AMERICAN LIBRARY DIRECTORY™ 2001-2002

The 54th edition of the *AMERICAN LIBRARY DIRECTORY*™
was prepared by Bowker's Database Production Group
in collaboration with the Information Technology Group

President and CEO
John A. Lawler

Vice President, Administrator
Drew Meyer

Vice President, Editorial Production
Dean Hollister

Vice President, Business Development
Michael Cairns

Product Manager, Directories
Art Stickney

Staff of the Database Production Group includes:

Editorial:
Managing Director: *Owen O'Donnell*
Managing Editor: *Beverley McDonough*
Senior Editor: *Mitra Purkayastha*
Associate Editors: *Jennifer Greve, Goretti Hampton*

Production:
Senior Director: *Carlton Dyce*
Senior Managing Editor: *Mitch Letterman*
Managing Editor: *Christopher Reid*
Desktop Publishing Specialist/Administrator: *Melanie Koserowski*
Associate Desktop Publishers: *Adesoji Akanbi, Colleen Crary*
Clarice D. Isaacs, Jocelyn Chloe Kwiatkowski
Kennard McGill, Richard Nagurka, Lorena Soriano

Information Technology:
Project Manager: *Frank Morris*
Programmer Analysts: *Dina Dvinyaninova, Chris Voser*

Data Collection:
Director: *Valerie Harris*
Production Manager: *Debra James*
Project Coordinator: *Carolyn Ollariu*
Associate Project Coordinator: *Paula Watts*

AMERICAN LIBRARY DIRECTORY™

2001 – 2002

54TH EDITION

VOL. 1

LIBRARIES IN THE UNITED STATES

Published by Bowker

International Standard Book Number: 0-8352-4404-0
Vol. 1 0-8352-4405-9, Vol. 2 0-8352-4406-7
International Standard Serial Number: 0065-910X
Library of Congress Catalog Card Number: 23-3581
Printed and bound in the United States of America

CONTENTS

VOLUME 1

VOLUME 2

PREFACE

Now in its 54th edition, the *American Library Directory*™ was edited and compiled by Bowker. Published biennially from 1908 until 1978, the directory is now updated year-round to reflect the increased importance of documenting change in library incomes, personnel, expenditures, and automated capabilities.

Updates for the directory can now be submitted at any time. Visit **www.bowker.com**. Click on menu choice Make Corrections, select Publishing/Media/Library Industries followed by American Library Directory.

ARRANGEMENT AND COVERAGE

The major section of the directory is a listing of public, academic, government and special libraries in the United States and regions administered by it and in Canada. Arranged geographically, the entries are alphabetized by state, region, or province; then by city; and finally by the institution or library name.

Each state, region, and province opens with statistical information regarding public libraries. These statistics were supplied by the state, regional, or provincial library.

Entries include the name and address of the library, names of key personnel, and information on the library's holdings. In addition, the entries for the majority of libraries provide information on some or all of these additional areas: Income; Expenditures, including salaries; E-Mail; Subject Interests; Special Collections; Automation; and Publications. Also included in each entry is a Standard Address Number (SAN), a unique address identification code. For SAN questions or assignments, contact *Diana Fumando* at 800-521-8110, ext. 7755. See the sample entry on page xi for a comprehensive guide to information which can be included in each entry.

Information within each library entry came either from the library itself or from public sources. Each library received a copy of the previous edition's entry for updating; if the material was not returned, the data were verified, as much as possible, through research. Entries verified from public sources are indicated by an asterisk (*) following the library name.

Libraries which the editors have learned about since the previous edition were sent questionnaires. If a library returned the form with sufficient information, it was included. Such entries, either new libraries or simply new to the directory, are indicated by a section indicator (§) to the left of the classification letter which precedes the entry.

Each library listed is identified by a code which indicates the type of library it is. The following codes are used:

A — Armed Forces
C — College and University
G — Government, from local to federal
J — Junior College
L — Law
M — Medical
P — Public
R — Religious
S — Special, including industry and company libraries as well as libraries serving associations, clubs, foundations, institutes, and societies.

ADDITIONAL SECTIONS

Library Award Recipients, 2000. This section includes awards for outstanding librarianship or services, major development grants and research projects.

Volume 2 of the directory serves as a support or auxiliary to the Library Section, and includes a variety of information:

1. *Networks, Consortia, and Other Cooperating Library Organizations* includes automation networks, statewide networking systems, book processing and purchasing centers, and other specialized cooperating organizations. Entries indicate the number of members and the primary functions of each.

2. *Library Schools and Training Courses* includes junior college, college, and university library science programs. Entries indicate entrance requirements, tuition, type of training offered, degrees and hours offered, and special courses offered. A dagger (†) indicates a program accredited by the American Library Association Committee on Accreditation.

3. *Library Systems* provides a listing of all state and provincial library systems. A brief statement indicating system functions within the state or province precedes the alphabetically arranged list of the state or province's systems. Cities are also included so that the user can locate a system's entry in the Library Section of the directory, or in cases where the state is followed by (N), in the Network Section of the directory.

4. *Libraries for the Blind and Physically Handicapped* provides a listing of all libraries designated by the National Library Service for the Blind and Physically Handicapped as regional and subregional libraries serving print handicapped patrons. It also includes Canadian libraries, which have facilities for assisting these patrons.

5. *Libraries Serving the Deaf and Hearing Impaired* provides a similar listing of all libraries which have indicated that they have a TDD reference service for deaf patrons. The list is arranged by state and within state by name. The city is included so that the user can find the entry in the Library Section and determine the TDD number as well as other services by reading the paragraph, "Special Services for the Deaf", in the library's entry.

6. *State and Provincial Public Library Agencies* indicates name, address, person-in-charge, and telephone number of the state agency which is responsible for public libraries.

7. *State School Library Agencies* indicates the same information for the state agency which is responsible for elementary and high school programs.

8. *The National Interlibrary Loan Code for the United States* is reprinted with the permission of the American Library Association.

9. *United States Armed Forces Libraries Overseas* is a listing, by military branch, of all overseas libraries arranged in geographical order. It includes name, address, person-in-charge, and Standard Address Number (SAN) of each library.

10. *The Organization Index* provides an alphabetical listing of all libraries and networks. Cross-references are included as needed.

11. *The Personnel Index* is an alphabetical listing of individuals who are included within entries for libraries, consortia, and schools.

CORRECTIONS VIA WEB SITE

Bowker has moved toward continuous data collection. Updated information for the *American Library Directory*™ can now be submitted at any time via the Bowker web site. Visit **www.bowker.com**. Click on menu choice Make Corrections, select Publishing/Media/Library Industries followed by American Library Directory. Once the information has been submitted, the editors will apply the changes to the database.

RELATED SERVICES

Mailing lists of libraries found in the *American Library Directory*™ can be requested from Cahners Business List, 1350 E Touhy Avenue, Des Plaines, IL 60018-3358. Telephone: 800-323-4958. Fax: 847-390-2779.

The *American Library Directory*™ is available online through Dialog (File 460) from The Dialog Corporation. For further information call 1-800-3-DIALOG (800-334-2564) or 919-462-8600; Internet: www.dialog.com or write to: The Dialog Corporation, 11000 Regency Parkway, Suite 400, Cary, NC 27511.

SilverPlatter Information offers an ERL-compliant CD-ROM of the directory. For more information on SilverPlatter's ERL CD-ROM, please contact SilverPlatter at 1-800-343-0064 or Bowker at 1-888-BOWKER2.

American Library Directory™ on CD-ROM, a powerful library tool, is now available from Bowker. For further information, please call 1-888-BOWKER2 (1-888-269-5372).

Library Resource Guide, A Catalog of Services and Suppliers for the library community is complimentary with *American Library Directory*™. For further information, call Lisa Tisi at 888-269-5372, ext. 3799 or visit **www.bowker.com**. You may also access *Library Resource Guide* on the internet at **www.libraryresource.com**.

The editors have made every effort to include all material submitted as accurately and completely as possible within the confines of format and scope. However, the publishers do not assume and hereby disclaim any liability to any party for any loss or damage caused by errors or omissions in *American Library Directory*™ whether such errors or omissions resulted from negligence, accident, or any other cause. In the event of a publication error, the sole responsibility of the publisher will be the entry of corrected information in succeeding editions.

ACKNOWLEDGEMENTS

The editors wish to thank all of those who responded to our requests for information; without their efforts, the *American Library Directory*™ could not be published.

The editors also wish to express their appreciation for the cooperation of the officers of the state, regional, and provincial libraries who have provided statistics and other information concerning libraries in their areas. We strongly encourage you to update your information online at **www.bowker.com** so that we can accurately reflect the changes in the industry.

Beverley McDonough
Managing Editor

Return this form to:

American Library Directory
121 Chanlon Road
New Providence, NJ 07974
Fax: (908) 771-7704 or (908) 771-8736

AMERICAN LIBRARY DIRECTORY™

EDITORIAL REVISION FORM

Library Name:____________________

The library listing is found on page number:____________________

☐ Please check here if you are nominating this library for a new listing in the directory

General Information

Address:____________________

City: __________ State/Country: __________ Postal Code:__________

Phone: __________ Fax:__________

E-mail: __________ Web Site:__________

Brief Description:____________________

Personnel

☐ Addition ☐ Deletion ☐ Correction

First Name:__________ Last Name: __________ Title:__________

☐ Addition ☐ Deletion ☐ Correction

First Name:__________ Last Name: __________ Title:__________

☐ Addition ☐ Deletion ☐ Correction

First Name:__________ Last Name: __________ Title:__________

☐ Addition ☐ Deletion ☐ Correction

First Name:__________ Last Name: __________ Title:__________

(continued on back)

Other Information

Indicate other information to be added to or corrected in this listing; please be as specific as possible, noting erroneous data to be deleted.

____

____

____

____

____

____

____

Verification

Data for this listing will not be updated without the following information.

Your First Name: ____________________ Your Last Name: ____________________

Organization Name: ____

Address: ____

City: ________________ State/Country: ________________ Postal Code: __________

Phone: ________________________ E-mail: ________________________

Indicate if you are a: ☐ Representative of this organization ☐ User of this directory ☐ Other

If other, please specify: ____

Thank you for helping Bowker maintain the most up-to-date information available. Please return by fax to 908-771-7704 or 908-771-8736, or visit our website at www.bowker.com and click on the option for Corrections.

SAMPLE ENTRY

[1]**P** [2]McNEIL & FOSTER, [3]Prescott Memorial Library, [4]500 Terra Cotta Dr, 85005-3126. [5]SAN 360-9070. [6]Tel: 602-839-9108. Toll Free Tel: 800-625-3848. FAX: 602-839-2020. TDD: 602-839-9202. E-Mail: mcneilfoster@prescott.org. Web Site: www.fosterpress.com. [7]*Dir* Troy Alan; Tel: 602-839-5522; *Asst Dir* Tasha Brunnell; *Tech Serv* Beverly Greene; *Pub Servs* Tanya Peeley. Subject Specialists: *Bus* Cecil Brown; *Folklore* Peggy Shoree.
[8]Staff 20 (MLS 15, Non-MLS 5)
[9]Founded 1903. Pop served 92,540; Circ 210,000
[10]July 2000-Jun 2001 Main library and branch library, Income $480,000 State $30,0000, City $139,518. Mats Exp $132,460, Books $53,000, Per/Ser (Incl.Access Fees)$72,900, Micro $1,160, AVEquip $5,100. Sal $97,100 (Prof $32,000)
[11]**Library Holdings**: Bk Vols 102,450; Bk Titles 72,000; Per subs 245
[12]**Special Collections**: Local History (Lehi Coll)
[13]**Subject Interests:** Child psychology, genetics
[14]**Automation Activity & Vendor Info**:(Acquisitions) Innovative Interfaces Inc.; (Cataloging) Innovative Interfaces Inc.; (Circulation) Gaylord
[15]**Database Vendor:** DRA, Ebsco-EbscoHost
[16]Mem of Southwestern Library System
[17]Partic in Amigos; BRS
[18]Special Services for the Deaf-TDD. Staff member who knows sign language; projector & captioned films
[19]Friends of Library Group
[20]**Bookmobiles:** 1
[21]**Branches:** 1
EASTSIDE, 9807 Post St, 85007-3184. SAN 360-9083. Tel 602-839-9178: *Librn* Linda Rhodes
Library Holdings: Bk Vols 23,000

1. Classification key (See "Arrangement & Coverage" for explanation.)
2. Official library name.
3. Other name by which library may be known
4. Address
5. SAN (Standard Address Number)
6. Communication numbers
7. Personnel
8. Number and status of staff
9. Library background–Data on enrollment and the highest degree offered are included for academic libraries.
10. Income figures–Library income is broken down by source, when reported.
    Expenditure figures–Material expenditure figures were requested for AV equipment, books, electronic reference materials (incl. access fees), manuscripts & archives, microforms, other print materials, periodicals/serials (incl. access fees) and preservation. In addition, salary figures are broken down by status when given.
11. Library holdings
12. Special collections
13. Subject interests
14. Automation activity & vendor
15. Database vendor
16. Library system to which the library belongs
17. Networks in which the library participates
18. Special services
19. Friends of library group
20. Bookmobiles
21. Branches (or departmental libraries for academic and special libraries)–Entries include library name, address, name of librarian and number of book volumes. Branch libraries are listed under the library of which they are a part. Branches located in towns different from the main library's seat are cross-referenced in the index.

LIBRARY COUNT

Provided here are totals for major types of libraries in the United States, its territories and Canada. Included are counts for Public, Academic, Armed Forces, Government and Special Libraries. Excluded from the counts are branch, departmental and divisional libraries not listed with a full address in the directory. Some categories, such as Academic, provide counts for specialized libraries such as Law or Medical libraries. As counts for only certain types of libraries are given, these sub-categories do not add up to the total count for each type of library.

PUBLIC—Each public library is counted once and then each branch is counted separately. Because the organization of systems varies from state to state, the method of counting these libraries varies also. In some cases, the libraries forming the systems were designated as member libraries, while in others they were given as branch libraries. In yet other instances, systems maintain branches as well as member libraries. If listed in this directory as a branch, the library was recorded in the branch count; however, member libraries were counted independently and recorded in the number of public libraries. Special public libraries are also included in the Total Special Libraries count.

ACADEMIC—The figure for academic libraries includes all libraries listed as part of academic institutions in the *AMERICAN LIBRARY DIRECTORY*™ whether they are main, departmental or special. Specialized libraries and library departments at these colleges, such as law, medical, religious or science libraries, are also counted in the Total Special Libraries figure.

GOVERNMENT and ARMED FORCES—Counts cover all government and armed forces-operated libraries listed in the directory, including specialized ones. Those libraries which are also defined as special libraries are included in the Total Special Libraries figure.

NOTE: Branch records for academics and government libraries are no longer counted within these breakdowns, causing some discrepancy when compared to previous editions. This does not affect the total number of libraries listed in *American Library Directory 2001-2002*.

SPECIAL—The Special Libraries count includes only specialized libraries which are not Public, Academic, Armed Forces or Government institutions. The Total Special Libraries count includes all law, medical, religious, business and other special libraries found in the *AMERICAN LIBRARY DIRECTORY*™ regardless of who operates them.

LIBRARIES IN THE UNITED STATES

A. **PUBLIC LIBRARIES** *16,512
- Public Libraries, excluding Branches 9,415
  - Main Public Libraries that have Branches 1,358
- Public Library Branches 7,097

B. **ACADEMIC LIBRARIES** *3,406
- Junior College Libraries 1,084
  - Departmental 177
  - Medical 4
  - Religious 6
- University & College 2,322
  - Departmental 1,535
  - Law 146
  - Medical 225
  - Religious 181

C. **ARMED FORCES LIBRARIES** *335
- Air Force 94
  - Medical 13
- Army 148
  - Medical 32
- Navy 91
  - Law 1
  - Medical 14

D. **GOVERNMENT LIBRARIES** *1,376
- Law 415
- Medical 216

E. **SPECIAL LIBRARIES** (Excluding Public, Academic, Armed Forces and Government) *9,763
- Law 1,123
- Medical 1,862
- Religious 604

F. **TOTAL SPECIAL LIBRARIES** (Including Public, Academic, Armed Forces and Government) 11,017
- Total Law 1,686
- Total Medical 2,366
- Total Religious 1,126

G. **TOTAL LIBRARIES COUNTED (*)** 31,392

LIBRARIES IN REGIONS ADMINISTERED BY THE UNITED STATES

A. **PUBLIC LIBRARIES** *30
- Public Libraries, excluding Branches 10
  - Main Public Libraries that have Branches 3
- Public Library Branches 20

B. **ACADEMIC LIBRARIES** *35
- Junior College Libraries 8
  - Departmental 4
  - Medical 0
- University & College 27
  - Departmental 22
  - Law 2
  - Medical 1
  - Religious 1

C. **ARMED FORCES LIBRARIES** *2
Air Force 1
Army 1
Navy 0

D. **GOVERNMENT LIBRARIES** *10
Law 4
Medical 2

E. **SPECIAL LIBRARIES** (Excluding Public, Academic, Armed Forces and Government) *19
Law 6
Medical 4
Religious 0

F. **TOTAL SPECIAL LIBRARIES** (Including Public, Academic, Armed Forces and Government) 29
Total Law 12
Total Medical 7
Total Religious 2

G. **TOTAL LIBRARIES COUNTED (*)** 96

LIBRARIES IN CANADA

A. **PUBLIC LIBRARIES** *1,697
Public Libraries, excluding Branches 706
Main Public Libraries that have Branches 124
Public Library Branches 991

B. **ACADEMIC LIBRARIES** *326
Junior College Libraries 83
Departmental 21
Medical 0
Religious 2
University & College 243
Departmental 204
Law 10
Medical 19
Religious 25

C. **GOVERNMENT LIBRARIES** *364
Law 24
Medical 5

D. **SPECIAL LIBRARIES** (Excluding Public, Academic, Armed Forces and Government) *1,311
Law 125
Medical 240
Religious 32

E. **TOTAL SPECIAL LIBRARIES** (Including Public, Academic, and Government) 1,396
Total Law 159
Total Medical 264
Total Religious 99

F. **TOTAL LIBRARIES COUNTED (*)** 3,698

SUMMARY

TOTAL UNITED STATES LIBRARIES 31,392

TOTAL LIBRARIES ADMINISTERED BY THE UNITED STATES 96

TOTAL CANADIAN LIBRARIES 3,698

GRAND TOTAL OF LIBRARIES LISTED 35,186

LIBRARY AWARD RECIPIENTS, 2000

Listed below are major awards given to libraries and librarians in the calendar year 2000. These entries were selected from the more inclusive list of scholarships and grants awards found in the *Bowker Annual*, 2001 edition. The editors attempted to include awards for outstanding librarianship or service, development grants and research projects larger than an essay or monographs.
Awards are listed alphabetically by organization.

• American Association of School Librarians (AASL)

AASL/HIGHSMITH RESEARCH GRANT (up to $5,000). To conduct innovative research aimed at measuring and evaluating the impact of school library media programs on learning and education. Donor: Highsmith Inc. Winner: Sharon Lee Vansickle.

DISTINGUISHED SERVICE AWARD AASL/BAKER & TAYLOR ($3,000). For outstanding contributions to librarianship and school library development. Donor: Baker & Taylor Books. Winner: Carol C. Kuhlthau.

• American Library Association (ALA)

ALA/INFORMATION TODAY LIBRARY OF THE FUTURE AWARD ($2,500). For a library, consortium, group of librarians, or support organization for innovative planning for, applications of, or development of patron training programs about information technology in a library setting. Donor: Information Today, Inc. Winner: Ocean County Library, New Jersey.

HUGH C. ATKINSON MEMORIAL AWARD ($2,000). For outstanding achievement (including risk-taking) by academic librarians that has contributed significantly to improvements in library automation, management, and/or development or research. Offered by: ACRL, ALCTS, LAMA, and LITA divisions. Winner: Kenneth L. Frazier.

CARROLL PRESTON BABER RESEARCH GRANT (up to $7,500). For innovative research that could lead to an improvement in library services to any specified group(s) of people. Donor: Eric C. Baber. Winner: Cheryl Knott Malone.

BETA PHI MU AWARD ($500). For distinguished service in library education. Donor: Beta Phi Mu International Library Science Honorary Society. Winner: Shirley Fitzgibbons.

DEMCO/BLACK CAUSCUS OF ALA AWARD FOR EXCELLENCE IN LIBRARIANSHIP ($5,000). To honor significant contributions to promoting the status of African Americans in the library profession. Winner: Satia Marshall Orange.

MELVIL DEWEY AWARD. To an individual or group for recent creative professional achievement in library management, training, cataloging and classification, and the tools and techniques of librarianship. Donor: OCLC/Forest Press. Winner: Paul Sybrowsky.

ELIZABETH FUTAS CATALYST FOR CHANGE AWARD ($1,000). To recognize and honor a librarian who invests time and talent to make positive change in the profession of librarianship. Donor: Elizabeth Futas Memorial Fund. Winner: Ann Symons.

LOLETA D. FYAN PUBLIC LIBRARY RESEARCH GRANT (up to $10,000). For projects in public library development. Winner: Noreen H. Bernstein for "Feed Me a Story."

GALE GROUP FINANCIAL DEVELOPMENT AWARD ($2,500). To a library organization for a financial development project to secure new funding resources for a public or academic library. Donor: Gale Group. Winner: Clute Public Library Association, Texas.

GROLIER NATIONAL LIBRARY WEEK GRANT ($4,000). To libraries or library associations of all types for a public awareness campaign in connection with National Library Week in the year the grant is awarded. Donor: Grolier Educational Corporation. Winner: Milwaukee Public Library.

JOSEPH W. LIPPINCOTT AWARD ($1,000). To a librarian for distinguished service to the profession. Donor: Joseph W. Lippincott, Jr. Winner: John Y. Cole.

MARSHALL CAVENDISH EXCELLENCE IN LIBRARY PROGRAMMING AWARD ($5,000). Recognizes either a school or public library that demonstrates excellence in library programming by providing programs that have community impact and respond to community need. Winner: Bad Axe Public Library, Michigan.

• Association for Library Collections and Technical Services (ALCTS)

BOWKER/ULRICH'S SERIALS LIBRARIANSHIP AWARD ($1,500). For demonstrated leadership in serials-related activities through participation in professional associations and/or library education programs, contributions to the body of serials literature, research in the area of serials, or development of tools or methods to enhance access to or management of serials. Donor: R. R. Bowker/Ulrich's. Winner: Trisha Davis.

LEADERSHIP IN LIBRARY ACQUISITIONS AWARDS ($1,500). For significant contributions by an outstanding leader in the field of library acquisitions. Donor: Harrassowitz Company. Winner: Frances Wilkinson.

ESTHER J. PIERCY AWARD ($1,500). To a librarian with fewer than ten years experience for contributions and leadership in the field of library collections and technical services. Donor: Yankee Book Peddler. Winner: Brian J. Baird.

• Association for Library Service to Children (ALSC)

DISTINGUISHED SERVICE TO ALSC AWARD ($1,000). To recognize significant contributions to, and an impact on, library services to children and/or ALSC. Winner: Peggy Sullivan.

• Association of College and Research Libraries (ACRL)

ACRL ACADEMIC OR RESEARCH LIBRARIAN OF THE YEAR AWARD ($3,000). For outstanding contribution to academic and research librarianship and library development. Donor: Baker & Taylor. Winner: Sharon A. Hogan.

ACRL EBSS DISTINGUISHED EDUCATION AND BEHAVIORAL SCIENCES LIBRARIAN AWARD. To an academic librarian who has made an outstanding contribution as an education and/or behavioral sciences librarian through accomplishments and service to the profession. Winner: Leslie Bjorncrantz.

ACRL WSS/GREENWOOD CAREER ACHIEVEMENT IN WOMEN'S STUDIES LIBRARIANSHIP ($1,000). Honors distinguished academic librarians who have made outstanding contributions to women's studies through accomplishments and service to the profession. Winner: Susan Ellis Searing.

ACRL WSS/ROUTLEDGE AWARD FOR SIGNIFICANT ACHIEVEMENT IN WOMEN'S STUDIES LIBRARIANSHIP ($1,000). Winner: Lynn Westbrook.

MIRIAM DUDLEY BIBLIOGRAPHIC INSTRUCTION LIBRARIAN AWARD ($1,000). For contribution to the advancement of bibliographic instruction in a college or research institution. Donor: JAI Press. Winner: Carol C. Kuhlthau.

• Association of Specialized and Cooperative Library Agencies (ASCLA)

FRANCIS JOSEPH CAMPBELL CITATION. For a contribution of recognized importance to library service for the blind and physically handicapped. Winner: Norman R. Coombs.

• Library and Information Technology Association (LITA)

LITA/GAYLORD AWARD FOR ACHIEVEMENT IN LIBRARY AND INFORMATION TECHNOLOGY ($1,000). Winner: William Gray Potter.

LITA/OCLC FREDERICK G. KILGOUR AWARD FOR RESEARCH IN LIBRARY AND INFORMATION TECHNOLOGY ($2,000 and expense paid attendance at ALA Annual Conference). To bring attention to research relevant to the development of information technologies. Winner: Gary Marchionini.

• Medical Library Association (MLA)

ESTELLE BRODMAN AWARD FOR THE ACADEMIC MEDICAL LIBRARIAN OF THE YEAR. To honor significant achievement, potential for leadership, and continuing excellence at mid-career in the area of academic health sciences librarianship. Winner: Jeanette C. McCray.

• Public Library Association (PLA)

EXCELLENCE IN SMALL AND/OR RURAL PUBLIC SERVICE AWARD ($1,000). Honors a library serving a population of 10,000 or less that demonstrates excellence of service to its community as exemplified by an overall service program or a special program of significant accomplishment. Donor: EBSCO Subscription Services. Winner: Clearwater County Free Library, Weippe, Idaho.

ALLIE BETH MARTIN AWARD ($3,000). Honors a librarian who, in a public library setting, has demonstrated extraordinary range and depth of knowledge about books or other library materials and has distinguished ability to share that knowledge. Donor: Baker & Taylor Books. Winner: Barbara Genco.

CHARLIE ROBINSON AWARD ($1,000). Honors a public library director who, over a period of seven years, has been a risk-taker, an innovator, and/or change agent in a public library. Donor: Baker & Taylor Books. Winner: William Ptacek.

• Reference and User Services Association (RUSA)

VIRGINIA BOUCHER-OCLC DISTINGUISHED ILL LIBRARIAN AWARD ($2,000). To a librarian for outstanding professional achievement, leadership, and contributions to interlibrary loan and document delivery. Winner: Joanne Halgren.

FACTS ON FILE GRANT ($2,000). To a library for imaginative programming that would make current affairs more meaningful to an adult audience. Donor: Facts on File, Inc. Winner: Carol Wads and the Adult Services staff, LeRoy Collins Leon County Public Library, Florida.

GALE GROUP AWARD FOR EXCELLENCE IN BUSINESS LIBRARIANSHIP (BRASS) ($1,000). To an individual for distinguished activities in the field of business librarianship. Donor: Gale Group Co. Winner: Catherine R. Friedman.

GALE GROUP AWARD FOR EXCELLENCE IN REFERENCE AND ADULT SERVICES. To a library or library system for developing an imaginative and unique library resource to meet patrons' reference needs ($1,000). Donor: Gale Group Co. Winner: Rutherford B. Hayes Presidential Center Library.

CANADA

• Canadian Library Association (CLA)

CLA OUTSTANDING SERVICE TO LIBRARIANSHIP AWARD. Donor: R. R. Bowker. Winner: Marianne Scott.

CLA RESEARCH AND DEVELOPMENT GRANT ($1,000). Winner: Alvin M. Schrader.

• Canadian Association of College and University Libraries (CACUL)

CACUL AWARD FOR OUTSTANDING ACADEMIC LIBRARIAN. Winner: Kewal Krishan.

• Canadian Association of Public Libraries (CAPL)

CAPL/BRODART OUTSTANDING PUBLIC LIBRARY SERVICE AWARD. Winner: Rowena Lunn.

CASLIS AWARD FOR SPECIAL LIBRARIANSHIP IN CANADA. Winner: Ruth Reedman.

• Canadian School Library Association (CSLA)

NATIONAL BOOK SERVICE TEACHER-LIBRARIAN OF THE YEAR AWARD. Winner: Holly Gunn.

KEY TO SYMBOLS AND ABBREVIATIONS

KEY TO SYMBOLS

A – Armed Forces libraries
C – College and university libraries
G – Government libraries
J – Junior college libraries
L – Law libraries
M – Medical libraries (including hospital, nursing school, and pharmaceutical libraries)
P – Public libraries
R – Religious libraries
S – Special libraries
* – No answer received directly from the library; data gathered from other sources
§ – New library and/or listed for the first time
† – Library school program accredited by the American Library Association Committee on Accreditation

KEY TO ABBREVIATIONS

A-tapes – Audio Tapes
Acad – Academic, Academy
Acctg – Accounting
Acq – Acquisition Librarian, Acquisitions
Actg – Acting
Ad – Adult Services Librarian
Add – Address
Admin – Administration, Administrative
Adminr – Administrator
Adv – Advisor, Advisory
Advan – Advanced, Advancement
Aeronaut – Aeronautics
AFB – Air Force Base
Agr – Agricultural, Agriculture
Ala – Alabama
Alta – Alberta
Am – America, American
Ann – Annual, Annually
Anthrop – Anthropology
APO – Air Force Post Office, Army Post Office
Approp – Appropriation
Approx – Approximate, Approximately
Appt – Appointment
Archaeol – Archaeological, Archaeology
Archit – Architecture
Ariz – Arizona
Ark – Arkansas
Asn – Association
Assoc – Associate
Asst – Assistant
AV – Audiovisual, Audiovisual Materials
Ave – Avenue
BC – British Columbia
Bd – Binding, Bound
Behav – Behavorial
Bibliog – Bibliographic, Bibliographical, Bibliography
Bibliogr – Bibliographer
Biog – Biographical, Biographically, Biography
Biol – Biology
Bk – Book
Bkmobile – Bookmobile
Bldg – Building
Blvd – Boulevard
Bot – Botany
Br – Branch
Bro – Brother
Bur – Bureau
Calif – California
Can – Canada, Canadian
Cap – Capital
Cat – Cataloging Librarian, Catalogs
CEGEP – College d'Enseignement General et Professional
Cent – Central
Ch – Children's Librarian, Children's Services
Chem – Chemical, Chemistry
Chmn – Chairman
Cht – Charts
Circ – Circulation
Cler – Clerical Staff
Co – Company
Col – College
Coll – Collection
Colo – Colorado
COM – Computer Output Microform
Commun – Community
Comn – Commission
Comt – Committee
Conn – Connecticut
Conserv – Conservation
Consult – Consultant
Coop – Cooperates, Cooperating, Cooperation, Cooperative
Coord – Coordinating
Coordr – Coordinator
Corp – Corporation
Coun – Council
CP – Case Postale
Ct – Court
Ctr – Center
Curric – Curriculum
DC – District of Columbia
Del – Delaware
Den – Denominational
Dent – Dentistry
Dep – Deputy, Depository
Dept – Department
Develop – Development
Dir – Director
Div – Division
Doc – Document
Dr – Doctor, Drive
E – East
Econ – Economic
Ed – Edited, Edition, Editor
Educ – Education, Educational
Elem – Elementary
Elec Mail – Electronic Mail
Eng – Engineering
Enrl – Enrollment
Ent – Entrance
Environ – Environmental
Equip – Equipment
ERDA – Energy Research & Development Administration
Est – Estimate, Estimation
Estab – Established
Excl – Excluding
Exec – Executive
Exp – Expenditure
Ext – Extension of Telephone
Exten – Extension
Fac – Faculty, Facilities
Fed – Federal
Fedn – Federation
Fel – Fellowship
Fla – Florida
Flm – Films
Found –Foundation
FPO – Fleet Post Office
Fr – French
Fs – Filmstrips
Ft – Fort
FT – Full Time
FTE – Full Time Equivalent
Ga – Georgia
Gen – General, Generated
Geog – Geographical, Geography
Geol – Geological, Geology
Govt – Government, Governmental
Grad – Graduate
Hist – Historical, History
Hort – Horticulture
Hq – Headquarters
Hrs – Hours
Hwy – Highway
Hydrol – Hydrology
Ill – Illinois
ILL – Interlibrary Loan
Illustr – Illustrator
Inc – Income, Incorporated
Incl – Including
Ind – Indiana
Indust – Industrial, Industry
Info – Information
Ins – Insurance
Inst – Institute, Institutions
Instrul – Instructional
Instr – Instructor
Int – International
Jr – Junior
Juv – Juvenile
Kans – Kansas
Ky – Kentucky
La – Louisiana
Lab – Laboratories, Laboratory
Lang – Language
Lectr – Lecturer
Legis – Legislative, Legislature

Libr – Libraries, Library
Librn – Librarian
Lit – Literature
Ltd – Limited
Mag – Magazine
Man – Manitoba
Mass – Massachusetts
Mat – Materials
Math – Mathematical, Mathematics
Md – Maryland
Med – Medical, Medicine
Media – Media Specialist
Mem – Member
Metaphys – Metaphysics
Metrop – Metropolitan
Mgr – Manager, Managerial
Mgt – Management
Mich – Michigan
Micro – Microform
Mil – Military
Misc – Miscellaneous
Miss – Mississippi
Minn – Minnesota
Mo – Missouri
Mont – Montana
Ms – Manuscript
Mus – Museum
N – North
NASA – National Aeronautics & Space Administration
Nat – National
NB – New Brunswick
NC – North Carolina
NDak – North Dakota
NE – Northeast, Northeastern
Nebr – Nebraska
Nev – Nevada
New Eng – New England
Newsp – Newspaper
Nfld – Newfoundland
NH – New Hampshire
NJ – New Jersey
NMex – New Mexico
NS – Nova Scotia
NW – Northwest, Northwestern
NY – New York
Oceanog – Oceanography
Off – Office, Official
Okla – Oklahoma
Ont – Ontario
Ore – Oregon
Orgn – Organizations
Ornith – Ornithology
Pa – Pennsylvania
Pac – Pacific
Partic – Participant, Participates
PEI – Prince Edward Island
Per – Periodical
Pharm – Pharmacy
Philos – Philosophical, Philosophy
Photog – Photograph, Photographical, Photography
Phys – Physical
Pkwy – Parkway
Pl – Place
PO – Post Office
Polit Sci – Political Science
Pop – Population
PR – Puerto Rico
Prep – Preparation, Preparatory
Pres – President
Presv – Preservation
Proc – Process, Processing
Prof – Professional, Professor
Prog – Program
Prov – Province, Provincial
Psychiat – Psychiatrist, Psychiatry
Psychol – Psychological, Psychology
PT – Part Time
Pub – Public
Pub Rel – Public Relations Head
Publ – Publisher, Publishing
Pvt – Private
Qtr – Quarter
Que – Quebec
R&D – Research & Development
Rd – Road
Read – Readable
Rec – Record, Recording
Ref – Reference
Relig – Religion, Religious
Rep – Representative
Reprod – Reproduction
Req – Requirement
Res – Research, Resources
RI – Rhode Island
RLIN – Research Libraries Information Network
Rm – Room
Rpt – Reports
Rte – Route
RR – Rural Route
S – South
Sal – Salary
SAN – Standard Address Number
Sask – Saskatchewan
SC – South Carolina
Sch – School
Sci – Science, Scientific
Sci Fict – Science Fiction
SDak – South Dakota
SE – Southeast, Southeastern
Secy – Secretary
Sem – Semester, Seminary
Ser – Serials, Serials Librarian
Serv – Service
Soc – Social, Societies, Society
Sociol – Sociology
Spec – Special
Sq – Square
Sr – Senor, Senior, Sister
St – Saint, Street
Sta – Station
Sub – Subscription
Subj – Subject
Sup – Supplies
Supv – Supervising, Supervision
Supvr – Supervisor
Supvry – Supervisory
SW – Southwest, Southwestern
Syst – System
TDD – Telecommunication Device for the Deaf
Tech – Technical, Technology
Tel – Telephone
Tenn – Tennessee
Tex – Texas
Theol – Theological, Theology
Tpk – Turnpike
Treas – Treasurer
TTY – Teletypewriter
TV – Television
TVA – Tennessee Valley Authority
UN – United Nations
Undergrad – Undergraduate
Univ – University
US – United States
VPres – Vice President
V-tapes – Video Tapes
Va – Virginia
Vet – Veteran
VF – Vertical Files
VI – Virgin Islands
Vis – Visiting
Vols – Volumes, Volunteers
Vt – Vermont
W – West
Wash – Washington
Wis – Wisconsin
WLN – Washington Library Network
WVa – West Virginia
Wyo – Wyoming
YA – Young Adult Librarian, Young Adult Services
Yr – Year
Zool – Zoology

AMERICAN LIBRARY DIRECTORY™

2001-2002

LIBRARIES IN THE UNITED STATES

ALABAMA

Date of Statistics: 1998-1999
Population, 1998 (est.) Census: 4,351,999
Population Served by Public Libraries: 4,351,999
Total Volumes in Public Libraries: 8,138,238
  Volumes Per Capita: 1.86
Total Public Library Circulation: 15,742,519
  Circulation Per Capita: 3.61
Total Public Library Income: $66,484,631
  Source of Income: Mainly public funds
  Expenditures Per Capita: $15.27
Number of County & Multi-county Public Library Systems: 20
  Counties Served: 67
Grants-in-Aid to Public Libraries:
  Federal (includes Title II): $2,276,650
  State: $4,799,347

ABBEVILLE

P ABBEVILLE MEMORIAL LIBRARY,* 301 Kirkland St, 36310. SAN 330-2822. Tel: 334-585-2818. FAX: 334-585-2818. *Librn*, Linda Floyd
Library Holdings: Bk Vols 20,095
Mem of Harrison Regional Library System
Friends of the Library Group

ADAMSVILLE

P ADAMSVILLE PUBLIC LIBRARY,* 5825 Main St, 35005-0241. (Mail add: PO Box 309, 35005-0241), SAN 376-7620. Tel: 205-674-3399. FAX: 205-674-5405. *Librn*, Clovis Hyde
Library Holdings: Bk Vols 11,000
Mem of Birmingham Pub & Jefferson County Free Libr Syst

AKRON

P AKRON PUBLIC LIBRARY, First Ave S, PO Box 8, 35441. SAN 300-0001. Tel: 205-372-3148. FAX: 205-372-3148. *Librn*, Josephine Williams; Staff 14 (MLS 5, Non-MLS 9)
1999-2000 Income $2,700, State $566. Mats Exp $378. Sal $111
Library Holdings: Bk Vols 235; Per Subs 10
Mem of Public Library Of Anniston & Calhoun County

ALABASTER

P ALBERT L SCOTT LIBRARY,* 100 Ninth St NW, 35007-9172. SAN 371-9332. Tel: 205-664-6822. FAX: 205-664-6839. *Dir*, Nan Abbott; E-Mail: nabbott@shelbycounty-al.org
Oct 1998-Sep 1999 Income $489,792, State $23,283, City $466,509. Mats Exp $60,700, Books $40,000, Per/Ser (Incl. Access Fees) $5,600. Sal $214,650 (Prof $119,955)
Library Holdings: Bk Vols 41,038; Per Subs 133
Special Collections: American Libraries, Library Journal, Booklist, Kirkus Review, School Library Journal
Mem of Harrison Regional Library System
Friends of the Library Group

ALBERTVILLE

P ALBERTVILLE PUBLIC LIBRARY, 200 Jackson St, 35950. (Mail add: PO Box 430, 35950), SAN 300-001X. Tel: 256-891-8290. *Dir*, Lisa Rowell; Staff 3 (MLS 1, Non-MLS 2)
Founded 2000. Pop 80,000; Circ 150,095
1999-2000 Income State $111
Library Holdings: Bk Vols 67,000; Bk Titles 85,000; Per Subs 100
Special Collections: Civil War Coll; Rare Books Room; War between the States
Mem of Public Library Of Anniston & Calhoun County
Partic in AALL
Friends of the Library Group

ALEXANDER CITY

P ADELIA MCCONNELL RUSSELL LIBRARY, 318 Church St, 35010-2516. SAN 376-5601. Tel: 256-329-6796. FAX: 256-329-6797. E-Mail: amrl@webshoppe.net. *Dir*, Sarah A Carlisle
Library Holdings: Bk Vols 36,500; Per Subs 87
Mem of Horseshoe Bend Regional Library

J CENTRAL ALABAMA COMMUNITY COLLEGE, Thomas D Russell Library, 1675 Cherokee Rd, PO Box 699, 35010. SAN 330-0005. Tel: 256-234-6346, Ext 6265. FAX: 205-234-0384. E-Mail: libscacc@core1.wwisp.net. Web Site: 207.98.224.1. *Dir Libr Serv*, Gerson Miles, III; E-Mail: gmilcacc@core1.wwisp.net; *Cat, Ref*, Carolyn Ingram; E-Mail: cingcacc@core1.wwisp.net; *Ser*, Karen Giangrosso; *Ser*, Denita Oliver; *Reader Servs*, Ola Mae Sims; Staff 5 (MLS 1, Non-MLS 4)
Founded 1965. Enrl 1,051; Fac 40; Highest Degree: Associate
Oct 1998-Sep 1999 Income (Main Library and Branch Library) $198,000. Mats Exp $28,000, Books $8,000, Micro $3,000, Other Print Mats $11,000, Electronic Ref Mat (Incl. Access Fees) $6,000. Sal $95,000
Library Holdings: Bk Titles 30,000; Per Subs 280
Special Collections: Alabama & Local History (Alabama Room)
Automation Activity & Vendor Info: (Cataloging) Athena; (Circulation) Athena; (OPAC) Athena
Database Vendor: Dialog, OCLC - First Search, OVID Technologies
Partic in Ala Union List & Serials
Friends of the Library Group
Departmental Libraries:
CHILDERSBURG CAMPUS, PO Box 389, Childersburg, 35044. SAN 370-4548. Tel: 205-378-5576. FAX: 205-378-5281. *In Charge*, Elaine Oliver
Partic in ABA/NET
Friends of the Library Group

ALICEVILLE

P ALICEVILLE PUBLIC LIBRARY, 416 Third Ave NE, 35442. SAN 300-0028. Tel: 205-373-6691. FAX: 205-373-3731. E-Mail: apl@pickens.net. *Librn*, Nelda Hudgins
Founded 1955. Pop 2,981; Circ 11,922
Library Holdings: Bk Vols 15,394; Bk Titles 14,217; Per Subs 30
Mem of Pickens County Coop Libr; Public Library Of Anniston & Calhoun County
Friends of the Library Group

ANDALUSIA

P ANDALUSIA PUBLIC LIBRARY, 212 S Three Notch St, 36420. SAN 300-0036. Tel: 334-222-6612. FAX: 334-222-6612. E-Mail: andylib@ala.com. Web Site: www.andylib.com. *Dir*, Karin Taylor; *Ch Servs*, Betty Harrelson; *Ref*, La Ferne D Griggs; *Tech Servs*, Joan Herring
Founded 1920. Pop 11,000; Circ 58,063
Library Holdings: Bk Titles 38,345; Per Subs 48
Special Collections: American Ancestors, bks, micro; One Hundred Years of County Newspapers, micro
Mem of Public Library Of Anniston & Calhoun County

J LURLEEN B WALLACE STATE JUNIOR COLLEGE LIBRARY, 1735 E Bypass, PO Box 1418, 36420. SAN 300-0044. Tel: 334-222-6591, Ext 2265. FAX: 334-222-6567. *Dir*, Marsha V Taylor; *Circ*, Susan B Evans; E-Mail: sbell@lbw.edu; *Dir Br Serv*, Mary Beth Green; Tel: 334-222-6591, Ext 2266, E-Mail: mbgreen@lbw.edu; Staff 4 (MLS 1, Non-MLS 3)
Founded 1969. Enrl 1,000; Fac 22
Oct 2000-Sep 2001 Income $123,359. Mats Exp $15,538, Books $11,000, Per/Ser (Incl. Access Fees) $4,538
Library Holdings: Bk Vols 28,755; Bk Titles 24,703; Per Subs 74
Special Collections: Alabama Coll; LBW Junior College Archives
Database Vendor: Ebsco - EbscoHost, GaleNet, OVID Technologies, ProQuest
Publications: Annual Report
Partic in Columbia Libr Syst; Novell
Special Services for the Deaf - Books on deafness & sign language

ANNISTON

M NORTHEAST ALABAMA REGIONAL MEDICAL CENTER, William Bruce Mitchell Medical Library, 400 E Tenth St, 36201. SAN 324-5950. Tel: 256-235-5877. FAX: 256-231-8760. Web Site: www.rmccares.org. *Coordr*, Janie Chitwood; E-Mail: canreg@hvps.com
Founded 1940
Library Holdings: Bk Vols 400; Bk Titles 400; Per Subs 80
Partic in Medline
Friends of the Library Group

R PARKER MEMORIAL BAPTIST CHURCH LIBRARY,* 1205 Quintard Ave, PO Box 2104, 36202. SAN 300-0052. Tel: 256-236-5628. FAX: 256-236-5441. *Librn*, Logene Griffin
Founded 1951
Library Holdings: Bk Vols 7,500

P PUBLIC LIBRARY OF ANNISTON & CALHOUN COUNTY, 108 E Tenth St, 36201. (Mail add: PO Box 308, 36202), SAN 330-003X. Tel: 256-237-8501. FAX: 256-238-0474. Web Site: www.anniston.lib.al.us. *Dir*, Bonnie G Seymour; E-Mail: bseymour@anniston.lib.al.us; *Bkmobile Coordr, Br Coordr, Commun Servs*, Linda Levens; *Acq*, Sandra Underwood; *Ad Servs*, Mary Connor; *Ad Servs, ILL, Ref*, Sunny Addison; *Cat, Tech Servs*, Lois Stahl; *Ch Servs, YA Servs*, Lanelle Striplin-Cova; *Rare Bks, Spec Coll*, Tom Mullins; Staff 19 (MLS 4, Non-MLS 15)
Founded 1965. Circ 169,295
Library Holdings: Bk Vols 106,658; Bk Titles 96,539; Per Subs 224
Subject Interests: Genealogy, Local history
Special Collections: Alabama History; Andrea Coll (Alabama Room); Anniston Room Coll; Genealogy (Alabama Room)
Automation Activity & Vendor Info: (Circulation) SIRSI
Publications: Serendipity Library Newsletter
Member Libraries: Akron Public Library; Albertville Public Library; Aliceville Public Library; Andalusia Public Library
Friends of the Library Group
Branches: 2
CARVER BRANCH, 722 W 14th St, 36201. SAN 330-0099. Tel: 256-237-7271. FAX: 256-237-7271. *Librn*, Brenda Manning

P LIBRARY FOR THE BLIND & PHYSICALLY HANDICAPPED, 108 E Tenth St, PO Box 308, 36202. SAN 330-0064. Tel: 256-237-8501. FAX: 256-238-0474. *Librn*, Deenie M Culver; Staff 1 (MLS 1)
Founded 1969. Circ 10,941
Provides services to nursing homes, nutrition sites, retirement homes & special education classes
Bookmobiles: 1

ARAB

P ARAB PUBLIC LIBRARY,* 325 Second St NW, 35016-1999. SAN 300-0060. Tel: 256-586-3366. FAX: 256-586-5638. E-Mail: arablib@airnet.net. *Tech Servs*, Danielle Houston
Founded 1963. Circ 71,269
1998-1999 Income $219,567, State $9,239, City $200,567, Locally Generated Income $5,000. Mats Exp $53,100, Books $40,000, Per/Ser (Incl. Access Fees) $8,100, Other Print Mats $5,000. Sal $102,886 (Prof $29,400)
Library Holdings: Per Subs 40
Subject Interests: Alabama, Civil War
Mem of Marshall County Cooperative Library
Friends of the Library Group

P MARSHALL COUNTY COOPERATIVE LIBRARY,* 325 Second St NW, 35016-1999. SAN 324-1424. Tel: 256-586-0565. FAX: 256-586-5638. *Librn*, Susan Delmas; *Bkmobile Coordr*, Janet Johnson
Founded 1974
Oct 1997-Sep 1998 Income $102,471, State $92,471, County $10,000. Mats Exp $12,839, Books $12,669, Per/Ser (Incl. Access Fees) $170. Sal $27,208 (Prof $8,234)
Library Holdings: Bk Titles 17,251
Member Libraries: Arab Public Library; Grant Public Library; Guntersville Public Library

ARITON

P ARITON PUBLIC LIBRARY,* Main St, 36311. SAN 330-2857. Tel: 334-762-2463. FAX: 334-762-2463. *Librn*, Nancy Hayward
Library Holdings: Bk Vols 3,344
Open Mon, Tues, Thurs & Fri 1-4:30
Friends of the Library Group

ARLEY

P ARLEY PUBLIC LIBRARY,* City Hall, PO Box 146, 35541. SAN 300-0079. Tel: 205-387-0103. FAX: 205-387-0105. *Librn*, Denise Childers
Founded 1974
Library Holdings: Bk Vols 3,402
Mem of Carl Elliott Regional Library System

ASHLAND

P ASHLAND CITY PUBLIC LIBRARY,* 113 N Second Ave W, PO Box 296, 36251-0296. SAN 376-561X. Tel: 256-354-3427. FAX: 256-354-3427. E-Mail: ashlibrary@aca-isp.com. *Librn*, Tina Nolen
Library Holdings: Bk Vols 13,412
Mem of Cheaha Regional Library

ASHVILLE

P SAINT CLAIR COUNTY LIBRARY,* PO Box 308, 35953-0308. SAN 330-3217. Tel: 205-884-1685. FAX: 205-884-1686. *Dir*, Judy Douglas
Founded 1957. Pop 55,930; Circ 89,615
1997-1998 Income $134,372, State $66,537, City $5,500, County $44,698, Other $17,637. Mats Exp $35,565, Books $33,350, Per/Ser (Incl. Access Fees) $1,363, Other Print Mats $400. Sal $45,680 (Prof $29,000)
Library Holdings: Bk Vols 50,000; Per Subs 27
Publications: History of St Clair County, 1539-1846
Branches: 7
ASHVILLE PUBLIC, Sixth Ave, PO Box 187, 35953. SAN 330-3241. Tel: 205-594-7954. *In Charge*, Barbara Stewart
Library Holdings: Bk Vols 10,660
MOODY PUBLIC, 2900 Daniel Dr, Moody, 35004. SAN 325-402X. Tel: 205-640-2517. *Librn*, Doris Stanley
Library Holdings: Bk Vols 9,519
ODENVILLE PUBLIC, PO Box 249, Odenville, 35120. SAN 330-3276. Tel: 205-629-5901. *Librn*, Mary Banks
Library Holdings: Bk Vols 3,013
PELL CITY BRANCH, 1923 First Ave N, Pell City, 35125. SAN 330-3306. Tel: 205-884-1015. *Librn*, Danny Stewart
Library Holdings: Bk Vols 45,735
Friends of the Library Group
RAGLAND BRANCH, Rte 2, Box 13B, Ragland, 35131. SAN 330-3330. Tel: 205-472-2007. *Librn*, Kim Jackson
Library Holdings: Bk Vols 7,378
SPRINGVILLE PUBLIC, 6496 US Hwy 11, Springville, 35146. SAN 374-6526. Tel: 205-467-2339. *Librn*, Connie Jo Rhudy
Library Holdings: Bk Vols 6,000; Per Subs 11
Friends of the Library Group
STEELE BRANCH, Rte 1, Box 548, Steele, 35987. SAN 330-339X. *Librn*, Jayne Ann Dearth; *Librn*, Jean Hunsucker
Library Holdings: Bk Vols 3,422
Bookmobiles: 1

ATHENS

C ATHENS STATE UNIVERSITY LIBRARY, 300 N Beaty St, 35611. SAN 300-0095. Tel: 256-233-8218. FAX: 256-233-6547. Web Site: www.athens.edu/library. *Dir*, Robert Burkhardt; E-Mail: burkhrr@athens.edu; *Cat*, Eugene Shockley; *Acq, Asst Dir*, Barbara Grigsby; *Circ*, Jonny Clendenon; *ILL*, Judy Stinnett; *Ref Serv*, Tim Williams; Staff 5 (MLS 5)
Founded 1842. Enrl 2,500; Fac 74; Highest Degree: Bachelor
Library Holdings: Bk Vols 102,475; Per Subs 317
Subject Interests: Local history, Rare books
Automation Activity & Vendor Info: (Acquisitions) DRA
Database Vendor: OCLC - First Search

Publications: Periodical Holdings List; WWW Resources by Subject
Partic in Library Management Network, Inc; Network of Alabama Academic Libraries; OCLC Online Computer Library Center, Inc; SE Libr Network
Friends of the Library Group

P ATHENS-LIMESTONE PUBLIC LIBRARY, 405 E South St, 35611. SAN 300-0087. Tel: 256-232-1233. FAX: 256-232-1250. *Dir*, Susan Todd; Staff 4 (MLS 1, Non-MLS 3)
Founded 1970
2000-2001 Income $281,000. Mats Exp $64,000. Sal $93,981
Library Holdings: Bk Vols 47,005; Per Subs 78
Special Collections: Nuclear Regulatory Commission, Local Public Document Coll
Automation Activity & Vendor Info: (Cataloging) DRA
Mem of Wheeler Basin Regional Library
Friends of the Library Group

S LIMESTONE COUNTY ARCHIVES, 310 W Washington St, 35611. SAN 373-3769. Tel: 256-233-6404. FAX: 256-233-6403. *Archivist*, Philip W Reyer; E-Mail: preyer@pclcable.com; *Archivist*, Sandra B Birdwell; E-Mail: sbirdwell@pclcable.com
Founded 1980
Oct 2000-Sep 2001 Income $88,000, County $86,000, Other $2,000. Mats Exp $14,450, Books $750, Per/Ser (Incl. Access Fees) $200, Presv $1,000, Micro $3,500, AV Equip $9,000. Sal $46,000
Library Holdings: Bk Vols 750
Special Collections: Walker-McClellan & Malvina Allen Moore
Friends of the Library Group

ATMORE

P ATMORE PUBLIC LIBRARY,* 700 E Church St, 36502. SAN 330-0153. Tel: 334-368-5234. FAX: 334-368-4130. E-Mail: library5@frontiernet.net. *Dir*, Joyce B Bolden; Staff 1 (MLS 1)
Founded 1923. Pop 15,000; Circ 27,197
Library Holdings: Bk Titles 50,000; Per Subs 54
Special Collections: Cancer & Heart Coll; Forestry (Atmores Industries Coll); Scout Books Coll
Friends of the Library Group

P ESCAMBIA COUNTY COOPERATIVE LIBRARY SYSTEM,* 700 E Church St, 36502. SAN 324-0754. Tel: 334-368-4130. FAX: 334-368-4130.; Staff 3 (MLS 1, Non-MLS 2)
Founded 1980
Library Holdings: Bk Vols 101,000
Special Collections: Alabama Room Coll; Audabon Print Coll; Madame Alexander Coll (Country Dolls of the World); Rare Book Coll
Special Services for the Blind - Talking book center
Books by mail service to Rural areas & Homebound

ATTALLA

P ATTALLA-ETOWAH COUNTY PUBLIC LIBRARY,* 604 N Fourth St, 35954. SAN 300-0109. Tel: 256-538-9266. FAX: 256-538-9223. *Dir*, Sue Cain; *Asst Librn*, Linda Bowen; E-Mail: lindabowen@hotmail.com
Founded 1967. Pop 8,000; Circ 14,284
Library Holdings: Bk Vols 23,000; Per Subs 72

AUBURN

P AUBURN PUBLIC LIBRARY, 161 N Ross St, 36830. SAN 300-0117. Tel: 334-887-4997. FAX: 334-887-4989. Web Site: www.auburnalabama.org/library. *Dir*, Margie Huffman; *Asst Dir*, Mary Simon; Staff 5 (MLS 4, Non-MLS 1)
Pop 40,000; Circ 133,465
Oct 1999-Sep 2000 Income $584,858, State $5,050, City $567,808, Other $12,000. Mats Exp $89,880, Books $59,000, Per/Ser (Incl. Access Fees) $14,000, AV Equip $16,880. Sal $391,695
Library Holdings: Bk Vols 43,900; Per Subs 119
Automation Activity & Vendor Info: (Cataloging) Gaylord; (Circulation) Gaylord; (Media Booking) Gaylord
Function: ILL available, Photocopies available, Reference services available
Mem of Horseshoe Bend Regional Library
Friends of the Library Group

AUBURN UNIVERSITY

C ARCHITECTURE Tel: 334-844-1752. FAX: 334-844-1756. *Librn*, Donna Anderson; Tel: 111-222-3333

C RALPH BROWN DRAUGHON LIBRARY, 231 Mell St, 36849. Tel: 334-844-4500. Interlibrary Loan Service Tel: 334-844-1728. Circulation Tel: 334-844-1701. Reference Tel: 334-844-1737. FAX: 334-844-4424. Interlibrary Loan Service FAX: 334-844-1753. Web Site: www.lib.auburn.edu/. *Dean of Libr*, Stella Bentley; *Asst Dean, Coll Develop*, Glenn Anderson; *Mgr*, Victor Bankston; Tel: 334-844-1712, E-Mail: banksvj@auburn.edu; *Cat*, Henry McCurley; *Acq*, Barbara A Nelson; *Asst Dean, Tech Servs*, Sherida Downer; *Asst Dean*, Harmon Straiton; Staff 51 (MLS 51)
Founded 1856. Enrl 21,778; Fac 1,145; Highest Degree: Doctorate
Oct 1999-Sep 2000 Income $11,429,970, State $24,856, Federal $74,782, Locally Generated Income $48,329, Parent Institution $10,863,868, Other $442,991. Mats Exp $10,220,052, Books $1,070,523, Per/Ser (Incl. Access Fees) $3,047,497, Presv $105,524, Other Print Mats $40,783. Sal $4,115,286 (Prof $2,366,533)
Library Holdings: Bk Vols 2,591,255; Per Subs 23,121
Subject Interests: Genealogy, Relig hist, Sports
Special Collections: Alabama Coll; Architecture Coll, slides; Auburn University Coll; US Government Publications; USGS Map Reference Coll
Automation Activity & Vendor Info: (Acquisitions) Endeavor; (Cataloging) Endeavor; (Circulation) Endeavor; (Serials) Endeavor
Mem of Asn of Research Libraries
Partic in BRS; CAS Online; Dialog Corporation; Nasa Libraries Information System - Nasa Galaxie; Nat Ground Water; Nat Libr of Med; RLIN; SDC Info Servs; SE Libr Network; USDC; Wilsonline

CM VETERINARY MEDICINE, 101 Greene Hall, 36849-5606. Tel: 334-844-1750. Circulation Tel: 334-844-1749. FAX: 334-844-1758. *Librn*, Yvonne Kovlowski; Staff 4 (MLS 1, Non-MLS 3)

G UNITED STATES FOREST SERVICE, Forest Engineering Research Library,* George W Andrews Forestry Sciences Lab, 520 Devall Dr, 36849-5418. SAN 373-3777. Tel: 334-826-8700. FAX: 334-821-0037.
Library Holdings: Bk Titles 10,000
Subject Interests: Forestry
Special Collections: Foreign publications; Forest Engineering; Forest operations literature

BAY MINETTE

P BAY MINETTE PUBLIC LIBRARY, 205 W Second St, 36507. SAN 300-0133. Tel: 334-580-1648. FAX: 334-937-0339. *Dir Libr Serv*, Charlotte J Cabaniss; E-Mail: ccabaniss@ci.bay-minette.al.us
Founded 1922. Pop 7,804; Circ 72,000
Oct 1999-Sep 2000 Income $363,954, State $10,146, City $133,808, Locally Generated Income $220,000. Mats Exp $22,708, Books $21,069, Per/Ser (Incl. Access Fees) $1,139, Electronic Ref Mat (Incl. Access Fees) $500. Sal $66,770 (Prof $32,500)
Library Holdings: Bk Vols 48,000; Per Subs 60
Subject Interests: Alabama, Genealogy
Automation Activity & Vendor Info: (Acquisitions) Athena; (Cataloging) Athena; (Circulation) Athena
Mem of Baldwin County Library Cooperative, Inc
Friends of the Library Group

J JAMES H FAULKNER STATE COMMUNITY COLLEGE, Austin R Meadows Library, 1900 Hwy 31 S, 36507. SAN 300-0141. Tel: 334-580-2145. FAX: 334-937-5140. *Dir*, Rheena Elmore; E-Mail: relmore@faulkner.cc.al.us; Staff 2 (MLS 2)
Founded 1965
Library Holdings: Bk Vols 54,000; Bk Titles 49,000; Per Subs 200; High Interest/Low Vocabulary Bk Vols 30
Automation Activity & Vendor Info: (Cataloging) Athena; (Circulation) Athena; (OPAC) Athena

BAYOU LA BATRE

P MOSE HUDSON TAPIA PUBLIC LIBRARY,* 13885 S Wintzell Ave, 36509. SAN 300-015X. Tel: 334-824-4213. E-Mail: tapialibrary@yahoo.com. *Librn*, Toni S Peppers
Library Holdings: Bk Vols 17,680; Per Subs 15

BESSEMER

P BESSEMER PUBLIC LIBRARY,* 400-19th St N, 35020. SAN 300-0168. Tel: 205-428-7882. FAX: 205-491-1480. E-Mail: bessemer@post.bham.lib.al.us. Web Site: www.bham.lib.al.us/bessemer. *Dir*, Carole McDowell Castine; E-Mail: ccastine@post.bham.lib.al.us; *Media Spec Ad*, Leslie Cost West; E-Mail: lwest@post.bham.lib.al.us; *Media Spec Ch*, Priscilla Renee Ward; E-Mail: pward@post.bham.lib.al.us; Staff 16 (MLS 2, Non-MLS 14)
Founded 1908. Pop 31,800; Circ 117,504
Oct 1999-Sep 2000 Income $552,984, State $27,228, City $491,756, Locally Generated Income $34,000. Mats Exp $172,100, Books $140,000, Per/Ser (Incl. Access Fees) $4,000, AV Equip $17,000, Electronic Ref Mat (Incl. Access Fees) $11,100. Sal $315,184
Library Holdings: Bk Vols 79,612; Bk Titles 79,460; Per Subs 123
Database Vendor: Ebsco - EbscoHost, IAC - Info Trac, Innovative Interfaces INN - View
Partic in Jefferson County Libr Coop

BIRMINGHAM

S ALABAMA POWER COMPANY RESEARCH SERVICES, 600 N 18th St, 35291-0277. (Mail add: PO Box 2641, 35291-0277), SAN 300-0184. Tel: 205-257-4466. FAX: 205-257-2075. *Res*, Sherie Mattox; E-Mail: samattox@

southernco.com; *Res*, Dawn Anderson; E-Mail: danderso@southernco.com; Staff 3 (MLS 2, Non-MLS 1)
Founded 1936
Library Holdings: Bk Vols 10,000; Bk Titles 8,000; Per Subs 50
Subject Interests: Business and management, Computer science, Engineering
Automation Activity & Vendor Info: (Acquisitions) EOS; (Cataloging) EOS; (Circulation) EOS; (Serials) EOS
Database Vendor: Dialog, Lexis-Nexis, ProQuest
Publications: New Acquisitions List; Newsletter
Partic in Solinet

M AMERICAN SPORTS MEDICINE INSTITUTE, Richard M Scrushy Library, 1313 13th St South, 35205. SAN 327-0327. Tel: 205-918-2131. FAX: 205-918-0800. Web Site: www.asmi.org. *Librn*, Susan Seay; E-Mail: susans@asmi.org
Library Holdings: Bk Titles 400; Per Subs 90
Subject Interests: Orthopedics
Partic in Alabama Health Libraries Association, Inc; Ga Health Scis Libr Asn; Jefferson County Hospital Librarians Association; Medical Libr Asn; Spec Libr Asn

S AMERICAN TRUCK HISTORICAL SOCIETY, Zoe James Memorial Library, 300 Office Park Dr Ste 120, 35223-2415. (Mail add: PO Box 531168, 35253-1168), Tel: 205-870-0566. FAX: 205-870-3069. E-Mail: aths@mindspring.com. Web Site: www.aths.org. *Mgr*, Larry L Scheef; *Archivist*, Maureen Palmer
Founded 1971
Library Holdings: Bk Titles 1,200; Per Subs 52; Spec Interest Per Sub 28
Special Collections: Ernie Sternberg - Sterling Truck; PIE; White Motor Company Archives
Publications: Antique Truck Registry (4th edition); ATHS Show Time; Wheels of Time (bi-monthly)

L BALCH & BINGHAM ATTORNEYS LIBRARY,* 1710 Sixth Ave N, PO Box 306, 35201. SAN 300-0192. Tel: 205-251-8100. FAX: 205-226-8798. E-Mail: lib-apco@balch.com. *Librn*, Terry Psarras; *Asst Librn*, Pam Acree; *Asst Librn*, Paula Webb; Staff 1 (MLS 1)
Library Holdings: Bk Vols 35,000; Per Subs 200
Restriction: Private library
Partic in Westlaw

M BIRMINGHAM BAPTIST MEDICAL CENTER PRINCETON, McMahon-Sibley Medical Library, 701 Princeton Ave, 35211. SAN 300-0206. Tel: 205-783-3078. FAX: 205-783-7076. *Dir*, Marian Morris
Founded 1945
Library Holdings: Bk Vols 2,000; Bk Titles 1,200; Per Subs 250
Partic in Alabama Health Libraries Association, Inc; RMLS

S BIRMINGHAM BOTANICAL GARDEN LIBRARY, 2612 Lane Park Rd, 35223. SAN 324-0061. Tel: 205-414-3920. FAX: 205-414-3906. Web Site: www.bbgardens.org. *Dir*, Gary Gerlach; *Librn*, Mindy Bodennamer; Staff 1 (MLS 1)
Founded 1973. Circ 3,000
Library Holdings: Bk Vols 6,000; Per Subs 150
Subject Interests: Horticulture
Automation Activity & Vendor Info: (OPAC) Innovative Interfaces Inc.
Partic in Jefferson County Libr Coop

S BIRMINGHAM EXPORT ASSISTANT CENTER,* Medical Forum Bldg Rm 707, 950 22nd St N, 35203-1128. SAN 370-2782. Tel: 205-731-1331. FAX: 205-731-0076. Web Site: www.usatrade.gov. *Dir*, George T Norton, Jr
Library Holdings: Bk Vols 175; Per Subs 10

S BIRMINGHAM MUSEUM OF ART, Clarence B Hanson Jr Library, 2000 Eighth Ave N, 35203-2278. SAN 300-0214. Tel: 205-254-2982. FAX: 205-254-2714. E-Mail: library@artsbma.org. Web Site: www.artsbma.org. *Adminr*, Grace Fealy Denson Reid; E-Mail: greid@artsbma.org; *Asst Librn*, Andrea Simpson Garrett; E-Mail: agarrett@artsbma.org. Subject Specialists: *Art*, Andrea Simpson Garrett; Staff 4 (MLS 2, Non-MLS 2)
Founded 1966
Library Holdings: Bk Vols 23,000; Bk Titles 21,500; Per Subs 100
Subject Interests: Art
Special Collections: Chellis Wedgwood Coll; The Dwight & Lucille Beeson Wedgwood Coll
Database Vendor: Ebsco - EbscoHost, GaleNet, OCLC - First Search, ProQuest, Wilson - Wilson Web
Restriction: Non-circulating
Function: For research purposes
Open Tues-Fri 10-12 & 1-4

S BIRMINGHAM NEWS, Reference Library,* 2200 Fourth Ave N, PO Box 2553, 35203. SAN 300-0222. Tel: 205-325-2409. FAX: 205-325-2495. *Librn*, Ann Hobbs; Staff 1 (MLS 1)
Founded 1950
Library Holdings: Bk Vols 1,000
Special Collections: Birmingham News 1888 - present, microfilm
Restriction: Not open to public

P BIRMINGHAM PUBLIC LIBRARY, 2100 Park Pl, 35203. SAN 330-0307. Tel: 205-226-3600. FAX: 205-226-3743. Web Site: www.bham.lib.al.us. *Dir*, Jack F Bulow; Tel: 205-226-3613, E-Mail: jack@bham.lib.al.us; *Assoc Dir*, Barbara Sirmans; Tel: 205-226-3614, E-Mail: barbara@bham.lib.al.us; *Coll Develop*, Deborah Dahlin; Tel: 205-226-3740, Fax: 205-226-3729; *Publ Servs*, Pamela Lyons; Tel: 205-226-3742, Fax: 205-226-3750; *Publ Servs*, Linda Wilson; Tel: 205-226-3746; *Automation Syst Coordr*, Phil Teague; Tel: 205-226-3701, Fax: 205-226-3703; *Res*, Anne Knight; Tel: 205-226-3742, Fax: 205-226-3743; *Br Coordr*, Sandra Crawley; Tel: 205-595-0714, Fax: 205-226-3750; *Br Coordr*, Virginia Guthrie; Tel: 205-786-6190, Fax: 205-226-3755; *Br Coordr*, Janine Langston; Tel: 205-322-6371, E-Mail: janine@bham.lib.al.us; *Br Coordr*, Jeffrey Northrup; Tel: 205-854-3700, Fax: 205-226-3765; *Br Coordr*, Marguerite Scott; Tel: 205-254-6449, Fax: 205-250-0725
Founded 1902. Pop 265,000; Circ 1,774,610
Jul 1998-Jun 1999 Income (Main Library and Branch Library) $12,890,311, State $229,270, City $12,391,041, County $270,000. Mats Exp $1,346,691, Books $966,517, Per/Ser (Incl. Access Fees) $141,500, Micro $197,674, Electronic Ref Mat (Incl. Access Fees) $41,000. Sal $8,657,229
Library Holdings: Bk Vols 973,936; Per Subs 2,810
Subject Interests: Genealogy
Special Collections: Ballet, Dance (Collins Coll of the Dance), bks, photog, programs; Cartography (Agee-Woodward Coll), bks, maps; Drama Coll; Early Children's Books (Hardie Coll); Genealogy, Southern History (Tutwiler Coll), bks, micro, pamphlets, per, VF; Philately (Scruggs Coll), bks, stamps, pamphlets; Rare Books (Bowron Coll)
Publications: A Bibliography of Birmingham, 1872-1972; A List of 19th Century Maps of the State of Alabama; A Singular Presence: Duard Le Grand, Newspaperman; Cemeteries of Jefferson County; Contemporary Literature in Birmingham: An Anthology; Creek Indian History; Eyewitness Accounts of the Civil War: Battle of the Crater; Five Cent Cotton: A Guide to the Collection of the Department of Archives & Manuscripts; Genealogical Research in the Tutwiler Collection of Southern History & Literature; George B Ward: Birmingham's Urban Statesman; Raid of the Confederate Calvary, Service of the Calvary in the Army of the Civil War & Synopsis of the Military Career of General Joseph Wheeler; Reprints of Robert Yates: Secret Proceedings of the Constitutional Convention; Research in Black History: A Guide to Resources; Rucker Agee Map Collection (16th, 17th & 18th Century); The Valley & The Hills: An Illustrated History of Birmingham & Jefferson County
Partic in Jefferson County Libr Coop
Special Services for the Deaf - TDD
Friends of the Library Group
Branches: 20
AVONDALE, 509 40th St, 35222. SAN 330-0390. Tel: 205-595-5821. FAX: 205-226-3750. Web Site: www.bham.lib.al.us. *Librn*, Sandra Crawley
Library Holdings: Bk Vols 56,708
EAST ENSLEY BRANCH, 900 14th St, Ensley, 35218. SAN 330-0455. Tel: 205-787-1928. FAX: 205-327-5360. Interlibrary Loan Service FAX: 205-785-7219. Web Site: www.bham.lib.al.us. *Librn*, Wilma Cottrell
Library Holdings: Bk Vols 30,225
EAST LAKE, 5 Oporto-Madrid Blvd, 35206. SAN 330-048X. Tel: 205-836-3341. FAX: 205-324-9861. Interlibrary Loan Service FAX: 205-833-8033. Web Site: www.bham.lib.al.us. *Librn*, Rochelle Sides-Renda
Library Holdings: Bk Vols 36,172
EASTWOOD, Eastwood Mall, 35210. SAN 330-0498. Tel: 205-591-4944. FAX: 205-595-3688. Web Site: www.bham.lib.al.us. *Librn*, Carla Starr
Library Holdings: Bk Vols 9,225
ENSLEY BRANCH, 1201 25th St, Ensley, 35218. SAN 330-051X. Tel: 205-785-2625. FAX: 205-785-6625. Web Site: www.bham.lib.al.us. *Librn*, Maxine Matthews
Library Holdings: Bk Vols 25,056
FIVE POINTS WEST, 4620 Avenue V, Ensley, 35208. SAN 330-0528. Tel: 205-780-8151. FAX: 205-226-3755. Web Site: www.bham.lib.al.us. *Librn*, Virginia Guthrie
Library Holdings: Bk Vols 54,672
INGLENOOK, 4100 N 40th Terrace, 35217. SAN 330-0595. Tel: 205-849-8739. FAX: 205-322-1088. Interlibrary Loan Service FAX: 205-841-2551. Web Site: www.bham.lib.al.us.
Library Holdings: Bk Vols 8,124
LITERACY, 730 Eighth Ave W, 35204. Tel: 205-322-6371. FAX: 205-322-7739. *Librn*, Janine Langston; E-Mail: janine@bham.lib.al.us
NORTH AVONDALE, 501 43rd St N, 35222. SAN 330-0544. Tel: 205-592-2082. FAX: 205-595-7392. Interlibrary Loan Service FAX: 205-595-9871. Web Site: www.bham.lib.al.us. *Librn*, Taneisha Chamblin
Library Holdings: Bk Vols 8,704
NORTH BIRMINGHAM, 2501 N 31st Ave, 35207. SAN 330-0633. Tel: 205-254-6454. FAX: 205-250-0725. *Librn*, Marguerite Scott
Library Holdings: Bk Vols 24,325
POWDERLY, 3301 Jefferson Ave SW, 35211. SAN 330-0684. Tel: 205-925-6178. FAX: 205-322-8752. Interlibrary Loan Service FAX: 205-923-3630. Web Site: www.bham.lib.al.us. *Librn*, Loretta Hasberry
Library Holdings: Bk Vols 13,869
PRATT CITY BRANCH, 1100 Hibernian St, Pratt City, 35214. SAN 330-0692. Tel: 205-798-5071. FAX: 205-791-3845. Web Site: www.bham.lib.al.us. *Librn*, Deborah Drake

Library Holdings: Bk Vols 14,465
SLOSSFIELD, 1916 25th Ct N, 35234. SAN 330-0722. FAX: 205-254-8817. *Assoc Dir*, Barbara Sirmans; Tel: 205-226-3614, Fax: 205-226-3743, E-Mail: barbara@bham.lib.al.us; *Govt Doc, Librn, Senior Librn*, Bettie Pruitt
Library Holdings: Bk Vols 16,774
SMITHFIELD, One Eighth Ave W, 35204. SAN 330-0757. Tel: 205-324-8428. FAX: 205-326-3135. Interlibrary Loan Service FAX: 205-254-8851. Web Site: www.bham.lib.al.us. *Librn*, Yolanda T Hardy
Library Holdings: Bk Vols 29,273
SOUTHSIDE, 1814 11th Ave S, 35205. SAN 330-0668. Tel: 205-933-7776. FAX: 205-918-0723. Web Site: www.bham.lib.al.us. *Librn*, Teresa Ceravolo
Library Holdings: Bk Vols 21,981
SPRINGVILLE ROAD, 1224 Springville Rd, 35215. SAN 330-0579. Tel: 205-856-0824. FAX: 205-226-3765. Web Site: www.bham.lib.al.us. *Librn*, Jeffrey Northrup
Library Holdings: Bk Vols 96,709
TITUSVILLE, 2 Sixth Ave SW, 35211. SAN 330-0781. Tel: 205-322-1140. FAX: 205-326-3646. Interlibrary Loan Service FAX: 205-328-2149. Web Site: www.bham.lib.al.us. *Librn*, Darlene Worford
Library Holdings: Bk Vols 14,215
WEST END, 1241 Tuscaloosa Ave SW, 35211. SAN 330-0811. Tel: 205-785-5518. FAX: 205-326-4121. Interlibrary Loan Service FAX: 205-780-5706. Web Site: www.bham.lib.al.us. *Librn*, Maya N Jones
Library Holdings: Bk Vols 15,010
WOODLAWN, 5709 First Ave N, 35212. SAN 330-0846. Tel: 205-595-2001. FAX: 205-595-7390. Interlibrary Loan Service FAX: 205-595-9654. Web Site: www.bham.lib.al.us. *Librn*, Darrell Blount
Library Holdings: Bk Vols 19,902
WYLAM BRANCH, 4300 Seventh Ave, Wylam, 35224. SAN 330-0870. Tel: 205-785-0349. FAX: 205-326-6012. Interlibrary Loan Service FAX: 205-781-6571. Web Site: www.bham.lib.al.us. *Librn*, Mary Ann Ellis
Library Holdings: Bk Vols 23,470
Bookmobiles: 2. Also have 1 bookvan

C BIRMINGHAM-SOUTHERN COLLEGE, Charles Andrew Rush Learning Center & N E Miles Library, 900 Arkadelphia Rd, PO Box 549020, 35254-9990. SAN 300-0230. Tel: 205-226-4740. Interlibrary Loan Service Tel: 205-226-4748. FAX: 205-226-4743. Web Site: www.bsc.edu. *Dir*, Billy Pennington; *Cat*, Janice J Poplau; *Head, Circ*, Eric Kennedy; Staff 12 (MLS 4, Non-MLS 8)
Founded 1856. Enrl 1,550; Fac 100; Highest Degree: Master
Library Holdings: Bk Vols 216,502; Bk Titles 164,217; Per Subs 1,040
Special Collections: Alabama Authors; Alabama History; Alabama Methodism; Americana
Automation Activity & Vendor Info: (Acquisitions) SIRSI
Partic in Network of Alabama Academic Libraries; SE Libr Network

L BRADLEY, ARANT, ROSE & WHITE, Law Library,* 2001 Park Pl, Ste 1400, 35203. SAN 300-0249. Tel: 205-521-8000. FAX: 205-521-8714. E-Mail: ldm@barw.com. *Head of Libr*, Lori D Martin
Library Holdings: Bk Vols 27,000
Restriction: Private library
Partic in Dialog Corporation; Westlaw

L BURR & FORMAN LIBRARY,* Southtrust Tower, Ste 3100, 420 20th St N, 35203. SAN 300-0419. Tel: 205-251-3000. FAX: 205-458-5100. *Librn*, Tim Lawson
Library Holdings: Bk Vols 18,000; Per Subs 25
Special Collections: Labor, Corporate law

M CALLAHAN EYE FOUNDATION HOSPITAL, John E Meyer Eye Library, 1720 University Blvd, 35233-1895. SAN 324-6523. Tel: 205-325-8505. *Librn*, Kenneth Tow
Library Holdings: Bk Titles 1,550; Per Subs 36
Subject Interests: Ophthalmology
Partic in Nat Libr of Med

M CARRAWAY METHODIST MEDICAL CENTER, Medical Library,* 1600 Carraway Blvd, 35234. SAN 300-0265. Tel: 205-502-6265. FAX: 205-502-5357. *Librn*, Bobby H Powell
Founded 1942
Library Holdings: Bk Vols 8,920; Per Subs 196
Subject Interests: Allied health, Medicine, Surgery
Restriction: Members only, Staff use only

GM DEPARTMENT OF VETERANS AFFAIRS, Medical Center Library Service (142D),* 700 S 19th St, 35233. SAN 300-0427. Tel: 205-933-8101, Ext 6474. FAX: 205-933-8101, Ext 6477. *Librn*, Jan Burns; E-Mail: burns.jan_p@forum.va.gov; *Tech Servs*, Jennifer Burt; Staff 3 (MLS 2, Non-MLS 1)
Founded 1952
1997-1998 Income $100,500. Mats Exp $94,000, Books $18,000, Per/Ser (Incl. Access Fees) $65,000
Library Holdings: Bk Titles 3,206; Per Subs 256
Publications: Newsletter
Partic in Dialog Corporation; Vets Admin Libr Network

SR INDEPENDENT PRESBYTERIAN CHURCH, John N Lukens Library, 3100 Highland Ave S, 35205-1400. SAN 328-5138. Tel: 205-933-1830. FAX: 205-933-1836. *Librn*, Ginni Robertson; Staff 7 (Non-MLS 7)
Library Holdings: Bk Vols 3,682
Special Collections: Theology & Bibles

GL JEFFERSON COUNTY LAW LIBRARY, 2121 Eighth Ave N, Ste 500, 35203-0072. SAN 300-029X. Tel: 205-325-5628. FAX: 205-322-5915. Web Site: www.jclawlib.org. *Librn*, Linda Marie Hand; E-Mail: hand@jcc.co.jefferson.al.us; *Tech Servs*, Dave B Lively; E-Mail: livelyd@jcc.co.jefferson.al.us; Staff 5 (MLS 1, Non-MLS 4)
Founded 1885
Oct 1999-Sep 2000 Income $507,477, County $110,250, Locally Generated Income $35,336, Other $361,891. Mats Exp $146,684, Books $53,182, Per/Ser (Incl. Access Fees) $5,999, Other Print Mats $2,209, Electronic Ref Mat (Incl. Access Fees) $85,294. Sal $143,658
Library Holdings: Bk Vols 55,148; Per Subs 78
Subject Interests: Law
Automation Activity & Vendor Info: (Cataloging) EOS

J JEFFERSON STATE COMMUNITY COLLEGE, James B Allen Library, 2601 Carson Rd, 35215-3098. SAN 300-0303. Tel: 205-856-8524. FAX: 205-856-8512. *Dir Libr Serv*, Dr William C Buchanan; Tel: 205-856-7785, E-Mail: bbuchan@jscc.cc.al.us; *Br Coordr*, Lynda Dickinson; Tel: 205-520-5930; *Circ*, Miriam Ford; Tel: 205-856-7788; *Ref*, Judy Dawson; Tel: 205-856-7786; Staff 8 (MLS 5, Non-MLS 3)
Founded 1965. Enrl 6,400; Highest Degree: Associate
Oct 1999-Sep 2000 Income $468,740. Mats Exp $108,040, Books $69,293, Per/Ser (Incl. Access Fees) $30,867, Presv $7,500, Micro $380, Electronic Ref Mat (Incl. Access Fees) $5,700. Sal $288,801 (Prof $201,182)
Library Holdings: Bk Vols 67,176; Per Subs 242
Automation Activity & Vendor Info: (Cataloging) SIRSI; (Circulation) SIRSI
Database Vendor: Ebsco - EbscoHost, OCLC - First Search, ProQuest
Publications: LRC (quarterly)

M L R JORDAN LIBRARY,* Ida V Moffett School of Nursing, 820 Montclair Rd, 35213. SAN 330-1052. Tel: 205-592-5103. FAX: 205-592-5861. *Coordr*, Roslyn Sewell
Founded 1922. Highest Degree: Bachelor
Library Holdings: Bk Vols 7,891; Bk Titles 8,000; Per Subs 80
Subject Interests: Nursing

J LAWSON STATE COMMUNITY COLLEGE LIBRARY,* 3060 Wilson Rd SW, 35221. SAN 320-5487. Tel: 205-925-2515, Ext 249. FAX: 205-929-6316. *Librn*, Cordell Adams; *Ref*, Mary Alyce Howard; *Automation Syst Coordr*, Gloria D Clark
Founded 1965. Enrl 700
Oct 1998-Sep 1999 Income $170,219, Federal $73,000. Mats Exp $70,000, Books $15,000, Per/Ser (Incl. Access Fees) $10,000, Micro $2,000
Library Holdings: Bk Vols 35,285; Per Subs 167
Special Collections: Martin Luther King Jr Afro-American Coll
Publications: annual report; Booktalk (newsletter); policy manual; student handbook
Friends of the Library Group

L MAYNARD, COOPER & GALE, Law Library,* Amsouth Harbert Plaza, Ste 2400, 1901 Sixth Ave N, 35203-2602. SAN 372-2627. Tel: 205-254-1993. FAX: 205-254-1999. *Dir*, Lorraine D Feld; E-Mail: feldlo@mcglaw.com; Staff 2 (MLS 1, Non-MLS 1)
Library Holdings: Bk Titles 10,000

C MILES COLLEGE, Learning Resources Center,* 5500 Myron Massey Blvd, 35064. (Mail add: PO Box 3800, 35208), SAN 300-0311. Tel: 205-929-1000. FAX: 205-929-1635. *Dir*, Geraldine Bell; *Publ Servs*, Kenneth Coachman; *Ref, Tech Servs*, Rose McLeod; *Tech Servs*, Gladys Madisson; *Media Spec*, Kim Gordon; *Per*, Patrice Tutt; *Publ Servs*, Lynne Bobbs
Founded 1905. Enrl 1,300; Fac 61; Highest Degree: Bachelor
1997-1998 Income $278,000. Mats Exp $111,200, Books $50,000, Per/Ser (Incl. Access Fees) $40,000, Micro $500, AV Equip $1,700, Other Print Mats $15,000, Manuscripts & Archives $1,000. Sal $85,531 (Prof $57,160)
Library Holdings: Bk Vols 97,000; Per Subs 365
Special Collections: Afro-American Coll; Instructional Materials Coll

P NORTH SHELBY COUNTY LIBRARY,* 5521 Cahaba Valley Rd, 35242. SAN 371-9367. Tel: 205-995-9931. FAX: 205-439-5503. *Dir*, Nancy Sims Donahoo
Library Holdings: Bk Vols 32,770; Per Subs 95
Mem of Harrison Regional Library System
Friends of the Library Group

S PEMCO AEROPLEX, INC, Engineering Technical Library,* Municipal Airport, PO Box 2287, 35201. SAN 300-0281. Tel: 205-591-7870. FAX: 205-591-5044. *Librn*, Belinda Holloway
Library Holdings: Bk Vols 500
Subject Interests: Technology

S RAYTHEON ENGINEERS & CONSTRUCTORS, INC,* Meadow Brook Corporate Park, 100 Corporate Pkwy, 35201-0101. (Mail add: PO Box 101, 35201-0101), SAN 300-032X. Tel: 205-995-6540. FAX: 205-995-6090. *Librn*, Calberta O Atkinson; E-Mail: cal_atkinson@ccgate.veci.com
Founded 1957
Library Holdings: Bk Vols 10,000; Per Subs 200
Subject Interests: Energy, Pulp and paper
Partic in Data Star; Dialog Corporation; OCLC Online Computer Library Center, Inc; Solinet

M SAINT VINCENT'S HOSPITAL, Cunningham Wilson Library, 810 St Vincent's Dr, 35202-2407. SAN 324-5306. Tel: 205-939-7830. FAX: 205-930-2182. E-Mail: xs00020@uabdpo.dpo.uab.edu. *Mgr*, C J Bryant; *Asst Librn*, Sister Anne-Marie; Staff 2 (MLS 1, Non-MLS 1)
Jul 1998-Jun 1999 Income $65,000. Mats Exp $35,548, Books $8,548, Per/Ser (Incl. Access Fees) $25,000. Sal $52,000
Library Holdings: Bk Vols 1,500; Per Subs 125
Subject Interests: Career develop, Consumer health, Nursing, Spiritual life
Partic in Jefferson County Hospital Librarians Association

C SAMFORD UNIVERSITY LIBRARY, 800 Lakeshore Dr, 35229. SAN 330-0900. Tel: 205-726-2846. Interlibrary Loan Service Tel: 205-726-2983. FAX: 205-726-2642. Web Site: www.samford.edu/library. *Dir*, Jean Thomason; *Librn*, Donna Fitch; *Automation Syst Coordr, Online Servs*, Ed Cherry; *Spec Coll*, Elizabeth Wells; *Coll Develop*, Sue Peterson; *Tech Servs*, Lynn Fetherston; *Circ*, Mike Hamilton; *Acq*, Marie Hooks; *Cat*, Tom Skinner; *Reader Servs*, Della Darbey; Staff 28 (MLS 10, Non-MLS 18)
Founded 1841. Highest Degree: Master
Library Holdings: Bk Vols 353,881; Per Subs 1,330
Special Collections: Alabama History & Literature, bks, maps, mss, newsp, microflm; Baptist History, bks, microfilm, mss; bks & critical works; Douglas McMurtrie, bks, pamphlets; Genealogy, per, bks, mss; Hearn; History & Genealogy (Casey Coll), bks, maps, mss; Irish; John Ruskin, first edition; Masefield first edition bks & critical works; Tennyson, first edition bks & critical works
Automation Activity & Vendor Info: (Acquisitions) VTLS
Publications: (S U Library Research Series, paper no.7); Folklore in the Samford University Library; History of Marion, Alabama, by Samuel A Townes (reprint of 1844 edition); Ireland, The Albert E Casey Collection & Other Irish Materials in the Samford University Library; Maps in the Samford University Library; Maud McLure Kelly, Alabama's First Woman Lawyer, by C Newman (S U Library Research Series, paper no.6)
Partic in Dialog Corporation; Network of Alabama Academic Libraries; SE Libr Network; VA Tech Libr Syst
Friends of the Library Group
Departmental Libraries:
LUCILLE STEWART BEESON LAW LIBRARY, 800 Lakeshore Dr, 35229. SAN 330-0994. Tel: 205-726-2714. FAX: 205-726-2644. *Dir, Librn*, Laurel R Clapp; *Acq*, Linda G Jones; *Cat*, Rebecca Hutto; *Ref*, Brenda K Jones; *Ref*, Edward L Craig, Jr; *Ser*, Robin McLendon; Staff 14 (MLS 7, Non-MLS 7)
Founded 1847. Enrl 636; Fac 30
Library Holdings: Bk Vols 180,505; Bk Titles 34,671; Per Subs 2,959
Partic in SE Libr Network
CURRICULUM MATERIALS CENTER, Beeson Education Bldg, 35229. SAN 330-096X. Tel: 205-726-2558. FAX: 205-726-2476. Web Site: www.samforduniversity.edu. *Dir*, Jan Baird; E-Mail: jkbaird@samford.edu
Library Holdings: Bk Titles 2,000
GLOBAL DRUG INFORMATION CENTER MCWHORTER SCHOOL OF PHARMACY, Ingalls Bldg, 35229. SAN 330-0935. Tel: 205-726-2161, 205-726-2891. FAX: 205-726-4012. *Dir*, Michael G Kendrach; *Librn*, Robert Schrimsher
Library Holdings: Bk Vols 1,150; Per Subs 60

L SIROTE & PERMUTT, PC, Law Library, 2311 Highland Ave S, PO Box 55727, 35205. SAN 326-3088. Tel: 205-930-5233. FAX: 205-930-5101. *Librn*, William Preston Peyton; E-Mail: ppeyton@sirote.com
Founded 1946
Library Holdings: Bk Vols 14,000
Database Vendor: Dialog, Lexis-Nexis
Restriction: Staff use only
Partic in AALL

CR SOUTHEASTERN BIBLE COLLEGE LIBRARY, 3001 Hwy 280 E, 35243. SAN 300-0346. Tel: 205-970-9233. FAX: 205-970-9207. E-Mail: info@sebc.edu. Web Site: www.sebc.edu. *Dir*, Rebecca Knight; E-Mail: rknight@sebc.edu
Founded 1935. Enrl 200; Fac 19; Highest Degree: Bachelor
Library Holdings: Bk Titles 37,000; Per Subs 180
Subject Interests: Education, Seminary
Partic in Asn of Christian Librs

S SOUTHERN COMPANY SERVICES, Corporate Research Library,* 42 Inverness Center Pkwy, 35242. SAN 300-0354. Tel: 205-992-7251. FAX: 205-992-6927. E-Mail: cilibrar@southerco.com. *In Charge*, Arnita Hines
Library Holdings: Bk Vols 10,000; Per Subs 500
Subject Interests: Business and management, Data processing, Electric power, Marketing
Publications: Brite Ideas Newsletter
Partic in Dialog Corporation

S SOUTHERN RESEARCH INSTITUTE, Thomas Martin Memorial Library, 2000 Ninth Ave S, 35255-5305. (Mail add: PO Box 55305, 35255-5305), SAN 300-0362. Tel: 205-581-2000, 205-581-2272. FAX: 205-581-2008. *Mgr, Online Servs*, Richard J Remy; E-Mail: r.remy@sri.org
Founded 1945
Library Holdings: Bk Vols 13,500; Per Subs 300
Subject Interests: Biology, Cancer, Chemistry, Engineering, Genetics, Mechanical engineering, Metallurgy, Microbiology, Physics, Pollution, Virology
Partic in CAS Online; Dialog Corporation

R TEMPLE EMANU-EL, William P Engel Library, 2100 Highland Ave, 35205. (Mail add: PO Box 55403, 35255), SAN 300-0397. Tel: 205-933-8037. FAX: 205-933-8099. *Librn*, Elinor Staff; E-Mail: elinorsue@aol.com
Founded 1914
Library Holdings: Bk Titles 4,500

UNIVERSITY OF ALABAMA AT BIRMINGHAM
CM DEPARTMENT OF ANESTHESIOLOGY LIBRARY, 619 19th St S, 35249-6810. SAN 324-5284. Tel: 205-934-4696. FAX: 205-975-5963. Web Site: www.anes.uab.edu. *Librn*, A J Wright; E-Mail: ajwright@uab.edu; Staff 1 (MLS 1)
Founded 1979
Library Holdings: Bk Vols 2,102; Per Subs 75
Subject Interests: Anesthesia, Critical care, Hist aspects of anesthesiology, Pain mgt, Res aspects of anesthesiology
Publications: A Core List of Anesthesia Monographs & Serials (semi-annual); Anesthesia & Critical Care Resources on the Internet (monthly); Serials Holdings List (semi-annual)
Partic in Dialog Corporation; Nat Libr of Med
CM LISTER HILL LIBRARY OF THE HEALTH SCIENCES, 1700 University Blvd, 35294-0013. (Mail add: 1530 Third Ave S, 35294-0013), SAN 330-1176. Tel: 205-934-5460. FAX: 205-934-3545. Web Site: www.uab.edu/lister. *Dir*, T Scott Plutchak; E-Mail: tscott@uab.edu; *Dep Dir*, Nancy W Clemmons; E-Mail: nclemmon@uab.edu; *Access Serv*, Jack Smith; E-Mail: jsmith@uab.edu; *Publ Servs*, Patricia Higginbottom; E-Mail: phiggin@uab.edu; *Automation Syst Coordr*, Tim Brown; E-Mail: tbrown@uab.edu; *Cat*, Valerie Gordon; E-Mail: vgordon@uab.edu; *Spec Coll*, Mike Flannery; E-Mail: flannery@uab.edu; *Tech Coordr*, Mike McBride; E-Mail: mmcbride@uab.edu; *Coll Develop*, Jay Harris; E-Mail: jharris@uab.edu; *Archivist*, Tim Pennycuff; E-Mail: archives@uab.edu; Staff 67 (MLS 14, Non-MLS 53)
Founded 1945. Highest Degree: Doctorate
Oct 1999-Sep 2000 Income $4,605,862. Mats Exp $1,426,009, Books $161,810, Per/Ser (Incl. Access Fees) $1,031,820. Sal $2,585,758
Library Holdings: Bk Vols 292,391; Bk Titles 92,761; Per Subs 1,860
Subject Interests: Allied health, Dentistry, Medicine, Nursing, Optometry, Public health
Special Collections: Alabama Museum of the Health Sciences; Reynolds Historical Library; UAB Archives
Automation Activity & Vendor Info: (Cataloging) epixtech, inc.; (Circulation) epixtech, inc.; (OPAC) epixtech, inc.; (Serials) epixtech, inc.
Database Vendor: epixtech, inc., IAC - Info Trac, OCLC - First Search, OVID Technologies
Publications: Lister Hill Letter; Newsletter of the Reynolds Library Assocs
Partic in Consortium Of Southern Biomedical Libraries (CONBLS); Network of Alabama Academic Libraries
Friends of the Library Group
C MERVYN H STERNE LIBRARY, 1530 Third Ave S, 35294-0014. Tel: 205-934-6364. Circulation Tel: 205-934-4338. Web Site: www.mhsl.uab.edu. *Dir, Librn*, Jerry W Stephens; Tel: 205-934-6360; *Tech Servs*, Susan Holt; Tel: 205-934-3512; *Ref*, Linda Harris; *Circ*, Jean Spradlin-Miller; Tel: 205-934-4338; *ILL*, Eddie Luster; *Coll Develop*, Paul H Spence; Tel: 205-934-6360; *Ref*, Richard H Harrison. Subject Specialists: *Bus*, Linda Harris; Staff 21 (MLS 16, Non-MLS 5)
Founded 1966. Enrl 16,252; Fac 406; Highest Degree: Doctorate
Oct 1999-Sep 2000 Income $5,621,750, Locally Generated Income $49,642, Parent Institution $5,572,108. Mats Exp $5,019,469, Books $627,145, Per/Ser (Incl. Access Fees) $1,253,314, Presv $61,218, AV Equip $36,500, Electronic Ref Mat (Incl. Access Fees) $274,927. Sal $1,825,784 (Prof $916,599)
Library Holdings: Bk Vols 1,375,339; Bk Titles 690,967; Per Subs 2,237
Special Collections: Proust Coll
Automation Activity & Vendor Info: (Acquisitions) Endeavor; (Cataloging) Endeavor; (Circulation) Endeavor; (Course Reserve) Endeavor; (ILL) Endeavor; (Media Booking) Endeavor; (OPAC) Endeavor; (Serials) Endeavor
Database Vendor: Dialog, Ebsco - EbscoHost, GaleNet, IAC - Info Trac, IAC - SearchBank, Lexis-Nexis, OCLC - First Search, ProQuest, Silverplatter Information Inc., Wilson - Wilson Web
Publications: Mervyn H Sterne Library Directions

Mem of Asn of Southeastern Research Libraries
Partic in Association Of Southeastern Research Libraries (ASERL); NAAL; SE Libr Network
Friends of the Library Group

BLOUNTSVILLE

P BLOUNTSVILLE PUBLIC LIBRARY,* 65 Chestnut St, 35031. (Mail add: PO Box 219, 35031), SAN 300-0443. Tel: 205-429-3156. FAX: 205-429-4806. *Head of Libr*, Yvonne Murphree; *Asst Librn*, Dorothy Yarbrough
Pop 1,400; Circ 23,000
Library Holdings: Bk Vols 22,737; Bk Titles 21,738; Per Subs 37
Subject Interests: Local history
Friends of the Library Group

BOAZ

P BOAZ PUBLIC LIBRARY,* 205 S Main St, 35957. SAN 300-0451. Tel: 256-593-8056. FAX: 256-593-8056. *Dir*, Doris Singleton; Staff 1 (MLS 1)
Founded 1971. Pop 8,000; Circ 10,000
Library Holdings: Bk Titles 40,000; Per Subs 100
Subject Interests: Alabama, Genealogy
Special Collections: Paperback Coll
Friends of the Library Group

J SNEAD STATE COMMUNITY COLLEGE, Virgil B McCain Learning Resource Center, 220 N Walnut, 35957. SAN 300-046X. Tel: 256-593-5120, Ext 274. FAX: 256-593-3098. Web Site: www.snead.cc.al.us/library/homepage/htm. *Dir*, Marsha V Taylor; E-Mail: mtaylor@snead.cc.al.us; *Asst Librn*, Dot Kennedy; *Asst Librn*, John Miller; Staff 3 (MLS 3)
Founded 1935. Enrl 1,676; Fac 40
Library Holdings: Bk Vols 36,640; Bk Titles 34,744; Per Subs 222
Special Collections: Alabama Authors (Borden Deal, Babs Deal, William B Huie, William Heath, Elise Sanguinetti, Thomas Wilkerson)

BRANTLEY

P BRANTLEY PUBLIC LIBRARY,* 9373 Main St, 36009. (Mail add: PO Box 13, 36009), SAN 300-0478. Tel: 334-527-8624. FAX: 334-527-3216. *Dir*, Margaret Colquett
Pop 1,151; Circ 4,207
Library Holdings: Bk Vols 3,519; Per Subs 24
Mem of Cross Trails Regional Library Service

BREWTON

P BREWTON PUBLIC LIBRARY, 206 W Jackson St, 36426. SAN 300-0494. Tel: 334-867-4626. FAX: 334-809-1749. E-Mail: bpl@brewton.escambia.net. Web Site: www.brewton.org/city/library. *Dir*, Brooke Walker; E-Mail: bwalker_1999-1942@yahoo.com; *Cat*, Wanda Wilson
Founded 1960. Pop 15,083; Circ 21,314
Oct 1999-Sep 2000 Income $240,370, State $7,200, City $173,170, Locally Generated Income $60,000. Mats Exp Books $10,000. Sal $106,120
Library Holdings: Bk Vols 44,500; Per Subs 48
Special Collections: Audubon Coll; Rare Books Coll; Wildflowers of Escambia County
Partic in Ethernet

J JEFFERSON DAVIS COMMUNITY COLLEGE, Leigh Library, 220 Alco Dr, 36426-2116. (Mail add: PO Box 958, 36427), SAN 300-0508. Tel: 334-809-1584. FAX: 334-867-7399. Web Site: www.jdcc.net. *Dir Libr Serv*, Jeffrey B Faust; E-Mail: jfaust@acet.net; *Tech Servs*, Kim Coale; Staff 3 (MLS 2, Non-MLS 1)
Founded 1965. Enrl 1,200
Library Holdings: Bk Vols 31,004
Special Collections: Alabama Coll; Local History & Genealogy Coll
Publications: Info Trac Health Reference Center
Partic in National Network Of Libraries Of Medicine - South Central Region

BRIDGEPORT

§P BRIDGEPORT PUBLIC LIBRARY, 116 Jim B Thomas Ave, 35740. (Mail add: PO Box 86, 35740-0086), Tel: 256-495-2259. FAX: 256-495-3611. E-Mail: blib@chattanooga.net. *Dir*, Charlean Rutherford
Oct 1998-Sep 1999 Income $25,422
Library Holdings: Bk Vols 7,697; Per Subs 23
Automation Activity & Vendor Info: (Acquisitions) Sagebrush Corporation; (Cataloging) Sagebrush Corporation; (Circulation) Sagebrush Corporation

G RUSSELL CAVE NATIONAL MONUMENT LIBRARY,* 3729 County Rd 98, 35740. SAN 323-6927. Tel: 256-495-2672. FAX: 256-495-9220. *In Charge*, William Springer
Founded 1962
Library Holdings: Bk Titles 400
Subject Interests: Archaeology

BRUNDIDGE

P TUPPER LIGHTFOOT MEMORIAL LIBRARY,* 164 S Main St, 36010. SAN 330-2911. Tel: 334-735-2145. *Dir*, Roslyn Holmes; *Librn*, Jean Carroll
Library Holdings: Bk Vols 17,300; Per Subs 36
Large print books & learning videos for day cares & schools

BUTLER

P CHOCTAW COUNTY PUBLIC LIBRARY,* 124 N Academy Ave, 36904. SAN 330-1206. Tel: 205-459-2542. FAX: 205-459-4122. E-Mail: ccpl@pinebelt.net. Web Site: www.pinebelt.net/~ccpl. *Dir*, Virginia Montgomery
Founded 1954. Pop 16,018; Circ 62,646
1998-1999 Income $107,000, State $18,000, City $25,000, County $5,000, Other $50,000. Mats Exp $15,000. Sal $51,421
Library Holdings: Bk Vols 72,000
Subject Interests: Alabama
Partic in SE Libr Network
Friends of the Library Group
Branches: 2
GILBERTOWN BRANCH, Gilbertown, 36908. (Mail add: 124 N Academy Ave, 36904), SAN 330-1230. *Librn*, Fay Cox
SILAS BRANCH, Silas, 36919. (Mail add: 124 N Academy Ave, 36904), SAN 330-1265. *Librn*, Fay Cox

CALERA

P CALERA PUBLIC LIBRARY,* 1241 17th Ave, PO Box 690, 35040. SAN 371-9340. Tel: 205-668-3514. FAX: 205-668-3514. E-Mail: cplib@mindspring.com. *Librn*, Janet Greathouse
Pop 4,000
1997-1998 Income $37,000, State $3,440. Mats Exp $2,400, Books $2,000, Per/Ser (Incl. Access Fees) $400. Sal $22,000
Library Holdings: Bk Vols 6,021; Per Subs 13
Mem of Harrison Regional Library System

CAMDEN

P WILCOX COUNTY LIBRARY,* 100 Broad St, 36726-1702. SAN 324-0738. Tel: 334-682-4355. FAX: 334-682-5437. *Dir*, Bettie Morgan; Staff 3 (MLS 1, Non-MLS 2)
Founded 1979. Pop 14,000
1997-1998 Income $119,334. Mats Exp $17,020. Sal $43,150
Library Holdings: Bk Titles 36,444; Per Subs 60
Special Collections: Alabamania Coll; Census Records Coll, micro; Genealogy Coll
Branches: 2
PINE APPLE BRANCH, 124 County Rd, No 59, Pine Apple, 36768. SAN 300-1881. *Librn*, Joyce Winters
Pop 298; Circ 763
Library Holdings: Bk Titles 5,000
PINE HILL BRANCH, 329 Church St, Pine Hill, 36769. SAN 324-2692. Tel: 334-963-4351. FAX: 334-963-4352. *Librn*, Brozime Morgan
Library Holdings: Bk Titles 10,000

CARBON HILL

P CARBON HILL CITY LIBRARY,* 414 NW Fifth Ave, PO Box 116, 35549. SAN 300-0524. Tel: 205-924-4254. *Dir, Librn*, Nancy Rhea Stewart; Staff 1 (MLS 1)
Founded 1931
Oct 1997-Sep 1998 Income $9,500. Mats Exp $9,800, Per/Ser (Incl. Access Fees) $80. Sal $4,500
Library Holdings: Bk Titles 4,505
Mem of Carl Elliott Regional Library System

CARROLLTON

P CARROLLTON PUBLIC LIBRARY,* Hwy 17 S, PO Box 92, 35447-0092. SAN 325-1551. Tel: 205-367-2142. Web Site: www.tusc.net/~cpl. *Librn*, Sue Yarbrough
Founded 1981. Pop 1,162; Circ 6,010
1997-1998 Income $23,959, State $1,394, City $15,000, Federal $5,000, Other $1,660. Mats Exp $3,264, Books $2,331, Per/Ser (Incl. Access Fees) $364. Sal $8,853 (Prof $7,995)
Library Holdings: Bk Titles 7,520; Per Subs 17
Open Mon, Wed & Thurs 12-5, Tues 9-3, Sat 9-12
Friends of the Library Group

§P PICKENS COUNTY COOPERATIVE LIBRARY HEADQUARTERS, Hwy 17 S, 35447. (Mail add: PO Box 489, 35447-0489), Tel: 205-367-8407. FAX: 205-367-8407. E-Mail: pccl@pickens.net. *Syst Coordr*, Susan Wolfe
Oct 1998-Sep 1999 Income $32,500, State $17,000, County $15,500
Library Holdings: Bk Vols 175

Special Collections: Pickens County Historical Coll
Automation Activity & Vendor Info: (Acquisitions) Sagebrush Corporation; (Cataloging) Sagebrush Corporation
Restriction: Not a lending library, Reference only to non-staff

CENTRE

P CHEROKEE COUNTY PUBLIC LIBRARY,* 310 Mary St, 35960. SAN 300-0532. Tel: 256-927-5838. FAX: 256-927-2800. *Librn*, Ginger White
Founded 1946. Pop 18,200; Circ 28,295
Library Holdings: Bk Vols 27,000; Bk Titles 26,000; Per Subs 15

CENTREVILLE

P BRENT-CENTREVILLE PUBLIC LIBRARY,* 20 Library St, 35042. SAN 300-0486. Tel: 205-926-4736. *Dir*, Cindy Suggs
Pop 16,000
Library Holdings: Bk Vols 15,000; Per Subs 16
Special Services for the Deaf - Captioned film depository
Friends of the Library Group

CHATOM

P WASHINGTON COUNTY PUBLIC LIBRARY,* Hwy 56 E, PO Box 1057, 36518. SAN 300-0540. Tel: 334-847-2097. FAX: 334-847-2098. *Dir*, Karen D Jessee; *Bkmobile Coordr*, Audrey Singleton; *Br Coordr*, Jenine Payne; *Coll Develop*, Cynthia Ciaburri
Pop 16,241; Circ 43,275
Library Holdings: Bk Vols 21,245; Per Subs 116
Subject Interests: Consumer health, Gardening
Special Collections: Washington County History Coll
Friends of the Library Group

CHEROKEE

§P CHEROKEE PUBLIC LIBRARY, 118 Church St, 35616. (Mail add: PO Box 333, 35616-0333), Tel: 256-359-4384. FAX: 256-359-4016. E-Mail: read@mail.getaway.net. *Head Librn*, Dorothy Todd; *Asst Librn*, Sheila Graham; Staff 2 (Non-MLS 2)
Circ 2,850
Library Holdings: Bk Vols 16,897
Special Services for the Blind - Bks on tape
Friends of the Library Group

CHICKASAW

P CHICKASAW CITY PUBLIC LIBRARY MEMORIAL LIBRARY, Ina Pullen Smallwood Memorial Library, 224 Grant St, 36611. (Mail add: PO Box 11449, 36671-0449), SAN 300-0559. Tel: 334-452-6465. FAX: 334-452-6465. E-Mail: smallwood@zebra.net. *Dir*, Barbara Jackson
Founded 1948. Pop 6,649; Circ 35,126
Library Holdings: Bk Vols 23,650; Per Subs 127

CHILDERSBURG

P EARLE A RAINWATER MEMORIAL LIBRARY,* 124 Ninth Ave SW, 35044. SAN 300-0567. Tel: 256-378-7239. FAX: 256-378-7239. E-Mail: bayridge@childersburg.org. *Dir*, Barbara Rich
Founded 1946. Pop 5,086; Circ 27,904
Library Holdings: Bk Vols 24,000; Per Subs 33
Mem of Cheaha Regional Library

CITRONELLE

P CITRONELLE MEMORIAL LIBRARY,* 7855 State St, 36522. SAN 300-0575. Tel: 334-866-7319. FAX: 334-866-7982. E-Mail: clib3@zebra.net. *Dir*, Debra Craft
Founded 1893. Pop 5,000; Circ 23,177
Library Holdings: Bk Titles 21,758; Per Subs 17

CLANTON

P CHILTON CLANTON LIBRARY, 100 First Ave, 35045. SAN 300-0583. Tel: 205-755-1768. FAX: 205-755-1374. E-Mail: ccpl@hiwaay.net. *Dir*, Mary Jo Abernathy
Founded 1963. Pop 34,197
Oct 1999-Sep 2000 Mats Exp $18,005, Books $12,265, Per/Ser (Incl. Access Fees) $4,240, AV Equip $1,500. Sal $117,358
Library Holdings: Bk Vols 58,831; Bk Titles 33,645; Per Subs 124
Subject Interests: Genealogy
Database Vendor: Ebsco - EbscoHost, OCLC - First Search
Partic in Birmingham Resource Ctr
Friends of the Library Group

Branches: 3
JEMISON PUBLIC LIBRARY, PO Box 609, Jemison, 35085. SAN 300-127X. Tel: 205-688-4492. *Librn*, Sandi L Drinkard
Founded 1945. Pop 1,828; Circ 3,669
Library Holdings: Bk Vols 557
MAPLESVILLE PUBLIC LIBRARY, 9400 Main St, AL Hwy 22, Maplesville, 36750. (Mail add: PO Box 9, Maplesville, 36750), SAN 300-1377. Tel: 334-366-4211. *Librn*, Evelyn Roebuck
Pop 754; Circ 3,099
Jan 1999-Dec 1999 Income City $500
Library Holdings: Bk Vols 127; Per Subs 4
THORSBY PUBLIC LIBRARY, PO Box 608, Thorsby, 35171. SAN 370-0909. Tel: 205-646-3575. *In Charge*, Debby Weldon

CLAYTON

P CLAYTON-TOWN & COUNTY LIBRARY, 45 N Midway St, PO Box 518, 36016. SAN 330-2946. Tel: 334-775-3506. FAX: 334-775-3506. E-Mail: tandclib@zebra.net. Web Site: towncountry.lib.al.us. *Dir*, Lois Warr
Library Holdings: Bk Vols 16,000; Per Subs 28
Friends of the Library Group

CLIO

P ELTON B STEPHENS LIBRARY,* 17 School St, 36017-9298. SAN 330-3012. Tel: 334-397-2911. E-Mail: ebslib@snowhill.com. *Librn*, Deborah Britt
Library Holdings: Bk Vols 1,500
Friends of the Library Group

COLLINSVILLE

P COLLINSVILLE PUBLIC LIBRARY,* 4299 Alabama Hwy 68, 35961-0743. (Mail add: PO Box 743, 35961-0743), SAN 376-740X. Tel: 256-524-2323. *Librn*, Jennifer Wilkins; E-Mail: jencollib@hotmail.com
Library Holdings: Bk Vols 6,000
Mem of DeKalb County Pub Libr

COLUMBIANA

P COLUMBIANA LIBRARY, 50 Lester St, 35051. (Mail add: PO Box 1459, 35051), SAN 321-6063. Tel: 205-669-5812. FAX: 205-669-5803. E-Mail: copl@mindspring.com. Web Site: www.shelby-al.org. *Dir, Head Librn*, Heather Johnston; E-Mail: hthrjhnstn@aol.com; Staff 3 (Non-MLS 3)
Pop 5,000
Library Holdings: Bk Titles 26,000; Per Subs 24
Mem of Harrison Regional Library System; Shelby County Regional Libr
Friends of the Library Group
Bookmobiles: 1

P HARRISON REGIONAL LIBRARY SYSTEM, 50 Lester St, 35051. SAN 330-129X. Tel: 205-669-3910 (Admin). Reference Tel: 205-669-3894 (Ref & ILL). FAX: 205-669-3940. E-Mail: info@shelbycounty-al.org. Web Site: www.shelbycounty-al.org. *Dir*, Barbara Roberts; Tel: 205-669-3893, E-Mail: director@shelbycounty-al.org; *Adminr*, Mary Hedrick; Tel: 205-669-3895, E-Mail: mhedrick@shelbycounty-al.org; *Mgr*, Kathy Arnett; Tel: 205-669-3891, E-Mail: karnett@shelbycounty-al.org; *Head Ref*, Cindy Reed; E-Mail: creed@shelbycounty-al.org; *Coll Develop, ILL, Ref*, Naomi Absher. Subject Specialists: *Reference*, Cindy Reed; *Syst mgt*, Mary Hedrick; Staff 12 (MLS 2, Non-MLS 10)
Founded 1940. Pop 140,000; Circ 590,000
Oct 1999-Sep 2000 Income $457,341, State $46,526, Federal $23,100, County $346,815, Locally Generated Income $5,500, Other $35,400. Mats Exp $32,000, Books $24,000, Per/Ser (Incl. Access Fees) $3,000, AV Equip $1,500, Electronic Ref Mat (Incl. Access Fees) $3,500. Sal $220,000 (Prof $45,000)
Library Holdings: Bk Vols 8,565; Bk Titles 8,032; Per Subs 53
Special Collections: Alabama & Shelby County History; George Washington Museum & Collection
Automation Activity & Vendor Info: (Cataloging) Gaylord; (Circulation) Gaylord; (OPAC) Gaylord
Database Vendor: Ebsco - EbscoHost, GaleNet, OCLC - First Search, ProQuest
Function: Some telephone reference
Member Libraries: Abbeville Memorial Library; Albert L Scott Library; Calera Public Library; Columbiana Library; Helena Public Library; Lallouise Florey McGraw Public Library; North Shelby County Library; Pelham Public Library; Wilsonville Public Library
Special Services for the Blind - Computers with Voice Synthesizer
Harrison Regional Library System is an administrative headquarters; for individual library statistical information, see individual listings

CORDOVA

P CORDOVA PUBLIC LIBRARY,* 130 Main St, 35550-5550. SAN 300-0605. Tel: 205-483-9578. FAX: 205-483-9578. *Librn*, Jimmie Ware
Library Holdings: Bk Vols 10,000; Per Subs 10
Mem of Carl Elliott Regional Library System

COTTONDALE

S AMERICAN COLLEGE OF HERALDRY LIBRARY, PO Box 710, 35453. SAN 326-0453.
Founded 1972
Library Holdings: Bk Titles 512
Subject Interests: Heraldry, History
Publications: The Armiger's News (quarterly); The Heraldic Register of America (occasional)
Restriction: Staff use only

COURTLAND

P COURTLAND PUBLIC LIBRARY,* 233 College St, PO Box 171, 35618-0171. SAN 376-7639. Tel: 256-637-9988. *Librn*, Dena Faye Eskridge
Library Holdings: Bk Vols 3,600
Mem of Wheeler Basin Regional Library

CROSSVILLE

§P CROSSVILLE PUBLIC LIBRARY, 80 Gaines St, 35962-3455. (Mail add: PO Box 308, 35962-0308), Tel: 205-528-2628. FAX: 256-528-2628. E-Mail: cplib@tds.net. *Librn*, Millie Bagwell
Oct 1999-Sep 2000 Income $6,484, State $1,484, City $2,000, County $2,500, Other $500
Library Holdings: Bk Vols 4,000
Automation Activity & Vendor Info: (Acquisitions) Brodart; (Cataloging) Brodart

CULLMAN

P CULLMAN COUNTY PUBLIC LIBRARY SYSTEM,* 200 Clark St NE, 35055. SAN 330-1567. Tel: 256-734-1068. FAX: 256-734-6902. E-Mail: ccpls@pcs-i.net. *Librn*, John Paul Myrick; *ILL*, Vivian Bailey; *Mgr*, Dorlene Daniel; *Tech Servs*, Wanda C Edge; *Ref*, Max Hand; *Ad Servs, Circ*, Lesia J Coleman; *Ch Servs, YA Servs*, Margaret W Wiley; Staff 7 (MLS 2, Non-MLS 5)
Founded 1928. Pop 71,278; Circ 121,000
Sep 1997-Aug 1998 Income $386,921. Mats Exp $37,641. Sal $229,067
Library Holdings: Bk Vols 78,529; Per Subs 128
Subject Interests: Alabama, Civil War
Special Collections: Genealogy (Daughters of the American Revolution Coll, United Daughters of the Confederacy Coll); Maps (Fuller Coll, Dan J Scott Coll); Photographs (Cullman-Johnson Coll, Hazel Karter-Daniel Coll)
Publications: A Friendly Reminder: Newletter of the Friends of CCPLS; programs calendar (quarterly)
Provides extension services in rural areas
Friends of the Library Group
Branches: 5
TOM BEVILL PUBLIC, 151 Byars Rd, Hanceville, 35077. SAN 330-1621. Tel: 205-287-1198.
Founded 1996. Pop 298
Library Holdings: Bk Vols 1,500; Per Subs 12
Subject Interests: Adult education, Afro-American
FAIRVIEW POET Tel: 205-796-5424. *Librn*, Bonnie Yarbrough
GARDEN CITY PUBLIC, Municipal Bldg, Hwy 31, Garden City, 35077. SAN 330-1591. Tel: 205-352-5408. FAX: 205-734-6902. *Mgr*, Althea Burnham
Founded 1946. Pop 604; Circ 5,504
Library Holdings: Bk Vols 5,200
Subject Interests: Local history
HANCEVILLE PUBLIC, 108 S Main St, Hanceville, 35077. SAN 377-7812. Tel: 205-352-6185. *Librn*, Sylvia Hicks
Bookmobiles: 1

DADEVILLE

P DADEVILLE PUBLIC LIBRARY,* 205 N West St, 36853. SAN 300-0613. Tel: 256-825-7820. FAX: 256-825-7820. E-Mail: dpl@lakemartin.net. *Librn*, Amy Huff
Founded 1907. Pop 3,263; Circ 43,728
1998-1999 Income $37,000. Mats Exp $5,926. Sal $24,970
Library Holdings: Bk Vols 16,642; Per Subs 13
Mem of Horseshoe Bend Regional Library
Friends of the Library Group

P HORSESHOE BEND REGIONAL LIBRARY,* 207 N West St, 36853. SAN 300-0621. Tel: 256-825-9232. FAX: 256-825-4314. E-Mail: hbrl@lakemartin.net. Web Site: www.mindspring.com/hbrl/hbrl.html. *Dir*, Susie Anderson; *Asst Dir*, Regina Strickland; *ILL*, Lorrie Harris Hammonds; Staff 3 (MLS 3)
Founded 1940. Pop 178,200
1997-1998 Income $231,919. Mats Exp $37,044
Library Holdings: Bk Vols 123,155; Per Subs 35
Member Libraries: Adelia McConnell Russell Library; Auburn Public Library; Dadeville Public Library; Goodwater Public Library; Lewis Cooper Junior Memorial Library & Arts Center; Millbrook Public Library; Rockford Public Library; Tallassee Community Library; Wetumpka Public Library
Partic in Academic Libraries of Brooklyn; Agricat; Veterans Affairs Library Network

DALEVILLE

P DALEVILLE PUBLIC LIBRARY,* 200 Warhawk Dr, 36322. SAN 330-3004. Tel: 334-503-9119. FAX: 334-503-9119. *Librn*, Kathryn Brown
1998-1999 Income $8,000. Mats Exp $7,000
Library Holdings: Bk Vols 18,000; Per Subs 20

DAPHNE

P DAPHNE PUBLIC LIBRARY, 2607 US Hwy 98, PO Box 1225, 36526. SAN 300-063X. Tel: 334-621-2818. FAX: 334-621-3086. E-Mail: daphlib3@bellsouth.net. Web Site: www.daphneal.com/. *Dir*, Dale Foster
Founded 1969. Pop 14,200; Circ 120,000
Oct 2000-Sep 2001 Income $392,641, State $17,739, City $349,065, Locally Generated Income $25,837. Mats Exp $69,539, Books $63,000, Per/Ser (Incl. Access Fees) $5,739, Presv $600, Electronic Ref Mat (Incl. Access Fees) $200. Sal $236,865 (Prof $83,885)
Library Holdings: Bk Vols 38,000; Bk Titles 36,700; Per Subs 71
Subject Interests: Local history
Automation Activity & Vendor Info: (Circulation) Athena
Mem of Baldwin County Library Cooperative, Inc
Friends of the Library Group

S UNITED STATES SPORTS ACADEMY LIBRARY,* One Academy Dr, 36526. SAN 324-5098. Tel: 334-626-3303, Ext 242. FAX: 334-626-1149. E-Mail: library@ussa-sport.ussa.edu. Web Site: www.sport.ussa.edu/library. *Librn*, Nancy Gray; Staff 3 (MLS 1, Non-MLS 2)
Enrl 220; Fac 11; Highest Degree: Doctorate
Library Holdings: Bk Vols 4,000; Bk Titles 3,600; Per Subs 247
Subject Interests: Fitness, Sport coaching, Sport med, Sport mgt, Sport research
Special Collections: Foreign Countries (International Coll), bks, flms, vf
Publications: Shelflist (monthly acquisitions list)
Partic in Nat Libr of Med; Network of Alabama Academic Libraries; OCLC Online Computer Library Center, Inc

DAUPHIN ISLAND

G DEPARTMENT OF CONSERVATION & NATURAL RESOURCES,* PO Box 189, 36528. SAN 327-8883. Tel: 334-861-2882. FAX: 334-861-8741. E-Mail: omrddi@gulftel.com. *Librn*, Don Bland
Library Holdings: Bk Vols 500

DECATUR

J CALHOUN COMMUNITY COLLEGE, Albert P Brewer Library, Hwy 31 N, 35609. (Mail add: PO Box 2216, 35609), SAN 330-1656. Tel: 256-306-2775. Circulation Tel: 256-306-2774. Reference Tel: 256-306-2777. FAX: 256-306-2780. Web Site: lib.calhoun.cc.al.us/lib. *Head Librn*, Lucinda M Beddow; Tel: 256-306-2784; *Librn*, Peggy D Campbell; Tel: 256-306-2564; *Head Ref*, Eva Randolph; *Coordr*, Phillip Parker; Tel: 256-306-2772, E-Mail: pep@calhoun.cc.al.us; *Cat*, Brenda P Sibley; Tel: 256-306-2778, E-Mail: bps@calhous.cc.al.us; Staff 8 (MLS 4, Non-MLS 4)
Founded 1965. Enrl 7,800; Fac 195; Highest Degree: Associate
Oct 1999-Sep 2000 Income $581,604, Locally Generated Income $11,471, Parent Institution $543,613, Other $26,520. Mats Exp $64,273, Books $18,168, Per/Ser (Incl. Access Fees) $15,741, Presv $1,250, Micro $955, Electronic Ref Mat (Incl. Access Fees) $28,159. Sal $378,532 (Prof $216,043)
Library Holdings: Bk Vols 49,881; Bk Titles 36,286; Per Subs 177
Subject Interests: Human resources
Special Collections: Alabama Coll; Center for the Study of Southern Political Culture
Automation Activity & Vendor Info: (Acquisitions) DRA; (Cataloging) DRA; (Circulation) DRA; (OPAC) DRA
Database Vendor: DRA, Ebsco - EbscoHost, GaleNet, ProQuest
Publications: Newsletter (twice per year)
Partic in Library Management Network, Inc
Special Services for the Blind - Screen enlargement software for people with visual disabilities

SR CENTRAL UNITED METHODIST CHURCH LIBRARY,* 616 Jackson St SE, 35601. SAN 373-3785. Tel: 256-353-6941. *Librn*, Betty Tull
Library Holdings: Bk Vols 5,000

S MONSANTO CHEMICAL GROUP, Technical Center Library,* PO Box 2204, 35609. SAN 300-0648. Tel: 256-552-2011.
Founded 1960
Library Holdings: Bk Vols 3,500; Bk Titles 2,500; Per Subs 200
Subject Interests: Chemical engineering, Chemistry, Polymer chemistry, Textiles
Restriction: Staff use only

G NORTH CENTRAL ALABAMA REGIONAL COUNCIL OF GOVERNMENTS LIBRARY,* 216 Jackson St, PO Box C, 35602. SAN 373-3793. Tel: 256-355-4515. FAX: 256-351-1380.
Subject Interests: Planning

P WHEELER BASIN REGIONAL LIBRARY, Decatur Public Library, 504 Cherry St NE, 35602-1970. (Mail add: PO Box 1766, 35602-1766), SAN 300-0656. Tel: 256-353-2993. FAX: 256-350-6736. *Dir*, Susan Delmas; *AV, Automation Syst Coordr*, Leslie Richard; *Ch Servs*, Jean Pace Hovey; *Circ*, Cathy Smothers; *ILL*, Jennifer Humiston; *Ref*, Margarete Lange; *Tech Servs*, Linda Dotzheimer; Staff 26 (MLS 3, Non-MLS 23)
Founded 1905. Pop 199,404; Circ 510,950
Oct 1999-Sep 2000 Income $1,253,317, State $235,729, City $473,000, Federal $36,675, County $170,240, Locally Generated Income $337,673. Mats Exp $261,588, Books $218,284, Per/Ser (Incl. Access Fees) $43,304
Library Holdings: Per Subs 273
Subject Interests: Genealogy, Local history
Database Vendor: DRA
Publications: INDEX-Friends of the Library Newsletter
Member Libraries: Athens-Limestone Public Library; Courtland Public Library; Eva Public Library; Falkville Public Library; Hartselle Public Library; Lawrence County Public Library
Friends of the Library Group

DEMOPOLIS

P MARENGO LIBRARY SYSTEM, Demopolis Public Library, 211 E Washington, 36732. SAN 300-0664. Tel: 334-289-1595. FAX: 334-289-8260. E-Mail: dpl@westal.net. *Dir*, Lindsy Gardner; *Asst Librn*, Ouida Kane; Staff 1 (MLS 1)
Founded 1922. Pop 25,000; Circ 41,170
Library Holdings: Bk Titles 23,307; Per Subs 66
Subject Interests: Genealogy
Special Collections: Demopolis History Coll
Friends of the Library Group

DORA

P DORA PUBLIC LIBRARY,* Dora Town Hall, 1485 Sharon Blvd, PO Box 700, 35062. SAN 300-0672. Tel: 205-648-3211. FAX: 205-648-3399. *Librn*, Janiece Chandler
Library Holdings: Bk Vols 4,241
Mem of Carl Elliott Regional Library System

DOTHAN

J GEORGE C WALLACE STATE COMMUNITY COLLEGE, Learning Resources Center, Rte 6 Box 62, 36303. SAN 300-0680. Tel: 334-983-3521, Ext 225. Toll Free Tel: 800-543-2426. TDD: 800-548-2546. FAX: 334-983-3600. Web Site: www.wallace.edu. *Dir*, Megan Johnson; E-Mail: mjohnson@wcc.cc.al.us; Staff 7 (MLS 3, Non-MLS 4)
Founded 1965. Enrl 3,800; Highest Degree: Associate
Sep 1998-Aug 1999 Mats Exp $334,000, Books $170,000, AV Equip $8,000, Electronic Ref Mat (Incl. Access Fees) $45,000. Sal $205,000 (Prof $135,000)
Library Holdings: Bk Vols 40,000; Bk Titles 35,000; Per Subs 350
Subject Interests: Alabama, Allied health, Aviation, Genealogy, Nursing
Automation Activity & Vendor Info: (Acquisitions) Endeavor; (Cataloging) Endeavor; (Circulation) Endeavor; (Course Reserve) Endeavor; (OPAC) Endeavor; (Serials) Endeavor

P HOUSTON LOVE MEMORIAL LIBRARY,* 212 W Burdeshaw St, PO Box 1369, 36302. SAN 330-1710. Tel: 334-793-9767. FAX: 334-793-6645. *Dir*, Bettye Forbus; *Asst Dir*, Dana Drumbelow; *Reader Servs*, Myrtis Merrow; *ILL, Ref*, Susan Veasey; *Ch Servs*, Anne McKee; *AV*, Brenda Muhammud; *Circ*, Glenda Cain; Staff 11 (MLS 4, Non-MLS 7)
Founded 1900. Pop 84,000; Circ 317,074
1997-1998 Income $825,530. Mats Exp $148,098, Books $121,658, Per/Ser (Incl. Access Fees) $18,665, Micro $476, Other Print Mats $20. Sal $433,320 (Prof $156,748)
Library Holdings: Bk Vols 181,952; Per Subs 282
Automation Activity & Vendor Info: (Circulation) SIRSI
Friends of the Library Group

Branches: 3
ASHFORD BRANCH, Sixth Ave, Ashford, 36312. SAN 330-1745. Tel: 334-899-3121. *Librn*, Gerry Rice
Library Holdings: Bk Vols 15,716; Bk Titles 15,040

P DIVISION FOR THE BLIND & PHYSICALLY HANDICAPPED, PO Box 1369, 36302. SAN 330-1729. Tel: 334-793-9767. *Librn*, Glenda Cain; *Librn*, Myrtis Merrow; Staff 2 (MLS 2)
Founded 1971. Circ 5,499
Special Collections: reference materials on blindness & other handicaps; Religious books on cassette & disc

ROSSIE PURCELL BRANCH, PO Box A2, Columbia, 36319. SAN 330-177X. Tel: 334-696-4417. *Librn*, Judy Potts
Library Holdings: Bk Vols 10,076; Bk Titles 9,517
Bookmobiles: 2

M SOUTHEAST ALABAMA MEDICAL CENTER, Medical Library, 1108 Ross Clark Circle, Hwy 84 E, 36301-3024. (Mail add: PO Box 6987, 36302-6987), SAN 320-362X. Tel: 334-793-8102. FAX: 334-793-8157. *Dir*, Pat McGee
Founded 1964
Library Holdings: Bk Titles 705; Per Subs 100
Subject Interests: Clinical medicine
Restriction: Staff use only
Partic in SE-Atlantic Regional Med Libr Servs

C TROY STATE UNIVERSITY DOTHAN LIBRARY, 501 University Dr, 36303. (Mail add: PO Box 8368, 36304), SAN 300-0885. Tel: 334-983-6556, Ext 320. Circulation Tel: 334-983-6556, Ext 323. Reference Tel: 334-983-6556, Ext 321. FAX: 334-983-6327. Web Site: www.tsud.edu. *Dir*, Julia Smith; Tel: 334-983-6556, Ext 320, E-Mail: jsmith@tsud.edu; *Media Spec*, Christopher Bryant; Tel: 334-983-6556, Ext 393, E-Mail: cbryant@tsud.edu; *Circ*, Daphne Harker; Tel: 334-983-6556, Ext 323, E-Mail: dharker@tsud.edu; *ILL, Per*, Mary McCruter; Tel: 334-983-6556, Ext 322, E-Mail: mmccruter@tsud.edu; *Spec Coll & Archives*, Tina Bernath; Tel: 334-983-6556, Ext 324, E-Mail: tbernath@tsud.edu; *Ref*, Donna Miller; Tel: 334-983-6556, Ext 321, E-Mail: dmiller@tsud.edu; *Per*, Rachel Hodges; *Tech Servs*, Robbin Glaser; Tel: 334-983-6556, Ext 325, E-Mail: rglase@tsud.edu; Staff 7 (MLS 3, Non-MLS 4)
Founded 1973. Enrl 1,864; Fac 95; Highest Degree: Master
1997-1998 Income $429,734, State $425,415. Mats Exp $140,409, Books $52,531, Per/Ser (Incl. Access Fees) $64,938, Presv $500, Micro $22,440. Sal $206,641 (Prof $123,007)
Library Holdings: Bk Vols 92,826; Bk Titles 91,560; Per Subs 869
Subject Interests: Business and management, Computer science, Criminal law and justice, Education, History, Personnel management
Special Collections: Annual Reports; College Catalogs; Microfiche: Slavery Documents; PCMI
Automation Activity & Vendor Info: (Cataloging) SIRSI; (Circulation) SIRSI; (Course Reserve) SIRSI; (OPAC) SIRSI
Database Vendor: Ebsco - EbscoHost, GaleNet, IAC - Info Trac, OCLC - First Search, ProQuest, Silverplatter Information Inc.
Publications: Library News
Partic in Network of Alabama Academic Libraries

DOUBLE SPRINGS

P DOUBLE SPRINGS PUBLIC LIBRARY, Blake Dr, PO Box 555, 35553. SAN 300-0699. Tel: 205-489-2412. FAX: 205-489-2412. *Librn*, Jean Overton
Library Holdings: Bk Vols 9,000
Mem of Carl Elliott Regional Library System
Open Mon-Thurs 9-5, Sat 9-12

EAST TALLASSEE

P TALLASSEE COMMUNITY LIBRARY,* 102 Freeman Ave, PO Box 671, 36023. SAN 300-2195. Tel: 334-283-2732. FAX: 334-283-2732. E-Mail: library@tallassee.net. *Librn*, William C Bryant
Pop 5,500; Circ 18,750
1997-1998 Income $19,750, State $5,000, Provincial $8,500, City $6,000, Locally Generated Income $250. Mats Exp $11,000, Books $7,500, Per/Ser (Incl. Access Fees) $1,400, Other Print Mats $2,100. Sal $14,100
Library Holdings: Bk Titles 19,210; Per Subs 12
Mem of Horseshoe Bend Regional Library

ELBA

P ELBA PUBLIC LIBRARY, 406 Simmons St, 36323. SAN 300-0710. Tel: 334-897-6921. FAX: 334-897-6921. E-Mail: elibrary@alaweb.com. Web Site: www.alaweb.com/~elibrary/index.htm. *Librn*, Kay Wilson; Staff 1 (MLS 1)
Pop 4,355; Circ 17,484
1999-2000 Income $53,056, State $10,650, City $34,358, Locally Generated Income $8,048. Mats Exp $16,107, Books $7,600, Per/Ser (Incl. Access Fees) $1,040, Micro $3,050, AV Equip $888, Other Print Mats $3,050,

Electronic Ref Mat (Incl. Access Fees) $479. Sal $33,636 (Prof $15,746)
Library Holdings: Bk Titles 20,459; Per Subs 28
Mem of Cross Trails Regional Library Service
Friends of the Library Group

ENTERPRISE

P ENTERPRISE PUBLIC LIBRARY, 101 E Grubbs St, 36330. SAN 300-0729. Tel: 334-347-2636. FAX: 334-393-6477. E-Mail: entplib@sanman.net. Web Site: www.enterprise-pub-library.net. *Dir*, Peggy B Samuels; *Asst Dir*, Warren Truitt; *Acq*, Jo Thompson; *Ch Servs*, Mary Rollins; *Circ*, Kay Knop; *Circ*, Margaret Gorum
Pop 22,000; Circ 82,000
Oct 1998-Sep 1999 Income $187,454, State $34,944, City $116,000, Federal $31,510, County $5,000, Locally Generated Income $47,188. Mats Exp $37,713, Books $34,112, Per/Ser (Incl. Access Fees) $3,600. Sal $89,495 (Prof $23,000)
Library Holdings: Bk Vols 35,000; Per Subs 70
Subject Interests: Alabama
Special Collections: Audio Books, Large Print, Videos
Automation Activity & Vendor Info: (Acquisitions) TLC; (Cataloging) TLC; (Circulation) TLC
Special Services for the Blind - Audio-cassettes; Large print bks
Friends of the Library Group

J ENTERPRISE STATE JUNIOR COLLEGE, Learning Resource Center,* 600 Plaza Dr, 36331. (Mail add: PO Box 1300, 36331), SAN 300-0737. Tel: 334-347-2623, Ext 271. FAX: 334-347-2623, Ext 306. E-Mail: escsss01@asc.edu. Web Site: www.esjc.cc.al.us/lrc_hp.htm. *Dir*, Susan Sumblin; *Bibliog Instr, Ref*, Jean Southwell; *Tech Servs*, Linda Stephens; *Automation Syst Coordr, Media Spec*, Brian Grimmer; Staff 3 (MLS 3)
Founded 1966. Enrl 1,925; Fac 52
1998-1999 Income $300,086. Mats Exp $37,075, Books $10,000, Per/Ser (Incl. Access Fees) $9,200, Presv $875, Micro $15,800, Other Print Mats $1,200. Sal $198,964
Library Holdings: Bk Vols 49,000; Per Subs 370
Subject Interests: Genealogy
Partic in OCLC Online Computer Library Center, Inc; SE Libr Network

R SAINT LUKE UNITED METHODIST CHURCH LIBRARY,* 201 Heath St, 36330. SAN 300-0745. Tel: 334-393-3879.
Library Holdings: Bk Vols 1,600

EUFAULA

P EUFAULA CARNEGIE LIBRARY, 217 N Eufaula Ave, 36027. SAN 330-3039. Tel: 334-687-2337. FAX: 334-687-8143. Web Site: www.zebra.net/~ecl/index.htm. *Librn*, Darryl Heritage
Library Holdings: Bk Vols 30,000; Per Subs 86
Friends of the Library Group

EVA

P EVA PUBLIC LIBRARY,* PO Box 99, 35621-0099. SAN 376-7647. Tel: 256-796-8638. *Librn*, Bonnie Holmes
Library Holdings: Bk Vols 12,000
Mem of Wheeler Basin Regional Library
Friends of the Library Group

EVERGREEN

P EVERGREEN-CONECUH PUBLIC LIBRARY,* 201 Park St, 36401. SAN 300-0753. Tel: 334-578-2670. FAX: 334-578-2316. *Librn*, Vern Steenwyk
Pop 15,500; Circ 27,000
Library Holdings: Bk Vols 34,000; Per Subs 91
Subject Interests: Genealogy
Special Collections: Heritage Section

FAIRFIELD

P WALTER J HANNA MEMORIAL LIBRARY,* 4615 Gary Ave, 35064. SAN 300-0761. Tel: 205-783-6007. FAX: 205-967-5376. *Dir*, Maftie Jackson; *Librn*, Yvonne Hollis
Circ 12,179
1998-1999 Income $299,107, State $7,448, City $266,300, Other $14,245. Mats Exp $48,710, Books $42,627, Per/Ser (Incl. Access Fees) $4,000, Micro $2,083. Sal $165,788 (Prof $41,500)
Library Holdings: Bk Vols 25,297; Per Subs 28

FAIRHOPE

P FAIRHOPE PUBLIC LIBRARY, 161 N Section St, 36532-2490. SAN 300-0788. Tel: 334-928-7483. Interlibrary Loan Service Tel: 334-947-7632. FAX: 334-928-9717. E-Mail: library@fairhope.com. *Dir*, Betty F Suddeth; *YA Servs*, Kathy Stone; *Librn*, Susan Diemert; *Librn*, Krick Ilse; *Librn*, Patricia Gipson; Staff 9 (MLS 2, Non-MLS 7)
Founded 1894. Pop 12,758; Circ 160,140
Oct 1999-Sep 2000 Income $280,200, State $14,200, City $240,000, Locally Generated Income $26,000. Mats Exp $60,000, Books $42,000, Per/Ser (Incl. Access Fees) $5,800, AV Equip $12,000, Other Print Mats $200. Sal $173,720 (Prof $60,000)
Library Holdings: Bk Vols 52,188; Bk Titles 52,188; Per Subs 128; High Interest/Low Vocabulary Bk Vols 99; Bks on Deafness & Sign Lang 21
Subject Interests: Local history, Theosophy
Special Collections: Alabama Poetry (Frances Ruffin Durham); Area History Coll; Local Authors Coll
Publications: Alabama A to Z
Mem of Baldwin County Library Cooperative, Inc
Open Wed 1-6
Friends of the Library Group

FALKVILLE

P FALKVILLE PUBLIC LIBRARY,* 17 North Ave, 35622-0407. (Mail add: PO Box 407, 35622-0407), SAN 376-737X. Tel: 256-784-5822. E-Mail: irbohn@yahoo.com. *Librn*, Irene Bohn
Library Holdings: Bk Vols 3,000
Mem of Wheeler Basin Regional Library

FAYETTE

J BEVILL STATE COMMUNITY COLLEGE, Learning Resources Center, 2631 Temple Ave N, 35555. SAN 300-0796. Tel: 205-932-3221, Ext 5141. FAX: 205-932-8821. Web Site: www.bevillst.cc.al.us. *Head Librn*, Sally Middleton; E-Mail: samiddleton@bevillst.cc.al.us; Staff 1 (MLS 1)
Founded 1969. Enrl 1,600; Fac 30
Library Holdings: Bk Vols 40,000
Special Collections: Albert P Brewer Coll
Database Vendor: Ebsco - EbscoHost, GaleNet, OCLC - First Search, ProQuest
Publications: BSCC LRC Handbook
Information reported includes 3 campuses: Brewer, Hamilton & Walker

P FAYETTE COUNTY MEMORIAL LIBRARY,* 326 Temple Ave N, 35555. SAN 300-080X. Tel: 205-932-6625. FAX: 205-932-4152. *Dir*, Gwen Lacey
Founded 1923. Circ 29,438
1997-1998 Income $64,000
Library Holdings: Bk Vols 35,000; Per Subs 35
Special Collections: Alabama Room, including Census Records through 1900; Genealogy Coll

FLOMATON

P FLOMATON PUBLIC LIBRARY,* 608 McCurdy St, 36441. SAN 300-0818. Tel: 334-296-3552. FAX: 334-296-3552. E-Mail: fplib@net1inc.net. *Librn*, Faye Knowles
Pop 1,800; Circ 18,073
Library Holdings: Bk Vols 16,680; Bk Titles 16,280; Per Subs 26

FLORALA

P FLORALA PUBLIC LIBRARY,* 510 N Fourth St, 36442. SAN 300-0826. Tel: 334-858-3525. FAX: 334-858-3525. E-Mail: floralapl@cyou.com. *Dir*, Barbara Parker; *Asst Librn*, Judy Petrey
Founded 1935. Pop 2,665; Circ 14,368
1998-1999 Income $41,990. Mats Exp $10,850. Sal $23,125
Library Holdings: Bk Vols 11,553; Per Subs 43
Special Collections: Historic photographs of Florala, AL
Mem of Cross Trails Regional Library Service

FLORENCE

P FLORENCE-LAUDERDALE PUBLIC LIBRARY, 218 N Wood Ave, 35630-4706. SAN 300-0834. Tel: 256-764-6564. FAX: 256-764-6629. E-Mail: library@florence.org. Web Site: www.library.florence.org. *Dir*, Elisabeth G South; E-Mail: egsouth@yahoo.com; *Asst Dir*, Terrye S Terry; E-Mail: terryeterry@yahoo.com. Subject Specialists: *Adult fiction*, Elisabeth G South; *Juvenile fiction*, Elisabeth G South; Staff 16 (MLS 2, Non-MLS 14)
Founded 1945. Pop 80,000; Circ 170,000
Oct 1999-Sep 2000 Income $506,000, State $69,000, City $352,115, County $32,500, Locally Generated Income $50,000. Mats Exp $86,000, Books $64,000, Per/Ser (Incl. Access Fees) $10,000, AV Equip $9,000. Sal $270,000 (Prof $50,000)
Library Holdings: Bk Vols 81,000; Bk Titles 78,000; Per Subs 130
Subject Interests: Genealogy, Local history
Automation Activity & Vendor Info: (Cataloging) DRA; (Circulation) DRA
Database Vendor: DRA, Ebsco - EbscoHost, OCLC - First Search,

ProQuest
Mem of Lauderdale County Regional Libr
Partic in Library Management Network, Inc
Friends of the Library Group

C UNIVERSITY OF NORTH ALABAMA, Collier Library, 100 Wesleyan Ave, Box 5028, 35632-0001. SAN 300-0850. Tel: 256-765-4241. Circulation Tel: 256-765-4467. Reference Tel: 256-765-4469. FAX: 256-765-4438. Web Site: www2.una.edu/library. *Dean of Libr*, Dr G Garry Warren; E-Mail: gwarren@unanov.una.edu; *Bibliog Instr*, Amy Gordon; Tel: 256-765-4266; *Ref*, Norman Elsner; Tel: 256-765-4473; *Syst Coordr*, Myra Harscheid; Tel: 256-765-4466; *Web Coordr*, Phillip Oliver; Tel: 256-765-4559; *ILL*, Celia Reynolds; Tel: 256-765-4625; *Archivist*, Cecile Nabors; Tel: 256-765-4468; *Per*, Marilyn Johnson; *Coll Develop*, Wayne O'Neal; Tel: 256-765-4470, E-Mail: woneal@unanov.una.edu; *Circ*, Doris McDaniel; Tel: 256-765-4669; Staff 12 (MLS 11, Non-MLS 1)
Founded 1830. Enrl 4,733; Fac 249
Oct 1999-Sep 2000 Income $2,061,230. Mats Exp $568,638, Books $129,537, Per/Ser (Incl. Access Fees) $212,262, Presv $11,529, Micro $58,056, AV Equip $41,201, Other Print Mats $27,604, Electronic Ref Mat (Incl. Access Fees) $88,449. Sal $1,321,300 (Prof $541,034)
Library Holdings: Bk Vols 343,468; Bk Titles 241,165; Per Subs 2,551
Subject Interests: Business and management, Education, History, Humanities, Nursing, Social sciences and issues
Special Collections: Alabama Historical Coll; Congressman Flippo Coll; Local History Archives
Automation Activity & Vendor Info: (Acquisitions) Endeavor; (Cataloging) Endeavor; (Circulation) Endeavor; (Course Reserve) Endeavor; (ILL) Endeavor; (Media Booking) Endeavor; (OPAC) Endeavor; (Serials) Endeavor
Database Vendor: Ebsco - EbscoHost, GaleNet, IAC - Info Trac, OCLC - First Search, ProQuest, Silverplatter Information Inc.
Publications: Pathfinder Series Finding Aids (Reference guide)
Function: ILL available
Partic in Network of Alabama Academic Libraries; SE Libr Network

FOLEY

P FOLEY PUBLIC LIBRARY,* 319 E Laurel Ave, 36535. SAN 300-0869. Tel: 334-943-7665. FAX: 334-943-8637. *Dir*, Donna Soto; E-Mail: dsoto@hotmail.com; Staff 7 (MLS 1, Non-MLS 6)
Founded 1923. Pop 6,000; Circ 110,054
Sep 1998-Oct 1999 Income $256,186, State $7,411, City $226,186, Locally Generated Income $22,589. Mats Exp Books $26,000
Library Holdings: Bk Vols 35,404; Per Subs 70
Subject Interests: Alabama, Genealogy
Mem of Baldwin County Library Cooperative, Inc
Friends of the Library Group

FORT PAYNE

P DE KALB COUNTY PUBLIC LIBRARY, 504 Grand Ave NW, 35967. SAN 300-0877. Tel: 256-845-2671. FAX: 205-845-2671. *Dir*, Elizabeth Tucker; *Asst Librn*, Yvonne Toombs
Circ 91,610
Oct 1998-Sep 1999 Income $240,102, City $73,202, Federal $64,000, County $68,500, Locally Generated Income $35,000. Mats Exp $43,900, Books $41,500, Per/Ser (Incl. Access Fees) $2,400. Sal $132,000 (Prof $32,000)
Library Holdings: Bk Vols 73,000; Per Subs 35
Subject Interests: Indians, Local history
Special Collections: Indian Coll
Automation Activity & Vendor Info: (Cataloging) DRA; (Circulation) DRA; (OPAC) DRA
Database Vendor: DRA
Partic in Library Management Network, Inc
Open Mon 10-8, Tues-Fri 10-6, Sat 10-3
Bookmobiles: 1

FORT RUCKER

UNITED STATES ARMY
AM AEROMEDICAL RESEARCH LABORATORY SCIENCE SUPPORT CENTER (Mail add: PO Box 620577, 36362-0577), Tel: 334-255-6907. Interlibrary Loan Service Tel: 334-255-6936. Reference Tel: 334-255-6936. FAX: 334-255-6067. *Dir*, Diana L Hemphill; *Ref*, Sharon A Fales; E-Mail: sharon.fales@sc.amedd.army.mil; Staff 2 (MLS 2)
Founded 1963
Library Holdings: Bk Titles 15,000; Per Subs 170
Subject Interests: Aviation med, Biomedical engineering, Mathematics, Medicine, Optics, Psychology, Statistics
Partic in BRS; Defense Technical Information Center; Dialog Corporation; Docline; OCLC Online Computer Library Center, Inc

A AVIATION CENTER LIBRARY, Bldg 212, 36362. SAN 330-1869. Tel: 334-255-9772. FAX: 334-255-1567. *Librn*, Leslie R Waltman Jr; *Ref*, Martha Lewis; Staff 6 (MLS 2, Non-MLS 4)
Founded 1954
Library Holdings: Bk Vols 70,000; Bk Titles 67,000; Per Subs 112
Subject Interests: German (Language)
Partic in BRS

A AVIATION TECHNICAL LIBRARY, Bldg 5906 & 5907, Fifth Ave & Skychief St, 36362. SAN 330-1923. Tel: 334-255-3177. FAX: 334-255-2838. E-Mail: atzqdptl@rucker.army.mil, redingtonj@rucker.army.mil. Web Site: www-rucker.army.mil/techlib/althome.htm. *Dir*, Beverly M Warf; E-Mail: warfb@rucker.army.mil; *Publ Servs*, Jill E Redington; *Ref*, Sherry Miller; Staff 3 (MLS 3)
Founded 1955
Library Holdings: Bk Vols 33,000; Bk Titles 31,244; Per Subs 431
Subject Interests: Aviation, Computer science, Military history
Special Collections: Army Regulations; DTIC Technical Reports; FAA Regulations
Publications: ATL Bulletin; Periodical Holdings List; specialized bibliographies
Partic in Defense Technical Information Center; Dialog Corporation; Nasa Libraries Information System - Nasa Galaxie; OCLC Online Computer Library Center, Inc; Wilsonline
College Cat, Lesson Plans, Poi's; Department of Army Publication & Military Standard/Specifications

AM MEDICAL LIBRARY, Lyster US Army Community Hospital, Bldg 301, 36362-5333. SAN 330-1931. Tel: 334-255-7350. FAX: 334-255-7714. Web Site: www.rucker.amedd.army.mil/lindex.htm. *Librn*, Mary Fran Prottsman; E-Mail: protts@entercomp.com
Library Holdings: Bk Vols 2,500; Bk Titles 2,000; Per Subs 148
Subject Interests: Clinical medicine, Dentistry
Partic in OCLC Online Computer Library Center, Inc

FULTONDALE

P FULTONDALE PUBLIC LIBRARY,* 1015 Walkers Chapel Rd, 35068. SAN 300-0893. Tel: 205-849-6335. FAX: 205-327-5692. E-Mail: fulton@bham.lib.al.us. Web Site: www.fultondale.lib.al.us. *Dir*, Christi Ware
Pop 7,000; Circ 42,000
Oct 1997-Sep 1998 Income $116,000
Library Holdings: Bk Vols 25,000; Per Subs 52

GADSDEN

R FIRST PRESBYTERIAN CHURCH OF GADSDEN LIBRARY,* 530 Chestnut St, PO Box 676, 35902-0676. SAN 300-0923. Tel: 256-547-5747. FAX: 256-547-5789. *Dir*, Brenda Hardeman
Founded 1960
Library Holdings: Bk Vols 3,000; Per Subs 10

J GADSDEN STATE COMMUNITY COLLEGE, Meadows Library, 1001 George Wallace Dr, 35902-0227. (Mail add: PO Box 227, 35902-0227), SAN 324-3435. Tel: 256-549-8333. Interlibrary Loan Service Tel: 256-549-8411. Reference Tel: 256-549-8411. FAX: 256-549-8401. Web Site: www.gadsdenst.cc.al.us/library/. *Branch Mgr*, Pat Norman; Tel: 256-549-8548, E-Mail: pnorman@gadsdenst.cc.al.us; *Head Librn*, Mary Dothard Cooper; Tel: 256-549-8410, E-Mail: mcooper@gadsdenst.cc.al.us; *Ref*, Melinda Jackson Harvey; Tel: 256-549-8412, E-Mail: mharvey@gadsdenst.cc.al.us; *Tech Servs*, Dorothy Burgess; Tel: 256-549-8496, E-Mail: dmburgess@gadsdenst.cc.al.us; Staff 8 (MLS 4, Non-MLS 4)
Founded 1965. Enrl 5,400; Fac 125
Oct 1999-Sep 2000 Income Parent Institution $500,197. Mats Exp $56,310, Books $28,322, Per/Ser (Incl. Access Fees) $13,107, Presv $881, Micro $14,000. Sal $327,611 (Prof $229,108)
Library Holdings: Bk Vols 107,041; Per Subs 325
Subject Interests: Alabama, Law, Southern lit
Special Collections: Gadsden State Archives
Automation Activity & Vendor Info: (Cataloging) DRA; (Circulation) DRA; (ILL) DRA; (OPAC) DRA
Database Vendor: DRA, Ebsco - EbscoHost, GaleNet, OCLC - First Search, ProQuest, Wilson - Wilson Web
Publications: Faculty Handbook; Library Skills Handbook; New-Acquisitions (annual); Student Handbook
Partic in Library Management Network, Inc
Special Services for the Blind - Low vision aids & talking readers

P GADSDEN-ETOWAH COUNTY LIBRARY, Gadsden Public Library, 254 College St, 35999-3101. SAN 330-1958. Tel: 256-549-4699. FAX: 256-549-4766. E-Mail: gpl@gadsden.com. Web Site: www.library.gadsden.com, www.lmn.lib.al.us. *Dir Libr Serv*, Rebecca Sledge Mitchell; *Circ*, Paula Spears; *Cat*, Phyllis Massenburg; *Res*, Barbara Reed; *Cat*, Dee Singleton; *ILL*, Paulette Makary; *Automation Syst Coordr*, Anita Brooks; Staff 25 (MLS 1, Non-MLS 24)
Founded 1906. Pop 103,975; Circ 252,593
Oct 1999-Sep 2000 Income (Main Library and Branch Library) $1,216,404, State $91,344, City $994,565, Federal $10,000, County $100,000, Other $20,495. Mats Exp $307,426, Books $128,998, Per/Ser (Incl. Access Fees) $8,500, Presv $2,684, Micro $26,411, Other Print Mats $140,833. Sal $762,205
Library Holdings: Bk Vols 195,232; Bk Titles 159,327

Subject Interests: Genealogy
Special Collections: Alabama History
Automation Activity & Vendor Info: (Cataloging) DRA; (Circulation) DRA; (ILL) DRA; (OPAC) DRA
Database Vendor: DRA, Ebsco - EbscoHost, GaleNet, OCLC - First Search
Publications: Ebsco Host
Partic in Library Management Network, Inc
Branches: 3
ALABAMA CITY, 2700 W Meighan Blvd, 35904. SAN 330-1982. Web Site: www.library.gadsden.com.; Staff 2 (Non-MLS 2)
CARVER MEMORIAL, 1030 Tuscaloosa Ave, 35901. SAN 330-2040. Web Site: www.library.gadsden.com.; Staff 1 (Non-MLS 1)
EAST GADSDEN, 919 Wilson St, 35903. SAN 330-2016. Web Site: www.library.gadsden.com.; Staff 1 (Non-MLS 1)

M RIVER REGIONAL HOSPITAL LIBRARY,* PO Box 268, 35999. SAN 375-6645. Tel: 256-543-5200. FAX: 256-543-5888.
Library Holdings: Bk Titles 250
Subject Interests: Nursing
Restriction: Not open to public

GARDENDALE

P GARDENDALE PUBLIC LIBRARY,* 995 Mt Olive Rd, 35071. SAN 300-0958. Tel: 205-631-6639. FAX: 205-631-0146. Web Site: www.gardendale.lib.al.us. *Coll Develop, Dir*, Wilma Burden; E-Mail: wburden@bham.lib.la.us; *Asst Dir*, Connie Smith; *Admin Assoc*, Vicki Morgan; *Cat*, Alice Cowart; *Cat*, Lisa Keith; *Ch Servs*, Lou Ellen Nichols; *Circ*, Angie Coburn; *Circ*, Sandy Bowman; *Circ*, Betty Williams
Founded 1959. Pop 15,000; Circ 119,350
Library Holdings: Bk Vols 43,655; Per Subs 120
Publications: Booklist; Library Journal; Public Libraries; Wilson Library Bulletin
Partic in Jefferson County Library System

GENEVA

P EMMA KNOX KENAN PUBLIC LIBRARY,* 312 S Commerce St, 36340-0550. (Mail add: PO Box 550, 36340-0550), SAN 300-0966. Tel: 334-684-2459. FAX: 334-684-2459. E-Mail: emma@alaweb.com. *Librn*, Carolyn Forehand
Pop 4,866; Circ 36,000
Library Holdings: Bk Vols 12,000; Per Subs 25
Mem of Cross Trails Regional Library Service

GERALDINE

P GERALDINE PUBLIC LIBRARY,* 13543 Alabama Hwy 227, 35974-0268. SAN 376-6454. Tel: 256-659-6663. FAX: 256-659-6663. *Librn*, Connie Taylor
Library Holdings: Bk Vols 15,429
Mem of DeKalb County Pub Libr

GOODWATER

P GOODWATER PUBLIC LIBRARY,* 36 Weogufka St, 35072. (Mail add: PO Box 140, 35072), SAN 300-0974. Tel: 256-839-5741. FAX: 256-839-5741. E-Mail: goodwaterl@wwisp.com. *Librn*, Judy Olmstead
Founded 1945. Pop 1,840; Circ 2,932
Library Holdings: Bk Vols 8,174; Bk Titles 7,999
Mem of Horseshoe Bend Regional Library

GORDO

P GORDO PUBLIC LIBRARY,* 287 Main St, 35466. (Mail add: PO Box 336, 35466), SAN 300-0982. Tel: 205-364-7148. FAX: 205-364-7148. E-Mail: gordolib@pickens.net. *Dir*, Melba Hollingsworth
Pop 4,250; Circ 10,500
Library Holdings: Bk Vols 7,500
Friends of the Library Group

GRANT

P GRANT PUBLIC LIBRARY,* PO Box 401, 35747-0401. SAN 376-5628. Tel: 256-728-5128. FAX: 256-728-5128. E-Mail: readme@neph.org. *Librn*, Beth Hilliard
Library Holdings: Bk Vols 13,738
Mem of Marshall County Cooperative Library
Friends of the Library Group

GRAYSVILLE

P GRAYSVILLE PUBLIC LIBRARY,* 315 S Main St, 35073. SAN 300-0990. Tel: 205-674-3040. FAX: 205-674-3296. *Librn*, Judy Moore
Founded 1978
Library Holdings: Bk Vols 12,000; Per Subs 45
Mem of Birmingham Pub & Jefferson County Free Libr Syst

GREENSBORO

P HALE COUNTY PUBLIC LIBRARY,* 1105 Main St, PO Box 399, 36744. SAN 300-1008. Tel: 334-624-3409. E-Mail: hcpl@westal.net. *Librn*, Carolyn Hemstreet; *Asst Librn*, Katherine Rugg; Staff 2 (Non-MLS 2)
Founded 1925. Pop 15,475
1997-1998 Income $25,000. Mats Exp $24,000
Library Holdings: Bk Titles 11,371; Per Subs 25
Special Collections: Alabama history & literature; Genealogy (area families)
Automation Activity & Vendor Info: (Cataloging) Athena; (Circulation) Athena
Friends of the Library Group

GREENVILLE

G BUTLER COUNTY HISTORICAL-GENEALOGICAL SOCIETY LIBRARY,* PO Box 561, 36037. SAN 375-8346. Tel: 334-382-3216. *Dir*, Judy Taylor
Library Holdings: Bk Titles 500; Per Subs 50

§P GREENVILLE-BUTLER COUNTY PUBLIC LIBRARY, 309 Ft Dale St, 36744-0399. Tel: 334-382-3216. FAX: 334-382-9769. E-Mail: gbcpl@alaweb.com. *Dir*, Burke McFerrin
Library Holdings: Bk Vols 40,000; Per Subs 55

GROVE HILL

P GROVE HILL PUBLIC LIBRARY,* 108 Dubose Ave, 36451. SAN 300-1016. Tel: 334-275-8157. FAX: 334-275-8157. E-Mail: grovelibrary@tds.net. *Librn*, Anita Long
Pop 2,266; Circ 10,800
Library Holdings: Bk Vols 19,000; Per Subs 25
Special Collections: Census Rec; Family Research

GULF SHORES

P THOMAS B NORTON PUBLIC LIBRARY,* 221 W 19th Ave, 36542. SAN 300-1024. Tel: 334-968-1176. FAX: 334-968-1184. E-Mail: gslibr@gulftel.com. *Librn*, Betty Wyman; Staff 6 (MLS 1, Non-MLS 5)
Founded 1963. Pop 4,900
Oct 1998-Sep 1999 Income $179,353, State $5,400, City $169,953, Other $4,000. Mats Exp $29,150, Books $25,000, Per/Ser (Incl. Access Fees) $4,150. Sal $112,800 (Prof $38,000)
Library Holdings: Bk Vols 33,000; Per Subs 135
Subject Interests: History
Special Collections: Alabama Room
Automation Activity & Vendor Info: (Acquisitions) Athena; (Cataloging) Athena; (Circulation) Athena; (OPAC) Athena
Mem of Baldwin County Library Cooperative, Inc
Friends of the Library Group

GUNTERSVILLE

P GUNTERSVILLE PUBLIC LIBRARY, 1240 O'Brig Ave, 35976. SAN 300-1032. Tel: 256-571-7595. FAX: 256-571-7596. E-Mail: books@netnav.com. *Coll Develop, Dir*, Joanne Savoie
Founded 1947. Pop 10,343; Circ 75,400
Oct 1999-Sep 2000 Income $224,491, State $10,491, City $181,000, Federal $8,000, Locally Generated Income $25,000. Mats Exp $35,018, Books $28,035, Per/Ser (Incl. Access Fees) $3,500, Other Print Mats $2,783, Electronic Ref Mat (Incl. Access Fees) $700. Sal $105,600 (Prof $50,000)
Library Holdings: Bk Vols 49,000; Per Subs 75
Special Collections: Genealogical materials of Marshall County; Historical Coll of Guntersville's newspapers
Automation Activity & Vendor Info: (Circulation) Sagebrush Corporation
Publications: Friends Newsletter; Library Notes (newsletter)
Mem of Alabama Library Exchange, Inc; Marshall County Cooperative Library
Friends of the Library Group

HALEYVILLE

P HALEYVILLE PUBLIC LIBRARY,* 913 20th St, 35565. SAN 300-1040. Tel: 205-486-7450. FAX: 205-486-7450. E-Mail: haleylib@sonet.net. *Librn*, Jacqulyn Arthur

Library Holdings: Bk Vols 10,000; Per Subs 45
Mem of Carl Elliott Regional Library System
Open Mon-Fri 8-5, Sat 9-12
Friends of the Library Group

HARTFORD

P HARTFORD PUBLIC LIBRARY,* 203 W Main St, 36344. SAN 300-1059. Tel: 334-588-2384. FAX: 334-588-2384. E-Mail: hpl@entercomp.ocm. *Dir*, Beverly McDuffie; *Asst Dir*, Dana Wesson
Pop 2,649; Circ 14,280
Library Holdings: Bk Vols 16,168; Per Subs 26
Mem of Cross Trails Regional Library Service

HARTSELLE

P HARTSELLE PUBLIC LIBRARY,* 152 NW Sparkman St, 35640. SAN 300-1067. Tel: 256-773-9880. FAX: 256-773-9884. *Librn*, Wendy Congiardo; *Asst Librn*, Robyn Carnes
Pop 10,860; Circ 47,280
Library Holdings: Bk Vols 24,153; Per Subs 38
Special Collections: William Bradford Huie Coll
Publications: Friends of the Library Newsletter
Mem of Wheeler Basin Regional Library
Friends of the Library Group

HAYNEVILLE

§P HAYNEVILLE-LOWNDES COUNTY PUBLIC LIBRARY, 4 Washington St, 36040. (Mail add: PO Box 425, 36040-0425), Tel: 334-548-2686. FAX: 334-548-2686. *Dir*, Jimmie Felder
Oct 1999-Sep 2000 Income $36,000, State $13,000, Other $22,000
Library Holdings: Bk Vols 18,229; Per Subs 36; High Interest/Low Vocabulary Bk Vols 100

HEADLAND

P BLANCHE R SOLOMON MEMORIAL LIBRARY,* 17 Park St, 36345. SAN 330-3063. Tel: 334-693-2706. FAX: 334-693-5023. Web Site: web.snowhill.com/~dede/index.html. *Librn*, Betty S Arnett; *Asst Librn*, Dede Coe; E-Mail: dede@snowhill.com
Nov 1997-Oct 1998 Income $63,000. Mats Exp $12,801. Sal $36,516
Library Holdings: Bk Vols 21,447; Per Subs 35

HEFLIN

P CHEAHA REGIONAL LIBRARY,* 935 Coleman St, 36264. SAN 320-1430. Tel: 256-463-7125. FAX: 256-463-7128. E-Mail: crl2@gte.net. *Dir*, Evi Jones; *Bkmobile Coordr*, Kayron Triplett
Founded 1976. Pop 65,000
Oct 1998-Sep 1999 Income $155,500, State $133,400, City $9,600, Federal $7,000, County $4,000, Locally Generated Income $1,000, Other $500. Mats Exp $25,500, Books $20,000, Per/Ser (Incl. Access Fees) $500, AV Equip $2,500, Electronic Ref Mat (Incl. Access Fees) $2,500. Sal $55,000 (Prof $27,000)
Library Holdings: Bk Titles 14,985; Per Subs 11
Automation Activity & Vendor Info: (Acquisitions) Follett; (Cataloging) Follett; (Circulation) Follett
Member Libraries: Annie L Awbrey Public Library; Ashland City Public Library; Earle A Rainwater Memorial Library; Lincoln Public Library; Lineville Public Library; Oxford Public Library
Bookmobiles: 2

P LUCILE L MORGAN PUBLIC LIBRARY,* 541 Ross St, 36264. (Mail add: PO Box 428, 36264), SAN 300-1075. Tel: 256-463-2259. *Dir*, Lorraine B Watson
Pop 3,014; Circ 8,952
Library Holdings: Bk Vols 36,000; Per Subs 25
Special Collections: Old Book Coll

HELENA

P HELENA PUBLIC LIBRARY, 230 Tucker Rd, 35080-7036. (Mail add: PO Box 262, 35080-0262), SAN 371-9359. Tel: 205-664-8308. FAX: 205-664-4593. *Librn*, Pat Valenti; E-Mail: pvalenti@shelbycounty-al.org; Staff 5 (MLS 1, Non-MLS 4)
Founded 1960. Pop 8,000
Oct 1999-Sep 2000 Income $11,397. Mats Exp $11,000, Books $8,000, Per/Ser (Incl. Access Fees) $300. Sal $60,000
Library Holdings: Bk Vols 5,000; Per Subs 23
Mem of Harrison Regional Library System
Friends of the Library Group

HOMEWOOD

P HOMEWOOD PUBLIC LIBRARY,* 1721 Oxmoor Rd, 35209-4085. SAN 300-1083. Tel: 205-877-8661. FAX: 205-802-6424. E-Mail: homewood@post.bham.al.us. Web Site: www.homewood.lib.al.us. *Dir*, Edith Harwell; *Ad Servs*, Norma Owen; *Ch Servs*, June Lacanski; *Circ*, Virginia Thompson; Staff 8 (MLS 8)
Founded 1942. Pop 23,156; Circ 282,558
Oct 1997-Sep 1998 Income $1,403,281, State $22,852, City $1,349,032, Other $31,397. Mats Exp $202,138, Books $124,272, Per/Ser (Incl. Access Fees) $12,000. Sal $938,578 (Prof $440,193)
Library Holdings: Bk Titles 77,140
Automation Activity & Vendor Info: (Circulation) Innovative Interfaces Inc.
Mem of Birmingham Pub & Jefferson County Free Libr Syst
Friends of the Library Group

HOOVER

P HOOVER PUBLIC LIBRARY,* 200 Municipal Dr, 35216. SAN 329-1839. Tel: 205-444-7800. FAX: 205-444-7878. Web Site: hoover.lib.al.us. *Dir*, Linda R Andrews; E-Mail: lindaa@bham.lib.al.us; *Ref*, Susan L Spafford; *Circ*, Sue C Simpson; *Ch Servs*, Vickie Shill; *Ad Servs*, David Ryan; Staff 6 (MLS 6)
Founded 1983. Pop 60,000
1997-1998 Income $2,795,571, State $38,277, City $2,757,294. Mats Exp $249,827, Books $158,477, Per/Ser (Incl. Access Fees) $35,250, Micro $12,000. Sal $104,905
Library Holdings: Bk Titles 105,402; Per Subs 314
Publications: Quarterly Calendar
Friends of the Library Group

HUEYTOWN

P HUEYTOWN PUBLIC LIBRARY,* 1372 Hueytown Rd, 35023. SAN 300-1091. Tel: 205-491-1443. FAX: 205-491-6319. Web Site: www.hueytown.com/htnlib.html. *Coll Develop, Librn*, Darryl K Heritage; E-Mail: dheritage@bham.lib.al.us; Staff 6 (MLS 1, Non-MLS 5)
Founded 1969. Pop 15,102; Circ 61,053
1998-1999 Income $80,000, State $15,000, City $65,000. Mats Exp $25,000, Books $17,000, Per/Ser (Incl. Access Fees) $2,000, Other Print Mats $6,000. Sal $58,000 (Prof $23,000)
Library Holdings: Bk Vols 42,500; Per Subs 42
Subject Interests: Alabama
Friends of the Library Group

HUNTSVILLE

P ALABAMA LIBRARY EXCHANGE, INC, 3218 Panorama Dr SE, 35801-1110. SAN 324-0762. Tel: 256-536-3458. FAX: 256-536-3458. *In Charge*, Christel L McCanless
Founded 1981
Member Libraries: Guntersville Public Library; Oakwood College
Alabama Library Exchange is a multitype library system. Its primary functions include continuing education, shared applications of technologies & staff development

S BOEING HUNTSVILLE, Technical Library,* 499 Boeing Blvd M/S JC-73, PO Box 240002, 35824-6402. SAN 373-3823. Tel: 205-461-2549. FAX: 205-461-3301. *Librn*, Harriet B McKay; E-Mail: harriet.b.mckay@boeing.com; *Librn*, Patricia D Countess; E-Mail: patricia.d.countess@boeing.com
Library Holdings: Bk Titles 700; Per Subs 25
Publications: Recent Acquisitions

SR FAITH PRESBYTERIAN CHURCH LIBRARY, 5003 Whitesburg Dr SE, 35802-1695. SAN 328-6762. Tel: 256-881-4811. *Librn*, Jerry Redus
Jan 1999-Dec 1999 Income $1,500, Parent Institution $500, Other $1,000. Mats Exp $1,500, Books $1,400
Library Holdings: Bk Vols 1,800

S HUNTSVILLE MUSEUM OF ART LIBRARY, 300 Church St S, 35801. SAN 373-3807. Tel: 256-535-4350. FAX: 256-532-1743. E-Mail: info@hsvmuseum.org. Web Site: www.hsvmuseum.org. *Pres*, B Shelley Joseph
Founded 1971
2000-2001 Mats Exp $2,515, Books $1,500, Per/Ser (Incl. Access Fees) $1,015
Library Holdings: Bk Titles 3,000; Per Subs 17
Subject Interests: Art, Ref
Restriction: In-house use for visitors
Function: Reference only

S THE HUNTSVILLE TIMES LIBRARY, 2317 S Memorial Pkwy, 35801. SAN 373-3815. Tel: 256-532-4414. FAX: 256-532-4420. Web Site: www.al.com. *Librn*, Kristina Gustafson
Library Holdings: Bk Titles 1,500; Per Subs 50

P HUNTSVILLE-MADISON COUNTY PUBLIC LIBRARY,* 915 Monroe, 35801. (Mail add: PO Box 443, 35804-0443), SAN 330-2105. Tel: 256-532-5940. Interlibrary Loan Service Tel: 256-532-5967. FAX: 256-532-5994. Web Site: hpl.lib.al.us. *Dir*, Donna B Schremser; *Asst Dir*, Susan B Royer; Tel: 256-532-5952; *Acq*, Regina Cooper; Tel: 256-532-5954, Fax: 256-532-5997; *Ref*, David Lilly; Tel: 256-532-5968; *Ch Servs*, Beth Dean; *Ad Servs*, Judy Purinton; *Cat, Tech Servs*, Barbara Liaw; Tel: 256-532-5976; *Circ*, Richard White; Tel: 256-532-5944; *Rare Bks*, Rane Pruitt; Tel: 256-532-5989; *ILL*, Sheila Gilbreath. Subject Specialists: *Internal medicine*, Gabrielle Liddon; *Local history*, Anne White Fuller
Founded 1817. Pop 258,000; Circ 2,039,352
Oct 1997-Sep 1998 Income $5,037,730, State $320,519, Provincial $769,151, City $3,005,980, Federal $41,806, County $393,270, Locally Generated Income $507,004. Mats Exp Books $357,171. Sal $2,997,640
Library Holdings: Bk Vols 501,000; Bk Titles 214,912; Per Subs 2,294
Subject Interests: Foreign Language
Special Collections: Civil War & Southern History (Zeitler Room Coll), bks, maps & newspapers; Foreign Language Materials; Genealogy & Local History (Heritage Room Coll), bks, mss & micro
Automation Activity & Vendor Info: (Circulation) SIRSI
Publications: Cover to Cover, Options
Subregional Library for Blind - Physically Handicapped
Friends of the Library Group
Branches: 13
BAILEY COVE, 1409 Weatherly Plaza, 35803. SAN 377-6581. Tel: 256-881-0257. Web Site: www.hpl.lib.al.us. *Branch Mgr*, Mary Wallace
Automation Activity & Vendor Info: (Circulation) SIRSI
Database Vendor: Dialog
BESSIE K RUSSELL BRANCH, 3011 C Sparkman Dr, 35810. SAN 330-2253. Tel: 205-859-9050. *Librn*, Nevada Easley
BLUE SPRING, 4600 Blue Spring Rd, 35810. SAN 377-6964. Tel: 205-851-7492. *Librn*, Kim Barley
COLLEGE OF DISCOVERY - OSCAR MASON BRANCH, 915 Monroe St, 35801. (Mail add: PO Box 443, 35804), SAN 376-8929. Tel: 256-532-5940. Web Site: www.hpl.lib.al.us. *Librn*, Beth Wheeler Dean; Tel: 256-532-5982, Fax: 256-532-5997
ELEANOR MURPHY BRANCH, 7910 Charlotte Dr SW, 35802. SAN 330-2164. Tel: 256-881-5620. FAX: 256-881-9181. *Branch Mgr, Librn*, Carolyn Courtenay
Library Holdings: Bk Vols 30,000
Friends of the Library Group
GURLEY BRANCH, 331 Walker St, Gurley, 35748. SAN 329-6121. Tel: 205-776-2102. *Librn*, Jerry Smith
HAZEL GREEN BRANCH, 14245 Hwy 231/431 N, Hazel Green, 35750. SAN 372-5103. *Librn*, Patti Ehman
MADISON BRANCH, 130 Plaza Dr, Madison, 35758. SAN 330-2229. Tel: 205-461-0046. *Librn*, Jeanelle Moritz
MADISON SQUARE MALL, 5901 University Dr, 35806. SAN 322-5569. Tel: 205-837-0783. *Librn*, Carol Miller
MONROVIA, 1960 Jeff Rd, 35806. SAN 377-6603. Tel: 205-837-6153. *Librn*, Marti Marlowe
NEW HOPE BRANCH, 5496 Main St, New Hope, 35760. SAN 329-6148. Tel: 205-723-2995. *Librn*, Priscilla Scott
P SUBREGIONAL LIBRARY FOR THE BLIND & PHYSICALLY HANDICAPPED Tel: 205-532-5980. *Librn*, Joyce Smith
TRIANA BRANCH, 280 Zierdt Rd, Triana, 35758. SAN 376-8937. Tel: 205-461-7598. *Librn*, Shirley Merrell
Bookmobiles: 1

S INTERNATIONAL ASSOCIATION OF EDUCATORS FOR WORLD PEACE, Research Center for Intercultural Information,* 2013 Orba Dr NE, 35811-2414. SAN 320-1147. Tel: 256-534-5501. FAX: 256-536-1018. E-Mail: mercieca@hiwaay.net. Web Site: www.earthportals.com/Portal_Messenger/mercieca.html. *Pres*, Charles Mercieca
Founded 1969
Library Holdings: Bk Titles 10,000; Per Subs 18
Subject Interests: Education, Government, History, Philosophy, Psychology, Securities, Sociology, Technology, United Nations
Publications: Administrative Skills & the Development of the Human Potentials, 1992; Education for Peace; Man's Search for Peace, 1985; Mismanagement in Higher Education, 1986; Peace Progress & Peace Education (International Journals of Education); Perspective of Yeltsin's Russia: Problems & Challenges, 1993; Teaching Methods: On Making Classroom Instruction More Effective & Relevant, 1990; Un News (published monthly in English & Korean); What It Entails, 1991; World Peace & Spirituality of the Third Millennium, 1996
Specializing in the development & implementation of peace education pilot schools project already developed successfully in a few countries including Russia

S NATIONAL SPELEOLOGICAL SOCIETY, NSS Library, 2813 Cave Ave, 35810-4431. SAN 326-2812. Tel: 256-852-1300. FAX: 256-851-9241. E-Mail: nss@caves.org. *Librn*, William W Torode
Library Holdings: Bk Titles 3,000
Subject Interests: Caves
Restriction: Non-circulating to the public

C OAKWOOD COLLEGE, Eva B Dykes Library,* 7000 Adventist Blvd, 35896. SAN 300-1164. Tel: 256-726-7246. Interlibrary Loan Service Tel: 256-726-7250. FAX: 256-726-7409. *Acq, Librn*, Dr Jannith L Lewis; *Cat, Tech Servs*, Morris Iheanacho; *Media Spec*, Ruth Swan; *Archivist*, Minneola Dixon; Staff 9 (MLS 5, Non-MLS 4)
Founded 1896. Enrl 1,158; Fac 83; Highest Degree: Bachelor
Library Holdings: Bk Vols 127,776; Per Subs 605
Special Collections: Black Studies; Oakwood College History; Seventh-Day Adventist Black History
Automation Activity & Vendor Info: (Acquisitions) SIRSI
Mem of Alabama Library Exchange, Inc
Partic in Coop Col Libr Ctr, Inc

S TELEDYNE BROWN ENGINEERING CO, Technical Library,* Cummings Research Park, 300 Sparkman Dr, 35807. SAN 300-1172. Tel: 256-726-1809. FAX: 256-726-2747. *Librn*, Mark Sutherland
Founded 1962
Library Holdings: Bk Vols 10,000; Per Subs 300
Restriction: Restricted access

S US SPACE & ROCKET CENTER, Von Braun Library & Archives, One Tranquility Base, 35805-3399. SAN 327-9340. Tel: 256-721-7167. FAX: 256-721-7180. *Exec Dir*, Larry Capps; *Curator*, David Alberg; *Archivist*, Irene Willhite; E-Mail: irenew@spacecamp.com
Library Holdings: Bk Vols 4,000

C UNIVERSITY OF ALABAMA IN HUNTSVILLE, M Louis Salmon Library, 301 Sparkman Dr NW, PO Box 2600, 35899. SAN 300-1199. Tel: 256-824-6530. Interlibrary Loan Service Tel: 256-890-6124. Reference Tel: 256-824-6529. FAX: 256-824-6552. Web Site: www.uah.edu/library. *Dean of Libr*, Dr Wilson Luquire; Tel: 256-824-6540, Fax: 256-824-6083, E-Mail: luqirew@email.uah.edu; *Librn*, John Warren; Tel: 256-824-6534, E-Mail: warrenjn@email.uah.edu; *Spec Coll & Archives*, Anne Coleman; Tel: 256-824-6523, E-Mail: colemana@email.uah.edu; *Govt Doc*, Susan D Herring; Tel: 256-824-6432, E-Mail: herrings@email.uah.edu; *Instrul Serv*, Margo B Mead; Tel: 256-824-6418, E-Mail: meadm@email.uah.edu; *Electronic Resources, Syst Coordr*, David Phillip Moore; Tel: 256-824-6285, Fax: 256-824-6083, E-Mail: mooredp@email.uah.edu; *ILL*, Lisa Hullett; Tel: 256-824-2185, Fax: 256-890-6862, E-Mail: hullettl@email.uah.edu; *Tech Servs*, Susan McCreless; Tel: 256-890-6537, E-Mail: mccrels@email.uah.edu; *Circ*, Lelon Oliver; Tel: 256-890-6530, E-Mail: oliverl@email.uah.edu; Staff 27 (MLS 9, Non-MLS 18)
Founded 1967. Enrl 4,304; Fac 301; Highest Degree: Doctorate
Oct 1998-Sep 1999 Income $2,038,373, State $1,988,373, Other $50,000. Mats Exp $1,061,901, Books $131,656, Per/Ser (Incl. Access Fees) $781,198, Presv $12,496, Micro $13,071, Manuscripts & Archives $20,066, Electronic Ref Mat (Incl. Access Fees) $103,414. Sal $762,963 (Prof $327,464)
Library Holdings: Bk Vols 331,448; Bk Titles 276,710; Per Subs 1,428
Subject Interests: Technology
Special Collections: Robert E Jones Congressional Papers; Saturn V History Documentation Coll; Willy Ley Coll
Automation Activity & Vendor Info: (Acquisitions) SIRSI; (Cataloging) SIRSI; (Circulation) SIRSI; (Course Reserve) SIRSI; (ILL) SIRSI; (OPAC) SIRSI; (Serials) SIRSI
Database Vendor: Ebsco - EbscoHost, GaleNet, IAC - Info Trac, IAC - SearchBank, OCLC - First Search, ProQuest, Silverplatter Information Inc.
Function: Research library
Partic in Network of Alabama Academic Libraries; OCLC Online Computer Library Center, Inc; SE Libr Network

IDER

P IDER PUBLIC LIBRARY,* 10808 Alabama Hwy 75, 35981-0202. (Mail add: PO Box 202, 35981-0202), SAN 376-5636. Tel: 256-657-2170. FAX: 256-657-3178. E-Mail: iderpl1@farmerstel.com. *Librn*, Virginia Adams
Library Holdings: Bk Vols 11,500
Mem of DeKalb County Pub Libr
Friends of the Library Group

IRONDALE

P IRONDALE PUBLIC LIBRARY, 105 S 20th St, 35210. SAN 300-1210. Tel: 205-951-1415. FAX: 205-951-7715. E-Mail: irondale@bham.lib.al.us. Web Site: www.irondalelibrary.com. *Dir*, Madelyn M Wilson
Founded 1951. Pop 9,704; Circ 63,840
Oct 1998-Sep 1999 Income City $300,204. Mats Exp $53,300, Books $50,000, Per/Ser (Incl. Access Fees) $3,300. Sal $168,958
Library Holdings: Bk Vols 34,454; Bk Titles 29,246; Per Subs 102
Automation Activity & Vendor Info: (Circulation) Innovative Interfaces Inc.; (OPAC) Innovative Interfaces Inc.
Publications: Book Remarks (quarterly)
Partic in Jefferson County Libr Coop
Friends of the Library Group

JACKSON

P WHITE SMITH MEMORIAL LIBRARY,* 213 College Ave, 36545. (Mail add: PO Box 265, 36545), SAN 300-1229. Tel: 334-246-4962. FAX: 334-246-4962. *Librn*, John Jessee
Founded 1937. Pop 6,073; Circ 29,521
Library Holdings: Bk Vols 19,902; Bk Titles 19,053; Per Subs 42
Special Collections: Video Coll
Open Mon 10-7, Tues-Thurs 10-5 & Sat 10-2

JACKSONVILLE

P JACKSONVILLE PUBLIC LIBRARY, 200 Pelham Rd S, 36265. SAN 300-1245. Tel: 256-435-6332. FAX: 256-435-4459. E-Mail: jpl@quicklink.net. *Actg Dir*, Barbara Rowell; *Coll Develop*, Diana Bryant
Founded 1957. Pop 11,000; Circ 86,965
Oct 1999-Sep 2000 Income $313,519. Mats Exp $50,000. Sal $165,000
Library Holdings: Bk Vols 45,000; Per Subs 50
Special Collections: Col John Pelham Papers; Jacksonville History Museum Coll; John Francis Papers (Civil War Roster & Letters)
Friends of the Library Group

C JACKSONVILLE STATE UNIVERSITY LIBRARY, N Pelham Rd, 36265. SAN 300-1237. Tel: 256-782-5255. Interlibrary Loan Service Tel: 256-782-5243. FAX: 256-782-5872. Web Site: jsucc.jsu.edu/depart/library. *Dir*, William J Hubbard; E-Mail: bhubbard@jsucc.jsu.edu; *Dir Libr Serv*, Sonja McAbee; *Acq, Per*, Mary Bevis; *AV*, Bob Campbell; *Bibliog Instr, Ref*, John Graham; *Cat*, Arland Henning; *Cat*, Jeanette Remer; *Cat*, Kim Weatherford; *ILL*, Debra Thompson. Subject Specialists: *Art*, George Whitesel; *Business and management*, Doug Taylor; *Geography*, Linda Cain; *History*, Linda Cain; *Language arts*, George Whitesel; *Literature*, Harry Nuttall; *Mathematics*, Paula Barnett-Ellis; *Music*, George Whitesel; *Science/technology*, Paula Barnett-Ellis; *Social sciences and issues*, Doug Taylor; *Technology*, Wang Hanrong; Staff 19 (MLS 18, Non-MLS 1)
Founded 1883. Enrl 8,000; Fac 300
Oct 1999-Sep 2000 Income $2,328,217, Parent Institution $2,301,631, Other $26,586. Mats Exp $646,949, Books $282,127, Per/Ser (Incl. Access Fees) $340,798, Presv $13,843, AV Equip $10,181. Sal $1,172,552
Library Holdings: Bk Vols 645,311; Bk Titles 420,583; Per Subs 1,695
Special Collections: Alabama; Old & Rare Books
Automation Activity & Vendor Info: (Acquisitions) Endeavor; (Cataloging) Endeavor; (Circulation) Endeavor; (Course Reserve) Endeavor; (ILL) Endeavor; (OPAC) Endeavor; (Serials) Endeavor
Database Vendor: Ebsco - EbscoHost, GaleNet, IAC - Info Trac, OCLC - First Search, ProQuest
Partic in Network of Alabama Academic Libraries; SE Libr Network
Friends of the Library Group

JASPER

J BEVILL STATE COMMUNITY COLLEGE, Irma D Nicholson Library, 1411 Indiana Ave, 35501-4967. SAN 300-1261. Tel: 205-387-0511, Ext 5718, 205-648-3271. FAX: 205-387-5190. Web Site: www.bevillst.cc.al.us. *Chief Librn*, Riette Susie Bryant Elliott; E-Mail: selliot@bevillst.cc.al.us; *Asst Librn*, Audie Davis; *Asst Librn*, Gail Peters; *Asst Librn*, Eloise Spivey; Staff 5 (MLS 4, Non-MLS 1)
Enrl 850; Highest Degree: Associate
Oct 1997-Sep 1998
Library Holdings: Bk Vols 27,000; Per Subs 166
Automation Activity & Vendor Info: (Cataloging) Athena; (Circulation) Athena; (OPAC) Athena

P CARL ELLIOTT REGIONAL LIBRARY SYSTEM,* 20 E 98th St, 35501. SAN 300-1253. Tel: 205-221-2568. FAX: 205-221-2584. *Dir*, Sandra Underwood; *Cat*, Martha R Baldwin
Founded 1957. Pop 90,000; Circ 190,000
Library Holdings: Bk Vols 89,000; Bk Titles 75,000; Per Subs 88
Special Collections: Literature (Musgrove Coll)
Publications: Regional Messenger
Member Libraries: Arley Public Library; Carbon Hill City Library; Cordova Public Library; Dora Public Library; Double Springs Public Library; Haleyville Public Library; Jasper Public Library; Sumiton Public Library

P JASPER PUBLIC LIBRARY,* 98 18th St E, 35501. SAN 320-8915. Tel: 205-221-8512. *Librn*, Colleen Miller
Oct 1998-Sep 1999 Income $168,000. Mats Exp $40,000
Library Holdings: Bk Titles 52,000; Per Subs 124
Mem of Carl Elliott Regional Library System

KILLEN

P KILLEN PUBLIC LIBRARY,* 229 J C Malden Hwy, 35645. SAN 376-5644. Tel: 256-768-0829. FAX: 256-768-0829. E-Mail: killib@getaway.net. *Librn*, Pamela White
Library Holdings: Bk Vols 9,900
Mem of Lauderdale County Regional Libr
Friends of the Library Group

LAFAYETTE

P LAFAYETTE PILOT PUBLIC LIBRARY,* 198 First St SE, 36862. SAN 300-1288. Tel: 334-864-0012. E-Mail: lafayettelibrary@mindspring.com. *Dir*, Jody Upton
Circ 3,104
Library Holdings: Bk Vols 6,000; Per Subs 21
Friends of the Library Group

LEEDS

P LEEDS JANE CULBRETH PUBLIC LIBRARY, 802 Parkway Dr SE, 35094. SAN 300-130X. Tel: 205-699-5962. FAX: 205-699-6843. E-Mail: leeds@bham.lib.al.us. Web Site: www.leedsalabama.com/library.htm. *Dir*, Doris L Jarvis; E-Mail: djarvis@bham.lib.al.us; Staff 5 (MLS 2, Non-MLS 3)
Pop 10,510; Circ 52,165
Oct 1999-Sep 2000 Income $214,253. Mats Exp $35,250, Books $29,000, Per/Ser (Incl. Access Fees) $3,250, AV Equip $3,000. Sal $134,055
Library Holdings: Bk Vols 34,532; Per Subs 93
Subject Interests: Alabama
Automation Activity & Vendor Info: (Circulation) Innovative Interfaces Inc.
Partic in Jefferson County Libr Coop
Special Services for the Deaf - Staff with knowledge of sign language
Open Mon & Thurs 9:30-8, Tues & Wed 9:30-5:30, Fri & Sat 9:30-5
Friends of the Library Group

LEIGHTON

P LEIGHTON PUBLIC LIBRARY, Main St, PO Box 484, 35646. SAN 300-1318. Tel: 256-446-5380. FAX: 256-446-5380. E-Mail: lepublib@hiwaay.net. *Librn*, Polly King
Pop 988; Circ 7,100
Library Holdings: Bk Vols 9,387; Per Subs 22
Open Tues-Fri 1-5, Sat 10-2
Friends of the Library Group

LEXINGTON

P BURCHELL CAMPBELL MEMORIAL LIBRARY, (Formerly Lexington Public Library), 11075 Hwy 101, 35648-0459. (Mail add: PO Box 459, 35648-0459), SAN 376-7590. Tel: 256-768-1196. FAX: 256-768-1196. E-Mail: lexlib@odyssey.net. *Librn*, Sherri Burgess
Library Holdings: Bk Vols 6,147
Mem of Lauderdale County Regional Libr
Friends of the Library Group

LINCOLN

P LINCOLN PUBLIC LIBRARY,* 49 Complex Dr, 35096-5096. SAN 376-5520. Tel: 205-763-7244. FAX: 205-763-7244. E-Mail: lpublib@coosavalley.net. *Librn*, Charlotte Mellon
Library Holdings: Bk Vols 12,000; Per Subs 27
Mem of Cheaha Regional Library

LINDEN

P MARENGO COUNTY PUBLIC LIBRARY,* 507 N Main St, PO Box 480519, 36748-0519. SAN 300-1326. Tel: 334-295-2246. FAX: 334-295-2247. *Librn*, Joyce Morgan; *Asst Librn*, Ann Young
Founded 1941. Pop 23,819; Circ 60,069
Library Holdings: Bk Vols 20,000; Per Subs 15

LINEVILLE

P LINEVILLE PUBLIC LIBRARY,* 60119 Hwy 49, 36266-0482. (Mail add: PO Box 482, 36266-0482), SAN 376-7388. Tel: 256-396-5162. FAX: 256-396-5162. E-Mail: lcl@claycom.com. *Librn*, Faye Cole
Library Holdings: Bk Vols 9,500
Mem of Cheaha Regional Library

LIVINGSTON

P SUMTER COUNTY LIBRARY SYSTEM, 201 Monroe St, PO Drawer U, 35470. SAN 324-0746. Tel: 205-652-2349. *Librn*, Margie Hutcheson; Staff 1 (MLS 1)
Founded 1979. Pop 17,000
Oct 1999-Sep 2000 Income $42,975, State $10,587, County $32,388. Mats Exp $22,326, Books $18,562, Per/Ser (Incl. Access Fees) $863, Other Print Mats $2,901. Sal $12,000
Library Holdings: Bk Titles 12,728
Member Libraries: Bushnell Public Library; George Nichols Public Library; Panasoffkee Community Library Inc; Ruby Pickens Tartt Public Library

P RUBY PICKENS TARTT PUBLIC LIBRARY, Livingston Public Library, 201 Monroe St, PO Drawer U, 35470. SAN 300-1342. Tel: 205-652-2349. *Librn*, Margie Hutcheson; Staff 3 (MLS 1, Non-MLS 2)
Founded 1905. Pop 30,780; Circ 34,571
Oct 1999-Sep 2000 Income $118,836, State $6,800, City $88,776, Federal $275, County $10,000, Other $12,985. Mats Exp $16,918, Books $12,605, Per/Ser (Incl. Access Fees) $1,194, Other Print Mats $3,119. Sal $78,726 (Prof $40,000)
Library Holdings: Bk Vols 23,895; Bk Titles 23,700; Per Subs 37
Mem of Sumter County Library System
Friends of the Library Group

C UNIVERSITY OF WEST ALABAMA, Julia Tutwiler Learning Resources Center,* Sta 12, 35470. SAN 300-1334. Tel: 205-652-3400. FAX: 205-652-2332. Web Site: www2.westal.edu/lrc. *Acq, Dir*, Dr Monroe C Snider; E-Mail: nsnider@univ.westal.edu
Founded 1835. Enrl 1,975; Fac 75
Library Holdings: Bk Vols 113,336; Bk Titles 102,049; Per Subs 200
Special Collections: Alabama Room; Folklore (Ruby Pickens Tartt Coll), mss; Microfiche Coll
Automation Activity & Vendor Info: (Acquisitions) Endeavor
Partic in SE Libr Network

LOUISVILLE

P LOUISVILLE PUBLIC LIBRARY,* City Hall, PO Box 125, 36048. SAN 330-3098. Tel: 334-266-5210. FAX: 334-266-5630. *Librn*, Debra Vinson
Oct 1997-Sep 1998 Income $4,252
Library Holdings: Bk Vols 6,000
Special Collections: Main Street
Mem of Barbour County Libr Syst

LOXLEY

P LOXLEY PUBLIC LIBRARY, 1001 Loxley Ave, PO Box 527, 36551-0527. SAN 300-1350. Tel: 334-964-5695. E-Mail: loxlib@gulftel. *Librn*, Iris Ann Kuklo
Circ 3,760
Library Holdings: Bk Vols 5,535
Mem of Baldwin County Library Cooperative, Inc
Open Mon, Wed & Fri 12-5, Tues 9-5, Sat 10-2

LUVERNE

P LUVERNE PUBLIC LIBRARY,* 148 E Third, 36049. SAN 300-1369. Tel: 334-335-5326. FAX: 334-335-6402. E-Mail: luvernelib@fcbl.net. *Librn*, Rene Lester
Pop 14,000; Circ 15,000
Library Holdings: Bk Vols 12,000; Per Subs 41
Mem of Cross Trails Regional Library Service
Friends of the Library Group

MARION

C JUDSON COLLEGE, Bowling Library, PO Box 120, 36756. SAN 300-1393. Tel: 334-683-5184. FAX: 334-683-5188. Web Site: home.judson.edu/library.html. *Actg Dir*, Kerry Douglas; Tel: 334-683-5182; *Cat*, Connie Cook
Founded 1839. Enrl 276; Fac 33; Highest Degree: Bachelor
Library Holdings: Bk Vols 60,000; Bk Titles 226; Per Subs 174
Subject Interests: Feminism, Religion
Special Collections: Alabama Women's Hall of Fame Coll
Automation Activity & Vendor Info: (Cataloging) Gaylord; (Circulation) Gaylord; (OPAC) Gaylord
Database Vendor: Ebsco - EbscoHost
Publications: Newsletter

J MARION MILITARY INSTITUTE, Baer Memorial Library, 1101 Washington St, 36756. SAN 300-1407. Tel: 334-683-2372. FAX: 334-683-2380. *Dir*, Audra Westbrook; Staff 3 (MLS 1, Non-MLS 2)
Founded 1930. Enrl 325
Library Holdings: Bk Vols 32,131; Bk Titles 22,853; Per Subs 76
Special Collections: H O Murfee Coll; US History (Thomas Perkins Abernethy Coll)

P MARION-PERRY COUNTY LIBRARY,* 202 Washington St, 36756. SAN 300-1415. Tel: 334-683-6411. FAX: 334-683-0599. E-Mail: mpclib@the-link.net. *Librn*, Astrid Knudsen
Founded 1934. Pop 14,872
Library Holdings: Bk Vols 17,944; Bk Titles 17,622; Per Subs 39
Special Collections: Art; A-V; Genealogy
Friends of the Library Group

MARSHALL SPACE FLIGHT CENTER

G MARSHALL TECHNICAL LIBRARY, (Formerly NASA), Marshall Space Flight Center, George C Marshall Space Flight Ctr, Code Ad33-Library, 35812. SAN 300-1423. Tel: 256-544-4524, 256-544-4525. FAX: 256-544-8610. *Librn*, Deborah R Wills; E-Mail: deborah.wills@msfc.nasa.gov; Staff 2 (MLS 1, Non-MLS 1)
Founded 1960
Library Holdings: Bk Titles 5,680; Per Subs 125
Subject Interests: Aerospace science, Engineering, Technology
Special Collections: Document Coll; NASA Microfiche Coll
Restriction: Restricted access
Partic in Dialog Corporation; Nasa Libraries Information System - Nasa Galaxie

MAXWELL AFB

A UNITED STATES AIR FORCE, Air University Library, 600 Chennault Circle, 36112-6424. SAN 300-1431. Interlibrary Loan Service Tel: 334-953-7223. Reference Tel: 334-953-2888. FAX: 334-953-6939. Web Site: www.au.af.mil/au/aul/aul.htm. *Dir*, Dr Shirley Laseter; Tel: 334-953-2606, E-Mail: shirley.laseter@maxwell.af.mil; *Assoc Dir*, Terry Hawkins; Tel: 334-953-2505, E-Mail: terry.hawkins@maxwell.af.mil; *Tech Coordr*, Jackie L Hatton; Tel: 334-953-2474, E-Mail: jackie.hatton@maxwell.af.mil; *Tech Servs*, Sarah Vickery; Tel: 334-953-7091, E-Mail: sarah.vickery@maxwell.af.mil; *ILL*, Rebecca Howze; E-Mail: rebecca.howze@maxwell.af.mil; *Automation Syst Coordr*, Martha Stewart; *Ref Serv*, A Sue Goodman; Tel: 334-953-8301, E-Mail: sue.goodman@maxwell.af.mil; *Circ*, Terry Kiss; Tel: 334-953-2230, E-Mail: terry.kiss@maxwell.af.mil; *Bibliogr*, Stephen B T Chun; Tel: 334-953-5042, E-Mail: stephen.chun@maxwell.af.mil; *Bibliogr*, Ron Fuller; Tel: 334-953-8302, E-Mail: marlow.peters@maxwell.af.mil; *Bibliogr*, Karen Hayward; Tel: 334-953-8302, E-Mail: karen.hayward@maxwell.af.mil; *Bibliogr*, Sandy Malladi; Tel: 334-953-5042, E-Mail: sandhya.malladi@maxwell.af.mil; *Bibliogr*, Joan Phillips; Tel: 334-953-5470, E-Mail: joan.phillips@maxwell.af.mil; *Bibliogr*, Janet Seymour; Tel: 334-953-8302, E-Mail: janet.seymour@maxwell.af.mil; *Bibliogr*, Diana Simpson; Tel: 334-953-5042, E-Mail: diana.simpson@maxwell.af.mil; *Electronic Resources*, Stephanie Havron; Tel: 334-953-8301, E-Mail: stephanie.havron@maxwell.af.mil; *Acq*, Lynn Lonergan; Tel: 334-953-2807, E-Mail: lynn.lonergan@maxwell.af.mil; *Automation Syst Coordr*, Perry Otis; Tel: 334-953-6498, E-Mail: perry.otis@maxwell.af.mil. Subject Specialists: *Canadiana*, Terry Kiss; *Latin America*, Ron Fuller; *Southeast Asia*, Diana Simpson; Staff 67 (MLS 33, Non-MLS 34)
Founded 1946. Enrl 2,100; Highest Degree: Master
Oct 2000-Sep 2001 Income Federal $3,375,000. Mats Exp $516,207, Books $204,107, Per/Ser (Incl. Access Fees) $250,000, Presv $1,000, Micro $18,000, Other Print Mats $17,000, Electronic Ref Mat (Incl. Access Fees) $26,100. Sal $2,375,000 (Prof $1,508,000)
Library Holdings: Bk Vols 789,814; Per Subs 1,863
Subject Interests: Business and management, Economics, Education, History, Mil sci
Special Collections: Air University Coll, rare bks & per related to flight
Automation Activity & Vendor Info: (Circulation) GEAC
Database Vendor: Dialog, Ebsco - EbscoHost, GaleNet, Lexis-Nexis, OCLC - First Search, ProQuest
Publications: Air University Library Index to Military Periodicals; Air University Library Master List of Periodicals; Roster of Subject Specialists; Special Bibliography Series
Restriction: Public use on premises
Partic in Association Of Southeastern Research Libraries (ASERL); Defense Technical Information Center; Fedlink; Military Educ Coordination Conf Libr Consortium; Network of Alabama Academic Libraries; Solinet

UNITED STATES AIR FORCE
AM HEALTH SCIENCE LIBRARY, Med Libr/SGSOL, 42nd Med Group, 330 Kirkpatrick Ave E, 36112-6219. SAN 330-2318. Tel: 334-953-5852. FAX: 334-953-3176. *Librn*, Josephine Turner
Founded 1956
Library Holdings: Bk Vols 3,700

A HISTORICAL RESEARCH AGENCY, AFHRA, 600 Chennault Circle, 36112-6424. SAN 330-2288. Tel: 334-953-5834. FAX: 334-953-7428. E-Mail: afhranews@maxwell.af.mil. Web Site: www.maxwell.af.mil/au/afhra/. *Archivist*, Lynn Gamma; Tel: 334-953-2395, E-Mail: lynn.gamma@maxwell.af.mil

Founded 1942
Special Collections: End of Tour Reports; German Air Force (Karlsruhe Document Coll) & GAF Monograph Series, doc, micro; Gulf War Coll; Historical Monographs; Histories of Air Force Organizations; Personal Papers of Air Force Leaders USAF (Individual Aircraft Record Card Coll), doc, micro

A MAXWELL AIR FORCE BASE LIBRARY FL3300, 42 SVS/SVMG, 481 Williamson St Bldg 1110 Gunter Annex, 36114-3117. SAN 330-2075. Tel: 334-416-3179. FAX: 334-416-5456.
Founded 1958. Pop 6,800
Oct 1998-Sep 1999 Income $430,235. Mats Exp $76,591. Sal $314,786
Library Holdings: Bk Vols 76,068; Per Subs 275

A MAXWELL GUNTER COMMUNITY LIBRARY SYSTEM, FL 3300, Bldg 28, 335 Kirkpatrick Ave E, 36112-5000. SAN 330-2342. Tel: 334-953-6484. FAX: 334-953-3178. *Librn*, J L Clark; *Tech Servs*, Dorothy King; Staff 16 (MLS 1, Non-MLS 15)

MIDFIELD

P MIDFIELD PUBLIC LIBRARY,* 400 Breland Dr, 35228-2732. SAN 376-5091. Tel: 205-923-1027. FAX: 205-923-1027. E-Mail: midfield@birmingham.lib.al.us. *Librn*, Gloria H Dutton
Library Holdings: Bk Vols 2,300; Per Subs 27
Mem of Birmingham Pub & Jefferson County Free Libr Syst

MIDLAND CITY

P MARY BERRY BROWN MEMORIAL LIBRARY,* Hinton Waters & Third St, 36350. (Mail add: PO Box 713, 36350), SAN 330-2881. Tel: 334-983-3511. *Librn*, Kay Armstrong
Library Holdings: Bk Vols 10,000; Per Subs 10

MILLBROOK

P MILLBROOK PUBLIC LIBRARY,* 3650 Grandview Rd, PO Box 525, 36054. SAN 300-144X. Tel: 334-285-6688. FAX: 334-285-0152. E-Mail: millbrook@mindspring.com. Web Site: www.mindspring.com/~millbrook/. *Dir*, Julia Alexander; *Librn*, Linda Moore
Founded 1964. Pop 10,500; Circ 48,000
1998-1999 Income $81,470. Mats Exp $36,500, Books $7,000, Per/Ser (Incl. Access Fees) $1,000. Sal $49,250
Library Holdings: Bk Vols 27,000; Per Subs 26
Mem of Horseshoe Bend Regional Library

MOBILE

J BISHOP STATE COMMUNITY COLLEGE LIBRARY,* 351 N Broad St, 36603-5898. SAN 300-1512. Tel: 334-690-6866. FAX: 334-438-2463. Web Site: www.bscc.cc.al.us. *Dir*, Robert L Parker; E-Mail: rparker@bscc.cc.al.us; *Asst Librn*, Arthurine Washington
Founded 1943
1997-1998 Income $737,637. Mats Exp $373,559. Sal $238,696
Library Holdings: Bk Vols 56,687; Per Subs 265
Special Collections: Black Coll
Special Services for the Deaf - Captioned film depository; Staff with knowledge of sign language

G CITY OF MOBILE, Mobile Municipal Archives, 457 Church St, 36602. SAN 328-2201. Tel: 334-208-7740. FAX: 334-208-7428. E-Mail: maf00527@maf.mobile.al.us. *Archivist*, Jay Higginbotham; Tel: 334-208-7736; *Asst Librn*, Ned Harkins. Subject Specialists: *History*, Jay Higginbotham; Staff 6 (MLS 2, Non-MLS 4)
Founded 1983
Library Holdings: Bk Vols 2,085; Bk Titles 1,050
Special Collections: History of Mobile (Mobile Official City Records Coll, 1814-present); Municipal; Urban Studies
Publications: Guide to the Mobile Municipal Archives
Restriction: Not a lending library
Function: Reference only

S HISTORIC MOBILE PRESERVATION SOCIETY, Mitchell Archives,* 300 Oakleigh Pl, 36604. SAN 327-8654. Tel: 334-432-6161. *In Charge*, Jean Wentworth
Library Holdings: Bk Vols 500
Open Mon-Fri 9-4

GL MOBILE COUNTY PUBLIC LAW LIBRARY, 205 Government St, 36644-2308. SAN 300-1482. Tel: 334-690-8436. FAX: 334-690-4757. *Librn*, Jacquelyn Carson
Library Holdings: Bk Vols 24,644; Bk Titles 20,000; Per Subs 59
Partic in Westlaw

P MOBILE PUBLIC LIBRARY,* 701 Government St, 36602-1499. SAN 330-2407. Tel: 334-208-7073, 334-208-7106 (Admin). Interlibrary Loan Service Tel: 334-208-7402. FAX: 334-208-7571. Web Site: www.mplonline.org. *Mgr*, Mary Laughlin; *Tech Servs*, Judy Walton; *Automation Syst Coordr*, Janet Silvernail; *Publ Servs*, Christina Bowersox; *Br Coordr*, Phyllis Jeffrey; *Ref*, Annette Huddle; *ILL*, Sarah Long; *Ch Servs*, Angela Mollise; *Coll Develop*, Dean Soldner; Staff 33 (MLS 33)
Founded 1928. Pop 389,234; Circ 1,326,578
Oct 1998-Sep 1999 Income $5,471,079, State $385,144, City $3,500,794, County $1,104,101, Locally Generated Income $481,040. Mats Exp $886,086, Books $573,296, Per/Ser (Incl. Access Fees) $53,980, Presv $3,889, Micro $19,110, AV Equip $128,255, Electronic Ref Mat (Incl. Access Fees) $107,556. Sal $3,631,169
Library Holdings: Bk Vols 455,719; Bk Titles 179,303; Per Subs 755
Subject Interests: Genealogy
Special Collections: Mobile History, 1702-present; Mobile Mardi Gras Coll, misc
Automation Activity & Vendor Info: (Acquisitions) SIRSI; (Circulation) SIRSI
Publications: MPL Today (public newsletter)
Special Services for the Deaf - Books on deafness & sign language; Staff with knowledge of sign language; TTY machine
Friends of the Library Group
Branches: 6
COTTAGE HILL, 5025 Cottage Hill Rd, 33609-4204. SAN 330-2431. Tel: 334-470-7772. FAX: 334-470-7711. *Librn*, Margie Calhoun
Library Holdings: Bk Vols 84,110
Friends of the Library Group
MONTE L MOORER BRANCH, 4 S McGregor Ave, 36608-1827. SAN 330-2466. Tel: 334-470-7770. FAX: 334-470-7774. *Librn*, Shirley Sheehan
Library Holdings: Bk Vols 72,029
Friends of the Library Group
PARKWAY, 1924-J Dauphin Island Pkwy, 36605-3004. SAN 330-2490. Tel: 334-470-7766. FAX: 334-470-7712. *Librn*, Janette Curry
Library Holdings: Bk Vols 49,932
SARALAND PUBLIC, 111 Saraland Loop Rd, Saraland, 36571-2418. SAN 330-2520. Tel: 334-675-2879. FAX: 334-679-5516. *Librn*, Lauryn Poynor
Library Holdings: Bk Vols 29,256
Friends of the Library Group
TILLMAN'S CORNER BRANCH, 5451 Halls Mill Rd, Ste 10, 33619-8803. SAN 371-9766. Tel: 334-661-4578. FAX: 334-661-4714. *Librn*, Gloria Williams
Library Holdings: Bk Vols 16,129
Friends of the Library Group
TOULMINVILLE, 2318 St Stephens Rd, 36617-3615. SAN 330-2555. Tel: 334-438-7075. FAX: 334-438-7058. *Librn*, Velma White
Library Holdings: Bk Vols 68,863
Friends of the Library Group
Bookmobiles: 1

S MOBILE REGISTER, INC LIBRARY,* 304 Government St, 36652. (Mail add: PO Box 2488, 36652), SAN 300-1490. Tel: 334-433-1551. FAX: 334-434-8662. *Librn*, Debra Stearns; E-Mail: bstearns@mobileregister.com
Library Holdings: Bk Vols 300
Restriction: Staff use only

S THE MUSEUMS OF MOBILE, Reference Library,* 355 Government St, 36602. SAN 300-1504. Tel: 334-208-7569. FAX: 334-208-7686. E-Mail: museum1@acan.net. *Dir*, George Ewert
Founded 1962
Library Holdings: Bk Titles 3,000
Subject Interests: Civil War

M PROVIDENCE HOSPITAL, Health Science Library,* PO Box 850724, 36685-0724. SAN 327-0041. Tel: 334-633-1373. FAX: 334-639-2061. *Librn*, Susan Deming
Library Holdings: Bk Vols 2,500; Per Subs 150
Subject Interests: Medicine, Nursing
Partic in Ala Health Sci Librn; Medical Libr Asn; Nat Libr of Med Region 2

CR SPRING HILL COLLEGE, Thomas Byrne Memorial Library, 4000 Dauphin St, 36608. SAN 300-1520. Tel: 334-380-3871. Interlibrary Loan Service Tel: 334-380-3880. Circulation Tel: 334-380-3870. Reference Tel: 334-380-3880. FAX: 334-460-2086. Web Site: camellia.shc.edu/byrne. *Dir*, Alice Harrison Bahr; E-Mail: bahr@azalea.shc.edu; *Access Serv*, Richard Weaver; *Cat*, Nancy Bolton; *Cat, Tech Servs*, Janie Mathews; *Doc, Instrul Serv*, Bret Heim; *Instrul Serv, Syst Coordr*, Patrick Quinn; Staff 18 (MLS 5, Non-MLS 13)
Founded 1830. Enrl 1,485; Highest Degree: Master
Jun 1999-May 2000 Income Parent Institution $278,640. Mats Exp $212,443, Books $107,545, Per/Ser (Incl. Access Fees) $67,142, Presv $4,280, Micro $19,100, Other Print Mats $12,376, Manuscripts & Archives $2,000. Sal $324,822
Library Holdings: Bk Vols 137,970; Bk Titles 91,410; Per Subs 538
Subject Interests: Rare books
Special Collections: Mobiliana Coll
Database Vendor: Dialog, Ebsco - EbscoHost, GaleNet, IAC - Info Trac, Lexis-Nexis, OCLC - First Search, ProQuest, Silverplatter Information Inc.
Publications: Friends of the Spring Hill College Newsletter

Function: Archival collection
Partic in Asn Jesuit & Univs; Network of Alabama Academic Libraries; OCLC Online Computer Library Center, Inc; SE Libr Network
Friends of the Library Group

C UNIVERSITY OF MOBILE, J L Bedsole Library, 5735 College Pkwy, 36663-0220. (Mail add: PO Box 13220, 36663-0220), SAN 330-2377. Tel: 334-442-2242. Interlibrary Loan Service Tel: 334-442-2431. Circulation Tel: 334-442-2246. FAX: 334-442-2515. Web Site: library.umobile.edu. *Coll Develop, Dir*, Jeffrey D Calametti; Tel: 334-442-2243, E-Mail: jeffc@mail.umobile.edu; *Cat, Tech Servs*, Donna Lewis-Christian; E-Mail: donnal@mail.umobile.edu; *Reader Servs*, Chris Cox; E-Mail: chrisc@mail.umobile.edu; Staff 4 (MLS 4)
Founded 1961. Enrl 2,000; Fac 90; Highest Degree: Master
1999-2000 Mats Exp $137,500, Books $65,000, Per/Ser (Incl. Access Fees) $58,000, Presv $3,000, AV Equip $11,500. Sal $189,000
Library Holdings: Bk Vols 62,046; Bk Titles 57,130; Per Subs 674
Subject Interests: Alabama, Civil War, Education, Local history, Religion
Special Collections: Southern Baptist History
Automation Activity & Vendor Info: (Cataloging) TLC; (Circulation) TLC; (Course Reserve) TLC; (OPAC) TLC
Partic in Network of Alabama Academic Libraries; OCLC Online Computer Library Center, Inc; SE Libr Network; Southern Baptist Libr Asn

UNIVERSITY OF SOUTH ALABAMA
CM BIOMEDICAL LIBRARY, Biomedical Library Bldg, 316 BLB, 36688. SAN 330-258X. Tel: 334-460-6885. Circulation Tel: 334-460-7043. Reference Tel: 334-460-7044. FAX: 334-460-7638. E-Mail: medlib@jaguar1.usouthal.edu. Web Site: www.usouthal.edu/usa/library/index.htm.; Staff 9 (MLS 9)
Founded 1972. Enrl 2,590; Fac 288; Highest Degree: Doctorate
Oct 1999-Sep 2000 Income $1,895,873. Mats Exp $849,000, Books $75,000, Per/Ser (Incl. Access Fees) $759,000, Presv $15,000. Sal $942,873
Library Holdings: Bk Vols 17,978; Bk Titles 16,620; Per Subs 1,237
Publications: Biofeedback (quarterly newsletter)
Partic in Consortium Of Southern Biomedical Libraries (CONBLS)
CM MEDICAL CENTER BRANCH, 2451 Fillingim, 36617. SAN 329-5788. Tel: 334-471-7855. FAX: 334-471-7857. E-Mail: medlib@jagur1.usouthal.edu. Web Site: southmed.usouthal.edu.; Staff 4 (MLS 1, Non-MLS 3)
Library Holdings: Bk Vols 12,500; Bk Titles 8,477
C UNIVERSITY LIBRARY, 310 Library Bldg, 36688. Tel: 334-460-7021. FAX: 334-460-7181. Web Site: southmed.usouthal.edu/univlib/southcat.html. *ILL*, Debbie Cobb; *Media Spec*, Dr Joaquin M Holloway Jr; *Cat*, Hannelore Miller; *Ref*, Mary Engebretson; *Bibliog Instr*, Jan Sauer; *Govt Doc*, Vicki Tate; *Circ*, Jim Norman; *Archivist*, Dr Michael Thomason; *Coll Develop*, Eugene V Sullivan
Founded 1964. Enrl 12,041; Fac 877; Highest Degree: Doctorate
Oct 1996-Sep 1997 Income $2,438,161. Mats Exp $832,572, Books $159,305, Per/Ser (Incl. Access Fees) $630,343, Micro $42,924. Sal $1,412,681 (Prof $787,487)
Library Holdings: Bk Titles 225,455; Per Subs 2,413
Subject Interests: Business and management, Education, Ethnic studies, Geriatrics and gerontology, History, Medicine
Special Collections: USA University Archives
Automation Activity & Vendor Info: (Acquisitions) NOTIS; (Circulation) NOTIS; (Serials) NOTIS
Publications: Library handbook
Partic in SE Libr Network
VTEK terminal for the disabled

MONROEVILLE

J ALABAMA SOUTHERN COMMUNITY COLLEGE, John Dennis Forte Library, Hwy 21 S, PO Box 2000, 36461. SAN 300-1547. Tel: 334-575-3156, Ext 242. FAX: 334-575-5116. Web Site: www.ascc.edu. *Head Librn*, Angela Roberts; E-Mail: aroberts@ascc.edu
Founded 1965. Enrl 688
Library Holdings: Bk Vols 48,000; Per Subs 250
Subject Interests: Careers
Special Collections: Alabamiana Coll; Professional Coll
Publications: Audiovisual Catalog; Index of Bicentennial Edition of Monroe Journal; Library handbook for students

P MONROE COUNTY PUBLIC LIBRARY,* 121 Pineville Rd, 36460. SAN 300-1539. Tel: 334-743-3818. FAX: 334-575-7357. E-Mail: monroli2@frontiernet.net. *Head of Libr*, Bunny Nobles; *Circ, Publ Servs*, Mary Ann Harris; *ILL*, Alene Brooks
Pop 23,968
Library Holdings: Bk Vols 24,000; Per Subs 57
Special Collections: Alabama Coll
Friends of the Library Group

MONTEVALLO

P PARNELL MEMORIAL LIBRARY, 845 Valley St, 35115. SAN 321-5660. Tel: 205-665-9207. FAX: 205-665-9214. *Dir*, Pauline Bouvier; Staff 1 (Non-MLS 1)
Founded 1958. Pop 4,500; Circ 24,806
Oct 2000-Sep 2001 Mats Exp $6,200, Books $5,900, Per/Ser (Incl. Access Fees) $300. Sal $46,000 (Prof $30,837)
Library Holdings: Bk Titles 15,493; Per Subs 10
Special Collections: Alabama Authors; Large Print; Native American Coll
Open Mon-Fri 10-5 & Sat 10-2

C UNIVERSITY OF MONTEVALLO, Oliver Cromwell Carmichael Library, Station 6100, 35115-6100. SAN 300-1555. Tel: 205-665-6100. FAX: 205-665-6112. Web Site: www.montevallo.edu/library/. *Dir*, Rosemary H Arneson; E-Mail: arnesonr@montevallo.edu; *Circ*, Donna Roose; *Ref*, Kathleen Barone; *Ref*, Patsy Sears; *Tech Servs*, William Shupe; *Coll Develop*, Pauline Williams; Staff 14 (MLS 6, Non-MLS 8)
Founded 1896. Highest Degree: Master
Oct 1999-Sep 2000 Income Parent Institution $918,859. Mats Exp $259,413, Books $172,061, Per/Ser (Incl. Access Fees) $55,055, Presv $5,902, Micro $23,348, Other Print Mats $956, Electronic Ref Mat (Incl. Access Fees) $2,091. Sal $390,475 (Prof $207,426)
Library Holdings: Bk Vols 248,132; Bk Titles 153,409; Per Subs 868
Special Collections: Alabama Authors; Alabama History & Descriptions
Database Vendor: epixtech, inc.
Publications: Recent Acquisitions (monthly)
Partic in Network of Alabama Academic Libraries; OCLC Online Computer Library Center, Inc; SE Libr Network

MONTGOMERY

S ALABAMA DEPARTMENT OF ARCHIVES & HISTORY REFERENCE ROOM, 624 Washington Ave, 36130-0100. SAN 300-1571. Tel: 334-242-4435. FAX: 334-240-3433. Web Site: www.archives.state.al.us. *Asst Dir*, Debbie Pendleton; *Ref*, Norwood A Kerr; E-Mail: nkerr@archives.state.al.us; *Ref*, Frazine Taylor
Founded 1901. Pop 135,200; Circ 524,517
Library Holdings: Bk Vols 250,000
Special Collections: Alabama newspapers; Historical Records of State of Alabama, bks, mss, maps, pamphlets & photog
Partic in OCLC Online Computer Library Center, Inc; RLIN; SE Libr Network
Open Tues-Fri 8-5, Sat 9-5
Friends of the Library Group

GM ALABAMA DEPARTMENT OF PUBLIC HEALTH, Communications Design,* 201 Monroe St, Ste 910, 36130-3017. SAN 320-4472. Tel: 334-206-5309. FAX: 334-206-5520. *In Charge*, Fran Edwards
Founded 1916
Library Holdings: Bk Vols 500; Per Subs 117
Special Collections: Medical Association Transactions State of Alabama, from 1852; Newsp clippings from 1938
Publications: Alabama's Health

G ALABAMA LEAGUE OF MUNICIPALITIES LIBRARY,* PO Box 1270, 36102. SAN 327-0114. Tel: 334-262-2566. FAX: 334-263-0200. *Librn*, Carrie Banks
Library Holdings: Bk Titles 1,500; Per Subs 42

P ALABAMA PUBLIC LIBRARY SERVICE,* 6030 Monticello Dr, 36130. SAN 330-2644. Tel: 334-213-3900. Toll Free Tel: 800-723-8459. TDD: 334-213-3905. FAX: 334-213-3993. Web Site: www.apls.state.al.us. *Dir*, Dr Lamar Veatch; E-Mail: lveatch@apls.state.al.us; *Assoc Dir*, Fred D Neighbors; E-Mail: fneighbors@apls.state.al.us; *Librn*, Hulen Bivins; E-Mail: hbivins@apls.state.al.us; *Librn*, Annie Brown; E-Mail: abrown@apls.state.al.us; *Librn*, Theresa Trawick; E-Mail: ttrawick@apls.state.al.us; *Librn*, Maureen Womack; E-Mail: mwomack@apls.state.al.us; *Librn*, Fara Zaleski; E-Mail: fzaleski@apls.state.al.us; *Librn*, Jim Smith; *Publ Servs*, Judy Shepard; E-Mail: jshepard@apls.state.al.us; *Tech Servs*, Janet Hamilton; E-Mail: jhamilton@apls.state.us; *Automation Syst Coordr*, Mary Payne; E-Mail: mpayne@apls.state.tn.us; *ILL, Online Servs*, Jane Marks; *AV*, Doradean Barnett; E-Mail: dbarnett@apls.state.al.us; *Govt Doc*, Vince Thacker; *Mgr*, Jim Dismukes; E-Mail: jdismukes@apls.state.al.us; *Coll Develop*, Gloria Norman. Subject Specialists: *Business*, Dr Lamar Veatch; *Personnel*, Dr Lamar Veatch; Staff 37 (MLS 22, Non-MLS 15)
Founded 1959. Pop 4,351,999
Oct 1998-Sep 1999 Income (Main Library Only) $10,827,453, State $7,930,839, Federal $2,896,614. Mats Exp $551,030, Books $359,047, Per/Ser (Incl. Access Fees) $55,298, Presv $2,250, Micro $47,591, Electronic Ref Mat (Incl. Access Fees) $86,844. Sal $1,858,340 (Prof $997,490)
Library Holdings: Bk Vols 176,415; Bk Titles 176,839; Per Subs 1,757
Subject Interests: Alabama
Automation Activity & Vendor Info: (Acquisitions) SIRSI; (Cataloging) SIRSI; (Circulation) SIRSI; (OPAC) SIRSI; (Serials) SIRSI
Database Vendor: Dialog, Ebsco - EbscoHost, IAC - Info Trac, OCLC - First Search, Wilson - Wilson Web
Publications: APLSauce (newsletters); Board Talk; Cottonboll; Director's

Chair; Four Star Review; WHAT's Line
Partic in Network of Alabama Academic Libraries; SE Libr Network
Special Services for the Deaf - Books on deafness & sign language; TDD
Regional library for the blind & physically handicapped
Branches: 1
DIVISION FOR THE BLIND & PHYSICALLY HANDICAPPED
See Separate Entry

P ALABAMA PUBLIC LIBRARY SERVICE, Division for the Blind & Physically Handicapped, 6030 Monticello Dr, 36130-6000. SAN 300-1598. Tel: 334-213-3906. Toll Free Tel: 800-392-5671. TDD: 334-213-3900. FAX: 334-213-3993. Web Site: www.apls.state.al.us. *Librn for Blind*, Fara L Zaleski; Tel: 334-213-3921, E-Mail: fzaleski@apls.state.al.us; Staff 8 (MLS 3, Non-MLS 5)
Founded 1978. Pop 5,600; Circ 139,894
Oct 1999-Sep 2000 Income $333,892, State $324,983, Federal $8,909
Library Holdings: Bk Vols 317,739; Bk Titles 51,239
Special Collections: Alabamiana; Blindness & Physically Handicapped (Core Coll)
Publications: What's Line (quarterly newsletter in braille, cassette & large print)
Restriction: Members only
Function: ILL available, Mail loans to members
Special Services for the Deaf - TDD
Special Services for the Blind - Brailling special requests; Duplicating special requests; Magazines on cassette; Videos on blindness & physical handicaps

C ALABAMA STATE UNIVERSITY, Levi Watkins Learning Resource Center,* 915 S Jackson St, 36101-0271. (Mail add: PO Box 271, 36101-0271), SAN 300-161X. Tel: 334-229-4106, 334-229-4591. FAX: 334-229-4940. Web Site: www.lib.alasu.edu. *Dir*, Dr Janice Franklin; E-Mail: frankln@alasa.edu; *Acq*, Keith Powell; *Circ*, Rebecca Mohr; *Publ Servs*, Patricia M Singleton; *Spec Coll*, Rubye Sullivan; *Tech Servs*, Freddie Siler; Staff 14 (MLS 14)
Founded 1921
Oct 1998-Sep 1999 Income $1,965,770. Mats Exp $943,774, Books $506,373, Per/Ser (Incl. Access Fees) $245,317. Sal $856,327 (Prof $725,275)
Library Holdings: Bk Vols 265,150; Per Subs 1,287
Subject Interests: Accounting, Allied health
Special Collections: E D Nixon Coll; Ollie L Brown Afro-American Heritage Coll, bks, micro
Publications: Libretto
Partic in SE Libr Network
Friends of the Library Group

GL ALABAMA SUPREME COURT & STATE LAW LIBRARY, Judicial Bldg, 300 Dexter Ave, 36104. SAN 300-1628. Tel: 334-242-4347. Interlibrary Loan Service Tel: 334-242-4953. Circulation Tel: 334-242-4953. Reference Tel: 334-242-4957. Toll Free Tel: 800-236-4069. FAX: 334-242-4484. Web Site: www.alalinc.net. *Dir, State Librn*, Timothy A Lewis; E-Mail: director@alalinc.net; *Res*, Dean Hartzg; Tel: 334-353-7225, E-Mail: deanh@alalinc.net; *Res*, Rick Hill; Tel: 334-353-7266, E-Mail: rick.hill@alalinc.net; *Res*, Lynne Thrower; Tel: 334-353-7249, E-Mail: lynnet@alalinc.net; *Tech Servs*, Sarah L Frins; Tel: 334-242-4934, E-Mail: sarah@alalinc.net; *Tech Servs*, Jane Garrett; Tel: 334-353-7228, E-Mail: jgarrett@alalinc.net; *Ser*, Lynn D Boyd; Tel: 334-242-4348, E-Mail: lboyd@alalinc.net; *Publ Servs*, Susan Wilkinson; Tel: 334-242-4949, E-Mail: susan@alalinc.net; *Publ Servs*, Alma Surles; Tel: 334-242-4948, E-Mail: alma@alalinc.net; *Automation Syst Coordr*, John Lazenby; Tel: 334-353-7317, E-Mail: johnl@alalinc.net; *Online Servs*, Debbie Keysor; Tel: 334-242-4952, E-Mail: dkeysor@alalinc.net; Staff 14 (MLS 6, Non-MLS 8)
Founded 1828
Oct 1999-Sep 2000 Income $1,701,727, State $1,614,101, Locally Generated Income $87,626. Mats Exp $420,517, Books $239,888, Per/Ser (Incl. Access Fees) $21,423, Presv $4,432, Micro $7,322, AV Equip $900, Electronic Ref Mat (Incl. Access Fees) $146,331. Sal $856,284 (Prof $658,279)
Library Holdings: Bk Vols 222,719; Bk Titles 52,112; Per Subs 752
Subject Interests: Alabama, Law
Special Collections: Government Printing Office
Automation Activity & Vendor Info: (Acquisitions) Innovative Interfaces Inc.; (Cataloging) Innovative Interfaces Inc.; (Circulation) Innovative Interfaces Inc.; (Course Reserve) Innovative Interfaces Inc.; (OPAC) Innovative Interfaces Inc.; (Serials) Innovative Interfaces Inc.
Database Vendor: GaleNet, Lexis-Nexis
Publications: Alabama Appellate Courts, Highlights
Function: Research library
Partic in OCLC Online Computer Library Center, Inc; SE Libr Network

C AUBURN UNIVERSITY, Southeast Regional Resource Center,* 7300 University Dr, 36119. (Mail add: PO Box 244023, 36124), SAN 327-4713. Tel: 334-244-3100, 334-244-3457. FAX: 334-244-3101. Web Site: www.edla.aum.edu/serrc/serrc/html. *Dir*, Dr Elizabeth Beale; E-Mail: bbeale@edla.aum
Library Holdings: Bk Vols 6,000; Per Subs 40
Special education of handicapped; law reports, Supreme Court proceedings, extensive textbook collection on special education; legal index to special education laws

C AUBURN UNIVERSITY MONTGOMERY LIBRARY, 7440 East Dr, 36117. (Mail add: PO Box 244023, 36124-4023), SAN 300-1636. Tel: 334-244-3200. FAX: 334-244-3720. Web Site: www.library.aum.edu/home/university/library. *Actg Dean, Coll Develop*, Rickey Best; E-Mail: rickey@library.aum.edu; *Ref*, Barbara Dekle; *Cat*, Phyllis Hytnen; *ILL*, Joyce Johnston; *Doc*, Betty Tims; *Circ*, Michael Grace
Founded 1969. Fac 213; Highest Degree: Doctorate
Oct 1999-Sep 2000 Income $1,669,938. Mats Exp $593,000, Books $270,000, Per/Ser (Incl. Access Fees) $311,000, Presv $2,000, Micro $10,000. Sal $691,720 (Prof $380,870)
Library Holdings: Bk Titles 292,586; Per Subs 1,480
Subject Interests: Genealogy
Special Collections: Local & Regional Studies; University Archives
Publications: Friends of the AUM Library Newsletter
Partic in Network of Alabama Academic Libraries; OCLC Online Computer Library Center, Inc; SE Libr Network
Friends of the Library Group

M BAPTIST MEDICAL CENTER LIBRARY,* 2055 East South Blvd, PO Box 11010, 36116-0010. SAN 324-5640. Tel: 334-286-2952. FAX: 334-286-3332. *Coordr*, Beverly Johnson
Founded 1963
Library Holdings: Bk Titles 1,247; Per Subs 63
Subject Interests: Dermatology, Gynecology, Internal medicine, Obstetrics, Orthopedics, Pediatrics, Surgery
Partic in Nat Libr of Med

GM CENTRAL ALABAMA VETERANS HEALTH CARE SYSTEM, West Campus Library Service, 215 Perry Hill Rd, 36109-3798. SAN 300-1725. Tel: 334-272-4670, Ext 4976. FAX: 334-260-4125. *Actg Mgr*, Sceiva Holland; Tel: 334-727-0550, Ext 3440; *Tech Servs*, Susan J Helms; Staff 1 (MLS 1)
Founded 1940
Library Holdings: Bk Titles 3,500; Per Subs 200; Spec Interest Per Sub 40
Subject Interests: Allied health, Medicine, Surgery
Partic in Vets Admin Libr Network

J FAULKNER UNIVERSITY, Gus Nichols Library, 5345 Atlanta Hwy, 36109-3398. SAN 300-1563. Tel: 334-386-7207. FAX: 334-386-7299. E-Mail: libref@faulkner.edu. Web Site: www.faulkner.edu/library/index.htm. *Dir*, Brenda Turner; E-Mail: bturner@faulkner.edu; *Exten Serv*, Dena Luce; Tel: 334-386-7482, E-Mail: dluce@faulkner.edu; *Coll Develop, Tech Servs*, Barbara Kelly; Tel: 334-386-7282, E-Mail: bkelly@faulkner.edu; *ILL*, Carolyn Benson; Tel: 334-386-7206, E-Mail: cbenson@faulkner.edu; *Ref*, Rodney Wooten; Staff 8 (MLS 4, Non-MLS 4)
Founded 1944. Enrl 1,800; Fac 50; Highest Degree: Doctorate
Jun 1999-May 2000 Income $455,440. Mats Exp $219,490, Books $182,810, Per/Ser (Incl. Access Fees) $36,680. Sal $145,783
Library Holdings: Bk Vols 106,128; Per Subs 504
Subject Interests: Art and architecture, Business and management, Economics, Education, Health sciences, History, Literature, Mathematics, Natural science, Psychology, Religion, Social sciences and issues
Special Collections: Churches of Christ Materials
Automation Activity & Vendor Info: (Acquisitions) Innovative Interfaces Inc.; (Cataloging) Innovative Interfaces Inc.; (Circulation) Innovative Interfaces Inc.; (Serials) Innovative Interfaces Inc.
Partic in Christian Col Libr; Montgomery Higher Education Librs; OCLC Online Computer Library Center, Inc; SE Libr Network
Departmental Libraries:
BIRMINGHAM CENTER, 2970 Lorma Rd, Birmingham, 35216. SAN 373-6008.
1996-1997 Income $7,000
Library Holdings: Bk Vols 1,500
Friends of the Library Group
HUNTSVILLE CENTER, 420 Wynn Dr, Huntsville, 35805. SAN 373-6024.
1996-1997 Income $7,000
Library Holdings: Bk Vols 1,700
Friends of the Library Group
MOBILE CENTER, 808 Western American Dr, Mobile, 36609. SAN 373-6032.
1996-1997 Income $7,000
Library Holdings: Bk Vols 950

C HUNTINGDON COLLEGE, Houghton Memorial Library, 1500 E Fairview Ave, 36106. SAN 300-1660. Tel: 334-833-4421. FAX: 334-263-4465. Web Site: www.huntingdon.edu/library/homepage.html. *Dir Libr Serv*, Eric A Kidwell; Tel: 334-833-4512, E-Mail: ekidwell@huntingdon.edu; *Admin Assoc*, Joel Godfrey; Tel: 334-833-4512, E-Mail: jgodfrey@huntingdon.edu; *AV, Per, Tech Coordr*, Brenda Kerwin; Tel: 334-833-4529, E-Mail: bkerwin@huntingdon.edu; *Circ*, Margaret Kinney; Tel: 334-833-4422, E-Mail: margaretk@huntingdon.edu; *ILL, Publ Servs*, Nordis Smith; Tel: 334-833-4537, E-Mail: nosmith@huntingdon.edu; *Archivist*, Mary Ann Pickard; Tel: 334-833-4413, E-Mail: mpickard@huntingdon.edu; *Tech Servs*,

Barbara Goss; Tel: 334-833-4511, E-Mail: bgoss@huntingdon.edu; Staff 12 (MLS 5, Non-MLS 7)
Founded 1854. Enrl 705; Fac 51; Highest Degree: Bachelor
Jun 1999-May 2000 Income $525,489. Mats Exp $301,568, Books $126,500, Per/Ser (Incl. Access Fees) $80,880, Presv $2,436, Micro $9,617, Electronic Ref Mat (Incl. Access Fees) $4,483. Sal $250,743 (Prof $137,059)
Library Holdings: Bk Vols 97,432; Per Subs 443
Special Collections: Alabama-West Florida Conference of the United Methodist Church; Alabamiana; Archives & History of United Methodist Church; Autographed Book Coll; College Archives; Rare Book Coll
Automation Activity & Vendor Info: (Acquisitions) Endeavor; (Cataloging) Endeavor; (Circulation) Endeavor; (Course Reserve) Endeavor; (ILL) Endeavor; (OPAC) Endeavor; (Serials) Endeavor
Database Vendor: Ebsco - EbscoHost, ProQuest, Silverplatter Information Inc.
Publications: New Book List (monthly acquisition list); The Book Report (bi-annual friends newsletter)
Partic in Ala Union List & Serials; ALICAT; Montgomery Higher Education Librs; SE Libr Network
Friends of the Library Group

M JACKSON HOSPITAL & CLINIC, INC, Medical Library,* 1725 Pine St, 36106. SAN 325-9501. Tel: 334-293-8696. FAX: 334-293-8742.
Library Holdings: Bk Vols 663; Bk Titles 340

S MONTGOMERY ADVERTISER LIBRARY,* 200 Washington Ave, PO Box 1000, 36101-1000. SAN 371-294X. Tel: 334-240-0157. FAX: 334-261-1505. Web Site: www.montgomeryadvertiser.com. *Head Librn*, Linda Harvey; Staff 2 (MLS 1, Non-MLS 1)
Library Holdings: Bk Vols 1,000

P MONTGOMERY CITY-COUNTY PUBLIC LIBRARY,* 245 High St, PO Box 1950, 36102-1950. SAN 330-2709. Tel: 334-240-4300. FAX: 334-240-4977. *Dir*, Jaunita McClain-Owes
Pop 197,360; Circ 480,556
Library Holdings: Bk Vols 400,000; Per Subs 240
Automation Activity & Vendor Info: (Acquisitions) Brodart; (Circulation) CLSI LIBS
Friends of the Library Group
Branches: 10
COLISEUM BOULEVARD BRANCH, 840 Coliseum Blvd, 36109. SAN 330-2768. Tel: 334-271-7005. *Branch Mgr*, Richard L Mobley; Tel: 334-271-7005, E-Mail: rmobley@mccpl.lib.al.us
Friends of the Library Group
E L LOWDER REGIONAL, 2590 Bell Rd, 36117. SAN 374-6879. *Librn*, Joseph Freedman
GOVERNOR SQUARE, 2885 B East South Blvd, 36116. SAN 330-2725. Tel: 334-284-7901. *Librn*, Linda Harvey
MAIN BRANCH, 245 High St, 36104. SAN 330-2717. Tel: 334-240-4999. *Librn*, Tommy Anderson
Friends of the Library Group
ROSA L PARKS BRANCH, 1276 Rosa Parks Ave, 36108. SAN 330-2733. Tel: 334-240-4979. *Librn*, Teresa Temple
PIKE ROAD BRANCH, PO Box 640036, Pike Road, 36064. SAN 378-1720. Tel: 334-244-8679. *In Charge*, Dale Collum
PINE LEVEL BRANCH, 310 School House Rd, PO Box 310, Pine Level, 36065. SAN 378-1747. Tel: 334-584-7144. Web Site: www.mccpl.lib.al.us/pine_level.html. *Librn*, Mrs Lynda Maddox; *Librn*, Dale E Collum; Tel: 334-284-7900, Fax: 334-284-7992, E-Mail: DCollum@mccpl.lib.al.us
Database Vendor: DRA, Ebsco - EbscoHost, OCLC - First Search
PINTLALA BRANCH, 255 Federal Dr, Pint Lala, 36043. SAN 378-1704. Tel: 334-281-8069. Web Site: www.mccpl.lib.al.us/pintlala.html. *In Charge, Librn*, Dale E Collum; Tel: 334-284-7900, Fax: 334-284-7992, E-Mail: DCollum@mccpl.lib.al.us; *Librn*, Olivia Anderson-Johnson; Staff 3 (MLS 1, Non-MLS 2)
Database Vendor: DRA, Ebsco - EbscoHost, OCLC - First Search
Friends of the Library Group
RAMER BRANCH, State Hwy 94, Ramer, 36069. SAN 330-2741. Tel: 334-562-3364. *Librn*, James Green
RUFUS A LEWIS REGIONAL, 3095 Mobile Hwy, 36108. SAN 374-6860. *Librn*, Julia Rutledge
Bookmobiles: 1

GL MONTGOMERY COUNTY LAW LIBRARY,* 251 S Lawrence St, PO Box 1667, 36102. SAN 300-1679. Tel: 334-832-1394. FAX: 334-265-9536. *Librn*, Dawn Howard

S MONTGOMERY MUSEUM OF FINE ARTS, Art Research Library,* One Museum Dr, PO Box 230819, 36123-0819. SAN 300-1687. Tel: 334-244-5700. FAX: 334-244-5774. *Librn*, Alice T Carter
Founded 1930
Library Holdings: Bk Vols 5,000; Bk Titles 3,000; Per Subs 13
Subject Interests: Arts and crafts (American), Sculpture

§C SOUTH COLLEGE LIBRARY, 122 Commerce St, 36104. SAN 375-4383. Tel: 334-263-1013. FAX: 334-834-9559. E-Mail: mtglib@southcollege.edu. Web Site: www.southcollege.edu. *Librn*, Donna Chow; Staff 2 (MLS 1, Non-MLS 1)
Library Holdings: Bk Vols 8,000; Per Subs 30
Automation Activity & Vendor Info: (Cataloging) Sagebrush Corporation; (Circulation) Sagebrush Corporation

SR SOUTHERN CHRISTIAN UNIVERSITY LIBRARY, 1200 Taylor Rd, 36117. SAN 371-9936. Tel: 334-387-3877, Ext 117. Toll Free Tel: 800-351-4040. FAX: 334-271-0002, 334-387-3878. E-Mail: library@southernchristian.edu. Web Site: www.southernchristian.edu. *Dir*, Kay Newman; *Librn*, Terence Sheridan; Staff 5 (MLS 2, Non-MLS 3)
Founded 1967. Enrl 125; Highest Degree: Master
Library Holdings: Bk Vols 65,000; Per Subs 200
Subject Interests: Theology
Database Vendor: OCLC - First Search, ProQuest
Partic in American Theological Library Association

L SOUTHERN POVERTY LAW CENTER, Intelligence Project,* PO Box 548, 36101-0548. SAN 329-3742. Tel: 334-264-0286. FAX: 334-264-8891. *Dir*, Joseph Roy Sr
Library Holdings: Bk Titles 500

C TROY STATE UNIVERSITY MONTGOMERY, Rosa Parks Library, 252 Montgomery St, 36104-3425. SAN 300-1709. Tel: 334-241-9576. FAX: 334-241-9590. Web Site: www.tsum.edu. *Chief Librn*, Kay Fowler; E-Mail: kfowler@tsum.edu; Staff 5 (MLS 5)
Founded 1970. Enrl 2,388; Fac 190
Library Holdings: Bk Vols 24,610; Bk Titles 21,517; Per Subs 469
Subject Interests: Nursing
Automation Activity & Vendor Info: (Circulation) SIRSI

G UNITED STATES ENVIRONMENTAL PROTECTION AGENCY, National Air & Radiation Environmental Laboratory,* 540 S Morris Ave, 36115-2601. SAN 373-384X. Tel: 334-270-3400, 334-270-3411. FAX: 334-270-3454.
Library Holdings: Bk Titles 2,500; Per Subs 23

S VALIDATA COMPUTER & RESEARCH CORP LIBRARY,* 428 S Perry St, PO Box 4719, 36104. SAN 373-3831. Tel: 334-834-2324. FAX: 334-262-5648. *Librn*, Warren Philips
Library Holdings: Bk Vols 7,000; Per Subs 10

MOULTON

P LAWRENCE COUNTY PUBLIC LIBRARY,* 401 College St, 35650. SAN 300-1733. Tel: 256-974-0883. FAX: 256-974-0890. *Librn*, Jane Day
Founded 1961. Pop 31,500; Circ 36,064
Sep 1997-Oct 1998 Income $45,000. Mats Exp $15,000
Library Holdings: Bk Vols 17,883; Per Subs 23
Mem of Wheeler Basin Regional Library

MOUNDVILLE

P MOUNDVILLE PUBLIC LIBRARY,* Market St, PO Box 336, 35474. SAN 300-1741. Tel: 205-371-2283. FAX: 205-371-2283. E-Mail: mpl@mound.net. *Librn*, Denise Gore
Pop 1,548; Circ 4,700
Library Holdings: Bk Vols 8,200
Special Collections: Alabamaian Coll
Open Mon-Fri 8-4:30, Sat 9:30-12

MOUNT VERNON

§P MOUNT VERNON PUBLIC LIBRARY, 1220 Military Rd, 36560. Tel: 334-829-9497. FAX: 334-829-5546. *Dir*, Mrs Willard Sims
Oct 1999-Sep 2000 Income $24,996, State $1,241, City $12,500, Federal $9,000, County $2,255
Library Holdings: Bk Vols 8,000; Per Subs 30

M SEARCY HOSPITAL PATIENT LIBRARY,* PO Box 1001, 36560. SAN 300-175X. Tel: 334-829-9411, Ext 249. FAX: 334-829-9075.
Library Holdings: Bk Vols 7,500; Bk Titles 7,000; Per Subs 85
Friends of the Library Group

MOUNTAIN BROOK

P EMMET O'NEAL LIBRARY, 50 Oak St, 35213. SAN 300-1768. Tel: 205-879-0459. FAX: 205-879-5388. Web Site: www.eolib.org. *Dir*, Susan DeBrecht Murrell; E-Mail: smurrell@bham.lib.al.us; *Asst Dir, Ref*, Jeff Hammack; E-Mail: jhammack@bham.lib.al.us; *Circ*, Doris Young; E-Mail: dyoung@bham.lib.al.us; *Ch Servs*, Lucia Chambers; *Acq, Cat*, Nancy D Sexton; E-Mail: nsexton@bham.lib.al.us; Staff 5 (MLS 2, Non-MLS 3)
Founded 1964. Pop 20,183; Circ 271,348
Library Holdings: Bk Vols 94,436; Bk Titles 79,435; Per Subs 132
Subject Interests: Gardening
Special Collections: Gardening Coll

Automation Activity & Vendor Info: (Circulation) Innovative Interfaces Inc.
Publications: Friends of the Library Bookends
Friends of the Library Group

MUSCLE SHOALS

S INTERNATIONAL FERTILIZER DEVELOPMENT CENTER, Travis P Hignett Memorial Library, PO Box 2040, 35662. SAN 325-9072. Tel: 256-381-6600. FAX: 256-381-7408. Web Site: www.ifdc.org. *Senior Librn*, Jean S Riley; E-Mail: jriley@ifdc.org
Library Holdings: Bk Titles 18,000
Subject Interests: Agriculture, Developing countries, Fertilizers, Marketing
Special Collections: Current Awareness Database; Developing Country File & International Agricultural Organization File; Fertaware Database; Patent Files; Training Programs
Automation Activity & Vendor Info: (Cataloging) EOS; (Circulation) EOS; (OPAC) EOS
Database Vendor: Dialog, OCLC - First Search
Publications: Library Handbook
Restriction: Open to employees & special libraries, Open to public for reference only
Function: Document delivery services, ILL available, Photocopies available, Reference services available, Research library, Some telephone reference

P MUSCLE SHOALS CITY PUBLIC LIBRARY,* 1918 E Avalon, 35661. SAN 300-1776. Tel: 256-386-9212. FAX: 256-386-9211. *Librn*, Hannah Jeffreys
Pop 9,000; Circ 42,540
Library Holdings: Bk Titles 26,000; Per Subs 62
Open Tues & Thurs 10-8, Wed, Fri & Sat 10-5, Sun 1-5
Friends of the Library Group

S TENNESSEE VALLEY AUTHORITY, TVA Environmental Research & Services,* PO Box 1010, 35662-1010. SAN 300-1784. Tel: 256-386-2417. FAX: 256-386-2453. *Librn*, Wendolyn Clark; E-Mail: whclark@tva.gov
Founded 1961
Library Holdings: Bk Titles 12,000; Per Subs 250
Subject Interests: Alternative sources (energy), Chemical engineering, Chemistry, Marketing
Publications: Library brochure; New Arrivals
Partic in Fedlink

NEWTON

P NEWTON PUBLIC LIBRARY,* Oates-Reynolds Bldg, 203 Oates Dr, 36352. SAN 330-3128. Tel: 334-299-3316. FAX: 334-299-3316. E-Mail: npl@alaweb.com. *Librn*, Mary Hall
Library Holdings: Bk Vols 10,950

NORMAL

C ALABAMA AGRICULTURAL & MECHANICAL UNIVERSITY, Joseph F Drake Memorial Learning Resources Center, 4900 Meridian St, PO Box 489, 35762. SAN 300-1792. Tel: 256-851-5764. Interlibrary Loan Service Tel: 256-858-4728. Circulation Tel: 256-858-4723. Reference Tel: 256-858-4712. Web Site: www.aamu.edu. *Coll Develop, Dir*, Patricia D Ford; E-Mail: pford@aamu.edu; *Acq, Tech Servs*, Wanda Cross; Tel: 256-858-4763, E-Mail: wcross@aamu.edu; *ILL*, Sebastine O Nwaneri; Fax: 256-858-5901, E-Mail: snwaneri@aamu.edu; *Govt Doc, Publ Servs, Ref Serv*, Mildred Stiger; Tel: 256-858-4717, E-Mail: mstiger@aamu.edu. Subject Specialists: *Administration*, Patricia D Ford; Staff 14 (MLS 7, Non-MLS 7)
Founded 1904. Enrl 5,215; Fac 280; Highest Degree: Doctorate
Library Holdings: Bk Vols 240,233; Bk Titles 203,183; Per Subs 1,285
Subject Interests: Agriculture, Art and architecture, Business and management, Economics, Education, Engineering, Food sci, Forestry, History, Humanities, Music, Natural science, Physics, Social sciences and issues, Technology, Urban planning
Special Collections: Archival & Historical Colls; Audio Visual Coll; Black Coll; Carnegie-Mydral Coll; Curriculum Coll; ERIC Coll; Government Documents Coll; International Studies Coll; J F Kennedy Memorial Coll; Schomburg Coll; Textbook Coll; YA Coll
Automation Activity & Vendor Info: (Acquisitions) epixtech, inc.; (Cataloging) epixtech, inc.; (Circulation) epixtech, inc.
Database Vendor: Ebsco - EbscoHost
Publications: LRC Fast Facts; LRC Weekly News; Mixed Media
Partic in Dialog Corporation; Network of Alabama Academic Libraries; SE Libr Network
Friends of the Library Group

ONEONTA

P ONEONTA PUBLIC LIBRARY,* 221 Second St S, 35121. SAN 300-1806. Tel: 205-274-7641. FAX: 205-274-7643. E-Mail: opls@yahoo.com. *Dir*, Kossie Buckelew; *Asst Librn*, Kay Butts; *Acq, Cat*, Pam Freeman; *Circ*, Marilyn Masters
Founded 1948. Circ 50,867
Sep 1997-Oct 1998 Income $138,124, State $37,106, City $79,659, County $11,250, Locally Generated Income $10,109. Mats Exp $21,397, Books $19,579, Per/Ser (Incl. Access Fees) $1,200. Sal $122,319
Library Holdings: Bk Vols 38,000; Per Subs 114
Special Collections: Genealogy Coll; Large Print; Rare Book Coll

OPELIKA

P LEWIS COOPER JUNIOR MEMORIAL LIBRARY & ARTS CENTER,* 200 S Sixth St, PO Box 125, 36801. SAN 300-1814. Tel: 334-705-5380. FAX: 334-705-5381. *Dir*, Michelle Jones; *Librn*, Diane Heard; *Ch Servs*, Karin Lindermann
Founded 1941. Pop 25,000; Circ 20,000
Oct 1997-Sep 1998 Income $5,200. Mats Exp $52,500, Books $47,000, Per/Ser (Incl. Access Fees) $5,500
Library Holdings: Bk Titles 57,000; Per Subs 85
Subject Interests: Art and architecture, Genealogy, History, Natural science, Religion
Mem of Horseshoe Bend Regional Library

OPP

P CROSS TRAILS REGIONAL LIBRARY SERVICE, 1604 N Main St, PO Drawer 770, 36467. SAN 300-1822. Tel: 334-493-9526. FAX: 334-493-7503. E-Mail: crosstra@alaweb.com. *Dir*, Mona Simon; *ILL, Ref*, Sharon Godwin; Staff 4 (MLS 1, Non-MLS 3)
Founded 1957. Pop 75,982; Circ 3,921
Oct 1999-Sep 2000 Income $117,071, State $83,792, County $22,650, Other $10,629. Mats Exp $7,984, Books $6,484, Per/Ser (Incl. Access Fees) $1,500. Sal $40,638 (Prof $12,000)
Library Holdings: Bk Vols 35,256; Bk Titles 30,805; Per Subs 30
Special Collections: Books-By-Mail (paperbacks)
Restriction: Not open to public
Member Libraries: Brantley Public Library; Elba Public Library; Emma Knox Kenan Public Library; Florala Public Library; Hartford Public Library; Luverne Public Library; Opp Public Library; Samson Public Library; Slocomb Public Library

P OPP PUBLIC LIBRARY,* 1604 N Main St, 36467. (Mail add: PO Drawer 770, 36467), SAN 300-1830. Tel: 334-493-6423. FAX: 334-493-6423. E-Mail: opplib@alaweb.com. *Dir*, William F Niblett, Jr
Pop 7,204; Circ 31,753
Library Holdings: Bk Vols 16,000; Per Subs 50
Mem of Cross Trails Regional Library Service

ORANGE BEACH

P ORANGE BEACH PUBLIC LIBRARY, 4101 Orange Beach Blvd, 36561-1649. (Mail add: PO Box 1649, 36561), SAN 373-7004. Tel: 334-981-2923. FAX: 334-981-2920. E-Mail: oblibrar@gulftel.com. Web Site: www.tlc.library.net/orangebeach. *Dir*, Marsha Owens; *Asst Librn*, Patti Underwood; *Ad Servs, ILL*, Angela Rand; *Ch Servs*, Patsy Rose; Staff 5 (MLS 1, Non-MLS 4)
Founded 1992. Pop 10,000; Circ 80,000
Oct 1999-Sep 2000 Income $258,895, City $252,895, Locally Generated Income $6,000. Mats Exp $51,200, Books $35,000, Per/Ser (Incl. Access Fees) $6,200, AV Equip $6,000, Electronic Ref Mat (Incl. Access Fees) $4,000. Sal $129,195 (Prof $43,000)
Library Holdings: Bk Vols 23,724; Bk Titles 22,325; Bks on Deafness & Sign Lang 26
Subject Interests: Ecology, Local history, Marine biology
Automation Activity & Vendor Info: (Cataloging) TLC; (Circulation) TLC; (OPAC) TLC
Database Vendor: Ebsco - EbscoHost, OCLC - First Search, ProQuest
Function: ILL available, Outside services via phone, cable & mail, Reference services available
Mem of Baldwin County Library Cooperative, Inc
Special Services for the Deaf - Books on deafness & sign language
Special Services for the Blind - Home delivery & demonstration of talking book machines & material to new readers
Book delivery service for handicapped patrons; Sponsor creative writing workshops
Friends of the Library Group

OXFORD

P OXFORD PUBLIC LIBRARY,* 213 Choccolocco St, 36203. SAN 300-1849. Tel: 256-831-1750. FAX: 256-835-6107. E-Mail: opl@nti.ent. Web Site: www.oxfordalabama.org. *Librn*, Irene Sparks
Founded 1927. Pop 10,990; Circ 37,311
Library Holdings: Bk Vols 21,242; Per Subs 41
Mem of Cheaha Regional Library
Open Tues-Fri 10-6:30, Sat 8-4:30, Closed Sun & Mon
Friends of the Library Group

OZARK

P OZARK-DALE COUNTY PUBLIC LIBRARY, INC,* 320 James St, 36360. SAN 330-2970. Tel: 334-774-2399, 334-774-5480. FAX: 334-774-9156. E-Mail: library@snowhill.com. Web Site: www.snowhill.com/~library/. *Dir*, Sandra Holmes; *Ch Servs*, Melanie Woodham; *Circ*, Gerry Nysewander; *Circ, ILL*, Angie Walsh
Library Holdings: Bk Vols 49,000
Special Collections: Autry Religious Coll; Creel R Richardson Genealogy Coll
Friends of the Library Group

J WALLACE COMMUNITY COLLEGE, Aviation Campus Learning Resource Center, Hwy 231 S, 36361-1209. (Mail add: PO Box 1209, 36361-1209), SAN 322-6824. Tel: 334-774-5113, Ext 656. Toll Free Tel: 800-624-3468, Ext 656. FAX: 334-774-6399. Web Site: www.wallace.edu. *Dir*, A P Hoffman
Founded 1980. Enrl 450; Fac 23; Highest Degree: Associate
Oct 1998-Sep 1999 Income State $30,000. Mats Exp $24,000, Books $2,000, Per/Ser (Incl. Access Fees) $17,000, AV Equip $5,000. Sal $70,000 (Prof $50,000)
Library Holdings: Bk Vols 10,500; Bk Titles 10,400; Per Subs 95
Subject Interests: Automotive, Aviation, Electronics
Special Collections: Civil, Commercial & General Aviation
Restriction: Open to faculty, students & qualified researchers
Departmental Libraries:
LEARNING RESOURCE CENTER, 243-B Club Manor, Mobile, 36615. SAN 370-0119. Tel: 334-438-2816. FAX: 334-438-2816.
Library Holdings: Bk Vols 2,000; Per Subs 15

PELHAM

P PELHAM PUBLIC LIBRARY,* Cummings St & Hwy 31 S, PO Box 1627, 35124. SAN 325-0407. Tel: 205-620-6418. FAX: 205-620-6469. E-Mail: library@pelhamonline.com. *Librn*, Barbara Roberts; Staff 9 (MLS 4, Non-MLS 5)
Founded 1975. Pop 12,000; Circ 115,000
Library Holdings: Bk Vols 31,000; Per Subs 50
Mem of Harrison Regional Library System

PHENIX CITY

P PHENIX CITY-RUSSELL COUNTY LIBRARY,* 1501 17th Ave, 36867. SAN 300-1857. Tel: 334-297-1139. FAX: 334-298-8452. *Dir*, Irma Duke
Founded 1957. Pop 45,394; Circ 85,745
Library Holdings: Bk Vols 68,703; Per Subs 90

PHIL CAMPBELL

J NORTHWEST-SHOALS COMMUNITY COLLEGE, James A Glasgow Library, 2080 College Rd, 35581. SAN 300-1865. Tel: 256-331-6271. FAX: 256-331-6202. *Coll Develop, Librn*, Rachel Trapp; Staff 2 (MLS 1, Non-MLS 1)
Founded 1963. Enrl 1,000; Fac 33
Library Holdings: Bk Vols 31,000; Per Subs 210
Subject Interests: Language arts, Nursing, Social sciences and issues
Special Collections: Alabama Room Coll, bks, microflm; Children's Coll; Nursing Coll, multi media mat
Publications: AV catalog; Policy & Procedures manual

PIEDMONT

P PIEDMONT PUBLIC LIBRARY,* 106 N Main St, 36272. SAN 300-1873. Tel: 256-447-3369. FAX: 256-447-3369. *Librn*, Kim Mills
Founded 1969. Circ 40,000
Library Holdings: Bk Vols 30,000
Mem of Anniston-Calhoun County Libr Syst

PLEASANT GROVE

P PLEASANT GROVE PUBLIC LIBRARY,* 501 Park Rd, 35127. (Mail add: PO Box 339, 35127), SAN 324-122X. Tel: 205-744-7221, Ext 42. FAX: 205-491-5472. *Dir*, Wynelle Anthony
Founded 1948. Pop 7,102; Circ 30,228
Library Holdings: Bk Vols 27,000; Per Subs 33

PRATTVILLE

P AUTAUGA-PRATTVILLE PUBLIC LIBRARY, 254 Doster St, 36067-3933. SAN 300-1903. Tel: 334-365-3396. FAX: 334-365-3397. Web Site: prattvillelibrary.compumise.com. *Dir*, Marjorie Mullins; *Asst Dir*, Anna-Beth Smith; *Cat*, Deanne Charlton; *Coll Develop*, Anna Beth Smith
Founded 1956. Pop 32,259; Circ 115,000
Library Holdings: Bk Vols 70,000; Per Subs 120
Special Collections: Alabama History Coll; Business Reference Center
Friends of the Library Group
Branches: 3
AUTAUGAVILLE PUBLIC, PO Box 178, Autaugaville, 36003. SAN 300-0125. Tel: 334-365-9322. Web Site: www.prattvillelibrary.compumise.com. *Librn*, Karen Milton
Friends of the Library Group
BILLINGSLEY PUBLIC, PO Box 34, Billingsley, 36006. SAN 300-0176. Tel: 205-755-9809. Web Site: www.prattvillelibrary.compumise.com. *Librn*, Mary Ellen Williams
Friends of the Library Group
MARBURY COMMUNITY, PO Box 200, Marbury, 36051. SAN 300-1385. Tel: 205-755-8575. Web Site: www.prattvillelibrary.compumise.com. *Librn*, Amelia Bishop
Friends of the Library Group

PRICHARD

P PRICHARD PUBLIC LIBRARY,* 300 W Love Joy Loop, 36610. SAN 300-1911. Tel: 334-452-7847. FAX: 334-452-7935. *Dir*, Sara Daughtry
Pop 39,000
Library Holdings: Bk Vols 10,000; Per Subs 110
Branches: 1
MITCHELL, 4440 Highpoint Blvd, Eight Mile, 36613. SAN 377-807X. Tel: 334-452-7846. *Librn*, Lucille Chapman

RAINBOW CITY

P RAINBOW CITY PUBLIC LIBRARY, 3702 Rainbow Dr, 35906. SAN 374-4604. Tel: 256-442-8477. FAX: 256-442-4128. Web Site: www.rbclibrary.org. *Dir*, Tina M Brooks; E-Mail: tbrooks@rainbow-city.com; *Cat*, Joan Roark; *Circ*, Kelly Johnson; *Circ*, Gloria Miller; Staff 8 (MLS 1, Non-MLS 7)
Founded 1981. Pop 8,694; Circ 67,500
Library Holdings: Bk Vols 41,146; Per Subs 52

RAINSVILLE

J NORTHEAST ALABAMA COMMUNITY COLLEGE, Cecil B Word Learning Resources Center, 138 Al Hwy 35, 35986. (Mail add: PO Box 159, 35986), SAN 300-192X. Tel: 256-228-6001, 256-638-4418. FAX: 256-228-4350. E-Mail: nac_circ@lmn.lib.al.us. Web Site: www.lmn.lib.al.us. *Dir*, Arlene E Grede; Tel: 256-228-6001, Ext 226; Staff 4 (MLS 3, Non-MLS 1)
Founded 1965. Enrl 1,700; Fac 39; Highest Degree: Doctorate
Oct 1999-Sep 2000 Income Parent Institution $210,227. Sal $130,495 (Prof $75,444)
Library Holdings: Bk Vols 47,000; Per Subs 134
Automation Activity & Vendor Info: (Cataloging) DRA; (Circulation) DRA; (ILL) DRA; (OPAC) DRA
Database Vendor: GaleNet, IAC - Info Trac, Wilson - Wilson Web
Function: ILL available
Partic in Library Management Network, Inc

P RAINSVILLE PUBLIC LIBRARY,* 941 E Main St, 35986. (Mail add: PO Box 509, 35986), SAN 300-1938. Tel: 256-638-3311. FAX: 256-638-3314. E-Mail: rpl1@farmers.com. Web Site: www.rplfarmers.com. *Dir*, Ruth Hammon; *Asst Librn*, Carolyn Wooten
Founded 1968. Pop 10,000; Circ 38,000
Oct 1997-Sep 1998 Income $101,000. Mats Exp $20,000
Library Holdings: Bk Vols 30,000; Per Subs 35
Mem of APLS

REDSTONE ARSENAL

UNITED STATES ARMY
A AVIATION & MISSILE COMMAND REDSTONE SCIENTIFIC INFORMATION CENTER, AMSAM-RD-AS-I-RSIC, Bldg 4484, 35898-5000. SAN 330-342X. Tel: 256-842-8434, 256-876-9309. Interlibrary Loan Service Tel: 256-876-0945. Reference Tel: 256-876-5195. FAX: 256-842-7415. E-Mail: rsic@redstone.army.mil. Web Site: library.redstone.army.mil. *Dir*, Martha Knott; *Tech Servs*, Paul Y Fritts; *Coll Develop*, Yvonne Stewart; Staff 14 (MLS 11, Non-MLS 3)
Founded 1949. Pop 7,300
Library Holdings: Bk Vols 240,000; Per Subs 2,000
Subject Interests: Aeronautics, Aviation, Chemistry, Computer science, Electrical engineering, Electronics, Mechanical engineering, Nuclear science, Physics
Special Collections: Guidance & Control; Helicopter; Metrication; Peenemuende Papers; Rocket Technology; Space Defense
Automation Activity & Vendor Info: (Cataloging) SIRSI; (Circulation) SIRSI; (OPAC) SIRSI
Database Vendor: OCLC - First Search
Partic in Defense Technical Information Center; Fed Libr & Info Network

A ORDNANCE MISSILE & MUNITIONS CENTER & SCHOOL TECHNICAL LIBRARY, Bldg 3323, 35897-6280. SAN 330-3454. Tel: 256-876-7425. FAX: 256-842-2193. *Chief Librn*, Mark Hines; E-Mail: hines_ma@redstone.army.mil
Founded 1952. Pop 3,500; Circ 21,557
Library Holdings: Bk Vols 17,500; Per Subs 140
Subject Interests: Education, Electronics, Military history
Publications: Acquisitions list; audiovisual catalog; library guide

REFORM

P REFORM PUBLIC LIBRARY, 302 First St S, 35481-0819. (Mail add: PO Box 819, 35481-0819), SAN 324-0630. Tel: 205-375-6240. FAX: 205-375-6240. E-Mail: reformlibrary@hotmail.com. *Librn*, Virginia Barton
Pop 2,100; Circ 5,030
Library Holdings: Bk Vols 9,704; Per Subs 25
Mem of Pickens County Coop Libr
Friends of the Library Group

ROANOKE

P ANNIE L AWBREY PUBLIC LIBRARY,* 736 College St, 36274-1617. SAN 300-1946. Tel: 334-863-2632. FAX: 334-863-8997. E-Mail: annielawbrey@yahoo.com. *Librn*, Glenda Brooks; Staff 1 (MLS 1)
Founded 1934. Pop 20,400
Library Holdings: Bk Vols 22,094; Bk Titles 20,716; Per Subs 50
Special Collections: Adult Readers; Audio Visual Coll; Books on Tape; Large Print Coll
Mem of Cheaha Regional Library
Library provides Dial-A-Story, a recorded children's story available 24 hours a day

ROBERTSDALE

P BALDWIN COUNTY LIBRARY COOPERATIVE, INC, (BCLC), 22743 Milwaukee St, PO Box 399, 36567. SAN 300-1954. Tel: 334-947-7632. FAX: 334-947-2651. E-Mail: bclc@gulftel.com. Web Site: www.gulftel.com/~bclc. *Dir*, Bonnie Lee Gray; *Tech Servs*, Kim Mumbower; *Electronic Resources*, Marie Fackler; E-Mail: bclcweb.gulftel.com; *ILL*, Susan Koler; E-Mail: bclcill@gulftel.com; Staff 1 (MLS 1)
Founded 1966
Oct 1999-Sep 2000 Income $198,166, State $83,073, County $93,573, Locally Generated Income $5,035, Parent Institution $11,025, Other $5,460. Mats Exp $15,507, Books $14,855, Per/Ser (Incl. Access Fees) $652. Sal $128,612 (Prof $33,500)
Library Holdings: Bk Vols 14,632; Bk Titles 14,320; Per Subs 12
Subject Interests: Adult education
Automation Activity & Vendor Info: (Cataloging) TLC; (Circulation) TLC; (OPAC) TLC
Function: ILL available, Reference services available, Some telephone reference
Member Libraries: Bay Minette Public Library; Daphne Public Library; Fairhope Public Library; Foley Public Library; Loxley Public Library; Orange Beach Public Library; Oscar Johnson Memorial Library; Robertsdale Public Library; Thomas B Norton Public Library
Bookmobiles: 1

P ROBERTSDALE PUBLIC LIBRARY,* 18301 Pennsylvania St, 36567. SAN 300-1962. Tel: 334-947-5720. FAX: 334-947-5521. E-Mail: roblib@gvlstel.com. *Dir*, Cynthia Nall; *Asst Librn*, Joyce Vaughn; *Asst Librn*, Pam White
Founded 1914. Pop 3,600; Circ 51,000
Library Holdings: Bk Titles 25,000; Per Subs 75
Mem of Baldwin County Library Cooperative, Inc

ROCKFORD

P ROCKFORD PUBLIC LIBRARY,* 110 Main St, 35136. (Mail add: PO Box 128, 35136), SAN 300-1970. Tel: 256-377-4911. FAX: 256-377-4489. E-Mail: rockfordpl@wwisp.com. *Librn*, Glenda Cardwell
Founded 1962. Pop 603; Circ 5,140
Library Holdings: Bk Vols 3,500; Per Subs 15
Mem of Horseshoe Bend Regional Library

ROGERSVILLE

P ROGERSVILLE PUBLIC LIBRARY,* 74 Bank St, 35652. (Mail add: PO Box 190, 35652), SAN 300-1989. Tel: 256-247-0151. FAX: 256-247-0144. E-Mail: ropublib@hiwaay.net. Web Site: www.ropublib.net. *Librn*, Tammy Russell
Pop 1,224; Circ 35,359
Library Holdings: Bk Vols 22,000; Per Subs 32
Friends of the Library Group

SAMSON

P SAMSON PUBLIC LIBRARY, 200 N Johnson St, 36477. (Mail add: PO Box 147, 36477), SAN 300-2012. Tel: 334-898-7806. FAX: 334-898-7806. *Librn*, Susie Dunn; E-Mail: sand@alaweb.com
Pop 2,300; Circ 8,297
Oct 1999-Sep 2001 Income $2,325, State $1,856, City $240, County $229. Sal $7,356
Library Holdings: Bk Titles 8,297
Mem of Cross Trails Regional Library Service
Open Mon-Fri 1-5

SATSUMA

R FIRST BAPTIST CHURCH & SATSUMA CHRISTIAN SCHOOL,* Old Hwy 43, PO Box 610, 36572. SAN 300-2020. Tel: 334-675-1295. FAX: 334-675-1282.
Founded 1964
Library Holdings: Bk Vols 4,700

§P SATSUMA PUBLIC LIBRARY, 5466 Old Hwy 43, 36572. (Mail add: PO Box 579, 36572-0579), Tel: 334-679-0700. FAX: 334-679-4993. E-Mail: splibrarydir@dibbs.net. Web Site: www.satsuma.qpg.com. *Dir*, Cindy Ingram
Oct 1998-Sep 1999 Income $28,305, State $6,836, City $7,031, County $12,985, Other $1,453
Library Holdings: Bk Vols 10,825; Bk Titles 10,113; Per Subs 18

SCOTTSBORO

P SCOTTSBORO PUBLIC LIBRARY,* 1002 S Broad St, 35768. SAN 300-2039. Tel: 256-574-4335. FAX: 256-259-4457. E-Mail: sborolib@hiwaay.net. Web Site: www.lmn.lib.al.us. *Librn*, Gloria Balentine; E-Mail: gloria_spl@lmn.lib.al.us
Founded 1929. Pop 49,900; Circ 101,183
1997-1998 Income $209,526, State $52,500, City $100,745, Federal $5,266, County $12,000, Locally Generated Income $37,115. Mats Exp $36,125, Books $28,291, Per/Ser (Incl. Access Fees) $7,834. Sal $122,003 (Prof $27,466)
Library Holdings: Bk Vols 36,973; Per Subs 103
Special Collections: Alabama Genealogy Coll; Nuclear Regulatory Commission on Public Document Room
Friends of the Library Group
Branches: 2
STEVENSON PUBLIC LIBRARY, 104 W Main St, Stevenson, 35772. SAN 374-4507. Tel: 256-437-3008. *Librn*, Juanita Powell
WOODVILLE PUBLIC LIBRARY, 26 Venson St, PO Box 116, Woodville, 35776. SAN 325-4402. Tel: 256-776-2796. Web Site: www.worldisp.net/1r/105. *Dir*, Karen Chambers
Founded 1985. Pop 1,200; Circ 19,176
Oct 1998-Sep 1999 Income (Main Library Only) $27,203, City $17,652, County $1,250, Locally Generated Income $7,389, Parent Institution $912. Mats Exp $3,906, Books $3,000, Per/Ser (Incl. Access Fees) $466, Micro $112, Other Print Mats $89, Electronic Ref Mat (Incl. Access Fees) $239. Sal $8,365 (Prof $4,405)
Library Holdings: Bk Vols 4,505; Bk Titles 6,180; Per Subs 22; High Interest/Low Vocabulary Bk Vols 135
Subject Interests: Genealogy
Bookmobiles: 1

SELMA

GL DALLAS COUNTY CIRCUIT COURT LIBRARY,* 105 Lauderdale St, PO Box 1158, 36701. SAN 325-9560. Tel: 334-874-2526. *Librn*, Barbara Rush

P PUBLIC LIBRARY OF SELMA & DALLAS COUNTY,* 1103 Selma Ave, 36703-4498. SAN 300-2055. Tel: 334-874-1725. FAX: 334-874-1729. E-Mail: selmalib@zebra.net. *Dir*, Becky Cothran Nichols
Founded 1903. Pop 55,000; Circ 72,000
Library Holdings: Bk Vols 61,493; Bk Titles 56,000; Per Subs 82
Subject Interests: Local history
Friends of the Library Group

C SELMA UNIVERSITY, Stone-Robinson Library,* 1501 Lapsley St, 36701. SAN 300-2063. Tel: 334-874-7673. FAX: 334-872-7746. *Dir*, Marietta Hatcher
Founded 1959. Highest Degree: Bachelor
Library Holdings: Bk Titles 35,000; Per Subs 154
Special Collections: Black Studies Coll

J WALLACE COMMUNITY COLLEGE, Selma Library,* 3000 Earl Goodwin Pkwy, PO Box 2530, 36702. SAN 300-2047. Tel: 334-876-9344. FAX: 334-876-9344. Web Site: wccs.cc.al.us. *Dir*, Hallie A Perry; Tel: 334-876-9345, Fax: 334-876-9394, E-Mail: halp@wccs.cc.al.us; Staff 4 (MLS 2, Non-MLS 2)
Founded 1971. Enrl 1,500; Fac 60; Highest Degree: Doctorate

Library Holdings: Bk Vols 19,000; Per Subs 185
Subject Interests: Literature, Nursing, Social sciences and issues, Technology
Database Vendor: Ebsco - EbscoHost

SHEFFIELD

P SHEFFIELD PUBLIC LIBRARY,* 316 N Montgomery Ave, 35660. SAN 300-2101. Tel: 256-386-5633. FAX: 256-386-5608. Web Site: www.lmn.lib.al.us. *Dir*, Christine Box; E-Mail: chris_msh@lmn.lib.al.us; *Asst Dir, Ch Servs*, Beth Ridgeway; *Cat*, Cindy Kirsch; *Tech Servs*, Evallou Richardson
Pop 11,903; Circ 53,647
Oct 1997-Sep 1998 Income $171,276. Mats Exp $70,000. Sal $95,000
Library Holdings: Bk Vols 50,000; Per Subs 106
Special Collections: Local History & Genealogy Coll
Database Vendor: DRA
Friends of the Library Group

SILVERHILL

P OSCAR JOHNSON MEMORIAL LIBRARY, 21967 Sixth St, PO Box 185, 36576-0185. Tel: 334-945-5201. E-Mail: shilib@gulftel.com. *Librn*, Elsie Chandler; Staff 1 (Non-MLS 1)
Founded 1907. Pop 613; Circ 3,050
Oct 1998-Sep 1999 Income $5,018, State $693, City $3,728, Locally Generated Income $597. Mats Exp $1,821, Per/Ser (Incl. Access Fees) $128, Other Print Mats $1,000, Electronic Ref Mat (Incl. Access Fees) $693
Library Holdings: Bk Vols 9,335
Mem of Baldwin County Library Cooperative, Inc

SLOCOMB

R FIRST BAPTIST CHURCH LIBRARY, PO Box 1298, 36375. SAN 300-2128. Tel: 334-886-3018. *Librn*, Gwen Ball; *Asst Librn*, Helen Trampe
Founded 1963
Library Holdings: Bk Titles 5,091; Per Subs 18
Subject Interests: Church history

P SLOCOMB PUBLIC LIBRARY,* PO Box 1026, 36375. SAN 376-7418. Tel: 334-886-9009. FAX: 334-886-3729. *Librn*, Mary Sue Newton
Library Holdings: Bk Titles 9,500
Mem of Cross Trails Regional Library Service

SUMITON

P SUMITON PUBLIC LIBRARY,* Town Hall, State St, 35148. (Mail add: PO Box 10, 35148), SAN 300-2136. Tel: 205-648-7451. FAX: 205-648-7451. E-Mail: sumiton@hotmail.com. *Librn*, Christine E Warren
Library Holdings: Bk Vols 6,000; Bk Titles 36,000; Per Subs 16
Mem of Carl Elliott Regional Library System

SYLACAUGA

P B B COMER MEMORIAL LIBRARY,* 314 N Broadway, 35150-2528. SAN 300-2144. Tel: 256-249-0961. FAX: 256-401-2492. E-Mail: bbclibrary@sylacauga.net. Web Site: www.sylacauga.net/index.htm. *Dir*, Dr Shirley K Spears; Staff 1 (MLS 1)
Founded 1939. Pop 25,000; Circ 125,577
Library Holdings: Bk Vols 71,097; Per Subs 160
Subject Interests: Genealogy
Special Collections: Alabama History Coll

TALLADEGA

P ALABAMA INSTITUTE FOR THE DEAF & BLIND, Library & Resource Center for the Blind & Physically Handicapped, 705 South St, 35160. (Mail add: PO Box 698, 35161), SAN 300-2152. Tel: 256-761-3237. FAX: 256-761-3561. Toll Free FAX: 800-848-4722. E-Mail: tlacy@aidb.state.al.us. Web Site: www.aidb.org. *Dir*, Teresa Lacy; *Reader Servs*, Martha Thompson; *Asst Dir*, Mike Jones; Staff 3 (MLS 1, Non-MLS 2)
Founded 1965
Library Holdings: Bk Vols 60,000; Per Subs 62
Special Collections: Alabama History, cassettes
Automation Activity & Vendor Info: (Acquisitions) Sagebrush Corporation; (Cataloging) Sagebrush Corporation; (Circulation) Sagebrush Corporation; (Course Reserve) Sagebrush Corporation; (ILL) Sagebrush Corporation; (Media Booking) Sagebrush Corporation; (OPAC) Sagebrush Corporation; (Serials) Sagebrush Corporation
Publications: Newsletter (irregular)
Serves blind & physically handicapped population of St Clair, Coosa & Talladega Counties
Friends of the Library Group

C TALLADEGA COLLEGE, Savery Library, 627 W Battle St, 35160. SAN 300-2160. Tel: 256-761-6279. FAX: 256-761-6382. Web Site: www.talladega.edu. *Librn*, Dr Helen Bush-Caver; E-Mail: hcaver@telledega.edu; *Archivist*, Louretta Wimberly; *Archivist*, Keith D Winsell; Staff 11 (MLS 4, Non-MLS 7)
Founded 1939. Enrl 660; Fac 48; Highest Degree: Bachelor
Library Holdings: Bk Titles 120,687; Per Subs 362
Special Collections: Amistad Mutiny - Murals; Black Studies
Publications: New Acquisitions; Student Handbook
Partic in Coop Col Libr Ctr, Inc

GL TALLADEGA COUNTY LAW LIBRARY, Talladega County Judicial Bldg, Northeast St, PO Box 459, 35161. SAN 300-2179. Tel: 256-761-2116. E-Mail: tallall@mindspring.com. *Librn*, Cindy Caudle
Founded 1955
Library Holdings: Bk Vols 30,000; Per Subs 100

P TALLADEGA PUBLIC LIBRARY, 202 South St E, 35160. SAN 300-2187. Tel: 205-362-4211. FAX: 205-362-0653. E-Mail: talladega@airnet.net. *Dir, Librn*, Deborah B Waller; Staff 7 (MLS 1, Non-MLS 6)
Founded 1906. Pop 72,601; Circ 118,641
Oct 1998-Sep 1999 Income $294,686, State $21,019, City $273,667. Mats Exp $43,836. Sal $173,008
Library Holdings: Bk Vols 75,000; Per Subs 110
Special Collections: Talladega History

TARRANT

P TARRANT PUBLIC LIBRARY,* 1143 Ford Ave, 35217-2437. SAN 300-2209. Tel: 205-849-2825. FAX: 205-327-5370. E-Mail: tarrant@bham.lib.al.us. *Librn*, Patrick Coleman; *Asst Librn*, Catherine Brown
Founded 1930. Pop 8,046
Library Holdings: Bk Vols 27,257; Bk Titles 25,528; Per Subs 48
Subject Interests: Alabama
Special Collections: Arrowhead Coll; Petrified Wood; Shell Coll
Publications: Newsletter
Partic in Jefferson County Public Libr Asn

THOMASVILLE

GM ALABAMA DEPARTMENT OF MENTAL HEALTH, Thomasville Mental Health Rehabilitation Center,* PO Box 309, 36784. SAN 300-2217. Tel: 334-636-5421, Ext 288. FAX: 334-636-5421, Ext 285. *Dir*, Beatrice McLean
Founded 1973
Oct 1997-Sep 1998 Mats Exp $15,870
Library Holdings: Bk Vols 5,000; Per Subs 27

C ALABAMA SOUTHERN COMMUNITY COLLEGE LIBRARY, 30755 Highway 43, PO Box 2000, 36784. SAN 322-8827. Tel: 334-636-9642. FAX: 334-636-1478. Web Site: www.ascc.edu. *Librn*, Angela Roberts
Enrl 500; Fac 21
Library Holdings: Bk Titles 43,000; Per Subs 250
Departmental Libraries:
GILBERTOWN CAMPUS, PO Box 2000, Gilbertown, 36908. Tel: 334-843-5265. FAX: 334-843-2420.

P THOMASVILLE PUBLIC LIBRARY,* 1000 Mosley Dr, 36784. SAN 300-2225. Tel: 334-636-5343. FAX: 334-636-5343. *Librn*, Kerry Q Phillips
Pop 5,000; Circ 18,000
1998-1999 Income $77,000, City $75,000, Locally Generated Income $2,000. Mats Exp $7,000, Books $5,500, Per/Ser (Incl. Access Fees) $500, Other Print Mats $1,000. Sal $40,000 (Prof $26,000)
Library Holdings: Bk Vols 15,000; Per Subs 26

TROY

P TROY PUBLIC LIBRARY, 300 N Three Notch Rd, 36081. SAN 330-3152. Tel: 334-566-1314. FAX: 334-566-4392. *Dir*, Margaret Stewart; *Asst Dir*, Karen Bullard; Staff 3 (MLS 1, Non-MLS 2)
Library Holdings: Bk Titles 50,000; Per Subs 250
Subject Interests: Genealogy
Friends of the Library Group

C TROY STATE UNIVERSITY LIBRARY,* 36082. SAN 330-3489. Tel: 334-670-3266. FAX: 334-670-3694. Web Site: www.tsulib.troyst.edu. *Dean of Libr*, Dr Henry Stewart; E-Mail: hrstewart@trojan.troyst.edu; *Coll Develop, Tech Servs*, Mary Beth Green; *ILL*, Belinda C Edwards; *Electronic Resources*, Jeremy Landry. Subject Specialists: *Business and management*, Lucy Farrow; *Education*, Susan Yarborough; *Humanities*, Betty Chancellor; *Social sciences and issues*, Brian Webb; Staff 9 (MLS 9)
Founded 1887. Enrl 5,664; Fac 202; Highest Degree: Doctorate
Sep 1998-Aug 1999 Income $1,656,514, Parent Institution $50,290,160, Other $4,730. Mats Exp $532,104, Books $156,152, Per/Ser (Incl. Access Fees) $272,952, Presv $15,000, Micro $67,000, AV Equip $1,000. Sal $757,305 (Prof $347,028)
Library Holdings: Bk Vols 306,857; Per Subs 1,681

Subject Interests: Education, Indians
Partic in OCLC Online Computer Library Center, Inc; SE Libr Network
Headquarters of the Troy State University Library System, coordinating services from various military bases in the United States & Europe

TRUSSVILLE

P TRUSSVILLE PUBLIC LIBRARY,* 201 Parkway Dr, 35173. SAN 300-2241. Tel: 205-655-2022. FAX: 205-226-3786. *Librn*, Brenda Brasher; E-Mail: bbrasher@bhan.lib.al.us
Circ 50,000
Library Holdings: Bk Vols 34,274; Per Subs 25
Special Collections: Trussville & Alabama History Coll
Friends of the Library Group

TUSCALOOSA

GM DEPARTMENT OF VETERANS AFFAIRS, Hospital Medical Center Library,* 3701 Loop Rd E, 35404. SAN 300-2284. Tel: 205-554-2000, Ext 2355. FAX: 205-554-2033. *Chief Librn*, Ruby Brown
Founded 1932
1997-1998 Income $48,000
Library Holdings: Bk Vols 1,692; Per Subs 191
Subject Interests: Geriatrics and gerontology
Special Collections: Alcoholism Coll, bk & tapes; Community Mental Health Coll, bks & tapes; Psychiatry Coll, bks & tapes
Partic in Medline; Vets Admin Libr Network

G GEOLOGICAL SURVEY OF ALABAMA LIBRARY,* Walter Bryan Jones Hall, PO Box O, 35486. SAN 300-2322. Tel: 205-349-2852, Ext 216. FAX: 205-349-2861. *Librn*, Alexander Sartwell; E-Mail: asartwell@ogb.gsa.tuscaloosa.al.us
Founded 1873
Oct 1996-Sep 1997 Income $30,000
Library Holdings: Bk Titles 150,911
Subject Interests: Geology, Paleontology
Special Collections: Aerial Photography; Satellite Imagery for Alabama
Publications: Bibliographies; publications of the Geological Survey of Alabama & State Oil & Gas Board
US Geological Survey - Earth Science Information Center for the State of Alabama

J SHELTON STATE COMMUNITY COLLEGE, Brooks-Cork Library, 9500 Old Greensboro Rd, 35405. SAN 300-225X. Tel: 205-391-3925. FAX: 205-391-3926. E-Mail: library@shelton.cc.al.us. Web Site: www.shelton.cc.al.us/library. *Dir*, Deborah Grimes; Tel: 205-391-2233, E-Mail: dgrimes@shelton.cc.al.us; *Librn*, Don Bell; Tel: 205-391-2245, E-Mail: dbell@shelton.cc.al.us; *Librn*, Sully Cochrane; Tel: 205-391-2248, E-Mail: scochrane@shelton.cc.al.us; *Per*, Kay Rable; E-Mail: krable@shelton.cc.al.us; *Publ Servs*, Glen Johnson; Tel: 205-391-2327, E-Mail: gjohnson@shelton.cc.al.us
Founded 1979. Enrl 6,000; Fac 200; Highest Degree: Associate
Oct 1999-Sep 2000 Income $559,000. Mats Exp $200,400, Books $45,000, Per/Ser (Incl. Access Fees) $51,000, Micro $7,000, AV Equip $40,000, Electronic Ref Mat (Incl. Access Fees) $10,000
Library Holdings: Bk Vols 41,000; Per Subs 400
Automation Activity & Vendor Info: (Cataloging) epixtech, inc.; (Circulation) epixtech, inc.; (Course Reserve) epixtech, inc.; (Media Booking) epixtech, inc.; (OPAC) epixtech, inc.
Partic in OCLC Online Computer Library Center, Inc; Solinet

C STILLMAN COLLEGE, William H Sheppard Library, 3601 Stillman Blvd, PO Box 1430, 35403. SAN 300-2268. Tel: 205-349-4240, Ext 651. FAX: 205-366-8996. Web Site: www.stillman.edu. *Dean*, Robert Heath; E-Mail: rheath@stillman.edu
Founded 1876. Enrl 766; Highest Degree: Bachelor
Library Holdings: Bk Vols 113,121; Per Subs 364
Subject Interests: Religion
Special Collections: Afro-American Coll; Black history & literature, 19th century & early 20th century, microfilm
Partic in OCLC Online Computer Library Center, Inc

P TUSCALOOSA PUBLIC LIBRARY, 1801 Jack Warner Pkwy, 35401-1099. SAN 330-3519. Tel: 205-345-5820, Ext 204. FAX: 205-758-1735. Web Site: www.tuscaloosa-library.org. *Dir*, Nancy C Pack; E-Mail: npack@tuscaloosa-library.org; *Asst Dir*, Judy Howington; E-Mail: jhowingt@tuscaloosa-library.org; *Librn for Blind*, Barbara B Jordan; Tel: 205-345-3994; *Tech Servs*, Claire Boone; *Automation Syst Coordr*, James Howard; Tel: 205-345-5820, Ext 331, E-Mail: jlhoward@tuscaloosa-library.org; *Ref Serv*, Elizabeth Bradt; *Outreach Serv*, Dawn Sheppard; Staff 40 (MLS 8, Non-MLS 32)
Founded 1921. Pop 158,779; Circ 299,824
Oct 1999-Sep 2000 Income (Main Library and Branch Library) $2,104,076, State $182,886, City $1,186,874, County $493,000, Locally Generated Income $241,316. Mats Exp $425,000, Books $400,000, Per/Ser (Incl. Access Fees) $15,000, Electronic Ref Mat (Incl. Access Fees) $10,000. Sal $1,007,169 (Prof $186,864)
Library Holdings: Bk Vols 139,000; Per Subs 159; Bks on Deafness & Sign Lang 28
Subject Interests: Genealogy
Special Collections: Local History & Genealogy
Automation Activity & Vendor Info: (Acquisitions) Innovative Interfaces Inc.; (Cataloging) Innovative Interfaces Inc.; (Circulation) Innovative Interfaces Inc.; (ILL) Innovative Interfaces Inc.; (OPAC) Innovative Interfaces Inc.; (Serials) Innovative Interfaces Inc.
Friends of the Library Group
Branches: 2

P SUBREGIONAL LIBRARY FOR THE BLIND & PHYSICALLY HANDICAPPED Tel: 205-345-3994. FAX: 205-752-8300. *Librn*, Barbara B Jordan
Founded 1974. Pop 218; Circ 8,159
Special Collections: Blindness & Physical Handicaps (Reference Coll)
Special Services for the Blind - Ednalite Hi-Vision scope & page magnifiers for in-house use; Home delivery & demonstration of talking book machines & material to new readers; Home delivery of replacement machines

WEAVER, 2937 18th St, 35401-8291. SAN 330-3578. Tel: 205-758-8291. FAX: 205-758-8291. Web Site: www.tuscaloosa-library.org. *Librn*, Corrine Harris
Friends of the Library Group
Bookmobiles: 1

UNIVERSITY OF ALABAMA

CL SCHOOL OF LAW LIBRARY, Box 870383, 35487-0383. SAN 330-3969. Tel: 205-348-5925. FAX: 205-348-1112. Web Site: www.law.ua.edu. *Dir*, James Leonard; E-Mail: jleonard@law.ua.edu; *Tech Servs*, Ruth Weeks; *Ref*, Penny Gibson; *Assoc Dir*, Robert Marshall; *Coll Develop*, Paul Pruitt; Staff 8 (MLS 8)
Founded 1872. Enrl 592; Fac 35; Highest Degree: Doctorate
Library Holdings: Bk Titles 76,782; Per Subs 3,148
Special Collections: Former US Supreme Court Justice Hugo L Black
Publications: CASE; UALL Newsletter; User Guides Series
Mem of Asn of Research Libraries
Partic in Dialog Corporation; NAAL; Westlaw

C UNIVERSITY LIBRARIES, Capstone Dr, 35487-0001. (Mail add: PO Box 870266, 35487-0154), SAN 330-3845. Tel: 205-348-7561. Interlibrary Loan Service Tel: 205-348-6345. Circulation Tel: 205-348-9748. Reference Tel: 205-348-6047. FAX: 205-348-8833. Web Site: www.lib.ua.edu. *Dean of Libr*, Charles B Osburn; E-Mail: cosburn@bama.ua.edu; *Assoc Dir*, Karen Croneis; Tel: 205-348-5569, E-Mail: kcroneis@bama.ua.edu; *Assoc Dir*, Anne Edwards; Tel: 205-348-4607, E-Mail: aedwards@bama.ua.edu; *Br Coordr*, Lee Pike; Tel: 205-348-1095, Fax: 205-348-0803, E-Mail: lpike@bruno.cba.ua.edu; *Br Coordr*, John Sandy; Tel: 205-348-2111, Fax: 205-348-2113, E-Mail: jsandy@bama.ua.edu; *Br Coordr*, Sharon L Stewart; Tel: 205-348-1506, Fax: 205-348-6602, E-Mail: sstewart@bama.ua.edu; *Head, Acq*, Beth Holley; Tel: 205-348-1493, Fax: 205-348-6358, E-Mail: bholley@bama.ua.edu; *Automation Syst Coordr*, Warren Murphy; Tel: 205-348-2299, E-Mail: wmurphy@bama.ua.edu; *Head, Cat*, Christine Thompson; Tel: 205-348-1488, Fax: 205-348-6358, E-Mail: cthompso@bama.ua.edu; *Head, Circ*, Janice Simpson; Tel: 205-348-8169, E-Mail: jsimpson@bama.ua.edu; *ILL*, Angela Wright; Tel: 205-348-6303, Fax: 205-348-9564, E-Mail: ajwright@bama.ua.edu; *Business*, Harriet Deason; Tel: 205-348-5540, Fax: 205-348-2399, E-Mail: hdeason@bama.ua.edu; *Planning Services*, Kate Ragsdale; Tel: 205-348-1484, E-Mail: kragsdal@bama.ua.edu; *Commun Relations*, Margaret Wilson; Tel: 205-348-1416, E-Mail: mawilson@bama.ua.edu; Staff 41 (MLS 35, Non-MLS 6)
Founded 1831. Enrl 18,324; Fac 756; Highest Degree: Doctorate
Oct 1999-Sep 2000 Mats Exp $3,856,194. Sal $3,352,577 (Prof $1,688,698)
Library Holdings: Bk Vols 1,930,706; Per Subs 13,777
Special Collections: First Editions (Sir Walter Scott, Lafcadio Hearn, Robinson Jeffers); Manuscript & Archive Coll; Rucker Agee Coll of Alabamiana; Southern Americana; William Campbell March & numerous Southern Authors; World War II Armed Services Editions
Database Vendor: Dialog, Ebsco - EbscoHost, GaleNet, IAC - Info Trac, Lexis-Nexis, OCLC - First Search, OVID Technologies, ProQuest, Silverplatter Information Inc., Wilson - Wilson Web
Publications: Library Horizons (newsletter); Rotunda (newsletter)
Partic in Network of Alabama Academic Libraries
Special Services for the Deaf - TTY machine
Special Services for the Blind - Adapted computers & special software with speech output to assist learning disabled, mentally retarded & uneducated
Friends of the Library Group

CM UNIVERSITY OF ALABAMA, Health Sciences Library,* DCH, 809 University Blvd E, 35401. (Mail add: Box 870378, 35487-0378), SAN 330-3608. Tel: 205-348-1360. FAX: 205-348-9563. Web Site: www.bama.ua.edu/~hslib/. *Actg Dir*, Nellie Williams; *Tech Servs*, Martha Cook; E-Mail: mcook@cchs.ua.edu; Staff 3 (MLS 3)
Founded 1973. Enrl 15,000; Fac 800; Highest Degree: Doctorate
1997-1998 Income $394,383. Mats Exp $54,849. Sal $262,939
Library Holdings: Bk Vols 17,700; Per Subs 347

Subject Interests: Medicine, Nursing
Partic in Alabama Biomedical Union List of Serials; Dialog Corporation; Medlars; OCLC Online Computer Library Center, Inc

R UNIVERSITY PRESBYTERIAN CHURCH, Ann Inglett Library, 1127 Eighth St, 35401. SAN 300-2276. Tel: 205-758-5422. E-Mail: upc35401@aol.com. *Head Librn*, Nancy Dupree
Founded 1964
Library Holdings: Bk Vols 3,000; Per Subs 10
Subject Interests: Biblical studies, Religion, Sociology, Theology

TUSCUMBIA

P HELEN KELLER PUBLIC LIBRARY,* 511 N Main St, 35674. SAN 300-2292. Tel: 256-383-7065. *Librn*, Judy Murphy
Founded 1893. Pop 9,137; Circ 32,794
Library Holdings: Bk Vols 19,000; Per Subs 25
Special Collections: Helen Keller Special Coll
Partic in Library Management Network, Inc
Friends of the Library Group

TUSKEGEE

P MACON COUNTY-TUSKEGEE PUBLIC LIBRARY, 302 S Main St, 36083-1894. SAN 330-3667. Tel: 334-727-5192. FAX: 334-727-5194, 334-727-5198. *Dir*, Maperal Clark; Fax: 334-727-5989, E-Mail: mclark@bellsouth.net; Staff 2 (Non-MLS 2)
Founded 1968. Pop 26,829
Library Holdings: Bk Vols 25,201; Bk Titles 24,957; Per Subs 63
Special Collections: Children's Literature (Sammy Young Coll), fs, A-tapes, flm
Automation Activity & Vendor Info: (Acquisitions) Gaylord
Publications: American Libraries; Library Journal; Library Scene
Books-By-Mail Program serves rural route residents & home bound citizens.

C TUSKEGEE UNIVERSITY, Hollis Burke Frissell Library,* 36088. SAN 330-3721. Tel: 334-727-8894. FAX: 334-727-9282. Web Site: www.tusk.edu. *ILL, Librn*, Juanita Roberts; E-Mail: jrobert@acd.tusk.edu; *Cat, Tech Servs*, Deborah Kilgore; *Ref*, Petre Bridges; *Spec Coll*, Cynthia Wilson; *Circ*, Deloris Player; *Media Spec*, Barry Williams; *Govt Doc*, Eunice Samuel; Staff 10 (MLS 10)
Founded 1881. Enrl 3,500
Library Holdings: Bk Vols 310,000; Per Subs 1,500
Special Collections: Blacks (Washington Coll)
Partic in Coop Col Libr Ctr, Inc
Friends of the Library Group
Departmental Libraries:
ARCHITECTURE, Wilcox A, 36088. Tel: 334-724-4269. FAX: 334-727-9282. *Librn*, Shakuntala Singh
ENGINEERING, Engineering Bldg, 36088. Tel: 334-727-8901. FAX: 334-727-9282. *Librn*, Frances F Davis

CM VETERINARY MEDICAL LIBRARY, Patterson Hall, 36088. Tel: 334-727-8780. FAX: 334-727-8442. *Librn*, Margaret Alexander
Library Holdings: Bk Vols 10,000; Per Subs 190

UNION SPRINGS

P UNION SPRINGS PUBLIC LIBRARY, 103 N Prairie, 36089. SAN 330-3187. Tel: 334-738-2760. FAX: 334-738-2760. *Librn*, Mary E Parr
Library Holdings: Bk Vols 10,309; Per Subs 26
Open Mon-Fri 11-5

UNIONTOWN

§P UNIONTOWN PUBLIC LIBRARY, Lucian St, 36786. (Mail add: PO Box 637, 36786-0637), Tel: 334-628-6681. *Librn*, Winnie Scott
Oct 2000-Sep 2001 Income $9,100, City $4,400, County $4,700
Library Holdings: Bk Vols 900

VALLEY

P H GRADY BRADSHAW CHAMBERS COUNTY LIBRARY,* 3419 20th Ave, 36854. SAN 320-1155. Tel: 334-768-2161. FAX: 334-768-7272. E-Mail: bradshaulibrary@mindspring.com. *Dir*, Anne K Alsobrook; *Ch Servs*, Tabitha Truitt; Staff 6 (MLS 1, Non-MLS 5)
Founded 1976. Pop 44,105; Circ 80,723
Library Holdings: Bk Vols 54,978; Bk Titles 48,229; Per Subs 126
Subject Interests: Genealogy
Special Collections: Cobb Memorial Archives
Friends of the Library Group

J SOUTHERN UNION STATE JUNIOR COLLEGE, Valley Campus Library, 321 Fob James Dr, 36854. SAN 300-1296. Tel: 334-756-4151. FAX: 334-756-5183. *Dir*, Kathy Reynolds; Tel: 256-395-2211, Ext 5130; *Librn*, Lucy Champion
Library Holdings: Bk Vols 90,000
Departmental Libraries:
OPELIKA BRANCH, 1701 Lafayette Pkwy, Opelika, 36801. Tel: 334-745-6437. FAX: 334-749-5505.

VESTAVIA HILLS

P VESTAVIA HILLS-RICHARD M SCRUSHY PUBLIC LIBRARY,* 1112 Montgomery Hwy, 35216. SAN 300-2349. Tel: 205-978-0155. FAX: 205-978-0156. Web Site: www.bham.lib.al.us. *Dir*, Grace F Reid; E-Mail: gfreid@bham.lib.al.us; *Ref*, Thomas M Lesley; *Tech Servs*, Lonny W Terry; *Ad Servs, Coll Develop*, Yvonne Chappell; *Automation Syst Coordr*, Carolyn S Key
Founded 1969. Pop 20,384; Circ 131,238
Oct 1998-Sep 1999 Income $712,842. Mats Exp $111,299, Books $81,953, Per/Ser (Incl. Access Fees) $9,733, Other Print Mats $19,613. Sal $546,434
Library Holdings: Bk Vols 79,960; Per Subs 135
Special Collections: American Heritage, National Geographic, 1955-82, Readers Digest
Automation Activity & Vendor Info: (Cataloging) Innovative Interfaces Inc.; (Circulation) Innovative Interfaces Inc.
Publications: American Libraries; Booklist
Partic in Jefferson County Libr Coop
Friends of the Library Group

VINCENT

P LALLOUISE FLOREY MCGRAW PUBLIC LIBRARY,* 42860 Hwy 25, PO Box 3, 35178. SAN 371-9375. Tel: 205-672-2749. FAX: 205-672-2749. *Librn*, Estelle Sumners
Library Holdings: Bk Vols 10,400; Per Subs 4
Mem of Harrison Regional Library System

WADLEY

J SOUTHERN UNION STATE COMMUNITY COLLEGE, McClintock-Ensminger Library, Robert St, 36276. (Mail add: PO Box 1000, 36276), SAN 300-2357. Tel: 256-395-2211, Ext 5130. FAX: 256-395-2215. *Dir*, Kathy E Reynolds; E-Mail: kreynolds@suscc.cc.al.us; *Tech Servs*, Kathy Thrash; *Tech Servs*, Dana Franklin; Staff 7 (MLS 2, Non-MLS 5)
Founded 1922
Library Holdings: Bk Vols 92,000; Per Subs 408
Automation Activity & Vendor Info: (Cataloging) SIRSI
Publications: A-V Catalog; Student Handbook
Partic in Ala Libr Asn; Am Libr Asn

WALNUT GROVE

P WESTSIDE PUBLIC LIBRARY,* 5151 Walnut Grove Rd, PO Box 100, 35990. SAN 374-5678. Tel: 205-589-6699. FAX: 205-589-6699. *Dir*, Rhonda Gibbs; Staff 2 (MLS 1, Non-MLS 1)
Founded 1991. Pop 3,500
Library Holdings: Bk Titles 7,000

WARRIOR

P EVELYN THORNTON-WARRIOR PUBLIC LIBRARY, 10 First St, 35180-1500. SAN 376-5539. Tel: 205-647-3006. FAX: 205-647-9280. E-Mail: warrior@bham.lib.al.us. Web Site: www.valcon.bham.lib.al.us/screens/warrior.html. *Librn*, Shirley Faye Pugh; *Asst Librn*, Lanette Williams
Library Holdings: Bk Vols 23,000; Bk Titles 22,800; Per Subs 32
Mem of Birmingham Pub & Jefferson County Free Libr Syst
Friends of the Library Group

WEST BLOCTON

§P WEST BLOCTON PUBLIC LIBRARY, 62 Walter Owens Dr, 35184. (Mail add: PO Box 292, 35184-0292), Tel: 205-938-3570. FAX: 205-938-7803. E-Mail: wbplib@toast.net. *Librn*, Emma Hicks
Oct 1998-Sep 1999 Income $20,000
Library Holdings: Bk Vols 15,000
Automation Activity & Vendor Info: (Acquisitions) Sagebrush Corporation; (Cataloging) Sagebrush Corporation; (Circulation) Sagebrush Corporation

WETUMPKA

P WETUMPKA PUBLIC LIBRARY,* 212 S Main St, 36092. (Mail add: PO Box 249, 36092), SAN 300-2365. Tel: 334-567-1308. FAX: 334-567-1309. E-Mail: wetumpkapl@mindspring.com. *Dir*, Shelby Bryson; *Librn*, Myrna Hays; *Librn*, Tammy Arnell
Founded 1957. Circ 39,036
Oct 1998-Sep 1999 Income $90,550. Mats Exp $24,617. Sal $59,545

Library Holdings: Bk Vols 23,000; Per Subs 55
Special Collections: Local Artists Art Coll
Mem of Horseshoe Bend Regional Library

WHITE HALL

§P WHITE HALL PUBLIC LIBRARY, 640 Freedom Rd, 36040-2830. Tel: 334-874-7323. FAX: 334-874-7323. *Dir*, Ethel J Williams; E-Mail: ewilliams@mindspring.com
Oct 1998-Sep 1999 Income State $900
Library Holdings: Bk Vols 11,000; High Interest/Low Vocabulary Bk Vols 3,000

WILSONVILLE

P WILSONVILLE PUBLIC LIBRARY,* 9905 N Main St, 35186. (Mail add: PO Box 70, 35186), SAN 371-9383. Tel: 205-669-6180. FAX: 205-669-6205. *Librn*, Vernice Stoudenmire
Library Holdings: Bk Titles 4,114
Mem of Harrison Regional Library System

WINFIELD

P NORTHWEST REGIONAL LIBRARY, 185 Ashwood Dr, PO Box 1527, 35594. SAN 330-4027. Tel: 205-487-2330. FAX: 205-487-4815. E-Mail: nwrl@sonet.net. *Dir*, Tracey Key
Founded 1961
Library Holdings: Bk Vols 78,000; Per Subs 14
Branches: 9
HAMILTON BRANCH, 350 Bexar Ave W, PO Box 1944, Hamilton, 35570. SAN 330-4051. Tel: 205-921-4290. FAX: 205-921-4290. *Librn*, Helen Palmer
Circ 33,400
Library Holdings: Bk Vols 13,500; Per Subs 27
Friends of the Library Group
KENNEDY BRANCH, 17885 Hwy 96, PO Box 70, Kennedy, 35574. SAN 330-4086. Tel: 205-596-3670. FAX: 205-596-3956. *Librn*, Avaleen Porter
Circ 800
Library Holdings: Bk Vols 3,700
MARY WALLACE COBB MEMORIAL LIBRARY, 110 First Ave, PO Box 357, Vernon, 35592. SAN 330-423X. Tel: 205-695-6123. FAX: 205-695-7718. *Librn*, Melisa McDaniel
Circ 16,000
Library Holdings: Bk Vols 6,000
MCHS COMMUNITY LIBRARY, 8115 US Hwy 43, PO Box 549, Guin, 35563. SAN 330-4116. Tel: 205-468-2544. FAX: 205-468-2544. *Librn*, Margaret Masengale
Circ 20,400
Library Holdings: Bk Vols 14,700
MILLPORT BRANCH, 480 Columbus St, PO Box 159, Millport, 35576. SAN 330-4124. Tel: 205-662-4286. FAX: 205-662-4286. *Librn*, Wylodine Prater
Circ 2,500
Library Holdings: Bk Vols 8,100
RUSSELLVILLE BRANCH, 110 E Lawrence St, Russellville, 35653. SAN 330-4175. Tel: 205-332-1535. FAX: 205-332-1535. *Librn*, Deborah Barnett
Circ 16,500
Library Holdings: Bk Vols 15,800
Friends of the Library Group
SULLIGENT BRANCH, 5518 Hwy 17, PO Box 215, Sulligent, 35586. SAN 330-4205. Tel: 205-698-8631. FAX: 205-698-8631. *Librn*, Kathy Bolin
Circ 13,000
Library Holdings: Bk Vols 10,000
WEATHERFORD, 307 Fourth Ave, PO Box 870, Red Bay, 35582. SAN 330-4140. Tel: 256-356-9255. *Librn*, Fran West
Founded 1974. Circ 13,300
Oct 1998-Sep 1999 Mats Exp $1,733
Library Holdings: Bk Vols 11,800; Bk Titles 12,000; Per Subs 11; Bks on Deafness & Sign Lang 10
Subject Interests: Biographies, Fiction
Friends of the Library Group
WINFIELD BRANCH, 185 Ashwood Dr, PO Box 688, 35594. SAN 330-4264. Tel: 205-487-2484. FAX: 205-487-5146. *Librn*, Hermine Russell
Circ 43,000
Library Holdings: Bk Vols 24,000
Friends of the Library Group

YORK

P HIGHTOWER MEMORIAL LIBRARY,* 630 Avenue A, 36925. SAN 300-2373. Tel: 205-392-2004. FAX: 205-392-9121. *Librn*, Thelma McCann
Pop 5,859; Circ 11,514
Library Holdings: Bk Vols 10,000; Per Subs 15

ALASKA

Date of Statistics: 1999
Population, 1999 Census (estimate): 622,000
Population Served by Public Libraries: 622,000
Total Volumes in Public Libraries: 2,319,108
Total Public Library Circulation: 3,833,528
Total Public Library Income: $22,617,752
Number of County Libraries: Alaska is divided into 14 organized boroughs and one unorganized borough. Nine boroughs fund borough-wide service.
Public Library Assistance & Interlibrary Cooperative Grants:
State Appropriations: $910,000

AKUTAN

§P AKUTAN PUBLIC LIBRARY, PO Box 26, 99553. Tel: 907-698-2230. FAX: 907-698-2230. *Librn*, Jessie Borenin; *Librn*, Antone Shelikoff
Jul 2000-Jun 2001 Income $22,000
Library Holdings: Bk Vols 7,000; Per Subs 13

ANCHOR POINT

§P ANCHOR POINT PUBLIC LIBRARY, Doc Fritz Rd, PO Box 129, 99556. Tel: 907-235-5692. FAX: 907-235-5692. *Librn*, Marcie Doner
Library Holdings: Bk Vols 9,000
Open Mon, Wed & Sat 9-2 (summer), 12-5 (after Labor Day)

ANCHORAGE

M ALASKA AIR NATIONAL GUARD, 176th Medical Squadron Library,* 5005 Raspberry Rd, MS No 9, Kulis Air National Guard Base, 99502-1998. SAN 374-9088. Tel: 907-249-1415. FAX: 907-249-1145. *Librn*, Mary Bramer
Library Holdings: Bk Titles 250

G ALASKA DEPARTMENT OF NATURAL RESOURCES, Public Information Center, 550 W Seventh Ave, Ste 1260, 99501-3557. SAN 374-602X. Tel: 907-269-8400. TDD: 907-269-8411. FAX: 907-269-8901. E-Mail: pic@dnr.state.ak.us. Web Site: www.dnr.state.ak.us. *Ref*, Kathy Johnson
Publications: Fact Sheets; Pamphlets on ADNR programs
Special Services for the Deaf - TTY machine
Open Mon-Fri 10-5

G ALASKA DEPARTMENT OF NATURAL RESOURCES, Division of Mining, Land & Water, 550 W Seventh Ave, Ste 1070, 99501. SAN 320-8095. Tel: 907-269-8600. FAX: 907-269-8904. *Dir*, Bob Loeffler; *Librn*, Cindy Evans
Library Holdings: Bk Vols 2,000; Per Subs 10
Subject Interests: Alaska
Special Collections: Coal Application Permits for Alaska; Division Reports; Geology & Mining Magazines; Large Mine Applications & Permitting in Alaska; US Bureaus of Mines Reports on Southeast Alaska

G ALASKA DIVISION OF ENERGY LIBRARY, Department of Community & Regional Affairs,* 333 W Fourth Ave, Ste 220, 99501-2341. SAN 373-0174. Tel: 907-269-4500. FAX: 907-269-4645. *Coordr*, Terri Ganthner; E-Mail: tganthner@comsegaf.state.ak.us
Library Holdings: Bk Vols 2,550; Per Subs 50
Subject Interests: Energy

S ALASKA HEALTH PROJECT, Resource Library,* 218 E Fourth Ave, 99501. SAN 373-7438. Tel: 907-276-2864. FAX: 907-279-3089. *Exec Dir*, Daniel Middaugh
Founded 1988
Library Holdings: Bk Titles 2,000; Per Subs 175
Publications: Annotated bibliographies
Restriction: Non-circulating to the public

S ALASKA HOUSING FINANCE CORP, (Formerly Alaska Housing Research & Information Center), Research Information Center Library, 4300 Boniface Pkwy, 99504. SAN 321-446X. Tel: 907-338-6100. FAX: 907-338-1747. E-Mail: ahfcric@corecom.net. Web Site: www.ahfc.state.ak.us. *In Charge*, Cary Bolling
Founded 1984
Library Holdings: Bk Titles 5,600; Per Subs 30

§M ALASKA NATIVE MEDICAL CENTER LIBRARY, 4315 Diplomacy Dr, 99508. Tel: 907-729-2943. FAX: 907-729-2945. *Librn*, Anne Girling; E-Mail: agirling@anmc.org. Subject Specialists: *Health sciences*, Anne Girling
Oct 1999-Sep 2000 Income $130,000
Library Holdings: Bk Vols 1,000; Per Subs 100
Automation Activity & Vendor Info: (Cataloging) CASPR; (OPAC) CASPR

G ALASKA OIL & GAS CONSERVATION COMMISSION LIBRARY,* 3001 Porcupine Dr, 99501-3192. SAN 373-3335. Tel: 907-793-1250. FAX: 907-276-7542. Web Site: www.state.ak.us/local/akpages/admin/ogc/homeogc.htm. *Admin Assoc*, Lori Taylor; E-Mail: lori_taylor@admin.state.ak.us
Library Holdings: Bk Vols 1,000; Per Subs 10
Publications: AOGCC monthly bulletin
Partic in Alaska Library Network
This is a reference library for oil & gas drilling & producing only. In those subjects we are specific to the state of Alaska & general to the rest of the US

S ALASKA PUBLIC UTILITIES COMMISSION LIBRARY,* 1016 W Sixth Ave, Ste 400, 99501. SAN 374-9169. Tel: 907-276-6222. FAX: 907-276-0160.
Library Holdings: Bk Titles 1,200; Per Subs 200

G ALASKA RESOURCES LIBRARY & INFORMATION SERVICES, (ARLIS),* 3150 C St, Ste 100, 99503. SAN 377-841X. Tel: 907-272-7547. FAX: 907-271-4742. E-Mail: arlis@ios.doi.gov. *Govt Doc*, Kevin Keating; *Cat, Ref*, Errol Locker; *ILL*, Sharon Prien; *Ref*, Juli Braund-Allen; *Syst Coordr*, Nancy Tileston; *Coll Develop*, Celia Rozen
Library Holdings: Bk Vols 159,000; Per Subs 700
Partic in Alaska Library Network; Anchorage LiNK; Fedlink; OCLC Online Computer Library Center, Inc
ARLIS is a partnership of eight Anchorage natural & cultural resource libraries & information centers including Alaska Dept of Fish & Game Habitat Library, Arctic Environmental Information & Data Center (Univ Alaska Anchorage), Bureau of Land Management/Alaska Resources Library, Fish & Wildlife Service Library, Minerals Management Service Library, National Park Service Library, Oil Spill Public Information Center & US Geological Survey Library in conjunction with the University of Alaska Anchorage

GL ALASKA STATE COURT LAW LIBRARY, 303 K St, 99501. (Mail add: 820 W Fourth Ave, 99501), SAN 300-2381. Tel: 907-264-0585. FAX: 907-264-0733. Web Site: www.alaska.net/~akctlib/homepage.htm. *State Librn*, Cynthia Fellows; *Coll Develop*, Peggy Michielsen; *Publ Servs*, Jessica Van Buren; *Tech Servs*, Beth Odsen
Founded 1959
Library Holdings: Bk Vols 60,000; Bk Titles 7,891
Automation Activity & Vendor Info: (Acquisitions) epixtech, inc.; (Cataloging) epixtech, inc.; (Circulation) epixtech, inc.; (OPAC) epixtech, inc.; (Serials) epixtech, inc.
Database Vendor: OCLC - First Search
Branches:
FAIRBANKS BRANCH, 604 Barnette St, Rm 139, Fairbanks, 99701. Tel: 907-452-9241. FAX: 907-452-9345. Web Site: www.state.ak.us. *Librn*, Christina Worker
Library Holdings: Per Subs 10
JUNEAU BRANCH, Dimond Court Bldg, 123 Fourth St, Juneau, 99811. (Mail add: PO Box 114100, Juneau, 99811-4100), Tel: 907-463-4761. FAX: 907-463-4784. Web Site: www.state.ak.us. *Librn*, Pat Wilson; E-Mail: pwilson@courts.state.ak.us
KETCHIKAN BRANCH, 415 Main St, Rm 206, Ketchikan, 99901. Tel: 907-225-0500. FAX: 907-225-7420. Web Site: www.state.ak.us. *Librn*, Clayton Jones

ALASKA STATE LIBRARY
S LIBRARY DEVELOPMENT-TALKING BOOK CENTER, 344 W Third Ave, Ste 125, 99501. SAN 375-2852. Tel: 907-269-6570. Toll Free Tel: 888-820-4525. FAX: 907-269-6580. E-Mail: aslanc@eed.state.ak.us. Web Site: www.educ.state.ak.us/lam/library.html. *Adminr, Librn*, Patience Frederiksen; Tel: 907-269-6566, E-Mail: patience_fredericksen@eed.state.ak.us; *Tech Coordr*, Tracy Swaim; Tel: 907-269-6567, E-Mail: tracy_swaim@eed.state.ak.us; *Coordr*, Della Matthis; Tel: 907-269-6569, E-Mail: della_matthis@eed.state.ak.us; *Media Spec*, Lois Petersen; Tel: 907-269-6569, E-Mail: lois_peterson@eed.state.ak.us; Staff 3 (MLS 3)
Library Holdings: Bk Vols 350
S TALKING BOOK CENTER, 344 W Third Ave, Ste 125, 99501. SAN 300-2403. Tel: 907-269-6575. FAX: 907-269-6580. Web Site: www.educ.state.ak.us/lam/library/dev/tbc.html. *Librn*, Mary Jennings; *Asst Librn*, Patricia Meek; E-Mail: patm@muskox.alaska.edu; Staff 1 (MLS 1)
Founded 1968
Special Collections: Alaska Native Oral Literature Cassette Coll (Stories & Legends Told in 7 Alaskan Native Languages)

§S ALASKA YUKON LIBRARY, 119 W Harvard Ave, 99501. Tel: 907-272-6647. FAX: 907-272-6647. Web Site: www.ankn.uaf.edu. *Librn*, Jean Anderson Graves; E-Mail: jgraves@alaska.net
Founded 1988
Library Holdings: Bk Vols 1,021
Subject Interests: Native Americans, Native people
Restriction: By appointment only, Non-circulating, Private library
Function: Research library
Partic in Alaska Libr Asn
$15.00 lifetime membership fee assessed after first visit

S ANCHORAGE DAILY NEWS LIBRARY,* 1001 Northway Dr. (Mail add: PO Box 14-9001, 99514-9001), SAN 329-7721. Tel: 907-257-4593. FAX: 907-258-2157. Web Site: www.adnsearch.com. *Librn*, Sharon Palmisano; E-Mail: spalmisano@adn.com; *Asst Librn*, David Willems; E-Mail: dwillems@adn.com; Staff 2 (MLS 2)
Library Holdings: Bk Titles 1,000; Per Subs 75

P ANCHORAGE MUNICIPAL LIBRARIES, 3600 Denali, 99503-6093. SAN 330-4329. Tel: 907-343-2975. Interlibrary Loan Service Tel: 907-343-2822. FAX: 907-562-1244. Web Site: lexicon.ci.anchorage.ak.us. *Dir*, Tim Lynch; Tel: 907-343-2983, E-Mail: lynchtp@ci.anchorage.ak.us; *Publ Servs*, Carrie Keene; *YA Servs*, Chrystal Carr Jeter; *Access Serv*, Paul Putz; *Coll Develop*, Mary Ellen Wilson; *Automation Syst Coordr*, Peg Thompson; *Ad Servs, ILL*, Chris Bristah; Staff 114 (MLS 43, Non-MLS 71)
Founded 1945. Pop 259,391; Circ 1,230,835
Jan 1999-Dec 1999 Income (Main Library and Branch Library) $9,310,546, State $66,574, City $8,343,325, Federal $285,076, Locally Generated Income $615,571. Mats Exp $1,279,328, Books $601,330, Per/Ser (Incl. Access Fees) $497,640, Other Print Mats $54,000, Electronic Ref Mat (Incl. Access Fees) $126,358. Sal $5,262,274
Library Holdings: Bk Vols 574,056
Special Collections: Alaska Coll, bks, maps, micro, photog, newsp clippings, mss, personal papers; Loussac Children's Literature Coll; Patent & Trademark
Automation Activity & Vendor Info: (Acquisitions) DRA; (Cataloging) DRA; (Circulation) DRA
Publications: Activities Calendar (monthly); Newsletter (quarterly); Topic Trails (irregularly)
Partic in OCLC Online Computer Library Center, Inc
Friends of the Library Group
Branches: 5
CHUGIAK-EAGLE RIVER BRANCH, 12400 Old Glenn Hwy, Eagle River, 99577. SAN 330-4353. Tel: 907-694-2500. FAX: 907-694-2955. *Librn*, Mary Williams
Library Holdings: Bk Vols 73,926
Friends of the Library Group
MOUNTAIN VIEW, 150 S Bragaw, 99508. SAN 375-6033. Tel: 907-272-4867. FAX: 907-272-8413. *In Charge*, Kim Pendleton
Library Holdings: Bk Vols 8,062
Friends of the Library Group
MULDOON, 5530 E Northern Lights Blvd, 99504. SAN 325-4380. Tel: 907-337-4223. FAX: 907-337-2122. Web Site: lexiconl.ci.anchorage.ak.us. *Librn*, Kim Pendleton
Library Holdings: Bk Vols 50,985
Publications: Business & Company ASAP; Computer Database; General Reference Center (Index to periodicals); Health Reference Center; National Newspapers Index (Index to newspapers)
Friends of the Library Group
SAMSON-DIMOND, 800 E Dimond, Ste 201, 99503. SAN 330-4507. Tel: 907-343-4049. FAX: 907-344-5161. *In Charge*, Charlotte Pendleton
Library Holdings: Bk Vols 45,058
Friends of the Library Group
SCOTT & WESLEY GERRISH LIBRARY, PO Box 169, Girdwood, 99587. SAN 330-4388. Tel: 907-783-2565. FAX: 907-783-3118. *Assoc Librn*, Denise Halliday
Library Holdings: Bk Vols 17,164
Friends of the Library Group

S ANCHORAGE MUSEUM OF HISTORY & ART ARCHIVES,* 121 W Seventh Ave, 99501. SAN 300-242X. Tel: 907-343-6189, 907-343-6191. FAX: 907-343-6149. *Archivist*, M Diane Brenner; E-Mail: brennermd@ci.anchorage.ak.us; *Coll Develop*, Mina Jacobs
Founded 1968
Library Holdings: Bk Vols 7,500; Bk Titles 7,000; Per Subs 15
Subject Interests: Alaska, Art, Ethnology, History
Special Collections: Alaska Railroad Coll, photogs; Alexander Creek (Fred Winters Coll), diaries; Barrow & Diomede Islands (Eide Coll), photogs; Federal Aviation Administration Coll, photogs; Reindeer Herding (Ickes Coll), photogs; Steve McCutcheon, photos; Valdez History (Hinchley-Alagco Coll), photogs; Ward Wells Coll, photogs
Mem of Alaska Libr Network

G ANCHORAGE SCHOOL DISTRICT, Bilingual Education Program Library, Anchorage School District - CISC Bldg, 1901 S Bragau, 99508. SAN 373-3858. Tel: 907-787-3088. FAX: 907-787-3040. *Librn*, Sally Quinto; *Coll Develop*, Vicki Lee Ross; E-Mail: vross@asd.k12.ak.us; Staff 3 (MLS 3)
Founded 1978
1999-2000 Income $9,300. Mats Exp Books $5,000. Sal $20,000 (Prof $10,000)
Library Holdings: Bk Titles 7,300
Special Collections: Japanese, Korean & second language acquisition; Spanish; Tagalog; Yupik

§C CHARTER COLLEGE LIBRARY, 2221 E Northern Lights Blvd, 99508. Tel: 907-777-1328. FAX: 907-274-3342. *Librn*, Colleen Tyrrell; E-Mail: ctyrrell@chartercollege.org
Jul 2000-Jun 2001 Income $120,000
Library Holdings: Bk Vols 4,000; Per Subs 60
Automation Activity & Vendor Info: (Cataloging) CASPR; (Circulation) CASPR; (OPAC) CASPR; (Serials) CASPR

S DEPARTMENT OF COMMERCE INTERNATIONAL TRADE ADMINISTRATION, Alaska Export Assistance Center, 550 W Seventh Ave Ste 1770, 99501. SAN 370-2472. Tel: 907-271-6237. FAX: 907-271-6242. *Dir*, Charles F Becker; E-Mail: cbecker@mail.goc.gov
Library Holdings: Bk Vols 1,000
Subject Interests: International trade

§GM DEPARTMENT OF VETERANS AFFAIRS, OC - RO Library, 2925 DeBarr Rd, 99508. Tel: 907-257-5452. FAX: 907-257-6723. *Librn*, Jarmila Henderson; E-Mail: jarmila.henderson@med.va.gov
Library Holdings: Bk Vols 25; Per Subs 50
Restriction: Staff use only

G NATIONAL ARCHIVES & RECORDS ADMINISTRATION, Pacific Alaska Region (Anchorage),* 654 W Third Ave, 99501-2145. Tel: 907-271-2441. FAX: 907-271-2442. E-Mail: archives@alaska.nara.gov. Web Site: www.nara.gov/regional/anchorag.html. *Archivist*, Thomas Wiltsey
Special Collections: Archival Records of Federal Agencies & Courts in Alaska; Indian Affairs Records, microfilm; Passenger Arrival & Naturalization Records, microfilm; Population Censuses for All States, 1790-1920, microfilm; Pre-Federal & Early Federal History, microfilm; Pre-World War I Military Service Records, microfilm; US Diplomacy Records, microfilm
Restriction: Reference only to non-staff
Open Mon-Fri 8-4; some Sat hours-call for schedule

S NATIONAL BANK OF ALASKA, Heritage Library, 301 W Northern Lights Blvd, 99503. (Mail add: PO Box 100600, 99510-0600), SAN 329-7209. Tel: 907-265-2834. FAX: 907-265-2002. *Librn*, Gail Hollinger
Founded 1968. Pop 300,000
Library Holdings: Bk Titles 2,500

Subject Interests: Arctic
Special Collections: Alaskan History (Bancoft's Works)
Publications: Heritage of Alaska
Function: Reference only
Partic in Alaska Libr Asn

S SPECIAL EDUCATION SERVICE AGENCY (SESA) LIBRARY, 2217 E Tudor Rd, Ste 1, 99507. SAN 371-7720. Tel: 907-562-7372. FAX: 907-562-0545. Web Site: www.sesa.org/agency/programs/library.html. *Librn*, Anne K Freitag; E-Mail: afreitag@sesa.org; Staff 1 (MLS 1)
Library Holdings: Bk Vols 9,720; Bk Titles 6,828; Per Subs 110; High Interest/Low Vocabulary Bk Vols 14; Bks on Deafness & Sign Lang 250
Subject Interests: Alaska, Maternal child health, Nutrition, Spec edc
Special Collections: Assistive Technology (ATA Coll), equip; State Infant Learning Program, Alaska School Psychologist Association
Automation Activity & Vendor Info: (Acquisitions) CASPR; (Cataloging) CASPR; (Circulation) CASPR; (OPAC) CASPR; (Serials) CASPR
Special Services for the Deaf - Books on deafness & sign language; Special interest periodicals
Special Services for the Blind - Braille & recorded books
ATA Collection is available to anyone in Alaska who has a need

GM THE LIBRARY AT AKEELA, INC, 4111 Minnesota Dr, 99503. SAN 373-3343. Tel: 907-258-6021 (Main), 907-565-1225. Toll Free Tel: 800-478-7738. FAX: 907-258-6052, 907-258-6052. E-Mail: prevent@mtaonline.net. Web Site: www.akeela.org. *Librn*, Anjana Roy; E-Mail: aroy@akeela.org; *Asst Librn*, Patty Donnelly; E-Mail: pdonnelly@akeela.org; Staff 3 (MLS 1, Non-MLS 2)
Founded 1979
Jul 2000-Jun 2001 Income State $200,000. Mats Exp $35,050, Books $12,000, Per/Ser (Incl. Access Fees) $8,050, AV Equip $10,000, Other Print Mats $5,000
Library Holdings: Bk Vols 3,000; Bk Titles 2,500; Per Subs 160
Subject Interests: Curric, Substance abuse, Videos
Automation Activity & Vendor Info: (Circulation) CASPR; (OPAC) CASPR
Database Vendor: Ebsco - EbscoHost, OCLC - First Search
Publications: Prevention Express (quarterly)
Partic in Alaska Library Network
Also acts as a RADAR Network Center

UNITED STATES ARMY
A ENGINEER DISTRICT, ALASKA LIBRARY, PO Box 898, 99506-0898. SAN 330-4590. Tel: 907-753-2527. FAX: 907-753-1177, 907-753-2526.
Library Holdings: Bk Vols 7,623; Per Subs 177

GL UNITED STATES COURTS LIBRARY, 222 W Seventh Ave, Rm 181, 99513-7586. SAN 300-2470. Tel: 907-271-5655. FAX: 907-271-5640. *Librn*, Catherine A Davidson; Staff 2 (MLS 1, Non-MLS 1)
Library Holdings: Bk Vols 27,000; Per Subs 88
Subject Interests: Law
Special Collections: Alaska National Interest Lands Conservation Act; Alaska Native Claims Settlement Act & other Alaska Titles
Publications: Audio Visual Holdings List; Library News (monthly newsletter); Microfiche Holdings List; Pathfinders; Periodicals List
Restriction: Staff use only
Partic in OCLC Online Computer Library Center, Inc; Westlaw

UNIVERSITY OF ALASKA ANCHORAGE
C CONSORTIUM LIBRARY, 3211 Providence Dr, 99508. SAN 300-2497. Tel: 907-786-1825. FAX: 907-786-6050. E-Mail: aylib@uaa.alaska.edu. Web Site: www.uaa.alaska.edu/lib/lib.html. *Dean of Libr*, Stephen Rollins; *ILL*, Nancy Lesh; *Archivist*, Dennis Walle; *Tech Servs*, Sylvia Fink; *Acq, Coll Develop*, Catherine Innes-Taylor; *Cat*, Tohsook Chang; *Publ Servs*, John Summerhill; *Ref, Syst Coordr*, Alden Rollins; Staff 18 (MLS 18)
Founded 1973. Enrl 17,535; Fac 440; Highest Degree: Master
Library Holdings: Bk Vols 676,745; Per Subs 3,840
Special Collections: Alaskana & Polar Regions Coll; Archives & Manuscripts Coll; Music Coll
Publications: LS101 Textbook; LS111 Textbook; Plugging Into the Electronic Library
Partic in Alaska Library Network; National Network Of Libraries Of Medicine - South Central Region; OCLC Online Computer Library Center, Inc

S ENVIRONMENT & NATURAL RESOURCES INSTITUTE ARCTIC ENVIRONMENTAL INFORMATION & DATA CENTER LIBRARY, 707 A St, 99501. SAN 300-2500. Tel: 907-257-2732. FAX: 907-257-2707. E-Mail: Internet: anjb1@uaa.alaska.edu. *Librn*, Juli Braund-Allen
Founded 1972
Library Holdings: Bk Titles 8,800
Subject Interests: Alaska climate rec, Alaska environ studies, Arctic res, Natural science
Special Collections: Alaska Department of Transportation & Public Facilities Statewide Research, rpts; Alaska Native Regional Corporations Annual Reports; Alaska Oil & Gas Association Reports; Alaska Oil Spill Commission Coll; Alyeska's Port Valdez Environmental Monitoring Studies; ARCO Arctic Environmental Reports; Arctic Petroleum Operators Association Publications; Climatological Data for Alaska; Depository for Arctic Petroleum Operators Association & for Alaska Oil & Gas Association; National Association of Corrosion Engineers, Alaska Section, Corrosion Book & Technical Reports Coll; Report Series of Various State Agencies; University of Alaska Institute Reports
Publications: Bibliographies; climate & environmental atlases; databases; maps; pamphlets; posters; technical reports
Partic in Alaska Library Network; OCLC
See also Alaska Resources Library & Information Services (ARLIS) in Anchorage

ANDERSON

P ANDERSON SCHOOL-VILLAGE LIBRARY,* First Ave, 99744. (Mail add: PO Box 3078, 99744), SAN 376-3617. Tel: 907-582-2628, 907-582-2700, Ext 17. FAX: 907-582-2000. *Librn*, Andrea Corbin; *Commun Relations*, Linda Graves
Jul 1998-Jun 1999 Income $10,500
Library Holdings: Bk Vols 14,000; Bk Titles 13,500; Per Subs 15

ATKA

P NETSVETOV ATKA SCHOOL LIBRARY,* PO Box 47050, 99547. SAN 376-6403. Tel: 907-839-2210. FAX: 907-839-2212. *In Charge*, Ethan Pettigrew
Library Holdings: Bk Vols 1,000; Per Subs 30

BARROW

P TUZZY CONSORTIUM LIBRARY,* PO Box 749, 99723. SAN 376-3609. Tel: 907-852-1720. FAX: 907-852-1729. *Dir*, David Ongley; E-Mail: dongley@co.north-slope.ak.us; *Publ Servs*, Chang Terrie
Jul 1999-Jun 2000 Income $751,500, State $56,000, Federal $190,000, Locally Generated Income $4,500, Parent Institution $501,000. Mats Exp $57,000, Books $47,000, Per/Ser (Incl. Access Fees) $10,000. Sal $541,000 (Prof $167,000)
Library Holdings: Bk Vols 30,000; Bk Titles 27,000; Per Subs 115
Special Collections: Arctic Related Rare Books

BETHEL

P KUSKOKWIM CONSORTIUM LIBRARY,* Pouch 1068, 99559. SAN 300-2535. Tel: 907-543-4516. FAX: 907-543-4503. *Head of Libr*, Christy Schink; E-Mail: christys@bethel.alaska.edu; *Asst Librn*, Maxine Beaver
Founded 1970. Pop 15,000
Jul 1997-Jun 1998 Income $186,511, State $8,023, City $65,000, Parent Institution $113,488. Mats Exp $24,099, Books $10,762, Per/Ser (Incl. Access Fees) $8,520. Sal $125,096 (Prof $40,000)
Library Holdings: Bk Vols 34,002; Per Subs 60
Special Collections: Alaska History
Library is consortium between Bethel & Kuskokwin Community College, a branch of University of Alaska. Serves as the area center library for the Yukon-Kuskokwim Delta
Friends of the Library Group

BIG LAKE

P BIG LAKE PUBLIC LIBRARY, Mile 4-S Big Lake Rd, PO Box 520829, 99652. SAN 376-3625. Tel: 907-892-6475. FAX: 907-892-6546. Web Site: www.biglake-ak.com/library/library.htm. *Librn*, Jo Cassidy; E-Mail: jcassidy@biglake-ak.com
Library Holdings: Bk Vols 11,000; Bk Titles 5,900; Per Subs 40
Friends of the Library Group

CHINIAK

P CHINIAK PUBLIC LIBRARY, 42650 Chiniak Hwy, PO Box 5610, 99615. SAN 376-3641. Tel: 907-486-3022. FAX: 907-486-3022. E-Mail: chiniakal@pti.net. Web Site: www.ptialaska.net/~chiniakl. *Dir*, Sue Baker
Pop 75; Circ 5,055
Library Holdings: Bk Vols 10,000; Bk Titles 17,000; Per Subs 23

COLD BAY

P COLD BAY PUBLIC LIBRARY,* PO Box 87, 99571-0087. SAN 376-3633. *Asst Librn*, Kristi Hicks
Library Holdings: Bk Vols 45,000; Bk Titles 19,000

COOPER LANDING

P COOPER LANDING COMMUNITY LIBRARY,* Bean Creek Rd, PO Box 517, 99572. SAN 322-8460. Tel: 907-595-1241. E-Mail: alibrary@arctic.net. *Dir*, Bee Wilson; Tel: 907-595-1697, E-Mail: rrbound@arctic.net
Founded 1984. Pop 500
Jan 1999-Dec 1999 Income $9,000, State $4,300, Locally Generated Income

$3,000. Mats Exp $5,700, Books $4,400, Per/Ser (Incl. Access Fees) $200
Library Holdings: Bk Titles 4,500
Subject Interests: Alaskana, Civil War
Special Collections: Alaskana
Mem of Alaska Libr Network
Open Mon-Sat 1-4
Friends of the Library Group

COPPER CENTER

§P KENNY LAKE PUBLIC LIBRARY, Mile 5 Edgerton Hwy, HC 60 Box 223, 99573-9703. Tel: 907-822-3015. FAX: 907-822-3015. E-Mail: yourlibrary@cvinternet.net. *Librn*, Lil Gilmore; *Librn*, Marian Lightwood
Jul 1999-Jun 2000 Income $9,500
Library Holdings: Bk Vols 5,000
Friends of the Library Group
Bookmobiles: 1

CORDOVA

S CORDOVA HISTORICAL MUSEUM ARCHIVES,* 622 First St, PO Box 391, 99574. SAN 329-9015. Tel: 907-424-6665. FAX: 907-424-6666. *Dir*, Cathy Sherman
Library Holdings: Bk Titles 350
Special Collections: Area News (Cordova Times Newspaper Coll), bk, micro

P CORDOVA PUBLIC LIBRARY, 622 First St, 99574. (Mail add: PO Box 1210, 99574), SAN 300-2543. Tel: 907-424-6667. FAX: 907-424-6666. E-Mail: cdvlib@ptialaska.net. *Dir*, Cathy Sherman; *Librn*, Susan Ogle; *YA Servs*, Linda McConnell
Founded 1908. Pop 3,000; Circ 27,397
Jan 2000-Dec 2000 Income $136,000. Mats Exp $8,800. Sal $114,000
Library Holdings: Bk Titles 21,086; Per Subs 70
Subject Interests: Alaskana, Arts and crafts, Education, Local history, Natural science, Technology
Friends of the Library Group

CRAIG

P CRAIG PUBLIC LIBRARY, PO Box 769, 99921. SAN 300-2551. Tel: 907-826-3281. FAX: 907-826-3278. *Librn*, Barb Hansen; E-Mail: bhansen@aptalaska.net
Founded 1935. Pop 1,637; Circ 11,382
Library Holdings: Bk Titles 10,900
Subject Interests: Alaska
Partic in OCLC

CUBE COVE

P CUBE COVE LIBRARY,* Cube Cove No 5, 99850-0360. SAN 376-365X. Tel: 907-799-2244. FAX: 907-799-2244. *Librn*, Mary Heath
Jul 1997-Jun 1998 Income $95,000. Mats Exp $50,000. Sal $35,000
Library Holdings: Bk Vols 40,000; Bk Titles 27,000; Per Subs 19

DEERING

P DEERING NATIVE VILLAGE, Ipnatchiaq Public Library, 59 Main St, 99736-9999. Tel: 907-363-2136. FAX: 907-363-2156. *Librn*, Nellie M Brown
Founded 1983. Pop 158; Circ 467
Jul 1999-Jun 2000 Income $14,800, State $6,300, City $4,000, Federal $4,500. Mats Exp $3,902, Books $1,102, Per/Ser (Incl. Access Fees) $1,100, AV Equip $800, Other Print Mats $900. Sal $9,505
Library Holdings: Bk Vols 8,184; Bk Titles 6,434; Per Subs 21

DELTA JUNCTION

§P DELTA COMMUNITY LIBRARY, 2288 Deborah St, 99737. (Mail add: PO Box 229, 99737), Tel: 907-895-4102. FAX: 907-895-4457. E-Mail: deltalibrary@knix.net. Web Site: www.knix.net/delta library. *Dir*, Joyce McCombs
Pop 1,746
Jul 2000-Jun 2001 Income $42,000
Library Holdings: Bk Vols 9,353; Bks on Deafness & Sign Lang 24
Automation Activity & Vendor Info: (Cataloging) Sagebrush Corporation; (Circulation) Sagebrush Corporation
Open Tues-Thurs 10-6, Sat 10-4

P RUTH RIGGS LIBRARY ASSOCIATION,* Horseshoe Lane & Jack Warren Rd, 99737. (Mail add: HC 60 Box 3780, 99737), SAN 328-1507. Tel: 907-895-4399. Web Site: www.akpub.com/akttt/riggs.html. *Librn*, Nanci Ruthschild-Kennedy; *Asst Librn*, Ruth E Madsen
Founded 1981. Pop 1,500; Circ 6,923
Library Holdings: Bk Titles 10,580; Per Subs 14
Special Collections: Alaskan Beer & Soda Cans; Antique Alaskan Items
Partic in Alaska Library Network
Special Services for the Deaf - Books on deafness & sign language
Open Wed & Sat 10-6

DENALI NATIONAL PARK

P DENALI NATIONAL PARK LIBRARY,* PO Box 9, 99755. SAN 376-3668. Tel: 907-683-2294. FAX: 907-683-9617. Web Site: www.nps.gov/dena. *In Charge*, Marisa James
Library Holdings: Bk Vols 5,000; Bk Titles 3,500; Per Subs 25

DILLINGHAM

P DILLINGHAM PUBLIC LIBRARY,* PO Box 870, 99576. SAN 322-6557. Tel: 907-842-5610. FAX: 907-842-5691. *Coordr*, Chris O'Connor; *Coordr*, Susan Ball; Staff 2 (MLS 1, Non-MLS 1)
Founded 1949. Pop 2,000; Circ 970
Library Holdings: Bk Titles 12,000; Per Subs 108
Subject Interests: Alaskana
Special Services for the Deaf - Books on deafness & sign language; Captioned film depository; High interest/low vocabulary books

DOUGLAS

G ALASKA DEPARTMENT OF FISH & GAME LIBRARY,* PO Box 240020, 99824. SAN 300-2640. Tel: 907-465-4119. FAX: 907-465-4944. *Librn*, Paul DeSloover; E-Mail: pauled@fishgame.state.ak.us
Founded 1959
Library Holdings: Bk Vols 623; Per Subs 52
Subject Interests: Arctic
Partic in OCLC

S JUNEAU MINERAL INFORMATION CENTER, Bureau of Land Management, Juneau Field Office, 100 Savikko Rd, 99824. SAN 300-2675. Tel: 907-364-1553. FAX: 907-364-1574. Web Site: juneau.ak.blm.gov. *Tech Servs*, Jane Albrecht; E-Mail: jalbrech@ak.blm.gov; Staff 1 (Non-MLS 1)
Founded 1952
Oct 1999-Sep 2000 Mats Exp $10,000, Books $2,100, Per/Ser (Incl. Access Fees) $3,500, AV Equip $250, Other Print Mats $1,700. Sal $38,000
Library Holdings: Bk Vols 20,000; Bk Titles 5,000; Per Subs 30
Subject Interests: Geology, Mineralogy, Mining engineering
Special Collections: Alaska Department Natural Resources Publications, selected geologic reports from Canada, emphasis on British Columbia & Yukon, submarine tailings disposal references, United States Geological Survey publications; Alaska Environmental Impact Statements; Mining & Mineral Deposits in Arctic; Permafrost; Submarine Tailings Disposal References; United States Geological Survey Publications
Publications: Bureau of Mines Publications on Alaska
Restriction: Non-circulating to the public
Function: ILL available
Partic in OCLC

EAGLE

P EAGLE PUBLIC LIBRARY,* PO Box 45, 99738. SAN 376-7957. Tel: 907-547-2334. FAX: 907-547-2232. E-Mail: eaglelib@alaska.net. *Pres*, Betty Borg; *Dir*, Theresa Dean; *Acq*, Elva Scott
Library Holdings: Bk Vols 16,000; Per Subs 40
Open Thurs 10-6 & Fri 12-9 during winter, Mon-Fri 10-2 during summer

EAGLE RIVER

S ALASKA STATE DEPARTMENT OF CORRECTIONS, Hiland Mountain Correctional Center Library,* PO Box 600, 99577-0600. SAN 321-026X. Tel: 907-694-9511, Ext 141. FAX: 907-694-4507, 907-694-9511. *Librn*, Janet Weiss; Staff 1 (Non-MLS 1)
Founded 1974
Library Holdings: Bk Vols 4,719; Bk Titles 4,000; Per Subs 27

EGEGIK

P EGEGIK VILLAGE LIBRARY,* PO Box 29, 99579. SAN 376-6535. Tel: 907-233-2208. FAX: 907-233-2312. E-Mail: evc233@aol.com. *Librn*, Natalie Fuller
Library Holdings: Bk Vols 4,500; Per Subs 126

EIELSON AFB

UNITED STATES AIR FORCE
A EIELSON AIR FORCE BASE LIBRARY, 3340 Central Ave, Ste 100, 99702-1299. SAN 330-4620. Tel: 907-377-3174. FAX: 907-377-1683. *Dir*, Cathy Rasmussen; E-Mail: cathy.rasmussen@eielson.af.mil; Staff 5 (MLS 1, Non-MLS 4)

Founded 1946 Sal $110,475 (Prof $41,489)
Library Holdings: Bk Vols 36,700; Per Subs 106
Special Collections: Arctic Coll; Professional Military Education; Total Quality Management (TQM)
Restriction: Not open to public
Partic in Alaska Library Network

ELIM

§P ELIM COMMUNITY LIBRARY, Ernest Nylin Memorial Library, 101 Hillside St, PO Box 39050, 99739-0050. Tel: 907-890-3501. FAX: 907-890-3811. E-Mail: elimlibrary@netscape.net. *Librn*, Jerri Nagaruk; E-Mail: jerrinagaruk@hotmail.com
Jun 2000-May 2001 Income $13,300
Library Holdings: Bk Vols 6,000; Per Subs 21

ELMENDORF AFB

UNITED STATES AIR FORCE

AM 3RD MEDICAL GROUP- SGSOL LIBRARY, 5955 Zeamer Ave, 99506-3700. SAN 330-468X. Tel: 907-580-6490. FAX: 907-580-5527. *Librn*, Donna M Hudson; E-Mail: donna.hudson@elmendorf.af.mil; Staff 1 (MLS 1)
Founded 1955
Library Holdings: Bk Vols 4,000; Per Subs 100
Subject Interests: Dentistry, Medicine, Nursing
Special Collections: Military Medicine
Partic in Alaska Library Network; Nat Libr of Med; WLM

A ELMENDORF AIR FORCE BASE LIBRARY-FL 5000, 10480 22nd St, 99506-2530. SAN 330-4655. Tel: 907-552-3787. FAX: 907-552-1707. Interlibrary Loan Service E-Mail: ill@gci.net. *Dir*, Martha K Sumpter; Tel: 907-552-5230, E-Mail: kay.sumpter@elmendorf.af.mil; *Ref*, Katherine S Black; Staff 8 (MLS 2, Non-MLS 6)
Founded 1950
Oct 1999-Sep 2000 Income $317,145. Mats Exp $71,150, Books $19,202, Per/Ser (Incl. Access Fees) $51,548. Sal $232,127
Library Holdings: Bk Titles 50,000; Per Subs 312
Special Collections: Air War College Coll; Alaskana Coll
Automation Activity & Vendor Info: (Cataloging) SIRSI; (Circulation) SIRSI
Database Vendor: OCLC - First Search

AM HOSPITAL LIBRARY, Third Medical Ctr/SGSOL, 5955 Zeamer Ave, 99506-3700. SAN 330-471X. Tel: 907-580-6490. FAX: 907-580-5527. *Librn*, Donna M Hudson; E-Mail: donna.hudson@elmendorf.af.mil; Staff 1 (MLS 1)
Library Holdings: Bk Vols 3,200
Special Collections: Alaskana; Popular Medicine
Automation Activity & Vendor Info: (Cataloging) ComPanion Corp; (OPAC) ComPanion Corp; (Serials) ComPanion Corp
Partic in Alaska Library Network

FAIRBANKS

§S ALYESKA PIPELINE SERVICE CO, Information Resource Center, 701 Bidwill Ave, Mailstop 811, 99701. Tel: 907-450-7832. FAX: 907-450-5540. *Librn*, Kay Kenyon Barboza; E-Mail: barbozakk@alyeska/pipeline.com
Library Holdings: Bk Vols 6,000; Per Subs 20
Automation Activity & Vendor Info: (Cataloging) Inmagic, Inc.
Restriction: Staff use only

G BUREAU OF LAND MANAGEMENT LIBRARY, 1150 University Ave, 99709-3844. SAN 300-256X. Tel: 907-474-2200. FAX: 907-474-2282. Web Site: aurora.ak.blm.gov.
Library Holdings: Bk Vols 500
Special Collections: 1874 to current; Alaska Statutes Coll; Department of the Interior Decisions Coll; Interior Board of Land Appeals (IBLA) decisions; United States Codes of Federal Regulations Coll; United States Statutes at Large Coll
Restriction: Staff use only

§SR CATHOLIC DIOCESE OF FAIRBANKS, Religious Education Resource Center, 1316 Peger Rd, 99709. Tel: 907-474-0753. FAX: 907-474-8009. E-Mail: library@cbna.org. Web Site: www.cbna.org. *Dir*, Jerry Finkler; E-Mail: jerry@cbna.org; *Coordr*, David Schienle
Jul 2000-Jun 2001 Income $17,000
Library Holdings: Bk Vols 3,739; Per Subs 25
Subject Interests: Theology
Special Collections: Alaskana Coll

S FAIRBANKS DAILY NEWS-MINER NEWSROOM LIBRARY,* 200 N Cushman St, PO Box 70710, 99707. SAN 373-336X. Tel: 907-459-7504. FAX: 907-452-7917. E-Mail: newsroom@newsminer.com. Web Site: www.newsminer.com. *Librn*, Marmian Grimes; E-Mail: mgrimes@newsminer.com; Staff 1 (MLS 1)
Library Holdings: Bk Titles 500; Per Subs 12
Subject Interests: Alaska

§M FAIRBANKS MEMORIAL HOSPITAL LIBRARY, 1650 Cowles St, 99701-5998. Tel: 907-458-5584. *Librn*, Doreen Smith; E-Mail: doreen.smith@bannerhealth.com
Jan 2000-Dec 2000 Income $120,000
Library Holdings: Bk Vols 1,000; Per Subs 150
Restriction: Medical staff only

S FAIRBANKS NATIVE ASSOCIATION LIBRARY,* 201 First Ave Ste 300, 99701-4892. SAN 373-3351. Tel: 907-452-1648. FAX: 907-456-4148. E-Mail: fnappd@alaska.net. *Dir*, Valerie Naquin
Library Holdings: Bk Titles 150; Per Subs 10

P FAIRBANKS NORTH STAR BOROUGH PUBLIC LIBRARY & REGIONAL CENTER, Noel Wien Library, 1215 Cowles St, 99701-4313. SAN 300-2578. Tel: 907-459-1020. FAX: 907-459-1024. Web Site: www.library.fnsb.lib.ak.us/. *Dir*, Greg Hill; *Publ Servs*, Jack Rasmussen; *Ref*, Ann Pittman; *Circ, Media Spec*, Maurine Canarsky; *Automation Syst Coordr*, Bill Galbraith; *Ch Servs*, Sue Sherif; *Coll Develop*, June Pinnell-Stephens
Founded 1909. Pop 82,875; Circ 593,266
Library Holdings: Bk Vols 272,520; Bk Titles 226,285; Per Subs 584
Subject Interests: Alaska
Special Collections: Arthur Rackham Coll
Automation Activity & Vendor Info: (Circulation) GEAC
Partic in OCLC
Friends of the Library Group
Branches: 1
NORTH POLE BRANCH, 601 Snowman, North Pole, 99705. SAN 324-2463. Tel: 907-488-6101. FAX: 907-488-8465. *Librn*, Ingrid Clauson
Library Holdings: Bk Vols 34,253
Friends of the Library Group

C GEOPHYSICAL INSTITUTE, Keith B Mather Library, Int Arctic Research Ctr, 930 Koyukuk, PO Box 757355, 99775-7355. SAN 330-4833. Tel: 907-474-7503. FAX: 907-474-7290. E-Mail: fygilib@aurora.alaska.edu. Web Site: www.gi.alaska.edu/services/library/. *Librn*, Julia Triplehorn; Staff 3 (MLS 2, Non-MLS 1)
Founded 1945
Library Holdings: Bk Vols 48,000; Per Subs 325
Subject Interests: Atmospheric scis, Geophysics, Glaciology, Remote sensing, Seismology, Space science, Volcanology

§R SALVATION ARMY LIBRARY, 1602 Tenth Ave, 99701. (Mail add: PO Box 70405, 99707-0405), Tel: 907-452-3103. FAX: 907-452-2397. *Librn*, Richard Greene
Library Holdings: Bk Vols 200

S SHANNON & WILSON INC, Arctic Alaska Testing Laboratories Library,* 2055 Hill Rd, 99709. SAN 370-3347. Tel: 907-479-0600. FAX: 907-479-5691. *Librn*, Julie Rowland
Library Holdings: Bk Titles 50
Restriction: Not open to public

C UNIVERSITY OF ALASKA FAIRBANKS, Elmer E Rasmuson Library, 310 Tanana Dr, PO Box 756800, 99775-6800. SAN 330-4779. Tel: 907-474-7224. Circulation Tel: 907-474-7481. Reference Tel: 907-474-7482. FAX: 907-474-6841. Interlibrary Loan Service FAX: 907-474-5744. E-Mail: fydir@uaf.edu. Web Site: www.uaf.edu/library. *Dir, Info Tech*, Paul McCarthy; *Media Spec*, Scott Kiefer; Tel: 907-474-6796, E-Mail: fnsrk@uaf.edu; *Bibliog Instr*, Debbie Kalvee; Tel: 907-474-7483, E-Mail: ffdhk@uaf.edu; *ILL*, Deb Knutsen; Tel: 907-474-6691, E-Mail: fyrill@uaf.edu; *Electronic Resources*, Lisa Lehman; Tel: 907-474-5350, E-Mail: fflml@uaf.edu; *Doc*, John Kawula; Tel: 907-474-6730, E-Mail: ffjdk@uaf.edu; *Head, Info Serv*, Rheba Dupras; Tel: 907-474-6692, E-Mail: ffrad1@uaf.edu; *Coll Develop*, Dennis Stephens; Tel: 907-474-6695, E-Mail: ffdjs1@uaf.edu; *Circ Media*, Karen Jensen; Tel: 907-474-5364, E-Mail: fnklj@uaf.edu; *Distance Educ*, Suzan Hahn; Tel: 907-474-5241, Fax: 907-474-5744, E-Mail: ffslh1@uaf.edu; *Ref*, Diane Ruess; Tel: 907-474-6349, E-Mail: ffder@uaf.edu; *Info Tech*, Richard Machida; Tel: 907-474-7102, E-Mail: richard.machida@uaf.edu; *Archivist*, Susan Grigg; Tel: 907-474-6593, E-Mail: ffslg@uaf.edu. Subject Specialists: *Arctic*, Susan Grigg; *Polar regions*, Susan Grigg; Staff 43 (MLS 13, Non-MLS 30)
Founded 1917. Enrl 4,552; Fac 514; Highest Degree: Doctorate
Jul 1999-Jun 2000 Income (Main Library and Branch Library) $5,498,566, State $3,591,122, Locally Generated Income $1,092, Parent Institution $1,906,353. Mats Exp $1,379,618, Books $418,441, Per/Ser (Incl. Access Fees) $521,144, Presv $64,655, Micro $73,321, AV Equip $10,569, Other Print Mats $28,513, Electronic Ref Mat (Incl. Access Fees) $262,974. Sal $3,348,522 (Prof $1,298,131)
Library Holdings: Bk Vols 926,199; Bk Titles 605,407; Per Subs 7,500
Special Collections: LS
Automation Activity & Vendor Info: (Circulation) VTLS
Database Vendor: CARL, Dialog, Ebsco - EbscoHost, GaleNet, IAC - Info Trac, OCLC - First Search, ProQuest, Silverplatter Information Inc.
Function: Research library
Departmental Libraries:
BIOSCIENCES LIBRARY, 186 Arctic Health Research Bldg, 901 S Koyukuk Dr, 99775. (Mail add: PO Box 757060, 99775-7060), Tel: 907-474-7442. FAX: 907-474-7820. E-Mail: fybmlib@uaf.edu. Web Site:

www.uaf.edu/library/collections/biosci.index.html. *Librn*, James H Anderson; Staff 4 (MLS 1, Non-MLS 3)
Founded 1949. Enrl 8,000; Fac 200; Highest Degree: Doctorate
Library Holdings: Bk Vols 70,679; Per Subs 468
Subject Interests: Agriculture, Aquaculture, Biochemistry, Botany, Ecology, Entomology, Environ chem, Fisheries, Forestry, Genetics, Limnology, Marine biology, Medicine, Microbiology, Molecular biology, Nutrition, Oceanography, Ornithology, Physiol, Soil science, Systematics, Veterinary medicine, Wildlife, Zoology
Automation Activity & Vendor Info: (Cataloging) VTLS; (Circulation) VTLS; (OPAC) DRA; (Serials) DRA
Database Vendor: OCLC - First Search
Partic in STN
Open Mon-Thurs 8am-9pm, Fri 8-5, Sat & Sun 12-5

UNIVERSITY OF ALASKA FAIRBANKS

C INSTITUTE OF ARTIC BIOLOGY, PO Box 757000, 99775-7000. Tel: 907-474-5799. FAX: 907-474-6967. E-Mail: fncjb@uaf.edu.
Library Holdings: Bk Vols 1,485

S WILDLIFE LIBRARY, 158 Arctic Health Research Bldg, PO Box 757000, 99775-7000. SAN 322-8967. Tel: 907-474-5799. FAX: 907-474-6967. E-Mail: fncjb@uaf.edu. *In Charge*, Carol Button; Staff 1 (Non-MLS 1)
Library Holdings: Bk Titles 400
Subject Interests: Behav, Biology, Ecol, Mgt, Physiology
Special Collections: AK Birds & Mammals, reprints

FORT RICHARDSON

P FORT RICHARDSON POST LIBRARY, 636 B St, 99505-6650. SAN 376-6314. Tel: 907-384-1648. FAX: 907-384-7534. *Dir*, Jud Erwin; Tel: 907-384-1797; *Tech Servs*, Jill Yahne; Tel: 907-384-1759; *Tech Servs*, Margaret Murphy; Tel: 907-384-1798
Founded 1950
Library Holdings: Bk Vols 48,000; Bk Titles 43,800; Per Subs 70
Subject Interests: Alaska, Military history
Automation Activity & Vendor Info: (Cataloging) EOS; (Circulation) EOS; (OPAC) EOS
Database Vendor: OCLC - First Search
Partic in OCLC Online Computer Library Center, Inc

FORT SMITH

S THE DARBY FOUNDATION, Museum & Heritage Centre,* 311 General Darby Rd, PO Box 1625, 72902-1625. SAN 375-3514. Tel: 501-782-3388, 501-783-7244. FAX: 501-783-7590. E-Mail: darby1945@aol.com. *Pres*, Emory S Dockery, Jr
Founded 1977
Library Holdings: Bk Vols 5,000
Special Collections: World War II Coll

FORT WAINWRIGHT

UNITED STATES ARMY

AM BASSET ARMY HOSPITAL MEDICAL LIBRARY, 1060 Gaffney Rd, 99703. Tel: 907-353-5194. FAX: 907-353-5357. *Librn*, George Kimmell
Oct 1996-Sep 1997 Income $30,000
Library Holdings: Bk Vols 2,000; Bk Titles 1,800; Per Subs 119
Subject Interests: Obstetrics and gynecology, Orthopedics, Surgery

A MILITARY OCCUPATIONAL SPECIALTY (MOS) LIBRARY, Bldg 2110, 99703. Tel: 907-353-7297. FAX: 907-353-7472. E-Mail: moslib@wainwright.army.mil. Web Site: mwr.polarnet.com/Education/Homepage.htm. *Librn*, Connie Miller
Library Holdings: Bk Vols 5,000
Use limited to servicemen & their families

A POST LIBRARY, Bldg 3700, Santiago Ave, 99703. (Mail add: 1060 Gaffney Rd, 99703-7130), SAN 330-4957. Circulation Tel: 907-353-2642. Reference Tel: 907-353-2642. FAX: 907-353-2609. E-Mail: postlib@wainwright.army.mil. *Dir, Librn*, Alfred L Preston; Tel: 907-353-2645, E-Mail: alfred.preston@wainwright.army.mil; *Head Tech Servs*, Betty Luebke; Tel: 907-353-2644; Staff 4 (MLS 1, Non-MLS 3)
Founded 1951. Pop 10,000; Circ 29,000
Oct 1998-Sep 1999 Mats Exp $17,270, Books $9,700, Per/Ser (Incl. Access Fees) $6,600, Micro $970. Sal $71,595
Library Holdings: Bk Vols 23,000; Bk Titles 22,000; Per Subs 200; High Interest/Low Vocabulary Bk Vols 12
Subject Interests: Alaska
Database Vendor: Ebsco - EbscoHost, OCLC - First Search
Partic in Western Libr Network

GALENA

P CHARLES EVANS COMMUNITY LIBRARY,* PO Box 229, 99741. SAN 376-6934. Tel: 907-656-1883, Ext 115. FAX: 907-656-1368. *Dir, Media Spec*, Patricia Knudsen; E-Mail: pknudsen@hotmail.com; *Librn*, Bonnie Warner; Staff 1 (MLS 1)
Jul 1998-Jun 1999 Income $119,500, State $58,000. Mats Exp $22,500, Books $20,000, Per/Ser (Incl. Access Fees) $2,500. Sal $75,000
Library Holdings: Bk Vols 16,600; Per Subs 85
Publications: Booklist; Library Journal; School Library Journal
Friends of the Library Group

GLENNALLEN

CR ALASKA BIBLE COLLEGE, Library Center, PO Box 289, 99588. SAN 300-2616. Tel: 907-822-3201. FAX: 907-822-5027. Web Site: www.akbible.edu. *Librn*, Pamela Horst; E-Mail: harley_bowerman@akbible.edu
Founded 1966. Enrl 69; Fac 12; Highest Degree: Bachelor
May 2000-Apr 2001 Mats Exp $10,000, Books $4,600, Per/Ser (Incl. Access Fees) $3,850
Library Holdings: Bk Titles 27,473; Per Subs 130
Subject Interests: Religion
Special Collections: Alaska-Arctic
Database Vendor: Ebsco - EbscoHost

P COPPER VALLEY COMMUNITY LIBRARY,* PO Box 173, 99588. SAN 372-5316. Tel: 907-822-5427. E-Mail: cvcla@alaska.net. *Dir*, Heike Wilmoth
Jul 1998-Jun 1999 Income $30,000
Library Holdings: Bk Vols 12,000; Per Subs 42
Open Tues-Thurs 1-6, Fri 1-8 & Sat 11-6

GUSTAVUS

§P GUSTAVUS PUBLIC LIBRARY, Gustavus Rd, PO Box 279, 99826-0279. Tel: 907-697-2350. FAX: 907-697-2249. E-Mail: kleary@gustavus.lib.ak.us. Web Site: www.gustavus.lib.ak.us. *Librn*, Lynne Jensen
Jul 1999-Jun 2000 Income $19,000
Library Holdings: Bk Vols 8,200; Per Subs 30

S NATIONAL PARK SERVICE, Glacier Bay National Park & Preserve Library, PO Box 140, 99826. SAN 300-2624. Tel: 907-697-2230. FAX: 907-697-2654. E-Mail: glva_administration@nps.gov. Web Site: www.nps.gov/glva/. *Dir*, Kris Nemeth; *Librn*, Elizabeth Hooge
Library Holdings: Bk Vols 2,000
Subject Interests: Marine biology

HAINES

P HAINES BOROUGH PUBLIC LIBRARY,* PO Box 1089, 99827-1089. SAN 300-2632. Tel: 907-766-2545. FAX: 907-766-2551. E-Mail: hnslib@seaknet.alaska.edu. *Librn*, Ann L Myren
Founded 1928. Pop 2,450; Circ 65,892
Jul 1999-Jun 2000 Income $209,977, State $6,700, County $180,000, Locally Generated Income $17,088, Other $12,889. Mats Exp $17,920, Books $15,000, Per/Ser (Incl. Access Fees) $2,038, Presv $350, Electronic Ref Mat (Incl. Access Fees) $532. Sal $134,760 (Prof $47,718)
Library Holdings: Bk Vols 22,993; Per Subs 118
Special Collections: Alaska Coll
Database Vendor: OCLC - First Search
Friends of the Library Group

S SHELDON MUSEUM & CULTURAL CENTER LIBRARY, 11 Main St, PO Box 269, 99827-0269. SAN 329-1995. Tel: 907-766-2366. FAX: 907-766-2368. Web Site: www.sheldonmuseum.org. *Curator*, Cindy Jones; E-Mail: curator@sheldonmuseum.org
Library Holdings: Bk Vols 1,150; Bk Titles 1,100
Subject Interests: Local history, State hist, Tlingit art, Tlingit culture
Restriction: Not a lending library
Serves the professional & reference needs of the staff & of people with particular interests in Alaskan history & Tlingit culture; Open Sun-Sat 1-5 (summer), Mon-Fri 1-4 (winter)

HEALY

P TRI-VALLEY COMMUNITY-SCHOOL LIBRARY,* Suntrana Rd, 99743. (Mail add: PO Box 400, 99743), SAN 376-3404. Tel: 907-683-2507. FAX: 907-683-2632. *Librn*, Katherine Hennigan; E-Mail: khennigan@mail.denali.k12.ak.us; *Librn*, Judy Engleman
Library Holdings: Bk Vols 22,000; Per Subs 45
Friends of the Library Group

HOLLIS

P HOLLIS PUBLIC LIBRARY, PO Box 5, 99950. SAN 376-3595. Tel: 907-530-7112. *Dir*, Patty Hiatt; *Librn*, Cathy Van Laar
Founded 1985
Jul 1998-Jun 1999 Income $10,320. Mats Exp $5,670
Library Holdings: Bk Vols 16,000; Bk Titles 9,500

HOMER

P HOMER PUBLIC LIBRARY, 141 W Pioneer Ave, 99603. SAN 320-1414. Tel: 907-235-3180. FAX: 907-235-3136. E-Mail: library@ci.homer.ak.us. Web Site: library.ci.homer.ak.us. *Dir*, Sister Marly Helm; Tel: 907-235-3180, Ext 21, E-Mail: mhelm@ci.homer.ak.us; Staff 1 (MLS 1)
Founded 1944. Pop 12,000; Circ 100,000
Jan 1999-Dec 1999 Income $291,042, State $6,300, City $284,742. Mats Exp $20,581, Books $16,400, Per/Ser (Incl. Access Fees) $3,853, AV Equip $328. Sal $198,623
Library Holdings: Bk Vols 34,333; Bk Titles 31,624; Per Subs 124
Automation Activity & Vendor Info: (Cataloging) Follett; (Circulation) Follett; (OPAC) Follett
Database Vendor: Ebsco - EbscoHost, OCLC - First Search
Friends of the Library Group

HYDER

P HYDER PUBLIC LIBRARY,* PO Box 50, 99923. SAN 328-0381. Tel: 250-636-9148. FAX: 250-636-2714. *Librn*, Caroline Gutierrez
Jul 1998-Jun 1999 Income $15,000. Mats Exp $7,500. Sal $6,900
Library Holdings: Bk Vols 15,000; Bk Titles 5,961; Per Subs 15

JUNEAU

GL ALASKA DEPARTMENT OF LAW, Attorney General's Library, Dimond Courthouse, PO Box 110300, 99811-0300. SAN 371-0270. Tel: 907-465-3600. FAX: 907-465-2520. *Librn*, Pamela Credo-Hayes
Library Holdings: Bk Vols 2,500; Per Subs 15

G ALASKA LEGISLATIVE AFFAIRS AGENCY, Reference Library,* State Capitol, 99801-1182. SAN 321-074X. Tel: 907-465-3808. FAX: 907-465-4844. *Librn*, Mary Pagenkopf; *Asst Librn*, Brien Daugherty; Staff 1 (MLS 1)
Special Collections: Alaska State Legislative Committee Records; Legislative Affairs Agency Publications Coll
Restriction: By appointment only

G ALASKA STATE ARCHIVES, 141 Willoughby Ave, 99811-1720. SAN 326-0321. Tel: 907-465-2270. FAX: 907-465-2465. E-Mail: archives@eed.state.ak.us. Web Site: www.eed.state.ak.us/am/archives. *Archivist*, John Stewart; *Archivist*, Lawrence E Hibpshman; *Archivist*, Judy Skagerberg; Staff 11 (MLS 5, Non-MLS 6)
Founded 1972
Jul 1998-Jun 1999 Income $710,000. Mats Exp $3,000, Books $800, Per/Ser (Incl. Access Fees) $2,200. Sal $565,000 (Prof $250,000)
Special Collections: Territorial & State of Alaska Government Records
Publications: Alaska State Archives: A Guide; Guide to Probate Records for Alaska, 1885-1960; informational pamphlet series
Partic in OCLC

G ALASKA STATE LIBRARY, 325 Willoughby Ave, State Office Bldg, 8th flr, 99811. (Mail add: PO Box 110571, 99811-0571), SAN 377-0036. Tel: 907-465-2910. FAX: 907-465-2151. E-Mail: asl@eed.state.ak.us. Web Site: www.eed.state.ak.us/lam/library.html. *Dir*, Karen Crane; E-Mail: karen_crane@eed.state.ak.us; *Dep Dir*, George Smith; Tel: 907-465-2912, E-Mail: george_smith@eed.state.ak.us; Staff 37 (MLS 17, Non-MLS 20)
Founded 1957
Library Holdings: Bk Titles 60,000; Per Subs 350
Branches:
ALASKA HISTORICAL COLLECTIONS, State Off Bldg, PO Box 110571, 99811-0571. SAN 300-2667. Tel: 907- 465-2910. FAX: 907-465-2665. E-Mail: asl@eed.state.ak.us. Web Site: www.eed.state.ak.us/lam/library.htm. *Librn*, Kathryn H Shelton; Staff 5 (MLS 3, Non-MLS 2)
Founded 1900
Library Holdings: Bk Vols 35,000
Subject Interests: Alaska, Arctic
Special Collections: (Alaska Packers Association Records); Alaska-Artic Research; Alaskana (Wickersham Coll); Marine History (L H Bayers), doc; Russian American Coll; Russian History-General and Military, (Dolgopolov Coll); Salmon Canneries; Trans-Alaska Pipeline Impact; Vinokouroff Coll; Winter & Pond Photograph Coll
Publications: Alaska Historical Monograph Series; Alaska Newspapers on Microfilm, 1866-1998; Some Books About Alaska Received (annual)
Restriction: Non-circulating to the public
Partic in OCLC Online Computer Library Center, Inc
Friends of the Library Group

P ALASKA STATE LIBRARY, ARCHIVES & MUSEUMS, Alaska Dept of Educ & Early Development, Div of State Libraries, State Office Bldg, PO Box 110571, 99811-0571. SAN 330-4981. Tel: 907-465-2910. Interlibrary Loan Service Tel: 907-465-2988. Reference Tel: 907-465-2921. FAX: 907-465-2665. E-Mail: asl@eed.state.ak.us. Web Site: www.library.state.ak.us. *Dir*, Karen R Crane; Tel: 907-465-2911, E-Mail: karen_crane@eed.state.ak.us; *Dep Dir*, George V Smith; Tel: 907-465-2912, E-Mail: george_smith@eed.state.ak.us; *Info Specialist*, Mike Mitchell; Tel: 907-465-2942, E-Mail: mike_mitchell.edd.state.ak.us; *Coll Develop*, Kay Shelton; Tel: 907-465-2926, Fax: 907-465-2990, E-Mail: kay_shelton@eed.state.ak.us; *Archivist*, John Stewart; Tel: 907-465-2275, Fax: 907-465-2465-, E-Mail: john_stewart@eed.state.ak.us; *Ref*, Catherine Wallen; Tel: 907-465-1315, E-Mail: catherine_wallen@eed.state.ak.us; *Curator*, Bruce Kato; Tel: 907-465-4866, Fax: 907-465-2976, E-Mail: bruce_kato@eed.state.ak.us; Staff 38 (MLS 18, Non-MLS 20)
Founded 1957. Pop 615,900
Jul 2000-Jun 2001 Income (Main Library and Branch Library) $4,620,700, State $3,945,200, Federal $675,500. Mats Exp $250,000. Sal $2,067,800
Library Holdings: Bk Vols 117,000; Per Subs 300
Subject Interests: History, Library and information science, State government
Special Collections: Alaska History (Wickersham Coll of Alaskana), photos; Alaska Marine History (L H Bayers Coll), doc; Can, Calif & Wash; Salmon Canneries (Alaska Packers Association Records), flm; Trans-Alaska Pipeline Impact, slides
Automation Activity & Vendor Info: (Cataloging) epixtech, inc.; (Circulation) epixtech, inc.; (OPAC) epixtech, inc.; (Serials) epixtech, inc.
Database Vendor: Ebsco - EbscoHost, IAC - Info Trac
Publications: Alaska Historical Monograph Series; Indexes to Collection; Information Empowered; Statistics of Alaska Public Libraries
Partic in Alliance Library System; Dialog Corporation; OCLC Online Computer Library Center, Inc
Special Services for the Blind - Talking book center
Branches: 1
COORDINATORS' OFFICE - TALKING BOOK CENTER, 344 W Third Ave, Ste 125, Anchorage, 99501. SAN 330-5074. Tel: 907-269-6570. TDD: 907-269-6575. FAX: 907-269-6580. Web Site: www.library.state.ak.us. *Coordr*, Pat Meek; Tel: 907-269-6575, E-Mail: pat_meek@eed.state.ak.us; Staff 4 (MLS 4)
Pop 2,000
Library Holdings: Bk Vols 65,000; Per Subs 45
Special Services for the Deaf - TDD

P JUNEAU PUBLIC LIBRARIES,* 292 Marine Way, 99801. SAN 330-5104. Tel: 907-586-5324. FAX: 907-586-5383. Web Site: www.juneau.lib.ak.us. *Dir*, Carol McCabe; *Circ*, Marian Christensen; *ILL*, Beth Bishop; *Ch Servs*, Sandra Strandtmann; *Acq*, Sue Fry; *Publ Servs*, Catherine Burnstead; *Electronic Resources*, Barbara Berg; Staff 5 (MLS 5)
Founded 1913. Pop 30,000; Circ 300,000
Jul 1998-Jun 1999 Income (Main Library and Branch Library) $1,695,318, State $28,464, City $1,480,354, Federal $186,500. Mats Exp $132,460, Books $53,300, Per/Ser (Incl. Access Fees) $72,900, Micro $1,160, AV Equip $5,100. Sal $971,552 (Prof $324,894)
Library Holdings: Bk Vols 64,426; Bk Titles 118,895; Per Subs 364
Subject Interests: Alaska
Database Vendor: DRA, epixtech, inc.
Publications: The Resource: A Directory of Juneau's Community Organizations
Friends of the Library Group
Branches: 2
DOUGLAS PUBLIC, Douglas, 99801. SAN 330-5139. Tel: 907-364-2378. FAX: 907-364-2627.
Library Holdings: Bk Vols 20,000
Friends of the Library Group
MENDENHALL VALLEY, 9105 Mendenhall Mall Rd, Ste 190, 99801. SAN 330-5163. Tel: 907-789-0125. FAX: 907-790-2213.
Library Holdings: Bk Vols 38,000
Friends of the Library Group

G NATIONAL MARINE FISHERIES SERVICE, Auke Bay Laboratory Library,* 11305 Glacier Hwy, 99801-8626. SAN 300-2519. Tel: 907-789-6010. FAX: 907-789-6094. *ILL, Librn*, Paula A Johnson; E-Mail: paula.johnson@noaa.gov
Founded 1960
Library Holdings: Bk Titles 20,000; Per Subs 84
Subject Interests: Ecology
Partic in Dialog Corporation

G UNITED STATES FOREST SERVICE, Juneau Forest Service Library, Forestry Sciences Laboratory, 2770 Sherwood Lane, Ste 2A, 99801-8545. SAN 321-527X. Tel: 907-586-7810, Ext 265. FAX: 907-586-8734. *Librn*, Lillian Petershoare; E-Mail: lpetersh/r10@fs.fed.us; Staff 1 (MLS 1)
Founded 1948
Oct 1998-Sep 1999 Income $200,000. Mats Exp $18,000, Books $2,000, Per/Ser (Incl. Access Fees) $16,000. Sal $80,000 (Prof $50,000)
Library Holdings: Bk Titles 3,600; Per Subs 47
Subject Interests: Botany, Ecology, Entomology, Forestry
Special Collections: Glaciology; Sitka Spruce Ecology
Partic in Alaska Library Network; Dialog Corporation; FS-Info; Western Libr Network

C UNIVERSITY OF ALASKA SOUTHEAST, JUNEAU, William A Egan Library, 11120 Glacier Hwy, 99801-8676. SAN 300-2691. Tel: 907-465-6466. Reference Tel: 907-465-6502. FAX: 907-465-6249. E-Mail: egan.library@uas.alaska.edu. Web Site: www.uas.alaska.edu/uas/library. *Actg Dir*, Carol Hedlin; Tel: 907-465-6467, Fax: 907-465-3612, E-Mail: carol.hedlin@usa.alaska.edu; *Asst Dir*, Lynn Shepherd; Tel: 907-465-6515, E-Mail: lynn.shepherd@uas.alaska.edu; *Outreach Serv*, Elise Tomlinson; Tel:

907-465-6285, E-Mail: elise.tomlinson@uas.alaska.edu; *Tech Servs*, Rebecca Moorman; Tel: 907-465-6345, E-Mail: rebecca.moorman@uas.alaska.edu; Staff 14 (MLS 5, Non-MLS 9)
Founded 1956. Enrl 1,942; Fac 88; Highest Degree: Master
Library Holdings: Bk Vols 128,696; Bk Titles 109,540; Per Subs 678
Automation Activity & Vendor Info: (Acquisitions) epixtech, inc.; (Cataloging) epixtech, inc.; (Circulation) epixtech, inc.; (Course Reserve) epixtech, inc.; (OPAC) epixtech, inc.; (Serials) epixtech, inc.
Database Vendor: Dialog, Ebsco - EbscoHost, epixtech, inc., OCLC - First Search, ProQuest

KAKTOVIK

P KAVOLOOK SCHOOL COMMUNITY LIBRARY,* PO Box 20, 99747. SAN 376-5911. Tel: 907-640-6626. FAX: 907-640-6718. *Librn*, Shelley Tetreau; E-Mail: stretreau@teachers@kaktovik
Library Holdings: Bk Vols 5,000

KASILOF

P KASILOF PUBLIC LIBRARY,* PO Box 177, 99610. SAN 320-4650. Tel: 907-262-4844. FAX: 907-262-8477. *Librn*, Cosette Kilfoyle; Staff 1 (MLS 1)
Founded 1962
Library Holdings: Bk Titles 5,409
Special Collections: Alaska Coll
Partic in Alaska Library Network

KENAI

P KENAI COMMUNITY LIBRARY, 163 Main St Loop, 99611. SAN 300-2705. Tel: 907-283-4378. FAX: 907-283-2266. E-Mail: library@ci.kenai.ak.us. Web Site: www.kenailibrary.org. *Dir*, Ewa Maria Jankowska; E-Mail: ejankowska@ci.kenai.ak.us; *Asst Dir*, Linda McNair; E-Mail: lmcnair@ci.kenai.ak.us; *YA Servs*, Corene Hall; E-Mail: chall@ci.kenai.ak.us; *ILL*, Julie Niederhauser; E-Mail: jniederhauser@ci.kenai.ak.us. Subject Specialists: *Preservation*, Julie Niederhauser; *Reference*, Julie Niederhauser; Staff 7 (MLS 1, Non-MLS 6)
Founded 1949. Pop 14,000; Circ 96,401
Jul 1999-Jun 2000 Income $448,568, State $11,090, City $437,478. Mats Exp $47,793, Books $39,375, Per/Ser (Incl. Access Fees) $6,717, Presv $2,000, Electronic Ref Mat (Incl. Access Fees) $9,500. Sal $207,116 (Prof $54,237)
Library Holdings: Bk Vols 77,772; Bk Titles 68,588; Per Subs 275; Bks on Deafness & Sign Lang 40
Subject Interests: Alaska, Genealogy
Special Collections: Alaskana Coll; Genealogy Coll
Automation Activity & Vendor Info: (Cataloging) epixtech, inc.; (Circulation) epixtech, inc.
Database Vendor: Ebsco - EbscoHost, GaleNet, IAC - Info Trac, OCLC - First Search, Wilson - Wilson Web
Publications: Alaska's Kenai Peninsula death records & cemetery inscriptions (Local historical information)
Function: ILL available
Mem of WLN
Partic in OCLC Online Computer Library Center, Inc
Friends of the Library Group

KETCHIKAN

P KETCHIKAN PUBLIC LIBRARY,* 629 Dock St, 99901. SAN 300-2721. Tel: 907-225-3331. FAX: 907-225-0153. Web Site: www.firstcitylib.org. *Dir*, Judith L Anglin; *Asst Librn*, Bridgit Stearns; *Ch Servs*, Charlotte Glover; Staff 3 (MLS 3)
Founded 1901. Pop 14,828
1998-1999 Income $917,000, State $7,000, City $415,000, County $375,000, Locally Generated Income $15,000. Mats Exp $70,000. Sal $462,000
Library Holdings: Bk Vols 52,000; Per Subs 171
Automation Activity & Vendor Info: (Cataloging) epixtech, inc.; (Circulation) epixtech, inc.; (OPAC) epixtech, inc.
Outreach services to homebound, jail & nursing homes
Friends of the Library Group

S TONGASS HISTORICAL MUSEUM, Reference Room, 629 Dock St, 99901. SAN 327-6805. Tel: 907-225-5600. FAX: 907-225-5602. *Dir*, Michael Naab; E-Mail: museumdir@city.ketchikan.ak.us; *Curator*, Chris Hanson; E-Mail: chrish@city.ketchikan.ak.us; Staff 3 (Non-MLS 3)
Founded 1961
Library Holdings: Bk Vols 2,500
Subject Interests: Ethnology
Publications: Bibliography of Ketchikan History
Partic in Alaska Hist Soc

C UNIVERSITY OF ALASKA SOUTHEAST, Ketchikan Campus Library, 2600 Seventh Ave, 99901. SAN 300-2713. Tel: 907-225-4722. FAX: 907-228-4520. E-Mail: cllib@firstcitylib.org. Web Site: www.ketch.alaska.edu/library.html. *Librn*, Kathleen Wiechelman; Tel: 907-228-4517, E-Mail: kbraecke@firstcitylib.org; Staff 2 (MLS 1, Non-MLS 1)
Founded 1954
Library Holdings: Bk Vols 45,000; Per Subs 225
Subject Interests: Native people, Western Americana
Database Vendor: Ebsco - EbscoHost, epixtech, inc., OCLC - First Search, ProQuest
Open Mon-Thurs 11-8, Fri 9-6

KODIAK

P A HOLMES JOHNSON MEMORIAL LIBRARY, Kodiak Public Library, 319 Lower Mill Bay Rd, 99615. SAN 300-273X. Tel: 907-486-8686. FAX: 907-486-8681. *Dir*, Joseph D'Elia; Tel: 907-486-8688, E-Mail: jdelia@city.kodiak.ak.us; *Acq*, Penny Boschee; Tel: 907-486-8685, E-Mail: pboschee@city.kodiak.ak.us; *Circ*, Theresa Dietrich; Tel: 907-486-8682, E-Mail: tdietrich@city.kodiak.ak.us; *Tech Servs*, Lisa Booch; Tel: 907-486-8684, E-Mail: lbooch@city.kodiak.ak.us; *Ch Servs*, Kristina Hinkle; Tel: 907-486-8683, E-Mail: khinkle@city.kodiak.ak.us; Staff 9 (MLS 1, Non-MLS 8)
Founded 1946. Pop 15,679; Circ 95,000
Jul 1999-Jun 2000 Income $545,011, State $7,000, City $535,011, County $3,000. Mats Exp $275,839, Books $54,822, Per/Ser (Incl. Access Fees) $10,862. Sal $269,184 (Prof $64,132)
Library Holdings: Bk Vols 64,095; Per Subs 250
Subject Interests: Fisheries
Special Collections: Alaska
Automation Activity & Vendor Info: (Cataloging) EOS; (Circulation) EOS; (OPAC) EOS
Publications: Library Lines (monthly newspaper column)
Partic in Alaska Library Network; OCLC
Friends of the Library Group

J KODIAK COLLEGE LIBRARY, Carolyn Floyd Library, 117 Benny Benson Dr, 99615-6643. SAN 320-5517. Tel: 907-486-1241. FAX: 907-486-1257. E-Mail: chatfield@kodiak.alaska.edu. Web Site: www.koc.alaska.edu/library/. *Dir*, Craig Ballain; Tel: 907-486-1238, E-Mail: cballain@kodiak.alaska.edu; *Media Spec*, Janet Bane; Tel: 907-486-1237, E-Mail: jbane@kodiak.alaska.edu; Staff 2 (MLS 1, Non-MLS 1)
Library Holdings: Bk Titles 26,500; Per Subs 40
Special Collections: Alaskana Coll
Database Vendor: DRA, Ebsco - EbscoHost, OCLC - First Search, OVID Technologies

G NATIONAL MARINE FISHERIES SERVICE, W F Thompson Memorial Library, 301 Research Ct, 99615-7400. SAN 300-2748. Tel: 907-481-1712. FAX: 907-481-1702. Web Site: www.afsc.noaa.gov/kodiak/library/libraryhomepage.htm. *Admin Assoc*, Beverly A Burns; E-Mail: beverly.a.burns@noaa.gov; Staff 1 (Non-MLS 1)
Founded 1971
Library Holdings: Bk Vols 6,300; Per Subs 70
Subject Interests: Biology, Chemistry, Ecology
Special Collections: International Halibut Commission, rpt; International Northern Pacific Fisheries Commission, doc, rpt; W F Thompson Coll
Restriction: Staff use only
Function: ILL by photocopy only
Partic in Dialog Corporation

R SAINT HERMAN'S THEOLOGICAL SEMINARY LIBRARY, 414 Mission Rd, 99615. SAN 320-5525. Tel: 907-486-3524. FAX: 907-486-5935. E-Mail: stherman@ptialaska.net. *Dir*, Beth Dunlop; Staff 2 (Non-MLS 2)
Founded 1973. Fac 4
Library Holdings: Bk Vols 4,074
Subject Interests: Rare books, Relig hist
Special Collections: Archives of the Diocese of Alaska
Automation Activity & Vendor Info: (Cataloging) Sagebrush Corporation
Restriction: Open to student, faculty & staff

KOTZEBUE

P CHUKCHI CONSORTIUM LIBRARY,* PO Box 297, 99752. SAN 376-3560. Tel: 907-442-2410. FAX: 907-442-2322. Web Site: zorba.ufadm.alaska.edu/cclib. *Librn*, Stacy Glaser
Library Holdings: Bk Vols 12,000; Bk Titles 9,000; Per Subs 100

KOYUKUK

P KOYUKUK COMMUNITY LIBRARY,* PO Box 29, 99754-4444. SAN 373-8612. Tel: 907-927-2245. *Chief Librn*, Harry Jones; *Librn*, Douglas Dayton
Founded 1983. Pop 110; Enrl 22; Fac 1
Library Holdings: Bk Titles 1,739; Per Subs 21
Mem of Fairbanks North Star Borough Pub Libr & Regional Ctr
Special Services for the Deaf - Staff with knowledge of sign language

MC GRATH

P MCGRATH COMMUNITY LIBRARY, Chinana Ave, PO Box 249, 99627-0249. SAN 374-437X. Tel: 907-524-3843. FAX: 907-524-3335. E-Mail: library@mcg.iasd.gcia.net. *Dir*, Carla Baumgartner; Staff 3 (MLS 1, Non-MLS 2)
Founded 1942. Pop 466; Circ 3,291
Library Holdings: Bk Titles 8,145; Per Subs 25
Special Collections: Alaskana, bks, per, res papers & v-tapes
Partic in Alaska Library Network

NAKNEK

§P MARTIN MONSEN REGIONAL LIBRARY, (Formerly King Salmon Branch Library), 101 Main St, 99633. (Mail add: PO Box 147, 99633-0147), Tel: 907-246-4465. FAX: 907-246-4465. E-Mail: library@bristonlbay.com. Web Site: www.theborough.com. *Librn*, Sheila Ring
Jul 1999-Jun 2000 Income (Main Library and Branch Library) $140,906
Library Holdings: Bk Vols 12,419; Per Subs 24; Bks on Deafness & Sign Lang 20
Automation Activity & Vendor Info: (Cataloging) Sagebrush Corporation; (Circulation) Sagebrush Corporation
Open Tues & Thurs 10-6, Wed, Fri & Sat 9-5
Branches: 1
SOUTH NAKNEK BRANCH, PO Box 70045, South Naknek, 99670. Tel: 907-246-6513. FAX: 907-246-6513. E-Mail: snnlibry@bristolbay.com. Web Site: www.theborough.com. *In Charge*, Anishia Elbie
Library Holdings: Bk Vols 4,826
Open Tues & Thurs 10-6, Wed, Fri & Sat 9-5

NENANA

§P NENANA PUBLIC LIBRARY, PO Box 40, 99760-0040. Tel: 907-832-5812. FAX: 907-832-5899. *Librn*, Mary J Harden; E-Mail: mjh@mtaonline.net
Jul 2000-Jun 2001 Income $29,000
Library Holdings: Bk Vols 10,000; Per Subs 12
Automation Activity & Vendor Info: (Cataloging) Sagebrush Corporation; (Circulation) Sagebrush Corporation

NIKOLAI

P NIKOLAI PUBLIC LIBRARY,* PO Box 9145, 99691. SAN 376-3684. Tel: 907-293-2113. FAX: 907-293-2115. *Adminr*, Roger Jenkins
Jul 1998-Jun 1999 Income $5,000. Mats Exp $4,200. Sal $2,000
Library Holdings: Bk Vols 25,000; Bk Titles 12,000; Per Subs 15

NINILCHIK

P NINILCHIK COMMUNITY LIBRARY, 15850 Sterling Hwy, 99639. (Mail add: PO Box 39165, 99639-0165), SAN 325-3031. Tel: 907-567-3333. *Librn*, Jackie Bear; Staff 1 (MLS 1)
Founded 1948. Pop 800; Circ 21,000

NOME

P KEGOAYAH KOZGA PUBLIC LIBRARY,* PO Box 1168, 99762. SAN 300-2756. Tel: 907-443-6628. FAX: 907-443-3762. *Admin Dir*, Debbie Cook
Founded 1902. Pop 3,656; Circ 26,126
Jul 1998-Jun 1999 Income $239,894, State $15,606, City $224,288. Mats Exp $27,279, Books $10,831, Per/Ser (Incl. Access Fees) $6,923. Sal $132,568
Library Holdings: Bk Titles 14,930; Per Subs 85
Subject Interests: Local history
Special Collections: Alaskana Rare Book Coll (Kozga); Bilingual Inupiat; Bilingual Inupiat/English; Elders Conference Recordings for the Inupiat Eskimo; Seward Peninsula; Siberian Yupik/English
Publications: A History of the Alaska Native as published in the headlines of the Nome Nugget from 1901 to 1976; I Remember History Series; Surah
Mem of Alaska Libr Network
Open Mon-Thurs 12-8, Fri & Sat 12-6

C UNIVERSITY OF ALASKA, NORTHWEST CAMPUS, Learning Resource Center, Pouch 400, 99762. SAN 322-8673. Tel: 907-443-2201, Ext 237. FAX: 907-443-2909. E-Mail: nnklh@aurora.alaska.edu. *Librn*, Kathleen Hansen
Founded 1980. Pop 4,000
1999-2000 Income $81,895. Mats Exp $78,333. Sal $60,352
Library Holdings: Bk Vols 12,719; Bk Titles 12,471; Per Subs 106
Partic in OCLC

NUIQSUT

P TRAPPER SCHOOL COMMUNITY LIBRARY,* General Delivery, 99789. SAN 376-3986. Tel: 907-480-6712. FAX: 907-480-6621. Web Site: www.nsbsd.k12.ak.us. *Librn*, Kim Bergey
Library Holdings: Bk Vols 30,000; Bk Titles 15,000; Per Subs 12

OUZINKIE

§S OUZINKIE TRIBAL COUNCIL, Media Center, PO Box 130, 99644. Tel: 907-680-2323. FAX: 907-680-2290. E-Mail: 105222.2407@compuserv.com. *Librn*, Tricia Squartsoff
Oct 1999-Sep 2000 Income $17,000
Library Holdings: Bk Vols 800

PALMER

R INTERACT MINISTRIES, Resource Center Library,* HC 04, Box 9100, 99645. SAN 320-5533. Tel: 907-745-3662. FAX: 907-745-7661. *Librn*, Donna Embree
Library Holdings: Bk Vols 750
Special Collections: Biblical Materials Coll

PALMER CORRECTIONAL CENTER

S MEDIUM SECURITY FACILITY LIBRARY, PO Box 919, 99645. Tel: 907-746-8270. FAX: 907-746-1574. *Coordr*, Mark Newell. Subject Specialists: *Edu*, Mark Newell
Library Holdings: Bk Vols 1,000

S MINIMUM SECURITY FACILITY LIBRARY, PO Box 919, 99645. Tel: 907-746-8250. FAX: 907-746-8248. *Coordr*, Paul Kroenung. Subject Specialists: *Edu*, Paul Kroenung
Library Holdings: Bk Vols 1,000

P PALMER PUBLIC LIBRARY,* 655 S Valley Way, 99645. SAN 300-2772. Tel: 907-745-4690. FAX: 907-746-3570. *Dir*, Janice Sanford; *ILL*, Jeanne Novosad; *YA Servs*, Candace Kopperud; Staff 5 (MLS 1, Non-MLS 4)
Founded 1945. Pop 17,000; Circ 100,000
Library Holdings: Bk Vols 38,000
Special Collections: Jewish Holocaust Memorial Coll; Johnson O'Malley Heritage Coll; Matanuska Valley Pioneer, Valley Settler & Matanuska Valley Record; Matanuska Valley Settlement Newspapers (1937-1959)
Publications: Friends of the Library Newsletter (quarterly)
Partic in Alaska Library Network; OCLC
Friends of the Library Group

J UNIVERSITY OF ALASKA ANCHORAGE MATANUSKA-SUSITNA COLLEGE, Alvin S Okeson Library, Mile Two Trunk Rd, 99645-5001. (Mail add: PO Box 5001, 99645-5001), SAN 300-2780. Tel: 907-745-9740. FAX: 907-745-9777. E-Mail: pylib@aaa.alaska.edu. Web Site: www.uaa.alaska.edu/matsu/. *Dir*, Leza Madsen; Staff 1 (MLS 1)
Founded 1961
Library Holdings: Bk Vols 47,382; Per Subs 195
Subject Interests: Agriculture, Computer science, Electronics
Special Collections: Local History
Mem of WLN
Partic in OCLC Online Computer Library Center, Inc

PELICAN

P PELICAN PUBLIC LIBRARY,* PO Box 712, 99832-0712. SAN 376-7302. Tel: 907-735-2500. *Librn*, Louisa Whitmarsh
Library Holdings: Bk Vols 7,000

PETERSBURG

P PETERSBURG PUBLIC LIBRARY, 12 Nordic Ave, PO Box 549, 99833-0549. SAN 300-2799. Tel: 907-772-3349. FAX: 907-772-3759. Web Site: ci.petersburg.ak.us/library/lib.html. *Librn*, Joyce Jenkins; E-Mail: joycej@ci.petersburg.ak.us; *Tech Servs*, Chris Weiss
Founded 1913. Circ 26,000
Jul 1999-Jun 2000 Income $172,289, State $6,300, City $160,794, Federal $267, Locally Generated Income $4,328, Other $600. Mats Exp $27,703, Books $22,296, Per/Ser (Incl. Access Fees) $3,428, AV Equip $1,979. Sal $118,351
Library Holdings: Bk Vols 27,036; Per Subs 72
Subject Interests: Scandinavia
Special Collections: Norwegian Coll
Publications: Petersburg, Heritage of the Sea
Partic in Alaska Library Network; OCLC Online Computer Library Center, Inc

POINT LAY

P CULLY SCHOOL-COMMUNITY LIBRARY,* 1029 Qasigialik St, 99759. (Mail add: PO Box 59077, 99759-0077), Tel: 907-833-2311. FAX: 907-833-2315. Web Site: www.nsbsd.k12.ak.us. *Librn*, Alverna Bresette; E-Mail: abresette@artic.nsbsd.k12.ak.us
Library Holdings: Bk Vols 9,000; Bk Titles 7,000; Per Subs 25

PORT LIONS

§P JESSE WAKEFIELD MEMORIAL LIBRARY, 207 Spruce Dr, PO Box 49, 99550-0049. Tel: 907-454-2288. FAX: 907-454-2588. E-Mail: jwmlcity@worldnet.att.net. *Head Librn*, Jessica Ursin
Jul 1999-Jun 2000 Income $19,200
Library Holdings: Bk Vols 11,356; Per Subs 45
Open Mon & Wed 6-9, Tues 9-12, Thurs-Sat 2-5

RUBY

§P RUBY COMMUNITY LIBRARY, PO Box 10, 99768. Tel: 907-468-4432. FAX: 907-468-4443. *Librn*, Karen Gurtler
Jul 2000-Jun 2001 Income $12,869
Library Holdings: Bk Vols 2,279

SAINT PAUL ISLAND

P ST PAUL SCHOOL COMMUNITY LIBRARY,* One Polstoi St, 99660. (Mail add: PO Box 901, 99660), SAN 376-3692. Tel: 907-546-2221, Ext 6. FAX: 907-546-2356. *Librn*, Irene Kochutin
Library Holdings: Bk Vols 12,000; Bk Titles 3,900; Per Subs 15

SELAWIK

P SELAWIK SCHOOL,* PO Box 119, 99770. SAN 376-5903. Tel: 907-484-2142. FAX: 907-484-2127. *Librn*, Victoria Ticket
Library Holdings: Bk Vols 6,000; Per Subs 20

SELDOVIA

P SELDOVIA PUBLIC LIBRARY,* 260 Seldovia St, 99663. (Mail add: Drawer H, 99663), SAN 376-3390. Tel: 907-234-7856. *Mgr*, Shirley Giles
Library Holdings: Bk Vols 10,000; Per Subs 20

SEWARD

§S ALASKA VOCATIONAL TECHNICAL CENTER, Jack Werner Memorial Library, 519 Fourth Ave, PO Box 889, 99664-0889. Tel: 907-224-6105. FAX: 907-224-6020. Web Site: www.eed.state.ak.us/avtec. *Librn*, Linda Corbin; E-Mail: linda_corbin@eed.state.ak.us
Jul 2000-Jun 2001 Income $75,000
Library Holdings: Bk Vols 7,500; Per Subs 60
Automation Activity & Vendor Info: (Cataloging) Follett; (Circulation) Follett; (OPAC) Follett

P SEWARD COMMUNITY LIBRARY, 238 Fifth Ave, PO Box 2389, 99664. SAN 300-2802. Tel: 907-224-3646. FAX: 907-224-3521. *Dir*, Patricia Linville; E-Mail: plinville@seward.net; *Tech Servs*, Doris Welch; E-Mail: doris@seward.net; *Ch Servs*, Maureen Callahan; E-Mail: maureen@seward.net; Staff 5 (MLS 1, Non-MLS 4)
Founded 1933. Pop 5,250; Circ 50,378
Jan 2000-Dec 2000 Income $291,000, State $6,300, City $220,000, Federal $3,000, Locally Generated Income $5,000. Mats Exp $28,000, Books $15,000, Per/Ser (Incl. Access Fees) $6,000, AV Equip $5,000, Other Print Mats $2,000. Sal $117,000 (Prof $42,000)
Library Holdings: Bk Titles 25,000; Per Subs 75; High Interest/Low Vocabulary Bk Vols 50
Subject Interests: Alaska, Japanese, Native Americans
Special Collections: Local Historical Photo Coll
Database Vendor: Ebsco - EbscoHost
Publications: Index to the Seward Gateway (1904-1910); Seward Gateway Prosperity, 1925 ed reprint
Function: Photocopies available
Friends of the Library Group

C UNIVERSITY OF ALASKA, INSTITUTE OF MARINE SCIENCE, Seward Marine Center Library, PO Box 730, 99664. SAN 328-6959. Tel: 907-224-5261. FAX: 907-224-3392. *In Charge*, Phyllis Shoemaker
Library Holdings: Bk Vols 2,000

SHISHMAREF

P NELLIE WEYIOUANNA ILISAAVIK LIBRARY,* PO Box 90, 99772. SAN 328-8366. Tel: 907-649-3011. FAX: 907-649-2201. *Librn*, Evelyn Olanna
Library Holdings: Bk Vols 4,000; Bk Titles 3,700; Per Subs 41

SITKA

P KETTLESON MEMORIAL LIBRARY,* 320 Harbor Dr, 99835-7553. SAN 300-2810. Tel: 907-747-8708. FAX: 907-747-8755. *Librn*, Nancy Gustavson; Staff 2 (MLS 2)
Founded 1923. Pop 8,700; Circ 121,635
Jul 1998-Jun 1999 Income $523,536, State $11,810, City $495,390, Locally Generated Income $16,336. Mats Exp $65,546, Books $44,351, Per/Ser (Incl. Access Fees) $13,095, Micro $8,000. Sal $303,712
Library Holdings: Bk Vols 51,000; Bk Titles 48,000; Per Subs 218
Special Collections: Local History (Louise Brightman Room), bk, micro
Automation Activity & Vendor Info: (Cataloging) epixtech, inc.; (Circulation) epixtech, inc.
Database Vendor: OCLC - First Search
Partic in OCLC

S NATIONAL PARK SERVICE, Sitka National Historical Park Library, 106 Metlakatla St, PO Box 738, 99835. SAN 323-8784. Tel: 907-747-6281. FAX: 907-747-5938. E-Mail: sitka_interpretation@nps.gov. *In Charge*, Mitzi Frank
Founded 1950
Library Holdings: Bk Titles 2,400
Special Collections: Russian American History, bks, tapes, film; SE Alaska Native Coll; Tlingit Indian Culture

C SHELDON JACKSON COLLEGE, Stratton Library, 801 Lincoln St, 99835-7699. SAN 300-2829. Tel: 907-747-5259. FAX: 907-747-5237. Web Site: www.sj-alaska.edu/stratton. *In Charge*, Dr Joseph McDonald
Founded 1944. Enrl 232
Library Holdings: Bk Vols 83,000; Per Subs 306
Subject Interests: Indians
Special Collections: Andrew's Coll of Books on Alaska; Children's Literature
Publications: Bibliography of Alaskana; Indexes to Verstovian; SJC Today
Mem of Alaska Libr Network, Western Libr Network
Partic in Dialog Corporation

SKAGWAY

P SKAGWAY PUBLIC LIBRARY, PO Box 394, 99840. SAN 300-2837. Tel: 907-983-2665. FAX: 907-983-2666. E-Mail: spl@aptalaska.net. *Librn*, Julene Fairbanks
Pop 811; Circ 17,290
Library Holdings: Bk Titles 13,125; Per Subs 67

G UNITED STATES NATIONAL PARK SERVICE, Klondike Gold Rush International Historical Park Library, Park Headquarters, Second Ave & Broadway, PO Box 517, 99840-0517. SAN 372-7157. Tel: 907-983-2921. TDD: 907-983-9200. FAX: 907-983-9249. *In Charge*, David Eslinger; E-Mail: david_eslinger@nps.gov
Founded 1976
Library Holdings: Bk Titles 1,000
Special Collections: Dyea & the Chilkoot Trail; Klondike Gold Rush, especially Skagway & the White Pass
Restriction: By appointment only
Special Services for the Deaf - TDD

SOLDOTNA

C KENAI PENINSULA COLLEGE LIBRARY, 34820 College Dr, 99669-9798. SAN 300-2845. Tel: 907-262-0385. Toll Free Tel: 800-392-8804. FAX: 907-262-0386. E-Mail: iylib@uaa.alaska.edu. *Librn*, Jane E Fuerstenau; E-Mail: ifjef@uaa.alaska.edu; *ILL*, Mary Broderson; Tel: 907-262-0384, E-Mail: inmjb@uaa.alaska.edu; Staff 2 (MLS 1, Non-MLS 1)
Founded 1964. Enrl 2,000; Fac 27; Highest Degree: Bachelor
1999-2000 Mats Exp $33,000, Books $11,000, Per/Ser (Incl. Access Fees) $11,000, Presv $100, Micro $3,000, AV Equip $2,000. Sal $55,000 (Prof $35,000)
Library Holdings: Bk Vols 25,000; Bk Titles 25,000; Per Subs 198
Subject Interests: Alaska
Automation Activity & Vendor Info: (Cataloging) DRA; (Circulation) DRA; (OPAC) DRA
Database Vendor: DRA, Ebsco - EbscoHost, OCLC - First Search, Wilson - Wilson Web
Function: ILL available
Partic in OCLC

P SOLDOTNA PUBLIC LIBRARY, Joyce Carver Memorial Library, 235 Binkley St, 99669. SAN 300-2853. Tel: 907-262-4227. FAX: 907-262-6856. E-Mail: sldlib5@ptialaska.net. *Librn*, Dorothy J Bishop
Founded 1965. Circ 80,000
Library Holdings: Bk Vols 35,823; Bk Titles 34,112; Per Subs 62
Automation Activity & Vendor Info: (Circulation) Follett
Database Vendor: Ebsco - EbscoHost

SUTTON

P SUTTON PUBLIC LIBRARY,* Jonesville Rd, PO Box 266, 99674. SAN 376-7329. Tel: 907-745-4467. FAX: 907-745-4467. *Librn*, Nancy Bertels; E-Mail: nbertels@msb.co.mat-su.ak.us
Jul 1997-Jun 1998 Income $85,000. Mats Exp $14,000. Sal $45,000
Library Holdings: Bk Vols 10,000; Bk Titles 9,700; Per Subs 30
Friends of the Library Group

TALKEETNA

P TALKEETNA PUBLIC LIBRARY,* PO Box 768, 99676. SAN 376-3706. Tel: 907-733-2359. FAX: 907-733-3017. *Librn*, Anna Lou Levinson
Jul 1997-Jun 1998 Income $88,000, State $7,000. Mats Exp $15,000. Sal $48,000
Library Holdings: Bk Vols 9,500; Bk Titles 5,000; Per Subs 60

TENAKEE SPRINGS

P DERMOTT O'TOOLE MEMORIAL LIBRARY,* PO Box 35, 99841. SAN 376-7965. Tel: 907-736-2248. *In Charge*, Taimane Scanlan
Library Holdings: Bk Titles 800

THORNE BAY

§P THORNE BAY COMMUNITY LIBRARY, PO Box 19110, 99919-0110. Tel: 907-828-3380. FAX: 907-828-3374. *Librn*, Karen Peterson
Library Holdings: Bk Vols 300; Per Subs 21

TOK

P TOK COMMUNITY LIBRARY,* PO Box 227, 99780-0227. SAN 322-7669. Tel: 907-883-5623. *Librn*, Kim Roth
Library Holdings: Bk Vols 16,000; Bk Titles 10,000; Per Subs 30

TRAPPER CREEK

P TRAPPER CREEK PUBLIC LIBRARY,* PO Box 13388, 99683. SAN 376-6497. Tel: 907-733-1546. FAX: 907-733-1547. E-Mail: tclib@matnet.com. *Librn*, Patty Christensen
Library Holdings: Bk Vols 8,000; Per Subs 20
Open Mon & Wed 12-7, Thurs 9-2, Sat 12-6

TULUKSAK

P TULUKSAK SCHOOL-COMMUNITY LIBRARY, Tulkisarmute Yupiit School,* PO Box 115, 99679. SAN 376-6926. Tel: 907-695-6313. FAX: 907-695-6989. *Librn*, Dora Napoka
Library Holdings: Bk Vols 1,000

UNALAKLEET

P TICASUK LIBRARY,* PO Box 28, 99684. SAN 325-2876. Tel: 907-624-3053. FAX: 907-624-3130.
Founded 1982. Pop 800; Circ 2,474
Library Holdings: Bk Vols 4,343
Subject Interests: Ethnography
Partic in Alaska Library Network

UNALASKA

§P UNALASKA PUBLIC LIBRARY, 64 Eleanor Dr, PO Box 1370, 99685-1370. Tel: 907-581-5060. FAX: 907-581-5266. E-Mail: akunak@ci.unalaska.ak.us. Web Site: www.ci.unalaska.ak.us. *Dir, Librn*, Daniel Masoni
Jul 2000-Jun 2001 Income $464,023, State $6,300, City $447,223, Locally Generated Income $2,000, Other $8,500
Library Holdings: Bk Vols 9,405; Bk Titles 9,303; Per Subs 77; High Interest/Low Vocabulary Bk Vols 451; Bks on Deafness & Sign Lang 58
Database Vendor: OCLC - First Search

VALDEZ

P VALDEZ CONSORTIUM LIBRARY, (VCL), Fairbanks St, PO Box 609, 99686. SAN 300-2861. Tel: 907-835-4632. FAX: 907-835-4876. E-Mail: vnvl@uaa.alaska.edu. Web Site: www.ci.valdez.ak.us/library/home.html. *Dir*, Karen Weiland; *Asst Librn*, Doreen Hodges; *Circ*, Bruce Good
Founded 1930. Pop 4,486; Circ 46,864
Library Holdings: Bk Vols 45,000; Bk Titles 42,640; Per Subs 117
Special Collections: Alaska Coll
Automation Activity & Vendor Info: (Cataloging) DRA; (Circulation) VTLS; (OPAC) VTLS
Partic in OCLC; University of Alaska GNOSIS Libr Syst
Open Mon & Fri 10am-6pm, Tues-Thurs 10am-8pm, Sat noon-5pm & Sun 1-5pm
Friends of the Library Group

WASILLA

P WASILLA PUBLIC LIBRARY, 391 N Main St, 99654-7085. SAN 300-287X. Tel: 907-376-5913. FAX: 907-376-2347. E-Mail: library@ci.wasilla.ak.us. *Dir*, Thomas Cornel; *Automation Syst Coordr*, Laura Salisbury; *Ch Servs*, Cathy Petrie; *ILL*, Trudy Toomey; Staff 9 (MLS 2, Non-MLS 7)
Founded 1938. Pop 23,000; Circ 170,000
Jul 1999-Jun 2000 Income $538,811, State $6,300, City $189,179, County $327,000, Locally Generated Income $21,332. Mats Exp $28,790, Books $20,429, Per/Ser (Incl. Access Fees) $8,361. Sal $300,573 (Prof $90,000)
Library Holdings: Bk Vols 51,000; Bk Titles 45,958; Per Subs 131
Automation Activity & Vendor Info: (Cataloging) epixtech, inc.; (Circulation) epixtech, inc.
Friends of the Library Group

WILLOW

P WILLOW PUBLIC LIBRARY,* Mile 70, Parks Hwy, PO Box 129, 99688. SAN 320-4677. Tel: 907-495-6424. FAX: 907-495-6424. *Librn*, Nicole Pease
Founded 1967. Pop 1,900; Circ 15,642
Jul 1996-Jun 1997 Income $101,402, State $7,000, County $94,402. Mats Exp $18,336. Sal $50,113
Library Holdings: Bk Vols 14,000; Per Subs 30
Special Collections: Alaskana
Friends of the Library Group

WRANGELL

P IRENE INGLE PUBLIC LIBRARY, 124 Second Ave, PO Box 679, 99929-0679. SAN 300-2888. Tel: 907-874-3535. FAX: 907-874-2520. E-Mail: library@seapac.net. Web Site: www.wrangell.com/community/library.htm. *Librn*, Kay Jabusch; *Assoc Librn*, Margaret Villarma
Founded 1921. Pop 2,675; Circ 36,000
2000-2001 Income $181,460, State $7,000, City $162,460, Locally Generated Income $12,000. Mats Exp $18,906, Books $16,511, Micro $1,395, Other Print Mats $1,000. Sal $75,860
Library Holdings: Bk Titles 31,000; Per Subs 64
Subject Interests: Alaska
Friends of the Library Group

ARIZONA

Date of Statistics: Fiscal 1998-99
Population, 1999 Census: 4,678,500
Population Served by Public Libraries: 4,678,500
Total Volumes in Public Libraries: 8,991,680
Volumes Per Capita: 1.9
Total Public Library Circulation: 29,113,222
Circulation Per Capita: 6.2
Total Public Library Income: $95,397,780
Number of County Libraries: 15
Counties Served: 15
Number of Bookmobiles in State: 18
Grants-in-Aid to Public Libraries (Fiscal 1998-99):
Federal: $1,602,918
State Aid: $565,565

AGUILA

P AGUILA PUBLIC LIBRARY,* 51321 Ray St W, PO Box 188, 85320. SAN 300-2896. Tel: 520-685-2214. FAX: 520-685-3233. *Librn*, Jenise Porter
Founded 1978. Pop 900; Circ 4,610
Library Holdings: Bk Vols 6,050; Bk Titles 5,914
Subject Interests: Southwestern Americana, Spanish (language)
Mem of Maricopa County Libr Syst
Friends of the Library Group

AJO

S DEPARTMENT OF INTERIOR NATIONAL PARK SERVICE, Organ Pipe Cactus National Monument Library, Rte 1, Box 100, 85321. SAN 370-2871. Tel: 520-387-6849. FAX: 520-387-7144. *Librn*, David DeWitt; E-Mail: david_dewitt@nps.gov
Library Holdings: Bk Vols 1,640

AMADO

S SMITHSONIAN INSTITUTION, Fred Lawrence Whipple Observatory Library, PO Box 97, 85645-0097. SAN 375-6556. Tel: 520-670-5701. FAX: 520-670-5113.
Library Holdings: Bk Titles 17; Per Subs 25
Subject Interests: Astronomy

APACHE JUNCTION

P APACHE JUNCTION PUBLIC LIBRARY, 1177 N Idaho Rd, 85219. SAN 300-290X. Tel: 480-474-8555. Circulation Tel: 480-474-8555. Reference Tel: 480-474-8556. TDD: 480-983-6012. FAX: 480-983-4540. Web Site: ajnet.ci.apache-jct.az.us/libtop1.htm. *Dir*, Pamela Loui; E-Mail: ploui@ajcity.net; *Mgr*, Spencer Paden; E-Mail: spaden@ajcity.net; *YA Servs*, Elizabeth Burks; Staff 5 (MLS 5)
Founded 1965. Pop 25,385; Circ 243,147
Jul 1999-Jun 2000 Income $845,831, City $818,257, Federal $14,000, County $13,574. Mats Exp $130,691, Books $90,871, Per/Ser (Incl. Access Fees) $11,363, AV Equip $14,333, Electronic Ref Mat (Incl. Access Fees) $14,124. Sal $529,009
Library Holdings: Bk Titles 96,902; Per Subs 179
Subject Interests: Large type print
Special Collections: Arizona Coll; Superstition Mountain Reserve Coll
Automation Activity & Vendor Info: (Acquisitions) epixtech, inc.; (Cataloging) epixtech, inc.; (Circulation) epixtech, inc.; (OPAC) epixtech, inc.
Database Vendor: Ebsco - EbscoHost, OCLC - First Search
Special Services for the Deaf - TDD; Videos & decoder
Adult literacy services
Friends of the Library Group

§C CENTRAL ARIZONA COLLEGE, Superstition Mountain Campus Learning Center, 273 E Old West Hwy (US 60), 85219-5223. Tel: 480-982-7261, Ext 128. Web Site: www.cac.cc.az.us/smclearningcenter/smc_lrngctr.html. *In Charge*, Julie Chelette-Vila; E-Mail: julie_chelette-vila@python.cac.cc.az.us
Jul 2000-Jun 2001 Mats Exp Books $195,000
Library Holdings: Bk Vols 10,000; Per Subs 10
Automation Activity & Vendor Info: (Cataloging) epixtech, inc.; (Circulation) epixtech, inc.; (OPAC) epixtech, inc.

ARIZONA CITY

P ARIZONA CITY COMMUNITY LIBRARY, 13254 S Sunland Gin Rd, PO Box 118, 85223-0118. SAN 300-2918. Tel: 520-466-5565. FAX: 520-466-6050. E-Mail: azcitylib@hotmail.com. Web Site: www.co.pinal.az.us/library/azcity/friends. *In Charge*, Mary J Klukas
Founded 1963. Pop 5,000; Circ 9,942
Jul 1998-Jun 1999 Income $16,376, County $1,075, Locally Generated Income $12,301, Other $3,000. Mats Exp $8,688, Books $4,000, Other Print Mats $830. Sal $6,721
Library Holdings: Bk Titles 17,800
Special Collections: Arizona Coll
Publications: Newsletter
Mem of Pinal County Library District
Special Services for the Blind - Audiotape library; Talking Books
Friends of the Library Group

ASH FORK

P ASH FORK PUBLIC LIBRARY,* 518 Lewis Ave, PO Box 695, 86320. SAN 323-7796. Tel: 520-637-2442. FAX: 520-637-0394. *Mgr*, Marion Schiffgen
Mem of Yavapai County Library District
Open Tues-Fri 10:00 am-12:30pm; 1:30 pm-4:00 pm

AVONDALE

P AVONDALE PUBLIC LIBRARY,* 328 W Western Ave, 85323. SAN 300-2926. Tel: 623-932-9415. FAX: 623-932-9418. *Dir*, Vince McCaul
Founded 1930. Circ 54,313
Library Holdings: Bk Vols 26,363
Subject Interests: Large type print, Spanish (language)
Automation Activity & Vendor Info: (Circulation) Follett
Friends of the Library Group

C ESTRELLA MOUNTAIN COMMUNITY COLLEGE, The Information Commons, 3000 N Dysart Rd, 85323-1000. SAN 374-7417. Tel: 623-935-8191. FAX: 623-935-8060. Web Site: www.emc.maricopa.edu. *Chair*, Edmund F SantaVicca; *Librn*, Terry Newbury; *Librn*, Karen Whitney; *Librn*, Terry Meyer; Staff 4 (MLS 4)
Enrl 4,250

Library Holdings: Bk Titles 10,000; Per Subs 100
Automation Activity & Vendor Info: (Acquisitions) DRA
Special Services for the Deaf - Staff with knowledge of sign language

BAGDAD

P BAGDAD PUBLIC LIBRARY,* 100 Main St, PO Box 95, 86321. SAN 323-7818. Tel: 520-633-2325. FAX: 520-633-2054. E-Mail: bag95a@aztec.asu.edu. *Mgr*, Yvonne Peppers
Library Holdings: Bk Titles 10,000
Mem of Yavapai County Library District

BEAVER DAN

P LITTLEFIELD-BEAVER DAN STATION LIBRARY,* PO Box 730, 86432. SAN 376-3218. Tel: 520-692-5785.
Library Holdings: Bk Titles 10
Mem of Mohave County Library District

BENSON

S APACHE NITROGEN PRODUCTS LIBRARY,* PO Box 700, 85602. SAN 370-3398. Tel: 520-720-2217, Ext 2111. FAX: 520-720-4158. *In Charge*, Jeanine Tracey
Library Holdings: Bk Titles 500
Subject Interests: Chemical engineering, Chemical technology

P BENSON PUBLIC LIBRARY, 300 S Huachuca, 85602-6650. (Mail add: PO Drawer 1480, 85602-6650), SAN 300-2934. Tel: 520-586-9535. FAX: 520-586-3224. Web Site: www.cochise.lib.az.us. *Dir*, Kay Whitehead; E-Mail: kwhiteh@bensonpl.lib.az.us; *Asst Librn*, Peggy Scott; Staff 7 (Non-MLS 7)
Founded 1916. Pop 7,000; Circ 58,500
Jul 1998-Jun 1999 Income $133,000, City $125,000, Locally Generated Income $8,000. Mats Exp $36,000, Books $20,000, Per/Ser (Incl. Access Fees) $1,000, Electronic Ref Mat (Incl. Access Fees) $15,000. Sal $90,500
Library Holdings: Bk Vols 28,541; Bk Titles 28,161; Per Subs 51
Subject Interests: Gen fiction
Special Collections: Arizoniana; Large Print, audio, video
Automation Activity & Vendor Info: (Cataloging) DRA; (Circulation) DRA
Database Vendor: DRA
Function: ILL available, Photocopies available, Professional lending library, Reference services available, Some telephone reference
Mem of Cochise County Library District
Special Services for the Deaf - Books on deafness & sign language; Special interest periodicals
Special Services for the Blind - Bks on tape

C WORLD UNIVERSITY LIBRARY, Desert Sanctuary Campus, PO Box 2470, 85602. SAN 300-4694. Tel: 520-586-2985. FAX: 520-586-4764. E-Mail: desertsanctuary@theriver.com. Web Site: www.worlduniversity.org. *Librn*, Howard John Zitko
Founded 1947
Library Holdings: Bk Vols 25,000; Bk Titles 25,000; Per Subs 25
Subject Interests: Occult, Peace studies, UFO phenomenon, World religion
Publications: Liftoff (international newsletter)
Function: Reference only
Friends of the Library Group

BISBEE

S ARIZONA CACTUS & SUCCULENT RESEARCH INC, Arizona Cactus Library, 8 S Cactus Lane, 85603. SAN 371-6430. Tel: 520-432-7040. E-Mail: azcactus@primenet.com. Web Site: www.arizonacactus.com. *Librn*, Judy Langer; *Cat, Publ Servs, Ref*, David Eppele
Founded 1983
Library Holdings: Bk Titles 1,930; Per Subs 18
Publications: Arizona Cactus News
Restriction: By appointment only

S BISBEE MINING & HISTORICAL MUSEUM, Lemuel C Shattuck Memorial Archival Library, 5 Copper Queen Plaza, PO Box 14, 85603-0014. SAN 300-2942. Tel: 520-432-7071. FAX: 520-432-7800. E-Mail: bisbeemuseum@theriver.com. Web Site: www.azstarnet.com/nonprofit/bisbeemuseum. *Dir*, Carri Gustavson; *Librn*, Boyd Nicholl; *Curator*, Boyd Nicholl; Staff 4 (MLS 1, Non-MLS 3)
Founded 1974
Library Holdings: Bk Titles 970
Subject Interests: Geology, Local history, Mining
Special Collections: 10 Cochise County Original Geological Survey Maps; Bisbee Newspapers 1898-1970, microfilm; City of Bisbee Voter Registration records; County Great Registers & County Census for 1880 (1882 Special Census), 1900 & 1910; Historic Preservation & Restoration File; Hospital Records, pre-1900; Manuscript Coll; microfilm; Photographic Coll of 25,000 historic images; Tombstone Newspapers 1877-1901
Friends of the Library Group

GL COCHISE COUNTY LAW LIBRARY,* PO Drawer P, 85603-0050. SAN 300-2950. Tel: 520-432-9339. FAX: 520-432-9293. *Librn*, Lucia Ventura
Founded 1930. Circ 1,200
Jul 1996-Jun 1997 Income $100,334. Mats Exp $103,508
Library Holdings: Bk Titles 27,000

P COCHISE COUNTY LIBRARY DISTRICT, Old Bisbee High School, PO Drawer AK, 85603. SAN 330-5228. Tel: 520-432-9250. FAX: 520-432-7339. Web Site: cochise.lib.az.us. *Dir*, Donna A Gaab; *Publ Servs*, Colleen Crowlie; *Tech Servs*, Susan Mathews; *Syst Coordr*, Kimberly Holman; Staff 9 (MLS 4, Non-MLS 5)
Founded 1970. Pop 120,000
Jul 1999-Jun 2000 Income $888,500, State $20,000, Federal $16,000, County $850,000, Other $2,500. Mats Exp $94,000, Books $80,000, Per/Ser (Incl. Access Fees) $4,000, Electronic Ref Mat (Incl. Access Fees) $10,000. Sal $300,000
Library Holdings: Bk Vols 100,000; Bk Titles 60,000
Automation Activity & Vendor Info: (Cataloging) DRA; (Circulation) DRA; (ILL) DRA; (OPAC) DRA
Database Vendor: DRA, OCLC - First Search
Member Libraries: Benson Public Library; Cochise County Library District; Cochise County Library District; Cochise County Library District; Cochise County Library District; Copper Queen Library; Douglas Public Library; Elsie S Hogan Community Library; Huachuca City Public Library; Sierra Vista Public Library; Tombstone Reading Station-Tombstone City Library
Provide support services to city libraries in district - Benson, Bisbee (Copper Queen), Douglas, Huachuca City, Sierra Vista, Tombstone, Willcox (Elsie S Hogan). Coordinates shared countywide DRA system
Friends of the Library Group
Branches: 4
ALICE WOODS SUNIZONA LIBRARY AT ASH CREEK SCHOOL, HCR 1, Box 260, Pearce, 85625. SAN 330-549X. Tel: 520-824-3340. FAX: 520-824-3410. Web Site: cochise.lib.az.us. *Br Coordr*, Trina Sue Riggs; Staff 1 (Non-MLS 1)
Founded 1979. Pop 300; Circ 7,500
Library Holdings: Bk Vols 7,500
Automation Activity & Vendor Info: (Cataloging) DRA; (Circulation) DRA; (ILL) DRA; (OPAC) DRA
Mem of Cochise County Library District
JIMMIE LIBHART LIBRARY, PO Box 417, Bowie, 85605. SAN 325-3910. Tel: 520-847-2522. FAX: 520-847-2522. Web Site: cochise.lib.az.us. *Br Coordr*, Pat Crowell; Staff 1 (Non-MLS 1)
Founded 1985. Pop 400; Circ 5,000
Library Holdings: Bk Vols 4,500
Automation Activity & Vendor Info: (Cataloging) DRA; (Circulation) DRA; (ILL) DRA; (OPAC) DRA
Mem of Cochise County Library District
MYRTLE KRAFT LIBRARY, Main St, PO Box 16552, Portal, 85632. SAN 330-5430. Tel: 520-558-2468. FAX: 520-558-2468. Web Site: cochise.lib.az.us. *Br Coordr*, Todd Malone; Staff 1 (Non-MLS 1)
Founded 1979. Pop 300; Circ 5,500
Library Holdings: Bk Vols 4,500
Automation Activity & Vendor Info: (Cataloging) DRA; (Circulation) DRA; (ILL) DRA; (OPAC) DRA
Mem of Cochise County Library District
SUNSITES COMMUNITY, 210 Ford Rd, PO Box 544, Pearce, 85625. SAN 330-5252. Tel: 520-826-3866. FAX: 520-826-3866. Web Site: cochise.lib.az.us. *Br Coordr*, Celia Skeeles; Staff 1 (Non-MLS 1)
Founded 1979. Pop 1,200; Circ 15,000
Library Holdings: Bk Vols 8,000
Automation Activity & Vendor Info: (Cataloging) DRA; (Circulation) DRA; (ILL) DRA; (OPAC) DRA
Mem of Cochise County Library District
Friends of the Library Group
Bookmobiles: 2. Also have 1 minibookmobile-courier van

P COPPER QUEEN LIBRARY, Bisbee City Library, 6 Main St, PO Box 1857, 85603. SAN 300-2969. Tel: 520-432-4232. FAX: 520-432-7061. Web Site: cochise.lib.az.us/bisbee/bisbee.htm. *Librn*, Janet M Ball; E-Mail: jball@bisbeepl.lib.az.us; *Librn*, Lise Gilliland; E-Mail: lgillil@bisbeepl.lib.az.us
Founded 1882. Pop 8,065; Circ 27,917
Jul 2000-Jun 2001 Income $122,700. Mats Exp $7,900, Books $6,100, Per/Ser (Incl. Access Fees) $900
Library Holdings: Bk Vols 29,000; Per Subs 40
Special Collections: Southwest & Arizona Coll
Automation Activity & Vendor Info: (Cataloging) DRA; (Circulation) DRA
Database Vendor: DRA
Mem of Cochise County Library District
Friends of the Library Group

BLACK CANYON CITY

P BLACK CANYON CITY COMMUNITY LIBRARY,* 34701 S Old Black Canyon Hwy, PO Box 87, 85324. SAN 323-7834. Tel: 623-374-5866. FAX: 623-374-0468. *Pres*, Trudy Dillard; *Librn*, Laura Seppala
1997-1998 Income $17,204. Mats Exp $3,700. Sal $5,700
Library Holdings: Bk Vols 12,000
Mem of Yavapai County Library District
Friends of the Library Group

BUCKEYE

§S ARIZONA DEPARTMENT OF CORRECTIONS - ADULT, Arizona State Prison Complex - Lewis Library, 26700 S Hwy 85, 85326. (Mail add: PO Box 70, 85326-0070), Tel: 623-386-6160. FAX: 623-386-2644. *Librn*, Deborah McKelvey; Tel: 623-386-6160, Ext 4908; *Librn*, Donna Hubbard; *Librn*, James McGee; *Librn*, Janet Tabor; *Librn*, Dawn Van Horn; Tel: 623-386-6160, Ext 4908
Library Holdings: Bk Vols 9,600

P BUCKEYE PUBLIC LIBRARY,* 310 N Sixth St, 85326-2439. SAN 300-2977. Tel: 623-386-2778. FAX: 623-393-0356. Web Site: guydbuckey.az.us. *Librn*, Jeanine Guy; *Ch Servs*, Cheryl Sedig; Staff 3 (Non-MLS 3)
Founded 1956
Library Holdings: Bk Vols 22,000; Per Subs 20
Special Collections: Arizona Highways Coll; Arizona History & Culture (Southwest Coll); National Geographics
Publications: Library Journal, booklist
Mem of Maricopa County Libr Syst
Friends of the Library Group

BULLHEAD CITY

M WESTERN ARIZONA REGIONAL MEDICAL CENTER, Medical Library,* 2735 Silver Creek Rd, 86442. SAN 375-7919. Tel: 520-763-2273. FAX: 520-763-0223. *Dir*, Ann Pierce
Library Holdings: Bk Titles 500; Per Subs 25

CAMP VERDE

P CAMP VERDE COMMUNITY LIBRARY, 130 Black Bridge Loop Rd, 86322. (Mail add: PO Box 566, 86322), SAN 323-7850. Tel: 520-567-3414. FAX: 520-567-9583. *Asst Librn*, Terry Ellison; *Tech Servs*, Jan Archull; *Ch Servs*, Peggy Schuler; E-Mail: pschuer@campverdecl.lib.az.us; Staff 4 (MLS 2, Non-MLS 2)
Founded 1975
Jul 2000-Jun 2001 Income $207,000, City $163,000, County $44,000. Mats Exp $24,600, Books $21,000, Per/Ser (Incl. Access Fees) $2,100, AV Equip $1,500. Sal $81,450 (Prof $30,450)
Library Holdings: Bk Vols 25,000; Per Subs 105
Subject Interests: Handicrafts
Special Collections: Southwest US Information & Culture
Automation Activity & Vendor Info: (Cataloging) epixtech, inc.; (Circulation) epixtech, inc.; (OPAC) epixtech, inc.
Database Vendor: Ebsco - EbscoHost
Publications: Subject handouts, Monthly Newsletter
Partic in Yavapai County Libr Network

S FORT VERDE STATE HISTORIC PARK LIBRARY, 125 E Hollamon, PO Box 397, 86322. SAN 374-5384. Tel: 520-567-3275. FAX: 520-567-4036. Web Site: www.pr.state.az.us. *Mgr*, Robert Munson; *Asst Librn*, Nora Graf; E-Mail: ngraf@pr.state.az.us
1998-1999 Mats Exp $1,003, Books $403, Micro $400, Manuscripts & Archives $200
Library Holdings: Bk Vols 250
Special Collections: Victorian Lifestyles, Clothing, bks, files; Western Military History, 1860-1900, bks, files

CASA GRANDE

P CASA GRANDE PUBLIC LIBRARY, 449 N Dry Lake, 85222. SAN 300-2993. Tel: 520-421-8710. TDD: 520-421-2035. FAX: 520-421-8701. *Dir*, David P Snider; E-Mail: dsnider@casa-grande.az.us; *Ad Servs*, John Olson; Staff 11 (MLS 3, Non-MLS 8)
Founded 1953. Pop 50,000; Circ 278,000
Library Holdings: Bk Vols 74,500; Per Subs 135
Subject Interests: Local history
Automation Activity & Vendor Info: (Cataloging) Gaylord; (Circulation) Gaylord; (OPAC) Gaylord
Database Vendor: Ebsco - EbscoHost, OCLC - First Search
Mem of Pinal County Library District
Friends of the Library Group

M CASA GRANDE REGIONAL MEDICAL CENTER, 1800 E Florence Blvd, 85222. Tel: 520-426-6517. *Asst Dir*, Kelly Carter; E-Mail: k.carter@cgrmc.org
Library Holdings: Bk Vols 125; Bk Titles 100; Per Subs 10

S CASA GRANDE VALLEY HISTORICAL SOCIETY, Museum Library, 110 W Florence Blvd, 85222. SAN 327-7089. Tel: 520-836-2223. Web Site: www.cguhs.org. *Librn*, Barbara Choen
Founded 1964
Library Holdings: Bk Titles 300
Subject Interests: Local history
Restriction: Non-circulating to the public

CAVE CREEK

P DESERT FOOTHILLS LIBRARY,* 38443 N Schoolhouse Rd, PO Box 4070, 85331. SAN 376-8414. Tel: 480-488-2286. FAX: 480-595-8353. *Dir*, Sandra Loveland
Library Holdings: Bk Vols 34,500; Bk Titles 33,600; Per Subs 25
Friends of the Library Group

CHANDLER

P CHANDLER PUBLIC LIBRARY,* 22 S Delaware, 85225. (Mail add: PO Box 4008 MS 601, 85244-4008), SAN 300-3000. Tel: 480-782-2800. TDD: 800-367-8939. FAX: 480-782-2790. Web Site: library.ci.chandler.az.us. *Dir*, Karen Drake; Tel: 480-782-2817, Fax: 480-782-2823, E-Mail: karen.drake@ci.chandler.az.us; *Assoc Dir*, Mary Johns; Tel: 480-782-2818, Fax: 480-782-2823, E-Mail: mary.johns@ci.chandler.az.us; *Ch Servs*, Phyllis Saunders; Tel: 480-782-2820, Fax: 480-782-2823, E-Mail: phyllis.saunders@ci.chandler.az.us; *Tech Coordr*, Daniel Lee; Tel: 480-782-2813, Fax: 480-782-2823, E-Mail: dan.lee@ci.chandler.az.us; *Coll Develop*, Lawrence Nelson; Tel: 480-782-2819, Fax: 480-782-2823, E-Mail: larry.nelson@ci.chandler.az.us; *Ad Servs*, Joseph Schallan; Tel: 480-782-2803, E-Mail: joe.schallan@ci.chandler.az.us; Staff 78 (MLS 16, Non-MLS 62)
Founded 1954. Pop 174,530
Jul 1998-Jun 1999 Income $2,812,983, State $51,199, City $2,705,209, Federal $37,500, Other $19,075. Mats Exp $756,830, Books $523,585, Per/Ser (Incl. Access Fees) $28,134, AV Equip $20,894, Electronic Ref Mat (Incl. Access Fees) $184,217. Sal $1,414,336
Library Holdings: Bk Vols 234,806; Per Subs 594
Special Collections: Arizona & Southwest Coll; Arizona Indian Coll; Large Print Book Coll; New Reader Coll; Spanish Language Coll
Automation Activity & Vendor Info: (Cataloging) SIRSI; (Circulation) SIRSI; (OPAC) SIRSI
Database Vendor: Ebsco - EbscoHost, GaleNet, IAC - SearchBank, OCLC - First Search
Publications: Library Times (newsletter)
Function: Reference services available
Services - Home delivery service; Adult & Family Literacy Programs
Friends of the Library Group
Branches: 2
HAMILTON, 3700 S Arizona Ave, 85248-4500. (Mail add: Mail Stop 917, PO Box 4008, 85244-4008), Tel: 480-782-2828. FAX: 480-782-2833. Web Site: library.chandler.az.us. *Br Coordr*, Delaslis George; Tel: 480-782-2831, E-Mail: george.delalis@ci.chandler.az.us
Library Holdings: Bk Vols 32,000; Per Subs 92; Bks on Deafness & Sign Lang 33
Automation Activity & Vendor Info: (Cataloging) SIRSI; (Circulation) SIRSI; (OPAC) SIRSI
SUNSET, 4930 W Ray Rd, 85226-6219. (Mail add: MS918, PO Box 4008, 85244-4008), Tel: 480-782-2846. FAX: 480-782-2848. *Br Coordr*, Ginger Miloserny; E-Mail: ginger.miloserney@ci.chandler.az.us
Library Holdings: Bk Vols 50,000; Per Subs 80; Bks on Deafness & Sign Lang 20
Automation Activity & Vendor Info: (Cataloging) SIRSI; (Circulation) SIRSI; (OPAC) SIRSI
Open Mon-Thurs 10-8, Fri & Sat 10-6

CHINLE

S NATIONAL PARK SERVICE, Canyon de Chelly National Monument Library, PO Box 588, 86503-0588. SAN 374-5600. Tel: 520-674-5500. FAX: 520-674-5507. E-Mail: gwenn_gallenstein@nps.gov.
Founded 1964. Circ 1,000
Library Holdings: Bk Titles 500
Special Collections: Cultural History, Canyon de Chelly; Natural History, Canyon de Chelly, bks, papers

CHINO VALLEY

P CHINO VALLEY PUBLIC LIBRARY, (Formerly Marion Lassa Chino Valley Public Library), 1020 W Palomino Rd, PO Box 1188, 86323-1188. SAN 323-7877. Tel: 520-636-2687. FAX: 520-636-9129. *Dir*, Scott A Bruner; *Asst Librn*, Julia A Diener; *Cat*, Patricia Lobdell; *Circ*, Patrick McAllister; *Ch Servs*, Darlene J Westcott; *Circ*, Betty Morrison; Staff 6

(MLS 1, Non-MLS 5)
Database Vendor: epixtech, inc.
Mem of Yavapai County Library District
Partic in Amninet; Aznet; Libr Network; Yavapai County Libr Network
Friends of the Library Group

CIBECUE

P CIBECUE COMMUNITY LIBRARY,* PO Box 8006, 85911. SAN 376-6047. Tel: 520-332-2621. FAX: 520-332-2415. *Librn*, Lena-Altaha Walker; *Asst Dir*, Elana Tessay
Library Holdings: Bk Vols 3,000

CLARKDALE

P CLARK MEMORIAL LIBRARY,* Ninth St, PO Box 357, 86324. SAN 323-7893. Tel: 520-634-9760. FAX: 520-639-0029. *In Charge*, Charlotte Hawken
Library Holdings: Bk Vols 9,000; Per Subs 15
Mem of Yavapai County Library District

CLAY SPRINGS

P CLAY SPRINGS PUBLIC LIBRARY,* PO Box 428, 85923. SAN 377-0737. Tel: 520-537-6027. *Librn*, Jackie Nelson
Library Holdings: Bk Vols 1,000; Bk Titles 925

CLIFTON

P CLIFTON-GREENLEE COUNTY PUBLIC LIBRARY,* 102 School St, PO Box 1226, 85533-1226. SAN 300-3027. Tel: 520-865-2461, Ext 3710. FAX: 520-865-3014. *Dir*, Rebecca B Oliver; *ILL*, Berta Manuz
Founded 1941. Pop 9,000
Library Holdings: Bk Vols 20,000; Per Subs 20
Special Collections: Arizona Coll
Member Libraries: Clifton Greenlee County
Friends of the Library Group

COLORADO CITY

P COLORADO CITY PUBLIC LIBRARY,* 140 S Pioneer, PO Box 1709, 86021. SAN 376-7299. Tel: 520-875-8015. FAX: 520-875-2778. *Dir*, Oliver B Barlow
Library Holdings: Bk Vols 16,000; Bk Titles 14,000
Mem of Mohave County Library District
Friends of the Library Group

CONGRESS

P CONGRESS PUBLIC LIBRARY, 400 Ranch Rd, 85332. (Mail add: PO Box 380, 85332), SAN 323-7915. Tel: 520-427-3945. FAX: 520-427-3945. E-Mail: conlib@yavapaicold.lib.az.us. Web Site: www.prescottlib.lib.az.us/conlib.htm. *Dir*, Mary Ann Paulic; Staff 1 (Non-MLS 1)
Founded 1984. Pop 1,200
Jun 1999-May 2000 Income County $11,156. Mats Exp Books $3,776. Sal $7,200
Library Holdings: Bk Titles 3,000
Mem of Yavapai County Library District

COOLIDGE

S ARIZONA DEPARTMENT OF ECONOMIC SECURITY, Arizona Training Program-Div of Developmental Disabilities at Coolidge,* 2800 N Hwy 87, PO Box 1467, 85228-1467. SAN 321-3234. Tel: 520-723-4151, Ext 1231. FAX: 520-723-7618. *In Charge*, Yvonne Height
Circ 3,650
Library Holdings: Bk Vols 3,650; Per Subs 10
Branches:
ANN C DEW LIBRARY, 2800 N Hwy 87, PO Box 1467, 85228-1467. SAN 330-5554. Tel: 520-723-4151, Ext 1306.
Founded 1969. Circ 5,000
Library Holdings: Bk Vols 4,000
Special Services for the Deaf - Captioned film depository; High interest/low vocabulary books; Staff with knowledge of sign language

C CENTRAL ARIZONA COLLEGE, Learning Resource Center,* 8470 N Overfield Rd, 85228. SAN 300-3043. Tel: 520-426-4286. FAX: 520-426-4284. *Dir*, Joddy McEuen; *Ref*, Janelle Pierce; *Ref*, Suzanne Delong; Staff 10 (MLS 5, Non-MLS 5)
Founded 1969. Circ 10,000
Library Holdings: Bk Vols 125,000; Per Subs 214
Partic in Amigos Library Services, Inc; OCLC Online Computer Library Center, Inc
Departmental Libraries:
ARAVAIPA CAMPUS LEARNING RESOURCE CENTER
See Separate Entry in Winkelman
SUPERSTITION MOUNTAIN CAMPUS LEARNING CENTER
See Separate Entry in Apache Junction

P COOLIDGE PUBLIC LIBRARY,* 160 W Central Ave, 85228-4406. SAN 300-3051. Tel: 520-723-9559. FAX: 520-723-7026. *Librn*, Jan Custis; E-Mail: jcustis@pinalcold.lib.az.us; Staff 1 (MLS 1)
Pop 6,859; Circ 48,840
1997-1998 Income $125,584
Library Holdings: Bk Titles 26,000; Per Subs 49
Special Collections: Large Print Coll; Southwest Coll
Friends of the Library Group

S UNITED STATES NATIONAL PARK SERVICE, Casa Grande Ruins National Monument Library, 1100 Ruins Dr, 85228. SAN 374-7697. Tel: 520-723-3172. FAX: 520-723-7209. *In Charge*, David Winchester
Library Holdings: Bk Vols 1,000

COTTONWOOD

P COTTONWOOD PUBLIC LIBRARY, 100 S Sixth St, 86326. SAN 300-306X. Tel: 520-634-7559. TDD: 520-634-7559. FAX: 520-634-0253. *Librn*, John R O'Neill; E-Mail: joneill@ci.cottonwood.az.us; Staff 9 (MLS 2, Non-MLS 7)
Founded 1960. Pop 35,000; Circ 220,201
Jul 2000-Jun 2001 Income $550,740, City $447,740, County $103,000. Mats Exp $78,460, Books $65,032, Per/Ser (Incl. Access Fees) $8,328, Presv $100, Micro $345, Other Print Mats $655, Electronic Ref Mat (Incl. Access Fees) $4,000. Sal $229,000 (Prof $76,000)
Library Holdings: Bk Titles 61,200; Per Subs 104
Subject Interests: Large type print
Automation Activity & Vendor Info: (Circulation) epixtech, inc.
Partic in Yavapai County Libr Network
Friends of the Library Group

M DAVID G WELLS MEMORIAL LIBRARY, Verde Valley Medical Center, 269 Saint Candy Lane, 86326. Tel: 520-639-6444. FAX: 520-639-6190. Web Site: na.health.com. *Assoc Librn*, Karen Fanning; E-Mail: fannink@nahealth.com
Library Holdings: Bk Vols 200; Bk Titles 300

DAVIS MONTHAN AFB

UNITED STATES AIR FORCE
A DAVIS MONTHAN AIR FORCE BASE LIBRARY FL4877, 355 SVS/SVMG, 5427 E Madera St Bldg 4339, 85707-4930. SAN 330-5619. Tel: 520-228-7148. FAX: 520-228-3998. *Coll Develop, Ref*, Charles Becker; E-Mail: beckerc@svs355.dm.af.mil; Staff 3 (MLS 2, Non-MLS 1)
Library Holdings: Bk Vols 32,000; Per Subs 158
Partic in Dialog Corporation; OCLC Online Computer Library Center, Inc

DOUGLAS

§S ARIZONA DEPARTMENT OF CORRECTIONS - ADULT, Arizona State Prison Complex - Douglas Library, 6911 N BDI Blvd, 85608. (Mail add: PO Drawer 3867, 85608-3867), Tel: 520-364-7521, Ext 7122. FAX: 520-364-7445. *Librn*, Eric Stracco
Library Holdings: Bk Vols 26,880

J COCHISE COLLEGE LIBRARY, Charles Di Peso Library, 4190 W Hwy 80, 85607. SAN 330-5643. Tel: 520-417-4144. FAX: 520-417-4120. E-Mail: library@cochise.cc.az.us. Web Site: www.cochise.cc.az.us/lib/index.html. *Dir*, Patricia Hotchkiss; *Librn*, Roberta Ibarra; *Librn*, Gail Staples; *Media Spec*, Larry McAlister; Staff 4 (MLS 4)
Founded 1964. Enrl 4,602; Fac 105
1998-1999 Income $584,637. Mats Exp $95,750, Books $35,852, Per/Ser (Incl. Access Fees) $22,500, Micro $14,148, AV Equip $13,250. Sal $417,092 (Prof $175,154)
Library Holdings: Bk Vols 62,841; Per Subs 318
Subject Interests: Aviation, History, Nursing
Publications: Annual Report; Audiocassette Catalog; Monthly Acquisitions Report; Periodical Holdings List; Videocassette Catalog
Partic in Amigos Library Services, Inc
Departmental Libraries:
ANDREA CRACCHIOLO LIBRARY, 901 N Colombo, Sierra Vista, 85635. SAN 300-4295. Tel: 520-515-5465. FAX: 520-515-5464. *Dir*, Patricia Hotchkiss; *Librn*, Gail Staples
Founded 1974
WILLCOX CENTER, 1110 W Freemont, Willcox, 85643. SAN 377-631X. *Dir*, Patricia Hotchkiss

P DOUGLAS PUBLIC LIBRARY,* 560 Tenth St, 85607. SAN 300-3078. Tel: 520-364-3851. FAX: 520-805-5503. *Dir*, Glenda Bavier; Staff 1 (MLS 1)
Founded 1902. Pop 21,000; Circ 46,378

Library Holdings: Bk Titles 33,000; Per Subs 58
Special Collections: Arizona Coll; Spanish Language Coll
Mem of Cochise County Library District
Friends of the Library Group

M SOUTHEAST ARIZONA MEDICAL CENTER LIBRARY,* Rte 1, Box 30, 85607. SAN 325-1209. Tel: 520-364-7931, Ext 3314. FAX: 520-364-2551.
Library Holdings: Bk Titles 125
Mem of SE Ariz Med Ctr Libr

DRAGOON

S AMERIND FOUNDATION, INC, Fulton-Hayden Memorial Library, 2100 N Amerind Rd, PO Box 400, 85609-0400. SAN 300-3086. Tel: 520-586-3666. FAX: 520-586-4679. E-Mail: amerind@amerind.org. Web Site: www.amerind.org. *Librn*, Celia Skeeles; E-Mail: libros@amerind.org
Founded 1962
Library Holdings: Bk Titles 25,000; Per Subs 150
Subject Interests: Anthropology, Archaeology
Special Collections: El Archivo de Hidalgo del Parral, 1631-1821, micro; Facsimile Editions of Major Mesoamerican Codices; Records of the Colonial Period of New Spain (northern Mexico); Southwest Americana
Restriction: By appointment only

DUNCAN

P DUNCAN PUBLIC LIBRARY, 122 N Hwy 75, PO Box 115, 85534. SAN 300-3094. Tel: 520-359-2094. *Librn*, Barbara Blackburn
Founded 1947
Library Holdings: Bk Titles 10,000
Subject Interests: American Indians
Special Collections: Southwest Coll

EAGAR

J NORTHLAND PIONEER COLLEGE, Springerville Eagar Center Library,* 578 N Main St, 85925. (Mail add: PO Box 180, 85938), SAN 329-0654. Tel: 520-333-2498. FAX: 520-333-0828. *Br Coordr*, Maggie Leef
Founded 1987. Enrl 165
Library Holdings: Bk Vols 1,500; Per Subs 14
Friends of the Library Group

EL MIRAGE

P EL MIRAGE PUBLIC LIBRARY,* 14010 N El Mirage Rd, PO Box 26, 85335. SAN 300-3108. Tel: 623-583-1030. FAX: 623-583-8757. *Librn*, Jeannie Ramsay
Founded 1964. Pop 2,979; Circ 7,900
Library Holdings: Bk Vols 10,000; Per Subs 20
Mem of Maricopa County Libr Syst

ELOY

P ELOY PUBLIC LIBRARY,* 624 N Main St, 85231. SAN 300-3116. Tel: 520-466-3814. FAX: 520-466-4433. Web Site: www.172.16.102.81. *Dir*, Russell Ketcham; E-Mail: rketcham@pinalcold.lib.az.us; *Ch Servs*, Mabelean White; *Asst Librn*, Maxine Nichols. Subject Specialists: *History*, Russell Ketcham; Staff 3 (MLS 1, Non-MLS 2)
Founded 1952. Pop 8,200; Circ 6,439
Jul 1999-Jun 2000 Income $102,628, State $1,475, City $93,000, County $8,153. Mats Exp $15,550, Books $13,000, Per/Ser (Incl. Access Fees) $1,050, Electronic Ref Mat (Incl. Access Fees) $1,500. Sal $55,364 (Prof $24,320)
Library Holdings: Bk Vols 10,000; Bk Vols 12,000; Per Subs 27; High Interest/Low Vocabulary Bk Vols 500
Special Collections: Adult Literacy Coll; African-American & Hispanic Coll; Arizona Coll; Audio Visual Coll; Southwest Coll
Automation Activity & Vendor Info: (Cataloging) Innovative Interfaces Inc.; (Circulation) Innovative Interfaces Inc.; (OPAC) Innovative Interfaces Inc.
Database Vendor: Innovative Interfaces INN - View
Mem of Pinal County Library District
Friends of the Library Group

FLAGSTAFF

§S ARIZONA HISTORICAL SOCIETY LIBRARY - NORTHERN ARIZONA DIVISION, 2340 N Fort Valley Rd, 86001. Tel: 520-774-6272. FAX: 520-774-1596. E-Mail: ahsnad@infomagic.net. Web Site: www.arizona.edu/~azhist/nadgeneral.htm. *Dir*, Joseph M Meehan; *Archivist*, James Dildine; *Curator*, Susan Wilcox
Library Holdings: Bk Vols 200

§C COCONINO COMMUNITY COLLEGE, Information Resources Center, 3000 N Fourth St, 86003. (Mail add: PO Box 8000, 86003-8000), Tel: 520-527-1222, Ext 272. FAX: 520-526-1821. Web Site: www.coco.cc.az.us. *Info Res, Media Spec*, Marcia Ostrowski; E-Mail: mostrows@coco.cc.az.us
Jul 2000-Jun 2001 Income $98,950
Library Holdings: Bk Vols 2,132

GL COCONINO COUNTY SUPERIOR COURT, Coconino County Law Library & Self-Help Center, 222 E Birch Ave, 86001. SAN 300-3124. Tel: 520-779-6535. E-Mail: cocolawlib@yahoo.com. *Librn*, Vicki Vega; Tel: 520-779-6743
Library Holdings: Bk Titles 15,000; Per Subs 154
Restriction: Not a lending library
Function: Research library

S CROSS-CULTURAL DANCE RESOURCES LIBRARY, (CCDR), 518 S Agassiz St, 86001-5711. SAN 375-1384. Tel: 520-774-8108. FAX: 520-774-8108. E-Mail: jwk3@jan.ucc.nau.edu. Web Site: www.ccdr.org/.
Founded 1981
Library Holdings: Bk Vols 11,500; Bk Titles 4,000; Per Subs 129
Subject Interests: Dance

P FLAGSTAFF CITY-COCONINO COUNTY PUBLIC LIBRARY SYSTEM, 300 W Aspen, 86001. SAN 330-5678. Tel: 520-779-7670. FAX: 520-774-9573. *Dir*, Kay Whitaker; E-Mail: kwhitak@fpl.lib.az.us; *Tech Servs*, Janine Veinus; *Assoc Dir, Publ Servs*, Dawn Gardner; *Acq*, Ilean Casey; *ILL*, Michal Goblet; *ILL*, Roabie Johnson; *Circ*, Barbara Griffiths; *Ch Servs*, Anna Del Paxton; Staff 11 (MLS 7, Non-MLS 4)
Founded 1890. Pop 106,000; Circ 752,724
Jul 2000-Jun 2001 Income $3,528,091, State $38,000, City $1,191,937, County $2,126,154, Other $172,000. Mats Exp $344,352, Books $249,748, Per/Ser (Incl. Access Fees) $39,309, Presv $3,085, AV Equip $12,450, Electronic Ref Mat (Incl. Access Fees) $39,760. Sal $1,179,951
Library Holdings: Bk Vols 200,000; Per Subs 400
Subject Interests: Arizona, Local history
Special Collections: Arizona Coll; Genealogy Coll; Local Hist; Southwest Coll
Publications: Newsletter
Partic in OCLC Online Computer Library Center, Inc
Special Services for the Deaf - High interest/low vocabulary books; Special interest periodicals
Special Services for the Blind - CCTV (VisualTex); Magnifying glasses/lamps; Reading machine; Talking Books
Adult literacy materials
Friends of the Library Group
Branches: 1
EAST FLAGSTAFF COMMUNITY LIBRARY, 3211 N Fourth St, 86004. SAN 330-5767. Tel: 520-774-8434. *Librn*, Pamela Joralmon; *Librn*, Shelley Heal
Bookmobiles: 2

S FLAGSTAFF MEDICAL CENTER, John B Jamison MD Memorial Library, 1200 N Beaver St, 86001. SAN 374-8235. Tel: 520-773-2418. FAX: 520-773-2253. *Assoc Librn*, Cludy Croft; E-Mail: croftc@nahealth.com
Library Holdings: Bk Vols 1,500; Per Subs 30

S LOWELL OBSERVATORY LIBRARY, 1400 W Mars Hill Rd, 86001. SAN 300-3132. Tel: 520-774-3358. FAX: 520-774-6296. E-Mail: asb@lowell.edu. Web Site: www.lowell.edu/. *Librn*, Antoinette Sansone-Beiser
Founded 1894
1999-2000 Income $35,000. Mats Exp $35,000, Books $4,000, Per/Ser (Incl. Access Fees) $30,000, Presv $1,000
Library Holdings: Per Subs 50
Subject Interests: Astronomy, Mathematics, Physics
Restriction: Staff use only

S MUSEUM OF NORTHERN ARIZONA-KATHARINE BARTLETT LEARNING CENTER, Harold S Colton Memorial Research Library, 3101 N Fort Valley Rd, 86001. SAN 300-3140. Tel: 520-774-5211, Ext 256. FAX: 520-779-1527. Web Site: www.musnaz.org. *Archivist, Assoc Librn*, F Michael O'Hara, III; E-Mail: mohara@mna.mus.az.us; Staff 1 (MLS 1)
Founded 1928
Library Holdings: Bk Vols 100,000; Per Subs 60
Subject Interests: Archaeology, Cultural hist, Ethnology, Natural history, Palentology, Southwestern Americana
Special Collections: Hopi & Navajo Culture
Restriction: Non-circulating to the public
Function: Research library

C NORTHERN ARIZONA UNIVERSITY, Cline Library, Knoles Dr, Bldg 028, 86011. (Mail add: PO Box 6022, 86011-6022), Tel: 520-523-6802. Circulation Tel: 520-523-2173. Reference Tel: 520-523-6805. FAX: 520-523-3770. Web Site: www.nau.edu/library/. *Admin Dir*, David F Finney; Tel: 520-523-6803, E-Mail: david.finney@nau.edu; *Dean of Libr, Librn*, Jean D Collins; E-Mail: jean.collins@nau.edu; *Assoc Librn*, Claudia J Bakula; Tel: 520-523-6817, E-Mail: claudia.bakula@nau.edu; *Assoc Librn*, Cynthia A Childrey; Tel: 520-523-5021, E-Mail: cynthia.childrey@nau.edu; *Assoc Librn*, T G McFadden; *Automation Syst Coordr*, Bruce W Palmer; *Online Servs*, Gary Gustafson; *Media Spec*, Emily Hill; *Archivist, Spec Coll*, Karen

J Underhill; Tel: 520-523-6502, E-Mail: karen.underhill@nau.edu; *Tech Servs*, David L Bruner; Tel: 520-523-9605, Fax: 520-523-8043, E-Mail: david.burner@nau.edu; *Coll Develop*, James Armour; *Distance Educ*, Karen Jaggers; Tel: 520-523-6834, E-Mail: karen.jaggers@nau.edu; *Selection of Gen Ref Mat*, Ann Eagan; *Circ*, Kathleen Smalldon; Tel: 520-523-0341, E-Mail: kathleen.smalldon@nau.edu; Staff 89 (MLS 33, Non-MLS 56)
Founded 1912. Enrl 20,131; Fac 614; Highest Degree: Doctorate
Jul 2000-Jun 2001 Income $6,319,903, State $6,239,303, Federal $54,600, Locally Generated Income $26,000. Mats Exp $2,793,606, Books $871,500, Per/Ser (Incl. Access Fees) $1,073,000, Presv $1,000, Micro $1,000, AV Equip $54,000, Other Print Mats $268,106, Manuscripts & Archives $20,000, Electronic Ref Mat (Incl. Access Fees) $505,000. Sal $2,772,366 (Prof $1,397,408)
Library Holdings: Bk Vols 1,411,945; Bk Titles 585,954; Per Subs 5,992
Special Collections: A F Whiting Coll; Arizona History (Historical Society Coll), archives, photos; Bruce Babbitt Coll; Colorado Plateau Coll; Elbert Hubbard-Roycroft Press (Floyd C Henning Coll); Emery Kolb Coll; Fred Harvey Coll; Harvey Butchart Coll; NAU Archives, mss, pictures; Philip Johnston Coll
Automation Activity & Vendor Info: (Acquisitions) Innovative Interfaces Inc.; (Cataloging) Innovative Interfaces Inc.; (Circulation) Innovative Interfaces Inc.; (ILL) Innovative Interfaces Inc.; (Media Booking) Innovative Interfaces Inc.; (OPAC) Innovative Interfaces Inc.
Database Vendor: Dialog, Ebsco - EbscoHost, GaleNet, IAC - Info Trac, Lexis-Nexis, OCLC - First Search, OVID Technologies, ProQuest, Silverplatter Information Inc.
Function: Reference services available
Partic in Amigos Library Services, Inc; Ariz Univ Consortium; AZHIN; Dialog Corporation; OCLC Online Computer Library Center, Inc

S THE ARBORETUM AT FLAGSTAFF LIBRARY, 4001 S Woody Mountain Rd, 86001. SAN 373-3866. Tel: 520-774-1442. FAX: 520-774-1441. E-Mail: arbor@flagstaffguide.com. Web Site: www.flagstaffguide.com/arboretum, www.thearb.org. *Dir*, Steve Yoder; Tel: 520-774-1442, Ext 109; *Cat*, Dana Vincil; *Asst Librn*, Lael Tennyson; Tel: 520-774-1442, Ext 103; Staff 3 (MLS 1, Non-MLS 2)
Founded 1981
Jan 2000-Dec 2000 Mats Exp Books $2,000
Library Holdings: Bk Titles 2,000; Per Subs 20
Subject Interests: Environ educ, Horticulture, Natural history, Photographs
Restriction: Staff use only
Function: Research library

G UNITED STATES GEOLOGICAL SURVEY LIBRARY, 2255 N Gemini Dr, 86001. SAN 300-3167. Tel: 520-556-7008. FAX: 520-556-7156. *In Charge*, Jenny Prennace
Founded 1964
Library Holdings: Bk Vols 40,000; Per Subs 210
Subject Interests: Earth science, Geology, Space science
Special Collections: Astro-Geology Coll

FLORENCE

§S ARIZONA DEPARTMENT OF CORRECTIONS - ADULT, Arizona State Prison Complex - Eyman Library, 4374 Butte Ave, 85232. (Mail add: PO Box 3500, 85232-3500), Tel: 520-868-0201. FAX: 520-868-5713. *Librn*, Kathy Cooper; Tel: 520-868-0201, Ext 6207; *Librn*, Patricia Dixon; Tel: 520-868-0201, Ext 6850; *Librn*, Terry Hernandez; Tel: 520-868-0201, Ext 4026; *Librn*, Elizabeth Miner; Tel: 520-868-0201, Ext 5022; *Librn*, Victor Ruboyianes; Tel: 520-868-0201, Ext 3006
Library Holdings: Bk Vols 28,952

S ARIZONA STATE PRISON COMPLEX LIBRARIES, 1305 E Butte Ave, PO Box 629, 85232-0629. SAN 324-1130. Tel: 520-868-4011, Ext 4045. FAX: 520-868-8228. *Librn*, Carolyn Rymer; Staff 1 (MLS 1)
Founded 1914. Pop 6,000; Circ 18,000
Library Holdings: Bk Titles 35,000; Per Subs 25
Special Services for the Deaf - Books on deafness & sign language; Staff with knowledge of sign language
Branches:
CENTRAL UNIT, 1305 East Butte Ave, 85232-0629. (Mail add: PO Box 629, 85232), Tel: 520-868-4011, Ext 5281. FAX: 520-868-4227. *Librn*, Karen Girrard; Staff 1 (Non-MLS 1)
Library Holdings: Bk Vols 34,023

P FLORENCE COMMUNITY LIBRARY, 1000 South Willow St, 85232. (Mail add: PO Box 985, 85232), SAN 300-3175. Tel: 520-868-9471. FAX: 520-868-4651. E-Mail: florencelibrary.florencelibrary@co.pinal.az.us. *Chief Librn*, Patricia Freeman; E-Mail: patty.freeman@co.pinal.az.us; Staff 6 (Non-MLS 6)
Pop 11,540; Circ 19,718
Library Holdings: Bk Titles 24,792; Per Subs 38
Automation Activity & Vendor Info: (ILL) Innovative Interfaces Inc.
Database Vendor: Ebsco - EbscoHost, OCLC - First Search
Function: ILL available
Mem of Pinal County Library District
Friends of the Library Group

S PINAL COUNTY HISTORICAL SOCIETY, INC LIBRARY, 715 S Main St, 85232. (Mail add: PO Box 851, 85232), SAN 328-672X. Tel: 520-868-4382. *Librn*, Louise Clark
Library Holdings: Bk Vols 600
Subject Interests: Local history, Sci
Special Collections: Yuma Territorial Prison & Early Arizona State Prison Inmates Records, microfilm
Restriction: Members only
Function: Reference only
Open Wed-Sun 12-4

P PINAL COUNTY LIBRARY DISTRICT, (PCLD), 92 W Butte Ave, PO Box 2974, 85232. SAN 300-3183. Tel: 520-868-6457. TDD: 520-868-6471. FAX: 520-868-6533. Web Site: co.pinal.az.us/library. *Dir*, Denise Keller; E-Mail: denise.keller@co.pinal.az.us; *Tech Servs*, Ellen Fallon; Tel: 520-868-6458, E-Mail: ellen.fallon@co.pinal.az.us; Staff 5 (MLS 3, Non-MLS 2)
Founded 1960. Pop 161,630
Jul 1999-Jun 2000 Income $508,729, State $20,498, Federal $37,400, County $447,331, Other $3,500. Mats Exp $111,456, Books $101,482, Per/Ser (Incl. Access Fees) $3,474, Electronic Ref Mat (Incl. Access Fees) $6,500. Sal $191,754 (Prof $125,735)
Library Holdings: Bk Vols 3,500; Per Subs 15
Subject Interests: Professional
Automation Activity & Vendor Info: (Acquisitions) Innovative Interfaces Inc.; (Cataloging) Innovative Interfaces Inc.; (Circulation) Innovative Interfaces Inc.; (Course Reserve) Innovative Interfaces Inc.; (ILL) Innovative Interfaces Inc.; (Media Booking) Innovative Interfaces Inc.; (OPAC) Innovative Interfaces Inc.; (Serials) Innovative Interfaces Inc.
Publications: PCLD Newsletter
Member Libraries: Arizona City Community Library; Arthur E Pomeroy Public Library; Casa Grande Public Library; Eloy Public Library; Florence Community Library; Ira H Hayes Memorial Library; Mammoth Public Library; Oracle Public Library; San Manuel Public Library; Stanfield Community Center Library; Superior Public Library
Special Services for the Deaf - TDD
PCLD is one of 28 Economic Development Centers (EDIC) in the State of Arizona

FOREST LAKES

P FOREST LAKES COMMUNITY LIBRARY,* 417 Old Rim Rd, PO Box 1799, 85931. SAN 376-320X. Tel: 520-535-9125. FAX: 520-535-4729. *Librn*, Cheryl Rife
Library Holdings: Bk Vols 7,700; Bk Titles 5,500
Mem of Flagstaff City-Coconino County Pub Libr District

FORT GRANT

S ARIZONA STATE PRISON-FORT GRANT, State Route 266, Spur Rd, 85644-4399. (Mail add: PO Box 4000, 85644-4399), Tel: 520-828-3393, Ext 4217. FAX: 520-828-3341. *Librn*, Catherine Fisher
Pop 750
Library Holdings: Bk Vols 4,541
Special Collections: Law Reference Coll

FORT HUACHUCA

UNITED STATES ARMY
A ARMY INTELLIGENCE CENTER & SCHOOL LIBRARY, Bldg 52065, 85613-6000. SAN 330-5880. Tel: 520-533-4101. FAX: 520-538-2119. *Chief Librn*, Chris Hurd; Staff 3 (MLS 1, Non-MLS 2)
Founded 1955. Circ 45,391
Oct 1997-Sep 1998 Income $20,000. Mats Exp $20,000. Sal $165,000
Library Holdings: Bk Titles 35,000; Per Subs 130
Subject Interests: Military history
Special Collections: Apache Indian Wars; Battle of Gettysburg
Publications: Bibliographies; local accessions list (monthly)
Partic in Tralinet
A INFORMATION RESOURCE CENTER, AFSC-HCI-R, Bldg 61801, 85613-5000. SAN 330-5945. Tel: 520-538-6201. FAX: 520-538-4731. *Tech Servs*, Rosemary Allen
Founded 1954
Oct 1997-Sep 1998 Mats Exp $40,097, Books $10,000, Per/Ser (Incl. Access Fees) $20,097, Micro $2,000, Other Print Mats $5,000, Manuscripts & Archives $3,000. Sal $59,096
Library Holdings: Bk Vols 8,469; Bk Titles 7,036; Per Subs 254
Subject Interests: Automation, Business and management, Computer science, Electrical engineering, Electronics, Mathematics, Optics, Physics, Telecommunications
Special Collections: Electronics Books; IEEE All-Society Periodicals; Telecommunications Books; Total Quality Management Books
Publications: Total Quality Management (TOM bibliography)
Partic in Fedlink
A LIBRARY BRANCH, Fort Huachuca Library Branch, Bldg 52065 ATZS-HRH-L, 85613-6000. SAN 330-5910. Tel: 520-533-2506. Interlibrary Loan Service Tel: 520-538-3041. FAX: 520-538-2119. *Chief Librn*, Chris Hurd;

Ref, Natalie Daiforth; Staff 2 (MLS 2)
Oct 1997-Sep 1998 Income $20,000
Library Holdings: Bk Vols 65,000; Per Subs 400
Special Collections: Military Affairs; Southwest Coll
Automation Activity & Vendor Info: (Circulation) LS 2000
Partic in Fedlink

AM RAYMOND W BLISS ARMY HEALTH CENTER, 85613-7040. Tel: 520-533-5668. FAX: 520-533-5580. *Librn*, Ann E Nichols; E-Mail: ann_nichols@smtplink.huachuca.amedd.army.mil
Oct 1997-Sep 1998 Mats Exp $14,421, Books $3,399, Per/Ser (Incl. Access Fees) $10,249. Sal $40,100
Library Holdings: Bk Vols 1,192; Per Subs 50
Subject Interests: Clinical medicine, Nursing
Special Collections: Dental Coll; Military Medicine

FREDONIA

P FREDONIA PUBLIC LIBRARY,* 118 N Main, PO Box 217, 86022-0217. SAN 300-3205. Tel: 520-643-7137. FAX: 520-643-7685. *Librn*, Marie Sadlier; Staff 1 (MLS 1)
Founded 1958. Pop 1,200
1997-1998 Income $39,000
Library Holdings: Bk Titles 14,000; Per Subs 19
Special Collections: Jonreed Lauritzen Books & Jensen Memorial Coll
Mem of Coconino County Libr Syst

P KAIBAB PAIUTE PUBLIC LIBRARY,* 250 N Pipe Springs Rd, HC 65, Box 2, 86022. SAN 376-317X. Tel: 520-643-7245. FAX: 520-643-7260. *In Charge*, Shirla Jessop
Library Holdings: Bk Vols 11,000; Bk Titles 10,000; Per Subs 12
Mem of Mohave County Library District

GANADO

G US NATIONAL PARK SERVICE, Hubbell Trading Post National Historic Site Library, PO Box 150, 86505. SAN 375-6459. Tel: 520-755-3475. FAX: 520-755-3405. Web Site: www.nps.gov/hutr.
Library Holdings: Bk Titles 15,000

GILA BEND

P GILA BEND PUBLIC LIBRARY,* 200 N Euclid, PO Box B, 85337. SAN 300-3221. Tel: 520-683-2061. FAX: 520-683-2463. *Librn*, Glenda McBrayer
Founded 1959. Pop 2,000; Circ 13,800
Library Holdings: Bk Vols 7,000; Bk Titles 6,000; Per Subs 20
Mem of Maricopa County Libr Syst
Friends of the Library Group

GLENDALE

M BANNER HEALTH ARIZONA, Thunderbird Samaritan Medical Center Library, 5555 W Thunderbird Rd, 85306. SAN 374-7638. Tel: 602-588-5863. FAX: 602-588-5963. *Dir Libr Serv*, Sally A Harvey; E-Mail: sally.harvey@bannerhealth.com; Staff 1 (MLS 1)
Library Holdings: Bk Vols 250; Per Subs 121
Subject Interests: Allied health, Consumer health, Medicine
Automation Activity & Vendor Info: (Cataloging) EOS
Database Vendor: OVID Technologies
Function: Document delivery services, Literary searches, Reference services available
Partic in Cent Ariz Biomed Librns; Med Libr Group of S Calif & Ariz
Open Mon-Fri 8:30-5:00

M CENTER FOR NEURO DEVELOPMENTAL STUDIES INCORPORATED LIBRARY,* 5430 W Glenn Dr, 85301. SAN 370-9590. Tel: 602-915-0345. FAX: 602-937-5425. *Dir*, Kay Marie King
Library Holdings: Bk Vols 400
Publications: Newsletter (every 3 months)
For Autistic & Special needs children

J GLENDALE COMMUNITY COLLEGE, Library Media Center, 6000 W Olive Ave, 85302. SAN 300-3256. Tel: 623-845-3109. Interlibrary Loan Service Tel: 623-845-3105. Reference Tel: 623-845-3112. FAX: 623-845-3102. Web Site: www.gc.maricopa.edu/lmc/. *Chairperson*, David Rodriguez; E-Mail: david.m.rodriguez@gcmail.maricopa.edu; *Ref*, Russell Searss; E-Mail: russell.sear@gcmail.maricopa.edu; *Coll Develop*, Dianna Dwyer; E-Mail: d.dwyer@gcmail.maricopa.edu; *Bibliog Instr*, Charlotte Cohen; E-Mail: charlotte.cohen@gcmail.maricopa.edu; *Media Spec*, Frank Gonzalez; E-Mail: frank.gonzalez@gcmail.maricopa.edu; Staff 18 (MLS 6, Non-MLS 12)
Founded 1965. Enrl 18,000; Fac 207
Library Holdings: Bk Vols 76,246; Bk Titles 63,248; Per Subs 439
Automation Activity & Vendor Info: (OPAC) DRA
Database Vendor: DRA, Ebsco - EbscoHost, GaleNet, IAC - Info Trac
Partic in Maricopa County Community College District

P GLENDALE PUBLIC LIBRARY,* 5959 W Brown St, 85302. SAN 300-3264. Tel: 623-930-3530. FAX: 623-842-2161. Web Site: www.lib.ci.glendale.az.us. *Dir*, Rodeane Widom; Tel: 623-930-3562, E-Mail: rwidom@ci.glendale.az.us; *Circ*, Louise Stephens; Tel: 623-930-3567, E-Mail: lstephens@ci.glendale.az.us; *Br Coordr*, Shelley Mosley; Tel: 623-930-3438, Fax: 623-937-8798; *Br Coordr*, Sue Komernicky; Tel: 623-930-3868, Fax: 623-930-3855; *Publ Servs*, Anne Caltabiano; Tel: 623-930-3569; *Tech Servs*, Cherrilynn Moore; Tel: 623-930-3565; *ILL*, Mary Walker; *Coll Develop*, Cathy Johnson; Staff 117 (MLS 34, Non-MLS 83)
Founded 1895. Pop 204,000; Circ 1,526,024
Jul 1998-Jun 1999 Income (Main Library and Branch Library) $5,170,022, State $5,360, City $5,139,787, Other $24,875. Mats Exp $853,079, Books $656,110, Per/Ser (Incl. Access Fees) $57,162. Sal $3,587,583 (Prof $33,021)
Library Holdings: Bk Vols 528,685; Bk Titles 97,795; Per Subs 994
Special Collections: Southwest Coll
Database Vendor: epixtech, inc.
Publications: Library Links
Partic in Amigos Library Services, Inc; OCLC Online Computer Library Center, Inc
Friends of the Library Group
Branches: 2
FOOTHILLS, 19055 N 57th Ave, 85308. Tel: 623-930-3830. Circulation Tel: 623-930-3830. Reference Tel: 623-930-3831. FAX: 623-930-3855. Web Site: www.lib.ci.glendale.az.us. *Branch Mgr*, Sue Komernicky; Tel: 623-930-3868, E-Mail: skomern@glenpub.lib.az.us; *YA Servs*, Karen-Marie Allen; Tel: 623-930-3837; *Head, Circ*, Margaret Horsman; *Ref Serv*, Cathy Johnson
Jul 2000-Jun 2001 Income $1,177,252
Library Holdings: Bk Vols 122,893; Per Subs 512
Automation Activity & Vendor Info: (Cataloging) epixtech, inc.; (Circulation) epixtech, inc.; (OPAC) epixtech, inc.
Database Vendor: OCLC - First Search
VELMA TEAGUE BRANCH, 7010 N 58th Ave, 85301. SAN 376-8821. Tel: 602-930-3438. FAX: 602-937-8798. Web Site: www.ci.glendale.az.us/localgov/library/index.htm. *Mgr*, Shelley Mosley
Library Holdings: Bk Vols 89,667; Bk Titles 35,867
Friends of the Library Group

C THUNDERBIRD, THE AMERICAN GRADUATE SCHOOL OF INTERNATIONAL MANAGEMENT, (IBIC), Merle A Hinrichs International Business Information Centre, 15249 N 59th Ave, Thunderbird Campus, 85306-6001. SAN 300-3248. Tel: 602-978-7232, 602-978-7300. Circulation Tel: 602-978-7232. Reference Tel: 602-978-7306. FAX: 602-978-7762. E-Mail: ibicdoc@t-bird.edu. Web Site: www.t-bird.edu/ibic. *Dir*, Carol Hammond; Tel: 602-978-7234, E-Mail: hammondc@t-bird.edu; *Cat, Coll Develop, Tech Servs*, Dixie Klatt; Tel: 602-978-7237, E-Mail: klattd@t-bird.edu; *ILL, Ser*, Fran Springer; Tel: 602-978-7235; *Instrul Serv*, Micaela Morales; Tel: 602-978-7231; *Electronic Resources*, Wes Edens; Tel: 602-978-7897, E-Mail: edensw@t-bird.edu; *Archivist*, Nelda Crowell. Subject Specialists: *Research*, Nelda Crowell; Staff 17 (MLS 7, Non-MLS 10)
Founded 1946. Enrl 1,500; Fac 110; Highest Degree: Master
Jul 2000-Jun 2001 Income $1,500,000. Mats Exp $578,000, Books $167,000, Per/Ser (Incl. Access Fees) $235,000, Electronic Ref Mat (Incl. Access Fees) $276,000. Sal $599,566 (Prof $222,508)
Library Holdings: Bk Titles 70,000; Per Subs 1,800
Subject Interests: Accounting, Finance, International, Marketing, Political science
Special Collections: Foreign Language Feature Films, video; Foreign Language Newspapers & Periodicals
Automation Activity & Vendor Info: (Acquisitions) SIRSI; (Cataloging) SIRSI; (Circulation) SIRSI; (Course Reserve) SIRSI; (ILL) SIRSI; (Media Booking) SIRSI; (OPAC) SIRSI; (Serials) SIRSI
Publications: Library Guides
Restriction: Open to student, faculty & staff
Partic in Amigos Library Services, Inc; OCLC Online Computer Library Center, Inc

GLOBE

§S ARIZONA DEPARTMENT OF CORRECTIONS - ADULT, Arizona State Prison Complex - Globe Library, PO Box 2799, 85502-2799. Tel: 520-425-8141. FAX: 520-425-0621.
Library Holdings: Bk Vols 2,930

M COBRE VALLEY COMMUNITY HOSPITAL, Medical Library,* 5880 South Hospital Dr, 85501. SAN 375-1503. Tel: 520-425-3261, Ext 1128. FAX: 520-425-7903. *Librn*, Donna Caldera
Library Holdings: Bk Vols 1,000; Per Subs 10

§C EASTERN ARIZONA COLLEGE, Gila Pueblo Campus Library, 6 Shooter Canyon, 85502. (Mail add: PO Box 2820, 85502-2820), Tel: 520-425-3151. FAX: 520-425-0554. Web Site: www.eac.cc.az.us/library/. *Librn*, Lynn Watts; E-Mail: watts@eac.cc.az.us

Jul 1999-Jun 2000 Income $148,145
Library Holdings: Bk Vols 10,924; Per Subs 90
Automation Activity & Vendor Info: (Cataloging) Gaylord; (Circulation) Gaylord; (OPAC) Gaylord

S GILA COUNTY HISTORICAL MUSEUM LIBRARY, 1330 N Broad St, PO Box 2891, 85502. SAN 374-8251. Tel: 520-425-7385. *Dir*, Dr Wilbur Haak
2000-2001 Mats Exp Per/Ser (Incl. Access Fees) $75
Library Holdings: Bk Vols 200
Subject Interests: Local history
Open Mon-Fri 10-4

GL GILA COUNTY LAW LIBRARY,* 1400 E Ash St, 85501. SAN 300-3272. Tel: 520-425-3231, Ext 275. FAX: 520-425-0319. *Librn*, Rosemary Bigando
Founded 1908
Library Holdings: Bk Vols 30,000; Per Subs 20

P GILA COUNTY LIBRARY DISTRICT,* 1400 E Ash St, 85501-1414. SAN 375-3182. Tel: 520-425-3231, Ext 303. TDD: 520-425-0839. FAX: 520-425-0319. Web Site: www.gila.lib.az.us. *Dir*, Jacque Griffin; *ILL*, Cecilia Amezcua; Staff 2 (MLS 1, Non-MLS 1)
Founded 1987. Pop 44,075
Jul 1997-Jun 1998 Income $161,135. Mats Exp $33,512. Sal $68,000
Library Holdings: Bk Titles 1,860
Publications: Large print catalog
Member Libraries: Globe Public Library; Hayden Public Library; Isabelle Hunt Memorial Public Library; Payson Public Library; San Carlos Public Library; Tonto Basin Public Library; Young Public Library
Special Services for the Deaf - TDD

P GLOBE PUBLIC LIBRARY,* 339 S Broad St, 85501-1744. SAN 300-3299. Tel: 520-425-6111. FAX: 520-425-3357. Web Site: gila.lib.az.us/globe/gpl.htm. *Librn*, Ellen Watters; E-Mail: elwatte@globepub.lib.az.us; *Asst Librn*, Marion Steele; *ILL*, Mary Stemm; Staff 3 (MLS 1, Non-MLS 2)
Jul 1998-Jun 1999 Income $132,176, State $1,800, City $7,922, County $116,849, Locally Generated Income $5,605. Mats Exp $19,696, Books $15,400, Per/Ser (Incl. Access Fees) $2,654, Presv $1,159, Micro $30, Electronic Ref Mat (Incl. Access Fees) $453. Sal $94,763 (Prof $28,114)
Library Holdings: Bk Vols 28,886; Per Subs 70
Special Collections: Arizona Southwest
Automation Activity & Vendor Info: (Cataloging) DRA; (Circulation) DRA; (OPAC) DRA
Mem of Gila County Library District
Friends of the Library Group

GOODYEAR

§S ARIZONA DEPARTMENT OF CORRECTIONS - ADULT, Arizona State Prison Complex - Perryville Library, 2014 N Citrus Rd, 85338. (Mail add: PO Box 3000, 85338-3000), Tel: 623-853-0304, Ext 6500. FAX: 623-853-0304, Ext 1074. *Librn*, Starla Cathcart; Tel: 623-853-0304, Ext 3119; *Librn*, Michael Maynard; Tel: 623-853-0304, Ext 2119; *Librn*, Lee Will; Tel: 623-853-0304, Ext 4119
Library Holdings: Bk Vols 17,400

GRAND CANYON

P GRAND CANYON COMMUNITY LIBRARY, PO Box 518, 86023-0518. SAN 300-3310. Tel: 520-638-2718. FAX: 520-638-2718. E-Mail: gccl@azaccess.com. *Head of Libr*, Rob Parker
Founded 1932. Pop 1,500; Circ 8,000
Library Holdings: Bk Vols 20,000; Per Subs 40
Special Collections: Southwest & Grand Canyon Coll
Mem of Coconino County Libr Syst
Friends of the Library Group

S GRAND CANYON NATIONAL PARK RESEARCH LIBRARY, One Village Loop, PO Box 129, 86023. SAN 300-3329. Tel: 520-638-7768. FAX: 520-638-7797. *Librn*, Sara T Stebbins; E-Mail: sara_st@nps.gov
Founded 1930. Pop 1,000; Circ 1,000
Jan 1999-Dec 1999 Mats Exp $9,000, Books $6,000, Per/Ser (Incl. Access Fees) $3,000. Sal $32,000
Library Holdings: Bk Vols 12,000; Per Subs 56
Subject Interests: Natural history
Special Collections: Photo Coll, prints
Restriction: By appointment only

GREENLEE

P CLIFTON GREENLEE COUNTY, 102 School St, PO Box 1226, 85533. SAN 377-5461. Tel: 520-865-2461. FAX: 520-865-3014. *Dir*, Rebecca Oliver; Tel: 520-865-3710, E-Mail: roliver@clifgreencopl.lib.az.us
Mem of Clifton-Greenlee County Public Library

HAYDEN

P HAYDEN PUBLIC LIBRARY,* 520 Velasco Ave, PO Box 99, 85235. SAN 300-3337. Tel: 520-356-7031. FAX: 520-356-7031. *Librn*, Anna Lash; *Asst Librn*, Mary Helen Lopez
Founded 1966. Pop 3,000; Circ 21,116
Library Holdings: Bk Vols 13,978; Bk Titles 11,500
Special Collections: Spanish, bks & records
Mem of Gila County Library District
Friends of the Library Group

HEBER

P RIM COMMUNITY LIBRARY, (RCL), 3401 Kimball St, 85928. (Mail add: PO Box 305, 85928-0305), Tel: 520-535-5749. FAX: 520-535-5749. *Dir*, Valerie Porter
Founded 1985. Pop 9,800
Jan 1998-Dec 1998 Income $3,800. Mats Exp $1,400, Books $1,000, Per/Ser (Incl. Access Fees) $150, Other Print Mats $250
Library Holdings: Bk Vols 12,800; Per Subs 17; Bks on Deafness & Sign Lang 10
Special Services for the Blind - Talking Books
Open Tues 1-7, Wed & Fri 1-5; Summer hours: Tues-Fri 11-5 (June-Aug)
Friends of the Library Group

HOLBROOK

P HOLBROOK PUBLIC LIBRARY,* 451 N First Ave, 86025. SAN 300-3345. Tel: 520-524-3732. FAX: 520-524-2159. E-Mail: wskvei83@fibertrails.com. *Librn*, Wendy Skevington; *Asst Librn*, Evelyn Cooley; Staff 2 (MLS 1, Non-MLS 1)
Founded 1958. Pop 4,500; Circ 18,949
1997-1998 Income $97,000. Mats Exp $14,000
Library Holdings: Bk Vols 19,000; Bk Titles 25,000; Per Subs 20
Partic in Ariz Resources Consortium
Friends of the Library Group

J NORTHLAND PIONEER COLLEGE LIBRARIES, PO Box 610, 86025. SAN 376-8791. Tel: 520-524-7320. FAX: 520-524-7321. *Head of Libr*, Trudy Bender; E-Mail: pctlb@northland.ec.az.us; *ILL*, Kathryn Melsted; Staff 3 (MLS 3)
Founded 1975. Enrl 2,100; Fac 250
Library Holdings: Bk Vols 50,000; Per Subs 400
Subject Interests: Art, History, Library and information science, Nursing, Photography
Special Collections: Grant's Coll
Partic in Amigos Library Services, Inc
Departmental Libraries:
DISTRICT LIBRARY-PAINTED DESERT CAMPUS, 993 E Hermosa Dr, 86025. (Mail add: 102 First Ave, PO Box 610, 86025), SAN 330-6003. Tel: 520-524-7320. FAX: 520-524-7321. *Head Librn*, Trudy Bender; *Tech Servs*, Barbara Cohen
Founded 1974. Enrl 3,886; Fac 52
Automation Activity & Vendor Info: (Cataloging) EOS; (Circulation) EOS; (OPAC) EOS
HEBER CENTER, PO Box 547, Heber, 85928. SAN 376-8732. Tel: 520-535-5937. FAX: 520-535-6253. *Media Spec YA Servs*, Patricia L Corbin
KEAMS CANYON CENTER, PO Box 1280, Keams Canyon, 86034. SAN 376-8759. Tel: 520-738-5585. FAX: 520-738-5587. *Tech Servs*, Wilma Adams
LITTLE COLORADO CAMPUS, 1400 E Third (Winslow). (Mail add: PO Box 610, 86025), SAN 300-4759. Tel: 520-289-6520. FAX: 520-289-6521. *Tech Servs*, Jeff Dawson; Staff 2 (MLS 2)
Founded 1975. Enrl 500; Fac 29
Library Holdings: Bk Vols 2,000; Bk Titles 1,500; Per Subs 25
Special Collections: Indian Americana
Partic in Ariz Resources Consortium; Channeled Ariz Info Network
SAINT JOHNS CENTER, PO Box 3150, Saint Johns, 85936. SAN 376-8767. Tel: 520-337-4768. FAX: 520-337-4768. *Tech Servs*, Janice DeGraff
SILVER CREEK CAMPUS, 1610 S Main (Snowflake), PO Box 610, 86025. SAN 300-4317. Tel: 520-536-6220. FAX: 520-524-2313. *Tech Servs*, Daphne Brimhall; Tel: 520-536-6223, Fax: 520-536-5221, E-Mail: daphnebrim@hotmail.com; *Tech Servs*, Margaret White; Tel: 520-536-6222, Fax: 520-536-6221; Staff 1 (MLS 1)
Founded 1975. Enrl 200; Fac 10
Library Holdings: Bk Vols 5,000; Bk Titles 2,000; Per Subs 40
Special Collections: Indian Americana Coll
Partic in Ariz Resources Consortium; Navajo County Libr Consortium
SPRINGERVILLE-EAGER CENTER, PO Box 1722, Springerville, 85925. SAN 376-8775. Tel: 520-333-2498. FAX: 520-333-0828. *Tech Servs*, Angie Trimbley
WHITE MOUNTAIN CAMPUS, 101 W Deuce of Clubs (Show Low). (Mail add: PO Box 610, 86025), SAN 300-4279. Tel: 520-532-6120. FAX: 520-532-6121. *Tech Servs*, Wendy Kochheiser; Staff 2 (MLS 2)
Founded 1975. Enrl 600; Fac 17
Library Holdings: Bk Vols 5,000; Bk Titles 4,500; Per Subs 50

Partic in Ariz Resources Consortium
WHITERIVER CENTER, PO Box 1599, Whiteriver, 85942. SAN 376-8783. Tel: 520-338-4662. FAX: 520-338-4662. *Tech Servs*, Denise Massey

HUACHUCA CITY

P HUACHUCA CITY PUBLIC LIBRARY,* 506 N Gonzales Blvd, 85616. SAN 300-3361. Tel: 520-456-1063. FAX: 520-456-1063. Web Site: www.cochise.lib.az.us/hcity.html. *Dir, Librn*, K C Cooper; E-Mail: kccooper@huachucapl.lib.az.us; *Cat*, Michelle R Ramirez; E-Mail: mramirez@huachucapl.lib.az.us
Founded 1961. Pop 12,000
Jul 1999-Jun 2000 Income City $24,600. Mats Exp Books $600. Sal $24,040 (Prof $12,162)
Library Holdings: Bk Vols 13,600; Bk Titles 12,090
Subject Interests: Audio, Large print, Literacy, Video
Special Collections: Arizona and Southwest Coll; Arizona History and Tourism; Cochise County History and Tourism
Automation Activity & Vendor Info: (Cataloging) DRA; (Circulation) DRA; (ILL) DRA; (OPAC) DRA
Database Vendor: DRA, Ebsco - EbscoHost, GaleNet, IAC - Info Trac, OCLC - First Search, Wilson - Wilson Web
Publications: The Bookmark (Newsletter)
Mem of Cochise County Library District
Friends of the Library Group

HUNTSVILLE

S INTERNATIONAL SOCIETY OF PARAMETRIC ANALYSTS, ISPA Library - Red Star Library, 6725 Odyssey Dr, 35806. SAN 375-7803. Tel: 256-971-6425. FAX: 256-971-6771. *Librn*, Mary Ellen Flourney
Library Holdings: Bk Titles 500

JEROME

P JEROME PUBLIC LIBRARY, 111 Jerome Ave & Hwy 89A, 86331. (Mail add: P O Drawer I, 86331-0247), SAN 300-337X. Tel: 520-639-0574. FAX: 520-639-0574. E-Mail: jerlib@yavapaicold.lib.az.us. Web Site: www.prescottlib.lib.az.us/jerlib.htm. *Librn*, Gaye Oberlin; Staff 1 (Non-MLS 1)
Founded 1919. Pop 600; Circ 1,245
Library Holdings: Bk Vols 10,000; Bk Titles 9,500
Special Collections: Arizona & the Southwest (National Geographic 1949-1976, Arizona Highways 1953-1977)
Mem of Yavapai County Library District
Friends of the Library Group

KAYENTA

J NORTHLAND PIONEER COLLEGE, Kayenta Center Library,* PO Box 248, 86033. SAN 330-5996. Tel: 520-697-8690. FAX: 520-697-8690. *In Charge*, Lorraine Benally; Staff 1 (MLS 1)
Founded 1983
Library Holdings: Bk Titles 1,000; Per Subs 15
Partic in Ariz Resources Consortium

KEAMS CANYON

J NORTHLAND PIONEER COLLEGE, Keans Canyon,* Learning Resource Ctr, PO Box 1280, 86034. SAN 300-3531. Tel: 520-738-5585. FAX: 520-738-5587. *Dir*, Louella Nahsonhoya; Staff 1 (MLS 1)
Founded 1975. Enrl 300; Fac 10
1997-1998 Income $177,283. Mats Exp $82,000
Library Holdings: Bk Titles 50,000; Per Subs 110
Partic in Ariz Resources Consortium; Channeled Ariz Info Network

KEARNY

P ARTHUR E POMEROY PUBLIC LIBRARY,* 912A Tilbury Rd, PO Box 220, 85237. SAN 300-3388. Tel: 520-363-5861. FAX: 520-363-5214. *Librn*, Mary Louise Eck; *Asst Librn*, Joyce Campbell
Founded 1958. Pop 2,500; Circ 39,399
Jul 1998-Jun 1999 Income $70,000. Mats Exp $15,000. Sal $33,200
Library Holdings: Bk Vols 20,000
Subject Interests: Local history
Special Collections: History (Southwestern Coll)
Publications: Booklist; Library Journal; School Library Journal
Mem of Pinal County Library District
Friends of the Library Group

KINGMAN

J MOHAVE COMMUNITY COLLEGE, District Library, 1971 Jagerson Ave, 86401. SAN 330-6186. Tel: 520-757-0856, 520-757-0883. FAX: 520-757-0871. Web Site: www.mohave.cc.az.us. *Coll Develop, Dir*, Robert Shupe; E-Mail: robshu@et.mohave.cc.az.us; Staff 5 (MLS 5)
Founded 1971. Enrl 1,872; Fac 50
Jul 1998-Jun 1999 Income $508,665. Mats Exp $111,266, Books $68,250, Per/Ser (Incl. Access Fees) $30,000, Presv $1,016, Micro $12,000. Sal $321,232
Library Holdings: Bk Vols 64,155; Bk Titles 52,132; Per Subs 523
Automation Activity & Vendor Info: (Circulation) DRA
All statistics include campus libraries
Departmental Libraries:
KINGMAN CAMPUS, 1971 Jagerson Ave, 86401-1299. Tel: 520-757-0856. FAX: 520-757-0896. Web Site: www.mohave.cc.az.us/library. *Librn*, Shirley Hall; E-Mail: shihal@et.mohave.cc.az.us
Library Holdings: Bk Vols 30,000; Per Subs 420
Automation Activity & Vendor Info: (Cataloging) DRA; (Circulation) DRA; (OPAC) DRA
Database Vendor: OCLC - First Search
LAKE HAVASU CITY CAMPUS, 1977 W Acoma Blvd, Lake Havasu City, 86403-2999. Tel: 520-453-5809. FAX: 520-453-8335. Web Site: www.mohave.cc.az.us/library. *Librn*, Beverly S Adler; E-Mail: bevadl@et.mohave.cc.az.us
Library Holdings: Bk Vols 20,000; Per Subs 420
Automation Activity & Vendor Info: (Cataloging) DRA; (Circulation) DRA; (OPAC) DRA
Database Vendor: OCLC - First Search
MOHAVE VALLEY CAMPUS, 3400 Hwy 95, Bullhead City, 86442-8204. Tel: 520-758-2420. FAX: 520-758-4436. Web Site: www.mohave.cc.az.us/library. *Ref*, Leatherwood Carol; E-Mail: carlea@ct.mohave.cc.az.us
Library Holdings: Bk Vols 20,000; Per Subs 420
Automation Activity & Vendor Info: (Cataloging) DRA; (Circulation) DRA; (OPAC) DRA
Database Vendor: OCLC - First Search
NORTH MOHAVE CENTER, 480 S Central, Colorado City, 86021. (Mail add: PO Box 980, Colorado City, 86021-0980), Tel: 520-875-2799, Ext 2224. FAX: 520-875-2831. Web Site: www.mohave.cc.az.us/library. *In Charge*, Lorie Wyler; E-Mail: lorwyl@et.mohave.cc.az.us
Library Holdings: Bk Vols 1,000; Per Subs 420
Automation Activity & Vendor Info: (Cataloging) DRA; (Circulation) DRA; (OPAC) DRA
Database Vendor: OCLC - First Search

S MOHAVE COUNTY HISTORICAL SOCIETY, Mohave Museum of History & Arts Library,* 400 W Beale St, 86401. SAN 300-3396. Tel: 520-753-3195. FAX: 520-753-3195. *Dir*, Jaynell Chambers; *Librn*, Linda Terrin
Founded 1966
1997-1998 Mats Exp $2,000
Library Holdings: Bk Titles 1,200
Subject Interests: Arizona, Indians, Mining
Special Collections: Camp Beale's Springs Coll, bks, mss, micro; Genealogical Coll; Maps; Photographs from 1880 related to Mohave County
Restriction: Non-circulating to the public

P MOHAVE COUNTY LIBRARY DISTRICT,* 3269 N Burbank St, PO Box 7000, 86402-7000. SAN 330-6038. Tel: 520-692-2665. FAX: 520-692-5788. *Dir*, Bonnie Campbell; *Mgr*, Mary Musgrave; Staff 6 (MLS 6)
Founded 1926
Library Holdings: Bk Titles 137,732; Per Subs 549
Subject Interests: Arizona
Member Libraries: Colorado City Public Library; Kaibab Paiute Public Library; Littlefield-Beaver Dan Station Library
Branches: 9
BULLHEAD CITY BRANCH, 1170 E Hancock Rd, Bullhead City, 86442. SAN 330-6062. Tel: 520-758-0714. FAX: 520-758-0720. *Mgr*, Julie Huelsbeck; E-Mail: jhuelsbe@mohave.lib.az; Staff 10 (MLS 2, Non-MLS 8)
Friends of the Library Group
CHARLES C ROYALL MEMORIAL LIBRARY, 1787 McCulloch Blvd, Lake Havasu City, 86403. SAN 330-6097. Tel: 520-453-0718. FAX: 520-458-0720. *Mgr*, Bonnie Campbell
Friends of the Library Group
CHLORIDE STATION, PO Box 111, Chloride, 86431. SAN 374-6348. Tel: 520-565-2200. FAX: 520-565-2200. *Coordr*, Jennifer Schramm
DOLAN SPRINGS STATION, PO Box 427, Dolan Springs, 86441. SAN 330-6151. Tel: 520-767-4292. FAX: 520-767-4292. *Coordr*, Marion Craig
Friends of the Library Group
GOLDEN SHORES-TOPOCK STATION, PO Box 1356, Topock, 86436-1356. SAN 371-361X. Tel: 520-768-2235. FAX: 520-768-2235. *Coordr*, Kay Slater
Friends of the Library Group
MEADVIEW COMMUNITY STATION, PO Box 187, Meadview, 86444. SAN 370-906X. Tel: 520-564-2535. FAX: 520-564-2535. *Coordr*, Pinkey Elliott

Friends of the Library Group
OATMAN STATION, PO Box 901, Oatman, 86433-0901. SAN 371-3628. Tel: 520-768-2323. FAX: 520-768-2323. *Coordr*, Marion Craig
Friends of the Library Group
SOUTH MOHAVE VALLEY STATION, PO Box 5661, Mohave Valley, 86440. SAN 373-191X. Tel: 520-768-1151. FAX: 520-768-1151. *Coordr*, Dorothy Diamians
Friends of the Library Group
VALLE VISTA STATION, 7193 Concho Dr, Ste B, 86401. SAN 378-1666. Tel: 520-692-7667. FAX: 520-692-7662. *Coordr*, Marion Craig
Friends of the Library Group

KYKOTSMOVI VILLAGE

P HOPI PUBLIC LIBRARY,* c/o Hopi Educ Dept, PO Box 123, 86039. SAN 377-5488. Tel: 520-734-3501. FAX: 520-734-3509. Web Site: hpaymella@hopi.nsn.us. *Dir*, Harvey Paymella
Oct 1996-Sep 1997 Mats Exp $4,000
Library Holdings: Bk Titles 1,050

LAKESIDE

P LARSON MEMORIAL PUBLIC LIBRARY, 1595 W Johnson Dr, 85929. (Mail add: PO Box 416, 85929-0416), SAN 300-340X. Tel: 520-368-6688. FAX: 520-368-8963. E-Mail: larmem@lib.az.us. *Dir*, Wendy A Kochheiser; Tel: 520-368-0624, E-Mail: wkochhei@lib.az.us; *Asst Librn*, Nancy Fish; Staff 2 (MLS 1, Non-MLS 1)
Founded 1954. Pop 22,000; Circ 41,000
Jul 2000-Jun 2001 Income $145,000, City $140,000, Locally Generated Income $5,000. Mats Exp $15,000. Sal $79,000 (Prof $30,000)
Library Holdings: Bk Vols 22,494; Bk Titles 20,180; Per Subs 60
Subject Interests: Arizona, Indians, Large type print
Special Collections: National Geographic Coll
Automation Activity & Vendor Info: (Circulation) SIRSI
Database Vendor: OVID Technologies
Function: ILL available
Partic in Navajo County Libr District
Special Services for the Blind - Talking Books
Friends of the Library Group

LITCHFIELD PARK

P LITCHFIELD PARK PUBLIC LIBRARY,* 101 W Wigwam Blvd, 85340-4634. SAN 300-3426. Tel: 623-935-4118. FAX: 623-935-1511. *Librn*, Gerard Saylor; Staff 5 (MLS 2, Non-MLS 3)
Founded 1965. Pop 3,000; Circ 55,300
Library Holdings: Bk Vols 32,000; Bk Titles 47,000; Per Subs 36
Mem of Maricopa County Libr Syst
Friends of the Library Group

LUKE AFB

UNITED STATES AIR FORCE
A LUKE AIR FORCE BASE LIBRARY, Bldg 219, 7424 N Homer Dr, 56 SVS/SVMG FL 4887, 85309-1220. SAN 330-6216. Tel: 623-856-3893, 623-856-7191. FAX: 623-935-2023. *Dir*, Katherine Gillen; E-Mail: katie.gillen@luke.af.mil; *Ref*, Janice Robrock
Founded 1951
1999-2000 Income $270,734. Mats Exp $57,400, Books $40,000, Per/Ser (Incl. Access Fees) $15,000, Micro $2,400. Sal $215,990 (Prof $80,000)
Library Holdings: Bk Vols 32,000; Per Subs 225
Subject Interests: Aeronautics, Military history
Special Collections: Arizona, Mission Support
Automation Activity & Vendor Info: (Cataloging) epixtech, inc.; (Circulation) epixtech, inc.
Database Vendor: OCLC - First Search
Publications: Bibliographies
Partic in Dialog Corporation; OCLC Online Computer Library Center, Inc

MAMMOTH

P MAMMOTH PUBLIC LIBRARY,* 125 N Clark St, PO Box 548, 85618-0548. SAN 300-3434. Tel: 520-487-2026. *Librn*, Mildretha Taylor
Founded 1962. Pop 2,500; Circ 7,833
Library Holdings: Bk Vols 8,500; Bk Titles 8,000; Per Subs 24
Mem of Pinal County Library District

MARICOPA

§P MARICOPA COMMUNITY LIBRARY, 44240 W Maricopa, Casa Grande Hwy, 85239. (Mail add: PO Box 123, 85239-0123), Tel: 520-568-2926. FAX: 520-568-2680. E-Mail: linda.wilmeth@co.pinal.az.us. Web Site: www.co.pinal.az.us/library. *Dir*, Linda Wilmeth; E-Mail: linda.wilmeth@co.pinal.az.us
Jul 1999-Jun 2000 Income $5,000, State $1,600, Other $3,400
Library Holdings: Bk Vols 12,000
Automation Activity & Vendor Info: (Cataloging) Innovative Interfaces Inc.; (Circulation) Innovative Interfaces Inc.
Open Tues & Thurs 9-5, Sat 9-1

MAYER

P CORDES LAKES PUBLIC LIBRARY,* 20445 Quailrun Dr, 86333. SAN 323-7931. Tel: 520-632-5492. FAX: 520-632-5492. *Mgr*, Violet Kalina; *Chair*, Marilyn Bryant
Library Holdings: Bk Vols 5,079

P MAYER PUBLIC LIBRARY,* PO Box 1016, 86333-1020. SAN 323-7974. Tel: 520-632-7370. FAX: 520-632-7370. *Mgr*, Dick Croisant
Library Holdings: Bk Vols 5,000
Mem of Yuma County Library District

MESA

S ARIZONA MUSEUM FOR YOUTH LIBRARY,* 35 N Robson, 85201. SAN 375-7161. Tel: 602-644-2468. FAX: 602-644-2466. *Curator*, Rebecca Akins
Library Holdings: Bk Titles 1,000

§C ARIZONA STATE UNIVERSITY, East Campus, Academic Center Bldg 20, Rm 110, 7001 E Williams Field Rd, 85212. Tel: 480-727-1037. FAX: 480-727-1077. E-Mail: eastlib@asu.edu. Web Site: www.east.asu.edu. *Dir*, Charles Brownson; Tel: 480-727-1974, E-Mail: brownson@asu.edu
Jul 1999-Jun 2000 Income $388,480
Library Holdings: Bk Vols 3,466; Per Subs 144
Automation Activity & Vendor Info: (Cataloging) Innovative Interfaces Inc.; (Circulation) Innovative Interfaces Inc.; (OPAC) Innovative Interfaces Inc.

S CHAMPLIN FIGHTER MUSEUM LIBRARY,* 4636 Fighter Aces Dr, 85215. SAN 376-0723. Tel: 602-830-4540. FAX: 602-830-4543. *Pres*, Douglas Champlin
Library Holdings: Bk Vols 500
Restriction: Private library

S CHURCH OF JESUS CHRIST OF LATTER-DAY SAINTS, Mesa Family History Center, 41 S Hobson, 85204. SAN 300-3450. Tel: 480-964-1200. FAX: 480-964-7137. *Dir*, Glenn Scott; *Asst Librn*, Robert Bryce; Staff 39 (Non-MLS 39)
Founded 1930
Library Holdings: Bk Titles 20,000
Subject Interests: Genealogy
Special Collections: Family Histories & Biographies; International Genealogical Index; US Census Records
Open Mon & Sat 9-5, Tues-Fri 9-9

M DESERT SAMARITAN MEDICAL CENTER, Health Science Library, 1400 S Dobson Rd, 85202. Tel: 480-835-3024. *Librn*, Kathy Bilko; E-Mail: kathy.bilko@bannerhealth.com
Library Holdings: Bk Vols 1,000; Bk Titles 50; Per Subs 200

S MCDONALD DOUGLAS HELICOPTER COMPANY LIBRARY, Bldg 530, Mail Sta B 223, 5000 E McDowell, 85215-9797. SAN 300-6972. Tel: 480-891-5677, Ext 5677. FAX: 480-891-6885. *Chief Librn*, Bonnie Rizzuto; E-Mail: bonnie.j.rizzuto@boeing.com; *Librn*, Judy Marker
Founded 1940
Library Holdings: Bk Vols 20,000; Per Subs 20
Subject Interests: Aeronautics, Mechanical engineering
Friends of the Library Group

J MESA COMMUNITY COLLEGE LIBRARY, Paul A Elsner Library & High Technology Complex, 1833 W Southern Ave, 85202. (Mail add: 2305 N Power Rd, 85215-2967), SAN 300-3469. Tel: 480-461-7671. Circulation Tel: 480-461-7680. Reference Tel: 480-461-7682. TDD: 480-969-5387. FAX: 480-462-7681. Web Site: www.mc.maricopa.edu/its/lib. *Chair*, Kaye Kaoru Sugiyama; Tel: 480-461-7664, E-Mail: k.sugiyama@mcmail.maricopa.edu; *Librn*, Marlene Forney; Tel: 480-461-7631, E-Mail: marlene.forney@mcmail.maricopa.edu; *Librn*, Sherry Peabody; Tel: 480-461-7691, E-Mail: sherry.peabody@mcmail.maricopa.edu; *Ref*, Florence Landon; Tel: 480-461-7663, E-Mail: f.landon@mcmail.maricopa.edu; *Ref*, James Theilmann; Tel: 480-461-7675, E-Mail: jim.theilmann@mcmail.maricopa.edu; *Head, Circ*, Jane Mente; Tel: 480-461-7694, E-Mail: jmente@mcmail.maricopa.edu; *Coll Develop*, Jill R Seymour; Tel: 480-461-7930, E-Mail: j.seymour@mcmail.maricopa.edu; *Electronic Resources*, Ann Tolzman; Tel: 480-461-7982, E-Mail: ann.tolzman@mcmail.maricopa.edu. Subject Specialists: *Asian studies*, Kaye Kaoru Sugiyama; *Audio*, Charles Moore; *Edu*, Sherry Peabody; *English*, Kaye Kaoru Sugiyama; *English*, Ann Tolzman; *Far East*, Kaye Kaoru Sugiyama; *History*, Jill R Seymour; *Libr*, Jill R Seymour; *Media*, Charles Moore; *Philosophy*, James Theilmann; *Religion*, James Theilmann; *Romance languages*, Marlene Forney; *Visual*, Charles Moore; Staff 32 (MLS 12, Non-MLS 20)
Founded 1963. Enrl 10,000
Jul 2000-Jun 2001 Income $2,400,000. Mats Exp $250,000, Books

$159,000, Per/Ser (Incl. Access Fees) $41,000, Micro $20,000, Electronic Ref Mat (Incl. Access Fees) $25,000. Sal $1,573,000 (Prof $621,000)
Library Holdings: Bk Vols 90,394; Bk Titles 89,923; Per Subs 612
Database Vendor: DRA, epixtech, inc., GaleNet, IAC - Info Trac, OCLC - First Search, OVID Technologies, ProQuest, Wilson - Wilson Web
Restriction: Open to student, faculty & staff
Mem of Maricopa County Libr Syst
Special Services for the Blind - ADA terminals for visually impaired
Open Mon-Thurs 7-10, Fri 7-5, Sat 9-5:30
Friends of the Library Group

M MESA GENERAL HOSPITAL MEDICAL CENTER, Medical Library,* 515 N Mesa Dr, 85201. SAN 374-986X. Tel: 602-844-6283. FAX: 602-844-4364. *Dir*, Jude Edelman
Library Holdings: Bk Titles 400; Per Subs 35

M MESA LUTHERAN HOSPITAL, Medical Library,* 525 W Brown Rd, 85201. SAN 373-0182. Tel: 480-461-2189, 480-834-2111. FAX: 480-461-2558. *In Charge*, Joyce Kern; E-Mail: jokern@bannerhealth.com
Library Holdings: Bk Titles 1,500; Per Subs 295
Subject Interests: Medicine
Partic in Cent Ariz Biomed Librns; MLGSCA

P MESA PUBLIC LIBRARY,* 64 E First St, 85201-6768. SAN 300-3477. Tel: 480-644-2702. Interlibrary Loan Service Tel: 480-644-2732. TDD: 480-644-2639. FAX: 480-644-3490. Interlibrary Loan Service FAX: 480-644-2991. Web Site: www.ci.mesa.az.us/library/. *Dir*, Patsy Hansel; *Librn*, Lanty Snelson; E-Mail: lanty_snelson@ci.mesa.az.us; *Cat*, Clarence Nelson; Tel: 480-644-2727, E-Mail: clarence_nelson@ci.mesa.az.us; *Circ*, Dawn Kucerak; Tel: 480-644-2739, E-Mail: dawn_kucera@ci.mesa.az.us; *Coll Develop*, Linda Mortland; Tel: 480-644-3554, E-Mail: linda_mortland@ci.mesa.az.us; *Coll Develop*, Pauline Savini; Tel: 480-644-2725, E-Mail: pauline_savini@ci.mesa.az.us; *Electronic Resources, Per, Ref*, Mary Beth Burgoyne; Tel: 480-644-3891, E-Mail: mary_beth_burgoyne@ci.mesa.az.us; *Exten Serv*, Molly Rice; Tel: 480-644-2704, E-Mail: molly_rice@ci.mesa.az.us; *Online Servs*, Kathryn Havris; Tel: 480-644-2711, E-Mail: kate_havris@ci.mesa.az.us; *Outreach Serv*, David Jenny; Tel: 480-644-2737, E-Mail: david_jenny@ci.mesa.az.us; *Publ Servs*, Jean Murphy; Tel: 480-644-2709, E-Mail: jean_murphy@ci.mesa.az.us; *Ref*, Barbara Seperich; Tel: 480-644-2710, E-Mail: barbara_seperich@ci.mesa.az.us; *Tech Servs*, Peggy Haney; Tel: 480-644-2726, E-Mail: peggy_haney@ci.mesa.az.us; *YA Servs*, Anne Britton; Tel: 480-644-2706, E-Mail: anne_britton@ci.mesa.az.us; *YA Servs*, Diane P Tuccillo; Tel: 480-644-2735, E-Mail: diane_tuccillo@ci.mesa.az.us
Founded 1926. Pop 380,000; Circ 2,508,850
Jul 1998-Jun 1999 Income (Main Library and Branch Library) $11,250,928, State $5,785, City $10,958,328, Federal $56,150, County $184,782, Other $45,745. Mats Exp $1,949,411, Books $1,144,681, Per/Ser (Incl. Access Fees) $272,800, Presv $153,000, Other Print Mats $164,930, Electronic Ref Mat (Incl. Access Fees) $214,000. Sal $6,909,361
Library Holdings: Bk Vols 736,618; Per Subs 2,999
Subject Interests: Large type print, Local history, Small business, Spanish (language)
Special Collections: Fed
Automation Activity & Vendor Info: (Acquisitions) EX Libris; (Circulation) epixtech, inc.; (Media Booking) epixtech, inc.; (OPAC) epixtech, inc.
Database Vendor: Ebsco - EbscoHost, OCLC - First Search
Publications: FRANK (young adult creative writing & illustration annual); Open Shelf (monthly young adult book review)
Partic in Amigos Library Services, Inc; Bibliographical Center For Research, Rocky Mountain Region, Inc; E Valley Info Network; OCLC Online Computer Library Center, Inc
Special Services for the Deaf - Staff with knowledge of sign language; TTY machine
Special Services for the Blind - Machine repair; Soundproof reading booth; Volunteer delivery & assistance service
Special Services for Homebound - Reader guidance; volunteer delivery & assistance; Spanish language staff & programs
Friends of the Library Group
Branches: 2
DOBSON, 2425 S Dobson Rd, 85202. SAN 328-6800. Tel: 602-644-3441. FAX: 602-644-3445. Web Site: www.ci.mesa.az.us/library/. *Librn*, Michael T Pitchford; *Ref*, Susan A Hopkins
EAST MESA REGIONAL, 635 N Power Rd, 85205. SAN 325-3791. Tel: 602-644-3184. FAX: 602-644-3559. Web Site: www.ci.mesa.az.us/library/. *Librn*, Brynn D Barkey; *Ch Servs*, Teresa Becker

MIAMI

P MIAMI MEMORIAL-GILA COUNTY LIBRARY,* 1052 Adonis Ave, 85539-1298. SAN 300-3493. Tel: 520-473-2621. FAX: 520-473-2567. *Librn*, Carol Ann Ciallella
Pop 37,098
Library Holdings: Bk Titles 41,000; Per Subs 35

MORENCI

P MORENCI COMMUNITY LIBRARY,* PO Box 1060, 85540. SAN 376-3269. Tel: 520-865-2775. FAX: 520-865-3130. *Dir*, John Lechtenberger
Jul 1997-Jun 1998 Income (Main Library Only) $95,000. Mats Exp $12,000. Sal $83,000 (Prof $42,000)
Library Holdings: Bk Vols 17,000; Bk Titles 12,000; Per Subs 65
Subject Interests: Arizona
Friends of the Library Group

NOGALES

P NOGALES-SANTA CRUZ COUNTY PUBLIC LIBRARY, Nogales Public Library,* 518 N Grand Ave, 85621. SAN 300-3507. Tel: 520-287-2911, 520-287-3343, 520-287-7417. FAX: 520-287-4823. *Dir*, Suzanne Haddock; *Ch Servs*, Susan Adame; *Coll Develop*, Mirna Navarro; *Branch Mgr*, Eunice Pinzon; Staff 10 (MLS 2, Non-MLS 8)
Founded 1923. Pop 36,500; Circ 141,500
Jul 1998-Jun 1999 Income (Main Library and Branch Library) $369,017, State $20,498, City $229,271, County $115,000. Mats Exp $45,347, Books $41,047, Per/Ser (Incl. Access Fees) $4,300. Sal $217,777 (Prof $24,000)
Library Holdings: Bk Titles 77,500; Per Subs 130
Special Collections: Arizona & Southwest History Coll; New Readers Coll (Literacy); Spanish Language Coll; Vocational Guidance & Career Coll
Mem of Santa Cruz Libr Syst
Partic in Amigos Library Services, Inc; OCLC Online Computer Library Center, Inc
Friends of the Library Group
Branches: 3
RIO RICO LIBRARY, 1060 Yavapai Dr, Rio Rico, 85648. SAN 320-9520. Tel: 520-281-8067. *Mgr*, Eunice Pinzon
Friends of the Library Group
SONOITA COMMUNITY, County Complex Bldg, 3147 State Rte 83, Hwy 82, Sonoita, 85637. SAN 373-1820. Tel: 520-455-5517. *Mgr*, Eunice Pinzon
Friends of the Library Group
TUBAC COMMUNITY LIBRARY, 3 Calle Baca, Tubac, 85646. SAN 326-7911. Tel: 520-398-9814. *Mgr*, Eunice Pinzon
Friends of the Library Group . Book van: 1

S PIMERIA ALTA HISTORICAL SOCIETY LIBRARY & MUSEUM,* 136 N Grand Ave, PO Box 2281, 85621. SAN 326-5609. Tel: 520-287-4621. FAX: 520-287-5201. *Archivist*, Susan Aycock-Williams
Library Holdings: Bk Vols 1,600; Bk Titles 1,500; Per Subs 10

ORACLE

P ORACLE PUBLIC LIBRARY, 565 American Ave, PO Box 1057, 85623-1057. SAN 300-3515. Tel: 520-896-2121. FAX: 520-896-2121. *Pres*, Jackie Buzan
Founded 1954. Pop 5,000; Circ 9,500
1998-1999 Income $8,000. Mats Exp $8,000
Library Holdings: Bk Titles 9,600; Per Subs 20
Special Collections: Southwest - 320
Mem of Pinal County Library District

PAGE

P PAGE PUBLIC LIBRARY, 479 S Lake Powell Blvd, PO Box 1776, 86040. SAN 300-354X. Tel: 520-645-4270. FAX: 520-645-5804. Web Site: www.ci.page.az.us/library.htm. *Dir*, Judy Hart; E-Mail: jhart@ci.page.az.us; *Acq*, Marjanne Supernaw; *Cat*, Dana Bennett; *Ref Servs YA*, Elaine Schulz; *Ch Servs*, Marilyn Jaques; *Ad Servs*, Lorraine Vigil; *Circ*, Linda Corn; *Circ*, Cynthia Smith; *Circ*, Christy Foster; *Circ*, Melissa Clark; *Circ*, Livia Howard; Staff 11 (MLS 1, Non-MLS 10)
Founded 1959
Library Holdings: Bk Vols 48,960; Bk Titles 46,069; Per Subs 78
Subject Interests: Arizona, Native Am
Automation Activity & Vendor Info: (Cataloging) TLC; (Circulation) TLC; (OPAC) TLC
Database Vendor: IAC - Info Trac, Innovative Interfaces INN - View, OVID Technologies
Publications: Annual Report; Library Board Policy Manual
Mem of Coconino County Libr Syst

S JOHN WESLEY POWELL MEMORIAL MUSEUM LIBRARY, 6 N Lake Powell Blvd, PO Box 547, 86040-0547. SAN 371-1560. Tel: 520-645-9496. Toll Free Tel: 888-597-6873. FAX: 520-645-3412. E-Mail: director@powellmuseum.org. Web Site: www.powellmuseum.org. *Dir*, Julia P Betz; Staff 2 (Non-MLS 2)
Founded 1969
Library Holdings: Bk Vols 500
Special Collections: State History - Glen Canyon Dam, Colorado River

PARKER

P COLORADO RIVER INDIAN TRIBES PUBLIC LIBRARY-ARCHIVE, Second Ave & Mohave Rd, Rte 1, Box 23-B, 85344. SAN 300-3558. Tel: 520-669-9211. FAX: 520-669-8262. E-Mail: alfhepah@hotmail.com. Web Site: www.critlibrary.com. *Dir*, Amelia Flores; *Chairperson*, Daniel Eddy Jr
Founded 1958. Circ 4,376
Library Holdings: Bk Vols 20,283; Bk Titles 11,230; Bks on Deafness & Sign Lang 16
Special Collections: Archival documents, History & Culture (Indian Coll), micro, photo
Automation Activity & Vendor Info: (Acquisitions) Sagebrush Corporation; (Cataloging) Sagebrush Corporation; (Circulation) Sagebrush Corporation
Internet restrictions

P PARKER PUBLIC LIBRARY, 1001 S Navajo Ave, 85344. SAN 300-3566. Tel: 520-669-2622. Toll Free Tel: 877-85-BOOKS. FAX: 520-669-8668. *Dir Libr Serv*, Jana Christine Ponce; E-Mail: jponce@parker.lib.az.us; *Ad Servs*, Donna Ellsworth; E-Mail: dellswor@parker.lib.az.us; *Ch Servs*, Jeannie Chavez; E-Mail: jeanjean@hotmail.com; Staff 4 (Non-MLS 4)
Founded 1957. Pop 12,000; Circ 43,000
Jul 2000-Jun 2001 Income $213,501, State $24,501, City $134,000, County $55,000. Mats Exp $18,000, Books $14,000. Sal $104,000 (Prof $33,000)
Library Holdings: Bk Vols 31,000
Subject Interests: Arizona, Young adult
Automation Activity & Vendor Info: (Cataloging) Sagebrush Corporation; (Circulation) Sagebrush Corporation
Database Vendor: OCLC - First Search
Function: ILL available
Special Services for the Deaf - Books on deafness & sign language; High interest/low vocabulary books
Special Services for the Blind - Bks on tape
Friends of the Library Group
Branches: 1
INDIAN HILLS, PO Box 309, Salome, 85348. SAN 377-0303. Tel: 520-859-4271. FAX: 520-859-4271. *Mgr*, Fay Wick
Library Holdings: Bk Titles 4,500

PATAGONIA

P PATAGONIA PUBLIC LIBRARY,* 346 Duquesne St, PO Box 415, 85624. SAN 320-2054. Tel: 520-394-2010. FAX: 520-394-2113. *Librn*, Amy Popadak; Staff 3 (MLS 1, Non-MLS 2)
Founded 1957. Pop 2,500
Library Holdings: Bk Titles 9,991; Per Subs 20
Special Collections: Classic Films, videos; Local History
Friends of the Library Group

PAYSON

P PAYSON PUBLIC LIBRARY, 510 W Main, 85541. SAN 300-3574. Tel: 520-474-5242. FAX: 520-474-2679. *Ch Servs, Dir*, Terry Morris
Founded 1923. Pop 13,000; Circ 101,000
Library Holdings: Bk Vols 72,000; Per Subs 72
Subject Interests: Large type print
Special Collections: History (Southwest Coll); Native Americans
Mem of Gila County Library District
Friends of the Library Group

PEORIA

P PEORIA PUBLIC LIBRARY, 8463 W Monroe, 85345. (Mail add: 8401 W Monroe, 85345), SAN 300-3590. Tel: 623-773-7555. Reference Tel: 623-773-7556. FAX: 623-773-7567. E-Mail: library@peoriaaz.com. Web Site: www.peoriaaz.com. *Mgr*, Brenda Brown; Tel: 623-773-7557, E-Mail: brendab@peoriaaz.com; *Coordr*, Ingrid Landon; Tel: 623-773-7511, E-Mail: ingridl@peoriaaz.com; *Acq*, Rosemary Sambora; Tel: 623-773-7540, E-Mail: rosemarys@peoriaaz.com; *Ch Servs*, Dawn M Schmidt; Tel: 623-773-7562, E-Mail: dawns@peoriaaz.com; *Ref Serv Ad*, Elizabeth Lucas; Tel: 623-773-7556, E-Mail: liz@peoriaaz.com; Staff 36 (MLS 7, Non-MLS 29)
Founded 1920. Pop 101,000; Circ 374,735
Jul 1999-Jun 2000 Income (Main Library Only) $1,331,642, City $1,311,542, Federal $20,100. Mats Exp $232,500, Books $113,500, Electronic Ref Mat (Incl. Access Fees) $20,000. Sal $766,290 (Prof $378,540)
Library Holdings: Bk Vols 155,539; Bk Titles 123,303; Per Subs 135
Subject Interests: Large type print, Spanish (language)
Automation Activity & Vendor Info: (Acquisitions) epixtech, inc.; (Cataloging) epixtech, inc.; (Circulation) epixtech, inc.; (Serials) epixtech, inc.
Database Vendor: epixtech, inc.
Partic in Amigos Library Services, Inc; OCLC Online Computer Library Center, Inc
Special Services for the Deaf - Staff with knowledge of sign language; TTY machine
Staff members who speak Spanish & German
Friends of the Library Group
Branches: 1
SUNRISE MOUNTAIN BRANCH LIBRARY, 21200 N 83rd Ave, 85381. SAN 377-7553. Tel: 623-487-5150. FAX: 623-487-5151. E-Mail: library@peoriaaz.com. Web Site: www.peoriaaz.com. *Branch Mgr*, David Hunenberg; Tel: 623-487-5152, E-Mail: dhunenber@peoriaaz.com; *Mgr*, Brown Brenda; Staff 9 (MLS 2, Non-MLS 7)
Founded 1996
Jul 1999-Jun 2000 Income City $312,331. Mats Exp $20,000, Books $10,000, Electronic Ref Mat (Incl. Access Fees) $10,000. Sal $89,460
Library Holdings: Bk Titles 78,183; Per Subs 78
Database Vendor: epixtech, inc.
Friends of the Library Group

PETRIFIED FOREST NATIONAL PARK

S NATIONAL PARK SERVICE, Petrified Forest National Park Library, One Park Rd, 86028-0217. (Mail add: PO Box 2217, 86028), SAN 300-3604. Tel: 520-524-6228. FAX: 520-524-3567.
Founded 1906
Library Holdings: Bk Vols 4,500
Subject Interests: Natural history
Special Collections: Triassic Period
Restriction: Staff use only

PHOENIX

S AG COMMUNICATION SYSTEMS INFORMATION RESOURCE CENTER, 2500 W Utopia Rd, PO Box 52179, 85072-2179. SAN 321-4699. Tel: 623-582-7000, 623-582-7268. FAX: 623-587-3378. *Dir*, Verlene Herrington; E-Mail: herringv@agcs.com; Staff 2 (MLS 1, Non-MLS 1)
Founded 1980
Library Holdings: Bk Vols 3,000; Bk Titles 2,200; Per Subs 60
Subject Interests: Electronic engineering
Restriction: Staff use only

S ALLIED-SIGNAL ENGINES, Engineering Library,* 1944 E Sky Harbor Circle, 85034. SAN 300-3612. FAX: 602-231-1681.
Founded 1956
Library Holdings: Bk Titles 19,000; Per Subs 200
Subject Interests: Aeronautics, Business and management, Ceramics, Chemistry, Energy, Engineering, Mathematics, Metallurgy
Publications: Library News
Restriction: Staff use only

S AMEC TECHNICAL LIBRARY, (Formerly AGRA Earth & Environmental Technical Library), 3232 W Virginia Ave, 85009. SAN 371-5191. Tel: 602-272-6848. Toll Free Tel: 800-248-2472. FAX: 602-272-7239. *Librn*, Elyse Rukkila; E-Mail: erukkila@agraus.com
1998-1999 Mats Exp $14,000, Books $6,000, Per/Ser (Incl. Access Fees) $2,400, Presv $100, Other Print Mats $200. Sal $9,600
Library Holdings: Bk Titles 1,300; Per Subs 120
Subject Interests: Engineering, Environment, Geology

SR AMERICAN INDIAN COLLEGE, Dorothy Cummings Memorial Library, 10020 N 15th Ave, 85021-2199. SAN 300-3639. Tel: 602-944-3335, Ext 251. FAX: 602-943-8299. *Dir*, John S Rose
Founded 1965
Library Holdings: Bk Vols 14,000; Per Subs 89
Subject Interests: American Indians, Theology

§S ARGOSY EDUCATIONAL GROUP, Arizona School of Professional Psychology Library, 2301 W Dunlap, Ste 211, 85021-2846. Tel: 602-216-2600. FAX: 602-674-3670. Web Site: www.aspp.edu. *Dir Libr Serv*, Karen Jeffers; E-Mail: kjeffers@azspp.edu
Library Holdings: Bk Titles 3,000; Per Subs 70

G ARIZONA DEPARTMENT OF AGRICULTURE, STATE AGRICULTURAL LABORATORY, Biology, 2422 W Holly, 85009. SAN 328-1736. Tel: 602-253-1920. FAX: 602-253-2247. *Librn*, David Mills
Founded 1909
Library Holdings: Bk Titles 3,200; Per Subs 10
Special Collections: Animal & Plant Coll; Botany Coll; Entomology (Technical & Popular Coll); Horticultural Coll; Plant Pathology Coll
Restriction: Staff use only

§S ARIZONA DEPARTMENT OF CORRECTIONS - ADULT, Arizona State Prison Complex - Phoenix Library, 2500 E Van Buren St, 85008. (Mail add: PO Box 52109, 85072-2109), Tel: 602-685-3100. FAX: 602-255-2244. *In Charge*, Chuck Poole; Tel: 602-255-1953
Library Holdings: Bk Vols 13,633

G ARIZONA DEPARTMENT OF ECONOMIC SECURITY, DES Authority Library, 1789 W Jefferson, 85007. SAN 375-4790. Tel: 602-542-4777. FAX: 602-364-0244.; Staff 2 (MLS 1, Non-MLS 1)

Founded 1977
Special Collections: Federal & State Regulations internal documents & codes
Restriction: Internal circulation only
Function: ILL available, Research library

G ARIZONA DEPARTMENT OF EDUCATION LIBRARY, 1535 W Jefferson St, 85007. SAN 300-3647. Tel: 602-542-5416. FAX: 602-542-0520. *Dir*, Linda Edgington; Staff 3 (MLS 1, Non-MLS 2)
Library Holdings: Bk Titles 10,000; Per Subs 130
Subject Interests: Education
Partic in Dialog Corporation

G ARIZONA DEPARTMENT OF ENVIRONMENTAL QUALITY, ADEQ Library, 3033 N Central Ave M0101A, 85012. SAN 374-9029. Tel: 602-207-4335. Circulation Tel: 602-207-4335. Reference Tel: 602-207-2217. Toll Free Tel: 800-234-5677 (AZ only). FAX: 602-207-4872. Web Site: www.adeq.state.az.us/comm/library. *Dir Libr Serv*, Lorraine E Akey; Tel: 602-207-2217, E-Mail: akey.lorraine@ev.state.az.us. Subject Specialists: *Reference*, Lorraine E Akey
Library Holdings: Bk Vols 10,000; Bk Titles 4,000
Subject Interests: Environ, Pollution prevention, Sustainable develop, Topographic maps
Database Vendor: OCLC - First Search
Restriction: Circulation limited, Public use on premises
Function: For research purposes

G ARIZONA DEPARTMENT OF HEALTH SERVICES, Public Health Library,* 1740 W Adams, 85007. SAN 300-3655. Tel: 602-542-1013. FAX: 602-542-1132. Web Site: www.hs.state.az.us/phl/phlib.htm. *Mgr*, Beverlee Hall; E-Mail: bhall@hs.state.az.us
Founded 1975
Library Holdings: Bk Titles 3,500; Per Subs 77
Subject Interests: Public health
Special Collections: Arizona Government Documents, Health-Related
Publications: Bibliographies on specific health topics; Media Catalog
Partic in BRS; Dialog Corporation
Branches:
FILM Tel: 602-542-1013. FAX: 602-542-1132. Web Site: www.hs.state.az.us/phl/phlib.htm.
Subject Interests: Public health

G ARIZONA DEPARTMENT OF TRANSPORTATION LIBRARY, 206 S 17th Ave, No 075R, 85007. SAN 374-5198. Tel: 602-712-3138. FAX: 602-256-6367, 602-712-3400. Web Site: www.dot.state.az.us/about/atrc/library.htm. *Librn*, Dale Steele
Jul 1999-Jun 2000 Income $20,000
Library Holdings: Bk Titles 25,000; Per Subs 240
Publications: Catalog of ATRC Publications
Partic in OCLC Online Computer Library Center, Inc

§S ARIZONA POST RESOURCE CENTER LIBRARY, 2643 E University Dr, 85034-6914. Tel: 602-223-2300. FAX: 602-244-0477. Web Site: www.azpost.state.az.us. *Dir*, Stacey Smith; E-Mail: ssmith@azpost.state.az.us
Library Holdings: Bk Vols 3,000; Per Subs 30
Automation Activity & Vendor Info: (Cataloging) EOS; (Circulation) EOS

S ARIZONA PUBLIC SERVICE COMPANY, Corporate Library,* PO Box 53999, Sta 8689, 85072. SAN 300-3671. Tel: 602-250-2844. FAX: 602-250-2136. *Librn*, Susan Opalka; *Librn*, Debbie Hekel
Founded 1947
Library Holdings: Bk Vols 2,650
Special Collections: 1964 Alaskan Earthquake (Seward Is Burning), slides

GL ARIZONA STATE ATTORNEY GENERAL, Water Rights Adjudication Team (WRAT) Research Room,* 1275 W Washington, 85007. SAN 373-3394. Tel: 602-542-1401. FAX: 602-542-1275. *Librn*, Lucy Trujillo
Library Holdings: Bk Titles 2,000; Per Subs 25

P ARIZONA STATE BRAILLE & TALKING BOOK LIBRARY,* 1030 N 32nd St, 85008. SAN 300-368X. Tel: 602-255-5578. Toll Free Tel: 800-255-5578. FAX: 602-255-4312. E-Mail: btbl@dlapr.lib.az.us. Web Site: www.dlapr.lib.az.us. *Dir*, Linda A Montgomery; *Asst Librn*, Sandra Everett; *Tech Servs*, Linda Eckhardt; *Coll Develop*, Kami Krenz
Founded 1970
Special Collections: Arizona & Spanish Language Cassettes, locally produced; Reference Materials on Blindness & Disablities, print
Automation Activity & Vendor Info: (Circulation) DRA
Publications: Newsletter (quarterly); Volunteer Monitor (quarterly)
Special Services - Statewide in WATS; patron newsletter; production of reading material to specialized format upon request of patron
Friends of the Library Group

G ARIZONA STATE HISTORIC PRESERVATION OFFICE - ARIZONA STATE PARKS,* 1300 W Washington, 2nd flr, 85007. SAN 374-9037. Tel: 602-542-7140. FAX: 602-542-4180. *Dir*, Bill Collins
Library Holdings: Bk Titles 1,000

M ARIZONA STATE HOSPITAL, Medical Library, 2500 E Van Buren St, 85008. SAN 330-6240. Tel: 602-220-6045. FAX: 602-220-6414. *Librn*, Gail Bacani; E-Mail: gbacani@hs.state.az.us
Founded 1965
Jul 1999-Jun 2000 Mats Exp $5,300, Books $1,000, Per/Ser (Incl. Access Fees) $3,300, AV Equip $1,000. Sal $28,000
Library Holdings: Bk Vols 4,600; Per Subs 127
Subject Interests: Drug abuse, Mental health, Nursing, Psychiatry, Psychology, Psychotherapy, Social service (social work)
Database Vendor: OCLC - First Search
Restriction: Non-circulating to the public
Partic in Pac SW Regional Med Libr

G ARIZONA STATE LAW LIBRARY, ARCHIVES & PUBLIC RECORDS, 1501 W Washington, 85007. Tel: 602-542-5297. FAX: 602-542-1111. E-Mail: slrefde@dlapr.lib.az.us. Web Site: www.dlapr.lib.az.us. *Dir*, Gladys-Ann Wells; *State Librn*, David Melillo; E-Mail: dmelillo@dlapr.lib.az.us
Library Holdings: Bk Vols 150,000; Per Subs 380
Special Collections: Arizona Revised Statutes
Automation Activity & Vendor Info: (Acquisitions) SIRSI; (Cataloging) SIRSI; (Circulation) SIRSI; (OPAC) SIRSI; (Serials) SIRSI
Database Vendor: OCLC - First Search
Restriction: Circulation limited
Function: ILL available
Partic in OCLC Online Computer Library Center, Inc

P ARIZONA STATE LIBRARY, Department of Library, Archives & Public Records, 1700 W Washington, Rm 200, 85007. SAN 300-3701. Tel: 602-542-4035. FAX: 602-542-4972. E-Mail: services@lib.az.us. Web Site: www.lib.az.us. *Dir*, GladysAnn Wells; *Adminr*, Carol Westwood; Tel: 602-542-4047, Fax: 602-542-8195, E-Mail: cwestwoo@lib.az.us; *Res*, Janet Fisher; Fax: 602-542-4400; *Coll Develop*, Bessie Platten; Staff 121 (MLS 33, Non-MLS 88)
Founded 1864
Jul 1999-Jun 2000 Income $9,371,106, State $7,425,700, Federal $2,305,406. Mats Exp $474,305, Books $303,666, Per/Ser (Incl. Access Fees) $93,073, Presv $20,000, Micro $28,262, Electronic Ref Mat (Incl. Access Fees) $29,304. Sal $3,319,715
Library Holdings: Bk Vols 1,139,780; Per Subs 429
Subject Interests: Arizona, Genealogy, Law, Maps
Special Collections: History (State Archives, Arizonia & SW), bks, film, mss, photogs, original rec; State Law Library
Automation Activity & Vendor Info: (Acquisitions) SIRSI; (Cataloging) SIRSI; (Circulation) SIRSI; (ILL) SIRSI; (OPAC) SIRSI; (Serials) SIRSI
Database Vendor: Dialog, DRA, Ebsco - EbscoHost, Lexis-Nexis, OCLC - First Search, ProQuest
Publications: Arizona Public Library Directory; Arizona Public Library Statistics; Arizona Reading Program Manual; County Library Handbook; Department Annual Report; Guide to Public Records in the Arizona State Archives; Records Management Manual for Arizona Municipalities; Roving Reporter; Talking Book News
Restriction: Open to public for reference only
Function: ILL available
Partic in Amigos Library Services, Inc; OCLC Online Computer Library Center, Inc

C ARIZONA STATE UNIVERSITY-WEST CAMPUS, Fletcher Library,* 4701 W Thunderbird Rd, PO Box 37100, 85069-7100. SAN 323-7788. Tel: 602-543-8501. FAX: 602-543-8540. E-Mail: westlib@asu.edu. Web Site: www.west.asu.edu/asuw/campus/lib/. *Dean of Libr*, Helen Gater; *Dir Info Resources & Res*, Marilyn Myers; Staff 46 (MLS 16, Non-MLS 30)
Founded 1984. Enrl 3,456; Fac 195; Highest Degree: Master
Jul 1998-Jun 1999 Income (Main Library Only) State $3,144,646. Mats Exp $1,046,921, Books $405,245, Per/Ser (Incl. Access Fees) $464,096, Presv $1,571, Micro $100,081, Electronic Ref Mat (Incl. Access Fees) $75,928. Sal $1,467,767 (Prof $629,646)
Library Holdings: Bk Vols 304,420; Per Subs 3,549
Database Vendor: Innovative Interfaces INN - View
Publications: Bibliographies; Library Guide Series; Library Guide to Programs & Services for Faculty; Services for Students
Partic in Amigos Library Services, Inc; Ariz Univ Librs Coun

L BEUS & GILBERT PLLC, Law Library, 3200 N Central Ave Ste 1000, 85012-2417. SAN 375-8362. Tel: 602-240-2923. FAX: 602-234-5893. *Librn*, Suzzanne Quinton; E-Mail: squinton@ix.netcom.com
Library Holdings: Bk Vols 14,000; Bk Titles 966; Per Subs 85

S BOLIN LABORATORIES, INC LIBRARY,* 17631 N 25th Ave, 85023. SAN 300-3728. Tel: 602-942-8220. FAX: 602-942-1050. *Librn*, Susan Grendahl
Subject Interests: Microbiology

L BROWN & BAIN LIBRARY,* 2901 N Central Ave, 85012. SAN 329-8191. Tel: 602-351-8039. FAX: 602-351-8516. *Librn*, Ellen Hepner; E-Mail: hepner@brownbain.com; Staff 3 (MLS 1, Non-MLS 2)

Library Holdings: Bk Vols 50,000; Per Subs 300
Subject Interests: Law
Database Vendor: epixtech, inc.
Restriction: Private library

L BURCH & CRACCHIOLO, Law Library, 702 E Osborn Rd, Ste 200, PO Box 16882, 85011. SAN 323-6854. Tel: 602-234-8704. FAX: 602-234-0341. *Librn*, Diane Abazarnia; Staff 1 (MLS 1)
Library Holdings: Bk Vols 12,000
Restriction: Staff use only

S CABLE SYSTEMS INTERNATIONAL,* 505 N 51st Ave, 85043. SAN 300-4031. Tel: 602-233-5592. FAX: 602-233-5069.
Founded 1972
Library Holdings: Bk Vols 534; Per Subs 53
Restriction: Not open to public

GM CARL T HAYDEN VA MEDICAL CENTER, Library (142-D), 650 E Indian School Rd, 85012. SAN 300-4023. Tel: 602-222-6411. FAX: 602-222-6472. *Librn*, Mark Simmons; E-Mail: mark.simmons@med.va.gov; *Tech Servs*, Vicki Armstrong; *Tech Servs*, Rayann Womack; E-Mail: rayann.womack@va.med.gov; Staff 4 (MLS 1, Non-MLS 3)
Founded 1951
Library Holdings: Bk Titles 2,100; Per Subs 300
Subject Interests: Consumer health, Medicine, Nursing
Automation Activity & Vendor Info: (Cataloging) EOS; (Circulation) EOS; (OPAC) EOS
Database Vendor: Dialog, IAC - Info Trac, OCLC - First Search, OVID Technologies
Mem of Valnet
Partic in AZHIN; Cent Ariz Biomed Librns; Valnet

G CITY OF PHOENIX PLANNING DEPARTMENT LIBRARY,* 200 W Washington St, 6th flr, 85003-1611. SAN 327-6600. Tel: 602-262-7577. FAX: 602-495-3793.
Library Holdings: Bk Titles 6,000; Per Subs 20

M COLUMBIA MEDICAL CENTER, PHOENIX, Medical Staff Library,* 1947 E Thomas Rd, 85016. SAN 370-5153. Tel: 602-241-7698. FAX: 602-241-7407.
Library Holdings: Bk Titles 275; Per Subs 100

G DEPARTMENT OF MINES & MINERAL RESOURCES LIBRARY, 1502 W Washington, 85007. SAN 300-3663. Tel: 602-255-3791. FAX: 602-255-3777.
Founded 1940
Library Holdings: Bk Vols 2,500; Bk Titles 2,000; Per Subs 20
Subject Interests: Minerals, Mining

S DESERT BOTANICAL GARDEN, (DBG), Richter Library, 1201 N Galvin Pky, 85008. SAN 321-0324. Tel: 480-481-8133. Interlibrary Loan Service Tel: 480-481-8133. Reference Tel: 480-481-8133. FAX: 480-481-8124. E-Mail: dbglibrary@uswest.net. Web Site: www.dbg.org. *Librn*, Jennifer Orf; Staff 1 (Non-MLS 1)
Founded 1937
Library Holdings: Bk Vols 13,000; Per Subs 175
Subject Interests: Agavaceae, Agro-ecology, Arid land plants, Cactaceae, Endangered, Ethnobotany, Rare plants
Special Collections: Cactaceae; Desert Landscape Design
Publications: AGAVE magazine (irregular); Index Seminum (semi-annual); Sonoran Quarterly (newsletter)
Partic in Council On Botanical Horticultural Libraries
Friends of the Library Group

C DEVRY INSTITUTE OF TECHNOLOGY LIBRARY, 2149 W Dunlap Ave, 85021-2982. Tel: 602-870-9222. FAX: 602-734-1999. E-Mail: spritchard@devry-phx.edu. Web Site: www.devry-phx.edu/lrnresrc/library/default.asp. *Dir*, Susan Pritchard; Tel: 602-870-9222, Ext 710
Founded 1931. Pop 2,000,000; Enrl 3,500; Fac 150; Highest Degree: Doctorate
Jul 2000-Jun 2001 Income $230,000. Mats Exp $90,000, Books $50,000, Per/Ser (Incl. Access Fees) $5,000, Presv $10,000, Micro $15,000, Other Print Mats $20,000, Electronic Ref Mat (Incl. Access Fees) $40,000. Sal $73,000 (Prof $43,000)
Library Holdings: Bk Vols 20,500; Bk Titles 20,000; Per Subs 110; Spec Interest Per Sub 20
Subject Interests: Computer science, Electronics
Special Collections: Directories: Arizona High Tech, Corporate Tech, Million Dollar, Moody's, Standard & Poor, Wards
Automation Activity & Vendor Info: (OPAC) Endeavor
Database Vendor: Ebsco - EbscoHost
Publications: Student Guide to the Library
Restriction: Non-circulating to the public

C DEVRY UNIVERSITY, (Formerly Athabasca Library), DeVry Institute of Technology, 2149 W Dunlap Ave, 85021-2982. SAN 375-7587. Tel: 602-870-9222. FAX: 602-734-1999. Web Site: www.devry-phx.edu. *Dir*, Susan V Pritchard; E-Mail: spritchard@devry-phx.edu; Staff 2 (MLS 1, Non-MLS 1)
Founded 1931. Enrl 3,500; Fac 150; Highest Degree: Doctorate
Jul 2000-Jun 2001 Income Locally Generated Income $4,500. Mats Exp $155,500, Books $75,000, Per/Ser (Incl. Access Fees) $15,000, Presv $5,000, Micro $5,000, AV Equip $5,000, Other Print Mats $4,000, Manuscripts & Archives $1,500, Electronic Ref Mat (Incl. Access Fees) $45,000. Sal $113,000 (Prof $43,000)
Library Holdings: Bk Vols 20,283; Bk Titles 20,100; Per Subs 125; High Interest/Low Vocabulary Bk Vols 20; Spec Interest Per Sub 10
Automation Activity & Vendor Info: (Acquisitions) Endeavor; (Cataloging) Endeavor; (Circulation) Endeavor; (Course Reserve) Endeavor; (ILL) Endeavor; (Media Booking) Endeavor; (OPAC) Endeavor; (Serials) Endeavor
Database Vendor: ProQuest
Restriction: In-house use for visitors, Not open to public, Open to student, faculty & staff
Function: Business archives, For research purposes, ILL available, Photocopies available, Reference services available

CR DIOCESE OF PHOENIX, Rausch Memorial Library at Kino Institute, 1224 E Northern, 85020. SAN 325-268X. Tel: 602-906-9798. FAX: 602-870-8871. *Librn*, Darcy Peletich
Founded 1975. Enrl 2,500; Fac 7
1999-2000 Mats Exp $25,000, Books $15,000, Per/Ser (Incl. Access Fees) $10,000. Sal $45,000 (Prof $27,000)
Library Holdings: Bk Titles 14,500; Per Subs 110
Subject Interests: Sacred scripture, Spirituality, Theology
Automation Activity & Vendor Info: (Circulation) Sagebrush Corporation
Publications: Cassette Lending Library Catalog; Video Catalog
Affiliated with University of San Francisco

L FENNEMORE & CRAIG, Law Library,* 3003 N Central Ave, Ste 2600, 85012-2913. SAN 372-3712. Tel: 602-916-5280. FAX: 602-916-5999. *Librn*, Charlene Trainor; E-Mail: ctrainor@fclaw.com
Library Holdings: Bk Vols 18,500; Per Subs 250

S FOUNDATION FOR BLIND CHILDREN LIBRARY & MEDIA CENTER, (AIRC), Arizona Instructional Resource Center, 1235 E Harmont Dr, 85020-3864. SAN 300-4163. Tel: 602-678-5810, 602-678-5816. FAX: 602-678-5811. E-Mail: info@the-fbc.org. Web Site: www.the-fbc.org/media.html. *Dir*, Inge Durre; E-Mail: idurre@the-fbc.org; *Media Spec*, Candy Chelsey
Founded 1958. Enrl 1,663; Highest Degree: Master
Library Holdings: Bk Vols 45,000; Bk Titles 15,000; Per Subs 25
Restriction: Visually impaired students & their teachers
Materials contained in depository consist mostly of braille & large type textbooks required to mainstream visually handicapped children in Arizona's public schools. A supplemental library of pleasure reading materials is also maintained in braille & large type for grades preschool through young adult & high school. A parent & professional library pertinent to the education of blind children is also on site

L GALLAGHER & KENNEDY, Law Library,* 2575 E Camelback Rd, 85016-4240. SAN 372-2619. Tel: 602-530-8000, 602-530-8149. FAX: 602-257-9459. E-Mail: nmr@gknet.com. Web Site: www.gknet.com. *Librn*, Nancy Riske
Library Holdings: Bk Titles 650; Per Subs 200

J GATEWAY COMMUNITY COLLEGE, Library Center,* 108 N 40th St, 85034-1704. SAN 300-3825. Tel: 602-392-5147. FAX: 602-392-5300. Web Site: www.gwc.maricopa.edus/lib/biblio/. *Dir*, Josefa Garcia; *Assoc Dir*, Kathy Lynch; Staff 2 (MLS 2)
Founded 1968. Enrl 3,000; Fac 110
Library Holdings: Bk Titles 34,000; Per Subs 175
Subject Interests: Allied health, Automotive engineering, Nursing

M GOOD SAMARITAN REGIONAL MEDICAL CENTER, Merril W Brown Health Sciences Library, 1111 E McDowell Rd, 85006. (Mail add: PO Box 2989, 85062-2989), SAN 300-3736. Tel: 602-239-4353. FAX: 602-239-3493. E-Mail: jacque@samaritan.edu. Web Site: www.samaritan.edu/library/banner/libs.htm. *Dir*, Jacqueline D Doyle; *Librn*, Lenore K Schnaitman; E-Mail: lenore.schnaitman@bannerhealth.com; Staff 7 (MLS 2, Non-MLS 5)
Founded 1965
Jan 1999-Dec 1999 Income $352,624. Mats Exp $240,000, Books $60,000, Per/Ser (Incl. Access Fees) $160,000, Electronic Ref Mat (Incl. Access Fees) $20,000
Library Holdings: Bk Vols 10,000; Per Subs 600
Subject Interests: Clinical medicine, Consumer health, Hospital administration, Nursing
Special Collections: GSRMC Heritage Coll
Database Vendor: IAC - Info Trac, OVID Technologies
Publications: Newsletter
Function: ILL limited
Partic in Ariz Health Info Network; Cent Ariz Biomed Librns; Med Libr Group of S Calif & Ariz

C GRAND CANYON UNIVERSITY, Fleming Library, 3300 W Camelback Rd, 85017-3030. SAN 300-3744. Tel: 602-589-2420. Toll Free Tel: 800-800-9776. FAX: 602-589-2895. Web Site: www.gculibrary.maricopa.gov. *Dir*, Margie Stites; *Ref*, Linda Graf; Tel: 602-589-2446, E-Mail: lgraf@yahoo.com; *Ref*, Julie Haase; Tel: 602-589-2424, E-Mail: julieh@aztex.asu.edu

Founded 1949. Fac 200; Highest Degree: Doctorate
Jul 1998-Jun 1999 Income $258,654. Mats Exp $96,181, Books $15,564, Per/Ser (Incl. Access Fees) $31,000, Micro $23,000, Other Print Mats $4,017. Sal $119,720 (Prof $74,672)
Library Holdings: Bk Vols 77,550; Per Subs 1,174
Subject Interests: Business, Education, Nursing, Religion
Special Collections: Children's Literature (Vera Butler Coll); Music Recordings (Brantner Coll); Rare Books (William Schattner Coll)
Automation Activity & Vendor Info: (Circulation) DRA; (OPAC) DRA
Database Vendor: Ebsco - EbscoHost
Partic in Amigos Library Services, Inc

§M GRIGG MEDICAL LIBRARY, 9202 N Second St, 85020. (Mail add: 250 E Dunlap Ave, 85020), Tel: 602-870-6328. FAX: 602-997-9325. Web Site: www.jcl.com. *Librn*, Jan Baum; E-Mail: jbaum@jcl.com; *Asst Librn*, David Conchado; E-Mail: dconoch@jcl.com; Staff 2 (MLS 2)
Founded 1983
Library Holdings: Bk Titles 5,000; Per Subs 300
Special Collections: Medical Libraries

S HALL OF FLAME, Richard S Fowler Memorial Library, 6101 E Van Buren, 85008. SAN 300-3752. Tel: 602-275-3473. FAX: 602-275-0896. Web Site: www.hallofflame.org. *Dir*, Peter Molloy; E-Mail: peter.molloy@hallofflame.org; *Actg Librn*, John Davee
Founded 1968
Library Holdings: Bk Vols 6,000; Per Subs 12

S HEARD MUSEUM, Billie Jane Baguley Library & Archives, 2301 N Central Ave, 85004-1323. SAN 300-3760. Tel: 602-251-0228, 602-252-8840. FAX: 602-251-0278. Web Site: www.heard.org/. *Archivist, Mgr*, Mario Nick Klimiades; *Archivist*, LaRee Bates; *Archivist*, James Reynolds; Staff 3 (MLS 1, Non-MLS 2)
Founded 1929
Library Holdings: Bk Titles 28,500; Per Subs 240
Subject Interests: Anthropology, Archaeology, Native Am art
Special Collections: Atlatl Coll; Fred Harvey Company Papers; Native American Artists Resource Coll; North American Indian (Curtis Coll); R Brownell McCrew Coll
Database Vendor: OCLC - First Search
Publications: Native American Artist Directory

S HONEYWELL, INC, Air Transport Systems Library,* 21111 N 19th Ave, PO Box 21111, 85036-1111. SAN 300-3957. Tel: 602-436-3311, 602-436-6414. FAX: 602-436-2252. *Librn*, Kay Heiberg
Founded 1959
Subject Interests: Electronic engineering
Partic in Dialog Corporation

L JABURG & WILK PC, Law Library, Great American Tower Ste 2000, 3200 N Central Ave, 85012. SAN 372-3720. Tel: 602-248-1000. FAX: 602-248-0522. E-Mail: rcp@jaburglaw.com. *Admin Assoc*, Pam Molnar
Library Holdings: Bk Vols 2,500

L JENNINGS, STROUSS & SALMON, Law Library,* One Renaissance Sq, 2 N Central Ste 1600, 85004-2393. SAN 372-3739. Tel: 602-495-2946. FAX: 602-495-2726. Web Site: www.jsslaw.com. *Librn*, Marcy McCahan; E-Mail: mmccahan@jsslaw.com
Library Holdings: Bk Vols 20,000

M JOHN C LINCOLN HOSPITAL DEER VALLEY, Chapman Memorial Medical Library, 19829 N 27th Ave, 85027. SAN 328-6703. Tel: 623-879-5288. FAX: 623-879-5369. *Head Librn*, Jan Baum; Tel: 602-870-6328, Fax: 602-997-9325, E-Mail: jbaum@jcl.com; *Librn*, Edith Hart; E-Mail: ehart@jcl.com; *Asst Librn*, Kathleen Carlson; E-Mail: kcarls@jcl.com; *Asst Librn*, David Conchado; E-Mail: dconch@jcl.com. Subject Specialists: *Medical*, David Conchado; *Medical*, Jan Baum; *Medical*, Kathleen Carlson; Staff 3 (MLS 2, Non-MLS 1)
Founded 1996
Library Holdings: Bk Titles 350; Per Subs 12
Database Vendor: OVID Technologies
Restriction: Not open to public
Function: Literary searches
Partic in AZHIN; MLGSCA
Open Mon & Wed 8:30-12:30, Tues & Thurs 1-4:30

L LEWIS & ROCA LIBRARY,* Renaisance Tower, No 2, 40 N Central Ave, Ste 1900, 85004-4429. SAN 326-5641. Tel: 602-262-5303. FAX: 602-262-5747. *Dir Libr Serv*, Michael Reddy; Staff 4 (MLS 2, Non-MLS 2)
Library Holdings: Bk Vols 40,000; Bk Titles 5,500; Per Subs 325
Subject Interests: Corporate law, Real estate
Publications: Law Library Guide
Restriction: Staff use only
Partic in Dialog Corporation; Westlaw

P MARICOPA COUNTY LIBRARY CENTER,* 17811 N 32nd St, 85032-1201. SAN 300-3809. Tel: 602-506-2950. FAX: 602-506-4689. E-Mail: library@library.maricopa.gov. *Mgr*, Ali Mattei-Majia; *Coll Develop*, Susan Wright
Founded 1929. Pop 427,982; Circ 1,683,268
Library Holdings: Bk Vols 570,606; Per Subs 300
Special Collections: Arizona History (Southwest Coll)
Automation Activity & Vendor Info: (Circulation) DRA
Partic in OCLC Western Service Center
Open Mon-Thurs 9-9, Fri & Sat 9-6, Sun 1-5
Friends of the Library Group
Branches: 11
AQULIA BRANCH, 51321 Ray St W, PO Box 188, Aqulia, 85320. SAN 378-2328. Tel: 520-685-2214. *Librn*, Jenise Porter
EL MIRAGE BRANCH, 14010 N El Mirage Rd, PO Box 26, El Mirage, 85335. SAN 378-2344. Tel: 602-583-1030. FAX: 602-583-5757. *Librn*, Jeannie Ramsey
FOUNTAIN HILLS BRANCH, Bldg C, 16836 E Palisades, Fountain Hills, 85268. SAN 376-8422. Tel: 602-837-9793. FAX: 602-837-7568. *Librn*, David Ellefssen
Library Holdings: Bk Vols 45,000; Bk Titles 40,000; Per Subs 50
Open Mon, Tues, Thurs & Fri 8-12:30 & 1-4, Sat 9-12 & 1-5
GILA BEND BRANCH, 202 W Euclid, PO Box B, Gila Bend, 85337. SAN 378-2387. Tel: 520-683-2061. FAX: 520-683-2463. *Librn*, Glenda McBrayer
GUADALUPE BRANCH, 9401 S Ave del Yaqui, Guadalupe, 85283. SAN 376-8449. Tel: 602-831-5467. FAX: 602-491-3247. *Head of Libr*, Lydia Flores
Pop 70,100; Circ 1,246,952
Library Holdings: Bk Vols 10,000; Bk Titles 9,000
Open Mon & Fri 8-5, Tues & Thurs 9-6, Wed 12-5, Sat 9-11
Friends of the Library Group
LAVEEN BRANCH, 9401 S 51st Ave, PO Box 618, Laveen, 85339. SAN 376-8104. Tel: 602-237-2904. *Librn, Mgr*, Sandra Griffin
Library Holdings: Bk Vols 4,500
Open Mon, Thurs & Fri 9-1 & 2-5, Tues 9-1 & 2-7
LITCHFIELD PARK BRANCH, 101 W Indian School Rd, Litchfield, 85340. SAN 378-2360. Tel: 602-935-4118. FAX: 602-935-1511. *Librn*, D L Hobert
QUEEN CREEK BRANCH, 22407 S Ellsworth Rd, Queen Creek, 85242. SAN 376-8465. Tel: 602-987-3600. FAX: 602-987-3787. *Mgr*, Joy Messer
Library Holdings: Bk Vols 18,000; Bk Titles 15,000; Per Subs 20
Open Tues, Wed, Fri & Sat 9-1 & 2-5, Thurs 10-1 & 2-7
SAN LUCY DISTRICT, 1129 B St, PO Box 66, San Lucy, Gila Bend, 85337. SAN 376-8473. Tel: 520-683-6406. FAX: 520-683-2008. *Librn*, Frances Benegas
Library Holdings: Bk Vols 15,000; Bk Titles 10,000; Per Subs 17
SUN LAKES BRANCH, 10440 East Riggs Rd Ste 207, Sun Lakes, 85248. SAN 376-8481. Tel: 480-895-5123. FAX: 480-895-2934. Web Site: www.mcld.maricopa.gov/.; Staff 2 (Non-MLS 2)
JulJun
Library Holdings: Bk Vols 30,000; Bk Titles 20,000; Per Subs 40
Database Vendor: DRA
Open Mon-Sat 8:30-5
Friends of the Library Group
SURPRISE BRANCH, 15844 N Hollyhock, Surprise, 85374. SAN 376-849X. Tel: 602-583-0626. FAX: 602-583-0636. *Head of Libr*, Pauline Wilke
Library Holdings: Bk Vols 2,000; Bk Titles 1,100; Per Subs 30
Open Tues-Fri 9-12:30 & 1-5, Sat 9-12:30 & 1-3
Bookmobiles: 4

M MARICOPA COUNTY MEDICAL SOCIETY LIBRARY, 326 E Coronado Ste 104, 85004-1576. SAN 371-6406. Tel: 602-252-2451. FAX: 602-256-2794. E-Mail: library@medical-society.com. *Head Librn*, Patricia K Sullivan; *Per*, Shirley McLeod; *Ref*, Kay Vargas
Founded 1930
Library Holdings: Per Subs 190
Partic in AZHIN; Cent Ariz Biomed Librns; Med Libr Group of S Calif & Ariz

M MARICOPA INTEGRATED HEALTH SYSTEM, Health Sciences Library, 2601 E Roosevelt St, PO Box 5099, 85010. SAN 300-3787. Tel: 602-344-5197. FAX: 602-344-1944. E-Mail: copanet@hcs.maricopa.gov. Web Site: www.maricopa.gov/medcenter/lib/libdescp.html. *Dir*, Michael Kronenfeld; E-Mail: mike.konenfeld@hcs.maricopa.gov; *Librn*, Rebecca Danner; E-Mail: rebecca.danner@hcs.maricopa.gov; Staff 3 (MLS 2, Non-MLS 1)
Founded 1958
Jul 1999-Jun 2000 Income $325,000. Mats Exp $151,000, Books $30,000, Per/Ser (Incl. Access Fees) $85,000, Micro $18,000, Electronic Ref Mat (Incl. Access Fees) $18,000. Sal $165,000
Library Holdings: Bk Titles 1,800; Per Subs 290
Subject Interests: Clinical medicine, Nursing
Automation Activity & Vendor Info: (Cataloging) DRA; (OPAC) DRA
Database Vendor: Ebsco - EbscoHost, OCLC - First Search, OVID Technologies
Restriction: Staff use only
Partic in AZHIN; Cent Ariz Biomed Librns

L MAYNARD MURRAY, CRONIN & O'SULLIVAN, Law Library,* 3200 N Central Ste 2300, 85012. SAN 375-8273. Tel: 602-279-8500. FAX: 602-263-8185. E-Mail: mmco@mmcolaw.com. *In Charge*, Nancy Lupo
Library Holdings: Bk Titles 13,000

SR ORANGEWOOD PRESBYTERIAN CHURCH LIBRARY,* 7321 N Tenth St, 85020. SAN 371-8492. Tel: 602-944-1508. FAX: 602-861-5997.; Staff 1 (MLS 1)
Founded 1975
Library Holdings: Bk Vols 790; Bk Titles 775

L OSBORN MALEDON, Law Library,* 2929 N Central 21st flr, 85012-2794. SAN 372-2635. Tel: 602-640-9000. FAX: 602-640-9050. *Librn*, Markita Martinez
Library Holdings: Bk Titles 5,000
Partic in Amigos Library Services, Inc; OCLC Online Computer Library Center, Inc

§J PARADISE VALLEY COMMUNITY COLLEGE LIBRARY, 18401 N 32nd St, 85032-1200. Tel: 602-787-7200. FAX: 602-787-7205. Web Site: www.pvc.maricopa.edu/library/. *Dir*, John U Chavez; Tel: 602-787-7222, E-Mail: j.chavez@pvmail.maricopa.edu
Jul 2000-Jun 2001 Income $780,990
Library Holdings: Bk Vols 30,000; Per Subs 250
Automation Activity & Vendor Info: (Cataloging) DRA; (Circulation) DRA; (OPAC) DRA
Database Vendor: OCLC - First Search

S PHOENIX ART MUSEUM LIBRARY, 1625 N Central Ave, 85004-1685. SAN 300-3868. Tel: 602-257-2136. FAX: 602-253-8662. E-Mail: info@phxart.org. *Librn*, Genevieve Houlihan; E-Mail: genni.houlihan@phxart.org; Staff 1 (MLS 1)
Founded 1959
Jul 1999-Jun 2000 Mats Exp $28,450, Books $7,500, Per/Ser (Incl. Access Fees) $13,950, Presv $1,200, Other Print Mats $5,000
Library Holdings: Bk Vols 40,000; Bk Titles 38,000; Per Subs 107
Subject Interests: Art and architecture, Decorative arts, European art, Fashion, Graphic arts, Sculpture
Special Collections: American Art Coll; Auction Records Coll; One-Person Exhibition Coll; Rembrandt Print Catalogs from 1751 (Orme Lewis Coll)
Automation Activity & Vendor Info: (OPAC) CARL
Restriction: Non-circulating to the public

M PHOENIX CHILDREN'S HOSPITAL, Emily Center Library, 909 E Brill St, 85006. SAN 373-3386. Tel: 602-239-6902. FAX: 602-239-4670. E-Mail: emilyc@phxchildrens.com. Web Site: www.phxchildrens.com/emilycenter. *Dir*, Irene Jacobs; Tel: 602-239-5975, E-Mail: ijacobs@phxchildrens.com; Staff 9 (Non-MLS 9)
Founded 1990
Library Holdings: Bk Titles 6,000; Per Subs 40
Special Collections: Spanish information about child health & illness issues
Friends of the Library Group

J PHOENIX COLLEGE LIBRARY,* 1202 W Thomas Rd, 85013. SAN 300-3876. Tel: 602-285-7457. FAX: 602-285-7368. Web Site: www.pc.maricopa.edu. *Ref*, J Lynn Marks; *Tech Servs*, Janet Johnston; *Circ*, David Laird; *AV*, Elizabeth Saliba; Staff 6 (MLS 6)
Founded 1925. Fac 181
Library Holdings: Bk Vols 78,117; Per Subs 330
Subject Interests: Arizona

S PHOENIX DAY SCHOOL FOR THE DEAF LIBRARY, 1935 W Hayward Ave, 85021-6997. SAN 300-371X. Tel: 602-336-6865. FAX: 602-336-6945. Web Site: www.hawbaker.cx:8000/pdsd/. *Media Spec, Tech Coordr*, Lori Elliott; *Media Spec*, Lisa Markham
Founded 1967. Enrl 300
Library Holdings: Bk Vols 10,000
Subject Interests: Deaf
Special Services for the Deaf - High interest/low vocabulary books

S PHOENIX JOB CORPS CENTER LIBRARY,* 518 S Third St, 85004-2599. SAN 300-3884. Tel: 602-254-5921. FAX: 602-340-1965.
Library Holdings: Bk Vols 50; Per Subs 16

M PHOENIX MEMORIAL HOSPITAL, Stepan Gulesserian Medical Library, 1201 S Seventh Ave, PO Box 21207, 85007. Tel: 602-238-3406, 602-258-5111. FAX: 602-238-3383. *Librn*, Mary Stumbough; E-Mail: mstum@phxmem.org
Library Holdings: Bk Titles 200; Per Subs 22

S PHOENIX NEWSPAPERS, INC LIBRARY,* PO Box 100, Mail Stop LI-18, 85001. SAN 300-3698. Tel: 602-444-8144. FAX: 602-444-8914. Web Site: www.azcentral.com. *Ref*, Heather Goebel; *Ref*, Paula Stevens; E-Mail: paulapni@aol.com; Staff 14 (MLS 5, Non-MLS 9)
Founded 1947
Library Holdings: Bk Vols 2,000
Subject Interests: Arizona
Special Collections: Newspaper clippings; photos, negatives
Produces full text database of news stories appearing in the Arizona Republic, The Phoenix Gazette & The Arizona Business Gazette. Database available online & CD. Also responsible for photo/article sales & reprint permission

P PHOENIX PUBLIC LIBRARY, Burton Barr Central Library, 1221 N Central Ave, 85004. SAN 330-6429. Tel: 602-262-6372. Interlibrary Loan Service Tel: 602-262-6066. FAX: 602-261-8836. Web Site: www.phoenixpubliclibrary.org. *Librn*, Toni Garvey; E-Mail: tgarvey@lib.ci.phoenix.az.us; *Adminr*, Rita Hamilton; E-Mail: rhamilt2@ci.phoenix.az.us; *Adminr, Tech Servs*, Ross McLachlan; E-Mail: rmclachl@lib.ci.phoenix.az.us; *Adminr*, Rosemary Nelson; E-Mail: rnelson@lib.ci.phoenix.az.us; *Adminr*, Kim van der Veen; E-Mail: kvanderv@lib.ci.phoenix.az.us; *Acq*, Leslie Steffes; E-Mail: lsteffes@lib.ci.phoenix.az.us; *ILL*, Carole H Towles; E-Mail: ctowles@lib.ci.phoenix.az.us; *Automation Syst Coordr*, William Kneedler; Tel: 602-262-4799, E-Mail: bkneedle@lib.ci.phoenix.az.us; *Coll Develop*, Kathleen Sullivan; E-Mail: ksullivan@lib.ci.phoenix.az.us; Staff 136 (MLS 79, Non-MLS 57)
Founded 1898. Pop 1,275,000; Circ 8,278,829
Jul 1999-Jun 2000 Income (Main Library and Branch Library) $23,475,303, State $63,570, City $23,092,863, County $202,000, Other $116,870. Mats Exp $3,244,556, Books $2,569,556, Per/Ser (Incl. Access Fees) $250,000, Presv $25,000, Electronic Ref Mat (Incl. Access Fees) $400,000. Sal $14,341,600
Library Holdings: Bk Vols 1,906,142; Bk Titles 604,378; Per Subs 4,500
Special Collections: Arizona History Coll; Art of Book Coll; Center for Children's Literature; Library of American Civilization Coll, microbk; Map Room; Rare Book Room
Automation Activity & Vendor Info: (Acquisitions) CARL; (Cataloging) CARL; (Circulation) CARL; (OPAC) CARL; (Serials) CARL
Database Vendor: OCLC - First Search
Partic in Amigos Library Services, Inc; OCLC Online Computer Library Center, Inc
Special Services for the Deaf - TTY machine
Friends of the Library Group
Branches: 12
ACACIA, 750 E Townley Ave, 85020. SAN 330-6453. Tel: 602-262-6223. FAX: 602-261-8694. *Librn*, Kathleen Birtciel
Library Holdings: Bk Vols 55,650
Friends of the Library Group
CENTURY, 1750 E Highland Ave, 85016. SAN 330-6488. Tel: 602-262-7412. FAX: 602-261-8655.
Library Holdings: Bk Vols 55,500
Friends of the Library Group
CHOLLA, 10050 Metro Pkwy E, 85051. SAN 330-6518. Tel: 602-534-3770. FAX: 602-261-8641. *Librn*, Deborah O'Keefe
Library Holdings: Bk Vols 155,000
Friends of the Library Group
DESERT SAGE, 7602 W Encanto Blvd, 85035. SAN 377-7960. Tel: 602-534-5276. FAX: 602-534-4367. *Librn*, Judy DeBolt
Library Holdings: Bk Vols 101,300
HARMON, 411 W Yavapai St, 85003. SAN 330-6542. Tel: 602-262-6362. FAX: 602-261-8591. *Librn*, Marshall Shore
Library Holdings: Bk Vols 30,800
Friends of the Library Group
IRONWOOD, 4333 E Chandler Blvd, 85044. SAN 372-0195. Tel: 602-534-1900. FAX: 602-261-8949.
Library Holdings: Bk Vols 120,000
Friends of the Library Group
JUNIPER, 1825 W Unionhills Dr, 85027. SAN 370-8098. Tel: 602-534-3900. FAX: 602-534-2762. *Librn*, Julaine Warner
Library Holdings: Bk Vols 112,500
Friends of the Library Group
MESQUITE, 4525 Paradise Village Pkwy N, 85032. SAN 330-6577. Tel: 602-262-7299. FAX: 602-261-8571. *Librn*, Shera Farnham
Library Holdings: Bk Vols 134,200
Friends of the Library Group
OCOTILLO, 102 W Southern, 85041. SAN 330-6607. Tel: 602-262-6694. FAX: 602-261-8516. *In Charge*, Billie Williams
Library Holdings: Bk Vols 61,000
Friends of the Library Group
PALO VERDE, 4402 N 51st Ave, 85031. SAN 330-6631. Tel: 602-262-6805. FAX: 602-261-8455. *Librn*, Meg Wolfe
Library Holdings: Bk Vols 97,500
Friends of the Library Group
SAGUARO, 2808 N 46th St, 85008. SAN 330-6666. Tel: 602-262-6802. FAX: 602-261-8386. *In Charge*, Janice Snodgras
Library Holdings: Bk Vols 83,900
Friends of the Library Group
YUCCA, 5648 N 15th Ave, 85015. SAN 330-6690. Tel: 602-262-6788. FAX: 602-261-8986. *Librn*, Jeanette Alarid
Library Holdings: Bk Vols 65,000
Friends of the Library Group

S PHOENIX ZOO LIBRARY,* 455 N Galvin Pkwy, 85008-3431. SAN 375-6394. Tel: 602-273-1341. FAX: 602-273-7078.
Library Holdings: Bk Titles 1,200

S PLANNED PARENTHOOD OF CENTRAL & NORTHERN ARIZONA, Alice Morrell Bogert Library, 5651 N Seventh St, 85014-2500. SAN 374-5821. Tel: 602-263-4244, 602-265-2495. FAX: 602-277-5243. Web Site:

www.ppcna.org. *Librn*, Diane Dudley
Founded 1937
Library Holdings: Bk Titles 3,000; Per Subs 30
Publications: Resource Guide; Sex Ed Workbook
Friends of the Library Group

S PUEBLO GRANDE MUSEUM, Research Library, 4619 E Washington St, 85034-1909. SAN 372-7629. Tel: 602-495-0901. FAX: 602-495-5645. E-Mail: prlpgstf@ci.phoenix.az.us. Web Site: www.pueblogrande.com. *Coordr*, Cathy Reigle
Jan 2000-Dec 2000 Income $1,975, City $300, Locally Generated Income $475, Other $1,200. Mats Exp $1,975, Books $1,625, Per/Ser (Incl. Access Fees) $300, Presv $50
Library Holdings: Bk Vols 4,400; Bk Titles 4,300; Per Subs 60
Subject Interests: Archaeology
Special Collections: Halseth Coll; Hayden Coll; Hohokam Coll, bks, mss; Pueblo Grande Museum Archives; Schroeder Coll
Restriction: Non-circulating to the public
Function: Archival collection, ILL by photocopy only, Photocopies available, Research library, Some telephone reference

M SAINT JOSEPH'S HOSPITAL & MEDICAL CENTER, Health Sciences Library, 350 W Thomas Rd, PO Box 2071, 85001-2071. SAN 300-3906. Tel: 602-406-3299. FAX: 602-406-4171. Web Site: www.chw.edu. *Mgr*, Molly Harrington; Staff 1 (MLS 1)
Founded 1942
Library Holdings: Bk Vols 5,000; Per Subs 350
Subject Interests: Medicine, Neuroscience, Nursing
Special Collections: Neurological Sciences (Barrow Neurological Institute of Neurological Sciences Coll)
Partic in AZHIN; Cent Ariz Biomed Librns

R SHEPHERD OF THE VALLEY LUTHERAN CHURCH LIBRARY, 1500 W Maryland Ave, 85015. SAN 300-3930. Tel: 602-249-1936. FAX: 602-249-1983. E-Mail: postmaster@shepherdofvalley.com. Web Site: www.shepherdofvalley.com. *In Charge*, Lois Francis; *In Charge*, Dottie Simons
Library Holdings: Bk Vols 1,221

M SMART PRACTICE, Reference Library,* 3400 E McDowell, 85008. SAN 327-6880. Tel: 602-225-9090. FAX: 602-225-0599. *Pres*, Curt Hamann
Library Holdings: Bk Vols 1,000

L SNELL & WILMER LAW LIBRARY,* One Arizona Ctr, 85004-0001. SAN 326-467X. Tel: 602-382-6050. FAX: 602-382-6070. Web Site: www.s.law.com. *Librn*, Arlen A Bristol; E-Mail: bristoa@swlaw.com; *Circ*, Eva Heard; *Ser*, Deborah Simon; Staff 3 (MLS 1, Non-MLS 2)
Founded 1938
Library Holdings: Bk Vols 45,000
Subject Interests: Construction, Corporate law, Immigration, Labor, Real estate, Securities
Publications: Acquisitions list (monthly)
Restriction: Staff use only
Partic in Amigos Library Services, Inc; Vutext; Westlaw

J SOUTH MOUNTAIN COMMUNITY COLLEGE LIBRARY,* 7050 S 24th St, 85040. SAN 320-9989. Tel: 602-243-8187. FAX: 602-243-8180. *Dir*, Gary Marks; *Librn*, Ora Wagoner; Staff 2 (MLS 2)
Founded 1980. Enrl 2,874
Library Holdings: Bk Titles 39,000
Partic in Amigos Library Services, Inc; Maricopa County Community College District

CR SOUTHWESTERN COLLEGE, Dr R S Beal Sr Library, 2625 E Cactus Rd, 85032-7097. SAN 300-3949. Tel: 602-992-6101, Ext 117. FAX: 602-404-2154. Toll Free FAX: 800-247-2697. *Librn*, Alice Eickmeyer; E-Mail: aeickme@southwestcl.lib.az.us; Staff 1 (Non-MLS 1)
Founded 1960. Enrl 204; Fac 9; Highest Degree: Bachelor
1998-1999 Income $95,356. Mats Exp $15,200, Books $6,000, Per/Ser (Incl. Access Fees) $8,000, Presv $1,200. Sal $58,204
Library Holdings: Bk Vols 29,543; Per Subs 181
Partic in Amigos Library Services, Inc; OCLC Online Computer Library Center, Inc

S STREICH LANG LIBRARY,* Renaissance One, 2 N Central Ave, 85004-2391. SAN 326-3320. Tel: 602-229-5325. *Librn*, Charlotte Henderson
Library Holdings: Bk Titles 2,000
Subject Interests: Commercial law
Partic in Dialog Corporation; Dow Jones News Retrieval; OCLC Online Computer Library Center, Inc; Westlaw

GL SUPERIOR COURT LAW LIBRARY,* 101 W Jefferson, 85003. SAN 300-3795. Tel: 602-506-3461. FAX: 602-506-3677. Web Site: www.maricopa.gov/lawlibrary/. *Asst Dir*, Richard Tennstra; E-Mail: rteenstr@smtpgw.maricopa.gov; *Automation Syst Coordr, Cat*, Michelle Dyer-Hurdon; *Acq*, Valerie Lerma; E-Mail: vlerma@smtpgw.maricopa.gov; *Coll Develop*, Corinne Guthrie; Staff 6 (MLS 6)
Founded 1913
Library Holdings: Bk Vols 140,000; Bk Titles 20,000
Subject Interests: Medicine
Publications: Court Informer (current awareness); En Banc (newsletter)
Partic in Dialog Corporation; Westlaw

S U-HAUL INTERNATIONAL, Library & Research Services, 2727 N Central Ave, PO Box 21502, 85036. SAN 300-3981. Tel: 602-263-6606. *Dir*, Ed Henderson; *Librn*, Meg Maher; E-Mail: meg-maher@fc.uhaul.com
Library Holdings: Bk Vols 6,850; Per Subs 550
Subject Interests: Business and management, Engineering, Industrial safety, Law, Manufacturing, Marketing, Transportation
Special Collections: Truck & Trailer Design & Safety
Publications: Publication Catalogs; Publication Index (for corporate publications)
Restriction: Access for corporate affiliates

S UFO INFORMATION RETRIEVAL CENTER, (UFOIRC), Points West, No 158, 3131 W Cochise Dr, 85051-9501. SAN 329-2525. Tel: 602-997-1523. FAX: 602-870-3178. Web Site: www.ufohelp.com. *In Charge*, Thomas M Olsen; E-Mail: tmolsen@csi.com; Staff 1 (Non-MLS 1)
Founded 1966
Jan 2000-Dec 2000 Mats Exp $100, Books $40, Per/Ser (Incl. Access Fees) $60
Library Holdings: Bk Titles 170
Subject Interests: UFO phenomenon
Restriction: Staff use only

GL US COURTS LIBRARY,* 6434 US Courthouse, 230 N First Ave, 85025-0074. SAN 321-8023. Tel: 602-514-7074. FAX: 602-514-7028. *Librn*, Timothy J Blake; E-Mail: tim_blake@ce9.uscourts.gov; *Tech Servs*, Evelyn Rayburn; Staff 2 (MLS 1, Non-MLS 1)
Founded 1980
Subject Interests: Law
Publications: Library guide; Library newsletter (monthly)
Partic in Illinois Library & Information Network; OCLC Online Computer Library Center, Inc; Westlaw

G UNITED STATES DEPARTMENT OF AGRICULTURE, Agriculture Research Service, US Water Conservation Laboratory, 4331 E Broadway, 85040. SAN 300-399X. Tel: 602-379-4356. Interlibrary Loan Service Tel: 602-379-4356, Ext 241. FAX: 602-379-4355. Web Site: www.uswcl.ars.ag.gov. *Dir*, Albert J Clemmens; Tel: 602-379-4356, Ext 269, E-Mail: bclemmens@uswcl.ars.ag.gov; *Librn*, Lisa DeGraw; E-Mail: ldegraw@uswcl.ars.ag.gov
Founded 1959
1999-2000 Mats Exp $12,000
Library Holdings: Bk Titles 2,000; Per Subs 30
Subject Interests: Agriculture, Chemistry, Engineering, Soil mechanics
Special Collections: Annual reports; ARS reports; USGS reports
Restriction: Open to public for reference only

M UNITED STATES PUBLIC HEALTH SERVICE, Phoenix Indian Medical Center Library, 4212 N 16th St, 85016. SAN 320-9075. Tel: 602-263-1676. FAX: 602-263-1577.; Staff 2 (MLS 1, Non-MLS 1)
Founded 1950
Library Holdings: Bk Vols 2,100; Bk Titles 2,000; Per Subs 170
Subject Interests: Endocrinology
Special Collections: Diseases of Native Americans Coll
Partic in Maricopa Biomed Libr

L VIAD CORP, Law Department Library, VIAD Tower, No 2212, 1850 N Central Ave, 85077. SAN 375-1406. Tel: 602-207-4950, 602-207-6675. FAX: 602-207-5480. *Librn*, Dianne Shay
Library Holdings: Bk Vols 3,000
Restriction: Not open to public

PIMA

P PIMA PUBLIC LIBRARY, 50 S 200 West, PO Box 426, 85543. SAN 300-404X. Tel: 520-485-2822. FAX: 520-485-0701. E-Mail: pimalib@eaznet.com. Web Site: www.eaznet.com/~pimalib/. *Librn*, Vicki Foote; *Asst Librn*, Frances Walker; Staff 2 (Non-MLS 2)
Founded 1960. Pop 2,600; Circ 9,800
Jul 1998-Jun 1999 Income $27,585. Mats Exp $22,029. Sal $8,302
Library Holdings: Bk Vols 16,000; Bk Titles 15,500
Special Collections: Arizona Coll
Automation Activity & Vendor Info: (Cataloging) Follett; (Circulation) Follett; (OPAC) Follett

PINE

P ISABELLE HUNT MEMORIAL PUBLIC LIBRARY,* PO Box 229, 85544-0229. SAN 300-4058. Tel: 520-476-3678. FAX: 520-476-2914. *Librn*, Linda Craft
Founded 1974. Pop 3,000; Circ 15,583
Jul 1997-Jun 1998 Income $56,000. Mats Exp $11,300. Sal $15,000

Library Holdings: Bk Vols 16,000
Special Collections: Arizona Coll, bks, pamphlets, vf
Mem of Gila County Library District
Friends of the Library Group

PORTAL

S SOUTHWESTERN RESEARCH STATION LIBRARY, PO Box 16553, 85632. SAN 375-0698. Tel: 520-558-2396. FAX: 520-558-2396. E-Mail: swrs@amnh.org. *Dir*, Wade C Sherbrooke
Library Holdings: Bk Titles 1,500; Per Subs 10

PRESCOTT

§S ARIZONA PIONEERS' HOME LIBRARY, 300 S McCormick St, 86303-4298. Tel: 520-445-2181. FAX: 520-778-1148. *In Charge*, Lucile Johnson; Tel: 520-445-1024, E-Mail: lucilejohnson@webtv.net
Library Holdings: Bk Vols 750

DEPARTMENT OF VETERANS AFFAIRS
G GENERAL LIBRARY, VA Med Ctr, 500 Hwy 89 N, 86313. SAN 321-2424. Tel: 520-445-4860, Ext 6492. FAX: 520-776-6094. *Tech Servs*, Linda Thomsen; E-Mail: lindathomsen@med.va.gov
Library Holdings: Bk Vols 1,300; Per Subs 120
Partic in Valnet
GM MEDICAL LIBRARY, 86313. Tel: 520-445-4860, Ext 6492. FAX: 520-776-6094. *Tech Servs*, Linda Thomsen; E-Mail: lindathomsen@med.va.gov
Founded 1923
Library Holdings: Bk Titles 1,200; Per Subs 200
Partic in Medline; Veterans Affairs Library Network

C EMBRY-RIDDLE AERONAUTICAL UNIVERSITY, Prescott Campus Library, 3200 Willow Creek Rd, 86301-8662. SAN 323-7621. Tel: 520-708-3811. FAX: 520-708-6988. E-Mail: library@pr.erau.edu. Web Site: library.pr.erau.edu. *Dir*, Sarah Thomas; Tel: 520-708-3812, E-Mail: sarah@pr.erau.edu; *Circ, ILL*, Peggy Law; *Tech Coordr*, Georgia Michalicek; *Tech Servs*, deLong Suzanne; Tel: 520-708-6658, E-Mail: delongs@pr.erau.edu; *Res*, Kathryn Hazlett Cline; Tel: 520-708-6656, E-Mail: hazlett@pr.erau.edu; *Publ Servs*, Dianne Bean; Tel: 520-708-3945, E-Mail: beand@pr.erau.edu; Staff 12 (MLS 5, Non-MLS 7)
Founded 1978. Enrl 1,700; Fac 94; Highest Degree: Master
May 2000-Apr 2001 Income Parent Institution $789,738. Mats Exp $383,080, Books $84,700, Per/Ser (Incl. Access Fees) $58,176, Presv $5,000, Micro $16,960, AV Equip $19,000, Electronic Ref Mat (Incl. Access Fees) $59,350. Sal $342,076 (Prof $137,777)
Library Holdings: Bk Vols 27,505; Bk Titles 26,130; Per Subs 575
Subject Interests: Aeronautical eng, Aeronautics, Aviation safety
Special Collections: Aviation History, Kalusa miniature aircraft collection to-scale, to-detail
Automation Activity & Vendor Info: (Acquisitions) epixtech, inc.; (Circulation) epixtech, inc.; (Serials) epixtech, inc.
Database Vendor: Ebsco - EbscoHost, epixtech, inc., IAC - SearchBank, OCLC - First Search, ProQuest
Publications: Annual Report; Media Catalog; Periodicals Holdings List; Strategic Plan
Mem of Yavapai County Library District
Partic in Amigos Library Services, Inc; Aznet; OCLC Online Computer Library Center, Inc; Yavapai County Libr Network

C PRESCOTT COLLEGE LIBRARY, 301 Grove Ave, 86301. SAN 321-4656. Tel: 520-778-2090, Ext 1300. FAX: 520-778-2090, Ext 1300. E-Mail: library@prescott.edu. Web Site: www.prescott.edu/library/libhome.html. *Dir*, Eileen Chalfoun; *Ref*, Linda Butterworth; Staff 6 (MLS 2, Non-MLS 4)
Founded 1966. Enrl 1,000; Fac 75; Highest Degree: Master
Jul 1998-Jun 1999 Income $223,400. Mats Exp $71,000, Books $50,000, Per/Ser (Incl. Access Fees) $21,000
Library Holdings: Bk Vols 23,000; Bk Vols 20,000; Per Subs 285
Subject Interests: Adventure, Counseling psychol, Environ sci, Environmental studies, Experimental educ
Database Vendor: epixtech, inc.
Mem of Yavapai County Library District
Partic in Amigos Library Services, Inc; OCLC Online Computer Library Center, Inc

S PRESCOTT HISTORICAL SOCIETY, Sharlot Hall Archives & Library, 415 W Gurley St, 86301. SAN 300-4074. Tel: 520-445-3122. FAX: 520-776-9053. Web Site: www.sharlot.org/archives. *In Charge*, Michael Wurtz
Founded 1928
Library Holdings: Bk Titles 10,000
Special Collections: Archives Coll; Arizona History Coll, newsp, mss; Early Arizona & Indian Coll, photog

P PRESCOTT PUBLIC LIBRARY, 215 E Goodwin St, 86303. SAN 330-6720. Tel: 520-445-8110. TDD: 520-771-0214. FAX: 520-445-1851. Web Site: www.prescottlib.lib.az.us. *Dir*, John Burton; Tel: 520-445-8110, Ext 111, E-Mail: john.burton@cityofprescott.net; *Asst Dir*, Toni Kaus; Tel: 520-445-8110, Ext 115, E-Mail: kaus@prescottlib.lib.a.us; *Ch Servs*, Constance Keremes; Tel: 520-445-8110, Ext 102, E-Mail: ckeremes@prescottlib.lib.az.us; Staff 22 (MLS 7, Non-MLS 15)
Founded 1903
Jul 2000-Jun 2001 Income $1,079,365. Mats Exp $200,434, Books $176,124, Per/Ser (Incl. Access Fees) $24,310. Sal $671,781 (Prof $222,274)
Library Holdings: Bk Vols 120,000; Bk Titles 112,197
Special Collections: Southwest Coll
Automation Activity & Vendor Info: (Circulation) epixtech, inc.
Database Vendor: Ebsco - EbscoHost, OCLC - First Search
Publications: Roundup
Mem of Yavapai County Library District
Partic in OCLC Online Computer Library Center, Inc; Yavapai County Libr Network
Special Services for the Deaf - TDD
Friends of the Library Group

S SMOKI MUSEUM, AMERICAN INDIAN ART & CULTURE, Smoki Museum Library, 147 N Arizona St, 86301. (Mail add: PO Box 10224, 86304-0224), SAN 375-3913. Tel: 520-445-1230. E-Mail: smoki@futureone.com. Web Site: www.smoki.com.
Founded 1995
Library Holdings: Bk Vols 800
Subject Interests: Anthropology, Archeology
Special Collections: E S Curtis Coll, photogravures; Kate T Cory Coll, diary, dictionary of Hopi words, paintings, photogs
Mem of Yavapai County Library District

M VA NORTH ARIZONA HEALTH CARE SYSTEM, 500 Hwy 89 N, 86313. Tel: 520-445-4860, Ext 6492. *Tech Servs*, Linda Thomsen
Library Holdings: Bk Titles 1,000; Per Subs 140

C YAVAPAI COLLEGE LIBRARY,* 1100 E Sheldon, 86301. SAN 300-4104. Tel: 520-776-2265. FAX: 520-776-2275. E-Mail: lib_glo@yavapai.cc.az.us. Web Site: www.yavapai.cc.az.us/library/yclpage.htm. *Dir*, Dennis Giovanetti; Tel: 520-776-2262; *Dir*, Jim Christopher; Tel: 520-776-2264, E-Mail: Jim_Christopher@yavapai.cc.az.us; *ILL*, Debra Orlando; Tel: 520-776-2263, E-Mail: Debby_Orlando@yavapai.cc.az.us; Staff 3 (MLS 3)
Founded 1969
Library Holdings: Bk Titles 74,000; Per Subs 800
Subject Interests: Southwest
Special Collections: College Archives
Automation Activity & Vendor Info: (Acquisitions) epixtech, inc.; (Circulation) epixtech, inc.
Database Vendor: Dialog, Ebsco - EbscoHost, OCLC - First Search, ProQuest
Mem of Yavapai County Library District
Departmental Libraries:
VERDE, 601 Black Hills Dr, Clarkdale, 86324. SAN 370-0224. Tel: 520-634-6542. FAX: 520-634-6543. *Librn*, Sheri Kinney
Library Holdings: Bk Vols 21,085; Bk Titles 20,000; Per Subs 320
Mem of Yavapai County Library District

GL YAVAPAI COUNTY LAW LIBRARY,* Yavapai County Courthouse, Rm 306, 86301. SAN 300-4090. Tel: 520-771-3309. *Librn*, Fred Smith
Library Holdings: Per Subs 44

P YAVAPAI COUNTY LIBRARY DISTRICT,* 172 E Merritt St, Ste E, 86301. SAN 323-8091. Tel: 520-771-3191. FAX: 520-771-3113. *Dir*, Barbara Kile; *Librn*, Cheryl Richardson; E-Mail: crichar@yavapaicold.lib.az.us; *Admin Assoc*, Arminta Tupper; *Tech Servs*, Ann Boles; *Online Servs*, Sharon Seymour; Staff 5 (MLS 2, Non-MLS 3)
Jul 1998-Jun 1999 Income $1,295,415, State $20,498, Federal $99,560, County $1,175,357. Mats Exp $51,728, Books $50,349, Per/Ser (Incl. Access Fees) $1,379. Sal $147,351 (Prof $40,747)
Library Holdings: Bk Titles 26,000; Per Subs 10
Automation Activity & Vendor Info: (Acquisitions) epixtech, inc.; (Cataloging) epixtech, inc.; (Circulation) epixtech, inc.; (Course Reserve) epixtech, inc.; (OPAC) epixtech, inc.; (Serials) epixtech, inc.
Database Vendor: epixtech, inc., OCLC - First Search
Member Libraries: Ash Fork Public Library; Bagdad Public Library; Black Canyon City Community Library; Chino Valley Public Library; Clark Memorial Library; Congress Public Library; Embry-Riddle Aeronautical University; Jerome Public Library; Prescott College Library; Prescott Public Library; Prescott Valley Public Library; Seligman Public Library; Smoki Museum, American Indian Art & Culture; Yarnell Public Library; Yavapai College Library; Yavapai College Library
Multi-type Library Network of public & academic libraries

S YAVAPAI-PRESCOTT TRIBAL LIBRARY,* 530 E Merritt, 86301-2038. SAN 375-1813. Tel: 520-445-8790. FAX: 520-778-9445. E-Mail: library@northlink.com. *Dir*, Debra Russell; *Tech Servs*, Amy M Ogo
Library Holdings: Bk Titles 4,000

PRESCOTT VALLEY

P PRESCOTT VALLEY PUBLIC LIBRARY,* 7501 Civil Circle, 86314. SAN 323-7990. Tel: 520-759-3040. FAX: 520-759-3122. E-Mail: library@ci.prescott.valley.92.us. *Dir*, Stuart Mattson; *Ch Servs*, Jo Ann Smith; *Ref*,

Scott Bruner; *Cat, Coll Develop*, Susan Lapis
Library Holdings: Bk Vols 40,000; Per Subs 20
Mem of Yavapai County Library District
Friends of the Library Group

QUARTZSITE

QUARTZSITE PUBLIC, (Formerly Parker Public Library), 465 N Plymouth Ave, 85346. (Mail add: PO Box 2812, 85346-2812), SAN 377-032X. Tel: 520-927-6593. FAX: 520-927-5411. Web Site: www.ci.quartzsite.az.us/community/public_library1.htm. *Mgr*, Alexandra Taft; E-Mail: ataft@quartzsite.lib.az.us
Library Holdings: Bk Vols 21,000; Bk Titles 10,000; Per Subs 30; High Interest/Low Vocabulary Bk Vols 100
Special Collections: Angona Coll
Automation Activity & Vendor Info: (Acquisitions) Sagebrush Corporation; (Cataloging) Sagebrush Corporation; (Circulation) Sagebrush Corporation
Open Mon-Fri 8-5, Sat 9-noon
Friends of the Library Group

RIO VERDE

S US DELEGATION FOR FRIENDSHIP AMONG WOMEN LIBRARY, 18926 Latigo Lane, 85263. SAN 323-8512. Tel: 480-471-3019. FAX: 480-471-0013. *Librn*, Mary Pomeroy
Founded 1970
Library Holdings: Bk Titles 670
Subject Interests: Children in developing countries, Women in developing countries

SACATON

P IRA H HAYES MEMORIAL LIBRARY,* Gila River Indian Community Church & Pima, PO Box 97, 85247. SAN 376-3188. Tel: 520-562-3225. FAX: 520-562-3903. *Librn*, Elaine Stephens
Library Holdings: Bk Titles 8,000
Mem of Pinal County Library District

M HUHUKAM MEMORIAL HOSPITAL LIBRARY, Seed Farm Rd At Career Center, PO Box 38, 85247. Tel: 520-562-1200, Ext 1230. *Librn*, Steve Schoffstall; E-Mail: stevef@grhc.org
Library Holdings: Bk Vols 100; Bk Titles 100; Per Subs 20

SAFFORD

§S ARIZONA DEPARTMENT OF CORRECTIONS - ADULT, Arizona State Prison Complex - Safford Library, Rte 1, Box 2222, 85548. Tel: 520-428-4698. *Librn*, Raymond Davis; Tel: 520-428-4698, Ext 2364
Library Holdings: Bk Vols 10,959

SR CHURCH OF JESUS CHRIST OF LATTER-DAY SAINTS, Family History Library, 515 11th St, 85546. SAN 375-2623. Tel: 520-428-7927. FAX: 520-428-7927. *Dir*, Fred Call; *Dir*, Karen Call
Library Holdings: Bk Vols 3,000

P SAFFORD CITY-GRAHAM COUNTY LIBRARY,* 808 Seventh Ave, 85546. SAN 300-4112. Tel: 520-428-1531. FAX: 520-348-3209. *Dir*, Glen Dowdle; E-Mail: gdowdle@saffordgrahco.lib.az.us; Staff 1 (MLS 1)
Founded 1962. Pop 24,200; Circ 95,582
Library Holdings: Bk Titles 73,000; Per Subs 68
Special Collections: Adult Basic Education Coll; Arizona Coll
Friends of the Library Group

SAINT DAVID

SR HOLY TRINITY MONASTERY LIBRARY, Hwy 80, Milepost 302, PO Box 298, 85630-0298. SAN 375-3832. Tel: 520-720-4642, Ext 22, 520-720-4754. FAX: 520-720-4202. E-Mail: trinitylib@theriver.com. Web Site: www.holytrinitymonastery.org. *Librn*, Sister Corinne Fair; Staff 2 (MLS 1, Non-MLS 1)
Founded 1974
Library Holdings: Bk Vols 49,000; Bk Titles 47,000; Per Subs 40
Special Collections: Monastic Coll, a-tapes, bks; Southwest/Native American Coll, bks, mags

SAINT JOHNS

P APACHE COUNTY LIBRARY DISTRICT, 205 W First S, PO Box 766, 85936-0766. SAN 300-4120. Tel: 520-337-3067, 520-337-4923. FAX: 520-337-2224. *Dir*, Judith M Pepple; E-Mail: jpepple@co.apache.az.us; *Tech Servs*, Vonda Cook; *Tech Servs*, Christina Maennche; Staff 3 (MLS 1, Non-MLS 2)
Founded 1976
Jul 1998-Jun 1999 Income (Main Library and Branch Library) $636,816, State $20,498, Federal $28,000, County $570,680, Other $17,638. Mats Exp $39,608, Books $34,304, Per/Ser (Incl. Access Fees) $3,510, Electronic Ref Mat (Incl. Access Fees) $1,794. Sal $233,345 (Prof $43,500)
Library Holdings: Bk Vols 64,551; Per Subs 114
Special Collections: Arizona Coll, bks & vf
Database Vendor: OCLC - First Search
Restriction: Not open to public
Branches: 6
ALPINE PUBLIC, Hwy 180, Alpine, 85920. (Mail add: PO Box 528, Alpine, 85920-0528), SAN 328-0314. Tel: 520-339-4925. FAX: 520-339-4925. Web Site: www.cybertrails.com/~rmaly47. *Mgr Libr*, Robin Maly; Tel: rmaly@co.apache.az.us; *Publ Servs*, Michele Ralston; Staff 1 (Non-MLS 1)
Friends of the Library Group
CONCHO PUBLIC, Evergreen St 119, County Rd 5051, PO Box 339, Concho, 85924-0339. SAN 371-3490. Tel: 520-337-2167. FAX: 520-337-2167. *Publ Servs*, Karen Christian; *Publ Servs*, Claudia Goodman; E-Mail: cgoodman@co.apache.az.us
GREER MEMORIAL, 109 Main St, PO Box 144, Greer, 85927-0144. SAN 371-3520. Tel: 520-735-7710. FAX: 520-735-7710. *Publ Servs*, Ramona K Harp; E-Mail: rharp@co.apache.az.us; *Publ Servs*, Linda Moriarty
Friends of the Library Group
ROUND VALLEY PUBLIC, 367 N Main St, Eagar, 85925. (Mail add: PO Box 1066, Springerville, 85938-1066), SAN 371-3482. Tel: 520-333-4694. FAX: 520-333-5682. *Mgr*, Carol Becker; E-Mail: cbecker@co.apache.az.us; *Publ Servs*, Fonda Brown; *Publ Servs*, Elnora Sayre; Staff 1 (Non-MLS 1)
Library Holdings: Bk Vols 12,100; Bk Titles 12,000; Per Subs 12
Friends of the Library Group
SAINT JOHNS PUBLIC, 205 W First S, PO Box 766, 85936-0766. SAN 371-3547. Tel: 520-337-4405. FAX: 520-337-2224. *Mgr Libr*, Linda Marley; E-Mail: lmarley@co.apache.az.us; *Publ Servs*, Lenora Charleston; *Publ Servs*, Traci Heap; *Circ*, Sue Ball; Staff 1 (Non-MLS 1)
SANDERS PUBLIC, Off 1-40, N Hwy 191, PO Box 1000, Sanders, 86512-1000. SAN 371-3539. Tel: 520-688-2677. FAX: 520-688-2677. *Mgr Libr*, Tresa Cox; E-Mail: tcox@apachecold.lib.az.us; *Publ Servs*, Helen Joe; Staff 1 (Non-MLS 1)

SAN CARLOS

P SAN CARLOS PUBLIC LIBRARY,* 58 San Carlos Ave, PO Box 545, 85550. SAN 300-4139. Tel: 520-475-2611. FAX: 520-475-2611. *Librn*, Bernice Phillips
Founded 1971. Pop 7,000
Library Holdings: Bk Vols 10,000; Per Subs 16
Special Collections: Arizona Indian Coll
Mem of Gila County Library District

SAN LUIS

§S ARIZONA DEPARTMENT OF CORRECTIONS - ADULT, Arizona State Prison Complex - Yuma Library, 7125 E Juan Sanchez Blvd, 85349. (Mail add: PO Box 13004, 85366-3004), Tel: 520-627-8871. FAX: 520-627-3048. *Librn*, Sharon Jones; Tel: 520-627-3048, Ext 3416; *Librn*, Randy Alkire
Library Holdings: Bk Vols 9,328

SAN MANUEL

P SAN MANUEL PUBLIC LIBRARY,* 108 Fifth St, 85631. SAN 300-4147. Tel: 520-385-4470. FAX: 520-385-2910. E-Mail: sanmanuellibrary@theriver.com. *Dir*, Sally Freitas
Founded 1959. Pop 5,000; Circ 18,112
Library Holdings: Bk Titles 10,500; Per Subs 17
Mem of Pinal County Library District
Open Mon-Thurs 4-7, Sat 10-1

SCOTTSDALE

THE DIAL CORP
S TECHNICAL CENTER, 15101 N Scottsdale Rd, 85254-2199. SAN 300-4155. Tel: 602-754-6120. FAX: 602-754-6137.
Founded 1975
Library Holdings: Bk Vols 3,241; Per Subs 255
Subject Interests: Chemistry, Cosmetics, Microbiology, Nutrition, Toxicology
Publications: Serial & Journal Holdings (annual)
Partic in BRS; CAS Online; CIS; Dialog Corporation; Dow Jones News Retrieval; OCLC Online Computer Library Center, Inc; SDC Info Servs; Vutext

C FRANK LLOYD WRIGHT SCHOOL OF ARCHITECTURE, William Wesley Peters Library, Taliesin West, 85261-4430. SAN 374-8243. Tel: 480-860-2700. FAX: 480-860-8472. E-Mail: wwplib@taliesin.edu. *Dir*, Elizabeth Dawsari; *Archivist*, Dennis Madden
Library Holdings: Bk Titles 17,000; Per Subs 100

Subject Interests: Architecture
Special Collections: Architectural Drawings; Extensive Archival Coll of Taliesin Architects
Publications: Subject Bibliographies (Architecture)

S GOOKIN ENGINEERS, LTD LIBRARY, 4203 N Brown Ave, 85251. SAN 323-4347. Tel: 602-947-3741. FAX: 602-947-0262. *In Charge*, Jackie Zinkhan
Library Holdings: Bk Titles 4,000

M MAYO CLINIC SCOTTSDALE LIBRARIES, 13400 E Shea Blvd, 85259. SAN 370-5366. Tel: 408-301-8443. FAX: 408-301-7005. *Dir*, Kay Wellik; E-Mail: wellik.kay@mayo.edu; *Librn*, Joseph Esposito; Staff 7 (MLS 2, Non-MLS 5)
Library Holdings: Bk Titles 1,800; Per Subs 325
Subject Interests: Clinical medicine, Molecular biology

S MOTOROLA, INC, Government & Systems Technology Group, Learning Centers,* 8201 E McDowell Rd, H1152, PO Box 1417, 85252-1417. SAN 300-418X. Tel: 602-441-3298, 602-441-3841. FAX: 602-441-8183. E-Mail: p22391@email.mot.com. *Mgr*, Don Guy; *Online Servs*, J E Stewart; *Librn*, Suzanne Henderson; Staff 3 (MLS 3)
Founded 1951
Library Holdings: Bk Titles 5,000; Per Subs 300
Subject Interests: Aeronautics, Business and management, Electronics, Mathematics, Physics, Radar, Solid state physics, Space science
Publications: Library Notes (newsletter, monthly)
Restriction: Staff use only

P SALT RIVER TRIBAL LIBRARY,* 10000 E McDowell Rd, 85256. SAN 300-4198. Tel: 480-850-8339. *Librn*, Leigh Thomas
Founded 1969. Pop 4,000; Circ 4,500
Library Holdings: Bk Vols 8,000; Per Subs 15
Mem of Maricopa County Libr Syst
Friends of the Library Group

J SCOTTSDALE COMMUNITY COLLEGE LIBRARY, 9000 E Chaparral Rd, 85256. SAN 300-4201. Tel: 480-423-6651. Circulation Tel: 480-423-6651. Reference Tel: 480-423-6650. FAX: 480-423-6666. Web Site: www.sc.maricopa.edu/library. *Dir*, Karen Biglin; Tel: 480-423-6434, E-Mail: karen.biglin@sccmail.maricopa.edu; *Syst Coordr*, Patricia Lokey; Tel: 480-423-6653, E-Mail: patricia.lokey@sccmail.maricopa.edu; *Media Spec*, Larry Bunting; E-Mail: larry.bunting@sccmail.maricopa.edu; *Bibliog Instr*, Sharon Howard; Tel: 480-423-6654, E-Mail: sharon.howard@sccmail.maricopa.edu; *Acq*, Marsha Ballard; Tel: 480-423-6638, E-Mail: marsha.ballard@sccmail.maricopa.edu; Staff 12 (MLS 4, Non-MLS 8)
Founded 1971. Enrl 10,000; Fac 143
Jul 2000-Jun 2001 Mats Exp $415,144, Books $85,000, Per/Ser (Incl. Access Fees) $26,000, Micro $4,144, Electronic Ref Mat (Incl. Access Fees) $300,000. Sal $371,000 (Prof $254,000)
Library Holdings: Bk Titles 50,000; Per Subs 350
Subject Interests: Careers, Foreign Language
Special Collections: Colleges and Careers Coll; Indians of the Southwest Coll
Database Vendor: Ebsco - EbscoHost, IAC - SearchBank, ProQuest, Wilson - Wilson Web

SCOTTSDALE HEALTHCARE

M DR ROBERT C FOREMAN HEALTH SCIENCES LIBRARY, Scottsdale Healthcare Osborn, 7400 E Osborn Rd, 85251. SAN 300-421X. Tel: 602-481-4870. FAX: 480-675-4200. *Librn*, Nita Mailander; Tel: 480-675-4870, E-Mail: nmailander@shc.org; Staff 2 (MLS 1, Non-MLS 1)
Founded 1968
Library Holdings: Bk Titles 2,000; Per Subs 250
Subject Interests: Internal medicine, Nursing, Obstetrics and gynecology, Orthopedics, Pediatrics, Radiology, Surgery
Special Collections: Family Practice, audio-digest tapes & v-tapes; Obstetrics, Gynecology & Urology
Database Vendor: Ebsco - EbscoHost, IAC - Info Trac, OVID Technologies
Restriction: Not open to public
Partic in AZHIN

M HEALTH SCIENCES LIBRARY, 9003 E Shea Blvd, 85260. SAN 375-2836. Tel: 602-860-3870. FAX: 602-860-3864.
Library Holdings: Bk Vols 1,500; Per Subs 200

P SCOTTSDALE PUBLIC LIBRARY SYSTEM, 3839 Drinkwater Blvd, 85251-4405. SAN 300-4228. Tel: 480-312-7323. TDD: 602-312-7670. FAX: 480-312-7993. Web Site: library.ci.scottsdale.az.us. *Dir*, Judy Register; Tel: 480-312-2454, E-Mail: jregister@ci.scottsdale.az.us; *Mgr*, Sharon Laser; Tel: 480-312-2692, E-Mail: slaser@ci.scottsdale.az.us; *Mgr*, Bill Pillow; E-Mail: bpillow@ci.scottsdale.az.us; *Mgr*, Debbie Tang; Tel: 480-312-6060, Fax: 480-312-6084, E-Mail: dtang@ci.scottsdale.az.us; *Coll Develop*, Joanne Hamilton-Selway; Staff 207 (MLS 40, Non-MLS 167)
Founded 1959. Pop 212,980
Jul 1999-Jun 2000 Income (Main Library and Branch Library) $7,161,276, State $2,812, City $6,974,178, Federal $15,000, Other $169,286. Mats Exp $1,019,047, Books $675,790, Per/Ser (Incl. Access Fees) $183,803, Presv $8,075. Sal $4,509,383
Library Holdings: Bk Titles 677,776; Per Subs 1,355
Subject Interests: Art and architecture, Business and management
Special Collections: Municipal Docs; Southwest Coll
Automation Activity & Vendor Info: (Acquisitions) DRA; (Cataloging) DRA; (Circulation) DRA; (OPAC) DRA
Database Vendor: DRA, GaleNet, IAC - Info Trac, IAC - SearchBank, OCLC - First Search, ProQuest
Partic in Amigos Library Services, Inc; OCLC Online Computer Library Center, Inc
Special Services for the Deaf - TDD
Friends of the Library Group
Branches: 3
ARABIAN, 10187 E McDowell Mountain Ranch Rd, 85259. SAN 376-8945. Tel: 602-312-6200. FAX: 602-312-6220. Web Site: library.ci.scottsdale.az.us. *Br Coordr*, Carolyn Malhoit
MUSTANG, 10101 N 90th St, 85258. SAN 374-4493. Tel: 602-312-6061. TDD: 602-312-6012. FAX: 602-312-6084. Web Site: library.ci.scottsdale.az.us. *Br Coordr*, Carol Damaso
Special Services for the Deaf - TDD
PALOMINO, 12575 E Via Linda, Ste 102, 85259. SAN 376-8953. Tel: 602-312-6100. FAX: 602-312-6120. Web Site: library.ci.scottsdale.az.us. *Br Coordr*, Deborah Tasnadi

R TEMPLE BETH ISRAEL LIBRARY,* 10460 N 56th St, 85253. SAN 300-3973. Tel: 602-951-0323. FAX: 602-951-7150. *Librn*, Norma D Sadick
Founded 1958
Library Holdings: Bk Titles 20,000; Per Subs 15
Special Collections: Yiddish (Judaica Coll), bks, per, cassettes, tapes & slides
Open Mon & Tues 10-2, Thurs 11-6 & Sun 9-12
Friends of the Library Group

SEDONA

P SEDONA PUBLIC LIBRARY,* 3250 White Bear Rd, 86336. SAN 300-4252. Tel: 520-282-7714. FAX: 520-282-5789. E-Mail: library@sedona.net. Web Site: users.sedona.net/~library. *Librn*, David W Keeber
Founded 1958. Pop 15,000; Circ 123,702
Jun 1997-May 1998 Income $357,041. Mats Exp $38,154, Books $33,194, Per/Ser (Incl. Access Fees) $4,960. Sal $202,290
Library Holdings: Bk Vols 63,000; Per Subs 187
Special Collections: Arizona Coll
Mem of Coconino County Libr Syst; Yuma County Library District
Friends of the Library Group

S WORLD RESEARCH FOUNDATION LIBRARY,* 41 Bell Rock Plaza, 86351. SAN 373-1030. Tel: 520-284-3300. FAX: 520-284-3530. E-Mail: info@wrf.org. *Pres*, Steve Ross
Library Holdings: Bk Vols 20,000

SELIGMAN

P SELIGMAN PUBLIC LIBRARY,* 325 N Main, PO Box 623, 86337. SAN 323-8016. Tel: 520-422-3633. *Mgr*, Elaine Crownover
Library Holdings: Bk Vols 3,000
Mem of Yavapai County Library District

SELLS

P PISINEMO MEDIA CENTER LIBRARY,* HC 02, Box 300, 85634. SAN 377-0753. Tel: 520-362-2806. *Coordr*, Frederick Pablo
Library Holdings: Bk Vols 200

M US PUBLIC HEALTH SERVICE INDIAN HOSPITAL, Medical Library, PO Box 548, 85634. Tel: 520-383-7251.
Library Holdings: Bk Vols 500; Bk Titles 300; Per Subs 10

SHOW LOW

SR GRACE LUTHERAN CHURCH LIBRARY,* 700 S 19th Ave, PO Box 174, 85901. SAN 326-0348. Tel: 520-537-4817. *Librn*, Irene Scheider
Library Holdings: Bk Titles 7,060; Per Subs 16
Subject Interests: Church history, Philosophy, Psychology, Theology

P SHOW LOW PUBLIC LIBRARY,* 20 N Sixth St, 85901. SAN 300-4287. Tel: 520-537-2447. FAX: 520-532-8669. E-Mail: slref@showlowpub.lib.az.us. *Librn*, Kris Bowen
Pop 10,000; Circ 80,556
Library Holdings: Bk Vols 26,300; Bk Titles 25,000; Per Subs 22
Mem of Navajo County Libr Syst
Partic in Amigos Library Services, Inc
Friends of the Library Group

SIERRA VISTA

P SIERRA VISTA PUBLIC LIBRARY, 2600 E Tacoma, 85635-1399. SAN 300-4309. Tel: 520-458-4225. FAX: 520-458-5377. Web Site: www.ci.sierra-vista.az.us/departments/library/lib.htm. *Dir Libr Serv*, David L Gunckel; E-Mail: dgunckl@sierravistapub.lib.az.us; *Ch Servs, Publ Servs*, Mona Baker; *Publ Servs*, Allison Dove; *ILL*, Debra Chatham; *Tech Servs*, Bonnie Goodrich; *Publ Servs*, Kate Draper
Founded 1958. Pop 40,000; Circ 310,000
Jul 1998-Jun 1999 Income City $586,000. Mats Exp $130,000, Per/Ser (Incl. Access Fees) $2,000. Sal $444,818 (Prof $152,000)
Library Holdings: Bk Vols 75,000; Per Subs 200
Special Collections: Arizona Collection
Automation Activity & Vendor Info: (Cataloging) DRA; (Circulation) DRA; (OPAC) DRA
Mem of Cochise County Library District
Partic in Amigos Library Services, Inc
Friends of the Library Group

SNOWFLAKE

P SNOWFLAKE-TAYLOR PUBLIC LIBRARY,* 418 S Fourth W, 85937. SAN 321-7779. Tel: 520-536-7103. FAX: 520-536-3057. E-Mail: cmcdow1@snowflakepub.lib.az.us. *Librn*, Cathryn McDowell
Founded 1965. Pop 7,000; Circ 35,000
Library Holdings: Bk Vols 21,000; Per Subs 55
Special Collections: Southwest Coll
Partic in Navajo County Libr District
Friends of the Library Group

SOMERTON

P COCOPAH TRIBAL LIBRARY,* 14250 S Ave I County 15th & Ave G, 85350. SAN 376-3196. Tel: 520-627-8026. FAX: 520-627-2510. E-Mail: cocopah1@yahoo.com. *Dir*, Frank A Molina
Library Holdings: Bk Titles 2,400; Per Subs 14

STANFIELD

P STANFIELD COMMUNITY CENTER LIBRARY,* 36680 W Cooper Dr, PO Box 699, 85272. SAN 376-3226. Tel: 520-424-3791. FAX: 520-424-3494. *Dir*, Phil Crabbe; E-Mail: pcrabbe@casagrande.com; *Librn*, Delise Christiansen
Jul 1997-Jun 1998 Income $4,767. Mats Exp $3,200
Library Holdings: Bk Vols 4,500; Bk Titles 4,000
Special Collections: National Geographic Magazines, 1950's to Present
Mem of Pinal County Library District

SUN CITY

M BOSWELL MEMORIAL HOSPITAL, Professional Library,* 13180 N 103rd Dr, 85351. SAN 373-3874. Tel: 602-977-7211, Ext 1745. FAX: 602-876-5574. E-Mail: boslid@primenet.com.
Library Holdings: Bk Vols 600; Per Subs 120
Subject Interests: Internal medicine, Surgery

P SUN CITY LIBRARY,* 16828 99th Ave, 85351. SAN 330-6992. Tel: 602-974-2569. FAX: 602-876-0283. Web Site: www.doitnow.com/~sclib. *Coll Develop, Dir*, Charles Youngman; *Asst Dir*, Grace Melody
Founded 1961. Pop 43,000; Circ 281,126
Jan 1998-Dec 1998 Income $393,000, State $3,800. Mats Exp $66,500, Books $58,000, Per/Ser (Incl. Access Fees) $7,000, Presv $500, Other Print Mats $1,000. Sal $327,000
Library Holdings: Bk Vols 100,000; Per Subs 220
Subject Interests: Investing
Special Collections: Arizona Coll; Large print Coll; Sun City Authors; Sun City History
Publications: The Bookworm
Special Services for the Deaf - Books on deafness & sign language; Special interest periodicals
Friends of the Library Group
Branches: 1
FAIRWAY, 10620 Peoria Ave, 85351. SAN 330-7026. Tel: 623-933-7433. *Mgr*, Martha Bard
Library Holdings: Bk Vols 14,200
Friends of the Library Group

SUN CITY WEST

P R H JOHNSON LIBRARY, 13801 Meeker Blvd, 85375. SAN 321-110X. Tel: 623-544-6130. E-Mail: scwlib@earthlink.net. *Librn*, Marcia Lea; *Asst Librn*, Margaret Anderson; Staff 6 (MLS 2, Non-MLS 4)
Founded 1979. Pop 30,000
Jul 1999-Jun 2000 Income $240,000. Mats Exp $69,250. Sal $142,000
Library Holdings: Bk Vols 44,000; Bk Titles 42,000; Per Subs 180
Subject Interests: Arizona
Automation Activity & Vendor Info: (Circulation) Athena; (Circulation) Sagebrush Corporation
Restriction: Members only
Friends of the Library Group

SUPAI

P HAVASUPAI VILLAGE LIBRARY,* PO Box 40, 86435. SAN 376-3161. Tel: 520-448-2901. FAX: 520-448-2551. *Librn*, Lenora Jones
Library Holdings: Bk Titles 100
Mem of Flagstaff City-Coconino County Pub Libr District

SUPERIOR

P SUPERIOR PUBLIC LIBRARY, 99 Kellner Ave, 85273. SAN 300-435X. Tel: 520-689-2327. FAX: 520-689-5809. *Ch Servs, Dir*, Josie O Campos; E-Mail: jcampos@pinalcold.lib.az.us
Founded 1952. Pop 3,400; Circ 24,000
Library Holdings: Bk Vols 12,300; Bk Titles 12,000; Per Subs 35
Publications: Library News (monthly newsletter)
Mem of Pinal County Library District
Friends of the Library Group

TEMPE

S ALLIED-SIGNAL AEROSPACE CO, Information Resource Center 1207-3M,* 1300 W Warner Rd, PO Box 22200, 85285-2200. SAN 323-6714. Tel: 480-592-7162. FAX: 480-592-4663. *Assoc Librn*, Janet Evory; E-Mail: janet.evory@alliedsignal.com
Founded 1986
Library Holdings: Bk Titles 4,000; Per Subs 260
Subject Interests: Careers, Engineering, Materials
Special Collections: Safety Videos
Partic in Nerac

S AMERICAN FEDERATION OF ASTROLOGERS, INC LIBRARY, 6535 S Rural Rd, PO Box 22040, 85285-2040. SAN 300-4368. Tel: 480-838-1751. FAX: 480-838-8293. E-Mail: afa@msn.com. *Librn*, Kris Brandt-Riske
Founded 1938
Library Holdings: Bk Vols 3,000
Special Collections: Various Out-of-Print Publications (1600-1800)
Publications: Today's Astrologer (monthly)
Restriction: Private library

S ARIZONA HISTORICAL FOUNDATION, Hayden Library, University Libraries Arizona State University, PO Box 871006, 85287-1006. SAN 327-5124. Tel: 480-965-3283, 480-966-8331. FAX: 480-966-1077. Web Site: www.asu.edu/lib/ahf. *Dir*, Evelyn Cooper
Founded 1959
Library Holdings: Bk Vols 8,000; Per Subs 10
Special Collections: Arizona Cattle & Cotton Growers Association, records; Congressional Papers of Senators Barry M Goldwater & Paul Fannin
Publications: Arizona Odyssey; Arizona's Angry Man; Camelback Mountain; Circle of Motion; Delightful Journey; Opportunity & Challenge; Tales of Superstitions; The Goldwaters of Arizona; The Shamrock Way; Wells Fargo in Arizona Territory
Friends of the Library Group

S ARIZONA HISTORICAL SOCIETY MUSEUM LIBRARY & ARCHIVES, 1300 N College Ave, 85281. SAN 321-8813. Tel: 480-929-0292. Reference Tel: 480-929-0292, Ext 174. FAX: 480-929-9973. E-Mail: library.reference@ahs.maricopa.gov. Web Site: www.tempe.gov./ahs. *Librn*, Anne Taylor; Tel: 480-929-0292, Ext 128, E-Mail: anne.taylor@ahs.maricopa.gov; *Archivist*, Dawn Nave; Tel: 480-929-0292, Ext 172, E-Mail: dawn.nave@ahs.maricopa.gov; *Archivist*, Dave Tackenberg; Tel: 480-929-0292, Ext 127, E-Mail: tackenberg@ahs.maricopa.gov; Staff 3 (MLS 1, Non-MLS 2)
Founded 1973
2000-2001 Mats Exp $7,200, Books $2,000, Per/Ser (Incl. Access Fees) $200, Presv $5,000
Library Holdings: Bk Titles 2,000; Per Subs 10
Subject Interests: Cent Ariz in 20th Century, Phoenix
Special Collections: A J Bayless Coll; Arizona Homebuilders Association Coll; Arizona Quilt Project; Charles A Stauffer Coll; Lescher-Mahoney Architectural Drawing Coll; Orpheus Men's Choir Coll; Phoenix History Project Coll; Photograph Coll; Robert Isbell Coll; Snell Family Papers
Restriction: Non-circulating to the public

C ARIZONA STATE UNIVERSITY LIBRARIES,* 85287-1006. SAN 330-7050. Tel: 480-965-3417. FAX: 480-965-9169. Web Site: www.lib.asu.edu. *Dean of Libr*, Sherrie Schmidt; *Spec Coll*, Marilyn Wurzburger; *Access Serv*, Ginny Sylvester; *Govt Doc*, Beckie Burke; *Cat*, David Reynolds; *Ref*, Lydia LaFaro; *Coll Develop*, Jeanne Richardson; Staff 363 (MLS 102, Non-MLS 261)
Founded 1891. Enrl 60,801; Fac 2,044; Highest Degree: Doctorate
Library Holdings: Bk Vols 3,372,529; Per Subs 33,034
Special Collections: Alberto Pradeau Archives; American Indian, Arizona &

Southwest History; Barry Goldwater Archives; Carl Hayden Archives; Jimmy Starr Archives; John R Rhodes Archives; Mexican Numismatics; Paolo Soleri Archives; Solar Energy Archives; Spain; Theatre for Youth Coll; Victorian Literature including Pre-Raphaelites & New; William Burroughs Archives
Automation Activity & Vendor Info: (Acquisitions) Innovative Interfaces Inc.; (Circulation) Innovative Interfaces Inc.; (Serials) Innovative Interfaces Inc.
Publications: ASU Libraries (newsletter); bibliographies
Mem of Asn of Research Libraries
Partic in OCLC Online Computer Library Center, Inc
Friends of the Library Group
Departmental Libraries:
ARCHITECTURE & ENVIRONMENTAL DESIGN LIBRARY Tel: 480-965-6400. FAX: 480-965-1130. Web Site: www.asu.edu/caed/aedlibrary.
Library Holdings: Bk Vols 30,000
ACQUISITIONS BIBLIOGRAPHIC RECORDS Tel: 480-965-5889. FAX: 480-965-1043.
COLLECTION DEVELOPMENT Tel: 480-965-5345. FAX: 480-965-9127. *Librn*, Jeanne Richardson
DANIEL E NOBEL SCIENCE & ENGINEERING LIBRARY, PO Box 871006, 85287. SAN 330-7123. Tel: 480-965-7607. FAX: 480-965-0883. Web Site: www.asu.edu/lib/. *In Charge*, Tom Turner

CL JOHN J ROSS - WILLIAM C BLAKLEY LAW LIBRARY, PO Box 877806, 85287-7806. SAN 330-714X. Tel: 480-965-6141. FAX: 480-965-4283. Web Site: www.lawlib.asu.edu. *Dir*, Victoria K Trotta; Tel: 480-965-2521, E-Mail: victoria.trotta@asu.edu; *Access Serv*, Alison Ewing; Tel: 480-965-4863; *Ref*, Marianne Alcorn; *Coll Develop*, Sharon Firestone; Tel: 480-965-4872; *Electronic Resources, Ref*, Rose Gavin; Tel: 480-965-1597; Staff 22 (MLS 8, Non-MLS 14)
Founded 1966. Enrl 450; Fac 31; Highest Degree: Doctorate
Library Holdings: Bk Vols 368,919; Per Subs 6,423
Subject Interests: Native Americans
Automation Activity & Vendor Info: (Course Reserve) Innovative Interfaces Inc.; (OPAC) Innovative Interfaces Inc.
Partic in OCLC Online Computer Library Center, Inc
MUSIC, Music Bldg, Rm W302, 3rd flr, PO Box 870505, 85287-0505. SAN 330-7174. Tel: 602-965-3513. FAX: 602-965-9598. *Librn*, Robert Follet

SR COOK COLLEGE & THEOLOGICAL SCHOOL, Mary M McCarthy Library, 708 S Lindon Lane, 85281. SAN 300-4384. Tel: 480-966-0822, Ext 136. FAX: 480-968-9357. E-Mail: cctslib@juno.com. *Librn*, Mark E Thomas
Founded 1943
Library Holdings: Bk Titles 14,500; Per Subs 40
Subject Interests: Religion, Theology
Specializes in theology education by extension; school for educating Indians for Christian leadership

S NATIONAL ASSOCIATION OF PURCHASING MANAGEMENT, Information Center,* 2055 E Centennial Circle, PO Box 22160, 85285-2160. SAN 311-9157. Tel: 602-752-6276, Ext 3076. FAX: 602-752-7890. E-Mail: infocenter@napm.org. Web Site: www.napm.org. *Librn*, Marnie Graham
Founded 1967
Library Holdings: Bk Vols 2,000; Per Subs 100
Subject Interests: Inventory control, Mat mgt, Purchasing
Restriction: Members only

J RIO SALADO COLLEGE, Library & Information Center,* 2323 W 14th St, 85281. SAN 321-4745. Tel: 480-517-8424. FAX: 480-517-8449. Web Site: www.rio.maricopa.edu/ci/riointernet/library/main.html. *Coll Develop, Dir*, Hazel Davis; *Coordr*, Sherry Peabody; E-Mail: peabody@rio.maricopa.edu
Founded 1982. Enrl 13,000; Fac 270
Library Holdings: Bk Titles 10,000; Per Subs 300
Subject Interests: Chem dependency

§CM SOUTHWEST COLLEGE OF NATUROPATHIC MEDICINE & HEALTH SCIENCES, Wade Boyle Memorial Library, 2140 E Broadway Rd, 85282-1751. Tel: 480-858-9100, Ext 247. FAX: 480-858-9116. Web Site: www.scnm.edu/library.htm. *Dir*, Dr Bryan Stansfield; Tel: 480-858-9100, Ext 245, E-Mail: b.stansfield@scnm.edu
Library Holdings: Bk Vols 3,400; Per Subs 50
Automation Activity & Vendor Info: (Cataloging) EOS; (Circulation) EOS; (OPAC) EOS; (Serials) EOS

SRP LIBRARY

S ISB LIBRARY, 1600 N Priest Dr, MS ISB552, PO Box 52025, 85281. Tel: 602-236-5676. FAX: 602-220-1191. *Librn*, Valerie Pomerenke; E-Mail: vafresch@srpnet.com; Staff 2 (MLS 1, Non-MLS 1)
Founded 1987. Pop 4,000
Subject Interests: Business and management, Computer tech, Finance, Utilities industry
Special Collections: Electric Utility Company Annual Reports; IBM Manuals; META Group Reports
Automation Activity & Vendor Info: (Acquisitions) Sydney; (Cataloging) Sydney; (Circulation) Sydney; (OPAC) Sydney; (Serials) Sydney
Database Vendor: Dialog, Lexis-Nexis
Restriction: Company library
Function: For research purposes, Some telephone reference
Partic in Amigos Library Services, Inc; SLA

S PAB LIBRARY, 1521 N Project Dr, 85281. (Mail add: PO Box 52025, MS PAB113, Phoenix, 85072-2025), SAN 300-4392. Tel: 602-236-2259. FAX: 602-236-2664. *Librn*, Cathy Large; E-Mail: calarge@srpnet.com; Staff 2 (MLS 1, Non-MLS 1)
Founded 1963. Pop 4,000
Library Holdings: Bk Titles 30,000; Per Subs 200
Subject Interests: Business and management, Electric utilities, Engineering, Utilities industry, Water
Special Collections: Career Resources; Electric Untility Co Annual Reports Coll; EPRI
Automation Activity & Vendor Info: (Acquisitions) Sydney; (Cataloging) Sydney; (Circulation) Sydney; (OPAC) Sydney; (Serials) Sydney
Database Vendor: Dialog, Lexis-Nexis
Restriction: Company library
Function: For research purposes, ILL available, Photocopies available, Some telephone reference
Partic in Amigos Library Services, Inc; SLA

S TEMPE HISTORICAL MUSEUM, Research Library, 809 E Southern Ave, 85282. SAN 374-4701. Tel: 480-350-5100. FAX: 480-350-5150. Web Site: www.tempe.gov/museum/. *Curator*, John Akers; E-Mail: john_akers@tempe.gov
Founded 1972
Library Holdings: Bk Titles 800
Special Collections: Arizona Genealogy, bks, database, files; Tempe History, bks, files, microforms
Restriction: By appointment only
Friends of the Library Group

P TEMPE PUBLIC LIBRARY, 3500 S Rural Rd, 85282-5405. SAN 300-4406. Tel: 480-350-5500. Circulation Tel: 480-350-5577. Reference Tel: 480-350-5511. TDD: 480-350-5050. FAX: 480-350-5544. Web Site: www.tempe.gov/library/. *Adminr*, Lee F Kornblum; Tel: 480-350-5552, E-Mail: lee_kornblum@tempe.gov; *Adminr*, Teri Metros; Tel: 480-350-5551, E-Mail: teri_metros@tempe.gov; *YA Servs*, Sherry Warren; E-Mail: sherry_warren@tempo.gov; *Ad Servs*, Gail R Rathbun; Tel: 480-350-5553, Fax: 480-350-5517, E-Mail: gail_ruthbun@tempe.gov; *Per*, Nancy Petrie; Tel: 480-350-5556, Fax: 480-350-5056, E-Mail: nancy_petrie@tempe.gov; *Coll Develop*, Kim S Garza; Tel: 480-350-5557, Fax: 480-350-5540, E-Mail: kim_garza@tempe.gov; *AV*, Judy Martin; Tel: 480-350-5546, Fax: 480-350-5540, E-Mail: judy_martin@tempe.gov; *Cat*, Clay Workman; Tel: 480-350-5540, E-Mail: clay_workman@tempe.gov; *Circ*, Theresa Ituarte; Tel: 480-350-5558, E-Mail: theresa_ituarte@tempe.gov; Staff 21 (MLS 21)
Founded 1935. Pop 160,802; Circ 1,107,473
Jul 1999-Jun 2000 Income $4,353,975, State $2,661, City $3,946,146, County $195,551, Locally Generated Income $209,617. Mats Exp $504,959, Books $487,294, Per/Ser (Incl. Access Fees) $32,870, Presv $1,927, Micro $36,697, AV Equip $57,883, Electronic Ref Mat (Incl. Access Fees) $135,636. Sal $1,981,953
Library Holdings: Bk Vols 435,676; Bk Titles 283,959; Per Subs 1,450
Special Collections: Foreign Language; Local History
Automation Activity & Vendor Info: (Acquisitions) Inlex; (Cataloging) Inlex; (Circulation) Inlex; (OPAC) Inlex; (Serials) EOS
Database Vendor: Ebsco - EbscoHost, IAC - SearchBank, OCLC - First Search, ProQuest
Partic in Amigos Library Services, Inc
Special Services for the Deaf - TDD
Friends of the Library Group

THATCHER

J EASTERN ARIZONA COLLEGE, Alumni Library, 600 Church St, 85552. SAN 300-4414. Tel: 520-428-8304. FAX: 520-428-7462. Web Site: www.eac.cc.az.us/library. *Dir Libr Serv*, Crystal Melton; E-Mail: melton@eac.cc.az.us; Staff 10 (MLS 2, Non-MLS 8)
Founded 1888. Enrl 2,500; Fac 85; Highest Degree: Associate
Jul 2000-Jun 2001 Mats Exp $70,500, Books $45,000, Per/Ser (Incl. Access Fees) $8,000, Micro $14,000, AV Equip $3,500
Library Holdings: Bk Titles 48,000; Per Subs 100; Bks on Deafness & Sign Lang 35
Special Collections: TV Social Issues
Automation Activity & Vendor Info: (Cataloging) Gaylord; (Circulation) Gaylord; (OPAC) Gaylord
Departmental Libraries:
GILA PUEBLO CAMPUS LIBRARY
See Separate Entry in Globe

TOLLESON

P TOLLESON PUBLIC LIBRARY,* 9555 W Van Buren St, 85353. SAN 300-4422. Tel: 602-936-2746. FAX: 602-936-7224. *Dir*, Sheryl Pieper; Staff 3 (MLS 1, Non-MLS 2)
Founded 1949. Pop 12,000; Circ 26,920

Jul 1997-Jun 1998 Income $135,874. Mats Exp $17,000, Books $14,350, Per/Ser (Incl. Access Fees) $900, Other Print Mats $1,000. Sal $99,723 (Prof $35,000)
Library Holdings: Bk Vols 19,225; Per Subs 134
Special Collections: Library of America; MacArthur Video classics Project; Prehistoric Arizona Indian pottery, Kachinas & Artifacts Coll; Southwestern Coll; Spanish Language Materials Coll
Partic in OCLC Online Computer Library Center, Inc
Friends of the Library Group

TOMBSTONE

P TOMBSTONE READING STATION-TOMBSTONE CITY LIBRARY, Fourth & Toughnut Sts, PO Box 218, 85638. SAN 300-4430. Tel: 520-457-3612. FAX: 520-457-3612. Web Site: www.cochise.lib.az.us. *Librn*, Jodie Hoffman; E-Mail: jhoffma@tombstonepl.lib.az.us; Staff 2 (Non-MLS 2)
Founded 1961
Library Holdings: Bk Vols 10,179
Subject Interests: Arizona
Mem of Cochise County Library District

TONTO BASIN

P TONTO BASIN PUBLIC LIBRARY,* One School St, PO Box 368, 85553. SAN 376-7280. Tel: 520-479-2355. FAX: 520-479-2830. E-Mail: comfran/tba@hotmail.com. *Mgr*, Fran Cain
Library Holdings: Bk Titles 15,000; Per Subs 10
Mem of Gila County Library District
Friends of the Library Group

TSAILE

J DINE COLLEGE, Naaltsoos Ba'Hooghan Library, 86556. SAN 300-4457. Tel: 520-724-6757. FAX: 520-724-3349. Web Site: crystal.ncc.cc.nm.us. *Per*, Cindy Slivers; *Tech Servs*, Rosita Klee; *Circ*, Ruby Johnson; *AV*, David Hurley; Staff 1 (MLS 1)
Founded 1969. Pop 140,000; Enrl 2,000; Fac 51
Library Holdings: Bk Vols 50,000; Per Subs 200
Special Collections: North American Indians (Moses Donner Coll), bks & film

TUBA CITY

P TUBA CITY PUBLIC LIBRARY, W Maple & Cedar, PO Box 190, 86045. SAN 300-4465. Tel: 520-283-5856. FAX: 520-283-6188. *Mgr*, Pearl G Yazzie; E-Mail: pyazzie@tubacity.pub.lib.az.us; *Mgr Libr*, Trish Polacca. Subject Specialists: *Literacy*, Trish Polacca
Founded 1957. Pop 10,000; Circ 14,031
Jul 1998-Jun 1999 Income $21,000
Library Holdings: Bk Vols 12,000; Per Subs 30
Subject Interests: Native Am
Special Collections: Navaho History & Culture
Automation Activity & Vendor Info: (Acquisitions) Follett
Database Vendor: OCLC - First Search
Mem of Coconino County Libr Syst
Open Mon-Wed 10-7, Thurs 9-5 & Fri 9-2

TUBAC

S TUBAC CENTER OF THE ARTS LIBRARY,* PO Box 1911, 85646. SAN 375-6343. Tel: 520-398-2371. FAX: 520-398-9511.
Library Holdings: Bk Titles 700
Subject Interests: Art history

TUCSON

S ARIZONA AEROSPACE FOUNDATION, Pima Air & Space Museum Library & Archives, 6000 E Valencia Rd, 85706. SAN 371-6678. Tel: 520-574-0462, Ext 116. FAX: 520-574-9238. Web Site: www.pimaair.org/library.htm. *Librn*, Cynthia J Coan; E-Mail: ccoan@pimaair.org; *Archivist*, Stephanie Mitchell; Tel: 520-574-0462, Ext 114, E-Mail: smitchell@pimaair.org; *Archivist*, Scott Thompson; Tel: 520-574-0462, Ext 168, E-Mail: sthompson@pimaair.org; Staff 3 (MLS 2, Non-MLS 1)
Founded 1988
Jul 2000-Jun 2001 Income Parent Institution $38,000. Mats Exp $4,485, Books $2,500, Per/Ser (Incl. Access Fees) $1,150, AV Equip $500, Manuscripts & Archives $335. Sal $59,000
Library Holdings: Bk Vols 9,300; Bk Titles 7,100; Per Subs 20
Subject Interests: Aviation hist, Space flight
Special Collections: Air Force Insignia & History (Robert F Schirmer Coll); Marauder Archive
Automation Activity & Vendor Info: (Cataloging) Inmagic, Inc.
Publications: Skywriting (quarterly newsletter)
Restriction: By appointment only, Non-circulating to the public
Function: Photocopies available, Reference services available

M ARIZONA AREA HEALTH EDUCATION CENTERS LIBRARY, (AHEC), 2501 E Elm St, 85716. SAN 375-717X. Tel: 520-626-7946. FAX: 520-321-7792. Web Site: www.rho.arizona.edu/mc/library.htm. *Coordr*, Patricia A Auflick; E-Mail: pauflick@rho.arizona.edu; Staff 1 (MLS 1)
Founded 1987
Jul 2000-Jun 2001 Income Federal $50,000. Mats Exp $5,500, Per/Ser (Incl. Access Fees) $500, Electronic Ref Mat (Incl. Access Fees) $5,000. Sal $43,000
Library Holdings: Per Subs 52
Subject Interests: Border studies, Managed care, Public health, Rural health
Publications: Arizona Medical Journals (Union list of serials)
Partic in AZHIN

S ARIZONA DAILY STAR LIBRARY, 4850 S Park Ave, PO Box 26807, 85726-6807. SAN 300-4481. Tel: 520-573-4160. FAX: 520-573-4190. *Chief Librn*, Elaine Raines; Staff 7 (MLS 1, Non-MLS 6)
Founded 1950
Library Holdings: Bk Titles 1,500
Subject Interests: Arizona
Special Collections: Back Issues Arizona Daily Star Coll, 1877 to present, micro; Tucson City Directories Coll, 1918 to present; Tucson Telephone Directories Coll, 1930 to present
Restriction: Staff use only

§S ARIZONA DEPARTMENT OF CORRECTIONS - ADULT, Arizona State Prison Complex - Tucson Library, 10,000 S Wilmot Rd, 85734. (Mail add: PO Box 24400, 85734-4400), Tel: 520-574-0024. FAX: 520-574-7308. *Librn*, Sally Berg; Tel: 520-574-0024, Ext 2115; *Librn*, Sue Boers; Tel: 520-574-0024, Ext 6830; *Librn*, Michele Canney; Tel: 520-574-0024, Ext 3037; *Librn*, Lisa Hussey; Tel: 520-574-0024, 5362; *Librn*, Gail Jeorgenson; Tel: 520-574-0024, Ext 3830; *Librn*, Starr Kirkland; Tel: 520-574-0024, Ext 4220
Library Holdings: Bk Vols 46,225

§G ARIZONA DEPARTMENT OF ECONOMIC SECURITY, Division of Developmental Disabilities - Tucson, 4710 E 29th St, 85711. (Mail add: PO Box 13178, 85732-3178), Tel: 520-745-5588, Ext 1014. FAX: 520-571-8871. Web Site: www.disabilitydepotaz.org. *Coordr*, Deni DuRoy-Cunningham
Library Holdings: Bk Vols 1,500; Bks on Deafness & Sign Lang 15

ARIZONA GEOLOGICAL SURVEY

S REFERENCE LIBRARY, 416 W Congress St, Ste 100, 85701. SAN 370-338X. Tel: 520-770-3500. FAX: 520-770-3505. *In Charge*, Tom McGarvin; E-Mail: mcgarvin_thomas@pop.state.az.us
Library Holdings: Bk Titles 300; Per Subs 10
Subject Interests: Geology
Special Collections: Arizona Theses & Dissertations; Mine Coll
Restriction: Open to public for reference only

S WELL SAMPLE & WELL FILE LIBRARY, 416 W Congress St, Ste 100, 85701. SAN 370-8241. Tel: 520-770-3500. FAX: 520-770-3505. Web Site: www.azgs.state.az.us. *Adminr*, Steven L Rauzi
Subject Interests: Gas, Oil

S ARIZONA HISTORICAL SOCIETY, Library Archives,* 949 E Second St, 85719. SAN 300-449X. Tel: 520-628-5774. FAX: 520-628-5695. E-Mail: azhist@azstarnet.com. Web Site: www.w3.arizona.edu.1.azhist. *Head Librn*, Deborah Shelton; *Librn*, Kim Frontz; *Archivist*, Rose Byrne; *Archivist*, Scott Denlinger; *Cat*, Debbie Newman
Founded 1884
Library Holdings: Bk Titles 50,000; Per Subs 40
Subject Interests: Arizona, Mexico

S ARIZONA STATE MUSEUM LIBRARY, University of Arizona, Bldg 26, PO Box 210026, 85721-0026. SAN 300-4678. Tel: 520-621-4695. FAX: 520-621-2976. Web Site: www.statemuseum.arizona.edu. *Librn*, Mary Graham; E-Mail: megraham@email.arizona.edu; Staff 3 (MLS 3)
Founded 1958
Library Holdings: Bk Vols 60,000; Bk Titles 35,000; Per Subs 30
Subject Interests: Anthropology, Archaeology, Museology
Restriction: Non-circulating

S ARIZONA STATE SCHOOLS FOR THE DEAF & BLIND LIBRARY, 1200 W Speedway, 85745. (Mail add: PO Box 85000, 85754), SAN 300-4503. Tel: 520-770-3671. FAX: 520-770-3752. *Librn*, Peg McCullough; E-Mail: pmccullough@asdb.org; Staff 3 (MLS 1, Non-MLS 2)
Circ 5,702
Library Holdings: Bk Vols 18,000; Per Subs 40
Special Collections: Braille; Captioned Film Depository; Deaf & Visually Impaired (Professional Coll); Deaf Studies; Parent Lending Library
Automation Activity & Vendor Info: (Cataloging) CASPR; (Circulation) CASPR
Mem of Amigos Bibliog Coun, Inc
Partic in Aznet
Special Services for the Deaf - TTY machine

S ARIZONA-SONORA DESERT MUSEUM LIBRARY, 2021 N Kinney Rd, 85743. SAN 330-7204. Tel: 520-883-1380, Ext 264. FAX: 520-883-2500. E-Mail: info@desertmuseum.org. Web Site: www.desertmuseum.org. *Librn*, Kimberly Buck. Subject Specialists: *Natural history*, Kimberly Buck; Staff 1 (MLS 1)

Founded 1952
Library Holdings: Bk Titles 6,300; Per Subs 85
Subject Interests: Botany, Ecology, Geology, Natural history, Zoology
Special Collections: Natural History Coll, slides
Restriction: By appointment only
Function: Research library

S BURR-BROWN CORP, Technical Library,* PO Box 11400, 85734. SAN 324-6531. Tel: 520-746-7788. FAX: 520-746-7467.
Founded 1980
Jan 1997-Dec 1998 Income $70,000. Mats Exp $34,000, Books $10,000, Per/Ser (Incl. Access Fees) $20,000, Micro $500, AV Equip $1,000, Other Print Mats $2,500
Library Holdings: Bk Titles 1,500; Per Subs 30
Subject Interests: Bus mgt, Electron device physics, High-tech, Hybrid assembly-manufacturing, Semiconductor fabrication, Semiconductor physics
Automation Activity & Vendor Info: (Cataloging) CASPR
Partic in Dialog Corporation; Nerac

M CARONDELET SAINT MARY'S HOSPITAL, Ralph Henry Fuller Medical Library, 1601 W St Mary's Rd, 85745. SAN 300-4600. Tel: 520-620-4974. FAX: 520-620-4936. *Librn*, Nancy Bart; E-Mail: njbart@azstarnet.com; *Librn*, Barbara Doose
Founded 1937
Library Holdings: Bk Titles 600; Per Subs 80
Subject Interests: Allied health, Medicine, Nursing
Publications: Serials list (annual)
Partic in Medline; Pacific SW Regional Med Libr Serv

G CATALINA MOUNTAIN SCHOOL, Department of Juvenile Corrections,* PO Box 8988-CRB, 85739. SAN 326-0186. Tel: 520-628-5351. FAX: 520-628-5940. *Librn*, Kathleen Stanley
Enrl 150; Fac 13
Library Holdings: Bk Titles 2,200
Friends of the Library Group

DEPARTMENT OF VETERANS AFFAIRS

GM MEDICAL CENTER LIBRARY SERVICE, 142-D, 3601 S Sixth Ave, 85723. SAN 300-4686. Tel: 520-629-1836. FAX: 520-629-4638. *Librn*, William E Azevedo; E-Mail: azevedo.bill@forum.za.gov; Staff 1 (MLS 1)
Library Holdings: Bk Vols 2,800; Per Subs 280
Subject Interests: Medicine, Nursing, Psychiatry, Psychology
Partic in Pac SW Regional Med Libr; Vets Admin Libr Network

GM PATIENT EDUCATION RESOURCE CENTER, 3601 S Sixth Ave, 85723. Tel: 520-792-1450, Ext 6516. FAX: 520-629-4638. *Librn*, William E Azevedo
Library Holdings: Bk Vols 300

S EDWARD F BARRINS MEMORIAL LIBRARY, 2023 E Adams St, 85719-4320. SAN 371-6422. Tel: 520-327-7956. *Librn*, Christine L Taylor-Parsil
Founded 1979
Library Holdings: Bk Titles 9,000; Per Subs 54; Bks on Deafness & Sign Lang 10
Subject Interests: Braille, Hypnotherapy in med, Nursing, Psychology, Reincarnation, Religion
Special Collections: Alexandria O'Sullivan Mystery Coll; Phyllis C Barrins Coll (complete works); Religion (Catherine M Willy Commemorative Coll)

R FIRST SOUTHERN BAPTIST CHURCH LIBRARY,* 445 E Speedway, 85705. SAN 300-4554. Tel: 520-623-5858. FAX: 520-629-0978.
Founded 1957
Library Holdings: Bk Titles 6,000; Per Subs 12
Restriction: Members only

S HONEYWELL TECHNICAL LIBRARY, (Formerly AlliedSignal Inc), PO Box 38001, 85740. SAN 374-9002. Tel: 520-469-6428. FAX: 520-469-6445. *Ref*, Pat Coates; E-Mail: pat.coates@alliedsignal.com; Staff 1 (MLS 1)
Automation Activity & Vendor Info: (OPAC) Inmagic, Inc.
Restriction: Staff use only

S INTERNATIONAL SOCIETY FOR VEHICLE PRESERVATION LIBRARY,* PO Box 50046, 85703-1046. SAN 373-3912. Tel: 520-622-2201. *Dir*, Elaine C Haessner
Subject Interests: Aviation

S JABA, INC LIBRARY,* 2766 N Country Club Rd, 85716. SAN 375-5045. Tel: 520-327-7440. FAX: 520-327-7450. Web Site: www.jaba.com. *Librn*, Robert J Macer; E-Mail: rmacer@jaba.com
Founded 1981
Library Holdings: Bk Titles 650; Per Subs 10

M KINO COMMUNITY HOSPITAL LIBRARY, 2800 E Ajo Way, 85713. SAN 327-859X. Tel: 520-741-6925. FAX: 520-741-9505. *Librn*, Barbara Edwards
Library Holdings: Bk Titles 633; Per Subs 59
Subject Interests: Pediatrics, Psychiatry
Publications: Bulletin M L A

S NATIONAL OPTICAL ASTRONOMY OBSERVATORIES LIBRARY, 950 N Cherry, 85726-4933. (Mail add: PO Box 26732, 85726-6732), SAN 300-4562. Tel: 520-318-8295. FAX: 520-318-8360. E-Mail: library@noao.edu. *Librn*, Mary Guerrieri; Staff 1 (MLS 1)
Founded 1958
Library Holdings: Bk Titles 15,000; Per Subs 100
Subject Interests: Astronomy, Astrophysics
Partic in Fedlink; OCLC Online Computer Library Center, Inc

S NATIONAL PARK SERVICE, Western Archeological & Conservation Center Library, 1415 N Sixth Ave, 85705. SAN 300-4570. Tel: 520-670-6501, Ext 245. FAX: 520-670-6525. *Librn*, Christine Simpson; E-Mail: chris_simpson@nps.gov
Founded 1952
Library Holdings: Bk Vols 4,000; Bk Titles 3,000; Per Subs 45
Subject Interests: Anthropology, Natural resources
Special Collections: Archives of archeological records of Southwestern US, (600 linear ft of mat); Stabilization & Environmental Impact Statements; Unpublished Reports & Manuscripts on Archaeological Excavations
Restriction: Staff use only
Partic in Fedlink; OCLC Online Computer Library Center, Inc
Reference access to document/photo archives

SR NEWMAN CATHOLIC STUDENT CENTER, Timothy Parkman Memorial Library, 1615 E Second St, 85719. SAN 300-4589. Tel: 520-327-6662. FAX: 520-327-6559. E-Mail: jhn@azstarnet.com. Web Site: arizona.edu/~newman. *Dir*, Albert Felice-Pace
Founded 1952
Library Holdings: Bk Vols 3,350; Bk Titles 3,300; Per Subs 61
Subject Interests: Catholicism, Philosophy, Psychology, Theology

J PIMA COMMUNITY COLLEGE, West Campus Library,* 2202 W Anklam Rd, 85709-0001. SAN 330-7328. Tel: 520-206-6821. FAX: 520-206-3059. *Dir*, Joseph Labuda; E-Mail: jlabuda@pimacc.pima.edu; *Librn*, Margaret A Holleman; *Ref*, Gretchen Graham; *Online Servs, Ref*, Nancy Buchanan; Staff 5 (MLS 5)
Founded 1970. Enrl 6,170; Fac 203
Library Holdings: Bk Vols 160,000; Per Subs 650
Subject Interests: Allied health, Criminal law and justice, Ethnic studies
Special Collections: Children's Coll; SAMS Photofacts; Spanish Language Coll
Automation Activity & Vendor Info: (Acquisitions) Innovative Interfaces Inc.; (Circulation) Innovative Interfaces Inc.; (Serials) Innovative Interfaces Inc.
Publications: Community & Junior College Libraries (bi-annual)
Partic in Dialog Corporation
Special Services for the Deaf - High interest/low vocabulary books; Special interest periodicals; Staff with knowledge of sign language
Special Services for the Blind - VisualTek closed circuit TV reading aid
Departmental Libraries:

COMMUNITY CAMPUS LIBRARY SERVICES, 401 N Bonita Ave, 85709-5060. SAN 372-0276. Tel: 520-206-6485. FAX: 520-206-6542. Web Site: www.library.pima.edu. *Dir Libr Serv*, Helen Meadors; *Librn*, Bob Baker; Fax: 520-206-6517, E-Mail: bbaker@pimacc.pima.edu
Enrl 2,336

DESERT VISTA, 5901 S Calle Santa Cruz, 85709-6055. SAN 373-0069. Tel: 520-206-5044. FAX: 520-206-5090. Web Site: dv.pima.edu/~aarroyo/library.htm. *Dir*, Diane Viewing Kruse; E-Mail: dkruse@pimacc.pima.edu
Library Holdings: Bk Titles 18,017; Per Subs 145
Automation Activity & Vendor Info: (Circulation) Innovative Interfaces Inc.

DOWNTOWN, 1255 N Stone, 85709-3035. SAN 330-7352. Tel: 520-206-6269. FAX: 520-206-6201. *Dir*, Kathy Curley; *Librn*, Sandy Chan; *Librn*, Charles Becker; *Librn*, Mary Stout
Founded 1974. Enrl 4,036; Fac 85; Highest Degree: Associate
Library Holdings: Bk Vols 24,764; Bk Titles 22,829; Per Subs 162
Subject Interests: Automotive engineering, Graphic arts, Technology

EAST, 8181 E Irvington Rd, 85709-4000. SAN 330-7387. Tel: 520-722-7693. FAX: 520-722-7690. *Dir*, Karl B Johnson; *Librn*, Becky Moore; Staff 5 (MLS 2, Non-MLS 3)
Founded 1976. Enrl 2,070; Fac 40
Library Holdings: Bk Vols 24,904; Bk Titles 23,619; Per Subs 181

LIBRARY TECHNICAL SERVICES, 4905B E Broadway Blvd, 85709-1140. SAN 374-8189. Tel: 520-206-4607. FAX: 520-206-4890. Web Site: www.library.pima.edu. *Dir Libr Serv*, Helen Meadors; Tel: 520-206-4608, E-Mail: hmeadors@pimacc.pima.edu; Staff 2 (MLS 2)
Founded 1969. Enrl 17,500; Fac 363; Highest Degree: Associate
Jul 1998-Jun 1999 Mats Exp $373,185, Books $167,561, Per/Ser (Incl. Access Fees) $182,705, AV Equip $22,919
Automation Activity & Vendor Info: (Acquisitions) Innovative Interfaces Inc.; (Cataloging) Innovative Interfaces Inc.; (Circulation) Innovative Interfaces Inc.; (Serials) Innovative Interfaces Inc.
Partic in Amigos Library Services, Inc; Aznet; OCLC Online Computer Library Center, Inc

S PIMA COUNCIL ON AGING LIBRARY, 5055 E Broadway, Ste C-104, 85711-3641. SAN 329-9163. Tel: 520-790-7262. FAX: 520-790-7577. *Librn*, Melissa S Morgan; Staff 1 (MLS 1)
Library Holdings: Per Subs 10,000
Subject Interests: Pub policy aspects of aging, Social aspects of aging

G PIMA COUNTY JUVENILE COURT CENTER LIBRARY, 2225 E Ajo Way, 85713-6295. SAN 326-3266. Tel: 520-740-2082. FAX: 520-628-5822. *Librn*, Gwen Reid
Founded 1976. Pop 590
Jul 2000-Jun 2001 Income County $13,000. Mats Exp $9,500, Books $5,000, Per/Ser (Incl. Access Fees) $1,500, Other Print Mats $3,000. Sal $6,000
Library Holdings: Bk Titles 1,050; Per Subs 33; Spec Interest Per Sub 10
Subject Interests: Juvenile delinquency

GL PIMA COUNTY LAW LIBRARY, Superior Court Bldg, 110 W Congress, Rm 256, 85701-1317. SAN 300-4597. Tel: 520-740-8456. FAX: 520-791-9122. E-Mail: pcll@azstarnet.com. Web Site: www.sc.co.pima.az.us/lawlib/. *Dir*, Brenda B Kelley; Staff 4 (MLS 1, Non-MLS 3)
Founded 1915
Jul 1999-Jun 2000 Income $390,614, County $164,933, Locally Generated Income $225,681. Mats Exp $269,446, Books $4,427, Per/Ser (Incl. Access Fees) $256,749, Electronic Ref Mat (Incl. Access Fees) $8,270. Sal $134,246 (Prof $60,000)
Library Holdings: Bk Vols 35,000; Bk Titles 2,000
Automation Activity & Vendor Info: (Cataloging) CASPR; (Circulation) CASPR; (OPAC) CASPR; (Serials) CASPR

G PIMA COUNTY PUBLIC WORKS LIBRARY, 201 N Stone Ave, 85701. SAN 326-2464. Tel: 520-740-6818. FAX: 520-623-5411. *Librn*, Paul Matty; E-Mail: pmatty@wwm.co.pima.az.us; Staff 1 (MLS 1)
Founded 1975
Library Holdings: Bk Titles 6,000; Per Subs 50
Subject Interests: Flood control, Land use planning, Transportation, Waste mgt
Publications: Converting to Access Software
Restriction: By appointment only

M PIMA MEDICAL INSTITUTE LIBRARY,* 3350 E Grant Rd, 85716. SAN 375-6785. Tel: 520-326-1600. FAX: 520-795-3463.
Library Holdings: Bk Vols 5,000; Bk Titles 2,000; Per Subs 78

S RAYTHEON TECHNICAL LIBRARY, 1151 E Hermans Rd, Bldg 811/T, 85706. (Mail add: PO Box 11337, Bldg 811/T, 85734), SAN 375-7722. Tel: 520-794-8807. *Librn*, Shannon Mack; E-Mail: slmack@west.raytheon.com; Staff 2 (MLS 1, Non-MLS 1)
Library Holdings: Bk Titles 16,408; Per Subs 300
Subject Interests: Aeronautics, Electronics, Mathematics, Physics, Radar
Database Vendor: Ebsco - EbscoHost, epixtech, inc., Silverplatter Information Inc.
Function: Research library

S RELIABILITY ENGINEERING & MANAGEMENT INSTITUTE, Technical Information Center, 7340 N La Oesta Ave, 85704-3119. SAN 373-0190. Tel: 520-621-2495, 520-621-6120. FAX: 520-621-8191. *Prof*, Dimitri B Kececioglu; Tel: 520-621-6120, E-Mail: dimitri@u.arizona.edu
Founded 1964. Enrl 35,000; Fac 2,200; Highest Degree: Doctorate
Library Holdings: Bk Vols 3,000
Subject Interests: Engineering

M SAINT JOSEPH'S HOSPITAL, Bruce Cole Memorial Library, 350 N Wilmot, 85711. SAN 328-588X. Tel: 520-721-3925. FAX: 520-721-6554. E-Mail: csjlibr@class.org. *Librn*, Michelle Bureau
Library Holdings: Bk Vols 800
Subject Interests: Ophthalmology

SR SAINT MARK'S PRESBYTERIAN CHURCH LIBRARY,* 3809 E Third St, 85716. SAN 373-3890. Tel: 520-325-1519. FAX: 520-327-4599. *Librn*, Don Dickinson; Tel: 520-325-1001
Library Holdings: Bk Vols 12,000; Bk Titles 10,000
Subject Interests: Counseling, Marriage, Philosophy, Religion, Theology

S SAN XAVIER LEARNING CENTER LIBRARY,* 2018 W San Xavier Rd, 85746. SAN 377-0761. Tel: 520-294-5727, 520-295-1025. FAX: 520-294-0613. *Librn*, Harlan Moreno
Library Holdings: Bk Vols 2,200

S SCOUT MUSEUM OF SOUTHERN ARIZONA, INC LIBRARY, 1937 E Blacklidge Dr, 85719. SAN 375-3824. Tel: 520-326-7669. *Pres*, Dr James Klein; Staff 12 (Non-MLS 12)
Founded 1986
Library Holdings: Bk Titles 500
Special Collections: Boy Scout History (Scout Museum of South Arizona Coll), bks, memorabilia
Publications: Messenger Newsletter

R TEMPLE EMANUEL LIBRARY,* 225 N Country Club Rd, 85716. SAN 300-4619. Tel: 520-327-4501, Ext 16. FAX: 520-327-4504.
Founded 1910
Library Holdings: Bk Titles 9,500; Per Subs 10
Subject Interests: Fiction, Judaica (lit or hist of Jews), Religious orders

S TOHONO CHUL PARK LIBRARY,* 7366 N Paseo del Norte, 85704. SAN 375-6572. Tel: 520-742-6455. FAX: 520-797-1213. E-Mail: general@tohonochulpark.org. *In Charge*, Jo Falls
Founded 1985
Library Holdings: Bk Titles 750
Special Collections: Desert Plants (Organic Gardening, Boyce Thompson Arboretum); Journal of Arizona Archaelogical & Historical Society; Journal of Arizona History
Restriction: Staff use only

S TUCSON CITY PLANNING DEPARTMENT LIBRARY,* PO Box 27210, 85726-7210. SAN 327-2923. Tel: 520-791-4234. FAX: 520-791-2663. *Librn*, Anna Sanchez; E-Mail: asanche1@ci.tucson.az.us
Library Holdings: Bk Titles 5,000; Per Subs 25
Subject Interests: Architecture, Planning
Publications: Publications catalog

S TUCSON ELECTRIC POWER CO LIBRARY, 3950 E Irvington, PO Box 711, 85714. SAN 300-4635. Tel: 520-745-3318. FAX: 520-571-4019. *In Charge*, Jana Swinney; E-Mail: jswinney@tucsonelectric.com
Founded 1974
Library Holdings: Bk Vols 1,100; Per Subs 325

M TUCSON MEDICAL CENTER LIBRARY,* 5301 E Grant Rd, 85712. (Mail add: PO Box 42195, 85733-2195), SAN 300-4651. Tel: 520-324-5140. FAX: 520-324-5363. E-Mail: library@tmcaz.com. Web Site: www.tmcaz.com. *Mgr*, Jeffrey W St Clair; *Librn*, Michelle Bureau; Staff 3 (MLS 2, Non-MLS 1)
Founded 1962
1998-1999 Mats Exp $83,000, Books $11,000, Per/Ser (Incl. Access Fees) $45,000
Library Holdings: Bk Titles 2,000; Per Subs 340
Subject Interests: Business and management, Clinical medicine, History of medicine, Nursing
Automation Activity & Vendor Info: (Acquisitions) EOS; (Cataloging) EOS; (Circulation) EOS; (OPAC) EOS
Partic in Ariz Health Info Network; MLGSCA; National Network Of Libraries Of Medicine - South Central Region; PSRMLS

S TUCSON MUSEUM OF ART LIBRARY, 140 N Main Ave, 85701-8290. SAN 300-466X. Tel: 520-624-2333, Ext 122. FAX: 520-624-7202. Web Site: www. tucsonarts.com. *Exec Dir*, Robert A Yassin; *Coll Develop, Mgr Libr*, Jill E Provan; E-Mail: jprovan@tucsonarts.com
Founded 1974
Jul 2000-Jun 2001 Mats Exp $13,834
Library Holdings: Bk Vols 10,500; Per Subs 35
Subject Interests: Art history, Folk art, Pre-Columbian art, Spanish colonial art
Special Collections: Archival papers of Arizona artists; Berta Wright Folk Art Coll, bks & pamphlets; John Maul, Charles Clement & Ray Strang; Pre-Columbian, African & Oceanic Arts (Fredrick Pleasant's Coll), bks, pamphlets, photogs, slides; Spanish Colonial, Western & 20th Century European & American Art, Folk Art
Publications: Bibliographies; Folk Art Resources; In-house Pre-Columbian Art Books, Pamphlets, Videos & Slides; Spanish Colonial Resources
Restriction: Circulation limited, Non-circulating to the public, Open to faculty, students & qualified researchers, Open to public for reference & circulation; with some limitations
Function: Reference services available, Research library, Some telephone reference
Friends of the Library Group

S TUCSON UNIFIED SCHOOL DISTRICT, (EMC), Educational Materials Center Library, 2025 E Winsett, 85719. SAN 375-6548. Tel: 520-617-7004. FAX: 520-617-7123. *Librn*, Obdulia Gonzalez; *Librn*, Judi Schwarz; *Librn*, Jan Strell; Staff 3 (MLS 3)
Library Holdings: Per Subs 50
Subject Interests: Bilingual Education, Education
Restriction: Circulation limited

P TUCSON-PIMA PUBLIC LIBRARY, 101 N Stone Ave, PO Box 27470, 85726-7470. SAN 330-7417. Tel: 520-791-4391. FAX: 520-791-3213. Web Site: www.lib.ci.tucson.az.us. *Dir*, Agnes M Griffen; *Asst Dir*, Patrick Corella; *Dep Dir*, Betsy Stunz-Hall; *ILL*, Michelle Graye; *Adminr, Coll Develop*, Annette Meyer; *Adminr, Outreach Serv*, Laura Thomas Sullivan; *Adminr*, Karen Thayer; *Adminr*, Jere Voigt. Subject Specialists: *Management*, Karen Thayer; *Technology*, Karen Thayer; Staff 87 (MLS 87)
Founded 1883. Pop 863,315; Circ 5,383,213
Jul 2000-Jun 2001 Income (Main Library and Branch Library) $19,211,654, State $60,629, City $9,454,440, County $9,454,440, Other $242,145. Mats Exp $3,207,550, Books $2,081,550, Per/Ser (Incl. Access Fees) $500,000, Presv $1,000, Micro $5,000, AV Equip $400,000, Electronic Ref Mat (Incl. Access Fees) $220,000. Sal $11,815,400 (Prof $3,207,550)

Library Holdings: Bk Vols 1,219,400; Bk Titles 203,260; Per Subs 2,695; Bks on Deafness & Sign Lang 200
Subject Interests: Arizona, Business and management, Government
Special Collections: Southwestern Literature for Children
Automation Activity & Vendor Info: (Acquisitions) Innovative Interfaces Inc.; (Cataloging) Innovative Interfaces Inc.; (Circulation) Innovative Interfaces Inc.; (OPAC) Innovative Interfaces Inc.
Partic in Amigos Library Services, Inc; OCLC Online Computer Library Center, Inc
Friends of the Library Group
Branches: 20
MILLER-GOLF LINKS, 9640 E Golf Links Rd, 85730. Tel: 520-791-5524. *Mgr Libr*, Midji Stephenson
Library Holdings: Bk Vols 75,700
CAVIGLIA-ARIVACA, 17050 W Arivaca Rd, 85601. SAN 371-9685. Tel: 520-398-2764. FAX: 520-791-5247. *Librn*, Mary Kasulaitis
Library Holdings: Bk Vols 15,400
Friends of the Library Group
COLUMBUS, 4350 E 22nd St, 85711. SAN 330-7476. Tel: 520-791-4081. FAX: 520-791-5344. *Mgr Libr*, Daphne Daly
Library Holdings: Bk Vols 71,300
DEWHIRST CATALINA, 15631 N Oracle Rd, Catalina, 85737. SAN 371-9693. Tel: 520-825-9541. FAX: 520-791-4659. *Senior Librn*, Kathleen Dannreuther
Library Holdings: Bk Vols 16,000
DUSENBERRY RIVER CENTER, 5605 E River Rd, No 105, 85715. SAN 371-9707. Tel: 520-791-4979. FAX: 520-791-4982. *Mgr Libr*, Bonny Bruce
Library Holdings: Bk Vols 84,300
EL PUEBLO, 101 W Irvington, 85714. SAN 330-7743. Tel: 520-791-4733. FAX: 520-791-5372. *Librn*, Frank De La Cruz
Library Holdings: Bk Vols 13,500
EL RIO, 1390 W Speedway, 85745. SAN 330-7778. Tel: 520-791-4468. FAX: 520-791-5373. *Librn*, Yolanda Sainz
Library Holdings: Bk Vols 11,000
G FREEMAN WOODS BRANCH, 3455 N First Ave, 85719. SAN 330-7506. Tel: 520-791-4548. FAX: 520-791-5246. *Mgr Libr*, Mary Robinson
Library Holdings: Bk Vols 102,000
HIMMEL PARK, 1035 N Treat, 85716. SAN 330-7565. Tel: 520-791-4397. FAX: 520-791-5339. *Librn*, Carol Ann Rott
Library Holdings: Bk Vols 48,000
JOYNER-GREEN VALLEY, 601 N La Canada Dr, Green Valley, 85614. SAN 330-7530. Tel: 520-625-8660. FAX: 520-791-5247. *Mgr Libr*, Sarajean Harwood
Library Holdings: Bk Vols 63,900
Friends of the Library Group
KIRK BEAR CANYON, 8959 E Tanque Verde Rd, 85749. SAN 371-9715. Tel: 520-791-5021. FAX: 520-791-5024. *Mgr Libr*, Roberta Barg
Library Holdings: Bk Vols 68,300
Friends of the Library Group
MAIN, 101 N Stone Ave, 85701. SAN 330-759X. Tel: 520-791-4010. FAX: 520-791-5248. *Adminr*, Jere Voigt; *Mgr Libr*, Joan Biggar
Library Holdings: Bk Vols 170,500
Friends of the Library Group
MARANA, 13370 Lon Adams Rd, 85653. SAN 330-7808. Tel: 520-682-4216. FAX: 520-791-4792. *Librn*, Meg Macleish
Library Holdings: Bk Vols 10,500
MISSION, 3770 S Mission Rd, 85713. SAN 330-762X. Tel: 520-791-4811. FAX: 520-791-5330. *Mgr Libr*, Elva Smithwhite
Library Holdings: Bk Vols 60,000
NANINI, 7300 N Shannon Rd, 85741. SAN 330-7654. Tel: 520-791-4626. FAX: 520-791-5245. *Mgr Libr*, Kristi Bradford
Library Holdings: Bk Vols 117,000
PIMA COUNTY DETENTION CENTER, 1270 W Silver Lake, PO Box 910, 85702. SAN 330-7832. *Senior Librn*, Jimmie Bevill
Library Holdings: Bk Vols 14,200
SALAZAR-AJO BRANCH, 33 Plaza, Ajo, 85321. SAN 330-7441. Tel: 520-387-6075. FAX: 520-387-5345. *In Charge*, James Schnell
Library Holdings: Bk Vols 17,300
SAM LENA SOUTH TUCSON, 1601 S Sixth Ave, 85713. SAN 330-7867. Tel: 520-791-4791. FAX: 520-791-5374. *Librn*, Ramona Grijalva
Library Holdings: Bk Vols 24,000
VALENCIA, 202 W Valencia Rd, 85706. SAN 330-7689. Tel: 520-791-4531. FAX: 520-791-5342. *Mgr Libr*, Amanda Castillo
Library Holdings: Bk Vols 81,200
WILMOT, 530 N Wilmot Rd, 85711. SAN 330-7719. Tel: 520-791-4627. FAX: 520-791-5343. *Mgr Libr*, Elaine Baarson
Library Holdings: Bk Vols 128,000
Bookmobiles: 3. Homebound vehicle - 1, Bookmobile - 1, Youth van - 1

SR UNITARIAN UNIVERSALIST CHURCH LIBRARY,* 4831 E 22nd St, 85711-4903. SAN 374-7719. Tel: 520-748-1551. FAX: 520-748-0178. E-Mail: uu@azstarnet.com.
Library Holdings: Bk Vols 300

G USDA AGRICULTURAL RESEARCH SERVICE, Southwest Watershed Research Center,* 2000 E Allen Rd, 85719. SAN 375-1821. Tel: 520-670-6381. FAX: 520-670-5550. *Librn*, E Sue Anderson
Library Holdings: Bk Titles 300; Per Subs 15

G UNITED STATES GEOLOGICAL SURVEY, Water Resources Division Library,* 520 N Park Ave, 85719-6644. SAN 374-7948. Tel: 520-670-6201, Ext 246. FAX: 520-670-5592. Web Site: www.daz.water.usgs.gov. *Librn*, Patsy Martinez; E-Mail: martinez@usgs.gov
Library Holdings: Bk Vols 5,000
Restriction: Open to public for reference only

C UNIVERSITY OF ARIZONA, Main Library, 1510 E University Blvd, PO Box 210055, 85721-0055. SAN 330-7891. Tel: 520-621-2101. Interlibrary Loan Service Tel: 520-621-6438. FAX: 520-621-9733. Web Site: dizzy.library.arizona.edu. *Dean of Libr*, Carla Stoffle; *Ref*, Janet Fore; *Govt Doc*, Cynthia Bower; *Ser*, Liz Bezanson; Staff 210 (MLS 69, Non-MLS 141)
Founded 1891. Enrl 32,783; Fac 1,623; Highest Degree: Doctorate
Library Holdings: Bk Vols 4,001,137; Per Subs 15,557
Special Collections: Arizoniana; Drama (T W Stevens Coll); Fiction; Fine Arts (Hanley Coll); Food & Agr Orgn & European Econ Community; History of Science; Mexican Colonial History; Photography as an Art Form (Center for Creative Photography); Private Press (Frank Holme Coll); Science; Southwestern Americana
Publications: Arizona Index; Azu Library Newsletter; Center for Creative Photography (journal); Guide to Chicano Resources; Index to Arizona News in the Arizona Daily Star; Libraries of the U of A; Library Information Guides; Library Skills Program Workbook
Mem of Asn of Research Libraries
Partic in Amigos Library Services, Inc; Center For Research Libraries
Special Services for the Deaf - Books on deafness & sign language; High interest/low vocabulary books; Special interest periodicals
Friends of the Library Group
Departmental Libraries:
ARID LANDS INFORMATION CENTER, College of Agriculture, 1955 E Sixth St, 85719. SAN 330-7913. Tel: 520-621-7897. FAX: 520-621-3816. Web Site: ag.arizona.edu/OALS/oals/alic/alic.html. *Dir, Librn*, Barbara Hutchinson; E-Mail: barbarah@ag.arizona.edu; Staff 7 (MLS 5, Non-MLS 2)
Founded 1968
Oct 1999-Sep 2000 Income $200,000, State $100,000, Locally Generated Income $100,000. Mats Exp $900, Books $300, Per/Ser (Incl. Access Fees) $500, Other Print Mats $100. Sal $200,000 (Prof $150,000)
Library Holdings: Bk Vols 35,000; Per Subs 15
Subject Interests: Water resources
Special Collections: Desert Slide Coll; Developing Country Profiles; Guayule; Jojoba
Publications: Arid Lands Newsletter
CM ARIZONA HEALTH SCIENCES LIBRARY, 1501 N Campbell Ave, 85724-5079. (Mail add: PO Box 245079, 85724-5079), SAN 330-7921. Tel: 520-626-6121. Interlibrary Loan Service Tel: 520-626-6840. Circulation Tel: 520-626-6241. Reference Tel: 520-626-6125. FAX: 520-626-2922. Interlibrary Loan Service FAX: 520-626-2831. E-Mail: refdesk@ahsl.arizona.edu. Web Site: www.ahsl.arizona.edu/. *Dep Dir*, Jeanette C McCray; Tel: 520-626-6143, E-Mail: mccray@ahsl.arizona.edu; *Res*, Zoe Stavri; Tel: 520-626-8537, E-Mail: zstavri@ahsl.arizona.edu; *Access Serv*, Joan B Schlimgen; Tel: 520-626-6140, E-Mail: joan@ahsl.arizona.edu; *Head, Info Serv*, Gerald J Perry; Tel: 520-626-6438, E-Mail: jperry@ahsl.arizona.edu; *Syst Coordr*, Kristin A Antelman; Tel: 520-626-1004, E-Mail: kaa@ahsl.arizona.edu; *Tech Servs*, Mary Holcomb; Tel: 520-626-2924, E-Mail: mholcomb@ahsl.arizona.edu; *Ref*, Hannah Fisher; Tel: 520-626-2933, E-Mail: hannah@ahsl.arizona.edu; *Ref*, Fred Heidenreich; Tel: 520-626-7724, E-Mail: fredheid@ahsl.arizona.edu; *Ref*, David Howse; Tel: 520-626-2934; *Info Tech*, Dave Piper; Tel: 520-626-2529, E-Mail: dpiper@ahsl.arizona.edu; *Ref*, Mary Riordan; Tel: 520-626-3510, E-Mail: mriordan@ahsl.arizona.edu; *Tech Servs*, Sue Trombley; Tel: 520-626-4656, E-Mail: susant@ahsl.arizona.edu; *Access Serv*, Pat Auflick; Tel: 520-626-6770, E-Mail: aauflick@ahsl.arizona.edu; Staff 51 (MLS 16, Non-MLS 35)
Founded 1965. Highest Degree: Doctorate
Jul 1999-Jun 2000 Income $3,740,422, State $2,901,248, Federal $39,875, Locally Generated Income $513,936, Parent Institution $234,432, Other $50,931. Mats Exp $1,235,285, Books $119,841, Per/Ser (Incl. Access Fees) $937,681, Presv $32,664, Micro $495, Other Print Mats $17,002, Electronic Ref Mat (Incl. Access Fees) $127,602. Sal $1,459,537 (Prof $812,489)
Library Holdings: Bk Vols 214,558; Bk Titles 86,006; Per Subs 2,047
Subject Interests: Health occupations, Medicine, Nursing, Pharmacy, Public health
Special Collections: Archives; Arizona Health Sciences Center & History of Health Care & The Healing Arts in the Southwest
Automation Activity & Vendor Info: (Acquisitions) SIRSI; (Cataloging) SIRSI; (Circulation) SIRSI; (OPAC) SIRSI; (Serials) SIRSI
Publications: Focus on Health Information (newsletter)
Partic in Amigos Library Services, Inc; Ariz Health Info Network; Ariz Univ Librs Coun; National Network of Libraries of Medicine - Greater

Midwest Region; Pac SW Regional Med Libr
Open Mon-Thurs 8-8, Fri 8-5, Sat & Sun 1-5 (reference hours); Open 24 hours
CENTER FOR CREATIVE PHOTOGRAPHY, 1030 N Olive, 85721. SAN 330-7956. Tel: 520-621-7968. FAX: 520-621-9444. Web Site: www.creativephotography.org. *Actg Dir*, Amy Rule; *Librn*, Miguel Juarez; Staff 18 (MLS 3, Non-MLS 15)
Founded 1975
Library Holdings: Bk Titles 7,100; Per Subs 75

CL COLLEGE OF LAW LIBRARY, 1201 E Speedway, PO Box 210176, 85721-0176. Tel: 520-621-1413. FAX: 520-621-3138. Web Site: www.law.arizona.edu/. *Dir*, Michael G Chiorazzi; E-Mail: chiorazzi@nt.law.arizona.edu; *Cat*, Astrid Norvelle; E-Mail: knorvelle@nt.law.arizona.edu; *Access Serv*, Maureen Garmon; E-Mail: garmon@nt.law.arizona.edu; *Publ Servs*, Shaun Esposito; E-Mail: esposito@nt.law.arizona.edu; *Tech Servs*, Robert Genovese; E-Mail: rgenovese@nt.law.arizona.edu; *Govt Doc, Ref*, Jacquelyn Kasper; E-Mail: kasper@nt.law.arizona.edu; *Ref*, Leah Sandwell-Weiss; E-Mail: sandwell@nt.law.arizona.edu; *Electronic Resources, Ref*, Iain Barksdale; E-Mail: barksdale@nt.law.arizona.edu. Subject Specialists: *Foreign law*, Francisco Avalos; *International law*, Francisco Avalos
Founded 1915
Library Holdings: Bk Vols 383,774; Bk Titles 65,556; Per Subs 4,449
Subject Interests: Natural resources
Restriction: Not a lending library, Open to faculty, students & qualified researchers
Function: Photocopies available
Partic in OCLC Online Computer Library Center, Inc
EAST ASIAN COLLECTION, 1510 E University Blvd, 85720-0055. Tel: 520-621-6382. FAX: 520-621-3655. *Librn*, Gene Hsiao; E-Mail: ghsiao@bird.library.arizona.edu; *Librn*, Hitoshi Kamada; Tel: 520-626-9303, E-Mail: kamadah@bird.library.arizona.edu
Subject Interests: Chinese, Japanese studies
FILM COLLECTION Tel: 520-621-3282. FAX: 520-621-9733.
GOVERNMENT DOCUMENTS DEPT Tel: 520-621-4872. FAX: 520-621-9733. *Librn*, Cynthia Bower
Library Holdings: Bk Vols 700,000
INFORMATION ACCESS TEAM Tel: 520-621-6444. FAX: 520-621-9733.
MEDIA CENTER Tel: 520-621-6406. FAX: 520-621-9733. *Librn*, Bonnie Travers
MUSEUM OF ART Tel: 520-621-7567. FAX: 520-621-8770. *Librn*, Barbara Kittle; *Librn*, Maurya Melton Smith; E-Mail: mauryas@u.arizona.edu; Staff 1 (MLS 1)
Library Holdings: Bk Titles 6,500; Per Subs 10
Subject Interests: Art history, Museology
Publications: Exhibit catalogues
MUSIC COLLECTION Tel: 520-621-7009. *Librn*, Robert Follet

CM RURAL HEALTH OFFICE LIBRARY, 2501 E Elm St, 85716. SAN 374-7298. Tel: 520-626-7946, Ext 132. FAX: 520-321-7792. Web Site: www.rho.arizona.edu/mc/library.htm. *Assoc Librn*, Patricia A Auflick; Tel: 520-626-7946, E-Mail: pauflick@rho.arizona.edu. Subject Specialists: *Public health*, Patricia A Auflick; Staff 1 (MLS 1)
Founded 1987
Jul 1999-Jun 2000 Income $50,200, Federal $50,000, Locally Generated Income $200. Mats Exp $6,000, Per/Ser (Incl. Access Fees) $1,000, Electronic Ref Mat (Incl. Access Fees) $5,000. Sal $43,000 (Prof $43,000)
Library Holdings: Per Subs 52
Subject Interests: Border studies, Health policy, Managed care, Public health, Rural health
Database Vendor: IAC - Info Trac, OVID Technologies
Function: ILL available
Partic in AZHIN; Cent Ariz Biomed Librns
SCIENCE-ENGINEERING, 744 N Highland, PO Box 210054, 85721. Tel: 520-621-6394. FAX: 520-621-3655. *In Charge*, Karen Holloway
SOCIAL SCIENCES, 1510 E University, 85721-0055. (Mail add: PO Box 210055, 85721-0055), Tel: 520-621-4869. FAX: 520-621-9733. Web Site: www.dizzy.library.arizona.edu/users/kollen/geog.htm, www.dizzy.library.arizona.edu/users/kollen/soced.htm. *Librn*, Chris Kollen; E-Mail: kollen@bird.library.arizona.edu
SPACE IMAGERY CENTER, Lunar & Planetary Laboratory, PO Box 210092, 85721-0092. SAN 321-6721. Tel: 520-621-4861. FAX: 520-621-4933. *Dir*, Robert Strom
Founded 1977
Subject Interests: Planetary sci
Special Collections: Apollo; Lunar Orbiter; Magellan, etc; Mariner 6, 7, 9, 10; Pioneer 10 & 11; Space Probes - Gemini; Viking 1 & 2; Voyager 1 & 2
Publications: library brochure; RPIF Consortium Newsletter
Regional Planetary Image Facilities: Flagstaff & Tempe, AZ; Pasadena, CA; Washington, DC; Honolulu, HI; St Louis, MO; Ithaca, NY; Providence, RI; Houston, TX; London, England; Oulu, Finland; Paris, France; Berlin, Germany; Rome, Italy; Kanagawa, Japan
SPECIAL COLLECTIONS DEPT Tel: 520-621-6423. FAX: 520-621-9733. *Librn*, Roger Myers; Tel: 520-621-4345, E-Mail: rmyers@bird.library.arizona.edu

W R BROWN MEMORIAL LIBRARY, (Formerly Arabian Hosre Owners Foundation), 4101 N Bear Canyon Rd, 85749. SAN 327-912X. Tel: 520-760-0682. Toll Free Tel: 800-892-0682. FAX: 520-749-2572. E-Mail: ahof001@aol.com. Web Site: www.ahof.org. *Exec Dir*, Howard Shenk; E-Mail: ahof001@aol.com; *Admin Dir*, Felicia LaBorde; E-Mail: shelnick816@aol.com
Founded 1956
Oct 1997-Sep 1998 Income $30,000. Mats Exp $15,000
Library Holdings: Bk Titles 2,300; Per Subs 17
Special Collections: Horse books dating from 1587

WHITERIVER

J NORTHLAND PIONEER COLLEGE, Whiteriver Center, Learning Resource Center,* PO Box 1599, 85941. SAN 300-4708. Tel: 520-338-4662. FAX: 520-338-4662. *Librn*, Denise Henry
Library Holdings: Bk Vols 500; Bk Titles 300; Per Subs 10
Special Collections: Indian Americana Coll
Partic in Ariz Resources Consortium

P WHITERIVER PUBLIC LIBRARY, Main St, PO Box 370, 85941. SAN 300-4716. Tel: 520-338-4884. FAX: 520-338-4470.
Founded 1934. Pop 10,000
Library Holdings: Bk Titles 12,000; Per Subs 100
Special Collections: Arizona Coll
Mem of Navajo County Libr Syst

WICKENBURG

S DESERT CABALLEROS WESTERN MUSEUM, Blossom Memorial Library, 21 N Frontier St, 85390. SAN 375-7579. Tel: 520-684-2272. FAX: 520-684-5794. E-Mail: dcwm@primenet.com. *Dir*, Michael Ettema
Library Holdings: Bk Titles 1,500

P WICKENBURG PUBLIC LIBRARY, 164 E Apache St, 85390. SAN 300-4724. Tel: 520-684-2665. FAX: 602-506-1580. E-Mail: wkbg.pub.library@juno.com. *Head Librn*, Linda Brown; E-Mail: lbrown@dlapr.lib.az.us; *Librn*, Rosemary Clark; E-Mail: rclark@dlapr.lib.az.us; *Asst Librn*, Sylvia Herndon; E-Mail: sylviaaz@excite.com
Founded 1942. Pop 11,000; Circ 120,000
Jul 1999-Jun 2000 Income $153,887, City $134,567, County $19,320. Mats Exp $131,064, Books $18,300, Per/Ser (Incl. Access Fees) $1,000. Sal $111,064
Library Holdings: Bk Vols 38,298; Bk Titles 36,200; Per Subs 30
Special Collections: History (Southwest Coll)
Automation Activity & Vendor Info: (Cataloging) Sagebrush Corporation; (Circulation) Sagebrush Corporation
Mem of Maricopa County Libr Syst
Friends of the Library Group

WILLCOX

P ELSIE S HOGAN COMMUNITY LIBRARY, 207 W Maley St, 85643. SAN 330-5376. Tel: 520-384-4271, Ext 503. FAX: 520-384-0126. Web Site: cochise.lib.az.us/willcoxhtm. *Dir*, Nancy Guerrero; E-Mail: nguerre@willcoxpl.lib.az.us; *Asst Librn*, Tom Miner; E-Mail: tminer@willcoxpl.lib.az.us
Pop 3,800; Circ 15,000
1998-1999 Income $123,000. Mats Exp Books $13,000. Sal $73,570
Library Holdings: Bk Titles 17,746; Per Subs 30
Mem of Cochise County Library District
Friends of the Library Group

G UNITED STATES NATIONAL PARK SERVICE, Chiricahua National Monument Library, 13063 E Bonita Canyon Rd, 85643. SAN 375-2259. Tel: 520-824-3560, Ext 103. FAX: 520-824-3421. Web Site: www.nps.gov/chir. *Librn*, Suzanne Moody; E-Mail: suzanne_moody@nps.gov
Founded 1924
Library Holdings: Bk Titles 4,000
Restriction: Access at librarian's discretion
Function: For research purposes

WILLIAMS

P WILLIAMS PUBLIC LIBRARY,* 113 S First St, 86046. SAN 300-4740. Tel: 520-262-6066, 520-635-2263. Interlibrary Loan Service Tel: 520-262-4606. FAX: 520-635-4495. *Librn*, Andrea Mary Dearing; E-Mail: adearin@williams.pub.lib.az.us; Staff 1 (Non-MLS 1)
Founded 1895. Pop 2,800; Circ 14,450
Jul 1998-Jun 1999 Income $50,082, State $1,320, City $18,972, County $22,528, Locally Generated Income $7,262. Mats Exp $6,442, Books $5,378, Per/Ser (Incl. Access Fees) $419, Presv $645. Sal $30,112 (Prof $23,957)
Library Holdings: Bk Vols 9,000; Bk Titles 8,800; Per Subs 17
Subject Interests: Arizona
Mem of Coconino County Libr Syst

WINDOW ROCK

P OFFICE OF NAVAJO NATION LIBRARY, PO Box 9040, 86515. SAN 321-0693. Tel: 520-871-6376, 520-871-7304. FAX: 520-871-7304. *Dir*, Irving Nelson; *Tech Servs*, Ruby Ashley; Staff 2 (MLS 2)
Founded 1941. Pop 160,000
Library Holdings: Bk Titles 31,000; Per Subs 97
Subject Interests: Archaeology
Special Collections: Navajo History and Culture
Branches: 3
NAVAJO COMMUNITY LIBRARY, PO Box 1296, Navajo, 86509. SAN 321-9275. Tel: 505-777-2598, 520-871-6376. *Tech Servs*, Emily Shurley
Library Holdings: Bk Vols 5,890
NAVAJO NATION LIBRARY *Mgr*, Irving Nelson
Library Holdings: Bk Vols 21,844
RESEARCH LIBRARY, NM Hwy 264 Loop Rd, PO Box 9040, 86515. SAN 321-0715. Tel: 520-871-6376, 520-871-6526, 520-871-7303. FAX: 520-871-7304. *Dir*, Irving Nelson; Staff 8 (Non-MLS 8)
Founded 1951. Pop 270,000
Oct 1998-Sep 1999 Income $267,434, Federal $4,400, Locally Generated Income $223,982, Other $39,052. Sal $181,237 (Prof $34,000)
Library Holdings: Bk Vols 6,145; Bk Titles 32,045; Per Subs 40
Special Collections: J Lee Correll Archival Coll; Native American Music Coll ONEO Coll; Navajo Times Preservation Project 1959 to Present; Navajo Tribal Documents Coll; Water Library
Automation Activity & Vendor Info: (Circulation) Sagebrush Corporation
Partic in NMex Libr Asn
Special collections usage - onsite only
Friends of the Library Group
Bookmobiles: 2

WINKELMAN

§C CENTRAL ARIZONA COLLEGE, Aravaipa Campus Learning Resource Center, 80440 E Aravaipa Rd, 85292. Tel: 520-357-2021. FAX: 520-426-4494. Web Site: www.cac.cc.az.us/avclearningcen/avc_lrngctr.html. *Coordr*, Larry Sheret; Tel: 520-357-2024, E-Mail: larry_sheret@python.cac.cc.az.us
Jul 2000-Jun 2001 Income $120,000
Library Holdings: Bk Vols 16,000; Per Subs 15
Automation Activity & Vendor Info: (Cataloging) epixtech, inc.; (Circulation) epixtech, inc.; (OPAC) epixtech, inc.

WINSLOW

§S ARIZONA DEPARTMENT OF CORRECTIONS - ADULT, Arizona State Prison Complex - Winslow Library, 2100 S Hwy 87, 86047. Tel: 520-289-9551. FAX: 520-289-9551, Ext 6553. *Librn*, Ralph Johnson; Tel: 520-337-4851, Fax: 520-337-4851; *Librn*, Mike Kaliher; Tel: 520-289-09551, Ext 2717
Library Holdings: Bk Vols 21,508

S ARIZONA STATE PARKS, Homolovi Ruins State Park Library, HCR 63, Box 5, 86047-9803. SAN 371-2788. Tel: 520-289-4106. FAX: 520-289-2021. E-Mail: homolovi@pr.state.az.us. *Librn*, Karen Berggren
Library Holdings: Bk Vols 23,000
Special Collections: Indian Culture Archeolology

P ROXANNE WHIPPLE MEMORIAL LIBRARY, (RWML), Winslow City Library, 420 W Gilmore, 86047. SAN 300-4767. Tel: 520-289-4982. FAX: 520-289-4182. E-Mail: win@roxwhimem.lib.az.us. Web Site: www.winslowarizona.com. *Ch Servs*, Sarah Greenwood; *Ad Servs*, Michele Hernandez; *Circ*, Sandy Fulton; Staff 4 (MLS 1, Non-MLS 3)
Founded 1969. Pop 10,800; Circ 52,000
Jul 1999-Jun 2000 Income $213,068, State $6,000, City $197,568, County $5,000, Locally Generated Income $4,500. Mats Exp $27,000, Books $19,500, Per/Ser (Incl. Access Fees) $3,000, Micro $500, Electronic Ref Mat (Incl. Access Fees) $4,000. Sal $93,181 (Prof $41,000)
Library Holdings: Bk Vols 37,000; Bk Titles 35,000; Per Subs 90; High Interest/Low Vocabulary Bk Vols 100
Subject Interests: Indians
Special Collections: Arizona History
Automation Activity & Vendor Info: (Cataloging) epixtech, inc.; (Circulation) epixtech, inc.; (OPAC) epixtech, inc.
Database Vendor: OCLC - First Search
Partic in Channeled Ariz Info Network; Navajo County Libr District
Special Services for the Deaf - TDD
Special Services for the Blind - Talking Books
Friends of the Library Group

WOODRUFF

§P WOODRUFF COMMUNITY LIBRARY, 6414 W First St, 85942. (Mail add: PO Box 77, 85942-0077), Tel: 520-524-3885. FAX: 520-524-3885. E-Mail: wcl@navajo.lib.az.us. Web Site: www.navajoco.lib.az.us. *Librn*, Merla Sauwen
Jan 2000-Dec 2000 Income County $2,000
Library Holdings: Bk Vols 3,000
Automation Activity & Vendor Info: (Cataloging) SIRSI; (Circulation) SIRSI
Database Vendor: OCLC - First Search

YARNELL

P YARNELL PUBLIC LIBRARY, Broadway & Crossway, PO Box 808, 85362. SAN 323-8032. Tel: 520-427-3191. FAX: 520-427-3191. *Mgr*, Richard V Arklin; E-Mail: yarlib@yavapaicold.lib.az.us
Special Collections: Local Archives
Mem of Yavapai County Library District

YOUNG

P YOUNG PUBLIC LIBRARY,* 150 Community Ctr Rd, PO Box 150, 85554. SAN 300-4783. Tel: 520-462-3588. FAX: 520-462-3588. *Librn*, Shirley Williams
Founded 1965. Pop 700; Circ 3,790
Jul 1997-Jun 1998 Income $46,949, State $5,200, County $35,769, Locally Generated Income $5,146. Mats Exp $5,855, Books $3,610, Per/Ser (Incl. Access Fees) $908, Presv $150. Sal $19,041
Library Holdings: Bk Vols 17,600
Subject Interests: Art, Large type print
Special Collections: Health Videos
Mem of Gila County Library District

YOUNGTOWN

P YOUNGTOWN PUBLIC LIBRARY,* 12035 Clubhouse Sq, 85363. SAN 300-4791. Tel: 623-974-3401. *Librn*, Florence Hinrichs; E-Mail: florh@aol.com; *Asst Dir*, Pearl Lane
Founded 1956. Pop 2,500; Circ 14,000
1997-1998 Income $8,000
Library Holdings: Bk Titles 10,000
Special Collections: Arizona & Southwestern
Completely volunteer library in Maricopa County

YUMA

S ARIZONA HISTORICAL SOCIETY LIBRARY - YUMA DIVISION, 240 Madison Ave, 85364. SAN 300-4821. Tel: 520-782-1841. FAX: 520-783-0680. E-Mail: azhistyuma@cybertrails.com. *Dir*, Megan Reid; *Curator*, Carol Brooks
Founded 1963
Library Holdings: Bk Titles 500
Special Collections: Lower Colorado River Area Historical Photographs; Military Oral History Tapes-WWII period, 150 tapes
Restriction: By appointment only
Collection non-circulating

J ARIZONA WESTERN COLLEGE & NAU-YUMA, (AZY), Academic Library, 9500 S Ave 8E, 85365. (Mail add: PO Box 929, 85366-0929), SAN 300-4805. Tel: 520-344-7777. FAX: 520-344-7751. Web Site: www.awc.cc.az.us/library. *Assoc Dean*, Tim Shove; *Ref*, Pam Blome; *Ref*, Angie Creel-Erb; *Ref*, Camille O'Neill; *Ref*, Alan Schuck; *ILL*, Rickley Prewitt; *Acq*, Renee Westphal; Staff 5 (MLS 4, Non-MLS 1)
Founded 1963. Enrl 5,315; Fac 86
Jul 1998-Jun 1999 Income $374,091. Mats Exp $148,000, Books $90,000, Per/Ser (Incl. Access Fees) $30,000, Micro $15,000, AV Equip $13,000. Sal $179,636 (Prof $100,479)
Library Holdings: Bk Titles 60,000; Per Subs 684
Special Collections: Southwest Arizona & Lower Colorado River Coll
Automation Activity & Vendor Info: (Acquisitions) SIRSI; (Cataloging) SIRSI; (Circulation) SIRSI; (Course Reserve) SIRSI; (OPAC) SIRSI
Database Vendor: OCLC - First Search
Mem of Yuma County Library District
Partic in Amigos Library Services, Inc; Aznet; OCLC Online Computer Library Center, Inc

UNITED STATES ARMY

A POST LIBRARY, Bldg 530, Yuma Proving Ground, 85365-9123. SAN 330-8286. Tel: 520-328-2558. FAX: 520-328-3055. E-Mail: post@libraryayuma-exchl.army.mil. Web Site: www.yuma.army.mil/mwr/postlibrary.htm. *Librn*, Katharine Ferguson; Staff 2 (MLS 1, Non-MLS 1)
Oct 1999-Sep 2000 Income (Main Library Only) $144,600. Mats Exp $37,500, Books $10,000, Per/Ser (Incl. Access Fees) $6,000, Electronic Ref Mat (Incl. Access Fees) $2,000. Sal $110,500
Library Holdings: Bk Vols 27,000; Per Subs 186
Subject Interests: Arizona
Database Vendor: OCLC - First Search
Partic in Fedlink; OCLC Online Computer Library Center, Inc

A TECHNICAL LIBRARY, Bldg 2105, Yuma Proving Ground, MTC-TC, 85365-9110. SAN 330-8316. Tel: 520-328-6549. FAX: 520-328-6222. *Librn*, Genifrances Williamson; E-Mail: gwilliam@yuma-emh-1.army.mil

Founded 1959
Library Holdings: Bk Vols 3,000; Per Subs 60
Partic in Defense Technical Information Center; Nat Tech Info Serv

UNITED STATES MARINE CORPS
A STATION LIBRARY MWR (MORALE, WELFARE & RECREATION), Bldg 633, PO Box 99119, 85369-9119. SAN 330-8340. Tel: 520-341-2785. FAX: 520-344-5592.
Founded 1948
Oct 1998-Sep 1999 Income $59,350. Mats Exp $19,900, Books $6,500, Per/Ser (Incl. Access Fees) $6,900. Sal $39,450
Library Holdings: Bk Vols 20,500; Per Subs 93
Subject Interests: Aviation

GL YUMA COUNTY LAW LIBRARY,* 219 W Second St, 85364. SAN 300-483X. Tel: 520-329-2255. *Librn*, Gerrie Regenscheid
Library Holdings: Bk Vols 16,000
Subject Interests: Law

P YUMA COUNTY LIBRARY DISTRICT, 350 Third Ave, 85364. SAN 330-8375. Tel: 520-782-1871. Circulation Tel: 520-782-1871, Ext 127. Reference Tel: 520-782-1871, Ext 123. TDD: 520-782-0316. FAX: 520-782-9420. Web Site: www.yumalibrary.org. *Dir*, Joan Heida Murray; Tel: 520-782-1871, Ext 118, E-Mail: director@yumalibrary.org; *Asst Dir*, Susan Evans; Tel: 520-782-1871, Ext 104, E-Mail: assistdirector@yumalibrary.org; *Mgr*, Carla Peterson; Tel: 520-782-1871, Ext 128, E-Mail: cpyouth@yumalibrary.org; *Head, Circ*, Sandra Nicasio; Tel: 520-782-1871, Ext 107, Fax: 520-782-0670, E-Mail: sncirc@yumalibrary.org; *Publ Servs*, June Turner; Tel: 520-782-1871, Ext 103, Fax: 520-782-0670, E-Mail: programlib@yumalibrary.org; *Coll Develop, Librn*, Rebecca Bush; Tel: 520-782-1871, Ext 117, E-Mail: collection@yumalibrary.org; *Librn*, Joanne Millard; Tel: 520-782-1871, Ext 124, Fax: 520-782-0670, E-Mail: speciallib@yumalibrary.org; *ILL*, James Patrick; Tel: 520-782-1871, Ext 116, Fax: 520-782-0670, E-Mail: infolib@yumalibrary.org; *Business*, Brian Franssen; Tel: 520-782-1871, Ext 106, Fax: 520-782-0670, E-Mail: businesslib@yumalibrary.org; *Govt Doc*, Iris Collard; Tel: 520-782-1871, Ext 103, Fax: 520-782-0670, E-Mail: docslib@yumalibrary.org; *Automation Syst Coordr*, Gen Smith; Tel: 520-782-1871, Ext 119, E-Mail: gsauto@yumalibrary.org. Subject Specialists: *Bus admin*, Steve Duran; *Displays*, June Turner; *Grants*, Cecilia Young; *Programs*, June Turner; *Youth*, Carla Peterson; Staff 58 (MLS 10, Non-MLS 48)
Founded 1921. Pop 139,650; Circ 546,512
Jul 1999-Jun 2000 Income (Main Library and Branch Library) $2,758,627, State $20,498, Federal $15,000, County $2,522,792, Other $200,337. Mats Exp $428,839, Books $208,418, Per/Ser (Incl. Access Fees) $38,950, Micro $27,816, Other Print Mats $107,741, Electronic Ref Mat (Incl. Access Fees) $45,914. Sal $1,325,686 (Prof $28,011)
Library Holdings: Bk Vols 336,724; Bk Titles 301,771; Per Subs 645
Subject Interests: Arizona, Business and management, Local history
Special Collections: Arizona Government Documents
Automation Activity & Vendor Info: (Acquisitions) SIRSI; (Cataloging) SIRSI; (Circulation) SIRSI; (ILL) SIRSI; (OPAC) SIRSI; (Serials) SIRSI
Database Vendor: OCLC - First Search
Publications: Calendar; webpage
Member Libraries: Arizona Western College & Nau-Yuma; Mayer Public Library; Sedona Public Library
Partic in OCLC Online Computer Library Center, Inc
Friends of the Library Group
Branches: 5
FOOTHILLS, 11279 S Glenwood Ave, Ste 2, 85367. SAN 328-6827. Tel: 520-342-1640. FAX: 520-305-0497. Web Site: www.yumalibrary.org.
Library Holdings: Bk Vols 18,350
Friends of the Library Group
ROLL BRANCH, 5151 S Ave 39E, Roll, 85347. SAN 376-8899. Tel: 520-785-4942. FAX: 520-785-9496. Web Site: www.yumalibrary.org.
Library Holdings: Bk Vols 2,684
SAN LUIS BRANCH, 23233 First St, San Luis, 85349. SAN 328-8900. Tel: 520-627-8344. FAX: 520-627-8296. Web Site: www.yumalibrary.org.
Library Holdings: Bk Vols 11,893
Friends of the Library Group
SOMERTON BRANCH, 240 Canal St, Somerton, 85350. SAN 330-8464. Tel: 520-627-2149. FAX: 520-627-8345. Web Site: www.yumalibrary.org.
Library Holdings: Bk Vols 11,187
Friends of the Library Group
WELLTON BRANCH, 30101 E Hwy 80, Wellton, 85356. SAN 330-8499. Tel: 520-785-9575. FAX: 520-785-4410. Web Site: www.yumalibrary.org.
Library Holdings: Bk Vols 23,663
Friends of the Library Group

ARKANSAS

Date of Statistics: 1999
Population, 1998 Census: 2,538,303
Population Served by Public Libraries: 2,455,934
Unserved: 82,369
Total Volumes in Public Libraries: 5,431,179
Volumes Per Capita: 2.21
Total Public Library Circulation: 9,599,519
Circulation Per Capita: 3.91
Total Public Library Income (including federal and state funds): $35,347,700
Sources of Income: Property tax, sales tax, state funds, gifts, and donations
Local Tax Rate: Varies from three-tenths mill to three mill
Expenditures Per Capita: $13.38

Number of County or Multi-County (Regional) Libraries:
City Public Libraries: 10
Single County Systems: 15
Multi-county Systems: 18
Counties Served: 72; Unserved: 3
Number of Bookmobiles in State: 6
Grants to Public Libraries:
State: $500,000 for public library construction
Federal (Title I LSCA): $14,557
Total State Aid (FY 1999): $3,987,872 (all for public libraries)
Total Federal Funds (spent for state library purposes-FY 1998): $1,428,562
Formula for Apportionment: Stratified
Special Uses of Two Funds: Regional library systems, automation, books, other library materials, bookmobile service.

ALMA

P ALMA PUBLIC LIBRARY,* 625 Fayetteville Ave, PO Box 375, 72921. SAN 330-9878. Tel: 501-632-4140. FAX: 501-632-4140. Web Site: www.crawfordcountylib.org. *Librn*, Linn Smith
Mem of Ozarks Regional Library
Friends of the Library Group

ARKADELPHIA

P CLARK COUNTY LIBRARY, 609 Caddo St, 71923. SAN 330-8553. Tel: 870-246-2271. FAX: 870-246-4189. E-Mail: library22@yahoo.com. *Dir*, Judy Golden
Founded 1897. Pop 24,932; Circ 116,586
2000-2000 Income (Main Library and Branch Library) $225,000. Mats Exp $25,700, Books $25,000, Per/Ser (Incl. Access Fees) $700. Sal $75,000 (Prof $24,000)
Library Holdings: Bk Titles 90,000; Per Subs 80
Special Collections: Genealogy (Daughters of the American Revolution); History of Arkansas
Automation Activity & Vendor Info: (Cataloging) Brodart; (Circulation) Brodart
Branches: 1
GURDON PUBLIC, 204 E Walnut, Gurdon, 71743. SAN 330-8618. Tel: 870-353-2911. *Librn*, Le'elna Davidson
Library Holdings: Bk Vols 20,000

C HENDERSON STATE UNIVERSITY, Huie Library, 1100 Henderson, 71999-0001. SAN 300-4848. Tel: 870-230-5258. FAX: 870-230-5365. E-Mail: yehlb@holly.hsu.edu. Web Site: www.library.hsu.edu. *Dir*, Robert Yehl; *Coll Develop, Tech Servs*, Kathie George; Tel: 870-230-5307; *Spec Coll*, Lea Ann Alexander; *Instrul Serv*, Marielle McFarland; *Publ Servs*, John Ragni; *Media Spec*, Dr Jim Shuff; Staff 21 (MLS 7, Non-MLS 14)
Founded 1890. Enrl 3,500; Highest Degree: Master
Library Holdings: Bk Titles 209,489; Per Subs 1,508
Special Collections: Graphic novels; History of comics
Partic in Amigos Library Services, Inc; BRS; Dialog Corporation
Friends of the Library Group

C OUACHITA BAPTIST UNIVERSITY, Riley-Hickingbotham Library,* 410 Ouachita, OBU-3742, 71998-0001. SAN 330-8677. Tel: 870-245-5119. FAX: 870-245-5500. *Dir*, Ray Granade; Tel: 870-245-5120, E-Mail: granade@alpha.obu.edu; *Tech Servs*, Anping Wu; Tel: 870-245-5113, E-Mail: wua@alpha.obu.edu; *Media Spec*, Margaret Reed; Tel: 870-245-5125, E-Mail: reedm@alpha.obu.edu; *Doc*, Janice Ford; Tel: 870-245-5122, E-Mail: fordj@alpha.obu.edu; *Archivist*, Wendy Richter; Tel: 870-245-5332, E-Mail: richterw@alpha.obu.edu; *Per*, Lindsay Van Sicklen; Tel: 870-245-5117, E-Mail: vansicklenl@alpha.obu.edu; *Circ*, Shirley Dumais; E-Mail: dumaiss@alpha.obu.edu; Staff 7 (MLS 7)
Founded 1886. Enrl 1,638; Highest Degree: Bachelor
Jun 1998-May 1999 Income (Main and Other College/University Libraries) Parent Institution $587,203. Mats Exp $211,915, Books $83,400, Per/Ser (Incl. Access Fees) $100,015, Presv $4,500, Electronic Ref Mat (Incl. Access Fees) $24,000. Sal $211,330
Library Holdings: Per Subs 1,032
Subject Interests: Education, Humanities, Music
Special Collections: Associational Minutes of the Arkansas Baptist State Convention; Papers of Senator John L McClellan 1940-1977
Automation Activity & Vendor Info: (Acquisitions) DRA; (Cataloging) DRA; (Circulation) DRA; (Course Reserve) DRA; (Media Booking) DRA; (OPAC) DRA; (Serials) DRA
Partic in Amigos Library Services, Inc
Departmental Libraries:
CHEMISTRY, Harvey Jones Sci Ctr, 71998-0001. SAN 330-8707.
MUSIC, Mabee Fine Arts Bldg, 71998-0001. SAN 330-8731. *Librn*, Russell Hodges

BATESVILLE

C LYON COLLEGE, Mabee-Simpson Library, 2300 Highland Rd, 72501-3699. SAN 300-4856. Tel: 870-698-4205. FAX: 870-698-4279. Web Site: www.lyon.edu/library. *Dir*, Dean Covington; Tel: 870-698-4206, E-Mail: covington@lyon.edu; *Asst Dir*, Camille Beary; Tel: 870-698-4267, E-Mail: beary@lyon.edu; *ILL*, Kathy Whittenton; Tel: 870-793-1744, E-Mail: whittenton@lyon.edu; *Bibliog Instr*, Gene Hyde; Tel: 870-793-1748, E-Mail: ghyde@lyon.edu; Staff 6 (MLS 3, Non-MLS 3)
Founded 1872. Enrl 471; Fac 48; Highest Degree: Bachelor
Jul 2000-Jun 2001 Income Parent Institution $302,081. Mats Exp $213,000, Books $79,000, Per/Ser (Incl. Access Fees) $95,000, Presv $2,000, Micro $6,000, AV Equip $1,000, Electronic Ref Mat (Incl. Access Fees) $30,000
Library Holdings: Bk Vols 147,062; Bk Titles 110,954; Per Subs 840
Special Collections: Arkansas & Ozark history & culture; John Quincy Wolf Folklore Coll
Database Vendor: CARL, Ebsco - EbscoHost, GaleNet, Lexis-Nexis, OCLC - First Search, ProQuest, Silverplatter Information Inc., Wilson - Wilson Web
Partic in Amigos Library Services, Inc

P WHITE RIVER REGIONAL LIBRARY,* 368 E Main St, 72501. SAN 300-4864. Tel: 870-793-8814. FAX: 870-793-8896. *Dir*, Debra Sutterfield; *ILL*, Janet Swaim; *Tech Servs*, Roberta McGuffey; *Bkmobile Coordr*, Sarah Cumnock; Staff 2 (MLS 2)
Founded 1978. Pop 91,428; Circ 394,482
Library Holdings: Bk Vols 151,905; Per Subs 462
Special Collections: Arkansas History (Vela Jernigan Memorial)
Member Libraries: Cleburne County Library; Cleburne County Library; Fulton County Library; Sharp County Library; Stone County Library
Branches: 5
FULTON COUNTY - MAMMOTH SPRING BRANCH, 315 Main St, Mammoth Spring, 72554. (Mail add: PO Box 256, Mammoth Spring, 72554-3205), Tel: 870-625-3205. *Librn*, Carole Howell
Library Holdings: Bk Vols 10,000; Per Subs 12
Open Mon, Wed-Fri 9-11 & 12-5, Sat 9-11 & 12-4
FULTON COUNTY - VIOLA BRANCH, 97 Foxmoor Trail, Viola, 72583.

Tel: 870-458-3070. *Librn*, Melenda Roberts
SHARP COUNTY - CAVE CITY BRANCH, 120 Spring St, Cave City, 72521. (Mail add: PO Box 240, Cave City, 72521-0240), Tel: 870-283-6947. *Librn*, Juanita Scoope
Library Holdings: Bk Vols 4,000; Per Subs 21
SHARP COUNTY - EVENING SHADE BRANCH, 222 Main St, Evening Shade, 72532. (Mail add: PO Box 235, Evening Shade, 72532-0235), Tel: 870-266-3873. *Librn*, Nancy Crabtree
SHARP COUNTY - WILLIFORD BRANCH, 232 Main St, Williford, 72482. (Mail add: PO Box 94, Williford, 72482-0094), Tel: 870-966-4227. *Librn*, Loretta D Jones
Library Holdings: Bk Vols 4,000

BEEBE

J ARKANSAS STATE UNIVERSITY, BEEBE, Abington Memorial Library, 1000 W Iowa St, 72012. SAN 300-4872. Tel: 501-882-8207. TDD: 501-882-8369. FAX: 501-882-8233. *Dir*, Carolyn Powers; E-Mail: cbpowers@asub.arknet.edu; *Selection of Gen Ref Mat*, Ron Russ; Tel: 501-882-8359, E-Mail: rsruss@asub.arknet.edu; *ILL*, Peggy Inns; Tel: 501-882-8208, E-Mail: painns@asub.arknet.edu; *Tech Servs*, Pam Sullivan; Tel: 501-882-8378, E-Mail: pbsullivan@asub.arknet.edu; *Ser*, John Clowers; Tel: 501-882-8379, E-Mail: jeclowers@asub.arknet.edu; Staff 7 (MLS 2, Non-MLS 5)
Founded 1929. Enrl 1,950; Fac 70
Jul 1999-Jun 2000 Mats Exp $158,697, Books $46,413, Per/Ser (Incl. Access Fees) $24,917, Presv $1,016, Micro $6,825, AV Equip $6,526, Electronic Ref Mat (Incl. Access Fees) $73,000
Library Holdings: Bk Titles 58,000; Per Subs 340
Subject Interests: Arkansas
Automation Activity & Vendor Info: (Cataloging) TLC; (Circulation) TLC; (Serials) TLC
Database Vendor: Ebsco - EbscoHost, IAC - Info Trac, Lexis-Nexis, OCLC - First Search, ProQuest
Function: ILL available
Partic in Amigos Library Services, Inc

BELLA VISTA

S BELLA VISTA HISTORICAL SOCIETY MUSEUM LIBRARY,* 1885 Bella Vista Way, 72714. SAN 371-7100. Tel: 501-855-2335. *Pres*, Carole Westby
Founded 1976
Library Holdings: Bk Titles 400; Per Subs 12
Subject Interests: Local history
Special Collections: Anthropology-Archaeology, bks, per, slides; history, bks, chts, docs, maps
Closed Dec-May

§P BELLA VISTA PUBLIC LIBRARY, 11 Dickens Pl, 72714-4603. Tel: 501-855-1753. FAX: 501-855-4475. *Dir*, Jana Pellusch; Staff 1 (MLS 1)
Founded 1981
Jan 1999-Dec 2000 Income $106,050
Library Holdings: Bk Vols 27,477; Per Subs 70; High Interest/Low Vocabulary Bk Vols 2,539; Bks on Deafness & Sign Lang 10
Special Collections: Classic Films Coll, video
Automation Activity & Vendor Info: (Cataloging) Brodart; (Circulation) Brodart; (OPAC) Brodart
Ongoing used books sale
Friends of the Library Group

BENTON

P SALINE COUNTY PUBLIC LIBRARY, 224 W South St, 72015. SAN 330-8855. Tel: 501-778-4766. Toll Free Tel: 800-476-4466. FAX: 501-778-0536. Web Site: www.saline.lib.ar.us. *Dir*, Julie C Hart; E-Mail: jhart@saline.lib.ar.us; *Head Ref*, Marilyn Schulte; *Ch Servs*, Ruth Hyatt; Staff 3 (MLS 3)
Founded 1928. Pop 64,183; Circ 140,000
Library Holdings: Bk Titles 66,000; Per Subs 100
Subject Interests: Arkansas
Automation Activity & Vendor Info: (Cataloging) epixtech, inc.; (Circulation) epixtech, inc.; (OPAC) epixtech, inc.
Database Vendor: OCLC - First Search
Branches: 1
BRYANT BRANCH, 107 Mills Park Rd, Bryant, 72210. SAN 330-888X. Tel: 501-847-2166. FAX: 501-847-2166. Web Site: www.saline.lib.ar.us. *Librn*, Pam Moore
Library Holdings: Bk Vols 17,000; Bk Titles 10,000
Friends of the Library Group

BENTONVILLE

P BENTONVILLE PUBLIC LIBRARY,* 125 W Central, 72712. SAN 300-4880. Tel: 501-271-3192. FAX: 501-271-3105. *Dir*, Lynn A Eldred
Founded 1947. Pop 16,500; Circ 80,000
Jan 1997-Dec 1998 Income $252,686, City $247,686, Other $5,000. Mats Exp $61,438, Books $45,000, Per/Ser (Incl. Access Fees) $2,885, Presv $1,000, Micro $688, AV Equip $10,000, Other Print Mats $1,540. Sal $136,621 (Prof $35,000)
Library Holdings: Bk Titles 54,739; Per Subs 92
Special Collections: Arkansas History, bk & microfilm; Benton County Democrat, micro, large print

BLYTHEVILLE

P MISSISSIPPI COUNTY LIBRARY SYSTEM & COLLEGE LIBRARY,* 200 N Fifth St, 72315-2791. SAN 330-891X. Tel: 870-762-2431. FAX: 870-762-2442. *Dir*, Joseph F Ziolko; *Asst Dir*, Bronwyn Morgan
Founded 1921. Pop 75,000; Circ 200,000
Library Holdings: Bk Vols 200,000
Publications: Two newspaper columns in five area newspapers
Partic in Amigos Library Services, Inc; OCLC Online Computer Library Center, Inc
Combined library services with Mississippi County Community College to form a combined public & community college library system in 1976
Branches: 7
BLYTHEVILLE PUBLIC Tel: 501-762-2431.
KEISER PUBLIC, 112 E Main, Keiser, 72351. SAN 330-8944. Tel: 501-526-2300. *Librn*, Mary Lee Bounds
LEACHVILLE PUBLIC, PO Box 216, Leachville, 72438-0216. SAN 330-8979. Tel: 501-539-6485. *Librn*, Ruth Johnson
LUXORA PUBLIC, 215 Washington, PO Box 160, Luxora, 72358. SAN 376-2408. Tel: 501-658-2421. *Librn*, Doris Dew
MANILA PUBLIC, PO Box 559, Manila, 72442-0559. SAN 330-9002. Tel: 501-561-3235. *Librn*, Jane Roth
OSCEOLA PUBLIC, 320 W Hale, Osceola, 72370-2530. SAN 330-9037. Tel: 870-563-2721. FAX: 870-563-2721. E-Mail: osceolapublib@hotmail.com. *Librn*, Kevin Dale Barron; *Asst Librn*, Laura B Giham
Jul 1999-Jun 2000 Mats Exp $540,000
Library Holdings: Bk Vols 34,419; Per Subs 80
Subject Interests: Local genealogy
Database Vendor: Ebsco - EbscoHost, IAC - Info Trac, OCLC - First Search
WILSON PUBLIC, Wilson, 72395. SAN 330-9061. Tel: 501-655-8414. *Librn*, Linda Dawson

CALICO ROCK

IZARD COUNTY LIBRARY, Calico Rock Public, PO Box 327, 72519. Tel: 870-297-3785. *Librn*, Mary Sexton
Friends of the Library Group

CAMDEN

J SOUTHERN ARKANSAS UNIVERSITY TECH-LIBRARY,* Tech Sta, 71701-1148. SAN 300-4961. Tel: 870-574-4518, 870-574-4544. FAX: 870-574-4568. E-Mail: library@sautech.edu. Web Site: www.sautech.edu/libhome.htm. *Dir*, Allison Malone; E-Mail: amalone@sautech.edu; Staff 4 (MLS 1, Non-MLS 3)
Founded 1967. Enrl 788; Fac 61
Jul 1999-Jun 2000 Income (Main Library Only) $181,730. Mats Exp $48,008, Books $28,508, Per/Ser (Incl. Access Fees) $5,000, Presv $1,000, Micro $1,500, AV Equip $7,000, Electronic Ref Mat (Incl. Access Fees) $5,000. Sal $92,915 (Prof $48,666)
Library Holdings: Bk Titles 15,934; Per Subs 100
Automation Activity & Vendor Info: (Cataloging) epixtech, inc.; (Circulation) epixtech, inc.; (OPAC) epixtech, inc.
Mem of Southern Ark Univ

CEDARVILLE

P CEDARVILLE PUBLIC LIBRARY,* PO Box 95, 639 Pirates Way, 72932. SAN 330-9908. Tel: 501-410-1853. FAX: 501-410-1853. *Librn*, Carla Lesley
Library Holdings: Bk Vols 2,500
Mem of Ozarks Regional Library
Friends of the Library Group

CLARKSVILLE

C UNIVERSITY OF THE OZARKS, Robson Library,* 415 N College Ave, 72830. SAN 300-4899. Tel: 501-979-1382. FAX: 501-979-1355. Web Site: www.eidos.ozarks.edu. *Dir*, Stuart P Stelzer; *Tech Servs*, Janice Blackard; Staff 3 (MLS 1, Non-MLS 2)
Founded 1891. Enrl 575; Fac 36; Highest Degree: Bachelor
Library Holdings: Bk Vols 85,000; Per Subs 500
Automation Activity & Vendor Info: (Cataloging) Endeavor
Partic in Amigos Library Services, Inc; Arknet; OCLC Online Computer Library Center, Inc

CONWAY

CR CENTRAL BAPTIST COLLEGE, JE Cobb Library, 1501 College Ave, 72032. SAN 300-4902. Tel: 501-329-6872. FAX: 501-329-2941. Web Site: www.cbc.edu. *Head Librn*, Ellen Courtney; E-Mail: ecourtney@admin.cbc.edu; *Asst Librn*, Anne L Clements; E-Mail: aclements@admin.cbc.edu; Staff 2 (MLS 2)
Founded 1952. Enrl 321
Jul 1998-Jun 1999 Income Parent Institution $167,052. Mats Exp $80,896, Books $58,060, Per/Ser (Incl. Access Fees) $15,591, Presv $629, Micro $498, AV Equip $618, Electronic Ref Mat (Incl. Access Fees) $5,500. Sal $81,000 (Prof $68,000)
Library Holdings: Bk Vols 45,192; Bk Titles 39,494; Per Subs 340
Subject Interests: Church history, Theology
Special Collections: Baptist Missionary Association of Arkansas History
Automation Activity & Vendor Info: (OPAC) CASPR
Database Vendor: IAC - Info Trac, ProQuest

P FAULKNER COUNTY LIBRARY, 1900 Tyler St, 72032. SAN 330-9126. Tel: 501-327-7482. FAX: 501-327-9098. *Dir*, Ruth Voss; *Asst Dir*, Cyntha Johnson; *Circ*, Karla Deckard; *Ch Servs*, Jo-Lynn James; *Cat*, Ginny Kopper; *Per*, Haskell Huffines; *Circ*, Vicky Works; *Tech Servs*, Tommy Nash; Staff 13 (MLS 3, Non-MLS 10)
Founded 1938. Pop 74,101; Circ 305,960
Library Holdings: Bk Vols 289,853; Per Subs 259
Special Collections: Arkansas Coll; Faulkner County Law Libr Coll
Automation Activity & Vendor Info: (Acquisitions) CASPR; (Cataloging) CASPR; (Circulation) CASPR; (OPAC) CASPR
Publications: Newsletter (irregularly)
Friends of the Library Group
Branches: 6
FAIRFIELD BAY BRANCH, Lakewood Village Mall, PO Box 1183, Fairfield Bay, 72088. SAN 330-9150. *Librn*, Marge Redford
Library Holdings: Bk Vols 5,000
Friends of the Library Group
GREENBRIER BRANCH, 13 Wilson Farm Rd, Greenbrier, 72058. SAN 377-7723. Tel: 501-679-6344. FAX: 501-679-6344. *Librn*, Laura McGee
MAYFLOWER BRANCH, 6 Ashmore Dr, Mayflower, 72106. SAN 377-774X. Tel: 501-470-9678. FAX: 501-470-9039. *Librn*, Brenda Reynold
TWIN GROVES BRANCH, No 10 Twin Groves Lane, Twin Groves, 72039. Tel: 501-335-8088. FAX: 501-335-8088. *Librn*, Michelle Burks
Library Holdings: Bk Vols 3,000
Automation Activity & Vendor Info: (Acquisitions) CASPR; (Cataloging) CASPR; (Circulation) CASPR
Open Mon-Fri 10-6
VAN BUREN COUNTY, Rte 6, Box 193, Clinton, 72031. SAN 330-9215. Tel: 501-745-2100. FAX: 501-745-5860. *Librn*, Karla Fultz
Library Holdings: Bk Vols 22,000
Friends of the Library Group
VILONIA, 3 Bise Dr, Vilonia, 72173. (Mail add: PO Box 388, Vilonia, 72173), SAN 374-4388. Tel: 501-796-8520. FAX: 501-796-8520. *Dir*, Julie Simoni

C HENDRIX COLLEGE, Olin C Bailey Library, 1600 Washington Ave, 72032-3080. SAN 300-4910. Tel: 501-450-1303. E-Mail: library@hendrix.edu. Web Site: www.hendrix.edu/baileylibrary. *Acq, Dir*, Robert W Frizzell; *Asst Librn*, Britt Anne Johnson; *Tech Servs*, Kirby Cheng; *Reader Servs*, Sheila Peters; Staff 9 (MLS 4, Non-MLS 5)
Founded 1876. Enrl 1,140; Fac 80; Highest Degree: Master
Aug 1998-Jul 1999 Mats Exp $350,699, Books $160,683, Per/Ser (Incl. Access Fees) $166,899, Presv $6,111, Micro $10,571, Electronic Ref Mat (Incl. Access Fees) $6,435. Sal $251,432 (Prof $157,166)
Library Holdings: Bk Vols 171,286; Bk Titles 149,063; Per Subs 719
Special Collections: Arkansas Methodism; Arkansasiana
Automation Activity & Vendor Info: (Cataloging) DRA; (Circulation) DRA; (OPAC) DRA
Database Vendor: OCLC - First Search
Partic in Amigos Library Services, Inc

C UNIVERSITY OF CENTRAL ARKANSAS, Torreyson Library, 201 Donaghey Ave, 72035. SAN 300-4929. Tel: 501-450-3129. Reference Tel: 501-450-5224. FAX: 501-450-5208. *Dean of Libr*, Willie Hardin; *Acq, Coll Develop*, Amanda Moore; *Cat*, Mary White; *Ref*, Tracy Swank; *Tech Servs*, Kaye Talley; *Ch Servs*, Ellen Johnson; *Archivist*, Jimmy Bryant; Staff 13 (MLS 13)
Founded 1907. Enrl 9,000; Fac 349; Highest Degree: Doctorate
1998-1999 Income $2,110,489. Mats Exp $681,220, Books $293,477, Per/Ser (Incl. Access Fees) $340,743, Manuscripts & Archives $47,000. Sal $835,903 (Prof $466,951)
Library Holdings: Bk Vols 538,836; Bk Titles 395,000; Per Subs 2,564
Subject Interests: Arkansas
Special Collections: Archives; Children's Literature (Laboratory Coll); Government Documents
Database Vendor: Innovative Interfaces INN - View
Publications: Torreyson Library Newsletter
Partic in Amigos Library Services, Inc; BRS; Dialog Corporation; OCLC Online Computer Library Center, Inc
Friends of the Library Group

CORNING

P NORTHEAST ARKANSAS REGIONAL LIBRARY, Corning Library, 613 Pine St, 72422. SAN 331-3239. Tel: 870-857-3453. FAX: 870-857-3453. *Librn*, Kathy Buchanan; Staff 4 (Non-MLS 4)

CROSSETT

P PAUL SULLINS PUBLIC LIBRARY,* 125 Main St, 71635. SAN 300-4937. Tel: 870-364-2230. FAX: 870-364-2231. *Dir*, Dolly Pruitt; Staff 2 (MLS 2)
Founded 1938. Pop 6,000; Circ 103,789
1997-1998 Income $115,000. Mats Exp $29,000. Sal $61,085
Library Holdings: Bk Vols 30,827; Bk Titles 35,000; Per Subs 65
Subject Interests: Arkansas
Friends of the Library Group

DARDANELLE

P ARKANSAS RIVER VALLEY REGIONAL LIBRARY SYSTEM,* Headquarters, 501 N Front St, 72834-3507. SAN 330-924X. Tel: 501-229-4418. FAX: 501-229-4456. E-Mail: arvlib@yell.com. *Dir*, Diana Skousen; *Online Servs, Tech Servs*, Virginia Hyde
Founded 1958. Pop 71,434; Circ 358,759
1998-1999 Income $1,036,775, State $127,609, City $6,431, Federal $18,872, County $783,697, Locally Generated Income $57,848, Other $42,318. Mats Exp $137,187, Books $105,673, Per/Ser (Incl. Access Fees) $11,000. Sal $393,137 (Prof $30,750)
Library Holdings: Bk Vols 132,263
Subject Interests: Local history
Special Collections: Arkansas
Publications: Handbook; Newsletter; Staff Manual
Partic in Amigos Library Services, Inc
Friends of the Library Group
Branches: 6
BOYD T & MOLLIE GATTIS LOGAN COUNTY LIBRARY, 100 E Academy, Paris, 72855-4432. SAN 330-9452. Tel: 501-963-2371. FAX: 501-963-2371. *Librn*, Alane Freerekson
Friends of the Library Group
CHARLESTON PUBLIC, PO Box 338, Charleston, 72933-0338. SAN 330-9304. Tel: 501-965-2605. FAX: 501-965-2605. *Librn*, Donna McDonald
FRANKLIN COUNTY, 407 W Market St, PO Box 222, Ozark, 72949-2727. SAN 330-9363. Tel: 501-667-2724. FAX: 501-667-2724. *Librn*, Nancy Smith
JOHNSON COUNTY PUBLIC, No 2 Taylor Circle, Clarksville, 72830-3653. SAN 330-9398. Tel: 501-754-3135. FAX: 501-754-6343. *Librn*, Linda Hildebrand
Library Holdings: Bk Titles 30,000
LOGAN COUNTY, 419 N Kennedy, Booneville, 72927-3630. SAN 330-9428. Tel: 501-675-2735. FAX: 501-675-2735. *Librn*, Darlene Wolenski
Friends of the Library Group
YELL COUNTY, 904 Atlanta St, PO Box 850, Danville, 72833-0850. SAN 330-9517. Tel: 501-495-2911. FAX: 501-495-2822. *Librn*, Joyce Cathy
Bookmobiles: 2

DECATUR

§P DECATUR PUBLIC LIBRARY, 249 Main St, 72722. (Mail add: PO Box 247, 72722-0247), Tel: 501-752-7323. E-Mail: decaturpubliclibrary@tds.net. *Librn*, Virginia Davis
Jan 1999-Dec 1999 Income $14,000, City $10,000, Other $4,000
Library Holdings: Bk Vols 5,300; High Interest/Low Vocabulary Bk Vols 10

DEWITT

P DEWITT PUBLIC LIBRARY,* 205 W Maxwell, 72042. SAN 300-4945. Tel: 870-946-1151. FAX: 870-946-1151. E-Mail: dewpl@hotmail.com. *Dir*, Virginia D Platt
Founded 1926. Pop 4,000; Circ 14,000
Library Holdings: Bk Vols 40,000
Branches: 1
CLEON COLLIER MEMORIAL LIBRARY, PO Box 310, Gillett, 72055. SAN 320-0817. Tel: 870-548-2821. FAX: 870-548-2821. *Librn*, Mildred Sanchez
Founded 1976. Circ 4,388
Library Holdings: Bk Titles 2,643

EDMONDSON

§P EDMONDSON PUBLIC LIBRARY, 61 Waterford St, PO Box 300, 72332-0300. Tel: 870-735-6946. FAX: 870-735-6988.
2000-2001 Income County $6,000

EL DORADO

P BARTON LIBRARY,* 200 E Fifth St, 71730-3897. SAN 330-9541. Tel: 870-863-5447. FAX: 870-862-3944. *Librn*, Nancy Arn; *ILL*, Irene Davis; Staff 1 (MLS 1)
Founded 1958. Pop 48,573; Circ 230,721
1997-1998 Income $314,644. Mats Exp $190,000, Books $23,000, Per/Ser (Incl. Access Fees) $5,500. Sal $194,480
Library Holdings: Bk Vols 75,476; Per Subs 102
Special Collections: Arkansas Coll, monographs; Genealogy Coll, micro, monographs; Large Print Coll, high interest-low vocabulary bks
Partic in OCLC Online Computer Library Center, Inc; South Arkansas Film Coop
Branches: 5
HARPER MEMORIAL, 301 N Myrtle, PO Box 730, Junction City, 71749. SAN 330-9606. Tel: 870-924-5556. FAX: 870-924-5556. *Librn*, Jo Ann Payne
Library Holdings: Bk Vols 5,255
Friends of the Library Group
HUTTIG BRANCH, PO Box 458, Frost St, Huttig, 71747. SAN 330-9576. Tel: 870-943-2965. FAX: 870-943-2965. *Librn*, Gelynn Little
Library Holdings: Bk Vols 4,659
NORPHLET PUBLIC, City Hall Bldg, PO Box 21, Norphlet, 71759. SAN 330-9630. Tel: 870-546-2274. FAX: 870-546-2274. *Librn*, Mary Gene Murphy
Library Holdings: Bk Vols 3,605
SMACKOVER PUBLIC, 700 N Broadway, Smackover, 71762. SAN 330-969X. Tel: 870-725-3741. FAX: 870-725-3741. *Librn*, Sally Farley
Library Holdings: Bk Vols 8,230
Subject Interests: Genealogy, Local history
Friends of the Library Group
STRONG PUBLIC, 246 W Second Ave, PO Box 157, Strong, 71765. SAN 330-972X. Tel: 870-797-2165. FAX: 870-797-2165. *Librn*, Rhonda Bagwell
Library Holdings: Bk Vols 5,203
Friends of the Library Group

L MURPHY OIL CORP, Law Department Library,* 200 Peach St, 71730. SAN 373-0204. Tel: 870-864-6486. FAX: 870-864-6489.
Library Holdings: Bk Vols 2,500

S SOUTH ARKANSAS ARTS CENTER LIBRARY, 110 E Fifth St, 71730. SAN 300-497X. Tel: 870-862-5474. FAX: 870-862-3944. *Dir*, Beth James
Library Holdings: Bk Vols 2,100

J SOUTH ARKANSAS COMMUNITY COLLEGE, Library Media Center, 300 Southwest Ave, 71730. SAN 321-1754. Tel: 870-862-8131, Ext 115. Interlibrary Loan Service Tel: 510-466-6192. Reference Tel: 870-864-7115. FAX: 870-864-7134. *Acq, Dir*, Phillip Arndt; E-Mail: parndt@southark.cc.ar.us; *Assoc Dir, Librn*, Joyce Adams; *Ser*, Ellen McGowan; *Syst Coordr*, Louri Wilson; Staff 4 (MLS 2, Non-MLS 2)
Founded 1976. Enrl 900; Fac 46; Highest Degree: Associate
Library Holdings: Bk Vols 29,000; Per Subs 220
Partic in Am Libr Asn; Ark Libr Asn

CM UNIVERSITY OF ARKANSAS FOR MEDICAL SCIENCES, Area Health Education Center Library - South Arkansas Library, 460 W Oak, 71730. SAN 300-4996. Tel: 870-881-4403, 870-881-4404. FAX: 870-862-0570. *Dir*, Vicki J de Yampert; Tel: 870-881-4404, E-Mail: deyampertv@ahecsa.uams.edu; *Tech Servs*, Debora G Johnson
Founded 1974
Library Holdings: Bk Vols 1,000; Per Subs 100
Partic in Amigos Library Services, Inc; Arkansas Area Health Education Center Consortium (AHEC); OCLC Online Computer Library Center, Inc; S Cent Regional Med Libr Program

ELKINS

P ELKINS PUBLIC LIBRARY,* 162 Doolin Dr, 72727. SAN 328-6843. Tel: 501-643-2904. *Librn*, Sherry Braker
Library Holdings: Bk Vols 5,000
Mem of Ozarks Regional Library
Friends of the Library Group

EUREKA SPRINGS

S CENTER ON WAR & THE CHILD LIBRARY,* 35 Benton St, PO Box 487, 72632. SAN 323-9578. Tel: 501-253-8900. FAX: 501-253-8900. *Librn*, Cheri White; *Dir*, Richard Parker
Founded 1987
Library Holdings: Bk Vols 1,600

SR SOCIETY FOR PROMOTING & ENCOURAGING ARTS & KNOWLEDGE OF THE CHURCH, Howard Lane Foland Library, 805 County Rd 102, 72632-9705. SAN 371-8824. Tel: 501-253-9701. FAX: 501-253-1277. E-Mail: speak@speakinc.org. *In Charge*, Tom Walker
Founded 1980
Library Holdings: Bk Titles 10,958

FAYETTEVILLE

GM DEPARTMENT OF VETERANS AFFAIRS, Library Service (142D),* 1100 N College Ave, 72703-6995. SAN 300-5011. Tel: 501-444-5060, 501-444-5096. FAX: 501-444-5054.; Staff 2 (MLS 1, Non-MLS 1)
Library Holdings: Bk Vols 3,362; Per Subs 167
Subject Interests: Allied health, Medicine, Nursing, Psychology
Publications: Journal Holdings list (annual); Patient Health Education AV Catalog (annual)
Partic in Veterans Affairs Library Network

P FAYETTEVILLE PUBLIC LIBRARY, 217 E Dickson, 72701. SAN 330-9932. Tel: 501-442-2242. FAX: 501-442-5723. E-Mail: fpl@fayettevillelibrary.org. Web Site: www.fayettevillelibrary.org. *Dir*, Louise Schaper; *Publ Servs*, Steven Thomas; Staff 27 (MLS 5, Non-MLS 22)
Founded 1916. Pop 60,000
Jan 2000-Dec 2000 Income $1,495,630, City $812,593, County $529,511, Locally Generated Income $139,261. Mats Exp $264,069
Library Holdings: Bk Vols 109,772; Per Subs 240
Subject Interests: Genealogy, Literacy
Automation Activity & Vendor Info: (Acquisitions) Innovative Interfaces Inc.; (Cataloging) Innovative Interfaces Inc.; (Circulation) Innovative Interfaces Inc.; (OPAC) Innovative Interfaces Inc.; (Serials) Innovative Interfaces Inc.
Mem of Washington County Libr Syst
Friends of the Library Group

P OZARKS REGIONAL LIBRARY,* 217 E Dickson St, 72701. SAN 330-9843. Tel: 501-442-6253. FAX: 501-442-6254. Web Site: www.orl.lib.ar.us.; Staff 5 (MLS 5)
Founded 1965. Pop 180,594; Circ 1,051,830
Jan 1997-Dec 1998 Income $3,404,850. Mats Exp $520,000. Sal $1,975,810
Library Holdings: Bk Vols 354,722
Subject Interests: Genealogy
Member Libraries: Alma Public Library; Cedarville Public Library; Elkins Public Library; Greenland Public Library; Lincoln Public Library; Mountainburg Public Library; Prairie Grove Public Library; West Fork Public Library

CM UNIVERSITY OF ARKANSAS FOR MEDICAL SCIENCES, (AHEC-NW), Area Health Education Center-Northwest Library, Washington Regional Medical Ctr, 1125 N College, 72703. SAN 324-7546. Tel: 501-521-7615, 501-713-1175. Toll Free Tel: 888-740-2432. FAX: 501-521-0624. *Librn*, Connie M Wilson; E-Mail: cwilson@ahecnwlibrary.uams.edu; *Asst Librn*, Elva Conditt; Staff 3 (MLS 1, Non-MLS 2)
Founded 1975
Library Holdings: Bk Vols 1,528; Bk Titles 2,500; Per Subs 175
Subject Interests: Allied health, Clinical medicine, Clinical nursing, Grad nursing, Med tech, Radiologic tech
Automation Activity & Vendor Info: (Cataloging) Innovative Interfaces Inc.
Publications: From the Shelf (Newsletter)
Restriction: In-house use for visitors
Function: ILL available, Reference only, Referrals accepted
Partic in Amigos Library Services, Inc; BRS; Nat Libr of Med; S Cent Regional Med Libr Program

C UNIVERSITY OF ARKANSAS LIBRARIES, Mullins Library 206, 72701-1201. SAN 331-0264. Tel: 501-575-6702. Interlibrary Loan Service Tel: 501-575-5311. Circulation Tel: 501-575-4101. Reference Tel: 501-575-6645. FAX: 501-575-6656. Interlibrary Loan Service FAX: 501-575-5558. Web Site: www.uark.edu/libinfo. *Dean of Libr*, Carolyn Henderson Allen; *Assoc Dean*, Juana R Young; Fax: 501-575-6656, E-Mail: jyoung@uark.edu; *Publ Servs*, Alberta Bailey; Tel: 501-575-7795, E-Mail: albertab@uark.edu; *Tech Servs*, Janet Parsch; Tel: 501-575-6694, E-Mail: jparsch@uark.edu; *Ser*, Marilyn Rogers; *Acq*, Ann Waligorski; *Head, Cat*, Cheryl Conway; *Selection of Gen Ref Mat*, Beth Juhl; Tel: 501-575-5313, E-Mail: bjuhl@uark.edu; *Govt Doc*, Sarah Santos; *Spec Coll*, Michael Dabrishus; Tel: 501-575-5576, E-Mail: mdabrish@uark.edu; Staff 66 (MLS 24, Non-MLS 42)
Founded 1872. Enrl 14,734; Fac 756
Jul 1999-Jun 2000 Income (Main Library and Branch Library) $8,021,953. Mats Exp $8,021,953, $3,411,572, Books $535,924, Per/Ser (Incl. Access Fees) $2,719,269, Presv $74,177, Electronic Ref Mat (Incl. Access Fees) $82,202. Sal $2,984,352 (Prof $1,807,172)
Library Holdings: Bk Vols 1,580,145; Per Subs 14,168
Subject Interests: Agriculture, Architecture, Creative writing, International relations
Special Collections: Arkansas Author Coll; Arkansas Coll; Edward Durrell Stone Coll; Folklore Coll; J William Fulbright Coll; Orval Faubus Collection; Ozarks History Coll; Rare Book Coll; Senator Dale Bumpers Coll; Senator David Pryor Coll; Senator Joe T Robinson Coll; William Gould Fletcher Coll; William Grant Still Coll
Automation Activity & Vendor Info: (OPAC) Innovative Interfaces Inc.
Database Vendor: CARL, Dialog, Ebsco - EbscoHost, GaleNet, IAC - Info Trac, Lexis-Nexis, OCLC - First Search, ProQuest, Wilson - Wilson Web
Publications: Annual Report; Books & Letters
Partic in Amigos Library Services, Inc; Arknet; Big Twelve Plus Libr Consortium

Departmental Libraries:
CHEMISTRY Tel: 501-575-2028. *Head of Libr*, Donna Johnson
Library Holdings: Bk Vols 32,262
Friends of the Library Group
FINE ARTS Tel: 501-575-4708. *Head of Libr*, Normastel Johnson
Library Holdings: Bk Vols 35,949
Friends of the Library Group
PHYSICS Tel: 501-575-2505. *Librn*, Usha Gupta
Library Holdings: Bk Vols 16,838
Friends of the Library Group

CL ROBERT A & VIVIAN YOUNG LAW LIBRARY, University of Arkansas School of Law, 72701-1201. SAN 331-0353. Tel: 501-575-5604. FAX: 501-575-2053. Web Site: www.law.uark.edu. *Dir*, Glen Peter Ahlers; *Ref*, Cathy Chick; *Ref*, W David Gay; *Ref*, Jim Jackson; *Tech Servs*, Lorraine Lorne; *Acq*, Peggy Melton; Staff 12 (MLS 5, Non-MLS 7)
Founded 1924. Enrl 400; Fac 35; Highest Degree: Doctorate
Library Holdings: Bk Vols 265,401; Bk Titles 89,462; Per Subs 545
Subject Interests: Law
Automation Activity & Vendor Info: (Acquisitions) Innovative Interfaces Inc.; (Cataloging) Innovative Interfaces Inc.; (Circulation) Innovative Interfaces Inc.; (Course Reserve) Innovative Interfaces Inc.; (ILL) Innovative Interfaces Inc.; (Media Booking) Innovative Interfaces Inc.; (OPAC) Innovative Interfaces Inc.; (Serials) Innovative Interfaces Inc.
Database Vendor: Lexis-Nexis
Publications: Young in a Nutshell (Newsletter)
Mem of Amigos Bibliog Coun, Inc
Partic in OCLC Online Computer Library Center, Inc
Friends of the Library Group

FORDYCE

P DALLAS COUNTY LIBRARY,* 501 E Fourth St, PO Box 584, 71742. SAN 331-0418. Tel: 870-352-3592. FAX: 870-352-8708. *Librn*, Kathryn Wright
Founded 1934. Pop 10,022; Circ 29,444
Library Holdings: Bk Vols 37,000
Branches: 1
SPARKMAN BRANCH, 186 Dallas 208, Sparkman, 71763. SAN 331-0477. *Librn*, Majorie Fleming

FORREST CITY

J EAST ARKANSAS COMMUNITY COLLEGE, Betty Jo Hodges Learning Resources Center, 1700 Newcastle Rd, 72335. SAN 320-1201. Tel: 870-633-4480, Ext 322. FAX: 870-633-7222. E-Mail: art@eacc.cc.ar.us. *Dir*, Art Berman; *Asst Dir*, Quanta Gwin; *AV*, Barbara Smith; Staff 5 (MLS 2, Non-MLS 3)
Founded 1974. Enrl 972
Library Holdings: Bk Vols 22,259; Bk Titles 20,313; Per Subs 123
Database Vendor: GaleNet, ProQuest

P FORREST CITY PUBLIC LIBRARY,* 421 S Washington, 72335-3839. SAN 300-502X. Tel: 870-633-5646. FAX: 870-633-5647. E-Mail: fcpl@ipa.net. *Dir*, Christine Maxam; E-Mail: cmaxam@ipa.net; Staff 5 (MLS 1, Non-MLS 4)
Founded 1921. Pop 13,364; Circ 34,019
Library Holdings: Bk Titles 29,156; Per Subs 31
Subject Interests: Arkansas

FORT SMITH

J BOREHAM LIBRARY, 5210 Grand Ave, PO Box 3649, 72913-3649. SAN 300-5062. Tel: 501-788-7200. Interlibrary Loan Service Tel: 501-788-7201. FAX: 501-788-7209. *Dir*, Wilma Cunningham; *Cat, Coll Develop*, Dennis Van Arsdale; *ILL, Ref*, Carolyn Filippelli; *Ser*, Martha Coleman; *Publ Servs*, Janet Sanders; Staff 5 (MLS 5)
Founded 1928. Enrl 5,800; Fac 192
Library Holdings: Bk Vols 58,000
Special Collections: Grantsmanship Coll; Wilder Historical Coll
Publications: Library Staff Policies & Procedures Manual; Monthly List of New Titles; Student Library Handbook
Partic in OCLC Online Computer Library Center, Inc

P FORT SMITH PUBLIC LIBRARY, 3201 Rogers Ave, 72903. SAN 331-0507. Tel: 501-783-0229. TDD: 501-783-5129. FAX: 501-782-8571. Web Site: www.fspl.lib.ar.us. *Dir*, Larry Larson; *Asst Dir*, Patricia Zabel; E-Mail: pzabel@fspl.lib.ar.us; *Librn*, Amy Hay; E-Mail: ahay@fspl.lib.ar.us; *Branch Mgr*, Kathy Hunt; Tel: 501-785-0405, Fax: 501-785-0431, E-Mail: khunt@fspl.lib.ar.us; *Branch Mgr*, Jacquie Mollenhauer; Tel: 501-484-5650, Fax: 501-484-5658, E-Mail: jacquiem@fspl.lib.ar.us; *Branch Mgr*, Anita Paddock; Tel: 501-646-3945, Fax: 501-646-3965; *Publ Servs*, James Miller; *Ch Servs*, Louise Turner; *Ref*, Roger Saft; *Syst Coordr*, Mary Marin; E-Mail: mmartin@fspl.lib.ar.us; *Bkmobile Coordr*, Mae Wellnitz. Subject Specialists: *Genealogy*, Amy Hay
Founded 1906. Pop 72,798; Circ 691,461
Jan 1999-Dec 1999 Income $1,692,000, State $145,000, City $1,422,000, Locally Generated Income $125,000. Mats Exp $375,000, Books $295,000, Electronic Ref Mat (Incl. Access Fees) $60,000. Sal $1,079,000
Library Holdings: Bk Vols 230,250; Bk Titles 134,753; High Interest/Low Vocabulary Bk Vols 125
Special Collections: Local, State History & Genealogy (Arkansas Coll), bks & micro; Vietnamese Coll
Database Vendor: Ebsco - EbscoHost, OCLC - First Search
Partic in Amigos Library Services, Inc; OCLC Online Computer Library Center, Inc
Friends of the Library Group
Branches: 4
DALLAS STREET, 8100 Dallas St, Forth Smith, 72903. Tel: 501-484-5650. Web Site: www.fspl.lib.ar.us. *Librn*, Jacqueline Mollenhauer; E-Mail: jacquiem@fspl.lib.ar.us
Library Holdings: Bk Vols 21,033
Database Vendor: OCLC - First Search

P LIBRARY FOR THE BLIND & PHYSICALLY HANDICAPPED FAX: 501-782-8571. *Librn*, Kelly Hamlin
Library Holdings: Bk Vols 25,000
Publications: Newletter (quarterly)
Friends of the Library Group
MILLER, 8701 S 28th St, 72908. Tel: 501-646-3945. FAX: 501-646-3965. Web Site: www.fspl.lib.ar.us. *Librn*, Anita Paddock; E-Mail: apadock@fspl.lib.ar.us
Library Holdings: Bk Vols 22,374
Database Vendor: OCLC - First Search
WINDSOR DRIVE, 4701 Windsor Dr, 72904. Tel: 501-785-0405. FAX: 501-785-0431. Web Site: www.fspl.lib.ar.us. *Librn*, Kathy Hunt; E-Mail: khunt@fspl.lib.ar.us
Library Holdings: Bk Vols 22,489
Database Vendor: OCLC - First Search

M REGIONAL MEDICAL CENTRE, Health Sciences Library,* 1311 South I St, PO Box 17006, 72917-7006. SAN 300-5054. Tel: 501-441-5338. FAX: 501-441-5339. Web Site: www.sparks.org. *Dir, Online Servs*, Grace Anderson; E-Mail: grace@sparks.org; *Asst Librn*, Barbara Redding
Founded 1972
Library Holdings: Bk Titles 3,000; Per Subs 227
Partic in Avid; Medline; OCLC Online Computer Library Center, Inc

M SAINT EDWARD MERCY MEDICAL CENTER LIBRARY,* PO Box 17000, 72917-7000. SAN 300-5038. Tel: 501-484-6000, Ext 6520. FAX: 501-478-5646. *Librn*, Sister Jackie Hittner; E-Mail: srjhittner@ftsm.smhs.com
Library Holdings: Bk Vols 1,600; Per Subs 75
Subject Interests: Medicine, Nursing

GL SEBASTIAN COUNTY LAW LIBRARY,* 623 Garrison Ave, 72901. SAN 300-5046. Tel: 501-783-4730. *Librn*, Jeri Kizer
Library Holdings: Bk Vols 15,000

GENTRY

§P GENTRY PUBLIC LIBRARY, 112 E Main St, 72734. (Mail add: PO Box 726, 72734-0726), Tel: 501-736-2054. E-Mail: gentrylibrary@cox-internet.com. *Head of Libr*, Darla Threet
Jan 2000-Dec 2000 Income $21,000, City $15,723
Library Holdings: Bk Vols 7,500; Per Subs 14
Open Mon-Wed 10-6, Thurs & Fri 10-5

GRAVETTE

§P GRAVETTE PUBLIC LIBRARY, 407 Charlotte St SE, 72736-9363. Tel: 501-787-6955. *Librn*, Jody Kanton
Jan 2000-Dec 2000 Income $36,000
Library Holdings: Bk Vols 20,000; Per Subs 10
Automation Activity & Vendor Info: (Acquisitions) Sagebrush Corporation; (Cataloging) Sagebrush Corporation; (Circulation) Sagebrush Corporation
Open Mon-Wed & Fri 9-1 & 1:30-5:30, Sat 9-1

GREENLAND

P GREENLAND PUBLIC LIBRARY,* City Hall, 72737. SAN 330-9967. Tel: 501-582-5992. *Librn*, Iva Sorrell
Mem of Ozarks Regional Library

GREENWOOD

P SCOTT-SEBASTIAN REGIONAL LIBRARY,* 18 N Adair, PO Box 400, 72936. SAN 331-0566. Tel: 501-996-2856. FAX: 501-996-2236. E-Mail: ssrlib@ipa.net. *Dir*, Judy Beth Clevenger; Staff 9 (MLS 1, Non-MLS 8)
Founded 1954. Pop 42,000
Jan 1999-Dec 1999 Income (Main Library and Branch Library) $235,000, County $155,000, Other $80,000. Mats Exp $38,500, Books $35,000, Per/Ser (Incl. Access Fees) $3,500

Library Holdings: Bk Vols 88,000
Special Collections: Arkansas History; Large Print Reference
Automation Activity & Vendor Info: (Circulation) Sagebrush Corporation
Database Vendor: OCLC - First Search
Mem of Ark Libr Develop District I
Branches: 5
HARTFORD LIBRARY, Hartford, 72938. SAN 331-0655. *In Charge*, Diana Roberts
Library Holdings: Bk Vols 4,000
LAVACA LIBRARY, Lavaca, 72941. SAN 331-071X. *In Charge*, Patricia Graham
Library Holdings: Bk Vols 1,300
MANSFIELD LIBRARY, Mansfield, 72944. SAN 331-0744. *In Charge*, Anna Carter
Library Holdings: Bk Vols 2,650
SCOTT COUNTY, Waldron, 72958. SAN 331-0809. Tel: 501-637-3516. *In Charge*, Shirley Maxey
Library Holdings: Bk Vols 29,000
Special Collections: Arkansas History
SEBASTIAN COUNTY Tel: 501-996-2856. *In Charge*, Gayle Taylor
Library Holdings: Bk Vols 58,000
Special Collections: Arkansas History; Gifted & Talented Children; Large Print; Reference

HAMBURG

P ASHLEY COUNTY LIBRARY,* 211 E Lincoln, 71646. SAN 300-5070. Tel: 870-853-2078. FAX: 870-853-2079. E-Mail: ashlib@cei.net. *Librn*, Henrietta Thompson
Founded 1935. Pop 24,319; Circ 85,637
Jan 1998-Dec 1999 Income $126,400, State $25,000, County $90,000, Locally Generated Income $11,400. Mats Exp $30,500, Books $23,000, Per/Ser (Incl. Access Fees) $1,500. Sal $59,400 (Prof $25,500)
Library Holdings: Bk Titles 50,126; Per Subs 54
Subject Interests: Genealogy
Publications: Weekly newspaper column

HAMPTON

S CALHOUN COUNTY REGIONAL LIBRARY,* PO Box 1162, 71744. SAN 373-1863. Tel: 870-798-4492. FAX: 870-234-5077. *Librn*, Mollie Wilson
Library Holdings: Bk Vols 30,000; Per Subs 30

HARDY

§P SHARP COUNTY LIBRARY, 201 Church St, 72542. Tel: 870-856-3934. *Librn*, Kathryn Newman
Jan 2000-Dec 2000 Income $133,764
Library Holdings: Bk Vols 28,000; Per Subs 49
Mem of White River Regional Library
Open Mon-Fri 8:30-5, Sat 9-1

HARRISBURG

P POINSETT COUNTY PUBLIC LIBRARY, 200 N East St, 72432. SAN 300-5089. Tel: 870-578-4465. FAX: 870-578-4466. *Librn*, Nechia Whittingham; E-Mail: nwhittin@crrl.lib.ar.us
Founded 1936
Library Holdings: Bk Vols 18,000; Per Subs 30
Mem of Crowley Ridge Regional Library
Friends of the Library Group
Branches: 3
LEPANTO BRANCH, 207 Greenwood St, PO Box 4756, Lepanto, 72354. SAN 331-197X. Tel: 870-475-6144. FAX: 870-475-6144. *Librn*, Carol Clukey
Library Holdings: Bk Vols 7,363
Friends of the Library Group
MARKED TREE BRANCH, 404 Liberty St, PO Box 215, Marked Tree, 72365. SAN 331-2003. Tel: 870-358-3190. FAX: 870-358-3190. *Librn*, Fran Bell
Library Holdings: Bk Vols 8,923
Friends of the Library Group
WEINER BRANCH, W Second & Washington, PO Box 124, Weiner, 72479. SAN 331-2062. Tel: 870-684-2235. FAX: 870-684-2235. *Librn*, Vikki Johnson
Library Holdings: Bk Vols 6,533
Friends of the Library Group

HARRISON

S ORPHAN VOYAGE, Museum of Orphanhood Library,* 601 S Birch St, 72601-5911. SAN 328-8307. Tel: 870-743-1487. *Coordr*, Jean Paton
Library Holdings: Bk Titles 975
Subject Interests: Opera
Friends of the Library Group

HEBER SPRINGS

P CLEBURNE COUNTY LIBRARY, 1010 W Searcy St, 72543. SAN 377-8592. Tel: 501-362-2477. FAX: 501-362-2606. *Librn*, Janet Cleary; Staff 5 (Non-MLS 5)
Founded 1935
Jan 2000-Dec 2000 Income (Main Library and Branch Library) $213,700
Library Holdings: Bk Vols 42,000; Per Subs 95
Mem of White River Regional Library
Friends of the Library Group
Branches: 1
GREERS FERRY BRANCH, PO Box 258, Greers Ferry, 72067. SAN 372-5138. Tel: 501-825-7172. FAX: 501-825-8029. *Librn*, Jean Stark
Founded 1974
Library Holdings: Bk Vols 1,200
Mem of White River Regional Library
Friends of the Library Group

HELENA

J PHILLIPS COMMUNITY COLLEGE OF THE UNIVERSITY OF ARKANSAS, Lewis Library, 1000 Campus Dr, PO Box 785, 72342. SAN 300-5097. Tel: 870-338-6474. FAX: 870-338-2783. E-Mail: dplaisted@pccc.cc.ar.us. Web Site: www.library.pccua.cc.ar.us. *Dir*, Jerrie Townsend; Tel: 870-673-4201, Ext 1818, Fax: 870-673-8166, E-Mail: jtownsend@pccua.cc.ar.us; *Coordr*, Deena Plaisted; Staff 1 (MLS 1)
Founded 1966. Enrl 1,486
Library Holdings: Bk Titles 43,550; Per Subs 344
Subject Interests: Art, Automotive engineering
Partic in Libr & Info Resources Network

P PHILLIPS-LEE-MONROE REGIONAL LIBRARY, 623 Pecan St, 72342-3298. SAN 331-1139. Tel: 870-338-3537. FAX: 870-338-7732. E-Mail: reflib@hnb.com. Web Site: www.geocities.com/athens/ithaca/4022. *Actg Dir*, Susan Hamilton; *ILL*, Judy Lederman; Staff 1 (Non-MLS 1)
Founded 1961. Pop 50,000; Circ 53,302
Library Holdings: Bk Vols 219,786; Per Subs 121
Subject Interests: Arkansas, Genealogy, Local history
Branches: 6
ELAINE PUBLIC, 126 Main St, Elaine, 72333-0328. SAN 331-1147. Tel: 870-827-6628. E-Mail: elib@hnb.com. *Librn*, Clara Williamson
Founded 1974
LEE COUNTY PUBLIC, 77 W Main St, Marianna, 72360-2297. SAN 321-8511. Tel: 870-295-2688. E-Mail: library@ipa.net. *Librn*, Betsy Bowman
MARVELL PUBLIC, 806 Carruth, PO Box 625, Marvell, 72366-0625. SAN 331-1163. Tel: 870-829-3183. E-Mail: mlib@hnb.com. *Librn*, Malissia Schaffhauser
Founded 1924
MONROE COUNTY PUBLIC, 270 Madison St, Clarendon, 72029-2792. SAN 331-1155. Tel: 870-747-5593. *Librn*, Juanita Ellis
PHILLIPS COUNTY PUBLIC Tel: 870-338-3537. *Dir*, Susan Hamilton; *Tech Servs*, Judy Lederman; *Circ*, Pat Ward; *Circ*, Kitty Norwood; *Circ*, Bridgette Cunningham
Founded 1939
WEST HELENA PUBLIC, 721 Plaza St, West Helena, 72390-2698. SAN 331-118X. Tel: 870-572-2861. E-Mail: p721w@hnb.com. *Circ*, Jean Smith; *Circ*, Susan Johns; *Circ*, Betty Inabinet
Founded 1916

HOPE

P SOUTHWEST ARKANSAS REGIONAL LIBRARY, 500 S Elm St, 71801. SAN 331-1198. Tel: 870-777-2957. FAX: 870-777-2957. E-Mail: swarklib@arkansas.net. *Dir*, Maybelle V James
Founded 1947. Pop 100,327; Circ 304,468
Jan 1999-Dec 1999 Income (Main Library and Branch Library) $862,869, State $188,815, City $13,000, Federal $190,061, County $416,612, Locally Generated Income $54,381. Mats Exp $95,408, Books $81,817, Per/Ser (Incl. Access Fees) $10,000, Electronic Ref Mat (Incl. Access Fees) $3,591. Sal $314,655 (Prof $64,404)
Library Holdings: Bk Vols 231,538; Bk Titles 80,000; Per Subs 340
Automation Activity & Vendor Info: (Cataloging) Brodart; (Circulation) Brodart; (OPAC) Brodart
Database Vendor: OCLC - First Search
Partic in OCLC Online Computer Library Center, Inc
Friends of the Library Group

Branches: 18
ASHDOWN BRANCH, 160 E Commerce, Ashdown, 71822. SAN 331-1228. Tel: 870-898-3233. FAX: 870-898-3233. *Librn*, Becky Burns
DELIGHT BRANCH, Delight, 71940. SAN 331-1252. Tel: 870-379-2422. *Librn*, Shirley Forbes
DEQUEEN BRANCH, 200 W Stillwell, DeQueen, 71832. SAN 331-1287. Tel: 870-584-4364. FAX: 870-642-8319. *Librn*, Betty Smith
DIERKS BRANCH, PO Box 10, Dierks, 71833. SAN 331-1317. *Librn*, Ruth White
FOREMAN BRANCH, PO Box 7, Foreman, 71836. SAN 331-1341. Tel: 870-542-7409. *Librn*, Billie Richmond
FULTON BRANCH, City Hall, Fulton, 71838. SAN 331-135X. Tel: 870-896-2740. *Librn*, Minnie Lou Weaver
GILLHAM BRANCH, PO Box 173, Gillham, 71841. SAN 331-1376. *Librn*, Pat Sheldon
GLENWOOD BRANCH, PO Box 370, Glenwood, 71943. SAN 331-1406. FAX: 370-356-4643. *Librn*, Lonetta Lock
HEMPSTEAD COUNTY LIBRARY (HEADQUARTERS LIBRARY) Tel: 870-777-4564. FAX: 870-777-2957. *Librn*, Judy Sooter
Friends of the Library Group
HORATIO BRANCH, PO Box 245, Horatio, 71842. SAN 331-1430. *Librn*, Sally Quinn
HOWARD COUNTY LIBRARY, 426 N Main St, Ste 5, Nashville, 71852. SAN 331-1643. Tel: 870-845-2566. FAX: 870-845-7532. *Librn*, Janice Curry; E-Mail: jcurry@pmail.net
Pop 6,000; Circ 34,000
Jan 1999-Dec 1999 Income County $107,500. Mats Exp $15,000. Sal $54,000
Library Holdings: Bk Titles 50,000; Per Subs 20; Bks on Deafness & Sign Lang 20
Subject Interests: Arkansas
LOCKESBURG BRANCH, 203 Shady Lane, Lockesburg, 71846-9705. SAN 331-1465. Tel: 870-289-3261. *Librn*, Martha Bell
MINERAL SPRINGS BRANCH, PO Box 309, Mineral Springs, 71851. SAN 331-152X. *Librn*, Wynema Autrey
NEVADA COUNTY, PO Box 613, Prescott, 71857. SAN 331-1619. Tel: 870-887-5846. FAX: 870-887-5846. *Librn*, Helen Miller
Friends of the Library Group
PIKE COUNTY LIBRARY, PO Box 153, Murfreesboro, 71958. SAN 331-149X. Tel: 870-285-3732. *Librn*, Malinda Stone
POLK COUNTY, 410 Eighth St, Mena, 71953. SAN 331-1589. Tel: 870-394-2314. FAX: 870-394-2314. *Librn*, Shirley Philpot
Friends of the Library Group
TOLLETTE BRANCH, 506 Plum St, Tollette, 71851. SAN 331-1651. Tel: 870-287-7166. *Librn*, Sophronia Tollette
WINTHROP BRANCH, PO Box 193, Winthrop, 71866. SAN 331-1554. Tel: 870-381-7580. *Librn*, Vonnie Chewning
Friends of the Library Group
Bookmobiles: 1

§J UNIVERSITY OF ARKANSAS COMMUNITY COLLEGE AT HOPE, Rapert Library Complex, 2500 S Main St, PO Box 140, 71801. SAN 375-4197. Tel: 870-777-5722. FAX: 870-777-5957. E-Mail: mjthomas@mail.uacch.cc.ar.us. Web Site: www.uacch.cc.ar.us/library/libhome.htm. *Dir*, Vicky Jackson; E-Mail: vjackson@mail.uacch.cc.ar.us; Staff 3 (MLS 1, Non-MLS 2)
Founded 1992
Database Vendor: Ebsco - EbscoHost, GaleNet, IAC - Info Trac, OCLC - First Search, OVID Technologies, ProQuest, Silverplatter Information Inc.
Partic in Amigos Library Services, Inc

HORSESHOE BEND

P IZARD COUNTY LIBRARY, Horseshoe Bend Public, 704 W Commerce, 72512. Tel: 870-670-5113. *Librn*, Shirley Alger; *Librn*, Marcia Wagner

HOT SPRINGS

J GARLAND COUNTY COMMUNITY COLLEGE LIBRARY, 101 College Dr, 71913. SAN 300-5100. Tel: 501-760-4101, 501-760-4110. FAX: 501-760-4106. Web Site: www.gccc.cc.ar.us/library/library.htm. *Dir*, Mary Farris; E-Mail: mfarris@admin.gccc.cc.ar.us; *Librn*, Marguerite Ogden; Staff 5 (MLS 2, Non-MLS 3)
Founded 1973. Enrl 2,300; Fac 90; Highest Degree: Associate
Library Holdings: Bk Vols 20,800; Bk Titles 20,053; Per Subs 250
Subject Interests: Arkansas, Art
Automation Activity & Vendor Info: (Circulation) epixtech, inc.
Publications: GCCC Libr Newsletter
Partic in Amigos Library Services, Inc; ARIEL; OCLC Online Computer Library Center, Inc

P GARLAND COUNTY LIBRARY, 1427 Malvern Ave, 71901. SAN 372-767X. Tel: 501-623-4161. FAX: 501-623-5647. E-Mail: gclhsar@hotmail.com/staff. Web Site: www.garcolib.com. *Dir*, John W Wells
Founded 1948. Pop 76,302; Circ 300,000
Library Holdings: Bk Vols 95,000; Per Subs 450
Automation Activity & Vendor Info: (Acquisitions) epixtech, inc.; (Cataloging) epixtech, inc.; (Circulation) epixtech, inc.
Mem of Tri-Lakes Regional Library
Friends of the Library Group

P TRI-LAKES REGIONAL LIBRARY, Garland County Library, 1427 Malvern Ave, 71901-5788. SAN 300-5119. Tel: 501-623-3943.
Founded 1948. Pop 101,013; Circ 518,460
Library Holdings: Bk Vols 134,099; Per Subs 214
Member Libraries: Garland County Library; Montgomery County Library
Friends of the Library Group

JEFFERSON

GM HHS-FDA, National Center for Toxicological Research Library, 3900 NCTR Rd, 72079-9502. SAN 300-5127. Tel: 870-543-7785. FAX: 870-543-7323. *Librn*, Susan Laney-Sheehan; E-Mail: ssheehan@nctr.fda.gov; Staff 5 (MLS 1, Non-MLS 4)
Founded 1972
Library Holdings: Bk Vols 17,000; Bk Titles 16,000; Per Subs 225
Subject Interests: Chemistry, Microbiology, Toxicology
Partic in Dialog Corporation; Nat Libr of Med; OCLC Online Computer Library Center, Inc

JONESBORO

C ARKANSAS STATE UNIVERSITY, Dean B Ellis Library, 108 Cooley Dr, 72401. (Mail add: PO Box 2040, 72467), SAN 331-1678. Tel: 870-972-3077. FAX: 870-972-3199. Web Site: www.library.astate.edu. *Dean of Libr*, Mary Moore; E-Mail: mmoore@choctaw.astate.edu; *Cat*, Myron Flugstad; *Bibliog Instr*, Robin Payn; *Coll Develop*, Peter Picerno; *Govt Doc*, Rod Miller; *Media Spec*, Deborah Bailey; *Publ Servs*, Jeff Bailey; *Ref*, Paul Kaupilla; *Ref*, Madeline Williams; *Archivist, Spec Coll*, Brady Banta; Staff 17 (MLS 13, Non-MLS 4)
Founded 1909
Library Holdings: Bk Vols 544,326
Special Collections: Cass Hough Aeronautica Coll; Children (Lois Lenski Coll); Iraf Twist Coll; Judd Hill Plantation Records; Legal Research Coll; Library Science (Reference & Periodical Coll); Midsouth Center for Oral History; Saint Francis Levee District Tax Coll Records; US Representative Bill Alexander Coll; US Representative E C Took Gathings Coll
Automation Activity & Vendor Info: (Acquisitions) Endeavor; (Circulation) Endeavor
Publications: Arkansas Union List of Periodicals
Partic in OCLC Online Computer Library Center, Inc
Friends of the Library Group

P CRAIGHEAD COUNTY & JONESBORO PUBLIC LIBRARY, (CCJPL), 315 W Oak Ave, 72401. SAN 331-1708. Tel: 870-935-5133, 870-935-5137. Interlibrary Loan Service Tel: 870-935-5133, Ext 34. Circulation Tel: 870-935-5133, Ext 10. Reference Tel: 870-935-5133, Ext 21. FAX: 870-935-7987. Web Site: www.crrl.lib.ar.us. *Dir*, Phyllis Burkett; Tel: 870-935-5133, Ext 29, E-Mail: phyllis@crrl.lib.ar.us; *Assoc Dir*, Rusty Dancer; Tel: 870-935-5133, Ext 16, E-Mail: rusty@crrl.lib.ar.us; *Circ*, Charlene Roberts; E-Mail: charlene@crrl.lib.ar.us; *Ch Servs*, Kay Taylor; E-Mail: kay@crrl.lib.ar.us; Staff 25 (MLS 4, Non-MLS 21)
Founded 1917. Pop 68,956; Circ 255,183
Jan 1999-Dec 1999 Income (Main Library and Branch Library) $985,960, City $728,697, County $257,263. Mats Exp $198,002, Books $172,494, Per/Ser (Incl. Access Fees) $11,396, Presv $1,777, Micro $1,842, Electronic Ref Mat (Incl. Access Fees) $10,493. Sal $498,234 (Prof $443,942)
Library Holdings: Bk Vols 120,000; Per Subs 336
Subject Interests: Genealogy
Special Collections: Arkansas History, bk, micro
Automation Activity & Vendor Info: (Circulation) epixtech, inc.; (OPAC) epixtech, inc.
Database Vendor: Ebsco - EbscoHost, epixtech, inc., IAC - Info Trac, OCLC - First Search, ProQuest
Function: ILL available
Friends of the Library Group
Branches: 3
CARAWAY BRANCH, 102 E State St, PO Box 249, Caraway, 72419. SAN 331-1732. Tel: 870-482-3394. FAX: 870-482-3394. *Librn*, Jane Blake
Library Holdings: Bk Vols 4,000
KOHN MEMORIAL, 103 S Edmund St, PO Box 510, 72447. SAN 331-1767. Tel: 870-486-2515. FAX: 870-486-2515. *Librn*, Martha Wallace
Library Holdings: Bk Vols 10,000
MCADAMS PUBLIC, 106 Cobean, PO Box 164, Lake City, 72437. SAN 331-1791. Tel: 870-237-4407. FAX: 870-237-4407. *Librn*, Donna Rolland
Library Holdings: Bk Vols 6,000

P CROWLEY RIDGE REGIONAL LIBRARY,* 315 W Oak Ave, 72401. SAN 331-1821. Tel: 870-935-5133, 870-935-5137. FAX: 870-935-7987. Web Site: www.crrl.lib.ar.us. *Dir*, Phyllis Burkett; Staff 3 (Non-MLS 3)
Founded 1966. Pop 93,620; Circ 368,031
Jul 1998-Jun 1999 Income Other $165,279. Mats Exp $123,320. Sal $54,509

Library Holdings: Bk Vols 153,827; Bk Titles 141,158; Per Subs 330
Automation Activity & Vendor Info: (OPAC) epixtech, inc.
Database Vendor: epixtech, inc., OCLC - First Search
Member Libraries: Poinsett County Public Library

CM UNIVERSITY OF ARKANSAS, Area Health Education Center Library-Northeast,* 223 E Jackson, 72401. SAN 300-5135. Tel: 870-972-1290. FAX: 870-931-0839. *Dir Libr Serv*, Karen Crosser; E-Mail: kcrosser@ahecne.uams.edu
Founded 1974
Library Holdings: Bk Vols 2,015; Per Subs 145
Subject Interests: Family practice
Publications: Updates (NE Arkansas Hosp Libr Consortium)
Partic in Docline; Northeast Arkansas Hospital Library Consortium; OCLC Online Computer Library Center, Inc; Univ of Ark for Med Sci

LINCOLN

P LINCOLN PUBLIC LIBRARY,* 107 W Bean, PO Box 555, 72744-0555. SAN 330-9991. Tel: 501-824-3294. FAX: 501-824-3294. *Librn*, Glynne Richey
Library Holdings: Bk Vols 18,000; Per Subs 30
Mem of Ozarks Regional Library

LITTLE ROCK

C ARKANSAS BAPTIST COLLEGE LIBRARY,* 1600 Bishop St, 72202. SAN 300-516X. Tel: 501-374-4923. FAX: 501-372-0321. *Dir*, Milrean Stockmon
Library Holdings: Bk Vols 60,000; Per Subs 98

S ARKANSAS DEMOCRAT GAZETTE NEWS LIBRARY,* 121 E Capitol, PO Box 2221, 72201. SAN 300-5194. Tel: 501-378-3498. FAX: 501-378-3489. *Mgr*, Rosie Dixon
Founded 1950
Library Holdings: Bk Vols 1,600
Special Collections: Gazette, from 1819 to present, micro

S ARKANSAS GEOLOGICAL COMMISSION LIBRARY, 3815 W Roosevelt Rd, 72204-6369. SAN 300-5208. Tel: 501-296-1877. FAX: 501-663-7360. E-Mail: agc@mac.state.ar.us. Web Site: www.state.ar.us/agc/agc.htm. *Librn*, Oleta Sproul
Founded 1923
Library Holdings: Bk Titles 10,000; Per Subs 11
Publications: Bulletins; guidebooks; information circulars, miscellaneous publications; water resources circulars & summaries

S ARKANSAS HISTORY COMMISSION LIBRARY,* One Capitol Mall, 72201. SAN 326-7008. Tel: 501-682-6900. FAX: 501-682-1364. Web Site: www.state.ar.us/ahc/ahc.html. *Dir*, John L Ferguson
Library Holdings: Bk Vols 20,000; Per Subs 1,000

S ARKANSAS SCHOOL FOR THE DEAF LIBRARY, (ASD), 2400 W Markham St, PO Box 3811, 72203. SAN 300-5240. Tel: 501-324-9515. FAX: 501-324-9553. *Librn*, Fran Miller; E-Mail: franm@asd.klz.ar.us
Library Holdings: Bk Vols 10,000; Per Subs 75; Bks on Deafness & Sign Lang 600
Automation Activity & Vendor Info: (Cataloging) Sagebrush Corporation; (Circulation) Sagebrush Corporation

G ARKANSAS STATE ENERGY OFFICE LIBRARY, One State Capitol Mall, Ste 4B-215, 72201. SAN 373-0212. Tel: 501-682-1370. FAX: 501-682-2703. *In Charge*, Reda Bowen
Library Holdings: Bk Vols 1,000; Per Subs 20
Subject Interests: Conservation

G ARKANSAS STATE HIGHWAY & TRANSPORTATION DEPARTMENT, Public Transportation Section Library,* PO Box 2261, 72203. SAN 374-9622. Tel: 501-569-2471. FAX: 501-569-2476.
Library Holdings: Bk Vols 200; Per Subs 10

P ARKANSAS STATE LIBRARY, One Capitol Mall 5th flr, 72201-1085. SAN 331-2097. Tel: 501-682-1527. Reference Tel: 501-682-2053. TDD: 501-682-1002. FAX: 501-682-1529. Web Site: www.asl.lib.ar.us. *State Librn*, Jack Mulkey; Tel: 501-682-1526, E-Mail: jmulkey@asl.lib.ar.us; *Cat*, Janet Berry; Tel: 501-682-2303, Fax: 501-682-1532, E-Mail: jberry@asl.lib.ar.us; *Circ, ILL, Reader Servs*, Mary Leckie; Tel: 501-682-2053, E-Mail: mleckie@asl.lib.ar.us; *Govt Doc*, Mary Brewer; Tel: 501-682-2326, Fax: 501-682-1532, E-Mail: mbrewer@asl.lib.ar.us; *Librn for Blind*, J D Hall; Tel: 501-682-1155, E-Mail: jhall@asl.lib.ar.us; *Exten Serv*, Carolyn Ashcraft; Tel: 501-682-5288, Fax: 501-582-1693, E-Mail: cashraf@asl.lib.ar.us; *Tech Servs*, Jenelle Stephens; Tel: 501-682-2550, Fax: 501-682-1532, E-Mail: jstephen@asl.lib.ar.us; *Tech Coordr*, Sarah Hawkes; Tel: 501-682-6052, Fax: 501-682-1531, E-Mail: shawkes@asl.lib.ar.us; Staff 52 (MLS 18, Non-MLS 34)
Founded 1935. Pop 2,538,303
Jun 1999-Jul 2000 Income $4,392,466, State $2,963,904, Federal $1,428,562. Mats Exp $896,204, Books $124,476, Per/Ser (Incl. Access Fees) $65,744, Micro $11,358, Electronic Ref Mat (Incl. Access Fees) $694,626
Library Holdings: Bk Vols 492,204; Per Subs 2,500
Subject Interests: Business and management, Computer science, Reference, US industries
Special Collections: Arkansiana; CIS microfiche; Patent Depository; Professional Coll (Library & Information Science)
Automation Activity & Vendor Info: (Acquisitions) SIRSI; (Circulation) SIRSI; (OPAC) SIRSI; (Serials) SIRSI
Database Vendor: Dialog, Ebsco - EbscoHost, GaleNet, OCLC - First Search, ProQuest, Wilson - Wilson Web
Publications: Arkansas Documents; directories; indexes; The News
Partic in Amigos Library Services, Inc; BRS; OCLC Online Computer Library Center, Inc
Federal Regional Library for the blind & physically handicapped; Federal Patents & Trademark Depository Library

P ARKANSAS STATE LIBRARY SERVICES FOR THE BLIND & PHYSICALLY HANDICAPPED, One Capitol Mall, 72201. SAN 300-5224. Tel: 501-682-1155. Toll Free Tel: 866-660-0885. TDD: 501-682-1002. FAX: 501-682-1155. E-Mail: nlsbooks@asl.lib.ar.us. *Coordr*, J D Hall; Fax: 501-682-1529, E-Mail: jhall@asl.lib.ar.us; *Reader Servs*, Eva Jane Harrison; Tel: 501-682-2871, Fax: 501-682-1529, E-Mail: eharriso@asl.lib.ar.us; *Reader Servs*, Claire Leheny; Tel: 501-682-2856, Fax: 501-682-1529, E-Mail: cleheny@asl.lib.ar.us; *AV*, Marty Lentz; Tel: 501-682-2858, Fax: 501-682-1529, E-Mail: mlentz@asl.lib.ar.us. Subject Specialists: *Children's*, Eva Jane Harrison; Staff 8 (MLS 2, Non-MLS 6)
Founded 1969. Pop 5,000; Circ 146,943
Jul 1999-Jun 2000 Income $524,820, State $344,235, Federal $180,000, Other $585
Library Holdings: Bk Vols 165,000; Bk Titles 50,000
Subject Interests: Audio bks, Braille
Function: Mail loans to members
Special Services for the Blind - Braille & recorded books

GL ARKANSAS SUPREME COURT LIBRARY,* 1310 Justice Bldg, 625 Marshall St, 72201-1080. SAN 300-5267. Tel: 501-682-2147. FAX: 501-682-6877. E-Mail: arsclib@mail.state.ar.us, sclibrary@ualr.edu. Web Site: www.courts.state.ar.us/sclib.htm. *Dir*, Timothy N Holthoff; E-Mail: Tim.Holthoff@mail.state.ar.us; *Asst Librn*, Ava M Hicks; E-Mail: Ava.Hicks@mail.state.ar.us; Staff 3 (MLS 2, Non-MLS 1)
Founded 1851
1999-2000 Income $409,107, State $284,107, Locally Generated Income $124,500. Mats Exp $409,106, Per/Ser (Incl. Access Fees) $200,000, Electronic Ref Mat (Incl. Access Fees) $25,000. Sal $122,796 (Prof $97,095)
Library Holdings: Bk Vols 90,000; Per Subs 5,000
Subject Interests: Law
Automation Activity & Vendor Info: (Acquisitions) Innovative Interfaces Inc.; (Cataloging) Innovative Interfaces Inc.; (Circulation) Innovative Interfaces Inc.; (OPAC) Innovative Interfaces Inc.; (Serials) Innovative Interfaces Inc.
Database Vendor: IAC - Info Trac, Lexis-Nexis, OCLC - First Search, Wilson - Wilson Web
Partic in Amigos Library Services, Inc; OCLC Online Computer Library Center, Inc

S ARKANSAS TERRITORIAL RESTORATION LIBRARY,* 200 E Third St, 72201. SAN 370-3355. Tel: 501-324-9351. FAX: 501-324-9345. *Dir*, W B Wothen; *Librn*, Georgann McKinney; *Circ*, Swannee Bennett
Library Holdings: Bk Vols 700

G ARKANSAS WORKERS' COMPENSATION COMMISSION LIBRARY,* 323 Spring St, 72201. (Mail add: PO Box 950, 72203-0950), SAN 371-0289. Tel: 501-682-2742. Toll Free Tel: 800-622-4472. FAX: 501-682-2048. Web Site: www.awcc.ar.us. *Librn*, Stark Ligon; E-Mail: sligon@awcc.state.ar.us
1998-1999 Income State $50,000. Mats Exp $45,000, Books $35,000, Per/Ser (Incl. Access Fees) $10,000
Library Holdings: Bk Vols 3,000; Per Subs 30

BAPTIST HEALTH

M MARGARET CLARK GILBREATH MEMORIAL LIBRARY, 9601 Interstate 630, 72205. SAN 331-2151. Tel: 501-202-2000. FAX: 501-202-1318. *Librn*, Kathryn Nikkel; E-Mail: knikkel@baptist_health.org
Founded 1974
Jan 1998-Dec 1999 Income $119,800. Mats Exp $60,000. Sal $84,000
Library Holdings: Bk Vols 3,500; Per Subs 230
Subject Interests: Medicine, Nursing
Special Collections: Consumer Health Information
Partic in Medline

P CENTRAL ARKANSAS LIBRARY SYSTEM, 100 Rock St, 72201-4698. SAN 331-2216. Tel: 501-918-3000. Interlibrary Loan Service Tel: 501-370-5950. FAX: 501-375-7451. Web Site: www.cals.lib.ar.us. *Dir*, Dr Bobby Roberts; *Dep Dir*, Linda Bly; *ILL*, Michael Chambers; *Pub Relations*, Susan Schallhorn; *Ref*, Carol Coffey; *Tech Servs*, Tracy Hamby; *Coll Develop*, Valerie Thwing; Staff 132 (MLS 20, Non-MLS 112)

Founded 1910. Pop 295,888; Circ 1,230,230
Jan 1999-Dec 1999 Income (Main Library and Branch Library) $5,889,644, State $361,608, Federal $32,629, County $5,024,762, Locally Generated Income $470,645. Mats Exp $646,886, Books $375,019, Per/Ser (Incl. Access Fees) $76,543, Presv $16,020, AV Equip $44,304, Electronic Ref Mat (Incl. Access Fees) $135,000. Sal $3,136,036
Library Holdings: Bk Vols 584,210; Bk Titles 252,959; Per Subs 800
Subject Interests: Genealogy, Local history, State hist
Special Collections: Charlie May Simon Awards Coll; Foundation Center Regional Coll
Database Vendor: Innovative Interfaces INN - View
Partic in Amigos Library Services, Inc
Special Services for the Deaf - TTY machine
Friends of the Library Group
Branches: 9
AEROSPACE, 3301 E Roosevelt Rd, 72206-6709. SAN 378-2476. Tel: 501-399-9401. *Librn*, Audrey Taylor
Library Holdings: Bk Vols 23,076
FLETCHER, 823 N Buchanan St, 72205-3211. SAN 331-2240. Tel: 501-663-5457. *Librn*, Melinda Jackson
Library Holdings: Bk Vols 64,735
MAUMELLE BRANCH, 10 Lake Pointe Dr, Maumelle, 72113-6230. SAN 378-2492. Tel: 501-851-2551. *Librn*, Mary Green
Library Holdings: Bk Vols 26,592
MILAM, Hwy 60 & Cedar, Perryville, 72126. SAN 331-2305. Tel: 501-889-2554. *Librn*, Janice Guffey
Library Holdings: Bk Vols 28,243
NIXON, 308 W Main St, Jacksonville, 72076-4507. SAN 331-2275. Tel: 501-982-5533. *Librn*, Mary Cantwell
Library Holdings: Bk Vols 49,044
SANDERS, 31 Shelby Dr, Sherwood, 72120-3197. SAN 331-233X. Tel: 501-835-7756. *Librn*, Genine Plunkett
Library Holdings: Bk Vols 37,069
SOUTHWEST, 5702 Dreher Lane, 72209-4810. SAN 331-2364. Tel: 501-568-7494. *Librn*, Almeta Smith
Library Holdings: Bk Vols 46,838
TERRY, 2015 Napa Valley Dr, 72212. SAN 370-5773. Tel: 501-228-0129. *Librn*, Margaret Yates
Library Holdings: Bk Vols 70,852
WILLIAMS, 1800 S Chester St, 72206-1010. SAN 378-2514. Tel: 501-376-4282.
Library Holdings: Bk Vols 22,237
Bookmobiles: 1

GM JOHN L MCCLELLAN MEMORIAL VETERANS HOSPITAL, Health Sciences Library, 4300 W Seventh St, 72205-5484. SAN 300-5321. Tel: 501-257-5620. FAX: 501-257-5619. *Chief Librn*, George Zumwalt; *Senior Librn*, Michael Blanton; *Senior Librn*, Glenna McCowan; Staff 3 (MLS 3)
Founded 1950
Oct 1999-Sep 2000 Mats Exp $145,359, Books $8,598, Per/Ser (Incl. Access Fees) $96,761, Electronic Ref Mat (Incl. Access Fees) $40,000. Sal $205,000 (Prof $173,000)
Library Holdings: Bk Titles 3,337; Per Subs 373
Automation Activity & Vendor Info: (Cataloging) Sagebrush Corporation; (Circulation) Sagebrush Corporation; (OPAC) Sagebrush Corporation
Database Vendor: OVID Technologies, Silverplatter Information Inc.
Partic in Vets Admin Libr Network
Statistics include North Little Rock Division

S METROPLAN (METROPOLITAN AREA PLANNING COMMISSION), Metroplan Information Center,* 501 W Markham Ste B, 72201. SAN 326-0607. Tel: 501-372-3300. FAX: 501-372-8060. *In Charge*, Richard Magee
Library Holdings: Bk Vols 3,000; Bk Titles 3,000
Subject Interests: Census records, City planning, Transportation studies, Water quality studies
Special Collections: County & City

L MITCHELL, WILLIAMS, SELIG, GATES & WOODYARD, Law Library, 425 W Capitol Ave, Ste 1800, 72201. SAN 372-2589. Tel: 501-688-8800. FAX: 501-688-8807. *Librn*, Catherine A Bruhn; E-Mail: cbruhn@mwsgw.com; Staff 2 (MLS 1, Non-MLS 1)
Library Holdings: Bk Vols 15,000; Per Subs 450

C PHILANDER SMITH COLLEGE, M L Harris Library, 812 W 13th St, 72202. SAN 300-5291. Tel: 501-370-5262. FAX: 501-370-5307. *Actg Dir*, Shawn Pierce; Staff 8 (MLS 1, Non-MLS 7)
Enrl 950; Highest Degree: Bachelor
1998-1999 Income $244,648, Federal $147,497, Parent Institution $97,151. Mats Exp $64,300, Books $34,800, Per/Ser (Incl. Access Fees) $22,000, Presv $1,000, AV Equip $6,500. Sal $127,396
Library Holdings: Bk Vols 62,000; Per Subs 280
Subject Interests: Arkansas, Black people (ethnic), Business and management, Ethnic studies
Special Collections: African American/Black History; PSC Archives
Automation Activity & Vendor Info: (Cataloging) Follett; (Circulation) Follett
Database Vendor: IAC - Info Trac, OCLC - First Search, ProQuest
Partic in Amigos Library Services, Inc

M SAINT VINCENT HEALTH SYSTEMS LIBRARY, Two Saint Vincent Circle, 72205. SAN 300-5305. Tel: 501-660-3231. FAX: 501-671-4311. *Coll Develop, Librn*, Mary King; E-Mail: mking@exchange.svime.com
Founded 1900
Library Holdings: Bk Vols 4,048; Per Subs 142
Subject Interests: Health sciences, Medicine

S THE ARKANSAS ARTS CENTER, Elizabeth Prewitt Taylor Memorial Library, MacArthur Park, 9th & Commerce, 72203. (Mail add: PO Box 2137, 72203-2137), SAN 300-5151. Tel: 501-396-0341. FAX: 501-375-8053. E-Mail: library@arkarts.com. Web Site: www.arkarts.com. *Librn*, Patrice O'Donoghue; Staff 1 (MLS 1)
Founded 1963
Library Holdings: Bk Vols 9,000; Per Subs 125
Subject Interests: Art, Decorative arts
Special Collections: George Fisher Political Cartoons; John Reid Coll of Early American Jazz
Restriction: Non-circulating

G UNITED STATES COURT OF APPEALS, Branch Library, 600 W Capitol Ave, Rm 224, 72201. SAN 324-6701. Tel: 501-604-5215. FAX: 501-604-5217. E-Mail: crata_castleberry@ared.uscourts.gov. Web Site: www.ca8.uscourts.gov/library/library.html. *Librn*, Crata Castleberry; Staff 1 (MLS 1)
Founded 1981
Library Holdings: Bk Vols 16,000; Bk Titles 500; Per Subs 65
Subject Interests: Fed law
Automation Activity & Vendor Info: (Acquisitions) SIRSI; (Cataloging) SIRSI; (Circulation) SIRSI; (Course Reserve) SIRSI; (ILL) SIRSI; (Media Booking) SIRSI; (OPAC) SIRSI
Partic in Dialog Corporation; Lexis, Solinet, Westlaw; OCLC Online Computer Library Center, Inc

C UNIVERSITY OF ARKANSAS AT LITTLE ROCK, Ottenheimer Library, 2801 S University, 72204. SAN 331-2429. Tel: 501-569-3122. Reference Tel: 501-569-8806. FAX: 501-569-3017. E-Mail: library@ualr.edu. Web Site: library.ualr.edu/marion. *Dir Libr Serv*, Kathy Sanders; Tel: 501-569-8802, Fax: 501-569-8814, E-Mail: kasanders@ualr.edu; *Asst Dir*, Bill Traylor; Tel: 501-569-8804, Fax: 501-569-8814, E-Mail: whtraylor@ualr.edu; *Syst Coordr*, Thomas Scott; Tel: 501-569-8057, E-Mail: tfscott@ualr.edu; *Doc*, Karen Russ; E-Mail: kmruss@ualr.edu; *Archivist*, Linda Pine; Tel: 501-569-8820, E-Mail: lrpine@ualr.edu; *Head Ref*, Sharon Kerr; E-Mail: shkerr@ualr.edu; *Head, Circ*, Linda Stipsky; Tel: 501-569-8817, E-Mail: lbstipsky@ualr.edu; *Head, Cat*, Donna Rose; Tel: 501-569-8817, E-Mail: dkrose@ualr.edu; *Acq, Coll Develop*, Maureen James-Barnes; Tel: 501-569-8816, E-Mail: mejames@ualr.edu; *Info Tech*, Regina Beach; Tel: 501-569-8813, E-Mail: rlbeach@ualr.edu; *Ref*, Carole Burke; E-Mail: crburke@ualr.edu; *Ref*, Carol Holstead-Macheak; E-Mail: ciholstead@ualr.edu; *Ref*, Abby Holt; E-Mail: aeholt@ualr.edu; *Ref*, Brent Nelson; E-Mail: banelson@ualr.edu; *Business*, Suzanne Martin; Tel: 501-569-8805, Fax: 501-569-8814, E-Mail: csmartin@ualr.edu; Staff 39 (MLS 11, Non-MLS 28)
Founded 1927. Enrl 11,000; Fac 445; Highest Degree: Doctorate
Jul 1999-Jun 2000 Income $2,914,381, State $349,121, Provincial $360,758, Locally Generated Income $66,524, Parent Institution $2,400,436, Other $52,095. Mats Exp $1,061,848, Books $460,484, Per/Ser (Incl. Access Fees) $506,329, Presv $24,886, Micro $33,389, AV Equip $6,060, Electronic Ref Mat (Incl. Access Fees) $30,700. Sal $1,156,283 (Prof $561,497)
Library Holdings: Bk Vols 371,156; Bk Titles 331,213; Per Subs 2,023
Subject Interests: Business and management, Education, Government, Humanities, Psychology, Social sciences, Technology
Special Collections: Architectural drawings, photos, maps, misc; Arkansas & Lower Mississippi Valley; Chet Lauck, Lum & Abner Coll; J N Heiskell; Myers Shakespeare Coll; Winthrop Rockefeller Papers
Automation Activity & Vendor Info: (Acquisitions) Innovative Interfaces Inc.; (Cataloging) Innovative Interfaces Inc.; (Circulation) Innovative Interfaces Inc.; (Course Reserve) Innovative Interfaces Inc.; (OPAC) Innovative Interfaces Inc.; (Serials) Innovative Interfaces Inc.
Database Vendor: Lexis-Nexis, OCLC - First Search, ProQuest
Special Services for the Deaf - TDD
Departmental Libraries:
CL PULASKI COUNTY LAW LIBRARY, 1201 McAlmont, 72202. SAN 331-2453. Tel: 501-324-9444. FAX: 501-324-9447. Web Site: www.ualr.edu/~lawlib. *Dir*, A Michael Beaird; E-Mail: ambeaird@ualr.edu; *Cat*, Susan Goldner; *Ref, Spec Coll*, Kathryn Fitzhugh; *Acq*, Jada Aitchison; *Tech Servs*, Melissa Serfass; *Circ*, Jessie Cranford; Staff 6 (MLS 6)
Founded 1965. Enrl 400; Fac 22; Highest Degree: Doctorate
Jul 1998-Jun 1999 Income $1,397,420, State $85,000, County $469,000, Parent Institution $843,420. Mats Exp $463,864, Books $39,146, Per/Ser (Incl. Access Fees) $407,373, Presv $9,710, Micro $7,304. Sal $471,631 (Prof $284,788)
Library Holdings: Bk Vols 164,039; Bk Titles 29,034; Per Subs 3,238
Special Collections: Arkansas Supreme Court Records and Briefs, 1836-1926
Database Vendor: Innovative Interfaces INN - View
Publications: Law Library Guide; Legal Reader Newsletter
Partic in Amigos Library Services, Inc; Dialog Corporation; OCLC Online Computer Library Center, Inc; Westlaw

CM UNIVERSITY OF ARKANSAS FOR MEDICAL SCIENCES LIBRARY, 4301 W Markham St, SLOT 586, 72205-7186. SAN 331-2488. Tel: 501-686-5980. Interlibrary Loan Service Tel: 501-686-6744. Reference Tel: 501-686-6734. FAX: 501-686-6745. Web Site: www.library.uams.edu. *Dir*, Mary Ryan; Tel: 501-686-6730, Fax: 501-296-1423; Staff 39 (MLS 10, Non-MLS 29)
Founded 1879. Enrl 1,861; Fac 1,030; Highest Degree: Doctorate
Jul 1999-Jun 2000 Income $2,499,160. Mats Exp $918,323, Books $92,858, Per/Ser (Incl. Access Fees) $825,465. Sal $1,217,877
Library Holdings: Bk Vols 46,120; Bk Titles 39,265; Per Subs 1,900
Special Collections: History of Medicine in Arkansas; Pathology (Schlumberger Coll)
Automation Activity & Vendor Info: (Acquisitions) Innovative Interfaces Inc.; (Cataloging) Innovative Interfaces Inc.; (Circulation) Innovative Interfaces Inc.; (Course Reserve) Innovative Interfaces Inc.; (ILL) Innovative Interfaces Inc.; (OPAC) Innovative Interfaces Inc.; (Serials) Innovative Interfaces Inc.
Publications: UAMS Library Newsletter
Partic in Amigos Library Services, Inc; OCLC Online Computer Library Center, Inc; South Central Academic Medical Libraries Consortium
Friends of the Library Group

L WILLIAMS & ANDERSON, Law Library,* 111 Center, 22nd flr, 72201. SAN 372-2597. Tel: 501-372-0800. FAX: 501-372-6453. E-Mail: library@williamsanderson.com. *Librn*, John Ferguson
Founded 1989. Pop 50
Library Holdings: Bk Vols 4,000
Subject Interests: Environmental law, Real estate, Securities

LITTLE ROCK AFB

UNITED STATES AIR FORCE
A LITTLE ROCK AIR FORCE BASE LIBRARY, 976 Cannon Dr, FL 4460, 72099-5289. SAN 331-2518. Tel: 501-987-6979. *Librn*, Bethry J Becker
Founded 1956
Library Holdings: Bk Vols 21,000
Subject Interests: Aeronautics, Business and management

LONOKE

P LONOKE PRAIRIE COUNTY REGIONAL LIBRARY HEADQUARTERS,* 204 E Second St, 72086-2858. SAN 324-041X. Tel: 501-676-6635. FAX: 501-676-7687. *Dir*, Philip Ross; Staff 8 (MLS 1, Non-MLS 7)
Founded 1937. Pop 49,000; Circ 122,000
Jan 1998-Dec 1998 Income $446,796, State $73,966, Provincial $322,830, City $22,000, County $28,000. Mats Exp $81,000. Sal $182,730 (Prof $33,979)
Library Holdings: Bk Vols 131,000; Bk Titles 80,000; Per Subs 240
Subject Interests: Genealogy, Local history
Branches: 8
ARLENE CHERRY MEMORIAL, 506 N Grant St, Cabot, 72023. SAN 324-0649. Tel: 501-843-7661. *Librn*, Devona Brannon
Friends of the Library Group
CARLISLE PUBLIC, City Park, PO Box 12, Carlisle, 72024-0012. SAN 324-0665. Tel: 870-552-3976. FAX: 870-552-3976. *Librn*, Frankie Dunn
DES ARC PUBLIC, 408 Curran St, PO Box 542, Des Arc, 72040-0542. SAN 373-5036. Tel: 870-256-3003. FAX: 870-256-3003. *Librn*, Mary Frances Calhoun
DEVALLS BLUFF PUBLIC, PO Box 504, Devalls Bluff, 72041-0504. SAN 373-5044. Tel: 870-998-7010. FAX: 870-998-7010. *Librn*, Brenda Prince
HAZEN PUBLIC, Hwy 70 E, PO Box 348, Hazen, 72064-0348. SAN 324-8070. Tel: 870-255-3576. FAX: 870-255-3576. *Librn*, Patsy McMullen
MARJORIE WALKER MCCRARY MEMORIAL Tel: 501-676-6635. FAX: 501-676-6635. *Librn*, Jamie C Frank
Friends of the Library Group
WARD PUBLIC, 100 Owens St, Ward, 72176. (Mail add: PO Box 609, Ward, 72176-0609), Tel: 501-941-3220. FAX: 501-941-3220. *Librn*, Carlyn Bray
Library Holdings: Bk Vols 9,000; Per Subs 11; Bks on Deafness & Sign Lang 17
WILLIAM F FOSTER PUBLIC, 100 E Taylor, England, 72046-2181. SAN 324-0673. Tel: 501-842-2051. FAX: 501-842-2051. *Librn*, Pam Guajardo

MAGNOLIA

P COLUMBIA-LAFAYETTE-OUACHITA-CALHOUN REGIONAL LIBRARY, (CLOC), Asa C Garrett Memorial Library, 220 E Main St, 71753-3530. (Mail add: PO Box 668, 71754-0668), SAN 331-2542. Tel: 870-234-1991. FAX: 870-234-5077. E-Mail: cloc@magnolia-net.com. *Dir*, Julie Metro; Staff 1 (MLS 1)
Founded 1947. Pop 71,734
Jan 1999-Dec 1999 Income (Main Library and Branch Library) $775,645, State $254,827, City $71,555, County $353,194, Other $96,069. Mats Exp $106,553. Sal $261,138 (Prof $36,000)
Library Holdings: Bk Vols 321,452; Bk Titles 147,791; Per Subs 224
Subject Interests: Arkansas, Genealogy
Database Vendor: OCLC - First Search
Branches: 10
BEARDEN PUBLIC LIBRARY, 110 N Cedar, Bearden, 71720. (Mail add: PO Box 536, Bearden, 71720-0536), SAN 331-2577. Tel: 870-687-2634. *Librn*, Mrs Hugh Thompson
CABE MEMORIAL PUBLIC LIBRARY, 312 Main St, Stamps, 71860. SAN 331-2755. Tel: 870-533-4424. FAX: 870-533-4424. *Librn*, Ruth Bales
CALHOUN COUNTY LIBRARY, 109 Second St, PO Box 1162, Hampton, 71744. SAN 331-2690. Tel: 870-798-4492. FAX: 870-798-4492. *Librn*, Molly Sue Wilson
CHIDESTER PUBLIC LIBRARY, 305 N Main, Chidester, 71726. SAN 331-2666. *Librn*, Sherrie Genn
LEWISVILLE COUNTY LIBRARY, 219 E Third St, Lewisville, 71845. SAN 331-2720. Tel: 870-921-4757. FAX: 870-921-4757. *Librn*, Dorothy Campbell
P LIBRARY FOR THE BLIND & PHYSICALLY HANDICAPPED, 220 E Main St, 71753. (Mail add: PO Box 668, 71754-0668), SAN 331-2550. Tel: 870-234-0399. Toll Free Tel: 866-234-8273. FAX: 870-234-5077. E-Mail: lbph@hotmail.com. *Librn*, Susan Walker
PUBLIC LIBRARY OF CAMDEN & OUACHITA COUNTY, 120 Harrison Ave SW, Camden, 71701. SAN 331-2631. Tel: 870-836-5083. FAX: 870-836-0163. *Dir*, Phyllis Stewart
STEPHENS PUBLIC LIBRARY, 108 W Ruby St, PO Box 104, Stephens, 71764. SAN 331-278X. Tel: 870-786-5231. *Librn*, Nettie Tribble
TAYLOR PUBLIC LIBRARY, 101 W Pope, Taylor, 71861. SAN 331-281X. Tel: 870-694-2051. *Librn*, Betty Ann Jackson
THORNTON PUBLIC LIBRARY, S Second St, Thornton, 71766. (Mail add: PO Box 102, Thornton, 71766-0102), SAN 331-2844. Tel: 870-352-5990. *Librn*, Vicky Davis

C SOUTHERN ARKANSAS UNIVERSITY, Magale Library, 100 E University, 71753-5000. (Mail add: SAU Box 9218, 71754-9218), SAN 300-533X. Tel: 870-235-4170. Reference Tel: 870-235-5083. FAX: 870-235-5018. Web Site: www.saumag.edu/library. *Dir*, Peggy Walters; Tel: 870-235-4171, E-Mail: ppwalters@saumag.edu; *Bibliog Instr, Publ Servs*, Martha Ann Bace; Tel: 870-235-5066, E-Mail: mabace@saumag.edu; *Govt Doc, Syst Coordr*, Margo Pierson; Tel: 870-235-4177, E-Mail: mmpierson@saumag.edu; *ILL, Ref*, Donna McCloy; Tel: 870-235-4178, E-Mail: dmmccloy@saumag.edu; *Per*, Peggy Rogers; Tel: 870-235-4174, E-Mail: pvrogers@saumag.edu; Staff 10 (MLS 5, Non-MLS 5)
Founded 1909. Enrl 2,600; Fac 135; Highest Degree: Master
Jul 1999-Jun 2000 Income $740,668, State $570,054, Federal $45,614, Locally Generated Income $125,000. Mats Exp $378,100, Books $145,560, Per/Ser (Incl. Access Fees) $82,058, Presv $500, Micro $45,460, AV Equip $22,040, Electronic Ref Mat (Incl. Access Fees) $74,280. Sal $253,053 (Prof $174,166)
Library Holdings: Bk Vols 149,006; Bk Titles 130,687; Per Subs 866; Bks on Deafness & Sign Lang 24
Subject Interests: Social work
Special Collections: Arkansiana
Automation Activity & Vendor Info: (Acquisitions) SIRSI; (Cataloging) SIRSI; (Circulation) SIRSI; (Course Reserve) SIRSI; (OPAC) SIRSI; (Serials) SIRSI
Database Vendor: CARL, Dialog, Ebsco - EbscoHost, GaleNet, IAC - Info Trac, OCLC - First Search, ProQuest, Silverplatter Information Inc.
Partic in Amigos Library Services, Inc; OCLC Online Computer Library Center, Inc

MALVERN

P HOT SPRING COUNTY LIBRARY, Mid-Arkansas Regional Library, 202 E Third, 72104. SAN 300-5348. Tel: 501-332-5441. FAX: 501-332-6679. *Dir*, Mary Ann Griggs
Founded 1928
Library Holdings: Bk Vols 60,000; Per Subs 70
Subject Interests: Arkansas, Genealogy
Mem of Mid-Arkansas Regional Libr Syst
Partic in SW Flm Coop

MARION

P CRITTENDEN COUNTY LIBRARY,* County Office Bldg, 116 Center St, 72364. SAN 300-5364. Tel: 870-739-3238. FAX: 870-739-3238. *Librn*, Pam Ervin
Pop 22,140; Circ 24,000
1997-1998 Income $125,000. Mats Exp $16,110, Books $15,000, Presv $1,000. Sal $80,188 (Prof $15,872)
Library Holdings: Bk Vols 41,000; Per Subs 75
Subject Interests: Arkansas
Branches: 4
CRAWFORDSVILLE BRANCH, Crawfordsville, 72327. SAN 321-9143.

Tel: 870-823-5204. *Librn*, Janis Lancaster
EARLE BRANCH, 703 Commerce St, Earle, 72331. SAN 321-9135. Tel: 870-792-8500. *Librn*, Dorothy Dickey
Friends of the Library Group
GILMORE BRANCH, Gilmore, 72339. SAN 321-916X. Tel: 870-343-2697. *Librn*, Cathy Moore
HORSESHOE BRANCH, Rte 2, Box A9, Horseshoe Lake, 72348. SAN 321-9178. Tel: 870-339-3862. *Librn*, Pat Lindsey

MELBOURNE

P IZARD COUNTY LIBRARY, Melbourne Public, Hwy 69, PO Box 343, 72556. SAN 326-7121. Tel: 870-368-7467. FAX: 870-368-7467. E-Mail: melbournelibrary@centurytel.net. *Head Librn*, Zennie Pollard
Founded 1957
Library Holdings: Per Subs 10

MONTICELLO

S DREW COUNTY HISTORICAL SOCIETY, Museum & Archives, 404 S Main St, 71655-4818. SAN 329-8434. Tel: 870-367-7446. *Chair*, Connie Mullis
Library Holdings: Bk Titles 460
Subject Interests: Ark, Drew County, Genealogy

P SOUTHEAST ARKANSAS REGIONAL LIBRARY,* 107 E Jackson St, 71655. SAN 331-2879. Tel: 870-367-8584. FAX: 870-367-5166. E-Mail: searlibr@seark.net. *Dir*, Kim Patterson; Staff 44 (MLS 1, Non-MLS 43)
Founded 1947. Pop 75,000; Circ 203,204
Jan 1998-Dec 1998 Income (Main Library and Branch Library) $685,248, State $151,031, City $10,836, Federal $7,469, County $455,726, Locally Generated Income $60,186. Mats Exp $201,509, Books $60,000, Per/Ser (Incl. Access Fees) $13,000, Presv $700, Electronic Ref Mat (Incl. Access Fees) $22,000. Sal $408,175 (Prof $35,500)
Library Holdings: Bk Vols 168,210; Bk Titles 42,622; Per Subs 495
Subject Interests: Arkansas
Friends of the Library Group
Branches: 15
ARKANSAS CITY BRANCH, PO Box 447, Arkansas City, 71630. SAN 331-2909. *Mgr*, Joyce Douthit
Library Holdings: Bk Vols 4,330
DERMOTT BRANCH, 117 S Freeman St, Dermott, 71638. SAN 321-9518. Tel: 870-538-3514. FAX: 870-538-3188. *Mgr*, LaTosha Williams
Library Holdings: Bk Vols 8,922
Friends of the Library Group
DUMAS BRANCH, 120 E Choctow, Dumas, 71639. SAN 331-2968. Tel: 870-382-5763. FAX: 870-382-5763. *Mgr*, Sandra Leek
Library Holdings: Bk Vols 21,237
Friends of the Library Group
EUDORA BRANCH, 161 N Cherry St, Eudora, 71640. SAN 321-9526. Tel: 870-355-2450. FAX: 870-355-2897. *Mgr*, Tina Toney
Library Holdings: Bk Vols 7,180
GOULD BRANCH, PO Box 683, Gould, 71643. SAN 331-2992.
Library Holdings: Bk Vols 2,324
HERMITAGE BRANCH, PO Box 98, Hermitage, 71647. SAN 331-3034. *Mgr*, Beverly Blankenship
Library Holdings: Bk Vols 2,106
LAKE VILLAGE BRANCH, 108 Church St, Lake Village, 71653. SAN 300-5143. Tel: 870-265-6116. FAX: 870-265-2078. *Mgr*, Ellen DiMaggio
Library Holdings: Bk Vols 11,424; Per Subs 12
Friends of the Library Group
MCGEHEE BRANCH, 211 N Fourth St, McGehee, 71654. SAN 331-3050. Tel: 870-222-4097. FAX: 870-222-4097. *Mgr*, Anna Bates
Library Holdings: Bk Vols 23,836
Friends of the Library Group
MONTICELLO BRANCH, 107 E Jackson, 71655. SAN 331-3069. Tel: 870-367-8583. FAX: 870-367-5166. *Mgr*, Carolyn Sledge
Library Holdings: Bk Vols 47,873
Friends of the Library Group
STAR CITY BRANCH, 206 S Lincoln, Star City, 71667. SAN 331-3085. Tel: 870-628-4711. FAX: 870-628-4711. *Mgr*, Judy Calhoun
Library Holdings: Bk Vols 14,249
Friends of the Library Group
TILLAR BRANCH, PO Box 136, Tillar, 71670. SAN 331-3115. *Mgr*, Joyce Douthit
Library Holdings: Bk Vols 1,630
WARREN BRANCH, 115 W Cypress, Warren, 71671. SAN 331-3131. Tel: 870-226-8420. FAX: 870-226-8420. *Mgr*, Gingy Cuthbertson
Library Holdings: Bk Vols 17,626
Friends of the Library Group
WATSON BRANCH, PO Box 205, Watson, 71674. SAN 331-314X. Tel: 870-644-3655. FAX: 870-644-3655. *Mgr*, Joyce Douthit
Library Holdings: Bk Vols 2,330
WILMAR BRANCH, PO Box 415, Wilmar, 71675. SAN 331-3174. *Mgr*, Mae Simpson
Library Holdings: Bk Vols 2,376

C UNIVERSITY OF ARKANSAS-MONTICELLO LIBRARY,* Hwy 425 S, 71656. (Mail add: PO Box 3599, 71656), SAN 300-5372. Tel: 870-460-1080. FAX: 870-460-1980. Web Site: www.cotton.uamont.edu/~uamlibrary/library.htmlx, www.rice.uamont.edu. *Dir*, Dr W F Droessler; *Assoc Librn, Reader Servs*, Sandra Dupree; *Cat, Spec Coll*, Jay Randall; *Electronic Resources, Ref*, Mark Shores; *Govt Doc*, Fran Hayden; *ILL*, Linda Forest; *Ser*, Helen Guenter; *Ser*, James Carter; Staff 4 (MLS 4)
Founded 1909. Enrl 2,500; Fac 96; Highest Degree: Master
Library Holdings: Bk Vols 146,000; Bk Titles 110,000; Per Subs 807
Subject Interests: Arkansas, Forestry
Database Vendor: DRA
Publications: Annual Report

MORRILTON

P CONWAY COUNTY LIBRARY HEADQUARTERS,* 101 W Church St, 72110-3399. SAN 300-5380. Tel: 501-354-5204. FAX: 501-354-5206. *Librn*, Zoe Butler
Founded 1915. Pop 19,505; Circ 64,840
Library Holdings: Bk Titles 49,653; Per Subs 30
Friends of the Library Group

S WINROCK INTERNATIONAL INSTITUTE FOR AGRICULTURAL DEVELOPMENT LIBRARY, 38 Winrock Dr, 72110. SAN 324-2757. Tel: 501-727-5435, Ext 303. FAX: 501-727-5242. Web Site: www.winrock.org. *Librn*, Melinda Pennington; E-Mail: mpennington@winrock.org; Staff 1 (MLS 1)
Founded 1975
Library Holdings: Bk Titles 20,000
Subject Interests: Agr educ, Agriculture, Crops, Forestry, Gender, Leadership training, Livestock, Pub policy, Renewable energy, Systs
Automation Activity & Vendor Info: (Cataloging) SIRSI; (OPAC) SIRSI
Publications: Publications Catalog
Partic in Amigos Library Services, Inc

MOUNT IDA

P MONTGOMERY COUNTY LIBRARY,* 145D Whittington St Civic Ctr, PO Box 189, 71957. SAN 300-5399. Tel: 870-867-3812. FAX: 870-867-3812. *Librn*, Joann Whisenhunt; E-Mail: montlib@hotmail
Founded 1958. Pop 7,841; Circ 22,291
1999-2000 Income $19,800
Library Holdings: Bk Vols 11,919
Mem of Tri-Lakes Regional Library
Friends of the Library Group

MOUNTAIN HOME

§P BAXTER COUNTY LIBRARY, 424 W Seventh St, 72653. Tel: 870-425-3598. FAX: 870-425-7226. *Librn*, Gwen Khayat
Jan 1999-Dec 1999 Income $396,812, State $45,474, Other $36,833
Library Holdings: Bk Vols 67,211; Per Subs 250; Bks on Deafness & Sign Lang 10
Automation Activity & Vendor Info: (Cataloging) TLC; (Circulation) TLC
Branches: 1
GASSVILLE BRANCH, 6469 Hwy 62 W, Gassville, 72635. Tel: 870-435-2180. *Librn*, Gwen Khayat
Library Holdings: Bk Vols 2,800
Automation Activity & Vendor Info: (Cataloging) TLC; (Circulation) TLC

MOUNTAIN VIEW

S OZARK FOLK CENTER LIBRARY, (OCRC), Ozark Cultural Resource Center, Hwy 382 Box 500, 72560. SAN 321-0332. Tel: www.library.edu. FAX: 870-269-2909. E-Mail: ofcmusic@mvtel.net. Web Site: www.ozarkfolkcenter.com. *Librn*, W K McNeil; *Cat*, Donna Deppe
Founded 1976
1998-1999 Income $9,100, State $500, Other $8,600. Mats Exp $7,100, Books $5,500, Per/Ser (Incl. Access Fees) $1,000, Per/Ser (Incl. Access Fees) $500, Manuscripts & Archives $100
Library Holdings: Bk Vols 8,600; Bk Titles 8,000; Per Subs 50
Subject Interests: Crafts, Music, Ozark folklore
Restriction: Not a lending library
Friends of the Library Group

§P STONE COUNTY LIBRARY, Bessie Boehm Moore Library, 326 W Washington St, 72560. (Mail add: PO Box 1105, 72560-1105), Tel: 870-269-3100. E-Mail: sclibrary99@hotmail.com. *Br Coordr*, Miriam Miller
Jan 2000-Dec 2000 Income $77,550
Library Holdings: Bk Vols 17,199; Per Subs 27
Automation Activity & Vendor Info: (Acquisitions) Sagebrush Corporation; (Cataloging) Sagebrush Corporation; (Circulation) Sagebrush Corporation
Mem of White River Regional Library
Open Tues & Fri 10-6, Wed 10-5, Thurs 10-7, Sat 9-1

MOUNTAINBURG

P MOUNTAINBURG PUBLIC LIBRARY,* 1300 Hwy 71 NE, 72946. SAN 331-0027. Tel: 501-369-1600. FAX: 501-369-1600. Web Site: www.crawfordcountylib.org. *Librn*, Helen Campbell
Mem of Ozarks Regional Library
Friends of the Library Group

MULBERRY

P MULBERRY PUBLIC LIBRARY, 207 Main St, PO Box 589, 72947. SAN 331-0051. Tel: 501-997-1226. Interlibrary Loan Service Tel: 501-471-3226. FAX: 501-997-1226. E-Mail: mulberrylibrary@hotmail.com. Web Site: www.crawfordcounty.lib.org. *Librn*, Cindy Whitson
Pop 1,600
Jan 2000-Dec 2000 Income $31,000, State $6,000, County $24,367, Parent Institution $633. Mats Exp $10,300, Books $10,000, Per/Ser (Incl. Access Fees) $300. Sal $16,494
Library Holdings: Bk Vols 12,000
Automation Activity & Vendor Info: (Acquisitions) TLC; (Cataloging) TLC; (Circulation) TLC; (OPAC) TLC
Database Vendor: OCLC - First Search
Mem of Crawford County Federated Library System
Friends of the Library Group

NEWPORT

P JACKSON COUNTY LIBRARY, W A Billingsley Memorial Library, 213 Walnut St, PO Box 190, 72112-0190. SAN 300-5402. Tel: 870-523-2952. FAX: 870-523-4283. *Dir, Librn*, Ila B Lacy; Staff 1 (MLS 1)
Founded 1930. Pop 21,646; Circ 84,000
Library Holdings: Bk Titles 45,000; Per Subs 57
Subject Interests: Arkansas, Genealogy
Automation Activity & Vendor Info: (Cataloging) Follett; (Circulation) Follett
Database Vendor: Ebsco - EbscoHost, OCLC - First Search
Branches: 1
TUCKERMAN BRANCH, 200 W Main St, Tuckerman, 72473. (Mail add: PO Box 1117, Tuckerman, 72473-1117), Tel: 870-349-5336. FAX: 870-349-5126. E-Mail: tuckermancitylibrary@alltel.net. *Librn*, Shirley Manuel
Jan 2000-Dec 2000 Income $14,400, City $13,800, County $600
Library Holdings: Bk Vols 58,624

NORTH LITTLE ROCK

FIRST ASSEMBLY OF GOD LIBRARY, 4501 Burrow Dr, 72116. SAN 300-5410. Tel: 501-758-8553. FAX: 501-758-3830. E-Mail: churchinfo@firstassemblynlr.com. Web Site: www.firstassembly.com. *Librn*, Joye Murry
Founded 1953
1999-2000 Income $2,500. Mats Exp $2,325, Books $2,000, Per/Ser (Incl. Access Fees) $125, AV Equip $200
Library Holdings: Bk Vols 5,400; Bk Titles 5,460
Subject Interests: Religion

P WILLIAM F LAMAN PUBLIC LIBRARY, 2801 Orange St, 72114-2296. SAN 300-5429. Tel: 501-758-1720. FAX: 501-758-3539. Web Site: www.laman.lib.ar.us. *Dir*, Jeffrey L Baskin; Fax: 501-753-0524, E-Mail: jbaskin@www.laman.lib.ar.us; Staff 15 (MLS 3, Non-MLS 12)
Founded 1945. Pop 64,388; Circ 230,037
Jan 2000-Dec 2000 Income $1,432,298, State $72,586, County $1,077,274, Locally Generated Income $57,690, Other $224,748. Mats Exp $310,811, Books $191,000, Per/Ser (Incl. Access Fees) $16,000, Presv $2,000, Micro $33,000, Electronic Ref Mat (Incl. Access Fees) $68,811. Sal $569,543 (Prof $234,196)
Library Holdings: Bk Vols 142,802; Per Subs 271
Special Collections: Ark History; Genealogy Coll
Automation Activity & Vendor Info: (OPAC) Gaylord
Partic in OCLC Online Computer Library Center, Inc

PARAGOULD

M ARKANSAS METHODIST HOSPITAL, Doctors' Memorial Library, 900 W Kings Hwy, PO Box 339, 72451. SAN 320-1236. Tel: 870-239-7894. FAX: 870-239-7400. *Librn*, Cheri Hutchison
Founded 1970
Library Holdings: Bk Vols 200; Bk Titles 800; Per Subs 20
Subject Interests: Medicine, Nursing
Restriction: Staff use only

J CROWLEY'S RIDGE COLLEGE LIBRARY, 100 College Dr, 72450. SAN 300-5445. Tel: 870-236-6901, Ext 23. FAX: 870-236-7748. Web Site: www.crc.paragould.ar.us. *Librn*, Adam Broom; E-Mail: adam@pioneer.crc.paragoud.as.us
Founded 1964. Enrl 100; Fac 8
Library Holdings: Bk Vols 13,500; Bk Titles 12,500; Per Subs 60
Subject Interests: Religion

P NORTHEAST ARKANSAS REGIONAL LIBRARY, Headquarters, 120 N 12th St, 72450. SAN 331-3204. Tel: 870-236-8711. FAX: 870-236-1442. *Dir*, Hal Hubener; Fax: 870-236-1442, E-Mail: hubener@gcl.lib.ar.us; Staff 1 (MLS 1)
Founded 1965. Pop 68,194; Circ 274,503
Branches: 5
CORNING BRANCH
See Separate Entry in Corning, Corning.
GREENE COUNTY BRANCH
See separate entry in Paragould.
PIGGOTT BRANCH
See Separate Listing in Piggott, Piggott.
RANDOLPH COUNTY BRANCH
See Separate Entry in Pocahontas, Pocahontas.
RECTOR BRANCH
See Separate Entry in Rector, Rector.

P NORTHEAST ARKANSAS REGIONAL LIBRARY, Greene County Library, 120 N 12th St, 72450. Tel: 870-236-8711. FAX: 870-236-1442. *Dir*, Sandra Rogers; Staff 14 (Non-MLS 14)
Founded 1965. Pop 68,194; Circ 274,503
Subject Interests: Arkansas, Genealogy

PEA RIDGE

§P PEA RIDGE COMMUNITY LIBRARY, 161 Pickens St, 72751. (Mail add: PO Box 29, 72751-0029), Tel: 501-451-8442. E-Mail: prcl@mczk.com. *Librn*, Jennifer Hook
Jan 2000-Dec 2000 Income $16,570
Library Holdings: Bk Vols 5,000; High Interest/Low Vocabulary Bk Vols 500

S US NATIONAL PARK SERVICE PEA RIDGE MILITARY PARK LIBRARY, PO Box 700, 72751. SAN 370-2855. Tel: 501-451-8122. FAX: 501-451-8639. *Librn*, Douglas Keller
1998-1999 Mats Exp Books $870
Library Holdings: Bk Vols 500
Special Collections: Battle of Pea Ridge (30 reels of microfilm, 15 rpts)
Restriction: Open to public for reference only

PIGGOTT

P NORTHEAST ARKANSAS REGIONAL LIBRARY, Piggott Library, 361 W Main, 72454. SAN 331-3263. Tel: 870-598-3666. FAX: 870-598-3666. *Librn*, Gay Johnson; Staff 3 (Non-MLS 3)

PINE BLUFF

P ARKANSAS DEPARTMENT OF CORRECTION LIBRARY SYSTEM,* 4218 W 28th St, 71603. SAN 326-5978. Tel: 870-879-5594. FAX: 870-879-1677. *Librn*, Marsha Moffitt
Circ 132,407
Jul 1997-Jun 1998 Income $85,435, Federal $9,305. Sal $73,130
Library Holdings: Bk Titles 61,000
Publications: Unit newsletters
Separate law library system

CM MELVILLE LIBRARY, UAMS-AHEC, Pine Bluff,* 4010 Mulberry, 71603. SAN 331-3387. Tel: 870-541-7625. FAX: 870-541-7628. *Dir Libr Serv*, Julie Dobbins; Tel: 870-541-7629, E-Mail: jdobbins@ahecpb.uams.edu
Library Holdings: Bk Vols 185,000
Subject Interests: Medicine, Nursing
Publications: The Collection (bimonthly newsletter)
Partic in Amigos Library Services, Inc; Arkansas Area Health Education Center Consortium (AHEC); OCLC Online Computer Library Center, Inc
Open Mon-Thurs 8-6, Fir 8-5

P PINE BLUFF & JEFFERSON COUNTY LIBRARY SYSTEM, 200 E Eighth Ave, 71601. SAN 300-5453. Tel: 870-534-4802. Circulation Tel: 870-534-4818. Reference Tel: 870-534-2159. FAX: 870-534-8707. E-Mail: pbjc-lib@pbjc-lib.state.ar.us. Web Site: pbjc-lib.state.ar.us. *Dir*, Dave Burdick; *Ch Servs*, Ann Lightsey; *Tech Servs*, Diana Lott; *Ref*, Brenda Tatum; *Br Coordr*, Mary Ellis; Tel: 870-267-1564, Fax: 870-247-2613; Staff 15 (MLS 1, Non-MLS 14)
Founded 1913. Pop 85,487
Jan 2000-Dec 2000 Income (Main Library and Branch Library) $1,125,000, State $115,000, City $507,000, County $440,000, Locally Generated Income $63,000. Mats Exp $987,045, Books $145,000, Per/Ser (Incl. Access Fees) $13,000, Presv $1,500, Micro $7,500, AV Equip $15,000, Electronic Ref Mat (Incl. Access Fees) $45,000. Sal $545,745 (Prof $56,200)
Library Holdings: Bk Vols 147,000; Bk Titles 92,500; Per Subs 250
Special Collections: Arkansas Coll; Genealogy with emphasis on Arkansas, North Carolina, South Carolina, Tennessee & Virginia; Regional History of Arkansas & Mississippi Valley, bks, maps, micro

Database Vendor: Ebsco - EbscoHost, GaleNet, OCLC - First Search
Partic in Amigos Library Services, Inc; OCLC Online Computer Library Center, Inc
Friends of the Library Group
Branches: 2
WATSON CHAPEL, 4120 Camden Rd, 71603. SAN 322-6204. Tel: 870-879-3406. FAX: 870-879-6437. *Br Coordr*, Mary Ellis; Tel: 870-267-1564, Fax: 870-247-2613; *Branch Mgr*, Elaine Stertmann
Library Holdings: Bk Vols 17,997
Database Vendor: Ebsco - EbscoHost, GaleNet, OCLC - First Search
P WHITE HALL PUBLIC LIBRARY, 300 Anderson St, White Hall, 71602. SAN 320-0825. Tel: 870-247-5064. FAX: 870-247-2613. *Dir*, Dave Burdick; Tel: 870-534-4802, Fax: 870-534-8707; *Br Coordr*, Mary Ellis; Tel: 870-267-1564; *Branch Mgr*, Jana Blankenship
Library Holdings: Bk Vols 29,694
Database Vendor: Ebsco - EbscoHost, GaleNet, OCLC - First Search
Friends of the Library Group
Bookmobiles: 1

C UNIVERSITY OF ARKANSAS, PINE BLUFF, Watson Memorial Library-Learning & Instructional Resources Centers, 1200 N University Dr, 71601. SAN 331-3352. Tel: 870-543-8000. Web Site: www.uapb.edu.com. *Dir*, E J Fontenette; E-Mail: fontenette_e@vx4500.uapb.edu; *Assoc Dir*, Delois D Johnson; *Ref*, Georgia Watley; *Cat*, Gwendolyn Cooper; *Acq*, Minnie L Greene; Staff 7 (MLS 7)
Founded 1938. Enrl 2,917; Fac 140; Highest Degree: Bachelor
Library Holdings: Bk Vols 257,007; Per Subs 1,068
Subject Interests: Agriculture, Education, Industrial arts, Nursing
Special Collections: Afro American Coll; Arkansas (Raley Coll); Literature (Rare Books Coll); State Government (Knox Nelson Coll)
Publications: Acquisitions List (monthly)
Partic in Amigos Library Services, Inc
Departmental Libraries:
FINE ARTS, PO Box 4925, 71611. Tel: 501-543-8236. FAX: 501-543-8232. *In Charge*, Henry Linton
HUMAN SCIENCES, PO Box 4971, 71611. *In Charge*, Edith Neal
MILITARY SCIENCE, 71611. Tel: 501-543-8445, 501-543-8451. FAX: 501-543-8039. *In Charge*, Melvin Banks
MUSIC LAB, PO Box 4956, 71611. Tel: 501-543-8905. *Dir*, Josephine Bell
NURSING LAB, PO Box 4973, 71611. Tel: 501-543-8221. FAX: 501-543-8229. *Dir*, Irene Henderson
SOCIAL & BEHAVIORAL SCIENCES, PO Box 4988, 71611. Tel: 501-543-8175. FAX: 501-543-8397. *In Charge*, Dr Ebo Tei

POCAHONTAS

P NORTHEAST ARKANSAS REGIONAL LIBRARY, Randolph County Library, 111 W Everett St, 72455. SAN 331-3298. Tel: 870-892-5617. FAX: 870-892-1142. E-Mail: racolib@yahoo.com. *Librn*, Brenda K White; Staff 5 (Non-MLS 5)
Founded 1939. Pop 16,000
Automation Activity & Vendor Info: (Cataloging) Brodart; (Circulation) Brodart; (OPAC) Brodart
Database Vendor: IAC - Info Trac, ProQuest
Function: ILL available
Friends of the Library Group

PRAIRIE GROVE

P PRAIRIE GROVE PUBLIC LIBRARY,* 123 S Neal St, PO Box 10, 72753. SAN 331-0086. Tel: 501-846-3782. FAX: 501-846-3428. E-Mail: prairiegrove@wcls.lib.ar.us. *Librn*, Maria Pendergraft
Library Holdings: Bk Vols 20,000
Mem of Ozarks Regional Library
Friends of the Library Group

PYATT

P NORTH ARKANSAS REGIONAL LIBRARY, 673 Foster St, 72672. SAN 331-0833. Tel: 870-427-2110. FAX: 870-427-2112. E-Mail: narlib@pyatt.net. *Dir*, Kuechmann Christopher
Founded 1944. Pop 66,617
Library Holdings: Bk Vols 80,000; Bk Titles 2,500; Per Subs 10
Subject Interests: Arkansas
Special Collections: Arkansas History Coll, bk & micro; Boone County Historical Photographs
Publications: Bi-monthly newsletter; NARL-ern Lights
Partic in OCLC Online Computer Library Center, Inc
Branches: 10
BERRYVILLE BRANCH, 104 Spring, Berryville, 72616. SAN 331-0922. Tel: 501-423-2323. FAX: 501-423-2323. E-Mail: bvpublib@cswnet.com. *Librn*, Carol Engskov; *Asst Librn*, Carla Youngblood
Founded 1978
Jan 2000-Dec 2000 Income $94,000, City $12,000, County $80,000, Locally Generated Income $2,000. Mats Exp Books $12,000
Library Holdings: Bk Vols 16,200; Bk Titles 22,000; Per Subs 20
Friends of the Library Group
BOONE COUNTY, 221 W Stephenson Ave, Harrison, 72601-4225. SAN 331-0892. Tel: 501-741-5913. FAX: 501-741-5913. *Librn*, Ted Odegard
Library Holdings: Bk Vols 51,000
Friends of the Library Group
BULL SHOALS LIBRARY, PO Box 406, Bull Shoals, 72619. SAN 329-5419. Tel: 501-445-4625.
Library Holdings: Bk Vols 20,000
EUREKA SPRINGS CARNEGIE PUBLIC, 194 Spring St, Eureka Springs, 72632. SAN 331-0957. Tel: 501-253-8754. FAX: 501-253-7807. *Librn*, Jean Elderwind; E-Mail: jean.elderwind@mail.state.ar.us; Staff 3 (MLS 1, Non-MLS 2)
Founded 1912. Pop 8,500; Circ 48,000
Jan 2000-Dec 2000 Income $90,000, County $80,000, Locally Generated Income $10,000. Mats Exp $11,500, Books $10,000, Per/Ser (Incl. Access Fees) $1,500. Sal $62,000 (Prof $25,500)
Library Holdings: Bk Vols 38,000; Per Subs 50; High Interest/Low Vocabulary Bk Vols 75; Spec Interest Per Sub 20; Bks on Deafness & Sign Lang 20
Subject Interests: Local history
Friends of the Library Group
GREEN FOREST PUBLIC, 206 E Main St, Green Forest, 72638. SAN 331-0981. Tel: 501-438-6700. FAX: 501-438-6700. *Librn*, Roberta O'Dell
Library Holdings: Bk Vols 12,000
Friends of the Library Group
KINGSTON COMMUNITY, Kingston, 72742. SAN 329-5435. Tel: 501-665-4139.
MADISON COUNTY, PO Box 745, Huntsville, 72740. SAN 331-1015. Tel: 501-738-2754. FAX: 501-738-2754. *Librn*, Billie Wharton
Library Holdings: Bk Vols 9,000
MARION, 308 Old Main, Yellville, 72687. (Mail add: 185 Ashwood Dr, PO Box 1527, Winfield, 35594), Tel: 501-449-6015. FAX: 501-449-6015. E-Mail: mcl@mtnhome.com. *Librn*, Anita Patton
Library Holdings: Bk Vols 21,000
Friends of the Library Group
NEWTON COUNTY, City Hall, Jasper, 72641. SAN 331-1074. Tel: 501-446-2983. FAX: 501-446-2983. *Librn*, Shirley Shelton
Library Holdings: Bk Vols 8,500
Friends of the Library Group
SEARCY COUNTY, HC80, Box 11, Marshall, 72650. SAN 331-1104. Tel: 501-448-2420. FAX: 501-448-5453. *Librn*, Pat Halsted
Library Holdings: Bk Vols 17,000
Friends of the Library Group
Bookmobiles: 1

RECTOR

P NORTHEAST ARKANSAS REGIONAL LIBRARY, Rector Public Library, 121 W Fourth St, 72461. SAN 331-3328. Tel: 870-595-2410. FAX: 870-595-2410. *Librn*, Geraldine Wagster; Staff 3 (Non-MLS 3)

REDFIELD

§P REDFIELD PUBLIC LIBRARY, 310 Brodie St, 72132. (Mail add: PO Box 70, 72132-0070), Tel: 501-397-5070. FAX: 501-397-5070. *Branch Mgr*, Patsy Johnson
Founded 1999
Database Vendor: Ebsco - EbscoHost, GaleNet, OCLC - First Search
Mem of Jefferson County Library System

RISON

P ROY & CHRISTINE STURGIS LIBRARY, Cleveland County Mid-Arkansas Regional Library, 203 W Magnolia St, PO Box 388, 71665. SAN 300-5461. Tel: 870-325-7270. FAX: 870-325-7008. E-Mail: clecolib@tds.net. *Librn*, Hilda Terry; *Asst Librn*, Belinda Winston
Pop 7,781; Circ 14,160
Library Holdings: Bk Vols 27,000; Per Subs 36
Friends of the Library Group

ROGERS

S NORTHWEST ARKANSAS GENEALOGY SOCIETY, Museum & Library-Archives,* PO Box 796, 72757-0796. SAN 371-1889. Tel: 501-273-3890. *Pres*, Marge Caskey; *Coll Develop*, Mary Marquess
Library Holdings: Bk Vols 200

P ROGERS PUBLIC LIBRARY, 711 S Dixieland, 72758. SAN 331-0116. Tel: 501-621-1152. FAX: 501-621-1165. Web Site: www.rogers-ar-us.org/library. *Coll Develop, Dir*, Alice Medin; Tel: 501-621-1152, Ext 11, E-Mail: alicem@rpl.lib.ar.us; *Coll Develop*, Teresa Davis; *Coll Develop*, Emma Henderson
Founded 1904. Pop 38,000; Circ 364,033
Jan 1999-Dec 1999 Income $1,315,828, State $42,029, City $803,953,

County $354,966, Other $114,880. Mats Exp $207,316. Sal $697,252 (Prof $257,424)
Library Holdings: Bk Vols 85,000
Publications: Check It Out (newsletter)
Friends of the Library Group

RUSSELLVILLE

C ARKANSAS TECH UNIVERSITY, Ross Pendergraft Library & Technology Center, 305 W "Q" St, 72801-2222. SAN 300-547X. Tel: 501-968-0289. Circulation Tel: 501-964-0568. Reference Tel: 501-964-0570. FAX: 501-964-0559, 501-968-2185. Web Site: www.atu.edu/acad/library/library.htm, www.library.atu.edu. *Dir*, Bill Parton; Tel: 501-968-0417, E-Mail: bill.parton@mail.atu.edu; *Librn*, Wilma Labahn; Tel: 501-968-0288, E-Mail: wilma.labahn@mail.atu.edu; *Cat*, Tess Connors; Tel: 501-964-0558, E-Mail: theresa.connors@mail.atu.edu; *Music*, Rachel Crane; *Acq*, Frances Hager; Tel: 501-964-0561, E-Mail: frances.hager@mail.atu.edu; *Publ Servs*, Renee Le Beau-Ford; Tel: 501-964-0571, E-Mail: renee.lebeau-ford@mail.atu.edu; *Syst Coordr*, Christine Kelly; Tel: 501-498-6042, E-Mail: christine.kelly@mail.atu.edu; Staff 14 (MLS 7, Non-MLS 7)
Founded 1909. Enrl 4,520; Fac 215; Highest Degree: Master
Jul 1999-Jun 2000 Income $1,084,231, State $1,071,217, Federal $13,014. Mats Exp $421,308, Books $74,491, Per/Ser (Incl. Access Fees) $160,402, Presv $6,703, Micro $24,712, Electronic Ref Mat (Incl. Access Fees) $155,000. Sal $518,900 (Prof $246,894)
Library Holdings: Bk Vols 229,450; Per Subs 1,240
Subject Interests: Engineering, Humanities, Music, Nursing
Special Collections: Parks & Recreation Administration, bk & micro
Automation Activity & Vendor Info: (Acquisitions) Endeavor; (Cataloging) Endeavor; (Circulation) Endeavor; (Course Reserve) Endeavor; (ILL) Endeavor; (Media Booking) Endeavor; (OPAC) Endeavor; (Serials) Endeavor
Publications: Arkansas Gazette Index (Index to newspapers)
Function: ILL limited
Partic in Amigos Library Services, Inc

P POPE COUNTY LIBRARY SYSTEM, Russellville Headquarters Branch,* 116 E Third St, 72801. SAN 371-7992. Tel: 501-968-4368. FAX: 501-968-3222. *Librn*, Grace F Berry; *Publ Servs*, Jackie Blaney; *Circ*, Carlene Austin; *Tech Servs*, Pat Cox; *Cat*, Katie Murdoch; *Ref*, Earlene Peak; *Ch Servs*, Kelly Bean; Staff 7 (MLS 1, Non-MLS 6)
Founded 1920. Pop 52,063; Circ 391,425
Jan 1998-Dec 1998 Income (Main Library and Branch Library) $1,051,451, Locally Generated Income $669,500. Mats Exp $210,200, Books $180,000, Per/Ser (Incl. Access Fees) $9,000, Presv $2,000, Micro $1,200, AV Equip $10,000, Other Print Mats $2,000, Electronic Ref Mat (Incl. Access Fees) $6,000. Sal $383,595 (Prof $40,000)
Library Holdings: Bk Vols 77,816; Bk Titles 60,012; Per Subs 145; High Interest/Low Vocabulary Bk Vols 150; Bks on Deafness & Sign Lang 25
Special Collections: Arkansas History, films; Genealogy (Katie Murdoch Coll), bks, docs
Automation Activity & Vendor Info: (Cataloging) Gaylord; (Circulation) Gaylord; (OPAC) Gaylord
Partic in Amigos Library Services, Inc
Special Services for the Deaf - Books on deafness & sign language; High interest/low vocabulary books; Staff with knowledge of sign language
Friends of the Library Group
Branches: 3
ATKINS CENTENNIAL BRANCH, 216 NE First St, Atkins, 72823. SAN 371-800X. Tel: 501-641-7904. FAX: 501-641-1169. *Head of Libr*, Robbie Duval
Library Holdings: Bk Vols 10,000
DOVER BRANCH, 81 Library Rd, Dover, 72837. SAN 371-8018. Tel: 501-331-2173. FAX: 501-331-4151. *Head of Libr*, Glenda McMillan
Library Holdings: Bk Vols 9,000
Friends of the Library Group
HECTOR BRANCH, PO Box 293, Hector, 72843. SAN 377-5925. Tel: 501-284-0907. FAX: 501-284-0907. *Head of Libr*, Ednita Condley
Library Holdings: Bk Vols 4,000
Open 16 hours per week
Bookmobiles: 1

SALEM

§P FULTON COUNTY LIBRARY, 103 Pickren St, 72576. (Mail add: PO Box 277, 72576-0277), Tel: 870-895-2014. FAX: 870-895-2014. *Librn*, Sharon L Carter
Jan 2000-Dec 2000 Income $82,555
Library Holdings: Bk Vols 20,260
Mem of White River Regional Library
Open Mon-Fri 8:30-4:30, Sat 9-12

SEARCY

CR HARDING UNIVERSITY, Brackett Library, Box 12267, 72143. SAN 300-5488. Tel: 501-279-4354. Circulation Tel: 501-279-4279. Reference Tel: 501-279-4775. FAX: 501-279-4012. Web Site: www.harding.edu/index.html. *Dir*, Ann Dixon; E-Mail: adixon@harding.edu; *Head, Info Serv*, Ann Hobby; Tel: 501-279-4237, E-Mail: ahobby@harding.edu; *ILL*, Gerald Cox; Tel: 501-279-4349, E-Mail: gcox@harding.edu; *Head Tech Servs*, Shirley Williams; Tel: 501-279-4376, E-Mail: swilliams@harding.edu; *Ser*, Henry Terrill; Tel: 501-279-4251, E-Mail: terrill@harding.edu; *Automation Syst Coordr*, Rick Fought; Tel: 501-279-4185, E-Mail: rfought@harding.edu; *Circ*, Gayla Hall; Tel: 501-279-4228, E-Mail: ghall@harding.edu; Staff 15 (MLS 7, Non-MLS 8)
Founded 1924. Enrl 3,903; Fac 214; Highest Degree: Doctorate
Jul 1998-Jun 1999 Income $897,204. Sal $453,317
Library Holdings: Bk Vols 439,457; Per Subs 1,357
Special Collections: LAC; Williams-Miles Science History Coll
Automation Activity & Vendor Info: (Acquisitions) Endeavor; (Cataloging) Endeavor; (Circulation) Endeavor; (ILL) Endeavor; (OPAC) Endeavor; (Serials) Endeavor
Database Vendor: CARL, Ebsco - EbscoHost, GaleNet, OCLC - First Search, ProQuest, Silverplatter Information Inc., Wilson - Wilson Web
Function: Archival collection, Document delivery services, ILL limited, Outside services via phone, cable & mail, Reference services available, Some telephone reference
Partic in Amigos Library Services, Inc; Arknet; OCLC Online Computer Library Center, Inc

P WHITE COUNTY REGIONAL LIBRARY SYSTEM, 113 E Pleasure Ave, 72143-7798. SAN 331-3417. Tel: 501-268-2449. FAX: 501-268-5682. *Librn*, Harriet (Susie) Boyett; E-Mail: susie.boyett@mail.state.ar.us; *Coll Develop*, Harriet (Susie) Boyett; Staff 1 (MLS 1)
Founded 1896. Pop 64,526
1998-1999 Income (Main Library and Branch Library) $629,487, State $106,825, City $95,050, County $414,238, Locally Generated Income $13,374. Mats Exp $91,900, Books $63,000, Per/Ser (Incl. Access Fees) $10,000, Presv $500, Micro $400, AV Equip $5,000, Electronic Ref Mat (Incl. Access Fees) $13,000. Sal $195,082 (Prof $36,660)
Library Holdings: Bk Vols 68,708; Bk Titles 60,000; Per Subs 720
Subject Interests: Arkansas
Automation Activity & Vendor Info: (Cataloging) SIRSI; (Cataloging) SIRSI; (OPAC) SIRSI
Friends of the Library Group
Branches: 6
BALDWIN MEMORIAL, 612 Van Buren, Judsonia, 72081. SAN 331-3476. Tel: 501-729-3995. FAX: 501-729-3995. *Librn*, Ruth Harris
Friends of the Library Group
BEEBE PUBLIC, Beebe, 72012-3245. SAN 331-3506. Tel: 501-882-3235. *Librn*, Eva McCulloch
Friends of the Library Group
BRADFORD BRANCH, Main St, Bradford, 72020. SAN 377-7707. Tel: 501-344-2558. FAX: 501-344-2558. *Librn*, Janet Suiter
Friends of the Library Group
LYDA MILLER LIBRARY, Hwy 367, PO Box 287, Bald Knob, 72010-0287. SAN 331-3441. Tel: 501-724-5452. *Librn*, Teresa Scritchfield
Friends of the Library Group
PANGBURN PUBLIC, Main St, PO Box 333, Pangburn, 72121-0333. SAN 331-3530. Tel: 501-728-4612. *Librn*, Kay Little
Friends of the Library Group
SEARCY PUBLIC, 113 E Pleasure Ave, 72143. SAN 331-3565. Tel: 501-268-2449. FAX: 501-268-5682. *Librn*, Joyce Turley

SHERIDAN

P GRANT COUNTY LIBRARY,* 210 N Oak St, 72150-2495. SAN 300-5496. Tel: 870-942-4436. FAX: 870-942-7500. *Librn*, Pam Withers; Staff 4 (MLS 1, Non-MLS 3)
Library Holdings: Bk Vols 26,652
Mem of Mid-Arkansas Regional Libr Syst

SILOAM SPRINGS

C JOHN BROWN UNIVERSITY, Arutunoff Learning Resources Center, 2000 W University, 72761. SAN 300-550X. Tel: 501-524-7202. Reference Tel: 501-524-7153. FAX: 501-524-7335. Web Site: library.jbu.edu. *Dir*, Larry L Blazer; Tel: 501-524-7203, E-Mail: lblazer@acc.jbu.edu; *Head Ref*, Mary Habermas; Tel: 501-524-7153, E-Mail: mhaberma@jbu.edu; *ILL*, Simone Schroder-Johnson; Tel: 501-524-7276, E-Mail: simones@jbu.edu; *Outreach Serv*, Li Ping Tan Blume; Tel: 501-524-7355, E-Mail: lblume@jbu.edu.
Subject Specialists: *Reference*, Mary Habermas; *Reference*, Li Ping Tan Blume; *Reference*, Simone Schroder-Johnson; Staff 10 (MLS 4, Non-MLS 6)
Founded 1956. Enrl 1,545; Fac 23; Highest Degree: Master
Jul 1999-Jun 2000 Income Other $392,610. Mats Exp $373,960, Books $35,000, Per/Ser (Incl. Access Fees) $36,500, Presv $6,358, Micro $4,100, AV Equip $5,900, Other Print Mats $2,030, Electronic Ref Mat (Incl. Access Fees) $18,549. Sal $235,542 (Prof $108,837)
Library Holdings: Bk Vols 110,000; Bk Titles 80,000; Per Subs 494; Spec

Interest Per Sub 10
Subject Interests: Disabilities, Gifted, Spanish (language), Special education
Special Collections: J Vernon McGee Coll, religious; Linda Romig Coll, juvenile
Automation Activity & Vendor Info: (Cataloging) TLC; (Circulation) TLC; (OPAC) TLC
Database Vendor: Lexis-Nexis, OCLC - First Search, ProQuest, Silverplatter Information Inc., Wilson - Wilson Web
Partic in OCLC Online Computer Library Center, Inc

S SILOAM SPRINGS MUSEUM, Museum Archives,* 112 N Maxwell, PO Box 1164, 72761. SAN 373-3939. Tel: 501-524-4011. E-Mail: ssmuseum@ipa.net. *Dir*, Don Warden
Subject Interests: Local history

P SILOAM SPRINGS PUBLIC LIBRARY,* 401 W University, 72761. SAN 300-5518. Tel: 501-524-4236. *Dir*, Elaine F Wilson; Staff 1 (MLS 1)
Founded 1966. Pop 11,000; Circ 65,000
Library Holdings: Bk Vols 22,000; Bk Titles 31,000; Per Subs 43

SPRINGDALE

S SHILOH MUSEUM OF OZARK HISTORY LIBRARY, 118 W Johnson Ave, 72764. SAN 373-3947. Tel: 501-750-8165. FAX: 501-750-8171. E-Mail: shiloh@springdaleark.org. Web Site: www.springdaleark.org/shiloh. *Dir*, Bob Besom; *Librn*, Manon Wilson
Library Holdings: Bk Vols 1,500
Special Collections: Photographs of Ozarks
Friends of the Library Group

P SPRINGDALE PUBLIC LIBRARY, 405 S Pleasant St, 72764. SAN 331-0140. Tel: 501-750-8180. FAX: 501-750-8182. Web Site: www.springdale.lib.ar.us. *Dir*, Marcia Ransom; E-Mail: mransom@spl.lib.ar.us; *Ad Servs*, Moncella Reed; *Ch Servs*, Ruth Ann Gentry; *Circ*, Angel Hutchison; Staff 7 (MLS 5, Non-MLS 2)
Jan 1999-Dec 1999 Income $906,087, State $75,432, City $416,585, County $372,650, Locally Generated Income $41,420. Mats Exp $187,405, Books $157,562, Per/Ser (Incl. Access Fees) $13,000, AV Equip $13,475, Electronic Ref Mat (Incl. Access Fees) $3,368. Sal $545,706 (Prof $223,421)
Library Holdings: Bk Vols 97,422; Per Subs 323
Automation Activity & Vendor Info: (Circulation) Innovative Interfaces Inc.; (OPAC) Innovative Interfaces Inc.
Publications: Newsletter (quarterly)
Mem of Washington County Libr Syst
Friends of the Library Group

STUTTGART

P STUTTGART PUBLIC LIBRARY, Arkansas County Library Headquarters,* 2002 S Buerkle St, 72160-6508. SAN 300-5526. Tel: 870-673-1966. FAX: 870-673-4295. *Dir*, Ted T Campbell
Founded 1922. Pop 21,653; Circ 85,465
Jan 2000-Dec 2000 Income $225,000, State $35,000, County $126,000, Locally Generated Income $6,500, Other $25,000. Mats Exp $32,450, Books $26,400, Per/Ser (Incl. Access Fees) $1,700, Presv $1,000, Micro $1,100, AV Equip $1,500, Manuscripts & Archives $250, Electronic Ref Mat (Incl. Access Fees) $500. Sal $90,000 (Prof $62,000)
Library Holdings: Bk Vols 85,465; Bk Titles 59,723; Per Subs 135
Subject Interests: Agriculture, Am Indians, Antiques, Genealogy
Special Collections: Arkansas Coll; Rare Books (Queeny Coll)
Publications: Newsletter (biannual)
Open Mon-Sat 9-6, Tues 9-8, Summer Mon-Sat 9-6
Friends of the Library Group

G US DEPT OF AGRICULTURE-AGRICULTURAL RESEARCH, PO Box 860, 72160. SAN 325-5271. Tel: 870-673-4483. FAX: 870-673-7710. Web Site: www.snarc.ars.usda.gov. *Librn*, Michele Wehner; E-Mail: mwehner@spa.avs.gov
Library Holdings: Bk Titles 985; Per Subs 125
Subject Interests: Aquaculture, Fish culture, Water quality
Special Collections: Reprint Coll - Cross indexed & filed numerically (subject & author)
Partic in OCLC Online Computer Library Center, Inc

SULPHUR SPRINGS

§P SULPHUR SPRINGS PUBLIC LIBRARY, 380 White St, 72768. (Mail add: PO Box 275, 72768-0275), Tel: 501-298-3753. *Librn*, Laurel Goforth
Jan 1999-Dec 1999 Income $2,171, City $1,000, Other $1,171
Library Holdings: Bk Vols 15,000

TEXARKANA

CM UNIVERSITY OF ARKANSAS FOR MEDICAL SCIENCES, (AHEC/SW), Area Health Education Center-Southwest Library, 300 E Sixth St, 71854. SAN 300-5534. Tel: 870-779-6023. FAX: 870-779-6050. *Dir*, Brenda Keays; Tel: 870-779-6053, E-Mail: b-keays@ahecsw.uams.edu; Staff 3 (MLS 1, Non-MLS 2)
Founded 1976
Library Holdings: Bk Titles 2,000; Per Subs 210
Subject Interests: Consumer health info
Publications: University of Arkansas for Medical Sciences, Area Health Education Centers, Union Catalog of Monographs; University of Arkansas for Medical Sciences, Area Health Education Centers, Union Catalog of Serials
Partic in OCLC Online Computer Library Center, Inc; S Cent Regional Med Libr Program

TRUMANN

P TRUMANN PUBLIC LIBRARY, W Main St, PO Box 73, 72472-0073. SAN 371-8379. Tel: 870-483-7744. *Librn*, Janie Teague; Staff 1 (Non-MLS 1)
Founded 1975. Pop 6,000; Circ 13,000
1999-2000 Mats Exp $6,000
Library Holdings: Bk Vols 12,000; Per Subs 10
Automation Activity & Vendor Info: (Cataloging) Athena; (Circulation) Athena
Special Services for the Blind - Bks on cassette

VAN BUREN

P VAN BUREN PUBLIC LIBRARY, 111 N 12th St, 72956. SAN 331-0175. Tel: 501-474-6045. FAX: 501-471-3226. Web Site: www.crawfordcountylib.org. *Librn*, Clara Meyers
Founded 1899
Jan 1999-Dec 1999 Income Parent Institution $89,000. Mats Exp Books $20,000. Sal $51,000
Library Holdings: Bk Vols 25,964
Automation Activity & Vendor Info: (Acquisitions) TLC; (Cataloging) TLC; (Circulation) TLC; (OPAC) TLC
Database Vendor: OCLC - First Search

WALNUT RIDGE

P LAWRENCE COUNTY LIBRARY,* 1315 W Main St, 72476. SAN 331-359X. Tel: 870-886-3222. FAX: 870-886-9520. *Librn*, Ashley Burris
Founded 1942. Pop 17,457; Circ 119,498
1997-1998 Income $153,402, State $25,441, City $8,104, Federal $8,440, County $105,564, Other $5,853. Mats Exp $39,270. Sal $73,896
Library Holdings: Bk Titles 32,000; Per Subs 51
Branches: 2
DRIFTWOOD, PO Box 94, Lynn, 72440. SAN 372-7866. *Librn*, Kathryn Bates
Library Holdings: Bk Vols 2,000
IMBODEN BRANCH, PO Box 718, Imboden, 72434. SAN 331-362X. *Librn*, Bobbie Jean
Library Holdings: Bk Vols 4,600

C WILLIAMS BAPTIST COLLEGE, Felix Goodson Library, PO Box 3667, 72476. SAN 300-5542. Tel: 501-886-6741, Ext 130. FAX: 501-886-5732. Web Site: www.wbc2.wbcoll.edu. *Bibliog Instr, Coll Develop, Online Servs*, Marilyn Goodwin; E-Mail: mgoodwin@wbcoll.edu; *ILL*, Debbie James; Staff 1 (MLS 1)
Founded 1941. Highest Degree: Bachelor
Jul 1999-Jun 2000 Income $133,151. Mats Exp $37,920, Books $15,000, Per/Ser (Incl. Access Fees) $18,000, Presv $2,520, Micro $400, AV Equip $2,000. Sal $56,770 (Prof $32,000)
Library Holdings: Bk Vols 75,107; Per Subs 200
Special Collections: Southern Baptist Convention Lab
Automation Activity & Vendor Info: (Circulation) Sagebrush Corporation; (OPAC) Sagebrush Corporation
Publications: Student Guide to the Felix Goodson Library

WASHINGTON

S SOUTHWEST ARKANSAS REGIONAL ARCHIVES, Old Washington Historic State Park, PO Box 134, 71862. SAN 328-3399. Tel: 870-983-2633. *Dir*, Lucille Westbrook
Subject Interests: Civil War, Hist SW Ark
Friends of the Library Group

WEST FORK

P WEST FORK PUBLIC LIBRARY,* PO Box 304, 72774. SAN 331-0205. Tel: 501-839-2626. FAX: 501-839-2626. E-Mail: westfork@wcls.lib.ar.us. Web Site: www.uark.edu/aladdin/publib/. *Librn*, Waneta Redfern
Library Holdings: Bk Vols 10,000
Mem of Ozarks Regional Library

WEST MEMPHIS

P WEST MEMPHIS PUBLIC LIBRARY,* 213 N Avalon, 72301. SAN 331-3654. Tel: 870-732-7590. FAX: 870-732-7636. *Dir*, Caroline Redfearn
Pop 29,800; Circ 50,000
Library Holdings: Bk Vols 50,000; Bk Titles 42,000; Per Subs 32
Friends of the Library Group

WINSLOW

P WINSLOW PUBLIC LIBRARY, 124 Main St, 72959. SAN 331-023X. Tel: 501-634-5405. E-Mail: winslow@orl.lib.ar.us. Web Site: www.uark.edu/aladdin/nwreasark/directory.html. *Librn*, Jo Ann Kyle; Tel: 501-634-3105, E-Mail: jo45@juno.com
Mem of Washington County Libr Syst

WYNNE

P EAST CENTRAL ARKANSAS REGIONAL LIBRARY,* 410 E Merriman Ave, 72396. SAN 324-0797. Tel: 870-238-3850. FAX: 870-238-5434. *Dir*, Lolly L Shaver; Staff 5 (MLS 1, Non-MLS 4)
Founded 1951. Pop 28,745; Circ 101,748
Library Holdings: Bk Titles 42,000; Per Subs 126
Friends of the Library Group
Branches: 2
CROSS COUNTY LIBRARY, 410 E Merriman Ave, 72396. SAN 300-5569. Tel: 870-238-3850. FAX: 870-238-5434. *Librn*, Lolly Shaver
Founded 1951
WOODRUFF COUNTY LIBRARY, 201 Mulberry St, Augusta, 72006. SAN 330-8766. Tel: 870-347-5331. FAX: 870-347-5331. *Dir, Librn*, Lolly L Shaver
Pop 11,566

CALIFORNIA

Date of Statistics: 1998-99
Population (est.): 35,755,460
Population Served by Public Libraries: 33,773,000
Total Volumes in Public Libraries: 61,254,000
Volumes Per Capita: 1.81
Total Public Library Circulation: 162,965,000
Circulation Per Capita: 4.83
Total Public Library Expenditure: $695,091,000
Expenditures Per Capita: $20.58
Number of County Libraries: 54
Counties Served: 58
Number of Bookmobiles: 55
Grants-in-Aid to Public Libraries:
Federal (Library Services & Construction Act): $13,171,479
Matching Local Funds: $17,001,045
State Aid: $48,004,172
Public Libraries' Share from Both Sources: $45,375,538
State Library's Share: $3,161,690

AGUANGA

S SCIENTIFIC RESOURCE SURVEYS, INC LIBRARY,* PO Box 669, 92536-0669. SAN 373-0247. Tel: 909-767-2555. FAX: 909-767-0305. *Pres*, Nancy Desautels
Library Holdings: Bk Vols 8,000; Per Subs 25
Subject Interests: Archaeology, Biology, Geology, History, Paleontology

ALAMEDA

P ALAMEDA FREE LIBRARY, 2200 A Central Ave, 94501-4506. SAN 331-3719. Tel: 510-748-4669. Circulation Tel: 510-748-4660. Reference Tel: 510-748-4661. TDD: 510-522-2072. FAX: 510-865-1230. Web Site: www.alamedafree.org. *Dir*, Susan Hardie; E-Mail: shardie@ci.alameda.ca.us; *Acq*, Sherry Carrai; *Cat, Online Servs, Tech Servs*, Elaine Hung; *Circ, Ref*, Donna Greenberg; *ILL*, Jane Chisaki; *YA Servs*, Karin Lundstrom; Staff 31 (MLS 10, Non-MLS 21)
Founded 1877. Pop 76,500; Circ 457,163
Jul 1999-Jun 2000 Income (Main Library and Branch Library) $2,190,524, State $134,418, City $1,712,604, County $300,856, Locally Generated Income $42,646. Mats Exp $242,700, Books $146,000, Per/Ser (Incl. Access Fees) $17,500, Micro $7,000, AV Equip $9,000, Electronic Ref Mat (Incl. Access Fees) $63,200. Sal $1,281,530 (Prof $373,514)
Library Holdings: Bk Vols 178,573; Bk Titles 120,000; Per Subs 422; High Interest/Low Vocabulary Bk Vols 90; Bks on Deafness & Sign Lang 60
Special Collections: Asian Languages; Books on Tape Coll; Chinese & Japanese Language Coll; City, County & State History Coll; Large Print Coll; Video Coll
Automation Activity & Vendor Info: (Cataloging) epixtech, inc.; (Circulation) epixtech, inc.; (OPAC) epixtech, inc.
Database Vendor: epixtech, inc., IAC - Info Trac, IAC - SearchBank, OCLC - First Search
Mem of Bay Area Libr & Info Syst
Special Services for the Deaf - Books on deafness & sign language; High interest/low vocabulary books; Staff with knowledge of sign language
Special Services for the Blind - CCTV (VisualTex); Kurzweil Reading Machine
Friends of the Library Group
Branches: 2
BAY FARM ISLAND, 3221 Mecartney Rd, 94501-6922. SAN 331-3727. Tel: 510-748-4668. FAX: 510-337-1426. *Librn*, Arta Benzieyoussef; Staff 2 (MLS 1, Non-MLS 1)
Founded 1980. Pop 12,039; Circ 99,636
Library Holdings: Bk Vols 23,862
Automation Activity & Vendor Info: (Cataloging) epixtech, inc.; (Circulation) epixtech, inc.
Partic in Bay Area Libr & Info Systs
WEST END, 788 Santa Clara Ave, 94501-3334. SAN 331-3743. Tel: 510-748-4667. FAX: 510-337-0877. *Librn*, Arta Benzieyoussef; Staff 3 (MLS 1, Non-MLS 2)
Founded 1933. Pop 25,078; Circ 64,407
Library Holdings: Bk Vols 32,131
Automation Activity & Vendor Info: (Cataloging) epixtech, inc.; (Circulation) epixtech, inc.
Partic in Bay Area Libr & Info Systs

C CALIFORNIA SCHOOL OF PROFESSIONAL PSYCHOLOGY, Rudolph Hurwich Library, 1005 Atlantic Ave, 94501. SAN 300-6085. Tel: 510-523-2300, Ext 172. FAX: 510-523-5943. *Dir*, Deanna Gaige; Staff 4 (MLS 2, Non-MLS 2)
Founded 1969. Enrl 700; Fac 32; Highest Degree: Doctorate
Library Holdings: Bk Vols 23,958; Per Subs 280
Subject Interests: Social sciences and issues
Special Collections: Psychological Assessment Coll
Partic in NCNMLG

J COLLEGE OF ALAMEDA, Library & Learning Resources Center, 555 Atlantic Ave, 94501. SAN 300-5577. Tel: 510-748-2365. FAX: 510-748-2380. *Head Librn*, Dr Mary K Holland; Tel: 510-748-2366, Fax: 510-748-2366, E-Mail: mholland@peralta.cc.ca.us; *AV*, Sami Ali; *Acq*, Bobby Snell; E-Mail: bsnell@peralta.cc.ca.us; *Circ*, Lili Tavassoli; Tel: 510-748-2251, E-Mail: ltavassoli@peralta.cc.ca.us; *Acq of New Ser*, Mary K Gulley-Pacheco; Tel: 510-748-2252, E-Mail: mgulley@peralta.cc.ca.us; *Cat*, Paticka Barnett; Tel: 510-748-2308, E-Mail: pbarnett@peralta.cc.ca.us; *Automation Syst Coordr*, David Hatfield Sparks; Tel: 510-748-2253, Fax: 510-748-2380, E-Mail: dsparks@peralta.cc.ca.us; Staff 10 (MLS 3, Non-MLS 7)
Founded 1970
Library Holdings: Bk Vols 32,000; Per Subs 200
Database Vendor: epixtech, inc., IAC - Info Trac, OCLC - First Search, ProQuest
Open Mon-Thurs 7:45 am-8:00 pm & Fri 7:45 am-4:45 pm

S LATHAM FOUNDATION LIBRARY, Latham Plaza, 1826 Clement St, 94501-1397. SAN 326-3290. Tel: 510-521-0920. FAX: 510-521-9861. E-Mail: lathm@aol.com. Web Site: www.latham.org. *Pres*, Hugh H Tebault, III
Founded 1917
Library Holdings: Bk Vols 300; Bk Titles 100
Special Collections: H/CAB (Human Companion Animal Bond), films & tapes 3/4"
Publications: Child Abuse, Domestic Abuse, Animal Abuse (1999); Teaching Compassion (1999)
Restriction: Not a lending library

ALBANY

G UNITED STATES DEPARTMENT OF AGRICULTURE, Agricultural Research Service, Western Regional Research Center Library,* 800 Buchanan St, 94710. SAN 300-5585. Tel: 510-559-5603. FAX: 510-559-5766. *Librn*, Rena Schonbrun; E-Mail: rschonbrun@pw.usda.gov; Staff 3 (MLS 1, Non-MLS 2)
Founded 1941
Library Holdings: Per Subs 170
Subject Interests: Chemistry, Microbiology, Nutrition
Partic in Fedlink; OCLC Online Computer Library Center, Inc

ALHAMBRA

P ALHAMBRA PUBLIC LIBRARY,* 410 W Main St, 91801-3488. SAN 331-3832. Tel: 626-570-5008. FAX: 626-457-1104. *Dir*, Stephanie Beverage; *ILL*, Estella Reyes; *Tech Servs*, Carol Higginbotham; *Ref*, Connie Chan; *Ref*, Robert Herberg; *Ref*, Mary Porrett; *Ref*, Heidi Nikpour; *Ref*, Patricia Todd; *Coll Develop*, Elke Schreiner; *Ref*, Sylvia Balero; Staff 8 (MLS 8)
Founded 1906. Pop 89,500; Circ 619,161
1997-1998 Income $1,617,189, State $144,467, City $1,472,388, Federal $334. Mats Exp $168,807, Books $113,740, Per/Ser (Incl. Access Fees) $18,800, Micro $1,800. Sal $955,640
Mem of Metropolitan Cooperative Library System
Special Services for the Blind - Talking book center
Literacy Services; Spanish & Chinese Language Outreach Services
Friends of the Library Group

R ALHAMBRA TRUE LIGHT PRESBYTERIAN CHURCH, Jack Miller Memorial Library, 20 W Commonwealth Ave, 91801. SAN 300-5607. Tel: 626-289-4106. FAX: 626-289-1313.
Library Holdings: Bk Vols 2,462

C CALIFORNIA SCHOOL OF PROFESSIONAL PSYCHOLOGY, Los Angeles Campus Library,* 1000 S Fremont Ave, 91803-1360. SAN 300-9009. Tel: 626-284-2777, Ext 3060. FAX: 626-284-1682. Web Site: www.library.cspp.edu. *Dir*, Tobeylynn Birch; E-Mail: tbirch@mail.cspp.edu; *Librn*, Janice Wilson; *ILL*, Dan DeNeve; *Tech Servs*, Vina Breslabsky; Staff 4 (MLS 2, Non-MLS 2)
Founded 1969. Enrl 536; Fac 42; Highest Degree: Doctorate
Jul 1997-Jun 1998 Income $308,165, Locally Generated Income $11,971, Parent Institution $296,194. Mats Exp $103,082, Books $28,954, Per/Ser (Incl. Access Fees) $56,878, Presv $10,346, Micro $2,077, Other Print Mats $4,827. Sal $174,665 (Prof $92,700)
Library Holdings: Bk Vols 25,770; Per Subs 300
Subject Interests: Mental health, Psychology, Women's studies
Special Collections: Psychology Fine Editions (Abbott Kaplan Memorial Coll)
Automation Activity & Vendor Info: (Acquisitions) Sydney; (Circulation) Sydney
Partic in CalPALs; OCLC Western Service Center; Pac SW Regional Med Libr

R DOROTHY HOOPER MEMORIAL LIBRARY OF THE FIRST UNITED METHODIST CHURCH, 9 N Almansor St, 91801-2699. SAN 300-5615. Tel: 626-289-4258. FAX: 626-289-4316. *Librn*, Elinor Salisbury
Founded 1940
Library Holdings: Bk Titles 5,500

ALISO VIEJO

S FLUOR DANIEL, INC, Knowledge Center, One Fluor Daniel Dr, 92698. SAN 332-1819. Tel: 949-349-2000. FAX: 949-349-3182. *Head of Libr*, Denise Franz; Tel: 949-349-4163
Founded 1972
Library Holdings: Bk Titles 6,000; Per Subs 25
Subject Interests: Chemistry, Construction, Petroleum
Automation Activity & Vendor Info: (Cataloging) Sydney; (Circulation) Sydney; (Serials) Sydney
Restriction: Staff use only

ALTADENA

P ALTADENA LIBRARY DISTRICT, 600 E Mariposa St, 91001. SAN 300-5631. Tel: 626-798-0834. FAX: 626-798-5351. E-Mail: aldpubl@netcom.com, spm@netcom.com, tema@earthlink.net. Web Site: scf.usc edu/s/owww.ald/library.html. *Dir*, William Tema; *Ad Servs*, Pauli Dutton; *Ch Servs*, Jacqueline Freeman; *YA Servs*, Connie Shair; *Circ*, Susan Heslin; *Tech Servs*, Steve Marsh; *Acq*, Tim Tran; *ILL*, Michelle Hoskins; Staff 7 (MLS 7)
Founded 1908. Pop 48,000; Circ 227,251
Jul 2000-Jun 2001 Income $1,585,914, State $33,400, City $1,407,330, Federal $21,730, Locally Generated Income $41,881. Mats Exp $102,800. Sal $1,505,738
Library Holdings: Bk Vols 120,200; Per Subs 230
Special Collections: Altadena History Coll
Publications: Friends of Altadena Newsletter
Mem of Metropolitan Cooperative Library System
Special Services for the Deaf - High interest/low vocabulary books; Staff with knowledge of sign language
Friends of the Library Group
Branches: 1
BOB LUCAS MEMORIAL LIBRARY & LITERACY CENTER, 2659 N Lincoln Ave, 91001-4963. SAN 375-524X. Tel: 626-798-8338. FAX: 626-798-3968. Web Site: libraryca.us/. *Librn*, Cora Forcell; Staff 2 (MLS 1, Non-MLS 1)
Friends of the Library Group

S BANNISTERS INTERNATIONAL BANANA CLUB, Museum & Library,* 2524 N El Molino Ave, 90001. SAN 371-1897. Tel: 626-798-2272. Web Site: www.banana-club.com.
Library Holdings: Bk Titles 35

S THEOSOPHICAL UNIVERSITY LIBRARY, 2416 N Lake Ave, 91001. SAN 300-5666. Tel: 626-798-8020. FAX: 626-798-4749. *Chief Librn*, James T Belderis; *Ref*, I Belderis
Founded 1919
Library Holdings: Bk Vols 45,000; Bk Titles 40,000; Per Subs 30
Subject Interests: Art and architecture, History, Mythology, Philosophy, Religion, Technology, Theosophy
Special Collections: Theosophy, bks, per
Publications: Sunrise Magazine

ALTURAS

P MODOC COUNTY LIBRARY,* 212 W Third St, 96101-3913. SAN 331-3891. Tel: 530-233-6340. FAX: 530-233-3375. E-Mail: libaltu1@hdo.net. Web Site: www.irifopeople.org/modoc. *Librn*, Cheryl Baker; *ILL*, Joanne Cain
Founded 1906. Pop 9,825
Library Holdings: Bk Vols 62,733; Per Subs 65
Special Collections: California Indian Library Coll; Modoc County History Coll
Mem of North State Cooperative Library System
Friends of the Library Group
Branches: 4
ADIN BRANCH, Adin Community Hall, Adin, 96006. SAN 331-3921. Tel: 916-299-3502. *Librn*, Kathy Nelson; Tel: 661-664-3254, Fax: 661-665-6910
Library Holdings: Bk Vols 5,000
Open Tues 3-8 & Thurs 1-6
CEDARVILLE BRANCH MEMORIAL, Main St, PO Box 573, Cedarville, 96104. SAN 331-4073. Tel: 916-279-2614. *Librn*, Margaret Schreiber
Library Holdings: Bk Vols 5,000
Open Tues & Fri 1-6
DAVIS CREEK BRANCH, Fire Hall, Davis Creek, 96108. SAN 331-3980. *Librn*, Margo Curtis
Library Holdings: Bk Vols 600
Open Thurs 3-5 & 2nd Tues of month 7-9
LOOKOUT BRANCH, Old School Bldg, Main St, Lookout, 96054. SAN 331-4049. Tel: 916-294-5776. *Librn*, Betty Hallberg
Library Holdings: Bk Vols 1,000
Open Tues & Thurs 1:30-6:30

ANAHEIM

M ANAHEIM MEMORIAL MEDICAL CENTER, Medical Library, 1111 W La Palma Ave, 92801. SAN 300-5674. Tel: 714-999-6020. FAX: 714-999-3907. E-Mail: amhml@deltanet.com. *Librn*, Robert Schroeder; E-Mail: rschroeder@memorialcare.org
Founded 1975
Library Holdings: Bk Vols 2,500; Per Subs 80
Restriction: Staff use only
Function: ILL available
Mem of Pac Southwest Regional Med Libr Serv
Partic in Medline

P ANAHEIM PUBLIC LIBRARY,* 500 W Broadway, 92805-3699. SAN 331-4103. Tel: 714-765-1880. FAX: 714-765-1731. *Dir*, Carol Stone; *Ad Servs, Bkmobile Coordr, Ref*, Kevin Moore; *ILL*, Bea North; *Coll Develop*, Estelle Williams; Staff 44 (MLS 44)
Founded 1901
Jul 1996-Jun 1997 Income $5,790,468
Library Holdings: Bk Vols 463,145
Subject Interests: Business and management, Law, Local history
Special Collections: Anaheim History Coll (Anaheim History Room), bks, pamphlets, pictures
Automation Activity & Vendor Info: (Acquisitions) epixtech, inc.; (Circulation) epixtech, inc.
Mem of Santiago Libr Syst
Friends of the Library Group
Branches: 4
CANYON HILLS, 400 Scout Trail, 92807-4763. SAN 331-412X. Tel: 714-974-7630. FAX: 714-998-7468. *Librn*, Cynthia Hicks
Library Holdings: Bk Vols 84,999
Friends of the Library Group
EUCLID, 1340 S Euclid St, 92802-2008. SAN 331-4138. Tel: 714-765-3625. FAX: 714-520-5998. *Librn*, Estelle Williams
Library Holdings: Bk Vols 53,626
Friends of the Library Group
HASKETT, 2650 W Broadway, 92804-2112. SAN 331-4162. Tel: 714-821-0551. FAX: 714-821-0403. *Mgr*, Marianne Hugo
Library Holdings: Bk Vols 32,647

Friends of the Library Group
SUNKIST, 901 S Sunkist St, 92806-4739. SAN 331-4197. Tel: 714-765-3576. FAX: 714-520-7955. *Librn*, Karen Gerloff
Library Holdings: Bk Vols 48,156
Friends of the Library Group
Bookmobiles: 1

S BOEING COMPANY, Library Services, 3370 Miraloma Ave, AA14, 92806-1911. SAN 300-5755. Tel: 714-762-1081. Interlibrary Loan Service Tel: 714-762-3180. FAX: 714-762-0834. *Mgr Libr*, Teresa G Powell; E-Mail: teresa.g.powell@boeing.com; *Librn*, Karen L Robertson; Fax: 714-762-0895, E-Mail: karen.l.robertson@boeing.com; *Librn*, Madeline C Rosario; E-Mail: madeline.c.rosario@boeing.com; Staff 3 (MLS 1, Non-MLS 2)
Founded 1955
Library Holdings: Bk Titles 10,776; Per Subs 125
Subject Interests: Controls, Electronics, GPS, Imaging tech, Navigation, Radar, Satellites
Automation Activity & Vendor Info: (OPAC) TechLIB
Database Vendor: Dialog, Ebsco - EbscoHost, IAC - SearchBank, Wilson - Wilson Web
Publications: Library Bulletin (Newsletter)
Restriction: Staff use only
Partic in Libr of Orange County Network

S FIGGIE INTERNATIONAL CORPORATION, Interstate Electronics Corporation Library, 1001 E Ball Rd, Dept 4543, PO Box 3117, 92803-3117. SAN 300-5690. Tel: 714-758-0500, Ext 4840. FAX: 714-758-3256. *Librn*, Grace Garcia
Founded 1957
Library Holdings: Per Subs 2,000
Subject Interests: Business and management, Electronics
Special Collections: Institute of Electrical & Electronics Engineers Transactions & Proceedings Coll, 1957 to present

CL SOUTH BAYLO UNIVERSITY LIBRARY,* 1126 N Brookhurst St, 92801-1704. SAN 300-6581. Tel: 714-533-1495. FAX: 714-533-6040. *Librn*, Toshiko Scott
Library Holdings: Bk Vols 10,000

M WESTERN MEDICAL CENTER HOSPITAL, Medical Library,* 1025 S Anaheim Blvd, 92805. SAN 300-5712. Tel: 714-563-2858. *Librn*, Barbara Garside
Founded 1973
Library Holdings: Bk Vols 1,200; Bk Titles 100; Per Subs 120
Subject Interests: Cardiology, Nursing, Surgery
Partic in Pacific Southwest Regional Med Libr Serv
Sister facility located in Santa Ana, Calif

ANGWIN

C PACIFIC UNION COLLEGE, W E Nelson Memorial Library,* One Angwin Ave, 94508-9705. SAN 300-5771. Tel: 707-965-6242, 707-965-6311. Interlibrary Loan Service Tel: 707-965-6244. FAX: 707-965-6504. E-Mail: aw@puc.edu. Web Site: www.library.puc.edu. *Dir*, Adu Worku; *Archivist, Spec Coll*, Gary Shearer; Tel: 707-965-6675, E-Mail: gshearer@puc.edu; *Cat*, Linda Maberla; Tel: 707-965-6640, E-Mail: lmaberly@puc.edu; *Media Spec*, Trevor Murtagh; Tel: 707-965-7221, E-Mail: tmurtagh@puc.edu; *Publ Servs, Syst Coordr*, Joel Lutes; Tel: 707-965-6674, E-Mail: jlutes@puc.edu; Staff 7 (MLS 7)
Founded 1882. Enrl 1,500; Fac 120; Highest Degree: Master
Jul 1998-Jun 1999 Income $809,569, Locally Generated Income $13,442, Parent Institution $796,127. Mats Exp $228,978, Books $101,773, Per/Ser (Incl. Access Fees) $116,004, AV Equip $11,201. Sal $513,395 (Prof $217,167)
Library Holdings: Bk Vols 133,014; Bk Titles 111,905; Per Subs 930
Subject Interests: Natural science
Special Collections: Ellen G White Study Center; Pitcairn Islands Study Center; Seventh-day Adventist Study Center
Publications: Morning Watch Index; Special Collection Bibliographies
Mem of North Bay Cooperative Library System
Partic in OCLC Online Computer Library Center, Inc

APTOS

J CABRILLO COLLEGE, Robert E Swenson Library, 6500 Soquel Dr, 95003-3198. SAN 300-578X. Tel: 831-479-6537. FAX: 831-479-6500. Web Site: www.cabrillo.cc.ca.us. *Dir*, Johanna Bowen; E-Mail: jobowen@cabrillo.cc.ca.us; *Librn*, Topsy Smalley; *Librn*, Sylvia Winder; *Tech Servs*, Stephanie Staley; *Publ Servs*, Georg Romero; Staff 8 (MLS 8)
Founded 1959. Enrl 13,000; Fac 220
Library Holdings: Bk Vols 63,530; Per Subs 400
Publications: Library Research Guides
Partic in Monterey Bay Area Coop Libr Syst

ARCADIA

S THE ARBORETUM OF LOS ANGELES COUNTY, Plant Science Library, 301 N Baldwin Ave, 91007-2697. SAN 300-581X. Tel: 626-821-3213. FAX: 626-445-1217. Web Site: www.arboretum.org. *Librn*, Joan DeFato; E-Mail: jdefato@co.la.ca.us; Staff 1 (MLS 1)
Founded 1948
Library Holdings: Bk Vols 28,000
Subject Interests: Botany, Horticulture, Local history

P ARCADIA PUBLIC LIBRARY, 20 W Duarte Rd, 91006. SAN 300-5798. Tel: 626-821-5567. Interlibrary Loan Service Tel: 626-821-4396. Reference Tel: 626-821-5569. FAX: 626-447-8050. Web Site: www.infopeople.org/arcadia. *Dir*, Kent C Ross; Tel: 626-821-5568, E-Mail: kross@ciarcadia.ca.us; *Ch Servs*, Kathy Meacham; Tel: 626-821-5574, E-Mail: kmeacham@ciarcadia.ca.us; *Cat*, Jackie Faust-Moreno; Tel: 626-821-5565, E-Mail: faust-moreno@ciarcadia.ca.us; *Doc*, Delia Blankquart; Tel: 626-821-4379, E-Mail: dblankquart@ciarcadia.ca.us; *Ref*, Janet Sporleder; Tel: 626-821-5572, E-Mail: jsporleder@ciarcadia.ca.us; *ILL*, Lisa Davis; Tel: 626-821-4396, E-Mail: ldavis@ciarcadia.ca.us; Staff 27 (MLS 10, Non-MLS 17)
Founded 1920. Pop 53,200; Circ 550,000
Jul 1999-Jun 2000 Income $1,804,150, State $89,600, City $1,714,550. Mats Exp $114,000, Books $100,000, Per/Ser (Incl. Access Fees) $14,000. Sal $870,320
Library Holdings: Bk Vols 132,000; Per Subs 248
Subject Interests: Local history
Automation Activity & Vendor Info: (Circulation) DRA; (OPAC) DRA
Mem of Metropolitan Cooperative Library System
Special Services for the Deaf - TDD
Special Services for the Blind - Braille; Magnifiers; Print scanner & software for conversion to speech
Friends of the Library Group

S CALIFORNIA THOROUGHBRED BREEDERS ASSOCIATION, Carleton F Burke Memorial Library, 201 Colorado Pl, PO Box 60018, 91066-6018. SAN 300-5801. Tel: 626-445-7800. Toll Free Tel: 800-573-2822. FAX: 626-574-0852. Web Site: www.ctba.com. *Librn*, Vivian Montoya; E-Mail: vivian@ctba.com
Founded 1964
Library Holdings: Bk Vols 10,000; Bk Titles 3,000; Per Subs 50
Special Collections: American Breeding (C C Moseley Coll), bks & flms; Foreign Racing & Breeding (Edward Lasker Coll); Kent Cochran Coll
Restriction: Open to public for reference only

M METHODIST HOSPITAL OF SOUTHERN CALIFORNIA, Medical Library,* 300 W Huntington Dr, 91007. SAN 300-5828. Tel: 626-445-4441. FAX: 626-574-3712. *Coordr*, Linda White
Library Holdings: Bk Vols 1,801; Per Subs 80
Library contracted with Health Sciences Library, Huntington Memorial Hospital

ARCATA

C HUMBOLDT STATE UNIVERSITY LIBRARY, 1 Harpst St, 95521-8299. SAN 300-5836. Tel: 707-826-3441. Interlibrary Loan Service Tel: 707-826-4889. Circulation Tel: 707-826-3431. Reference Tel: 707-826-3418. FAX: 707-826-3440. Interlibrary Loan Service FAX: 707-826-5590. Web Site: library.humboldt.edu. *Dean of Libr*, Sharnon H Kenyon; *Head Tech Servs*, Wayne Perryman; Tel: 707-826-5598, E-Mail: wrp1@humbolt.edu; *Head Ref*, Robert Sathrum; Tel: 707-826-4953, Fax: 707-826-4900, E-Mail: rls2@humbolt.edu; *Coll Develop*, Mary H Kay; Tel: 707-826-3414, Fax: 707-826-4900, E-Mail: mhk1@humbolt.edu; *Spec Coll*, Joan Berman; Tel: 707-826-4939, E-Mail: jrb1@humbolt.edu; *Govt Doc*, Ray Wang; Tel: 707-826-5614, E-Mail: rw6@humbolt.edu; *Syst Coordr*, Jeremy Shellhase; E-Mail: jcs7001@humbolt.edu; Staff 43 (MLS 15, Non-MLS 28)
Founded 1913. Highest Degree: Master
Jul 1999-Jun 2000 Income $3,547,378, State $3,446,472, Federal $43,091, Locally Generated Income $57,815. Mats Exp $1,138,992, Books $452,399, Per/Ser (Incl. Access Fees) $463,764, Presv $8,499, Micro $11,303, AV Equip $22,598, Other Print Mats $148, Electronic Ref Mat (Incl. Access Fees) $180,281. Sal $1,945,916 (Prof $1,041,889)
Library Holdings: Bk Vols 538,731; Per Subs 2,799
Special Collections: Childrens Coll; History (Humboldt County Coll, Humboldt State University Archives)
Automation Activity & Vendor Info: (Acquisitions) Endeavor; (Cataloging) Endeavor; (Circulation) Endeavor
Database Vendor: CARL, Dialog, Ebsco - EbscoHost, epixtech, inc., Lexis-Nexis, OCLC - First Search, OVID Technologies, ProQuest, Silverplatter Information Inc.
Mem of North State Cooperative Library System
Partic in OCLC Online Computer Library Center, Inc

ARMONA

§P ARMONA COMMUNITY LIBRARY, 11115 C St, 93202. (Mail add: PO Box 368, 93202-0368), Tel: 559-583-5005. FAX: 559-583-5004. Web Site: www.sjvls.lib.ca.us/kings. *In Charge*, Mary Diaz

Library Holdings: Bk Vols 11,000
Automation Activity & Vendor Info: (Acquisitions) epixtech, inc.; (Cataloging) epixtech, inc.; (Circulation) epixtech, inc.; (OPAC) epixtech, inc.

ATASCADERO

S ATASCADERO HISTORICAL SOCIETY MUSEUM LIBRARY,* 6500 Palma Ave, 93423. (Mail add: PO Box 1047, 93423), SAN 370-341X. Tel: 805-466-8341. *Curator*, Helen Lindsay
Jan 1999-Dec 1999 Income $11,000
Library Holdings: Bk Vols 300
Special Collections: Photo Coll of E G Lewis, founder Atascadero Newspapers & High School Yearbooks
Open Mon-Sat 1-4

ATASCADERO STATE HOSPITAL
S LOGAN PATIENT'S LIBRARY, 10333 El Camino Real, PO Box 7001, 93423-7001. SAN 331-4227. Tel: 805-468-2491, 805-468-2520. FAX: 805-466-6011. *Senior Librn*, Richard Maynard; Fax: 805-468-3111, E-Mail: rmaynard@dmhash.state.ca.us; *In Charge*, Kimberly Williams; Tel: 805-468-3111; *Info Specialist*, Alicia Rocha; Tel: 805-468-3343; Staff 4 (MLS 1, Non-MLS 3)
Founded 1957
Jul 2000-Jun 2001 Mats Exp $22,500, Books $21,000, Per/Ser (Incl. Access Fees) $1,500
Library Holdings: Bk Vols 13,000; Bk Titles 9,000; Per Subs 41; High Interest/Low Vocabulary Bk Vols 100
Subject Interests: Law
Restriction: Not open to public
M LOGAN PROFESSIONAL LIBRARY, 10333 El Camino Real, PO Box 7001, 93423-7001. SAN 331-4251. Tel: 805-468-2491. FAX: 805-468-3111. E-Mail: athl@rain.org. *Senior Librn*, Richard Maynard; E-Mail: rmaynard@dmhash.state.ca.us; Staff 5 (MLS 1, Non-MLS 4)
Founded 1957. Pop 1,250
Jul 2000-Jun 2001 Income $100,000. Mats Exp $43,500, Books $10,000, Per/Ser (Incl. Access Fees) $26,000, Electronic Ref Mat (Incl. Access Fees) $7,500
Library Holdings: Bk Vols 9,000; Bk Titles 8,500; Per Subs 126
Subject Interests: Medicine, Nursing, Psychiatry, Psychotherapy
Special Collections: Psychological Assessment; Psychopathy & Forensic Psychiatry
Automation Activity & Vendor Info: (Cataloging) Sydney; (Circulation) Sydney; (Serials) Sydney
Database Vendor: Dialog
Restriction: Not open to public
Function: ILL by photocopy only
Partic in Med Libr Group of S Calif & Ariz; Medical Libr Asn

ATHERTON

C MENLO COLLEGE, Bowman Library, 1000 El Camino Real, 94027-4301. SAN 301-0511. Tel: 650-543-3825. Reference Tel: 650-543-3826. FAX: 650-462-1396. Web Site: rosie.menlo.edu. *Dean of Libr*, Keith Brehmer; Tel: 650-543-3827, E-Mail: kbrehmer@menlo.edu; *Tech Servs*, Sally Lancaster; Tel: 650-543-3933, E-Mail: slancaster@menlo.edu; *Ref*, Michele Speck; Tel: 650-543-3828, E-Mail: mspeck@menlo.edu; Staff 4 (MLS 3, Non-MLS 1)
Founded 1962. Enrl 654; Fac 41; Highest Degree: Bachelor
Jul 2000-Jun 2001 Income Parent Institution $504,000. Mats Exp $115,000, Books $75,000, Per/Ser (Incl. Access Fees) $18,000, Electronic Ref Mat (Incl. Access Fees) $22,000. Sal $276,000
Library Holdings: Bk Vols 65,000; Per Subs 138
Subject Interests: Business and management
Automation Activity & Vendor Info: (Acquisitions) Innovative Interfaces Inc.; (Cataloging) Innovative Interfaces Inc.; (Circulation) Innovative Interfaces Inc.; (Course Reserve) Innovative Interfaces Inc.; (ILL) Innovative Interfaces Inc.; (Media Booking) Innovative Interfaces Inc.; (OPAC) Innovative Interfaces Inc.; (Serials) Innovative Interfaces Inc.
Partic in Bay Area Library & Information Network; Central Association Of Libraries; OCLC Online Computer Library Center, Inc; Southnet

AUBURN

P AUBURN-PLACER COUNTY LIBRARY,* 350 Nevada St, 95603-3789. SAN 331-4286. Tel: 530-886-4500, 530-886-4550. FAX: 530-886-4555. E-Mail: apclau@garlic.com, au@placer.lib.ca.us. Web Site: www.placer.ca.gov/library. *Dir*, Elaine Paez Reed; *Coll Develop*, Jim Hickson
Founded 1937. Pop 145,500; Circ 732,106
Jul 1998-Jun 1999 Income $2,302,540, State $172,401, City $12,000, Federal $43,960, County $1,930,142, Locally Generated Income $144,037. Mats Exp $181,967, Books $153,009, Per/Ser (Incl. Access Fees) $25,319, Electronic Ref Mat (Incl. Access Fees) $3,639. Sal $1,236,876 (Prof $489,927)
Library Holdings: Bk Vols 271,666; Per Subs 471
Mem of Mountain-Valley Library System
Includes Placer County Law Library
Friends of the Library Group
Branches: 10
APPLEGATE BRANCH, 18018 Applegate Rd, PO Box 267, Applegate, 95703-0267. SAN 331-4316. Tel: 530-878-2721. *In Charge*, Karen Russell
Friends of the Library Group
COLFAX BRANCH, 2000 Church St, PO Box 153, Colfax, 95713-0153. SAN 331-4340. Tel: 530-346-8211. *In Charge*, Andrea Spark
Friends of the Library Group
FORESTHILL BRANCH, 24580 Main St, PO Box 393, Foresthill, 95631-0393. SAN 331-4405. Tel: 530-367-2785. FAX: 530-367-4721. *In Charge*, Robin Guthrie
Friends of the Library Group
GRANITE BAY BRANCH, 6475 Douglas Blvd, Granite Bay, 95746. SAN 373-5737. Tel: 916-791-5590. FAX: 916-791-1837. *Librn*, Bron Cancilla
Library Holdings: Bk Titles 34,221
Friends of the Library Group
KINGS BEACH BRANCH, 301 Secline Dr, PO Box 246, Kings Beach, 96143-0246. SAN 331-443X. Tel: 530-546-2021. FAX: 530-546-2126. *In Charge*, Louise Jensen
Friends of the Library Group
LOOMIS BRANCH, 6050 Library Dr, PO Box 610, Loomis, 95650-0610. SAN 331-4464. Tel: 916-652-7061. FAX: 530-652-5156. *In Charge*, Beth Enright
Friends of the Library Group
PENRYN BRANCH, 2215 Rippey Rd, PO Box 405, Penryn, 95663-0405. SAN 331-4499. Tel: 916-663-3621.
Friends of the Library Group
PLACER COUNTY LAW, 1523 Lincoln Way, 95603. SAN 377-7766. Tel: 530-823-2573. FAX: 530-823-9470. *In Charge*, Christopher Christman
ROCKLIN BRANCH, 5460 Fifth St, Rocklin, 95677-2547. SAN 331-4529. Tel: 916-624-3133. FAX: 916-632-9152. *Librn*, Mary George
Friends of the Library Group
TAHOE CITY BRANCH, 740 N Lake Blvd, PO Box 6570, Tahoe City, 96145-6579. SAN 331-4553. Tel: 530-583-3382. FAX: 530-583-5805. *In Charge*, Beverly Edholm
Friends of the Library Group
Bookmobiles: 1

AZUSA

P AZUSA CITY LIBRARY,* 729 N Dalton Ave, 91702-2586. SAN 300-5844. Tel: 626-812-5232. FAX: 626-334-4868. E-Mail: azusalib@ix.netcom.com, azusalibrary@azusa.ca.gov. Web Site: www.azusa.ca.gov. *Dir*, Paymaneh Maghsoudi; *ILL*, Betty Donnelson; *Tech Servs*, Norma Levy; *Ch Servs*, Cheryl Stewart; Staff 7 (MLS 7)
Founded 1909. Pop 43,500
Library Holdings: Bk Vols 110,000; Per Subs 163
Subject Interests: Local history
Special Collections: Indians of North America Coll; Spanish Language Coll
Mem of Metropolitan Cooperative Library System
Friends of the Library Group

C AZUSA PACIFIC UNIVERSITY, Marshburn Memorial Library and Hugh & Hazel Darling Library, 701 E Foothill Blvd, 91702-7000. (Mail add: 901 E Alosta Ave, 91702), SAN 300-5852. Tel: 626-815-6000. Circulation Tel: 626-815-6000, Ext 3847 & 5060. Reference Tel: 626-815-6000, Ext 3270 & 5066. FAX: 626-815-5064, 626-969-6611. Web Site: www.apu.edu. *Dean of Libr*, Paul Gray; Tel: 626-815-6000, Ext 5062, E-Mail: pgray@apu.edu; *Assoc Librn*, Elizabeth Leahy; Tel: 626-815-6000, Ext 3250, E-Mail: lleahy@apu.edu; *Assoc Librn*, Dorcas Szeto; Tel: 626-815-6000, Ext 5264, E-Mail: dszeto@apu.edu; *Librn*, David Harmeyer; Tel: 626-815-6000, Ext 3255, E-Mail: dharmeyer@apu.edu; *Librn*, David Holifield; Tel: 626-815-6000, Ext 5266, E-Mail: dholifield@apu.edu; *Librn*, Kenneth Otto; Tel: 626-815-6000, Ext 5263, E-Mail: kotto@apu.edu; *Librn*, Steve Brewster; *Librn*, Debra Quast; E-Mail: dquast@apu.edu; *Coll Develop*, Irene Robinson; Tel: 626-815-6000, Ext 3442, E-Mail: irobinson@apu.edu; *Librn*, Jacquelyn Swinney; Staff 19 (MLS 10, Non-MLS 9)
Founded 1899. Pop 6,495; Circ 35,404; Enrl 6,495; Highest Degree: Doctorate
Jul 1999-Jun 2000 Income (Main and Other College/University Libraries) $2,022,630. Mats Exp $358,545, Books $325,567, Per/Ser (Incl. Access Fees) $11,772, Micro $21,206. Sal $847,290 (Prof $574,302)
Library Holdings: Bk Vols 157,371; Bk Titles 128,178; Per Subs 1,736
Special Collections: Azusa Foothill Citrus Company Coll, mss, ephemera; Biography (MacNeil Family Coll), papers, rec; Dobson Coll; George Fullerton Cattle Business Coll
Database Vendor: CARL, Dialog, Ebsco - EbscoHost, GaleNet, Lexis-Nexis, OCLC - First Search, OVID Technologies, ProQuest, Silverplatter Information Inc.
Publications: Update
Partic in CalPALs; Inland Empire Acad Libr Coop; Southern Calif Area Theol Librns Asn

BAKER

C CALIFORNIA STATE UNIVERSITY, Desert Studies Center Library,* PO Box 490, 92309. SAN 373-4935. Tel: 760-733-4266. FAX: 760-733-4266. *Mgr*, Robert Fulton
Jul 1997-Jun 1998 Income $500. Mats Exp Books $450
Library Holdings: Bk Titles 650
Restriction: Open to public for reference only

BAKERSFIELD

J BAKERSFIELD COLLEGE, Grace Van Dyke Bird Library, 1801 Panorama Dr, 93305-1298. SAN 300-5879. Tel: 661-395-4461. FAX: 661-395-4397. Web Site: www.bc.cc.ca.us/library. *Dir*, Anna Agenjo; E-Mail: aagenjo@bc.cc.ca.us; *Tech Servs*, Kirk Russell; *Ref*, Patty Brommelsiek; Staff 7 (MLS 3, Non-MLS 4)
Founded 1913. Enrl 12,239; Fac 236
Library Holdings: Bk Vols 54,000; Per Subs 319
Subject Interests: California
Special Collections: Bell British Plays, 1776-1795; Grove Plays of the Bohemian Club of San Francisco, 1911-1958
Publications: Bulletin

C CALIFORNIA STATE UNIVERSITY, (WSL), Walter W Stiern Library, 9001 Stockdale Hwy, 93311-1099. SAN 300-5895. Tel: 661-664-3172. Interlibrary Loan Service Tel: 661-664-2218. Reference Tel: 661-664-3231. FAX: 661-664-3238. E-Mail: csub_library@csub.edu. Web Site: www.lib.csub.edu. *Dir*, Rodney M Hersberger; Tel: 661-664-3042, E-Mail: rhersberger@csubak.edu; *Librn*, Christy Gavin; Tel: 661-664-3237, E-Mail: cgavin@csub.edu; *Asst Librn*, Curt Asher; Tel: 661-664-3251, E-Mail: casher@csub.edu; *Asst Librn*, Norm Hutcherson; Tel: 661-664-2061, E-Mail: nhutcherson@csub.edu; *Asst Librn*, Shayne Knapp; Tel: 661-664-3119, E-Mail: sknapp@csub.edu; *Asst Librn*, David Kosakowski; Tel: 661-664-3259, E-Mail: dkosakowski@csub.edu; *Asst Librn*, Patricia A Robles; Tel: 661-664-3235, Fax: 661-664-2259, E-Mail: probles@csub.edu; *Circ*, Mark Dowdle; Tel: 661-664-3233, Fax: 661-664-2259, E-Mail: mdowdle@csub.edu; *Circ*, Liz McDannold; Tel: 661-664-3174, Fax: 661-664-2259, E-Mail: lmcdannold@csub.edu; *Circ*, Vickie Melton; Tel: 661-664-3236, Fax: 661-664-2259, E-Mail: vmelton@csub.edu; *Circ*, Aide Zaragoza; Tel: 661-664-3234, Fax: 661-664-2259, E-Mail: azaragoza@csub.edu; *Ref*, Johanna Alexander; Tel: 661-664-3256, E-Mail: jalexander@csub.edu; *Syst Coordr*, Frank Aguirre; Tel: 661-664-2274, E-Mail: faguirre@csub.edu; *Tech Servs*, Sherry Bennett; Tel: 661-664-3254, Fax: 661-665-6910, E-Mail: sbennett@csub.edu; *Tech Servs*, Bonnie Dixon; Tel: 661-664-3263, Fax: 661-665-6910, E-Mail: bdixon@csub.edu; *ILL*, Janet Gonzales; Tel: 661-664-2129, Fax: 661-664-2259, E-Mail: jgonzales@csub.edu; *ILL*, Ariel Lauricio; Tel: 661-664-2218, Fax: 661-664-2259, E-Mail: alauricio@csub.edu; *Ser*, Dawn Jackson; Tel: 661-664-3249, Fax: 661-665-6910, E-Mail: djackson@csub.edu; *Ser*, Denise Marquez; Tel: 661-664-3250, Fax: 661-665-6910, E-Mail: dmarquez@csub.edu; *Cat*, Elaine Olsen; Tel: 661-664-3257, Fax: 661-664-6910, E-Mail: eolsen@csub.edu; *Cat*, Roxanne Starbuck; Tel: 661-664-3258, Fax: 661-664-6910, E-Mail: rstarbuck@csub.edu; *Acq*, Darline Norris; Tel: 661-664-3262, Fax: 661-664-6910, E-Mail: dnorris@csub.edu
Founded 1970. Enrl 5,610; Fac 408; Highest Degree: Master
Jul 1999-Jun 2000 Income $2,594,214, State $2,577,652, Locally Generated Income $16,562. Mats Exp $2,531,555, Books $341,539, Per/Ser (Incl. Access Fees) $358,319, Presv $21,000, Micro $13,157, Electronic Ref Mat (Incl. Access Fees) $74,209. Sal $1,260,425 (Prof $638,631)
Library Holdings: Bk Vols 419,085; Bk Titles 307,776; Per Subs 1,959; Spec Interest Per Sub 1,504
Automation Activity & Vendor Info: (Acquisitions) GEAC; (Cataloging) GEAC; (Circulation) GEAC; (ILL) GEAC; (Serials) GEAC
Database Vendor: CARL, Ebsco - EbscoHost, GaleNet, Lexis-Nexis, Silverplatter Information Inc., Wilson - Wilson Web
Partic in Dialog Corporation; OCLC Online Computer Library Center, Inc; SDC Search Serv; Southern Calif Answering Network
Friends of the Library Group

G CALIFORNIA WELL SAMPLE REPOSITORY,* 9001 Stockdale Hwy, 93311-1099. SAN 375-7889. Tel: 805-664-2324. FAX: 805-664-3194. *Curator*, Russ Robinson; E-Mail: rrobinson@csubak.edu
Library Holdings: Bk Titles 350

GL KERN COUNTY LAW LIBRARY, 1415 Truxtun Ave, Rm 301, 93301. SAN 300-5917. Tel: 661-868-5320. FAX: 661-868-5368. *Librn*, Annette Heath
Founded 1891 Income (Main Library Only) Federal $11,910
Library Holdings: Bk Vols 25,000; Per Subs 56

P KERN COUNTY LIBRARY,* 701 Truxtun Ave, 93301-4816. SAN 331-4588. Tel: 661-868-0700. FAX: 661-868-0799. Web Site: www.netxn.com/~kclib. *Dir*, Diane R Duquette; *Dep Dir*, Barbara Swanson; *Mgr*, Connie Bartlett; *ILL*, Linda Self; *Ch Servs*, Georgia Wages; *Automation Syst Coordr*, George App; *Tech Servs*, Laura Gardner; *AV*, Louann Nickerson; Staff 31 (MLS 31)
Founded 1911. Pop 628,200; Circ 1,884,744
Library Holdings: Bk Vols 1,058,405; Per Subs 817
Subject Interests: History, Natural science, Technology
Special Collections: California Geology-Mining-Petroleum Coll, bks & micro; Kern County Historical Coll, bks & micro
Publications: Kern County Library Scuttlebutt (staff newsletter)
Mem of San Joaquin Valley Library System
Friends of the Library Group
Branches: 28

ARVIN BRANCH, 201 Campus Dr, Arvin, 93203-1111. SAN 331-4596. Tel: 661-854-5934. Web Site: www.netxn.com/~kclib. *Librn*, Marcus Clough
Library Holdings: Bk Vols 26,785
Open Tues 12-8, Wed-Fri 10-6, Sat 9-5
Friends of the Library Group

BAKER STREET, 1400 Baker St, 93305-3731. SAN 331-4618. Tel: 661-861-2390. Web Site: www.netxn.com/~kclib. *Librn*, Josie Lopez
Library Holdings: Bk Vols 17,684
Open Mon, Wed, Fri & Sat 10-6
Friends of the Library Group

BEALE MEMORIAL, 701 Truxtun Ave, 93301. SAN 331-4642. Tel: 661-861-2135. FAX: 661-631-9439. Web Site: www.netxn.com/~kclib. *Librn*, Louann Nickerson
Library Holdings: Bk Vols 298,288
Special Collections: Genealogy; Geology Mining & Petroleum Coll; Kern County History Coll
Open Mon-Thurs 10-9, Fri & Sat 10-6
Friends of the Library Group

BKM I, 701 Truxton Ave, 93301. SAN 378-2050. Tel: 661-861-2130. *In Charge*, Woody White

BKM III, 7054 Lake Isabella Blvd, Isabella, 93240. SAN 378-2077. Tel: 760-379-8022.

BORON BRANCH, 26967 20-Mule Team Rd, Boron, 93516-1103. SAN 331-460X. Tel: 760-762-5606. Web Site: www.netxn.com/~kclib. *Librn*, Lee Williams
Library Holdings: Bk Vols 16,316
Open Mon, Wed & Thurs 10-6

BUTTONWILLOW BRANCH, 116 S Buttonwillow Ave, PO Box 476, Buttonwillow, 93206. SAN 331-4626. Tel: 661-764-5337. Web Site: www.netxn.com/~kclib. *Librn*, Olivia Barulich
Library Holdings: Bk Vols 11,327
Open Tues-Thurs 9-5

CALIFORNIA CITY BRANCH, 9507 California City Blvd, California City, 93505-2291. SAN 331-4634. Tel: 760-373-4757. Web Site: www.netxn.com/~kclib. *Librn*, Shelia Izmirian-Rader
Library Holdings: Bk Vols 25,423
Open Mon & Wed 9-6, Tues & Thurs 9-7, Fri 9-1
Friends of the Library Group

DELANO BRANCH, 925 Tenth Ave, Delano, 93215-2229. SAN 331-4677. Tel: 661-725-1078. Web Site: www.netxn.com/~kclib. *Librn*, Gail Lancaster; E-Mail: glancast@sjvls.lib.ca.us; Staff 4 (MLS 1, Non-MLS 3)
Library Holdings: Bk Vols 37,500; Per Subs 20
Database Vendor: epixtech, inc.
Open Mon & Wed 10-8, Tues & Thurs 10-6, Sat 10-2
Friends of the Library Group

ELEANOR N WILSON BRANCH, 1901 Wilson Rd, 93304-5696. SAN 331-4790. Tel: 805-834-4044. Web Site: www.netxn.com/~kclib. *Librn*, Nancy Hughes
Library Holdings: Bk Vols 42,189
Open Mon-Wed 10-8, Thurs 10-6, Sat 9-5
Friends of the Library Group

FIRE DEPARTMENT, 5642 Victor St, 93308-4044. Tel: 661-391-7106. FAX: 661-399-5763. Web Site: www.netxn.com/~kelib. *In Charge*, Tracy Garber
Library Holdings: Bk Vols 8,236; Per Subs 10
Automation Activity & Vendor Info: (Circulation) DRA; (OPAC) DRA

FRAZIER PARK BRANCH, 3015 Mt Pinos Way Unit 101, PO Box 1718, Frazier Park, 93225-0718. SAN 321-8686. Tel: 661-245-1267. Web Site: www.netxn.com/~kclib. *Librn*, Judith Waters
Library Holdings: Bk Vols 13,585
Open Tues-Fri 10-5, Sat 10-2
Friends of the Library Group

HOLLOWAY-GONZALES, 506 E Brundage Lane, 93307-3399. SAN 331-4707. Tel: 661-861-2083. Web Site: www.netxn.com/~kclib. *Librn*, Owen Nelson
Library Holdings: Bk Vols 31,395
Open Tues-Thurs 10-6, Sat 9-5

KERN RIVER VALLEY, 7054 Lake Isabella Blvd, Isabella, 93240-2698. SAN 331-4685. Tel: 760-379-8022. Web Site: www.netxn.com/~kclib. *Librn*, Karen Leifeld
Library Holdings: Bk Vols 37,462
Open Mon-Thurs & Sat 10-6
Friends of the Library Group

KERNVILLE BRANCH, 48 Tobias St, PO Box W, Kernville, 93238-9999. SAN 331-4693. Tel: 760-376-6180. Web Site: www.netxn.com/~kclib. *Librn*, Linda Dierck
Library Holdings: Bk Vols 7,695
Open Wed & Fri 12-6

Friends of the Library Group
LAMONT BRANCH, 8304 Segrue Rd, Lamont, 93241-2123. SAN 331-4715. Tel: 661-845-3471. Web Site: www.netxn.com/~kclib. *In Charge*, Ramon Barajas
Library Holdings: Bk Vols 32,206
Open Mon & Wed 12-8, Tues, Thurs & Fri 10-6
Friends of the Library Group
MCFARLAND BRANCH, 500 Kern Ave, McFarland, 93250. SAN 377-6662. Tel: 661-792-2318. FAX: 661-792-6588. *In Charge*, Tina Garcia
Library Holdings: Bk Vols 13,000; Per Subs 26
Open Mon-Thurs & Sat 10-6
MOJAVE BRANCH, 16916 1/2 Hwy 14 Sp D-2, Mojave, 93501-1607. SAN 331-474X. Tel: 661-824-2243. Web Site: www.netxn.com/~kclib. *Librn*, Syble Thomas
Library Holdings: Bk Vols 14,266
Open Mon, Wed & Sat 10-6
Friends of the Library Group
NORTHEAST BAKERSFIELD, 3725 Columbus St, 93306. SAN 331-4847. Tel: 661-871-9017. Web Site: www.netxn.com/~kclib.
Library Holdings: Bk Vols 49,181
Open Mon-Thurs 10-8, Fri & Sat 10-6
Friends of the Library Group
RATHBUN, 200 W China Grade Loop, Oildale, 93308-1735. SAN 331-4731. Tel: 661-393-6431. Web Site: www.netxn.com/~kclib. *Librn*, Mary Jane Weerts
Library Holdings: Bk Vols 51,754
Open Mon, Tues & Thurs 10-8, Wed 10-6, Sat 9-5
Friends of the Library Group
RIDGECREST BRANCH, 131 E Las Flores, Ridgecrest, 93555-1735. SAN 331-4766. Tel: 760-375-7666. FAX: 619-384-3211. Web Site: www.netxn.com/~kclib. *Librn*, Marsha Lloyd
Library Holdings: Bk Vols 52,847
Special Collections: Flora & Fauna of Indian Wells Valley
Open Mon-Wed 10-8, Fri 10-6, Sat 9-5
Friends of the Library Group
ROSAMOND BRANCH, 3611 Rosamond Blvd, Rosamond, 93560. SAN 378-2093. Tel: 661-256-3236. *In Charge*, Barbara Rogers
Open Tues & Wed 10-8, Thurs-Sat 10-6
SHAFTER BRANCH, 236 James St, Shafter, 93263-2031. SAN 331-4774. Tel: 661-746-2156. Web Site: www.netxn.com/~kclib. *Librn*, Judy Knox
Library Holdings: Bk Vols 31,245
Open Mon-Thurs 11-7
Friends of the Library Group
SOUTHWEST BAKERSFIELD BRANCH, 8301 Ming Ave, 93311. SAN 331-4839. Tel: 661-664-7716. Web Site: www.netxn.com/~kclib. *Librn*, Norm Hutcherson
Library Holdings: Bk Vols 74,382
Open Mon-Thurs 10-9, Fri & Sat 10-6
Friends of the Library Group
TAFT BRANCH, 27 Emmons Park Dr, Taft, 93268-2317. SAN 331-4820. Tel: 661-763-3294. Web Site: www.netxn.com/~kclib. *Librn*, Catherine Edgecomb
Library Holdings: Bk Vols 35,062
Open Tues-Thurs 10-8, Fri 10-5, Sat 10-2
Friends of the Library Group
TEHACHAPI BRANCH, 450 West F St, Tehachapi, 93561-1639. SAN 331-4782. Tel: 661-822-4938. Web Site: www.netxn.com/~kclib. *Librn*, Kris Duke
Library Holdings: Bk Vols 37,560
Open Tues-Thurs 10-8, Fri 10-6, Sat 10-5
Friends of the Library Group
WASCO BRANCH, 1102 Seventh St, Wasco, 93280-1801. SAN 331-4804. Tel: 661-758-2114. Web Site: www.netxn.com/~kclib. *Librn*, Linda Anderson
Library Holdings: Bk Vols 29,758
Open Mon-Thurs 11-7
Friends of the Library Group
WOFFORD HEIGHTS BRANCH, 7 Oak St, PO Box 748, Wofford Heights, 93285-0748. SAN 331-4812. Tel: 760-376-6160. Web Site: www.netxn.com/~kclib. *Librn*, Linda Dierck
Library Holdings: Bk Vols 11,605
Open Tues & Thurs 9-5
Friends of the Library Group
Bookmobiles: 3

S KERN COUNTY MUSEUM, Historical Reference Library, 3801 Chester Ave, 93301-1395. SAN 300-5925. Tel: 661-852-5000. FAX: 661-322-6415. Web Site: www.kcmuseum.org. *Curator*, Jeff Nickell; E-Mail: jenickell@kern.org; Staff 3 (Non-MLS 3)
Founded 1941
Library Holdings: Bk Vols 2,500
Subject Interests: Archaeology, California, Local history, Museology
Special Collections: 60+ Structure Village; Historical Museum; Product Catalogs, 1890-1970
Publications: A Kern County Diary: The Forgotten Photographs of Carleton E Watkins, 1881-1888
Restriction: By appointment only
Associated archives of Kern County, manuscript collections & photographs (over 350,000)

M KERN MEDICAL CENTER, Health Sciences Library,* 1830 Flower St, 93305-4197. SAN 300-5933. Tel: 661-326-2227. FAX: 661-326-2687. *Librn*, Paul Amrit; Tel: 661-326-2228, Fax: 661-323-7178, E-Mail: Paula@kernmedctr.com
Founded 1945
Library Holdings: Bk Vols 9,112; Per Subs 288

M MERCY HEALTHCARE, Medical Library,* 2215 Truxtun Ave, 93302-0119. (Mail add: PO BOX 119, 93302-0119), SAN 323-598X. Tel: 661-632-5386. *Librn*, Brooke Lilly
Library Holdings: Bk Titles 156; Per Subs 200
Subject Interests: Oncology
Friends of the Library Group

BANNING

S MALKI MUSEUM, INC ARCHIVES,* 11-795 Fields Rd, Morongo Indian Reservation, PO Box 578, 92220. SAN 370-1751. Tel: 909-849-7289. *Pres*, Katherine Saubel
Library Holdings: Bk Titles 35
Subject Interests: Manuscripts, Oral hist tapes, Photographs
Special Collections: John Peabody Harrington, Anthropologist Coll
Restriction: Open to public for reference only

M SAN GORGONIO MEMORIAL HOSPITAL, Medical Library,* 600 N Highland Springs Ave, 92220. SAN 327-5930. Tel: 909-845-1121. FAX: 909-845-2836.
Library Holdings: Bk Vols 151
Restriction: Staff use only

BARSTOW

J BARSTOW COLLEGE, Thomas Kimball Library, 2700 Barstow Rd, 92311. SAN 300-595X. Tel: 760-252-2411, Ext 7270. FAX: 760-252-6725. *Dir*, Joseph A Clark; Staff 3 (Non-MLS 3)
Founded 1960
Library Holdings: Bk Vols 37,558; Per Subs 218

BAY POINT

P BAYPOINT CONTRA COSTA COUNTY LIBRARY,* 205 Pacifica Ave, 94565. SAN 377-5453. Tel: 925-458-2215. FAX: 925-458-2215. *Asst Librn*, Carolina Montufar
Library Holdings: Bk Vols 2,000

BEALE AFB

UNITED STATES AIR FORCE
A BEALE AIR FORCE BASE LIBRARY FL4686, 9 SVS/SVMG, 17849 16th St Bldg 25219, 95903-1612. SAN 331-4944. Tel: 530-634-2314. FAX: 530-634-2032. *Dir*, Janet Parker; E-Mail: parkerj@sptg9.beale.as.mil; *Ref*, Judith Roberts
Library Holdings: Bk Vols 29,000; Per Subs 1,300
Special Collections: Aeronautics & California

BEAUMONT

P BEAUMONT LIBRARY DISTRICT, 125 E Eighth St, 92223-2194. SAN 300-5968. Tel: 909-845-1357. FAX: 909-845-6217. E-Mail: beaumontlib@telis.org. Web Site: www.bld.lib.ca.us. *Dir*, Clara DiFelice; *Ch Servs*, Linda Johnson; *Ref*, Antonov Yetena; Staff 5 (MLS 4, Non-MLS 1)
Founded 1911. Pop 24,750; Circ 101,205
Jul 1999-Jun 2000 Income $392,000, State $37,000, Federal $10,000, Locally Generated Income $345,000. Mats Exp $62,000, Books $57,000, Per/Ser (Incl. Access Fees) $5,000. Sal $218,000
Library Holdings: Bk Vols 57,000; Bk Titles 52,000; Per Subs 100
Automation Activity & Vendor Info: (Cataloging) TLC; (Circulation) TLC; (OPAC) TLC
Database Vendor: OCLC - First Search
Mem of Inland Library System
Partic in OCLC Online Computer Library Center, Inc
Friends of the Library Group

BELLFLOWER

R CALIFORNIA MISSIONARY BAPTIST INSTITUTE & SEMINARY LIBRARY,* 9246 Rosser St, 90706. SAN 300-5976. Tel: 562-925-4082. FAX: 562-804-0413. *Actg Librn*, Kathy Wood
Founded 1957
Library Holdings: Bk Vols 5,000
Restriction: Students only

M KAISER PERMANENTE MEDICAL CENTER, Health Sciences Library & Media Center, 9400 E Rosecrans Ave, 90706. SAN 300-5984. Tel: 562-461-4247. FAX: 562-461-4948. *Dir*, Mary E White; E-Mail: mary.e.white@kp.org
Founded 1965
Library Holdings: Bk Vols 8,720; Per Subs 500
Subject Interests: Hospital administration, Medicine, Nursing
Partic in Kaiser Permanente Library System - Southern California Region
Video teleconferencing for Medical Center

BELMONT

C COLLEGE OF NOTRE DAME LIBRARY, 1500 Ralston Ave, 94002-9974. SAN 300-5992. Tel: 650-508-3748. FAX: 650-508-3697. Web Site: www.library.cnd.edu. *Actg Dir*, Kip Hussey; E-Mail: khussey@cnd.edu; *Acq*, Judy Castillo; Tel: 650-508-3746, E-Mail: jcastillo@cnd.edu; *Ref*, Jennifer Altenberg; Tel: 650-508-3747, E-Mail: jaltenberg@cnd.edu; *Ref*, Mary Guedon; Tel: 650-508-3747, E-Mail: mguedon@cnd.edu; *Ref*, Kip Hussey; Tel: 650-508-3747, E-Mail: khussey@cnd.edu; *Cat*, Hai Huynh; Tel: 650-508-3486, E-Mail: hhuynh@cnd.edu; *Circ*, Jeanne Gallagher; E-Mail: jgallagher@cnd.edu; *Circ*, Reena Maharaji; E-Mail: rmaharaj@cnd.edu; *Circ*, Sasan Yousefpour; Tel: 650-508-3750, E-Mail: syousefpour@cnd.edu.
Subject Specialists: *Bus*, Kip Hussey; *Humanities*, Mary Guedon; *Music*, Jennifer Altenberg; Staff 9 (MLS 4, Non-MLS 5)
Founded 1922. Pop 1,754; Circ 60,000; Enrl 1,754; Fac 110; Highest Degree: Master
Jul 1999-Jun 2000 Income Parent Institution $559,802. Mats Exp $272,871, Books $46,106, Per/Ser (Incl. Access Fees) $88,099, Electronic Ref Mat (Incl. Access Fees) $59,220. Sal $286,931 (Prof $168,597)
Library Holdings: Bk Vols 100,000; Bk Titles 80,000; Per Subs 732
Subject Interests: Art and architecture, Business and management, Education, Music, Religion, Social sciences and issues
Special Collections: California Coll
Database Vendor: GaleNet, IAC - SearchBank, OCLC - First Search, Silverplatter Information Inc.
Partic in CAL/PALS

BENICIA

P BENICIA PUBLIC LIBRARY, 150 East L St, 94510-3281. SAN 300-6018. Tel: 707-746-4343. FAX: 707-747-8122. Web Site: www.ci.benicia.ca.us/library.html. *Dir*, Monique le Conge; E-Mail: mleconge@ci.benicia.ca.us; *Ch Servs*, Allison Angell; *Ch Servs*, Nicole Reader; *Publ Servs*, Fran Martinez-Scott; *Head Tech Servs*, Daveta Cooper; *YA Servs*, Charlotte Gerstein; Staff 41 (MLS 8, Non-MLS 33)
Founded 1911. Pop 29,000; Circ 242,670
Jul 1998-Jun 1999 Income $1,260,015, State $122,245, City $776,000, Locally Generated Income $361,770
Library Holdings: Bk Vols 90,000; Per Subs 275
Subject Interests: Art and architecture, Local history
Special Collections: Antiques Coll; California Coll; North Point Press Coll
Automation Activity & Vendor Info: (Circulation) CARL
Function: ILL available
Mem of North Bay Cooperative Library System
Partic in N Bay Coop Libr Syst; Snap
Friends of the Library Group

BERKELEY

R ACADEMY OF AMERICAN FRANCISCAN HISTORY LIBRARY, 1712 Euclid Ave, 94709-1208. SAN 326-4351. Tel: 510-548-1755. FAX: 510-549-9466. E-Mail: acadafh@aol.com. Web Site: www.aafh.org. *Dir*, John F Schwaller; Staff 1 (Non-MLS 1)
Founded 1944
Library Holdings: Bk Titles 20,000; Per Subs 100
Special Collections: Archives of the Indies (Seville Coll), Franciscan related docs; Archivo Historico Nacional de Mexico, docs; History of Southwest (Mary Coleman Powell Coll), 700 vols
Publications: Various texts on Franciscan history in Latin America, California, Florida & Arizona
Restriction: By appointment only
Bulk of collection now located at Washington Theological Union Library Archives in Maryland

S ALCOHOL RESEARCH GROUP LIBRARY,* 2000 Hearst Ave Ste 300, 94709-2176. SAN 329-8272. Tel: 510-642-5208. FAX: 510-642-7175. E-Mail: salis@arg.org. Web Site: www.arg.org, www.salis.org. *Dir, Librn*, Andrea L Mitchell; E-Mail: amitchell@arg.org
Library Holdings: Bk Vols 6,100; Per Subs 80
Subject Interests: Alcohol abuse, Drug abuse, Other drug use, Smoking, Socio-cultural aspects of alcohol, Tobacco

ALTA BATES MEDICAL CENTER
M ASHBY HEALTH SCIENCES LIBRARY, 2450 Ashby Ave, 94705. SAN 300-6042. Tel: 510-204-1696. FAX: 510-204-4091. *Librn*, Gerald Saunders; E-Mail: gerald-saunders@altabates.com
Founded 1975
Jan 1999-Dec 2000 Income $130,000. Mats Exp $45,000, Books $3,150, Per/Ser (Incl. Access Fees) $24,350. Sal $48,000
Library Holdings: Bk Titles 1,250; Per Subs 220
M HERRICK HEALTH SCIENCES LIBRARY, 2001 Dwight Way, 94704. SAN 331-572X. Tel: 510-204-4517. FAX: 510-204-3521. *Librn*, Laurie Bagley; E-Mail: laurie_bagley@altabates.com
Founded 1957
Library Holdings: Bk Vols 4,500; Bk Titles 4,000; Per Subs 115
Subject Interests: Neurology, Psychiatry, Psychoanalysis, Psychology, Psychotherapy
Special Collections: Vintage Library Coll
Partic in Dialog Corporation; Medline; Pacific SW Regional Med Libr Serv

M BAYER CORP, Berkeley Library & Information Services,* 800 Dwight Way, PO Box 1986, 94701. SAN 300-6107. Tel: 510-705-7815. FAX: 510-705-7819. *Librn*, H Wen Ng
Founded 1948
Library Holdings: Bk Vols 24,380; Per Subs 372
Subject Interests: Pharmaceutical science
Publications: Acquisitions List (quarterly); Current Awareness Biological (weekly); Periodical Holdings List
Partic in Dialog Corporation

P BERKELEY PUBLIC LIBRARY, 2090 Kittredge St, 94704. SAN 331-5428. Tel: 510-644-6095. Interlibrary Loan Service Tel: 510-649-3932. Reference Tel: 510-644-6648. TDD: 510-548-1240. FAX: 510-845-7598. Web Site: www.infopeople.org/bpl/. *Dep Dir*, MaryLou Mull; *Circ, ILL*, Dolores Wright; *Mgr*, Trarie Kottkamp; *Ch Servs*, Linda Perkins; *Coll Develop, Ref*, Diane Davenport; *Br Coordr*, Audrey Powers; Staff 71 (MLS 71)
Founded 1893. Pop 105,900; Circ 1,229,991
Jul 1999-Jun 2000 Income $9,308,783, State $314,051, City $8,373,525, Federal $16,456, Locally Generated Income $410,135, Other $194,616. Mats Exp $804,970, Books $599,833, Per/Ser (Incl. Access Fees) $126,747, Presv $18,700. Sal $6,564,779
Library Holdings: Bk Vols 434,748; Per Subs 1,539
Subject Interests: Art and architecture, Civil rights, Ethnic studies, Feminism, Music
Special Collections: Swingle Collection of Berkeley History, bks, maps, oral hist, pamphlets, photog, misc; World War I & World War II Poster Coll
Automation Activity & Vendor Info: (Circulation) Innovative Interfaces Inc.; (OPAC) Innovative Interfaces Inc.
Database Vendor: OCLC - First Search
Mem of Bay Area Libr & Info Syst
Partic in Dialog Corporation
Special Services for the Deaf - TDD
Special Services for the Blind - Reading edge system
Friends of the Library Group
Branches: 4
CLAREMONT, 2940 Benvenue Ave, 94705. SAN 331-5452. Tel: 510-644-6880. FAX: 510-843-1603. *Librn*, Karen Joseph-Smith
Library Holdings: Bk Vols 61,854
Friends of the Library Group
NORTH, 1170 The Alameda, 94707. SAN 331-5487. Tel: 510-644-6850. FAX: 510-528-8975. *In Charge*, Barbara Alesandrini
Library Holdings: Bk Vols 57,295
Friends of the Library Group
SOUTH, 1901 Russell St, 94703. SAN 331-5517. Tel: 510-644-6860. FAX: 510-549-3054. *Librn*, Jeri Ewart
Library Holdings: Bk Vols 43,396
Friends of the Library Group
WEST, 1125 University Ave, 94702. SAN 331-5541. Tel: 510-644-6870. *Librn*, Richard Serrato
Library Holdings: Bk Vols 51,071
Friends of the Library Group

GM CALIFORNIA STATE DEPARTMENT OF HEALTH SERVICES, Division of Communicable Diseases,* 2151 Berkeley Way, Rm 708, 94704-1011. SAN 328-2368. Tel: 510-540-2356. FAX: 510-540-3666.
Library Holdings: Bk Titles 3,000
Subject Interests: Applied surveillance, Control methodologies, Diseases transmitted to man via arthropods

S CITIZENS RESEARCH FOUNDATION, UC Berkeley-Institute of Governmental Studies Library, 109 Moses Hall, IGS-UC Berkeley, 94720. Tel: 510-642-1472. FAX: 510-642-0866. *Chair*, Nelson W Posby; *Librn*,

Ron Heckart
Library Holdings: Bk Vols 3,000; Bk Titles 1,500; Per Subs 30
Restriction: Restricted public use

CR GRADUATE THEOLOGICAL UNION LIBRARY, 2400 Ridge Rd, 94709. SAN 331-5630. Tel: 510-649-2500. Reference Tel: 510-649-2501. FAX: 510-649-2508. E-Mail: libref@gtu.edu. Web Site: www.gtu.edu/library/. *Dir*, Dr Bonnie Hardwick; Tel: 510-649-2540, E-Mail: hardwick@gtu.edu; *Librn*, Cheryl Miller Maddox; Tel: 510-649-2510, E-Mail: cmaddox@gtu.edu; *Librn*, Michael Peterson; Tel: 415-258-6635, Fax: 415-453-2050, E-Mail: mpeterson@sfts.edu; *Librn*, Mehry Samadi; Tel: 510-649-2532, E-Mail: msamadi@gtu.edu; *Librn*, Kristine Veldheer; Tel: 510-649-2504, E-Mail: veldheer@gtu.edu; *Head, Circ*, Patricia Boucher; Tel: 510-649-2506, E-Mail: pboucher@gtu.edu; *Head, Info Serv*, Ann Hotta; Tel: 510-649-2512, E-Mail: ahotta@gtu.edu; *Acq*, Dana Spottswood; Tel: 510-649-2508, E-Mail: dspotts@gtu.edu; *Archivist*, Lucinda Glenn Rand; Tel: 510-649-2507, E-Mail: lglenn@gtu.edu; *Coll Develop*, Clay-Edward Dixon; Tel: 510-649-2509, E-Mail: cedixon@gtu.edu; *Head, Cat*, Mark Takaro; Tel: 510-649-2521, E-Mail: mtakaro@gtu.edu; *Ser*, Nang-Kai Lahpai; Tel: 510-649-2528, E-Mail: nlahpai@gtu.edu; Staff 35 (MLS 10, Non-MLS 25)
Founded 1969. Enrl 1,335; Fac 281; Highest Degree: Doctorate
Jul 1999-Jun 2000 Mats Exp $338,530, Books $235,854, Per/Ser (Incl. Access Fees) $76,528, Presv $4,950, Micro $6,043, AV Equip $6,351, Electronic Ref Mat (Incl. Access Fees) $8,804. Sal $897,560 (Prof $464,606)
Library Holdings: Bk Vols 409,455; Per Subs 1,452
Subject Interests: Biblical studies, Christianity, Religion, Theology, World religion
Special Collections: Archival Collections with emphasis in the area of Ecumenical & Inter-Religious Activity in the Western United States & Pacific Rim
Automation Activity & Vendor Info: (Acquisitions) Innovative Interfaces Inc.; (Circulation) Innovative Interfaces Inc.; (Course Reserve) Innovative Interfaces Inc.; (OPAC) Innovative Interfaces Inc.; (Serials) Innovative Interfaces Inc.
Database Vendor: OVID Technologies, ProQuest
Restriction: Public use on premises
Function: Research library
Special Services for the Blind - Reading machine
Library serves: American Baptist Seminary of the West, Church Divinity School of the Pacific, Dominican School of Philosophy & Theology, Franciscan School of Theology, Jesuit School of Theology at Berkeley; Pacific Lutheran Theological Seminary, Pacific School of Religion, San Francisco Theological Seminary, Starr King School for the Ministry; Richard S Dinner Center for Jewish Studies; Center for Ethics & Social Policy; Center for Women & Religion, Institute for Buddhist Studies, Center for the Arts, Religion & Education; Center for the Theology & the Natural Sciences; New College for Advanced Christian Studies, Pacific & Asian American Center for Theology & Strategies; Patriarch Athenagoras Orthodox Institute, School of Applied Theology, Center for the Study of Culture & Religion
Friends of the Library Group

S INTERNATIONAL BIRD RESCUE RESEARCH CENTER,* 699 Potter St, 94710. SAN 373-3963. Tel: 510-841-9086. FAX: 510-841-9089. *Dir*, Jay Holcomb
Library Holdings: Bk Titles 205; Per Subs 6
Open 9-5

S INTERNATIONAL CHILD RESOURCE INSTITUTE,* 1581 Leroy Ave, 94708. SAN 370-2278. Tel: 510-644-1000. FAX: 510-525-4106. E-Mail: icrichild@aol.com. *Dir*, Ken Jaffe
Library Holdings: Bk Vols 13,000

S LAWRENCE BERKELEY NATIONAL LABORATORY LIBRARY,* Bldg 50B, Rm 4206, One Cyclotron Rd, 94720-0001. SAN 331-5754. Tel: 510-486-5621. FAX: 510-486-6406. E-Mail: library@lbl.gov. Web Site: www-library.lbl.gov/. *Head of Libr*, Carol Backhus; *Circ, ILL, Ref*, Rita LaBrie; Staff 8 (MLS 5, Non-MLS 3)
Founded 1946
Library Holdings: Bk Vols 24,729; Bk Titles 25,000; Per Subs 600
Subject Interests: Chemistry, Computer science, Earth science, Electronic engineering, Energy, Nuclear medicine, Nuclear science, Physics
Special Collections: High energy physics preprints
Restriction: Staff use only, Use of others with permission of librarian
Partic in RLIN
Lawrence Berkeley Laboratory is operated by the University of California for the US Dept of Energy
Branches:
BUILDING 62 LIBRARY Tel: 510-486-5971. Web Site: www-library.lbl.gov/.
DONNER LABORATORY LIBRARY, Bldg 1, Rm 201, 94720. SAN 331-5789. Tel: 510-486-6201. FAX: 510-486-6427. Web Site: www-library.lbl.gov/. *In Charge*, Cheryl Weisenmiller
Subject Interests: Biochemistry, Biology, Cancer

JUDAH L MAGNES MEMORIAL MUSEUM
S BLUMENTHAL LIBRARY, 2911 Russell St, 94705. SAN 331-5878. Tel: 510-549-6939. FAX: 510-849-3673. *Archivist, Librn*, Tova Gazit. Subject Specialists: *Jewish art*, Tova Gazit; *Jewish hist*, Tova Gazit
Founded 1967
Library Holdings: Bk Vols 25,000; Bk Titles 20,000
Subject Interests: Archival, Jewish art, Jewish hist, Jewish lit, Music
Special Collections: 15th to the Present Rare Printed Editions, bks, mss; Community Collections from Cochin, India, Egypt, Morocco & Czechoslovakia; Heine & other German authors, letters; Holocaust Material (Institute for Righteous Acts Coll); Illustrated Bks; Karaite Community; Passover Haggadot; Ukrainian Pogroms (Belkin Coll), doc
Restriction: Non-circulating to the public
S WESTERN JEWISH HISTORY CENTER, 2911 Russell St, 94705. SAN 331-5908. Tel: 510-549-6956. FAX: 510-849-3673. E-Mail: wjhc@magnesmuseum.org. *Archivist*, Kim Klausner; *Archivist*, Julia Bazar; Staff 1 (Non-MLS 1)
Founded 1967
Library Holdings: Bk Vols 1,570; Per Subs 15
Subject Interests: Jewish history and literature
Special Collections: David Lubin-Harris Weinstock & Families; Institution Records, Secular & Religious; Jewish Chicken Ranchers of Petaluma; Jewish Community Center Coll; Jewish Community Federation Coll of San Francisco, Marin & Sonoma Counties & the Peninsula; Jewish Life, Jewish Individuals (Florence Prag Kahn, Judah Magnes, David Lubin, Alvin Fine) and Jewish religious and secular Institutions (Mt. Zion Hospital, national Council of Jewish Women-SF, Congregation Sherith Israel) in the Western United States since 1850, archives, mss, photog, doc, artifacts; Jews of China; Judah Magnes Archives, mss, photog, doc, graphs, bks, pamphlets; N Calif Jews from Harbin, Manchuria; Oral Histories of San Fancisco Jews of Eastern European Origin; Petaluma Project; San Francisco Jews of Eastern European origin (1880-1940) Coll; Western Jewish Americana, mss, doc, archives, bks, micro, per, photog, VF; Western Jewish Periodicals Coll
Publications: Catalog of Western Jewish Periodicals; Western Jewish Americana Bibliography Series, 22 publications dealing with Western Jewish History; WJHC: Guide to Archival & Oral History Coll
Restriction: Non-circulating to the public
Function: Archival collection
Mem of Bay Area Libr & Info Syst

L MEIKLEJOHN CIVIL LIBERTIES INSTITUTE LIBRARY, PO Box 673, 94701-0673. SAN 300-6158. Tel: 510-848-0599. FAX: 510-848-6008. E-Mail: mcli@igc.org. Web Site: www.sfsu.edu/~mclicfc. *Dir*, Ann Fagan Ginger
Founded 1965
Subject Interests: Civil rights, Cold War, Human rights, Nuclear weapons, Peace studies, United Nations
Publications: Alexander Meiklejohn: Teacher of Freedom; Cold War Against Labor; Human Rights Organizations & Periodicals Directory, 9th ed 1998; Human Rights Protections: A Guide to UN & Their Application in US; MCLI Issue Sheets: for the First US Report to UN Committee Against Torture (9/99); MCLI Issue Sheets: for the First US Report to UN Committee on Elimination of All Forms of Racial Discrimination (8/97); MCLI Issue Sheets: for the First US Report to UN Human Rights Committee (1994); Peace Law Packets; Relevant Lawyers; The Ford Hunger March Human Rights & Peace Law Docket: 1945-1993, 5th ed 1995
Function: Reference only, Research library
Friends of the Library Group

S NATIONAL CLEARINGHOUSE ON MARITAL & DATE RAPE, Women's History Library, 2325 Oak St, 94708. SAN 327-9200. Tel: 510-524-1582. FAX: 510-524-7768. Web Site: ncmdr.org.
Subject Interests: Law, Mental health

S PREVENTION RESEARCH CENTER LIBRARY, 2150 Shattuck Ave, Ste 900, 94704. SAN 374-8553. Tel: 510-486-1111. FAX: 510-644-0594. *Librn*, Christina Miller
Library Holdings: Bk Titles 1,000; Per Subs 30
Restriction: Staff use only

CL UNIVERSITY OF CALIFORNIA EXTENSION, Continuing Education of the Bar Library,* 2300 Shattuck Ave, 94704-1576. SAN 300-6204. Tel: 510-642-5343. FAX: 510-642-3788. *Dir*, Rebecca Lhermitte; E-Mail: lhermir@ceb.ucop.edu; Staff 1 (MLS 1)
Founded 1960
Library Holdings: Bk Vols 9,000; Bk Titles 2,000; Per Subs 230

C UNIVERSITY OF CALIFORNIA, BERKELEY, 245 Doe Library, 94720-6000. SAN 331-6025. Tel: 510-642-3773. TDD: 510-642-0704. FAX: 510-643-8179. Web Site: www.lib.berkeley.edu. *Actg Librn*, Thomas C Leonard; *Assoc Librn*, Patricia Iannuzzi; *Assoc Librn*, Lee Leighton; *Assoc Librn*, Alan Ritch; *Assoc Librn*, Isabelle Stirling; *ILL*, Charlotte Rubens
Founded 1871. Enrl 32,000; Fac 1,482; Highest Degree: Doctorate
Library Holdings: Per Subs 89,948
Special Collections: Foreign; Letters, Literary Manuscripts & Scrapbooks of Samuel Clemens (Mark Twain Coll); Music History, bks, mss, scores; Radio Carbon Date Cards, Photographic Plates, Rubbings, University Archive Photographs, Aerial Photographs, VF mat; Recollections of Persons Who

Have Contributed to the Development of the West (Regional Oral History Office)
Publications: A Program for the Conservation & Preservation of Library Materials in the General Library; Bene Legere Newsletter for Library Associates; bibliographic guides to research resources in selected subjects; Collection Development Policy Statement; faculty newsletter (quarterly); orientation leaflets; Titles Classified by the Library of Congress Classification: National Shelflist Count
Mem of Asn of Research Libraries; Bay Area Libr & Info Syst
Partic in BRS; Dialog Corporation; Medline; OCLC Online Computer Library Center, Inc; RLG; RLIN; STN; Westlaw; Wilsonline
Special Services for the Deaf - TDD
Special Services for the Blind - Blind Students Center; Kurzweil Reading Machine; Rental typewriters & computers
Friends of the Library Group
Departmental Libraries:
ANTHROPOLOGY, 230 Kroeber Hall, 94720-6000. SAN 331-6173. Tel: 510-642-2400. FAX: 510-643-9293. *Librn*, Suzanne Calpestri
Library Holdings: Bk Vols 69,273
ART HISTORY-CLASSICS, 308 Doe Library, 94720-6000. SAN 331-684X. Tel: 510-642-5358. FAX: 510-643-6650. *Librn*, Kathryn Wayne
ASTRONOMY-MATHEMATICS-STATISTICS, 100 Evans Hall, 94720-6000. SAN 331-6688. Tel: 510-642-3381. FAX: 510-642-8257. E-Mail: math@library.berkeley.edu. Web Site: www.lib.berkeley.edu/ams. *In Charge*, Ann Jensen
Library Holdings: Bk Vols 87,219
BANCROFT LIBRARY, 94720-6000. Tel: 510-642-3781. FAX: 510-642-7589. Web Site: www.lib.berkeley.edu/banc/. *Dir*, Charles Faulhaber
Library Holdings: Bk Vols 400,000
Special Collections: Fine Printing Coll; History of Science & Technology (Rare Books Coll); History of Western North America, especially California & Mexico (Bancroft Coll), bks, mss; Humanities Coll; Mark Twain Coll, mss, bks; Modern Poetry Coll; North & South America Coll; Rare Imprints of Western Europe; University Archives
BUSINESS & ECONOMICS, Haas School of Business, Rm S352, 94720-6000. SAN 331-6327. Tel: 510-642-0370. FAX: 510-643-5277. Web Site: www.lib.berkeley.edu/busi/. *Librn*, Milton Ternberg
Library Holdings: Bk Vols 130,000
Subject Interests: Economics
CENTER FOR CHINESE STUDIES, 2223 Fulton, Ground flr, 94720. SAN 331-6068. Tel: 510-642-6510. FAX: 510-642-3817.
Library Holdings: Bk Vols 54,041
CHEMISTRY, 40 Doe, 94720-6000. SAN 331-6718. Tel: 510-642-3753. FAX: 510-643-9041. Web Site: www.lib.berkeley.edu/chem. *In Charge*, Mary Ann Mahoney
Library Holdings: Bk Vols 67,003
EARTH SCIENCES & MAPS, 50 McCone Hall, 94720-6000. SAN 331-6742. Tel: 510-642-2997. FAX: 510-643-6576. E-Mail: eartmaps@library.berkeley.edu. Web Site: www.lib.berkeley.edu/eart. *Head Librn*, Katie Frohmberg; Tel: 510-643-2684; Staff 6 (MLS 1, Non-MLS 5)
2000-2000 Mats Exp $350,000. Sal $250,000
Library Holdings: Bk Vols 118,228; Per Subs 2,000
Automation Activity & Vendor Info: (Acquisitions) Innovative Interfaces Inc.; (Serials) Innovative Interfaces Inc.
Database Vendor: OCLC - First Search
EARTHQUAKE ENGINEERING RESEARCH CENTER, 453 Richmond Field Sta, 1301 S 46th St, Richmond, 94804. SAN 331-6912. Tel: 510-231-9403. Reference Tel: 510-231-9401. FAX: 510-231-9461. Web Site: www.eerc.berkeley.edu/.
Founded 1972
Library Holdings: Bk Vols 51,000
Subject Interests: Earthquakes, Engineering, Geotech eng, Seismology, Structural engineering
Special Collections: Earthquake Engineering Abstracts Database; Godden International Structural Slide Library; Steinbrugge Image Coll
Database Vendor: OCLC - First Search
EAST ASIAN, Durant Hall, Rm 208, 94720-6000. SAN 331-6084. Tel: 510-642-2556. FAX: 510-642-3817.
Library Holdings: Bk Vols 796,147
EDUCATION PSYCHOLOGY, 2600 Tolman Hall, 94720-6000. SAN 331-6203. Tel: 510-642-4209. Circulation Tel: 510-642-4209. Reference Tel: 510-642-2475. FAX: 510-642-8224. Web Site: www.lib.berkeley.edu/edp/. *Librn*, Barbara Glendenning; Tel: 510-643-6224, E-Mail: bglenden@library.berkeley.edu; Staff 5 (MLS 2, Non-MLS 3)
Highest Degree: Doctorate
Library Holdings: Bk Vols 176,474; Per Subs 802
ENVIRONMENTAL DESIGN, Moffitt Library, 5th flr, 94720-6000. SAN 331-6238. Tel: 510-642-4818. Reference Tel: 510-643-7421. FAX: 510-642-8266. Web Site: www.lib.berkeley.edu/envi. *Head Librn*, Elizabeth D Byrne; *Librn*, Deborah Sommer; *Librn*, Susan Koskinen. Subject Specialists: *Architecture*, Susan Koskinen; *Architecture*, Elizabeth D Byrne; *Landscaping*, Deborah Sommer; *Planning*, Deborah Sommer; Staff 7 (MLS 3, Non-MLS 4)
Founded 1903. Enrl 1,100; Fac 70; Highest Degree: Doctorate
Library Holdings: Bk Vols 185,000; Per Subs 1,000
Subject Interests: Architecture, City planning, Landscape architecture
Special Collections: Beatrix Farrand Rare Books
ETHNIC STUDIES, 30 Stephens Hall, No 2360, 94720-2360. SAN 376-9518. Tel: 510-643-1234. FAX: 510-643-8433. E-Mail: esl@library.berkeley.edu. Web Site: eslibrary.berkeley.edu. *Head Librn*, Lillian Castillo-Speed; Tel: 510-642-3947; Staff 5 (MLS 3, Non-MLS 2)
Subject Interests: Chicano studies, Ethnic studies, Native Am studies
Special Collections: AAS Archives; AAS Special Coll; Asian American Studies; CS A/V; CS Archives; CS Locked Case; NAS California Coll & NAS A/V Coll
Partic in Berkeley Libr Info Network
GIANNINI FOUNDATION LIBRARY, 248 Giannini Hall, 94720-3310. SAN 331-6890. Tel: 510-642-7121. FAX: 510-643-8911. Web Site: are.berkeley.edu/library. *Librn*, Grace Dote; Staff 3 (MLS 1, Non-MLS 2)
Founded 1930. Fac 15; Highest Degree: Doctorate
2000-2000 Mats Exp $44,000. Sal $120,000 (Prof $68,000)
Library Holdings: Bk Vols 20,829; Per Subs 300
Subject Interests: Agricultural economics, Natural resources
Special Collections: Federal-State market reports on microfilm form 1900 to 1982
Automation Activity & Vendor Info: (Cataloging) Inmagic, Inc.
Database Vendor: Ebsco - EbscoHost
Publications: Economic Research of Interest to Agriculture (triennial); Materials added to the Giannini Foundation Library (10 times per year)
Restriction: Staff use only
INSTITUTE OF GOVERNMENTAL STUDIES, 109 Moses Hall, Ground flr, 94720-2370, 94720. SAN 331-6920. Tel: 510-642-1472. FAX: 510-643-0866. Web Site: www.igs.berkeley.edu:8880/library. *Dir*, Ron Heckart
Library Holdings: Bk Vols 437,299
Closed Sat & Sun
INSTITUTE OF INDUSTRIAL RELATIONS, 2521 Channing Way, No 5555, 94720-5555. SAN 331-6955. Tel: 510-642-1705. FAX: 510-642-6432. E-Mail: iirl@library.berkeley.edu. Web Site: iir.berkeley.edu. *Librn*, Terence Huwe
Founded 1945. Enrl 30,000; Fac 65; Highest Degree: Doctorate
Library Holdings: Bk Vols 64,081
INSTITUTE OF TRANSPORTATION STUDIES, 412 McLaughlin Hall, 94720. SAN 331-7013. Tel: 510-642-3604. FAX: 510-642-9180. *Librn*, Catherine Cortelyou; *Librn*, Daniel Krummes
Founded 1948
Library Holdings: Bk Vols 149,426
Special Collections: San Francisco Bay Area Transit Coll, 1941-date, newsp clippings, VF
Partic in OCLC Online Computer Library Center, Inc
KRESGE ENGINEERING LIBRARY, 110 Bechtel Engineering Ctr, 94720-1796. SAN 331-6777. Tel: 510-642-3532. Reference Tel: 510-642-3339. FAX: 510-643-6771. Web Site: www.lib.berkeley.edu/engi. *Librn*, Camille Wanat; Staff 3 (MLS 3)
Library Holdings: Bk Vols 215,948; Per Subs 1,804
Subject Interests: Engineering
LAW, 225 Boalt Hall, 94720. SAN 331-7072. Tel: 510-642-4044. FAX: 510-643-5039. *Librn*, Robert Berring
Founded 1912. Highest Degree: Doctorate
Special Collections: Anglo-American, Foreign & International Law Research Coll; Canon, Medieval & Roman Law Coll
Publications: Acquisitions list
Partic in RLIN; Westlaw
MARIAN KOSHLAND BIOSCIENCE & NATURAL RESOURCES LIBRARY, 2101 VLSB, No 6500, 94720-6500. SAN 331-6475. Tel: 510-642-2531. FAX: 510-642-8217. Web Site: www.lib.berkeley.edu/bios/. *Librn*, Beth Weil; Staff 4 (MLS 4)
Library Holdings: Bk Vols 500,000; Per Subs 6,500
MUSIC, 240 Morrison Hall, 94720-6000. SAN 331-6297. Tel: 510-642-2623. FAX: 510-642-8237. *Librn*, John Roberts
Library Holdings: Bk Vols 165,326
OPTOMETRY, 490 Minor Hall, 94720-6000. SAN 331-6599. Tel: 510-642-1020. FAX: 510-841-4232. Web Site: www.lib.berkeley.edu/opto/. *Librn*, Bette Anton; Staff 4 (MLS 1, Non-MLS 3)
Library Holdings: Bk Vols 11,490
PHILOSOPHY, 305 Moses Hall, 94720. SAN 331-7021. Tel: 510-642-6516.
Library Holdings: Bk Vols 9,711
PHYSICS, 351 LeConte Hall, 94720-6000. SAN 331-6807. Tel: 510-642-3122. FAX: 510-642-8350. *Librn*, Diane Fortner
Library Holdings: Bk Vols 48,321
PUBLIC HEALTH, 42 Warren Hall, No 7360, 94720-7360. SAN 331-6629. Tel: 510-642-2511. FAX: 510-642-7623. E-Mail: publ@library.berkeley.edu. Web Site: www.lib.berkeley.edu/publ/.; Staff 11 (MLS 5, Non-MLS 6)
Founded 1955
Library Holdings: Bk Vols 93,158
ROSBERG INTERNATIONAL STUDIES LIBRARY, 340 Stephens Hall, 94720. SAN 331-698X. Tel: 510-642-3633. FAX: 510-643-5045. Web Site: www.ias.berkeley.edu/rosberglib.html. *In Charge*, Linda Blum
Library Holdings: Bk Vols 8,200
Subject Interests: Political science
Special Collections: Asian Development Bank Coll
SOCIAL WELFARE, 227 Haviland Hall, 94720-6000. SAN 331-6351. Tel: 510-642-4432. FAX: 510-643-1476. Web Site: www.lib.berkeley.edu/socw.

Head of Libr, Lora L Graham
Library Holdings: Bk Vols 27,954
SOUTH-SOUTHEAST ASIA LIBRARY SERVICE, 120 Doe Library, 94720-6000. SAN 331-6831. Tel: 510-642-3095. FAX: 510-643-8817. *Asst Librn*, Virginia Jing-yi Shih; Tel: 510-643-0850, E-Mail: vshih@library.berkeley.edu
Library Holdings: Bk Vols 16,548
TECHNICAL SERVICES, 250 Moffit Library, 94720-6000. SAN 320-944X. Tel: 510-643-8239. FAX: 510-642-8331. *Head of Libr*, Armanda Barone
THE TEACHING LIBRARY, 302 Moffitt Library, 94720-6000. SAN 331-6114. Tel: 510-643-9959. FAX: 510-642-9454. *Head of Libr*, Ellen Meltzer
WATER RESOURCES CENTER ARCHIVES, 410 O'Brien Hall, 94720. SAN 331-7048. Tel: 510-642-2666. FAX: 510-642-1943. *Librn*, Linda Vida
Library Holdings: Bk Vols 108,986

J VISTA COLLEGE LIBRARY,* 2020 Milvia St, 94704. SAN 323-5726. Tel: 510-981-2800, 510-981-2821, 510-981-2823. FAX: 510-540-8132, 510-841-7333. *Dir*, Timothy Hackett
Enrl 5,000
Library Holdings: Bk Vols 1,000; Per Subs 33
Open Mon-Thurs 11-7, Fri 9-2 & Sat 9-1

S WRIGHT INSTITUTE LIBRARY, 2728 Durant Ave, 94704. SAN 323-4649. Tel: 510-841-9230, Ext 121. FAX: 510-841-0167. Web Site: www.wrightinst.edu. *Librn*, Lona French; E-Mail: lfrench@wrightinst.edu
Library Holdings: Bk Titles 10,000; Per Subs 115
Subject Interests: Psychology

BEVERLY HILLS

S ACADEMY OF MOTION PICTURE ARTS & SCIENCES, Margaret Herrick Library, 333 S La Cienega Blvd, 90211. SAN 300-6212. Tel: 310-247-3000. Reference Tel: 310-247-3020. FAX: 310-657-5193. *Dir*, Linda Harris Mehr; Tel: 310-247-3000, Ext 201; *Ref*, Sandra Archer; Tel: 310-247-3000, Ext 205; *Acq, Archivist*, Howard Prouty; Tel: 310-247-3000, Ext 225; *Ser*, Lucia Schultz; Tel: 310-247-3000, Ext 217; *Curator*, Robert Cushman; Tel: 310-247-3000, Ext 221; *Archivist, Res*, Barbara Hall; Tel: 310-247-3000, Ext 218; *Archivist, Coll Develop*, Val Almendarez; Tel: 310-247-3000, Ext 224; *Info Tech*, Vionnette Dover Sellers; Tel: 310-247-3000, Ext 211; Staff 55 (MLS 8, Non-MLS 47)
Founded 1927
Library Holdings: Bk Vols 30,375; Bk Titles 27,325; Per Subs 200
Special Collections: Adolph Zukor Coll; Alfred Hitchcock Coll; Andrew Marton Coll; Arthur Hiller Coll; Barry Lyndon Coll; Buster Keaton (vaudeville) Coll; Cary Grant Coll; Cecil B DeMille Coll, stills; Charlton Heston Coll; Colleen Moore Coll, scrapbks, stills; David Niven Coll; Edith Head Coll, sketches & stills; Elmer-Dyer Coll; Endre Bohem Coll; Fred Renaldo Coll; Fred Zinnemann Coll; George Cukor Coll, correspondence & scripts; George Steven Coll, correspondence, financial rec, production files, scripts & stills; Gregory Peck Coll; Hal B Wallis Coll; Hedda Hopper Coll; J Roy Hunt Coll, correspondence, scripts & stills; Jackie Coogan Coll; James Wong Howe Coll; Jean Hersholt Coll; John Engstead Coll; John Paxton Coll; John Sturges Coll; Joseph Biroc Coll; Jules White Coll; Kay Van Pipper Coll; Leo Kuter Coll; Leonard Goldstein Coll; Lewis Milestone, Mary Pickford, Martin Ritt, Paul Mazursky, William Friedkin, Hal Ashby, George Roy Hill & Bryan Forbes (Hollywood Museum Coll), papers & stills; Louella Parsons Coll; Mack Sennett Coll, contracts, financial rec, scripts & stills; Merle Oberon Coll; Metro-Goldwyn-Mayer Inc, stills; MGM Scripts Coll; Milton Krims Coll; MPAA Production Code, case files; Paramount Pictures, scripts, still bks & stills; Paul Ivano Coll; Pete Smith Coll; Ring Lardner Jr Coll; RKO Radio Pictures Coll, stills; Robert Lees Coll; Sam Peckinpah Coll; Saul Bass Coll; Selig Coll, copyrights, scripts & stills; Sid Avery Coll, stills; Sidney Skolsky Coll; Steve McQueen Coll; Thomas Ince Coll; Valentine Davies Coll; William Beaudine Coll
Publications: Acquisitions list (monthly); Annual Index to Motion Picture Credits; Motion Picture Scripts: A Union List

P BEVERLY HILLS PUBLIC LIBRARY, 444 N Rexford Dr, 90210-4877. SAN 300-6239. Tel: 310-288-2201. FAX: 310-278-3387. Web Site: www.ci.beverly-hills.ca.us (City of Beverly Hills). *Dir*, Michael Steinfeld; *ILL*, Loc Huynh; *Ch Servs*, Christina Garcia; *Media Spec, Rare Bks, Spec Coll*, Stefan Klima; *Acq, Cat, Tech Servs*, Karen Buth; *Coll Develop, Ref*, Frank Piontek; *Circ*, Elena Panajotovic
Founded 1929. Pop 34,050; Circ 718,609
Jul 1999-Jun 2000 Income $6,653,689. Mats Exp $1,200,292. Sal $2,995,969
Library Holdings: Bk Vols 291,468; Per Subs 700
Subject Interests: Art, Dance
Special Collections: 19th & 20th Century Art & Artists; Beverly Hills Coll
Mem of Metropolitan Cooperative Library System
Friends of the Library Group

BEVERY HILLS PUBLIC LIBRARY, Roxbury Park Senior Adult Library, 471 S Roxbury Dr, 90212-4113. Tel: 310-550-4947. Web Site: www.bhpl.org. *Dir*, Michael Steinfeld
Library Holdings: Bk Vols 1,700; Per Subs 50

S SOUTHERN CALIFORNIA PSYCHOANALYTIC INSTITUTE, Franz Alexander Library, 9024 Olympic Blvd, 90211. SAN 300-6271. Tel: 310-276-2455, Ext 2. Interlibrary Loan Service Tel: 310-272-7620. FAX: 310-276-3057. E-Mail: scpilib@earthlink.net. Web Site: www.socalpsa.com. *Librn*, Marilyn Slater; *ILL*, Lena Pincus
Founded 1958
Library Holdings: Bk Vols 4,500; Bk Titles 3,200; Per Subs 27
Subject Interests: Humanities, Psychiatry, Psychoanalysis, Psychology, Social sciences and issues
Partic in Pacific SW Regional Med Libr Serv

S THOMSON & THOMSON, (Formerly Deforest Research), DeForest Research, 8383 Wilshire Blvd, Ste 450, 90211. SAN 300-9815. Tel: 310-273-2900. Toll Free Tel: 800-431-8133. FAX: 310-888-3270. Toll Free FAX: 800-431-4031. Web Site: www.thomson-thomson.com.
Founded 1913
Library Holdings: Bk Vols 10,000; Per Subs 12
Subject Interests: Film, Television

BIG CREEK

P FRESNO COUNTY PUBLIC LIBRARY, Big Creek Station,* 51190 Point Rd, PO Box 25, 93605-0025. SAN 377-3426. Tel: 559-893-6614. Web Site: www.sjvls.lib.ca.us/fresno. *In Charge*, Kathy Richmond
Library Holdings: Bk Vols 8,000; Per Subs 20
Mem of San Joaquin Valley Library System

BISHOP

S LAWS RAILROAD MUSEUM & HISTORICAL SITE LIBRARY, Libr & Arts Bldg, Silver Canyon Rd, PO Box 363, 93515. SAN 375-4685. Tel: 760-873-5950. E-Mail: lawsmuseum@aol.com. Web Site: www.sierralibrary.com. *In Charge*, Barbara Moss
Founded 1966
Library Holdings: Bk Vols 500

M NORTHERN INYO HOSPITAL, Medical Library,* 150 Pioneer Lane, 93514. SAN 325-0962. Tel: 760-873-5811, Ext 2279. FAX: 760-873-6734. E-Mail: ninyohosplib@telis.org. *Librn*, Annette Gaskin
1997-1998 Income $71,244. Mats Exp $21,864, Books $14,664, Per/Ser (Incl. Access Fees) $7,200. Sal $32,100
Library Holdings: Bk Titles 551; Per Subs 51
Subject Interests: Health care
Special Collections: High Altitude Sickness, Pulmonary Edema; Mountain, Wilderness Emergencies

BLYTHE

J PALO VERDE COLLEGE, Harry A Faull Library Resource Center,* 811 W Chanslorway, 92225-1199. SAN 300-628X. Tel: 760-921-5332. FAX: 760-922-0230. Web Site: www.paloverde.cc.ca.us/library. *Assoc Dean*, Scott Connell; Staff 1 (MLS 1)
Founded 1947
1998-1999 Mats Exp $38,000. Sal $81,000 (Prof $70,000)
Library Holdings: Bk Vols 17,246; Bk Titles 14,792; Per Subs 167
Automation Activity & Vendor Info: (Cataloging) Sagebrush Corporation; (Circulation) Sagebrush Corporation
Database Vendor: IAC - Info Trac
Partic in SIRCULS

P PALO VERDE VALLEY DISTRICT LIBRARY, 125 W Chanslorway, 92225-1293. SAN 300-6298. Tel: 760-922-5371. FAX: 760-922-5371. E-Mail: pvvalleylib@ispchannel.com. Web Site: www.paloverdevalleylibrary.com. *Dir*, Rosita Smith
Founded 1959. Pop 41,380; Circ 44,680
Jul 1999-Jun 2000 Income $249,192, State $69,412, City $18,851, County $123,675, Locally Generated Income $7,984, Other $29,270. Mats Exp $28,501, Books $21,731, Per/Ser (Incl. Access Fees) $3,225, Electronic Ref Mat (Incl. Access Fees) $3,545. Sal $86,378 (Prof $34,070)
Library Holdings: Bk Vols 53,752; Bk Titles 46,660; Per Subs 79; Bks on Deafness & Sign Lang 10
Special Collections: Palo Verde Times (local) 1911 to present (microfilm); Palo Verde Valley Local History (complete set)
Automation Activity & Vendor Info: (Cataloging) Brodart; (Circulation) epixtech, inc.
Mem of Inland Library System
Friends of the Library Group

BRANDEIS

S BRANDEIS-BARDIN INSTITUTE, The Molle Library, 1101 Peppertree Lane, 93064. SAN 300-6301. Tel: 805-582-4450. FAX: 805-526-1398. Web Site: www.thebbi.org. *Librn*, Hannah R Kuhn
Founded 1973

Library Holdings: Bk Vols 10,000; Bk Titles 8,000
Special Collections: Books in Hebrew (Dr Shlomo Bardin)
Publications: Torah at Brandeis Institute: The Layman Expounds

BRAWLEY

P BRAWLEY PUBLIC LIBRARY,* 400 Main, 92227-2491. SAN 300-631X. Tel: 760-344-1891. FAX: 760-344-0212. *Dir*, Marjo Mello; Staff 1 (MLS 1)
Founded 1927. Pop 20,000; Circ 72,961
Library Holdings: Bk Titles 43,500; Per Subs 109
Mem of Serra Cooperative Library System
Open Mon-Thurs 12-8, Sat 9-5
Friends of the Library Group

BREA

L UNOCAL CORP, Law Library, 376 S Valencia Ave, N-120, 92823. SAN 301-0074. Tel: 714-577-3237. FAX: 714-577-3236. *Librn*, Ellen Chang; Staff 1 (MLS 1)
Library Holdings: Bk Vols 50,000
Subject Interests: Commercial law, Labor, Mining, Natural resources, Real estate, Securities
Automation Activity & Vendor Info: (Cataloging) TechLIB; (OPAC) TechLIB
Database Vendor: Dialog, Lexis-Nexis
Restriction: Company library
Partic in Dialog Corporation; Saegis

BRIDGEPORT

P MONO COUNTY FREE LIBRARY SYSTEM-NORTHERN REGION,* 94 N School St, PO Box 398, 93517-0398. SAN 300-6344. Tel: 760-932-7482. FAX: 760-932-7539. Web Site: www.monocoe.k12.ca.us/library/lib0215.htm. *Librn*, Vineca Hess; E-Mail: vineca_hess@eee.org
Founded 1965. Pop 11,200; Circ 63,391
Library Holdings: Bk Vols 26,000; Per Subs 19
Subject Interests: Geology
Publications: Bibliographies
Mem of Mountain-Valley Library System
Open Tues 10-5:30, Wed 10-8, Thurs & Fri 10-5, Sat 10-2:30
Friends of the Library Group

GL MONO COUNTY LAW LIBRARY,* Courthouse, PO Box 617, 93517. SAN 320-555X. Tel: 760-932-5223. FAX: 760-932-5283. *In Charge*, Maureen Pollock
Pop 10,000
Library Holdings: Bk Vols 2,258
Restriction: Not a lending library

BRISBANE

S AIRCRAFT TECHNICAL PUBLISHERS LIBRARY, 101 S Hill Dr, 94005-1251. SAN 321-9089. Tel: 415-330-9500. Toll Free Tel: 800-227-4610. FAX: 415-468-1596.
Founded 1973
Library Holdings: Bk Titles 3,500
Subject Interests: Aviation maintenance
Publications: Library services & research tools for the aviation industry

BUENA PARK

P BUENA PARK LIBRARY DISTRICT, 7150 La Palma Ave, 90620-2547. SAN 300-6352. Tel: 714-826-4100. FAX: 714-826-5052. E-Mail: bplstaff@buenapark.lib.ca.us. Web Site: www.buenapark.lib.ca.us. *Dir*, Linda Katsouleas; *ILL, Ref*, Kathleen Wade; *Circ*, Mary McCasiand; Staff 12 (MLS 5, Non-MLS 7)
Founded 1919. Pop 77,300; Circ 390,790
Jul 1999-Jun 2000 Income (Main Library Only) $1,727,950. Mats Exp $1,366,380, Books $105,452, Per/Ser (Incl. Access Fees) $10,356, Electronic Ref Mat (Incl. Access Fees) $17,250. Sal $679,877
Library Holdings: Bk Vols 126,381; Bk Titles 106,160; Per Subs 405
Subject Interests: Asia, Spain
Automation Activity & Vendor Info: (Acquisitions) epixtech, inc.; (Cataloging) epixtech, inc.; (Circulation) epixtech, inc.; (OPAC) epixtech, inc.
Function: ILL available, Photocopies available, Reference services available
Mem of Santiago Libr Syst
Open Mon-Thurs 9-9, Fri & Sat 9-6
Friends of the Library Group

S SPEECH & LANGUAGE DEVELOPMENT CENTER LIBRARY,* 8699 Holder St, 90620. SAN 300-6360. Tel: 714-821-3620, Ext 35. FAX: 714-821-5683. *Librn*, Robert Tipton
Founded 1955. Enrl 60
Library Holdings: Bk Vols 12,000; Per Subs 10
Subject Interests: Speech and hearing
Restriction: Staff use only
Friends of the Library Group

BURBANK

P BURBANK PUBLIC LIBRARY, 110 N Glenoaks Blvd, 91502-1203. SAN 331-7161. Tel: 818-238-5600. Interlibrary Loan Service Tel: 818-238-5580. FAX: 818-238-5553. E-Mail: bplref@ix.netcom.com, refbpl@ci.burbank.ca.us. Web Site: www.ci.burbank.ca.us. *Ad Servs*, Dr Kay Bruce; Tel: 714-484-7302, E-Mail: kbruce@bypress.cc.ca.us; *Ad Servs*, Helen Wang; *ILL*, Liz Avery; *Ref*, Nancy Tidwell; *Ch Servs*, Ellen Tanner; *Circ, Tech Servs*, Sharon Cohen; Staff 29 (MLS 29)
Founded 1938. Pop 105,000; Circ 655,635
Jul 1998-Jun 1999 Income $3,798,713. Mats Exp $554,014, Books $226,269, Per/Ser (Incl. Access Fees) $41,935, Presv $277,744, Micro $8,066. Sal $2,915,242
Library Holdings: Bk Titles 365,804; Per Subs 474
Subject Interests: Television
Special Collections: Motion Picture & Television Production Research; Production & Script Research Files; Warner Research Coll (Special Research Division)
Automation Activity & Vendor Info: (Circulation) SIRSI
Mem of Metropolitan Cooperative Library System
Partic in OCLC Online Computer Library Center, Inc; Southern Calif Answering Network
Friends of the Library Group
Branches: 2
BUENA VISTA, 401 N Buena Vista, 91505-3208. SAN 331-7196. Tel: 818-238-5620. FAX: 818-238-5623. Web Site: burbank.acityline.com. *Librn*, John Coultas
Library Holdings: Bk Vols 68,000
NORTHWEST, 3323 W Victory Blvd, 91505-1543. SAN 331-7226. Tel: 818-238-5640. FAX: 818-238-5642. Web Site: burbank.acityline.com. *Librn*, Christine Rodriguez
Library Holdings: Bk Vols 43,608
Friends of the Library Group

S CRANE CO, Hydro-Aire Engineering Library,* 3000 Winona Ave, PO Box 7722, 91510. SAN 300-6395. Tel: 818-526-2693. FAX: 818-842-6117.
Founded 1955
Library Holdings: Bk Vols 1,750; Per Subs 50

S WALT DISNEY COMPANY, Walt Disney Archives, 500 S Buena Vista St, 91521-3040. SAN 300-6409. Tel: 818-560-5424. *Archivist*, David R Smith; Staff 8 (MLS 3, Non-MLS 5)
Founded 1970
Special Collections: annual reports; awards; biographies; personal memorabilia, recordings & transcripts of speeches, office furnishings; product samples; Walt Disney Coll
Publications: Brochure
Restriction: Company staff only
Function: Some telephone reference

M PROVIDENCE SAINT JOSEPH MEDICAL CENTER, Health Science Library, 501 S Buena Vista St, 91505-4866. SAN 300-6425. Tel: 818-238-2865. FAX: 818-238-2887. *Librn*, Lisa Marks; E-Mail: lmarks@phsca.org; Staff 2 (MLS 1, Non-MLS 1)
Founded 1943
Library Holdings: Bk Vols 7,314; Per Subs 514
Subject Interests: Nursing
Automation Activity & Vendor Info: (Cataloging) EOS; (Circulation) EOS; (Serials) EOS
Restriction: Circulates for staff only, In-house use for visitors
Partic in Medlars; Pacific SW Regional Med Libr Serv

S SOUTHERN CALIFORNIA GENEALOGICAL SOCIETY FAMILY RESEARCH LIBRARY, 417 Irving Dr, 91504-2408. SAN 324-5675. Tel: 818-843-7247. FAX: 818-843-7262. E-Mail: scgs@annex.com. Web Site: www.scgsgenealogy.com. *Pres*, Douglas J Miller; *Acq*, Sally Emerson; *Per*, Beverly Truesdale
Founded 1964
Library Holdings: Bk Vols 30,000; Bk Titles 20,000; Per Subs 1,200
Subject Interests: California, Fr Canadian, Genealogy, Hispanic, Periodicals
Special Collections: California; French-Canadian; Hispanic-America; Periodicals
Publications: The Searcher (bi-monthly journal)
Restriction: Open to public for reference only
Partic in Genealogical Alliance

S WARNER BROS STUDIOS, Research Library, 2777 N Ontario St, 91504. SAN 300-6964. Tel: 818-506-8693. FAX: 818-506-8079. *Dir*, Anne G Schlosser; Tel: 818-977-5050, Fax: 818-567-4366; Staff 3 (MLS 2, Non-MLS 1)
Founded 1928
Library Holdings: Bk Titles 65,000; Per Subs 92

Subject Interests: Art and architecture, Costume design, Transportation, World War II
Special Collections: Historical Location Picture/Photograph Coll
Partic in Metronet

C WOODBURY UNIVERSITY LIBRARY,* 7500 Glenoaks Blvd, PO Box 7846, 91510-7846. SAN 301-0236. Tel: 818-767-0888, Ext 206. FAX: 818-767-4534. Web Site: www.woodburyu.edu/library. *Dir*, Barbara Bowley; *Ref*, Mary Turtle; *Tech Servs*, Marti Pike; Staff 5 (MLS 5)
Founded 1884. Enrl 1,096; Fac 134; Highest Degree: Master
Library Holdings: Bk Vols 63,574; Per Subs 646
Subject Interests: Architecture, Fashion, Interior design
Special Collections: Masters Theses; Senior Papers
Partic in SCELC
Friends of the Library Group

BURLINGAME

P BURLINGAME PUBLIC LIBRARY, 480 Primrose Rd, 94010-4083. SAN 331-7315. Tel: 650-342-1038. Interlibrary Loan Service Tel: 650-342-9797. Circulation Tel: 650-342-1036. Reference Tel: 650-342-1037, Ext 135. FAX: 650-342-1948. Web Site: www.pls.lib.ca.us/pls/bpl/bpl.html. *Librn*, Alfred H Escoffier; E-Mail: escoffia@pls.lib.ca.us; *ILL*, Patti Flynn; *Ch Servs, YA Servs*, Joan Riordan Manini; Tel: 650-342-1283; *Ref*, Patricia Harding; Tel: 650-342-9797, Ext 110, E-Mail: hardingp@pls.lib.ca.us; *Cat, Tech Servs*, Vera Warrick; E-Mail: warrickv@pls.lib.ca.us; *Commun Servs*, Susan Reiterman; E-Mail: reiterma@pls.lib.ca.us; *Br Coordr*, Lisa Dunseth; E-Mail: dunsetul@pls.lib.ca.us; *AV*, Linda Santo; *Per*, Dorothy Ezquerro; Staff 11 (MLS 11)
Founded 1909. Pop 35,880; Circ 400,346
Jul 2000-Jun 2001 Mats Exp $283,350, Books $243,350, Per/Ser (Incl. Access Fees) $40,000. Sal $1,981,475
Library Holdings: Bk Vols 221,835; Bk Titles 210,685; Per Subs 433
Database Vendor: epixtech, inc.
Mem of Peninsula Library System
Friends of the Library Group
Branches: 1
EASTON DRIVE, 1800 Easton Drive, 94010. Tel: 650-343-1794. Web Site: www.pls.lib.ca.us/pls/bpl/bpl.html. *Librn*, Lisa Dunseth
Library Holdings: Bk Vols 30,000; Bk Titles 25,000
Friends of the Library Group

S CENTER FOR LIBERTARIAN STUDIES LIBRARY,* 851 Burlway Rd Ste 202, 94010. SAN 376-0855. Tel: 650-692-8456. FAX: www.libertarianstudies.org. *Pres*, Burton Blumert
Library Holdings: Bk Vols 5,000
Publications: Journal of Libertarian Studies
Non-profit, academic organization

S COEN COMPANY, INC, Technical Library,* 1510 Rollins Rd, 94010-2306. SAN 375-6890. Tel: 650-697-0440. FAX: 650-686-5655.
Library Holdings: Bk Titles 400; Per Subs 15

M MILLS-PENINSULA HEALTH SERVICES LIBRARY,* 1783 El Camino Real, 94010, SAN 300-6433. Interlibrary Loan Service Tel: 650-696-5621. FAX: 650-696-5484. *Librn*, Debbie Martin
Library Holdings: Bk Vols 5,000; Per Subs 328
Subject Interests: Medicine, Nursing
Partic in Nat Libr of Med

S TECHNICAL INSTRUMENT CO,* 1826 Rollins Rd, 94010-2200. SAN 328-2821. Tel: 415-431-8231. FAX: 415-431-6491. *Tech Servs*, F E Lundy
Library Holdings: Bk Titles 500

CALABASAS

§P CALABASAS PUBLIC LIBRARY, 26135 Mureau Rd, Ste 100, 91302. Tel: 818-878-9585. FAX: 818-878-9784. *Librn*, Barbara Lockwood; E-Mail: barbaral@lssi.com; *Circ*, Jemima Perry
Library Holdings: Bk Vols 18,000; Bk Titles 17,500
Automation Activity & Vendor Info: (Acquisitions) Follett; (Cataloging) Follett; (Circulation) Follett; (ILL) Follett; (OPAC) Follett; (Serials) Follett
Mem of Metropolitan Cooperative Library System
Open Tues-Thurs 10-9, Fri & Sat 10-5, Sun 12-5
Friends of the Library Group

CALEXICO

P CAMARENA MEMORIAL LIBRARY, 850 Encinas Ave, 92231. SAN 300-6441. Tel: 760-768-2170. FAX: 760-357-0404. Web Site: www.calexico.k12.ca.us/cml/. *Dir*, Sandra Tauler; Staff 6 (MLS 2, Non-MLS 4)
Founded 1919. Pop 26,150
Jul 1998-Jun 1999 Income $449,188, State $34,000, City $415,188. Mats Exp $74,050, Books $62,000, Per/Ser (Incl. Access Fees) $12,000, Micro $50. Sal $245,938 (Prof $95,000)
Library Holdings: Bk Vols 60,000; Bk Titles 55,000; Per Subs 90; High Interest/Low Vocabulary Bk Vols 150
Special Collections: History of Imperial Valley
Mem of Serra Cooperative Library System
Friends of the Library Group
Branches: 1

C SAN DIEGO STATE UNIVERSITY, Imperial Valley Campus Library, 720 Heber Ave, 92231-0550. SAN 331-7374. Tel: 760-768-5585. FAX: 760-768-5525. E-Mail: interll@mail.sdsu.edu. Web Site: www.lib.sdsu.edu. *Dir*, Frank Bruno; E-Mail: bruno@mail.sdsu.edu; *Librn*, Cathy Zazuzta; *Circ*, Karina Ramirez; *ILL*, Lupita Lopez; *Media Spec, Ref*, Patrick Hall; Staff 6 (MLS 6)
Founded 1959. Highest Degree: Master
Library Holdings: Bk Vols 107,000; Bk Titles 50,000; Per Subs 290
Subject Interests: Bilingual Education, Criminal law and justice, Education, International, Psychology, Social service (social work)
Special Collections: Border Coll
Automation Activity & Vendor Info: (Cataloging) Innovative Interfaces Inc.; (Circulation) Innovative Interfaces Inc.
Database Vendor: Innovative Interfaces INN - View
Partic in Bestnet; OCLC Online Computer Library Center, Inc; San Diego Greater Metro Area Libr & Info Agency Coun; Serra Cooperative Library System

CAMARILLO

G CALIFORNIA YOUTH AUTHORITY, CYA Ventura Youth Correctional Facility Library, 3100 Wright Rd, 93010-8307. SAN 322-8681. Tel: 805-485-7951. FAX: 805-485-2801. *In Charge*, Claudia Deardorff
Founded 1962. Enrl 950; Fac 42
1998-1999 Income $1,100. Mats Exp Per/Ser (Incl. Access Fees) $1,100
Library Holdings: Bk Titles 12,500; Per Subs 85
Subject Interests: Law, Sociology
Special Collections: Law Coll

S ENSR, CORP LIBRARY, 1220 Avenida Acaso, 93012. SAN 329-3068. Tel: 805-388-3775, Ext 230. FAX: 805-388-3577. Web Site: www.ensr.com. *Librn*, Elaine Houston
Founded 1977
Library Holdings: Bk Vols 319; Bk Titles 300; Per Subs 60
Subject Interests: Air pollution, Environ chem, Environ impact
Restriction: Staff use only

R SAINT JOHN'S SEMINARY, Edward Laurence Doheny Memorial Library, 5012 Seminary Rd, 93012-2598. SAN 331-7463. Tel: 805-482-2755, Ext 1081. FAX: 805-987-0885. *Dir*, Pat Basu; *Coll Develop, Librn*, Alyson Kaye; Staff 3 (MLS 2, Non-MLS 1)
Founded 1940. Enrl 88; Fac 22; Highest Degree: Master
Library Holdings: Bk Vols 35,637; Per Subs 339
Subject Interests: Biblical studies, Church history, Theology
Partic in American Theological Library Association; OCLC Online Computer Library Center, Inc; Total Interlibrary Exchange
Branches:
CARRIE ESTELLE DOHENY MEMORIAL LIBRARY, 5118 Seminary Rd, 93012. SAN 331-7498. Tel: 805-482-2755, Ext 2043. FAX: 805-987-5097. *Dir*, Pat Basu; *Librn*, Rita Mann
Founded 1962. Enrl 61 Mats Exp Presv $550
Library Holdings: Bk Vols 64,590; Per Subs 198
Subject Interests: Humanities, Philosophy
Partic in OCLC Online Computer Library Center, Inc; Total Interlibrary Exchange

CAMP PENDLETON

UNITED STATES MARINE CORPS

A SEASIDE SQUARE LIBRARY, San Onofre, Bldg 51093, 92055. Tel: 760-725-7325. FAX: 760-725-7325. *Tech Servs*, Geraldine Hagen
Library Holdings: Bk Vols 10,124; Per Subs 70

UNITED STATES NAVY

A CREW'S LIBRARY, Naval Hospital, Box 555191, 92055-5191. SAN 331-7587. Tel: 760-725-1229. FAX: 760-725-1229. E-Mail: pen1kdt@pen10.med.navy.mil. *Librn*, Kathleen Dunning-Torbett
Library Holdings: Bk Vols 10,000; Per Subs 87
Restriction: Not open to public

A MARINE CORPS BASE BRIG, PO Box 555226, 92055. Tel: 760-725-8144. FAX: 760-725-8564. *Dir*, Patrick J Carney
Library Holdings: Bk Vols 3,703; Per Subs 45

AM MEDICAL LIBRARY, Naval Hospital, PO Box 555191, 92055-5191. SAN 331-7617. Tel: 760-725-1322. FAX: 760-725-1116. Web Site: 159.71.170.42/nhcp/library.htm. *Head of Libr*, Kathy Susan Parker; E-Mail: ksparker@cpen.med.navy.mil; Staff 2 (MLS 1, Non-MLS 1)
Founded 1947
Oct 1999-Sep 2000 Income $174,416. Mats Exp $90,200, Books $12,000, Per/Ser (Incl. Access Fees) $44,000, Presv $1,500, Other Print Mats $2,500, Electronic Ref Mat (Incl. Access Fees) $12,000. Sal $84,216 (Prof

$56,800)
Library Holdings: Bk Titles 1,800; Per Subs 202
Subject Interests: Dentistry, Nursing
Automation Activity & Vendor Info: (Cataloging) epixtech, inc.
Database Vendor: Dialog, Ebsco - EbscoHost, IAC - Info Trac, Lexis-Nexis, OVID Technologies, Silverplatter Information Inc.
Publications: Newsletter
Partic in Consortium of Navy Librs; Docline; Fed Libr & Info Network; MLA; National Network Of Libraries Of Medicine - South Central Region; OCLC Online Computer Library Center, Inc; Pacific SW Regional Med Libr Serv; PSRMLS

A MOBILE LIBRARY, Bldg 1122, E St, 92055-5005. Tel: 760-725-5104, 760-725-5973. FAX: 760-725-6177. *Dir*, Patrick J Carney
Library Holdings: Bk Vols 8,400; Bk Titles 8,000

A SOUTH MESA LIBRARY, Bldg 200090, Oceanside, 92054. Tel: 760-725-2032. FAX: 760-725-6177. *Librn*, Aurora M Ulatan
Library Holdings: Bk Vols 23,000; Per Subs 72

A UNITED STATES MARINE CORPS LIBRARY SERVICES, Bldg 1122, PO Box 555005, 92055-5005. SAN 331-7528. Tel: 760-725-5104. FAX: 760-725-6177. *Dir*, Patrick J Carney; *Asst Librn*, Ariel Gasper; Staff 19 (MLS 4, Non-MLS 15)
Founded 1950
Library Holdings: Bk Vols 167,272; Bk Titles 122,805; Per Subs 425
Subject Interests: Military history
Partic in San Diego Greater Metro Area Libr & Info Agency Coun

CAMPBELL

C JOHN F KENNEDY UNIVERSITY, Campbell Campus Library, One W Campbell Ave, Bldg A, No 1, 95008. SAN 370-1123. Tel: 408-874-7750. FAX: 408-874-7777. Web Site: library.jfku.edu. *Dir*, Denyse Gantenbein; Staff 2 (MLS 1, Non-MLS 1)
Jul 1999-Jun 2000 Income Parent Institution $127,735. Mats Exp $54,444, Books $22,047, Per/Ser (Incl. Access Fees) $30,119, Electronic Ref Mat (Incl. Access Fees) $2,278
Library Holdings: Bk Vols 8,110; Bk Titles 7,096; Per Subs 131
Subject Interests: Psychology
Automation Activity & Vendor Info: (Acquisitions) Innovative Interfaces Inc.; (Cataloging) Innovative Interfaces Inc.; (Circulation) Innovative Interfaces Inc.; (Course Reserve) Innovative Interfaces Inc.; (ILL) Innovative Interfaces Inc.; (OPAC) Innovative Interfaces Inc.; (Serials) Innovative Interfaces Inc.
Database Vendor: Silverplatter Information Inc.
Open Mon-Thurs 12-8, Fri 12-4, Sat 10-3

CARLSBAD

P CARLSBAD CITY LIBRARY,* 1775 Dove Lane, 92009-4048. SAN 300-6492. Tel: 760-602-2011. FAX: 760-602-7942. Web Site: www.ci.carlsbad.ca.us. *Dir*, Clifford E Lange; Tel: 760-602-2010; *Asst Dir*, Geoff Armour; *Ch Servs*, John Quartarone; *Media Spec*, Bill Richmond; *Cat, Tech Servs*, Chris Pickavet; *Ref Serv Ad*, Mary Van Orsdol; Tel: 760-602-2038; *Acq, Coll Develop*, Susan Simpson; *ILL*, Leila Dooley; *Ref*, Charlene Kennedy; Staff 30 (MLS 16, Non-MLS 14)
Founded 1956. Pop 70,000
Jul 1997-Jun 1998 Income $3,280,860, State $256,000, City $2,735,003, Federal $5,000, Locally Generated Income $284,857. Mats Exp $424,000, Books $218,371, Presv $15,181, Micro $32,266, Other Print Mats $158,182. Sal $1,747,953
Library Holdings: Bk Vols 234,302; Per Subs 649
Subject Interests: Genealogy, Local history
Automation Activity & Vendor Info: (Circulation) Inlex
Publications: Carlsbad: A Village by the Sea; Carlsbad: An Unabashed History of the Village by the Sea; Seekers of the Spring: A History of Carlsbad
Mem of Serra Cooperative Library System
Partic in Dialog Corporation; OCLC Online Computer Library Center, Inc
Special Services for the Deaf - Captioned film depository; TDD
Special Services for the Blind - Vantage closed circuit TV magnifier
Friends of the Library Group
Branches: 2
CENTRO DE INFORMACION, 3333 Harding St, Rm 11, 92008. SAN 375-5428. Tel: 760-729-6907. *Librn*, Lizeth Simonson
GEORGINA COLE LIBRARY, 1250 Carlsbad Village Dr, 92009-1991. SAN 322-5550. Tel: 760-434-2870. FAX: 760-434-9975. *Librn*, Christine Holt
Friends of the Library Group
Bookmobiles: 1

S GEMOLOGICAL INSTITUTE OF AMERICA, Richard T Liddicoat Gemological Library & Information Center, 5345 Armada Dr, 92008. SAN 301-5866. Tel: 760-603-4000, Ext 4068. Reference Tel: 760-603-4046. Toll Free Tel: 800-421-7250. FAX: 760-603-4256. E-Mail: library@gia.edu. Web Site: www.gia.edu/education/library.cfm. *Dir*, Dona Mary Dirlam; Tel: 760-603-4154, E-Mail: ddirlam@gia.edu; *Mgr*, Glenn Meyer; Tel: 760-603-4174, E-Mail: glenn.meyer@gia.edu; *Senior Librn*, Rosemary Tozer; Tel: 760-603-4016, E-Mail: rtozer@gia.edu. Subject Specialists: *Visual*, Judy Colbert; Staff 11 (MLS 1, Non-MLS 10)
Founded 1931
Library Holdings: Bk Titles 20,000; Per Subs 380
Subject Interests: Jewelry, Mineralogy
Special Collections: Auction Catalog Coll; Clifford Awald Coll; John & Marjorie Jane Sinkankas Mineralogy & Gemology Coll
Automation Activity & Vendor Info: (Cataloging) EOS; (OPAC) EOS; (Serials) EOS
Database Vendor: OCLC - First Search
Publications: Gems & Gemology (partial abstracts & articles)
Restriction: Students only
Partic in OCLC Online Computer Library Center, Inc
Open Mon-Fri 7:30-5

CARMEL

P HARRISON MEMORIAL LIBRARY,* Ocean & Lincoln, PO Box 800, 93921. SAN 300-6514. Tel: 831-624-4629. FAX: 831-624-0407. Web Site: www.hm-lib.org. *Dir*, Margaret Pelikan
Founded 1906. Pop 14,864; Circ 125,550
Jul 1998-Jun 1999 Income $846,667, State $27,921, City $576,092, Locally Generated Income $24,109, Other $218,545. Mats Exp $143,408, Books $97,673, Per/Ser (Incl. Access Fees) $9,850, Micro $5,871. Sal $576,092 (Prof $425,866)
Library Holdings: Bk Vols 76,004
Special Collections: Carmel History Coll (photogs); Edward Weston Photographs; Robinson Jeffers
Mem of Monterey Bay Area Cooperative Library System
Special Services for the Deaf - TTY machine
Friends of the Library Group
Branches: 1
PARK, Mission & Sixth St, 93921-0800. SAN 377-8657. Tel: 831-624-4629. FAX: 831-624-0407. Web Site: www.hm-lib.org. *Librn*, Kennon Bowen; *Librn*, Susan Jones
Library Holdings: Bk Vols 20,000

CARMICHAEL

M MERCY HEALTH CARE SACRAMENTO, Regional Library,* 6501 Coyle Ave, 95608. SAN 300-6530. Tel: 916-537-5218. FAX: 916-537-5399. E-Mail: mhslibrary@chw.edu. *Librn*, Catherine Hanson-Tracy; E-Mail: chanson-tracy@chw.edu; Staff 2 (MLS 1, Non-MLS 1)
Founded 1965
Library Holdings: Bk Vols 1,300; Bk Titles 1,100; Per Subs 140
Subject Interests: Medicine
Database Vendor: Dialog, IAC - Info Trac
Partic in Dialog Corporation; Pacific SW Regional Med Libr Serv

CARSON

C CALIFORNIA STATE UNIVERSITY DOMINGUEZ HILLS, Educational Resources Center,* 1000 E Victoria St, 90747. SAN 300-6549. Tel: 310-243-3700. FAX: 310-516-4219. E-Mail: dhvx2o@csudh.edu. Web Site: www.csudh.edu/library/ulib/lib.htm/library.csudh.edu. *Librn*, Sandra Parham; *Ref*, Gail Cook; *Cat*, Cecilia Chen; *Bibliog Instr*, Jim Hunt; *Coll Develop*, John Calhoun; Staff 16 (MLS 16)
Founded 1963. Fac 782; Highest Degree: Master
1997-1998 Income $2,636,069. Mats Exp $544,391, Books $214,570, Per/Ser (Incl. Access Fees) $265,501, Presv $6,023, Micro $58,297. Sal $1,774,552 (Prof $914,387)
Library Holdings: Bk Vols 435,627; Per Subs 2,200
Special Collections: American Best Sellers (Claudia Buckner Coll); Archives of California State Univ Syst
Automation Activity & Vendor Info: (Acquisitions) GEAC; (Cataloging) GEAC; (Circulation) GEAC
Partic in OCLC Online Computer Library Center, Inc
Friends of the Library Group

CARUTHERS

P FRESNO COUNTY PUBLIC LIBRARY, Caruthers Neighborhood Library, 13357 S Henderson, PO Box 95, 93609. SAN 377-3361. Tel: 559-864-8766. Web Site: www.sjvls.lib.ca.us/fresno. *Librn*, Tammie Wenter
Library Holdings: Bk Vols 8,294; Bk Titles 8,048
Open Mon 10:30-3:30 & Tues & Thurs 1:30-6:30
Friends of the Library Group

CERRITOS

P CITY OF CERRITOS PUBLIC LIBRARY,* 18025 Bloomfield Ave, 90703. SAN 300-6611. Tel: 562-916-1350. FAX: 562-916-1375. E-Mail: library@ci.cerritos.ca.us. Web Site: library.ci.cerritos.ca.us. *Dir*, Waynn Pearson; *Ch Servs*, Hedy Harrison; *Tech Servs*, John Batjiaka; *Ref*, Padmini Prabakar; Staff 8 (MLS 8)

Founded 1973. Pop 53,800; Circ 701,232
Jul 1997-Jun 1998 Income $2,316,793, State $45,203, City $2,271,590. Mats Exp $364,343, Books $257,766, Per/Ser (Incl. Access Fees) $17,816, Presv $12,947, Micro $6,162. Sal $1,701,278
Library Holdings: Bk Titles 152,859; Per Subs 304
Special Collections: First Ladies' Coll; Performing Arts
Automation Activity & Vendor Info: (Circulation) Bestseller
Mem of Metropolitan Cooperative Library System
Partic in OCLC Online Computer Library Center, Inc
Friends of the Library Group

CHATSWORTH

P CHATSWORTH HISTORICAL SOCIETY, Frank H Schepler Jr Memorial Library, 10385 Shadow Oak Dr, 91311. SAN 371-2435. Tel: 818-882-5614. *Curator*, Virginia Watson
Library Holdings: Bk Titles 200
Subject Interests: Geography, Local authors
Special Collections: Photographs of San Fernando Valley History; Slide Coll

S GRINBERG FILM LIBRARIES, INC, 21011 Itasca St, Unit D, 91311. SAN 373-3432. Tel: 818-709-2450. FAX: 818-709-8450. Web Site: www.grinberg.com. *Mgr*, Bill Brewington

CHERRY VALLEY

S RIVERSIDE COUNTY MUSEUM DEPARTMENT, Edward-Dean Museum,* 9401 Oak Glen Rd, 92223. SAN 300-6638. Tel: 909-845-2626. *Dir*, Richard Doluttle
Founded 1958
Library Holdings: Bk Vols 1,200; Per Subs 10
Special Collections: 17th-19th Century Decorative Arts; Ceramics; Furniture; Glass; Paintings; Sculpture; Textiles; Works on Paper

CHESTER

P PLUMAS COUNTY LIBRARY, Chester Branch, 210 First Ave, 96020-0429. (Mail add: PO Box 429, 96020-0429), SAN 377-8142. Tel: 530-258-2742. FAX: 530-258-3725. E-Mail: pclibc@thegrid.net. Web Site: www.psln.com/pclibq. *Asst Librn*, Elise Tuma
Library Holdings: Bk Vols 9,000; Per Subs 32
Automation Activity & Vendor Info: (OPAC) TLC
Friends of the Library Group

CHICO

C CALIFORNIA STATE UNIVERSITY, CHICO, Meriam Library, 400 W First St, 95929-0295. SAN 300-6646. Tel: 530-898-5862. Interlibrary Loan Service Tel: 530-898-6881. FAX: 530-898-4443. Web Site: www.csuchico.edu.library. *Info Res*, Frederick Ryan; *Dir*, Carolyn Dusenbury; E-Mail: cdusenbury@csuchico.edu; *Coordr*, Sarah Blakeslee; *Access Serv*, Joseph Crotts; *Spec Coll*, William Jones; *Coll Develop, Tech Servs*, Julie Rankin; *Ref*, Barbara Pease; *Coll Develop*, James Dwyer; Staff 16 (MLS 16)
Founded 1887. Enrl 13,434; Fac 632; Highest Degree: Master
Library Holdings: Bk Vols 909,961; Per Subs 674,762
Special Collections: Calif & Rand Corp; Northeast California Coll, print & photog
Mem of North State Cooperative Library System
Friends of the Library Group

CHINA LAKE

UNITED STATES NAVY
A NAVAL AIR WARFARE STATION, 861000D, 93555-6001. SAN 331-7706. Tel: 760-939-2595. FAX: 760-927-0825. *Head of Libr*, Elsa Pendleton; Staff 3 (MLS 1, Non-MLS 2)
Founded 1945
Oct 1996-Sep 1997 Income $150,000. Mats Exp $50,000. Sal $100,000
Library Holdings: Bk Titles 40,000; Per Subs 116
Special Collections: Military Aviation Coll
A TECHNICAL LIBRARY, Naval Air Warfare Ctr, Weapons Division, 93555-6001. (Mail add: Bldg 02327, Code 4TL000D, NAWCWD, One Admin Circle, 93555-6100), Tel: 760-939-3389. Interlibrary Loan Service Tel: 760-939-4668. Reference Tel: 760-939-1017. FAX: 760-939-2431. Web Site: www.chinalake.navy.mil/~teclib. *Dir*, Sandy Bradley; *Coll Develop*, Craig Pelz; Staff 15 (MLS 3, Non-MLS 12)
Founded 1946
1998-1999 Income $1,500,000. Mats Exp $525,000, Books $75,000, Per/Ser (Incl. Access Fees) $450,000. Sal $600,000
Library Holdings: Bk Titles 30,500; Per Subs 300
Subject Interests: Aerospace, Chemistry, Computer science, Electronics, Engineering, Mathematics, Naval sci, Optics, Physics, Weapons
Automation Activity & Vendor Info: (Cataloging) SIRSI
Database Vendor: Dialog, ProQuest, Silverplatter Information Inc.
Publications: Bibliographies (various); new books list; periodicals book; User Manual
Partic in Consortium of Navy Librs; Coop Libr Agency for Syst & Servs; Fedlink; RLIN

CHINO

§S CALIFORNIA YOUTH AUTHORITY, Herman G Stark Youth Correctional Facility Library, 15180 Euclid Ave, 91710. Tel: 909-606-5000, Ext 2331. FAX: 909-606-5053. *Librn*, Rose Lepley
Library Holdings: Bk Vols 10,000; Per Subs 12

CHULA VISTA

S AMERICAN SCIENTIFIC CORP LIBRARY, 3250 Holly Way, 91910-3217. SAN 328-1388. Tel: 619-422-1754. FAX: 619-426-1280. Web Site: www.americanscientific.com. *Librn*, S Gerken; *Asst Librn*, C Gerken; E-Mail: gerkenlc@cs.com; *Tech Servs*, V Brault
Founded 1980
Library Holdings: Bk Titles 500; Per Subs 10
Subject Interests: World War II

P CHULA VISTA PUBLIC LIBRARY, 365 F St, 91910-2697. SAN 300-6662. Tel: 619-691-5168. Interlibrary Loan Service Tel: 619-476-5312. FAX: 619-427-4246. Web Site: www.chulavista.lib.ca.us. *Dir*, David Palmer; Tel: 619-691-5179, E-Mail: davidp@libris.chulavista.lib.ca.us; *Asst Dir*, Paula Brown; Tel: 619-691-5068, E-Mail: pbrown@libris.chulavista.lib.ca.us; *Tech Servs*, Margaret Blue; *Tech Servs*, John Corbett; Tel: 619-691-5138, E-Mail: jcorbett@chulavista.lib.ca.us; *Ch Servs*, Susie Ward; *Ref*, Eric Rhee; *Coll Develop*, Stephanie Loney; Staff 102 (MLS 24, Non-MLS 78)
Founded 1891. Pop 166,900; Circ 1,246,433
Jul 1998-Jun 1999 Mats Exp $4,331,880. Sal $3,194,761
Library Holdings: Bk Vols 467,132; Per Subs 898
Subject Interests: Local history
Database Vendor: Ebsco - EbscoHost, GaleNet, Innovative Interfaces INN - View
Publications: Library Brochure
Mem of Serra Cooperative Library System
Partic in OCLC Online Computer Library Center, Inc
Special Services for the Disabled - Library materials delivered to homebound; Special Services for Spanish Speaking Patrons - Materials collection, storytimes in Spanish & bi-lingual staff
Friends of the Library Group
Branches: 4
CIVIC CENTER-MAIN LIBRARY, 365 F St, 91910. SAN 370-2839. Tel: 619-691-5161. Circulation Tel: 619-691-5064. Reference Tel: 619-691-5715. FAX: 619-427-4246. *Asst Dir*, Paula Brown; Tel: 619-691-5068, E-Mail: pbrown@chulavista.lib.ca.us
Library Holdings: Bk Vols 240,480
Friends of the Library Group
EASTLAKE, 1120 Eastlake Pkwy, 91915-2102. SAN 373-8728. Tel: 619-656-0314. *Branch Mgr*, Eric Rhee; Tel: 619-656-0486, E-Mail: erhee@chulavista.lib.ca.us
Founded 1993
Library Holdings: Bk Vols 41,225
Friends of the Library Group
LITERACY TEAM, 389 Orange Ave, 91911-4116. SAN 376-2157. Tel: 619-585-5757. FAX: 619-420-1328. *Mgr*, Patrice O'Halloran; E-Mail: pohallor@chulavista.lib.ca.us; *Asst Dir*, Paula Brown; Tel: 619-691-5068, Fax: 619-427-4246, E-Mail: pbrown@libris.chulavista.lib.ca.us
1999-1999 Mats Exp $126,417. Sal $117,657
SOUTH CHULA VISTA, 389 Orange Ave, 91911-4116. SAN 370-2952. Tel: 619-585-5750. FAX: 619-420-1591. *Branch Mgr*, Maureen Roeber; E-Mail: mroeber@chulavista.lib.ca.us; *Asst Dir*, Paula Brown; Tel: 619-691-5068, Fax: 619-427-4246, E-Mail: pbrown@chulavista.lib.ca.us
Pop 21,000; Circ 140,000
Library Holdings: Bk Vols 168,231
Friends of the Library Group

J SOUTHWESTERN COLLEGE LIBRARY, 900 Otay Lakes Rd, 91910-7299. SAN 300-6689. Tel: 619-482-6373. TDD: 619-482-6490. FAX: 619-482-6417. Web Site: www.swc.cc.ca.us/~library/. *Dean*, Dr John Newhouse; Tel: 619-482-6347, E-Mail: jnewhouse@swc.cc.ca.us; *Chair*, Karen Smith; Tel: 619-482-6430, E-Mail: ksmith@swc.cc.ca.us; *Tech Servs*, Ron Vess; Tel: 619-482-6431, E-Mail: rvess@swc.cc.ca.us; *Online Servs*, Anthony McGee; Tel: 619-482-6474, E-Mail: tmcgee@swc.cc.ca.us; *Br Coordr*, Diane Gustafson; Tel: 619-482-6433, E-Mail: dgustafson@swc.cc.ca.us; Staff 9 (MLS 4, Non-MLS 5)
Founded 1961. Enrl 17,456; Fac 832; Highest Degree: Associate
Jul 1999-Jun 2000 Income State $860,391. Mats Exp $135,451, Books $75,442, Per/Ser (Incl. Access Fees) $27,495, Presv $1,488, Micro $13,328, Other Print Mats $200, Electronic Ref Mat (Incl. Access Fees) $17,498. Sal $677,980 (Prof $445,021)
Library Holdings: Bk Vols 84,833; Bk Titles 78,499; Per Subs 434; High Interest/Low Vocabulary Bk Vols 558
Automation Activity & Vendor Info: (Cataloging) epixtech, inc.;

(Circulation) epixtech, inc.
Database Vendor: Ebsco - EbscoHost, epixtech, inc., IAC - Info Trac, OCLC - First Search, ProQuest
Publications: (Newsletter); Academic Information Services, "Resources for Learning"
Partic in OCLC Online Computer Library Center, Inc
Friends of the Library Group

CITY OF INDUSTRY

S INDUSTRY HILLS SHERATON RESORT, Ralph W Miller Golf Library & Museum,* One Industry Hills Pkwy, 91744. SAN 320-1538. Tel: 626-854-2354. FAX: 626-854-2425. E-Mail: golflore@earthlink.net. *Librn*, Saundra Sheffer; *Mgr*, Marge Dewey
Founded 1976
Library Holdings: Bk Titles 5,000; Per Subs 25
Subject Interests: Scotland
Special Collections: Golf art, photogs, sports bks; golf articles from non-golf magazines; museum articles-golf (postcards, clubs & balls); tournament programs; Videotapes

S WORKMAN & TEMPLE FAMILY HOMESTEAD MUSEUM LIBRARY,* 15415 E Don Julian Rd, 91745-1029. SAN 374-793X. Tel: 626-968-8492. FAX: 626-968-2048. E-Mail: library@homesteadmuseum.org. Web Site: www.homesteadmuseum.org.
1997-1998 Income $3,500. Mats Exp $1,500, Books $1,000, Per/Ser (Incl. Access Fees) $500
Library Holdings: Bk Vols 1,000; Per Subs 45
Subject Interests: Architecture, Decorative arts, Interior design

CLAREMONT

C CLAREMONT COLLEGES LIBRARIES,* 800 Dartmouth Ave, 91711. SAN 331-7765. Tel: 909-621-8045. Interlibrary Loan Service FAX: 909-621-8629. Web Site: voxlibris.claremont.edu. *Circ, ILL*, Dr Kay Bruce; *Dir*, Bonnie J Clemens; *Assoc Dir*, Alberta C Walker; *Asst Dir, Spec Coll*, Judy H Sahak; *Ref*, Cindy Snyder; *Acq*, Linda Osborn; *Cat*, Judy Moser; *Coll Develop*, Meg Garrett. Subject Specialists: *Asia*, Isamu Miura; *Government publications*, Mary Martin
Founded 1952. Enrl 5,633; Fac 698; Highest Degree: Doctorate
Jul 1996-Jun 1997 Mats Exp $1,225,258, Books $406,660, Per/Ser (Incl. Access Fees) $727,267, Presv $61,239, Micro $30,092. Sal $2,156,012 (Prof $1,373,416)
Library Holdings: Bk Vols 1,971,686; Per Subs 5,967
Subject Interests: Art, Business and management, Economics, Education, Environmental studies, History, Law, Literature, Music, Natural science, Religion, Social sciences and issues, Technology, Women's studies
Special Collections: Cartography of the Pacific Coast; Claremont Colleges Archives; Honnold Library: Calif & Western Americana; Irving Wallace; Northern Europe & Scandinavia; Oxford & its Colleges; Philbrick Library of Dramatic Arts; Renaissance; Water Resources of Southern Calif, bk, mss
Automation Activity & Vendor Info: (Acquisitions) Innovative Interfaces Inc.; (Cataloging) Innovative Interfaces Inc.; (Circulation) Innovative Interfaces Inc.; (Serials) Innovative Interfaces Inc.
Publications: Faculty & staff newsletters
Partic in Colorado Alliance Of Research Libraries; OCLC Online Computer Library Center, Inc; RLIN
This library system, jointly supported by Claremont Graduate University, Pomona College, Scripps College, Claremont Mckenna College, Harvey Mudd College & Pitzer College, comprises the Honnold/Mudd Library Complex, The Denison Library, Sprague Library & The Seeley G Mudd Science Library
Departmental Libraries:
ELLA STRONG DENISON LIBRARY, Scripps College Campus, 1030 Columbia Ave, 91711. SAN 331-779X. Tel: 909-607-3941. FAX: 909-621-8283. *Librn*, Judy Harvey Sahak; E-Mail: jharveysahak@rocky.claremont.edu
Library Holdings: Bk Vols 104,106
Subject Interests: Art and architecture, Humanities, Women's studies
Special Collections: Bookplates; Ellen Browning Scripps; Gertrude Stein Coll; History of Book & Book Arts; Latin America Coll; Macpherson Collection on Women; Melville Coll; Robert & Elizabeth Browning Coll; Southwest Coll
NORMAN F SPRAGUE MEMORIAL LIBRARY, 301 E 12th St, 91711-5990. SAN 331-782X. Tel: 909-621-8920. FAX: 909-621-8681. *Librn*, Brian Ebersole
Subject Interests: Engineering, Natural science, Technology
Special Collections: Carruthers Aviation Coll; Herbert Hoover Collection on the History of Science & Metallic Arts
SEELEY G MUDD SCIENCE LIBRARY, 640 N College Ave, 91711-6345. SAN 331-7854. Tel: 909-621-8924. *Librn*, Brian Ebersole
Library Holdings: Bk Vols 99,740
Subject Interests: Astronomy, Botany, Chemistry, Geology, Mathematics, Physics, Zoology
Special Collections: A O Woodford Geology Library

S CLAREMONT GRADUATE UNIVERSITY, George G Stone Center for Children's Books, 131 E Tenth St, 91711-6188. SAN 300-6743. Tel: 909-607-3670. *Dir*, Doty Hale; *Assoc Dir*, Carolyn Angus; Tel: 909-607-1186, E-Mail: carolyn.angus@cgu.edu
Library Holdings: Bk Titles 35,000
Subject Interests: Children's literature, Education
Publications: Gifts to Open Again & Again (annual booklist)
Friends of the Library Group

CR CLAREMONT SCHOOL OF THEOLOGY LIBRARY,* 1325 N College Ave, 91711-3199. SAN 300-676X. Tel: 909-626-3521, Ext 1-286. FAX: 909-626-7062. Web Site: www.cst.edu/library/libhome.htm. *Dir*, Michael P Boddy; Tel: 909-626-3521, Ext 1-263; *Cat*, Eugene Fieg; *Bibliog Instr, Ref*, Betty Clements; Tel: 909-626-3521, Ext 1-270; Staff 7 (MLS 4, Non-MLS 3)
Founded 1957. Enrl 395; Fac 33; Highest Degree: Doctorate
Library Holdings: Bk Vols 175,000; Per Subs 600
Subject Interests: Biblical studies
Special Collections: James C Baker Manuscripts; Kirby Page Manuscripts; Robert H Mitchell Hymnology Coll
Partic in OCLC Online Computer Library Center, Inc
Departmental Libraries:
CENTER FOR PROCESS STUDIES Tel: 909-621-5330, 909-626-3521, Ext 224. FAX: 909-621-2760. E-Mail: process@ctr4process.org. *Librn*, John Quiring
Library Holdings: Bk Vols 1,400
Subject Interests: Philosophy, Theology
Special Collections: Charles Hartshorn Archive
Publications: Process Studies

S RANCHO SANTA ANA BOTANIC GARDEN LIBRARY, 1500 N College Ave, 91711. SAN 300-6751. Tel: 909-625-8767, Ext 236. FAX: 909-626-7670. Web Site: www.cgu.edu/inst/rsa. *Librn*, Beatrice M Beck; E-Mail: bea.beck@cgu.edu
Founded 1927
Library Holdings: Bk Vols 42,000
Subject Interests: Biology, Botany, Evolution, Horticulture
Special Collections: Californiana; Marcus E Jones Archival materials
Database Vendor: OCLC - First Search
Partic in Coop Librs in Claremont; OCLC Online Computer Library Center, Inc; OCLC Western Service Center

CLOVIS

CL SAN JOAQUIN COLLEGE OF LAW LIBRARY, 901 Fifth St, 93612. SAN 300-7669. Tel: 559-323-2100. FAX: 559-323-5566. *Librn*, Kathryn McTigue-Floyd; E-Mail: kmctigue@sjcl.edu
Founded 1969
Library Holdings: Bk Vols 22,606

COALINGA

P COALINGA-HURON LIBRARY DISTRICT,* 305 N Fourth St, 93210. SAN 331-8060. Tel: 559-935-1676. FAX: 559-935-1058. *Tech Servs*, Diana Baker; *Librn*, Judy Ramirez; *Circ*, Hilda Crawford; Staff 1 (MLS 1)
Founded 1912. Pop 14,590; Circ 101,633
Jul 1999-Jun 2000 Income $411,000, State $10,381, City $1,600. Mats Exp $42,500, Books $35,000, Per/Ser (Incl. Access Fees) $5,000, Micro $1,500, Other Print Mats $1,000. Sal $301,431
Library Holdings: Bk Vols 75,092; Per Subs 114
Subject Interests: California, Genealogy, Local history, Native Am
Automation Activity & Vendor Info: (Acquisitions) epixtech, inc.
Mem of San Joaquin Valley Library System
Branches: 1
HURON BRANCH, 36050 O St, PO Box 190, Huron, 93234. SAN 331-8095. Tel: 209-945-2284. FAX: 209-945-2855. *Librn*, Judy Ramirez
Library Holdings: Bk Vols 14,500

J WEST HILLS COMMUNITY COLLEGE, Fitch Library, 300 Cherry Lane, 93210. SAN 331-8125. Tel: 559-935-0801, Ext 3247. FAX: 559-935-3312. Web Site: www.westhills.cc.ca.us. *Chief Librn*, Jon F Noland; E-Mail: nolandj@whccd.cc.ca.us; Staff 7 (MLS 1, Non-MLS 6)
Founded 1956. Enrl 2,100; Fac 41
1999-2000 Mats Exp $66,000, Books $54,000, Per/Ser (Incl. Access Fees) $10,000, AV Equip $2,000
Library Holdings: Bk Vols 44,000; Bk Titles 44,000; Per Subs 1,800; High Interest/Low Vocabulary Bk Vols 2,000
Subject Interests: Chicano studies
Special Collections: Critical Thinking
Database Vendor: Ebsco - EbscoHost
Restriction: Open to students
Partic in Awlnet

COLEVILLE

P COLEVILLE LIBRARY,* 111591 Hwy 395, 96107. SAN 377-8428. Tel: 530-495-2788. FAX: 530-495-2295. E-Mail: cvb@gbis.com. *Librn*, Olga Gilbert
Library Holdings: Bk Vols 27,000
Mem of Mono County Free Libr Syst
Open Tues-Thurs (hours vary)
Friends of the Library Group

COLTON

M ARROWHEAD REGIONAL MEDICAL CENTER, (Formerly San Bernardino County Medical Center Library), Health Sciences Library, 400 N Pepper Ave, 92324-1819. SAN 301-3014. Tel: 909-580-1300. FAX: 909-580-1310. E-Mail: mnourok@co.san-bernardine.ca.us. *Dir Libr Serv*, Gloria Arredondo; Tel: 909-580-1385, E-Mail: arredondog@armc.ca.san-bernardino.ca.us; *ILL*, Michelle Long; Tel: 909-580-1308; Staff 2 (MLS 1, Non-MLS 1)
Jul 1999-Jun 2000 Income $258,704
Library Holdings: Bk Titles 1,300; Per Subs 334
Subject Interests: Medicine
Automation Activity & Vendor Info: (Acquisitions) EOS; (Cataloging) EOS; (Circulation) EOS; (Serials) EOS
Database Vendor: Dialog, Ebsco - EbscoHost, Silverplatter Information Inc.
Publications: San Bernardino County Medical Center Libr Brouchure
Restriction: Medical staff only
Function: Research library
Mem of MLGSCA, PSRMLS
Partic in Dialog Corporation; Docline; Inland Empire Med Libr Coop; Medline; Pacific SW Regional Med Libr Serv; San Bernardino, Inyo, Riverside Counties United Library Services

P COLTON PUBLIC LIBRARY, 656 N Ninth St, 92324. SAN 300-6778. Tel: 909-370-5083. FAX: 909-422-0873. E-Mail: coltonpl@colton.lib.ca.us. Web Site: www.co.riverside.ca.us/colton/library. *City Librn*, David Michael Davis; Tel: 909-370-5084; *Asst City Librn*, Mary Ann Ponder; E-Mail: mponder@ci.colton.ca.us; *Tech Servs*, Diana Lynn Fraser; E-Mail: diana@colton.lib.ca.us. Subject Specialists: *Info servs*, Diana Lynn Fraser; Staff 3 (MLS 2, Non-MLS 1)
Founded 1906. Pop 47,350
Jul 2000-Jun 2001 Income $1,001,917, State $119,460, City $798,435, Other $84,022. Mats Exp $140,026, Books $69,476, Per/Ser (Incl. Access Fees) $11,756. Sal $583,447
Library Holdings: Bk Vols 97,468; Bk Titles 85,141; Per Subs 300
Special Collections: Books on Tape; Compact Discs; DVD's; Videocassettes
Automation Activity & Vendor Info: (Circulation) epixtech, inc.
Database Vendor: epixtech, inc.
Mem of Inland Library System
Friends of the Library Group
Branches: 1
LUQUE BRANCH LIBRARY, 294 E 0 St, 92324. SAN 329-2673. Tel: 909-370-5182. *Mgr*, Irene Pedroza

M WORLD LIFE RESEARCH INSTITUTE LIBRARY,* 23000 Grand Terrace Rd, 92324. SAN 300-6786. Tel: 909-825-4773. FAX: 909-783-3477. *Dir*, Bruce Halstead
Founded 1959
Library Holdings: Bk Vols 30,000
Subject Interests: Marine biology, Nutrition, Pollution, Toxicology

COLUSA

P COLUSA COUNTY FREE LIBRARY,* 738 Market St, 95932-2398. SAN 376-3722. Tel: 530-458-7671. FAX: 530-458-7358. Web Site: colusanet.com/ccl. *Dir*, Susan Rawlins; E-Mail: srawlins@colusa-coc.kia.ca.us
Library Holdings: Bk Vols 70,000; Bk Titles 45,000; Per Subs 50
Mem of North State Cooperative Library System
Friends of the Library Group
Branches: 6
ARBUCKLE BRANCH, 610 King St, Arbuckle, 95912. (Mail add: PO Box 893, Arbuckle, 95912-0893), Tel: 530-476-2526. FAX: 530-476-2526. Web Site: www.colusanet.com/ccl/. *In Charge*, Barbara Johnson
Library Holdings: Bk Vols 2,500
GRIMES BRANCH, 240 Main St, Grimes, 95950. (Mail add: PO Box 275, Grimes, 95950-0275), Tel: 530-437-2428. FAX: 530-437-2428. Web Site: www.colusanet.com/ccl/. *In Charge*, Roseann Ellis
Library Holdings: Bk Vols 7,600
MAXWELL BRANCH, 34 Oak St, Maxwell, 95955. (Mail add: PO Box 613, Maxwell, 95955-0613), Tel: 530-438-2250. FAX: 530-438-2250. Web Site: www.colusanet.com/ccl/. *In Charge*, Darlene Word
Library Holdings: Bk Vols 10,000
PRINCETON BRANCH, 232 Prince St, Princeton, 95970. (Mail add: PO Box 97, Princeton, 95970-0097), Tel: 530-439-2235. FAX: 530-439-2235. Web Site: www.colusanet.com/ccl/. *In Charge*, Mary Beth Massa
Library Holdings: Bk Vols 10,000
STONYFORD BRANCH, 5080 Stonyford-Lodoga Rd, Stonyford, 95979. (Mail add: PO Box 238, Stonyford, 95979-0238), Tel: 530-963-3722. FAX: 530-963-3722. Web Site: www.colusanet.com/ccl/. *In Charge*, Debbie Alloway
Library Holdings: Bk Vols 1,500
WILLIAMS BRANCH, 901 E St, Williams, 95987. (Mail add: PO Box 517, Williams, 95987-0517), Tel: 530-473-5955. FAX: 530-473-5955. Web Site: www.colusanet.com/ccl/. *In Charge*, Dixie Armfield
Library Holdings: Bk Vols 8,500

§L COLUSA COUNTY LAW LIBRARY, 547 Market St, 95932. Tel: 530-458-0430. FAX: 530-458-4242. *Librn*, Vivian Pearson; Tel: 530-458-0683
Jul 2000-Jun 2001 Income $26,000
Library Holdings: Bk Vols 3,000

COMMERCE

P COMMERCE PUBLIC LIBRARY,* 5655 Jillson St, 90040-1485. SAN 331-8338. Tel: 323-722-6660. FAX: 323-724-1978. Web Site: www.mcls.org/bin/entity/25. *Ch Servs*, Marie Kaneko; *Circ*, Yolanda Cardenas-Parra; *Ref*, Pamela Cibbarelli; Staff 11 (MLS 11)
Founded 1961. Pop 12,250; Circ 87,696
Library Holdings: Bk Titles 45,081; Per Subs 237
Subject Interests: Law
Special Collections: Coatings (Varnish & Paint)
Publications: Bibliography of the Los Angeles Society of Coatings Technology
Partic in Metropolitan Cooperative Library System; OCLC Online Computer Library Center, Inc
Branches: 3
ATLANTIC, 2269 S Atlantic Blvd, 90040. SAN 377-5712. Tel: 323-780-1176. FAX: 323-780-0308. Web Site: www.mcls.org/bin/entity/25. *Mgr*, Olivia Audoma
Library Holdings: Bk Vols 21,000; Bk Titles 9,000
Partic in Metro Coop Libr Syst
BRISTOW PARK BRANCH, 1466 S McDonnell Ave, 90040. SAN 378-1852. Tel: 323-265-1787. FAX: 323-269-6608. Web Site: www.mcls.org/bin/entity/66. *Coll Develop, Mgr*, Maria Christina Muniz
Library Holdings: Bk Vols 12,000; Bk Titles 9,214; Per Subs 50
Partic in Metro Coop Libr Syst
GREENWOOD, 6134 Greenwood Ave, 90040. SAN 378-1879. Tel: 562-927-1516. FAX: 562-927-2976. Web Site: www.mcls.org/bin/entity/67. *Mgr*, Martha Urrea
Library Holdings: Bk Vols 29,000; Bk Titles 10,000; Per Subs 50
Partic in Metropolitan Cooperative Library System

COMPTON

J EMILY B HART HOLIFIELD LIBRARY, Compton Community College, 1111 E Artesia Blvd, 90221-5393. SAN 300-6816. Tel: 310-900-1648. FAX: 310-900-1693. Web Site: www.compton.cc.ca.us/library. *Coordr*, Ann Stevens; E-Mail: stevens_a@compton.cc.ca.us; *Librn*, Roberta Hawkins; *Librn*, Estina Pratt; *Librn*, Andree Valdry; Staff 6 (MLS 4, Non-MLS 2)
Founded 1927. Highest Degree: Associate
Jul 1998-Jun 1999 Income $376,501. Mats Exp $136,698, Books $34,824, Per/Ser (Incl. Access Fees) $8,509, Micro $3,042, Electronic Ref Mat (Incl. Access Fees) $5,895. Sal $188,618 (Prof $135,207)
Library Holdings: Bk Vols 35,632; Bk Titles 30,675
Automation Activity & Vendor Info: (Acquisitions) Endeavor; (Cataloging) Endeavor; (Circulation) Endeavor; (OPAC) Endeavor

CONCORD

S CALRECOVERY INC LIBRARY, 1850 Gateway Blvd, Ste 1060, 94520. SAN 373-4951. Tel: 925-356-3700. FAX: 925-356-7956. *Librn*, Linda Eggerth
Library Holdings: Bk Vols 4,000; Per Subs 20

S INTERNATIONAL SOCIETY FOR GENERAL SEMANTICS LIBRARY, 2465 Salvio St, Ste A & B, 94520-2138. (Mail add: P O Box 728, 94522-0728), SAN 301-4185. Tel: 925-798-0311. FAX: 925-798-0312. E-Mail: isgs@generalsemantics.org. Web Site: www.generalsemantic.org. *Exec Dir*, Paul Dennithorne Johnston
Founded 1943
Library Holdings: Bk Vols 200

CORONA

P CORONA PUBLIC LIBRARY, 650 S Main St, 92882. SAN 300-6824. Tel: 909-736-2382. Interlibrary Loan Service Tel: 909-279-3730. FAX: 909-736-2499. Web Site: www.ci.corona.ca.us/library. *Actg Dir*, Emma B Harris; *Actg Mgr*, Gloria Freel; *Ad Servs, Senior Librn*, Dottie Laird; *Circ*, Geeta Puttaneik; *Ch Servs, Senior Librn*, Suzanne MacConnell; Staff 9 (MLS 9)
Founded 1899. Pop 123,000; Circ 370,002
Library Holdings: Bk Vols 143,000; Per Subs 220

Subject Interests: Local history
Special Collections: Calif; Corona Newspaper Archives, photographs
Automation Activity & Vendor Info: (Acquisitions) SIRSI; (Cataloging) SIRSI; (Circulation) SIRSI; (Course Reserve) SIRSI; (ILL) SIRSI; (Media Booking) SIRSI; (OPAC) SIRSI; (Serials) SIRSI
Mem of Inland Library System
Friends of the Library Group

CORONA DEL MAR

S SHERMAN RESEARCH LIBRARY, 614 Dahlia Ave, 92625-2101. SAN 300-6832. Tel: 949-673-1880. FAX: 949-675-5458. *Dir*, W O Hendricks; Staff 2 (MLS 1, Non-MLS 1)
Founded 1966
Library Holdings: Bk Vols 20,000
Subject Interests: Regional history
Restriction: Not a lending library

CORONADO

P CORONADO PUBLIC LIBRARY, 640 Orange Ave, 92118-1526. SAN 300-6840. Tel: 619-522-7390. FAX: 619-435-4205. Web Site: coronado.lib.ca.us. *Cat, Tech Servs*, Sharyn Oakes; Tel: 619-522-7887, E-Mail: s.oakes@coronado.lib.ca.us; *Dir*, Christian R Esquevin; E-Mail: c.esquevin@coronado.lib.ca.us; *Ch Servs*, Ellen Joy Weber; Tel: 619-522-7886, E-Mail: e.weber@coronado.lib.ca.us; *Ad Servs, Coll Develop*, Anne Clifford; Tel: 619-522-7885, E-Mail: a.clifford@coronado.lib.ca.us; *Circ*, Sarah Brown; Tel: 619-522-7884, E-Mail: sbrown@coronado.lib.ca.us; *Automation Syst Coordr*, Phyllis Belter; Tel: 619-522-7889, E-Mail: p.belter@coronado.lib.ca.us; Staff 9 (MLS 9)
Founded 1890. Pop 28,550; Circ 361,348
Jul 1999-Jun 2000 Income $1,477,000, State $71,450, City $1,402,000, Locally Generated Income $75,000. Mats Exp $160,900, Books $108,400, Per/Ser (Incl. Access Fees) $15,700, Presv $1,800, Micro $10,000, AV Equip $8,000, Electronic Ref Mat (Incl. Access Fees) $17,000. Sal $808,615
Library Holdings: Bk Vols 141,034; Bk Titles 128,239; Per Subs 344
Subject Interests: Gardening, Local history, World War II
Special Collections: Coronado government documents
Automation Activity & Vendor Info: (Circulation) Innovative Interfaces Inc.; (OPAC) Innovative Interfaces Inc.
Publications: Calendar of Events; Library Lookout Newsletter; Summer Reading Brochure
Mem of Serra Cooperative Library System
Partic in OCLC Online Computer Library Center, Inc
Circulating Puppet & Puzzle Collections
Friends of the Library Group

COSTA MESA

M FAIRVIEW DEVELOPMENTAL CENTER, Staff Library, 2501 Harbor Blvd, 92626. SAN 320-1546. Tel: 714-957-5394. FAX: 714-957-5510. E-Mail: ddsfair@ix.netcom.com. *Chief Librn*, Barbara Rycroft; *Tech Servs*, Raj Malhotra; Staff 2 (MLS 1, Non-MLS 1)
Founded 1959
Jul 2000-Jun 2001 Mats Exp $26,000. Sal $80,000
Library Holdings: Bk Vols 2,768; Per Subs 72; Bks on Deafness & Sign Lang 15
Subject Interests: Developmental disabilities, Mental retardation
Automation Activity & Vendor Info: (Cataloging) Sydney; (Circulation) Sydney; (OPAC) Sydney; (Serials) Sydney
Publications: AV Holdings List; Journal holdings list; Library brochure
Restriction: Open to public for reference only
Partic in NLM; Pac SW Regional Med Libr

S FASHION INSTITUTE OF DESIGN & MERCHANDISING, Resource & Research Center,* 3420 S Bristol St Ste 400, 92626. SAN 328-6622. Tel: 714-546-0930. FAX: 714-540-8118. *Asst Librn*, Kim Eldien
Library Holdings: Bk Vols 2,100; Per Subs 65

L LATHAM & WATKINS, Law Library,* 650 Town Ctr, Ste 2000, 92626. SAN 374-9452. Tel: 714-755-8273. FAX: 714-755-8290.
Library Holdings: Bk Vols 100; Per Subs 50

J ORANGE COAST COLLEGE LIBRARY, 2701 Fairview Rd, PO Box 5005, 92628-5005. SAN 300-6905. Tel: 714-432-5705. FAX: 714-432-5739. Web Site: www.lib.occ.cccd.edu/library/libhomepage.html. *Dir*, Donald Ackley; E-Mail: dackley@mail.occ.cccd.edu; *Bibliog Instr*, Jodie Della Marna; *Cat, Syst Coordr*, Joanna Brand; *Circ*, Edith Rietstra; *Ser*, Debbie Webb; *Media Spec*, Vinta Shumway; *Acq, Coll Develop*, Carl Morgan
Founded 1948. Fac 425
Library Holdings: Bk Vols 92,107; Bk Titles 80,266; Per Subs 453
Subject Interests: Horticulture, Photography
Partic in OCLC Online Computer Library Center, Inc
Friends of the Library Group

L RUTAN & TUCKER LIBRARY,* 611 Anton, Ste 1400, 92626. SAN 301-5424. Tel: 714-641-5100. FAX: 714-546-9035. Web Site: www.rutan.com/libinfo. *Asst Librn*, Christine Helper
Library Holdings: Bk Vols 30,000; Per Subs 150

C VANGUARD UNIVERSITY OF SOUTHERN CALIFORNIA, (Formerly Southern California College), O Cope Budge Library, 55 Fair Dr, 92626. SAN 300-6913. Tel: 714-556-3610, Ext 419 or 303. FAX: 714-966-5478. *Head of Libr*, Alison English; *Per*, Melvyn Covetta; *Cat*, Nanako Kodaira; *Ref*, Mary Wilson; *Circ*, Heather Barrington; Staff 6 (MLS 4, Non-MLS 2)
Founded 1920. Enrl 1,307; Fac 70; Highest Degree: Master
Library Holdings: Bk Vols 124,000; Bk Titles 66,367; Per Subs 800
Special Collections: Christian Religion & Judaic Coll; Pentecostal Coll
Automation Activity & Vendor Info: (Cataloging) Sagebrush Corporation; (Circulation) Sagebrush Corporation; (OPAC) Sagebrush Corporation
Partic in OCLC Online Computer Library Center, Inc; SCELC
Friends of the Library Group

CL WHITTIER COLLEGE, School of Law Library, 3333 Harbor Blvd, 92626. SAN 301-0201. Tel: 714-444-4141. Interlibrary Loan Service Tel: 714-444-4141, Ext 487. Circulation Tel: 714-444-4141, Ext 482. Reference Tel: 714-444-4141, Ext 482. FAX: 714-444-3609. Web Site: wollfpac.law.whittier.edu. *Dir*, J Denny Haythorn; E-Mail: dhaythorn@law.whittier.edu; *Assoc Dir*, Rosanne Krikorian; *Cat*, Bill Nazarro; *Govt Doc*, George Allen; *Ser*, Christa Balz; *Ref*, Thomas Watts; *Circ*, Curt Jones; *Online Servs*, Rod Morgan; Staff 8 (MLS 8)
Founded 1976. Enrl 670; Fac 27; Highest Degree: Doctorate
Library Holdings: Bk Vols 330,000; Per Subs 4,700
Automation Activity & Vendor Info: (Cataloging) Innovative Interfaces Inc.; (Circulation) Innovative Interfaces Inc.; (Course Reserve) Innovative Interfaces Inc.; (OPAC) Innovative Interfaces Inc.
Database Vendor: Innovative Interfaces INN - View

COVINA

C AMERICAN GRADUATE UNIVERSITY LIBRARY,* 733 N Dodsworth Ave, 91724. SAN 373-0239. Tel: 626-966-4576. FAX: 626-915-1709. E-Mail: agu@ix.netcom.com. Web Site: www.agu.edu. *Librn*, Marie Sirney
Library Holdings: Bk Titles 3,500; Per Subs 30

P COVINA PUBLIC LIBRARY, 234 N Second Ave, 91723-2198. SAN 300-6921. Tel: 626-858-7297. Circulation Tel: 626-967-3935. Reference Tel: 626-331-7675. FAX: 626-915-8915. E-Mail: covinats@lightside.com. Web Site: ci.covina.ca.us/departments/library/librarymain.htm. *Dir*, Roger Possner; E-Mail: rpossner@ci.covina.ca.us; *Asst City Librn*, Alan Burkin; E-Mail: aburkin@ci.covina.ca.us; *Ad Servs, Ref*, Deanna Smith; *ILL*, Susan Mita; *Tech Coordr*, Robin Masters; Tel: 626-858-7926, E-Mail: rmasters@ci.covina.ca.us; *Ch Servs*, Joy Shaup; Tel: 626-967-3936, E-Mail: jshaup@ci.covina.ca.us; *Ref Serv Ad*, Greg Ullman; Tel: 626-332-4575, E-Mail: gullman@ci.covina.ca.us; *Senior Librn*, Lisa Valore; Tel: 626-858-5553, E-Mail: lvalore@ci.covina.ca.us; *Circ*, Diane Huchinson; Tel: 626-967-3935, E-Mail: dhutchin@ci.covina.ca.us; *Asst Librn*, Frances Rouse; Tel: 626-967-3936, E-Mail: frouse@ci.covina.ca.us; *Asst Librn*, Steve Smith; Tel: 626-858-5553, E-Mail: ssmith@ci.covina.ca.us; Staff 28 (MLS 6, Non-MLS 22)
Founded 1887. Pop 47,988; Circ 237,551
Jul 1999-Jun 2000 Income $1,029,430, State $121,310, City $882,950, County $4,800, Other $20,370. Mats Exp $214,260, Books $152,880, Per/Ser (Incl. Access Fees) $13,820, Electronic Ref Mat (Incl. Access Fees) $47,560. Sal $214,260
Library Holdings: Bk Vols 95,648; Bk Titles 79,271; Per Subs 184
Automation Activity & Vendor Info: (Circulation) epixtech, inc.
Database Vendor: epixtech, inc., GaleNet, IAC - Info Trac, IAC - SearchBank
Function: Reference services available
Mem of Metropolitan Cooperative Library System
Partic in Metro Coop Libr Syst
Friends of the Library Group

CRESCENT CITY

S DEL NORTE COUNTY HISTORICAL SOCIETY LIBRARY,* 577 H St, 95531. SAN 327-3202. Tel: 707-464-3922. *In Charge*, Mary Lu Saunier
Library Holdings: Bk Vols 1,000
Subject Interests: Local history
Special Collections: Historical Files of Settlement of Del Norte County Area (circa 1800-1900)

GL DEL NORTE COUNTY LAW LIBRARY,* Courthouse, 450 H St, 95531. SAN 300-6948. Tel: 707-464-7217. *Librn*, Margot E McGuire
Founded 1954
Library Holdings: Bk Vols 7,500

P DEL NORTE COUNTY LIBRARY DISTRICT, 190 Price Mall, 95531-4395. SAN 300-693X. Tel: 707-464-9793. FAX: 707-464-6726. E-Mail: delnl@cc.northcoast.com. *Librn*, Liz McCumsey; Staff 1 (MLS 1)
Founded 1978. Pop 25,000; Circ 70,000
Jul 1999-Jun 2000 Income $235,000. Sal $137,000 (Prof $30,000)

Library Holdings: Bk Vols 35,000; Per Subs 60
Special Collections: California Indian Library Coll - Del Norte; Del Norte County History
Automation Activity & Vendor Info: (Cataloging) TLC; (Circulation) TLC; (OPAC) TLC
Mem of North State Cooperative Library System
Friends of the Library Group

M SUTTER COAST HOSPITAL LIBRARY,* 800 E Washington Blvd, 95531-3699. SAN 325-2566. Tel: 707-464-8880. FAX: 707-464-8886. *Dir*, Toni Brixey
Founded 1960
Library Holdings: Bk Titles 300; Per Subs 80

CULVER CITY

S PROSPEROS SERVERS' CENTER LIBRARY,* PO Box 4969, 90231-4969. SAN 371-3407. Tel: 310-287-1663. FAX: 310-287-0157. *In Charge*, Clair Gold
Library Holdings: Bk Vols 1,200; Per Subs 2
Subject Interests: History, Psychology

S STEREO CLUB OF SOUTHERN CALIFORNIA LIBRARY,* PO Box 2368, 90231. SAN 329-3769. Tel: 310-837-2368. FAX: 310-558-1653. *Dir*, Susan Pinsky
Library Holdings: Per Subs 50

J WEST LOS ANGELES COLLEGE LIBRARY, Heldman Learning Resource Center,* 4800 Freshman Dr, 90230. SAN 309-4618. Tel: 310-287-4302. FAX: 310-836-2867. Web Site: www.geocities.com/athens/4800/home.html. *Chair, Per*, Ken Lee; *Acq, Coll Develop*, Catherine A Froloff; *Cat*, Yanzi Lin; *Ref*, Judy Chow; Staff 5 (MLS 5)
Founded 1969. Enrl 8,000
Jul 1997-Jun 1998 Income $390,000. Mats Exp $36,050, Books $20,000, Per/Ser (Incl. Access Fees) $13,350, Micro $2,200, AV Equip $500. Sal $300,000 (Prof $210,000)
Library Holdings: Bk Titles 65,000
Special Collections: Law Coll (support paralegal program)
Database Vendor: DRA

CUPERTINO

S COMPAQ COMPUTER CORPORATION, Silicon Valley Library, 10400 N Tantau, Loc CAC14-7, 95014. Tel: 408-285-3160. FAX: 408-285-3150. Web Site: www.compaq.com. *Mgr*, Patricia Turner; Staff 5 (MLS 3, Non-MLS 2)
Library Holdings: Bk Vols 16,000; Per Subs 350
Open Mon-Fri 8-5
Friends of the Library Group

J DE ANZA COLLEGE, A Robert DeHart Learning Center,* 21250 Stevens Creek Blvd, 95014-5793. SAN 300-6999. Tel: 408-864-8761. FAX: 408-864-8603. *Dean of Libr*, Ralph Steinke; *Coll Develop, Librn*, Jan Redd; *Ref*, George W Sloan; *Online Servs, Ref*, Kwan Chan; *Publ Servs*, Judith Mowrey; Staff 7 (MLS 7)
Founded 1967. Enrl 28,000; Fac 800
Library Holdings: Bk Vols 73,000; Per Subs 250
Subject Interests: Art and architecture, History, Special education
Friends of the Library Group

S HEWLETT-PACKARD COMPANY, Cupertino Site Information & Learning Center,* 19483 Pruneridge Ave, 95014. SAN 300-7006. Tel: 408-447-1307. FAX: 408-447-5809. *Librn*, Nancy Lewis; E-Mail: nlewis@hp.com; Staff 2 (MLS 1, Non-MLS 1)
Founded 1969
Library Holdings: Bk Vols 4,000; Per Subs 110
Subject Interests: Business, Computer science, Marketing
Partic in Dialog Corporation

CYPRESS

J CYPRESS COLLEGE LIBRARY,* 9200 Valley View St, 90630-5897. SAN 300-7049. Tel: 714-484-7124, 714-826-0130. FAX: 714-826-6723. Web Site: www.cypress.cc.ca.us/library/library.htm. *Dean*, Dr Kay Bruce; *Acq, ILL, Tech Servs*, Bonnie Fast; *Ref*, Judy Koike; *Coll Develop*, Monica Doman; Staff 4 (MLS 4)
Founded 1966. Circ 42,563
Jul 1998-Jun 1999 Mats Exp $265,910, Books $66,540, Per/Ser (Incl. Access Fees) $44,223, AV Equip $2,000. Sal $439,581 (Prof $228,683)
Library Holdings: Bk Vols 60,348; Bk Titles 60,065; Per Subs 252
Automation Activity & Vendor Info: (Serials) Endeavor
Database Vendor: Ebsco - EbscoHost

DALY CITY

P DALY CITY PUBLIC LIBRARY, 40 Wembley Dr, 94015-4399. SAN 331-8664. Tel: 650-991-8025. Circulation Tel: 650-991-8023. FAX: 650-991-8225. E-Mail: dcpl@pls.lib.ca.us. Web Site: www.pls.lib.ca.us/pls/srm/srm.html. *Dir*, Susanna C Gilden; E-Mail: gildens@pls.lib.ca.us; *Librn*, Kristi Bell; E-Mail: bellk@pls.lib.ca.us; *Librn*, Lolly Pineda; E-Mail: pinedal@pls.lib.ca.us; *Cat*, Kathy Rivera; E-Mail: riverak@pls.lib.ca.us; *Ch Servs*, Cathie Scalice; Tel: 650-991-8244, E-Mail: scalicec@pls.lib.ca.us; Staff 68 (MLS 7, Non-MLS 61)
Founded 1911. Pop 103,400; Circ 410,565
Jul 2000-Jun 2001 Income (Main Library and Branch Library) $2,402,749, State $175,000, City $1,978,449, County $120,000, Locally Generated Income $114,500, Other $14,800. Mats Exp $281,105, Books $242,100, Per/Ser (Incl. Access Fees) $13,600, Presv $5,000, Micro $4,300, Electronic Ref Mat (Incl. Access Fees) $21,150. Sal $1,040,522 (Prof $390,000)
Library Holdings: Bk Vols 158,801; Per Subs 461
Special Collections: Daly City History Coll, hist photogs; Sam Chandler Historical Coll
Automation Activity & Vendor Info: (Cataloging) epixtech, inc.; (Circulation) epixtech, inc.; (OPAC) epixtech, inc.
Database Vendor: Ebsco - EbscoHost, epixtech, inc., OCLC - First Search
Function: ILL available
Mem of Peninsula Library System
Friends of the Library Group
Branches: 3
BAYSHORE, 2960 Geneva Ave, 94014-1525. SAN 331-8699. Tel: 650-991-8074.
Friends of the Library Group
JOHN D DALY BRANCH, 6351 Mission St, 94014-2012. SAN 331-8729. Tel: 650-991-8073. FAX: 650-746-8373.
Friends of the Library Group
WESTLAKE, 275 Southgate Ave, 94015-3471. SAN 331-8753. Tel: 650-991-8071. FAX: 650-991-8180. *Librn*, Tom Goward; E-Mail: gowardt@pls.lib.ca.us; Staff 1 (MLS 1)
Friends of the Library Group

M SETON MEDICAL CENTER LIBRARY,* 1900 Sullivan Ave, 94015. SAN 300-7057. Tel: 650-991-6700. FAX: 650-991-6638. *Librn*, Janice Perlman-Stites
Library Holdings: Bk Vols 1,000; Per Subs 190
Subject Interests: Medicine

DANVILLE

S THE BLACKHAWK MUSEUM, Automotive Research Library, 3700 Blackhawk Plaza Circle, 94506. SAN 300-7812. Tel: 925-736-2277, Ext 228. FAX: 925-736-4818. Web Site: www.blackhawkauto.org. *Librn*, Thomas Behring
Founded 1914
Library Holdings: Bk Titles 400; Per Subs 40
Special Collections: J Frank Duryea & the First American Gas Auto (Duryea Brothers Coll), bks, ephemera, letters, photogs, personal papers of W Everett Miller, Auto Designer
Open Tues-Fri 9-5

DAVIS

S CENTER FOR SUSTAINABLE AGRICULTURE LIBRARY,* 723 A St, 95616. SAN 373-398X. Tel: 530-753-2931. FAX: 530-756-7188. *Librn*, Karen Van Epen
Library Holdings: Bk Titles 6,000; Per Subs 40
Subject Interests: Agriculture, Forestry, Horticulture, Natural resources

R DAVIS COMMUNITY CHURCH LIBRARY,* 412 C St, 95616. SAN 300-7073. Tel: 530-753-2894. FAX: 530-753-2896. *Librn*, Carol May; *Librn*, Mary L Stephens
Library Holdings: Bk Vols 3,015

SR DAVIS FRIENDS MEETING LIBRARY, 345 L St, 95616. SAN 371-6562. Tel: 530-758-8492. *Librn*, Noel Peattie; E-Mail: nrpeattie@earthlink.net; Staff 1 (MLS 1)
Oct 1999-Sep 2000 Income $450. Mats Exp Books $400
Library Holdings: Bk Titles 1,375; Per Subs 20
Subject Interests: Quaker info
Special Collections: Quaker History
Publications: Annual report (cumulative 1986-1993); Subject headings with supplements

M KESSLER-HANCOCK INFORMATION SERVICES, INC, 203 F St, Ste E, 95616. SAN 371-9251. Tel: 530-756-4636. FAX: 530-756-6943. E-Mail: orders@khinfo.com. Web Site: www.khinfo.com. *Dir*, Greg W Kessler; E-Mail: greg_kessler@khinfo.com; Staff 13 (MLS 4, Non-MLS 9)
Founded 1989
1999-2000 Income $1,500,000. Mats Exp $25,027, Books $15,000, Per/Ser (Incl. Access Fees) $5,000, Presv $220, Micro $550, AV Equip $952, Other Print Mats $1,500, Manuscripts & Archives $900. Sal $350,000 (Prof $200,000)
Library Holdings: Bk Vols 549; Bk Titles 500; Per Subs 20
Partic in Coop Libr Agency for Syst & Servs

S MONSANTO INFORMATION RESOURCES & SERVICES LIBRARY, 1920 Fifth St, 95616. SAN 325-0539. Tel: 530-792-2206. FAX: 530-792-2453. *Br Coordr*, Deanna Johnson; E-Mail: deanne.johnson@monsanto.com; Staff 1 (MLS 1)
Founded 1982
Jan 2000-Dec 2000 Income $200,000. Mats Exp $54,900, Books $8,400, Per/Ser (Incl. Access Fees) $45,000, Micro $1,500. Sal $50,000
Library Holdings: Bk Vols 1,850; Per Subs 55; Spec Interest Per Sub 55
Subject Interests: Genetic eng, Molecular biology, Plant sci
Automation Activity & Vendor Info: (Acquisitions) CASPR; (Cataloging) CASPR; (Circulation) CASPR; (OPAC) CASPR; (Serials) CASPR
Database Vendor: Dialog, epixtech, inc., OCLC - First Search
Restriction: Company staff only
Function: Research library

UNITED STATES ARMY
A CORPS OF ENGINEERS, HYDROLOGIC ENGINEERING CENTER LIBRARY, 609 Second St, 95616. SAN 321-8937. Tel: 530-756-1104, Ext 308. FAX: 530-756-8250. Web Site: www.wvc-hec.usace.army.mil. *In Charge*, Arlen Feldman; E-Mail: arlen.d.feldman@usace.army.mil
Founded 1980
Library Holdings: Bk Titles 700; Per Subs 84
Subject Interests: Hydraulic eng, Hydrologic eng, Water resources mgt, Water resources planning

C UNIVERSITY OF CALIFORNIA, DAVIS, General Library, 100 N W Quad, 95616-5292. SAN 331-8788. Tel: 530-752-2110, 530-752-2256 (Lending). Interlibrary Loan Service Tel: 530-752-2251. FAX: 530-752-6899. Web Site: www.lib.ucdavis.edu. *Librn*, Marilyn J Sharrow; *Assoc Librn*, George Bynon; *Assoc Librn, Syst Coordr*, Gail Yokote; *Cat, Ser, Spec Coll*, Clinton Howard; *Acq*, Sharon D Baker; *Doc*, Linda M Kennedy; *ILL*, Gail Nichols. Subject Specialists: *Agriculture*, Tejinder S Sibia; *Agriculture*, Susan Casement; *Biological*, Tejinder S Sibia; *Health sciences*, JoAnne Boorkman; *Physical science*, Karen Andrews; Staff 201 (MLS 50, Non-MLS 151)
Founded 1908. Enrl 25,092; Fac 1,652; Highest Degree: Doctorate
Jul 1999-Jun 2000 Income $18,498,425. Mats Exp $8,666,110, Books $2,280,845, Per/Ser (Incl. Access Fees) $5,830,106, Presv $270,698, Micro $9,532, Other Print Mats $274,929. Sal $8,412,806
Library Holdings: Bk Vols 2,830,420; Per Subs 39,640
Subject Interests: Agricultural economics, Agriculture, Art and architecture, Biochemistry, Biology, Botany, Business and management, Chemistry, Developmental biology, Economics, Education, Entomology, Ethnic studies, Genetics, Geology, History, Horticulture, Law, Literature, Mathematics, Medicine, Music, Natural science, Nutrition, Philosophy, Physics, Physiology, Theater, Toxicology, Veterinary medicine, Women's studies
Special Collections: 16th, 17th, 18th, 19th & 20th century British), bks, pamphlets; Agricultural Technology, advertising mat, archives, bks, mss, manufacturer's cat, pamphlets, per, photog, repair manuals; Apiculture, bks, cat, mss, pamphlets, per, photog; Asian History, bks, mss, pamphlets; Botany, bks, mss, per, photog; California Agricultural & Northern California history, bks, mss, oral hist, pamphlets, per, photog, promotional materials; California Artists & Architecture, bibliographies, cat, drawings & paintings, mss, photog; Chicano History, bks, mss, oral history, pamphlets; Civil Rights, bks, broadsides, mss, pamphlets; Ecology, archives, bks, mss, pamphlets; Enology & Viticulture, bks, mss, oral hist, pamphlets, per, photog, posters, promotional materials; Fine Printing, bks, broadsides, pamphlets; Food Industry & Technology, archives, bks, mss, menus, pamphlets, photog; French Revolution, doc, engravings, mss; German Literature, bks, clippings, mss; History & Literature (18th, 19th & early 20th century American; Horticulture & Pomology, advertising materials, archives, bks, cat, drawings & paintings, mss, pamphlets, photog, posters; Michael & Margaret B Harrison Western Research Center, Fair Oaks, Calif; Native American History, bks, broadsides, mss, pamphlets; Performing Arts, archives, bks, clippings, engravings, mss, photog, playbills, posters, programs, scripts, stage & lighting designs; Poetry (US Avant Garde & British 1789-1972), bks, broadsides, mss, pamphlets, per; Russian History, engravings, mss, photog; Water & Irrigation, archives, bks, mss, pamphlets, photog; Western American History & Thought, Fair Oaks, Calif, bks, clippings, ethnographic reports, pamphlets, photog, pictures; World War I & II, bks, mss, pamphlets, posters
Automation Activity & Vendor Info: (Acquisitions) Innovative Interfaces Inc.; (Cataloging) DRA; (Circulation) DRA; (Course Reserve) DRA; (Serials) Innovative Interfaces Inc.
Publications: Library Perspective
Mem of Asn of Research Libraries; Center for Res Librs; Mountain-Valley Library System
Partic in OCLC Online Computer Library Center, Inc; Pacific SW Regional Med Libr Serv; Univ of Calif Librs
Special Services for the Blind - Magnifiers; Television screen magnifiers
Friends of the Library Group
Departmental Libraries:
AGRICULTURAL & RESOURCE ECONOMICS LIBRARY, One Shields Ave, 95616-8512. SAN 331-8966. Tel: 530-752-1540. FAX: 530-752-5614. E-Mail: arel@ucdavis.edu. Web Site: www.agecon.ucdavis.edu/library/homepage.html. *Librn*, Susan Casement; Staff 3 (MLS 1, Non-MLS 2)
Library Holdings: Bk Vols 8,484; Per Subs 290
Subject Interests: Agriculture, Economics, Land
INSTITUTE OF GOVERNMENTAL AFFAIRS LIBRARY & DATA ARCHIVE, 360 Shields, 95616-8617. SAN 331-8877. Tel: 530-752-2045. FAX: 530-752-2835. Web Site: www.iga.ucdavis.edu/. *Res*, Jean Stratford; E-Mail: jsstratford@ucdavis.edu
Library Holdings: Bk Vols 6,852; Per Subs 371
Subject Interests: Economics, Social sciences and issues, Statistics, Telecommunications
Special Collections: East Asian Business Archives
Partic in Dialog Corporation
CL LAW LIBRARY Tel: 530-752-3327. FAX: 530-752-8766. Web Site: lawlibrary.ucdavis.edu. *Librn*, George Grossman; E-Mail: gsgrossman@ucdavis.edu; Staff 6 (MLS 6)
Founded 1964. Enrl 518; Fac 33
Library Holdings: Bk Vols 285,603; Per Subs 5,359
CM LOREN D CARLSON HEALTH SCIENCES LIBRARY, One Shields Ave, 95611-5291. SAN 331-8990. Tel: 530-752-1162. Interlibrary Loan Service Tel: 530-752-6379. FAX: 530-752-4718. Web Site: www.lib.ucdavis.edu/hsl/hslhome.htm. *Librn*, Jo Anne Boorkman; Tel: 530-752-6585, E-Mail: jaboorkman@ucdavis.edu; *Cat, Tech Servs*, Karleen Darr; Tel: 530-754-9301, E-Mail: kldarr@ucdavis.edu; *Ref*, Rebecca Davis; Tel: 530-752-3271, E-Mail: radavis@ucdavis.edu; *Coll Develop*, Carolyn Kopper; Tel: 530-752-6205, E-Mail: cskopper@ucdavis.edu; Staff 23 (MLS 7, Non-MLS 16)
Founded 1966. Enrl 844; Fac 546; Highest Degree: Doctorate
Library Holdings: Bk Vols 287,942; Per Subs 2,362
Special Collections: Veterinary Historical Coll
Partic in OCLC Online Computer Library Center, Inc; Pacific SW Regional Med Libr Serv
MEDICAL CENTER LIBRARY
See Separate Entry in Sacramento
PHYSICAL SCIENCES & ENGINEERING LIBRARY, One Shields Ave, 95616-8676. SAN 331-9059. Tel: 530-752-0459. TDD: 530-752-2170. FAX: 530-752-4719. E-Mail: pse@ucdavis.edu. Web Site: www.lib.ucdavis.edu/pse/. *Head of Libr*, Karen Andrews
Library Holdings: Bk Vols 330,936; Per Subs 4,195
Subject Interests: Astronomy, Chemistry, Engineering, Geology, Meteorology, Physics
Special Services for the Deaf - TDD
TOXICOLOGY DOCUMENTATION CENTER, Environ Toxicology Dept, 95616-8588. SAN 331-8842. Tel: 530-752-2587. FAX: 530-752-3394. *In Charge*, Loreen Kleinschmidt
Library Holdings: Bk Vols 6,000; Per Subs 100

DEATH VALLEY

S NATIONAL PARK SERVICE, Death Valley National Park Research Libraries, PO Box 579, 92328. SAN 300-7081. Tel: 760-786-2331, Ext 287. FAX: 760-786-3283. *Curator*, Blair Davenport; E-Mail: blair_davenport@nps.gov
Founded 1958
Library Holdings: Bk Titles 10,000
Special Collections: Death Valley National Park; Natural Sciences, Chiefly Geology (Theses & Dissertations based upon Field Studies Completed in
Friends of the Library Group

DIXON

P DIXON UNIFIED SCHOOL DISTRICT, Dixon Public Library, 230 N First St, 95620-3028. SAN 300-712X. Tel: 707-678-5447. FAX: 707-678-3515. E-Mail: dixonlib@wheel.dcn.davis.ca.us. Web Site: www.dixon.lib.ca.us. *Librn*, Marilyn Costamagna; Tel: 707-678-2967, Fax: 707-678-3515, E-Mail: mpc@wsheel.dcn.davis.ca.us; Staff 11 (MLS 1, Non-MLS 10)
Founded 1913. Pop 19,100; Circ 38,857
Library Holdings: Bk Titles 27,000; Per Subs 32
Special Collections: Local History Photograph & Scrapbook Coll
Mem of Mountain-Valley Library System
Friends of the Library Group

DOWNEY

P COUNTY OF LOS ANGELES PUBLIC LIBRARY, Executive Office, 7400 E Imperial Hwy, 90242-3375. (Mail add: PO Box 7011, 90241-7011), SAN 332-3765. Tel: 562-940-8462. Interlibrary Loan Service Tel: 562-940-8561. TDD: 310-679-4316, 661-945-2503, 661-945-2503. FAX: 562-803-3032. E-Mail: exec@lhqsmtp.colapl.org. Web Site: www.colapublib.org/. *Dir*, Margaret Donnellan Todd; *Asst Dir*, David Flint; *Asst Dir*, Wendy Romano; *Asst Dir*, Fred Hungerford; *ILL*, Juanita Montoya; *Ad Servs*, Mary T Anderson; *YA Servs*, Penny Markey; *Acq*, Maria Price; *Bibliogr*, Maria Blume; *Coll Develop*, Phyllis Young; Staff 281 (MLS 243, Non-MLS 38)
Founded 1912. Pop 3,506,500; Circ 14,761,515
Jul 1999-Jun 2000 Income (Main Library and Branch Library) $68,923,421, State $6,364,009, Federal $300,160, County $57,186,931, Locally Generated Income $5,072,321. Mats Exp $8,147,470, Books $5,787,259, Per/Ser (Incl. Access Fees) $886,937, Presv $58,619, Micro $162,058, AV Equip

$851,420, Other Print Mats $8,614, Electronic Ref Mat (Incl. Access Fees) $392,563. Sal $34,267,304
Library Holdings: Bk Vols 7,743,803; Bk Titles 712,419; Per Subs 14,171
Special Collections: American Indian Resource Center, multi-media; Arkel Erb Memorial Mountaineering; Asian Pacific Resource Center, multi-media; Black Resource Center, multi-media; Californiana, multi-media; Chicano Resource Center, multi-media; Consumer Health Information Program & Services (CHIPS), multi-media; Document & Information Services Center, periodicals; Granger Poetry Coll; HIV Information Center; Judaica, multi-media; Nautical, multi-media; Sams Photofact
Automation Activity & Vendor Info: (Acquisitions) DRA; (Cataloging) DRA; (Circulation) DRA; (OPAC) DRA
Publications: Dispatch (volunteer newsletter) (Newsletter); Kidbeat (children's newsletter); Libraries of the County of Los Angeles Public Library (directory); Literacy LINK (Newsletter); READ (Newsletter); READ ALL ABOUT IT (Newsletter)
Mem of South State Cooperative Library System
Partic in OCLC Online Computer Library Center, Inc
Special Services for the Deaf - High interest/low vocabulary books; Staff with knowledge of sign language; TDD
Friends of the Library Group
Branches: 94

ALONDRA BRANCH, 11949 Alondra Blvd, Norwalk, 90650-7108. SAN 332-4303. Tel: 562-868-7771. FAX: 562-863-8620. Web Site: www.colapublib.org/libs/alondra. *Librn*, Cathy Saldin
Circ 101,814
Library Holdings: Bk Vols 51,460; Per Subs 110
Database Vendor: DRA
Friends of the Library Group

ANGELO M IACOBONI BRANCH, 4990 Clark Ave, Lakewood, 90712-2676. SAN 332-5415. Tel: 562-866-1777. FAX: 562-866-1217. Web Site: www.colapublib.org/libs/iacoboni/. *Librn*, Donna Walters
Circ 447,337
Library Holdings: Bk Vols 231,906; Per Subs 539
Database Vendor: DRA
Friends of the Library Group

ANTELOPE VALLEY BOOKMOBILE, 601 W Lancaster Blvd, Lancaster, 93534. Tel: 661-948-8270. FAX: 661-949-7386. Web Site: www.colapublib.org/libs/antelopevalley/bookmobile.html. *In Charge*, Diane Gavin
Circ 59,379
Library Holdings: Bk Vols 6,580; Per Subs 25
Database Vendor: DRA

ARTESIA BRANCH, 18722 S Clarkdale Ave, Artesia, 90701-5817. SAN 332-4338. Tel: 562-865-6614. FAX: 562-924-4644. Web Site: www.colapublib.org/libs/artesia/. *Librn*, Janet Fattahi
Circ 81,011
Library Holdings: Bk Vols 46,476; Per Subs 54
Database Vendor: DRA
Friends of the Library Group

AVALON BRANCH, 215 Sumner Ave, PO Box 535, Avalon, 90704-0535. SAN 332-4362. Tel: 310-510-1050. FAX: 310-510-1645. Web Site: www.colapublib.org/libs/avalon/. *In Charge*, Linda Cookman
Circ 29,136
Library Holdings: Bk Vols 18,288; Per Subs 66
Database Vendor: DRA
Friends of the Library Group

BALDWIN PARK BRANCH, 4181 Baldwin Park Blvd, Baldwin Park, 91706-3203. SAN 332-4397. Tel: 626-962-6947. FAX: 626-337-6631. Web Site: www.colapublib.org/libs/baldwinpark/. *Librn*, Rafael Gonzalez
Circ 151,935
Library Holdings: Bk Vols 103,552; Per Subs 112
Database Vendor: DRA
Friends of the Library Group

BELL BRANCH, 4411 E Gage Ave, Bell, 90201-1216. SAN 332-4427. Tel: 323-560-2149. FAX: 323-773-7557. Web Site: www.colapublib.org/libs/bell/. *Librn*, Hsiao-Yung Fang
Circ 88,029
Library Holdings: Bk Vols 52,676; Per Subs 92
Database Vendor: DRA
Friends of the Library Group

BELL GARDENS BRANCH, 7110 S Garfield Ave, Bell Gardens, 90201-3244. SAN 332-4451. Tel: 562-927-1309. FAX: 562-928-4512. Web Site: www.colapublib.org/libs/bellgardens/. *Librn*, Naomi Engle
Circ 118,147
Library Holdings: Bk Vols 59,355; Per Subs 95
Database Vendor: DRA
Friends of the Library Group

A C BILBREW BRANCH, 150 E El Segundo Blvd, Los Angeles, 90061-2356. SAN 332-4516. Tel: 310-538-3350. FAX: 310-327-0824. Web Site: www.colapublib.org/libs/bilbrew/. *Librn*, Fannie Love
Circ 94,275
Library Holdings: Bk Vols 72,374; Per Subs 199
Special Collections: Black Resource Center
Database Vendor: DRA
Friends of the Library Group

CLIFTON M BRAKENSIEK BRANCH, 9945 E Flower St, Bellflower, 90706-5486. SAN 332-4575. Tel: 562-925-5543. FAX: 562-920-9249. Web Site: www.colapublib.org/libs/brakensiek/. *Librn*, Linda Larsen
Circ 239,341
Library Holdings: Bk Vols 128,329; Per Subs 227
Database Vendor: DRA
Friends of the Library Group

CANYON COUNTY BRANCH, 18536 Soledad Canyon Rd, Santa Clarita, 91351. SAN 332-4605. Tel: 661-251-2720. FAX: 661-298-7137. Web Site: www.colapublib.org/libs/canyoncountry/. *Librn*, Geraldine Matthews
Circ 219,380
Library Holdings: Bk Vols 73,383; Per Subs 119
Database Vendor: DRA
Friends of the Library Group

CARSON BRANCH, 151 E Carson St, Carson, 90745-2797. SAN 332-463X. Tel: 310-830-0901. FAX: 310-830-6181. Web Site: www.colapublib.org/libs/carson/. *Librn*, Nina David
Circ 404,482
Library Holdings: Bk Vols 205,477; Per Subs 530
Special Collections: Consumer Health Information Program & Services
Database Vendor: DRA
Friends of the Library Group

CENTRAL JUVENILE HALL, 1605 Eastlake Ave, Los Angeles, 90033-1093. SAN 376-9372. Tel: 323-226-8469. FAX: 323-225-3274. *In Charge*, Frank A Martinez
Pop 25,406
Library Holdings: Bk Vols 5,243
Database Vendor: DRA

CENTRAL REGIONAL OFFICE, 1550 W Beverly Blvd, Montebello, 90640-3993. SAN 332-379X. Tel: 323-722-5621. FAX: 323-722-9683. *Adminr*, Roger Woelfel; *Admin Assoc*, Helen Tsai
Circ 1,152
Library Holdings: Bk Vols 8,584; Per Subs 50
Subject Interests: California, Geography, History, Literature
Special Collections: American Indian Resource Center; Asian Pacific Resource Center; Californiana Collection; Chicano Resource Center; Granger Poetry Collection

CHARTER OAK BRANCH, 20540-K Arrow Hwy, 91724-1238. SAN 332-4664. Tel: 626-339-2151. FAX: 626-339-2799. Web Site: www.colapublib.org/libs/charteroak/. *Librn*, Denise Dilley
Circ 162,713
Library Holdings: Bk Vols 56,184; Per Subs 59
Database Vendor: DRA
Friends of the Library Group

CITY TERRACE BRANCH, 4025 E City Terrace Dr, Los Angeles, 90063-1297. SAN 332-4699. Tel: 323-261-0295. FAX: 323-261-1790. Web Site: www.colapublib.org/libs/cityterrace/. *Librn*, Olga Garcia
Circ 76,011
Library Holdings: Bk Vols 56,382; Per Subs 85
Database Vendor: DRA
Friends of the Library Group

CLAREMONT BRANCH, 208 N Harvard Ave, Claremont, 91711. SAN 332-4729. Tel: 909-621-4902. FAX: 909-621-2366. Web Site: www.colapublib.org/libs/claremont/. *Librn*, Charles Kaufman
Circ 215,828
Library Holdings: Bk Vols 155,421; Per Subs 375
Database Vendor: DRA
Friends of the Library Group

COMPTON BRANCH, 240 W Compton Blvd, Compton, 90220-3109. SAN 332-4753. Tel: 310-637-0202. FAX: 310-537-1141. Web Site: www.colapublib.org/libs/compton/. *Librn*, Sharon Johnson
Circ 64,178
Library Holdings: Bk Vols 106,866; Per Subs 164
Database Vendor: DRA
Friends of the Library Group

CUDAHY BRANCH, 5218 Santa Ana St, Cudahy, 90201-6098. SAN 332-4788. Tel: 323-771-1345. FAX: 323-771-6973. Web Site: www.colapublib.org/libs/cudahy/. *Librn*, Gerard Billard
Circ 58,470
Library Holdings: Bk Vols 49,138; Per Subs 78
Database Vendor: DRA
Friends of the Library Group

CULVER CITY BRANCH, 4975 Overland Ave, Culver City, 90230-4299. SAN 332-4818. Tel: 310-559-1676. FAX: 310-559-2994. Web Site: www.colapublib.org/libs/culvercity/. *Librn*, Josephine Zoretich
Circ 446,091
Library Holdings: Bk Vols 209,046; Per Subs 725
Special Collections: Judaica Coll
Database Vendor: DRA
Friends of the Library Group

DIAMOND BAR BRANCH, 1061 S Grand Ave, Diamond Bar, 91765-2299. SAN 332-4877. Tel: 909-861-4978. FAX: 626-860-3054. Web Site: www.colapublib.org/libs/diamondbar/. *Librn*, Irene Wang
Circ 268,456
Library Holdings: Bk Vols 99,946; Per Subs 134
Database Vendor: DRA

Friends of the Library Group
DUARTE BRANCH, 1301 Buena Vista St, Duarte, 91010-2410. SAN 332-4931. Tel: 626-358-1865. FAX: 626-303-4917. Web Site: www.colapublib.org/libs/duarte/. *Librn*, Peter Rosenwald
Circ 116,565
Library Holdings: Bk Vols 75,207; Per Subs 171
Database Vendor: DRA
Friends of the Library Group
EAST LOS ANGELES BRANCH, 4801 E Third St, Los Angeles, 90022-1601. SAN 332-4990. Tel: 323-264-0155. FAX: 323-264-5465. Web Site: www.colapublib.org/libs/eastla/. *Librn*, Ruth Morse
Circ 184,732
Library Holdings: Bk Vols 106,223; Per Subs 219
Subject Interests: Chicano studies
Database Vendor: DRA
Friends of the Library Group
EAST RANCHO DOMINGUEZ BRANCH, 4205 E Compton Blvd, East Rancho Dominguez, 90221-3664. SAN 332-4966. Tel: 310-632-6193. FAX: 310-608-0294. Web Site: www.colapublib.org/libs/dominguez/. *In Charge*, Betty Marlow
Circ 45,016
Library Holdings: Bk Vols 46,457; Per Subs 96
Database Vendor: DRA
Friends of the Library Group
EAST REGIONAL OFFICE, 1601 W Covina Pkwy, West Covina, 91790-2786. SAN 332-382X. Tel: 626-960-2861. FAX: 626-337-4495. *Adminr*, Albert Tovar; *Admin Assoc*, Michael McClintock
Circ 3,855
Library Holdings: Bk Vols 5,711; Per Subs 35
Subject Interests: Art, Recreation
EL CAMINO REAL BRANCH, 4264 E Whittier Blvd, Los Angeles, 90023-2036. SAN 332-5059. Tel: 323-269-8102. FAX: 323-268-5186. Web Site: www.colapublib.org/libs/elcaminoreal/. *In Charge*, Rebecca Garcia
Circ 61,021
Library Holdings: Bk Vols 43,594; Per Subs 68
Database Vendor: DRA
Friends of the Library Group
EL MONTE BRANCH, 3224 Tyler Ave, El Monte, 91731-3356. SAN 332-5083. Tel: 626-444-9506. FAX: 626-443-5864. Web Site: www.colapublib.org/libs/elmonte/. *Librn*, Tony Ramirez
Circ 204,465
Library Holdings: Bk Vols 86,321; Per Subs 149
Database Vendor: DRA
Friends of the Library Group
FLORENCE BRANCH, 1610 E Florence Ave, Los Angeles, 90001-2522. SAN 332-5113. Tel: 323-581-8028. FAX: 323-587-3240. Web Site: www.colapublib.org/libs/florence/. *Librn*, Stephen Kight
Circ 107,066
Library Holdings: Bk Vols 47,714; Per Subs 88
Database Vendor: DRA
GARDENA MAYME DEAR BRANCH, 1731 W Gardena Blvd, Gardena, 90247-4726. SAN 332-5148. Tel: 310-323-6363. FAX: 310-327-0992. Web Site: www.colapublib.org/libs/gardena/. *Librn*, Julie Fu
Circ 268,594
Library Holdings: Bk Vols 139,902; Per Subs 407
Database Vendor: DRA
Friends of the Library Group
GEORGE NYE JR BRANCH, 6600 Del Amo Blvd, Lakewood, 90713-2206. SAN 332-6136. Tel: 562-421-8497. FAX: 562-496-3943. Web Site: www.colapublib.org/libs/nye/. *Librn*, Linda Gahan
Circ 90,007
Library Holdings: Bk Vols 71,048; Per Subs 120
Database Vendor: DRA
Friends of the Library Group
GRAHAM BRANCH, 1900 E Firestone Blvd, Los Angeles, 90001-4126. SAN 332-5172. Tel: 323-582-2903. FAX: 323-581-8478. Web Site: www.colapublib.org/libs/graham/. *In Charge*, Martha Martinez
Circ 100,904
Library Holdings: Bk Vols 48,429; Per Subs 100
Database Vendor: DRA
Friends of the Library Group
HACIENDA HEIGHTS BRANCH, 16010 La Monde St, Hacienda Heights, 91745-4299. SAN 332-5202. Tel: 626-968-9356. FAX: 626-336-3126. Web Site: www.colapublib.org/libs/haciendahts/. *Librn*, John McClellan
Circ 418,401
Library Holdings: Bk Vols 107,551; Per Subs 205
Database Vendor: DRA
Friends of the Library Group
HAWAIIAN GARDENS BRANCH, 12100 E Carson St, No E, Hawaiian Gardens, 90716-1137. SAN 332-5229. Tel: 562-496-1212. FAX: 562-425-0410. Web Site: www.colapublib.org/libs/hawaiiangardens/. *In Charge*, Clairene Almond
Circ 62,622
Library Holdings: Bk Vols 36,677; Per Subs 57
Database Vendor: DRA
HAWTHORNE BRANCH, 12700 S Grevillea Ave, Hawthorne, 90250-4396. SAN 332-5237. Tel: 310-679-8193. FAX: 310-679-4846. Web Site: www.colapublib.org/libs/hawthorne/. *Librn*, Cindy Miller
Circ 231,619
Library Holdings: Bk Vols 169,502; Per Subs 397
Database Vendor: DRA
Friends of the Library Group
HERMOSA BEACH BRANCH, 550 Pier Ave, Hermosa Beach, 90254-3892. SAN 332-5261. Tel: 310-379-8475. FAX: 310-374-0746. Web Site: www.colapublib.org/libs/hermosa/. *Librn*, Ronald Schneider
Circ 101,618
Library Holdings: Bk Vols 53,138; Per Subs 171
Database Vendor: DRA
Friends of the Library Group
CHET HOLIFIELD BRANCH, 1060 S Greenwood Ave, Montebello, 90640-6030. SAN 332-5296. Tel: 323-728-0421. FAX: 323-888-6053. Web Site: www.colapublib.org/libs/holifield/. *Librn*, Beverly Harada
Circ 52,142
Library Holdings: Bk Vols 37,250; Per Subs 73
Database Vendor: DRA
Friends of the Library Group
HOLLYDALE BRANCH, 12000 S Garfield Ave, South Gate, 90280-7894. SAN 332-5326. Tel: 562-634-0156. FAX: 562-531-9530. Web Site: www.colapublib.org/libs/hollydale/. *Librn*, Cherie Shih
Circ 64,953
Library Holdings: Bk Vols 53,653; Per Subs 44
Database Vendor: DRA
Friends of the Library Group
HUNTINGTON PARK BRANCH, 6518 Miles Ave, Huntington Park, 90255-4388. SAN 332-5385. Tel: 323-583-1461. FAX: 323-587-2061. Web Site: www.colapublib.org/libs/huntingtonpark/. *Librn*, Norma Montero
Circ 165,537
Library Holdings: Bk Vols 140,849; Per Subs 257
Subject Interests: N Am Indians
Database Vendor: DRA
Friends of the Library Group
LA CANADA FLINTRIDGE BRANCH, 4545 N Oakwood Ave, La Canada Flintridge, 91011-3358. SAN 332-544X. Tel: 818-790-3330. FAX: 818-952-1754. Web Site: www.colapublib.org/libs/lacanada/. *Librn*, Sue Renyer
Circ 305,676
Library Holdings: Bk Vols 117,669; Per Subs 286
Database Vendor: DRA
Friends of the Library Group
LA CRESCENTA BRANCH, 4521 La Crescenta Ave, La Crescenta, 91214-2999. SAN 332-5474. Tel: 818-248-5313. FAX: 818-248-1289. Web Site: www.colapublib.org/libs/lacrescenta/. *Librn*, Victoria Guagliardo
Circ 195,335
Library Holdings: Bk Vols 66,662; Per Subs 126
Database Vendor: DRA
Friends of the Library Group
LA MIRADA BRANCH, 13800 La Mirada Blvd, La Mirada, 90638-3098. SAN 332-5504. Tel: 562-943-0277. FAX: 562-943-3920. Web Site: www.colapublib.org/libs/lamirada/. *Librn*, Virginia Haussmann
Circ 228,151
Library Holdings: Bk Vols 123,038; Per Subs 268
Database Vendor: DRA
Friends of the Library Group
LA PUENTE BRANCH, 15920 E Central Ave, La Puente, 91744-5499. SAN 332-5563. Tel: 626-968-4613. FAX: 626-369-0294. Web Site: www.colapublib.org/libs/lapuente/. *Librn*, Debby Yashar
Circ 135,490
Library Holdings: Bk Vols 83,320; Per Subs 189
Database Vendor: DRA
Friends of the Library Group
LA VERNE BRANCH, 3640 D St, La Verne, 91750-3572. SAN 332-5628. Tel: 909-596-1934. FAX: 909-596-7303. Web Site: www.colapublib.org/libs/laverne/. *Librn*, Stuart Rosenberg
Circ 147,970
Library Holdings: Bk Vols 71,664; Per Subs 123
Database Vendor: DRA
Friends of the Library Group
LAKE LOS ANGELES, 16921 E Ave O, No A, Palmdale, 93591. SAN 373-563X. Tel: 661-264-0593. FAX: 661-264-0859. Web Site: www.colapublib.org/libs/lakelosangeles/. *In Charge*, Mary MacTaggart
Circ 111,654
Library Holdings: Bk Vols 47,214; Per Subs 54
Database Vendor: DRA
Friends of the Library Group
LANCASTER BRANCH, 601 W Lancaster Blvd, Lancaster, 93534. SAN 332-5539. Tel: 661-948-5029. FAX: 661-945-0480. Web Site: www.colapublib.org/libs/lancaster/. *Librn*, Charles Billodeaux
Circ 585,193
Library Holdings: Bk Vols 269,426; Per Subs 695
Database Vendor: DRA
Friends of the Library Group
LAS VIRGENES, 29130 W Roadside Dr, Agoura Hills, 91301-4599. SAN 332-5598. Tel: 818-889-2278. FAX: 818-991-5019. Web Site: www.colapublib.org/libs/lasvirgenes/. *Librn*, Raya Sagi
Circ 232,099

Library Holdings: Bk Vols 101,625; Per Subs 171
Database Vendor: DRA
Friends of the Library Group
LAS VIRGENES BOOKMOBILE, 23519 W Civic Ctr Way, Malibu, 90265. Tel: 310-456-8572. FAX: 310-456-8681. Web Site: www.colapublib.org/libs/lasvirgenes/bookmobile.html. *In Charge*, Donna Serra
Circ 24,398
Library Holdings: Bk Vols 7,575; Per Subs 18
Database Vendor: DRA
LAWNDALE BRANCH, 14615 Burin Ave, Lawndale, 90260-1431. SAN 332-5652. Tel: 310-676-0177. FAX: 310-973-0498. Web Site: www.colapublib.org/libs/lawndale/. *Librn*, Elmita Brown
Circ 73,116
Library Holdings: Bk Vols 42,306; Per Subs 174
Database Vendor: DRA
Friends of the Library Group
LENNOX BRANCH, 4359 Lennox Blvd, Lennox, 90304-2398. SAN 332-5687. Tel: 310-674-0385. FAX: 310-673-6508. Web Site: www.colapublib.org/libs/lennox/. *Librn*, Peter Hsu
Circ 210,064
Library Holdings: Bk Vols 59,046; Per Subs 132
Database Vendor: DRA
Friends of the Library Group
LITTLEROCK BRANCH, 35119 80th St E, Littlerock, 93543. SAN 332-5717. Tel: 661-944-4138. FAX: 661-944-4150. Web Site: www.colapublib.org/libs/littlerock/. *Librn*, Susan Broman
Circ 104,618
Library Holdings: Bk Vols 50,082; Per Subs 108
Database Vendor: DRA
Friends of the Library Group
LIVE OAK BRANCH, 4153-55 E Live Oak Ave, Arcadia, 91006-5895. SAN 332-5741. Tel: 626-446-8803. FAX: 626-446-9418. Web Site: www.colapublib.org/libs/liveoak/. *Librn*, Brian Trygstad
Circ 155,839
Library Holdings: Bk Vols 46,503; Per Subs 96
Database Vendor: DRA
Friends of the Library Group
LOMITA BRANCH, 24200 Narbonne Ave, Lomita, 90717-1188. SAN 332-5776. Tel: 310-539-4515. FAX: 310-534-8649. Web Site: www.colapublib.org/libs/lomita/. *Librn*, Linda Shimane
Pop 143,793; Circ 146,334
Library Holdings: Bk Vols 47,428; Per Subs 190
Database Vendor: DRA
Friends of the Library Group
LOS NIETOS, 11644 E Slauson Ave, Whittier, 90606-3396. SAN 332-5806. Tel: 562-695-0708. FAX: 562-699-3876. Web Site: www.colapublib.org/libs/losnietos/. *In Charge*, Theresa Stout-Cazares
Circ 69,573
Library Holdings: Bk Vols 38,322; Per Subs 57
Database Vendor: DRA
LYNWOOD BRANCH, 11320 Bullis Rd, Lynwood, 90262-3661. SAN 332-5830. Tel: 310-635-7121. FAX: 310-635-4967. Web Site: www.colapublib.org/libs/lynwood/. *Librn*, Glorieta Navo
Circ 152,324
Library Holdings: Bk Vols 90,564; Per Subs 135
Database Vendor: DRA
Friends of the Library Group
MALIBU BRANCH, 23519 W Civic Center Way, Malibu, 90265-4804. SAN 332-5865. Tel: 310-456-6438. FAX: 310-456-8681. Web Site: www.colapublib.org/libs/malibu/. *Librn*, Sherri Smith
Circ 121,359
Library Holdings: Bk Vols 88,632; Per Subs 185
Special Collections: Arkel Erb Memorial Mountaineering Coll
Database Vendor: DRA
Friends of the Library Group
MANHATTAN BEACH BRANCH, 1320 Highland Ave, Manhattan Beach, 90266-4789. SAN 332-589X. Tel: 310-545-8595. FAX: 310-545-5394. Web Site: www.colapublib.org/libs/manhattan/. *Librn*, Lila Held
Circ 302,879
Library Holdings: Bk Vols 123,714; Per Subs 401
Database Vendor: DRA
Friends of the Library Group
MASAO W SATOW BRANCH, 14433 S Crenshaw Blvd, Gardena, 90249-3142. SAN 332-6462. Tel: 310-679-0638. FAX: 310-970-0275. Web Site: www.colapublib.org/libs/satow/. *Librn*, Alice Tang
Circ 71,244
Library Holdings: Bk Vols 55,414; Per Subs 137
Database Vendor: DRA
Friends of the Library Group
MAYWOOD CESAR CHAVEZ BRANCH, 4323 E Slauson Ave, Maywood, 90270-2837. SAN 332-5989. Tel: 323-771-8600. FAX: 323-560-0515. Web Site: www.colapublib.org/libs/maywood/. *Librn*, Rosemary Gurrola
Circ 87,187
Library Holdings: Bk Vols 40,892; Per Subs 113
Database Vendor: DRA
MONTEBELLO BRANCH, 1550 W Beverly Blvd, Montebello, 90640-3993. SAN 332-6012. Tel: 323-722-6551. FAX: 323-722-3018. Web Site: www.colapublib.org/libs/montebello/. *Librn*, Lisa Castaneda
Circ 230,272
Library Holdings: Bk Vols 201,325; Per Subs 486
Database Vendor: DRA
Friends of the Library Group
NEWHALL BRANCH, 22704 Ninth St, Newhall, 91321-2808. SAN 332-6047. Tel: 661-259-0750. FAX: 661-254-5760. E-Mail: ac@104.colapl.org. Web Site: www.colapublib.org/libs/newhall/. *Librn*, Judith Hist
Founded 1916. Circ 162,374
Library Holdings: Bk Vols 65,461; Per Subs 109
Database Vendor: DRA
Friends of the Library Group
NORTH REGIONAL OFFICE, 601 W Lancaster Blvd, Lancaster, 93534. SAN 332-3889. Tel: 661-948-0796. FAX: 661-949-7386. *In Charge*, Catherine Bowen
Circ 425
Library Holdings: Bk Vols 3,972
Subject Interests: Philosophy, Religion
Special Collections: Arkel Erb Mountaineering Coll; Sams Photofact Coll
NORWALK BRANCH, 12350 Imperial Hwy, Norwalk, 90650-3199. SAN 332-6071. Tel: 562-868-0775. FAX: 562-929-1130. Web Site: www.colapublib.org/libs/norwalk/. *Librn*, Linda Chavez-Doyle
Circ 286,710
Library Holdings: Bk Vols 258,293; Per Subs 594
Subject Interests: Business
Special Collections: Edelman Public Policy Coll
Database Vendor: DRA
Friends of the Library Group
NORWOOD, 4550 N Peck Rd, El Monte, 91732-1998. SAN 332-6101. Tel: 626-443-3147. FAX: 626-350-6099. Web Site: www.colapublib.org/libs/norwood/. *Librn*, Pat Libby
Circ 148,496
Library Holdings: Bk Vols 70,577; Per Subs 155
Database Vendor: DRA
Friends of the Library Group
PARAMOUNT BRANCH, 16254 Colorado Ave, Paramount, 90723-5085. SAN 332-6160. Tel: 562-630-3171. FAX: 562-630-3968. Web Site: www.colapublib.org/libs/paramount/. *Librn*, Leticia Tan
Circ 129,372
Library Holdings: Bk Vols 71,448; Per Subs 116
Database Vendor: DRA
Friends of the Library Group
PICO RIVERA BRANCH, 9001 Mines Ave, Pico Rivera, 90660-3098. SAN 332-6195. Tel: 562-942-7394. FAX: 562-942-7779. Web Site: www.colapublib.org/libs/picorivera/. *Librn*, Kathi Grant
Circ 76,503
Library Holdings: Bk Vols 71,819; Per Subs 105
Database Vendor: DRA
Friends of the Library Group
QUARTZ HILL BRANCH, 42018 N 50th St W, Quartz Hill, 93536-3509. SAN 332-6225. Tel: 661-943-2454. FAX: 661-943-6337. Web Site: www.colapublib.org/libs/quartzhill/. *In Charge*, Virginia Tenneson
Circ 135,363
Library Holdings: Bk Vols 56,276; Per Subs 78
Database Vendor: DRA
Friends of the Library Group
ANTHONY QUINN BRANCH, 3965 Cesar E Chavez Ave, Los Angeles, 90063. SAN 332-4486. Tel: 323-264-7715. FAX: 323-262-7121. Web Site: www.colapublib.org/libs/quinn/. *Librn*, Joshua Cloner
Circ 84,235
Library Holdings: Bk Vols 53,786; Per Subs 44
Database Vendor: DRA
RIVERA BRANCH, 7828 S Serapis Ave, Pico Rivera, 90660-4600. SAN 332-625X. Tel: 562-949-5485. FAX: 562-948-3455. Web Site: www.colapublib.org/libs/rivera/. *Librn*, Joe Olvera
Circ 41,257
Library Holdings: Bk Vols 37,196; Per Subs 63
Database Vendor: DRA
Friends of the Library Group
ROSEMEAD BRANCH, 8800 Valley Blvd, Rosemead, 91770-1788. SAN 332-6284. Tel: 626-573-5220. FAX: 626-280-8523. Web Site: www.colapublib.org/libs/rosemead/. *Librn*, Susana Rogers
Circ 240,103
Library Holdings: Bk Vols 164,264; Per Subs 309
Special Collections: California Coll
Database Vendor: DRA
Friends of the Library Group
ROWLAND HEIGHTS BRANCH, 1850 Nogales St, Rowland Heights, 91748-2945. SAN 332-6314. Tel: 626-912-5348. FAX: 626-810-3538. Web Site: www.colapublib.org/libs/rowlandhts/. *Librn*, Sherna Kopple-Svensson
Pop 50,000; Circ 533,667
Library Holdings: Bk Vols 135,953; Per Subs 292
Database Vendor: DRA
Friends of the Library Group
SAN DIMAS BRANCH, 145 N Walnut Ave, San Dimas, 91773-2603. SAN 332-6349. Tel: 909-599-6738. FAX: 909-592-4490. Web Site: www.colapublib.org/libs/sandimas/. *Librn*, Mary Noonan

Circc 211,201
Library Holdings: Bk Vols 107,307; Per Subs 138
Database Vendor: DRA
Friends of the Library Group
SAN FERNANDO BRANCH, 1050 Library St, San Fernando, 91340-2433. SAN 332-6373. Tel: 818-365-6928. FAX: 818-365-3820. Web Site: www.colapublib.org/libs/sanfernando/. *Librn*, Kathleen Coakley
Circ 148,536
Library Holdings: Bk Vols 74,055; Per Subs 132
Database Vendor: DRA
Friends of the Library Group
SAN GABRIEL BRANCH, 500 S Del Mar Ave, San Gabriel, 91776-2408. SAN 332-6403. Tel: 626-287-0761. FAX: 626-285-2610. Web Site: www.colapublib.org/libs/sangabriel/. *Librn*, Miling Maria Yap
Circ 159,254
Library Holdings: Bk Vols 94,362; Per Subs 115
Database Vendor: DRA
Friends of the Library Group
SANTA CLARITA VALLEY BOOKMOBILE, 22704 W Ninth St, Santa Clarita, 91321. Tel: 661-260-1792. FAX: 661-254-5760. Web Site: www.colapublib.org/libs/santaclarita/bookmobile.html. *In Charge*, Irene Beltran
Circ 48,987
Library Holdings: Bk Vols 11,771; Per Subs 29
Database Vendor: DRA
SORENSEN BRANCH, 11405 E Rose Hedge Dr, Whittier, 90606-1994. SAN 377-6549. Tel: 562-248-5313. FAX: 562-695-8925. Web Site: www.colapublib.org/libs/sorensen/. *In Charge*, Ellie Weismiller
Circ 41,819
Library Holdings: Bk Vols 22,546; Per Subs 46
Database Vendor: DRA
SOUTH EL MONTE BRANCH, 1430 N Central Ave, South El Monte, 91733-3302. SAN 332-6527. Tel: 626-443-4158. FAX: 626-575-7450. Web Site: www.colapublib.org/libs/selmonte/. *Librn*, Roberta Marquez
Circ 95,929
Library Holdings: Bk Vols 51,009; Per Subs 75
Database Vendor: DRA
Friends of the Library Group
SOUTH REGIONAL OFFICE, 12348 Imperial Hwy, Norwalk, 90650-3199. SAN 332-3919. Tel: 562-868-0770. FAX: 562-868-3088. *Adminr*, Stephen Klein; *Admin Assoc*, Billie Frierson
Circ 1,039
Library Holdings: Bk Vols 9,473; Per Subs 29
Subject Interests: Business and management, Social sciences and issues
Special Collections: Black Resource Center; Business
SOUTH WHITTIER BRANCH, 14433 Leffingwell Rd, Whittier, 90604-2966. SAN 332-6551. Tel: 562-946-4415. FAX: 562-941-6138. Web Site: www.colapublib.org/libs/swhittier/. *Librn*, Verna Dunning
Circ 102,990
Library Holdings: Bk Vols 63,180; Per Subs 114
Database Vendor: DRA
Friends of the Library Group
SUNKIST, 840 N Puente Ave, 91746-1316. SAN 332-6586. Tel: 626-960-2707. FAX: 626-338-5141. Web Site: www.colapublib.org/libs/sunkist/. *Librn*, Deborah Anderson
Circ 160,024
Library Holdings: Bk Vols 74,275; Per Subs 149
Database Vendor: DRA
Friends of the Library Group
LLOYD TABER-MARINA DEL REY BRANCH, 4533 Admiralty Way, Marina del Rey, 90292-5416. SAN 332-5954. Tel: 310-821-3415. FAX: 310-306-3372. Web Site: www.colapublib.org/libs/marina/. *Librn*, Claudia Fishler
Circ 65,943
Library Holdings: Bk Vols 59,779; Per Subs 210
Database Vendor: DRA
Friends of the Library Group
TEMPLE CITY BRANCH, 5939 Golden West Ave, Temple City, 91780-2292. SAN 332-6640. Tel: 626-285-2136. FAX: 626-285-2314. Web Site: www.colapublib.org/libs/templecity/. *Librn*, Joseph Zagami
Circ 254,914
Library Holdings: Bk Vols 108,276; Per Subs 208
Database Vendor: DRA
Friends of the Library Group
VALENCIA, 23743 W Valencia Blvd, Santa Clarita, 91355-2191. SAN 332-6675. Tel: 661-259-8942. FAX: 616-259-7187. Web Site: www.colapublib.org/libs/valencia/. *Librn*, Andera Kish
Circ 808,172
Library Holdings: Bk Vols 231,956; Per Subs 546
Database Vendor: DRA
Friends of the Library Group
VALENCIA REGIONAL OFFICE, 23710 W Magic Mountain Pkwy, Santa Clarita, 91355. SAN 376-9380. Tel: 661-259-8946. FAX: 661-254-5999. *Admin Dir*, Sandra Duncan; *Admin Assoc*, Josefina Reyes
Circ 777
Library Holdings: Bk Vols 2,110; Per Subs 22
VICTORIA PARK, 17906 S Avalon Blvd, Carson, 90746-1598. SAN 332-6705. Tel: 310-327-4830. FAX: 310-327-3630. Web Site: www.colapublib.org/libs/victoria/. *Librn*, Cynthia Nickelson
Circ 32,706
Library Holdings: Bk Vols 40,266; Per Subs 112
Database Vendor: DRA
Friends of the Library Group
VIEW PARK, 3854 W 54th St, Los Angeles, 90043-2297. SAN 332-673X. Tel: 323-293-5371. FAX: 323-292-4330. Web Site: www.colapublib.org/libs/viewpark/. *Librn*, Anthony Lynch
Circ 63,276
Library Holdings: Bk Vols 61,427; Per Subs 170
Database Vendor: DRA
Friends of the Library Group
WALNUT BRANCH, 21155 La Puente Rd, Walnut, 91789-2017. SAN 332-6829. Tel: 909-595-0757. FAX: 909-595-7553. Web Site: www.colapublib.org/libs/walnut/. *Librn*, Jenny Cheng
Circ 195,309
Library Holdings: Bk Vols 88,178; Per Subs 105
Database Vendor: DRA
Friends of the Library Group
LELAND R WEAVER BRANCH, 4035 Tweedy Blvd, South Gate, 90280-6199. SAN 332-6853. Tel: 323-567-8853. FAX: 323-563-1046. Web Site: www.colapublib.org/libs/weaver/. *Librn*, Eileen Tokar
Circ 149,538
Library Holdings: Bk Vols 122,750; Per Subs 252
Database Vendor: DRA
Friends of the Library Group
WEST COVINA BRANCH, 1601 W Covina Pkwy, West Covina, 91790-2786. SAN 332-6888. Tel: 626-962-3541. FAX: 626-962-1507. Web Site: www.colapublib.org/libs/wcovina/. *Librn*, Linda Siggins; Staff 50 (MLS 12, Non-MLS 38)
Circ 448,374
Library Holdings: Bk Vols 259,627; Per Subs 547
Database Vendor: DRA
Friends of the Library Group
WEST HOLLYWOOD BRANCH, 715 N San Vicente Blvd, West Hollywood, 90069-5020. SAN 332-6438. Tel: 310-652-5340. FAX: 310-652-2580. Web Site: www.colapublib.org/libs/whollywood/. *Librn*, Laura Frakes
Circ 150,038
Library Holdings: Bk Vols 85,077; Per Subs 144
Subject Interests: HIV-AIDS
Database Vendor: DRA
Friends of the Library Group
WEST REGIONAL OFFICE, 150 E 216th St, Carson, 90745-2797. SAN 332-3943. Tel: 310-830-0231. FAX: 310-834-4097. *Admin Dir*, Jean Alexander; *Admin Assoc*, Ruth Venerable
Circ 765
Library Holdings: Bk Vols 5,353; Per Subs 22
Subject Interests: Medicine
Special Collections: Consumer Health Information Program & Services (CHIPS); HIV Information Center; Judaica; Nautical
WESTLAKE VILLAGE BRANCH, 4371 Park Terrace Dr, Westlake Village, 91361. SAN 373-5648. Tel: 818-865-9230. FAX: 818-865-0724. Web Site: www.colapublib.org/libs/westlake/. *Librn*, Marie Scherb-Clift
Circ 116,154
Library Holdings: Bk Vols 47,365; Per Subs 145
Database Vendor: DRA
Friends of the Library Group
WILLOWBROOK BRANCH, 11838 Wilmington Ave, Los Angeles, 90059-3016. SAN 332-6918. Tel: 323-564-5698. FAX: 323-564-7709. Web Site: www.colapublib.org/libs/willowbrook/. *In Charge*, Lydia Hammons
Circ 67,548
Library Holdings: Bk Vols 27,651; Per Subs 52
Database Vendor: DRA
WISEBURN, 5335 W 135th St, Hawthorne, 90250-4948. SAN 332-6942. Tel: 310-643-8880. FAX: 310-536-0749. Web Site: www.colapublib.org/libs/wiseburn/. *Librn*, Barbara Johnson
Circ 91,714
Library Holdings: Bk Vols 50,146; Per Subs 206
Database Vendor: DRA
Friends of the Library Group
WOODCREST, 1340 W 106th St, Los Angeles, 90044-1626. SAN 332-6977. Tel: 323-757-9373. FAX: 323-756-4907. Web Site: www.colapublib.org/libs/woodcrest/. *Librn*, Joan Mead
Circ 150,906
Library Holdings: Bk Vols 68,093; Per Subs 150
Database Vendor: DRA
Friends of the Library Group
Bookmobiles: 3. Librns, Pat Cowman, Gloria Pearson, Irene Beltran. Santa Clarita Valley Bookmobile - Bk vols 10307. Tel: 661-260-1792, Fax: 661-254-5760, Website: www.colapublib.org/libs/santaclarita/bookmobile.html

P DOWNEY CITY LIBRARY, 11121 Brookshire, PO Box 7015, 90241-7015. SAN 300-7146. Tel: 562-904-7360. Interlibrary Loan Service Tel: 562-904-7360, Ext 20. Circulation Tel: 562-904-7360, Ext 28. Reference Tel: 562-904-7360, Ext 32. FAX: 562-923-3763. Web Site: www.downey.lib.ca.us. *Dir*, Victoria L Jenkins; E-Mail: vjenkins@downey.lib.ca.us; *Cat*, Marion Scichilone; *Ref*, Thad Phillips; *Ch Servs*, Gina Probst; Staff 9 (MLS 9)
Founded 1958. Pop 102,100; Circ 468,168
Jul 1999-Jun 2000 Income $2,020,657, State $223,839, City $1,646,933, Federal $32,500, Locally Generated Income $117,385. Mats Exp $229,403, Books $175,488, Per/Ser (Incl. Access Fees) $18,178, Micro $5,917, Electronic Ref Mat (Incl. Access Fees) $19,164. (Prof $774,330)
Library Holdings: Bk Titles 116,080; Per Subs 315
Automation Activity & Vendor Info: (Circulation) epixtech, inc.
Mem of Metropolitan Cooperative Library System
Open Mon-Thurs 10-9, Fri & Sat 10-5, Sun 1-5
Friends of the Library Group

S DOWNEY HISTORICAL SOCIETY, Downey History Center Library,* 12540 Rives Ave, PO Box 554, 90241. SAN 328-2406. Tel: 562-862-2777, 562-927-5255. *Dir*, Barbara Callarman
Library Holdings: Bk Titles 800
Subject Interests: Aerospace, Governor Downey, Local history, Los Nietos Valley pioneers
Special Collections: Aerospace; Clipping File; Downey Court Dockets (1871-1957); Local Newspapers (1888-present); Los Angeles County District Attorney's Records of Arrests (1883- 1919); Photographs; School, Insurance & Agriculture Records

S LOS ANGELES COUNTY OFFICE OF EDUCATION, Library Services, Bell Flower Annex, 9300 Imperial Hwy, 90242. (Mail add: 12757 Bell Flower Blvd, 90242), SAN 324-4687. Tel: 562-922-6359. FAX: 562-940-1699. E-Mail: prc_reference_desk@lacoe.edu. Web Site: www.lacoe.edu/doc/prc/prc.html. *Info Res*, Sharon McNeil; E-Mail: mcnneil_sharon@lacoe.edu; Staff 2 (MLS 2)
Founded 1974
Library Holdings: Per Subs 300
Subject Interests: Curric, Education
Publications: Funding brief newsletter (weekly)
Partic in Coop Libr Agency for Syst & Servs; Dialog Corporation

M RANCHO LOS AMIGOS MEDICAL CENTER, Health Sciences Library, 7601 E Imperial Hwy, Rm 1109, 90242-3456. SAN 300-7154. Tel: 562-401-7696. *In Charge*, Evelyn Marks
Founded 1959
Library Holdings: Bk Titles 9,010; Per Subs 450
Subject Interests: Orthopedics, Physical therapy
Partic in BRS; Dialog Corporation; Medline; SDC Info Servs
Open Mon-Thurs 8-9, Fri 8-5 & Sat 9-1
Friends of the Library Group

DOWNIEVILLE

L SIERRA COUNTY LAW LIBRARY, Courthouse, PO Box 457, 95936. SAN 373-1871. Tel: 530-289-3269. FAX: 530-289-0130. *Librn*, Sheri Johnson
Library Holdings: Bk Vols 3,000
Subject Interests: State law

DUARTE

S BAXTER HYLAND RESEARCH LIBRARY,* 1720 Flower Ave, 91010-2923. SAN 300-6867. Tel: 626-305-5017. FAX: 626-305-5092.
Founded 1955
Library Holdings: Bk Titles 100; Per Subs 250
Subject Interests: Biochemistry, Hematology, Microbiology, Virology
Partic in Dialog Corporation; Pacific SW Regional Med Libr Serv
Branches:
BAXTER HEALTHCARE INFORMATION MANAGEMENT CENTER, Rte 120 Wilson Rd, Round Lake, 60073. SAN 377-8630. Tel: 847-270-5360. *Mgr*, Ardys Chang; *Tech Servs*, John Chu

M CITY OF HOPE NATIONAL MEDICAL CENTER, Graff Medical & Scientific Library, 1500 E Duarte Rd, 91010-0269. SAN 300-7170. Tel: 626-301-8497. FAX: 626-357-1929. E-Mail: Internet: library@coh.org. *Dir*, Anne Dillibe; E-Mail: adillibe@coh.org; Staff 6 (MLS 2, Non-MLS 4)
Founded 1954
Library Holdings: Bk Vols 36,000; Per Subs 818
Subject Interests: Biology, Cancer, Endocrinology, Genetics, Hematology, Immunology, Pathology, Psychiatry, Respiratory diseases
Partic in OCLC Online Computer Library Center, Inc

DUBLIN

S NATIONAL FOOD LABORATORY,* 6363 Clark Ave, 94568-3097. SAN 300-7189. Tel: 925-828-1440, Ext 274. FAX: 925-833-8795. *In Charge*, Patricia Troutman
Library Holdings: Bk Titles 2,250; Per Subs 100
Restriction: Staff use only
Partic in Dialog Corporation

EDWARDS AFB

G NASA, Dryden Flight Research Center Library, PO Box 273, 93523-0273. SAN 300-7197. Tel: 661-276-3702. FAX: 661-276-2244. Web Site: nasagalaxie.larc.nasa.gov. *Librn*, Barbara Rogers
Library Holdings: Bk Titles 3,100; Per Subs 85
Subject Interests: Aeronautics
Special Collections: NACA Wartime Reports & RM's
Partic in Dialog Corporation; Nasa Libraries Information System - Nasa Galaxie; OCLC Online Computer Library Center, Inc
Friends of the Library Group

UNITED STATES AIR FORCE
A AIR FORCE FLIGHT TEST CENTER TECHNICAL LIBRARY, 412 TW/TSDL, 307 E Popson Ave Bldg 1400 Rm 110, 93524-6630. SAN 331-9113. Tel: 661-277-3606. TDD: 805-277-2124. FAX: 661-277-6451. E-Mail: edu@mhs.elan.af.mil, lamb%ts@mhs.elan.af.mil. *Chief Librn*, Jolaine Lamb; E-Mail: jolaine.lamb@edwards.af.mil; *Asst Librn*, Darrell Shiplett; *Librn*, Ted Miles
Founded 1955
Library Holdings: Bk Vols 31,474; Per Subs 513
Subject Interests: Aeronautics, Chemistry, Electrical engineering, Mathematics, Physics
Restriction: Staff use only
Partic in Defense Technical Information Center; Dialog Corporation; OCLC Online Computer Library Center, Inc
Special Services for the Deaf - TDD
A EDWARDS AIR FORCE BASE LIBRARY, 95th SPTG/SVMG, 5 W Yeager Blvd Bldg 2665, 93524-1295. SAN 331-9083. Tel: 805-277-2375, 805-277-4881. FAX: 805-277-6100. *Librn*, Michael Moyer
Founded 1942
Library Holdings: Bk Vols 40,000; Per Subs 430
Subject Interests: Education, Recreation
Restriction: Non-circulating to the public
Partic in OCLC Online Computer Library Center, Inc

EL CAJON

CR CHRISTIAN HERITAGE COLLEGE LIBRARY, 2100 Greenfield Dr, 92019-1157. SAN 331-9148. Tel: 619-441-2200, Ext 1224, 1223. FAX: 619-440-0209. Web Site: www.christianheritage.edu. *Dir, Online Servs*, Mona Hsu; *Dir Libr Serv*, Ruth Martin; Staff 2 (MLS 2)
Founded 1970. Enrl 600; Fac 75; Highest Degree: Bachelor
1998-1999 Mats Exp $150,000, Books $60,000, Per/Ser (Incl. Access Fees) $20,000. Sal $95,000 (Prof $80,000)
Library Holdings: Bk Vols 70,000; Bk Titles 55,400; Per Subs 220
Subject Interests: Biblical studies, Business and management, Counseling, Education, History, Humanities, Music, Psychology
Database Vendor: Ebsco - EbscoHost, ProQuest, Wilson - Wilson Web
Partic in Coop Libr Agency for Syst & Servs; New York Metrop Ref & Res Libr Agency; OCLC Online Computer Library Center, Inc

J CUYAMACA COLLEGE LIBRARY, 900 Rancho San Diego Pkwy, 92019-4304. SAN 322-872X. Tel: 619-660-4416. Reference Tel: 619-660-4421. FAX: 619-660-4493. Web Site: www.cuyamaca.net. *Assoc Dean*, Pei-Hua Chou; *Librn*, Janice Camp; *Librn*, Kate Dunn; *Librn*, Angela Nesta; *Librn*, Jeri Resto; *Librn*, Lawrence Sherwood; *Librn*, Virginia Sherwood; *Librn*, Bruce Thompson; *Librn*, John Tibbals; Staff 9 (MLS 4, Non-MLS 5)
Founded 1978. Enrl 7,000; Fac 89; Highest Degree: Doctorate
Jul 1999-Jun 2000 Income $733,900. Mats Exp $67,800, Books $46,000, Per/Ser (Incl. Access Fees) $21,000, AV Equip $800. Sal $563,700 (Prof $362,770)
Library Holdings: Bk Vols 32,000; Bk Titles 24,958; Per Subs 283

SR FIRST PRESBYTERIAN CHURCH, El Cajon Library, 500 Farragut Circle, 92020. SAN 374-8448. Tel: 619-442-2583. FAX: 619-442-2588. Web Site: www.forministry.com/92020fpcoe. *Librn*, Elva Colbeth; *Librn*, Michele Blackman; Staff 2 (MLS 1, Non-MLS 1)
Founded 1981
Jan 1999-Dec 1999 Mats Exp $500, Books $200, Per/Ser (Incl. Access Fees) $125
Library Holdings: Bk Vols 4,000; Per Subs 25; Spec Interest Per Sub 50
Subject Interests: Religion
Partic in Church & Synagogue Libr Asn

J GROSSMONT COLLEGE, Lewis F Smith Learning Resource Center Library, 8800 Grossmont College Dr, 92020-1799. SAN 300-7200. Tel: 619-644-7355. FAX: 619-644-7921. Web Site: grossmont.gccd.cc.ca.us/library.

Dir, Thomas U Foster; E-Mail: tom_foster@gcccd.cc.ca.us; *Tech Servs*, Richard L Johnson; *Chairperson*, Dr Curtis Stevens; *Bibliog Instr*, Michelle Blackman; Staff 5 (MLS 5)
Founded 1961. Enrl 16,660; Fac 1,393
Library Holdings: Bk Vols 106,149; Per Subs 650
Special Collections: Career Information; Reference Resources

S PHOTOPHILE STOCK PHOTOGRAPHY AGENCY LIBRARY, PMB 281, 2650 Jamacha Rd, No 147, 92019. SAN 374-5554. Tel: 619-660-1130. FAX: 619-660-1920. Web Site: www.photo-phile.com. *In Charge*, Nancy Masten
Founded 1967

EL CENTRO

P EL CENTRO PUBLIC LIBRARY,* 539 State St, 92243-2973. SAN 331-9202. Tel: 760-337-4565. FAX: 760-352-1384. Web Site: www.eclib.org. *Actg Librn*, Lois Shelton; E-Mail: lshelton@eclib.org; Staff 2 (MLS 2)
Founded 1909. Pop 31,650; Circ 147,000
1997-1998 Income $265,433. Mats Exp $57,335. Sal $208,098
Library Holdings: Bk Titles 95,000; Per Subs 45
Special Collections: Imperial Valley California Coll, bks & pamphlets
Mem of Serra Cooperative Library System
Branches: 1
EL CENTRO COMMUNITY CENTER, 375 S First, 92243. SAN 331-9237. Tel: 760-337-4565. Web Site: www.eclib.org. *Librn*, Alma Vargas
Library Holdings: Bk Vols 1,500

P IMPERIAL COUNTY FREE LIBRARY,* 1125 Main St, 92243. SAN 332-1606. Tel: 760-337-4565. FAX: 760-352-1384.
Founded 1912. Pop 41,730; Circ 153,738
Library Holdings: Bk Vols 61,000
Subject Interests: Agriculture, Social sciences and issues
Special Collections: California & Imperial Valley Coll
Mem of Serra Cooperative Library System
Branches: 8
CALIPATRIA BRANCH, PO Box 707, Calipatria, 92233-0707. SAN 332-1630. Tel: 760-348-2630. FAX: 760-348-5575. *In Charge*, Theresa Woelke
DESERT SHORES BRANCH, 801 N Palm, Desert Shores, 92275. (Mail add: PO Box 5319, Desert Shores, 92275-5319), *In Charge*, Rita Hunt
Library Holdings: Bk Vols 3,000
HEBER BRANCH, 1136 Heber Ave, Heber, 92249. (Mail add: PO Box 1530, Heber, 92249-1530), Tel: 760-336-0737. *In Charge*, Guadalupe Delgado
Pop 1,241; Circ 14,084
Jul 1998-Jun 1999
Library Holdings: Bk Vols 2,300
Friends of the Library Group
HOLTVILLE BRANCH, PO Box 755, Holtville, 92250. SAN 332-1665. Tel: 760-356-2385. FAX: 760-356-2385. *In Charge*, Sally Henthorne
NILAND BRANCH, 8106 Hwy III, Niland, 92257. (Mail add: PO Box 70, Niland, 92257-0070), *In Charge*, Laveda Thetford
Library Holdings: Bk Vols 2,200
OCOTILLO BRANCH, 1159 N Imperial, Ocotillo, 92259. (Mail add: PO Box 23, Ocotillo, 92259-0023),
Library Holdings: Bk Vols 2,100
SALTON CITY BRANCH, 2098 Frontage Rd, Salton City, 92275. (Mail add: PO Box 5539, Salton City, 92275-5539), Tel: 760-394-5503. *In Charge*, Rita Hunt
Library Holdings: Bk Vols 3,500
WESTMORLAND BRANCH, 335 S Center St, Westmorland, 92281. (Mail add: PO Box 398, Westmorland, 92281-0398), *In Charge*, Evelyn Ford
Library Holdings: Bk Vols 5,000

GL IMPERIAL COUNTY LAW LIBRARY, Courthouse, 939 W Main St, 92243. SAN 300-7227. Tel: 760-482-4374. FAX: 760-352-3184. *Librn*, Ramona Gieck
Library Holdings: Bk Vols 12,100

UNITED STATES NAVY
A NAVAL AIR GENERAL LIBRARY, MWR Library, 2003 D St, Bldg 318, 92243. SAN 331-9261. Tel: 760-339-2470. FAX: 760-339-2470. *Librn*, Alma Zuniga-Foley; E-Mail: foleya@nasni_emh.navy.mil
Library Holdings: Bk Titles 8,000; Per Subs 14

EL CERRITO

S LARRY MARKS INFORMATION FOR BUSINESS LIBRARY, 7806 Potrero Ave, 94530. SAN 371-1471. Tel: 510-232-3767. E-Mail: thefolks@lx.netcom.com. *Dir*, Larry Marks; Staff 1 (Non-MLS 1)
Highest Degree: Bachelor
1998-1999 Income $25,000. Mats Exp $1,850, Books $50, Per/Ser (Incl. Access Fees) $1,800
Library Holdings: Bk Vols 200; Per Subs 30
Subject Interests: Humor
Partic in Dialog Corporation

EL MONTE

S AMERICAN SOCIETY OF MILITARY HISTORY LIBRARY,* 1918 N Rosemeade Blvd, 91733. SAN 328-039X. Tel: 626-442-1776. FAX: 626-443-1776. *Exec Dir*, Don Michelson
Founded 1962
Library Holdings: Bk Titles 30,000; Per Subs 10

S CALIFORNIA AIR RESOURCES BOARD, Agency Library,* 9480 Telstar Ave Ste 4, 91731. SAN 320-5576. Tel: 626-575-7065. FAX: 626-575-6685. *Tech Servs*, Karen Woo
Library Holdings: Bk Vols 267; Per Subs 40
Restriction: Staff use only

S EL MONTE MUSEUM OF HISTORY LIBRARY, Museum Library, 3150 N Tyler Ave, 91731. SAN 327-3148. Tel: 626-444-3813, 626-580-2232. *Curator*, Donna Crippen; *Librn*, Fred Love
Library Holdings: Bk Vols 3,000; Bk Titles 1,700; Per Subs 20

EL SEGUNDO

S AEROSPACE CORP, Charles C Lauritsen Library, 2350 E El Segundo Blvd, 90245-4691. (Mail add: PO Box 80966, Mail Sta M1-199, 90080-0966), SAN 300-7251. Tel: 310-336-6093. FAX: 310-336-1467. *Dir Info Resources & Res*, Patricia W Green; E-Mail: patricia.w.green@aero.org; *Archivist*, Kay J Wade; Fax: 310-336-5912, E-Mail: kay.j.wade@aero.org; *Res*, Benita T Campbell; Tel: 310-336-6178, E-Mail: benita.t.campbell@aero.org; *Res*, Susan Clifford; *Tech Servs*, Chris Lincoln
Founded 1960
Library Holdings: Bk Vols 100,000; Bk Titles 99,800; Per Subs 700
Subject Interests: Aeronautics, Aerospace science, Astronautics, Engineering
Special Collections: Aerospace Corporation Authors
Automation Activity & Vendor Info: (Acquisitions) SIRSI; (Cataloging) SIRSI; (Circulation) SIRSI; (OPAC) SIRSI; (Serials) SIRSI
Publications: Library Services Announcements; Professional Papers
Restriction: By appointment only, Circulation to military employees only
Partic in Defense Technical Information Center; Dialog Corporation; Nasa Libraries Information System - Nasa Galaxie; OCLC Online Computer Library Center, Inc; Pergamon Infoline; Pergamon Orbit; RLIN; UCLA-Orion

S COMPUTER SCIENCES CORP, Corporate Library,* 2100 E Grand Ave, 90245-2299. SAN 300-7278. Tel: 310-615-1709. FAX: 310-322-3685. *Mgr*, Michael L Shapiro; E-Mail: michaelcsc@aol.com
Founded 1964
Library Holdings: Bk Titles 500; Per Subs 80
Subject Interests: Business and management, Marketing
Special Collections: Annual Fortune 500 reports
Publications: Newsletter (quarterly)
Partic in Coop Libr Agency for Syst & Servs; Metronet
Friends of the Library Group

G DEFENSE TECHNICAL INFORMATION CENTER, Western Regional Office,* DTIC-BRNL Bldg 80, 2420 Vela Way Ste 1467, 90245-4659. SAN 323-8067. Tel: 310-363-8980. FAX: 310-363-8972. E-Mail: losangel@dtic.mil. Web Site: www.dtic.mil/dtic/dticb/dticbln/western.html. *Br Coordr, Mgr*, Janet Hodges; Staff 3 (MLS 1, Non-MLS 2)
Founded 1975

P EL SEGUNDO PUBLIC LIBRARY, 111 W Mariposa Ave, 90245-2299. SAN 300-7286. Tel: 310-524-2722. Reference Tel: 310-524-2728. TDD: 310-222-4889. FAX: 310-648-7560. Web Site: www.elsegundo.org. *Dir*, Debra Brighton; E-Mail: brighton@elsegundo.org; Staff 5 (MLS 4, Non-MLS 1)
Founded 1930
Library Holdings: Bk Vols 90,156; Bk Titles 134,827; Per Subs 337; High Interest/Low Vocabulary Bk Vols 300
Subject Interests: Genealogy, Local history, World War II
Special Collections: Adult Literacy; California; High-Interest; Large Type
Publications: Blue ButterFlyer
Mem of Metropolitan Cooperative Library System
Special Services for the Deaf - High interest/low vocabulary books; Staff with knowledge of sign language; TDD
Special Services for the Blind - Arkenstone, a computer system for the visually handicapped
Friends of the Library Group

S NORTHROP GRUMNAN LIBRARY, (Formerly Northrop Grumnan Corp), Air Combat Systems Business & Technology Research Center, One Hornet Way, Dept VK10/W7, 90245. SAN 300-8088. Tel: 310-331-7105. FAX: 310-332-5562. E-Mail: acs_Library@mail.northgrum.com. *Acq*, Linda L Long; E-Mail: longli@mail.northgrum.com; Staff 3 (MLS 2, Non-MLS 1)
Founded 1942
Library Holdings: Bk Vols 1,500; Bk Titles 1,000; Per Subs 14
Subject Interests: Aerospace, Business, Defense
Special Collections: Military Specifications, micro; Technical Reports

Database Vendor: Dialog, Lexis-Nexis
Publications: Library Guide
Restriction: Staff use only
Function: Research library

S RAYTHEON ELECTRONIC SYSTEMS, (Formerly Raytheon Systems Co), Bldg E-01 MS/E117, 2000 E El Segundo Blvd, 90245-0902. (Mail add: PO Box 902, 90245-0902), SAN 331-8451. Tel: 310-647-2000. FAX: 310-647-1324. E-Mail: libraryе01@west.raytheon.com. *Mgr*, Jeff Sevier; Tel: 310-647-1324, E-Mail: jasevier@west.raytheon.com; *Info Specialist*, Don Matsumiya; Tel: 310-647-1339, Fax: 310-647-1312, E-Mail: dhmatsumiya@west.raytheon.com; *Info Specialist*, Joanna Sutton; Tel: 310-647-1323, E-Mail: jmsutton@west.raytheon.com; Staff 10 (MLS 3, Non-MLS 7)
Founded 1950
Library Holdings: Bk Vols 20,000; Per Subs 200
Subject Interests: Aerospace, Computer science, Defense, Electrical engineering, Optics, Radar
Automation Activity & Vendor Info: (Acquisitions) epixtech, inc.; (Cataloging) epixtech, inc.; (Circulation) epixtech, inc.; (OPAC) epixtech, inc.; (Serials) epixtech, inc.
Database Vendor: epixtech, inc.
Restriction: Company library, Not open to public

S RAYTHEON SYSTEMS CO, Microelectronics Library,* PO Box 902, 90245-0902. SAN 324-0924. Tel: 949-759-2411. FAX: 949-759-2050.
Founded 1958
Library Holdings: Bk Titles 4,500; Per Subs 2,500
Subject Interests: Bus, Chemistry, Computers, Electronics, Engineering, Metallurgy, Mgt, Microelectronics, Physics, Semiconductors, Solid state devices

S WYLE LABORATORIES, Research Library,* 128 Maryland St, 90245-4115. SAN 326-6346. Tel: 310-322-1763, Ext 6641. FAX: 310-322-9799. *Librn*, Linda Meneses
Library Holdings: Bk Titles 400; Per Subs 40
Subject Interests: Aeronautics, Noise pollution

S XEROX CORPORATION, Technical Information Center,* 701 S Aviation Blvd, Mail Stop ESAE-325, 90245. SAN 300-7308. Tel: 310-333-5222. FAX: 310-333-8424. *Mgr*, Ellen Chang
Founded 1968
Library Holdings: Bk Titles 7,000; Per Subs 400
Subject Interests: Business and management, Computer science, Electrical engineering
Publications: Journal Holdings; What's New (quarterly newsletter)
Restriction: Access for corporate affiliates
Partic in BRS; Coop Libr Agency for Syst & Servs; Dialog Corporation; OCLC Online Computer Library Center, Inc; SDC Info Servs

ELDRIDGE

M SONOMA DEVELOPMENTAL CENTER, Staff Library, PO Box 1493, 95431-1493. SAN 331-9385. Tel: 707-938-6244. FAX: 707-938-6289. *Librn*, Angela Brunton; E-Mail: abrunton@sonic.net
Founded 1951. Pop 1,800
1998-1999 Mats Exp $17,000
Library Holdings: Bk Vols 4,800; Per Subs 104
Subject Interests: Mentally retarded, Pediatrics, Psychiatry, Psychology, Social service (social work)
Special Collections: History of Sonoma State Hospital, bks, journals & newsp
Publications: Journal Holdings
Restriction: Staff use only
Partic in N Bay Health Sci Libr Consortium; Pac SW Regional Med Libr

EMERYVILLE

S CHIRON CORP, Library & Information Center,* 4560 Horton St, 94608. SAN 328-1914. Tel: 510-923-2591. FAX: 510-923-4134. *Dir*, George McGregor; E-Mail: george_mcgregor@cc.chiron.com; *Coll Develop*, Dorrie Slutsker
Library Holdings: Bk Vols 8,000

S INNOVATIVE INTERFACES INC LIBRARY,* 5850 Shellmound Way, 94608. SAN 372-2643. Tel: 510-655-6200. FAX: 510-450-6350. E-Mail: info@iii.com. Web Site: www.iii.com. *Pres*, Gerald M Kline; *VPres*, Leslie Straus; *VPres*, Sandy Westall
Library Holdings: Bk Vols 200; Per Subs 30

ENCINITAS

S QUAIL BOTANICAL GARDENS FOUNDATION INC LIBRARY,* PO Box 230005, 92023-0005. SAN 373-3998. Tel: 760-436-3036. FAX: 760-632-0917. Web Site: www.qbgardens.com. *Librn*, Kenneth Hayward
Library Holdings: Bk Vols 2,000; Per Subs 8
Subject Interests: Botany, Gardening, Horticulture
Special Collections: Out-of-Print Botanical Coll, bks, slides & videos

S SOLUTION MINING RESEARCH INSTITUTE LIBRARY,* 3336 Lone Hill Lane, 92024. SAN 328-1078. Tel: 858-759-7532. *Exec Dir*, H W Diamond; E-Mail: bdiamond@mcs.com
Founded 1959

ENCINO

S PHILLIPS GRADUATE INSTITUTE LIBRARY, 5445 Balboa Blvd, 91316. SAN 300-8908. Tel: 818-386-5640. FAX: 818-386-5696. E-Mail: uribe@pgi.edu. Web Site: www.pgi.edu/library.htm. *Dir Libr Serv*, Lydia M Uribe; Tel: 818-386-5641, E-Mail: uribe@pgi.edu; *Publ Servs*, Ankara McPherson; Tel: 818-386-5642, E-Mail: ankara@pgi.edu; *Circ*, Linda Folse; Staff 3 (MLS 1, Non-MLS 2)
Founded 1981
Library Holdings: Bk Vols 6,000; Bk Titles 5,000; Per Subs 150
Subject Interests: Marriage, Organizational behavior, Psychology, Sch counseling
Automation Activity & Vendor Info: (Acquisitions) EOS; (Cataloging) EOS; (Circulation) EOS; (OPAC) EOS; (Serials) EOS
Database Vendor: Silverplatter Information Inc.
Function: Research library
Partic in OCLC Online Computer Library Center, Inc; SCELC

ESCONDIDO

S ESCONDIDO HISTORICAL SOCIETY & HERITAGE WALK MUSEUM LIBRARY,* 321 N Broadway, PO Box 263, 92033. SAN 373-4013. Tel: 760-743-8207. FAX: 760-743-8267. E-Mail: ehs@connectnet.com. *Chair*, Janean Young
1998-1999 Mats Exp Per/Ser (Incl. Access Fees) $30
Library Holdings: Bk Vols 919
Subject Interests: Furniture, History
Restriction: Open to public for reference only

P ESCONDIDO PUBLIC LIBRARY, 239 S Kalmia St, 92025. SAN 300-7340. Tel: 760-839-4601. Interlibrary Loan Service Tel: 760-839-4840. Reference Tel: 760-839-4839. TDD: 760-738-9042. FAX: 760-741-4255. Web Site: www.ci.escondido.ca.us/library. *City Librn*, Laura Mitchell; E-Mail: lmitchell@ci.escondido.ca.us; *Librn*, Jo Ann Greenberg; Tel: 760-839-4825, E-Mail: jgreenberg@ci.escondido.ca.us; *Publ Servs*, Loretta McKinney; Tel: 760-839-4329, E-Mail: lmckinney@ci.escondido.ca.us; *Media Spec*, David Curtis; Tel: 760-839-4828, E-Mail: dcurtis@ci.escondido.ca.us; *Tech Servs*, Chris Reeske; Tel: 760-839-4624, E-Mail: creeske@ci.escondido.ca.us; *Ref*, Pat Buscher; Tel: 760-839-4814, E-Mail: pbuscher@ci.escondido.ca.us; *Coll Develop*, Neva Robinson; Tel: 760-839-4214, E-Mail: nrobinson@ci.escondido.ca.us; Staff 82 (MLS 18, Non-MLS 64)
Founded 1894. Pop 128,000
Jul 1999-Jun 2000 Income (Main Library and Branch Library) $2,525,338, State $165,721, City $2,095,820, Federal $55,850, Other $207,947. Mats Exp $443,910, Books $376,030, Per/Ser (Incl. Access Fees) $25,000, Presv $5,200, Micro $6,160, Manuscripts & Archives $5,000, Electronic Ref Mat (Incl. Access Fees) $26,520. Sal $1,842,955
Library Holdings: Bk Titles 344,085; Per Subs 320; High Interest/Low Vocabulary Bk Vols 15,630
Subject Interests: Business and management, Local history
Special Collections: Pioneer Room (local & family history)
Automation Activity & Vendor Info: (Circulation) epixtech, inc.
Publications: 100 Years of Library History in Escondido
Special Services for the Deaf - TDD
Open Mon, Tues & Thurs 10-9, Wed, Fri & Sat 10-6
Friends of the Library Group
Branches: 1
EAST VALLEY, 2245 E Valley Pkwy, 92027. Tel: 760-839-4394. TDD: 760-738-9042. FAX: 760-746-2052. Web Site: www.ci.escondido.ca.us/library. *Branch Mgr*, Paul Crouthamel
Jul 1999-Jun 2000 Income $60,500
Library Holdings: Bk Vols 51,110; Per Subs 73; Bks on Deafness & Sign Lang 12
Automation Activity & Vendor Info: (Cataloging) epixtech, inc.; (OPAC) epixtech, inc.
Special Services for the Deaf - TDD

M PALOMAR POMERADO HEALTH SYSTEMS, Palomar Medical Center Library, 555 E Valley Pkwy, 92025. SAN 371-6325. Tel: 760-739-3146. FAX: 760-739-3229. E-Mail: uxa@pphs.org. *Librn*, Ursula Avakian; Staff 1 (MLS 1)
Founded 1988
Library Holdings: Bk Vols 560; Bk Titles 520; Per Subs 125
Subject Interests: Allied health, Nursing
Partic in Med Libr Group of S Calif & Ariz; National Network Of Libraries Of Medicine

R WESTMINSTER THEOLOGICAL SEMINARY LIBRARY,* 1725 Bear Valley Pkwy, 92027. SAN 321-236X. Tel: 760-480-8474. FAX: 760-480-0252. *Librn*, James T Dennison Jr; *ILL*, Jack Dundas; Staff 1 (MLS 1)
Founded 1980

Jul 1997-Jun 1998 Mats Exp $107,351, Books $42,977, Per/Ser (Incl. Access Fees) $17,985. Sal $89,106 (Prof $71,106)
Library Holdings: Bk Titles 110,000; Per Subs 245
Subject Interests: Biblical studies, Theology
Special Collections: 16th/17th Century Reformation and Puritanism (microforms)

EUREKA

J COLLEGE OF THE REDWOODS LIBRARY, 7351 Tompkins Hill Rd, 95501. SAN 300-7375. Tel: 707-476-4260. Interlibrary Loan Service Tel: 707-476-4256. Circulation Tel: 707-476-4260, Ext 4695. Reference Tel: 707-476-4263. FAX: 707-476-4432. E-Mail: library@eureka.redwoods.cc.ca.us. Web Site: www.redwoods.cc.ca.ws/main/services/library/index.htm. *Librn*, Ruth Coughlin; E-Mail: ruth-coughlin@eureka.redwoods.cc.ca.us; *Coordr*, John Mayeski; E-Mail: john-mayeski@eureka.redwoods.cc.ca.us; Staff 2 (MLS 2)
Founded 1965. Enrl 6,602; Fac 122
Jul 1999-Jun 2000 Mats Exp $23,463, Books $13,918, Per/Ser (Incl. Access Fees) $8,962, Presv $250, Micro $333. Sal $224,650 (Prof $70,096)
Library Holdings: Bk Vols 67,442; Bk Titles 66,767; Per Subs 102
Subject Interests: Nursing
Special Collections: Civil War
Automation Activity & Vendor Info: (Cataloging) Endeavor; (Circulation) Endeavor; (Course Reserve) Endeavor; (OPAC) Endeavor
Database Vendor: Ebsco - EbscoHost, ProQuest
Mem of North State Cooperative Library System
Partic in OCLC Online Computer Library Center, Inc
Departmental Libraries:
DEL NORTE CAMPUS, 883 W Washington Blvd, Crescent City, 99531-8361. SAN 372-798X. Tel: 707-464-2330. FAX: 707-464-6867. *In Charge*, Terry Compton; E-Mail: terry-compton@delnorte.redwoods.cc.ca.us
Automation Activity & Vendor Info: (Cataloging) Endeavor; (Circulation) Endeavor; (Course Reserve) Endeavor; (OPAC) Endeavor
Database Vendor: Ebsco - EbscoHost, ProQuest
MENDOCINO COAST, 1211 Del Mar Dr, Fort Bragg, 95437-3295. SAN 372-7998. Tel: 707-961-2609. FAX: 707-961-0943. *In Charge*, Mary Schaffler; E-Mail: mary-schaffler@mendocino.redwoods.cc.ca.us; Staff 1 (Non-MLS 1)
Automation Activity & Vendor Info: (Cataloging) Endeavor; (Circulation) Endeavor; (Course Reserve) Endeavor; (OPAC) Endeavor
Database Vendor: Ebsco - EbscoHost, ProQuest

GL HUMBOLDT COUNTY LAW LIBRARY, Courthouse, 825 Fifth St, Rm 812, 95501. SAN 300-7383. Tel: 707-269-1270. FAX: 707-445-7201. *Librn*, Betty Finley
Founded 1907
Library Holdings: Bk Vols 21,000; Per Subs 20

P HUMBOLDT COUNTY LIBRARY,* 1313 Third St, 95501-0553. SAN 331-9415. Tel: 707-269-1918. TDD: 718-442-0462. FAX: 707-269-1997. *Dir*, Judy Klapproth; *Asst Dir*, Lisa Naef; *Circ*, Ronda Wittenberg; *Ch Servs*, Jo Ann Bauer; *Ref*, Richard C Pollard; *Cat*, Janet Smith; Staff 12 (MLS 12)
Founded 1878. Pop 121,000
Library Holdings: Bk Vols 239,625; Bk Titles 148,308; Per Subs 332
Special Collections: American Indians Coll, especially California Indians; Humboldt County History Coll; NRC Nuclear Power Plants LDR
Automation Activity & Vendor Info: (Circulation) CLSI LIBS
Mem of North State Cooperative Library System
Special Services for the Deaf - TDD
Friends of the Library Group
Branches: 10
ARCATA BRANCH, 500 Seventh St, Arcata, 95521-6315. SAN 331-944X. Tel: 707-822-5954. *Librn*, Maggie Nystrom
Library Holdings: Bk Vols 12,000
BLUE LAKE BRANCH, City Hall, 111 Greenwood Ave, Blue Lake, 95525-0236. SAN 331-9474. Tel: 707-668-4207. *In Charge*, Kay Walstad
Library Holdings: Bk Vols 3,000
Friends of the Library Group
EUREKA MAIN LIBRARY, 1313 Third St, 95501. SAN 331-9490. Tel: 707-269-1900.
Library Holdings: Bk Vols 161,860
Friends of the Library Group
FERNDALE BRANCH, 807 Main St, PO Box 397, Ferndale, 95536-0397. SAN 331-9504. Tel: 707-786-9559. *In Charge*, Melinda Candry
Library Holdings: Bk Vols 10,000
FORTUNA BRANCH, 14th & N Sts, Fortuna, 95540-2113. SAN 331-9539. Tel: 707-725-3460. *In Charge*, Linnie Ault
Library Holdings: Bk Vols 7,000
Friends of the Library Group
GARBERVILLE BRANCH, 715 Cedar St, Garberville, 95542-3201. SAN 331-9563. Tel: 707-923-2230. *Librn*, Margaret Taylor
Library Holdings: Bk Vols 7,000
KLAMATH-TRINITY BRANCH, Hwy 299 & Hwy 96, Willow Creek, 95573-0466. SAN 331-9628. Tel: 530-629-2146. *Librn*, Kay Walstad
Library Holdings: Bk Vols 5,458
MCKINLEYVILLE BRANCH, 1606 Pickett Rd, McKinleyville, 95519. SAN 331-9652. Tel: 707-839-4459. *In Charge*, Joy Moore
Library Holdings: Bk Vols 2,500
Friends of the Library Group
RIO DELL BRANCH, 715 Wildwood Ave, Rio Dell, 95562-1321. SAN 331-9687. Tel: 707-764-3333. *In Charge*, Sharon Phillips
Library Holdings: Bk Vols 3,600
Friends of the Library Group
TRINIDAD BRANCH, PO Box 856, Trinidad, 95570-0856. SAN 331-9717. Tel: 707-677-0227. *In Charge*, Kenzie Mullen
Library Holdings: Bk Vols 2,500
Friends of the Library Group
Bookmobiles: 2

S KIM YERTON INDIAN ACTION LIBRARY, 2725 Myrtle Ave, No A, 95501. SAN 324-2773. Tel: 707-443-8401. FAX: 707-443-9281. *Dir*, Coleen Holbrook
Founded 1974
Library Holdings: Bk Titles 6,000
Special Collections: American Indians; California Northwest Coast Tribes (Yurok, Hupa, Karok Coll), bks, flms, photogs, tapes; Photographs (Ericson, Curtis, Boyle, Roberts Coll), bd vols

M SAINT JOSEPH HOSPITAL, Medical Library,* 2700 Dolbeer St, 95501. SAN 300-7391. Tel: 707-445-8121, Ext 7514. FAX: 707-269-3897. *Dir, Librn, Online Servs*, Elizabeth Brown
Founded 1950
Library Holdings: Bk Vols 300; Per Subs 100
Publications: SJH Library flyer, SJH-Table of Contents
Restriction: By appointment only
Partic in Docline; Medline; Pacific SW Regional Med Libr Serv
Open Mon-Thurs 8:30-2

FAIRFIELD

GL SOLANO COUNTY LAW LIBRARY, Hall of Justice, 600 Union Ave, 94533. SAN 300-7405. Tel: 707-421-6520. FAX: 707-421-6516. *Coll Develop, Librn*, Marianna G Moore; E-Mail: mmoore@solanocounty.com
Founded 1911
1998-1999 Income $307,570. Mats Exp Presv $500. Sal $101,013 (Prof $50,000)
Library Holdings: Bk Titles 24,000; Per Subs 99
Special Collections: California Statutes; Codes of Solano Co & Cities therein

P SOLANO COUNTY LIBRARY,* 1150 Kentucky St, 94533-5799. SAN 331-9741. Tel: 707-421-6510. TDD: 707-421-6500. FAX: 707-421-7474. Web Site: www.snap.lib.ca.us. *Dir Libr Serv*, Ann Cousineau; E-Mail: acousine@snap.lib.ca.us; *Assoc Dir*, Bonnie A Katz; Tel: 707-421-6512, E-Mail: bkatz@snap.lib.ca.us; *Tech Coordr*, Lynne E Williams; Tel: 707-421-6560, E-Mail: lwilliam@snap.lib.ca.us; *Coll Develop*, Shirley Coronado; Staff 67 (MLS 34, Non-MLS 33)
Founded 1914. Pop 373,100
Jul 1997-Jun 1998 Income (Main Library and Branch Library) $6,305,992, State $458,380, Federal $16,718, Locally Generated Income $5,459,126, Other $371,768. Mats Exp $541,177, Books $312,298, Per/Ser (Incl. Access Fees) $40,383, Micro $17,925, AV Equip $39,618, Electronic Ref Mat (Incl. Access Fees) $130,953. Sal $3,052,463
Library Holdings: Bk Vols 569,516; Bk Titles 526,809; Per Subs 1,006
Special Collections: Printing (Donovan J McCune Coll), rare bks, specimens; Solano County History; Vallejo History
Automation Activity & Vendor Info: (Acquisitions) CARL; (Circulation) CARL
Database Vendor: CARL
Mem of North Bay Cooperative Library System
Provides minimal jail outreach service, administers County Law Library
Friends of the Library Group
Branches: 6
FAIRFIELD-SUISUN COMMUNITY BRANCH, 1150 Kentucky St, 94533. SAN 331-9776. Tel: 707-421-6500. FAX: 707-421-7207. Web Site: www.snap.lib.ca.us. *Librn*, Laurelle Martin
Friends of the Library Group
JOHN F KENNEDY BRANCH, 505 Santa Clara St, Vallejo, 94590. SAN 331-9806. Tel: 707-553-5568. FAX: 707-553-5667. Web Site: www.snap.lib.ca.us. *Librn*, Andrea Voss
Friends of the Library Group
RIO VISTA BRANCH, 44 S Second St, Rio Vista, 94571. SAN 331-9830. Tel: 707-374-2664. FAX: 707-374-2919. Web Site: www.snap.lib.ca.us. *Librn*, Suzanne Olawski
Friends of the Library Group
SPRINGSTOWNE, 1003 Oakwood Ave, Vallejo, 94591. SAN 331-9865. Tel: 707-553-5546. FAX: 707-553-5656. Web Site: www.snap.lib.ca.us. *Librn*, Leslie Westbrook
Friends of the Library Group
SUISUN CITY BRANCH, 333 Sunset, Ste 280, Suisun City, 94585. SAN 373-8760. Tel: 707-421-6937. FAX: 707-421-6941. Web Site:

www.snap.lib.ca.us. *Librn*, Mary Falcon
Friends of the Library Group
VACAVILLE BRANCH, 1020 Ulatis Dr, Vacaville, 95687. SAN 331-989X. Tel: 707-449-6290. FAX: 707-451-0987. Web Site: www.snap.lib.ca.us. *Librn*, Jeanette Stevens
Friends of the Library Group
Bookmobiles: 1

FIREBAUGH

P FRESNO COUNTY PUBLIC LIBRARY, Firebaugh Neighborhood Library, 1315 O St, 93622. SAN 377-3442. Tel: 559-659-2820. Web Site: www.sjvls.lib.ca.us/fresno. *Asst Librn*, Nellie Serna
Library Holdings: Bk Vols 6,000; Per Subs 15
Open Mon & Tues 10-6, Wed &Thurs 11-7, Fri & Sat 11-3

FOLSOM

P FOLSOM PUBLIC LIBRARY, 300 Persifer St, 95630. SAN 375-4987. Tel: 916-355-7374. FAX: 916-355-7332. E-Mail: folib@windjammer.net. *Librn*, Kathleen Connors; *YA Servs*, Jacquelyn Foster; *Circ*, Mary Alice McClarin; *Ref*, Julie Rinaldi; *Tech Servs*, Phyllis Bulaga; *Tech Servs*, Diane Knight
Founded 1993. Pop 40,850; Circ 225,000
Library Holdings: Bk Vols 53,090; Per Subs 91
Automation Activity & Vendor Info: (Cataloging) Innovative Interfaces Inc.; (Circulation) Innovative Interfaces Inc.
Mem of Mountain-Valley Library System
Friends of the Library Group

FONTANA

M KAISER-PERMANENTE MEDICAL CENTER, Health Sciences Library,* 9961 Sierra Ave, 92335. SAN 300-743X. Tel: 909-427-5085. FAX: 909-427-6288. *Librn*, Shirley Younce; E-Mail: shirley.younce@kp.org; Staff 4 (MLS 2, Non-MLS 2)
Founded 1950
Jan 1998-Dec 1998 Income $241,000. Mats Exp $93,000, Books $18,000, Per/Ser (Incl. Access Fees) $60,100. Sal $125,000 (Prof $86,000)
Library Holdings: Bk Vols 15,500; Per Subs 415
Subject Interests: Dermatology, Internal medicine, Neurology, Obstetrics and gynecology, Orthopedics, Pediatrics, Radiology, Surgery, Urology
Publications: Inland Empire Service Area Newsletter
Partic in Inland Empire Med Libr Coop; Kaiser Permanente Library System - Southern California Region; Medical Libr Asn; San Bernardino, Inyo, Riverside Counties United Library Services

FORESTVILLE

P FORESTVILLE LIBRARY,* 107 First St, PO Box 1718, 95436-9425. SAN 376-396X. Tel: 707-887-7654. *In Charge*, Bonnie Smith
Library Holdings: Bk Vols 4,900; Bk Titles 2,300
Mem of North Bay Cooperative Library System

FORT IRWIN

UNITED STATES ARMY
A FORT IRWIN POST LIBRARY, National Training Ctr, Bldg 331, Box 105091, 92310-5091. SAN 321-8716. Tel: 760-380-3462. FAX: 760-380-5071. *Librn*, Kimberly Bryan; Staff 4 (MLS 1, Non-MLS 3)
Founded 1981
Library Holdings: Bk Vols 40,000; Per Subs 112
Subject Interests: Mil sci, Military history
Special Collections: Calif
Partic in Fedlink; OCLC Online Computer Library Center, Inc; San Bernardino, Inyo, Riverside Counties United Library Services
AM WEED ARMY COMMUNITY HOSPITAL, MEDICAL LIBRARY, PO Box 105109, 92310-5109. SAN 324-153X. Tel: 760-380-6889. FAX: 760-380-5734. *Librn*, Rosa Lee Furr; Fax: 703-858-0794
Library Holdings: Bk Vols 900; Bk Titles 512; Per Subs 35
Subject Interests: Dentistry, Emergency room, Nursing, Pharm, Preventive med

FOUNTAIN VALLEY

M FOUNTAIN VALLEY REGIONAL HOSPITAL, Medical Library, 17100 Euclid St, 92708. SAN 375-7641. Tel: 714-966-7200, 714-966-8028. FAX: 714-966-3312. *Librn*, Evelyn Simpson; Staff 1 (MLS 1)
Library Holdings: Bk Titles 450; Per Subs 125
Subject Interests: Medicine, Nursing

FREMONT

P ALAMEDA COUNTY LIBRARY,* 2450 Stevenson Blvd, 94538-2326. SAN 332-091X. Tel: 510-745-1500. FAX: 510-793-2987. Web Site: www.aclibrary.org. *Librn*, Linda M Wood; *Ch Servs*, Bonnie Janssen; *Commun Servs*, Sandi Pantages; *Cat*, Nancy Baca; *Ref*, Joan Galvez; *Bkmobile Coordr*, Amy Cheney
Founded 1910. Pop 541,287; Circ 3,536,764
Jul 1997-Jun 1998 Income $13,797,150, State $467,260, City $1,610,548, Federal $58,591, County $10,137,540, Locally Generated Income $841,616, Other $403,951. Mats Exp $1,605,181, Books $1,051,165, Per/Ser (Incl. Access Fees) $111,691, Presv $261, Micro $15,022. Sal $9,372,692
Library Holdings: Bk Vols 1,205,965; Per Subs 2,970
Subject Interests: Business and management, Local history, Spanish (language)
Automation Activity & Vendor Info: (Acquisitions) Innovative Interfaces Inc.; (Circulation) Innovative Interfaces Inc.; (Serials) Innovative Interfaces Inc.
Mem of Bay Area Libr & Info Syst
Friends of the Library Group
Branches: 10
ALBANY BRANCH, 1247 Marin Ave, Albany, 94706-1796. SAN 332-0944. Tel: 510-526-3720. FAX: 510-526-8754. Web Site: www.aclibrary.org. *Librn*, Ronnie Davis
Library Holdings: Bk Vols 79,263
Friends of the Library Group
CASTRO VALLEY BRANCH, 20055 Redwood Rd, Castro Valley, 94546-4382. SAN 332-1002. Tel: 510-670-6280. FAX: 510-537-5991. Web Site: www.aclibrary.org. *Librn*, Carolyn Moskovitz
Library Holdings: Bk Vols 90,728
Friends of the Library Group
CENTERVILLE, 3801 Nicolet Ave, 94536-3493. SAN 332-1037. Tel: 510-795-2629. FAX: 510-790-5734. Web Site: www.aclibrary.org. *Librn*, Elinore Tandowsky
Library Holdings: Bk Vols 55,706
Friends of the Library Group
DUBLIN BRANCH, 7606 Amador Valley Blvd, Dublin, 94568-2383. SAN 332-1061. Tel: 510-828-1315. FAX: 510-828-9296. Web Site: www.aclibrary.org. *Librn*, Pat Zahn
Library Holdings: Bk Vols 85,398
Friends of the Library Group
FREMONT MAIN LIBRARY, 2400 Stevenson Blvd, 94538-2325. SAN 332-1096. Tel: 510-745-1400. TDD: 510-796-9749. FAX: 510-797-6557. Web Site: www.aclibrary.org. *Librn*, Sandra Pantages
Library Holdings: Bk Vols 322,140
Special Services for the Deaf - Books on deafness & sign language; Staff with knowledge of sign language; TDD
Friends of the Library Group
IRVINGTON, 41825 Greenpark Dr, 94538-4084. SAN 332-1150. Tel: 510-795-2631. FAX: 510-490-5622. Web Site: www.aclibrary.org. *Librn*, Elinore Tandowsky
Library Holdings: Bk Vols 40,890
Friends of the Library Group
NEWARK BRANCH, 6300 Civic Terrace Ave, Newark, 94560-3795. SAN 332-1185. Tel: 510-795-2627. FAX: 510-797-3019. Web Site: www.aclibrary.org. *Librn*, Elizabeth Silva
Library Holdings: Bk Vols 65,975
Friends of the Library Group
NILES, 150 I St, 94536-2998. SAN 332-1215. Tel: 510-795-2626. Web Site: www.aclibrary.org. *Librn*, Rayne Meyers
Library Holdings: Bk Vols 14,682
Friends of the Library Group
SAN LORENZO BRANCH, 395 Paseo Grande, San Lorenzo, 94580-2491. SAN 332-1274. Tel: 510-670-6283. FAX: 510-317-8497. Web Site: www.aclibrary.org. *Branch Mgr*, Anthony Dos Santos; Tel: 510-670-6283, Ext 11, E-Mail: adoslz@alam1.lib.co.alameda.ca.us; Staff 18 (MLS 3, Non-MLS 15)
Library Holdings: Bk Vols 102,891
Database Vendor: Ebsco - EbscoHost, IAC - Info Trac, Innovative Interfaces INN - View
Friends of the Library Group
UNION CITY BRANCH, 34007 Alvarado-Niles Rd, Union City, 94587-4498. SAN 332-1304. Tel: 510-745-1464. FAX: 510-487-7241. Web Site: www.aclibrary.org. *Librn*, Linda Harris
Library Holdings: Bk Vols 79,033
Subject Interests: Spanish (language)
Friends of the Library Group

S CALIFORNIA SCHOOL FOR THE BLIND, Library Media Center,* 500 Walnut Ave, 94536. SAN 300-6069. Tel: 510-794-3800, Ext 259. FAX: 510-794-3813. *Librn*, Elizabeth Hart; E-Mail: ehart@csb.cde.ca.gov
Founded 1926. Enrl 200
Library Holdings: Bk Vols 7,000; Bk Titles 6,500; Per Subs 27
Special Collections: large print, Braille & 4-Track Tapes; Professional Coll, bks, manipulative & tactile items for students; Recreational &

Supplementary materials for students
Special Services for the Deaf - Captioned media; High interest/low vocabulary books; Special interest periodicals

J OHLONE COLLEGE, Blanchard Learning Resources Center, 43600 Mission Blvd, 94539. SAN 300-7480. Tel: 510-659-6160. Interlibrary Loan Service Tel: 510-659-6171. Circulation Tel: 510-659-6160. Reference Tel: 510-659-6171. FAX: 510-659-6265. Web Site: www.ohlone.cc.ca.us/org/library. *Dean*, Dr Shirley Peck; Tel: 510-659-6166, E-Mail: speck@ohlone.cc.ca.us; *Librn*, Jim Landavazo; Tel: 510-659-6000, Ext 5025, E-Mail: jlandavazo@ohlone.cc.ca.us; *Librn*, KG Greenstein; Tel: 510-659-6000, Ext 5272, E-Mail: kgreenstein@ohlone.cc.ca.us; *Tech Servs*, Kathy Sklar; Tel: 510-659-6164, E-Mail: ksklar@ohlone.cc.ca.us; Staff 14 (MLS 4, Non-MLS 10)
Founded 1967. Enrl 10,634; Fac 400; Highest Degree: Associate
Jul 1999-Jun 2000 Income $917,230. Mats Exp $144,738, Books $50,000, Per/Ser (Incl. Access Fees) $25,378, Presv $2,000, AV Equip $42,922, Electronic Ref Mat (Incl. Access Fees) $24,438. Sal $647,839 (Prof $287,577)
Library Holdings: Bk Titles 62,424; Per Subs 191
Subject Interests: Art and architecture, History, Indians, Law
Automation Activity & Vendor Info: (Acquisitions) Endeavor; (Cataloging) Endeavor; (Circulation) Endeavor; (OPAC) Endeavor; (Serials) Endeavor
Database Vendor: Ebsco - EbscoHost, OCLC - First Search
Function: Reference services available
Partic in Bay Area Library & Information Network

J QUEEN OF THE HOLY ROSARY COLLEGE LIBRARY, 43326 Mission Blvd, PO Box 3908, 94539-0391. SAN 321-4265. Tel: 510-657-2468. FAX: 510-657-1734. *Librn*, Mary Ellen D Parker; E-Mail: qhrcparker@mailcity.com; *Asst Librn*, Claudine Hammer; Staff 3 (MLS 1, Non-MLS 2)
Founded 1908. Pop 500
Aug 1998-Jul 1999 Income Parent Institution $27,109. Mats Exp $9,700, Books $6,300, Per/Ser (Incl. Access Fees) $3,400
Library Holdings: Bk Vols 24,002; Bk Titles 19,406; Per Subs 150
Subject Interests: Philosophy, Religion, Theology
Special Collections: Art (Dresden Coll), slides
Publications: Lumen (student publication)

FRENCH CAMP

M SAN JOAQUIN GENERAL HOSPITAL, Medical Library, 500 W Hospital Rd, 95231. (Mail add: PO Box 1010, 95201), SAN 300-7499. Tel: 209-468-6628. FAX: 209-468-6642. E-Mail: sjghml@mail.softcom.net. *Librn*, Berta Keizur; Staff 1 (Non-MLS 1)
Jul 1998-Jun 1999 Mats Exp $46,500, Books $5,000, Per/Ser (Incl. Access Fees) $37,000. Sal $28,500
Library Holdings: Bk Vols 2,305; Bk Titles 1,000; Per Subs 238
Subject Interests: Medicine, Nursing
Special Collections: Ethics Management
Partic in 49-99 Coop Libr Syst; Docline; NCNMLG

FRESNO

L BAKER, MANOCK & JENSEN, Law Library,* 5260 N Palm Ave, Ste 321, 93704. SAN 372-266X. Tel: 559-432-5400. FAX: 559-432-5620. *Librn*, Jamie Ohanesian
Library Holdings: Bk Vols 13,000; Per Subs 50
Partic in Area Wide Library Network

C CALIFORNIA CHRISTIAN COLLEGE LIBRARY,* 4881 E University Ave, 93703. SAN 300-7502. Tel: 559-251-2998, 559-251-4215. FAX: 559-251-4231. *Actg Librn*, Melisa Scroggins
Founded 1955
Library Holdings: Bk Vols 13,348; Per Subs 30
Subject Interests: Religion
Special Collections: California Free Will Baptist History; Free Will Baptist Denominational History

L CALIFORNIA COURT OF APPEAL FIFTH APPELLATE DISTRICT LIBRARY,* 2525 Capitol St, 93721. SAN 372-2678. Tel: 559-445-5491. FAX: 559-445-5769. *Librn*, Kathleen Pearce; Tel: 559-445-5686
Library Holdings: Bk Vols 35,000; Per Subs 250

C CALIFORNIA SCHOOL OF PROFESSIONAL PSYCHOLOGY, Kauffman Library, 5130 E Clinton Way, 93727. SAN 300-7510. Tel: 209-253-2265. FAX: 209-253-2223. Web Site: library.cspp.edu. *Dir*, Louise A Colbert; E-Mail: lcolbert@mail.cspp.edu; Staff 3 (MLS 1, Non-MLS 2)
Founded 1973. Enrl 420; Fac 30; Highest Degree: Doctorate
Jul 1999-Jun 2000 Mats Exp $94,540, Books $18,000, Per/Ser (Incl. Access Fees) $49,500, Presv $4,000, Micro $150, Other Print Mats $1,000. Sal $134,436 (Prof $74,436)
Library Holdings: Bk Vols 18,500; Bk Titles 13,000; Per Subs 200
Subject Interests: Psychology
Database Vendor: Innovative Interfaces INN - View
Publications: Acquisitions list (monthly); Guide to Services (annual); serials holdings list (annual); video resources listing (annual)
Mem of San Joaquin Valley Library System
Partic in Area Wide Library Network; National Network Of Libraries Of Medicine - South Central Region; OCLC Online Computer Library Center, Inc

CALIFORNIA STATE UNIVERSITY, FRESNO

C HENRY MADDEN LIBRARY, 5200 N Barton, Mail Stop ML-34, 93740-8014. SAN 300-7529. Tel: 559-278-2403. Circulation Tel: 559-278-2551. Reference Tel: 559-278-2174. FAX: 559-278-6952. Web Site: www.lib.csufresno.edu. *Dean of Libr*, Michael Gorman; E-Mail: michaelg@csufresno.edu; *Assoc Dean*, Sandra Gothe; Tel: 559-278-4051, E-Mail: sandyg@csufresno.edu; *ILL*, Jean M Tempesta; *Spec Coll*, Tammy Lau; *Media Spec, Music*, Janet Bochin; Tel: 559-278-2158, E-Mail: janetbo@csufresno.edu; *Curator*, Angelica Carpenter; Tel: 559-278-8116, E-Mail: angelica@csufresno.edu; *Govt Doc*, Carol Doyle; Tel: 559-278-2335, E-Mail: caroldo@csufresno.edu; *Head, Acq*, Ruth Kallenberg; Tel: 559-278-2024, E-Mail: ruthk@csufresno.edu; *Head, Info Serv*, Hye Ok Park; Tel: 559-278-6628, E-Mail: hyeok@csufresno.edu; *Head, Circ*, Patricia Lavigna; Tel: 559-278-4024, E-Mail: pati@csufresno.edu; *Head Ref*, Dave Tyckoson; Tel: 559-278-5678, E-Mail: davety@csufresno.edu; *Coll Develop*, Marcia Morrison; Tel: 559-278-7177, E-Mail: marciamo@csufresco.edu; *ILL*, Suzanne M Cates; *Librn*, Tilman Mike; Tel: 559-278-2054, E-Mail: miket@csufresno.edu; *Head, Cat*, Vincent Smith; Tel: 559-278-2786, E-Mail: vinces@csufresno.edu; *Admin Assoc*, Susan Mangini; Tel: 559-278-2403, E-Mail: susanm@csufresno.edu. Subject Specialists: *Curriculum mat*, Tilman Mike; *Curriculum planning*, Tilman Mike; *Juv*, Tilman Mike; Staff 72 (MLS 27, Non-MLS 45)
Founded 1911. Enrl 18,000; Fac 1,000; Highest Degree: Master
Jul 1999-Jun 2000 Mats Exp $1,915,931, Books $880,067, Per/Ser (Incl. Access Fees) $771,092, Micro $107,800, AV Equip $29,100, Other Print Mats $27,880, Electronic Ref Mat (Incl. Access Fees) $99,992. Sal $3,550,214 (Prof $1,868,141)
Library Holdings: Bk Vols 813,263; Bk Titles 658,864; Per Subs 2,640
Special Collections: Arne Nixon Center for the Study of Children's Literature; Central Valley Political Archives; Credit Foncier Colony, Topolobampo, Sinaloa (Mexico Coll); Enology; History (Roy J Woodward Memorial Library of California); International Exhibitions; Literature (William Saroyan Coll)
Automation Activity & Vendor Info: (Acquisitions) GEAC; (Cataloging) GEAC; (Circulation) GEAC; (ILL) GEAC; (OPAC) GEAC
Database Vendor: CARL, IAC - Info Trac, Lexis-Nexis, Silverplatter Information Inc.
Publications: Madden Library Update & Friendscript
Mem of California State University
Partic in OCLC Online Computer Library Center, Inc
Special Services for the Deaf - TDD
Friends of the Library Group

S SAHATDJIAN LIBRARY, Armenian Studies Program, 5245 N Backer Ave PB4, 93740-8001. Tel: 209-278-2669. FAX: 209-278-2129. Web Site: www.csufresno.edu/ArmenianStudies/. *Dir*, Dickran Kouymjian; E-Mail: dickrank@csufresno.edu
Founded 1988. Enrl 150; Fac 3; Highest Degree: Doctorate
Library Holdings: Bk Titles 2,000; Per Subs 30
Subject Interests: Archives, Photographs
Special Collections: Armenian Film Archive; Index of Armenian Art; William Saroyan Coll
Restriction: In-house use for visitors

M COMMUNITY MEDICAL CENTER-FRESNO, Community Medical Library, Fresno & R Sts, PO Box 1232, 93715-1232. SAN 300-7588. Tel: 559-459-3968. FAX: 559-459-6451. *Librn*, Roberto Urzua; E-Mail: rurzua@communitymedical.org. Subject Specialists: *Medical*, Roberto Urzua; Staff 2 (MLS 2)
Founded 1974
Library Holdings: Bk Titles 4,372; Per Subs 387
Subject Interests: Allied health, Clinical medicine, Nursing
Special Collections: Historical & Rare Medical Books
Restriction: Circulates for staff only
Partic in Area Wide Library Network; MLGSCA; NCNMLG

GM DEPARTMENT OF VETERANS AFFAIRS, Medical Center Library,* 2615 E Clinton Ave, 93703-2286. SAN 300-7707. Tel: 559-228-5341. FAX: 559-228-6924. *Tech Servs*, Daphne Perry; Staff 3 (MLS 1, Non-MLS 2)
Founded 1975
Library Holdings: Bk Titles 4,250; Per Subs 354
Subject Interests: Nursing
Special Collections: Reprint file on Coccidioidomycosis, 1880s-1972
Partic in Nat Libr of Med Region 2; Northern California & Nevada Medical Library Group; Veterans Affairs Library Network

S FRESNO BEE, Editorial Library,* 1626 E St, 93786-0001. SAN 300-7545. Tel: 209-441-6380. FAX: 209-441-6436. *Head of Libr*, Mabel Wilson; E-Mail: mwilson@fresnobee.com
Founded 1922
Library Holdings: Bk Vols 963

Special Collections: Newspaper clippings, fiche, microfilm from 1922-present
Restriction: By appointment only
Partic in Area Wide Library Network; Dialog Corporation; Dow Jones News Retrieval

S FRESNO CITY & COUNTY HISTORICAL SOCIETY ARCHIVES,* 7160 W Kearney Blvd, 93706. (Mail add: PO Box 2029, 93718), SAN 300-7553. Tel: 559-441-0862. FAX: 559-441-1372. E-Mail: fhsarchiv@aol.com. Web Site: www.valleyhistory.org. *Dir*, Jill Moffat; *Archivist*, Kelly Hobbs
Founded 1919
Library Holdings: Bk Titles 3,000
Subject Interests: California
Special Collections: Arthur H Drew, papers; B W Gearhart, papers; Ben Walker Coll, clippings; Chester Rowell, papers; Fresno County (A W Peters, Hutchinson, Porteous), glass negative plates; Municipal & County Records; R W Riggs Coll, photog & glass negatives

J FRESNO CITY COLLEGE, Learning Resources Center,* 1101 E University Ave, 93741. SAN 300-7561. Tel: 559-442-8206. FAX: 559-265-5708. *Dir*, Jannett N Jackson; E-Mail: jannett.jackson@do1.scccd.cc.ca.us; *Librn, Ref*, David K Racki; *Cat*, Ron Byrd; *Acq, Circ, Per*, Tanya Liscano; Staff 7 (MLS 7)
Founded 1910. Enrl 19,000; Fac 530
1998-1999
Library Holdings: Bk Titles 75,000; Per Subs 540

S FRESNO COUNTY GENEALOGICAL SOCIETY LIBRARY,* 2420 Mariposa, PO Box 1429, 93721-1429. SAN 370-6834. Tel: 559-483-3439, 559-488-6720. Web Site: sjvls.lib.ca.us/fresno/reference.html, telnet://pac.sjvls.lib.ca./fresno (Loginas Library), www.sjvls.lib.ca.us/fresno/fgs/resource.html. *Librn*, Mary Lou Talens
Founded 1965
Nov 1998-Oct 1999 Income $3,000, Locally Generated Income $813. Mats Exp $4,000, Books $1,640, Per/Ser (Incl. Access Fees) $344
Library Holdings: Bk Titles 5,000; Per Subs 87
Subject Interests: Genealogy
Automation Activity & Vendor Info: (Cataloging) epixtech, inc.
Publications: Ash Tree Echo; The Jotted Line (monthly newsletter)
Friends of the Library Group

GL FRESNO COUNTY LAW LIBRARY, Rm 600, Fresno County Courthouse, 1100 Van Ness Ave, 93721-2098. SAN 300-7626. Tel: 209-237-2227. *Dir*, Sharon E Borbon; E-Mail: sborbon@lightspeed.net
Founded 1891
Jul 1999-Jun 2000 Income $570,471. Mats Exp $440,367. Sal $135,905
Library Holdings: Bk Vols 44,715; Bk Titles 3,072; Per Subs 233
Subject Interests: Philosophy
Special Collections: Frank E Wells Memorial Coll

P FRESNO COUNTY LIBRARY,* 2420 Mariposa St, 93721-2285. SAN 331-9989. Tel: 559-488-3185. TDD: 559-488-1642. FAX: 559-488-1971. Web Site: www.sjvls.lib.ca.us/fresno/. *Librn*, John K Kallenberg; E-Mail: jkallenb@sjvls.lib.ca.us; *Assoc Librn*, Karen Bosch Cobb; Tel: 559-488-3438, E-Mail: kboschco@sjvls.lib.ca.us; *Mgr*, John Freitas; *Br Coordr*, Jeanne Johnson; *Br Coordr*, Pat Pondexter; *Br Coordr*, Rebecca Jennings; *Ad Servs, Coll Develop, YA Servs*, Lydia Kuhn; *Online Servs, Ref*, Marie Stanley; *Ref*, Joe Hoyt; *YA Servs*, Cynthia MacDonald. Subject Specialists: *Business and management*, Louise Richardson; *Children's literature*, Martha Connor; *History*, Ray Silvia; Staff 30 (MLS 30)
Founded 1910. Pop 768,850; Circ 1,553,604
1997-1998 Income $1,246,799, State $442,412, Federal $87,209, County $282,143, Locally Generated Income $435,035. Mats Exp $591,006, Books $327,668, Per/Ser (Incl. Access Fees) $165,435, Presv $5,026, Micro $1,604. Sal $3,668,977
Library Holdings: Bk Vols 869,393; Per Subs 1,478
Subject Interests: California, Genealogy, Japanese (Language)
Special Collections: City & County; Leo Politi Bks; Mono, Miwok & Yokut Native American Coll, bks, photos, reprints; Mother Goose Coll; William Saroyan Coll
Publications: Impulse; Information & Referral; Talking Book for the Blind Newsletter
Mem of San Joaquin Valley Library System
Partic in Area Wide Library Network; OCLC Online Computer Library Center, Inc
Special Services for the Deaf - TDD
Friends of the Library Group
Branches: 33
AUBERRY BRANCH, 33049 Auberry Rd, Auberry, 93602. (Mail add: PO Box 279, Auberry, 93602), Tel: 559-855-8523. FAX: 559-855-8523. Web Site: www.psnw.com/~foothill/library.html. *Librn*, Anne Neal; E-Mail: aneal@sjvls.lib.ca.us; Staff 7 (MLS 1, Non-MLS 6)
Library Holdings: Bk Vols 18,453
Special Collections: California Indian Library Coll
Automation Activity & Vendor Info: (Circulation) epixtech, inc.; (OPAC) epixtech, inc.
Friends of the Library Group
BEAR MOUNTAIN LIBRARY & ACTIVITY CENTER, 30733 E Kings Canyon, Squaw Valley, 93675-9601. SAN 378-2239. Tel: 559-332-2528. Web Site: www.fresnolibrary.org. *In Charge*, Marilyan Coxan; Staff 2 (MLS 1, Non-MLS 1)
Library Holdings: Bk Vols 8,662
Friends of the Library Group
BIG CREEK STATION, PO Box 25, Big Creek, 93605-0025. SAN 378-2255. Tel: 559-893-6614. Web Site: www.fresnolibrary.org. *Librn*, Kathleen Richmond; *Assoc Librn*, Karen Bosch Cobb; Tel: 559-488-3438, Fax: 559-488-1971, E-Mail: kboschco@sjvls.lib.ca.us; Staff 1 (Non-MLS 1)
Library Holdings: Bk Vols 4,490
CARUTHERS NEIGHBORHOOD, 13357 S Henderson, Caruthers, 93609-9501. SAN 378-2271. Tel: 559-864-8766. Web Site: www.fresnolibrary.org. *In Charge*, Tammie Wenter; *Assoc Librn*, Karen Bosch Cobb; Tel: 559-488-3438, Fax: 559-488-1971, E-Mail: kboschco@sjvls.lib.ca.us
Library Holdings: Bk Vols 8,449
Friends of the Library Group
CEDAR CLINTON NEIGHBORHOOD, 4150 E Clinton Ave, 93703-2520. SAN 378-2298. Tel: 559-442-1770. Web Site: www.fresnolibrary.org. *In Charge*, Will Cooper; E-Mail: wcooper@sjvls.lib.ca.us; Staff 1 (MLS 1)
Library Holdings: Bk Vols 40,888
CLOVIS REGIONAL, 1155 Fifth St, Clovis, 93612-1391. SAN 332-0103. Tel: 559-299-9531. Web Site: www.fresnolibrary.org. *Librn*, Joseph Augustino; E-Mail: jaugusti@sjvls.lib.ca.us; *Assoc Librn*, Karen Bosch Cobb; Tel: 559-488-3438, Fax: 559-488-1971, E-Mail: kboschco@sjvls.lib.ca.us; Staff 3 (MLS 3)
Library Holdings: Bk Vols 41,097
Special Collections: Westerns
EASTON NEIGHBORHOOD, 25 E Fantz, 93706-5813. SAN 378-231X. Tel: 559-237-3929. Web Site: www.fresnolibrary.org. *In Charge*, Karel Chavez; *Assoc Librn*, Karen Bosch Cobb; Tel: 559-488-3438, Fax: 559-488-1971, E-Mail: kboschco@sjvls.lib.ca.us
Library Holdings: Bk Vols 11,421
FIG GARDEN REGIONAL, 3071 W Bullard, 93711. SAN 332-0162. Tel: 559-438-4071. Web Site: www.fresnolibrary.org. *Librn*, Alan Lessel; Tel: 2, E-Mail: alessel@sjvls.lib.ca.us; *Assoc Librn*, Karen Bosch Cobb; Tel: 559-488-3438, Fax: 559-488-1971, E-Mail: kboschco@sjvls.lib.ca.us
Library Holdings: Bk Vols 30,442; Per Subs 30
FIREBAUGH NEIGHBORHOOD, 1315 O St, Firebaugh, 93622-2319. SAN 378-2336. Tel: 559-659-2820. Web Site: www.fresnolibrary.org. *In Charge*, Nellie Serna; *Assoc Librn*, Karen Bosch Cobb; Tel: 559-488-3438, Fax: 559-488-1971, E-Mail: kboschco@sjvls.lib.ca.us
Library Holdings: Bk Vols 10,353
FOWLER NEIGHBORHOOD, 119 E Merced St, Fowler, 93625. SAN 377-6387. Tel: 559-834-3114. Web Site: www.fresnolibrary.org. *In Charge*, Sandra Zendner; *Assoc Librn*, Karen Bosch Cobb; Tel: 559-488-3438, Fax: 55-488-1971, E-Mail: kboschco@sjvls.lib.ca.us
Library Holdings: Bk Vols 10,265
Friends of the Library Group
FRESNO COUNTY JAIL, 2200 Fresno St, 93721. SAN 377-6409. Tel: 559-488-3723. FAX: 559-488-1971. Web Site: www.fresnolibrary.org. *In Charge*, Tim Jacoby
Library Holdings: Bk Vols 8,000
GILLIS NEIGHBORHOOD, 629 W Dakota, 93705. SAN 377-6425. Tel: 559-225-0140. Web Site: www.fresnolibrary.org. *Librn*, Cheryl Phelps
Library Holdings: Bk Vols 24,107
IVY CENTER NEIGHBORHOOD, 1350 E Annadale, 93706. SAN 377-6441. Tel: 559-264-6119. Web Site: www.sjvls.lib.ca.us/fresno. *In Charge*, Connie Gatewood
Library Holdings: Bk Vols 9,000
KERMAN NEIGHBORHOOD, 662 S Madera Ave, Kerman, 93630. SAN 377-6093. Tel: 559-846-8804. Web Site: www.fresnolibrary.org. *In Charge*, Rita Del Testa
Library Holdings: Bk Vols 8,460; Per Subs 35
KINGSBURG NEIGHBORHOOD, 1399 Draper, Kingsburg, 93631. SAN 377-6115. Tel: 559-897-3710. Web Site: www.fresnolibrary.org. *In Charge*, Sara Wever; E-Mail: swever@sjvls.lib.ca.us
Library Holdings: Bk Vols 9,540
Friends of the Library Group
LATON STATION, 6313 DeWoody St, Laton, 93242. SAN 377-6131. Tel: 559-923-4554. Web Site: www.fresnolibrary.org. *In Charge*, Pixie Pizarro
Library Holdings: Bk Vols 4,837
MENDOTA NEIGHBORHOOD, 667 Quince St, Mendota, 93640-2334. SAN 378-2352. Tel: 559-655-3391. Web Site: www.fresnolibrary.org. *In Charge*, Sonia Bautista
Library Holdings: Bk Vols 5,393
MIRAMONTE STATION, 46034 Dunlap Rd, Miramonte, 93641. SAN 377-6158. Tel: 559-336-2355. Web Site: www.fresnolibrary.org. *In Charge*, Kaysia Barr
Library Holdings: Bk Vols 907
MOSQUEDA NEIGHBORHOOD, 4670 E Butler, 93702. SAN 377-6174. Tel: 559-453-4072. Web Site: www.fresnolibrary.org. *In Charge*, Andrea Sartain

Library Holdings: Bk Vols 9,935
ORANGE COVE NEIGHBORHOOD, 523 Park Blvd, Orange Cove, 93646-0356. SAN 378-2379. Tel: 559-626-7942. Web Site: www.fresnolibrary.org. *In Charge*, Sandra Kuykendall
Library Holdings: Bk Vols 8,159
Friends of the Library Group
PARLIER NEIGHBORHOOD, 1130 E Parlier Ave, Parlier, 93648. SAN 377-6190. Tel: 559-646-3835. Web Site: www.fresnolibrary.org. *In Charge*, Abby Rivera
Library Holdings: Bk Vols 11,722
PIEDRA STATION, 25385 Trimmer Spring Rd, Piedra, 93649. SAN 377-6212. Tel: 559-787-3266. Web Site: www.fresnolibrary.org. *In Charge*, Beverley Henson
Library Holdings: Bk Vols 1,429
Friends of the Library Group
PINEDALE NEIGHBORHOOD, 7170 N San Pablo, Pinedale, 93650. SAN 377-6239. Tel: 559-439-0486. Web Site: www.fresnolibrary.org. *Actg Librn*, Robyn Aguiar
Library Holdings: Bk Vols 7,097
POLITI NEIGHBORHOOD, 5771 N First, 93710-6269. SAN 378-2395. Tel: 559-431-6450. Web Site: www.fresnolibrary.org. *In Charge*, Maureen Pollard
Library Holdings: Bk Vols 27,472
REEDLEY BRANCH, 1027 E St, Reedley, 93654-2982. SAN 332-0227. Tel: 559-638-2818. Web Site: www.fresnolibrary.org. *Librn*, Deb Janzen; E-Mail: djanzen@sjvls.lib.ca.us
Library Holdings: Bk Vols 26,459
Friends of the Library Group
RIVERDALE NEIGHBORHOOD, 20975 Malsbary, Riverdale, 93656. SAN 377-6255. Tel: 559-867-3381. Web Site: www.fresnolibrary.org. *In Charge*, Tamara Mattos
Library Holdings: Bk Vols 11,801
Friends of the Library Group
SAN JOAQUIN NEIGHBORHOOD, 8781 Main St, San Joaquin, 93660. SAN 377-6271. Tel: 559-693-2171. Web Site: www.sjvls.lib.ca.us/fresno. *In Charge*, Beth Goering
Library Holdings: Bk Vols 10,643
SANGER BRANCH, 1812 Seventh St, Sanger, 93657-2805. SAN 332-0251. Tel: 559-875-2435. FAX: 559-875-2435. Web Site: www.fresnolibrary.org. *Librn*, Barbara Light; E-Mail: blight@sjvls.lib.ca.us
Library Holdings: Bk Vols 41,471
SELMA BRANCH, 2200 Selma St, Selma, 93662-3151. SAN 332-0286. Tel: 559-896-3393. Web Site: www.fresnolibrary.org. *Librn*, Penny Hill; E-Mail: phill@sjvls.lib.ca.us
Library Holdings: Bk Vols 36,939
Special Collections: Sister City Collection
Friends of the Library Group
SHAVER LAKE STATION, 41344 Tollhouse Rd, Shaver Lake, 93664-0169. SAN 378-2417. Tel: 559-841-3330. Web Site: www.fresnolibrary.org. *In Charge*, Chris Rickert
Library Holdings: Bk Vols 5,397
SUNNYSIDE REGIONAL, 5566 E Kings Canyon Rd, 93727-4526. SAN 378-2433. Tel: 559-255-6594. Web Site: www.fresnolibrary.org. *Actg Librn*, Lyn MacEachron; E-Mail: lmaceach@sjvls.lib.ca.us
Library Holdings: Bk Vols 23,295
P TALKING BOOK LIBRARY FOR THE BLIND, 770 N San Pablo, 93728-3640. SAN 332-0014. Tel: 559-488-3217. Web Site: www.fresnolibrary.org. *Librn*, Wendy Eisenberg; E-Mail: weisenbe@sjvls.lib.ca.us
Founded 1975
Library Holdings: Bk Vols 1,500
Publications: Newsletter
Friends of the Library Group
TRANQUILITY NEIGHBORHOOD, 5831 S Juanche Ave, Tranquility, 93668. SAN 377-6298. Tel: 559-698-5158. Web Site: www.fresnolibrary.org. *In Charge*, Juanita McPhetridge
Library Holdings: Bk Vols 4,884
Bookmobiles: 2

G FRESNO COUNTY OFFICE OF EDUCATION, School Library Media Services,* 1111 Van Ness Ave, 93721. SAN 300-7596. Tel: 559-265-3000, 559-265-3091. FAX: 559-237-3525. *Circ*, Maria Villalpando; Staff 7 (MLS 1, Non-MLS 6)
Founded 1945
Library Holdings: Bk Vols 70,000; Per Subs 90
Special Collections: Adult Basic Education-English as a Second Language; Best of the Best, Children's Coll; Instructional Material Display; Literature Sets; Microcomputer/Software Evaluation Coll: Publishers' Samples; Teachers Professional Library
Partic in Area Wide Library Network; San Joaquin Valley Libr Syst

C FRESNO PACIFIC UNIVERSITY, Hiebert Library, 1717 S Chestnut Ave, 93702. SAN 300-7642. Tel: 559-453-2090. FAX: 559-453-2007. Web Site: www.fresno.edu/dept/library. *Dir*, Steven Brandt; Tel: 559-453-2222, E-Mail: srbrandt@fresno.edu; *Archivist*, Kevin Enns-Rempel; Tel: 559-453-2225, E-Mail: kennsrem@fresno.edu; *ILL, Publ Servs*, Anne Guenther; Tel: 559-453-2121, E-Mail: aguenthe@fresno.edu; *Acq*, Chris Brown; Tel: 559-453-2131, E-Mail: cbrown@fresno.edu; *Circ*, William P Ishmael; Tel: 559-453-2087, E-Mail: bishmael@fresno.edu; Staff 4 (MLS 4)
Founded 1944. Enrl 1,667; Fac 96; Highest Degree: Master
1998-1999 Mats Exp $211,916, Books $104,856, Per/Ser (Incl. Access Fees) $66,679, Presv $18,321, Micro $22,060. Sal $256,839 (Prof $220,660)
Library Holdings: Bk Vols 148,320; Per Subs 1,114
Subject Interests: History, Religion
Special Collections: Center for Mennonite Brethren Studies
Partic in Coop Libr Agency for Syst & Servs; OCLC Online Computer Library Center, Inc
Jointly operated with Mennonite Brethren Biblical Seminary

L MCCORMICK, BARSTOW, SHEPPARD, WAYTE & CARRUTH, Law Library, 5 River Park Pl E, 93720. SAN 373-7446. Tel: 559-433-2190. FAX: 559-433-2485, Attn: Library. E-Mail: library@sirius.net. *Librn*, Elizabeth A Shea; E-Mail: bshea@mbswc.com
Library Holdings: Bk Vols 12,000; Bk Titles 1,300

SR ROMAN CATHOLIC DIOCESE OF FRESNO LIBRARY, 1550 N Fresno St, 93703-3788. SAN 300-7537. Tel: 559-488-7400. FAX: 559-488-7464.
Founded 1934
1998-1999 Income $2,000
Library Holdings: Bk Vols 20,000
Subject Interests: Religion, Western Americana

M SAINT AGNES MEDICAL CENTER LIBRARY, 1303 E Herndon Ave, 93720-1234. SAN 320-5592. Tel: 559-449-3322. FAX: 559-449-3315. E-Mail: medlib@samc.com.; Staff 2 (MLS 1, Non-MLS 1)
Jul 2000-Jun 2001 Mats Exp $63,940, Books $10,000, Per/Ser (Incl. Access Fees) $53,940. Sal $82,260
Library Holdings: Per Subs 165
Subject Interests: Cancer, Cardiology, Medicine, Nursing
Automation Activity & Vendor Info: (OPAC) SIRSI
Partic in Area Wide Library Network; Med Libr Group of S Calif & NMex; Northern California & Nevada Medical Library Group; Pac SW Regional Med Libr

P SAN JOAQUIN VALLEY LIBRARY SYSTEM, 2420 Mariposa St, 93721. SAN 300-7677. Tel: 559-488-3185. Interlibrary Loan Service Tel: 559-488-3199. FAX: 559-488-1971. Web Site: www.sjvls.lib.ca.us. *Librn*, John K Kallenberg; E-Mail: jkallenb@sjvls.lib.ca.us; *Coordr*, Sharon Vandercook; Tel: 559-488-3229, E-Mail: sharonv@sjvls.lib.ca.us; *Automation Syst Coordr*, Mary Ellen Tyckoson; Tel: 559-488-3462, E-Mail: metyck@sjvls.lib.ca.us; Staff 9 (MLS 5, Non-MLS 4)
Founded 1960. Pop 2,097,000; Circ 5,439,613
Jul 1999-Jun 2000 Income $1,874,076, State $580,817, Federal $12,238, Locally Generated Income $1,066,296, Other $214,725. Mats Exp $103,596, Books $15,096, Per/Ser (Incl. Access Fees) $2,500, Electronic Ref Mat (Incl. Access Fees) $86,000. Sal $283,852 (Prof $202,137)
Automation Activity & Vendor Info: (Cataloging) epixtech, inc.; (Circulation) epixtech, inc.; (Course Reserve) epixtech, inc.; (ILL) epixtech, inc.; (OPAC) epixtech, inc.
Database Vendor: GaleNet, IAC - Info Trac
Publications: News & Clues (Newsletter)
Member Libraries: California Department of Corrections Library System; California School of Professional Psychology; Cerro Coso Community College; Coalinga-Huron Library District; Fresno County Library; Fresno County Public Library; Kern County Library; Kings County Library; Madera County Library; Mariposa County Library; Porterville Public Library; Reedley College Library; Tulare County Library; Tulare Public Library
Special Services for the Blind - Talking Books

SR TEMPLE BETH ISRAEL LIBRARY,* 6622 N Maroa Ave, 93704. SAN 320-5606. Tel: 209-432-3600. FAX: 209-432-3685.
Library Holdings: Bk Vols 1,400; Per Subs 12
Special Collections: Holocaust Coll
Partic in Area Wide Library Network
Open Mon-Thurs 9-12:30 & 1-4, Fri 9-3:30

L UNITED STATES COURTS LIBRARY, 1130 O St, Rm 4690, 93721. SAN 372-2686. Tel: 559-498-7334. FAX: 559-498-7295. *Librn*, Nedra Grubel; E-Mail: nedra_grubel@ce9.uscourts.gov
Library Holdings: Bk Vols 14,500

G UNITED STATES DEPARTMENT OF AGRICULTURE, Agricultural Research Service-Horticultural Crops Research Laboratory,* 2021 S Peach Ave, 93727. SAN 300-7685. Tel: 209-453-3002. FAX: 209-453-3088.
Library Holdings: Bk Vols 4,000
Subject Interests: Entomology
Publications: Pamphlets; reports

M UNIVERSITY MEDICAL CENTER LIBRARY, 445 S Cedar Ave, 93702. SAN 300-7693. Tel: 559-459-5030. FAX: 559-459-3841. *Librn*, Vicky Christianson; Staff 1 (Non-MLS 1)
Founded 1921
Library Holdings: Bk Vols 5,000; Bk Titles 2,000; Per Subs 190
Restriction: By appointment only

S THE VINEYARD, Real Estate Library, 100 W Shaw Ave, 93704. SAN 300-7650. Tel: 559-222-0182. *Librn*, Richard Erganian
Founded 1956
Library Holdings: Bk Titles 3,000
Subject Interests: Architecture, Urban planning
Special Collections: Mixed Use Development; Real Estate (Shopping Center Development), Hotels and Motels
Restriction: Staff use only

FULLERTON

S BECKMAN COULTER INC, Research Library,* 4300 N Harbor Blvd, 92834-3100. SAN 300-7731. Tel: 714-773-8906. Interlibrary Loan Service Tel: 714-961-3775. FAX: 714-773-8969. *Librn, Online Servs*, Carol Blankmeyer; *Coll Develop*, Marie Navrotska-Poff; Staff 7 (MLS 3, Non-MLS 4)
Founded 1955
Library Holdings: Bk Titles 7,500; Per Subs 450
Subject Interests: Microbiology, Optics, Physical chemistry
Publications: New Booklist; Periodicals Holdings List
Partic in Coop Libr Agency for Syst & Servs; Dialog Corporation

J FULLERTON COLLEGE, William T Boyce Library, 321 E Chapman Ave, 92832-2095. SAN 300-7758. Tel: 714-992-7061. FAX: 714-992-1786. Web Site: www.fullcoll.edu. *Dean of Libr*, John L Ayala; E-Mail: jayala@fullcoll.edu; *Head Ref*, Michele Fitzsimmons; Tel: 714-992-7072, E-Mail: mfitzsimmons@fullcoll.edu; *Asst Librn*, Ruth Ristow; E-Mail: rristow@fullcoll.edu; *Syst Coordr*, Jenny Langrell; Tel: 714-992-7069, Fax: 714-992-7069, E-Mail: jlangrell@fullcoll.edu; *Cat*, Sandy Smith; Tel: 714-992-7075, E-Mail: ssmith@fullcoll.edu; *Acq*, Goldie Eggers; Tel: 714-992-7003, E-Mail: geggers@fullcoll.edu; *Bibliog Instr*, Jackie Boll; Tel: 714-992-7068, E-Mail: jboll@fullcoll.edu; *Circ*, Anita Varela; Tel: 714-992-7067, E-Mail: avarela@fullcoll.edu; Staff 19 (MLS 9, Non-MLS 10)
Founded 1913. Enrl 19,862; Fac 336; Highest Degree: Associate
Jul 1999-Jun 2000 Mats Exp $119,250, Books $75,898, Per/Ser (Incl. Access Fees) $37,107, Micro $4,550, AV Equip $1,500, Other Print Mats $195, Electronic Ref Mat (Incl. Access Fees) $35,165. Sal $964,771
Library Holdings: Bk Vols 103,033; Bk Titles 85,923; Per Subs 443
Subject Interests: California, Library and information science, Literary criticism, Local history, Music, Women's studies
Special Collections: Topographic Maps of California (United States Geological Survey Coll)
Automation Activity & Vendor Info: (Acquisitions) Endeavor; (Cataloging) Endeavor; (Circulation) Endeavor; (Course Reserve) Endeavor; (OPAC) Endeavor; (Serials) Endeavor
Database Vendor: Ebsco - EbscoHost, GaleNet, OCLC - First Search, ProQuest
Partic in OCLC Online Computer Library Center, Inc
Friends of the Library Group

P FULLERTON PUBLIC LIBRARY, 353 W Commonwealth Ave, 92832-1796. SAN 332-0340. Tel: 714-738-6380. Circulation Tel: 714-738-5371. Reference Tel: 714-738-6327. FAX: 714-447-3280. E-Mail: alm@ci.fullerton.ca.us. Web Site: www.ci.fullerton.ca.us/library. *Dir*, Albert J Milo; E-Mail: alm@ci.fullerton.ca.us; *Librn*, Joanne Hardy; *Ch Servs*, Carolyn Eckert; *YA Servs*, Melinda Willeford-West; *Tech Servs*, Michael O'Brien; *Cat*, Carol Wright; *Ref*, Tim Mountain; *Bkmobile Coordr*, Barbara Weber; Staff 30 (MLS 15, Non-MLS 15)
Founded 1906. Pop 128,000; Circ 1,200,000
Jul 1999-Jun 2000 Income (Main Library and Branch Library) $2,800,570, State $150,000, City $2,444,940, Federal $3,191, Locally Generated Income $205,630. Mats Exp $289,730, Books $197,730, Per/Ser (Incl. Access Fees) $40,000, Electronic Ref Mat (Incl. Access Fees) $52,000. Sal $1,776,820
Library Holdings: Bk Titles 240,000; Per Subs 450
Subject Interests: Chinese Language, Korean (Language), Spanish (language)
Special Collections: Albert Launer Local History Room; Mary Campbell Children's Coll
Automation Activity & Vendor Info: (Circulation) GEAC
Database Vendor: Ebsco - EbscoHost, IAC - Info Trac
Mem of Santiago Libr Syst
Friends of the Library Group
Branches: 1
HUNT PUBLIC, 201 S Basque, 92833-3372. SAN 332-0375. Tel: 714-738-3122. FAX: 714-992-2946. Web Site: www.ci.fullerton.ca.us. *Librn*, Kathy Dasney
Library Holdings: Bk Vols 30,024
Friends of the Library Group
Bookmobiles: 1

C HOPE INTERNATIONAL UNIVERSITY, Hugh & Hazel Darling Library, 2500 E Nutwood Ave, 92831. SAN 300-7782. Tel: 714-879-3901. FAX: 714-879-1041. Web Site: www.hiu.edu/library. *Dir*, Armand Ternak; E-Mail: aternak@hiu.edu; Staff 8 (MLS 3, Non-MLS 5)
Founded 1928. Highest Degree: Master
Library Holdings: Bk Vols 65,000; Per Subs 300
Special Collections: Rare book coll, primarily related to history of Restoration Movement
Partic in OCLC Online Computer Library Center, Inc; SCELC

C PAULINA JUNE & GEORGE POLLAK LIBRARY, (Formerly California State University), 800 N State College Blvd, PO Box 4150, 92834-4150. SAN 300-774X. Tel: 714-278-2714. FAX: 714-278-2439. E-Mail: libadm@fullerton.edu. Web Site: www.library.fullerton.edu. *Librn*, Richard C Pollard; E-Mail: rpollard@fullerton.edu; *Ser, Tech Servs*, Teresa Malinowski; *Spec Coll*, Sharon Perry; *Cat, Tech Servs*, Jerri Harrison; *Acq*, Floyd Zula; *Ref*, Doug Highsmith; *Cat*, Verna Wheeler; *Publ Servs*, Francisco Garcia; *Coll Develop*, Patricia Bril; Staff 62 (MLS 25, Non-MLS 37)
Founded 1959. Enrl 27,000; Fac 714; Highest Degree: Master
Jul 1999-Jun 2000 Income $4,802,803. Mats Exp $5,872,924, Books $432,466, Per/Ser (Incl. Access Fees) $621,669, Micro $621,669, Other Print Mats $174,479. Sal $2,989,730 (Prof $1,567,999)
Library Holdings: Bk Vols 1,096,803; Bk Titles 728,854; Per Subs 2,437
Automation Activity & Vendor Info: (Cataloging) Innovative Interfaces Inc.; (Circulation) Innovative Interfaces Inc.
Publications: Exhibition Catalogue for Maps Illustrating the History of Cartography; Reference Department Bibliographies & Guides
Partic in BRS; Dow Jones News Retrieval; Medline; OCLC Online Computer Library Center, Inc; SDC Info Servs
Friends of the Library Group

M SAINT JUDE MEDICAL CENTER, Medical Library, 101 E Valencia Mesa Dr, 92835. SAN 327-4098. Tel: 714-871-3280. FAX: 714-447-6481. *Librn*, Carol Bondurant; E-Mail: cbondura@sjf.stjoe.org
Library Holdings: Bk Vols 1,000; Per Subs 130
Subject Interests: Medicine, Nursing
Automation Activity & Vendor Info: (Cataloging) Inmagic, Inc.; (OPAC) Inmagic, Inc.
Partic in Med Libr Group of S Calif & Ariz

C SOUTHERN CALIFORNIA COLLEGE OF OPTOMETRY, M B Ketchum Memorial Library, 2575 Yorba Linda Blvd, 92831-1699. SAN 300-7790. Tel: 714-449-7440. FAX: 714-879-0481. Web Site: www.scco.edu. *Dir*, Doreen Keough; E-Mail: dkeough@scco.edu
Founded 1950. Enrl 400; Fac 100; Highest Degree: Doctorate
Library Holdings: Bk Titles 10,000; Per Subs 346
Subject Interests: Ophthalmology, Optics, Optometry
Special Collections: Historical Vision Coll
Publications: Faculty publications; Library's latest additions (bimonthly); student research papers (annual)
Partic in Coop Libr Agency for Syst & Servs; OCLC Online Computer Library Center, Inc

CL WESTERN STATE UNIVERSITY, Reis Law Library, 1111 B State College Blvd, 92831-3014. SAN 300-7804. Tel: 714-738-1000. FAX: 714-871-4806. Web Site: www.wsulaw.edu. *Dir*, Carol L P Ebbinghouse; E-Mail: carole@wsulaw.edu; *Asst Dir, Ref*, Anne Rimmer; *Ref*, Cindy Parkhurst; *Tech Servs*, Pat Plumb
Library Holdings: Bk Vols 168,033; Per Subs 25,448
Subject Interests: Anglo-American law
Partic in OCLC Online Computer Library Center, Inc

GARDENIA

S NISSAN NORTH AMERICA, Corporate Library,* 18501 S Figueroa St, 90248. SAN 300-6557. Tel: 310-532-3111. FAX: 310-771-3343.
Founded 1972
1997-1998 Mats Exp $10,000
Library Holdings: Bk Vols 500
Subject Interests: Automotive engineering, Business and management

GILROY

J GAVILAN COLLEGE LIBRARY, 5055 Santa Teresa Blvd, 95020. SAN 300-7839. Tel: 408-848-4812. Circulation Tel: 408-848-4810. Reference Tel: 408-848-4806. FAX: 408-846-4927. Web Site: www.gavilan.cc.ca.us/library/. *Dir*, Shukchun Auyeung; Tel: 408-848-4809, E-Mail: sauyeung@gavilan.cc.ca.us; *ILL*, Diana Hanks; E-Mail: dhanks@gavilan.cc.ca.us; *Ref*, JoAnne Howell; E-Mail: jhowell@gavilan.cc.ca.us; Staff 2 (MLS 2)
Founded 1963. Enrl 1,996; Fac 70
Jul 1999-Jun 2000 Mats Exp $91,932, Books $52,283, Per/Ser (Incl. Access Fees) $10,970, Micro $3,511, Electronic Ref Mat (Incl. Access Fees) $14,935. Sal $243,727
Library Holdings: Bk Vols 46,720; Bk Titles 42,303; Per Subs 2,513
Automation Activity & Vendor Info: (Acquisitions) Endeavor; (Cataloging) Endeavor; (Circulation) Endeavor; (Course Reserve) Endeavor; (OPAC) Endeavor; (Serials) Endeavor
Database Vendor: Ebsco - EbscoHost, ProQuest
Publications: Bibliographies; Handouts
Partic in MOBAC; Monterey Bay Area Coop Libr Syst; RLIN

S LUCAS SIGNATONE CORP LIBRARY,* 393 Tomkins Ct Ste J, 95020. SAN 328-2031. Tel: 408-848-2851. FAX: 408-848-5763. E-Mail: sales@signatone.com. Web Site: www.signatone.com. *Librn*, Richard Dixon
Library Holdings: Bk Vols 1,000

GLEN ELLEN

S JACK LONDON RESEARCH CENTER LIBRARY, 14300 Arnold Dr, PO Box 337, 95442. SAN 325-5301. Tel: 707-996-2888. FAX: 707-996-4107. E-Mail: jlondon@vom.com. *Cat, Librn*, Winnie Kingman
Founded 1972
Library Holdings: Bk Vols 500; Bk Titles 500
Subject Interests: Jack London, San Francisco Bay literary figures (1876-1916)

S JACK LONDON STATE HISTORIC PARK, Betty Hageman Memorial Library, 2400 London Ranch Rd, 95442. SAN 373-4021. Tel: 707-938-5216. FAX: 707-938-4827. Web Site: www.parks.sonoma.net. *Librn*, Jane Merryman
Library Holdings: Bk Titles 90; Per Subs 20
Special Collections: Jack London Literature
Restriction: Not open to public

GLENDALE

S WALT DISNEY IMAGINEERING, Information Research Center,* 1401 Flower St, PO Box 25020, 91221-5020. SAN 300-7952. Tel: 818-544-6594. FAX: 818-544-7845. Web Site: www.irc@disney.com. *In Charge*, Aileen Barkley; E-Mail: aileen_kutaka-barkley@disney.com; *Info Specialist*, Saundra Murray; *Cat*, Joseph Geissler; *Circ*, Al Simpson; Staff 6 (MLS 4, Non-MLS 2)
Founded 1962
Library Holdings: Bk Vols 50,000; Per Subs 500
Subject Interests: Art and architecture, Business and management, Costume design, Engineering, History, Interior design, Technology, Travel
Special Services for the Deaf - Staff with knowledge of sign language

S FOREST LAWN MUSEUM LIBRARY,* 1712 S Glendale Ave, 91205. SAN 300-7847. Tel: 323-340-4707. FAX: 323-254-8152. *Dir*, Stephanie Olmeda-Vance
Founded 1951
Library Holdings: Bk Vols 3,000
Special Collections: American Bronze Statuary; American History; Autographs; Gems; Pre-Christian & Christian Era Coins
Restriction: Staff use only

M GLENDALE ADVENTIST MEDICAL CENTER LIBRARY,* 1509 Wilson Terrace, PO Box 871, 91209-0871. SAN 300-7855. Tel: 818-409-8034. FAX: 818-546-5633. *Dir*, June Levy
Founded 1957
Library Holdings: Bk Titles 8,500; Per Subs 650
Subject Interests: Allied health, Medicine, Nursing
Automation Activity & Vendor Info: (Cataloging) Sydney; (Circulation) Sydney
Partic in BRS; Dialog Corporation; Medline; Paper Chase; Wilsonline

S GLENDALE CITY PLANNING DIVISION, Technical Library,* 633 E Broadway, Rm 103, 91206-4386. SAN 327-6899. Tel: 818-548-2140. FAX: 818-240-0392.
Library Holdings: Bk Vols 2,000; Per Subs 12

J GLENDALE COMMUNITY COLLEGE LIBRARY, 1500 N Verdugo Rd, 91208-2894. SAN 300-7863. Tel: 818-240-1000, Ext 5574. FAX: 818-246-5107. Web Site: www.glendale.cc.ca.us/library. *Dean of Libr*, Ruth Thompson McKernan; *Tech Servs*, Brenda Jones; *Publ Servs*, Linda Winters; *Instrul Serv*, Shelley Aronoff; *Circ*, Russell Beckett; *Ref*, Ramchandran Sethuraman
Founded 1927. Enrl 15,000; Fac 534
Jul 1999-Jun 2000 Income $1,201,583. Mats Exp $218,032, Books $109,000, Per/Ser (Incl. Access Fees) $23,362, Presv $1,000, Electronic Ref Mat (Incl. Access Fees) $84,670. Sal $888,198
Library Holdings: Bk Vols 112,431; Bk Titles 81,177; Per Subs 331
Automation Activity & Vendor Info: (Acquisitions) Endeavor; (Cataloging) Endeavor; (Circulation) Endeavor; (Serials) Endeavor
Publications: Library Research Guide
Partic in Cal Coun of Chief Librns; OCLC Online Computer Library Center, Inc

P GLENDALE PUBLIC LIBRARY, 222 E Harvard St, 91205-1075. SAN 332-043X. Tel: 818-548-2030. Interlibrary Loan Service Tel: 818-548-6430. Circulation Tel: 818-548-2021. Reference Tel: 818-548-2027. TDD: 818-543-0368. FAX: 818-548-7225. Web Site: www.library.ci.glendale.ca.us. *Dir Libr Serv*, Laurel Patric; E-Mail: lpatric@ci.glendale.ca.us; *Asst Dir*, Marie Fish; Tel: 818-548-4019, E-Mail: mfisg@ci.glendale.ca.us; *Ad Servs*, Cindy Cleary; Tel: 818-548-2043, Fax: 818-409-7030, E-Mail: ccleary@ci.glendale.ca.us; *Ch Servs*, Carolyn Flemming; Tel: 818-548-3999, Fax: 818-409-7030, E-Mail: cflemming@ci.glendale.ca.us; *Head Tech Servs*, Nora Goldsmith; Tel: 818-548-4020, E-Mail: ngoldsmith@ci.glendale.ca.us; *Automation Syst Coordr*, Nancy Hunt-Coffey; Tel: 818-548-6459, Fax: 818-247-5888, E-Mail: nhunt-coffey@ci.glendale.ca.us; Staff 56 (MLS 33, Non-MLS 23)
Founded 1906. Pop 203,734; Circ 937,943
Jul 1999-Jun 2000 Income (Main Library and Branch Library) $5,753,910. Mats Exp $687,075, Books $510,175, Per/Ser (Incl. Access Fees) $52,128, Presv $10,000, Micro $31,772, Electronic Ref Mat (Incl. Access Fees) $83,000. Sal $3,746,202
Library Holdings: Bk Vols 518,653; Per Subs 901
Subject Interests: California, Local history, Music
Special Collections: Domestic Cat Genealogy; Original Art Coll; Piano Roll Coll; Sheet Music Coll
Automation Activity & Vendor Info: (Acquisitions) GEAC; (Circulation) GEAC; (OPAC) GEAC
Database Vendor: Dialog, GaleNet, IAC - Info Trac, IAC - SearchBank
Mem of Metropolitan Cooperative Library System
Partic in Dialog Corporation; OCLC Online Computer Library Center, Inc
Special Services for the Deaf - TDD
Special Services for the Blind - Cassettes; Large print bks; Records; Talking Books
Friends of the Library Group
Branches: 5
BRAND ART & MUSIC, 1601 W Mountain St, 91201-1209. SAN 332-0464. Tel: 818-548-2051. TDD: 818-543-0367. FAX: 818-548-5079. Web Site: www.library.ci.glendale.ca.us. *Librn*, Jill Conner; Tel: 818-548-2010, E-Mail: jconner@ci.glendale.ca.us; *Librn*, Joe Fuchs; Tel: 818-548-2026, E-Mail: jfuchs@ci.glendale.ca.us. Subject Specialists: *Art*, Jill Conner; *Music*, Joe Fuchs; Staff 3 (MLS 3)
Circ 140,043
Library Holdings: Bk Vols 98,854
Subject Interests: Art, Music
Special Collections: Art; cassettes; discs; piano rolls; sheet music & scores
Special Services for the Deaf - TDD
Friends of the Library Group
CASA VERDUGO, 1151 N Brand Blvd, 91202-2503. SAN 332-0499. Tel: 818-548-2047. FAX: 818-548-8052. Web Site: library.ci.glendale.ca.us. *Librn*, Mary Alice Wollam; E-Mail: mwollam@ci.glendale.ca.us; Staff 2 (MLS 2)
Founded 1951. Pop 26,526; Circ 46,236
Library Holdings: Bk Vols 46,656
Friends of the Library Group
CHEVY CHASE, 3301 E Chevy Chase Dr, 91206-1416. SAN 332-0529. Tel: 818-548-2046. FAX: 818-548-7713. Web Site: www.library.ci.glendale.ca.us. *Librn*, Mary Alice Wollam; Tel: 818-548-2047, E-Mail: mwollam@ci.glendale.ca.us
Circ 6,914
Library Holdings: Bk Vols 30,971
Friends of the Library Group
GRANDVIEW, 1535 Fifth St, 91205-1985. SAN 332-0553. Tel: 818-548-2049. FAX: 818-549-0678. Web Site: www.library.ci.glendale.ca.us. *Librn*, Mary Alice Toomey; E-Mail: mtoomey@ci.glendale.ca.us; Staff 5 (MLS 2, Non-MLS 3)
Pop 41,775; Circ 48,569
Library Holdings: Bk Vols 43,609
Friends of the Library Group
MONTROSE-CRESCENTA BRANCH, 2465 Honolulu Ave, Montrose, 91020-1803. SAN 332-0588. Tel: 818-548-2048. TDD: 818-548-2048. FAX: 818-248-6987. Web Site: library.ci.glendale.ca.us. *Librn*, Patricia Zeider; E-Mail: pzeider@ci.glendale.ca.us; Staff 2 (MLS 2)
Pop 33,895; Circ 87,306
Library Holdings: Bk Vols 63,205
Special Services for the Deaf - TDD
Friends of the Library Group
Bookmobiles: 1. Librn, Mindy Libertman. Bk vols 7777

CL GLENDALE UNIVERSITY, College of Law Library,* 220 N Glendale Ave, 91206. SAN 300-7871. Tel: 818-247-0770. FAX: 818-247-0872. E-Mail: admit@glendalelaw.edu. Web Site: www.glendalelaw.edu. *Librn*, Judy Greitzer
Founded 1967
Library Holdings: Bk Vols 65,000; Per Subs 290
Special Collections: English Common Law Coll; Rare Law Books
Friends of the Library Group

L KNAPP, PETERSON & CLARKE, Law Library,* 500 N Brand Blvd, 91203. SAN 372-3194. Tel: 818-547-5050. FAX: 818-547-5329.
Library Holdings: Bk Vols 14,250; Per Subs 28

S NESTLE USA, INC, 800 N Brand Blvd, 91203. SAN 370-9671. Tel: 818-549-6655. FAX: 818-549-6912. *Dir*, Mary Beth Rymers
Library Holdings: Bk Titles 100; Per Subs 40
Restriction: Not open to public

S SONS OF THE REVOLUTION LIBRARY, 600 S Central Ave, 91204-2009. SAN 300-7928. Tel: 818-240-1775. E-Mail: sr@walika.com. Web Site: www.walika.com/sr.htm. *Dir*, Edwin W Coles; *Librn*, Anne Coe
Founded 1893

Library Holdings: Bk Vols 35,000; Per Subs 10
Subject Interests: American revolution, Genealogy
Special Collections: Family Histories; Vital Records
Friends of the Library Group

GLENDORA

J CITRUS COLLEGE, Hayden Memorial Library, 1000 W Foothill Blvd, 91741-1899. SAN 300-5860. Tel: 626-914-8640. Interlibrary Loan Service Tel: 626-914-8644. FAX: 626-963-2531. Web Site: www.citruscollege.com/library.htm. *Dean, Librn*, John R Thompson; *Bibliog Instr, Online Servs, Publ Servs*, Barbara Rugeley; Staff 16 (MLS 6, Non-MLS 10)
Founded 1915
Library Holdings: Bk Titles 39,439; Per Subs 125
Subject Interests: Art and architecture, Music, Railroads, Social sciences and issues
Special Collections: Astronomy (Schlesinger Coll)
Automation Activity & Vendor Info: (Circulation) Gaylord
Partic in Dialog Corporation; OCLC Online Computer Library Center, Inc

P GLENDORA PUBLIC LIBRARY, 140 S Glendora Ave, 91741. SAN 300-7979. Tel: 626-852-4891. FAX: 626-852-4899. E-Mail: library@ci.glendora.ca.us. Web Site: www.ci.glendora.ca.us/library. *Actg Dir*, Hal Watson; *Senior Librn*, Carmen Hernandez; *ILL*, Caroline Nance; *Circ*, Anne Pankow; *Tech Servs*, Frances Bockhoven; Staff 6 (MLS 6)
Founded 1912. Circ 372,958
Library Holdings: Bk Vols 110,000; Per Subs 375
Automation Activity & Vendor Info: (Cataloging) Gaylord; (Circulation) Gaylord
Publications: Children's Programs; Community Calendar; Computer Center; Gateway to Knowledge; Literacy Program; Monthly Calendar; Your Elected Officials
Mem of Metropolitan Cooperative Library System
Special Services - Homebound delivery, community information, referral & adult literacy. Open Mon, Tues & Wed 10-9, Thurs, Fri & Sat 10-5:30
Friends of the Library Group

GOLETA

S RAYTHEON SYSTEMS CO, E W Library, 6380 Hollister Ave, 93117. SAN 300-8053. Tel: 805-879-3004. FAX: 805-879-3079. *Librn*, Sheila Anderson
Founded 1957
Library Holdings: Bk Titles 3,500; Per Subs 80
Subject Interests: Aerospace science, Computer science, Electronics, Engineering

GRASS VALLEY

J SIERRA COLLEGE LIBRARY, Nevada County Campus, 250 Sierra College Dr, 95945. SAN 375-4243. Tel: 530-274-5304. FAX: 530-274-5333. Web Site: www.sierra.cc.ca.us. *Librn, Ref*, Patricia Saulsbury; E-Mail: psaulsbury@scmail.sierra.cc.ca.us
Library Holdings: Bk Vols 11,000; Bk Titles 10,000; Per Subs 100
Automation Activity & Vendor Info: (Cataloging) Endeavor; (Circulation) Endeavor

M SIERRA NEVADA MEMORIAL HOSPITAL, Health Sciences Library, 155 Glasson Way, 95945-5723. (Mail add: PO Box 1029, 95945-1029), SAN 370-6753. Tel: 530-274-6064. FAX: 530-274-6627. *Dir Libr Serv*, Tonya Kraft; E-Mail: tkraft@chw.edu
Founded 1981
Library Holdings: Bk Vols 1,200; Per Subs 120
Partic in Sacramento Area Health Sciences Librs

HANFORD

GL KINGS COUNTY LAW LIBRARY,* Kings County Government Ctr, 1400 W Lacey Blvd, 93230. SAN 320-5649. Tel: 209-582-3211, Ext 4430. *Librn*, Cheryl Lehn
Founded 1898
Library Holdings: Bk Vols 15,000; Per Subs 16

P KINGS COUNTY LIBRARY,* 401 N Douty St, 93230. SAN 332-0618. Tel: 559-582-0261. FAX: 559-583-6163. Web Site: www.sjvls.lib.ca.us/kings, www.sjvls.lib.ca.us/kings. *Dir*, Ivan Edelman; Tel: 559-582-0262, E-Mail: iedelman@co.kings.ca.us; *Dep Dir*, Louise Hodges; Tel: 559-582-0262, E-Mail: lhodges@sjvls.lib.ca.us; *Ad Servs, Ref*, Janet Harader; *Ad Servs, Ref*, Jeff Crosby; E-Mail: jcrosby@sjvls.lib.ca.us; *Ch Servs*, Theresa Goedde; Staff 5 (MLS 5)
Founded 1911. Pop 118,000; Circ 386,551
Jul 1998-Jun 1999 Income (Main Library and Branch Library) $857,000, State $68,400, Locally Generated Income $30,000. Mats Exp $140,000, Books $135,000, Presv $5,000. Sal $584,967
Library Holdings: Bk Vols 174,168; Per Subs 300
Automation Activity & Vendor Info: (Acquisitions) epixtech, inc.; (Cataloging) epixtech, inc.; (Circulation) epixtech, inc.
Database Vendor: epixtech, inc., IAC - Info Trac, OCLC - First Search
Mem of San Joaquin Valley Library System
Friends of the Library Group
Branches: 6
AVENAL BRANCH, 501 E King St, Avenal, 93204. SAN 332-0677. Tel: 559-386-5741. *Librn*, Sheryl Tune
Library Holdings: Bk Vols 14,033
Friends of the Library Group
CORCORAN BRANCH, 1001-A Chittenden, Corcoran, 93212. SAN 332-0731. Tel: 559-992-3314. *Librn*, Joyce Cravens
Library Holdings: Bk Vols 13,210
HANFORD, 401 N Douty St, 93230. SAN 332-0790. Tel: 559-582-0261. FAX: 559-583-6163. Web Site: www.sjvls.lib.ca.us/kings/. *Librn*, Jeff Crosby
Library Holdings: Bk Vols 89,326
Friends of the Library Group
KETTLEMAN CITY BRANCH, 104 Becky Pease St, Kettleman City, 93239. SAN 332-0820. Tel: 559-386-9804. *Librn*, Barbara Ervin
Library Holdings: Bk Titles 11,807
Friends of the Library Group
LEMOORE BRANCH, 457 C St, Lemoore, 93245. SAN 332-0855. Tel: 559-924-2188. FAX: 559-924-1521. *Librn*, Chris Baize
Library Holdings: Bk Vols 28,796
STRATFORD BRANCH, 20300 Main St, Stratford, 93266. SAN 332-088X. Tel: 559-947-3003. *Librn*, Clarice Wilkins
Library Holdings: Bk Vols 12,504

S PIRELLI TIRE CORP LIBRARY,* 10701 Idaho Ave, 93230. SAN 302-251X. Tel: 209-583-2764. FAX: 209-583-2722.
Founded 1960
Library Holdings: Bk Vols 600; Per Subs 50
Special Collections: Industry Technical Papers; Internal Reports; Product Test Data

HARBOR CITY

M BAY HARBOR HOSPITAL, Medical Library,* 1437 W Lomita Blvd, 90710. SAN 324-7589. Tel: 310-325-1221. *Librn*, Maureen Neeley
1997-1998 Income $3,000. Mats Exp $2,000, Books $1,000, Per/Ser (Incl. Access Fees) $1,000. Sal $1,000
Library Holdings: Bk Titles 865; Per Subs 12
Subject Interests: Medicine, Nursing
Restriction: Staff use only
Partic in Meditech

M KAISER FOUNDATION HOSPITAL, Medical Library,* 25825 S Vermont Ave, 90710-3599. SAN 322-774X. Tel: 310-517-2090. FAX: 310-517-4212. E-Mail: harbor-city.medical-library@kp.org.; Staff 2 (MLS 2)
Library Holdings: Bk Titles 4,686; Per Subs 233
Subject Interests: Health sci, Nursing
Publications: Newsletter (quarterly)
Partic in Pac SW Regional Med Libr

HAYWARD

S AQUATIC RESEARCH INSTITUTE LIBRARY, 2242 Davis Ct, 94545-1114. SAN 300-8118. Tel: 510-785-2216. FAX: 510-784-0945. *Dir*, Robert R Rofen; E-Mail: rofen@prado.com; *Librn*, Verle Jean Parker
Founded 1961
Library Holdings: Bk Titles 10,000; Per Subs 1,000
Subject Interests: Ichthyology, Marine biology, Oceanography
Publications: Aquatica 1-3; Journal of Aquariculture & Aquatic Sciences

C CALIFORNIA STATE UNIVERSITY, HAYWARD LIBRARY,* 25800 Carlos Bee Blvd, 94542-3052. SAN 300-8142. Tel: 510-885-3664. FAX: 510-885-2049. Web Site: www.csuhayward.edu/library/. *Dir*, Noreen Alldredge; *Dep Dir, Ref*, Ilene Rockman; *Acq, Coll Develop, Tech Servs*, Carol Castagnozzi; *Coordr*, Pat Dixon; Staff 34 (MLS 13, Non-MLS 21)
Founded 1959. Enrl 12,583; Fac 628; Highest Degree: Master
Jul 1998-Jun 1999 Income (Main Library and Branch Library) $4,021,029. Mats Exp $1,449,995. Sal $1,642,673
Library Holdings: Bk Vols 892,847; Per Subs 3,493
Special Collections: Bay Area Poetry Coll; Cameos Coll; Early Voyages & Travels Coll; Marco Polo Coll
Automation Activity & Vendor Info: (Acquisitions) Innovative Interfaces Inc.; (Cataloging) Innovative Interfaces Inc.; (Circulation) Innovative Interfaces Inc.; (Course Reserve) Innovative Interfaces Inc.; (ILL) Innovative Interfaces Inc.; (Media Booking) Innovative Interfaces Inc.; (OPAC) Innovative Interfaces Inc.; (Serials) Innovative Interfaces Inc.
Partic in Bay Area Libr & Info Systs; OCLC Online Computer Library Center, Inc
Departmental Libraries:
CONTRA COSTA CAMPUS LIBRARY, 4700 Ygnacio Valley Rd, Concord, 94521. SAN 321-8554. Tel: 925-602-6725. FAX: 925-602-6751.

Web Site: www.library.csuhayward.edu/ccc/. *Librn*, Steve Philibosian; *Librn*, Caroline Whitcomb; E-Mail: cwhitcom.bay.csuhayward.edu
Founded 1982. Enrl 1,300; Fac 1; Highest Degree: Master

J CHABOT COLLEGE, Learning Resource Center,* 25555 Hesperian Blvd, 94545. SAN 332-1339. Tel: 510-786-6762. Interlibrary Loan Service Tel: 510-786-6764. FAX: 510-782-9315. Web Site: www.clpccd.cc.ca.us. *Librn*, David W Butler; *Coordr*, James Matthews; *Circ*, Diana Immisch; *Ref*, Valerie Hicks; *Acq*, Barbara Olson; Staff 4 (MLS 4)
Founded 1961. Enrl 14,783; Fac 264
Library Holdings: Bk Titles 83,460; Per Subs 290
Special Collections: California History Coll

S HAYWARD AREA HISTORICAL SOCIETY MUSEUM LIBRARY, 22701 Main St, 94541. SAN 300-8150. Tel: 510-581-0223. FAX: 510-581-0217. E-Mail: haywdhist@aol.com. *Librn*, Bernard Golumb
Founded 1956
2000-2001 Income $500. Mats Exp Presv $500
Library Holdings: Bk Vols 3,000; Bk Titles 2,000
Special Collections: Cemetary Records; City Records from 1856, mss; Honchorenko Coll; Local History Coll, negatives, photogs, slides, magazines, clippings
Publications: Adobe Trails (quarterly)
Restriction: Non-circulating to the public, Not a lending library
Function: Archival collection, Business archives, Photocopies available, Research fees apply, Some telephone reference

P HAYWARD PUBLIC LIBRARY, 835 C St, 94541-5120. SAN 332-1363. Tel: 510-881-7954. Circulation Tel: 510-293-8685. Reference Tel: 510-881-7942. TDD: 510-293-1590. FAX: 510-733-6669. E-Mail: librarypo@cityofhaywood.com. Web Site: www.library.cityofhaywood.com. *Dir*, Marilyn Baker-Madsen; Tel: 510-881-7956, E-Mail: marilynb@ci.hayward.ca.us; *Syst Coordr*, Cheryl Armstrong; *Ad Servs*, John Hebel; Tel: 510-881-7976, E-Mail: john@ci.hayward.ca.us; *YA Servs*, Sherry Kumler; Tel: 510-881-7948; Staff 17 (MLS 13, Non-MLS 4)
Founded 1897. Pop 127,700
Jul 1999-Jun 2000 Income $2,354,366, City $2,052,178, Locally Generated Income $71,604, Other $10,000. Mats Exp $222,271, Books $152,082, Per/Ser (Incl. Access Fees) $18,500, AV Equip $23,200, Electronic Ref Mat (Incl. Access Fees) $27,000. Sal $2,023,071
Library Holdings: Bk Vols 189,665; Bk Titles 104,973; Per Subs 338
Subject Interests: Local history
Automation Activity & Vendor Info: (Acquisitions) Innovative Interfaces Inc.
Mem of Bay Area Libr & Info Syst
Partic in Bay Area Libr & Info Serv
Friends of the Library Group
Branches: 1
WEEKES, 27300 Patrick Ave, 94544. SAN 332-1398. Tel: 510-782-2155. FAX: 510-259-0429. *Dir*, Marilyn Baker-Madsen; Tel: 510-881-7956, Fax: 510-733-6669, E-Mail: marilynb@ci.hayward.ca.us
Library Holdings: Bk Vols 52,569; Bk Titles 40,958
Friends of the Library Group

M KAISER PERMANENTE MEDICAL CENTER, Health Sciences Library,* 27400 Hesperian Blvd, 94545. SAN 300-8169. Tel: 510-784-4420. FAX: 510-784-4992. *Librn*, Cynthia Seay; E-Mail: cynthia.seay@ncal.kaiperm.org; *Asst Librn*, Rebecca Hoxsey
Library Holdings: Bk Titles 1,000; Per Subs 180
Subject Interests: Allied health, Medicine, Nursing

JM LIFE CHIROPRACTIC COLLEGE-WEST LIBRARY, 25001 Industrial Blvd, 94545. SAN 327-9162. Tel: 510-780-4507. Reference Tel: 510-780-4500, Ext 2930. FAX: 510-276-4893. Web Site: www.lifewest.edu. *Dir*, Annette Osenga; E-Mail: aosenga@lifewest.edu; *Syst Coordr*, Barbara Delli-Gatti
Founded 1981. Enrl 685; Highest Degree: Doctorate
Jul 1999-Jun 2000 Income $582,000, Locally Generated Income $12,000, Parent Institution $570,000. Mats Exp $99,100, Books $25,000, Per/Ser (Incl. Access Fees) $38,000, Presv $6,000, AV Equip $20,000, Other Print Mats $600, Electronic Ref Mat (Incl. Access Fees) $9,500. Sal $528,000 (Prof $130,500)
Library Holdings: Bk Vols 12,500; Bk Titles 11,230; Per Subs 250
Special Collections: Chiropractic (rare bk coll); College archives
Automation Activity & Vendor Info: (Cataloging) epixtech, inc.; (Circulation) epixtech, inc.; (Course Reserve) epixtech, inc.; (OPAC) epixtech, inc.
Publications: Audiovisuals (quarterly); New Books (quarterly); Pathfinders (5 per year); What's New in the Library: Periodicals (approx monthly)
Restriction: In-house use for visitors
Function: Document delivery services, Photocopies available, Research fees apply, Some telephone reference
Partic in Chiropractic Libr Consortium; National Network Of Libraries Of Medicine - South Central Region; OCLC Online Computer Library Center, Inc

HEALDSBURG

P HEALDSBURG REGIONAL LIBRARY,* 139 Piper St, 95448. SAN 376-3897. Tel: 707-433-3772. FAX: 707-433-7946. *Mgr*, Catherine Bassett
Library Holdings: Bk Vols 16,000; Bk Titles 10,000
Mem of North Bay Cooperative Library System

HEMET

P HEMET PUBLIC LIBRARY,* 510 E Florida Ave, 92543. SAN 300-8177. Tel: 909-765-2440. TDD: 909-765-2447. FAX: 909-765-2446. *ILL*, Martha Vieten; *Tech Servs*, Maxine Watters; Staff 3 (MLS 3)
Founded 1907. Pop 57,502; Circ 244,778
Jul 1997-Jun 1998 Income $927,000. Mats Exp $86,000. Sal $599,000
Library Holdings: Bk Vols 67,000; Bk Titles 56,500; Per Subs 216
Special Collections: California Coll; Large Print Bks
Automation Activity & Vendor Info: (Circulation) epixtech, inc.
Mem of Inland Library System
Partic in San Bernardino, Inyo, Riverside Counties United Library Services
Special Services for the Deaf - TDD
Friends of the Library Group

L HEMET VALLEY HOSPITAL, Medical Library, 1117 E Devonshire Ave, 92543. SAN 327-5957. Tel: 909-652-2811, Ext 6144. FAX: 909-765-4809. *Coordr*, Sudi Sajed; Staff 1 (MLS 1)
Library Holdings: Bk Vols 750; Bk Titles 719; Per Subs 110
Partic in Inland Empire Acad Libr Coop

HOLLISTER

P SAN BENITO COUNTY FREE LIBRARY, 470 Fifth St, 95023-3885. SAN 300-8185. Tel: 831-636-4107. FAX: 831-636-4099. E-Mail: sbclib@hollinet.com. Web Site: sbclib.com. *Librn*, Josephine Barrios Wahdan; Tel: 831-636-4097; Staff 9 (MLS 2, Non-MLS 7)
Founded 1918. Pop 48,100
Jul 2000-Jun 2001 Income $385,651, State $89,894, City $13,000, County $269,307, Locally Generated Income $13,450. Mats Exp $44,900, Books $30,564, Per/Ser (Incl. Access Fees) $8,741, Presv $800, AV Equip $2,825, Electronic Ref Mat (Incl. Access Fees) $1,970. Sal $303,659 (Prof $88,754)
Library Holdings: Bk Vols 75,948; Per Subs 186
Subject Interests: Art, California, Japanese (Language), Local history, Spanish (language)
Automation Activity & Vendor Info: (Cataloging) TLC; (Circulation) TLC; (OPAC) TLC
Database Vendor: Wilson - Wilson Web
Function: ILL available, Some telephone reference
Mem of Monterey Bay Area Cooperative Library System
Friends of the Library Group
Bookmobiles: 1. 1982 Chevrolet Pioneer II, Model #CG31603

GL SAN BENITO COUNTY LAW LIBRARY,* Courthouse, Rm 206, 440 Fifth St, 95023. SAN 320-5665. Tel: 408-636-4040. FAX: 408-636-4044. *In Charge*, Maria Alfaro
Library Holdings: Bk Vols 12,537; Bk Titles 5,200

HOLLYWOOD

M HOLLYWOOD COMMUNITY HOSPITAL, Medical Staff Library,* 6245 DeLongpre Ave, 90028. SAN 371-1447. Tel: 213-462-2271. FAX: 213-467-5108.
Library Holdings: Bk Vols 6,000

S HOLLYWOOD FILM ARCHIVE LIBRARY, PMB 321, 8391 Beverly Blvd, 90048. SAN 320-1570. Tel: 323-933-3345. E-Mail: cabaret66@aol.com. *Dir*, D Richard Baer
Founded 1973
Library Holdings: Bk Titles 2,300
Subject Interests: Television
Special Collections: Computerized review indexes, Motion Picture Exhibitor, Monthly Film Bulletin, Harrison's Reports; Film Reference (The Hollywood Film Archive Catalog), computer printout
Restriction: Staff use only, Use of others with permission of librarian

HOPLAND

S HOPLAND RESEARCH & EXTENSION CENTER LIBRARY,* 4070 University Rd, 95449. SAN 373-4943. Tel: 707-744-1424. FAX: 707-744-1040. E-Mail: uchrec@ucdavis.edu. *Mgr*, Robert M Timm
1998-1999 Income $250. Mats Exp $250, Books $100, Per/Ser (Incl. Access Fees) $50, Other Print Mats $50, Manuscripts & Archives $50
Library Holdings: Bk Vols 200; Per Subs 50

HUNTINGTON BEACH

S BOEING COMPANY, Library & Information Services,* 5301 Bolsa Ave, H010-B001, 92647-2099. SAN 370-1735. Tel: 714-896-2319. FAX: 714-896-1737. *Cat, Online Servs, Ref*, Grace Lo; *Cat, Online Servs, Ref*, Diane Brenes; *Cat, Online Servs, Ref*, Sharon Olson
Library Holdings: Bk Vols 11,000; Per Subs 176
Partic in Dialog Corporation

J GOLDEN WEST COLLEGE, R Dudley Boyce Library & Learning Center, 15744 Golden West St, 92647. SAN 300-8215. Tel: 714-895-8741 (Admin). FAX: 714-895-8916. Web Site: www.gwc.cccd.edu/library/library.html. *Dean*, Marilyn M Dorfman; *Chair*, Maryann McManus; *Media Spec*, Roxanna Ross; Tel: 714-895-8741 Ext 51209, E-Mail: rross@gwc.cccd.edu; *Dean of Libr*, Douglas Larson; Tel: 714-895-8384, E-Mail: dlarson@gwc.cccd.edu; *Librn*, Lou Ann Hobbs; *Head Tech Servs*, Jeanette Onishi; *Head, Ser Acq*, Susan Berman; Staff 14 (MLS 5, Non-MLS 9)
Founded 1966. Enrl 12,200; Highest Degree: Associate
Jul 1999-Jun 2000 Income $746,585. Mats Exp $91,000, Books $37,000, Per/Ser (Incl. Access Fees) $25,000, Presv $300, Micro $3,500, AV Equip $900, Other Print Mats $5,300, Electronic Ref Mat (Incl. Access Fees) $19,000. Sal $788,626 (Prof $327,000)
Library Holdings: Bk Vols 96,000; Bk Titles 87,000; Per Subs 290; High Interest/Low Vocabulary Bk Vols 30; Bks on Deafness & Sign Lang 160
Subject Interests: Art, Nursing, Social sciences and issues
Database Vendor: Ebsco - EbscoHost, GaleNet
Function: ILL available
Open Mon-Thurs 8am-9pm, Fri 8-3 & Sat 10-3. Student ID is library card. Non-students may purchase for $10 per year

P HUNTINGTON BEACH PUBLIC LIBRARY SYSTEM, Information & Cultural Resource Center, 7111 Talbert Ave, 92648. SAN 332-1428. Tel: 714-842-4481. FAX: 714-375-5180. E-Mail: library@hbpl.org. Web Site: www.hbpl.org. *Dir Libr Serv*, Ronald Hayden; E-Mail: haydenr@hbpl.org; *Mgr Libr Serv*, Jan Halvorsen; E-Mail: halvorsj@hbpl.org; *Head Ref*, Daugherty Sherrie; E-Mail: daughers@hbpl.org; *Head Tech Servs*, Roger Hiles; E-Mail: hilesr@hbpl.org; *Ch Servs*, Nanci Williams; E-Mail: williamn@hbpl.org; Staff 38 (MLS 11, Non-MLS 27)
Founded 1909. Pop 200,000; Circ 1,120,058
Oct 2000-Sep 2001 Income (Main Library and Branch Library) $4,804,556, State $142,000, City $3,523,893, Federal $124,000, Locally Generated Income $1,014,570, Other $310,315. Mats Exp $711,738, Books $478,118, Per/Ser (Incl. Access Fees) $62,994, Micro $14,490, Electronic Ref Mat (Incl. Access Fees) $122,945. Sal $2,319,390
Library Holdings: Bk Vols 438,878; Bk Titles 244,691; Per Subs 585
Subject Interests: Business and management, Careers, Technology
Special Collections: Genealogy (Orange County Genealogical Society Coll)
Automation Activity & Vendor Info: (Cataloging) GEAC; (Circulation) GEAC; (OPAC) GEAC
Database Vendor: Ebsco - EbscoHost, IAC - Info Trac
Friends of the Library Group
Branches: 4
BANNING BRANCH, 9281 Banning Ave, 92646-8302. SAN 332-1517. Tel: 714-375-5005. FAX: 714-375-5091. *In Charge*, Lee Beltz
Friends of the Library Group
GRAHAM BRANCH, 15882 Graham St, 92649-1724. SAN 332-1487. Tel: 714-375-5006. FAX: 714-373-3088.
Friends of the Library Group
MAIN STREET BRANCH, 525 Main St, 92648-5133. SAN 332-1452. Tel: 714-375-5071. FAX: 714-375-5072.
Friends of the Library Group
OAK VIEW, 17241 Oak Lane, 92648. SAN 377-0265. Tel: 714-375-5068. FAX: 714-375-5073. *In Charge*, Claudia de Locke
Friends of the Library Group

M UNITED STATES LIFESAVING ASSOCIATION,* PO Box 366, 92648. SAN 370-2545. Tel: 714-968-9360. FAX: 714-962-9370. *Pres*, Bill Richardson; E-Mail: wj_richardson@compuserve.com
Restriction: Not open to public

HUNTINGTON PARK

P SOUTH STATE COOPERATIVE LIBRARY SYSTEM,* 6518 Miles Ave, 90255. SAN 320-5797. Tel: 323-583-1292. FAX: 323-583-2314. E-Mail: ssclscnd@pacbell.net, ssclshq@pacbell.net. *Ref*, Chris Cockroft; Staff 3 (MLS 2, Non-MLS 1)
Founded 1978. Pop 3,553,430
Jul 1996-Jun 1997 Income $237,300, State $174,900, Locally Generated Income $28,400. Mats Exp $17,000
Publications: South State Express
Member Libraries: City Of Inglewood Public Library; City Of Pasadena Department Of Information Services Library; County of Los Angeles Public Library; Palmdale City Library
Partic in State of Calif Answering Network

IMPERIAL

P IMPERIAL PUBLIC LIBRARY, 200 W Ninth St, PO Box 38, 92251-0038. SAN 300-8231. Tel: 760-355-1332. FAX: 760-355-4857. *In Charge*, Fred Fontaine
Founded 1904. Pop 7,800; Circ 9,780
Library Holdings: Bk Vols 25,500
Mem of Serra Cooperative Library System
Open Mon-Thurs 10-1 & 2-7

J IMPERIAL VALLEY COLLEGE, Spencer Library Media Center, 380 E Ira Aten Rd, PO Box 158, 92251. SAN 300-824X. Tel: 760-355-6378. FAX: 760-355-1090. Web Site: www.imperial.cc.ca.us/departments/library. *Dir*, Eileen Ford; Tel: 760-355-6377, E-Mail: eileen@imperial.cc.ca.us; *Asst Librn, Cat*, Larry Welch; Tel: 760-355-6382, E-Mail: larryw@imperial.cc.ca.us; *Per, Ref*, Hope Navarro; Tel: 760-355-6381, E-Mail: hopen@imperial.cc.ca.us; *Tech Servs*, Tricia Grijalva; Tel: 760-355-6409, E-Mail: triciag@imperial.cc.ca.us; *Acq*, Toni Gamboa; *Circ, ILL, Ref*, Mary Ann Smith; Tel: 760-355-6380; *AV*, Jesus Valenzuela; Tel: 760-355-6389, E-Mail: jesusv@imperial.cc.ca.us; Staff 2 (MLS 2)
Founded 1922. Enrl 6,373; Fac 119; Highest Degree: Associate
Jul 2000-Jun 2001 Income Parent Institution $1,128,016. Mats Exp $245,192, Books $61,046, Per/Ser (Incl. Access Fees) $22,841, Micro $9,116, AV Equip $118,865, Electronic Ref Mat (Incl. Access Fees) $33,324. Sal $370,483 (Prof $159,703)
Library Holdings: Bk Vols 58,733; Bk Titles 54,685; Per Subs 425
Special Collections: Local History
Automation Activity & Vendor Info: (Circulation) SIRSI; (OPAC) SIRSI
Database Vendor: OCLC - First Search
Mem of Serra Cooperative Library System
Partic in OCLC Online Computer Library Center, Inc
Open Mon-Thurs 8am-9pm, Fri 8-5 & Sat 9-1

INDEPENDENCE

P INYO COUNTY FREE LIBRARY, 168 N Edwards St, Drawer K, 93526. SAN 332-169X. Tel: 760-878-0260. Reference Tel: 760-873-5122. FAX: 760-878-0360. E-Mail: inyocolib@qnet.com. *Dir*, Bill Michael; Tel: 760-878-0359, E-Mail: bilmichael@qnet.com; *Librn*, Ulla Lipp; *Librn*, Nancy Masters; *Cat*, Patricia Hunter; Tel: 760-878-0262; *Purchasing*, Sharon Brewer; Tel: 760-878-0262; *ILL*, Carol Ann Mitchell
Founded 1913. Pop 18,400; Circ 164,028
Jul 1998-Jun 1999 Income (Main Library and Branch Library) $594,700, State $13,700, County $567,000, Locally Generated Income $14,000. Mats Exp Books $46,000. Sal $440,786
Library Holdings: Bk Vols 84,026; Bk Titles 79,164; Per Subs 48
Subject Interests: Mining
Special Collections: Mary Hunter Austen Coll
Mem of Inland Library System
Partic in San Bernardino, Inyo, Riverside Counties United Library Services
Branches: 6
BIG PINE BRANCH, 201 N Main, PO Box 760, Big Pine, 93513-0760. SAN 377-6018. Tel: 760-938-2420. E-Mail: bplibrary@qnet.com. *Mgr*, Juanita Hunter
Library Holdings: Bk Vols 6,000; Bk Titles 5,800; Per Subs 30
Friends of the Library Group
BISHOP BRANCH, 210 Academy Ave, Bishop, 93514-2693. SAN 375-5509. Tel: 760-873-5115. Reference Tel: 760-873-5119. FAX: 760-873-5356. E-Mail: bishoplib@qnet.com. *Librn*, Sue Franz; Tel: 760-873-5119; *Librn*, Annie Kothman; Tel: 760-873-5119; *ILL*, Carol Ann Mitchell; Tel: 760-873-5122
Founded 1913
Library Holdings: Per Subs 41
Friends of the Library Group
FURNACE CREEK, Cow Creek, Death Valley, 92328. Tel: 760-786-2408. *In Charge*, Margaret Anderson
Library Holdings: Bk Vols 888; Per Subs 15
INYO COUNTY LAW LIBRARY, Courthouse, 168 N Edwards St, PO Drawer K, 93526. SAN 320-1562. *In Charge*, Diane Gray
1997-1998 Income $14,000. Mats Exp Books $11,000. Sal $2,555
Library Holdings: Bk Vols 2,500
Subject Interests: California
LONE PINE BRANCH, 145 W Bush St, PO Box 756, Lone Pine, 93545. SAN 377-6034. Tel: 619-876-5031. E-Mail: lplibrary@qnet.com. *Librn*, Beverly Brown
Library Holdings: Bk Vols 10,000; Per Subs 20
Friends of the Library Group
TECOPA BRANCH, Tecopa Hot Springs Rd, Tecopa, 92389. (Mail add: PO Box 177, Tecopa, 92389-0177), Tel: 760-852-4171. *In Charge*, Andrea Morgan
Library Holdings: Bk Vols 1,144; Per Subs 14

INDIO

M JOHN F KENNEDY MEMORIAL HOSPITAL, Medical & Nursing Library, 47-111 Monroe St, 92201. SAN 323-4622. Tel: 760-775-8101. FAX: 760-775-8424.
Library Holdings: Bk Vols 500; Per Subs 100
Restriction: Medical staff only

G RIVERSIDE COUNTY LAW LIBRARY, Indio Branch,* 46-200 Oasis St, 92201. SAN 300-8258. Tel: 760-863-8316. FAX: 760-342-2581. *In Charge*, Patricia Stewart
Library Holdings: Bk Vols 22,450
Subject Interests: Law
Open Mon-Fri 8-5, Sat 9-4

INGLEWOOD

M CENTINELA HOSPITAL MEDICAL CENTER, Edwin W Dean Sr Memorial Library, 555 E Hardy St, PO Box 720, 90307-0720. SAN 321-1258. Tel: 310-673-4660, Ext 7266. FAX: 310-672-5208. E-Mail: Internet: centhosp@class.org.
Founded 1975
Library Holdings: Bk Titles 2,000; Per Subs 200
Subject Interests: Medicine, Orthopedics

P CITY OF INGLEWOOD PUBLIC LIBRARY,* 101 W Manchester Blvd, 90301-1771. SAN 332-172X. Tel: 310-412-5397. Interlibrary Loan Service Tel: 310-412-5380. FAX: 310-412-8848. E-Mail: inglewod@class.org, publiclibrary@cityofinglewood.org. Web Site: www.cityofinglewood.org/depts/library/iplhmp.html. *Dir*, Miguel J C Alaniz; *ILL*, Frank Francis; *Ch Servs, YA Servs*, Robin Hunter; *Tech Servs*, Richard Siminski; *Circ, Media Spec*, Sue Kamm; *Br Coordr*, Ulla Roden-Davis; *Ref*, Kay Ikuta; Staff 15 (MLS 15)
Founded 1962. Pop 120,500; Circ 408,540
Oct 1997-Sep 1998 Income $2,600,000, State $95,354, City $400,000, Federal $9,510, Locally Generated Income $67,157. Mats Exp $452,109, Books $250,869, Per/Ser (Incl. Access Fees) $99,769, Presv $26,705, Micro $38,802, Other Print Mats $5,747. Sal $1,740,423
Library Holdings: Bk Vols 421,374; Bk Titles 259,283; Per Subs 1,526
Special Collections: Large Print Books Coll; Spanish Books Coll
Publications: Cursos de Accion en la Seleccion de Materiales Bibliotecarios; Formats Used in the Library Multimedia Union Catalog; Large Print Book Catalog; Library Community Services; Library Information Service; Library Materials Selection Policy; Library Objectives, Goals & Activities; Library of Congress Classification Adapted for Children's Materials; Library Reference Service; Library Service to the Spanish Speaking; Servicio de Informacion en la Biblioteca
Mem of South State Cooperative Library System
Friends of the Library Group
Branches: 2
CRENSHAW-IMPERIAL, 11141 Crenshaw Blvd, 90303-2338. SAN 332-1754. Tel: 310-412-5403. *Librn*, Ulla Roden-Davis
Library Holdings: Bk Vols 38,620
MORNINGSIDE PARK, 3202 W 85th St, 90305-1910. SAN 332-1789. Tel: 310-412-5400. *Librn*, Ulla Roden-Davis
Library Holdings: Bk Vols 18,724

M DANIEL FREEMAN MEMORIAL HOSPITAL, Health Sciences Library,* 333 N Prairie Ave, PO Box 100, 90301. SAN 300-8266. Tel: 310-674-7050, Ext 3230. FAX: 310-419-8275. *Dir*, Linda Moore; E-Mail: lmoore@danielfreeman.org
Founded 1954
Library Holdings: Bk Titles 1,000; Per Subs 200
Special Collections: CME Programs, A-tapes
Publications: (Update) Newsletter
Partic in Medline
Open Mon, Wed & Fri 8:30-4, Tues & Thurs 8:30-4

CL UNIVERSITY OF WEST LOS ANGELES, Law School Library,* 1155 W Arbor Vitae St, 90301. SAN 331-863X. Tel: 310-342-5200, Ext 230. FAX: 310-342-5298. *Librn*, Linda Rauhauser
Founded 1968. Enrl 700
Library Holdings: Bk Vols 31,000; Per Subs 237
Partic in Westlaw

IONE

§S CALIFORNIA YOUTH AUTHORITY, Preston Youth Correctional Facility Library, 201 Waterman Rd, 95640. Tel: 209-274-8134. FAX: 209-274-4068. *Senior Librn*, John Lafferty
Library Holdings: Bk Vols 6,000; Per Subs 50

IRVINE

CR CONCORDIA UNIVERSITY LIBRARY, 1530 Concordia W, 92612. SAN 322-7065. Tel: 949-854-8002, Ext 1505. FAX: 949-854-6893. E-Mail: librarian@cui.edu. Web Site: library.cui.edu. *Dir Libr Serv*, Diane Gaylor; Tel: 949-854-8002, Ext 1531, E-Mail: gaylor@cui.edu. Subject Specialists: *Education*, Diane Gaylor; Staff 5 (MLS 3, Non-MLS 2)
Founded 1976. Enrl 1,200; Fac 55
Library Holdings: Bk Vols 79,000; Bk Titles 90,000; Per Subs 850
Subject Interests: Lutheran theol, Reformation hist
Automation Activity & Vendor Info: (Acquisitions) SIRSI; (Cataloging) SIRSI; (Circulation) SIRSI; (Course Reserve) SIRSI; (OPAC) SIRSI; (Serials) SIRSI
Database Vendor: IAC - SearchBank, Silverplatter Information Inc., Wilson - Wilson Web
Function: Professional lending library
Partic in CalPALs; Concordia Univ Syst; SCELC
Open Mon-Thurs 7:30-12, Fri 7:30-5, Sat 9-5 & Sun 2-12

J IRVINE VALLEY COLLEGE LIBRARY,* 5500 Irvine Center Dr, 92720-4399. SAN 324-7333. Tel: 949-451-5261. Interlibrary Loan Service Tel: 949-451-5266. FAX: 949-451-5796. Web Site: www.ivc.cc.ca.us/infoserv/library/library.html. *Chair, Librn*, Fred Forbes; E-Mail: fforbes@ivc.cc.ca.us; Staff 4 (MLS 4)
Founded 1979. Enrl 14,768; Fac 70
Library Holdings: Bk Vols 43,000; Per Subs 240
Partic in Dialog Corporation; OCLC Online Computer Library Center, Inc

M DR RAY WILLIAM LONDON & ASSOCIATES INTERNATIONAL LIBRARY,* 17955 Sky Park Circle, Ste E, 92614-6373. SAN 327-2672. Tel: 714-505-0873. FAX: 714-505-0874. *Dir*, Linda Garcia
Library Holdings: Bk Vols 10,000; Bk Titles 9,000; Per Subs 25

L MORRISON & FOERSTER, Law Library,* 19900 MacArthur Blvd, 12th flr, 92612. SAN 372-2716. Tel: 949-251-7539. FAX: 949-251-0900. E-Mail: rhu@mofo.com. *Assoc Librn*, Robert Hu; Staff 1 (MLS 1)
Library Holdings: Bk Vols 9,000; Per Subs 100

S MOTORCYCLE INDUSTRY COUNCIL,* 2 Jenner St Ste 150, 92618-3806. SAN 373-0255. Tel: 949-727-4211. FAX: 949-727-4217. Web Site: www.mic.org. *Dir, Res*, Pat Murphy
Library Holdings: Bk Vols 150; Per Subs 25

L PARKER HANNIFIN CORP, Engineering Library,* 18321 Jamboree Blvd, 92612. SAN 377-4244. Tel: 949-851-3352. FAX: 714-476-3931. *Librn*, Kristy Anderson
1997-1998 Mats Exp $10,000
Library Holdings: Bk Vols 25,000
Partic in Spec Libr Asn

M PHARMACIA IOVISION RESEARCH & DEVELOPMENT LIBRARY,* 15350 Barranka Pkwy, 92618. SAN 375-6793. Tel: 949-789-9000, Ext 5372. FAX: 949-789-9036.
Library Holdings: Bk Titles 2,000; Per Subs 16

C UNIVERSITY OF CALIFORNIA LIBRARY, PO Box 19557, 92623-9557. SAN 300-8355. Tel: 949-824-6836. FAX: 949-824-5740. Web Site: www.lib.uci.edu/. *Librn*, Judy Kaufman; *Librn*, Susan Lessick; *Librn*, Gerald Munoff; *Spec Coll*, Jackie Dooley; *Acq*, Tim McAdam; *Coordr*, John Barefoot; *Coordr*, Pamela La Zarr; Staff 52 (MLS 52)
Founded 1965. Enrl 16,716; Fac 1,003; Highest Degree: Doctorate
Library Holdings: Bk Vols 2,136,232; Per Subs 18,187
Special Collections: (Bibliotheca Neurologica Courville Coll), artifacts, bks; Book Art Coll; Book Arts Coll; British Naval History Coll; Contemporary Small Press Poetry Coll; Dance Coll; History of Literary Criticism (Wellek Coll); Neurology, Neuropathology (Courville Coll); Orchids & Horticulture (Menninger Coll); Regional California History Coll; Southeast Asian Archive; Thomas Mann (Waldmuller Coll)
Publications: Library Items; Library Update
Mem of Asn of Research Libraries
Partic in BRS; Center For Research Libraries; Dialog Corporation; Libr of Orange County Network; OCLC Online Computer Library Center, Inc; SDC Info Servs; Univ of Calif Librs
Friends of the Library Group
Departmental Libraries:
CM MEDICAL CENTER, 101 City Dr S, Orange, 92868. SAN 326-713X. Tel: 714-456-5585. FAX: 714-634-9252. Web Site: www.lib/uci.edu/. *Head of Libr*, Rochelle Minchow
SCIENCE, PO Box 19556, 92713-9556. SAN 326-7091. Tel: 949-824-6836. FAX: 949-824-3114. Web Site: www.lib.uci.edu/.

IRWINDALE

P IRWINDALE PUBLIC LIBRARY, 5050 N Irwindale Ave, 91706. SAN 300-8363. Tel: 626-430-2229.
Founded 1961. Pop 1,160
Jul 1999-Jun 2000 Income $244,183. Mats Exp $4,673, Books $2,684, Per/Ser (Incl. Access Fees) $1,556, Electronic Ref Mat (Incl. Access Fees) $433. Sal $91,346 (Prof $59,765)
Library Holdings: Bk Vols 25,000; Bk Titles 14,775; Per Subs 24
Subject Interests: History
Special Collections: Irwindale City History Coll

JACKSON

§GL AMADOR COUNTY LAW LIBRARY, 108 Court St, 95642. Tel: 209-223-6463. FAX: 209-223-6640. *Librn*, Mary Lou Haueter
Library Holdings: Bk Vols 1,000

P AMADOR COUNTY LIBRARY,* 530 Sutter St, 95642-2379. SAN 300-8371. Tel: 209-223-6400. FAX: 209-223-6303. *Adminr*, Judy Ramm
Pop 32,250; Circ 141,037
Library Holdings: Bk Vols 121,238; Per Subs 102
Special Collections: Amador County Hist; Bancrofts Works & Hist of Calif; Index of Amador County Newspapers on microfilm; Mines & Mineral Res Coll
Publications: Friends of Library Bulletin
Mem of 49-99 Cooperative Library System
Friends of the Library Group
Branches: 6
AMADOR CITY BRANCH, Old School House, School St, Amador City, 95601. *In Charge*, June Biagi
Library Holdings: Bk Vols 370
IONE BRANCH, 25 E Main St, Ione, 95640. (Mail add: PO Box 194, Ione, 95640-0194), Tel: 209-274-2560. *In Charge*, Donnel Junes
Library Holdings: Bk Vols 8,000
PINE GROVE BRANCH, 19889 Hwy 88, Pine Grove, 95665. Tel: 209-296-3111. E-Mail: director@boise.basin.lib.id.us. *In Charge*, Laura Mueller
Library Holdings: Bk Vols 6,360
PIONEER BRANCH, 25070 Buckhorn Ridge Rd, Pioneer, 95666. (Mail add: PO Box 821, Pioneer, 95666-0821), Tel: 209-295-7330. *In Charge*, Rebecca Powers
Library Holdings: Bk Vols 5,000
PLYMOUTH BRANCH, 9375 Main St, Plymouth, 95669. (Mail add: PO Box 61, Plymouth, 95669-0061), Tel: 209-245-6476. *In Charge*, Irene Cranford
Library Holdings: Bk Vols 7,600
SUTTER CREEK BRANCH, 35 Main St, Sutter Creek, 95685. SAN 377-7545. Tel: 209-267-5489. *In Charge*, Beverly Gunther
Library Holdings: Bk Vols 6,089; Per Subs 20
Friends of the Library Group

JAMESTOWN

P TUOLUMNE COUNTY FREE LIBRARY, Jamestown Library,* Community Hall, 18299 Fifth St, 95327. SAN 377-5151. Tel: 209-984-0371. *Librn*, Eileen Steerman
Library Holdings: Bk Vols 600

JOSHUA TREE

J COPPER MOUNTAIN COLLEGE, Greenleaf Library, 6162 Rotary Way, 92252. (Mail add: PO Box 1398, 92251-0879), SAN 301-6722. Tel: 760-366-3791. FAX: 760-366-1182. Web Site: www.cmccd.cc.ca.us. *Librn*, Carolyn Hopkins; E-Mail: chopkins@cmccd.cc.ca.us; Staff 4 (MLS 1, Non-MLS 3)
Enrl 2,400; Fac 23; Highest Degree: Associate
Jul 2000-Jun 2001 Mats Exp $45,000, Books $18,000, Per/Ser (Incl. Access Fees) $20,000, AV Equip $7,000
Library Holdings: Bk Vols 10,600; Bk Titles 9,100; Per Subs 1,300
Special Collections: Desert Studies
Automation Activity & Vendor Info: (Circulation) TLC; (OPAC) TLC
Database Vendor: Ebsco - EbscoHost
Partic in SIRCULS

JUNE LAKE

P JUNE LAKE LIBRARY,* 90 W Granite Ave, 93529. SAN 377-8444. Tel: 760-648-7284. FAX: 760-648-7284. *Librn*, Brenda M Chambers
Library Holdings: Bk Vols 12,000; Per Subs 12
Mem of Mono County Free Libr Syst
Open Tues 4-6, Weds 2-7, Thurs 4-6 & Sat 1-5
Friends of the Library Group

KENTFIELD

J COLLEGE OF MARIN LIBRARY,* 835 College Ave, 94904. SAN 300-8398. Tel: 415-485-9470. FAX: 415-457-5395. Web Site: www.marin.cc.ca.us. *Dean of Libr*, Terri Frongia; E-Mail: terrifrongia@marin.cc.ca.us; *Ref*, Carl Cox; *Media Spec*, Clarke Bugbee; Staff 5 (MLS 5)
Founded 1926
Library Holdings: Bk Vols 137,000; Bk Titles 92,100; Per Subs 331
Mem of North Bay Cooperative Library System
Friends of the Library Group

LA CANADA

SR CHURCH OF THE LIGHTED WINDOW LIBRARY, 1200 Foothill Blvd, 91011. SAN 375-2658. Tel: 818-790-1185. FAX: 818-790-5886. *Librn*, Bobbe Parsons
Library Holdings: Bk Vols 1,300
Friends of the Library Group

LA JOLLA

S CENTER FOR US-MEXICAN STUDIES, Research Library, University of California, San Diego, 9500 Gilman Dr, 92093-0510. SAN 371-2443. Tel: 619-534-4309. FAX: 619-534-6447. Web Site: www.weber.uesd.edu/depts/usmex/welcome.htm. *Res*, Anna Eastman; E-Mail: anneastmn@hotmail.com; *Res*, Cecilia Vega; E-Mail: cevega@ucsd.edu; *Res*, Vicente Hernandez; E-Mail: jvhdez@hotmail.com
Library Holdings: Bk Titles 1,000; Per Subs 100
Subject Interests: Latin America, Mexico

S COPLEY PRESS INCORPORATED, James S Copley Library, 1134 Kline St, PO Box 1530, 92038. SAN 300-8444. Tel: 858-729-8040. FAX: 858-729-8051. *Mgr*, Carol Beales; E-Mail: carol.beales@copleypress.com
Founded 1966
Library Holdings: Bk Vols 16,000
Subject Interests: American revolution, California
Special Collections: Fine Press Books, 20th Century English & American Author Correspondence
Partic in OCLC Online Computer Library Center, Inc

S LIBRARY ASSOCIATION OF LA JOLLA, Athenaeum Music & Arts Library, 1008 Wall St, 92037. SAN 300-8479. Tel: 619-454-5872. FAX: 619-454-5835. *Dir*, Erika Torri; Staff 7 (MLS 2, Non-MLS 5)
Founded 1899
Jul 1999-Jun 2000 Income $980,000, State $7,500, City $100,000, County $10,000, Locally Generated Income $862,500. Mats Exp $40,000, Books $16,000, Per/Ser (Incl. Access Fees) $6,000, Micro $14,300. Sal $486,000 (Prof $250,000)
Library Holdings: Bk Titles 13,000; Per Subs 98
Subject Interests: Art, Music
Special Collections: Artists Books; Music (Bach Gesselschaft Coll)
Publications: Annual Report; Newsletter (bi-monthly); School Brochures (quarterly)
Restriction: Non-circulating to the public

S MINGEI INTERNATIONAL MUSEUM, Art Reference Library,* PO Box 553, 92038. SAN 373-1359. Tel: 619-239-0003. FAX: 619-239-0605. *Librn*, Rob Cerello
Library Holdings: Bk Vols 3,750
Subject Interests: Ceramics, Sculpture
Special Collections: Florence Temko Paper Coll; Japanese Ceramics; Meirs Mexico Coll
Restriction: Not a lending library

S MUSEUM OF CONTEMPORARY ART, SAN DIEGO, Helen Palmer Geisel Library, 700 Prospect St, 92037. SAN 300-8460. Tel: 858-454-3541, Ext 132. FAX: 858-454-6985. Web Site: www.mcasandiego.org. *Librn*, Virginia Abblitt; E-Mail: vabblitt@san.rr.com; Staff 5 (MLS 1, Non-MLS 4)
Founded 1941
Library Holdings: Bk Titles 4,500; Per Subs 43
Subject Interests: Contemporary art, Modern art
Special Collections: Artists Vertical Files
Restriction: Not a lending library

S SALK INSTITUTE FOR BIOLOGICAL STUDIES, Salk Institute Library, 10010 N Torrey Pines Rd, 92037-1099. (Mail add: PO Box 85800, 92186-5800), SAN 300-8495. Tel: 858-453-4100, Ext 1235. FAX: 858-452-7472. E-Mail: library@salk.edu. *Librn*, Kimberlee K Antrim; Tel: 858-453-1400, Ext 1044, E-Mail: antrim@salk.edu; Staff 4 (MLS 1, Non-MLS 3)
Founded 1962. Fac 56
Jul 1999-Jun 2000 Mats Exp $258,000. Sal $129,000
Library Holdings: Bk Vols 15,000; Per Subs 185
Subject Interests: AIDS, Biochemistry, Cancer, Genetics, Immunology, Molecular biology, Neuroscience, Virology
Database Vendor: Ebsco - EbscoHost
Restriction: Open to public with supervision only
Function: Research library

M THE SCRIPPS RESEARCH INSTITUTE, Kresge Library, 10550 N Torrey Pines Rd, 92037. SAN 300-8509. Tel: 858-784-8705. FAX: 858-784-2035. E-Mail: helplib@scripps.edu. Web Site: www.scripps.edu. *Dir*, Paula King; *Ref*, Michaeleen Trimarchi; Staff 6 (MLS 2, Non-MLS 4)
Founded 1962
Library Holdings: Bk Vols 2,000; Per Subs 800
Subject Interests: Biochemistry, Cell biology, Chemistry, Immunology, Medicine, Molecular biology, Neurobiol
Automation Activity & Vendor Info: (OPAC) Innovative Interfaces Inc.
Database Vendor: IAC - Info Trac, OVID Technologies
Partic in Nat Libr of Med; OCLC Online Computer Library Center, Inc

G UNITED STATE DEPARTMENT OF COMMERCE, NATIONAL OCEANIC & ATMOSPHERIC ADMINISTRATION, NATIONAL MARINE FISHERIES SERVICE, (SWFSC), (Formerly National Marine Fisheries Service), Southwest Fisheries Science Center Library, 8604 La Jolla Shores Dr, 92037. (Mail add: PO Box 271, 92038-0271), SAN 300-8487. Tel: 619-546-7038, 619-546-7196. FAX: 619-546-7003. *Librn*, Debra A Losey; E-Mail: debra.losey@noaa.gov; Staff 2 (MLS 1, Non-MLS 1)
Founded 1965
Oct 1999-Sep 2000 Income Federal $165,100. Mats Exp $75,900, Books $6,000, Per/Ser (Incl. Access Fees) $58,000, Electronic Ref Mat (Incl. Access Fees) $3,000
Library Holdings: Per Subs 100
Subject Interests: Antarctic, Fisheries, Marine biology
Special Collections: Inter-American Tropical Tuna Commission
Publications: FYI (inhouse, irregular); New Acquisitions (inhouse, irregular)
Restriction: Open to others by appointment, Restricted access
Partic in Fedlink; Int Asn of Aquatic & Marine Sci Libr & Info Centers; OCLC Online Computer Library Center, Inc; Southern Calif Online Users Group

C UNIVERSITY OF CALIFORNIA, SAN DIEGO, University Libraries, 9500 Gilman Dr, Mail Code 0175G, 92093-0175. SAN 332-1878. Tel: 858-534-3336. Interlibrary Loan Service Tel: 858-534-2528. FAX: 858-534-4970. Web Site: www.ucsd.edu/library/index.html. *Librn*, Brian E C Schottlaender; *Dep Dir*, Phyllis S Mirsky; *Assoc Librn*, R Bruce Miller; *Assoc Librn*, Susan Starr; *Assoc Librn*, Jacqueline Hanson; *Acq*, Karen Cargille; *Cat*, Linda Barnhart; *Spec Coll*, Lynda Claassen; *Syst Coordr*, Geri Ingram; *Online Servs*, James Jacobs; *ILL*, Tammy Dearie. Subject Specialists: *Architecture*, Leslie Abrams; *Art*, Leslie Abrams; *Music*, Leslie Abrams; Staff 99 (MLS 49, Non-MLS 50)
Founded 1959. Enrl 19,282; Fac 1,350; Highest Degree: Doctorate
Jul 1999-Jun 2000 Income (Main and Other College/University Libraries) $23,585,281. Mats Exp $6,489,326, Books $1,832,547, Per/Ser (Incl. Access Fees) $4,431,593, Presv $4,281, Micro $215,185, Other Print Mats $10,001. Sal $10,681,649 (Prof $4,153,474)
Library Holdings: Bk Vols 2,654,094; Per Subs 26,536
Special Collections: Baja, CA; Contemporary American Poetry (Archive for New Poetry); Contemporary Music; European Communities Common Market Publications; Melanesian Ethnography; Pacific Voyages; Renaissance; Science & Public Policy; Spanish Civil War
Automation Activity & Vendor Info: (Acquisitions) Innovative Interfaces Inc.; (Circulation) Innovative Interfaces Inc.; (OPAC) Innovative Interfaces Inc.; (Serials) Innovative Interfaces Inc.
Database Vendor: OCLC - First Search
Publications: Faculty/Friends Newsletter; Melanesian Acquisition; Pacific Voyages Collection Bibliography; Renaissance Collection Bibliography
Mem of Asn of Research Libraries
Partic in Am Asn of Health Sci Librs; Center For Research Libraries; Coalition for Networked Info; Coun of Libr Info Resources; Dialog Corporation; MLA; National Initiative for a Networked Cultural Heritage; OCLC Online Computer Library Center, Inc; Pacific SW Regional Med Libr Serv; Scholarly Publ & Acad Resources Coalition; SDC Search Serv
Friends of the Library Group
Departmental Libraries:
ART & ARCHITECTURE Tel: 858-534-4811. FAX: 858-534-0189. *Head of Libr*, Leslie Abrams; E-Mail: labrams@ucsd.edu
Library Holdings: Bk Vols 65,222; Per Subs 180
CM BIOMEDICAL, 9500 Gilman Dr 0699, 92093-0699. Tel: 858-534-3253. FAX: 858-534-1202. *Librn*, Susan Starr
Founded 1963
Library Holdings: Bk Vols 221,467; Per Subs 2,142
CENTER FOR LIBRARY & INSTRUCTIONAL COMPUTING SERVICES Tel: 858-534-3065. *Librn*, Kari Lucas
Library Holdings: Bk Vols 19,809; Per Subs 36
Closed for renovation
INTERNATIONAL RELATIONS & PACIFIC STUDIES Tel: 858-534-0926. FAX: 858-534-8526. E-Mail: klo@ucsd.educ. Web Site: www.irpslibrary.ucsd.edu. *Librn*, Karl Lo
Library Holdings: Bk Vols 91,452; Per Subs 1,630
Publications: Pacific Scope
MANDEVILLE SPECIAL COLLECTIONS Tel: 858-534-2533. FAX: 858-534-5950. *Spec Coll*, Lynda C Claassen
Library Holdings: Bk Vols 156,365
CM MEDICAL CENTER, 200 W Arbor, San Diego, 92103. SAN 332-1967. Tel: 619-543-6520. FAX: 619-543-3289. *Librn*, Craig Haynes
Library Holdings: Bk Vols 24,671; Per Subs 639
MUSIC Tel: 858-534-2759. FAX: 858-534-0189. *Librn*, Leslie Abrams
Library Holdings: Bk Vols 28,813
SCIENCE & ENGINEERING Tel: 858-534-3258. FAX: 858-534-5583. E-Mail: scilib@ucsd.edu. *Librn*, Anna Keller Gold
Library Holdings: Bk Vols 254,549; Per Subs 562
SCRIPPS INSTITUTION OF OCEANOGRAPHY Tel: 858-534-3274. FAX: 858-534-5296. E-Mail: scrippsill@ucsd.edu. *Librn*, Peter Brueggeman; E-Mail: pbrueggeman@ucsd.edu
Library Holdings: Bk Vols 226,598; Per Subs 2,330

LA MESA

C COLEMAN COLLEGE LIBRARY,* 7380 Parkway Dr, 91942. SAN 321-5350. Tel: 619-465-3990, Ext 64, 619-698-3512. FAX: 619-463-0162. Web Site: www.coleman.edu. *Librn*, Manuel Bernad; Staff 1 (MLS 1)
Highest Degree: Master
Jul 1996-Jun 1997 Mats Exp $7,200, Books $5,000, Per/Ser (Incl. Access Fees) $1,200, Presv $1,000. Sal $76,720 (Prof $26,800)
Library Holdings: Bk Titles 27,386
Subject Interests: Computers
Publications: Library guides

S PRICE-POTTENGER NUTRITION FOUNDATION LIBRARY,* PO Box 2614, 91943-2614. SAN 371-4268. Tel: 619-574-7763. FAX: 619-574-1314. E-Mail: info@price-pottenger.org. Web Site: www.price-pottenger.org. *Curator*, Marion Patricia Connolly
Library Holdings: Bk Titles 10,000
Subject Interests: Ecology, Gardening
Publications: Health Journal
We are a Special Library within a non-profit education foundation. Our library is non-lending & is intended for research purposes for the interested layperson or professional. Open Mon-Fri 8-4

LA MIRADA

C BIOLA UNIVERSITY LIBRARY, 13800 Biola Ave, 90639-0001. SAN 300-8525. Tel: 562-903-4834. Interlibrary Loan Service Tel: 562-903-4833. Circulation Tel: 562-903-4835. Reference Tel: 562-903-4838. FAX: 562-903-4840. E-Mail: library@peter.biola.edu. Web Site: www.biola.edu/admin/library/. *Dir*, Rodney M Vilet; E-Mail: rodney.vliet@biola.net; *Syst Coordr*, Sue Whitehead; E-Mail: sue.whitehead@truth.biola.edu; *Ref*, Beth Patton; E-Mail: beth_patton@peter.biola.edu; *Tech Servs*, Susan Johnson; E-Mail: susan.johnson@truth.biola.edu; *Ser*, Bob Krauss; E-Mail: bob.krauss@truth.biola.edu; *Media Spec, Music*, John Redford; E-Mail: john.redford@truth.biola.edu; Staff 16 (MLS 6, Non-MLS 10)
Founded 1908. Enrl 35,999; Fac 174; Highest Degree: Doctorate
Jul 1999-Jun 2000 Income $1,541,452, Locally Generated Income $83,671, Parent Institution $1,457,781. Mats Exp $431,585, Books $132,266, Per/Ser (Incl. Access Fees) $183,982, Micro $18,617, AV Equip $35,076, Electronic Ref Mat (Incl. Access Fees) $61,644. Sal $594,694 (Prof $259,109)
Library Holdings: Bk Vols 267,186; Bk Titles 192,831; Per Subs 994
Subject Interests: Music, Nursing, Psychology, Religion
Special Collections: Bible Versions & Translations Coll
Automation Activity & Vendor Info: (Acquisitions) DRA; (Cataloging) DRA; (Circulation) Inlex; (Course Reserve) Inlex; (OPAC) DRA; (OPAC) Inlex
Database Vendor: Ebsco - EbscoHost, OCLC - First Search, Silverplatter Information Inc.
Function: Document delivery services, ILL available, Reference services available, Referrals accepted
Partic in Dialog Corporation; Southern Calif Area Theol Librns Asn; Southern Calif Libr Consortium
Special Services for the Blind - Braille
Bible Braille; Adaptive technology available to Biola students only

LA VERNE

S GERMAN GENEALOGICAL SOCIETY OF AMERICA LIBRARY, (GGSA), 2125 Wright Ave, Ste C-9, 91750-5816. SAN 373-4080. Tel: 909-593-0509. E-Mail: german_genealogical_society_of_america@hotmail.com. Web Site: feefhs.org/ggsa/frg-ggsa.html. *Pres*, T M Schoenky
Founded 1986
Library Holdings: Bk Vols 3,500; Per Subs 65
Subject Interests: Genealogy, History
Publications: Library User's Guide; Shelf Lists
Open Wed & Sat 1-5
Friends of the Library Group

C UNIVERSITY OF LA VERNE, Wilson Library, 2040 Third St, 91750. SAN 332-205X. Tel: 909-593-3511, Ext 4301. FAX: 909-392-2711. Web Site: www.ulv.edu. *Head of Libr*, Dr Marlin L Heckman; E-Mail: heckmann@ulv.edu
Founded 1891
Library Holdings: Bk Vols 5,000; Per Subs 4,500
Special Collections: Bunnelle of California; Genealogy & Church of the Brethren
Partic in OCLC Online Computer Library Center, Inc
Friends of the Library Group
Departmental Libraries:
COLLEGE OF LAW AT LA VERNE, 1950 Third St, 91750. SAN 329-6679. Tel: 909-392-2717. FAX: 909-392-2707. Web Site: www.ulv.edu. *Dir*, Lawrence R Meyer; E-Mail: meyerl@ulv.edu; Staff 3 (MLS 1, Non-MLS 2)
Founded 1970. Enrl 137; Fac 8; Highest Degree: Doctorate

Library Holdings: Bk Vols 117,000; Per Subs 400
Publications: Journal of Juvenile Law
Partic in Inland Empire Acad Libr Coop; OCLC Online Computer Library Center, Inc; Westlaw

LAFAYETTE

R LAFAYETTE-ORINDA PRESBYTERIAN CHURCH LIBRARY, 49 Knox Dr, 94549. SAN 300-855X. Tel: 925-283-8722. FAX: 925-283-0138. Web Site: www.lopc.org. *Librn*, Betty Graves
Library Holdings: Bk Vols 1,957

S SOYFOODS CENTER LIBRARY, 1021 Dolores Dr, 94549-2907. (Mail add: PO Box 234, 94549-0234), SAN 325-4925. Tel: 925-283-2991. *Librn*, William Shurtleff; Staff 1 (MLS 1)
Founded 1976
Jan 1999-Dec 1999 Income $14,700. Mats Exp $15,600, Books $1,800, Per/Ser (Incl. Access Fees) $800, Other Print Mats $13,000
Library Holdings: Bk Titles 2,235; Per Subs 34
Subject Interests: Soybeans, Soyfoods
Special Collections: Soybeans & Soyfoods Coll, archives, bks, reprints & databases
Publications: Bibliographies of Soya Series (40 vols); SoyaScan Publications (Bibliographic database of 56,800 plus references, 1100 BC-present); Soyfoods Industry & Market Directory & Databook; Thesaurus for Soya
Friends of the Library Group

§R TEMPLE ISAIAH, Cantor Ted Cotler Memorial Library, 3800 Mount Diablo Blvd, 94549. Tel: 925-283-8575, Ext 322. Web Site: www.temple-isaiah.org. *Librn*, Alida Field; Staff 1 (MLS 1)
Jul 1999-Jun 2000 Income $26,000. Sal $16,000
Library Holdings: Bk Vols 4,500; Per Subs 15
Subject Interests: Judaica
Special Collections: Jewish Parenting Coll; Multicultural Judaism Coll
Automation Activity & Vendor Info: (Cataloging) Sagebrush Corporation; (Circulation) Sagebrush Corporation
Restriction: In-house use for visitors, Non-circulating to the public
Open Mon & Wed 9:30-7 (summer)

LAGUNA NIGUEL

G NATIONAL ARCHIVES & RECORDS ADMINISTRATION, Pacific Region (Laguna Niguel),* 24000 Avila Rd, 92677-3497. (Mail add: PO Box 6719, 92607-6719), Tel: 949-360-2641. FAX: 949-360-2624. E-Mail: archives@laguna.nara.gov. Web Site: www.nara.gov/regional/laguna.html. *Archivist*, Paul Wormser
Special Collections: Archival Records from Federal Agencies & Courts in Arizona, Southern California, Hawaii & Clark County, Nevada; Indian Affairs Records, microfilm; Passenger Arrival & Naturalization Records, microfilm; Population Censuses for All States, 1790-1920, microfilm; Pre-Federal & Early Federal History, microfilm; Pre-World War I Military Service Records, microfilm; US Diplomacy Records, microfilm
Restriction: Reference only to non-staff
Open Mon-Fri 8-4:30 & first Tues each month 4:30pm-8:30pm (microfilm research only)

LAKEPORT

GL LAKE COUNTY LAW LIBRARY, 255 N Forbes, 95453. SAN 320-5673. Tel: 707-263-2205. FAX: 707-263-2207. *Librn*, Robert Peterson
Pop 50,000
Jul 1999-Jun 2000 Income $33,000, Locally Generated Income $32,000, Other $1,000. Mats Exp $29,000, Books $24,000, Per/Ser (Incl. Access Fees) $3,000, Micro $2,000. Sal $700
Library Holdings: Bk Vols 6,000
Special Collections: Federal cases on Microfiche; Local ordances
Open Mon-Fri 12:30-4:30

P LAKE COUNTY LIBRARY, Lakeport Library, 1425 N High St, 95453-3800. SAN 332-2114. Tel: 707-263-8816. FAX: 707-263-6796. *Librn*, Kathleen M Jansen; *Circ, ILL*, Darcine Egan; *Ad Servs*, Naida Frey; *Tech Servs*, Jan Cook; *Tech Servs*, Amy Patton; Staff 2 (MLS 2)
Founded 1974. Pop 57,500; Circ 191,314
Library Holdings: Bk Vols 98,000; Per Subs 174
Special Collections: Geothermal Resources; Lake County History; Pomo Indians
Mem of North Bay Cooperative Library System
Friends of the Library Group
Branches: 3
MIDDLETOWN BRANCH, Calistoga & Collayami Sts, PO Box 578, Middletown, 95461-0478. SAN 332-2149. Tel: 707-987-3674.
Friends of the Library Group
REDBUD, 14785 Burns Valley Rd, Clearlake, 95422-0600. SAN 332-2173. Tel: 707-994-5115. FAX: 707-995-6012. *Librn*, Irwin Feldman; Staff 1 (MLS 1)
Friends of the Library Group
UPPER LAKE BRANCH, 310 Second St, PO Box 486, Upper Lake, 95485-0486. SAN 332-2203. Tel: 707-275-2049.
Friends of the Library Group

S LAKE COUNTY MUSEUM LIBRARY,* 255 N Main St, 255 N Forbes, 95453. SAN 329-966X. Tel: 707-263-4555. Web Site: www.museum.lake.kiz.ca.us. *Curator*, Donna Howard
Library Holdings: Bk Vols 1,000
Subject Interests: Genealogy
Open Wed-Sat 11-4
Friends of the Library Group

LANCASTER

J ANTELOPE VALLEY COLLEGE, Library, 3041 W Avenue K, 93536-5426. SAN 300-8584. Tel: 661-722-6533. FAX: 661-722-6456. E-Mail: library@avc.edu. Web Site: www.avc.edu/avclibrary/index.html. *Chief Librn*, Diana Gonzalez; *Librn*, Marilyn Baird; *Tech Servs*, Lida Bushloper; Staff 3 (MLS 3)
Founded 1962. Enrl 8,800; Fac 320
Library Holdings: Bk Vols 45,000; Per Subs 200

GM LOS ANGELES COUNTY HIGH DESERT HOSPITAL, Richard E Osgood MD Medical Library, 44900 N 60th St W, 93536. SAN 321-5997. Tel: 661-945-8350. FAX: 661-948-7061. *Dir*, Kimberly Orr; E-Mail: korr@dhs.co.la.ca.us
Founded 1975
2000-2001 Mats Exp $41,000, Books $3,000, Per/Ser (Incl. Access Fees) $38,000. Sal $39,000
Library Holdings: Bk Titles 1,650; Per Subs 200
Subject Interests: Medical, Nursing
Database Vendor: Ebsco - EbscoHost, OVID Technologies
Restriction: Open to others by appointment, Staff use only
Function: Document delivery services, Reference services available
Partic in Los Angeles County Hosp Libr; Med Libr Group of S Calif & Ariz; Pacific SW Regional Med Libr Serv

LARKSPUR

P LARKSPUR PUBLIC LIBRARY, 400 Magnolia Ave, PO Box 525, 94977. SAN 300-8592. Tel: 415-927-5005. FAX: 415-927-5022. E-Mail: lk_library@ci.larkspur.ca.us. Web Site: www.ci.larkspur.ca.us. *Librn*, Frances Gordon
Pop 12,000; Circ 115,000
2000-2000 Mats Exp $65,000
Library Holdings: Bk Titles 55,000; Per Subs 100
Friends of the Library Group

LEMOORE

J WEST HILLS COMMUNITY COLLEGE LIBRARY,* 1200 Cinnimon, 93245. SAN 300-7421. Tel: 559-924-9524. FAX: 559-924-8293. *Librn*, Gail Beck; E-Mail: beckgg@whccd.cc.ca.us
Library Holdings: Bk Vols 3,000; Per Subs 70
Open Mon-Thurs 7:30am-8pm, Fri 7:30-4:30

LINCOLN

P LINCOLN PUBLIC LIBRARY, 590 Fifth St, 95648. SAN 300-8622. Tel: 916-645-3607. FAX: 916-645-7924. E-Mail: lincolnlibrary@starstream.net. *Dir*, Esther Peden; Staff 2 (Non-MLS 2)
Founded 1906. Pop 8,000; Circ 12,000
Library Holdings: Bk Vols 15,000; Per Subs 14
Mem of Mountain-Valley Library System
Friends of the Library Group

LIVERMORE

GM DEPARTMENT OF VETERANS AFFAIRS MEDICAL CENTER & PALO ALTO HEALTHCARE SYSTEMS, Medical Library,* 4951 Arroyo Rd, 94550. SAN 300-8673. Tel: 925-447-2560, Ext 36363. FAX: 925-455-7424. *Librn*, Sandy Lynch; Staff 2 (MLS 1, Non-MLS 1)
Founded 1925
Library Holdings: Bk Vols 400; Per Subs 75
Special Collections: Medical Library - Health Sciences

J LAS POSITAS COLLEGE, Las Positas Learning Resources Center, 3033 Collier Canyon Rd, 94550-7650. SAN 300-8630. Tel: 925-373-4950. Circulation Tel: 925-373-4951. FAX: 925-606-7249. Web Site: www.lpcl.clpccd.cc.ca.us/lpc/lrc. *Dean of Libr*, Pamela Luster; *Coordr*, Frances Hui; *Ref*, Peggy Carter; *Ref*, Aileen Furuyama; *Ref*, Barbara Hardy; Staff 4 (MLS 4)
Founded 1975. Enrl 4,665
Library Holdings: Bk Titles 32,000; Per Subs 226
Automation Activity & Vendor Info: (Acquisitions) DRA; (Cataloging)

DRA; (Circulation) DRA; (OPAC) DRA
Partic in Bay Area Library & Information Network; OCLC Online Computer Library Center, Inc
Open Mon-Thurs 8am-9pm, Fri 8-2, Sat 9-4

P LIVERMORE PUBLIC LIBRARY, 1000 S Livermore Ave, 94550. SAN 300-8649. Tel: 925-373-5500, 925-373-5509. Circulation Tel: 925-373-5501. Reference Tel: 925-373-5505. FAX: 925-373-5503. Web Site: www.ci.livermore.ca.us/library. *Dir Libr Serv*, Susan R Gallinger; E-Mail: srgallinger@ci.libermore.ca.us; *Asst Dir*, Julia Casamajor; E-Mail: jccasamajor@ci.livermore.ca.us; *Asst Dir*, Wendy Muchmore; E-Mail: wmmuchmore@livermore.ca.us; *ILL*, John Clarefield; Staff 10 (MLS 10)
Founded 1896. Pop 73,500; Circ 777,039
Jul 1999-Jun 2000 Income $2,840,736, State $159,676, City $2,435,963, Federal $97,979, Locally Generated Income $147,118. Mats Exp $312,300, Books $247,190, Per/Ser (Incl. Access Fees) $24,666, Micro $6,723, Electronic Ref Mat (Incl. Access Fees) $33,721. Sal $1,771,560 (Prof $728,126)
Library Holdings: Bk Vols 247,190; Bk Titles 163,145; Per Subs 350
Subject Interests: Local history
Special Collections: Story & Folk Tale Coll
Automation Activity & Vendor Info: (Acquisitions) DRA; (Cataloging) DRA; (Circulation) DRA; (OPAC) DRA
Database Vendor: IAC - Info Trac
Publications: Annual Report; Long Range Plan; Monthly Calendar
Mem of Bay Area Libr & Info Syst
Friends of the Library Group
Branches: 3
RINCON, 725 Rincon Ave, 94550. SAN 377-5933. Tel: 925-373-5540. FAX: 925-373-5543. Web Site: www.ci.livermore.ca.us/library. *Branch Mgr*, Donna Pontay; Tel: 925-373-5541; Staff 2 (MLS 1, Non-MLS 1)
Founded 1992. Pop 25,000; Circ 155,786
Jul 1999-Jun 2000 Income City $165,610. Mats Exp $54,788, Books $45,469, Per/Ser (Incl. Access Fees) $3,227, AV Equip $6,092. Sal $153,296 (Prof $69,524)
Library Holdings: Bk Vols 44,143; Bk Titles 29,134; Per Subs 85
SPRINGTOWN, 998 Bluebell Dr, 94550. SAN 377-595X. Tel: 925-373-5517. FAX: 925-773-5534. Web Site: www.ci.livermore.ca.us/library.; Staff 1 (MLS 1)
Founded 1986. Pop 13,500; Circ 154,388
Jul 1999-Jun 2000 Income City $153,620. Mats Exp $39,654, Books $31,545, Per/Ser (Incl. Access Fees) $3,205, AV Equip $4,904. Sal $140,686 (Prof $68,640)
Library Holdings: Bk Vols 34,802; Bk Titles 22,969; Per Subs 40
SUMMER, 94550. SAN 377-5976. Tel: 925-373-5500.
Founded 1989. Pop 11,000
Jul 1999-Jun 2000 Income Locally Generated Income $12,500. Mats Exp Books $3,000. Sal $8,255
Library Holdings: Bk Vols 5,073; Bk Titles 5,000
Open June-Aug only

S SANDIA NATIONAL LABORATORIES, Technical Library, 7011 East Ave, 94550. (Mail add: PO Box 969, 94551-0969), SAN 300-8657. Tel: 925-294-2525. Circulation Tel: 925-294-1029. FAX: 925-294-2355.; Staff 5 (MLS 2, Non-MLS 3)
Founded 1956
Library Holdings: Bk Titles 12,000; Per Subs 575
Subject Interests: Chemistry, Computer science, Energy, Engineering, Mathematics, Nuclear science, Physics
Automation Activity & Vendor Info: (Acquisitions) epixtech, inc.; (Cataloging) epixtech, inc.
Restriction: Not open to public
Function: Research library

S UNIVERSITY OF CALIFORNIA, Lawrence Livermore National Laboratory Main Library, 7000 East Ave, PO Box 5500, 94550. SAN 300-8665. Tel: 925-423-8063. FAX: 424-2921. E-Mail: library-reference@llnl.gov. Web Site: www.llnl.gov/tid/Library.html. *Dir*, Isom Harrison; Staff 20 (MLS 20)
Founded 1952
Oct 1998-Sep 1999 Income $4,000,000
Library Holdings: Bk Vols 335,000; Per Subs 7,179
Subject Interests: Technology
Automation Activity & Vendor Info: (Acquisitions) SIRSI; (Cataloging) SIRSI; (Circulation) SIRSI; (Course Reserve) SIRSI; (ILL) SIRSI; (Media Booking) SIRSI; (OPAC) SIRSI; (Serials) SIRSI
Publications: New Titles
Restriction: Staff use only
Partic in BRS; Defense Technical Information Center; Dialog Corporation; Medline; Nasa Libraries Information System - Nasa Galaxie; RLIN; STN

LODI

P LODI PUBLIC LIBRARY,* 201 W Locust, 95240-2099. SAN 300-8681. Tel: 209-333-8507. FAX: 209-367-5944. E-Mail: library@lodi.gov. Web Site: www./odi.gov/library/index.html. *Dir*, Nancy Martinez; E-Mail: nmartin@lodinet.net; *Tech Servs*, Christine Mitchell; *Ch Servs*, Dorothy W Maas; *Ref*, Behjat Kerdegari; *Ref*, Sandra Smith; *ILL*, Dianna Murphy; Staff 5 (MLS 5)
Founded 1907. Pop 55,700; Circ 306,170
Jul 1997-Jun 1998 Income $1,015,780, State $65,897, City $874,886, Locally Generated Income $65,300, Other $6,619. Mats Exp $137,542. Sal $691,000
Library Holdings: Bk Vols 147,499; Bk Titles 129,500; Per Subs 252
Special Collections: Lodi History & Californiana, micro, photog
Automation Activity & Vendor Info: (Circulation) GEAC
Mem of 49-99 Cooperative Library System
Partic in Cent Valley Asn of Librs
Friends of the Library Group

S SAN JOAQUIN COUNTY HISTORICAL MUSEUM, Gerald D Kennedy Reference Library, 11793 N Micke Grove Rd, PO Box 30, 95241. SAN 327-8905. Tel: 209-331-2055. FAX: 209-331-2057. E-Mail: info@sanjoaquinhistory.org. Web Site: wwwsanjoaquinhistory.org. *Archivist, Librn*, Dr Donald Walker; E-Mail: dwalker@uop.edu; Staff 1 (MLS 1)
Library Holdings: Bk Vols 3,000; Per Subs 12
Subject Interests: Local county hist
Special Collections: Perino (Carmen) Papers; San Joaquin County 19th Century Archives; Weber Family Papers
Restriction: By appointment only, In-house use for visitors, Not a lending library
Function: Archival collection, Photocopies available, Reference only, Research library

S SRI AUROBINDO SADHANA PEETHAM LIBRARY, 2621 W Hwy 12, 95242. SAN 327-1668. Tel: 209-339-1342, 209-339-3710. FAX: 209-339-3715. E-Mail: sasp@lodinet.com. *Librn*, Dakshina Vanzetti
Library Holdings: Bk Titles 2,000
Special Collections: Ayurveda & Health; Classical Indian Spiritual Tradition; Collected Works of Sri Aurobindo; Collected Works of the Mother; Yoga
Restriction: By appointment only

LOGANSPORT

J IVY TECH STATE COLLEGE,* 2815 E Market St, 46947. SAN 372-722X. Tel: 219-753-5101. FAX: 219-753-5103. Web Site: www.ivy.tech.in.us. *In Charge*, Gloria Carvey; E-Mail: gcarvey@ivy.tec.in.us
Founded 1992. Enrl 500; Fac 5
Library Holdings: Bk Titles 661
Friends of the Library Group

LOMA LINDA

GM DEPARTMENT OF VETERANS AFFAIRS, Medical Center Library Service, 11201 Benton St, 92357. SAN 300-869X. Tel: 909-422-3063. FAX: 909-422-3164. *Tech Servs*, Lynn LaVigueur; Staff 2 (MLS 1, Non-MLS 1)
Founded 1977
Oct 1999-Sep 2000 Income $64,000. Mats Exp $56,318, Books $6,723, Per/Ser (Incl. Access Fees) $49,595
Library Holdings: Bk Titles 2,000; Per Subs 201
Subject Interests: Medicine
Automation Activity & Vendor Info: (Cataloging) Innovative Interfaces Inc.; (Circulation) Innovative Interfaces Inc.
Partic in Inland Empire Med Libr Coop; San Bernardino, Inyo, Riverside Counties United Library Services; Vets Admin Libr Network

LOMA LINDA UNIVERSITY
C DEL E WEBB MEMORIAL LIBRARY, 11072 Anderson St, 92350-0001. SAN 332-2297. Tel: 909-558-4581. Interlibrary Loan Service Tel: 909-558-4925. FAX: 909-558-4188. E-Mail: webblibrary@dwebb.llu.edu. Web Site: www.llu.edu/llu/library. *Tech Servs*, Nelia Wurangian; *Publ Servs*, Carlene Bogle; *Rare Bks, Spec Coll*, Merlin D Burt; *Per*, Shirley Graves; *Coll Develop*, Sylvia Goss; Staff 10 (MLS 10)
Founded 1907. Enrl 3,235; Highest Degree: Doctorate
Library Holdings: Bk Vols 188,633; Per Subs 1,438
Subject Interests: Health sciences, Medicine, Religion
Special Collections: Archival Coll; History of; Human Relations Area Files, micro; Medicine (Peter C Remondino Coll), bks, Archives of American Dental Society of Anesthesiology; Seventh-Day Adventist (Heritage Coll), bks, VF
Automation Activity & Vendor Info: (Acquisitions) Innovative Interfaces Inc.; (Cataloging) Innovative Interfaces Inc.
Database Vendor: Innovative Interfaces INN - View
Partic in Adventist Librs Info Coop; Inland Empire Acad Libr Coop; Nat Libr of Med; San Bernardino, Inyo, Riverside Counties United Library Services; Southern Calif Electronic Libr Consortium
CM MEDICAL CENTER LIBRARY & INFORMATION CENTER, 11234 Anderson St, 92354. (Mail add: PO Box 2000, 92354), Tel: 909-558-4620. FAX: 909-558-4722. E-Mail: mclibrary@llu.edu. Web Site: www.jmlic.llu.edu. *Actg Dir*, David D Rios; *Assoc Dir*, Laura Brown; *ILL, Ser*, Shirley Rayis; *Publ Servs*, Betty Allanson
Jan 1999-Dec 1999 Income $490,000
Library Holdings: Bk Titles 4,500; Per Subs 370

Automation Activity & Vendor Info: (Acquisitions) Innovative Interfaces Inc.; (Cataloging) Innovative Interfaces Inc.; (Circulation) Innovative Interfaces Inc.; (OPAC) Innovative Interfaces Inc.; (Serials) Innovative Interfaces Inc.

M NATIONAL COUNCIL FOR RELIABLE HEALTH INFORMATION, National Council Against Health Fraud Library, PO Box 1276, 92354-1276. SAN 373-4048. Tel: 909-824-4690. FAX: 909-824-4838. Web Site: www.ncahf.org, www.quackwatch.com. *Exec Dir*, Dr William Jarvis; *Pres*, William M London
Founded 1977
Library Holdings: Bk Vols 500; Per Subs 20
Publications: NCAHF Newsletter, NCAHF Bulletin Board

S WILDERNESS LEADERSHIP INTERNATIONAL LIBRARY, Outdoor Living Library,* 24414 University Ave, No 34, 92354. SAN 374-5392. Tel: 909-796-8501. FAX: 909-799-7122. *Asst Librn*, Len Kramer
Library Holdings: Bk Titles 1,000

LOMPOC

S LA PURISIMA MISSION ARCHIVES,* La Purisima Mission State Historic Park, 2295 Purisima Rd, 93436. SAN 373-4056. Tel: 805-733-3713. FAX: 805-733-2497. *In Charge*, Joe McCummins
Library Holdings: Bk Vols 375

S LOMPOC MUSEUM ASSOCIATES INC, Research Library,* 200 South H St, 93436. SAN 373-4064. Tel: 805-736-3888. FAX: 805-736-2840. *Curator, Dir*, Debra Argel
Library Holdings: Bk Vols 1,500
Subject Interests: Archaeology

P LOMPOC PUBLIC LIBRARY,* 501 E North Ave, 93436-3498. SAN 332-2351. Tel: 805-736-3477. FAX: 805-736-6440. E-Mail: lref@rain.org. Web Site: www.rain.org/lomplyn. *Dir*, Nina K Taylor; *Ad Servs*, Molly Blaschke; *Ch Servs*, Patrice Doctor
Founded 1969. Pop 67,470; Circ 313,715
Jul 1997-Jun 1998 Income $947,167, State $27,283, City $566,833, County $263,800. Mats Exp $71,500. Sal $426,000
Library Holdings: Bk Vols 100,000; Bk Titles 98,000; Per Subs 325
Subject Interests: Gardening, Horticulture
Special Collections: Local History
Mem of Black Gold Cooperative Library System
Friends of the Library Group
Branches: 2
BUELLTON BRANCH, PO Box 187, Buellton, 93427. SAN 332-2386. Tel: 805-688-3115. FAX: 805-688-3115. *Librn*, Judith Just
Library Holdings: Bk Titles 13,000
VILLAGE, 3755 Constellation Rd, 93436. SAN 332-2416. Tel: 805-733-3323. *Librn*, Melinda Farris
Library Holdings: Bk Titles 15,000

LONG BEACH

S BOEING LIBRARY SERVICE, 3855 Lakewood Blvd, DO 36-0084, 90846. SAN 300-8789. Tel: 562-593-7687. FAX: 562-496-5696. *Mgr*, Brewsaugh Sue
Library Holdings: Bk Titles 20,000; Per Subs 800

S BOEING NORTH AMERICAN BMA, Technical Information Center CO52-0180,* Longbeach Bldg 52, 4201 E Wardlow Rd, 90807. SAN 331-9326. Tel: 562-593-8172.
Founded 1935
Library Holdings: Bk Vols 10,000; Bk Titles 9,610; Per Subs 194
Subject Interests: Aeronautics, Computer science
Restriction: Staff use only
Partic in Defense Technical Information Center; Dialog Corporation; Nasa Libraries Information System - Nasa Galaxie; SDC Info Servs

C CALIFORNIA STATE UNIVERSITY, LONG BEACH, University Library, 1250 Bellflower Blvd, 90840-1901. SAN 300-8711. Tel: 562-985-4047. FAX: 562-985-8131. Web Site: www.csulb.edu/library. *Dean*, Roman V Kochan; *Assoc Dean*, Henry DuBois; *Assoc Dir*, Gretchen A Johnson; *Bibliog Instr*, Patricia Matzke; Tel: 562-985-1751, E-Mail: matzke@csulb.edu; Staff 72 (MLS 21, Non-MLS 51)
Founded 1949. Enrl 28,763; Fac 1,423; Highest Degree: Master
Jul 1999-Jun 2000 Mats Exp $2,678,907, Books $406,895, Per/Ser (Incl. Access Fees) $1,992,574, Presv $33,783, Micro $45,422, Electronic Ref Mat (Incl. Access Fees) $245,655. Sal $3,707,916 (Prof $1,252,087)
Library Holdings: Bk Vols 1,455,805; Bk Titles 803,715; Per Subs 3,589
Special Collections: Abolition Movement (Dumond Coll); Art Prints & Photography Coll; Arts in Southern California Archive; California History (Bekeart Coll); Radical Politics in California (Dorothy Healey Coll); Theater History (Pasadena Playhouse Coll), playscripts; United States Revolutionary War; University Archives
Automation Activity & Vendor Info: (Acquisitions) Innovative Interfaces Inc.; (Cataloging) Innovative Interfaces Inc.; (Circulation) Innovative Interfaces Inc.; (Course Reserve) Innovative Interfaces Inc.; (OPAC) Innovative Interfaces Inc.; (Serials) Innovative Interfaces Inc.
Publications: Library Skills (course book for library component of general education requirement)
Mem of California State University
Partic in Link; OCLC Online Computer Library Center, Inc
Friends of the Library Group

GM DEPARTMENT OF VETERANS AFFAIRS MEDICAL CENTER, Health Care Sciences Library,* Bldg 2, Rm 345, 5901 E Seventh St, 90822-5201. SAN 300-8835. Tel: 562-494-5465. FAX: 562-494-5447. *Online Servs*, Thomas Hanson; Staff 5 (MLS 2, Non-MLS 3)
Founded 1946
Library Holdings: Bk Titles 9,405; Per Subs 524
Subject Interests: Medicine
Special Collections: Management Coll
Partic in Docline; Vets Admin Libr Network

R FIRST BAPTIST CHURCH OF LAKEWOOD LIBRARY,* 5336 Arbor Rd, 90808. SAN 300-872X. Tel: 562-420-1471. FAX: 562-420-9140. *In Charge*, Sonja Friese
Founded 1950
Library Holdings: Bk Vols 7,300; Per Subs 3
Subject Interests: Biblical studies, Children's literature, Marriage, Missions and missionaries
Special Collections: Pastor's Sermons, A-tapes
Open Thurs 9-noon

R FIRST BAPTIST CHURCH OF LONG BEACH LIBRARY,* 1000 Pine Ave, 90813. SAN 300-8738. Tel: 562-432-8447. FAX: 562-983-1794. *Librn*, Ella Allen
Library Holdings: Bk Vols 3,000

M FIRST CONSULTING GROUP, Information Resource Center,* 111 W Ocean Blvd, 4th flr, PO Box 22676, 90801-5676. SAN 375-7617. Tel: 562-624-5200, 562-624-5239. FAX: 562-432-5774. Web Site: www.fcg.com.; Staff 1 (MLS 1)
Library Holdings: Bk Titles 500

S HISTORICAL SOCIETY OF LONG BEACH, 40 S Locust, 90802. (Mail add: PO Box 1869, 90801), SAN 326-4807. Tel: 562-495-1210. FAX: 562-495-1281. E-Mail: hslb@thegrid.net. Web Site: www.thegrid.net/hslb. *Exec Dir*, Jullie Bartolotto; *Coll Develop*, Dominique Brummond; Staff 2 (Non-MLS 2)
Founded 1962. Circ 350,000
Library Holdings: Bk Titles 400
Subject Interests: Local history
Special Collections: Artifacts; Maps; Photograph Coll, Scrap bks, Pamphlets
Publications: Photograph journals
Function: Reference only

L KEESAL, YOUNG & LOGAN, Law Library,* 400 Oceangate, 90801. SAN 372-3763. Tel: 562-436-2000. FAX: 562-436-7416. Web Site: www.kyl.com. *Librn*, Marilyn R Wills; E-Mail: mrwills@class.org
Library Holdings: Bk Vols 15,000
Subject Interests: Employment, Securities

LONG BEACH CITY COLLEGE
J LIBERAL ARTS CAMPUS & PACIFIC COAST CAMPUS LIBRARIES, 4901 E Carson St, 90808. SAN 332-2475. Tel: 562-938-4025. FAX: 562-938-4777. Web Site: www.2.lbcc.cc.ca.us/lib. *Head of Libr*, Monica White; Tel: 562-938-4582, E-Mail: mwhite@lbcc.cc.ca.us; *Br Coordr*, Marion Flowers Hinton; Tel: 562-938-3129, Fax: 562-938-3062, E-Mail: mhinton@lbcc.cc.ca.us; *Bibliog Instr*, Kim Barclay; Tel: 562-938-4708, E-Mail: kbarclay@lbcc.cc.ca.us; *Cat*, Dele Ukwu; *Per*, Nenita Buenaventura; Tel: 562-938-4576, E-Mail: nbuena@lbcc.cc.ca.us; Staff 18 (MLS 9, Non-MLS 9)
Founded 1927. Enrl 24,828
Jul 1998-Jun 1999 Income $1,224,507. Mats Exp $110,286, Books $67,862, Per/Ser (Incl. Access Fees) $42,424. Sal $898,513 (Prof $518,019)
Library Holdings: Bk Vols 145,639; Per Subs 466
Automation Activity & Vendor Info: (Cataloging) VTLS; (Circulation) VTLS; (OPAC) VTLS; (Serials) TLC
Database Vendor: IAC - Info Trac, OCLC - First Search, ProQuest
Friends of the Library Group

S LONG BEACH JEWISH COMMUNITY CENTER, Stanley S Zack Library, 3801 E Willow St, 90815. SAN 300-8762. Tel: 562-426-7601. FAX: 562-424-3915. E-Mail: jcclb@aol.com. *Exec Dir*, Michael Wittenstein
Founded 1961
Library Holdings: Bk Vols 3,500; Bk Titles 3,500; Per Subs 20
Subject Interests: Judaica (lit or hist of Jews)

M LONG BEACH MEMORIAL MEDICAL CENTER, Parks Library Resource Center,* 2801 Atlantic Ave, PO Box 1428, 90801-1428. SAN 300-8797. Tel: 562-933-3841. FAX: 562-981-1205. *Dir*, Marion N Scichilone; Staff 4 (MLS 2, Non-MLS 2)
Founded 1927

Library Holdings: Bk Vols 11,540; Per Subs 650
Subject Interests: Allied health, Medicine, Nursing
Publications: Fact Sheet, newsletter (quarterly)
Partic in BRS; Dialog Corporation; Docline; Ontyme; SDC Search Serv

S LONG BEACH MUSEUM OF ART LIBRARY,* 2300 E Ocean Blvd, 90803. SAN 300-8770. Tel: 562-439-2119. FAX: 562-439-3587. *Dir*, Harold B Nelson
Founded 1957
Library Holdings: Bk Vols 2,600; Bk Titles 2,000

P LONG BEACH PUBLIC LIBRARY & INFORMATION CENTER, 101 Pacific Ave, 90822-1097. SAN 332-2564. Tel: 562-570-7500. Interlibrary Loan Service Tel: 562-570-6053. TDD: 562-570-6744. FAX: 562-570-7408. Web Site: www.lbpl.org. *Dir*, Eleanore Schmidt; *Assoc Dir*, Louise Mazerov; *Assoc Dir*, Nancy Messineo; *YA Servs*, Christine Burcham; *Acq*, Toni Sorenson; *Per*, Glenda Williams. Subject Specialists: *History*, Claudine Burnett; *Literature*, Claudine Burnett; Staff 140 (MLS 53, Non-MLS 87)
Founded 1896. Pop 457,000; Circ 2,411,815
Library Holdings: Bk Vols 1,344,556; Per Subs 2,136
Special Collections: Bertrand L Smith Rare Book; California History Rancho Period (Rancho Los Cerritos Library); Films; Long Beach History; Marilyn Horne Archives, pictures, press clippings, rec; Petroleum; Videocassettes
Automation Activity & Vendor Info: (Acquisitions) epixtech, inc.; (Cataloging) epixtech, inc.; (Circulation) epixtech, inc.; (OPAC) epixtech, inc.; (Serials) epixtech, inc.
Mem of Metropolitan Cooperative Library System
Partic in Coop Libr Agency for Syst & Servs; Southern Calif Interlibr Loan Network
Friends of the Library Group
Branches: 11
ALAMITOS, 1836 E Third St, 90802. SAN 332-2599. Tel: 562-570-1037. *Librn*, Josephine Caron
Library Holdings: Bk Vols 44,344
BAY SHORE, 195 Bay Shore Ave, 90803. SAN 332-2653. Tel: 562-570-1039. *Librn*, Cliff Phillips
Library Holdings: Bk Vols 42,174
Friends of the Library Group
BRET HARTE BRANCH, 1595 W Willow St, 90810. SAN 332-2807. Tel: 562-570-1044. *Librn*, Karol Seehaus
Library Holdings: Bk Vols 54,438
BREWITT, 4036 E Anaheim St, 90804. SAN 332-2688. Tel: 562-570-1040. *Librn*, Karen Cressy
Library Holdings: Bk Vols 41,880
BURNETT, 560 E Hill St, 90806. SAN 332-2718. Tel: 562-570-1041. *Librn*, Mary Hopman
Library Holdings: Bk Vols 56,822
Friends of the Library Group
DANA, 3680 Atlantic Ave, 90807. SAN 332-2742. Tel: 562-570-1042. *Librn*, Steve Quinney
Library Holdings: Bk Vols 49,952
EL DORADO, 2900 Studebaker Rd, 90815. SAN 332-2777. Tel: 562-570-1043. *Librn*, Mary Heggdale
Library Holdings: Bk Vols 67,509
LOS ALTOS, 5614 Britton Dr, 90815. SAN 332-2831. Tel: 562-570-1045. *Librn*, Lynda Fritz
Library Holdings: Bk Vols 57,506
MARK TWAIN BRANCH, 1325 E Anaheim St, 90813. SAN 332-2890. Tel: 562-570-1046. *Librn*, Diane Olivos-Posher
Library Holdings: Bk Vols 27,958
NORTH, 5571 Orange Ave, 90805. SAN 332-2920. Tel: 562-570-1047. *Mgr*, Marge Holleman
Library Holdings: Bk Vols 55,888
RUTH BACH BRANCH, 4055 Bellflower Blvd, 90808. SAN 332-2629. Tel: 562-570-1038. FAX: 562-570-1276. Web Site: www.lbpl.org. *Branch Mgr*, Candy Powell; E-Mail: cpowell@lbpl.org
Library Holdings: Bk Vols 47,852
Friends of the Library Group

M PACIFIC HOSPITAL OF LONG BEACH, Harris Memorial Library, 2776 Pacific Ave, 90806. SAN 300-8800. Tel: 562-424-7422, Ext 3291. FAX: 562-595-0271. *Librn*, Katherine Halcrow; *Librn*, Irene M Lovas; Staff 1 (MLS 1)
Founded 1964
Library Holdings: Bk Titles 1,350; Per Subs 100
Subject Interests: Acupuncture, Medicine, Nursing, Osteopathology, Osteopathy, Podiatry

S RMS FOUNDATION, INC, Hotel Queen Mary Historical Archives, 1126 Queens Hwy, 90802. SAN 326-2936. Tel: 562-435-3511. FAX: 562-437-4531. E-Mail: queenmry@gte.net. Web Site: www.queenmary.com. *Archivist*, Ron Smith; Staff 4 (MLS 3, Non-MLS 1)
Founded 1967
Library Holdings: Bk Titles 200
Special Collections: Original logbooks, manuals, plans and misc recs

M SAINT MARY MEDICAL CENTER, Bellis Medical Library, 1050 Linden Ave, PO Box 887, 90801. SAN 300-8819. Tel: 562-491-9295. FAX: 562-491-9293. *Mgr*, Linda Rubin; E-Mail: lrubin@chw.edu
Founded 1955
Library Holdings: Bk Vols 30,000
Subject Interests: Hospital administration, Nursing
Publications: Medical Library Newsletter
Restriction: Medical staff only
Partic in Dialog Corporation; Medline
Friends of the Library Group

S SCS ENGINEERS LIBRARY, 3711 Long Beach Blvd 9th Flr, 90807-3315. SAN 373-028X. Tel: 562-426-9544. FAX: 562-427-0805. Web Site: www.scsengineers.com. *Librn*, Loran Bures; E-Mail: lbures@scsengineers.com; Staff 1 (Non-MLS 1)
Founded 1970
Library Holdings: Bk Vols 55,000; Per Subs 120
Restriction: Access at librarian's discretion
Function: Research library

S SELF WINDING CLOCK ASSOCIATION LIBRARY,* 1165 E San Antonio Dr Ste A, 90807-2374. SAN 372-655X. Tel: 562-422-5158. *Librn*, Bengt E Honning
Founded 1979
Library Holdings: Bk Vols 2,500; Bk Titles 2,500; Per Subs 10
Restriction: Members only

LOS ALTOS HILLS

R CONGREGATION BETH AM LIBRARY, 26790 Arastradero Rd, 94022. SAN 300-8878. Tel: 650-493-4661. FAX: 650-494-8248. *Librn*, Diane Rauchwerger
Library Holdings: Bk Vols 6,000
Special Collections: Judaica

FOOTHILL COLLEGE
J HUBERT H SEMANS LIBRARY, 12345 El Monte Rd, 94022-4599. SAN 300-8894. Tel: 650-949-7390, 650-949-7608. FAX: 650-949-7123. Web Site: www.fhda.edu/foothill/. *Dean of Libr*, Dr Penny Patz; E-Mail: patz@admin.fhda.edu; *Coordr*, Walter Scott; *Bibliog Instr*, Charlotte Thunen; *Automation Syst Coordr*, Dr Roxanne Mendrinos; *Coll Develop, Tech Servs*, John Broadwin; *Publ Servs*, Karen Gillette
Founded 1958. Enrl 10,191; Fac 334
Jul 1997-Jun 1998 Income $986,443, State $986,443. Mats Exp $11,291, Books $1,450, Micro $9,841. Sal $430,524
Library Holdings: Bk Vols 82,757; Per Subs 477
Subject Interests: Art, Literature, Philosophy, Religion
Publications: Introduction to Library Skills; Principles of Library Research; Student Handbook
Mem of South Bay Coop Libr Syst
Partic in Colorado Alliance Of Research Libraries; OCLC Online Computer Library Center, Inc

LOS ANGELES

L ALSCHULER, GROSSMAN, STEIN & KAHAN, (Formerly Alschuler, Grossman & Pines), Law Library, 2049 Century Park E, 39th flr, 90067. SAN 372-2732. Tel: 310-277-1226, 310-551-9155. FAX: 310-552-6077. *Dir*, Denise Julie Grigst; E-Mail: dgrigst@agsk.com; *Librn*, George M Mood; Tel: 310-277-1226, Ext 465, E-Mail: gmood@agsk.com; *Asst Librn*, Lisa Marie Burke; Tel: 910-551-9135, E-Mail: lburke@agsk.com. Subject Specialists: *Law*, Denise Julie Grigst; *Law*, George M Mood; *Law*, Lisa Marie Burke; Staff 3 (Non-MLS 3)
1997-1998 Mats Exp $350,000
Library Holdings: Bk Vols 10,000
Automation Activity & Vendor Info: (Acquisitions) Inmagic, Inc.; (Cataloging) Inmagic, Inc.; (ILL) Inmagic, Inc.; (OPAC) Inmagic, Inc.
Database Vendor: Lexis-Nexis
Mem of Metropolitan Cooperative Library System
Open Mon-Fri 8:30-6

S AMATEUR ATHLETIC FOUNDATION OF LOS ANGELES LIBRARY, 2141 W Adams Blvd, 90018. SAN 300-9076. Tel: 323-730-4646. FAX: 323-730-0546. E-Mail: library@aafla.org. Web Site: www.aafla.org. *VPres*, Wayne Wilson; *Ref*, Shirley Ito; *Cat, Ref*, Michael Salmon; Staff 4 (MLS 3, Non-MLS 1)
Founded 1936
Library Holdings: Bk Vols 30,000; Bk Titles 27,000; Per Subs 400
Subject Interests: Sports
Special Collections: Olympic Games, sport photographs, sport films
Automation Activity & Vendor Info: (OPAC) epixtech, inc.; (Serials) epixtech, inc.
Database Vendor: Dialog, OCLC - First Search, Silverplatter Information Inc.
Publications: Sportsletter (bi-monthly)
Restriction: By appointment only

Function: Archival collection, ILL by photocopy only, Outside services via phone, cable & mail, Photocopies available, Research library
Partic in OCLC Online Computer Library Center, Inc

S AMERICAN FILM INSTITUTE, Louis B Mayer Library, 2021 N Western Ave, 90027. SAN 300-6220. Tel: 323-856-7654. FAX: 323-856-7803. Web Site: www.afionline.org. *Coll Develop, Librn*, Caroline Sisneros; Tel: 323-856-7661, Fax: 323-856-7803, E-Mail: csisneros@afionline.org; Staff 5 (MLS 1, Non-MLS 4)
Founded 1969. Enrl 250; Highest Degree: Master
Library Holdings: Bk Titles 5,000; Per Subs 100
Subject Interests: Television
Special Collections: Film Daily Coll (1923-1969); Film Index (1930-1969); Fritz Lang Coll; Manuscript Coll; Martin Scorsese Coll; Motion Picture & Television Scripts Coll; Oral History Transcripts Coll; Radio-TV Daily (1939-1964); RKO Radio Flash Coll (1932-1955); Robert Aldrich Coll; Seminar Transcripts & Tape Coll; TV Guide (1948-present)
Automation Activity & Vendor Info: (Circulation) CASPR
Restriction: Non-circulating to the public
Partic in Southern Calif Electronic Libr Consortium

L ANDERSON, MCPHARLIN & CONNERS LLP LIBRARY, 624 S Grand Ave 1900, 90017. Tel: 213-236-1677. FAX: 213-622-7594. E-Mail: sml@amclaw.com. *Librn*, Shihmei Lin; Staff 1 (MLS 1)
Founded 1947
Jan 2000-Dec 2000 Mats Exp $100,000. Sal $40,000 (Prof $30,000)
Library Holdings: Bk Vols 5,000; Bk Titles 1,000; Per Subs 20; High Interest/Low Vocabulary Bk Vols 30
Database Vendor: Lexis-Nexis
Publications: (Collection catalog)
Function: For research purposes

L ARTER & HADDEN LIBRARY,* 725 S Figueroa St, Ste 3400, 90017. SAN 300-9459. Tel: 213-430-3240. FAX: 213-617-9255. *Librn*, Anna Delgado; E-Mail: adelgado@arterhadden.com; Staff 3 (MLS 2, Non-MLS 1)
Library Holdings: Bk Vols 10,000; Per Subs 40
Restriction: Not open to public

S ASOCIACION NACIONAL PRO PERSONAS MAYORES LIBRARY,* 1452 W Temple St, 90026. (Mail add: 234 E Colorado Blvd Ste 300, 91101), SAN 371-0025. Tel: 213-487-1922. FAX: 213-202-5905. E-Mail: anppm@aol.com. *Pres*, Carmela G Lacayo
Library Holdings: Bk Titles 4,200; Per Subs 77
Friends of the Library Group

ATLANTIC RICHFIELD CO
S TAX LIBRARY, 333 S Hope St, 90071. SAN 370-0356. Tel: 213-486-1485. FAX: 213-486-2408. *Librn*, Chris Gilbertson
Library Holdings: Bk Vols 2,070; Per Subs 10

S AUTOMOBILE CLUB OF SOUTHERN CALIFORNIA, Public Affairs Library,* 2601 S Figueroa St, 90007-3289. SAN 321-8945. Tel: 213-741-3686. FAX: 213-741-4670. *In Charge*, Laurie Bychowski
Founded 1972
Library Holdings: Bk Vols 17,000; Bk Titles 15,000; Per Subs 100
Subject Interests: Automotive engineering, Highway eng, Traffic safety
Special Collections: Westways Magazine (Touring Topic) 1909-present
Publications: Acquisitions list
Restriction: Open to public for reference only
Partic in Dialog Corporation

S AUTRY MUSEUM OF WESTERN HERITAGE, Research Center, 4700 Western Heritage Way, 90027-1462. SAN 372-6606. Tel: 323-667-2000. FAX: 323-953-8735. E-Mail: rroom@autry-museum.org. Web Site: www.autry-museum.org. *Dir*, Kevin Mulroy; *Ref*, Marva Felchlin; *Archivist*, Jeanette Hoskinson; Tel: 323-667-2000, Ext 321, E-Mail: jhoskinson@autry-museum.org; Staff 6 (MLS 5, Non-MLS 1)
Founded 1988
Library Holdings: Per Subs 100
Subject Interests: Western Americana
Special Collections: Rosenstock Coll; West of Imagination (Autry Coll), multimedia
Automation Activity & Vendor Info: (Cataloging) Innovative Interfaces Inc.; (OPAC) Innovative Interfaces Inc.
Partic in Dialog Corporation

L BAKER & HOSTETLER, Law Library, 333 S Grand Ave, 90071. SAN 300-9629. Tel: 213-624-2400. FAX: 213-975-1740. Web Site: www.bakerlaw.com. *Librn*, Stewart Annand; E-Mail: sannand@bakerlaw.com; Staff 2 (MLS 1, Non-MLS 1)
Library Holdings: Bk Titles 30,000
Partic in Westlaw

L BANK OF AMERICA - SOUTHERN CALIFORNIA HEADQUARTERS, Law Library,* Legal Dept 24017, 555 S Flower St, 90071. SAN 300-8959. Tel: 213-228-3148. FAX: 213-228-4968. *Librn*, Elizabeth Cobarrubias; E-Mail: elizabeth.s.corbarrubias@bankamerica.com; *Asst Librn*, Christina Levia
Library Holdings: Bk Vols 15,000; Per Subs 15
Subject Interests: Banks and banking, Commercial law
Special Collections: ALR 1st, 2nd, 3rd & 4th; Federal Reporters 1st & 2nd Series

M BARLOW RESPIRATORY HOSPITAL, Elks Tuberculosis Library,* 2000 Stadium Way, 90026-2696. SAN 300-8967. Tel: 213-250-4200, Ext 3345. FAX: 213-250-5032. *Librn*, Rose Thompson
Founded 1947
Library Holdings: Bk Titles 3,400; Per Subs 70
Subject Interests: Respiratory diseases
Restriction: Medical staff only

L BLECHER & COLLINS, Law Library,* 611 W Sixth St, 20th flr, 90017. SAN 372-2775. Tel: 213-622-4222. FAX: 213-622-1656. *Librn*, Antoinette V Shilkevich
Library Holdings: Bk Vols 10,000

S BOEING SATTELITE SYSTEM S24 LIBRARY, (Formerly Hughes Electronics Co), Bldg S24 M/S D538 2020 E Imperial Hwy, PO Box 92919, 90009. SAN 331-8575. Tel: 310-364-6002. FAX: 310-364-6424. E-Mail: hsc.library@hsc.com. *Mgr*, Patricia Adorno; E-Mail: patricia.adorno@hsc.com; *Librn*, L Morris; *Librn*, M Deeds; *Librn*, B Hinz
Founded 1963
Library Holdings: Bk Vols 20,000; Per Subs 300
Subject Interests: Business and management, Chemistry, Electronics, Mathematics, Physics
Database Vendor: epixtech, inc.
Restriction: Staff use only
Partic in SCOUG

S BOSTON CONSULTING GROUP LIBRARY,* 355 S Grand Ave 33rd flr, 90071. SAN 370-9531. Tel: 213-621-2772. FAX: 213-621-1639. Web Site: www.bcg.com. *Dir Info Resources & Res*, Linda Adams
Library Holdings: Bk Vols 1,700; Per Subs 100
Subject Interests: Industry

P BRAILLE INSTITUTE LIBRARY SERVICES, 741 N Vermont Ave, 90029-3594. SAN 300-8975. Tel: 323-660-3880. Toll Free Tel: 800-808-2555. FAX: 323-663-0867. E-Mail: bils@brailib.org. Web Site: www.brailleinstitute.org/books.html. *Dir Libr Serv*, Dr Henry C Chang; E-Mail: dls@brailib.org; *Outreach Serv*, Tina Herbison; E-Mail: supports@brailib.org; *Reader Servs*, Brent Cooper; E-Mail: ism@brailib.org; *Circ*, Cris Sipin; E-Mail: circulation@brailib.org; *Info Tech*, John W Brewster; *Automation Syst Coordr*, Ming Cheng; E-Mail: systeml@brailib.org; *Ref*, Julie Uyeno; E-Mail: reference@brailib.org; Staff 43 (MLS 5, Non-MLS 38)
Founded 1919. Pop 32,000; Circ 1,080,500
Jul 2000-Jun 2001 Income (Main Library and Branch Library) $2,450,000, State $577,000, Parent Institution $1,873,000. Mats Exp $52,000, Books $50,000, Per/Ser (Incl. Access Fees) $2,000. Sal $1,400,000
Library Holdings: Bk Vols 903,236; Bk Titles 71,717; Per Subs 12
Subject Interests: Blindness, Physically handicapped
Special Collections: Blindness & Other Handicap Reference Material; Southern California Coll
Automation Activity & Vendor Info: (Circulation) DRA
Database Vendor: Dialog, DRA
Publications: Fiction Classics Catalog; Librarian Newsletter; Record Books on Tapes about California; Subject Bibliographies; Transcribe Books into Braille
Partic in National Library Service For The Blind & Physically Handicapped, Library Of Congress
Branches: 4
DESERT CENTER, 70-251 Ramon Rd, Rancho Mirage, 92270. SAN 372-7637. Tel: 760-321-1111. FAX: 760-321-9715. Web Site: www.brailleinstitute.org. *Coordr*, Judith Vander Pol
Library Holdings: Bk Vols 6,183
Special Collections: Braille Reference Books
Friends of the Library Group
ORANGE COUNTY CENTER, 527 N Dale Ave, Anaheim, 92801. SAN 372-7645. Tel: 714-821-5000. FAX: 714-527-7621. Web Site: www.brailleinstitute.org. *Br Coordr*, Nancy Stanton
Library Holdings: Bk Vols 9,909
Special Collections: Braille Reference Books
Friends of the Library Group
SAN DIEGO CENTER, 4555 Executive Dr, Ste 100, San Diego, 92121. SAN 372-7653. Tel: 619-452-1111. FAX: 619-452-1688. E-Mail: ism@braillib.org. Web Site: www.brailleinstitute.org. *Coordr*, Wayne Perrill; *Reader Servs*, Brent Cooper; Tel: 323-660-3880, Fax: 323-663-0867
Library Holdings: Bk Vols 6,183
Special Collections: Braille Reference Books
Friends of the Library Group
SANTA BARBARA CENTER, 2031 De la Vina, Santa Barbara, 93105. SAN 372-7661. Tel: 805-682-6222. FAX: 323-663-0867. E-Mail: ism@braillib.org. Web Site: www.brailleinstitute.org. *Coordr*, Ami Woodmansee; *Reader Servs*, Brent Cooper; Tel: 323-660-3880

Library Holdings: Bk Vols 4,740
Subject Interests: Reading, Recreation
Special Collections: Braille Reference Books
Friends of the Library Group

L BROBECK, PHLEGER & HARRISON LIBRARY,* 550 S Hope St, Ste 2100, 90071. SAN 326-6907. Tel: 213-745-3406. FAX: 213-745-3345. *Chief Librn*, Jane McMahon; E-Mail: jmcmahon@brobeck.com; *Asst Librn*, Kathleen Terada; Staff 1 (MLS 1)
Library Holdings: Bk Vols 15,000; Per Subs 60
Subject Interests: Corporate law
Special Collections: Bankruptcy, bks, per
Publications: Newsletter
Partic in RLIN; Westlaw

L BUCHALTER, NEMER, FIELDS & YOUNGER, Law Library,* 601 S Figueroa St Ste 2400, 90017. SAN 372-2740. Tel: 213-891-0700. FAX: 213-896-0400. Web Site: www.buchalter.com. *In Charge*, Gilbert Romero
Library Holdings: Bk Vols 20,000

GL CALIFORNIA DEPARTMENT OF JUSTICE LIBRARY, North Tower, 7th flr, 300 S Spring St, 90013. SAN 300-8991. Tel: 213-897-2342. FAX: 213-897-2335. *Head Librn*, Janet Raffalow; *Librn*, Kathryn Lee; Staff 5 (MLS 2, Non-MLS 3)
Library Holdings: Bk Vols 40,000
Restriction: Not open to public
Partic in Westlaw

C CALIFORNIA GRADUATE INSTITUTE LIBRARY,* 1145 Gayle Ave, 90024. SAN 325-1497. Tel: 310-208-4240. FAX: 310-208-0684. E-Mail: cgi@ix.netcom.com.; Staff 6 (MLS 1, Non-MLS 5)
Enrl 500; Fac 186
Library Holdings: Bk Vols 4,850; Bk Titles 4,350; Per Subs 125
Subject Interests: Behavioral med, Psychiatry, Psychoanalysis, Psychology, Psychotherapy

M CALIFORNIA HOSPITAL MEDICAL CENTER LOS ANGELES, Information Center Medical Library, 1401 S Grand Ave, 90015. SAN 320-4448. Tel: 213-742-5872. FAX: 213-765-4046.; Staff 2 (MLS 1, Non-MLS 1)
Founded 1964
Library Holdings: Bk Vols 1,600; Bk Titles 680; Per Subs 114
Subject Interests: Clinical medicine, Nursing, Oncology
Partic in Nat Libr of Med

G CALIFORNIA STATE DEPARTMENT OF CORPORATIONS LIBRARY, 320 W Fourth St, Ste 750, 90013. SAN 321-6438. Tel: 213-576-7667. FAX: 213-576-7182. *Librn*, Sharon Akey; E-Mail: sakey@corp.ca.gov; Staff 1 (MLS 1)
Library Holdings: Bk Vols 12,000; Bk Titles 3,500; Per Subs 100
Subject Interests: Corporate securities
Library holdings includes branches holdings

C CALIFORNIA STATE UNIVERSITY, LOS ANGELES, John F Kennedy Memorial Library, 5151 State University Dr, 90032-8300. SAN 300-9017. Tel: 323-343-3955. FAX: 323-343-5600. Web Site: calstate.edu.htm, web.calstatela.edu/library/index/htm. *Librn*, Doug Davis; E-Mail: ddavis2@calstatela.edu; *Assoc Librn*, Margo Young; *ILL*, Chris Kurtnaker; *Per*, Andrew Shroyer; *Circ*, Deborah Schaeffer; *Acq, Coll Develop*, Wayne Gladish; *Cat*, Jack Robb; Staff 16 (MLS 16)
Founded 1947. Enrl 13,330; Fac 608; Highest Degree: Master
Library Holdings: Bk Vols 1,168,054; Per Subs 1,771
Special Collections: Anthony Quinn Coll of Film Scripts; Arthur M Applebaum Theatre Arts Coll; Eugene List & Carol Glenn Coll of Musical Scores; Joseph Wambaugh Manuscript Coll; Otto Klemperer Coll of Musical Scores; Perry R Long Coll of Books on Printing; Public Officials Papers: Mervyn Dymally, Julian Nava, Edward Roybal; Roy Harris & Stan Kenton Music Archives
Partic in Los Angeles Libr Coop; Metronet; OCLC Online Computer Library Center, Inc
Friends of the Library Group

S CAPITAL GROUP COMPANIES, INC, Research Library, 333 S Hope St, 90071. SAN 300-9025. Tel: 213-486-9261. FAX: 213-486-9571. E-Mail: vht@capgroup.com. *VPres*, Vickie H Taylor; Staff 12 (MLS 5, Non-MLS 7)
Founded 1965
Library Holdings: Bk Vols 3,000; Per Subs 3,000
Subject Interests: Business and management, Economics, Stock market
Special Collections: Economic & Financial Information on 7000 American & Foreign Companies
Automation Activity & Vendor Info: (Acquisitions) Sydney; (Cataloging) Sydney; (OPAC) Sydney; (Serials) Sydney

M CEDARS-SINAI MEDICAL CENTER, Medical Library, 8700 Beverly Blvd, PO Box 48956, 90048-1865. SAN 300-9033. Tel: 310-423-3751. FAX: 310-423-0138. E-Mail: library@cshs.org. Web Site: www.csmc.edu/mlic. *Mgr*, Phyllis Soben
Library Holdings: Bk Vols 10,000
Publications: Current Book List

S CG JUNG INSTITUTE OF LOS ANGELES, Max & Lore Zeller Library, 10349 W Pico Blvd, 90064. SAN 300-9378. Tel: 310-556-1196. FAX: 310-556-2290. E-Mail: junginla@earthlink.net. Web Site: www.junginla.earthlink.net. *Librn*, John Sweeney
Founded 1948
1998-1999 Income $49,000, Locally Generated Income $15,000, Parent Institution $34,000. Mats Exp $4,900, Books $4,000, Per/Ser (Incl. Access Fees) $500. Sal $36,000
Library Holdings: Bk Vols 7,300; Per Subs 21
Subject Interests: Analytical chemistry
Special Collections: Analytical Psychology Club of Los Angeles, lectures 1944-76; ARAS (Archive for Research in Archetypal Symbolism) photogs, cat sheets, slides
Restriction: Members only, Non-circulating to the public
Friends of the Library Group

M CHILDREN'S HOSPITAL OF LOS ANGELES, Health Sciences Library, 4650 Sunset Blvd, 90027-0700. SAN 300-9068. Tel: 323-669-2254. FAX: 323-662-7019. Web Site: www.chla.us.edu.
Founded 1928
Library Holdings: Bk Vols 5,000; Per Subs 324
Subject Interests: Pediatrics

S CITICORP-TRANSACTION TECHNOLOGY, INC, Technical Library,* 12731 W Jefferson Blvd, 90066. SAN 301-0015. Tel: 310-302-4000. FAX: 310-302-4100. *Mgr*, Holly Geil
Founded 1973
Library Holdings: Bk Titles 4,000; Per Subs 300
Subject Interests: Banks and banking, Computer science, Electronic engineering
Partic in OCLC Online Computer Library Center, Inc

CM CLEVELAND CHIROPRACTIC COLLEGE LIBRARY,* 590 N Vermont Ave, 90004. SAN 325-0350. Tel: 323-660-6166, Ext 53. FAX: 323-660-7468. E-Mail: clechiro@class.org. Web Site: www.clevelandchiropractic.edu. *Dir*, Marian Hicks; Staff 5 (MLS 1, Non-MLS 4)
Founded 1978. Enrl 550
Library Holdings: Bk Vols 19,198
Special Collections: Chiropractic
Partic in Dialog Corporation

L COURT OF APPEALS, Second Appellate District Library,* 300 S Spring St, Rm 3547, 90013. SAN 300-9114. Tel: 213-897-5113. FAX: 213-897-5811. *Librn*, C David Carlburg; E-Mail: dcarlbrg@cogent.net; Staff 3 (MLS 2, Non-MLS 1)
Founded 1967
1997-1998 Mats Exp $388,300
Library Holdings: Bk Vols 65,000
Subject Interests: California
Partic in Dialog Corporation; Westlaw

L COX, CASTLE & NICHOLSON LLP LIBRARY,* 2049 Century Park E, 28th flr, 90067. SAN 300-9122. Tel: 310-277-4222, Ext 444. FAX: 310-277-7889. *Librn*, Janet Kasabian; E-Mail: jkasabian@ccnlaw.com
Library Holdings: Bk Vols 17,000; Per Subs 500

S DANIEL, MANN, JOHNSON & MENDENHALL, Information Services,* 3250 Wilshire Blvd, 90010. SAN 300-9157. Tel: 213-381-3663. FAX: 213-383-3656.
Founded 1956
Library Holdings: Bk Titles 8,500; Per Subs 275
Subject Interests: Architecture, Engineering, Environmental studies, Transportation, Urban planning, Water resources, Water treatment
Publications: What's New in the DMJM Library

S DELOITTE & TOUCHE INFORMATION SERVICES, 350 S Grand Ave, Ste 200, 90071-3462. SAN 373-3319. Tel: 213-688-4103, 213-688-5359. FAX: 213-694-5359. *Mgr*, Kathleen Tice; E-Mail: ktice@deloitte.com; *Res*, Linda Hamilton; E-Mail: linhamilton@deloitte.com; Staff 3 (MLS 2, Non-MLS 1)
Library Holdings: Per Subs 300
Subject Interests: Accounting, Consulting

M DOHENY EYE INSTITUTE, Norris Visual Science Library, 1450 San Pablo St, 90033. SAN 321-6128. Tel: 323-442-7149. FAX: 323-442-7117. *Actg Librn*, Susan Clarke; Tel: 323-442-7139, E-Mail: sclarke@hsc.usc.edu; Staff 2 (Non-MLS 2)
Founded 1976
Library Holdings: Bk Vols 1,000; Per Subs 75
Subject Interests: Ophthalmology
Database Vendor: Ebsco - EbscoHost, OVID Technologies
Partic in Association of Vision Science Librarians (AVSL); Med Libr Group of S Calif & Ariz; PSRMLS

L DOLE FOOD COMPANY LIBRARY,* 10900 Wilshire Blvd, Ste 1600, 90024. SAN 323-4215. Tel: 310-834-4501. FAX: 310-824-2159. *Librn*, Dan Picciotto
Library Holdings: Bk Vols 1,500; Per Subs 50
Subject Interests: Regulatory doc, Trademarks

S ECONOMICS RESEARCH ASSOCIATES LIBRARY, 10990 Wilshire Blvd, Ste 1500, 90024. SAN 300-9173. Tel: 310-477-9585. FAX: 310-478-1950. E-Mail: jar@la.econres.com. Web Site: www.econres.com.; Staff 2 (MLS 1, Non-MLS 1)
Founded 1968
Library Holdings: Bk Vols 14,000; Bk Titles 1,000; Per Subs 500
Subject Interests: Recreation

S EDUCATIONAL COMMUNICATIONS, INC, Environmental Resources Library, PO Box 351419, 90035-9119. SAN 326-1654. Tel: 310-559-9160. FAX: 310-559-9160. E-Mail: ecnp@aol.com. Web Site: www.ecoprojects.org. *Dir*, Nancy Pearlman
Founded 1958
Library Holdings: Per Subs 400
Subject Interests: Ecology
Special Collections: Environment & Ecology (ECONEWS Television Series & Environmental Directions Radio Series Coll), a-tapes, v-tapes
Publications: Directory of Environmental Organizations; Directory on ACSII & PC diskettes; The Compendium Newsletter
Restriction: By appointment only

S ERNST & YOUNG, Center for Business Knowledge,* 2049 Century Park E, Ste 1600, 90067. SAN 300-9408. Tel: 213-277-0880, Ext 4035. FAX: 310-284-8644. *In Charge*, Vladimir Reyes; Staff 5 (MLS 2, Non-MLS 3)
Founded 1973
Library Holdings: Bk Titles 4,000; Per Subs 388
Subject Interests: Accounting, Auditing, Business and management, Real estate
Publications: Acquisitions List
Partic in Dialog Corporation; OCLC Online Computer Library Center, Inc
Open Mon-Fri 8:30-5:30

S ERNST & YOUNG LLP, Center for Business Knowledge, 725 S Figueroa 8th Flr, 90071. SAN 300-9181. Tel: 213-977-3167, 213-977-3193, 213-977-3581, 213-977-3708, 213-977-3737, 213-977-4216. FAX: 213-977-5897. *Librn*, Linda Denney; Tel: 213-977-3353, E-Mail: lindadenney@ey.com; *Librn*, Verleen Jones; Tel: 213-971-3651, E-Mail: verleen.jones@ey.com; *Business*, Jeffrey M Lambert; E-Mail: jeffrey.lambert@ey.com; Staff 9 (Non-MLS 9)
Founded 1977
Library Holdings: Per Subs 150
Subject Interests: Accounting, Tax
Database Vendor: Dialog, Ebsco - EbscoHost, Lexis-Nexis
Restriction: Staff use only
Partic in Dow Jones News Retrieval; Profound; SDC
Ernst & Young is a merger of Arthur Young & Ernst & Whinney

S FARMERS INSURANCE GROUP LIBRARY,* 4680 Wilshire Blvd, PO Box 2478, Terminal Annex, 90051. SAN 300-919X. Tel: 323-932-3615. FAX: 323-932-3101. *Librn*, Maria Palma
Library Holdings: Bk Vols 5,800
Restriction: Staff use only

S FASHION INSTITUTE OF DESIGN & MERCHANDISING, Resource & Research Center, 919 S Grand Ave, 90015-1421. SAN 375-4774. Tel: 213-624-1200, Ext 3368. FAX: 213-624-9365. Web Site: www.fidm.com/. *Exec Dir*, Kaycee Hale; E-Mail: kchale@fidm.com; *Librn*, Trinity Donias; E-Mail: tdonias@fidm.com; *Per*, Justine Mandlebaum; Staff 16 (MLS 1, Non-MLS 15)
Founded 1969
Library Holdings: Bk Vols 10,716; Per Subs 205
Special Collections: Apparel Industry, bks, per, slides, CDs & videos

L FOLEY & LARDNER, 2029 Century Park E Ste 3500, 90067-3021. SAN 371-6007. Tel: 310-277-2223. FAX: 310-557-8475. *Head Librn*, Lisa H Marks; Tel: 310-975-7738, E-Mail: lmarks@foleylaw.com; *Ref*, Stefanie Frame; Tel: 310-975-7739, E-Mail: sframe@foleylaw.com; Staff 3 (MLS 2, Non-MLS 1)
Library Holdings: Bk Vols 8,000; Bk Titles 800; Per Subs 142
Subject Interests: Health law

L FRIED, FRANK, HARRIS, SHRIVER & JACOBSON, Law Library,* 350 S Grand Ave, 32nd flr, 90071. SAN 372-2791. Tel: 213-473-2083. FAX: 213-473-2222. *Librn*, Karen Campbell; E-Mail: campbka@ffhsj.com
Library Holdings: Bk Vols 50,000

L FULBRIGHT & JAWORSKI LLP, Law Library, 865 S Figueroa St, 29th flr, 90017. SAN 372-2805. Tel: 213-892-9262. FAX: 213-680-4518. Web Site: www.fulbright.com. *Librn*, Nina A Clark; E-Mail: naclark@fulbright.com
Library Holdings: Bk Vols 25,000

G GERMAN CULTURAL CENTER, Goethe-Institute Library, 5750 Wilshire Blvd, Ste 100, 90036. SAN 329-2851. Tel: 323-525-3388. FAX: 323-934-3597. Web Site: www.goethe.de/losangeles. *In Charge*, Stefan Kloo
Founded 1986
1998-1999 Mats Exp $3,000, Books $1,000, Per/Ser (Incl. Access Fees) $1,000, Other Print Mats $1,000
Library Holdings: Bk Vols 4,000; Bk Titles 3,900; Per Subs 34
Publications: AV Catalog; Union List of Periodicals-Goethe Institute Libraries in the US & Canada

S THE GETTY RESEARCH INSTITUTE LIBRARY, 1200 Getty Center Dr Ste 1100, 90049-1688. SAN 301-0325. Tel: 310-440-7390. Reference Tel: 310-440-7390. FAX: 310-440-7780. E-Mail: reference@getty.edu. Web Site: www.getty.edu/gri. *Chief Librn*, Susan M Allen; E-Mail: sallen@getty.edu; *Tech Servs*, Sally Crosby; E-Mail: scrosby@getty.edu; *Res*, Kathleen Salomon; E-Mail: ksalomon@getty.edu
Founded 1983
Library Holdings: Bk Vols 808,770; Bk Titles 533,154; Per Subs 4,244
Subject Interests: Archaeology, Architecture, Archives, Drawings, Manuscripts, Photographs, Prints, Rare books, Western European Arts from the 13th to 20th centuries
Automation Activity & Vendor Info: (Acquisitions) Innovative Interfaces Inc.; (Cataloging) Innovative Interfaces Inc.; (Circulation) Innovative Interfaces Inc.; (OPAC) Innovative Interfaces Inc.; (Serials) Innovative Interfaces Inc.
Publications: Bibliography of the History of Art (BHA) (Bibliographies); Provenance Index
Restriction: Authorized scholars by appointment
Partic in Research Libraries Group, Inc; Southern Calif Electronic Libr Consortium
Open Mon-Sat 9-6

L GIBSON, DUNN & CRUTCHER, Law Library, 333 S Grand Ave, 90071-3197. SAN 300-9238. Tel: 213-229-7000. FAX: 213-229-7520. *Dir*, Pamela Soreide; *Librn*, Dena Hollingsworth; Staff 12 (MLS 6, Non-MLS 6)
Library Holdings: Bk Vols 50,000
Partic in Dialog Corporation; OCLC Online Computer Library Center, Inc; Westlaw

M GOOD SAMARITAN HOSPITAL, Medical Library,* 616 S Witmer St, 90017. SAN 300-9300. Tel: 213-977-2326. FAX: 213-977-4185. *Librn*, Linda Rubin; Staff 2 (MLS 1, Non-MLS 1)
Founded 1941. Pop 1,800
Library Holdings: Bk Vols 2,500; Per Subs 150
Restriction: Non-circulating to the public
Partic in Nat Libr of Med
Open Mon-Fri 8am-4pm

S GRANTSMANSHIP CENTER LIBRARY,* PO Box 17220, 90017. SAN 328-459X. Tel: 213-482-9860. FAX: 213-482-9863. *Pres*, Norton Kirritz; E-Mail: norton@tgci.com
Library Holdings: Bk Vols 4,000
Restriction: Not open to public

L GREENBERG, GLUSKER, FIELDS, CLAMAN & MACHTINGER LLP LIBRARY, 1900 Avenue of the Stars Ste 2100, 90067. SAN 300-9246. Tel: 310-553-3610. FAX: 310-553-0687. *Head Librn*, Marjorie Jay; E-Mail: mjay@ggfcm.com; Staff 2 (MLS 2)
Library Holdings: Bk Vols 27,220; Bk Titles 3,320; Per Subs 700
Subject Interests: Law

S GRIFFITH OBSERVATORY LIBRARY,* 2800 E Observatory Rd, 90027. SAN 300-9254. Tel: 323-664-1181. FAX: 323-663-4323. Web Site: www.griffithobs.org. *Dir*, E C Krupp
Founded 1935
Library Holdings: Bk Vols 6,600; Per Subs 20
Subject Interests: Astronomy
Publications: Griffith Observer
Restriction: Non-circulating to the public

S HEBREW UNION COLLEGE, JEWISH INSTITUTE OF RELIGION, Frances-Henry Library, 3077 University Ave, 90007. SAN 300-9262. Tel: 213-749-3424. Circulation Tel: 213-749-4227. Reference Tel: 213-749-4225. Toll Free Tel: 800-899-0925. FAX: 213-749-1937. Web Site: www.huc.edu/libraries. *Head Librn*, Dr Yaffa Weisman; Tel: 213-749-3424, Ext 4270, E-Mail: yweisman@huc.edu; *Librn*, Harvey P Horowitz; Tel: 213-749-3424, Ext 4226, E-Mail: hhorowitz@huc.edu. Subject Specialists: *Hebrew*, Dr Yaffa Weisman; *Judaica*, Dr Yaffa Weisman; Staff 5 (MLS 2, Non-MLS 3)
Founded 1958. Enrl 150; Highest Degree: Doctorate
Library Holdings: Bk Vols 100,000; Per Subs 500; Bks on Deafness & Sign Lang 20
Subject Interests: Ethics, Jewish history and literature, Judaica (lit or hist of Jews), Religion
Special Collections: American Jewish Archives, West Coast Microfilm branch; American Jewish Periodical Center, West Coast Microfilm branch
Partic in RLG; RLIN
Special Services for the Blind - Audio-cassettes; Audiobooks; Braille
Library serves as resource for Judaic Studies GE classes offered by the University of Southern CA. Open to patrons who are not students
Friends of the Library Group

L HILL, FARRER & BURRILL, Law Library,* 300 S Grand Ave, 37th flr, 90071-3147. SAN 300-9270. Tel: 213-620-0460, Ext 1848. FAX: 213-624-4840. *Librn*, Nina A Hall
Library Holdings: Bk Vols 14,400; Per Subs 67
Subject Interests: Environmental law, Labor, Real estate, Securities
Restriction: Staff use only

L HILLSINGER & CONSTANZO, Law Library,* 3055 Wilshire Blvd, 12th flr, 90010. SAN 372-3690. Tel: 213-388-9441. FAX: 213-388-1592. *Librn*, Mercedes Perez
Library Holdings: Bk Vols 10,000

M HOUSE EAR INSTITUTE, Athalie Irvine Clarke Library, 2100 W Third St, 90057-1922. SAN 325-7215. Tel: 213-483-4431, Ext 7004. FAX: 213-413-6754. *Dir Libr Serv*, Liz Gnerre; E-Mail: gnerre@hei.org
Library Holdings: Bk Vols 2,800; Per Subs 136
Subject Interests: Audiology, Biomedical engineering, Otolaryngology
Special Collections: Rare books
Partic in Med Libr Group of S Calif & Ariz

L HOWREY & SIMON,* 550 S Hope, Ste 1400, 90071. SAN 323-7494. Tel: 213-892-1800. FAX: 213-892-2300. *Librn*, Leslie Snyder; E-Mail: snyderl@howrey.com
Library Holdings: Bk Vols 1,000; Per Subs 42
Subject Interests: Corporate law
Publications: Scall Union List (Southern California Association of Law Libraries)

S HUGHES ELECTRONICS CO, El Segundo North Library,* Bldg S24, M/S D538, 2020 E Imperial Hwy. (Mail add: PO Box 92919, 90009), SAN 332-3285. Tel: 310-364-6002. E-Mail: hec.libary@hsc.com. *Mgr*, Patricia Adorno; *Librn*, B Hinz; *Librn*, Margaret Deeds; *Librn*, L Morris; Staff 5 (MLS 5)
Founded 1963
Library Holdings: Bk Vols 30,000; Per Subs 300
Subject Interests: Computer science, Electronics, Mathematics, Physics, Radar
Publications: Monthly Telecommications & Space Bibliography
Restriction: Staff use only
Partic in Defense Technical Information Center; Dialog Corporation; OCLC Online Computer Library Center, Inc

L IRELL & MANELLA LLP LIBRARY, 1800 Avenue of the Stars, Ste 500, 90067. SAN 300-9351. Tel: 310-203-7010. FAX: 310-203-7199. E-Mail: llieb@irell.com. Web Site: www.irell.com. *Dir*, Louise Lieb
Founded 1968
Library Holdings: Bk Vols 70,000
Subject Interests: Law
Publications: Library Bulletin

R JEWISH COMMUNITY LIBRARY, (Formerly JewishCommunity Library), Peter M Khan Memorial, 6505 Wilshire Blvd, 90048. SAN 300-936X. Tel: 323-761-8648. FAX: 323-761-8647. Web Site: www.jclla.org. *Dir*, Abigail Yasgur; Tel: 323-761-8644; Staff 3 (MLS 1, Non-MLS 2)
Founded 1947
Library Holdings: Bk Titles 30,000; Per Subs 75
Subject Interests: Israel, Judaism (religion)
Special Collections: History of the Local Jewish Community Documents (Archives of the Jewish Community of Los Angeles and; Vicinity), books, newspapers, documents, photographs, microfilm
Publications: Anthologies; bibliographies
Friends of the Library Group

L JONES, DAY, REAVIS & POGUE, Law Library,* 555 W Fifth St Ste 4600, 90013-1025. SAN 329-9953. Tel: 213-489-3939. FAX: 213-243-2539. *Mgr*, Elizabeth Elliot; *Ref*, James Center
Library Holdings: Bk Vols 18,000

M KAISER PERMANENTE MEDICAL CENTER, Irving P Ackerman Health Sciences Library, 4747 Sunset Blvd, 4th flr, 90027. SAN 300-9394. Tel: 213-783-8568. FAX: 213-783-4192. *Librn*, Anne Fraser; *Asst Librn*, Kati Kreie; Staff 5 (MLS 2, Non-MLS 3)
Founded 1953
Library Holdings: Bk Titles 7,000; Per Subs 450
Subject Interests: Clinical medicine, Nursing, Psychiatry, Psychology
Publications: Acquisitions Lists (quarterly)
Restriction: Staff use only
Partic in Medline

M KAISER-PERMANENTE MENTAL HEALTH CENTER, Professional Library,* 765 W College St, 90012. SAN 323-4304. Tel: 213-580-7260. FAX: 213-580-7288. *Librn*, Nicky Garganta
Library Holdings: Bk Vols 5,750; Per Subs 142
Special Collections: Psychology of Women

L KAYE, SCHOLER, FIERMAN, HAYS & HANDLER, Law Library,* 1999 Avenue of the Stars, Ste 1600, 90067. SAN 372-2694. Tel: 310-788-1000. FAX: 310-788-1200. *Librn*, Elinor Martin; E-Mail: emartin@kayescholer.com
Library Holdings: Bk Vols 12,000

S KOREAN CULTURAL CENTER LIBRARY, (KCCLA), 5505 Wilshire Blvd, 90036. SAN 327-5795. Tel: 323-936-7141. FAX: 323-936-5712. E-Mail: librarian@kccla.org. Web Site: kccla.org. *Librn*, Sejung Kim
Library Holdings: Bk Vols 12,000; Per Subs 52
Publications: Korean Culture (quarterly)

S KPMG LLP, (Formerly KPMG Peat Marwick), Tax Library, 355 S Grand Ave, Ste.2000, 90017-1568. SAN 300-9823. Tel: 213-955-8638. FAX: 213-630-2279. *Librn*, Brian H Aby; E-Mail: baby@kpmg.com. Subject Specialists: *Tax*, Brian H Aby; Staff 1 (Non-MLS 1)
Library Holdings: Bk Vols 4,100; Bk Titles 3,000; Per Subs 250
Subject Interests: Auditing, Federal, Gen bus, International, State, Tax
Special Collections: Company Annual Reports Coll; Historic tax reference books; IRCB volumes; tax journals
Automation Activity & Vendor Info: (Serials) Sydney
Database Vendor: Lexis-Nexis
Publications: Industry Profile Series; New Acquisitions; Serials List
Function: Research library

L LEGAL AID FOUNDATION OF LOS ANGELES LAW LIBRARY, 1102 S Crenshaw Blvd, 90019. SAN 372-2937. Tel: 323-801-7940. FAX: 323-801-7921. *Librn*, Pamela L Hall; Fax: 323-801-7921, E-Mail: phall@lafla.org; Staff 1 (MLS 1)
Library Holdings: Bk Vols 22,000
Subject Interests: Benefits, Consumer, Employment, Government, Housing, Immigration
Special Collections: Govt agency regulation manuals; Govt agency regulation manuals
Database Vendor: Lexis-Nexis
Restriction: Not open to public
Function: Research library

L LEWIS, D'AMATO, BRISBOIS & BISGAARD LLP, Law Library, 221 N Figueroa St Ste 1200, 90012. SAN 372-2708. Tel: 213-580-7908. FAX: 213-250-7900. E-Mail: library@ldbb.com. *Dir*, Mary T Kamraczewski; Staff 2 (MLS 1, Non-MLS 1)
Founded 1978
Library Holdings: Bk Titles 2,000
Subject Interests: Environmental law

S LOS ANGELES AREA CHAMBER OF COMMERCE, Business Information & International Commerce Library,* 350 S Bixel St, PO Box 513696, 90051-1696. SAN 300-9483. Tel: 213-580-7500, Ext 552. FAX: 213-580-7511.
Library Holdings: Bk Vols 500; Bk Titles 400; Per Subs 30
Subject Interests: Local history
Special Collections: International Trade & Commerce

S LOS ANGELES CENTER FOR PHOTOGRAPHIC STUDIES LIBRARY,* 400 S Main St, 90013-1314. SAN 370-1719. Tel: 323-466-6232. FAX: 323-466-3203. *Exec Dir*, Tanya Martinez-Lemke
Subject Interests: Photo-related arts, Photog

J LOS ANGELES CITY COLLEGE LIBRARY,* 855 N Vermont Ave, 90029. SAN 300-9491. Tel: 323-953-4406. FAX: 323-953-4407. Web Site: citywww.lacc.cc.ca.us. *Cat, Chief Librn, Circ*, Dorothy Fuhrmann; E-Mail: fuhrmadm@email.lacc.cc.ca.us; *Acq*, Ana Lya Sater; E-Mail: sateral@email.lacc.cc.ca.us; *Ref*, Barbara Vasquez; E-Mail: vasqueb@email.lacc.cc.ca.us; Staff 3 (MLS 3)
Founded 1929. Enrl 15,000; Fac 250
Jul 1998-Jun 1999 Mats Exp $415,982, Books $30,991, Per/Ser (Incl. Access Fees) $16,283, Micro $3,472. Sal $406,232 (Prof $243,407)
Library Holdings: Bk Vols 150,000; Per Subs 130
Database Vendor: DRA, IAC - SearchBank
Partic in Southern Calif Interlibr Loan Network

M LOS ANGELES COUNTY, Martin Luther King Jr, Drew Medical Center Health Sciences Library,* 1731 E 120th St, 90059. SAN 300-9424. Tel: 323-563-4869. FAX: 323-563-4861. Web Site: www.cdrewu.edu/kdhs/lib_home.htm. *Dir*, John Carney; E-Mail: jocarney@cdrewu.edu; *Coll Develop*, Terri Ottosen; *Ser*, Charles P Hobbs; Staff 10 (MLS 3, Non-MLS 7)
Founded 1972
Library Holdings: Bk Vols 48,000; Bk Titles 14,000; Per Subs 760
Special Collections: Clinical Medicine
Restriction: Medical staff only
Partic in Medline

L LOS ANGELES COUNTY COUNSEL LAW LIBRARY,* 500 W Temple St Rm 610, 90012. SAN 372-3704. Tel: 213-974-1982. FAX: 213-626-7446. *Librn*, Eugene S Drayton; E-Mail: edrayton@mail.com.la.ca.us
Library Holdings: Bk Vols 18,000

M LOS ANGELES COUNTY HEALTH ADMINISTRATION-MANAGEMENT LIBRARY,* 313 N Figueroa St, Rm MZ2, 90012. SAN 300-9513. Tel: 213-240-7780. FAX: 213-250-3909. *Librn*, Sharon Pruhs; *Asst Librn*, Ann Phelps
Founded 1928
Library Holdings: Bk Titles 150; Per Subs 600
Subject Interests: Public health
Partic in Dialog Corporation; Medline

L LOS ANGELES COUNTY LAW LIBRARY, 301 W First St, 90012-3100. SAN 332-334X. Tel: 213-629-3531. FAX: 213-613-1329. E-Mail: lacll@lalaw.lib.ca.us. Web Site: www.lalaw.lib.ca.us/. *Dir*, Richard T Iamele; Tel: 213-629-3531, Ext 319, Fax: 213-680-1727, E-Mail: richard@lalaw.lib.ca.us; *Tech Servs*, Melody Lembke; Tel: 213-629-3531, Ext. 331, Fax: 213-680-1758, E-Mail: melody@lalaw.lib.ca.us; *Publ Servs*, Diane C Reynolds; Tel: 213-629-3531, Ext 0, E-Mail: diane@lalaw.lib.ca.us; *Automation Syst Coordr*, Meiling Li; Tel: 213-629-3531, Ext 334, Fax: 213-680-1758, E-Mail: meiling@lalaw.lib.ca.us; Staff 91 (MLS 14, Non-MLS 77)
Founded 1891
Jul 1999-Jun 2000 Income (Main Library and Branch Library) $5,966,952, Locally Generated Income $169,469, Other $5,797,483. Mats Exp $2,198,330, Books $81,321, Per/Ser (Incl. Access Fees) $2,051,834, Presv $65,175. Sal $2,284,887
Library Holdings: Bk Vols 788,613; Bk Titles 186,011; Per Subs 11,968
Subject Interests: Comparative law, Fed law, Foreign law, International law, State law
Automation Activity & Vendor Info: (Cataloging) Endeavor; (Circulation) Endeavor; (OPAC) Endeavor; (Serials) Endeavor
Database Vendor: Dialog
Partic in Research Libraries Group, Inc; RLIN
Serving officials, attorneys & pub in Los Angeles
Branches:
BEVERLY HILLS BRANCH, Court Bldg, Rm 405, 9355 Burton Way, Beverly Hills, 90210. SAN 332-3374. Tel: 310-288-1269.
Subject Interests: Fed law, State law
COMPTON BRANCH, County Courts Bldg, Rm 201, Compton, 90220. SAN 332-3404. Tel: 310-603-7239.
Subject Interests: Fed law, State law
LONG BEACH BRANCH, County Bldg, Rm 505, 415 W Ocean Blvd, Long Beach, 90802. SAN 332-3439. Tel: 562-491-5970.
Subject Interests: Fed law, State law
NORWALK BRANCH, SE Superior Courts Bldg, Rm 714, 12720 Norwalk Blvd,, Norwalk, 90650. SAN 332-3463. Tel: 562-807-7310.
Subject Interests: Fed law, State law
PASADENA BRANCH, County Courthouse, 300 E Walnut Ave, Rm 300, Pasadena, 91101. SAN 332-3498. Tel: 818-356-5253.
Subject Interests: Fed law, State law
POMONA BRANCH, East District Superior Courts Bldg, 400 Civic Center Plaza, Rm 102, Pomona, 91766. SAN 332-3528. Tel: 909-620-3091.
Subject Interests: Fed law, State law
SANTA MONICA BRANCH, County Bldg, 1725 Main St, Rm 219, Santa Monica, 90401. SAN 332-3552. Tel: 310-260-3644.
Subject Interests: Fed law, State law
TORRANCE BRANCH, County Bldg, 825 Maple Ave, Rm 110, Torrance, 90503. SAN 332-3587. Tel: 310-222-8816.
Subject Interests: Fed law, State law
VAN NUYS BRANCH, Van Nuys Courts Bldg, 6230 Sylmar Ave, Rm 350, Van Nuys, 91401. SAN 332-3617. Tel: 818-374-2499.
Subject Interests: Fed law, State law

G LOS ANGELES COUNTY METROPOLITAN TRANSPORTATION AUTHORITY, Information Center Library, One Gateway Plaza, 15th flr, 90012. SAN 325-4933. Tel: 213-922-4859. FAX: 213-922-7955. *Dir*, Dorothy Peyton Gray; E-Mail: grayd@mta.net; *Cat*, Glenda Mariner; Staff 4 (MLS 2, Non-MLS 2)
Founded 1976
Library Holdings: Bk Vols 200,000; Bk Titles 40,000; Per Subs 165
Subject Interests: Transportation
Special Collections: Deeds; Local Transit; Photographs early 1900 to present
Publications: Acquisitions List
Special Services for the Deaf - TDD
Open Mon-Fri 8-4

L LOS ANGELES COUNTY MUNICIPAL COURTS, Planning & Research Unit Library,* 110 N Grand Rm 620, 90012. SAN 372-2759. Tel: 213-974-6181. Web Site: www.web.pru.co.la.ca.us. *In Charge*, Leslie Admire
Library Holdings: Bk Vols 1,500

S LOS ANGELES COUNTY MUSEUM OF ART, Mr & Mrs Allan C Balch Art Research Library, 5905 Wilshire Blvd, 90036-4597. SAN 332-3641. Tel: 323-857-6118. FAX: 323-857-4790. E-Mail: library@lacma.org. Web Site: www.lacma.org. *Head Librn*, Deborah Barlow Smedstad; Tel: 323-857-6122, E-Mail: smedstad@lacma.org; Staff 9 (MLS 5, Non-MLS 4)
Founded 1965
Jul 1999-Jun 2000 Income (Main Library Only) $544,718, County $61,200, Parent Institution $483,518. Mats Exp $235,483, Books $81,400, Per/Ser (Incl. Access Fees) $30,000, Electronic Ref Mat (Incl. Access Fees) $3,000. Sal $309,235
Library Holdings: Bk Vols 130,000; Bk Titles 115,000; Per Subs 452
Subject Interests: Art history
Special Collections: Art (Knoedler Library), micro
Automation Activity & Vendor Info: (Acquisitions) SIRSI; (Cataloging) SIRSI; (Circulation) SIRSI; (Course Reserve) SIRSI; (OPAC) SIRSI; (Serials) SIRSI
Restriction: Non-circulating to the public
Partic in OCLC Online Computer Library Center, Inc
Branches:
VISUAL RESOURCE CENTER, 5905 Wilshire Blvd, 90036-4597. SAN 332-3706. Tel: 323-857-6116. FAX: 323-857-6216. *Librn*, Naomi Weiss
Founded 1966
1997-1998 Income $4,000. Mats Exp $10,000
Subject Interests: Art and architecture, East Asia, European art
Special Collections: Ancient Near East (G Heeramaneck Coll); European Art & Architecture (William Keighley Coll)

S LOS ANGELES COUNTY MUSEUM OF ART, Robert Gore Rifkind Center for German Expressionist Studies, Los Angeles County Museum of Art, 5905 Wilshire Blvd, 90036. SAN 320-3646. Tel: 323-857-6165. FAX: 323-857-4752. Web Site: www.lacma.org/lacma.asp. *Librn*, Susan Trauger; E-Mail: trauger@lacma.org
Founded 1979
Library Holdings: Bk Vols 7,700; Bk Titles 6,000
Special Collections: German Expressionist Graphics Coll
Automation Activity & Vendor Info: (Acquisitions) SIRSI; (Cataloging) SIRSI
Publications: Bibliography of German Expressionism: Catalog of the Robert Gore Rifkind Center for German Expressionist Studies at the Los Angeles County Museum of Art (G K Hall, 1990)

L LOS ANGELES COUNTY SUPERIOR COURT, Law Library, 111 N Hill St, Rm 344, 90012. SAN 372-2953. Tel: 213-974-4867. FAX: 213-217-4823.
Library Holdings: Bk Vols 200,000

M LOS ANGELES COUNTY-UNIVERSITY OF SOUTHERN CALIFORNIA, General Hospital Medical Library, LAC & USC Healthcare Network, 1200 N State St, Rm 2050, 90033. SAN 332-7000. Tel: 323-226-3234. *Chief Librn*, Bella Kwong; Staff 4 (MLS 1, Non-MLS 3)
Founded 1914
Library Holdings: Bk Vols 10,000; Per Subs 1,000
Subject Interests: Clinical medicine, Nursing
Partic in BRS; Dialog Corporation; Docline; Medline
Branches:
WOMEN & CHILDREN'S HOSPITAL MEDICAL LIBRARY, 1240 N Mission Rd, Rm 3L3, 90033. SAN 332-7094. Tel: 213-226-3234. FAX: 213-226-3360.; Staff 2 (MLS 1, Non-MLS 1)
Library Holdings: Bk Vols 3,461
Subject Interests: Obstetrics and gynecology

S LOS ANGELES MASTER CHORALE ASSOCIATION, Music Library,* 135 N Grand Ave, 90012. SAN 370-4866. Tel: 213-626-0631. FAX: 213-626-0196. *Exec Dir*, Joan Cumming

S LOS ANGELES PHILHARMONIC ASSOCIATION, Orchestral Library,* 135 N Grand Ave, 90012. SAN 370-4858. Tel: 213-972-7313. *Librn*, Kazue McGregor

S LOS ANGELES PSYCHOANALYTIC SOCIETY & INSTITUTE, Simmel-Fenichel Library, 2014 Sawtelle Blvd, 90025. SAN 300-9572. Tel: 310-478-6541. FAX: 310-477-5968. E-Mail: lapsi@aol.com. Web Site: www.lapsi.org. *Dir*, Erchelle Rigsby
Founded 1948
Library Holdings: Bk Titles 5,100; Per Subs 25
Subject Interests: Psychoanalysis
Special Collections: Chicago Psycho-analytic Index; Freudiana, bks, articles, letters, photog
Restriction: Private library

P LOS ANGELES PUBLIC LIBRARY SYSTEM, 630 W Fifth St, 90071-2097. SAN 332-7124. Tel: 213-228-7515. FAX: 213-228-7429. Web Site: www.lapl.org. *Dir*, Joan Bartle; *Asst Dir*, Elizabeth Higbie; *Br Coordr*, Patricia Kiefer; *Publ Servs*, Peter Persic; *Mgr*, Betsey Hoage; Tel: 213-228-7578, Fax: 213-228-7519, E-Mail: ehoage@lapl.org; *Mgr*, Kris Morita; *Acq*, Marilyn Webster; *Cat*, Violet Kuroki; *Ad Servs*, Joyce Albers; Staff 393 (MLS 393)
Founded 1872. Pop 3,681,708; Circ 10,964,844
Jul 1999-Jun 2000 Income (Main Library and Branch Library) $84,686,085, State $6,559,736, City $74,393,406, Federal $1,102,098, Other $2,630,845. Mats Exp $7,824,617. Sal $36,620,948
Library Holdings: Bk Titles 6,066,546; Per Subs 15,000
Special Collections: Automotive Repair Manuals; California History; California in Fiction; Catholicism of Early Spanish Southwest; Children's Literature; City & County; Cookery; Corporation Records; Dobinson Coll of Drama & Theatre, bks, programs; Fiction by & about Blacks; Film Study; Genealogy; Government Specifications & Standards; Japanese Prints; Language Study; Large Type Books; Menus Coll; microfiche; Orchestral Scores & Parts; Rare Books; United States Patents

Mem of Metropolitan Cooperative Library System
Partic in OCLC Online Computer Library Center, Inc
Special Services for the Deaf - Captioned media; Staff with knowledge of sign language; TDD
Special Services - Service to shut-ins; Multilingual services in Asian & Spanish languages; Library Adult Reading Project, 6 reading centers for adult literacy; Homework centers at branches
Friends of the Library Group
Branches: 74
ANGELES MESA, 2700 W 52nd St, 90043-1999. SAN 332-7272. Tel: 213-292-4328. FAX: 213-296-3508. Web Site: www.lapl.org. *Librn*, Cathy Chang
Library Holdings: Bk Vols 31,765
Friends of the Library Group
ARROYO SECO REGIONAL, 6145 N Figueroa St, 90042-3593. SAN 332-7302. Tel: 213-237-1181. FAX: 213-612-0543. Web Site: www.lapl.org. *Librn*, Eugene Estrada
Library Holdings: Bk Vols 84,261
Friends of the Library Group
ASCOT, 256 W 70th St, 90003-1831. SAN 332-7337. Tel: 323-759-4817. FAX: 323-612-0438. Web Site: www.lapl.org. *Librn*, Camille Carter
Library Holdings: Bk Vols 43,263
ATWATER, 3379 Glendale Blvd, 90039-1812. SAN 332-7361. Tel: 323-664-1353. FAX: 323-913-4765. Web Site: www.lapl.org. *Librn*, Andree Matton
Library Holdings: Bk Vols 34,801
Friends of the Library Group
BALDWIN HILLS, 2906 S La Brea Ave, 90016-3902. SAN 332-7396. Tel: 323-733-1196. FAX: 323-612-0429. Web Site: www.lapl.org. *Librn*, Laura Dwan
Library Holdings: Bk Vols 37,814
Friends of the Library Group
BENJAMIN FRANKLIN BRANCH, 2200 E First St, 91011. SAN 332-7426. Tel: 323-263-6901. FAX: 323-526-3043. Web Site: www.lapl.org. *Librn*, Kent Brinkmeyer; E-Mail: kbrink@lapl.org; Staff 9 (MLS 4, Non-MLS 5)
Founded 1916
Library Holdings: Bk Vols 57,066
Friends of the Library Group
CAHUENGA, 4591 Santa Monica Blvd, 90029-1827. SAN 332-7485. Tel: 323-664-6418. FAX: 323-612-0446. Web Site: www.lapl.org. *Librn*, Joel Rane
Library Holdings: Bk Vols 49,706
Friends of the Library Group
CANOGA PARK, 7260 Owensmouth Ave, Canoga Park, 91303-1529. SAN 332-7515. Tel: 818-887-0320. FAX: 818-756-9284. E-Mail: cngopk@lapl.org. Web Site: www.lapl.org. *Librn*, Renee Ardon
Library Holdings: Bk Vols 58,781
Friends of the Library Group
CENTRAL SOUTHERN AREA, 931 S Gaffey St, San Pedro, 90731. SAN 332-7140. Tel: 310-548-7785. FAX: 310-548-7453. Web Site: www.lapl.org. *Mgr*, Janine Goodale
CHATSWORTH, 21052 Devonshire St, Chatsworth, 91311-2314. SAN 332-754X. Tel: 818-341-4276. FAX: 818-756-9177. Web Site: www.lapl.org. *Librn*, Bruce Seidman
Library Holdings: Bk Vols 56,599
Friends of the Library Group
CHINATOWN, 536 W College St, 90012-2386. SAN 332-7574. Tel: 213-620-0925. FAX: 213-612-0401. Web Site: www.lapl.org. *Librn*, Carol Duan
Library Holdings: Bk Vols 88,438
Friends of the Library Group
CYPRESS PARK, 3320 Pepper Ave, 90065-1605. SAN 332-7604. Tel: 213-612-0460. FAX: 213-612-0420. Web Site: www.lapl.org. *Librn*, Jennie Rodriguez-Combs
Library Holdings: Bk Vols 31,148
Friends of the Library Group
DONALD BRUCE KAUFMAN -BRENTWOOD BRANCH, 11820 San Vincente Blvd, 90049-5055. SAN 332-7450. Tel: 310-575-8273. FAX: 310-578-8276. Web Site: www.lapl.org. *Librn*, Youngsil Lee
Library Holdings: Bk Vols 55,150
Friends of the Library Group
EAGLE ROCK, 5027 Caspar Ave, 90041-1901. SAN 332-7639. Tel: 323-258-8078. FAX: 323-485-8154. Web Site: www.lapl.org. *Librn*, Tom Johnson
Library Holdings: Bk Vols 64,788
Friends of the Library Group
EAST VALLEY AREA, 5211 Tujunga Ave, 91601. SAN 332-7159. Tel: 818-755-7648. FAX: 818-755-7649. Web Site: www.lapl.org. *Mgr*, Arthur Pond
ECHO PARK, 1410 W Temple St, 90026-5017. SAN 332-7663. Tel: 213-250-7808. FAX: 213-580-3744. Web Site: www.lapl.org. *Librn*, Connie Dosch
Library Holdings: Bk Vols 50,092
Friends of the Library Group
EL SERENO, 4990 Huntington Dr S, 90032-2656. SAN 332-7698. Tel: 323-225-9201. FAX: 323-612-0422. Web Site: www.lapl.org. *Librn*, Ann Maupin
Library Holdings: Bk Vols 40,222
Friends of the Library Group
ENCINO-TARZANA BRANCH, 18231 Ventura Blvd, Tarzana, 91356-3620. SAN 332-7728. Tel: 818-343-1983. FAX: 818-756-9285. Web Site: www.lapl.org. *Librn*, Chris Parsons
Library Holdings: Bk Vols 53,384
Friends of the Library Group
EXPOSITION PARK - DR MARY MCLEOD BETHUNE REGIONAL BRANCH, 3665 S Vermont Ave, 90007-3946. SAN 332-7752. Tel: 323-732-0169. FAX: 323-612-0540. Web Site: www.lapl.org. *Librn*, Cecily Thomas
Library Holdings: Bk Vols 67,298
Friends of the Library Group
FAIRFAX, 161 S Gardner St, 90036-2717. SAN 332-7787. Tel: 323-936-6191. FAX: 323-933-0719. Web Site: www.lapl.org. *Librn*, Roy Stone
Library Holdings: Bk Vols 60,784
Friends of the Library Group
FELIPE DENEVE BRANCH, 2820 W Sixth St, 90057-3204. SAN 332-7817. Tel: 213-384-7676. FAX: 213-368-7667. Web Site: www.lapl.org. *Librn*, Christine Metro
Library Holdings: Bk Vols 63,558
Friends of the Library Group
FRANCES HOWARD GOLDWYN-HOLLYWOOD REGIONAL BRANCH, 1623 N Ivar Ave, 90028-6305. SAN 332-7906. Tel: 323-467-1821. FAX: 323-467-5707. Web Site: www.lapl.org. *Librn*, Dan Strehl; E-Mail: dstrehl@lapl.org
Library Holdings: Bk Vols 98,959
Subject Interests: Motion pictures
Friends of the Library Group
GRANADA HILLS BRANCH, 10640 Petit Ave, Granada Hills, 91344-6305. SAN 332-7876. Tel: 818-368-5687. FAX: 818-756-9286. Web Site: www.lapl.org. *Librn*, Christina Hanson
Library Holdings: Bk Vols 62,671
Friends of the Library Group
HARBOR GATEWAY - HARBOR CITY, 1555 W Sepulveda Blvd, 90501. SAN 377-6492. Tel: 310-548-7791. Web Site: www.lapl.org. *Librn*, Norma Anders
Library Holdings: Bk Vols 33,198
HOLLYWOOD AREA, 1623 N Ivar Ave, 90028. SAN 332-7167. Tel: 323-467-3628. FAX: 323-467-5707. Web Site: www.lapl.org.
HYDE PARK, 6527 Crenshaw Blvd, 90043-4197. SAN 332-7930. Tel: 323-750-7241. FAX: 213-612-0436. Web Site: www.lapl.org. *Librn*, Hosneya Khattab
Library Holdings: Bk Vols 28,607
Friends of the Library Group
WASHINGTON IRVING BRANCH, 4117 W Washington Pl, 90018-1053. SAN 332-7965. Tel: 323-734-6303. FAX: 213-612-0435. Web Site: www.lapl.org. *Librn*, Hosneya Khattab
Library Holdings: Bk Vols 53,533
Friends of the Library Group
JOHN C FREMONT BRANCH, 6121 Melrose Ave, 90038-3339. SAN 332-7841. Tel: 323-962-3521. FAX: 323-962-4553. E-Mail: jcfrmt@lapl.org. Web Site: www.lapl.org. *Senior Librn*, Denice Nossett; Staff 10 (MLS 4, Non-MLS 6)
Library Holdings: Bk Vols 41,021
Friends of the Library Group
JOHN MUIR BRANCH, 1005 W 64th St, 90044-3715. SAN 332-8236. Tel: 323-789-4800. FAX: 323-789-5758. Web Site: www.lapl.org. *Librn*, Margaret Murphy
Library Holdings: Bk Vols 42,633
Friends of the Library Group
JUNIPERO SERRA, 4607 S Main St, 90037-2641. SAN 332-8023. Tel: 323-234-1685. FAX: 213-612-0432. Web Site: www.lapl.org. *Librn*, JoAnn Morgan
Library Holdings: Bk Vols 45,362
Friends of the Library Group
LA BIBLIOTECA DEL PUEBLO DE LINCOLN HEIGHTS, 2530 Workman St, 90031-2202. SAN 332-8058. Tel: 323-226-1692. FAX: 323-226-1691. Web Site: www.lapl.org. *Librn*, Ivan Lorpeno-Chacvz
Library Holdings: Bk Vols 40,282
Friends of the Library Group
LEON H WASHINGTON JR MEMORIAL-VERNON BRANCH, 4504 S Central Ave, 90011-9623. SAN 332-8953. Tel: 213-234-9106. FAX: 213-485-8155. Web Site: www.lapl.org. *Librn*, Brenda Hicks
Library Holdings: Bk Vols 44,025
Friends of the Library Group
LITTLE TOKYO, 244 S Alameda St, 90013. SAN 329-658X. Tel: 213-612-0525. FAX: 213-612-0424. Web Site: www.lapl.org. *Librn*, Susan Thompson
Library Holdings: Bk Vols 45,152
Friends of the Library Group
LOS FELIZ, 1801 Hillhurst Ave, 90027-2794. SAN 332-8082. Tel: 323-913-4710. FAX: 323-913-4714. Web Site: www.lapl.org. *Librn*, Pearl Yonezawa
Library Holdings: Bk Vols 52,679

Friends of the Library Group
LOYOLA VILLAGE, 7114 W Manchester Ave, 90045-3581. SAN 332-8112. Tel: 310-670-5436. FAX: 310-612-0426. Web Site: www.lapl.org. *Librn*, Laura Dwan
Library Holdings: Bk Vols 39,003
Friends of the Library Group
MALABAR, 2801 Wabash Ave, 90033-2604. SAN 332-8147. Tel: 323-263-1497, 323-268-0874. FAX: 213-612-0416. Web Site: www.lapl.org. *Librn*, Judy Donovan
Library Holdings: Bk Vols 39,685
Friends of the Library Group
MAR VISTA, 12006 Venice Blvd, 90066-3810. SAN 332-8171. Tel: 213-390-3455. FAX: 213-756-9282. Web Site: www.lapl.org. *Librn*, Kuang-Pei Tu
Library Holdings: Bk Vols 44,910
Friends of the Library Group
MARK TWAIN BRANCH, 9621 S Figueroa St, 90003. SAN 332-8716. Tel: 323-755-4088. FAX: 323-612-0437. Web Site: www.lapl.org. *Senior Librn*, Stella Nahapetian; Staff 8 (MLS 2, Non-MLS 6)
Library Holdings: Bk Vols 37,866
Friends of the Library Group
MEMORIAL, 4625 W Olympic Blvd, 90019-3810. SAN 332-8201. Tel: 323-934-0855, 323-938-2732. FAX: 323-938-3378. Web Site: www.lapl.org. *Librn*, Maggie Johnson
Library Holdings: Bk Vols 45,073
Friends of the Library Group
MID-VALLEY REGIONAL & BOOKMOBILE HEADQUARTERS, 16244 Nordhoff St, North Hills, 91343. SAN 377-6476. Tel: 818-895-3650. FAX: 818-895-3657. Web Site: www.lapl.org. *Librn*, Dan Dupill
Library Holdings: Bk Vols 123,809
Friends of the Library Group
NORTH HOLLYWOOD REGIONAL, 5211 Tujunga Ave, North Hollywood, 91601-3179. SAN 332-8260. Tel: 818-766-7185. FAX: 818-756-9135. Web Site: www.lapl.org. *Librn*, Harriet Newton
Library Holdings: Bk Vols 97,928
Friends of the Library Group
NORTHEAST AREA, 6145 N Figueroa St, 90042. SAN 332-7175. Tel: 213-237-1185. FAX: 213-612-0543. Web Site: www.lapl.org. *Mgr*, Sylva Galan-Garcia
NORTHRIDGE BRANCH, 9051 Darby Ave, Northridge, 91325-2708. SAN 332-8295. Tel: 818-886-3640. FAX: 818-756-9178. Web Site: www.lapl.org. *Librn*, Collette Nower; *Librn*, Yvonne Wong
Library Holdings: Bk Vols 59,724
Friends of the Library Group
PACOIMA BRANCH, 13605 Van Nuys Blvd, Pacoima, 91331-3697. SAN 332-8325. Tel: 818-899-5203. FAX: 818-756-9280. Web Site: www.lapl.org. *Librn*, Angelica Gracia
Library Holdings: Bk Vols 48,464
Friends of the Library Group
PALISADES BRANCH, 861 Alma Real Dr, Pacific Palisades, 90272-3797. SAN 332-835X. Tel: 310-459-2754. FAX: 310-459-3304. Web Site: www.lapl.org. *Librn*, Barbara Dave
Library Holdings: Bk Vols 43,687
Friends of the Library Group
PALMS-RANCHO PARK, 2920 Overland Ave, 90064-4299. SAN 332-8384. Tel: 310-838-2157. FAX: 310-612-0427. Web Site: www.lapl.org. *Librn*, Lizbeth Caccese
Library Holdings: Bk Vols 50,853
Friends of the Library Group
PANORAMA CITY BRANCH, 14345 Roscoe Blvd, Panorama City, 91402-4222. SAN 332-8414. Tel: 818-894-4071. FAX: 818-891-5960. Web Site: www.lapl.org. *Librn*, Cathy Ortiz
Library Holdings: Bk Vols 61,950
Friends of the Library Group
PIO PICO-KOREATOWN, 695 S Serrano Ave, 90006-2810. SAN 332-8449. Tel: 213-368-7282, 213-381-1453. FAX: 213-612-0433. Web Site: www.lapl.org. *Librn*, Myungcha Miki Lim; *Librn*, Jae Min Roh
Library Holdings: Bk Vols 68,904
Friends of the Library Group
PLATT, 23600 Victory Blvd, Woodland Hills, 91367. SAN 377-0117. Tel: 818-340-9386. FAX: 818-340-9645. Web Site: www.lapl.org. *Librn*, Janet Metzler
Library Holdings: Bk Vols 72,333
Friends of the Library Group
PORTER RANCH, 11371 Tampa Ave, Northridge, 91326. SAN 377-0095. Tel: 818-360-5706. FAX: 818-360-3106. Web Site: www.lapl.org. *Librn*, Lina Daukas
Library Holdings: Bk Vols 56,098
Friends of the Library Group
ROBERT L STEVENSON BRANCH, 803 Spence St, 90023-1728. SAN 332-8562. Tel: 323-268-4710. FAX: 213-612-0425. Web Site: www.lapl.org. *Branch Mgr*, Dora Suarez
Library Holdings: Bk Vols 38,621
Friends of the Library Group
ROBERTSON, 1719 S Robertson Blvd, 90035-4316. SAN 332-8473. Tel: 213-837-1239. Web Site: www.lapl.org. *Librn*, Cheryl Collins
Library Holdings: Bk Vols 46,986
Friends of the Library Group
SAN PEDRO REGIONAL, 931 S Gaffey St, San Pedro, 90731-1349. SAN 332-8503. Tel: 310-548-7779. FAX: 310-548-7453. Web Site: www.lapl.org. *Librn*, John Kralick
Library Holdings: Bk Vols 117,642
SHERMAN OAKS BRANCH, 14245 Moorpark St, Sherman Oaks, 91423. SAN 332-8538. Tel: 818-981-7850. FAX: 818-756-9288. Web Site: www.lapl.org. *Senior Librn*, Michaella Johnson; E-Mail: michaela@lapl.org
Library Holdings: Bk Vols 53,804
Friends of the Library Group
STUDIO CITY BRANCH, 4400 Babcock Ave, Studio City, 91604-1399. SAN 332-8597. Tel: 818-769-5212. FAX: 818-612-0403. Web Site: www.lapl.org. *Librn*, Ann Maupin
Library Holdings: Bk Vols 57,382
Friends of the Library Group
SUN VALLEY BRANCH, 7935 Vineland Ave, Sun Valley, 91352-4498. SAN 332-8627. Tel: 818-764-7907. FAX: 818-756-9289. Web Site: www.lapl.org. *Librn*, Judy Tetove
Library Holdings: Bk Vols 56,036
Friends of the Library Group
SUNLAND-TUJUNGA BRANCH, 7771 Foothill Blvd, Tujunga, 91042-2197. SAN 332-8651. Tel: 818-352-4481. FAX: 818-352-2501. Web Site: www.lapl.org. *Librn*, Vivien Fidder
Library Holdings: Bk Vols 55,723
Friends of the Library Group
SYLMAR BRANCH, 13059 Glenoaks Blvd, Sylmar, 91342-3924. SAN 332-8686. Tel: 818-367-6102. FAX: 818-756-9290. Web Site: www.lapl.org. *Librn*, Irene Galvan
Library Holdings: Bk Vols 52,360
Friends of the Library Group
VALLEY PLAZA, 12311 Vanowen St, North Hollywood, 91605. SAN 332-9100. Tel: 818-765-0805. FAX: 323-756-9292. E-Mail: vpya@lapl.org. Web Site: www.lapl.org. *Librn*, Gloria Glover
Library Holdings: Bk Vols 45,937
Friends of the Library Group
VAN NUYS BRANCH, 6250 Sylmar Ave Mall, Van Nuys, 91401-2787. SAN 332-8740. Tel: 818-756-8453. FAX: 818-756-9291. E-Mail: vnnuys@lapl.org. Web Site: www.lapl.org. *Librn*, Guadalupe Canales
Library Holdings: Bk Vols 67,828
Friends of the Library Group
VASSIE D WRIGHT MEMORIAL-JEFFERSON BRANCH, 2211 W Jefferson Blvd, 90018-3798. SAN 332-799X. Tel: 323-734-8573. FAX: 213-612-0431. Web Site: www.lapl.org. *Librn*, Gladys Cole
Library Holdings: Bk Vols 36,383
Friends of the Library Group
VENICE-ABBOT KINNEY MEMORIAL, 501 S Venice Blvd, Venice, 90291-3440. SAN 332-9070. Tel: 310-821-2065. FAX: 310-756-9283. Web Site: www.lapl.org. *Librn*, Lucille Cappas
Library Holdings: Bk Vols 53,807
Friends of the Library Group
VERMONT SQUARE, 1201 W 48th St, 90037-3787. SAN 332-8864. Tel: 323-290-7406. FAX: 323-290-7408. Web Site: www.lapl.org. *Librn*, Judy A Hermann; Staff 8 (MLS 3, Non-MLS 5)
Library Holdings: Bk Vols 36,317
Subject Interests: Black history
Friends of the Library Group
WATER & POWER, 111 N Hope St, Rm 516, 90012. (Mail add: PO Box 51111, 90051-0100), SAN 332-7248. Tel: 213-367-1995. FAX: 213-367-5088. E-Mail: irc@ladwp.com. *Librn*, Joyce Purcell; Staff 7 (MLS 2, Non-MLS 5)
Library Holdings: Bk Vols 13,527
Subject Interests: Civil engineering
Special Collections: Electric Power Institute Coll, microfiche
Restriction: Staff use only
Open Mon-Fri 8-4
WEST LOS ANGELES REGIONAL, 11360 Santa Monica Blvd, 90025-3152. SAN 332-9046. Tel: 310-575-8323. FAX: 310-312-8309. Web Site: www.lapl.org. *Librn*, Kathleen Strelioff
Library Holdings: Bk Vols 70,583
Friends of the Library Group
WEST VALLEY AREA, 16244 Nordhoff St, North Hills, 91343. SAN 332-7213. Tel: 818-345-4394. FAX: 818-996-1855. Web Site: www.lapl.org. *Mgr*, Lawrence M Eisenberg
WEST VALLEY REGIONAL, 19036 Vanowen St, 91335. SAN 332-8929. Tel: 818-345-4393. FAX: 818-996-1855. Web Site: www.lapl.org. *Librn*, Frank Navarro
Library Holdings: Bk Vols 111,186
Friends of the Library Group
WESTCHESTER, 145D Whittington St Civic Ctr, PO Box 189, Mount Ida, 71957. Tel: 310-645-6082. FAX: 310-342-3123. Web Site: www.lapl.org. *Librn*, Judy Sanchez-Moorehead
Library Holdings: Bk Vols 47,177
Friends of the Library Group
WESTERN AREA, 1719 S Robertson Blvd, 90035. SAN 332-7221. Tel: 310-840-2153. FAX: 310-840-2155. Web Site: www.lapl.org. *Mgr*,

Suzanne Gray
WILL & ARIEL DURANT BRANCH, 1403 N Gardner St, 90046-4101. SAN 332-8899. Tel: 323-876-2741. FAX: 213-612-0410. Web Site: www.lapl.org. *Librn*, Hannah Kramer
Library Holdings: Bk Vols 43,719
Friends of the Library Group
WILMINGTON, 1300 N Avalon Blvd, 90744. SAN 332-883X. Tel: 310-834-1082. FAX: 310-548-7418. Web Site: www.lapl.org. *Librn*, June Cheng
Library Holdings: Bk Vols 60,427
Friends of the Library Group
WILSHIRE, 149 N Saint Andrew Pl, 90004. SAN 332-8805. Tel: 323-957-4550. FAX: 323-957-4555. E-Mail: wlshre@lapl.org. Web Site: www.lapl.org. *Librn*, Ruth E Seid
Library Holdings: Bk Vols 53,121
Hours Mon & Wed 12:30-8, Tues & Sat 10-5:30, Thurs & Fri 12:30-5:30
Friends of the Library Group
WOODLAND HILLS BRANCH, 22200 Ventura Blvd, Woodland Hills, 91364-1599. SAN 332-8988. Tel: 818-887-0160. FAX: 818-756-9287. Web Site: www.lapl.org. *Librn*, Diana Lisignoli-Cochran
Library Holdings: Bk Vols 53,346
Friends of the Library Group
ALMA REAVES WOODS -WATTS BRANCH, 10205 Compton Ave, 90002-3308. SAN 332-8775. Tel: 213-228-7578. FAX: 213-228-7519. Web Site: www.lapl.org. *Mgr*, Betsey Hoage; E-Mail: ehoage@lapl.org; *Librn*, Lucille Vestal
Library Holdings: Bk Vols 49,282
Friends of the Library Group
Bookmobiles: 5

G LOS ANGELES REGIONAL FAMILY PLANNING COUNCIL
REPRODUCTIVE HEALTH LIBRARY,* 3600 Wilshire Blvd, Ste 600, 90010-0605. SAN 329-0808. Tel: 213-368-4401. FAX: 213-368-4410. *Librn*, Sam Stackhouse
Library Holdings: Bk Vols 1,200; Bk Titles 1,000; Per Subs 60
Special Collections: History of Family Planning (Cynthia Goldstein Coll)
Publications: Bilingual Bibliography (English & Spanish), film catalogue, AV catalogue
Family Planning; USA & International, Reproductive Health; Spanish language bks & videos & Multicultural info

J LOS ANGELES SOUTHWEST COLLEGE LIBRARY,* 1600 W Imperial Hwy, 90047. SAN 300-9580. Tel: 323-241-5235. FAX: 323-241-5221. *Head of Libr*, Patricia H McCollum; *Per, Ref*, Hebert Cobbs; *Cat*, Gabrielle Arvig
Founded 1967. Enrl 5,000; Fac 97
1997-1998 Income $330,176,000. Mats Exp $21,747,485, Books $30,000, Per/Ser (Incl. Access Fees) $21,712,000, Micro $5,485. Sal $271,364 (Prof $181,000)
Library Holdings: Bk Vols 61,000; Per Subs 360
Subject Interests: Afro-American, Hispanic
Publications: Library handbook; Los Angeles Southwest College - a selected list of new books; periodicals holdings list

S LOS ANGELES TIMES, Editorial Library,* Times-Mirror Sq, 90053-0267. SAN 300-9599. Tel: 213-237-7181. FAX: 213-237-4641, 237-4502. Web Site: www.latimes.com. *Dir*, Dorothy Ingebretsen; Tel: 213-237-3351; *Archivist*, Mildred Simpson; *Acq*, Carla Barbula; Staff 45 (MLS 25, Non-MLS 20)
Founded 1905
Library Holdings: Bk Titles 10,000
Subject Interests: Current events
Special Collections: Core Reference Coll; Los Angeles Times, clippings, flm, photogs
Publications: Library Information Notes; Library Updates
Partic in Metropolitan Cooperative Library System; OCLC Online Computer Library Center, Inc
Los Angeles Times full-text database is available on Bell & Howell, ProQuest, Nexis, Dialog & Dialog CD-ROM, Dow Jones, Newsbank CD-ROM, Reuters, Financial Times & latimes.com. Research & reprint service available from Times on Demand 1-800-788-8804

J LOS ANGELES TRADE TECHNICAL COLLEGE LIBRARY,* 400 W Washington Blvd, 90015. SAN 300-9602. Tel: 213-744-9025. Reference Tel: 213-744-9027. FAX: 213-749-0002. *Chairperson*, Joyce Livingston; Tel: 213-744-9027, E-Mail: joyce_livingston@laccd.cc.ca.us; *Ref*, David Aragon; *Cat*, Leslie S Kite; Tel: 213-744-9028, E-Mail: leslie_s._kite@laccd.cc.ca.us; Staff 2 (MLS 2)
Founded 1927. Enrl 6,440; Fac 500
Library Holdings: Bk Vols 73,439; Bk Titles 70,706; Per Subs 320
Subject Interests: Fashion
Automation Activity & Vendor Info: (Circulation) DRA
Database Vendor: DRA
Mem of Los Angeles Community Col District

S LOS ANGELES ZOO, Research Library,* 5333 Zoo Dr, 90027-1498. SAN 324-1661. Tel: 323-644-4216. FAX: 323-662-6879. *Librn*, Luz Morales; E-Mail: lmorales@zoo.ci.la.ca.us
Founded 1964
1998-1999 Income $35,000, City $15,000, Parent Institution $20,000. Mats Exp $19,000, Books $5,000, Per/Ser (Incl. Access Fees) $14,000
Library Holdings: Bk Titles 4,500; Per Subs 85
Subject Interests: Birds, Mammals, Reptiles
Special Collections: Zoo Archive

LOYOLA MARYMOUNT UNIVERSITY
C CHARLES VON DER AHE LIBRARY, 7900 Loyola Blvd, 90045-8203. SAN 332-9135. Tel: 310-338-2788. Reference Tel: 310-338-2790. FAX: 310-338-4366, 310-338-7683. Web Site: www.lib.lmu.edu. *Dir*, G Edward Evans; Tel: 310-338-4593, Fax: 310-338-4484, E-Mail: eevans@lmumail.lmu.edu; *Bibliog Instr*, Anthony Amodeo; Tel: 310-338-7681, E-Mail: aamodeo@lmu.edu; *Cat*, Naomi Zahavi; Tel: 310-338-7685, E-Mail: nzahavi@lmu.edu; *Acq, Ser*, Janet Lai; Tel: 310-338-3088, Fax: 310-338-4366, E-Mail: jlai@lmumail.lmu.edu; *Online Servs*, Sachi Yagyu; Tel: 310-338-7680, Fax: 310-338-4366, E-Mail: syagyu@lmumail.lmu.edu; *Coll Develop*, Marcia Findley; Tel: 310-338-7686, E-Mail: mfindley@lmumail.lmu.edu; *Spec Coll*, Errol Stevens; Tel: 310-338-3048, E-Mail: estevens@lmumail.lmu.edu; Staff 34 (MLS 14, Non-MLS 20)
Founded 1929. Enrl 5,961; Fac 415; Highest Degree: Master
Library Holdings: Bk Vols 347,231; Per Subs 10,681
Special Collections: 20th Century Theater & Film Coll; Arthur P Jacobs Coll; Oliver Goldsmith Coll; Rare Books; Saint Thomas Moore Coll
Automation Activity & Vendor Info: (Acquisitions) Innovative Interfaces Inc.; (Cataloging) Innovative Interfaces Inc.; (Circulation) Innovative Interfaces Inc.; (OPAC) Innovative Interfaces Inc.
Database Vendor: Ebsco - EbscoHost, GaleNet, Innovative Interfaces INN - View, Lexis-Nexis, OCLC - First Search, ProQuest, Silverplatter Information Inc.
Publications: Faculty newsletter
Partic in OCLC Online Computer Library Center, Inc; SCELC
CL WILLIAM M RAINS LAW LIBRARY, 919 S Albany St, 90015-1211. SAN 332-916X. Tel: 213-736-1117. Interlibrary Loan Service Tel: 213-736-1142. Reference Tel: 213-736-1177. FAX: 213-487-2204. Web Site: lucy.lls.edu. *Dir*, Robert J Nissenbaum; Tel: 213-736-1197, Fax: 213-385-5950, E-Mail: robert.nissenbaum@lls.edu; *Assoc Dir*, Karen Verdugo; Tel: 213-736-1181, E-Mail: karen.verdugo@lls.edu; *Selection of Gen Ref Mat*, Don Buffaloe; Tel: 213-736-1141, E-Mail: don.buffaloe@lls.edu; *Ref*, Ruth Hill; Tel: 213-736-1174, E-Mail: ruth.hill@lls.edu; *Ref*, Paul Howard; Tel: 213-736-1417, E-Mail: paul.howard@lls.edu; *Cat*, Vera Aronoff; Tel: 213-736-1419, E-Mail: vera.aronoff@lls.edu; *Acq*, Marlene Bubrick; Tel: 213-736-1410, E-Mail: marlene.bubrick@lls.edu; *Tech Servs*, Edward St John; Tel: 213-736-1146, E-Mail: edward.stjohn@lls.edu; *Govt Doc*, Gwendolyn Lohman; Tel: 213-736-8145, E-Mail: gwen.lohmann@lls.edu; *ILL*, Demetrio Orlino; Tel: 213-736-1142, E-Mail: demetrio.orlino@lls.edu; *Automation Syst Coordr*, David Burch; Tel: 213-736-1115, E-Mail: david.burch@lls.edu; Staff 30 (MLS 12, Non-MLS 18)
Founded 1920. Highest Degree: Doctorate
Jul 1998-Jun 1999 Income $3,286,660. Mats Exp $1,914,498, Books $170,090, Per/Ser (Incl. Access Fees) $1,308,608, Other Print Mats $435,800. Sal $1,512,585 (Prof $631,236)
Library Holdings: Bk Vols 498,942; Bk Titles 227,493; Per Subs 6,795
Subject Interests: Acid rain
Special Collections: Loyola Law School Archive Coll; Rare Books on Law
Database Vendor: Dialog, Lexis-Nexis, OCLC - First Search
Publications: Acid Rain; Annual report; Brainstorms; Occasional Showers

S MASONRY INSTITUTE OF AMERICA LIBRARY, 2550 Beverly Blvd, 90057. SAN 370-1778. Tel: 213-388-0472. FAX: 213-388-6958. E-Mail: masinst@aol.com. Web Site: masonryinstitute.org. *Exec Dir*, John Chrysler
Library Holdings: Bk Vols 2,000; Per Subs 10
Subject Interests: Construction, Earthquakes
Restriction: Open to public for reference only

L MAYER, BROWN & PLATT, Law Library,* 350 S Grand Ave, 25th flr, 90071. SAN 372-2929. Tel: 213-229-9565. FAX: 213-625-0248. *Librn*, Michael Whalen
Library Holdings: Bk Vols 13,000

S MCKINSEY & COMPANY, Information Center, 400 S Hope St, Ste 800, 90071. SAN 300-9637. Tel: 213-624-1414. FAX: 213-622-9399. *In Charge*, Kim Esser; E-Mail: kim_esser@mckenzie.com; Staff 8 (MLS 6, Non-MLS 2)
Library Holdings: Bk Titles 1,500; Per Subs 250
Subject Interests: Electronics, Energy
Restriction: Staff use only
Partic in Data Time; Dialog Corporation; Dow Jones News Retrieval; SDC Info Servs; Vutext

S MCMILLAN SCIENCE ASSOCIATES, INC LIBRARY, 3736 Tuller Ave, 90034-6810. SAN 300-9645. Tel: 310-313-4545. FAX: 310-313-4547. *Librn*, Nancy C McMillan
Founded 1971
Library Holdings: Bk Vols 2,000; Per Subs 40
Special Collections: Military History Coll
Function: Reference services available

L MESERVE, MUMPER & HUGHES, Law Library, 555 S Flower St 18th flr, 90071-2319. SAN 328-4093. Tel: 213-620-0300. FAX: 213-625-1930. *Librn*, James Rollins; E-Mail: jrollins@mmhllp.com
Library Holdings: Bk Vols 13,000
Subject Interests: Labor
Restriction: Not open to public

L MILBANK, TWEED, HADLEY & MCCLOY, Law Library, 601 S Figueroa St, 30th Flr, 90017. SAN 372-3046. Tel: 213-892-4468. FAX: 213-629-5063. *Librn*, Glen Gustafson; Staff 3 (MLS 2, Non-MLS 1)
2000-2000 Mats Exp $442,000, Books $97,000, Per/Ser (Incl. Access Fees) $30,000, Other Print Mats $15,000, Electronic Ref Mat (Incl. Access Fees) $300,000
Library Holdings: Bk Vols 10,000; Bk Titles 2,141; Per Subs 218
Restriction: Not a lending library, Not open to public
Partic in OCLC Online Computer Library Center, Inc

L MITCHELL, SILBERBERG & KNUPP LLP, Law Library, 11377 W Olympic Blvd, 90064-1683. SAN 300-9696. Tel: 310-312-2000. FAX: 310-312-3100. *Librn*, Carolyn A Pratt; *Asst Librn*, Sunan Xing; Staff 4 (MLS 2, Non-MLS 2)
Library Holdings: Bk Vols 35,000

S MORRISON & FOERSTER LLP LIBRARY, 555 W Fifth St, Ste 3500, 90013-1024. SAN 370-1662. Tel: 213-892-5359. FAX: 213-892-5454. Web Site: www.mofo.com. *Librn*, Lee Nemchek
Library Holdings: Bk Titles 20,000; Per Subs 500
Subject Interests: Labor, Law, Real estate
Special Collections: California City Charters; California Municipal Planning & Zoning Ordinances
Partic in CDB Infotek; CourtLink; Dialog Corporation; Dun & Bradstreet Info Servs; Westlaw

C MOUNT SAINT MARY'S COLLEGE, Charles Willard Coe Memorial Library, 12001 Chalon Rd, 90049-1599. SAN 332-9194. Tel: 310-954-4370. FAX: 310-954-4379. Web Site: www.msmc.la.edu. *Dir*, Claudia Reed; E-Mail: creed@msmc.la.edu; *Media Spec*, Carolyn Douglas; *Ref*, Rouzica Popovitch-Krekic; Staff 6 (MLS 6)
Founded 1925. Enrl 1,200; Fac 89; Highest Degree: Master
Library Holdings: Bk Vols 132,201; Bk Titles 115,000; Per Subs 800
Subject Interests: Humanities, Nursing, Physical therapy
Special Collections: Cardinal Newman Coll
Partic in Dialog Corporation; Medline; Nat Libr of Med; OCLC Online Computer Library Center, Inc
Departmental Libraries:
DOHENY CAMPUS LIBRARY, 10 Chester Pl, 90007. SAN 332-9224. Tel: 213-477-2750. FAX: 213-749-8111. *Librn*, Mary Kranz

L MUNGER, TOLLES & OLSON LLP, Law Library, 355 S Grand Ave, 35th flr, 90071-1560. SAN 300-970X. Tel: 213-683-9100. FAX: 213-687-3702. *Assoc Librn*, Helen Kim; Staff 4 (MLS 3, Non-MLS 1)
Founded 1963
Library Holdings: Bk Vols 15,000
Partic in Dow Jones News Retrieval; Westlaw

L MUSICK, PEELER & GARRETT LIBRARY,* One Wilshire Bldg, 624 S Grand Ave, Ste 2000, 90017. SAN 300-9718. Tel: 213-629-7600. FAX: 213-624-1376. *Librn*, Lisa L Baker
Library Holdings: Bk Vols 35,000; Per Subs 400
Subject Interests: Labor, Law, Real estate

S NATIONAL ECONOMIC RESEARCH ASSOCIATES, INC LIBRARY, 777 S Figueroa St, Ste 4200, 90017. SAN 300-9726. Tel: 213-346-3000. FAX: 213-346-3030. Web Site: www.nera.com.
Library Holdings: Bk Vols 2,500; Per Subs 95
Subject Interests: Antitrust law

S NATURAL HISTORY MUSEUM OF LOS ANGELES COUNTY, Research Library, 900 Exposition Blvd, 90007. SAN 300-9734. Tel: 213-763-3466. FAX: 213-746-2999. Web Site: www.nhm.org. *Chief Librn*, Donald W McNamee; Tel: 213-763-3388, E-Mail: dmcnamee@nhm.org; *Asst Librn*, Mark Herbert; Staff 3 (MLS 2, Non-MLS 1)
Founded 1913
Library Holdings: Bk Vols 125,000; Bk Titles 95,000; Per Subs 500
Subject Interests: Anthropology, Archaeology, Botany, California, Entomology, Herpetology, Ichthyology, Indians, Mammals, Ornithology, Paleontology
Special Collections: Automotive Hist (Indust Tech Coll); Bookplate Coll Natural History Art & ILL; Herpetology (Pope Coll); LaBrea Tar Pits; Lepidoptera (Paddy McHenry Coll); Newspaper (Pre-1900 Southern California Newspaper Coll); Seaver Center for Western History Research, bks, journals, maps, photogs, mss; The Library of the Lepidopterists' Society; The Southern California Academy of Science Library; Theatrical Programs (Los Angeles Theatre Program Coll)
Restriction: By appointment only
Partic in OCLC Online Computer Library Center, Inc
Friends of the Library Group

NORTHROP GRUMMAN CORP

S B-2 DIVISION, BUSINESS RESEARCH CENTER LIBRARY, 1840 Century Park E, 90067. SAN 328-2872. Tel: 310-553-6262. FAX: 310-201-3023. Web Site: www.northgrum.com. *Acq, ILL*, Linda Long; *Ref*, Marilyn Durkin; Staff 14 (MLS 8, Non-MLS 6)
Library Holdings: Bk Titles 500
Special Collections: Military/DOD Specifications & Standards; NASA Reports Coll
Publications: New Acquisitions List
Partic in Coop Libr Agency for Syst & Servs

S CORPORATE RESEARCH LIBRARY, 1840 Century Park E, 90067-2199. SAN 371-7232. Tel: 310-201-3107. FAX: 310-553-2076. *Mgr*, Brad Kuperstein; Staff 3 (MLS 2, Non-MLS 1)
1997-1998 Income $200,000. Mats Exp $65,000, Books $30,000, Per/Ser (Incl. Access Fees) $35,000
Library Holdings: Bk Titles 3,245; Per Subs 90
Partic in OCLC Western Service Center

L NOSSAMAN, GUTHNER, KNOX & ELLIOTT,* Union Bank Bldg, 31st flr, 445 S Figueroa St, 90071-1602. SAN 300-9742. Tel: 213-612-7822. FAX: 213-612-7801. *Librn*, Arlene Junior
Library Holdings: Bk Vols 12,000

L O'MELVENY & MYERS LLP, Law Library, 400 S Hope St, 90071-2899. SAN 300-9769. Tel: 213-430-6000. FAX: 213-430-6407. *Librn*, Ian Beste; E-Mail: ibeste@omm.com; *Coll Develop*, Gail Okazaki; Staff 14 (MLS 8, Non-MLS 6)
Founded 1885
Library Holdings: Bk Vols 45,000; Per Subs 500
Automation Activity & Vendor Info: (Cataloging) Sydney
Restriction: Staff use only
Partic in Dialog Corporation; Dow Jones News Retrieval; OCLC Online Computer Library Center, Inc; Westlaw

C OCCIDENTAL COLLEGE, Mary Norton Clapp Library, 1600 Campus Rd, 90041-3314. SAN 300-9750. Tel: 323-259-2832. Interlibrary Loan Service Tel: 323-259-2914. Reference Tel: 323-259-2818. FAX: 323-341-4991. Web Site: www.oxy.edu/departments/library. *Dir*, Alfred Gonsalves; Tel: 323-259-2814, E-Mail: alfred@oxy.edu; *Cat, Syst Coordr*, Mark Braden; Tel: 323-259-2668, E-Mail: marker@oxy.edu; *Coll Develop*, Emily Bergman; Tel: 323-259-2935, E-Mail: bergman@oxy.edu; *Electronic Resources*, John Dobbins; Tel: 323-259-2833, E-Mail: dobbins@oxy.edu; *Info Specialist, Instrul Serv*, Dian Teigler; Tel: 323-259-2817, E-Mail: diant@oxy.edu; *Spec Coll*, Michael Sutherland; Tel: 323-259-2852, E-Mail: bun@oxy.edu; *Doc Delivery*, John De La Fontaine; Tel: 323-259-2914, E-Mail: delafo@oxy.edu. Subject Specialists: *Science/technology*, Dian Teigler; Staff 11 (MLS 9, Non-MLS 2)
Founded 1887. Enrl 1,712; Fac 135; Highest Degree: Master
Jun 2000-Jun 2001 Mats Exp $708,545, Books $178,843, Per/Ser (Incl. Access Fees) $444,479, Presv $19,885, AV Equip $6,045, Electronic Ref Mat (Incl. Access Fees) $59,293. Sal $718,244 (Prof $526,929)
Library Holdings: Bk Vols 484,903; Per Subs 1,135
Automation Activity & Vendor Info: (Acquisitions) Innovative Interfaces Inc.; (Cataloging) Innovative Interfaces Inc.; (Circulation) Innovative Interfaces Inc.; (Course Reserve) Innovative Interfaces Inc.; (ILL) Innovative Interfaces Inc.; (Media Booking) Innovative Interfaces Inc.; (OPAC) Innovative Interfaces Inc.; (Serials) Innovative Interfaces Inc.
Publications: Robinson Jeffers Newsletter (quarterly)
Partic in CalPALs; Coop Libr Agency for Syst & Servs; CSU Link; OCLC Online Computer Library Center, Inc
Friends of the Library Group

S ONE INSTITUTE & ARCHIVES, (Formerly Homosexual Information Center Library), International Gay & Lesbian Heritage-Research Center, 909 W Adams Blvd, 90007. SAN 300-9297. Tel: 213-741-0094. Web Site: www.oneinstitute.org. *Librn*, Leslię Colfax
Founded 1952
Library Holdings: Bk Vols 4,000
Special Collections: Homosexual Movement records from 1948 (incl the movement's orgn, social & polit hist)
Publications: A Few Doors West of Hope, the Life & Times of Dauntless Don Slater; HIC Newsletter; Prostitution is Legal; Reader at Large; Seeds of the Amrrican Sexual Revolution; Selected Bibliography of Homosexuality; Subject heading guides for libraries; The Lesbian Paperback
Branches:

S ONE INSTITUTE AT UCS, International Gay & Lesbian Archives, 909 W Adams Blvd, 90007-2406. SAN 300-9777. Tel: 213-741-0094. E-Mail: oneigla@usc.edu. Web Site: www.oneinstitute.org. *Librn*, Misha Schutt; E-Mail: mishagmcla@aol.com
Founded 1952
Library Holdings: Bk Titles 200,000; Per Subs 2,000
Subject Interests: Gay liberation
Special Collections: Collections in Dutch, French, German, Japanese, Scandinavian, Spanish, Catalan & Basque
The Baker Library is part of ONE Institute, a non-profit organization. The majority of books, periodicals & other material is donated by members of the gay & lesbian communities in US & Europe

M ORTHOPAEDIC HOSPITAL, Lt Robert J Rubel Memorial Library, 2400 S Flower St, PO Box 60132, 90007. SAN 300-9785. Tel: 213-742-1530. FAX: 213-742-1100. *Dir*, Mina R Mandal; E-Mail: mmandel@laoh.ucla.edu. Subject Specialists: *Orthopedic*, Mina R Mandal; Staff 1 (MLS 1)
Founded 1945
Library Holdings: Bk Titles 3,600; Per Subs 117
Subject Interests: Orthopedics
Database Vendor: Ebsco - EbscoHost
Restriction: Not open to public
Partic in Pacific SW Regional Med Libr Serv

S OTIS COLLEGE OF ART & DESIGN LIBRARY, 9045 Lincoln Blvd, 90045. SAN 300-9793. Tel: 310-665-6800, Ext 6930. FAX: 310-665-6998. E-Mail: otislib@otisart.edu. Web Site: otisart.edu. *Coll Develop, Dir*, Sue Maberry; E-Mail: maberry@otisart.edu; *Cat*, Cathy Chambers; *Circ*, Andreea Theodore; Staff 3 (MLS 2, Non-MLS 1)
Founded 1917. Enrl 960; Fac 100; Highest Degree: Master
Jul 2000-Jun 2001 Mats Exp $47,000, Books $26,000, Per/Ser (Incl. Access Fees) $15,000, Electronic Ref Mat (Incl. Access Fees) $6,000
Library Holdings: Bk Vols 30,000; Per Subs 139
Subject Interests: Fashion, Fine arts, Photography
Special Collections: Artists bks
Restriction: By appointment only
Partic in RLIN

C PACIFIC STATES UNIVERSITY LIBRARY,* 1516 S Western Ave, 90006. SAN 300-9807. Tel: 323-731-2383. FAX: 323-731-7276. E-Mail: library@psuca.edu. *Actg Librn*, Nelia C Virtucio; Staff 2 (MLS 1, Non-MLS 1)
Founded 1928. Enrl 550; Fac 35; Highest Degree: Master
Library Holdings: Bk Vols 15,450; Per Subs 110; Spec Interest Per Sub 12
Database Vendor: IAC - Info Trac, ProQuest, Wilson - Wilson Web

L PAUL, HASTINGS, JANOFSKY & WALKER LLP, Law Library, 555 S Flower, 23rd Flr, 90071. SAN 329-9333. Tel: 213-683-6000. Interlibrary Loan Service Tel: 213-683-5074. FAX: 213-627-0705. Web Site: www.phjw.com. *Chief Librn*, Susan Streiker; E-Mail: slstreiker@phjw.com; *Tech Servs*, Rosalind A Srivasta va; *ILL*, Andres Victorin; *Ref*, Lee Neugebauer
Library Holdings: Bk Vols 30,000; Per Subs 400
Subject Interests: Labor law

S PERFORMING ARTS CENTER OF LOS ANGELES COUNTY ARCHIVES, (Formerly Music Center Operating Company Archives), 135 N Grand Ave, 90012-3013. SAN 332-9259. Tel: 213-972-7499. FAX: 213-972-3132. *Archivist*, Julio C Gonzalez
Founded 1969
Library Holdings: Bk Vols 500; Bk Titles 381
Subject Interests: Music, Performing arts
Special Collections: costumes; Los Angeles (Raymond Barnes Coll), bks, programs, clippings, photogs; Los Angeles Philharmonic Orchestra-Hollywood Bowl (John Orlando Northcutt Coll), bks, photogs; Opera (Richard Crooks Coll), stage; Otto Rothschild Photo Coll; Theatre-Early; Theatre-New York, Los Angeles (Kenneth Randall Coll), bks, programs, clippings, photogs
Restriction: By appointment only

S PHILOSOPHICAL RESEARCH SOCIETY LIBRARY,* 3910 Los Feliz Blvd, 90027. SAN 300-9831. Tel: 323-663-2167. FAX: 323-663-9443. E-Mail: info@prs.org. Web Site: www.prs.org. *Librn*, Nora Slobodo
Founded 1934
Library Holdings: Bk Vols 50,000
Subject Interests: Astrology, Comparative law, Mythology, Occult, Psychology
Special Collections: Edwin Parker Coll; Le Plongeon Coll; Manly P Hall Coll, bks & art; Philosophy & Psychology (Oliver L Reiser Coll)

L PILLSBURY WINTHROP, Attorneys at Law Library, 725 S Figueroa St, Ste 2700, 90017-5406. SAN 327-5752. Tel: 213-488-7100. FAX: 213-629-1033. *Info Res*, Hui-Chuan Chen; Staff 4 (MLS 2, Non-MLS 2)
Subject Interests: Real estate
Partic in Dialog Corporation; Dow Jones News Retrieval; Westlaw

G POLAND'S MILLENNIUM LIBRARY IN LOS ANGELES, 3424 W Adams Blvd, 90018. SAN 327-6414. Tel: 310-234-0279. *Coll Develop*, Danuta Zawadzki; Staff 4 (MLS 1, Non-MLS 3)
Founded 1966
Library Holdings: Bk Vols 16,000; Bk Titles 14,000
Subject Interests: Poland
Special Collections: Poles Under German Occupation, 1939-1945

S PRICE WATERHOUSE COOPERS, Information Center,* 400 S Hope St, 90071-2889. SAN 300-984X. Tel: 213-236-3515. FAX: 213-236-3098. *Mgr*, Daniel Beardt
Founded 1961
Library Holdings: Bk Vols 2,341; Per Subs 343
Subject Interests: Accounting, Auditing
Publications: Library Office Newsletter
Restriction: Staff use only

L PROSKAUER ROSE LLP, Law Library, 2049 Century Park E, Ste 3200, 90067. SAN 372-3054. Tel: 310-284-5683, 310-557-2900. FAX: 310-557-2193. Web Site: www.proskauer.com. *Head of Libr*, Lisa Winslow; *Asst Librn*, Audrey Gauna; Staff 2 (MLS 1, Non-MLS 1)
Founded 1875
Library Holdings: Bk Vols 15,000; Per Subs 100

M QUEEN OF ANGELS, Hollywood Presbyterian Medical Center,* 1300 N Vermont, 90027. SAN 300-9866. Tel: 213-413-3000, Ext 6695. FAX: 213-913-4848. *Librn*, Pacita Estepa
Founded 1943
Library Holdings: Bk Vols 3,000; Bk Titles 400; Per Subs 67
Restriction: Staff use only

S REISS-DAVIS CHILD STUDY CENTER, Research Library, 3200 Motor Ave, 90034-3710. SAN 300-9874. Tel: 310-204-1666, Ext 359. FAX: 310-838-4637. E-Mail: saundersdawn@yahoo.com. *Librn*, Dawn Saunders
Founded 1950
Library Holdings: Bk Vols 14,500; Bk Titles 9,000; Per Subs 95
Special Collections: Freud Coll
Partic in Pacific SW Regional Med Libr Serv

L RICHARDS, WATSON & GERSHON LIBRARY, 333 S Hope St, 38th flr, 90071-1469. SAN 300-9882. Tel: 213-626-8484, Ext 369. FAX: 213-626-0078. E-Mail: la@rwglaw.com. Web Site: www.rwglaw.com. *Librn*, Francine Biscardi; E-Mail: fbiscardi@rwglaw.com
Library Holdings: Bk Titles 1,300
Subject Interests: Environment, Insurance, Labor, Pub law, Real estate

L RIORDAN & MCKINZIE, Law Library,* 300 S Grand Ave, Ste 2900, 90071. SAN 372-3798. Tel: 213-629-4824. FAX: 213-229-8550. E-Mail: mckinzie@netcom.com. Web Site: www.riordan.com. *Librn*, Mary Dryden
Library Holdings: Bk Vols 21,000; Per Subs 100
Restriction: Private library

S ROUNCE & COFFIN CLUB ARCHIVES,* Occidental College Library, 1600 Campus Rd, 90041. SAN 325-7118. Tel: 323-259-2852. FAX: 323-341-4991. *Spec Coll*, Michael C Sutherland
Library Holdings: Bk Vols 2,300

M ST VINCENT MEDICAL CENTER, Health Science Library,* 2131 W Third St, 90057. SAN 325-7177. Tel: 213-484-5530. FAX: 213-484-7092. *Librn*, Evelyn Walker; E-Mail: ewalker@chw.edu
Library Holdings: Bk Titles 2,000; Per Subs 200
Subject Interests: Cardiology, Oncology
Partic in National Network Of Libraries Of Medicine - Pacific Northwest Region

S SAVING & PRESERVING ARTS & CULTURAL ENVIRONMENTS, Spaces Library & Archives, 1804 N Van Ness Ave, 90028. SAN 328-2139. Tel: 323-463-1629. *Dir*, Seymour Rosen
Subject Interests: Architecture, Art

L SEYFARTH, SHAW, FAIRWEATHER & GERALDSON LIBRARY, 2029 Century Park E, Ste 3300, 90067. SAN 325-7614. Tel: 310-277-7200. FAX: 310-201-5219. *Librn*, Beth Bernstein
Library Holdings: Bk Vols 9,472; Per Subs 300

S SHAKESPEARE SOCIETY OF AMERICA, New Place Rare Book Library,* 1107 N Kings Rd, 90069. SAN 371-134X. Tel: 323-654-5623. *Pres*, R Thad Taylor
Library Holdings: Bk Vols 7,500

L SHEPPARD, MULLIN, RICHTER & HAMPTON LIBRARY, 333 S Hope, 42nd flr, 90071. SAN 300-9912. Tel: 213-617-4127. FAX: 213-620-1398. *Head Librn*, Martin Korn; Staff 5 (MLS 2, Non-MLS 3)
Library Holdings: Bk Vols 50,000; Bk Titles 6,500; Per Subs 300
Subject Interests: Antitrust law, Banking, Intellectual property, Labor, Litigation, Real estate, Securities
Restriction: Staff use only

L SIDLEY & AUSTIN LIBRARY, 555 W Fifth St, Ste 4000, 90013. SAN 371-6309. Tel: 213-896-6193. FAX: 213-896-6600. *Dir*, Elisabeth A Lamartine; E-Mail: elamarti@sidley.com; *Assoc Librn*, Lisa Kiguchi; Staff 4 (MLS 2, Non-MLS 2)
Founded 1980
Library Holdings: Bk Vols 25,000
Subject Interests: Law
Special Collections: Bankruptcy; Environmental Law; Tax
Restriction: Not open to public

L SIEMPRA ENERGY, Law Library,* 633 W Fifth St, Ste 5100. (Mail add: PO Box 4690, 90051), SAN 300-9947. Tel: 213-895-5195. FAX: 213-629-9621. *Chief Librn*, Rosemary Rodriguez
Library Holdings: Bk Vols 18,000; Per Subs 600

C SIMON WIESENTHAL CENTER LIBRARY & ARCHIVES,* 1399 S Roxbury Dr. (Mail add: 9760 W Pico Blvd, 90035-4792), SAN 320-5681. Tel: 310-772-7605. FAX: 310-277-6568. E-Mail: library@wiesenthal.com. Web Site: library.weisenthal.com, www.weisenthal.com. *Dir*, Adaire J Klein;

Librn, Margo Gutstein; *Archivist, Ser*, Fama Mor; *Ref*, Nancy Saul
Library Holdings: Bk Vols 40,000; Per Subs 400
Subject Interests: Holocaust, Judaica (lit or hist of Jews)
Special Collections: Books By & About Simon Wiesenthal; Primary Anti-semitica & Holocaust Denial

SR SINAI TEMPLE, Blumenthal Library, 10400 Wilshire Blvd, 90024. SAN 300-9920. Tel: 310-474-1518, Ext 3215. FAX: 310-470-4165. E-Mail: rbflibrary@aol.com. *Dir*, Lisa Handelman; E-Mail: hanlgt@aol.com
Founded 1969
Library Holdings: Bk Vols 22,500; Bk Titles 20,899; Per Subs 38
Subject Interests: Children's literature, Judaica (lit or hist of Jews), Literature
Special Collections: Haggadot Coll; Parenting Coll; Sinai Akiba Day School Coll for General Studies; William R Blumenthal Rare Book Coll
Publications: Articles for Association of Jewish Libraries (bulletins); Articles on children's literature with Jewish themes; Assorted special topic bibliographies; Central Cataloging Service for Libraries of Judaica; Reform Judaism; regular columns in monthly in-house newsletter; reviews in Los Angeles Jewish Journal
Partic in Metronet

S SOCIETY FOR CALLIGRAPHY LIBRARY,* PO Box 64174, 90064. SAN 373-4099. Tel: 323-936-7395. *Librn*, Andree Weinman
Library Holdings: Bk Vols 500; Per Subs 10
Subject Interests: Typography

C SOUTHERN CALIFORNIA INSTITUTE OF ARCHITECTURE (SCI-ARC), Kappe Library, 350 Merrick St, 90013-1829. SAN 301-5947. Tel: 213-613-2200. FAX: 213-613-2260. *Mgr*, Kevin McMahon
Founded 1974. Enrl 380; Fac 50; Highest Degree: Master
Library Holdings: Bk Vols 50,325; Bk Titles 50,000; Per Subs 120
Subject Interests: Art and architecture, Urban planning
Special Collections: Victor Gruen Speeches, project reprints
Open Mon-Fri 9-6

S SOUTHERN CALIFORNIA LIBRARY FOR SOCIAL STUDIES & RESEARCH, 6120 S Vermont Ave, 90044. SAN 300-9955. Tel: 323-759-6063. FAX: 323-759-2252. E-Mail: archives@socallib.org. Web Site: www.socallib.org. *Dir*, Sarah H Cooper; *Electronic Resources*, Mary Tyler
Founded 1963
Library Holdings: Bk Titles 25,000; Per Subs 100
Special Collections: Calif Democratic Council Records; Chicano & Black Liberation, newsp files; Civil Rights Congress Records; Committee for The Protection of Foreign Born Files; Folk Music (Earl Robinson & William Wolff Colls); Harry Bridges Deportation Case Records; Morris Kominsky Coll (American Right); Organization History (Peace, Civil Rights, Political & Social Action Groups as well as Civil Rights & Civil Liberties Ad Hoc Committees), files from turn of century to present; Smith Act Case Records
Publications: Heritage (quarterly newsletter)

S SOUTHWEST MUSEUM, Braun Research Library, 234 Museum Dr. (Mail add: PO Box 41558, 90041-0558), SAN 300-9963. Tel: 323-221-2164, Ext 255. Reference Tel: 323-221-2164, Ext 252. FAX: 323-224-8223. E-Mail: library@southwestmuseum.org. Web Site: www.southwestmuseum.org. *Dir*, Kim G Walters. Subject Specialists: *Archaeology*, Kim G Walters; *SW Am*, Kim G Walters; Staff 2 (MLS 1, Non-MLS 1)
Founded 1907
Jul 2000-Jun 2001 Income $79,000. Mats Exp $9,000, Books $3,000, Per/Ser (Incl. Access Fees) $4,000, Presv $2,000
Library Holdings: Bk Vols 60,000; Per Subs 125
Special Collections: Archaeology (Hector Alliot Memorial Library of Archaeology); Arizona & the Southwest (Munk Library of Arizoniana); Californiana (George Wharton James Library); Charles F Lummis Manuscript Coll; Frank Hamilton Cushing Papers; Frederick Webb Hodge Papers; George Bird Grinnell Papers, mss; Historic Map Coll; John Charles Fremont Papers; Linguistic materials for Native American languages; Photo Coll of Am Indian, Missions, Adobes, California & Arizona history & archaeology of the Southwest; Redproduction of Aztec & Mayan Codices; Spanish Language, California and the Southwest, folklore and music (Charles Fletcher Lummis Library)
Automation Activity & Vendor Info: (Acquisitions) Endeavor; (Cataloging) Endeavor; (Circulation) Endeavor; (OPAC) Endeavor
Restriction: Non-circulating
Function: Photocopies available
Partic in OCLC Western Service Center

CL SOUTHWESTERN UNIVERSITY, Law Library, 3050 Wilshire Blvd, 90010. (Mail add: 675 S Westmoreland Ave, 90005-3992), Tel: 213-738-5771, 213-738-6723. Interlibrary Loan Service Tel: 213-738-6728. Reference Tel: 213-738-6725. FAX: 213-738-5792. Web Site: www.swlaw.edu/. *Dir*, Linda Whisman; *Cat*, Connie Deng; *Cat*, Tracy Tsui; *Assoc Dir*, Carole Weiner; *Ref*, David McFadden; *Ref*, Dennis Ladd; *Ref*, Sharrel Gerlach; Staff 10 (MLS 7, Non-MLS 3)
Founded 1911. Enrl 829; Fac 45; Highest Degree: Doctorate
Jul 1999-Jun 2000 Income Parent Institution $2,430,879. Mats Exp $1,306,270, Books $134,582, Per/Ser (Incl. Access Fees) $871,719, Presv $18,289, Micro $53,819, Electronic Ref Mat (Incl. Access Fees) $93,465. Sal $1,124,609
Library Holdings: Bk Vols 242,942; Bk Titles 55,305; Per Subs 4,611
Automation Activity & Vendor Info: (Acquisitions) Innovative Interfaces Inc.; (Cataloging) Innovative Interfaces Inc.; (Circulation) Innovative Interfaces Inc.; (Course Reserve) Innovative Interfaces Inc.; (ILL) Innovative Interfaces Inc.; (Media Booking) Innovative Interfaces Inc.; (OPAC) Innovative Interfaces Inc.; (Serials) Innovative Interfaces Inc.
Restriction: Not open to public
Function: ILL available
Partic in RLIN
Open Mon-Thurs 7am-12am, Fri 7am-8pm, Sat 9-7, Sun 10-10

R STEPHEN S WISE TEMPLE LIBRARY, 15500 Stephen S Wise Dr, 90077-1598. SAN 301-0228. Tel: 310-889-2241. FAX: 310-476-2353. *Dir*, Roberta Wise; Fax: 310-476-3587, E-Mail: rlloyd@swes.org; *Librn*, Christie Hamm; E-Mail: chamm@swes.org; *Librn*, Teri Markson; E-Mail: tmarkson@swes.org; *AV*, Michael Saul; *Head of Libr*, Roberta Lloyd; *Tech Servs*, Shamis Katebi; Staff 4 (MLS 3, Non-MLS 1)
Founded 1967
Subject Interests: Judaica (lit or hist of Jews)
Friends of the Library Group

S RALPH STONE & CO, INC, Engineers Library,* 10954 Santa Monica Blvd, 90025. SAN 300-9971. Tel: 310-478-1501. FAX: 310-478-7359.
Founded 1950
Library Holdings: Bk Vols 5,094; Per Subs 13
Subject Interests: Chemistry, Environmental engineering
Restriction: Staff use only

L STROOCK & LAVAN, Law Library,* 2029 Century Park E, Ste 1800, 90067. SAN 372-3747. Tel: 310-556-5800. FAX: 310-556-5959. *Librn*, Judith Ciasulli; E-Mail: ciasulli@ix.netcom.com
Library Holdings: Bk Vols 12,000

L TRANSAMERICA OCCIDENTAL LIFE INSURANCE, Law Library, 1150 S Olive St, Ste T-2100, 90015-2211. SAN 370-4106. Tel: 213-742-3123. FAX: 213-741-6623.
Library Holdings: Bk Vols 9,000; Per Subs 11

L TROY & GOULD, Law Library,* 1801 Century Park E 16th flr, 90067. SAN 372-3755. Tel: 310-553-4441. FAX: 310-201-4746. Web Site: www.troygould.com. *Librn*, Stacey Steadman; E-Mail: srsteadman@troygould.com
Library Holdings: Bk Vols 5,000; Per Subs 12

L TUTTLE & TAYLOR, INC, Law Library,* 355 S Grand, 40th flr, 90071. SAN 372-378X. Tel: 213-683-0260. FAX: 213-683-0225. E-Mail: gbrusca818@aol.com. *Librn*, Ginger G Brusca
Library Holdings: Bk Vols 10,000

S 20TH CENTURY FOX FILM CORP, Frances C Richardson Research Center,* 10201 W Pico Blvd No 89/105, 90035. (Mail add: PO Box 900, 90213), SAN 301-0031. Tel: 310-369-2782. FAX: 310-369-3645. *Dir*, Lisa Fredsti; E-Mail: lisafr@fox.com; Staff 4 (MLS 1, Non-MLS 3)
Founded 1928
Library Holdings: Bk Vols 50,000; Per Subs 20
Subject Interests: Art and architecture, Costume design, History
Special Collections: US & German Armies; WW II Combat Photos
Restriction: Staff use only

S UNION BANK OF CALIFORNIA LIBRARY,* 445 S Figueroa St, 90071. SAN 301-0066. Tel: 213-236-4040. FAX: 213-236-4039.
Founded 1965
Library Holdings: Bk Titles 2,500; Per Subs 90
Subject Interests: Banks and banking, Business and management, Economics
Partic in Dialog Corporation

CR UNITED CHURCH OF RELIGIOUS SCIENCE, Johnson Metaphysical Library, 3251 W Sixth St, PO Box 75127, 90075. SAN 327-599X. Tel: 213-388-2181. FAX: 213-388-1926. *Librn*, Dee Down
Founded 1972. Enrl 80; Fac 12
Library Holdings: Bk Titles 10,000; Per Subs 45
Subject Interests: Philosophy, Psychology
Special Collections: New Thought, bks & magazines; Religious Science (Ernest Holmes) writings, Emerson, Troward, Quimby
Partic in Metronet
International headquarters library for the United Church of Religious Science

GL UNITED STATES COURTS LIBRARY,* 1702 United States Courthouse, 312 N Spring St, 90012. SAN 301-0104. Tel: 213-894-3636. FAX: 213-894-7171.
Library Holdings: Bk Vols 27,036; Per Subs 1,400
Subject Interests: Law
Partic in OCLC Online Computer Library Center, Inc; Westlaw

GL UNITED STATES DEPARTMENT OF JUSTICE, United States Attorney Central District of California Library,* 1214 US Courthouse, 312 N Spring St, 90012. SAN 301-0090. Tel: 213-894-2419. FAX: 213-894-0141. *Librn*,

Dennis Yanaihara
Founded 1888
Library Holdings: Bk Vols 15,000

G UNITED STATES FOOD & DRUG ADMINISTRATION LIBRARY,* 1521 W Pico, 90015. SAN 301-0120. Tel: 213-252-7592. FAX: 213-251-7142.
Library Holdings: Bk Titles 914; Per Subs 92
Restriction: Staff use only

C UNIVERSITY OF CALIFORNIA LOS ANGELES LIBRARY,* 11334 University - Young Research Library, PO Box 951575, 90095-1575. SAN 332-9615. Tel: 310-825-1201. Interlibrary Loan Service Tel: 310-825-1263. FAX: 310-206-4109. Web Site: www.library.ucla.edu. *Librn*, Gloria Werner; *Publ Servs*, Janice Koyama; *Coll Develop*, Cindy Shelton; *Ref*, Marie Waters; *Ser*, Mike Randall; *Cat*, Carol Hixson; *Acq*, Andy Stancliffe; *Spec Coll*, Charlotte Brown. Subject Specialists: *Africa*, Ruby Bell-Gam; *Biomedical*, Alison Bunting; *Judaica (lit or hist of Jews)*, David Hirsch; *Latin America*, Dora Loh; *Near East*, David Hirsch; *Slavic history and literature*, Leon Ferder; Staff 413 (MLS 134, Non-MLS 279)
Founded 1919. Enrl 37,842; Fac 5,601; Highest Degree: Doctorate
Jul 1998-Jun 1999 Mats Exp $8,598,521, Books $4,258,522, Per/Ser (Incl. Access Fees) $4,339,999
Library Holdings: Bk Vols 7,304,000; Per Subs 94,863
Special Collections: 19th & 20th Century British & American Literature; 19th Century British Fiction (Michael Sadlier Coll); British Commonwealth History, especially Australia & New Zealand; British History; California History; Contemporary Western Writers, including special collections on individual authors; Early English Children's Books; Early Italian Printing (Ahmanson-Murphy Coll); Elmer Belt Library of Vinciana; Folklore; History of Medicine; Latin American Studies; Mazarinades; Mountaineering Literature (Farquhar Coll); National Parks & Conservation (Albright Coll); Organizational; Southern California Imprints, pamphlets; Spinoza Coll; Western Americana
Publications: Faculty News From the Department of Special Collections; UCLA Librarian; UCLA Library Guide
Mem of Asn of Research Libraries
Partic in Metronet
Friends of the Library Group
Departmental Libraries:
THE ARTS LIBRARY, 2250 Dickson Art Ctr, 90095-1392. SAN 332-9704. Tel: 310-825-3817. FAX: 310-825-1303. *Librn*, Gordon Theil
Library Holdings: Bk Vols 224,814; Per Subs 2,042
Subject Interests: Art, Art and architecture, Ceramics, Photography, Textiles
Special Collections: Art of the Low Countries Decimal Index; Bookworks & Artist Publications (Hoffberg Coll); Christian Art - Princeton Index; Jewish Art Index; Leonardo da Vinci (Elmer Belt Library of Vinciana); Marburger Index
Publications: Art Catalogs
Partic in BRS; OCLC Online Computer Library Center, Inc
COLLEGE UNDERGRADUATE, Powell Library Bldg, 90095. SAN 332-964X. Tel: 310-825-4134. FAX: 310-206-9312. Web Site: www.library.ucla.edu. *Librn*, Eleanor Mitchell; *Ref*, Deborah Costa; *Ref*, Esther Grassian; *Ref*, Lise Snyder; *Circ*, Stan Patrick; *Ref*, Stephanie Brasley; *Ref*, Cathy Brown; *Ref*, Alice Kawakami
Library Holdings: Bk Vols 192,261; Per Subs 868
Publications: General Information Guide; Self-Guided Tour
ENGLISH READING ROOM, 1120 Rolfe Hall, 90095. SAN 332-9887. Tel: 310-825-4511. *Coll Develop*, Teresa Omidsalar
Library Holdings: Bk Vols 28,691; Per Subs 165
Subject Interests: American literature, English literature, Literary criticism
Special Collections: Josephine Miles Poetry Coll; Modern Contemporary Poetry (1500 vols)
HENRY J BRUMAN MAPS & GOVERNMENT INFORMATION LIBRARY, A5410 YRL, 90095-1575. SAN 333-0001. Tel: 310-825-3135. FAX: 310-206-3374. *Librn*, Lauri Kram
Subject Interests: California, Latin America, Near East, Pacific Islands, Urban planning
Special Collections: Historical Facsimile Maps; Mental Maps, maps & articles; Pictoral Maps
Publications: Latitudes

CL HUGH & HAZEL DARLING LAW LIBRARY, 1106 Law Bldg, Box 951458, 90095-1458. SAN 332-9941. Tel: 310-825-3960, 310-825-7826. FAX: 310-825-1372. Web Site: www.law.ucla.edu/library. *Librn*, Myra Saunders; *Ref*, Kevin Gerson; *Ref*, Laura Cadra; *Ref*, Cindy Spadoni; *Ref*, Karen Lasnick-McNeil; *Ref*, Linda Maisner; *Tech Servs*, Kathleen Pecarovich; *Cat*, Rhonda Lawrence; *Ref*, Linda Karr O'Connor; *Coll Develop*, Adrienne Adan
Library Holdings: Bk Vols 482,041; Per Subs 7,248
Subject Interests: East Asia, Latin America
Special Collections: David Bernard Memorial Aviation Law Library
Partic in Legal Lexis; OCLC Online Computer Library Center, Inc; Westlaw

CM LOUISE M DARLING BIOMEDICAL LIBRARY, 12-077 Center for Health Science, 90095-1798. SAN 332-9739. Tel: 310-825-5781. Interlibrary Loan Service Tel: 310-825-4904. FAX: 310-825-0465. *Librn*, Alison Bunting; *Dir*, Elaine Graham; *Ref*, Janice Contini
Library Holdings: Bk Vols 583,040; Per Subs 4,752
Subject Interests: Dentistry, Medicine, Neurology, Nursing, Public health
Special Collections: Dr M N Beigelman Coll (opthalmology); Florence Nightingale Coll; History of the Health Sciences; History of the Life Sciences; Japanese Medical Books & Prints, 17th-19th Centuries; S Weir Mitchell Coll; Slide, Portrait, Realia & Print Collections
Partic in Cap Area Libr Network Inc; Coop Libr Agency for Syst & Servs; Medline
MANAGEMENT, Rosenfeld Library E-302, 90095. SAN 332-9976. Tel: 310-825-2356, 310-825-3138. *Librn*, Robert Bellanti; *Coll Develop, Ref*, Rita Costello; *Publ Servs, Ref*, Eloisa Borah
Library Holdings: Bk Vols 160,043; Per Subs 2,874
Subject Interests: Accounting, Computer science, Marketing, Real estate
Special Collections: Corporate History; Dean Emeritus Neil H Jacoby Coll; Goldsmiths-Kress Library of Economic Literature, micro fiche; Rare Books in Business & Economics (Robert E Gross Coll)
Partic in BRS; Coop Libr Agency for Syst & Servs; Dialog Corporation; Dow Jones News Retrieval; OCLC Online Computer Library Center, Inc
RICHARD C RUDOLPH EAST ASIAN LIBRARY, 21617 Research Library YRL, 90095. SAN 333-0060. Tel: 310-825-1401. FAX: 310-206-4960. *Coll Develop*, Ching Fen (Amy) Tsiang; *Coll Develop*, Toshie Marra; *Coll Develop*, Mikyung Kang
Library Holdings: Per Subs 5,247
Subject Interests: East Asia
Special Collections: Chinese Archeology; Fine Arts; Japanese Buddhism; Korean Literature - Classical & Modern; Religion
Publications: Richard C Rudolph East Asian Library Bibliographic Series
Partic in OCLC Online Computer Library Center, Inc
SCIENCE & ENGINEERING LIBRARIES, 8270 Boelter Hall, 90095. SAN 332-9852. Tel: 310-825-3398. Interlibrary Loan Service Tel: 310-825-3646. FAX: 310-206-9872. Interlibrary Loan Service FAX: 310-206-3908. *Head of Libr*, Audrey Jackson
Library Holdings: Bk Vols 524,452; Per Subs 6,082
Subject Interests: Astronomy
Special Collections: Technical Reports Coll (including depository items from DOE, NASA, NTIS, Rand Corp)
Partic in Dialog Corporation
UNIVERSITY ELEMENTARY SCHOOL, 1017 UES, 90095. SAN 333-015X. Tel: 310-825-4928. *Head of Libr*, Judith Kanter
Library Holdings: Bk Vols 18,071; Per Subs 29
Subject Interests: Children's literature
Special Collections: Folk Literature; Poetry Coll
WILLIAM ANDREWS CLARK MEMORIAL LIBRARY, 2520 Cimarron St, 90018. SAN 332-9798. Tel: 323-731-8529. *Dir*, Peter Reill; *Librn*, Bruce Whiteman
Library Holdings: Bk Vols 90,400; Per Subs 196
Special Collections: 17th & early 18th Century English Civilization; Eric Gill Coll; John Dryden Coll; Modern Fine Printing; Montana History; Oscar Wilde & the Nineties; Robert Boyle Coll; Robert Gibbings Coll

UNIVERSITY OF CALIFORNIA, LOS ANGELES

C CENTER FOR AFRICAN-AMERICAN STUDIES LIBRARY, 44 Haines Hall, Box 951545, 90095-1545. SAN 332-9550. Tel: 310-825-6060. FAX: 310-206-3421. E-Mail: imz@ucla.edu. Web Site: www.sscnet.uclaedu/caas/library/about.html. *Librn*, Itibari M Zulu
Founded 1969
Library Holdings: Bk Vols 6,343; Bk Titles 8,124; Per Subs 40
Subject Interests: Afro-American
Special Collections: Afro-Americans & Blacks in the Caribbean & Central & South America, av mat, bks, ser, vf
Publications: Lexican of African American Subject Headings
Mem of Asn of Research Libraries
Friends of the Library Group

C INSTRUCTIONAL MEDIA LIBRARY, Powell Library, Rm 46, 90095-1517. SAN 332-9585. Tel: 310-825-0755. FAX: 310-206-5392. E-Mail: imlib@ucla.edu. Web Site: www.oid.ucla.edu/imlib/index.html. *Mgr*, Patricia O'Donnell-Rough
Founded 1963
Subject Interests: Business and management, Ethnic studies, History, Performing arts, Social sciences and issues
Publications: Video periodicals & directories

CR UNIVERSITY OF JUDAISM LIBRARY,* 15600 Mulholland Dr, 90077. SAN 301-0155. Tel: 310-476-9777, Ext 238. FAX: 310-476-5423. *Librn*, Rick Burke; E-Mail: rburke@uj.edu
Library Holdings: Bk Vols 105,000; Per Subs 390
Subject Interests: Education, Humanities, Judaica (lit or hist of Jews)
Special Collections: Judaica & Hebraica Coll
Publications: S'farim (pub irregularly)

C UNIVERSITY OF SOUTHERN CALIFORNIA, Edward L Doheny Memorial Library, University Park, 90089-0182. SAN 333-0184. Tel: 213-740-2543. FAX: 213-749-1221. E-Mail: jtoscan@calvin.usc.edu. Web Site: www.usc.edu/isd/elecresources/catalogs.html. *Asst Librn*, Christopher

Furguson; *Asst Librn*, Anne Lynch; *Govt Doc*, Julia Johnson; *Archivist*, Paul Christopher; *Coll Develop*, Lynn Sipe; Staff 52 (MLS 52)
Founded 1880. Enrl 43,201; Fac 1,717; Highest Degree: Doctorate
Library Holdings: Bk Vols 3,480,853; Bk Titles 2,580,183; Per Subs 28,534
Special Collections: American Literature Coll (1850-); Can; Cinema Coll, mixed; East Asian Coll; German Literature in Exile Coll; International Relations Coll; Latin American (Boeckmann Coll); Philosophy (Gomperz Coll)
Automation Activity & Vendor Info: (Acquisitions) GEAC; (Cataloging) GEAC; (Circulation) GEAC
Publications: CORANTO; Literati
Mem of Asn of Research Libraries
Partic in Center For Research Libraries; OCLC Online Computer Library Center, Inc; Research Libraries Group, Inc
Closed in 1999 for renovations. Expected to reopen in the Fall/2001
Friends of the Library Group
Departmental Libraries:
ANDRUS GERONTOLOGY, University Park, MC-0191, 90089-0191. SAN 333-063X. Tel: 213-740-5990. FAX: 213-740-8983. Web Site: www.usc.edu/isd/locations/science/gerontology. *Head of Libr*, Stella Fu; E-Mail: stellafu@usc.edu
Library Holdings: Bk Vols 13,000; Per Subs 100
Subject Interests: Geriatrics and gerontology
Special Collections: Scan Microfiche Coll
Publications: Acquisitions List
ASA V CALL LAW LIBRARY, University Park, 90089-0072. SAN 333-0753. Tel: 213-740-6482. FAX: 213-740-7179. Web Site: www.usc.edu/dept/law-lib/index.html. *Assoc Dean*, Albert O Brecht, II; *Asst Dir*, Brian Raphael; *Circ, ILL*, Hazel Lord; *Cat*, Wendy Nobunaga; *Tech Servs*, Leonette Williams; *Ref*, Lee Neugebauer; *Res*, Diana Jaque; *Res*, Will Geeslin
Founded 1896. Enrl 650; Fac 45; Highest Degree: Doctorate
Jul 1997-Jun 1998 Income $2,006,589. Mats Exp $579,806, Books $60,448, Per/Ser (Incl. Access Fees) $79,372, Micro $4,636, Other Print Mats $430,989. Sal $999,395 (Prof $573,161)
Library Holdings: Bk Titles 67,000; Per Subs 4,450
Database Vendor: Innovative Interfaces INN - View
Publications: Asa V Call Law Guide to Legal Secondary Source in the Law Library; Asa V Call Law Library Bibliography Series
Partic in Westlaw
FEUCHTWANGER MEMORIAL LIBRARY, Department of Special Collections, 90089-0182. SAN 333-0338. Tel: 213-740-7119. FAX: 213-740-2343. Web Site: www.usc.edu/isd/locations/collections/fml/. *Curator, Librn*, Marje Schuetze-Coburn; E-Mail: schuetze@calvin.usc.edu
HANCOCK LIBRARY OF BIOLOGY & OCEANOGRAPHY, University Park, 90089-0372. SAN 333-0664. Tel: 213-740-7542. FAX: 213-740-5142. Web Site: www.usc.edu/isd/locations/science/hancock. *Mgr*, Suzanne Henderson
Library Holdings: Bk Vols 120,000; Per Subs 1,751
Subject Interests: Earth science, Marine biology, Oceanography, Paleontology
Special Collections: Rare Natural History & Ocean Expeditions
HELEN TOPPING ARCHITECTURE & FINE ARTS LIBRARY, Watt Hall Rm 4, 90089-0182. SAN 333-0214. Tel: 213-740-1956. FAX: 213-749-1221. E-Mail: afalib@usc.edu. Web Site: www.usc.edu/library/afa. *In Charge*, Mike Bonnet; Staff 5 (MLS 3, Non-MLS 2)
Library Holdings: Bk Vols 78,000
Special Collections: Art & Architecture Ephemera; Artist's Books
Partic in OCLC Online Computer Library Center, Inc; Research Libraries Group, Inc
HOOSE LIBRARY OF PHILOSOPHY, Mudd Memorial Hall of Philos, 90089-0182. SAN 333-0397. Tel: 213-740-7434. Web Site: www.usc.edu/library/phil/. *Librn*, Ross Scimeca; E-Mail: scimeca@calvin.usc.edu
Library Holdings: Bk Vols 55,000; Per Subs 150
Special Collections: Western European Philosophers, First & Early Editions, 1700-1850
CM JENNIFER ANN WILSON DENTAL LIBRARY & LEARNING CENTER, Den 21 University Park MC0641, 90089-0641. SAN 333-0729. Tel: 213-740-6476. FAX: 213-748-8565. E-Mail: dentalib@hsc.usc.edu. Web Site: www.usc.edu/hsc/dental/library.html. *Coll Develop, Dir*, Frank Mason; *Bibliog Instr, Online Servs*, John P Glueckert; Staff 2 (MLS 2)
Founded 1897. Enrl 696; Fac 100; Highest Degree: Doctorate
Jul 1997-Jun 1998 Mats Exp $108,581, Books $21,891, Per/Ser (Incl. Access Fees) $85,107, Micro $1,583
Library Holdings: Bk Vols 36,718; Per Subs 700
Special Collections: Dentistry Rare Books Coll
Partic in Nat Libr of Med; Pac SW Regional Med Libr
CL LAW LIBRARY, 699 Exposition Blvd, 90089-0073. (Mail add: MC0072, 90089-0072), Tel: 213-740-0072. FAX: 213-740-7179. Web Site: www.usc.edu/dept/law-lib. *Assoc Dean*, Albert Brecht
Library Holdings: Bk Vols 358,193; Per Subs 4,197
Automation Activity & Vendor Info: (Acquisitions) Innovative Interfaces Inc.; (Cataloging) Innovative Interfaces Inc.; (Circulation) Innovative Interfaces Inc.; (OPAC) Innovative Interfaces Inc.; (Serials) Innovative Interfaces Inc.
MICROGRAPHICS, Doheny Memorial Libr, 90089. SAN 333-0486. Tel: 213-740-3572. *Head of Libr*, Hari Rorlich; E-Mail: rorlich@calvin.usc.edu
Subject Interests: Art, History, Literature, Social sciences and issues
MUSIC, Doheny Memorial Libr, 90089. SAN 333-0516. Tel: 213-740-2926. FAX: 213-747-4176. *Librn*, Rodney Rolfs; E-Mail: rolfs@calvin.usc.edu
CM NORRIS MEDICAL LIBRARY, 2003 Zonal Ave, 90089-9130. SAN 333-0788. Tel: 323-442-1116. Interlibrary Loan Service Tel: 323-442-1115. FAX: 323-221-1235. E-Mail: medlib@hsc.usc.edu. Web Site: www.usc.edu/nml/. *Dir*, Nelson J Gilman; *Tech Servs*, Margaret Wineburgh-Freed; *Ref*, Jan Nelson; *Info Specialist*, Russell Smith; *Info Res*, Bill Clintworth; *Info Specialist*, Pamela Corley; *Access Serv*, Judy Kraemer; *Web Coordr*, Joan Mircheff; *Ref*, Eileen Eandi; *Ref*, Candice Benjes; *Coll Develop*, David Morse; Staff 14 (MLS 14)
Founded 1928. Enrl 3,300; Fac 1,247; Highest Degree: Doctorate
Jul 1997-Jun 1998 Income $3,686,936, Locally Generated Income $249,945, Parent Institution $2,560,519, Other $13,464. Mats Exp $1,218,078, Books $123,398, Per/Ser (Incl. Access Fees) $868,519, Presv $31,886. Sal $1,776,656 (Prof $742,879)
Library Holdings: Bk Vols 46,163; Bk Titles 44,288; Per Subs 2,113
Subject Interests: Medicine, Nursing, Physical therapy
Special Collections: American Indian Ethnopharmacology Coll; Far West Medicine Coll; Salerni Collegium History of Medicine Coll
Publications: Bibliography of Spanish Medical Books; Creating a World Wide Web Presence; Guide to Drug Information & Literature; Information Sheets; Library Newsletter; Medical Subject Headings (MESH) & NLM Classification for Catalogers: Syllabus, MedInfo Search Guide
Partic in National Network Of Libraries Of Medicine - South Central Region; OCLC Online Computer Library Center, Inc
Friends of the Library Group
SCIENCE & ENGINEERING, Seaver Science Ctr, 90089-0481. SAN 333-0540. Tel: 213-740-4419, 213-740-8507. FAX: 213-740-0558. Web Site: www.isd.lib.usc.edu/info/sci. *Head of Libr*, Najwa Hanel; E-Mail: nhanel@usc.edu; Staff 9 (MLS 4, Non-MLS 5)
Library Holdings: Bk Vols 250,000; Per Subs 2,500
Automation Activity & Vendor Info: (Cataloging) SIRSI
VON KLEINSMID CENTER LIBRARY, Von KleinSmid Ctr, 90089-0182. SAN 333-0605. Tel: 213-740-1768. FAX: 213-749-1221. Web Site: www.usc.edu/isd/locations/international/vkc. *Dir*, Robert Labaree; *Ref*, Janice Hanks; E-Mail: jhanks@usc.edu
Library Holdings: Bk Vols 195,000; Per Subs 450
Subject Interests: International relations, Political science, Public admin, Urban planning
Special Collections: International Documents; Planning Documents
Automation Activity & Vendor Info: (Cataloging) SIRSI

GM VA GREATER LOS ANGELES HEALTH CARE SYSTEM, West Los Angeles Library Service, 11301 Wilshire Blvd, B142D, 90073. SAN 333-0842. Tel: 310-268-3110. FAX: 310-268-4919. *Chief Librn*, Nina Hull; E-Mail: hull_nina@va.med.gov; Staff 4 (MLS 2, Non-MLS 2)
Founded 1936
Library Holdings: Bk Vols 12,250; Per Subs 784
Subject Interests: Medicine, Psychiatry, Psychology
Partic in Dialog Corporation

S VISUAL COMMUNICATIONS, Asian Pacific American Photographic Archives,* 120 Judge John Also St, 90012. SAN 373-3327. Tel: 213-680-4462. FAX: 213-687-4848. E-Mail: viscom@apanet.org. *Exec Dir*, Linda Mabalot; *Archivist*, Amy Kato
Library Holdings: Per Subs 10

S WESTERN CENTER ON LAW & POVERTY, INC LIBRARY,* 3701 Wilshire Blvd Ste 208, 90010-2809. SAN 373-0301. Tel: 213-487-7211, Ext 16. FAX: 213-487-0242.
Library Holdings: Bk Vols 1,500; Per Subs 405

M WHITE MEMORIAL MEDICAL CENTER, Courville-Abbott Memorial Library, 1720 Cesar E Chavez Ave, 90033-2462. SAN 301-0198. Tel: 323-260-5715. FAX: 323-260-5748. *Librn, Online Servs*, Zahra Fotovat; E-Mail: zfotovat@earthlink
Founded 1920
Library Holdings: Bk Vols 43,000; Per Subs 350
Subject Interests: Medicine, Nursing
Special Collections: History & Religion (Percy T Magan Coll); History Coll; History of Medicine (Margaret & H James Hara Memorial Coll)
Restriction: Staff use only
Partic in Medline; National Network Of Libraries Of Medicine - Pacific Northwest Region
Friends of the Library Group

SR WILSHIRE BOULEVARD TEMPLE, Sigmund Hecht Library, 3663 Wilshire Blvd, 90010. SAN 301-021X. Tel: 213-388-2401. FAX: 213-388-2595. *Exec Dir*, Steve Breuer
Founded 1929
Library Holdings: Bk Vols 17,050
Special Collections: Judaica

LOS GATOS

SR CALIFORNIA PROVINCE OF THE SOCIETY OF JESUS, Jesuit Center Library,* 300 College Ave, PO Box 128, 95031. SAN 301-0252. Tel: 408-354-9240. FAX: 408-354-1773. *Librn*, Edward T Burke; Staff 1 (MLS 1)
Founded 1851
Library Holdings: Bk Titles 40,000
Special Collections: Catholic Theology; Ecclesiastical History; Jesuitica
Restriction: Not a lending library

M COMMUNITY HEALTH LIBRARY OF LOS GATOS, 815 Pollard Rd, 95032. SAN 370-5676. Tel: 408-866-4044. FAX: 408-866-3829.; Staff 7 (MLS 1, Non-MLS 6)
Founded 1989
Jan 1999-Dec 1999 Income $100,000. Mats Exp $25,000
Library Holdings: Bk Titles 1,100; Per Subs 160
Subject Interests: Consumer health, Medicine, Nursing
Partic in Coop Libr Agency for Syst & Servs
Friends of the Library Group

P LOS GATOS PUBLIC LIBRARY, 110 E Main St, 95030-6981. SAN 301-0260. Tel: 408-354-6891. Reference Tel: 408-354-6896. FAX: 408-399-5755. Web Site: www.town.los-gatos.ca.us. *Dir*, Peggy Conaway
Founded 1898. Pop 28,200
Library Holdings: Bk Vols 114,000; Per Subs 350
Subject Interests: Local history
Database Vendor: epixtech, inc.
Mem of Silicon Valley Library System
Friends of the Library Group

LYNWOOD

M SAINT FRANCIS MEDICAL CENTER, Medical Library,* 3630 Imperial Hwy, 90262. SAN 301-0287. Tel: 310-603-6045. FAX: 310-639-5936. *Coordr*, Beth Araya; Staff 2 (MLS 1, Non-MLS 1)
Founded 1971
Library Holdings: Bk Vols 4,500; Bk Titles 4,200; Per Subs 325
Friends of the Library Group

MADERA

S CANANDAIGUA WINE COMPANY INC, Research Center,* 12667 Rd 24, 93637. SAN 301-0317. Tel: 559-673-7071, Ext 2386. FAX: 559-673-0334. *Librn*, Jennifer Van Buren
Library Holdings: Bk Vols 725; Per Subs 45
Partic in Area Wide Library Network
Friends of the Library Group

G MADERA COUNTY DEPARTMENT OF EDUCATION, School Library,* 28123 Ave 14, 93638. SAN 301-0295. Tel: 209-673-6051, Ext 263. FAX: 209-673-5569. *Media Spec*, Sara Robison
Special Collections: Professional Books Coll
Partic in Area Wide Library Network

S MADERA COUNTY HISTORICAL SOCIETY, Museum-Library,* 210 W Yosemite Ave, PO Box 478, 93639. SAN 371-7267. Tel: 559-673-0291. FAX: 559-674-5114. *Curator*, Dorothy Foust
Library Holdings: Bk Vols 130
Special Collections: County

GL MADERA COUNTY LAW LIBRARY,* County Government Ctr, 209 W Yosemite Ave, 93637-3596. SAN 301-0309. Tel: 209-673-0378. *Librn*, Darla Hix
Founded 1909
Jul 1996-Jun 1997 Income $54,786, County $52,960, Locally Generated Income $1,826. Mats Exp $49,195, Books $47,120, Per/Ser (Incl. Access Fees) $450. Sal $8,000
Library Holdings: Bk Titles 8,112

P MADERA COUNTY LIBRARY, 121 North G St, 93637-3592. SAN 333-0966. Tel: 559-675-7871. FAX: 559-675-7998. Web Site: www.psnw.com/~maderalib. *Mgr Libr*, John Taylor; *Head Librn*, Linda Sitterding; *Ch Servs*, Donna Hopson; *Ref*, Stan Matli
Founded 1910
Library Holdings: Bk Vols 74,874; Per Subs 316
Subject Interests: California, Civil War, Genealogy
Publications: Friends of Madera County Library Newsletter
Mem of San Joaquin Valley Library System
Partic in Area Wide Library Network
Friends of the Library Group
Branches: 4
CHOWCHILLA BRANCH, 621 Robertson Blvd, Chowchilla, 93610-2859. SAN 333-0990. Tel: 559-665-2630. FAX: 559-665-2630. *In Charge*, June Sullivan
Library Holdings: Bk Vols 17,153
Friends of the Library Group
NORTH FORK BRANCH, 32908 Rd 200, PO Box 428, North Fork, 93643. SAN 333-1024. Tel: 559-877-2387. FAX: 559-877-3527. Web Site: sjvls.lib.ca.us. *In Charge*, Paula Gonzalez
Library Holdings: Bk Vols 17,727
Friends of the Library Group
OAKHURST BRANCH, 49044 Civic Circle, Oakhurst, 93644-0484. SAN 333-1059. Tel: 559-683-4838. FAX: 559-642-4591. Web Site: sjvls.lib.ca.us. *In Charge*, Joan Wandell
Library Holdings: Bk Vols 30,000; Per Subs 114
Friends of the Library Group
RANCHOS BRANCH, 37167 Ave 12, Ste 4C, 93638-8725. SAN 371-9537. Tel: 559-645-1214. FAX: 559-645-1216. *In Charge*, Elaine Paisley
Library Holdings: Bk Vols 11,911
Friends of the Library Group

M VALLEY CHILDRENS HOSPITAL, Pediatric Sciences Library, 9300 Valley Children's Pl, 93638-8762. SAN 320-5614. Tel: 559-353-6170. Interlibrary Loan Service Tel: 559-353-6178. FAX: 559-353-6176. *Librn*, Paul Connor; E-Mail: connor@ucsfresno.edu. Subject Specialists: *Graphics*, Tom Warren; Staff 4 (MLS 1, Non-MLS 3)
Founded 1989
Library Holdings: Bk Vols 1,500; Per Subs 240
Subject Interests: Pediatrics
Automation Activity & Vendor Info: (Circulation) SIRSI
Database Vendor: OVID Technologies
Restriction: Circulates for staff only, Public use on premises
Function: Photocopies available
Partic in Area Wide Library Network; Northern California & Nevada Medical Library Group

MALIBU

S HRL LABORATORIES, LLC, 3011 Malibu Canyon Rd, 90265. SAN 301-0333. Tel: 310-317-5373. FAX: 310-317-5624. E-Mail: hrl_library@hrl.com. *Head of Libr*, Stephanie Tiffany; Staff 2 (MLS 1, Non-MLS 1)
Founded 1959
Library Holdings: Bk Titles 10,000; Per Subs 200
Subject Interests: Chemistry, Computer science, Electronics, Physics, Telecommunications
Automation Activity & Vendor Info: (Cataloging) CASPR; (Circulation) CASPR; (OPAC) CASPR; (Serials) CASPR
Database Vendor: Dialog
Publications: Quarterly acquisition list
Partic in OCLC Online Computer Library Center, Inc

C PEPPERDINE UNIVERSITY, Payson Library, 24255 Pacific Coast Hwy, 90263. SAN 333-1083. Tel: 310-456-4252, 310-456-4786. FAX: 310-456-4117. Web Site: www.rigel.pepperdine.edu. *Dir*, Nancy J Kitchen; E-Mail: nancy.kitchen@pepperdine.edu; *Tech Servs*, Rosita Kwok; *Per*, Elizabeth Parang; *ILL*, Melissa Nicholls; *Cat*, Christopher Thomas; *Cat*, Patricia Richmond; *Ref*, Marc Vinyard; *Ref*, William P Deese; *Coordr*, Camay Jennings; *Coll Develop*, Herbert Gore; Staff 24 (MLS 13, Non-MLS 11)
Founded 1937. Enrl 6,206; Fac 382; Highest Degree: Doctorate
Library Holdings: Bk Vols 285,812; Per Subs 1,590
Special Collections: French Collection on 19th Century Paris (Mlynarsky Coll); Religious History (Churches of Christ)
Partic in OCLC Online Computer Library Center, Inc
Friends of the Library Group
Departmental Libraries:
LONG BEACH CENTER, One World Trade Ctr, Ste 200, Long Beach, 90831. SAN 373-5575. Tel: 562-495-0288.
1997-1998 Income $5,380. Mats Exp Per/Ser (Incl. Access Fees) $1,109
Subject Interests: Business and management
ORANGE COUNTY CENTER, Lakeshore Towers III, 18111 Von Karman Ave, Irvine, 92612. SAN 321-4044. Tel: 949-833-8221. Circulation Tel: 949-223-2520. Reference Tel: 949-223-2520. *Librn*, Toby Berger
1997-1998 Income $308,044. Mats Exp $83,025, Books $17,492, Per/Ser (Incl. Access Fees) $17,969, Micro $7,716, Other Print Mats $39,848. Sal $187,659 (Prof $79,038)
Library Holdings: Bk Vols 6,688; Per Subs 132
Subject Interests: Business and management, Education, Psychology
Function: ILL available
Open Mon-Thurs 12-9, Fri 12-7, Sat 9-5, Sun 1-7 (circulation services only)
PEPPERDINE UNIVERSITY PLAZA, 400 Corporate Pointe, Culver City, 90230. SAN 332-9402. Tel: 310-568-5684. *Ref*, Monica Hagan
1997-1998 Income $670,786. Mats Exp $180,289, Books $17,380, Per/Ser (Incl. Access Fees) $77,333, Micro $17,702, Other Print Mats $64,441. Sal $459,087 (Prof $215,629)
Subject Interests: Business and management, Education, Psychology
SAN FERNANDO VALLEY CENTER, 16830 Ventura Blvd, Encino, 91436. SAN 373-5567. Tel: 818-501-1615. *Librn*, Kay White
1997-1998 Income $125,318. Mats Exp $20,870, Books $244, Per/Ser (Incl. Access Fees) $2,082, Other Print Mats $18,544. Sal $80,999 (Prof $43,971)
Subject Interests: Business and management, Education, Psychology
SCHOOL OF LAW, 24255 Pacific Coast Hwy, 90263. Tel: 310-456-4643. FAX: 310-456-4836. Web Site: pepperdine.edu/law_library/index.html. *Librn*, Daniel Martin; *Ref*, Katie Kerr; *Ref*, Mona Stahl; *Ref*, John Peele

Library Holdings: Bk Vols 290,000; Bk Titles 23,648; Per Subs 1,403
VENTURA COUNTY CENTER, Westlake Ctr 2, 2829 Townsgate Rd Ste 180, Westlake Village, 91361. Tel: 805-449-1181. *In Charge*, Bill Corum

MAMMOTH LAKES

P MONO COUNTY FREE LIBRARY, 960 Forest Trail, PO Box 1120, 93546. SAN 377-8576. Tel: 760-934-4777. FAX: 760-934-6268. Web Site: www.monocoe.k12.ca.us. *Librn*, Diane Hurlburt; Tel: 760-934-8670, E-Mail: dhurlburt@monocoe.k12.ca.us
Pop 10,800; Circ 70,000
Jul 1998-Jun 1999 Income $439,472. Sal $285,000
Library Holdings: Bk Vols 100,000; Per Subs 80
Automation Activity & Vendor Info: (Circulation) DRA; (OPAC) DRA
Database Vendor: DRA, OCLC - First Search
Publications: Library News (quarterly)
Friends of the Library Group
Bookmobiles: 1

MARINA

S MONTEREY INSTITUTE FOR RESEARCH & ASTRONOMY, Priscilla Fairfield Bok Library, 200 Eighth St, 93933. SAN 327-7119. Tel: 831-883-1000. FAX: 831-883-1031. E-Mail: mira@mira.org. Web Site: www.mira.org. *Librn*, Clasina Shane; E-Mail: cs@mira.org
Library Holdings: Bk Vols 1,000; Per Subs 6,600
Restriction: By appointment only

MARINA DEL REY

C UNIVERSITY OF SOUTHERN CALIFORNIA, Information Sciences Institute Library,* 4676 Admiralty Way, 90292-6695. SAN 301-0384. Tel: 310-822-1511, Ext 88282. FAX: 310-823-6714. E-Mail: techlib@isi.edu. *Librn*, Linda Mizushima
Founded 1972
Library Holdings: Bk Titles 5,800; Per Subs 125
Subject Interests: Computer science, Linguistics, Mathematics
Publications: ISI Library Newsletter
Restriction: Staff use only
Partic in Coop Libr Agency for Syst & Servs; Dialog Corporation; RLIN

MARIPOSA

L MARIPOSA COUNTY LAW LIBRARY,* 5088 Bullion, PO Box 189, 95338-0189. SAN 324-3532. Tel: 209-966-3222. FAX: 209-966-5147. *Librn*, Sandra V Adams
Library Holdings: Bk Vols 1,993

P MARIPOSA COUNTY LIBRARY, 4978 Tenth St, PO Box 106, 95338. SAN 374-6291. Tel: 209-966-2140. FAX: 209-742-7527. E-Mail: library@yosemite.net. *Librn*, Jacque Meriam; *Asst Librn*, Catherine Adams; *Ref*, Janet Chase-Williams; Staff 1 (MLS 1)
Founded 1926. Pop 16,000; Circ 81,133
Library Holdings: Bk Vols 33,000; Per Subs 75
Mem of San Joaquin Valley Library System
Special Services for the Deaf - Books on deafness & sign language; Captioned film depository; High interest/low vocabulary books
Closed on Sun & Mon
Friends of the Library Group
Branches: 4
EL PORTAL BRANCH, PO Box 160, El Portal, 95318-0160. SAN 374-6305. Tel: 209-379-2401. *Head of Libr*, Roseann Mulvey; Staff 4 (Non-MLS 4)
Friends of the Library Group
RED CLOUD, 10304 Fiske Rd, Coulterville, 95311-9544. SAN 374-6313. Tel: 209-878-3692. *Head of Libr*, Cynthia Brown; Staff 3 (Non-MLS 3)
Friends of the Library Group
WAWONA BRANCH, PO Box 2008, Wawona, 95389-2008. SAN 374-6321. Tel: 209-375-6510. *Head of Libr*, Doris Linn; Staff 4 (Non-MLS 4)
Friends of the Library Group
YOSEMITE BRANCH, PO Box 395, Yosemite, 95389-0395. SAN 374-633X. Tel: 209-372-4552. *Head of Libr*, Marcia Luger; Staff 4 (Non-MLS 4)
Friends of the Library Group

S MARIPOSA MUSEUM & HISTORY CENTER, INC, Research Library,* 5119 Jessie St, PO Box 106, 95338. SAN 301-0392. Tel: 209-966-2140. FAX: 209-742-7527. *In Charge*, Jacque Meriam; E-Mail: jmeriam@sjuls.lib.ca.us
Founded 1971
Library Holdings: Bk Titles 29,000
Publications: Guide to the Mother Lode Country; The Dear Charlie Letters
Open Tues & Thurs 10-7, Wed, Fri & Sat 10-5
Branches:
BASSETT MEMORIAL, Wawona, 95389. SAN 378-1097. Tel: 209-375-6510.
EL PORTAL BRANCH, El Portal, 95318. SAN 378-1119. Tel: 209-379-2401.
RED CLOUD, Coulterville, 95311. SAN 378-1135. Tel: 209-878-3692.
YOSEMITE NATIONAL PARK BRANCH, Yosemite National Park, 95389. SAN 378-1178. Tel: 209-372-4552.

MARKLEEVILLE

P ALPINE COUNTY FREE LIBRARY,* 270 Laramie St, PO Box 187, 96120-0187. SAN 301-0406. Tel: 530-694-2120. FAX: 530-694-2408.
Founded 1969. Pop 1,190; Circ 15,000
1997-1998 Income $164,000. Sal $122,000
Library Holdings: Bk Titles 13,000; Per Subs 62
Special Collections: Local History Coll
Publications: Library Corner in Alpine Enterprise (monthly newspaper)
Mem of Mountain-Valley Library System
Friends of the Library Group
Branches: 1
BEAR VALLEY BRANCH, 367 Creekside Dr, PO Box 5237, Bear Valley, 95223. SAN 370-4904. Tel: 209-753-6219. FAX: 209-753-2219. *Branch Mgr*, Thea Schoettgen
Friends of the Library Group
Bookmobiles: 1

S HISTORICAL SOCIETY OF ALPINE COUNTY, Museum Library, One School St, PO Box 517, 96120-0517. SAN 371-7038. Tel: 530-694-2317. FAX: 530-694-1087. E-Mail: alpinecountymuseum@gbis.com. *Dir*, Richard C Edwards; E-Mail: alpcomu@hotmail.com
Founded 1964
Library Holdings: Bk Titles 600
Special Collections: Alpine County First Familes Coll; Spicer Archealogical Coll

MARTINEZ

GL CONTRA COSTA COUNTY LAW LIBRARY,* 1020 Ward St, 1st flr, 94553-1276. SAN 301-0414. Tel: 925-646-2783. FAX: 925-646-2438. Web Site: www.cccllib.com.
1998-1999 Income $636,000. Mats Exp $303,000
Library Holdings: Bk Vols 50,000; Per Subs 100
Branches:
LAW LIBRARY, 100 37th St, No 216, Richmond, 94805. SAN 323-5556. Tel: 510-374-3019. FAX: 510-374-3019.
Library Holdings: Bk Vols 17,000

M CONTRA COSTA HEALTH SERVICES, Degnan Medical Library, 2500 Alhambra Ave, 94553. SAN 370-5552. Tel: 925-370-5530. FAX: 925-370-5911. E-Mail: schu@hsd.co.contra-costa.ca.us. *Librn*, Sally Chu
Founded 1975
Library Holdings: Bk Vols 1,125; Bk Titles 1,500; Per Subs 150
Subject Interests: Medicine
Automation Activity & Vendor Info: (Cataloging) EOS; (Circulation) EOS; (OPAC) EOS

GM DEPARTMENT OF VETERANS AFFAIRS, Medical Staff Library,* 150 Muir Rd, 94553. SAN 301-0422. Tel: 925-372-2196. FAX: 925-372-2306.
Founded 1946
Library Holdings: Bk Vols 1,000; Per Subs 110
Partic in Veterans Affairs Library Network

MARYSVILLE

J YUBA COMMUNITY COLLEGE, Learning Resources Center,* 2088 N Beale Rd, 95901. SAN 301-0449. Tel: 530-741-6762. FAX: 530-741-6824. *Dir*, Stephen Cato
Founded 1927. Enrl 3,100; Fac 145
Library Holdings: Bk Titles 65,000; Per Subs 250
Mem of Mountain-Valley Library System

§GL YUBA COUNTY LAW LIBRARY, 215 Fifth St, 95901-5788. (Mail add: Courthouse, 2nd flr, 95901-5788), Tel: 530-749-7565. FAX: 530-749-7513. *In Charge*, Esther O Davis
Library Holdings: Bk Vols 2,500

P YUBA COUNTY LIBRARY,* 303 Second St, 95901-6099. SAN 301-0430. Tel: 530-741-6241. FAX: 530-741-3098. *Dir*, Deborah Graf; *ILL*, Jackie Bean; *Ad Servs*, Barbara Lawson; *Ch Servs*, Regina Zurakowski; Staff 2 (MLS 2)
Founded 1858. Pop 65,000; Circ 130,000
Library Holdings: Bk Vols 96,000; Per Subs 100
Subject Interests: History, Travel
Special Collections: California History
Mem of Mountain-Valley Library System
Friends of the Library Group

MENDOCINO

S MENDOCINO ART CENTER LIBRARY,* 45200 Little Lake St, PO Box 765, 95460. SAN 333-1202. Tel: 707-937-5818. FAX: 707-937-1764. E-Mail: mendoart@mcn.org. Web Site: www.mendocinoartcenter.org. *Dir*, Dena Berry Nye
Founded 1962. Enrl 1,000
Library Holdings: Bk Vols 10; Bk Vols 3,200
Restriction: Members only
Branches:
CERAMICS, 45200 Little Lake St, PO Box 765, 95460. Tel: 707-937-5818. FAX: 707-937-1764. E-Mail: mendoart@mcn.org. Web Site: www.mendocinoartcenter.org. *Dir*, Dena Berry Nye
FINE ARTS, 45200 Little Lake St, PO Box 765, 95460. Tel: 707-937-5818. FAX: 707-937-1764. E-Mail: mendoart@mcn.org. Web Site: www.mendocinoartcenter.org. *Dir*, Dena Berry Nye
JEWELRY, 45200 Little Lake St, PO Box 765, 95460. Tel: 707-937-5818. FAX: 707-937-1764. E-Mail: mendoart@mcn.org. Web Site: www.mendocinoartcenter.org. *Dir*, Dena Berry Nye
SCULPTURE, 45200 Little Lake St, PO Box 765, 95460. Tel: 707-937-5818. FAX: 707-937-1764. E-Mail: mendoart@mcn.org. Web Site: www.mendocinoartcenter.org. *Dir*, Dena Berry Nye
WEAVING-TEXTILES, 45200 Little Lake St, PO Box 765, 95460. Tel: 707-937-5818. FAX: 707-937-1764. E-Mail: mendoart@mcn.org. Web Site: www.mendocinoartcenter.org. *Dir*, Vicki Fraser
Library Holdings: Bk Vols 50; Per Subs 10

P MENDOCINO COMMUNITY LIBRARY,* 10591 William St, PO Box 585, 95460-0585. SAN 301-0457. Tel: 707-937-5773. *In Charge*, Ted Hendershot
Founded 1947. Pop 5,000; Circ 16,000
1997-1998 Income $27,000, Locally Generated Income $10,000, Parent Institution $3,000. Mats Exp $9,200, Books $9,000, Per/Ser (Incl. Access Fees) $200
Library Holdings: Bk Vols 8,000; Per Subs 24
Subject Interests: Am Indians, Local authors

S MENDOCINO HISTORICAL RESEARCH INC, Kelley House Museum, 45007 Albion St, PO Box 922, 95460. SAN 373-4102. Tel: 707-937-5791. FAX: 707-937-2156. E-Mail: mgx@mgx.com. *Pres*, Don Tucker; *Exec Dir*, Katherine Bicknell
Library Holdings: Bk Vols 300

MENLO PARK

SR ARCHDIOCESE OF SAN FRANCISCO, Chancery Archives,* 320 Middlefield Rd, 94025. SAN 328-1752. Tel: 650-328-6502. *Archivist*, Dr Jeffrey M Burns
Friends of the Library Group

S CARNEGIE FOUNDATION FOR THE ADVANCEMENT OF TEACHING, Information Center, 555 Middlefield Rd, 94025. SAN 300-6093. Tel: 650-566-5100. FAX: 650-326-0278. Web Site: www.carnegiefoundation.org. *In Charge*, Kathleen Blair; E-Mail: blair@carnegiefoundation.org
Founded 1967
Library Holdings: Bk Vols 8,500; Per Subs 100
Special Collections: Higher Education Coll
Restriction: Open to others by appointment, Staff use only
Partic in Consortium Of Foundation Libraries

S EXPONENT FAILURE ANALYSIS ASSOCIATES, Information Resources, 149 Commonwealth Dr, 94025. SAN 371-7453. Tel: 650-688-7171. FAX: 650-329-9526. *Mgr*, Lee Pharis; Tel: 650-688-7141, E-Mail: lpharis@exponent.com; Staff 5 (MLS 3, Non-MLS 2)
Founded 1984
Library Holdings: Bk Vols 8,500; Bk Titles 6,000; Per Subs 25
Subject Interests: Electronics, Engineering
Database Vendor: Dialog, Lexis-Nexis
Restriction: Private library

P MENLO PARK PUBLIC LIBRARY, 800 Alma St, Alma & Ravenswood, 94025-3460. SAN 301-052X. Tel: 650-858-3460. FAX: 650-858-3466. Web Site: www.plsinfo.org. *Librn*, Karen Fredrickson
Founded 1916. Pop 28,400; Circ 293,932
Library Holdings: Bk Vols 132,000
Publications: Friends of the Library - Bookmark
Mem of Peninsula Library System
Open Mon-Thurs 10-9, Fri & Sat 10-6, Sun 12-5
Friends of the Library Group
Branches: 1
BELLE HAVEN, 413 Ivy Dr, 94025. Tel: 650-329-0145. Web Site: www.pls.lib.ca.us/pls/mpl/mpl.html. *Branch Mgr*, Judy Fagerholm
Library Holdings: Bk Vols 10,000; Per Subs 30; Bks on Deafness & Sign Lang 24
Automation Activity & Vendor Info: (Cataloging) epixtech, inc.; (Circulation) epixtech, inc.; (OPAC) epixtech, inc.
Open Mon-Fri 10-5 during school session, summers: call

S RAYCHEM CORP, Corporate Library,* 123 Library, 300 Constitution Dr, 94025. SAN 301-0538. Tel: 650-361-3282. FAX: 650-361-2655.
Library Holdings: Bk Vols 10,000; Per Subs 450
Subject Interests: Radiation
Restriction: Staff use only

R SAINT PATRICK'S SEMINARY, McKeon Memorial Library, 320 Middlefield Rd, 94539. SAN 301-0546. Tel: 650-321-5655. FAX: 650-322-0997. E-Mail: stpats@ix.netcom.com. *Dir Libr Serv*, Cecil R White; E-Mail: cecilrwhite@juno.com; *Cat*, Molly Lyons; *Tech Servs*, Patricia Wittman. Subject Specialists: *Theology*, Cecil R White; Staff 4 (MLS 3, Non-MLS 1)
Founded 1898. Highest Degree: Master
Jul 1999-Jun 2000 Income Parent Institution $219,609. Mats Exp $49,404, Books $31,365, Per/Ser (Incl. Access Fees) $17,524, AV Equip $515. Sal $154,442 (Prof $117,985)
Library Holdings: Bk Vols 92,571; Per Subs 283
Subject Interests: Theology
Special Collections: Library of Archbishop Alemany (First Archbishop of San Francisco Coll)
Automation Activity & Vendor Info: (OPAC) EOS
Restriction: Restricted borrowing privileges
Function: Photocopies available
Partic in OCLC Online Computer Library Center, Inc

S SRI INTERNATIONAL, Research Information Services,* 333 Ravenswood Ave, 94025. SAN 333-1261. Tel: 650-859-5981. FAX: 650-859-2757. E-Mail: library@sri.com. *Mgr*, Lisa Beffa; Staff 5 (Non-MLS 5)
Founded 1948
Library Holdings: Bk Titles 55,000; Per Subs 350
Special Collections: SRI Reports Coll - Archival
Restriction: Staff use only
Branches:
LIFE SCIENCES, 333 Ravenswood Ave, 94025. SAN 333-1296. Tel: 690-859-3549. *Librn*, Juan Pedro De La Mora; E-Mail: juan.delamoya@sri.com

G UNITED STATES GEOLOGICAL SURVEY LIBRARY, (GIM), 345 Middlefield Rd, MS 955, 94025-3591. SAN 301-0554. Tel: 650-329-5027. Circulation Tel: 650-329-5026. FAX: 650-329-5132. E-Mail: men_lib@usgs.gov. Web Site: www.library.usgs.gov. *Ref*, Angelica Bravos; *Ref*, Philip Stoffer; Staff 15 (MLS 3, Non-MLS 12)
Founded 1953
Library Holdings: Bk Titles 350,000; Per Subs 1,000
Subject Interests: California, Earth science, Maps
Publications: Internal Newsletter
Partic in Dialog Corporation; OCLC Online Computer Library Center, Inc

MERCED

J MERCED COLLEGE, Lesher Library, 3600 M St, 95348-2898. SAN 333-1326. Tel: 209-384-6080. Interlibrary Loan Service Tel: 209-384-6083. Reference Tel: 209-384-6083. FAX: 209-384-6084. E-Mail: lrcstaff@elite.net. Web Site: www.merced.cc.ca.us/lrc/. *Dir*, Dr Susan Walsh; *Assoc Librn*, Ed Brush; Tel: 209-384-6283, E-Mail: brushe@merced.cc.ca.us; *AV*, Gilbert Arguelles; *Ref*, Dee Near; Staff 9 (MLS 2, Non-MLS 7)
Founded 1972. Enrl 2,980; Fac 310
Jul 1999-Jun 2000 Income Parent Institution $756,754. Mats Exp $137,800, Books $71,563, Per/Ser (Incl. Access Fees) $43,619, Micro $4,285, AV Equip $7,801, Electronic Ref Mat (Incl. Access Fees) $10,532. Sal $531,434 (Prof $214,473)
Library Holdings: Bk Vols 40,886; Bk Titles 34,753; Per Subs 253
Automation Activity & Vendor Info: (Circulation) SIRSI; (Course Reserve) SIRSI; (OPAC) SIRSI; (Serials) SIRSI
Database Vendor: Ebsco - EbscoHost, OCLC - First Search, ProQuest
Mem of 49-99 Cooperative Library System
Friends of the Library Group

GL MERCED COUNTY LAW LIBRARY,* 670 W 22nd St, 95340-3780. SAN 301-0570. Tel: 209-385-7332. FAX: 209-725-9223. *Coll Develop, Librn*, Gloria Calistro
Library Holdings: Bk Titles 585
Partic in Westlaw

P MERCED COUNTY LIBRARY, 2100 O St, 95340-3637. SAN 333-1350. Tel: 209-385-7484, 209-385-7643. FAX: 209-726-7912. Web Site: www.co.merced.ca.us/library/library.html. *Head Librn*, Charleen Renteria; Staff 12 (MLS 2, Non-MLS 10)
Founded 1910. Pop 198,800; Circ 230,945
Library Holdings: Bk Vols 372,920; Bk Titles 191,537; Per Subs 211
Special Collections: California History Coll; California Telephone Books Coll; Cookery Coll; Genealogy
Mem of 49-99 Cooperative Library System
Partic in OCLC Online Computer Library Center, Inc
Open Tues-Thurs 12-8, Fri 10-6, Sat 12-6
Friends of the Library Group
Branches: 16
ATWATER BRANCH, 1600 Third St, Atwater, 95301-3691. SAN 333-1415. Tel: 209-358-6651. *In Charge*, Amanda Kelly

Library Holdings: Bk Vols 24,435
Friends of the Library Group
CRESSEY BRANCH, 9257 N Cressey Way, PO Box 25, Cressey, 95312-0025. SAN 333-1504. Tel: 209-394-3656. *In Charge*, Verda Jantz
Library Holdings: Bk Vols 7,996
DELHI EDUCATIONAL PARK COMMUNITY, 16114 Schendal Rd, PO Box 338, Delhi, 95315-9543. SAN 333-1539. Tel: 209-669-3169. *In Charge*, Joy Freeman
Library Holdings: Bk Vols 5,643
DOS PALOS BRANCH, 2002 Almond, Dos Palos, 93620-2304. SAN 333-1563. Tel: 209-392-2155. *In Charge*, Patricia Leisman
Library Holdings: Bk Vols 13,076
Friends of the Library Group
GUSTINE BRANCH, 205 Sixth St, Gustine, 95322-1112. SAN 333-1687. Tel: 209-854-3013. *In Charge*, Nola Ramirez
Library Holdings: Bk Vols 7,473
Friends of the Library Group
IRWIN-HILMAR BRANCH, 20041 W Falke St, Hilmar, 95324-0970. SAN 333-1717. Tel: 209-632-0746. *In Charge*, Debbie Hutchins
Library Holdings: Bk Vols 10,036
Friends of the Library Group
LE GRAND BRANCH, 12949 Le Grand Rd, Le Grand, 95333. SAN 333-1741. Tel: 209-389-4541. Web Site: www.co.merced.ca.us/library/index.html. *In Charge*, Dana Moroni
Founded 1910. Circ 4,000
Library Holdings: Bk Vols 9,000
Friends of the Library Group
LIVINGSTON BRANCH, 1212 Main St, Livingston, 95334-1297. SAN 333-1776. Tel: 209-394-7330. *In Charge*, Yvette Enos
Library Holdings: Bk Vols 17,161
Friends of the Library Group
LOS BANOS BRANCH, 1312 Seventh St, Los Banos, 93635-4753. SAN 333-1806. Tel: 209-826-5254. *In Charge*, Lenny Costa
Library Holdings: Bk Vols 16,464
Friends of the Library Group
SANTA NELLA, 29188 W Centinella Ave, Gustine, 95322-0733. SAN 333-1911. Tel: 209-826-6059. *In Charge*, Kathryn Currie
Library Holdings: Bk Vols 7,900
Friends of the Library Group
SNELLING BRANCH, 15916 N Hwy 59, PO Box 5, Snelling, 95369-0005. SAN 333-192X. Tel: 209-563-6616. *In Charge*, Margaret Wise
Library Holdings: Bk Vols 3,419
Friends of the Library Group
SOUTH DOS PALOS BRANCH, 21961 S Reynolds Ave, PO Box 26, South Dos Palos, 93665-0026. SAN 333-1954. Tel: 209-392-6354. *In Charge*, Barbara Weaver
Library Holdings: Bk Vols 9,767
Friends of the Library Group
STEVINSON BRANCH, 20314 W Third Ave, PO Box 127, Stevinson, 95374-0127. SAN 333-1989. Tel: 209-634-5796. *In Charge*, Michelle Douglas
Library Holdings: Bk Vols 8,204
Friends of the Library Group
WILLIAM J GEORGE BRANCH, 1345 W Fourth St, 95340. SAN 378-2166. Tel: 209-725-3909. *In Charge*, Sharon Wilkins
WINTON BRANCH, 7057 W Walnut, PO Box 38, Winton, 95388-0038. SAN 333-2012. Tel: 209-358-3651. *In Charge*, Ellie Smith
Library Holdings: Bk Vols 5,230
Friends of the Library Group

M SUTTER MERCED MEDICAL CENTER, William E Fountain Health Sciences Library, 301 E 13th St, 95340. SAN 301-0562. Tel: 209-385-7000, 209-385-7058. FAX: 209-385-7038. E-Mail: smced@elite.net. Web Site: www.sutterhealth.org. *Librn*, Mary Silva
Library Holdings: Bk Titles 1,087; Per Subs 179
Subject Interests: Allied health, Business and management, Medicine, Nursing
Partic in Merced County Health Info Consortium; Pacific SW Regional Med Libr Serv

MILL VALLEY

R GOLDEN GATE BAPTIST THEOLOGICAL SEMINARY LIBRARY, 201 Seminary Dr No 37, 94941-3197. SAN 301-0589. Tel: 415-380-1660. FAX: 415-380-1652. E-Mail: library@ggbts.edu. Web Site: www.ggbts.edu. *Dir Libr Serv*, Barbara Dabney; *Tech Servs*, Hae-Sook Kim; *Publ Servs, Reader Servs*, Michelle Sponer; Staff 7 (MLS 2, Non-MLS 5)
Founded 1944. Enrl 1,307; Fac 30
Aug 1999-Jul 2000 Income $747,820. Mats Exp $66,084, Books $35,166, Per/Ser (Incl. Access Fees) $28,195, Presv $2,723, Other Print Mats $230. Sal $344,977 (Prof $72,849)
Library Holdings: Bk Titles 154,857; Per Subs 801; Bks on Deafness & Sign Lang 40
Subject Interests: Music, Religion, Theology
Special Collections: Baptist History
Automation Activity & Vendor Info: (Acquisitions) Endeavor; (Cataloging) Endeavor; (Circulation) Endeavor; (OPAC) Endeavor; (Serials) Endeavor
Partic in OCLC Online Computer Library Center, Inc

P MILL VALLEY PUBLIC LIBRARY, 375 Throckmorton Ave, 94941-2698. SAN 301-0597. Tel: 415-389-4292. FAX: 415-388-8929. Web Site: millvalleylibrary.org. *Head of Libr*, Anne Montgomery; E-Mail: amontgomery@millvalleylibrary.org; *Ch Servs*, Marilyn Simons; *Ref*, Joyce Crews; *Ref*, Allen Testa; *ILL*, Lynne Foster; *City Librn*, Catherne Blumberg; E-Mail: cblumberg@millvalleylibrary.org; Staff 7 (MLS 7)
Founded 1908. Pop 14,100; Circ 290,965
Jul 1999-Jun 2000 Income City $1,335,099. Mats Exp $154,115, Books $110,656, Per/Ser (Incl. Access Fees) $25,468, Presv $1,491, Electronic Ref Mat (Incl. Access Fees) $16,500. Sal $730,964
Library Holdings: Bk Vols 123,862; Per Subs 359
Special Collections: Jungian Psychology; Lucretia Little History Room, bks, clippings, pamphlets, photog; Miwok Indians; Native Plants Coll; Theatre & Movies Coll
Automation Activity & Vendor Info: (Circulation) Innovative Interfaces Inc.
Database Vendor: Ebsco - EbscoHost, GaleNet
Function: ILL available
Mem of North Bay Cooperative Library System
Partic in OCLC Online Computer Library Center, Inc; Ontyme
Friends of the Library Group

MILPITAS

M FIRST PRESBYTERIAN CHURCH MILPITAS LIBRARY,* 1000 S Park Victoria Dr, 95035-7099. SAN 374-4981. Tel: 408-262-8000, Ext 113. FAX: 408-262-1635. *Librn*, Emily Smith; Staff 1 (MLS 1)
Founded 1981
Library Holdings: Bk Titles 7,000
Special Collections: Bibles, 50 variations & languages

C HEALD COLLEGE LIBRARY, (Formerly Heald Institute Of Technology Library), Learning Resource Center, 341A Great Mall Pkwy, 95035-8027. SAN 326-4165. Tel: 408-934-4900. FAX: 408-934-7777. Web Site: www.heald.edu. *Mgr*, Richard Stuart; *Mgr*, Valeh Dabiri; Staff 2 (MLS 1, Non-MLS 1)
Founded 1980. Enrl 1,800; Fac 70; Highest Degree: Associate
Library Holdings: Bk Titles 1,500; Per Subs 40
Subject Interests: Accounting, Audio visual mats, Business, Career educ, Computers, Electronics, Networks
Special Collections: Databooks & Technical Manuals
Publications: Research procedures; Subject bibliographies
Partic in Southnet

MINERAL

S NATIONAL PARK SERVICE, Lassen Volcanic National Park Library, PO Box 100, 96063-0100. SAN 301-0619. Tel: 530-595-4444, Ext 5130. FAX: 530-595-3262. Web Site: www.nps.gov/lavo. *In Charge*, Scott Isaacson; E-Mail: scott_isaacson@nps.gov
Library Holdings: Bk Vols 800; Per Subs 10
Subject Interests: Natural history

MISSION HILLS

M PROVIDENCE HOLY CROSS MEDICAL CENTER, Health Sciences Library, 115031 Rinaldi St, 91345. SAN 329-3963. Tel: 818-898-4545. FAX: 818-898-4481. *Librn*, Beverly Gardner; *Librn*, Lucille R Moss; *Tech Servs*, Pamela Gay
Library Holdings: Bk Vols 2,500; Per Subs 269
Partic in Nat Libr of Med

SR ROMAN CATHOLIC ARCHDIOCESE OF LOS ANGELES, Archival Center Library & Historical Museum,* 15151 San Fernando Mission Blvd, 91345. SAN 371-1099. Tel: 818-365-1501. *Archivist*, Francis J Weber
Library Holdings: Bk Vols 15,000
Friends of the Library Group

MISSION VIEJO

§P MISSION VIEJO LIBRARY, 25209 Marguerite Pkwy, 92692. SAN 375-4227. Tel: 949-830-7100. Circulation Tel: 949-830-7100, Ext 4001. Reference Tel: 949-830-7100, Ext 4008. FAX: 949-586-8447. Web Site: www.cmvl.org. *Dir*, Valerie Meyer; Tel: 949-830-7100, Ext 4002, E-Mail: vmeyer@mission-viejo.com; *Mgr*, Alexandra Woodcock; Tel: 949-830-7100, Ext 4016, E-Mail: swoodcock@mission-viejo.com; *Senior Librn*, Thea Blair; Tel: 949-830-7100, Ext 4015, E-Mail: tblair@mission-viejo.com; Staff 25 (MLS 9, Non-MLS 16)
Founded 1997. Pop 98,000; Circ 550,000
Jul 1999-Jun 2000 Income $1,600,000. Mats Exp $250,000
Library Holdings: Bk Vols 121,000; Per Subs 250
Subject Interests: Genealogy, Local history

Automation Activity & Vendor Info: (Acquisitions) epixtech, inc.; (Cataloging) epixtech, inc.; (Circulation) epixtech, inc.; (OPAC) epixtech, inc.
Database Vendor: GaleNet
Mem of Santiago Libr Syst
Friends of the Library Group

J SADDLEBACK COLLEGE, James B Utt Library, 28000 Marguerite Pkwy, 92692. SAN 301-0635. Tel: 949-582-4523. Interlibrary Loan Service Tel: 949-582-4515. FAX: 949-582-4753. Web Site: www.saddleback.cc.ca.us. *Dean of Libr*, Dr Kevin O'Connor; Tel: 949-582-4366; *Librn*, Anna Maria Cobos; *Librn*, Gita Satyendra; *Librn, Tech Servs*, Steve Tash; *Acq*, Tom Weisrock; *Cat*, Sue Kosmides; *Ref*, Wendy Lewis; Staff 12 (MLS 12)
Founded 1968. Enrl 25,000; Fac 270
Library Holdings: Bk Vols 101,438; Bk Titles 87,611; Per Subs 283
Publications: Library Skills Workbook
Partic in Coop Libr Agency for Syst & Servs; Dialog Corporation; OCLC Online Computer Library Center, Inc
Friends of the Library Group

S UNISYS CORP, (WCIC), West Coast Information Center, 25725 Jeronimo Rd, MS-260, 92691. SAN 301-0627. Tel: 949-380-5061. FAX: 949-380-5332. *Mgr*, Patricia Feeney; E-Mail: pat.feeney@unisys.com; Staff 1 (MLS 1)
Founded 1975
Library Holdings: Bk Vols 7,200; Per Subs 200
Special Collections: Computer Science Technical Reports
Publications: Newsletter (monthly)
Restriction: Not open to public
Function: ILL limited
Partic in Dialog Corporation

MODESTO

M DOCTORS MEDICAL CENTER, Professional Library,* 1441 Florida Ave, PO Box 4138, 95350. SAN 321-5628. Tel: 209-576-3782. FAX: 209-576-3595. E-Mail: library@tenethealth.com. *Librn*, Jane Johnson; Staff 1 (MLS 1)
Founded 1966
Library Holdings: Bk Vols 625; Bk Titles 586; Per Subs 166
Subject Interests: Medicine, Nursing
Partic in Nat Libr of Med

S E & J GALLO WINERY, Research Library, 600 Yosemite Blvd, PO Box 1130, 95353-2760. SAN 301-0651. Tel: 209-341-3230. FAX: 209-341-3083. *Librn*, Susan J Visser; Tel: 209-341-3266, E-Mail: susan.visser@ejgallo.com; *Assoc Librn*, Susan E Timmons; E-Mail: susan.timmons@ejgallo.com; Staff 2 (MLS 1, Non-MLS 1)
Founded 1950
Library Holdings: Bk Vols 5,000; Per Subs 500
Subject Interests: Chemistry, Science/technology, Winemaking
Database Vendor: Dialog
Mem of 49-99 Cooperative Library System

S MCHENRY MUSEUM, 1402 I St, 95354. SAN 375-8192. Tel: 209-577-5366. FAX: 209-491-4407. Web Site: www.division.net/mchenry. *Curator*, Wayne Mathes
Special Collections: City Records; Court & School Transcripts; Photographs
Function: Reference only

M MEMORIAL HOSPITALS ASSOCIATION, Health Sciences Library, 1800 Coffee Rd Ste 43, 95355. (Mail add: PO Box 942, 95353), SAN 328-4344. Tel: 209-526-4500, Ext 8200. FAX: 209-569-7469. *Dir*, Nancy Mangum; E-Mail: mangumn@sutterhealth.org; Staff 2 (MLS 1, Non-MLS 1)
Jan 2000-Dec 2000 Income $120,275. Mats Exp $52,050, Books $17,000, Per/Ser (Incl. Access Fees) $30,000, Electronic Ref Mat (Incl. Access Fees) $4,000. Sal $73,000 (Prof $46,000)
Library Holdings: Bk Vols 1,500; Per Subs 200
Subject Interests: Medicine, Nursing, Pharmacology
Partic in MLA; Nevada Medical Library Group

S MODESTO BEE, Editorial Library,* 1325 H St, PO Box 3928, 95352. SAN 301-066X. Tel: 209-578-2370. FAX: 209-578-2207. Web Site: www.modbee.com. *Librn*, Iris Carroll; Tel: 209-578-2333, E-Mail: icarroll@modbee.com; Staff 4 (MLS 1, Non-MLS 3)
Library Holdings: Bk Vols 160; Per Subs 31
Restriction: Staff use only

J MODESTO JUNIOR COLLEGE LIBRARY,* 435 College Ave, 95350. SAN 301-0678. Tel: 209-575-6062. FAX: 209-575-6669. Web Site: www.virtual.yosemite.cc.ca.us/mjc_library/. *Dir*, Margo Sasse; E-Mail: sassem@yosemite.cc.ca.us; *Librn*, Le-Huong Pham; *Librn*, Sue Adler; *Librn*, Kathleen Ennis
Founded 1920. Enrl 5,273; Fac 300
Library Holdings: Bk Titles 69,865
Special Collections: College Archives
Partic in OCLC Online Computer Library Center, Inc
Friends of the Library Group

P STANISLAUS COUNTY FREE LIBRARY,* 1500 I St, 95354-1166. SAN 333-2101. Tel: 209-558-7800, 209-558-7801. FAX: 209-529-4779. Web Site: www.hinet.com/scfl/scfl.htm. *Librn*, Denise Peterson; *Publ Servs*, Mary Moore; *Acq*, Sara Thompson; Staff 29 (MLS 29)
Founded 1912. Pop 412,000; Circ 1,268,696
Library Holdings: Bk Vols 600,000; Per Subs 1,290
Subject Interests: Genealogy
Special Collections: Californiana; Selections in Spanish & Vietnamese; Song File; Stanislaus County Hist Coll, bks
Automation Activity & Vendor Info: (Acquisitions) Brodart
Mem of 49-99 Cooperative Library System
Partic in Central Association Of Libraries
Friends of the Library Group
Branches: 13
DENAIR BRANCH, 4801 Kersey Rd, Denair, 95316-0190. SAN 333-2160. Tel: 209-634-1283. Web Site: www.ainet.com/scfl/welcome.html. *Librn*, Kathy Andrews
Library Holdings: Bk Vols 9,246
Open Tues-Sat 12-6
EMPIRE BRANCH, 18 S Abbie St, Empire, 95319-0007. SAN 333-2195. Tel: 209-524-5505. *Librn*, Yolanda Sandoval
Library Holdings: Bk Vols 7,206
Open Tues-Sat 12-6
CERES BRANCH (FLORENCE L GONDRING LIBRARY), 2250 Magnolia, Ceres, 95307-3209. SAN 333-2136. Tel: 209-537-8938. Web Site: www.ainet.com/scfl/welcome.html. *Librn*, K Qualls
Library Holdings: Bk Vols 23,058
Friends of the Library Group
HUGHSON BRANCH, 2412 Third St, Hughson, 95326-1025. SAN 333-2225. Tel: 209-883-2293. Web Site: alhet.com/scfl/welcome.html. *Librn*, Isabel Fiqueroa
Library Holdings: Bk Vols 8,170
KEYES BRANCH, 4420 Maud Ave, Keyes, 95328-0367. SAN 333-225X. Tel: 209-664-8006. *Librn*, Kathy Davis
Library Holdings: Bk Vols 9,204
Open Mon, Weds & Fri 9-5, Thurs 9-7 & Sat 12-6
MODESTO-STANISLAUS (CENTRAL LIBRARY), 1500 I St, 95354-1166. SAN 333-2128. Tel: 209-558-7800. FAX: 209-529-4779. Web Site: www.ainet.com/scfl/welcome.html. *Librn*, Denise Peterson
Library Holdings: Bk Vols 362,159
Open Mon-Thurs 10-9, Fri & Sat 10-5, Sun 12-5
Friends of the Library Group
NEWMAN BRANCH, 1305 Kern, Newman, 95360-1603. SAN 333-2284. Tel: 209-862-2010. *Branch Mgr*, Joie Phillips-Rainey
Founded 1909. Pop 6,000; Circ 37,868
Library Holdings: Bk Vols 14,483
Mem of 49-99 Cooperative Library System
Friends of the Library Group
WATERFORD BRANCH (NORA BALLARD LIBRARY), 324 E St, Waterford, 95386-0007. SAN 333-2497. Tel: 209-874-2191. *Librn*, Roseanne Derose
Library Holdings: Bk Vols 19,440
Friends of the Library Group
OAKDALE BRANCH (DAVID F BUSH LIBRARY), 151 S First Ave, Oakdale, 95361-3902. SAN 333-2314. Tel: 209-847-4204. FAX: 209-847-4205. *Librn*, Diane Bartlett; E-Mail: bartlett@scfl.lib.ca.us
Library Holdings: Bk Vols 39,474
Friends of the Library Group
PATTERSON BRANCH, 46 N Salado, Patterson, 95363-2587. SAN 333-2349. Tel: 209-892-6473. FAX: 209-892-5100. *Librn*, Sandie Segoviano; E-Mail: sgoviano@scfl.lib.ca.us
Founded 1976. Pop 10,400
Library Holdings: Bk Vols 26,302
Automation Activity & Vendor Info: (OPAC) epixtech, inc.
Friends of the Library Group
RIVERBANK BRANCH, 3442 Santa Fe Ave, Riverbank, 95367-2319. SAN 333-2373. Tel: 209-869-7008. *Librn*, Kathy Johnson
Library Holdings: Bk Vols 21,592
Friends of the Library Group
SALIDA BRANCH, 4520 Broadway St, No C, Salida, 95368-0617. SAN 333-2403. Tel: 209-543-7353. *Librn*, Karen White
Library Holdings: Bk Vols 7,204
TURLOCK BRANCH, 550 Minaret Ave, Turlock, 95380. SAN 333-2438. Tel: 209-664-8100. FAX: 209-664-8102. Web Site: www.ainet.com/scfl/scfl.htm. *Librn*, Jim Griffin
Library Holdings: Bk Vols 74,728
Friends of the Library Group

GL STANISLAUS COUNTY LAW LIBRARY, 1101 13th St, 95354. SAN 301-0716. Tel: 209-558-7759. FAX: 209-558-8284. E-Mail: colawlib@ainet.com. Web Site: www.co.stanislaus.ca.us/courts/lawlib.htm. *Librn*, Janice K Milliken
Jul 1999-Jun 2000 Income $350,620, Locally Generated Income $26,261. Mats Exp $343,106. Sal $62,926
Library Holdings: Bk Vols 25,500; Per Subs 55
Special Collections: Local Municipal & County Codes

M STANISLAUS COUNTY MEDICAL LIBRARY,* 830 Scenic Dr. (Mail add: PO Box 3271, Stanislaus Medical Ctr, 95353), SAN 301-0708. Tel: 209-558-7162. FAX: 209-558-7538. *Librn*, Jane Johnson
Founded 1957
Library Holdings: Bk Vols 5,911; Bk Titles 5,036; Per Subs 152

MOFFETT FIELD

NASA AMES RESEARCH CENTER

G LIFE SCIENCES LIBRARY, Mail Stop 239-13, 94035-1000. SAN 333-2527. Tel: 650-604-5387. FAX: 650-604-7741. *Librn*, Esther Johnson; E-Mail: ejohnson@mail.arc.nasa.gov; *Tech Servs*, Kim Kranovich; E-Mail: kkranovich@mail.arc.nasa.gov; Staff 2 (MLS 1, Non-MLS 1)
Founded 1965
Library Holdings: Bk Titles 16,254; Per Subs 240
Subject Interests: Aerospace med, Aviation med, Biochemistry, Human factors, Physiology, Planetary sci
Special Collections: Aerospace Biology & Medicine; Biochemistry (Origin of Life Coll); Biogenesis Coll; Evolution Genetics
Partic in Dialog Corporation; OCLC Online Computer Library Center, Inc

S TECHNICAL LIBRARY, N-202-3, 94035-1000. SAN 333-2551. Tel: 650-604-6325. FAX: 650-604-4988. E-Mail: library@mail.arc.nasa.gov. Web Site: mainlib.arc.nasa.gov. *Mgr*, Catherine Andrejak; *Chief Librn*, Mary Walsh; *Asst Librn*, Joe Langdon; *ILL*, Jay Onchongco; *Cat*, Marle Schneider; *Ref*, Dan Pappas; *Ref*, Robert Schwier; Staff 12 (MLS 5, Non-MLS 7)
Founded 1940
Library Holdings: Per Subs 900
Subject Interests: Astronomy, Astrophysics, Chemistry, Computer science, Engineering, Mathematics
Special Collections: NASA & NACA Reports
Partic in Aerospace Res Info Network; Dialog Corporation; DROLS; OCLC Online Computer Library Center, Inc

MONROVIA

S AEROVIRONMENT, INC LIBRARY,* 222 E Huntington Dr, Ste 200, 91016. SAN 301-1887. Tel: 626-357-9983. FAX: 626-359-9628. *Librn*, Heideh Nikpour
Library Holdings: Per Subs 160

R FIRST PRESBYTERIAN CHURCH LIBRARY,* 101 E Foothill Blvd, 91016. SAN 374-843X. Tel: 626-358-3297. FAX: 626-358-5997. *Mgr*, Alicia Noonan
Library Holdings: Bk Vols 100; Per Subs 20

P MONROVIA PUBLIC LIBRARY,* 321 S Myrtle Ave, 91016-2848. SAN 301-0732. Tel: 626-256-8250. FAX: 626-256-8255. Web Site: www.acityline.com/monrovia/. *In Charge*, Monica Greening; Tel: 626-256-8251, E-Mail: mgreening@ci.monrovia.ca.us; *YA Servs*, Melinda Steep; Tel: 626-256-8254, E-Mail: msteep@ci.monrovia.ca.us; *Ad Servs, ILL*, Leila Kair; Staff 8 (MLS 8)
Founded 1895. Pop 39,750; Circ 179,382
Jul 1998-Jun 1999 Income (Main Library Only) $899,205, State $46,713, City $852,492. Mats Exp $100,322. Sal $590,947
Library Holdings: Bk Vols 134,227; Per Subs 321
Database Vendor: epixtech, inc.
Mem of Metropolitan Cooperative Library System
Friends of the Library Group

S WORLD VISION INTERNATIONAL, Resource Center,* 840 W Chestnut Ave, 91016-3198. SAN 326-5730. Tel: 626-303-8811, Ext 7602. FAX: 626-301-7786. *Librn*, Maria Quay
Library Holdings: Bk Titles 2,000; Per Subs 64
Subject Interests: Religion

MONTEBELLO

M BEVERLY HOSPITAL, Breitman Memorial Library, 309 W Beverly Blvd, 90640. SAN 373-4129. Tel: 323-726-1222. FAX: 323-889-2424. E-Mail: mr1.mdj@bhmail.org. *Librn*, Margot D Jensen
Library Holdings: Bk Vols 800; Per Subs 125
Subject Interests: Medicine, Nursing, Nutrition, Pharmacology
Open Mon-Thurs 8-1 & Fri 8-12

S MEXICAN AMERICAN OPPORTUNITY FOUNDATION, Child Care Resource & Referral Service,* 401 N Garfield Ave, 90640. SAN 328-4050. Tel: 323-890-9616. FAX: 323-890-9636. *In Charge*, Leanne Cisneros
Library Holdings: Bk Vols 1,900
Subject Interests: Parenting
Our Foundation is funded by the State of California Dept of Education. Referrals are provided for parents seeking child care. We also keep an up to date base of licensed child care providers & centers in our service area. A small Bilingual/Bicultural Early Childhood Educ Resource & Toy Lending Libr is open to providers & parents, Mon-Fri, 8:00-5:00 & the first Saturday of each month from 9:30-12:00

MONTEREY

S COLTON HALL MUSEUM LIBRARY,* Civic Ctr, 93940. SAN 327-8158. Tel: 831-646-3851, 831-646-5640. FAX: 831-646-3422. E-Mail: museumpt@ci.monterey.ca.us. *In Charge*, Susan Klusmire
Library Holdings: Bk Vols 2,500; Per Subs 15
Special Collections: Monterey History American Period - 1846-present
Open Sun-Sat 10am-4pm

M COMMUNITY HOSPITAL OF THE MONTEREY PENINSULA, Medical Library,* 23625 Holman Hwy, 93940. (Mail add: PO Box HH, 93942), SAN 300-6506. Tel: 831-625-4550. FAX: 831-625-4937. *Librn*, Susan Ulrich; E-Mail: susan.ulrich@chomp.org; Staff 1 (MLS 1)
Founded 1928
1997-1998 Mats Exp $45,350, Books $7,500, Per/Ser (Incl. Access Fees) $25,000, Presv $3,850
Library Holdings: Bk Vols 1,500; Per Subs 225
Subject Interests: Medical
Restriction: Not open to public
Mem of Monterey Bay Area Cooperative Library System
Partic in Nevada Medical Library Group

S CTB MCGRAW-HILL LIBRARY, 20 Ryan Ranch Rd, 93940-5703. SAN 301-0759. Tel: 831-393-0700, 831-393-7008. FAX: 831-393-7825. Web Site: www.ctb.com. *Chief Librn*, Laurel Wilson
Founded 1965
Library Holdings: Bk Vols 9,000; Per Subs 150
Subject Interests: Education, Psychology, Statistics
Special Collections: Test Archives
Publications: Acquisitions List (monthly)
Partic in Cooperative Information Network

S DEFENSE LANGUAGE INSTITUTE, Aiso Library, 543 Lawton Rd Ste 617A, 93944-3214. SAN 301-2212. Tel: 831-242-5206, 831-242-5572. FAX: 831-242-5816. Web Site: 160.133.206.67/aisoweb/aisolib.htm. *Dir*, Margaret Groner; E-Mail: gronerm@pom-emh1.army.mil; *Cat*, Robbie Forrest; *Syst Coordr*, Dewey Mace; *Ref*, Lynn Herrick; *Access Serv*, Carl Chan; *Acq*, Rita Smith; Staff 12 (MLS 6, Non-MLS 6)
Founded 1943. Enrl 2,800; Fac 900
Library Holdings: Bk Vols 95,000; Per Subs 600
Subject Interests: Foreign Language
Publications: New Acquisitions List (monthly)
Mem of Monterey Bay Area Cooperative Library System
Partic in OCLC Online Computer Library Center, Inc

S MARITIME MUSEUM OF MONTEREY LIBRARY,* 5 Custom House Plaza, 93940. SAN 301-0767. Tel: 831-372-2608, 831-375-2553 (Administrative Office). FAX: 831-655-3054. Web Site: www.mhaamm.org. *In Charge*, Linda Jaffe
Library Holdings: Bk Vols 2,500
Special Collections: Maritime & Naval History; Sailing Ships, photog

S MONTEREY BAY AQUARIUM LIBRARY,* 886 Cannery Row, 93940-1085. SAN 373-031X. Tel: 831-648-4849. FAX: 831-648-4884. Web Site: www.mbayag.org. *Mgr*, Fran Wolfe; E-Mail: fwolfe@mbayaq.org; *Cat*, Gail Skidmore
Library Holdings: Bk Vols 5,000; Per Subs 100
Subject Interests: Oceanography

P MONTEREY BAY AREA COOPERATIVE LIBRARY SYSTEM,* Library Bldg, 980 Fremont St, 93940-4799. SAN 301-2921. Tel: 831-646-4256. FAX: 831-646-4111. E-Mail: mobac@library.monterey.edu. *Ref*, Rosy Brewer; *ILL*, Laney Humphrey
Founded 1968. Pop 661,450
Jul 1998-Jun 1999 Income $288,527, State $163,620, Other $124,907. Mats Exp $13,700
Publications: MOBAC Union List of Periodicals
Member Libraries: Community Hospital Of The Monterey Peninsula; Defense Language Institute; Harrison Memorial Library; Monterey County Free Libraries; Monterey County Free Libraries; Monterey Institute of International Studies; Monterey Peninsula College Library; Naval Postgraduate School; Pacific Grove Public Library; Salinas Public Library; San Benito County Free Library; San Juan Bautista City Library; Santa Cruz City-County Library System Headquarters; University of California; Watsonville Public Library
Partic in Dialog Corporation; OCLC Online Computer Library Center, Inc

S MONTEREY COUNTY HERALD, News Library,* 8 Upper Ragsdale Dr, 93942. (Mail add: PO Box 271, 93940), SAN 329-7888. Tel: 831-372-3311. FAX: 831-372-8401. Web Site: www.angelfire.com/ky/toddcopl. *Librn*, Elizabeth Roberts
Library Holdings: Bk Titles 100
Restriction: Not open to public

S MONTEREY HISTORY & ART ASSOCIATION, Mayo Hayes O'Donnell Library, 5 Custom House Plaza, 93940-0805. SAN 301-0775. Tel: 831-375-2553. Web Site: www.mntmh.org. *Dir*, Linda Jaffe
Founded 1970

Library Holdings: Bk Vols 2,500; Per Subs 12
Subject Interests: California
Special Collections: Californiana; Western United States, especially Monterey

C MONTEREY INSTITUTE OF INTERNATIONAL STUDIES, Barnet J Segal Building Library, 425 Van Buren St, 93940. SAN 301-0783. Tel: 831-647-4133. Interlibrary Loan Service Tel: 831-647-4134. FAX: 831-647-3518. Web Site: www.mouti.miis.edu. *Cat*, Wang Hsueh-Ying; *ILL*, Zooey Lober; *Ref*, Ann Flower; Staff 9 (MLS 4, Non-MLS 5)
Founded 1955. Enrl 640; Fac 70; Highest Degree: Master
Jul 1998-Jun 1999 Income Parent Institution $835,000. Mats Exp $325,000, Books $100,000, Per/Ser (Incl. Access Fees) $156,000, Presv $3,000, Micro $6,000, Electronic Ref Mat (Incl. Access Fees) $60,000. Sal $389,000 (Prof $215,000)
Library Holdings: Bk Vols 80,000; Per Subs 567
Subject Interests: Economics, Humanities, International, Languages, Literature, Trade
Special Collections: Foreign Language; General & Technical Dictionaries (English & foreign languages); International Business; MIIS Theses; Monterey Institute of International Studies
Automation Activity & Vendor Info: (Acquisitions) Innovative Interfaces Inc.; (Cataloging) Innovative Interfaces Inc.; (Circulation) Innovative Interfaces Inc.; (Course Reserve) Innovative Interfaces Inc.; (OPAC) Innovative Interfaces Inc.; (Serials) Innovative Interfaces Inc.
Database Vendor: Innovative Interfaces INN - View
Publications: MIIS/List of Periodicals
Mem of Monterey Bay Area Cooperative Library System
Partic in Research Libraries Group, Inc; SCELC

S MONTEREY MUSEUM OF ART LIBRARY,* 559 Pacific St, 93940. SAN 328-1000. Tel: 831-372-5477. FAX: 831-372-5680. E-Mail: mtry-art@mbay.net. Web Site: www.montereyart.org. *Dir*, Richard Gadd
Library Holdings: Bk Titles 5,000
Subject Interests: Art history, Fine arts
Special Collections: Regional California Artists

J MONTEREY PENINSULA COLLEGE LIBRARY,* 980 Fremont Blvd, 93940-4704. SAN 301-0791. Tel: 831-646-4095. FAX: 831-645-1308. Web Site: www.mpc.edu/library. *Dir*, Mary Anne Teed; *Tech Servs*, Bernadine Abbott; *Ref*, Deborah Ruiz; *Ref*, Julia Batchev
Founded 1947. Enrl 12,500; Highest Degree: Associate
Library Holdings: Bk Vols 55,000; Per Subs 288
Automation Activity & Vendor Info: (Acquisitions) Endeavor; (Cataloging) Endeavor; (Circulation) Endeavor; (Course Reserve) Endeavor; (ILL) Endeavor; (OPAC) Endeavor; (Serials) Endeavor
Mem of Monterey Bay Area Cooperative Library System
Partic in OCLC Online Computer Library Center, Inc

P MONTEREY PUBLIC LIBRARY, 625 Pacific St, 93940-2866. SAN 301-0805. Tel: 831-646-3932. Interlibrary Loan Service Tel: 831-646-3743. Circulation Tel: 831-646-3930. Reference Tel: 831-646-3933. FAX: 831-646-5618. E-Mail: refdesk@ci.monterey.ca.us. Web Site: www.monterey.org/library. *Dir*, Paula Simpson; Tel: 831-646-5601, E-Mail: simpson@ci.monterey.ca.us; *Asst Dir*, Nancy Quelland; Tel: 831-646-5602, E-Mail: quelland@ci.monterey.ca.us; *Ref Serv*, Douglas Holtzman; Tel: 831-646-3745, E-Mail: holtzman@ci.monterey.ca.us; *ILL*, Bridget McConnell; E-Mail: mcconnel@ci.monterey.ca.us; *Ch Servs*, Karen Brown; Tel: 831-646-3744, E-Mail: brownk@ci.monterey.ca.us; *Reader Servs*, Kim Bui-Burton; Tel: 831-646-3477, E-Mail: buiburto@ci.monterey.ca.us; Staff 10 (MLS 10)
Founded 1849. Pop 32,000; Circ 422,200
Jul 1999-Jun 2000 Income $2,085,000, State $39,700, City $1,917,000, Locally Generated Income $127,000. Mats Exp $205,000, Books $149,000, Per/Ser (Incl. Access Fees) $22,000, Micro $6,300. Sal $1,480,000
Library Holdings: Bk Titles 109,000; Per Subs 360
Special Collections: Monterey History
Automation Activity & Vendor Info: (Acquisitions) Innovative Interfaces Inc.; (Cataloging) Innovative Interfaces Inc.; (Circulation) Innovative Interfaces Inc.; (OPAC) Innovative Interfaces Inc.; (Serials) Innovative Interfaces Inc.
Publications: Annual Report; Calendar of Events
Partic in MOBAC
Friends of the Library Group
Bookmobiles: 1

C NAVAL POSTGRADUATE SCHOOL, Dudley Knox Library, 411 Dyer Rd Rm 110, 93943-5101. SAN 301-0813. Tel: 831-656-2341, 831-656-2441. FAX: 831-656-5137. Web Site: web.nps.navy.mil/~library/. *Dir*, Dr M Reneker; *Reader Servs*, Greta Marlatt; Staff 15 (MLS 15)
Founded 1946. Enrl 2,992; Fac 400; Highest Degree: Doctorate
Library Holdings: Bk Vols 262,000; Per Subs 1,257
Subject Interests: Business and management, Economics, History, Social sciences and issues, Technology
Special Collections: Naval History & the Sea (Christopher Buckley Jr Coll)
Automation Activity & Vendor Info: (Cataloging) NOTIS
Publications: Periodical Holdings
Mem of Coop Libr Agency For Systs & Servs; Monterey Bay Area Cooperative Library System; South Bay Coop Libr Syst
Partic in Dialog Corporation; DROLS; Fedlink; RLIN

UNITED STATES NAVY
A NAVAL RESEARCH LABORATORY, MARINE METEOROLOGY DIVISION LIBRARY, MONTEREY, 7 Grace Hopper Ave, 93943-5502. SAN 333-2616. Tel: 831-656-4791. FAX: 831-656-4769. *Librn*, Joanne M May; E-Mail: jmay@fnoc.navy.mil
Founded 1971
Oct 1997-Sep 1998 Income $25,000
Library Holdings: Bk Titles 3,200; Per Subs 150
Subject Interests: Meteorology

MONTEREY PARK

P BRUGGEMEYER MEMORIAL LIBRARY, Monterey Park Public Library, 318 S Ramona Ave, 91754-3399. SAN 301-0821. Tel: 626-307-1418. Interlibrary Loan Service Tel: 626-307-1368. Circulation Tel: 626-307-1366. Reference Tel: 626-307-1368. FAX: 626-288-4251. E-Mail: Library@MontereyPark.ca.gov. Web Site: www.ci.monterey-park.ca.us/Library. *Dir*, Linda Wilson; E-Mail: lindalwilson@juno.com; *Acq, Head Tech Servs, Per*, Evena Shu; Tel: 626-307-1379, E-Mail: EShu@MontereyPark.ca.gov; *Circ*, Jeannie Lam; E-Mail: JLam@MontereyPark.ca.gov; *ILL*, Bonnie Apalategui; Tel: 626-307-1399, E-Mail: BApalategui@MontereyPark.ca.gov; *Ch Servs*, Christina Yueh; Tel: 626-307-1412, E-Mail: CYueh@MontereyPark.ca.gov; Staff 57 (MLS 9, Non-MLS 48)
Founded 1929. Pop 65,500; Circ 67,400
Jul 1999-Jun 2000 Income $1,672,830, State $219,584, City $1,322,905, Federal $55,508, Locally Generated Income $74,833. Mats Exp $207,270, Books $162,620, Per/Ser (Incl. Access Fees) $9,665, Presv $5,010, Micro $4,690, AV Equip $12,837, Electronic Ref Mat (Incl. Access Fees) $12,448. Sal $1,083,926 (Prof $361,415)
Library Holdings: Bk Vols 153,668; Bk Titles 135,000; Per Subs 240
Subject Interests: California, Local history
Special Collections: Beatrix Potter Figuerine Coll; Chinese, Japanese, Vietnamese, Korean & Spanish Languages, Materials
Automation Activity & Vendor Info: (Cataloging) Innovative Interfaces Inc.; (Circulation) Innovative Interfaces Inc.; (OPAC) Innovative Interfaces Inc.
Database Vendor: Ebsco - EbscoHost, OCLC - First Search
Publications: Lamppost (semi-annual newsletter for literacy tutors, students & contributors); Library Footnotes (quarterly publication on library services); Life (newsletter for area educators-three times during school year)
Mem of Metropolitan Cooperative Library System
Partic in OCLC Online Computer Library Center, Inc
Administers Literacy Program for adult functional illiterates in West San Gabriel Valley Area
Friends of the Library Group

C EAST LOS ANGELES COLLEGE, Helen Miller Bailey Library, 1301 Avenida Cesar Chaves, 91754. SAN 301-083X. Tel: 323-265-8758. FAX: 323-265-8759. Web Site: www.elac.cc.ca.us/library. *Chairperson*, Evelyn Escatiola; Tel: 323-265-8757, E-Mail: escatie@laccd.cc.ca.us; Staff 9 (MLS 4, Non-MLS 5)
Founded 1946. Enrl 15,000; Fac 250; Highest Degree: Associate
Library Holdings: Bk Vols 136,000; Bk Titles 100,000; Per Subs 200
Special Collections: Afro-American; Mexican-American
Automation Activity & Vendor Info: (OPAC) DRA
Database Vendor: DRA, ProQuest
Publications: Bibliographic Instructional Handouts; Library handbook
Partic in State of Calif Answering Network
Friends of the Library Group

MOORPARK

J MOORPARK COLLEGE LIBRARY,* 7075 Campus Rd, 93021-1695. SAN 301-0848. Tel: 805-378-1450. FAX: 805-378-1470. Web Site: www.moorpark.cc.ca.us. *Dir*, Edward F Tennen; E-Mail: etennen@vccd.net; *Ref*, Mary LaBarge; *Tech Servs*, Penny Penaflor; Staff 3 (MLS 3)
Founded 1967. Enrl 9,362; Fac 312
Library Holdings: Bk Vols 65,000; Per Subs 300
Publications: A-V Manager (audio-visual database management system instruction manual)
Partic in Total Interlibrary Exchange

S SCHUYLER TECHNICAL LIBRARY, 4519 N Ashtree St, 93021. SAN 317-3607. *In Charge*, Gilbert S Bahn
Founded 1952
Special Collections: Professional Papers of Gilbert S Bahn
Restriction: Staff use only

MORAGA

S MORAGA HISTORICAL SOCIETY ARCHIVES, 1500 Saint Mary's Rd, 94556-2037. (Mail add: PO Box 103, 94556-0103), SAN 372-7343. Tel: 925-377-8734. FAX: 925-376-3034. Web Site: www.moragahistory.org. *Archivist*, Margaret Skinner; Staff 1 (MLS 1)
Library Holdings: Bk Titles 600

Subject Interests: Genealogy
Special Collections: Rancho Land Case No 590 (1852)
Publications: El Rancho (historical journal); Newsletter
Restriction: Open to public for reference only
Open Mon, Wed & Fri 1-3 or by appointment
Friends of the Library Group

C SAINT MARY'S COLLEGE OF CALIFORNIA, Saint Albert Hall Library, 1928 Saint Mary's Rd, PO Box 4290, 94575-4290. SAN 301-0856. Tel: 925-631-4229. FAX: 925-376-6097. Web Site: gaelnet.stmarys-ca.edu/library/index.html. *Media Spec*, Larry Dyer; *Archivist*, Linda Wobbe; *Ref*, Patricia Wade; *Syst Coordr*, Martin Cohen; *Instrul Serv*, Kris Rankka; Staff 21 (MLS 12, Non-MLS 9)
Founded 1863. Enrl 3,803; Fac 127; Highest Degree: Master
Jul 1999-Jun 2000 Income (Main Library Only) $1,448,675, Parent Institution $1,366,675, Other $82,000. Mats Exp $542,000, Books $240,000, Per/Ser (Incl. Access Fees) $164,000, Presv $7,000, Micro $19,000, Electronic Ref Mat (Incl. Access Fees) $112,000. Sal $798,000
Library Holdings: Bk Vols 199,000; Bk Titles 160,000; Per Subs 1,066
Subject Interests: History, Philosophy, Religion
Special Collections: Byron Bryant Film Coll, v-tapes; Califorina Mathematical Society Archives; College Archives; Easley Guitar Music Coll, flm; Oxford Movement (Newman Coll); Spirituality of 17th & 18th Century (Lasallian Research Center)
Automation Activity & Vendor Info: (Cataloging) Innovative Interfaces Inc.; (Circulation) Innovative Interfaces Inc.; (Course Reserve) Innovative Interfaces Inc.; (OPAC) Innovative Interfaces Inc.
Partic in Michigan Library Consortium; OCLC Online Computer Library Center, Inc; RLIN

MORENO VALLEY

P MORENO VALLEY PUBLIC LIBRARY,* 25480 Alessandro Blvd, 92553. SAN 378-2565. Tel: 909-242-5500. FAX: 909-247-8346. Web Site: www.ci.moreno-valley.ca.us. *Publ Servs*, Rebecca Manley; *Circ*, Sylvia Chavira; *Ref*, Dana Pearson; *Ch Servs*, Meghan Kennedy; Staff 13 (MLS 4, Non-MLS 9)
Pop 132,000
1998-1999 Income $993,630. Mats Exp $130,000. Sal $437,020
Library Holdings: Bk Vols 90,000; Bk Titles 68,000; Per Subs 75
Automation Activity & Vendor Info: (Acquisitions) DRA; (Cataloging) DRA; (Circulation) DRA; (Serials) DRA
Mem of Inland Library System
Friends of the Library Group

J RIVERSIDE COMMUNITY COLLEGE DISTRICT, Moreno Valley Campus Library, 16130 Lasselle St, 92551-2045. SAN 371-9626. Tel: 909-571-6112. Reference Tel: 909-571-6109. FAX: 909-571-6191. Web Site: rcclamp.rccd.cc.ca.us, www.rccd.cc.ca.us. *Assoc Prof*, Friedrich K Brose; Tel: 909-571-6109, E-Mail: fbrose@rccd.cc.ca.us; Staff 3 (MLS 2, Non-MLS 1)
Founded 1991. Enrl 2,000; Fac 46; Highest Degree: Associate
Library Holdings: Bk Vols 20,000; Per Subs 150
Publications: Library pamphlet

M RIVERSIDE COUNTY REGIONAL MEDICAL CENTER LIBRARY,* 26520 Catus Ave, 92555. SAN 301-2557. Tel: 909-486-5101. *Coordr*, Sherry Natour; E-Mail: snatour@co.riverside.ca.us
Founded 1957
Library Holdings: Bk Vols 1,025; Bk Titles 995; Per Subs 209
Subject Interests: Bacteriology, Dermatology, Internal medicine, Mental health, Neurology, Nursing, Obstetrics and gynecology, Ophthalmology, Otolaryngology, Pediatrics, Radiology, Surgery
Restriction: Medical staff only

MOSS LANDING

S CALIFORNIA STATE UNIVERSITY, Moss Landing Marine Laboratories Library, 8272 Moss Landing Rd, 95039. SAN 301-0864. Tel: 831-632-4400. FAX: 831-753-2826. Web Site: www.mlml.calstate.edu. *Dir*, Joan Parker; E-Mail: parker@mlml.calstate.edu
Founded 1966. Enrl 126; Fac 9; Highest Degree: Master
Library Holdings: Bk Vols 15,000; Per Subs 120
Subject Interests: California, Mammals, Marine biology, Oceanography
Special Collections: Elkhorn Slough Coll

MOUNTAIN VIEW

S AEROTHERM CORP, Technical Library,* 580 Clyde Ave, 94043. SAN 301-0872. Tel: 650-961-6100, Ext 2580. FAX: 650-964-8349. *Mgr*, Karen Milos; *Asst Librn*, Kelly Pettigrew; Staff 2 (MLS 1, Non-MLS 1)
Library Holdings: Bk Titles 3,000; Per Subs 100
Subject Interests: Electronics
Automation Activity & Vendor Info: (Cataloging) Inmagic, Inc.

S ALZA, INC, Research Library, 1900 Charleston Rd, 94043. SAN 301-1658. Tel: 650-564-5597. FAX: 650-564-5554. Web Site: www.alza.com.; Staff 7 (MLS 5, Non-MLS 2)
Founded 1968
Library Holdings: Bk Titles 5,500; Per Subs 500
Subject Interests: Dermatology, Medicine, Obstetrics and gynecology, Ophthalmology, Pharmacology, Physiology
Restriction: By appointment only
Partic in Calif Libr Authority for Systs & Servs; Cooperative Information Network

S CATALYTICA, INC, Information Center,* 430 Ferguson Dr, 94043-5272. SAN 327-7097. Tel: 650-940-6326. FAX: 650-960-0127. *Librn, Mgr*, Silvia Lee; E-Mail: slee@mv.catalytica-inc.com
Library Holdings: Bk Vols 5,000; Per Subs 200
Subject Interests: Chemical engineering, Chemistry
Restriction: Staff use only
Partic in Class; Southnet

M EL CAMINO HOSPITAL LIBRARY & INFORMATION CENTER,* 2500 Grant Rd, PO Box 7025, Mail Stop ECH156, 94039-7025. SAN 370-2006. Tel: 650-940-7210. FAX: 650-940-7299. E-Mail: echline@six.netcon.com. *Mgr*, Margaret Goya; *Coll Develop*, Caroline Edmonds
Circ 2
Jul 1997-Jun 1998 Income $250,000. Mats Exp $65,000, Books $25,000, Per/Ser (Incl. Access Fees) $40,000. Sal $75,000
Library Holdings: Bk Vols 4,460; Per Subs 200
Subject Interests: Medicine, Nursing
Publications: Holdings Lists; occasional Newsletter; Special Selected Bibliographies
Partic in Northern California & Nevada Medical Library Group; Southnet

S GENERAL DYNAMICS-ELECTRONIC SYSTEMS, (Formerly GTE Government Systems Corp), Information Resource Center, 100 Ferguson Dr, PO Box 7188, 94039. SAN 301-0880. Tel: 650-966-3082. FAX: 650-966-2449. Web Site: eol.gd-es.com/irc. *In Charge*, Julie del Fierro; E-Mail: julie.delfierro@gd.es.com; Staff 2 (MLS 1, Non-MLS 1)
Founded 1953
Library Holdings: Bk Titles 5,000; Per Subs 450
Subject Interests: Electronics
Partic in Coop Libr Agency for Syst & Servs

S INTERNATIONAL DATA CORP LIBRARY,* 2131 Landings Dr, 94043. SAN 375-9164. Tel: 650-962-6481. FAX: 650-691-0518.
Library Holdings: Bk Vols 350

P MOUNTAIN VIEW PUBLIC LIBRARY,* 585 Franklin St, 94041-1998. SAN 301-0899. Tel: 650-903-6335. FAX: 650-962-0438. Web Site: www.library.ci.mtnview.ca.us. *Dir*, Susan Ozubko; *Coll Develop*, Kent Pettey; Staff 14 (MLS 14)
Founded 1905. Pop 71,300; Circ 720,000
Library Holdings: Bk Vols 266,955; Bk Titles 207,027; Per Subs 675
Special Collections: Automobiles, Maintenance & Repair; Local History
Automation Activity & Vendor Info: (Circulation) Innovative Interfaces Inc.
Publications: Bittersweet: Memoirs of Old Mountain View, An Oral History; Mountain View Library Community Analysis for Responsive Library Services
Mem of South Bay Coop Libr Syst
Friends of the Library Group

S NIELSEN ENGINEERING & RESEARCH, INC LIBRARY, 526 Clyde Ave, 94043-2212. SAN 301-0902. Tel: 650-968-9457, Ext 236. FAX: 650-968-1410. E-Mail: lib@nearinc.com. Web Site: www.nearinc.com. *Mgr*, Judy Faltz; Staff 1 (MLS 1)
Founded 1966
Library Holdings: Bk Vols 1,000; Per Subs 60
Publications: New Accessions List
Restriction: Staff use only

S PACIFIC STUDIES CENTER,* 222B View St, 94041. SAN 320-1597. Tel: 650-969-1545. FAX: 650-968-1126. *Dir*, Lenny Siegel; E-Mail: lsiegel@cpeo.org
Founded 1969
Library Holdings: Bk Titles 4,500; Per Subs 30
Special Collections: alternative magazines; Vertical file coll of newspaper clippings
Publications: Global Electronics (monthly)

MURRIETA

§P MURRIETA CITY LIBRARY, 39589 Los Alamos Rd, 92653. Tel: 909-304-2665. FAX: 909-696-0165. Web Site: www.ci.murrieta.ca.us. *City Librn*, Diane Alter; E-Mail: dalter@ci.murrieta.ca.us
Library Holdings: Bk Vols 18,000; Per Subs 68
Automation Activity & Vendor Info: (Cataloging) DRA; (Circulation) DRA; (OPAC) DRA; (Serials) DRA
Mem of Riverside County Library System

NAPA

P COMMUNITY RESOURCES FOR CHILDREN, Toy Library,* 5 Financial Plaza, Ste 224, 94558. SAN 326-1956. Tel: 707-253-0376. FAX: 707-253-2735. E-Mail: crc@napanet.net. *Librn*, Yvonne Robertson

P NAPA CITY-COUNTY LIBRARY, 580 Coombs St, 94559-3396. SAN 301-0929. Tel: 707-253-4241. TDD: 707-253-6088. FAX: 707-253-4615. Web Site: www.co.napa.ca.us/library. *Dir*, Thomas G Trice; E-Mail: ttrice@co.napa.ca.us; *Asst Dir*, Janet McCoy; *ILL*, Candace Ruise; *Tech Servs*, Maryll Telegdy; *Ref*, Norman Badion; Staff 9 (MLS 9)
Founded 1916. Pop 118,500; Circ 574,656
Jul 1999-Jun 2000 Income (Main Library and Branch Library) $3,041,159, State $349,347, Federal $10,000, County $2,431,552, Locally Generated Income $208,600, Other $41,660. Mats Exp $3,286,684, Books $278,270, Per/Ser (Incl. Access Fees) $24,920, Micro $860, Other Print Mats $50, Electronic Ref Mat (Incl. Access Fees) $342,752. Sal $1,386,869
Library Holdings: Bk Vols 149,926; Per Subs 398
Subject Interests: California
Special Collections: Calistoga Local History; Local History Newspaper Index
Automation Activity & Vendor Info: (Acquisitions) CARL; (Cataloging) CARL; (Circulation) CARL; (OPAC) CARL
Database Vendor: CARL, OCLC - First Search
Publications: Local History Indexer's Manual
Mem of North Bay Cooperative Library System
Special Services for the Deaf - TDD
Special Services for the Blind - Optelek 20/20 video magnification system
Common circulation system with Napa Valley College Library, Solano County Library & St Helen Public Library; Literacy Program for adult learners
Friends of the Library Group
Branches: 2
CALISTOGA PUBLIC, 1108 Myrtle, Calistoga, 94515-1730. SAN 321-7353. Tel: 707-942-4833. FAX: 707-942-0941.
Pop 4,950; Circ 32,058
Jul 1999-Jun 2000 Mats Exp $171,229
Library Holdings: Bk Vols 16,479
Subject Interests: Local history
Friends of the Library Group
YOUNTVILLE BRANCH LIBRARY, Town Hall Bldg, 6548 Yount St, Yountville, 94599-1271. SAN 328-7769. Tel: 707-944-1888.
Pop 3,770; Circ 9,687
1999-2000 Mats Exp $65,712
Library Holdings: Bk Vols 6,262
Friends of the Library Group

S NAPA COUNTY HISTORICAL SOCIETY RESEARCH LIBRARY,* Goodman Library Bldg, 1219 First St, 94559. SAN 326-6338. Tel: 707-224-1739. FAX: 707-224-5933. *Exec Dir*, Diane S Ballard; *Ref*, Ned Soderholm; Staff 14 (MLS 1, Non-MLS 13)
Founded 1975
Library Holdings: Bk Vols 3,686; Bk Titles 7,000
Special Collections: City & Co of Napa
Publications: Memoirs of the Vallejos; Wall Kennedy (booklets)
Restriction: Non-circulating to the public

GL NAPA COUNTY LAW LIBRARY, Old Courthouse, 1st Flr, 825 Brown St, 94559. SAN 301-0945. Tel: 707-253-4481. FAX: 707-259-8318. *Librn*, Maxine C Oellien
Library Holdings: Bk Vols 14,696

M NAPA STATE HOSPITAL, Wrenshall A Oliver Professional Library, 2100 Napa-Vallejo Hwy, 94558-6293. SAN 332-1541. Tel: 707-253-5000, 707-253-5477. *Librn*, B Fetesoff
Founded 1957
Library Holdings: Bk Titles 5,000; Per Subs 120
Subject Interests: Mentally retarded, Neurology, Psychiatry, Psychology, Social service (social work)
Special Collections: Contemporary Psychotherapies (Laskay Coll); History of Psychiatry (Argens Coll)
Restriction: Staff use only
Partic in Pacific SW Regional Med Libr Serv
Branches:
JOHN STEWART RICHIE PATIENTS' LIBRARY Tel: 707-253-5351. FAX: 707-253-5513. *Librn*, Patricia Bowen
Library Holdings: Bk Vols 6,500; Per Subs 55

J NAPA VALLEY COLLEGE LIBRARY, 2277 Napa Vallejo Hwy, 94558-6236. SAN 301-0937. Tel: 707-253-3011. Reference Tel: 707-253-3067. FAX: 707-253-3015. Web Site: www.nvc.cc.ca.us. *Asst Dean*, Bonnie Thoreen; Tel: 707-253-3014, E-Mail: bthoreen@campus.nvc.cc.ca.us; *Ref*, Carolyn Fruchtenicht; Tel: 707-253-3013, E-Mail: cfruchtenicht@campus.nvc.cc.ca.us; Staff 5 (MLS 2, Non-MLS 3)
Founded 1942. Enrl 10,000; Fac 200; Highest Degree: Associate
Jul 2000-Jun 2001 Income State $317,190. Mats Exp $47,645, Books $24,285, Per/Ser (Incl. Access Fees) $13,305, Micro $3,825, Other Print Mats $6,230. Sal $220,590 (Prof $96,600)
Library Holdings: Bk Vols 56,500; Bk Titles 55,000; Per Subs 203
Automation Activity & Vendor Info: (Acquisitions) CARL; (Circulation) CARL; (Course Reserve) CARL; (OPAC) CARL
Database Vendor: CARL, Ebsco - EbscoHost, GaleNet, IAC - Info Trac, OCLC - First Search, ProQuest
Mem of North Bay Cooperative Library System
Partic in N Bay Coop Libr Syst; Snap
Affiliated with Napa City-County Library & Solano County Libraries (SNAP)

NATIONAL CITY

S BEAUCHAMP BOTANICAL LIBRARY, 1434 E 24th St, PO Box 985, 91951-0985. SAN 324-7325. Tel: 619-477-0295. FAX: 619-477-5380. *Librn*, R Mitchel Beauchamp; E-Mail: mitch@psbs.com
Founded 1970
Jan 1999-Dec 1999 Mats Exp $1,200, Books $500, Per/Ser (Incl. Access Fees) $700
Library Holdings: Bk Titles 6,200; Per Subs 54
Subject Interests: Petaloid monocots (esp amaryllidaceae), Vascular floras of the world
Special Collections: Floristic Monographs

P NATIONAL CITY PUBLIC LIBRARY,* 200 E 12th St, 91950-3314. SAN 301-0953. Tel: 619-336-4350. FAX: 619-336-4368. Web Site: www.sdcoe.k12.ca.us/ncpl. *Dir*, Anne Campbell; E-Mail: acamp@sdcoe.k12.ca.us; *Head of Libr*, Lupe Sanchez; *Ch Servs*, Kenna Payne; Staff 8 (MLS 4, Non-MLS 4)
Founded 1896. Pop 55,600; Circ 303,370
Library Holdings: Bk Titles 110,500; Per Subs 350
Subject Interests: Ethnic studies, History
Special Collections: Local History, bks, tapes; Spanish bks, per
Publications: Pee Wee Press; Project READ (newsletter); Teacher's Topics (newsletter)
Mem of Serra Cooperative Library System
Partic in San Diego Greater Metro Area Libr & Info Agency Coun
Friends of the Library Group

M PARADISE VALLEY HOSPITAL, Medical Staff Library, 2400 E Fourth St, 91950. SAN 329-9945. Tel: 619-470-4120. FAX: 619-472-4573. *Asst Librn*, Marilyn Carnes
Library Holdings: Bk Titles 190; Per Subs 25
Restriction: Medical staff only
Partic in MLGSCA; National Network of Libraries of Medicine - Southeastern Atlantic Region

NEVADA CITY

S AMERICAN HERB ASSOCIATION LIBRARY,* PO Box 1673, 95959. SAN 370-9914. Tel: 530-274-3140. FAX: 530-274-3140. *Dir*, Kathi Keville
Library Holdings: Bk Vols 6,000; Per Subs 40

S NEVADA COUNTY HISTORICAL SOCIETY, Searls Historical Library, 214 Church St, 95959. SAN 301-0961. Tel: 530-265-5910. *Librn*, Edwin L Tyson; Staff 1 (MLS 1)
Founded 1972
Library Holdings: Bk Titles 1,125
Subject Interests: California, Local history, Nevada

L NEVADA COUNTY LAW LIBRARY, 201 Church St, Ste 9, 95959. SAN 301-097X. Tel: 530-265-2918. FAX: 530-265-7082. E-Mail: lawlibrary@co.nevada.ca.us. *Librn*, Lucifer Mellado
Library Holdings: Bk Titles 5,000

P NEVADA COUNTY LIBRARY,* Government Ctr, 980 Helling Way, 95959-2592. SAN 333-2640. Tel: 530-265-1407, 530-265-7078. FAX: 530-265-7241. *Librn*, Francisco Pinneli; E-Mail: fpinneli@hotmail.com; *ILL*, Joan Parkan; *Branch Mgr*, Mary Ann Trygg; Tel: 530-265-7078, E-Mail: limtrygg@er_excl.co.nevada.ca.us; Staff 18 (MLS 3, Non-MLS 15)
Founded 1972. Pop 89,000
Jul 1997-Jun 1998 Income $654,929. Mats Exp $60,217. Sal $420,591
Library Holdings: Bk Vols 116,492; Per Subs 310
Subject Interests: Nevada
Automation Activity & Vendor Info: (Circulation) epixtech, inc.
Mem of Mountain-Valley Library System
Friends of the Library Group
Branches: 4
GRASS VALLEY BRANCH, 207 Mill St, Grass Valley, 95945-6789. SAN 333-2675. Tel: 530-273-4117. FAX: 530-273-5619. *Librn*, Judith Mariaz; Staff 13 (MLS 3, Non-MLS 10)
Library Holdings: Bk Vols 52,305
Friends of the Library Group
MADELYN HELLING COUNTY LIBRARY, Government Ctr, 980 Helling Way, 95959. SAN 373-5931. Tel: 530-265-7050. FAX: 530-265-7241. *Librn*, Mary Ann Trygg
Library Holdings: Bk Vols 63,299

Friends of the Library Group
LOCAL HISTORY, 211 N Pine St, 95959-2592. SAN 333-2705. Tel: 530-265-4606. *Tech Servs*, Nadya Henry
Library Holdings: Bk Vols 1,178
Subject Interests: Local history, Mining
Friends of the Library Group
TRUCKEE BRANCH, 10031 Levone Ave, Truckee, 96161-4800. SAN 333-273X. Tel: 530-582-7846. Web Site: www.nccn.net/~nclib/index.htm. *In Charge*, Lauri Ferguson
Founded 1976. Pop 11,000
Library Holdings: Bk Vols 26,000; Per Subs 35
Subject Interests: Local history
Friends of the Library Group

NEWPORT BEACH

S CONEXANT SYSTEMS INC, (Formerly Rockwell Semiconductor Systems), Library & Information Center, 4311 Jamboree Rd, E01-100, 92660. SAN 301-1054. Tel: 949-483-5628. FAX: 949-483-6977. *Librn, Mgr*, Jill Foreman; E-Mail: jill.foreman@conexant.com; *Assoc Librn*, Debra Lozano; E-Mail: debra.lozano@conexant.com; *Web Coordr*, Magan Stephens; E-Mail: magan.stephens@conexant.com; Staff 4 (MLS 2, Non-MLS 2)
1998-1999 Mats Exp $500,000
Library Holdings: Bk Vols 4,000; Bk Titles 3,000; Per Subs 250
Subject Interests: Telecommunications
Special Collections: Commercial, Industry Coll
Restriction: Company library

L CUMMINS & WHITE, Law Library,* 2424 SE Bristol St No 300, 92660. SAN 375-7552. Tel: 949-852-1800. FAX: 949-852-8510. *Adminr*, Donna T Funa
Library Holdings: Bk Titles 12,000; Per Subs 25

M FULTON SKIN RESEARCH INSTITUTE LIBRARY,* 1617 Westcliff Dr, No 100, 92660. SAN 375-765X. Tel: 949-631-3376. FAX: 949-631-1284. *Dir*, Dr James E Fulton Jr
Library Holdings: Per Subs 15

M HOAG MEMORIAL HOSPITAL PRESBYTERIAN, Robert & Winifred Bacon Memorial Medical Library,* One Hoag Dr, PO Box 6100, 92648-6100. SAN 301-102X. Tel: 949-760-2308. FAX: 949-760-5729. *Librn*, Cathy Drake; E-Mail: cdrake@hoaghospital.org; Staff 1 (MLS 1)
Founded 1959
Library Holdings: Bk Vols 3,000; Per Subs 300
Subject Interests: Nursing
Special Collections: Psychiatry (Krukas Memorial Coll)

S NEWPORT AERONAUTICAL SALES LIBRARY, 1542 Monrovia Ave, 92663-2807. SAN 373-0263. Tel: 949-574-4100. FAX: 949-574-4106. E-Mail: nwptaero@primenet.com. *Pres, Res*, George M Posey
Library Holdings: Bk Vols 100,000

P NEWPORT BEACH PUBLIC LIBRARY, 1000 Avocado Ave, 92660-6301. SAN 333-2764. Tel: 949-717-3800. FAX: 949-640-5681. E-Mail: nbplref@city.newport-beach.ca.us. Web Site: www.newportbeachlibrary.org. *City Librn*, LaDonna T Kienitz; Tel: 949-644-3157, Fax: 949-644-3155, E-Mail: lkienitz@city.newport-beach.ca.us; *Asst City Librn*, Darlene Gaetano; Tel: 949-717-3805, E-Mail: dgaetano@city.newport-beach.ca.us; *ILL*, Janet Bandel; *Acq*, Eileen Harrington; Tel: 949-717-3822; *Ch Servs, YA Servs*, Judy Kelley; Tel: 949-717-3807, E-Mail: jkelley@city.newport-beach.ca.us; *Ref Serv*, Susan Hubbs; Tel: 949-717-3806, Fax: 949-640-5648, E-Mail: slamb@city.newport-beach.ca.us; *Coll Develop*, Susan Warren; Tel: 949-717-3828, E-Mail: swarren@city.newport-beach.ca.us; *Circ*, Melissa Kelly; Tel: 949-717-3852, E-Mail: mkelly@city.newport-beach.ca.us; Staff 22 (MLS 20, Non-MLS 2)
Founded 1920. Pop 70,100; Circ 1,246,952
Jul 1998-Jun 1999 Income (Main Library and Branch Library) $5,016,577. Mats Exp $649,926, Books $421,826, Per/Ser (Incl. Access Fees) $47,000, Micro $46,100, Electronic Ref Mat (Incl. Access Fees) $135,000. Sal $2,102,640
Library Holdings: Bk Vols 374,361; Bk Titles 280,758; Per Subs 905
Special Collections: Nautical Coll; Newport Beach History
Automation Activity & Vendor Info: (Acquisitions) epixtech, inc.; (Cataloging) Brodart; (Circulation) epixtech, inc.; (OPAC) epixtech, inc.
Database Vendor: Ebsco - EbscoHost, GaleNet, OCLC - First Search, ProQuest
Publications: Bookends (Friends newsletter); Check it Out (newsletter); Lighthouse (literacy newsletter)
Mem of Santiago Libr Syst
Partic in Metro Coop Libr Syst; OCLC Online Computer Library Center, Inc
Friends of the Library Group
Branches: 4
BALBOA BRANCH, 100 E Balboa Blvd, Balboa, 92661. SAN 333-2799. Tel: 949-717-3800. FAX: 949-675-8524. *Librn*, Judy Booth; E-Mail: jbooth@city.newport-beach.ca.us
Library Holdings: Bk Vols 49,090
Special Collections: Nautical Coll
CENTRAL LIBRARY, 1000 Avocado Ave, 92660-6301. SAN 333-2888. Tel: 949-717-3800. FAX: 949-640-5681. *Librn*, Darlene Gaetano
Library Holdings: Bk Vols 226,811
Subject Interests: American history, Art, Business and management
CORONA DEL MAR BRANCH, 420 Marigold Ave, Corona del Mar, 92625. SAN 333-2829. Tel: 949-717-3800. FAX: 949-673-4917. *Librn*, Jana Pratt; E-Mail: jpratt@city.newport-beach.ca.us; Staff 1 (MLS 1)
Library Holdings: Bk Vols 31,718
MARINERS, 2005 Dover Dr, 92660. SAN 333-2853. Tel: 949-717-3800. FAX: 949-642-4848. *Librn*, Phyllis Scheffler; E-Mail: pscheff@city.newport-beach.ca.us; Staff 2 (MLS 2)
Library Holdings: Bk Vols 66,742

L O'MELVENY & MYERS, Law Library, 610 Newport Center Dr, 92660. SAN 372-3801. Tel: 949-760-9600. FAX: 949-823-6994. *Dir*, Gary Singer; Tel: 949-823-6915, E-Mail: gsinger@omm.com; *Librn*, Aleta Benjamin; E-Mail: abenjamin@amm.com
Founded 1979
Library Holdings: Bk Vols 5,000

S ORANGE COUNTY MUSEUM OF ART LIBRARY,* 850 San Clemente Dr, 92660. SAN 301-1046. Tel: 949-759-1122. FAX: 949-759-5623. *Librn*, Ruth E Roe
Founded 1965
Library Holdings: Bk Titles 200
Subject Interests: California
Restriction: Staff use only

S STRADLING, YOCCA, CARLSON & RAUTH, Law Library, 660 Newport Ctr, Ste 1600, 92660. SAN 373-9007. Tel: 949-725-4000. FAX: 949-725-4100. *Librn*, Lynn Connor Merring; Staff 3 (MLS 1, Non-MLS 2)
Library Holdings: Bk Vols 7,000; Bk Titles 1,000; Per Subs 200

NORTH HIGHLANDS

R ZION LUTHERAN CHURCH,* 3644 Bolivar Ave, 95660. SAN 301-1070. Tel: 916-332-4001. FAX: 916-332-4030. *Librn*, Marilyn Weinrich
Library Holdings: Bk Vols 600

NORTH HOLLYWOOD

S PACIFICA FOUNDATION, Radio Archive, 3729 Cahuenga Blvd W, 91604. (Mail add: PO Box 8092 Department B, 91608), SAN 326-0577. Tel: 818-506-1077. Toll Free Tel: 800-735-0230. FAX: 818-506-1084. E-Mail: pacarchive@aol.com. Web Site: www.pacifica.org. *Cat*, J Brian DeShazor; Tel: 818-506-1077, Ext 265; Staff 2 (MLS 1, Non-MLS 1)
Founded 1970
Library Holdings: Bk Titles 40,000
Subject Interests: Political science, Pub affairs
Automation Activity & Vendor Info: (Cataloging) Inmagic, Inc.
Publications: Annual Cassette & Reel to Reel Catalogues (print)
Function: Archival collection
Partic in OCLC Online Computer Library Center, Inc
Cassette sales to public (individuals). Reel to Reel to public radio stations. Facility is open to public to listen to tapes in house, by appointment

S WESTERN COSTUME CO, Research Library,* 11041 Vanowen St, 91605. SAN 326-3800. Tel: 818-760-0902, Ext 148. FAX: 818-508-2182. Web Site: www.westerncostume.com. *Dir, Res*, Sally Nelson-Harb; Staff 1 (MLS 1)
Founded 1915
Library Holdings: Bk Vols 13,500; Bk Titles 12,500; Per Subs 60
Special Collections: Godey, Peterson & Vogue, mags; Sears & Montgomery Ward Catalogs (1895 to present); Twentieth Century Fox Costume Still Coll

NORTHRIDGE

C CALIFORNIA STATE UNIVERSITY, NORTHRIDGE, Delmar T Oviatt Library, 18111 Nordhoff St, 91330-8326. SAN 333-2918. Tel: 818-677-2271. Interlibrary Loan Service Tel: 818-677-2294. FAX: 818-677-2676. E-Mail: libweb@csun.edu. Web Site: library.csun.edu. *Dean of Libr*, Susan C Curzon; E-Mail: susan.curzon@csun.edu; *Assoc Dean*, Susan E Parker; Tel: 818-677-2272, E-Mail: susan.parker@csun.edu; *Cat*, Snowdy Dodson; Tel: 818-677-2261, E-Mail: snowdy.dodson@csun.edu; *Ref*, Michael Barrett; Tel: 818-677-2277, E-Mail: michael.barrett@csun.edu; *Per*, Lisle Wenberg; Tel: 818-677-3282, E-Mail: lisle.wenberg@csun.edu; *Bibliog Instr*, Kris Eckland; Tel: 818-677-2281, E-Mail: kris.eckland@csun.edu; *ILL*, Felicia Cousin; E-Mail: felicia.cousin@csun.edu; *Rare Bks, Spec Coll*, Tony Gardner; Tel: 818-677-2832, E-Mail: tony.gardner@csun.edu; *Coll Develop*, David Perkins; Tel: 818-677-7830, E-Mail: david.perkins@csun.edu; *Govt Doc*, Mary Finley; Tel: 818-677-5001, E-Mail: mary.finley@csun.edu; *Archivist*, Virginia Elwood; Tel: 818-677-5336, E-Mail: virginia.elwood@csun.edu; *Ref*, Monica Burdex-Esposito; Tel: 818-677-4679, E-Mail: monica.burdex@csun.edu; *Ref*, Angela Lew; Tel: 818-677-2600, E-Mail: angela.lew@csun.edu; *Ref, Spec Coll*, Caroline Russom; Tel: 818-677-4887, E-Mail: caroline.russom@csun.edu; *Cat, Doc Delivery*, Jina Wakimoto; *Cat*, Mary Woodley; Tel: 818-677-2261, E-Mail: mary.woodley@csun.edu. Subject

Specialists: *Business and management*, Karen Anderson; *Deaf*, Mara Houdyshell; *Economics*, Karen Anderson; *Education*, Mara Houdyshell; *Foreign Language*, Kris Ecklund; *Health sciences*, Marcia Henry; *Philosophy*, Kris Ecklund; *Political science*, Darrin Gitisetan; *Religion*, Kris Ecklund; *Women studies*, Virginia Elwood; Staff 25 (MLS 25)
Founded 1958. Enrl 27,653; Fac 1,580; Highest Degree: Master
1998-1999 Income $6,076,464. Mats Exp $1,684,550, Books $889,952, Per/Ser (Incl. Access Fees) $794,598. Sal $3,918,442 (Prof $1,773,541)
Library Holdings: Bk Vols 1,180,917; Bk Titles 694,582; Per Subs 2,551
Subject Interests: Local history, Music
Special Collections: 19th Century English & American Playbills (Theater Program Coll, 1809-1930); 19th Century English Theatre Playbills Coll; American Plantation Documents (Legal & Financial Documents on slaves & slavery, 1756-1869); California & Local History, per; California Tourism & Promotional Literature Coll; Carl Sandburg Coll, bks, pamphlets & news clippings; Contemporary 20th Century American Writers (McDermott Coll); Edwin Booth Coll, migrant farm labor camp newsletters 1930s, Francis Gilbert Webb correspondence 1898-1934; Gwen Driston papers; Haldeman-Julius Publications, Big & Little Blue Books, etc; History of printing (Lynton Kistler-Merle Armitage Coll); Human Sexuality (Vern & Bonnie Bullough Coll); Japanese-American World War II Relocation Camps, newsp & documents; Radio & Film Scripts, NBC radio plays 1935-1943, Milton Geiger papers; Ray Martin Coll, music scores; Revolutionary & Political Movements in Russia 1875-1937 (Patrick Coll); Vern & Bonnie Bullough Coll; Women Music Composers (Aaron Cohen Coll, Ruth Shaw Wylie Scores, Ardis O Higgin Coll)
Automation Activity & Vendor Info: (Acquisitions) GEAC; (Cataloging) GEAC; (Circulation) GEAC; (Serials) GEAC
Publications: Faculty Guide; Oviatt Friends, University Library Annual Report; Reference Department Bibliographies; Santa Susana Press; University Library News
Partic in Center For Research Libraries; OCLC Online Computer Library Center, Inc
Special Services for the Deaf - Books on deafness & sign language; Special interest periodicals; Staff with knowledge of sign language; TTY machine
Special Services for the Blind - Braille typewriter; Kurzweil Reading Machine; Talking books from Braille Institute; Talking calculator
PC software & hardware setups for differing disabilities
Friends of the Library Group
Departmental Libraries:
GEOGRAPHY MAP LIBRARY, Sierra Hall 135, 91330-8249. SAN 333-2977. Tel: 818-677-3465. FAX: 818-677-7840. E-Mail: map.library@csun.edu. Web Site: www.maplibrary.csun.edu. *Curator*, Michael Swift; Staff 2 (Non-MLS 2)
NATIONAL CENTER ON DEAFNESS, 18111 Nordhoff St, 91330-8267. SAN 333-2942. Tel: 818-677-2611. FAX: 818-677-4899. E-Mail: wrocc@csun.edu. Web Site: www.ncod.csun.edu. *Dir*, Marrie C Pearson; *Info Res*, Anthony Ivan Kovic
Library Holdings: Bk Vols 3,000; Per Subs 25

M NORTHRIDGE HOSPITAL, Atcherley Medical Library, 18300 Roscoe Blvd, 91328. SAN 321-5601. Tel: 818-885-8500, Ext 4608. FAX: 818-885-0372. *Librn*, Theresa Sase; *Asst Librn*, Joyce Machynia
Founded 1975
Library Holdings: Bk Titles 3,000; Per Subs 190

NORWALK

§S CALIFORNIA YOUTH AUTHORITY, Southern Youth Correctional Reception Center & Clinic Library, 13200 S Bloomfield Ave, 90650. Tel: 562-868-9979, Ext 2363. FAX: 562-868-2899. *Senior Librn*, Phyllis Nemeth
Library Holdings: Bk Vols 4,000; Per Subs 40
Open Mon, Wed &Thurs 8-11 & 1-4:30

J CERRITOS COLLEGE LIBRARY,* 11110 Alondra Blvd, 90650. SAN 301-1127. Tel: 562-860-2451, Ext 2412. FAX: 562-467-5002. Web Site: www.library.cerritos.edu. *Dean*, John McGinnis; E-Mail: mcginnis@cerritos.edu; *Coll Develop, Librn*, Lynda Sampson; *Librn*, Val Mitchell; *Librn*, Judy Ohye
Founded 1957. Enrl 23,000
Jul 1997-Jun 1998 Income $734,000. Mats Exp $277,427, Books $228,942, Per/Ser (Incl. Access Fees) $48,485. Sal $606,320 (Prof $338,749)
Library Holdings: Bk Vols 86,184; Bk Titles 72,546; Per Subs 434
Partic in OCLC Online Computer Library Center, Inc
Friends of the Library Group

METROPOLITAN STATE HOSPITAL
S PATIENTS LIBRARY, 11400 Norwalk Blvd, 90650. SAN 333-306X. Tel: 562-651-3274. FAX: 562-651-4439. *In Charge*, Arno Nappi; E-Mail: a.nappi@dreamsoft.com
Founded 1950
Library Holdings: Bk Vols 2,500; Per Subs 30
Subject Interests: Psychiatry, Psychology, Sociology
M STAFF LIBRARY, 11401 S Bloomfield Ave, 90650. SAN 333-3124. Tel: 562-651-4334. Reference Tel: 562-651-2295. FAX: 562-651-4439. E-Mail: stafflibrary@dreamsoft.com. *In Charge*, Arno Nappi; E-Mail: a.nappi@dreamsoft.com. Subject Specialists: *Psychiatry*, Arno Nappi; *Psychology*, Arno Nappi; *Psychotherapy*, Arno Nappi; Staff 2 (MLS 1, Non-MLS 1)
Founded 1957
Jul 1999-Jun 2000 Income $145,000. Mats Exp $24,450, Books $8,000, Per/Ser (Incl. Access Fees) $15,000, Presv $1,200, Electronic Ref Mat (Incl. Access Fees) $250. Sal $140,000 (Prof $110,000)
Library Holdings: Bk Vols 9,500; Per Subs 71
Subject Interests: Psychiatry, Psychology, Psychotherapy
Automation Activity & Vendor Info: (Circulation) Inmagic, Inc.; (OPAC) Inmagic, Inc.; (Serials) Inmagic, Inc.
Database Vendor: Dialog
Restriction: Staff use only
Function: Archival collection
Partic in Pacific SW Regional Med Libr Serv

NOVATO

S FIREMAN'S FUND INSURANCE CO LIBRARY, 777 San Marin Dr, 94998. SAN 301-4053. Tel: 415-899-2871. FAX: 415-899-2195. E-Mail: library@ffic.com. *Head of Libr*, Lori Deibel; Staff 5 (MLS 2, Non-MLS 3)
Founded 1969
Library Holdings: Bk Vols 5,000; Per Subs 225
Subject Interests: Insurance
Automation Activity & Vendor Info: (Acquisitions) Sydney; (Cataloging) Sydney; (Circulation) Sydney; (OPAC) Sydney; (Serials) Sydney
Restriction: Staff use only

C INDIAN VALLEY COLLEGES LIBRARY,* 1800 Ignacio Blvd, 94949. SAN 320-5703. Tel: 415-883-2211. FAX: 415-883-6980. Web Site: www.marin.cc.ca.us. *Tech Servs*, Joan Nilsen
Founded 1971
Library Holdings: Bk Vols 85,000; Per Subs 45
Partic in OCLC Online Computer Library Center, Inc
Open Tues-Thurs 9-2:30

S MARIN INDEPENDENT JOURNAL, Newspaper Library,* 150 Alameda del Prado, PO Box 6150, 94948-6150. SAN 327-2613. Tel: 415-382-7236. FAX: 415-883-5458. *Chief Librn*, Carol Farrand
Library Holdings: Bk Vols 500
Special Collections: Clippings & Photo Files; Historical Photographs; Newspaper Archives

S MARIN MUSEUM OF THE AMERICAN INDIAN LIBRARY, (MMAI), Miwok Park 2200 Novato Blvd, 94948. (Mail add: PO Box 864, 94948), SAN 329-0662. Tel: 415-897-4064. FAX: 415-892-7804. *Exec Dir*, Shirly Schaufel
Founded 1973
Library Holdings: Bk Vols 600
Subject Interests: Am Indian art, California, Native people
Function: Reference only
Open Tues-Fri 10am-3pm & Sat-Sun noon-4pm, call for appointment

OAKLAND

M ALAMEDA COUNTY MEDICAL CENTER, Medical Library, 1411 E 31st St, 94602. SAN 301-1135. Tel: 510-437-4701. FAX: 510-437-4696. Web Site: library1@acmedctr.org. *Librn*, Kathy C Yue; E-Mail: cyue@acmedctr.org; Staff 1 (MLS 1)
Founded 1917
Oct 1999-Sep 2000 Mats Exp $65,000, Books $10,000, Per/Ser (Incl. Access Fees) $45,000, Electronic Ref Mat (Incl. Access Fees) $10,000
Library Holdings: Bk Titles 2,200; Per Subs 130
Subject Interests: Clinical medicine
Automation Activity & Vendor Info: (Acquisitions) EOS; (OPAC) EOS; (Serials) EOS
Database Vendor: OVID Technologies
Restriction: Employees & their associates
Partic in Northern California & Nevada Medical Library Group; Pacific SW Regional Med Libr Serv

C ARMSTRONG UNIVERSITY LIBRARY,* 1608 Webster St, 94612. SAN 300-6034. Tel: 510-835-7900. FAX: 510-835-8935. E-Mail: library@armstrong.u.edu. *Librn*, Steve Lavoie; Staff 5 (MLS 1, Non-MLS 4)
Founded 1918. Enrl 100; Fac 20; Highest Degree: Doctorate
Library Holdings: Bk Vols 12,250; Bk Titles 10,000; Per Subs 100
Subject Interests: Accounting, Economics, International, Marketing
Special Collections: Annual Report Coll; Armstrong College Archives; Biography Coll; Business History Coll

S BERKELEY PLANNING ASSOCIATES LIBRARY,* 440 Grand Ave, Ste 500, 94610. SAN 371-2389. Tel: 510-465-7884. FAX: 510-465-7885. Web Site: www.bpa.com. *Librn*, Sabrina Williams
Library Holdings: Bk Vols 550; Per Subs 20
Open Mon-Fri 8:30-5

GL BERNARD E WITKIN ALAMEDA COUNTY LAW LIBRARY, 12th & Oak Street Bldg, 125 Twelfth St, 94607-4912. SAN 301-1143. Tel: 510-208-4800. Circulation Tel: 510-208-4835. Reference Tel: 510-208-4832. FAX: 510-208-4836. E-Mail: csun@co.alameda.ca.us. Web Site:

www.co.alameda.ca.us/law/index.htm. *Dir*, Cossette T Sun; *Publ Servs*, Robert Podlech; *Cat, Ref*, Greg Fite; Staff 4 (MLS 4)
Founded 1891. Pop 1,356,612
Jul 1999-Jun 2000 Income $1,350,402, Locally Generated Income $121,085, Other $1,229,317. Mats Exp $264,634, Books $84,289, Per/Ser (Incl. Access Fees) $7,329, Micro $8,187, Other Print Mats $164,829. Sal $621,132 (Prof $209,335)
Library Holdings: Bk Vols 126,030; Bk Titles 15,418
Special Collections: California Supreme Court & Appellate Briefs; Federal & State Statutes, indexes & digests; Legal Periodical Coll; Legal Practice Material
Automation Activity & Vendor Info: (Cataloging) Sydney; (Circulation) Sydney; (OPAC) Sydney; (Serials) Sydney
Publications: (Serials catalog); ACLL Newsletter; Recent Acquisitions List
Restriction: Members only, Residents only
Partic in RLIN; Westlaw
Branches:
SOUTH COUNTY BRANCH, 224 W Winton Ave, Rm 162, Hayward, 94544. SAN 300-810X. Tel: 510-670-5230. FAX: 510-670-5292. Web Site: www.co.alameda.ca.us/law/index.htm. *Dir*, Cossette T Sun; *Ref*, Gregory Fite; Staff 1 (MLS 1)
Founded 1967
Library Holdings: Bk Vols 23,307
Special Collections: Local Municipal Codes & City Ordinances
Automation Activity & Vendor Info: (OPAC) Sydney
Function: Research library

C CALIFORNIA COLLEGE OF ARTS & CRAFTS, Meyer Library, 5212 Broadway, 94618. SAN 301-1186. Tel: 510-594-3658. FAX: 510-594-3711. *Dir*, Mary Manning; *Librn*, Alice Egan; *Librn*, Michael Lordi
Founded 1907. Enrl 1,058; Fac 200
Library Holdings: Bk Titles 43,937; Per Subs 300
Subject Interests: Architecture, Fine arts
Special Collections: Industrial Design (Jo Sinel Coll)

S CALIFORNIA REGIONAL WATER QUALITY CONTROL BOARD, San Francisco Bay Region Library, 1515 Clay St Ste 1400, 94612. SAN 371-246X. Tel: 510-622-2300. FAX: 510-622-2460. Web Site: www.swrcb.ca.gov/~rwqcb2. *In Charge*, Lawrence Kolb
Library Holdings: Bk Vols 1,500; Per Subs 20
Open Mon-Fri 8-5

§G CALIFORNIA STATE DEPARTMENT OF HEALTH SERVICES, Occupational & Environmental Health Library, 1515 Clay St, 16th flr, 94612. Tel: 510-622-3204, 510-622-3205. FAX: 510-622-3197. Web Site: www.lib.berkeley.edu/publ/dhs/oehlindex.html. *Head Librn*, Charleen Kubota; E-Mail: ckubota@oehha.ca.gov
Library Holdings: Bk Vols 6,400; Per Subs 40
Restriction: Staff use only

G CALIFORNIA STATE DEPARTMENT OF TRANSPORTATION, District 4 Library,* 111 Grand Ave, PO Box 23660, 94623-0660. SAN 301-3812. Tel: 510-286-5243. FAX: 510-286-5244. *In Charge*, Alice Y Whitten; E-Mail: awhitten@trmx3.dot.ca.gov
Founded 1972
Jul 1997-Jun 1998 Mats Exp $15,106, Books $9,780, Per/Ser (Incl. Access Fees) $5,326
Library Holdings: Bk Titles 11,375; Per Subs 180
Subject Interests: Environmental engineering, Transportation
Special Collections: California Division of Highways Statutes, 1929 to Date, Budget Reports, 1925 to Date, Specifications, 1925 to Date, Public Works & Highways, 1924-66, per; Highway Research Board, pamphlets, per
Publications: News from the Library (list of new publications)
Partic in Triangle Research Libraries Network

S CHABOT SPACE & SCIENCE CENTER LIBRARY, (Formerly Chabot Observatory & Science Center Library), 10000 Skyline Blvd, 94619. SAN 301-1194. Tel: 510-336-7300. FAX: 510-336-7491. Web Site: www.chabotspace.org. *Exec Dir*, Dr Michael D Reynolds
Founded 1883
Library Holdings: Bk Titles 2,500
Subject Interests: Astronomy
Restriction: By appointment only

M CHILDREN'S HOSPITAL OAKLAND, Gordon Health Sciences Library, 744 52nd St, 94609. (Mail add: 747 52nd St, 94609), SAN 301-1208. Tel: 510-428-3448. FAX: 510-601-3963. E-Mail: cholibrary@mail.cho.org. *Mgr Libr Serv*, Jane A Irving; E-Mail: jirving@mail.cho.org; Staff 2 (MLS 2)
Founded 1938
Jul 1999-Jun 2000 Income $268,000. Mats Exp $161,020, Books $34,420, Per/Ser (Incl. Access Fees) $79,000, Electronic Ref Mat (Incl. Access Fees) $47,600. Sal $90,000
Library Holdings: Bk Vols 4,283; Bk Titles 3,929; Per Subs 350
Subject Interests: Pediatrics
Publications: Online Acquisitions List; Online Newsletter; Serials Holdings
Friends of the Library Group

L CROSBY, HEAFEY, ROACH & MAY, Law Library, 1999 Harrison St, 94612. SAN 301-1232. Tel: 510-466-6195. Interlibrary Loan Service Tel: 510-466-6192. Reference Tel: 510-466-6194. FAX: 510-273-8898. *Dir Libr Serv*, Nora Levine; E-Mail: nlevine@chrm.com; Staff 6 (MLS 3, Non-MLS 3)
Founded 1967
Library Holdings: Bk Vols 25,000; Bk Titles 5,000; Per Subs 600
Automation Activity & Vendor Info: (Acquisitions) EOS; (Serials) EOS
Branches:
LAW LIBRARY, 700 S Flower St, Ste 2200, Los Angeles, 90017. SAN 370-7571. Tel: 213-689-6418. FAX: 213-896-8080. *Librn*, Malinda Muller; E-Mail: mmuller@chrm.com; Staff 2 (MLS 1, Non-MLS 1)
Library Holdings: Bk Vols 5,000; Bk Titles 200; Per Subs 24
Automation Activity & Vendor Info: (Acquisitions) EOS; (Serials) EOS

S DATACENTER LIBRARY,* 1904 Franklin St, Ste 900, 94612. SAN 326-4955. Tel: 510-835-4692. FAX: 510-835-3017. E-Mail: datacenter@igc.apc.org. Web Site: datacenter.org. *Dir*, Catherine Powell
Founded 1976
Library Holdings: Bk Titles 4,000; Per Subs 600
Subject Interests: Human rights
Publications: Culture Watch; Information Services Lat America; ISLA; Plant Shutdowns Monitor

L FITZGERALD, ABBOTT & BEARDSLEY, Law Library,* 1221 Broadway, 21st flr, 94612. SAN 301-1259. Tel: 510-451-3300. FAX: 510-451-1527. *Librn*, Virginia Meadowcroft
Founded 1906
Library Holdings: Bk Vols 12,000
Restriction: Staff use only

C HOLY NAMES COLLEGE, Paul J Cushing Library, 3500 Mountain Blvd, 94619. SAN 301-1267. Interlibrary Loan Service Tel: 510-436-1332. FAX: 510-436-1199. Web Site: www.hnc.edu. *Dir*, Joyce McLean; E-Mail: hui@academ.hnc.edu; Staff 5 (MLS 3, Non-MLS 2)
Founded 1880. Enrl 734; Fac 90; Highest Degree: Master
Library Holdings: Bk Vols 110,695; Per Subs 457
Subject Interests: Music, Nursing, Religion
Special Collections: Book plates

S WILSON IHRIG & ASSOCIATES LIBRARY,* 5776 Broadway, 94618. SAN 325-4674. Tel: 510-658-6719. FAX: 510-652-4441. E-Mail: info@wiai.com. Web Site: www.wiai.com. *Librn*, Beverly Milam; Staff 17 (MLS 9, Non-MLS 8)
Founded 1966
Library Holdings: Bk Vols 800; Bk Titles 620; Per Subs 55
Subject Interests: Acoustics
Restriction: By appointment only
Partic in Dialog Corporation

S INDEPENDENT INSTITUTE LIBRARY,* 100 Swan Way, 94621. SAN 371-7410. Tel: 510-632-1366. FAX: 510-568-6040. E-Mail: info@independent.org. Web Site: www.independent.org.
Library Holdings: Bk Titles 5,200; Per Subs 85
Subject Interests: History, Law

S K T ANALYTICS INC LIBRARY,* 885 Rosemount Rd, 94610. SAN 373-4137. Tel: 510-839-7702. FAX: 510-839-9887. *Mgr, VPres*, Thomas Higgins
Library Holdings: Bk Vols 2,500

M KAISER-PERMANENTE MEDICAL CENTER, Health Sciences Library,* 280 W MacArthur Blvd, 94611-5693. SAN 301-1283. Tel: 510-596-6158. FAX: 510-596-1500. *Librn*, Ysabel Bertolucci; Staff 2 (MLS 1, Non-MLS 1)
Founded 1969
Library Holdings: Bk Titles 2,000; Per Subs 350
Subject Interests: Arthritis, Cancer, Nutrition
Publications: AV list; book list; pamphlet list
Restriction: Not open to public

J LANEY COLLEGE, Library-Learning Resources Center,* 900 Fallon St, 94607. SAN 301-1291. Tel: 510-464-3498, Ext 3495. FAX: 510-464-3264. Web Site: www.peralta.cc.ca.us. *Chief Librn, Publ Servs*, Shirley Coaston; *Cat*, Evelyn Lord; *Ref*, Margaret Traylor; *Acq*, May Frances Moore; Staff 5 (MLS 5)
Founded 1956. Enrl 10,508; Fac 177
Library Holdings: Bk Vols 78,882; Bk Titles 72,000; Per Subs 285
Open Mon-Thurs 8-9, Fri 8-2 & Sat 8:30-2

C LINCOLN UNIVERSITY LIBRARY,* 401 15th St, 94612. SAN 321-9380. Tel: 510-628-8011. *Librn*, Mei Hung; Staff 1 (MLS 1)
Founded 1962. Enrl 385; Highest Degree: Master
Library Holdings: Bk Vols 21,500; Per Subs 657
Partic in Dialog Corporation

J MERRITT COLLEGE LIBRARY, 12500 Campus Dr, 94619-3196. SAN 301-1305. Tel: 510-436-2462. Circulation Tel: 510-436-2457. Reference Tel: 510-436-2557. FAX: 510-531-4960. Web Site: www.merritt.edu:80/~lrc. *Tech Servs*, Eva Ng-Chin; E-Mail: engchin@merrit.edu
Founded 1954. Enrl 2,198; Fac 128

Library Holdings: Bk Titles 60,000; Per Subs 120
Automation Activity & Vendor Info: (Acquisitions) epixtech, inc.; (Cataloging) epixtech, inc.; (Circulation) epixtech, inc.; (Course Reserve) epixtech, inc.; (OPAC) epixtech, inc.
Partic in Bay Area Libr & Info Systs
Special Services for the Blind - ADA PC (OPAC) with JAWS & Zoom Text; Kurzweil Reader

G METROPOLITAN TRANSPORTATION COMMISSION, Association of Bay Area Governments (ABAG) Library, 101 Eighth St, 94607. SAN 331-5363. Tel: 510-464-7836. FAX: 510-464-7852. E-Mail: library@mtc.ca.gov. Web Site: www.mtc.ca.gov. *Chief Librn*, Joan Friedman; Tel: 510-464-7833, E-Mail: jfriedman@mtc.ca.gov; *Librn*, Jane McKenna; Tel: 510-464-7835, E-Mail: jmcken@mtc.ca.gov; Staff 3 (MLS 2, Non-MLS 1)
Founded 1972
Library Holdings: Bk Vols 25,000; Per Subs 1,000
Subject Interests: Census, City planning, Regional planning, Transportation
Special Collections: Environmental Impact Reports; San Francisco Bay Region Planning & Transportation History
Publications: New Acquisitions Periodical (quarterly)
Partic in Dialog Corporation; OCLC Online Computer Library Center, Inc
Special Services for the Blind - DECTalk/JAWS for synthetic voice output of computer screen contents

C MILLS COLLEGE LIBRARY, F W Olin Library, 5000 MacArthur Blvd, 94613. SAN 333-3159. Tel: 510-430-2385. Interlibrary Loan Service Tel: 510-430-2180. Circulation Tel: 510-430-2196. FAX: 510-430-2278. Web Site: www.mills.edu/library. *Dir Libr Serv*, Renee Jadushlever; Tel: 510-430-2033, E-Mail: reneejad@mills.edu; *Ref*, Susan Garbarino; Tel: 510-430-2051, E-Mail: susang@mills.edu; *Ref*, Carol Jarvis; E-Mail: carolj@mills.edu; *Tech Servs*, Nancy MacKay; Tel: 510-430-2028, E-Mail: mackay@mills.edu; *Ser*, Stella Tang; Tel: 510-430-2382, E-Mail: stellat@mills.edu; *Spec Coll & Archives*, Janice Braun; Tel: 510-430-2047, E-Mail: jbraun@mills.edu; Staff 12 (MLS 6, Non-MLS 6)
Founded 1852. Enrl 1,027; Fac 94; Highest Degree: Master
Jun 2000-May 2001 Income Parent Institution $1,296,599. Mats Exp $343,736, Books $169,211, Per/Ser (Incl. Access Fees) $99,457, Presv $8,350, Micro $17,019, AV Equip $12,441, Electronic Ref Mat (Incl. Access Fees) $37,258. Sal $587,688 (Prof $288,721)
Library Holdings: Bk Vols 275,172; Bk Titles 162,936; Per Subs 944
Subject Interests: Art, Bk arts, Dance, Literature, Music, Shakespeare
Special Collections: 19th & 20th Century English & American; Dance (Jane Bourne Parton Coll); Fine Press Books; Music (Darius Milhaud Archive); Rare Americana
Automation Activity & Vendor Info: (Acquisitions) epixtech, inc.; (Cataloging) epixtech, inc.; (Circulation) epixtech, inc.; (Course Reserve) epixtech, inc.; (ILL) epixtech, inc.; (OPAC) epixtech, inc.; (Serials) epixtech, inc.
Database Vendor: CARL, Dialog, Ebsco - EbscoHost, epixtech, inc., GaleNet, Lexis-Nexis, OCLC - First Search, Silverplatter Information Inc., Wilson - Wilson Web
Publications: Literary & Cultural Journeys: Selected Letters to Arturo Torres-Rioseco; Salon at Larkmead; The Flying Cloud & Her First Passengers
Function: For research purposes
Partic in Michigan Library Consortium; SCELC

S OAKLAND CITY PLANNING DEPARTMENT LIBRARY,* 3rd flr, Ste 330, 250 Frank H Ogawa Plaza, 94612. SAN 327-7151. Tel: 510-238-3941, 510-238-7200. FAX: 510-238-6538. *Librn*, Deborah Diamond
Library Holdings: Bk Vols 1,000; Per Subs 20

S OAKLAND MUSEUM, Paul C Mills Archive of California Art Library,* 1000 Oak St, 94607-4892. SAN 301-1321. Tel: 510-238-3005. FAX: 510-238-6925. *Res*, Kathy Borgogno
Founded 1954
Library Holdings: Bk Vols 2,000
Subject Interests: Art, California
Special Collections: California Art & Artists' Files
Restriction: Not open to public

P OAKLAND PUBLIC LIBRARY, 125 14th St, 94612. SAN 333-3213. Tel: 510-238-3281. Circulation Tel: 510-238-3144. Reference Tel: 510-238-3134. TDD: 510-834-7446. FAX: 510-238-2232. E-Mail: esche-ma@oaklandlibrary.org. Web Site: www.oaklandlibrary.org. *City Librn, Dir*, Carmen Martinez; E-Mail: cmartinez@oaklandlibrary.org; *Adminr*, Mae Bolton; Tel: 510-238-6716; *Adminr*, Julie Odofin; Tel: 510-238-6610, E-Mail: odof#ju@oaklandlibrary.org; *Librn*, Richard Mull; Tel: 510-238-6615; *Librn*, Jan Wiggins; Tel: 510-482-7841, E-Mail: wiggi#jk@oaklandlibrary.org; *Publ Servs*, Kathleen Hirooka; Tel: 510-238-6713, Fax: 510-238-4923, E-Mail: hiroo_kg@oaklandlibrary.org; *Acq, Coll Develop*, Dana Heidrick; Tel: 510-238-4704, E-Mail: heid#dj@oaklandlibrary.org; *Computer Services*, Mairi McFall; Tel: 510-238-3270, E-Mail: mcfal#mk@oaklandlibrary.org
Founded 1878. Pop 421,050; Circ 1,800,000
Jul 1999-Jun 2000 Income (Main Library and Branch Library) $14,882,714, State $705,579, City $8,763,776, Locally Generated Income $4,511,654, Other $1,607,284. Mats Exp $1,068,000. Sal $10,575,446
Library Holdings: Bk Vols 1,151,616; Per Subs 2,910
Subject Interests: Art, Asia, Business, Govt docs, Local history, Music
Special Collections: African-American Museum, archives, photogs, primary doc; Bilingual Spanish, Cambodian, Chinese, Japanese, Korean, Laotian, Tagalog & Vietnamese Materials; Black Studies; Jack London Coll; Pacific Rim Business; USGS Topographical Maps; Local History
Automation Activity & Vendor Info: (Acquisitions) epixtech, inc.; (Cataloging) epixtech, inc.; (Circulation) epixtech, inc.; (OPAC) epixtech, inc.; (Serials) epixtech, inc.
Database Vendor: OCLC - First Search
Publications: Annual Reports; Calendar of Events; Staff Newsletter
Function: ILL available, Reference services available
Mem of Bay Area Libr & Info Syst
Special Services for the Deaf - Books on deafness & sign language; TTY machine
Special Services for the Blind - ADA PC (OPAC) with JAWS & Zoom Text; Descriptive videos; Kurzweil Reading Machine; Large print bks; VisualTek; ZoomText software to enlarge computer screen
Friends of the Library Group
Branches: 18
ASIAN, 388 Ninth St, Ste 190, 94612. SAN 333-3248. Tel: 510-238-3400. FAX: 510-238-4732. *Branch Mgr*, Dorothy Chang; E-Mail: chang#dy@oaklandlibrary.org
Friends of the Library Group
BROOKFIELD, 9255 Edes Ave, 94603. SAN 333-3272. Tel: 510-615-5725. FAX: 510-615-5862.
Friends of the Library Group
CESAR E CHAVEZ BRANCH, 1900 Fruitvale Ave, 94601. SAN 333-3515. Tel: 510-535-5620. FAX: 510-535-5622. *Branch Mgr*, Rodrigo Quintanilla; E-Mail: quint#rc@oaklandlibrary.org
Friends of the Library Group
DIMOND, 3565 Fruitvale Ave, 94602. SAN 333-3302. Tel: 510-482-7844. FAX: 510-482-7824. *Branch Mgr*, Catherine Nichols; E-Mail: nicho#cj@oaklandlibrary.org
Friends of the Library Group
EASTMONT, Eastmont Town Center, Ste 211, 7200 Bancroft Ave, 94605. SAN 333-3337. Tel: 510-615-5726. FAX: 510-615-5863. *Branch Mgr*, Bella Madana; E-Mail: madar#bj@oaklandlibrary.org
Friends of the Library Group
ELMHURST, 1427 88th Ave, 94621. SAN 333-3361. Tel: 510-615-5727. FAX: 510-615-5869. *Branch Mgr*, Shirley Mack
GOLDEN GATE, 5606 San Pablo Ave, 94608. SAN 333-3426. Tel: 510-597-5023. FAX: 510-597-5030. *Branch Mgr*, Gracie Woodard; E-Mail: wooda#gg@oaklandlibrary.org
Friends of the Library Group
LAKEVIEW, 550 El Embarcadero, 94610. SAN 333-3485. Tel: 510-238-7344. FAX: 510-238-6576. *Branch Mgr*, Lynda Williams
BUSINESS INFORMATION CENTER MAGAZINE & NEWSPAPER ROOM Tel: 510-238-3176. FAX: 510-238-3934. Web Site: www.oaklandlibrary.org. *Librn*, Daniel Hersh
MAIN LIBRARY & GENERAL REFERENCE, 125 14th St, 94612. SAN 333-3221. Tel: 510-238-3134. TDD: 510-834-7446. FAX: 510-238-2232. E-Mail: esche_ma@oaklandlibrary.org. Web Site: www.oaklandlibrary.org. *Librn*, Gerry Garzon
Special Services for the Blind - Descriptive videos; Kurzweil Reading Machine; ZoomText software to enlarge computer screen
MARTIN LUTHER KING BRANCH, 6833 International Blvd, 94621. SAN 333-3450. Tel: 510-615-5728. FAX: 510-615-5739. *Branch Mgr*, Jamie Turner; E-Mail: turner#jl@oaklandlibrary.org
MELROSE, 4805 Foothill Blvd, 94601. SAN 333-3574. Tel: 510-535-5623. *Branch Mgr*, Roberta Frye; E-Mail: frye#rd@oaklandlibrary.org; Staff 4 (MLS 2, Non-MLS 2)
1999-2000 Mats Exp $20,000
Friends of the Library Group
MONTCLAIR, 1687 Mountain Blvd, 94611. SAN 333-3604. Tel: 510-482-7810. FAX: 510-482-7865. *Branch Mgr*, Leon Cho; E-Mail: cho#lc@oaklandlibrary.org
OAKLAND HISTORY ROOM Tel: 510-238-3222. FAX: 510-238-2232. *Librn*, William Sturm
1999-2000 Mats Exp $3,600, Books $3,100, Presv $500
Library Holdings: Bk Vols 5,300; Bk Titles 5,100
Subject Interests: Photographs, State hist
Special Collections: Birth & death certificates; City block books; Postcards; Sanborn maps
Publications: (Index to newspapers); (Index to ethnic materials)
PIEDMONT AVENUE, 160 41st St, 94611. SAN 333-3663. Tel: 510-597-5011. Web Site: oaklandlibrary.org. *Branch Mgr*, Jamie McGrath; Fax: 510-597-5056, E-Mail: jamiemc@prodigy.net
Friends of the Library Group
ROCKRIDGE, 5366 College Ave, 94618. SAN 333-3698. Tel: 510-597-5017. FAX: 510-597-5067. Web Site: www.oaklandlibrary.org. *Branch Mgr*, Gail Wiemann; E-Mail: wiema#jg@oaklandlibrary.org; Staff 18 (MLS 4, Non-MLS 14)
Founded 1919. Pop 18,000; Circ 244,000
Library Holdings: Bk Vols 50,000
Database Vendor: epixtech, inc., IAC - Info Trac

Friends of the Library Group
TEMESCAL, 5205 Telegraph Ave, 94609. SAN 333-3728. Tel: 510-597-5049. FAX: 510-597-5062. *Branch Mgr*, Martha Bergmann; E-Mail: bergm#mr@oaklandlibrary.org
Friends of the Library Group
WEST OAKLAND, 1801 Adeline St, 94607. SAN 333-3752. Tel: 510-238-7352. FAX: 510-238-6585. *Branch Mgr*, Christine Saed; E-Mail: saed#ck@oaklandlibrary.org
Bookmobiles: 1

S OAKLAND TRIBUNE, INC LIBRARY,* 401 13th St, 94612. SAN 301-1356. Tel: 510-208-6420. FAX: 510-208-6477. *Librn*, Essie Chan; Staff 3 (MLS 1, Non-MLS 2)
Founded 1912
Library Holdings: Bk Titles 5,000
Subject Interests: Local history
Special Collections: Doc Rogers Coll
Publications: Time Capsule, Sunday column
Restriction: Not open to public

C PATTEN COLLEGE, Harry & Dorothy Blumenthal Library, 2433 Coolidge Ave, 94601. SAN 301-133X. Tel: 510-261-8500. FAX: 510-534-8564. Web Site: www.patten.edu. *Dir*, Peggy Jo Zemens; Tel: 510-261-8500, Ext 775, E-Mail: pzemens@yahoo.com; *Ref*, David Fleischer; Tel: 510-261-8500, Ext 721; *AV*, Shondrel Slaughter; Tel: 510-261-8500, Ext 717. Subject Specialists: *Genealogy*, Peggy Jo Zemens; *Religion*, Peggy Jo Zemens; Staff 4 (MLS 1, Non-MLS 3)
Founded 1960. Enrl 465; Fac 34; Highest Degree: Master
Aug 2000-Jul 2001 Income Parent Institution $112,000. Mats Exp $21,100, Books $10,000, Per/Ser (Incl. Access Fees) $5,100, AV Equip $1,000, Electronic Ref Mat (Incl. Access Fees) $5,000. Sal $74,000 (Prof $30,000)
Library Holdings: Bk Vols 35,500; Bk Titles 35,000; Per Subs 210; Bks on Deafness & Sign Lang 15
Subject Interests: Archaeology, Biblical studies, Church history, Education
Special Collections: Dienstein Criminology Coll
Restriction: Not open to public
Partic in Bay Area Library & Information Network; SCELC
K-12 Academy

S REDWOOD EMPIRE ASSOCIATION, Visitor Information Center, 1925 13th Ave, No 103, 94606-3161. SAN 370-4351. Tel: 510-536-8808. FAX: 510-536-8824. E-Mail: reavisit@aol.com. *Dir*, Cedar Kennan
Library Holdings: Bk Titles 100
Subject Interests: NW Calif, Photos
Publications: Adventures: Visitors Guide to the Redwood Empire; Visitors Guide to the Redwood Empire

CM SAMUEL MERRITT COLLEGE, John A Graziano Memorial Library, 400 Hawthorne Ave, 94609. SAN 301-1313. Tel: 510-869-8900. FAX: 510-869-6633. Web Site: www.samuelmerritt.edu. *Dir*, Harry Hosel; Tel: 510-869-6833, E-Mail: hhosel@samuelmerritt.edu; *Tech Servs*, Ann Barnard; Tel: 510-869-8693, E-Mail: abarnard@samuelmerritt.edu; *Access Serv*, Huyen Ho; Tel: 510-869-8694, E-Mail: hho@samuelmerritt.edu; *Coll Develop, Publ Servs*, Barbara Ryken; Tel: 510-869-8692, E-Mail: bryken@samuelmerritt.edu; *Circ*, LaTonya Vunters; Staff 2 (MLS 2)
Founded 1909. Enrl 700; Fac 102; Highest Degree: Master
Jul 1999-Jun 2000 Income $360,000. Mats Exp $165,000, Books $28,000, Per/Ser (Incl. Access Fees) $80,000, Presv $10,000, Electronic Ref Mat (Incl. Access Fees) $45,000. Sal $195,000
Library Holdings: Bk Titles 10,500; Per Subs 530
Subject Interests: Health sciences, Nursing, Occupational therapy, Physical therapy
Automation Activity & Vendor Info: (Acquisitions) epixtech, inc.; (Cataloging) epixtech, inc.; (Circulation) epixtech, inc.; (Course Reserve) epixtech, inc.; (OPAC) epixtech, inc.; (Serials) epixtech, inc.
Database Vendor: ProQuest, Silverplatter Information Inc.
Restriction: Non-circulating to the public
Mem of Bay Area Libr & Info Syst
Partic in Docline; National Network Of Libraries Of Medicine - South Central Region; Northern Calif Consortium of Psychol Librs; Northern California & Nevada Medical Library Group; PAC SW Regional Libr Serv
Open Mon-Thurs 8-10, Fri 8-5, Sat 10-5 & Sun 11-10

G SAN FRANCISCO BAY AREA RAPID TRANSIT DISTRICT LIBRARY, 101 Eighth St, MET-G, Rm 9, PO Box 12688, 94607. SAN 377-3973. Tel: 510-464-6848. FAX: 510-464-6197. *Dir, Librn*, Jacqueline R Edwards; E-Mail: jedward@bart.gov
Jul 1999-Jun 2000 Mats Exp $37,000, Books $30,500, Per/Ser (Incl. Access Fees) $1,000
Library Holdings: Bk Vols 2,500; Per Subs 15

S SOCIETY OF MAYFLOWER DESCENDANTS IN THE STATE OF CALIFORNIA LIBRARY,* 405 14th St, Terrace Level, 94612. SAN 301-4681. Tel: 510-451-9599. *Librn*, Donald W Stewart
Founded 1907
Library Holdings: Bk Titles 2,200
Special Collections: Folger Family Group Sheets; Genealogy (Mayflower Descendants); NYGB Complete; Vital Records of New England - NEHGR Complete, Essex Institute to 1934
Restriction: Non-circulating to the public
Open Mon 9am-4pm & Wed 9am-noon
Branches:
EAST BAY GENEALOGICAL SOCIETY LIBRARY *Librn*, Lois J Kline
Library Holdings: Bk Titles 300
Special Collections: Alameda County, Microfilm; Ancestry charts of members; Births 1870-1904; Death 1870-1893
Open Mon 9am-4pm & Wed 9am-noon

G UNITED STATES DEPARTMENT OF ENERGY, Oakland Operations Office, Energy Information Center & Public Reading Room,* 1301 Clay St, Rm 700 N, 94612. SAN 375-0825. Tel: 510-637-1764. FAX: 510-637-2011.
Library Holdings: Bk Vols 1,500; Per Subs 20
Restriction: Open to public for reference only

S WOODWARD-CLYDE CONSULTANTS LIBRARY,* 500 12th St, Ste 200, 94607-4014. SAN 301-4908. Tel: 510-893-3600, Ext 3147. FAX: 510-874-3268. Web Site: ursgreiner@urscorp.com. *Librn*, Beverly Walton
Library Holdings: Bk Vols 5,000; Per Subs 250
Subject Interests: Environmental studies
Restriction: Not open to public

OCEANSIDE

J MIRACOSTA COLLEGE LIBRARY, One Barnard Dr, 92056-3899. SAN 301-1372. Tel: 760-795-6715. FAX: 760-795-6723. Web Site: www.miracosta.cc.ca.us/library. *Dean of Libr*, Joseph A Moreau; Tel: 760-795-6720, E-Mail: jmoreau@yar.miracosta.cc.ca.us; *Coll Develop, Publ Servs*, Janet Megill; *Tech Servs*, Patricia McClure; *Bibliog Instr*, Marion Foerster; *Librn*, Myla Stokes Kelly; Tel: 760-944-4449, Ext 7736, E-Mail: mskelly@miracosta.cc.ca.us; Staff 4 (MLS 4)
Founded 1934. Enrl 8,380
Jul 1999-Jun 2000 Income (Main Library and Branch Library) $1,305,191. Mats Exp $251,261, Books $140,119, Per/Ser (Incl. Access Fees) $18,863, Micro $4,742, AV Equip $55,450, Electronic Ref Mat (Incl. Access Fees) $32,087. Sal $965,884 (Prof $566,496)
Library Holdings: Bk Vols 60,956; Bk Titles 52,854; Per Subs 205
Subject Interests: Art and architecture, Ethnic studies, Feminism
Automation Activity & Vendor Info: (Cataloging) SIRSI; (Circulation) SIRSI; (Serials) SIRSI
Publications: Citation Guides (Reference guide)
Partic in N County Higher Educ Alliance; OCLC Online Computer Library Center, Inc; San Diego & Imperial Counties College Learning Resources Cooperative

P OCEANSIDE PUBLIC LIBRARY, 330 N Coast Hwy, 92054-2824. SAN 301-1380. Tel: 760-435-5600. Reference Tel: 760-435-5580. TDD: 760-435-5566. FAX: 760-435-5567. E-Mail: public.library@ci.oceanside.ca.us. Web Site: www.library.ci.oceanside.ca.us. *Dir*, Deborah Polich; Tel: 760-435-5560, E-Mail: dpolich@ci.oceanside.ca.us; *Ad Servs*, Margaret Taylor; Tel: 760-435-5579, E-Mail: mtaylor@ci.oceanside.ca.us; *Cat*, Mary Cappadonna; Tel: 760-435-5608, E-Mail: mcappadonna@ci.oceanside.ca.us; *Ch Servs*, Nancy Carstensen; Tel: 760-435-5594, E-Mail: ncarstensen@ci.oceanside.ca.us; *Ch Servs*, Nisa Kalambaheti; Tel: 760-435-5597, E-Mail: nkalambaheti@@ci.oceanside.ca.us; *Ch Servs*, Carol Naegele; Tel: 760-435-5591, E-Mail: cnaegele@ci.oceanside.ca.us; *Ch Servs*, Leida Nuez Rodriquez; *Ch Servs*, Kathie Phoenix; Tel: 760-435-5593, E-Mail: kphoenix@ci.oceanside.ca.us; *Circ*, Sherri Cosby; Tel: 760-435-5609, E-Mail: scosby@@ci.oceanside.ca.us; *Electronic Resources*, Cathrine Greene; Tel: 760-435-5578, E-Mail: cgreene@ci.oceanside.ca.us; *Tech Coordr*, Donna Arnold; Tel: 760-435-5606, E-Mail: darnold@ci.oceanside.ca.us; *YA Servs*, Joyce Lea Brown; Tel: 760-435-5577, E-Mail: jbrown@ci.oceanside.ca.us; *Bkmobile Coordr*, Adeline Pinon; E-Mail: apinon@ci.oceanside.ca.us; Staff 72 (MLS 14, Non-MLS 58)
Founded 1904. Pop 160,800; Circ 683,790
Jul 1999-Jun 2000 Income $5,153,975. Mats Exp $487,168, Books $364,525, Per/Ser (Incl. Access Fees) $33,220, Micro $11,328, AV Equip $40,135, Electronic Ref Mat (Incl. Access Fees) $37,960. Sal $1,416,790 (Prof $714,823)
Library Holdings: Bk Vols 907,935; Bk Titles 181,555; Per Subs 560
Subject Interests: Art and architecture, Business and management, Children's literature, Employment, Parenting, Religion
Special Collections: Caldecott-Newberry Memorial Coll; Martin Luther King Coll; Parents Resource Coll; Samoan Culture Coll; Teachers Resource Center
Automation Activity & Vendor Info: (Acquisitions) SIRSI; (Circulation) SIRSI; (ILL) SIRSI; (OPAC) SIRSI; (Serials) SIRSI
Database Vendor: GaleNet, IAC - Info Trac, OCLC - First Search, ProQuest, Silverplatter Information Inc.
Publications: See Gull
Function: ILL available
Mem of Serra Cooperative Library System
Special Services for the Deaf - TDD
Friends of the Library Group

Branches: 3
COMMUNITY COMPUTER CENTER, 321 N Nevada St, 92054-2811. SAN 378-0457. Tel: 760-966-4110. FAX: 760-966-4111. *Branch Mgr*, James Jones; Tel: 760-966-4112, E-Mail: jjones@ci.oceanside.ca.us; Staff 12 (Non-MLS 12)
Founded 1997
OCEANSIDE READS LEARNING CENTER, 321 N Nevada St, 92054. SAN 378-1240. Tel: 760-966-4677. FAX: 760-966-4102.
OLD MISSION, 3861 B Mission Ave, 92054. SAN 370-3819. Tel: 760-435-5630. FAX: 760-435-5643. Web Site: www.ci.oceanside.ca.us. *Branch Mgr*, Barbara Sullivan; E-Mail: bsullivan@ci.oceanside.ca.us
Bookmobiles: 2

SR ROSICRUCIAN FELLOWSHIP LIBRARY,* 2222 Mission Ave, 92054-0112. SAN 328-3755. Tel: 760-757-6600, Ext 211. FAX: 760-721-3806. E-Mail: rosfshp@cts.com. *Librn*, Gloria Hayes
Library Holdings: Bk Vols 1,000
Open Mon-Fri 8:30-4

OJAI

S KRISHNAMURTI FOUNDATION OF AMERICA LIBRARY, 1130 McAndrew Rd, 93023. SAN 374-4817. Tel: 805-646-4948. E-Mail: klibrary@kfa.org. Web Site: www.kfa.org/library.htm. *Librn*, Douglas Evans
Founded 1984
Library Holdings: Bk Vols 2,000
Special Collections: J Krishnamurti, bks & teachings
Open Wed-Sun 1-5, closed Mon & Tues

SR KROTONA INSTITUTE OF THEOSOPHY LIBRARY, Krotona Hill, No 2, 93023. SAN 301-1399. Tel: 805-646-2653. FAX: 805-646-5381. *Head of Libr*, Lakshmi Narayan
Founded 1926
Library Holdings: Bk Titles 10,000
Subject Interests: Astrology, Eastern philosophy, Philosophy, Psychology, Religion, Theosophy

ONTARIO

P ONTARIO CITY LIBRARY, 215 East C St, 91764-4198. SAN 301-1429. Tel: 909-395-2004. FAX: 909-395-2043. E-Mail: library@cl.ontario.ca.us. Web Site: www.ci.ontario.ca.us/ontario/library/index.htm. *Dir*, Judy Evans; Tel: 909-395-2223, E-Mail: jevans@ci.ontario.ca.us; *Ad Servs*, Joanne Boyajian; Tel: 909-395-2233, E-Mail: jboya@ci.ontario.ca.us; *Cat*, Joan Jordon; Tel: 909-395-2234, E-Mail: jjordan@ci.ontario.ca.us; *ILL*, Rachel Marquez-Morales; Tel: 909-395-2216, E-Mail: rmarq@ci.ontario.ca.us; *Ch Servs*, Susan Umpleby; Tel: 909-395-2208, E-Mail: sumple@ci.ontario.ca.us; *Media Spec*, Gary Friedman; Tel: 909-395-2528, E-Mail: gfriedman@ci.ontario.ca.us; *Coll Develop*, Paul Johnson; Tel: 909-395-2217, E-Mail: pjohn@ci.ontario.ca.us. Subject Specialists: *Local history*, Terry Carter; Staff 67 (MLS 8, Non-MLS 59)
Founded 1885. Pop 151,500
Jul 1999-Jun 2000 Income (Main Library and Branch Library) City $2,842,000. Mats Exp $376,500, Books $231,000, Per/Ser (Incl. Access Fees) $42,500, Presv $1,000, Micro $16,000, AV Equip $51,000, Electronic Ref Mat (Incl. Access Fees) $35,000. Sal $2,111,500
Library Holdings: Bk Vols 174,000; Bk Titles 140,000; Per Subs 625
Subject Interests: Large type print, Local history
Automation Activity & Vendor Info: (Circulation) epixtech, inc.
Friends of the Library Group
Branches: 1
SOUTH ONTARIO, 2403-D S Vineyard, 91761. Tel: 909-395-2014. FAX: 909-930-0836. *Librn*, Carl Barthelette; E-Mail: cbart@ci.ontario.ca.us; *Ch Servs*, Celest Fong; E-Mail: cmfong@ci.ontario.ca.us; Staff 13 (MLS 2, Non-MLS 11)
Library Holdings: Bk Vols 42,500; Per Subs 57

ORANGE

S BERGEN BRUNSWIG BUSINESS RESEARCH LIBRARY, 4000 Metropolitan Dr, 92868. SAN 371-2486. Tel: 714-385-6903. Web Site: www.bergenbrunswig.com. *Dir*, Shannon Jager; *Librn*, Mayumi Devera
Library Holdings: Bk Vols 700; Per Subs 110
Restriction: Not open to public
Open Mon-Fri 8-4

C CHAPMAN UNIVERSITY, Thurmond Clarke Memorial Library, 333 N Glassell, 92866-1099. SAN 301-1437. Tel: 714-997-6806. FAX: 714-744-7063. Web Site: www.chapman.edu/library/homepage.html. *Dean*, Charlene Baldwin; *Assoc Dean*, Ron Rodriguez; E-Mail: ronr@chapman.edu; *Circ*, Gregory Farmer; *Librn*, Lorraine Attarian; *Librn*, Nancy Gonzalez; *Librn*, Claudia Horn; *Librn*, Heather Tunender
Founded 1923. Enrl 3,800; Highest Degree: Master
Jun 1998-May 1999 Income $24,006, Locally Generated Income $24,006. Mats Exp $488,501, Books $78,837, Per/Ser (Incl. Access Fees) $266,661, Presv $1,500, Micro $32,531, AV Equip $50,413, Electronic Ref Mat (Incl. Access Fees) $58,559. Sal $560,795 (Prof $212,650)
Library Holdings: Bk Vols 220,000; Bk Titles 118,949; Per Subs 2,111
Subject Interests: County hist
Special Collections: Charles C Chapman Rare Book Coll; Disciple of Christ Church History
Automation Activity & Vendor Info: (Acquisitions) Innovative Interfaces Inc.; (Cataloging) Innovative Interfaces Inc.; (Circulation) Innovative Interfaces Inc.; (Course Reserve) Innovative Interfaces Inc.; (OPAC) Innovative Interfaces Inc.; (Serials) Innovative Interfaces Inc.
Function: ILL available, Reference services available
Partic in OCLC Online Computer Library Center, Inc; SCELC

P ORANGE PUBLIC LIBRARY,* 101 N Center St, 92866-1594. SAN 333-483X. Tel: 714-288-2400. FAX: 714-771-6126. E-Mail: library@cityoforange.org. Web Site: www.library.cityoforange.org. *Commun Servs, Dir Libr Serv*, Gary Wann; *Mgr*, Eugenia Wong; *Ref*, Yolanda Moreno; *Ref Serv Ad*, Rosemarie Williams; *ILL*, Karen Klan; Staff 11 (MLS 11)
Founded 1894. Pop 117,956; Circ 695,539
Library Holdings: Bk Vols 301,959; Bk Titles 151,501; Per Subs 375
Subject Interests: Biology, Children's literature, Local history
Special Collections: Spanish Coll
Publications: Adult Literacy Program (newsletter); Orange Public Library Newsletter; Partners in Reading
Mem of Santiago Libr Syst
Partic in Coop Libr Agency for Syst & Servs; OCLC Online Computer Library Center, Inc
Friends of the Library Group
Branches: 2
CHARLES P TAFT BRANCH, 740 E Taft Ave, 92865-4404. SAN 333-4899. Tel: 714-288-2430. FAX: 714-282-8663. *In Charge*, Belva Teegarden
Library Holdings: Bk Vols 42,680; Bk Titles 29,786
Friends of the Library Group
EL MODENA BRANCH, 380 S Hewes St, 92869-4060. SAN 333-4864. Tel: 714-288-2450. FAX: 714-997-1041. *Librn*, Beth Irish
Library Holdings: Bk Vols 56,348; Bk Titles 36,654

S PLANNED PARENTHOOD ASSOCIATION OF ORANGE & SAN BERNADINO COUNTIES, Health Education Department Resource Library,* 700 S Tustin Ave, 92866. SAN 301-1461. Tel: 714-744-9764. FAX: 714-744-9780. *Librn*, Cheryl Van Allen
Founded 1974
Library Holdings: Bk Titles 230; Per Subs 20
Subject Interests: Birth control, Sexuality
Partic in Libr of Orange County Network

M SAINT JOSEPH HOSPITAL & CHILDRENS HOSPITAL OF ORANGE COUNTY, Burlew Medical Library, 1100 W Stewart Dr, 92868. (Mail add: PO Box 5600, 92863-5600), SAN 301-147X. Tel: 714-771-8291. FAX: 714-744-8533. *Dir*, Julie L Smith; E-Mail: jsmith@sjo.stjoe.org; *Tech Servs*, Jan Grabowski; Staff 3 (MLS 1, Non-MLS 2)
Founded 1955
Library Holdings: Bk Titles 8,000; Per Subs 400
Subject Interests: Cardiology, Ethics, Internal medicine, Nursing, Orthopedics, Pediatrics, Surgery
Automation Activity & Vendor Info: (Cataloging) Sydney; (Serials) Sydney
Database Vendor: OVID Technologies
Restriction: In-house use for visitors, Lending to staff only
Function: Document delivery services, ILL available, Reference services available, Research library
Partic in BRS; Coop Libr Agency for Syst & Servs; National Network Of Libraries Of Medicine - Pacific Northwest Region; SDC

C SAINT JOSEPH LIBRARY, 480 S Batavia St, 92868-3907. SAN 333-3965. Tel: 714-633-8121, Ext 7765. FAX: 714-744-3166. E-Mail: csjlib@earthlink.net. *Dir*, Sister A Hennessy; *Tech Servs*, A Sprang. Subject Specialists: *Theology*, Sister A Hennessy; Staff 2 (Non-MLS 2)
Founded 1953
Library Holdings: Bk Titles 17,000; Per Subs 80
Subject Interests: Art, California, Philosophy, Religion, Theology
Departmental Libraries:
TAPE CENTER (AUDIO CASSETTE LIBRARY), 480 S Batavia St, 92868-3907.

L WOODRUFF, SPRADLIN & SMART LIBRARY,* 701 S Parker St, Ste 7000, 92868. SAN 301-5416. Tel: 714-558-7000. FAX: 714-835-7787.
Library Holdings: Bk Vols 5,000
Subject Interests: Law

ORANGE COVE

P FRESNO COUNTY PUBLIC LIBRARY, Orange Cove Neighborhood Library, 523 Park Blvd, PO Box 357, 93646. SAN 377-4929. Tel: 559-626-7942. *In Charge*, Sandra Kuykendall
Library Holdings: Bk Vols 9,000; Per Subs 30
Open Tues & Wed 11-5, Thurs 11-5:30

ORINDA

C JOHN F KENNEDY UNIVERSITY, Fisher Library, 12 Altarinda Rd, 94563. SAN 301-150X. Tel: 925-258-2233. FAX: 925-254-8136. Web Site: library.jfku.edu. *Dir*, Ann Patterson; E-Mail: apatters@jfku.edu; *Tech Servs*, Claudia Chester
Founded 1964. Enrl 1,665; Fac 781; Highest Degree: Doctorate
Jul 1999-Jun 2000 Income (Main Library Only) Parent Institution $612,474. Mats Exp $162,302, Books $66,569, Per/Ser (Incl. Access Fees) $73,502, AV Equip $2,530, Electronic Ref Mat (Incl. Access Fees) $19,701. Sal $352,895 (Prof $198,911)
Library Holdings: Bk Vols 63,622; Bk Titles 40,000; Per Subs 750
Subject Interests: Education, Liberal arts, Museology, Psychology
Automation Activity & Vendor Info: (Acquisitions) Innovative Interfaces Inc.; (Cataloging) Innovative Interfaces Inc.; (Circulation) Innovative Interfaces Inc.; (Course Reserve) Innovative Interfaces Inc.; (ILL) Innovative Interfaces Inc.; (OPAC) Innovative Interfaces Inc.; (Serials) Innovative Interfaces Inc.
Database Vendor: Ebsco - EbscoHost, Silverplatter Information Inc.
Publications: JFKU Library Handbook
Partic in Bay Area Library & Information Network; Coop Libr Agency for Syst & Servs; Northern Calif Consortium of Psychol Librs
Departmental Libraries:
BUSINESS, 1250 Arroyo Way, Walnut Creek, 94596. SAN 373-5893. Tel: 510-295-0605. FAX: 510-295-0604. Web Site: www.jfku.edu/~library/. *Librn*, Susan Brown; E-Mail: sbrown@jftu.edu; Staff 2 (MLS 1, Non-MLS 1)
Library Holdings: Bk Vols 5,608; Bk Titles 5,458; Per Subs 61
Subject Interests: Business and management, International
Automation Activity & Vendor Info: (Acquisitions) Innovative Interfaces Inc.; (Cataloging) Innovative Interfaces Inc.; (Circulation) Innovative Interfaces Inc.; (Course Reserve) Innovative Interfaces Inc.; (ILL) Innovative Interfaces Inc.; (OPAC) Innovative Interfaces Inc.; (Serials) Innovative Interfaces Inc.
CAMPBELL CAMPUS LIBRARY
See Separate Entry in Campbell
CAREER RESOURCES, 1250 Arroyo Way, Walnut Creek, 94596. Tel: 510-295-0611. FAX: 510-295-0615.; Staff 1 (Non-MLS 1)
Jul 1999-Jun 2000 Mats Exp $3,156, Books $1,500, Per/Ser (Incl. Access Fees) $1,656
Library Holdings: Bk Vols 2,000; Per Subs 21
Subject Interests: Careers, Counseling
Special Collections: Richard Bolles Coll
LAW LIBRARY, 547 Ygnacio Valley Rd, Walnut Creek, 94596. SAN 321-4400. Tel: 925-295-1810. Web Site: www.jfku.edu. *Librn*, Tina Miller; *Librn*, Jane Minor; *Librn*, Susan Smith; Staff 7 (MLS 3, Non-MLS 4)
Jul 1999-Jun 2000 Income (Main Library Only) $398,642, Locally Generated Income $4,000, Parent Institution $394,642. Mats Exp $186,105, Books $56,921, Per/Ser (Incl. Access Fees) $113,751, Electronic Ref Mat (Incl. Access Fees) $15,433. Sal $201,186 (Prof $129,405)
Library Holdings: Bk Vols 31,170; Bk Titles 3,300; Per Subs 160
Friends of the Library Group

ORLAND

P ORLAND FREE LIBRARY,* 333 Mill St, 95963. SAN 333-4929. Tel: 530-865-1640. FAX: 530-865-2124. E-Mail: orlandlib@glenncounty.net. *Dir*, Marilyn Cochran; Staff 6 (MLS 1, Non-MLS 5)
Founded 1909. Pop 13,200; Circ 87,509
Jul 1997-Jun 1998 Income $213,264, City $128,981, County $84,283. Mats Exp $30,390, Books $27,037, Per/Ser (Incl. Access Fees) $3,353. Sal $128,544 (Prof $37,000)
Library Holdings: Bk Vols 63,500; Per Subs 92
Subject Interests: History
Mem of North State Cooperative Library System
Friends of the Library Group

OROVILLE

J BUTTE COMMUNITY COLLEGE, Frederick S Montgomery Library, 3536 Butte Campus Dr, 95965. SAN 301-1518. Tel: 530-895-2511, 530-895-2596. Circulation Tel: 530-895-2596. Reference Tel: 530-895-2452. FAX: 530-895-2924. Web Site: www.butte.cc.ca.us/library. *Dir Libr Serv*, Tabzeera Dosu; Tel: 530-895-2596, E-Mail: dosuta@butte.cc.ca.us; Staff 7 (MLS 4, Non-MLS 3)
Founded 1967. Enrl 10,000; Fac 400
Library Holdings: Bk Vols 53,000; Per Subs 184
Subject Interests: Art, Literature
Database Vendor: GaleNet, IAC - Info Trac, ProQuest, Wilson - Wilson Web
Mem of North State Cooperative Library System
Partic in OCLC Online Computer Library Center, Inc

GL BUTTE COUNTY LAW LIBRARY,* One Court St, 95965. SAN 301-1526. Tel: 530-538-7122. FAX: 530-538-6827. *Librn*, John A Zorbas
Founded 1907
Library Holdings: Bk Vols 19,000; Per Subs 31

P BUTTE COUNTY LIBRARY, 1820 Mitchell Ave, 95966-5387. SAN 333-4988. Tel: 530-538-7525. Circulation Tel: 530-538-7355. Reference Tel: 530-538-7642. FAX: 530-538-7235. E-Mail: lib@buttecounty.net. Web Site: www.buttecounty.net/library/. *Dir*, Nancy D Brower; E-Mail: nbrower@buttecounty.net; *Ref*, Brenda Crotts; E-Mail: bcrotts@buttecounty.net; Staff 25 (MLS 4, Non-MLS 21)
Founded 1913. Pop 201,300; Circ 513,413
Jul 1999-Jun 2000 Income (Main Library and Branch Library) $1,893,841, State $403,808, County $1,271,867, Locally Generated Income $218,166. Mats Exp $242,731, Books $220,574, Per/Ser (Incl. Access Fees) $18,005, Micro $4,152, Electronic Ref Mat (Incl. Access Fees) $1,500. Sal $634,171
Library Holdings: Bk Vols 203,091; Per Subs 382
Subject Interests: County hist, Reference
Special Collections: Butte County Hist
Automation Activity & Vendor Info: (Cataloging) TLC; (Circulation) TLC; (OPAC) TLC
Database Vendor: GaleNet, IAC - Info Trac
Function: ILL available
Mem of North State Cooperative Library System
Partic in OCLC Online Computer Library Center, Inc
Special Services for the Deaf - TDD
Friends of the Library Group
Branches: 5
BIGGS BRANCH, 464A B St, PO Box 516, Biggs, 95917. SAN 370-7938. Tel: 530-868-5724.
CHICO BRANCH, 1108 Sherman Ave, Chico, 95926-3575. SAN 333-5046. Tel: 530-891-2762. FAX: 916-891-2978. *Librn*, Susan Rauen; Staff 1 (MLS 1)
Friends of the Library Group
DURHAM BRANCH, 2545 Durham-Dayton Hwy, Durham, 95938-0119. SAN 333-5100. Tel: 530-343-4094.
Friends of the Library Group
GRIDLEY BRANCH, 299 Spruce St, Gridley, 95948-0397. SAN 333-516X. Tel: 530-846-3323. *In Charge*, Julie Piontek
Friends of the Library Group
PARADISE BRANCH, 5922 Clark Rd, Paradise, 95969-4896. SAN 333-5194. Tel: 530-872-6320. FAX: 530-872-6322. *Librn*, Elizabeth Stewart
Friends of the Library Group
Bookmobiles: 1

M OROVILLE HOSPITAL, Goddard Memorial Library, 2767 Olive Hwy, 95966. SAN 301-1534. Tel: 530-532-8657. FAX: 530-532-8434. E-Mail: rbrudno@orohosp.com.; Staff 1 (MLS 1)
Founded 1968
Library Holdings: Bk Titles 250; Per Subs 78
Restriction: Not open to public, Open to researchers by request
Partic in Nat Libr of Med; Northern California & Nevada Medical Library Group; Pacific SW Regional Med Libr Serv; Sacramento Area Health Sciences Librs

OXNARD

J OXNARD COLLEGE LIBRARY,* 4000 S Rose Ave, 93033-6699. SAN 321-4788. Tel: 805-986-5819. FAX: 805-986-5880. Web Site: www.oxnard.cc.ca.us/library/libmain.htm. *Dean of Libr*, Delois J Flowers; *Assoc Librn*, Harmony Rodriguez; *Assoc Librn*, Tom Stough; E-Mail: stough@vcccd.net; *ILL, Tech Servs*, Betty Newlee; *Circ*, Colleen Wilson; Staff 2 (MLS 2)
Founded 1975. Enrl 6,500; Fac 88
Library Holdings: Bk Titles 31,000; Per Subs 212
Subject Interests: Soc sci
Partic in Total Interlibrary Exchange
Open Mon-Thurs 8-9 & Fri 8-5

P OXNARD PUBLIC LIBRARY, 251 South A St, 93030. SAN 301-1542. Tel: 805-385-7500. Circulation Tel: 805-486-5370. Reference Tel: 805-487-7532. FAX: 805-385-7526. E-Mail: opl@rain.org. Web Site: www.oxnard.org. *Dir*, Barbara J Murray; *Librn*, Tony Ramirez; *Ref*, Steve Alcorta; *Ref*, Sofia Bollos; *Ref*, Brenda Crispin; *Ref*, Doug McLaughlin; *Ref*, Carol Summers; *Ch Servs*, Kay Driscoll; *Ch Servs*, Sharon Dykstra; *Circ*, Robin Middleton; *Coll Develop*, Peggy O'Donnell; Staff 13 (MLS 13)
Founded 1907. Pop 158,300; Circ 599,604
Jul 1998-Jun 1999 Income (Main Library and Branch Library) $2,535,854, State $183,326, City $2,310,665, Federal $3,300, Locally Generated Income $38,563. Mats Exp $310,702, Books $256,702, Per/Ser (Incl. Access Fees) $25,112, Presv $7,578, Micro $21,310. Sal $1,520,350 (Prof $776,637)
Library Holdings: Bk Titles 325,773; Per Subs 485
Subject Interests: Large type print, Local government, Local history, Spanish (language)
Automation Activity & Vendor Info: (Cataloging) epixtech, inc.; (Circulation) epixtech, inc.
Database Vendor: epixtech, inc., IAC - Info Trac, OCLC - First Search
Mem of Metropolitan Cooperative Library System
Partic in Metro Coop Libr Syst

Special Services for the Deaf - TDD
Special Services for the Blind - Braille books on tape; Kurzweil Reader; Voice OPAC
Friends of the Library Group
Branches: 2
COLONIA MINI, 1500 Camino del Sol, No 21, 93030. SAN 377-5917. Tel: 805-385-8108. Web Site: www.oxnard.org/opl.html.
Library Holdings: Bk Vols 8,458
SOUTH OXNARD BRANCH, 200 E Bard Rd, 93033. SAN 377-8401. Tel: 805-385-8129. Web Site: www.oxnard.org/opl.html.
Library Holdings: Bk Vols 42,497; Per Subs 86

M SAINT JOHN'S REGIONAL MEDICAL CENTER, Health Sciences Library, 1600 N Rose Ave, 93030. SAN 301-1550. Tel: 805-988-2820. FAX: 805-981-4419. Web Site: www.stjohns.org. *Librn*, Joanne Kennedy; E-Mail: jkennedy@ch.edu
Founded 1973
Library Holdings: Bk Titles 3,500; Per Subs 100
Restriction: Staff use only
Open Mon-Fri 7:30-4

PACIFIC GROVE

P PACIFIC GROVE PUBLIC LIBRARY, 550 Central Ave, 93950-2789. SAN 301-1585. Tel: 831-648-5760. Reference Tel: 831-648-5762. FAX: 831-373-3268. Web Site: www.pacificgrove.lib.ca.us. *Dir*, Barbara Morrison; Tel: 831-648-5765, E-Mail: bmorriso@pacificgrove.lib.ca.us; *Ad Servs*, Ellen G Pastore; Tel: 831-648-5760, Ext 17, E-Mail: epastore@pacificgrove.lib.ca.us; *Ch Servs*, Lisa Maddalena; Tel: 831-648-5760, Ext 14, E-Mail: lmaddale@pacificgrove.lib.ca.us. Subject Specialists: *Children's literature*, Lisa Maddalena; *Reference*, Ellen G Pastore; Staff 18 (MLS 6, Non-MLS 12)
Founded 1908. Pop 17,300; Circ 214,736
Jul 1999-Jun 2000 Income $863,200, State $46,666, City $782,178, Federal $5,000, Locally Generated Income $29,356. Mats Exp $119,967, Books $96,534, Per/Ser (Incl. Access Fees) $8,055, Presv $4,262, Micro $2,343, Electronic Ref Mat (Incl. Access Fees) $5,086. Sal $645,500 (Prof $228,252)
Library Holdings: Bk Vols 96,568; Bk Titles 87,000; Per Subs 305
Automation Activity & Vendor Info: (Acquisitions) Innovative Interfaces Inc.; (Cataloging) Innovative Interfaces Inc.; (Circulation) Innovative Interfaces Inc.; (OPAC) Innovative Interfaces Inc.; (Serials) Innovative Interfaces Inc.
Database Vendor: IAC - Info Trac, Innovative Interfaces INN - View, OCLC - First Search, ProQuest
Function: ILL available
Mem of Monterey Bay Area Cooperative Library System
Partic in Monterey Bay Area Coop Libr Syst
Special Services for the Deaf - TDD
Special Services for the Blind - Reading edge system; VisualTek closed circuit TV reading aid
Friends of the Library Group

PACIFIC PALISADES

R KEHILLATH ISRAEL JEWISH CONGREGATION OF PACIFIC PALISADES, Berrie Library, 16019 Sunset Blvd, 90272. SAN 301-1607. Tel: 310-459-2328. FAX: 310-573-2098. *Exec Dir*, Betty Greenstine; *Librn*, Ann Salenger
Founded 1968
Library Holdings: Bk Titles 2,500; Per Subs 25
Subject Interests: Judaica (lit or hist of Jews)
Special Collections: Reconstructionist Judaism
Restriction: Members only
Open Mon-Thurs 9-5, Fri 9-3:30

PALM DESERT

J COLLEGE OF THE DESERT LIBRARY, 43-500 Monterey, 92260. SAN 301-1615. Tel: 760-773-2563, 760-776-0105. FAX: 760-776-0134. Web Site: www.desert.cc.ca.us. *Coordr*, Char Whitaker; E-Mail: cwhitaker@dccd.cc.ca.us; *Instrul Serv*, Claudia Derum; E-Mail: cderum@dccd.cc.ca.us; Staff 6 (MLS 2, Non-MLS 4)
Founded 1962. Enrl 5,100
Jul 2000-Jun 2001 Income State $315,053. Mats Exp $92,181, Books $51,294, Per/Ser (Incl. Access Fees) $21,211, Presv $418, Micro $11,830, Electronic Ref Mat (Incl. Access Fees) $7,428. Sal $210,286 (Prof $113,945)
Library Holdings: Bk Vols 45,000; Per Subs 240
Subject Interests: Rare books
Special Collections: Desert Coll, rare books; Winston S Churchill Coll, bks, pamphlets, rare bks
Partic in Coop Libr Agency for Syst & Servs; Inland Empire Acad Libr Coop; San Bernardino, Inyo, Riverside Counties United Library Services
Open Mon-Thurs 8-9, Fri 8-5
Friends of the Library Group

S LIVING DESERT, Haynes Memorial Library, 47-900 Portola Ave, 92260. SAN 327-6112. Tel: 760-346-5694. FAX: 760-568-9685. *Exec Dir*, Karen Sausman
Library Holdings: Bk Titles 475
Restriction: By appointment only

PALM SPRINGS

S PALM SPRINGS DESERT MUSEUM LIBRARY, 101 Museum Dr, PO Box 2310, 92263. SAN 301-1631. Tel: 760-325-7186. FAX: 760-327-5069. E-Mail: psmuseum@aol.com. Web Site: www.palmsprings.com/points/museum.html. *Librn*, Kenneth Plate; Tel: 760-325-7186, Ext 133, E-Mail: kplate@psmuseum.org; Staff 1 (MLS 1)
Founded 1938
Library Holdings: Bk Vols 9,500; Per Subs 23
Subject Interests: Art, Natural science
Automation Activity & Vendor Info: (Cataloging) Follett
Restriction: Non-circulating to the public

P PALM SPRINGS PUBLIC LIBRARY,* 300 S Sunrise Way, 92262-7699. SAN 333-5224. Tel: 760-322-7323. Reference Tel: 760-323-8294. FAX: 760-320-9834. E-Mail: 74111.3302@compuserve.com. Web Site: www.ci.palm-springs.ca.us. *Dir*, Margaret Roades; *Circ, Tech Servs*, Ann Morris; *Media Spec*, Shelly Thacker; *Asst Librn*, Josette McNary; *Ch Servs, YA Servs*, Nancy Fritzal; Staff 8 (MLS 8)
Founded 1940. Pop 42,509; Circ 491,582
Jul 1996-Jun 1997 Income $1,868,208. Mats Exp $205,000, Books $135,400, Per/Ser (Incl. Access Fees) $27,000, Micro $12,600. Sal $887,419
Library Holdings: Bk Vols 139,252; Per Subs 527
Subject Interests: Art and architecture, Genealogy, History
Special Collections: Local Artists; Robinson Jeffers Coll, bks, letters, mss; Southern Californiana (Rothman)
Automation Activity & Vendor Info: (Circulation) Inlex
Publications: New Reader News
Mem of Inland Library System
Partic in OCLC Online Computer Library Center, Inc; San Bernardino, Inyo, Riverside Counties United Library Services
Friends of the Library Group

PALMDALE

P PALMDALE CITY LIBRARY, 700 E Palmdale Blvd, 93550. SAN 324-2781. Tel: 661-267-5601. Reference Tel: 661-267-5647. FAX: 661-267-5606. E-Mail: pcl@qnet.com. Web Site: www.palmdale.lib.ca.us. *Dir*, Linda Storsteen; *Ad Servs, Coordr*, Sandra Marsh; *Tech Servs*, Sheila Dumas; *Ch Servs*, Harriet Miles; Staff 7 (MLS 6, Non-MLS 1)
Founded 1977. Pop 122,934; Circ 357,513
2000-2001 Mats Exp Books $250,860. Sal $922,150
Library Holdings: Bk Vols 111,542; Bk Titles 105,000; Per Subs 427
Special Collections: Aerospace Coll; Genealogy Coll; Law
Automation Activity & Vendor Info: (Acquisitions) epixtech, inc.; (Circulation) epixtech, inc.
Mem of South State Cooperative Library System
Friends of the Library Group
Branches: 1
YOUTH, 38510 N Sierra Hwy, 93550. Tel: 661-267-5222. FAX: 661-267-5227. Web Site: www.palmdale.lib.ca.us. *Ch Servs*, Harriet Miles
Library Holdings: Bk Vols 40,000; Per Subs 80
Automation Activity & Vendor Info: (Cataloging) epixtech, inc.; (Circulation) epixtech, inc.; (OPAC) epixtech, inc.

PALO ALTO

L AGILENT TECHNOLOGIES, INC, (Formerly Hewlett-Packard Co), Legal Department Library, 395 Page Mill Rd, MS A3-19, 94306. SAN 372-3828. Tel: 650-857-5692. *Res*, Marissa Andrea; E-Mail: marissa_andrea2@agilent.com
Library Holdings: Bk Vols 7,000
Subject Interests: Corporate law

S AMERICAN INSTITUTE FOR RESEARCH,* 1791 Arastradero Rd, PO Box 1113, 94302. SAN 301-1666. Tel: 650-493-3550. FAX: 650-858-0958. Web Site: www.air-dc.org.
Founded 1967
Library Holdings: Bk Vols 3,400; Bk Titles 3,200; Per Subs 300
Subject Interests: Education, Psychology, Social sciences and issues
Special Collections: American Institutes for Research Technical Reports
Open Mon-Fri 8am-midnight

S BECKMAN INSTRUMENTS, INC, Spinco Div, 1050 Page Mill Rd, 94304-0809. SAN 301-1674. Tel: 650-859-1734. FAX: 650-859-1550. Web Site: www.beckmancoulter.com. *Librn*, Sumedha Shende; E-Mail: sshende@beckman.com; Staff 1 (MLS 1)
Founded 1958
Library Holdings: Bk Vols 5,000; Per Subs 70

Subject Interests: Biomechanics, Biotechnology, Molecular biology
Publications: Current Literature Checklist; What's New
Partic in Coop Libr Agency for Syst & Servs; Dialog Corporation; RLIN

GM DEPARTMENT OF VETERANS AFFAIRS MEDICAL CENTER, Medical Library (142 D),* 3801 Miranda Ave, 94304. SAN 301-1828. Tel: 650-493-5000, Ext 65703. FAX: 650-852-3258. *Chief Librn*, Susan Shyshka
Founded 1935
Library Holdings: Bk Titles 12,000; Per Subs 450
Restriction: Staff use only

S DNAX RESEARCH INSTITUTE LIBRARY, 901 California Ave, 94304-1104. SAN 370-8497. Tel: 650-852-9196. FAX: 650-496-1289. *Librn*, Jonathan Silver
Library Holdings: Bk Vols 1,200; Per Subs 60

S EPRI LIBRARY, 3412 Hillview Ave, 94304-1395. SAN 321-4907. Tel: 650-855-2354. FAX: 650-855-2295. E-Mail: library@epri.com. *Info Specialist*, Mark Graham; *Info Specialist*, Margaret May; Staff 3 (MLS 2, Non-MLS 1)
Founded 1972
Library Holdings: Bk Titles 7,500; Per Subs 260
Subject Interests: Electric power, Energy, Engineering
Special Collections: EPRI Reports
Automation Activity & Vendor Info: (Circulation) Sydney
Restriction: Company staff only, Not open to public
Partic in OCLC Online Computer Library Center, Inc; RLIN

L FENWICK & WEST LIBRARY,* 2 Palo Alto Sq, Ste 800, 94306. SAN 373-739X. Tel: 650-858-7163, Ext 7163. FAX: 650-494-1417. Web Site: www.fenwick.com. *Librn*, Carla Cardona; Staff 3 (MLS 1, Non-MLS 2)
Founded 1975
Library Holdings: Bk Vols 10,000; Bk Titles 2,000; Per Subs 300

R FIRST CONGREGATIONAL CHURCH LIBRARY,* 1985 Louis Rd, 94303-3499. SAN 301-1720. Tel: 650-856-6662. FAX: 650-856-6664. *Librn*, Carol Murden
Library Holdings: Bk Titles 2,100
Subject Interests: Fiction
Open Mon-Fri 8:30am-4:30pm

SR FIRST UNITED METHODIST CHURCH LIBRARY, 625 Hamilton Ave, 94301. SAN 301-1739. Tel: 650-323-6167. FAX: 650-323-3923. *Librn*, Florence Jensen
Founded 1964
1999-2000 Income Locally Generated Income $4,000. Mats Exp $3,200, Books $2,000, AV Equip $1,000, Other Print Mats $200
Library Holdings: Bk Vols 5,500; High Interest/Low Vocabulary Bk Vols 400

L GRAY, CARY, WARE & FREIDENRICH, Law Library,* 400 Hamilton Ave, 94301. SAN 372-2570. Tel: 650-328-6561, Ext 2341. FAX: 650-327-3699. Web Site: www.graycary.com. *Librn*, Ann Levy
Library Holdings: Bk Vols 10,000; Per Subs 100
Open Mon-Fri 8am-6pm

S HEWLETT-PACKARD LABORATORIES, Research Library, 1501 Page Mill Rd, PO Box 10490, 94303-0969. SAN 333-5283. Tel: 650-857-6620. Circulation Tel: 650-857-3092. Reference Tel: 650-857-3091. FAX: 650-852-8187. E-Mail: research_library@hp.com. Web Site: lib.hpl.hp.com. *Dir*, Eugenie E Prime; E-Mail: eugenie_prime@hp.com; *Doc Delivery*, Jon De Bord; Tel: 650-857-6627; *ILL*, Rosemary Gillespie; Staff 20 (MLS 8, Non-MLS 12)
Founded 1952
Library Holdings: Bk Vols 55,000; Per Subs 550
Subject Interests: Business and management, Chemistry, Electronics, Marketing, Physics, Solid state physics
Automation Activity & Vendor Info: (Cataloging) SIRSI; (Circulation) SIRSI; (Serials) SIRSI
Database Vendor: Dialog, Lexis-Nexis, ProQuest
Publications: Library Line (Acquisition list)
Restriction: By appointment only

S INSTITUTE OF TRANSPERSONAL PSYCHOLOGY LIBRARY, 744 San Antonio Rd, 94303. SAN 326-4483. Tel: 650-493-4430. FAX: 650-493-3297. E-Mail: itplib@ix.netcom.com. Web Site: www.itp.edu/resources/library.html. *Dir*, Peter I Hirose; Staff 2 (MLS 1, Non-MLS 1)
Highest Degree: Doctorate
Library Holdings: Bk Titles 13,050; Per Subs 150
Subject Interests: Psychology
Special Collections: Collected Works of C G Jung; Complete Psychological Works of Sigmund Freud; Spirituality (Classics of Western Spirituality Coll)
Partic in BRS; Coop Libr Agency for Syst & Servs; Northern California Consortium Of Psychology Libraries; Psychol Studies Librns
Open Mon-Thurs 9-9, Fri 9-5, Sat 10-4, Sun noon-6
Friends of the Library Group

S LOCKHEED MARTIN MISSILES & SPACE, Technical Information Center,* Dept 90-11, Bldg 201, 3251 Hanover St, 94304-1187. SAN 301-1763. Tel: 650-424-2869. FAX: 650-424-3124. *Mgr*, Angela Cookson; E-Mail: cookson@lmsc.lockheed.com; *Acq*, Jan Thomas; *Online Servs*, Carolyn Yandle; *Ref*, Audrey L Bryant; Staff 15 (MLS 10, Non-MLS 5)
Founded 1955
Library Holdings: Bk Vols 40,000; Bk Titles 30,000; Per Subs 228
Subject Interests: Aerospace science, Chemistry, Energy, Marketing, Space science
Automation Activity & Vendor Info: (Cataloging) TechLIB
Publications: What's New (acquisitions list)
Partic in Dialog Corporation; DMS; DOE-Recon; DTIC; Environet; Nasa Libraries Information System - Nasa Galaxie; Newsnet; STN
Friends of the Library Group
Branches:
PALO ALTO RESEARCH LABORATORY, 3251 Hanover St, 94304-1187. SAN 328-8617.
SUNNYVALE LIBRARY - TECHNICAL INFORMATION CENTER, Bldg 157, PO Box 3504, Sunnyvale, 94088. SAN 328-803X. Tel: 408-742-4969. *Librn*, Doris Robinson
Subject Interests: Aerospace science

C PACIFIC GRADUATE SCHOOL OF PSYCHOLOGY, Research Library, 935 E Meadow Dr, 94303-4233. SAN 371-8425. Tel: 650-843-3508. FAX: 650-856-6734. Web Site: www.pgsp.edu. *Librn*, Christine Dassoff; E-Mail: c.dassoff@pgsp.edu; Staff 5 (MLS 2, Non-MLS 3)
Founded 1975. Fac 60
1998-1999 Income $250,000. Mats Exp $43,500, Books $10,000, Per/Ser (Incl. Access Fees) $30,000, Micro $2,500, AV Equip $1,000
Library Holdings: Bk Vols 7,000; Bk Titles 6,000; Per Subs 218
Subject Interests: Psychiatry, Psychology
Automation Activity & Vendor Info: (Circulation) CASPR; (OPAC) CASPR
Partic in Northern Calif Consortium of Psychol Librs; Northern California & Nevada Medical Library Group
Friends of the Library Group

P PALO ALTO CITY LIBRARY, 1213 Newell Rd, 94303. (Mail add: PO Box 10250, 94303), SAN 333-5348. Tel: 650-329-2436. Circulation Tel: 650-329-2438. Reference Tel: 650-329-2664. FAX: 650-327-2033. E-Mail: pa_library@city.palo-alto.ca.us. Web Site: www.city.palo-alto.ca.us/library. *Dir*, Mary Jo Levy; Tel: 650-329-2516, Fax: 650-327-7568, E-Mail: maryjo_levy@city.palo-alto.ca.us; *Coll Develop, Mgr Libr Serv*, Diane Jennings; Tel: 650-329-2668, Fax: 650-327-7266, E-Mail: diane_jennings@city.palo-alto.ca.us; *Senior Librn*, Deborah Angel; Tel: 650-329-2586, E-Mail: deborah_angel@city.palo-alto.ca.us; *ILL, Senior Librn*, Faith VanLiere; E-Mail: faith_vanliere@city.palo-alto.ca.us; *Assoc Librn, Ser*, Daphne Lee; Tel: 650-329-2308; *Cat, Tech Servs*, Mary Minto; Tel: 650-329-2517, E-Mail: mary_minto@city.palo-alto.ca.us; *Acq*, Vicki Tran; Tel: 650-329-2511, E-Mail: vicki_tran@city.palo-alto.ca.us; *Circ*, Rose Sebastian; Tel: 650-329-2478, E-Mail: rose_sebastian@city.palo-alto.ca.us; *Ref*, Sylvia Baker; Tel: 650-329-2620, E-Mail: sylvia_baker@city.palo-alto.ca.us; *Ch Servs, Librn*, Katy Obringer; Tel: 650-329-2134, Fax: 650-322-1150, E-Mail: katy_obringer@city.palo-alto.ca.us; Staff 26 (MLS 22, Non-MLS 4)
Founded 1904. Pop 60,500; Circ 926,128
Jul 1999-Jun 2000 Income (Main Library and Branch Library) $4,458,405, State $105,235, City $4,262,052, Other $91,118. Mats Exp $521,105, Books $202,613, Per/Ser (Incl. Access Fees) $175,891, Presv $6,584, Micro $26,878, AV Equip $41,620, Electronic Ref Mat (Incl. Access Fees) $67,519. Sal $2,190,827
Library Holdings: Bk Vols 238,636; Bk Titles 166,858; Per Subs 952
Subject Interests: Local history
Special Collections: Palo Alto Historical Association files
Automation Activity & Vendor Info: (Acquisitions) epixtech, inc.; (Cataloging) epixtech, inc.; (Circulation) epixtech, inc.; (ILL) epixtech, inc.; (OPAC) epixtech, inc.; (Serials) epixtech, inc.
Database Vendor: epixtech, inc., IAC - Info Trac
Publications: Foreword (Newsletter of Friends of the Library)
Restriction: Circulation limited
Mem of Silicon Valley Library System
Friends of the Library Group
Branches: 5
CHILDREN'S, 1276 Harriet St, 94301. SAN 333-5372. Tel: 650-329-2134. FAX: 650-322-1150. Web Site: www.city.palo-alto.ca.us/library.
Founded 1940. Circ 253,902
Library Holdings: Bk Vols 33,984; Bk Titles 26,898
Friends of the Library Group
COLLEGE TERRACE, 2300 Wellesley St, 94306. SAN 333-5402. Tel: 650-329-2298. FAX: 650-494-7145. Web Site: www.city.palo-alto.ca.us/library. *Librn*, Katy Obringer; Tel: 650-329-2205, Fax: 650-322-1150, E-Mail: katy_obringer@city.palo-alto.ca.us
Founded 1936. Circ 64,075
Library Holdings: Bk Vols 20,704; Bk Titles 20,097
Friends of the Library Group
DOWNTOWN, 270 Forest Ave, 94301. SAN 333-5437. Tel: 650-329-2641. FAX: 650-327-7568. Web Site: www.city.palo-alto.ca.us/library. *Coordr*, Barbara Geibel; Tel: 650-329-2644, E-Mail: barbara_geibel@city.palo-alto.ca.us
Founded 1904. Circ 45,297
Library Holdings: Bk Vols 16,672; Bk Titles 16,143

Friends of the Library Group
MITCHELL PARK, 3700 Middlefield Rd, 94303. SAN 333-5461. Tel: 650-329-2586. TDD: 650-856-6839. FAX: 650-856-7925. Web Site: www.city.polo-alto.ca.us/library. *Librn*, Marilyn Gillespie; Tel: 650-329-2322, E-Mail: marilyn_gillespie@city.palo-alto.ca.us
Founded 1958. Circ 264,081
Library Holdings: Bk Vols 61,065; Bk Titles 56,617
Special Services for the Deaf - TDD
Special Services for the Blind - Internet workstation with adaptive software for use by people with visual limitations; Print enlarger, reading machine & an adaptive terminal to enlarge screen information when using library catalog
Friends of the Library Group
TERMAN PARK, 661 Arastradero Rd, 94306. SAN 328-7521. Tel: 650-329-2606. FAX: 650-494-3718. Web Site: www.city.palo-alto.ca.us/library. *Librn*, Marilyn Gillespie; Tel: 650-329-2322, Fax: 650-322-1150, E-Mail: marilyn_gillespie@city.palo-alto.ca.us
Founded 1985. Circ 18,405
Library Holdings: Bk Vols 9,547; Bk Titles 8,785
Friends of the Library Group

M PALO ALTO MEDICAL FOUNDATION, Barnett-Hall Library, 860 Bryant St, 94301-2799. SAN 301-178X. Tel: 650-326-8120, Ext 4831. FAX: 650-853-2909. *Chief Librn*, Judith Cummings; *Ser*, Charlotte A Steinmetz
Founded 1950
Library Holdings: Bk Vols 12,107; Per Subs 229
Subject Interests: Clinical medicine
Publications: Annual report; newsletter (quarterly)
Partic in Nat Libr of Med; Northern California & Nevada Medical Library Group; Pacific SW Regional Med Libr Serv; Spec Libr Asn

S PENINSULA CONSERVATION CENTER FOUNDATION LIBRARY,* 3921 E Bayshore Rd, 94303. SAN 326-1352. Tel: 650-962-9876. FAX: 650-962-8234. E-Mail: info@pccf.org, library@pccf.org. *Librn*, Rosemary Jorde; *Asst Librn*, Ann Schwabecher; Staff 1 (MLS 1)
Founded 1970
Library Holdings: Bk Vols 6,500; Bk Titles 6,000; Per Subs 30
Special Collections: Backpacking & Trails; Birding, bks, per; Energy; Environmental Careers; Environmental Volunteers Coll; Wildlife & Endangered Species Coll
Publications: The Center View (parent publication bi-monthly)
The library's strength is a collection of pamphlet & newspaper clippings on environmental subjects
Friends of the Library Group

S ROCHE BIOSCIENCE LIBRARY & INFORMATION CENTER, Corporate Library-Information Services,* 3401 Hillview Ave, MS AZ-060, 94304-1397. SAN 301-1798. Tel: 650-855-5431, 650-855-5432. FAX: 650-354-7741. *Mgr*, Pamela Jaiko; Staff 11 (MLS 6, Non-MLS 5)
Founded 1961
Library Holdings: Bk Titles 6,000; Per Subs 500
Subject Interests: Biochemistry, Clinical medicine, Organic chemistry, Pharmacology, Physiology, Veterinary medicine
Special Collections: Syntex Personnel Reprints
Partic in OCLC Online Computer Library Center, Inc

M STANFORD UNIVERSITY HOSPITAL, Health Library,* 2-B Stanford Shopping Ctr, 94305. SAN 374-5376. Tel: 650-725-8400. FAX: 650-725-1444. *Librn*, Howard Fuller; Staff 3 (MLS 2, Non-MLS 1)
Founded 1989
Library Holdings: Bk Titles 3,000; Per Subs 100
Subject Interests: Consumer health, Medicine

S VARIAN ASSOCIATES, Corporate Library,* 3075 Hansen Way, K-100, 94304-1025. SAN 333-5496. Tel: 650-424-5071. FAX: 650-424-6988. *Coll Develop, Librn*, Ailya Rose; E-Mail: ailya.rose@grc.varian.com
Founded 1961
Library Holdings: Bk Vols 20,000; Bk Titles 15,000
Subject Interests: Business and management, Chemistry, Computer science, Electronics, Mathematics, Physics
Publications: Technical Library Bulletin
Partic in Dialog Corporation; Dow Jones News Retrieval; OCLC Online Computer Library Center, Inc

L WILSON, SONSINI, GOODRICH & ROSATI, Library,* 650 Page Mill Rd, 94304. SAN 372-2988. Tel: 650-493-9300. FAX: 650-493-6811. *Librn*, Leiza D MacMorris
Library Holdings: Bk Vols 40,000; Per Subs 300

S XEROX CORP, Palo Alto Research Center Information Center,* 3333 Coyote Hill Rd, 94304-1314. SAN 301-1844. Tel: 650-812-4042. FAX: 650-812-4028. E-Mail: library.parc@xerox.com. *Mgr*, Katherine Jarvis; *Doc*, Lisa Alfke; Staff 15 (MLS 8, Non-MLS 7)
Founded 1971
Library Holdings: Bk Titles 15,000; Per Subs 800
Subject Interests: Electronics, Physics
Automation Activity & Vendor Info: (Circulation) TechLIB
Publications: Acquisition List (monthly); Competitive Flyer (monthly); IC News (weekly); Monday Teller (monthly); Update (weekly); Xerox PARC Information Services User Manual
Restriction: Staff use only

PANORAMA CITY

M KAISER-PERMANENTE MEDICAL CENTER, Panorama City Health Science Library,* 13652 Cantara St, 91402. SAN 375-7749. Tel: 818-375-2239. *Librn*, Winnie Lee
Library Holdings: Bk Titles 1,800

PASADENA

C ART CENTER COLLEGE OF DESIGN, James Lemont Fogg Memorial Library, 1700 Lida St, 91109-1999. SAN 301-1895. Tel: 626-396-2231. FAX: 626-568-0428. Web Site: www.galloway.artcenter.edu. *Dir*, Elizabeth Galloway; E-Mail: galloway@artcenter.edu; *Cat*, Alison Holt; E-Mail: aholt@artcenter.edu; *Acq*, George Porcari; *Ref*, C Michelle Betty; E-Mail: cbetty@artcenter.edu
Founded 1930. Highest Degree: Master
Library Holdings: Bk Vols 100,000; Bk Titles 75,000; Per Subs 425
Subject Interests: Advertising, Commercial art, Films and filmmaking, Fine arts, Graphic arts, Photography
Automation Activity & Vendor Info: (Cataloging) epixtech, inc.; (Circulation) epixtech, inc.
Partic in OCLC Online Computer Library Center, Inc; OCLC Western Service Center
Open Mon-Thurs 8:30-10, Fri 8:30-5 & Sat 8:30-4

S AVERY DENNISON RESEARCH & INFORMATION CENTER,* 2900 Bradley St, 91107-1599. SAN 301-1909. Tel: 626-398-2550, Ext 2579. FAX: 626-398-2553.
Founded 1968
Library Holdings: Bk Vols 2,000; Per Subs 150
Subject Interests: Films and filmmaking
Special Collections: Patents Coll
Restriction: Staff use only
Open Mon-Fri 8am-5pm

S BROWN & ROOT, INC, Information Resource Center,* 790 E Colorado Blvd, Ste 600, 91101-2186. SAN 300-5593. Tel: 626-300-1010. Interlibrary Loan Service Tel: 626-300-2330. FAX: 626-300-1020.
Founded 1935
Library Holdings: Bk Titles 7,500; Per Subs 100
Subject Interests: Business and management, Chemistry, Energy
Publications: Library Bulletin (monthly, internal distribution only)
Restriction: Not open to public
Partic in Dialog Corporation

C CALIFORNIA INSTITUTE OF TECHNOLOGY, Caltech Library System 1-32, M/C 1-32, 1201 E California Blvd, 91125. SAN 333-5704. Tel: 626-395-6401. FAX: 626-792-7540. E-Mail: library@caltech.edu. Web Site: www.library.caltech.edu. *Dir*, Kimberly Douglas; *Mgr*, Judith Brott; E-Mail: brott@library.caltech.edu; *Librn*, Anne M Buck; E-Mail: buck@its.caltech.edu; *Br Coordr*, Caroline Smith; *Br Coordr*, Jim O'Donnell; *Ref*, George Porter; *Ref*, Judy Nollar; *Ref*, Daniel Taylor; *Ref*, Louisa Toot; *Ref*, Dana Roth; Staff 20 (MLS 14, Non-MLS 6)
Founded 1891. Enrl 2,100; Fac 400; Highest Degree: Doctorate
Oct 1999-Sep 2000 Mats Exp $3,416,570, Books $376,958, Per/Ser (Incl. Access Fees) $2,001,062, Presv $58,988, Electronic Ref Mat (Incl. Access Fees) $500,232. Sal $1,053,916 (Prof $1,003,168)
Library Holdings: Bk Vols 548,752; Per Subs 3,144
Subject Interests: Engineering, History of science, Social sciences and issues, Technology
Special Collections: NACA/NASA Technical Reports
Automation Activity & Vendor Info: (Acquisitions) Innovative Interfaces Inc.; (Cataloging) Innovative Interfaces Inc.; (Circulation) Innovative Interfaces Inc.; (Serials) Innovative Interfaces Inc.
Publications: CLS Guide to SciSearch Services; CLS Online Resources; CLS Rules of Access
Partic in CAL/PALS; G4; IATUL; SCELC
Friends of the Library Group
Departmental Libraries:
ASTROPHYSICS, 109 Robinson, 91125. SAN 333-5763. Tel: 626-395-4008. *Librn*, Caroline Smith
EARTHQUAKE ENGINEERING RESEARCH, 201 Thomas, 91125. SAN 333-5852. Tel: 626-395-4227. *Librn*, Jim O'Donnell
SHERMAN FAIRCHILD LIBRARY OF ENGINEERING & APPLIED SCIENCE, Fairchild Library I-43, 91125. SAN 376-8961. Tel: 626-395-3404. FAX: 626-431-2681. *Dir*, Kimberly Douglas

S CALIFORNIA INSTITUTE OF TECHNOLOGY, (LARS), Jet Propulsion Laboratory Library, Archives, & Records Section, 4800 Oak Grove Dr, MS 111-113, 91109-8099. SAN 301-195X. Tel: 818-354-3007. Interlibrary Loan Service Tel: 818-354-9258. Circulation Tel: 818-354-3840. Reference Tel: 818-354-4200. FAX: 818-393-6752. Web Site: beacon.jpl.nasa.gov. *Archivist*,

Dr Michael Hooks; Tel: 818-354-8804, E-Mail: michael.q.hooks@jpl.nasa.gov; *Circ, Ref*, Eric Hines; Tel: 818-354-4202, E-Mail: eric.l.hines@jpl.nasa.gov; *Cat*, Jennifer Momjian; Tel: 818-354-5540, E-Mail: jennifer.c.momjian@jpl.nasa.gov; *Acq*, Barbara Amago; Tel: 818-354-3183, E-Mail: barbara.j.amago@jpl.nasa.gov; *Coll Develop*, Judith Castagno; Tel: 818-354-5469, E-Mail: judith.m.castagno@jpl.nasa.gov; Staff 22 (MLS 12, Non-MLS 10)
Founded 1948
Library Holdings: Bk Vols 84,827; Bk Titles 40,977; Per Subs 1,030
Subject Interests: Aerospace, Astronomy, Astrophysics, Business and management, Engineering, Physical science
Special Collections: JPL Archives
Automation Activity & Vendor Info: (Acquisitions) SIRSI; (Cataloging) SIRSI; (Circulation) SIRSI; (OPAC) SIRSI; (Serials) SIRSI
Partic in Nasa Libraries Information System - Nasa Galaxie; OCLC Online Computer Library Center, Inc

P CITY OF PASADENA DEPARTMENT OF INFORMATION SERVICES LIBRARY,* 285 E Walnut St, 91101. SAN 333-6212. Tel: 626-405-4033, 626-744-3867, 626-744-4052. FAX: 626-449-2165. Web Site: www.ci.pasadena.ca.us. *Dir Libr Serv*, Luis Herrera; E-Mail: lherrera@ci.pasadena.ca.us; *Info Res*, Beth Walker; *Info Tech*, Bryan Sands; *Admin Assoc*, Barbara Ayala; *Commun Servs*, Susan Gegenhuber; Staff 118 (MLS 43, Non-MLS 75)
Founded 1882. Pop 130,000; Circ 1,554,000
Library Holdings: Bk Vols 712,358; Per Subs 1,450
Subject Interests: Art, Business and management, Economics, History, Music, Technology
Special Collections: Annual Reports; Local History Coll
Automation Activity & Vendor Info: (Circulation) GEAC
Mem of South State Cooperative Library System
Partic in BRS; Dialog Corporation; Dow Jones News Retrieval; OCLC Online Computer Library Center, Inc; Vutext; Wilsonline
Friends of the Library Group
Branches: 9
ALLENDALE, 1130 S Marengo Ave, 91106. SAN 333-6247. Tel: 626-744-7260. *Librn*, Diane Walker
Library Holdings: Bk Vols 34,286
HASTINGS, 3325 E Orange Grove Blvd, 91107. SAN 333-6271. Tel: 626-744-7262. *Librn*, Donna Watkins
Library Holdings: Bk Vols 57,792
HILL AVENUE, 55 S Hill Ave, 91106. SAN 333-6301. Tel: 626-744-7264. *Librn*, Thelma Watson
Library Holdings: Bk Vols 46,622
Special Collections: Asian languages and subjects
LA PINTORESCA, 1355 N Raymond Ave, 91103. SAN 333-6360. Tel: 626-744-7268. *Librn*, Barbara Martin
Library Holdings: Bk Vols 42,301
Special Collections: Career material
LAMANDA PARK, 140 S Altadena Dr, 91107. SAN 333-6336. Tel: 626-744-7266. *Librn*, Kathryn Currey
Library Holdings: Bk Vols 58,643
LINDA VISTA, 1281 Bryant St, 91103. SAN 333-6395. Tel: 626-744-7278. *Librn*, Robin Reidy
Library Holdings: Bk Vols 28,840
SAN RAFAEL, 1240 Nithsdale Rd, 91105. SAN 333-6425. Tel: 626-744-7270. *Librn*, Christine Reeder
Library Holdings: Bk Vols 34,277
SANTA CATALINA, 999 E Washington Blvd, 91104. SAN 333-645X. Tel: 626-744-7272. *Librn*, Bernadette Glover
Library Holdings: Bk Vols 47,946
Special Collections: Armenian language and subjects
VILLA PARKE INFORMATION STOP, 363 E Villa St, 91101. SAN 374-8103. Tel: 626-744-6510. *Librn*, Rosa Martin

SR FIRST UNITED METHODIST CHURCH LIBRARY,* 500 E Colorado Blvd, 91101. SAN 373-0344. Tel: 626-796-0157. FAX: 626-568-1615. Web Site: www.fumcpas.org ((church)). *Librn*, Ruth McPhearson
Library Holdings: Bk Vols 4,000
Subject Interests: Religion

R FULLER THEOLOGICAL SEMINARY, McAlister Library, 135 N Oakland Ave, 91182. SAN 301-1933. Tel: 626-584-5218. FAX: 626-584-5613. *Acq, Dir*, John Dickason; E-Mail: dickason@fuller.edu; *Per*, Steve Magnuson; *Online Servs, Ref*, Sharon Ralston; *Cat*, E Yeung
Founded 1948. Enrl 1,334; Fac 93; Highest Degree: Doctorate
Library Holdings: Bk Vols 220,000; Per Subs 960
Subject Interests: Biblical studies, Church history, Feminism, Philosophy, Psychology, Religion, Theology
Partic in Metronet; OCLC Online Computer Library Center, Inc
Open Mon-Fri 8am-10:30pm & Sat 9am-10:30pm
Friends of the Library Group

M HUNTINGTON MEMORIAL HOSPITAL, Health Sciences Library,* 100 W California Blvd, PO Box 7013, 91109-7013. SAN 301-1941. Tel: 626-397-5161. FAX: 626-397-8009. *Dir Libr Serv*, Samir Maurice Zeind; *Ref*, Suzanne Huddleson; *Circ*, Jennifer Edmonson
Library Holdings: Bk Vols 5,500; Per Subs 680
Special Collections: Medical & Paramedical Texts, bks, journals, AV
Restriction: Members only
Partic in Dialog Corporation; Docline; Nat Libr of Med; Pacific SW Regional Med Libr Serv
Open Mon-Fri 7:30-6
Friends of the Library Group

M KAISER PERMANENTE, Management Effectiveness Library,* 393 E Walnut St, 5th flr, 91188. SAN 321-1762. Tel: 626-405-3089. FAX: 626-405-6715. *Dir Libr Serv*, Henri Mondschein; E-Mail: henri.x.mondschein@kp.org; *Asst Librn*, Edward Reaser
Founded 1976
Library Holdings: Bk Titles 4,400; Per Subs 255
Subject Interests: Law

P METROPOLITAN COOPERATIVE LIBRARY SYSTEM, 3675 E Huntington Dr, Ste 100, 91107. SAN 301-1968. Tel: 626-683-8244. FAX: 626-683-8097. E-Mail: mclshq@mclsys.org. Web Site: www.mcls.org. *Exec Dir*, Barbara Custen; E-Mail: bcusten@mclsys.org; Staff 14 (MLS 5, Non-MLS 9)
Founded 1965. Pop 6,192,785
Publications: Beyond Standard & Poor's; Directory of AV Equipment, Materials & Services; Fines & Fees in MCLS Libraries; Guide to Government Officials; MCLS News; MCLS Program Resource List; MCLS/SLS Tax Packet; Reference Hotline; Survey of Special Collections & Staff Expertise; Union List of Periodicals
Member Libraries: Alhambra Public Library; Alschuler, Grossman, Stein & Kahan; Altadena Library District; Arcadia Public Library; Azusa City Library; Beverly Hills Public Library; Bruggemeyer Memorial Library; Burbank Public Library; Calabasas Public Library; City Of Cerritos Public Library; City Of Commerce Public Library; Covina Public Library; Downey City Library; El Segundo Public Library; Glendale Public Library; Glendora Public Library; Long Beach Public Library & Information Center; Los Angeles Public Library System; Monrovia Public Library; Oxnard Public Library; Palos Verdes Library District; Pomona Public Library; Redondo Beach Public Library; San Marino Public Library; Santa Ana Public Library; Santa Fe Springs City Library; Santa Monica Public Library; Sierra Madre Public Library; Signal Hill Public Library; South Pasadena Public Library; Thousand Oaks Library; Torrance Public Library; Whittier Public Library

S MONTGOMERY WATSON LIBRARY,* 250 N Madison Ave, 91101. SAN 328-0640. Tel: 626-568-6583. FAX: 626-568-6367. *Librn*, Fern Willis; E-Mail: fern.willis@mw.com; Staff 4 (MLS 2, Non-MLS 2)
Subject Interests: Water treatment

S OBSERVATORIES OF THE CARNEGIE INSTITUTION OF WASHINGTON, Hale Library, 813 Santa Barbara St, 91101. SAN 371-0297. Tel: 626-304-0228. FAX: 626-795-8136. Web Site: www.ociw.edu. *Librn*, John Grula; E-Mail: jgrula@ociw.edu; Staff 1 (MLS 1)
Library Holdings: Bk Vols 30,000; Bk Titles 4,000; Per Subs 55
Subject Interests: Astronomy, Astrophysics, Physics
Database Vendor: OCLC - First Search

S PACIFIC ASIA MUSEUM LIBRARY,* 46 N Los Robles, 91101. SAN 326-2413. Tel: 626-449-2742, Ext 24. FAX: 626-449-2754. E-Mail: libraryPAM@aol.com, pacasiamus@aol.com. *Librn*, Sarah McKay; Staff 1 (MLS 1)
Sep 1998-Aug 1999 Income $8,711, Locally Generated Income $4,530, Parent Institution $4,181. Mats Exp $3,327, Books $2,898, Per/Ser (Incl. Access Fees) $429. Sal $4,732
Library Holdings: Bk Vols 7,000; Per Subs 8
Subject Interests: Art, Asian art, Culture, Pacific
Special Collections: India (Paul Sherbert Coll)
Partic in Metronet

C PACIFIC OAKS COLLEGE, Andrew Norman Library, 6 Westmoreland Pl, 91103. SAN 301-1976. Tel: 626-397-1354, 626-397-1360. Toll Free Tel: 800-684-0500. FAX: 626-397-1356. Web Site: www.pacificoaks.edu. *Librn*, Margaret Connors; E-Mail: mconnors@pacificoaks.edu; *Ref*, Ed Armstrong; Tel: 626-666-1227
Founded 1945. Enrl 275; Fac 20; Highest Degree: Master
Jul 1998-Jun 1999 Income $193,017. Mats Exp $39,450, Books $16,500, Per/Ser (Incl. Access Fees) $22,950. Sal $139,003 (Prof $114,003)
Library Holdings: Bk Vols 19,600; Bk Titles 18,600; Per Subs 110
Special Collections: Children's Coll, books, records; Historical Development of Children's Literature (Critical); Society of Friends
Open Mon-Thurs 12-10, Sat 10-4 & Sun 11-4

S PARSON'S CORPORATION, Technical Library, 100 W Walnut St, 91124. SAN 301-1984. Tel: 626-440-3998. FAX: 626-440-2630. *In Charge*, Claire Hammond; E-Mail: claire_hammond@parsons.com
Library Holdings: Bk Vols 10,000; Per Subs 38,000
Subject Interests: Mining, Transportation
Partic in Southern Calif Interlibr Loan Network

S PARSONS INFRASTRUCTURE & TECHNOLOGY, Technical Library,* 100 W Walnut, 91124. SAN 320-5789. Tel: 626-440-3998. FAX: 626-440-2630. *Librn*, Claire Hammond; E-Mail: claire_hammond@parsons.com
Founded 1949

Library Holdings: Bk Vols 10,000
Subject Interests: Aviation, Transportation
Special Collections: Company Project Reports; Published Articles
Publications: TIPS (monthly newsletter)

J PASADENA CITY COLLEGE LIBRARY,* 1570 E Colorado Blvd, 91106-2003. SAN 301-1992. Tel: 626-585-7360. Interlibrary Loan Service Tel: 626-585-7835. FAX: 626-585-7913. Web Site: www.paccd.cc.ca.us. *Asst Dir*, Jennifer Cooper; *Dir*, Mary Ann Laun; E-Mail: malaun@paccd.cc.ca.us; *Acq, Coll Develop*, Joanne Kim; *Automation Syst Coordr, Ref*, Daniel Haley; *Bibliog Instr*, Dona Mitoma; *Tech Servs*, Dorothy Potter
Founded 1924
1997-1998 Income $1,165,678. Mats Exp $129,000, Books $65,000, Per/Ser (Incl. Access Fees) $21,000, Micro $18,000, AV Equip $25,000. Sal $786,708
Library Holdings: Bk Vols 160,000; Per Subs 613
Subject Interests: Education, History, Local history
Automation Activity & Vendor Info: (Circulation) VTLS

S PASADENA HISTORICAL MUSEUM, Research Library & Archives, 470 W Walnut St, 91103-3594. SAN 301-200X. Tel: 626-577-1660. FAX: 626-577-1662. E-Mail: trizzo@pasadenahistory.org. Web Site: www.pasadenahistory.org. *Archivist*, Tania Rizzo; Tel: 626-577-1660, Ext 12, E-Mail: trizzo@pasadenahistory.org; Staff 1 (MLS 1)
Founded 1924
Jan 2000-Dec 2000 Income Locally Generated Income $2,500. Mats Exp Presv $2,000. Sal $15,000
Library Holdings: Bk Vols 1,500; Bk Titles 1,000
Subject Interests: Architecture, Local history, Maps, Photog, Real estate, Women's studies
Special Collections: J. Allen Hawkins Photo Coll; Pasadena Star-News Photo Archive; Sylvanus Marston; Tournament of Roses
Publications: A Southern California Paradise; Historic Pasadena (Lund); Pasadena Photographs and Photographers 1880-1920; Pasadena's Super Athletes; Walter Raymond, A Gentleman of the Old School
Restriction: Open to public for reference only
Function: Archival collection, Photocopies available, Research fees apply, Research library

S RIGHT TO LIFE LEAGUE OF SOUTHERN CALIFORNIA LIBRARY, 1028 N Lake Ave, Ste 104, 91104. SAN 370-4327. Tel: 626-398-6100. FAX: 626-398-6101. E-Mail: rtll@pabell.net. Web Site: rtllsc.org.
Founded 1969
Subject Interests: Abortion, Abstinence educ, Euthanasia, Genetic eng, Human experimentation, Infanticide, Pop control, Pre-natal develop, Sex educ

M SAINT LUKE MEDICAL CENTER, (STML), William P Long Memorial Medical Library, 2632 E Washington Blvd, Bin 7021, 91109-7021. SAN 320-572X. Tel: 626-797-1141, Ext 280. FAX: 626-794-7407. Web Site: www.tenethealth.com. *Librn*, Christine DeCicco; E-Mail: christine.decicco@tenethealth.com
Founded 1932
Library Holdings: Bk Vols 640; Per Subs 70
Subject Interests: Clinical medicine
Restriction: Staff use only
Mem of MLGSCA, PSRMLS
Partic in Pacific SW Regional Med Libr Serv

S SKYNET UFO RESEARCH LIBRARY, 257 Sycamore Glen, 91105-1350. SAN 329-0921. Tel: 323-256-8655. *Acq, Coordr*, Ann Druffel
Founded 1965
2000-2001 Mats Exp $11,000, Books $3,000, AV Equip $4,000, Manuscripts & Archives $4,000
Library Holdings: Bk Titles 860; Per Subs 35
Special Collections: UFO Research (Ann Druffel Coll), acad papers, AV, bks, photos, rpts, slides, transparencies, videos
Publications: Skynet Guide
Publication list of 185 published articles ans 3 books on UFO subject by Druffel, copies available for fees. Inquires for information must be accompanied by SASE. Research on specific aspects UFO - $60 per hour. By appointment

L US COURT OF APPEALS, NINTH CIRCUIT LIBRARY, 125 S Grand Ave, 91105. SAN 323-7680. Tel: 626-229-7190. FAX: 626-229-7460. *Librn*, Kathryn A Way; Staff 1 (MLS 1)
Founded 1985
Library Holdings: Bk Vols 27,000; Bk Titles 1,710; Per Subs 90
Subject Interests: Law

C WILLIAM CAREY INTERNATIONAL UNIVERSITY, Kenneth Scott Latourette Library, 1530 E Elizabeth St, 91104-2608. (Mail add: 1539 E Howard St, 91104-2635), SAN 328-3542. Tel: 626-398-2155, 626-797-1200. FAX: 626-398-2101. *Librn*, Dwight P Baker
Library Holdings: Bk Vols 40,000; Per Subs 480
Subject Interests: Sociological cultural studies

S XEROX SPECIAL INFORMATION SYSTEMS LIBRARY, 250 N Halstead St, 91109-7018. SAN 301-2050. Tel: 626-351-4403. FAX: 626-351-4433. *Librn*, Frances A McCrary; E-Mail: fmccrary@xsis.xerox.com; Staff 1 (MLS 1)
Founded 1984
Library Holdings: Bk Vols 3,001; Bk Titles 1,900; Per Subs 64
Subject Interests: Business, Computer science, Engineering
Publications: annual periodical list; Weekly new acquisitions list
Restriction: Staff use only

PASO ROBLES

§S CALIFORNIA YOUTH AUTHORITY, El Paso de Robles Youth Correctional Facility Library, 4545 Airport Rd, 93446. (Mail add: PO Box 7008, 93447-7008), Tel: 805-238-4040, Ext 3060. FAX: 805-239-5954.
Library Holdings: Bk Vols 5,139; Per Subs 47

P PASO ROBLES PUBLIC LIBRARY,* 1000 Spring St, 93446-2207. SAN 301-2069. Tel: 805-237-3870. FAX: 805-238-3665. *Librn*, Ann Robb; E-Mail: annie@prcity.com; *Ad Servs*, Karen Cushing; *Ref*, Barbara Bilyeu; *Ch Servs*, Julie Dahlen
Founded 1903. Pop 22,000; Circ 138,711
Library Holdings: Bk Vols 50,000; Per Subs 150
Special Collections: Paso Robles Newspapers from 1892, micro
Mem of Black Gold Cooperative Library System
Friends of the Library Group

PATTON

PATTON STATE HOSPITAL

M PATIENTS' LIBRARY, 3102 E Highland Ave, 92369. SAN 320-1600. Tel: 909-425-6039. FAX: 909-425-6162. *Senior Librn*, Frederick Brenion; Staff 1 (MLS 1)
Library Holdings: Bk Vols 13,000; Bk Titles 10,300; Per Subs 50
Partic in San Bernardino, Inyo, Riverside Counties United Library Services

M STAFF LIBRARY, 3102 E Highland Ave, 92369. SAN 320-1619. Tel: 909-425-7484. FAX: 909-425-6053. *Librn*, Laurie Piccolotti; E-Mail: lpiccolo@dmhpsh.state.ca.us; Staff 1 (MLS 1)
Founded 1941
Jul 1999-Jun 2000 Income State $43,000. Mats Exp $41,000, Books $15,000, Per/Ser (Incl. Access Fees) $18,000, Electronic Ref Mat (Incl. Access Fees) $8,000. Sal $50,000
Library Holdings: Bk Titles 3,300; Per Subs 130
Subject Interests: Psychiatry
Automation Activity & Vendor Info: (Acquisitions) Sydney; (Cataloging) Sydney; (Circulation) Sydney; (OPAC) Sydney; (Serials) Sydney
Database Vendor: Silverplatter Information Inc.
Restriction: By appointment only
Function: Reference only
Partic in Med Libr Group of S Calif & Ariz; San Bernardino, Inyo, Riverside Counties United Library Services

PEBBLE BEACH

S HYDRO RESEARCH SCIENCE LIBRARY,* 1138 Porque Lane, PO Box 1321, 93953. SAN 377-4902. Tel: 831-624-1640. FAX: 831-624-7880. *Dir*, Dr Alexander Rudawsky
Library Holdings: Bk Vols 250

PETALUMA

P PETALUMA REGIONAL LIBRARY, 100 Fairgrounds Dr, 94952-3369. SAN 376-3919. Tel: 707-763-9801. FAX: 707-763-0288. Web Site: www.sonomalibrary.org. *Mgr*, Kiyo Okazaki; E-Mail: kiyo@sonoma.lib.ca.us
Library Holdings: Bk Vols 100,000; Bk Titles 52,000; Per Subs 220
Special Collections: Petaluma History Room
Mem of North Bay Cooperative Library System
Friends of the Library Group

PICO RIVERA

S ARMENIAN NUMISMATIC SOCIETY LIBRARY, 8511 Beverly Park Pl, 90660-1920. SAN 374-4825. Tel: 562-695-0380. E-Mail: armnumsoc@aol.com. *Librn*, W Gewenian; *Asst Librn*, Y T Nercessian
Founded 1971

PLACENTIA

P PLACENTIA LIBRARY DISTRICT,* 411 E Chapman Ave, 92870. SAN 301-1488. Tel: 714-528-1906. FAX: 714-528-8236. E-Mail: plalibd@cosmoslink.net. *Dir*, Elizabeth Minter; *Ad Servs*, Suad Ammar; *Ch Servs*, Cyrise Smith; *Ref*, Cindy McClain; Staff 12 (MLS 5, Non-MLS 7)
Founded 1919. Pop 2,326,200

Library Holdings: Bk Vols 147,463; Per Subs 253
Special Collections: Arabic Language Coll; California Coll; Placentia Local History, bks, microfilm
Automation Activity & Vendor Info: (Circulation) epixtech, inc.
Publications: Ethnic Orange County - resources directory, 4th ed, 1989; Newsletter (quarterly); OCULP, Orange County Union List of Periodicals, 8th ed, 1990
Provide second-level reference service (via contract with Inland Library System) to member libraries; provide inter-library deliveries of books & mail; have federal LSCA Title I grant to develop automated information and referral operation in public libraries & human services agencies throughout Orange County. Open Sun 1-5, Mon-Wed 12-9, Thurs 10-6
Friends of the Library Group

PLACERVILLE

GL EL DORADO COUNTY LAW LIBRARY, 550 Main St, Ste A, 95667-5699. SAN 301-2123. Tel: 530-621-6423. FAX: 530-626-1932.
Library Holdings: Bk Titles 10,311
Subject Interests: California
Special Collections: Calif & fed legal materials
Open Mon-Fri 8-5 (closed 12-1 lunch)

P EL DORADO COUNTY LIBRARY, 345 Fair Lane, 95667-4196. SAN 333-6484. Tel: 530-621-5540, 530-621-5546. FAX: 530-622-3911. E-Mail: lib-pl@eldoradolibrary.org. Web Site: www.el-dorado.ca.us/~lib-pl/welcome.shtml. *Dir*, Jeanne Amos; Tel: 530-621-5546, E-Mail: jamos@co.el-dorado.ca.us; *Ref*, Bonnie Battaglia; *ILL*, Nancy Leonti; Staff 8 (MLS 8)
Founded 1947. Pop 150,800; Circ 600,000
Jul 1999-Jun 2000 Income (Main Library and Branch Library) $2,000,000, State $280,000, Locally Generated Income $1,720,000. Mats Exp $331,000, Books $275,000, Per/Ser (Incl. Access Fees) $41,500, Micro $2,500, AV Equip $12,000. Sal $1,200,000 (Prof $300,000)
Library Holdings: Bk Vols 305,533; Bk Titles 158,030; Per Subs 325
Subject Interests: California
Automation Activity & Vendor Info: (Acquisitions) DRA; (Cataloging) DRA; (Circulation) DRA; (OPAC) DRA
Database Vendor: DRA, OCLC - First Search
Mem of Mountain-Valley Library System
Friends of the Library Group
Branches: 5
CAMERON PARK BRANCH, 2500 Country Club Dr, Cameron Park, 95682. SAN 374-6852. Tel: 530-621-5500. FAX: 530-672-1346.
Library Holdings: Bk Vols 31,754
Friends of the Library Group
GEORGETOWN BRANCH, PO Box 55, Georgetown, 95634. SAN 333-6549. Tel: 916-333-4724. FAX: 916-333-0843. *Mgr*, Barbara Ingle
Library Holdings: Bk Vols 12,721
Friends of the Library Group
OAKRIDGE - EL DORADO HILLS BRANCH, 1120 Harvard Way, El Dorado Hills, 95630. SAN 333-6514. Tel: 916-933-6982. FAX: 916-933-6987. *Librn*, Kym Woolston
Library Holdings: Bk Vols 7,774
Friends of the Library Group
POLLOCK PINES BRANCH, PO Box 757, Pollock Pines, 95726. SAN 333-6603. Tel: 916-644-2498. *Mgr*, Judy Brush
Library Holdings: Bk Vols 15,735
SOUTH LAKE TAHOE BRANCH, 1000 Rufus Allen Blvd, South Lake Tahoe, 96150. SAN 333-6573. Tel: 916-573-3185. FAX: 916-544-8954. *Mgr*, Sally Neitling
Library Holdings: Bk Vols 48,761
Friends of the Library Group

PLEASANT HILL

S BROWN & CALDWELL LIBRARY,* 3480 Buskirk Ave, 94523. SAN 320-6106. Tel: 925-210-2364. FAX: 925-937-9026. *Librn*, Paula Spurlock; E-Mail: pspurlock@brwneald.com
Library Holdings: Bk Vols 8,000; Per Subs 125
Subject Interests: Civil engineering, Water treatment
Publications: Monthly Acquisitions List
Restriction: Staff use only
Partic in Bay Area Library & Information Network
Open Mon-Fri 8-5

P CONTRA COSTA COUNTY LIBRARY,* 1750 Oak Park Blvd, 94523-4497. SAN 333-6662. Tel: 925-646-6423. Interlibrary Loan Service Tel: 925-646-6354. FAX: 925-646-6461. Web Site: www.contra-costa.lib.ca.us. *Librn*, Anne Cain; *Publ Servs*, Rose-Marie Kennedy; *Publ Servs*, Melinda Sisson; *Acq, Coll Develop*, John Pardee; *Automation Syst Coordr*, Cindy Brittain; Staff 166 (MLS 55, Non-MLS 111)
Founded 1913. Pop 787,900; Circ 3,658,228
Library Holdings: Bk Vols 1,202,797; Per Subs 2,787
Special Collections: California History; Contra Costa History; Food Technology (Vincent Davi Coll)
Automation Activity & Vendor Info: (Circulation) CARL
Mem of Bay Area Libr & Info Syst
Special Services for the Blind - Closed circuit radio for broadcast services; Talking bks & player equipment
Project Second Chance - Literacy Program
Friends of the Library Group
Branches: 23
ANTIOCH BRANCH, 501 W 18th St, 94509-2292. SAN 333-6697. Tel: 510-757-9224. FAX: 510-427-8540. Web Site: www.contra-costa.lib.ca.us. *Librn*, P Chan
Library Holdings: Bk Vols 72,192
Friends of the Library Group
BAY POINT BRANCH, 205 Pacifica Ave, Bay Point, 94565. SAN 377-6654. Tel: 510-458-9597. FAX: 510-458-2215. Web Site: www.contra-costa.lib.ca.us. *Librn*, Carolina Montufar
Library Holdings: Bk Vols 6,367
Friends of the Library Group
BRENTWOOD BRANCH, 751 Third St, Brentwood, 94513-1359. SAN 333-6727. Tel: 510-634-4101. FAX: 510-634-0157. Web Site: www.contra-costa.lib.ca.us. *Librn*, Leonard Roudman
Library Holdings: Bk Vols 38,376
Friends of the Library Group
CENTRAL, 1750 Oak Park Blvd, 94523-4497. SAN 333-6751. Tel: 510-646-6434. FAX: 510-646-6040. Web Site: www.contra-costa.lib.ca.us. *In Charge*, Linda Saltzer
Library Holdings: Bk Vols 215,515
Friends of the Library Group
CLAYTON BRANCH, 6125 Clayton Rd, Clayton, 94517. SAN 377-6670. Tel: 925-673-0659. FAX: 925-673-0359. Web Site: www.contra-costa.lib.ca.us. *Librn*, Susan Reeve; Staff 4 (MLS 2, Non-MLS 2)
Library Holdings: Bk Vols 60,000
Friends of the Library Group
CONCORD BRANCH, 2900 Salvio St, Concord, 94519-2597. SAN 333-6786. Tel: 510-646-5455. FAX: 510-646-5453. Web Site: www.contra-costa.lib.ca.us. *In Charge*, Maureen Kilmurray
Library Holdings: Bk Vols 78,473
Friends of the Library Group
CROCKETT BRANCH, 991 Loring Ave, Crockett, 94525-1168. SAN 333-6816. Tel: 510-787-2345. FAX: 510-787-7275. Web Site: www.contra-costa.lib.ca.us. *In Charge*, C Tucker-Watt
Library Holdings: Bk Vols 7,977
Friends of the Library Group
DANVILLE BRANCH, 400 Front St, Danville, 94526-3465. SAN 333-7235. Tel: 510-837-4889. FAX: 510-831-1299. Web Site: www.contra-costa.lib.ca.us. *Librn*, S VanOgtrop
Library Holdings: Bk Vols 52,700
Friends of the Library Group
EL CERRITO BRANCH, 6510 Stockton Ave, El Cerrito, 94530-3189. SAN 333-6840. Tel: 510-526-7512. FAX: 510-526-6375. Web Site: www.contra-costa.lib.ca.us. *Librn*, J Hildebrand
Library Holdings: Bk Vols 47,291
Friends of the Library Group
EL SOBRANTE BRANCH, 4191 Appian Way, El Sobrante, 94803-2298. SAN 333-6875. Tel: 510-374-3991. FAX: 510-222-4137. Web Site: www.contra-costa.lib.ca.us. *Librn*, Jan Aaronian
Library Holdings: Bk Vols 45,347
Friends of the Library Group
KENSINGTON BRANCH, 61 Arlington Ave, Kensington, 94707-1098. SAN 333-6905. Tel: 510-524-3043. FAX: 510-528-2567. Web Site: www.contra-costa.lib.ca.us. *Librn*, B Furgason
Library Holdings: Bk Vols 42,981
Friends of the Library Group
LAFAYETTE BRANCH, 952 Moraga Rd, Lafayette, 94549-4594. SAN 333-693X. Tel: 510-283-3872. FAX: 510-283-8231. Web Site: www.contra-costa.lib.ca.us. *Librn*, Laura O'Donoghue
Library Holdings: Bk Vols 62,594
Friends of the Library Group
MARTINEZ BRANCH, 740 Court St, Martinez, 94553-1218. SAN 333-6964. Tel: 510-646-2898. FAX: 510-646-4291. Web Site: www.contra-costa.lib.ca.us. *Librn*, Jan Aaronian
Library Holdings: Bk Vols 41,409
Friends of the Library Group
MORAGA BRANCH, 1500 Saint Mary's Rd, Moraga, 94556-2099. SAN 333-6999. Tel: 510-376-6852. FAX: 510-376-3034. Web Site: www.contra-costa.lib.ca.us. *Librn*, Laura O'Donoghue
Library Holdings: Bk Vols 64,066
Friends of the Library Group
OAKLEY BRANCH, 118 E Ruby St, Oakley, 94561-2195. SAN 333-7022. Tel: 510-625-2400. FAX: 510-625-2400. Web Site: www.contra-costa.lib.ca.us. *Librn*, Julie Italiano
Library Holdings: Bk Vols 12,349
Friends of the Library Group
ORINDA BRANCH, 2 Irwin Way, Orinda, 94563-2555. SAN 333-7057. Tel: 510-254-2184. FAX: 510-253-8629. Web Site: www.contra-costa.lib.ca.us. *Librn*, A DeFraga
Library Holdings: Bk Vols 60,350

Friends of the Library Group
PINOLE BRANCH, 2935 Pinole Valley Rd, Pinole, 94564-1494. SAN 333-7111. Tel: 510-758-2741. FAX: 510-758-2745. Web Site: www.contra-costa.lib.ca.us. *Librn*, J Hildebrand
Library Holdings: Bk Vols 52,334
Friends of the Library Group
RODEO BRANCH, 220 Pacific Ave, Rodeo, 94572-1118. SAN 333-7170. Tel: 510-799-2606. FAX: 510-799-2606. Web Site: www.contra-costa.lib.ca.us. *In Charge*, C Tucker-Watt
Library Holdings: Bk Vols 7,927
Friends of the Library Group
SAN PABLO BRANCH, 2101 Market Ave, San Pablo, 94806-4452. SAN 371-3350. Tel: 510-374-3998. FAX: 510-374-3225. Web Site: www.contra-costa.lib.ca.us. *Librn*, B Furgason
Library Holdings: Bk Vols 34,846
Friends of the Library Group
SAN RAMON BRANCH, 100 Montgomery St, San Ramon, 94583-4707. SAN 333-7200. Tel: 510-866-8467. FAX: 510-866-6720. Web Site: www.contra-costa.lib.ca.us. *Librn*, J Gunn
Library Holdings: Bk Vols 80,662
Friends of the Library Group
VINCENT A DAVI BRANCH, 80 Power Ave, Pittsburg, 94565-3842. SAN 333-7146. Tel: 510-427-8390. FAX: 510-427-8137. Web Site: www.contra-costa.lib.ca.us. *Librn*, Marian Partridge
Library Holdings: Bk Vols 44,033
Friends of the Library Group
WALNUT CREEK BRANCH, 1644 N Broadway, Walnut Creek, 94596-4297. SAN 333-726X. Tel: 510-646-6773. FAX: 510-646-6048. Web Site: www.contra-costa.lib.ca.us. *Librn*, A Shelton
Library Holdings: Bk Vols 71,580
Friends of the Library Group
YGNACIO VALLEY (THURMAN G CASEY MEMORIAL), 2661 Oak Grove Rd, Walnut Creek, 94598-3627. SAN 333-7294. Tel: 510-938-1481. FAX: 510-646-6026. Web Site: www.contra-costa.lib.ca.us. *Librn*, A Shelton
Library Holdings: Bk Vols 67,923
Friends of the Library Group
Bookmobiles: 1

S CONTRA COSTA COUNTY OFFICE OF EDUCATION, Learning Resource Center, 77 Santa Barbara Rd, 94523. SAN 324-4504. Tel: 925-942-5332. FAX: 925-942-5398. *Dir*, Susan Magnone; Staff 3 (MLS 3)
Founded 1952
Library Holdings: Bk Titles 4,000; Per Subs 75
Subject Interests: Education, Grants, Libr sci
Special Collections: ERIC; Grant Resources; State-adopted materials; State-adopted Textbooks
Database Vendor: Ebsco - EbscoHost, Innovative Interfaces INN - View
One of ten high-tech IMDCs in CALIF. (Display of K-8 State adopted text materials)

J DIABLO VALLEY COLLEGE LIBRARY, 321 Golf Club Rd, 94523-1576. SAN 301-2131. Tel: 925-685-1230, Ext 241. Interlibrary Loan Service Tel: 925-685-1230, Ext 246. Circulation Tel: 925-685-1230, Ext 441. Reference Tel: 925-685-1230, Ext 246. FAX: 925-798-3588. Web Site: www.dvc.edu/library. *Dir*, Mary Dolven; Tel: 925-685-1230, Ext 237, E-Mail: mdolven@dvc.edu; *Coll Develop*, Lorrita Ford; Tel: 925-685-1230, Ext 242, E-Mail: lford@dvc.edu; *Cat*, Marva DeLoach; Tel: 925-685-1230, Ext 780, E-Mail: mdo1ven@dvc.edu; *Instrul Serv*, Ruth Sison; Tel: 925-685-1230, Ext 681, E-Mail: rsison@dvc.edu; *Ref*, Betty Bortz; E-Mail: bbortz@dvc.edu; *Ref*, Andy Kivel; Tel: 925-685-1230, Ext 1105, E-Mail: akivel@dvc.edu; Staff 13 (MLS 6, Non-MLS 7)
Founded 1950. Enrl 23,000; Fac 784; Highest Degree: Associate
Jul 1999-Jun 2000 Income State $1,672,837. Mats Exp $218,969, Books $97,130, Per/Ser (Incl. Access Fees) $24,737, Micro $11,559, Manuscripts & Archives $1,143, Electronic Ref Mat (Incl. Access Fees) $84,400. Sal $791,430 (Prof $416,933)
Library Holdings: Bk Vols 88,498; Bk Titles 79,000; Per Subs 324
Subject Interests: Art and architecture, Ethnic studies
Special Collections: Californiana
Automation Activity & Vendor Info: (Acquisitions) Innovative Interfaces Inc.; (Cataloging) Innovative Interfaces Inc.; (Circulation) Innovative Interfaces Inc.; (Course Reserve) Innovative Interfaces Inc.; (OPAC) Innovative Interfaces Inc.; (Serials) Innovative Interfaces Inc.
Database Vendor: GaleNet, IAC - Info Trac, Wilson - Wilson Web
Partic in Bay Area Library & Information Network
Friends of the Library Group

PLEASANTON

S CLOROX SERVICES CO, Technical Center Library, 7200 Johnson Dr, PO Box 493, 94566. SAN 326-0682. Tel: 925-847-6621. FAX: 925-847-8112. Web Site: www.clorox.com. *Acq, ILL, Per*, Dale Dorman; E-Mail: dale.dorman@clorox.com; Staff 1 (Non-MLS 1)
Founded 1974
Library Holdings: Bk Vols 6,000; Bk Titles 5,000; Per Subs 200
Automation Activity & Vendor Info: (Acquisitions) Sydney; (Cataloging) Sydney; (Circulation) Sydney; (Course Reserve) Sydney; (ILL) Sydney; (Media Booking) Sydney; (OPAC) Sydney; (Serials) Sydney

S KAISER ALUMINUM & CHEMICAL CORP, Technical Information Center,* 6177 Sunol Blvd, 94566. SAN 301-214X. Tel: 925-847-4264. FAX: 925-847-4245.
Founded 1969
Library Holdings: Bk Vols 39,000; Per Subs 400
Subject Interests: Chemistry, Metallurgy
Publications: Accession List (monthly)
Partic in Dialog Corporation; OCLC Online Computer Library Center, Inc

P PLEASANTON PUBLIC LIBRARY, 400 Old Bernal Ave, 94566-7012. SAN 332-124X. Tel: 925-931-3400. FAX: 925-846-8517. Web Site: www.ci.pleasanton.ca.us/library.html. *Dir*, Billie Dancy; Tel: 925-931-3406; Staff 10 (MLS 9, Non-MLS 1)
Founded 1999. Pop 65,900; Circ 542,686
Jul 1999-Jun 2000 Income $2,606,945, State $108,330, City $2,478,615, Other $20,000. Mats Exp $302,714, Books $248,937, Per/Ser (Incl. Access Fees) $13,777, AV Equip $20,000, Electronic Ref Mat (Incl. Access Fees) $20,000. Sal $1,118,064
Library Holdings: Bk Vols 168,000; Bk Titles 105,000; Per Subs 329
Automation Activity & Vendor Info: (Acquisitions) Innovative Interfaces Inc.; (Cataloging) Innovative Interfaces Inc.; (Circulation) Innovative Interfaces Inc.; (OPAC) Innovative Interfaces Inc.; (Serials) Innovative Interfaces Inc.
Database Vendor: IAC - Info Trac
Special Services for the Deaf - TDD
Friends of the Library Group

POINT MUGU

UNITED STATES NAVY
A NAVAL BASE VENTURA COUNTY LIBRARY/RESOURCE CENTER, Point Mugu Sta, Bldg 221, Code NW 400, 93042-5000. (Mail add: 10000 23rd Ave, Code MW400, Port Hueneme, 94043-4301), SAN 333-7359. Tel: 805-989-7771. FAX: 805-989-3948. *Mgr*, Diana Hoslett; *Tech Servs*, Christie Taylor
Founded 1946
Library Holdings: Bk Vols 30,000; Per Subs 100
Subject Interests: Aeronautics, Military history
Partic in Total Interlibrary Exchange

POINT REYES STATION

G US NATIONAL PARK SERVICE, Point Reyes National Seashore Library, 94956. SAN 323-7168. Tel: 415-663-8054. FAX: 415-663-8132. *Librn*, Loretta Farley
Library Holdings: Bk Titles 1,150
Restriction: By appointment only

POINT RICHMOND

C AMERICAN SCHOOL OF PROFESSIONAL PSYCHOLOGY-SAN FRANCISCO BAY AREA LIBRARY, 999 A Canal Blvd, 94804. SAN 321-6217. Tel: 510-215-0277, Ext 215. FAX: 510-215-0299. Web Site: www.aspp.edu. *Librn*, Julie Griffith
Founded 1998. Enrl 75; Fac 10; Highest Degree: Doctorate
Library Holdings: Bk Titles 4,500; Per Subs 31
Publications: Annual report
Partic in Northern Calif Consortium of Psychol Librs

POMONA

C CALIFORNIA STATE POLYTECHNIC UNIVERSITY LIBRARY,* Bldg 15, 3801 W Temple Ave, 91768. SAN 301-2158. Tel: 909-869-3090. FAX: 909-869-6922. Web Site: www.csupomona.edu/~library/. *Dir*, Harold B Schleifer; E-Mail: hbschleifer@csupomora.edu; *Cat*, Yvonne Zhang; *Coordr*, Sue Benney; *Coll Develop, Ref*, Kathleen Dunn; Staff 49 (MLS 12, Non-MLS 37)
Founded 1938. Enrl 14,248; Fac 670; Highest Degree: Master
Library Holdings: Bk Vols 621,184; Bk Titles 415,000; Per Subs 2,855
Special Collections: Twentieth Century English & American Literature (First Editions); WK Kellogg Library, bks, per
Automation Activity & Vendor Info: (Acquisitions) Innovative Interfaces Inc.; (Circulation) Innovative Interfaces Inc.; (Serials) Innovative Interfaces Inc.
Publications: Annual Report; Arabian Horse Bibliography
Partic in Coop Libr Agency for Syst & Servs; Dialog Corporation; OCLC Online Computer Library Center, Inc
Open Mon-Thurs 7:30-10:30, Fri 7:30-5, Sat 12-5 & Sun 12-9
Departmental Libraries:
ENVIRONMENTAL DESIGN LIBRARY, Bldg 7, 3801 W Temple Ave, 91768. SAN 329-0352. Tel: 909-869-2665 (Library), 909-869-2666 (Environ Design), 909-869-7659 (Information). *Curator*, Christine Delany

Founded 1975. Enrl 1,150; Highest Degree: Master
Library Holdings: Bk Titles 11,497; Per Subs 125
Special Collections: Architect Craig Elwood Coll, letters, papers, photographs; Architect Raphael Soriano, drawings, letters, papers; Richard Nentra sketches, papers

LANTERMAN DEVELOPMENTAL CENTER
S RESIDENTS' LIBRARY & LISTENING CENTER, 3530 W Pomona Blvd, PO Box 100, 91769. SAN 333-7383. Tel: 909-444-7267. FAX: 909-598-4352.
Founded 1959
Library Holdings: Bk Titles 350; Per Subs 17
Friends of the Library Group

M STAFF LIBRARY, 3530 W Pomona Blvd, PO Box 100, 91769. SAN 333-7413. Tel: 909-444-7264. FAX: 909-444-7524. E-Mail: inlib1@ix.netcom.com. *Librn*, Treva Fredericks
Founded 1954
Jul 1996-Jun 1997 Income $28,000. Mats Exp $20,411, Books $3,716, Per/Ser (Incl. Access Fees) $14,795, Presv $700, Other Print Mats $1,200. Sal $34,000
Library Holdings: Bk Vols 15,000; Bk Titles 8,000; Per Subs 131
Subject Interests: Mentally retarded
Mem of MLGSCA, PSRMLS
Partic in Dialog Corporation; Nat Libr of Med

P POMONA PUBLIC LIBRARY,* 625 S Garey Ave, 91766-3322. (Mail add: PO Box 2271, 91769-2271), SAN 301-2174. Tel: 909-620-2043. TDD: 909-620-3690. FAX: 909-620-3713. E-Mail: library@ci.pomona.ca.us. Web Site: www.mcls.org/bin/entity/53. *Dir*, Gregory Shapton; Tel: 909-620-2473, E-Mail: greg_shapton@ci.pomona.ca.us; *Ch Servs*, Marguerite Raybould; Tel: 909-620-2018, E-Mail: marguerite_raybould@ci.pomona.ca.us; *Ad Servs*, Bruce Guter; Tel: 909-620-2049, E-Mail: bruce_guter@ci.pomona.ca.us; *Tech Servs*, Pat Lambert; Tel: 909-620-2022, E-Mail: pat_lambert@ci.pomona.ca.us; *Circ*, Pat Williams; Tel: 909-620-2474, E-Mail: pat_williams@ci.pomona.ca.us; *Coordr*, Muriel Spill; Tel: 909-620-2048, E-Mail: muriel_spill@ci.pomona.ca.us; Staff 55 (MLS 13, Non-MLS 42)
Founded 1887. Pop 145,000; Circ 350,000
Jul 1997-Jun 1998 Income $1,959,688. Mats Exp $183,315, Books $146,753, Per/Ser (Incl. Access Fees) $21,089, Presv $1,000, Micro $10,473. Sal $1,169,070
Library Holdings: Bk Vols 272,134; Per Subs 357
Subject Interests: Local history, Photography
Special Collections: Laura Ingalls Wilder Coll, bks, dolls & papers; Orange Crate Labels; Postcard Coll; Wine Labels
Function: ILL available
Mem of Metropolitan Cooperative Library System
Partic in OCLC Online Computer Library Center, Inc
Open Mon-Thurs 9-8, Fri & Sat noon-5; special collections open Mon, Tue & Thurs noon-6, Wed noon-8, Fri & Sat noon-5; $30 annual fee for non-residents
Friends of the Library Group

M POMONA VALLEY HOSPITAL MEDICAL CENTER, Medical Library,* 1798 N Garey Ave, 91767. SAN 333-7448. Tel: 909-865-9878. FAX: 909-865-9770. *Librn*, Deborah Klein
Founded 1950
Library Holdings: Bk Vols 850; Per Subs 180
Restriction: Medical staff only
Partic in Nat Libr of Med; Pac SW Regional Med Libr
Open Mon, Tues, Thurs & Fri 8:30-2:30

CM WESTERN UNIVERSITY OF HEALTH SCIENCES, Health Sciences Library, 309 E Second St, 91766-1854. SAN 322-8894. Tel: 909-469-5323. FAX: 909-469-5486. E-Mail: lib@westernu.edu. *Dir*, Pat Vader; E-Mail: pvader@westernu.edu; Staff 9 (MLS 1, Non-MLS 8)
Enrl 1,400 Sal $195,400
Library Holdings: Bk Vols 11,000; Per Subs 466
Subject Interests: Medicine
Special Collections: Osteopathic Lit, bks, jour
Automation Activity & Vendor Info: (Cataloging) SIRSI; (ILL) SIRSI; (OPAC) SIRSI; (Serials) SIRSI
Publications: Library Newsletter
Open Mon-Fri 7am-11pm, Sat & Sun 11am-7pm

PORT HUENEME

UNITED STATES NAVY
A NAVAL CONSTRUCTION BATTALION CENTER LIBRARY-THE RESOURCE CENTER, Code 193, Bldg 1180, 1000 23rd Ave, 93043-4301. SAN 333-7502. Tel: 805-982-4411, 805-982-4746. FAX: 805-982-3514. *Head of Libr*, Diana Hoslett; E-Mail: djhoslett@cbeph.navy.mil; Staff 2 (MLS 1, Non-MLS 1)
Founded 1947
Library Holdings: Bk Titles 40,000; Per Subs 53
Subject Interests: World War II
Partic in Black Gold Coop; Total Information Exchange

A NAVAL SCHOOL, CIVIL ENGINEER CORPS OFFICERS, MOREELL LIBRARY, 3502 Goodspeed St, Ste 1, 93043-4336. SAN 333-7561. Tel: 805-982-2826. FAX: 805-982-2918. Web Site: www.cnet.navy.mil/cecos/cecos.htm. *Dir*, Deborah M Gunia; E-Mail: dgunia@cbcph.navy.mil; Staff 2 (MLS 1, Non-MLS 1)
Founded 1946
Oct 1996-Sep 1997 Income $6,000. Mats Exp Presv $1,000
Library Holdings: Bk Vols 34,032; Bk Titles 8,093; Per Subs 46
Subject Interests: Civil engineering, Construction
Special Collections: Admiral Ben Moreell Coll; Admiral Robert E Peary Coll
Restriction: By appointment only
Partic in OCLC Online Computer Library Center, Inc; Total Interlibrary Exchange

A NFESC TECHNICAL INFORMATION CENTER, Tech Info Ctr, 1100 23rd Ave, 93043-4370. SAN 333-7537. Tel: 805-982-1124. FAX: 805-982-1409. *Dir*, Bryan Thompson; E-Mail: thompsonbp@nfesc.navy.mil; *Bibliog Instr, Librn, Online Servs*, Jo Ann Van Reenan; Tel: 805-982-1078, E-Mail: vanreenanjm@nfesc.navy.mil; *ILL*, Ray Acosta; Staff 4 (MLS 2, Non-MLS 2)
Founded 1948
Oct 1998-Sep 1999 Income $460,000. Mats Exp $221,225, Books $100,000, Per/Ser (Incl. Access Fees) $100,000, Presv $3,225, Micro $18,000. Sal $270,000 (Prof $110,000)
Library Holdings: Bk Vols 70,000; Per Subs 450
Subject Interests: Civil engineering, Construction, Energy, Ocean engineering, Soil mechanics
Automation Activity & Vendor Info: (Cataloging) SIRSI
Publications: New on the Shelf; Periodical Holdings
Restriction: Staff use only, Use of others with permission of librarian

PORTERVILLE

J PORTERVILLE COLLEGE LIBRARY, 100 E College Ave, 93257-5901. SAN 301-2182. Tel: 209-791-2318. FAX: 209-791-2289. Web Site: www.pc.ca.us. *Dir*, Jeff R Spalsbury; Tel: 559-791-2317, E-Mail: jspalsbu@pc.cc.ca.us; *Librn*, M Linda Bailey; Tel: 559-791-2293, E-Mail: lbailey@pc.cc.ca.us; *Librn*, Lorie Barker; Tel: 559-791-2370, E-Mail: lebarker@pc.cc.ca.us; Staff 7 (MLS 3, Non-MLS 4)
Founded 1927. Enrl 3,554; Fac 315; Highest Degree: Associate
Jun 2000-Jul 2001 Income State $496,941. Mats Exp $55,400, Books $16,300, Per/Ser (Incl. Access Fees) $16,100, Electronic Ref Mat (Incl. Access Fees) $23,000. Sal $447,597 (Prof $171,965)
Library Holdings: Bk Vols 36,414; Bk Titles 33,104; Per Subs 223; Bks on Deafness & Sign Lang 29
Special Collections: Anthropology Library containing 341 titles
Automation Activity & Vendor Info: (Cataloging) Follett; (Circulation) Follett
Database Vendor: Ebsco - EbscoHost, IAC - Info Trac, ProQuest
Publications: Library Handbook
Partic in Coop Libr Agency for Syst & Servs; San Joaquin Valley Libr Syst

PORTERVILLE DEVELOPMENTAL CENTER
M PROFESSIONAL LIBRARY, 26501 Ave 140, PO Box 2000, 93258-2000. SAN 333-7650. Tel: 559-782-2609. FAX: 559-784-5630. *In Charge*, Diana Upton; E-Mail: dupton@ocsnet.net; Staff 1 (Non-MLS 1)
Founded 1954
Jul 1999-Jun 2000 Income State $56,044. Mats Exp $11,263, Books (MEX) $4,263, Per/Ser (Incl. Access Fees) $7,000. Sal $42,623
Library Holdings: Bk Titles 4,607; Per Subs 89
Subject Interests: Mentally retarded
Special Collections: Mental Health
Restriction: In-house use for visitors
Partic in Area Wide Library Network; Pac SW Regional Med Libr

S RESIDENTS' RESOURCE CENTER, 26501 Ave 140, PO Box 2000, 93258-2000. SAN 333-7685. Tel: 209-782-2021. FAX: 209-784-5630. *Dir*, Myrt Ellis Mats Exp Per/Ser (Incl. Access Fees) $25,000
Library Holdings: Bk Vols 10,000; Bk Titles 1,000

P PORTERVILLE PUBLIC LIBRARY,* 41 W Thurman, 93257-3652. SAN 301-2190. Tel: 559-784-0177. FAX: 559-781-4396. *Ref, Ser, Tech Servs*, Kathie Poundstone; *Librn*, Carolyn Johnson; *Asst Librn, Ch Servs*, Sonja Kreitzer; *Acq*, Melanie Wells; *AV*, Billie Clark
Founded 1904. Pop 34,450
Library Holdings: Bk Vols 70,000; Per Subs 151
Special Collections: Local History, bks, photos
Mem of San Joaquin Valley Library System
Friends of the Library Group

M SIERRA VIEW DISTRICT HOSPITAL, Medical Library,* 465 W Putnam, 93257-3320. SAN 301-2204. Tel: 209-788-6108. FAX: 209-788-6135.
Library Holdings: Bk Vols 130; Per Subs 50
Partic in Area Wide Library Network

POWAY

S SAN DIEGO CULTURAL LIBRARY, 16934 Chabad Way, 92064. SAN 371-1110. Tel: 858-487-0981. FAX: 858-673-0299. Web Site: www.chabadpoway.org. *Dir*, Yisroel Goldstein; *Asst Librn*, Kathy Taylor; *Br Coordr*, Bernice Levine; *Circ*, Patricia Kadosch; *Publ Servs*, Renee Mazlen; Staff 6 (MLS 6)
Founded 1990
Library Holdings: Bk Vols 2,000
Subject Interests: Religion
Special Services for the Deaf - Books on deafness & sign language; High interest/low vocabulary books; Special interest periodicals; Staff with knowledge of sign language

QUINCY

J FEATHER RIVER COLLEGE LIBRARY,* 570 Golden Eagle Ave, 95971-9124. SAN 301-2220. Tel: 530-283-0202, Ext 236. FAX: 530-283-4097. E-Mail: library@frcc.cc.ca.us. Web Site: www.frcc.cc.ca.us/library/welcome.htm. *Librn*, Tom Davis; Staff 3 (MLS 1, Non-MLS 2)
Founded 1969. Enrl 594; Fac 24
1998-1999 Mats Exp $18,769, Books $12,010, Per/Ser (Incl. Access Fees) $6,438, AV Equip $321. Sal $96,155
Library Holdings: Bk Vols 17,900; Bk Titles 17,500; Per Subs 117
Subject Interests: Business and management, Environmental studies, Forestry, Natural science
Database Vendor: Dialog
Mem of North State Cooperative Library System
Open Mon-Thurs 8-9 & Fri 8-4:30

GL PLUMAS COUNTY LAW LIBRARY,* 520 W Main St, Rm 413, 95971. SAN 301-2239. Tel: 530-283-6325. FAX: 530-283-0946. *Librn*, Tom Van Rossem
Founded 1905
Library Holdings: Bk Vols 6,800; Per Subs 4
Subject Interests: California, Law
Open Mon, Tues, Thurs & Fri 9-2

P PLUMAS COUNTY LIBRARY, 445 Jackson St, 95971-9410. SAN 301-2247. Tel: 530-283-6310. FAX: 530-283-3242. E-Mail: pclibq@psln.com. Web Site: www.psln.com/pclibq. *Dir*, Margaret Miles; *Tech Servs*, Jeannette Legg; *Ch Servs*, Jeanette Brauner; Staff 3 (MLS 2, Non-MLS 1)
Founded 1916. Pop 24,440; Circ 105,138
Library Holdings: Bk Vols 71,668; Per Subs 231
Subject Interests: Botany
Special Collections: Local History & Local Mining Colls
Automation Activity & Vendor Info: (Cataloging) TLC; (Circulation) TLC; (OPAC) TLC
Mem of North State Cooperative Library System
Open Mon-Wed 10-6, Thurs 12-8, Fri & Sat 10-2
Friends of the Library Group
Branches: 3
CHESTER BRANCH
See Separate Entry in Chester
GREENVILLE BRANCH, 204 Ann St, Greenville, 95947-0635. (Mail add: PO Box 635, Greenville, 95947-0635), Tel: 530-284-7416. FAX: 530-284-7416. Web Site: www.plumas.library.org. *In Charge*, Judy Wallace; Staff 1 (Non-MLS 1)
Library Holdings: Bk Vols 10,000; Per Subs 20
Automation Activity & Vendor Info: (Circulation) TLC
Database Vendor: IAC - Info Trac
Open Mon-Wed 10-1 & 1:30-5:30, Thurs 12-4 & 4:30-7:30, Fri 9:30-1 & 1:30-5, Sat 10-2
Friends of the Library Group
PORTOLA BRANCH, 34 Third Ave, Portola, 96122. Tel: 530-832-4241. FAX: 530-832-4241. Web Site: www.plumaslibrary.org.; Staff 1 (Non-MLS 1)
Library Holdings: Bk Vols 10,000; Bk Titles 30
Automation Activity & Vendor Info: (Circulation) TLC
Database Vendor: IAC - Info Trac
Open Mon-Wed & Fri 10:30-1 & 2-6, Thurs 12-9, Sat 10-12
Friends of the Library Group

G PLUMAS COUNTY MUSEUM LIBRARY,* 445 Jackson St, 95971. SAN 372-4069. Tel: 530-283-6310, 530-283-6320. FAX: 530-6415. *Curator, Dir*, Scott Lawson; *Curator*, Evelyn Whisman
Library Holdings: Bk Titles 1,000; Per Subs 300
Special Collections: County; Native Americans (Maidu Indian Coll), baskets, docs, photogs; Plumas County History Railroad Coll, bks, docs, maps, photogs
Publications: Newsletter (bi-annual)
Friends of the Library Group

RANCHO CORDOVA

S VRYONIS CENTER LIBRARY,* 3140 Gold Camp Dr No 50, 95670-6023. SAN 375-362X. Tel: 916-631-9099. FAX: 916-631-7175. Web Site: www.glavx.org. *Librn*, Janet Coles; E-Mail: colesj@glavx.org; Staff 2 (Non-MLS 2)
Founded 1986
Library Holdings: Bk Vols 65,000; Bk Titles 40,000; Per Subs 200
Special Collections: Twentieth Century Modern Greek/Greek American History, (Vlavianos Coll), archives, bks & photog
Automation Activity & Vendor Info: (Cataloging) IME
Publications: Recent Acquisitions List

RANCHO CUCAMONGA

J CHAFFEY COLLEGE LIBRARY,* 5885 Haven Ave, 91737-3002. SAN 300-5623. Tel: 909-941-2400. FAX: 909-466-2821. *Librn*, Frank R Pinkerton; *Librn*, Priscilla Fernandez; Staff 3 (MLS 3)
Founded 1916. Enrl 16,000; Fac 251
Library Holdings: Bk Vols 73,000; Per Subs 250
Partic in San Bernardino, Inyo, Riverside Counties United Library Services
Open Mon-Thurs 8-8, Fri 8-4, Sat 9-2

P RANCHO CUCAMONGA PUBLIC LIBRARY, 7368 Archibald Ave, 91730. SAN 376-6756. Tel: 909-477-2720. Circulation Tel: 909-477-2720, Ext 5000. Reference Tel: 909-477-2720, Ext 5008. FAX: 909-477-2721. E-Mail: reference@ci.rancho-cucamonga.ca.us. Web Site: www.rcpl.lib.ca.us. *Dir*, Deborah K Clark; Tel: 909-477-2720, Ext 5020, E-Mail: dclark@ci.rancho-cucamonga.ca.us; *Mgr Libr Serv*, Robert Karatsu; Tel: 909-477-2720, Ext 5022, E-Mail: rkaratsu@ci.rancho-cucamonga.ca.us; *Ch Servs*, Renee Tobin; Tel: 909-477-2720, Ext 5024, E-Mail: rtobin@ci.rancho-cucamonga.ca.us; *Ref Serv Ad*, Michelle Perera; Tel: 909-477-2720, Ext 5033, E-Mail: mperera@ci.rancho-cucamonga.ca.us; Staff 59 (MLS 9, Non-MLS 50)
Founded 1994. Pop 117,000; Circ 700,000
Jul 2000-Jun 2001 Income $1,500,000. Mats Exp $325,000. Sal $883,000
Library Holdings: Bk Titles 115,000; Per Subs 215
Automation Activity & Vendor Info: (Cataloging) epixtech, inc.; (Circulation) epixtech, inc.; (OPAC) epixtech, inc.
Database Vendor: epixtech, inc., GaleNet, IAC - Info Trac, IAC - SearchBank
Mem of Inland Library System
Friends of the Library Group

GL SAN BERNARDINO COUNTY LAW LIBRARY, West End,* 8303 Haven Ave, 91730. SAN 328-2899. Tel: 909-944-5108. *Librn*, Carolyn Poston
Library Holdings: Bk Titles 9,236

§S WLC ARCHITECTS LIBRARY, 10470 Foothill Blvd, 91730-3754. Tel: 909-987-0909. FAX: 909-980-9980. E-Mail: ability@wlc-architects.com. Web Site: www.wlc-architects.com. *Librn*, Tiffany Alver
Library Holdings: Bk Vols 2,500
Restriction: Staff use only

RANCHO MIRAGE

M EISENHOWER MEDICAL CENTER, Del E Webb Memorial Medical Information Center, 39000 Bob Hope Dr, 92270. SAN 301-2255. Tel: 760-773-1400. FAX: 760-773-1577. E-Mail: medlib@emc.org. *Librn*, Barbara Potts; Staff 1 (MLS 1)
Founded 1973
Library Holdings: Per Subs 175
Subject Interests: Clinical medicine
Restriction: Staff use only
Partic in Pacific Southwest Regional Med Libr Serv; San Bernardino, Inyo, Riverside Counties United Library Services

P RANCHO MIRAGE PUBLIC LIBRARY, 42-520 Bob Hope Dr, 92270. SAN 375-3549. Tel: 760-341-7323. FAX: 760-341-5213. E-Mail: librarian@miragenet.org. Web Site: www.miragenet.org. *Dir*, Tom Johnson; *Circ*, Heather Hurley; *Ref*, Stella Baker; *ILL*, Denee Phillips; *Ch Servs*, Carol Lloyd; Staff 5 (MLS 5)
Founded 1994. Pop 15,500; Circ 250,534
Jul 1999-Jun 2000 Income $1,249,654. Mats Exp $1,257,349
Library Holdings: Bk Vols 51,339; Per Subs 1,487
Subject Interests: Golf, Investments, Local authors, Medical
Automation Activity & Vendor Info: (Cataloging) DRA; (Circulation) DRA; (OPAC) DRA
Publications: Monthly Program & Exhibits Calendar; The Bookworm (newsletter)
Mem of Inland Library System
Partic in Metropolitan Cooperative Library System; OCLC Online Computer Library Center, Inc
Friends of the Library Group

RANCHO PALOS VERDES

SR CRESTMONT COLLEGE SALVATION ARMY, (Formerly Salvation Army College for Officer Training), Elftman Memorial Library, 30840 Hawthorne Blvd, 90275. SAN 301-2271. Tel: 310-544-6475. FAX: 310-265-6514. E-Mail: mukbill@msn.com. *Dir*, Misty Jesse; Staff 4 (MLS 2, Non-MLS 2)
Founded 1923. Enrl 105
Oct 1998-Sep 1999 Income $25,000. Mats Exp $18,000, Books $15,000, Per/Ser (Incl. Access Fees) $3,000
Library Holdings: Bk Titles 36,000; Per Subs 153
Subject Interests: Psychology, Religion
Special Collections: Salvation Army Publications

J MARYMOUNT COLLEGE LIBRARY,* 30800 Palos Verdes Dr E, 90275-6299. SAN 301-2263. Tel: 310-377-5501, Ext 260. FAX: 310-377-6223. *Dir*, Becky J Gifford; E-Mail: bgifford@marymountpv.edu; *Librn*, Alice Cornelio
Founded 1932. Enrl 750; Fac 55
Library Holdings: Bk Vols 26,000; Per Subs 231
Publications: Library Guides; Library Newsletter
Partic in Metronet; SCELC
Friends of the Library Group

RED BLUFF

§GL TEHAMA COUNTY LAW LIBRARY, Courthouse, Rm 38, 633 Washington St, 96080. Tel: 530-529-5033. FAX: 530-529-0980. *In Charge*, Nancy Camba
Jul 2000-Jun 2001 Income $36,792
Library Holdings: Bk Vols 10,000

P TEHAMA COUNTY LIBRARY,* 645 Madison St, 96080-3383. SAN 333-7804. Tel: 530-527-0607. FAX: 530-527-1562. *Librn*, Ray Schroff; *Tech Servs*, Linda Logan; Staff 3 (MLS 3)
Founded 1916. Pop 54,700; Circ 207,940
1996-1997 Income $281,655, State $9,040, County $272,615
Library Holdings: Bk Vols 95,716; Bk Titles 74,702; Per Subs 115
Special Collections: Tehama County History
Mem of North State Cooperative Library System
Friends of the Library Group
Branches: 2
CORNING BRANCH, 740 Third St, Corning, 96021-2517. SAN 333-7839. Tel: 916-824-7050. FAX: 916-824-7051. *Librn*, Ray Schroff
Friends of the Library Group
LOS MOLINOS BRANCH, 7881 Hwy 99E, Los Molinos, 96055-9701. SAN 329-6598. Tel: 916-384-2772. FAX: 916-384-2772. *Librn*, Ray Schroff
Friends of the Library Group

REDDING

S CH2M HILL, Information Center, 2525 Airpark Dr, PO Box 49-2478, 96001-2478. SAN 301-228X. Tel: 530-243-5831. FAX: 530-243-1654. Web Site: www.ch2m.com. *In Charge*, Marlene Bishop
Founded 1968
Library Holdings: Bk Vols 7,156; Bk Titles 7,000; Per Subs 50
Subject Interests: Agriculture, California, Civil engineering, Environmental studies, Geology
Special Collections: North American Weather Charts & Rainfall Records (1942-1978); Soil Surveys
Restriction: Staff use only, Use of others with permission of librarian
Mem of North State Cooperative Library System
Partic in Dialog Corporation

J SHASTA COLLEGE LIBRARY, Learning Resources Center, 11555 Old Oregon Trail, PO Box 496006, 96049. SAN 301-2298. Tel: 530-225-4777. Circulation Tel: 530-225-4977. Reference Tel: 530-225-4975. FAX: 530-225-4830. E-Mail: webmaster@library.shastacollege.edu. *Dir*, Ed Neroda; *Tech Servs*, Maureen Stephens; *Acq*, Janet Albright; *Ref*, Elaine Crowe; *Ref*, Carolyn Singh. Subject Specialists: *Sci educ*, Philip Roche; *Technology*, Philip Roche; Staff 14 (MLS 5, Non-MLS 9)
Founded 1948. Enrl 10,615; Fac 146; Highest Degree: Associate
Library Holdings: Bk Vols 100,000; Bk Titles 70,000; Per Subs 200
Subject Interests: Local history
Mem of North State Cooperative Library System
Partic in OCLC Online Computer Library Center, Inc
Open Mon-Thurs 7:45-8:45, Fri 7:45-3:45, closed weekends & holidays

GL SHASTA COUNTY LAW LIBRARY, Court House, B-7, 1500 Court St, 96001. SAN 370-4246. Tel: 530-245-6243. FAX: 530-245-6966. E-Mail: lawlib@snowcrest.net. *Librn*, Jeanne Sweat
Founded 1968 Sal $27,393
Library Holdings: Bk Titles 8,900; Per Subs 12

P SHASTA COUNTY LIBRARY,* 1855 Shasta St, 96001. SAN 333-8010. Tel: 530-225-5769. FAX: 530-241-7169. E-Mail: redlib@shasta.com, techserv@shasta.com. *Dir*, Carolyn J Chambers; Staff 15 (MLS 3, Non-MLS 12)
Founded 1949. Pop 165,000; Circ 286,049
Jul 1997-Jun 1998 Income $834,138, State $94,784, City $177,000, County $431,998, Locally Generated Income $45,697, Other $25,000. Mats Exp $43,229, Books $33,346, Per/Ser (Incl. Access Fees) $7,134, Micro $1,544. Sal $322,219 (Prof $116,410)
Library Holdings: Bk Vols 173,288
Subject Interests: California
Special Collections: Californiana Coll
Mem of North State Cooperative Library System
Partic in RLIN
Friends of the Library Group
Branches: 2
ANDERSON BRANCH, 3200 W Center, Anderson, 96007. SAN 333-8045. Tel: 530-365-7685. FAX: 530-365-7685. E-Mail: andlib@shasta.com. *Librn*, Martee Boban
Friends of the Library Group
EASTERN SHASTA COUNTY REGIONAL LIBRARY (BURNEY), 37038 Siskiyou St, Burney, 96013. SAN 333-807X. Tel: 530-335-4317. FAX: 530-335-4317. E-Mail: burneylibrary@norcalis.net. *Librn*, Connie Clecker
Friends of the Library Group

S SHASTA HISTORICAL SOCIETY, Research Library, 1449 Market St, 96001. SAN 375-1945. Tel: 530-243-3720. *In Charge*, Diane Kathleen; Fax: 530-246-3708, E-Mail: shs@c-zone.net; Staff 2 (Non-MLS 2)
Founded 1933
Library Holdings: Bk Vols 1,000

CR SIMPSON COLLEGE, Start-Kilgour Memorial Library, 2211 College View Dr, 96003-8606. SAN 301-4665. Tel: 530-226-4117. FAX: 530-224-2056. E-Mail: library@simpsonca.edu. Web Site: www.simpsonca.edu. *Dir Libr Serv*, Larry L Haight; Tel: 530-226-4110, E-Mail: lhaight@simpsonca.edu; *Reader Servs*, Miles S Compton; Tel: 530-226-4115, E-Mail: scompton@simpsonca.edu; *Reader Servs*, R Curt Rice; Tel: 530-226-4943, E-Mail: crice@simpsonca.edu; Staff 5 (MLS 3, Non-MLS 2)
Founded 1921. Enrl 1,186; Fac 42; Highest Degree: Master
May 1999-Apr 2000 Income (Main Library Only) Parent Institution $262,906. Mats Exp $53,255, Books $32,998, Per/Ser (Incl. Access Fees) $5,871, Presv $1,808, Micro $2,600, Electronic Ref Mat (Incl. Access Fees) $9,978. Sal $196,369 (Prof $123,002)
Library Holdings: Bk Vols 69,916; Bk Titles 61,793; Per Subs 73
Subject Interests: Religion
Special Collections: Christian & Missionary Alliance Denominational History (A B Simpson Memorial)
Database Vendor: Lexis-Nexis, OCLC - First Search, ProQuest, Silverplatter Information Inc.
Function: ILL available
Mem of North State Cooperative Library System
Friends of the Library Group

REDLANDS

R REDLANDS CHRISTIAN REFORMED CHURCH LIBRARY,* 1135 N Church St, 92374. SAN 301-2301. Tel: 909-798-2221. FAX: 909-798-4133. *Librn*, Barbara Hirzel
Library Holdings: Bk Vols 3,500

P A K SMILEY PUBLIC LIBRARY, 125 W Vine St, 92373. SAN 301-2344. Tel: 909-798-7565. FAX: 909-798-7566. E-Mail: admin@akspl.org. Web Site: www.aksmiley.org. *Dir*, Larry E Burgess; *Ad Servs, Ref*, Lorraine Estelle; E-Mail: lestelle@akspl.org; *Cat*, Jean Macomber; E-Mail: jmacomber@akspl.org; *Rare Bks, Spec Coll*, Don McCue; Tel: 909-798-7632, E-Mail: dmccue@akspl.org; *Ch Servs*, Blanca Rodriguez; *ILL*, Ann Pearson; E-Mail: reference@akspl.org; *Tech Servs*, Sandra Sanchez; Tel: 908-798-7676, E-Mail: ssanchez@akspl.org; Staff 5 (MLS 2, Non-MLS 3)
Founded 1894. Pop 67,800; Circ 273,110
Jul 1999-Jun 2000 Income $1,335,912, State $112,711, City $1,022,060, Locally Generated Income $75,543, Other $125,598. Mats Exp $174,556, Books $107,319, Per/Ser (Incl. Access Fees) $25,954, Presv $1,189, Micro $5,801, Manuscripts & Archives $34,293. Sal $897,184 (Prof $346,284)
Library Holdings: Bk Vols 90,539; Bk Titles 66,459; Per Subs 277
Subject Interests: Art and architecture, Civil War
Special Collections: Californiana, Redlands Heritage, bks & pamphlets, mss, maps, photogs; Lincoln Shrine, bks, pamphlets, photos, tapes, ephemera; Smiley Family Letters, papers; Lincoln (Watchorn Memorial Shrine), bks, pamphlets, photogs, tapes & ephemera; Smiley Family Letters, papers
Automation Activity & Vendor Info: (Cataloging) epixtech, inc.; (Circulation) epixtech, inc.; (OPAC) epixtech, inc.
Database Vendor: epixtech, inc.
Publications: A K Smiley Public Library, A Brief History; A Lost Letter Found; Encountering the Lincoln Scholarly Zareba; Horace Greely, Lincoln & the War for the Union; Powderly, Lincoln & the Shrine; The Archives of the A K Smiley Public Library; The Lincoln Memorial Shrine Golden Jubilee; The Lincoln Memorial Shrine, Redlands, California; What is Patron Saint's Day?
Friends of the Library Group

C UNIVERSITY OF REDLANDS, (CUR), George & Verda Armacost Library, 1249 E Colton Ave, 92374-3758. SAN 301-2352. Tel: 909-335-4022. FAX: 909-335-3403. Web Site: newton.uor.edu/libraries.html. *Coll Develop, Dir*, Klaus Musmann; E-Mail: kmusmann@uor.edu; *Dir Br Serv*, Linda Salem; *Bibliog Instr, Ref*, Leslie Canterbury; *Bibliog Instr, Ref*, Angelynn King; *Ref*, William Kennedy; *Tech Servs*, Jean Swanson; Staff 17 (MLS 6, Non-MLS 11)
Founded 1907. Enrl 3,800; Fac 190; Highest Degree: Master
Jul 1999-Jun 2000 Income Parent Institution $1,356,739. Mats Exp $591,400, Books $175,000, Per/Ser (Incl. Access Fees) $295,000, Presv $13,000, Electronic Ref Mat (Incl. Access Fees) $108,400. Sal $636,335 (Prof $300,257)
Library Holdings: Bk Vols 241,314; Per Subs 1,859
Special Collections: Californiana & the Great Southwest (Vernon & Helen Farquhar Coll); Harley Farnsworth & Florence Ayscough McNair Far Eastern Library; James Irvine Foundation Map Coll
Automation Activity & Vendor Info: (Acquisitions) Innovative Interfaces Inc.; (Cataloging) Innovative Interfaces Inc.; (Circulation) Innovative Interfaces Inc.; (Course Reserve) Innovative Interfaces Inc.; (ILL) Innovative Interfaces Inc.; (Media Booking) Innovative Interfaces Inc.; (OPAC) Innovative Interfaces Inc.; (Serials) Innovative Interfaces Inc.
Partic in Coop Libr Agency for Syst & Servs; Inland Empire Acad Libr Coop; OCLC Online Computer Library Center, Inc; San Bernardino, Inyo, Riverside Counties United Library Services; Southern Calif Electronic Libr Consortium

REDONDO BEACH

P REDONDO BEACH PUBLIC LIBRARY, 303 N Pacific Coast Hwy, 90277. SAN 333-8525. Tel: 310-318-0675. FAX: 310-318-3809. E-Mail: lb@redondo.org. Web Site: www.redondo.org/library. *Dir*, Jean M Scully; E-Mail: jean.scully@redondo.org; *Senior Librn*, Erin Schoonover; *Ch Servs*, Maret Rank; *Tech Servs*, Margaret Menninger; *Circ*, Tyna Carson; *AV*, Steve Fritch Morris; Staff 29 (MLS 10, Non-MLS 19)
Founded 1908. Circ 714,045
Jul 1999-Jun 2000 Income (Main Library and Branch Library) $1,922,550, State $183,207, City $1,577,725, Locally Generated Income $161,618. Mats Exp $202,290. Sal $1,169,180
Library Holdings: Bk Vols 154,779; Per Subs 506
Database Vendor: epixtech, inc., IAC - SearchBank, OCLC - First Search, ProQuest
Function: ILL available
Mem of Metropolitan Cooperative Library System
Special Services for the Blind - Kurzweil Reading Machine
Friends of the Library Group
Branches: 1
NORTH, 2000 Artesia Blvd, 90278. SAN 333-855X. Tel: 310-318-0677. FAX: 310-374-3768.
Friends of the Library Group

S TRW, Technical Information Center, One Space Park Bldg S Rm 1316, 90278-1099. SAN 301-2379. Tel: 310-812-4185. FAX: 310-814-3203. E-Mail: techinfo.center@trw.com. *Mgr*, Pat Artiago; *Librn*, Barbara Molinelli; Staff 6 (MLS 4, Non-MLS 2)
Founded 1954
Library Holdings: Bk Titles 25,000; Per Subs 300
Subject Interests: Aerospace science, Business and management, Chemistry, Electronics, Energy, Mathematics, Physics
Special Collections: AIAA Papers; CPIA; IEEE; NASA; TRW Technical Doc
Publications: Serials Holdings List (bi-monthly)

REDWOOD CITY

J CANADA COLLEGE LIBRARY, 4200 Farm Hill Blvd, 94061-1099. SAN 301-2395. Tel: 650-306-3267. FAX: 650-306-3434. Web Site: www.smcccd.cc.ca.us/pls/smcccd/con/can.html. *Coordr*, Marilyn Hayward; E-Mail: haywardm@pls.lib.ca.us; Staff 4 (MLS 2, Non-MLS 2)
Founded 1968. Enrl 3,460; Fac 111
Special Collections: Center for the American Musical Library, Archives
Database Vendor: Ebsco - EbscoHost, GaleNet, Wilson - Wilson Web
Mem of Peninsula Library System
Partic in Coop Libr Agency for Syst & Servs

M KAISER-PERMANENTE MEDICAL CENTER, Health Sciences Library,* 1150 Veterans Blvd, 94063. SAN 301-2409. Tel: 650-299-2437. FAX: 650-299-2488. *Librn*, Florence Fong
Library Holdings: Bk Vols 1,500
Mem of Pac Southwest Regional Med Libr Serv

P REDWOOD CITY PUBLIC LIBRARY,* 1044 Middlefield Rd, 94063-1868. SAN 333-8584. Tel: 650-780-7018, 650-780-7061 (Admin). FAX: 650-780-7069. Web Site: www.ci.redwood_city.ca.us/index.html. *Dir*, Yvonne Chen; *Tech Servs*, Linda Hedges; *Ch Servs*, Charles Ashton; Staff 19 (MLS 19)
Founded 1865. Pop 70,500; Circ 727,321
Library Holdings: Bk Vols 197,749; Per Subs 871
Subject Interests: Technology
Automation Activity & Vendor Info: (Circulation) GEAC
Mem of Peninsula Library System
Partic in Coop Libr Agency for Syst & Servs
Friends of the Library Group
Branches: 2
FAIR OAKS, 2510 Middlefield Rd, 94063-3402. SAN 333-8614. Tel: 650-780-7261. FAX: 650-568-3371. E-Mail: balabang@pls.lib.ca.us. Web Site: www.redwoodcity.org/library/fair_oaks/fair_oaks.html. *Librn*, Linda Hedges
Library Holdings: Bk Vols 17,000
Friends of the Library Group
SCHABERG BRANCH, 2140 Euclid Ave, 94061-1327. SAN 333-8649. Tel: 650-780-7010. FAX: 650-568-1702. Web Site: www.redwoodcity.org/library/schaberg/schaberg.html. *Librn*, Linda Hedges
Library Holdings: Bk Vols 36,000
Friends of the Library Group

L ROPERS, MAJESKI, KOHN & BENTLEY, Law Library,* 1001 Marshall St, 94063. SAN 323-6919. Tel: 650-780-1614. FAX: 650-367-0997. *Librn*, Chris Bolioni
Library Holdings: Bk Vols 10,000; Bk Titles 1,800; Per Subs 12
Automation Activity & Vendor Info: (Acquisitions) Inmagic, Inc.
Open Mon-Fri 8am-6pm

S SAN MATEO COUNTY HISTORICAL MUSEUM ARCHIVES, 777 Hamilton St, 94063. SAN 301-522X. Tel: 650-299-0104. FAX: 650-299-0141. Web Site: www.sanmateocountyhistory.com. *Archivist*, Carol Peterson
Founded 1935
Library Holdings: Bk Vols 1,500; Bk Titles 1,378
Subject Interests: County hist
Publications: La Peninsula (a journal published 2-3 times a year); news report (monthly)
Restriction: Non-circulating to the public
Open Tues-Thurs 10-12 & 12:30-4, Sun 12-4
Friends of the Library Group

GL SAN MATEO COUNTY LAW LIBRARY,* 710 Hamilton St, 94063. SAN 301-2417. Tel: 650-363-4913. FAX: 650-367-8040. E-Mail: smcll@ix.netcom.com. Web Site: pwl.netcom.com/~smcll/smcll.htm. *Dir*, Karen M Lutke; *Asst Librn*, Janet L Fischer; Staff 8 (MLS 2, Non-MLS 6)
1997-1998 Income $518,088. Mats Exp $368,335, Books $279,302, Per/Ser (Incl. Access Fees) $8,159, Other Print Mats $20,569. Sal $149,831
Library Holdings: Bk Vols 34,588

S SAN MATEO COUNTY OFFICE OF EDUCATION, The SMERC Library, 101 Twin Dolphin Dr, 94065-1064. SAN 371-1250. Tel: 650-802-5655. FAX: 650-802-5665. Web Site: www.smcoe.k12.ca.us/smerc. *Dir*, Karol Thomas; Tel: 650-802-5637, E-Mail: kthomas@smcoe.k12.ca.us; Staff 3 (MLS 2, Non-MLS 1)
1999-2000 Mats Exp $70,000, Books $30,000, Per/Ser (Incl. Access Fees) $25,000, Electronic Ref Mat (Incl. Access Fees) $15,000
Library Holdings: Bk Vols 30,000; Bk Titles 25,000; Per Subs 400
Database Vendor: epixtech, inc., OCLC - First Search
Publications: Directory of Librarians; Hot Topics (for educators); News Notes (for librns)

REEDLEY

R FIRST MENNONITE CHURCH LIBRARY, 1208 L St, PO Box 111, 93654. SAN 301-2433. Tel: 559-638-2917. FAX: 559-637-8826. E-Mail: mennonite@morynet.com. *Librn*, Marie Boldt; *Librn*, Ellen Ewy
Library Holdings: Bk Vols 2,000
Subject Interests: Mennonites

J REEDLEY COLLEGE LIBRARY,* 995 N Reed Ave, 93654-2099. SAN 301-2441. Tel: 559-638-0352. FAX: 559-638-0384. *Librn*, Lloyd C Dry; *Librn*, Wilifred Louise Alire; Staff 2 (MLS 2)
Founded 1956. Enrl 6,000; Fac 91
1998-1999 Mats Exp $51,456, Books $27,167, Per/Ser (Incl. Access Fees) $22,411. Sal $293,000 (Prof $160,000)
Library Holdings: Bk Titles 40,000; Per Subs 215
Mem of San Joaquin Valley Library System
Open Mon-Thurs 7:30-5 & 6:30-9, Fri 8-4 & Sat 9-12

REPRESA

S FOLSOM STATE PRISON LIBRARY, (FSP), Prison Rd, PO Box 71, 95671. SAN 301-245X. Tel: 916-985-2561, Ext 4236. FAX: 916-351-3002. *Senior Librn*, Robert Morris; Staff 21 (MLS 3, Non-MLS 18)
Founded 1949
Jul 1998-Jun 1999 Mats Exp $56,000, Books $36,000, Per/Ser (Incl. Access Fees) $5,000, AV Equip $5,000, Other Print Mats $5,000, Electronic Ref Mat (Incl. Access Fees) $5,000. (Prof $48,000)
Library Holdings: Bk Vols 40,000; Bk Titles 32,000; Per Subs 65; High Interest/Low Vocabulary Bk Vols 2,000; Spec Interest Per Sub 3,000; Bks on

Deafness & Sign Lang 50
Subject Interests: African-American, American Indians, Law, Literacy, Mental health, Self help, Spanish (language)
Automation Activity & Vendor Info: (Cataloging) Sagebrush Corporation

RICHMOND

S BERLEX BIOSCIENCES LIBRARY, 15049 San Pablo Ave, 94804. SAN 329-2444. Tel: 510-262-5401. FAX: 510-669-4249. *Mgr*, Charlie Sodano; E-Mail: charlie_sodano@berlex.com; Staff 2 (MLS 1, Non-MLS 1)
Library Holdings: Bk Titles 2,000; Per Subs 200
Subject Interests: Biochemistry, Biology, Immunology, Molecular biology, Neurology, Oncology, Virology
Partic in OCLC Online Computer Library Center, Inc

S CHEVRON SERVICES CO, Technical Library, 100 Chevron Way, PO Box 1627, 94802-0627. SAN 301-2468. Tel: 510-242-4755. FAX: 510-242-5621. E-Mail: fdlo@chevron.com. *In Charge*, F D Lopez; Staff 14 (MLS 7, Non-MLS 7)
Founded 1920
Subject Interests: Chemical engineering, Chemistry, Patents, Petroleum
Special Collections: Patents
Publications: Library bulletin
Branches:
TOXICOLOGY & HEALTH RISK ASSESSMENT UNIT Tel: 510-242-7053. FAX: 510-242-7022.; Staff 1 (MLS 1)
Library Holdings: Bk Titles 1,700
Subject Interests: Toxicology
Publications: Acquisitions List (quarterly)

S EUREKA, The California Career Information System Library, PO Box 647, 94808-0647. SAN 326-0550. Tel: 415-884-0818. FAX: 415-884-0824. Web Site: www.eurekanet.org. *Exec Dir*, Sumyyah Bilal; Staff 10 (MLS 6, Non-MLS 4)
Founded 1977
Publications: Computerized Career Information (user's handbook, counselor's manual)

S RICHMOND MUSEUM OF HISTORY, 400 Nevin Ave, 94801-3017. (Mail add: PO Box 1267, 94802-0267), SAN 375-6351. Tel: 510-235-7387. FAX: 510-235-4345. *Pres*, Lois Boyle; *Curator*, Kathleen Rupley
Library Holdings: Bk Titles 200

P RICHMOND PUBLIC LIBRARY,* 325 Civic Center Plaza, 94804-9991. SAN 333-8673. Tel: 510-620-6555. TDD: 510-233-2348. FAX: 510-620-6850. E-Mail: rplref@hotmail.com. Web Site: www.ci.richmond.ca.us/~library. *Librn*, Joseph Green; *Ch Servs*, Kathy Haug; *Media Spec*, Geoffrey Miller; *Bkmobile Coordr*, Rosa Casazza; Staff 17 (MLS 17)
Founded 1907. Pop 89,300; Circ 421,979
Library Holdings: Bk Vols 312,030; Bk Titles 176,322; Per Subs 558
Special Collections: Afro-American History & Literature; California History Coll; Richmond History Coll
Automation Activity & Vendor Info: (Circulation) Innovative Interfaces Inc.
Publications: Monthly Booklist
Mem of Bay Area Libr & Info Syst; North Bay Cooperative Library System
Partic in Coop Libr Agency for Syst & Servs; OCLC Online Computer Library Center, Inc
Special Services for the Deaf - TDD; TTY machine; Videos & decoder
Open Thurs & Sat 10-5, Fri & Sun 1-5
Friends of the Library Group
Branches: 2
BAYVIEW BRANCH, 5100 Hartnett Ave, 94804-4700. SAN 333-8703. Tel: 510-620-6566. FAX: 510-620-6908. Web Site: www.ci.richmond.ca.us/~library/. *Librn*, Lucile Meinhardt
Library Holdings: Bk Vols 7,000
Open Mon & Tues 2-7, Wed & Thurs 10:30-5 & Fri 2-5
Friends of the Library Group
WEST SIDE BRANCH, 135 Washington Ave, 94801-3946. SAN 333-8738. Tel: 510-620-6567. *Librn*, Lynn Whitson
Enrl 300; Highest Degree: Bachelor
Library Holdings: Bk Vols 8,800
Open Mon & Tues 12-7, Wed - Fri 12-5
Friends of the Library Group
Bookmobiles: 1. Also have 1 Outreach Van

C UNIVERSITY OF CALIFORNIA, Forest Products Library,* 1301 S 46th St, 94804. SAN 333-8797. Tel: 510-215-4255. FAX: 510-215-4299. *Librn*, Myriam Aroner
Library Holdings: Bk Titles 12,000; Per Subs 235
Subject Interests: Adhesives, Composites, Forest products, Indigenous hardwoods, Wood machining

S ZENECA AG PRODUCTS INC, Western Research Center Libraries, 1200 S 47th St, 94804. SAN 301-2476. Tel: 510-231-1410. FAX: 510-231-1332. Web Site: www.zenecaagproducts.com. *In Charge*, Ginger Gutherie; Staff 7 (MLS 5, Non-MLS 2)
Library Holdings: Bk Titles 5,000; Per Subs 160
Subject Interests: Agriculture, Biol sci, Biology
Special Collections: Patents
Restriction: Not open to public
Partic in OCLC Online Computer Library Center, Inc

RIDGECREST

J CERRO COSO COMMUNITY COLLEGE, Walter Stiern Memorial Library, 3000 College Heights Blvd, 93555-9571. SAN 333-8827. Tel: 760-384-6318. FAX: 760-384-6321. Web Site: www.cc.cc.ca.us/library/. *Dir*, Dr Dennis I VanderWerff; *ILL*, Virjean Miller; *Media Spec*, Suzanne Bequette; *Acq*, Susan Parker; *Circ*, Janet Wilson; Staff 1 (MLS 1)
Founded 1973. Enrl 4,871; Fac 42
Jul 1998-Jun 1999 Income $217,772. Mats Exp $20,876, Books $14,649, Per/Ser (Incl. Access Fees) $6,227. Sal $186,166
Library Holdings: Bk Vols 22,000; Bk Titles 20,000; Per Subs 100
Automation Activity & Vendor Info: (Acquisitions) epixtech, inc.; (Cataloging) epixtech, inc.; (Circulation) epixtech, inc.; (Course Reserve) epixtech, inc.; (OPAC) epixtech, inc.
Mem of San Joaquin Valley Library System

S MATURANGO MUSEUM, Resource Library, 100 E Las Flores St, 93555. SAN 375-8184. Tel: 760-375-6900. FAX: 760-375-0479. E-Mail: matmus@ridgenet.net. Web Site: www.maturango.org. *Curator*, Elva Younkin
Library Holdings: Bk Titles 2,000

RIVERSIDE

G BUREAU OF LAND MANAGEMENT, Riverside District Office Library,* 6221 Box Springs Blvd, 92507. SAN 301-2484. Tel: 909-697-5297. FAX: 909-697-5299. *Librn*, Arzaretta Shelton; *Commun Servs*, Doran Sanchez
Library Holdings: Bk Vols 5,000; Per Subs 20
Restriction: Staff use only
Open Mon-Fri 7:45-4:30

CR CALIFORNIA BAPTIST UNIVERSITY, Annie Gabriel Library, 8432 Magnolia Ave, 92504. SAN 301-2492. Tel: 909-343-4352. FAX: 909-343-4523. Web Site: www.calbaptist.edu/library. *Dir Libr Serv*, Barbara Holohan; E-Mail: bholohan@calbaptist.edu; *Cat*, Helen Xu; Tel: 909-343-4354, E-Mail: hxu@calbaptis.edu; *Tech Servs*, Rose Lilley; Tel: 909-343-4353, E-Mail: rlilley@calbaptist.edu; *ILL, Online Servs, Ref*, Tori Koch; Tel: 909-343-4415, E-Mail: vbauer@calbaptist.edu; *Ser*, Dr Barry Parker; Tel: 909-343-4242, E-Mail: bparker@calbaptist.edu; *Coll Develop*, Erica McLaughlin; Tel: 909-343-4333, E-Mail: emclaugh@calbaptist.edu; *Circ*, Charlotte Sandoval; Tel: 909-343-4331, E-Mail: csandova@calbaptist.edu; Staff 9 (MLS 5, Non-MLS 4)
Founded 1950. Enrl 2,000; Highest Degree: Master
Jul 1999-Jun 2000 Income (Main Library Only) Parent Institution $675,190. Mats Exp $132,748, Books $35,333, Per/Ser (Incl. Access Fees) $68,761, Micro $5,000, Electronic Ref Mat (Incl. Access Fees) $18,000. Sal $266,036 (Prof $200,936)
Library Holdings: Bk Vols 123,989; Per Subs 919
Subject Interests: Education, Fine arts, Psychology, Religion
Special Collections: Hymnology (P Boyd Smith Coll); Nie Wieder Coll
Automation Activity & Vendor Info: (Cataloging) SIRSI; (Circulation) SIRSI; (OPAC) SIRSI
Database Vendor: Ebsco - EbscoHost, GaleNet, IAC - Info Trac, OCLC - First Search
Function: ILL available
Partic in ELVIS; Inland Empire Acad Libr Coop; OCLC Online Computer Library Center, Inc; San Bernardino, Inyo, Riverside Counties United Library Services; SCELC

S CALIFORNIA CACTUS GROWERS ASSOCIATION LIBRARY,* 11152 Palm Terrace Lane, 92505. SAN 375-7900. Tel: 909-687-1809. FAX: 909-687-9055. *Librn*, James Welton
Library Holdings: Bk Titles 154
Restriction: Members only

S CALIFORNIA SCHOOL FOR THE DEAF LIBRARY,* 3044 Horace St, 92506. SAN 320-5746. Tel: 909-782-6500. Web Site: www.cde.ca.gov/csdr. *Librn*, Helen Johnson Peterson
Library Holdings: Bk Vols 13,000
Subject Interests: Deaf, Special education
Special Collections: American Annals for the Deaf; Volta Review
Partic in San Bernardino, Inyo, Riverside Counties United Library Services
Special Services for the Deaf - TTY machine

G CALIFORNIA STATE COURT OF APPEAL, Fourth Appellate District, Division Two Library, 3389 12th St, 92501. SAN 327-1587. Tel: 909-248-0220. FAX: 909-248-0235. *Librn*, Terry R Lynch; E-Mail: terry.lynch@jud.ca.gov
Library Holdings: Bk Vols 30,000

CALVARY PRESBYTERIAN CHURCH USA LIBRARY, 4495 Magnolia Ave, 92501. SAN 301-2506. Tel: 909-686-0761. FAX: 909-686-1488. Web Site: www.calvarypresch.org.
Library Holdings: Bk Vols 3,500

P INLAND LIBRARY SYSTEM, 3581 Mission Inn Ave, 92501. (Mail add: PO Box 468, 92502), SAN 301-231X. Tel: 909-369-7995. FAX: 909-784-1158. E-Mail: ils@inlandlib.org. Web Site: www.inlandlib.org. *Exec Dir*, Kathleen Aaron; E-Mail: kaaron@inlandlib.org; *Ref*, Linda Taylor; E-Mail: ltaylor@inlandlib.org; *Ref*, Cecelia Mestas-Holm; E-Mail: cmholm@inlandlib.org
Founded 1966
Jul 1998-Jun 1999 Income $326,000. Sal $211,000
Publications: Inland Messenger (occasional newsletter)
Restriction: Member organizations only
Member Libraries: Banning Public Library; Beaumont Library District; Colton Public Library; Corona Public Library; Hemet Public Library; Inyo County Free Library; Moreno Valley Public Library; Palm Springs Public Library; Palo Verde Valley District Library; Rancho Cucamonga Public Library; Rancho Mirage Public Library; Riverside Public Library; San Bernardino County Library; San Bernardino Public Library; Upland Public Library
Partic in Coop Libr Agency for Syst & Servs; OCLC Online Computer Library Center, Inc

M KAISER-PERMANENTE MEDICAL CENTER, Health Sciences Library, 10800 Magnolia Ave, 92505. SAN 377-5208. Tel: 909-353-3659. FAX: 909-353-3262. *Librn*, William Paringer; *Asst Librn*, Grace Johnson
Library Holdings: Bk Vols 50

C LA SIERRA UNIVERSITY LIBRARY,* 4700 Pierce St, 92515. SAN 333-8851. Tel: 909-785-2397. Interlibrary Loan Service Tel: 909-785-2402. FAX: 909-785-2445. Web Site: www.lasierra.edu/library/. *Actg Dir, Publ Servs*, Gilbert Abella; *Acq, Ref, Tech Servs*, Kitty Simmons; E-Mail: ksimmons@lasierra.edu; *Cat*, James Walker; *Per*, Vera May Schwarz; *Rare Bks, Spec Coll*, Tony Zbaraschuk
Founded 1927. Enrl 1,472; Fac 100
1998-1999 Income $949,308. Mats Exp $263,068, Books $112,028, Per/Ser (Incl. Access Fees) $129,746. Sal $374,776 (Prof $284,959)
Library Holdings: Bk Vols 196,976; Per Subs 1,480
Special Collections: Far Eastern; History (W A Scharffenberg Coll); Library of American Civilization, micro; Library of English Literature, micro; Reformation History (William M Landeen Coll); Seventh Day Adventist Coll
Automation Activity & Vendor Info: (Cataloging) Innovative Interfaces Inc.; (Circulation) Innovative Interfaces Inc.; (Serials) Innovative Interfaces Inc.
Partic in Inland Empire Acad Libr Coop; OCLC Online Computer Library Center, Inc; San Bernardino, Inyo, Riverside Counties United Library Services

S PRESS-ENTERPRISE NEWSPAPER LIBRARY,* 3512 14th St, PO Box 792, 92502-0792. SAN 301-2514. Tel: 909-782-7580. FAX: 909-782-7572. *Dir*, Jackie Chamberlain; E-Mail: jchamberlain@pe.com
Library Holdings: Bk Vols 300
Library prepares & maintains an index of our publications from 1968-Sept 1992, available on microfiche for a charge

J RIVERSIDE COMMUNITY COLLEGE, Dr Martin Luther King Jr Library, 4800 Magnolia Ave, 92506-1299. SAN 301-2530. Tel: 909-222-8654. FAX: 909-222-8034. Web Site: www.rccd.cc.ca.us. *Coll Develop*, Linda Chang; Staff 9 (MLS 9)
Founded 1919. Enrl 34,000; Fac 710; Highest Degree: Associate
1999-2000 Income $1,972,397. Mats Exp $879,188, Books $470,269, Per/Ser (Incl. Access Fees) $233,919, AV Equip $175,000. Sal $1,216,600 (Prof $657,574)
Library Holdings: Bk Titles 141,000; Per Subs 740
Automation Activity & Vendor Info: (Acquisitions) Innovative Interfaces Inc.; (Cataloging) Innovative Interfaces Inc.; (Circulation) Innovative Interfaces Inc.; (Course Reserve) Innovative Interfaces Inc.; (ILL) Innovative Interfaces Inc.; (Media Booking) Innovative Interfaces Inc.; (OPAC) Innovative Interfaces Inc.; (Serials) Innovative Interfaces Inc.
Partic in San Bernardino, Inyo, Riverside Counties United Library Services
Open Mon-Thurs 7:30am-9pm, Fri 7:30-4:30

S RIVERSIDE COUNTY HISTORICAL COMMISSION LIBRARY,* 4600 Crestmore Rd, 92509-6858. SAN 301-2611. Tel: 909-955-4310. FAX: 909-955-4305. Web Site: www.co.riverside.ca.us/parks.; Staff 17 (MLS 2, Non-MLS 15)
Founded 1968
Library Holdings: Bk Titles 600
Subject Interests: Historic preservation
Special Collections: Audio Tapes; Local History, bks, ms
Publications: Local History Books

GL RIVERSIDE COUNTY LAW LIBRARY, 3989 Lemon St, 92501-3674. SAN 301-2549. Tel: 909-955-6390. FAX: 909-955-6394. *Librn*, Gayle E Webb; Tel: 909-955-6395, E-Mail: gwebb@co.riverside.ca.us; *Coll Develop*, Laura Stockton; Tel: 909-955-6397, E-Mail: lstockto@co.riverside.ca.us; *Tech Servs*, Elizabeth Manouchehri; Tel: 909-955-6396, E-Mail: emanouch@co.riverside.ca.us; Staff 3 (MLS 2, Non-MLS 1)
Jul 1999-Jun 2000 Income $1,188,276, County $1,020,090, Locally Generated Income $154,814, Other $13,372. Mats Exp $515,358, Books $6,622, Per/Ser (Incl. Access Fees) $474,714, AV Equip $18,732, Electronic Ref Mat (Incl. Access Fees) $15,290. Sal $357,842
Library Holdings: Bk Vols 86,366; Bk Titles 5,587
Special Collections: Municipal Codes
Automation Activity & Vendor Info: (Acquisitions) DRA; (Cataloging) DRA; (Serials) DRA
Publications: Bookmark (publicity info)

§P RIVERSIDE COUNTY LIBRARY SYSTEM, 4080 Lemon St, 12th flr, 92501. Tel: 909-955-1100. FAX: 909-955-1105. Web Site: www.co.riverside.ca.us/community/rccpl. *Adminr, VPres*, Gordon Conable; Tel: 909-369-3003, Fax: 909-369-6801, E-Mail: gordonc@lssi.com; *Librn*, Gary Christmas; E-Mail: gchristm@co.riverside.ca.us
Jul 1998-Jun 1999 Income $7,622,158, State $889,000, Federal $43,318, County $5,625,453, Locally Generated Income $546,317, Other $518,070
Library Holdings: Bk Vols 758,870; Per Subs 700
Automation Activity & Vendor Info: (Acquisitions) DRA; (Cataloging) DRA; (Circulation) DRA; (ILL) DRA; (OPAC) DRA; (Serials) DRA
Member Libraries: Murrieta City Library
Branches: 24
ANZA BRANCH, 57430 Mitchell Rd, Anza, 92539. Tel: 909-763-4216. FAX: 909-763-0652. *Branch Mgr*, Bertha Estrella; Fax: 909-763-0657, E-Mail: bertha_anz@riverside.lib.ca.us
Automation Activity & Vendor Info: (Acquisitions) DRA; (Cataloging) DRA; (Circulation) DRA; (ILL) DRA; (OPAC) DRA; (Serials) DRA
CALIMESA BRANCH, 974 Calimesa Blvd, Calimesa, 92320. Tel: 909-795-2287. FAX: 909-795-4399. *Branch Mgr*, Sandra Jefferson; E-Mail: sandra_cal@riverside.lib.ca.us
Automation Activity & Vendor Info: (Acquisitions) DRA; (Cataloging) DRA; (Circulation) DRA; (ILL) DRA; (OPAC) DRA; (Serials) DRA
CANYON LAKE BRANCH, 31516 Railroad Canyon Rd, Canyon Lake, 92587. Tel: 909-244-9181. FAX: 909-244-7382. *Branch Mgr*, Connie Rynning; E-Mail: connie_cnl@riverside.lib.ca.us
Automation Activity & Vendor Info: (Acquisitions) DRA; (Cataloging) DRA; (Circulation) DRA; (ILL) DRA; (OPAC) DRA; (Serials) DRA
CATHEDRAL CITY BRANCH, 33-520 Date Palm Dr, Cathedral City, 92234. Tel: 760-328-4262. FAX: 760-770-9828. *Branch Mgr*, Roger Clements; E-Mail: roger_cat@riverside.lib.ca.us
Automation Activity & Vendor Info: (Acquisitions) DRA; (Cataloging) DRA; (Circulation) DRA; (ILL) DRA; (OPAC) DRA; (Serials) DRA
COACHELLA BRANCH, 1538 Seventh St, Coachella, 92236. Tel: 760-398-5148. FAX: 760-398-1068. *Branch Mgr*, Elia Gentry; E-Mail: elia_coa@riverside.lib.ca.us
Automation Activity & Vendor Info: (Acquisitions) DRA; (Cataloging) DRA; (Circulation) DRA; (ILL) DRA; (OPAC) DRA; (Serials) DRA
DESERT HOT SPRINGS BRANCH, 11691 West Dr, Desert Hot Springs, 92240. Tel: 760-329-5926. FAX: 760-329-3593. *Branch Mgr*, Helen Kerrigan; E-Mail: helen_dhs@riverside.lib.ca.us
Automation Activity & Vendor Info: (Acquisitions) DRA; (Cataloging) DRA; (Circulation) DRA; (ILL) DRA; (OPAC) DRA; (Serials) DRA
GLEN AVON, 9244 Galena, 92509. Tel: 909-685-8121. FAX: 909-685-7158. *Branch Mgr*, Diane Drake; E-Mail: diane_gav@riverside.lib.ca.us
Automation Activity & Vendor Info: (Acquisitions) DRA; (Cataloging) DRA; (Circulation) DRA; (ILL) DRA; (OPAC) DRA; (Serials) DRA
HIGHGROVE BRANCH, 690 W Center St, Highgrove, 92507. Tel: 909-682-1507. FAX: 909-321-4107. *Branch Mgr*, Louise Martinez; E-Mail: louise_hig@riverside.lib.ca.us
Automation Activity & Vendor Info: (Acquisitions) DRA; (Cataloging) DRA; (Circulation) DRA; (ILL) DRA; (OPAC) DRA; (Serials) DRA
IDYLLWILD BRANCH, 54185 Pinecrest Rd, Idyllwild, 92549. Tel: 909-659-2300. FAX: 909-659-2453. *Branch Mgr*, Teresa Brouwer; E-Mail: teresa_idl@riverside.lib.ca.us
Automation Activity & Vendor Info: (Acquisitions) DRA; (Cataloging) DRA; (Circulation) DRA; (ILL) DRA; (OPAC) DRA; (Serials) DRA
INDIO BRANCH, 200 Civic Ctr Mall, Indio, 92201. Tel: 760-347-2383. FAX: 760-347-3159. *Branch Mgr*, Donna McCune; E-Mail: donna_ind@riverside.lib.ca.us
Automation Activity & Vendor Info: (Acquisitions) DRA; (Cataloging) DRA; (Circulation) DRA; (ILL) DRA; (OPAC) DRA; (Serials) DRA
LA QUINTA BRANCH, 78-080 Calle Estado, La Quinta, 92253. Tel: 760-564-4767. FAX: 760-771-0237. *Branch Mgr*, Miguel Guitron-Rodriquez; E-Mail: miguel_laq@riverside.lib.ca.us
Automation Activity & Vendor Info: (Acquisitions) DRA; (Cataloging) DRA; (Circulation) DRA; (ILL) DRA; (OPAC) DRA; (Serials) DRA
LAKE ELSINORE BRANCH, 600 W Graham, Lake Elsinore, 92530. Tel: 909-657-4517. FAX: 909-245-7715. *Branch Mgr*, Emily Gerstbacher; E-Mail: emily_lke@riverside.lib.ca.us
Automation Activity & Vendor Info: (Acquisitions) DRA; (Cataloging) DRA; (Circulation) DRA; (ILL) DRA; (OPAC) DRA; (Serials) DRA
LAKE TAMARISK, 43880 Lake Tamarisk Dr, Desert Center, 92239. Tel: 760-227-3273. FAX: 760-227-0043. *Branch Mgr*, Charlene Carney; E-Mail: charlene_lkt@riverside.lib.ca.us
Automation Activity & Vendor Info: (Acquisitions) DRA; (Cataloging) DRA; (Circulation) DRA; (ILL) DRA; (OPAC) DRA; (Serials) DRA
MECCA BRANCH, 65-250A Coahuilla St, Mecca, 92254. Tel: 760-396-2363. FAX: 760-396-1503. *Branch Mgr*, Elia Gentry; E-Mail: elia_mec@riverside.lib.ca.us

Automation Activity & Vendor Info: (Acquisitions) DRA; (Cataloging) DRA; (Circulation) DRA; (ILL) DRA; (OPAC) DRA; (Serials) DRA

NORCO BRANCH, 3954 Old Hamner, Norco, 92860. Tel: 909-735-5329. FAX: 909-735-0263. *Branch Mgr*, Debra Langguth; E-Mail: debbie_nor@riverside.lib.ca.us

Automation Activity & Vendor Info: (Acquisitions) DRA; (Cataloging) DRA; (Circulation) DRA; (ILL) DRA; (OPAC) DRA; (Serials) DRA

NUVIEW, 29990 Lake View, Nuevo, 92567. Tel: 909-928-0769. FAX: 909-928-3360. *Branch Mgr*, Louise Martinez; E-Mail: louise_nuv@riverside.lib.ca.us

Automation Activity & Vendor Info: (Acquisitions) DRA; (Cataloging) DRA; (Circulation) DRA; (ILL) DRA; (OPAC) DRA; (Serials) DRA

PALM DESERT BRANCH, 73-300 Fred Waring Dr, Palm Desert, 92260. Tel: 760-346-6552. FAX: 760-341-7862. *Branch Mgr*, Beth Zieglar; E-Mail: bethz_pld@riverside.lib.ca.us

Automation Activity & Vendor Info: (Acquisitions) DRA; (Cataloging) DRA; (Circulation) DRA; (ILL) DRA; (OPAC) DRA; (Serials) DRA

PERRIS BRANCH, 163 E San Jacinto, Perris, 92570. Tel: 909-657-2358. FAX: 909-657-9849. *Branch Mgr*, Ron Stump; E-Mail: ron_per@riverside.lib.ca.us

Automation Activity & Vendor Info: (Acquisitions) DRA; (Cataloging) DRA; (Circulation) DRA; (ILL) DRA; (OPAC) DRA; (Serials) DRA

ROBIDOUX, 5763 Tilton Ave, 92509. Tel: 909-682-5485. FAX: 909-682-8641. *Branch Mgr*, Laura Mae Leach; E-Mail: lauramae_rob@riverside.lib.ca.us

Automation Activity & Vendor Info: (Acquisitions) DRA; (Cataloging) DRA; (Circulation) DRA; (ILL) DRA; (OPAC) DRA; (Serials) DRA

SAN JACINTO BRANCH, 500 Idyllwild Dr, San Jacinto, 92583. Tel: 909-654-8625. FAX: 909-654-8344. *Branch Mgr*, Lia Bushong; E-Mail: lia_saj@riverside.lib.ca.us

Automation Activity & Vendor Info: (Acquisitions) DRA; (Cataloging) DRA; (Circulation) DRA; (ILL) DRA; (OPAC) DRA; (Serials) DRA

SUN CITY BRANCH, 26982 Cherry Hills Blvd, Sun City, 92586. Tel: 909-679-3534. FAX: 909-672-8293. *Branch Mgr*, Nancy Smith; E-Mail: nancy_scy@riverside.lib.ca.us

Automation Activity & Vendor Info: (Acquisitions) DRA; (Cataloging) DRA; (Circulation) DRA; (ILL) DRA; (OPAC) DRA; (Serials) DRA

TEMECULA BRANCH, 41000 County Ctr, Temecula, 92591. Tel: 909-600-6263. FAX: 909-600-6265. *Branch Mgr*, Rosie Vanderhaak; Tel: 909-600-6266, E-Mail: rosie_tem@riverside.lib.ca.us

Automation Activity & Vendor Info: (Acquisitions) DRA; (Cataloging) DRA; (Circulation) DRA; (ILL) DRA; (OPAC) DRA; (Serials) DRA

THOUSAND PALMS BRANCH, 72-715 La Canada Way, Thousand Palms, 92276. Tel: 760-343-1556. FAX: 760-343-0957. *Branch Mgr*, Sharon Ballard; E-Mail: sharon_tps@riverside.lib.ca.us

Automation Activity & Vendor Info: (Acquisitions) DRA; (Cataloging) DRA; (Circulation) DRA; (ILL) DRA; (OPAC) DRA; (Serials) DRA

VALLE VISTA, 43975 E Florida Ave, Hemet, 92544. Tel: 909-927-2611. FAX: 909-927-7902. *Mgr*, Mark Smith; Tel: 909-369-3003, Ext 27, Fax: 909-369-6801, E-Mail: mark_tem@riverside.lib.ca.us

Automation Activity & Vendor Info: (Acquisitions) DRA; (Cataloging) DRA; (Circulation) DRA; (ILL) DRA; (OPAC) DRA; (Serials) DRA

P RIVERSIDE PUBLIC LIBRARY, 3581 Mission Inn Ave, 92501. SAN 333-8886. Tel: 909-826-5201. E-Mail: hluley@ci.riverside.ca.us. Web Site: www.co.riverside.ca.us/library. *Dir*, Judith Auth; *Cat*, John Crane; *Coll Develop*, Patricia McGuckian; Staff 15 (MLS 15)

Founded 1888. Pop 245,800; Circ 1,008,107

Library Holdings: Bk Vols 396,112; Bk Titles 161,692

Special Collections: Black History Coll; Genealogy Coll; Historical Children's Books (Dorothy Daniels Memorial Coll); Local History Coll; Mexican American Coll; Sight Handicapped Coll, bks, per, cassettes

Automation Activity & Vendor Info: (Acquisitions) DRA

Mem of Inland Library System

Partic in San Bernardino, Inyo, Riverside Counties United Library Services

Special Services for the Deaf - Staff with knowledge of sign language; TDD

Friends of the Library Group

Branches: 4

ARLINGTON, 9556 Magnolia, 92503-3698. SAN 333-8916. FAX: 909-689-6612. *Librn*, Charlene Swanson

Library Holdings: Bk Vols 38,751; Bk Titles 8,170

Friends of the Library Group

CASA BLANCA, 2985 Madison St, 92504-4480. SAN 333-8940. Tel: 909-688-3825.

Library Holdings: Bk Vols 18,461; Bk Titles 3,123

Friends of the Library Group

LA SIERRA, 4600 La Sierra, 92505-2722. SAN 333-9181. Tel: 909-688-7740. FAX: 909-352-7578. *Librn*, Pat Atwal

Library Holdings: Bk Vols 52,969; Bk Titles 5,993

Friends of the Library Group

MARCY BRANCH, 3711 Central Ave, 92506-2468. SAN 333-9270. Tel: 909-826-5201. FAX: 909-682-5524. *Librn*, Carolyn Denny

Library Holdings: Bk Vols 36,369; Bk Titles 4,859

Friends of the Library Group

Bookmobiles: 2

C UNIVERSITY OF CALIFORNIA, RIVERSIDE, University Library, PO Box 5900, 92517-5900. SAN 333-9696. Tel: 909-787-3221. Interlibrary Loan Service Tel: 909-787-3234, 909-787-6387 (Science). FAX: 909-787-2255 (Admin), 909-787-3285. Web Site: www.library.ucr.edu. *Librn*, James C Thompson; *Assoc Librn, Coll Develop*, Peter Briscoe; *Asst Librn, Publ Servs*, Venita Jorgensen; *Assoc Librn, Tech Servs*, John W Tanno; E-Mail: john.tanno@ucr.edu; *Acq*, Stefanie Wittenbach; *Science*, Diana Lane; *Coll Develop*, Kuei Chiu; *Coll Develop*, Nancy Koller; *Spec Coll, Spec Coll & Archives*, Sheryl Davis; *Cat*, Nancy Douglas. Subject Specialists: *Art*, Kuei Chiu; *Asia*, Kuei Chiu; *Social sciences and issues*, Nancy Koller; Staff 123 (MLS 45, Non-MLS 78)

Founded 1954. Enrl 9,469; Fac 429; Highest Degree: Doctorate

Jul 1999-Jun 2000 Income (Main Library Only) $10,951,271. Mats Exp $4,222,501, Books $1,298,744, Per/Ser (Incl. Access Fees) $2,531,779, Presv $215,864, Other Print Mats $176,114. Sal $4,922,541 (Prof $2,451,102)

Library Holdings: Bk Vols 2,018,234; Per Subs 12,814

Special Collections: B Traven Coll; Boys Books Coll, 1870-1900; Citrus History Coll; English Civil War Coll, 1640-1680, pamphlets; English Deism Coll, 1680-1710; European Socialism Coll, 1870-1920; Ezra Pound Coll; Field Photographic Archive of Riverside, Riverside Municipal Archive); Filibustering in Mexico & Nicaragua; First editions of 19th & 20th Century British Literature; History of Photography Coll; J Lloyd Eaton Coll of Science Fiction & Fantasy Literature Coll; Niels Gade Coll; Osuna & Casasola Photographic Archives of the Mexican Revolution; Oswald Jones Memorial Coll, including Heinrich Schenker Archives; Paraguayan History & Literature (Diaz-Perez & Godoi Collections); Paris, France Coll; Regional History (California Deserts & Anthropology; Robert Lowell Coll; Sadakichi Hartmann Archive Coll; The Tomas Rivera Archives; Thomas Hardy Coll; Utopianism Coll; William Blake (Trianon Press Coll)

Database Vendor: OCLC - First Search

Publications: Sadakichi Hartmann Papers

Partic in Asn of Research Libraries; San Bernardino, Inyo, Riverside Counties United Library Services

Friends of the Library Group

Departmental Libraries:

MEDIA LIBRARY Tel: 909-787-5606. *Head of Libr*, Jim Glenn

MUSIC Tel: 909-787-3137. Interlibrary Loan Service Tel: 909-787-3234. *Head of Libr*, Lia Schaafsma

RUPERT COSTO LIBRARY OF THE AMERICAN INDIAN, PO Box 5900, 92517-5900. SAN 328-8935. Tel: 909-787-3233. FAX: 909-787-4673. *Assoc Librn*, John Tanno; Tel: 909-787-3221, Fax: 909-787-2255, E-Mail: john.tanno@ucr.edu; *Spec Coll & Archives*, Sheryl Davis; *Coll Develop*, Peter Briscoe

Founded 1985

Library Holdings: Bk Vols 3,500

ROCKLIN

J SIERRA JOINT COMMUNITY COLLEGE DISTRICT, Learning Resource Center, 5000 Rocklin Rd, 95677. SAN 301-2565. Tel: 916-624-3333, Ext 2567, 916-781-0567. Circulation Tel: 916-789-2636. Reference Tel: 916-781-0566. FAX: 916-789-2893. Web Site: lrc.sierra.cc.ca.us. *Dean*, Brian Haley; *Coll Develop, Ref Serv*, Tina Sixt; *Ref*, Sandra Montgomery; *Cat*, Deirdre Campbell

Founded 1914.

Library Holdings: Bk Titles 65,879; Per Subs 189

Subject Interests: California, Mining

Special Collections: Rare books 169, Realia 60

Automation Activity & Vendor Info: (Cataloging) Endeavor; (Circulation) Endeavor; (Course Reserve) Endeavor; (OPAC) Endeavor

Partic in Mountain Valley Libr Syst

Friends of the Library Group

ROHNERT PARK

P ROHNERT PARK-COTATI REGIONAL LIBRARY,* 6600 Hunter Dr, 95428-2418. SAN 376-3927. Tel: 707-584-9121. FAX: 707-584-8561. Web Site: www.sinoma.lib.ca.us. *Mgr*, Donald Gass

Library Holdings: Bk Vols 55,000; Bk Titles 32,000; Per Subs 50

Mem of North Bay Cooperative Library System

Friends of the Library Group

C SONOMA STATE UNIVERSITY LIBRARY, Jean & Charles Schultz Information Center, 1801 E Cotati Ave, 94928. SAN 301-2573. Tel: 707-664-2397. FAX: 707-664-2090. Web Site: www.libweb.sonoma.edu. *Dean*, Barbara Butler; E-Mail: barbara.butler@sonoma.edu; *Cat, Doc*, Sandy Heft; *Bibliog Instr*, Karen Brodsky; *ILL, Online Servs*, Gail Cosmo; *Coll Develop*, Sandra Walton; *Ref*, Raye Lynn Thomas; Staff 11 (MLS 11)

Founded 1961. Enrl 7,200; Highest Degree: Master

1998-1999 Mats Exp $750,000. Sal $1,880,000 (Prof $831,194)

Library Holdings: Bk Vols 516,032

Special Collections: Celtic Coll; North Bay Regional Information Center; Small California Press

Automation Activity & Vendor Info: (Circulation) DRA
Mem of North Bay Cooperative Library System
Partic in CNI; EDUCOM
Friends of the Library Group

ROLLING HILLS ESTATES

P PALOS VERDES LIBRARY DISTRICT, Peninsula Center Library, 701 Silver Spur Rd, 90274. SAN 333-5550. Tel: 310-377-9584. Interlibrary Loan Service Tel: 310-377-9584, Ext 235. Circulation Tel: 310-377-9584, Ext 260. Reference Tel: 310-377-9584, Ext 601. FAX: 310-541-6807. Web Site: www.palos-verdes.lib.ca.us. *Dir*, Diana Moreno; Tel: 310-377-9584, Ext 200, E-Mail: diana@palos-verdes.lib.ca.us; *Dir*, Peg Tarbox; Tel: 310-377-9584, Ext 236, E-Mail: peg@palos-verdes.lib.ca.us; *Mgr*, Marian Heslenfeld; Tel: 310-377-9584, Ext 552, E-Mail: marian@palos-verdes.lib.ca.us; *Mgr*, Janet Judson; Tel: 310-377-9584, Ext 453, E-Mail: janet@palos-verdes.lib.ca.us; *Coll Develop, Ref*, Lanny Swallow; Tel: 310-377-9584, Ext 210, E-Mail: lanny@palos-verdes.lib.ca.us; Staff 16 (MLS 13, Non-MLS 3)
Founded 1928. Pop 70,847; Circ 812,330
Jul 1998-Jun 1999 Income $4,085,534, State $153,484, Federal $35,516, County $3,088,808, Locally Generated Income $282,372, Other $525,354. Mats Exp $559,084, Books $454,318, Per/Ser (Incl. Access Fees) $57,370, Micro $15,000, Other Print Mats $25,000, Electronic Ref Mat (Incl. Access Fees) $7,396. Sal $1,434,673
Library Holdings: Bk Vols 267,772; Bk Titles 189,981; Per Subs 541
Subject Interests: Art, Genealogy, Local history, Travel
Automation Activity & Vendor Info: (Acquisitions) Brodart; (Cataloging) epixtech, inc.; (Circulation) epixtech, inc.; (OPAC) epixtech, inc.; (Serials) epixtech, inc.
Database Vendor: OCLC - First Search
Publications: Friends of the Library Newsletter; Library Advisory Committee Newsletters; Library Update
Mem of Metropolitan Cooperative Library System
Friends of the Library Group
Branches: 2
MALAGA COVE PLAZA, 2400 Via Campesina, Palos Verdes Estates, 90274-3662. SAN 333-5585. Tel: 310-377-9584, Ext 550. FAX: 310-373-7594. Web Site: www.muse.palos.verdes.lib.ca.us. *Mgr*, Marian Heslenfeld; Tel: 310-377-9584, Ext 551, E-Mail: marian@palos-verdes.lib.ca.us; Staff 1 (MLS 1)
Library Holdings: Bk Vols 36,034; Bk Titles 34,900
Subject Interests: Local history
Friends of the Library Group
MIRALESTE, 29089 Palos Verdes Dr E, Rancho Palos Verdes, 90275. SAN 333-5615. Tel: 310-377-9584, Ext 452. FAX: 310-547-4067. Web Site: www.muse.palos-verdes.lib.ca.us. *Mgr*, Janet Judson; Tel: 310-377-9584, Ext 453, E-Mail: janet@palos-verdes.lib.ca.us; Staff 1 (MLS 1)
Library Holdings: Bk Vols 40,687; Bk Titles 38,500
Friends of the Library Group

ROSEMEAD

J DON BOSCO TECHNICAL INSTITUTE, Lee Memorial Library, 1151 San Gabriel Blvd, 91770. SAN 301-2581. Tel: 626-940-2035. FAX: 626-940-2001. Web Site: www.boscotech.org. *Librn*, Margaret Pedregon; E-Mail: mpedregon@boscotech.tec.net.ca.us; Staff 3 (MLS 2, Non-MLS 1)
Founded 1957
Library Holdings: Bk Vols 9,500; Bk Titles 7,500; Per Subs 30
Subject Interests: Art, Religion, Technology
Automation Activity & Vendor Info: (Cataloging) Sagebrush Corporation; (Circulation) Sagebrush Corporation
Database Vendor: ProQuest
Open Mon-Fri 7:30-5
Friends of the Library Group

S SOUTHERN CALIFORNIA EDISON CO, Corporate Library,* 2244 Walnut Grove Ave, Rm G-55, 91770-3714. SAN 301-259X. Tel: 626-302-8971, 626-302-8973. FAX: 626-302-8015. *Librn*, Paul Morton; *Asst Librn*, Steven D Lowry; *Asst Librn*, William D Lee
Library Holdings: Bk Vols 15,500; Per Subs 640
Subject Interests: Business and management, Chemistry, Nuclear engineering, Solar energy
Special Collections: EPRI Reports
Restriction: By appointment only
Partic in Dialog Corporation; Dow Jones News Retrieval

ROSEVILLE

P ROSEVILLE PUBLIC LIBRARY, 225 Taylor St, 95678-2681. SAN 333-9815. Tel: 916-774-5221. FAX: 916-773-5594. E-Mail: library@roseville.ca.us. Web Site: roseville.ca.us/library.html. *Dir*, Susan L Nickerson; *Asst Dir*, Dianne Bish; *Circ*, Edna Esparza; *Ch Servs, YA Servs*, Rosemary Dukelow; *Tech Servs*, Sallie Odom; *Bibliog Instr, Ref*, Rick Lurie; Staff 29 (MLS 10, Non-MLS 19)
Founded 1912. Pop 64,000
Jul 1999-Jun 2000 Income (Main Library and Branch Library) $2,471,000, State $209,000, City $2,262,000. Mats Exp $194,336, Books $155,586, Per/Ser (Incl. Access Fees) $17,000, Presv $600, Micro $21,000, Other Print Mats $150. Sal $1,199,000 (Prof $503,000)
Library Holdings: Bk Vols 152,000; Bk Titles 142,000; Per Subs 395
Subject Interests: Railroads
Special Collections: Local History, photogs
Automation Activity & Vendor Info: (Acquisitions) epixtech, inc.; (Circulation) epixtech, inc.; (OPAC) epixtech, inc.
Database Vendor: OCLC - First Search
Mem of Mountain-Valley Library System
Partic in Mountain Valley Libr Syst
Special Services for the Deaf - Staff with knowledge of sign language
Friends of the Library Group
Branches: 1
MAIDU, 1530 Maidu Dr, 95661. SAN 333-984X. Tel: 916-774-5900. FAX: 916-773-0972. E-Mail: library@roseville.ca.us. Web Site: roseville.ca.us/library.html. *Branch Mgr*, Sharon Troxel; Staff 9 (MLS 4, Non-MLS 5)
Founded 1990. Pop 11,000
Library Holdings: Bk Vols 48,365
Friends of the Library Group

M SUTTER ROSEVILLE MEDICAL CENTER LIBRARY, One Medical Plaza, 95661. SAN 301-2603. Interlibrary Loan Service Tel: 916-781-1580. FAX: 916-781-1582. *Librn*, Dorothy Thurmond; E-Mail: thurmod@sutterhealth.org
Founded 1968
Library Holdings: Bk Titles 1,000; Per Subs 65
Subject Interests: Surgery
Special Collections: Medical Coll
Publications: Book Lists; Library Brochure
Partic in Sacramento Area Health Sciences Librs
Open Mon-Fri 8-2:30

SACRAMENTO

AEROJET GENERAL CORP
S SACRAMENTO TECHNICAL INFORMATION CENTER, PO Box 13222, 95813. SAN 329-4366. Tel: 916-355-3401. FAX: 916-355-2104.
Library Holdings: Bk Vols 7,100; Per Subs 65
Publications: Current awareness bulletin (bi-monthly); Library information pamphlet

S AMERICAN DOWN ASSOCIATION, ADA-Library Section,* 3216 Eastwood Rd, 95821. SAN 325-5530. Tel: 916-971-1135. FAX: 916-971-3151. *Librn, Publ Servs*, Jeff Helms
Subject Interests: Consumer info, Down, Feathers, Research, Statistics, Testing

J AMERICAN RIVER COLLEGE LIBRARY,* 4700 College Oak Dr, 95841. SAN 333-9874. Tel: 916-484-8457. Interlibrary Loan Service Tel: 916-484-8458. FAX: 916-484-8657. *Dean*, Henry Burnett; *Online Servs, Tech Servs*, Kathy Champion; *Ser*, Larry Fisher
Founded 1955. Enrl 22,000
Library Holdings: Bk Vols 77,895
Subject Interests: California, Careers
Automation Activity & Vendor Info: (Circulation) epixtech, inc.
Mem of Mountain-Valley Library System
Partic in OCLC Online Computer Library Center, Inc
Friends of the Library Group

SR BETHANY PRESBYTERIAN CHURCH LIBRARY,* 5625 24th St, 95822. SAN 301-262X. Tel: 916-428-5281. FAX: 916-428-3716. *In Charge*, Vicki McNamee
Library Holdings: Bk Vols 4,000

P BRAILLE & TALKING BOOK LIBRARY, (Formerly California State Braille & Talking Book Library), 900 N St, 95814. (Mail add: PO Box 942837, 94237-0001), Tel: 916-654-0640. Toll Free Tel: 800-952-5666. FAX: 916-654-1119. E-Mail: btbl@library.ca.gov. Web Site: www.library.ca.gov. *Mgr*, Donine S Hedrick; Tel: 916-654-6414, Fax: 916-654-1119, E-Mail: dhedrick@library.ca.gov; Staff 26 (MLS 4, Non-MLS 22)
Founded 1905. Circ 671,746
Jul 2000-Jun 2001 Income $1,118,831. Mats Exp $4,500, Books $2,000, Per/Ser (Incl. Access Fees) $1,500, Other Print Mats $1,000. Sal $851,348
Library Holdings: Bk Titles 55,000; Per Subs 15
Special Collections: Blindness & Other Disabilities Reference Material
Automation Activity & Vendor Info: (Circulation) DRA
Publications: Borrower's Handbook; BTBL Recorded Books on California
Special Services for the Blind - Braille & recorded books

GM CALIFORNIA DEPARTMENT OF ALCOHOL & DRUG PROGRAMS, Resource Center Library, 1700 K St, 95814-4037. SAN 328-5014. Tel: 916-324-5439. Toll Free Tel: 800-879-2772. FAX: 916-323-1270. E-Mail: resourcecenter@adp.state.ca.us. Web Site: www.adp.state.ca.us. *Librn*, Cynthia Castillo; E-Mail: ccastillo@adp.state.ca.us. Subject Specialists: *Alcohol and drugs*, Cynthia Castillo; Staff 2 (Non-MLS 2)
Jul 2000-Jun 2001 Income Parent Institution $45,000. Mats Exp $30,000, Books $10,000, Per/Ser (Incl. Access Fees) $20,000

Library Holdings: Bk Vols 7,350; Bk Titles 5,400; Per Subs 117
Subject Interests: Substance abuse
Automation Activity & Vendor Info: (Cataloging) CASPR
Database Vendor: Ebsco - EbscoHost
Restriction: Open to government employees only
Function: Reference services available

P CALIFORNIA DEPARTMENT OF CORRECTIONS LIBRARY SYSTEM, 1515 South St, 95814-7243. (Mail add: c/o Educ & Inmates Prog Unit, PO Box 942883, 94283-0001), SAN 371-8026. Tel: 916-324-4615. FAX: 916-324-1416. *Head Librn*, Janice Cesolini-Stuter; Staff 141 (MLS 74, Non-MLS 67)
Pop 160,000; Circ 2,100,000
JulJun
Library Holdings: Bk Vols 469,838; Per Subs 1,660
Branches: 34
AVENAL STATE PRISON, One Kings Way, PO Box 8, Avenal, 93204. SAN 371-8034. Tel: 209-386-0587, Ext 6644. *Librn*, Judy Salter; *Asst Librn, Tech Servs*, Sharon Blanton; *Asst Librn, Tech Servs*, Wanda Lee Gipson; *Asst Librn, Tech Servs*, Karen Raymond; *Asst Librn, Tech Servs*, Linda Bozner
1998-1999 Mats Exp $39,000
CALIFORNIA CORRECTIONAL CENTER, PO Box 790, Susanville, 96130. SAN 371-8042. Tel: 530-257-2181. FAX: 530-252-3020. *Librn*, Howard Cron; Staff 3 (MLS 3)
Circ 5,000
1999-2000 Mats Exp $39,000
CALIFORNIA CORRECTIONAL INSTITUTION, End of Hwy 202, Tehachapi, 93581. SAN 301-6544. Tel: 805-822-4402. *Senior Librn*, Harold Stanford; Tel: 661-822-4402, Ext 3675, Fax: 661-823-5003; *Librn*, June Williams; *Librn*, Juel Ratzlaff; *Librn*, Gillian Ray; Staff 6 (MLS 1, Non-MLS 5)
1998-1999 Mats Exp $39,000
Library Holdings: Bk Vols 4,400; Per Subs 22
Subject Interests: Law
CALIFORNIA INSTITUTION FOR MEN, 14901 Central Ave, PO Box 128, Chino, 91710. SAN 300-6654. Tel: 909-597-1821. *Librn*, Brian Maughan; *Librn*, Carolyn Carotenuti; *Librn*, Christopher Maughan; *Librn*, Raghbir Jassel
1998-1999 Mats Exp $43,000
CALIFORNIA INSTITUTION FOR WOMEN, 16756 Chino-Corona Rd, Frontera, 91720-9508. SAN 300-7723. Tel: 909-606-4954. FAX: 909-604-4936. *Senior Librn*, Juming Tong Davis
Founded 1952
1998-1999 Mats Exp $12,000
Library Holdings: Bk Titles 25,000; Per Subs 38
Subject Interests: Women studies
Automation Activity & Vendor Info: (Cataloging) Sagebrush Corporation; (Circulation) Sagebrush Corporation
Friends of the Library Group
CALIFORNIA MEDICAL FACILITY, 1600 California Dr, PO Box 2000, Vacaville, 95696-2000. SAN 335-2056. Tel: 707-448-6841. FAX: 707-448-1467. *Senior Librn*, Yaoming Cheng; Staff 2 (MLS 2)
1998-1999 Mats Exp $21,000
CALIFORNIA MEN'S COLONY-EAST, Hwy 1, PO Box 8101, San Luis Obispo, 93409. SAN 301-5122. Tel: 805-547-7900. *Librn*, Joan Lienemann; *Librn*, Patrick Moloney; Staff 1 (MLS 1)
Founded 1961. Pop 3,500
1998-1999 Mats Exp $44,000
Library Holdings: Bk Titles 25,000; Per Subs 125
Subject Interests: Law
Mem of Black Gold Cooperative Library System
Partic in Total Interlibrary Exchange
CALIFORNIA MEN'S COLONY-WEST, Hwy 1, 3 miles North, San Luis Obispo, 93403. (Mail add: PO Box 8103, San Luis Obispo, 93403), Tel: 805-547-7900, Ext 7185. FAX: 805-547-7792. *Senior Librn*, Patrick Moloney
Library Holdings: Bk Vols 20,000; Per Subs 65
Automation Activity & Vendor Info: (Cataloging) Sagebrush Corporation; (Circulation) Sagebrush Corporation; (Serials) Sagebrush Corporation
CALIFORNIA REHABILITATION CENTER, Fifth St & Western, PO Box 1841, Norco, 91760. SAN 301-1062. Tel: 909-689-4552. *Librn*, Linda Humphrey
1998-1999 Mats Exp $33,000
CALIFORNIA STATE PRISON, CORCORAN, 4001 King Ave, PO Box 8800, Corcoran, 93212. SAN 371-8050. Tel: 209-992-8800, Ext 5558. *Librn*, Gerald Squyres; *Librn*, John Richard; *Librn*, Ron Oxford; *Asst Librn, Tech Servs*, Dava Nunes; *Asst Librn, Tech Servs*, Sherry Parks
1998-1999 Mats Exp $33,000
CALIFORNIA STATE PRISON, LOS ANGELES COUNTY, 44750 60th St W, Lancaster, 93536-7620. SAN 375-5819. Tel: 661-729-2000. FAX: 661-729-6930. *Senior Librn*, Linda Rowe; *Librn*, Carl Seele; *Asst Librn, Tech Servs*, Pat Boetsch; *Asst Librn, Tech Servs*, George Riippi; *Asst Librn, Tech Servs*, Karen Hebert
1998-1999 Mats Exp $27,000
CALIFORNIA STATE PRISON, SACRAMENTO INMATE LIBRARY, 100 Prison Rd, PO Box 290001, Represa, 95671-0001. SAN 371-8069. Tel: 916-985-8610. FAX: 916-985-3407. *Senior Librn*, Dennis McCargar; Tel: 916-985-8610, Ext 6121; Staff 3 (MLS 1, Non-MLS 2)
Library Holdings: Bk Vols 33,000; Per Subs 10; High Interest/Low Vocabulary Bk Vols 300
Subject Interests: Genealogy, Law
Restriction: Residents only
Mem of Mountain-Valley Library System
Partic in State Libr Network
CALIFORNIA STATE PRISON-SOLANO, 2100 Peabody Rd, PO Box 4000, Vacaville, 95696-4000. SAN 375-5789. Tel: 707-451-0182. *Librn*, Helene Kosher
1998-1999 Mats Exp $37,000
CALIFORNIA SUBSTANCE ABUSE TREATMENT FACILITY & STATE PRISON AT CORCORON, 900 Quebec Ave, PO Box 7100, Corcoran, 93212. SAN 377-8002. Tel: 559-992-7100. FAX: 559-992-7182. *Senior Librn*, Julia Schneider; Staff 5 (MLS 1, Non-MLS 4)
Circ 6,300
1998-1999 Mats Exp $31,000
Library Holdings: Bk Vols 50,000; Bk Titles 40,000; Per Subs 72
Subject Interests: Law ref bks
Automation Activity & Vendor Info: (Circulation) Follett
Partic in Awlnet
Special Services for the Blind - Extensive large print collection; Talking book center
CALIPATRIA STATE PRISON, PO Box 5001, Calipatria, 92233. SAN 371-8085. Tel: 760-348-7000. FAX: 760-348-7155. *Librn*, Waheed Jawadi; *Asst Librn, Tech Servs*, Amidio Arteaga; *Tech Servs*, Kathy Rasky; *Asst Librn, Tech Servs*, Maria Davidosky
1998-1999 Mats Exp $27,000
CENTINELA STATE PRISON, 2302 Brown Rd, PO Box 731, Imperial, 92251-0731. SAN 375-5827. Tel: 760-337-7900. FAX: 760-337-7633. *Librn*, Rosa Pitones; *Asst Librn, Tech Servs*, Laura Hopkins; *Asst Librn, Tech Servs*, Patricia D Robb; *Asst Librn, Tech Servs*, Mark Selay; *Asst Librn, Tech Servs*, Tiffany Torrez
1998-1999 Mats Exp $30,000
CENTRAL CALIFORNIA WOMEN'S FACILITY, 23377 Rd 22, PO Box 1501, Chowchilla, 93610-1501. SAN 371-8093. Tel: 209-665-5531. *Librn*, Phil Renteria; *Tech Servs*, Dawn Duxbury
1998-1999 Mats Exp $24,000
CHUCKAWALLA VALLEY STATE PRISON, 19025 Wiley's Well Rd, PO Box 2289, Blythe, 92226. SAN 371-8107. Tel: 760-922-5300. *Librn*, Florita G Lariba; *Asst Librn, Tech Servs*, Donna Teskey; *Asst Librn, Tech Servs*, Lois Coulter; *Asst Librn, Tech Servs*, Betty Chavez; *Asst Librn, Tech Servs*, Reyna Jimenez; *Asst Librn, Tech Servs*, Timothy June
1998-1999 Mats Exp $24,000
CORRECTIONAL TRAINING FACILITY, Hwy 101 N, PO Box 686, Soledad, 93960. SAN 301-6137. Tel: 408-678-3951. *Librn*, Crystal Bailey; *Librn*, Kara Schmidt; *Librn*, Julie Stenner; *Librn*, Gerry Vassallo
1998-1999 Mats Exp $47,000
FOLSOM STATE PRISON, Prison Rd, PO Box 71, Represa, 95671. SAN 371-8077. Tel: 916-985-2561. *Librn*, Robert Morris; *Librn*, Nina Jensen; *Librn*, Simon Fuller
1998-1999 Mats Exp $26,000
HIGH DESERT STATE PRISON, 475-750 Rice Canyon Rd, Susanville, 96130. SAN 375-5835. Tel: 530-251-5100. FAX: 530-251-5003. *Librn*, Iris Ruiz; *Asst Librn, Tech Servs*, Barbara Hamilton; *Asst Librn, Tech Servs*, John Gamble; *Asst Librn, Tech Servs*, Valerie Brazil
1998-1999 Mats Exp $26,000
IRONWOOD STATE PRISON, PO Box 2229, Blythe, 92226. SAN 375-5843. Tel: 760-921-3000. *Librn*, Brenda Scott; *Asst Librn, Tech Servs*, Art Lariba; *Asst Librn, Tech Servs*, Cindy Sanford; *Asst Librn, Tech Servs*, Emily Rutherford; *Asst Librn, Tech Servs*, Micky Miller
1998-1999 Mats Exp $29,000
MULE CREEK STATE PRISON, 4001 Hwy 104, PO Box 409099, Ione, 95640. SAN 371-8115. Tel: 209-274-4911, Ext 6510. FAX: 209-274-5904. *Senior Librn*, Leon Robinson; *Tech Servs*, Maxine Cova; *Tech Servs*, Janet Varcoe; Tel: 209-274-4911, Ext 6510; Staff 4 (MLS 1, Non-MLS 3)
1998-1999 Mats Exp $24,000
Library Holdings: Bk Titles 60,000; Per Subs 15
NORTH KERN STATE PRISON, 2737 W Cecil Ave, PO Box 567, Delano, 93216-0567. SAN 375-5851. Tel: 661-721-2345, Ext 7610. FAX: 661-721-6224. *Dir*, Ken Clark; *Senior Librn*, Lilly Brook; *Tech Servs*, David Amaro; *Tech Servs*, Denise Carr; *Tech Servs*, Marylove McMullen; *Tech Servs*, Della Picklesimer
Founded 1993
Jul 2000-Jun 2001 Income State $31,000. Mats Exp $31,000
Library Holdings: Bk Vols 24,000; Per Subs 22; High Interest/Low Vocabulary Bk Vols 500
Subject Interests: Fed law, State law
Automation Activity & Vendor Info: (Acquisitions) Follett
Function: For research purposes
Mem of San Joaquin Valley Library System
Special Services for the Blind - Cassette bks; Optelek 20/20 video

magnification system
NORTHERN CALIFORNIA WOMEN'S FACILITY, 7150 E Arch Rd, PO Box 213006, Stockton, 95213-9006. SAN 371-8123. Tel: 209-943-1600. *Librn*, Gautam Sarkar
1998-1999 Mats Exp $6,000
PELICAN BAY STATE PRISON, 5905 Lake Earl Dr, PO Box 7000, Crescent City, 95532-7000. SAN 371-8131. Tel: 707-465-1000. *Librn*, Tisa Jewell; *Asst Librn, Tech Servs*, Helen Griffin; *Asst Librn, Tech Servs*, Richard Miles
1998-1999 Mats Exp $24,000
PLEASANT VALLEY STATE PRISON, 24863 W Jayne Ave, Coalinga, 93210. (Mail add: PO Box 8500, Coalinga, 93210-8500), Tel: 559-935-4900, Ext 6565. FAX: 209-935-7093. *Senior Librn*, Harold Overstreet; *Librn*, Pauline Castillo; Tel: 559-935-7090; *Librn*, Roger Kavorkian; Fax: 559-935-7089; *Asst Librn, Tech Servs*, Beverly Russell; Fax: 559-935-4991; *Asst Librn, Tech Servs*, Delia Rios; Fax: 539-935-7094
Jul 1998-Jun 1999 Mats Exp $30,000
Library Holdings: Bk Titles 32,466; Per Subs 55
Special Services for the Blind - Arkenstone, a computer system for the visually handicapped
RICHARD J DONOVAN CORRECTIONAL FACILITY AT ROCK MOUNTAIN, 480 Alta Rd, San Diego, 92179. SAN 371-814X. Tel: 619-661-6500. FAX: 619-661-6253. *Senior Librn*, Anita Peterson; Staff 4 (MLS 1, Non-MLS 3)
1998-1999 Mats Exp $31,000
Library Holdings: Bk Titles 40,000; Per Subs 30
Restriction: Not open to public
Mem of Serra Cooperative Library System
SALINAS VALLEY STATE PRISON, 31625 Hwy 101, PO Box 1020, Soledad, 93960-1020. SAN 375-5878. Tel: 408-678-5500. FAX: 408-678-5141. *Librn*, John Burk; *Asst Librn, Tech Servs*, Sandra MacDonald; *Asst Librn, Tech Servs*, Steff Duck; *Asst Librn, Tech Servs*, Charlene Pickering; *Asst Librn, Tech Servs*, Tenny Burke
1998-1999 Mats Exp $28,000
SAN QUENTIN STATE PRISON, San Quentin, 94964. SAN 334-8695. Tel: 415-454-1460. *Librn*, Doug Jeffrey
1998-1999 Mats Exp $39,000
SIERRA CONSERVATION CENTER, 5100 O'Byrnes Ferry Rd, PO Box 497, Jamestown, 95327. SAN 300-838X. Tel: 209-984-5291. *Librn*, Dennis F Ward; *Librn*, Christine Long; *Librn*, Ron Rutherford; *Asst Librn, Tech Servs*, Mike Parsons; Staff 18 (MLS 2, Non-MLS 16)
Founded 1966
1999-2000 Mats Exp $36,000
Library Holdings: Bk Vols 39,062; Per Subs 160
Special Collections: Federal & California Law, cases & statutes
Partic in Central Association Of Libraries
VALLEY STATE PRISON FOR WOMEN, 21633 Avenue 24, PO Box 99, Chowchilla, 93610-0099. SAN 375-5886. Tel: 209-665-6100. FAX: 209-665-6113. *Librn*, Jean Leonard; *Asst Librn, Tech Servs*, Lucy Babb; *Asst Librn, Tech Servs*, Olga Del Torro
1998-1999 Mats Exp $22,000
WASCO STATE PRISON-RECEPTION CENTER, 701 Scofield Ave, PO Box 8800, Wasco, 93280. SAN 371-8158. Tel: 805-758-8400. *Librn*, Norman Olsen; *Asst Librn, Tech Servs*, Lupe Armendariz; *Asst Librn, Tech Servs*, Robin Tinsley
1998-1999 Mats Exp $37,000

G CALIFORNIA DEPARTMENT OF JUSTICE, Division of Law Enforcement Library Services, 4949 Broadway, Rm A-107, 95820. SAN 371-6554. Tel: 916-227-3575. FAX: 916-454-5433. *Librn*, Jawadi Waheed; E-Mail: jawadiw@hdcdojnet.state.ca.us; Staff 2 (MLS 1, Non-MLS 1)
Founded 1987
Library Holdings: Bk Titles 8,000; Per Subs 72
Special Collections: California Criminal Statistics
Automation Activity & Vendor Info: (Cataloging) Sydney; (Circulation) Sydney; (OPAC) Sydney; (Serials) Sydney
Restriction: Not open to public
Mem of Mountain-Valley Library System
Partic in Northern California & Nevada Medical Library Group

G CALIFORNIA DEPARTMENT OF PARKS & RECREATION, Northern Service Center Library,* 1725 23rd St, Ste 200, 95816. SAN 374-440X. Tel: 916-323-0975. FAX: 916-324-0888. *Librn*, Rob Ueltzen; *Asst Librn*, Jim Woodward
Library Holdings: Bk Titles 5,000; Per Subs 20
Special Collections: California State Parks (Interpretive Services Coll), rpts & res archives
Restriction: Non-circulating to the public

G CALIFORNIA DEPARTMENT OF PESTICIDE REGULATION LIBRARY, 1001 I St, 95814. (Mail add: PO Box 4015, 95812-4015), SAN 372-6487. Tel: 916-324-3548. FAX: 916-324-1619. E-Mail: librarydesk@cdpr.ca.gov. *Librn*, Chizuko Kawamoto; Tel: 916-324-3556, Fax: 916-324-1619, E-Mail: ckawamoto@cdpr.ca.gov; Staff 7 (MLS 1, Non-MLS 6)
Founded 1981
Library Holdings: Bk Vols 58,000; Bk Titles 4,500; Per Subs 157
Subject Interests: Pesticides
Automation Activity & Vendor Info: (Acquisitions) Inmagic, Inc.; (Cataloging) Inmagic, Inc.; (Serials) Inmagic, Inc.

S CALIFORNIA ENERGY COMMISSION LIBRARY,* 1516 Ninth St, MS10, 95814-5512. SAN 320-5754. Tel: 916-654-4292. FAX: 916-446-5218. Web Site: www.energy.ca.gov. *Librn*, Diana Fay Watkins; E-Mail: dwatkins@energy.state.ca.us
Library Holdings: Bk Vols 18,000; Per Subs 275
Partic in Dialog Corporation; OCLC Online Computer Library Center, Inc

S CALIFORNIA ENVIRONMENTAL PROTECTION AGENCY PUBLIC LIBRARY, (Formerly California Air Resources Board Library), 1001 I St, PO Box 2815, 95812-2815. SAN 320-1627. Tel: 916-323-8377. FAX: 916-322-4357. E-Mail: medwards@arb.ca.gov. Web Site: www.arb.ca.gov/db/library/libsrch.htm. *Librn*, Mark T Edwards; Staff 2 (MLS 1, Non-MLS 1)
Founded 1976
Library Holdings: Bk Titles 10,500; Per Subs 600
Subject Interests: Air pollution
Special Collections: Air Pollution Technical Information Center, rpts & micro

S CALIFORNIA HIGHWAY PATROL, Headquarters Library, 2555 First Ave Rm 130, 95818. SAN 320-5762. Tel: 916-657-7220. FAX: 916-657-7252. *Librn*, Lucille Morgan
Library Holdings: Bk Vols 2,500; Per Subs 132
Special Collections: Codes, Federal Register, Reports & Studies

S CALIFORNIA INSTITUTE OF PUBLIC AFFAIRS LIBRARY, 517 19th St, 95818. (Mail add: PO Box 189040, 95818-9040), SAN 300-6735. Tel: 916-442-2472. FAX: 916-442-2478. Web Site: www.cipahq.org. *Dir*, Thaddeus C Trzyna; Staff 1 (Non-MLS 1)
Founded 1969
Library Holdings: Bk Titles 2,500; Per Subs 200
Subject Interests: California, Environ concerns
Publications: Numerous directories & bibliog
Restriction: Staff use only
Partic in Honnold Libr of Claremont Cols

§G CALIFORNIA INTEGRATED WASTE MANAGEMENT BOARD LIBRARY, 1001 I St, 95814. (Mail add: PO Box 4025, 95812-4025), Tel: 916-341-6000. FAX: 916-322-7060. Web Site: www.ciwmb.ca.gov/library/. *Senior Librn*, Donna Khalili; Tel: 916-341-6197
Jul 1999-Jun 2000 Income $43,000
Library Holdings: Bk Vols 8,000; Per Subs 117
Subject Interests: Recycling, Technology, Waste mgt
Automation Activity & Vendor Info: (Cataloging) EOS; (Circulation) EOS; (Serials) EOS
Restriction: In-house use for visitors, Open to public for reference only
Open Mon-Fri 8-12 & 1-4

G CALIFORNIA REAL ESTATE SERVICES DIVISION PROFESSIONAL SERVICES, Design Services Quality Control Library, 1102 Q St, Ste 4000, 95814. SAN 333-9939. Tel: 916-445-5327. FAX: 916-322-4064. *Librn*, Donna M Brakowiecki
Library Holdings: Bk Vols 5,736; Bk Titles 5,000; Per Subs 30
Special Collections: California Code of Regulations; Deerings Annotated Code; ICBO Research Reports; Sweet's Building Design File
Restriction: Staff use only
Open Mon-Fri 8am-5pm

G CALIFORNIA STATE ARCHIVES,* 1020 O St, 95814. SAN 326-5706. Tel: 916-653-7715. Reference FAX: 916-653-7363. E-Mail: archivesweb@ss.ca.gov. Web Site: www.ss.ca.gov. *Dir*, Walter P Gray III; *Ref*, Genevieve Troka; *Tech Servs*, Nancy Zimmelman; Staff 12 (MLS 4, Non-MLS 8)
Founded 1850
Special Collections: California State History & Government
Partic in RLIN
Friends of the Library Group

GL CALIFORNIA STATE BOARD OF EQUALIZATION, Law Library,* 450 N St, 95814. SAN 301-2697. Tel: 916-445-7356. FAX: 916-323-3387. *Librn*, Marilyn Johnson
Library Holdings: Bk Titles 10,000
Special Collections: State Taxation
Restriction: By appointment only

GL CALIFORNIA STATE COURT OF APPEAL, Law Library, 914 Capitol Mall, 95814. (Mail add: 900 N St, Ste 400, 95814), SAN 301-2700. Tel: 916-653-0207. FAX: 916-653-0324. E-Mail: cta3@jps.net. *Librn*, Linda Wallihan
Library Holdings: Bk Vols 25,000; Bk Titles 1,500; Per Subs 50
Special Collections: California Law Coll
Restriction: Staff use only

§G CALIFORNIA STATE DEPARTMENT OF FOOD & AGRICULTURE, Plant Industry Div Library, 3294 Meadowview Rd, 95832-1448. Tel: 916-262-1157. FAX: 916-262-1191. Web Site: www.cdfa.ca.gov. *Senior Librn*,

Khiet D Le
Library Holdings: Bk Vols 25,000
Restriction: Open to government employees only

§G CALIFORNIA STATE DEPARTMENT OF HOUSING & COMMUNITY DEVELOPMENT, Housing Resource Center, 1800 Third St, Rm 430, 95814. (Mail add: PO Box 952055, 94252-2055), Tel: 916-322-9648. FAX: 916-327-2643. Web Site: www.hcd.ca.gov/. *Coordr*, Rosalie Robison
Library Holdings: Bk Vols 638; Per Subs 333
Restriction: Open to others by appointment

§G CALIFORNIA STATE DEPARTMENT OF MOTOR VEHICLES, Research Library, 2415 First Ave, 6th flr, MS F-126, 95818. Tel: 916-657-5805. FAX: 916-657-8589. Web Site: www.dmv.ca.gov. *Tech Servs*, Douglas Luong; E-Mail: dluong@dmv.ca.gov
Library Holdings: Bk Vols 2,000
Restriction: Staff use only

CALIFORNIA STATE DEPARTMENT OF TRANSPORTATION
GL LAW LIBRARY, 1120 N St, PO Box 1438, MS 57, 95812-1438. SAN 333-9998. Tel: 916-654-2630, Ext 79. FAX: 916-654-6128. *Librn*, Lorna J Flesher; Staff 2 (MLS 1, Non-MLS 1)
Library Holdings: Bk Vols 15,000; Per Subs 179
Subject Interests: Environmental law
Restriction: Not open to public
Partic in Westlaw

L CALIFORNIA STATE DEPARTMENT OF WATER RESOURCES, Law Library, 1416 Ninth St, Rm 1118-13, 95814. (Mail add: PO Box 942836, 94236-0001), SAN 371-5590. Tel: 916-653-8001. FAX: 916-653-0952. *Librn*, Mary Ann Parker; E-Mail: mparker@water.ca.gov; Staff 2 (MLS 1, Non-MLS 1)
Founded 1966
Library Holdings: Bk Vols 20,000; Per Subs 30
Subject Interests: Law
Restriction: Staff use only

G CALIFORNIA STATE EMPLOYMENT DEVELOPMENT DEPARTMENT, Labor Market Information Division Library, Bldg 1100, 7000 Franklin Blvd, 95823-1859. SAN 372-6118. Tel: 916-262-2162. FAX: 916-262-2443. E-Mail: lmid.webmaster@edd.ca.gov. Web Site: www.calmis.ca.gov.
Library Holdings: Bk Vols 3,100; Per Subs 2,000
Special Collections: Labor Market Information; Unemployment Insurance
Automation Activity & Vendor Info: (Acquisitions) CASPR; (Cataloging) CASPR; (Circulation) CASPR; (Serials) CASPR
Publications: Labor Market Information Publications Directory
Restriction: Not open to public, Open to government employees only
Partic in Mountain Valley Libr Syst

GL CALIFORNIA STATE LEGISLATIVE COUNSEL, Law Library, 925 L St, Lower Level, 95814-3772. SAN 301-2727. Tel: 916-445-2609. Web Site: www.leginfo.ca.gov. *Librn*, Linda Heatherly; E-Mail: lheather@lc.ca.gov; Staff 11 (MLS 1, Non-MLS 10)
Founded 1951
Library Holdings: Bk Vols 45,000; Per Subs 152
Subject Interests: Legislation
Special Collections: Legal Coll
Restriction: Staff use only

P CALIFORNIA STATE LIBRARY, Library & Courts Bldg No 1, 914 Capitol Mall, 95814. (Mail add: PO Box 942837, 94237-0001), SAN 334-0058. Tel: 916-654-0183. Interlibrary Loan Service Tel: 916-654-0206. Reference Tel: 916-654-0261. TDD: 916-653-0692. FAX: 916-654-0241. E-Mail: cslsirc@library.ca.gov. Web Site: www.library.ca.gov/. *State Librn*, Dr Kevin Starr; *Info Tech*, Kathy Hudson; Staff 83 (MLS 63, Non-MLS 20)
Founded 1850. Pop 33,000,000
Jul 1999-Jun 2000 Income (Main Library and Branch Library) $23,274,951, State $20,274,951, Federal $3,000,000. Mats Exp $2,290,275. Sal $10,291,972
Library Holdings: Bk Vols 768,808; Per Subs 9,641
Subject Interests: Agriculture, California, Education, Genealogy, Government publications, History, Law
Automation Activity & Vendor Info: (Acquisitions) DRA; (Cataloging) DRA; (Circulation) DRA; (OPAC) DRA; (Serials) DRA
Publications: California Library Directory; California Library Statistics; California State Publications
Partic in Nat Libr of Med
Open Mon-Fri 9:30-4
Friends of the Library Group
Branches: 1
BRAILLE & TALKING BOOK LIBRARY, 900 N St, 95814. (Mail add: PO Box 942837, 94237-0001), Tel: 916-654-0640. Toll Free Tel: 800-952-5666. FAX: 916-654-1119. Web Site: www.library.ca.gov. *In Charge*, Donine Hedrick
Friends of the Library Group

S CALIFORNIA STATE RAILROAD MUSEUM LIBRARY, 111 I St, 95814. SAN 321-6470. Tel: 916-323-8073. FAX: 916-327-5655. E-Mail: csrmlibrary@csrmf.org. Web Site: www.csrmf.org. *Senior Librn*, Ellen Halteman; *Curator*, Stephen Drew; Tel: 916-323-8075, E-Mail: sedrew@cwo.com; *Archivist*, Kathryn Jigursky; Tel: 916-322-0375; Staff 3 (MLS 2, Non-MLS 1)
Founded 1981
Library Holdings: Bk Vols 10,000; Per Subs 80
Special Collections: Corporate Records (Central Pacific, Southern Pacific & Western Pacific Railroads), mss; Correspondence & Business Records (Collis P Huntington Papers, 1856-1901, on micro); Drawings & Specifications (Lima Locomotive Works); Railroad Equipment (Pullman Company), glass plate negatives; Railroad History (Gerald M Best, Grahame H Hardy, Gilbert H Kneiss, Stanley F Merritt, Louis L Stein Jr Coll), bks, mss, artifacts, ephemera; Railroad History (Railway & Locomotive Historical Society), bks, mss, artifacts; Railroad History, photog & negatives; Specifications (Baldwin Locomotive Works Engine Specification Books, 1869-1938, on micro)
Automation Activity & Vendor Info: (Cataloging) Inmagic, Inc.; (OPAC) Inmagic, Inc.
Database Vendor: OCLC - First Search
Publications: Pullman Company Negative Collection Guide; Research & Restoration Reports for CSRM Locomotive & Cars
Restriction: Open to public for reference only
Reading room open Tues-Sat 1-5

S CALIFORNIA STATE RESOURCES AGENCY LIBRARY,* 1416 Ninth St, Rm 117, 95814. SAN 301-2743. Tel: 916-653-2225. FAX: 916-653-1856.
Founded 1927
Library Holdings: Bk Vols 32,000; Bk Titles 30,000; Per Subs 400
Subject Interests: Conservation, Fish, Forestry, Natural resources, Water resources, Wildlife

C CALIFORNIA STATE UNIVERSITY, SACRAMENTO LIBRARY, 2000 State University Dr E, 95819-6039. SAN 301-2751. Tel: 916-278-5679. Interlibrary Loan Service Tel: 916-278-6395. TDD: 916-278-5679. FAX: 916-278-5917. Interlibrary Loan Service FAX: 916-278-7089. Web Site: www.csus.edu/csuslibr. *Dean of Libr*, Patricia Larsen; E-Mail: plarsen@csus.edu; *ILL*, Kathyrn King; E-Mail: kathyking@csus.edu; *Coll Develop, Tech Servs*, Tamara Frost Trujillo; Tel: 916-278-7508, E-Mail: tftrujillo@csus.edu; *Acq*, Jennifer Ware; Tel: 916-278-7223, E-Mail: jdware@csus.edu; *Publ Servs*, Fred Batt; Tel: 916-278-5657, E-Mail: fredbatt@csus.edu; *Circ*, Rhonda Rios-Kravitz; Tel: 916-278-5477, E-Mail: rrioskravitz@csus.edu; *Doc*, Ben Amata; Tel: 916-278-5672, E-Mail: bamata@csus.edu; *Bibliog Instr*, Linda Goff; Tel: 916-278-5981, E-Mail: ljgoff@csus.edu; Staff 26 (MLS 24, Non-MLS 2)
Founded 1947. Enrl 19,159; Fac 1,134; Highest Degree: Master
Jul 1999-Jun 2000 Income $6,605,269, State $6,456,533, Federal $103,679, Locally Generated Income $24,057, Other $21,000. Mats Exp $1,975,838, Books $674,458, Per/Ser (Incl. Access Fees) $903,394, Presv $40,000, Micro $94,141, AV Equip $2,499, Other Print Mats $498, Electronic Ref Mat (Incl. Access Fees) $260,848. Sal $4,284,504 (Prof $1,748,817)
Library Holdings: Bk Vols 1,175,617; Bk Titles 770,779; Per Subs 4,040
Subject Interests: Education, Humanities, Social sciences and issues, Technology
Special Collections: Archives & Special Coll; Congressman John Moss Papers; Dissent & Social Change Coll; Florin Japanese-American Citizens League Oral History Project; Japanese American Archival Coll
Database Vendor: Innovative Interfaces INN - View
Mem of Mountain-Valley Library System
Special Services for the Deaf - TDD
Friends of the Library Group

S CALIFORNIA TAXPAYERS ASSOCIATION LIBRARY,* 215 K St No 1250, 95814. SAN 301-276X. Tel: 916-441-0490. FAX: 916-441-1619. Web Site: www.calpax.org. *Pres*, Larry McCarthy
Library Holdings: Bk Vols 2,000; Per Subs 30

GL CALIFORNIA WATER RESOURCES CONTROL BOARD, Law Library,* 901 P St, PO Box 100, 95812. SAN 301-2662. Tel: 916-657-2412. FAX: 916-653-0428. *Librn*, Keith Blean; E-Mail: kblean@gwgate.swrcb.ca.gov
Library Holdings: Bk Vols 19,500
Subject Interests: Environmental law
Special Collections: California State Water Quality Orders; State Board Resolutions; State Water Rights Orders & Decisions

J CALIFORNIA YOUTH AUTHORITY, Northern Youth Reception Center Clinic Library, Madline Magazina High School,* 3001 Ramona Ave, 95826. SAN 371-9278. Tel: 916-733-2350. FAX: 916-227-1370. *Librn*, Linda Krenzler
Library Holdings: Bk Titles 3,381
Subject Interests: Law
Automation Activity & Vendor Info: (Cataloging) Follett
Special Services for the Deaf - Books on deafness & sign language; High interest/low vocabulary books
Open Mon-Fri 8-5

J COSUMNES RIVER COLLEGE, Learning Resources Center, 8401 Center Pkwy, 95823-5799. SAN 301-2778. Tel: 916-691-7257. Interlibrary Loan Service Tel: 916-691-7266. Circulation Tel: 916-691-7266. Reference Tel: 916-691-7265. FAX: 916-691-7349. Web Site: wserver.crc.losrios.cc.ca.us/library/index.htm. *Mgr*, Stephen McGloughlin; E-Mail: mcglous@crs.losrios.cc.ca.us; *Automation Syst Coordr, Tech Servs*, Rosalie Amer; Tel: 916-691-7249, E-Mail: ammer@crc.losrios.cc.ca.us; *Bibliog Instr, Publ Servs*, Sandy Marsh; Tel: 916-691-7340, E-Mail: marshs@crc.losrios.cc.ca.us; *Bibliog Instr, Publ Servs*, Terri Clark; Tel: 916-691-7621, E-Mail: clarkt@crc.losrios.cc.c.us; Staff 14 (MLS 3, Non-MLS 11)
Founded 1970. Enrl 9,923; Fac 670; Highest Degree: Associate
Jul 1999-Jun 2000 Income $743,869. Mats Exp $115,944, Books $64,617, Per/Ser (Incl. Access Fees) $11,710, Presv $500, Micro $4,782, AV Equip $3,743, Electronic Ref Mat (Incl. Access Fees) $8,420. Sal $607,922 (Prof $226,149)
Library Holdings: Bk Vols 65,154; Bk Titles 57,314; Per Subs 380; High Interest/Low Vocabulary Bk Vols 300; Bks on Deafness & Sign Lang 25
Special Collections: California History, examples of fine printing; Campus Oral History
Automation Activity & Vendor Info: (Acquisitions) epixtech, inc.; (Cataloging) epixtech, inc.; (Circulation) epixtech, inc.; (Course Reserve) epixtech, inc.; (OPAC) epixtech, inc.; (Serials) epixtech, inc.
Database Vendor: OCLC - First Search
Publications: Library Lines & Media Center News
Mem of Mountain-Valley Library System
Partic in Coop Libr Agency for Syst & Servs; MVLS; OCLC Online Computer Library Center, Inc
Special Services for the Blind - Braille printer & software
Open Mon-Thurs 7:30-9, Fri 7:30-4:30 & Sat 10

S DEPARTMENT OF CONSERVATION, California Division of Mines & Geology Library, 801 K St, Mail Stop 14-34, 95814-3532. SAN 323-553X. Tel: 916-327-1850. FAX: 916-327-1853. E-Mail: dmglib@consrv.ca.gov. *Librn*, Rosemary Guerin-Place
Library Holdings: Bk Vols 30,000; Per Subs 130
Special Collections: California Fieldtrip Guidebooks; Historic Mine Files & Maps; United States Bureau of Mines Publications
Automation Activity & Vendor Info: (Acquisitions) Inmagic, Inc.; (Cataloging) Inmagic, Inc.; (Circulation) Inmagic, Inc.; (Serials) Inmagic, Inc.
Database Vendor: OCLC - First Search
Restriction: Open to public for reference only

G DEPARTMENT OF TOXIC SUBSTANCES CONTROL, Technical Reference Library,* PO Box 806, 95812-0806. SAN 372-3038. Tel: 916-324-5898. FAX: 916-324-1788. *In Charge*, Bridget Bonilla
Library Holdings: Bk Vols 7,000

S JONES & STOKES ASSOCIATES LIBRARY, 2600 V St, 95818-1914. SAN 373-0352. Tel: 916-737-3000. FAX: 916-737-3030. Web Site: www.jsanet.com. *In Charge*, Andrea Morais; E-Mail: amorais@jsanet.com
Library Holdings: Bk Vols 18,500; Per Subs 500
Subject Interests: Water resources
Special Collections: JSA Reports
Open Tues & Thurs 8-12

M KAISER PERMANENTE MEDICAL CENTER, Health Sciences Library,* 2025 Morse Ave, 95825. SAN 324-508X. Tel: 916-973-6944. FAX: 916-973-6999. *Librn*, Michael Bennett; *Asst Librn*, Marlene Swaim; Staff 2 (MLS 1, Non-MLS 1)
Founded 1965
Jan 1999-Dec 1999 Income $225,000. Mats Exp $100,000, Books $15,000, Per/Ser (Incl. Access Fees) $85,000. Sal $75,000 (Prof $25,000)
Library Holdings: Bk Titles 3,500; Per Subs 305
Subject Interests: Clinical medicine
Partic in Nat Libr of Med

S WILLIAMS KUEBELBECK & ASSOCIATES INC LIBRARY,* 1337 Howe Ave, Ste 104, 95825-3314. SAN 323-4436. Tel: 916-564-0600. FAX: 916-564-7186. *Librn*, Bobbi Gallagher
Library Holdings: Bk Titles 1,800; Per Subs 150

S MEN'S RIGHTS INC, Reading Center, PO Box 163180, 95816. SAN 375-1589. Tel: 916-484-7333. FAX: 916-484-7333. *Exec Dir*, Fredric Hayward
Founded 1977
Library Holdings: Bk Vols 250; Bk Titles 250

P MOUNTAIN-VALLEY LIBRARY SYSTEM, 828 I St, Ste 524, 95814-2508. SAN 301-2808. Tel: 916-264-2722. FAX: 916-441-3425. E-Mail: mvls@ns.net. Web Site: www.mvls.lib.ca.us. *Coordr*, Gerald Maginnity; *ILL, Ref*, Judith Lane; Staff 6 (MLS 3, Non-MLS 3)
Founded 1969. Pop 1,900,000
Jul 2000-Jun 2001 Income $800,000. Sal $332,000 (Prof $200,000)
Member Libraries: Alpine County Free Library; American River College Library; Auburn-Placer County Library; California Department of Corrections Library System; California Department Of Justice; California State University, Sacramento Library; Cosumnes River College; Dixon Unified School District; El Dorado County Library; Folsom Public Library; Lake Tahoe Community College; Lincoln Public Library; Mono County Free Library System-Northern Region; Nevada County Library; Roseville Public Library; Sacramento County Law Library; Sacramento Public Library; Sutter County Free Library; Sutter Resource; University Of California, Davis; University of California, Davis; Woodland Public Library; Yolo County Library; Yuba Community College; Yuba County Library

S SACRAMENTO ARCHIVES & MUSEUM COLLECTION CENTER LIBRARY, 551 Sequoia Pacific Blvd, 95814-0229. SAN 320-6009. Tel: 916-264-7072. FAX: 916-264-7582. E-Mail: samcc@cityofsacramento.org. Web Site: www.sacramentities/history/. *Mgr*, James E Henley; *Archivist*, Patricia J Johnson; E-Mail: pjohnson@cityofsacramento.org; *Archivist*, Annastasia S Wolfe; E-Mail: swolfe@cityofsacramento.org
Founded 1954
Library Holdings: Bk Vols 5,000
Subject Interests: Local history
Special Collections: Entire repository consists of special collections relating to Sacramento region. Collections are from local government agencies as well as from private families, organization, and businesses.
Restriction: Non-circulating to the public
Function: Archival collection

S SACRAMENTO AREA COUNCIL OF GOVERNMENTS LIBRARY, 3000 S St Ste 300, 95816. SAN 327-1684. Tel: 916-457-2264. FAX: 916-457-3299. E-Mail: data_center@sacog.org. Web Site: www.sacog.org. *Info Specialist, Librn*, Florene Kunder; Staff 1 (Non-MLS 1)
Library Holdings: Bk Titles 4,168; Per Subs 85
Subject Interests: Planning
Special Collections: Census data
Publications: New Library Acquisitions (monthly); SACOG Publications (irregular)
Open Mon-Fri 8-12 & 1-4

J SACRAMENTO CITY COLLEGE, Learning Resources Division Library,* 3835 Freeport Blvd, 95822. SAN 301-2824. Tel: 916-558-2253. FAX: 916-558-2114. *Dean*, Kirk Wiecking; *Acq*, Kathy Campbell
Founded 1916. Enrl 18,000
Library Holdings: Bk Vols 68,894; Per Subs 410
Partic in OCLC Online Computer Library Center, Inc
Friends of the Library Group

GL SACRAMENTO COUNTY LAW LIBRARY,* Sacramento County Courthouse, 720 Ninth St, Rm 16, 95814-1397. SAN 301-2832. Tel: 916-874-6011. FAX: 916-874-5691. *Dir*, Shirley H David; *Tech Servs*, Tana E Smith; *Publ Servs*, Ruth Nunez-Schaldach; Staff 6 (MLS 6)
Subject Interests: Law
Special Collections: Municipal Court Judges (1991-present); Portraits of Sacramento County Superior Court Judges (1850-present)
Automation Activity & Vendor Info: (Acquisitions) epixtech, inc.; (Serials) epixtech, inc.
Publications: Annual Report
Mem of Mountain-Valley Library System
Partic in RLIN

P SACRAMENTO PUBLIC LIBRARY,* 828 I St, 95814-2589. SAN 334-0112. Tel: 916-264-2700, 916-264-2858. Reference Tel: 916-264-2920. FAX: 916-264-2755. Web Site: www.saclib.org. *Dir*, Richard M Killian; *Assoc Dir*, Janet Larson; *Cat*, George Newton; *Coll Develop*, Wally Hoffsis; Staff 208 (MLS 87, Non-MLS 121)
Founded 1857. Pop 1,114,140
Jul 1998-Jun 1999 Income $22,913,650, State $639,000, City $9,559,260, County $9,001,271, Locally Generated Income $1,186,228, Other $1,900,000. Mats Exp $3,241,000, Books $2,399,000, Per/Ser (Incl. Access Fees) $229,000, Micro $46,000, Other Print Mats $250,000, Manuscripts & Archives $3,000. Sal $11,803,911 (Prof $4,796,767)
Library Holdings: Bk Vols 1,800,000
Subject Interests: Art and architecture, Business and management, Genealogy, Music
Special Collections: Art; Californiana; City & County; City Planning & Urban Development; Genealogical; History of Printing
Publications: Library News
Mem of Mountain-Valley Library System
Special Services for the Deaf - TDD
Friends of the Library Group
Branches: 24
ARCADE COMMUNITY, 2443 Marconi Ave, 95821. SAN 334-0147. Tel: 916-264-2700. FAX: 916-575-2163. Web Site: www.saclib.org. *Librn*, Tanis Groth
Library Holdings: Bk Titles 61,704
Friends of the Library Group
ARDEN, 891 Watt Ave, 95864. SAN 334-0171. Tel: 916-264-2700. FAX: 916-575-2173. Web Site: www.saclib.org. *Librn*, Glenda Adams
Library Holdings: Bk Titles 87,000
Friends of the Library Group
CARMICHAEL REGIONAL, 5605 Marconi Ave, Carmichael, 95608. SAN 334-0201. Tel: 916-264-2700. FAX: 916-575-2155. Web Site: www.saclib.org. *Librn*, Ruth Craft
Library Holdings: Bk Titles 121,000
Special Collections: California

Friends of the Library Group
CENTRAL, 828 I St, 95814. SAN 334-0236. Tel: 916-264-2700. FAX: 916-264-2854. Web Site: www.saclib.org. *Librn*, Judy Eitzen
Library Holdings: Bk Titles 240,000
Subject Interests: Art, Local history, Music
Special Collections: Sacramento Authors and Printing History
COLONIAL HEIGHTS COMMUNITY, 4799 Stockton Blvd, 95820. SAN 329-5958. Tel: 916-264-2700. FAX: 916-277-2191. Web Site: www.saclib.org. *Librn*, Phyllis Martin
Library Holdings: Bk Titles 62,000
Friends of the Library Group
BELLE COOLEDGE BRANCH, 5600 S Land Park Dr, 95822. SAN 334-0260. Tel: 916-264-2700. FAX: 916-433-2033. Web Site: www.saclib.org. *Librn*, Dave Rater
Library Holdings: Bk Titles 65,000
Friends of the Library Group
COURTLAND BRANCH, PO Box 536, Courtland, 95615. SAN 374-714X. Tel: 916-264-2700. Web Site: www.saclib.org.
Friends of the Library Group
DEL PASO HEIGHTS, 920 Grand Ave, 95838. SAN 334-0325. Tel: 916-264-2700. FAX: 916-566-2146. Web Site: www.saclib.org. *Tech Servs*, Kathryn Howard
Library Holdings: Bk Titles 27,000
Friends of the Library Group
E K MCCLATCHY BRANCH, 2112 22nd St, 95818. SAN 334-0627. Tel: 916-264-2700. Web Site: www.saclib.org. *Tech Servs*, JoAnn Severson
Library Holdings: Bk Titles 19,000
Friends of the Library Group
ELK GROVE BRANCH, 8962 Elk Grove Blvd, Elk Grove, 95624. SAN 334-035X. Tel: 916-264-2700. FAX: 916-685-5266. Web Site: www.saclib.org. *Librn*, Pat Sandefur
Library Holdings: Bk Titles 52,000
Friends of the Library Group
FAIR OAKS BRANCH, 11601 Fair Oaks Blvd, Fair Oaks, 95628. SAN 334-0384. Tel: 916-264-2700. FAX: 916-867-2203. Web Site: www.saclib.org. *Librn*, Frances Atkins
Library Holdings: Bk Titles 65,000
Friends of the Library Group
GALT BRANCH, 1000 Caroline Ave, Galt, 95632. SAN 334-0473. Tel: 209-264-2700. FAX: 209-745-7685. Web Site: www.saclib.org. *Tech Servs*, Sally Faubion
Library Holdings: Bk Titles 22,709
Friends of the Library Group
ISLETON BRANCH, 412 Union St, Isleton, 95641. SAN 374-7158. Tel: 916-264-2700. Web Site: www.saclib.org. *In Charge*, Natalie Beaver
Library Holdings: Bk Titles 14,000
Friends of the Library Group
MARTIN LUTHER KING JR REGIONAL, 7340 24th St Bypass, 95822. SAN 334-0597. Tel: 916-264-2700. FAX: 916-433-2045. Web Site: www.saclib.org. *Librn*, Terry Chekon
Library Holdings: Bk Titles 101,000
Friends of the Library Group
MCKINLEY, 601 Alhambra Blvd, 95816. SAN 334-0651. Tel: 916-264-2700. FAX: 916-264-2872. Web Site: www.saclib.org. *Tech Servs*, Shari Nichelini
Library Holdings: Bk Titles 35,000
Friends of the Library Group
NORTH HIGHLANDS BRANCH, 3601 Plymouth Dr, North Highlands, 95660. SAN 334-0686. Tel: 916-264-2700. FAX: 916-575-2168. Web Site: www.saclib.org. *Librn*, Matthew Hall
Library Holdings: Bk Titles 44,000
Friends of the Library Group
NORTH SACRAMENTO-HAGGINWOOD BRANCH, 2109 Del Paso Blvd, 95815. SAN 334-0716. Tel: 916-264-2700. FAX: 916-566-2128. Web Site: www.saclib.org.
Library Holdings: Bk Titles 33,000
Friends of the Library Group
ORANGEVALE BRANCH, 8820 Greenback Lane, No D, Orangevale, 95662. SAN 374-7166. Tel: 916-264-2700. FAX: 916-986-2079. Web Site: www.saclib.org. *In Charge*, Cindy Cantin
Library Holdings: Bk Titles 16,000
RANCHO CORDOVA COMMUNITY, 9845 Folsom Blvd, 95827. SAN 334-0775. Tel: 916-264-2700. FAX: 916-228-2114. Web Site: www.saclib.org.
Library Holdings: Bk Titles 69,000
Friends of the Library Group
RIO LINDA BRANCH, 902 Oak Lane, Rio Linda, 95673. SAN 334-0805. Tel: 916-264-2700. FAX: 916-566-2140. Web Site: www.saclib.org. *Tech Servs*, Eric Noblet
Library Holdings: Bk Titles 32,000
Friends of the Library Group
SOUTH NATOMAS, 1620 W El Camino Ave, Ste 148, 95833. SAN 374-7174. Tel: 916-264-2700. FAX: 916-566-2135. Web Site: www.saclib.org. *Tech Servs*, Coral Procter
Library Holdings: Bk Titles 14,000
Friends of the Library Group
SOUTHGATE COMMUNITY, 6132 66th Ave, 95823. SAN 334-083X. Tel: 916-264-2700. FAX: 916-433-2038. Web Site: www.saclib.org. *Librn*, Rosemary Aschwanden
Library Holdings: Bk Titles 71,000
Friends of the Library Group
SYLVAN OAKS COMMUNITY, 6700 Auburn Blvd, Citrus Heights, 95621. SAN 334-0864. Tel: 916-264-2700. FAX: 916-867-2213. Web Site: www.saclib.org. *Librn*, Barbara Kerhoulas
Library Holdings: Bk Titles 66,000
Friends of the Library Group
WALNUT GROVE BRANCH, 14177 Market St, PO Box 40, Walnut Grove, 95690. SAN 334-0899. Tel: 916-264-2700. Web Site: www.sna.com/saclib. *Tech Servs*, Ward Hirstein
Founded 1919
Library Holdings: Bk Titles 15,000
Open Mon & Wed 9-12 & 1-4, Tues & Thurs 9-12 & 1-5, Fri 1-5, first Sat of each month 9-12 & 1-5
Friends of the Library Group
Bookmobiles: 2

S SEARCH GROUP, INC LIBRARY,* 7311 Greenhaven Dr Ste 145, 95831. SAN 370-4262. Tel: 916-392-2550. FAX: 916-392-8440. Web Site: www.search.org. *In Charge*, Twyla Cunningham
Library Holdings: Bk Titles 250; Per Subs 24
Subject Interests: Law enforcement

§S SIERRA RESEARCH LIBRARY, 1801 J St, 95814. Tel: 916-444-6666. FAX: 916-444-8373. Web Site: www.sierraresearch.com. *Librn*, Gabriel C McAuliffe; E-Mail: gmcauliffe@sierraresearch.com
Library Holdings: Bk Titles 14,981; Per Subs 12
Restriction: Staff use only

G STATE OF CALIFORNIA OFFICE OF ADMINISTRATIVE LAW LIBRARY, 555 Capitol Mall Ste 1290, 95814. SAN 329-1189. Tel: 916-323-6225. FAX: 916-323-6826. *Librn*, Mike Ibold; Tel: 916-323-8906, E-Mail: mibold@oal.ca.gov; Staff 1 (Non-MLS 1)
Founded 1980
Jul 1999-Jun 2000 Mats Exp $23,070. Sal $42,000
Library Holdings: Bk Vols 9,000; Bk Titles 525; Per Subs 12
Subject Interests: State codes
Special Collections: California Code of Regulations Registers & Notices-original 1945 titles to present
Restriction: Non-circulating

GL STATE PUBLIC DEFENDER, Law Library,* 801 K St, Ste 1100, 95814. SAN 323-9039. Tel: 916-322-0136. FAX: 916-324-9792. *Asst Librn*, Trystan Colston; Staff 3 (MLS 1, Non-MLS 2)
Library Holdings: Bk Vols 25,000
Special Collections: Brief bank, paper
Open Mon-Fri 8-5

UNITED STATES ARMY
A CORPS OF ENGINEERS SACRAMENTO DISTRICT-TECHNICAL INFORMATION CENTER, 1325 J St, 95814-2922. SAN 334-0929. Tel: 916-557-6657. FAX: 916-557-7091. Web Site: lepac1.brodart.com/search/am/. *Librn*, Beatrice Alger; *Tech Servs*, Frances Sweeney
Founded 1945
Library Holdings: Bk Titles 5,500; Per Subs 350
Subject Interests: Engineering, Geology
Publications: Library Bulletin; News & New Books in the District Library
Partic in Fedlink

CM UNIVERSITY OF CALIFORNIA, DAVIS, Medical Center Library, 2252 45th St, 95817. SAN 301-2875. Tel: 916-734-3529. Interlibrary Loan Service Tel: 916-734-3533. FAX: 916-734-7418. E-Mail: libraryref@ucdmc.ucdavis.edu. Web Site: www.lib.ucdavis.edu/hsl/hshome.html. *Head Librn*, Terri L Malmgren; E-Mail: tlmalmgren@ucdavis.edu; Staff 10 (MLS 3, Non-MLS 7)
Founded 1929
Library Holdings: Bk Vols 34,588; Per Subs 606
Subject Interests: Allied health, Bioethics, Birth defects, Medicine, Nursing
Mem of Mountain-Valley Library System
Partic in Dialog Corporation; Docline; Medline; NLM; OCLC Online Computer Library Center, Inc; Pacific SW Regional Med Libr Serv

CL UNIVERSITY OF THE PACIFIC - MCGEORGE SCHOOL OF LAW, Gordon D Schaber Law Library, 3282 Fifth Ave, 95817. SAN 301-2883. Tel: 916-739-7131. Interlibrary Loan Service Tel: 916-739-7164. FAX: 916-739-7273. Web Site: www.mcgeorge.edu.; Staff 8 (MLS 8)
Founded 1924. Enrl 1,300; Fac 85; Highest Degree: Doctorate
Library Holdings: Bk Vols 445,000
Partic in RLIN; Westlaw
Open Sun-Thurs 8am-midnight & Fri-Sat 8am-11pm (school time)

G US BUREAU OF LAND MANAGEMENT-US FISH & WILDLIFE SERVICE, Field Office Interagency Library, 2800 Cottage Way, 95825-1886. SAN 375-636X. Tel: 916-978-4302. FAX: 916-978-4305. *Tech Servs*,

Patricia Arentz
Founded 1992
Library Holdings: Bk Titles 3,500; Per Subs 15
Automation Activity & Vendor Info: (Cataloging) EOS; (Circulation) EOS

G US DEPARTMENT OF THE INTERIOR, BUREAU OF RECLAMATION, Mid-Pacific Regional Library, 2800 Cottage Way, Rm W-1825, 95825-1898. SAN 301-2867. Tel: 916-978-5593. FAX: 916-978-5599. *Regional Librarian*, Stephen Jones; E-Mail: sjones@mp.usbr.gov
Founded 1946
Library Holdings: Bk Vols 21,000; Per Subs 120
Subject Interests: Water resources
Special Collections: Project Histories - Mid-Pacific Region BOR; San Joaquin Valley Drainage Program
Restriction: Not a lending library

L WEINTRAUB, GENSHLEA & SPROUL, Law Library,* 400 Capitol Mall, Ste 1100, 95814. SAN 372-302X. Tel: 916-558-6081. FAX: 916-446-1611. *Librn*, Noami Nagano
Library Holdings: Bk Vols 10,000; Per Subs 50
Special Collections: General Legal

S WESTERN FAIRS ASSOCIATION LIBRARY,* 1776 Tribute Rd Ste 210, 95815-4410. SAN 323-5882. Tel: 916-927-3100. FAX: 916-927-6397. E-Mail: wfa@fairsnet.org. Web Site: www.fairsnet.org. *Exec Dir*, Stephen Chambers
Founded 1936
Special Collections: Oral histories - fairs

S WESTERN HIGHWAY INSTITUTE, Research Library,* 3251 Beacon Blvd, 95691. SAN 328-4913. Tel: 307-577-1225. FAX: 307-577-1716. E-Mail: whi@creative.net. *Librn*, John Paquette
Library Holdings: Bk Vols 5,000; Per Subs 20

SAINT HELENA

P SAINT HELENA PUBLIC LIBRARY, George & Elsie Wood Public Library, 1492 Library Lane, 94574-1143. SAN 301-2891. Tel: 707-963-5244. Interlibrary Loan Service Tel: 707-963-5245. FAX: 707-963-5264. Web Site: www.shpl.org. *Dir*, Clayla Davis; *Ch Servs*, Leslie Stanton; *Publ Servs*, Allie La Centra; Staff 5 (MLS 3, Non-MLS 2)
Founded 1892. Pop 6,225; Circ 187,000
Jul 2000-Jun 2001 Income $817,000, State $90,133, City $696,504. Mats Exp $148,000, Per/Ser (Incl. Access Fees) $10,082, Presv $1,200, Micro $800, AV Equip $7,000, Electronic Ref Mat (Incl. Access Fees) $18,997. Sal $342,506
Library Holdings: Bk Vols 76,217; Per Subs 226
Subject Interests: Wine
Special Collections: Wine & Wine Making (Napa Valley Wine Library), bks, flm, rec, tapes
Automation Activity & Vendor Info: (Circulation) CARL; (OPAC) CARL
Database Vendor: CARL
Publications: Napa Valley Wine Library Report
Mem of North Bay Cooperative Library System
Partic in Snap
Open Sun 1-5, Mon & Wed 12-9, Tues, Thurs & Fri 10-6 & Sat 10-4
Friends of the Library Group

SALINAS

J HARTNELL COLLEGE LIBRARY, 156 Homestead Ave, 93901. SAN 301-2913. Tel: 831-755-6872. FAX: 831-759-6084. Web Site: www.hartnell.cc.ca.us. *Dir*, Gary Hughes; Tel: 831-755-6870, E-Mail: ghughes@hartnell.cc.ca.us; *Tech Servs*, Peggy Mayfield; E-Mail: mayfiel@hartnell.cc.ca.us; Staff 11 (MLS 3, Non-MLS 8)
Founded 1936. Fac 147
Library Holdings: Bk Vols 57,434; Bk Titles 50,334; Per Subs 257
Special Collections: Ornithology (O P Silliman Memorial Library of Natural History), bks, ser
Automation Activity & Vendor Info: (Acquisitions) Endeavor; (Media Booking) Endeavor; (OPAC) Endeavor; (Serials) Endeavor
Database Vendor: Ebsco - EbscoHost, OCLC - First Search, ProQuest
Partic in MOBAC; OCLC Online Computer Library Center, Inc

P MONTEREY COUNTY FREE LIBRARIES,* 26 Central Ave, 93901-2628. SAN 334-0953. Tel: 831-755-5838. FAX: 831-755-5839. E-Mail: mcfl@co.monterey.ca.us. Web Site: www.co.monterey.ca.us. *Dir*, Robert A McElroy; *Mgr, Tech Servs*, Ruth Forsberg; *Ad Servs, Mgr*, Rosellen Brewer; *Mgr*, Marilyn May Kanemura; E-Mail: kanemuram@co.monterey.ca.us; *Mgr, YA Servs*, Chris Mayer; Staff 19 (MLS 14, Non-MLS 5)
Founded 1912. Pop 202,140; Circ 821,183
Jul 1998-Jun 1999 Income $4,007,579. Mats Exp $298,084, Books $258,324, Per/Ser (Incl. Access Fees) $38,960, Micro $800. Sal $2,321,656
Library Holdings: Bk Vols 360,803; Per Subs 655
Special Collections: Californiana
Automation Activity & Vendor Info: (Cataloging) epixtech, inc.; (Circulation) epixtech, inc.; (OPAC) epixtech, inc.
Database Vendor: epixtech, inc.
Publications: Contact (quarterly newsletter)
Mem of Monterey Bay Area Cooperative Library System
Partic in Coop Libr Agency for Syst & Servs; OCLC Online Computer Library Center, Inc
Special Services - Books by Mail service
Friends of the Library Group
Branches: 17
AROMAS BRANCH, Blohm St, PO Box 298, Aromas, 95004. SAN 334-0988. Tel: 831-726-3240. FAX: 831-726-0102. *Mgr*, Jane Ward
Library Holdings: Bk Vols 11,012
Friends of the Library Group
BIG SUR BRANCH, Ripplewood Resort, PO Box 217, Big Sur, 93920. SAN 334-1135. Tel: 831-667-2537. FAX: 831-667-0708.
Library Holdings: Bk Vols 10,061
Friends of the Library Group
BRADLEY BRANCH, Dixie St, PO Box 330, Bradley, 93426. SAN 334-1046. Tel: 805-472-9407. FAX: 805-472-9565. *Mgr*, Darlene Lloyd
Library Holdings: Bk Vols 4,333
BUENA VISTA, 18250 Tara Dr, 93908. SAN 378-0376. Tel: 831-455-9699. FAX: 831-455-0369. *Librn*, Adriana Greenawalt
Library Holdings: Bk Vols 1,887
CARMEL VALLEY BRANCH, 65 W Carmel Valley Rd, Carmel Valley, 93924. SAN 334-1070. Tel: 831-659-2377. FAX: 831-659-0589. *Librn*, Anne Petersen Burk
Library Holdings: Bk Vols 23,103
Friends of the Library Group
CASTROVILLE BRANCH, 11266 Merritt, Castroville, 95012. SAN 334-1100. Tel: 831-633-2829. FAX: 831-633-6315. *Librn*, Shirley Dawon
Library Holdings: Bk Vols 27,706
Friends of the Library Group
GONZALES BRANCH, 851 V Fifth St, Gonzales, 93926. SAN 334-116X. Tel: 831-675-2209. FAX: 831-675-9525. *Librn*, Elizabeth Lopez
Library Holdings: Bk Vols 15,796
GREENFIELD BRANCH, 315 El Camino Real, Greenfield, 93927. SAN 334-1194. Tel: 831-674-2614. FAX: 831-674-2688. *Librn*, Anne Burk
Pop 54,338; Circ 804,102
Library Holdings: Bk Vols 25,960
Friends of the Library Group
KING CITY BRANCH, 402 Broadway, King City, 93930. SAN 370-7946. Tel: 831-385-3677. FAX: 831-385-0918. *Head of Libr*, Liz Cecchi-Ewing
Library Holdings: Bk Vols 27,763
Friends of the Library Group
MARINA BRANCH, 266 Reservation Rd, Marina, 93933. SAN 334-1224. Tel: 831-384-6971. FAX: 831-384-1829.
Library Holdings: Bk Vols 15,485
Friends of the Library Group
PAJARO BRANCH, 29 Bishop St, Pajaro, 95076. SAN 376-9186. Tel: 831-761-2545. FAX: 831-768-7782.
Library Holdings: Bk Vols 6,173
PARKFIELD, 70643 Parkfield-Coalinga Rd, San Miguel, 93451. SAN 334-1283. Tel: 805-463-2347. FAX: 805-463-2347.
Library Holdings: Bk Vols 4,033
PRUNEDALE BRANCE, 17822 Moro Rd, Prunedale, 93907. SAN 334-1313. Tel: 831-663-2292. FAX: 831-663-0203. *Head of Libr*, Reggie Bradford
Library Holdings: Bk Vols 49,782
Friends of the Library Group
SAN ARDO BRANCH, 62350 College St, PO Box 192, San Ardo, 93450. SAN 334-1348. Tel: 831-627-2503. FAX: 831-627-4229. *Mgr*, Joyce Lombardi
Library Holdings: Bk Vols 9,022
Friends of the Library Group
SAN LUCAS BRANCH, 54692 Teresa St, PO Box 2, San Lucas, 93954. SAN 334-1372. Tel: 831-382-4382. FAX: 831-382-4677. *Mgr*, Linda Larson
Library Holdings: Bk Vols 7,509
Friends of the Library Group
SEASIDE BRANCH, 550 Harcourt Ave, Seaside, 93955. SAN 334-1402. Tel: 831-899-2055. FAX: 831-899-2735. Web Site: www.library.monterey.edu/mcfl/se.html. *In Charge*, Myra Kong; E-Mail: libmcfl2@redshift.com; Staff 7 (MLS 3, Non-MLS 4)
Library Holdings: Bk Vols 73,161
Mem of Monterey Bay Area Cooperative Library System
Friends of the Library Group
SOLEDAD BRANCH, 179 Main St, Soledad, 93960. SAN 334-1437. Tel: 831-678-2430. FAX: 831-678-3087. *Librn*, Angie Lopez
Library Holdings: Bk Vols 24,453
Friends of the Library Group
Bookmobiles: 2

GL MONTEREY COUNTY LAW LIBRARY, 100 W Alisal, Ste 144, 93901. SAN 301-293X. Tel: 831-755-5046. FAX: 831-422-9593. E-Mail: mcolawlib@redshift.com. Web Site: fp.redshift.com/mcolawlib. *Librn*, Joseph Wyatt; Staff 1 (Non-MLS 1)
Jul 1999-Jun 2000 Income (Main Library and Branch Library) $200,443, County $500, Other $195,434. Mats Exp Books $118,235. Sal $57,348 (Prof

$35,000)
Library Holdings: Bk Vols 15,984
Special Collections: California Legal
Function: For research purposes
Branches:
MONTEREY BRANCH, Monterey County Court House, 1200 Aguajito Rd, Rm 202, Monterey, 93940. SAN 377-015X. Tel: 831-647-7746. FAX: 831-372-6036. E-Mail: mcolawlib@redshift.com. Web Site: fp.redshift.com/mcolawlib. *Librn*, Joseph Wyatt; *Asst Librn*, Christopher Cobb; Staff 1 (Non-MLS 1)
Library Holdings: Bk Vols 15,653
Function: For research purposes

P SALINAS PUBLIC LIBRARY, John Steinbeck Library, 350 Lincoln Ave, 93901. SAN 334-1496. Tel: 831-758-7311. FAX: 831-758-7336. *Dir*, Julia Orozco; Tel: 831-758-7391; *Mgr*, Jan Neal; Tel: 831-758-7454, E-Mail: nealj@salinas.lib.ca.us; *Tech Servs*, Shannon Lucas; Tel: 831-758-7365; Staff 17 (MLS 8, Non-MLS 9)
Founded 1892. Pop 131,100; Circ 440,000
Jul 2000-Jun 2001 Mats Exp $278,500
Library Holdings: Bk Vols 154,200; Per Subs 400
Subject Interests: Agriculture
Automation Activity & Vendor Info: (Acquisitions) epixtech, inc.; (Cataloging) epixtech, inc.; (Circulation) epixtech, inc.; (OPAC) epixtech, inc.; (Serials) epixtech, inc.
Database Vendor: OCLC - First Search
Function: ILL available, Some telephone reference
Mem of Monterey Bay Area Cooperative Library System
Partic in MOBAC
Friends of the Library Group
Branches: 2
CESAR CHAVEZ LIBRARY, 615 Williams Rd, 93905. SAN 334-1526. Tel: 831-758-7345. FAX: 831-758-9172. E-Mail: cclib@salinas.lib.ca.us. *Branch Mgr*, Patricia Oliverez; Tel: 831-758-7346; Staff 2 (MLS 2)
Pop 52,000; Circ 140,000
Jul 1999-Jun 2000 Mats Exp $48,000
Library Holdings: Bk Vols 55,000; Per Subs 86
Special Collections: Chicano Cultural Resource Center
Automation Activity & Vendor Info: (Acquisitions) epixtech, inc.; (Cataloging) epixtech, inc.; (Circulation) epixtech, inc.; (OPAC) epixtech, inc.; (Serials) epixtech, inc.
Partic in MOBAC
Friends of the Library Group
EL GABILAN, 1400 N Main St, 93906. SAN 334-1550. Tel: 831-758-7302. FAX: 831-442-0817. E-Mail: eglib@salinas.lib.ca.us. *Branch Mgr*, Susan Dvorak; Tel: 831-758-7303; Staff 2 (MLS 2)
Pop 55,000; Circ 165,000
Jul 1999-Jun 2000 Mats Exp $50,300
Library Holdings: Bk Vols 54,000; Per Subs 55
Automation Activity & Vendor Info: (Acquisitions) epixtech, inc.; (Cataloging) epixtech, inc.; (Circulation) epixtech, inc.; (OPAC) epixtech, inc.; (Serials) epixtech, inc.
Partic in MOBAC
Friends of the Library Group

SAN ANDREAS

S CALAVERAS COUNTY ARCHIVES, 46 N Main St, PO Box 1281, 95249. SAN 301-2964. Tel: 209-754-3918. *Archivist*, Lorrayne Kennedy
Founded 1976
Special Collections: County of Calaveras (1850 to present), bks & flm; Mother Lode History
Publications: Trips to the Mines
Partic in 49-99 Coop Libr Syst
Friends of the Library Group

L CALAVERAS COUNTY LAW LIBRARY, c/o County Counsel, Government Ctr, 95249. SAN 326-0526. Tel: 209-754-6314. *Librn*, Mike Ibold
Pop 39,000
Jul 2000-Jun 2001 Income $21,144. Mats Exp $27,829. Sal $1,340
Library Holdings: Bk Vols 8,500

P CALAVERAS COUNTY LIBRARY, 891 Mountain Ranch Rd, 95249-0338. (Mail add: PO Box 338, 95249-0338), SAN 301-2956. Tel: 209-754-6510. FAX: 209-754-6512. *Dir*, Maurie Hoekstra; Tel: 209-754-6701, E-Mail: mhoekstra@co.calaveras.ca.us; *Circ*, Elizabeth Castor; *ILL*, Gayle Nordby; *Tech Servs*, Lynn Cuneo
Founded 1939. Pop 35,000; Circ 118,544
Jul 1999-Jun 2000 Income $537,215, State $153,849, County $340,522, Other $42,844. Mats Exp $38,795, Books $34,368, Per/Ser (Incl. Access Fees) $4,427. Sal $257,214 (Prof $48,000)
Library Holdings: Bk Vols 72,983; Per Subs 171
Subject Interests: Local history, Mining
Mem of 49-99 Cooperative Library System
Partic in OCLC Online Computer Library Center, Inc
Friends of the Library Group
Branches: 7
ANGELS CAMP BRANCH, 185 S Main St, Angels Camp, 95222. (Mail add: PO Box 456, Angels Camp, 95222), SAN 324-2382. Tel: 209-736-2198. E-Mail: anglib@co.calaveras.ca.us. *In Charge*, Diana Lewis; *Dir*, Maurie Hoekstra; Tel: 209-754-6701, Fax: 209-754-6512, E-Mail: mhoekstra@co.calaveras.ca.us
Circ 12,796
Library Holdings: Bk Vols 7,332
Friends of the Library Group
ARNOLD BRANCH, 1065 Blagen Rd, Arnold, 95223. (Mail add: PO Box 788, Arnodl, 95223), SAN 324-2390. Tel: 209-795-1009. *In Charge*, Hahn Knutsen; *Dir*, Maurie Hoekstra; Tel: 209-754-6701, Fax: 207-754-6512, E-Mail: mhoekstra@co.calaveras.ca.us
Circ 20,465
Library Holdings: Bk Vols 5,612
Friends of the Library Group
COPPEROPOLIS BRANCH, 49 Cosmic Ct, Unit C, Copperopolis, 95249. Tel: 209-785-0920. *In Charge*, Valerie Dean; Staff 1 (MLS 1)
Founded 1998. Pop 1,000; Circ 5,024
Library Holdings: Bk Vols 3,864
Database Vendor: epixtech, inc.
Friends of the Library Group
MURPHYS BRANCH LIBRARY, 480 Park Lane, Murphys, 95247. (Mail add: PO Box 702, Murphys, 95247), SAN 324-2412. Tel: 209-728-3036. E-Mail: mvlib@goldrush.com. *In Charge*, Jane Lind; *Dir*, Maurie Hoekstra; Tel: 209-754-6701, Fax: 209-754-6512, E-Mail: mhoekstra@co.calaveras.ca.us
Circ 8,156
Library Holdings: Bk Vols 5,194
Friends of the Library Group
VALLEY SPRINGS BRANCH, 240 Pine St, Valley Springs, 95252-0029. SAN 324-2447. Tel: 209-772-1318. *In Charge*, Althea Geleta; *Dir*, Maurie Hoekstra; Tel: 209-754-6701, Fax: 209-754-6512, E-Mail: mhoekstra@co.calaveras.ca.us
Circ 19,521
Library Holdings: Bk Vols 10,965
Friends of the Library Group
WEST POINT BRANCH, 291 Main St, West Point, 95255. SAN 324-2455. Tel: 209-293-7020. *In Charge*, Geri Austen; *Dir*, Maurie Hoekstra; Tel: 209-754-6701, Fax: 209-754-6512, E-Mail: mhoekstra@co.calaveras.ca.us
Circ 2,977
Library Holdings: Bk Vols 3,362
Friends of the Library Group

SAN ANSELMO

P SAN ANSELMO PUBLIC LIBRARY, 110 Tunstead Ave, 94960-2617. SAN 301-2972. Tel: 415-258-4656. FAX: 415-258-4666. Web Site: www.townofsananselmo.org/library. *Librn*, Sara Loyster; E-Mail: sloyster@marlin.org
Founded 1915. Pop 12,300; Circ 58,121
Library Holdings: Bk Vols 43,000; Per Subs 142
Special Collections: San Anselmo Historical Museum Coll
Mem of North Bay Cooperative Library System
Friends of the Library Group

S YWCA MARIN COUNTY CENTER, Resource Library, 1000 Sir Francis Drake Blvd, 94960. SAN 370-3193. Tel: 415-456-0782. FAX: 415-456-1950. *Dir*, Ann Kennedy
Library Holdings: Bk Vols 250; Per Subs 12
Subject Interests: Career, Law
Restriction: Open to public for reference only

SAN BERNARDINO

C CALIFORNIA STATE UNIVERSITY, SAN BERNARDINO LIBRARY,* 5500 University Pkwy, 92407-2397. SAN 301-2980. Tel: 909-880-5102. Interlibrary Loan Service Tel: 909-880-5093. FAX: 909-880-7048. Interlibrary Loan Service FAX: 909-880-5906. Web Site: www.lib.csusb.edu. *Librn*, Johnnie Ann Ralph; E-Mail: jralph@csusb.edu; *Automation Syst Coordr*, Buckley B Barrett; Tel: 909-880-5104, E-Mail: bbarrett@csusb.edu; *Bibliog Instr*, Renee Nesbitt; *Publ Servs*, Les Kong; Tel: 909-880-5111, E-Mail: lkong@csusb.edu; *Coll Develop, Tech Servs*, Michael Burgess; Tel: 909-880-5109, E-Mail: mburgess@csusb.edu; Staff 11 (MLS 11)
Founded 1963. Enrl 14,000; Fac 400; Highest Degree: Master
Jul 1998-Jun 1999 Income $4,720,815. Mats Exp $1,061,471, Books $368,957, Per/Ser (Incl. Access Fees) $462,174, Micro $25,058, AV Equip $57,962, Electronic Ref Mat (Incl. Access Fees) $147,320. Sal $1,663,992 (Prof $672,290)
Library Holdings: Bk Vols 632,840; Bk Titles 496,536; Per Subs 3,214
Database Vendor: Ebsco - EbscoHost, epixtech, inc., GaleNet, Lexis-Nexis, OCLC - First Search, Wilson - Wilson Web
Publications: Faculty Handbook; Pfau Library Newsletter (Newsletter)

Partic in Inland Empire Acad Libr Coop; San Bernardino, Inyo, Riverside Counties United Library Services
Open Mon-Thurs 8am-11pm, Fri 8am-5pm, Sat 9am-5pm & Sun 2-11pm
Friends of the Library Group

M COMMUNITY HOSPITAL OF SAN BERNARDINO, Medical Library, 1805 Medical Center Dr, 92411-1288. SAN 324-5071. Tel: 909-887-6333, Ext 1540.
Library Holdings: Bk Titles 700; Per Subs 107
Restriction: Staff use only
Partic in Dialog Corporation; Nat Libr of Med, Coop Libr Agency for Systems & Servs

SR INTERNATIONAL SCHOOL OF THEOLOGY LIBRARY,* 24600 Arrowhead Springs Rd, 92414-0001. SAN 301-2999. Tel: 909-886-7876, Ext 205. FAX: 909-882-8458. *Coll Develop, Dir*, Dr Paul Hamm; E-Mail: phamm@isot.org.net; *ILL, Per*, Linda Green
Founded 1978
Sep 1997-Aug 1998 Income $115,680, Locally Generated Income $726, Parent Institution $114,954. Mats Exp $29,089, Books $7,370, Per/Ser (Incl. Access Fees) $17,344, Presv $3,514, Micro $685. Sal $71,546 (Prof $40,000)
Library Holdings: Bk Titles 39,244; Per Subs 4,000
Subject Interests: Biblical studies, Counseling, Evangelicalism, Theology
Partic in OCLC Online Computer Library Center, Inc

GL LAW LIBRARY FOR SAN BERNARDINO COUNTY,* PO Box 213, 92402. SAN 334-1585. Tel: 909-885-3020. FAX: 909-885-1869. E-Mail: lawlib@eee.org. *Librn*, Carolyn Poston
Founded 1891
Library Holdings: Bk Vols 104,683
Special Collections: American Law & Foreign Law
Publications: Video tape of legal research guide
Branches:
HIGH DESERT, 15455 Seneca Rd, Victorville, 92392. SAN 373-8477. Tel: 760-243-2044. FAX: 760-243-2009. *Mgr*, Ed Butler
RANCHO CUCAMONGA
See Separate Entry in Rancho Cucamonga

M SAINT BERNARDINE MEDICAL CENTER, Medical Library,* 2101 N Waterman Ave, 92404. SAN 320-3662. Tel: 909-883-8711. FAX: 909-881-7171. *Librn*, Kathy Crumpacker; E-Mail: crumpack@eee.org; Staff 1 (MLS 1)
Founded 1964
Library Holdings: Bk Vols 5,400; Bk Titles 1,500; Per Subs 78
Subject Interests: Allied health, Medicine, Nursing
Partic in Inland Empire Med Libr Coop

P SAN BERNARDINO COUNTY LIBRARY, 104 W Fourth St, 92415-0035. SAN 334-164X. Tel: 909-387-5728. FAX: 909-387-5724. Web Site: www.co.san-bernardino.ca.us/library/intres.htm. *Dir*, Ed Kieczykowski; Tel: 909-387-5721, E-Mail: ekieczykowski@lib.co.san-bernardino.ca.us; *Tech Servs*, Richard Watts; E-Mail: rwatts@lib.co.san-bernardino.ca.us; *Mgr*, Rick Erickson; E-Mail: rerickson@lib.co.san-bernardino.ca.us; *YA Servs*, Susan Erickson; Tel: 909-387-5738, E-Mail: serickson@lib.co.san-bernardino.ca.us; *Ref*, Nannette Bricker-Barrett; Tel: 909-387-5716, E-Mail: nbricker-barrett@lib.co.san-bernardino.ca.us; *Commun Servs*, Kathy Wessels; Tel: 909-387-5729, E-Mail: kwessels@lib.co.san-bernardino.ca.us; *Automation Syst Coordr*, Pat Franco; Tel: 909-387-5682, E-Mail: pfranco@lib.co.san-bernardino.ca.us; *Coll Develop*, Carolyn Bowse; Tel: 909-387-5716, E-Mail: cbowse@lib.co.san-bernardino.ca.us; Staff 133 (MLS 21, Non-MLS 112)
Founded 1914. Pop 1,020,000; Circ 2,800,000
Jul 1999-Jun 2000 Income $9,067,270, State $1,450,000, County $7,617,270. Mats Exp $1,296,700, Books $1,200,000, Per/Ser (Incl. Access Fees) $88,000, Micro $8,700. Sal $4,780,000 (Prof $2,234,400)
Library Holdings: Bk Vols 1,210,000
Special Collections: Mines & Mineral Resources Coll; San Bernardino County History Coll
Automation Activity & Vendor Info: (Circulation) DRA
Database Vendor: DRA, OCLC - First Search
Publications: San Bernardino County Newsletter
Mem of Inland Library System
Friends of the Library Group
Branches: 28
ADELANTO BRANCH, 11744 Bartlett, Adelanto, 92301. SAN 334-1674. Tel: 760-246-5661. FAX: 760-246-5661. *In Charge*, Carollee Stater
Founded 1971
Library Holdings: Bk Vols 23,504
Friends of the Library Group
APPLE VALLEY BRANCH, 15001 Wakita Rd, Apple Valley, 92307. SAN 334-1704. Tel: 760-247-2022. FAX: 760-247-9729. *Librn*, Gretchen Kellems
Founded 1952
Library Holdings: Bk Vols 67,356
Friends of the Library Group
BARSTOW BRANCH, 304 E Buena Vista, Barstow, 92311. SAN 334-1739. Tel: 760-256-4850. FAX: 760-256-4852. Web Site: www.co.san-bernardino.ca.us/library/. *Librn*, Linda Williams; Staff 3 (MLS 1, Non-MLS 2)
Pop 50,000
Library Holdings: Bk Vols 56,009; Per Subs 50
Friends of the Library Group
BIG BEAR LAKE BRANCH, 41930 Garstin Dr, Big Bear Lake, 92315. SAN 334-1763. Tel: 909-866-0162. FAX: 909-866-0187. *Librn*, Pamela Heiman
Founded 1988
Library Holdings: Bk Vols 43,356
Friends of the Library Group
BLOOMINGTON BRANCH, 10145 Orchard St, Bloomington, 92316. SAN 334-1798. Tel: 909-877-1453. FAX: 909-820-0533. *In Charge*, Adelle Hansen
Founded 1966
Library Holdings: Bk Vols 25,361
Friends of the Library Group
CHINO BRANCH, 13180 Central Ave, Chino, 91710. SAN 334-1828. Tel: 909-517-1526. FAX: 909-590-4928. E-Mail: chiref@lib.co.san-bernardino.ca.us. Web Site: www.cosan-bernardino.ca.us/library/main.htm, www.members.aol.com/frchinolib. *Librn*, Jennifer Fukunaga; Tel: 909-517-1527
Library Holdings: Bk Vols 60,102
Friends of the Library Group
CHINO HILLS BRANCH, 2003 Grand Ave, Chino Hills, 91709. SAN 373-5885. Tel: 909-590-5380. FAX: 909-590-5267. *Librn*, Susan Wenger
Founded 1992
Library Holdings: Bk Vols 56,009
Friends of the Library Group
CRESTLINE BRANCH, 23555 Knapp's Cutoff, PO Box 1087, Crestline, 92325. SAN 334-1852. Tel: 909-338-3294. FAX: 909-338-0964. *In Charge*, Betty Chamberlin
Founded 1919
Library Holdings: Bk Vols 19,140
Friends of the Library Group
FONTANA BRANCH, 8334 Emerald St, Fontana, 92335. SAN 334-1941. Tel: 909-822-2321, 909-822-8330. FAX: 909-823-0489. *Mgr*, Renee Lovato
Founded 1963
Library Holdings: Bk Vols 79,441
Friends of the Library Group
GRAND TERRACE BRANCH, 22795 Barton Rd, Grand Terrace, 92313. SAN 325-4453. Tel: 909-783-0147. FAX: 909-783-1913. *Librn*, Laurie Shearer
Founded 1985
Library Holdings: Bk Vols 32,431
Friends of the Library Group
HESPERIA BRANCH, 9565 Seventh Ave, Hesperia, 92345. SAN 334-1976. Tel: 760-244-4898. FAX: 760-244-1530. *Librn*, Ann Marie Wentworth
Founded 1970
Library Holdings: Bk Vols 51,244
Friends of the Library Group
HIGHLAND BRANCH, 27167 Base Line, Highland, 92346. SAN 334-1917. Tel: 909-862-8549. FAX: 909-864-0816. *Librn*, Harriet Foucher
Founded 1975
Library Holdings: Bk Vols 63,330
Friends of the Library Group
JOSHUA TREE BRANCH, 6465 Park Blvd, Joshua Tree, 92252. SAN 334-200X. Tel: 760-366-8615. FAX: 760-366-8615. *In Charge*, Peggy Bryant
Founded 1945
Library Holdings: Bk Vols 15,220
Friends of the Library Group
LAKE ARROWHEAD, 27235 Hwy 189, PO Box 766, Blue Jay, 92317. SAN 334-2034. Tel: 909-337-3118. FAX: 909-337-2287. *Librn*, Irene Wickstrom
Founded 1924
Library Holdings: Bk Vols 31,303
Friends of the Library Group
LOMA LINDA BRANCH, 25581 Barton Rd, Loma Linda, 92354. SAN 334-2069. Tel: 909-796-8621. FAX: 909-796-4221. *Librn*, Stan Sewell
Founded 1989
Library Holdings: Bk Vols 42,138
Friends of the Library Group
LUCERNE VALLEY BRANCH, 33103 Old Woman Springs Rd, PO Box 408, Lucerne Valley, 92356. SAN 334-2093. Tel: 760-248-7521. FAX: 760-248-7521. *In Charge*, Myra Andrest
Founded 1988
Library Holdings: Bk Vols 28,589
Friends of the Library Group
MENTONE BRANCH, 1870 Mentone Blvd, Mentone, 92359. SAN 334-2123. Tel: 909-794-2657. FAX: 909-794-2657. *In Charge*, Margaret Griffith
Founded 1939
Library Holdings: Bk Vols 15,802
Friends of the Library Group
MONTCLAIR BRANCH, Civic Center, 9955 Fremont, Montclair, 91763. SAN 334-2158. Tel: 909-624-4671. FAX: 909-391-7775. *Librn*, Yvonne Woytovich

Founded 1963
Library Holdings: Bk Vols 60,153
Friends of the Library Group
NEEDLES BRANCH, 1111 Bailey, Needles, 92363. SAN 334-2182. Tel: 760-326-9255. FAX: 760-326-9238. *Librn*, Barbara De Gidio
Founded 1979
Library Holdings: Bk Vols 25,451
Friends of the Library Group
RIALTO BRANCH, 251 W First St, Rialto, 92376. SAN 334-2212. Tel: 909-875-0144. FAX: 909-875-2801. *Librn*, Joyce Martell
Founded 1914
Library Holdings: Bk Vols 60,967
Friends of the Library Group
RUNNING SPRINGS BRANCH, 31976 Hilltop Blvd, PO Box 248, Running Springs, 92382. SAN 334-2247. Tel: 909-867-2554. FAX: 909-867-2554. *In Charge*, Janet Parsons
Founded 1938
Library Holdings: Bk Vols 13,738
Friends of the Library Group
SAN BERNARDINO ARCHIVES, 777 E Rialto Ave, 92415-0795. SAN 329-6229. Tel: 909-387-2030. *Archivist*, James D Hofer
Library Holdings: Bk Vols 550
TRONA BRANCH, 82805 Mountain View St, Trona, 93562. SAN 334-2271. Tel: 760-372-5847. FAX: 760-372-5847. *In Charge*, Joan Nordseth
Founded 1971
Library Holdings: Bk Vols 17,880
Friends of the Library Group
TWENTYNINE PALMS BRANCH, 6078 Adobe Rd, Twentynine Palms, 92277. SAN 334-2301. Tel: 760-367-9519. FAX: 760-361-0703. *Librn*, Linda Muller
Founded 1959
Library Holdings: Bk Vols 36,948
Friends of the Library Group
VICTORVILLE BRANCH, 15011 Circle Dr, Victorville, 92392. SAN 334-2336. Tel: 760-245-4222. FAX: 760-245-2273. *Librn*, Suzanne Oliver
Founded 1971
Library Holdings: Bk Vols 59,775
Friends of the Library Group
WRIGHTWOOD BRANCH, 6014 Park Dr, PO Box 1962, Wrightwood, 92397. SAN 334-2344. Tel: 760-249-4577. FAX: 760-249-3263. *In Charge*, Linda Felgar
Founded 1971
Library Holdings: Bk Vols 15,807
Friends of the Library Group
YUCAIPA BRANCH, 12040 Fifth St, Yucaipa, 92399. SAN 334-2360. Tel: 909-790-3146. FAX: 909-790-3151. *Librn*, Cheryl Erickson
Founded 1969
Library Holdings: Bk Vols 70,349
Friends of the Library Group
YUCCA VALLEY BRANCH, 57098 Twentynine Palms Hwy, Yucca Valley, 92284. SAN 334-2395. Tel: 760-228-5455. FAX: 760-228-5459. *Librn*, Peg Bryant
Founded 1973
Library Holdings: Bk Vols 44,323
Friends of the Library Group
Bookmobiles: 2

S SAN BERNARDINO COUNTY SUN LIBRARY,* 399 North D St, 92401. SAN 329-4382. Tel: 909-386-3850. FAX: 909-885-8741. *Librn*, Peggy Hardy
Library Holdings: Bk Titles 900

P SAN BERNARDINO PUBLIC LIBRARY, Norman F Feldheym Public Library, 555 W Sixth St, 92410-3001. SAN 334-2425. Tel: 909-381-8215. Circulation Tel: 909-381-8201. Reference Tel: 909-381-8226. FAX: 909-381-8229. Web Site: www.sbpl.org. *Dir*, Ophelia Roop; E-Mail: oroop@sbpl.org; *Assoc Dir*, Michael Clark; *Ref*, Millicent Price; *Ch Servs*, Irene Thomsen; *ILL*, Rosemary DuBois; *Acq*, Connie Griffin-Woodring; *Tech Servs*, Ellen Lanto; *Doc, Per*, Gerald Linxwiler. Subject Specialists: *California*, Millicent Price; *Local history*, Millicent Price; Staff 10 (MLS 10)
Founded 1891. Pop 185,000; Circ 539,875
Jul 1999-Jun 2000 Income $2,395,245, State $310,723, City $1,795,200, Federal $62,645, Locally Generated Income $75,000, Other $151,677. Mats Exp $253,200, Books $215,200, Per/Ser (Incl. Access Fees) $30,000, Micro $8,000. Sal $1,410,800 (Prof $398,632)
Library Holdings: Bk Vols 214,350; Per Subs 502
Special Collections: California History (California Coll)
Automation Activity & Vendor Info: (Circulation) TLC; (OPAC) TLC
Mem of Inland Library System
Partic in OCLC Online Computer Library Center, Inc; San Bernardino, Inyo, Riverside Counties United Library Services
Friends of the Library Group
Branches: 3
INGHRAM, 1505 W Highland Ave, 92411. SAN 334-2484. Tel: 909-887-4494. FAX: 909-887-6594. E-Mail: inghram@sbpl.org. Web Site: www.sbpl.org. *Branch Mgr*, Debra Bemben
Pop 15,000; Circ 41,806
Library Holdings: Bk Vols 14,138
Special Collections: Black History Coll
Automation Activity & Vendor Info: (OPAC) TLC
Friends of the Library Group
ROWE, 108 E Marshall Blvd, 92404. SAN 334-2514. Tel: 909-883-3411. FAX: 909-882-4941. E-Mail: rowe@sbpl.org. Web Site: www.sbpl.org. *Branch Mgr*, Mary Chartier
Pop 60,000; Circ 170,301
Library Holdings: Bk Vols 39,583
Automation Activity & Vendor Info: (OPAC) TLC
Friends of the Library Group
VILLASENOR, 525 N Mount Vernon Ave, 90411. SAN 334-2549. Tel: 909-383-5156. FAX: 909-381-1766. E-Mail: villa@sbpl.org. Web Site: www.sbpl.org. *Branch Mgr*, Angela Encinas
Pop 12,500; Circ 27,010
Library Holdings: Bk Vols 19,160
Special Collections: Bilingual Material; Spanish language material

J SAN BERNARDINO VALLEY COLLEGE, Samuel E Andrews Memorial Library, 701 S Mount Vernon Ave, 92410-2748. SAN 301-3022. Tel: 909-888-6511. Circulation Tel: 909-888-6511, Ext 1231. Reference Tel: 909-888-6511, Ext 1233. FAX: 909-383-2802. Web Site: lr.valley.sbccd.cc.ca.us/libhome.htm. *Dean*, Robin J Calote; Tel: 909-888-6411, Ext 1628, E-Mail: rcalotea@sbccd.cc.ca.us; *Head Tech Servs*, Dr Marie D Mestas; Tel: 909-888-6511, Ext 1229, E-Mail: mmestas@sbccd.cc.ca.us; *Bibliog Instr*, Celia J McKinley; Tel: 909-888-6511, Ext 1237, E-Mail: cmckinl@sbccd.cc.ca.us; Staff 11 (MLS 3, Non-MLS 8)
Founded 1926. Enrl 11,500; Highest Degree: Associate
Library Holdings: Bk Vols 101,043; Per Subs 389
Automation Activity & Vendor Info: (Acquisitions) Innovative Interfaces Inc.; (Cataloging) Innovative Interfaces Inc.; (Circulation) Innovative Interfaces Inc.; (Course Reserve) Innovative Interfaces Inc.; (OPAC) Innovative Interfaces Inc.; (Serials) Innovative Interfaces Inc.
Database Vendor: Ebsco - EbscoHost, Innovative Interfaces INN - View

SAN BRUNO

S NATIONAL ARCHIVES & RECORDS ADMINISTRATION, Pacific Region (San Francisco), 1000 Commodore Dr, 94066-2350. SAN 301-3030. Tel: 650-876-9009. FAX: 650-876-9233. E-Mail: archives@sanbruno.nara.gov. Web Site: www.nara.gov/regional/sanfranc.html. *Dir*, Daniel Nealand; Staff 8 (MLS 3, Non-MLS 5)
Founded 1969
Subject Interests: Aeronautics, Afro-American, Agricultural economics, Agriculture, California, Environmental studies, Hawaii, Labor, Land, Maritime, Natural resources, Navy hist, Nevada, Petroleum engineering, World War II
Special Collections: Bureau of Indian Affairs, California & Nevada, 1859-1960, micro & doc; Bureau of Land Management, 1853-1960, micro & doc; Chinese Immigration Records, 1882-1955, doc; Department of Energy, 1915-1970, doc; Government of American Samoa, 1900-1966, doc; National Park Service, 1910-1969, doc; San Francisco Mint, 1853-1960, doc; United States Army Corps of Engineers, 1853-1976, doc; United States Attorneys (San Francisco), 1913-1971,doc; United States Census, 1790-1920, micro; United States Committee on Fair Employment Practice, 1941-46, doc; United States Court of Appeals for Ninth Circuit, 1891-1969, doc; United States District Court, Eastern District of California, 1900-1973, doc; United States District Court, Hawaii, 1900-1968, doc; United States District Court, Nevada (Reno/Carson City), 1865-1963, micro & doc; United States District Courts for Northern District of California, 1851-1972, micro & doc; United States Forest Service, 1870-1970, doc; United States National War Labor Board, 1942-47; United States Naval Shipyards (Mare Island, Pearl Harbor & San Francisco), 1854-1965, doc; United States Penitentiary at Alcatraz, 1934-1964, doc
Publications: Chinese Immigration & Chinese in the United States: Records in the Regional Archives of the National Archives and Records Administration; Guide to Records in the National Archives-Pacific Sierra Region; Records in the National Archives-Pacific Sierra Region for Study of Science, Technology, Natural Resources & the Environment; Records in the National Archives-Pacific Sierra Region for the Study of Ethnic History; Records in the National Archives-Pacific Sierra Region for the Study of Labor & Business History
Restriction: Public use on premises
Function: Archival collection
Partic in Cooperative Information Network

P SAN BRUNO PUBLIC LIBRARY,* 701 Angus Ave W, 94066-3490. SAN 301-3049. Tel: 650-616-7078. FAX: 650-876-0848. E-Mail: sbpl@pls.lib.ca.us. Web Site: www.pls.lib.ca.us/pls.sbl.html. *Dir*, Terry Jackson; *Ch Servs*, JoJo Hilliard; Staff 19 (MLS 6, Non-MLS 13)
Founded 1916. Pop 40,850; Circ 252,981
Library Holdings: Bk Vols 100,000
Special Collections: San Bruno Historical Pictures
Mem of Peninsula Library System
Friends of the Library Group

J SKYLINE COLLEGE LIBRARY,* 3300 College Dr, 94066-1698. SAN 301-3057. Tel: 650-738-4311. FAX: 650-738-4149. Web Site: www.pls.lib.ca.us/pls/smcccd/sky/sky.html. *Dir*, Thomas Hewitt; *Bibliog Instr*, Eric Brenner; Staff 3 (MLS 3)
Founded 1969. Enrl 6,455; Fac 156
Library Holdings: Bk Vols 45,000; Bk Titles 50,000; Per Subs 240
Subject Interests: Feminism
Partic in OCLC Online Computer Library Center, Inc; PLS

M STAYWELL, Library & Resource Center, 1100 Grundy Lane, 94066. SAN 370-1670. Tel: 650-742-0400. Web Site: www.staywell.com. *Mgr*, Daniel Angel; Tel: 650-244-4532
Library Holdings: Bk Titles 3,000; Per Subs 400
Partic in Dialog Corporation; Nat Libr of Med

SAN CARLOS

S LITTON INDUSTRIES, Electron Devices Division Library,* 960 Industrial Rd, 94070-4194. SAN 301-3073. Tel: 650-591-8411, Ext 2517. FAX: 650-595-3136. *Librn*, Tim Wilcox
Library Holdings: Bk Vols 1,870
Subject Interests: Electronics
Automation Activity & Vendor Info: (Cataloging) Inmagic, Inc.
Publications: Monthly Bulletin
Partic in Dialog Corporation

M PSORIASIS RESEARCH ASSOCIATION LIBRARY,* 107 Vista del Grande, 94070. SAN 375-1937. Tel: 650-593-1394.
Library Holdings: Bk Vols 200

S RAGUSAN PRESS, Croatian Immigration Library, 2527 San Carlos Ave, 94070. SAN 326-4858. Tel: 650-592-1190. Web Site: www.croations.com. *Librn*, Adam S Eterovich; E-Mail: adam@croatians.com
Library Holdings: Bk Titles 10,000
Subject Interests: Immigration
Special Collections: 70,000 Pioneers Coll (prior to 1900)
Publications: Ragusan Research Bulletin

SAN CLEMENTE

R SAN CLEMENTE PRESBYTERIAN CHURCH,* 119 Ave de la Estrella, 92672. SAN 301-3111. Tel: 949-492-6158. FAX: 949-492-6158.
Founded 1956
Library Holdings: Bk Vols 2,500
Open Mon-Fri 8-5 & Sun during services

S SOUTHERN CALIFORNIA EDISON COMPANY LIBRARY,* San Onofre Nuclear Generating Sta, E-50B, MESA, PO Box 128, 92674-0128. SAN 328-2996. Tel: 949-368-3000. FAX: 949-368-8996.
Library Holdings: Bk Titles 2,300
Restriction: Not open to public

SAN DIEGO

C ALLIANT UNIVERSITY SAN DIEGO CAMPUS LIBRARY, (Formerly California School Of Professional Psychology Library), 6160 Cornerstone Ct E, 92121-3725. SAN 301-3154. Tel: 858-623-2777, Ext 306. Interlibrary Loan Service Tel: 858-623-2777, Ext 340. Circulation Tel: 858-723-2777, Ext 332. Reference Tel: 858-623-2777, Ext 308. FAX: 858-452-0331. Web Site: www.library.cspp.edu. *Dir Libr Serv*, Deborah A Fleming; E-Mail: dfleming@cspp.edu; *Cat*, Trudy Snell; Tel: 858-623-2777, Ext 307, E-Mail: tsnell@cspp.edu; *Head, Circ*, Nick Page; E-Mail: npage@cspp.edu; *ILL, Ser*, Karen Yochum; E-Mail: kyochum@cspp.edu; Staff 4 (MLS 2, Non-MLS 2)
Founded 1972. Enrl 600; Fac 30; Highest Degree: Doctorate
Jul 2000-Jun 2001 Income $221,241. Mats Exp $106,145, Books $16,895, Per/Ser (Incl. Access Fees) $71,500, Presv $7,200, Micro $3,600, AV Equip $2,950, Electronic Ref Mat (Incl. Access Fees) $4,000. Sal $101,296 (Prof $41,150)
Library Holdings: Bk Vols 27,000; Bk Titles 20,250; Per Subs 376; Spec Interest Per Sub 376; Bks on Deafness & Sign Lang 54
Subject Interests: Psychology
Special Collections: American Indian Counseling Coll; Friends of Jung Coll; Psychological Test Materials
Automation Activity & Vendor Info: (Acquisitions) Innovative Interfaces Inc.; (Cataloging) Innovative Interfaces Inc.; (Circulation) Innovative Interfaces Inc.; (Course Reserve) Innovative Interfaces Inc.; (ILL) Innovative Interfaces Inc.; (OPAC) Innovative Interfaces Inc.; (Serials) Innovative Interfaces Inc.
Database Vendor: OVID Technologies, ProQuest, Silverplatter Information Inc.
Publications: Library Guide
Restriction: Internal circulation only
Lending to students, faculty & staff; Affilated with other Alliant libraries in Fesno, Alhambra, Alameda & Sacramento

S ANACOMP, Datagraphix Engineering Research Library, PO Box 509005, 92150-9005. SAN 301-3197. Tel: 858-679-9797, Ext 5801. FAX: 858-486-8729. *Librn*, Connie Soliday
Founded 1963
Library Holdings: Bk Vols 15,000; Per Subs 93
Subject Interests: Optics
Restriction: Staff use only

S ARINC, INC, Technical Library,* 4055 Hancock St, 92110. SAN 324-4237. Tel: 619-222-7447, Ext 202. FAX: 619-225-1750.
1996-1997 Income $26,000. Mats Exp $26,000, Books $13,000, Per/Ser (Incl. Access Fees) $1,000, Other Print Mats $1,000
Library Holdings: Per Subs 100
Subject Interests: Computer specifications, Electrical, Engineering, Military specifications
Partic in Dialog Corporation

L BROBECK, PHLEGER & HARRISON, Law Library,* 12390 El Camino Rio, 92130. SAN 323-6218. Tel: 619-234-1966, 858-720-2500. FAX: 858-720-2555. E-Mail: mhabianbph@class.org. Web Site: www.brobeck.com. *Librn*, Michelle Habian
Founded 1987
Library Holdings: Bk Vols 15,000
Restriction: Staff use only

S C P KELCO LIBRARY & INFORMATION SERVICES, 8355 Aero Dr, 92123-1718. SAN 301-3308. Tel: 858-292-4900. FAX: 858-467-6570. *Mgr*, Susan J Shepherd; *Res*, Ann M Willard; *Tech Servs*, Penny Coppernoll-Blach; Staff 5 (MLS 3, Non-MLS 2)
Founded 1954
Library Holdings: Bk Vols 5,000; Per Subs 350
Subject Interests: Biochemistry, Biology, Chemical technology, Chemistry, Food sci, Food tech, Microbiology, Nutrition
Publications: Bibliographies; internal alerting services; literature surveys
Restriction: By appointment only
Function: Archival collection, Research library
IDI BASIS Plus software for published and internal documents control, full-text applications, and proprietary product data

S CALBIOCHEM CORPORATION LIBRARY,* 10394 Pacific Center Ct, PO Box 12087, 92121-4180. SAN 370-9523. Tel: 619-450-9600. Toll Free Tel: 800-776-0999. FAX: 619-453-3552.
Library Holdings: Bk Vols 1,000; Per Subs 12
Subject Interests: Biochemistry

GL CALIFORNIA COURT OF APPEAL, Fourth Appellate District-Division One Law Library,* 750 B St Ste 300, 92101-8196. SAN 301-312X. Tel: 619-645-2833. FAX: 619-645-2850. *Librn*, Nanna Frye; E-Mail: nfrye@ix.netcom.com; Staff 1 (MLS 1)
Founded 1929
Library Holdings: Bk Vols 40,000
Subject Interests: State law
Restriction: Staff use only
Partic in Dialog Corporation; Westlaw

GL CALIFORNIA DEPARTMENT OF JUSTICE LIBRARY,* 110 West A St, Ste 1311, 92101. SAN 301-3138. Tel: 619-645-2162. *Librn*, Fay Henexson; E-Mail: henexson@class.org; Staff 2 (MLS 1, Non-MLS 1)
Founded 1972
Library Holdings: Bk Titles 26,000; Per Subs 50
Publications: Newsletter

CL CALIFORNIA WESTERN SCHOOL OF LAW LIBRARY, 290 Cedar St, 92101. (Mail add: 225 Cedar St, 92101), SAN 301-3162. Tel: 619-525-1418. Interlibrary Loan Service Tel: 619-525-1426. Reference Tel: 619-525-1419. FAX: 619-685-2918. Web Site: www.cwsl.edu/library/. *Dir*, Phyllis Marion; E-Mail: pmarion@cwsl.edu; *Ref*, Bill Bookheim; E-Mail: bbookheim@cwsl.edu; *Ref*, Bobbi Weaver; E-Mail: bweaver@cwsl.edu; *ILL*, Linda Weathers; E-Mail: lweathers@cwsl.edu; *Cat*, James W Dopp; E-Mail: jdopp@cwsl.edu; *Assoc Dir*, Mary E Garcia; E-Mail: mgarcia@cwsl.edu; *Acq*, Carmen Brigandi; E-Mail: cbrigandi@cwsl.edu; *Ref*, Amy Moberly; E-Mail: amoberly@cwsl.edu; Staff 16 (MLS 9, Non-MLS 7)
Founded 1958. Enrl 735; Fac 41; Highest Degree: Doctorate
Aug 1999-Jul 2000 Income Parent Institution $1,140,253. Mats Exp $1,140,303, Books $100,042, Per/Ser (Incl. Access Fees) $664,499, Presv $11,743, Micro $46,067, Other Print Mats $215,253, Electronic Ref Mat (Incl. Access Fees) $102,699
Library Holdings: Bk Vols 279,907; Bk Titles 46,613; Per Subs 3,750
Subject Interests: Law
Special Collections: Congressional Information Service (US Congress Coll), micro; US Supreme Court Records & Briefs, micro
Automation Activity & Vendor Info: (Acquisitions) Innovative Interfaces Inc.; (Cataloging) Innovative Interfaces Inc.; (Circulation) Innovative Interfaces Inc.; (Course Reserve) Innovative Interfaces Inc.; (OPAC) Innovative Interfaces Inc.; (Serials) Innovative Interfaces Inc.
Database Vendor: Innovative Interfaces INN - View, OCLC - First Search
Restriction: Not open to public, Private library

Partic in Law Libr Microfilm Consortium; OCLC Online Computer Library Center, Inc
Open Mon-Fri 7am-11pm & Sat-Sun 8am-11pm

M CHILDREN'S HOSPITAL & HEALTH CENTER, Health Sciences Library, 3020 Children's Way, Mailcode 5043, 92123-4282. SAN 325-0369. Tel: 858-966-7474. FAX: 858-966-4934. Web Site: www.chsd.org. *Mgr*, Anna Habetler; E-Mail: ahabetler@chsd.org; *Librn*, Charlotte McClammer; Staff 3 (MLS 2, Non-MLS 1)
Founded 1955
Jul 1998-Jun 1999 Income $283,067. Mats Exp $70,030, Books $16,000, Per/Ser (Incl. Access Fees) $49,530, Presv $4,500. Sal $159,234
Library Holdings: Bk Vols 3,500; Bk Titles 2,500; Per Subs 190
Subject Interests: Pediatrics
Partic in Dialog Corporation; Med Libr Group of S Calif & Ariz; Medical Libr Asn; Nat Libr of Med; OCLC Online Computer Library Center, Inc

S CUBIC DEFENSE SYSTEMS, INC, Technical Library, 9333 Balboa Ave, PO Box 85587, 92186-5587. SAN 301-3189. Tel: 858-505-2326. FAX: 858-505-1542. *Mgr*, Kathleen Cook; E-Mail: kathy.cook@cubic.com; Staff 1 (MLS 1)
Founded 1952
Oct 1998-Sep 1999 Income (Main Library Only) $130,000. Mats Exp $130,000, Books $62,000, Per/Ser (Incl. Access Fees) $68,000
Library Holdings: Bk Titles 6,000; Per Subs 320
Subject Interests: Aeronautics, Communications, Computer science, Electronic engineering, Electronics, Management, Mathematics, Physics, Radar
Publications: Acquisition List; Index to Periodicals; Library guide
Restriction: By appointment only
Partic in Dialog Corporation

GM DEPARTMENT OF VETERANS AFFAIRS MEDICAL CENTER LIBRARY, 3350 La Jolla Village Dr, 92161. SAN 301-3588. Tel: 619-552-8585. FAX: 619-552-7537. *Chief Librn*, Deborah Batey; Tel: 858-552-8585, Ext 3421, E-Mail: deborah.batey@med.va.gov
Founded 1972
Library Holdings: Bk Vols 4,400
Subject Interests: Dentistry, Internal medicine, Nursing, Psychiatry, Surgery
Special Collections: Patient Information, EEO
Database Vendor: Ebsco - EbscoHost, Innovative Interfaces INN - View, OVID Technologies
Publications: Library Update (monthly)
Partic in Depart of Vet Affairs Libr Network; Nat Libr of Med

S ENVITECH,* 2924 Emerson St, No 320, 92106-2758. SAN 375-7870. Tel: 619-623-9925. FAX: 619-623-9605.
Library Holdings: Bk Titles 850
Restriction: Not open to public

J FASHION INSTITUTE OF DESIGN & MERCHANDISING, Resource & Research Center,* 1010 Second St, 2nd Fl, 92101. SAN 370-2197. Tel: 619-235-4515. FAX: 619-232-4322. *Coordr*, Kathryn Harris
Library Holdings: Bk Vols 1,700; Per Subs 86

R FIRST PRESBYTERIAN CHURCH OF SAN DIEGO LIBRARY, 320 Date St, 92101. SAN 301-3219. Tel: 619-232-7513. FAX: 619-232-8469. *Librn*, Jim Meals
Founded 1940
Library Holdings: Bk Titles 4,000; Per Subs 45
Open Mon-Fri 8:30-12:15 & 1-4

S GEORGE S PATTON JR HISTORICAL SOCIETY LIBRARY, 3116 Thorn St, 92104-4618. SAN 374-8219. Tel: 619-282-4201. FAX: 619-282-1920. E-Mail: pattonhq@utm.net. Web Site: members.aol.com/pattonsghq/homeghq.html. *Pres*, Charles M Province
Library Holdings: Bk Vols 300

S GEOSCIENCE LIMITED LIBRARY,* 6260-B Marindustry Dr, 92121. SAN 301-6129. Tel: 619-453-5483. FAX: 619-453-4694. Web Site: www.electriciti.com/~geosci. *Pres*, H F Poppendiek
Founded 1961
Library Holdings: Bk Vols 700
Subject Interests: Physics

L GRAY, CARY, WARE & FREIDENRICH, Law Library,* 401 B St Ste 1700, 92101-4297. SAN 329-7977. Tel: 619-699-2770. FAX: 619-236-1048. Web Site: www.graycary.com. *Mgr Libr Serv*, June F Mac Leod; E-Mail: jmacleod@graycary.com
Library Holdings: Bk Vols 60,000; Per Subs 300
Restriction: Staff use only

M HELICON FOUNDATION LIBRARY,* 4622 Santa Fe St, 92109. SAN 370-2227. Tel: 858-272-3884. FAX: 858-272-1621. *In Charge*, Laura Ryan
Library Holdings: Bk Vols 150

S HEWLETT-PACKARD COMPANY, San Diego Research Library,* 16399 W Bernardo Dr, 92127-1899. SAN 329-1294. Tel: 858-655-4687. FAX: 858-655-4587. *In Charge*, Roberta Cabulong; Staff 1 (Non-MLS 1)
Founded 1980
Library Holdings: Bk Titles 3,000

L HIGGS, FLETCHER & MACK LLP, Law Library, 401 West A St, Ste 2600, 92101-7913. SAN 301-3243. Tel: 619-236-1551. FAX: 619-696-1410.
Founded 1939
Library Holdings: Bk Vols 12,000
Partic in Westlaw

S HUBBS-SEA WORLD RESEARCH INSTITUTE,* 2595 Ingraham St, 92109. SAN 326-4084. Tel: 619-226-3870. FAX: 619-226-3944. *Librn*, Suzanne Bond
Library Holdings: Bk Vols 620; Per Subs 30
Publications: Currents

S INSTITUTE FOR WORLD UNDERSTANDING OF PEOPLES, CULTURES & LANGUAGES LIBRARY,* 4370 La Jolla Village Dr, Ste 1000, 92122-1253. SAN 373-0271. Tel: 858-454-0705. *Dir*, Dr Bernard (Burt) W Aginsky
Library Holdings: Bk Vols 1,000

M KAISER PERMANENTE MEDICAL CENTER, Health Sciences Library,* 4647 Zion Ave, 92120. SAN 301-3294. Tel: 619-528-7323. FAX: 619-528-3444. *Librn*, Sheila Latus; *Online Servs*, Laurel Windrem; Staff 6 (MLS 2, Non-MLS 4)
Founded 1967
Library Holdings: Bk Titles 6,500; Per Subs 500
Subject Interests: Medicine, Nursing

L LATHAM & WATKINS, Law Library,* 701 B St, Ste 2100, 92101. SAN 371-1021. Tel: 619-236-1234. FAX: 619-696-7419. *Librn*, Carolyn L Vega
Library Holdings: Bk Vols 2,700; Bk Titles 1,000
Open Mon-Fri 8:30-6

S LOGICON, INC, Tactical Systems Div Library,* 4010 Sorrento Valley Blvd, 92121-1498. SAN 301-3324. Tel: 858-597-7179. FAX: 858-552-1021. Web Site: www.logicon.com. *Librn*, Paula Oquita; *Asst Librn*, Diane Morgan
Library Holdings: Bk Vols 5,000; Per Subs 100
Special Collections: Specifications & Standards
Publications: Acquisitions list; brochure; flier
On-Line access to a number of information services as well as electronic bulletin boards

L LUCE, FORWARD, HAMILTON & SCRIPPS, Law Library,* 600 W Broadway, Ste 2600, 92101. SAN 301-3332. Tel: 619-236-1414. FAX: 619-232-8311. *Librn*, Carmen Valero; E-Mail: cvalero@luce.com; *Asst Librn*, Michelle Schmidt
Library Holdings: Bk Vols 50,000; Per Subs 260
Special Collections: International Business; Pacific Rim
Publications: In-house newsletter; New Books List
Restriction: Staff use only
Open Mon-Fri 8:30-5

S MAXWELL TECHNOLOGIES INC, Technical Library,* 8888 Balboa Ave, 92123. SAN 301-3537. Tel: 619-279-5100. FAX: 619-576-7710. Web Site: www.maxwell.com/maxwell/library/. *Librn*, LaDonna Rowe
Founded 1969
Library Holdings: Bk Vols 3,500; Bk Titles 3,000; Per Subs 161
Subject Interests: Analytical chemistry
Partic in Dialog Corporation; San Diego Greater Metro Area Libr & Info Agency Coun; SDC Info Servs

J MIRAMAR COLLEGE, Learning Resource Center, 10440 Black Mountain Rd, 92126-2999. SAN 301-3359. Tel: 619-388-7310. Reference Tel: 619-388-7316. FAX: 619-388-7918. Web Site: www.miramar.sdccd.net/depts/library. *Chair, Librn*, Sandra V Pesce; E-Mail: spesce@sdccd.net; *Librn*, Eric M Mosier; Staff 10 (MLS 4, Non-MLS 6)
Founded 1973. Enrl 8,685
Jul 1999-Jun 2000 Mats Exp $83,656. Sal $420,139
Library Holdings: Bk Vols 21,707; Per Subs 102
Subject Interests: Automotive, Diesel, Emergency med, Fire science, Law, Transportation
Special Collections: Law Library
Automation Activity & Vendor Info: (Acquisitions) epixtech, inc.; (Cataloging) epixtech, inc.; (Circulation) epixtech, inc.; (Course Reserve) epixtech, inc.; (OPAC) epixtech, inc.; (Serials) epixtech, inc.
Database Vendor: Ebsco - EbscoHost, GaleNet, IAC - SearchBank, ProQuest
Partic in OCLC Online Computer Library Center, Inc; San Diego & Imperial Counties College Learning Resources Cooperative

S NATIONAL ASSOCIATION FOR YEAR-ROUND EDUCATION LIBRARY, 5404 Napa St Ste A, 92110. SAN 371-2508. Tel: 619-276-5296. FAX: 858-571-5754. E-Mail: info@nayre.org. Web Site: www.nayre.org.

Exec Dir, Marilyn J Stenvall; *Coll Develop*, Jeanne Walsh
Library Holdings: Bk Vols 300
Restriction: Staff use only
Open Mon-Fri 7-4

S NATIONAL STEEL & SHIPBUILDING CO, Engineering Library,* 28th & Harbor Dr, PO Box 85278, 92138. SAN 301-3383. Tel: 619-544-7661. FAX: 619-544-3543. *Librn*, Alta Sadler
Library Holdings: Bk Vols 2,000
Special Collections: Ships' Plans & Blueprints, microfilm

C NATIONAL UNIVERSITY LIBRARY, 9393 Lightwave Ave, 92123-1447. (Mail add: PO Box 639023, 92163-9023), SAN 301-3391. Tel: 858-541-7900. Toll Free Tel: 800-628-8648, Ext 7900. FAX: 858-541-7994. Toll Free FAX: 888-840-8288. E-Mail: refdesk@nu.edu. Web Site: www.nu.edu/library/. *Dir Libr Serv*, Anne Marie Secord; Tel: 858-541-7913, E-Mail: asecord@nu.edu; *Publ Servs*, Mary Brandt; Tel: 858-541-7915, E-Mail: mbrandt@nu.edu; *Tech Servs*, Jeffrey Earnest; Tel: 858-541-7916, E-Mail: jearnest@nu.edu; *Business*, Bud Sonka; Tel: 858-541-7914, Fax: 858-541-7992, E-Mail: bsonka@nu.edu; *Automation Syst Coordr, Syst Coordr*, Joe Simpson; Tel: 858-541-7911, E-Mail: jsimpson@nu.edu; *Head, Circ*, Michael Morganson; Tel: 858-541-7478, E-Mail: mmorgans@nu.edu; *Cat*, Leticia Gumban; *ILL*, Patrick Pemberton; Tel: 858-541-7909, Fax: 858-541-7992, E-Mail: ppembert@nu.edu; Staff 35 (MLS 21, Non-MLS 14)
Founded 1975. Enrl 17,000; Fac 450; Highest Degree: Master
2000-2001 Mats Exp $3,365,206
Library Holdings: Bk Vols 220,000; Per Subs 4,398
Subject Interests: Bus, Education, Human behav, Psychology
Special Collections: Adult Learners
Automation Activity & Vendor Info: (Acquisitions) DRA; (Cataloging) DRA; (Circulation) DRA; (OPAC) DRA; (Serials) DRA
Database Vendor: Ebsco - EbscoHost, GaleNet, ProQuest, Wilson - Wilson Web
Publications: Library Connections (Newsletter)
Partic in CalPALs; Dialog Corporation; SCELC; Serra Cooperative Library System

S NCR CORPORATION LIBRARY, Dept 8714, 17095 Via Del Campo, 92127. SAN 301-3367. Tel: 858-485-3291. FAX: 858-485-3567. *Librn*, Mary Hill; E-Mail: mary.hill@sandiegoca.ncr.com
1998-1999 Income $150,000
Library Holdings: Bk Vols 10,000; Per Subs 150
Subject Interests: Electronics
Automation Activity & Vendor Info: (Acquisitions) EOS; (Cataloging) EOS; (Circulation) EOS; (Serials) EOS

C POINT LOMA NAZARENE COLLEGE, Ryan Library, 3900 Lomaland Dr, 92106-2899. SAN 301-3405. Tel: 619-849-2355. FAX: 619-222-0711. E-Mail: dirli@ptloma.edu. Web Site: www.ptloma.edu. *Dir*, James Newburg; Tel: 619-849-2355, Ext 2338; *Bibliog Instr, Online Servs, Ref*, Ann Ruppert; *Bibliog Instr, Online Servs, Ref*, Beryl Pagan; *Cat, Syst Coordr*, Anne Elizabeth Powell; *Bibliog Instr, Online Servs, Ref*, Douglas Fruehling
Founded 1902
Library Holdings: Bk Vols 165,000; Per Subs 613
Subject Interests: Religion
Special Collections: Armenian-Wesleyan Theological Library; Religion (Holiness Authors)
Partic in Coop Libr Agency for Syst & Servs; Dialog Corporation; OCLC Online Computer Library Center, Inc

S SAN DIEGO AERO-SPACE MUSEUM, INC, N Paul Whittier Historical Aviation Library, 2001 Pan American Plaza, Balboa Park, 92101-1636. SAN 321-2653. Tel: 619-234-1531, Ext 33. FAX: 619-233-4526. Web Site: www.aerospacemuseum.org. *Librn*, Pamela Gay; *Archivist*, Ron Bulinski; Staff 4 (MLS 3, Non-MLS 1)
Founded 1978
Library Holdings: Bk Vols 24,500; Bk Titles 24,000; Per Subs 18
Subject Interests: Aerospace, Aviation, Mil aircraft
Special Collections: Air Mail Pioneers (Edwin Cooper Coll); Convair Corporate Files; Ed Heinemann Coll; Flying Cars (T P Hall Coll); Flying Wings Engineering (Wilhelm F Schult Coll); Frank T Courtney, Early Birds; George E A Hallett, Adm Marc Mitscher, John J Montgomery, Waldo D Waterman; Gliding & Soaring (Wally Wiberg Coll); John & Helen Sloan (Fokker); Ray Fife & Tex LaGrone Coll; RH Fleet Coll (Consolidated); Ryan Aeronautical Libr Coll
Partic in Serra Cooperative Library System

L SAN DIEGO CITY ATTORNEY LIBRARY,* 1200 Third Ave Ste 1307, 92101. SAN 371-8786. Tel: 619-236-6078. FAX: 619-236-7215. E-Mail: mbh@sdcity.sannet.gov. *Librn*, Mary Lynn Hyde
1999-2000 Income $75,000. Mats Exp $80,000, Books $64,000, Per/Ser (Incl. Access Fees) $11,000
Library Holdings: Bk Vols 13,500; Bk Titles 550; Per Subs 75
Subject Interests: Government, Law
Partic in Westlaw

J SAN DIEGO CITY COLLEGE, Learning Resource Center,* 1313 12th Ave, 92101-4712. SAN 301-3421. Tel: 619-230-2535. FAX: 619-230-2063. *Librn*, Cecilia Cheung; *Ref*, Curtis E Lang; *Media Spec*, Sidney Forman; Staff 6 (MLS 6)
Founded 1916. Enrl 13,280; Fac 295
Library Holdings: Bk Vols 62,025; Per Subs 425
Open Mon-Thurs 8-9:50, Fri 8-4:20, closed Sat & Sun
Friends of the Library Group

P SAN DIEGO COUNTY LIBRARY, Bldg 15, 5555 Overland Ave, 92123-1296. SAN 334-2573. Tel: 858-694-2414, 858-694-2484 (Public Info). Interlibrary Loan Service Tel: 858-694-3996. Circulation Tel: 858-505-6353. FAX: 858-495-5981. E-Mail: info@sdcl.org. Web Site: www.sdcl.org. *Actg Dir*, Valerie Rodak; *Dep Dir*, Cheryl Cline; *Ch Servs, YA Servs*, Audrey Jones; *Automation Syst Coordr*, Kathleen Honeysett; *Outreach Serv*, Teresa Osburn; *Coll Develop, Tech Servs*, Betty Waznis; *Business*, Carolyn Brain; Staff 176 (MLS 43, Non-MLS 133)
Founded 1913. Pop 965,413; Circ 3,205,898
Jul 1998-Jun 1999 Income (Main Library and Branch Library) $13,819,246, State $1,383,228, Federal $4,322, Locally Generated Income $11,699,666, Other $732,030. Mats Exp $1,556,471, Books $1,232,273, Per/Ser (Incl. Access Fees) $158,446, Presv $1,470, Micro $16,248, Electronic Ref Mat (Incl. Access Fees) $148,034. Sal $6,661,655
Library Holdings: Bk Vols 1,199,687; Bk Titles 270,000; Per Subs 2,598
Special Collections: Arabic; Chinese; Korean; Spanish; Tagalog; Vietnamese
Automation Activity & Vendor Info: (Circulation) DRA; (OPAC) DRA
Database Vendor: GaleNet, IAC - Info Trac, OCLC - First Search
Publications: Library Services Brochures
Mem of Serra Cooperative Library System
Special Services for the Deaf - Captioned media
Special Services for the Blind - Newsline for the Blind; Sub-lending agent for Braille Institute Library; Talking Books
Friends of the Library Group
Branches: 31

ALPINE BRANCH, 2130 Arnold Way, Alpine, 92001-9499. SAN 334-2603. Tel: 619-445-4221. FAX: 619-445-4856. Web Site: www.sdcl.org. *In Charge*, Susan Peralta
Library Holdings: Bk Vols 20,912
Open Tues 12-8, Wed-Thurs 10-6, Fri & Sat 10-4
Friends of the Library Group

BONITA-SUNNYSIDE BRANCH, 5047 Central Ave, Bonita, 91902-2698. SAN 334-2638. Tel: 619-475-4642. FAX: 619-475-4366. Web Site: www.sdcl.org. *In Charge*, Linda Julian
Library Holdings: Bk Vols 22,131
Open Mon & Tues 12-8, Wed & Thurs 10-6, Fri & Sat 10-5
Friends of the Library Group

BORREGO SPRINGS BRANCH, 500 The Mall, Borrego Springs, 92004-0297. (Mail add: PO Box 685, Borrego Springs, 92004-0685), SAN 334-2662. Tel: 760-767-5761. FAX: 760-767-3619. Web Site: www.sdcl.org. *In Charge*, Valerie Guelke
Library Holdings: Bk Vols 8,251
Open Tues & Fri 9-3, Wed-Thurs 10-6, Sat 9-2

CAMPO BRANCH, 31466 Hwy 94, Campo, 91906-0207. SAN 334-2697. Tel: 619-478-5945. FAX: 619-478-2446. Web Site: www.sdcl.org. *In Charge*, Sheri Davis
Library Holdings: Bk Vols 5,978
Open Tues 9-12, Wed 9-12 & 1-5, Thurs 1-8, Fri 1-4, Sat 9-12
Friends of the Library Group

CARDIFF BRANCH, 2027 San Elijo Ave, Cardiff, 92007-1896. SAN 334-3480. Tel: 760-753-4027. FAX: 760-753-4267. Web Site: www.sdcl.org. *In Charge*, Faith Niles
Library Holdings: Bk Vols 16,409
Open Tues 10-6; Wed & Thurs 10-8; Fri 10-5; Sat 10-2
Friends of the Library Group

CASA DE ORO BRANCH, 9628 Campo Rd, Ste L, Spring Valley, 91977-1286. SAN 334-2727. Tel: 619-463-3236. FAX: 619-463-8670. Web Site: www.sdcl.org. *In Charge*, Teresa Omahen
Library Holdings: Bk Vols 27,860
Open Mon & Tues 12-8; Wed & Thurs 11-6; Fri 10-4
Friends of the Library Group

CREST BRANCH, 105 Juanita Lane, El Cajon, 92021-4399. SAN 334-2786. Tel: 619-442-7083. FAX: 619-442-4972. Web Site: www.sdcl.org. *In Charge*, Elisa James
Library Holdings: Bk Vols 10,208
Open Tues 1-6; Wed & Thurs 12-5; Sat 11-4

DEL MAR BRANCH, 1309 Camino del Mar, Del Mar, 92014-2693. SAN 334-2816. Tel: 858-755-1666. FAX: 858-755-9168. E-Mail: dmbl@cts.com. *Mgr Libr*, Gretchen Schmidt
Library Holdings: Bk Vols 21,072
Open Tues 10-6; Wed & Thurs 10-8; Fri & Sat 10-5; Sun 1-5
Friends of the Library Group

DESCANSO BRANCH, 9545 River Dr, Descanso, 91916-0185. SAN 334-2840. Tel: 619-445-5279. FAX: 619-445-4891. Web Site: www.sdcl.org. *In Charge*, Peggy Machado
Library Holdings: Bk Vols 8,488
Open Mon & Fri 1-5; Wed &Thurs 11:30-1, 1:30-6; Sat 10-1
Friends of the Library Group

EL CAJON BRANCH, 201 E Douglas, El Cajon, 92020. SAN 334-2875. Tel: 619-579-4454. FAX: 619-579-4018. *Mgr Libr*, Suzanne Hess
Library Holdings: Bk Vols 144,110

Open Mon & Thurs 12-8; Tues & Wed 10-6; Fri 10-5; Sat 10-4:30
Friends of the Library Group
ENCINITAS BRANCH, 540 Cornish Dr, Encinitas, 92024-4599. SAN 334-2905. Tel: 760-753-7376. FAX: 760-753-0582. Web Site: www.sdcl.org. *Mgr Libr*, Jose Clark
Library Holdings: Bk Vols 34,792
Open Mon & Tues 12-8; Wed & Thurs 10-6; Fri & Sat 10-5
Friends of the Library Group
FALLBROOK BRANCH, 124 S Mission Rd, 92028-2896. SAN 334-293X. Tel: 760-728-2373. FAX: 760-728-4731. Web Site: www.sdcl.org. *Mgr Libr*, Jennifer McKenzie
Library Holdings: Bk Vols 55,124
Open Tues & Wed 10-6; Thurs 12-8; Fri & Sat 10-5; Sun 1-5
Friends of the Library Group
FLETCHER HILLS BRANCH, 576 Garfield Ave, El Cajon, 92020-2792. SAN 334-2964. Tel: 619-466-1132. FAX: 619-466-4682. Web Site: www.sdcl.org. *In Charge*, Leslie Ward
Library Holdings: Bk Vols 20,015
Open Tues, Thurs, Fri & Sat 10-5 & Wed 12-8
Friends of the Library Group
IMPERIAL BEACH BRANCH, 810 Imperial Beach Blvd, Imperial Beach, 91932-2798. SAN 334-2999. Tel: 619-424-6981. FAX: 619-424-8749. Web Site: www.sdcl.org. *In Charge*, Loueida Robinson
Library Holdings: Bk Vols 34,002
Open Mon 12-8, Tues-Thurs 10-6, Fri-Sat 10-4
Friends of the Library Group
JACUMBA BRANCH, 44605 Old Hwy 80, PO Box 186, Jacumba, 91934-0186. SAN 334-3022. Tel: 619-766-4608. FAX: 619-766-9206. Web Site: www.sdcl.org. *In Charge*, Sheri Davis
Library Holdings: Bk Vols 10,056
Open Tues 1-8; Wed 9-12 & 1-5, Thurs & Fri 9-12; Sat 1-4
Friends of the Library Group
JULIAN BRANCH, 2133 Fourth St, Julian, 92036-0326. SAN 334-3057. Tel: 760-765-0370. FAX: 760-765-2748. Web Site: www.sdcl.org. *In Charge*, Rosa Mejia
Library Holdings: Bk Vols 11,268
Open Tues 12-8; Wed & Thurs 10-6; Fri & Sat 10-4
Friends of the Library Group
LA MESA BRANCH, 8055 University Ave, La Mesa, 91941-5097. SAN 334-3111. Tel: 619-469-2151. FAX: 619-697-3751. Web Site: www.sdcl.org. *Mgr Libr*, Bryndis Rubin
Library Holdings: Bk Vols 84,809
Open Mon & Thurs 10-6, Tues & Wed 12-8, Fri & Sat 10-5
Friends of the Library Group
LAKESIDE BRANCH, 9839 Vine St, Lakeside, 92040-3199. SAN 334-3081. Tel: 619-443-1811. FAX: 619-443-8002. Web Site: www.sdcl.org. *Mgr Libr*, Dorothy Stamper
Library Holdings: Bk Vols 36,712
Open Tues 12-8; Wed & Thurs 10-6; Fri & Sat 10-5; Sun 1-5
Friends of the Library Group
LEMON GROVE BRANCH, 8073 Broadway, Lemon Grove, 91945-2599. SAN 334-3146. Tel: 619-463-9819. FAX: 619-463-8069. Web Site: www.sdcl.org. *Mgr Libr*, Sonya Heiserman
Library Holdings: Bk Vols 48,635
Open Tues 10-8; Wed 12-8; Thurs 10-6; Fri & Sat 10-4
Friends of the Library Group
LINCOLN ACRES BRANCH, 2725 Granger Ave, National City, 91950-0168. SAN 334-3170. Tel: 619-475-9880. FAX: 619-475-4382. Web Site: www.sdcl.org. *In Charge*, Jose Ogadiz
Library Holdings: Bk Vols 8,447
Open Tues 12-4:30, 5-8; Wed 10-12:30, 1-5; Thurs 12-5; Sat 10-3
Friends of the Library Group
PINE VALLEY BRANCH, 28857 Old Hwy 80, Pine Valley, 91962-0592. SAN 334-3200. Tel: 619-473-8022. FAX: 619-473-9638. Web Site: www.sdcl.org. *In Charge*, Sherry Markham
Library Holdings: Bk Vols 7,971
Open Tues 1-8; Wed & Fri 11-3; Thurs 1-6; Sat 11-2
Friends of the Library Group
POTRERO BRANCH, 24955 Library Lane, Potrero, 91963-0051. SAN 334-3235. Tel: 619-478-5978. FAX: 619-478-2695. Web Site: www.sdcl.org. *In Charge*, Candy Bonner
Library Holdings: Bk Vols 7,383
Open Tues & Thurs 10-5; Wed 5-8; Fri & Sat 10-1
Friends of the Library Group
POWAY BRANCH, 13137 Poway Rd, Poway, 92064-4687. SAN 334-326X. Tel: 858-513-2900. Web Site: www.ci.poway.ca.us. *Mgr Libr*, Matthew Beatty
Library Holdings: Bk Vols 76,766
Open Mon -Thurs 10-8; Fri & Sat 10-5; Sun 1-5
Friends of the Library Group
RAMONA BRANCH, 1406 Montecito Rd, Ramona, 92065-2296. SAN 334-3294. Tel: 760-738-2434. FAX: 760-738-2475. Web Site: www.sdcl.org. *Mgr Libr*, Hari Bhalla
Library Holdings: Bk Vols 36,499
Open Tues 12-8; Wed & Thurs 10-6; Fri & Sat 10-5; Sun 1-5
Friends of the Library Group
RANCHO SANTA FE BRANCH, 17040 Avenida de Acacias, Rancho Santa Fe, 92067-0115. SAN 334-3324. Tel: 858-756-2512. FAX: 858-756-3485. Web Site: www.sdcl.org. *Librn*, Josephine Moeller
Library Holdings: Bk Vols 39,968
Open Mon & Tues 10-6; Wed 10-8; Thurs, Fri & Sat 10-5
Friends of the Library Group
SAN MARCOS BRANCH, Civic Center Dr, No 2, San Marcos, 92069-2919. SAN 334-3359. Tel: 760-736-2160. FAX: 760-736-2170. Web Site: www.sdcl.org. *Mgr Libr*, Ann Terrell
Library Holdings: Bk Vols 58,282
Open Tues 10-6; Wed & Thurs 10-8; Fri & Sat 10-4
Friends of the Library Group
SANTEE BRANCH, 9225 Carlton Hills Blvd, No 17, Santee, 92071-3192. SAN 334-3383. Tel: 619-448-1863. FAX: 619-448-1497. Web Site: www.sdcl.org. *Mgr Libr*, Josephine Routhier
Library Holdings: Bk Vols 46,893
Open Tues & Wed 12-8; Thurs 10-6; Fri & Sat 10-5
Friends of the Library Group
SOLANA BEACH BRANCH, 981 Lomas Santa Fe Dr, No F, Solana Beach, 92075-1873. SAN 334-3413. Tel: 858-755-1404. FAX: 858-755-9327. Web Site: www.sdcl.org. *Librn*, Sue Dess
Library Holdings: Bk Vols 33,149
Open Tues 12-8; Wed 10-8; Thurs 10-6; Fri & Sat 10-5
Friends of the Library Group
SPRING VALLEY BRANCH, 1043 Elkelton Blvd, Spring Valley, 91977-4796. SAN 334-3448. Tel: 619-463-3006. FAX: 619-463-8917. Web Site: www.sdcl.org. *Mgr Libr*, Beth Watson
Library Holdings: Bk Vols 34,148
Open Mon & Tues 10-8; Wed & Thurs 10-6; Fri 10-5; Sat 10-4
Friends of the Library Group
VALLEY CENTER BRANCH, 29115 Valley Center Rd, Valley Center, 92082-9699. SAN 334-3472. Tel: 760-749-1305. FAX: 760-749-1764. Web Site: www.sdcl.org. *In Charge*, Sandy Puccio
Library Holdings: Bk Vols 25,111
Open Tues 10-6; Wed 12-8; Thurs 10-8; Fri 10-5; Sat 10-3
Friends of the Library Group
VISTA BRANCH, 700 Eucalyptus Ave, Vista, 92084-6245. SAN 334-3502. Tel: 760-945-5116. FAX: 760-945-5140. Web Site: www.sdcl.org. *Mgr Libr*, Jane Marmack
Library Holdings: Bk Vols 120,175
Open Mon & Thurs 10-6; Tues & Wed 10-8; Fri 10-5; Sat 10-4
Friends of the Library Group
Bookmobiles: 2

GL SAN DIEGO COUNTY PUBLIC LAW LIBRARY,* 1105 Front St, 92101-3999. SAN 301-343X. Tel: 619-531-3904. FAX: 619-238-7716. Web Site: www.sdcll.org. *Dir*, Charles R Dyer; *Acq, Coll Develop, Tech Servs*, Colleen Buskirk; *Ref*, Mewail Mebrahtu; Staff 44 (MLS 18, Non-MLS 26)
Founded 1891
1997-1998 Income $2,360,499, Locally Generated Income $196,563. Mats Exp $632,766, Books $215,387, Micro $12,835, Other Print Mats $400,256
Library Holdings: Bk Vols 333,655; Per Subs 1,181
Special Collections: California Appellate Court Briefs since 1950; Local Legal History
Publications: Guide to Collections & Services; Newsletters
Mem of Serra Cooperative Library System
Partic in Coop Libr Agency for Syst & Servs; Dialog Corporation; OCLC Online Computer Library Center, Inc; Westlaw
Branches:
CHULA VISTA BRANCH, 500 Third Ave, Chula Vista, 91910-5617. SAN 321-4109. Tel: 619-691-4929. FAX: 619-427-7521. *Librn*, Edna Thiel
Library Holdings: Bk Vols 16,456
EL CAJON BRANCH, 250 E Main, El Cajon, 92020-3941. SAN 321-9364. Tel: 619-441-4444. FAX: 619-441-0235. *Librn*, Carolyn Dulude
Library Holdings: Bk Vols 10,838
VISTA BRANCH, 325 S Melrose, Ste 300, Vista, 92083-6697. SAN 321-4117. Tel: 760-940-4386. FAX: 760-724-7694. *Librn*, Joan Allen-Hart
Library Holdings: Bk Vols 20,000
Friends of the Library Group

S SAN DIEGO FAMILY HISTORY CENTER, Family History Center, 4195 Camino Del Rio S, 92108. SAN 329-2118. Tel: 619-584-7668. *Dir*, Robert Chambers; E-Mail: robert30@wans.net
Founded 1966
Library Holdings: Bk Vols 12,000; Per Subs 60
Special Services for the Deaf - Staff with knowledge of sign language

S SAN DIEGO HISTORICAL SOCIETY, Research Archives, Balboa Park, 1649 El Prado, 92101. (Mail add: PO Box 81825, 92138), SAN 301-3448. Tel: 619-232-6203. Reference Tel: 619-232-6203, Ext 127. FAX: 619-232-1059. Web Site: www.sandiegohistory.org. *Curator*, Greg Williams; Tel: 619-232-6203, Ext 116, E-Mail: williams@sandiegohistory.org. Subject Specialists: *Photog*, Greg Williams
Founded 1929
Library Holdings: Bk Vols 10,000; Per Subs 30
Subject Interests: Local history
Special Collections: Architectural Drawings; Maps; Public Records (city,

county, superior court)
Publications: Guide to Photograph Coll (1998); Guide to the Public Records Collection (1987); Journal of San Diego History (Historical Society Publications); Stranger Than Fiction (1995)

S SAN DIEGO MARITIME MUSEUM, Jerry MacMullen Library, 1306 N Harbor Dr, 92101. SAN 371-5604. Tel: 619-234-9153, Ext 110. FAX: 619-234-8345. Web Site: www.stmaritime.com. *Librn*, Charles Bencik; Staff 1 (MLS 1)
Founded 1981
Library Holdings: Bk Vols 7,000; Per Subs 170
Special Collections: Ship Plans & Blueprints; Ships' Logs
Publications: Mains'l Haul: A Journal of Maritime History

J SAN DIEGO MESA COLLEGE LIBRARY, 7250 Mesa College Dr, 92111-4998. SAN 301-3456. Tel: 619-388-2695. FAX: 858-627-2922. Web Site: www.sdmesa.sdccd.net/library. *Chairperson, Publ Servs*, Jack Forman; E-Mail: jforman@sdccd.net; *AV, Coll Develop*, Devin Milner; *Per*, Jean Smith; *Tech Servs*, Roger Olson; *Instrul Serv*, Val Ontell; Staff 5 (MLS 5)
Founded 1963. Enrl 23,000; Highest Degree: Associate
Jul 1999-Jun 2000 Mats Exp $180,000, Books $120,000, Per/Ser (Incl. Access Fees) $60,000. Sal $924,000 (Prof $350,000)
Library Holdings: Bk Vols 94,000; Per Subs 500
Automation Activity & Vendor Info: (Cataloging) epixtech, inc.; (Circulation) epixtech, inc.; (Course Reserve) epixtech, inc.; (OPAC) epixtech, inc.; (Serials) epixtech, inc.
Database Vendor: Ebsco - EbscoHost, GaleNet, ProQuest, Wilson - Wilson Web
Partic in San Diego & Imperial Counties College Learning Resources Cooperative; San Diego Greater Metro Area Libr & Info Agency Coun
Friends of the Library Group

S SAN DIEGO MODEL RAILROAD MUSEUM LIBRARY, 1649 El Prado, 92101. SAN 374-5651. Tel: 619-696-0199. FAX: 619-696-0239. E-Mail: sdmodrailm@abac.com. Web Site: www.sdmodelrailroad.com. *Exec Dir*, John Rotsart; Staff 1 (MLS 1)
Founded 1994
Jul 1998-Jun 1999 Income (Main Library Only) Locally Generated Income $1,600. Mats Exp $1,150, Manuscripts & Archives $500
Library Holdings: Bk Titles 45,000
Subject Interests: Railroads
Function: Research library
Friends of the Library Group

S SAN DIEGO MUSEUM OF ART LIBRARY, PO Box 2107, 92112-2107. SAN 301-3464. Tel: 619-696-1959. FAX: 619-232-9367. E-Mail: sdmalib@pacbell.net. *Librn*, Nancy Emerson; E-Mail: nemerson@class.org; *Librn*, James Grebl
Founded 1926
Library Holdings: Bk Vols 30,000; Per Subs 95
Subject Interests: Art
Special Collections: Binney Collection - books & catalogues in subject area of Indian miniature painting; Exhibition & Auction Catalogues Coll
Partic in Coop Libr Agency for Syst & Servs; OCLC Online Computer Library Center, Inc

S SAN DIEGO MUSEUM OF MAN, Scientific Library,* Balboa Park, 1350 El Prado, 92101. SAN 301-3472. Tel: 619-239-2001. FAX: 619-239-2749. Web Site: www.museumofman.org. *Librn*, Jane Bentley; *Asst Librn*, Joyce Antorietto
Founded 1915
1998-1999 Mats Exp $10,000
Library Holdings: Bk Vols 18,800; Per Subs 300
Subject Interests: Anthropology, Archaeology, Egypt, Ethnology

P SAN DIEGO PUBLIC LIBRARY,* 820 E St, 92101-6478. SAN 334-3650. Tel: 619-236-5830. FAX: 619-236-5878. E-Mail: axt@citymgr.sannet.gov. Web Site: ci.san_diego.ca.us/public_library/index.html. *Dir*, Anna Tatar; *Dep Dir*, Helga Moore; *Dep Dir*, Meryl Balko; *Ref*, Ellen Sneberger; *ILL*, Lynn Whitehouse; *Spec Coll*, Jane Selvar; *Ch Servs*, Jean Stewart; *Coll Develop*, Joanne Anderson. Subject Specialists: *History*, Lynn Whitehouse; *Language arts*, John Vanderby; *Literature*, John Vanderby; *Science/technology*, Nora Brooks; *Social sciences and issues*, Fran Bookheim; Staff 109 (MLS 109)
Founded 1882. Pop 1,197,700; Circ 6,573,161
Library Holdings: Bk Vols 2,670,375; Bk Titles 87,900; Per Subs 3,663
Special Collections: Baja California, San Diego & Southern California History (California Room), Rare Books & History of Printing (Wangenheim); City & County
Publications: Check Us Out (quarterly); Tideline (quarterly)
Mem of Serra Cooperative Library System
Friends of the Library Group
Branches: 33
BALBOA, 4255 Mt Abernathy Ave, 92117. SAN 334-3685. Tel: 858-573-1390. FAX: 858-573-1391. Web Site: www.sannet.gov/public-library/. *Mgr*, Aina Celms; *YA Servs*, Joan Raphael; Staff 5 (MLS 2, Non-MLS 3)
Founded 1971. Pop 38,530
Library Holdings: Bk Vols 65,120; Per Subs 47
Friends of the Library Group
BECKWOURTH, 721 San Pasqual St, 92113. SAN 334-3715. Tel: 619-527-3404. Web Site: www.sannet.gov/public-library/. *Mgr*, Anna Der Parseghian
Library Holdings: Bk Vols 50,153
Friends of the Library Group
BENJAMIN, 5188 Zion St, 92120. SAN 334-374X. Tel: 619-533-3970. Web Site: www.sannet.gov/public-library/. *Mgr*, Leean Knetzer
Library Holdings: Bk Vols 53,374
Friends of the Library Group
CARMEL MOUNTAIN RANCH, 12095 World Trade Dr, 92128. SAN 377-6808. Tel: 858-538-8181. FAX: 858-674-7372. Web Site: www.sannet.gov/public-library. *Mgr*, Sandy Steele
Library Holdings: Bk Vols 28,081
CARMEL VALLEY, 3919 Townsgate Dr, 92130. SAN 373-9228. Tel: 858-552-1668. FAX: 858-552-1672. Web Site: www.sannet.gov/public-library/. *Mgr*, Susan Roberts
Library Holdings: Bk Vols 80,670
Friends of the Library Group
CLAIREMONT, 2920 Burgener Blvd, 92110. SAN 334-3774. Tel: 858-581-9935. Web Site: www.sannet.gov/public-library/. *Mgr*, Dee Gantz
Library Holdings: Bk Vols 44,254
Friends of the Library Group
COLLEGE HEIGHTS, 4710 College Ave, 92115. SAN 334-3804. Tel: 619-533-3902. Web Site: www.sannet.gov/public-library/. *Mgr*, Harriet Cohen
Library Holdings: Bk Vols 43,628
Friends of the Library Group
KENSINGTON-NORMAL HEIGHTS, 4121 Adams Ave, 92116. SAN 334-4010. Tel: 619-533-3974. Web Site: www.sannet.gov/public-library/. *Mgr*, Jack Albrecht
Library Holdings: Bk Vols 30,588
Friends of the Library Group
LA JOLLA RIFORD BRANCH, 7555 Draper Ave, La Jolla, 92037. SAN 334-3863. Tel: 858-552-1657. Web Site: www.sannet.gov/public-library/. *Mgr*, Richard Burke
Library Holdings: Bk Vols 78,338
Friends of the Library Group
LINDA VISTA, 2160 Ulric St, 92111. SAN 334-3898. Tel: 858-573-1399. Web Site: www.sannet.gov/public-library/. *Mgr*, Lowell Waxman
Library Holdings: Bk Vols 72,397
Friends of the Library Group
LOGAN HEIGHTS, 811 S 28th St, 92113. SAN 334-3928. Tel: 619-533-3968. FAX: 619-235-5243. Web Site: www.sannet.gov/public-library/. *Mgr*, Juan Ortiz
Library Holdings: Bk Vols 37,605
Friends of the Library Group
MALCOM X BRANCH, 5148 Market St, 92114. SAN 334-4495. Tel: 619-527-3405. FAX: 619-527-5456. Web Site: www.sannet.gov/public-library/. *In Charge*, Shery Marc
Library Holdings: Bk Vols 68,964
MIRA MESA, 8405 New Salem St, 92126. SAN 334-3952. Tel: 858-538-8165. Web Site: www.sannet.gov/public-library/. *Mgr*, Charles Wyborney
Library Holdings: Bk Vols 98,029
Friends of the Library Group
MISSION HILLS, 925 W Washington St, 92103. SAN 334-3987. Tel: 619-692-4910. Web Site: www.sannet.gov/public-library/. *Mgr*, Philip Detwiler
Library Holdings: Bk Vols 44,415
Friends of the Library Group
NORTH CLAIREMONT, 4616 Clairemont Dr, 92117. SAN 334-4045. Tel: 858-581-9931. Web Site: www.sannet.gov/public-library/. *Mgr*, Lien Dao
Library Holdings: Bk Vols 44,388
Friends of the Library Group
NORTH PARK, 3795 31st St, 92104. SAN 334-407X. Tel: 619-533-3972. Web Site: www.sannet.gov/public-library/. *Mgr*, Jean Hughes
Library Holdings: Bk Vols 79,063
Friends of the Library Group
OAK PARK, 2802 54th St, 92105. SAN 334-410X. Tel: 619-527-3406. Web Site: www.sannet.gov/public-library/. *Mgr*, Kathy Ford
Library Holdings: Bk Vols 40,630
Friends of the Library Group
OCEAN BEACH, 4801 Santa Monica Ave, 92107. SAN 334-4134. Tel: 619-531-1532. Web Site: www.sannet.gov/public-library/. *Mgr*, Heather Reed
Library Holdings: Bk Vols 45,129
Friends of the Library Group
OTAY MESA, 3003 Coronado Ave, 92154. SAN 334-4169. Tel: 619-424-0474. Web Site: www.sannet.gov/public-library/. *Mgr*, Christine Gonzalez
Library Holdings: Bk Vols 66,208
Friends of the Library Group
PARADISE HILLS, 5922 Rancho Hills Dr, 92139. SAN 334-4223. Tel: 619-527-3461. Web Site: www.sannet.gov/public-library/. *Mgr*, Pat Fickling
Library Holdings: Bk Vols 35,997
Friends of the Library Group
POINT LOMA, 2130 Poinsettia Dr, 92107. SAN 334-4258. Tel: 619-531-1539. Web Site: www.sannet.gov/public-library/. *Mgr*, Bruce Johnson
Library Holdings: Bk Vols 58,509

Friends of the Library Group
RANCHO BERNARDO, 17110 Bernardo Center Dr, 92128. SAN 334-4282. Tel: 858-538-8163. Web Site: www.sannet.gov/public-library/. *Mgr*, Anna Marie Hain
Library Holdings: Bk Vols 90,458
Friends of the Library Group
RANCHO PENASQUITOS, 13330 Salmon River Rd, 92129. SAN 322-5577. Tel: 858-538-8159. FAX: 858-538-8160. Web Site: www.sannet.gov/public-library/. *Mgr*, John Lima
Library Holdings: Bk Titles 95,326
Friends of the Library Group
SAN CARLOS, 7265 Jackson Dr, 92119. SAN 334-4312. Tel: 619-527-3430. Web Site: www.sannet.gov/public-library/.
Library Holdings: Bk Vols 73,096
Friends of the Library Group
SAN YSIDRO, 101 W San Ysidro Blvd, 92173. SAN 334-4347. Tel: 619-690-8375. Web Site: www.sannet.gov/public-library/. *Mgr*, James Frazier
Library Holdings: Bk Vols 45,208
Friends of the Library Group
SCRIPPS RANCH, 10301 Scripps Lake Dr, 92131. SAN 328-7904. Tel: 619-538-8158. FAX: 858-538-8154. Web Site: www.sannet.gov/public-library/. *Mgr*, Nancy Assaf
Library Holdings: Bk Vols 76,095
Friends of the Library Group
SERRA MESA, 3440 Sandrock Rd, 92123. SAN 334-4371. Tel: 858-573-1396. Web Site: www.sannet.gov/public-library/. *Mgr*, Marilyn Gibbs
Library Holdings: Bk Vols 46,370
Friends of the Library Group
SKYLINE HILLS, 480 S Meadowbrook Dr, 92114. SAN 334-4401. Tel: 619-527-3485. Web Site: www.sannet.gov/public-library/. *Mgr*, Cora Dompor
Library Holdings: Bk Vols 36,147
Friends of the Library Group
TAYLOR-PACIFIC BEACH, 4275 Cass St, 92109. SAN 334-4193. Tel: 858-581-9934. Web Site: www.sannet.gov/public-library/. *Mgr*, Sharon Stevelman; E-Mail: ecu@library.sannet.gov
Library Holdings: Bk Vols 76,323
Friends of the Library Group
TIERRASANTA, 4985 La Cuenta Dr, 92124. SAN 334-4428. Tel: 619-573-1384. Web Site: www.sannet.gov/public-library/. *Mgr*, Judith Castiano
Library Holdings: Bk Vols 75,246
Friends of the Library Group
UNIVERSITY COMMUNITY, 4155 Governor Dr, 92122. SAN 334-4460. Tel: 858-552-1655. Web Site: www.sannet.gov/public-library/. *Mgr*, Ginny Boylls
Library Holdings: Bk Vols 71,452
Friends of the Library Group
UNIVERSITY HEIGHTS, 4193 Park Blvd, 92103. SAN 334-4436. Tel: 619-692-4912. Web Site: www.sannet/gov/public-library/. *Mgr*, Leslie Simmons
Library Holdings: Bk Vols 41,736
Friends of the Library Group
CITY HEIGHTS WEINGART, 3795 Fairmount Ave, 92105. SAN 334-3839. Tel: 619-641-6100. Web Site: www.sannet.gov/public-library/. *Mgr*, Ramiro Gonzalez
Library Holdings: Bk Vols 48,274
Friends of the Library Group

S SAN DIEGO SOCIETY OF NATURAL HISTORY LIBRARY,* PO Box 121390, 92112-1390. SAN 301-3480. Tel: 619-232-3821. FAX: 619-232-0248. E-Mail: library@sdnhm.org. Web Site: www.sdnhm.org/research/library/libdept/html. *Dir*, Margaret Dykens
Founded 1874
Jul 1997-Jun 1998 Income $83,616. Mats Exp $40,281, Books $10,445, Per/Ser (Incl. Access Fees) $29,836. Sal $34,188
Library Holdings: Bk Vols 91,000
Subject Interests: Botany, Mammals
Special Collections: Bird Paintings (Sutton & Brooks Coll); Geology & Paleontology (Anthony W Vodges Coll); Herpetology (Lawrence Klauber Coll); Photo Archives; Wild Flower Paintings (Valentien Coll)
Publications: Occasional Papers; Proceedings; Transactions & Memoirs superseded by Proceedings of the San Diego Society of Natural History 1990-
Partic in Coop Libr Agency for Syst & Servs; OCLC Online Computer Library Center, Inc; San Diego Greater Metro Area Libr & Info Agency Coun

C SAN DIEGO STATE UNIVERSITY LIBRARY, 5500 Campanile Dr, 92182-8050. SAN 334-4525. Tel: 619-594-6724. FAX: 619-594-2700. Web Site: libweb.sdsu.edu. *Online Servs*, Bruce Harley; *Bibliog Instr*, Linda Muroi; *Cat*, Carol Lea Goyne; *Spec Coll*, Lyn Olsson; *Ser*, Marsha Shea; *Ref*, Catherine Freeman; *Coll Develop*, Douglas Cargille; Staff 45 (MLS 45)
Founded 1897. Enrl 23,281; Fac 1,238; Highest Degree: Doctorate
Library Holdings: Bk Vols 1,273,603; Bk Titles 875,790; Per Subs 3,490
Special Collections: 20th Century San Diego History; Adams Postcard Coll; Astronomy & History of Astronomy (Ernst Zinner Coll); Bookbinding (Wallace A Pearce Coll); Chesterfield Coll; Early Botanical Works Coll; H L Mencken Coll; History of Biology (Norland Coll); JFK Coll; Jiddu Krishnamurti Coll; Modern Rare Editions (Paul L Pfaff Coll); Orchidology (Reginald S Davies Coll); San Diego State University Archives; Science Fiction (Chater Coll)
Publications: SDSU Library Newsletter
Partic in OCLC Online Computer Library Center, Inc; San Diego Greater Metro Area Libr & Info Agency Coun
Special Services for the Deaf - Books on deafness & sign language; Special interest periodicals; Staff with knowledge of sign language; TTY machine
Friends of the Library Group

S SCOTTISH RITE MASONIC LIBRARY,* 1895 Camino del Rio S, 92108. SAN 301-3499. Tel: 619-293-4888. FAX: 619-297-2751. *In Charge*, Robert Norris
Founded 1974
Library Holdings: Bk Vols 4,000; Per Subs 20
Special Collections: Taped Lectures (Masonic & related subjects)
Publications: Monthly Newsletter

M SCRIPPS MERCY HOSPITAL, Jean Farb Memorial Medical Library, 4077 Fifth Ave, 92103-2180. SAN 301-3340. Tel: 619-260-7024. FAX: 619-260-7262. E-Mail: library.mercy@scrippshealth.org. *Mgr*, Penny Ward; *Librn*, Michaele Robinson; Staff 2 (MLS 2)
Founded 1937
Oct 2000-Sep 2001 Income $285,626. Mats Exp $174,586. Sal $111,040 (Prof $111,040)
Library Holdings: Bk Vols 4,300; Bk Titles 4,000; Per Subs 285
Subject Interests: Archives, Clinical medicine, Nursing, Psychiatry
Automation Activity & Vendor Info: (Cataloging) EOS; (Circulation) EOS; (OPAC) EOS; (Serials) EOS
Database Vendor: Dialog, OCLC - First Search, OVID Technologies
Publications: Connections (electronic newsletter)
Restriction: Not open to public
Partic in Med Libr Group of S Calif & Ariz; Nat Libr of Med; OCLC Online Computer Library Center, Inc
Library maintains a homepage on Scripps Health intranet.

S SEA WORLD LIBRARY, 500 Sea World Dr, 92109-7995. SAN 301-3502. Tel: 619-222-6363, Ext 3965. TDD: 800-TD-SHAMU. FAX: 619-226-3634. Web Site: www.seaworld.com. *Dir*, Joy Wolf
Founded 1972
Library Holdings: Bk Titles 800; Per Subs 25
Subject Interests: Ichthyology, Mammals, Oceanography
Special Collections: Children's Marine Life Titles
Special Services for the Deaf - TDD

L SELTZER, CAPLAN, WILKINS & MCMAHON, Law Library,* 750 B St, Ste 2100, 92101. SAN 372-3011. Tel: 619-685-3003. FAX: 619-685-3100. *Librn*, Jean Evelyn Waters
Library Holdings: Bk Vols 8,500; Per Subs 100

P SERRA COOPERATIVE LIBRARY SYSTEM,* Bldg 15, 5555 Overland Ave, 92123. SAN 301-3510. Tel: 858-694-3600. Interlibrary Loan Service Tel: 619-232-1225. FAX: 858-495-5905. E-Mail: hq@serralib.org. Web Site: www.serralib.org. *Syst Coordr*, Susan Swisher; Staff 9 (MLS 4, Non-MLS 5)
Jul 1998-Jun 1999 Income $567,345. Mats Exp $546,470
Publications: bibliographies; Serra Newsletter; union lists
Member Libraries: Brawley Public Library; California Department of Corrections Library System; Camarena Memorial Library; Carlsbad City Library; Chula Vista Public Library; Coronado Public Library; El Centro Public Library; Imperial County Free Library; Imperial Public Library; Imperial Valley College; National City Public Library; Oceanside Public Library; San Diego County Library; San Diego County Public Law Library; San Diego Public Library
Partic in Dialog Corporation; OCLC Online Computer Library Center, Inc

M SHARP MEMORIAL HOSPITAL, Health Sciences Library, 7901 Frost St, 92123. SAN 301-3529. Tel: 858-541-3242. FAX: 858-541-3248. *Coll Develop, Head of Libr*, Laura Stubblefield; E-Mail: laura.stubblefield@sharp.com; *Asst Librn*, George Brundrett; *Asst Librn*, Dolly Bucsit
Founded 1970
Library Holdings: Bk Vols 1,100; Per Subs 250
Subject Interests: Health sciences, Medicine, Nursing
Partic in Dialog Corporation; Medline

S SOLAR TURBINES, INC LIBRARY,* 2200 Pacific Hwy, PO Box 85376, 92186-5376. SAN 301-3278. Tel: 619-544-2548. FAX: 619-544-5528. *Librn*, George Hall
Library Holdings: Bk Vols 1,000
Partic in Dialog Corporation

S UNION-TRIBUNE PUBLISHING CO LIBRARY, 350 Camino de la Reina, PO Box 120191, 92112. SAN 301-3561. Tel: 619-299-3131. Web Site: www.uniontrib.com. *Mgr*, Sharon Stewart Reeves; *Admin Assoc*, Anne Magill; *Res*, Marie Monteagudo; Staff 16 (MLS 3, Non-MLS 13)
Founded 1945
Library Holdings: Bk Vols 4,000; Bk Titles 3,100; Per Subs 50
Subject Interests: Current events, History

G UNITED STATES COURTS LIBRARY, 940 Front St, Rm 3185, 92101-8920. SAN 372-3003. Tel: 619-557-5066. FAX: 619-557-5077. *Librn*, Elizabeth Carroll; *Asst Librn*, Valerie Railey; Staff 4 (MLS 2, Non-MLS 2)
Library Holdings: Bk Vols 52,000
Restriction: Not open to public
Partic in OCLC Online Computer Library Center, Inc
Judges, court personnel, attorneys admitted to practice in Southern District of California & Ninth Circuit Court of Appeals

C UNITED STATES INTERNATIONAL UNIVERSITY, Walter Library, 10455 Pomerado Rd, 92131-1799. SAN 301-357X. Tel: 858-635-4511. Interlibrary Loan Service Tel: 858-635-4605. FAX: 858-635-4689. Web Site: www.usiu.edu/academic/waltlibr.htm. *Dir*, Connie E Cos; *Acq*, Drew Selvar; Staff 13 (MLS 4, Non-MLS 9)
Founded 1952. Enrl 1,225; Fac 200; Highest Degree: Doctorate
Jul 2000-Jun 2001 Income $565,000, Locally Generated Income $5,000, Parent Institution $560,000. Mats Exp $120,000, Books $25,000, Per/Ser (Incl. Access Fees) $55,000, Micro $10,000, Electronic Ref Mat (Incl. Access Fees) $30,000. Sal $423,151
Library Holdings: Bk Vols 130,000; Per Subs 1,500
Subject Interests: Business, Education, Global issues, Psychology
Automation Activity & Vendor Info: (Cataloging) Athena; (Circulation) Athena
Partic in SCELC
USIU also has libraries on campuses in Irvine, CA, Nairobi, Africa & Mexico City, Mexico
Friends of the Library Group

UNITED STATES NAVY

A THE COMMAND LIBRARY, Fleet Anti-Sub Warfare Training Ctr, 32444 Echo Lane, Ste 100, 92147-5199. SAN 334-4703. Tel: 619-524-1908. FAX: 619-524-6875.
Founded 1967
Library Holdings: Bk Vols 18,000; Bk Titles 3,100; Per Subs 30

A MARINE CORPS RECRUIT DEPOT LIBRARY, Bldg 7, 92140-5011. SAN 334-4762. Tel: 619-524-1849, 524-1850. FAX: 619-524-8243. *Librn*, Rebecca B Young; *Tech Servs*, Christina Rappin; Staff 1 (MLS 1)
Founded 1927
Library Holdings: Bk Vols 45,000; Per Subs 75
Special Collections: Marine Corps History
Publications: Book lists (5 per yr)
Partic in Serra Cooperative Library System

A NAVAL BASE CORONADO LIBRARY, MWR Base Library, 2478 Munda Rd, 92155-5396. SAN 334-4797. Tel: 619-437-3026. FAX: 619-437-3891. *Tech Servs*, Suzi Siemer
Founded 1944
Oct 1997-Sep 1998 Income $25,000
Library Holdings: Bk Vols 25,000; Per Subs 130
Subject Interests: Vietnam

AM NAVAL MEDICAL CENTER, Libr Bldg 5-2, Naval Med Ctr, 92134. SAN 334-4940. Tel: 619-532-7950. FAX: 619-532-9293. E-Mail: snd1mws@snd10.med.navy.mil. *Chief Librn*, Marilyn Schwartz; *Librn*, Donna Murico; *Librn*, Jan B Dempsey; Staff 8 (MLS 3, Non-MLS 5)
Founded 1922
Oct 1997-Sep 1998 Income $500,000
Library Holdings: Per Subs 950
Subject Interests: Dentistry, Medicine, Nursing
Special Collections: Layman Health Information
Partic in Dialog Corporation; Medline

A NAVY PERSONNEL RESEARCH STUDIES & TECHNOLOGY, PERS 102, 5720 Integrity Dr, Millington, 38055. SAN 334-5122. Tel: 901-874-2116. E-Mail: library@nprdc.navy.mil.
Founded 1953
Library Holdings: Bk Vols 15,000; Bk Titles 10,000; Per Subs 330
Subject Interests: Statistics
Publications: Accession list (weekly); Journal list (annually)
Partic in Calif Union List of Periodicals; Fedlink; LVIS; OCLC Online Computer Library Center, Inc

A SPAWAR SYSTEMS CENTER TECHNICAL LIBRARY, Code D0274, 53560 Hull St, 92152-5001. SAN 334-4851. Tel: 619-553-4902. FAX: 619-553-4882. E-Mail: library@spawar.navy.mil. *Head Librn*, Kathy Wright; Staff 12 (MLS 5, Non-MLS 7)
Founded 1949
Library Holdings: Bk Vols 225,000; Bk Titles 60,000; Per Subs 700
Subject Interests: Computer science, Electronics, Engineering, Marine biology, Mathematics, Ocean engineering, Physics
Special Collections: Navy Radio & Sound Laboratory Reports; War Research (National Defense Research Committee, University of California Division of
Publications: Periodical Holdings
Partic in Defense Technical Information Center; Dialog Corporation; OCLC Online Computer Library Center, Inc

A SUPERVISOR OF SHIPBUILDING CONVERSION & REPAIR LIBRARY, PO Box 368119, 92136-5066. SAN 334-5157. Tel: 619-556-3385. FAX: 619-556-3456. *In Charge*, Pat Parker; E-Mail: parkerpat@exchange.sssd.navy.mil
Founded 1950
Library Holdings: Bk Vols 20,000

AM WILKINS BIOMEDICAL LIBRARY-NAVAL HEALTH RESEARCH CENTER, PO Box 85122, 92186-5122. SAN 334-4916. Tel: 619-553-8425. FAX: 619-553-9389. *Librn*, Mary Aldous; E-Mail: aldous@nhrc.navy.mil; *Tech Servs*, Betty Croft; Staff 3 (MLS 1, Non-MLS 2)
Founded 1959
Library Holdings: Bk Titles 10,000; Per Subs 354
Subject Interests: Biochemistry, Immunology, Medicine, Military history, Psychiatry, Psychology, Sociology, Statistics
Special Collections: Naval Medicine (United States Naval Medical Bulletin, 1907-1949); Prisoner of War Studies Publications
Publications: Journal holdings list; new acquisitions list
Restriction: Staff use only
Partic in Defense Technical Information Center; Dialog Corporation; Fedlink; OCLC Online Computer Library Center, Inc

UNIVERSITY OF SAN DIEGO

C HELEN K & JAMES COPLEY LIBRARY, 5998 Alcala Park, 92110. SAN 334-5181. Tel: 619-260-2370. Interlibrary Loan Service Tel: 619-260-2364. Reference Tel: 619-260-4765. FAX: 619-260-4617. Web Site: www.acusd.edu/academic/library.shtml. *Dir*, Edward D Starkey; E-Mail: estarkey@acusd.edu; *Assoc Dir*, Marjo Gray; *Publ Servs*, Steve Staninger; *Head Tech Servs*, Margit Smith; *ILL*, Alex Moran; *Spec Coll & Archives*, Diane Maher; *Coll Develop*, Tony Harvell; *Bibliog Instr*, Karen Sharpe; *Access Serv*, Bill Hall. Subject Specialists: *Business*, Steve Staninger; *Education*, Karen Sharpe; *Humanities*, Diane Maher; *Humanities*, Edward D Starkey; *Sciences*, Marjo Gray; *Social sciences*, Margit Smith; *Social sciences*, Tony Harvell; Staff 12 (MLS 10, Non-MLS 2)
Founded 1949. Enrl 6,900
Jul 2000-Jun 2001 Income (Main Library Only) Parent Institution $3,200,000. Mats Exp $1,267,669, Books $380,200, Per/Ser (Incl. Access Fees) $583,500, Presv $25,619, Micro $53,350, Electronic Ref Mat (Incl. Access Fees) $225,000. Sal $1,729,975 (Prof $610,165)
Library Holdings: Bk Vols 370,000; Bk Titles 290,000; Per Subs 2,500
Subject Interests: Catholicism, History, Literature, Philosophy, Religion
Database Vendor: Innovative Interfaces INN - View
Partic in San Diego Library Circuit; SCELC
Friends of the Library Group

CL LEGAL RESEARCH CENTER, 5998 Alcala Park, 92110-2491. SAN 334-5211. Tel: 619-260-4542. FAX: 619-260-4616. E-Mail: ncc@acusd.edu. Web Site: www.acusd.edu/lrc. *Dir*, Nancy Carol Carter; *Assoc Dir*, L Ruth Levor; *Publ Servs*, Franklin A Weston; *Ref*, John Adkins; *Ref*, Owen Smith; *Ref*, Patricia Bermel; *Cat*, Kathy Whistler; *Cat*, Margaret McDonald; Staff 10 (MLS 10)
Founded 1954. Enrl 1,080; Fac 82; Highest Degree: Doctorate
1996-1997 Income $2,363,259. Mats Exp $355,508, Books $109,508, Presv $20,956, Micro $225,044. Sal $899,569 (Prof $505,936)
Library Holdings: Bk Vols 196,978; Bk Titles 192,068; Per Subs 5,405
Publications: Guide series; Information Series
Partic in OCLC Online Computer Library Center, Inc; Westlaw
Friends of the Library Group

S URS CORPORATION, Woodward-Clyde International Library, 1615 Murray Canyon Rd, Ste 1000, 92108-4324. SAN 321-3838. Tel: 619-294-9400. Toll Free Tel: 800-697-1550. FAX: 619-293-7920. Web Site: www.wcc.com. *Librn*, Margo Treihaft; E-Mail: margo_treihaft@urscorp.com
Founded 1959
Library Holdings: Bk Vols 3,500; Per Subs 85
Subject Interests: Environmental law, Environmental regulations, Geology, Geotech eng, Groundwater, Hazardous waste
Publications: Acquisitions List (bi-monthly)

§S US NATIONAL PARK SERVICES, Cabrillo National Monument Library, 1800 Cabrillo Memorial Dr, 92106-3601. Tel: 619-557-5450. TDD: 619-222-8211. FAX: 619-557-5469. E-Mail: cabr_administration@nps.gov. Web Site: www.nps.gov/cabr. *In Charge*, Karl Pierce
Library Holdings: Bk Vols 2,700; Per Subs 20
Special Collections: 216,000 archives-Park Records & manuscripts
Restriction: Open to public for reference only
Special Services for the Deaf - TDD
Open Sun-Sat 9-5:15

S ZOOLOGICAL SOCIETY OF SAN DIEGO LIBRARY,* San Diego Zoo, PO Box 120-551, 92112-0551. SAN 301-3596. Tel: 619-557-3908. FAX: 619-595-1717. *Librn, Online Servs*, Linda L Coates; Staff 2 (MLS 1, Non-MLS 1)
Founded 1916
Library Holdings: Bk Vols 13,000; Per Subs 680
Subject Interests: Horticulture, Veterinary medicine
Special Collections: Ernst Schwarz Coll, reprints; Herpetology (Charles E Shaw Coll), bks, reprints; Zoo Publications (annual reports, guidebooks, newsletters)
Publications: Accessions list (monthly)
Partic in Coop Libr Agency for Syst & Servs; Dialog Corporation; OCLC Online Computer Library Center, Inc; San Diego Greater Metro Area Libr & Info Agency Coun

SAN DIMAS

S INTERNATIONAL INSTITUTE OF MUNICIPAL CLERKS, Management Information Center,* 1212 N San Dimas Canyon Rd, 91773. SAN 328-5154. Tel: 909-592-4462. FAX: 909-592-1555. *In Charge*, Ani Kevorkian
Library Holdings: Bk Titles 400
Open Mon-Fri 7-4

R LIFE BIBLE COLLEGE ALUMNI LIBRARY,* 1100 Covina Blvd, 91773. SAN 300-9467. Tel: 909-599-5433. FAX: 909-599-6690. E-Mail: lifebibl@tstonramp.com. Web Site: www.tsonramp.com/~lifebibl. *Librn*, Keith Dawson
Founded 1925. Enrl 397; Fac 26; Highest Degree: Bachelor
Library Holdings: Bk Vols 34,500; Bk Titles 32,000; Per Subs 250
Subject Interests: Education, Religion
Special Collections: Archive of International Church of the Foursquare Gospel

SAN FRANCISCO

S ACADEMY OF ART COLLEGE LIBRARY, 180 New Montogomery, 6th flr, 94105. SAN 372-6452. Tel: 415-274-2270. FAX: 415-263-8803. Web Site: www.academyart.edu. *Dir*, John Winsor; Staff 11 (MLS 3, Non-MLS 8)
Founded 1929. Enrl 5,200; Fac 900
Library Holdings: Bk Vols 26,000; Bk Titles 18,000; Per Subs 300
Subject Interests: Visual arts
Special Collections: Art & Applied Art, bks, slides, videos, cd-rom
Database Vendor: Innovative Interfaces INN - View
Partic in Coop Libr Agency for Syst & Servs

M AMERICAN ACADEMY OF OPHTHALMOLOGY LIBRARY, PO Box 7424, 94120-7424. SAN 374-8995. Tel: 415-561-8500. FAX: 415-561-8533. Web Site: www.eyenet.org. *Mgr*, Beverly Taugher; E-Mail: btaugher@aao.org; Staff 2 (MLS 1, Non-MLS 1)
Library Holdings: Bk Titles 500; Per Subs 62

S ARTHUR ANDERSEN & CO, San Francisco Office Library, 101 Second St, Ste 1100, 94105. SAN 324-7856. Tel: 415-546-8466. FAX: 415-543-1827. *Dir Libr Serv*, Martha Kassin; *Librn*, Kurt W Shuck; E-Mail: kurt.w.shuck@us.arthurandersen.com. Subject Specialists: *Accounting*, Kurt W Shuck; *Tax*, Kurt W Shuck; Staff 3 (MLS 1, Non-MLS 2)
Library Holdings: Bk Vols 500; Bk Titles 300; Per Subs 200
Subject Interests: Accounting, Auditing, Bus, Mgt consulting, Tax
Database Vendor: Lexis-Nexis
Restriction: Staff use only
Function: Research library
Partic in Coop Libr Agency for Syst & Servs; Dialog Corporation; Dow Jones News Retrieval

S ANNUAL REPORTS LIBRARY & MUSEUM,* 369 Broadway, PO Box 2006, 94126. SAN 374-5082. Tel: 415-956-6808, 415-956-8665. FAX: 415-421-2544. Web Site: www.zpub.com/sf/arl. *Librn*, Jim Milner; E-Mail: jimilner@hotmail.com; *Asst Librn, Tech Servs*, Jane S Cynthia; *Ref*, Richard Wahlberg; Staff 4 (MLS 2, Non-MLS 2)
Founded 1979
Library Holdings: Per Subs 15
Special Collections: Corporate Reports (JLM Coll), bks on annual report presentations
Publications: Newsletter on annual reports
Friends of the Library Group

S ANSHEN & ALLEN, ARCHITECTS LIBRARY,* 901 Market St, Ste 600, 94103. SAN 325-6375. Tel: 415-882-9500. FAX: 415-882-9523. *Librn*, Nancy Bruer-Hufford
Library Holdings: Bk Vols 600; Per Subs 100
Restriction: Staff use only

§S ART INSTITUTES INTERNATIONAL AT SAN FRANCISCO LIBRARY, 1170 Market St, 94102-4908. SAN 378-3782. Tel: 415-865-0198. Toll Free Tel: 888-493-3261. FAX: 415-863-5831. Web Site: www.aisf.artinstitutes.edu. *Dir*, David Briggs; E-Mail: david@info.sims.berkeley.edu
Library Holdings: Bk Titles 3,000; Per Subs 100
Automation Activity & Vendor Info: (OPAC) Sagebrush Corporation

S ASTRONOMICAL SOCIETY OF THE PACIFIC LIBRARY, 390 Ashton Ave, 94112. SAN 325-6677. Tel: 415-337-1100. FAX: 415-337-5205. E-Mail: membership@aspsky.org. Web Site: www.aspsky.org. *Exec Dir*, James C White, II; E-Mail: jwhite@aspsky.org
Founded 1889
Library Holdings: Bk Titles 1,600; Per Subs 50
Subject Interests: Astronomy, History of science, Space science
Special Collections: People & objects in astronomy, photo archive
Publications: Bibliographies; journals; newsletter

L BAKER & MCKENZIE LIBRARY, 2 Embarcadero Ctr, Ste 2400, 94111-3909. SAN 321-4028. Tel: 415-576-3066. FAX: 415-576-3099. *Librn*, Donna Purvis; E-Mail: dpurvis@bakernet.com; *Ref*, Caren Doyle; Staff 4 (MLS 2, Non-MLS 2)
Founded 1970
Library Holdings: Bk Vols 10,000; Bk Titles 2,000; Per Subs 400
Subject Interests: Law

BANK OF AMERICA

L LAW LIBRARY, Dept 13220, 555 California St, 7th flr, 94104. SAN 334-5246. Tel: 415-622-6601. FAX: 415-622-9238. *Dir*, Lauri R Flynn; *Librn*, Trish McCurdy; E-Mail: patricia.mccurdy@bankamerica.com
Library Holdings: Bk Vols 22,000
Subject Interests: Commercial law
Restriction: Not open to public
Partic in Dialog Corporation; Westlaw

S TECHNOLOGY LIBRARY, 1755 Grant, CAY-703-01-23, Concord, 94520. SAN 324-752X. Tel: 925-675-1361. FAX: 925-675-3411. *Mgr*, Larry White; *Ref*, Lee Stoney; Staff 3 (MLS 2, Non-MLS 1)
Founded 1978
Library Holdings: Bk Titles 9,000
Subject Interests: Data processing, Internet, Programming, Telecommunications
Automation Activity & Vendor Info: (Cataloging) EOS; (Circulation) EOS; (OPAC) EOS
Restriction: Staff use only

S BECHTEL CORPORATE LIBRARY,* 50 Beale St, PO Box 193965, 50/2/C32, 94119-3965. SAN 301-3707. Tel: 415-768-5306. FAX: 415-768-0837. E-Mail: jxmah@bechtel.com. *Chief Librn*, Jeffery Mah
Founded 1951
Library Holdings: Bk Titles 40,000; Per Subs 250
Subject Interests: Business and management, Construction, Energy, Engineering
Partic in Dialog Corporation; Dow Jones News Retrieval; Dun & Bradstreet Info Servs; Profound; RLIN
Branches:
COMPUTER SERVICES, 50 Beale St, 5th flr, Rm D75, 94105. SAN 322-8959. Tel: 415-768-9015. FAX: 415-768-7327. *Librn*, Mercedes Dumlao; *Tech Servs*, Vijaya Vasireddi; Staff 2 (MLS 1, Non-MLS 1)
Founded 1973
Library Holdings: Bk Vols 2,000; Bk Titles 400; Per Subs 5
Special Collections: BECCAT, computer readable materials on tape & disks; Program documentation; Vendor software manual, computer program software catalogs
Publications: Bechtel Standards for Production Computer Application; Computer Program Catalog

S BECHTEL ENTERPRISES, Research & Information Center,* 50 California, PO Box 193965, 50C/2207, 94119. SAN 370-8438. Tel: 415-768-5100. FAX: 415-951-0846. *Res*, Geradine Kaman; E-Mail: gmkaman@ben.bechtel.com; Staff 1 (MLS 1)
Library Holdings: Bk Vols 650; Per Subs 120
Restriction: Not open to public

L BEVERIDGE & DIAMOND, Law Library,* One Sansome St, Ste 3400, 94104. SAN 375-0205. Tel: 415-397-0100. FAX: 415-397-4243. *Librn*, Darlene Kaskie
Library Holdings: Bk Vols 4,000
Subject Interests: Environmental law

S BOHEMIAN CLUB LIBRARY, 624 Taylor St, 94102. SAN 301-3723. Tel: 415-885-2440. FAX: 415-567-2332. *Head Librn*, Matthew W Buff; E-Mail: mbuff@bc-owl.org; Staff 1 (MLS 1)
Publications: Library Notes (occasional)
Restriction: Members only, Private library

L BROBECK, PHLEGER & HARRISON LIBRARY,* One Market Spear Tower, 94105. SAN 301-374X. Tel: 415-979-2619. Interlibrary Loan Service Tel: 415-979-2623. FAX: 415-442-1010. Web Site: www.brobeck.com. *Ref*, Alan R MacDougall
Library Holdings: Bk Vols 39,100
Subject Interests: Law
Partic in Dialog Corporation; Dow Jones News Retrieval; Lexis, RLIN; Westlaw

R BUREAU OF JEWISH EDUCATION, Jewish Community Library, 601 14th Ave, 94118. SAN 301-3766. Tel: 415-751-6983, Ext 106. FAX: 415-668-1816. Web Site: www.bjesf.org. *Librn*, Jonathan Schwartz
Library Holdings: Bk Vols 30,000; Per Subs 84
Subject Interests: Children's literature, Hebrew (Language), Holocaust, Russian (language), Yiddish (Language)
Friends of the Library Group

S C G JUNG INSTITUTE OF SAN FRANCISCO, Virginia Allan Detloff Library, 2040 Gough St, 94109. SAN 372-5928. Tel: 415-771-8055. FAX: 415-771-8926. E-Mail: library@sfjung.org. Web Site: www.sfjung.org. *Coll Develop, Librn*, Marianne Morgan; E-Mail: mmorgan@sfjung.org; Staff 2 (MLS 1, Non-MLS 1)
Founded 1965. Enrl 40; Fac 27
Jul 2000-Jun 2001 Income $52,800, Locally Generated Income $8,800, Parent Institution $44,000. Mats Exp $8,550, Books $4,000, Per/Ser (Incl. Access Fees) $4,000, Presv $500, Micro $50. Sal $35,000 (Prof $18,000)

Library Holdings: Bk Titles 8,500; Per Subs 20
Subject Interests: Art, Jungian psychol, Mythology, Psychology
Special Collections: Archive of Historical Jungiana, Audio & Video
Automation Activity & Vendor Info: (Acquisitions) Inmagic, Inc.; (Cataloging) Inmagic, Inc.
Publications: Acquisitions list (quarterly)
Function: ILL available, Reference services available
Partic in Northern Calif Consortium of Psychol Librs
Open Mon-Fri 9-5

S CALIFORNIA ACADEMY OF SCIENCES LIBRARY, Golden Gate Park, 94118. SAN 301-3774. Tel: 415-750-7102. FAX: 415-750-7106. E-Mail: library@calacademy.org. Web Site: www.calacademy.org/research/library. *Head Librn*, Anne Marie Malley; Tel: 415-750-7101, E-Mail: amalley@calacademy.org; *Assoc Librn*, David Acheson; Tel: 415-750-7103, E-Mail: dacheson@calacademy.org; *Assoc Librn*, Stella Tang; Tel: 415-750-7103, E-Mail: stang@calacademy.org; *Asst Librn*, Laura Burkhart; E-Mail: lburkhart@calacademy.org; *Asst Librn*, Lawrence Currie; Tel: 415-750-7108, E-Mail: lcurrie@calacademy.org; *Asst Librn*, Diane Sands; Tel: 415-750-7361, E-Mail: dsands@calacademy.org; *Archivist*, Michele Wellck; Tel: 415-750-7301, E-Mail: mwellck@calacademy.org; *Spec Coll*, Carrie Burroughs; Tel: 415-750-7104, E-Mail: cburroughs@calacademy.org. Subject Specialists: *Natural history*, Anne Marie Malley; *Natural history*, Laura Burkhart; *Natural history*, Diane Sands; *Natural history*, Lawrence Currie; Staff 15 (MLS 8, Non-MLS 7)
Founded 1853
Jul 1999-Jun 2000 Income Parent Institution $558,750. Mats Exp $223,950, Books $27,500, Per/Ser (Incl. Access Fees) $81,500, AV Equip $5,000. Sal $334,800
Library Holdings: Bk Vols 190,000; Per Subs 2,500
Subject Interests: Anthropology, Astronomy, Botany, Entomology, Geography, Geology, Herpetology, Ichthyology, Marine biology, Museology, Natural history, Ornithology, Paleontology, Zoology
Special Collections: Academy Archives; Natural history image clippings files; Natural history photography coll
Automation Activity & Vendor Info: (Cataloging) DRA; (Circulation) DRA
Database Vendor: DRA, Ebsco - EbscoHost, OCLC - First Search, Silverplatter Information Inc.
Publications: Accessions List (bi-monthly); Selected New Acquisitions (newsletter, monthly)
Function: Research library
Partic in Bay Area Library & Information Network; OCLC Online Computer Library Center, Inc
OCLC records included in University of California MELVYL database, accessible through the Internet

CM CALIFORNIA COLLEGE OF PODIATRIC MEDICINE, Schmidt Medical Library, 1210 Scott St, 94115. SAN 301-3782. Tel: 415-292-0409. FAX: 415-292-0467. Web Site: www.ccpm.edu. *Dir, Per*, Ronald E Schultz; E-Mail: rschultz@ccpm.edu; *Asst Librn, Tech Servs*, Tilly Roche; E-Mail: troche@ccpm.edu; *ILL*, Tanya Fimby; E-Mail: tfimby@ccpm.edu; Staff 3 (MLS 2, Non-MLS 1)
Founded 1963. Enrl 400; Fac 75; Highest Degree: Doctorate
Jul 1999-Jun 2000 Income $160,000. Mats Exp $45,000, Books $16,000, Per/Ser (Incl. Access Fees) $24,000. Sal $111,000 (Prof $64,000)
Library Holdings: Per Subs 200
Special Collections: Orthopedics Coll, bk, per, tape; Podiatry Coll, bk, per, tape; Sports Medicine Coll, bk, per, tape
Automation Activity & Vendor Info: (Acquisitions) Sydney; (Circulation) SIRSI; (OPAC) Sydney
Publications: Library handbook (biennial); newsletter/acquisitions list (quarterly); serials holding list (annual)
Partic in Northern California & Nevada Medical Library Group; Pacific SW Regional Med Libr Serv
Friends of the Library Group

S CALIFORNIA HISTORICAL SOCIETY, North Baker Research Library, 678 Mission St, 94105. SAN 320-1635. Tel: 415-357-1848, Ext 20. FAX: 415-357-1850. E-Mail: bakerlib@calhist.org. Web Site: www.calhist.org. *Dir*, Tanya Hollis; *Cat*, Brenda Baldwin; Staff 3 (MLS 3)
Founded 1922
1998-1999 Mats Exp $2,800, Books $500, Per/Ser (Incl. Access Fees) $300, Presv $2,000. Sal $74,500 (Prof $74,500)
Library Holdings: Bk Vols 56,000; Bk Titles 30,000; Per Subs 52
Subject Interests: California, History, Rare books
Special Collections: Manuscript & Archival Coll; Photograph Coll; Taylor & Taylor (S F) Archives; Western Printing & Publishing (Edward C Kemble Coll)
Restriction: By appointment only, Not a lending library
Partic in Melvyl; RLIN
Friends of the Library Group

C CALIFORNIA INSTITUTE OF INTEGRAL STUDIES, Laurance S Rockefeller Library, 1453 Mission St, 94103. SAN 320-6025. Tel: 415-575-6180. Interlibrary Loan Service Tel: 415-575-6187. Reference Tel: 415-575-6186. FAX: 415-575-1264. E-Mail: lib@ciis.edu. *Dir*, Olive C R James; Tel: 415-755-6181, E-Mail: olivej@ciis.edu; *Online Servs*, Joshua Boatright; Tel: 415-575-6187, E-Mail: joshuab@ciis.edu; *Res*, Lee J Olivier; Tel: 415-575-6183, E-Mail: leeo@ciis.edu; Staff 6 (MLS 2, Non-MLS 4)
Founded 1968. Enrl 1,000; Fac 45; Highest Degree: Doctorate
Jul 2000-Jun 2001 Income $319,000, Parent Institution $312,000. Sal $185,000 (Prof $97,000)
Library Holdings: Bk Vols 30,000; Bk Titles 22,000; Per Subs 200
Subject Interests: East-West relations, Philosophy, Psychology, Religion, Spirituality, Women relig
Automation Activity & Vendor Info: (Cataloging) Sagebrush Corporation; (Circulation) Sagebrush Corporation; (OPAC) Sagebrush Corporation
Database Vendor: Ebsco - EbscoHost, OCLC - First Search, ProQuest, Silverplatter Information Inc.
Partic in Northern Calif Consortium of Psychol Librs; SCELC

GL CALIFORNIA JUDICIAL CENTER LIBRARY,* South Tower, Rm 8047, 303 Second St, 94107. SAN 301-4746. Tel: 415-396-9439. FAX: 415-396-9585. *Librn*, Karen Toran; E-Mail: karen_toran@jud.ca.gov
Founded 1868
Library Holdings: Bk Vols 150,000; Per Subs 150
Partic in Bay Area Library & Information Network; Coop Libr Agency for Syst & Servs; Westlaw

M CALIFORNIA PACIFIC MEDICAL CENTER, DAVIES CAMPUS, Dr OW Jones Jr Library, Castro & Duboce Sts, 94114. SAN 301-3960. Tel: 415-565-6352. FAX: 415-241-5619. *Librn*, Anne L Shew
Library Holdings: Bk Vols 1,400; Bk Titles 900; Per Subs 156
Publications: Acquisition List
Restriction: Staff use only
Partic in Coop Libr Agency for Syst & Servs; Medline; Pacific Southwest Regional Med Libr Serv; San Francisco Biomedical Library Network

CM CALIFORNIA PACIFIC MEDICAL CENTER-UNIVERSITY OF THE PACIFIC SCHOOL OF DENTISTRY, Health Sciences Library, 2395 Sacramento St, 94115. (Mail add: PO Box 7999, 94115-7999), SAN 301-4851. Tel: 415-923-3240. FAX: 415-923-6597. E-Mail: cpmclib@sutterhealth.org. Web Site: www.cpmc.org/health_library. *Mgr*, Douglas Varner; E-Mail: varnerd@sutterhealth.org; Staff 7 (MLS 2, Non-MLS 5)
Founded 1870. Enrl 415; Fac 115
Library Holdings: Bk Vols 35,635; Bk Titles 18,790; Per Subs 685
Subject Interests: Dentistry, Medicine, Ophthalmology, Orthopedics
Partic in Asn for Vision Sci Librns; San Francisco Biomedical Library Network
Departmental Libraries:
ARTHUR E GUEDEL MEMORIAL ANESTHESIA CENTER LIBRARY Tel: 415-923-3240. FAX: 415-923-6597. E-Mail: varnerd@sutterhealth.org. Web Site: www.cpmc.org/health_library/guedel.
Founded 1968
Library Holdings: Bk Titles 1,242; Per Subs 55
Subject Interests: Anesthesiology
Publications: Catalog

G CALIFORNIA STATE COURT OF APPEAL, First District Library,* 303 Second St, Ste 600 S Tower, 94107. SAN 322-6638. Tel: 415-396-9758. FAX: 415-396-9668. *Librn*, Bonnie Lee; Staff 2 (MLS 1, Non-MLS 1)
Library Holdings: Bk Vols 60,000; Per Subs 125
Subject Interests: Law
Restriction: Staff use only

S CALIFORNIA STATE LIBRARY, Sutro Library, 480 Winston Dr, 94132. SAN 301-4754. Tel: 415-731-4477. FAX: 415-557-9325. *Dir*, Clyde Janes; E-Mail: cjanes@library.ca.gov; *Ref*, Frank Glover; *Ref*, Martha Whittaker
Founded 1870
Special Collections: Ancient Hebrew Manuscripts and Scrolls Coll; English History and Literature from Shakespeare to Victoria Coll; Genealogy and Local History Coll; History of Printing and Book Illustrations Coll; History of the Pure and Applied Sciences to 1900 Coll; Mexican History and Literature from the Conquest to 1900 Coll; Papers of Sir Joseph Banks Coll; Voyages and Travel from Columbus to Byrd Coll
Publications: A Quarterly List; New Arrivals in American Local History and Genealogy
Branch of California State Library, Sacramento
Friends of the Library Group

L CARROLL, BURDICK & MCDONOUGH, Law Library,* 44 Montgomery St, Ste 400, 94104. SAN 372-2996. Tel: 415-989-5900. FAX: 415-989-0932. *Librn*, Nancy Castor
Library Holdings: Bk Vols 10,000
Partic in OCLC Online Computer Library Center, Inc

S CHANDLER, WOOD, HARRINGTON & MAFFLY LIBRARY,* One Maritime Plaza 4th flr, 94111. SAN 323-4142. Tel: 415-421-5484. FAX: 415-986-4874. E-Mail: harr@well.com. *Librn*, Carol Brenner
Library Holdings: Bk Vols 500
Subject Interests: Law

CITY & COUNTY OF SAN FRANCISCO
GL LAW LIBRARY, SAN FRANCISCO CITY ATTORNEY, 1390 Market St, Ste 500, 94102. SAN 301-3871. Tel: 415-554-3821. FAX: 415-554-4318. *Librn*, Maria Protti

Library Holdings: Bk Vols 24,250; Per Subs 26
Subject Interests: Municipal law
Special Collections: Municipal Reports 1862 to date; San Francisco City Attorney Opinions 1893 to date; Statutes & Amendments to Codes of California Coll
Publications: San Francisco City Attorney Opinions (annual)
Partic in Westlaw

J CITY COLLEGE OF SAN FRANCISCO LIBRARY,* 50 Phelan Ave, 94112. SAN 301-388X. Tel: 415-452-5454. Interlibrary Loan Service Tel: 415-239-3267. FAX: 415-452-5588. Web Site: www.ccsf.cc.ca.us.librar. *Dean*, Rita W Jones; E-Mail: rjones@ccsf.cc.ca.us; *AV*, Philip Paulsen; *Media Spec*, Alexander Valentine; *Online Servs*, Julia Bergman; *Cat*, Agnes Szombathy; *Archivist, Coordr*, John Few; *Ref*, Karen Saginor; *Ref*, James Lim; *Ref*, Brian Lym; *Ref*, Mark Fan; *Per*, Christopher Cox; *Ref*, Kate Connell; *Ref*, Margaret Brickner; *Bibliog Instr*, Bonnie Gratch; Staff 12 (MLS 12)
Founded 1935. Enrl 34,918; Fac 2,692
Library Holdings: Bk Vols 153,180; Per Subs 39
Special Collections: Hotel-Restaurant (Alice Statler Coll), bks, microflm, reels
Automation Activity & Vendor Info: (Acquisitions) epixtech, inc.; (Cataloging) epixtech, inc.; (Circulation) epixtech, inc.
Publications: Library Tips
Partic in Bay Area Library & Information Network; Coop Libr Agency for Syst & Servs; OCLC Online Computer Library Center, Inc

S COMMONWEALTH CLUB OF CALIFORNIA, Stuart Richardson Ward Library,* 595 Market St, 94105. SAN 301-3901. Tel: 415-597-6700. FAX: 415-597-6729. E-Mail: cwc@sirius.com. Web Site: www.commonwealthclub.org. *Mgr*, Cara Lane
Founded 1903
Library Holdings: Bk Titles 6,000; Per Subs 150

S COMMUNICATIONS LIBRARY, Lock Box 472139, Marina Sta, 94147-2139. SAN 371-5817. Tel: 415-626-5050. FAX: 415-626-5050 (Fax upon arrangement). E-Mail: ComLibrary@aol.com. Web Site: www.nvo.com/cinst. *Admin Dir*, Phillip D'Artagnan Greenleaf; Staff 8 (MLS 2, Non-MLS 6)
Founded 1965
Jan 2000-Dec 2000 Income $200,000, Locally Generated Income $100,000, Parent Institution $100,000. Mats Exp $27,500, Per/Ser (Incl. Access Fees) $1,500, Presv $1,000, Other Print Mats $10,000, Manuscripts & Archives $15,000. Sal $60,000 (Prof $45,000)
Library Holdings: Bk Vols 20,000; Per Subs 125; Spec Interest Per Sub 100
Subject Interests: Cable indust, Communications
Special Collections: Cable Television History in United States 1950-1999; Communications Worldwide Courses & Degrees; Open-ended Directory of Institutions of Higher Education Worldwide Offering Studies in Communications; Open-ended Non-cumulative Bibliography on Cable Television
Automation Activity & Vendor Info: (Cataloging) Inmagic, Inc.
Database Vendor: Ebsco - EbscoHost, GaleNet
Publications: BCTV: Bibliography on Cable Television (non-cumulative annual); BCTV: Bibliography on Cable Television, 1975-1984; CINCOM - 2000: Courses in Communications (Reference guide)
Restriction: By appointment only, Staff use only, Students only
Function: Research library
Friends of the Library Group

L COOLEY GODWARD LLP LIBRARY, One Maritime Plaza, 20th flr, 94111-3580. SAN 301-391X. Tel: 415-693-2000. FAX: 415-951-3699. *In Charge*, Yvonne Boyer; E-Mail: boyery@cooley.com; *Ref*, Margaret Baer; *Tech Servs*, Vera Janour; *Tech Servs*, Alla Medvinsky; Staff 4 (MLS 2, Non-MLS 2)
Library Holdings: Bk Vols 20,000
Subject Interests: Law
Partic in Dialog Corporation; Westlaw

L COOPER, WHITE & COOPER, Law Library, 201 California St, 17th flr, 94111-5002. SAN 372-3917. Tel: 415-433-1900. FAX: 415-433-5530. Web Site: cwclaw.com. *Mgr*, Cindy Beck Weller; Tel: 415-433-1900, Ext 6269, E-Mail: cweller@cwclaw.com; *Ref*, Phyllis Cronin; Tel: 415-433-1900, Ext 6231, E-Mail: pcronin@cwclaw.com. Subject Specialists: *Law*, Phyllis Cronin; Staff 2 (MLS 2)
Founded 1896
1999-2000 Mats Exp Electronic Ref Mat (Incl. Access Fees) $180,000. Sal $110,000
Library Holdings: Bk Vols 20,000; Per Subs 200
Subject Interests: Construction, Corporate law, Employment, Labor, Telecommunications law
Special Collections: Law
Automation Activity & Vendor Info: (Cataloging) Inmagic, Inc.; (Serials) Inmagic, Inc.
Database Vendor: Dialog, Lexis-Nexis
Restriction: Private library
Function: For research purposes
Partic in Northern Calif Asn of Law Librs

S DEGENKOLB ENGINEERS LIBRARY,* 225 Bush St, Ste 1000, 94104. SAN 327-6864. Tel: 415-392-6952. FAX: 415-981-3157. *Librn*, Wess-John Murdough; E-Mail: murdough@degenkolb.com
Library Holdings: Bk Vols 3,200
Special Collections: EERC Reports; Technical papers
Restriction: By appointment only
Partic in Bay Area Library & Information Network

GM DEPARTMENT OF VETERANS AFFAIRS LIBRARY,* Medical Library, 4150 Clement St, 94121. SAN 301-4878. Tel: 415-221-4810, Ext 3302. FAX: 415-750-6919. Web Site: www.sf.med.va.gov/medlib. *Chief Librn*, William Koch; Tel: 415-221-4810, Ext 3302, E-Mail: william.koch@med.va.gov; *Librn*, Anne Ludvik
Founded 1949
Library Holdings: Bk Vols 4,500; Bk Titles 4,000; Per Subs 335
Special Collections: Patient Education
Database Vendor: IAC - Info Trac, OVID Technologies
Partic in Vets Admin Libr Network

L DERBY, COOK, QUINBY & TWEEDT, Law Library,* 333 Market St Ste 2800, 94105. SAN 372-2961. Tel: 415-777-0505. FAX: 415-546-5896.
Library Holdings: Bk Vols 9,000; Per Subs 200

S DOLBY LABORATORIES, INC, Technical Library,* 100 Potrero Ave, 94103. SAN 370-2286. Tel: 415-558-0268. FAX: 415-863-1373. E-Mail: tlh@dolby.com. *In Charge*, Tamara Horacek
Library Holdings: Bk Vols 2,700; Per Subs 250

S DRESDNER RCM GLOBAL INVESTORS, Research Library, 4 Embarcadero Ctr, Ste 2900, 94111-4189. SAN 320-6068. Tel: 415-954-5400. FAX: 415-954-8200. *Head of Libr*, Biff Moshe
Library Holdings: Bk Vols 300; Per Subs 162
Restriction: Not open to public

S EARTH ISLAND INSTITUTE LIBRARY,* 300 Broadway, Ste 28, 94133. SAN 370-2170. Tel: 415-788-3666. FAX: 415-788-7324. E-Mail: earthisland@earthisland.org. Web Site: www.earthisland.org.
Library Holdings: Bk Vols 2,000

S ESHERICK, HOMSEY, DODGE & DAVIS LIBRARY,* 500 Treat Ave No 201, 94110. SAN 301-3987. Tel: 415-285-9193. FAX: 415-285-3866. Web Site: www.ehdd.com. *Librn*, Judith Paquette; E-Mail: judithpaquette@ehdd.com; Staff 1 (MLS 1)
Founded 1970
Library Holdings: Bk Titles 2,800; Per Subs 140
Subject Interests: Architecture, Planning
Restriction: Staff use only

§S EXPLORATORIUM LEARNING STUDIO LIBRARY, 3601 Lyon St, 94123. Tel: 415-353-0343. FAX: 415-561-0370. Web Site: www.exploratorium.edu/ls. *Actg Mgr*, Jo Falcon; *Senior Info Specialist*, Rosemarie E Falanga; E-Mail: rosef@exploratorium.edu
Library Holdings: Bk Vols 8,000; Per Subs 100
Automation Activity & Vendor Info: (Cataloging) Bestseller; (Circulation) Bestseller; (OPAC) Bestseller; (Serials) Bestseller
Restriction: Open to others by appointment, Staff use only

S FARALLONE'S MARINE SANCTUARY ASSOCIATION LIBRARY, Old Coast Guard Station Presido, PO Box 29386, 94129-0386. SAN 375-2453. Tel: 415-561-6625. FAX: 415-561-6616. Web Site: www.farallones.org. *Dir*, Maria Brown
Library Holdings: Bk Vols 5,000

L FARELLA, BRAUN & MARTEL, Law Library,* 235 Montgomery St, 19th flr, 94104. SAN 372-297X. Tel: 415-954-4451. FAX: 415-954-4480. *Librn*, Mary Staats
Library Holdings: Bk Vols 20,000

J FASHION INSTITUTE OF DESIGN & MERCHANDISING, Cyril Magnin Resource & Research Center, 55 Stockton St 5th flr, 94108. SAN 326-8918. Tel: 415-675-5200, 415-675-5218. FAX: 415-296-7299. Web Site: www.fidm.com. *Coordr*, Rob Gillian; Staff 2 (MLS 2)
Enrl 500
Library Holdings: Bk Titles 4,200; Per Subs 130
Subject Interests: Fashion, Interior design
Special Collections: Advertising Art (Joseph Magnin Coll), ad slicks, scrapbks, cats; Costume Coll 1860s to present; Roos-Atkins Coll, scrapbks of newsp clippings

S FEDERAL HOME LOAN BANK OF SAN FRANCISCO LIBRARY,* 600 California, PO Box 7948, 94120. SAN 301-4010. Tel: 415-616-2701. FAX: 415-616-2626. *Librn*, Inga Govaars
Pop 200
Library Holdings: Bk Vols 3,000; Per Subs 700
Subject Interests: Finance, Housing
Publications: Selected Additions (monthly)

S FEDERAL RESERVE BANK OF SAN FRANCISCO, Research Library, 101 Market St, PO Box 7702, 94105. SAN 301-4029. Tel: 415-974-3216. FAX: 415-974-3429. *Mgr*, Miriam Ciochon; *Ref*, Tim DeWolf; *Ref*, Patricia

Rea; *Tech Servs*, Diane Rosenberger
Library Holdings: Bk Vols 35,000; Bk Titles 18,000; Per Subs 350
Restriction: By appointment only

G FEDERAL TRADE COMMISSION, San Francisco Regional Office Library,* 901 Market St, Ste 570, 94103. SAN 301-4037. Tel: 415-356-5270. FAX: 415-356-5284.

S FINE ARTS MUSEUMS OF SAN FRANCISCO RESEARCH LIBRARY, M H de Young Memorial Museum,* Golden Gate Park, 94118. SAN 301-4045. Tel: 415-750-3600. FAX: 415-750-7692. *Librn*, Allison Pennell
Founded 1955
Library Holdings: Bk Titles 42,000; Per Subs 150
Special Collections: Bothin American Art Library Coll - Achenbach Foundation for Graphic Arts Library
Consists of the combined libraries of the M H de Young Memorial Museum (founded 1955) & the California Palace of the Legion of Honor (founded 1930). The California Palace of the Legion of Honor includes the Achenbach Foundation for Graphic Arts Library

L FOLGER, LEVIN & KAHN, Law Library,* Embarcadero Ctr W, 275 Battery St 23rd flr, 94111. SAN 372-3062. Tel: 415-986-2800. FAX: 415-986-2827. *Librn*, Carolyn Applegate-London
Library Holdings: Bk Vols 10,000

S FORBES NORRIS MDA-ALS CENTER, Patient Support Group Library,* 2324 Sacramento St, 94115. SAN 323-5009. Tel: 415-923-3604. FAX: 415-673-5184. *Dir*, Robert G Miller
Founded 1984
Library Holdings: Bk Vols 500
Open Mon-Fri 9-5

S FOUNDATION CENTER-SAN FRANCISCO LIBRARY, 312 Sutter St, No 606, 94108. SAN 301-4061. Tel: 415-397-0902. FAX: 415-397-7670. E-Mail: jfc@fdncenter.org. Web Site: www.fdncenter.org. *Actg Dir*, Janet Camarena; Staff 5 (MLS 3, Non-MLS 2)
Founded 1977
Library Holdings: Bk Titles 1,400; Per Subs 50
Special Collections: Foundation Annual Reports; IRS 990-PF; Tax Returns
Publications: This Month in the Foundation Center - San Francisco
Partic in Dialog Corporation
Foundation Center is a Database producer available through Dialog. Open Mon-Fri 10-5, Wed 10-8

S FOUNDATION FOR SAN FRANCISCO ARCHITECTURAL HERITAGE LIBRARY,* 2007 Franklin St, 94109. SAN 371-6589. Tel: 415-441-3000. FAX: 415-441-3015. E-Mail: info@sfheritage.org. Web Site: www.sfheritage.org. *In Charge*, Donald Andreini
Founded 1971
Library Holdings: Bk Titles 1,500
Subject Interests: Architecture
Special Collections: History of San Francisco Architecture

L FREED & HEINEMANN ATTORNEYS AT LAW,* 633 Baffery St, Ste 620, 94111. SAN 323-6803. Tel: 415-986-0707. FAX: 415-986-0999. *Librn*, Jean Mahoney

C GOLDEN GATE UNIVERSITY, University Library,* 536 Mission St, 94105-2967. SAN 334-5300. Tel: 415-442-7255. FAX: 415-543-6779. Web Site: internet.ggu.edu/university_library/. *Dean of Libr*, Joshua Adarkwa; E-Mail: jadarkwa@ggu.edu; *Ref*, Gilles Poitsas
Founded 1851. Enrl 9,400; Fac 47; Highest Degree: Doctorate
Library Holdings: Bk Vols 300,000; Bk Titles 78,000; Per Subs 1,500
Publications: General Library Newsletter
Departmental Libraries:

CL SCHOOL OF LAW LIBRARY, 536 Mission St, 94105. SAN 334-5335. Tel: 415-442-6680. FAX: 415-512-9395. Web Site: internet.ggu.edu/law_library/index.html. *Dir*, Sarah Hooke Lee; E-Mail: shlee@ggu.edu; *Asst Dir, Publ Servs*, Margaret Arnold; E-Mail: marnold@ggu.edu; *Tech Servs*, Melodie Frances; E-Mail: mfrances@ggu.edu; *Doc, Media Spec*, Kristine Ogilvie; E-Mail: kogilvie@ggu.edu; Staff 6 (MLS 6)
Founded 1901. Enrl 650; Fac 38
Library Holdings: Bk Vols 230,155; Per Subs 3,225
Subject Interests: Anglo-American law, California, Law
Publications: Guide Series; Information Series; Policy & Procedure Series
Partic in Dialog Corporation; Westlaw

L GORDON & REES, Law Library,* 275 Battery St, 19th flr, 94111. SAN 372-3143. Tel: 415-986-5900. FAX: 415-986-8054. *Librn*, Amerisa Hernandez
Library Holdings: Bk Vols 20,000
Subject Interests: Medicine

S GRAND LODGE FREE & ACCEPTED MASONS OF CALIFORNIA, (Formerly Institute For Masonic Studies Library & Museum), Henry Wilson Coil Library & Museum, 1111 California St, 94108. SAN 301-4088. Tel: 415-776-7000, Ext 143. FAX: 415-929-0690. E-Mail: ims@freemason.org. Web Site: www.freemason.org. *Dir*, Joel H Springer, III; E-Mail: jhspringer@freemason.org
Founded 1949
Library Holdings: Bk Vols 12,000; Per Subs 30
Special Collections: Annual Proceedings of Masonic Grand Lodge, California 1850-present
Publications: Current Book List

L HANCOCK, ROTHERT & BUNSHOFT, Law Library,* 4 Embarcadero Ctr 3rd flr, 94111. SAN 372-316X. Tel: 415-981-5550. FAX: 415-955-2599. *Librn*, Kathy Skinner; E-Mail: kskinner@hrblaw.com
Library Holdings: Bk Vols 12,000

L HANSON, BRIDGETT, MARCUS, VLAHOS & RUDY, Law Library,* 333 Market St, 23rd flr, Ste 2300, 94105. SAN 372-3429. Tel: 415-995-5142, 415-995-5150. FAX: 415-541-9366. *Librn*, Lydia H Freeman; E-Mail: lfreeman@hbmvr.com; *ILL*, Helen Brobst
Library Holdings: Bk Vols 24,000
Open Mon-Fri 6:30am-3:30pm

L HASSARD & BONNINGTON, Law Library,* 2 Embarcadero Ctr, Ste 1800, 94111. SAN 324-1335. Tel: 415-288-9800. FAX: 415-288-9801. *Librn*, Jeanne Shea
Library Holdings: Bk Vols 12,000; Bk Titles 2,000; Per Subs 200
Subject Interests: Health care, Medicine

S HELEN BROWN LOMBARDI LIBRARY OF INTERNATIONAL AFFAIRS, World Affairs Council of Northern California, 312 Sutter St, Ste 300, 94108. SAN 301-4916. Tel: 415-293-4600. FAX: 415-982-5028. E-Mail: library@wacsf.org. Web Site: www.wacsf.org/library. *Mgr Libr Serv*, Mary Anne McGill; Tel: 415-293-4647. Subject Specialists: *International*, Mary Anne McGill
Founded 1947
Library Holdings: Bk Vols 7,000; Per Subs 100
Subject Interests: International relations
Publications: Spotlight on World Affairs
Restriction: Open to public for reference only
Partic in Bay Area Library & Information Network

L HELLER, EHRMAN, WHITE & MCCAULIFFE LLP LIBRARY, 333 Bush St, 94104-2878. SAN 301-4126. Tel: 415-772-6812. Interlibrary Loan Service Tel: 415-772-6103. FAX: 415-772-6268. *Librn*, Loretta Mak; E-Mail: lmak@hewm.com; Staff 7 (MLS 4, Non-MLS 3)
Founded 1921
Library Holdings: Bk Vols 30,004; Per Subs 396
Subject Interests: Law
Partic in RLIN

S HELLMUTH, OBATA & KASSABAUM, INC LIBRARY,* 71 Stevenson St, Ste 2200, 94105. SAN 329-3947. Tel: 415-243-0555. FAX: 415-882-7763. Web Site: www.hok.com. *Mgr*, Mark Maloy; E-Mail: mark.maloy@hok.com
Library Holdings: Bk Vols 1,200; Per Subs 45
Friends of the Library Group

S HOLOCAUST CENTER OF NORTHERN CALIFORNIA LIBRARY,* 601 14th Ave, 94118. (Mail add: 639 14th Ave, 94118), SAN 326-064X. Tel: 415-751-6040. FAX: 415-751-6735. E-Mail: library@holocaust.sf.org. Web Site: www.holocaust.sf.org. *Exec Dir*, Adrian Schrek; *Librn, Tech Servs*, Elizabeth Houdek; Staff 2 (Non-MLS 2)
Founded 1979
Library Holdings: Bk Vols 13,000; Bk Vols 9,000
Special Collections: Holocaust Atrocity Sites (Holocaust Database), computer programs; Nuremberg Trials (Nuremberg Transcripts Coll), docs
Publications: Bulletin of Events (monthly); Kristalnacht-1988, WWII & the Holocaust-1989
Open Mon & Wed 10-4, Tues & Thurs 12-6 & Sun 12-4

L HOWARD, RICE, NEMEROVSKI, CANADY, FALK & RABKIN LIBRARY,* 3 Embarcadero Ctr, Ste 600, 94111. SAN 327-5760. Tel: 415-399-3043. FAX: 415-217-5910. *Librn*, Marlowe Griffith
Library Holdings: Bk Vols 13,000
Subject Interests: Law

S INSTITUTE FOR ADVANCED STUDY OF HUMAN SEXUALITY, Research Library, 1523 Franklin St, 94109. SAN 327-5787. Tel: 415-928-1133. FAX: 415-928-8284. *Librn*, Jerry Zientara
Founded 1974
2000-2000 Mats Exp Presv $200,000
Library Holdings: Bk Titles 250,000; Per Subs 250,000
Restriction: Not open to public

S INSTITUTE FOR CHILDHOOD RESOURCES, Family Information Center, 268 Bush St, 94104. SAN 324-5128. Tel: 415-864-1169. FAX: 510-540-0111. Web Site: www.drtoy.com. *Dir*, S Auerbach; Staff 4 (MLS 2, Non-MLS 2)
Library Holdings: Bk Titles 5,000; Per Subs 10
Subject Interests: Child care, Early childhood, Parenting educ
Special Collections: toys

Publications: Choosing Childcare: A Guide for Parents; Toychest: A Sourcebook; Whole Child: A Sourcebook
Restriction: By appointment only

M INSTITUTE FOR HEALTH & HEALING LIBRARY, Planetree Health Resource Center, 2040 Webster St, 94115. SAN 327-5744. Tel: 415-600-3681. FAX: 415-673-2629. *Mgr*, Sarah Federman
Library Holdings: Bk Vols 2,500
Open Tues, Thurs-Sat 11-5, Wed 11-7

S INTERNATIONAL LONGSHORE & WAREHOUSE UNION, Anne Rand Research Library, 1188 Franklin St, 94109. SAN 301-4177. Tel: 415-775-0533. FAX: 415-775-1302. *Librn*, Eugene Dennis Vrana
Founded 1942
Library Holdings: Bk Titles 3,000; Per Subs 125

S JAPANESE AMERICAN NATIONAL LIBRARY, 1619 Sutter St, 94109. (Mail add: PO Box 590598, 94159-0598), SAN 374-7751. Tel: 415-567-5006. *Dir*, Karl K Matsushita
Founded 1969
Library Holdings: Bk Vols 20,000; Per Subs 55
Special Collections: Japanese American Redress
Restriction: Open to public for reference only
Function: Archival collection, Reference services available, Research library

M KAISER-PERMANENTE MEDICAL CENTER, Health Sciences Library, 2425 Geary Blvd, 94115. SAN 301-4207. Tel: 415-202-3837. FAX: 415-202-3257. E-Mail: sfovjl@ncal.kaiperm.org. *Dir Libr Serv*, Sara Pimental; Tel: 415-202-3835, E-Mail: sara.pimental@kp.org; *ILL*, Tony Cesnik; Staff 2 (MLS 1, Non-MLS 1)
Founded 1954
Library Holdings: Bk Titles 3,700; Per Subs 190
Subject Interests: Paramedics
Special Collections: Hypnosis, staff reprints
Database Vendor: Ebsco - EbscoHost, IAC - SearchBank, OVID Technologies
Publications: Journal list; Recent acquisitions
Partic in Northern California & Nevada Medical Library Group; San Francisco Biomedical Library Network

S KAPLAN, MCLAUGHLIN & DIAZ, Architects & Planners Library, 222 Vallejo St, 94111. SAN 327-5809. Tel: 415-399-4931. FAX: 415-394-7158. *Librn*, Rachel Ginsberg; E-Mail: ginsberg@kmd-arch.com; *Librn*, Michelle Lieggi; E-Mail: lieggi@kmd-arch.com. Subject Specialists: *Architecture*, Rachel Ginsberg; Staff 1 (MLS 1)
Library Holdings: Bk Titles 4,600; Per Subs 100
Subject Interests: Architecture, Design, Planning
Special Collections: Architectural Library
Restriction: By appointment only

S KENNEDY-JENKS CONSULTANTS, INC LIBRARY,* 303 Second St, 10th flr N, 94107-1366. SAN 301-4215. Tel: 415-243-2531. FAX: 415-896-0999. *Librn*, Alice F Sullivan
Library Holdings: Bk Vols 3,600; Per Subs 84
Publications: Library Bulletin
Restriction: Not open to public

L LANDELS, RIPLEY & DIAMOND LIBRARY,* 350 The Embarcadero, 94105-1250. SAN 321-5261. Tel: 415-512-8700. FAX: 415-512-8750. *Librn*, C Mitchell; *Asst Librn*, D Graham; Staff 2 (MLS 2)
Founded 1975
Library Holdings: Bk Titles 14,500
Subject Interests: Law
Partic in Dialog Corporation

L LASKY, HAAS & COHLER LIBRARY,* 505 Sansome St, Ste 1200, 94111-3183. SAN 321-8759. Tel: 415-788-2700. FAX: 415-981-4025. *Librn*, Patricia Dammann
Library Holdings: Bk Vols 8,000; Per Subs 12
Partic in Westlaw

L LATHAM & WATKINS, Law Library,* 505 Montgomery St, Ste 1900, 94111. SAN 372-2910. Tel: 415-395-8039. FAX: 415-395-8095. *Coll Develop, Mgr*, Frank Lee; E-Mail: frank.lee@lw.com; *Librn*, Ann Hardham; E-Mail: ann.hardham@lw.com; *ILL*, Patricia Allen
Library Holdings: Bk Vols 20,000
Partic in OCLC Online Computer Library Center, Inc

L LEBOEUF, LAMB, GREENE & MACRAE, LLP, Law Library, One Embarcadero Ctr, Ste 400, 94111. SAN 374-4612. Tel: 415-951-1306. FAX: 415-951-1180. Web Site: www.llgm.com. *Librn*, Nancy J Carlin; E-Mail: ncarlin@llgm.com
Founded 1983
Library Holdings: Bk Vols 20,000; Bk Titles 400; Per Subs 100
Restriction: Staff use only

S LEVI STRAUSS & COMPANY, Law Library,* 1155 Battery St LS/7, 94111. SAN 327-926X. Tel: 415-501-7064. FAX: 415-501-7650. *Librn*, Tom Martin; E-Mail: tmartinz@levi.com
Library Holdings: Bk Titles 300
Subject Interests: Antitrust law

L LITTLER MEDELSON LIBRARY,* 650 California St, 20th flr, 94108-2693. SAN 325-5212. Tel: 415-433-1940, Ext 280. FAX: 415-399-8478. *Librn*, Joanne Block; *Librn*, Yarka Odvarko; *Mgr*, Suzie Campbell; Staff 7 (MLS 4, Non-MLS 3)
Founded 1953
Subject Interests: Employment law, Labor law
Automation Activity & Vendor Info: (Acquisitions) Inmagic, Inc.; (Cataloging) Inmagic, Inc.; (Serials) Inmagic, Inc.

§S MANALYTICS INTERNATIONAL LIBRARY, 301 Howard St, Ste 1320, 94105. Tel: 415-777-3500. FAX: 415-777-0540. E-Mail: inbox@manalytics.net. *In Charge*, Jane Miller
Library Holdings: Bk Vols 2,000; Per Subs 300

L MCCUTCHEN, DOYLE, BROWN & ENERSEN, Law Library, 3 Embarcadero Ctr, 94111. SAN 301-4274. Tel: 415-393-2560. FAX: 415-393-2286. *Mgr*, Jo Caporaso; *Ref*, Maeve Roche; *Tech Servs*, Bess Moffitt
Library Holdings: Bk Vols 50,000

L MCKENNA & CUNEO, Law Library, One Market Plaza, Steuart St Tower, 27th flr, 94105. SAN 372-3437. Tel: 415-267-4000. FAX: 415-267-4198. *Coordr*, Eric Carlson
Library Holdings: Bk Vols 15,000; Per Subs 50
Partic in OCLC Online Computer Library Center, Inc

S MCKINSEY & CO, INC LIBRARY, 555 California St, Ste 4700, 94104. SAN 301-4282. Tel: 415-981-0250. FAX: 415-954-5200. *Librn*, Sara Nichols
Library Holdings: Bk Titles 4,000; Per Subs 150
Subject Interests: Business and management
Restriction: Staff use only, Use of others with permission of librarian
Partic in Dialog Corporation; Dow Jones News Retrieval

S MCQUAID, METZLER, BEDFORD & VAN ZANDT LIBRARY, 221 Main St, 16th flr, 94105. SAN 374-9150. Tel: 415-905-0200. FAX: 415-905-0202. *Librn*, Diane Camacho

S MECHANICS' INSTITUTE LIBRARY, 57 Post St, 94104-5003. SAN 301-4304. Tel: 415-393-0101. Reference Tel: 415-393-0102. FAX: 415-397-8747. E-Mail: reference@milibrary.org. Web Site: www.milibrary.org. *Dir*, Inez Shor Cohen; Tel: 415-393-0103, Fax: 415-421-4192, E-Mail: icohen@milibrary.org; *Head Ref*, A C Jackson; Tel: 415-393-0111, E-Mail: acjackson@milibrary.org; *Ref*, Erika Schmidt; Tel: 415-393-0115, E-Mail: eschmidt@milibrary.org; *Ref*, Lucinda Walker; Tel: 415-393-0123, E-Mail: lwalker@milibrary.org; *Acq*, Herbert E Childs; Tel: 415-393-0104, E-Mail: hechilds@milibrary.org; *Cat*, William Schubert; Tel: 415-393-0115, E-Mail: bschubert@milibrary.org; Staff 14 (MLS 7, Non-MLS 7)
Founded 1855
Sep 2000-Aug 2001 Income $875,000, Locally Generated Income $33,600, Parent Institution $875,000. Mats Exp $227,000, Books $105,500, Per/Ser (Incl. Access Fees) $84,000, Micro $13,000, AV Equip $7,500, Electronic Ref Mat (Incl. Access Fees) $25,000. Sal $438,000
Library Holdings: Bk Vols 165,000; Per Subs 500
Subject Interests: Fiction, Local history
Special Collections: Business; California History Coll; Chess; Finance; Investment; Local Authors
Automation Activity & Vendor Info: (Acquisitions) Innovative Interfaces Inc.; (Cataloging) Innovative Interfaces Inc.; (Circulation) Innovative Interfaces Inc.; (OPAC) Innovative Interfaces Inc.; (Serials) Innovative Interfaces Inc.
Database Vendor: IAC - Info Trac
Publications: New titles list (Monthly); Newsletter (bi-annually)
Function: Professional lending library
Partic in Bay Area Library & Information Network

S MEXICO CITY CONSULTING GROUP LIBRARY,* 1306 Montgomery St, 94133. SAN 375-8044. Tel: 415-788-4444, 415-981-5495. FAX: 415-788-4447. *Pres*, John Schick
Library Holdings: Bk Titles 350

L MILLS LAW LIBRARY, 220 Montgomery St, 1st flr, 94104. SAN 371-5825. Tel: 415-781-2665. FAX: 415-781-1116. *Librn*, Jacob Koff; *ILL*, Vicki Guthrie; Staff 2 (MLS 1, Non-MLS 1)
Founded 1987
Library Holdings: Bk Vols 35,000; Bk Titles 5,000; Per Subs 170
Publications: Newsletter

L MURPHY, SHENEMAN, JULIAN & ROGERS, Law Library,* 101 California St, 39th flr, 94111. SAN 372-3178. Tel: 415-398-4700. FAX: 415-421-7879. Web Site: www.msjr.com. *Librn*, Leslie Ann Forrester
Library Holdings: Bk Vols 11,000; Per Subs 200
Automation Activity & Vendor Info: (Acquisitions) Inmagic, Inc.; (Cataloging) Inmagic, Inc.; (Circulation) Inmagic, Inc.; (ILL) Inmagic, Inc.; (Serials) Inmagic, Inc.

S MUSEUM OF CRAFT & FOLK ART LIBRARY, Landmark Bldg A, Fort Mason Ctr, 94123-1382. SAN 371-7348. Tel: 415-775-0991. FAX: 415-775-1861. Web Site: www.mocfa.org. *Librn*, Barbara Rogers; E-Mail: barbara@mocfa.org; Staff 1 (MLS 1)
Founded 1983
Library Holdings: Bk Titles 1,800; Per Subs 26
Restriction: Not a lending library

S MUSEUM OF RUSSIAN CULTURE, INC LIBRARY, 2450 Sutter St, 94115. SAN 320-605X. Tel: 415-921-4082. *Pres*, Demitri Brown; *VPres*, Georgy Tarala
Library Holdings: Bk Vols 20,000

S NATIONAL ASSOCIATION FOR VISUALLY HANDICAPPED, (NAVH), 3201 Balboa St, 94121. SAN 372-6169. Tel: 415-221-3201. FAX: 415-221-8754. E-Mail: staff@navh.org, staffca@navh.org. Web Site: www.navh.org. *Librn*, Cecelia Chang
Founded 1954
Library Holdings: Bk Titles 2,000

S NATIONAL PARK SERVICE, Pacific - Great Basin Resources Library,* 600 Harrison St, Ste 600, 94107-1372. SAN 301-4371. Tel: 415-427-1300, 415-427-1436. FAX: 415-744-4043.
Founded 1937
Subject Interests: Archaeology, History

C NEW COLLEGE OF CALIFORNIA LIBRARY, Law Library, 50 Fell St, 94102. SAN 326-4572. Tel: 415-241-1376. FAX: 415-241-1391. Web Site: www.newcollege.edu/lib/library.html. *Acq*, S S Cush; Staff 3 (MLS 3)
Founded 1973. Enrl 700; Fac 40; Highest Degree: Doctorate
Library Holdings: Bk Vols 40,000; Bk Titles 30,000; Per Subs 50
Subject Interests: Humanities, Law, Psychology
Special Collections: Modern American Poets (Poetics Coll), tapes, journals
Partic in Northern Calif Consortium of Psychol Librs
Departmental Libraries:
HUMANITIES, 777 Valencia St, 94110. Tel: 415-437-3460. *Librn*, Karen Prescher

L ORRICK, HERRINGTON & SUTCLIFFE, Law Library, Old Federal Reserve Bank Bldg, 400 Sansome St, 94111-3143. SAN 301-4398. Tel: 415-392-1122. FAX: 415-773-5759. Web Site: www.orrick.com. *Librn*, Debi Mazor; E-Mail: dmazor@orrick.com; Staff 4 (MLS 3, Non-MLS 1)
Founded 1884
Library Holdings: Bk Vols 48,000; Bk Titles 12,000; Per Subs 700
Subject Interests: California, Corporate law
Publications: OHS Library News
Restriction: Staff use only
Partic in Northern Calif Asn of Law Librs

S PACIFIC GAS & ELECTRIC COMPANY, Energy Resource Center Library, 851 Howard St, 94103. SAN 375-1422. Tel: 415-973-7206. FAX: 415-896-1280. E-Mail: mxv6@pge.com. Web Site: www.pge.com/pec. *In Charge*, Marlene Vogelsang; Staff 1 (MLS 1)
Founded 1991
1999-1999 Mats Exp $50,000, Books $5,000, Per/Ser (Incl. Access Fees) $10,000, Other Print Mats $10,000, Electronic Ref Mat (Incl. Access Fees) $25,000. Sal $55,000
Library Holdings: Bk Titles 1,000; Per Subs 90
Subject Interests: Energy, Energy efficiency
Special Collections: Calif Energy Comn Doc
Restriction: Circulates for staff only

S PESTICIDE ACTION NETWORK NORTH AMERICAN REGIONAL CENTER, International Information Program,* 47 Powell St, Ste 500, 94102. SAN 372-6827. Tel: 415-981-1771. FAX: 415-981-1991. Web Site: www.panna.org/panna.
Founded 1988
Library Holdings: Bk Titles 4,000; Per Subs 350
Subject Interests: Agriculture, Pesticides
Special Collections: Pesticides, Agriculture & International Development, bks; US Environmental Protection Agency, reports & bd doc
Automation Activity & Vendor Info: (Cataloging) Inmagic, Inc.
Restriction: By appointment only

L PILLSBURY WINTHROP LLP, (Formerly Pillsbury Madison & Sutro LLP), Law Library, 50 Fremont St, 94105. SAN 301-4460. Tel: 415-983-1130. Interlibrary Loan Service Tel: 415-983-1420. FAX: 415-983-1200. *ILL*, Karen Calarco
Library Holdings: Bk Vols 100,000; Per Subs 1,500

S PKF CONSULTING, (Formerly PKF Consulting), Hospitality Research Group Library, 425 California St, Ste 1650, 94104. SAN 374-8502. Tel: 415-421-5378. FAX: 415-956-7708. Web Site: www.pkfonline.com. *Dir*, Gary Carr; E-Mail: gcarr@pkfc.com; *Res*, Robert Mandelbaum
Library Holdings: Bk Titles 200

S ROSE RESNICK LIGHTHOUSE FOR THE BLIND, Free Lending-Browsing Braille Library, 214 Van Ness Ave, 94102. SAN 301-4606. Tel: 415-431-1481. FAX: 415-863-7568. Web Site: www.lighthouse-sf.org. *In Charge*, Molly Pearson
Founded 1949
Library Holdings: Bk Vols 1,900; Bk Titles 600
Subject Interests: Fiction, Philosophy, Religion
Special Collections: Braille Codes, Thesaurus, Unabridged Dictionary, World Book
Special Services for the Deaf - TTY machine

M SAINT FRANCIS MEMORIAL HOSPITAL, Walter F Schaller Memorial Library, 900 Hyde St, PO Box 7726, 94120. SAN 301-4487. Tel: 415-353-6320. FAX: 415-353-6323. E-Mail: sfmhlibrary@chw.edu. *Dir*, Maryann Zaremska; E-Mail: zaremska@hooked.net
Founded 1972
Library Holdings: Bk Vols 2,000; Bk Titles 1,845; Per Subs 240
Subject Interests: Plastic surgery
Partic in Docline; Northern California & Nevada Medical Library Group; San Francisco Biomedical Library Network

M SAINT LUKE'S HOSPITAL, Medical Library, 3555 Cesar Chavez, 94110. SAN 301-4509. Tel: 415-647-8600. *Librn*, Patricia Forrest
Founded 1959
Restriction: Staff use only
Partic in Medline

M SAINT MARY'S MEDICAL CENTER, Solomon Library, 450 Stanyan St, 94117-1079. SAN 301-4517. Tel: 415-750-5784. FAX: 415-750-4954. *Librn*, Lise M Dyckman; Staff 4 (MLS 1, Non-MLS 3)
Founded 1937
Library Holdings: Bk Vols 5,000; Bk Titles 4,000; Per Subs 340
Subject Interests: Medicine, Nursing, Orthopedics, Psychiatry
Special Collections: Management; Patient Education
Automation Activity & Vendor Info: (Cataloging) Inmagic, Inc.
Partic in Catholic Healthcare W; Nat Libr of Med; Northern California & Nevada Medical Library Group; Pacific SW Regional Med Libr Serv

S SAN FRANCISCO AFRICAN-AMERICAN HISTORICAL & CULTURAL SOCIETY, Library of San Francisco,* 762 Fulton St, 2nd Flr, 94102. SAN 301-3618. Tel: 415-292-6172. FAX: 415-440-4231. E-Mail: aahs@sfpl.lib.ca.us. *Pres*, Jesse Byrd
Founded 1955
Library Holdings: Bk Vols 35,892; Per Subs 10
Publications: A Walking Tour of Black Presence in California during the 19th Century; Ascension - Literary Anthology
Partic in Bay Area Ref Ctr
Friends of the Library Group

C SAN FRANCISCO ART INSTITUTE, Anne Bremer Memorial Library, 800 Chestnut St, 94133. SAN 301-4533. Tel: 415-749-4559. E-Mail: library@sfai.edu. *Librn*, Jeff Gunderson; *Cat*, Carolyn Franklin; *Media Spec*, Charles Stephanian; Staff 3 (MLS 2, Non-MLS 1)
Founded 1871. Enrl 700; Highest Degree: Master
Jul 1998-Jun 1999 Income $350,000. Mats Exp $50,000, Books $20,000, Per/Ser (Incl. Access Fees) $10,000. Sal $200,000
Library Holdings: Bk Vols 30,500; Bk Titles 29,000; Per Subs 210
Subject Interests: Art, Films and filmmaking, Photography
Special Collections: California Art, 1871 - present; History (San Francisco Art Institute), archives, bks, doc, photogs
Publications: Hey You; Read This First (quarterly)
Restriction: Open to faculty, students & qualified researchers

S SAN FRANCISCO CAMERAWORK, Reference Library,* 115 Natoma, 94105. SAN 328-1140. Tel: 415-764-1001. FAX: 415-764-1063.
Founded 1974
Library Holdings: Bk Vols 5,000
Special Collections: Artist's bks; Exhibition cats
Publications: SF Camerawork (mag)

S SAN FRANCISCO CHRONICLE NEWSPAPER PUBLISHING CO LIBRARY, 901 Mission St, 94103. SAN 301-4541. Tel: 415-777-7230. FAX: 415-896-0668. Web Site: www.sfgate.com/chronicle.shtml. *Dir*, Judy Canter; E-Mail: jcanter@sfchronicle.com; *Res*, Richard Geiger; E-Mail: rgeiger@sfchronicle.com; *Archivist*, Bill Van Niekerken; E-Mail: bvaniekerken@sfchronicle.com. Subject Specialists: *Archives*, Bill Van Niekerken; Staff 17 (MLS 9, Non-MLS 8)
Library Holdings: Bk Vols 2,000
Partic in Data Time; Dialog Corporation; Dow Jones News Retrieval

S SAN FRANCISCO COLLEGE OF MORTUARY SCIENCE LIBRARY, 1598 Dolores St, 94110-4927. SAN 301-455X. Tel: 415-824-1313. FAX: 415-824-1390. E-Mail: info@sfcms.org. Web Site: www.sfcms.org. *Pres*, Jacquie Taylor; E-Mail: jtsfcms@ix.netcom.com; Staff 1 (Non-MLS 1)
Founded 1930. Enrl 70; Fac 8; Highest Degree: Master
Library Holdings: Bk Vols 750; Per Subs 35

S SAN FRANCISCO CONSERVATORY OF MUSIC, Bothin Library, 1201 Ortega St, 94122. SAN 301-4568. Tel: 415-564-8086. FAX: 415-759-3499. Web Site: www.sfcm.edu. *Head of Libr*, Deborah Smith; Tel: 415-759-3453, E-Mail: dls@sfcm.edu; Staff 2 (MLS 1, Non-MLS 1)
Founded 1957. Enrl 247; Fac 25; Highest Degree: Master
Library Holdings: Bk Vols 63,345; Bk Titles 37,968; Per Subs 73
Subject Interests: Humanities, Music
Automation Activity & Vendor Info: (Acquisitions) Innovative Interfaces Inc.; (Cataloging) Innovative Interfaces Inc.; (Circulation) Innovative Interfaces Inc.; (Course Reserve) Innovative Interfaces Inc.; (OPAC) Innovative Interfaces Inc.
Publications: Semi-annual acquisitions lists

M SAN FRANCISCO GENERAL HOSPITAL, Barnett-Briggs Medical Library, 1001 Potrero Ave, Bldg 30, 94110. SAN 301-4584. Tel: 415-206-3114. Interlibrary Loan Service Tel: 415-206-3113. FAX: 415-206-6102. E-Mail: sfghlib@itsa.ucsf.edu. Web Site: sfghdean.ucsf.edu/barnett/index.htm. *Dir*, Joan Fierberg; *Tech Servs*, Richard Scott
Founded 1966
Library Holdings: Bk Titles 18,120; Per Subs 420
Partic in Coop Libr Agency for Syst & Servs; Northern California & Nevada Medical Library Group; Pacific SW Regional Med Libr Serv; San Francisco Biomedical Library Network

GL SAN FRANCISCO LAW LIBRARY,* 401 Van Ness Ave, Rm 400, 94102-4672. SAN 334-5424. Tel: 415-554-6821. FAX: 415-554-6820. *Librn*, Marcia R Bell
Founded 1870
Library Holdings: Bk Vols 308,000; Per Subs 492
Branches:
MARKET STREET, 685 Market St, Ste 420, 94105. SAN 334-5459. Tel: 415-882-9310. FAX: 415-882-9594. *Dir*, John M Moore
Library Holdings: Bk Vols 45,563; Per Subs 53

L SAN FRANCISCO LAW SCHOOL LIBRARY,* 20 Haight St, 94102. SAN 301-4592. Tel: 415-626-5550. FAX: 415-626-5584. *Librn*, Gloria Lopez
Founded 1909
Library Holdings: Bk Vols 21,000

S SAN FRANCISCO MARITIME NATIONAL HISTORICAL PARK, J Porter Shaw Library & Historic Documents Department,* Library, Bldg E, 3rd flr, Fort Mason Ctr, 94123. SAN 301-4363. Tel: 415-556-9870. FAX: 415-556-3540. E-Mail: safr_maritime_library@nps.gov. *Head of Libr*, David Hull; *Tech Servs*, Heather Hawkins; *Ref*, Irene Stachura
Founded 1959
Library Holdings: Bk Vols 32,000; Per Subs 160
Special Collections: Alaska Packers Asn Coll; Barbara Johnson Whaling Coll; Bethlehem Shipbuilding Coll; David W Dickie Coll; Hester Coll; John Lyman Coll; John W Proctor Coll; Mawdeley Coll; Plummer Beaton Coll; Proctor Coll; Reardon Coll
Automation Activity & Vendor Info: (Cataloging) Athena; (OPAC) Athena
Publications: Sea Letter
Restriction: Non-circulating to the public
Partic in Fedlink; OCLC Online Computer Library Center, Inc
Friends of the Library Group

G SAN FRANCISCO MUNICIPAL RAILWAY LIBRARY, 949 Presidio Ave, Rm 204, 94115-3399. SAN 321-9682. Tel: 415-923-6089. FAX: 415-923-6306. *Librn*, Dr Marc Hofstadter; E-Mail: marc_hofstadter@ci.sf.ca.us. Subject Specialists: *Transit*, Dr Marc Hofstadter; Staff 1 (MLS 1)
Founded 1980
Jul 2000-Jun 2001 Income $22,207. Mats Exp $5,707, Books $500, Per/Ser (Incl. Access Fees) $850, Other Print Mats $92, Electronic Ref Mat (Incl. Access Fees) $500. Sal $17,000
Library Holdings: Bk Vols 8,000; Bk Titles 6,000; Per Subs 50
Subject Interests: City planning, Transit, Transportation
Special Collections: San Francisco Municipal Railway, charts, doc, maps, plans
Database Vendor: OCLC - First Search
Publications: Acquisitions List
Partic in OCLC Online Computer Library Center, Inc

S SAN FRANCISCO MUSEUM OF MODERN ART LIBRARY, 151 Third St, 94103-3107. SAN 301-4614. Tel: 415-357-4121. FAX: 415-357-4038. *Librn*, Eugenie Candau; E-Mail: ecandau@sfmoma.org; Staff 3 (MLS 1, Non-MLS 2)
Founded 1935
Library Holdings: Bk Titles 44,000; Per Subs 425
Special Collections: Modern Art, exhibition catalogs; Photography (Margery Mann Coll)

S SAN FRANCISCO PERFORMING ARTS LIBRARY & MUSEUM, (SFPALM), 401 VanNess Ave, 4th flr, 94102. SAN 372-5774. Tel: 415-255-4800. FAX: 415-255-1913. E-Mail: info@sfpalm.org. Web Site: www.sfpalm.org. *Exec Dir*, David Humpherey; *Librn*, Kirsten Tanaka; Staff 5 (MLS 3, Non-MLS 2)
Founded 1983
Library Holdings: Bk Vols 12,000; Per Subs 29
Subject Interests: Dance, Music, Opera, Theater
Special Collections: Dance (San Francisco Ballet Archives); Music (San Francisco Symphony Archives; Musical Theater Recording Coll; San Francisco Opera Archives; Theatrical Design Research Coll
Publications: San Francisco Performing Arts Library & Museum Series
Restriction: Non-circulating to the public
Function: Archival collection, Research library

S SAN FRANCISCO PSYCHOANALYTIC INSTITUTE, Erik Erikson Library, 2420 Sutter St, 94115. SAN 301-4622. Tel: 415-563-4477. FAX: 415-563-8406. E-Mail: 72774.3114@compuserve.com. *Dir*, Susanna Bonetti; Staff 1 (Non-MLS 1)
Founded 1950
Library Holdings: Bk Titles 5,600; Per Subs 50
Subject Interests: Psychoanalysis
Special Collections: Bernice S Engle Coll; Emmanuel Windholz Coll
Publications: Dialogue
Partic in Pac SW Regional Med Libr
Friends of the Library Group

P SAN FRANCISCO PUBLIC LIBRARY, 100 Larkin St, 94102-4734. SAN 334-5483. Tel: 415-557-4236, 415-557-4400. FAX: 415-557-4239. Web Site: www.sfpl.org. *Actg Librn*, Susan Hildreth; *Ch Servs*, Toni Bernardi; *Tech Servs*, Vivian Pisano
Founded 1878. Pop 801,400; Circ 5,166,843
Jul 1999-Jun 2000 Income (Main Library and Branch Library) $46,474,806, State $1,331,806, City $44,993,000, Other $150,000. Mats Exp $4,680,597, Books $2,636,914, Per/Ser (Incl. Access Fees) $691,886, AV Equip $371,707, Other Print Mats $218,081, Electronic Ref Mat (Incl. Access Fees) $762,009. Sal $27,518,362
Library Holdings: Bk Vols 2,208,749; Per Subs 11,923
Special Collections: Calligraphy (Richard Harrison); Chinese language & interest (Chinatown Branch); Eric Hoffer Manuscripts; Fine Printing & Binding (Kuhl); Gay & Lesbian Archives; History of Printing & Development of the Book (Robert Grabhorn); San Francisco; San Francisco Newspaper Morgues; Science Fiction & Fantasy (McComas); Spanish language & interest (Mission Branch); Wit & Humor (Schmulowitz)
Automation Activity & Vendor Info: (Acquisitions) DRA; (Circulation) DRA; (OPAC) DRA; (Serials) Innovative Interfaces Inc.
Mem of Bay Area Libr & Info Syst
Special Services for the Deaf - Special interest periodicals; Staff with knowledge of sign language; TTY machine
Friends of the Library Group
Branches: 26
ANZA, 550 37th Ave, 94121-2691. SAN 334-5548. Tel: 415-666-7160. FAX: 415-876-0379. *Branch Mgr*, Isabel Delgadillo-Romo
Library Holdings: Bk Vols 47,870
Friends of the Library Group
BAYVIEW-ANNA E WAYDEN, 5075 Third St, 94124-2311. SAN 334-6269. Tel: 415-468-1323. FAX: 415-671-0736. *Branch Mgr*, Linda Brooks-Burton
Library Holdings: Bk Vols 43,665
BERNAL HEIGHTS, 500 Cortland Ave, 94110-5612. SAN 334-5572. Tel: 415-695-5160. FAX: 415-642-9951. *Branch Mgr*, Steve Cody
Library Holdings: Bk Vols 37,912
CHINATOWN, 1135 Powell St, 94108. SAN 334-5637. Tel: 415-274-0275. FAX: 415-274-0277. *Branch Mgr*, Elsie Wong
Founded 1921
Library Holdings: Bk Vols 110,531
EUREKA VALLEY-HARVEY MILK MEMORIAL, 3555 16th St, 94114-1621. SAN 334-5661. Tel: 415-554-9445. FAX: 415-552-2584. *Branch Mgr*, Karen Sundheim
Library Holdings: Bk Vols 40,958
EXCELSIOR, 4400 Mission St, 94112-1927. SAN 334-5696. Tel: 415-337-4735. FAX: 415-337-4738. *Actg Mgr*, Katie Lynds
Library Holdings: Bk Vols 67,620
GLEN PARK, 653 Chenery, 94131-3092. SAN 334-5726. Tel: 415-337-4740. FAX: 415-587-8425. *Branch Mgr*, Mark Hall
Library Holdings: Bk Vols 24,740
GOLDEN GATE VALLEY, 1801 Green St, 94123-4921. SAN 334-5750. Tel: 415-292-2195. FAX: 415-563-7068. *Branch Mgr*, Eileen Wampole
Library Holdings: Bk Vols 27,685
INGLESIDE, 387 Ashton Ave, 94112-1745. SAN 334-5785. Tel: 415-337-4745. *Branch Mgr*, Jan Nunes
Library Holdings: Bk Vols 26,131
MARINA, 1890 Chestnut St, 94123-2804. SAN 334-5815. Tel: 415-292-2150. FAX: 415-673-1197. *Branch Mgr*, Valentin Porras
Library Holdings: Bk Vols 51,270
MERCED, 155 Winston Dr, 94132-2032. SAN 334-584X. Tel: 415-337-4780. FAX: 415-587-6491. *Branch Mgr*, Sue Bizio
Library Holdings: Bk Vols 44,511
MISSION, 300 Bartlett St, 94110-3801. SAN 334-5874. Tel: 415-695-5090. FAX: 415-648-6566. E-Mail: mismgr@sfpl.lib.ca.us. *Branch Mgr*, Gloria Hanson
Library Holdings: Bk Vols 97,558
NOE VALLEY-SALLY BRUNN, 451 Jersey St, 94114-3632. SAN 334-5904. Tel: 415-695-5095. FAX: 415-642-4267. *Branch Mgr*, Roberta Griefer

Library Holdings: Bk Vols 34,690
NORTH BEACH, 2000 Mason St, 94133-2354. SAN 334-5939. Tel: 415-274-0270. FAX: 415-772-8251. *Branch Mgr*, Gardner Haskell
Library Holdings: Bk Vols 42,518
OCEAN VIEW, 345 Randolph St, 94132-3119. SAN 334-5963. Tel: 415-337-4785. FAX: 415-452-8584. *Branch Mgr*, Sarah Lester; Staff 6 (MLS 1, Non-MLS 5)
Library Holdings: Bk Vols 16,261
ORTEGA, 3223 Ortega St, 94122-4098. SAN 334-5998. Tel: 415-753-7120. FAX: 415-504-6053. *Branch Mgr*, Chris Ahrens
Library Holdings: Bk Vols 48,718
PARK, 1833 Page St, 94117-1909. SAN 334-6021. Tel: 415-666-7155. FAX: 415-933-8853. *Branch Mgr*, Anne Hyatt
Library Holdings: Bk Vols 28,828
PARKSIDE, 1200 Taraval St, 94116-2454. SAN 334-6056. Tel: 415-753-7125. FAX: 415-682-9642. *Branch Mgr*, Pat Dimmick
Library Holdings: Bk Vols 41,793
PORTOLA, 2565 San Bruno Ave, 94134-1504. SAN 334-6080. Tel: 415-715-4090. FAX: 415-657-0376. *Branch Mgr*, Roz Chang
Library Holdings: Bk Vols 23,972
POTRERO, 1616 20th St, 94107-2811. SAN 334-6110. Tel: 415-285-3022. FAX: 415-401-8147. *Branch Mgr*, Toba Singer
Library Holdings: Bk Vols 31,916
PRESIDIO, 3150 Sacramento St, 94115-2090. SAN 334-5513. Tel: 415-292-2155. FAX: 415-567-1580. *Branch Mgr*, Catherine Bremer; Staff 6 (MLS 2, Non-MLS 4)
Founded 1926
Library Holdings: Bk Vols 33,711
RICHMOND, 351 Ninth Ave, 94118-2210. SAN 334-617X. Tel: 415-666-7165. FAX: 415-666-7019. *Branch Mgr*, Tim Williams
Library Holdings: Bk Vols 78,608
SUNSET, 1305 18th Ave, 94122-1899. SAN 334-620X. Tel: 415-753-7130. FAX: 415-753-7002. *Branch Mgr*, Jane Hudson
Library Holdings: Bk Vols 61,970
VISITACION VALLEY, 45 Leland Ave, 94134-2895. SAN 334-6234. Tel: 415-337-4790. FAX: 415-337-4741. *Branch Mgr*, Dede Puma
Library Holdings: Bk Vols 24,028
WEST PORTAL, 190 Lenox Way, 94127-1113. SAN 334-6293. Tel: 415-753-7135. FAX: 415-753-7034. *Branch Mgr*, Cathie Helmick; E-Mail: cathieh@sfpl.lib.ca.us
Library Holdings: Bk Vols 62,290
WESTERN ADDITION, 1550 Scott St, 94115-3512. SAN 334-6323. Tel: 415-292-2160. FAX: 415-292-7511. *Branch Mgr*, Robert Carlson
Library Holdings: Bk Vols 69,269
Bookmobiles: 2

C SAN FRANCISCO STATE UNIVERSITY, J Paul Leonard Library, 1630 Holloway Ave, 94132-1789. SAN 301-4630. Tel: 415-338-1854. FAX: 415-338-1504. Web Site: www.library.sfsu.edu. *Dir Libr Serv*, Deborah Masters; Tel: 415-338-1681, E-Mail: dmasters@sfsu.edu; *Mgr*, Linda Madden; Tel: 415-338-2953, E-Mail: lmadden@sfsu.edu; *Acq, Mgr*, Nancy Noda; *Head Librn*, Dora Ng; Tel: 415-338-7324, E-Mail: dlng@sfsu.edu; *Librn*, Ned Fielden; Tel: 415-338-1454, E-Mail: fielden@sfsu.edu; *Librn*, Maria Garrido; Tel: 415-338-1455, E-Mail: garrido@sfsu.edu; *Coll Develop, Syst Coordr*, Judy Ganson; Tel: 415-338-6953, E-Mail: ganson@sfsu.edu; *Syst Coordr*, Richard Blood; Tel: 415-338-2646, E-Mail: rblood@sfsu.edu; *Cat*, Sara Berlowitz; Tel: 415-338-1146, E-Mail: berlwitz@sfsu.edu; *Ser*, Mitch Turitz; *Ref*, C Stuart Hall; *Coordr*, Kathleen Messer; Tel: 415-338-1744, Fax: 415-338-6199, E-Mail: kmesser@sfsu.edu; *Ser*, Mitch Turitz; Tel: 415-338-7883, Fax: 415-338-6940, E-Mail: turitz@sfsu.edu. Subject Specialists: *Govt publications*, Dora Ng; Staff 110 (MLS 26, Non-MLS 84)
Founded 1899. Pop 27,446; Enrl 26,500; Fac 1,500; Highest Degree: Doctorate
Jul 1998-Jun 1999 Income Parent Institution $7,991,725. Mats Exp $2,763,612, Books $829,944, Per/Ser (Incl. Access Fees) $1,213,429, Presv $35,802, Micro $155,499, Electronic Ref Mat (Incl. Access Fees) $528,938. Sal $4,501,509 (Prof $1,816,999)
Library Holdings: Bk Vols 997,578; Bk Titles 742,167; Per Subs 6,335
Subject Interests: Art and architecture, Business and management, Economics, Education, History
Special Collections: Archer Children's Book Coll; Bay Area TV Archives; Frank V deBellis Coll; Labor Archives & Research Center
Automation Activity & Vendor Info: (Acquisitions) Innovative Interfaces Inc.; (Cataloging) Innovative Interfaces Inc.; (Circulation) Innovative Interfaces Inc.; (Course Reserve) Innovative Interfaces Inc.; (ILL) Innovative Interfaces Inc.; (OPAC) Innovative Interfaces Inc.; (Serials) Innovative Interfaces Inc.
Database Vendor: Innovative Interfaces INN - View
Publications: Bibliographies; information guides; library resource workbook; research guides
Mem of California State University
Partic in Consortium of Western Univ & Col; CSU Link; OCLC Online Computer Library Center, Inc; San Francisco Biomedical Library Network
Friends of the Library Group

S SAN FRANCISCO UNIFIED SCHOOL DISTRICT, Helen Boutin Professional Library, 2550 25th Ave, 94116. SAN 327-6228. Tel: 415-759-2985. FAX: 415-731-6620. Web Site: www.sfdusd.klz.ca.us/. *Librn*, Philip Crawford; E-Mail: cfarrell@sfusd.klz.ca.us
Library Holdings: Bk Vols 10,000

C SAYBROOK GRADUATE SCHOOL & RESEARCH CENTER LIBRARY, 450 Pacific Ave, 94133-4640. SAN 378-2212. Tel: 415-394-5062. Interlibrary Loan Service Tel: 415-394-5061. Circulation Tel: 415-394-5061. FAX: 415-433-9271. *Dir Libr Serv*, Steven Gerstle; E-Mail: sgerstle@saybrook.edu; *Circ, ILL*, Floyd Fox; E-Mail: ffox@saybrook.edu; Staff 2 (MLS 1, Non-MLS 1)
Enrl 420; Fac 20; Highest Degree: Doctorate
1998-1999
Library Holdings: Bk Vols 1,500; Bk Titles 1,000
Subject Interests: Psychology
Automation Activity & Vendor Info: (Cataloging) Athena; (Circulation) Athena
Partic in Northern Calif Consortium of Psychol Librs

L SEDGWICK, DETERT, MORAN & ARNOLD LIBRARY, One Embarcadero Ctr, 16th Flr, 94111. SAN 327-800X. Tel: 415-781-7900. FAX: 415-781-2635. *Librn*, Mark Newman; E-Mail: mnewman@sdma.com
Library Holdings: Bk Vols 15,000; Bk Titles 1,500
Partic in Class

L SHEARMAN & STERLING LIBRARY,* 555 California St, 19th flr, 94104. SAN 373-1006. Tel: 415-616-1100. FAX: 415-616-1199. *Librn*, Debbie Giahos
Library Holdings: Bk Vols 10,000; Per Subs 100

S SIERRA CLUB, William E Colby Memorial Library, 85 Second St, 2nd Flr, 94105-3441. SAN 301-4657. Tel: 415-977-5506. FAX: 415-977-5799. Web Site: www.sierraclub.org.; Staff 1 (Non-MLS 1)
Founded 1892
Library Holdings: Bk Vols 11,000; Per Subs 350
Subject Interests: Conservation, Natural history, Pollution
Special Collections: Early International & North American Mountaineering (Sierra Club Mountaineering Coll), bd vols, bks, photog
Publications: Recent Acquisitions
Partic in OCLC Online Computer Library Center, Inc
Friends of the Library Group

S SMITH GROUP, INC, Health Planning & Programming Library, 225 Bush St, 11th flr, 94104. SAN 301-472X. Tel: 415-227-0100. FAX: 415-495-5091. Web Site: www.smpshg.com. *Librn*, Halsted Bernard
Founded 1967
Library Holdings: Bk Vols 2,500; Per Subs 112
Subject Interests: Architecture
Restriction: Not open to public

S SMITH-KETTLEWELL EYE RESEARCH FOUNDATION LIBRARY,* 2318 Fillmore St, 94115. SAN 327-7038. Tel: 415-345-2000. FAX: 415-348-8455. Web Site: www.ski.org. *In Charge*, Norberto Grizywacz
Library Holdings: Bk Vols 400
Restriction: Not open to public

L STEEFEL, LEVITT & WEISS, Law Library,* 31st flr, Ste 3000, One Embarcadero Ctr, 94111. SAN 372-3070. Tel: 415-788-0900. FAX: 415-788-2019. *Librn*, Kathryn Ranharter
Library Holdings: Bk Vols 10,000

S STRYBING ARBORETUM SOCIETY OF GOLDEN GATE PARK, (HCRL), Helen Crocker Russell Library of Horticulture, Ninth Ave at Lincoln Way, 94122. SAN 301-4738. Tel: 415-661-1316, Ext 303. FAX: 415-661-3539. E-Mail: library@strybing.org. Web Site: www.strybing.org. *Coll Develop, Head of Libr*, Barbara M Pitschel; E-Mail: bpitschel@strybing.org; *Asst Librn*, Kathleen Fisher; Staff 2 (MLS 2)
Founded 1972
Jan 1999-Dec 1999 Income $110,000, Locally Generated Income $50,000, Parent Institution $60,000. Mats Exp $21,500, Books $10,000, Per/Ser (Incl. Access Fees) $9,000, Presv $2,500. Sal $68,000 (Prof $68,000)
Library Holdings: Bk Vols 18,500; Per Subs 500
Subject Interests: Botany, Horticulture
Special Collections: Nursery & Seed Catalogs
Publications: Bibliography Series
Restriction: Non-circulating to the public
Partic in CDB-S; Council On Botanical Horticultural Libraries; OCLC Online Computer Library Center, Inc
Friends of the Library Group
Bookmobiles: 1

S THE BOOK CLUB OF CALIFORNIA, 312 Sutter St, No 510, 94108-4320. SAN 326-6249. Tel: 415-781-7532. Toll Free Tel: 800-869-7656. FAX: 415-781-7537. E-Mail: www.bcc@slip.net. Web Site: bccbooks.org.
Founded 1912
Library Holdings: Bk Vols 3,200; Bk Titles 2,200
Subject Interests: Bk arts, Western hist

Special Collections: Printing History
Publications: annual keepsake; Quarterly Newsletter; three press books annually
Restriction: Members only

L THELEN, REID, PREIST, LLP, Law Library, 101 Second St, 94105-3672. SAN 301-4762. Interlibrary Loan Service Tel: 415-369-7093, 415-369-7105. FAX: 415-371-1211. *Librn*, Ann Borkin; *Assoc Librn*, Todd Bennett
Library Holdings: Bk Vols 30,000; Per Subs 200
Subject Interests: Construction, Corporate law
Restriction: Members only
Partic in Dialog Corporation; Westlaw

S THEOSOPHICAL SOCIETY LIBRARY,* 809 Mason St, 94102. SAN 301-4649. Tel: 415-771-8777. *Librn*, Peggy Tahir; *Coll Develop*, Shawn Phillips
Founded 1893
Library Holdings: Bk Titles 4,500; Per Subs 16
Subject Interests: Astrology, Occult, Theosophy
Special Collections: History, Metaphysics (San Francisco Occult Archives), bks, doc; Metaphysics (Manly P Hall Lectures), bd mss

M UCSF MEDICAL CENTER AT MOUNT ZION, (Formerly UCSF Stanford Health Care), Harris M Fishbon Memorial Library, 1600 Divisadero St, Rm A-116, 94115. SAN 301-4347. Tel: 415-885-7378. Web Site: mzweb.his.ucsf.edu. *Dir*, Gail Sorrough
Library Holdings: Bk Titles 11,000; Per Subs 210
Subject Interests: Cardiology, Geriatrics and gerontology, Internal medicine, Oncology, Orthopedics, Pediatrics, Surgery
Special Collections: History of Medicine Coll; Psychiatry
Partic in National Network Of Libraries Of Medicine - South Central Region; Northern California & Nevada Medical Library Group; Pac SW Regional Med Libr; San Francisco Biomedical Library Network
This is a hospital library, owned by UCSF Stanford Health Care Mount Zion Medical Center; it is not part of UCSF Campus Library

UNITED STATES ARMY
A CORPS OF ENGINEERS, SAN FRANCISCO AREA TECHNICAL LIBRARY, 333 Market St, Rm 925, 94105-2197. SAN 334-6358. Tel: 415-977-8601. FAX: 415-977-8423. *In Charge*, Frank Conway; E-Mail: fconway@_spd.usac.army.mil
Library Holdings: Bk Titles 14,000; Per Subs 300
Special Collections: CE Projects (Corps of Engineers Annual Reports); San Francisco Bay-Delta; Wetlands
Partic in Fedlink

GL UNITED STATES COURT OF APPEALS LIBRARY,* PO Box 193939, 94119-3939. SAN 301-4789. Tel: 415-556-9500. FAX: 415-556-9927. *Librn*, Elisabeth Knauff; *Cat*, Jim Moldevin; *Coll Develop*, Cheryl Blare; Staff 12 (MLS 7, Non-MLS 5)
Founded 1891
Library Holdings: Per Subs 2,500
Subject Interests: Law
Partic in Fedlink; OCLC Online Computer Library Center, Inc

GL UNITED STATES DISTRICT COURT, Law Library, 450 Golden Gate Ave, PO Box 36060, 94102-3489. SAN 301-4800. Tel: 415-436-8130. FAX: 415-436-8134. *Librn*, Lynn Lundstrom; E-Mail: lynn_lundstrom@cand.uscourts.gov; *Asst Librn*, Susan Wong Caulder; Staff 2 (MLS 1, Non-MLS 1)
Founded 1960
Library Holdings: Bk Vols 34,701; Bk Titles 2,114; Per Subs 1,105
Restriction: Staff use only

G UNITED STATES ENVIRONMENTAL PROTECTION AGENCY, Region IX Library,* 75 Hawthorne St, 94105. SAN 301-3979. Tel: 415-744-1510. FAX: 415-744-1474. E-Mail: library-reg9@epamail.epa.gov. Web Site: www.epa.gov. *Head of Libr*, Colette Myles; Staff 5 (MLS 3, Non-MLS 2)
Founded 1970
1997-1998 Income $375,000. Mats Exp $82,000, Books $25,000, Per/Ser (Incl. Access Fees) $50,000, Micro $7,000. Sal $175,000 (Prof $125,000)
Library Holdings: Bk Titles 8,000; Per Subs 200
Subject Interests: Air pollution, Environmental law, Pesticides, Water pollution
Special Collections: Topographical Maps
Publications: Library Line (quarterly newsletter)
Partic in Fedlink; OCLC Online Computer Library Center, Inc

CL UNIVERSITY OF CALIFORNIA, Hastings College of the Law Library, 200 McAllister St, 94102-4978. SAN 301-4835. Tel: 415-565-4757. Circulation Tel: 415-565-4750. Reference Tel: 415-565-4751. FAX: 415-621-4859. Web Site: www.uchastings.edu/library. *Dir*, Jenni Parrish; *Assoc Dir*, Faye Jones; *Circ*, John Borden; *Publ Servs*, Linda Weir; *Head Tech Servs*, Mary Glennon; *Online Servs*, Dan Taysom; *Cat*, Grace Takatani; *Ref*, Charles Marcus; *Ref*, Vincent Moyer; *Ser*, Barbara Roush; Staff 24 (MLS 11, Non-MLS 13)
Founded 1878. Pop 1,344; Enrl 1,208; Fac 136; Highest Degree: Doctorate
Jul 1999-Jun 2000 Income $2,770,427. Mats Exp $1,277,303. Sal $1,277,303
Library Holdings: Bk Vols 406,097; Bk Titles 122,700; Per Subs 8,273
Subject Interests: Criminal law and justice, Law
Database Vendor: Dialog, IAC - Info Trac, Innovative Interfaces INN - View, Lexis-Nexis, OCLC - First Search
Open Mon-Fri 8-6, evening & weekend hours are restricted to faculty

C UNIVERSITY OF CALIFORNIA SAN FRANCISCO, Library & Center for Knowledge Management,* 530 Parnassus Ave, Rm 128, 94143-0840. SAN 301-4843. Tel: 415-476-8293. FAX: 415-476-4653. E-Mail: kab@library.ucsf.edu. Web Site: www.library.ucsf.edu. *Coll Develop*, Glennda Vandegrift; Staff 23 (MLS 23)
Founded 1864. Enrl 3,730; Fac 1,461; Highest Degree: Doctorate
Jul 1997-Jun 1998 Income $6,301,037, State $5,184,998, Locally Generated Income $947,497, Other $168,542. Mats Exp $1,240,385, Books $183,195, Per/Ser (Incl. Access Fees) $1,001,354, Presv $55,836. Sal $2,619,306 (Prof $685,709)
Library Holdings: Bk Vols 739,464; Per Subs 2,473
Subject Interests: Health sciences, Tobacco
Special Collections: California Medicine (special concentration in communicable diseases, high altitude physiology, industrial/organizational medicine); East Asian Medicine; History of Health Sciences; University Archives
Partic in OCLC Online Computer Library Center, Inc; Pacific SW Regional Med Libr Serv

C UNIVERSITY OF SAN FRANCISCO, (GLE - GRC), Richard A Gleeson Library - Charles & Nancy Geschke Resource Center, 2130 Fulton St, 94117-1049. SAN 334-6471. Tel: 415-422-6167. Interlibrary Loan Service Tel: 415-422-5634. Circulation Tel: 415-422-2660. Reference Tel: 415-422-2039. FAX: 415-422-5949. Web Site: www.usfca.edu/usf/library/gleeson.html. *Distance Educ, Regional Librarian*, Vicki Rosen; Tel: 415-422-5387, E-Mail: rosen@usfca.edu; *Dean of Libr*, Tyrone H Cannon; E-Mail: cannont@usfca.edu; *Coordr*, Carmen Fernandez-Baybay; Tel: 415-422-2035, E-Mail: fernandezc@usfca.edu; *Head, Acq*, Hille Novak; Tel: 415-422-6417, E-Mail: novak@usfca.edu; *Head, Cat*, Eric Ewen; Tel: 415-422-5361, E-Mail: ewene@usfca.edu; *Cat*, Benjamin Watson; Tel: 415-422-5633, E-Mail: watson@usfca.edu; *Head Ref*, Locke Morrisey; Tel: 415-422-5399, E-Mail: morrisey@usfca.edu; *Ref Serv*, Sherise Kimura; Tel: 415-422-5379, E-Mail: kimura@usfca.edu; *Ref Serv*, Randy Souther; Tel: 415-422-5388, E-Mail: southerr@usfca.edu; *Head, Circ*, Mary Sue Grant; Tel: 415-422-5660, E-Mail: grantm@usfca.edu; *Per, Ref Serv*, Debbie Malone; Tel: 415-422-5352, E-Mail: maloned@usfca.edu; *Per*, Kathleen Woo; Tel: 415-422-5351, E-Mail: woo@usfca.edu; *ILL*, Marion Gin; Tel: 415-422-5385, E-Mail: ginm@usfca.edu; *Rare Bks*, John Hawk; Tel: 415-422-2036, E-Mail: hawkj@usfca.edu; *Govt Doc*, Kathryn Brazee; Tel: 415-422-5389, E-Mail: brazee@usfca.edu; *Syst Coordr*, Karen Johnson; Tel: 415-422-2759, E-Mail: johnsonka@usfca.edu; *Archivist*, Michael Kotlanger; Tel: 415-422-5932, E-Mail: kotlanger@usfca.edu; *Instrul Serv*, Joe Garity; Tel: 415-422-5386, E-Mail: garity@usfca.edu; *Instrul Serv*, Richard Nicolopulos; Tel: 415-422-2415, E-Mail: nicolopulos@usfca.edu; *Media Spec*, Pat Steacy; Tel: 415-422-2002, E-Mail: steacy@usfca.edu; *Doc Delivery*, Eric Shappy; Tel: 415-422-2045, E-Mail: shappy@usfca.edu; *Dir Info Resources & Res*, Mark Stephen Mir; Tel: 415-422-5981, Ext 6401, E-Mail: mir@usfca.edu; Staff 22 (MLS 22)
Founded 1855. Enrl 7,383; Fac 1,132; Highest Degree: Doctorate
Jun 1999-May 2000 Income (Main Library and Branch Library) $4,403,162, Parent Institution $4,084,197, Other $318,965. Mats Exp $1,560,194, Books $536,383, Per/Ser (Incl. Access Fees) $576,166, Presv $41,694, Micro $2,821, Electronic Ref Mat (Incl. Access Fees) $403,130. Sal $1,534,585 (Prof $874,981)
Library Holdings: Bk Vols 747,062; Bk Titles 433,211; Per Subs 2,418; Bks on Deafness & Sign Lang 235
Special Collections: 1890's English Literature; A E & Lawrence Housman; Book Club of California; Carrollton; Charles Carroll of; Eric Gill; Fine Printing; Grabhorn Press; John Henry Nash; Recusant Literature; Richard Le Gallienne; Robert Graves; Sir Thomas More & Contemporaries; Victor Hammer
Automation Activity & Vendor Info: (Acquisitions) Innovative Interfaces Inc.; (Cataloging) Innovative Interfaces Inc.; (Circulation) Innovative Interfaces Inc.; (ILL) Innovative Interfaces Inc.; (OPAC) Innovative Interfaces Inc.; (Serials) Innovative Interfaces Inc.
Database Vendor: Dialog, OCLC - First Search, ProQuest, Silverplatter Information Inc., Wilson - Wilson Web
Restriction: In-house use for visitors, Non-circulating to the public, Not open to public, Open to students, Private library
Function: Archival collection, Document delivery services, ILL available, Some telephone reference
Mem of Asn of Research Libraries; Bay Area Libr & Info Syst
Partic in Am Libr Asn; Asn Jesuit & Univs; Coop Libr Agency for Syst & Servs; OCLC Online Computer Library Center, Inc; San Francisco Biomedical Library Network; Southern Calif Electronic Libr Consortium
Friends of the Library Group
Departmental Libraries:
CL SCHOOL OF LAW LIBRARY, 2130 Fulton St, Ignatian Heights, 94117-1080. SAN 334-6536. Tel: 415-422-6679. FAX: 415-422-2345. Web Site: www.usfca.edu/law_library/. *Dir*, Virginia J Kelsh; *Ref*, Leslie Campbell; *Tech Servs*, Nancy Hoebelheinrick; *Ref*, Lee Ryan; Staff 6 (MLS 6)
Founded 1912. Enrl 582; Fac 30

Jun 1999-May 2000 Income $1,721,920. Mats Exp $736,524, Books $65,970, Per/Ser (Incl. Access Fees) $530,745, Presv $10,809, Micro $58,000, Electronic Ref Mat (Incl. Access Fees) $71,000. Sal $872,337 (Prof $388,996)
Library Holdings: Bk Vols 302,348; Bk Titles 28,247; Per Subs 2,757

S WELLS FARGO BANK LIBRARY, 633 Folsom St, A0149-011, 94107. SAN 334-6560. Tel: 415-396-0777. Interlibrary Loan Service Tel: 415-396-0772. FAX: 415-396-7662. E-Mail: northp@wellsfargo.com. *Mgr*, Paul North; E-Mail: northp@wellsfargo.com; Staff 6 (MLS 4, Non-MLS 2)
Founded 1890
Library Holdings: Bk Vols 5,400; Per Subs 600
Subject Interests: Banks and banking
Automation Activity & Vendor Info: (Cataloging) Sydney
Publications: Column (in-house organ)
Branches:
HISTORICAL SERVICES LIBRARY, 420 Montgomery, 2nd flr, 94163. SAN 334-6595. Tel: 415-396-4157. FAX: 415-391-8644.
Library Holdings: Bk Vols 6,000; Per Subs 22
Special Collections: California Gold Rush & Mining; Californiana; History of Banking & Finance; San Francisco History; Staging & Western Transportation; Wells Fargo & Co History

L WEST GROUP, B E Witkin Law Library, 50 California St, 94111. SAN 301-3685. Tel: 415-732-8500. FAX: 415-732-8873. *Coordr*, Michael Christensen
Founded 1858
Library Holdings: Bk Titles 135,000; Per Subs 430
Subject Interests: California

S WINE INSTITUTE LIBRARY,* 425 Market St, Ste 1000, 94105. SAN 301-4886. Tel: 415-512-0151. FAX: 415-442-0742. Web Site: www.wineinstitute.org. *Librn*, Robert Zerkowitz
Founded 1934
Library Holdings: Bk Vols 3,100; Per Subs 150
Subject Interests: Wine
Special Collections: Oral Hist on Ca wine indust

S ALAN WOFSY FINE ARTS, Reference Library, 1109 Geary Blvd, 94109. SAN 374-8979. Tel: 415-986-3030. Reference Tel: 415-292-6500. FAX: 415-512-0130. E-Mail: beauxarts@earthlink.net. Web Site: www.art-books.com. *Dir*, Mark Hyman; *Coll Develop*, Buzzard Cohen
Library Holdings: Bk Titles 100
Subject Interests: Art

SAN JACINTO

J MOUNT SAN JACINTO COLLEGE, Milo P Johnson Library, 1499 N State St, 92583-2399. SAN 301-4924. Tel: 909-487-6752, Ext 1580. FAX: 909-654-8387. *Librn*, David King; Tel: 909-487-6752, Ext 1532, E-Mail: ddking@msjc.cc.ca.us; *Circ*, Lydia Herrera-Soren; E-Mail: lherrera@msjc.cc.ca.us; *Per*, Robert Pipes; *Cat*, Pam Quintana; E-Mail: pamquintana@msjac.cc.ca.usa
Founded 1963. Enrl 2,930; Highest Degree: Associate
Jul 1998-Jun 1999 Mats Exp $62,456, Books $22,069, Per/Ser (Incl. Access Fees) $35,587, AV Equip $3,000, Electronic Ref Mat (Incl. Access Fees) $1,800. Sal $129,000
Library Holdings: Bk Vols 36,000; Bk Titles 34,175; Per Subs 325
Automation Activity & Vendor Info: (Cataloging) DRA; (Circulation) DRA; (OPAC) DRA
Database Vendor: DRA
Partic in Inland Empire Acad Libr Coop; San Bernardino, Inyo, Riverside Counties United Library Services
Departmental Libraries:
MENIFEE VALLEY, 28237 La Piedra, Menifee Valley, 92584. SAN 378-2085. Tel: 909-487-6752, Ext 2525. FAX: 909-672-0874. Web Site: www.msjc.cc.ca.us/mvclibrary. *Librn*, Sherri Moore; Staff 3 (MLS 1, Non-MLS 2)
Highest Degree: Associate
Library Holdings: Bk Vols 11,000; Per Subs 45

SAN JOSE

AGNEWS DEVELOPMENTAL CENTER
S REACH PROGRAM, 3500 Zanker Rd, 95134. SAN 334-665X. Tel: 408-451-6483. FAX: 408-451-6037. E-Mail: adcrch@pacbell.net.
Founded 1948
Library Holdings: Bk Titles 500; Per Subs 20
M STAFF LIBRARY, 3500 Zanker Rd, 95134-2299. SAN 334-6625. Tel: 408-451-6118. FAX: 408-451-6439. E-Mail: aglib@dds.ca.gov. *Senior Librn*, Roberta Ling. Subject Specialists: *Developmental disabilities*, Roberta Ling; Staff 1 (MLS 1)
Founded 1957
Library Holdings: Bk Titles 1,000
Restriction: Staff use only, Students only

L BERLINER COHEN, Law Library, 10 Almaden Blvd, 11th flr, 95113-2233. SAN 372-3186. Tel: 408-286-5800. FAX: 408-998-5388. *Librn*, Gayle Hittle; Tel: 408-938-2458, E-Mail: gh@berliner.com; Staff 1 (MLS 1)
Library Holdings: Bk Vols 7,000
Subject Interests: California, Fed law, Law

§S DADE BEHRING-A SYVA COMPANY, Research Library, 3403 Yerba Buena Rd, 95135. (Mail add: PO Box 49013, 95161-9013), Tel: 408-239-2533. FAX: 408-239-2553. *In Charge*, Kim Kubik; E-Mail: kim_kubik@dadebehring.com
Library Holdings: Bk Vols 4,500; Per Subs 350
Restriction: Staff use only

S EARTH TECH LIBRARY,* 695 River Oaks Pkwy, 95134-1907. SAN 301-1836. Tel: 408-232-2800. FAX: 408-232-2801.
Founded 1978
Library Holdings: Bk Vols 4,000; Per Subs 32
Mem of South Bay Coop Libr Syst

J EVERGREEN VALLEY COLLEGE LIBRARY, 3095 Yerba Buena Rd, 95135-1598. SAN 320-166X. Tel: 408-270-6433. Reference Tel: 408-274-7900, Ext 6661. TDD: 408-531-8512. FAX: 408-532-1925. Web Site: www.library.sjeccd.cc.ca.us. *Dir*, Victoria Atherton; Tel: 408-274-7900, Ext 6503, E-Mail: victoria.atherton@sjeccd.cc.ca.us; *Acq, Cat, Online Servs*, Carol Bristow; Tel: 408-274-7900, Ext 6510, E-Mail: carol.bristow@sjeccd.cc.ca.us; *Circ*, Joy Chase; Tel: 408-274-7900, Ext 6821, E-Mail: joy.chase@sjeccd.cc.ca.us; Staff 10 (MLS 4, Non-MLS 6)
Founded 1975. Fac 282
Jul 1999-Jun 2000 Income $661,396. Mats Exp $80,257, Books $51,117, Per/Ser (Incl. Access Fees) $7,788, Electronic Ref Mat (Incl. Access Fees) $21,352. Sal $475,116 (Prof $262,612)
Library Holdings: Bk Vols 45,611; Bk Titles 37,450; Per Subs 154
Automation Activity & Vendor Info: (Cataloging) Innovative Interfaces Inc.; (Circulation) Innovative Interfaces Inc.
Database Vendor: Ebsco - EbscoHost, GaleNet, IAC - SearchBank, Innovative Interfaces INN - View
Restriction: Staff use only, Students only
Partic in Calif Commun Col Libr Coop - Desert Area
Open Mon-Thurs 8am-9pm & Fri 8am-4pm

S GARTNER GROUP - DATAQUEST, Information Resource Center,* 251 River Oaks Pkwy, 95134-1913. SAN 370-212X. Tel: 408-468-8000. FAX: 408-468-8021.
Library Holdings: Per Subs 100
Subject Interests: Telecommunications
Special Collections: Proprietary Research Reports
Restriction: Not open to public

S GE NUCLEAR ENERGY LIBRARY, 175 Curtner Ave, MC 728, 95125. SAN 301-4967. Tel: 408-925-3523. FAX: 408-925-3536. *Librn*, Phyllis Reyburn; E-Mail: phyllis.reyburn@gene.ge.com
Founded 1955
Library Holdings: Bk Vols 8,000
Subject Interests: Nuclear engineering
Publications: Monthly bulletin of new acquisitions
Partic in Class; OCLC Online Computer Library Center, Inc

S HISTORY MUSEUMS OF SAN JOSE, Research Center, 1650 Senter Rd, 95112. SAN 323-9519. Tel: 408-918-1054. FAX: 408-287-2291. E-Mail: research@historysj.org. Web Site: www.historysanjose.org. *Archivist*, Paula Jabloner; E-Mail: pjabloner@sjhistory.org; Staff 1 (MLS 1)
Founded 1970
Library Holdings: Bk Titles 500
Subject Interests: San Jose, Santa Clara Valley, Victoria mats
Special Collections: New Almaden Mines Coll; San Jose Pueblo Records, early local government records, maps; Santa Clara Valley historical photos; Sempervirens Club Coll
Restriction: Non-circulating

L HOPKINS & CARLEY LIBRARY,* PO Box 1469, 95109. SAN 329-4919. Tel: 408-286-9800. FAX: 408-998-4790. *Librn*, Paul Reavis; E-Mail: preavis@hopkins.carley.com
Library Holdings: Bk Vols 3,000; Per Subs 75

INTERNATIONAL BUSINESS MACHINES CORP
S RESEARCH LIBRARY, Dept K 74/H2A, 650 Harry Rd, 95120-6099. SAN 334-6714. Tel: 408-927-1060, 408-927-1580. FAX: 408-927-3105. *Mgr*, W T Gallagher
Founded 1952
Library Holdings: Bk Vols 27,000; Per Subs 300
Subject Interests: Chemistry, Computer science, Engineering, Mathematics, Physics
Partic in BRS; Cooperative Information Network; Dialog Corporation; RLIN; STN
S STL LIBRARY, 555 Bailey Ave, 95141. SAN 301-1755. Tel: 408-463-4050. FAX: 408-463-3261. *Librn*, Beverly Delavigne; Staff 2 (MLS 1, Non-MLS 1)

Library Holdings: Bk Titles 4,000; Per Subs 300
Subject Interests: Computer science
Special Collections: IBM SRL Manuals

CL LINCOLN LAW SCHOOL OF SAN JOSE LIBRARY,* One N First, 95113. SAN 301-424X. Tel: 408-271-0712. FAX: 408-977-7228. Web Site: www.lincolnlaw.sj.edu. *Dean of Libr*, Maya Harris; *Librn*, Bridgett Lawley
Founded 1919. Enrl 42; Highest Degree: Doctorate
Library Holdings: Bk Vols 23,300; Per Subs 25
Special Collections: Philippines
Partic in OCLC Online Computer Library Center, Inc

C NATIONAL HISPANIC UNIVERSITY, 14271 Story Rd, 95127-3823. SAN 327-7135. Tel: 408-273-2773. FAX: 408-254-1369. E-Mail: rlitwin@rhu.edu. Web Site: www.nhu.edu/library. *Dir*, Rory Litwin; E-Mail: rlitwin@nhu.edu; *Coll Develop*, Paul R Martinez
Enrl 311; Highest Degree: Bachelor
Library Holdings: Bk Vols 15,500; Per Subs 50
Subject Interests: Women's studies
Special Collections: American Coll; Bilingual Materials Coll; Gerald Wheeler's Latin Coll; Jacob Drucaroff Coll; M Huston Women's Coll
Automation Activity & Vendor Info: (Circulation) Sagebrush Corporation
Database Vendor: OCLC - First Search

M O'CONNER HOSPITAL LIBRARY, Medical Library,* 2105 Forest Ave, 95128. SAN 370-7490. Tel: 408-947-2647. FAX: 408-947-2819. E-Mail: och@netcom.com. *Librn*, Nancy Firchow; Staff 1 (MLS 1)
Founded 1985
Library Holdings: Bk Titles 800; Per Subs 140
Restriction: Staff use only

CM PALMER COLLEGE OF CHIROPRACTIC-WEST LIBRARY, 90 E Tasman Dr, 95134. SAN 326-4602. Tel: 408-944-6142. FAX: 408-944-6181. Web Site: www.palmer.edu. *Coll Develop, Dir, Librn*, Patricia McGrew; E-Mail: mcgrew_p@palmer.edu; *Circ*, Wendy Kubow; *Tech Servs*, Alexandra Teris; Staff 4 (MLS 1, Non-MLS 3)
Founded 1978. Enrl 600; Fac 52; Highest Degree: Doctorate
Library Holdings: Bk Vols 15,000; Bk Titles 14,000; Per Subs 165
Subject Interests: Chiropractic medicine
Special Collections: Chiropractic Archives, bks
Publications: Newsletter
Partic in Coop Libr Agency for Syst & Servs; OCLC Online Computer Library Center, Inc

S PRATT & WHITNEY, (Formerly United Technologies Corp), CSD Library-Space Propulsion Operations, 600 Metcalf Rd, 95138-9602. SAN 301-6463. Tel: 408-776-4957. Interlibrary Loan Service Tel: 408-776-4673. Reference Tel: 408-776-4452. FAX: 408-776-5995. *Librn*, Karen S Schaffer; E-Mail: schaffer@csd.com
Founded 1960
Library Holdings: Bk Titles 9,500; Per Subs 100
Subject Interests: Organic chemistry
Publications: Guide to the CSD Library
Restriction: Staff use only
Partic in Defense Technical Information Center; Dialog Corporation

M REGIONAL MEDICAL CENTER OF SAN JOSE, Ismael Medical Library, 225 N Jackson Ave, 95116-1603. SAN 322-8797. Tel: 408-259-5000, Ext 2230. FAX: 408-729-2881. *Librn*, Elizabeth A Mason; Staff 1 (MLS 1)
Library Holdings: Bk Vols 585; Per Subs 75
Subject Interests: Medicine
Publications: Journal List (semi-yearly); List of Holdings (yearly)

S ROSICRUCIAN ORDER, AMORC, Research Library,* Rosicrucian Park, 1342 Naglee Ave, 95191. SAN 301-4983. Tel: 408-947-3600. FAX: 408-947-3677. *Librn*, Myra Marsh
Founded 1939
Library Holdings: Bk Vols 16,000; Per Subs 21
Subject Interests: Egypt
Publications: Rosicrucian Indexes
Restriction: Members only
Friends of the Library Group

CR SAN JOSE CHRISTIAN COLLEGE, Memorial Library,* 790 S 12th St, PO Box 1090, 95112. SAN 301-4991. Tel: 408-278-4370, 408-293-9058. FAX: 408-293-7352. E-Mail: sjcc1939@aol.com. Web Site: www.sschristiancoc.edu. *Dir*, May Wu; *Librn*, Tonya Persall; Staff 2 (MLS 2)
Founded 1939. Pop 17,000; Circ 17,000; Enrl 287; Fac 38; Highest Degree: Bachelor
1997-1998 Income $155,729. Mats Exp $14,390, Books $7,800, Per/Ser (Incl. Access Fees) $4,510, Presv $550, AV Equip $1,530
Library Holdings: Bk Vols 34,000; Per Subs 177
Subject Interests: Restoration, Theology
Special Collections: Bible Commentaries; Restoration History

J SAN JOSE CITY COLLEGE LIBRARY, 2100 Moorpark Ave, 95128-2799. SAN 301-5009. Tel: 408-288-3775. Interlibrary Loan Service Tel: 408-288-3776. Circulation Tel: 408-288-3776. Reference Tel: 408-298-2181, Ext 3899. FAX: 408-293-4728. Web Site: www.sjcc.edu. *Coordr*, Joseph King; Tel: 408-298-2181, Ext 3544, E-Mail: jking@sjeccd.cc.ca.us; *Cat*, Robert Wing; Tel: 408-298-2181, Ext 3945, E-Mail: robert.wing@sjeccd.cc.ca.us; *Doc, Per, Ref*, Todd Williams; Tel: 408-298-2181, Ext 3721, E-Mail: todd.williams@sjeccd.cc.ca.us; *Bibliog Instr*, Anh Nguyen; Tel: 408-298-2181, Ext 3949, E-Mail: anguyen@sjeccd.cc.ca.us; *Acq, Ref Serv*, Russell Fischer; Tel: 408-298-2181, Ext 3944, E-Mail: russ.fischer@sjeccd.cc.ca.us; *Ref Serv*, Hilde Borror; Tel: 408-298-2181, Ext 3944, E-Mail: hborror@sjeccd.cc.ca.us; Staff 6 (MLS 6)
Founded 1921. Enrl 10,549; Highest Degree: Associate
Jul 1999-Jun 2000 Income $718,343. Sal $583,836
Library Holdings: Bk Vols 60,035; Per Subs 241
Automation Activity & Vendor Info: (Acquisitions) Innovative Interfaces Inc.; (Circulation) Innovative Interfaces Inc.; (Course Reserve) Innovative Interfaces Inc.; (ILL) Innovative Interfaces Inc.; (Media Booking) Innovative Interfaces Inc.; (OPAC) Innovative Interfaces Inc.; (Serials) Innovative Interfaces Inc.
Publications: Recent Acquisitions, Library Newsletter, Information Sheets, Resource Guides, Library Instruction Workbook
Partic in RLIN

M SAN JOSE MEDICAL CENTER, Health Sciences Library, 675 E Santa Clara St, 95112. SAN 334-6749. Tel: 408-977-4638. FAX: 408-993-7031. *Librn*, Judy Gehman; Staff 1 (MLS 1)
Founded 1924
Library Holdings: Bk Titles 3,200; Per Subs 450
Subject Interests: Allied health, Hospital administration, Medicine, Nursing
Restriction: Staff use only
Partic in Docline; Med Libr Consortium of Santa Clara County

S SAN JOSE MERCURY NEWS LIBRARY, 750 Ridder Park Dr, 95190. SAN 301-5025. Tel: 408-920-5346. FAX: 408-920-5345. Web Site: www.sjmercurycenter.com. *Head Librn*, Chris Hardesty
Founded 1928
Library Holdings: Bk Vols 2,600; Per Subs 60
Subject Interests: Electronics
Special Collections: Newspaper photographs & clipping
Partic in Vutext

S SAN JOSE MUSEUM OF ART LIBRARY, 110 S Market St, 95113. SAN 321-6454. Tel: 408-271-6840. FAX: 408-294-2977. E-Mail: info@sjmusart.org. Web Site: www.sjmusart.org. *Librn*, Jean Wheeler; Staff 1 (MLS 1)
Founded 1978
Library Holdings: Bk Vols 2,790
Subject Interests: Art
Special Collections: Children's Art Books Coll
Restriction: Staff use only

P SAN JOSE PUBLIC LIBRARY, 180 W San Carlos St, 95113. SAN 334-6773. Tel: 408-277-4822. Circulation Tel: 408-277-4846. Reference Tel: 408-277-4815. TDD: 408-277-2858. FAX: 408-277-3187. E-Mail: admin.sjpl@ci.sj.ca.us. Web Site: lib.ci.sj.ca.us. *Dir*, Jane Light; E-Mail: jane.light@ci.sj.ca.us; *Mgr Libr*, Joy Macari; E-Mail: joy.macari@ci.sj.ca.us; *Mgr Libr*, Elsi Stotts; E-Mail: elsi.stotts@ci.sj.ca.us; *Mgr Libr*, Gordon Yusko; E-Mail: gordon.yusko@ci.sj.ca.us; *Librn*, Peggy Conaway; *Librn*, Hannah Slocum; *Asst Librn*, Paul Underwood; *Acq, Cat*, Rhonda Lakatos; Tel: 408-277-4831, E-Mail: rhonda.lakatos@ci.sj.ca.us; *Circ*, Jeanne Lofranco; Tel: 408-277-4997, E-Mail: jeanne.lofranco@ci.sj.ca.us; *Automation Syst Coordr*, Linda Dydo; Tel: 408-277-5323, E-Mail: linda.dydo@ci.sj.ca.us; *Online Servs*, Brian Fowler; *Coordr*, Cornelia Van Aken-Sanks; E-Mail: cornelia.vanaken-sanks@ci.sj.ca.us. Subject Specialists: *Language arts*, Rita Torres; *Youth*, Cornelia Van Aken-Sanks; Staff 457 (MLS 113, Non-MLS 344)
Founded 1872. Pop 924,000; Circ 7,886,647
Jul 1999-Jun 2000 Income (Main Library and Branch Library) $38,509,540, State $1,447,008, City $36,565,846, Federal $131,577, Locally Generated Income $36,565,846, Other $385,099. Mats Exp $3,644,640, Books $2,618,797, Per/Ser (Incl. Access Fees) $240,360, Presv $5,720, Micro $18,471, Electronic Ref Mat (Incl. Access Fees) $249,067. Sal $19,427,242
Library Holdings: Bk Vols 1,451,073
Subject Interests: Business and management, Music
Special Collections: Aging-Handicapped; California Room; Mexican-American Literature & Spanish Language
Automation Activity & Vendor Info: (Acquisitions) epixtech, inc.; (Cataloging) epixtech, inc.; (Circulation) epixtech, inc.; (OPAC) epixtech, inc.; (Serials) epixtech, inc.
Database Vendor: Dialog, Ebsco - EbscoHost, epixtech, inc., GaleNet, IAC - Info Trac, OCLC - First Search, Wilson - Wilson Web
Mem of Silicon Valley Library System
Friends of the Library Group
Branches: 17
ALMADEN, 6455 Camden Ave, 95120-2823. SAN 334-6803. Tel: 408-268-7601. FAX: 408-927-6106. Web Site: www.lib.ci.sj.ca.us. *Librn*, Judy Kristofferson
Library Holdings: Bk Vols 99,051
Friends of the Library Group
ALVISO, 1060 Taylor St, 95002. SAN 334-6838. Tel: 408-263-3626. FAX: 408-956-9435. Web Site: www.lib.ci.sj.ca.us.

Library Holdings: Bk Vols 12,042
Friends of the Library Group
BERRYESSA, 3311 Noble Ave, 95132-3198. SAN 334-6862. Tel: 408-272-3555. FAX: 408-926-6627. Web Site: www.lib.ci.sj.ca.us. *Librn*, Dave Genesy
Library Holdings: Bk Vols 87,548
Friends of the Library Group
BIBLIOTECA LATINO AMERICANA, 690 Locust St, 95110-2939. SAN 334-6897. Tel: 408-294-1237. FAX: 408-297-4278. Web Site: www.lib.ci.sj.ca.us. *Librn*, Linda Mendez-Ortiz
Library Holdings: Bk Vols 36,704
Subject Interests: Spanish (language)
Friends of the Library Group
CALABAZAS, 1230 Blaney Ave, 95129-3799. SAN 334-6927. Tel: 408-996-1536. FAX: 408-255-7597. Web Site: www.lib.ci.sj.ca.us. *Librn*, Marianne Pridemore
Library Holdings: Bk Vols 80,466
Friends of the Library Group
CAMBRIAN, 1780 Hillsdale Ave, 95124-3199. SAN 334-6951. Tel: 408-269-5063. FAX: 408-269-6106. Web Site: www.lib.ci.sj.ca.us. *Librn*, Charlotte Sakai
Library Holdings: Bk Vols 114,162
Friends of the Library Group
EAST SAN JOSE CARNEGIE, 1102 E Santa Clara St, 95116-2246. SAN 334-6986. Tel: 408-998-2069. FAX: 408-971-4542. Web Site: www.lib.ci.sj.ca.us. *Librn*, David Nashelsky
Library Holdings: Bk Vols 48,894
Friends of the Library Group
EDUCATIONAL PARK, 1770 Educational Park Dr, 95133-1703. SAN 334-701X. Tel: 408-272-3663. FAX: 408-251-6971. Web Site: www.lib.ci.sj.ca.us. *Librn*, Nora Sepulveda-Conte
Library Holdings: Bk Vols 69,898
Friends of the Library Group
EMPIRE, 491 E Empire St, 95112-3308. SAN 334-7044. Tel: 408-286-5627. FAX: 408-971-4577. Web Site: www.lib.ci.sj.ca.us.
Library Holdings: Bk Vols 42,991
Friends of the Library Group
EVERGREEN, 2635 Aborn Rd, 95121-1294. SAN 334-7079. Tel: 408-238-4434. FAX: 408-274-9548. Web Site: www.lib.ci.sj.ca.us. *Librn*, Wendy Kay
Library Holdings: Bk Vols 93,263
Friends of the Library Group
HILLVIEW, 2255 Ocala Ave, 95122-1199. SAN 334-7109. Tel: 408-272-3100. FAX: 408-926-6641. Web Site: www.lib.ci.sj.ca.us. *Librn*, Gloria Heinzl
Library Holdings: Bk Vols 63,590
Friends of the Library Group
PEARL AVENUE, 4270 Pearl Ave, 95136-1899. SAN 334-7133. Tel: 408-265-7834. FAX: 408-269-6211. Web Site: www.lib.ci.sj.ca.us. *Librn*, Gayleen Thomas
Library Holdings: Bk Vols 83,298
Friends of the Library Group
ROSEGARDEN, 1580 Naglee Ave, 95126-2097. SAN 334-7168. Tel: 408-998-1512. FAX: 408-971-4955. Web Site: www.lib.ci.sj.ca.us.
Founded 1960
Library Holdings: Bk Vols 64,849
Friends of the Library Group
SANTA TERESA, 290 International Circle, 95119-1132. SAN 334-7176. Tel: 408-281-1879. FAX: 408-363-0620. Web Site: www.lib.ci.sj.ca.us. *Librn*, Anne Proudfoot
Library Holdings: Bk Vols 131,173
Friends of the Library Group
SEVENTREES, 3597 Cas Dr, 95111-2499. SAN 334-7192. Tel: 408-629-4536. FAX: 408-365-1736. Web Site: www.lib.ci.sj.ca.us. *Librn*, Gloria Heinzl
Library Holdings: Bk Vols 59,561
Friends of the Library Group
WEST VALLEY, 1243 San Tomas Aquino Rd, 95117-3399. SAN 334-7222. Tel: 408-244-4766. FAX: 408-984-3736. Web Site: www.lib.ci.sj.ca.us. *Librn*, Wayne Disher
Library Holdings: Bk Vols 81,155
Friends of the Library Group
WILLOW GLEN, 1157 Minnesota Ave, 95125-3324. SAN 334-7257. Tel: 408-998-2053. FAX: 408-971-6043. Web Site: www.lib.ci.sj.ca.us. *Librn*, Maurice Stevenson
Library Holdings: Bk Vols 53,266
Friends of the Library Group
Bookmobiles: 1

C SAN JOSE STATE UNIVERSITY, Clark Library, 1 Washington Sq, 95192-0028. SAN 301-5033. Tel: 408-924-2700. Interlibrary Loan Service Tel: 408-924-2720. Circulation Tel: 408-924-2710. Reference Tel: 408-924-2730. TDD: 408-924-2745. FAX: 408-924-2701. Web Site: www.library.sjsu.edu/. *Dean*, Dr Patricia Senn Breivik; Tel: 408-924-2419, Fax: 408-924-2800, E-Mail: pbreivik@email.sjsu.edu; *Asst Dean*, Donna Z Pontau; Tel: 408-924-2818, Fax: 408-924-2800, E-Mail: dpontau@email.sjsu.edu; *Admin Dir*, Florence Cappelloni; Tel: 408-924-2744, E-Mail: cappello@email.sjsu.edu; *Librn*, Sandra Belanger; Tel: 408-924-2719, E-Mail: belanger@email.sjsu.edu; *Librn*, Judith Reynolds; Tel: 408-924-2725, E-Mail: judyr@email.sjsu.edu; *Head, Acq*, Lucy Yonemura; Tel: 408-924-2834, E-Mail: lyonemur@email.sjsu.edu; *Automation Syst Coordr*, Jeff Paul; Tel: 408-924-2815, Fax: 408-924-2800, E-Mail: jpaul@email.sjsu.edu; *AV, Media Spec*, Lorraine Lance; Tel: 408-924-2801, E-Mail: llance@email.sjsu.edu; *Head, Circ*, Julie Kowalewski-Ward; Tel: 408-924-2708, E-Mail: jaward@email.sjsu.edu; *Doc*, Lorene Sisson; *ILL*, Cathy Perez; Tel: 408-924-2811, E-Mail: ceperez@sjsu.edu; *Outreach Serv*, Robert McDermand; Tel: 408-924-2761, E-Mail: miicem@email.sjsu.edu; *Head Ref*, Rosemary Thorne; Tel: 408-924-2827, E-Mail: thorne@sjsu.edu; *Spec Coll*, Cecilia Mullen; Tel: 408-924-2813, E-Mail: mullen@sjsu.edu; *Head Tech Servs*, Celia Bakke; Tel: 408-924-2717, 924-2781, E-Mail: cbakke@email.sjsu.edu. Subject Specialists: *Academic*, Sandra Belanger; *Education*, Judith Reynolds; Staff 74 (MLS 26, Non-MLS 48)
Founded 1857. Enrl 26,000; Fac 1,200; Highest Degree: Master
Jul 1999-Jun 2000 Income $7,501,722, Federal $68,619, Locally Generated Income $30,866, Parent Institution $7,191,061, Other $211,176. Mats Exp $2,188,984, Books $664,323, Per/Ser (Incl. Access Fees) $1,102,811, Presv $53,940, Micro $41,359, Electronic Ref Mat (Incl. Access Fees) $326,551. Sal $3,720,513 (Prof $1,760,675)
Library Holdings: Bk Vols 1,143,500; Bk Titles 981,854; Per Subs 2,422
Special Collections: Beethoven Studies; British Parliamentary Papers; World War II Diplomatic & Military History (John Steinbeck Coll)
Automation Activity & Vendor Info: (Acquisitions) Innovative Interfaces Inc.; (Cataloging) Innovative Interfaces Inc.; (Circulation) Innovative Interfaces Inc.; (Course Reserve) Innovative Interfaces Inc.; (ILL) Innovative Interfaces Inc.; (Media Booking) Innovative Interfaces Inc.; (OPAC) Innovative Interfaces Inc.; (Serials) Innovative Interfaces Inc.
Database Vendor: GaleNet, Lexis-Nexis, ProQuest, Silverplatter Information Inc., Wilson - Wilson Web
Mem of California State University
Partic in Dialog Corporation; OCLC Online Computer Library Center, Inc; RLIN
Special Services for the Deaf - TTY machine

P SANTA CLARA COUNTY FREE LIBRARY, (SCCL), 1095 N Seventh St, 95112-4434. SAN 334-7281. Tel: 408-293-2326. FAX: 408-287-9826. E-Mail: webmaster@santaclaracountylib.org. Web Site: www.santaclaracountylib.org. *Dir*, Susan Fuller; *Ad Servs, ILL, YA Servs*, Carol Jaech; *Dep Dir*, Julie Farnsworth; *Tech Servs*, Evelyn Howard; *Tech Servs*, Bonnie Natsuhara; *Ch Servs*, Davi Evans; Staff 61 (MLS 61)
Founded 1912. Pop 403,990; Circ 7,140,715
Jul 1998-Jun 1999 Income (Main Library and Branch Library) $4,988,794, State $2,439,100, Locally Generated Income $1,331,900, Other $1,217,794. Mats Exp $20,601,077, Books $2,947,975, Per/Ser (Incl. Access Fees) $122,936, Electronic Ref Mat (Incl. Access Fees) $108,908. Sal $11,836,433
Library Holdings: Bk Vols 1,513,379; Bk Titles 342,783; Per Subs 2,850; High Interest/Low Vocabulary Bk Vols 2,950
Special Collections: California Western Americana
Automation Activity & Vendor Info: (Cataloging) epixtech, inc.; (Circulation) epixtech, inc.
Database Vendor: Ebsco - EbscoHost, epixtech, inc., IAC - Info Trac, OCLC - First Search
Mem of Silicon Valley Library System
Friends of the Library Group
Branches: 9
ALUM ROCK, 75 S White Rd, 95127-2994. SAN 334-7311. Tel: 408-251-1280. FAX: 408-258-5694. *Librn*, Karen Burnett
Library Holdings: Bk Vols 86,035
Friends of the Library Group
CAMPBELL PUBLIC, 77 Harrison Ave, Campbell, 95008-1499. SAN 334-7370. Tel: 408-866-1991. FAX: 408-866-1433. *Librn*, Theresa Lehan
Library Holdings: Bk Vols 164,460
Friends of the Library Group
CUPERTINO PUBLIC, 10400 Torre Ave, Cupertino, 95014-3254. SAN 334-7435. Tel: 408-446-1677. FAX: 408-252-8749. *Librn*, Mary-Ann Wallace
Library Holdings: Bk Vols 312,614
Friends of the Library Group
GILROY PUBLIC, 7387 Rosanna St, Gilroy, 95020-6193. SAN 334-746X. Tel: 408-842-8207. FAX: 408-842-0489. *Librn*, Lani Yoshimura; Tel: 408-842-8208, E-Mail: lyoshimu@scinet.co.santa-clara.ca.us
Library Holdings: Bk Vols 127,007
Friends of the Library Group
LOS ALTOS MAIN, 13 S San Antonio Rd, Los Altos, 94022-3049. SAN 334-7494. Tel: 650-948-7683. FAX: 650-941-6308. Web Site: www.santaclaracountylib.org. *Librn*, Catharine Fouts
Pop 40,000; Circ 1,100,000
Library Holdings: Bk Vols 214,501
Friends of the Library Group
LOS ALTOS-WOODLAND BRANCH, 1975 Grant Rd, Los Altos, 94022-6984. SAN 334-7672. Tel: 650-969-6030. FAX: 650-969-4922. *Librn*, Catharine Fouts
Library Holdings: Bk Vols 45,887
Friends of the Library Group
MILPITAS COMMUNITY, 40 N Milpitas Blvd, Milpitas, 95035-4495. SAN 334-7346. Tel: 408-262-1171. FAX: 408-262-5806. *Librn*, Karen Burnett

Library Holdings: Bk Vols 207,729
Friends of the Library Group
MORGAN HILL BRANCH, 17575 Peak Ave, Morgan Hill, 95037-4128. SAN 334-7524. Tel: 408-779-3196. FAX: 408-779-0883. *Librn*, Sarah Flowers
Library Holdings: Bk Vols 157,565
Friends of the Library Group
SARATOGA COMMUNITY, 13650 Saratoga Ave, Saratoga, 95070-5099. SAN 334-7559. Tel: 408-867-6129. FAX: 408-867-9806. *Librn*, Dolly Barnes
Library Holdings: Bk Vols 179,948
Friends of the Library Group
Bookmobiles: 2

GL SANTA CLARA COUNTY LAW LIBRARY, 360 N First St, 95113. SAN 301-505X. Tel: 408-299-3568. FAX: 408-286-9283. *Dir*, Susan Kuklin; *Circ, Ref*, Elaine Taranto; Staff 12 (MLS 2, Non-MLS 10)
Founded 1874
Library Holdings: Bk Vols 70,000; Per Subs 302
Friends of the Library Group

S SANTA CLARA COUNTY OFFICE OF EDUCATION, Professional Library, 1290 Ridder Park Dr, Mail Code 232, 95131. SAN 329-8140. Tel: 408-453-6800. FAX: 408-453-6815. E-Mail: professional_library@sccoe.k12.ca.us. Web Site: sccoe.k12.ca.us/proflibr.htm. *Mgr*, Susan Martimo Choi; *Coll Develop*, Donna Wheelehan; Staff 6 (MLS 2, Non-MLS 4)
Library Holdings: Bk Vols 15,000; Per Subs 152
Subject Interests: Educ mat for professionals
Database Vendor: epixtech, inc.

M SANTA CLARA VALLEY MEDICAL CENTER, (SCVMC), Milton J Chatton Medical Library, 751 S Bascom Ave, 95128. SAN 334-7702. Tel: 408-885-5650. FAX: 408-885-5655. E-Mail: medlib@hhs.co.santa-clara.ca.us. Web Site: www.scvmed.org. *Librn*, Connie Kwan; *Librn*, Shirley L Lin; Staff 5 (MLS 2, Non-MLS 3)
Founded 1930
Jul 1999-Jun 2000 Mats Exp $101,187, Books $9,995, Per/Ser (Incl. Access Fees) $91,192
Library Holdings: Bk Titles 4,000; Per Subs 500
Subject Interests: Medicine, Nursing, Public health
Automation Activity & Vendor Info: (Acquisitions) EOS; (Cataloging) Follett; (Circulation) Follett; (OPAC) Follett
Database Vendor: OVID Technologies
Restriction: Lending to staff only, Restricted public use
Partic in Dialog Corporation; Med Libr Consortium of Santa Clara County; Medline

G SANTA CLARA VALLEY WATER DISTRICT LIBRARY, 1020 Blossom Hill Rd, 95123. (Mail add: 5750 Almaden Expressway, 95118), SAN 375-5533. Tel: 408-265-2600, Ext 2487. FAX: 408-267-5039. Web Site: www.scvwd.dst.ca.us/fyi/library.htm. *Librn*, Robert J Teeter; Fax: 408-267-5039, E-Mail: bteeter@scvwd.dst.ca.us; Staff 2 (MLS 1, Non-MLS 1)
Library Holdings: Bk Vols 18,000; Bk Titles 14,000; Per Subs 400
Subject Interests: Engineering, Environment, Public admin, Water
Special Collections: SCVWD documents
Database Vendor: OCLC - First Search
Restriction: Circulation limited, In-house use for visitors

L UNITED STATES DISTRICT COURT LIBRARY,* 280 S First St, 95113. SAN 372-3127. Tel: 408-535-5323. FAX: 408-535-5322. *Librn*, Nancy B Selan
Library Holdings: Bk Vols 12,000; Per Subs 40
Partic in OCLC Online Computer Library Center, Inc

SAN JUAN BAUTISTA

P SAN JUAN BAUTISTA CITY LIBRARY,* 801 Second St, 95045. (Mail add: PO Box 1420, 95045), SAN 301-5068. Tel: 831-623-4687. FAX: 831-623-4093. E-Mail: sjblib@hollinet.com, sjblib@hotmail.com. *Dir*, Dr Patricia Larkin; Staff 3 (MLS 1, Non-MLS 2)
Founded 1896. Pop 1,300; Circ 4,800
Library Holdings: Bk Vols 9,118
Automation Activity & Vendor Info: (Cataloging) Sagebrush Corporation
Mem of Monterey Bay Area Cooperative Library System
Open Mon 10-8, Tues & Thurs 8-8, Wed & Fri 10-6, Sat 9-5
Friends of the Library Group

SAN JUAN CAPISTRANO

M AIDS EDUCATION GLOBAL INFORMATION SYSTEM, PO Box 184, 92693-0184. SAN 375-7234. Tel: 949-248-5843. FAX: 949-248-2839. Web Site: www.aegis.org. *Dir*, Sister Mary Elizabeth
Library Holdings: Bk Titles 20; Per Subs 27

M QUEST DIAGNOSTICS, INC, (Formerly Smithkline Beecham Clinical Laboratories Library), Corporate Medical Library, 33608 Ortega Hwy, 92690-6130. SAN 301-6846. Tel: 949-728-4689. FAX: 949-728-4047. *In Charge*, Bonnie Stephenson; E-Mail: stephenb@questdiagnostics.com; Staff 1 (MLS 1)
Founded 2000
Library Holdings: Bk Vols 200; Bk Titles 800; Per Subs 180
Subject Interests: Clinical labs, Endocrinology, Genetics, Oncology, Pathology, Toxicology
Restriction: Not open to public, Private library
Function: For research purposes

SAN JUAN CAPISTRANO LIBRARY
See Orange County Public Library, Santa Ana , .

SAN LEANDRO

S PORTUGUESE UNION OF THE STATE OF CALIFORNIA, J A Freitas Library, 1120 E 14th St, 94577. SAN 301-5092. Tel: 510-483-7676. FAX: 510-483-5015. E-Mail: upec@worldnet.att.net. Web Site: www.upec.org. *Librn*, Duarte Batista
Founded 1967
Library Holdings: Bk Titles 10,000
Special Collections: Portuguese Newspapers of California 1880s

S PRIMEX PHYSICS INTERNATIONAL CO LIBRARY,* 2700 Merced St, PO Box 5010, 94577-0599. SAN 301-5084. Tel: 510-357-4610. FAX: 510-577-7283.
Library Holdings: Bk Vols 500
Subject Interests: Physics
Restriction: Not open to public

P SAN LEANDRO COMMUNITY LIBRARY, 300 Estudillo Ave, 94577. SAN 334-7761. Tel: 510-577-3970. Interlibrary Loan Service Tel: 510-577-3971. FAX: 510-562-9564. Web Site: infopeople.berkeley.edu:8000/slpl/. *Dir*, David R Bohne; Tel: 510-577-3940, Fax: 510-577-3967, E-Mail: dbohne@ci.san-leandro.ca.us; *City Librn*, Nancy Fong; Tel: 510-577-3947, Fax: 510-577-3967
Founded 1906. Pop 72,000; Circ 631,831
Jul 1999-Jun 2000 Income (Main Library and Branch Library) City $2,992,900. Mats Exp $225,096, Books $189,064, Per/Ser (Incl. Access Fees) $25,573, Presv $4,427, Micro $6,032. Sal $1,384,024
Library Holdings: Bk Vols 207,232; Per Subs 415
Special Collections: Californiana
Automation Activity & Vendor Info: (Acquisitions) epixtech, inc.; (Cataloging) epixtech, inc.; (Circulation) epixtech, inc.; (OPAC) epixtech, inc.; (Serials) epixtech, inc.
Database Vendor: epixtech, inc., OVID Technologies
Friends of the Library Group
Branches: 3
MANOR, 1307 Manor Blvd, 94579-1501. SAN 334-7850. Tel: 510-357-6252. *Librn*, Mary Litvinchuck
Library Holdings: Bk Vols 20,604
MULFORD-MARINA, 13699 Aurora Dr, 94577-4036. SAN 334-7885. Tel: 510-357-3850. *Librn*, Lois Jessee
Library Holdings: Bk Vols 12,601
SOUTH, 14799 E 14th St, 94578-2818. SAN 334-7915. Tel: 510-357-5464. *Librn*, Sue Belchik
Library Holdings: Bk Vols 11,814

M VENCOR HOSPITAL, San Leandro Library,* 2800 Benedict Dr, 94577. SAN 301-5106. Tel: 510-357-8300, Ext 4562. FAX: 510-357-2391.
Library Holdings: Bk Vols 250; Per Subs 5

SAN LUIS OBISPO

C CALIFORNIA POLYTECHNIC STATE UNIVERSITY, Robert E Kennedy Library, One Grand Ave, 93407. SAN 301-5130. Tel: 805-756-2345. FAX: 805-756-2346. E-Mail: library@calpoly.edu. Web Site: www.lib.calpoly.edu. *Dean of Libr*, Hiram L Davis; *Acq*, Johanna Brown; *Cat*, Judi Pinkerton; *Ref*, Paul Adalian; *Archivist, Spec Coll*, Nancy Loe; Staff 18 (MLS 18)
Founded 1901. Enrl 15,000; Fac 800; Highest Degree: Master
Library Holdings: Bk Vols 731,878; Bk Titles 554,566; Per Subs 2,306
Subject Interests: Agriculture, Art and architecture, Graphic arts
Special Collections: California Promotional & Travel Literature; Fairs & Expositions; Healy Newspaper Coll; Hearst Castle Architectural Drawings; John Henry Nash Coll; Josephine Miles Coll; Julia Morgan Coll; Local History; Upton Sinclair Coll; William F Cody Coll; William McDill Railroad Coll
Publications: Archival Descriptive Guides; Library Connections; Library Information Guides; OPAC Searching Guides
Mem of California State University
Partic in Dialog Corporation; Medline; Melvyl; OCLC Online Computer Library Center, Inc; RLIN
Special Services for the Deaf - High interest/low vocabulary books; Staff with knowledge of sign language; TTY machine
Disabled student services equipment in library
Friends of the Library Group

C CUESTA COLLEGE LIBRARY, (Formerly Cuesta College), Hwy 1, 93403-8106. (Mail add: P O Box 8106, 93403-8106), SAN 301-5149. Tel: 805-546-3155. Reference Tel: 805-546-3157. FAX: 805-546-3109. Web Site: library.cuesta/cc/ca/us. *Dir*, Dr David Dowell; Tel: 805-546-3159, E-Mail: ddowell@bass.cuesta.cc.ca.us; *Tech Servs*, Christina Lau; *Tech Servs*, Keith Lilley; Staff 15 (MLS 5, Non-MLS 10)
Founded 1965. Enrl 8,656; Fac 397
Jul 1999-Jun 2000 Mats Exp $154,350, Books $54,989, Per/Ser (Incl. Access Fees) $27,617, Micro $4,739, AV Equip $67,005. Sal $616,425 (Prof $228,551)
Library Holdings: Bk Vols 64,814; Bk Titles 55,750; Per Subs 584
Special Collections: Career Transfer Center; Health Coll; Morro Bay Coll
Database Vendor: Ebsco - EbscoHost, GaleNet
Publications: Expanding Horizons (bibliographic instruction workbook)
Function: ILL available
Partic in OCLC Online Computer Library Center, Inc; Total Interlibrary Exchange
Friends of the Library Group

P SAN LUIS OBISPO CITY-COUNTY LIBRARY, 995 Palm St, PO Box 8107, 93403-8107. SAN 334-794X. Tel: 805-781-5784. FAX: 805-781-1320. E-Mail: ipslolib@slonet.org. Web Site: www.slonet.org/vv/slo_library/index.html. *Dir*, Brian A Reynolds; E-Mail: breynolds@co.slo.ca.us; *Asst Dir*, Mary H McGee; Tel: 805-781-5990, E-Mail: mmcgee@co.slo.ca.us. Subject Specialists: *Accounting*, Sherry L Ferris; Staff 63 (MLS 14, Non-MLS 49)
Founded 1919. Pop 222,300; Circ 1,618,676
Jul 1999-Jun 2000 Income (Main Library and Branch Library) $5,687,918, State $675,001, County $291,947, Other $4,720,970. Mats Exp $404,953, Books $349,915, Per/Ser (Incl. Access Fees) $31,526, Micro $8,339, Electronic Ref Mat (Incl. Access Fees) $15,173. Sal $2,779,174
Library Holdings: Bk Vols 424,459; Per Subs 669
Subject Interests: Local history
Special Collections: History of San Luis Obispo County (especially Hearst Family)
Automation Activity & Vendor Info: (Acquisitions) epixtech, inc.; (Cataloging) epixtech, inc.; (Circulation) epixtech, inc.; (OPAC) epixtech, inc.
Database Vendor: epixtech, inc.
Mem of Black Gold Cooperative Library System
Partic in Black Gold Coop
Friends of the Library Group
Branches: 15
ATASCADERO BRANCH, 6850 Morro Rd, Atascadero, 93422. SAN 334-8008. Tel: 805-461-6161. FAX: 805-461-6045. E-Mail: atascaderolibrary@thegrid.net. *Librn*, Marcia Cunningham; Staff 8 (MLS 2, Non-MLS 6)
Friends of the Library Group
CAMBRIA BRANCH, 900 Main St, Cambria, 93428. SAN 334-8032. Tel: 805-927-4336. FAX: 805-927-3524. *Librn*, Kathleen Neve
Friends of the Library Group
CAYUCOS BRANCH, 248 Ocean Ave, Cayucos, 93430. SAN 334-8067. Tel: 805-995-3312. *Librn*, Shera Hill
Friends of the Library Group
CRESTON BRANCH, PO Box 1, Creston, 93432. SAN 334-8091. Tel: 805-239-3010. *Librn*, Kathleen Saffell
Friends of the Library Group
MAIN LIBRARY, PO Box 8107, 93403-8107. SAN 334-8458. Tel; 805-781-5991. FAX: 805-781-1166. *Librn*, Judy Rohr
Friends of the Library Group
MORRO BAY BRANCH, 625 Harbor St, Morro Bay, 93442. SAN 334-8180. Tel: 805-772-6394. FAX: 805-772-6396. *Librn*, Jude Long
Friends of the Library Group
NIPOMO BRANCH, 918 W Tefft, Nipomo, 93444. SAN 334-8210. Tel: 805-929-3994. FAX: 805-929-5476. *Librn*, Rosalyn Pierini
Friends of the Library Group
POZO BRANCH, 250 W Pozo Rd, Santa Margarita, 93453. SAN 334-8245. Tel: 805-438-3705. *Librn*, Stephen Wise
SAN MIGUEL BRANCH, PO Box 86, San Miguel, 93451. SAN 334-827X. Tel: 805-467-3224. *Librn*, Judy Brown
Friends of the Library Group
SANTA MARGARITA BRANCH, PO Box 960, Santa Margarita, 93453. SAN 334-830X. Tel: 805-438-5622. *Librn*, Debra Jurey
Friends of the Library Group
SHANDON BRANCH, PO Box 196, Shandon, 93461. SAN 334-8334. Tel: 805-237-3009. *Librn*, Maureen Vestal
SHELL BEACH BRANCH, Veterans Bldg, 230 Leeward Ave, Shell Beach, 93449. SAN 334-8369. Tel: 805-773-2263. *Librn*, Catherine Marvier
Friends of the Library Group
SIMMLER BRANCH, PO Box 3108, California Valley, 93453. SAN 334-8393. Tel: 805-475-2603. *Librn*, Maureen Vestal
SOUTH BAY, 2075 Palisades Ave, Los Osos, 93402. SAN 334-8423. Tel: 805-528-1862. FAX: 805-528-7835. *Librn*, Carolyn Mueller
Friends of the Library Group
SOUTH COUNTY, 800 W Branch St, Arroyo Grande, 93420. SAN 334-7974. Tel: 805-473-7161. FAX: 805-473-7173. *Librn*, Deborah Schlanser; Staff 10 (MLS 3, Non-MLS 7)
Friends of the Library Group
Bookmobiles: 1

GL SAN LUIS OBISPO COUNTY LAW LIBRARY, County Government Ctr, Rm 125, 1050 Monterey St, 93408. SAN 301-5157. Tel: 805-781-5855. FAX: 805-781-4172. E-Mail: slolawli@rain.org. Web Site: www.thegrid.net/slocll. *Librn*, Kathleen Boyd; Staff 1 (MLS 1)
Founded 1896
Jul 1999-Jun 2000 Income $177,283, Locally Generated Income $20,836, Other $156,447. Mats Exp Books $103,516. Sal $52,448 (Prof $35,700)
Library Holdings: Bk Vols 23,632; Per Subs 59
Subject Interests: California
Restriction: Non-circulating

G SAN LUIS OBISPO COUNTY PLANNING DEPARTMENT LIBRARY,* County Govt Ctr, 93408. SAN 328-543X. Tel: 805-781-5600. FAX: 805-781-1242.
Library Holdings: Bk Titles 600

SAN MARCOS

C CALIFORNIA STATE UNIVERSITY, San Marcos Library, 333 S Twin Oaks Valley Rd, 92096-0001. SAN 323-911X. Tel: 760-750-4340. Interlibrary Loan Service Tel: 760-750-4345. Circulation Tel: 760-750-4348. Reference Tel: 760-750-4342. TDD: 760-750-3163. FAX: 760-750-3287. Web Site: www.csusm.edu/library/. *Dean of Libr*, Marion T Reid; Tel: 760-750-4330, E-Mail: mreid@csusm.edu; *Asst Dean*, Bonnie Biggs; Tel: 760-750-4337, E-Mail: bbiggs@csusm.edu; *Librn*, Sharon Berglund; Tel: 760-750-4375, E-Mail: sberglund@csusm.edu; *Librn*, Jacqueline M Borin; Tel: 760-750-4336, E-Mail: jborin@csusm.edu; *Librn*, Ann M Fiegen; Tel: 760-750-4365, E-Mail: afiegen@csusm.edu; *Librn*, Kit Herlihy; Tel: 760-750-4357, E-Mail: kherlihy@csusm.edu; *Librn*, Susan M Thompson; Tel: 760-750-4373, E-Mail: sthompsn@csusm.edu; *Librn*, Hua Yi; Tel: 760-750-4368, E-Mail: hyi@csusm.edu; *Coordr*, Gloria L Rhodes; Tel: 760-750-4369, E-Mail: grhodes@csusm.edu; *Coordr*, Gabriela Sonntag; Tel: 760-750-4356, E-Mail: gsg@csusm.edu; Staff 11 (MLS 11)
Founded 1989. Enrl 4,355; Fac 230; Highest Degree: Master
Jul 1999-Jun 2000 Income $2,548,663. Mats Exp $830,881, Books $190,359, Per/Ser (Incl. Access Fees) $226,769, Presv $23,636, Micro $26,463, AV Equip $787, Other Print Mats $226,769, Electronic Ref Mat (Incl. Access Fees) $136,098. Sal $1,486,778 (Prof $729,181)
Library Holdings: Bk Vols 188,116; Bk Titles 147,784; Per Subs 2,138
Special Collections: Spanish Literature, bks, cat
Automation Activity & Vendor Info: (Acquisitions) Innovative Interfaces Inc.; (Cataloging) Innovative Interfaces Inc.; (Circulation) Innovative Interfaces Inc.; (Course Reserve) Innovative Interfaces Inc.; (ILL) Innovative Interfaces Inc.; (Media Booking) Innovative Interfaces Inc.; (OPAC) Innovative Interfaces Inc.; (Serials) Innovative Interfaces Inc.
Database Vendor: CARL, Ebsco - EbscoHost, GaleNet, Innovative Interfaces INN - View, Lexis-Nexis, OCLC - First Search, ProQuest, Silverplatter Information Inc.
Publications: Library & Information Services Notes; Library & Information Services Report
Restriction: Open to student, faculty & staff
Partic in San Diego Circuit
Special Services for the Blind - ADA terminals for visually impaired

J PALOMAR COLLEGE LIBRARY - MEDIA CENTER, 1140 W Mission Rd, 92069-1487. SAN 334-8482. Tel: 760-744-1150, Ext 2848. TDD: 760-736-0246. FAX: 760-761-3500. E-Mail: library@palomar.edu. Web Site: daphne.palomar.edu/library. *Dir*, Dr George Mozes; E-Mail: gmozes@palomar.edu; *Librn*, Daniel C Arnsan; *Librn*, Carolyn Funes; *Librn*, Jennifer Paris; *Publ Servs*, Alexis K Ciurczak; *Acq*, Judy Cater; *Syst Coordr*, Tamera Weintraub; *Cat*, Byung Kang; Staff 5 (MLS 5)
Founded 1946. Enrl 22,926; Fac 350
Library Holdings: Bk Titles 108,400; Per Subs 900
Subject Interests: Art and architecture, Ethnic studies
Special Collections: California History Coll; Early California & Iowa Frontier, newsp on microfilm; Iceland; Indians of North America; World War I Posters
Automation Activity & Vendor Info: (Acquisitions) SIRSI; (Cataloging) SIRSI; (Circulation) SIRSI; (Serials) SIRSI
Publications: A Guide to the Palomar College Library; Aging in the 1980s; Controversial Issues; Faculty in Print; Grants Bibliog; Library Self Help Bulletins
Partic in BRS; Coop Libr Agency for Syst & Servs; Dialog Corporation; OCLC Online Computer Library Center, Inc; San Diego Greater Metro Area Libr & Info Agency Coun
Special Services for the Deaf - TDD; Videos & decoder
Special Services - Accessible to handicapped; photocopier

SAN MARINO

S HUNTINGTON LIBRARY, 1151 Oxford Rd, 91108. SAN 301-5165. Tel: 626-405-2191. FAX: 626-449-5720. Web Site: www.huntington.org. *Dir*, David S Ziedberg; *Curator*, Mary L Robertson; *Curator*, Jennifer Watts; *Curator*, Cathy Cherbosque; *Curator*, Sara S Hodson; *Curator*, William Frank; *Curator*, John Rhodehamel; *Curator*, Alan Jutzi; *Curator*, Peter Blodgett; *Curator*, Stephen Tabor; *Curator*, Jennifer Martinez; *Curator*, Olga Tsapina; *Curator*, Dan Lewis; *Acq*, Lorraine Perrotta; *Admin Assoc*, Melanie Pickett; *Reader Servs*, Romaine Ahlstrom; *Ref*, Jill Cogen; *Tech Servs*, Laura Stalker; *Cat*, Kathleen Martin; *Cat*, Richard Jackson; Staff 30 (MLS 19, Non-MLS 11)
Founded 1919
Library Holdings: Bk Titles 686,154; Per Subs 600
Special Collections: American Photography, History, Pirnts, Printmaking & Desing; American Sheet Music; California; Colonial & Early Federal Americana; Early Hispanic Americana; Early Modern England; Manuscript Coll-Medieval; 19th Century Americana; 19th Century England; Restoration & 18th Century England; 20th Century American Literature & Letters; 20th Century British Literature; Western Americana
Publications: Guide to American Historical Manuscripts in the Huntington Library; Guide to British Historical Manuscripts in the Huntington Library; Guide to Literary Manuscripts in the Huntington Library; Guide to Medieval & Renaissance Manuscripts; The Huntington Library Quarterly
Partic in RLIN
Friends of the Library Group

SR SAN MARINO COMMUNITY PRESBYTERIAN CHURCH LIBRARY,* 1750 Virginia Rd, 91108. SAN 371-893X. Tel: 626-282-4181. FAX: 626-282-4185. *Librn*, Jeannie Cornwell
Founded 1941
Library Holdings: Bk Titles 4,000; Per Subs 6
Publications: Bulletin insert

P SAN MARINO PUBLIC LIBRARY, 1890 Huntington Dr, 91108-2595. SAN 301-5173. Tel: 626-300-0777. FAX: 626-284-0766. Web Site: www.smnet.org. *City Librn*, Carolyn Crain; E-Mail: carolyn@ci.san-marino.ca.us; *Ad Servs*, Rex Mayreis; *Ch Servs*, Ann Marie Biden; *Ref, Syst Coordr*, Irene McDermott
Founded 1932. Pop 13,700; Circ 160,023
1997-1998 Income $875,726, State $15,800, City $645,264, Other $214,662. Mats Exp $137,509, Books $100,326, Per/Ser (Incl. Access Fees) $7,500, Micro $6,374. Sal $338,496
Library Holdings: Bk Vols 95,901; Per Subs 225
Subject Interests: Art and architecture, California, Travel
Mem of Metropolitan Cooperative Library System
Friends of the Library Group

S SMITHSONIAN INSTITUTION ARCHIVES OF AMERICAN ART, Huntington Library, 1151 Oxford Rd, 91108. SAN 320-913X. Tel: 626-583-7847. FAX: 626-583-7207. E-Mail: aaawcrc@aaa.si.edu. *Dir*, Dr Paul Karlstrom
Founded 1954
Special Collections: Artists, architects, designers, craftsmen, institutions, museums & galleries in America from colonial times to the present, microfilm, tapes, transcripts
Publications: A Checklist of the Collection; Archives of American Art Journal, quarterly; Archives of American Art: A Directory of Resources; Arts in America: A Bibliography; Catalog of the Oral History Collection of the Archives of Americal Art; Collection of Exhibition Catalogs; The Card Catalog of the Manuscript Collection of the Archives of American Art
The Archives of American Art holds the world's largest collection of material documenting the history of the visual arts in the US. A bureau of the Smithsonian Institution since 1970, the Archives preserves its original documents in Washington with microfilm copies in its regional branches. Microfilm is available throughout the world on interlibrary loan

S THE GAMBLE HOUSE, U S C Greene & Greene Library, Virginia Steele Scott Gallery of the Huntington Library, 1151 Oxford Rd, 91108. SAN 328-431X. Tel: 626-405-2232. *Dir*, Edward R Bosley, III
Library Holdings: Bk Titles 800; Per Subs 1,100
Special Collections: Archival material on architects Charles & Henry Greene & their contemporaries; Arts & Crafts Movement
Open to the public by appointment, Tues & Thurs 1-4

SAN MATEO

S BAY MEADOWS, William P Kyne Memorial Library, 2600 S Delaware St, PO Box 5050, 94402. SAN 327-7364. Tel: 650-574-7223, Ext 4509. FAX: 650-573-4671.
Restriction: By appointment only

J COLLEGE OF SAN MATEO LIBRARY,* 1700 W Hillsdale Blvd, 94402-3795. SAN 301-5181. Tel: 650-574-6100. FAX: 650-358-6797. *Dir*, Gregg T Atkins; Staff 8 (MLS 4, Non-MLS 4)
Founded 1923. Enrl 13,800; Fac 300
Library Holdings: Bk Vols 115,000; Bk Titles 102,000; Per Subs 475
Subject Interests: Art and architecture, Ethnic studies, Feminism, Music, Natural science, Nursing, Social sciences and issues, Technology
Special Collections: American History (LAC, Library of American Civilization)
Mem of Peninsula Library System

S LEIGH FISHER ASSOCIATES LIBRARY,* 160 Bovet Rd Ste 300. (Mail add: PO Box 8007, San Francisco Int'l Airport, 94128-8007), SAN 301-4444. Tel: 650-571-7722. FAX: 650-571-5220. Web Site: www.leighfisher.com. *Coll Develop, Librn*, K A Mayers; Tel: 650-571-2357, E-Mail: karenm@leighfisher.com; Staff 3 (MLS 1, Non-MLS 2)
Founded 1945
Library Holdings: Bk Titles 500; Per Subs 100
Subject Interests: Airport planning, Transportation
Restriction: Staff use only

S PENINSULA COMMUNITY FOUNDATION, Peninsula Nonprofit Center,* 1700 S El Camino Real No 201, 94402-3049. SAN 327-5876. Tel: 650-358-9392. FAX: 650-358-0141. E-Mail: georgia@pcf.org. Web Site: www.pcfnonprofitcenter.org. *Mgr*, Georgia W McDaniel
Library Holdings: Bk Titles 2,200; Per Subs 30
Special Collections: Fed Register; Foundation Center Coll; Volunteer Center Coll
Publications: Ways & Means Newsletter (quarterly)

P PENINSULA LIBRARY SYSTEM, 25 Tower Rd, 94402-4000. SAN 300-7065. Tel: 650-349-5538. FAX: 650-349-5089. Web Site: www.pls.lib.ca.us. *Dir*, Linda Crowe; *Ref*, Susan Holmer; Staff 21 (MLS 13, Non-MLS 8)
Founded 1970. Pop 670,000
Library Holdings: Bk Titles 525,000
Publications: Library Events (monthly); San Mateo County Directory of Human Services; Union List of Periodicals (yearly)
Member Libraries: Burlingame Public Library; Canada College Library; College Of San Mateo Library; Daly City Public Library; Menlo Park Public Library; Redwood City Public Library; San Bruno Public Library; San Mateo County Library; San Mateo County Library; San Mateo County Library; San Mateo Public Library; South San Francisco Public Library

R PENINSULA TEMPLE BETH EL LIBRARY,* 1700 Alameda de Las Pulgas, 94403. SAN 301-5203. Tel: 650-341-7701. FAX: 650-570-7183. *Librn*, Stephanie Hoffman
Library Holdings: Bk Vols 5,500
Subject Interests: Judaica (lit or hist of Jews)

G SAN MATEO COUNTY, Medical Library,* 222 W 39th Ave, 94403. SAN 301-5211. Tel: 650-573-2520. FAX: 650-573-3510. E-Mail: hs*mconstant3@co.sanmateo.ca.us. *Librn*, Mark Q Constantz
Founded 1967
Library Holdings: Bk Vols 3,000; Per Subs 100
Subject Interests: Geriatrics and gerontology, Psychiatry, Public health
Partic in Nat Libr of Med

P SAN MATEO COUNTY LIBRARY, Administrative Office, 25 Tower Rd, 94402-4000. SAN 331-4979. Tel: 650-312-5258. FAX: 650-312-5382. Web Site: www.pls.lib.ca.us/pls/ccd/ccd.html. *Dir*, Paul Underwood; Tel: 650-312-5258, E-Mail: underwood@pls.lib.ca.us; *Asst Dir*, Jannette Engel; Tel: 650-312-5245, E-Mail: engelj@pls.lib.ca.us; *Ref*, Freda Hofland; Tel: 650-312-5296, E-Mail: hoflandf@pls.lib.ca.us; *Tech Servs*, Carol Bowles; Tel: 650-312-5255, E-Mail: bowlesc@pls.lib.ca.us; *Coll Develop*, Vicki Jacobs; Tel: 650-312-5274, E-Mail: jacobsv@pls.lib.ca.us; *Ch Servs*, Jeanine Asche; Tel: 650-312-5263, E-Mail: aschej@pls.lib.ca.us; Staff 44 (MLS 44)
Founded 1915. Pop 274,800; Circ 1,828,948
Jul 1999-Jun 2000 Income (Main Library and Branch Library) $12,536,673, State $728,144, City $56,057, Federal $15,341, County $10,868,482, Locally Generated Income $868,649. Mats Exp $1,412,447, Books $991,661, Per/Ser (Incl. Access Fees) $126,530, AV Equip $229,139, Electronic Ref Mat (Incl. Access Fees) $65,117. Sal $7,042,695
Library Holdings: Bk Vols 448,335; Bk Titles 230,000; Per Subs 1,738
Subject Interests: Library and information science
Special Collections: California Coll; San Mateo County
Automation Activity & Vendor Info: (Acquisitions) epixtech, inc.; (Circulation) epixtech, inc.; (OPAC) epixtech, inc.
Database Vendor: OCLC - First Search
Mem of Peninsula Library System
Partic in OCLC Online Computer Library Center, Inc; Peninsula Libraries Automated Network
Friends of the Library Group
Branches: 12
ATHERTON BRANCH, 2 Dinklespiel Station Lane, Atherton, 94027. SAN 331-5002. Tel: 650-328-2422. FAX: 650-328-4138. Web Site: www.athertonlibrary.org. *Branch Mgr*, Thom Ball; E-Mail: ballt@pls.lib.ca.us; Staff 2 (MLS 2)
Pop 15,000; Circ 65,740
Library Holdings: Bk Vols 23,000
Friends of the Library Group
BELMONT BRANCH, 1110 Alameda, Belmont, 94002. SAN 331-5037. Tel: 650-591-8286. FAX: 650-591-1195. Web Site: www.belmontlibrary.org. *Mgr*, Linda Chiochios; E-Mail: chiochio@pls.lib.ca.us; Staff 3 (MLS 3)
Pop 26,150; Circ 155,850

Library Holdings: Bk Vols 46,000
Friends of the Library Group
BRISBANE BRANCH, 250 Visitacion Ave, Brisbane, 94005. SAN 331-5061. Tel: 415-467-2060. FAX: 415-467-4824. Web Site: www.brisbanelibrary.org. *Mgr*, Chet Mulawka; E-Mail: mulawkac@pls.lib.ca.us; Staff 2 (MLS 2)
Pop 4,060; Circ 37,409
Library Holdings: Bk Vols 18,500
Friends of the Library Group
EAST PALO ALTO BRANCH, 2415 University Ave, East Palo Alto, 94303. SAN 331-5096. Tel: 650-321-7712. FAX: 650-326-8961. Web Site: www.eastpaloaltolibrary.org. *Mgr*, Rebecca Hill-Long; E-Mail: hilllong@pls.lib.ca.us; Staff 4 (MLS 4)
Pop 25,100; Circ 50,056
Library Holdings: Bk Vols 32,000
Function: Reference services available
Friends of the Library Group
FOSTER CITY BRANCH, 1000 E Hillsdale Blvd, Foster City, 94404. SAN 331-5126. Tel: 650-574-4842. FAX: 650-572-1875. Web Site: www.fostercitylibrary.org. *Mgr*, Barbara Escoffier; E-Mail: escoffif@pls.lib.ca.us; Staff 5 (MLS 5)
Pop 30,900; Circ 407,204
Library Holdings: Bk Vols 87,000
Special Services for the Blind - Kurzweil Personal Reader
Friends of the Library Group
HALF MOON BAY BRANCH, 620 Correas St, Half Moon Bay, 94019. SAN 331-5150. Tel: 650-726-2316. FAX: 650-726-9282. *Mgr*, Maya Kennedy; E-Mail: kennedym@pls.lib.ca.us; Staff 4 (MLS 4)
Pop 25,000; Circ 252,106
Library Holdings: Bk Vols 66,000
Friends of the Library Group
MILLBRAE BRANCH, One Library Ave, Millbrae, 94030. SAN 331-5185. Tel: 650-697-7607. FAX: 650-692-4747. Web Site: www.millbraelibrary.org. *Mgr*, Ruth Stout; E-Mail: stoutr@pls.lib.ca.us; Staff 4 (MLS 4)
Pop 21,400; Circ 205,313
Library Holdings: Bk Vols 68,000
Friends of the Library Group
PACIFICA BRANCH, 104 Hilton, Pacifica, 94044. SAN 331-5215. Tel: 650-355-5196. FAX: 650-355-6658. Web Site: www.pacificalibrary.org. *Mgr*, Elizabeth Sor; E-Mail: sore@pls.lib.ca.us; Staff 2 (MLS 2)
Pop 22,300; Circ 128,524
Library Holdings: Bk Vols 46,000
Friends of the Library Group
PORTOLA VALLEY BRANCH, 765 Portola Rd, Portola Valley, 94028. SAN 331-524X. Tel: 650-851-0560. FAX: 650-851-8365. Web Site: www.portolavalleylibrary.org. *Branch Mgr*, Thom Ball; E-Mail: ballt@pls.lib.ca.us; Staff 2 (MLS 2)
Founded 1968. Pop 6,500; Circ 50,556
Library Holdings: Bk Vols 22,000
Mem of Peninsula Library System
Friends of the Library Group
SAN CARLOS BRANCH, 610 Elm St, San Carlos, 94070. SAN 331-5274. Tel: 650-591-0341. FAX: 650-591-1585. Web Site: www.sancarloslibrary.org. *Mgr*, Chet Mulawka; E-Mail: mulawkac@pls.lib.ca.us; Staff 5 (MLS 5)
Pop 28,950; Circ 285,066
Library Holdings: Bk Vols 72,000
Special Services for the Blind - CCTV for print enlargement
Friends of the Library Group
SANCHEZ BRANCH, 1111 Terra Nova Blvd, Pacifica, 94044. SAN 331-5304. Tel: 650-359-3397. FAX: 650-359-3808. Web Site: www.sanchezlibrary.org. *Mgr*, eLIZABETH Sor; E-Mail: SORE@PLS.LIB.CA.US; Staff 2 (MLS 2)
Pop 18,750; Circ 114,854
Library Holdings: Bk Vols 37,000
Friends of the Library Group
WOODSIDE BRANCH, 3140 Woodside Rd, Woodside, 94062. Tel: 650-851-0147. FAX: 650-851-2695. Web Site: www.woodsidelibrary.org. *Mgr*, ThomRuth Ball; E-Mail: ballt@pls.lib.ca.us; Staff 2 (MLS 2)
Library Holdings: Bk Vols 23,000
Mem of Peninsula Library System
Friends of the Library Group
Bookmobiles: 1

P SAN MATEO PUBLIC LIBRARY, 55 W Third Ave, 94402-1592. SAN 334-8571. Tel: 650-522-7802. Circulation Tel: 650-522-7833. Reference Tel: 650-522-7818. FAX: 650-522-7801. Web Site: www.plsinfo.org/pls/smp/smp.html. *Dir*, Kathleen G Ouye; *ILL*, Sonja Moss; *Ref, Tech Servs*, Linda Lubovich; Staff 12 (MLS 12)
Founded 1899. Pop 94,200; Circ 642,498
Library Holdings: Bk Vols 280,000; Per Subs 794
Subject Interests: California, Music
Special Collections: Californiana, maps
Automation Activity & Vendor Info: (Circulation) epixtech, inc.
Publications: Annual Report; Business Reference (bibliography)
Mem of Peninsula Library System
Partic in Coop Libr Agency for Syst & Servs
Friends of the Library Group
Branches: 2
HILLSDALE, 205 W Hillsdale Blvd, 94403-4217. SAN 334-8601. Tel: 650-522-7880. Circulation Tel: 650-522-7882. Reference Tel: 650-522-7885. FAX: 650-522-7881. Web Site: www.plsinfo.org/pls/smp/smp.html.
Library Holdings: Bk Vols 46,903
MARINA, 1530 Susan Ct, 94403-1193. SAN 334-8660. Tel: 650-522-7890. Interlibrary Loan Service Tel: 650-522-7802. Circulation Tel: 650-522-7892. Reference Tel: 650-522-7893. FAX: 650-522-7891. Web Site: www.plsinfo.org/pls/smp/smp.html.
Library Holdings: Bk Vols 32,431

P SILICON VALLEY LIBRARY SYSTEM, (SVLS), 25 Tower Rd, 94402. SAN 301-5777. Tel: 650-349-5538. Reference Tel: 408-294-2345. FAX: 650-349-5089. E-Mail: srch@ix.netcom.com. Web Site: www.svls.lib.ca.us. *Dir*, Linda Crowe
Founded 1970. Pop 1,516,000
Jul 1999-Jun 2000 Income $773,000, State $133,000, Federal $26,000, Locally Generated Income $548,000, Other $66,000. Mats Exp $353,000, Books $3,000, Electronic Ref Mat (Incl. Access Fees) $350,000
Publications: Search (the quarterly newsletter of the Silicon Valley Library System); SVLS Union List of Periodicals (annual)
Member Libraries: Los Gatos Public Library; Palo Alto City Library; San Jose Public Library; Santa Clara City Library; Santa Clara County Free Library; Sunnyvale Public Library

SAN PABLO

M BROOKSIDE HOSPITAL, Medical Staff Library,* 2000 Vale Rd, 94806. SAN 301-5254. Tel: 510-235-7000, Ext 5709. *Librn*, Diane Douglas
Founded 1964
Library Holdings: Bk Titles 350; Per Subs 127
Partic in Pacific SW Regional Med Libr Serv

J CONTRA COSTA COLLEGE LIBRARY, 2600 Mission Bell Dr, 94806-3195. SAN 301-5262. Tel: 510-235-7800, Ext 4318. FAX: 510-234-8161. Web Site: www.contracosta.cc.ca.us/library/index.htm. *Circ, Mgr*, Bruce Carlton; Tel: 510-235-7800, Ext 4449, E-Mail: bcarlton@contracosta.cc.ca.us; *Acq*, Gloria Gideon; Tel: 510-235-7800, Ext 4447, E-Mail: ggideon@contracosta.cc.ca.us; *Media Spec*, Ellen Geringer; Tel: 510-235-7800, Ext 4457, E-Mail: egeringer@contracosta.cc.ca.us; *Bibliog Instr*, Judith Flum; Tel: 510-235-7800, Ext 4445, E-Mail: jflum@contracosta.cc.ca.us; Staff 4 (MLS 4)
Founded 1950. Enrl 8,000; Fac 122; Highest Degree: Associate
Library Holdings: Bk Vols 57,863; Per Subs 220
Special Collections: Ethnic Studies Coll; Topographic maps; Vocational Information Coll
Partic in Coop Libr Agency for Syst & Servs
Special Services for the Deaf - High interest/low vocabulary books
Friends of the Library Group

SAN PEDRO

S AMERICAN CETACEAN SOCIETY LIBRARY,* 745 Paseo del Mar, PO Box 1391, 90737. SAN 329-1324. Tel: 310-548-6279. FAX: 310-548-6950. E-Mail: acs@pobox.com.
Library Holdings: Bk Vols 1,200
Subject Interests: Marine mammals
Special Collections: Cetaceans (Ray Gilmore Coll), bks, reprints
Publications: WhaleWatcher (quarterly)
Partic in Metronet

S LOGICON, INC, Information Center, 222 W Sixth St, PO Box 471, 90733-0471. SAN 301-5289. Tel: 310-831-0611, Ext 2504. Reference Tel: 310-831-0611, Ext 2500. FAX: 310-521-2699. *Mgr*, Shirley Lee Tanaka; E-Mail: stanaka@logicon.com; Staff 4 (MLS 3, Non-MLS 1)
Founded 1967
Library Holdings: Bk Titles 5,000; Per Subs 200
Automation Activity & Vendor Info: (Cataloging) Inmagic, Inc.
Restriction: Not open to public

S LOS ANGELES DEPARTMENT OF RECREATION & PARKS, Cabrillo Marine Aquarium Library, 3720 Stephen White Dr, 90731. SAN 301-5270. Tel: 310-548-7562. TDD: 310-548-2052. FAX: 310-548-2649. E-Mail: info@cabrilloaq.org, webmaster@cabrilloaq.org. Web Site: www.cabrilloaq.org. *Dir*, Dr Susanne Lawrenz Miller; Tel: 310-548-7562, Ext 7010, E-Mail: slawmil@rap.lacity.org; *Curator*, Steve Vogel; Tel: 310-548-7562, Ext 5026, E-Mail: steve.vogel@cabrilloaq.org; Staff 2 (Non-MLS 2)
Founded 1935
Library Holdings: Bk Titles 2,500; Per Subs 25; Spec Interest Per Sub 20

Subject Interests: California, Ecology, Marine biology
Restriction: Non-circulating to the public
Open Tues-Fri noon-5pm & Sat-Sun 10am-5pm
Friends of the Library Group

M SAN PEDRO PENINSULA HOSPITAL, Medical Library,* 1300 W Seventh St, 90732-3593. SAN 301-5297. Tel: 310-832-3311, Ext 6298. FAX: 310-514-5306. E-Mail: spmedllibrary@lcmhs.org. *Librn*, Maureen Neeley
Founded 1940
1998-1999 Income $21,000. Mats Exp $10,000, Books $1,000, Per/Ser (Incl. Access Fees) $9,000. Sal $12,000 (Prof $8,500)
Library Holdings: Bk Vols 2,000; Per Subs 50
Subject Interests: Medicine, Nursing
Restriction: By appointment only

SAN RAFAEL

CR DOMINICAN COLLEGE OF SAN RAFAEL, Archbishop Alemany Library, 50 Acacia Ave, 94901-2298. SAN 301-5319. Tel: 415-485-3251. Reference Tel: 415-485-3252. FAX: 415-459-2309. E-Mail: library@dominican.edu. Web Site: www.dominican.edu/library. *Head, Acq*, Alan Schut; Tel: 415-458-3703, E-Mail: schut@dominican.edu; *Head Ref*, Laurie Isenberg; Tel: 415-257-0197, E-Mail: isenberg@dominican.edu; *Publ Servs*, Kathlene Hanson; *Tech Servs*, Jean P Gordon; *Acq, Ser*, Judith Parle; Tel: 415-257-0195, E-Mail: parle@dominican.edu; Staff 6 (MLS 2, Non-MLS 4)
Founded 1917. Enrl 1,667; Fac 54; Highest Degree: Master
Jul 1999-Jun 2000 Income $740,342, Locally Generated Income $1,837, Parent Institution $720,580, Other $17,925. Mats Exp $214,451, Books $116,052, Per/Ser (Incl. Access Fees) $62,775, Presv $2,750, Micro $3,922, Electronic Ref Mat (Incl. Access Fees) $28,952. Sal $278,869 (Prof $169,292)
Library Holdings: Bk Vols 102,813; Bk Titles 77,418; Per Subs 389
Special Collections: Ansel Adams Coll
Automation Activity & Vendor Info: (Cataloging) Innovative Interfaces Inc.; (Circulation) Innovative Interfaces Inc.
Database Vendor: Ebsco - EbscoHost, GaleNet, Lexis-Nexis, OCLC - First Search, OVID Technologies, ProQuest, Silverplatter Information Inc.
Publications: Dominican College Library Newsletter
Partic in OCLC Online Computer Library Center, Inc

SR DOMINICAN SISTERS-CONGREGATION OF THE HOLY NAME, Archives,* 1520 Grand Ave, 94901-2236. SAN 370-2057. Tel: 415-257-4947. FAX: 415-453-8367. *Archivist*, Sister Gerald LaVoy
Subject Interests: Hist of the congregation

S LUCASFILM LTD, Research Library,* PO Box 2009, 94912. SAN 327-7305. Tel: 415-662-1912. FAX: 415-662-1628. *Res*, Jo Donaldson; *Res*, Cheryl Edwards; *Res*, Jennifer Craik; Staff 5 (MLS 2, Non-MLS 3)
Library Holdings: Bk Vols 18,000; Per Subs 75
Special Collections: Paramount Studios Library

P MARIN COUNTY FREE LIBRARY,* 3501 Civic Center Dr, Rm 414, 94903-4177. SAN 334-8784. Tel: 415-499-3220. Interlibrary Loan Service Tel: 415-499-6776. FAX: 415-499-3726. Web Site: www.co.marin.ca.us/libs/marinet.html. *Dir*, Carol Starr
Founded 1927. Pop 144,655; Circ 1,112,480
Library Holdings: Bk Vols 450,000; Per Subs 1,400
Subject Interests: Art and architecture, Local history
Special Collections: Art, Indians, California
Mem of North Bay Cooperative Library System
Partic in Coop Libr Agency for Syst & Servs
Friends of the Library Group
Branches: 10
BOLINAS BRANCH, Wharf Rd, PO Box 10, Bolinas, 94924. SAN 334-8806. Tel: 415-868-1171. FAX: 415-868-1171. *In Charge*, Lynn Murray
Library Holdings: Bk Vols 7,070
CIVIC CENTER, 3501 Civic Center Dr, Rm 427, 94903-4177. SAN 334-8814. Tel: 415-499-6057. FAX: 415-499-3726. *Librn*, David Dodd
Library Holdings: Bk Vols 95,000
CORTE MADERA, 707 Meadowsweet, Corte Madera, 94925-1717. SAN 334-8849. Tel: 415-924-4844. FAX: 415-924-8227. *Actg Librn*, Nancy Davis
Library Holdings: Bk Vols 62,862
Open Mon-Thurs 10-9, Sat 10-6 & Sun 1-5, closed Fri
FAIRFAX, 2097 Sir Francis Drake Blvd, Fairfax, 94930-1198. SAN 334-8873. Tel: 415-453-8092. FAX: 415-453-7154. *In Charge*, Nora Harris
Library Holdings: Bk Vols 47,275
INVERNESS BRANCH, 15 Park Ave, PO Box 160, Inverness, 94937-0160. SAN 334-8822. Tel: 415-669-1288. FAX: 415-669-1288. *In Charge*, Ann Taylor
Library Holdings: Bk Vols 9,414
MARIN CITY BRANCH, 164 Donahue, Marin City, 94965. SAN 334-8830. Tel: 415-332-6158.
Friends of the Library Group
NOVATO REGIONAL BRANCH, 1720 Novato Blvd, Novato, 94947. SAN 334-8903. Tel: 415-897-1141. FAX: 415-898-3454. Web Site: countylibrary.marin.org, www.marin.org. *Branch Mgr*, Donna Evans; E-Mail: devans@marin.org
Library Holdings: Bk Vols 85,000
Database Vendor: Dialog, Innovative Interfaces INN - View
Mem of North Bay Cooperative Library System
Partic in N Bay Coop Libr Syst
Friends of the Library Group
POINT REYES STATION BRANCH, W Marin Shops, 11431 State Rte 1, PO Box 1330, Point Reyes Station, 94956-1330. SAN 334-8857. Tel: 415-663-8375. *In Charge*, Ann Taylor
Library Holdings: Bk Vols 5,563
SAN GERONIMO VALLEY BRANCH, Sir Francis Drake Blvd & Meadow Way, PO Box 423, San Geronimo, 94963. SAN 334-8865. Tel: 415-488-0430. FAX: 415-488-0430. *In Charge*, Ann Taylor
Library Holdings: Bk Vols 6,500
STINSON BEACH BRANCH, 3470 Shoreline Hwy, PO Box 578, Stinson Beach, 94970-0578. SAN 334-8881. Tel: 415-868-0252. FAX: 415-868-0252. *In Charge*, Ann Taylor
Library Holdings: Bk Vols 5,801
Bookmobiles: 1. Also have 1 outreach van

G MARIN COUNTY HISTORICAL SOCIETY, Archives & Library, 1125 B St, 94901. SAN 327-6546. Tel: 415-454-8538. E-Mail: infomchs@pacbell.net. Web Site: www.marinhistory.org. *Curator, Librn*, Jocelyn Moss
Founded 1935
Library Holdings: Bk Vols 1,000
Subject Interests: Genealogy, Local history
Special Collections: Bound newspapers (1868 - present), land grants
Publications: Marin People (3 vols)
Restriction: By appointment only
Function: Archival collection, Photocopies available, Reference services available, Research fees apply
Open Thurs-Sat 1-4

GL MARIN COUNTY LAW LIBRARY,* 20 N San Pedro Rd, Ste 2015, 94903. SAN 301-5327. Tel: 415-499-6356. FAX: 415-499-6837. *Librn*, Barbara Gately
Founded 1891
Library Holdings: Bk Vols 30,000
Special Collections: Continuing Education of the Bar Coll

M MARIN GENERAL HOSPITAL, Medical Library,* PO Box 8010, 94912-8010. SAN 322-8886. Tel: 415-925-7000, Ext 7393. FAX: 415-925-7117. Web Site: www.marin-gh.org. *Librn*, Katherine Renick; E-Mail: krenick@hooked.net
Library Holdings: Bk Vols 2,500
Subject Interests: Medicine

S MARIN INSTITUTE FOR THE PREVENTION OF ALCOHOL & OTHER DRUG PROBLEMS, Resource Center, 24 Belvedere St, 94901. SAN 372-0012. Tel: 415-456-5692. FAX: 415-456-0491. Web Site: www.marininstitute.org. *Dir, Librn*, Kristi Wessenberg; Staff 2 (MLS 1, Non-MLS 1)
Founded 1989
Library Holdings: Bk Titles 10,000; Per Subs 60
Automation Activity & Vendor Info: (Cataloging) Inmagic, Inc.; (Serials) Inmagic, Inc.
Restriction: Restricted public use, Staff & professional research
Partic in Bay Area Libr & Info Serv; Dialog Corporation

P SAN RAFAEL PUBLIC LIBRARY, 1100 E St, 94901-1900. SAN 301-5335. Tel: 415-485-3323. FAX: 415-485-3112. Web Site: www.marinet.marin.org. *Dir*, Vaughn Stratford; E-Mail: vaughn.stratford@ci.san-rafael.ca.us; *Ad Servs*, Gail Lockman; *Ch Servs*, Hollie Stanaland; Staff 6 (MLS 6)
Founded 1887. Pop 49,750; Circ 302,604; Fac 54,000
Jul 1998-Jun 1999 Income $1,342,411, State $92,987, City $1,170,575, Federal $78,849. Mats Exp $141,000, Books $125,600, Per/Ser (Incl. Access Fees) $9,800, Micro $5,600. Sal $739,759
Library Holdings: Bk Titles 120,000; Per Subs 302
Subject Interests: Art and architecture, Business and management
Special Collections: California Coll
Mem of North Bay Cooperative Library System
Friends of the Library Group

S WILD CARE,* 76 Albert Park Lane, PO Box 150930, 94915-0930. SAN 327-6449. Tel: 415-453-1000, 415-456-7283. FAX: 415-456-0594. *Exec Dir*, Bruce Truitt
Library Holdings: Bk Titles 300

SAN RAMON

S CHEVRON PETROLEUM TECHNOLOGY CO, Library & Records Management,* 6001 Bollinger Canyon Rd, 94583. SAN 300-8428. Tel: 925-842-1000.
Founded 1947
Library Holdings: Bk Vols 30,000; Per Subs 250
Subject Interests: Chemistry, Geology, Mathematics, Oceanography, Petroleum, Physics

Restriction: By appointment only
Partic in Dialog Corporation; OCLC Online Computer Library Center, Inc; RLIN; Sci & Tech Info Network; SDC Info Servs

§S CHEVRON SERVICES CO, Library Services, 6001 Bollinger Canyon Rd, E1300, 94583-2324. (Mail add: PO Box 5060, 94583-5060), Tel: 925-842-4426. E-Mail: libpark@chevron.com. *In Charge*, Mildred Andrews
Library Holdings: Bk Vols 100,000; Per Subs 400
Automation Activity & Vendor Info: (Acquisitions) SIRSI; (Cataloging) SIRSI; (Circulation) SIRSI; (Serials) SIRSI
Restriction: Staff use only

S KVAERNER METALS, Library Center,* 12657 Alcosta Blvd, Ste 200, 94583. SAN 327-2656. Tel: 925-866-1166. FAX: 925-866-6520. *Librn*, Maryann Blunden
Library Holdings: Bk Vols 15,000

S PACIFIC BELL, Corporate Intelligence Center,* 2600 Camino Ramon Rm 1CS95, 94583-9958. SAN 327-5841. Tel: 925-823-8000. FAX: 925-867-8516. Web Site: www.home.sbc.com/cic. *Mgr*, Jan Keiser; Staff 3 (MLS 3)
Library Holdings: Bk Vols 7,000
Subject Interests: Telecommunications
Publications: Bulletin
Restriction: Not open to public

SAN SIMEON

§S HEARST SAN SIMEON STATE HISTORICAL MONUMENT, (Formerly Califnornia State Department Of Parks & Recreastion), Hearst Castle Staff Library, 750 Hearst Castle Rd, 93452-9741. Tel: 805-927-2076. FAX: 805-927-2117. E-Mail: library@hearstcastle.com. Web Site: www.hearstcastle.com. *Coordr*, Judy Anderson
Library Holdings: Bk Vols 3,655; Per Subs 75
Restriction: Not open to public, Staff use only
Open Sun-Sat 9-4, some evening tours

SANTA ANA

S AMERICAN AVIATION HISTORICAL SOCIETY, AAHS Reference Library,* 2333 Otis St, 92704. SAN 371-2834. Tel: 714-549-4818. FAX: 714-549-3657. *Pres*, Tim Williams
Library Holdings: Bk Vols 1,000
Restriction: Members only

S BOWERS MUSEUM OF CULTURAL ART, Research Library,* 2002 N Main St, 92706. SAN 373-2835. Tel: 714-567-3600, 714-567-3649, 714-567-3652. FAX: 714-567-3650.
Founded 1932
Library Holdings: Bk Titles 7,000; Per Subs 20
Subject Interests: Africa, Archaeology, Art history, Asia, Latin America, Thailand
Special Collections: African Art Coll; Ban Chiang Coll; Native American Coll, bks, film, objects & photos; Orange County History, bks & photos; Pacific Rim Coll
Publications: Monographs; museum exhibit catalog; newsletters
Partic in Metronet
Open Tues-Fri 8-5

GL ORANGE COUNTY LAW LIBRARY, 515 N Flower St, 92703-2354. SAN 334-8997. Tel: 714-834-3397. FAX: 714-834-4375. Web Site: www.oc.ca.gov/lawlib. *Dir*, Maryruth Storer; Staff 22 (MLS 5, Non-MLS 17)
Founded 1891
Jul 1999-Jun 2000 Income (Main Library and Branch Library) $2,554,992, Locally Generated Income $55,533. Mats Exp $944,758, Presv $8,573, Micro $48,965. Sal $892,517 (Prof $309,987)
Library Holdings: Bk Vols 318,595; Per Subs 898
Special Collections: California SC (Records & Briefs), 1960-64, 1969-, fiche; USSC (Records & Briefs), 1950, fiche
Automation Activity & Vendor Info: (Acquisitions) Innovative Interfaces Inc.; (Cataloging) Innovative Interfaces Inc.; (Circulation) Innovative Interfaces Inc.; (OPAC) Innovative Interfaces Inc.; (Serials) Innovative Interfaces Inc.
Publications: Acquisition list; bibliographies
Branches:
GL COURTHOUSE, 700 Civic Center Dr W, 92703. SAN 334-9020. Tel: 714-834-4649. Web Site: www.oc.ca.gov/lawlib.
Library Holdings: Bk Vols 20,006

G ORANGE COUNTY PFRD/PDSD LIBRARY, 300 N Flower St, 92703-5001. (Mail add: PO Box 4048, 97202-4048), SAN 334-8938. Tel: 714-834-3497. FAX: 714-834-5188. *Librn*, Sallie Jones; E-Mail: joness@pfrd.co.orange.ca.us; Staff 1 (Non-MLS 1)
Founded 1963
Library Holdings: Bk Titles 10,000
Subject Interests: Flood control, Harbors, Local history, Parks, Transportation
Special Collections: Flood & Flood Control Photographs, 1919-
Automation Activity & Vendor Info: (Acquisitions) EOS; (Cataloging) EOS; (Circulation) EOS; (OPAC) EOS
Restriction: By appointment only
Partic in Metronet

P ORANGE COUNTY PUBLIC LIBRARY, 1501 E St Andrew Pl, 92705-4048. SAN 333-4023. Tel: 714-566-3000. FAX: 714-566-3042. Web Site: www.ocpl.org. *Regional Manager*, Lynn Eisenhut; *Regional Manager*, Dan Josslin; *Regional Manager*, Georgia Weddle; *Librn*, John M Adams; Tel: 714-566-3040, E-Mail: jmadams@ocpl.org; *ILL*, Deann Irwin; *Ad Servs, Ch Servs*, Julie Fredericksen; *Coll Develop*, Jan Tapley; *ILL*, Carol Manley; Staff 206 (MLS 126, Non-MLS 80)
Founded 1921. Pop 1,346,125
Jul 2000-Jun 2001 Income (Main Library and Branch Library) $25,440,873, State $2,667,234, County $22,773,639. Mats Exp $4,110,003, Books $2,566,901, Per/Ser (Incl. Access Fees) $926,754, Presv $8,240, Micro $105,271, Electronic Ref Mat (Incl. Access Fees) $502,837. Sal $13,279,953
Library Holdings: Bk Vols 2,659,307; Bk Titles 401,352; Per Subs 5,070
Subject Interests: Business, Chinese Language, Japanese (Language), Korean (Language), Popular music, Spanish (language)
Automation Activity & Vendor Info: (Acquisitions) epixtech, inc.; (Cataloging) epixtech, inc.; (Circulation) epixtech, inc.; (OPAC) epixtech, inc.; (Serials) epixtech, inc.
Database Vendor: GaleNet, OCLC - First Search, ProQuest
Mem of Santiago Libr Syst
Partic in Metro Coop Libr Syst
Friends of the Library Group
Branches: 27
ALISO VIEJO BRANCH, One Journey, Aliso Viejo, 92656. SAN 378-2506. Tel: 949-360-1730. FAX: 949-360-1728. *Dir*, Hilary McAllister
BREA BRANCH, One Civic Center Circle, Brea, 92821. SAN 333-4058. Tel: 714-671-1722. FAX: 714-990-0581. Web Site: www.ocpl.org. *Chief Librn*, Cheryl Nakaji
Library Holdings: Bk Vols 75,153; Bk Titles 72,422
Subject Interests: Spanish (language)
Friends of the Library Group
CHAPMAN, 9182 Chapman Ave, Garden Grove, 92841-2590. SAN 333-4082. Tel: 714-539-2115. FAX: 714-530-9363. Web Site: www.ocpl.org. *Chief Librn*, Carol Ann Helsel
Library Holdings: Bk Vols 53,147
Friends of the Library Group
COSTA MESA BRANCH, 1855 Park Ave, Costa Mesa, 92627-2778. SAN 333-4112. Tel: 949-646-8845. FAX: 949-631-3112. Web Site: www.ocpl.org. *Chief Librn*, Dolores Madrigal
Library Holdings: Bk Vols 63,001; Bk Titles 62,060
Subject Interests: Spanish (language)
Friends of the Library Group
CYPRESS BRANCH, 5331 Orange Ave, Cypress, 90630-2985. SAN 333-4147. Tel: 714-826-0350. FAX: 714-828-1103. Web Site: www.ocpl.org. *Chief Librn*, Helen Richardson
Library Holdings: Bk Vols 104,088; Bk Titles 97,001
Subject Interests: Adult literature, Music
Friends of the Library Group
DANA POINT BRANCH, 33841 Niguel Rd, Dana Point, 92629-4010. SAN 333-4171. Tel: 949-496-5517. FAX: 949-240-7650. Web Site: www.ocpl.org. *Chief Librn*, John Dunham
Library Holdings: Bk Vols 81,758; Bk Titles 76,209
Friends of the Library Group
EL TORO BRANCH, 24672 Raymond Way, Lake Forest, 92630-4489. SAN 333-4228. Tel: 949-855-8173. FAX: 949-586-7412. Web Site: www.ocpl.org. *Chief Librn*, Phyllis Brown
Library Holdings: Bk Vols 112,488; Bk Titles 111,500
Special Services for the Deaf - TTY machine
Friends of the Library Group
FOUNTAIN VALLEY BRANCH, 17635 Los Alamos St, Fountain Valley, 92708-5299. SAN 333-4236. Tel: 714-962-1324. FAX: 714-964-8164. Web Site: www.ocpl.org. *Chief Librn*, Carol Davis
Library Holdings: Bk Vols 84,321; Bk Titles 82,137
Subject Interests: Adult literature
Friends of the Library Group
GARDEN GROVE REGIONAL LIBRARY, 11200 Stanford Ave, Garden Grove, 92640-5398. SAN 333-4260. Tel: 714-530-0711. FAX: 714-530-0961. Web Site: www.ocpl.org. *Chief Librn*, Su Chung Chay; Tel: 714-530-0718, 539-2167; Staff 18 (MLS 5, Non-MLS 13)
Library Holdings: Bk Vols 162,258; Bk Titles 154,772
Subject Interests: California, Consumer health, Korean (Language), Native Americans
Friends of the Library Group
HERITAGE PARK REGIONAL LIBRARY, 14361 Yale Ave, Irvine, 92704-1901. SAN 328-9788. Tel: 949-936-4040. FAX: 949-551-9283. Web Site: www.ocpl.org. *Mgr*, Barbara Brook; *Ad Servs, Librn*, Patrick O'Halloran; E-Mail: ocplhpr@fea.net; Staff 27 (MLS 7, Non-MLS 20)
Founded 1988. Pop 150,000; Circ 500,000
Library Holdings: Bk Vols 133,000; Per Subs 350
Special Collections: Audio 4100; Video 2500
Database Vendor: IAC - Info Trac

Friends of the Library Group
LA HABRA BRANCH, 221 E La Habra Blvd, La Habra, 90631-5437. SAN 333-4325. Tel: 562-694-0078, 714-526-7728. FAX: 562-691-8043. Web Site: www.ocpl.org. *Branch Mgr*, Jill Paterson
Library Holdings: Bk Vols 87,473; Bk Titles 86,261
Subject Interests: Spanish (language)
Friends of the Library Group
LA PALMA BRANCH, 7842 Walker St, La Palma, 90623-1721. SAN 333-435X. Tel: 714-523-8585. FAX: 714-521-5551. Web Site: www.ocpl.org. *Chief Librn*, Susan Sassone
Library Holdings: Bk Vols 59,951; Bk Titles 54,832
Subject Interests: Japanese (Language)
Friends of the Library Group
LAGUNA BEACH BRANCH, 363 Glenneyre St, Laguna Beach, 92651-2310. SAN 333-4295. Tel: 949-497-1733. FAX: 949-497-2876. Web Site: www.ocpl.org. *Chief Librn*, Marianna Hof
Library Holdings: Bk Vols 75,496; Bk Titles 72,687
Subject Interests: Art
Friends of the Library Group
LAGUNA NIGUEL BRANCH, 30341 Crown Valley Pkwy, Laguna Niguel, 92677-6326. SAN 328-9745. Tel: 949-249-5252. FAX: 949-249-5258. Web Site: www.ocpl.org. *Chief Librn*, Loretta Farley
Library Holdings: Bk Vols 77,190; Bk Titles 72,425
Friends of the Library Group
LOS ALAMITOS-ROSSMOOR, 12700 Montecito Rd, Seal Beach, 90740-2745. SAN 333-4414. Tel: 562-430-1048, 714-846-3240. FAX: 562-431-2931. Web Site: www.ocpl.org. *Chief Librn*, Kim Nissen
Library Holdings: Bk Vols 79,333; Bk Titles 74,298
MESA VERDE, 2969 Mesa Verde Dr E, Costa Mesa, 92626-3699. SAN 333-4473. Tel: 714-546-5274. FAX: 714-540-8413. Web Site: www.ocpl.org. *Chief Librn*, Nancy McQuillan
Library Holdings: Bk Vols 59,204; Bk Titles 54,630
Friends of the Library Group
RANCHO SANTA MARGARITA BRANCH, 30902 LaPromesa, Rancho Santa Margarita, 92688-2821. SAN 376-2440. Tel: 949-459-6094. FAX: 949-459-8391. Web Site: www.ocpl.org. *Branch Mgr*, Trish Noa
Library Holdings: Bk Vols 102,937; Bk Titles 90,270
SAN CLEMENTE BRANCH, 242 Avenida Del Mar, San Clemente, 92672-4005. SAN 333-4538. Tel: 949-492-3493. FAX: 949-498-5749. Web Site: www.ocpl.org. *Branch Mgr*, Terry Pringle
Library Holdings: Bk Vols 72,590
Friends of the Library Group
SAN JUAN CAPISTRANO REGIONAL LIBRARY, 31495 El Camino Real, San Juan Capistrano, 92675-2600. SAN 333-4562. Tel: 949-493-1752. FAX: 949-240-7680. Web Site: www.ocpl.org. *Chief Librn*, Renee Welling
Library Holdings: Bk Vols 81,996
Subject Interests: Architecture, California, Spanish (language)
Friends of the Library Group
SEAL BEACH-MARY WILSON BRANCH, 707 Electric Ave, Seal Beach, 90740-6196. SAN 333-4449. Tel: 562-431-3584, 714-840-6759. FAX: 562-431-3374. Web Site: www.ocpl.org. *Chief Librn*, Diane Gayton
Library Holdings: Bk Vols 54,904; Bk Titles 50,871
Friends of the Library Group
SILVERADO BRANCH, 28192 Silverado Canyon Rd, Silverado, 92676. (Mail add: PO Box 535, Silverado, 92676-0535), Tel: 714-649-2216. FAX: 714-649-2121. Web Site: www.ocpl.org. *Chief Librn*, Lucille Cruz
Library Holdings: Bk Vols 15,386; Bk Titles 14,657
Friends of the Library Group
STANTON BRANCH, 7850 Katella Ave, Stanton, 90680-3195. SAN 333-4651. Tel: 714-898-3302. FAX: 714-898-0040. Web Site: www.ocpl.org. *Chief Librn*, Tom Fitch
Library Holdings: Bk Vols 62,040; Bk Titles 59,381
Subject Interests: Spanish (language)
Friends of the Library Group
TUSTIN BRANCH, 345 E Main St, Tustin, 92680-4491. SAN 333-4686. Tel: 714-544-7725. FAX: 714-832-4279. Web Site: www.ocpl.org. *Chief Librn*, Emily Moore
Library Holdings: Bk Vols 117,004; Bk Titles 116,511
Friends of the Library Group
UNIVERSITY PARK, 4512 Sandburg Way, Irvine, 92612-2794. SAN 333-4716. Tel: 949-786-4001. FAX: 949-857-1029. Web Site: www.ocpl.org. *Chief Librn*, Joy Johnson
Library Holdings: Bk Vols 91,464; Bk Titles 91,399
Friends of the Library Group
VILLA PARK BRANCH, 17865 Santiago Blvd, Villa Park, 92861-4105. SAN 333-4740. Tel: 714-998-0861. FAX: 714-998-2752. Web Site: www.ocpl.org. *Branch Mgr*, Joyce Hensley
Library Holdings: Bk Vols 24,744
Friends of the Library Group
WEST GARDEN GROVE BRANCH, 11962 Bailey St, Garden Grove, 92645. SAN 333-4775. Tel: 714-897-2594. FAX: 714-895-2761. Web Site: www.ocpl.org. *Chief Librn*, Dennis McGuire
Library Holdings: Bk Vols 53,452
Friends of the Library Group
WESTMINSTER BRANCH, 8180 13th St, Westminster, 92683-8118. SAN 333-4805. Tel: 714-893-5057. FAX: 714-898-0229. Web Site: www.ocpl.org. *Chief Librn*, Mary Ann Hutton
Library Holdings: Bk Vols 140,614; Bk Titles 134,707
Subject Interests: Adult literature
Special Collections: Vietnamese Language Coll
Special Services for the Blind - Braille & cassetes; Kurzweil Reader
Friends of the Library Group

G ORANGE COUNTY SHERIFF-CORONER, (OCSDFSSL), Forensic Science Services Library,* 320 N Flower St, PO Box 449, 92703. SAN 301-5394. Tel: 714-834-4510. FAX: 714-834-4519. E-Mail: ocsdfss@telis.org. *Dir*, Frank Fitzpatrick; Staff 1 (Non-MLS 1)
Founded 1948
Jul 1999-Jun 2000 Mats Exp $5,000, Books $2,500, Per/Ser (Incl. Access Fees) $2,500. Sal $29,000
Library Holdings: Bk Titles 4,156; Per Subs 25
Subject Interests: Biochemistry, Chemistry, Forensic medicine, Mathematics, Microscopy, Spectroscopy, Toxicology
Special Collections: Forensic Science, 3200 reprints of journal articles
Restriction: Not open to public
Partic in National Network Of Libraries Of Medicine - Pacific Southwest Regional Medical Library

J SANTA ANA COLLEGE, Nealley Library, 1530 W 17th St, 92706-9990. SAN 301-5432. Tel: 714-564-6700. FAX: 714-564-6729. *Dir*, Maria Sungranes; *Acq*, Denise Phillips; Staff 8 (MLS 8)
Founded 1915. Enrl 24,035; Fac 329
Library Holdings: Bk Vols 103,000; Per Subs 619
Automation Activity & Vendor Info: (Cataloging) epixtech, inc.
Partic in Class
Orange County Fire Services Library, a membership library serving fire departments, is housed & operated by Nealley Library
Departmental Libraries:
SANTIAGO CANYON COLLEGE, 8045 E Chapman Ave, Orange, 92869. SAN 329-3017. Tel: 714-564-4700. FAX: 714-633-2842. *Librn*, Linda Cucovatz
1999-2000 Mats Exp Electronic Ref Mat (Incl. Access Fees) $16,507
Library Holdings: Bk Vols 27,781; Per Subs 336
Database Vendor: Ebsco - EbscoHost, epixtech, inc., IAC - Info Trac

P SANTA ANA PUBLIC LIBRARY, 26 Civic Center Plaza, 92701-4010. SAN 334-9055. Tel: 714-647-5250. Interlibrary Loan Service Tel: 714-647-5267. FAX: 714-647-5356. Web Site: www.ci.santa-ana.ca.us/library/default.html. *Dir*, Rob Richard; *Ch Servs*, Angie Nguyen; *Mgr Libr Serv*, Margaret Jean Owens; *Ref*, Heather Folmar; *Outreach Serv*, Martha Garcia-Almarzouk; *Circ*, Sylvia Morales. Subject Specialists: *Local history*, Anne Harder
Founded 1891. Pop 331,460; Circ 1,083,165
Jul 2000-Jun 2001 Income $3,920,600
Library Holdings: Bk Vols 354,000; Per Subs 400
Special Collections: Business, bks, cassettes; California History, bks, VF; Hispanic & Asian American Heritage; Santa Ana & Orange County History, bks, VF; Spanish Language, bks, rec, cassettes
Automation Activity & Vendor Info: (Acquisitions) Brodart; (Cataloging) Brodart; (Circulation) epixtech, inc.; (OPAC) epixtech, inc.
Database Vendor: Ebsco - EbscoHost
Restriction: Open to student, faculty & staff
Mem of Metropolitan Cooperative Library System
Friends of the Library Group
Branches: 2
MCFADDEN LIBRARY LEARNING CENTER, 2627 W McFadden, 92704. SAN 334-908X. Tel: 714-647-5790. FAX: 714-835-2289.
Library Holdings: Bk Vols 55,415; Per Subs 102
NEWHOPE LIBRARY LEARNING CENTER, 122 N Newhope, 92703. SAN 334-9098. Tel: 714-647-5792. FAX: 714-554-9633.
Library Holdings: Bk Vols 52,477; Per Subs 103
Bookmobiles: 2. Lead Librn, Sylvia Morales

SR TRINITY UNITED PRESBYTERIAN CHURCH LIBRARY, 13922 Prospect Ave, 92705. SAN 301-5459. Tel: 714-544-7850. FAX: 714-544-6837. *Librn*, Lois Boyer; Tel: 714-505-6254, Ext 121, E-Mail: loisb@tupcsa.org
Founded 1955
Library Holdings: Bk Vols 7,000; Per Subs 20
Subject Interests: Theology

CL TRINITY UNIVERSITY, Law Library & Information Center, 2200 N Grand Ave, 92705-7016. SAN 326-5412. Tel: 714-796-7171. FAX: 714-796-7190. *Coll Develop, Librn*, Michael Bryant; E-Mail: mbryant@tiu.edu
Founded 1980. Enrl 200; Fac 6; Highest Degree: Doctorate
1998-1999 Income $200,000. Mats Exp $100,000, Books $50,000, Per/Ser (Incl. Access Fees) $25,000, Other Print Mats $3,000. Sal $81,000
Library Holdings: Bk Vols 55,000; Bk Titles 32,000; Per Subs 56
Subject Interests: Human rights
Special Collections: Arthur Henry Robertson Coll (int law & human rights), mss, bks; European Commission and Court of Human Rights; Rarisma (15th-18th century classical, legal and apologetic books, including numerous English Reporters)

Automation Activity & Vendor Info: (Acquisitions) ComPanion Corp; (Cataloging) ComPanion Corp; (Circulation) ComPanion Corp; (OPAC) ComPanion Corp; (Serials) ComPanion Corp

M WESTERN MEDICAL CENTER, Medical Library,* 1001 N Tustin Ave, 92705. SAN 301-5440. Tel: 714-953-3406. FAX: 714-530-7318. *Librn*, Phyllis Dowling
Founded 1968
Library Holdings: Bk Titles 4,000; Per Subs 160
Subject Interests: Dentistry, Medicine, Nursing, Surgery
Partic in Docline; Medline
Sister facility located in Anaheim, Calif

S WOODWARD-CLYDE INTERNATIONAL, Library-Information Center,* 2020 E First St, Ste 400, 92705. SAN 321-4001. Tel: 714-835-6886, Ext 500. FAX: 714-667-7147. *Librn*, Karien Hudock
Founded 1978
Library Holdings: Bk Titles 9,000; Per Subs 50
Subject Interests: Engineering, Geology
Special Collections: Company Project Reports
Publications: Inmagic On-line catalog
Restriction: By appointment only

SANTA BARBARA

S ABC CLIO LIBRARY, 130 Cremona Dr, 93117. SAN 301-5467. Tel: 805-968-1911. FAX: 805-685-9685. E-Mail: library@abc-clio.com. Web Site: www.abc-clio.com. *Mgr*, Deborah Looker; E-Mail: dlooker@abc-clio.com; *Mgr Libr Serv*, Luke Howe; Staff 5 (Non-MLS 5)
Founded 1967
Library Holdings: Bk Vols 4,800; Bk Titles 1,050; Per Subs 2,200
Subject Interests: Social sciences and issues, World history
Publications: List of Periodicals
Restriction: Staff use only
Function of this library is to acquire scholarly historical periodicals & have the articles abstracted and covered for publication in ABC-CLIO's serial products Historical Abstracts, America: History & Life, EXEGY: The Source for Current World Information, Kalediescope: Current World Data, and ABC Pol-Sci. In addition, the library meets the reference & information needs of the company

C BROOKS INSTITUTE, School of Photography Library,* 801 Alston Rd, 93108. SAN 301-5475. Tel: 805-966-3888, Ext 237. FAX: 805-564-1475. E-Mail: library@brooks.edu. Web Site: www.brooks.edu. *Dir*, Susan Shiras; *Asst Librn*, Debbie Webber; Staff 4 (MLS 2, Non-MLS 2)
Founded 1972. Enrl 420; Highest Degree: Master
Library Holdings: Bk Vols 8,000; Per Subs 101
Subject Interests: Photography

S COMMUNITY ENVIRONMENTAL COUNCIL, Easton Library,* 930 Miramonte Dr, 93109-1384. SAN 327-2699. Tel: 805-963-0583. FAX: 805-962-9080. *Coordr*, Heidi Seward
Library Holdings: Bk Titles 500

M COTTAGE HOSPITAL, David L Reeves Medical Library, Pueblo & Bath, PO Box 689, 93102. SAN 301-5548. Tel: 805-569-7240. FAX: 805-569-7588. Web Site: www.cottagehealthsystem.org. *Dir*, Lucy B Thomas; E-Mail: lthomas@sbch.org; Staff 3 (MLS 3)
Founded 1941
Jan 1999-Dec 1999 Income $215,000, Locally Generated Income $15,000, Parent Institution $200,000. Mats Exp $90,000, Books $20,000, Per/Ser (Incl. Access Fees) $40,000. Sal $110,000
Library Holdings: Bk Vols 4,100; Bk Titles 3,500; Per Subs 325
Subject Interests: Medicine, Surgery
Special Collections: Medical History Coll
Automation Activity & Vendor Info: (OPAC) EOS
Publications: Newsletter (quarterly)
Restriction: Non-circulating to the public
Partic in NNLM/SCR, OCLC Online Computer Libr Ctr, Inc; Pac SW Regional Med Libr; Total Interlibrary Exchange
Friends of the Library Group

C FIELDING INSTITUTE LIBRARY,* 2112 Santa Barbara St, 93105. SAN 375-6874. Tel: 805-687-1099, Ext 3148. FAX: 805-898-4122. E-Mail: library@fielding.edu. Web Site: www.fielding.edu. *Dir Libr Serv*, Stefan Kramer; Tel: 805-898-4022, E-Mail: skramer@fielding.edu; Staff 1 (MLS 1)
Highest Degree: Doctorate
Library Holdings: Bk Titles 300; Per Subs 100
Database Vendor: OCLC - First Search
Restriction: Non-circulating to the public

SR FIRST UNITED METHODIST CHURCH, Memorial Library, 305 E Anapamu St, 93101. SAN 323-861X. Tel: 805-963-3579. *Librn*, Homer W Freeman; *Asst Librn*, Ruth Bosworth
1998-1999 Income $350
Library Holdings: Bk Vols 2,500

S GRC INTERNATIONAL, INC, Science & Technology Div Library,* 5383 Hollister Ave, PO Box 6770, 93160-6770. SAN 301-5491. Tel: 805-964-7724, Ext 266. FAX: 805-967-7094. *Librn*, Phil Morlan
Library Holdings: Bk Vols 7,000; Per Subs 135
Subject Interests: Computer science, Economics, Radar, Transportation

S INTERNATIONAL ACADEMY AT SANTA BARBARA LIBRARY, 5385 Hollister Ave, No 210, 93111. SAN 301-5513. Tel: 805-964-0790. Toll Free Tel: 800-530-2682. FAX: 805-964-0890. E-Mail: info@iasb.org. Web Site: www.iasb.org. *Pres*, Joanne St John; *Dir*, Janice E Warren
Founded 1972
Subject Interests: Energy, International relations, Nutrition, Political science, Water resources
Publications: Environmental Knowledge base on CD-ROM; Environmental Periodicals Bibliography on CD-ROM; Environmental Periodicals Bibliography Online
Restriction: Staff use only

GL MCMAHON LAW LIBRARY OF SANTA BARBARA COUNTY, County Court House, 93101. SAN 301-5572. Tel: 805-568-2296. FAX: 805-568-2299. Web Site: www.rain.org/~sblaw. *Dir*, Raymond MacGregor; *Librn*, Stephen Zaharias
Founded 1891
Library Holdings: Bk Vols 33,210
Open Mon-Fri 8-5, Sat 12-4:45

S MISSION RESEARCH CORP, Technical Library,* 735 State St, 93101. SAN 301-5521. Tel: 805-963-8761. FAX: 805-962-8530. *In Charge*, Jackie Newman
Library Holdings: Bk Vols 8,000; Per Subs 75
Subject Interests: Technology

S SANTA BARBARA BOTANIC GARDEN LIBRARY,* 1212 Mission Canyon Rd, 93105-2199. SAN 301-5556. Tel: 805-682-4726. FAX: 805-563-0352. Web Site: www.sbbg.org. *Librn*, Laurie Hannah
Founded 1942
Jan 1997-Dec 1998 Mats Exp $11,627, Books $4,430, Per/Ser (Incl. Access Fees) $5,759, Presv $1,438
Library Holdings: Bk Vols 12,000; Per Subs 195
Subject Interests: Botany, California, Horticulture
Restriction: Non-circulating to the public
Partic in Council On Botanical Horticultural Libraries; OCLC Online Computer Library Center, Inc

J SANTA BARBARA CITY COLLEGE, Eli Luria Library, 721 Cliff Dr, 93109-2394. SAN 301-5564. Tel: 805-965-0581, Ext 2638. Interlibrary Loan Service Tel: 805-965-0581, Ext 2635. Circulation Tel: 805-965-0581, Ext 2630. TDD: 805-965-8853. FAX: 805-965-0771. Web Site: www.sbcc.net/studentservices/library/. *Coordr*, David Kiley; Tel: 805-965-0581, Ext 2635, E-Mail: kiley@sbcc.net; *Ref*, M'Liss Garza; Tel: 805-965-0581, Ext 2634, E-Mail: garza@sbcc.net; *Cat*, Richard Hoffman; Tel: 805-965-0581, Ext 2643, E-Mail: hoffman@sbcc.net; Staff 13 (MLS 6, Non-MLS 7)
Founded 1909. Enrl 13,199; Fac 902; Highest Degree: Associate
Jul 1999-Jun 2000 Income $649,433, Locally Generated Income $17,000, Parent Institution $632,433. Mats Exp $105,620, Books $57,469, Per/Ser (Incl. Access Fees) $36,300, Presv $1,985, Micro $4,773, Electronic Ref Mat (Incl. Access Fees) $5,093. Sal $443,004 (Prof $265,591)
Library Holdings: Bk Vols 105,412; Bk Titles 101,124; Per Subs 356
Automation Activity & Vendor Info: (Cataloging) epixtech, inc.; (Circulation) epixtech, inc.; (Course Reserve) epixtech, inc.; (OPAC) epixtech, inc.; (Serials) epixtech, inc.
Database Vendor: OCLC - First Search
Partic in OCLC Online Computer Library Center, Inc
Special Services for the Blind - Magnifiers
Friends of the Library Group

S SANTA BARBARA COUNTY GENEALOGICAL SOCIETY, (SBCGS), Sahyun Library, 316 Castillo St, 93101-3814. (Mail add: PO Box 1303, 93116-1303), SAN 376-0790. Tel: 805-884-9909. E-Mail: sbcgs@juno.com. Web Site: www.cagenweb.com/~santabarbara/sbcgs. *Dir*, Marion Denniston; Tel: 805-968-9364; *Dir*, Ted Denniston; Tel: 805-968-9364, E-Mail: teditor@earthlink.net
Founded 1972
Jul 2000-Jun 2001 Income $55,000. Mats Exp $32,000
Library Holdings: Bk Titles 6,200; Per Subs 100
Subject Interests: Europe, Genealogy, US
Publications: Ancestors West (quarterly); Tree Tips (monthly)
Restriction: Public use on premises
Function: Photocopies available
For research purposes

S SANTA BARBARA HISTORICAL SOCIETY GLEDHILL LIBRARY, 136 E De La Guerra St, 93101. (Mail add: PO Box 578, 93102), SAN 301-5599. Tel: 805-966-1601. FAX: 805-966-1603. *Exec Dir*, George Anderjack; E-Mail: gmanderjack@sbhistorical.org; *Librn*, Michael E Redmon; E-Mail: mredmon@sbhistorical.org
Founded 1943
Library Holdings: Bk Vols 5,000; Per Subs 20

Subject Interests: Genealogy, Local history
Publications: Noticias (quarterly)
Restriction: Non-circulating to the public

S SANTA BARBARA MISSION, (SBMAL), Archive-Library, Old Mission, 2201 Laguna St, 93105. SAN 301-5602. Tel: 805-682-4713. FAX: 805-682-6067. *Dir*, Virgilio Biasiol
Founded 1786
Library Holdings: Bk Vols 22,000
Special Collections: California Missions (Father Junipero Serra Coll, covers all 21 California missions), docs; Early California (Webb Coll, Smilie Coll, Baer Coll and Wilson Coll), mss, papers, bks & docs; Original Spanish & Mexican Missionary Coll, bks; Spanish & Hispanic American Coll, bks; Spanish & Latin Coll, docs
Publications: Spanish California Revisited (Francis Guest, OFM); The Voyage of the Princesa to Southern California in 1782
Friends of the Library Group

S SANTA BARBARA MUSEUM OF ART, Fearing Library,* 1130 State St, 93101. SAN 320-1678. Tel: 805-963-4364, Ext 351. FAX: 805-966-6840. *Librn*, Ron Crozier
Founded 1974
Library Holdings: Bk Vols 50,000; Bk Titles 15,000; Per Subs 50
Subject Interests: Art
Special Collections: Group Exhibition Catalogues Coll; Individual Artist File Coll; Institutional Art Coll; Sale Catalogues Coll

S SANTA BARBARA MUSEUM OF NATURAL HISTORY LIBRARY, (SBN), 2559 Puesta del Sol Rd, 93105. SAN 301-5610. Tel: 805-682-4711, Ext 328. FAX: 805-569-3170. Web Site: www.sbnature.org. *Librn*, Terri Sheridan; E-Mail: tsheridan@sbnature2.org; Staff 2 (MLS 1, Non-MLS 1)
Founded 1920
Jan 2001-Dec 2001 Mats Exp $11,000, Books $2,000, Per/Ser (Incl. Access Fees) $6,000, Presv $2,000, Other Print Mats $1,000
Library Holdings: Bk Vols 40,000; Bk Titles 12,000; Per Subs 420
Subject Interests: Indians, Natural history, Systematics, Zoology
Special Collections: Channel Islands Archive; John Peabody Harrington California Indian Archives
Database Vendor: OCLC - First Search
Restriction: Non-circulating to the public
Partic in OCLC Online Computer Library Center, Inc

S SANTA BARBARA NEWS PRESS LIBRARY, 715 Anacapa St, PO Box 1359, 93102-1359. SAN 327-6104. Tel: 805-564-5200, Ext 251. FAX: 805-966-6258. Web Site: www.newspress.com. *Librn*, Susan DeLapa
Library Holdings: Bk Vols 15,000
News press back issues on microfiche

P SANTA BARBARA PUBLIC LIBRARY,* 40 E Anapamu St, PO Box 1019, 93102. SAN 334-9179. Tel: 805-564-5608. Interlibrary Loan Service Tel: 805-564-5610. FAX: 805-962-6304. E-Mail: Reference: sbplref@rain.org. *Dir*, Carol L Keator; E-Mail: sbkeator@rain.org; *ILL*, Sarah Dunn; *Tech Servs*, Mona Escobar-Ornelas; *Mgr Libr Serv*, Myra J Nicholas; Staff 15 (MLS 15)
Pop 218,300; Circ 1,379,493
Jul 1997-Jun 1998 Income $3,392,295. Mats Exp $635,565. Sal $2,000,375
Library Holdings: Bk Vols 193,888; Per Subs 421
Subject Interests: Local history
Mem of Black Gold Cooperative Library System
Partic in Dialog Corporation; OCLC Online Computer Library Center, Inc
Friends of the Library Group
Branches: 8
CARPINTERIA BRANCH, 5141 Carpinteria Ave, Carpinteria, 93013. SAN 334-9209. Tel: 805-684-4314. *In Charge*, Tara O'Reilly
Friends of the Library Group
CENTRAL LIBRARY Tel: 805-962-7653. FAX: 805-962-8972. *Dir*, Carol L Keator
Friends of the Library Group
EASTSIDE, 1102 E Montecito St, 93103. SAN 334-9268. Tel: 805-963-3727. E-Mail: sbeast@rain.org. Web Site: www.ci.santa-barbara.ca.us/library. *Librn*, Marge Fauver; Fax: 617-344-0433, E-Mail: mfauver@ci.santa-barbara.ca.us; *Ch Servs*, Chris Pedersen; Fax: 617-344-0433
Database Vendor: epixtech, inc.
Partic in Black Gold Coop; Total Interlibrary Exchange
Friends of the Library Group
GOLETA BRANCH, 500 N Fairview Ave, Goleta, 93117. SAN 334-9292. Tel: 805-964-7878. *Librn*, Pam Bury
Friends of the Library Group
LOS OLIVOS, Grange Hall, PO Box 306, 93441. SAN 377-7790. *In Charge*, Teresa McNeil-Maclean
Library Holdings: Bk Vols 1,800
MONTECITO, 1469 E Valley Rd, 93108. SAN 334-9357. Tel: 805-969-5063. *In Charge*, Luise Bird-Robinson
Friends of the Library Group
SANTA YNEZ BRANCH, 3598 Sagunto St, Santa Ynez, 93460. (Mail add: PO Box 186, Santa Ynez, 93460-0186), Web Site: www.ci.santa-barbara.ca.us/departments/library/.
Library Holdings: Bk Titles 300
Automation Activity & Vendor Info: (Circulation) Innovative Interfaces Inc.
Open Fri 2-5
SOLVANG BRANCH, 1745 Mission Dr, Solvang, 93463. SAN 334-9411. Tel: 805-688-4214. *In Charge*, Carey McKinnon
Friends of the Library Group
Bookmobiles: 1

S STONEHENGE STUDY GROUP, Stonehenge Viewpoint Library, PO Box 30887, 93130. SAN 327-6120. Tel: 805-687-6029. E-Mail: stonevue@aol.com. *Librn*, Joan L Cyr
Library Holdings: Bk Vols 5,000
Subject Interests: Archaeology, Astronomy, Geology
Special Collections: Bob Forrest Coll; Colo Epigraphy photos; Donald L Cyr Coll; Isaac N Vail Coll; Louis K Bell Coll; Paul Karlsson Johnstone Coll

R TRINITY EPISCOPAL CHURCH LIBRARY, 1500 State St, 93101. SAN 301-5645. Tel: 805-965-7419. FAX: 805-965-8840. *In Charge*, Lou Smitheram; Staff 3 (MLS 2, Non-MLS 1)
Library Holdings: Bk Vols 2,500

C UNIVERSITY OF CALIFORNIA, Davidson Library, 93106. SAN 301-5653. Tel: 805-893-2478, 805-893-2741 (Admin). FAX: 805-893-7010. Web Site: www.library.ucsb.edu. *Assoc Librn*, Cecily Johns; *Librn*, Sarah Pritchard; *Acq, Cat*, Lynne Hayman; *Rare Bks, Spec Coll*, David Tambo; *Online Servs*, Carol Gibbens; *Access Serv*, Marlayna Gates; *Ser*, Catherine Nelson
Founded 1909. Enrl 19,000; Fac 850; Highest Degree: Doctorate
Library Holdings: Bk Vols 2,500,000; Per Subs 18,825
Subject Interests: Nuclear engineering
Special Collections: 20th Century American & British Writers Coll; Art Exhibition Catalog Coll; Balkan History (Nikic Coll); Conservation in Southern California (Pearl Chase Coll); Evolution (Darwin Coll); History of Printing 19th & 20th Century (Skofield Coll); Humanistic Psychology Archive; Late 19th & 20th Century Trade Catalogs (Romaine Coll); Lincoln, Civil War & American Westward Expansion (Wyles Coll); Lotte Lehmann Archives Coll; Rare Bibles Coll
Automation Activity & Vendor Info: (Circulation) NOTIS
Publications: Soundings
Partic in Asn of Research Libraries; Center For Research Libraries; Dialog Corporation; OCLC Online Computer Library Center, Inc; Research Libraries Group, Inc; Total Interlibrary Exchange
Friends of the Library Group
Departmental Libraries:
ARTS LIBRARY Tel: 805-893-2850. *Librn*, Catherine Nelson

C WESTMONT COLLEGE, Roger John Voskuyl Library, 955 La Paz Rd, 93108-1099. SAN 301-5661. Tel: 805-565-6000, 805-565-6175. Interlibrary Loan Service Tel: 805-565-6000, Ext 6146. FAX: 805-565-6220. Web Site: www.westmont.edu. *Dir*, John D Murray; E-Mail: jmurray@westmont.edu; *Acq, Bibliog Instr, Ref Serv*, Kristyn Thurman; E-Mail: kthurman@westmont.edu; *Acq, Assoc Dir, Cat*, Marilyn Nichols; E-Mail: mnichols@westmont.edu; *Media Spec*, Karin J Holmes; *Asst Dir, Ref*, Diane Ziliotto; E-Mail: dziliotto@westmont.edu; *Access Serv, Asst Dir*, Richard Burnweit; E-Mail: burnweit@westmont.edu; *ILL*, Ruth Angelos; E-Mail: rangel@westmont.edu; Staff 7 (MLS 6, Non-MLS 1)
Founded 1940. Enrl 1,200; Fac 64; Highest Degree: Bachelor
Library Holdings: Bk Vols 123,012; Per Subs 700
Subject Interests: History, Literature
Special Collections: Interaction of Christian Faith & Culture (Christ & Culture Coll)
Automation Activity & Vendor Info: (Cataloging) epixtech, inc.
Partic in OCLC Online Computer Library Center, Inc; Total Interlibrary Exchange

SANTA CLARA

S AGILENT TECHNOLOGIES, Santa Clara Site Library, 5301 Stevens Creek Blvd, 55/27, 95052-8059. SAN 301-5726. Tel: 408-553-2593. FAX: 408-553-7755. *In Charge*, Diana M Robba; E-Mail: diana_robba@agilent.com
Founded 1973
Library Holdings: Bk Titles 4,800; Per Subs 163

S FAMILY RESOURCE CENTER, (PHP), Parents Helping Parents Library, 3041 Olcott St, 95054-3222. SAN 372-8439. Tel: 408-727-5775. FAX: 408-727-0182. Web Site: www.php.com. *Coordr*, Judy Bower; Tel: 408-727-5775, Ext 110, E-Mail: judy.bower@php.com; Staff 2 (Non-MLS 2)
Founded 1981
Library Holdings: Bk Titles 3,500; Bks on Deafness & Sign Lang 15
Subject Interests: Disability, Parenting
Special Services for the Deaf - Videos & decoder
Open 9-5

S HMS BOUNTY SOCIETY, INTERNATIONAL, Historical & Genealogical Research Library & Depository,* 1656 Betty Ct, 95051-2910. SAN 301-6609. Tel: 408-241-7517. *Dir*, Scott Christian

Founded 1971
Subject Interests: Genealogy
Special Collections: History of Pitcairn & Norfolk Islands & People

S INTEL CORPORATION, Library & Information Services,* 2200 Mission College Blvd, PO Box 58119, RN1-31, 95052-8119. SAN 321-0766. Tel: 408-765-8892. FAX: 408-765-8080.
Founded 1979
Library Holdings: Bk Titles 15,000; Per Subs 650
Subject Interests: Electronics
Automation Activity & Vendor Info: (Cataloging) TechLIB; (Circulation) TechLIB
Partic in RLIN
Open Mon-Fri 8-5

C MISSION COLLEGE LIBRARY, 3000 Mission College Blvd, 95054-1897. SAN 301-5742. Tel: 408-855-5150. Reference Tel: 408-855-5151. FAX: 408-855-5462. Web Site: www.wvmccd.cc.ca.us/mc/lib.html. *Dir*, Win-Shin Chiang; Tel: 408-855-5167, E-Mail: win_shin_chiang@wvmccd.cc.ca.us; *Publ Servs*, Judie Smith; Tel: 408-855-5163, E-Mail: judie_smith@wvmccd.cc.ca.us; *Coll Develop*, Erlinda Estrada; Tel: 408-855-5164, E-Mail: erlinda_estrada@wvmccd.cc.ca.us; *Electronic Resources*, Cathy Cox; Tel: 408-855-5165, E-Mail: cathy_cox@wvmccd.cc.ca.us; Staff 12 (MLS 5, Non-MLS 7)
Founded 1975. Enrl 11,350; Fac 200
Library Holdings: Bk Titles 54,000; Per Subs 110
Subject Interests: Allied health, Fire science
Database Vendor: Innovative Interfaces INN - View
Publications: Basic Library Research Skills: A Self-Paced Course
Partic in Coop Libr Agency for Syst & Servs

S NATIONAL SEMICONDUCTOR CORP, Information Resource Center,* 2900 Semiconductor Dr, MS-DT-05, 95052-8090. SAN 325-0385. Tel: 408-721-3810. FAX: 408-721-7060. E-Mail: library@library.nsc.com. *Mgr*, Mary Holland; *Ref*, Jennifer Armstrong; *Ser*, Catherine Lee; *Circ*, Andrea Rematore; Staff 7 (MLS 3, Non-MLS 4)
Founded 1979
Library Holdings: Bk Vols 9,000; Bk Titles 7,000; Per Subs 450
Subject Interests: Electronics, Semiconductors
Publications: Acquisition List; Brochure on Service; Holdings List; Specifications & Standards Holdings
Partic in Coop Libr Agency for Syst & Servs

P SANTA CLARA CITY LIBRARY, 2635 Homestead Rd, 95051. SAN 301-5750. Tel: 408-615-2900. FAX: 408-247-9657. E-Mail: library@ci.santa-clara.ca.us. Web Site: www.library.ci.santa-clara.ca.us. *Dir*, Karen Rollin Duffy; Tel: 408-615-2999; *Cat*, Mary Jo Bosteels; Tel: 408-615-2941; *Circ*, Darla Wegener; Tel: 408-615-2971; *ILL*, Anita Gower; *Ad Servs*, Trish Taylor; Tel: 408-615-2902; *Ref*, Jane Botsford; Tel: 408-615-2904; *Coordr*, Kathy St John; Tel: 408-615-2957; *YA Servs*, Julie Passalacqua; Tel: 408-615-2921; *Bkmobile Coordr*, Judy Brown; Tel: 408-615-2955; *Coll Develop*, Nancy Crabbe; Tel: 408-615-2903. Subject Specialists: *Literacy*, Kathy St John; Staff 54 (MLS 17, Non-MLS 37)
Founded 1904. Pop 103,000; Circ 1,600,000
Jul 1999-Jun 2000 Income (Main Library and Branch Library) City $4,367,456. Mats Exp $677,914. Sal $2,954,798
Library Holdings: Bk Vols 302,000; Bk Titles 251,383; Per Subs 690
Subject Interests: Business and management, Genealogy
Special Collections: Genealogy Coll
Automation Activity & Vendor Info: (Circulation) Innovative Interfaces Inc.; (OPAC) Innovative Interfaces Inc.
Mem of Silicon Valley Library System
Friends of the Library Group
Branches: 1
MISSION, 1098 Lexington St, 95050. SAN 371-358X. Tel: 408-615-2964. FAX: 408-249-2486. *Coordr*, Kathy St John; Tel: 408-615-2957. Subject Specialists: *Literacy*, Kathy St John
Library Holdings: Bk Vols 17,966
Friends of the Library Group
Bookmobiles: 1

C SANTA CLARA UNIVERSITY, Michel Orradre Library, 500 El Camino Real, 95053-0500. SAN 334-9470. Tel: 408-554-5020. Interlibrary Loan Service Tel: 408-554-5428. Reference Tel: 408-554-4658. FAX: 408-554-6827. Web Site: www.scu.edu/library. *Dir*, Elizabeth M Salzer; Tel: 408-554-6829, E-Mail: esalzer@scu.edu; *Assoc Dir*, Taeock Kim; Tel: 408-554-5429, E-Mail: tkim@scu.edu; *Tech Servs*, Paula Popma; Tel: 408-554-5431, E-Mail: ppopma@scu.edu; *Tech Coordr*, Fred Gertler; Tel: 408-554-6808, Fax: 408-555-1805, E-Mail: fgertler@scu.edu; *Res*, Alice Whistler; Tel: 408-554-6927, Fax: 408-554-2124, E-Mail: awhistler@scu.edu; *Circ*, Marian Fricano; Tel: 408-554-5439, E-Mail: mfricano@scu.edu; *Acq*, Anthony Raymond; Tel: 408-554-5430, E-Mail: araymond@scu.edu; *Archivist*, Anne McMahon; Tel: 408-554-4117, Fax: 408-554-5179, E-Mail: amcmahon@scu.edu; *Doc*, George Carlson; Tel: 408-554-5436, E-Mail: gcarson@scu.edu; *Cat*, Lynne Toribara; Tel: 408-554-5437, E-Mail: ltoribara@scu.edu; Staff 49 (MLS 13, Non-MLS 36)
Founded 1851. Enrl 6,706; Fac 468; Highest Degree: Doctorate
Jul 1999-Jun 2000 Income (Main Library and Branch Library) Locally Generated Income $5,136,555. Mats Exp $2,294,493, Presv $30,581. Sal $1,909,498 (Prof $769,283)
Library Holdings: Bk Vols 712,996; Bk Titles 455,268; Per Subs 5,201
Special Collections: California: Denise Levertov, Jose Antonio Villarreal; Labor Relations in California
Automation Activity & Vendor Info: (Acquisitions) Innovative Interfaces Inc.; (Cataloging) Innovative Interfaces Inc.; (Circulation) Innovative Interfaces Inc.; (ILL) Innovative Interfaces Inc.; (OPAC) Innovative Interfaces Inc.; (Serials) Innovative Interfaces Inc.
Database Vendor: Dialog, Ebsco - EbscoHost, GaleNet, Innovative Interfaces INN - View, Lexis-Nexis, OCLC - First Search, Silverplatter Information Inc.
Function: Archival collection, Literary searches
Partic in Link; OCLC Online Computer Library Center, Inc; Southern Calif Electronic Libr Consortium
Departmental Libraries:
ARCHIVES Tel: 408-554-4117. FAX: 408-554-5179. E-Mail: jokeefe@scu.bitnet. Web Site: www.scu.edu/archives.
Special Collections: Alaska (Bernard R Hubbard, S J Coll), ms, photog, Botany (George Schoener Coll); Early Aviation (John J Montgomery), ms, photog; Local History

CL HEAFEY LAW LIBRARY, School of Law, 500 El Camino Real, 95053-0430. SAN 334-9500. Tel: 408-554-4451. FAX: 408-554-5318. E-Mail: memery@scu.edu. Web Site: www.scu.edu/law/depts/library/library.html. *Dir*, Mary B Emery; Tel: 408-554-4010, E-Mail: memery@scu.edu; *Assoc Dir*, Mary D Hood; Tel: 408-554-2732, E-Mail: mhood@scu.edu; *Librn*, Katherine Hall; Tel: 408-554-2167, E-Mail: khall@scu.edu; *Ref*, David Bridgman; Tel: 408-554-4452; *Publ Servs*, Ellen J Platt; Tel: 408-554-5139, E-Mail: eplatt@scu.edu; *Head Ref*, Prano Amjadi; Tel: 408-554-5320, E-Mail: pamjadi@scu.edu; *Cat*, Marilyn Dreyer; Tel: 408-554-5307, E-Mail: mdreyer@scu.edu; *Tech Servs*, Whitney Alexander; Tel: 408-554-2733, E-Mail: walexander@scu.edu; Staff 16 (MLS 8, Non-MLS 8)
Founded 1912. Enrl 926; Fac 37; Highest Degree: Master
Jul 1999-Jun 2000 Income $1,877,685. Mats Exp $1,166,292, Books $73,690, Per/Ser (Incl. Access Fees) $630,952, Presv $11,370, Electronic Ref Mat (Incl. Access Fees) $105,153. Sal $711,393 (Prof $351,423)
Library Holdings: Bk Vols 143,751; Bk Titles 28,864; Per Subs 3,668
Special Collections: Proceedings of the House Judiciary Committee on the Watergate Hearings
Automation Activity & Vendor Info: (Cataloging) Innovative Interfaces Inc.; (Circulation) Innovative Interfaces Inc.; (Course Reserve) Innovative Interfaces Inc.; (ILL) Innovative Interfaces Inc.; (OPAC) Innovative Interfaces Inc.; (Serials) Innovative Interfaces Inc.
Database Vendor: Dialog, IAC - Info Trac, Innovative Interfaces INN - View, Lexis-Nexis
Publications: Heafey Headnotes
Partic in Coop Libr Agency for Syst & Servs; Dialog Corporation; Jesuit Law Libr Consortium; RLIN; S Bay Area Ref Network; Westlaw

S TRITON MUSEUM OF ART LIBRARY,* 1505 Warburton Ave, 95050. SAN 301-5793. Tel: 408-247-3754. FAX: 408-247-3796. E-Mail: triton246@aol.com. Web Site: www.tritonmuseum.org. *Dir*, George Rivera; *Asst Dir*, Beth Bowman
Founded 1968
Library Holdings: Bk Vols 1,600
Subject Interests: Art, Art history
Publications: Aassen (Frelmark) Middlebrook-Horse of a Different Color; Crime & Punishment-Reflections of Violence in Contemporary Art; Day of the Dead-Tradition & Change in Contemporary Mexico; Elizabeth Boott Duveneck-Her Life & Times; Frank Duveneck-Lost Paintings Found; Native American Artifacts of California & the Southwest; New Furnishings-A Survey of Post of Post Modern Bay Area Furniture; Our Heritage in Clothing; Robot Sculptures; The Art & Tradition of Mexican Indian Dance Masks; The Family of Appliances You Can Believe In; Theodore Wores-Permanent Collection Catalogue of the Triton Museum; Three From the Northern Island -Contemporary Sculptors from Hokkaido; Two Thousand Years of Santa Clara Valley Architecture; Winslow Homer-Prints from Harper's Weekly
Restriction: By appointment only

S UNITED DEFENSE LP, GSD Library PO5, PO Box 58123, 95052. SAN 301-4959. Tel: 408-289-4336. FAX: 408-289-2868. *Mgr*, Karen Venema; *Ref*, Lynn Russell; Staff 3 (MLS 2, Non-MLS 1)
Library Holdings: Bk Titles 1,500; Per Subs 30
Automation Activity & Vendor Info: (Cataloging) Inmagic, Inc.; (Circulation) Inmagic, Inc.
Publications: Acquisition List; Bibliographies; Newsletter
Mem of South Bay Coop Libr Syst
Partic in Coop Libr Agency for Syst & Servs

SANTA CLARITA

J COLLEGE OF THE CANYONS LIBRARY,* 26455 Rockwell Canyon Rd, 91355-1899. SAN 301-6811. Tel: 661-259-7800, Ext 3330. FAX: 661-253-1845. Web Site: www.coc.cc.ca.us/library/default.htm. *Dean of Libr*, Jan K Keller; E-Mail: keller_j@mail.coc.cc.ca.us; *Publ Servs*, Leslie Bretall; Tel: 661-259-7800, Ext 3302, E-Mail: bretall_l@mail.coc.cc.ca.us; *Tech Servs*,

Isad Uesugi; Tel: 661-259-7800, Ext 3607, E-Mail: uesugi_i@mail.coc.cc.ca.us; Staff 10 (MLS 4, Non-MLS 6)
Founded 1969. Enrl 14,089; Fac 97; Highest Degree: Associate
Jul 1998-Jun 1999 Income State $582,433. Mats Exp $89,640, Books $52,666, Per/Ser (Incl. Access Fees) $10,529, Micro $4,545, Electronic Ref Mat (Incl. Access Fees) $21,900. Sal $460,640 (Prof $155,818)
Library Holdings: Bk Vols 45,803; Per Subs 225
Automation Activity & Vendor Info: (Acquisitions) DRA; (Cataloging) DRA; (Circulation) DRA; (Course Reserve) DRA; (ILL) DRA; (OPAC) DRA
Database Vendor: DRA
Partic in Santa Clarita Interlibrary Network; Total Interlibrary Exchange
Special Services for the Deaf - TTY machine
Special Services for the Blind - DECTalk/JAWS for synthetic voice output of computer screen contents
Friends of the Library Group

CR ROBERT L POWELL LIBRARY (THE MASTER'S COLLEGE), 21726 W Placerita Canyon Rd, 91321-1200. SAN 301-0996. Tel: 661-259-3540. Toll Free Tel: 800-568-6248. FAX: 661-222-9159. Web Site: www.masters.edu/libraries/welcome.htm. *Dir*, John W Stone; E-Mail: jstone@masters.edu; *Head Librn*, James F Stitzinger; E-Mail: jstitz@pacbell.net; *Ref*, Janet L Tillman; E-Mail: jtillman@masters.edu. Subject Specialists: *Liberal arts*, Janet L Tillman; *Theology*, John W Stone; Staff 7 (MLS 3, Non-MLS 4)
Founded 1927. Enrl 1,050; Fac 128; Highest Degree: Master
Jul 1999-Jun 2000 Mats Exp $473,856, Books $79,270, Per/Ser (Incl. Access Fees) $45,190, Electronic Ref Mat (Incl. Access Fees) $35,060. Sal $188,000 (Prof $97,500)
Library Holdings: Bk Titles 135,000; Per Subs 460
Subject Interests: Biblical studies
Automation Activity & Vendor Info: (Acquisitions) Endeavor; (Cataloging) Endeavor; (Circulation) Endeavor; (OPAC) Endeavor; (Serials) Endeavor
Database Vendor: GaleNet, Lexis-Nexis, OCLC - First Search, ProQuest
Function: ILL available
Partic in Southern Calif Electronic Libr Consortium; Southern Calif Interlibr Loan Network

SANTA CRUZ

M DOMINICAN HOSPITAL, (Formerly Dominican Santa Cruz Hospital), Medical Library, 1555 Soquel Dr, 95065. SAN 324-5063. Tel: 831-462-7738. FAX: 831-462-7705. *Librn*, Candace Walker; Staff 2 (MLS 1, Non-MLS 1)
Founded 1975
Library Holdings: Bk Vols 1,200; Bk Titles 1,000; Per Subs 70
Subject Interests: Medicine
Partic in Nat Libr of Med; Northern California & Nevada Medical Library Group

S MUSEUM OF ART & HISTORY LIBRARY,* 705 Front St, 95060-4508. SAN 371-7860. Tel: 831-429-1964. FAX: 831-429-1954. E-Mail: mah@cruzio.com. Web Site: www.santacruzmah.org. *Res*, Rachel McKay
Library Holdings: Bk Titles 600
Subject Interests: Local history
Special Collections: Evergreen Cemetery Records
Publications: Santa Cruz County History Journal
Friends of the Library Group

S OTTAWAY NEWS, INC, Sentinel News Library,* 207 Church St, PO Box 638, 95061. SAN 329-7829. Tel: 831-423-4242, Ext 263. FAX: 831-429-9620. Web Site: www.santacruz.sentinel.com. *Librn*, Christine A Watson; E-Mail: cwatson@santa-cruz.com
Library Holdings: Bk Titles 100
Subject Interests: History, Local government
Special Collections: Film Negatives, photo; Historical Mat, clips

S SAN FRANCISCO ACADEMY OF COMIC ART LIBRARY, 170 West Cliff Dr, Bldg 15, 95060. SAN 301-4525. Tel: 831-427-1737. FAX: 831-427-1737. *Dir*, Bill Blackbeard; *Online Servs*, B Tyger
Founded 1967
Library Holdings: Bk Titles 62,000; Per Subs 31
Subject Interests: Graphic arts, Science fiction
Special Collections: Comic Strips (Charles Knabenschuh Coll); De Frantz Mystery & Crime Fiction Coll; Newspapers (Los Angeles Times Bequest Coll), bd vols; Popular Fiction Magazines (Pulps Coll)
Publications: 19th Century Gothic Novels; Comic Strip Century; Complete Krazy Kat; Complete Terry & the Pirates; Great Comic Cats; Hyperion Classic Comic Strip Reprint Series; Science Fiction in the Comics; Sherlock Holmes in America; Smithsonian Collection of Newspaper Comics; The Complete Yellow Kid; The Kin-Der-Kids
Restriction: By appointment only
Partic in Bay Area Ref Ctr

P SANTA CRUZ CITY-COUNTY LIBRARY SYSTEM HEADQUARTERS, 1543 Pacific Ave, 95060-3873. SAN 334-9659. Tel: 831-420-5600. Interlibrary Loan Service Tel: 831-429-3520. FAX: 831-420-5601. Web Site: www.santacruzpl.org. *Dir*, Anne M Turner; Tel: 831-420-5612, E-Mail: turnera@santacruzpl.org; *Asst Dir*, Susan Elgin; Tel: 831-420-5610, E-Mail: elgins@santacruzpl.org; *Branch Mgr*, Barbara Snider; Tel: 831-420-5704, Fax: 831-420-5701, E-Mail: sniderb@santacruzpl.org; *Head Ref*, Gary Decker; Tel: 831-420-5661, E-Mail: deckerg@santacruzpl.org; *Head Tech Servs*, Margaret Souza; Tel: 831-420-5660, E-Mail: souzam@santacruzpl.org; *Tech Coordr*, Robert Easley; Tel: 831-420-5763, E-Mail: easleyd@santacruzpl.org; *YA Servs*, Janis O'Driscoll; Tel: 831-420-5662, E-Mail: odriscollj@santacruzpl.org; Staff 28 (MLS 28)
Founded 1868. Pop 215,100; Circ 1,488,951
Jul 2000-Jun 2001 Income (Main Library and Branch Library) $10,141,519, State $356,446, Locally Generated Income $9,785,073. Mats Exp $1,309,800. Sal $6,241,006
Library Holdings: Bk Vols 560,510; Bk Titles 225,119; Per Subs 1,400
Subject Interests: California, Local history, Sheet music
Automation Activity & Vendor Info: (Acquisitions) DRA; (Cataloging) DRA; (Circulation) DRA; (OPAC) DRA
Database Vendor: DRA, Ebsco - EbscoHost
Mem of Monterey Bay Area Cooperative Library System
Special Services for the Deaf - TTY machine
Friends of the Library Group
Branches: 10
APTOS BRANCH, 7695 Soquel Dr, Aptos, 95003. SAN 334-9683. Tel: 831-688-5688. *Branch Mgr*, Julie Richardson
Library Holdings: Bk Vols 53,535
BOULDER CREEK BRANCH, 13390 W Park Ave, Boulder Creek, 95006. SAN 334-9772. Tel: 408-338-6340. *Branch Mgr*, Barbara Kiehl
Library Holdings: Bk Vols 31,731
BRANCIFORTE, 230 Gault St, 95062. SAN 334-9802. Tel: 408-429-3176. *Branch Mgr*, Merritt Taylor
Library Holdings: Bk Vols 52,950
CAPITOLA BRANCH, 2005 Wharf Rd, Capitola, 95010. SAN 378-0694.
CENTRAL, 224 Church St, 95060-3873. SAN 322-5666. FAX: 408-425-4927. *Branch Mgr*, Barbara Snider
Library Holdings: Bk Vols 213,336
FELTON BRANCH, 6299 Gushee St, PO Box 56, Felton, 95018. SAN 334-9861. Tel: 408-335-4052. *Branch Mgr*, Dorcas Abbott
Library Holdings: Bk Vols 18,846
GARFIELD PARK, 705 Woodrow Ave, 95060. SAN 334-9926. Tel: 831-420-6345. FAX: 831-420-6345. E-Mail: garfieldlib@santacruzpl.org. Web Site: www.garfieldlib.com. *Branch Mgr*, Sandra Imperio; Tel: 831-420-6347, E-Mail: imperios@santacruzpl.org; Staff 5 (Non-MLS 5)
Founded 1915
Library Holdings: Bk Vols 14,798; Per Subs 60
LA SELVA BEACH BRANCH, 316 Estrella, La Selva Beach, 95076. SAN 334-9950. Tel: 408-722-1958. *In Charge*, Sonya Birkel
Library Holdings: Bk Vols 12,076
LIVE OAK, 2380 Portola Dr, 95062. SAN 323-8423. Tel: 408-476-9193. *Branch Mgr*, Lillian Dobbs
Library Holdings: Bk Vols 20,031
SCOTTS VALLEY BRANCH, 230-D Mt Hermon Rd, Scotts Valley, 95066. SAN 334-9985. Tel: 408-438-2855. *Branch Mgr*, Gale Farthing
Library Holdings: Bk Vols 24,183
Bookmobiles: 1

GL SANTA CRUZ COUNTY LAW LIBRARY,* 701 Ocean St Rm 070, 95060. SAN 301-5815. Tel: 831-457-2525. FAX: 831-457-2255. E-Mail: librarian@lawlibrary.org. Web Site: www.lawlibrary.org. *Librn*, Patricia J Pfremmer; *Asst Librn*, Dolores Wiemers
Founded 1896
1997-1998 Income $174,337, State $134,254, Locally Generated Income $40,083. Mats Exp Books $92,024. Sal $73,500
Library Holdings: Bk Vols 25,000

C UNIVERSITY OF CALIFORNIA, University Library, 95064. SAN 335-0045. Tel: 831-459-2076. Interlibrary Loan Service Tel: 831-459-2234. FAX: 831-459-8206. Web Site: library.ucsc.edu. *Dir*, Allan J Dyson; *Asst Dir*, Kate McGirr; *Asst Dir*, Robert White; *Head Tech Servs*, Larry Millsap; *Spec Coll*, Rita Bottoms; *Bibliog Instr, Head Ref*, Cheryl Gomez; *Bibliogr*, Paul Machlis; *Bibliogr*, Karen Mokrzycki; *Bibliogr*, Martha Ramirez; *Bibliogr*, Elizabeth Remak-Honnef; *Access Serv*, Deborah Turner; *Govt Doc*, Cynthia Johns. Subject Specialists: *Archives*, Rita Bottoms; *Maps*, Cynthia Johns; Staff 28 (MLS 28)
Founded 1965. Enrl 11,306; Fac 616; Highest Degree: Doctorate
Jul 1999-Jun 2000 Income $9,411,334, State $9,245,657, Other $165,677. Mats Exp $3,188,212, Books $904,881, Per/Ser (Incl. Access Fees) $1,974,619, Presv $147,551, Electronic Ref Mat (Incl. Access Fees) $161,161. Sal $5,730,885 (Prof $2,144,436)
Library Holdings: Bk Vols 1,302,295; Per Subs 13,360
Special Collections: Gregory Bateson Coll; Kenneth Patchen Archive; Lime Kiln Press Archive; Mary Lea Shane Archives of the Lick Observatory; Robert Heinlein Archive; Santa Cruz County History Coll; Strouse Coll of Thomas Carlyle; Trianon Press Archive; Turtle Island Press Archive
Automation Activity & Vendor Info: (Acquisitions) Innovative Interfaces Inc.; (Cataloging) Innovative Interfaces Inc.; (Circulation) Innovative Interfaces Inc.; (Media Booking) Innovative Interfaces Inc.; (OPAC) Innovative Interfaces Inc.; (Serials) Innovative Interfaces Inc.
Database Vendor: OCLC - First Search
Publications: Catalog of South Pacific Collection (1978); Catalog of the

Carlyle Coll (1980); Norman & Charlotte Strouse Lectures on Carlyle & His Era (Series)
Mem of Monterey Bay Area Cooperative Library System
Friends of the Library Group
Departmental Libraries:
SCIENCE Tel: 831-459-2886. FAX: 831-459-2797. *Librn*, Catherine Soehner; Staff 5 (MLS 5)
Founded 1969
Library Holdings: Bk Vols 315,394
Subject Interests: Astronom, Biology, Chemistry, Earth science, Environ toxicology, Mathematics, Ocean sci, Physics
Friends of the Library Group

SANTA FE SPRINGS

P SANTA FE SPRINGS CITY LIBRARY,* 11700 E Telegraph Rd, 90670-3600. SAN 301-5831. Tel: 562-868-7738. FAX: 562-929-3680. Web Site: www.santafesprings.org/library.htm. *Dir*, Monica Penninger; *Ad Servs*, Diane Catlin; *Ch Servs*, Linda Furey; *AV*, Shannon Dailey; Staff 11 (MLS 5, Non-MLS 6)
Founded 1961. Pop 16,000; Circ 122,000
Library Holdings: Bk Vols 90,000; Per Subs 235
Special Collections: Whittier Area Genealogical Society Coll
Automation Activity & Vendor Info: (Circulation) epixtech, inc.
Mem of Metropolitan Cooperative Library System
Partic in Metropolitan Cooperative Library System
Open Mon & Tues 10-9:30
Friends of the Library Group
Branches: 2
BETTY WILSON CENTER LIBRARY STATION, 11641 Florence Ave, 90670. Tel: 562-929-7431. E-Mail: library@santafesprings.org. Web Site: www.santafesprings.org/libindex.htm. *Dir*, Monica Penninger
Library Holdings: Bk Vols 500; Per Subs 15
NEIGHBORHOOD CENTER LIBRARY STATION, 9255 Pioneer Blvd, 90670. Tel: 562-692-0261. E-Mail: library@santafesprings.org. Web Site: www.santafesprings.org/libindex.htm. *Dir*, Monica Penninger
Library Holdings: Bk Vols 500; Per Subs 15

SANTA JOSE

S SOCIETY FOR INFORMATION DISPLAY LIBRARY,* 31 E Julian St, 95112. SAN 370-4408. Tel: 408-977-1013. E-Mail: office@sid.org. Web Site: www.sid.org. *Exec Dir*, Dee Dumont; *Coordr*, Jenny Needham
Library Holdings: Bk Vols 5,000

SANTA MARIA

J ALLAN HANCOCK COLLEGE, Learning Resources Center, 800 S College Dr, 93454. SAN 301-584X. Tel: 805-922-6966, Ext 3224. Reference Tel: 805-922-6966, Ext 3322. FAX: 805-922-3763. Web Site: www.hancock.cc.ca.us. *Assoc Dean*, Lil Clary; Tel: 805-922-6966, Ext 3475, E-Mail: clary@hancock.cc.ca.us; *Acq*, Mildred Carpenter; Tel: 805-922-6966, Ext 3637, E-Mail: mcarpenter@hancock.cc.ca.us; *Distance Educ*, Joanne Britton; Tel: 805-922-6966, Ext 3320, E-Mail: jbritton@hancock.cc.ca.us; *Librn*, Kathy Headtke; Tel: 805-922-6966, Ext 5474, Fax: 805-735-1554, E-Mail: headtked@yahoo.sjsu.edu; *Librn*, Nancy Meddings; Tel: 805-922-6966, Ext 3474, E-Mail: mmeddings@hotmail.com; *Librn*, Leslie Mosson; Tel: 805-922-6966, Ext 3758, E-Mail: imosson@utech.net; *Circ*, Chana Ortiz; Tel: 805-922-6966, Ext 5475, E-Mail: cortiz@hancock.cc.ca.us; *Circ*, Anna Rice; E-Mail: arice@hancock.cc.ca.us; Staff 1 (MLS 1)
Founded 1920. Enrl 9,195; Fac 151
Library Holdings: Bk Vols 44,478; Bk Titles 38,509; Per Subs 337
Special Collections: Theatre
Automation Activity & Vendor Info: (Cataloging) Endeavor; (Circulation) Endeavor; (OPAC) Endeavor
Partic in Total Interlibrary Exchange

GL SANTA BARBARA COUNTY LAW LIBRARY, (SMLL), Santa Maria Branch, 312-E Cook St, 93454. SAN 301-5858. Tel: 805-346-7548. FAX: 805-346-7692. E-Mail: smlaw@rain.org. Web Site: www.rain.org/~sblaw/santamaria.htm. *Head of Libr*, Ray MacGregor; Tel: 805-568-2296, 568-2297, Fax: 805-568-2299, E-Mail: sblaw@rain.org; *Librn*, Stephen Zaharais
2000-2001 Income $302,000. Mats Exp $132,000, Books $72,000, Per/Ser (Incl. Access Fees) $54,000. Sal $133,858 (Prof $84,000)
Library Holdings: Bk Vols 16,665

P SANTA MARIA PUBLIC LIBRARY, 420 S Broadway, 93454-5199. SAN 335-0134. Tel: 805-925-0994. Interlibrary Loan Service FAX: 805-928-7432. E-Mail: smref@rain.org. Web Site: www.ci.santa-maria.ca.us/library. *Dir*, Jack Buchanan; E-Mail: jbuchanan@ci.santa-maria.ca.us; *Asst Dir*, Marcia Frasier; E-Mail: mfrasie@rain.org; Staff 8 (MLS 5, Non-MLS 3)
Founded 1909. Pop 111,130; Circ 632,397
Jul 1998-Jun 1999 Mats Exp $210,596, Books $144,327, Per/Ser (Incl. Access Fees) $18,200, Micro $2,300, Electronic Ref Mat (Incl. Access Fees) $7,439. Sal $732,076
Library Holdings: Bk Vols 168,816; Per Subs 380
Subject Interests: Careers, Genealogy, Local history
Automation Activity & Vendor Info: (Cataloging) epixtech, inc.; (Circulation) epixtech, inc.; (ILL) epixtech, inc.; (OPAC) epixtech, inc.
Database Vendor: OCLC - First Search
Mem of Black Gold Cooperative Library System
Friends of the Library Group
Branches: 3
CUYAMA BRANCH, PO Box 176, New Cuyama, 93254. SAN 335-0169. Tel: 661-766-2490. Web Site: www.ci.santa_maria.ca.us/library. *In Charge*, Grace Sullano
GUADALUPE STATION, 1005 Guadalupe, Guadalupe, 93434. SAN 335-0193. Tel: 805-343-1405. *In Charge*, Melinda Arreola
Library Holdings: Bk Vols 3,850; Bk Titles 3,050
Friends of the Library Group
ORCUTT BRANCH, 1157 E Clark, Ste K, 93455. SAN 335-0258. Tel: 805-937-6483. *In Charge*, Cheryl Whitmeyer
Library Holdings: Bk Vols 11,500; Bk Titles 10,500
Friends of the Library Group

S THEOSOPHICAL BOOK ASSOCIATION FOR THE BLIND, Baker Memorial Library, 516 N Lucas Dr, 93454-3828. SAN 301-1410. Tel: 805-646-2121. E-Mail: tbab@compuserve.com.
Founded 1923
Library Holdings: Bk Titles 1,200
Subject Interests: Occult, Philosophy
Publications: The Braille Star Theosophist

SANTA MONICA

L BRYAN CAVE LLP, Law Library, 120 Broadway, Ste 300, 90401. SAN 327-6287. Tel: 310-576-2100. FAX: 310-576-2200. *Librn*, Karen Lasnick; E-Mail: kslasnick@bryancave.com; *Librn*, Karen Olson; E-Mail: kkolson@bryancave.com
Library Holdings: Bk Vols 30,000
Subject Interests: Aviation, Labor
Restriction: Private library

S CALIFORNIA RESEARCH CORP LIBRARY,* 2118 Wilshire Blvd, Ste 163, 90403-5784. SAN 329-0476. Tel: 310-829-9865. FAX: 310-459-1234. *Librn*, Barry Rubens
Founded 1977
Library Holdings: Bk Titles 275; Per Subs 29
Publications: California Research Report; Monthly financial newsletter
Restriction: Not open to public

S LEAR ASTRONICS CORP, Technical Library,* 3400 Airport Ave, 90405. SAN 375-8109. Tel: 310-915-6000, 310-915-6726. FAX: 310-915-8369.
Library Holdings: Bk Titles 1,150; Per Subs 120

S MARKETEMPS, Marketing Intelligence Center,* 3435 Ocean Park Blvd, Ste 112, 90405. SAN 370-176X. Tel: 310-471-5590. FAX: 310-471-0932. *Pres*, Clifford S Lightfoot
Library Holdings: Bk Titles 800; Per Subs 40
Special Collections: Advanced Technology; Business Plans; Corporate Image & Turnaround; Creativity; Inventor; Small Industry Studies
Publications: Marketing Business Services (for law firms & accounting firms); Marketing Intelligence Manual

S RAND LIBRARY, 1700 Main St, 90401. (Mail add: PO Box 2138, 90407-2138), Tel: 310-393-0411, Ext 7788. Interlibrary Loan Service Tel: 310-451-7029. FAX: 310-451-6920. Web Site: www.rand.org. *Dir Libr Serv*, Lucy Wegner; Tel: 310-451-6940; *Librn*, Susan Adler; *Branch Mgr*, Gail Kouril; *Syst Coordr*, Kara Speiniger; *Coll Develop, Ref*, Roberta Shanman; *Head, Circ*, Walter Nelson; *Head, Cat*, Chris Fox; *Acq, Doc Delivery, Ser*, Lorraine Gersitz
Founded 1948
Oct 1998-Sep 1999 Income $2,470,000, Locally Generated Income $300,000, Parent Institution $1,970,000, Other $200,000
Library Holdings: Bk Titles 51,000; Per Subs 2,300
Subject Interests: Behav sci, Criminal justice, Data coll, Economics, Education, Environ sci, Foreign Language, Health science, Labor, Mil sci, Population, Science/technology, Terrorism
Automation Activity & Vendor Info: (Acquisitions) SIRSI; (Cataloging) SIRSI; (Circulation) SIRSI; (OPAC) SIRSI; (Serials) SIRSI
Database Vendor: Dialog, GaleNet, Lexis-Nexis, OVID Technologies, Silverplatter Information Inc.
Publications: Electronic Accessions Lists (biweekly); Library Notes (irregular) (Newsletter); New Videos in the Library; What's New in ROBIN (biweekly electronic accessions list)
Restriction: Staff use only, Use of others with permission of librarian
Function: Document delivery services, ILL available, Reference services available
Partic in Capcon Library Network; OCLC Online Computer Library Center, Inc; RLIN

J SANTA MONICA COLLEGE LIBRARY,* 1900 W Pico Blvd, 90405-1628. SAN 301-5939. Tel: 310-434-4334, 310-434-4692. FAX: 310-434-4387. Web Site: www.smc.edu. *Tech Servs*, Patricia Burson; *Asst Dean*, Mona Martin; *Coll Develop*, Brenda Antrim; *Syst Coordr*, Steve Hunt; *Bibliog Instr*, Teresa Grenot; *Ref*, Anne Powers; Staff 6 (MLS 6)
Founded 1929. Fac 228
Library Holdings: Bk Vols 105,000; Bk Titles 98,000; Per Subs 475
Partic in Calif Libr Authority for Systs & Servs; OCLC Online Computer Library Center, Inc

P SANTA MONICA PUBLIC LIBRARY, 1343 Sixth St, 90401. (Mail add: PO Box 1610, 90406), SAN 335-0282. Tel: 310-458-8600. Reference Tel: 310-451-8859. TDD: 310-395-8499. FAX: 310-394-8951. Web Site: www.smpl.org. *Dir*, Wini Allard; Tel: 310-458-8607, Fax: 310-393-5702, E-Mail: wallard@pen.ci.santa-monica.ca.us; *Asst City Librn*, Greg Mullen; Tel: 310-458-8611, E-Mail: gmullen@pen.ci.santa-monica.ca.us; *Ch Servs*, Ellen Braby; Tel: 310-458-8922, E-Mail: ebraby@pen.ci.santa-monica.ca.us; *Head, Info Serv*, Migell Acosta; Tel: 310-458-8625, E-Mail: migell-acosta@santa-monica.org; *Publ Servs*, Susan Annett; Tel: 310-458-8640, E-Mail: sannett@pen.ci.santa-monica.ca.us; *Head Ref*, Nancy O'Neill; Tel: 310-458-8629, E-Mail: oneill@pen.ci.santa-monica.ca.us; *YA Servs*, Penny Bohn; Tel: 310-458-8976, E-Mail: penny-bohn@santa-monica.org; *Ref*, Cynni Murphy; Staff 105 (MLS 30, Non-MLS 75)
Founded 1890. Pop 90,000; Circ 1,100,000
Jul 2000-Jun 2001 Income (Main Library and Branch Library) $4,852,817. Mats Exp $664,000. Sal $3,333,593
Library Holdings: Bk Vols 350,000; Bk Titles 240,000; Per Subs 850
Special Collections: Santa Monica History & Biography Coll, card file & photogs
Automation Activity & Vendor Info: (Acquisitions) SIRSI; (Cataloging) SIRSI; (Circulation) SIRSI
Database Vendor: GaleNet, IAC - Info Trac, IAC - SearchBank, OCLC - First Search
Function: Some telephone reference
Mem of Metropolitan Cooperative Library System
Partic in Metropolitan Cooperative Library System
Friends of the Library Group
Branches: 3
FAIRVIEW, 2101 Ocean Park Blvd, 90405-5013. SAN 335-0312. Tel: 310-450-0443. FAX: 310-450-5749. Web Site: www.smpl.org. *Branch Mgr*, Louix Escobar-Matute; E-Mail: lescobar@pen.ci.santa-monica.ca.us; *Admin Assoc*, Rachel Foyt; Tel: 310-458-8608, Fax: 310-394-8951, E-Mail: rachel-foyt@santa-monica.org; Staff 6 (MLS 3, Non-MLS 3)
Library Holdings: Bk Vols 37,442
Automation Activity & Vendor Info: (Circulation) SIRSI
Database Vendor: GaleNet, IAC - Info Trac, IAC - SearchBank, OCLC - First Search
Friends of the Library Group
MONTANA AVENUE, 1704 Montana Ave, 90403-1908. SAN 335-0347. Tel: 310-829-7081. FAX: 310-829-3691. Web Site: www.smpl.org. *Branch Mgr*, Janet Hunt; E-Mail: jhunt@pen.ci.santa-monica.ca.us; *Admin Assoc*, Rachel Foyt; Tel: 310-458-8608, Fax: 310-394-8951, E-Mail: rachel-foyt@santa-monica.org; Staff 5 (MLS 2, Non-MLS 3)
Library Holdings: Bk Vols 37,373
Automation Activity & Vendor Info: (Circulation) SIRSI
Database Vendor: GaleNet, IAC - Info Trac, IAC - SearchBank, OCLC - First Search
Friends of the Library Group
OCEAN PARK, 2601 Main St, 90405-4001. SAN 335-0371. Tel: 310-392-3804. FAX: 310-399-6739. Web Site: www.smpl.org. *Branch Mgr*, Celia Carroll; E-Mail: ccarroll@pen.ci.santa-monica.ca.us; *Admin Assoc*, Rachel Foyt; Tel: 310-458-8608, Fax: 310-694-8951, E-Mail: rachel-foyt@santa-monica.org; Staff 4 (MLS 1, Non-MLS 3)
Library Holdings: Bk Vols 18,910
Automation Activity & Vendor Info: (Circulation) SIRSI
Database Vendor: GaleNet, IAC - Info Trac, IAC - SearchBank, OCLC - First Search
Friends of the Library Group

M SANTA MONICA-UCLA MEDICAL CENTER LIBRARY, 1250 16th St, 90404. SAN 329-9929. Tel: 310-319-4000, Ext 93055. FAX: 310-319-4889. *Librn*, Lenore F Orfirer; E-Mail: lorfirer@mednet.ucla.edu; Staff 1 (MLS 1)
Library Holdings: Bk Vols 1,700; Per Subs 175
Subject Interests: Clin med, Health sci

M SHACKNOVE - SAINT JOHN'S MEDICAL STAFF LIBRARY, (Formerly Saint John's Hospital & Health Center), 2200 Santa Monica Blvd, 90404. SAN 301-5920. Tel: 310-582-7141. FAX: 310-582-7353. *Librn*, John Wright; Staff 1 (Non-MLS 1)
Founded 1952
Library Holdings: Bk Vols 100
Subject Interests: Allied health, Medicine, Nursing
Partic in Medline

M SPECIALTY LABORATORIES INC LIBRARY,* 2211 Michigan Ave, 90404. SAN 375-6696. Tel: 310-828-6543. FAX: 310-828-5173.
Library Holdings: Bk Vols 140; Bk Titles 100; Per Subs 70
Subject Interests: Immunology
Partic in National Network Of Libraries Of Medicine - South Central Region

SANTA PAULA

P BLANCHARD-SANTA PAULA PUBLIC LIBRARY DISTRICT, (BSP), Blanchard Community Library, 119 N Eighth St, 93060-2784. SAN 301-5963. Tel: 805-525-3615. FAX: 805-933-2324. E-Mail: irockman@rain.org, spblref@rain.org. Web Site: www.rain.org/~stapaula. *Coll Develop, Librn*, Daniel O Robles; E-Mail: drobles@rain.org; *Publ Servs, Ref*, Paula Clarke; *Ch Servs, YA Servs*, Ilene Gavenman; *ILL*, Penny Sjolund; Tel: 805-525-2394; Staff 23 (MLS 2, Non-MLS 21)
Founded 1909. Pop 27,100; Circ 60,984
Jul 2000-Jun 2001 Income $510,464, State $45,657, County $453,307, Locally Generated Income $11,500. Mats Exp $510,464, Books $22,000, Per/Ser (Incl. Access Fees) $2,600, AV Equip $6,000, Electronic Ref Mat (Incl. Access Fees) $2,500. Sal $311,655 (Prof $72,000)
Library Holdings: Bk Vols 69,214; Bk Titles 57,447; Per Subs 113; High Interest/Low Vocabulary Bk Vols 512; Spec Interest Per Sub 17
Subject Interests: California, Genealogy, Local authors, Local history
Special Collections: Hispanic Bilingual (Preciado Coll)
Automation Activity & Vendor Info: (Acquisitions) epixtech, inc.; (Cataloging) epixtech, inc.; (Circulation) epixtech, inc.; (ILL) epixtech, inc.; (OPAC) epixtech, inc.
Database Vendor: IAC - Info Trac
Function: ILL available, Outside services via phone, cable & mail, Some telephone reference
Mem of Black Gold Cooperative Library System
Partic in Black Gold Coop
Special Services for the Blind - Bks on tape
Open Mon-Thurs & Sat
Friends of the Library Group

C THOMAS AQUINAS COLLEGE, Saint Bernardine Library, 10000 N Ojai Rd, 93060-9980. SAN 321-4621. Tel: 805-525-4417. Toll Free Tel: 800-634-9797. FAX: 805-525-0620. E-Mail: admissions@thomasaquinas.edu. Web Site: www.thomasaquinas.edu. *Librn*, V A Jatulis
Founded 1971. Enrl 277; Fac 35; Highest Degree: Bachelor
Library Holdings: Bk Vols 47,000; Per Subs 50
Subject Interests: Philosophy, Theology
Restriction: Open to faculty, students & qualified researchers

SANTA ROSA

S AGILENT TECHNOLOGIES, Research Library, 1400 Fountaingrove Pkwy, 95403. SAN 301-598X. Tel: 707-577-3500. FAX: 707-577-3579. *Librn*, Annette Brahms; Tel: 707-577-2893, E-Mail: annette_brahms@agilent.com; *Librn*, Marion Larsen; Tel: 707-577-3419, E-Mail: marion_larsen@agilent.com
Subject Interests: Electrical engineering

S MALEDICTA INTERNATIONAL RESEARCH CENTER FOR VERBAL AGGRESSION LIBRARY, PO Box 14123, 95402-6123. SAN 322-8975. Tel: 707-523-4761. FAX: 707-523-4761. Web Site: www.sonic.net/maledicta. *Librn*, Reinhold A Aman; E-Mail: aman@sonic.net
Founded 1965
Library Holdings: Bk Titles 4,500; Per Subs 10
Subject Interests: Censorship, Curses, Folklore, Humor, Insults, Lexicography, Slurs, Stereotypes, Verbal aggression
Publications: Maledicta Journal; Maledicta Monographs

P NORTH BAY COOPERATIVE LIBRARY SYSTEM,* 55 E St, 95404-4728. SAN 301-5998. Tel: 707-544-0142. FAX: 707-544-8411. E-Mail: annetnbc@sonic.net, refnbcls@sonic.net. Web Site: www.nbcls.org.; Staff 8 (MLS 4, Non-MLS 4)
Founded 1960. Pop 1,317,125
Jul 1999-Jun 2000 Income $674,478, State $223,647, Federal $2,000, Other $448,831. Mats Exp $2,710, Books $1,810, Per/Ser (Incl. Access Fees) $400. Sal $334,194
Publications: Directory of Libraries; Newsletter; Union List of Automobile Manuals; Union List of Government Docs; Union List of Newspapers; Union List of Periodicals
Member Libraries: Benicia Public Library; Cloverdale Regional Library; College Of Marin Library; Forestville Library; Guerneville Regional Library; Healdsburg Regional Library; Lake County Library; Marin County Free Library; Marin County Free Library; Mendocino County Library; Mill Valley Public Library; Napa City-County Library; Napa Valley College Library; Northwest Regional Library; Pacific Union College; Petaluma Regional Library; Richmond Public Library; Rohnert Park-Cotati Regional Library; Saint Helena Public Library; San Anselmo Public Library; San Rafael Public Library; Santa Rosa Junior College; Sausalito Public Library; Sebastopol Regional Library; Solano County Library; Sonoma County

Library; Sonoma State University Library; Sonoma Valley Regional Library; United States Air Force
Partic in OCLC Online Computer Library Center, Inc; RLIN

S THE PRESS DEMOCRAT, News Research Center, PO Box 910, 95402. SAN 325-0512. Tel: 707-526-8520. FAX: 707-521-5411. E-Mail: library@pressdemo.com. Web Site: www.pressdemo.com. *Actg Dir, Ref*, Vonnie Matthews; E-Mail: vonnie@pressdemo.com; *Ref, Res*, Michelle Van Hoeck; E-Mail: mvanhoeck@pressdemo.com; *Res*, Teresa Meikle; E-Mail: tmeikle@pressdemo.com; Staff 5 (MLS 3, Non-MLS 2)
Founded 1950
Subject Interests: Local history
Special Collections: Glossy Photographs (In-house Photography Coll); Newspaper Clippings (Subject & Biographical Info Coll); Rare Local Photographs
Open Tues & Fri 1-5

J SANTA ROSA JUNIOR COLLEGE, Bernard C Plover Library, 1501 Mendocino Ave, 95401. SAN 301-6005. Tel: 707-527-4261 (Media Servs), 707-527-4391. Interlibrary Loan Service Tel: 707-527-4554. FAX: 707-527-4545. Web Site: www.santarosa.edu/library. *Actg Dir*, Will Baty; *AV*, Russ Bowden; *Bibliog Instr, Ref*, Marjorie Grossman; *Circ*, Joseph Friedman; *ILL*, JoAnne Black; *Ref*, Liz Tynan; *Ref*, Linda Wilson; *Tech Servs*, Paula Burkes; Staff 6 (MLS 6)
Founded 1918
Library Holdings: Bk Vols 101,500; Per Subs 610
Subject Interests: Computer science, Dentistry, Horticulture, Nutrition, Patents, Theater
Mem of North Bay Cooperative Library System
Partic in Coop Libr Agency for Syst & Servs; OCLC Online Computer Library Center, Inc

GL SONOMA COUNTY LAW LIBRARY, Hall of Justice, Rm 213-J, 600 Administration Dr, 95403-2879. SAN 301-6013. Tel: 707-565-2668. FAX: 707-565-1126. Web Site: www.sonomacountylawlibrary.org. *Librn*, Marilyn Josi
Founded 1891
Library Holdings: Bk Vols 30,000
Publications: List of Holdings; Union List of Legal Periodicals in Sonoma County (published infrequently)

P SONOMA COUNTY LIBRARY, Third & E Sts, 95404-4400. SAN 335-0401. Tel: 707-545-0831. TDD: 707-575-1206. FAX: 707-575-0437. Web Site: www.sonomalibrary.org. *Dir*, Roger Pearson; E-Mail: rpearson@sonoma.lib.ca.us; *Asst Dir*, Molly E McDermott; *Tech Servs*, Jim Rosaschi; *Ch Servs*, Patricia Lewis; *Ad Servs*, Nancy Persons; *Publ Servs*, Virginia McLaren; *Cat*, Joan E Seim; Staff 124 (MLS 47, Non-MLS 77)
Founded 1965. Pop 453,092; Circ 2,301,931
Jul 1999-Jun 2000 Income (Main Library and Branch Library) $9,459,911, State $830,903, Federal $26,089, County $7,371,232, Locally Generated Income $1,231,687. Mats Exp $1,170,107, Books $640,844, Per/Ser (Incl. Access Fees) $179,652, Micro $29,798, AV Equip $34,960, Other Print Mats $46,536, Electronic Ref Mat (Incl. Access Fees) $238,317. Sal $5,153,325 (Prof $2,616,183)
Library Holdings: Bk Vols 666,201; Per Subs 1,539
Special Collections: County; Sonoma County History; Sonoma County Wine Library
Automation Activity & Vendor Info: (Acquisitions) epixtech, inc.; (Cataloging) epixtech, inc.; (Circulation) epixtech, inc.; (OPAC) epixtech, inc.; (Serials) epixtech, inc.
Database Vendor: OCLC - First Search
Mem of North Bay Cooperative Library System
Special Services for the Deaf - TDD
Friends of the Library Group
Branches: 13
CENTRAL, Third & E Sts, 95404. SAN 376-8988. Tel: 707-545-0831. FAX: 707-575-0437. *Mgr*, Virginia McLaren
Friends of the Library Group
CLOVERDALE REGIONAL, 401 N Cloverdale Blvd, Cloverdale, 95425-3322. SAN 376-8996. Tel: 707-894-5271. FAX: 707-894-1861. Web Site: www.sonoma.lib.ca.us. *Mgr*, Debbie Hand; E-Mail: deb@sonoma.lib.ca.us; Staff 5 (MLS 2, Non-MLS 3)
Library Holdings: Bk Vols 26,000; Bk Titles 17,000; Per Subs 46
Friends of the Library Group
FORESTVILLE, 107 First St, PO Box 1781, Forestville, 95436. SAN 376-9097. Tel: 707-887-7654.
Friends of the Library Group
GUERNEVILLE REGIONAL, 14107 Armstrong Woods Rd, Guerneville, 95446. SAN 376-9003. Tel: 707-869-9004. FAX: 707-869-1267. *Mgr*, Sue Plummer
Friends of the Library Group
HEALDSBURG REGIONAL, Piper & Center Sts, Healdsburg, 95448. SAN 376-9011. Tel: 707-433-3772. Circulation Tel: 707-433-3772, Ext 7. Reference Tel: 707-433-3772, Ext 5. FAX: 707-433-7946. *Mgr*, Catherine Bassett; Staff 7 (MLS 3, Non-MLS 4)
Library Holdings: Bk Vols 41,164
Special Collections: Sonoma County Wine Library
Friends of the Library Group
OCCIDENTAL, 73 Main St, PO Box 703, Occidental, 95465. SAN 376-9100. Tel: 707-874-3080.
Friends of the Library Group
PETALUMA REGIONAL, 100 Fairgrounds Dr, Petaluma, 94952. SAN 376-902X. Tel: 707-763-9801. FAX: 707-763-0288. *Mgr*, Kiyo Okazaki
Friends of the Library Group
ROHNERT PART-COTATI REGIONAL, 6600 Hunter Dr, Rohnert, 94928. SAN 376-9038. Tel: 707-584-9121. FAX: 707-584-8561. *Mgr*, Kathy Dennison
Library Holdings: Bk Vols 55,000; Bk Titles 32,000; Per Subs 50
Friends of the Library Group
SANTA ROSA: NORTHWEST REGIONAL, 150 Coddington Ctr, 95401. SAN 376-9046. Tel: 707-546-2265. FAX: 707-546-2510. *Mgr*, Beverly Dalum
Friends of the Library Group
SANTA ROSA: RINCON VALLEY REGIONAL, 6959 Montecito Blvd, 95409. SAN 376-9054. Tel: 707-537-0162. FAX: 707-537-0174. *Mgr*, Jain Erla
Friends of the Library Group
SEBASTOPOL REGIONAL, 7140 Bodega Ave, Sebastopol, 95472. SAN 376-9062. Tel: 707-823-7691. FAX: 707-823-7172. *Mgr*, Del Guidinger
Jul 1999-Jun 2000 Mats Exp Books $70,646
Library Holdings: Bk Titles 49,278; Per Subs 104
Friends of the Library Group
SONOMA VALLEY REGIONAL, 755 W Napa St, Sonoma, 95476. SAN 376-9070. Tel: 707-996-5217. FAX: 707-996-5918. *Mgr*, Stephan Buffy
Friends of the Library Group
WINDSOR REGIONAL, 9291 Old Redwood Hwy, No 100, Windsor, 95492. SAN 376-9089. Tel: 707-838-1020. FAX: 707-838-8329. *Mgr*, Anne Marie Murphy; Tel: 707-838-1020, Ext 11, E-Mail: annem@sonoma.lib.ca.us; Staff 6 (MLS 2, Non-MLS 4)
Founded 1996
Library Holdings: Bk Vols 25,757
Friends of the Library Group

M SUTTER MEDICAL CENTER OF SANTA ROSA, Medical Library, 3325 Chanate Rd, 95404-1794. SAN 301-5971. Tel: 707-576-4675. FAX: 707-573-5196. *Librn*, Joan Chilton; E-Mail: chiltonj@sutterhealth.org
1999-2000 Mats Exp $53,927, Books $13,041, Per/Ser (Incl. Access Fees) $33,032. Sal $66,000
Library Holdings: Bk Titles 3,000; Per Subs 150
Subject Interests: History of medicine
Partic in Medlars; N Bay Health Sci Libr Consortium; Northern California & Nevada Medical Library Group; Pacific SW Regional Libr Syst

SANTA YNEZ

S SANTA YNEZ VALLEY HISTORICAL SOCIETY, Ellen Gleason Library, 3596 Sagunto, 93460. (Mail add: PO Box 181, 93460), SAN 328-3364. Tel: 805-688-7889. FAX: 805-688-1109. *Pres*, Bill Luton
Library Holdings: Bk Titles 1,500
Subject Interests: Local history
Open Tues-Thurs 10am-4pm & Fri-Sun 1-4pm

SANTEE

J GROSSMONT HEALTH OCCUPATIONS CENTER LIBRARY,* 9368 Oakbourne Rd, 92071-2314. SAN 371-9138. Tel: 619-596-3676. FAX: 619-579-4779. *Librn*, Kathleen A Johnson; E-Mail: johnsonk@grossmont.k12.ca.us
Founded 1970. Enrl 2,200; Fac 50
Library Holdings: Bk Titles 1,100; Per Subs 30
Subject Interests: Medicine

S INSTITUTE FOR CREATION RESEARCH LIBRARY, 10946 Woodside Ave N, 92071. (Mail add: PO Box 2667, 92071), SAN 326-4580. Tel: 619-448-0900, Ext 6045. FAX: 619-448-3469. Web Site: www.icr.org. *Librn*, Richard LaHaye; E-Mail: dlahaye@icr.org
Library Holdings: Bk Vols 13,143; Bk Titles 11,269; Per Subs 466; Spec Interest Per Sub 568
Special Collections: Religion (Harald F J Ellingson Coll)

SARATOGA

J WEST VALLEY COMMUNITY COLLEGE LIBRARY,* 14000 Fruitvale Ave, 95070-5698. SAN 301-6021. Tel: 408-741-2140. FAX: 408-741-2134. Web Site: www.wvmccd.cc.ca.us/wvc/pat. *Dean*, Dave Fishbaugh; E-Mail: dave_fishbaugh@wvmccd.cc.ca.us; *Acq*, Janice Bonnet; *Automation Syst Coordr*, Bill Proudfoot; *Circ, Tech Servs*, Betsy Sandford; *Publ Servs*, Yanghee Kim; Staff 15 (MLS 6, Non-MLS 9)
Founded 1964. Enrl 11,478; Fac 469
Library Holdings: Bk Vols 93,484; Per Subs 400
Automation Activity & Vendor Info: (Circulation) Innovative Interfaces

Inc.
Partic in Dialog Corporation; RLIN
Special Services for the Deaf - Captioned media; High interest/low vocabulary books

SAUSALITO

S INSTITUTE OF NOETIC SCIENCES LIBRARY,* 475 Gate Five Rd, Ste 300, 94965. SAN 327-5590. Tel: 415-331-5650, Ext 225. FAX: 415-331-5673. *Librn*, Nola Lewis
Library Holdings: Bk Vols 7,000
Restriction: Staff use only

P SAUSALITO PUBLIC LIBRARY, 420 Litho St, 94965-1933. SAN 301-603X. Tel: 415-289-4121. FAX: 415-331-7943. Web Site: www.ci.sausalito.ca.us. *Coll Develop, Librn*, Mary Richardson; *Librn*, Penny Greene; Staff 3 (MLS 3)
Founded 1907. Pop 7,825; Circ 109,920
Jul 1999-Jun 2000 Income $493,092. Mats Exp $100,200, Books $83,000, Per/Ser (Incl. Access Fees) $10,000, Presv $1,200, AV Equip $6,000. Sal $286,791
Library Holdings: Bk Vols 67,479; Per Subs 180
Subject Interests: Boating, Boats, Local history
Automation Activity & Vendor Info: (Acquisitions) Innovative Interfaces Inc.; (Cataloging) Brodart; (Circulation) Innovative Interfaces Inc.; (OPAC) Innovative Interfaces Inc.
Database Vendor: Innovative Interfaces INN - View
Mem of North Bay Cooperative Library System
Partic in Marynet
Friends of the Library Group

SCOTTS VALLEY

S ASBESTOS VICTIMS OF AMERICA LIBRARY,* PO Box 66594, 95067. SAN 326-2650. Tel: 831-661-0282. FAX: 831-661-0282. *Dir*, Heather Bechtel
Founded 1981
Library Holdings: Bk Vols 100
Subject Interests: Toxicology
Partic in AFL-CIO; Am Trial Lawyers Asn; Calif Trial Lawyers Asn; Community Colleges in US; EPA

CR BETHANY COLLEGE, Wilson Library, 800 Bethany Dr, 95066-2898. SAN 301-6048. Tel: 831-438-3800, Ext 1450. FAX: 831-438-4517. E-Mail: liboff@mail.bethany.edu. *Dir*, Arnold McLellan
Founded 1919. Circ 10,858; Enrl 600; Fac 32; Highest Degree: Master
Library Holdings: Bk Vols 62,000; Bk Titles 51,000; Per Subs 386
Publications: Libr Handbook
Partic in Coop Libr Agency for Syst & Servs

S BORLAND INTERNATIONAL, Technical Library,* 100 Borland Way, 95066-3249. SAN 377-2551. Tel: 831-431-4218. FAX: 831-431-4102. *Librn*, Jane Bomberger
Library Holdings: Bk Vols 6,000; Bk Titles 5,000; Per Subs 55

SEASIDE

C CALIFORNIA STATE UNIVERSITY, Monterey Bay Library, 100 Campus Ctr, Bldg 12, 93955-8001. SAN 378-2530. Tel: 831-582-3733. FAX: 831-582-3354. E-Mail: library_circulation@monterey.edu. Web Site: library.monterey.edu. *Dir*, Bill Robnett; Tel: 831-582-4448, E-Mail: bill_robnett@monterey.edu; *Bibliog Instr*, Pam Baker; Tel: 831-582-3887, E-Mail: pam_baker@monterey.edu; *Coll Develop*, Eddy Hogan; Tel: 831-582-3794, E-Mail: eddy_hogan@monterey.edu; *Online Servs*, Kathlene Hanson; Tel: 831-582-3883, E-Mail: kathlene_hanson@monterey.edu; *Reader Servs*, Janie B Silveria; Tel: 831-582-3727, E-Mail: janie_silveria@monterey.edu; *Tech Servs*, Lisa Rowlison; Tel: 831-582-4642, E-Mail: lisa_rowlison@monterey.edu; *Tech Coordr*, Steve Watkins; Tel: 831-582-3793, E-Mail: steve_watkins@monterey.edu; Staff 14 (MLS 7, Non-MLS 7)
Founded 1995. Highest Degree: Master
Jul 1999-Jun 2000 Income Parent Institution $1,398,596. Mats Exp $271,634, Books $88,135, Per/Ser (Incl. Access Fees) $55,556, Presv $17,076, Electronic Ref Mat (Incl. Access Fees) $110,867. Sal $736,501 (Prof $508,425)
Library Holdings: Bk Vols 48,947; Bk Titles 44,552; Per Subs 363
Special Collections: Environmental Clean-up (Ford Ord Reuse Coll)
Automation Activity & Vendor Info: (Acquisitions) Endeavor; (Cataloging) Endeavor; (Circulation) Endeavor; (Serials) Endeavor
Database Vendor: Ebsco - EbscoHost, GaleNet, IAC - Info Trac, Lexis-Nexis, OCLC - First Search, ProQuest, Silverplatter Information Inc.
Member Libraries: California Maritime Academy Library; California Polytechnic State University; California State University, Fresno; California State University, Long Beach; San Francisco State University; San Jose State University
Friends of the Library Group

SEBASTOPOL

P SEBASTOPOL REGIONAL LIBRARY,* 7140 Bodega Ave, 95472-3712. SAN 376-3951. Tel: 707-823-7691. FAX: 707-823-7172. *Mgr*, Del Guidinger
Pop 50,000
Jul 1999-Jun 2000 Mats Exp Books $70,646
Library Holdings: Bk Titles 49,278; Per Subs 104
Mem of North Bay Cooperative Library System
Friends of the Library Group

SEPULVEDA

GM DEPARTMENT OF VETERANS AFFAIRS, Library Service (142D),* 16111 Plummer St, 91343. SAN 301-6072. Tel: 818-891-7711, Ext 9253. FAX: 818-895-9553. E-Mail: casep@forum.va.gov.
Founded 1955
Library Holdings: Bk Vols 7,000; Per Subs 450

SIERRA MADRE

P SIERRA MADRE PUBLIC LIBRARY,* 440 W Sierra Madre Blvd, 91024-2399. SAN 301-6102. Tel: 626-355-7186. FAX: 626-355-6218. Web Site: www.sierramadre.lib.ca.us. *Dir*, Toni Gollands Buckner
Founded 1887. Pop 10,850
Library Holdings: Bk Titles 50,000; Per Subs 182
Mem of Metropolitan Cooperative Library System
Friends of the Library Group

SIGNAL HILL

P SIGNAL HILL PUBLIC LIBRARY,* 1770 E Hill St, 90806. SAN 301-6110. Tel: 562-989-7323. FAX: 562-989-7392. E-Mail: sigpl@ix.netcom.com. *Dir*, Carole A Molloy; *Librn*, Pamela May
Founded 1928. Pop 8,775; Circ 29,499
Library Holdings: Bk Vols 22,000; Per Subs 70
Subject Interests: Local history
Mem of Metropolitan Cooperative Library System
Partic in Metropolitan Cooperative Library System
Friends of the Library Group

SIMI VALLEY

S MEDIA CENTER LIBRARY, 101 W Cochran Ave, 93065. SAN 300-7944. Tel: 805-955-7657. FAX: 805-955-7703. Web Site: www.vop.com. *Librn*, Eldyn Karr
Library Holdings: Bk Titles 7,540
Subject Interests: Religion, Theology

S NATIONAL ARCHIVES & RECORDS ADMINISTRATION, Ronald Reagan Presidential Library & Museum, 40 Presidential Dr, 93065. SAN 373-0956. Tel: 805-522-8444. Toll Free Tel: 800-410-8354. FAX: 805-522-9621. E-Mail: library@reagan.nara.gov. Web Site: www.reagan.utexas.edu. *Publ Servs*, Lynda Schuler; *Archivist, Librn*, Diane Barrie; Tel: 800-410-8354, Ext 2039, E-Mail: diane.barrie@reagan.nara.gov; Staff 23 (MLS 11, Non-MLS 12)
Founded 1991
Library Holdings: Bk Vols 2,700; Bk Titles 2,000; Per Subs 12
Subject Interests: American history, Polit hist of the US, Presidents (US)
Special Collections: American Presidency, Ronald Reagan; Politics & Government, 1964-1989
Automation Activity & Vendor Info: (Cataloging) Inmagic, Inc.
Function: Archival collection
Manuscript depository
Friends of the Library Group

S SIMI VALLEY HISTORICAL SOCIETY, Archives,* 137 Strathearn Pl, PO Box 351, 93065. SAN 370-4238. Tel: 805-526-6453. FAX: 805-526-6462. *Dir*, Patricia Havens
Library Holdings: Bk Vols 1,200
Open Tues-Fri 9-1, tour hours: Wed 1:00, Sat & Sun 1-4

M SIMI VALLEY HOSPITAL & HEALTH CARES SERVICES, Medical Library, 2975 N Sycamore Dr, 93065. SAN 320-1694. Tel: 805-955-6900. FAX: 805-955-6063.
Founded 1965
Library Holdings: Bk Titles 480; Per Subs 30
Subject Interests: Medicine
Restriction: Medical staff only
Function: Reference only

SONOMA

P SONOMA VALLEY REGIONAL LIBRARY,* 755 W Napa St, 95476-6412. SAN 376-3943. Tel: 707-996-5217. FAX: 707-996-5918. Web Site: www.sonoma.lib.ca.us. *Mgr*, Stephan Buffy; E-Mail: stephan@

sonoma.lib.ca.us
Jul 1998-Jun 1999 Income $340,000. Mats Exp $42,384. Sal $223,000
Library Holdings: Bk Titles 53,000; Per Subs 20
Mem of North Bay Cooperative Library System
Friends of the Library Group

SONORA

J COLUMBIA COLLEGE LIBRARY,* 11600 Columbia College Dr, 95370-8581. SAN 300-6794. Tel: 209-588-5118. Interlibrary Loan Service Tel: 209-588-5119. FAX: 209-588-5121. Web Site: columbia.yosmite.cc.ca.us. *Dir*, Larry R Steuben; *Ser*, Adele Wikner; *Circ, ILL*, Linn Greeley; *Media Spec*, Wendy Link; *Tech Servs*, Nancy Brooks; Staff 1 (MLS 1)
Founded 1968. Enrl 3,656; Fac 168
Subject Interests: Forestry
Special Collections: History of the Mother Lode, bk, per, micro, maps, ephemera
Publications: Mother Lode History (bibliography)
Partic in Central Association Of Libraries; OCLC Online Computer Library Center, Inc

P TUOLUMNE COUNTY FREE LIBRARY,* 480 Greenley Rd, 95370-5956. SAN 301-6145. Tel: 209-533-5507. FAX: 209-533-0936. *Librn*, Constance T Corcoran; *ILL*, Kathy Meyer; *Ch Servs*, Lorraine Vogt; *Tech Servs*, Margaret Durgin; Staff 9 (MLS 3, Non-MLS 6)
Founded 1917. Pop 53,100; Circ 150,231
Jul 1998-Jun 1999 Income (Main Library and Branch Library) $610,598, State $45,553, County $553,045, Locally Generated Income $12,000. Mats Exp $72,399, Books $66,199, Per/Ser (Incl. Access Fees) $4,000, Presv $500, Micro $500, Electronic Ref Mat (Incl. Access Fees) $1,200. Sal $360,379
Library Holdings: Bk Vols 82,096; Bk Titles 71,000; Per Subs 135
Subject Interests: Mining
Special Collections: Tuolumne County History, tapes
Automation Activity & Vendor Info: (Cataloging) epixtech, inc.; (Circulation) epixtech, inc.; (OPAC) epixtech, inc.
Database Vendor: epixtech, inc.
Mem of 49-99 Cooperative Library System
Partic in OCLC Online Computer Library Center, Inc
Friends of the Library Group
Branches: 5
GROVELAND BRANCH, Community Hall, Groveland, 95321. (Mail add: PO Box 1275, Groveland, 95321-1275), Tel: 209-962-6144. *In Charge*, Donna Manship
Library Holdings: Bk Vols 5,700; Per Subs 10
Automation Activity & Vendor Info: (Circulation) epixtech, inc.
MIWUK BRANCH, Sierra Rd, Miwuk Village, 95346. (Mail add: PO Box 446, Miwuk Village, 95346-0446), Tel: 209-586-6251. *In Charge*, Janet Brady
Library Holdings: Bk Vols 900
PINECREST BRANCH, Old Firehouse Rd, Pinecrest, 95364. (Mail add: PO Box 1038, Pinecrest, 95364-1038), Tel: 209-965-4225. *In Charge*, Alice Smith
Library Holdings: Bk Vols 2,300
Automation Activity & Vendor Info: (Circulation) epixtech, inc.
TUOLUMNE CITY BRANCH, Tuolumne Square, 18880 Birch St, Tuolumne, 95379. (Mail add: PO Box 1077, Tuolumne, 95379-1077), Tel: 209-928-3612. *In Charge*, Trisha Davis
Library Holdings: Bk Vols 2,200
Automation Activity & Vendor Info: (Circulation) epixtech, inc.
TWAIN HARTE BRANCH, 18752 Joaquin Gully Rd, Twain Harte, 95383. (Mail add: PO Box 666, Twain Harte, 95383-0666), Tel: 209-586-4501. *In Charge*, Sharon Alomia
Library Holdings: Bk Vols 3,800; Per Subs 10
Automation Activity & Vendor Info: (Circulation) epixtech, inc.

S TUOLUMNE COUNTY GENEALOGICAL SOCIETY LIBRARY,* 158 W Bradford St, PO Box 3956, 95370. SAN 322-6956. Tel: 209-532-1317. *Coordr*, Louise Leedy; *Asst Librn*, Anne Williams; *Asst Librn*, Dythe-Mary Egleston
Founded 1979
Jun 1997-May 1998 Income $1,600, Locally Generated Income $400. Mats Exp $1,100, Books $500, Per/Ser (Incl. Access Fees) $100, Micro $500
Library Holdings: Bk Vols 1,200; Per Subs 10
Special Collections: Tuolumne County, California Cemeteries, 1850-1920 Census on micro, Church, School & Voter Registers, Local Family Histories, Obituaries, Vital Records on micro
Publications: 1890 Great Register Tuolumne Country; CH Burden Undertaking Co Records 1890-1943; Gold Digger (newsletter); Golden Roots; Toulumne County Marriages 1875-1910
Housed in the County Museum & shared with the Historical Society

GL TUOLUMNE COUNTY LAW LIBRARY, 68 N Washington St, 95370. SAN 301-6153. Tel: 209-536-0308. *Librn*, David Holstrom
Library Holdings: Bk Vols 18,934; Bk Titles 17,000
Restriction: Not a lending library, Open to public for reference only
Function: Research library

SOUTH EL MONTE

S LEE PHARMACEUTICALS, Polymer Science Library,* 1434 Santa Anita Ave, PO Box 3638, 91733. SAN 301-6161. Tel: 626-442-3141. FAX: 626-443-8745.
Founded 1966
Library Holdings: Bk Titles 2,000; Per Subs 100
Subject Interests: Chemical engineering, Chemistry, Dentistry, Environmental engineering, Environmental law
Special Collections: Polymer Science
Restriction: Staff use only

SOUTH LAKE TAHOE

J LAKE TAHOE COMMUNITY COLLEGE, Library-Media Services,* One College Dr, 96150. SAN 301-617X. Tel: 530-541-4660, Ext 232. FAX: 530-541-7852. Web Site: www.ltcc.cc.ca.us. *Librn*, William F Scoble; E-Mail: scoble@ltcc.cc.ca.us
Founded 1976
Library Holdings: Bk Titles 40,000; Per Subs 187
Mem of Mountain-Valley Library System

S LAKE TAHOE HISTORICAL SOCIETY, Museum Library, 3058 Hwy 50, PO Box 404, 96156. SAN 374-5694. Tel: 530-541-5458.
Library Holdings: Bk Titles 50

SOUTH PASADENA

P SOUTH PASADENA PUBLIC LIBRARY, (SPPL), 1100 Oxley St, 91030-3198. SAN 301-6188. Tel: 626-403-7330. Circulation Tel: 626-403-7340. Reference Tel: 626-403-7350. FAX: 626-403-7331. *Dir*, Terri Maguire; E-Mail: tmaguire@ci.south-pasadena.ca.us; *Ad Servs*, Ellen Fusco; *Ch Servs*, Maida Wong; *Tech Servs*, Barbara Posner; Staff 31 (MLS 7, Non-MLS 24)
Founded 1895. Pop 26,000; Circ 351,141
Jul 2000-Jun 2001 Income City $1,169,797. Mats Exp $125,500, Books $107,000, Presv $2,500, AV Equip $8,000, Electronic Ref Mat (Incl. Access Fees) $8,000. Sal $719,759
Library Holdings: Bk Vols 117,000; Per Subs 400
Subject Interests: Art, Drama, Local history
Special Collections: Plays
Automation Activity & Vendor Info: (Cataloging) Inlex; (Circulation) Inlex; (OPAC) Inlex
Database Vendor: DRA, Ebsco - EbscoHost, GaleNet, IAC - Info Trac
Publications: South Pasadena: A Centennial History, 1888-1988; The South Pasadena Public Library: A History 1895-1982
Function: ILL available
Mem of Metropolitan Cooperative Library System
Partic in OCLC Online Computer Library Center, Inc
Friends of the Library Group

SOUTH SAN FRANCISCO

M KAISER PERMANENTE MEDICAL CENTER LIBRARY, 1200 El Camino Real, 94080. SAN 320-1708. Tel: 650-742-2540. FAX: 650-742-2239. *Librn*, Geri Bodeker; E-Mail: geri.bodeker@kp.org
Founded 1973
Library Holdings: Bk Vols 3,100; Bk Titles 1,000; Per Subs 185
Subject Interests: Health sciences, Medicine, Nursing

P SOUTH SAN FRANCISCO PUBLIC LIBRARY,* 840 W Orange Ave, 94080-3124. SAN 335-0495. Tel: 650-829-3872. Interlibrary Loan Service Tel: 650-829-3862. FAX: 650-829-3865. E-Mail: ssfpladm@pls.lib.ca.us. Web Site: www.ci.ssf.ca.us, www.plsinfo.org. *Dir*, Valerie Sommer; *Coll Develop, Ref*, Banny Rucker; Staff 57 (MLS 12, Non-MLS 45)
Founded 1916. Pop 59,200; Circ 395,246
Jul 1996-Jun 1997 Income $2,302,336, State $178,176, City $1,928,036, Federal $13,135, Locally Generated Income $116,439. Mats Exp $185,118, Books $150,318, Per/Ser (Incl. Access Fees) $16,000, Presv $1,000, Micro $2,800. Sal $1,046,796
Library Holdings: Bk Vols 180,000; Per Subs 400
Subject Interests: Consumer health, Local history, Medicine
Automation Activity & Vendor Info: (Circulation) epixtech, inc.
Mem of Peninsula Library System
Friends of the Library Group
Branches: 1
GRAND AVENUE, 306 Walnut Ave, 94080-2700. SAN 335-0525. Tel: 650-877-8530. FAX: 650-829-6615. Web Site: www.ci.ssf.ca.us, www.plsinfo.org. *Librn*, Banny Rucker
Library Holdings: Bk Vols 48,040
Friends of the Library Group

STANFORD

S CARNEGIE INSTITUTION OF WASHINGTON, Department of Plant Biology Library,* 260 Panama St, 94305. SAN 370-9612. Tel: 650-325-1521, Ext 203. FAX: 650-325-6857. *Dir*, Chris Somerville
Library Holdings: Bk Vols 5,000
Publications: Newsletter

S CENTER FOR ADVANCED STUDY IN THE BEHAVIORAL SCIENCES LIBRARY, 75 Alta Rd, 94305. SAN 301-6196. Tel: 650-321-2052. FAX: 650-321-1192. *Librn*, Cynthia Ziegler; E-Mail: cynthia@casbs.stanford.edu; Staff 2 (MLS 1, Non-MLS 1)
Founded 1954
Library Holdings: Bk Vols 7,000; Per Subs 290
Subject Interests: Anthropology, History, Philosophy, Political science, Psychiatry, Sociology
Special Collections: Ralph Tyler Coll
Automation Activity & Vendor Info: (Cataloging) SIRSI; (Circulation) SIRSI; (Serials) SIRSI
Publications: Annual Reports; The Ralph W Tyler Collection, 1954-1979 & 1954-1994
Partic in Dialog Corporation; RLIN

C STANFORD UNIVERSITY LIBRARIES, Cecil H Green Library, 557 Escondido Mall, 94305-6004. SAN 335-055X. Tel: 650-723-9108. FAX: 650-725-6874. Web Site: www-sul.stanford.edu, www-sul.stanford.edu/. *Dir*, Michael A Keller; Tel: 650-723-5553. Subject Specialists: *Americana*, William McPheron; *German (Language)*, Henry Lowood; *Great Britain*, William McPheron; *Latin America*, Adan Griego; *Music*, Barbara Sawka; *Romance languages*, Mary Jane Parrine; *Slavic history and literature*, Wojciech Zalewski; Staff 94 (MLS 94)
Founded 1892. Enrl 14,002; Fac 1,408; Highest Degree: Doctorate
Library Holdings: Bk Vols 7,000,000; Per Subs 43,211
Subject Interests: Agricultural economics, Art and architecture, Business and management, Computer science, Education, History, Law, Literature, Marine biology, Mathematics, Medicine, Music, Natural science, Physics, Social sciences and issues, Technology
Special Collections: American; California (Borel Coll); Chicano Coll, mss; Children's Literature (Schofield Coll); Engineering Mechanics (Timoshenko Coll); English & American Literature of the 19th & 20th Centuries (Felton, Kline/Roethke & Starling Colls); Gunst Memorial Library (Book Arts), bks, mss; Hebraica & Judaica, bks & mss (Taube/Baron Coll.); History (Elmer E Robinson Coll); History of Science (Barchas, Brasch & Dudley Colls); Hopkins Transportation Library; Irish Literature, bks, mss (Healy Coll); Memorial Library of Music, bks, mss; Theatre Coll
Publications: Archive of Recorded Sound Recording Series; Bettini Catalog Reprints, micro; David Starr Jordan Papers 1861-1964, guide, micro; Dealers of Polish & Russian Books; Disasters; El Espectador, 1937-1960, micro; Francis B Loomis Papers 1835-1959, micro; Guide to Research on Martin Luther King Jr; Index to the Library of Congress Cataloging Service Bulletins, micro; John Steinbeck Catalogue; Prevention & Coping; Project South, micro; Scholars, Texts & Traditions; Slavic Colls; Stanford: A History; Strength of Art: Poets & Poetry in the Lives of Yvor Winters & Juliet Lewis; The Barchas Coll: The Making of Modern Science; User's Guide to Conservation of Library Materials; William R Shafter Papers 1862-1938, micro
Partic in Coop Libr Agency for Syst & Servs; Research Libraries Group, Inc
Friends of the Library Group
Departmental Libraries:
ART, 102 Cummings Art Bldg Main Bldg, 94305-2018. SAN 335-0614. Tel: 650-723-3408, 650-725-1037. FAX: 650-725-0140. *Librn*, Alex Ross
Library Holdings: Bk Vols 155,000; Per Subs 535
BRANNER EARTH SCIENCES, Mitchell Bldg 2nd flr, 94305. Tel: 650-723-2746, 650-725-1102. FAX: 650-725-2534. *Librn*, Charlotte Derksen
Library Holdings: Bk Vols 116,000; Per Subs 2,003
Subject Interests: Geochemistry, Geology, Petroleum engineering
Special Collections: Geothermal Engineering; State Geological Survey, open-file reports
ROBERT CROWN LAW LIBRARY, Stanford Law School, 559 Nathan Abbott Way, 94305-8612. SAN 335-1068. Tel: 650-723-2477. Interlibrary Loan Service Tel: 650-723-1932. FAX: 650-723-1933. E-Mail: reference@law.stanford.edu. Web Site: www.law.stanford.edu/library/. *Dir*, Lance E Dickson; Tel: 650-723-2721, Fax: 650-723-8657, E-Mail: ldickson@stanford.edu; *Tech Servs*, Regina Wallen; Tel: 650-723-2475, Fax: 650-723-8657, E-Mail: rwallen@stanford.edu; *Cat*, Kathleen Winzer; Tel: 650-723-0343, Fax: 650-723-8657, E-Mail: kwinzer@stanford.edu; *Ref*, Paul Lomio; Tel: 650-725-0804, E-Mail: plomio@stanford.edu; Staff 9 (MLS 8, Non-MLS 1)
Founded 1897. Enrl 631; Fac 40; Highest Degree: Doctorate
Sep 1998-Aug 1999 Income (Main Library Only) $2,929,497. Mats Exp $1,467,826. Sal $1,461,671
Library Holdings: Bk Vols 496,000; Bk Titles 185,000; Per Subs 7,619
Subject Interests: Law
Partic in OCLC Online Computer Library Center, Inc; RLIN
CUBBERLEY EDUCATION, Education Bldg Rm 202-205, 94305-3096. Tel: 650-723-2121. FAX: 650-725-1068. *Librn*, Barbara Celone
Library Holdings: Bk Vols 151,031; Per Subs 670
ENGINEERING, Terman Engineering Ctr 2nd flr, 94305. Tel: 650-723-0001. FAX: 650-725-1096. *Actg Librn*, Karen Greig
Library Holdings: Bk Vols 112,241; Per Subs 1,800
Special Collections: Timoshenko Coll
FALCONER BIOLOGY, Herrin Hall 3rd flr, 94305. Tel: 650-723-1528. FAX: 650-725-7712. *Librn*, Michael Newman
Library Holdings: Bk Vols 105,000; Per Subs 1,242
Publications: Falconer Biology Library Serials List
HOOVER INSTITUTION ON WAR, REVOLUTION & PEACE LIBRARY Tel: 650-723-1754, 650-723-3166. FAX: 650-723-1687. *Dir*, John Raisian; *Dep Dir*, Charles G Palm; *Head Librn*, Paul Thomas; *Head Librn*, Ramon Meyers
Founded 1919
Library Holdings: Bk Vols 1,557,879; Per Subs 3,339
Special Collections: E Asian Coll; Hoover Institution Archives; Western Language Coll
Publications: Guide to Hoover Institution Archives (Hoover Institution Press, 1980); The Library Catalogs of the Hoover Institution on War, Revolution & Peace (G K Hall, 1969-77); The Library of the Hoover Institution on War, Revolution & Peace (Hoover Institution Press, 1985)
Partic in RLIN
J HUGH JACKSON LIBRARY, Graduate School of Business, 350 Memorial Way, 94305-5016. SAN 335-1009. Tel: 650-723-2162. FAX: 650-723-0281. E-Mail: jackson.library@gsb.stanford.edu. Web Site: www-gsb.stanford.edu/services/library/. *Dir*, Karen Wilson; *Dir*, Shirley Hallblade; *Res*, Paul Reist; Staff 9 (MLS 9)
Founded 1933. Enrl 882; Fac 120; Highest Degree: Doctorate
Sep 1998-Aug 1999 Income $1,968,272. Sal $1,541,958 (Prof $670,465)
Library Holdings: Bk Vols 434,102; Per Subs 2,120
Subject Interests: Business and management, Economics
Special Collections: Pacific Northwest Economic History (Favre Coll)
Automation Activity & Vendor Info: (Circulation) CARL
Database Vendor: CARL
Publications: Selected Additions to the J Hugh Jackson Library (6 issues yearly)
Partic in Dialog Corporation

CM LANE MEDICAL LIBRARY, Stanford University Medical Ctr, 300 Pasteur Dr, Rm L109, 94305-5123. SAN 335-1033. Tel: 650-723-6831, 650-723-7198. FAX: 650-725-7471. E-Mail: laneinto@lanelib.stanford.edu. Web Site: www.med.stanford.edu/lane/. *Dir*, Tom Rindflesch; *Tech Servs*, Dick Miller; *Coll Develop*, Mary Buttner; Staff 17 (MLS 17)
Founded 1906. Highest Degree: Master
Library Holdings: Bk Vols 355,200; Per Subs 2,912
Special Collections: Fleischmann Learning; History of Medicine
Automation Activity & Vendor Info: (Acquisitions) CARL; (Cataloging) CARL; (Serials) CARL
Partic in National Network Of Libraries Of Medicine - South Central Region; Research Libraries Group, Inc
LINEAR ACCELERATOR CENTER LIBRARY, 2575 Sand Hill Rd, MS82, Menlo Park, 94025. (Mail add: PO Box 4349, MS82, 94309), Tel: 650-926-2411. Interlibrary Loan Service Tel: 650-926-2411. FAX: 650-926-4905. E-Mail: library@slac.stanford.edu. Web Site: www.slac.stanford.edu/library. *Dir Libr Serv*, Patricia Kreitz; Tel: 650-926-4385, E-Mail: pkreitz@slac.stanford.edu; *Librn*, Ann Redfield; Tel: 650-926-4396, E-Mail: redfield@slac.stanford.edu; *Ser*, Arsella Raman; *Publ Servs*, Molly M Moss; Tel: 650-926-4388, E-Mail: mmoss@slac.stanford.edu; *Archivist*, Jean Marie Deken; Tel: 650-926-3091, E-Mail: jmdeken@slac.stanford.edu; Staff 12 (MLS 3, Non-MLS 9)
Founded 1962
Oct 1998-Sep 1999 Income (Main Library Only) $1,000,000. Mats Exp $230,000
Library Holdings: Bk Vols 26,000; Per Subs 600
Special Collections: High-energy Physics Archives; SLAC Archives & History Office; SPIRES-HEP Databases
Function: Research library
Partic in Unix-Spires
MATHEMATICS & COMPUTER SCIENCES, Sloan Mathematics Ctr, Bldg 380 4th flr, 94305. Tel: 650-723-0864, 650-723-4672. FAX: 650-725-8998. *Librn*, Linda Yamamoto
Library Holdings: Bk Vols 63,000; Per Subs 800
Subject Interests: Computer science, Mathematics, Statistics
Special Collections: Technical Reports in Computer Science
J HENRY MEYER MEMORIAL Tel: 650-723-2434, 650-724-5600. FAX: 650-725-8495. *Librn*, Ed McGuigan
Library Holdings: Bk Vols 85,000
Special Collections: Foreign Language Instruction; Instructional Maps; Media Coll; Snowglobes
MILLER LIBRARY AT HOPKINS MARINE STATION, Pacific Grove, 93950-3094. SAN 371-1501. Tel: 831-655-6228, 831-655-6229. FAX: 831-373-7859. *Librn*, Joseph G Wible
Library Holdings: Bk Vols 45,000; Per Subs 352
MUSIC - BRAUN ARCHIVE OF RECORDED SOUND, Braun Music Ctr, 541 Lasuen Mall, 94305. Tel: 650-723-1211. FAX: 650-725-1145. *Librn*, Barbara Sawka
Library Holdings: Bk Vols 90,335; Per Subs 612

Special Collections: Archive of Recorded Sound
PHYSICS, Varian Bldg 3rd flr, 94305. Tel: 650-723-4342, 650-723-9577. FAX: 415-725-2079. *Librn*, Catherine Candee
Library Holdings: Bk Vols 55,000; Per Subs 521
STANFORD AUXILIARY, 691 Pampas Lane, 94305. Tel: 650-723-9201. FAX: 650-723-3048. *Mgr*, Paul Davis
Library Holdings: Bk Vols 737,098
SWAIN LIBRARY OF CHEMISTRY & CHEMICAL ENGINEERING, Organic Chemistry Bldg NW End, 94305. Tel: 650-723-9237. FAX: 650-725-2274. *Librn*, Grace Baysinger
Library Holdings: Bk Vols 54,000; Per Subs 619

STEWARTS POINT

S CALIFORNIA ENVIRONMENTAL RESEARCH GROUP LIBRARY,* PO Box 177, 95480-0177. SAN 378-1380. Tel: 916-341-7790. FAX: 916-341-7795. *Exec Dir*, Tom Sparks
Library Holdings: Bk Vols 2,500

STINSON BEACH

S POINT REYES BIRD OBSERVATORY LIBRARY, 4990 Shoreline Hwy, 94970. SAN 374-8472. Tel: 415-868-1221 Ext 13. FAX: 415-868-1946. *Librn*, Gareth Penn; E-Mail: gpenn@prbo.org; Staff 1 (MLS 1)
Founded 1965
Library Holdings: Bk Titles 3,500; Per Subs 150
Subject Interests: Ornithology
Restriction: Not open to public

STOCKTON

§S CALIFORNIA YOUTH AUTHORITY, N A Chaderjian Youth Correctional Facility Library, 7650 S Newcastle Rd, 95213. (Mail add: PO Box 213014, 95213-9014), Tel: 209-944-6444, Ext 6755. FAX: 209-944-6167. *Senior Librn*, Deborah Bennett
Library Holdings: Bk Vols 9,360; Per Subs 46

CALIFORNIA YOUTH AUTHORITY
S DEWITT NELSON YOUTH CORRECTIONAL FACILITY LIBRARY, 7650 S Newcastle Rd, 95213-9003. (Mail add: PO Box 213003, 95213-9003), Tel: 209-944-6168. FAX: 209-465-2968. *Senior Librn*, Gwen Chen
Library Holdings: Bk Vols 2,000; Per Subs 12
S KARL HOLTON YOUTH CORRECTIONAL FACILITY LIBRARY, 7650 S Newcastle Rd, 95213-9002. (Mail add: PO Box 213002, 95213-9002), Tel: 209-944-6373. FAX: 209-465-4164. *Librn*, Steve Thurm
Jul 1999-Jun 2000 Income $20,000
Library Holdings: Bk Vols 4,700; Per Subs 40
S O H CLOSE YOUTH CORRECTIONAL FACILITY LIBRARY, 7650 S Newcastle Rd, 95213-9001. (Mail add: PO Box 213001, 95213-9001), Tel: 209-944-6346. FAX: 209-944-6136. *Senior Librn*, James Morgan
Library Holdings: Per Subs 10

R CHRISTIAN LIFE COLLEGE LIBRARY,* 9023 N West Lane, 95210. SAN 301-6323. Tel: 209-476-7882. FAX: 209-476-7868. *Librn*, Mary Lou Myrick
Founded 1955
Library Holdings: Bk Vols 18,371; Per Subs 68

P 49-99 COOPERATIVE LIBRARY SYSTEM, Central Association of Libraries,* 605 N El Dorado St, 95202-1999. SAN 301-6218. Tel: 209-937-8649. FAX: 209-937-8292. E-Mail: 4999@stockton.lib.ca.us.; Staff 2 (MLS 2)
Founded 1968
Special Collections: Bi-Folkal Kits; Film Coll
Publications: Directory; Large Print Book Catalog; Union List of Serials
Member Libraries: Amador County Library; Calaveras County Library; California Department of Corrections Library System; California State University; E & J Gallo Winery; Haggin Museum; Lodi Public Library; Merced College; Merced County Library; San Joaquin County Public Health Services; Stanislaus County Free Library; Stanislaus County Free Library; Stockton-San Joaquin County Public Library; Tuolumne County Free Library; University of the Pacific Library

S HAGGIN MUSEUM, Petzinger Library of Californiana, 1201 N Pershing Ave, 95203-1699. SAN 301-6234. Tel: 209-940-6300. FAX: 209-462-1404. E-Mail: info@hagginmuseum.org. Web Site: www.hagginmuseum.org. *Archivist, Librn*, Susan Benedetti
Founded 1949
Library Holdings: Bk Titles 7,000; Per Subs 35
Subject Interests: Local history
Special Collections: California History; Farm Machinery; Holt Manufacturing Company History; Industrial History Archives; Ralph Yardley Cartoons; Stephens Bros Boat Builders, marine drawings & photogs; Stockton & The San Joaquin Valley
Restriction: By appointment only, Not a lending library
Mem of 49-99 Cooperative Library System

C HUMPHREYS COLLEGE LIBRARY,* 6505 Inglewood Ave, 95207. SAN 301-6226. Tel: 209-478-0800. *Librn*, Darla Marie Barton-Knoles; Tel: 209-478-0800, Ext 128, E-Mail: dbarton@humphreys.edu
Library Holdings: Bk Vols 20,702; Per Subs 113
Subject Interests: Law
Database Vendor: Ebsco - EbscoHost, OCLC - First Search

M SAINT JOSEPH'S MEDICAL CENTER LIBRARY,* 1800 N California St, 95204. SAN 320-6076. Tel: 209-467-6332. FAX: 209-461-5098. *Librn*, Colleen Lamkin
Library Holdings: Bk Titles 1,200; Per Subs 140
Subject Interests: Human relations, Medicine, Nursing

GL SAN JOAQUIN COUNTY LAW LIBRARY, Courthouse, Rm 410, 222 E Weber Ave Fourth Flr, 95202. SAN 301-6242. Tel: 209-468-3920. FAX: 209-468-9968. E-Mail: sjcll@pacbell.net. *Dir*, Barbara M Zaruba; Staff 3 (MLS 1, Non-MLS 2)
Library Holdings: Bk Vols 30,000

GM SAN JOAQUIN COUNTY PUBLIC HEALTH SERVICES, Health Education Services,* 1601 E Hazelton Ave, PO Box 2009, 95201. SAN 301-6277. Tel: 209-468-3415. FAX: 209-468-8032. *Librn*, Jeanette Hinsz
Special Collections: Public health, rpts
Mem of 49-99 Cooperative Library System

J SAN JOAQUIN DELTA COLLEGE, Goleman Library, 5151 Pacific Ave, 95207-6370. SAN 301-6250. Tel: 209-954-5139. Interlibrary Loan Service Tel: 209-954-5148. Circulation Tel: 209-954-5143. Reference Tel: 209-954-5145. FAX: 209-954-5691. Web Site: www.sjdccd.cc.ca.usl/library. *Dir*, Evia Briggs Moore; *Bibliog Instr*, Dr Jun Wang; *Tech Servs*, Steve Schermerhorn; *Coll Develop*, Jan Mullen; *Publ Servs*, Lynn Welch; Staff 15 (MLS 5, Non-MLS 10)
Founded 1948. Enrl 17,199; Fac 230; Highest Degree: Associate
Jul 1999-Jun 2000 Mats Exp $320,053, Books $120,737, Per/Ser (Incl. Access Fees) $74,929, Presv $1,376, Micro $6,812, AV Equip $33,959, Electronic Ref Mat (Incl. Access Fees) $44,526. Sal $702,942 (Prof $398,022)
Library Holdings: Bk Vols 93,073; Bk Titles 81,241; Per Subs 629
Automation Activity & Vendor Info: (Acquisitions) DRA; (Cataloging) DRA; (Circulation) DRA; (Course Reserve) DRA; (ILL) DRA; (OPAC) DRA
Database Vendor: OCLC - First Search
Publications: Handbook for Instructors; Instructor of Record Handbook; Library Handbook; Library Research Workbook; Library Skills Workbook
Partic in Central Association Of Libraries; Coop Libr Agency for Syst & Servs; OCLC Online Computer Library Center, Inc
Friends of the Library Group

S STOCKTON RECORD LIBRARY,* 530 E Market St, PO Box 900, 95201. SAN 301-6285. Tel: 209-546-8290. FAX: 209-547-8186. *Librn*, Thai Strom
Founded 1952
Library Holdings: Bk Vols 400

P STOCKTON-SAN JOAQUIN COUNTY PUBLIC LIBRARY, (Formerly Stockton-San Joaquin County Public Library, Stockton), 605 N El Dorado St, 95202. SAN 335-1122. Tel: 209-937-8362. Circulation Tel: 209-937-8416. Reference Tel: 209-937-8221. FAX: 209-937-8683. Web Site: www.stockton.lib.ca.us. *Dir*, Nicky Stanke; Tel: 209-937-8365, E-Mail: nicky.stanke@ci.stockton.ca.us; *Dep Dir*, Patty Wong; *Mgr Libr Serv*, Diane Freggiaro; Tel: 209-937-8384, E-Mail: diane.freggiaro@ci.stockton.ca.us; *Mgr Libr Serv*, Lydia Tiuder; Tel: 209-937-8394, E-Mail: ltinder@stockton.lib.ca.us; *Mgr Libr Serv*, Ken Yamashita; Tel: 209-937-8467, E-Mail: kyamashita@stockton.lib.ca.us; *Automation Syst Coordr*, Robert Lombardi; Staff 108 (MLS 37, Non-MLS 71)
Founded 1880. Pop 508,600; Circ 1,697,727
Jul 1998-Jun 1999 Income (Main Library and Branch Library) $8,845,460, State $633,304, City $4,930,396, Federal $11,000, County $2,395,709, Locally Generated Income $372,694, Other $502,357. Mats Exp $1,054,582, Books $738,242, Per/Ser (Incl. Access Fees) $98,760, Presv $9,303, Micro $40,522, AV Equip $56,438, Other Print Mats $62,851, Electronic Ref Mat (Incl. Access Fees) $48,466. Sal $4,240,105
Library Holdings: Bk Vols 992,373; Per Subs 1,661
Subject Interests: Chinese Language, Japanese (Language), Spanish (language)
Special Collections: Local History; Online Community Info Database; Picture Book Subject Index; Southeast Asian Language; Spanish Language; Stockton & San Joaquin County History; Stockton Record Index
Automation Activity & Vendor Info: (Acquisitions) DRA; (Cataloging) DRA; (Circulation) DRA; (OPAC) DRA
Database Vendor: Dialog, DRA, Ebsco - EbscoHost, IAC - Info Trac, OCLC - First Search
Publications: Connections (Newsletter); Library News
Mem of 49-99 Cooperative Library System
Partic in OCLC Online Computer Library Center, Inc
Holdings: High interest/low vocabulary bk vols; Community Information Database (information & referral)
Friends of the Library Group

Branches: 10
ANGELOU BRANCH, 2324 Pock Lane, 95205. SAN 335-1270. Tel: 209-937-7700. FAX: 209-937-7702. Web Site: www.stockton.lib.ca.us. *Branch Mgr*, Janice (Alex) Bailey; Tel: 209-937-7701, E-Mail: jbailey@stockton.lib.ca.us
Library Holdings: Bk Vols 51,665
Subject Interests: Afro-American, History, Spanish (language)
Friends of the Library Group
ESCALON BRANCH, 1540 Second St, Escalon, 95320. SAN 335-1157. Tel: 209-838-2478. FAX: 209-838-2032. Web Site: www.stockton.lib.ca.us. *Branch Mgr*, Beverly Hine; E-Mail: bjhine@stockton.lib.ca.us
Library Holdings: Bk Vols 53,660
Friends of the Library Group
FAIR OAKS, 2370 E Main St, 95205. SAN 335-1181. Tel: 209-937-7100. FAX: 209-937-7102. Web Site: www.stockton.lib.ca.us. *Branch Mgr*, Anita Young; E-Mail: ayoung@stockton.lib.ca.us
Library Holdings: Bk Vols 101,667
Subject Interests: Spanish (language)
Friends of the Library Group
LINDEN BRANCH, 19012 E Main St, Linden, 95236. SAN 335-136X. Tel: 209-887-3370. FAX: 209-887-2075. Web Site: www.stockton.lib.ca.us. *Branch Mgr*, Tom Hindman; E-Mail: thindman@stockton.lib.ca.us
Library Holdings: Bk Vols 20,697
Friends of the Library Group
MANTECA BRANCH, 320 W Center St, Manteca, 95336. SAN 335-1211. Tel: 209-825-2380. FAX: 209-825-2394. Web Site: www.stockton.lib.ca.us. *Branch Mgr*, Diane Bills; E-Mail: dbills@stockton.lib.ca.us
Library Holdings: Bk Vols 119,366
Subject Interests: Large type print, Spanish (language)
Friends of the Library Group
MARGARET K TROKE BRANCH, 502 W Benjamin Holt Dr, 95207. SAN 335-1300. Tel: 209-937-7000. FAX: 209-937-7721. Web Site: www.stockton.lib.ca.us. *Branch Mgr*, David Gouker; E-Mail: dgouker@stockton.lib.ca.us
Library Holdings: Bk Vols 160,235
Subject Interests: Chinese Language, Large type print
Friends of the Library Group
RIPON BRANCH, 430 W Main St, Ripon, 95336. SAN 335-1246. Tel: 209-599-3326. FAX: 209-599-5530. Web Site: www.stockton.lib.ca.us. *Branch Mgr*, Melinda Scanlon; E-Mail: mscanlon@stockton.lib.ca.us
Library Holdings: Bk Vols 41,934
Friends of the Library Group
THORNTON BRANCH, 26341 N Thornton Rd, Thornton, 95686. SAN 335-1394. Tel: 209-794-2621. FAX: 209-794-0617. Web Site: www.stockton.lib.ca.us. *Branch Mgr*, Tom Hindman; E-Mail: thindman@stockton.lib.ca.us
Library Holdings: Bk Vols 23,942
Friends of the Library Group
TRACY BRANCH, 20 E Eaton Ave, Tracy, 95376. SAN 335-1335. Tel: 209-831-4250. FAX: 209-831-4252. Web Site: www.stockton.lib.ca.us. *Branch Mgr*, Susan Johnston; E-Mail: sjohnston@stockton.lib.ca.us; Staff 7 (MLS 2, Non-MLS 5)
Library Holdings: Bk Vols 131,977
Subject Interests: Spanish (language)
Special Collections: Kiersh Memorial Music; Tugel Memorial Natural History
Friends of the Library Group
Bookmobiles: 1. Librn, Beverly Schlesser

C UNIVERSITY OF THE PACIFIC LIBRARY, 3601 Pacific Ave, 95211. SAN 335-1459. Tel: 209-946-2434. Interlibrary Loan Service Tel: 209-946-2196. Reference Tel: 209-946-2433. FAX: 209-946-2805. Web Site: www.library.uop.edu. *Dean*, Jean M Purnell; E-Mail: jpurnell@uop.edu; *Asst Dean*, Kathlin Ray; Tel: 209-946-2939, E-Mail: kray@uop.edu; *Tech Servs*, Mary Lang; *Circ*, Gail Stovall; *Ref*, Craig Hawbaker; *Spec Coll*, Daryl Morrison; Staff 12 (MLS 12)
Founded 1851. Enrl 4,100; Fac 270; Highest Degree: Doctorate
Jul 1999-Jun 2000 Income (Main and Other College/University Libraries) $1,829,338, Parent Institution $1,814,272. Mats Exp $722,583, Books $207,313, Per/Ser (Incl. Access Fees) $515,270. Sal $1,074,036 (Prof $496,477)
Library Holdings: Bk Vols 392,562; Per Subs 2,695
Special Collections: Folk Dance (Lawton Harris), rec; John Muir Papers; Methodist History (Fry Research Library)
Automation Activity & Vendor Info: (Acquisitions) Innovative Interfaces Inc.; (Cataloging) Innovative Interfaces Inc.; (Circulation) Innovative Interfaces Inc.; (Course Reserve) Innovative Interfaces Inc.; (OPAC) Innovative Interfaces Inc.; (Serials) Innovative Interfaces Inc.
Mem of 49-99 Cooperative Library System
Partic in OCLC Western Service Center
Friends of the Library Group
Departmental Libraries:
HEALTH SCIENCE & CHEMISTRY, School of Pharmacy Bldg, 3601 Pacific Ave, 95211. SAN 335-1602. Tel: 209-946-2940. FAX: 209-946-2041. Web Site: www.library.uop.edu. *Librn*, Kimberly Lyons-Mitchell; E-Mail: klyons@uop.edu; Staff 3 (MLS 1, Non-MLS 2)
Subject Interests: Chemistry, Pharmacy, Physical therapy
HOLT-ATHERTON DEPARTMENT OF SPECIAL COLLECTIONS, 3601 Pacific Ave, 95211. Tel: 209-946-2404. Web Site: library.uop.edu. *Head of Libr*, Daryl Morrison; E-Mail: dmorrison@uop.edu; Staff 3 (MLS 1, Non-MLS 2)
Subject Interests: California, Western Americana
METHODIST ARCHIVES-JAB FRY RESEARCH LIBRARY, 3601 Pacific Ave, 95211. Tel: 209-946-2404. Web Site: library.uop.edu. *Librn*, Nadine Johnson
Founded 1952
Library Holdings: Bk Titles 2,000; Per Subs 11
Restriction: By appointment only
Open Mon 2-4

SUISUN CITY

S BAY AREA ELECTRIC RAILROAD ASSOCIATION INC, (Formerly Western Railway Museum), F M Smith Memorial Library, Western Railway Museum, 5848 Hwy 12, Rio Vista Junction, 94585. SAN 301-6331. Tel: 707-374-2978. FAX: 707-374-6742. *Chief Librn*, Bart Nadeau; *Librn*, Chas Vercelli
Founded 1969
Library Holdings: Bk Titles 5,000; Per Subs 20
Special Collections: Abandonment of Interurban Lines (Pacific Electric Railway of Los Angeles, California Coll), correspondence files; California Railroad Commission, rpts; Charles D Savage Memorial Coll of Western Interurban Negatives; Construction of the San Francisco-Oakland Bay Bridge Interurban Railway Coll, files; Fresno Traction Company Coll, correspondence files; Joseph P McTigeu Coll, photogs, proceedings; Key System Transit Co & Predecessor Companies Coll, corp records; L M Clement Coll, correspondence, drawings, glass plate negatives, maps; Monterey & Pacific Grove Street Railway Company Coll, valuation rpt; Oakland, Antioch & Eastern Railway, Northern Electric Railway & Sacramento Northern Railway Coll, correspondence files, valuation rec; Peninsular Railway & San Jose Railroads Coll, rpts, valuation files; Railroads (A H Loflin, Proffer & Estacaille Coll), bks, photogs; Roy Healey Coll, bks, photogs; Southern Pacific Railroad Timetable Coll, 1900-1912; Vernon J Sappers Coll, photogs, correspondence files; Visalia Electric Railroad Coll, construction correspondence files
Publications: Bay Area Review (monthly)

J SOLANO COMMUNITY COLLEGE LIBRARY, 4000 Suisun Valley Rd, 94585. SAN 301-6838. Tel: 707-864-7132. FAX: 707-864-7231. Web Site: www.solano.cc.ca.us/lrc/lib/scclib.html. *Head Librn*, Jeanne DeMars; Tel: 707-864-7243, E-Mail: jdemars@solano.cc.ca.us; *Publ Servs*, Quentin Carter; E-Mail: qcarter@solano.cc.ca.us; *Tech Servs*, Elizabeth Tsai; Tel: 707-864-7173, E-Mail: etsai@solano.cc.ca.us; Staff 8 (MLS 4, Non-MLS 4)
Founded 1965. Enrl 10,377; Fac 146; Highest Degree: Associate
Jul 1998-Jun 1999 Income (Main Library Only) $602,994. Mats Exp $69,847, Books $29,950, Per/Ser (Incl. Access Fees) $31,992, Presv $250, Micro $4,655, Electronic Ref Mat (Incl. Access Fees) $3,000. Sal $414,221
Library Holdings: Bk Vols 36,500; Bk Titles 30,550; Per Subs 165; High Interest/Low Vocabulary Bk Vols 200
Automation Activity & Vendor Info: (Circulation) CARL; (OPAC) CARL
Database Vendor: Ebsco - EbscoHost, OCLC - First Search
Partic in Coop Libr Agency for Syst & Servs; N Bay Coop Libr Syst; OCLC Online Computer Library Center, Inc; Snap

SUN VALLEY

SR THE MASTER'S GRACE LIBRARY, 13248 Roscoe Blvd, 91352. SAN 323-620X. Tel: 818-909-5634. FAX: 818-909-5680. Web Site: www.mastersem.edu. *Dir*, James F Stitzinger; *Librn*, Dennis M Swanson; E-Mail: dswanson@mastersem.edu; *Tech Servs*, Anna Lois Kroll; *Per*, Linda Pettegrew; *Acq*, Michael Bush; Staff 3 (MLS 3)
Founded 1986. Enrl 260; Fac 19
Library Holdings: Bk Vols 105,000; Bk Titles 85,000; Per Subs 750
Partic in Dialog Corporation; OCLC Online Computer Library Center, Inc

SUNNYVALE

S ADVANCED MICRO DEVICES, INC, Technical Library MS-No 169,* One AMD Pl, PO Box 3453, MS 169, 94088. SAN 301-634X. Tel: 408-749-2260. *Librn*, John Owen
Founded 1971
Library Holdings: Bk Titles 8,000; Per Subs 190
Subject Interests: Chemistry, Solid state physics
Special Collections: United States & International Proceedings on Semiconductor Technology
Publications: Acquisitions List (monthly)
Restriction: Staff use only
Partic in Dialog Corporation; S Bay Coop Libr Syst

S AMDAHL CORPORATION, Corporate Library,* 1250 E Arques Ave MS 247, 94088. SAN 327-6147. Tel: 408-746-6000, 408-746-8021. FAX: 408-245-8760.
Library Holdings: Bk Vols 70,000; Per Subs 250
Partic in OCLC Online Computer Library Center, Inc

C COGSWELL POLYTECHNICAL COLLEGE LIBRARY,* 1175 Bordeaux Dr, 94089. SAN 301-3898. Tel: 408-541-0100, Ext 144. FAX: 408-747-0764. E-Mail: library@cogswell.edu. Web Site: www.cogswell.edu. *Librn*, Bruce G Dahms; Staff 6 (MLS 2, Non-MLS 4)
Founded 1887. Enrl 400; Fac 50; Highest Degree: Bachelor
Library Holdings: Bk Titles 13,000; Per Subs 100
Subject Interests: Electrical engineering
Special Collections: Manufacturers' Data Manuals
Automation Activity & Vendor Info: (Cataloging) CASPR
Publications: Cogswell Contact (quarterly college-wide newsletter); The Source (library irregular acquisitions newsletter)
Partic in Coop Libr Agency for Syst & Servs

R SAINT THOMAS EPISCOPAL CHURCH LIBRARY,* 231 S Sunset Ave, 94086-5938. SAN 328-1884. Tel: 408-736-4155. FAX: 408-736-8655. E-Mail: stthomasch.stc@aol.com. *Librn*, Carol Campbell; Staff 5 (MLS 1, Non-MLS 4)
Founded 1979
Library Holdings: Bk Titles 4,000
Subject Interests: Religion
Special Services for the Deaf - Books on deafness & sign language

P SUNNYVALE PUBLIC LIBRARY, 665 W Olive Ave, 94088-3714. SAN 301-6455. Tel: 408-730-7314. Interlibrary Loan Service Tel: 408-730-7323. FAX: 408-735-8767. E-Mail: adultref@ci.sunnyvale.ca.us. Web Site: www.ci.sunnyvale.ca.us/library. *Dir*, Victoria L Johnson; *Circ*, Ellen Giarrizzo; *Publ Servs*, Susan Denniston; *Adminr*, Karen Willes; *Ch Servs*, Nancy Jackson; *Cat*, Marsha Pollak; *Coll Develop*, Christine Doxtad. Subject Specialists: *Sciences*, Mary Clare Sprott; Staff 36 (MLS 36)
Founded 1960. Pop 131,127; Circ 1,358,078
Jul 1999-Jun 2000 Income (Main Library and Branch Library) $6,871,304, State $225,191, Federal $174,272, Locally Generated Income $871,952, Parent Institution $5,599,889. Mats Exp $455,206, Books $335,078, Per/Ser (Incl. Access Fees) $110,983, Presv $9,145. Sal $3,237,868
Library Holdings: Bk Vols 261,807; Per Subs 506
Subject Interests: Art and architecture, Business and management, Electronics
Special Collections: California History; Sunnyvale
Automation Activity & Vendor Info: (Acquisitions) Inlex; (Cataloging) Inlex; (Circulation) Inlex; (OPAC) Inlex
Mem of Silicon Valley Library System
Partic in Coop Libr Agency for Syst & Servs; OCLC Online Computer Library Center, Inc
Library has over 5.7 million patents in collection
Friends of the Library Group
Branches: 1
SCI 3 SUNNYVALE CENTER FOR INNOVATION, INVENTION & IDEAS, 465 S Mathilda Ave, Ste 3, 94086. SAN 326-3789. Tel: 408-730-7290. FAX: 408-735-8762. Web Site: www.sci3.com.; Staff 3 (MLS 3)
Founded 1965
Jul 1999-Jun 2000 Income $1,398,086, City $713,442, Locally Generated Income $684,644. Sal $358,320
Library Holdings: Bk Titles 200; Per Subs 3
Subject Interests: Patents
Special Collections: US Patent
Publications: Newsletter (quarterly)
Access to US Patent & Trademark Office databases. Fee-based professional services or patron direct access
Bookmobiles: 1

S TRW ESL RESEARCH LIBRARY, 1330 Geneva Dr, PO Box 3510, 94088-3510. SAN 301-6382. Tel: 408-738-2888, Ext 6795. FAX: 408-743-6449. *Librn*, Jane Talbot; Staff 1 (Non-MLS 1)
Founded 1966
Library Holdings: Bk Vols 11,200; Bk Titles 5,600; Per Subs 150
Subject Interests: Electronics, Engineering, Telecommunications
Special Collections: IEEE Conference Proceedings up to 1997
Automation Activity & Vendor Info: (Cataloging) Inmagic, Inc.
Database Vendor: Dialog
Restriction: Staff use only
Function: For research purposes
Partic in Coop Libr Agency for Syst & Servs; Dialog Corporation
Subsidiary of TRW

S WEATHERNEWS OCEANROUTES, Technical Library,* 333 W El Camino Real, Ste 300, 94087. SAN 324-3885. Tel: 408-731-2300. FAX: 408-245-5787. *Librn*, Lisa Bail
Library Holdings: Bk Vols 1,000; Bk Titles 750; Per Subs 50
Subject Interests: Meteorology, Naval sci
Restriction: Not open to public
Partic in Dialog Corporation; OCLC Online Computer Library Center, Inc; S Bay Coop Libr Syst

S WESTERN PHILATELIC LIBRARY, Bldg 6, 1500 Partridge Ave, Rm 6, PO Box 2219, 94087. SAN 324-3524. Tel: 408-733-0336. *Pres*, Stuart Levin
Library Holdings: Bk Vols 10,000; Per Subs 50
Subject Interests: Stamp collecting
Publications: The Bay Phil
Library is housed in Sunnyvale City, Raynor Activity Center
Friends of the Library Group

SUSANVILLE

C LASSEN COLLEGE LIBRARY, 478-200 Hwy 139, PO Box 3000, 96130. SAN 301-6498. Tel: 530-251-8830. FAX: 530-257-8964. Web Site: www.lassen.cc.ca.us/library/webpage.htm. *Librn*, Rosanna Brown; E-Mail: rbrown@lassen.cc.ca.us; Staff 1 (MLS 1)
Founded 1926. Enrl 2,357; Fac 122
Library Holdings: Bk Titles 21,000; Per Subs 217
Subject Interests: Criminal law and justice
Special Collections: California Col; N American Indian Coll
Automation Activity & Vendor Info: (Cataloging) TLC; (Circulation) TLC; (Course Reserve) TLC; (OPAC) TLC
Mem of North State Cooperative Library System

P SUSANVILLE DISTRICT LIBRARY, 1618 Main St, 96130-4515. SAN 301-6501. Tel: 530-257-8113 (Admin). Circulation Tel: 530-251-8127. FAX: 530-257-8115. *Librn*, Linda Pack; Tel: 530-257-8113
Founded 1915. Pop 27,595; Circ 96,563
Library Holdings: Bk Titles 47,897; Per Subs 101
Subject Interests: Indians, Local history
Special Collections: California History
Mem of North State Cooperative Library System
Friends of the Library Group

SYLMAR

J LOS ANGELES MISSION COLLEGE LIBRARY,* 13356 Eldridge Ave, 91342-3200. SAN 301-360X. Tel: 818-364-7750. FAX: 818-364-7749. E-Mail: lamission@cc.ca.us. Web Site: www.lamission.cc.ca.us. *Cat, Tech Servs*, Ed Casson; *Librn*, Sandy Thomsen; *Publ Servs, Ref*, David Garza; Staff 3 (MLS 3)
Founded 1975. Enrl 8,500; Fac 57
Library Holdings: Bk Vols 44,000; Per Subs 193
Special Collections: Los Angeles Mission College Archives
Publications: Bibliographies & Study Aids
Partic in Metronet

M OLIVE VIEW-UCLA MEDICAL CENTER, Health Science Library, 14445 Olive View Dr, 91342. SAN 373-6660. Tel: 818-364-4240. FAX: 818-364-4632. Web Site: www.149.142.193.6/education/ovlibrary/. *Librn*, Marsha Gelman Kmec; E-Mail: mkmec@ucla.edu; *Tech Servs*, Grace Dominguez
Fac 180
Library Holdings: Bk Titles 3,000; Per Subs 400
Subject Interests: Medicine, Nursing
Publications: Newsletter

M ST JUDE MEDICAL INC - CARDIAC RHYTHM MANAGEMENT DIV, Library & Resource Center, 15900 Valley View Ct, 91342. (Mail add: PO Box 9221, 91392-9221), SAN 373-286X. Tel: 818-493-3101. Toll Free Tel: 800-423-5611, Ext 3101. FAX: 818-362-8142. E-Mail: library@sjm.com. Web Site: www.sjm.com. *Mgr*, Sandra Crumlish; Staff 1 (Non-MLS 1)
Founded 1990
Jan 1999-Dec 1999 Mats Exp $149,000, Books $10,000, Per/Ser (Incl. Access Fees) $45,000, AV Equip $2,000, Other Print Mats $10,000, Manuscripts & Archives $10,000, Electronic Ref Mat (Incl. Access Fees) $58,000. Sal $46,000
Library Holdings: Bk Titles 1,500; Per Subs 103
Subject Interests: Cardiology
Automation Activity & Vendor Info: (Acquisitions) EOS; (Cataloging) EOS; (Circulation) EOS; (OPAC) EOS; (Serials) EOS
Partic in Med Libr Group of S Calif & Ariz; Medical Libr Asn; Spec Libr Asn

TAFT

J TAFT COLLEGE LIBRARY, 29 Emmons Park Dr, 93268-2317. SAN 301-6536. Tel: 661-763-7707. FAX: 805-763-7778. Web Site: www.taft.cc.ca.us/TCLibrary/. *Dir Libr Serv*, Dr Mimi Collins; Tel: 661-763-7764, E-Mail: mcollins@taft.org; *Tech Servs*, Linda Silveira; E-Mail: lsilveira@taft.org; *Tech Servs*, Mabel Yetter; E-Mail: myetter@taft.org; Staff 1 (MLS 1)
Founded 1922
Library Holdings: Bk Vols 32,000; Per Subs 150
Database Vendor: GaleNet, IAC - Info Trac, ProQuest
Mem of West Kern Community Col District

TARZANA

J COLUMBIA COLLEGE - HOLLYWOOD, Joseph E Bluth Memorial Library, 18618 Oxnard St, 91356. SAN 328-2449. Tel: 818-345-8414. FAX: 818-345-9053. E-Mail: cchadmin@columbiacollege.edu. Web Site: www.columbiacollege.edu. *Librn*, Mary Huang; Staff 5 (MLS 2, Non-MLS 3)
Founded 1952. Enrl 250; Fac 43; Highest Degree: Bachelor
Library Holdings: Bk Titles 9,800; Per Subs 33
Special Collections: Hollywood Museum Coll; Motion Picture & Revision Script Coll, scripts; Society of Motion Picture & Television Engineers, jrnls, 1910-present
Friends of the Library Group

TEMPLE CITY

TEMPLE CITY NAZARENE CHURCH, Carl W Mischke Memorial Library, 9953 Las Tunas, 91780. SAN 301-6552. Tel: 626-287-1136. FAX: 626-287-7818. *Librn*, Irene Craig; Tel: 626-287-7463
Founded 1971
Library Holdings: Bk Titles 250
Subject Interests: Fiction, Missions and missionaries
Special Collections: Missionary Reading Books

THOUSAND OAKS

S AMGEN INCORPORATED LIBRARY,* One Amgen Center Dr, 91320. SAN 329-5745. Tel: 805-447-4636. FAX: 805-447-1981. Web Site: www.amgen.com. *Mgr*, Larry Markworth; E-Mail: larrym@amgen.com; *Coll Develop*, Janine Pitt; Staff 28 (MLS 19, Non-MLS 9)
Founded 1981
Library Holdings: Bk Vols 6,000; Bk Titles 5,000; Per Subs 425
Partic in Coop Libr Agency for Syst & Servs; Pac SW Regional Med Libr

C CALIFORNIA LUTHERAN UNIVERSITY, Pearson Library, 60 W Olsen Rd, MC 5100, 91360-2787. SAN 301-6560. Tel: 805-493-3250. FAX: 805-493-3842. E-Mail: libcirc@clunet.edu. Web Site: www.clunet.edu. *ILL*, Kathy Horneck; *Cat*, Donald Powell; Staff 9 (MLS 4, Non-MLS 5)
Founded 1961. Pop 2,766; Circ 25,547; Enrl 2,766; Fac 111; Highest Degree: Master
Jun 1999-May 2000 Income Parent Institution $630,768. Mats Exp $630,768, Books $63,230, Per/Ser (Incl. Access Fees) $79,340, Electronic Ref Mat (Incl. Access Fees) $90,174. Sal $295,704 (Prof $171,900)
Library Holdings: Bk Vols 123,147; Per Subs 657
Subject Interests: Counseling, Marriage, Pacific Islands
Special Collections: Scandinavian
Automation Activity & Vendor Info: (Acquisitions) DRA; (Cataloging) DRA; (Circulation) DRA; (OPAC) DRA; (Serials) DRA
Database Vendor: Lexis-Nexis, OCLC - First Search, ProQuest, Silverplatter Information Inc.
Partic in Pac Net

M LOS ROBLES REGIONAL MEDICAL CENTER, Medical Staff Library, 215 W Janss Rd, 91360. SAN 301-6579. Tel: 805-497-2727. FAX: 805-446-8843. *Dir*, Linda Carvotta
Library Holdings: Bk Vols 350; Per Subs 66
Subject Interests: Medicine

S ROCKWELL INTERNATIONAL, Science Center Library,* 1049 Camino Dos Rios, 91360. SAN 301-6587. Tel: 805-373-4722. FAX: 805-373-4296. *Bibliog Instr, Librn, Online Servs*, Yolanda O Fackler; E-Mail: yofackler@rscrockwell.com
Founded 1962
Library Holdings: Bk Vols 13,000; Per Subs 350
Subject Interests: Chemistry, Mathematics, Metallurgy, Physics
Partic in BRS; Dialog Corporation; Dow Jones News Retrieval; Orbit
Friends of the Library Group

P THOUSAND OAKS LIBRARY, 1401 E Janss Rd, 91362-2199. SAN 335-2323. Tel: 805-449-2660. Interlibrary Loan Service Tel: 805-497-2195. FAX: 805-373-6858. Web Site: www.tol.lib.ca.us. *Dir*, Stephen R Brogden; Tel: 805-449-2660, Ext 200, E-Mail: sbrogden@mx.tol.lib.ca.us; *Dep Dir*, Nancy Sevier; Tel: 805-449-2660, Ext 227, E-Mail: nsevier@mx.tol.lib.ca.us; *Branch Mgr*, Roxanne Burg; Tel: 805-498-2139, Ext 226, Fax: 805-498-7034, E-Mail: rburg@mx.tol.lib.ca.us; *Mgr Libr Serv*, Nadia Dagher; Tel: 805-449-2660, Ext 251, E-Mail: ndagher@mx.tol.lib.ca.us; *Coll Develop*, Kathy Cresto; *Ch Servs*, Anne Landon; *Tech Servs*, Sue Pelman; *Automation Syst Coordr*, Brad Miller; Staff 85 (MLS 22, Non-MLS 63)
Founded 1982. Pop 120,744; Circ 1,424,997
Jul 1999-Jun 2000 Income (Main Library and Branch Library) $5,624,680. Mats Exp $717,755, Books $296,328, Per/Ser (Incl. Access Fees) $226,478, Presv $2,555, Micro $19,584, AV Equip $55,811, Other Print Mats $38,220, Manuscripts & Archives $6,129, Electronic Ref Mat (Incl. Access Fees) $72,650. Sal $2,858,682
Library Holdings: Bk Vols 291,059; Per Subs 752
Subject Interests: Genealogy, Hist of radio, Local history, TV broadcasting
Special Collections: Radio & Television Broadcasting
Automation Activity & Vendor Info: (Cataloging) GEAC
Database Vendor: Dialog, IAC - Info Trac, Innovative Interfaces INN - View
Publications: Bibliographies; Brochures; Fliers; Pathfinders; Programs
Mem of Metropolitan Cooperative Library System
Support Organizations: Thousand Oaks Library Foundation; Friends of the Thousand Oaks Library
Friends of the Library Group
Branches: 1
NEWBURY PARK BRANCH, 2331 Borchard Rd, Newbury Park, 91320-3206. SAN 372-5626. Tel: 805-498-2139. *Librn*, Nancy Sevier
Library Holdings: Bk Vols 35,000
Friends of the Library Group

THREE RIVERS

S SEQUOIA & KINGS CANYON NATIONAL PARKS, Park Headquarters Library, 93271. SAN 301-6595. Tel: 559-565-3132, 559-565-3341. FAX: 559-565-3730. *Librn*, Tom Burge; E-Mail: tom-burge@nps.gov
Library Holdings: Bk Titles 3,700
Subject Interests: Nevada

TIBURON

P BELVEDERE-TIBURON LIBRARY, 1501 Tiburon Blvd, 94920. Tel: 415-789-2665. FAX: 415-789-2650. Web Site: bel-tib-lib.org. *Dir*, Deborah Mazzolini; E-Mail: dmazzolini@bel-tib-lib.org; *Ad Servs*, Joan Garrett; *Ch Servs*, Alicia Bell; *Circ*, Phil Brown; *ILL*, Andrea Wheeler; *Tech Servs*, Elaine Crepeau; *Tech Coordr*, Heather Lamb; Staff 16 (MLS 7, Non-MLS 9)
Founded 1997. Pop 11,500; Circ 155,000
Jul 2000-Jun 2001 Income $1,018,641
Library Holdings: Bk Vols 55,200; Per Subs 325; Bks on Deafness & Sign Lang 10
Automation Activity & Vendor Info: (Acquisitions) Innovative Interfaces Inc.; (Cataloging) Innovative Interfaces Inc.; (Circulation) Innovative Interfaces Inc.; (OPAC) Innovative Interfaces Inc.; (Serials) Innovative Interfaces Inc.
Database Vendor: Ebsco - EbscoHost, GaleNet, Innovative Interfaces INN - View
Library is 4 yrs old

G NATIONAL MARINE FISHERIES SERVICE, Tiburon Laboratory Library,* 3150 Paradise Dr, 94920. SAN 301-6617. Tel: 415-435-3149, Ext 220. FAX: 415-435-3675. *Librn*, Gareth Penn; E-Mail: gareth.penn@noaa.gov
Founded 1962
1998-1999 Mats Exp $21,500, Books $3,000, Per/Ser (Incl. Access Fees) $17,000, Presv $1,500. Sal $38,429
Subject Interests: Oceanography
Publications: Laboratory staff reprints
Partic in Dialog Corporation; OCLC Online Computer Library Center, Inc

TOLLHOUSE

S PEOPLE FOOD & LAND FOUNDATION, Sun Mountain Center Library, 35751 Oak Springs Dr, 93667. SAN 374-8529. Tel: 559-855-3710. FAX: 559-855-4774. E-Mail: sunmt@sunmt.org. Web Site: www.sunmt.org. *Dir*, George Ballis
Founded 1975
Library Holdings: Bk Titles 1,000
Special Collections: Activist Actions, films & videos

TORRANCE

S DYNAMICS TECHNOLOGY, INC LIBRARY,* 21311 Hawthorne Blvd, Ste 300, 90503. SAN 328-7912. Tel: 310-543-5433. FAX: 310-543-2117. *Librn*, Seruia Thompson; E-Mail: sthompson@dynatec.com
Library Holdings: Bk Vols 16,000; Per Subs 74

J EL CAMINO COLLEGE, 16007 S Crenshaw Blvd, 90506. SAN 301-6625. Tel: 310-660-3525. FAX: 310-660-3513. Web Site: www.libweb.elcamino.cc.ca.us. *Dean*, Raymond Roney; *Ref*, Vincent Robles; *Ref*, Claudia Striepe; *Media Spec*, Howard Story; *Circ*, Edward Martinez; *Cat*, Alice Grigsby; *Music*, Don Brown; *Coll Develop*, Judy Harris; Staff 7 (MLS 7)
Founded 1948. Enrl 23,486; Fac 425
Library Holdings: Bk Vols 116,046; Bk Titles 103,075; Per Subs 496
Subject Interests: Japanese (Language), Music
Automation Activity & Vendor Info: (Acquisitions) GEAC; (Cataloging) GEAC; (Circulation) GEAC; (Course Reserve) GEAC; (OPAC) GEAC; (Serials) GEAC
Database Vendor: Ebsco - EbscoHost, ProQuest, Wilson - Wilson Web
Publications: Bibliographies; Lamppost (quarterly newsletter)
Friends of the Library Group

S HONEYWELL INTERNATIONAL INC, (Formerly Allied-Signal Equipment Systems Library), Honeywell Engines & Systems Technical Library, 2525 W 190th St, 90504-6099. SAN 301-6633. Tel: 310-512-3666. FAX: 310-512-1604. *Librn*, Yanghoon Rhee; E-Mail: momo.rhee@honeywell.com; *Librn*, Louise Y Sakamoto; E-Mail: louise.sakamoto@honeywell.com; Staff 2 (MLS 2)
Founded 1941
Library Holdings: Per Subs 125
Subject Interests: Aeronautics, Engineering
Publications: Index of Honeywell Engineering Reports
Partic in OCLC Online Computer Library Center, Inc

M LOS ANGELES COUNTY HARBOR UCLA MEDICAL CENTER, A F Parlow Library of Health Sciences, 1000 W Carson St, PO Box 18, 90509-2910. SAN 335-1637. Tel: 310-222-2372. *Dir*, Mary Ann Berliner; *Asst Dir*, Marilouise Gil-Gomez
Founded 1964
Library Holdings: Bk Titles 29,778; Per Subs 794
Subject Interests: Hospital administration, Medicine, Nursing, Social service (social work)
Publications: Library Newsline (every 2 months)
Restriction: Circulates for staff only, Lending to staff only, Non-circulating to the public
Function: Professional lending library
Partic in Nat Libr of Med; OCLC Online Computer Library Center, Inc

S PHENOMENEX LIBRARY,* 2320 W 205th, 90501. SAN 323-4991. Tel: 310-212-0555. FAX: 310-328-7768. *In Charge*, Shelley Colbos
Library Holdings: Bk Vols 500; Per Subs 15
Subject Interests: Gas chromatography, Gel permeation chromatography, High performance liquid chromatography

M TORRANCE MEMORIAL MEDICAL CENTER, Medical Library, 3330 W Lomita Blvd, 90505. SAN 301-6668. Tel: 310-517-4720. *Librn, Online Servs*, Anita N Klecker; Staff 1 (MLS 1)
Founded 1972
Library Holdings: Bk Titles 450; Per Subs 100
Subject Interests: Medicine, Nursing
Publications: Serials Holding List
Partic in National Network Of Libraries Of Medicine; Pacific Southwest Regional Med Libr Serv

P TORRANCE PUBLIC LIBRARY, 3301 Torrance Blvd, 90503-5059. SAN 335-1696. Tel: 310-618-5959. FAX: 310-618-5952. Web Site: www.library.tornet.com. *Dir*, James W Buckley; Tel: 310-618-5950, E-Mail: jbuckley@tornet.com; *Mgr*, Norman Reeder; E-Mail: nreeder@tornet.com; *Mgr*, Paula Weiner; E-Mail: pweiner@tornet.com; *Librn*, Evelyn Harris; Tel: 310-618-5974, Fax: 310-320-3421, E-Mail: eharris@tornet.com; *Automation Syst Coordr*, Patrice Deleget; Tel: 310-618-5968, Fax: 310-781-7583, E-Mail: pdeleget@tornet.com; *Tech Servs*, Nancy Applegate Coffey; *Ch Servs*, Cynthia Olsen; Tel: 310-618-5964, E-Mail: colsen@tornet.com; Staff 25 (MLS 25)
Founded 1967. Pop 152,500; Circ 1,500,250
Jul 1999-Jun 2000 Mats Exp $635,400, Books $471,100, Per/Ser (Incl. Access Fees) $130,300, Presv $5,000, Micro $29,000. Sal $3,590,175
Library Holdings: Bk Vols 493,000; Bk Titles 495,989; Per Subs 1,029
Subject Interests: Art and architecture, History, Radio
Automation Activity & Vendor Info: (Cataloging) DRA
Mem of Metropolitan Cooperative Library System
Special Services for the Deaf - Staff with knowledge of sign language
Friends of the Library Group
Branches: 5
EL RETIRO, 126 Vista Del Parque, 90277. SAN 335-1726. Tel: 310-375-0922. FAX: 310-375-6588. *Librn*, Rosalee Greenberg; *Librn*, Tina Chen
Library Holdings: Bk Vols 32,411
Friends of the Library Group
ISABEL HENDERSON BRANCH, 4805 Emerald St, 90503-2899. SAN 335-1750. Tel: 310-371-2075. FAX: 310-371-5025. *Librn*, Lilian Hung
Library Holdings: Bk Vols 34,284
Friends of the Library Group
NORTH TORRANCE, 3604 W Artesia Blvd, 90504-3315. SAN 335-1785. Tel: 310-323-7200. FAX: 310-323-9687. *Librn*, Christine Downey
Library Holdings: Bk Vols 33,666
Friends of the Library Group
SOUTHEAST, 23115 S Arlington Ave, 90501-5816. SAN 335-1815. Tel: 310-530-5044. FAX: 310-530-5181. *Librn*, Shawna Thorup
Library Holdings: Bk Vols 48,658
Friends of the Library Group
WALTERIA, 3815 W 242nd St, 90505-6410. SAN 335-184X. Tel: 310-375-8418. FAX: 310-375-8325. *Librn*, Patrice Deleget
Library Holdings: Bk Vols 31,171
Friends of the Library Group

TRAVIS AFB

UNITED STATES AIR FORCE
AM DAVID GRANT MEDICAL CENTER LIBRARY, 101 Bodin Circle, 94535-1800. SAN 335-1874. Tel: 707-423-7963. FAX: 707-423-7965. *Head Librn*, Regina Ann Rowell; Tel: 707-423-5344, E-Mail: regina.rowell@60mdg.travis.af.mil; *Librn*, John Sims; E-Mail: john.sims@60mdg.travis.af.mil; *Tech Servs*, Connie Clarkson; E-Mail: connie.clarkston@60mdg.travis.af.mil; *ILL*, Nanette G Phillips; Tel: 707-423-7963, E-Mail: nanette.phillips@60mdg.travis.af.mil; Staff 2 (MLS 1, Non-MLS 1)
Library Holdings: Bk Vols 8,600; Per Subs 470
Subject Interests: Dentistry, Hospital administration, Medicine, Nursing
Database Vendor: OVID Technologies
Restriction: Staff use only
Function: ILL available
Partic in BRS; Medline; OCLC Online Computer Library Center, Inc
A TRAVIS AIR FORCE BASE LIBRARY FL4427, 60 SVS/SVMG, 510 Travis Ave, 94535-2168. SAN 335-1904. Tel: 707-424-3279. FAX: 707-424-3809.
Founded 1943
Library Holdings: Bk Vols 40,000; Per Subs 242
Mem of North Bay Cooperative Library System

TUJUNGA

S HENRY GEORGE SCHOOL OF LOS ANGELES, Research Library,* 10242 Mahogany Trail, PO Box 655, 91042. SAN 326-2510. Tel: 818-352-4141. *Librn*, Gwen Pollard
Founded 1945. Fac 30
Library Holdings: Bk Titles 2,000
Publications: Good Society (AG Letter)

TULARE

P TULARE PUBLIC LIBRARY, 113 North F St, 93274-3857. SAN 301-6684. Tel: 559-685-2341. FAX: 559-685-2345. Web Site: www.sjvls.lib.ca.us/tularepub/. *Dir*, Michael C Stowell; E-Mail: mstowell@sjuls.lib.ca.us; Staff 8 (MLS 3, Non-MLS 5)
Founded 1878. Pop 40,300; Circ 122,971
Jul 1999-Jun 2000 Income $426,530. Mats Exp $70,600, Books $65,000, Per/Ser (Incl. Access Fees) $5,600. Sal $261,430
Library Holdings: Bk Vols 71,107; Bk Titles 61,276; Per Subs 120
Subject Interests: Art, California, Genealogy, History, Music, Religion
Automation Activity & Vendor Info: (Circulation) epixtech, inc.
Database Vendor: Ebsco - EbscoHost, epixtech, inc.
Mem of San Joaquin Valley Library System
Partic in Area Wide Library Network
Friends of the Library Group

TULELAKE

S NATIONAL PARK SERVICE, Lava Beds National Monument Research Library, PO Box 865, 96134. SAN 370-0046. Tel: 530-667-2282. FAX: 530-667-2737. Web Site: www.nps.gov/labe. *In Charge*, Craig Dorman
Library Holdings: Bk Vols 2,550; Bk Titles 2,500
Restriction: By appointment only

TURLOCK

C CALIFORNIA STATE UNIVERSITY, Stanislaus Library, 801 W Monte Vista Ave, 95382. SAN 301-6692. Tel: 209-667-3232. Circulation Tel: 209-667-3234. Reference Tel: 209-667-3233. FAX: 209-667-3164. Web Site: www.library.csustan.edu. *Dean of Libr*, Carl E Bengston; Tel: 209-667-3607, E-Mail: cbengston@stan.csustan.edu; *Librn*, Laura Boyer; E-Mail: lboyer@toto.csustan.edu; *Librn*, Arthur Buell; E-Mail: abuell@toto.csustan.edu; *Librn*, Priscilla Peters; Tel: 209-667-3492, E-Mail: pechi@altair.csustan.edu; *Online Servs*, Paula Crawford; Tel: 209-667-3232, Ext 6055, E-Mail: paula@toto.csustan.edu; *ILL*, Julie Reuben; Tel: 209-667-3236, E-Mail: jreuben@toto.csustan.edu; *Archivist*, Bob Santos; E-Mail: bsantos@toto.csustan.edu; *Head Tech Servs*, Annie Hor; Tel: 209-667-3709, E-Mail: ahor@toto.csustan.edu; *Tech Servs*, Annie Yuen-Mun Hor; Tel: 209-667-3232, Ext 3709, E-Mail: ahor@toto.custan.edu; *Coll Develop*, Kenneth Potts; Tel: 209-667-3332, E-Mail: kpotts@toto.csustan.edu; Staff 25 (MLS 9, Non-MLS 16)
Founded 1960. Enrl 7,050; Fac 477; Highest Degree: Master
Jul 1999-Jun 2000 Income $2,778,455. Mats Exp $807,363, Books $138,266, Per/Ser (Incl. Access Fees) $583,406, Presv $6,191, Electronic Ref Mat (Incl. Access Fees) $79,500. Sal $1,478,172 (Prof $651,606)
Library Holdings: Bk Vols 336,418; Bk Titles 280,622; Per Subs 1,994
Subject Interests: Business, Liberal arts, Sciences, Teacher educ
Special Collections: Californiana; Portuguese Culture Photographs; Religious Assyriana; Stanislaus County History; Stanislaus County Photographs; Western US Fine Printing
Automation Activity & Vendor Info: (Acquisitions) GEAC; (Cataloging) GEAC; (Circulation) GEAC; (Course Reserve) GEAC; (ILL) GEAC;

(OPAC) GEAC; (Serials) GEAC
Database Vendor: CARL, Dialog, Ebsco - EbscoHost, GaleNet, IAC - Info Trac, Lexis-Nexis, OCLC - First Search, ProQuest, Silverplatter Information Inc., Wilson - Wilson Web
Mem of 49-99 Cooperative Library System
Partic in Central Association Of Libraries; OCLC Online Computer Library Center, Inc

M EMANUEL MEDICAL CENTER LIBRARY,* PO Box 819005, 95381-9005. SAN 301-6706. Tel: 209-667-4200, Ext 5450. FAX: 209-669-2377. *In Charge*, Sharon Speer
Founded 1971
Library Holdings: Bk Vols 769; Per Subs 84
Partic in N San Joaquin Health Sci Libr Consortium

TWENTYNINE PALMS

UNITED STATES MARINE CORPS
A AIR GROUND COMBAT CENTER LIBRARY, Center Library-Bldg 1528, MCCS Box 788150, 92278-8150. SAN 335-1939. Tel: 760-830-6875. FAX: 760-830-4497. *Librn*, Kay Emerson
Founded 1957
Library Holdings: Bk Vols 28,200; Per Subs 84
Subject Interests: Military history
Partic in San Bernardino, Inyo, Riverside Counties United Library Services

S UNITED STATES NATIONAL PARK SERVICE, Joshua Tree National Park Research Library, 74485 National Park Dr, 92277. SAN 371-7879. Tel: 760-367-5571. FAX: 760-367-5588. *In Charge*, Charlotte Hunter
Founded 1994
Library Holdings: Bk Vols 4,000
Subject Interests: Local history
Restriction: Not a lending library
Function: Reference only

UKIAH

G BUREAU OF LAND MANAGEMENT, Ukiah Field Office Library,* 2550 N State St, 95482-3023. SAN 301-6730. Tel: 707-468-4000. FAX: 707-468-4027. *Librn*, Deborah McAfee
Library Holdings: Bk Vols 2,500; Per Subs 15

J MENDOCINO COLLEGE LIBRARY, 1000 Hensley Creek Rd, 95482. (Mail add: PO Box 3000, 95482), SAN 301-6749. Tel: 707-468-3053. Interlibrary Loan Service Tel: 707-468-3052. Circulation Tel: 707-468-3158. Reference Tel: 707-468-3051. FAX: 707-468-3056. Web Site: www.mendocino.cc.ca.us. *Chief Librn*, Yvonne Sligh; E-Mail: ysligh@mendocino.cc.ca.us; Staff 3 (MLS 1, Non-MLS 2)
Founded 1973. Fac 200; Highest Degree: Associate
Jul 1999-Jun 2000 Income $200,681. Mats Exp $200,681. Sal $176,241 (Prof $82,244)
Library Holdings: Bk Vols 30,000; Per Subs 177
Automation Activity & Vendor Info: (Circulation) Sagebrush Corporation; (OPAC) Sagebrush Corporation
Restriction: Non-circulating to the public
Partic in OCLC Online Computer Library Center, Inc

S MENDOCINO COUNTY HISTORICAL SOCIETY, Held-Poage Historical Research Library, 603 W Perkins St, 95482-4726. SAN 301-6757. Tel: 707-462-6969. *Dir*, Lila Lee; Staff 8 (Non-MLS 8)
Founded 1970
Jul 2000-Jun 2001 Income Locally Generated Income $10,000. Mats Exp $4,500, Books $1,000, Micro $2,500, Manuscripts & Archives $1,000
Library Holdings: Bk Titles 5,200
Subject Interests: Genealogy
Special Collections: Americana (Estelle Beard Coll); California Indians; Civil War (William P Held Coll); Mendocino County; Mendocino County (Robert J Lee Coll) film; notebooks
Publications: Newsletter (quarterly)

GL MENDOCINO COUNTY LAW LIBRARY, Courthouse Rm 307, 95482. SAN 301-6765. Tel: 707-463-4201. E-Mail: lawlib@pacific.net. *Dir*, Tom Anderson
Library Holdings: Bk Vols 8,000

P MENDOCINO COUNTY LIBRARY, 105 N Main St, 95482. SAN 335-1963. Tel: 707-463-4490. Interlibrary Loan Service Tel: 707-463-4154. Reference Tel: 404-463-4493. FAX: 707-463-5472. E-Mail: mendolib@pacificnet.com. *Dir*, Erika Condon; Tel: 707-463-4492, E-Mail: erikacondon@yahoo.com; *Branch Mgr*, Donna Kerr; *Reader Servs*, Dorothy Anderson; Tel: 707-463-4493; *Info Specialist*, Srah Haman; Tel: 707-463-4493; *Ch Servs*, Ina Gordon; Tel: 707-463-4153; *Bkmobile Coordr*, Wendy Norris; Tel: 707-463-4694; Staff 10 (MLS 5, Non-MLS 5)
Founded 1964. Pop 88,900; Circ 297,063
Jul 2000-Jun 2001 Income (Main Library and Branch Library) $1,182,410, State $143,000, County $991,410, Locally Generated Income $48,000. Mats Exp $303,135, Books $28,000, Per/Ser (Incl. Access Fees) $4,000. Sal $685,275
Library Holdings: Bk Vols 159,500; Bk Titles 93,000; Per Subs 110
Subject Interests: Art, Fishing, Forestry, Genealogy, Indians, Logging, Wines
Special Collections: Native Americans of Mendocino County
Database Vendor: Ebsco - EbscoHost, epixtech, inc., IAC - Info Trac
Mem of North Bay Cooperative Library System
Partic in OCLC Online Computer Library Center, Inc
Friends of the Library Group
Branches: 4
COAST COMMUNITY, PO Box 808, Point Arena, 95468. SAN 376-8139. Tel: 707-882-3114. *Librn*, Patricia Augustine
Library Holdings: Bk Vols 10,000
Friends of the Library Group
FORT BRAGG BRANCH, 499 Laurel St, Fort Bragg, 95437. SAN 335-1998. Tel: 707-964-2020. FAX: 707-961-2623. *Librn*, Carl Danis
Library Holdings: Bk Vols 22,000
Friends of the Library Group
ROUND VALLEY, PO Box 620, Covelo, 95428. SAN 372-7858. Tel: 707-983-6736. *Tech Servs*, Georgina Wright
Library Holdings: Bk Vols 10,000
Friends of the Library Group
WILLITS BRANCH, 390 E Commercial St, Willits, 95490. SAN 335-2021. Tel: 707-459-5908. FAX: 707-459-7819. *Librn*, Peggy Rhoads
Pop 12,000
1999-2000 Mats Exp $30,000
Library Holdings: Bk Vols 31,500; Per Subs 35
Special Collections: Calif History Coll; Western Americana Coll
Automation Activity & Vendor Info: (Circulation) epixtech, inc.
Friends of the Library Group
Bookmobiles: 1

UPLAND

R FIRST PRESBYTERIAN CHURCH LIBRARY,* 869 N Euclid Ave, 91786. SAN 301-6781. Tel: 909-982-8811. FAX: 909-985-8014. *Librn*, Lillian McGlibery; *Asst Librn*, Frieda Simpson
Library Holdings: Bk Vols 1,650

M SAN ANTONIO COMMUNITY HOSPITAL, Weber Memorial Library, 999 San Bernardino Rd, 91786. SAN 327-4152. Tel: 909-920-4972. FAX: 714-931-0102. *Librn*, Ardis Weiss
Library Holdings: Bk Vols 4,800; Per Subs 620
Partic in Inland Empire Acad Libr Coop

P UPLAND PUBLIC LIBRARY,* 450 N Euclid Ave, 91786-4732. SAN 301-679X. Tel: 909-931-4200. FAX: 909-931-4209. Web Site: uplandpl.lib.ca.us. *Dir*, Linda Yao; *ILL*, Barbara Reifenrath; *Ch Servs*, Penny Garris; Staff 4 (MLS 4)
Founded 1913. Pop 67,453; Circ 313,566
Jul 1997-Jun 1998 Income $1,218,186, State $62,822, Locally Generated Income $107,100, Other $73,938. Mats Exp $150,029, Books $119,795, Per/Ser (Incl. Access Fees) $13,216. Sal $736,772
Library Holdings: Bk Titles 108,680; Per Subs 244
Mem of Inland Library System
Partic in San Bernardino, Inyo, Riverside Counties United Library Services
Friends of the Library Group

VALENCIA

C CALIFORNIA INSTITUTE OF THE ARTS, Division of Library & Information Resources, 24700 McBean Pkwy, 91355-2397. SAN 301-6803. Tel: 661-253-7885. Circulation Tel: 661-253-7889. Reference Tel: 661-291-3024. FAX: 661-254-4561. E-Mail: library@calarts.edu. Web Site: library.calarts.edu. *Dean*, Frederick B Gardner; E-Mail: fred@calarts.edu; *Assoc Dean*, Susan Lowenberg; Tel: 661-253-7888, E-Mail: susan@calarts.edu; *Ref*, Coco Halverson; E-Mail: coco@calarts.edu; *Bibliogr*, Evy Horigan; Tel: 661-253-7880, E-Mail: ehorigan@calarts.edu; *Bibliogr*, Kevin McLaughlin; Tel: 661-253-7882, E-Mail: kevin@calarts.edu. Subject Specialists: *Biblioq instruction*, Coco Halverson; *Performing arts*, Kevin McLaughlin; *Technology*, Susan Lowenberg; *Visual arts*, Evy Horigan; Staff 18 (MLS 5, Non-MLS 13)
Founded 1968. Enrl 1,191; Highest Degree: Master
Jul 2000-Jun 2001 Income $1,183,194. Mats Exp $151,500, Books $97,500, Per/Ser (Incl. Access Fees) $34,000, Electronic Ref Mat (Incl. Access Fees) $20,000. Sal $690,415 (Prof $292,095)
Library Holdings: Bk Vols 88,505; Per Subs 372
Subject Interests: Art, Dance, Films and filmmaking, Music, Theater, Writing
Special Collections: Artists Books; Film History; MCA Coll; Viola Hegyi Swisher Dance Coll
Database Vendor: DRA, OCLC - First Search, OVID Technologies, ProQuest, Wilson - Wilson Web
Publications: CalArts Library Handbook; CalArts Library Workbook
Restriction: Circulation limited, In-house use for visitors
Function: ILL available

S US BORAX INC, Information Department, 26877 Tourney Rd, 91355. SAN 300-5763. Tel: 661-287-6063. FAX: 661-287-6062. *Mgr*, Chitra Krishnaswamy; Staff 3 (MLS 1, Non-MLS 2)
Founded 1956
Library Holdings: Bk Vols 9,250; Per Subs 200
Subject Interests: Chemistry
Publications: acquisition list; Pats Bull; Toxicology Bull; Weekly Bull

VALLEJO

C CALIFORNIA MARITIME ACADEMY LIBRARY, 200 Maritime Academy Dr, PO Box 1392, 94590. SAN 301-682X. Tel: 707-654-1090. Reference Tel: 707-654-1092. FAX: 707-654-1094. Web Site: www.csum.edu/library/. *Dir*, Carl D Phillips; Tel: 707-654-1093, E-Mail: carlphillips@csum.edu; *Tech Servs*, Simone Brooks; Tel: 707-654-1091, E-Mail: sbrooks@csum.edu; *Publ Servs*, Bruce Boylen; E-Mail: bboylen@csum.edu. Subject Specialists: *Maritime*, Simone Brooks; *Maritime*, Bruce Boylen; *Sci-tech*, Carl D Phillips; Staff 5 (MLS 2, Non-MLS 3)
Founded 1939. Enrl 575; Fac 20; Highest Degree: Bachelor
Jul 1999-May 2000 Income (Main Library and Branch Library) Parent Institution $348,680. Mats Exp $177,105, Books $57,695, Per/Ser (Incl. Access Fees) $46,577, Presv $7,725, Other Print Mats $43,653, Electronic Ref Mat (Incl. Access Fees) $22,619. Sal $171,838 (Prof $159,858)
Library Holdings: Bk Vols 28,308; Bk Titles 24,562; Per Subs 275; Spec Interest Per Sub 111
Subject Interests: Marine eng, Marine tech, Marine transportation, Maritime law
Special Collections: Academy Historical Archives
Automation Activity & Vendor Info: (Cataloging) epixtech, inc.; (Circulation) epixtech, inc.; (Course Reserve) epixtech, inc.; (OPAC) epixtech, inc.
Database Vendor: CARL, Dialog, Ebsco - EbscoHost, epixtech, inc., IAC - Info Trac, Lexis-Nexis, OCLC - First Search, ProQuest, Silverplatter Information Inc.
Function: Research library
Mem of California State University
Partic in CSU Pharos, OCLC Online Computer Libr Ctr, Inc

G USDA FOREST SERVICE PACIFIC SOUTHWEST RESEARCH STATION, Pacific Southwest Library & Infromation Center, 1323 Club Dr, 94592. SAN 324-5659. Tel: 707-562-8670. FAX: 707-562-9032. E-Mail: mailroom_r5@fs.fed.us Subj:pswlic. Web Site: library. psw.fs.fed.us. *Librn*, Patricia Pepin; Tel: 707-562-8658, E-Mail: ppepin@fs.fed.us; Staff 4 (MLS 1, Non-MLS 3)
Founded 1960
Library Holdings: Per Subs 30
Subject Interests: Fire, Forest injury, Forest mgt, Forest pathology, Wildland mgt
Special Collections: US Forest Service
Partic in Forest Service Library Network; OCLC Online Computer Library Center, Inc

S VALLEJO NAVAL & HISTORICAL MUSEUM, 734 Marin St, 94590. SAN 326-5048. Tel: 707-643-0077. FAX: 707-643-2443. E-Mail: valmuse@pacbell.net. Web Site: www.vallejomuseum.org. *Librn*, Arlene Valdez
Founded 1974
Library Holdings: Bk Titles 5,200; Per Subs 10
Subject Interests: Local history, Maritime history
Special Collections: Solano County & City of Vallejo
Restriction: Non-circulating

VALLEY GLEN

J LOS ANGELES VALLEY COLLEGE LIBRARY, 5800 Fulton Ave, 91401-4096. SAN 301-6900. Tel: 818-947-2425. Circulation Tel: 818-947-2756. Reference Tel: 818-947-2763. FAX: 818-947-2751. Web Site: www.lavc.cc.ca.us/library.html. *Chairperson*, David G May; E-Mail: maydg@laccd.cc.ca.us; Staff 4 (MLS 4)
Founded 1949. Enrl 18,300; Fac 320; Highest Degree: Associate
Library Holdings: Bk Vols 123,000; Bk Titles 97,000; Per Subs 375
Subject Interests: Art and architecture, Ethnic studies, Humanities, Social sciences and issues
Automation Activity & Vendor Info: (Cataloging) DRA; (Circulation) DRA; (Course Reserve) DRA; (ILL) DRA; (OPAC) DRA; (Serials) DRA

VAN NUYS

S INTERNATIONAL STAMP COLLECTORS SOCIETY LIBRARY, PO Box 854, 91408. SAN 325-528X. Tel: 818-997-6496. *Librn*, Lorraine Pollak
Founded 1970
Library Holdings: Bk Titles 500; Per Subs 25

S NATIONAL INVESTIGATIONS COMMITTEE ON UNIDENTIFIED FLYING OBJECTS, Research Library, 14617 Victory Blvd, Ste 4, 91411. SAN 375-1570. Tel: 818-989-5942. FAX: 818-989-2165. E-Mail: drfes@earthlink.net. Web Site: www.nicufo.org. *Pres*, Dr Frank Stranges; Tel: 818-989-5942, Fax: 818-989-2165, E-Mail: drfes@earthlink.net; Staff 7 (MLS 7)
Founded 1967
Library Holdings: Bk Vols 25; Per Subs 450

S US BUREAU OF THE CENSUS, Information Services Program - Los Angeles Regional Office, 15350 Sherman Way, Ste 310, 91406. SAN 370-2510. Tel: 818-904-6339. FAX: 818-904-6614. Web Site: www.census.gov. *Librn*, Maria Mochulski
Open Mon-Fri 9-4:30

M VALLEY PRESBYTERIAN HOSPITAL, Richard O Myers Library, 15107 Vanowen St, 91409-9102. SAN 301-6935. Tel: 818-902-2973. FAX: 818-902-3990. *Dir*, Francine Kubrin
Library Holdings: Bk Titles 1,550; Per Subs 365
Restriction: Staff use only
Partic in Medline

VANDENBERG AFB

G ITT INDUSTRIES LIBRARY, (Formerly ITT- Federal Services Corporation Library), 5130 Doc Repository, PO Box 5728, 93437. SAN 375-779X. Tel: 805-606-3288.
Library Holdings: Bk Titles 28,000
Restriction: Not open to public

UNITED STATES AIR FORCE

A TECHNICAL LIBRARY, 30TH SPACE WING, 30 SPW/XPOT, 806 13th St Bldg 7015 Ste A, 93437-5223. SAN 335-217X. Tel: 805-734-8232, Ext 69745. FAX: 805-734-8232, Ext 58941. E-Mail: techlib@plansvaft.af.mil. *Dir*, Michele Knight; *Cat, Ref*, Brenda Shintaku; *Per*, Eleanor Potts
Library Holdings: Per Subs 480
Subject Interests: Computer science, Engineering, Fuel, Optics, Radar
Publications: Monthly acquisitions; periodicals
Partic in Coop Libr Agency for Syst & Servs; Dialog Corporation; OCLC Online Computer Library Center, Inc

A VANDENBERG AIR FORCE BASE LIBRARY FL4610, 30 SVS/SVMG, 100 Community Loop Bldg 10343-A, 93437-6111. SAN 326-0720. Tel: 805-734-8232, Ext 66414. FAX: 805-734-1201. E-Mail: spaceprt@rain.org. *Librn*, Joseph Carlson; *Asst Librn*, Richard Kempton; *Tech Servs*, Janice Murphy; Staff 6 (MLS 2, Non-MLS 4)
Founded 1959
Library Holdings: Bk Titles 48,312; Per Subs 133
Subject Interests: Aerospace science, California
Special Collections: Air Force History (Air War College Coll), bks, per
Mem of Black Gold Cooperative Library System

VENTURA

P BLACK GOLD COOPERATIVE LIBRARY SYSTEM, 4882 McGrath St, Ste 230, 93003-7721. SAN 301-5114. Tel: 805-650-7732. FAX: 805-642-9095. Web Site: goldcoastlibraries.org. *Syst Coordr*, Judith Segel; Tel: 805-650-7733, E-Mail: jsegel@rain.org; Staff 3 (MLS 3)
Founded 1963. Pop 1,400,700; Circ 4,390,000
Jul 1999-Jun 2000 Income $1,206,296, State $423,172, Federal $13,333, Locally Generated Income $769,791. Mats Exp $308,727, Per/Ser (Incl. Access Fees) $74,000, Other Print Mats $900, Electronic Ref Mat (Incl. Access Fees) $233,827. Sal $439,858 (Prof $235,840)
Automation Activity & Vendor Info: (Acquisitions) Innovative Interfaces Inc.; (Cataloging) Innovative Interfaces Inc.; (Circulation) Innovative Interfaces Inc.; (ILL) Innovative Interfaces Inc.; (OPAC) Innovative Interfaces Inc.; (Serials) Innovative Interfaces Inc.
Member Libraries: Blanchard-Santa Paula Public Library District; California Department of Corrections Library System; Lompoc Public Library; Paso Robles Public Library; San Luis Obispo City-County Library; Santa Barbara Public Library; Santa Maria Public Library; United States Air Force; Ventura County Library
Partic in OCLC Online Computer Library Center, Inc; Total Interlibrary Exchange

S THE CHURCH OF JESUS CHRIST OF LATTER-DAY SAINTS, Family History Center Ventura Stake,* 76 Saint Paul Dr, 93003. SAN 329-1790. Tel: 805-643-5607. *Librn*, Rosemarie Salmon; *Dir*, Joan Beem; Staff 6 (MLS 1, Non-MLS 5)
Founded 1978
Library Holdings: Bk Vols 1,000; Per Subs 10
Special Collections: IgI Ancestral File; Social Security Death Index

S E W SCRIPPS, (VCS), Ventura County Star Library, 5250 Ralston St, 93003-7392. (Mail add: PO Box 6711, 93003-6711), SAN 329-1561. Tel: 805-655-5803. FAX: 805-644-6123. Web Site: insidevc.com. *Librn*, Wanda Woessner; E-Mail: woessner@insidevc.com
Database Vendor: Lexis-Nexis
Function: Newspaper reference library

S FUGRO WEST, Ventura Library,* 5855 Olivas Park Dr, 93003. SAN 320-3689. Tel: 805-650-7000. FAX: 805-650-7010. *In Charge*, Robin Martin
Library Holdings: Bk Vols 4,500; Per Subs 162
Subject Interests: Geophysics

J VENTURA COLLEGE, D R Henry Library, 4667 Telegraph Rd, 93003-3889. SAN 301-6986. Tel: 805-654-6482. FAX: 805-648-8900. *Dean*, Dr Diane Moore; Tel: 805-654-6468, E-Mail: dmoore@vcccd.net; *Assoc Librn*, David A Breslin; Tel: 805-654-6400, Ext 3257, E-Mail: dbreslin@vcccd.net; *Assoc Librn*, Octavio A Sifuentes; Tel: 805-654-6400, Ext 3258, E-Mail: osifuentes@vcccd.net; Staff 6 (MLS 3, Non-MLS 3)
Founded 1926. Enrl 11,695; Fac 530; Highest Degree: Associate
Jul 1999-Jun 2000 Income State $663,209. Mats Exp $99,130, Books $44,326, Per/Ser (Incl. Access Fees) $14,834, Micro $11,833, AV Equip $10,000, Electronic Ref Mat (Incl. Access Fees) $18,137. Sal $406,123 (Prof $173,060)
Library Holdings: Bk Vols 66,357; Bk Titles 54,061; Per Subs 494
Subject Interests: Art, Ethnic studies, Feminism, Geology
Automation Activity & Vendor Info: (Cataloging) TLC; (Circulation) TLC; (OPAC) TLC
Database Vendor: GaleNet, ProQuest, Wilson - Wilson Web
Function: ILL available
Partic in Coop Libr Agency for Syst & Servs; Total Interlibrary Exchange

GL VENTURA COUNTY LAW LIBRARY,* 800 S Victoria Ave, 93009-2020. SAN 301-7001. Tel: 805-642-8982. FAX: 805-642-7177. E-Mail: vcll@rain.org. *Librn*, Jane G Meyer; Staff 3 (MLS 1, Non-MLS 2)
Founded 1891
Library Holdings: Bk Vols 81,292; Per Subs 328
Special Collections: Law Coll

P VENTURA COUNTY LIBRARY, 800 S Victoria Ave, 93009-1950. SAN 335-220X. Tel: 805-662-6756. Interlibrary Loan Service Tel: 805-641-4445. Circulation Tel: 805-641-4450. Reference Tel: 805-648-2716. FAX: 805-662-6758. E-Mail: vclsaa2@rain.org. Web Site: www.vencolibrary.org. *Dir*, Starrett Kreissman; Tel: 805-662-6750, E-Mail: starrett@rain.org; *Dep Dir*, Alan Langville; Tel: 805-662-6751, E-Mail: langvill@rain.org; *ILL*, Romero Liz; *Acq*, Lori Karns; Tel: 805-641-4449; Staff 20 (MLS 20)
Founded 1915. Pop 433,559; Circ 1,254,001
Jul 1999-Jun 2000 Income $7,528,900. Mats Exp $839,514. Sal $3,523,253
Library Holdings: Bk Vols 731,471; Per Subs 1,078
Special Collections: Ventura County Local History, slides, tapes, bks, per, pamphlets
Automation Activity & Vendor Info: (Circulation) epixtech, inc.
Mem of Black Gold Cooperative Library System
Partic in Total Interlibrary Exchange
Special Services for the Deaf - High interest/low vocabulary books; TTY machine
Friends of the Library Group
Branches: 16
ALBERT H SOLIZ LIBRARY, 2820 Jourdan, El Rio, 93030. SAN 335-2358. Tel: 805-485-4515. FAX: 805-604-7966. Web Site: www.vencolibrary.org. *In Charge*, Cathy Brady
Library Holdings: Bk Vols 16,294
Open Mon-Thurs 10-6, Fri 10-5 & Sat 10-3
Friends of the Library Group
AVENUE, 606 N Ventura Ave, 93001. SAN 335-2234. Tel: 805-643-6393. FAX: 805-648-3791. Web Site: www.vencolibrary.org. *In Charge*, Priscilla Becker
Library Holdings: Bk Vols 22,862
Open Mon 11-1 & 2-6, Tues & Thurs 2-6, Wed 12-6 & Sat 10-3
Friends of the Library Group
CAMARILLO LIBRARY, 3100 Ponderosa Dr, Camarillo, 93010. SAN 335-2269. Tel: 805-482-1952. FAX: 805-987-5241. Web Site: www.ventura.org/vclib/venlsa.htm. *Librn*, Sandi Banks
Library Holdings: Bk Vols 105,319
Friends of the Library Group
E P FOSTER LIBRARY, 651 E Main St, 93001. SAN 335-2412. Tel: 805-648-2715. FAX: 805-648-3696. Web Site: www.ventura.org/vclib/venlsa.htm.
Library Holdings: Bk Vols 122,440
Friends of the Library Group
FILLMORE LIBRARY, 502 Second St, Fillmore, 93015. SAN 335-2382. Tel: 805-524-3355. FAX: 808-524-4636. Web Site: www.ventura.org/vclib/venlsa.htm. *Librn*, Cathy Thomason
Library Holdings: Bk Vols 27,646
Friends of the Library Group
H P WRIGHT LIBRARY, 57 Day Rd, 93003. SAN 335-2714. Tel: 805-642-0336. FAX: 805-644-8725. Web Site: www.vencolibrary.org. *Librn*, Mary Lynch
Library Holdings: Bk Vols 77,085
Open Mon & Tues 10-8, Wed-Fri 2-6 & Sat 10-5
Friends of the Library Group
MEINERS OAKS LIBRARY, 114 N Padre Juan Ave, Meiners Oaks, 93023. SAN 335-2447. Tel: 805-646-4804. FAX: 805-646-8007. Web Site: www.ventura.org/vclib/venlsa.htm. *In Charge*, Dayna Canada
Library Holdings: Bk Vols 12,245
Friends of the Library Group
MOORPARK LIBRARY, 699 Moorpark Ave, Moorpark, 93021. SAN 335-2471. Tel: 805-529-0440. FAX: 805-523-1879. Web Site: www.ventura.org/vclib/venlsa.htm. *Librn*, Bernadette McDowell
Library Holdings: Bk Vols 40,219
Friends of the Library Group
OAK PARK LIBRARY, 899 N Kanan Rd, Agoura, 91301. SAN 335-2528. Tel: 818-889-2239. Web Site: www.ventura.org/vclib/venlsa.htm. *Librn*, Janet Weaver
Library Holdings: Bk Vols 17,040
Friends of the Library Group
OAK VIEW LIBRARY, 469 N Ventura Ave, Oak View, 93022. SAN 335-2536. Tel: 805-649-1523. FAX: 805-649-3511. Web Site: www.ventura.org/vclib/venlsa.htm. *In Charge*, Aleta Rodriguez
Library Holdings: Bk Vols 16,879
Friends of the Library Group
OJAI LIBRARY, 111 E Ojai Ave, Ojai, 93023. SAN 335-2560. Tel: 805-646-1639. FAX: 805-646-4693. Web Site: www.ventura.org/vclib/venlsa.htm. *Librn*, Kit Willis
Library Holdings: Bk Vols 47,590
Friends of the Library Group
PIRU LIBRARY, 3811 Center St, Piru, 93040. SAN 329-7527. Tel: 805-521-1753. FAX: 805-521-0729. Web Site: www.ventura.org/vclib/venlsa.htm. *In Charge*, Cindy Escoto
Library Holdings: Bk Vols 15,496
Friends of the Library Group
RAY D PRUETER LIBRARY, 510 Park Ave, Port Hueneme, 93041. SAN 335-2595. Tel: 805-486-5460. FAX: 805-487-9190. Web Site: www.vencolibrary.org. *Librn*, Cathy Thomason
Library Holdings: Bk Vols 53,692
Open Mon & Tues 3-8, Weds & Thurs 10-6, Sat 12-5, closed Fri & Sun
Friends of the Library Group
SATICOY LIBRARY, 11426 Violeta St, 93004. SAN 376-2084. Tel: 805-647-5736. FAX: 805-672-0406. Web Site: www.vencolibrary.org. *In Charge*, Evelyn Cuevas
Library Holdings: Bk Vols 20,466
Open Mon-Thurs 1-6, Sat 10-2, closed Fri & Sun
Friends of the Library Group
SIMI VALLEY LIBRARY, 2969 Tapo Canyon Rd, Simi Valley, 93063. SAN 335-265X. Tel: 805-526-1735. FAX: 805-526-1738. Web Site: www.vencolibrary.org. *Librn*, Dale Redfield
Library Holdings: Bk Vols 125,986
Open Mon-Thurs 11-9, Fri & Sun 1-5, Sat 10-5
Friends of the Library Group

S VENTURA COUNTY MEDICAL CENTER, Lillian Smolt Memorial Library, 3291 Loma Vista Rd, 93003. SAN 301-6978. Tel: 805-652-6030. FAX: 805-652-6158. E-Mail: library@venturafpr.com. *Dir*, Stella Castaneda; *Librn*, Janet Parker
Library Holdings: Bk Vols 1,200; Per Subs 150
Restriction: Medical staff only
Open Mon-Fri 9-3

S VENTURA COUNTY MUSEUM OF HISTORY & ART, (VCMHA), Historical Research Library, 100 E Main St, 93001. SAN 301-6994. Tel: 805-653-0323, Ext 13. FAX: 805-653-5267. E-Mail: library@vcmha.org. Web Site: www.vcmha.org. *Coll Develop, Librn*, Charles Johnson; Staff 1 (MLS 1)
Founded 1913
Library Holdings: Bk Titles 5,000; Per Subs 16
Special Collections: California Ventura County History, bks, photos, newspapers, 1871 to 1935; Indian Artifacts; Newspapers, 1850-1935; Ventura County Historical Society Quarterlies, 1955-present
Publications: Historical Journal; Ventura County Historical Society (quarterly)
Restriction: Non-circulating

VERNON

P VERNON PUBLIC LIBRARY,* 4305 Santa Fe Ave, 90058-0805. SAN 301-701X. Tel: 323-583-8811. FAX: 323-581-7924. *Librn*, Leonis Malburg
Pop 90
Library Holdings: Bk Vols 1,112

VICTORVILLE

J VICTOR VALLEY COMMUNITY COLLEGE LIBRARY,* 18422 Bear Valley Rd, 92392-9699. SAN 301-7028. Tel: 760-245-4271, Ext 262. FAX: 760-245-4373. *Librn*, Janet Ashton-Beazie; E-Mail: jbeazie@victor.cc.ca.us; *Coll Develop, Librn*, Fran Elgin; *Librn*, John Akins
Founded 1961
Jul 1996-Jun 1997 Income $769,282. Mats Exp $199,279, Books $55,000, Per/Ser (Incl. Access Fees) $28,000, Presv $725, Micro $5,911, AV Equip $20,027. Sal $466,596 (Prof $198,700)
Library Holdings: Bk Vols 54,000; Bk Titles 50,000; Per Subs 492
Special Collections: Mojave Desert
Partic in OCLC Online Computer Library Center, Inc; San Bernardino, Inyo, Riverside Counties United Library Services
Friends of the Library Group

VISALIA

J COLLEGE OF THE SEQUOIAS LIBRARY,* 915 S Mooney Blvd, 93277. SAN 301-7036. Tel: 559-730-3824. FAX: 559-737-4835. Web Site: giant.sequoias.cc.ca.us/academic/library/homepage/library_homepage.htm. *Dir*, Nancy Finney; *Ref*, Linda Yamakawa; Staff 5 (MLS 5)
Founded 1926. Enrl 7,909; Fac 384
Library Holdings: Bk Vols 78,000; Per Subs 430
Partic in Area Wide Library Network

M KAWEAH DELTA HEALTH CARE DISTRICT LIBRARY,* 400 W Mineral King Ave, 93291-6263. SAN 320-6084. Tel: 209-625-7167, 209-625-7216. FAX: 209-635-4051. *Librn*, Jeannine Hinkel; E-Mail: jhinkel@kdhcd.org
Jul 1996-Jun 1997 Mats Exp $54,650, Books $28,650, Per/Ser (Incl. Access Fees) $26,000. Sal $68,856 (Prof $49,735)
Subject Interests: Clinical medicine, Hospital administration, Nursing
Partic in Nat Libr of Med

GL TULARE COUNTY LAW LIBRARY, County Courthouse, Rm 1, 221 S Mooney Blvd, 93291. SAN 301-7052. Tel: 559-733-6395. *Dir*, Anne R Bernardo; E-Mail: abernard@co.tulare.ca.us; Staff 4 (Non-MLS 4)
Founded 1892
Jul 1999-Jun 2000 Income $299,151, County $227,013, Locally Generated Income $72,138. Mats Exp $186,638, Books $134,155, Per/Ser (Incl. Access Fees) $3,317, Presv $610, AV Equip $17,768, Electronic Ref Mat (Incl. Access Fees) $30,788. Sal $102,908
Library Holdings: Bk Vols 18,566; Bk Titles 1,674; Per Subs 110
Database Vendor: Lexis-Nexis
Function: Reference only
Partic in Area Wide Library Network

P TULARE COUNTY LIBRARY, 200 W Oak Ave, 93291-4993. SAN 335-2749. Tel: 559-733-6954. Circulation Tel: 559-733-6954, Ext 210. Reference Tel: 559-733-6954, Ext 228. FAX: 559-730-2524, 559-737-4586 (Admin). Web Site: www.sjvls.lib.ca.us. *Automation Syst Coordr, Dir*, Brian G Lewis; Tel: 559-733-6954, Ext 201, E-Mail: blewis@sjvls.lib.ca.us; *Asst Dir*, Jeff Crosby; Tel: 559-733-6954, Ext 222, E-Mail: jcrosby@sjvls.lib.ca.us; *ILL*, Deb Florez; *Head Ref*, Van Quine; Tel: 559-733-6954, Ext 216, E-Mail: vquine@sjvls.lib.ca.us; Staff 7 (MLS 7)
Founded 1910. Pop 288,600
Jul 1999-Jun 2000 Income (Main Library and Branch Library) $2,677,472, State $479,989, Federal $11,000, Locally Generated Income $149,682, Other $2,036,801. Mats Exp $2,677,472, Books $272,809, Per/Ser (Incl. Access Fees) $33,112, Presv $8,000, Micro $3,086. Sal $956,704 (Prof $211,300)
Library Holdings: Bk Vols 397,151; Bk Titles 295,300; Per Subs 746
Special Collections: George W Stewart Coll, mss; History of Kings & Sequoia National Park; Tulare County
Database Vendor: OCLC - First Search
Mem of San Joaquin Valley Library System
Partic in Area Wide Library Network; OCLC Online Computer Library Center, Inc
Friends of the Library Group
Branches: 17
ALPAUGH BRANCH, 3816 Ave 54, PO Box 69, Alpaugh, 93201. SAN 335-2773. Tel: 559-949-8355. FAX: 559-949-8225. *Branch Mgr*, Daniel Rhoads; *Librn*, Joy Foster
Founded 1910. Pop 927
Library Holdings: Bk Vols 8,438
DINUBA BRANCH, 150 S I St, Dinuba, 93618. SAN 335-2838. Tel: 559-591-5828. FAX: 559-591-5886. *Branch Mgr*, Celia Morales; *Branch Mgr*, Deanna Warkentin
Founded 1910. Pop 16,000
Library Holdings: Bk Vols 31,363
Friends of the Library Group
EARLIMART BRANCH, 780 E Washington St, PO Box 12153, Earlimart, 93219-2153. SAN 335-2897. Tel: 661-849-2525. FAX: 661-849-1517. *Branch Mgr*, Daniel Rhoads
Founded 1914. Pop 2,000
Library Holdings: Bk Vols 10,153
EXETER BRANCH, 230 E Chestnut, Exeter, 93221. SAN 335-2927. Tel: 559-592-5361. FAX: 559-592-4452. *Branch Mgr*, Kathryn Ramsey
Founded 1910. Pop 7,200
Library Holdings: Bk Vols 30,787
Friends of the Library Group
FARMERSVILLE BRANCH, 147 N Front, Farmersville, 93223. Tel: 559-747-2123.
Founded 1915. Pop 7,000
Library Holdings: Bk Vols 3,000
FARMERSVILLE VOLUNTEER BRANCH, 147 N Front St, Farmersville, 93223. Tel: 559-747-2123. Web Site: www.sjvls.lib.ca.us/tulareco, www.tularecolib.net.
Library Holdings: Bk Vols 3,000
Open Mon-Fri 2-5
IVANHOE BRANCH, 15964 Heather, Ivanhoe, 93235. SAN 335-3044. Tel: 559-798-1264. FAX: 559-798-5634. *Branch Mgr*, Irene Gomez; E-Mail: igomez@sjvls.lib.ca.us
Founded 1914. Pop 4,100
Library Holdings: Bk Vols 11,051
LINDSAY BRANCH, 165 N Gale Hill St, Lindsay, 93247. SAN 335-3079. Tel: 559-562-3021. FAX: 559-562-5066. *Branch Mgr*, Deanna Pettus
Founded 1910. Pop 10,100
Library Holdings: Bk Vols 23,381
Friends of the Library Group
OROSI BRANCH, 12646 Ave 416, Orosi, 93647. SAN 335-3133. Tel: 559-519-5830. FAX: 559-528-9156. *Branch Mgr*, Augustina Ortiz
Founded 1911. Pop 6,800
Library Holdings: Bk Vols 9,342
Friends of the Library Group
PIXLEY BRANCH, 300 N School, PO Box K, Pixley, 93256. (Mail add: 200 W Oak Ave, 93291), SAN 335-3192. Tel: 559-733-6954, Ext 213. FAX: 559-737-4586. *Librn*, Marisol Rodriguez
Founded 1913. Pop 3,100
Library Holdings: Bk Vols 13,353
Pixley School District has a joint agreement with the County of Tulare in the operations of a joint school & public library
SPRINGVILLE BRANCH, 35800 Hwy 190, PO Box 257, Springville, 93265. SAN 335-3257. Tel: 559-539-2624. FAX: 559-539-6307. *Branch Mgr*, Donna Ellis
Founded 1911. Pop 1,545
Library Holdings: Bk Vols 8,789
Friends of the Library Group
STRATHMORE BRANCH, 19646 Rd 230, PO Box 595, Strathmore, 93267. SAN 335-3281. Tel: 559-568-1067. FAX: 559-568-0633. *Branch Mgr*, Donna Ellis; Tel: 559-568-1087
Founded 1911. Pop 3,000
Library Holdings: Bk Vols 16,416
Friends of the Library Group
TERRA BELLA BRANCH, 23825 Ave 92, PO Box 442, Terra Bella, 93270. SAN 335-3311. Tel: 559-535-5583. *Branch Mgr*, Donna Ellis
Founded 1912. Pop 3,400
Library Holdings: Bk Vols 9,096
Terra Bella School District shares in the operations of a school & public library with Tulare County Library
THREE RIVERS BRANCH, 42052 Eggers Dr, PO Box 216, Three Rivers, 93271. SAN 335-3346. Tel: 559-561-4564. FAX: 559-561-7318. *Branch Mgr*, Rita Pena
Founded 1910. Pop 930
Library Holdings: Bk Vols 18,498
Friends of the Library Group
TIPTON BRANCH, 301 E Woods Ave, PO Box 39, Tipton, 93272. SAN 335-3370. Tel: 559-752-4236. FAX: 559-752-7307. *Branch Mgr*, Cindy Little
Library Holdings: Bk Vols 8,540
VISALIA HEADQUARTERS BRANCH, 200 W Oak Ave, 93291. SAN 335-3435. Tel: 559-733-6954. FAX: 559-737-4586. Web Site: www.sjvls.lib.ca.us.tulareco. *Asst Dir*, Jeff Crosby; E-Mail: jcrosby@sjvls.lib.ca.us; *Branch Mgr*, Rita Pena; Tel: 559-564-8424, Fax: 559-564-6725; *Head Ref*, Van Quine; Tel: 559-733-6954, Ext 216, E-Mail: vquine@sjvls.lib.ca.us; *Librn*, Jane Cothron; Staff 7 (MLS 7)
Founded 1910. Pop 93,500
Library Holdings: Bk Vols 150,450
Database Vendor: IAC - SearchBank, OCLC - First Search
Friends of the Library Group
WOODLAKE BRANCH, 400 W Whitney Ave, Woodlake, 93286. SAN 335-346X. Tel: 559-564-8424. FAX: 559-564-6725. *Librn*, Carol Demmers; *Librn*, Rita Pena
Library Holdings: Bk Vols 13,221
Bookmobiles: 2

G TULARE COUNTY OFFICE OF EDUCATION, Educational Resource Services,* 7000 Doe, Ste A, 93291. SAN 301-7044. Tel: 559-651-3031. FAX: 559-651-1012. Web Site: www.tcoe.k12.ca.us. *Media Spec*, George Pilling; *Mgr*, Elaine Scott; Tel: 559-651-3042, E-Mail: escott@tcoe.k12.ca.us; Staff 12 (MLS 2, Non-MLS 10)
Founded 1927. Enrl 76,574; Fac 3,169; Highest Degree: Doctorate
Library Holdings: Bk Vols 250,000; Bk Titles 100,000; Per Subs 50
Special Collections: Instructional Materials Display Center of Textbooks & Media
Special Services for the Deaf - Captioned film depository

WALNUT

J MOUNT SAN ANTONIO COLLEGE LIBRARY,* 1100 N Grand Ave, 91789. SAN 301-7079. Tel: 909-594-5611, Ext 4260. FAX: 909-468-4011. *Dean of Libr*, Kerry C Stern; E-Mail: kstern@ibm.mtsac.edu; *Librn*, Tula Demas; *Ref*, Joan Conger; *Acq, Circ*, Charles Varnes; *Automation Syst Coordr*, Ligia Kralert; Staff 5 (MLS 5)
Founded 1946
Library Holdings: Bk Titles 77,296
Partic in Inland Empire Acad Libr Coop

WALNUT CREEK

S CONTRA COSTA TIMES NEWS RESEARCH DEPARTMENT,* 2640 Shadelands Dr, PO Box 5088, 94596-1088. SAN 324-4245. Tel: 925-943-8190. FAX: 925-943-8362.; Staff 3 (MLS 2, Non-MLS 1)
Founded 1978
Library Holdings: Bk Vols 500; Bk Titles 480; Per Subs 20
Special Collections: Contra Costa Times, clippings, micro
Publications: Orientation Handbook
Restriction: Staff use only

M JOHN MUIR MEDICAL CENTER LIBRARY,* 1601 Ygnacio Valley Rd, 94598-3194. SAN 326-5110. Tel: 925-947-5231. FAX: 925-947-3237. *Librn*, Helen M Doughty
Library Holdings: Bk Vols 3,750
Subject Interests: History of medicine
Publications: Infoline (newsletter)
Partic in Balin; Dialog Corporation; National Network Of Libraries Of Medicine - Pacific Northwest Region

S SHADELANDS RANCH HISTORICAL MUSEUM, Shadelands History Room Library,* 2660 Ygnacio Valley Rd, 94598. SAN 301-7117. Tel: 925-935-7871. FAX: 925-935-7885. *Librn*, Audrey Veregge
Founded 1972
Library Holdings: Bk Titles 500
Subject Interests: California
Special Collections: Albert Johnson Business Papers; Concord Journal 1957-1967; Hutchinson Family photos; James P Howe Coll, papers; Joseph Reddeford Walker & Family, photog; Local Newspaper Coll: Concord Journal 1957-1967, Pleasant Hill Post 1957-1967, Walnut Creek Independent, Walnut Creek Sentinel, Walnut Kennel Newspaper 1932-1967; Pleasant Hill Post 1957-1967; Rogers Hotel, photog; Seely Family Letters; Seely-Hodges Family Letters; Shadelands Ranch Business Documents; Walnut Creek (Robert Thain Coll), photog; Walnut Creek City Documents; Walnut Kennel Newspaper 1932-1967

WATSONVILLE

S PAJARO VALLEY HISTORICAL ASSOCIATION LIBRARY,* 332 E Beach St, PO Box 95077, 95076. SAN 301-7125. Tel: 831-722-0305. FAX: 831-722-5501.
Founded 1964
Library Holdings: Bk Titles 381
Special Collections: Local History, papers & photogs
Publications: Newsletter (bi-monthly)

P WATSONVILLE PUBLIC LIBRARY, 310 Union St, 95076. SAN 301-7133. Tel: 831-728-6040. FAX: 831-763-4015. E-Mail: library@watsonville.lib.ca.us. Web Site: www.watsonville.lib.ca.us. *Dir*, Deborah Barrow; E-Mail: dbarrow@watsonville.lib.ca.us; *Cat*, Ted Harris; *Publ Servs*, Carol C Heitzig; E-Mail: cheitzig@ci.watsonville.ca.us; *Circ*, Alicia Martinez; E-Mail: amartine@ci.watsonville.ca.us; *Ch Servs*, Karen Sherman; E-Mail: ksherman@ci.watsonville.ca.us; *Tech Servs*, Steven Silveria; E-Mail: ssilveri@ci.watsonville.ca.us; Staff 9 (MLS 9)
Founded 1895. Pop 36,000
Jul 2000-Jun 2001 Income (Main Library and Branch Library) $2,083,000, State $50,000, City $541,000, County $1,422,000, Locally Generated Income $70,000. Mats Exp $200,000, Books $150,000, Electronic Ref Mat (Incl. Access Fees) $50,000. Sal $683,301
Library Holdings: Bk Vols 111,000; Per Subs 349
Subject Interests: Spanish (language)
Database Vendor: OCLC - First Search, ProQuest
Mem of Monterey Bay Area Cooperative Library System
Partic in MOBAC
Friends of the Library Group
Branches: 1
FREEDOM BRANCH, 2021 Freedom Blvd, Freedom, 95019. Tel: 831-763-4141. FAX: 831-763-4141. Web Site: www.watsonville.lib.ca.us. *Librn*, Rachel Harwood
Jul 2000-Jun 2001 Income $32,000
Library Holdings: Bk Vols 13,500; Per Subs 28
Automation Activity & Vendor Info: (Cataloging) Innovative Interfaces Inc.; (Circulation) Innovative Interfaces Inc.; (OPAC) Innovative Interfaces Inc.

WEAVERVILLE

GL TRINITY COUNTY LAW LIBRARY,* Courthouse, 101 Court St, PO Box 1258, 96093-1258. SAN 328-6665. Tel: 916-623-1369. FAX: 916-623-3762. *Librn*, Donna Regnani

P TRINITY COUNTY LIBRARY,* 211 N Main St, PO Box 1226, 96093-1226. SAN 301-7141. Tel: 530-623-1373. FAX: 530-623-4427. E-Mail: trill@tcoe.trinity.k12.ca.us. *Dir*, Godelieve Uyttenhoven
Founded 1916. Pop 13,900; Circ 103,000
Jul 1997-Jun 1998 Income $197,601
Library Holdings: Bk Vols 30,000; Per Subs 57
Special Collections: Trinity County History; Trinity River Basin Coll
Mem of North State Cooperative Library System
Friends of the Library Group
Branches: 2
HAYFORK BRANCH, Hayfork, 96041. SAN 329-3599. Tel: 530-628-5427. FAX: 530-628-5427. E-Mail: haylib@tcoe.trinity.k12.ca.us. *Librn*, Sharon Boone
Friends of the Library Group
TRINITY CENTER BRANCH, Trinity Center, 96091. SAN 370-4386. Tel: 530-266-3242. *Librn*, Marion Teitzel
Friends of the Library Group

WEED

J COLLEGE OF THE SISKIYOUS LIBRARY, 800 College Ave, 96094. SAN 301-715X. Tel: 530-938-5331. FAX: 530-938-5226. E-Mail: library@siskiyous.edu. Web Site: www.siskiyous.edu. *Dir*, Dennis R Freeman
Founded 1957. Pop 3,077; Circ 25,643; Enrl 2,270; Fac 164
Library Holdings: Bk Vols 42,640; Per Subs 175
Subject Interests: Local history, Philosophy, Religion
Automation Activity & Vendor Info: (Circulation) SIRSI
Mem of North State Cooperative Library System
Partic in Coop Libr Agency for Syst & Servs; N Calif Telecommunications Consortium

WEST HILLS

§C DEVRY INSTITUTE OF TECHNOLOGY LIBRARY, 22801 Roscoe Blvd, 91304. SAN 375-4294. Tel: 818-932-3028. FAX: 818-932-3107. *Librn*, Kimberly Embleton; Tel: 818-932-3027, E-Mail: kembleto@socal.devry.edu; Staff 2 (MLS 1, Non-MLS 1)
Founded 1999
Library Holdings: Bk Vols 5,000; Per Subs 85
Subject Interests: Bus mgt, Computer info systs, Technology
Automation Activity & Vendor Info: (Cataloging) Endeavor; (Circulation) Endeavor; (OPAC) Endeavor
Database Vendor: ProQuest

WEST HOLLYWOOD

S CENTER FOR EARLY EDUCATION LIBRARY, 563 N Alfred St, 90048. SAN 300-9041. Tel: 323-651-0707. FAX: 323-651-0860. *Librn*, Lucy Rafael; Staff 1 (MLS 1)
Founded 1965
Jul 1998-Jun 1999 Income $20,000
Library Holdings: Bk Vols 20,622; Bk Titles 19,560; Per Subs 99
Subject Interests: Child development, Children's literature, Education
Automation Activity & Vendor Info: (Acquisitions) Follett; (Cataloging) Follett; (Circulation) Follett; (Media Booking) Follett
Children's Collections serving students (toddler-grade 6), their teachers & parents; Adult Collection of child development resources for parents & teachers; Teacher's Resource Library of hands-on classroom materials for teacher use only

WHITTIER

§S CALIFORNIA YOUTH AUTHORITY, Fred C Nelles Youth Correctional Facility-Manuel R Gallegos Memorial Library, 11850 E Whittier Blvd, 90601. Tel: 562-698-6781, Ext 4346. FAX: 562-907-9761. *Senior Librn*, Juel Blanchard
Jul 1999-Jun 2000 Income $34,000
Library Holdings: Bk Vols 10,000; Per Subs 96

M PRESBYTERIAN INTERCOMMUNITY HOSPITAL, Medical Library,* 12401 E Washington Blvd, 90602. SAN 301-7184. Tel: 562-698-0811, Ext 2583. *Librn*, Cybil Balletine
Library Holdings: Bk Titles 600; Per Subs 165
Partic in Nat Libr of Med; Pacific SW Regional Med Libr Serv

J RIO HONDO COMMUNITY COLLEGE LIBRARY, 3600 Workman Mill Rd, 90601. SAN 301-7192. Tel: 562-908-3417. Circulation Tel: 562-908-3416. Reference Tel: 562-908-3484. FAX: 562-692-9948. E-Mail: library@rh.cc.ca.us. Web Site: www.rh.cc.ca.us/library. *Coordr*, Adele Enright; E-Mail: aenright@rh.cc.ca.us; *Coll Develop*, Stephanie Wells; E-Mail: swells@rh.cc.ca.us; *Syst Coordr*, Jan Coe; E-Mail: jcoe@rh.cc.ca.us; *Bibliog Instr*, Judy Sevilla-Marzona; E-Mail: jsevilla@rh.cc.ca.us; *Coll Develop*, Robin Babou; E-Mail: rbabou@rh.cc.ca.us; Staff 16 (MLS 5, Non-MLS 11)
Founded 1965. Enrl 13,303; Fac 406
1999-2000 Mats Exp $109,850, Books $49,600, Per/Ser (Incl. Access Fees) $36,400, Micro $2,000, AV Equip $2,000, Electronic Ref Mat (Incl. Access Fees) $19,850. Sal $402,935 (Prof $748,005)
Library Holdings: Bk Vols 84,761; Bk Titles 75,558; Per Subs 205
Subject Interests: Art and architecture, Labor, Law, Photography
Automation Activity & Vendor Info: (Acquisitions) SIRSI; (Cataloging)

SIRSI; (Circulation) SIRSI; (Course Reserve) SIRSI; (OPAC) SIRSI; (Serials) SIRSI
Database Vendor: CARL, IAC - Info Trac, ProQuest
Partic in Metropolitan Cooperative Library System

CM SOUTHERN CALIFORNIA UNIVERSITY OF HEALTH SCIENCES, (Formerly Los Angeles College of Chiropractic), Learning Resource Center, 16200 E Amber Valley Dr, 90604-4098. (Mail add: PO Box 1166, 90609-1166), SAN 300-7898. Tel: 562-902-3368. FAX: 562-902-3323. E-Mail: library@lacc.edu. Web Site: www.deltanet.com/lacc. *Dir*, Nehmat Saab; Tel: 562-947-8755, Ext 367; *Librn*, Diana Gonzalez; Tel: 562-947-8755, Ext 564
Founded 1911. Enrl 1,000
Sep 1999-Aug 2000 Mats Exp $139,024, Books $42,000, Per/Ser (Incl. Access Fees) $52,000, Micro $8,500, AV Equip $1,524, Electronic Ref Mat (Incl. Access Fees) $35,000. Sal $161,665 (Prof $108,000)
Library Holdings: Bk Vols 24,925; Bk Titles 10,387; Per Subs 222
Subject Interests: Anatomy, Chiropractic medicine, Neurology, Nutrition, Osteopathology, Physical therapy, Physiology, Sports
Special Collections: Chiropractic History; Nutrition & Natural Therapeutics
Automation Activity & Vendor Info: (Acquisitions) Endeavor; (Cataloging) Endeavor; (Circulation) Endeavor; (Serials) Endeavor
Database Vendor: Ebsco - EbscoHost, OVID Technologies, ProQuest
Partic in Chiropractic Libr Consortium; CLS; Med Libr Group of S Calif & Ariz

WHITTIER COLLEGE

C BONNIE BELL WARDMAN LIBRARY, 7031 Founders Hill Rd, 90608-9984. SAN 335-3524. Tel: 562-907-4247. FAX: 562-698-7168. Web Site: library.whittier.edu. *Dir*, Philip M O'Brien; E-Mail: pobrien@whittier.edu; *Bibliog Instr, ILL, Ref*, Ann Topjon; *Cat, Tech Servs*, Mary Ellen Vick; *Govt Doc*, Shelley Urbizagastegui; *Ser, Spec Coll*, Joe Dmohowski; *Syst Coordr*, Peggy Gaugy; Staff 6 (MLS 6)
Founded 1901. Enrl 1,305; Fac 93; Highest Degree: Master
Jul 1998-Jun 1999 Income Parent Institution $888,728. Mats Exp $423,957, Books $202,894, Per/Ser (Incl. Access Fees) $175,731, Presv $11,171, Micro $1,200, Electronic Ref Mat (Incl. Access Fees) $32,961. Sal $403,511 (Prof $289,330)
Library Holdings: Bk Vols 232,031; Per Subs 660
Special Collections: Jan de Hartog Coll, bks & mss; Jessamyn West Coll, bks, mss; John Greenleaf Whittier Coll; Richard M Nixon Coll; Society of Friends (Clifford & Susan Johnson Library of Quaker Literature), bks, micro, pamphlets
Automation Activity & Vendor Info: (Acquisitions) Innovative Interfaces Inc.; (Cataloging) Innovative Interfaces Inc.; (Circulation) Innovative Interfaces Inc.; (Course Reserve) Innovative Interfaces Inc.; (ILL) Innovative Interfaces Inc.; (Media Booking) Innovative Interfaces Inc.; (OPAC) Innovative Interfaces Inc.; (Serials) Innovative Interfaces Inc.
Database Vendor: Innovative Interfaces INN - View
Publications: Discovery
Partic in CAL/PALS; OCLC Online Computer Library Center, Inc; SCELC

C FAIRCHILD AERIAL PHOTOGRAPHY COLLECTION, 13615 Earlham Dr, Science Bldg, 2nd flr, 90601. Tel: 562-907-4220. FAX: 562-693-6117. E-Mail: fairchild@whittier.edu. Web Site: www.whittier.edu/fairchild/home.html. *Dir*, Stephanie Breaux
Founded 1965. Enrl 1,250; Fac 95; Highest Degree: Master
Subject Interests: Aerial photos
Restriction: By appointment only
Function: Archival collection, Research fees apply
Partic in Nat Cartographic Info Ctr

C MEDIA CENTER, 13406 E Philadelphia St, PO Box 634, 90608. SAN 335-3559. Tel: 562-907-4267. FAX: 562-907-4922. *In Charge*, Richard Cheatham; E-Mail: rcheatham@whittier.edu
Founded 1971
Jul 1996-Jun 1997 Income $10,000. Mats Exp $8,000, Micro $3,000, AV Equip $3,000
Subject Interests: Education, Environmental studies, Ethnic studies, Feminism, History

P WHITTIER PUBLIC LIBRARY, 7344 S Washington Ave, 90602. SAN 335-3583. Tel: 562-464-3450. FAX: 562-464-3569. E-Mail: wpl1@jps.net. *Actg Dir*, Bonnie Weber; *ILL*, Carolyn Rory; *Media Spec*, Edward Montano; *Acq*, Diana Erickson; *Ref*, Cynthia Birt; Staff 14 (MLS 14)
Founded 1900. Pop 83,000; Circ 636,930
Library Holdings: Bk Vols 251,991
Special Collections: Margaret Fulmer Peace Coll; Whittier Hills Archives; Whittier History
Automation Activity & Vendor Info: (Circulation) epixtech, inc.
Mem of Metropolitan Cooperative Library System
Friends of the Library Group
Branches: 1
WHITTWOOD, 10537 Santa Gertrudes Ave, 90603-2760. SAN 335-3613. Tel: 562-464-3470. FAX: 562-464-3479. *Librn*, Rae Beverage; *Circ*, Martha Hidalgo; *Per, Ref*, Debi Shulkatis; Staff 9 (MLS 5, Non-MLS 4)
Circ 192,148
Library Holdings: Bk Vols 66,413; Bk Titles 47,196; Per Subs 90
Partic in Metropolitan Cooperative Library System
Friends of the Library Group

WILDOMAR

S NORTH AMERICAN RADIO ARCHIVES, The Farm Rd, 92595. SAN 329-0751. Tel: 909-244-5242. FAX: 909-244-0022. *Librn*, Don Aston; E-Mail: aston@cosmosaccess.net
Founded 1972
Library Holdings: Bk Titles 475
Publications: The NARA News (quarterly)

WILLITS

M FRANK R HOWARD MEMORIAL HOSPITAL LIBRARY,* One Nadrone St, 95490. SAN 322-6476. Tel: 707-459-6801, Ext 254. FAX: 707-459-3163. *Librn*, Sue Atherton
Founded 1974
Library Holdings: Bk Vols 539; Bk Titles 476

WILLOWS

P NORTH STATE COOPERATIVE LIBRARY SYSTEM, (NSCLS), 259 N Villa Ave, 95988-2607. SAN 301-7206. Tel: 530-934-2173. Reference Tel: 530-538-7326. FAX: 530-934-7156. Web Site: www.nscls.library.net. *Syst Coordr*, James H Kirks, Jr; E-Mail: jkirks@glenncounty.net; *Ref*, Terry Simas; Fax: 530-538-7235, E-Mail: nscref@buttecounty.net; Staff 16 (MLS 2, Non-MLS 14)
Founded 1969. Pop 736,290
Jul 1999-Jun 2000 Income $1,408,958, State $267,172, Federal $439,199, Locally Generated Income $268,855, Other $433,732. Mats Exp $212,231, Books $33,972, Per/Ser (Incl. Access Fees) $1,227, AV Equip $29,956, Electronic Ref Mat (Incl. Access Fees) $147,076. Sal $348,880 (Prof $136,310)
Subject Interests: Compact discs, Video cassettes
Automation Activity & Vendor Info: (Cataloging) TLC
Publications: Children's Services Correspondence Course; ILL & ILR Manual; Listen-In Catalog (audio cassette & compact disc); Reference Correspondence Courses; Resources Directory (special libraries in NSCLS area); VHS Videocassette Catalog
Member Libraries: Butte Community College; Butte County Library; California State University, Chico; CH2M Hill; College of the Redwoods Library; College Of The Siskiyous Library; Colusa County Free Library; Del Norte County Library District; Feather River College Library; Humboldt County Library; Humboldt State University Library; Lassen College Library; Modoc County Library; Orland Free Library; Plumas County Library; Shasta College Library; Shasta County Library; Simpson College; Susanville District Library; Tehama County Library; Trinity County Library; Willows Public Library
Special Services for the Deaf - Captioned media
Special Services for the Blind - Audio-cassettes

P WILLOWS PUBLIC LIBRARY,* 201 N Lassen St, 95988-3010. SAN 301-7214. Tel: 530-934-5156. FAX: 530-934-2225. *Librn*, Don Hampton; Staff 2 (MLS 2)
Founded 1906. Pop 11,275; Circ 75,778
Library Holdings: Bk Vols 64,297; Bk Titles 58,114; Per Subs 120
Special Collections: Californiana Coll
Mem of North State Cooperative Library System
Partic in Class; RLIN
Friends of the Library Group
Branches: 2
BAYLISS, 7830 Rd 39, Glenn, 95943. SAN 376-2599. Tel: 530-934-2287. FAX: 530-934-8082. *Br Coordr*, Linda Peelle-Haddeman
Founded 1914. Pop 1,000
Library Holdings: Bk Vols 3,570; Per Subs 15
ELK CREEK BRANCH, 120 Church St, Elk Creek, 95939. (Mail add: PO Box 133, Elk Creek, 95939-0133), Tel: 530-968-5238. Web Site: www.glenn-co.k12.ca.us/wil_lib/. *Branch Mgr*, Corinne Reid
Library Holdings: Bk Vols 1,300; Per Subs 11
Open Mon & Wed 12-4, Thurs 9-1

WILMINGTON

S GENERAL PHINEAS BANNING RESIDENCE MUSEUM LIBRARY,* PO Box 397, 90748. SAN 374-8200. Tel: 310-548-7777. FAX: 310-548-2644. Web Site: www.banning.org. *Curator*, Michael Sanborn
Library Holdings: Bk Vols 500
Restriction: Private library

J LOS ANGELES HARBOR COLLEGE, Camille L Baxter Learning Resource Center, 1111 Figueroa Pl, 90744-2397. SAN 301-7222. Tel: 310-522-8292. FAX: 310-522-8435. Web Site: www.lahc.cc.ca.us/library. *Chairperson*, Sally Gogin; Tel: 310-522-8434, E-Mail: gogins@laccd.cc.ca.us; *Coll Develop*, Elisabeth Campbell; *Cat*, Jonathon Lee; *Acq*, Ibtesam Dessouky; Staff 3 (MLS 3)
Founded 1949. Pop 7,519; Enrl 7,519; Fac 115; Highest Degree: Associate
Jul 1999-Jun 2000 Income $426,526. Mats Exp $62,664, Books $32,360, Per/Ser (Incl. Access Fees) $13,604, Electronic Ref Mat (Incl. Access Fees)

$16,700. Sal $408,619 (Prof $271,467)
Library Holdings: Bk Vols 82,904; Per Subs 206
Special Collections: Los Angeles Harbor Area History (Los Angeles Harbor College Historical Project), clippings, photogs
Automation Activity & Vendor Info: (Cataloging) DRA; (Circulation) DRA; (Course Reserve) DRA; (OPAC) DRA
Database Vendor: IAC - Info Trac, ProQuest
Restriction: Open to faculty, students & qualified researchers
Mem of Los Angeles Community Col District
Friends of the Library Group

WOODLAND

P WOODLAND PUBLIC LIBRARY,* 250 First St, 95695-3411. SAN 301-7249. Tel: 530-661-5981. FAX: 530-666-5408. *Dir*, Marie Bryan; *Ch Servs*, Carol Beckham; *Ref*, Jane Derry; Staff 8 (MLS 8)
Founded 1904. Pop 42,250; Circ 234,106
Library Holdings: Bk Vols 92,000; Per Subs 237
Automation Activity & Vendor Info: (Circulation) CLSI LIBS
Mem of Mountain-Valley Library System
Partic in OCLC Online Computer Library Center, Inc
Open Mon-Thurs 11-8, Fri & Sat 10-5
Friends of the Library Group

GL YOLO COUNTY LAW LIBRARY,* 625 Court St, 95695. SAN 301-7257. Tel: 530-666-8918. FAX: 530-666-8618. E-Mail: lawlib@cndcn.davis.ca.us. *Librn*, Laura Reed
Library Holdings: Bk Titles 13,000
Open Mon-Thurs 9-5, Fri 9-2

P YOLO COUNTY LIBRARY, Admin Off, 226 Buckeye St, 95695-2600. SAN 335-3648. Tel: 530-666-8005. FAX: 530-666-8006. Web Site: www.yolocounty.org/org/library. *Dir*, Mary L Stephens; *Asst Dir*, Marilyn Corcoran; *Tech Servs*, Kim Sheppard; *Ch Servs*, Peggy Rollins; Staff 10 (MLS 9, Non-MLS 1)
Founded 1910. Pop 113,200; Circ 741,680
Jul 1999-Jun 2000 Income $2,478,603, State $208,228, Locally Generated Income $339,628. Mats Exp $291,785, Books $272,180, Per/Ser (Incl. Access Fees) $19,605. Sal $1,460,003
Library Holdings: Bk Vols 306,080; Per Subs 568
Special Collections: Geography (Beulah Hughes Coll); Spanish Language Coll; Yolo County History Coll
Database Vendor: DRA
Mem of Mountain-Valley Library System
Friends of the Library Group
Branches: 7
CLARKSBURG BRANCH, 52915 Netherlands Ave, PO Box 229, Clarksburg, 95612. SAN 335-3672. Tel: 916-744-1755. FAX: 916-744-1755. *Librn*, Rebecca Frame
Library Holdings: Bk Vols 20,097
Friends of the Library Group
DAVIS BRANCH, 315 E 14th St, Davis, 95616. SAN 335-3702. Tel: 530-757-5593. Circulation Tel: 530-757-5592. FAX: 530-757-5590. *Librn*, Jay Johnstone
Library Holdings: Bk Vols 160,416
Friends of the Library Group
ESPARTO BRANCH, 17065 Yolo Ave, Esparto, 95627. SAN 335-3737. Tel: 530-787-3426. FAX: 530-787-4874. *Librn*, Nadine DeSmet
Library Holdings: Bk Vols 17,160
Friends of the Library Group
KNIGHTS LANDING BRANCH, 42351 Third St, PO Box 517, Knights Landing, 95645. SAN 335-3761. Tel: 530-735-6593. FAX: 530-735-6593. *Librn*, Nora Gortze
Library Holdings: Bk Vols 12,632
Friends of the Library Group
ARTHUR F TURNER BRANCH, 1212 Merkley Ave, West Sacramento, 95691. SAN 335-3796. Tel: 916-375-6465. FAX: 916-371-5612. *Librn*, Dale Gilliard
Library Holdings: Bk Vols 71,710
Friends of the Library Group
WINTERS BRANCH, 201 First St, Winters, 95694. SAN 335-3826. Tel: 530-795-4955. FAX: 530-795-4955. *Librn*, Barbara Wright; *Librn*, Karla Knabke
Library Holdings: Bk Vols 34,948
Friends of the Library Group
YOLO BRANCH, 37750 Sacramento St, PO Box 447, Yolo, 95697. SAN 335-3850. Tel: 530-662-2363. FAX: 530-662-2363. *Librn*, Nora Gortze
Library Holdings: Bk Vols 7,297

WOODLAND HILLS

S LITTON INDUSTRIES, Guidance & Control Systems,* 5500 Canoga Ave, 91367. SAN 301-7273. Tel: 818-712-7355. FAX: 818-712-7151. *Tech Servs*, Manuela Wood
Founded 1954
Library Holdings: Bk Vols 40,500
Subject Interests: Business and management, Electronics, Engineering, Mathematics, Physics
Publications: Acquisitions List; Journals List

L LITTON INDUSTRIES, Corporate & Law Library,* 21240 Burbank Blvd, 91367. SAN 329-9031. Tel: 818-598-5141. FAX: 818-598-3318. *Librn*, Larry Zamora; Staff 3 (MLS 1, Non-MLS 2)
Library Holdings: Bk Vols 10,000
Subject Interests: Bus, Finance, Legal
Special Services for the Deaf - TTY machine

S LOS ANGELES DAILY NEWS, Editorial Library,* PO Box 4200, 91365. SAN 370-1727. Tel: 818-713-3656. FAX: 818-713-3037. E-Mail: dnlalib@aol.com. Web Site: www.dailynews.com. *Chief Librn*, Margaret Douglas; *Librn*, Miriam Velasquez; Staff 4 (MLS 1, Non-MLS 3)
Library Holdings: Per Subs 50
Special Collections: Newspaper 1911-present on microfilm
Publications: Daily News of LA
Restriction: Not open to public
Partic in Dialog Corporation; Dow Jones News Retrieval

J LOS ANGELES PIERCE COLLEGE LIBRARY, 6201 Winnetka Ave, 91371. SAN 301-7281. Tel: 818-719-6409. Reference Tel: 818-710-2833. FAX: 818-719-9058. Web Site: www.piercecollege.com/homel.html. *Acq, Dir, Ref*, Florence Robin; E-Mail: florence_k._robin@laccd.cc.ca.us; *Cat, Tech Servs*, Luise Ehrhardt; *Acq, Per, Ref*, Anne Gibson-Lott; Staff 4 (MLS 4)
Founded 1947. Enrl 12,800; Fac 350; Highest Degree: Associate
Jul 1999-Jun 2000 Income $48,000. Mats Exp $48,000, Books $25,000, Per/Ser (Incl. Access Fees) $23,000. Sal $428,176 (Prof $250,944)
Library Holdings: Bk Vols 105,000; Bk Titles 91,651; Per Subs 297
Subject Interests: Agriculture
Special Collections: Beachy Library (San Fernando Valley Coll)
Automation Activity & Vendor Info: (Acquisitions) DRA
Mem of Los Angeles Community Col District

S MOSQUITO ASSOCIATION, INC, Library & Archives, 5942 Salamea Dr, 91367. SAN 371-7003. Tel: 818-884-1857. FAX: 818-712-9957. *Archivist*, Jerry L Allen
Founded 1962
2000-2001 Mats Exp Presv $200
Library Holdings: Per Subs 20
Special Collections: Mosquito Albums, photos & ephemera
Publications: Newsletter (quarterly)
Restriction: By appointment only

M MOTION PICTURE & TELEVISION FUND, Judy Garland Library, 23388 Mulholland Dr, 91364. SAN 301-729X. Tel: 818-876-1888, Ext 2449. FAX: 818-225-1359. *Librn*, Fran Beattie
Library Holdings: Bk Titles 300; Per Subs 66
Partic in Nat Libr of Med

SR WOODLAND HILLS PRESBYTERIAN CHURCH, Norman E Nygaard Library, 5751 Platt Ave, 91367. SAN 328-3585. Tel: 818-346-7894. FAX: 818-346-7826. *Dir*, Kim Henry
Library Holdings: Bk Titles 1,000

WRIGHTWOOD

S FIRE & ACCIDENT RECONSTRUCTION LIBRARY, PO Box 620, 92397-0620. SAN 372-5693. Tel: 760-249-6837. FAX: 760-249-1078. E-Mail: m1892@earthlink.net. Web Site: www.home.earthlink.net/~m1892. *Pres*, J A Caudron
Founded 1985
Library Holdings: Bk Vols 320; Bk Titles 250; Per Subs 12
Special Collections: Fires, Accident Research & all Phases of Engineering, Tech Evaluations

YORBA LINDA

S RICHARD NIXON LIBRARY & BIRTHPLACE, 18001 Yorba Linda Blvd, 92886. SAN 375-9636. Tel: 714-993-5075, Ext 214. Web Site: www.nixonfoundation.org. *Archivist*, Susan Naulty
Library Holdings: Bk Titles 3,000
Special Collections: American Political History 1946-1994; Richard Nixon

P YORBA LINDA PUBLIC LIBRARY, 18181 Imperial Hwy, 92886-3437. SAN 301-7303. Tel: 714-777-2873. TDD: 714-777-4812. FAX: 714-777-0640. E-Mail: ylpl@deltanet.com. Web Site: www.ylpl.lib.ca.us. *Dir*, Carol Ann Tassios; Tel: 714-777-2466, E-Mail: tassios@ylpl.lib.ca.us; *Asst Dir*, Diane Schwarzmann; E-Mail: dianes@ylpl.lib.ca.us; *ILL*, Karen Pomykata; *Ad Servs, AV, Ref*, Mary Ellen Bowman; E-Mail: meb@ylpl.lib.ca.us; *Ch Servs*, Danis Kreimeier; E-Mail: danisk@ylpl.lib.ca.us; *Circ, Tech Servs*, Marie Hemmer; E-Mail: marich@ylpl.lib.ca.us; Staff 5 (MLS 5)
Founded 1913. Pop 62,136; Circ 632,441
Jul 1998-Jun 1999 Income $2,567,023. Mats Exp $362,479, Books $258,892, Per/Ser (Incl. Access Fees) $16,290, Electronic Ref Mat (Incl. Access Fees) $55,413. Sal $878,653

Library Holdings: Bk Vols 124,000; Per Subs 265
Subject Interests: Local history
Automation Activity & Vendor Info: (Acquisitions) epixtech, inc.; (Cataloging) Brodart; (Circulation) epixtech, inc.; (OPAC) epixtech, inc.; (Serials) epixtech, inc.
Database Vendor: epixtech, inc., IAC - Info Trac
Publications: California Missions; Yorba Legacy
Mem of Santiago Libr Syst
Special Services for the Deaf - TDD
Friends of the Library Group

YOSEMITE

G YOSEMITE NATIONAL PARK SERVICE, Research Library, Museum Bldg, 95389. (Mail add: PO Box 577, 95389), SAN 301-7311. Tel: 209-372-0280. FAX: 209-372-0255. *Librn*, Linda S Eade; E-Mail: linda_eade@nps.gov; Staff 1 (Non-MLS 1)
Founded 1923
Library Holdings: Bk Titles 10,000; Per Subs 80
Subject Interests: History

YOUNTVILLE

S DEPARTMENT OF VETERANS AFFAIRS, VETERANS HOME OF CALIFORNIA, Lincoln Memorial Library, Veterans Home, PO Box 1200, 94599-1297. SAN 335-3885. Tel: 707-944-4915, 707-944-4916. *Librn*, Carole DeBell; *Asst Librn*, Phyllis Bush
Founded 1886
Library Holdings: Bk Titles 40,000; Per Subs 100
Subject Interests: Large print bks, World War I, World War II
Special Collections: Spanish American War
Partic in N Bay Health Sci Libr Consortium; Northern California & Nevada Medical Library Group
Branches:
WILLIAM K MURPHY HEALTH SCIENCES MEMORIAL LIBRARY, Holderman Hospital, 94599. SAN 335-394X. Tel: 707-944-4715. *Librn*, Carole DeBell; E-Mail: carole.debell@cdva.ca.gov
Library Holdings: Bk Titles 400; Per Subs 125
Subject Interests: Geriatrics and gerontology

YREKA

GL SISKIYOU COUNTY LAW LIBRARY, Courthouse, 311 Fourth St. (Mail add: PO Box 1026, 96097), SAN 301-732X. Tel: 530-842-8390. FAX: 530-842-8339.
Library Holdings: Bk Titles 5,536

S SISKIYOU COUNTY MUSEUM,* 910 S Main St, 96097. SAN 328-3658. Tel: 530-842-3836. FAX: 530-842-3166. *Dir*, Mike Hendryx
Library Holdings: Bk Vols 1,000; Per Subs 12
Subject Interests: Local history
Special Collections: Bancroft History, complete set; local newspapers 1917-1956 272 vols

P SISKIYOU COUNTY PUBLIC LIBRARY, 719 Fourth St, 96097. SAN 335-3974. Tel: 530-841-4175. Reference Tel: 530-841-4178. FAX: 530-842-7001. E-Mail: siskiyouilibrary@snowcrest.net. Web Site: www.snowcrest.net/siskiyoulibrary/index.html. *Dir*, Patricia Harper; Tel: 530-841-4179, E-Mail: phar@co.siskiyou.ca.us; *Ref*, Kathy Fueston; Staff 17 (MLS 4, Non-MLS 13)
Founded 1915. Pop 44,500
Jul 1999-Jun 2000 Income (Main Library and Branch Library) $789,498, State $74,719, City $11,000, County $631,200, Locally Generated Income $9,081, Other $63,569. Mats Exp $90,000, Books $80,000, Electronic Ref Mat (Incl. Access Fees) $10,000. Sal $434,250 (Prof $163,000)
Library Holdings: Bk Vols 140,000; Bk Titles 110,000; Per Subs 260
Subject Interests: California, Genealogy, Local Native Am, Mining
Database Vendor: OCLC - First Search
Function: ILL available
Open Mon 10-7, Tues & Wed 10-6, Thurs & Fri 12-5, Sat 1-5
Friends of the Library Group
Branches: 11
DORRIS BRANCH, PO Box 649, Dorris, 96023-0288. SAN 335-4008. Tel: 530-397-4932. *Dir*, Pat Harper; Tel: 530-841-4179, E-Mail: phar@co.siskiyou.ca.us; *Branch Mgr*, Anne Larkin; *Librn*, Lorraine Fine
Library Holdings: Bk Titles 4,977
Open Mon 12:30-5, Tues & Wed 12:30-5:30
DUNSMUIR BRANCH, 5714 Dunsmuir Ave, Dunsmuir, 96025. SAN 335-4032. Tel: 530-235-2035. *Dir*, Pat Harper; Tel: 530-842-7001, E-Mail: phar@co.siskiyou.ca.us; *Branch Mgr*, Ann De Rosa
Library Holdings: Bk Titles 11,628
Open Mon-Wed 1-8, Thurs 1-5, Sat 10-2
Friends of the Library Group
ETNA BRANCH, 121 Collier Way, Etna, 96027-0130. SAN 335-4067. Tel: 530-467-3661. *Dir*, Pat Harper; Tel: 530-841-4179, Fax: 530-842-7001, E-Mail: phar@co.siskiyou.ca.us; *Librn*, Pam Reimer
Library Holdings: Bk Titles 10,423
Open Mon-Wed & Fri 12-5, Thurs 10-5
Friends of the Library Group
FORT JONES BRANCH, 119 Sixty E, PO Box 632, Fort Jones, 96032-0446. SAN 335-4091. Tel: 530-468-2383. *Librn*, Julie Mitchell
Library Holdings: Bk Titles 7,236
Open Mon-Fri 12:30-5:30
Friends of the Library Group
HAPPY CAMP BRANCH, 143 Buckhorn Rd, Happy Camp, 96039. (Mail add: PO Box 317, Happy Camp, 96039-0317), SAN 335-4121. Tel: 530-493-2964. *Librn*, Dorothy LaHue
Library Holdings: Bk Titles 7,878
Open Mon-Thurs 1:30-5:30
MCCLOUD BRANCH, 300 E Colombero Dr, PO Box 425, McCloud, 96057-0425. SAN 335-4156. Tel: 530-964-2169. *Librn*, Lydia Grigsby
Library Holdings: Bk Titles 8,927
Open Mon & Wed 11-4, Tues & Thurs 10-5:30
Friends of the Library Group
MONTAGUE BRANCH, City Hall, 230 S 13th St, PO Box 428, Montague, 96064-0428. SAN 335-4164. Tel: 530-459-5473. *Librn*, Essie Biggs
Library Holdings: Bk Titles 3,912
Open Mon & Fri 12-5, Tues 1-4
Friends of the Library Group
MOUNT SHASTA BRANCH, 515 E Alma St, Mount Shasta, 96067. SAN 335-4180. Tel: 530-926-2031. *Librn*, Terry Thompson
Library Holdings: Bk Titles 17,251
Open Mon & Wed 1-6, Tues 12-6, Thurs & Sat 1-5
Friends of the Library Group
SCOTT BAR BRANCH, 27233 Scott River Rd, Scott Bar, 96085-9998. Tel: 530-496-3248. Web Site: www.snowcrest.net/siskiyoulibrary/index.html. *Librn*, Genetta Clark
Library Holdings: Bk Vols 400
Open Mon-Fri 8-4:30, Sat 11:30-1:30
TULELAKE BRANCH, 451 Main St, Tulelake, 96134-9527. (Mail add: PO Box 757, Tulelake, 96134-0757), Tel: 530-667-2291. *Librn*, Margaret McAuliffe
Library Holdings: Bk Titles 8,968
Open Mon 9-1 & 2-5, Tues-Thurs 10-1 & 2-5
WEED BRANCH, 780 S Davis St, PO Box 470, Weed, 96094. SAN 335-4210. Tel: 530-938-4769. *Librn*, Shelley Green
Library Holdings: Bk Titles 8,984
Open Wed-Fri 1-6

YUBA CITY

P SUTTER COUNTY FREE LIBRARY,* 750 Forbes Ave, 95991-3891. SAN 335-4245. Tel: 530-822-7137. FAX: 530-671-6539. E-Mail: suttlibr@yahoo.com. *Dir*, Roxanna Darley; *ILL*, Harumi Oki; Staff 3 (MLS 3)
Founded 1917. Pop 62,500; Circ 240,970
Library Holdings: Bk Vols 98,000; Bk Titles 88,000; Per Subs 159
Special Collections: Sutter County History Coll
Mem of Mountain-Valley Library System
Friends of the Library Group
Branches: 4
BARBER, 10321 Live Oak Blvd, Live Oak, 95953. SAN 335-427X. Tel: 530-695-2021. *Mgr*, Arlene Wheeler
Circ 6,358
Library Holdings: Bk Vols 13,500
Friends of the Library Group
BROWNS, 1248 Pacific Ave, Rio Oso, 95674. SAN 335-430X. Tel: 530-633-2170. *Mgr*, Mona White
Circ 11,516
Library Holdings: Bk Vols 6,043
Friends of the Library Group
PLEASANT GROVE BRANCH, 3093 Howsley Rd, Pleasant Grove, 95668. SAN 335-4369. Tel: 916-655-3484. *Mgr*, Mary Henderson
Circ 4,090
Library Holdings: Bk Vols 5,237
SUTTER BRANCH, 2147 California St, PO Box 286, Sutter, 95982. SAN 335-4393. Tel: 530-755-0485. *Mgr*, Karen Crocker
Circ 6,045
Library Holdings: Bk Vols 8,717

GM SUTTER COUNTY LAW LIBRARY,* Courthouse, 446 Second St, 95991. SAN 370-422X. Tel: 530-822-7360. FAX: 530-741-7159.
Library Holdings: Bk Vols 8,000

YUCAIPA

J CRAFTON HILLS COLLEGE LIBRARY,* 11711 Sand Canyon Rd, 92399. SAN 301-7338. Tel: 909-389-3307, 909-389-3323. FAX: 909-794-9524. Web Site: www.sbccd.cc.ca.us/index.htm. *Chief Librn*, Betty Byron; E-Mail: bbyron@sbccd.cc.ca.us; *Librn*, Laura Winningham; E-Mail: lwinningham@sbccd.cc.ca.us; *Librn*, Sam Job; Tel: 909-389-3322, E-Mail: sejob@sbccd.cc.ca.us; Staff 6 (MLS 3, Non-MLS 3)
Founded 1972. Enrl 5,500; Fac 76; Highest Degree: Associate
1999-1999 Mats Exp $137,069, Books $35,000, Per/Ser (Incl. Access Fees)

$49,839, Presv $5,000, Micro $14,500, Electronic Ref Mat (Incl. Access Fees) $32,730. Sal $312,019 (Prof $214,220)
Library Holdings: Bk Titles 67,556; Per Subs 414
Automation Activity & Vendor Info: (Course Reserve) Innovative Interfaces Inc.; (ILL) Innovative Interfaces Inc.; (Media Booking) Innovative Interfaces Inc.; (OPAC) Innovative Interfaces Inc.; (Serials) Innovative Interfaces Inc.
Mem of San Bernardino Commun Col District
Partic in Calif Commun Col Libr Coop - Desert Area; Inland Empire Acad Libr Coop; San Bernardino, Inyo, Riverside Counties United Library Services

COLORADO

Date of Statistics: 1999
Population, 1998 Estimate: 4,154,269
Population Served by Public Libraries: 4,041,796
Total Volumes in Public Libraries: 10,756,149
Volumes Per Capita: 2.66
Total Public Library Circulation: 37,955,457
Circulation Per Capita: 9.3
Total Public Library Income: (Local) $128,329,473
Total Public Library Expenditures: $122,049,115
Expenditure Per Capita: $30.20
Source of Income: Mainly public funds from property tax
Grants-in-Aid to Public Libraries:
2001 State (County Equalization Grants): $134,114
2001 State (State Grants for Libraries): $1,950,000
2001 (Regional Library Service Systems): $2,449,893
2000 Federal (Library Services & Technology Act): $2,019,623

AGUILAR

P AGUILAR PUBLIC LIBRARY,* 146 W Main St, PO Box 578, 81020-0586. SAN 301-7346. FAX: 719-941-4426. *Dir*, Julie Chavez; Tel: 719-555-1212, E-Mail: chavez-julie@hotmail.com
Pop 700; Circ 1,400
Library Holdings: Bk Vols 5,779
Mem of Arkansas Valley Regional Library Service System
Friends of the Library Group

AKRON

P AKRON PUBLIC LIBRARY,* 302 Main, 80720-1437. SAN 301-7354. Tel: 970-345-6818. FAX: 970-345-0122. E-Mail: akronpl@rmi.net. *Librn*, Jan Vaughn
Founded 1921. Pop 4,800; Circ 8,339
Library Holdings: Bk Vols 8,338
Mem of High Plains Regional Library Service System

S USDA AGRICULTURAL RESEARCH SERVICE, Central Great Plains Research Station Library, 40335 County Rd GG, 80720. SAN 370-2499. Tel: 970-345-2259. FAX: 970-345-2088. Web Site: www.akron.ars.usda.gov. *Res*, Merle L Vigil. Subject Specialists: *Agronomy*, Merle L Vigil
Library Holdings: Bk Vols 250; Per Subs 10
Restriction: Open to public for reference only

ALAMOSA

C ADAMS STATE COLLEGE NIELSEN LIBRARY,* 81102. SAN 301-7362. Tel: 719-587-7781. FAX: 719-587-7590. Web Site: www.adams.edu/academics/library/library.html. *Acq, Dir*, Dianne L Machado; E-Mail: dlmachad@adams.edu; *Automation Syst Coordr, Syst Coordr*, Glenda Geu; *Cat, Circ*, David Goetzman; *ILL, Ref*, Debra West; *Coll Develop*, Dianne Machado; Staff 6 (MLS 6)
Founded 1925. Enrl 2,040; Fac 123; Highest Degree: Master
Jul 1997-Jun 1998 Income $318,563. Mats Exp $259,197, Books $57,193, Per/Ser (Incl. Access Fees) $102,353, Presv $2,651. Sal $318,563 (Prof $194,784)
Library Holdings: Bk Vols 143,865; Bk Titles 144,709; Per Subs 1,002
Subject Interests: Education, History, Latin America, Law
Special Collections: Colorado Room
Automation Activity & Vendor Info: (Circulation) CARL; (OPAC) CARL
Database Vendor: IAC - Info Trac, OCLC - First Search
Mem of Bibliog Ctr for Res, Rocky Mountain, Inc; Southwest Regional Library Service System
Special Services for the Deaf - TDD

P SOUTHERN PEAKS PUBLIC LIBRARY,* 423 Fourth St, 81101-2601. SAN 301-7370. Tel: 719-589-6592. FAX: 719-589-3786. *Dir*, Margaret Morris; Staff 8 (Non-MLS 8)
Founded 1908. Pop 14,000; Circ 76,700
Library Holdings: Bk Vols 28,000; Per Subs 30
Subject Interests: Colorado, Genealogy, Parenting, Spanish (language)
Special Collections: Colorado Children with Disabilities
Mem of Southwest Regional Library Service System
Friends of the Library Group

ARVADA

S AMC WORLD CLUBS, INC, American Motors Historical Collection Library, 7963 Depew St, 80003-2527. SAN 372-5839. Tel: 303-428-8760. *Dir*, Larry Mitchell
Library Holdings: Bk Vols 350,000
Special Collections: American Motors Automobiles 1955-88, bks, mag & sales lit; Toys, Models & Promotional Items 1955-88

ASPEN

S ASPEN HISTORICAL SOCIETY LIBRARY,* 620 W Bleeker St, 81611. SAN 328-5073. Tel: 970-925-3721. FAX: 970-925-5347. E-Mail: ahistory@rof.net. Web Site: www.aspenhistory.org. *Curator*, Lisa Hancock
Library Holdings: Bk Titles 800

S THE ASPEN INSTITUTE, Clarke Library, 1000 N Third St, 81611-1361. SAN 301-7397. Tel: 970-925-7010. FAX: 544-7983, 970-925-4188.
Founded 1963
Library Holdings: Bk Titles 4,000

P PITKIN COUNTY LIBRARY,* 120 N Mill St, 81611. SAN 301-7400. Tel: 970-925-4025. FAX: 970-925-3935. *Dir*, Kathleen Chandler; *Asst Dir*, Jocelyn Durrance; *Ch Servs*, Susan S Keenan; *Tech Servs*, Carol McArdell; *ILL*, Helen Palmer. Subject Specialists: *Music*, David V Gollon; Staff 4 (MLS 4)
Founded 1940. Pop 11,500; Circ 79,512
Library Holdings: Bk Titles 66,731; Per Subs 202
Special Collections: Aspen Newspapers, 1888-present, microfilm; Music, rec & scores
Mem of Three Rivers Regional Library Service System
Partic in Marmot Western Colo Libr Network
Friends of the Library Group

AULT

P AULT PUBLIC LIBRARY,* 105 W First St, PO Box 147, 80610-0147. SAN 301-7419. Tel: 970-834-1259. FAX: 970-834-1259. *Dir*, Karen Haberman
Founded 1926. Pop 3,000; Circ 13,365
Library Holdings: Bk Vols 12,000; Per Subs 56
Mem of High Plains Regional Library Service System; Weld Libr Dist
Friends of the Library Group

AURORA

P AURORA PUBLIC LIBRARY, Library & Recreation Services, 14949 E Alameda Dr, 80012. SAN 335-4458. Tel: 303-739-6640. Interlibrary Loan Service Tel: 303-739-6618. FAX: 303-739-6586. Web Site: www.ci.aurora.co.us. *Dir*, Thomas P Nicholas; *ILL*, Terri Hurst; *Publ Servs*, Yvonne Harding; *Coll Develop*, Diane Long; Staff 23 (MLS 23)
Founded 1929. Circ 1,719,870
1998-1999 Income $4,599,000, City $4,519,000, Federal $80,000. Mats Exp $1,140,000. Sal $3,150,000
Library Holdings: Bk Vols 439,006
Subject Interests: Spanish (language)
Automation Activity & Vendor Info: (Circulation) Innovative Interfaces Inc.
Publications: Annual Report; Aurora Public Library General Brochure; Aurora Public Library Long Range Plan; Facts & Profile; Leisure for Life; Library Times
Mem of Cent Colorado Libr Syst
Partic in OCLC Online Computer Library Center, Inc
Friends of the Library Group
Branches: 5
ILIFF SQUARE, 2245 S Peoria St, 80014. SAN 371-3369. Tel: 303-751-4871. FAX: 303-745-4608. Web Site: www.ci.aurora.co.us.
Friends of the Library Group
MARTIN LUTHER KING JR LIBRARY, 9901 E 16th Ave, 80010. SAN 335-4547. Tel: 303-341-4173. FAX: 303-364-6503. Web Site: www.ci.aurora.co.us. *Dir*, Thomas Nicholas
Friends of the Library Group
NORTH, 1298 Peoria St, 80011-6207. SAN 335-4512. Tel: 303-361-2928. FAX: 303-344-1166. Web Site: www.ci.aurora.co.us. *Librn*, Pam Szot
Friends of the Library Group
NORTHEAST, 15008 E 17th Ave, 80011. SAN 335-4520. Tel: 303-363-6115. FAX: 303-361-0850. Web Site: www.ci.aurora.co.us.
Friends of the Library Group
SOUTH, 15324 E Hampden Circle, 80013-2408. SAN 335-4571. Tel: 303-693-1440. FAX: 303-680-4041. Web Site: www.ci.aurora.co.us. *Librn*, Chris Bradley
Friends of the Library Group

S AURORA PUBLIC SCHOOLS, District Resource Center,* 15751 E First Ave, 80011. SAN 301-7427. Tel: 303-340-0854. FAX: 303-326-1283. *Dir*, William Carter; Staff 9 (MLS 1, Non-MLS 8)
Founded 1950
Library Holdings: Bk Titles 700; Per Subs 450
Subject Interests: Education, Special education
Publications: Bibliographies; Elementary, Middle School, High School Media Curriculum for Teachers & Media Specialists (three publications); Film/video materials list (bi-annually); Media Equipment Training Manual
Partic in Central Colorado Library System

R LUTHERAN CHURCH-MISSOURI SYNOD, Rocky Mountain District Library, 14334 E Evans Ave, 80014. SAN 301-8539. Tel: 303-695-8001. FAX: 303-695-4047. *Librn*, Martha Palmreuter
Library Holdings: Bk Vols 475
Special Collections: Church Documents
Restriction: Employees & their associates
Open Mon-Fri 8-4

SR MEDICAL CENTER OF AURORA LIBRARY,* 700 Potomac St, 80011. SAN 377-4651. Tel: 303-360-3105. FAX: 303-360-3355. *Librn*, Sharon Martin; E-Mail: smartin@csn.net
Library Holdings: Bk Vols 250; Per Subs 78
Partic in Medical Libr Asn

S MID-CONTINENT RESEARCH FOR EDUCATION & LEARNING, Resource Center, 2550 S Parker Rd, No 500, 80014. SAN 309-0469. Tel: 303-337-0990. FAX: 303-337-3005. E-Mail: info@mcrel.org. Web Site: www.mcrel.org. *Exec Dir*, Timothy Waters; *Coordr*, Terry Young
Founded 1966
Subject Interests: Education

S NATIONAL WRITERS ASSOCIATION LIBRARY, 3140 S Peoria St, No 295PMB, 80014. SAN 301-7443. Tel: 303-841-0246. FAX: 303-841-2607. Web Site: www.nationalwriters.com. *Dir*, Sandy Whelchel
Founded 1937
Library Holdings: Bk Vols 4,200
Subject Interests: Literature
Publications: Authorship
This is a specialized library supported by the National Writers Association

C PARKS COLLEGE LIBRARY,* 6 Abilene St, 80011. SAN 377-4686. Tel: 303-367-2757. FAX: 303-361-9706. *Pres*, Nick Davis; *Librn*, Anna Andrews; Staff 1 (MLS 1)
Library Holdings: Bk Vols 57; Bk Titles 3,611; Per Subs 13

BAILEY

P PARK COUNTY PUBLIC LIBRARY,* 350 Bulldogger Rd, PO Box 282, 80421-0282. SAN 335-4636. Tel: 303-838-5539. FAX: 303-838-2351. *Dir*, Willanne Dye; E-Mail: willanned@hotmail.com; *Asst Librn*, Judy Owen; Staff 2 (MLS 2)
Founded 1966. Circ 64,000
Library Holdings: Bk Titles 28,481; Per Subs 10
Subject Interests: Art, Arts and crafts, Indians
Special Collections: Book Classics; History (Colorado)
Mem of Plains & Peaks Regional Library System
Partic in Bibliographical Center For Research, Rocky Mountain Region, Inc
Friends of the Library Group

BASALT

P BASALT REGIONAL LIBRARY DISTRICT, 99 Midland Ave, 81621-8305. SAN 320-1724. Tel: 970-927-4311. FAX: 970-927-1351. Web Site: www.aclin.org. *Dir*, Jean J Winkler
Founded 1976. Pop 9,825; Circ 44,957
Library Holdings: Bk Vols 21,674; Per Subs 77
Subject Interests: Colorado
Automation Activity & Vendor Info: (Circulation) CARL; (OPAC) CARL
Mem of Three Rivers Regional Library Service System
Partic in Marmot Western Colo Libr Network

BAYFIELD

P PINE RIVER PUBLIC LIBRARY,* 15 E Mill St, PO Box 227, 81122-0227. SAN 301-746X. Tel: 970-884-2222. *Librn*, Donnalee Baxstrom
Founded 1934. Pop 1,700; Circ 8,000
Library Holdings: Bk Vols 12,000; Bk Titles 10,000
Mem of Southwest Regional Library Service System
Friends of the Library Group

BERTHOUD

P BERTHOUD PUBLIC LIBRARY,* 236 Welch Ave, PO Box 1259, 80513. SAN 301-7478. Tel: 970-532-2757. FAX: 970-532-4372. Web Site: pyramid.cudenver.edu/berthoud. *Dir*, Roberta Depp; E-Mail: rdepp@pyramid.cudenver.edu; Staff 4 (MLS 1, Non-MLS 3)
Founded 1931. Pop 7,500
Jan 1998-Dec 1998 Income $86,856, City $66,858, County $9,698, Locally Generated Income $10,300. Mats Exp $12,648, Books $8,258, Per/Ser (Incl. Access Fees) $1,650, AV Equip $300. Sal $44,374 (Prof $31,680)
Library Holdings: Bk Vols 21,000; Per Subs 50
Subject Interests: Colorado
Special Collections: Berthoud Bulletin on microfilm; Xeriscape Materials
Automation Activity & Vendor Info: (Circulation) Sagebrush Corporation
Mem of High Plains Regional Library Service System
Friends of the Library Group

BLACK HAWK

P GILPIN COUNTY PUBLIC LIBRARY, 15131 Hwy 119, 80403. (Mail add: PO Box 551, 80422), SAN 378-0163. Tel: 303-582-5777. FAX: 303-582-5777. E-Mail: gilpinlib@gilpincounty.com. Web Site: www.peaknet.org/webpages/gilpinlilb. *Dir*, Lawrence Grieco; Tel: 303-582-0161, E-Mail: lgrieco@usa.com; *Automation Syst Coordr*, Cynthia Gribble; *Info Tech*, George Blevins; *Ch Servs*, Sandra Fuller; Staff 5 (MLS 1, Non-MLS 4)
Founded 1978. Pop 4,000
Library Holdings: Bk Vols 20,000; Bk Titles 19,000; Per Subs 50
Subject Interests: Colorado, State hist
Automation Activity & Vendor Info: (Circulation) Sagebrush Corporation
Mem of Cent Colorado Libr Syst
Partic in Am Libr Asn; Central Colorado Library System; Colo Libr Asn
Friends of the Library Group
Bookmobiles: 1

BOULDER

S BALL AEROSPACE & TECHNOLOGIES CORPORATION, Library Services, 1600 Commerce St, 80301-2734. SAN 301-7486. Tel: 303-939-5755. FAX: 303-939-4142. *In Charge*, Vicky Schneller; E-Mail: vschnell@ball.com; *Online Servs*, Fran Brown; Staff 4 (MLS 2, Non-MLS 2)
Founded 1961
Library Holdings: Bk Vols 5,000; Per Subs 200
Subject Interests: Astronomy, Cryogenics, Electronics, Engineering, Optics, Physics
Restriction: Not open to public
Partic in Bibliographical Center For Research, Rocky Mountain Region, Inc

M BOULDER COMMUNITY HOSPITAL, Medical Library,* N Broadway & 1100 Balsam Ave, PO Box 9019, 80301-9019. SAN 301-7508. Tel: 303-440-2091. FAX: 303-938-3483. *Librn*, Connie Cencich Myers

Founded 1922
Library Holdings: Bk Vols 365; Per Subs 32
Subject Interests: Medicine, Nursing

S BOULDER COUNTY CORRECTIONS LIBRARY,* 3200 Airport Rd, 80301. SAN 377-0788. Tel: 303-441-4686. FAX: 303-441-4608. E-Mail: dhosh@co.boulder.co.us. Web Site: www.co.boulder.co.us/sheriff. *Dir*, Donald O'Hara
Library Holdings: Bk Vols 5,000; Per Subs 22

P BOULDER PUBLIC LIBRARY,* 1000 Canyon Blvd, PO Drawer H, 80306. SAN 335-4695. Tel: 303-441-3100. FAX: 303-442-1808. E-Mail: gralappm@boulder.lib.co.us. Web Site: www.boulder.lib.co.us. *Dir*, Marcelee Gralapp; *Asst Dir*, Randy Smith; *Ch Servs, YA Servs*, Mary Jane Holland; *Info Res*, Lynn Reed; *Ch Servs*, Judith Volc; *Tech Servs*, Ray Ingraham; *Branch Mgr*, Priscilla Hudson
Pop 119,160; Circ 1,407,291
Jan 1998-Dec 1999 Income (Main Library and Branch Library) $5,007,695, City $4,847,663, Locally Generated Income $102,500. Mats Exp $528,000, Books $319,000, Per/Ser (Incl. Access Fees) $76,000, AV Equip $50,000, Electronic Ref Mat (Incl. Access Fees) $83,000. Sal $3,633,714
Library Holdings: Bk Vols 434,747; Per Subs 1,100
Special Collections: Boulder Arts Resource Coll; Children's Literature Reference; Local History; Municipal Government
Automation Activity & Vendor Info: (Circulation) CARL
Publications: BookLook (children's publication); Boulder Municipal Govt 1871-1946, 1965-1974, 1975-1979 & 1980-1984; Colorado Business; Colorado History; Taking Care of Business (business newsletter); Word (Young Adult Magazine)
Mem of Cent Colorado Libr Syst
Branches: 3
CARNEGIE BRANCH, 1125 Pine St, PO Drawer H, 80306. SAN 335-4709. Tel: 303-441-3110. FAX: 303-441-3110. *Mgr*, Wendy Hall
Subject Interests: Colorado
Special Collections: Boulder Historical Society Photograph Coll; Digitized OPAC Images
GEORGE R REYNOLDS BRANCH, 3595 Table Mesa Dr, 80303. SAN 335-4725. Tel: 303-441-3120. FAX: 303-441-4094. *Mgr*, Steve Austin
Library Holdings: Bk Vols 25,000
MEADOWS BRANCH, 4800 Baseline Rd, PO Drawer H, 80303. SAN 323-9381. Tel: 303-441-4390. FAX: 303-441-4490. *Branch Mgr*, Patty Kellicker

S COLORADO CHAUTAUQUA ASSOCIATION, Archives & History Room,* 900 Baseline Rd, 80302. SAN 375-751X. Tel: 303-442-3282, 303-545-6924. FAX: 303-449-0790. E-Mail: chau@usa.net. *Exec Dir*, Leslie Durgin

S DAILY CAMERA LIBRARY,* 1048 Pearl St, 80302. SAN 374-9819. Tel: 303-473-1303. FAX: 303-449-9358. Web Site: www.bouldernews.com.
Library Holdings: Bk Titles 100

S EDUCAUSE LIBRARY,* 4772 Walnut St Ste 206, 80301. SAN 376-0812. Tel: 303-449-4430. FAX: 303-440-0461. E-Mail: info@educause.edu. Web Site: www.educause.edu/information-resources/ir-library.html. *Pres*, Brian L Hawkins; *Coordr*, Julia Rudy

R FIRST UNITED METHODIST CHURCH LIBRARY,* 1421 Spruce, 80302. SAN 301-7516. Tel: 303-442-3770. FAX: 303-442-4752.
Founded 1952
Library Holdings: Bk Vols 2,200
Subject Interests: Education, Psychology, Religion, Social sciences and issues

M MENTAL HEALTH CENTER OF BOULDER COUNTY INC, Mental Health Center Library,* 1333 Iris Ave, 80304-2296. SAN 325-2132. Tel: 303-443-8500, Ext 273. FAX: 303-449-6029. *Librn*, Marilyn Rothman
Library Holdings: Bk Titles 3,000; Per Subs 30
Subject Interests: Psychiatry, Psychology, Res
Publications: Annual Report
Restriction: Staff use only
Partic in Colorado Alliance Of Research Libraries; Colorado Council Of Medical Librarians; OCLC Online Computer Library Center, Inc

C NAROPA UNIVERSITY LIBRARY, 2130 Arapahoe Ave, 80302. SAN 320-443X. Tel: 303-546-3507. FAX: 303-444-0410. Web Site: www.naropa.edu. *Actg Dir*, John Burns
Founded 1974. Highest Degree: Master
Library Holdings: Bk Vols 26,000; Bk Titles 20,000; Per Subs 200
Subject Interests: Buddhism, Poetry, Psychology, Tibetan (language)
Special Collections: Modern Poetry Coll
Partic in OCLC Online Computer Library Center, Inc

G NATIONAL CENTER FOR ATMOSPHERIC RESEARCH LIBRARY, 1850 Table Mesa Dr, 80305. (Mail add: PO Box 3000, 80307-3000), SAN 335-4784. Tel: 303-497-1180. Interlibrary Loan Service Tel: 303-497-1177. FAX: 303-497-1170. Web Site: www.ucar.edu/library. *Actg Librn*, Gayl Gray; E-Mail: gayl@ucar.edu; *Tech Servs*, Terry Murray; Tel: 303-497-1178, E-Mail: tmurray@ucar.edu
Founded 1962
Library Holdings: Bk Vols 35,000; Bk Titles 31,000; Per Subs 642
Subject Interests: Chemistry, Computer science, Electrical engineering, Electronics, Mathematics, Mechanical engineering, Meteorology, Oceanography, Physics
Special Collections: Meteorological Atlases & Data
Automation Activity & Vendor Info: (Acquisitions) SIRSI; (Cataloging) SIRSI; (Circulation) SIRSI; (OPAC) SIRSI; (Serials) SIRSI
Database Vendor: Dialog, OCLC - First Search
Partic in Central Colorado Library System; Dialog Corporation; Fedlink; OCLC Online Computer Library Center, Inc

L NATIONAL INDIAN LAW LIBRARY, Native Americans Rights Fund, 1522 Broadway, 80302-6217. SAN 321-8007. Tel: 303-447-8760. FAX: 303-443-7776. Web Site: www.narf.org/nill/nillindex.html. *In Charge*, David Selden; E-Mail: dselden@narf.org; Staff 2 (MLS 1, Non-MLS 1)
Founded 1972
2000-2001 Mats Exp $82,000, Books $7,000, Per/Ser (Incl. Access Fees) $50,000, Electronic Ref Mat (Incl. Access Fees) $25,000. Sal $110,000 (Prof $100,000)
Library Holdings: Bk Titles 3,000; Per Subs 200
Special Collections: National Indian Law Library (cases, briefs, pleadings, legal opinions, rulings, treatises, studies, articles, reports, and legislative materials on Federal Indian Law); Tribal Codes & Constitutions; Tribal Court Cases
Automation Activity & Vendor Info: (Acquisitions) Inmagic, Inc.; (Cataloging) Inmagic, Inc.; (Circulation) Inmagic, Inc.; (Course Reserve) Inmagic, Inc.; (ILL) Inmagic, Inc.; (OPAC) Inmagic, Inc.; (Serials) Inmagic, Inc.
Publications: Indian Claims Commission Decisions & Index, Top Fifty Cases
Restriction: Open to public for reference only
This library is a national repository for Native American legal materials & resources
Friends of the Library Group

G NATIONAL OCEANIC & ATMOSPHERIC ADMINISTRATION, Mountain Administrative Support Center-Information Resources Div Library, 325 Broadway MC5, 80305-3328. SAN 335-4814. Tel: 303-497-3271. Interlibrary Loan Service Tel: 303-497-5569. FAX: 303-497-3890. E-Mail: main.library@noaa.gov. Web Site: www.bldrdoc.gov/library/library.htm. *Chief Librn*, John Welsh; *Ref*, Jane Watterson; *Electronic Resources*, Joan St Germain; *Ref*, Katherine Day; *Head Tech Servs*, Sara Martin; Staff 12 (MLS 5, Non-MLS 7)
Founded 1954
Library Holdings: Bk Titles 46,884; Per Subs 621
Subject Interests: Chemistry, Computer science, Cryogenics, Electronics, Mathematics, Meteorology, Telecommunications
Special Collections: Radio Science & Physics (Technical Reports, 1940-1970), bks & micro
Automation Activity & Vendor Info: (Acquisitions) Endeavor; (Cataloging) Endeavor; (Circulation) Endeavor; (OPAC) Endeavor; (Serials) Endeavor
Database Vendor: Dialog, OCLC - First Search
Publications: Library Brochure; Library Notes
Restriction: Open to public for reference only
Mem of Cent Colorado Libr Syst
Partic in Bibliographical Center For Research, Rocky Mountain Region, Inc; Dialog Corporation; Fedlink; Nasa Libraries Information System - Nasa Galaxie; OCLC Online Computer Library Center, Inc
Branches:
RESEARCH LABORATORY NO 3, 30th & Marine, 80303. SAN 335-4849.

C UNIVERSITY OF COLORADO AT BOULDER, University Libraries,* Campus Box 184, 80309-0184. SAN 335-4903. Tel: 303-492-7511. FAX: 303-492-1881. Web Site: www-libraries.colorado.edu. *Dean of Libr, Dir*, James F Williams, II; E-Mail: james.williams@colorado.edu; *Publ Servs*, Susan H Anthes; *Tech Servs*, Janet Swan Hill; *Admin Assoc*, Scott Seaman; *Circ*, Brice Austin; *Acq*, Harriet Rebuldela; *Cat*, William Garrison; *Info Res*, Yem Fong; *Ref*, Lori Arp; *Ser*, Pat Wallace; *Publ Servs*, Deborah Fink; *Coll Develop*, Sue Williams; *Syst Coordr*, John Culshaw; Staff 179 (MLS 56, Non-MLS 123)
Founded 1876. Enrl 28,157; Fac 1,217; Highest Degree: Doctorate
Jul 1998-Jun 1999 Income (Main and Other College/University Libraries) $16,626,011. Mats Exp $8,154,813, Books $1,676,318, Per/Ser (Incl. Access Fees) $4,858,433, Micro $779,471, Electronic Ref Mat (Incl. Access Fees) $33,593. Sal $6,836,104 (Prof $2,326,561)
Library Holdings: Bk Vols 2,850,114; Per Subs 26,082
Special Collections: History of Silver (Leavens Coll); Human Area Relations File; Human Rights; Juvenile Literature (Epstein & Block Colls); Labor Archives; Miller Milton Coll; Mountaineering (John J Jerome Hart Coll); Tippit Photobook Coll; Western History
Automation Activity & Vendor Info: (Acquisitions) Innovative Interfaces Inc.; (Cataloging) Innovative Interfaces Inc.; (Circulation) Innovative Interfaces Inc.; (Course Reserve) Innovative Interfaces Inc.; (OPAC) Innovative Interfaces Inc.; (Serials) Innovative Interfaces Inc.
Mem of Asn of Research Libraries

Partic in Bibliographical Center For Research, Rocky Mountain Region, Inc; Center For Research Libraries; Central Colorado Library System; Colorado Alliance Of Research Libraries; OCLC Online Computer Library Center, Inc
Friends of the Library Group
Departmental Libraries:
ARCHIVES DEPARTMENT, Norlin, Campus Box 184, 80309-0184. SAN 372-5391. Tel: 303-492-7247. FAX: 303-492-3960. Web Site: www-libraries.colorado.edu. *Archivist*, Harvey Gardiner
Library Holdings: Bk Vols 18,748
Subject Interests: Colorado, History, Human rights
ART & ARCHITECTURE, Norlin, Campus Box 184, 80309-0184. SAN 335-4938. Tel: 303-492-7955. FAX: 303-492-1881. Web Site: www-libraries.colorado.edu.
Library Holdings: Bk Vols 99,991
Subject Interests: Architecture, Art history, Fine arts, Graphic arts, Landscape architecture, Photography, Urban planning

S BUSINESS RESEARCH DIVISION, TRAVEL REFERENCE CENTER, Campus Box 420, 80309. SAN 335-5179. Tel: 303-492-8227. FAX: 303-492-3620. Web Site: www.libraries.colorado.edu.
Founded 1969
Library Holdings: Bk Titles 10,000; Per Subs 40
Mem of Asn of Research Libraries
Friends of the Library Group
EAST ASIAN, Norlin, Campus Box 184, 80309-0184. SAN 371-0572. Tel: 303-492-8822. FAX: 303-492-1881. Web Site: www.libraries.colorado.edu.
Library Holdings: Bk Vols 42,563
Subject Interests: Chinese Language
GEMMILL ENGINEERING, Mathematics Bldg, Rm 135, Campus Box 184, 80309-0184. SAN 335-5020. Tel: 303-492-5396. FAX: 303-492-6488. Web Site: www-libraries.colorado.edu.
Library Holdings: Bk Vols 135,136
Subject Interests: Engineering, Technology
GOVERNMENT PUBLICATIONS, Norlin, Campus Box 184, 80309-0184. SAN 372-5375. Tel: 303-492-8834. FAX: 303-492-1881. *Librn*, Debbie Hollis; *Librn*, Peggy Jobe
Special Collections: European Communities Dep; GATT Dep

S INSTITUTE OF ARCTIC & ALPINE RESEARCH LIBRARY, 1560 30th St, Campus Box 450, 80309-0450. SAN 335-5144. Tel: 303-492-1867. FAX: 303-492-6388. Web Site: www.libraries.colorado.edu. *Dir*, Martha Andrews
Library Holdings: Bk Vols 3,100; Per Subs 212
Subject Interests: Arctic
JERRY CRAIL JOHNSON EARTH SCIENCES LIBRARY, Benson Earth Science Bldg, Campus Box 184, 80309-0184. SAN 335-4997. Tel: 303-492-6133. FAX: 303-4735-4879. Web Site: www.libraries.colorado.edu. *Librn*, Suzanne Larsen
Library Holdings: Bk Vols 45,000; Per Subs 225
Subject Interests: Geochemistry, Geology, Geophysics, Mineralogy, Oceanography, Paleontology

CL LAW LIBRARY, Campus Box 402, 80309. SAN 335-5055. Tel: 303-492-7534. Reference Tel: 303-492-3522. FAX: 303-492-2707. E-Mail: lawlib@stripe.colorado.edu. Web Site: www.colorado.edu/Law/lawlib/. *Dir*, Barbara A Bintliff; Tel: 303-492-1233, E-Mail: barbara.bintliff@colorado.edu; *Assoc Dir, Head Tech Servs*, Georgia K Briscoe; Tel: 303-492-7312, E-Mail: briscoe@colorado.edu; *Cat*, Karen Selden; Tel: 303-492-7535, E-Mail: karen.selden@colorado.edu; *Publ Servs*, Mitchell Fontenot; Tel: 303-492-1181, E-Mail: mitch.fontenot@colorado.edu; *Tech Servs*, Robert C Richards; Tel: 303-492-2706, E-Mail: rrichard@stripe.colorado.edu; *ILL, Ref Serv*, Bev Agnew; Tel: 303-492-2704, E-Mail: agnew@colorado.edu; Staff 7 (MLS 7)
Founded 1892. Enrl 450; Fac 32; Highest Degree: Doctorate
Jul 1999-Jun 2000 Income $1,659,873, State $1,649,381, Federal $10,492. Mats Exp $937,435, Books $51,314, Per/Ser (Incl. Access Fees) $672,862, Micro $89,917, AV Equip $11,180, Electronic Ref Mat (Incl. Access Fees) $112,162. Sal $693,013 (Prof $428,032)
Library Holdings: Bk Vols 400,000; Per Subs 4,058
Subject Interests: Constitutional law, Environmental law, Native Am law
Special Collections: Commonwealth & Foreign Law; International Law
Automation Activity & Vendor Info: (Acquisitions) Innovative Interfaces Inc.; (Cataloging) Innovative Interfaces Inc.; (Circulation) Innovative Interfaces Inc.; (Course Reserve) Innovative Interfaces Inc.; (OPAC) Innovative Interfaces Inc.; (Serials) Innovative Interfaces Inc.
Database Vendor: IAC - Info Trac, Lexis-Nexis, OCLC - First Search, Wilson - Wilson Web
Mem of Asn of Research Libraries
Partic in Bibliographical Center For Research, Rocky Mountain Region, Inc; Central Colorado Library System; Colorado Alliance Of Research Libraries; OCLC Online Computer Library Center, Inc
MUSIC, Music Bldg, N250, Campus Box 184, 80309-0184. SAN 335-5098. Tel: 303-492-8093. FAX: 303-492-5619. Web Site: www-libraries.colorado.edu. *Head of Libr*, Laurie Sampsel; E-Mail: laurie.sampsel@spot.colorado.edu
Library Holdings: Bk Vols 60,000
Special Collections: 18th Century Comic Opera; American Music Research Center; California Mission Music; Early New England Singing Schools; Limpkin Folk Song; Moravian Music; Music of Colorado Composers; Popular Sheet Music
OLIVER C LESTER LIBRARY OF MATHEMATICS & PHYSICS, Duane Physical Labs G-140, Campus Box 184, 80309-0184. SAN 335-508X. Tel: 303-492-8231. FAX: 303-492-1881. Web Site: www.libraries.colorado.edu.
Library Holdings: Bk Vols 80,000
Subject Interests: Astronomy, Astrophysics, Mathematics, Physics
SCIENCE, Norlin, Campus Box 184, 80309-0184. SAN 335-511X. Tel: 303-492-5136. FAX: 303-492-1881. Web Site: www.libraries.colorado.edu. *Librn*, Daria O Carle
Library Holdings: Bk Vols 245,000
Subject Interests: Biochemistry, Biology, Chemistry, Psychology

S SPECIAL COLLECTIONS DEPARTMENT, Norlin, Campus Box 184, 80309-0184. SAN 372-5383. Tel: 303-492-6144. FAX: 303-492-1881. Web Site: www-libraries.colorado.edu.
Library Holdings: Bk Vols 72,556; Per Subs 23
Subject Interests: American literature, Bk arts, Colorado, English literature, Fine printing, Illustrated bks, Incunabula, Mountaineering, Natural history, Photography
Special Collections: Epsteen & Bloch Children's Literature Coll; Tippit Photobook Coll; Twentieth Century Photography, John Milton Coll
Friends of the Library Group
WILLIAM M WHITE BUSINESS LIBRARY, Campus Box 184, 80309-0184. SAN 335-4962. Tel: 303-492-3194, 303-492-8367. Toll Free Tel: 303-492-3194. FAX: 303-735-0333. Web Site: www-libraries.colorado.edu. *Librn*, Martha Jo Sani; *Librn*, Jean Whelan
Library Holdings: Bk Vols 95,000; Per Subs 675
Subject Interests: Accounting, Finance, Marketing, Real estate, Transportation

S WESTERN INTERSTATE COMMISSION FOR HIGHER EDUCATION LIBRARY,* 1540 30th St, PO Box 9752, 80301-9752. SAN 301-7540. Tel: 303-541-0285. E-Mail: econway@wiche.edu. Web Site: www.wiche.edu.; Staff 2 (MLS 1, Non-MLS 1)
Founded 1955
Library Holdings: Bk Vols 3,500; Bk Titles 3,000; Per Subs 250
Subject Interests: Mental health, Nursing
Publications: Acquisitions List
Mem of Cent Colorado Libr Syst
Partic in First Search

S WORLD DATA CENTER-A FOR GLACIOLOGY LIBRARY,* CIRES, Univ of Colo, Campus Box 449, 80309-0449. SAN 335-4873. Tel: 303-492-5171. FAX: 303-492-2468. E-Mail: nsidc@kryos.colorado.edu.; Staff 3 (MLS 1, Non-MLS 2)
Founded 1957
Library Holdings: Bk Vols 9,000; Per Subs 90
Publications: Glaciological Data; New Accessions List
Partic in Dialog Corporation

BROOMFIELD

P MAMIE DOUD EISENHOWER PUBLIC LIBRARY, Broomfield Public Library, One Des Combes Dr, 80020-2495. SAN 301-7575. Tel: 303-469-1821. FAX: 303-438-6294. *Dir*, Helen Martin; Tel: 303-438-6203, E-Mail: hmartin@boulder.lib.co.us; *Ch Servs*, Lesly Clayton; Tel: 303-438-6206, E-Mail: lclayton@ci.broomfield.co.us; *YA Servs*, Gigi Yang; Tel: 303-438-6209, E-Mail: gyang@ci.broomfield.co.us; *ILL*, Barbara Livsey; Tel: 303-438-6204, E-Mail: blivsey@ci.broomfield.co.us; *Ref*, Susan Simmons; Tel: 303-438-6207; *Cat*, Yolanda Maloney; Tel: 303-438-6210; *Cat*, Barbara Thorne; Tel: 303-438-6210, E-Mail: bthorne@ci.broomfield.co.us; *Circ*, Jean Patterson; Tel: 303-438-6200, E-Mail: jpatterson@ci.broomfield.co.us; Staff 26 (MLS 9, Non-MLS 17)
Founded 1960. Pop 38,500; Circ 244,615
Library Holdings: Bk Vols 83,127; Bk Titles 60,000; Per Subs 214
Special Collections: Mamie Doud Eisenhower Coll
Automation Activity & Vendor Info: (Cataloging) Innovative Interfaces Inc.; (Circulation) Innovative Interfaces Inc.; (Course Reserve) Innovative Interfaces Inc.; (ILL) Innovative Interfaces Inc.; (Media Booking) Innovative Interfaces Inc.; (OPAC) Innovative Interfaces Inc.
Database Vendor: CARL, GaleNet, IAC - Info Trac, IAC - SearchBank, OVID Technologies
Mem of Cent Colorado Libr Syst
Partic in Bibliographical Center For Research, Rocky Mountain Region, Inc
Friends of the Library Group

BRUSH

P EAST MORGAN COUNTY LIBRARY DISTRICT, 500 Clayton St, 80723-2016. SAN 301-7583. Tel: 970-842-4596. FAX: 970-842-2450. E-Mail: emcl_98@yahoo.com. *Dir, Librn*, Deborah Johnson
Founded 1915. Pop 7,624; Circ 76,660
Jan 1999-Dec 1999 Income $337,894, Locally Generated Income $196,621, Parent Institution $72,377, Other $68,896. Mats Exp $14,430, Books $2,600, Per/Ser (Incl. Access Fees) $2,130, Presv $800, AV Equip $8,000, Electronic Ref Mat (Incl. Access Fees) $900. Sal $102,940 (Prof $36,340)
Library Holdings: Bk Vols 27,700; Bk Titles 26,080; Per Subs 81
Special Collections: Colorado Coll; Hospes; Local History; Photographs;

Taped interviews
Automation Activity & Vendor Info: (Acquisitions) epixtech, inc.; (Cataloging) epixtech, inc.; (Circulation) epixtech, inc.; (OPAC) epixtech, inc.
Publications: Bibliographies; Friends Brochure; Friends Newsletter; Newspaper column (weekly); Subject
Mem of High Plains Regional Library Service System
Friends of the Library Group

BUENA VISTA

S BUENA VISTA CORRECTIONAL COMPLEX LIBRARY, PO Box 2017, 81211-2017. SAN 301-7605. Tel: 719-395-2404, Ext 7354. FAX: 719-395-7214. E-Mail: bvcflibi@amigo.net. *Dir*, Alison Guild; E-Mail: aguild@amigo.net
Library Holdings: Bk Vols 16,327; Per Subs 48
Partic in Arkansas Valley Regional Library Service System (AVRLSS)

P BUENA VISTA PUBLIC LIBRARY, Northern Chaffee County Regional Library, 131 Linderman Ave, PO Box 2019, 81211-2019. SAN 301-7591. Tel: 719-395-8700. FAX: 719-395-6426. E-Mail: bvbooks@chaffee.net. *Dir*, Gail Nottingham
Founded 1898
Library Holdings: Bk Vols 13,428; Bk Titles 13,735
Mem of Arkansas Valley Regional Library Service System

BURLINGTON

P BURLINGTON PUBLIC LIBRARY,* 321 14th St, 80807-1607. SAN 301-7613. Tel: 719-346-8109. FAX: 719-346-8672. *Dir*, Della Yersin
Founded 1921. Pop 3,500; Circ 31,000
Library Holdings: Bk Vols 18,000; Per Subs 35
Mem of High Plains Regional Library Service System

CANON CITY

P CANON CITY PUBLIC LIBRARY,* 516 Macon Ave, 81212-3380. SAN 301-7621. Tel: 719-269-9021. FAX: 719-269-9031. *Dir*, Charlotte Davis; *Tech Servs*, Suzanne Lasha; *Publ Servs*, Michael Clark; Staff 3 (MLS 3)
Founded 1886
Library Holdings: Bk Titles 54,000; Per Subs 130
Subject Interests: Local history
Mem of Arkansas Valley Regional Library Service System

COLORADO DEPARTMENT OF CORRECTIONS

S ARROWHEAD CORRECTIONAL CENTER LIBRARY, 57500 US Hwy 50 E. (Mail add: PO Box 300, 81215), SAN 373-6369. Tel: 719-269-5601, Ext 3923. FAX: 719-269-5650.; Staff 1 (MLS 1)
Founded 1991
Jul 1997-Jun 1998 Income $15,855, State $15,124, Federal $731. Mats Exp $11,876, Books $5,817, Per/Ser (Incl. Access Fees) $1,588, AV Equip $1,079. Sal $59,256 (Prof $36,000)
Library Holdings: Bk Titles 9,900; Per Subs 37
Mem of Arkansas Valley Regional Library Service System
Special Services for the Deaf - Books on deafness & sign language; High interest/low vocabulary books

S CENTENNIAL CORRECTIONAL FACILITY LIBRARY, PO Box 600, 81215-0600. SAN 301-763X. Tel: 719-275-4181, Ext 3741. FAX: 719-269-5545. *Librn*, Chuck Rose; *Tech Servs*, Ladell Marta; Staff 8 (MLS 8)
Library Holdings: Bk Vols 8,000
Mem of Arkansas Valley Regional Library Service System

S COLORADO STATE PENITENTIARY LIBRARY,* PO Box 777, 81215-0777. SAN 377-080X. Tel: 719-269-5268. FAX: 719-269-5125. *Librn*, Charles M Sakai
Library Holdings: Bk Vols 9,500

S COLORADO TERRITORIAL CORRECTIONAL FACILITY LIBRARY,* PO Box 1010, 81215-1010. SAN 370-7660. Tel: 719-275-4181, Ext 3167. FAX: 719-269-4115. E-Mail: ctcflib1@sni.net. *Librn*, Linda Hyatt
Founded 1985. Pop 489
Library Holdings: Bk Vols 12,971; Per Subs 42
Subject Interests: Poetry
Partic in Arkansas Valley Regional Library Service System (AVRLSS)

S COLORADO WOMEN'S CORRECTIONAL FACILITY LIBRARY, 3800 Grandview Ave, PO Box 500, 81215-0500. SAN 301-7648. Tel: 719-269-4707, Ext 3818. FAX: 719-269-4716. *Librn*, Tina Bell; *Librn*, Stacey Cleine
Pop 350
Library Holdings: Bk Vols 10,000; Per Subs 24
Partic in Arkansas Valley Regional Library Service System (AVRLSS)

S FREMONT CORRECTIONAL FACILITY LIBRARY, US Hwy 50, Evans Blvd, 81215. (Mail add: PO Box 999, 81215-0999), Tel: 719-275-4181, Ext 3566. FAX: 719-269-5020. E-Mail: fcflib@amigo.net. *Librn*, Z Oreada Mitchell; *Ad Servs*, Darlene M Cole; Fax: 719-269-5048; Staff 3 (MLS 1, Non-MLS 2)
Founded 1957
Library Holdings: Bk Vols 1,850; Bk Titles 1,800; Per Subs 59
Function: ILL available
Partic in Arkansas Valley Regional Library Service System (AVRLSS)

S SKYLINE CORRECTIONAL FACILITY LIBRARY,* PO Box 800, 51215-0800. SAN 325-3635. Tel: 719-275-4181, Ext 3351. FAX: 719-269-5404. *Tech Servs*, Nola Dieringer; Staff 1 (MLS 1)
Jul 1999-Jun 2000 Mats Exp $1,500
Library Holdings: Bk Vols 3,000; Per Subs 25

CASTLE ROCK

P DOUGLAS PUBLIC LIBRARY DISTRICT,* 961 S Plum Creek Blvd, 80104-2788. SAN 335-5268. Tel: 303-688-8752. FAX: 303-688-1942. E-Mail: jlarue@csn.net. Web Site: douglas.lib.co.us. *Dir*, James LaRue; *Assoc Dir*, Holly Deni
Founded 1966. Pop 156,306; Circ 1,305,174
Jan 1998-Dec 1998 Income (Main Library Only) $7,000,758, Locally Generated Income $644,489, Parent Institution $6,356,269. Mats Exp $690,500, Books $625,000, Per/Ser (Incl. Access Fees) $35,000, Micro $500, Electronic Ref Mat (Incl. Access Fees) $30,000. Sal $2,092,589 (Prof $1,104,984)
Library Holdings: Bk Vols 335,512; Bk Titles 153,639; Per Subs 501; High Interest/Low Vocabulary Bk Vols 58; Bks on Deafness & Sign Lang 111
Special Collections: Local History; Newspapers of Douglas County 1881-1992, micro; Photographs
Automation Activity & Vendor Info: (Cataloging) epixtech, inc.; (Circulation) epixtech, inc.; (OPAC) epixtech, inc.
Mem of Cent Colorado Libr Syst
Friends of the Library Group
Branches: 5
HIGHLANDS RANCH BRANCH, 48 W Springer Dr, Highlands Ranch, 80126. SAN 371-9510. Tel: 303-791-7703. FAX: 303-791-9963. Web Site: douglas.lib.co.us. *Branch Mgr*, Pam Nissler; E-Mail: pnissler@csn.net
Library Holdings: Bk Vols 82,280
Friends of the Library Group
LONE TREE, 8827 Lone Tree Pkwy, Lone Tree, 80124. SAN 335-5357. Tel: 303-799-4446. FAX: 303-799-4275. Web Site: douglas.lib.co.us. *Branch Mgr*, Claudine Perrault; E-Mail: cperrault@mail.douglas.lib.co.us
Library Holdings: Bk Vols 50,862
Friends of the Library Group
LOUVIERS BRANCH, 7885 Louviers Blvd, Louviers, 80131. (Mail add: PO Box 282, Louviers, 80131), SAN 335-5292. Tel: 303-791-7323. FAX: 303-791-7323. Web Site: douglas.lib.co.us. *Librn*, Peg Hooper
Library Holdings: Bk Vols 6,325
Open Mon & Thurs 3-7
PARKER BRANCH, 10851 S Crossroads Dr, Parker, 80134-9081. SAN 335-5322. Tel: 303-841-3503. FAX: 303-841-7892. Web Site: douglas.lib.co.us. *Branch Mgr*, Patt Paul; Tel: 303-841-6344, E-Mail: p.paul@sni.org
Library Holdings: Bk Vols 94,170
Friends of the Library Group
PHILIP S MILLER BRANCH, 961 S Plum Creek Blvd, 80104-2726. SAN 370-4955. Tel: 303-688-5157. FAX: 303-688-1942. Web Site: douglas.lib.co.us. *Branch Mgr*, Greg Mickells; E-Mail: gmickells@mail.douglas.lib.co.us
Library Holdings: Bk Vols 101,875
Special Collections: Local History
Friends of the Library Group
Bookmobiles: 1. Immobile bookmobile, open Mon & Wed 3-8:30, Fri 9-12 & Sat 1-5. 720-981-3040. Librn, Peg Hooper. Bk Vols 3321

COLORADO SPRINGS

S AMERICAN NUMISMATIC ASSOCIATION LIBRARY,* 818 N Cascade, 80903-3279. SAN 301-7664. Tel: 719-632-2646. FAX: 719-632-5208. E-Mail: analib@money.org. Web Site: www.money.org. *Librn*, Nawana Britenriker; Staff 2 (MLS 1, Non-MLS 1)
Founded 1891
Library Holdings: Bk Vols 25,000; Bk Titles 7,300; Per Subs 75
Subject Interests: Numismatics
Special Collections: Arthur Braddan Coole Library of Oriental Numismatics
Publications: The Numismatist

S ARJUNA LIBRARY,* 1025 Garner St, D Space 18, 80905-1774. SAN 326-3029. *Dir*, Joseph A Uphoff Jr
Founded 1963
Library Holdings: Bk Titles 2,100
Subject Interests: Art, Mathematics
Publications: Journal of Regional Criticism, Arjuna Library Press
Restriction: By appointment only
Theoretical database

J BLAIR COLLEGE LIBRARY,* 828 Wooten Rd, 80915. SAN 326-4394. Tel: 719-574-1082. FAX: 719-574-4493. *Pres*, Joel Boyd; Staff 7 (MLS 1, Non-MLS 6)

Enrl 600
Library Holdings: Bk Vols 4,500; Per Subs 23
Subject Interests: Business and management, Computer science, Medical, Travel
Special Collections: Computer Science; Travel, bks, pamphlets

S CHEYENNE MOUNTAIN ZOOLOGICAL PARK LIBRARY,* 4250 Cheyenne Mountain Zoo Rd, 80906. SAN 328-2317. Tel: 719-633-0917. FAX: 719-633-2254. Web Site: www.cmzoo.org. *Curator*, Frogard Ryan
Library Holdings: Bk Vols 3,000
Subject Interests: Zoology
Open 9-5; 7 days a week

S CHRISTIAN & MISSIONARY ALLIANCE, Albert B Simpson Historical Library, PO Box 35000, 80935-3500. SAN 329-8671. Tel: 719-599-5999. FAX: 719-593-8692. E-Mail: info@cmalliance.org. Web Site: www.cmalliance.org. *Archivist, Dir*, Dr Joseph C Wenninger
Library Holdings: Bk Vols 3,000
Special Collections: The Christian & Missionary Alliance (1887)
Open Wed 8-4:30

S CITY OF COLORADO SPRINGS, Office of City Attorney Library, 30 S Nevada Ave Ste 501, 80903. (Mail add: PO Box 1575 Mail Code 510, 80901-1575), Tel: 719-385-5909. FAX: 719-578-6209. *Librn*, Corine Ownbey
Library Holdings: Bk Titles 300; Per Subs 70
Restriction: Staff use only

C COLORADO COLLEGE, Charles Leaming Tutt Library, 1021 N Cascade Ave, 80903-3252. SAN 301-7680. Tel: 719-389-6658. Interlibrary Loan Service Tel: 719-389-6664. FAX: 719-389-6859. Web Site: coloradocollege.edu/library. *Dir*, Carol Dickerson; *Tech Servs*, Nancy Knipe; *Doc*, Julie Jones-Eddy; *ILL*, Diane Broderson; *Syst Coordr*, Karl Henson; *Spec Coll*, Ginny Kiefer; *Circ, Publ Servs*, Debra Hoke. Subject Specialists: *Soc sci*, Robin Satterwhite
Founded 1874. Enrl 1,998
Library Holdings: Bk Vols 465,000; Per Subs 1,400
Special Collections: Autographs of the British Poets (Alice Bemis Taylor Coll); Chess Books (Alfred R Justice Coll); Colorado &; Colorado College Archives, Colorado Springs, files of early newspapers, also bks, clippings & pamphlets & mss relating to development of Colorado Springs; Colorado Imprints; Dickens (Carruthers Coll); Edmund van Diest Papers; Helen Hunt Jackson Papers; Hendee Collection of Lincolniana; Rare Books (Coll of mss & early printed leaves, Incunabula, drawings & prints from the Romanesque period to the Renaissance); Southwestern United States; United States Relocation Center, Granada, Colorado; Western Americana
Automation Activity & Vendor Info: (Acquisitions) Innovative Interfaces Inc.; (Cataloging) Innovative Interfaces Inc.
Publications: The Chronicle (irregular newsletter),
Mem of Plains & Peaks Regional Library System
Partic in OCLC Online Computer Library Center, Inc
Friends of the Library Group

S COLORADO SCHOOL FOR THE DEAF & BLIND, Media Center,* 33 N Institute St, 80903-3599. SAN 301-7699. Tel: 719-578-2206. FAX: 719-578-2239. Web Site: www.csdb.org. *Librn*, Marianne Arnold; E-Mail: marnold@csdb.org; *Media Spec*, Janet Rose; E-Mail: jrose@csdb.org
1998-1999 Mats Exp $2,000, Books $1,300, Per/Ser (Incl. Access Fees) $700. Sal $90,000 (Prof $90,000)
Library Holdings: Bk Vols 10,000; Per Subs 75
Subject Interests: Blindness
Special Collections: Braille & Large Print Books for Children; Professional Books on Deafness & Blindness; Videotapes on Sign Language
Partic in Plains & Peaks Regional Libr Syst

S COLORADO SPRINGS FINE ARTS CENTER LIBRARY,* 30 W Dale St, 80903. SAN 301-7702. Tel: 719-634-5581, Ext 327. FAX: 719-634-0570. *Librn*, Roderick Dew; E-Mail: rdew@csfineartscenter.org; Staff 1 (MLS 1)
Founded 1936
Library Holdings: Bk Vols 30,000; Per Subs 50
Special Collections: 20th Century American Art; Anthropology of the Southwest (Taylor Museum Coll), bks, series, pamphlets

S COLORADO SPRINGS PIONEERS MUSEUM, Starsmore Center for Local History,* 215 S Tejon St, 80903. SAN 301-7818. Tel: 719-578-6650. FAX: 719-578-6718. *Archivist*, Leah Davis Witherow; E-Mail: lwitherow@ci.colospqs.co.us
Founded 1938
Library Holdings: Bk Titles 8,000; Per Subs 25
Subject Interests: Colorado
Special Collections: Southwest (Francis W Cragin Coll), mss; Western US Coll, photogs; William J Palmer Coll; Winfield Scott Stratton Coll
Partic in Plains & Peaks Regional Libr Syst

C COLORADO TECHNICAL UNIVERSITY LIBRARY, 4435 N Chestnut, 80907. SAN 322-7456. Tel: 719-598-0200. FAX: 719-598-3740. *Dir*, Kay Burman; Tel: 719-590-6708, E-Mail: kburman@cos.colotechu.edu; Staff 3 (MLS 1, Non-MLS 2)
Highest Degree: Doctorate
Library Holdings: Bk Vols 23,000; Bk Titles 14,000
Subject Interests: Bus, Careers, Computer science, Electrical engineering, Mgt, Videos
Special Collections: Dissertations & Thesis
Automation Activity & Vendor Info: (Cataloging) TLC; (OPAC) TLC

S COMPAQ COMPUTER CORP, CXO Library,* 301 Rockrimmon Blvd, 80919-2398. SAN 324-5314. Tel: 719-548-2113. FAX: 719-548-2922.
Founded 1979
Library Holdings: Bk Vols 5,000; Per Subs 50
Subject Interests: Bus, Computer science, Engineering
Partic in Dialog Corporation

GM EL PASO COUNTY DEPARTMENT OF HEALTH & ENVIRONMENT LIBRARY, 301 S Union Blvd, 80910-3123. SAN 377-2578. Tel: 719-578-3113. FAX: 719-575-8644.
Library Holdings: Bk Vols 500

GL EL PASO COUNTY LAW LIBRARY,* 104 Judicial Bldg, 20 E Vermijo, 80903-2290. SAN 301-7710. Tel: 719-448-7780. FAX: 719-448-7685. *Coll Develop, Librn*, Kathleen Clark Edie; E-Mail: kclark@csn.org
Founded 1973
Library Holdings: Bk Vols 22,000; Per Subs 40
Partic in Colorado Alliance Of Research Libraries; OCLC Online Computer Library Center, Inc; Westlaw

R FIRST CONGREGATIONAL CHURCH-UNITED CHURCH OF CHRIST, Gregg Memorial Library, 20 E Saint Vrain St, 80903. SAN 301-7729. Tel: 719-635-3549. FAX: 719-633-4715. *Chair*, Wes Burnett
Founded 1935
Library Holdings: Bk Vols 2,000
Open Mon-Fri 9-4

R FIRST PRESBYTERIAN CHURCH, John C Gardner Memorial Library, 219 E Bijou, 80903. SAN 301-7737. Tel: 719-471-3763, Ext 452. FAX: 719-540-7528.
Founded 1945
Library Holdings: Bk Vols 4,000; Per Subs 26
Mem of Plains & Peaks Regional Library System
Friends of the Library Group

S THE GAZETTE, Newsroom Library, PO Box 1779, 80901. SAN 323-5211. Tel: 719-476-1600, 719-632-5511. FAX: 719-636-0202. E-Mail: research@gazette.com. Web Site: www.gazette.com. *In Charge*, Jeff Thomas; *Librn*, Pula Davis
Library Holdings: Bk Vols 400; Per Subs 10

S HEWLETT PACKARD, Southern Colorado Learning Center,* 4920 Centennial Blvd, 80919-2404. SAN 301-7745. Tel: 719-590-1900, 719-590-2708. FAX: 719-590-3008. *Chief Librn*, Audrey Tolle
Founded 1970
Library Holdings: Bk Titles 1,400; Per Subs 125
Subject Interests: Computer science, Electronics
Partic in Dialog Corporation; RLIN

S ITT INDUSTRIES INC, ADVANCED ENGINEERING & SCIENCES DIVISION LIBRARY, (Formerly ITT Industries Inc, Systems Div Library), 5009 Centennial Blvd, PO Box 39550, 80949-9550. SAN 301-7753. Tel: 719-599-1500. FAX: 719-599-1942. *Librn*, Barbara A Kinslow
Founded 1963
Library Holdings: Bk Titles 8,200; Per Subs 85
Subject Interests: Chemistry, Electronics, Energy, Mechanical engineering, Nuclear engineering, Optics, Physics, Software engineering
Partic in DTIC

M MEMORIAL HOSPITAL, Health Sciences Library, 1400 E Boulder, Rm 2406, 80909-5599. SAN 301-7761. Tel: 719-365-5182. FAX: 719-365-5184. *Mgr*, Char Longwell; Staff 1 (MLS 1)
Founded 1950
Library Holdings: Bk Vols 3,500
Subject Interests: Cardiology, Nursing, Obstetrics and gynecology, Pediatrics, Surgery
Special Collections: Historical Medical Works Coll; Rare Book Coll
Mem of Plains & Peaks Regional Library System
Partic in Medline; Midcontinental Regional Med Libr Program; OCLC Online Computer Library Center, Inc

MOTOROLA, INC

S BUSINESS RESEARCH LIBRARY, 1303 E Algonquin, Schaumburg, 60196. SAN 376-0405. Tel: 847-576-1948. FAX: 847-538-2250. *In Charge*, Nancy A Talend; E-Mail: ant002e@america.mot.com; Staff 4 (MLS 3, Non-MLS 1)
Library Holdings: Bk Titles 250; Per Subs 30

S RESEARCH & TECHNICAL LIBRARY, 1301 E Algonquin Rd Rm 1914, Schaumburg, 60196-1078. SAN 304-6354. Tel: 847-576-8580. FAX: 847-576-4716. *Info Specialist*, Nancy Snyder; Staff 3 (MLS 1, Non-MLS 2)
Founded 1978
Library Holdings: Bk Vols 10,000; Bk Titles 9,800; Per Subs 450
Subject Interests: Electronics

Special Collections: Communications Coll
Database Vendor: Dialog, epixtech, inc., OCLC - First Search, ProQuest
Publications: Acquisitions; dissertations; journals; technical reports
Function: ILL by photocopy only
Mem of North Suburban Library System

CR NAZARENE BIBLE COLLEGE, Trimble Library, 1111 Academy, Park Loop, 80910-3717. SAN 301-777X. Tel: 719-596-5110, Ext 110. FAX: 719-550-9437. E-Mail: info@nbc.edu, library@nbc.edu. Web Site: www.nbc.edu. *Dir*, Vernell Posey; E-Mail: vwposey@nbc.edu; Staff 1 (MLS 1)
Founded 1967. Enrl 417; Fac 24; Highest Degree: Bachelor
Jul 1999-Jun 2000 Mats Exp $122,000
Library Holdings: Bk Vols 43,277; Per Subs 208
Subject Interests: Biblical studies, Theology
Special Collections: Wesleyana Coll

M PENROSE HOSPITAL, Webb Memorial Library, 2215 N Cascade Ave, PO Box 7021, 80933. SAN 301-7788. Tel: 719-776-5288. FAX: 719-776-5603. *Dir*, Richard Maxwell; E-Mail: richardmaxwell@centura.org; *Librn*, Mary Kircher; Staff 2 (MLS 2)
Founded 1959
Library Holdings: Bk Vols 1,656; Per Subs 200
Subject Interests: Medicine
Special Collections: History of Medicine
Database Vendor: OVID Technologies
Partic in Medline; Midcontinental Regional Med Libr Program; OCLC Online Computer Library Center, Inc

J PIKES PEAK COMMUNITY COLLEGE, Learning Resources Center,* 5675 S Academy Blvd, 80906-5498. SAN 301-780X. Tel: 719-576-7711. FAX: 719-540-7523. Web Site: www.ppcc.cccdes.edu. *Dir*, Mary Jo Berger; E-Mail: berger@ppcc.colorado.edu; *Head Ref*, Audrey Tolle; Tel: 719-540-7506, E-Mail: audrey.tolle@ppcc.cccoes.edu; *Media Spec*, Bob Armintor; *Circ, ILL*, Susan Dodson
Founded 1969. Enrl 6,000; Fac 403
Jul 1997-Jun 1998 Mats Exp $41,855, Books $5,725, Per/Ser (Incl. Access Fees) $21,820, Other Print Mats $13,810
Library Holdings: Bk Vols 42,356; Per Subs 290
Special Collections: PPCC Archives
Automation Activity & Vendor Info: (OPAC) CARL
Database Vendor: CARL, IAC - Info Trac, OCLC - First Search, ProQuest
Publications: LRC Express; Piecing the Puzzle Together
Mem of Plains & Peaks Regional Library System
Partic in BCR

P PIKES PEAK LIBRARY DISTRICT, 5550 N Union Blvd, 80918. (Mail add: PO Box 1579, 80901), SAN 335-5381. Tel: 719-531-6333. TDD: 719-471-1770. FAX: 719-389-8989. Web Site: library.ppld.org. *Dir*, Patrick A Losinski; Staff 75 (MLS 75)
Founded 1905. Pop 432,320; Circ 3,620,498
Library Holdings: Bk Vols 1,263,816; Per Subs 1,790
Subject Interests: Local history
Automation Activity & Vendor Info: (Acquisitions) CARL; (Serials) CARL
Publications: Check It Out
Mem of Plains & Peaks Regional Library System
Partic in Colorado Alliance Of Research Libraries
Special Services for the Deaf - Books on deafness & sign language; High interest/low vocabulary books; Special interest periodicals; Staff with knowledge of sign language
Friends of the Library Group
Branches: 12
CHEYENNE MOUNTAIN BRANCH, 1791-D S Eighth St, 80906. SAN 335-5411. Tel: 719-633-6278. FAX: 719-389-8976. Web Site: library.ppld.org. *Librn*, Deborah Bonifas
EAST LIBRARY & INFORMATION CENTER, 5550 N Union Blvd, 80918. SAN 335-5446. Tel: 719-531-6333. FAX: 719-528-5289. Web Site: www.library.ppld.org.
Friends of the Library Group
EL POMAR NONPROFIT RESOURCE, 1661 Mesa Ave, 80906. SAN 376-0332. Tel: 719-577-7000. Toll Free Tel: 800-554-7711. Web Site: library.ppld.org.
Special Collections: Foundation Center Core Coll
FOUNTAIN BRANCH, 501 E Iowa, Fountain, 80817. SAN 335-5608. Tel: 719-382-5347. FAX: 719-382-8217. Web Site: library.ppld.org. *In Charge*, Jan Knauer
RUTH HOLLEY BRANCH, 923 N Murray Blvd, 80915. SAN 329-6350. Tel: 719-597-5377. FAX: 719-597-1214. Web Site: library.ppld.org. *Librn*, Patty Van Eysden
Friends of the Library Group
MONUMENT HILL BRANCH, Mine Shopping Ctr, PO Box 1688, Monument, 80132. SAN 335-5535. Tel: 719-488-2370. FAX: 719-488-0621. Web Site: library.ppld.org. *Mgr*, Beth Barrett
Friends of the Library Group
OLD COLORADO CITY, 2418 W Pikes Peak, 80904. SAN 335-556X. Tel: 719-634-1698. FAX: 719-389-8975. Web Site: ppld.library.org. *Dir*, Amy Holzworth
Friends of the Library Group
PALMER LAKE BRANCH, 66 Lower Glenway, Palmer Lake, 80133. SAN 335-5594. Tel: 719-481-2587. FAX: 719-481-2587. Web Site: library.ppld.org. *Librn*, June Legg
Friends of the Library Group
PENROSE PUBLIC LIBRARY, 20 N Cascade Ave, 80903. SAN 329-6334. Tel: 719-531-6333. FAX: 719-389-8989. Web Site: library.ppld.org. *Dir*, Patrick Losinski
Friends of the Library Group
ROCKRIMMON LIBRARY, 832 Village Center Dr, 80919. SAN 370-4505. Tel: 719-593-8000. FAX: 719-528-3952. Web Site: library.ppld.org. *Librn*, Susan Douglass
Friends of the Library Group
SAND CREEK, 1821 S Academy Blvd, 80916. SAN 329-6377. Tel: 719-597-7070. FAX: 719-597-0985. Web Site: library.ppld.org. *Librn*, Lisa Garcia
Friends of the Library Group
UTE PASS, 8010 Severy, Cascade, 80809. SAN 335-5624. Tel: 719-684-9342. FAX: 719-684-9342. Web Site: library.ppld.org. *Librn*, Elaine Weseman
Bookmobiles: 3

P PLAINS & PEAKS REGIONAL LIBRARY SYSTEM,* 530 Communications Circle, Ste 205, 80905-1743. SAN 301-7826. Tel: 719-473-3417. FAX: 719-632-9645. E-Mail: mjo@csn.org. Web Site: www.csn.net/pprlss. *Dir*, Mary Jeanne Owen; Staff 4 (MLS 4)
Founded 1976. Pop 525,980
Oct 1998-Sep 1999 Income $409,686, State $30,702. Mats Exp $2,500. Sal $153,166 (Prof $76,905)
Special Collections: Professional Tools
Publications: Plainspeaking (newsletter)
Member Libraries: Colorado College; Elbert County Library; First Presbyterian Church; Franklin Ferguson Memorial Library; Hugo Public Library; Limon Memorial Public Library; Manitou Springs Public Library; Memorial Hospital; Park County Public Library; Pikes Peak Community College; Pikes Peak Library District; Rampart Regional Library District; Security Public Library; United States Army; Victor Public Library
Professional collection on NEAR database at Pikes Peak Library District, Colorado Springs, Colorado, 719-551-5531, Website: http://www.ppld.org. NEAR lists holdings of small libraries in eastern Colorado & the professional collections of three regional library service systems including Plains & Peaks

S PRO RODEO HALL OF FAME LIBRARY,* 101 Pro Rodeo Dr, 80919. SAN 371-5396. Tel: 719-528-4762. FAX: 719-548-4874. *Curator, Dir*, Patricia Hildebrand
Founded 1979
Library Holdings: Bk Titles 600
Special Collections: Rodeo Coll

L SHEPARD'S LAW LIBRARY,* 555 Middle Creek Pkwy, 80921-3630. SAN 301-7842. Tel: 719-481-7508, 719-481-7832. Toll Free Tel: 800-743-7393, Ext 7832. FAX: 719-481-7387.
Founded 1873
Library Holdings: Bk Vols 100,000; Per Subs 700
Special Collections: West Reporter System, official state court reports, official codes & laws, legal periodicals
Publications: Shepard's Citations Series
Restriction: Private library
Partic in Westlaw

S UNITED STATES OLYMPIC COMMITTEE, Information Resource Center,* One Olympic Plaza, 80909-5760. SAN 325-5220. Tel: 719-578-4622. FAX: 719-632-5352. Web Site: www.usoc.org. *Dir*, Cindy Slater; *Info Res*, Ruth Larson
Library Holdings: Bk Vols 4,800; Bk Titles 4,500; Per Subs 475
Subject Interests: Athletic training, Biomechanics, Coaches educ, Exercise, Exercise physiology, Nutrition, Physical fitness, Sports for disabled, Sports med
Automation Activity & Vendor Info: (Cataloging) Sydney; (Circulation) Sydney; (Serials) Sydney
Partic in BCR; OCLC Online Computer Library Center, Inc

C UNIVERSITY OF COLORADO AT COLORADO SPRINGS, Kraemer Family Library, 1420 Austin Bluffs Pkwy, PO Box 7150, 80933-7150. SAN 301-7850. Tel: 719-262-3286. FAX: 719-528-5227. E-Mail: refdesk@mail.uccs.edu. Web Site: web.uccs.edu/library. *Dean of Libr*, Leslie Manning; *Tech Servs*, Rita M Hug; *Doc*, Judith Rice-Jones; *Online Servs*, Susan Byerley; Staff 8 (MLS 8)
Founded 1965. Enrl 4,800; Fac 250; Highest Degree: Doctorate
Jul 1998-Jun 1999 Income $1,488,322. Mats Exp $701,039. Sal $669,868
Library Holdings: Bk Vols 300,381; Per Subs 2,171
Subject Interests: Business, Education, Electrical engineering, Psychology
Automation Activity & Vendor Info: (Acquisitions) Innovative Interfaces Inc.; (Cataloging) Innovative Interfaces Inc.; (Circulation) Innovative Interfaces Inc.; (OPAC) Innovative Interfaces Inc.; (Serials) Innovative Interfaces Inc.
Partic in BCR; OCLC Online Computer Library Center, Inc

S WESTERN MUSEUM OF MINING & INDUSTRY LIBRARY, 1025 N Gate Rd, I-25 Exit 156-A, 80921. SAN 326-3371. Tel: 719-495-2182. FAX: 719-488-9261. Web Site: www.wmmi.org. *Dir*, Linda LeMieux
Library Holdings: Bk Vols 14,000; Per Subs 11
Subject Interests: Mining
Publications: Annual Report; quarterly newsletter
Restriction: Open to others by appointment
Open Mon-Sat 9-4, Sun 12-4
Friends of the Library Group

P ZEBULON PIKE YOUTH SERVICES CENTER LIBRARY,* 1427 W Rio Grande, 80906. SAN 327-7682. Tel: 719-633-8713. FAX: 719-633-5302. *Dir*, Jema Hill
Library Holdings: Bk Vols 3,500
Friends of the Library Group

COMMERCE CITY

S ROCKY MOUNTAIN ARSENAL, Technical Information Center, Bldg 129, 72nd & Quebec, 80022-1748. SAN 373-1251. Tel: 303-289-0342. FAX: 303-289-0205. *Librn*, Amira Hamdy; E-Mail: ahamdy@rma.army.mil; Staff 2 (MLS 1, Non-MLS 1)
Founded 1983
Library Holdings: Bk Titles 15,000; Per Subs 75
Subject Interests: Environmental engineering
Special Collections: RMA Archives
Publications: Monthly newsletter
Partic in Dialog Corporation; Nat Libr of Med; OCLC Online Computer Library Center, Inc

CORTEZ

P CORTEZ PUBLIC LIBRARY,* 802 E Montezuma Ave, 81321-3355. SAN 301-7869. Tel: 970-565-8117. FAX: 970-565-8117. *Dir*, Joanie Howland; Staff 5 (MLS 1, Non-MLS 4)
Founded 1932. Pop 22,000; Circ 85,000
Library Holdings: Bk Titles 36,000; Per Subs 65
Special Collections: Southwest Historical Coll
Database Vendor: OCLC - First Search
Mem of Southwest Regional Library Service System
Partic in Marmot Western Colo Libr Network
Friends of the Library Group

S CROW CANYON ARCHAEOLOGICAL RESEARCH LIBRARY,* 23390 County Rd K, 81321. SAN 377-0958. Tel: 970-565-8975. FAX: 970-565-4859. Web Site: www.crowcanyon.org. *Dir*, Melita Romasco; *Dir Info Resources & Res*, Mark Barien
Library Holdings: Bk Vols 3,000

CRAIG

G BUREAU OF LAND MANAGEMENT, Little Snake Field Office Library,* 455 Emerson St, 81625-1129. SAN 301-7877. Tel: 970-826-5000. FAX: 970-826-5002.
Library Holdings: Bk Vols 1,200
Restriction: Not open to public
Open Mon-Fri 8-4

P MOFFAT COUNTY LIBRARIES, 570 Green St, 81625-3027. SAN 301-7885. Tel: 970-824-5116. FAX: 970-824-5525. E-Mail: moffat@marmot.org. *Dir*, Donna J Watkins; E-Mail: watkinsd@marmot.org; Staff 21 (MLS 1, Non-MLS 20)
Founded 1911. Pop 13,000
Jan 2000-Dec 2000 Income $802,874, County $802,874. Mats Exp $82,015, Books $66,000, Per/Ser (Incl. Access Fees) $15, AV Equip $16,000. Sal $500,206 (Prof $49,006)
Library Holdings: Bk Vols 51,000; Per Subs 73
Subject Interests: Local history
Automation Activity & Vendor Info: (Circulation) CARL; (OPAC) CARL
Database Vendor: CARL
Mem of Three Rivers Regional Library Service System
Friends of the Library Group

CREEDE

P MINERAL COUNTY REGIONAL LIBRARY,* La Garite Ave, PO Box 429, 81130. SAN 376-2831. Tel: 719-658-2313. FAX: 719-658-2942. *Librn*, Francis Kolisch
Library Holdings: Bk Vols 10,000; Per Subs 26
Mem of Southwest Regional Library Service System

CRIPPLE CREEK

P FRANKLIN FERGUSON MEMORIAL LIBRARY,* PO Box 975, 80813. SAN 301-7893. Tel: 719-689-2800. FAX: 719-689-3187. *Dir*, Mike McDonald; *Asst Librn*, Nancy Fromm; Staff 1 (MLS 1)
Founded 1976. Pop 700; Circ 4,830
Library Holdings: Bk Titles 21,165
Subject Interests: History
Special Collections: Colorado History; Local history
Mem of Plains & Peaks Regional Library System
Combination school public library

CROOK

P CROOK COMMUNITY LIBRARY,* PO Box 143, 80726-0143. SAN 301-7907. Tel: 970-886-2451. *Dir*, Grace Stump
Founded 1928. Circ 3,016
Library Holdings: Bk Vols 5,300
Mem of High Plains Regional Library Service System
Open Tues 2-4pm

CROWLEY

S COLORADO DEPARTMENT OF CORRECTIONS, Arkansas Valley Correctional Facility Library, PO Box 1000, 81034. SAN 376-5768. Tel: 719-267-3520, Ext 3251. FAX: 719-267-5024. E-Mail: avcflibn@ria.com. *Librn*, Linda Hollis
Jul 1998-Jun 1999 Income $14,090, State $3,550, Parent Institution $10,540. Mats Exp $3,450, Books $1,850, Per/Ser (Incl. Access Fees) $1,600. Sal $31,000 (Prof $54,000)
Library Holdings: Bk Vols 14,500; Per Subs 45
Automation Activity & Vendor Info: (Cataloging) EOS; (Circulation) EOS; (OPAC) EOS

DACONO

P DACONO PUBLIC LIBRARY,* 512 Cherry St, PO Box 186, 80514-0186. SAN 372-8021. Tel: 303-833-2317, Ext 129. FAX: 303-833-5528. *Librn*, Sharmaine Martinez; Staff 1 (MLS 1)
Founded 1978. Pop 2,228; Circ 5,002
Library Holdings: Bk Vols 7,000; Per Subs 12

DEL NORTE

P DEL NORTE PUBLIC LIBRARY,* 790 Grand Ave, 81132. SAN 301-7915. Tel: 719-657-2633. FAX: 719-657-2633. *Dir*, Kathy Gilliam; E-Mail: kathy.gilliam@amigo.net; *Librn*, Benita Pacheco
Founded 1899. Pop 10,770
Library Holdings: Bk Titles 18,000; Per Subs 50
Special Collections: Local newspaper, 1923-present
Mem of Southwest Regional Library Service System
Friends of the Library Group

DELTA

P COLORADO DEPARTMENT OF CORRECTIONS, Delta Correctional Center Library, 1140 E-10 Rd, 81416. SAN 376-5784. Tel: 970-874-7614. FAX: 970-874-5810. *Tech Servs*, Connie Syas
Library Holdings: Bk Titles 13,000; Per Subs 34

P DELTA COUNTY PUBLIC LIBRARY, 211 W Sixth St, 81416. SAN 335-5659. Tel: 970-874-9630. FAX: 970-874-8605. *Dir*, Maureen Burns; *ILL*, Alice Lister
Founded 1911. Pop 21,275; Circ 228,550
Library Holdings: Bk Titles 106,048; Per Subs 185
Subject Interests: Coal, Mining, Recreational
Mem of Pathfinder Regional Library Service System
Friends of the Library Group
Branches: 4
CEDAREDGE PUBLIC, 180 SW Sixth Ave, PO Box 548, Cedaredge, 81413. SAN 335-5683. Tel: 970-856-3518. *Librn*, Lynnette Reed
CRAWFORD COMMUNITY, 42 Hwy 22, PO Box 201, Crawford, 81415-0201. SAN 335-5713. Tel: 970-921-3500. *Librn*, Cathy Little
HOTCHKISS PUBLIC, PO Box 540, Hotchkiss, 81419-0540. SAN 335-5748. Tel: 970-872-3253. *Librn*, Rhonda Duclo
PAONIA PUBLIC, PO Box 969, Paonia, 81428-0969. SAN 335-5772. Tel: 970-527-3470. FAX: 970-527-3871. *Librn*, Myrna Westerman

DENVER

S AMERICAN SOCIETY OF SUGAR BEET TECHNOLOGISTS LIBRARY,* 800 Grant St, Ste 500, 80203. SAN 374-9304. Tel: 303-832-4460. FAX: 303-832-4468.
Library Holdings: Bk Titles 250; Per Subs 15

S AMERICAN WATER WORKS ASSOCIATION, Library & Information Services Department,* 6666 W Quincy, 80235. SAN 301-7958. Tel: 303-347-6170, 303-794-7711. FAX: 303-795-1440. Web Site: www.awwa.org. *In Charge*, Kurt M Keeley; *Tech Servs*, Heidi Chiacchieri; Staff 5 (MLS 4, Non-MLS 1)

Founded 1977
Library Holdings: Bk Titles 5,000; Per Subs 300
Subject Interests: Water treatment
Publications: Specialized Subject Annotated Bibliographies
Partic in Bibliographical Center For Research, Rocky Mountain Region, Inc; Dialog Corporation

S ARTHUR ANDERSEN LLP BUSINESS INFORMATION CENTER, 1225 17th St, Ste 3100, 80202-5607. SAN 326-5382. Tel: 303-291-9444. FAX: 303-291-9200. *Res*, Steve Rosas; Staff 1 (MLS 1)
Library Holdings: Bk Titles 300; Per Subs 100
Subject Interests: Accounting, Finance

M AORN CENTER FOR LIBRARY SERVICES & ARCHIVES, 2170 S Parker Rd, 80231-5711. SAN 301-7982. Tel: 303-755-6304, Ext 314. FAX: 303-368-4460. Web Site: www.aorn.org. *Dir*, Sara Katsh; Tel: 303-755-6304, Ext 288, E-Mail: skatsh@aorn.org; *Librn*, Margaret Stewart; Tel: 303-755-6304, Ext 276, E-Mail: mstewart@aorn.org; *Librn*, Susan Osborn; Tel: 303-755-6304, Ext 291, E-Mail: sosborn@aorn.org
Founded 1972
Jul 1999-Jun 2000 Mats Exp $121,000, Books $25,000, Per/Ser (Incl. Access Fees) $43,000. Sal $180,500
Library Holdings: Bk Vols 5,000; Bk Titles 4,500; Per Subs 400
Subject Interests: Health sciences, Medicine, Nursing
Special Collections: AORN Publications, archives, thesis
Automation Activity & Vendor Info: (OPAC) Innovative Interfaces Inc.; (Serials) Innovative Interfaces Inc.
Database Vendor: GaleNet, OCLC - First Search, OVID Technologies
Partic in Bibliographical Center For Research, Rocky Mountain Region, Inc; Central Colorado Library System; Colorado Council Of Medical Librarians; National Network Of Libraries Of Medicine - South Central Region

R ARCHBISHOP VEHR THEOLOGICAL LIBRARY & ARCHIVES,* 1300 S Steele St, 80210-2599. SAN 301-8741. Tel: 303-715-3146. FAX: 303-715-2037. *Dir*, Sylvia Rael; E-Mail: library1@archden.org; *Assoc Dir*, Michael Woodward; E-Mail: library2@archden.com; Staff 4 (MLS 1, Non-MLS 3)
Founded 1908. Enrl 57; Fac 25
Library Holdings: Bk Vols 137,000
Subject Interests: Philosophy, Theology
Special Collections: Anglican Studies; Hispanic Pastoral Ministry Coll
Partic in OCLC Online Computer Library Center, Inc
Friends of the Library Group

R AUGUSTANA LUTHERAN CHURCH LIBRARY,* 5000 E Alameda Ave, 80246. SAN 301-7990. Tel: 303-388-4678. FAX: 303-388-1338. *Librn*, Eloise Pearson
Founded 1963
Library Holdings: Bk Vols 5,308

C AURARIA LIBRARY,* 1100 Lawrence St, 80204-2096. SAN 335-5802. Tel: 303-556-2805. Interlibrary Loan Service Tel: 303-556-2562. FAX: 303-556-3528. Web Site: www.cudenver.edu/public/library. *Dean*, David Gleim; E-Mail: dgleim@carbon.cudenver.edu; *Asst Dir, Tech Servs*, Ellen Greenblatt; Tel: 303-556-6704, E-Mail: egreenbl@carbon.cudenver.edu; *Access Serv, Asst Dir*, Tony Dedrick; Tel: 303-556-2843, E-Mail: adedrick@carbon.cudenver.edu; *Asst Dir, Info Res*, Kathy Payne; Tel: 303-556-4766, E-Mail: klpayne@carbon.cudenver.edu; *Assoc Dir*, Jean F Hemphill; Tel: 303-556-3523, E-Mail: jhemphill@carbon.cudenver.edu; *Coll Develop*, Terry Leopold; Tel: 303-556-3452, E-Mail: tleopold@carbon.cudenver.edu; *Coordr*, Eveline Yang; Tel: 303-556-6381, E-Mail: eyang@carbon.cudenver.edu; *Acq*, Cindy Hashert; Tel: 303-556-5256, E-Mail: chashert@carbon.cudenver.edu; *Head Ref*, Judith Valdez; Tel: 303-556-4999, E-Mail: jvaldez@carbon.cudenver.edu; *Cat*, Florence Jones; Tel: 303-556-4762, E-Mail: fjones@carbon.cudenver.edu; *ILL, Per*, Robb Waltner; Tel: 303-556-2876, E-Mail: rwaltner@carbon.cudenver.edu; *Govt Doc*, Louise Treff-Gangler; Tel: 303-556-3532, E-Mail: ltreff@carbon.cudenver.edu; *Instrul Serv*, Liz D'Antonio; Tel: 303-556-2791, E-Mail: edantoni@carbon.cudenver.edu; Staff 25 (MLS 25)
Founded 1976. Enrl 23,000; Fac 1,050; Highest Degree: Doctorate
Jul 1998-Jun 1999 Income State $6,040,279. Mats Exp $2,077,890. Sal $3,425,273 (Prof $1,559,829)
Library Holdings: Bk Vols 612,507; Bk Titles 556,774; Per Subs 3,083
Subject Interests: Architecture
Special Collections: Civil Liberties in Colorado; Higher Education (Auraria Higher Education Center Archives); HUD; Literature & Literary Criticism (Donald Sutherland Coll); State & Local Policy (Seasongood Library, National Municipal League, Conservative Think Tanks)
Automation Activity & Vendor Info: (Acquisitions) Innovative Interfaces Inc.; (Cataloging) Innovative Interfaces Inc.; (Circulation) Innovative Interfaces Inc.; (Course Reserve) Innovative Interfaces Inc.; (Media Booking) Innovative Interfaces Inc.; (OPAC) Innovative Interfaces Inc.; (Serials) Innovative Interfaces Inc.
Database Vendor: OCLC - First Search
Mem of Cent Colorado Libr Syst
Partic in BCR; Colorado Alliance Of Research Libraries; Dialog Corporation; OCLC Online Computer Library Center, Inc
Special Services for the Deaf - Staff with knowledge of sign language; TTY machine
Special Services for the Blind - VisualTek closed circuit TV reading aid
Combined Computer Access Center
Friends of the Library Group

G BUREAU OF LAND MANAGEMENT LIBRARY,* Bldg 50, RS 150 A, Denver Federal Ctr, PO Box 25047, 80225-0047. SAN 335-5926. Tel: 303-236-6650. FAX: 303-236-4810. *Ref*, Barbara Campbell; *Tech Servs*, Joan Penzien; *Tech Servs*, Talitha Cumi; *Tech Servs*, Barbara Klassen; Staff 7 (MLS 3, Non-MLS 4)
Founded 1971
Library Holdings: Bk Vols 40,000
Publications: BLM Monthly Alert
Partic in Central Colorado Library System; Fedlink

S CAMP, DRESSER & MCKEE, Environmental Library,* 1331 17th St Ste 1200, 80202. SAN 302-0320. Tel: 303-298-1311. FAX: 303-293-8236. *In Charge*, Gary Sagehorn
Founded 1975
Library Holdings: Bk Vols 5,000; Per Subs 80
Subject Interests: Air pollution, Mining, Water pollution
Partic in Dialog Corporation; SDC Info Servs

S CENTURY ENERGIES LIBRARY,* PO Box 840, 80201. SAN 301-8644. Tel: 303-294-2620. FAX: 303-294-2799. *Librn*, Mary Ann Hamm; E-Mail: mhamm@psco.com
Founded 1950
Library Holdings: Bk Titles 8,000; Per Subs 400
Subject Interests: Electricity, Energy
Special Collections: American Gas Association Coll; Edison Electric Institute Coll; Electric Power Research Institute Coll; Gas Research Institute Coll
Restriction: Staff use only
Mem of Colo Tech Ref Center
Open Mon-Fri 7:30-4:30

THE CHILDREN'S HOSPITAL

M FAMILY HEALTH LIBRARY, 1056 E 19th Ave, 80218-1088. SAN 378-1739. Tel: 303-861-6378. FAX: 303-861-6786, 303-864-5385. E-Mail: family.resource@tchden.org. Web Site: www.tchden.org. *Librn*, Kate Smith
Library Holdings: Bk Vols 2,000; Per Subs 10
Restriction: Staff use only

M FORBES MEDICAL LIBRARY, 1056 E 19th Ave, 80218-1088. SAN 326-3185. Tel: 303-861-6400. *Mgr*, Linda Van Wert; Staff 4 (MLS 3, Non-MLS 1)
Library Holdings: Bk Titles 3,800; Per Subs 285
Automation Activity & Vendor Info: (Acquisitions) Innovative Interfaces Inc.; (Cataloging) Innovative Interfaces Inc.; (Circulation) Innovative Interfaces Inc.; (OPAC) Innovative Interfaces Inc.; (Serials) Innovative Interfaces Inc.
Database Vendor: OCLC - First Search
Restriction: Staff use only

S COLORADO AGENCY FOR JEWISH EDUCATION, 300 S Dahlia St, Ste 101, 80246. SAN 377-9041. Tel: 303-321-3191, Ext 20. FAX: 303-321-5436. E-Mail: library@caje-co.org. Web Site: www.caje-co.org. *Dir*, Bernice Tarlie
Library Holdings: Bk Vols 9,000; Bk Titles 9,000; Per Subs 20
Subject Interests: Education, Holocaust, Judaica, Special education
Special Collections: Children's Judaica Library; Judaic teacher materials; Video coll
Automation Activity & Vendor Info: (Cataloging) Sagebrush Corporation; (Circulation) Sagebrush Corporation
Partic in Asn of Jewish Librs; BCR; Central Colorado Library System
Friends of the Library Group

G COLORADO DEPARTMENT OF LOCAL AFFAIRS LIBRARY,* 1313 Sherman St, Rm 521, 80203. SAN 301-8067. Tel: 303-866-2156. FAX: 303-866-4819.
Library Holdings: Bk Vols 500

S COLORADO DEPARTMENT OF PUBLIC HEALTH & ENVIRONMENT, Rocky Flats Reading Room & Information Center Library, 4300 Cherry Creek Dr S, 80246-1530. SAN 377-8983. Tel: 303-692-2037. Toll Free Tel: 800-886-7689. FAX: 303-691-1979. *Librn*, Kay Juricek; E-Mail: kay.juricek@state.co.us; Staff 1 (MLS 1)
Library Holdings: Bk Vols 5,000; Bk Titles 3,000; Per Subs 150
Restriction: Not a lending library
Partic in Access Colo Libr Info Network; Colorado Alliance Of Research Libraries

G COLORADO DEPARTMENT OF TRANSPORTATION LIBRARY,* 4340 E Louisiana Ave, Rm L203, 80246. SAN 301-8164. Tel: 303-757-9972. FAX: 303-757-9242. Web Site: www.dot.state.co.us/business/library/index.htm. *Librn*, Joan Pinamont; E-Mail: joan.pinamont@dot.state.co.us
Founded 1949
Library Holdings: Bk Vols 18,000; Per Subs 800
Subject Interests: Safety, Transportation

G COLORADO DEVELOPMENTAL DISABILITIES PLANNING COUNCIL LIBRARY,* 777 Grant St, Ste 304, 80203-3534. SAN 375-9113. Tel: 303-894-2345. FAX: 303-894-2880. *Librn*, Sylvia Nicodemus
Library Holdings: Bk Vols 600

G COLORADO DIVISION OF STATE ARCHIVES & PUBLIC RECORDS LIBRARY,* 1313 Sherman St, Rm 1B20, 80203-2236. SAN 373-8175. Tel: 303-866-2055. FAX: 303-866-2257. E-Mail: webmaster@state.co.us. Web Site: www.state.co.us/gov-dir/gss/archives/index. *Dir*, Terry Ketelsen; Staff 8 (MLS 8)
Founded 1943
Jul 1996-Jun 1997 Income $561,000
Special Collections: Colorado Public Officials; Records of Territory & State of Colorado, flm original docs, vols
Restriction: Staff use only
Friends of the Library Group

G COLORADO GOVERNOR'S OFFICE OF ENERGY MANAGEMENT & CONSERVATION LIBRARY, 225 E 16th Ave, Ste 650, 80203. SAN 323-4843. Tel: 303-894-2383. FAX: 303-894-2388. Web Site: www.state.co.us/oemc. *Dir*, Rick Grice; *Librn*, Martha Blackwell
Library Holdings: Bk Vols 300
Subject Interests: Energy
Open Mon-Fri 8-5

S COLORADO HISTORICAL SOCIETY, Stephen H Hart Library, 1300 Broadway, 80203-2137. SAN 301-8083. Tel: 303-866-2305. FAX: 303-866-4600. Web Site: www.coloradohistory.org. *Dir*, Rebecca Lintz; *Curator*, Eric Paddock; Staff 15 (MLS 10, Non-MLS 5)
Founded 1879
Library Holdings: Bk Vols 47,000
Subject Interests: Colorado, Mining, Railroads, Social history
Special Collections: Aultman Studio Photo Coll; Colorado Newspapers; Denver & Rio Grande Railroads; H A W Tabor Coll, mss, W H Jackson Photo & Mss Coll
Restriction: Not a lending library
Partic in OCLC Online Computer Library Center, Inc

S COLORADO LEGISLATIVE COUNCIL, Joint Legislative Library, State Capitol Bldg Rm 048, 200 E Colfax Ave, 80203-1784. SAN 375-4510. Tel: 303-866-3521. FAX: 303-866-2167. *Mgr, Senior Librn*, Molly Oho; *Librn*, Gay Roesch
Founded 1973
Library Holdings: Bk Vols 2,500; Per Subs 100
Special Collections: Bills, Colorado General Assembly materials, Fiscal Notes, Interim Committee Reports
Restriction: Non-circulating to the public
Mem of Cent Colorado Libr Syst

M COLORADO MENTAL HEALTH INSTITUTE AT FORT LOGAN, Medical Library,* 3520 W Oxford Ave, 80236. SAN 301-8385. Tel: 303-866-7844. FAX: 303-866-7048. *Dir Libr Serv*, Kate Elder; E-Mail: kate.elder@state.co.us
Founded 1961
Library Holdings: Bk Vols 9,480; Bk Titles 5,000; Per Subs 90
Subject Interests: Mental health, Nursing, Psychiatry, Psychology, Social sciences and issues
Special Collections: Refugee mental health - reports
Publications: The Supplement (bimonthly newsletter)
Mem of Cent Colorado Libr Syst; Colo Coun of Med Librns
Partic in Assn of Mental Health Librns, Mid Continental Regional Med Libr Group
Branches:
CHILDREN'S DIVISION LIBRARY, 4055 S Lowell Blvd, 80236. SAN 328-8404. Tel: 303-866-7882. FAX: 303-866-4260. *Librn*, Sarah Triffleman
Library Holdings: Bk Titles 8,000
Special Collections: Consumer/Parent; Mental Health

L COLORADO STATE BANK BUILDING, Law Library,* 1600 Broadway, Ste 510, 80202-4915. SAN 321-804X. Tel: 303-837-0287.
Founded 1976
Library Holdings: Bk Vols 17,000
Subject Interests: Bankruptcy, Labor law, Litigation, Tax

G COLORADO STATE DEPARTMENT OF LABOR & EMPLOYMENT, Division of Employment & Training, Labor Market Information Section Library,* Tower 2, Ste 300, 1515 Arapahoe St, 80202. SAN 301-8121. Tel: 303-620-4859. FAX: 303-620-4988. *Dir*, Marvin Wojahn
Founded 1964
Library Holdings: Bk Vols 200; Per Subs 2,000
Special Collections: Colorado Labor Force Review Series, 1964 to present; Official Colorado Labor Force Estimates

COLORADO STATE DEPARTMENT OF NATURAL RESOURCES

G COLORADO GEOLOGICAL SURVEY LIBRARY, 1313 Sherman St, Rm 715, 80203. SAN 335-6019. Tel: 303-866-2611. FAX: 303-866-2461. Web Site: www.dnr.state.co.us/geosurvey. *Dir*, Vicki Cowart
Founded 1969
Library Holdings: Bk Titles 6,200; Per Subs 201
Subject Interests: Geology

G COLORADO WATER CONSERVATION BOARD LIBRARY, 1313 Sherman St, Rm 721, 80203. SAN 335-6043. Tel: 303-866-3441. FAX: 303-866-4474. *Actg Dir*, Peter Evans
Library Holdings: Bk Vols 2,806

S DIVISION OF WILDLIFE LIBRARY, 6060 Broadway, 80216. SAN 335-6078. Tel: 303-291-7319, 303-297-1192, Ext 319. FAX: 303-291-7113. *Librn*, Rita Green; E-Mail: rita.green@state.co.us
Jul 1997-Jun 1998 Income $45,000. Mats Exp $6,000, Books $1,500, Per/Ser (Incl. Access Fees) $1,500, AV Equip $1,000. Sal $35,000
Library Holdings: Bk Vols 7,000; Per Subs 36
Partic in Central Colorado Library System

P COLORADO STATE LIBRARY, Colorado Department of Education, 201 E Colfax Ave, No 309, 80203-1799. SAN 335-6108. Tel: 303-866-6900. FAX: 303-866-6940. Web Site: www.cde.state.co.us/library_index.htm. *Dir*, Eugene Hainer; E-Mail: hainer_e@cde.state.co.us; *Dir Libr Serv*, James Schubert; *State Librn*, Nancy M Bolt; E-Mail: nancybolt@earthlink.net; *Res*, Keith Lance
Founded 1876
Jul 1998-Jun 1999 Income $8,618,694. Mats Exp $101,899. Sal $1,926,129
Library Holdings: Bk Titles 26,935; Per Subs 75
Subject Interests: Education, Library and information science
Special Collections: Adult Literacy; Standards & Assessment Resource Bank; State Publications
Automation Activity & Vendor Info: (OPAC) CARL; (Serials) CARL
Database Vendor: OCLC - First Search
Publications: Annual Report; Information Literacy Guidelines; Long Range Plan; Public Library Standards; Resource Sharing Study; School Media Guidelines; Standards for Adult Correctional Institutions; Statistical Summaries by Type of Library; The Impact of School Library Media Centers on Academic Achievement; The Library Collection & The Community: A Handbook for Small Public Libraries
Partic in BCR; OCLC Online Computer Library Center, Inc
Branches: 3
COLORADO STATE PUBLICATIONS FAX: 303-866-6940. Web Site: www.cde.state.co.us/slstpubs.htm.
COLORADO LITERACY RESOURCE CENTER FAX: 303-830-0793. Web Site: www.cde.state.co.us/sladserv.htm. *Dir*, Keith Curry Lance
COLORADO TALKING BOOK LIBRARY
See Separate Entry

GL COLORADO SUPREME COURT LIBRARY,* B112 State Judicial Bldg, 2 E 14th Ave, 80203-2116. SAN 301-8180. Tel: 303-837-3720. FAX: 303-837-3702. *Librn*, Lois Calvert; E-Mail: lcalvert@csn.net; *Librn*, Linda Gruenthal; *Asst Librn*, Martha Campbell
Founded 1874
Library Holdings: Bk Vols 90,000; Per Subs 500
Subject Interests: Law
Partic in OCLC Online Computer Library Center, Inc

P COLORADO TALKING BOOK LIBRARY,* 180 Sheridan Blvd, 80226. SAN 301-8172. Tel: 303-727-9277. Toll Free Tel: 800-685-2136. FAX: 303-727-9281.; Staff 3 (MLS 3)
Founded 1931
Special Collections: Blindness & Other Handicaps Reference Materials; Spanish Language, cassettes; Volunteer Produced Books & Magazines
Publications: Newsletter
Friends of the Library Group

§SR CONGREGATION EMMANUEL LIBRARY, 51 Grape St, 80220. SAN 378-3790. Tel: 303-388-4013. FAX: 303-388-6328. *Librn*, Susan Bersen
Library Holdings: Bk Titles 7,000; Per Subs 30
Automation Activity & Vendor Info: (Cataloging) Sagebrush Corporation

L DAVIS, GRAHAM & STUBBS LLP, Law Library, 1550 17th St, 80202. SAN 301-8229. Tel: 303-892-7306. FAX: 303-893-1379. *Dir*, Tom Duggin; Staff 4 (MLS 2, Non-MLS 2)
Library Holdings: Bk Vols 20,000

S DENVER ACADEMY LIBRARY,* 1101 S Race St, 80210. SAN 377-9068. Tel: 303-777-5870. FAX: 303-777-5893. Web Site: www.denveracademy.org. *Librn*, Jolene Gutierrez; E-Mail: jgutierrez@denveracademy.org
Library Holdings: Bk Titles 7,200; Per Subs 20
Partic in Am Libr Asn; Central Colorado Library System; Colo Educ Media Asn; Colo Independent Sch Librs; Colo Libr Asn

S DENVER ART MUSEUM LIBRARY,* 100 W 14th Ave Pkwy, 80204-2788. SAN 301-8245. Tel: 303-640-1613. FAX: 303-640-5627. *Dir*, Nancy Simon
Founded 1935
Oct 1997-Sep 1998 Income $15,000
Library Holdings: Bk Vols 20,000

Subject Interests: Anthropology, Fine arts
Special Collections: Douglas Coll of Native Arts
Partic in OCLC Online Computer Library Center, Inc

S DENVER BOTANIC GARDENS, Helen Fowler Library, 909 York St, 80206-3799. SAN 301-8253. Tel: 720-865-3570. FAX: 720-865-3730. E-Mail: library@botanicgardens.org. Web Site: www.botanicgardens.org. *Senior Librn*, Susan Eubank; E-Mail: eubanks@botanicgardens.org; Staff 2 (MLS 2)
Founded 1947
Jan 1999-Dec 1999 Income $150,000, Locally Generated Income $20,000, Other $130,000. Mats Exp $28,000, Books $17,000, Per/Ser (Incl. Access Fees) $8,500, Presv $1,000, AV Equip $500, Electronic Ref Mat (Incl. Access Fees) $1,000. Sal $68,500
Library Holdings: Bk Vols 27,000; Bk Titles 25,000; Per Subs 500; Spec Interest Per Sub 403
Subject Interests: Botany, Horticulture
Special Collections: Waring Rare Book Room
Partic in Bibliographical Center For Research, Rocky Mountain Region, Inc; Central Colorado Library System

S DENVER CENTER FOR THE PERFORMING ARTS, National Theatre Conservatory Library, 1101 13th St, 80204. SAN 377-9084. Tel: 303-446-4869. FAX: 303-825-2117. *Librn*, Linda M Eller; E-Mail: eller@dcpa.org. Subject Specialists: *Theater*, Linda M Eller; Staff 1 (MLS 1)
Founded 1991
Jul 1999-Jun 2000 Mats Exp $10,000, Books $7,000, Per/Ser (Incl. Access Fees) $1,000, AV Equip $2,000
Library Holdings: Bk Vols 17,000; Per Subs 15; Spec Interest Per Sub 15
Subject Interests: Dance, Performance, Theater
Automation Activity & Vendor Info: (Cataloging) Sagebrush Corporation; (Circulation) Sagebrush Corporation
Partic in Central Colorado Library System; Colo Libr Asn; Theatre Libr Asn

R DENVER CONSERVATIVE BAPTIST SEMINARY, Carey S Thomas Library, 3401 S University Blvd, 80110. (Mail add: PO Box 100000, 80250), SAN 301-9004. Tel: 303-761-2482, Ext 1403. FAX: 303-761-8060. *Mgr*, Pearl Saylor; Tel: 303-762-6963, E-Mail: sarah@densem.edu; *Asst Librn*, Jeannette France; Tel: 303-762-6964, E-Mail: jeannette@densem.edu; *Cat*, Randy Kemp; Tel: 303-761-2482, Ext 1410, E-Mail: randyk@densem.edu; *Cat*, Robin Ottoson; Staff 8 (MLS 2, Non-MLS 6)
Founded 1950. Pop 575; Circ 2,575; Enrl 575; Fac 20; Highest Degree: Doctorate
Library Holdings: Bk Vols 152,000; Bk Titles 143,750; Per Subs 575
Subject Interests: Theology
Database Vendor: Dialog, Ebsco - EbscoHost, epixtech, inc., OCLC - First Search
Function: Some telephone reference
Partic in BRS; OCLC Online Computer Library Center, Inc

M DENVER HEALTH MEDICAL CENTER, Medical Library, 777 Bannock St, 80204-4507. SAN 301-8261. Tel: 303-436-6360. FAX: 303-436-6476. E-Mail: mlibrary@dhha.org. Web Site: www.denverhealth.org. *Mgr*, W Robin Waters; Staff 2 (MLS 1, Non-MLS 1)
Founded 1944
1999-2000 Income $160,400. Mats Exp $61,500, Books $12,000, Per/Ser (Incl. Access Fees) $48,500, Other Print Mats $1,000. Sal $49,500 (Prof $34,000)
Library Holdings: Bk Vols 1,200; Per Subs 200
Subject Interests: Medicine, Nursing
Automation Activity & Vendor Info: (Acquisitions) Innovative Interfaces Inc.; (Cataloging) Innovative Interfaces Inc.; (Circulation) Innovative Interfaces Inc.; (Course Reserve) Innovative Interfaces Inc.; (ILL) Innovative Interfaces Inc.; (Media Booking) Innovative Interfaces Inc.; (OPAC) Innovative Interfaces Inc.; (Serials) Innovative Interfaces Inc.
Database Vendor: OCLC - First Search
Restriction: Medical staff only
Function: ILL available
Partic in Central Colorado Library System
Open Mon-Fri 8-4:30

S DENVER MUSEUM OF NATURAL HISTORY LIBRARY-ARCHIVES,* 2001 Colorado Blvd, 80205-5798. SAN 301-8288. Tel: 303-370-6362, 303-370-8353. FAX: 303-331-6492. *Archivist*, Kristine Haglund; E-Mail: khaglund@dmnh.org; *Librn*, Katherine B Gully; E-Mail: kgully@dmnh.org; *Archivist*, Liz Clancy; *Asst Librn*, Nancy Kall; *Cat*, Eloise Howerton
Founded 1900
Library Holdings: Bk Vols 30,000; Bk Titles 20,000; Per Subs 300; Spec Interest Per Sub 300
Subject Interests: Anthropology, Archaeology, Entomology, Geology, Life sciences, Ornithology, Paleontology, Space science, Zoology
Special Collections: Institutional Archives for Museum; Photo Archives; Rare books
Automation Activity & Vendor Info: (Acquisitions) EOS; (Cataloging) EOS; (Circulation) EOS; (Course Reserve) EOS; (ILL) EOS; (Media Booking) EOS; (OPAC) EOS; (Serials) EOS
Database Vendor: OCLC - First Search
Mem of Cent Colorado Libr Syst
Partic in Access Colo Libr Info Network
Most periodicals & special/rare collections for on-site use only. Conducts limited research for long-distance inquiries

S DENVER POST LIBRARY,* 1560 Broadway, 80202. SAN 301-8296. Tel: 303-820-1443. FAX: 303-832-4511. *Librn*, Vickie Makings; E-Mail: vmakings@denverpost.com
Library Holdings: Bk Titles 400
Restriction: Not open to public

P DENVER PUBLIC LIBRARY, 10 W 14th Ave Pkwy, 80204-2731. SAN 335-6167. Tel: 720-865-1111. Circulation Tel: 303-691-0458. FAX: 720-865-2087. Web Site: www.denver.lib.co.us. *Librn*, Rick J Ashton; *Asst Librn*, Rich Patton; *Tech Servs*, Gail M Dow; *Circ, ILL*, Lynn Taylor; *Bibliog Instr*, Sue Sterner; *Materials Manager*, Merveit Alkhoudairy; *Coll Develop, Mgr*, Carol King; *Mgr, Pub Relations*, Celeste Jackson; Staff 85 (MLS 85)
Founded 1889. Pop 501,473
Library Holdings: Bk Vols 1,882,487
Subject Interests: Aeronautics, Art and architecture, Business and management, Environmental studies, Genealogy, History, Music, Natural science, Technology
Special Collections: Aeronautics (Ross-Barrett Historical Aeronautical); Eugene Field, letters; Fine Printing (Douglas); Folk Music, popular v-tapes, scores; Genealogy; Mountaineering; Napoleon, bks, mss; Western History
Automation Activity & Vendor Info: (Acquisitions) CARL; (Circulation) CARL
Publications: Bonded to Build; Dewey's Dispatch; Viewpoint
Mem of Cent Colorado Libr Syst
Partic in Colorado Alliance Of Research Libraries
Special Services for the Deaf - TTY machine
Friends of the Library Group
Branches: 27
ATHMAR PARK, 1055 S Tejon St, 80223-2520. SAN 335-6469. Tel: 303-935-0721. FAX: 303-934-9388. *Mgr*, Susan Kotarba
BEAR VALLEY, 5171 W Dartmouth, 80236-2006. SAN 335-6493. Tel: 303-935-0616. FAX: 303-934-9403. *Mgr*, Iris Espino
BYERS, 675 Santa Fe Dr, 80204. SAN 335-6523. Tel: 303-571-1665. FAX: 303-572-4787. *Mgr*, Pilar Castro-Reino
CHILDREN'S LIBRARY Tel: 303-640-6384. FAX: 303-640-6323. *Mgr*, Kelly Campbell
Library Holdings: Bk Vols 125,761
Friends of the Library Group
DECKER, 1501 S Logan, 80210. SAN 335-6612. Tel: 303-733-7584. FAX: 303-733-8665. *Mgr*, Linda Metcalf
EUGENE FIELD, 810 S University, 80210. SAN 335-6647. Tel: 303-777-2301. FAX: 303-722-7331. *Mgr*, Anne Phillips
FIVE POINTS, 2855 Tremont Pl, 80205. SAN 328-6908. Tel: 303-297-0106. FAX: 303-295-4093. *Mgr*, Sondra Harris
FORD WARREN, 2825 High St, 80205. SAN 335-6671. Tel: 303-294-0907. FAX: 303-295-4090. *Mgr*, Sondra Harris
GENERAL REFERENCE & NON FICTION Tel: 303-640-6280. *Actg Mgr*, Karen Kelley
Library Holdings: Bk Vols 472,399
GOVERNMENT PUBLICATIONS & BUSINESS Tel: 303-640-6226. FAX: 303-640-6228. *Mgr*, Elena Wenzel
Library Holdings: Bk Vols 10,742
HADLEY, 1890 S Grove St, 80219. SAN 335-6701. Tel: 303-935-4267. FAX: 303-934-1294. *Mgr*, Iris Espino
HAMPDEN, 9755 E Girard Ave, 80231. SAN 335-6736. Tel: 303-750-3885. FAX: 303-751-4878. *Mgr*, Fred Yonce
BURNHAM HOYT (POPULAR, FICTION, AV & YOUNG ADULTS) Tel: 303-640-6262. FAX: 303-640-6264. *Mgr*, Georgiana Foley
Library Holdings: Bk Vols 116,271
MONTBELLO, 12955 Albrook Dr, 80239-4704. SAN 335-6795. Tel: 303-373-0767. FAX: 303-371-3542. *Mgr*, Sondra Harris
MONTCLAIR, 932 Jersey St, 80220. SAN 335-6825. Tel: 303-331-4061. FAX: 303-388-2331. *Mgr*, Cori Jackamore
PARK HILL, 4705 Montview Blvd, 80207-3760. SAN 335-685X. Tel: 303-331-4063. FAX: 303-388-2335. *Mgr*, Judy Stovall
PAULINE ROBINSON BRANCH, 5575 E 33rd Ave, 80207. SAN 376-107X. Tel: 303-370-1530. FAX: 303-370-1541. *Mgr*, Judy Stovall
VALDEZ PERRY BRANCH, 4690 Vine St, 80216. SAN 376-1088. Tel: 303-295-4302. *Mgr*, Pilar Castro-Reino
ROSS-BARNUM BRANCH, 3570 W First Ave, 80219. SAN 335-6884. Tel: 303-935-1891. FAX: 303-934-9324. *Mgr*, Susan Kotarba
ROSS-BROADWAY, 33 E Bayaud Ave, 80209-1503. SAN 335-6914. Tel: 303-777-4845. FAX: 303-733-8601. *Mgr*, Anne Phillips
ROSS-CHERRY CREEK, 305 Milwaukee St, 80206-4329. SAN 335-6949. Tel: 303-331-4016. FAX: 303-331-3860. *Mgr*, Cori Jackamore
ROSS-UNIVERSITY HILLS, 4310 E Amherst Ave, 80222. SAN 335-6973. Tel: 303-757-2714. FAX: 303-692-0712. *Mgr*, Linda Metcalf
SMILEY, 4501 W 46th Ave, 80212-2582. SAN 335-7007. Tel: 303-477-3622. FAX: 303-433-1294. *Mgr*, Teresa Burkert
VIRGINIA VILLAGE, 1500 S Dalhia, 80222-3509. SAN 335-7031. Tel: 303-757-6662. FAX: 303-692-0721. *Mgr*, Fred Yonce
WESTERN HISTORY & GENEALOGY Tel: 303-640-6291. FAX: 303-640-6298. *Actg Mgr*, Jim Kroll

Library Holdings: Bk Vols 137,753
WESTWOOD, 1000 S Lowell Blvd, 80219-3339. SAN 328-6886. Tel: 303-936-8808. FAX: 303-937-4454. *Mgr*, Susan Kotarba
WOODBURY, 3265 Federal Blvd, 80211-3211. SAN 335-7066. Tel: 303-455-3930. FAX: 303-455-5613. *Mgr*, Teresa Burkert
Bookmobiles: 1

S DENVER PUBLIC SCHOOL DISTRICT, Professional Library,* 1330 Fox St S 3rd Flr, 80204. SAN 328-4565. Tel: 303-405-8117. FAX: 303-405-8100. Web Site: www.denver.k12.co.us/departments/ers/index.html. *Mgr*, Jody Gehrig; Tel: 303-405-8101, E-Mail: jody_gehrig@dpsk12.org; *Coll Develop*, Susan L Potter; Tel: 303-405-8107, E-Mail: susan_potter@dpsk12.org; *Tech Servs*, Melinda Way; Tel: 303-405-8106, E-Mail: melinda_way@dpsk12.org
Library Holdings: Bk Vols 100,000; Per Subs 149
Automation Activity & Vendor Info: (Circulation) Innovative Interfaces Inc.
Database Vendor: Innovative Interfaces INN - View, OCLC - First Search, ProQuest
Partic in Bibliofile: The Dialog Corp, PLC

S DENVER RECEPTION & DIAGNOSTIC CENTER LIBRARY,* 10900 Smith Rd, PO Box 392004, 80239-8004. SAN 371-6066. Tel: 303-371-4804, Ext 3305. FAX: 303-375-2015. *Tech Servs*, Irene Betin; E-Mail: ibetin@csn.net
Founded 1991
Library Holdings: Bk Titles 9,673; Per Subs 25
Partic in Central Colorado Library System
Special Services for the Deaf - Books on deafness & sign language; High interest/low vocabulary books
Special Services for the Blind - Brailling & large print projects
Spanish language holdings

S DENVER WOMEN'S CORRECTIONAL FACILITY, General Library,* 3600 Havana, 80239. Tel: 303-307-2500, Ext 3608. FAX: 303-307-2674. E-Mail: dwcflib1@rmi.net. *In Charge*, Irene A Betin; Staff 1 (Non-MLS 1)
Founded 1999
Library Holdings: Bk Vols 3,500; Per Subs 36

S DENVER ZOOLOGICAL GARDEN LIBRARY,* 2300 Steele St, 80205. SAN 329-2304. Tel: 303-376-4898. FAX: 303-376-4839. *Librn*, Debbie Moody
Founded 1970
Library Holdings: Bk Titles 663; Per Subs 150

GM DEPARTMENT OF VETERANS AFFAIRS, Medical Center Library (142D), 1055 Clermont St, 80220. SAN 301-8873. Tel: 303-393-2821. FAX: 303-393-4647. *Chief Librn*, Nancy E Myer; *Asst Librn*, Elizabeth Alme; Staff 2 (MLS 2)
Oct 1998-Sep 1999 Income Federal $99,245. Mats Exp $95,163, Books $10,659, Per/Ser (Incl. Access Fees) $76,767, Electronic Ref Mat (Incl. Access Fees) $7,737
Library Holdings: Bk Vols 3,308; Bk Titles 3,300; Per Subs 382
Subject Interests: Allied health, Medicine, Nursing, Patient health educ
Database Vendor: Silverplatter Information Inc.
Restriction: Non-circulating to the public
Partic in Veterans Affairs Library Network

L DUFFORD & BROWN PC, Law Library, 1700 Broadway, Ste 1700, 80290-1701. SAN 375-2135. Tel: 303-861-8013. FAX: 303-832-3804. *Dir, Librn*, Craig Sorensen; E-Mail: sorensc@duffordbrown.com
Library Holdings: Bk Vols 6,000; Bk Titles 3,000; Per Subs 35

M EXEMPLA-SAINT JOSEPH HOSPITAL, Medical Library,* 1835 Franklin St, 80218-1191. SAN 301-8733. Tel: 303-837-7375. FAX: 303-837-7977. *Librn*, Margaret Bandy
Founded 1965
Library Holdings: Bk Vols 2,800; Per Subs 130
Subject Interests: Consumer health, Medicine, Nursing
Partic in Colorado Alliance Of Research Libraries

S GAS RESEARCH INSTITUTE INFORMATION CENTER,* 518 17th St, Ste 610, 80202. SAN 326-4793. Tel: 303-575-9030. FAX: 303-575-9129. E-Mail: gricentr@ix.netcom.com. *Res*, Ann Priestman
Founded 1984
Library Holdings: Bk Vols 10,000
Subject Interests: Geology, Geophysics
Publications: GRI publications

S GATES RUBBER CO, Information Center, 900 S Broadway, 80209. (Mail add: PO Box 5887, 80209), SAN 301-8393. Tel: 303-744-4150. FAX: 303-744-4745. E-Mail: rainwatr@csn.net. *Librn*, Kathleen Rainwater; Staff 1 (MLS 1)
Founded 1945
Library Holdings: Bk Titles 3,000; Per Subs 90
Subject Interests: Business and management, Chemistry, Mechanical engineering, Organic chemistry, Physical chemistry
Automation Activity & Vendor Info: (Cataloging) EOS; (OPAC) EOS; (Serials) EOS
Database Vendor: OCLC - First Search
Publications: Information News (quarterly)
Restriction: Staff use only
Partic in BCR; BCS

S GILLIAM YOUTH CENTER LIBRARY,* 2844 Downing St, 80205. SAN 378-0570. Tel: 303-291-8950. FAX: 303-291-8990. *Dir*, Vel Gardner
Library Holdings: Bk Titles 1,000

M HEALTH ONE PRESBYTERIAN-SAINT LUKE'S MEDICAL CENTER, Denver Medical Library, 1719 E 19th Ave, 80218-1281. SAN 335-721X. Tel: 303-839-6670. FAX: 303-863-8112. *Dir*, Sue Coldren; E-Mail: scoldren@yahoo.com; Staff 6 (MLS 4, Non-MLS 2)
Founded 1893
Jan 1999-Dec 1999 Income Parent Institution $475,000
Library Holdings: Bk Vols 54,000; Bk Vols 55,000; Per Subs 425
Subject Interests: Allied health, Cardiology, Geriatrics and gerontology, Neonatology, Obstetrics and gynecology, Pediatrics
Special Collections: History of Colorado Medicine; History of Medicine
Automation Activity & Vendor Info: (Cataloging) Innovative Interfaces Inc.; (Circulation) Innovative Interfaces Inc.; (OPAC) Innovative Interfaces Inc.; (Serials) Innovative Interfaces Inc.
Database Vendor: GaleNet, OCLC - First Search, OVID Technologies, Wilson - Wilson Web
Restriction: Private library, Staff & members only
Function: ILL available
Mem of Cent Colorado Libr Syst
Partic in Colorado Council Of Medical Librarians

S HEMLOCK SOCIETY USA LIBRARY, PO Box 101810, 80250-1810. SAN 329-4005. Tel: 303-639-1202. Toll Free Tel: 800-247-7421. FAX: 303-639-1224. E-Mail: legislate@hemlock.org. Web Site: www.hemlock.org. *Librn*, Lois Schafer
Library Holdings: Bk Vols 150
Special Collections: End of Life Decisions Coll

L HOLLAND & HART, Law Library, PO Box 8749, 80201-8749. SAN 301-8458. Tel: 303-295-8091. FAX: 303-295-8261. *Mgr*, Holly Kulikowski; E-Mail: hkulikowski@hollandhart.com; Staff 5 (MLS 3, Non-MLS 2)
Founded 1948
Library Holdings: Bk Vols 23,000
Restriction: Staff use only
Partic in Bibliographical Center For Research, Rocky Mountain Region, Inc

L HOLME ROBERTS & OWEN LLC, Law Library,* 1700 Lincoln, Ste 4100, 80203. SAN 301-8466. Tel: 303-861-7000, Ext 380. FAX: 303-866-0200. E-Mail: mestes@csn.net. *Librn*, Mark E Estes
Library Holdings: Bk Vols 35,000
Partic in OCLC Online Computer Library Center, Inc

CR ILIFF SCHOOL OF THEOLOGY, Ira J Taylor Library, 2201 S University Blvd, 80210. SAN 301-8474. Tel: 303-765-3173. Circulation Tel: 303-765-3172. Reference Tel: 303-765-3179. FAX: 303-777-0164. Web Site: www.iliff.edu. *Actg Librn*, Elmer J O'Brien; Tel: 303-765-3170, E-Mail: eobrien@iliff.edu; *Librn*, Sara J Myers; Tel: 303-765-3170, E-Mail: smyers@iliff.edu; *Tech Servs*, Alice I Runis; *Ref*, Marshall Edison; E-Mail: meidson@iliff.edu; *Cat*, Anita Schuneman; E-Mail: aschuneman@iliff.edu. Subject Specialists: *Theology*, Sara J Myers; *Theology*, Marshall Edison; Staff 4 (MLS 4)
Founded 1892. Circ 18,583; Enrl 267; Fac 29; Highest Degree: Doctorate
Jun 1999-May 2000 Income Parent Institution $460,811. Mats Exp $145,950, Books $107,944, Per/Ser (Incl. Access Fees) $37,957, Micro $49. Sal $255,784 (Prof $161,719)
Library Holdings: Bk Vols 196,330; Per Subs 711
Subject Interests: Religion
Special Collections: Hymnody (Van Pelt Hymnal Coll); Local Methodism (Archives of Iliff School of Theology & Rocky Mountain Conference of the United Methodist Church); Methodistica
Partic in Bibliographical Center For Research, Rocky Mountain Region, Inc; OCLC Online Computer Library Center, Inc

S INTERNATIONAL FEDERATION OF PETROLEUM & CHEMICAL WORKERS LIBRARY, 435 S Newport Way, 80224-1321. SAN 301-8490. Tel: 303-333-7605. *In Charge*, C J Hogan
Founded 1965

S LIPPER INC (A REUTERS COMPANY), Corporate Library, 1380 Lawrence St, Ste 950, 80204. SAN 375-8125. Tel: 303-534-3472. *Head of Libr*, Carol Mobley
Library Holdings: Bk Titles 400; Per Subs 55

S LOCKHEED MARTIN, Library Information Center,* PO Box 179, 80201-0179. SAN 301-8547. Tel: 303-977-5512. FAX: 303-977-6412. *Librn*, Janna Jantz; E-Mail: janna.jantz@lmco.com
Founded 1955

Library Holdings: Bk Titles 19,000; Per Subs 450
Subject Interests: Aerospace science, Electronics
Partic in BRS; Dialog Corporation; DROLS; Nasa Libraries Information System - Nasa Galaxie

L MILE HIGH CENTER, Law Library,* 1700 Broadway, Ste 1215, 80290-1201. SAN 301-8806. Tel: 303-832-3335. *Librn*, Gayle Walter
Founded 1951
Library Holdings: Bk Vols 25,000
Special Collections: Colorado History Statutes since Statehood

L MORRISON & FOERSTER LLP, Law Library, 5200 Republic Plaza Bldg, 370 17th St, 80202. SAN 328-5863. Tel: 303-592-2259. FAX: 303-592-1510. Web Site: www.mofo.com. *Mgr*, Pamela K Lewis; E-Mail: pklewis@mofo.com; Staff 2 (MLS 1, Non-MLS 1)
Library Holdings: Bk Vols 4,700; Per Subs 25
Restriction: Not open to public
Partic in Am Asn of Law Librs

S MOUNTAIN STATES EMPLOYERS COUNCIL LIBRARY, 1799 Pennsylvania St, 80203-1310. (Mail add: PO Box 539, 80201-0539), SAN 301-8598. Tel: 303-233-5331. FAX: 303-233-8326. Web Site: www.msec.org. *Mgr*, Mariwayne Scully; E-Mail: mscully@msec.org; Staff 2 (MLS 1, Non-MLS 1)
Founded 1939
Library Holdings: Bk Vols 2,000; Per Subs 90
Subject Interests: Business and management
Automation Activity & Vendor Info: (Cataloging) EOS; (Serials) EOS

S NATIONAL ENVIRONMENTAL HEALTH ASSOCIATION LIBRARY, 720 S Colorado Blvd, Ste 970-S, 80246-1925. SAN 374-9878. Tel: 303-756-9090. FAX: 303-691-9490. E-Mail: staff@neha.org. Web Site: www.neha.org. *Exec Dir*, Nelson E Fabian; Tel: 303-756-9090, Ext 301, E-Mail: nfabian@neha.org
Founded 1938
Library Holdings: Bk Titles 2,500
Subject Interests: Environmental studies

M NATIONAL JEWISH MEDICAL & RESEARCH CENTER, Gerald Tucker Memorial Medical Library, 1400 Jackson St, 80206-2762. SAN 301-861X. Tel: 303-398-1482. FAX: 303-270-2149. E-Mail: library@njc.org. Web Site: www.library.nationaljewish.org. *Librn*, Rosalind F Dudden; Tel: 303-398-1483, E-Mail: duddenr@njc.org. Subject Specialists: *Respiratory med*, Rosalind F Dudden; Staff 3 (MLS 2, Non-MLS 1)
Founded 1935
Jul 2000-Jun 2001 Mats Exp $280,839, Books $31,476, Per/Ser (Incl. Access Fees) $179,760, Electronic Ref Mat (Incl. Access Fees) $28,692. Sal $164,487 (Prof $100,000)
Library Holdings: Bk Titles 3,000; Per Subs 250
Subject Interests: Allergies, Immunology, Molecular biology, Respiratory med
Special Collections: Patient & Consumer Health Information
Automation Activity & Vendor Info: (Acquisitions) Innovative Interfaces Inc.; (Cataloging) Innovative Interfaces Inc.; (Circulation) Innovative Interfaces Inc.; (Course Reserve) Innovative Interfaces Inc.; (OPAC) Innovative Interfaces Inc.; (Serials) Innovative Interfaces Inc.
Database Vendor: Dialog, OCLC - First Search, OVID Technologies
Mem of Cent Colorado Libr Syst
Partic in Bibliographical Center For Research, Rocky Mountain Region, Inc; Colorado Council Of Medical Librarians

M PORTER ADVENTIST HOSPITAL, Harley E Rice Memorial Medical Library, 2525 S Downing St, 80210-5241. SAN 301-8636. Tel: 303-778-5656. FAX: 303-778-5608. Web Site: www.centura.org. *Librn, Mgr*, Patricia Perry; E-Mail: patperry@centura.org; *Tech Servs*, Deanna Malament
Founded 1934
Library Holdings: Bk Vols 2,445; Per Subs 300
Subject Interests: Medicine, Nursing
Partic in BRS; Colorado Council Of Medical Librarians; OCLC Online Computer Library Center, Inc

C REGIS UNIVERSITY, Dayton Memorial Library, 3333 Regis Blvd, 80221-1099. SAN 301-8660. Tel: 303-458-4030. FAX: 303-964-5497. Web Site: www.regis.edu. *Actg Dean*, Dr David Suiter; *Librn*, Ann James-Herron; *Media Spec*, Andrew Dorfman; *Circ*, Caren Clark; *ILL*, Mary Sponsel; *Tech Servs*, Janet Lee; Staff 11 (MLS 11)
Founded 1877. Enrl 3,739; Fac 379; Highest Degree: Master
Library Holdings: Bk Vols 261,791; Bk Titles 162,727; Per Subs 2,623
Subject Interests: Religion
Special Collections: Archives of Loretto Heights College; Archives of Regis College; Archives of the American Academy of Religion; Archives of the Society of Biblical Literature; Early 18th Century Religious Coll, pamphlets (American); Western Jesuitica Coll; Women's Coll
Publications: The periodicals list of the Regis college libraries
Partic in BRS; Colorado Alliance Of Research Libraries; Dialog Corporation; OCLC Online Computer Library Center, Inc
The Teikyo Loretto Heights College Library of Denver was added to the Regis libraries in 1988 (106,000 bk vols)

Departmental Libraries:
COLORADO SPRINGS CAMPUS, 7450 Campus Dr, Colorado Springs, 80920. SAN 370-5005. Tel: 719-264-7080. FAX: 719-264-7082. Web Site: www.regis.edu. *Dir*, Janice Marie; *Ref*, Phyllis Wells; *Circ*, Susan Stewart; Staff 2 (MLS 2)
Library Holdings: Bk Vols 14,000; Per Subs 464
Subject Interests: Computer science, Religion
Partic in Colorado Alliance Of Research Libraries

C ROCKY MOUNTAIN COLLEGE OF ART & DESIGN LIBRARY, 6875 E Evans Ave, 80224. SAN 377-9017. Tel: 303-753-6046, Ext 368. FAX: 303-759-4970. Web Site: www.rmcad.edu. *Dir*, Hugh Thurlow; E-Mail: hthurlow@rmcad.edu
Founded 1983. Enrl 450; Fac 44; Highest Degree: Bachelor
Library Holdings: Bk Titles 12,000; Per Subs 100
Automation Activity & Vendor Info: (Cataloging) Follett; (Circulation) Follett; (OPAC) Follett
Partic in Bibliographical Center For Research, Rocky Mountain Region, Inc; Central Colorado Library System; OCLC Online Computer Library Center, Inc

S ROCKY MOUNTAIN JEWISH HISTORICAL SOCIETY, Ira M Beck Memorial Archives,* Center for Judaic Studies, 2040 E Evans, Rm 217, Columbine E, 80208-0292. SAN 375-0485. Tel: 303-871-3020. FAX: 303-871-3037. *Archivist*, Dr Jeanne Abrams
Library Holdings: Bk Vols 200

S DENVER ROCKY MOUNTAIN NEWS EDITORIAL LIBRARY, 400 W Colfax Ave, 80204-2607. SAN 301-8695. Tel: 303-892-2649. FAX: 303-892-2577. E-Mail: newsquest@denver-rmn.com. Web Site: www.insidedenver.com. *Asst Dir, Coll Develop*, Carol Kasel. Subject Specialists: *Photos*, Sarah Lander You; Staff 8 (MLS 3, Non-MLS 5)
Founded 1950
Library Holdings: Bk Titles 1,160

M ROSE MEDICAL CENTER, Medical Library,* 4567 E Ninth Ave, 80220-3908. SAN 301-8709. Tel: 303-320-2160. FAX: 303-320-2661. *Librn*, Martha Libster
Founded 1949

L ROTHGERBER, JOHNSON & LYONS, Law Library,* One Tabor Ctr, Ste 3000, 1200 17th St, 80202. SAN 372-3240. Tel: 303-623-9000. FAX: 303-623-9222. Web Site: www.rothgerber.com. *Librn*, Dianne Kulesa
Library Holdings: Bk Vols 6,000; Per Subs 50

M SAINT ANTHONY'S HOSPITAL SYSTEMS, Memorial Medical Library, 4231 W 16th Ave, 80204. SAN 301-8725. Tel: 303-629-3790. FAX: 303-629-2234. *Coordr*, Yolanda Crespin; E-Mail: yolandacrespin@centura.org; Staff 2 (MLS 1, Non-MLS 1)
Founded 1946
Library Holdings: Bk Titles 1,500; Per Subs 250
Subject Interests: Medicine, Nursing
Restriction: Medical staff only
Partic in Dialog Corporation; Medline
Open 8-4

SR SAINT JOHN'S CATHEDRAL LIBRARY, 1313 Clarkson St, 80218-1807. SAN 375-3468. Tel: 303-831-7115. FAX: 303-831-7119. Web Site: www.sjc.den.org. *Librn*, Joyce L White; Staff 5 (MLS 2, Non-MLS 3)
Founded 1950
Library Holdings: Bk Vols 3,500; Bk Titles 3,000; Per Subs 28
Subject Interests: Church history, Theology
Special Collections: Old Prayer Books (BCP)
Partic in OCLC Online Computer Library Center, Inc

S SECURITY LIFE OF DENVER, Corporate Library,* 1290 Broadway, 80203-5699. SAN 376-1878. Tel: 303-860-2338. FAX: 303-860-2134. *Librn*, Beth Engelsman
Library Holdings: Bk Vols 2,000

L SHERMAN & HOWARD, Law Library,* 633 17th St, Ste 2400, 80202. SAN 301-8237. Tel: 303-299-8041. FAX: 303-298-0940. *Librn*, Linda Rose; Staff 7 (MLS 3, Non-MLS 4)
Library Holdings: Bk Vols 20,000; Per Subs 350
Publications: Newsletter
Partic in BRS; Data Time; Dialog Corporation; Legislate; OCLC Online Computer Library Center, Inc; Outext; Westlaw
Open Mon-Fri 8:30-11, 1:30-4

S STAGECOACH LIBRARY FOR GENEALOGICAL RESEARCH,* 1840 S Wolcott Ct, 80219-4309. SAN 326-5951. Tel: 303-922-8856.; Staff 2 (MLS 1, Non-MLS 1)
Founded 1980
Library Holdings: Bk Titles 5,000; Per Subs 175

S STONE & WEBSTER ENGINEERING CORP LIBRARY,* 7677 E Berry Ave, PO Box 5406, 80217. SAN 301-8776. Tel: 303-741-7700. FAX: 303-741-7670. *In Charge*, Ted Farrell
Founded 1975
Library Holdings: Bk Vols 6,000; Per Subs 25
Open Mon-Fri 7am-3:45pm

C TEIKYO LORETTO HEIGHTS UNIVERSITY LIBRARY,* 3001 S Federal Blvd, 80236. SAN 373-594X. Tel: 303-937-4246. FAX: 303-937-4224. Web Site: www.tlhu.edu. *Dir*, Larry Grieco; E-Mail: lgrieco@tlhu.edu; Staff 4 (MLS 2, Non-MLS 2)
Founded 1989. Enrl 303; Fac 14; Highest Degree: Bachelor
Library Holdings: Bk Vols 118,000; Per Subs 273
Special Collections: East Asian Coll
Automation Activity & Vendor Info: (Acquisitions) CARL; (Circulation) CARL; (Serials) CARL
Partic in Central Colorado Library System; Colorado Alliance Of Research Libraries

L US BANK, Law Library, U S Bank Tower Bldg, 950 17th St, 80202. SAN 301-8105. Tel: 303-825-8400. FAX: 303-825-6525. *Librn*, Ann Marie Wills; E-Mail: awills@ojrnr.com
Founded 1975
Library Holdings: Bk Vols 33,000; Bk Titles 750; Per Subs 96
Publications: Handbook; newsletter
Restriction: Private library
Partic in OCLC Online Computer Library Center, Inc
Partners with Otten, Johnson, Robbinson, Neff & Ragonetti

GL UNITED STATES COURT OF APPEALS, Tenth Circuit Library,* US Courthouse, Rm C 411, 1929 Stout St, 80294-0001. SAN 301-8822. Tel: 303-844-3591. FAX: 303-844-5958. *Librn*, J Terry Hemming; *Publ Servs*, Catherine Eason; *Br Coordr*, Jerry Stephens; *Br Coordr*, Leslie McGuire; *ILL*, Inez Larson; *Tech Servs*, Ruthann Rehnborg; *Coll Develop*, Donna Stegner; Staff 13 (MLS 10, Non-MLS 3)
Founded 1929
Library Holdings: Bk Vols 50,000
Subject Interests: Law
Partic in Dialog Corporation; Fedlink; OCLC Online Computer Library Center, Inc; Westlaw

UNITED STATES DEPARTMENT OF DEFENSE
A DEFENSE FINANCE & ACCOUNTING SERVICE - DENVER CENTER - LEARNING CENTER, 6760 E Irvington Pl, 80279-8000. SAN 335-7279. Tel: 303-676-7566. FAX: 303-676-6003.
Founded 1951
Oct 1998-Sep 1999 Income $175,000. Mats Exp $275,060, Books $175,060, Per/Ser (Incl. Access Fees) $90,000, Micro $5,000
Library Holdings: Bk Vols 9,685
Subject Interests: Accounting, Computer science
Restriction: Not open to public
Partic in Dialog Corporation; Fedlink; OCLC Online Computer Library Center, Inc

G UNITED STATES DEPARTMENT OF LABOR, OSHA Library,* 1999 Broadway, Ste 1690, 80202-5716. SAN 323-7028. Tel: 303-844-1603, Ext 326. FAX: 303-844-1616. *Librn*, Carolyn Leslie; E-Mail: leslie_carolyn@dol.gov
Library Holdings: Bk Vols 1,000; Bk Titles 450; Per Subs 50
Special Collections: Occupation Safety & Health, AV, bks, compact discs, docs, microfiche
Partic in Colorado Alliance Of Research Libraries; Dialog Corporation; Fedlink; OCLC Online Computer Library Center, Inc

UNITED STATES DEPARTMENT OF THE INTERIOR
G BUREAU OF RECLAMATION, RECLAMATION SERVICE CENTER LIBRARY, Denver Fed Ctr D7925 - Sixth Ave & Kipling St, PO Box 25007, 80225. SAN 335-7392. Tel: 303-445-2072. FAX: 303-445-6303. E-Mail: lib@do.usbr.gov. Web Site: www.library.usbr.gov.
Founded 1945
Library Holdings: Bk Vols 60,000; Per Subs 1,000
Subject Interests: Construction
Special Collections: Construction Specifications
Partic in Dialog Corporation; Fedlink; OCLC Online Computer Library Center, Inc

G UNITED STATES ENVIRONMENTAL PROTECTION AGENCY, Region 8 Library,* 80C-L 999-18th St, Ste 500, 80202-2466. SAN 301-8334. Tel: 303-312-6312. FAX: 303-312-7061. E-Mail: library-reg8@group.epamail.epa.gov. Web Site: www.epa.gov/region08. *Head of Libr*, Marybeth Homiack; E-Mail: homiackmarybeth@epamail.epa.gov
Founded 1973
Subject Interests: Air pollution, Pesticides, Radiation, Water pollution
Automation Activity & Vendor Info: (Circulation) TechLIB

G UNITED STATES ENVIRONMENTAL PROTECTION AGENCY, National Enforcement Investigations Center,* Bldg 53 DFC, Box 25227, 80225. SAN 329-0786. Tel: 303-236-6136. FAX: 303-236-3218. Web Site: www.epa.gov/oeca/oceft/neic. *Librn*, Dorothy Biggs; *ILL, Librn*, Kim O'Neill; E-Mail: oneill.kim@epa.gov; *ILL*, Stacey Nagle; Staff 3 (MLS 2, Non-MLS 1)
Library Holdings: Bk Titles 2,000; Per Subs 150
Subject Interests: Analytical chemistry, Environmental law, Forensic sci
Special Collections: EPA Methods Collection
Automation Activity & Vendor Info: (Serials) EOS
Database Vendor: OCLC - First Search
Publications: NEIC newsletter
Partic in EPA; Fedlink

G UNITED STATES GEOLOGICAL SURVEY LIBRARY,* Bldg 20 Rm C2002, Denver Federal Ctr. (Mail add: PO Box 25046, Stop 914, 80225-0046), SAN 320-1260. Tel: 303-236-1000. TDD: 303-236-0098. FAX: 303-236-0015. E-Mail: den_lib@usgs.gov. Web Site: library.usgs.gov. *Librn*, Tommie Ann Gard; Tel: 303-236-1004, E-Mail: tagard@usgs.gov; Staff 12 (MLS 4, Non-MLS 8)
Founded 1948
Library Holdings: Bk Titles 230,000; Per Subs 700
Subject Interests: Earth science
Special Collections: Field Records Library (original field notes & maps of USGS research); GEO Center (K-12 educational materials on geoscience); Photo Library (USGS photographs of geologic subjects)
Partic in Central Colorado Library System; Dialog Corporation; Fedlink; OCLC Online Computer Library Center, Inc
Special Services for the Deaf - TDD

UNIVERSITY OF COLORADO HEALTH SCIENCES CENTER
CM DENISON MEMORIAL LIBRARY, 4200 E Ninth Ave, 80262. SAN 335-7600. Tel: 303-315-5125. FAX: 303-315-0294. Web Site: www.uchsc.edu/library/. *Dir*, Rick Forsman; *Assoc Dir*, Marla Graber; *Asst Dir*, Pat Nelson; *Ref*, Sandra Parker; *Circ*, Carole Hirschfield; *Acq, Syst Coordr*, Sandra Arnesen; *Coll Develop, ILL*, Catherine Reiter; Staff 15 (MLS 15)
Founded 1924. Enrl 2,000; Highest Degree: Doctorate
Jul 1997-Jun 1998 Income $3,200,000. Mats Exp $963,145, Books $90,783, Per/Ser (Incl. Access Fees) $872,362. Sal $1,499,287 (Prof $726,058)
Library Holdings: Bk Vols 96,919; Bk Titles 90,783; Per Subs 1,647
Subject Interests: Medicine
Publications: Connections (bimonthly newsletter)
Mem of Midcontinental Regional Med Libr
Partic in Dialog Corporation; Nat Libr of Med; OCLC Online Computer Library Center, Inc

C UNIVERSITY OF DENVER, Penrose Library, 2150 E Evans, 80208-2007. SAN 335-766X. Tel: 303-871-2007. Interlibrary Loan Service Tel: 303-871-3150. FAX: 303-871-2290. Web Site: www.penlib.du/edu/. *Dean of Libr*, Nancy Allen; E-Mail: nallen@du.edu; *Assoc Dir, Publ Servs*, Thomas Fry; *Assoc Dir*, Pat Clark; *Cat*, Lois Jones; *Online Servs*, Esther Gil; *Rare Bks, Spec Coll*, Steven Fisher; *Coll Develop*, Patricia A Fisher; *Ref*, Peggy Keeran; *Ref*, Michael Levine-Clark; *Ref*, Joe Kraus; *Ref*, Nonny Schlotzhauer; *Ref*, Chris Brown; Staff 19 (MLS 19)
Founded 1864. Enrl 7,390; Fac 424; Highest Degree: Doctorate
Library Holdings: Bk Vols 909,100; Per Subs 5,540
Special Collections: Ira M Beck Memorial Archives; Levette J Davidson Folklore Coll; Margaret Husted Culinary Coll; Papers of Congressman Wayne Aspinall; Papers of Senator Peter Dominick
Automation Activity & Vendor Info: (Acquisitions) Innovative Interfaces Inc.; (Cataloging) Innovative Interfaces Inc.; (Circulation) Innovative Interfaces Inc.; (Serials) Innovative Interfaces Inc.
Partic in Colorado Alliance Of Research Libraries; OCLC Online Computer Library Center, Inc
Friends of the Library Group
Departmental Libraries:
BRANCH MUSIC LIBRARY, 711 Montview Blvd, 80220. SAN 301-8199. Tel: 303-871-6421. FAX: 303-871-6886. *Librn*, Suzanne Moulton-Gertig; E-Mail: smoulton@du.edu
Founded 1985
Library Holdings: Bk Titles 15,860; Per Subs 27
WESTMINSTER LAW LIBRARY, 1900 Olive St, 80220. SAN 335-7694. Tel: 303-871-6153 (Admin), 303-871-6188. Interlibrary Loan Service Tel: 303-871-6191. FAX: 303-871-6999. Web Site: www.law.du.edu/library/. *Dir*, Gary Alexander; *Coll Develop, Tech Servs*, Barbara Allen; *Ref*, Sheila Green; *Ref*, Martha Keister; *Ref*, Patti Wellinger; *Access Serv*, Paul Sharpe; Staff 12 (MLS 12)
Founded 1892. Enrl 871; Highest Degree: Doctorate
1998-1999 Mats Exp $772,000. Sal $972,000 (Prof $663,000)
Library Holdings: Bk Vols 330,000; Per Subs 4,348
Special Collections: Howard Jenkins Manuscripts, Lowell Thomas Coll
Publications: Newsletter
Partic in Colorado Alliance Of Research Libraries; OCLC Online Computer Library Center, Inc

DOLORES

P DOLORES LIBRARY DISTRICT,* 420 Railroad Ave, PO Box 847, 81323-0847. SAN 301-892X. Tel: 970-882-4127. FAX: 970-882-2224. E-Mail: library@fone.net. Web Site: www.doloreslibrary.org. *Dir*, Carole Arnold;

E-Mail: carole@fone.net
Founded 1956. Pop 8,000; Circ 15,000
1999-2000 Income $217,000. Mats Exp $15,000. Sal $71,797
Library Holdings: Bk Titles 16,000; Per Subs 30
Subject Interests: Colorado, Local history
Special Collections: Archeology 200; Spanish (Children's Dual-Language Books)
Automation Activity & Vendor Info: (Cataloging) Sagebrush Corporation; (Circulation) Sagebrush Corporation
Publications: Book list
Mem of Southwest Regional Library Service System
Partic in OCLC Online Computer Library Center, Inc
Friends of the Library Group

DOVE CREEK

P DOLORES COUNTY PUBLIC LIBRARY, PO Box 578, 81324-0578. SAN 376-2823. Tel: 970-677-2389. *Dir*, Donna Brackett; *Librn*, Laurie Ernst; E-Mail: lernst@hubwest.com
Library Holdings: Bk Titles 15,000
Mem of Southwest Regional Library Service System

DURANGO

P DURANGO PUBLIC LIBRARY,* 1188 E Second Ave, 81301-5164. SAN 301-8938. Tel: 970-385-2970. FAX: 970-247-5214. *Dir*, Sherrie Taber; *Ad Servs*, Paula Lafrenierre; *Ch Servs*, Rita Curtis; *Tech Servs*, Veronica Valdez; *Br Coordr*, Susan Mooney; Staff 3 (MLS 3)
Founded 1889. Pop 30,000; Circ 196,355
Library Holdings: Bk Vols 72,000; Bk Titles 66,000; Per Subs 131
Special Collections: Archaeology (Helen Sloan Daniels); Local History, photogs; Southwestern US History (Helen Sloan Daniels)
Mem of Southwest Regional Library Service System
Friends of the Library Group
Branches: 1
FORT LEWIS MESA, 11274 Hwy 140, Hesperus, 81326. SAN 321-9313. Tel: 970-588-3331. *Librn*, Laurel Penwell
Library Holdings: Bk Vols 5,000

C FORT LEWIS COLLEGE LIBRARY, John F Reed Library, 1000 Rim Dr, 81301-3999. SAN 301-8946. Tel: 970-247-7250. Interlibrary Loan Service Tel: 970-247-7233. Circulation Tel: 970-247-7270. Reference Tel: 970-247-7551. FAX: 970-247-7149. E-Mail: frisbie_j@fortlewis.edu. Web Site: www.library.fortlewis.edu. *Dir*, Margaret Landrum; E-Mail: landrum_m@fortlewis.edu; *Actg Dir, Science*, Jeffrey Frisbie; E-Mail: frisbie_j@fortlewis.edu; *ILL*, Phyllis Kroupa; Tel: 970-247-7233, E-Mail: kroupa_p@fortlewis.edu; *Media Spec*, Ross Worley; Tel: 970-247-7418, E-Mail: worley_r@fortlewis.edu; *Acq, Coll Develop*, John Crowder; Tel: 970-247-7315, E-Mail: crowder_j@fortlewis.edu; *Circ, Tech Servs*, Alice McKinney; Tel: 970-247-7507, E-Mail: mckinney_a@fortlewis.edu; *Electronic Resources, Ref Serv*, Minna Sellers; Tel: 970-247-7149, E-Mail: sellers_m@fortlewis.edu; *Outreach Serv*, Elayne Walstedter; Tel: 970-247-7662, E-Mail: walstedter_e@fortlewis.edu; *Admin Assoc*, Ruth R Appleby; E-Mail: appleby_r@fortlewis.edu. Subject Specialists: *Maps*, Jeffrey Frisbie; Staff 8 (MLS 8)
Founded 1911. Enrl 4,287; Fac 250; Highest Degree: Bachelor
Jul 1999-Jun 2000 Income $1,400,000. Mats Exp $313,031, Books $101,520, Per/Ser (Incl. Access Fees) $127,161, Presv $5,154, AV Equip $11,340, Electronic Ref Mat (Incl. Access Fees) $67,856. Sal $699,247
Library Holdings: Bk Vols 183,977; Bk Titles 150,000; Per Subs 972
Automation Activity & Vendor Info: (Acquisitions) Innovative Interfaces Inc.; (Cataloging) Innovative Interfaces Inc.; (Circulation) Innovative Interfaces Inc.; (OPAC) Innovative Interfaces Inc.; (Serials) Innovative Interfaces Inc.
Database Vendor: CARL, Ebsco - EbscoHost, Innovative Interfaces INN - View, OCLC - First Search, Silverplatter Information Inc., Wilson - Wilson Web
Mem of Southwest Regional Library Service System
Partic in ACLIN
Friends of the Library Group

P SOUTHWEST REGIONAL LIBRARY SERVICE SYSTEM,* Drawer B, 81302-1090. SAN 301-8954. Tel: 970-247-4782. FAX: 970-247-5087. Web Site: www.colosys.net//swrlss. *Dir*, S Jane Ulrich; E-Mail: sjulrich@frontier.net
Founded 1976. Pop 106,000
Library Holdings: Bk Titles 150
Subject Interests: Library and information science
Publications: Swirls (newsletter)
Member Libraries: Adams State College Nielsen Library; Allerton Public Library; Anita Public Library; Bailey Memorial Library; Benson Village Library; Carnegie Public Library; Castleton Free Library; Conejos County Library; Cornwall Free Public Library; Cortez Public Library; Costilla County Library; Del Norte Public Library; Dolores County Public Library; Dolores Library District; Dorset Public Library Association, Inc; Durango Public Library; Edwin M Davis Memorial Library; Elk Horn Public Library; Exira Public Library; Fort Lewis College Library; Frederic D Barstow Memorial Library; Hubbardton Community Library; Ignacio Community Library District; Kuna School Community Library; Maclure Library; Mancos Public Library; Mark Skinner Library; Middletown Springs Public Library; Mineral County Regional Library; Mount Ayr Public Library; National Park Service; Orwell Free Library; Owen Memorial Library; Pawlet Public Library; Pine River Public Library; Proctor Free Library; Roger Clark Memorial Library; S L Griffith Memorial Library; Saguache County Public Library; Shrewsbury Public Library; Silverton Public Library; Sisson Memorial Library; Solomon Wright Library; Southern Peaks Public Library; Tinmouth Public Library; Wells Village Library; Whiting Free Library
Special Services - Provides consulting, continuing education, ILL coordination, cataloging & other services to member agencies

EADS

P KIOWA COUNTY PUBLIC LIBRARY, 1305 Goff, PO Box 790, 81036-0790. SAN 301-8962. Tel: 719-438-5581. FAX: 719-438-5325. E-Mail: kcpld@eads.lib.co.us. *Dir*, Sharon Johnson; *Asst Librn*, Phyllis Koch
Founded 1939. Pop 1,825; Circ 5,000
Library Holdings: Bk Vols 8,000; Per Subs 30
Mem of Arkansas Valley Regional Library Service System

EAGLE

P EAGLE VALLEY LIBRARY DISTRICT,* 600 Broadway, PO Box 240, 81631-0240. SAN 335-7724. Tel: 970-328-8800. FAX: 970-328-6901. *Head Librn*, Jan Fedrizzi; *Dir*, Charlyn Canada; *Asst Dir*, Anne Johnson; E-Mail: ajohnson@colosys.net; *Ch Servs, YA Servs*, Robyn Bryant; Staff 21 (MLS 4, Non-MLS 17)
Founded 1993. Pop 26,000; Circ 152,163
Jan 2000-Dec 2000 Income Other $3,034,878. Mats Exp $1,500,000, Books $217,000, Per/Ser (Incl. Access Fees) $50,000, AV Equip $55,000, Electronic Ref Mat (Incl. Access Fees) $13,500. Sal $1,124,904
Library Holdings: Bk Vols 111,314; Per Subs 420
Subject Interests: Colorado
Special Collections: Eagle County Hist Coll
Automation Activity & Vendor Info: (Circulation) CARL; (OPAC) CARL
Mem of Three Rivers Regional Library Service System
Partic in Marmot Western Colo Libr Network; OCLC Online Computer Library Center, Inc
Friends of the Library Group
Branches: 2
AVON PUBLIC, 200 Benchmark Rd, PO Box 977, Avon, 81620-0977. SAN 335-7740. Tel: 970-949-6797. FAX: 970-949-0233. *Mgr*, Kelly Mitchell
Library Holdings: Bk Vols 22,000
Friends of the Library Group
GYPSUM PUBLIC, 753 Valley Rd, PO Box 979, Gypsum, 81637. SAN 377-7227. *Mgr*, Tia Vallas-Hancock
Library Holdings: Bk Vols 3,000

EATON

P EATON PUBLIC LIBRARY,* 132 Maple Ave, 80615. SAN 301-8970. Tel: 970-454-2189. FAX: 970-454-2189. Web Site: www.weld.lib.co.us. *Librn*, Linda MacNeil
Founded 1901. Pop 2,136; Circ 19,600
Library Holdings: Bk Vols 15,000; Per Subs 15
Mem of High Plains Regional Library Service System

ENGLEWOOD

S THE AMERICAN HUMANE ASSOCIATION, Children's Division Library,* 63 Inverness Dr E, 80112-5117. SAN 323-6307. Tel: 303-792-9900. FAX: 303-792-5333. E-Mail: children@americanhumane.org. Web Site: www.americanhumane.org. *Coll Develop, Librn*, Robyn Alsop
Founded 1986
Jul 1999-Jun 2000 Mats Exp $5,000, Books $4,000, Per/Ser (Incl. Access Fees) $1,000. Sal $45,000
Library Holdings: Bk Titles 3,000; Per Subs 100
Mem of Cent Colorado Libr Syst

S APPLIED GEOLOGIC STUDIES, INC LIBRARY,* 2875 W Oxford Ste 3, 80110. SAN 370-3428. Tel: 303-761-5624. FAX: 303-761-5625. E-Mail: ags@webaccess.net. *In Charge*, Jim Hardy
Library Holdings: Bk Vols 3,000
Subject Interests: Geology, Mining
Special Collections: CF&I Coll; Duval Coll; Grace Coll
Restriction: Staff & members only
Open Mon-Fri 9-5

S CHERRY CREEK PROFESSIONAL LIBRARY,* 14188 E Briarwood Ave, 80112. SAN 301-875X. Tel: 303-486-4080. FAX: 303-486-4085. Web Site: www.media.ccsol.k12.co.us. *In Charge*, Sue Eckhardt; Staff 4 (MLS 1, Non-MLS 3)
Founded 1968

Library Holdings: Bk Vols 10,000
Subject Interests: Education
Special Collections: Children & Young Adult Preview; Textbook Preview
Mem of Cent Colorado Libr Syst

P ENGLEWOOD PUBLIC LIBRARY,* 3400 S Elati St, 80110-2304. SAN 301-9012. Tel: 303-762-2560, 303-762-2572 (Admin). Interlibrary Loan Service Tel: 303-762-2565. FAX: 303-762-2576. Web Site: www.ci.englewood.co.us. *Dir Libr Serv*, Hank Long; E-Mail: hlong@englewood.lib.co.us; *Mgr*, Mary Lou Tatum; Tel: 303-762-2569, E-Mail: mtatum@englewood.lib.co.us; *Automation Syst Coordr, Cat, Coll Develop, Mgr*, Pat Jurgens; Tel: 303-762-2552, E-Mail: pjurgens@englewood.lib.co.us; Staff 7 (MLS 7)
Founded 1920. Pop 30,000; Circ 250,541
Jan 2000-Dec 2000 Income $1,170,671, City $1,170,671. Mats Exp $210,372, Books $138,654, Per/Ser (Incl. Access Fees) $18,533, Micro $8,245, AV Equip $9,765, Electronic Ref Mat (Incl. Access Fees) $35,175. Sal $832,755
Library Holdings: Bk Vols 104,000; Per Subs 300
Special Collections: Englewood Local History General Coll, newsp & other mat; Englewood Local History Photograph Coll
Automation Activity & Vendor Info: (Cataloging) epixtech, inc.; (Circulation) epixtech, inc.; (ILL) epixtech, inc.; (OPAC) epixtech, inc.
Database Vendor: Ebsco - EbscoHost, epixtech, inc., GaleNet, OCLC - First Search, ProQuest
Mem of Cent Colorado Libr Syst
Special Services for the Deaf - TTY machine
Special Services for the Blind - Braille translation & printing software & equipment
Kids Komputers with educational programs for ages 2-12
Friends of the Library Group
Bookmobiles: 1

R FIRST PLYMOUTH CONGREGATIONAL CHURCH LIBRARY,* 3501 S Colorado Blvd, 80110. SAN 301-9020. Tel: 303-762-0616. FAX: 303-789-2783. *Librn*, Linda Glenn
Library Holdings: Bk Vols 3,000

S GLOBAL ENGINEERING DOCUMENTS,* 15 Inverness Way E, 80112-5710. SAN 376-074X. Tel: 314-726-0444. FAX: 314-726-6418.

S INFORMATION HANDLING SERVICES LIBRARY,* 15 Inverness Way E, MS A107, 80112. SAN 370-968X. Tel: 303-790-0600, Ext 2820. *Librn*, Barb Whitney
Library Holdings: Bk Titles 500; Per Subs 100

S MEDICAL GROUP MANAGEMENT ASSOCIATION, Information Center, 104 Inverness Terrace E, 80112. SAN 301-8555. Tel: 303-397-7887. FAX: 303-397-1823. Web Site: www.mgma.com. *Dir*, Cynthia Kiyotake; Staff 8 (MLS 4, Non-MLS 4)
Founded 1972
Library Holdings: Bk Titles 5,500; Per Subs 225
Subject Interests: Business and management, Health care
Special Collections: American College of Medical Practice Executives Bound Professional Papers; Group Practice Survey Reports
Automation Activity & Vendor Info: (Cataloging) EOS
Publications: Resources Catalog (annual)
Restriction: Open to public for reference only
Partic in Bibliographical Center For Research, Rocky Mountain Region, Inc

S NATIONAL STROKE ASSOCIATION LIBRARY,* 9707 E Easter Lane, 80112-3747. SAN 372-7610. Tel: 303-649-9299. TDD: 303-771-1887. FAX: 303-649-1328. Web Site: www.stroke.org. *Librn*, Carrie Mahan Groce; Tel: 303-754-0932, E-Mail: cmgroce@stroke.org; Staff 1 (Non-MLS 1)
Library Holdings: Bk Vols 100; Per Subs 10
Subject Interests: Stroke
Special Services for the Deaf - TDD

S NEWMONT MINING CORP, Technical Library, 10101 E Dry Creek, 80112. SAN 311-970X. Tel: 303-708-4116. FAX: 303-708-4060. *Head Librn*, Mary Cytrynbaum; E-Mail: mcyt4116@corp.newmont.com; *Res, Senior Librn*, Charlene Gendill; Tel: 303-708-4176, E-Mail: cgen5849@corp.newmont.com; *Adminr*, Patricia Jefferson; Tel: 303-708-4119, E-Mail: patti@nel.newmont.com; Staff 3 (MLS 1, Non-MLS 2)
Founded 1965
Library Holdings: Bk Titles 6,000; Per Subs 90
Subject Interests: Bus develop, Develop, Exploration, Geology, Geophysics, Metals
Special Collections: Extensive property file collection worldwide
Restriction: Company library

S RAYTHEON ENGINEERS & CONSTRUCTORS WESTERN OPERATIONS, Technical Information Center,* 5555 Greenwood Plaza Blvd, 80111-2203. SAN 327-3288. Tel: 303-843-2256. FAX: 303-843-2208. *Librn*, Kate Anver
Library Holdings: Bk Vols 5,000; Per Subs 150
Subject Interests: Chemical engineering, Mechanical engineering
Open Mon-Fri 7:30-4:30

S STANDARD & POOR'S INSTITUTIONAL MARKET SERVICES, Data Resource Center, 7400 S Alton Ct, 80112-2394. SAN 375-0965. Tel: 303-771-6510. Toll Free Tel: 800-523-4534. FAX: 303-721-4432, 303-721-4652. *Dir*, Catrin Novak
Library Holdings: Per Subs 15

M SWEDISH MEDICAL CENTER LIBRARY,* 501 E Hampton Ave, 80110. SAN 301-9047. Tel: 303-788-5000, 303-788-6669. FAX: 303-788-6840. *Librn*, Katherine Artus; *ILL*, Suzanne Kaller
Founded 1967
Library Holdings: Bk Titles 4,000; Per Subs 350
Subject Interests: Medicine, Nursing
Partic in ACLIN; Impulse

ESTES PARK

P ESTES PARK PUBLIC LIBRARY, 335 E Elkhorn Ave, PO Box 1687, 80517-1687. SAN 301-9055. Tel: 970-586-8116. FAX: 970-586-0189. Web Site: www.estes.lib.co.us. *Dir*, Ed Volz; E-Mail: evolz@estes.lib.co.us
Founded 1922. Pop 12,615; Circ 134,743
Jan 1999-Dec 1999 Income $558,000, Locally Generated Income $10,979, Other $39,003. Mats Exp $68,000, Books $57,000, Per/Ser (Incl. Access Fees) $11,000. Sal $367,359
Library Holdings: Bk Vols 51,000; Per Subs 197
Subject Interests: Local history
Automation Activity & Vendor Info: (Circulation) CARL
Publications: Diversion Colorado-Big Thompson Water Project - A slide-tape production done with Colorado Endowment for the Humanities grant.
Mem of High Plains Regional Library Service System
Friends of the Library Group

G NATIONAL PARK SERVICE, Rocky Mountain National Park Library, 80517-8397. SAN 301-9063. Tel: 970-586-1362. FAX: 970-586-4702. *Tech Servs*, Sybil Barnes
Founded 1915
Library Holdings: Bk Vols 2,550; Bk Titles 1,800
Subject Interests: Biology, Ecology
Special Collections: Doctoral & Master's Thesis Coll; Ecology (Enos Mills Coll); Historical Maps of Rocky Mountain National Park; Published Works (William Allen White Coll)

FLAGLER

P FLAGLER COMMUNITY LIBRARY,* PO Box 367, 80815-0367. SAN 301-9071. Tel: 719-765-4310. FAX: 719-765-4498. *Librn*, Shirley Trimmer
Founded 1920. Pop 2,325; Circ 3,337
1997-1998 Income $10,703, City $8,474, Other $2,229. Mats Exp Books $3,000. Sal $4,300
Library Holdings: Bk Vols 6,500
Special Collections: BiCentennial Book Shelf; Hal Borland Coll; Page History Room, American History
Mem of High Plains Regional Library Service System

FLEMING

P FLEMING COMMUNITY LIBRARY,* 506 N Fremont Ave, 80728. SAN 301-908X. Tel: 970-265-2046. FAX: 970-265-2255. *Librn*, Lee Ann Nichols; Staff 2 (MLS 1, Non-MLS 1)
Pop 500; Circ 5,400
Library Holdings: Bk Vols 10,000; Per Subs 44
Mem of High Plains Regional Library Service System
Friends of the Library Group

FLORENCE

P FLORENCE PUBLIC LIBRARY, Second & Pikes Peak, 81226. SAN 301-9098. Tel: 719-784-4649. FAX: 719-784-4937. E-Mail: papac@people.pc. *Librn*, Jean Newell; Staff 1 (Non-MLS 1)
Founded 1908. Pop 6,000; Circ 41,000
Library Holdings: Bk Vols 24,000; Per Subs 24
Mem of Arkansas Valley Regional Library Service System

FORT CARSON

UNITED STATES ARMY
A GRANT LIBRARY, 4950 Flint St, 80913-4105. SAN 335-7813. Tel: 719-526-2350. FAX: 719-526-8139. *Chief Librn*, Rebecca Harris; E-Mail: harrisr@carson.army.mil; *Ref*, Janice Haines; Staff 9 (MLS 2, Non-MLS 7)
Founded 1942. Circ 116,064
Oct 1997-Sep 1998 Income $60,000. Mats Exp $57,411, Books $47,113, Per/Ser (Incl. Access Fees) $10,298. Sal $240,000
Library Holdings: Bk Titles 48,000; Per Subs 250
Special Collections: Colorado; Military Arts & Sciences; World War II
Mem of Plains & Peaks Regional Library System
Partic in Fedlink; OCLC Online Computer Library Center, Inc

AM MEDICAL LIBRARY, Evans US Army Community Hospital, 7500 Cochran Circle, MEDDAC (EACH), Attn Medical Library, 80913-4604. SAN 335-7848. Tel: 719-526-7286. FAX: 719-526-7113. *In Charge*, Roma A Marcum; E-Mail: roma_a_marcum@smtplink.carson.amedd.army.mil; Staff 1 (MLS 1)
Founded 1952
Oct 1998-Sep 1999 Income $126,000. Mats Exp $88,000, Books $20,000, Per/Ser (Incl. Access Fees) $68,000. Sal $86,507 (Prof $44,000)
Library Holdings: Bk Vols 6,000; Bk Titles 4,000; Per Subs 199
Subject Interests: Dentistry, Medicine, Mental health, Nursing, Orthopedics, Physical therapy, Veterinary medicine
Special Collections: Consumer's Coll
Automation Activity & Vendor Info: (Acquisitions) Endeavor; (Cataloging) Endeavor; (Circulation) Endeavor; (Course Reserve) Endeavor; (ILL) Endeavor; (Media Booking) Endeavor; (OPAC) Endeavor; (Serials) Endeavor
Publications: Patients Health
Partic in Colorado Council Of Medical Librarians; Dialog Corporation; Fedlink; OCLC Online Computer Library Center, Inc

FORT COLLINS

GM CENTERS FOR DISEASE CONTROL & PREVENTION, Division of Vector-Borne Infectious Diseases Library,* US Public Health Serv, Foothill Campus, PO Box 2087, 80522-2087. SAN 374-7603. Tel: 970-221-6400. FAX: 970-221-6476. *Purchasing*, Cookie Cloninger
Library Holdings: Per Subs 100

S COLORADO DIVISION OF WILDLIFE, Research Center Library, 317 W Prospect, 80526-2097. SAN 301-9101. Tel: 970-472-4353. FAX: 970-472-4457. *Coll Develop, Librn*, Jackie Boss; E-Mail: jackie.boss@state.co.us
Founded 1967
Library Holdings: Bk Vols 12,274; Per Subs 125
Subject Interests: Environmental studies, Zoology
Special Collections: Wildlife (Federal Aid in Fish & Wildlife Restoration, Colorado)
Publications: Division Reports; Outdoor Facts; Special Reports; Technical Publications
Mem of High Plains Regional Library Service System

C COLORADO STATE UNIVERSITY, William E Morgan Library, 80523-1019. SAN 335-7872. Tel: 970-491-1838. FAX: 970-491-1195. Web Site: www.manta.library.colostate.edu/. *Dean of Libr*, Camila Alire; E-Mail: calire@manta.colostate.edu; *Asst Dean*, Teri Switzer; *Access Serv*, Jim Farmer; *Acq*, Patricia Smith; *Archivist*, John Newman; *Coll Develop, Ref*, Anna DeMiller; *Coll Develop*, Pam Jones; *Govt Doc*, Fred Schmidt; *ILL*, Tom Delaney; *Publ Servs*, Julie Wessling; *Ref*, Allison Cowgill; *Ref*, Polly Thistlethwaite; *Tech Servs*, Carmel Bush; Staff 44 (MLS 44)
Founded 1870. Enrl 21,038; Fac 990; Highest Degree: Doctorate
Library Holdings: Bk Vols 1,803,493; Per Subs 21,208
Subject Interests: Agricultural economics, Agriculture, Engineering, Natural resources
Special Collections: Germans From Russia; International Poster Coll; Vietnam War Fiction
Database Vendor: Innovative Interfaces INN - View
Publications: Library Connection
Mem of Asn of Research Libraries
Partic in ACLIN; Bibliographical Center For Research, Rocky Mountain Region, Inc; Big Twelve Plus Libr Consortium; Colorado Alliance Of Research Libraries; High Plains Regional Library Service System; OCLC Online Computer Library Center, Inc
Departmental Libraries:
ATMOSPHERIC SCIENCE, Atmospheric Science Bldg, Foothills Campus, 80523. SAN 328-6924. Tel: 970-491-8532. Web Site: www.manta.library.colostate.edu/research/. *Librn*, Mike Culbertson; E-Mail: mculbertson@manta.library.colostate.edu
Library Holdings: Bk Vols 9,000; Per Subs 62

CM VETERINARY TEACHING HOSPITAL Tel: 970-491-1213. FAX: 970-491-4141. *Librn*, Tom Moothart

P FORT COLLINS PUBLIC LIBRARY,* 201 Peterson St, 80524-2990. SAN 301-9128. Tel: 970-221-6742. TDD: 970-224-6005. FAX: 970-221-6398. E-Mail: support@libsys.ci.fort-collins.co.us. Web Site: www.ci.fort-collins.co.us/c_library/index.htm. *Dir*, Brenda Carns; Tel: 970-221-6670, E-Mail: bcarns@ci.fort-collins.co.us; *Coll Develop*, Dean Wilms; Staff 61 (MLS 15, Non-MLS 46)
Founded 1900. Pop 138,974; Circ 1,397,125
Jan 1998-Dec 1998 Income (Main Library and Branch Library) $3,183,930. Mats Exp $2,959,065. Sal $1,915,613
Library Holdings: Bk Vols 317,906; Bk Titles 199,438; Per Subs 454
Special Collections: Local History, photogs
Automation Activity & Vendor Info: (Circulation) epixtech, inc.
Mem of High Plains Regional Library Service System
Special Services for the Deaf - Staff with knowledge of sign language
Special Services for the Blind - Assistive Technology Center for Persons who are blind or physically handicapped
Friends of the Library Group
Branches: 1
HARMONY, 4616 S Shields, 80526. SAN 378-1054. Tel: 970-204-8206. FAX: 970-226-4644. *Librn*, Ellen Willis

J FRONT RANGE COMMUNITY COLLEGE, Larimer Campus Harmony Library, 4616 S Shields, 80526. SAN 301-9144. Tel: 970-204-8206. FAX: 970-226-4644. Web Site: frcc.cc.co.us/la/library/index.html. *Librn*, Karen Dornseif
Founded 1989
Library Holdings: Bk Vols 100,000; Per Subs 300
Subject Interests: Nursing
Partic in Colorado Alliance Of Research Libraries
Friends of the Library Group

S HEWLETT-PACKARD COMPANY, Fort Collins Global Library & Information Services, 3404 E Harmony Rd, 80528-9599. SAN 329-479X. Tel: 970-898-3830. FAX: 970-898-3430. E-Mail: library@fc.hp.com. *Mgr Libr Serv*, Jane St Germain; *ILL*, Marlyce Trujillo; *Res*, Susan Charles; *Res*, Pamela Clements; *Res*, Robyn Hutson; Staff 4 (MLS 3, Non-MLS 1)
Founded 1978
Library Holdings: Bk Vols 8,900; Bk Titles 6,200; Per Subs 380
Automation Activity & Vendor Info: (Acquisitions) Sydney; (Cataloging) Sydney; (Circulation) Sydney; (OPAC) Sydney; (Serials) Sydney
Publications: Library News
Partic in OCLC Online Computer Library Center, Inc

S PLATTE RIVER POWER AUTHORITY LIBRARY, 2000 E Horsetooth Rd, 80525. SAN 325-6928. Tel: 970-229-5230. FAX: 970-229-5244. Web Site: www.prpa.org. *Librn*, Rosalie Feldman; E-Mail: feldmanr@prpa.org; Staff 2 (MLS 1, Non-MLS 1)
Founded 1977
1998-1999 Mats Exp $20,000
Library Holdings: Bk Titles 2,000; Per Subs 200
Subject Interests: Electric power production
Restriction: Open to others by appointment, Staff use only
Mem of High Plains Regional Library Service System

M POUDRE VALLEY HOSPITAL, Medical Library,* 1024 Lemay Ave, 80524-3998. SAN 301-9152. Tel: 970-495-7323. FAX: 970-495-7652. E-Mail: gmc@libra.pvh.org. Web Site: www.pvhs.org. *Librn*, Gerald M Carlson; Staff 1 (MLS 1)
Founded 1969
Jan 1998-Dec 1998 Mats Exp $39,500, Books $6,500, Per/Ser (Incl. Access Fees) $33,000. Sal $42,000
Library Holdings: Bk Vols 4,000; Per Subs 120
Subject Interests: Allied health, Medicine, Nursing
Special Collections: Bioethics
Mem of High Plains Regional Library Service System
Partic in Bibliographical Center For Research, Rocky Mountain Region, Inc; Colorado Council Of Medical Librarians; Medline; Midcontinental Regional Med Libr Group

G UNITED STATES DEPARTMENT OF AGRICULTURE, National Wildlife Research Center Library, 4101 La Porte Ave, 80521-2154. SAN 335-7422. Tel: 970-266-6000. FAX: 970-266-6010. Web Site: www.aphis.usda.gov/ws/nwrc. *Librn*, Diana Dwyer; *Librn*, Laurie Paulik; Staff 3 (MLS 2, Non-MLS 1)
Founded 1967
Library Holdings: Bk Titles 10,000; Per Subs 130
Subject Interests: Ornithology, Physiology, Toxicology
Special Collections: Author Reprints Coll; Predator Coll; United States Fish & Wildlife Service Publications
Publications: Annual Publications List
Partic in Bibliographical Center For Research, Rocky Mountain Region, Inc; Dialog Corporation; Fedlink; OCLC Online Computer Library Center, Inc

G UNITED STATES FOREST SERVICE, Rocky Mountain Research Station,* 240 W Prospect, 80526. SAN 301-9179. Tel: 970-498-1268. FAX: 970-498-1010. *Tech Servs*, Robert W Dana
Library Holdings: Bk Vols 20,000; Per Subs 500
Special Collections: Reports, pioneer research 1910
Open Mon-Fri 8-5

G US GEOLOGICAL SURVEY, Mid-Continent Ecological Science Center Library, 4512 McMurry Ave, 80525-3400. SAN 375-653X. Tel: 970-226-9403. FAX: 970-226-9230. Web Site: www.mesc.usgs.gov. *Librn*, Liz Lucke; E-Mail: liz_lucke@usgs.gov
Oct 1998-Sep 1999 Income $117,000. Mats Exp $26,000, Books $1,800, Per/Ser (Incl. Access Fees) $13,000. Sal $91,000 (Prof $51,000)
Library Holdings: Bk Vols 12,000; Per Subs 80
Subject Interests: Biology, Ecology, Fisheries, Wildlife
Mem of High Plains Regional Library Service System
Partic in Fedlink; OCLC Online Computer Library Center, Inc

FORT LUPTON

P FORT LUPTON PUBLIC & SCHOOL LIBRARY,* 425 S Denver Ave, 80621-1303. SAN 301-9187. Tel: 303-857-7180. FAX: 303-857-7190. Web Site: internet-plaza.net/ftlupton. *Dir*, Janice Fisher-Giles; Staff 7 (MLS 3, Non-MLS 4)
Founded 1978
Jul 1997-Jun 1998 Income $254,991. Mats Exp $25,500. Sal $200,198
Library Holdings: Bk Vols 25,000; Bk Titles 20,000; Per Subs 124
Mem of High Plains Regional Library Service System
Open Mon & Wed 8am-5pm, Tues & Thurs 8am-9pm, Fri 8am-4pm & Sat 10am-2pm

FORT LYON

GM DEPARTMENT OF VETERANS AFFAIRS, Medical Center Library,* 81038. SAN 301-9195. Tel: 719-384-3130. FAX: 719-384-3189. *Chief Librn*, Helen S Scalzi; Staff 2 (MLS 1, Non-MLS 1)
Library Holdings: Bk Vols 5,000; Per Subs 319
Subject Interests: Geriatrics and gerontology, Psychiatry, Psychology
Mem of Arkansas Valley Regional Library Service System
Partic in BRS; Medline; Valnet

FORT MORGAN

P FORT MORGAN PUBLIC LIBRARY, 414 Main St, 80701. SAN 301-9209. Tel: 970-867-9456. FAX: 970-867-2988. Web Site: pyramid.cudenver.edu/ftmorgan/. *Asst Dir*, Catherine Bosley; E-Mail: cbosley@pyramid.cudenver.edu; *Head, Cat*, Josie Diaz; E-Mail: jodi@pyramid.cudenver.edu; *Tech Coordr*, Lanny Page; E-Mail: pager@pyramid.cudenver.edu; *Ref*, Marcia Iverson; E-Mail: miverson@pyramid.cudenver.edu; *Circ*, Ella Mae Walker; E-Mail: emwalker@pyramid.cudenver.edu; *Ch Servs*, Claudia Nickell; E-Mail: claudia@pyramid.cudenver.edu; *Cat*, Vanita McIlvanie; E-Mail: vmac@pyramid.cudenver.edu; Staff 8 (MLS 2, Non-MLS 6)
Founded 1893. Pop 11,000
Jan 2000-Jan 2001 Income $424,457. Mats Exp $47,495, Books $40,500, Per/Ser (Incl. Access Fees) $5,000, Presv $500, Electronic Ref Mat (Incl. Access Fees) $1,495. Sal $176,800 (Prof $56,000)
Library Holdings: Bk Titles 45,000; Per Subs 117
Special Collections: Lute Johnson Collection; Western History
Automation Activity & Vendor Info: (Cataloging) CARL; (Circulation) CARL; (OPAC) CARL
Database Vendor: CARL
Publications: FMPL Update (Newsletter)
Function: ILL available
Mem of High Plains Regional Library Service System
Friends of the Library Group

J MORGAN COMMUNITY COLLEGE LIBRARY,* 17800 Rd 20, 80701-4399. SAN 301-9217. Tel: 970-542-3185. Toll Free Tel: 800-622-0216. FAX: 970-867-6608. *Asst Librn*, Maureen Kahl; Staff 2 (MLS 1, Non-MLS 1)
Founded 1972. Enrl 850; Fac 93
Library Holdings: Bk Vols 15,459; Per Subs 99
Partic in High Plains Regional Library Service System

FOWLER

P FOWLER PUBLIC LIBRARY, 114 E Cranston Ave, 81039-1198. SAN 301-9225. Tel: 719-263-4472. FAX: 719-263-5845. Web Site: www.geocities.tarynnlibrary/library.html. *Librn*, Tarynn P McMahan; E-Mail: fowler.library@fowler.lib.co.us
Founded 1891. Pop 1,570; Circ 13,600
Library Holdings: Bk Vols 8,500
Mem of Arkansas Valley Regional Library Service System
Friends of the Library Group

FRISCO

P SUMMIT COUNTY LIBRARY,* 37 County Rd 1005, PO Box 770, 80443. SAN 335-7937. Tel: 970-668-5555. FAX: 970-668-5556. *Dir*, Joyce Dierauer; Tel: 970-668-4130, E-Mail: joyced@colosys.net; *Dep Dir*, Sarah Nordholm; Tel: 970-668-4131, E-Mail: sarahn@co.summit.co.us; *Branch Mgr*, Vanessa Woodford; Tel: 970-468-5887, Fax: 970-513-0854, E-Mail: vanw@colosys.net; *Branch Mgr*, Julie Commons; Tel: 970-453-6098, Fax: 970-547-9637, E-Mail: jcommons@colosys.net; *ILL*, Becky Astuto; Tel: 970-668-4135, E-Mail: beckya@co.summit.co.us; Staff 1 (MLS 1)
Founded 1962. Pop 18,557; Circ 124,046
Jan 2000-Dec 2000 Income (Main Library and Branch Library) $762,898, County $736,898, Locally Generated Income $26,000. Mats Exp $139,900, Books $106,000, Per/Ser (Incl. Access Fees) $12,500, Presv $400, AV Equip $11,000, Electronic Ref Mat (Incl. Access Fees) $10,000. Sal $419,615 (Prof $51,342)
Library Holdings: Bk Vols 76,532; Per Subs 220
Special Collections: Colorado History (Summit County History); Skiing
Automation Activity & Vendor Info: (Circulation) CARL; (OPAC) CARL
Database Vendor: CARL, IAC - Info Trac
Mem of Reg Libr Servs Syst; Three Rivers Regional Library Service System
Partic in Marmot Western Colo Libr Network; OCLC Online Computer Library Center, Inc
Friends of the Library Group
Branches: 2
NORTH BRANCH, PO Box 1248, Silverthorne, 80498-1248. SAN 335-7996. Tel: 970-468-5887. *Br Coordr*, Vanessa Woodford
Library Holdings: Bk Vols 12,823
Friends of the Library Group
SOUTH BRANCH, 504 Airport Rd, PO Box 96, Breckenridge, 80424-0096. SAN 335-7961. Tel: 970-453-6098. *Br Coordr*, Julie Commons
Library Holdings: Bk Vols 12,762
Friends of the Library Group

GEORGETOWN

P JOHN TOMAY MEMORIAL LIBRARY, Georgetown Library,* 605 Sixth St, PO Box 338, 80444-0338. SAN 301-9233. Tel: 303-569-2620. FAX: 303-569-3003. Web Site: www.sni.net/~bennhoff/. *Dir*, Laura S Craig
Founded 1882. Pop 2,732; Circ 9,583
1999-2000 Income $98,360. Mats Exp $30,332, Books $9,703, Per/Ser (Incl. Access Fees) $620. Sal $61,205
Library Holdings: Bk Titles 15,247
Mem of Cent Colorado Libr Syst
Friends of the Library Group

GLENWOOD SPRINGS

J COLORADO MOUNTAIN COLLEGE-SPRING VALLEY CENTER LIBRARY,* 3000 County Rd 114, 81601. SAN 335-802X. Tel: 970-947-8271. FAX: 970-947-8288. *Asst Librn*, D Abbott; Staff 1 (MLS 1)
Founded 1966. Enrl 400; Fac 70
Library Holdings: Bk Titles 27,000; Per Subs 150
Mem of Three Rivers Regional Library Service System
Partic in Colorado Alliance Of Research Libraries; Eric Processing & Reference Facility; OCLC Online Computer Library Center, Inc

P THREE RIVERS REGIONAL LIBRARY SERVICE SYSTEM,* 710 Cooper Ave, Ste 111, 81601. SAN 301-9934. Tel: 970-945-2626. FAX: 970-945-9396. Web Site: www.colosys.net/three. *Dir*, Sandra Scott; E-Mail: sandra@colosys.net; Staff 5 (MLS 3, Non-MLS 2)
Founded 1969. Pop 160,000
Oct 1998-Sep 1999 Income $555,292, State $324,106, Other $231,186. Mats Exp $2,771. Sal $151,198
Library Holdings: Bk Vols 475; Per Subs 15
Subject Interests: Library and information science
Database Vendor: OCLC - First Search
Publications: Annual membership directory
Member Libraries: Basalt Regional Library District; Bud Werner Memorial Library; Colorado Mountain College-Alpine Campus Library; Colorado Mountain College-Spring Valley Center Library; Colorado Mountain College-Timberline Campus; Colorado Northwestern Community College Library; Eagle Valley Library District; Garfield County Public Library System; Grand County Library District; Jackson County Public Library; Lake County Public Library; Meeker Regional Library District; Moffat County Libraries; Oak Creek Public Library; Pitkin County Library; Rangely Regional Library; Rifle Correctional Facility; Summit County Library; Vail Public Library; West Routt Library District-Hayden Public Library; Yampa Public Library
Partic in Bibliographical Center For Research, Rocky Mountain Region, Inc; TriPath Internet Access Network

GOLDEN

S AMERICAN ALPINE CLUB LIBRARY,* 710 Tenth St Ste 15, 80401. SAN 311-5674. Tel: 303-384-0110, Ext 21, 303-384-0112. FAX: 303-384-0113. E-Mail: library@americanalpineclub.org. *Dir*, Francine Loft
Founded 1902 Sal $36,000
Subject Interests: Alps, Antarctic, Arctic, Glaciology, Himalayas, Mountaineering
Partic in BCR

S BUFFALO BILL MEMORIAL MUSEUM, Information Center,* 987 1/2 Lookout Mountain Rd, 80401. SAN 371-1676. Tel: 303-526-0744. FAX: 303-526-0197. *Curator*, Steve Friesen
Library Holdings: Bk Vols 175
Special Collections: Buffalo Bill Cody Coll, archival doc

S COLORADO CORRECTIONAL CENTER,* 15445 Old Golden Rd, PO Box 4020, 80401-4020. SAN 377-2594. Tel: 303-273-1620. FAX: 303-279-4407. *Librn*, Mary Alice Newton
Library Holdings: Bk Vols 3,000; Per Subs 25

S COLORADO RAILROAD HISTORICAL FOUNDATION, INC, Robert W Richardson Railroad Library, 17155 W 44th Ave, 80403-1621. (Mail add: PO Box 10, 80402-0010), SAN 301-925X. Tel: 303-279-4591. FAX: 303-279-4229. E-Mail: mail@crrm.org. Web Site: www.crrm.org. *Dir*, Steve Mason; *Archivist*, Kenton Forrest
Founded 1959
Library Holdings: Bk Titles 15,000; Per Subs 50
Special Collections: Railroad History, Rare Old Papers, Photogs & Artifacts; Railroad Mechanical & Operating Instructions (Colorado & Southern, Denver & Interurban, Denver Tramway, Rio Grande; Railroadiana Coll, Narrow & Standard Gauge Locomotives & Cars; Southern & Denver Rio Grande Western Railroads), original doc
Publications: Journal of Colorado Railroad Museum Library
Restriction: Open to public for reference only
Friends of the Library Group

C COLORADO SCHOOL OF MINES, Arthur Lakes Library, 14th & Illinois St, 80401-1887. SAN 301-9268. Tel: 303-273-3911. Circulation Tel: 303-273-3698. Reference Tel: 303-273-3694. FAX: 303-273-3199. Web Site: www.mines.edu/library/. *Dir*, Joanne V Lerud; E-Mail: jlerud@mines.edu; *Cat*, Janice Christopher; *Publ Servs*, Lisa Dunn; *Coll Develop*, Robert Sorgenfrei; Staff 8 (MLS 8)
Founded 1874
Library Holdings: Bk Vols 150,000; Per Subs 2,000
Subject Interests: Chemistry, Energy, Engineering, Environmental studies, Geology, Geophysics, Metallurgy, Mining, Petroleum engineering, Physics
Special Collections: Colorado & Mining History Coll; Energy, Environmental & Public Policy Coll
Publications: Links to Lakes (newsletter)
Partic in Bibliographical Center For Research, Rocky Mountain Region, Inc; Central Colorado Library System; Colorado Alliance Of Research Libraries

S COORS BREWING COMPANY, Technical Library,* PO Box 4030 - BC 520, 80401-0030. SAN 325-7363. Tel: 303-277-3506, 303-279-6565. FAX: 303-277-2805. *Chief Librn*, Steve Boss
Library Holdings: Bk Vols 5,500; Per Subs 300

S FOOTHILLS ART CENTER, Mary S Robinson Art Library, 809 15th St, 80401. SAN 301-9292. Tel: 303-279-3922. FAX: 303-279-9470. E-Mail: fac@foothillsartcenter.org. Web Site: www.foothillsartcenter.org. *Exec Dir*, Carol Dickenson
Library Holdings: Bk Vols 2,200
Subject Interests: Art, Poetry

S JEFFERSON COUNTY PUBLIC SCHOOLS, (Formerly Jefferson County School District R-1), Professional Library & Archives, 13950 W 20th Ave, 80401-3104. (Mail add: PO Box 4001, 80401-0001), SAN 324-3443. Tel: 303-982-5946. FAX: 303-982-5959. Web Site: 204.98.1.2/plmc/. *Dir*, Shelley Shea; E-Mail: sshea@jeffco.k12.co.us; *ILL, Ref*, Lynn Strickler; E-Mail: lstrickl@jeffco.k12.co.us; Staff 5 (MLS 3, Non-MLS 2)
Library Holdings: Bk Titles 34,000; Per Subs 250
Subject Interests: Education
Special Collections: Curriculum Materials
Automation Activity & Vendor Info: (Cataloging) Sagebrush Corporation; (Circulation) Sagebrush Corporation; (OPAC) Sagebrush Corporation
Publications: New Materials List
Mem of Cent Colorado Libr Syst
Partic in Bibliographical Center For Research, Rocky Mountain Region, Inc; Dialog Corporation; OCLC Online Computer Library Center, Inc

G NATIONAL RENEWABLE ENERGY LABORATORY LIBRARY, 1617 Cole Blvd, 80401-3393. SAN 321-5644. Tel: 303-275-4215. FAX: 303-275-4222. E-Mail: library@nrel.gov. *Mgr*, Mary Donahue; Tel: 303-275-4092, Fax: 303-275-4250, E-Mail: mary_donahue@nrel.gov; *Cat, ILL*, Soon Duck Kim; *Online Servs, Ref*, Annette Berger; *Automation Syst Coordr*, Carol Fitzgerald; *Coll Develop*, Judy Oberg; Staff 10 (MLS 6, Non-MLS 4)
Founded 1977
Oct 1997-Sep 1998
Library Holdings: Bk Vols 75,000; Per Subs 700
Subject Interests: Alternative fuels, Energy efficiency, Energy policy, Photovoltaic cells, Renewable energy, Solar energy, Solid state physics
Automation Activity & Vendor Info: (OPAC) Sydney
Database Vendor: CARL, Dialog, Ebsco - EbscoHost, GaleNet, Lexis-Nexis, OCLC - First Search
Publications: Serials List
Mem of Cent Colorado Libr Syst
Partic in Bibliographical Center For Research, Rocky Mountain Region, Inc
National Renewable Energy Laboratory is operated for the US Dept. of Energy by Midwest Research Institute, Battelle.Bechtel

GRANBY

P GRAND COUNTY LIBRARY DISTRICT,* PO Box 1050, 80446. SAN 335-8054. Tel: 970-887-9411. FAX: 970-887-3227. E-Mail: library@rkymtnhi.com. *Dir*, Marlys Swalboski; Staff 9 (MLS 9)
Founded 1933. Pop 11,438; Circ 63,579
Jan 1997-Dec 1998 Income $1,594,479, State $250,000, City $14,575, Federal $52,500, Locally Generated Income $24,100, Other $700,997. Mats Exp $45,432, Books $40,882, Per/Ser (Incl. Access Fees) $4,550. Sal $221,218
Library Holdings: Bk Vols 63,260; Per Subs 100
Subject Interests: Colorado
Mem of Three Rivers Regional Library Service System
Friends of the Library Group
Branches: 5
FRASER VALLEY BRANCH, PO Box 160, Fraser, 80442. SAN 335-8089. Tel: 970-726-5689. FAX: 970-726-9226. E-Mail: sclib@rkymtnhi.com. Web Site: www.colosys.net/grand.co. *Librn*, Mary Anne Wilcox
Friends of the Library Group
GRANBY, PO Box 1049, 80446. SAN 335-8119. Tel: 970-887-2149. FAX: 970-887-2621. *Librn*, John Wright
Friends of the Library Group
HOT SULPHUR SPRINGS BRANCH, 105 Moffat, PO Box 336, Hot Sulphur Springs, 80451. SAN 335-8143. Tel: 970-725-3942. FAX: 970-725-3942. *Librn*, Lynn Shirley
Friends of the Library Group
JUNIPER LIBRARY AT GRAND LAKE, 315 Pitkin, PO Box 506, Grand Lake, 80447-0506. SAN 329-613X. Tel: 970-627-8353. FAX: 970-627-8353. *Librn*, Sue Luton
Friends of the Library Group
KREMMLING BRANCH, 300 S Eighth St, PO Box 1240, Kremmling, 80459-1240. SAN 335-8178. Tel: 970-724-9228. FAX: 970-724-3419. E-Mail: kremlib@rkymtnhi.com. *Librn*, Marilyn Huff; *Librn*, Margaret Perry
Friends of the Library Group

GRAND JUNCTION

S AGAPITO ASSOCIATES INC LIBRARY,* 715 Horizon Dr, Ste 340, 81506. SAN 374-7778. Tel: 970-242-4220. FAX: 970-245-9234. *Librn*, Anissa Hatcher
Library Holdings: Bk Vols 400
Subject Interests: Engineering

S BUREAU OF LAND MANAGEMENT LIBRARY,* 2815 H Rd, 81506. SAN 301-9349. Tel: 970-244-3000. FAX: 970-244-3083. *In Charge*, Richard Arcand; *Mgr*, Kathy Crone
Library Holdings: Bk Vols 1,200; Per Subs 21
Partic in LRL
Open Mon-Fri 7:30-4:30

GM DEPARTMENT OF VETERANS AFFAIRS, Medical Center Libraries,* 2121 North Ave, 81501-6428. SAN 301-9403. Tel: 970-242-0731, Ext 2254. FAX: 970-244-1309. *Librn*, Lynn Bragdon
Founded 1951
1998-1999 Income $80,000. Mats Exp $64,200, Books $14,000, Per/Ser (Incl. Access Fees) $28,000, Micro $8,200, AV Equip $6,000. Sal $72,000 (Prof $42,000)
Subject Interests: Colorado
Mem of Pathfinder Regional Library Service System
Partic in BRS; Coop Libr Agency for Syst & Servs; Dialog Corporation; Nat Libr of Med; Veterans Affairs Library Network

P MESA COUNTY PUBLIC LIBRARY DISTRICT, 530 Grand Ave, 81502. (Mail add: PO Box 20000-5019, 81502-5019), SAN 335-8208. Tel: 970-243-4783. Circulation Tel: 970-243-4443. Reference Tel: 970-241-5251. TDD: 970-241-0500. FAX: 970-243-4744. Web Site: www.mcpld.org. *Dir*, Terry Pickens; E-Mail: tpickens@colosys.net; *Asst Dir, Publ Servs*, Mark A Rose; E-Mail: mrose@colosys.net; *Br Coordr*, Shana Wade; Tel: 970-464-6936, E-Mail: swade@colosys.net; *Head Tech Servs*, Penny Shiel; E-Mail: pshiel@colosys.net; *Ch Servs*, Maxine Curley; Tel: 970-241-4726, E-Mail: mcurley@colosys.net; *Ref*, Kay Oxer; E-Mail: koxer@colosys.net; *Reader Servs*, Linda Garey; Tel: 970-241-4807, E-Mail: lgarey@colosys.net; Staff 43 (MLS 12, Non-MLS 31)
Founded 1967. Pop 115,150; Circ 704,908
Jan 2000-Dec 2000 Income (Main Library and Branch Library) $2,692,053, County $2,531,542, Locally Generated Income $111,011, Other $49,500. Mats Exp $367,660, Books $285,160, Per/Ser (Incl. Access Fees) $22,000, Micro $46,000, AV Equip $14,500. Sal $1,194,003 (Prof $390,720)
Library Holdings: Bk Vols 270,092; Bk Titles 185,455; Per Subs 425
Subject Interests: Agriculture, Local history, Railroads
Special Collections: Western Fiction
Automation Activity & Vendor Info: (Cataloging) CARL; (Circulation) CARL; (OPAC) CARL; (Serials) CARL
Database Vendor: CARL
Mem of Pathfinder Regional Library Service System
Partic in OCLC Online Computer Library Center, Inc
Special Services for the Deaf - High interest/low vocabulary books; TDD; TTY machine
Open Mon-Thurs 9-9, Fri & Sat 9-5, Sun 1-5
Friends of the Library Group
Branches: 7
CLIFTON BRANCH, Peach Tree Shopping Ctr, 3225 I 70b Bus Lp A-1, Clifton, 81520. SAN 335-8232. Tel: 970-434-6936. FAX: 970-434-7045. *Librn*, Melvin Vogel

Library Holdings: Bk Vols 13,000
Open Tues-Thurs 9-6, Fri & Sat 9-5
Friends of the Library Group
COLLBRAN BRANCH, 111 Main St, PO Box 88, Collbran, 81624. SAN 335-8267. Tel: 970-487-3545. FAX: 970-487-3716. *Librn*, Sharon Jordan
Library Holdings: Bk Titles 7,551
Open Tues, Thurs & Fri 10-noon & 1-6, Sat 9-1
Friends of the Library Group
DEBEQUE JOINT BRANCH, 730 Minter Ave, DeBeque, 81630. SAN 335-8291. Tel: 970-283-5596. FAX: 970-283-5213. *Librn*, Rose Varner
Library Holdings: Bk Titles 8,184
Open Mon-Fri 8-12 & 12:30-4:30 (Sept-May); Mon-Fri 9-12 (June-Aug)
Friends of the Library Group
FRUITA BRANCH, 325 E Aspen, Fruita, 81521. SAN 335-8321. Tel: 970-858-7703. FAX: 970-858-3254. *Librn*, Lila Wills
Library Holdings: Bk Titles 10,005
Open Tues, Thurs-Sat 9-1 & 2-6, Wed 3-6
Friends of the Library Group
GATEWAY BRANCH, 42700 Hwy No 141, Gateway, 81522. SAN 335-833X. Tel: 970-931-2428. *Librn*, June Blaisdale
Library Holdings: Bk Titles 2,859
Open Mon, Tues & Thurs 9-1, Wed 5-8, Fri 9-11
ORCHARD MESA, 2736 Unaweep Ave, 81503. SAN 375-0531. Tel: 970-243-0181. FAX: 970-241-9762. *Librn*, Brian Hiebert
Library Holdings: Bk Titles 14,000
PALISADE BRANCH, 175 E Third St, Palisade, 81526. SAN 335-8356. Tel: 970-464-7557. FAX: 970-464-7904. *Librn*, Mary Faye Hampton
Library Holdings: Bk Titles 14,529
Open Mon, Tues & Thurs 9-12 & 1-6, Wed 1-6, Fri 9-12 & 1-5
Friends of the Library Group

C MESA STATE COLLEGE LIBRARY, 1200 College Pl, 81501. SAN 301-9365. Tel: 970-248-1862. Interlibrary Loan Service Tel: 970-248-1844. Reference Tel: 970-248-1860. FAX: 970-248-1930. Web Site: mesastate.edu/library. *Dir*, Valerie Horton; E-Mail: vhorton@mesastate.edu; *Ref*, Elizabeth W Brodak; E-Mail: ebrodak@mesastate.edu; *ILL*, Jane Heitman; *Acq*, Linda Chamberlin; *Media Spec*, Mark Kasselhut; *Coordr*, Barbara Borst; *Circ*, Georgette Gerlach; *Cat*, Jo Hunter; *Govt Doc, Spec Coll*, Kathleen Tower; Staff 18 (MLS 7, Non-MLS 11)
Founded 1925. Enrl 5,200; Fac 202; Highest Degree: Master
Jul 1999-Jun 2000 Income $1,228,336. Mats Exp $376,976, Books $137,316, Per/Ser (Incl. Access Fees) $134,460, Presv $7,453, Micro $15,193, AV Equip $8,458, Electronic Ref Mat (Incl. Access Fees) $74,096. Sal $844,414 (Prof $412,966)
Library Holdings: Bk Vols 195,804; Bk Titles 147,805; Per Subs 1,050
Special Collections: Ethridge Indian Pottery Coll; Mesa College Archives; Walter Walker Memorial Coll; Wayne Aspinall Coll
Automation Activity & Vendor Info: (Cataloging) CARL; (Circulation) CARL; (Course Reserve) CARL; (OPAC) CARL; (Serials) CARL
Partic in BCR
Friends of the Library Group

S MUSEUM OF WESTERN COLORADO, Loyd Files Research Library, 462 Ute Ave, 81501. (Mail add: PO Box 20000, 81502-5020), SAN 301-9381. Tel: 970-242-0971, Ext 210. FAX: 970-242-3960. Web Site: www.wcmuseum.org. *Curator, Librn*, Judy Prosser-Armstrong; E-Mail: judypa@colosys.net
Founded 1965
Jan 2000-Dec 2000 Mats Exp $3,800, Books $1,000, Presv $1,800, Micro $250, AV Equip $500, Electronic Ref Mat (Incl. Access Fees) $250. (Prof $42,060)
Library Holdings: Bk Vols 5,000; Bk Titles 4,000; Per Subs 12
Subject Interests: Archaeology, Paleontology, Railroads
Special Collections: Al Look Papers; Grand Junction Fire Department Coll; Local History (Western Colorado, Mesa County, Grand Junction); Mesa County Genealogical Society; Mesa County Historical Society Coll; Mesa County Newspapers, hardcopy, micro; Mesa County Oral History Coll, tapes (2400 hrs); Quahada Chapter Colorado Archaeological Society; Warren Kiefer Railroad Coll (1940-present)
Publications: Museum Times (monthly newsletter)
Restriction: By appointment only, Non-circulating, Open to public for reference only
Function: Archival collection
Mem of Pathfinder Regional Library Service System
Partic in Pathfinder Libr Syst
Friends of the Library Group

S NATIONAL ASSOCIATION OF PRIVATE, NONTRADITIONAL SCHOOLS & COLLEGES, Accreditation Library,* 182 Thompson Rd, 81503-2246. SAN 326-8837. Tel: 970-243-5441. FAX: 970-242-4392. Web Site: www.napnsc.org. *Librn*, H Earl Heusser; *Asst Librn*, Dolly Heusser
Founded 1974
Library Holdings: Bk Vols 1,500; Bk Titles 1,355; Per Subs 12
Special Collections: Depository for Theses and Dissertations completed by students of nontraditional-alternative colleges and universities (360 bound volumes)
Publications: Accreditation Brochure; Accreditation Fact Sheet; General Information Brochure; Handbook for Accreditation, Volumes I & II; On-site Evaluation Reports

P PATHFINDER REGIONAL LIBRARY SERVICE SYSTEM, 1048 Independent Ave Ste A119, 81505-6120. SAN 301-9918. Tel: 970-242-2418. Toll Free Tel: 800-356-1212. FAX: 970-244-2947. Web Site: www.colosys.net. *Dir*, John Campbell; E-Mail: john@colosys.net; *Librn*, Judy Maki; E-Mail: judy@colosys.net; *ILL*, Susan Hartman; E-Mail: susan@colosys.net; *ILL*, Connie Zortman; E-Mail: czortman@colosys.net
Founded 1967. Pop 143,321
Oct 1998-Sep 1999 Income $538,670, State $250,771, Locally Generated Income $287,899. Mats Exp $5,500, Books $500, AV Equip $5,000. Sal $164,680 (Prof $142,680)
Library Holdings: Bk Vols 100
Special Collections: Small prof coll
Database Vendor: CARL
Publications: Second Tuesday (newsletter)
Member Libraries: Belt Public Library; Blaine County Library; Choteau Public Library; Chouteau County Library; Conrad Public Library; Delta County Public Library; Department Of Veterans Affairs; Dutton Public Library; Fairfield Public Library; Gunnison County Public; Gunnison County Public; Havre Hill County Library; Hinsdale County Library District; Liberty County Library; Mesa County Public Library District; Montrose Library District; Museum of Western Colorado; Nucla Public Library; San Miguel County Public Library District No 1; San Miguel Library District 2; Toole County Free Library; Valier Public Library; Wedsworth Memorial Library; Western State College Of Colorado
Partic in Bibliographical Center For Research, Rocky Mountain Region, Inc; OCLC Online Computer Library Center, Inc

M ST MARY'S HOSPITAL, Dr E H Munro Library, PO Box 1628, 81502-1628. SAN 301-9373. Tel: 970-244-2171. FAX: 970-244-7509. *Librn*, Joan E Paine; E-Mail: jpaine@stmarygj.com
Founded 1945
Partic in Colorado Council Of Medical Librarians; Medical Libr Asn; Midcontinental Regional Med Libr Program

S UNITED STATES GEOLOGICAL SURVEY, Water Resources Library,* 764 Horizon Dr Ste 125, 81506. SAN 370-2693. Tel: 970-245-5257. FAX: 970-245-1026. Web Site: www.usgs.gov, www.webserver.cr.usgs.gov. *In Charge*, Paul Von Guerard
Library Holdings: Bk Titles 1,100

GREELEY

J AIMS COMMUNITY COLLEGE, Kiefer Library,* 5401 W 20th St, PO Box 69, 80632-0069. SAN 301-942X. Tel: 970-330-8008, Ext 6237. FAX: 970-339-6568. Web Site: www.aims.edu/vp/library. *Coll Develop, Dir*, Jean Warnke; E-Mail: jwarnke@aims.edu; *Acq*, Judy Novak; *Cat*, Judy Alcott; *Publ Servs*, Darlin Jean Krause; Staff 4 (MLS 4)
Founded 1970. Enrl 4,242; Fac 326
Jul 1996-Jun 1997 Income $274,429. Mats Exp $90,574, Books $44,006, Per/Ser (Incl. Access Fees) $11,000, Presv $500, Micro $10,000. Sal $186,701 (Prof $166,360)
Library Holdings: Bk Vols 39,770; Bk Titles 30,137; Per Subs 257
Special Collections: Colorado History Coll
Mem of High Plains Regional Library Service System
Partic in Bibliographical Center For Research, Rocky Mountain Region, Inc; CCLINK; CLA N Cent; Colorado Alliance Of Research Libraries; OCLC Online Computer Library Center, Inc

S CITY OF GREELEY, Municipal Museum Archives,* 919 Seventh St, 80631. SAN 301-9454. Tel: 970-350-9220. FAX: 970-350-9570. *Res*, Peggy A Ford
Founded 1968
Jan 1998-Dec 1998 Income $680,000
Library Holdings: Bk Titles 4,000
Special Collections: Greeley Early History (Union Colony Records)
Publications: History of Greeley & Weld County pamphlets
Restriction: Open to public for reference only
Friends of the Library Group

R FIRST CONGREGATIONAL CHURCH LIBRARY,* 2101 16th St, 80631. SAN 301-9438. Tel: 970-353-0828. *In Charge*, Jane Bateman; *Ch Servs*, Laurie McCarty
Library Holdings: Bk Vols 1,600
Subject Interests: Religion

P HIGH PLAINS REGIONAL LIBRARY SERVICE SYSTEM,* 800 Eighth Ave, No 341, 80631. SAN 301-9470. Tel: 970-356-4357. FAX: 970-353-4355. Web Site: www.highplains.org. *Dir*, Elizabeth Hager; E-Mail: bhager@csn.net
Founded 1967. Pop 368,929
Library Holdings: Bk Vols 500; Per Subs 20
Special Collections: Library Science Coll
Publications: No Silence

Member Libraries: Aims Community College; Akron Public Library; Ault Public Library; Berthoud Public Library; Burlington Public Library; Colorado Division of Wildlife; Crook Community Library; East Morgan County Library District; Eaton Public Library; Estes Park Public Library; Flagler Community Library; Fleming Community Library; Fort Collins Public Library; Fort Lupton Public & School Library; Fort Morgan Public Library; Glenn A Jones Memorial Library; Haxtun Public Library; Heginbotham Library; Hudson Public Library; Julesburg Public Library; Loveland Public Library; Northeast Colorado Bookmobile Services; Northeastern Junior College; Ovid Public Library; Platte River Power Authority Library; Platteville Public Library; Poudre Valley Hospital; Sterling Public Library; Stratton Public Library; University of Northern Colorado; US Geological Survey; Weld Library District; Weld Library District; Windsor-Severance Library District; Wray Public Library; Yuma Public Library

C UNIVERSITY OF NORTHERN COLORADO, James A Michener Library, 501 20th St, 80639. SAN 335-8380. Tel: 970-351-2601. FAX: 970-351-2963. Web Site: www.unco.edu/library. *Dean of Libr*, Gary M Pitkin; E-Mail: gmpitki@unco.edu; *Librn*, Bette Rathe; Tel: 970-351-2476, E-Mail: bdrathe@unco.edu; *Acq, Purchasing*, Joan Lamborn; Tel: 970-351-1547, E-Mail: jlamborn@unco.edu; *Archivist*, Mary Linscome; Tel: 970-351-2854, E-Mail: mlinscom@unco.edu; *Automation Syst Coordr*, Craig McWhirter; Tel: 970-351-2775, E-Mail: camcwhi@unco.edu; *Cat*, Kay Lowell; Tel: 970-351-2183, E-Mail: kelowell@unco.edu; *Govt Doc*, Mark Anderson; Tel: 970-351-1474, E-Mail: manderson@unco.edu; *ILL*, Jane Smith; Tel: 970-351-1446, E-Mail: mjsmith@unco.edu; *Music*, Stephen Luttmann; Tel: 970-351-2281, E-Mail: sfluttm@unco.edu; *Publ Servs*, George Jaramillo; E-Mail: gjaramil@unco.edu; *Ref*, Jan Squire; Tel: 970-351-1521, E-Mail: jsquire@unco.edu; *Spec Coll*, Roiann Baird; Tel: 970-351-3035. Subject Specialists: *Music*, Stephen Luttmann; Staff 18 (MLS 18)
Founded 1890. Enrl 413; Fac 9,700; Highest Degree: Doctorate
Jul 1998-Jun 1999 Mats Exp $1,148,085, Books $389,363, Per/Ser (Incl. Access Fees) $727,222, Presv $26,900, Micro $4,600. Sal $1,890,030 (Prof $879,228)
Library Holdings: Bk Vols 992,074; Per Subs 3,219
Subject Interests: Education, Music
Special Collections: James A Michener Archives; University Archives
Automation Activity & Vendor Info: (Acquisitions) Innovative Interfaces Inc.; (Cataloging) Innovative Interfaces Inc.; (Circulation) Innovative Interfaces Inc.; (OPAC) Innovative Interfaces Inc.; (Serials) Innovative Interfaces Inc.
Publications: Bibliotech
Partic in Bibliographical Center For Research, Rocky Mountain Region, Inc; Colorado Alliance Of Research Libraries; OCLC Online Computer Library Center, Inc
Friends of the Library Group
Departmental Libraries:
MUSIC Tel: 970-351-2439. FAX: 970-351-2540.
Library Holdings: Bk Vols 51,064
Friends of the Library Group

GL WELD COUNTY DISTRICT COURT, Law Library,* 915 Tenth St, PO Box C, 80632-0138. SAN 301-9446. Tel: 970-351-7300, Ext 4515. FAX: 970-356-4356.
Founded 1918
Subject Interests: Colorado, Law
Open Mon & Wed 8-12 & 1-5, Thurs 1-5

P WELD LIBRARY DISTRICT,* 2227 23rd Ave, 80634. SAN 301-9489. Tel: 970-330-0208. Toll Free Tel: 800-331-7182. FAX: 970-330-9408. Web Site: www.weld.lib.co.us. *Dir*, Steve Cottrell; Staff 21 (MLS 6, Non-MLS 15)
Founded 1931. Pop 137,888; Circ 736,645
Library Holdings: Bk Vols 360,019; Per Subs 711
Subject Interests: Colorado, Genealogy
Special Collections: New Adult Reader
Automation Activity & Vendor Info: (Acquisitions) epixtech, inc.; (Cataloging) epixtech, inc.; (Circulation) epixtech, inc
Publications: READ (Newsletter)
Mem of High Plains Regional Library Service System
Friends of the Library Group
Branches: 3
CARBON VALLEY BRANCH, 601 Fourth St, PO Box 118, Frederick, 80530. SAN 371-3601. Tel: 303-833-3510. FAX: 303-833-2576. Web Site: www.weld.lib.co.us. *Librn*, Nancy Presley; Staff 3 (MLS 1, Non-MLS 2)
Library Holdings: Bk Titles 12,500
Automation Activity & Vendor Info: (Circulation) epixtech, inc.
Mem of Cent Colorado Libr Syst
Friends of the Library Group
CENTENNIAL PARK, 2227 23rd Ave, 80631-1110. SAN 372-4891. Tel: 970-330-0208. Toll Free Tel: 800-331-7182. FAX: 970-330-9408. Web Site: www.weld.lib.co.us. *Branch Mgr*, Susan E Hurt; Tel: 970-330-7691, Ext 22, E-Mail: sehurt@weld.lib.co.us; *Dir*, Steve Cottrell; E-Mail: cottrell@weld.lib.co.us; Staff 44 (MLS 6, Non-MLS 38)
Founded 1985
Database Vendor: epixtech, inc.
Friends of the Library Group
LINCOLN PARK BRANCH, 919 Seventh St, 80631. SAN 301-9462. Tel: 970-350-9210. FAX: 970-350-9215. *Mgr*, Charlene Parker; *Ref*, Margaret Langley
Founded 1877. Pop 58,254; Circ 179,558
Special Collections: Colorado History bks, per & oral hist tapes; Greeley & Weld County, bks, per, oral hist tapes; History of Germans from Russia (German-Russian Coll), bk, pamphlets, flm, genealogy, maps
Mem of High Plains Regional Library Service System
Friends of the Library Group
Bookmobiles: 2

GREENWOOD VILLAGE

S APOLLO GROUP, College for Financial Planning Library, 6161 S Syracuse Way, 80111-4707. Tel: 303-220-4835. FAX: 303-220-4941. E-Mail: fki@fp.edu. Web Site: www.fp.edu. *Dir*, Faith Ioannides
Library Holdings: Bk Vols 3,000; Per Subs 100; Spec Interest Per Sub 70
Partic in Central Colorado Library System; Colo Libr Syst; Spec Libr Asn

S COBANK LIBRARY, 5500 S Quebec St, 80111. SAN 377-9106. Tel: 303-694-5865. FAX: 303-224-2586. Web Site: www.cobank.com. *In Charge*, Connie Raines; E-Mail: craines@cobank.com
Library Holdings: Bk Titles 200; Per Subs 200
Partic in Spec Libr Asn

S SCIENCE APPLICATIONS INTERNATIONAL CORPORATION, Foreign Systems Research Center,* 6021 S Syracuse Way, Ste 300, 80111-4732. SAN 326-6095. Tel: 303-773-6900. FAX: 303-770-3297. *Librn*, Dave Beachley; *Cat*, John Scafe; Staff 3 (MLS 2, Non-MLS 1)
Founded 1979
Library Holdings: Bk Titles 14,000; Per Subs 175
Subject Interests: International relations, Technology
Publications: Newsletter & User manual
Partic in Dialog Corporation

GUNNISON

P GUNNISON COUNTY PUBLIC, Ann Zugelder Library, 307 N Wisconsin, 81230-2627. SAN 335-847X. Tel: 970-641-3485. FAX: 970-641-4653. Web Site: www.colosys.net/gunnison. *Dir*, Peggy Martin
Founded 1939. Pop 12,000
Library Holdings: Bk Titles 40,000; Per Subs 70
Mem of Pathfinder Regional Library Service System
Friends of the Library Group
Branches: 1
CRESTED BUTTE BRANCH, 507 Maroon St, Crested Butte, 81224. (Mail add: Old Rock Community Library, PO Box 489, Crested Butte, 81224-0489), Tel: 970-349-6535. FAX: 970-349-0348. *Librn*, Mary Jo Laird; Staff 3 (Non-MLS 3)
Library Holdings: Bk Titles 5,000; Per Subs 50
Database Vendor: OCLC - First Search
Mem of Pathfinder Regional Library Service System
Friends of the Library Group

C WESTERN STATE COLLEGE OF COLORADO, Leslie J Savage Library, 600 N Adams St, 81231. SAN 301-9497. Tel: 970-943-2054. Interlibrary Loan Service Tel: 970-943-2103. FAX: 970-943-2042. Web Site: www.western.edu/lib/Welcome.html. *Acq*, Deborah Keller Brown; E-Mail: dbrown@western.edu; *Bibliog Instr*, Nancy Gauss; E-Mail: ngauss@western.edu; *Coll Develop, Publ Servs*, Patrick Muckleroy; E-Mail: pmuckleroy@western.edu; *Per*, Karla Knaussman Duran; E-Mail: kduran@western.edu; *Publ Servs*, Wendy Highby; E-Mail: whighby@western.edu; *Spec Coll, Tech Servs*, Ethel Rice; E-Mail: erice@western.edu; Staff 8 (MLS 6, Non-MLS 2)
Founded 1901. Enrl 2,400; Fac 81; Highest Degree: Bachelor
Jul 1999-Jun 2000 Income $697,729. Mats Exp $164,623, Books $78,420, Per/Ser (Incl. Access Fees) $54,303, Presv $900, Micro $31,000. Sal $463,029 (Prof $345,362)
Library Holdings: Bk Vols 432,601; Bk Titles 156,266; Per Subs 854
Special Collections: Colorado History (Western Americana); Western Colorado Newspapers, micro
Automation Activity & Vendor Info: (Cataloging) DRA; (Circulation) DRA; (Course Reserve) DRA; (OPAC) DRA; (Serials) DRA
Mem of Pathfinder Regional Library Service System
Partic in Bibliographical Center For Research, Rocky Mountain Region, Inc; Dialog Corporation; OCLC Online Computer Library Center, Inc

HAXTUN

P HAXTUN PUBLIC LIBRARY,* 137 S Colorado Ave, PO Box 446, 80731. SAN 301-9500. Tel: 970-774-6106. FAX: 970-774-6288. *Dir*, Glenna J Mooney
Founded 1925. Pop 1,050; Circ 16,500
Library Holdings: Bk Vols 12,500

Subject Interests: Agriculture, Art and architecture, Business and management, Economics, Education
Mem of High Plains Regional Library Service System

HAYDEN

P WEST ROUTT LIBRARY DISTRICT-HAYDEN PUBLIC LIBRARY,* PO Box 1813, 81639-1813. SAN 336-0008. Tel: 970-276-3777. FAX: 970-276-3778. *Dir*, Jacquelyn Boyd; E-Mail: jboyd@colosys.net; Staff 1 (MLS 1)
Founded 1932. Pop 2,450
Jan 1998-Dec 1999 Income $89,930, Locally Generated Income $3,900, Other $1,750. Mats Exp $14,600, Books $12,300, Per/Ser (Incl. Access Fees) $1,400, Presv $200. Sal $55,534 (Prof $33,700)
Library Holdings: Bk Titles 20,000; Per Subs 57
Mem of Three Rivers Regional Library Service System
Friends of the Library Group

HOLLY

P HOLLY PUBLIC LIBRARY, 302 S Main, PO Box 706, 81047. SAN 301-9527. Tel: 719-537-6520. FAX: 719-537-6621. E-Mail: hpl@holly.k12.co.us. *Dir*, Nolamae S Ice; Staff 1 (Non-MLS 1)
Founded 1911. Pop 993; Circ 4,715
Library Holdings: Bk Vols 6,832
Partic in Arkansas Valley Regional Library Service System (AVRLSS)

HOLYOKE

P HEGINBOTHAM LIBRARY,* 539 S Baxter St, 80734-1497. SAN 301-9535. Tel: 970-854-2597. FAX: 970-854-2636. *Dir*, Laura Roth; *Asst Librn*, Julie Koberstein; *Librn*, Caroline Daise
Founded 1920. Pop 2,000; Circ 25,004
Library Holdings: Bk Titles 13,000
Mem of High Plains Regional Library Service System
Open Mon, Wed & Fri 11am-5pm, Tues & Thurs 1-5pm & Sat 11am-3pm
Friends of the Library Group

HOT SULPHUR SPRINGS

S GRAND COUNTY HISTORICAL ASSOCIATION LIBRARY,* 110 E Byers Ave, PO Box 165, 80451-0165. SAN 372-5731. Tel: 970-725-3939. FAX: 970-725-0129. E-Mail: gcha@rkymtnhi.com.
Library Holdings: Bk Vols 200
Publications: Grand County Historical Association Journal
Open Wed-Sat 10-5
Friends of the Library Group

HUDSON

P HUDSON PUBLIC LIBRARY,* 555 Main St, PO Box 188, 80642. SAN 301-9543. Tel: 303-536-4550. FAX: 303-536-4404. *Dir*, Carolyn Peters
Founded 1951. Pop 3,200; Circ 5,925
1997-1998 Income $31,300, County $30,500, Locally Generated Income $800. Mats Exp Books $2,600. Sal $14,600
Library Holdings: Bk Vols 6,725; Bk Titles 6,500
Mem of High Plains Regional Library Service System

HUGO

P HUGO PUBLIC LIBRARY,* PO Box 429, 80821-0429. SAN 301-9551. Tel: 719-743-2325. *Dir*, Dora Mae Vassios
Founded 1921. Pop 773; Circ 8,206
Library Holdings: Bk Titles 7,459
Mem of Plains & Peaks Regional Library System

IDAHO SPRINGS

P IDAHO SPRINGS PUBLIC LIBRARY, 219 14th Ave, 80452-1509. (Mail add: PO Box 1509, 80452-1509), SAN 301-956X. Tel: 303-567-2020. FAX: 303-567-2020. E-Mail: ilibrary@purplemtn.com. Web Site: www.purplemtn.com/library. *Dir*, Marilyn E Blacker; *Asst Libr Dir*, Paula Dreith. Subject Specialists: *Education*, Paula Dreith; Staff 4 (MLS 1, Non-MLS 3)
Founded 1904. Pop 7,000; Circ 27,859
Jan 2000-Dec 2000 Income $139,359, County $137,359, Locally Generated Income $2,000. Mats Exp $23,858, Books $22,058, Per/Ser (Incl. Access Fees) $1,700, Electronic Ref Mat (Incl. Access Fees) $100. Sal $69,200 (Prof $30,703)
Library Holdings: Bk Vols 18,500; Per Subs 100
Subject Interests: Colorado, Mineralogy
Special Collections: Local Newspaper (1888-present), micro
Automation Activity & Vendor Info: (Cataloging) Sagebrush Corporation; (Circulation) Sagebrush Corporation; (OPAC) Sagebrush Corporation
Restriction: Residents only
Function: ILL available
Mem of Cent Colorado Libr Syst
Partic in BCR

IGNACIO

P IGNACIO COMMUNITY LIBRARY DISTRICT, Butch McClanahan Memorial Library, 470 Goddard Ave, PO Box 886, 81137-0886. SAN 371-8522. Tel: 970-563-9287. FAX: 970-563-9296. Web Site: www.ignacio.co.us. *Dir*, Debbie Winlock
Founded 1991. Pop 5,500
Library Holdings: Bk Vols 18,000
Mem of Southwest Regional Library Service System
Open Mon & Tues 1-6, Wed & Thurs 10-8 & Sun 1-5
Friends of the Library Group

JOHNSTOWN

P GLENN A JONES MEMORIAL LIBRARY,* Idaho & Jay Sts, PO Box 457, 80534. SAN 301-9578. Tel: 970-587-2459. FAX: 970-587-2352. *Dir*, Pat Betz; *Asst Dir*, Jill Schraeder; Staff 1 (Non-MLS 1)
Founded 1965. Pop 4,000; Circ 31,000
Library Holdings: Bk Titles 12,000
Special Collections: MacArthur Foundation Video Coll
Publications: What's New at Library, Johnstown Breeze 1969-present (weekly column)
Mem of High Plains Regional Library Service System
Library broadcasts story-time program on local access cable TV

JULESBURG

P JULESBURG PUBLIC LIBRARY,* 320 Cedar St, 80737-1545. SAN 301-9586. Tel: 970-474-2608. FAX: 970-474-2787. E-Mail: juleslibrary@sosinc.net. *Dir*, Shirley Allen
Founded 1922. Pop 1,576; Circ 10,994
1998-1999 Income $8,400. Mats Exp $3,900, Books $3,600, Per/Ser (Incl. Access Fees) $100
Library Holdings: Bk Vols 8,000
Subject Interests: History, Natural science
Mem of High Plains Regional Library Service System
Open Mon-Tues & Thurs-Sat 2-5
Friends of the Library Group

KIOWA

P ELBERT COUNTY LIBRARY,* PO Box 56, 80117-0056. SAN 335-8534. Tel: 303-621-2754. FAX: 303-621-2343.
Founded 1937. Pop 6,850; Circ 10,564
Library Holdings: Bk Titles 12,855
Subject Interests: Agriculture, Antiques, Local history
Mem of Plains & Peaks Regional Library System
Open Tues 9-8, Thurs 10:30-8, Fri 9-5 & Sat 9-noon
Friends of the Library Group
Branches: 2
ELIZABETH BRANCH, 207 S Main St, PO Box 70, Elizabeth, 80107. SAN 335-8569. Tel: 303-646-3416. *Librn*, Jan Gabehart
Circ 6,200
Library Holdings: Bk Vols 12,000
Friends of the Library Group
SIMLA BRANCH, 325 Pueblo Ave, PO Box 323, Simla, 80835-0323. SAN 335-8593. Tel: 719-541-2573. FAX: 719-541-2152. *Librn*, Gwen Gordon
Circ 4,500
Library Holdings: Bk Vols 2,500
Friends of the Library Group
Bookmobiles: 1

LA JARA

P CONEJOS COUNTY LIBRARY,* PO Box 63, 81140. SAN 376-2815. Tel: 719-274-5858. FAX: 719-274-5858. *Dir*, Maria Deherrera
Library Holdings: Bk Vols 19,500; Per Subs 30
Mem of Southwest Regional Library Service System
Friends of the Library Group

LA JUNTA

S KOSHARE INDIAN MUSEUM LIBRARY, 115 W 18th St, PO Box 580, 81050-0580. SAN 321-2394. Tel: 719-384-4411. FAX: 719-384-8836. Web Site: www.ruralnet.net/~koshare. *Spec Coll*, Jo Kent; E-Mail: joann.kent@ojc.cccoes.edu; Staff 2 (Non-MLS 2)
Founded 1950
Library Holdings: Bk Titles 4,000
Subject Interests: Native Americans

J OTERO JUNIOR COLLEGE, Wheeler Library,* 20 Pinon Ave, 81050-3347. SAN 301-9594. Tel: 719-384-6882. FAX: 719-384-6883. *Tech Servs*, Kendra Schwindtswope
Founded 1941
Library Holdings: Bk Vols 34,310; Bk Titles 32,131; Per Subs 230
Special Collections: Phonograph - 33LP Coll
Mem of Arkansas Valley Regional Library Service System

S UNITED STATES NATIONAL PARK SERVICE, Bent's Old Fort National Historic Site Library, 35110 Hwy 194 E, 81050. SAN 374-7956. Tel: 719-383-5010. FAX: 719-383-5031. *In Charge*, Donald C Hill
Library Holdings: Bk Vols 1,500

P WOODRUFF MEMORIAL LIBRARY, City Library of La Junta,* 522 Colorado Ave, 81050-2308. (Mail add: PO Box 479, 81050-0479), SAN 301-9608. Tel: 719-384-4612. FAX: 719-383-2514. *Dir*, Debora Cosper
Founded 1888. Pop 12,300; Circ 91,000
Jan 1999-Dec 1999 Income $270,000, City $267,000, County $3,000. Mats Exp $44,000, Books $34,800, Per/Ser (Incl. Access Fees) $6,100, Presv $1,200, Micro $200, Electronic Ref Mat (Incl. Access Fees) $1,700. Sal $169,000 (Prof $40,000)
Library Holdings: Bk Titles 32,000; Per Subs 156
Subject Interests: Local history
Special Collections: Affiliate Dat Center-1990 Census; Area Newspaper Coll
Automation Activity & Vendor Info: (Cataloging) Follett; (Circulation) Follett; (OPAC) Follett
Publications: Centennial Brochure, 1988; Otero County Centennial Brochure, 1989
Mem of Arkansas Valley Regional Library Service System
Friends of the Library Group

LA PORTE

S HOLMAN, INC, Technical Support Laboratory,* PO Box 1468, 80535-1468. SAN 301-9136. Tel: 970-482-5600. FAX: 970-482-5608.
Founded 1953
Library Holdings: Bk Vols 2,200; Per Subs 30

LA VETA

P LA VETA PUBLIC LIBRARY, 310 Main St, PO Box 28, 81055. SAN 301-9616. Tel: 719-742-3572. E-Mail: books1@rmi.net. *Dir*, Cindy Pierotti
Founded 1974. Pop 900; Circ 12,000
Library Holdings: Bk Vols 18,000
Special Collections: History (Colorado Coll), large print
Mem of Arkansas Valley Regional Library Service System

LAFAYETTE

P LAFAYETTE PUBLIC LIBRARY,* 775 W Baseline Rd, 80026. SAN 301-9624. Tel: 303-665-5200. FAX: 303-665-8936. Web Site: www.ci.lafayette.co.us/library. *Dir*, Michele Seipp; E-Mail: micheles@cityoflafayette.com; *Coll Develop*, Sandra Lindberg
Founded 1923
Jan 2000-Dec 2000 Income $776,122. Mats Exp Books $99,000. Sal $531,014
Library Holdings: Bk Vols 106,000; Bk Titles 110,000; Per Subs 260
Special Collections: Local History Coll
Database Vendor: epixtech, inc., IAC - Info Trac, OCLC - First Search
Mem of Cent Colorado Libr Syst

LAKE CITY

P HINSDALE COUNTY LIBRARY DISTRICT, Lake City Public Library, 221 Silver St, PO Box 607, 81235-0607. SAN 376-284X. Tel: 970-944-2615. FAX: 970-944-4102. *Librn*, Elaine Gray; *Asst Librn*, Taffy Bolger
Library Holdings: Bk Vols 16,000; Bk Titles 9,350
Mem of Pathfinder Regional Library Service System
Friends of the Library Group

LAKEWOOD

M AMC CANCER RESEARCH CENTER, Robert A Silverberg Family Research Library, 1600 Pierce St, 80214. SAN 301-9632. Tel: 303-239-3368. FAX: 303-233-9562. *Librn*, Doris Borchert; E-Mail: borchert@amc.org
Founded 1970
Library Holdings: Bk Titles 3,000; Per Subs 160
Subject Interests: Cancer
Partic in Dialog Corporation; Docline; Medline; OCLC Online Computer Library Center, Inc; Wilsonline

M COBE BLOOD COMPONENT TECHNOLOGY, INC LIBRARY,* 1201 Oak St, 80215-4498. SAN 375-6882. Tel: 303-231-4278. FAX: 303-239-2115. *Librn*, Zelda Hawkins
Library Holdings: Bk Titles 1,000; Per Subs 125
Restriction: Staff use only

C COLORADO CHRISTIAN UNIVERSITY LIBRARY,* 180 S Garrison St, 80226. SAN 301-8679. Tel: 303-963-3250. FAX: 303-274-7560. Web Site: www.ccu.edu/library/. *Actg Dir, Tech Servs*, Paul Murdock; Staff 5 (MLS 4, Non-MLS 1)
Founded 1914. Enrl 850; Fac 60; Highest Degree: Master
Jul 1998-Jun 1999 Income $402,000, Locally Generated Income $2,000, Parent Institution $400,000. Mats Exp $172,000, Books $76,000, Per/Ser (Incl. Access Fees) $60,000, AV Equip $2,000, Electronic Ref Mat (Incl. Access Fees) $34,000. Sal $165,000 (Prof $98,000)
Library Holdings: Bk Vols 56,000; Bk Titles 50,000; Per Subs 1,450
Subject Interests: Education, Humanities, Music, Religion
Automation Activity & Vendor Info: (OPAC) epixtech, inc.
Database Vendor: epixtech, inc.
Publications: Library News
Partic in Central Colorado Library System

S COLORADO PREVENTION RESOURCE CENTER,* Rocky Mountain Ctr for Health Promotion & Education, 7525 W Tenth Ave, 80215. SAN 377-8754. Tel: 303-239-8633. FAX: 303-239-8428. Web Site: www.rmc.org. *Dir*, Anne Zanders; Tel: 303-239-6976, Ext 114, E-Mail: annez@rmc.org
Library Holdings: Bk Titles 3,000; Per Subs 45
Partic in Central Colorado Library System; Colo Prevention Resource Syst; Regional Alcohol And Drug Abuse Resource Network; Substance Abuse Librarians & Information Specialists

M JEFFERSON CENTER FOR MENTAL HEALTH LIBRARY, 9808 W Cedar Ave, 80226. SAN 375-7765. Tel: 303-432-5446. FAX: 303-234-0117. *Librn*, Barbara Wessel; E-Mail: barbw@jcmh.org; Staff 1 (MLS 1)
1998-1999 Mats Exp $14,750, Books $3,500, Per/Ser (Incl. Access Fees) $7,500, AV Equip $750, Electronic Ref Mat (Incl. Access Fees) $3,000. Sal $35,000
Library Holdings: Bk Titles 3,500; Per Subs 50
Subject Interests: Psychiatry, Psychology
Database Vendor: Ebsco - EbscoHost

P JEFFERSON COUNTY PUBLIC LIBRARY, 10200 W 20th Ave, 80215. SAN 335-8623. Tel: 303-232-7114. FAX: 303-275-2202. Web Site: www.jefferson.lib.co.us. *Dir*, William Knott; Tel: 303-275-2200, E-Mail: wknott@jefferson.lib.co.us; *Admin Dir*, Paddy Correia; Tel: 303-275-2206, E-Mail: pcorreia@jefferson.lib.co.us; *Publ Servs*, Margaret Owens; Tel: 303-275-2216, E-Mail: mowens@jefferson.lib.co.us; *Publ Servs*, Barbara Yost; E-Mail: byost@jefferson.lib.co.us; *Coll Develop, Coordr*, Martha Reid; *Commun Relations*, Kay Pride; Tel: 303-275-2203, E-Mail: kpride@jefferson.lib.co.us; Staff 215 (MLS 54, Non-MLS 161)
Founded 1952. Pop 511,800; Circ 3,146,394
Jan 1999-Dec 1999 Income Locally Generated Income $16,552,065. Mats Exp $2,242,600, Books $1,515,000, Per/Ser (Incl. Access Fees) $293,000, Electronic Ref Mat (Incl. Access Fees) $150,000. Sal $8,339,311
Library Holdings: Bk Vols 978,522; Bk Titles 375,042; Per Subs 1,326
Subject Interests: Art, Colorado, Consumer health, Folk music, Govt docs, Law, Railroads
Special Collections: Jefferson County Archives Coll
Database Vendor: CARL, Ebsco - EbscoHost, GaleNet, Innovative Interfaces INN - View, OCLC - First Search, Wilson - Wilson Web
Publications: Exploring Your Library
Mem of Cent Colorado Libr Syst
Friends of the Library Group
Branches: 12
ARVADA BRANCH, 8555 W 57th Ave, Arvada, 80002. SAN 335-8658. Tel: 303-424-5527. *Mgr*, Larry Domingues
COLUMBINE, 7706 W Bowles Ave, Littleton, 80123. SAN 335-8682. Tel: 303-932-2690.
CONIFER PUBLIC, 10441 Hwy 73, Conifer, 80433. SAN 376-9119. Tel: 303-982-5310. *Mgr*, Susann Guillaumin; *Librn*, Bonnie Jensen
DANIELS, 1301 Union St, Golden, 80401. SAN 335-8747. Tel: 303-238-2130. *Librn*, Theresa Bailey
EDGEWATER BRANCH, 5843 W 25th Ave, Edgewater, 80214. SAN 335-8771. Tel: 303-237-3395. *Librn*, Theresa Bailey
EVERGREEN BRANCH, 5000 State Hwy 73, Evergreen, 80439. SAN 335-8801. Tel: 303-674-0780. *Mgr*, Priscilla Winter; E-Mail: pwinter@jefferson.lib.co.us
EXTENSION SERVICES *Librn*, Theresa Bailey
GOLDEN, 1019 Tenth St, Golden, 80401. SAN 335-8836. Tel: 303-279-4585. Web Site: www.jefferson.lib.co.us. *Librn*, Kathy Husband; Tel: 303-279-4585, Ext 15, E-Mail: kathyh@jefferson.lib.co.us; Staff 15 (MLS 5, Non-MLS 10)
Pop 520,000
LAKEWOOD, 10200 W 20th Ave, 80215. SAN 335-8860. Tel: 303-232-9507. FAX: 303-275-2234. *Mgr*, Brett Lear
LIBRARY SERVICE CENTER, 10550 W 38th Ave, Wheat Ridge, 80033. SAN 376-9127. Tel: 303-375-4049.
STANDLEY LAKE, 8485 Kipling St, 80005. SAN 371-4918. Tel: 303-456-0806. *Librn*, Larry Domingues
VILLA, 455 S Pierce St, 80226. SAN 335-8895. Tel: 303-936-7407. *Mgr*, Elizabeth Bergstrom; E-Mail: libbyb@jefferson.lib.co.us
Bookmobiles: 1

S LAKEWOOD ENVIRONMENTAL LIBRARY, Property Management Division & Central Records,* 445 S Allison Pkwy, 80226-3106. SAN 377-1849. Tel: 303-987-7190. FAX: 303-987-7194. *In Charge*, Brian Nielsen
Library Holdings: Bk Vols 75

S LAKEWOOD'S HERITAGE CENTER LIBRARY, 797 S Wadsworth Blvd, 80226. SAN 374-9258. Tel: 303-987-7850. Reference Tel: 303-987-7855. FAX: 303-987-7851. *Adminr*, Kris Anderson; *Curator*, Win Ferrill; *Curator*, Elizabeth Nosek
Founded 1976
Library Holdings: Bk Vols 2,500
Subject Interests: Local history, Native Am, Railroad

S NATIONAL PARK SERVICE LIBRARY,* 12795 W Alameda Pkwy, PO Box 25287, 80225-0287. SAN 301-9667. Tel: 303-969-2716. FAX: 303-969-2557. *Librn*, Bess Lloyd; E-Mail: bess_lloyd@nps.gov
Founded 1971
Oct 1997-Sep 1998 Income $154,000. Mats Exp $25,000, Books $10,000, Per/Ser (Incl. Access Fees) $15,000. Sal $155,000 (Prof $96,000)
Library Holdings: Bk Vols 20,000; Per Subs 300
Subject Interests: Construction, Ecology, Engineering, History, Landscape architecture
Restriction: Open to public for reference only
Partic in Fedlink; OCLC Online Computer Library Center, Inc

RED ROCKS COMMUNITY COLLEGE
J MARVIN BUCKELS LIBRARY, 13300 W Sixth Ave, 80228-1255. SAN 301-9276. Tel: 303-914-6740. FAX: 303-914-6741. E-Mail: library@rrcc.cccoes.edu. Web Site: www.rrcc.cccoes.edu/library. *Coll Develop, Librn*, Tom Connole; Tel: 303-914-6743, E-Mail: tom.connole@rrcc.cocoes.edu; *Coordr*, Larry Rouch; Tel: 303-914-6742, E-Mail: larry.rouch@rrcc.cocoes.edu; *ILL*, Fran Ortega; Tel: 303-914-6746, E-Mail: fran.ortega@rrcc.cocoes.edu; Staff 6 (MLS 4, Non-MLS 2)
Founded 1969. Enrl 4,000; Fac 65; Highest Degree: Associate
Jul 1998-Jun 1999 Income $300,000. Mats Exp $109,000, Books $25,000, Per/Ser (Incl. Access Fees) $32,000, Micro $7,000. Sal $128,000
Library Holdings: Bk Vols 42,000; Bk Titles 38,000; Per Subs 320
Automation Activity & Vendor Info: (Cataloging) CARL; (Circulation) CARL; (OPAC) CARL; (Serials) CARL
Database Vendor: CARL, OCLC - First Search

G US BUREAU OF THE CENSUS LIBRARY, 6900 W Jefferson Ave, 80235-2032. SAN 326-2731. Tel: 303-969-7750. FAX: 303-969-7022. Web Site: www.census.gov. *Coordr*, Jerry O'Donnell

LAMAR

J LAMAR COMMUNITY COLLEGE, Learning Resources Center,* Bowman Bldg, 2401 S Main St, 81052-3999. SAN 301-9691. Tel: 719-336-2248, Ext 256. FAX: 719-336-2448. *Librn*, Dorothy D Wilcox; E-Mail: dorothy.wilcox@lcc.cccoes.edu
Founded 1937. Enrl 609; Fac 44
1998-1999 Mats Exp $28,490
Library Holdings: Bk Titles 23,500; Per Subs 130
Subject Interests: Colorado, Horses, Nursing
Database Vendor: CARL
Publications: Online media catalog
Mem of Arkansas Valley Regional Library Service System
Affiliate Data Center, State of Colorado, Department of Local Affairs

P LAMAR PUBLIC LIBRARY,* 104 E Parmenter St, 81052-3239. SAN 301-9705. Tel: 719-336-4632. FAX: 719-336-2787. E-Mail: lamarpo@hotmail.com. *Dir*, Susan C Ooton; *Asst Librn*, Lois Wilger; Staff 5 (MLS 1, Non-MLS 4)
Founded 1908. Pop 14,100; Circ 39,500
Library Holdings: Bk Vols 39,000; Per Subs 150
Special Collections: Colorado History Coll
Publications: The View From the Stacks (weekly)
Mem of Arkansas Valley Regional Library Service System
Friends of the Library Group

S PROWERS COUNTY HISTORICAL SOCIETY, Big Timbers Museum Library,* 7515 US Hwy 50, PO Box 362, 81052. SAN 370-436X. Tel: 719-336-2472. FAX: 719-336-2472. *Curator*, Jeanne Clark
Library Holdings: Bk Titles 250
Subject Interests: Local history
Friends of the Library Group

LAS ANIMAS

P LAS ANIMAS-BENT COUNTY PUBLIC LIBRARY,* 306 Fifth St, 81054. SAN 301-9713. Tel: 719-456-0111, 719-456-0112. FAX: 719-456-0112. *Dir*, Donna Burns
Founded 1922. Pop 6,100; Circ 22,251
Library Holdings: Bk Titles 15,000; Per Subs 57
Special Collections: Bent County Coll & Llewellyn Thompson Coll
Mem of Arkansas Valley Regional Library Service System

P LOWER ARKANSAS VALLEY REGIONAL LIBRARY, 510 Carson Ave, 81054-1732. SAN 301-9721. Tel: 719-456-1770. FAX: 719-456-1770. E-Mail: books@ria.net. *Librn*, Marcia McElroy; *Asst Librn*, Misty Warren
Pop 9,899; Circ 24,542
1998-1999 Income $30,522, State $1,722, County $24,100, Other $4,700. Mats Exp $2,000. Sal $20,000
Library Holdings: Bk Vols 28,176; Bk Titles 27,682
Subject Interests: Colorado, Genealogy
Mem of Arkansas Valley Regional Library Service System
Friends of the Library Group
Bookmobiles: 1

LEADVILLE

J COLORADO MOUNTAIN COLLEGE-TIMBERLINE CAMPUS, Learning Resources Center, 901 S Hwy 24, 80461. SAN 335-895X. Tel: 719-486-4250. Interlibrary Loan Service Tel: 719-486-4249. FAX: 719-486-4221. Web Site: www.coloradomtn.edu/library/. *Dir*, Sharon C Moller; E-Mail: smoller@coloradomtn.edu; Staff 1 (MLS 1)
Founded 1967. Enrl 158
Jul 1998-Jun 1999 Income $137,850. Mats Exp $25,500, Books $12,500, Per/Ser (Incl. Access Fees) $7,200, Presv $300, Electronic Ref Mat (Incl. Access Fees) $5,500. Sal $110,500 (Prof $44,800)
Library Holdings: Bk Vols 17,000; Bk Titles 15,100; Per Subs 171
Special Collections: Documents relating to EPA California Gulch Superfund Site (Lake County, Colorado)
Mem of Three Rivers Regional Library Service System
Have dedicated line to MARMOT, a computerized Public Access Catalog

P LAKE COUNTY PUBLIC LIBRARY, 1115 Harrison Ave, 80461-3398. SAN 335-8984. Tel: 719-486-0569. FAX: 719-486-3544. *Dir*, Nancy S McCain; *Circ, ILL*, Debbie Cisneros; *Ch Servs*, Glenda Dunn; *Ch Servs*, Robin Deisten; Staff 4 (MLS 1, Non-MLS 3)
Founded 1897. Pop 6,000; Circ 40,894
Jan 1999-Dec 1999 Income $144,411, State $7,881, Locally Generated Income $127,983, Other $8,547. Mats Exp $20,021, Books $15,612, Per/Ser (Incl. Access Fees) $2,090, AV Equip $879, Electronic Ref Mat (Incl. Access Fees) $1,440. Sal $87,797 (Prof $32,000)
Library Holdings: Bk Vols 22,140; Bk Titles 21,750; Per Subs 108
Special Collections: Early Newspapers, micro, memorabilia; Local History (Colorado Mountain History Coll), bks, photos, pamphlets
Mem of Three Rivers Regional Library Service System

LIMON

P LIMON MEMORIAL PUBLIC LIBRARY,* 205 E Ave, 80828. SAN 301-973X. Tel: 719-775-2163. FAX: 719-775-8808. *Librn*, Marjorie Monks
Founded 1948. Circ 18,000
Library Holdings: Bk Vols 10,000
Special Collections: Eastern Colorado History Coll; Historical Picture Coll; Local Historical Audio Coll
Mem of Plains & Peaks Regional Library System
Special Services for the Deaf - Books on deafness & sign language; High interest/low vocabulary books; Special interest periodicals

LITTLETON

J ARAPAHOE COMMUNITY COLLEGE LIBRARY,* 5900 S Santa Fe Dr, PO Box 9002, 80160-9002. SAN 301-9748. Interlibrary Loan Service Tel: 303-797-5726. FAX: 303-798-4173. Web Site: www.arapahoe.edu. *Dir*, Malcolm Brantz; Tel: 303-797-5739, E-Mail: mbrantz@arapahoe.edu; *Tech Servs*, Marilyn Munsterman; Tel: 303-797-5728, E-Mail: mmunsterman@arapahoe.edu; *Publ Servs*, Jan Dawson; Tel: 303-797-5731, E-Mail: jdawson@arapahoe.edu; *Instrul Serv*, Gene Hayworth; Staff 8 (MLS 4, Non-MLS 4)
Founded 1966. Enrl 4,200
Jul 1998-Jun 1999 Income State $503,043. Mats Exp $113,650. Sal $310,643 (Prof $118,180)
Library Holdings: Bk Vols 43,500; Per Subs 404
Automation Activity & Vendor Info: (Cataloging) CARL; (Circulation) CARL; (OPAC) CARL
Database Vendor: OCLC - First Search
Publications: Serials listing, film & video tape catalog
Mem of Cent Colorado Libr Syst
Partic in Bibliographical Center For Research, Rocky Mountain Region, Inc

P ARAPAHOE LIBRARY DISTRICT,* 2305 E Arapahoe Rd, 80122-1583. SAN 335-9042. Tel: 303-798-2444. FAX: 303-798-2485. Web Site: www.arapahoelibraries.org. *Dir*, Eloise May; *Branch Mgr*, Marilyn Hobbs; *Acq, Coll Develop*, Fran Schrag; *Exten Serv*, Candice Brown; Staff 60 (MLS 60)
Founded 1966. Pop 174,000
Jan 1999-Dec 1999 Income $10,994,081. Mats Exp $789,046, Books $753,112, Per/Ser (Incl. Access Fees) $35,934. Sal $4,899,267 (Prof $2,082,188)
Library Holdings: Bk Vols 425,343

Publications: By the Book (monthly newsletter); Community Information Guide
Mem of Cent Colorado Libr Syst
Send acquisition inquiries to Collection Development at Koelbel Library only
Friends of the Library Group
Branches: 9
CASTLEWOOD, 6739 S Uinta, Englewood, 80112. SAN 335-9190. Tel: 303-771-3197. FAX: 303-771-3264. Web Site: www.arapahoelibraries.org. *Mgr*, Laurie Christensen; *Ad Servs*, Jane Seidl; *Ch Servs*, Jane Herbel; *AV*, Lesley Hardt; *Circ*, Bobby Keil
Library Holdings: Bk Vols 71,000
DAVIES PUBLIC LIBRARY, 350 Second Ave, Deer Trail, 80105. SAN 335-9131. Tel: 303-769-4310. FAX: 303-769-4350. Web Site: www.arapahoelibraries.org. *Mgr*, Charmaine Ness
Library Holdings: Bk Vols 17,000
Friends of the Library Group
EXTENSION SERVICES, 5955 S Holly St, 80121. SAN 370-9337. Tel: 303-220-0482. FAX: 303-741-9599. Web Site: www.arapahoelibraries.org. *Mgr*, Candice Brown
Library Holdings: Bk Vols 7,000
GLENDALE BRANCH, 999 S Clermont St, Glendale, 80246. SAN 335-914X. Tel: 303-691-0331. FAX: 303-691-0332. Web Site: www.arapahoelibraries.org. *Mgr*, Annette Choszczyk
Library Holdings: Bk Vols 22,000
KELVER PUBLIC LIBRARY, 404 E Front St, Byers, 80103. SAN 335-9077. Tel: 303-822-9392. FAX: 303-822-9393. Web Site: www.arapahoelibraries.org. *Mgr*, Carol Gottlob
Library Holdings: Bk Vols 27,000
Friends of the Library Group
KOELBEL LIBRARY, 5955 S Holly St, 80121. SAN 335-9107. Tel: 303-220-7704. FAX: 303-220-1651. Web Site: www.arapahoelibraries.org. *Ad Servs*, Jean Angler; *Ch Servs*, Sabroma Speight; *Circ*, Donna Walker; *AV*, Jan Derks
Library Holdings: Bk Vols 162,000
Friends of the Library Group
SHERIDAN PUBLIC BRANCH, 3201 W Oxford Ave, Sheridan, 80236. SAN 335-9166. Tel: 303-789-5422. FAX: 303-789-2611. Web Site: www.arapahoelibraries.org. *Mgr*, Mollie Hagen
Library Holdings: Bk Vols 32,000
SOUTHGLENN PUBLIC, 7500 S University Blvd, No 101, 80122. SAN 373-5753. Tel: 303-221-3998. FAX: 303-740-8356. Web Site: www.arapahoelibraries.org. *Mgr*, Linda Downs
Library Holdings: Bk Vols 34,862
SMOKY HILL PUBLIC LIBRARY, 15460 E Orchard Rd, Aurora, 80015. SAN 335-9174. Tel: 303-693-7449. FAX: 303-690-4572. Web Site: www.arapahoelibraries.org. *Mgr*, Sharon Edstrom; E-Mail: sedstrom@ald.lib.co.us; Staff 30 (MLS 4, Non-MLS 26)
Library Holdings: Bk Vols 49,500; Per Subs 117
Database Vendor: Innovative Interfaces INN - View
Friends of the Library Group
Bookmobiles: 1. (Also have 1 van)

P EDWIN A BEMIS PUBLIC LIBRARY, Littleton Public Library, 6014 S Datura St, 80120-2636. SAN 301-9756. Tel: 303-795-3961. TDD: 303-795-3998. FAX: 303-795-3996. E-Mail: bemisl@csn.org. Web Site: www.littletongov.org/bemis/index.htm. *Dir*, Margery Smith; E-Mail: mesmith@mail.littleton.org; *ILL*, Becky Fenn; *Ref*, Phyllis Larison; Staff 11 (MLS 11)
Founded 1897. Pop 39,300; Circ 312,255
Jan 1999-Dec 1999 Income $1,590,890, City $1,545,890, Other $45,000. Mats Exp $175,226, Books $126,628, Per/Ser (Incl. Access Fees) $23,764, Micro $4,788, Other Print Mats $182, Electronic Ref Mat (Incl. Access Fees) $19,864. Sal $1,132,430
Library Holdings: Bk Vols 125,000; Per Subs 279
Subject Interests: Genealogy
Automation Activity & Vendor Info: (Circulation) CARL; (OPAC) CARL
Mem of Cent Colorado Libr Syst
Special Services - TTY for Deaf, video magnifier for visually impaired, personal computer for public use with magnification & voice amplification
Friends of the Library Group

S FEDERAL CORRECTIONAL INSTITUTION LIBRARY,* 9595 W Quincy Ave, 80123. SAN 377-8770. Tel: 303-985-1566. FAX: 303-763-2599. *Librn*, Monty Wiest
Library Holdings: Bk Titles 6,000
Partic in Central Colorado Library System

S LITTLETON HISTORICAL MUSEUM LIBRARY, 6028 S Gallup, 80120. SAN 301-9764. Tel: 303-795-3950. FAX: 303-730-9818. *Dir*, Mary Allman; *Curator*, Lorena Donohue
Founded 1969
Library Holdings: Bk Vols 800; Per Subs 10
Special Collections: Early Exploration Maps; Littleton History Coll, bks, micro, doc, photog
Open Tues-Fri 8-5, Sat 10-5 & Sun 1-5
Friends of the Library Group

S JOHNS MANVILLE CORPORATE LIBRARY,* R-21, PO Box 625005, 80162-5005. SAN 373-6733. Tel: 303-978-5388. FAX: 303-978-5094. *In Charge*, Pat Klug; E-Mail: klugp@jm.com
Founded 1946
Library Holdings: Bk Vols 3,728; Per Subs 270
Publications: Articles; Library brochure; new book list; patents

S MUTUAL UFO NETWORK, INC, MUFON Library, 10143 W Chatfield Ave, Unit No 4, 80127. (Mail add: PO Box 369, 80465-0369), SAN 329-1626. Tel: 303-932-7709. FAX: 303-932-9279. E-Mail: mufonhq@aol.com. Web Site: www.mufon.com. *Acq, Dir*, John F Schuessler; *Circ*, Kathy Schuessler; E-Mail: kathyschu@mho.com; *Publ Servs*, Robert H Bletchman; Staff 1 (MLS 1)
Founded 1969
Library Holdings: Bk Titles 300; Per Subs 65
Special Collections: Unidentified Flying Objects, bks, flms
Publications: Annual MUFON INTERNATIONAL UFO Symposium Proceedings; MUFON UFO Journal (monthly)
Restriction: By appointment only

S NATIONAL CABLE TELEVISION INSTITUTE LIBRARY,* 801 W Mineral Ave, 80120. SAN 371-2524. Tel: 303-797-9393. FAX: 303-797-9394. E-Mail: info@ncti.com. Web Site: www.ncti.com. *Exec Dir*, Roland D Hieb
Library Holdings: Bk Vols 190; Per Subs 5

LONGMONT

P LONGMONT PUBLIC LIBRARY,* 409 Fourth Ave, 80501-6006. SAN 301-9780. Tel: 303-651-8471. FAX: 303-651-8911. *Dir*, Tony Brewer; *Circ*, Becky Williamson; *Ch Servs*, Sandra Pendergraff; Staff 20 (MLS 12, Non-MLS 8)
Founded 1871. Pop 68,000; Circ 615,000
Library Holdings: Bk Vols 160,000; Per Subs 358
Mem of Cent Colorado Libr Syst
Partic in ALA; Colo Libr Asn; Dynix Consortium; OCLC
Friends of the Library Group

M LONGMONT UNITED HOSPITAL, Resource Library,* 1950 W Mountainview Ave, 80501. SAN 301-9799. Tel: 303-651-5180. FAX: 303-651-3851. *Librn*, Carol McMurry
Library Holdings: Bk Vols 130; Per Subs 20

S NOVARTIS SEEDS INC-SUGARBEETS-NASTA, Research Library,* 1020 Sugarmill Rd, 80501. SAN 374-7786. Tel: 303-776-1802. FAX: 303-776-0392. *Dir*, Gerald Simantel
Library Holdings: Bk Vols 650; Per Subs 25
Restriction: By appointment only

G UNITED STATES DEPARTMENT OF JUSTICE, National Institute of Corrections Information Center,* 1860 Industrial Circle, Ste A, 80501. SAN 323-6579. Tel: 303-682-0213. Toll Free Tel: 800-877-1461. TDD: 202-724-3156. FAX: 303-682-0558. E-Mail: asknicic@nicic.org. Web Site: www.nicic.org. *Librn*, Eileen Conway; *Cat*, Jeff White
Library Holdings: Bk Titles 15,000; Per Subs 200
Subject Interests: Prisons
Mem of Cent Colorado Libr Syst
Special Services for the Deaf - TDD

LOUISVILLE

P LOUISVILLE PUBLIC LIBRARY, 950 Spruce St, 80027. SAN 301-9810. Tel: 303-666-6037. FAX: 303-666-9664. Web Site: www.ci.louisville.co.us/library/. *Dir*, Anne Mojo; E-Mail: mojo@louisville.lib.co.us; *Acq, Ser*, Ann Stoffel; *YA Servs*, Carol Purfurst; *Ad Servs*, Kathy Kelly; Staff 7 (MLS 6, Non-MLS 1)
Founded 1925. Pop 20,000; Circ 283,000
Jan 2000-Dec 2000 Income City $735,000. Mats Exp $102,000, Books $71,000, Per/Ser (Incl. Access Fees) $11,000, Electronic Ref Mat (Incl. Access Fees) $20,000. Sal $530,000
Library Holdings: Bk Titles 53,000; Per Subs 189
Special Collections: History of Louisville
Publications: Newsletter
Mem of Cent Colorado Libr Syst
Friends of the Library Group

S STORAGE TECHNOLOGY CORPORATION, Corporate Information Center,* 2270 S 88th St, MS 5218, 80028-5218. SAN 320-9830. Tel: 303-673-5867. FAX: 303-673-5019. *Librn*, Kathy Carton; E-Mail: cartojk@louisville.stortek.com; Staff 1 (MLS 1)
Founded 1978
Library Holdings: Bk Vols 2,100; Bk Titles 1,536; Per Subs 175
Subject Interests: Engineering

LOVELAND

S AGILENT TECHNOLOGIES, Loveland Facility Library, 815 SW 14th St, 80537-6330. SAN 321-8252. Tel: 970-679-2460. FAX: 970-679-2023. *Info Specialist*, Rose Finch; E-Mail: rose_finch@agilent.com; Staff 3 (MLS 1, Non-MLS 2)
Founded 1965
Library Holdings: Bk Titles 8,000; Per Subs 325
Subject Interests: Bus, Computer science, Electronics, Quality control
Automation Activity & Vendor Info: (Circulation) SIRSI
Database Vendor: CARL, Dialog, Ebsco - EbscoHost, IAC - SearchBank, Lexis-Nexis, OCLC - First Search, ProQuest
Publications: Monthly newsletter
Partic in BCR; BRS; Coop Libr Agency for Syst & Servs; Dialog Corporation; RLIN

P LOVELAND PUBLIC LIBRARY, 300 N Adams Ave, 80537-5754. SAN 301-9837. Tel: 970-962-2665. Circulation Tel: 970-962-2586. Reference Tel: 970-962-2402. TDD: 970-962-2407. FAX: 970-962-2905. Web Site: www.ci.loveland.co.us/city10.htm. *Dir*, Ted Schmidt; Tel: 970-962-2400, E-Mail: schmit@ci.loveland.co.us; *Asst Librn*, Marcia Lewis; Tel: 970-962-2404; *Ref*, Carol Hammang; *Ch Servs*, Susan Peterson; Tel: 970-962-2587; *Circ*, Lupe Saldana; Staff 44 (MLS 6, Non-MLS 38)
Founded 1905. Pop 61,766; Circ 582,459
Jan 2000-Dec 2000 Income $1,577,890, City $1,392,890, County $62,000, Locally Generated Income $85,000, Other $77,950. Mats Exp $196,605, Books $161,010, Per/Ser (Incl. Access Fees) $20,319, Presv $390, Micro $2,886, AV Equip $12,000. Sal $1,116,510 (Prof $638,278)
Library Holdings: Bk Vols 150,635; Bk Titles 123,754; Per Subs 288; High Interest/Low Vocabulary Bk Vols 1,500
Special Collections: Loveland History; Oral History Coll; Western Americana Books Coll
Automation Activity & Vendor Info: (Acquisitions) Innovative Interfaces Inc.; (Cataloging) Innovative Interfaces Inc.; (Circulation) Innovative Interfaces Inc.; (OPAC) Innovative Interfaces Inc.; (Serials) Innovative Interfaces Inc.
Database Vendor: OCLC - First Search, ProQuest
Publications: Through Zethyl's Eyes: A Loveland History (Local historical information)
Function: Business archives
Mem of High Plains Regional Library Service System
Special Services for the Deaf - TDD
Special Services for the Blind - Descriptive videos

LYONS

P LYONS DEPOT LIBRARY,* PO Box 49, 80540. SAN 377-9858. Tel: 303-823-5165. FAX: 303-823-8257, 303-823-9532. *Dir*, Merlyn Williams
Library Holdings: Bk Titles 12,224; Per Subs 62
Partic in Central Colorado Library System

MANCOS

P MANCOS PUBLIC LIBRARY, 111 N Main, PO Box 158, 81328-0158. SAN 301-9845. Tel: 970-533-7569. E-Mail: mancospl@fone.net.; Staff 4 (Non-MLS 4)
Founded 1946. Pop 1,555; Circ 11,051
Jan 1999-Dec 1999 Income $90,896, State $84,521, City $2,000, Other $4,375. Mats Exp $6,200, Books $6,000, Per/Ser (Incl. Access Fees) $200. Sal $34,000 (Prof $15,768)
Library Holdings: Bk Titles 9,949
Special Collections: Southwest Coll
Mem of Southwest Regional Library Service System
Friends of the Library Group

MANITOU SPRINGS

P MANITOU SPRINGS PUBLIC LIBRARY,* 701 Manitou Ave, 80829-1810. SAN 301-9853. Tel: 719-685-5206. FAX: 719-685-1169. E-Mail: manitou@oldcolo.com. *Librn*, Carol Mehlhaff
Founded 1910. Pop 4,475; Circ 18,000
Library Holdings: Bk Titles 13,900; Per Subs 21
Subject Interests: Large type print
Special Collections: Colo History Coll, bks & clipings; Indian Coll
Mem of Plains & Peaks Regional Library System

MANZANOLA

P MANZANOLA PUBLIC LIBRARY,* 300 S Catalata St, PO Box 148, 81058-0148. SAN 301-9861. Tel: 719-462-5542. FAX: 719-462-5780. *In Charge*, Kathy Bauserman; E-Mail: kathy.bauserman@manzanola.k12.co.us
Pop 451
Library Holdings: Bk Vols 6,748
Mem of Arkansas Valley Regional Library Service System

MEEKER

P MEEKER REGIONAL LIBRARY DISTRICT, 200 Main St, 81641. SAN 301-987X. Tel: 970-878-5911. FAX: 970-878-5495. E-Mail: meekerp@hotmail.com. *Dir*, Mike Bartlett; Staff 2 (MLS 1, Non-MLS 1)
Founded 1913. Pop 2,053; Circ 25,397
Library Holdings: Bk Titles 26,000; Per Subs 64
Mem of Three Rivers Regional Library Service System
Friends of the Library Group

MESA VERDE NATIONAL PARK

S NATIONAL PARK SERVICE, Mesa Verde Research Library, PO Box 8, 81330. SAN 301-9888. Tel: 970-529-4627, 970-529-5079. FAX: 970-529-4637.
Founded 1929
Oct 1999-Sep 2000 Mats Exp $3,000. (Prof $30,000)
Library Holdings: Bk Vols 10,000; Per Subs 45
Subject Interests: Anthropology, Archaeology, Ethnic studies, Natural history
Special Collections: Colorado Conservation Corp Historical Files on Park Development; Fact Files; Historical Park Records; Interpretative Ranger Reference Manuals; Negative & Photo Files
Mem of Southwest Regional Library Service System
Library is part of the National Park System, operating in Mesa Verde National Park. The budget is part of the Interpretation fiscal budget. The Chief of Interpretation is the Supervisor of the Library Tech. The library falls in the Interpretation Division of Mesa Verde National Park's operation

MONTE VISTA

P CARNEGIE PUBLIC LIBRARY,* 120 Jefferson St, 81144-1797. SAN 301-9896. Tel: 719-852-3931. FAX: 719-852-0821. *Dir*, Carol Lee Dugan
Founded 1885. Pop 10,000; Circ 41,245
1998-1999 Income $101,500, City $2,500, County $99,000. Mats Exp $12,915, Books $11,000, Per/Ser (Incl. Access Fees) $1,200, Presv $50, AV Equip $65, Other Print Mats $500, Manuscripts & Archives $100. Sal $56,495
Library Holdings: Bk Titles 24,000; Per Subs 77
Special Collections: Colorado History Coll; County Newspapers, microflm; Spanish Language Coll
Mem of Southwest Regional Library Service System
Friends of the Library Group
Branches: 1
RUTH TABOR MEMORIAL LIBRARY, 254 Hwy 149, South Fork, 81154. SAN 320-0833. *Librn*, Rose Mae Fairchild

MONTROSE

G BUREAU OF LAND MANAGEMENT, Montrose District Office Library,* 2465 S Townsend, 81401. SAN 301-990X. Tel: 970-240-5300, 970-240-5333. FAX: 970-240-5368. *Librn*, Rosemary Gibbs
Library Holdings: Bk Vols 5,000; Per Subs 15
Partic in Fedlink
Open Mon-Fri 8-5

G LEAGUE FOR ECONOMIC ASSISTANCE & PLANNING, Region 10 Library,* 300 N Cascade, Ste 1, PO Drawer 849, 81402. SAN 375-8095. Tel: 970-249-2436. FAX: 970-249-2488. *Librn*, Dot Kropp
Library Holdings: Bk Titles 200; Per Subs 27

P MONTROSE LIBRARY DISTRICT, 320 S Second Ave, 81401-3909. SAN 335-9255. Tel: 970-249-9656. FAX: 970-240-1901. Web Site: www.colosys.net/montrose. *Dir*, Paul H Paladino; E-Mail: ppaladin@colosys.net; *Ref*, Rickie Wertz; E-Mail: uwertz@fred.colosys.net; *Ref*, Tania Hajjar; E-Mail: thajjar@colosys.net; *Ch Servs*, Janet Oslund; E-Mail: joslund@colosys.net; Staff 14 (MLS 4, Non-MLS 10)
Founded 1969. Pop 33,509; Circ 182,578
Jan 1999-Dec 1999 Income (Main Library and Branch Library) $565,842, State $7,820, County $362,069, Locally Generated Income $35,122, Other $160,831. Mats Exp $86,905, Books $67,666, Per/Ser (Incl. Access Fees) $6,607, AV Equip $3,711, Electronic Ref Mat (Incl. Access Fees) $8,921. Sal $353,655
Library Holdings: Bk Titles 69,000; Per Subs 200
Subject Interests: Genealogy, Local history
Automation Activity & Vendor Info: (Cataloging) Innovative Interfaces Inc.; (Circulation) Innovative Interfaces Inc.; (ILL) Innovative Interfaces Inc.; (OPAC) Innovative Interfaces Inc.; (Serials) Innovative Interfaces Inc.
Database Vendor: Innovative Interfaces INN - View
Mem of Pathfinder Regional Library Service System
Friends of the Library Group
Branches: 4
NATURITA BRANCH, Naturita Town Park, PO Box 466, Naturita, 81422. SAN 335-928X. Tel: 970-865-2848. *Librn*, Joan Swavely
OLATHE BRANCH, PO Box 756, Olathe, 81425-0756. SAN 335-931X.

Tel: 970-323-5601. *Librn*, Martha Macintosh
PARADOX BRANCH, Paradox Fire Sta, Paradox, 81429. SAN 335-9344. Tel: 970-859-7330. *Librn*, Enid Case
REDVALE BRANCH, 450 Redvale Rd, PO Box 64, Redvale, 81431. SAN 335-9379. Tel: 970-327-4387. *Librn*, Arlene Wilson

MOSCA

S US NATIONAL PARK SERVICE, Great Sand Dunes National Monument Library, 11999 Hwy 150, 81146. SAN 375-9318. Tel: 719-378-2312, Ext 221. Web Site: www.nps.gov/grsa/. *Librn*, Patrick Myers
Library Holdings: Bk Vols 2,000; Per Subs 10
Subject Interests: Biology, Botany, Natural history, Zoology

NEW CASTLE

P GARFIELD COUNTY PUBLIC LIBRARY SYSTEM,* PO Box 320, 81647-0320. SAN 335-9433. Tel: 970-984-2347. FAX: 970-984-2081. Web Site: www.colosys.net/garfield/index.htm. *Dir*, Jacilyn Spuhler; E-Mail: jspuhler@colosys.net; *Ref*, Sharon Puckett
Founded 1938. Pop 37,627; Circ 226,229
Library Holdings: Bk Vols 137,040
Subject Interests: Agriculture, Alternative sources (energy), Art, Colorado
Database Vendor: CARL
Mem of Three Rivers Regional Library Service System
Friends of the Library Group
Branches: 6
GLENWOOD SPRINGS BRANCH, 413 Ninth St, Glenwood Springs, 81601-3607. SAN 335-9492. Tel: 970-945-5958. FAX: 970-945-5958.
Library Holdings: Bk Vols 22,356
Friends of the Library Group
GORDON COOPER BRANCH, 76 S Fourth St, Carbondale, 81623-2014. SAN 335-9468. Tel: 970-963-2889. FAX: 970-963-2889. *Librn*, Marilyn Murphy
Library Holdings: Bk Vols 20,386
Friends of the Library Group
NEW CASTLE BRANCH, PO Box 320, 81647. SAN 373-5249. Tel: 970-984-2346. FAX: 970-984-2081. *Librn*, Jimmie Finnell
Library Holdings: Bk Vols 48,713
Friends of the Library Group
PARACHUTE BRANCH, 244 Grand Valley Way, Parachute, 81635-9608. SAN 335-9506. Tel: 970-285-9870. FAX: 970-285-9870. *Librn*, Holly Klinzman
Library Holdings: Bk Vols 11,656
Friends of the Library Group
RIFLE BRANCH, 107 E Second St, Rifle, 81650-2313. SAN 335-9522. Tel: 970-625-3471. FAX: 970-625-3471. *Librn*, Judy Martens
Library Holdings: Bk Vols 18,074
Friends of the Library Group
SILT BRANCH, PO Box 10, Silt, 81652-0010. SAN 335-9530. Tel: 970-876-5500. FAX: 970-876-5500. *Librn*, Diane Smith
Library Holdings: Bk Vols 9,723
Friends of the Library Group

NORWOOD

P SAN MIGUEL LIBRARY DISTRICT 2, Norwood Public Library, 1110 Lucerne St, PO Box 127, 81423-0127. SAN 376-2858. Tel: 970-327-4833. FAX: 970-327-4129. *Dir*, Barbara Youngblood
Library Holdings: Bk Vols 4,800; Bk Titles 2,500; Per Subs 18
Mem of Pathfinder Regional Library Service System
Friends of the Library Group

NUCLA

P NUCLA PUBLIC LIBRARY,* PO Box 129, 81424. SAN 301-9942. Tel: 970-864-2166. *Librn*, Gayle Alverado
Pop 1,027; Circ 6,500
Library Holdings: Bk Vols 6,500
Mem of Pathfinder Regional Library Service System
Friends of the Library Group

OAK CREEK

P OAK CREEK PUBLIC LIBRARY,* 227 Dodge Ave, PO Box 175, 80467-0175. SAN 336-0032. Tel: 970-736-8371. FAX: 970-736-8371. *Librn*, Lexie Iacovetto
Library Holdings: Bk Titles 4,215
Mem of Three Rivers Regional Library Service System
Friends of the Library Group

OLNEY SPRINGS

P LOUIS GOODRICH MEMORIAL LIBRARY, 403 Warner, 81062. (Mail add: PO Box 97, 81062-0097), SAN 301-9950. Tel: 719-267-3111. *Dir*, Adele R Chwalek; Tel: 202-319-4735, E-Mail: chwalek@cua.edu
Founded 1958. Pop 300
Library Holdings: Bk Vols 2,000
Open Tues 7pm-8pm & Sat 1-5
Friends of the Library Group

ORDWAY

P ORDWAY PUBLIC LIBRARY,* 105 E Fourth St, 81063-1316. SAN 301-9969. Tel: 719-267-3823. *Librn*, Barbara Henry; Tel: 202-319-5091, Fax: 202-319-4735, E-Mail: henry@cua.edu
Circ 4,154
Library Holdings: Bk Vols 6,700; Bk Titles 6,300
Mem of Arkansas Valley Regional Library Service System
Friends of the Library Group

OURAY

P OURAY PUBLIC LIBRARY,* 320 Sixth Ave, PO Box 625, 81427-0625. SAN 301-9985. Tel: 970-325-4616. *Librn*, Mary Ann Dismant
Pop 1,046; Circ 12,000
Library Holdings: Bk Vols 11,100

OVID

P OVID PUBLIC LIBRARY,* 213 Main St, PO Box 245, 80744-0245. SAN 301-9993. Tel: 970-463-5524. *Librn*, Caroline Peterson
Founded 1927. Pop 350; Circ 1,142
Library Holdings: Bk Vols 5,050
Mem of High Plains Regional Library Service System
Open Tues 2-5, Thurs 4-6

PAGOSA SPRINGS

P SISSON MEMORIAL LIBRARY,* PO Box 849, 81147. SAN 302-0002. Tel: 970-264-2209. FAX: 970-264-4764. *Dir*, Lenore Bright; E-Mail: lbright@frontier.net
Founded 1960. Pop 10,000; Circ 60,000
1999-2000 Income $297,235
Library Holdings: Bk Titles 24,965; Per Subs 48
Special Collections: Hershey Coll (Southwest Literature); Southwest Coll
Automation Activity & Vendor Info: (Cataloging) Follett
Mem of Southwest Regional Library Service System
Partic in Santa Clarita Interlibrary Network
Special Services for the Blind - Bks on cassette
Friends of the Library Group

PENROSE

P PENROSE COMMUNITY LIBRARY,* 415 Fourth Ave, 81240-0318. SAN 376-4966. Tel: 719-372-0606. FAX: 719-372-9226. *Dir*, Kristi Lindsey
Library Holdings: Bk Vols 12,000; Bk Titles 8,500; Per Subs 27
Mem of Arkansas Valley Regional Library Service System
Friends of the Library Group

PETERSON AFB

UNITED STATES AIR FORCE
A PETERSON AIR FORCE BASE LIBRARY FL2500, 21 SVS'SVMG, 201 W Stewart Ave Bldg 1171, 80914-1600. SAN 335-976X. Tel: 719-556-7462. FAX: 719-556-6752. E-Mail: svrl@tdka.afsv.af.mil. *Librn*, Kathleen Kucharski
Founded 1950
Library Holdings: Bk Vols 40,000; Per Subs 200
Subject Interests: Aeronautics, Business and management, Space science

PINE

P PINE PUBLIC LIBRARY,* 16720 Hwy 126, 80470. SAN 378-018X. Tel: 303-838-6093. *Librn*, Eleanor Miller
Library Holdings: Bk Titles 6,000; Per Subs 12
Partic in Central Colorado Library System

PLATTEVILLE

P PLATTEVILLE PUBLIC LIBRARY,* 504 Marion Ave, PO Box 567, 80651-0567. SAN 302-0010. Tel: 970-785-2231. FAX: 970-785-0708. Web Site: www.weld.lib.co.us/plattevil.html. *Dir*, Dianne Norgren; E-Mail: dianne.n@usa.net; *Asst Librn*, Donna Galusha

Founded 1932. Pop 2,500; Circ 20,000
Library Holdings: Bk Vols 16,000
Subject Interests: World War II
Mem of High Plains Regional Library Service System
Partic in Weld Libr District

PUEBLO

P ARKANSAS VALLEY REGIONAL LIBRARY SERVICE SYSTEM,* 635 W Corona, Ste 113, 81004. SAN 302-0029. Tel: 719-542-2156. FAX: 719-542-3155. Web Site: www.uscolo.edu/arkvally. *Dir*, Donna Jones Morris; E-Mail: dmorris@uscolo.edu
Founded 1972. Pop 240,875
Oct 1999-Sep 2000 Income $396,941, State $342,391, Locally Generated Income $54,550. Mats Exp $21,000, Books $20,000, Per/Ser (Incl. Access Fees) $1,000. Sal $175,012 (Prof $92,106)
Special Collections: Professional, Children's Preview
Member Libraries: Aguilar Public Library; Baca County Public Library; Buena Vista Public Library; Canon City Public Library; Carnegie Public Library; Colorado Department Of Corrections; Colorado Department Of Corrections; Department Of Veterans Affairs; Florence Public Library; Fowler Public Library; Kiowa County Public Library; La Veta Public Library; Lamar Community College; Lamar Public Library; Las Animas-Bent County Public Library; Lower Arkansas Valley Regional Library; Manzanola Public Library; Ordway Public Library; Otero Junior College; Penrose Community Library; Pueblo Community College Library; Pueblo Library District; Rocky Ford Public Library; Salida Regional Library; Spanish Peaks Library District; Trinidad State Junior College; University of Southern Colorado Library; West Custer County Library District; Woodruff Memorial Library

G CITY OF PUEBLO MUNICIPAL REFERENCE LIBRARY,* 211 East D St, 81003. SAN 326-0488. Tel: 719-543-6006. FAX: 719-543-0572. *Librn*, Don R Vest; E-Mail: donvest@iex.net
Founded 1960
Library Holdings: Bk Titles 2,500; Per Subs 10
Subject Interests: Local government
Publications: Pueblo Quarterly Economic Indicators (data book)
Special Services for the Deaf - TTY machine

P COLORADO DEPARTMENT OF CORRECTIONS, San Carlos Correctional Facility Library, PO Box 3, 81003. SAN 376-5792. Tel: 719-544-4800. FAX: 719-583-5510. E-Mail: sccflib@amigo.net. *Librn*, Jerome Halpin
Library Holdings: Bk Titles 4,500; Per Subs 35

COLORADO MENTAL HEALTH INSTITUTE OF PUEBLO

GM HOSPITAL COMMUNITY LIBRARY, 1600 W 24th St, 81003. SAN 335-9794. Tel: 719-546-4197. FAX: 719-546-4484. *Librn*, Carol Ann Smith; E-Mail: carol.smith@state.co.us
Jul 1997-Jun 1998 Income $6,853. Mats Exp $6,702, Books $3,000, Per/Ser (Incl. Access Fees) $950, AV Equip $1,552, Other Print Mats $200
Library Holdings: Bk Vols 10,945; Bk Titles 9,192; Per Subs 52

GM PROFESSIONAL LIBRARY, 1600 W 24th St, 81003. SAN 335-9824. Tel: 719-546-4677. FAX: 719-546-4484. *Librn*, Carol Ann Smith; E-Mail: carol.smith@state.co.us
Founded 1925
Jul 1997-Jun 1998 Income $22,996. Mats Exp $17,750, Books $2,300, Per/Ser (Incl. Access Fees) $14,950. Sal $59,200 (Prof $32,400)
Library Holdings: Bk Vols 6,490; Bk Titles 5,695; Per Subs 118
Subject Interests: Medicine, Psychiatry, Psychology, Social sciences and issues
Restriction: Open to public with supervision only
Partic in BRS; Colorado Council Of Medical Librarians; Nat Libr of Med

M PARKVIEW EPISCOPAL MEDICAL CENTER, Medical Library,* 400 W 16th St, 81003-2729. SAN 302-0037. Tel: 719-584-4582. *Librn*, Alma Williams
Founded 1959
Library Holdings: Bk Vols 3,000; Per Subs 136
Subject Interests: Nursing, Obstetrics and gynecology, Respiratory diseases
Publications: Acquisitions List
Partic in Arkansas Valley Regional Library Service System (AVRLSS); Nat Libr of Med
Serves college students in AA & LPN programs in Respiratory Therapy & Radiological Technology & Laboratory School of Technology

S PUEBLO CHIEFTAIN NEWSPAPER LIBRARY,* 825 W Sixth St, PO Box 4040, 81003. SAN 323-570X. Tel: 719-544-3520, Ext 491. FAX: 719-544-5897. E-Mail: library@chieftain.com. Web Site: www.chieftain.com. *Librn*, Margie Strescino
Special Collections: The Pueblo Chieftain 1868 to present; The Star Journal 1946-1984
All holdings on microfilm

J PUEBLO COMMUNITY COLLEGE LIBRARY,* 900 W Orman Ave, 81004-1430. SAN 325-2264. Tel: 719-549-3308. FAX: 719-549-3309. Web Site: www.pcc.cccoes.edu/library/. *Librn*, W Jeanne Gardner; E-Mail: jeanne.gardner@pcc.cccoes.edu; *Tech Servs*, Kerry Cook; *Circ*, Ruth Mahoney; *Asst Librn, Circ*, Effie Romero; *Ref*, Michael Thomason; Staff 5 (MLS 2, Non-MLS 3)
Founded 1979. Enrl 4,275; Fac 94
Jul 1997-Jun 1998 Income $277,491. Mats Exp $82,684, Books $25,439, Per/Ser (Incl. Access Fees) $18,464, Presv $1,998, Micro $4,504, AV Equip $3,642. Sal $152,266 (Prof $78,896)
Library Holdings: Bk Vols 23,993; Bk Titles 20,467; Per Subs 211
Subject Interests: Criminal justice, Dental hygiene
Special Collections: College Archives
Publications: Periodical List
Mem of Arkansas Valley Regional Library Service System
Partic in Peaks & Valleys Library Consortium

P PUEBLO LIBRARY DISTRICT, McClelland Public Library, 701 Court St, 81003-4290. SAN 335-9859. Tel: 719-562-5600. FAX: 719-562-5610. Web Site: www.pueblolibrary.org. *Exec Dir*, Charles E Bates; Tel: 719-562-5607, Fax: 719-562-5609, E-Mail: cebates@pueblo.lib.co.us; *Mgr*, Jerry King; Tel: 719-562-5652, Fax: 719-562-5655, E-Mail: kingj@pueblo.lib.co.us; *Mgr*, Helen Tomicich; Tel: 719-562-5632, Fax: 719-562-5619, E-Mail: helent@pueblo.lib.co.us; *Commun Relations*, Joanne Dodds; Tel: 719-562-5605, Fax: 719-562-5619, E-Mail: jdodds@pueblo.lib.co.us; *Ad Servs*, Charles T Turner; Tel: 719-562-5624, E-Mail: charles@pueblo.lib.co.us; *YA Servs*, Jan Irving; *Circ*, Heinz Bergann; Tel: 719-562-5621, E-Mail: hbergann@pueblo.lib.co.us; *Tech Servs*, Barbara Carol; Tel: 719-562-5629, E-Mail: bcarol@pueblo.lib.co.us; *ILL*, Mary Margaret Lucero; Tel: 719-562-5637, E-Mail: mmlucero@mail.pueblo.lib.co.us; *Tech Coordr*, Ben Taylor; Tel: 719-562-5622, Fax: 719-562-5620, E-Mail: btaylor@pueblo.lib.co.us; *Res*, Richard Tucey; Tel: 719-562-5627, Fax: 719-562-5619, E-Mail: richard@pueblo.lib.co.us; *Govt Doc*, Melissa Blackmore; Tel: 719-562-5601, E-Mail: melissa@pueblo.lib.co.us; *Spec Coll*, Noreen Riffe; Tel: 719-562-5625, E-Mail: noreen@pueblo.lib.co.us; *Publ Servs*, Richard Lee; Tel: 719-562-5625, Fax: 719-562-5635, E-Mail: richardl@pueblo.lib.co.us; Staff 97 (MLS 17, Non-MLS 80)
Founded 1891. Pop 136,311; Circ 850,365
Library Holdings: Bk Vols 365,422; Per Subs 690
Subject Interests: Genealogy, Hispanic studies, Local history
Special Collections: Business (Frank I Lamb Memorial Coll); Western-American History (Western Research Coll)
Automation Activity & Vendor Info: (Cataloging) DRA; (Circulation) DRA; (OPAC) DRA; (Serials) DRA
Database Vendor: DRA, GaleNet, IAC - Info Trac, OCLC - First Search, ProQuest
Publications: Monthly Calendar of Events; Pueblo County Health & Human Services Directory
Mem of Arkansas Valley Regional Library Service System
Partic in Peaks & Valleys Library Consortium
Special Services for the Deaf - TTY machine
Friends of the Library Group
Branches: 3
FRANK & MARIE BARKMAN BRANCH, 1300 Jerry Murphy Rd, 81001-1858. SAN 335-9883. Tel: 719-562-5680. FAX: 719-562-5685. Web Site: www.pueblo.lib.co.us. *In Charge*, Ronda Gettel; E-Mail: rond@pueblo.lib.co.us; Staff 9 (MLS 2, Non-MLS 7)
Library Holdings: Bk Vols 51,612
Database Vendor: DRA
Friends of the Library Group
FRANK I LAMB BRANCH, 2525 S Pueblo Blvd, 81005-2700. SAN 322-5801. Tel: 719-562-5680. FAX: 719-562-5685. Web Site: www.pueblo.lib.co.us. *In Charge*, Kathleen Knox
Library Holdings: Bk Vols 41,886
Database Vendor: DRA
Friends of the Library Group
MAHLON THATCHER WHITE BRANCH, 298 S Joe Martinez Blvd, Pueblo West, 81007-2740. SAN 377-6360. Tel: 719-562-5660. FAX: 719-562-5665. Web Site: www.pueblolibrary.org. *In Charge*, Betsy Berg
Founded 1997
Library Holdings: Bk Vols 25,557
Database Vendor: DRA
Friends of the Library Group
Bookmobiles: 2

M SAINT MARY CORWIN HOSPITAL, Finney Memorial Library, 1008 Minnequa Ave, 81004-9988. SAN 302-0045. Tel: 719-560-5598. FAX: 719-560-4646, 719-564-3018. Web Site: www.uscolo.edu/smc/. *Asst Librn*, Shannon O'Grady; E-Mail: shannono'grady@centura.org
Founded 1818
Library Holdings: Bk Vols 400; Per Subs 100
Subject Interests: Cardiology, Internal medicine, Nursing, Obstetrics and gynecology, Oncology, Pediatrics, Surgery
Partic in Arkansas Valley Regional Library Service System (AVRLSS)

C UNIVERSITY OF SOUTHERN COLORADO LIBRARY, 2200 Bonforte Blvd, 81001-4901. SAN 302-0053. Tel: 719-549-2361. Interlibrary Loan Service Tel: 719-549-2362. FAX: 719-549-2738. Web Site: www.uscolo.edu/library. *Dean of Libr*, Beverly Moore; E-Mail: moore@uscolo.edu; *Chair*, Tony Moffeit; *Acq, Coll Develop*, Dan Sullivan; *Cat, Circ*, Gayle Abrahamson; *Commun Servs, Doc, Ref*, Ann Kuntzman; *Per*, Margaret

Kleszynski; *Bibliog Instr*, Rhonda Gonzalez; Staff 9 (MLS 9)
Founded 1933. Enrl 4,000; Fac 185; Highest Degree: Master
Library Holdings: Bk Vols 199,748; Per Subs 1,257
Special Collections: University Archives; US Western History, pamphlets, bks
Automation Activity & Vendor Info: (Acquisitions) epixtech, inc.; (Cataloging) epixtech, inc.; (Circulation) epixtech, inc.
Mem of Arkansas Valley Regional Library Service System
Partic in Peaks & Valleys Library Consortium

RANGELY

J COLORADO NORTHWESTERN COMMUNITY COLLEGE LIBRARY,* 500 Kennedy Dr, 81648-3502. SAN 302-0061. Tel: 970-675-3229. FAX: 970-675-3267. *Actg Dir*, Deborah Reynolds; E-Mail: dreynolds@chcc.cc.co.us; Staff 1 (MLS 1)
Founded 1962. Enrl 350; Fac 45
Library Holdings: Bk Vols 21,625; Per Subs 105
Subject Interests: Aviation, Criminal law and justice
Mem of Three Rivers Regional Library Service System

P RANGELY REGIONAL LIBRARY,* 109 E Main, 81648-2737. SAN 302-007X. Tel: 970-675-8811. FAX: 970-675-8811. *Dir*, Lorna Heath
Founded 1960. Pop 2,400; Circ 13,000
Library Holdings: Bk Vols 28,200; Per Subs 25
Mem of Three Rivers Regional Library Service System
Open Mon 1-8pm, Tues-Thurs 10am-8pm, Fri 10am-6pm & Sat 10am-3pm

RIFLE

S RIFLE CORRECTIONAL FACILITY,* 0200 County Rd 219, 81650. SAN 327-7666. Tel: 970-625-1700. FAX: 970-625-1706. *Mgr*, Warren Leonard
Library Holdings: Bk Vols 1,200; Per Subs 13
Mem of Three Rivers Regional Library Service System

ROCKY FORD

P ROCKY FORD PUBLIC LIBRARY,* 400 S Tenth St, 81067. SAN 302-0096. Tel: 719-254-6641. *Dir*, Marilyn S Dean
Founded 1905. Pop 10,000; Circ 41,253
Library Holdings: Bk Vols 23,500; Bk Titles 19,000; Per Subs 48
Mem of Arkansas Valley Regional Library Service System

SAGUACHE

P SAGUACHE COUNTY PUBLIC LIBRARY,* Eighth & Pitkin Ave, PO Box 448, 81149-0448. SAN 335-9913. Tel: 719-655-2551. FAX: 719-655-2579. *Dir*, Charlotte McKee
Founded 1950. Circ 16,000
Jan 1998-Dec 1998 Income $87,545, State $3,274, City $2,000, County $80,000, Other $654. Mats Exp $6,000, Books $4,000, Per/Ser (Incl. Access Fees) $2,000. Sal $62,819 (Prof $21,769)
Library Holdings: Bk Vols 20,000; Per Subs 52
Subject Interests: American history, Colorado
Special Collections: American History & Memorials; Bicentennial History; Colorado & Southwest History; Cookbooks; Juvenile; Saguache & Saguache County; Southwest Fiction & Nonfiction
Automation Activity & Vendor Info: (Cataloging) Sagebrush Corporation; (Circulation) Sagebrush Corporation
Mem of Southwest Regional Library Service System
Friends of the Library Group
Branches: 1
CENTER LIBRARY, 400 S Worth, Center, 81125-0306. SAN 335-9948. Tel: 719-754-3156. FAX: 719-655-2579. *Dir*, Charlotte McKee
Subject Interests: Fiction
Friends of the Library Group
Bookmobiles: 1. Librn, Willis Bennett. Bk titles 500

SALIDA

P SALIDA REGIONAL LIBRARY,* 405 E St, 81201-2642. SAN 302-010X. Tel: 719-539-4826. FAX: 719-539-2318. *Dir*, Jeff Donlan; *Ch Servs, ILL*, Becky Nelson
Circ 59,370
Library Holdings: Bk Vols 18,500; Per Subs 173
Subject Interests: Local history
Special Collections: Sheet Music Coll of several thousand titles
Publications: Library Information Brochure
Mem of Arkansas Valley Regional Library Service System
Friends of the Library Group

SAN LUIS

P COSTILLA COUNTY LIBRARY,* PO Box 351, 81152. SAN 302-0118. Tel: 719-672-3309. *Dir*, Jessica Aragon
Founded 1972. Pop 3,400
Library Holdings: Bk Titles 5,941; Per Subs 22
Special Collections: Bilingual (Children; Bilingual-Bicultural); Literature (Adult Spanish Book); Minority Studies (Southwest Chicano); Solar Energy Coll
Mem of Southwest Regional Library Service System

SECURITY

P SECURITY PUBLIC LIBRARY,* 715 Aspen Dr, 80911-1807. SAN 302-0126. Tel: 719-391-3191. FAX: 719-392-7641. E-Mail: hudson@wsd3.k12.co.us. Web Site: www.wsd3.k12.co.us/spl/. *Dir*, Barbara Hudson; *Ch Servs*, Erma Gallob; *ILL, Ref*, Susan Garrett; E-Mail: garretts@wsd3.k12.co.us; Staff 1 (Non-MLS 1)
Founded 1961. Pop 40,000; Circ 140,000
Library Holdings: Bk Titles 56,000; Per Subs 120
Subject Interests: Colorado
Publications: Newsletter (monthly)
Mem of Plains & Peaks Regional Library System
Open Mon-Thurs 10-8, Fri & Sat 9-5
Friends of the Library Group

SILVERTON

P SILVERTON PUBLIC LIBRARY,* 1117 Reese, PO Box 68, 81433-0068. SAN 302-0142. Tel: 970-387-5770. FAX: 970-387-0217. *Dir*, Jackie Leithauser; E-Mail: jleithau@frontier.net
Founded 1901. Pop 800; Circ 8,700
Library Holdings: Bk Titles 12,000; Per Subs 21
Subject Interests: Local history
Mem of Southwest Regional Library Service System
Friends of the Library Group

SNOWMASS

SR SAINT BENEDICT'S MONASTERY LIBRARY, 1012 Monastery Rd, 81654. SAN 302-0150. Tel: 970-927-3311, Ext 40. FAX: 970-927-3399. *Librn*, Father William Meninger
Founded 1958
Library Holdings: Bk Vols 8,000
Subject Interests: Religion, Theology

SPRINGFIELD

P BACA COUNTY PUBLIC LIBRARY,* 733 Main St, 81073-1542. SAN 302-0169. Tel: 719-523-6962. FAX: 719-523-6962. *Librn*, Beulah Collins
Founded 1925. Circ 6,000
Library Holdings: Bk Vols 9,500
Mem of Arkansas Valley Regional Library Service System

STEAMBOAT SPRINGS

J COLORADO MOUNTAIN COLLEGE-ALPINE CAMPUS LIBRARY,* 1330-50 Bob Adams Dr, 80487. (Mail add: PO Box 774688, 80477), Tel: 970-870-4445. FAX: 970-870-4490. *Librn*, Margaret E Dorr; Tel: 970-870-4451, E-Mail: mdorr@cmc1.coloradomtn.edu; *ILL*, Kristin Weber; Tel: 970-870-4449; Staff 3 (MLS 2, Non-MLS 1)
Founded 1983. Enrl 600; Fac 16
1999-2000 Income $186,500, State $46,500, County $92,000, Locally Generated Income $46,500, Other $1,500. Mats Exp $47,500, Books $25,000, Per/Ser (Incl. Access Fees) $20,000, Electronic Ref Mat (Incl. Access Fees) $2,500. Sal $128,233 (Prof $47,160)
Library Holdings: Bk Vols 20,000; Bk Titles 19,200; Per Subs 210
Subject Interests: Resort mgt, Ski bus, Small business
Special Collections: Colorado State Documents
Automation Activity & Vendor Info: (Circulation) CARL
Publications: Steamboat Pilot Index
Mem of Three Rivers Regional Library Service System
Open Sun 2-10, Mon-Thurs 8-10 & Fri-Sat 8-5

P BUD WERNER MEMORIAL LIBRARY,* 1289 Lincoln Ave, 80487. SAN 335-9972. Tel: 970-879-0240. FAX: 970-879-3476. Web Site: www.marmot.org/bud. *Dir*, Christine Painter; E-Mail: cpainter@marmot.org; *Ref*, Lauren Stara; E-Mail: lstara@marmot.org; Staff 15 (MLS 3, Non-MLS 12)
Founded 1967. Pop 12,050; Circ 234,260
Jan 1998-Dec 1998 Income $769,276, Locally Generated Income $92,230. Mats Exp $145,726, Books $85,965, Per/Ser (Incl. Access Fees) $17,345, Presv $5,473, AV Equip $22,699, Electronic Ref Mat (Incl. Access Fees) $14,244. Sal $348,238 (Prof $77,973)
Library Holdings: Bk Vols 50,000; Per Subs 214

Special Collections: Western Coll
Automation Activity & Vendor Info: (Circulation) CARL; (OPAC) CARL
Mem of Three Rivers Regional Library Service System
Partic in Marmot Western Colo Libr Network; OCLC Online Computer Library Center, Inc

STERLING

J NORTHEASTERN JUNIOR COLLEGE, Monahan Library, 100 College Dr, 80751-2399. SAN 302-0177. Tel: 970-521-6600, Ext 6612. Reference Tel: 970-521-6663. FAX: 970-521-6759. Web Site: nejc.cc.co.us/library/library.html. *Dir*, Candace Havely; Tel: 970-521-6721, E-Mail: candace.havely@njc.cccoes.edu; Staff 9 (MLS 1, Non-MLS 8)
Founded 1941. Enrl 1,795; Fac 95
Library Holdings: Bk Vols 33,691; Per Subs 236
Subject Interests: Colorado
Database Vendor: CARL, IAC - Info Trac, ProQuest
Publications: Video/film catalog
Mem of High Plains Regional Library Service System
Open Mon-Thurs 8-10, Fri 8-5, Sun 3-10

P STERLING PUBLIC LIBRARY,* Centennial Sq, 80751-3399. SAN 302-0185. Tel: 970-522-2023. FAX: 970-522-2657. Web Site: www.sterlingcolo.com. *Librn*, Sandy VanDusen; Staff 1 (MLS 1)
Founded 1918. Pop 17,000; Circ 98,000
Library Holdings: Bk Titles 57,000; Per Subs 125
Special Collections: Aviation Coll; Western History (Otto C Unfug Coll & T M Rogers Coll)
Mem of High Plains Regional Library Service System
Friends of the Library Group

STRASBURG

S COMANCHE CROSSING MUSEUM LIBRARY,* PO Box 647, 80136. SAN 375-1376. Tel: 303-622-4690. *Curator*, Sandy Miller
1997-1998 Mats Exp $500

STRATTON

P STRATTON PUBLIC LIBRARY,* 331 New York Ave, PO Box 267, 80836-0267. SAN 302-0193. Tel: 719-348-5922. FAX: 719-348-5922. *In Charge*, Ester Lewis
Pop 500; Circ 5,420
Library Holdings: Bk Vols 3,350
Mem of High Plains Regional Library Service System

TELLURIDE

P SAN MIGUEL COUNTY PUBLIC LIBRARY DISTRICT NO 1, Wilkinson Public Library, 100 W Pacific Ave, 81435-2189. (Mail add: PO Box 2189, 81435), SAN 302-0215. Tel: 970-728-4519. FAX: 970-728-3340. Web Site: www.telluride.lib.co.us. *Dir*, Robin Magee; E-Mail: robinmac@csn.net; Staff 9 (MLS 2, Non-MLS 7)
Founded 1975. Pop 5,550; Circ 84,970
Library Holdings: Bk Vols 20,650; Per Subs 163
Special Collections: Books about Film; Classic Movie Video Coll
Automation Activity & Vendor Info: (OPAC) CARL
Mem of Pathfinder Regional Library Service System
Open Mon-Thurs 10-8, Fri & Sat 10-6, Sun 12-5
Friends of the Library Group

THORNTON

P ADAMS COUNTY LIBRARY SYSTEM, Administration, 8992 N Washington, 80229-4537. SAN 335-9557. Tel: 303-288-2001. FAX: 303-286-8467. *Dir*, Nancy K Buchanan
Founded 1953. Pop 213,000; Circ 826,000
Jan 1999-Dec 1999 Income (Main Library and Branch Library) $2,443,359, State $13,765, County $2,299,594, Locally Generated Income $130,000. Mats Exp $229,797, Books $203,555, Per/Ser (Incl. Access Fees) $23,045, Micro $3,197. Sal $1,677,099 (Prof $687,002)
Library Holdings: Bk Vols 344,000; Bk Titles 174,000; Per Subs 224; High Interest/Low Vocabulary Bk Vols 1,900
Subject Interests: Colorado, Poetry
Automation Activity & Vendor Info: (Cataloging) epixtech, inc.; (Circulation) epixtech, inc.; (OPAC) epixtech, inc.
Mem of Cent Colorado Libr Syst
Friends of the Library Group
Branches: 7
BENNETT BRANCH, 495 Seventh St, PO Box 332, Bennett, 80102-0332. SAN 335-9581. Tel: 303-644-3303. FAX: 303-893-1640. *Librn*, Jim Houston
BRIGHTON BRANCH, 575 S Eighth Ave, Brighton, 80601-3122. SAN 335-9611. Tel: 303-659-2572. FAX: 303-654-0793. *Librn*, Dodie Stewart
COMMERCE CITY BRANCH, 7185 Monaco, Commerce City, 80022-2051. SAN 335-9646. Tel: 303-287-0063. FAX: 303-289-6313. *Librn*, Annette Martinez
NORTHGLENN BRANCH, 10530 N Huron, Northglenn, 80234-4011. SAN 335-9670. Tel: 303-452-7534. FAX: 303-450-2578.
Subject Interests: Poetry
PERL MACK, 7611 Hilltop Circle, Denver, 80221. SAN 335-9700. Tel: 303-428-3576. FAX: 303-428-1358. *Librn*, Ruth DeChant
Subject Interests: Computer science
STRASBURG BRANCH, c/o Bennett Branch, PO Box 332, Bennett, 80102-0332. SAN 325-4089. Tel: 303-622-4268. *Librn*, Jim Houston
THORNTON BRANCH, 8992 N Washington, 80229. SAN 335-9735. Tel: 303-287-2514. FAX: 303-286-8467.
Subject Interests: Colorado
Bookmobiles: 1

M NORTH SUBURBAN MEDICAL CENTER LIBRARY, 9191 Grant St, 80229. SAN 377-8797. Tel: 303-450-3568. FAX: 303-450-4504. *Librn*, Jenny Garcia; E-Mail: jenny.garcia@healthonecares.com; Staff 1 (MLS 1)
Jul 1998-Jun 1999 Mats Exp $6,500, Books $3,000, Per/Ser (Incl. Access Fees) $3,500
Library Holdings: Bk Titles 300; Per Subs 23
Partic in Cnt Colo Libr Syst; Colorado Council Of Medical Librarians; Medical Libr Asn; Mid Continental Med Libr Asn

C PARKS COLLEGE LIBRARY, Jay Johnson Memorial Library, 9065 Grant St, 80229. SAN 377-466X. Tel: 303-457-2757. FAX: 303-457-4030. *Pres*, Catherine Knox; *Librn*, Jane Watson. Subject Specialists: *Music*, Jane Watson
Library Holdings: Bk Vols 5,000; Bk Titles 1,200; Per Subs 31

TRINIDAD

P CARNEGIE PUBLIC LIBRARY,* 202 N Animas St, 81082. SAN 302-0223. Tel: 719-846-6841. FAX: 719-846-0885. *Dir*, Sara Murphy; *Ch Servs*, Judy Veris-Decker; *Tech Servs*, Shaleen Martinez; *ILL*, Martinez Carmen
Founded 1882. Pop 10,000; Circ 173,507
Jan 1998-Dec 1999 Income $150,000, City $109,000, County $6,000. Mats Exp $30,000, Books $18,000, Per/Ser (Incl. Access Fees) $2,000, Micro $1,000
Library Holdings: Bk Titles 31,000; Per Subs 108
Subject Interests: Genealogy, Local history
Mem of Arkansas Valley Regional Library Service System
Friends of the Library Group

J TRINIDAD STATE JUNIOR COLLEGE, Samuel Freudenthal Memorial Library, 600 Prospect, 81082. SAN 302-0231. Tel: 719-846-5593. FAX: 719-846-5667, 719-846-7343. Web Site: www.tsjc.cccoes.edu/library/. *Dir*, Craig Larson; *ILL*, Evelyn Rios; Staff 1 (MLS 1)
Founded 1925. Enrl 2,009; Fac 127
Library Holdings: Bk Titles 52,000; Per Subs 154
Subject Interests: Law enforcement, Local history, Nursing
Automation Activity & Vendor Info: (Cataloging) CARL
Database Vendor: CARL
Mem of Arkansas Valley Regional Library Service System
Partic in Colorado Alliance Of Research Libraries

USAF ACADEMY

C UNITED STATES AIR FORCE ACADEMY LIBRARY,* 2354 Fairchild Dr, Ste 3A10, 80840-6214. SAN 336-0067. Tel: 719-333-2590. FAX: 719-333-2999, 719-333-4754. Web Site: www.usafa.af.mil/dfsel. *Dir*, Edward A Scott; E-Mail: edward.scott@usafa.af.mil; *Assoc Dir*, Steven E Maffeo; E-Mail: steven.maffeo@usafa.af.mil; *Cat*, Rita A Jones; Tel: 719-333-4783, E-Mail: rita.jones@usafa.af.mil; *Acq*, Alice R Roy; Tel: 719-333-4654, E-Mail: alice.roy@usafa.af.mil; *Ref*, Sue E Neufeld; Tel: 719-333-4406, E-Mail: sue.neufeld@usafa.af.mil; *Spec Coll*, Duane J Reed; Tel: 719-333-6919, E-Mail: duane.reed.usafa.af.mil; *Online Servs*, M Douglas Johnson; E-Mail: douglas.johnson@usafa.af.mil; Staff 57 (MLS 17, Non-MLS 40)
Founded 1955. Enrl 4,100; Fac 530; Highest Degree: Bachelor
Oct 1998-Sep 1999 Income Parent Institution $2,716,749. Mats Exp $854,524, Books $347,700, Per/Ser (Incl. Access Fees) $480,600, Micro $24,710, AV Equip $1,514. Sal $1,612,200 (Prof $915,434)
Library Holdings: Bk Vols 712,200; Bk Titles 3,232,365; Per Subs 1,676
Subject Interests: Aviation, Military history
Special Collections: Aeronautics Hist before 1910 (Col Richard Gimbel Coll); US Air Force Academy Archives
Automation Activity & Vendor Info: (Acquisitions) epixtech, inc.; (Cataloging) epixtech, inc.; (Circulation) epixtech, inc.; (Course Reserve) epixtech, inc.; (ILL) epixtech, inc.; (Media Booking) epixtech, inc.; (OPAC) epixtech, inc.; (Serials) epixtech, inc.
Restriction: Staff use only, Students only
Partic in BCR; MECC; Merlin
Friends of the Library Group

Departmental Libraries:
COMMUNITY CENTER, 5136 Red Tail, Ste H103, 80841. SAN 336-0091. Tel: 719-333-4665. *Librn*, Christine Bowman
Library Holdings: Bk Vols 31,000; Per Subs 102
LAW
Library Holdings: Bk Vols 4,486
CM MEDICAL (SGAL), USAF Acad, 4310 Pinion Dr, 80840-4000. SAN 336-0156. Tel: 719-333-5107. *Librn*, Jeanne Entze
Library Holdings: Bk Vols 5,128; Per Subs 300

VAIL

S COLORADO SKI MUSEUM - SKI HALL OF FAME, Library & Research Center, 231 S Frontage Rd E, PO Box 1976, 81658. SAN 371-8263. Tel: 970-476-1876. FAX: 970-476-1879. E-Mail: skimuse@vail.net. Web Site: www.vailsoft.com/museum/. *Exec Dir*, Marjorie Plath
Founded 1990
Library Holdings: Bk Titles 500; Per Subs 300

P VAIL PUBLIC LIBRARY,* 292 W Meadow Dr, 81657. SAN 302-024X. Tel: 970-479-2184. FAX: 970-479-2192. *Dir*, Annie Fox; *Asst Dir, Coll Develop*, Susan Boyd; E-Mail: susann@teal.csm.org; *Ad Servs, Ch Servs*, Annie Murray
Founded 1972. Pop 18,500; Circ 53,007
Library Holdings: Bk Titles 50,000; Per Subs 201
Special Collections: Mountain Environment (Alpine Coll); Skiing Coll
Publications: Friends of Library
Mem of Three Rivers Regional Library Service System
Friends of the Library Group

VICTOR

P VICTOR PUBLIC LIBRARY,* 124 S Third St, PO Box 5, 80860. SAN 302-0258. Tel: 719-689-2011. FAX: 719-689-3157. *Librn*, Belinda Brown
Circ 15,000
Library Holdings: Bk Vols 10,000
Special Collections: Colorado Local History Coll
Mem of Plains & Peaks Regional Library System

WALDEN

P JACKSON COUNTY PUBLIC LIBRARY,* 412 Fourth St, PO Box 398, 80480-0398. SAN 302-0266. Tel: 970-723-4602. FAX: 970-723-4602. *Dir*, Carol Jean Wofford
Founded 1954. Pop 1,700; Circ 17,423
Library Holdings: Bk Vols 14,842; Bk Titles 14,774; Per Subs 40
Subject Interests: Local history
Publications: Library Journal
Mem of Three Rivers Regional Library Service System
Friends of the Library Group

WALSENBURG

P SPANISH PEAKS LIBRARY DISTRICT, 323 Main St, 81089-1842. SAN 302-0274. Tel: 719-738-2774. FAX: 719-738-2468. E-Mail: spld@spld.org. Web Site: www.spld.org. *Dir*, Rebecca McPhearson; *Circ*, John Thomas
Founded 1906. Pop 6,600; Circ 8,124
Library Holdings: Bk Vols 14,000; Bk Titles 12,650; Per Subs 20
Mem of Arkansas Valley Regional Library Service System
Friends of the Library Group

WELLINGTON

P WELLINGTON PUBLIC LIBRARY,* 3800 Wilson Ave, PO Box 416, 80549. SAN 370-6710. Tel: 970-568-3040. FAX: 970-568-9713. *Librn*, Diane Montgomery; E-Mail: dmontgom@csn.net
Founded 1980. Pop 2,500; Circ 14,002
Library Holdings: Bk Titles 11,000; Per Subs 40
Open Mon 10am-8pm, Tues & Thurs 1-6pm, Wed 4-8pm & Fri-Sat 9am-noon
Friends of the Library Group

WESTCLIFFE

P WEST CUSTER COUNTY LIBRARY DISTRICT,* 209 Main St, 81252. SAN 302-0290. Tel: 719-783-9138. FAX: 719-783-2155. *Dir*, Marty Frick
Founded 1939. Pop 2,300; Circ 3,100
Library Holdings: Bk Titles 10,991
Special Collections: Local History
Mem of Arkansas Valley Regional Library Service System
Friends of the Library Group

WESTMINSTER

S ARABIAN HORSE TRUST LIBRARY & SPECIAL COLLECTIONS,* 12000 Zuni St, 80234. SAN 329-1014. Tel: 303-450-4710. FAX: 303-450-4707. E-Mail: arabiantrust@earthlink.net. Web Site: www.arabianhorsetrust.com. *Res*, Linda Gruver
Founded 1974
Library Holdings: Bk Vols 1,650; Bk Titles 1,500; Per Subs 20
Special Collections: Arabian Heritage Video Coll; Arabian horse (Rare Book Room); Arabian horse history (Pioneer Scrapbooks); Arabian horse photographs (Smith Coll); Twenty interviews
Publications: A Catalog of Travelers Rest Arabian Horses; Arabian Heritage Video Library; Beyond Oats; The Arabian Horse Bibliography; The Arabian Horse Through History

C BELLEVIEW CHRISTIAN SCHOOL LIBRARY,* 3455 W 83rd Ave, 80031. SAN 302-0304. Tel: 303-430-0105. *Librn*, RaeNell Hunter
Library Holdings: Bk Vols 17,950; Per Subs 12

J FRONT RANGE COMMUNITY COLLEGE, College Hill Library & Media Center, 3705 W 112th Ave, 80031-2140. SAN 302-0312. Tel: 303-404-5504. FAX: 303-404-5135. Web Site: www.frcc.cc.co.us. *Dir*, Dr Warren Taylor; *Circ*, Karen Shoemaker; *Coll Develop, Tech Servs*, Ann Marie Obarski; *Automation Syst Coordr*, Veronica Smith; *Bibliog Instr*, Kathleen Cain; E-Mail: caink@csn.net; *Media Spec*, B Candelaria; *Media Spec*, Dave Sacher; *ILL*, Dale White; *Media Spec*, T Theobald; *Ref*, Mary Wilder; *Instr*, Grundel Tami
Founded 1968
Library Holdings: Bk Vols 150,000; Bk Titles 144,000; Per Subs 395
Automation Activity & Vendor Info: (Cataloging) epixtech, inc.
Publications: New in the LMC (acquisitions list)
Mem of Cent Colorado Libr Syst
Partic in Bibliographical Center For Research, Rocky Mountain Region, Inc; Colorado Alliance Of Research Libraries; OCLC Online Computer Library Center, Inc

P WESTMINSTER PUBLIC LIBRARY, 3705 W 112th Ave, 80031. SAN 375-409X. Tel: 303-430-2400, Ext 2315. FAX: 303-657-9784. Web Site: www.westminster.lib.co.us. *Mgr*, Kathy Sullivan; Tel: 303-404-5111; *Ad Servs*, Terry Sterling; *Ch Servs*, Vicky Sisto; *Tech Servs*, Mary Oswalt; *Automation Syst Coordr*, Veronica Smith
Founded 1951. Pop 96,000; Circ 650,000
1998-1999 Income $1,861,000. Mats Exp $379,000, Books $286,100, Per/Ser (Incl. Access Fees) $14,000, Micro $11,500. Sal $1,152,372 (Prof $472,438)
Library Holdings: Bk Vols 186,000; Per Subs 300
Automation Activity & Vendor Info: (Acquisitions) epixtech, inc.; (Cataloging) epixtech, inc.; (Circulation) epixtech, inc.
Mem of Cent Colorado Libr Syst
Friends of the Library Group
Branches: 1
76TH AVE, 3031 W 76th Ave, 80030. SAN 377-8371. Tel: 303-430-2400, Ext 2315. Web Site: www.ci.westminster.co.us.
Bookmobiles: 1

WHEAT RIDGE

M LUTHERAN MEDICAL CENTER, Health Resources Library,* 8300 W 38th Ave, 80033-8270. SAN 302-0339. Tel: 303-425-8662. FAX: 303-467-8794. *Mgr*, Susan Brandes; *Tech Servs*, Sherry Muniz; E-Mail: sherrym@primera.org
Library Holdings: Bk Vols 5,000; Per Subs 260
Subject Interests: Business and management, Consumer health, Medicine, Nursing, Surgery
Partic in Colorado Council Of Medical Librarians; Dialog Corporation; OCLC Online Computer Library Center, Inc; RML

S WHEAT RIDGE HISTORICAL SOCIETY LIBRARY,* 4610 Robb St, 80033. (Mail add: PO Box 1833, 80034-1833), Tel: 303-467-0023. FAX: 303-467-2539. *Pres*, Claudia Worth; E-Mail: cworth@aol.com; *Librn*, Charlotte Whettsel
Founded 1974
Library Holdings: Bk Vols 600; Bk Titles 400
Special Collections: School Coll, mss, vf
Publications: Guide to collections
Restriction: Non-circulating to the public

WINDSOR

P WINDSOR-SEVERANCE LIBRARY DISTRICT,* 720 Third St, 80550. SAN 302-0355. Tel: 970-686-5603. FAX: 970-686-2502. Web Site: windsor.colorado.library.net/. *Dir*, Carol A Ingle
Founded 1922. Circ 102,793
Jan 1999-Dec 2000 Income $317,000. Mats Exp $55,000. Sal $143,000
Library Holdings: Bk Vols 48,426
Mem of High Plains Regional Library Service System
Friends of the Library Group

WOODLAND PARK

P RAMPART REGIONAL LIBRARY DISTRICT, Woodland Park Public Library, 821 W Lafayette Ave, PO Box 336, 80866. SAN 302-0363. Tel: 719-687-9281. FAX: 719-687-6631. *Dir*, Sharon Quay
Founded 1966. Pop 19,000; Circ 92,002
Library Holdings: Bk Vols 25,000; Bk Titles 20,205; Per Subs 66
Subject Interests: Local history
Mem of Plains & Peaks Regional Library System
Friends of the Library Group
Branches: 1
FLORISSANT PUBLIC, 2001 Teller 31, PO Box 252, Florissant, 80816. SAN 320-9687. Tel: 719-748-3939. FAX: 719-748-3939. *Librn*, Judy Scott
Friends of the Library Group

WRAY

P NORTHEAST COLORADO BOOKMOBILE SERVICES, 325 W Seventh St, 80758. SAN 302-0371. Tel: 970-332-4715. Toll Free Tel: 800-306-4715. FAX: 970-332-3439. E-Mail: necbs@plains.net.; Staff 4 (Non-MLS 4)
Founded 1961. Pop 68,586; Circ 156,459
1999-2000 Income $122,000, County $112,650, Other $9,350. Mats Exp Books $16,500. Sal $66,000 (Prof $38,264)
Library Holdings: Bk Vols 49,000; Bk Titles 38,000
Mem of High Plains Regional Library Service System
Friends of the Library Group
Bookmobiles: 1

P WRAY PUBLIC LIBRARY,* 621 Blake St, 80758-1619. SAN 302-038X. Tel: 970-332-4744. FAX: 970-332-4784. *Dir*, Mary Ellen Hayes; *Asst Librn*, Shara Berghuis
Founded 1913. Circ 31,000
Library Holdings: Bk Titles 13,500; Per Subs 29
Mem of High Plains Regional Library Service System

YAMPA

P YAMPA PUBLIC LIBRARY,* PO Box 10, 80483-0010. SAN 302-0398. Tel: 970-638-4654. FAX: 970-638-4654. *Librn*, Mary Jean Perry
Founded 1934
Library Holdings: Bk Titles 5,000
Special Collections: Local History Coll; Old Western Novels
Mem of Three Rivers Regional Library Service System
Friends of the Library Group

YUMA

P YUMA PUBLIC LIBRARY,* 114 W Third Ave, 80759-2402. SAN 302-0401. Tel: 970-848-2368. FAX: 970-848-0423. E-Mail: ypl@plains.net. *Dir*, Kelly Rayl
Founded 1924. Pop 3,000; Circ 18,581
Library Holdings: Bk Titles 19,000; Per Subs 52
Mem of High Plains Regional Library Service System

CONNECTICUT

Date of Statistics: 1998-99
Population, 1998 Estimate: 3,274,069
Population Served by Public Libraries: 3,274,069
Total Volumes in Public Libraries: 13,365,871
Volumes Per Capita: 4.1
Total Public Library Circulation: 25,670,136
Circulation Per Capita: 7.8
Total Public Library Expenditures: $123,169,170
Source of Income: Local taxes: 78%; State & Federal Funds: 3%; Investments: 5%; all other: 14%
Operating Expenditures Per Capita: $30.78
Number of Bookmobiles in State: 6

Grants-in-Aid to Public Libraries:
Federal LSTA 1998-99
Competitive: $148,002
Targeted: $10,000
State Aid: $453,776
Connecticard: $697,835
State Grants Public Library Construction: $2,500,000
State Grants Cooperating Library Service Units : $807,829
State aid: $1200 to each of 164 principal public libraries plus equalization and incentive grants.
Connecticard: Half of total annual appropriation is distributed to all participating libraries on a transaction basis; other half distributed to libraries with net plus transactions.

ABINGTON

P ABINGTON SOCIAL LIBRARY,* 536 Hampton Rd, 06230. SAN 302-041X. Tel: 860-974-0415. *Librn*, Karen Stevens
Founded 1793. Pop 1,000; Circ 8,300
Library Holdings: Bk Titles 12,500; Per Subs 11

ANDOVER

P ANDOVER PUBLIC LIBRARY, 355 Rte 6, 06232. (Mail add: PO Box 117, 06232), SAN 302-0428. Tel: 860-742-7428. FAX: 860-742-7428. E-Mail: andoverpl@neca.com. *Librn*, Amy E Orlomoski; Staff 1 (MLS 1)
Founded 1896. Pop 2,700; Circ 15,000
Jul 1999-Jun 2000 Income $80,908, State $1,500, City $77,031, Locally Generated Income $2,377. Mats Exp $9,200, Books $7,890, Per/Ser (Incl. Access Fees) $1,310. Sal $46,880 (Prof $24,675)
Library Holdings: Bk Vols 15,500; Bk Titles 15,350; Per Subs 43
Mem of Eastern Conn Librs, Inc
Friends of the Library Group

ANSONIA

P ANSONIA LIBRARY, 53 S Cliff St, 06401-1909. SAN 302-0436. Tel: 203-734-6275. FAX: 203-732-4551. Web Site: www.biblio.org/ansonia. *Dir*, Joyce Ceccarelli; *Asst Dir*, Mary Ann Capone; *Ch Servs*, Janet Fitol; Staff 7 (MLS 3, Non-MLS 4)
Founded 1896. Pop 18,403; Circ 81,380
Library Holdings: Bk Vols 60,562; Per Subs 137
Subject Interests: Local history
Special Collections: Daughters of American Revolution
Automation Activity & Vendor Info: (Cataloging) CARL; (Circulation) CARL; (OPAC) CARL; (Serials) CARL
Database Vendor: CARL
Friends of the Library Group

L LAW OFFICE OF DANIEL D SKURET PC LIBRARY,* 215 Division St, 06401. (Mail add: PO Box 158, 06401), SAN 370-3436. Tel: 203-736-9934. FAX: 203-734-3484. E-Mail: attydds@aol.com. *In Charge*, Daniel D Skuret
Library Holdings: Bk Titles 2,000; Per Subs 15

ASHFORD

P BABCOCK LIBRARY, 25 Pompey Hollow Rd, PO Box 360, 06278-0360. SAN 323-6455. Tel: 860-429-0287. FAX: 860-429-6829. *Head Librn*, Denise Bachand; Staff 7 (MLS 4, Non-MLS 3)
Founded 1866. Pop 4,000; Circ 36,077
Library Holdings: Bk Vols 21,825; Per Subs 75
Subject Interests: Genealogy, Local history
Mem of Eastern Conn Librs, Inc
Friends of the Library Group

AVON

P AVON FREE PUBLIC LIBRARY, 281 Country Club Rd, 06001. SAN 302-0452. Tel: 860-673-9712. TDD: 860-673-3431. FAX: 860-675-6364. Web Site: www.avon.lib.ct.us. *Dir*, Virginia Vocelli; E-Mail: vvocelli@avon.lib.ct.us; *Asst Dir*, Donna Miller; E-Mail: dmiller@avon.lib.ct.us; *Tech Servs*, Susan Turner; E-Mail: sturner@avon.lib.ct.us; *Circ*, Linda LaChase; E-Mail: llachase@avon.lib.ct.us; *Ch Servs*, Karen McNulty; E-Mail: kmcnulty@avon.lib.ct.us; Staff 33 (MLS 12, Non-MLS 21)
Founded 1798. Pop 15,500; Circ 231,990
Jul 1999-Jun 2000 Income $916,144, State $13,076, City $830,543, Other $72,525. Mats Exp $110,000, Books $77,424, Per/Ser (Incl. Access Fees) $11,941, Micro $3,444, AV Equip $2,192, Electronic Ref Mat (Incl. Access Fees) $15,000. Sal $500,692 (Prof $271,926)
Library Holdings: Bk Titles 71,061; Per Subs 258
Subject Interests: Local history
Automation Activity & Vendor Info: (Cataloging) CARL; (Circulation) CARL; (OPAC) SIRSI
Database Vendor: CARL, Ebsco - EbscoHost, OCLC - First Search
Publications: Friends Newsletter
Mem of Capitol Regional Libr Council
Partic in Capital Region Libr Coun
Friends of the Library Group

SR CHRIST EPISCOPAL CHURCH, Richard W Dunne Library, 35 Harris Rd, 06001. (Mail add: 118 Fox Den Rd, 06001), SAN 375-281X. Tel: 860-673-6382. FAX: 860-673-8690. *Librn*, Sally C Levin
Library Holdings: Bk Vols 900

BALTIC

P SPRAGUE PUBLIC LIBRARY,* One Main St, PO Box 162, 06330. SAN 376-5334. Tel: 860-822-3012. E-Mail: spraguelibrary@netscape.net. *Librn*, Ann Jones
Library Holdings: Bk Vols 25,000

BEACON FALLS

P BEACON FALLS PUBLIC LIBRARY, 10 Maple Ave, 06403. SAN 302-0460. Tel: 203-729-1441. FAX: 203-720-1078. E-Mail: beaconfalls.library@snet.net. Web Site: www.electronicvalley.org/beacon-falls/lib/index.html. *Librn*, Marsha Durley
Founded 1957. Pop 6,100; Circ 10,380
Library Holdings: Bk Vols 12,000
Partic in Western Connecticut Library Council, Inc
Friends of the Library Group

BERLIN

P BERLIN FREE LIBRARY,* 834 Worthington Ridge, 06037. SAN 302-0479. Tel: 860-828-3344. *Dir, Librn*, Barbara Lewis
Circ 9,907

Library Holdings: Bk Vols 17,500; Per Subs 15
Mem of Conn Libr Asn
Open Mon & Fri 2:30-5 & 7-8:30, Wed 9-11:30 & 7-8:30

P BERLIN-PECK MEMORIAL LIBRARY, 234 Kensington Rd, 06037. SAN 302-2005. Tel: 860-828-7125. FAX: 860-829-1848. Web Site: www.berlinpeck.lib.ct.us. *Dir*, Sara Munson; E-Mail: saramunson@hotmail.com; *Asst Dir, Ch Servs*, Cathy Nelson; *Cat*, Andrew J Fal; Staff 8 (MLS 5, Non-MLS 3)
Founded 1829. Pop 17,061; Circ 232,022
Jul 1999-Jun 2000 Income $709,415. Mats Exp $114,000, Books $108,000, Per/Ser (Incl. Access Fees) $5,000, Presv $200, Electronic Ref Mat (Incl. Access Fees) $6,000. Sal $525,000
Library Holdings: Bk Titles 83,058; Per Subs 199
Subject Interests: Local history
Automation Activity & Vendor Info: (Cataloging) CARL; (Circulation) CARL; (ILL) CARL; (OPAC) CARL
Database Vendor: CARL, Ebsco - EbscoHost, GaleNet
Mem of Capitol Regional Libr Council
Partic in Connect; OCLC Online Computer Library Center, Inc
Special Services for the Blind - Optelek 20/20 video magnification system
Friends of the Library Group

BETHANY

P CLARK MEMORIAL LIBRARY,* 538 Amity Rd, 06524-3015. SAN 302-0495. Tel: 203-393-2103. *Librn*, Mary Relyea
Founded 1930. Pop 4,600; Circ 50,400
Jul 1998-Jun 1999 Income $74,500, State $1,400, City $64,600, Locally Generated Income $8,500. Mats Exp $14,000. Sal $33,000
Library Holdings: Bk Vols 30,000
Friends of the Library Group

BETHEL

P BETHEL PUBLIC LIBRARY, 189 Greenwood Ave, 06801-2598. SAN 302-0509. Tel: 203-794-8756. FAX: 203-794-8761. E-Mail: bethelp@bethel-ct.org. Web Site: www.biblio.org/bethel/bethel. *Dir*, Lynn M Rosato; *Ch Servs*, Joanne Grumman; *Ad Servs*, Barbara Van Achterberg; *YA Servs*, Amy Schumann; Staff 22 (MLS 4, Non-MLS 18)
Founded 1909. Pop 18,000; Circ 143,000
Jul 2000-Jun 2001 Income $606,996, State $2,521, City $604,475. Mats Exp $117,424, Books $83,150, Per/Ser (Incl. Access Fees) $8,500, Micro $3,600, AV Equip $10,174, Electronic Ref Mat (Incl. Access Fees) $12,000. Sal $428,025 (Prof $176,370)
Library Holdings: Bk Vols 84,988; Per Subs 264; High Interest/Low Vocabulary Bk Vols 75
Subject Interests: Local history
Automation Activity & Vendor Info: (Cataloging) CARL; (Circulation) CARL; (ILL) CARL; (OPAC) CARL
Database Vendor: CARL, Ebsco - EbscoHost, GaleNet
Publications: Newsletter (bimonthly)
Mem of Western Conn Libr Coun
Partic in Bibliomation
Friends of the Library Group

S GROLIER, INC, Grolier Library, 6 Parklawn Dr, 06801. SAN 302-1041. Tel: 203-797-3848. FAX: 203-797-3428. *Librn*, Chun C Chang; E-Mail: cchang@grolier.com; Staff 2 (MLS 1, Non-MLS 1)
Founded 1936
Library Holdings: Bk Titles 14,000; Per Subs 150
Restriction: Open to public for reference only

BETHLEHEM

SR ABBEY OF REGINA LAUDIS LIBRARY, Flanders Rd, 06751. SAN 302-0517. Tel: 203-266-7727. *Librn*, Mother Lucia Kuppens; Staff 2 (MLS 1, Non-MLS 1)
Founded 1947
Library Holdings: Bk Vols 23,100; Per Subs 34
Subject Interests: Art and architecture, Church history, Ecumenism, Judaism (religion), Liturgy, Near East, Theology
Special Collections: Art & Art History (Lauren Ford Coll); English Monastic History (Hope Emily Allen Coll); Gregorian Chant (Rev Thomas F Dennehy Coll); Literature (Heinrich Brunning & Lloyd B Holsapple Coll); Medieval Mystics; Patristics (Sources Chretiennes, Migne & Corpus Christianorum); Sacred Music (T F Dennehy Coll); Social Science (Sage Coll)
Restriction: Not open to public
Mem of Region One Coop Libr Servs Unit

P BETHLEHEM PUBLIC LIBRARY, 32 Main St S, PO Box 99, 06751. SAN 302-0525. Tel: 203-266-7792. FAX: 203-266-6157. Web Site: ci.bethlehem.ct.us/. *Dir*, Anne Small
Founded 1857. Pop 3,286
Jul 1999-Jun 2000 Income $77,454, State $1,400, City $73,354, Locally Generated Income $2,700. Mats Exp Books $9,185. Sal $50,623 (Prof $32,110)
Library Holdings: Bk Vols 23,100; Per Subs 33
Subject Interests: Local history
Publications: Grapevine (monthly newsletter)
Partic in Western Connecticut Library Council, Inc
Friends of the Library Group

BLOOMFIELD

S ANDERSEN LABORATORIES, INC LIBRARY,* 45 Old Iron Ore Rd, 06002. SAN 302-0533. Tel: 860-286-9090, Ext 368. FAX: 860-242-4472. *Librn*, Marie Hemmingway; E-Mail: mhemingway@anlabs.com
Founded 1971
Library Holdings: Bk Vols 464; Per Subs 23
Restriction: In-house use for visitors

S CIGNA, CO LIBRARY,* 900 Cottage Grove Rd, 06002. SAN 302-0541. Tel: 860-726-4414. FAX: 860-726-5128. *Dir*, Patricia Malahan; *Info Specialist*, David MacHenry; *Info Specialist*, Jessie Liu-Snyder; *Tech Servs*, Roberta Merrigan; Staff 10 (MLS 5, Non-MLS 5)
Founded 1922
Library Holdings: Bk Titles 35,000; Per Subs 500
Subject Interests: Business and management, Economics, Investing, Law
Partic in Capitol Region Library Council; OCLC Online Computer Library Center, Inc

S KAMAN AEROSPACE LIBRARY,* Old Windsor Rd, 06002-0002. (Mail add: PO Box 2, 06002-0002), SAN 302-055X. Tel: 860-242-4461, Ext 2241. FAX: 860-243-6142. E-Mail: parenta-kac@kaman.com. *Librn*, Angela Parent
Library Holdings: Bk Vols 6,000

P PROSSER PUBLIC LIBRARY,* One Tunxis Ave, 06002-2476. SAN 336-0245. Tel: 860-243-9721. FAX: 860-242-1629. E-Mail: prosser@connix.com. Web Site: www.crlc.org/prosser/. *Dir*, Beverly Lambert; *Ch Servs*, Linda Gabianelli; *Commun Servs*, Elaine Kittler; *Tech Servs*, Thomas Schadlich; Staff 7 (MLS 2, Non-MLS 5)
Founded 1901. Pop 19,070; Circ 172,635
Library Holdings: Bk Vols 112,230; Per Subs 183
Publications: Monthly calendar; newsletter
Partic in Can Asn of Res Librs; Capitol Region Library Council; Nelinet, Inc
Friends of the Library Group
Branches: 1
WINTONBURY BRANCH LIBRARY, 1015 Blue Hills Ave, 06002. Tel: 860-242-0041. Web Site: www.crlc.org:80/prosser. *Librn*, Claudia Wright
Library Holdings: Bk Vols 22,000; Bk Titles 22,000; Per Subs 25

R SAINT THOMAS SEMINARY-HARTFORD ARCHDIOCESE, Archbishop Henry J O'Brien Library, 467 Bloomfield Ave, 06002. SAN 302-0576. Tel: 860-242-5573, Ext 114. FAX: 860-242-4886. E-Mail: stthomasseminary@snet.net. Web Site: pages.cthome.net/obrienlibrary/library.htm. *Dir*, Karen Hubbard; *Circ*, David Pontreli; Staff 2 (MLS 1, Non-MLS 1)
Founded 1897. Enrl 100; Fac 6; Highest Degree: Doctorate
Jul 1999-Jun 2000 Income $97,700, Locally Generated Income $7,700, Parent Institution $20,000, Other $70,000. Mats Exp $20,000, Books $9,000, Per/Ser (Incl. Access Fees) $3,574, Presv $1,427, Other Print Mats $200. Sal $42,000 (Prof $33,000)
Library Holdings: Bk Vols 30,000; Per Subs 87
Subject Interests: Catholicism, Philosophy, Theology
Special Collections: 15th-17th Century Coll; Bibles; Early Catholic Americana Coll
Automation Activity & Vendor Info: (Cataloging) Nicholas; (Cataloging) Sagebrush Corporation; (Cataloging) Athena; (Circulation) Sagebrush Corporation; (Circulation) Athena; (Circulation) Nicholas; (OPAC) Nicholas; (OPAC) Sagebrush Corporation; (OPAC) Athena
Database Vendor: OCLC - First Search
Publications: Link
Function: ILL available
Partic in Capitol Region Library Council; Hartford Consortium For Higher Education

BOLTON

P BENTLEY MEMORIAL LIBRARY,* 206 Bolton Center Rd, 06043. SAN 302-0584. Tel: 860-646-7349. FAX: 860-649-9059. E-Mail: bentley@connix.com. Web Site: www.state.ct.vf/munic/bolton/bolton.htm. *Dir*, Elizabeth E Thornton; Staff 5 (MLS 1, Non-MLS 4)
Founded 1915. Pop 4,600; Circ 45,562
Jul 1998-Jun 1999 Income $153,316. Mats Exp $37,535. Sal $104,951
Library Holdings: Bk Vols 35,000; Per Subs 140
Special Collections: Dolls from around the World (Private Coll)
Mem of Eastern Conn Librs, Inc
Friends of the Library Group

BRANFORD

P JAMES BLACKSTONE MEMORIAL LIBRARY, 758 Main St, 06405-3697. SAN 302-0592. Tel: 203-488-1441. FAX: 203-481-6077. Web Site: www.blackstone.lioninc.org. *Dir*, Donna Lolos; *Ch Servs*, Jane Ash; *Ch Servs*, Bonnie Lalor; *Ref*, Barbara Cangiano; *Tech Servs*, Gennett Grinnell; Staff 20 (MLS 9, Non-MLS 11)
Founded 1893. Pop 28,000; Circ 172,547
Jul 1998-Jun 1999 Income $571,026, State $4,184, City $522,669, Locally Generated Income $22,285, Other $21,888. Mats Exp $59,146, Books $50,022, Per/Ser (Incl. Access Fees) $8,798, Micro $326. Sal $415,269 (Prof $306,969)
Library Holdings: Per Subs 211
Subject Interests: Genealogy, Local history
Publications: Marble Columns (newsletter)
Partic in Libraries Online, Inc
Friends of the Library Group

BRIDGEPORT

G BRIDGEPORT DEPARTMENT OF ARCHIVES, RECORDS & INFORMATION SERVICES, City Hall Rm 13, 45 Lyon Terrace, 06604. SAN 323-6757. Tel: 203-576-8192. FAX: 203-576-8193. *Archivist*, Mollie Keller; E-Mail: kellem0@ci.bridgeport.ct.us
Founded 1983
Jul 1998-Jun 1999 Income $83,995. Mats Exp $22,000, Micro $5,000. Sal $64,500 (Prof $60,000)
Special Collections: Bridgeport City Records
Restriction: By appointment only

M BRIDGEPORT HOSPITAL, Reeves Memorial Library, 267 Grant St, PO Box 5000, 06610. SAN 302-0622. Tel: 203-384-3254. FAX: 203-384-3107. *Dir*, Janice Swiatek-Kelley; Staff 4 (MLS 3, Non-MLS 1)
Library Holdings: Bk Vols 4,400; Bk Titles 3,500; Per Subs 300
Subject Interests: Health sciences
Partic in Conn Asn of Health Scis Librs; Univ Halifax

P BRIDGEPORT PUBLIC LIBRARY, 925 Broad St, 06604. SAN 336-0334. Tel: 203-576-7777. FAX: 203-576-8255. Web Site: bridgeport.lib.ct.us/bpl. *Librn*, Michael Golrick; Fax: 203-333-0253, E-Mail: mgolrick@brdgprtpl.lib.ct.us; *Asst Dir*, Ann Osbon; E-Mail: aosbon@brdgprtpl.lib.ct.us; *Ch Servs*, Eileen Sheridan; *Commun Servs*, Michael Bielawa; *ILL*, John Soltis; *Ref*, Anne Maio; *Tech Servs*, Sylvia Boyd. Subject Specialists: *Business and management*, Barbara Bennorth; *History*, Mary Witkowski; *Technology*, Barbara Bennorth; Staff 95 (MLS 31, Non-MLS 64)
Founded 1881. Pop 139,160; Circ 142,563
Jul 1999-Jun 2000 Income (Main Library and Branch Library) $3,613,834. Mats Exp $400,000. Sal $2,526,538
Library Holdings: Bk Vols 491,593
Subject Interests: Art and architecture, Business and management, Literature, Technology
Special Collections: Local History; P T Barnum Circus
Automation Activity & Vendor Info: (Circulation) epixtech, inc.
Publications: Monthly Newsletter
Partic in Nelinet, Inc; Western Connecticut Library Council, Inc
Special Services for the Deaf - Books on deafness & sign language; High interest/low vocabulary books
Branches: 4
BLACK ROCK, 2705 Fairfield Ave, 06605. SAN 336-0369. Tel: 203-576-7427. Web Site: bridgeport.lib.ct.us/bpl/branches/br/index.htm. *Librn*, Nancy Sweeney; E-Mail: nsweeney@brdgprtpl.lib.ct.us
Library Holdings: Bk Vols 17,897
NEWFIELD, 1230 Stratford Ave, 06607. SAN 336-0423. Tel: 203-576-7828, 203-576-7834. Web Site: bridgeport.lib.ct.us/bpl/branches/new/nf.htm. *Librn*, Renate Ferree; E-Mail: rferree@brdgprtpl.lib.ct.us
Library Holdings: Bk Vols 14,000
NORTH, 3455 Madison Ave, 06606. SAN 336-0458. Tel: 203-576-7423. FAX: 203-576-7752. Web Site: bridgeport.lib.ct.us/bpl/branches/nor/northlib.htm. *Br Coordr*, Paula Keegan; E-Mail: pkeegan@brdgprtpl.lib.ct.us
Library Holdings: Bk Vols 50,000
OLD MILL GREEN, 1677-81 E Main St, 06608. SAN 336-0393. Tel: 203-576-7634. Web Site: bridgeport.lib.ct.us/bpl/branches/omg/index.htm. *Librn*, Diane Kurtz; Tel: 203-696-0849, E-Mail: dkurtz@brdgprtpl.lib.ct.us; Staff 5 (MLS 2, Non-MLS 3)
Library Holdings: Bk Vols 29,170
Subject Interests: Spanish lang
Bookmobiles: 1

R CONGREGATION B'NAI ISRAEL LIBRARY, 2710 Park Ave, 06604. SAN 302-0649. Tel: 203-336-1858. FAX: 203-367-7889. *Librn*, Melissa Volman; Staff 1 (MLS 1)
Founded 1960
Library Holdings: Bk Vols 4,000
Subject Interests: Judaica (lit or hist of Jews)

GL CONNECTICUT JUDICIAL BRANCH, Law Library at Bridgeport,* Court House, 1061 Main St 7th flr, 06604. SAN 336-1802. Tel: 203-579-6237. FAX: 203-579-6512. Web Site: www.jud.state.connecticut.us/directory/. *In Charge*, Willie E Jackson
Library Holdings: Bk Vols 38,000; Per Subs 92

J HOUSATONIC COMMUNITY COLLEGE LIBRARY, (Formerly Housatonic Community-Technical College Library), 900 Lafayette Blvd, 06604. SAN 302-0657. Tel: 203-332-5070. FAX: 203-332-5252. Web Site: www.hctc.commnet.edu/library/index.html. *Dir*, Bruce Harvey; Tel: 203-332-5075, E-Mail: ho_harvey@commnet.edu; *Librn*, Ompa Chukwurah; Tel: 203-332-5179, E-Mail: ho_chukwurah@commnet.edu; *Publ Servs*, Nancy Blomstrom; Tel: 203-332-5075, E-Mail: ho_blomstrom@commnet.edu; *Circ*, Mark Gore; Tel: 203-332-5069, E-Mail: ho_gore@commnet.edu; *Ref*, Peter Everett; Tel: 203-332-5074, E-Mail: ho_everett@commnet.edu; *Tech Servs*, Qiming Han; Tel: 203-332-5073, E-Mail: ho_han@commnet.edu; *Media Spec*, Lois McCracken; Tel: 203-332-5076, E-Mail: ho_mccracken@commnet.edu; Staff 8 (MLS 6, Non-MLS 2)
Founded 1967. Enrl 3,800; Highest Degree: Associate
Jul 1998-Jun 1999 Income State $478,616. Mats Exp $153,036. Sal $324,422
Library Holdings: Bk Vols 34,575; Per Subs 240
Database Vendor: Ebsco - EbscoHost, Lexis-Nexis, OCLC - First Search
Restriction: Circulation limited
Partic in OCLC Online Computer Library Center, Inc

S JEWISH CENTER FOR COMMUNITY SERVICES LIBRARY, 4200 Park Ave, 06604. SAN 302-0665. Tel: 203-372-6567. FAX: 203-374-0770. E-Mail: info@jccs.org. Web Site: www.jccs.org. *Pres*, Dan Baker
Library Holdings: Bk Vols 1,000; Per Subs 15

M SAINT VINCENT'S MEDICAL CENTER, Daniel T Banks Health Science Library, 2800 Main St, 06606. SAN 302-0703. Tel: 203-576-5336. FAX: 203-576-5645. Web Site: www.stvincents.org. *Dir*, Kathy Giotsas; E-Mail: kgiotsas@svhs-ct.org; Staff 6 (MLS 2, Non-MLS 4)
Founded 1976
Library Holdings: Bk Vols 4,583; Per Subs 275
Subject Interests: Allied health, Medicine, Nursing
Special Collections: Archives (hospital history)

C UNIVERSITY OF BRIDGEPORT, Magnus Wahlstrom Library, 126 Park Ave, 06604-5694. SAN 302-0711. Tel: 203-576-4740. Interlibrary Loan Service Tel: 203-576-4748. Circulation Tel: 203-576-4745. Reference Tel: 203-576-4747. FAX: 203-576-4791. E-Mail: reference@bridgeport.edu. Web Site: www.bridgeport.edu/indexhtml/library. *Librn*, Karen R Smiga; E-Mail: karen@bridgeport.edu; *Head Ref, Instrul Serv*, Jo-Anne Frenkel; Tel: 203-576-4748, E-Mail: jfrenkel@bridgeport.edu; *Ref*, Valerie Haines; Tel: 203-576-4748, E-Mail: vhaines@bridgeport.edu; *Cat*, Doug Apicella; Tel: 203-576-4753, E-Mail: apicella@bridgeport.edu; *Access Serv*, Allison Carboni; Tel: 203-576-4746, E-Mail: acarboni@bridgeport.edu; *Coll Develop, Head, Acq*, Olga M Majewski; Tel: 203-576-4754, E-Mail: majewski@bridgeport.edu; *Head Tech Servs, Syst Coordr*, Jianxin Yang; Tel: 203-576-4657, E-Mail: jianxin@bridgeport.edu. Subject Specialists: *Art*, Olga M Majewski; *Business*, Jo-Anne Frenkel; *Design*, Olga M Majewski; *Health sciences*, Valerie Haines; *Science/technology*, Allison Carboni; *Social sciences*, Doug Apicella; Staff 25 (MLS 14, Non-MLS 11)
Founded 1927. Enrl 3,000; Fac 93; Highest Degree: Doctorate
Jul 1999-Jun 2000 Income $1,188,398, Locally Generated Income $2,817, Parent Institution $1,185,581. Mats Exp $401,815, Books $54,391, Per/Ser (Incl. Access Fees) $241,279, Presv $10,326, Micro $29,627, AV Equip $9,172, Other Print Mats $9,717, Electronic Ref Mat (Incl. Access Fees) $47,303. Sal $614,803 (Prof $275,307)
Library Holdings: Bk Vols 215,644; Per Subs 1,136
Subject Interests: Acupuncture, American literature, Chiropractic, Computer science, Education, Engineering, History, Naturopathic med
Special Collections: English Books 1475-1640, micro; ERIC, microfiche; Library of American Civilization, ultrafiche; Lincolniana, monographs, clippings, photo; Socialism in Connecticut, monographs, pamphlets
Automation Activity & Vendor Info: (Acquisitions) Endeavor; (Cataloging) Endeavor; (Circulation) Endeavor; (Course Reserve) Endeavor; (OPAC) Endeavor; (Serials) Endeavor
Database Vendor: Dialog, Ebsco - EbscoHost, Lexis-Nexis, OCLC - First Search, ProQuest
Restriction: Circulation limited, Private library
Function: For research purposes, ILL available, Photocopies available, Reference services available
Partic in Coun of Conn Acad Libr Dirs; Nelinet, Inc; New England Libr Info Network; OCLC Online Computer Library Center, Inc; Western Connecticut Library Council, Inc
Financial figures include funding provided by the College of Chiropractic, Naturopathic Medicine & Oriental Medicine for library materials & by the College of Chiropractic for personnel support. Library holdings are only for the main library

BRIDGEWATER

P BRIDGEWATER LIBRARY ASSOCIATION, Burnham Library, 62 Main St S, 06752-9998. (Mail add: PO Box 430, 06752-9998), SAN 302-0738. Tel: 860-354-6937. FAX: 860-354-4583. *Dir*, Sandra Neary; *Head Librn*, Patricia Mesnig; Staff 2 (Non-MLS 2)
Founded 1926. Pop 1,739; Circ 21,949
Jul 1999-Jun 2000 Income $86,933, State $8,423, City $52,318, Locally Generated Income $7,295, Parent Institution $17,881, Other $1,016. Mats Exp $14,940. Sal $59,180 (Prof $37,222)
Library Holdings: Bk Titles 28,514; Per Subs 57
Special Collections: Bridgewater Authors; Civil War Letters; Van Wyck Brooks
Publications: Friends of the Library Events Postcard (monthly)
Friends of the Library Group

BRISTOL

S AMERICAN CLOCK & WATCH MUSEUM, INC, Edward Ingraham Library, 100 Maple St, 06010-5092. SAN 302-0746. Tel: 860-583-6070. FAX: 860-583-1862. *Actg Dir*, Chris H Bailey
Founded 1952
Library Holdings: Bk Vols 2,000

M BRISTOL HOSPITAL HEALTH SCIENCES LIBRARY, Brewster Rd, PO Box 977, 06011-0977. Tel: 860-585-3239. Web Site: www.bristolhospital.org. *Dir*, Marilyn Pitman; E-Mail: mpitman@brishosp.chime.org; *Mgr Libr Serv*, Julie Simard; Staff 2 (MLS 1, Non-MLS 1)
Library Holdings: Bk Titles 1,300; Per Subs 180

P BRISTOL PUBLIC LIBRARY,* 5 High St, 06010. SAN 336-0571. Tel: 860-584-7787. FAX: 860-584-7696. *Dir*, Francine Petosa; *Asst Librn*, Harriet Lorenz
Founded 1892. Pop 60,790; Circ 296,315
Jul 1998-Jun 1999 Income $1,335,446, City $1,297,107. Mats Exp $1,311,311. Sal $850,467
Library Holdings: Bk Vols 140,272; Per Subs 328
Subject Interests: Agriculture, Art and architecture, Education, Environmental studies, Music
Special Collections: Local & State History Coll
Partic in Connect
Friends of the Library Group
Branches: 1
MANROSS MEMORIAL, 260 Central St, Forestville, 06010. (Mail add: PO Box 730, Forestville, 06011), SAN 336-0601. Tel: 860-584-7790. *Librn*, Doris Camire
Library Holdings: Bk Vols 45,000
Friends of the Library Group

BROAD BROOK

P BROAD BROOK PUBLIC LIBRARY, 78 Main St, 06016. Tel: 860-623-1334. FAX: 860-627-0493. *Librn*, Marilyn Rajala
Library Holdings: Bk Vols 6,000; Bk Titles 6,000; Per Subs 10

BROOKFIELD

P THE BROOKFIELD LIBRARY,* 182 Whisconier Rd, 06804. SAN 302-0762. Tel: 203-775-6241. FAX: 203-740-7723. Web Site: www.brookfieldct.org/library.htm. *Ch Servs*, Valerie Annis; *Cat*, Marilyn Schmidt; *Circ*, Mary Proudfoot; *Ad Servs*, Natasha Goodman; E-Mail: ngoodman@biblio.org; Staff 19 (MLS 3, Non-MLS 16)
Founded 1951. Pop 14,475; Circ 126,450
Jul 1998-Jun 1999 Income $467,389, State $2,954, City $390,926, Locally Generated Income $73,509. Mats Exp $72,848, Books $53,638, Per/Ser (Incl. Access Fees) $5,158, Micro $3,763, Electronic Ref Mat (Incl. Access Fees) $10,289. Sal $268,950 (Prof $142,293)
Library Holdings: Bk Vols 58,014; Per Subs 138
Automation Activity & Vendor Info: (Cataloging) CARL; (Circulation) CARL
Partic in Bibliomation, Inc; Western Connecticut Library Council, Inc
Friends of the Library Group

BROOKLYN

P BROOKLYN TOWN LIBRARY ASSOCIATION,* 10 Canterbury Rd, 06234. (Mail add: PO Box 357, 06234), SAN 302-0770. Tel: 860-774-0649. FAX: 860-774-0649. E-Mail: brookl@neca.com. *Librn*, Catherine Tucker
Pop 6,600; Circ 15,070
Library Holdings: Bk Vols 18,000
Subject Interests: Local history
Partic in Eastern Connecticut Libraries
Friends of the Library Group

BURLINGTON

P BURLINGTON PUBLIC LIBRARY, 34 Library Lane, PO Box 1379, 06013-0379. SAN 302-0789. Tel: 860-673-3331. FAX: 860-673-0897. E-Mail: burltnpl@crlc.org. *Librn*, Anne Walluk; Staff 3 (MLS 3)
Founded 1896. Pop 7,800
Jul 1999-Jun 2000 Income $150,000. Mats Exp $9,200, Books $8,000, Per/Ser (Incl. Access Fees) $1,200. Sal $96,000 (Prof $65,000)
Library Holdings: Bk Vols 35,000
Subject Interests: Local history
Automation Activity & Vendor Info: (Circulation) SIRSI; (OPAC) SIRSI
Database Vendor: OCLC - First Search
Partic in Capital Region Libr Coun
Friends of the Library Group

CANAAN

P DOUGLAS LIBRARY,* 108 Main St, PO Box 608, 06018. SAN 302-0797. Tel: 203-824-7863. E-Mail: douglas.libr@snet.net. *Librn*, Norma DeMay; *Asst Librn*, Joan Weber
Founded 1821. Pop 3,000; Circ 20,694
Jul 1998-Jun 1999 Income $42,435, State $1,367. Mats Exp Books $9,650. Sal $27,275
Library Holdings: Bk Vols 18,513; Per Subs 43
Partic in Region I Coop Libr Servs Unit
Friends of the Library Group

CANTERBURY

P CANTERBURY PUBLIC LIBRARY, 8 Library Rd, 06331-1512. SAN 376-3234. Tel: 860-546-9022. FAX: 860-546-9022. E-Mail: canterpl@neca.com. Web Site: www.users.neca.com/canterpl. *Librn*, Marion Sheehan; Staff 1 (Non-MLS 1)
Founded 1925
2000-2001 Mats Exp $6,300, Books $6,000, Per/Ser (Incl. Access Fees) $300
Library Holdings: Bk Vols 14,000; Per Subs 14
Database Vendor: GaleNet
Function: ILL available, Some telephone reference
Mem of Conn Libr Asn
Partic in Eastern Connecticut Libraries
Friends of the Library Group

S CONNECTICUT HISTORICAL COMMISSION, Prudence Crandall Museum Library, Rte 14 & 169, PO Box 58, 06331-0058. SAN 325-0431. Tel: 860-546-9916. FAX: 860-546-7803. E-Mail: crndll@snet.net. *Curator*, Kazimiera Kozlowski
Founded 1983
Library Holdings: Bk Vols 600; Bk Titles 600
Subject Interests: Black hist

CANTON

P CANTON PUBLIC LIBRARY, 40 Dyer Ave, 06019. SAN 302-0878. Tel: 860-693-5800. FAX: 860-693-5804. E-Mail: cantonpl@tiac.net. Web Site: www.tiac.net/users/cantonpl. *Dir*, Kathleen Cockroft; *Tech Servs*, Win Purrington
Pop 8,453; Circ 70,000
Jul 2000-Jun 2001 Income $319,742. Mats Exp Books $37,000. Sal $240,000
Library Holdings: Bk Vols 46,000
Subject Interests: Connecticut, Local history
Partic in Capitol Region Library Council
Friends of the Library Group

CENTRAL VILLAGE

P CENTRAL VILLAGE PUBLIC LIBRARY,* 51 Black Hill Rd, 06332. (Mail add: PO Box 158, 06332), SAN 376-3250. Tel: 860-564-7753. FAX: 860-564-2738. *Dir*, Shirley DeFosse
Jul 1998-Jun 1999 Income $42,000. Mats Exp $22,000. Sal $20,000
Library Holdings: Bk Vols 8,500; Bk Titles 8,000; Per Subs 12
Partic in Eastern Connecticut Libraries

CHAPLIN

P WILLIAM ROSS PUBLIC LIBRARY,* 130 Chaplin St, 06235-2302. SAN 302-0819. Tel: 860-455-9424. *Librn*, Geraldine Helmer
Founded 1911. Pop 1,900
Library Holdings: Bk Vols 11,684; Per Subs 28
Subject Interests: Local history
Partic in Eastern Connecticut Libraries
Open Mon 3-6, Wed 2-5 & 6-8, Thurs 2-6, Sat 1-5

CHESHIRE

S ARCH CHEMICALS INC, Chemical Research Library, 350 Knotter Dr, 06410-0586. SAN 302-2595. Tel: 203-271-4000. FAX: 203-271-4060. Web Site: www.archchemicals.com.
Library Holdings: Bk Titles 14,000; Per Subs 150
Subject Interests: Chemistry, Engineering, Environmental studies, Patents
Publications: Bulletin (monthly); search reports list
Partic in Nat Libr of Med

P CHESHIRE PUBLIC LIBRARY, 104 Main St, 06410-2499. SAN 302-0827. Tel: 203-272-2245. FAX: 203-272-7714. E-Mail: chesire@kaplibraries.org. Web Site: www.cheshirelib.org. *Dir*, Ann S Wrege; *Coll Develop, Dep Dir*, Deborah Rutter; *Ch Servs*, Susan Hartley; *Circ*, Noureen Hakim; *Commun Servs*, Maria Poirier; *Online Servs*, Karen Kramer; *Ref*, Mary Beeckman; *Ser*, Carrie-Ann Crowe; *Tech Servs*, Gail Roberts; Staff 32 (MLS 19, Non-MLS 13)
Founded 1892. Pop 26,471; Circ 287,260
Jul 1999-Jun 2000 Income $1,094,447, State $8,322, City $1,000,462, Locally Generated Income $44,036, Other $41,627. Mats Exp $133,537. Sal $869,985
Library Holdings: Bk Vols 105,232; Per Subs 478
Automation Activity & Vendor Info: (Cataloging) GEAC; (Circulation) GEAC
Database Vendor: OCLC - First Search
Partic in Southern Connecticut Library Council
Friends of the Library Group

S CONNECTICUT CORRECTIONAL INSTITUTION, 900 Highland Ave, 06410. Tel: 203-250-2600, Ext 2124. *Librn*, Candace Hall
Library Holdings: Bk Vols 2,000; Bk Titles 1,800; Per Subs 30

R FIRST CONGREGATIONAL CHURCH LIBRARY,* 111 Church Dr, 06410. SAN 302-0835. Tel: 203-272-5323. *Librn*, Ruth Eppler
Library Holdings: Bk Vols 1,500

CHESTER

P CHESTER PUBLIC LIBRARY, W Main St, PO Box 310, 06412. SAN 302-0843. Tel: 860-526-0018. *Dir*, Gloria Eustis; *Asst Librn*, Pam Larson; *Asst Librn*, Patricia Petrus
Founded 1789. Pop 3,700; Circ 32,120
Jul 1999-Jun 2000 Mats Exp $17,920, Books $16,720, Per/Ser (Incl. Access Fees) $1,200. Sal $45,378
Library Holdings: Bk Vols 13,500; Per Subs 53
Subject Interests: Local history
Partic in Southern Connecticut Library Council
Friends of the Library Group

CLINTON

P HENRY CARTER HULL LIBRARY, INC,* 10 Killingworth Tpk, 06413. SAN 302-0851. Tel: 860-669-2342. FAX: 860-669-8318. Web Site: www.ct.com. *Librn*, Gary J Cummings; *Ch Servs*, Lynn Hidek; Staff 3 (MLS 1, Non-MLS 2)
Founded 1925. Pop 11,224
Library Holdings: Bk Vols 50,000; Per Subs 120
Publications: H C Hull Libr News
Friends of the Library Group

COLCHESTER

P CRAGIN MEMORIAL LIBRARY, 8 Linwood Ave, 06415. SAN 302-086X. Tel: 860-537-5752. FAX: 860-537-4559. E-Mail: cragin@colchesterpl.libct.org. *Dir*, Siobhan M Grogan
Pop 13,000; Circ 70,000
Jul 1998-Jun 1999 Income $242,000. Mats Exp $50,000. Sal $132,000
Library Holdings: Bk Vols 41,000; Per Subs 160
Friends of the Library Group

COLLINSVILLE

S CANTON HISTORICAL SOCIETY LIBRARY, 11 Front St, 06019. SAN 329-8418. Tel: 860-693-2793. *Librn*, Cynthia Griggs
Library Holdings: Bk Vols 350
Subject Interests: Local history
Special Collections: Local Census, 1790-1910; Samuel W Collins & the Collins Company Coll, 1826-1966
Restriction: Open to public for reference only

COLUMBIA

P SAXTON B LITTLE FREE LIBRARY, INC,* 319 Rte 87, 06237-1143. SAN 302-0886. Tel: 860-228-0350. FAX: 860-228-1569. E-Mail: slslib@necd.com. Web Site: www.state.ct.us/munic/columbia. *Dir*, Janice Benda; *Ad Servs*, Carol Kubala; Staff 6 (MLS 3, Non-MLS 3)
Pop 4,864; Circ 36,115
Jul 1998-Jun 1999 Income $168,960, State $1,800, City $155,610, Federal $1,800, Locally Generated Income $5,700, Other $4,050. Mats Exp $33,100, Books $26,500, Per/Ser (Incl. Access Fees) $6,600. Sal $87,611
Library Holdings: Bk Vols 25,500; Per Subs 110
Subject Interests: Local history
Publications: Friends Newsletter
Mem of Eastern Conn Librs, Inc
Friends of the Library Group

CORNWALL

P CORNWALL FREE LIBRARY, Pine St, PO Box 126, 06753. SAN 302-0908. Tel: 860-672-6874. E-Mail: cornwall.library@snet.net. *Librn*, Virginia Potter; Staff 2 (Non-MLS 2)
Pop 1,414; Circ 14,000
Jul 1999-Jun 2000 Income $4,050, State $1,250, City $2,800. Mats Exp $5,400, Books $5,200, Per/Ser (Incl. Access Fees) $200. Sal $33,150
Library Holdings: Bk Vols 14,800; Per Subs 10
Friends of the Library Group

COS COB

S HISTORICAL SOCIETY OF THE TOWN OF GREENWICH, William E Finch Jr Archives, 39 Strickland Rd, 06807. SAN 302-0924. Tel: 203-869-6899. FAX: 203-869-6727. Web Site: www.hstg.org. *Archivist*, Susan Richardson; E-Mail: srichardson@hstg.org
Founded 1931
Library Holdings: Bk Vols 500
Subject Interests: Decorative arts, Genealogy, History
Special Collections: Connecticut History Coll; Impressionist Literature Coll
Restriction: Open to public for reference only

COVENTRY

P BOOTH & DIMOCK MEMORIAL LIBRARY, 1134 Main St, 06238-3157. (Mail add: PO Box 129, 06238-0129), SAN 302-0932. Tel: 860-742-7606. FAX: 860-742-7491. Web Site: www.coventrypl.org. *Dir*, Sharon Pacholski; E-Mail: spacholski@coventrypl.libct.org
Founded 1880. Pop 11,200; Circ 86,000
Jul 1999-Jun 2000 Income $212,300. Mats Exp $25,700, Books $21,500, Per/Ser (Incl. Access Fees) $3,800, Electronic Ref Mat (Incl. Access Fees) $400. Sal $119,500 (Prof $62,000)
Library Holdings: Bk Titles 45,000; Per Subs 80
Special Collections: History of Coventry; Nathan Hale Coll
Automation Activity & Vendor Info: (Cataloging) Sagebrush Corporation; (Circulation) Sagebrush Corporation
Publications: Newsletter
Partic in Eastern Connecticut Libraries
Friends of the Library Group

CROMWELL

P CROMWELL BELDEN PUBLIC LIBRARY,* 39 West St, 06416. SAN 302-0959. Tel: 860-632-3460. FAX: 860-635-5741. Web Site: www.state.ct.us/munic/cromwell. *Dir*, Eileen Branciforte; *Asst Dir, Ch Servs*, Lois Meltzer; *Ad Servs*, Lynn Caley
Founded 1888
Jul 1998-Jun 1999 Income $342,545. Mats Exp $54,944. Sal $246,338
Library Holdings: Bk Vols 60,000
Subject Interests: Local history
Special Collections: Local History Coll
Automation Activity & Vendor Info: (Cataloging) CARL; (Circulation) CARL
Partic in Cap Region Libr Coun; Southern Connecticut Library Council
Open Mon & Wed 1-8, Tues & Thurs 10-8, Fri & Sat 10-5
Friends of the Library Group

C HOLY APOSTLES COLLEGE & SEMINARY LIBRARY, 33 Prospect Hill Rd, 06416-2005. SAN 302-0967. Tel: 860-632-3009. FAX: 860-632-3090. E-Mail: hacslibrary@hotmail.com. *Dir*, Philip S Kiley; *Assoc Librn*, Clare Adamo; *Asst Librn*, Robert Whitton; Staff 4 (MLS 2, Non-MLS 2)
Founded 1957. Enrl 100; Fac 29; Highest Degree: Master
Library Holdings: Bk Titles 62,000; Per Subs 220
Subject Interests: History, Philosophy, Religion
Partic in Nelinet, Inc; OCLC; ReQuest OPAC Catalog

DANBURY

G CONNECTICUT JUDICIAL BRANCH, Danbury Law Library, Courthouse, 146 White St, 06810. SAN 302-1009. Tel: 203-207-8625. FAX: 203-207-8627. *Librn*, Diana Nolan; E-Mail: diana.nolan@jud.state.ct.us; Staff 2 (MLS 1, Non-MLS 1)
Library Holdings: Bk Vols 28,000; Bk Titles 400; Per Subs 30

Subject Interests: Connecticut, Law
Special Collections: Connecticut Legislative Histories; Historical Information (Connecticut Law)
Open Mon-Fri 9-5

M DANBURY HOSPITAL, Health Sciences Library,* 24 Hospital Ave, 06810. SAN 302-0991. Tel: 203-797-7035. FAX: 203-731-8662. Web Site: www.danbury.lib.ct.us. *Librn*, Michael Schott; E-Mail: mschott@pcngt.com
Founded 1956
Library Holdings: Bk Vols 3,200; Per Subs 400
Subject Interests: Allied health, Hospital administration, Medicine, Nursing

P DANBURY PUBLIC LIBRARY, 170 Main St, 06810. SAN 302-1017. Circulation Tel: 203-797-4505. Reference Tel: 203-797-4527. FAX: 203-797-4501. Web Site: www.danbury.org/library. *Dir*, Elizabeth McDonough; Tel: 203-797-4512, Fax: 203-796-1677, E-Mail: emcdon@danbury.lib.ct.us; *Asst Dir*, Diane Greenwald; E-Mail: dmg@danbury.lib.ct.us; *Asst Dir*, Laura McLaughlin; E-Mail: ldmcl@danbury.lib.ct.us; *Commun Servs*, Maryellen De Jong; *Ref*, Marcella Jenkins; Fax: 203-796-1518, E-Mail: marcella@danbury.lib.ct.us; *Automation Syst Coordr*, Tony Booth; Tel: 203-796-1607, Fax: 203-797-4573, E-Mail: Tony@danbury.lib.ct.us; *Ch Servs*, Veronica Stevenson-Moudamane; Tel: 203-797-4528, E-Mail: vstevens@danbury.lib.ct.us; *Circ*, Laura Eisenberg; E-Mail: laura@danbury.lib.ct.us; *AV*, Susan Horton; Tel: 203-797-4533, E-Mail: sh@danbury.lib.ct.us; Staff 29 (MLS 14, Non-MLS 15)
Founded 1869. Pop 65,829; Circ 395,456
Jul 1999-Jun 2000 Income City $1,618,647. Mats Exp $241,338, Books $141,104, Per/Ser (Incl. Access Fees) $19,835, Manuscripts & Archives $3,314, Electronic Ref Mat (Incl. Access Fees) $33,418. Sal $1,328,870
Library Holdings: Bk Vols 96,924; Per Subs 239
Subject Interests: Local history
Database Vendor: GaleNet, IAC - SearchBank
Friends of the Library Group

S DANBURY SCOTT-FANTON MUSEUM & HISTORICAL SOCIETY, Research Library,* 43 Main St, 06810. SAN 302-1025. Tel: 203-743-5200. FAX: 203-743-1131. *Exec Dir*, Maryann R Root
Founded 1942
Library Holdings: Bk Vols 600
Subject Interests: Antiques, Genealogy, Local history
Special Collections: Charles Ives; Hat Making

S FEDERAL CORRECTIONAL INSTITUTION, Department of Justice Centralized Library,* Pembroke Sta, 06811. SAN 302-1033. Tel: 203-743-6471, Ext 410. FAX: 203-312-5138. *Librn*, Dorothy Baker
Founded 1979
Library Holdings: Bk Vols 2,000; Per Subs 25
Special Collections: World War I & II Coll

P LONG RIDGE LIBRARY,* 191 Long Ridge Rd, 06810. SAN 321-6578. Tel: 203-748-1011.
Founded 1919. Pop 600
Library Holdings: Bk Titles 14,000
Open Wed 4-8 & Sat 1-5

S NEUROCOMMUNICATION RESEARCH LABORATORIES, INC LIBRARY,* 36 Mill Plain Rd, Ste 412, 06811. SAN 324-7392. Tel: 203-744-7474. FAX: 203-744-7488. *Pres*, Curt Weinstein
Library Holdings: Bk Titles 1,200
Subject Interests: Dermatology, Physiological psychol

S RAYTHEON COMPANY LIBRARY, 100 Wooster Heights Rd M/S 856, 06810. Circulation Tel: 203-797-5324. *Acq, Senior Info Specialist*, Joyce H Pierce; Tel: 203-797-6239, E-Mail: joyce_h_pierce@raytheon.com; Staff 1 (Non-MLS 1)
Library Holdings: Bk Titles 1,600; Per Subs 500
Database Vendor: Dialog
Function: For research purposes

S RSA CORP LIBRARY, 36 Old Sherman Tpk, 06810. SAN 328-0993. Tel: 203-790-8100. FAX: 203-790-1709. *Librn*, Stephanie Weber; E-Mail: rsasteph@cs.com
Library Holdings: Bk Vols 2,000; Per Subs 30
Open Mon-Fri 9-5

UNION CARBIDE CORP
L LAW & BUSINESS LIBRARY, 39 Old Ridgebury Rd, Rm N2, 06817-0001. SAN 353-8117. Tel: 203-794-5314. FAX: 203-794-5055. *Mgr*, Roger Miller; *Ref*, Margaret Houghton-Capozzi; E-Mail: houghtma@ucarb.com
Founded 1935
Library Holdings: Bk Titles 15,000; Per Subs 250
Subject Interests: Antitrust, Chemical, Corp, Financing, Industry, Labor, Mktg, Patent environmental law
Partic in Dialog Corporation; Dow Jones News Retrieval; Westlaw

C WESTERN CONNECTICUT STATE UNIVERSITY, Ruth A Haas Library, 181 White St, 06810-6885. SAN 302-1076. Tel: 203-837-9100. FAX: 203-837-9108. Web Site: www.wcsu.cstateu.edu/library. *Dir Libr Serv*, Ralph Holibaugh; Tel: 203-837-9109, E-Mail: holibaugh@wcsu.edu; *Circ*, Russell Gladstone; Tel: 203-837-9101; *Ser*, Barbara Heuer; Tel: 203-837-9115, E-Mail: heuer@wcsu.edu; *Ref*, Vijay Nair; Tel: 203-837-9116, E-Mail: nair@wcsu.edu; *Cat*, Alesia Szabo; Tel: 203-837-9104, Fax: 203-837-9103, E-Mail: szabo@wcsu.edu; *ILL*, Joanne Elpern; *Acq*, Xiao Hua Yang; Tel: 203-837-9105, Fax: 203-837-9103, E-Mail: yangx@wcsu.edu; *Bibliog Instr*, Joan Reitz; Tel: 203-837-8308, E-Mail: reitz@wcsu.edu; *Per*, Lorraine Furtick; Tel: 203-837-8296, E-Mail: furtick@wcsu.edu; *Acq*, Deborah Barrett; Tel: 203-837-9106, E-Mail: barrettd@wcsu.edu; Staff 11 (MLS 11)
Founded 1905. Highest Degree: Master
1999-1999 Mats Exp $472,000, Books $66,000, Per/Ser (Incl. Access Fees) $300,000, Micro $55,000, Electronic Ref Mat (Incl. Access Fees) $51,000
Library Holdings: Bk Vols 250,000; Bk Titles 105,000; Per Subs 1,821
Subject Interests: Local history
Special Collections: Fairfield County & Connecticut History (Connecticut Room), bks, doc; Music Education , bks, rec; Teacher Educ (Curriculum Center)
Automation Activity & Vendor Info: (Acquisitions) Innovative Interfaces Inc.; (Cataloging) Innovative Interfaces Inc.; (Circulation) Innovative Interfaces Inc.
Database Vendor: Ebsco - EbscoHost
Publications: Guide to Library
Partic in BRS; Dialog Corporation; Nelinet, Inc; OCLC Online Computer Library Center, Inc
Departmental Libraries:
ROBERT S YOUNG BUSINESS LIBRARY Tel: 203-837-9139. FAX: 203-837-9108. Web Site: www.wcsu.ctstateu.edu/library. *Librn*, Jane Fowler; *Librn*, Mary Kay Loomis
Library Holdings: Bk Vols 6,000; Per Subs 250

DANIELSON

P KILLINGLY PUBLIC LIBRARY, 25 Westcott Rd, 06239. SAN 302-1092. Tel: 860-779-5383. FAX: 860-779-1823. Web Site: www.state.ct.us/munic/killingly/killingly.htm. *Dir*, Marie C Chartier; E-Mail: mchartier@biblio.org; *Asst Dir*, Laura Zipkin; E-Mail: lzipkin@biblio.org; *Ch Servs, YA Servs*, Mary Tiebout; E-Mail: mtiebout@biblio.org; *Ref*, Louis Leveillee; E-Mail: llevei@biblio.org; Staff 12 (MLS 4, Non-MLS 8)
Founded 1854. Pop 16,127; Circ 128,880
Jul 1999-Jun 2000 Income $579,567, State $14,475, City $547,468, Other $17,624. Mats Exp $68,045, Books $67,595, Micro $450. Sal $272,302
Library Holdings: Bk Vols 51,972; Per Subs 152
Special Collections: Local History (Windham County Coll)
Automation Activity & Vendor Info: (Cataloging) CARL; (Circulation) CARL
Database Vendor: CARL
Partic in Bibliomation; Eastern Connecticut Libraries; Nelinet, Inc; OCLC Online Computer Library Center, Inc
Friends of the Library Group

J QUINEBAUG VALLEY COMMUNITY COLLEGE LIBRARY, 742 Upper Maple St, 06239. SAN 302-1106. Tel: 860-774-5967. FAX: 860-779-3287. E-Mail: qv_library@commnet.edu. Web Site: www.commnet.edu/qvctc/home.html. *Dir*, Hyunyong C Kim; *Ref*, Sharon Moore; E-Mail: qv_moore@commnet.edu
Founded 1971. Enrl 1,200
Library Holdings: Bk Vols 27,000; Per Subs 135
Automation Activity & Vendor Info: (Circulation) Endeavor; (Course Reserve) Endeavor; (OPAC) Endeavor; (Serials) Endeavor
Database Vendor: Ebsco - EbscoHost, OCLC - First Search, ProQuest
Mem of Conn Libr Asn
Partic in Bibliomation; Eastern Connecticut Libraries; Nelinet, Inc

DARIEN

S DARIEN HISTORICAL SOCIETY, INC LIBRARY,* 45 Old Kings Hwy N, 06820. SAN 302-1114. Tel: 203-655-9233. *Exec Dir*, Madeline Hart
Founded 1953
Library Holdings: Bk Vols 1,600; Per Subs 10
Subject Interests: Decorative arts, Genealogy, Local history, New England

P DARIEN LIBRARY, 35 Leroy Ave, 06820-4497. SAN 302-1122. Tel: 203-655-1234. FAX: 203-655-1547. E-Mail: circ@darien.lib.ct.us. Web Site: www.darien.lib.ct.us. *Dir*, Louise Berry; E-Mail: lberry@darien.lib.ct.us; *Assoc Dir*, Kathleen K Stalker; *ILL*, Blanche Parker; *Ch Servs*, Christine Ginsberg; *Acq*, Anita Ekern; *Ref*, Linda Fenster
Founded 1894. Pop 18,152; Circ 466,326
Library Holdings: Bk Vols 153,112; Per Subs 287
Subject Interests: Genealogy, Large type print, Literature, Local history, Travel
Database Vendor: Dialog, Ebsco - EbscoHost, GaleNet, Innovative Interfaces INN - View, Lexis-Nexis, OCLC - First Search
Partic in Western Connecticut Library Council, Inc
Friends of the Library Group

SR NOROTON PRESBYTERIAN CHURCH LIBRARY, PO Box 3401, 06820. SAN 371-5639. Tel: 203-655-1451. *Librn*, Marlene Eldridge
Founded 1940
Library Holdings: Bk Vols 3,500; Bk Titles 3,200

S ZOTOS INTERNATIONAL LIBRARY, 100 Tokeneke Rd, 06820-1005. SAN 320-6149. Tel: 203-656-7700, 203-656-7805. FAX: 203-656-7963. *In Charge*, Judy Landau
Founded 1932
Library Holdings: Bk Titles 5,300; Per Subs 50
Subject Interests: Dermatology, Organic chemistry, Pharmacology, Toxicology
Publications: Newsletters
Partic in Dialog Corporation; Univ Halifax

DEEP RIVER

P DEEP RIVER PUBLIC LIBRARY, 150 Main St, 06417. SAN 302-1157. Tel: 860-526-6039. FAX: 860-526-6040. Web Site: www.deepriverct.com/library. *Dir*, Ann Paietta; E-Mail: apaietta@att.net; Staff 1 (MLS 1)
Founded 1900. Pop 4,333; Circ 18,236
Library Holdings: Bk Titles 25,000; Per Subs 75
Partic in ReQuest OPAC Catalog
Friends of the Library Group

DERBY

P DERBY NECK LIBRARY, 307 Hawthorne Ave, 06418-1199. SAN 302-1165. Tel: 203-734-1492. FAX: 203-734-1492. Web Site: www.electronicvalley.org/derby/lib/derbyneck.htm. *Head Librn*, Judith W Augusta; E-Mail: jaugusta@biblio.org; *Asst Librn*, Margaret Borchers; E-Mail: mborchers@biblio.org; Staff 2 (MLS 2)
Founded 1897. Pop 11,760
Jul 1999-Jun 2000 Mats Exp $5,362, Books $3,606, Per/Ser (Incl. Access Fees) $525, AV Equip $1,231. Sal $73,747 (Prof $62,247)
Library Holdings: Bk Vols 49,426; Bk Titles 44,427
Subject Interests: Cooking, Fiction, Historic preservation
Special Collections: Audiobooks; Large Print Books; Videotapes
Partic in Bibliomation Consortium
Library in temporary storefront during construction with limited hours and materials

P DERBY PUBLIC LIBRARY, 313 Elizabeth St, 06418. SAN 302-1173. Tel: 203-736-1482. TDD: 800-842-9710. FAX: 203-736-1419. Web Site: www.derbypubliclibrary.org. *Dir*, Karen Higginson; E-Mail: khiggins@biblio.org; *Ad Servs*, Joan Driscoll; E-Mail: derbycir@biblio.org; *Ch Servs*, Catherine Williams; E-Mail: cwilliams@biblio.org; Staff 11 (MLS 2, Non-MLS 9)
Founded 1902. Pop 11,704; Circ 34,000
Jul 1999-Jun 2000 Income $250,000. Mats Exp $42,500, Books $30,000, Per/Ser (Incl. Access Fees) $3,000, Presv $500, Micro $1,000, AV Equip $2,500, Manuscripts & Archives $500, Electronic Ref Mat (Incl. Access Fees) $5,000. Sal $180,000 (Prof $38,500)
Library Holdings: Bk Vols 40,000; Per Subs 205; High Interest/Low Vocabulary Bk Vols 50
Subject Interests: Bks on tape, Compact discs, Employment, Finance, Genealogy, History, Large print, Literacy, Literature, Local history, Sheet music, Videos
Special Collections: Genealogy; Large Print; Literacy; Local History; Parent's Place; Sheet Music Coll
Publications: Darby Public Library (Newsletter); Newsletter
Function: Internet access, Reference services available
Partic in Southern Connecticut Library Council
Special Services for the Deaf - Staff with knowledge of sign language; TDD
Special Services for the Blind - Bks on tape; Large print bks
Friends of the Library Group

M GRIFFIN HOSPITAL, Health Resource Center, 130 Division St, 06418. SAN 371-5264. Tel: 203-732-7399. FAX: 203-732-1390. E-Mail: iflib@giffinhealth.org. *Coordr*, Kerry Dennigan; Staff 2 (MLS 1, Non-MLS 1)
Founded 1994
Library Holdings: Bk Titles 1,000; Per Subs 250
Subject Interests: Consumer health
Partic in Conn Asn of Health Scis Librs

DURHAM

P DURHAM PUBLIC LIBRARY, 7 Maple Ave, 06422. SAN 302-1181. Tel: 860-349-9544. FAX: 860-349-9853. Web Site: www.lioninc.org/durham. *Coll Develop, Dir*, Valerie Harrod; E-Mail: vharrod@durhamlibrary.lioninc.inc
Founded 1894. Pop 6,300; Circ 104,339
Jul 1999-Jun 2000 Income $304,877. Mats Exp $40,250, Books $30,000, Per/Ser (Incl. Access Fees) $6,000, Presv $250, Other Print Mats $4,000. Sal $195,279 (Prof $114,209)
Library Holdings: Bk Vols 48,651; Per Subs 75
Subject Interests: Local history
Automation Activity & Vendor Info: (Circulation) epixtech, inc.
Database Vendor: epixtech, inc.
Partic in Libraries Online, Inc
Friends of the Library Group

EAST BERLIN

P EAST BERLIN LIBRARY ASSOCIATION,* 80 Main St, 06023. (Mail add: PO Box 334, 06023), SAN 302-119X. Tel: 860-828-3123. *Librn*, Francine Sencio
Circ 6,000
Library Holdings: Bk Vols 7,168; Per Subs 24
Open Summer Hours May 1-Sept 30, Mon & Thurs 3-5 & 6:30-8:30; Winter Hours Oct 1-Apr 30, Mon 3-5, Wed 3:30-5:30, Thurs 3-5 & 6:30-8:30

EAST GRANBY

P EAST GRANBY PUBLIC LIBRARY, 27 School St, PO Box G, 06026-9998. SAN 302-1203. Tel: 860-653-3002. FAX: 860-653-3936. E-Mail: east.granby.pub.lib@snet.net. Web Site: pages.cthome.net/egpl/. *Librn*, Linda Veirs; Staff 9 (MLS 1, Non-MLS 8)
Founded 1922. Pop 4,500; Circ 33,990
Jul 1999-Jun 2000 Income $77,555, State $1,350, City $53,045, Locally Generated Income $23,160. Mats Exp $13,897, Books $10,698, Per/Ser (Incl. Access Fees) $1,261. Sal $50,237 (Prof $10,000)
Library Holdings: Bk Vols 24,737; Per Subs 24
Subject Interests: Careers, Consumer info, Education, Local history
Publications: Literally Speaking
Partic in Capitol Region Library Council
Friends of the Library Group

EAST HADDAM

S MUSICAL THEATRE, Goodspeed Opera House Library, 8 Norwich Rd, 06423-1344. (Mail add: PO Box A, 06423-0281), SAN 370-6044. Tel: 860-873-8664. FAX: 860-873-2329. E-Mail: library@goodspeed.org. Web Site: www.goodspeed.org. *Librn*, Lisa Viall; Staff 1 (Non-MLS 1)
Founded 1979
Library Holdings: Bk Vols 3,000; Bk Titles 2,500; Per Subs 25
Subject Interests: Music therapy
Special Collections: Geo Gershwin Coll, Tuit Gershwin Coll, bks, rec, sheet music; NBC Sheet Music Coll
Publications: Show Music
Restriction: Open to public for reference only
Friends of the Library Group

P RATHBUN FREE MEMORIAL LIBRARY,* 36 Main St, PO Box G, 06423. SAN 302-122X. Tel: 860-873-8210. FAX: 860-873-3601. Web Site: www.rathbunlibrary.org. *Dir*, Kathleen Marszyeky; *Circ*, Polly Ayer
Founded 1935. Circ 59,604
Library Holdings: Bk Vols 23,000; Per Subs 68
Special Collections: East Haddam History Coll, clippings, micro
Friends of the Library Group

EAST HAMPTON

P EAST HAMPTON PUBLIC LIBRARY,* 105 Main St, 06424. SAN 302-1238. Tel: 860-267-6621. FAX: 860-267-4427. E-Mail: ehplct@hotmail.com. Web Site: www.lioninc.org. *Ch Servs, Dir*, Monica Kangley; *Ref, YA Servs*, Sue Bercescik; Staff 6 (MLS 2, Non-MLS 4)
Founded 1898. Pop 11,600; Circ 67,520
1998-1999 Income $304,362. Mats Exp $48,175, Books $40,000, Per/Ser (Incl. Access Fees) $4,100, Electronic Ref Mat (Incl. Access Fees) $4,075. Sal $207,747 (Prof $75,000)
Library Holdings: Bk Titles 56,000; Per Subs 138
Subject Interests: Local history
Special Collections: East Hampton Room
Partic in Southern Connecticut Library Council
Friends of the Library Group

EAST HARTFORD

S CONNECTICUT SOCIETY OF GENEALOGISTS, INC LIBRARY,* 175 Maple St, 06118-2364. (Mail add: PO Box 435, 06033-0435), SAN 372-6525. Tel: 860-569-0002. Web Site: www.csginc.org. *Mgr*, Helen Hodge; Staff 1 (MLS 1)
Library Holdings: Bk Titles 3,500

P EAST HARTFORD PUBLIC LIBRARY, Raymond Memorial Library, 840 Main St, 06108. SAN 336-0636. Tel: 860-289-6429. FAX: 860-291-9166. Web Site: www.easthartford.lib.ct.us. *Dir*, Patrick Michael Jones; *Ref*, Sharon Jarush
Founded 1879. Pop 59,000; Circ 250,000

Library Holdings: Bk Vols 332,000; Per Subs 400
Special Collections: Aviation Coll; Tobacco Coll
Partic in Capitol Region Library Council
Friends of the Library Group
Branches: 3
HOCKANUM, 165 Main St, 06118. SAN 336-0695. Tel: 860-568-1690. *Mgr*, Edith Sylvester
Library Holdings: Per Subs 15
Friends of the Library Group
PENNEY ALUMNI, 869 Forbes St, 06118. SAN 336-0725. Tel: 860-569-1000. *Mgr*, Wendy Russell
WICKHAM, 656 Burnside Ave, 06108. SAN 336-075X. Tel: 860-528-4664. *Mgr*, Jose Maldenado
Friends of the Library Group

S UTC INFORMATION NETWORK, Research Ctr, 411 Silver Lane, 06108. SAN 302-1246. Tel: 860-610-7478. FAX: 860-610-7316. Web Site: www.utc.com. *Dir*, Jeanne Mayhew; Staff 46 (MLS 25, Non-MLS 21)
Founded 1939
Library Holdings: Bk Vols 49,000; Per Subs 1,000
Subject Interests: Energy, Fuel, Physical science, Transportation
Publications: Bulletin; Business Contents; Technology Topics
Partic in BRS; Dialog Corporation; DOE-Recon; Dow Jones News Retrieval; SDC Info Servs
United Technologies Library & Information Services consists of twelve sites

EAST HAVEN

P HAGAMAN MEMORIAL LIBRARY, 227 Main St, 06512. SAN 302-1262. Tel: 203-468-3890. FAX: 203-468-3892. Web Site: www.leaplibraries.org/ehaven. *Dir*, Nancy McNicol; E-Mail: nmcnicol@leaplibraries.org; Staff 20 (MLS 4, Non-MLS 16)
Founded 1909. Pop 26,100; Circ 133,720
Jul 1999-Jun 2000 Income $506,035, State $7,576, City $460,731, Locally Generated Income $37,494. Mats Exp $68,200, Books $64,500, Per/Ser (Incl. Access Fees) $3,700. (Prof $152,681)
Library Holdings: Bk Titles 58,891; Per Subs 142
Automation Activity & Vendor Info: (Cataloging) TLC; (Circulation) GEAC
Database Vendor: epixtech, inc.
Function: ILL available
Partic in Library Exchange Aids Patrons
Friends of the Library Group

S THE SHORE LINE TROLLEY MUSEUM LIBRARY, 17 River St, 06512. SAN 302-1254. Tel: 203-467-6927. Web Site: www.bera.org. *Curator*, Michael H Schreiber; *Dir*, Geo Boucher
Library Holdings: Bk Vols 3,500
Special Collections: Technical & Social History of the Street Railway & Electric Railway Industry, equip, blueprints, doc, trade journals & photos

EAST WINDSOR

S CONNECTICUT ELECTRIC RAILWAY ASSOCIATION, INC, Connecticut Trolley Museum Library, 58 North Rd, 06088-0360. (Mail add: PO Box 360, 06088-0360), SAN 326-3983. Tel: 860-627-6540. FAX: 860-627-6510. E-Mail: information@ceraonline.org. Web Site: www.ceraonline.org. *Chairperson*, James Haury; *Librn*, Steve Kellner
Founded 1940
Library Holdings: Bk Vols 3,000

P LIBRARY ASSOCIATION OF WAREHOUSE POINT,* 107 Main St, 06088. SAN 302-4091. Tel: 860-623-5482. FAX: 860-627-6823. Web Site: www.connect.crlc.org. *Dir*, Adele R Chwalek; Tel: 202-319-4735; Staff 1 (MLS 1)
Founded 1811. Pop 9,100; Circ 37,218
Library Holdings: Bk Titles 35,000; Per Subs 85
Partic in Capitol Region Library Council
Friends of the Library Group

EAST WOODSTOCK

S EAST WOODSTOCK LIBRARY ASSOCIATION, May Memorial Library, 15 Prospect St, PO Box 14, 06244-0014. SAN 323-7249. Tel: 860-928-0284. *Librn*, Judith D Schumacher
Pop 2,500
Library Holdings: Bk Titles 7,500
Friends of the Library Group

EASTFORD

P EASTFORD PUBLIC LIBRARY,* 179 Eastford Rd, PO Box 908, 06242-0908. SAN 302-1270. Tel: 860-974-0125. FAX: 860-974-1751. *Librn*, Barbara Pakenham; Staff 1 (MLS 1)
Founded 1896
Jul 1998-Jun 1999 Income $25,000, State $1,200, City $23,800. Mats Exp $6,225, Books $4,325, Per/Ser (Incl. Access Fees) $900. Sal $15,000 (Prof $10,613)
Library Holdings: Bk Titles 10,943
Partic in Eastern Connecticut Libraries
Closed for renovations until June 2000

EASTON

P EASTON PUBLIC LIBRARY, 691 Morehouse Rd, PO Box 2, 06612. SAN 302-1289. Tel: 203-261-0134. FAX: 203-261-0708. E-Mail: easton.public.lib@snet.net. Web Site: www.eastonlibrary.org. *Dir*, Bernadette Baldino; *Asst Dir, Ch Servs*, Diane Conroy; Staff 8 (MLS 2, Non-MLS 6)
Founded 1934. Pop 6,700; Circ 92,831
Jun 1999-Jul 2000 Income $331,498. Mats Exp $50,000. Sal $200,868 (Prof $79,851)
Library Holdings: Bk Vols 52,596
Automation Activity & Vendor Info: (Cataloging) Follett; (Circulation) Follett; (OPAC) Follett
Partic in Western Connecticut Library Council, Inc
Friends of the Library Group

ELLINGTON

P HALL MEMORIAL LIBRARY, Ellington Public Library, 93 Main St, 06029. (Mail add: PO Box 280, 06029), SAN 302-1297. Tel: 860-870-3160. FAX: 860-870-3163. E-Mail: hallmlib@biblio.org. Web Site: www.biblio.org/ellington/hall.htm. *Dir*, Susan J Phillips; *Ch Servs*, Patricia W Grundman
Founded 1903. Pop 11,197; Circ 91,986
Jul 1998-Jun 1999 Income $360,530, State $4,252, City $329,361, Locally Generated Income $26,917. Mats Exp $45,332. Sal $184,011
Library Holdings: Bk Vols 46,183; Per Subs 150
Special Collections: Ellington History, docs, pamphlets
Partic in Bibliomation; Eastern Connecticut Libraries
Friends of the Library Group

ENFIELD

J ASNUNTUCK COMMUNITY TECHNICAL COLLEGE, Learning Resource Center,* 170 Elm St, 06082-0068. SAN 302-1300. Tel: 860-253-3174. FAX: 860-253-9310. E-Mail: as_lrcref@commnet.edu. Web Site: www.asctc.commnet.edu. *Dir*, Michael J Moran; Tel: 860-253-3171, E-Mail: as_moran@commnet.edu; *Librn*, Beverly G Himelstein; Tel: 860-253-3169, E-Mail: as_bev@commnet.edu; *Librn*, Sherry Gelbwasser; Tel: 860-253-3161, E-Mail: as_gelbwasser@commnet.edu; *Circ*, Madeline Pease; Tel: 860-253-3172, E-Mail: as_pease@commnet.edu; *AV*, Ben Durant; Tel: 860-253-3074, E-Mail: as_durant@commnet.edu; Staff 7 (MLS 3, Non-MLS 4)
Founded 1972. Enrl 671; Highest Degree: Associate
Jul 1997-Jun 1998 Income $404,771, State $404,771. Mats Exp $122,073, Books $14,206, Per/Ser (Incl. Access Fees) $53,629, Micro $1,503, AV Equip $14,234, Other Print Mats $3,798, Electronic Ref Mat (Incl. Access Fees) $34,663. Sal $282,698 (Prof $161,454)
Library Holdings: Bk Vols 29,954; Bk Titles 26,793; Per Subs 324; Bks on Deafness & Sign Lang 30
Special Collections: Copernicus Coll (Polish History & Culture); Literacy Volunteers
Automation Activity & Vendor Info: (Circulation) CARL; (Course Reserve) CARL; (OPAC) CARL
Database Vendor: Ebsco - EbscoHost, GaleNet, OCLC - First Search
Publications: Course Pathfinders; News of Note (newsletter)
Partic in Cap Region Libr Coun; Nelinet, Inc

S CARL ROBINSON CORRECTIONAL INSTITUTION LIBRARY,* 285 Shaker Rd, 06083. (Mail add: PO Box 1400, 06083-1400), SAN 324-4466. Tel: 860-763-6230. FAX: 860-763-6393. *Librn*, Nafi Donat; Staff 1 (MLS 1)
Library Holdings: Bk Titles 7,000; Per Subs 30

S CONNECTICUT CORRECTIONAL INSTITUTION, Enfield-Medium Library, 289 Shaker Rd, PO Box 1500, 06083-1500. SAN 371-5760. Tel: 860-763-7383. *Librn*, Edwin Wilmot; Staff 6 (MLS 1, Non-MLS 5)
Pop 754; Circ 8,700
Library Holdings: Bk Titles 10,000; Per Subs 30
Special Collections: Law - Connecticut, Federal & State

P ENFIELD PUBLIC LIBRARY, Central Library, 104 Middle Rd, 06082. SAN 336-0784. Tel: 860-763-7510. FAX: 860-763-7514. Web Site: www.enfield.lib.ct.us/enfield/. *Dir*, Henry Dutcher; E-Mail: hdutcher@enfield.org; *Asst Dir*, Mary Palomba; *Br Coordr*, Barbara Nosal; Tel: 860-253-6433; *AV*, Ann Bell; *Ch Servs*, Linda Adamczyk; E-Mail: ladamczyk@enfield.lib.ct.us; *Ch Servs*, Suzanne Lott; *Ch Servs*, Jeanne Smith; *ILL*, Eleanor Varnet; *Ref*, Betsy Marks; E-Mail: bmarks@enfield.lib.ct.us; *Tech Servs*, Phyllis Gleeson; *Circ*, Yvonne Wollenberg; Staff 28 (MLS 4, Non-MLS 24)
Founded 1874. Pop 43,075; Circ 256,662
Jul 1999-Jun 2000 Income (Main Library and Branch Library) $972,708. Mats Exp $137,800, Books $115,000, Per/Ser (Incl. Access Fees) $6,000, Presv $500, Micro $6,800, AV Equip $9,500. Sal $726,894

Library Holdings: Bk Titles 146,545; Per Subs 275
Special Collections: Local History/Shaker History (Enfield Centennial Coll), bks
Automation Activity & Vendor Info: (Cataloging) CARL; (Circulation) CARL; (OPAC) CARL
Publications: Annual Report; Enfield Centennial Coll Catalog; History of Enfield Public Library; Town Newsletter
Partic in Capitol Region Library Council
Branches: 1
PEARL STREET, 159 Pearl St, 06082. Tel: 860-253-6433. Web Site: www.enfield.lib.ct.us/. *Librn*, Barbara Nosal; Staff 2 (Non-MLS 2)

S PHOENIX HOME LIFE LIBRARY,* 100 Bright Meadow Blvd, 06083. SAN 302-1904. Tel: 860-403-2325. FAX: 860-403-1352. *Librn*, Elaine Loehr; E-Mail: elianeloehr_@phl.com
Founded 1915
Library Holdings: Bk Titles 2,000; Per Subs 100
Subject Interests: Business and management, Finance
Open 8:30-4

ESSEX

P ESSEX LIBRARY ASSOCIATION, INC, 33 West Ave, 06426-1196. SAN 302-1327. Tel: 860-767-1560. FAX: 860-767-2500. Web Site: www.essexlibrary.lioninc.org. *Dir*, Bridget Quinn-Carey; E-Mail: bquinn@essexlibrary.lioninc.org; *Asst Dir*, Mary Attridge; E-Mail: mattridge@essexlibrary.lioninc.org; *Cat*, Elizabeth Nash; E-Mail: enash@essexlibrary.lioninc.org; *Ch Servs*, Beverly Page; E-Mail: bpage@essexlibrary.lioninc.org; *Ref*, Anita Amos; E-Mail: aamos@essexlibrary.lioninc.org; Staff 4 (MLS 1, Non-MLS 3)
Founded 1890. Pop 6,000; Circ 44,991
Jul 1998-Jun 1999 Income $232,063, State $2,107, City $63,000, Locally Generated Income $166,956. Mats Exp $27,050, Books $20,000, Per/Ser (Incl. Access Fees) $4,500, Presv $250, AV Equip $1,300, Electronic Ref Mat (Incl. Access Fees) $1,000. Sal $110,458 (Prof $100,051)
Library Holdings: Bk Titles 26,200; Per Subs 45
Automation Activity & Vendor Info: (Cataloging) epixtech, inc.; (Circulation) epixtech, inc.; (OPAC) epixtech, inc.
Publications: Ex Libris (quarterly)
Mem of Southern Conn Libr Coun
Partic in Libraries Online, Inc
Friends of the Library Group

S SEAWORTHY SYSTEMS INC LIBRARY, PO Box 965, 06426. SAN 375-1724. Tel: 860-767-9061. FAX: 860-767-1263. Web Site: www.seaworthysys.com. *Librn*, Martin Toyen; E-Mail: mtoyen@seaworthysys.com

FAIRFIELD

S CONNECTICUT AUDUBON SOCIETY LIBRARY,* 2325 Burr St, 06430. SAN 326-9159. Tel: 203-259-6305. FAX: 203-254-7673. *Dir*, Milan Bull
Library Holdings: Bk Vols 3,000
Restriction: Members only

S FAIRFIELD HISTORICAL SOCIETY LIBRARY, 636 Old Post Rd, 06430. SAN 302-1335. Tel: 203-259-1598. FAX: 203-255-2716. Web Site: www.fairfieldhistoricalsoc.org. *Librn*, Dennis A Barrow; Staff 2 (MLS 1, Non-MLS 1)
Founded 1903
Jul 1999-Jun 2000 Mats Exp $4,300, Books $550, Per/Ser (Incl. Access Fees) $350, Presv $3,000
Library Holdings: Bk Titles 10,000; Per Subs 18
Subject Interests: Decorative arts, Genealogy, Local history
Special Collections: Manuscript Coll, account books, diaries, local church & cemetery records, local organization records, school & town records, business & family papers, shipping logs, vf, scrapbooks, ephemera, city directories, architectural records
Publications: Newsletter
Restriction: Not a lending library
Partic in OCLC Online Computer Library Center, Inc; Western Connecticut Library Council, Inc

P FAIRFIELD PUBLIC LIBRARY, 1080 Old Post Rd, 06430-5996. SAN 336-0873. Tel: 203-256-3155. FAX: 203-256-3162. Web Site: www.fairfieldpubliclibrary.org. *Dir*, Tom Geoffino; Tel: 203-256-3158; *Acq, Asst Dir*, Carol Alexander; Tel: 203-256-3154; *Cat, Tech Servs*, Marilyn Rice; *Ch Servs*, Constance Cleary; *ILL, YA Servs*, Ina Goldstein; *Media Spec*, Lillian Ray; Tel: 203-256-3063; *Ref*, Maura Ritz; Staff 24 (MLS 12, Non-MLS 12)
Founded 1877. Pop 52,960; Circ 786,655
Jul 1999-Jun 2000 Income $2,942,355, State $4,872. Mats Exp $514,852, Per/Ser (Incl. Access Fees) $36,104. Sal $2,007,513
Library Holdings: Bk Vols 226,840; Per Subs 770
Automation Activity & Vendor Info: (Circulation) CARL; (OPAC) CARL
Partic in Bibliomation
Branches: 1
FAIRFIELD WOODS, 1147 Fairfield Woods Rd, 06430. SAN 336-0903. Tel: 203-255-7307. FAX: 203-255-7311. *Librn*, Susan Radel
Library Holdings: Bk Vols 64,113

C FAIRFIELD UNIVERSITY, Gustav & Dagmar Nyselius Library, 1073 N Benson Rd, 06430-5195. SAN 302-1343. Tel: 203-254-4044. Circulation Tel: 203-254-4000, Ext 2188. Reference Tel: 203-254-4000, Ext 2178. FAX: 203-254-4135. E-Mail: refdesk1@fair1.fairfield.edu. Web Site: library.fairfield.edu, www.fairfield.edu/academic/nyseliu/newweb/html/index.htm. *VPres*, James Estrada; Fax: 203-254-4133; *Assoc Librn*, Joan T Overfield; Fax: 203-254-4133; *Res*, Teresa Faust; *ILL*, Nancy Romanello; *Cat*, Mona Hefzallah; *Circ*, Barbara Kravec; *Tech Coordr*, Peter Morris; *Cat*, Jonathan Hodge; *Coll Develop*, Keith Stetson; *Media Spec Ad*, Ramona Islam; *ILL*, John Cayer; Staff 23 (MLS 11, Non-MLS 12)
Founded 1948. Enrl 3,972; Fac 280; Highest Degree: Certificate
Jul 1999-Jun 2000 Income Parent Institution $2,382,102. Mats Exp $763,965, Books $310,071, Per/Ser (Incl. Access Fees) $382,637, Presv $15,322, Micro $55,935. Sal $997,950 (Prof $599,220)
Library Holdings: Bk Vols 243,191; Per Subs 1,790
Subject Interests: Education, Nursing, Religion
Special Collections: American Studies (Early American Imprints, incl Evans, Shaw-Shoemaker), microprint; History of Science (Landmarks of Science), microprint
Automation Activity & Vendor Info: (Acquisitions) DRA; (Cataloging) DRA; (Circulation) DRA; (Course Reserve) DRA; (ILL) DRA; (OPAC) DRA; (Serials) DRA
Database Vendor: Dialog, DRA, GaleNet, IAC - Info Trac, Lexis-Nexis, OCLC - First Search, ProQuest, Silverplatter Information Inc.
Publications: A Bibliography for the Administrator (1981); semi-annual faculty newsletter (Notes from Nyselius Library)
Mem of Western Conn Libr Coun
Partic in CCLAD; Nelinet, Inc; Western Connecticut Library Council, Inc
Friends of the Library Group

L GENERAL ELECTRIC CO, Corporate Information Research Center,* 3135 Easton Tpk, 06431. SAN 302-1351. Tel: 203-373-2105. FAX: 203-373-2799. *Librn*, Jose Escarilla
Founded 1974
Library Holdings: Bk Titles 40,000; Per Subs 200
Subject Interests: Administrative law, Patents, Securities
Special Collections: Briefs File; Company History; Customs Law; Foreign Commercial & Company Law
Restriction: Staff use only
Partic in Dialog Corporation; Dow Jones News Retrieval; Newsnet; RLIN; Vutext; Westlaw

C SACRED HEART UNIVERSITY LIBRARY, Ryan-Matura Library, 5151 Park Ave, 06432-1023. SAN 302-069X. Tel: 203-371-7700. FAX: 203-374-9968. Web Site: www.sacredheart.edu/. *Actg Librn*, Susan Bradstone; *Ref*, Mary Ellen Bowen; *Ref*, William Etzel; *Ref*, Melanie Ferko; *Ref*, Lisa Kelley. Subject Specialists: *Periodicals*, Mary Ellen Bowen; Staff 15 (MLS 6, Non-MLS 9)
Founded 1967. Enrl 5,500; Fac 150; Highest Degree: Master
Jul 1999-Jun 2000 Income $904,000. Mats Exp $362,500, Books $53,500, Per/Ser (Incl. Access Fees) $215,000, Presv $3,000, Micro $21,000, Electronic Ref Mat (Incl. Access Fees) $70,000. Sal $518,515 (Prof $261,000)
Library Holdings: Bk Vols 263,146; Bk Titles 130,957; Per Subs 2,157
Subject Interests: Business and management, Religion
Special Collections: World Children's Books
Automation Activity & Vendor Info: (Cataloging) Innovative Interfaces Inc.; (Circulation) Innovative Interfaces Inc.; (OPAC) Innovative Interfaces Inc.; (Serials) Innovative Interfaces Inc.
Database Vendor: CARL, Ebsco - EbscoHost, Lexis-Nexis, OCLC - First Search, OVID Technologies, ProQuest, Wilson - Wilson Web
Partic in Bibliomation; Nelinet, Inc; OCLC Online Computer Library Center, Inc

FALLS VILLAGE

P DAVID M HUNT LIBRARY, 63 Main St, PO Box 217, 06031-0217. SAN 324-5152. Tel: 860-824-7424. *Librn*, June Kubarek; *Ch Servs*, Erica Joncyk
Founded 1891. Pop 1,052; Circ 17,284
Jul 1999-Jun 2000 Income $79,867, State $1,300, City $30,000. Mats Exp $8,272, Books $7,000, Other Print Mats $1,272. Sal $42,618
Library Holdings: Per Subs 42
Subject Interests: Local history
Friends of the Library Group

S FALLS VILLAGE - CANAAN, Historical Society Library,* Depot Bldg, Railroad St, 06031. (Mail add: PO Box 206, 06031-0206), SAN 374-4906. Tel: 860-824-0707. FAX: 860-824-4506. *Curator*, Marion Stock
Library Holdings: Bk Vols 250
Open Fri 2-4

FARMINGTON

P THE FARMINGTON LIBRARY,* 6 Monteith Dr, 06034. (Mail add: PO Box 407, 06034), SAN 336-0938. Tel: 860-673-6791. FAX: 860-675-7148. Web Site: www.farmington.lib.ct.us/. *Dir*, Barbara H Gibson; *Ref*, Pamela Bombara; Staff 17 (MLS 17)
Founded 1890. Pop 20,000; Circ 368,520
Library Holdings: Bk Vols 165,000; Per Subs 500
Special Collections: Framed art; Local History (Farmington Room Coll), bks, pamphlets, pictures, maps; Toy Lending Library (Realia)
Automation Activity & Vendor Info: (Circulation) CARL
Publications: Bookends; Business Member Newsletter; Monthly Calendar
Partic in Capitol Region Library Council
Friends of the Library Group
Branches: 1
VILLAGE BRANCH, 71 Main St, 06032. SAN 336-0962. Tel: 860-677-6866. FAX: 860-677-5993. *Librn*, Kathleen Lescoe
Library Holdings: Bk Vols 35,000
Friends of the Library Group

S HILL-STEAD MUSEUM ARCHIVE, 35 Mountain Rd, 06032. SAN 302-1408. Tel: 860-677-4787. FAX: 860-677-0174. E-Mail: hillstead@juno.com. Web Site: www.hillstead.org. *Archivist*, Polly Huntington; *Archivist*, Sandra Wheeler
Founded 1946
Library Holdings: Bk Titles 4,000
Subject Interests: Art, History, International relations
Special Collections: Psychical Research (Theodate Pope Riddle Coll)
Restriction: Non-circulating
Function: Research library

L LEVY & DRONEY, Law Library,* 74 Batterson Park Rd, 06032. SAN 372-3372. Tel: 860-676-3000. FAX: 860-676-3200. E-Mail: levy_droney@compuserv.com. *Librn*, Patty Mackiewicz
Library Holdings: Bk Vols 15,000

J TUNXIS COMMUNITY - COLLEGE LIBRARY, 271 Scott Swamp Rd, 06032. SAN 302-1416. Tel: 860-679-9544. FAX: 860-676-0021. Web Site: www.tunxis.cc.ct.us/library/. *Dir*, Judith Markiewicz; Staff 4 (MLS 4)
Founded 1970. Enrl 1,400
Library Holdings: Bk Vols 38,000; Per Subs 251
Subject Interests: Dentistry, Fine arts, Graphic arts, Literature, Photography, Technology
Special Collections: American Literature Coll; Art Coll; Criminal Justice Coll
Automation Activity & Vendor Info: (Cataloging) CARL; (Circulation) CARL
Partic in Capitol Region Library Council; OCLC Online Computer Library Center, Inc

CM UNIVERSITY OF CONNECTICUT HEALTH CENTER, Lyman Maynard Stowe Library, 263 Farmington Ave, 06030-4003. (Mail add: PO Box 4003, 06034-4003), Tel: 860-679-2839. Interlibrary Loan Service Tel: 860-679-2940. FAX: 860-679-1230. E-Mail: library@nso.uchc.edu. Web Site: library.uchc.edu. *Dir*, Ralph D Arcari; Tel: 860-793-2860, E-Mail: arcari@nso.uchc.edu; *Assoc Dir*, Marion Holena Levine; Tel: 860-679-3323, E-Mail: levine@nso.uchc.edu; *Circ, ILL*, Jacqueline Lewis; *Automation Syst Coordr, Tech Servs*, Lorna Wright; Tel: 860-679-4058, E-Mail: wright@nso.uchc.edu; *Bibliog Instr, Online Servs, Ref*, Hongjie Wang; Tel: 860-679-4033, E-Mail: wang@nso.uchc.edu; *Coll Develop*, Arta Dobbs; Tel: 860-679-2432, E-Mail: dobbs@nso.uchc.edu; *Regional Librarian*, John Stey; Tel: 860-679-4790, E-Mail: stey@nso.uchc.edu; *Network Services*, Sheryl Bai; Tel: 860-679-8371, E-Mail: bai@nso.uchc.edu; Staff 34 (MLS 22, Non-MLS 12)
Founded 1965. Enrl 1,624; Fac 533; Highest Degree: Doctorate
Jul 1999-Jun 2000 Income $3,539,451, Federal $492,129, Locally Generated Income $178,245, Parent Institution $2,869,077. Mats Exp $1,340,421, Books $121,721, Per/Ser (Incl. Access Fees) $955,222, Presv $26,297, AV Equip $7,639, Other Print Mats $40,590, Electronic Ref Mat (Incl. Access Fees) $188,952. Sal $1,943,994 (Prof $1,208,765)
Library Holdings: Bk Vols 194,570; Bk Titles 58,180; Per Subs 1,747
Subject Interests: Dentistry, Medicine, Nursing
Special Collections: History of Medicine
Automation Activity & Vendor Info: (Acquisitions) Endeavor; (Cataloging) Endeavor; (Circulation) Endeavor; (Course Reserve) Endeavor; (OPAC) Endeavor; (Serials) Endeavor
Database Vendor: OVID Technologies
Publications: Newsletter (quarterly); Regional Medical Library Newsletter (bimonthly)
Restriction: Circulates for staff only, Open to public for reference only
Function: ILL available, Outside services via phone, cable & mail, Photocopies available, Reference services available
Partic in Nat Libr of Med
Serves as the Regional Medical Library for New England as part of the National Network of Libraries of Medicine supported by the National Library of Medicine
Friends of the Library Group

GALES FERRY

SR ST DAVID EPISCOPAL CHURCH LIBRARY,* Corner Rte 12 & Rte 214, PO Box 296, 06335. SAN 372-5162. Tel: 860-464-6516. *Librn*, Charlotte S Sanford; Staff 1 (MLS 1)
Founded 1968
Library Holdings: Bk Titles 2,700

GLASTONBURY

P EAST GLASTONBURY PUBLIC LIBRARY, 1389 Neipsic Rd, 06033. SAN 324-279X. Tel: 860-633-5637. *Librn*, Virginia McGill
Founded 1960. Pop 28,238; Circ 15,744
Jul 1998-Jun 1999 Income $19,926, City $5,000, Locally Generated Income $1,958, Other $12,967. Mats Exp $8,950, Books $8,389, Per/Ser (Incl. Access Fees) $561
Library Holdings: Bk Vols 17,217
Friends of the Library Group

S THE FUTURES GROUP INTERNATIONAL LIBRARY, 80 Glastonbury Blvd, 06033-4409. SAN 302-1432. Tel: 860-633-3501. FAX: 860-657-3918. *Mgr*, Katherine H Willson; E-Mail: k.willson@tfgi.com; Staff 1 (MLS 1)
Founded 1971
Library Holdings: Bk Titles 15,000; Per Subs 150
Subject Interests: Family planning, Health policy, HIV-AIDS
Restriction: Staff use only
Function: For research purposes

P WELLES-TURNER MEMORIAL LIBRARY, 2407 Main St, 06033. SAN 302-1440. Tel: 860-652-7719. Reference Tel: 860-652-7720. FAX: 860-652-7721. Web Site: www.wtmlib.com. *Automation Syst Coordr, Dir*, Barbara J Bailey; E-Mail: bailey@glasct.org; *Ad Servs*, Barbara J Bailey; *Ch Servs*, Renee Pease; Tel: 860-652-7725, E-Mail: pease@glasct.org; *Coll Develop*, Elizabeth Twarkins; *Ref*, Rosalyn Gutterman; *ILL, Ref*, Sally Ruef; E-Mail: ruef@glasct.org; *Ref*, Wendy Ureiuoli; *Ch Servs, Ref*, Margy Pelka; Tel: 860-652-7718, E-Mail: pelka@glasct.org; *Ch Servs, YA Servs*, Miriam Neiman; E-Mail: neiman@glasct.org; *Coll Develop*, Barbara Bailey; *Outreach Serv*, Carole Noble; E-Mail: noble@glasct.org; Staff 31 (MLS 9, Non-MLS 22)
Founded 1895. Pop 29,000; Circ 384,730
Jul 1999-Jun 2000 Income City $1,121,755. Mats Exp $226,575, Books $206,696, Electronic Ref Mat (Incl. Access Fees) $19,879. Sal $641,826
Library Holdings: Bk Vols 111,550; Per Subs 318
Subject Interests: Gardening, Local history, Parenting
Special Collections: Connecticut Down Syndrome Congress
Automation Activity & Vendor Info: (Cataloging) SIRSI; (Circulation) SIRSI; (OPAC) SIRSI
Database Vendor: Ebsco - EbscoHost
Publications: Newsletter (Newsletter)
Partic in Cap Region Libr Coun
Special Services for the Deaf - Videos & decoder
Special Services for the Blind - Descriptive videos; Large print bks
Outreach programs include daycare story programs, depository collections in senior housing centers & deliver to the homebound
Friends of the Library Group

GOSHEN

S GOSHEN HISTORICAL SOCIETY LIBRARY, 21 Old Middle Rd, 06756-2001. (Mail add: PO Box 457, 06756-0457), SAN 302-1459. Tel: 860-491-9610. Web Site: www.goshenhistoricalsociety.org. *Pres*, Margaret K Wood; *Curator*, Henrietta C Horvay
Founded 1955
Library Holdings: Bk Vols 1,000
Subject Interests: Local history
Special Collections: Furniture; Glass; Natural Science; Pewter; Tools; Toys
Publications: Annual letter to members
Friends of the Library Group

P GOSHEN PUBLIC LIBRARY, 42 North St, 067561509. (Mail add: PO Box 158, 06756-0158), SAN 376-2726. Tel: 860-491-3234. FAX: 860-491-0100. *Dir*, Ann Davis; E-Mail: amdavis@connix.com; Staff 1 (MLS 1)
Founded 1901
Jul 2000-Jun 2001 Income $82,472, State $1,400, City $81,072. Mats Exp $21,000, Books $18,500, Per/Ser (Incl. Access Fees) $1,000, AV Equip $1,500. Sal $51,867 (Prof $30,030)
Library Holdings: Bk Titles 23,896; Per Subs 26
Partic in Western Connecticut Library Council, Inc
Friends of the Library Group

GRANBY

P GRANBY PUBLIC LIBRARY, 15 N Granby Rd, 06035. SAN 302-1467. Tel: 860-653-8955. E-Mail: staff@granbypl.libct.org. *Dir*, Joan Fox; Staff 14 (MLS 2, Non-MLS 12)
Founded 1869. Pop 9,399
Jul 1999-Jun 2000 Income (Main Library and Branch Library) $28,310, State $3,495, City $24,815. Mats Exp $46,652, Books $36,936, Per/Ser

(Incl. Access Fees) $6,000, Electronic Ref Mat (Incl. Access Fees) $3,716. Sal $252,961 (Prof $93,427)
Library Holdings: Bk Vols 55,998; Per Subs 223
Subject Interests: Large type print
Publications: Collections
Partic in Capitol Region Library Council
Friends of the Library Group
Branches: 1
FREDERICK H COSSITT LIBRARY, 388 N Granby Rd, North Granby, 06060. SAN 374-3594. Tel: 860-653-8958. *Librn*, Evelyn Caranchim; Tel: 860-653-8957; Staff 4 (MLS 1, Non-MLS 3)
Founded 1890
Friends of the Library Group

S SALMON BROOK HISTORICAL SOCIETY, Reference & Educational Center, 208 Salmon Brook St, 06035. SAN 302-1475. Tel: 860-653-9713. Web Site: www.salmonbrookhistorical.org. *Librn*, Carol Laun
Founded 1975
Library Holdings: Bk Titles 1,000
Subject Interests: Genealogy
Special Collections: American History (State 19th Century Newspapers); Connecticut History, doc; Granby Town Records (1786-1853); Home Guard, doc; Local Document Colls, account books, business papers, deeds, letters
Publications: Collections 1979, 1980, 1987, 1989, 1995, 1999
Restriction: By appointment only
Open Thurs 9-12

SR SOUTH CONGREGATIONAL CHURCH, Ethel L Austin Library, 242 Salmon Brook St, 06035. SAN 302-1483. Tel: 860-653-7289. FAX: 860-653-7952. E-Mail: schurch@connix.com. *Librn*, Joyce Burbank
Library Holdings: Bk Vols 2,400
Subject Interests: Psychology, Theology

GREENWICH

S BRUCE MUSEUM LIBRARY, One Museum Dr, 06830. SAN 302-1505. Tel: 203-869-0376. FAX: 203-869-0963. E-Mail: brucemus@netaxis.com. Web Site: www.brucemuseum.org. *Actg Dir*, Homer Rees
Founded 1925
Library Holdings: Bk Vols 3,500; Per Subs 15
Subject Interests: Asian art, Connecticut, Native Am, Natural history
Restriction: By appointment only

S DATABASE AMERICA, (Formerly Ed Burnett Consultants, Inc), Donnelley Marketing Library, One American Lane, 06831. SAN 311-6611. Tel: 203-552-6700, Ext 6427. Toll Free Tel: 800-390-6009. FAX: 203-552-6346. *Librn*, Anna Lima
Founded 1973
Library Holdings: Bk Titles 2,000
Subject Interests: Bus, Consumer buying patterns, Database bldg, Institutional, Maintenance, Marketing, Prof directories
Publications: Database Marketing; Direct Mail Lists Handbook; Guide to Mailing Lists; How to Use & Test Mailing Lists; Newsnotes...from Ed Burnett; The Basics of Business List Merge-Purge

GREENWICH DEPARTMENT OF HEALTH LIBRARY, 101 Field Point Rd, 06836. (Mail add: PO Box 2540, 06836), Tel: 203-622-6488. FAX: 203-622-7770. *Dir*, Caroline Baisley
Library Holdings: Bk Vols 1,000; Per Subs 45

M GREENWICH HOSPITAL, Gray Carter Library,* 5 Perryridge Rd, 06830. SAN 302-1521. Tel: 203-863-3285. FAX: 203-863-4664. *Mgr*, Hirem Baran; E-Mail: hiremb@greenhosp.chime.org
Founded 1965
Library Holdings: Bk Titles 2,000; Per Subs 173
Restriction: Staff use only
Partic in BRS; Conn Asn of Health Scis Librs; Health Info Librs of Westchester; Nat Libr of Med; SW Health Sci Libr Consortium

P GREENWICH LIBRARY, 101 W Putnam Ave, 06830-5387. SAN 336-1144. Tel: 203-622-7900. Interlibrary Loan Service Tel: 203-622-7944. Reference Tel: 203-622-7910. FAX: 203-622-7939. Web Site: www.greenwich.lib.ct.us. *Dir*, Mario Gonzalez; Tel: 203-622-7961, E-Mail: mgonzalez@greenwich.lib.ct.us; *Dep Dir*, Inga Boudreau; Tel: 203-622-7962, E-Mail: iboudreau@greenwich.lib.ct.us; *Ref*, Vera Skop; Tel: 203-622-7931, E-Mail: vskop@greenwich.lib.ct.us; *ILL*, Louise Gudelis; Tel: 203-622-7971, E-Mail: lgudelis@greenwich.lib.ct.us; Staff 62 (MLS 23, Non-MLS 39)
Founded 1878. Pop 58,400; Circ 951,599
2000-2001 Mats Exp $904,781, Books $532,000, Per/Ser (Incl. Access Fees) $230,000, Electronic Ref Mat (Incl. Access Fees) $142,781
Library Holdings: Bk Vols 293,214; Bk Titles 176,370; Per Subs 620
Subject Interests: Local history
Automation Activity & Vendor Info: (Acquisitions) Innovative Interfaces Inc.; (Circulation) Innovative Interfaces Inc.; (OPAC) Innovative Interfaces Inc.; (Serials) Innovative Interfaces Inc.
Database Vendor: Ebsco - EbscoHost, GaleNet, OCLC - First Search, ProQuest
Partic in Nelinet, Inc
Special Services for the Deaf - TTY machine
Special Services for the Blind - Kurzweil Reader
Friends of the Library Group
Branches: 2
BYRAM SHUBERT BRANCH, 21 Mead Rd, 06830-6812. SAN 336-1179. Tel: 203-531-0426. FAX: 203-531-0789. Web Site: www.greenwich.lib.ct.us. *Librn*, Mary Ann Moore; E-Mail: mmoore@greenwich.lib.ct.us; Staff 4 (MLS 1, Non-MLS 3)
Library Holdings: Bk Vols 29,350; Bk Titles 25,120
Special Collections: Byram Historical Vertical File
Automation Activity & Vendor Info: (Acquisitions) Innovative Interfaces Inc.; (Circulation) Innovative Interfaces Inc.; (OPAC) Innovative Interfaces Inc.; (Serials) Innovative Interfaces Inc.
Database Vendor: Ebsco - EbscoHost, GaleNet, OCLC - First Search, ProQuest
Partic in Nelinet, Inc
Special Services for the Deaf - TTY machine
Special Services for the Blind - Kurzweil Reader
Friends of the Library Group
COS COB BRANCH, 5 Sinawoy Rd, Cos Cob, 06807-2701. SAN 336-1209. Tel: 203-622-6883. FAX: 203-661-5315. Web Site: www.greenwich.lib.ct.us. *Librn*, Wendy Silver; E-Mail: wsilver@greenwich.lib.ct.us; Staff 4 (MLS 1, Non-MLS 3)
Library Holdings: Bk Vols 24,646; Bk Titles 26,083
Automation Activity & Vendor Info: (Acquisitions) Innovative Interfaces Inc.; (Circulation) Innovative Interfaces Inc.; (OPAC) Innovative Interfaces Inc.; (Serials) Innovative Interfaces Inc.
Database Vendor: Ebsco - EbscoHost, GaleNet, OCLC - First Search, ProQuest
Partic in Nelinet, Inc
Special Services for the Deaf - TTY machine
Special Services for the Blind - Kurzweil Reader
Friends of the Library Group
Bookmobiles: 1

S NEWSPAPER FEATURES COUNCIL, Library Information Center, 22 Byfield Lane, 06830. SAN 371-2311. Tel: 203-661-3386. FAX: 203-661-7337. *Dir*, Corinta Kotula
Founded 1955
Library Holdings: Bk Vols 410
Restriction: Staff use only
Archives are stored at the Ohio State Univesity Cartoon Research Library

GROTON

P BILL MEMORIAL LIBRARY, 240 Monument St, 06340. SAN 302-1556. Tel: 860-445-0392. FAX: 860-449-8971. Web Site: www.billmemorial.org. *Dir*, Hali R Keeler; E-Mail: hkeeler@billmemorial.libet.org; Staff 4 (MLS 1, Non-MLS 3)
Founded 1890
Library Holdings: Bk Vols 20,000
Subject Interests: Genealogy, Local history
Mem of Eastern Conn Librs, Inc
Friends of the Library Group

S GENERAL DYNAMICS CORP, Electric Boat Company Library, Eastern Point Rd, Dept 400, 06340. SAN 302-1564. Tel: 860-433-3481. FAX: 860-433-1400. *Chief Librn*, Jack Barclay; E-Mail: jbarclay@ebmail.gdeb.com
Founded 1955
Library Holdings: Bk Vols 12,000; Bk Titles 8,000; Per Subs 450
Subject Interests: Oceanography

P GROTON PUBLIC LIBRARY, 52 Newtown Rd, 06340. SAN 302-1572. Tel: 860-441-6750. FAX: 860-448-0363. E-Mail: grotonpl@mail1.nai.net. Web Site: www.town.groton.ct.us. *Dir Libr Serv*, Alan G Benkert; *Ad Servs*, Elizabeth Anne Reiter; *AV*, Shawn P Greeley; *Admin Assoc*, Kathy G Catalano; *Ch Servs*, Jane L Glover; *Circ*, Patricia Zalesny; *Govt Doc*, Jean Schweid; *ILL, Ser*, Sarah B Sutton; *Tech Servs*, Cynthia R Wright; *YA Servs*, Anne S Campbell
Founded 1959. Pop 41,284; Circ 343,220
Jul 1999-Jun 2000 Income $1,576,090. Mats Exp $229,513
Library Holdings: Bk Vols 123,388
Subject Interests: Genealogy, Local history
Special Collections: Local Doc Dep
Publications: Bibliographies; Local history books
Friends of the Library Group

M PFIZER, INC, Information Resources Group,* Eastern Point Rd, 06340. SAN 302-1580. Tel: 860-441-5507. FAX: 860-441-8519. *Dir*, Dr Roger P Nelson; Staff 19 (MLS 12, Non-MLS 7)
Founded 1959
Library Holdings: Bk Titles 2,200; Per Subs 1,150
Subject Interests: Medicine, Organic chemistry, Pharmacology
Special Collections: Drug Information Systems; Patents
Publications: Infosource
Restriction: By appointment only
Partic in SE Conn Libr Asn

A US COAST GUARD RESEARCH & DEVELOPMENT CENTER, Technical Library, 1082 Shennecossett Rd, 06340-6096. SAN 323-8970. Tel: 860-441-2648. FAX: 860-441-2792. Web Site: www.rdc.uscg.mil. *In Charge*, Sandra A Brown; E-Mail: mkendall@rdc.uscq.mil
Library Holdings: Bk Vols 10,000; Bk Titles 4,000; Per Subs 100
Subject Interests: Ocean engineering
Special Collections: Coast Guard reports
Partic in Fedlink

UNITED STATES NAVY

A BASE LIBRARY, Naval Submarine Base New London, Bldg 164, PO Box 14, 06349-5014. SAN 336-1233. Tel: 860-694-2578, 860-694-3723. *Dir*, Mary Parker; *YA Servs*, Mame M Jennings; Staff 4 (MLS 1, Non-MLS 3)
Founded 1942
Oct 1998-Sep 1999 Mats Exp $8,000. Sal $40,800
Library Holdings: Bk Titles 20,000; Per Subs 70
Partic in Eastern Connecticut Libraries; OCLC Online Computer Library Center, Inc

AM DEPUTY READING ROOM, Naval Hospital Bldg 449, Naval Ambulatory Care Center, PO Box 600, Code 17-1 Wahoo Dr, 06349-5600. SAN 336-1322. Tel: 860-694-3049, 860-694-4883. FAX: 860-694-4226.
Library Holdings: Bk Vols 3,400; Per Subs 47
Subject Interests: Medicine

A HISTORIC SHIP NAUTILUS-SUBMARINE FORCE MUSEUM, Naval Submarine Base, 06349-5571. SAN 336-1292. Tel: 860-694-4276. FAX: 860-694-4150. *Librn*, Wendy S Gulley
Library Holdings: Bk Vols 7,600
Special Collections: Copies of World War II Patrol Reports-US; Histories of General Dynamics-Electric Boat, (1915-1964), and Naval Submarine Base, Groton, (1868-); John P Holland & Simon Lake Papers; Photograph Coll; Scrapbook binders on all US Submarines; Submarines & related topics; Submarines & their inventors prior to 1900
Restriction: By appointment only

AM NAVAL SUBMARINE MEDICAL RESEARCH LAB, PO Box 900, 06349-5900. SAN 336-1268. Tel: 860-694-2558. FAX: 860-694-4809. *Actg Librn*, Thomas Tremblay
Founded 1945
Library Holdings: Bk Titles 4,405; Per Subs 150
Partic in BRS; Dialog Corporation; Docline; DROLS; Nat Libr of Med

C UNIVERSITY OF CONNECTICUT AT AVERY POINT LIBRARY, 1084 Shennecossett Rd, 06340-6097. SAN 302-1599. Tel: 860-405-9146. FAX: 860-405-9150. E-Mail: hbladm58@uconnvm.uconn.edu. Web Site: www.lib.uconn.edu/averypoint. *Librn*, Jan E Heckman; *Mgr*, Mary Ann Davison. Subject Specialists: *Marine sciences*, Jan E Heckman; Staff 2 (MLS 1, Non-MLS 1)
Founded 1967. Enrl 700; Fac 50; Highest Degree: Doctorate
Library Holdings: Bk Titles 29,272; Per Subs 298
Subject Interests: Marine sciences
Special Collections: Dredging Data; Hydrographic Charts (East Coast) 1832-1876; Literature of the Sea
Database Vendor: GaleNet, IAC - Info Trac, Lexis-Nexis, OCLC - First Search, ProQuest, Silverplatter Information Inc.
Mem of Eastern Conn Librs, Inc; Eastern Conn Librs, Inc
Partic in Nelinet, Inc

GUILFORD

P GUILFORD FREE LIBRARY, 67 Park St, 06437. SAN 302-1602. Tel: 203-453-8282. FAX: 203-453-8288. Web Site: www.lioninc.org/guilford. *Dir*, Sandra Ruoff; E-Mail: sruoff@guilford.ub.ct.us; *Asst Dir*, Lana Ferguson; E-Mail: l.ferguson@guilford.lib.ct.us; *Ch Servs*, Heinrich Suellen; *Ref*, Jacqueline Stevens; E-Mail: j.stevens@guilford.lib.ct.us; Staff 13 (MLS 6, Non-MLS 7)
Founded 1888. Pop 20,000; Circ 250,000
Jul 1998-Jun 1999 Income $850,000. Mats Exp $87,000
Library Holdings: Bk Vols 117,000; Per Subs 200
Subject Interests: Poetry
Special Collections: Guilford History & Genealogy
Publications: Steiner's History of Guilford & Madison
Partic in Libraries Online, Inc; Southern Connecticut Library Council
Friends of the Library Group

S SUNSEARCH, INC LIBRARY,* 393A Soundview Rd, PO Box 590, 06437. SAN 375-2496. Tel: 203-453-6591. FAX: 203-458-9011. *Pres*, Everett Barber
Library Holdings: Bk Vols 300; Per Subs 3

S WIRE ASSOCIATION INTERNATIONAL LIBRARY, 1570 Boston Post Rd, PO Box 578, 06437. SAN 324-783X. Tel: 203-453-2777. FAX: 203-453-8384. Web Site: www.wirenet.org.
Library Holdings: Bk Titles 600; Per Subs 26
Subject Interests: Cable indust, Wire indust
Publications: Conference proceedings, technical reports
Partic in Dialog Corporation

HADDAM

S BRAINERD MEMORIAL LIBRARY,* 920 Saybrook Rd, 06438. SAN 302-1610. Tel: 860-345-2204. FAX: 860-345-7735. E-Mail: brainerd@ct2.nai.net. *Dir*, Suzanne Risley; Staff 5 (MLS 1, Non-MLS 4)
Founded 1908. Pop 6,900; Circ 15,284
Library Holdings: Bk Titles 20,000
Special Collections: Genealogy & Haddam History Coll
Friends of the Library Group

HAMDEN

R CONGREGATION MISHKAN ISRAEL LIBRARY, 785 Ridge Rd, 06517. SAN 302-1629. Tel: 203-288-3877. FAX: 203-248-2148. *Librn*, Linda K Cohen
Founded 1840
1998-1999 Income $1,600
Library Holdings: Bk Titles 4,000; Per Subs 6
Subject Interests: Judaica (lit or hist of Jews)
Special Collections: Archives of Congregation (founded 1840); Rabbi Robert E Goldburg Coll

P HAMDEN LIBRARY SYSTEM, Miller Memorial Library, 2901 Dixwell Ave, 06518-3135. SAN 336-1357. Tel: 203-287-2686 (Administration). Circulation Tel: 203-287-2682. Reference Tel: 203-287-2680. TDD: 203-287-2680. FAX: 203-287-2685. Web Site: www.hamdenlibrary.org. *Info Tech, Ref Serv*, Krista Eberl; E-Mail: keberl@yahoo.com; *Dir*, Louise A Brundage; E-Mail: lbrundage@snet.net; *Asst Dir*, Robert Gualtieri; E-Mail: bgual@yahoo.com; *Tech Servs*, Marisa Kalt; Tel: 203-287-2687; *Circ*, Ella Baldwin; *Ch Servs*, Nancy McLaughlin; Tel: 203-230-3770; *Coll Develop, Publ Servs*, Irene Nolan; *Ref*, Doina Lucas; E-Mail: doina_lucas@hotmail.com; Staff 16 (MLS 14, Non-MLS 2)
Founded 1943. Pop 51,093
Jul 2000-Jun 2001 Income (Main Library and Branch Library) $1,590,371, City $1,545,371, Locally Generated Income $45,000. Mats Exp $185,000, Books $149,000, Per/Ser (Incl. Access Fees) $13,500, Micro $5,500, Electronic Ref Mat (Incl. Access Fees) $17,000. Sal $1,235,751 (Prof $634,912)
Library Holdings: Bk Vols 162,790; Bk Titles 138,112; Per Subs 417; High Interest/Low Vocabulary Bk Vols 1,800
Special Collections: ADA; Business Resource Center; Career Resource Center; Hamden History; Literacy
Automation Activity & Vendor Info: (Circulation) epixtech, inc.
Special Services for the Deaf - TDD
Friends of the Library Group
Branches: 2
COMMUNITY, 91 Circular Ave, 06514. SAN 336-1381. Tel: 203-287-2675. FAX: 203-287-2675. *Librn*, Barbara Florentino; Staff 2 (MLS 1, Non-MLS 1)
Special Collections: Italian Coll
Friends of the Library Group
WHITNEYVILLE, 125 Carleton St, 06517. SAN 336-1446. Tel: 203-287-2677. FAX: 203-287-2677. *Librn*, Barbara Welfare; Staff 2 (MLS 1, Non-MLS 1)
Friends of the Library Group

C PAIER COLLEGE OF ART, INC LIBRARY, 20 Gorham Ave, 06514-3902. SAN 324-2803. Tel: 203-287-3023. FAX: 203-287-3021. E-Mail: info@paierart.com. Web Site: www.paierart.com. *Coll Develop, Dir*, Beth R Harris; Staff 1 (MLS 1)
Enrl 260; Fac 40; Highest Degree: Bachelor
Jun 1998-May 1999 Income $42,797. Mats Exp $12,000, Books $10,000, Per/Ser (Incl. Access Fees) $2,000. Sal $33,000
Library Holdings: Bk Vols 11,808
Subject Interests: Fine arts, Literature, Photog, Tech arts
Special Collections: Picture Reference File
Automation Activity & Vendor Info: (OPAC) Athena
Publications: ARLIS Newsletter; Book Alert; Syllabus

C QUINNIPIAC UNIVERSITY, Arnold Bernhard Library, Mt Carmel Ave, 06518. SAN 302-1645. Tel: 203-582-8632. FAX: 203-582-3451. Web Site: www.quinnipiac.edu/libraries. *Dir*, Charles M Getchell, Jr; Tel: 203-582-8631, E-Mail: charles.getchell@quinnipiac.edu; *ILL*, Norma Keegan; *Automation Syst Coordr*, Terry Ballard; Tel: 203-582-8945, E-Mail: terry.ballard.quinnipiac.com; *Cat*, Susan Pfister; *Online Servs*, Linda Hawkes; Tel: 203-582-8633, E-Mail: linda.hawkes@quinnipiac.edu; *Acq*, June DeGennaro; Tel: 203-582-8944; *Reader Servs*, Janet L Valeski; Tel: 203-582-8633, E-Mail: janet.valeski@quinnipiac.edu; Staff 20 (MLS 8, Non-MLS 12)
Founded 1929. Pop 5,000; Enrl 5,000; Fac 5; Highest Degree: Doctorate
Jun 1999-Jun 2000 Mats Exp $750,000, Books $200,000, Per/Ser (Incl. Access Fees) $200,000, Presv $500, Micro $10,000, Electronic Ref Mat (Incl. Access Fees) $200,000
Library Holdings: Bk Vols 165,000; Bk Titles 120,000; Per Subs 500
Subject Interests: Holocaust
Special Collections: The Great Famine (Ireland)
Database Vendor: GaleNet, IAC - SearchBank, Lexis-Nexis, OCLC - First

Search, OVID Technologies, ProQuest, Silverplatter Information Inc., Wilson - Wilson Web
Partic in Coun of Conn Acad Libr Dirs; Nelinet, Inc

J SACRED HEART ACADEMY, Mary & James Dimeo Library, c/o Sacred Heart Academy, 265 Benham St, 06514. SAN 302-1637. Tel: 203-288-2309. FAX: 203-230-9680. E-Mail: library@sha-excelsior-org. Web Site: sha-excelsior.org. *Librn*, Sister Mary Matthew Papallo; *Librn*, Mary Jo Lee
Founded 1946. Pop 580; Enrl 480; Fac 46; Highest Degree: Doctorate
2000-2000 Mats Exp Electronic Ref Mat (Incl. Access Fees) $3,495
Library Holdings: Bk Vols 40,000; Per Subs 150
Automation Activity & Vendor Info: (Cataloging) Follett; (Circulation) Follett; (OPAC) Follett

R TEMPLE BETH SHOLOM, Esther Swinkin Memorial Library, 1809 Whitney Ave, 06517. SAN 302-1653. Tel: 203-288-7748. FAX: 203-288-0582. *Librn*, Nancy Smith
Founded 1960
Library Holdings: Bk Titles 1,500
Subject Interests: Holocaust

HAMPTON

P FLETCHER MEMORIAL LIBRARY,* 257 Main St, 06247. SAN 302-1661. Tel: 860-455-9295. *Librn*, Mrs Ray P Fuller
Pop 1,350; Circ 12,000
Library Holdings: Bk Vols 14,000
Partic in Eastern Connecticut Libraries

HARTFORD

AETNA INC
L LAW LIBRARY, 151 Farmington Ave-RC4A, 06156. SAN 336-156X. Tel: 860-273-8183. FAX: 860-273-8340. *Librn*, Frances Bertelli; Staff 3 (MLS 1, Non-MLS 2)
Founded 1975
Library Holdings: Bk Vols 15,000; Per Subs 50
Subject Interests: Corporate law, Health law
Automation Activity & Vendor Info: (Cataloging) epixtech, inc.; (Circulation) epixtech, inc.
Restriction: Staff use only, Use of others with permission of librarian
Function: Research library

S ARTHUR ANDERSEN, LLP LIBRARY, One Financial Plaza, 06103. SAN 326-9965. Tel: 860-280-0526. FAX: 860-280-0554. *Librn*, Marianne Cirrito; Staff 1 (MLS 1)
Library Holdings: Bk Titles 500; Per Subs 300
Partic in Spec Libr Asn

J CAPITAL COMMUNITY TECHNICAL COLLEGE, Woodland Campus Library,* 61 Woodland St, 06105. SAN 302-1777. Tel: 860-520-7891. FAX: 860-520-7909. Web Site: www.cctc.commnet.edu. *Dir*, Mary Ann Affleck; E-Mail: affleck@commnet.edu; *Coll Develop*, Karen DeLoatch; Staff 5 (MLS 5)
Founded 1967
Jul 1997-Jun 1998 Income $516,839. Mats Exp $81,188. Sal $345,567 (Prof $275,142)
Library Holdings: Bk Titles 51,183; Per Subs 445
Automation Activity & Vendor Info: (Circulation) CARL
Publications: Guide to Research; Library Workbook
Partic in Capitol Region Library Council; OCLC Online Computer Library Center, Inc

S CAPITOL REGION EDUCATION COUNCIL, CREC Resource Center,* 111 Charter Oak Ave, 06106. SAN 372-6398. Tel: 860-524-4017. FAX: 860-246-3304. Web Site: www.crec.org. *Res*, Nancy Goff; E-Mail: ngoff@crec.org
Jul 1998-Jun 1999 Income $70,000. Mats Exp $5,000. Sal $50,000
Subject Interests: Adult education

SR CATHOLIC LENDING LIBRARY - ARCHDIOCESE OF HARTFORD,* 125 Market St, 06103. SAN 302-167X. Tel: 860-522-0602. FAX: 860-247-3490. *Dir*, Rev Edward J McLean
Founded 1935
Library Holdings: Bk Titles 10,000
Subject Interests: Liturgy, Philosophy, Theology
Special Collections: Drawings (G K Chesterton Coll); Etchings (Childe Hassam); Guerre & Miserere (G Rouault Coll); Madonna (Robert Newman Coll); Monotypes (Eugene Higgins Coll)

S CONNECTICUT DEPARTMENT OF CHILDREN & FAMILIES, DCF Library, 505 Hudson St, 6th Flr, 06106-7107. SAN 375-5053. Tel: 860-550-6442. FAX: 860-550-6362. *Librn*, Mark Sosnowski; E-Mail: mark.sosnowski@po.state.ct.us
Founded 1992
Library Holdings: Bk Titles 2,000
Subject Interests: Child welfare
Partic in LVIS; OCLC Online Computer Library Center, Inc

S THE CONNECTICUT HISTORICAL SOCIETY LIBRARY, One Elizabeth St, 06105. SAN 302-1696. Tel: 860-236-5621. FAX: 860-236-2664. E-Mail: libchs@chs.org. Web Site: www.chs.org. *Dir*, David M Kahn; *Archivist*, Ruth Blair; *Coll Develop*, Gary Wait; *Ref*, Margaret Maier; Staff 12 (MLS 8, Non-MLS 4)
Founded 1825
Library Holdings: Bk Vols 100,000; Bk Titles 70,000; Per Subs 200
Subject Interests: Children's literature, Connecticut, Genealogy, Local history, New England, Religion
Special Collections: Connecticut Imprints; Historical Manuscripts; Juvenile (Bates & Caroline Hewins Coll); Sermons
Publications: Loan Collection Catalogue
Partic in OCLC Online Computer Library Center, Inc

GL CONNECTICUT JUDICIAL DEPARTMENT, Hartford Law Library, Superior & Appellate Courthouse, Rm 201, 95 Washington St, 06106. SAN 336-1837. Tel: 860-548-2866. FAX: 860-548-2868. Web Site: www.jud.state.ct.us. *Librn*, Carole Martin; E-Mail: carole.martin@jud.state.ct.us
Library Holdings: Bk Vols 40,000

S CONNECTICUT STATE DEPARTMENT OF HIGHER EDUCATION, 61 Woodland St, 06105. SAN 323-5068. Tel: 860-947-1842. FAX: 860-947-1311. Web Site: www.ctdhe.org. *In Charge*, Dr Jan W Lyddon; E-Mail: jlyddon@commnet.edu
Library Holdings: Bk Vols 1,000

P CONNECTICUT STATE LIBRARY, 231 Capitol Ave, 06106. SAN 336-1594. Tel: 860-757-6510. Interlibrary Loan Service Tel: 860-757-6530. Circulation Tel: 860-757-6530. Reference Tel: 860-757-6500. FAX: 860-757-6503. E-Mail: isref@cslib.org. Web Site: www.cslib.org. *Dir Libr Serv*, Lynne Newell; Tel: 860-757-6565, E-Mail: lnewell@clsib.org; *Admin Dir*, Richard L Kingston; Tel: 860-566-1021, E-Mail: rkingston@cslib.org; *State Librn*, Kendall Wiggin; E-Mail: kwiggin@cslib.org; *Ref Serv*, Denise Jernigan; Tel: 860-757-6590, Fax: 860-757-6539, E-Mail: djernigan@cslib.org; *Ref Serv*, Richard C Roberts; Tel: 860-757-6590, Fax: 860-757-6521, E-Mail: rroberts@cslib.org; *Ref Serv*, Julie Schwartz; Tel: 860-757-6570, Fax: 860-757-6569, E-Mail: jschwartz@cslib.org; *Cat*, Stephen Slovasky; Tel: 860-757-6546, E-Mail: sslovasky@cslib.org; *Coll Develop*, Diane Pizzo; Tel: 860-757-6561, Fax: 860-757-6559, E-Mail: dpizzo@cslib.org; *Archivist*, Mark H Jones; Tel: 860-757-6595, Fax: 860-757-6542, E-Mail: mjones@cslib.org; *ILL*, Joseph Starkowski; Fax: 860-757-6559, E-Mail: jstarkowski@cslib.org. Subject Specialists: *Genealogy*, Richard C Roberts; *Govt info*, Julie Schwartz; *History*, Richard C Roberts; *Law*, Denise Jernigan; Staff 50 (MLS 39, Non-MLS 11)
Founded 1854. Fac 162
Jul 1999-Jun 2000 Income (Main Library Only) $18,340,364, State $14,323,978, Federal $2,775,268, Other $1,241,118. Mats Exp $944,745, Books $117,356, Per/Ser (Incl. Access Fees) $87,255, Presv $14,138, Micro $99,408, Other Print Mats $569,088, Electronic Ref Mat (Incl. Access Fees) $57,500. Sal $5,550,040 (Prof $2,184,559)
Library Holdings: Bk Vols 1,045,448; Per Subs 2,838
Subject Interests: Government, Law, Political science, Pub policy, State hist for genealogy
Special Collections: Archives & Historical Manuscripts; Cemetery Inscriptions; Census Records; Charter of 1662; Church, Town & Vital Records; Colt Firearms; Connecticut - Aerial Photographic Survey Maps; Connecticut Shelf Clock Coll; Fraternal Orders; Governor's Portraits; Law; Law Reports; Legislative Reference; Legislative Transcripts; Map Coll; Medals, Coins & Indian Relics; Military Records & War Posters; Newspapers; Old Houses of Connecticut; State & Local History; State Statutes
Automation Activity & Vendor Info: (Acquisitions) Innovative Interfaces Inc.; (Cataloging) Innovative Interfaces Inc.; (Circulation) Innovative Interfaces Inc.; (OPAC) Innovative Interfaces Inc.; (Serials) Innovative Interfaces Inc.
Database Vendor: Dialog, Ebsco - EbscoHost, GaleNet, IAC - Info Trac, Lexis-Nexis, OCLC - First Search
Publications: Checklist of Connecticut State Documents; Connecticut Union List of Serials; The Connector
Function: Research library
Partic in Conn State Univ Libr Syst; New England Law Library Consortium, Inc
Branches: 3
LIBRARY FOR THE BLIND & PHYSICALLY HANDICAPPED
See Separate Entry in Rocky Hill
MIDDLETOWN LIBRARY SERVICE CENTER, 786 S Main St, Middletown, 06457. SAN 336-1683. Tel: 860-344-2972. FAX: 860-344-2537. Web Site: www.cslib.org. *Dir*, Mary Engels; E-Mail: mengels@cslib.org; Staff 4 (MLS 2, Non-MLS 2)
Library Holdings: Bk Titles 77,000; Per Subs 50
Subject Interests: Librarianship
Database Vendor: OCLC - First Search
WILLIMANTIC LIBRARY SERVICE CENTER, 1216 Main St, Willimantic, 06226. SAN 302-4504. Tel: 860-456-1717. Toll Free Tel: 800-253-7944. FAX: 860-423-5874. Web Site: www.cslib.org. *Dir*, Susan Cormier; E-Mail: scormier@cslib.org; Staff 6 (MLS 2, Non-MLS 4)
Library Holdings: Bk Titles 80,000

L DAY, BERRY & HOWARD LIBRARY,* City Pl I, 185 Asylum St, 06103-3499. SAN 302-1769. Tel: 860-275-0100, 860-275-0320, 860-275-0322. FAX: 860-275-0343. *Librn*, Karen Hannigan; *Librn*, Sara Zagorski; *Librn*, Carla Simmons; *Librn*, Linda Howey
Library Holdings: Bk Vols 25,000; Per Subs 170
Subject Interests: Law
Partic in Dialog Corporation; Westlaw

SR EPISCOPAL DIOCESE OF CONNECTICUT, Diocesan Library & Archives, 1335 Asylum Ave, 06105. SAN 325-7541. Tel: 860-233-4481. FAX: 860-523-1410. Web Site: www.tiac.net/users/diocese/new.htm. *Archivist*, Robert G Carroon; E-Mail: jcarroon@ctdiocese.org
Founded 1784
Library Holdings: Bk Vols 12; Bk Titles 10,010
Subject Interests: Religion
Special Collections: Bishop's Papers; Colonial Connecticut Church Records

S HARRIET BEECHER STOWE CENTER LIBRARY, 77 Forest St, 06105-3296. SAN 336-2647. Tel: 860-522-9258. FAX: 860-522-9259. E-Mail: stowelib@hartnet.org. Web Site: www.hartnet.org/stowe. *Dir*, Katherine Kane; *Librn*, Jacqueline McKiernan; Staff 1 (Non-MLS 1)
Founded 1965
Library Holdings: Bk Vols 15,000; Per Subs 40
Subject Interests: 19th Century Am decorative arts, 19th Century women's hist, Afro-American hist
Special Collections: Conservancy photo survey & data sheets on Hartford; Harriet Beecher Stowe Coll; Lyman Beecher Family Coll, photogs; Warner Family Coll; William H Gillette Coll
Publications: The Papers of Harriet Beecher Stowe, microfilm edition of the papers of Isabella Beecher Hooker
Restriction: By appointment only
Partic in OCLC Online Computer Library Center, Inc

J HARTFORD COLLEGE FOR WOMEN, Bess Graham Library, 1265 Asylum Ave, 06105. SAN 302-1785. Tel: 860-768-5600. FAX: 860-768-5693. Web Site: libaxp.hartford.edu/llr/online.htm. *Librn*, Sara Metcalfe; Tel: 860-768-5693, E-Mail: metcalfe@mail.hartford.edu
Founded 1939. Fac 27
Library Holdings: Bk Titles 40,000; Per Subs 135
Subject Interests: Humanities, Legal, Literature, Women's studies
Partic in Nelinet, Inc; OCLC Online Computer Library Center, Inc

S HARTFORD CONSERVATORY, Carolyn B Taylor Library, 834 Asylum Ave, 06105. Tel: 860-246-2588, Ext 11. E-Mail: hartfordconservatory@snet.net. Web Site: www.hartfordconservatory.org. *Dir*, Marilyn Huntington
Library Holdings: Bk Vols 2,000; Bk Titles 2,012

S HARTFORD COURANT NEWS LIBRARY,* 285 Broad St, 06115. SAN 302-1793. Tel: 860-241-6200. FAX: 860-520-6906. *Librn*, Kathleen McKula; Tel: 860-241-6664
Library Holdings: Bk Vols 700
Special Collections: Clipping Files; Hartford Courant News (1764-present)
Mem of Datatimes

M HARTFORD HOSPITAL, Health Science Libraries,* Conklin Bldg-3, 80 Seymour St, PO Box 5037, 06102-5037. SAN 336-2108. Tel: 860-545-2971. FAX: 860-545-2415. *ILL*, Barbara Bradley; Staff 17 (MLS 7, Non-MLS 10)
Founded 1855
Library Holdings: Bk Titles 7,144; Per Subs 871
Subject Interests: Allied health, Clinical medicine, Hospital administration, Nursing
Special Collections: History of Nursing (Foley Coll) bks, archives
Partic in Bibliog Retrieval Servs Inc; Capital Area Health Consortium; Conn Asn of Health Scis Librs; Medline; OCLC Online Computer Library Center, Inc
Branches:
INSTITUTE OF LIVING-RESEARCH BUILDING, 400 Washington St, 06106. SAN 302-1866. Tel: 860-545-7282. FAX: 860-545-7275.
JEFFERSON HOUSE GERONTOLOGY RESOURCE CENTER, One John H Stewart Dr, Newington, 06111. SAN 336-2124. Tel: 860-594-5327. FAX: 860-667-4459. *Dir*, Arlene Freed; *Dir*, Janice Kaplan
MEDICAL LIBRARY, Conklin Bldg-3, 80 Seymour St, 06102. SAN 336-2167. Tel: 860-545-2971. FAX: 860-545-2572. *Dir*, Janice Kaplan
ROBINSON LIBRARY, 560 Hudson St, 06106. SAN 336-2132. Tel: 860-545-2250. FAX: 860-545-4250. *Dir*, Janice Kaplan
Library Holdings: Bk Vols 4,000; Per Subs 300

THE HARTFORD INSURANCE GROUP
L LAW LIBRARY, Hartford Plaza, HO-1-09, 06115. SAN 328-3836. Tel: 860-547-2710. FAX: 860-547-6959. *Librn*, Marion Moebus
Library Holdings: Bk Vols 2,100; Per Subs 33
Publications: Newsletter
Partic in Dialog Corporation; Phinet; Westlaw
S LOSS CONTROL DEPARTMENT LIBRARY, Hartford Plaza, 06115. SAN 336-2221. Tel: 860-547-3099. FAX: 860-547-6004. Web Site: www.thehartford.com. *Dir*, Sarah Hager Johnston; Staff 1 (MLS 1)
Founded 1970
Library Holdings: Bk Vols 7,500; Bk Titles 5,000; Per Subs 150
Subject Interests: Engineering, Occupational safety
Publications: Focus on Loss Control; Library Bulletin; Technical Bulletin
Restriction: Staff use only
Partic in Dialog Corporation; Nelinet, Inc; OCLC Online Computer Library Center, Inc

M HARTFORD MEDICAL SOCIETY LIBRARY,* 230 Scarborough St, 06105-1129. SAN 302-1823. Tel: 860-236-5613. FAX: 860-236-8401. *Librn*, Dr H David Crombie Jr
Founded 1889
Library Holdings: Bk Vols 34,300; Per Subs 10
Subject Interests: Medicine
Special Collections: Gershom Bulkeley, mss; Hartford Imprints; History of Anesthesia; History of Medicine
Partic in Capitol Region Library Council

P HARTFORD PUBLIC LIBRARY, 500 Main St, 06103-3075. SAN 336-2280. Tel: 860-543-8628. FAX: 860-722-6900. E-Mail: webmaster@hartfordpl.lib.ct.us. Web Site: www.hartfordpl.lib.ct.us. *Chief Librn*, Louise Blalock; Tel: 860-543-8652, E-Mail: lblalock@hartfordpl.lib.ct.us; *Assoc Librn*, Lucy Gangone; Tel: 860-543-8563, E-Mail: lgangone@hartfordpl.lib.ct.us; *Assoc Librn*, Marlene Melcher; Tel: 860-543-8632, E-Mail: mmelcher@hartfordpl.lib.ct.us; *Coll Develop, Tech Servs*, Mary Billings; Tel: 860-543-8535, E-Mail: billings@hartfordpl.lib.ct.us; *Ch Servs*, Patricia O'Malley; Tel: 860-543-8654, E-Mail: pomalley@hartfordpl.lib.ct.us; *Ch Servs*, Debra Perry; *Br Coordr*, Anwar Ahmad; Tel: 860-722-6888; *Tech Coordr*, David Balesky; Tel: 860-543-8561, E-Mail: dbalesky@hartfordpl.lib.ct.us; *Bibliogr*, Cynthia Yoscik; Tel: 860-522-4888, Ext 6452; *Bkmobile Coordr*, Ida McGhee; Tel: 860-522-4888, Ext 6161; Staff 214 (MLS 37, Non-MLS 177)
Founded 1774. Pop 133,280; Circ 539,660
Jul 1998-Jun 1999 Income (Main Library and Branch Library) $5,653,790, State $43,465, Federal $40,110, Locally Generated Income $65,000, Other $352,078. Mats Exp $572,752, Books $430,162, Per/Ser (Incl. Access Fees) $46,720, AV Equip $72,695, Electronic Ref Mat (Incl. Access Fees) $23,175. Sal $4,328,716
Library Holdings: Bk Vols 485,000; Bk Titles 255,000; Per Subs 805
Subject Interests: Art, Business and management, Economics, Education, History, Literary criticism, Music, Technology
Special Collections: Center Cooperating Coll; Chamber Music Parts (Helen Rice Memorial Coll); Foundation Center Cooperating Coll; Hartford Coll; Outstanding Children's Books (Caroline M Hewins); Patent & Trademark
Database Vendor: Innovative Interfaces INN - View
Publications: annual reports; Companion to the Arts (quarterly); Hartford Public Library Programs & Events (monthly, programs); Readings (quarterly publication of Connecticut Center for the Book); special lists
Partic in Capitol Region Library Council; Nelinet, Inc
Friends of the Library Group
Branches: 9
ALBANY AVENUE, 1250 Albany Ave, 06112. SAN 336-2310. Tel: 860-722-6871. FAX: 860-722-6901. Web Site: www.hartfordpl.lib.ct.us. *Librn*, Tracie Hall; E-Mail: thall@hartfordpl.lib.ct.us
Library Holdings: Bk Vols 19,021
BARBOUR, 281 Barbour St, 06120. SAN 336-2345. Tel: 860-722-6872. Web Site: www.hartfordpl.lib.ct.us. *Asst Librn*, Erica Dean Glenn
Library Holdings: Bk Vols 14,971
BLUE HILLS, 655 Blue Hills Ave, 06112. SAN 336-237X. Tel: 860-722-6873. Web Site: www.hartfordpl.lib.ct.us. *Asst Librn*, Cynthia F Turner
Library Holdings: Bk Vols 15,028
CAMP FIELD, 30 Campfield Ave, 06114. SAN 336-240X. Tel: 860-722-6874. Web Site: www.hartfordpl.lib.ct.us. *Librn*, Dorothy Ni; E-Mail: dni@hartfordpl.lib.ct.us; Staff 4 (MLS 2, Non-MLS 2)
Library Holdings: Bk Vols 23,400
DWIGHT, 7 New Park Ave, 06106. SAN 336-2434. Tel: 860-722-6875. Web Site: www.hartfordpl.lib.ct.us. *Librn*, Melissa Yurechko; E-Mail: myurechk@hartfordpl.lib.ct.us
Library Holdings: Bk Vols 10,746
GOODWIN, 460 New Britain Ave, 06106. SAN 336-2469. Tel: 860-722-6876. Web Site: www.hartfordpl.lib.ct.us. *Librn*, Judith Pachnieski; E-Mail: jpachnie@hartfordpl.lib.ct.us
Library Holdings: Bk Vols 14,300
MARK TWAIN BRANCH, 256 Farmington Ave, 06105. SAN 336-2493. Tel: 860-722-6877. Web Site: www.hartfordpl.lib.ct.us. *Librn*, Helen Rusnak; E-Mail: prusnak@hartfordpl.lib.ct.us
Library Holdings: Bk Vols 17,700
PARK, 744 Park St, 06106. SAN 336-2523. Tel: 860-722-6878. Web Site: www.hartfordpl.lib.ct.us. *Asst Librn*, Elizabeth Perez-Balesky; E-Mail: epb@hartfordpl.lib.ct.us
Library Holdings: Bk Vols 13,200
ROPKINS, 1700 Main St, 06120. SAN 336-2558. Tel: 860-722-6879. Web Site: www.hartfordpl.lib.ct.us. *Br Coordr*, Anwar Ahmad; E-Mail: aahmad@hartfordpl.lib.ct.us
Library Holdings: Bk Vols 11,900
Bookmobiles: 1

SR HARTFORD SEMINARY LIBRARY,* 77 Sherman St, 06105. SAN 302-1831. Tel: 860-509-9561. FAX: 860-509-9509. Web Site: library.hartsem.edu. *Coll Develop, Librn*, Jackie Ammerman; E-Mail: jwa@

hartsem.edu; *Coordr*, Caroline Sperl; E-Mail: csperl@hartsem.edu; Staff 3 (MLS 1, Non-MLS 2)
Founded 1834
Library Holdings: Bk Vols 72,000; Per Subs 300
Subject Interests: Islam, Theology
Special Collections: Arabic Manuscripts; Koran, illuminated mss; New England Theologians; papers & sermons
Partic in Greater Hartford Consortium for Higher Educ; OCLC Online Computer Library Center, Inc

S HARTFORD STEAM BOILER INSPECTION & INSURANCE CO, Virtual Information Center, One State St, 9th Flr, 06102-5024. SAN 324-4423. Tel: 860-722-5486. FAX: 860-722-5530. Web Site: www.hsb.com. *Mgr*, Peter S Moon; Staff 1 (MLS 1)
Founded 1988
Library Holdings: Bk Titles 12,000; Per Subs 70
Subject Interests: Bus, Engineering, Hitech (computers), Ins
Special Collections: ASME Boiler & Pressure Vessel Code
Automation Activity & Vendor Info: (Acquisitions) CASPR; (Cataloging) CASPR; (Circulation) CASPR; (OPAC) CASPR; (Serials) CASPR
Database Vendor: Dialog, Lexis-Nexis, OCLC - First Search
Restriction: By appointment only, Company library
Partic in Cap Region Libr Coun; Hoover; Nelinet, Inc; Northern Lights Library Network; Spec Libr Asn

S INDUSTRIAL RISK INSURERS LIBRARY, 85 Woodland St, PO Box 5010, 06102-5010. SAN 302-1858. Tel: 860-520-7412. Toll Free Tel: 800-243-8308, Ext 7412. FAX: 860-520-6133. Web Site: www.industrialrisk.com. *Librn*, Patricia A Sasso; E-Mail: trish.sasso@industrialrisk.com; Staff 1 (MLS 1)
Founded 1890
Jan 2000-Dec 2000 Mats Exp $23,200, Books $8,000, Per/Ser (Incl. Access Fees) $7,000, Presv $200, Electronic Ref Mat (Incl. Access Fees) $8,000. Sal $44,000
Library Holdings: Bk Titles 3,000; Per Subs 200
Subject Interests: Chemistry, Fire, Insurance, Manufacturing
Special Collections: NFPA Codes; NFPA Fire Journal; NFPA Fire Technology; UL Reports
Function: Research library

S LEGISLATIVE LIBRARY,* Legislative Off Bldg, Rm 5400, 06106-1591. SAN 372-3844. Tel: 860-240-8888. FAX: 860-240-8881. *Dir*, Susan M Southworth; *Librn*, Barbara Karp; *Librn*, Jennifer Bernier
Library Holdings: Bk Vols 10,000

S MASSACHUSETTS MUTUAL LIFE INSURANCE CO, Corporate Library, 140 Garden St, H201, 06154. SAN 302-170X. Tel: 860-987-2195. FAX: 860-987-6800.

L MURTHA, CULLINA, RICHTER & PINNEY LIBRARY,* City Pl, 06103. SAN 371-6503. Tel: 860-240-6092. FAX: 860-240-6150. *Librn*, Judith Vanotta; Staff 1 (MLS 1)
Library Holdings: Bk Titles 20,000; Per Subs 300
Publications: Acquisition List; Handbook

L REID & RIEGE PC,* One State St, 06103-3185. Tel: 860-240-1150. FAX: 860-240-1002. Web Site: www.reidriege.com. *Librn*, Mary Ann Veenstra; Tel: 860-278-1150, Ext 1205, E-Mail: mveenstra@reidandriege.com

C RENSSELAER AT HARTFORD, Robert L & Sara Marcy Cole Library, 275 Windsor St, 06120-2991. SAN 302-1807. Tel: 860-548-2490. FAX: 860-278-0180. E-Mail: lib-info@rh.edu. Web Site: www.rh.edu/dept/library. *Dir*, Barbara J Vizoyan
Founded 1955. Highest Degree: Master
Library Holdings: Bk Vols 38,728; Per Subs 885
Subject Interests: Business and management, Computer science
Special Collections: Computer Science, Corporate Annual Reports
Automation Activity & Vendor Info: (Circulation) SIRSI
Publications: Library Periodicals List; Newsources (newsletter)
Partic in Capitol Region Library Council; Greater Hartford Consortium for Higher Educ

S ROBINSON & COLE LLP LIBRARY,* 280 Trumbull St, 06103-3597. SAN 326-1557. Tel: 860-275-8200. FAX: 860-275-8299. *Mgr*, Robert Riger; Tel: 860-275-8321; Staff 1 (MLS 1)
Library Holdings: Bk Vols 31,000; Bk Titles 8,500; Per Subs 222
Restriction: Staff use only
Partic in Westlaw

M SAINT FRANCIS HOSPITAL & MEDICAL CENTER, Health Sciences Library,* 114 Woodland St, 06105. SAN 336-2582. Tel: 860-714-4406. FAX: 860-714-8022. E-Mail: library@stfranciscare.org. *Dir*, Mark Gentry; *Asst Dir*, Carolyn Wilcox
Oct 1998-Sep 1999 Mats Exp $210,000, Books $30,000, Per/Ser (Incl. Access Fees) $160,000, Electronic Ref Mat (Incl. Access Fees) $20,000. Sal $340,000
Library Holdings: Bk Vols 15,000; Per Subs 625
Special Collections: Hospital Archives
Publications: Library Notes
Partic in Conn Asn of Health Scis Librs; Dialog Corporation; Nat Libr of Med; North Atlantic Health Sciences Libraries, Inc; OCLC Online Computer Library Center, Inc
Friends of the Library Group
Branches:

SR SAINT MONICA'S CHURCH LIBRARY, 31 Mather St, 06120. SAN 375-1740. Tel: 860-522-7761. FAX: 860-524-8458. *Librn*, Himie-Budu Shannon Jr
Library Holdings: Bk Vols 100

L SOROKIN, GROSS & HYDE PC, Law Library,* One Corporate Ctr, 06103. SAN 372-3380. Tel: 860-525-6645. FAX: 860-522-1781. E-Mail: sorokin@sorokinlaw.com. Web Site: www.sorokinlaw.com. *Librn*, Catherine Bayer
Library Holdings: Bk Vols 5,000

S THE VILLAGE FOR FAMILIES & CHILDREN, INC, Frances & C Rollin Zane Library, 1680 Albany Ave, 06105-1001. SAN 372-736X. Tel: 860-297-0558. FAX: 860-231-8449. E-Mail: zanelib@aol.com. *Librn*, Pat McCurdy-Crescimanno
Jul 1998-Jun 1999 Income Parent Institution $9,635. Mats Exp $4,111, Books $1,834, Per/Ser (Incl. Access Fees) $2,014, Electronic Ref Mat (Incl. Access Fees) $263. Sal $5,424 (Prof $5,424)
Library Holdings: Bk Vols 2,600; Bk Titles 2,000; Per Subs 16
Subject Interests: Child welfare, Psychology, Social work
Restriction: Staff use only
Mem of Capitol Regional Libr Council

§S TRAVELERS INSURANCE CO, Loss Prevention & Engineering Library, One Town Square, 13 CR, 06183-4070. Tel: 860-277-5279. FAX: 860-954-6727. *Librn*, William Boston
Library Holdings: Bk Vols 3,600; Per Subs 13
Restriction: Not open to public

C TRINITY COLLEGE LIBRARY, 300 Summit St, 06106. SAN 336-2701. Tel: 860-297-2248. Interlibrary Loan Service Tel: 860-298-2242. FAX: 860-297-2251. Web Site: www.trincoll.edu/depts/library/. *Dir*, Richard S Ross; Tel: 860-297-2258, Fax: 860-987-6232, E-Mail: richard.ross@trincoll.edu; *Acq*, George Graf; Tel: 860-297-2246, E-Mail: george.graf@mail.trincoll.edu; *Archivist*, Peter Knapp; Tel: 860-297-2269, E-Mail: peter.knapp@mail.trincoll.edu; *Head, Cat*, Thomas Zaharevich; Tel: 860-297-2243, E-Mail: thomas.zaharevich@trincoll.edu; *Circ*, Alice Angelo; Tel: 860-297-2247, E-Mail: alice.angelo@mail.trincoll.edu; *Circ*, Renee Counts; Tel: 860-297-5184, E-Mail: renee.counts@mail.trincoll.edu; *Coll Develop*, Doris Kammradt; Tel: 860-297-5352, E-Mail: doris.kammradt@mail.trincoll.edu; *Coll Develop*, Ann Crawford; Tel: 860-297-5120, E-Mail: ann.crawford@mail.trincoll.edu; *ILL*, Mary Curry; E-Mail: mary.curry@mail.trincoll.edu; *Rare Bks*, Jeffrey H Kaimowitz; *Selection of Gen Ref Mat*, Patricia Bunker; Tel: 860-297-2254, E-Mail: patricia.bunker@mail.trincoll.edu; *Spec Coll*, Trudy Jacoby; Tel: 860-297-2194, E-Mail: trudy.jacoby@mail.trincoll.edu; *Spec Coll*, Jeffrey Kaimowitz; Tel: 860-297-2266, E-Mail: jeffrey.kaimowitz@mail.trincoll.edu; *Tech Coordr*, Vincent Boisselle; Tel: 860-297-2234, E-Mail: vincent.boissele@mail.trincoll.edu; *Tech Servs*, Bronzell Dinkins; Tel: 860-297-2271; Staff 34 (MLS 17, Non-MLS 17)
Founded 1823. Enrl 2,151; Fac 195; Highest Degree: Master
Jul 1999-Jun 2000 Income (Main Library Only) Parent Institution $3,187,420. Mats Exp $1,557,922, Books $664,752, Per/Ser (Incl. Access Fees) $659,177, Presv $41,858, Micro $21,474, Electronic Ref Mat (Incl. Access Fees) $137,687. Sal $1,226,986 (Prof $775,809)
Library Holdings: Bk Vols 962,703; Per Subs 2,689
Subject Interests: Education, History, Music
Special Collections: American Education (Henry Barnard Coll); American Indian; Americana; Bibliography & History of Printing; Charles Dudley Warner Coll, mss; Charles Nodier Coll; Civil War; Cruikshank Coll; Early American Sheet Music & Periodicals; Early American Textbooks (Henry Barnard Coll); Early Voyages & Discoveries; Edna St Vincent Millay Coll; Edwin Arlington Robinson Coll; Folklore; Horology; Incunabula (Trumbull-Prime Coll); Philology; Private Press Books; Psalm & Hymn Books; Robert Frost Coll; Slavery; Walter de la Mare Coll; Witchcraft; World War I
Automation Activity & Vendor Info: (Acquisitions) SIRSI; (Cataloging) SIRSI; (Circulation) SIRSI; (Course Reserve) SIRSI; (OPAC) SIRSI; (Serials) SIRSI
Database Vendor: Dialog, IAC - Info Trac, IAC - SearchBank, OCLC - First Search
Publications: Exhibition catalogs; Gatherings; Ornithology Books in the Library of Trinity College, Hartford 1983
Restriction: Open to faculty, students & qualified researchers
Function: Some telephone reference
Partic in Capitol Region Library Council; CTW Library Consortium; Greater Hartford Consortium for Higher Educ; Nelinet, Inc
Friends of the Library Group

Departmental Libraries:
WATKINSON Tel: 860-297-2268. FAX: 860-297-2251. Web Site: www.trincoll.edu/depts/library/main/watkin.html. *Curator, Librn*, Jeffrey H Kaimowitz; Staff 3 (MLS 3)
Subject Interests: Education, History, Music
Friends of the Library Group

SR UNITED CHURCH OF CHRIST, Connecticut Conference Archives,* 125 Sherman St, 06105. SAN 325-7665. Tel: 860-233-5564. FAX: 860-231-8111. *Archivist*, Dr Evans Sealand
Library Holdings: Bk Vols 5,000
Special Collections: Church Records, doc; Early Americana; Missionary Papers

CL UNIVERSITY OF CONNECTICUT, School of Law Library,* 39 Elizabeth St, 06105-2213. SAN 336-5492. Tel: 860-570-5200. Interlibrary Loan Service Tel: 860-570-5072. FAX: 860-570-5104. Web Site: www.law.uconn.edu. *Dir*, Darcy Kirk; Tel: 860-570-5109, E-Mail: dkirk@law.uconn.edu; *Acq, Ser*, Jeannine Uppgard; Tel: 860-570-5016, Fax: 860-570-5036, E-Mail: juppgard@law.uconn.edu; *Bibliogr*, Charles S L Marlor; *Cat*, Barbara Plante; Tel: 860-570-5009, Fax: 860-570-5036, E-Mail: bplante@law.uconn.edu; *Doc Delivery*, Andrea S Joseph; Fax: 860-570-5116, E-Mail: ajoseph@law.uconn.edu; *Info Tech*, Robert P Simonds; Tel: 860-570-5059, Fax: 860-570-5036, E-Mail: rsimonds@law.uconn.edu; Staff 14 (MLS 14)
Founded 1921. Enrl 658; Fac 55; Highest Degree: Doctorate
Library Holdings: Bk Vols 471,556; Per Subs 5,994
Subject Interests: Law
Automation Activity & Vendor Info: (Acquisitions) Innovative Interfaces Inc.; (Cataloging) Innovative Interfaces Inc.; (Circulation) Innovative Interfaces Inc.; (Course Reserve) Innovative Interfaces Inc.; (OPAC) Innovative Interfaces Inc.; (Serials) Innovative Interfaces Inc.
Database Vendor: Innovative Interfaces INN - View, Lexis-Nexis, OCLC - First Search
Partic in Nelinet, Inc; New England Law Library Consortium, Inc; OCLC Online Computer Library Center, Inc; RLIN; Westlaw

L UPDIKE, KELLY & SPELLACY, Law Library,* One State St, 06123. SAN 372-3836. Tel: 860-548-2600. FAX: 860-548-2680. E-Mail: slapointe@uks.com. *Librn*, Susan Lapointe
Library Holdings: Bk Vols 10,000

S WADSWORTH ATHENEUM, Auerbach Art Library, 600 Main St, 06103. SAN 302-1955. Tel: 860-278-2670, Ext 3115. FAX: 860-527-0803. *Chief Librn*, John Teahan; E-Mail: john.teahan@wadsworthatheneum.org; *Asst Librn*, William Staples
Founded 1934
Library Holdings: Bk Vols 36,000; Per Subs 90
Subject Interests: Costume design, Decorative arts, Fine arts, Local history, Museology, Photography
Special Collections: Art (Watkinson Coll); Bookplates (Baker Coll)
Restriction: Non-circulating to the public, Open to public for reference only
Partic in Capital Region Libr Coun
Friends of the Library Group

HARWINTON

P HARWINTON PUBLIC LIBRARY,* 80 Bentley Dr, 06791. SAN 302-198X. Tel: 860-485-9113. FAX: 860-485-0051. *Librn*, Stasia Motuzick
Founded 1909. Pop 5,000; Circ 21,000
Library Holdings: Bk Vols 18,500; Bk Titles 18,000; Per Subs 55
Subject Interests: Local history
Partic in Region I Coop Libr Servs Unit
Friends of the Library Group

HEBRON

P DOUGLAS LIBRARY OF HEBRON, 22 Main St, 06248. SAN 302-1998. Tel: 860-228-9312. FAX: 860-228-4372. Web Site: www.douglaslibrary.org. *Librn*, Anne Burgan; E-Mail: anne@douglaslibrary.org
Founded 1899. Pop 8,200; Circ 41,852
Jul 1999-Jun 2000 Income $190,408, City $106,593. Mats Exp $27,461. Sal $134,783 (Prof $41,800)
Library Holdings: Bk Titles 33,000; Per Subs 70
Subject Interests: Connecticut, Genealogy
Database Vendor: Ebsco - EbscoHost, GaleNet
Publications: Our Town's Heritage (by John Sibun)
Function: ILL available
Mem of Eastern Conn Librs, Inc
Friends of the Library Group

INFIELD

L PHOENIX HOME LIFE LIBRARY, 100 Bright Meadow Blvd, 06082. SAN 372-3860. Tel: 860-403-2325. FAX: 860-403-1352. *Librn*, Briza Bisillon
Library Holdings: Bk Vols 10,000

IVORYTON

P IVORYTON LIBRARY ASSOCIATION,* 106 Main St, 06442. (Mail add: PO Box 515, 06442), SAN 324-2811. Tel: 860-767-1252. FAX: 860-767-3157. E-Mail: ivoryton.library@snet.net. Web Site: www.ivoryton.com. *Librn*, Robbie Storms
Founded 1887. Pop 1,500; Circ 12,000
Library Holdings: Bk Titles 7,000; Per Subs 30

JEWETT CITY

P SLATER LIBRARY,* 26 Main St, Griswold, 06351. SAN 376-2629. Tel: 860-376-0024. FAX: 860-376-0024.
Library Holdings: Bk Vols 15,000; Bk Titles 10,000; Per Subs 25
Partic in Eastern Connecticut Libraries
Friends of the Library Group

KENT

S KENT HISTORICAL SOCIETY LIBRARY,* 38 Main St, 06757. SAN 320-6157. Tel: 860-927-3419. *Pres*, Emily Hopson; *VPres*, Margaret McAvoy
Founded 1954
Library Holdings: Bk Vols 200
Subject Interests: Local history, Mining
Special Collections: Art (George Laurence Nelson Coll), engravings, paintings
Publications: George Laurence Nelson, artist; Kent Tales (monographic series): Barzillai Slosson's History of Kent; Rufus Fuller & the South Kent Orebed; Sherm Chase Remembers; The Pratts of Macedonia
Restriction: By appointment only

P KENT LIBRARY ASSOCIATION, Kent Memorial Library, 32 N Main St, 06757-0127. (Mail add: PO Box 127, 06757-0127), SAN 302-2013. Tel: 860-927-3761. FAX: 860-927-1427. E-Mail: kentlib@mohawk.net. *Librn*, Deborah P Custer; *Ch Servs*, Cheryl McDowell
Founded 1915. Pop 3,020; Circ 29,708
Library Holdings: Bk Vols 32,000; Per Subs 37
Partic in Western Connecticut Library Council, Inc

KILLINGWORTH

P KILLINGWORTH LIBRARY, 301 Rte 81, 06419-1218. (Mail add: PO Box 725, 06419-0725), SAN 302-2021. Tel: 860-663-2000. FAX: 860-663-2783. E-Mail: kla@killingworthlibrary.org. Web Site: www.killingworthlibrary.org. *Head Librn*, Virginia W Chapman; E-Mail: vchapman@killingworthla.libet.org; Staff 3 (MLS 1, Non-MLS 2)
Founded 1964. Pop 5,694; Circ 51,732
Jul 1999-Jun 2000 Income $212,960. Sal $85,739
Library Holdings: Bk Vols 27,700; Per Subs 94
Automation Activity & Vendor Info: (Circulation) Athena
Database Vendor: Ebsco - EbscoHost

LAKEVILLE

S THE HOTCHKISS SCHOOL, Edsel Ford Memorial Library, 11 Interlaken Rd, 06039-2101. (Mail add: PO Box 800, 06039-0800), SAN 326-0224. Tel: 860-435-3247. FAX: 860-435-8116. Web Site: www.hotchkiss.pvt.k12.ct.us/library/. *Dir*, Walter E DeMelle, Jr; E-Mail: wdemelle@hotchkiss.pvt.k12.ct.us; *Asst Librn*, David Ward; *Access Serv*, Kimberly Gnerre; *Archivist, Ref Serv*, Jennifer Tolpa; Staff 12 (MLS 4, Non-MLS 8)
Founded 1893. Enrl 550; Fac 111
Library Holdings: Bk Vols 80,000; Bk Titles 70,000; Per Subs 275
Automation Activity & Vendor Info: (Acquisitions) Innovative Interfaces Inc.; (Cataloging) Innovative Interfaces Inc.; (Circulation) Innovative Interfaces Inc.; (Course Reserve) Innovative Interfaces Inc.; (OPAC) Innovative Interfaces Inc.
Database Vendor: Ebsco - EbscoHost, Lexis-Nexis, OCLC - First Search
Partic in CLSC; Nelinet, Inc; OCLC Online Computer Library Center, Inc; Western Connecticut Library Council, Inc

LEBANON

P JONATHAN TRUMBULL LIBRARY, 580 Exeter Rd, PO Box 145, 06249. SAN 302-203X. Tel: 860-642-7763. FAX: 860-642-7763. E-Mail: j.trum.pub.libr@snet.net. Web Site: www.lebanonct.org/lib/library.htm. *Dir*, Linda Wallace; E-Mail: lwallace@lebanonpl.libct.org; *Ch Servs*, Linda Slate; Staff 6 (MLS 1, Non-MLS 5)
Founded 1896. Pop 6,400
Jul 2000-Jun 2001 Income $107,000, City $92,000, Other $15,000. Mats Exp $22,000, Books $18,000, Per/Ser (Incl. Access Fees) $1,000, AV Equip $2,000, Electronic Ref Mat (Incl. Access Fees) $1,000. Sal $53,900
Library Holdings: Bk Vols 50,000; Bk Titles 4,800; Per Subs 60
Open Mon 9-5, Tues & Thurs 1-8 & Sat 9-2
Friends of the Library Group

LEDYARD

P LEDYARD PUBLIC LIBRARY, Gales Ferry & Bill Library, 718 Col Ledyard Hwy, PO Box 225, 06339. SAN 302-2048. Tel: 860-464-9912. E-Mail: bill-lib@ledyard.lioninc.org. Web Site: www.lioninc.org/ledyard. *Dir*, Gale F Bradbury; Tel: 860-464-9917, E-Mail: gbradbur@ledyard.lib.ct.us; *Asst Dir*, Anne King; E-Mail: aking@ledyard.lioninc.org; *Asst Librn*, Mary Ellen Osborne; Tel: 860-464-6943, Fax: 860-464-2208, E-Mail: mosborne@ledyard.lioninc.org
Founded 1863. Pop 14,400; Circ 150,449
Jul 1999-Jun 2000 Income $479,049, State $3,897, City $463,469, Locally Generated Income $11,683. Mats Exp $82,425. Sal $295,724 (Prof $159,390)
Library Holdings: Bk Vols 86,836; Bk Titles 68,942; Per Subs 202
Subject Interests: Local history
Automation Activity & Vendor Info: (OPAC) epixtech, inc.
Database Vendor: Ebsco - EbscoHost, epixtech, inc.
Publications: Books & Beyond (Newsletter)
Partic in Eastern Connecticut Libraries; Libraries Online, Inc
Friends of the Library Group

LITCHFIELD

§GL CONNECTICUT JUDICIAL BRANCH, Law Library at Litchfield, Courthouse, 15 West St, 06759. Tel: 860-567-0598. FAX: 860-567-4533. *Librn*, Janet Zigadto; E-Mail: janet.zigadto@jud.state.ct.us
Special Collections: Law - primary & secondary sources with a concentration on Connecticut materials
Open Mon-Fri 9-5

S LITCHFIELD HISTORICAL SOCIETY, H J Ingraham Memorial Research Library, 7 South St, 06759-0385. (Mail add: PO Box 385, 06759-0385), SAN 302-2056. Tel: 860-567-4501. FAX: 860-567-3565. E-Mail: lhsoc@snet.net. *Dir*, Catherine Fields
Founded 1856
Library Holdings: Bk Vols 8,000; Bk Titles 6,150; Per Subs 11
Subject Interests: Local history
Special Collections: American History; Litchfield Female Academy Coll (1792-1833); Litchfield Law Coll (1784-1833); Local Economic History (Account Bk (571) Coll); Local History (Litchfield Newspaper)
Friends of the Library Group

P OLIVER WOLCOTT LIBRARY, Litchfield Public Library, 160 South St, PO Box 187, 06759-0187. SAN 302-2064. Tel: 860-567-8030. FAX: 860-567-4784. E-Mail: owlib@owlibrary.org. Web Site: www.biblio.org/owl/home.htm. *Dir*, Karen M Bohrer; E-Mail: kbohrer@library.org; *Ch Servs*, Ann Marie White; Staff 9 (MLS 2, Non-MLS 7)
Founded 1862. Pop 8,747; Circ 69,601
Jul 1999-Jun 2000 Income $554,072. Mats Exp $370,619, Books $49,531. Sal $238,118
Library Holdings: Bk Vols 45,427; Per Subs 99
Subject Interests: Local history
Automation Activity & Vendor Info: (Cataloging) CARL; (Circulation) CARL; (OPAC) CARL
Database Vendor: CARL, Ebsco - EbscoHost, GaleNet
Publications: Newsletter
Partic in Bibliomation; Western Connecticut Library Council, Inc

LYME

P LYME PUBLIC LIBRARY, 482 Hamburg Rd, 06371-3110. SAN 302-2072. Tel: 860-434-2272. FAX: 860-434-9972. E-Mail: lymepl@neca.com. Web Site: users.neca.com/lymepl/home.htm. *Dir*, Theresa R Conley; E-Mail: tconley@neca.com; *Ch Servs*, Barbara L Carlson; *Tech Servs*, Mary Schaaf; *Circ*, Elizabeth Alvord; *Circ*, LynnAnn Baldi; Staff 5 (MLS 1, Non-MLS 4)
Founded 1913. Pop 1,969; Circ 18,366
Jul 1998-Jun 1999 Income $115,819, State $1,676, City $81,978, Locally Generated Income $11,060, Other $20,105. Mats Exp $17,028, Books $9,529, Per/Ser (Incl. Access Fees) $1,489, AV Equip $5,343, Electronic Ref Mat (Incl. Access Fees) $667. Sal $60,912 (Prof $36,572)
Library Holdings: Bk Vols 23,406; Per Subs 75
Special Collections: Donald Barr Chidsey History Coll; Gertrude Jewett Eno Cookbook Coll; Tucky Jewett Garden Book Coll
Partic in Eastern Connecticut Libraries
Friends of the Library Group

MADISON

P E C SCRANTON MEMORIAL LIBRARY,* 801 Boston Post Rd, PO Box 631, 06443-0631. SAN 302-2080. Tel: 203-245-7365. FAX: 203-245-7821. Web Site: www.madisonct.com/library/. *Dir*, Sandra R Long; *Asst Dir*, Marcia Sokolnicki; *ILL*, Clara Flath; *Ch Servs*, Suzanne Maryeski; *Ref, Tech Servs*, Laurie Alper; Staff 15 (MLS 5, Non-MLS 10)
Founded 1900. Pop 15,956; Circ 193,443
Jul 1998-Jun 1999 Income $817,241, State $4,676, City $650,409, Locally Generated Income $13,032, Other $149,124. Mats Exp $151,174, Books $105,642, Per/Ser (Incl. Access Fees) $7,230, Micro $225, Electronic Ref Mat (Incl. Access Fees) $25,768. Sal $348,192 (Prof $177,661)
Library Holdings: Bk Vols 89,401; Bk Titles 75,274; Per Subs 191
Database Vendor: epixtech, inc.
Partic in Southern Connecticut Library Council
Friends of the Library Group

MANCHESTER

M EASTERN CONNECTICUT HEALTH NETWORK, Medical Library, 71 Haynes St, 06040-4188. SAN 302-2110. Tel: 860-647-6853. FAX: 860-647-6443. *Dir*, Jeannine Cyr Gluck; E-Mail: jgluck@mmhosp.chime.org
Founded 1948
Library Holdings: Bk Titles 11,000; Per Subs 200
Subject Interests: Allied health, Medical, Nursing
Friends of the Library Group

S FUSS & O'NEILL INC, 146 Hartford Rd, 06040-5921. Tel: 860-646-2469. Web Site: www.fando.com. *Librn*, Charles G Murphy; E-Mail: cmurphy@fando.com; Staff 1 (MLS 1)
Library Holdings: Bk Vols 5,200; Bk Titles 5,000; Per Subs 200
Subject Interests: Civil engineering, Environmental engineering
Database Vendor: Dialog
Restriction: Not open to public
Partic in Capitol Region Library Council

J MANCHESTER COMMUNITY COLLEGE LIBRARY, Great Path, PO Box 1046, 06045-1046. SAN 302-2102. Tel: 860-647-6164, 860-647-6167. FAX: 860-647-6238. E-Mail: ma_antonucci@commnet.edu. Web Site: www.mcc.commnet.edu/library/new/library.htm. *Actg Dir*, Randy Fournier; *Ref*, Carl Antonucci; *Ref*, Jorge Cervera; *Ref*, Paula Cook; *Tech Servs*, Diana Paris; *Circ*, Donna Brice; *ILL*, Melissa Rivera; *Per*, Pamela Perll; *Ref*, Evelyn Angry-Smith; Staff 9 (MLS 4, Non-MLS 5)
Founded 1963. Circ 26,162; Enrl 2,767; Fac 201
Library Holdings: Bk Vols 42,053; Bk Titles 38,453; Per Subs 461
Automation Activity & Vendor Info: (Circulation) CARL
Partic in Cap Region Libr Coun; Dialog Corporation; OCLC Online Computer Library Center, Inc

P MANCHESTER PUBLIC LIBRARY, Mary Cheney Library, 586 Main St, 06040. SAN 302-2129. Tel: 860-643-2471. Reference Tel: 860-645-0821. TDD: 860-646-4232. FAX: 860-643-9453. Web Site: library.ci.manchester.ct.us. *Assoc Librn*, Noreen Quinn-Lake; *Dir*, Douglas McDonough; *Asst Dir*, Ramona A Harten; Tel: 860-645-0577, E-Mail: rharten@ci.manchester.ct.us; *Head Ref*, Janet Nocek; *Head, Circ*, Katherine Byroade; Staff 58 (MLS 12, Non-MLS 46)
Founded 1871. Pop 51,618; Circ 772,586
Jul 1999-Jun 2000 Income (Main Library and Branch Library) $2,014,657, State $46,289, City $1,953,368, Federal $15,000. Mats Exp $246,000, Books $228,000, Per/Ser (Incl. Access Fees) $14,000, Presv $1,000, Electronic Ref Mat (Incl. Access Fees) $3,000. Sal $1,414,995
Library Holdings: Bk Vols 207,402; Per Subs 360
Automation Activity & Vendor Info: (Circulation) SIRSI; (OPAC) SIRSI
Partic in Capitol Region Library Council
Friends of the Library Group
Branches: 1
WHITON MEMORIAL, 100 N Main St, 06040. SAN 371-3571. Tel: 860-643-6892. FAX: 860-533-1251. *Asst Dir*, Ramona Harten; Tel: 860-645-0577, Fax: 860-643-9453, E-Mail: rharten@ci.manchester.ct.us; *Branch Mgr*, Thomas Burnham
Bookmobiles: 1

MANSFIELD CENTER

P MANSFIELD LIBRARY, 54 Warrenville Rd, 06250. SAN 302-2137. Tel: 860-423-2501. FAX: 860-423-9856. Web Site: www.biblio.org/mansfield. *Dir*, Louise Bailey; E-Mail: lbailey@neca.com; *Ch Servs*, Susan Schur; *Ref*, Valerie Toner; Staff 3 (MLS 3)
Founded 1906. Pop 18,000; Circ 250,000
Jul 2000-Jun 2001 Income $512,698, State $12,738, City $476,960, Locally Generated Income $23,000. Mats Exp $87,400, Books $64,310, Per/Ser (Incl. Access Fees) $3,140, Other Print Mats $14,450, Electronic Ref Mat (Incl. Access Fees) $5,500. Sal $357,110 (Prof $173,310)
Library Holdings: Bk Vols 65,000; Per Subs 128
Automation Activity & Vendor Info: (Circulation) CARL; (OPAC) CARL; (Serials) CARL
Partic in Bibliomation
Friends of the Library Group

MARLBOROUGH

P RICHMOND MEMORIAL LIBRARY,* 15 School Dr, PO Box 387, 06447. SAN 302-2145. Tel: 860-295-6210. FAX: 860-295-6212. E-Mail: librml@neca.com. Web Site: www.crlc.org. *Dir*, Nancy M Wood; *Asst Dir*, Ann Grybko
Founded 1924. Pop 5,737; Circ 106,061
Jul 1997-Jun 1998 Income $210,818, State $6,585, City $167,942, Locally

Generated Income $12,238, Other $24,053. Mats Exp $32,698, Books $24,057, Per/Ser (Incl. Access Fees) $3,775, Micro $700. Sal $113,550
Library Holdings: Bk Titles 25,525; Per Subs 90
Partic in Can Asn of Res Librs
Friends of the Library Group

MASHANTUCKET

P MASHANTUCKET PEQUOT RESEARCH LIBRARY,* 110 Pequot Trail, PO Box 3180, 06339. SAN 376-5814. Tel: 860-396-6800. FAX: 860-396-6874. *Dir*, Cheryl Metoyer; Staff 16 (MLS 10, Non-MLS 6)
Library Holdings: Bk Titles 32,000; Per Subs 810
Special Collections: Native American Research Library for children; Popular Culture & Ephemera with Native American Themes; Tribal Archives

MERIDEN

G CONNECTICUT POLICE ACADEMY, Police Officer Standards & Training Council, Law Enforcement Resource Center,* 285 Preston Ave, 06450. SAN 302-2188. Tel: 203-238-6531. FAX: 203-238-6643. *Librn*, Gerald Seagrave
Founded 1972
Library Holdings: Bk Vols 3,875; Bk Titles 2,300; Per Subs 60
Subject Interests: Criminal law and justice, Law enforcement
Special Collections: Connecticut Appellate Reports; Connecticut Laws & Court Cases; Connecticut Reports; Connecticut Supplement
Publications: Audio-Visual Catalog

P MERIDEN PUBLIC LIBRARY, 105 Miller St, PO Box 868, 06450-4285. SAN 302-217X. Tel: 203-238-2344. Interlibrary Loan Service Tel: 203-630-2346. Reference Tel: 203-630-2346. FAX: 203-238-3647. Web Site: www.cityofmeriden.com/services/library. *Dir*, Marcia Trotta; Tel: 203-630-6352, E-Mail: mtrotta@mail.ci.mrd.ct.us; *ILL*, Sara Porter; *Ch Servs*, Kathie Matsil; *Cat*, Susan O'Brien; *Bibliog Instr*, Rebecca Hagstrom; *Bkmobile Coordr*, Alexis Burgess; *Commun Servs*, Victoria Navin; *Publ Servs*, Roxanne Moreau; *Coll Develop*, Nancy Lauretano; Staff 11 (MLS 11)
Founded 1903. Pop 59,479; Circ 348,874
Jul 1999-Jun 2000 Income City $1,643,293. Mats Exp $189,000, Books $140,000, Per/Ser (Incl. Access Fees) $3,400, Presv $200, Micro $2,200, Other Print Mats $32,800, Manuscripts & Archives $400, Electronic Ref Mat (Incl. Access Fees) $10,000. Sal $1,239,077 (Prof $581,818)
Library Holdings: Bk Vols 220,213; Per Subs 147
Subject Interests: Local history
Special Collections: Silver Industry; US Census Bureau
Automation Activity & Vendor Info: (Acquisitions) epixtech, inc.; (Cataloging) epixtech, inc.; (Circulation) epixtech, inc.; (OPAC) epixtech, inc.
Publications: Friends of the Library (Newsletter)
Partic in Libraries Online, Inc
Open Mon & Tues 10-9, Thurs, Fri & Sat 10-5, Sun 1-5 (Oct-Mar)
Friends of the Library Group
Bookmobiles: 1

M MID STATE MEDICAL CENTER, Tremaine Resource Center, 435 Lewis Ave, 06451. SAN 336-2760. Tel: 203-694-8131. FAX: 203-694-7618. *Librn*, Wendy Urcuioli; E-Mail: wurciuo@harthosp.org
Library Holdings: Bk Titles 1,000; Per Subs 35
Subject Interests: Cardiology, Nursing
Partic in Basic Health Sciences Library Network; Conn Asn of Health Scis Librs

MIDDLE HADDAM

P MIDDLE HADDAM PUBLIC LIBRARY,* Middle Haddam Rd, PO Box 221, 06456-0221. SAN 302-2196. Tel: 860-267-9093. E-Mail: middle.haddam.lib@snet.net. *Librn*, Lynn Biega
Founded 1909. Pop 600; Circ 5,650
Library Holdings: Bk Vols 16,000
Subject Interests: Antiques, Gardening, Local history
Publications: 80 Years of Progress
Library in a 1799 building recycled into a library in 1909. Children's wing added 1965

MIDDLEBURY

S CROMPTON CORPORATION, (Formerly CK Witco Corporation), Information Services-Library, Benson Rd, 06749. SAN 302-2218. Tel: 203-573-4508. FAX: 203-573-2890. *Librn*, Patricia Ann Harmon; E-Mail: ann_harmon@cromptoncorp.com; Staff 1 (MLS 1)
Founded 1914
Library Holdings: Bk Vols 20,000; Per Subs 200
Subject Interests: Agricultural chemistry, Chemistry, Engineering, Rubber chemistry
Special Collections: Encyclopedia of Polymer Science & Engineering; Kirk-Othmer Encyclopedia of Chemical-Technology; Organic Chemistry (Beilsteins Handbuch Coll); Organic Chemistry (Houben-Weyl-Methoden Coll)
Partic in Western Connecticut Library Council, Inc

S GENERAL DATACOMM, INC, Engineering Library,* PO Box 1299, 06762-1299. SAN 326-5897. Tel: 203-574-1118, Ext 6154. FAX: 203-598-7173. *Librn*, John F Wiehn; E-Mail: wiehn@gdc.com
Founded 1975
Library Holdings: Bk Vols 1,550; Bk Titles 3,250; Per Subs 85
Subject Interests: Electrical engineering
Special Collections: ITU/CCITT Publications
Restriction: By appointment only
Partic in Western Connecticut Library Council, Inc

P MIDDLEBURY PUBLIC LIBRARY, Crest Rd, 06762. SAN 302-220X. Tel: 203-758-2634. FAX: 203-577-4164. *Dir*, Jane O Gallagher; *Asst Dir*, Janice LeDuc; Staff 3 (MLS 3)
Founded 1794. Pop 6,000; Circ 83,632
2000-2001 Mats Exp Books $45,000
Library Holdings: Bk Vols 55,000; Per Subs 90
Publications: Newsletter (monthly)
Mem of Western Conn Libr Coun
Friends of the Library Group

MIDDLEFIELD

P LEVI E COE LIBRARY,* 414 Main St, 06455-0458. SAN 302-2226. Tel: 203-349-3857. FAX: 203-349-2131. *Dir*, Karen T Smith; *Ch Servs*, Lucia Ginter
Founded 1893. Pop 4,000; Circ 37,892
Partic in Libraries Online, Inc

MIDDLETOWN

M AETNA INC, Medical Library, 1000 Middle St, 06457. SAN 371-6511. Tel: 860-636-1419. FAX: 860-636-2180. *Tech Servs*, Kathy Erzen; E-Mail: erzenka@aetna.com
Founded 1988
Library Holdings: Bk Titles 300; Per Subs 140

CONNECTICUT VALLEY HOSPITAL

M HALLOCK MEDICAL LIBRARY, Silver St, PO Box 351, 06457. SAN 302-2234. Tel: 860-262-5059. FAX: 860-262-5049. *Librn*, Pauline A Kruk; E-Mail: pauline.kruk@po.state.ct.us; *Librn*, Stephen Curtin; Tel: 860-262-5079; *Librn*, Julia Traver; Staff 3 (MLS 3)
Founded 1950
Jul 1999-Jun 2000 Mats Exp $68,000, Books $5,000, Per/Ser (Incl. Access Fees) $45,000, Electronic Ref Mat (Incl. Access Fees) $18,000. Sal $130,000
Library Holdings: Bk Titles 10,000; Per Subs 150
Subject Interests: Mental health, Psychiatric nursing, Psychiatry, Psychology
Database Vendor: Ebsco - EbscoHost
Restriction: Staff use only
Function: ILL available
Partic in Basic Health Sciences Library Network; Conn Asn of Health Scis Librs; OCLC Online Computer Library Center, Inc

M WILLIS ROYLE LIBRARY, Silver St, 06457. (Mail add: PO Box 351, 06457), SAN 324-3303. Tel: 860-262-5520. FAX: 860-262-5570. E-Mail: wroyle@connix.com. *Librn*, Storm Beverly Somers; *Reader Servs*, Heather Insull; Staff 2 (MLS 1, Non-MLS 1)
Founded 1980
Jul 1999-Jun 2000 Mats Exp $6,973, Books $491, Per/Ser (Incl. Access Fees) $1,552, AV Equip $285, Other Print Mats $1,420, Electronic Ref Mat (Incl. Access Fees) $3,225. Sal $82,000 (Prof $52,000)
Library Holdings: Bk Vols 4,400; Bk Titles 4,202; Per Subs 40; High Interest/Low Vocabulary Bk Vols 50
Subject Interests: Addictions, Community living, Fiction, Mental health, Psychology, Soc sci
Special Collections: Daily Living Skills; Entertainment videos; High interest - low reading level materials; Large Print; Music Cassettes & CD's; Spanish Language
Automation Activity & Vendor Info: (Cataloging) Sagebrush Corporation; (Circulation) Sagebrush Corporation
Database Vendor: Ebsco - EbscoHost
Restriction: By appointment only, Residents only
Function: ILL available

S GODFREY MEMORIAL LIBRARY, 134 Newfield St, 06457. SAN 302-2242. Tel: 860-346-4375. FAX: 860-347-9874. E-Mail: godfrey@connix.com. Web Site: www.godfrey.org. *Dir*, Nancy Doane. Subject Specialists: *Genealogy*, Nancy Doane; Staff 1 (Non-MLS 1)
Founded 1950
Library Holdings: Bk Vols 18,000
Subject Interests: Genealogy, History

Publications: American Genealogical-Biographical Index (5 vols per yr)
Restriction: Private library
Special Services for the Deaf - Staff with knowledge of sign language
Friends of the Library Group

J MIDDLESEX COMMUNITY COLLEGE, Jean Burr Smith Library, 100 Training Hill Rd, 06457-4889. SAN 302-2250. Tel: 860-343-5830. FAX: 860-343-5874. Web Site: www.mxctc.commnet.edu/rsrcs/library/library.htm. *Dir*, Howard Einsohn; E-Mail: mx_einsohn@commnet.edu; *Per, Ref*, Anne Paluck; Tel: 860-343-5831, E-Mail: mx_paluck@commnet.edu; *Circ, ILL*, Alma Zyko; Tel: 860-343-5834, E-Mail: mx_zyko@commnet.edu; *Circ*, Carol Nelson; Tel: 860-343-5832, E-Mail: mx_nelson@commnet.edu; *Tech Servs*, Lan Liu; Tel: 860-343-5833, E-Mail: mx_liu@commnet.edu; Staff 8 (MLS 4, Non-MLS 4)
Founded 1966. Enrl 2,309; Fac 45; Highest Degree: Associate
Jul 2000-Jun 2001 Income Locally Generated Income $81,775. Mats Exp $73,610, Books $18,296, Per/Ser (Incl. Access Fees) $15,407, Micro $5,907, Electronic Ref Mat (Incl. Access Fees) $34,000
Library Holdings: Bk Vols 44,965; Per Subs 166
Automation Activity & Vendor Info: (Acquisitions) Endeavor; (Cataloging) Endeavor; (Circulation) Endeavor; (Course Reserve) Endeavor; (ILL) Endeavor; (Media Booking) Endeavor; (OPAC) Endeavor; (Serials) Endeavor
Database Vendor: Ebsco - EbscoHost, GaleNet, OCLC - First Search
Publications: New Stuff (irregular); News Bank; Newsfile
Mem of Voyageur Regional Libr
Partic in Nelinet, Inc; OCLC Online Computer Library Center, Inc; Southern Connecticut Library Council

S MIDDLESEX COUNTY HISTORICAL SOCIETY LIBRARY,* 151 Main St, 06457-3423. SAN 326-159X. Tel: 860-346-0746. FAX: 860-346-0746. *Dir*, Dione Longley; Staff 1 (MLS 1)
Founded 1901
Library Holdings: Bk Vols 7,000
Special Collections: Genealogy (Frank Farnsworth Starr Coll), bks, mss; Local History; Town

M MIDDLESEX HOSPITAL, Tremaine Library, 28 Crescent St, 06457-7005. SAN 302-2269. Tel: 860-344-6286. FAX: 860-344-6115. Web Site: www.midhosp.org. *Dir*, Evelyn Breck Morgen; E-Mail: evelyn-breck-morgen@midhosp.org; *Ref*, Sandra Chamberlain
Founded 1972
Library Holdings: Bk Titles 2,000; Per Subs 210
Subject Interests: Medicine, Nursing
Partic in Conn Asn of Health Scis Librs; Docline; Regional Med Libr Network

GM RIVERVIEW HOSPITAL FOR CHILDREN & YOUTH LIBRARY,* 915 River Rd, PO Box 2797, 06457. SAN 377-4163. Tel: 860-704-4199. FAX: 860-704-4002. *Librn*, Margaret Stewart
Library Holdings: Bk Vols 850

P RUSSELL LIBRARY, 123 Broad St, 06457. SAN 302-2277. Tel: 860-347-2528. TDD: 860-347-2520. FAX: 860-347-4048. E-Mail: russlib@russelllibrary.org. Web Site: www.russelllibrary.org. *Dir*, Arthur S Meyers; Tel: 860-347-2528, Ext 141, E-Mail: ameyers@russell.lioninc.org; *Asst Dir*, Linda A Rusczek; Tel: 860-347-0196, E-Mail: lrusczek@russell.lioninc.org; *Head Tech Servs*, Isabel Danforth; *Head, Circ*, Janet Cavanagh; *Ch Servs*, Richard Alleva; *Ch Servs*, Judith Stoughton; Tel: 860-347-8479, E-Mail: jstough@russell.lioninc.org; *Ref*, Valerie Grate; *Ref*, Phyllis Nathanson; *Selection of Gen Ref Mat*, Cathy Ahern; Tel: 860-347-2520, E-Mail: cahern@russell.lioninc.org; *AV*, Gail Thompson-Allen; Tel: 860-347-2528, Ext 132; *Cat*, Ann Juknis; Staff 76 (MLS 20, Non-MLS 56)
Founded 1875. Pop 43,398; Circ 508,833
Jul 1998-Jun 1999 Income $2,303,837, State $47,988, City $2,134,207, Federal $10,557, Locally Generated Income $89,767, Other $21,318. Mats Exp $294,384, Other Print Mats $250,828, Electronic Ref Mat (Incl. Access Fees) $43,556. Sal $1,521,559
Library Holdings: Bk Vols 173,089; Per Subs 358
Subject Interests: Genealogy, Local history
Special Collections: Adult Basic Education (ABE); literacy materials; NRC Haddam Neck Plant
Automation Activity & Vendor Info: (Cataloging) epixtech, inc.; (Circulation) epixtech, inc.; (OPAC) epixtech, inc.
Database Vendor: Ebsco - EbscoHost, epixtech, inc., GaleNet, IAC - Info Trac, IAC - SearchBank
Publications: Russell Reminder (newsletter)
Partic in Libraries Online, Inc
Special Services for the Deaf - TDD
Special Services for the Blind - Page magnifiers
Special Services for the Disabled - Magnifier, TDD, Delivery for Homebound
Friends of the Library Group

S SERC LIBRARY, 25 Industrial Park Rd, 06457-1520. SAN 324-5497. Tel: 860-632-1485. FAX: 860-632-8870. Web Site: www.serc.rh.edu. *Dir*, Marianne Kirner; *Asst Librn*, Virginia Smyth; Tel: 860-632-1485, Ext 235; *Coordr*, Stephen Krasner; Tel: 860-632-1485, Ext 218; *Syst Coordr*, Donna-Lee Rulli; Tel: 860-632-1485, Ext 219; *Circ*, Barbara Wallach; Tel: 860-632-1485, Ext 235; *Circ*, Susan Cohen-Chase; Tel: 860-632-1485, Ext 235; Staff 6 (Non-MLS 6)
Founded 1969
Library Holdings: Bk Titles 6,382; Per Subs 300; Spec Interest Per Sub 275; Bks on Deafness & Sign Lang 100
Subject Interests: Children lit, Disability, Family
Publications: Bibliographies; Computer Software at SERC; How to do Research in Special Education; Newsletter; Test List
Function: Research library

C WESLEYAN UNIVERSITY, Olin Memorial Library, 252 Church St, 06459-0108. SAN 336-2825. Tel: 860-685-2600, 860-685-3844. FAX: 860-685-2661. Web Site: www.wesleyan.edu/libr. *Librn*, J Robert Adams; E-Mail: radams@wesleyan.edu; *Coll Develop*, Edwin Allen; *Archivist, Spec Coll*, Suzy Taraba; *Doc*, Erhard Konerding; *Ser*, Helen Aiello; Staff 17 (MLS 17)
Founded 1831. Enrl 2,905; Fac 250; Highest Degree: Doctorate
Jul 1998-Jun 1999 Income $4,963,000. Mats Exp $2,310,510, Books $890,108, Per/Ser (Incl. Access Fees) $1,158,012, Presv $73,484. Sal $2,009,143 (Prof $1,016,184)
Library Holdings: Bk Vols 1,187,027; Bk Titles 835,313; Per Subs 3,167
Publications: Numerous guides & pathfinders
Partic in CTW Library Consortium; Nelinet, Inc
Friends of the Library Group
Departmental Libraries:
ART Tel: 860-685-3327. *Librn*, Susanne Javorski
Library Holdings: Bk Vols 23,823
PSYCHOLOGY Tel: 860-685-2770. *Librn*, Roberta Raczka
Library Holdings: Bk Vols 19,117
SCIENCE Tel: 860-685-2860. *Librn*, Tim Klassen
Library Holdings: Bk Vols 166,642
Subject Interests: Astronomy, Biology, Chemistry, Geology, Mathematics, Physics
SCORES & RECORDINGS COLLECTION Tel: 860-685-3898. *Librn*, Alec McLane
Library Holdings: Bk Vols 20,000
Special Collections: World Music Archives (4000 items)

G WHITING FORENSIC INSTITUTE LIBRARY,* 70 O'Brien Dr, PO Box 70, 06457. SAN 326-0097. Tel: 860-262-5400, Ext 2522, 860-262-5469. FAX: 860-344-7585. *Librn*, Timothy E Sweeney
Founded 1970
Library Holdings: Bk Vols 3,600; Bk Titles 3,500; Per Subs 50
Mem of State of Conn Institutional Librs
Partic in Conn Asn of Health Scis Librs; Inter-Conn Orgn

MILFORD

S DORR-OLIVER, INC, Technical Library,* 612 Wheelers Farms Rd, 06460-1673. SAN 302-3753. Tel: 203-876-5537. FAX: 203-876-5432. *Librn*, William D Kallaway
Founded 1937
Library Holdings: Bk Vols 9,000; Per Subs 300
Subject Interests: Pulp and paper, Waste disposal
Partic in Dialog Corporation; SDC; Univ Halifax

P MILFORD PUBLIC LIBRARY,* 57 New Haven Ave, 06460. SAN 336-2973. Tel: 203-783-3290. FAX: 203-877-1072. E-Mail: mulford.public.lib@snet.net. *Dir, Librn*, Salvatore L Stingo; *Asst Librn, Cat*, Jean Tsang; *Automation Syst Coordr*, Monica Slomski; *Circ*, Phyllis Cullen; *Media Spec*, Arthur Bargar; *Ref*, Josephine Pan
Founded 1895. Pop 52,000; Circ 214,151
Jul 1998-Jun 1999 Income $803,858. Mats Exp $120,910. Sal $588,199 (Prof $198,229)
Library Holdings: Bk Vols 215,000; Per Subs 250
Special Collections: Milford & Connecticut History & Genealogy
Partic in Phoenix Video; SC Conn Libr Coun, Inc
Open Mon-Wed 10-8:30, Thurs, Fri & Sat 10-5
Friends of the Library Group

G NATIONAL MARINE FISHERIES SERVICE, US Dept of Commerce, Milford Laboratory Library,* 212 Rogers Ave, 06460. SAN 302-2307. Tel: 203-783-4200. *Actg Librn*, Steven Pitchford; E-Mail: steven.pitchford@noaa.gov
Library Holdings: Bk Vols 2,800; Per Subs 15
Special Collections: Food & Agriculture Organization of the United Nations (fisheries items); NOAA documents; United States Bureau of Fisheries
Partic in Dialog Corporation

MONROE

P MONROE PUBLIC LIBRARY, 7 Fan Hill Rd, 06468. SAN 302-2315. Tel: 203-452-5458. Reference Tel: 203-452-5481. FAX: 203-261-3359. E-Mail: monroe-ref@biblio.org. Web Site: www.biblio.org/monroe/monlib2.html. *Dir*, Robert R Gallucci; E-Mail: rgallucci@biblio.org; *Ad Servs*, Frederick Danowski; *Ch Servs*, Sally Markiewicz; Tel: 203-452-5459; Staff 18 (MLS 4, Non-MLS 14)

Founded 1954. Pop 18,827; Circ 148,430
Jul 1999-Jun 2000 Income $506,656, State $3,567, City $449,316, Federal $14,236, Locally Generated Income $20,365, Other $19,172. Mats Exp $95,040, Books $64,314. Sal $285,006
Library Holdings: Bk Vols 72,172; Per Subs 202
Special Collections: Environmental Resources Information Center; Loveland Newspaper Clippings of Monroe History
Automation Activity & Vendor Info: (Acquisitions) Sagebrush Corporation; (Cataloging) CARL; (Circulation) CARL; (OPAC) CARL
Database Vendor: CARL, Ebsco - EbscoHost, GaleNet
Mem of Western Conn Libr Coun
Partic in Bibliomation, Inc; Western Connecticut Library Council, Inc
Friends of the Library Group

MOODUS

P EAST HADDAM FREE PUBLIC LIBRARY, 18 Plains Rd, 06469. (Mail add: PO Box 372, 06469), SAN 302-1211. Tel: 860-873-8248. FAX: 860-873-1269. Web Site: www.ehfp.lib.ct.us. *Dir*, Judith A Westcott; E-Mail: jwestcot@chaddampl.libct.org; Staff 4 (Non-MLS 4)
Pop 7,175; Circ 15,406
Library Holdings: Bk Vols 22,656; Per Subs 28
Subject Interests: Genealogy
Special Services - Home bound delivery for handicapped people; story hour once a week for children; night time story hour on occasion
Friends of the Library Group

MOOSUP

P ALDRICH FREE PUBLIC LIBRARY, 299 Main St, 06354. SAN 302-2331. Tel: 860-564-8760. FAX: 860-564-8760. E-Mail: libafl@neca.com. Web Site: www.commnct.edu/qvctc/educ/khart.html. *Librn*, Kathleen Hart; Staff 5 (MLS 1, Non-MLS 4)
Founded 1896. Pop 15,000; Circ 19,532
Library Holdings: Bk Titles 25,881; Per Subs 34
Open Mon-Thurs 2-8pm, Fri 2-5:30pm & Sat 1-4pm, Sun Nov-Apr 12-3

MORRIS

P MORRIS PUBLIC LIBRARY, 4 North St, 06763-1415. (Mail add: PO Box 85, 06763-0085), SAN 302-234X. Tel: 860-567-7440. FAX: 860-567-7432. *Dir*, Lee S Cook; Staff 5 (MLS 1, Non-MLS 4)
Founded 1900. Pop 2,000; Circ 21,251
Jul 1999-Jun 2000 Income $56,686, State $1,700, City $47,986, Locally Generated Income $7,000. Mats Exp $7,000. Sal $34,890
Library Holdings: Bk Titles 14,254; Per Subs 30
Mem of Western Conn Libr Coun
Open Tues 10-8, Wed, Thurs & Fri 1-8, Sat 10-3

MYSTIC

P MYSTIC & NOANK LIBRARY, INC, 40 Library St, 06355. SAN 302-2358. Tel: 860-536-7721. Interlibrary Loan Service Tel: 860-536-3019. FAX: 536-2350, 860-536-7160. E-Mail: mnl@juno.com. Web Site: www.mysticnoanklibrary.com. *Dir*, Joanna M Case; *Ch Servs*, Roberta Donahue; *Ad Servs, Coll Develop*, Hanneli Ansel; Staff 4 (MLS 3, Non-MLS 1)
Founded 1893. Pop 15,000; Circ 90,000
Oct 1999-Sep 2000 Income $378,200, State $10,000, City $160,500, Locally Generated Income $74,400, Parent Institution $40,500. Mats Exp $44,710, Books $33,860, Per/Ser (Incl. Access Fees) $4,350. Sal $201,600
Library Holdings: Bk Vols 45,000; Per Subs 134
Subject Interests: Genealogy, Local history
Automation Activity & Vendor Info: (Circulation) GEAC
Publications: Annual Report
Partic in Eastern Connecticut Libraries
Friends of the Library Group

S MYSTIC AQUARIUM, Research Library, 55 Coogan Blvd, 06355. SAN 375-1600. Tel: 860-572-5955. FAX: 572-5984, 860-572-5969. Web Site: www.mysticaquarium.org. *Librn*, Gayle Sirpenski; E-Mail: gsirpenski@mysticaquarium.org
Library Holdings: Bk Titles 2,000; Per Subs 10
Subject Interests: Chemistry, Marine fisheries, Marine mammals, Water quality
Restriction: Not open to public
Function: Research library

S MYSTIC RIVER HISTORICAL SOCIETY, William A Downes Building Archives, 74 High St, 06355. (Mail add: PO Box 245, 06355-0245), SAN 371-7658. Tel: 860-536-4779. *Archivist, Coll Develop, Librn, Mgr*, Janet B Godwin; *Curator*, Helen Keith; Staff 1 (MLS 1)
Founded 1973
Subject Interests: Genealogy, Local history, Manuscripts, Photographs
Restriction: Not a lending library, Open to public with supervision only
Function: Archival collection
Open Tues 9-12, Wed & Thurs 12-4

S MYSTIC SEAPORT MUSEUM, G W Blunt White Library, 75 Greenmanville Ave, PO Box 6000, 06355-0990. SAN 302-2366. Tel: 860-572-5367. FAX: 860-572-5394. E-Mail: library_desk@mysticseaport.org. Web Site: www.mysticseaport.org. *Librn, Ref*, Paul J O'Pecko; *Archivist*, Leah Prescott; *Cat*, Susan M Filupeit
Founded 1929
Library Holdings: Bk Vols 60,000; Bk Titles 30,000; Per Subs 404
Special Collections: American Maritime Studies, mss
Publications: Rutter (quarterly)
Partic in SE Conn Libr Asn
Also has a "Fellows of the G W Blunt White Library"
Friends of the Library Group

NAUGATUCK

P HOWARD WHITTEMORE MEMORIAL LIBRARY,* 243 Church St, 06770-4198. SAN 336-3090. Tel: 203-729-4591. FAX: 203-723-1820. Web Site: www.biblio.org.whittemore. *Dir*, Joan Lamb; E-Mail: jlamb@biblio.org; *Circ*, Glenda Grieder; Staff 3 (MLS 3)
Founded 1894. Pop 29,000; Circ 110,000
Library Holdings: Bk Vols 65,000; Per Subs 120
Subject Interests: Art and architecture, Connecticut, Local history
Special Collections: Large Print Books
Partic in Bibliomation Automated Network; Region I Coop Libr Servs Unit
Friends of the Library Group

NEW BRITAIN

C CENTRAL CONNECTICUT STATE UNIVERSITY, Elihu Burritt Library, 1615 Stanley St, 06050. SAN 302-2382. Tel: 860-832-2097. Circulation Tel: 860-832-2055. Reference Tel: 860-832-2060. FAX: 860-832-3409. Web Site: www.library.ccsu.edu. *Dir*, Jeanne Sohn; *Assoc Dir*, Frank Gagliardi; *Circ*, Janice Kozovich; *Bibliog Instr*, Nick Tomaiuolo; *Coll Develop*, Lynn Johnson-Corcoran; *Govt Doc*, Richard Churchill; *ILL*, Stephen Cauffman; *Online Servs*, Emily Chasse; *Ref*, Joan Packer; *Tech Servs*, Priya Rai; *Syst Coordr*, John Rutherford; Staff 40 (MLS 23, Non-MLS 17)
Founded 1849. Enrl 12,252; Fac 354
Jul 1998-Jun 1999 Income $3,603,407, State $1,838,019, Parent Institution $1,765,388. Mats Exp $1,270,415, Books $341,585, Per/Ser (Incl. Access Fees) $732,733, Presv $26,659, Micro $47,623, Electronic Ref Mat (Incl. Access Fees) $121,815. Sal $1,677,260 (Prof $1,061,036)
Library Holdings: Bk Vols 620,958; Per Subs 2,813
Subject Interests: Education, Humanities, Technology
Special Collections: Bruce Rogers Coll; Daniel Webster Coll; Elihu Burritt Coll, bks, mss; Frederic W Goudy Coll; Gender Equity Coll, incl Htfd Feminist Libr; Polish Heritage Coll; Walter Hart Blumenthal Coll; World's Fairs Coll
Automation Activity & Vendor Info: (Acquisitions) Innovative Interfaces Inc.; (Cataloging) Innovative Interfaces Inc.; (Circulation) Innovative Interfaces Inc.; (Course Reserve) Innovative Interfaces Inc.; (OPAC) Innovative Interfaces Inc.; (Serials) Innovative Interfaces Inc.
Database Vendor: Dialog, Ebsco - EbscoHost, GaleNet, Lexis-Nexis, OCLC - First Search, OVID Technologies, ProQuest
Publications: CCSU Library Newsletter
Partic in Capital Region Libr Coun; Hartford Consortium For Higher Education; Nelinet, Inc; OCLC Online Computer Library Center, Inc

S HERALD PUBLISHING CO LIBRARY,* One Herald Sq, 06050. SAN 324-5942. Tel: 860-225-4601, Ext 302. FAX: 860-225-2611. E-Mail: nbnews@ctcentral.com. Web Site: www.ctcentral.com. *Librn*, Virginia Blanchfield
Library Holdings: Bk Vols 275; Bk Titles 185
Special Collections: Herald 1880, 1886-date, vols bd, 1921-present, micro

M NEW BRITAIN GENERAL HOSPITAL, Health Sciences Library,* 100 Grand St, 06050. SAN 302-2390. Tel: 860-224-5900, Ext 2570. FAX: 860-224-5970. Web Site: www.nbgh.org/library.html.; Staff 3 (MLS 2, Non-MLS 1)
Founded 1946
Library Holdings: Per Subs 250
Subject Interests: Clinical medicine, Health sciences, History of medicine
Publications: Library Newsletter Quarterly; Patient Education (bibliography, annual update)
Partic in Conn Asn of Health Scis Librs; Nat Libr of Med; Nelinet, Inc; OCLC Online Computer Library Center, Inc

S NEW BRITAIN MUSEUM OF AMERICAN ART LIBRARY, 56 Lexington St, 06052. SAN 371-232X. Tel: 860-229-0257. FAX: 860-229-3445. Web Site: www.nbmaa.org. *Curator, Dir*, Douglas Hyland
Library Holdings: Bk Vols 4,000
Restriction: Open to public for reference only

P NEW BRITAIN PUBLIC LIBRARY,* 20 High St, 06051. SAN 336-3155. Tel: 860-224-3155. FAX: 860-223-6729. Web Site: www.nbpl.lib.ct.us. *Dir*, Robert Gallucci; *Ch Servs*, Nancy Jordan; *Circ*, Allen Butte; *Tech Servs*, Elzbieta Cyran; *Ref*, Daniel J Palmer; Staff 55 (MLS 16, Non-MLS 39)
Founded 1853. Pop 71,911; Circ 331,901
Library Holdings: Bk Vols 260,602; Per Subs 471
Subject Interests: Local history
Special Collections: Elihu Burritt, bks, mss, pamphlets; Foreign Language Materials
Automation Activity & Vendor Info: (Circulation) CARL
Publications: Monthly Calendar, program flyers
Partic in Capitol Region Library Council
Friends of the Library Group
Branches: 2
CHAMBERLAIN, 120 Newington Ave, 06051. SAN 336-318X. Tel: 860-223-3832. Web Site: nbpl.lib.ct.us. *Librn*, Linda McNair
Library Holdings: Bk Vols 16,000
Friends of the Library Group
JEFFERSON, 140 Horse Plain Rd, 06053. SAN 336-321X. Tel: 860-225-4700. Web Site: nbpl.lib.ct.us. *Librn*, Linda Pouliot
Library Holdings: Bk Vols 15,000
Friends of the Library Group

§J NEW ENGLAND TECHNICAL INSTITUTE OF CONNECTICUT LIBRARY, 200 John Downey Dr, 06051. Tel: 860-225-8641. FAX: 860-224-2983. Web Site: www.gonewenglandtech.com. *Dir*, Robert Dockendorff
Library Holdings: Bk Vols 500; Per Subs 100

S POLISH GENEALOGICAL SOCIETY OF CONNECTICUT, Archive & Resource Center, 8 Lyle Rd, 06053-2104. SAN 370-6974. Tel: 860-223-5596. E-Mail: pgsne2@aol.com. Web Site: members.aol.com/pgsne2. *Archivist, Dir*, Jonathan D Shea; Staff 1 (MLS 1)
Founded 1984
Library Holdings: Bk Vols 3,000; Per Subs 15
Special Collections: Cartography Coll; Cemetery Inscriptions; Marriage & Immigrant Origins Databases; Polish & Lithuanian Telephone Directories; Polish Diocesan Church Directories; Polish-American Church Histories
PGS provides speakers for workshops & lectures upon request
Friends of the Library Group

NEW CANAAN

S NEW CANAAN HISTORICAL SOCIETY LIBRARY, 13 Oenoke Ridge, 06840. SAN 302-2420. Tel: 203-966-1776. FAX: 203-972-5917. E-Mail: newcanaan.historical@snet.net. Web Site: www.nchistory.org. *Exec Dir*, Janet Lidstrom
Founded 1889
Library Holdings: Bk Titles 6,000; Per Subs 30
Subject Interests: Art and architecture, Costume design, Genealogy
Special Collections: Historical Society Biographical & Genealogical Index, 1640-present, filecards; Historical Society Newspaper File & Subject Index, 1868-present, bd vols & microfilm; Hoyt Nursery Coll; Noyes Family; Price & Lee New Canaan Darien Directories, original to 1903 & current; Silliman Coll; Weed Colleciton of Paul Prindle FASG
Publications: A Guide to God's Acre; A New Canaan Private in the Civil War (Letters of Justus M Silliman, 17th Connecticut Volunteers); Annuals; John Rogers & the Rogers Groups; My Impressions of the Hour - The Diary of an Early New Canaan Teacher; Philip Johnson in New Canaan; The Hanford Silliman House; The Merritt Parkway; Wampum to Wall Street
Restriction: Open to public for reference only

P NEW CANAAN LIBRARY, 151 Main St, 06840. SAN 302-2439. Tel: 203-801-2665. FAX: 203-801-2665. Web Site: newcanaanlibrary.org. *Dir*, David Bryant; Tel: 203-801-2664, E-Mail: dbryant@newcanaanlibrary.org; *Asst Dir*, Cynde Bloom Lahey; E-Mail: clahey@newcanaanlibrary.org; *Ch Servs*, Rose Marie Zaharek; E-Mail: rzaharek@newcanaanlibrary.org; *Circ*, Suzanne Albright
Founded 1877. Pop 17,864; Circ 322,468
Jul 1999-Jun 2000 Income $1,558,837, State $9,294, City $1,240,608, Locally Generated Income $308,935. Mats Exp $263,529, Books $177,421, Per/Ser (Incl. Access Fees) $21,894, Other Print Mats $29,667, Electronic Ref Mat (Incl. Access Fees) $34,547. Sal $901,095 (Prof $538,965)
Library Holdings: Bk Vols 163,191; Per Subs 383
Subject Interests: Art and architecture, Natural science, Popular
Special Collections: Alice A & Helen C Bristow-Nature Coll; Arturo Alfandari Coll (European Art, 476-1900); Chester Hansen WWII Coll; Chinese Japanese Art & Culture; Howard Schless Medieval Coll; Richard Salant Room with Eric Sevareid Coll on broadcast journalism
Automation Activity & Vendor Info: (Acquisitions) Innovative Interfaces Inc.; (Circulation) Innovative Interfaces Inc.; (Course Reserve) Innovative Interfaces Inc.; (ILL) Innovative Interfaces Inc.; (Media Booking) Innovative Interfaces Inc.; (OPAC) Innovative Interfaces Inc.; (Serials) Innovative Interfaces Inc.
Database Vendor: OCLC - First Search
Publications: New Canaan Library News (newsletter); Polished Apple (newsletter)
Special Services for the Blind - Optelek 20/20 video magnification system; Reading edge system
Friends of the Library Group

M SILVER HILL HOSPITAL, Medical Research Library, 208 Valley Rd, 06840. Tel: 203-966-3561, Ext 2270. FAX: 203-966-2058. Web Site: www.silverhillhospital.com. *Dir*, Anne Marie Romano
Library Holdings: Bk Titles 1,110; Per Subs 157

NEW FAIRFIELD

P NEW FAIRFIELD FREE PUBLIC LIBRARY,* 2 Brush Hill Rd, PO Box F, 06812. SAN 302-2463. Tel: 203-312-5679. FAX: 203-312-5687. E-Mail: nflibweb@ct2.nai.net. Web Site: www.nai.net/~nflibweb/home.htm. *Dir*, Linda Fox
Founded 1897. Pop 13,110
Jul 1999-Jun 2000 Income Locally Generated Income $341,668. Mats Exp $53,560. Sal $260,791
Library Holdings: Bk Vols 53,879; Per Subs 207
Subject Interests: Large type print, Local history
Special Collections: Census records
Automation Activity & Vendor Info: (Cataloging) Gaylord; (Circulation) Gaylord; (OPAC) Gaylord
Open Sun 1-4pm (Oct-May), Mon & Fri 1-9pm, Tues, Thurs & Sat 10-5, Wed 10-9
Friends of the Library Group

NEW HARTFORD

P BAKERVILLE LIBRARY, 6 Maple Hollow Rd, 06057. SAN 302-2471. Tel: 860-482-8806. FAX: 860-482-8806. *Librn*, Mary Auclair
Founded 1949. Pop 5,810
Library Holdings: Per Subs 39
Subject Interests: Agriculture, Art, Gardening
Special Collections: Bicentennial of the Constitution Bookshelf
Publications: Friends of Bakerville Library Newsletter
Partic in Region I Coop Libr Servs Unit
Friends of the Library Group

P NEW HARTFORD MEMORIAL LIBRARY, INC,* 10 Central Ave, 06057. SAN 302-248X. Tel: 860-379-7235. FAX: 860-379-5806. *Dir*, Nancy Crilly-Kirk; *Asst Librn*, Betsy Whittemore; *Ch Servs, Ref*, Evelyn Caranchini
Founded 1907. Pop 6,000
Jul 1998-Jun 1999 Income $368,000, State $4,000, City $137,000, Locally Generated Income $10,000, Other $217,000. Mats Exp $62,000, Books $60,000, Per/Ser (Incl. Access Fees) $2,000. Sal $175,000
Library Holdings: Bk Vols 32,000
Publications: Bookmarks; Newsletter; Program brochures
Friends of the Library Group

NEW HAVEN

S ACES EDUCATIONAL CENTER FOR THE ARTS, 55 Audubon St, 06510-1294. (Mail add: 670 State St, 06511), Tel: 203-777-5451. Web Site: www.aces.k12.ct.us/eca. *Dir*, Robert D Parker. Subject Specialists: *Art history*, Robert D Parker; *Hist of photog*, Robert D Parker
Library Holdings: Bk Vols 300; Bk Titles 300; Per Subs 10

CR ALBERTUS MAGNUS COLLEGE LIBRARY, 700 Prospect St, 06511. SAN 302-2498. Tel: 203-773-8594. Reference Tel: 203-773-8511. FAX: 203-773-8588. E-Mail: refdesk@albertus.edu. Web Site: www.albertus.edu/library/index.htm, www.albertus.edu/libsvcctrs/libinside.html. *Dir*, Dr Samuel Brown; E-Mail: brown@albertus.edu; *Asst Dir, Head, Cat*, Joanne Day; E-Mail: day@albertus.edu; *Head, Circ, Head Ref*, Anne Leeney-Panagrossi; E-Mail: panagrossi@albertus.edu; *Head, Ser Acq, ILL*, Patricia Dawson; E-Mail: dawson@albertus.edu; *Ref*, Carissa DeLizio; E-Mail: carissa_delizio@hotmail.com; *Ref*, John McCann; E-Mail: mccann@albertus.edu; Staff 10 (MLS 5, Non-MLS 5)
Founded 1925. Enrl 2,009; Highest Degree: Master
2000-2001 Income $380,801
Library Holdings: Bk Vols 103,488; Per Subs 582
Special Collections: Donald Grant Mitchell Coll; Louis Imogen Guiney Coll; Samuel Flagg Bemis Coll
Automation Activity & Vendor Info: (Acquisitions) Endeavor; (Cataloging) Endeavor; (Circulation) Endeavor; (OPAC) Endeavor; (Serials) Endeavor
Database Vendor: Ebsco - EbscoHost, Lexis-Nexis, Silverplatter Information Inc.
Partic in Nelinet, Inc

S CONNECTICUT AGRICULTURAL EXPERIMENT STATION, Thomas B Osborne Library, 123 Huntington St, PO Box 1106, 06504-1106. SAN 302-2528. Tel: 203-974-8447. FAX: 203-974-8502. Web Site: www.state.ct.us/caes. *Librn*, Vickie Bomba; E-Mail: vickie.bomba@po.state.ct.us
Founded 1875
Library Holdings: Bk Vols 11,000; Per Subs 500

Subject Interests: Analytical chemistry, Biochemistry, Climatology, Entomology, Environmental studies, Genetics, Tobacco
Automation Activity & Vendor Info: (OPAC) Sagebrush Corporation

GL CONNECTICUT JUDICIAL BRANCH, Law Library at New Haven, County Courthouse, 235 Church St, 06510. SAN 336-1926. Tel: 203-503-6828. FAX: 203-789-6499. Web Site: www.jud.state.ct.us, www.jud.state.ct.us/lawlib/index.html. *In Charge*, Martha J Sullivan
Library Holdings: Bk Vols 55,000; Per Subs 75

M CONNECTICUT MENTAL HEALTH CENTER LIBRARY,* 34 Park St, 06508. SAN 302-2536. Tel: 203-974-7311. *Librn*, Russell Edward Aldrich
Founded 1965
Library Holdings: Bk Vols 1,200; Per Subs 69
Subject Interests: Psychiatry, Psychology

J GATEWAY COMMUNITY-TECHNICAL COLLEGE LONG WHARF CAMPUS, Library-Media Services, 60 Sargent Dr, 06511-5970. SAN 302-2617. Tel: 203-285-2057. FAX: 203-285-2055. Web Site: www.gwctc.comnet.edu/libwebpage/html. *Dir*, Michele Cone; *Librn*, Carolyn Boulay; *Librn*, Bonnie Pease
Founded 1968. Enrl 2,026
Library Holdings: Bk Vols 53,000; Per Subs 624
Partic in Colorado Alliance Of Research Libraries
Departmental Libraries:
NORTH HAVEN CAMPUS, 88 Bassett Rd, North Haven, 06473. SAN 377-7650. Tel: 203-285-2340. FAX: 203-285-2342. Web Site: www.gwctc.comnet.edu/libwebpage/libwebpage.html. *Dir*, Michele Cone; *Librn*, Nora Bird

S HASKINS LABORATORIES LIBRARY, 270 Crown St, 06511-6695. SAN 302-2544. Tel: 203-764-9353, 203-865-6163. FAX: 203-865-6963. E-Mail: story@haskins.yale.edu. Web Site: www.haskins.org. *Coll Develop, Librn*, Linda Story; E-Mail: story@haskins.yale.edu
Founded 1937
Library Holdings: Bk Vols 3,700; Bk Titles 3,400; Per Subs 100
Subject Interests: Linguistics, Physiology, Reading, Speech
Special Collections: Status Report on Speech Research
Publications: Haskins Laboratories Status Report on Speech Research
Partic in CDP

M HOSPITAL OF SAINT RAPHAEL, (Formerly Saint Raphael Healthcare System), Health Sciences Library, 1450 Chapel St, 06511. SAN 302-2552. Tel: 203-789-3330. FAX: 203-789-5176. *Dir*, Patricia L Wales; E-Mail: pwales@srhs.org; Staff 2 (MLS 1, Non-MLS 1)
Founded 1941
Oct 2000-Sep 2001 Income Parent Institution $166,000. Mats Exp $75,000, Books $10,000, Per/Ser (Incl. Access Fees) $50,000, Micro $500, Manuscripts & Archives $1,000, Electronic Ref Mat (Incl. Access Fees) $5,000. Sal $55,000 (Prof $36,000)
Library Holdings: Bk Vols 2,200; Bk Titles 2,000; Per Subs 260
Subject Interests: Allied health, Health care, Medicine, Nursing
Database Vendor: Ebsco - EbscoHost, OVID Technologies, Silverplatter Information Inc.
Restriction: Not open to public
Function: Research library
Partic in Basic Health Sciences Library Network; Conn Asn of Health Scis Librs; Medical Libr Asn; North Atlantic Health Sciences Libraries, Inc

S KNIGHTS OF COLUMBUS SUPREME COUNCIL ARCHIVES, One State St, 06511. SAN 372-6126. Tel: 203-772-2130. FAX: 203-773-3000. Web Site: www.kofc.org. *Archivist, Librn*, Susan H Brosnan; E-Mail: brosnan@kofc-supreme.com; Staff 1 (MLS 1)
Founded 1882
Special Collections: Christopher Columbus, bks & articles; Knights of Columbus, bks & archival material
Restriction: By appointment only

S NEW HAVEN COLONY HISTORICAL SOCIETY, Whitney Library, 114 Whitney Ave, 06510-1025. SAN 302-2579. Tel: 203-562-4183. FAX: 203-562-2002. *Librn*, James W Campbell; E-Mail: jcampbel@csunet.ctstateu.edu; *Ref*, Frances H Skelton; *Curator*, Amy Trout; Staff 5 (MLS 5)
Founded 1863
Library Holdings: Per Subs 20
Subject Interests: Genealogy
Special Collections: Genealogy (Lewis, Sedgwick & Sperry Family Colls), mss; Local History (business, civic & religious organizations)
Publications: A Guide to the Manuscripts & Archives in the Whitney Library of the New Haven Colony Historical Society
Friends of the Library Group

P NEW HAVEN FREE PUBLIC LIBRARY,* 133 Elm St, 06510. SAN 336-3244. Tel: 203-946-8130. FAX: 203-946-8140. Web Site: www.nhfpl.lib.ct.us. *Dir*, Howard F McGinn; Tel: 203-946-8139, E-Mail: hmcginn@nhfpl.org; *Br Coordr*, Cathleen De Nigris; Tel: 203-946-8124, E-Mail: cdenigris@nhfpl.org; *Business*, Frank Aiello; *Publ Servs*, Dale Johnson; Tel: 203-946-8131, E-Mail: djohnson@nhfpl.org; *Tech Servs*, Carole Ross; Tel: 203-946-8127, E-Mail: cross@nhfpl.org; *Tech Coordr*, John Glendon; Tel: 203-946-8697, E-Mail: john.glendon@nhfpl.org; *Coll Develop*, Christine Stempinski; Staff 72 (MLS 47, Non-MLS 25)
Founded 1887. Pop 126,000; Circ 200,000
Jul 1999-Jun 2000 Income (Main Library and Branch Library) $3,885,323, State $15,910, City $3,282,380, Federal $134,264, Locally Generated Income $168,933, Other $283,836. Mats Exp $596,826, Books $383,460, AV Equip $28,540, Electronic Ref Mat (Incl. Access Fees) $184,826. Sal $2,330,695
Library Holdings: Bk Vols 623,762; Per Subs 389
Automation Activity & Vendor Info: (Cataloging) Innovative Interfaces Inc.
Database Vendor: Ebsco - EbscoHost, IAC - Info Trac
Friends of the Library Group
Branches: 3
FAIR HAVEN, 182 Grand Ave, 06513. SAN 336-3368. Tel: 203-946-8115. Web Site: www.nhfpl.lib.ct.us. *Librn*, Nancy Moscoso-Guzman
Library Holdings: Bk Vols 25,140
Friends of the Library Group
MITCHELL, 37 Harrison St, 06515. SAN 336-3422. Tel: 203-946-8117. Web Site: www.nhfpl.lib.ct.us. *Librn*, Joan Silverman
Library Holdings: Bk Vols 49,776
Friends of the Library Group
STETSON BRANCH, 200 Dixwell Ave, 06511. SAN 336-3457. Tel: 203-946-8119. FAX: 203-946-6782. *Branch Mgr*, Maria Tonelli; Tel: 203-946-6786, E-Mail: mtonelli@nhfpl.org; Staff 4 (MLS 2, Non-MLS 2)
Function: ILL available
Friends of the Library Group

P PLANNED PARENTHOOD OF CONNECTICUT LIBRARY,* 129 Whitney Ave, 06510. SAN 376-1932. Tel: 203-865-5158. FAX: 203-624-1333. Web Site: www.ppct.org. *Librn*, Susan Killheffer
Library Holdings: Bk Vols 4,400

C SOUTHERN CONNECTICUT STATE UNIVERSITY, Hilton C Buley Library, 501 Crescent St, 06515. SAN 302-2625. Tel: 203-392-5750. Interlibrary Loan Service Tel: 203-392-7009. Circulation Tel: 203-392-5756. Reference Tel: 203-392-5732. FAX: 203-392-5740. Web Site: www.library.southernct.edu. *Dir Libr Serv*, Susan E Cirillo; Tel: 203-392-5742, E-Mail: cirillo@scsu.ctstateu.edu; *Access Serv*, Shirley Cavanagh; Tel: 203-392-5768; *Per*, Merle Bunco; *Ref*, Winnie Shyam; Tel: 203-392-5762; *Spec Coll*, Paul Holmer; Tel: 203-392-5746; *Tech Servs*, Cindy Schofield-Bodt; Tel: 203-392-5778; Staff 23 (MLS 22, Non-MLS 1)
Founded 1895. Enrl 12,800; Fac 541; Highest Degree: Master
Jul 2000-Jun 2001 Income Parent Institution $4,226,481. Mats Exp $1,841,440, Books $826,440, Per/Ser (Incl. Access Fees) $750,000, Presv $30,000, Micro $35,000, Electronic Ref Mat (Incl. Access Fees) $200,000. Sal $2,179,609
Library Holdings: Bk Vols 438,770; Bk Titles 350,000; Per Subs 2,788
Special Collections: African artifacts; Children's Books (Caroline Sherwin Bailey Historical Coll), early Am textbks; Connecticut books, pamphlets, photogs, maps, artifacts (Connecticut Room)
Automation Activity & Vendor Info: (Acquisitions) Innovative Interfaces Inc.; (Cataloging) Innovative Interfaces Inc.; (Circulation) Innovative Interfaces Inc.; (ILL) Innovative Interfaces Inc.; (OPAC) Innovative Interfaces Inc.; (Serials) Innovative Interfaces Inc.
Database Vendor: Dialog, Ebsco - EbscoHost, GaleNet, Lexis-Nexis, OCLC - First Search, OVID Technologies, ProQuest
Partic in Nelinet, Inc; OCLC Online Computer Library Center, Inc

§S SOUTHWESTERN BELL COMMUNICATIONS, Corporate Research Center, 545 Long Wharf Dr, 1st flr, 06511. Tel: 203-771-8383. FAX: 203-495-9349. Web Site: www.snet.com. *Dir*, Kathy Straka; E-Mail: kstraka@snet.com
Library Holdings: Bk Vols 3,000; Per Subs 65
Subject Interests: Computer science, Data processing, Telecommunications
Restriction: Not open to public

L TYLER, COOPER & ALCORN, Law Library,* 205 Church St, 06510. (Mail add: PO Box 1936, 06510), SAN 372-3259. Tel: 203-784-8200. FAX: 203-789-2133. *Dir*, Sally Salancy; E-Mail: salancy@tylercooper.com
Library Holdings: Bk Vols 15,000
Restriction: Private library

S THE UNITED ILLUMINATING CO LIBRARY,* 157 Church St, PO Box 1564, 06510. SAN 325-2469. Tel: 203-499-2316. FAX: 203-499-3626. *In Charge*, Julia Ficklin; E-Mail: julia.ficklin@usnet.com
Founded 1979
Library Holdings: Bk Vols 1,500; Per Subs 150
Subject Interests: Electricity generation, Energy, Engineering, Human res, Mgt
Special Collections: EPRS Technical Reports
Publications: Newsletter (quarterly)
Restriction: By appointment only
Partic in Dialog Corporation

L WIGGIN & DANA INFORMATION CENTER, 265 Church St, 06510. Tel: 203-498-4413. FAX: 203-782-2889. *Dir*, Ana Oman; E-Mail: amo@wiggin.com; *Electronic Resources*, Veronica Salaam; Tel: 203-498-4403, E-Mail: vms@wiggin.com; Staff 6 (MLS 2, Non-MLS 4)

Library Holdings: Bk Vols 17,000
Subject Interests: Law
Automation Activity & Vendor Info: (Acquisitions) EOS; (Cataloging) EOS; (OPAC) EOS; (Serials) EOS
Partic in Dialog Corporation; Dow Jones News Retrieval; Westlaw

C YALE UNIVERSITY LIBRARY, 120 High St, PO Box 208240, 06520-8240. SAN 336-3546. Tel: 203-432-2798. Interlibrary Loan Service Tel: 203-432-1789. FAX: 203-432-1294. E-Mail: libweb@www.library.yale.edu. Web Site: www.library.yale.edu. *Adminr*, Carolyn V Claflin; Tel: 203-432-1818, E-Mail: carolyn.claflin@yale.edu; *Adminr*, Diane Turner; *Chief Librn*, Scott Bennett; Tel: 203-432-1818; *Assoc Librn*, Ralph W Franklin; *Assoc Librn*, Danuta Nitecki; *Assoc Librn*, Ann L Okerson; *Business*, Deborah McGraw
Founded 1701. Enrl 10,832; Fac 1,496; Highest Degree: Doctorate
Jul 1998-Jun 1999 Income $69,000,000. Mats Exp $15,269,000, Books $3,516,000, Per/Ser (Incl. Access Fees) $6,289,000, Other Print Mats $5,464,000. Sal $19,019,000
Mem of Asn of Research Libraries
Partic in Dialog Corporation; Dow Jones News Retrieval; Westlaw
Special Services for the Blind - Kurzweil Reading Machine
Friends of the Library Group
Departmental Libraries:
AMERICAN ORIENTAL SOCIETY, 329 Sterling Memorial Library, 06520. SAN 336-3635. Tel: 203-432-1842. FAX: 203-432-4087. *Librn*, Stanley Insler; E-Mail: sihsler@yalevm
Library Holdings: Bk Vols 22,774
Subject Interests: History, Language arts, Literature
Publications: American Oriental Series (77 vols); Journal of the American Oriental Society
Partic in RLIN
ART & ARCHITECTURE, 180 York St, 06520. SAN 336-3694. Tel: 203-432-2640. FAX: 203-432-0549. E-Mail: arcs.library@yale.edu. Web Site: library.yale.edu/art/aa.htm. *Librn*, Max Marmor; *Asst Librn*, Christine de Vallet; *Instrul Serv*, Barbara Rockenbach; Staff 6 (MLS 5, Non-MLS 1)
Library Holdings: Bk Vols 115,000
Subject Interests: Architecture, Graphic arts, Photography, Sculpture
Special Collections: Books on Color (Faber Birren Coll)
Partic in RLIN
ASTRONOMY, J W Gibbs Lab, Rm 217, 260 Whitney Ave, PO Box 208101, 06520-8101. SAN 336-4356. Tel: 203-432-3033. FAX: 203-432-5048. Web Site: www.astro.yale.edu/kimm/index.html.
Library Holdings: Bk Vols 26,279
Subject Interests: Astronomy, Astrophysics, Mathematics, Physics
Special Collections: Astronomy Slides; Domestic & Foreign Observatory Publications
Friends of the Library Group
BABYLONIAN, 130 Wall St, 06520. (Mail add: Sterling Memorial Library, Rm 322, PO Box 208240, 06520-8240), Tel: 203-432-1837. FAX: 203-432-7231. E-Mail: bab33@pantheon.yale.edu. *Curator*, William W Hallo
Founded 1911
Library Holdings: Bk Vols 15,000
Subject Interests: Archaeology, Art history, History, Literature
Publications: Catalogue of the Babylonian Coll of Yale; Yale Near Eastern Researches; Yale Oriental Series - Babylonian Texts
Partic in RLIN
Largest collection of cuneiform tablets and cylinder seals in the US
Friends of the Library Group
BEINECKE RARE BOOK & MANUSCRIPT, 121 Wall St, 06520. (Mail add: PO Box 208240, 06520-8240), Tel: 203-432-2977. FAX: 203-432-4047. Web Site: www.library.yale.edu/beinecke/. *Dir*, Ralph W Franklin; Tel: 203-432-2959, E-Mail: ralph.franklin@yale.edu; *Curator*, Patricia Willis; Tel: 203-432-2962, E-Mail: patricia.willis@yale.edu; *Curator*, George A Miles; Tel: 203-432-2958, E-Mail: george.miles@yale.edu; *Curator*, Stephen R Parks; Tel: 203-432-2967, E-Mail: stephen.parks@yale.edu; *Curator*, Christa A Sammons; Tel: 203-432-2964, E-Mail: christa.sammons@yale.edu; *Curator*, Robert Babcock; Tel: 203-432-2968, E-Mail: robert.babcock@yale.edu; *Curator*, Vincent Giroud; Tel: 203-432-2872, E-Mail: vincent.giroud@yale.edu; *Publ Servs*, Ellen R Cordes; Tel: 203-432-2973, E-Mail: ellen.cordes@yale.edu; *Tech Servs*, Suzanne Rutter; Tel: 203-432-2975, E-Mail: suzanne.rutter@yale.edu; *Mgr*, Regina Romero; Tel: 203-432-2955, E-Mail: regina.romero@yale.edu; *Syst Coordr*, Brian Kupiec; Tel: 203-432-2965, E-Mail: brian.kupiec@yale.edu; Staff 52 (MLS 29, Non-MLS 23)
Founded 1963
Library Holdings: Bk Vols 575,092
Subject Interests: Alchemy, Children's literature, European history, History of science, Judaica (lit or hist of Jews), Latin America, Literature, Music, Theology, Travel
Special Collections: Aldus Manutius; Arthus Davison Ficke; Asch; Barrett Clark; Barrie; Baskerville; Baskin; Boccaccio; Boswell; Browning; Bruce Rogers; Bryon; Buchan; Burney; Cabell; Carlyle; Coleridge; Conrad; Cooper; D H Lawrence; David Low; Defoe; Dickens; Dorothy Richardson; Dryden; Edith Wharton; Edmund Wilson; Eleanor Wylie; Erza Stiles; Ezra Pound; F T Marinetti; Fielding; Garrick; George Eliot; George MacDonald; George Moore; Gertrude Stein; Gissing; Goethe; Hardy; Herman Hagedorn; Hermann Broch; Hilda Doolittle; Hogg; Hutchins & Neith Boyce Hapgood; James Gates Percival; James Purdy; James Weldon Johnson; Jean Giono; Joel Barlow; John Gould Fletcher; John Hersey; Jonathan Edwards; Joseph Ireland; Joyce; Katherine Dreier; Kipling; Kurt & Helen Wolff; Landor; Langston Hughes; Leo Stein; Leonie Adams; Mabel Luhan; MacLeish; Maria Edgeworth; Marquand; Marsden Hartley; Masefield; Matthew Arnold; Mencken; Meredith; Milosz; Milton; Muriel Draper; Norman Douglas; Norman MacLeod; O'Neill; Paul Horgan; Paul Leicester Ford; Pope; Rachel Carson; Rebecca West; Richard Wright; Rilke; Robert Nathan; Robert Penn Warren; Robinson Jeffers; Ruskin; S V Benet; Samuel Johnson; Samuel Richardson; Shakespeare; Sheridan; Sinclair Lewis; Sir Thomas More; Sir Winston Churchill; Spenser; Spinelli Family; Stevenson; Stieglitz; Swinburne; Tennyson; Thackeray; Theatre Guild; Thomas Mann; Tocqueville; Toklas; Trollope; Van Vechten; Vardis Fisher; W R Benet; Walter Crane; Walton; Washington Irving; Whitman; Wilder; William Beckford; William Carlos Williams; William McFee; Wordsworth
Publications: The Yale University Library Gazette
Partic in RLIN
Visiting Fellowship Program for post-doctoral or equivalent research. Application deadline mid-January for next academic year
Friends of the Library Group
CENTER FOR BRITISH ART, 1080 Chapel St, PO Box 208280, 06520-8280. SAN 336-3783. Tel: 203-432-2814 (Rare Bks). Reference Tel: 203-432-2818. FAX: 203-432-9695. Web Site: www.yale.edu/ycba/library/library/htm. *Curator, Rare Bks*, Elisabeth Fairman; *Librn*, Susan Brady; Staff 10 (MLS 3, Non-MLS 7)
Library Holdings: Bk Vols 42,576; Per Subs 55
Subject Interests: Anatomy, Genealogy, Optics, Paintings, Prints, Sculpture
Special Collections: British Art Photograph Archive; British Topography (Rupert Gunnis Coll); Color-Plate Books (J R Abbey Coll); Jennings Album of Historical English Portraits; Sotheby & Christie Catalogs on British Art
Function: Research library
Partic in RLIN
CHEMISTRY LIBRARY, Sterling Chemistry Laboratory, 225 Prospect St, PO Box 208107, 06520-8107. SAN 336-4216. Tel: 203-432-6144. FAX: 203-432-3960. Web Site: www.library.yale.edu/scilib/chem/chemnav.html. *Librn*, Jennifer Kostelnik; E-Mail: jennifer.kostelnik@yale.edu
Library Holdings: Bk Vols 13,160
Subject Interests: Biochemistry, Chemistry, Inorganic chemistry, Organic chemistry, Physical chemistry
CLASSICS, Phelps Hall, 344 College St, Rm 505, 06520. SAN 336-3813. Tel: 203-432-0854.
Library Holdings: Bk Vols 23,200
Subject Interests: Ancient history, Mythology, Numismatics, Religion
COWLES FOUNDATION FOR RESEARCH IN ECONOMICS, 30 Hillhouse Ave, PO Box 208281, 06520-8281. SAN 336-3848. Tel: 203-432-3697. FAX: 203-432-6167. Web Site: www.econ.yale.edu.; Staff 1 (Non-MLS 1)
Library Holdings: Bk Vols 13,334
Subject Interests: Economics
Special Collections: Cowles Foundation Papers
CROSS CAMPUS, 120 High St, 06520-8240. SAN 336-3872. Tel: 203-432-1870. FAX: 203-432-1876. *Librn*, Susan Crockford-Peters; *Circ*, Judith Parker; *Circ*, Mary Beth Bran
Library Holdings: Bk Vols 202,224
Special Collections: Mountaineering Coll
Partic in RLIN
Special Services for the Blind - Kurzweil Reading Machine
Non-print media: selected audio, video & computer hardware available

CR DIVINITY SCHOOL, 409 Prospect St, 06511-2108. SAN 336-3902. Tel: 203-432-5290. FAX: 203-432-3906. Web Site: www.library.yale.edu/div/divhome.htm. *Librn*, Paul Stuehrenberg; Tel: 203-432-5294; *Ref*, Martha Smalley; Tel: 203-432-6374; *Ser*, Rolfe Gjellstad; Tel: 203-432-5295; *Circ*, Susan Burdick; Tel: 203-432-5288; *Acq*, Mary Ellen Barbarito; Staff 12 (MLS 4, Non-MLS 8)
Founded 1932. Enrl 367; Fac 34; Highest Degree: Master
Library Holdings: Bk Vols 420,000
Special Collections: American Home Missionary Society; China Missions; Day Historical Library of Foreign Missions; Ghana Archives of the Basel Mission; Historical Sermons Coll; International Missionary Council & Conference of British Missionary Societies; Jansenism; John R Mott Papers; Kenneth Scott Latourette Papers; Liston Pope Collection of Christian Social Ethics; Methodist Missionary Society; Mircofilm/Fiche Collection-Council for World Mission; Missions Pamphlets; Religious Education Association Archives; Student Volunteer Movement Archives; The United Board for Christian Higher Education in Asia Archives; World Student Christian Federation Archives
Partic in RLIN
Friends of the Library Group
DRAMA, University Theatre, 222 York St, PO Box 208244, 06520-8244. SAN 336-3937. Tel: 203-432-1554. FAX: 203-432-1550. Web Site: www.library.yale.edu/eas/.
Library Holdings: Bk Vols 28,436
Subject Interests: Costume design
Special Collections: Abel Thomas; George Pierce Baker Coll; History of

Costume, sl; Interiors & Furnishings; Rockefeller Prints Coll, photos
Partic in RLIN

ENGINEERING & APPLIED SCIENCE, 15 Prospect St, 06520. (Mail add: PO Box 208284, 06520-8284), SAN 336-3961. Tel: 203-432-2928. FAX: 203-432-7465. E-Mail: engineering.library@yale.edu. Web Site: www.library.yale.edu/eas. *Librn*, Andrew Shimp
Jul 1998-Jun 1999 Income (Main Library Only) $646,597. Mats Exp $482,096. Sal $123,280
Library Holdings: Bk Vols 49,646; Per Subs 792
Subject Interests: Computer science, Engineering
Automation Activity & Vendor Info: (Acquisitions) NOTIS; (Cataloging) NOTIS; (Circulation) NOTIS; (Course Reserve) NOTIS; (OPAC) NOTIS; (Serials) NOTIS

CM EPIDEMIOLOGY & PUBLIC HEALTH, Epidemiology & Public Health, 60 College St, PO Box 208034, 06520-8034. SAN 336-3996. Tel: 203-785-2835, 203-785-5680. FAX: 203-785-4998. *Librn*, William Uricchio; Fax: 860-570-9027, E-Mail: hbladm14@uconnvm.uconn.edu; *Librn*, Matthew Wilcox; E-Mail: matthew.wilcox@yale.edu
Founded 1940. Enrl 300; Fac 192; Highest Degree: Doctorate
Library Holdings: Bk Vols 16,686; Per Subs 256
Subject Interests: Anthropology, Public health
Special Collections: World Health Organization, National Center for Health Statistics

FORESTRY & ENVIRONMENTAL STUDIES, Sage Hall, 205 Prospect St, 4th flr, 06511. SAN 336-402X. Tel: 203-432-5130. *Librn*, Rochelle Smith
Subject Interests: Environmental studies, Forestry

GEOLOGY, Kline Geology Lab, 210 Whitney Ave Rm 328, 06520-8109. (Mail add: PO Box 208109, 06520-8109), SAN 336-4054. Tel: 203-432-3157. FAX: 203-432-3441. E-Mail: science.reference@yale.ed. Web Site: www.library.yale.edu/scilib/geol.html.
Library Holdings: Bk Vols 110,049
Subject Interests: Geochemistry, Geology, Geophysics, Meteorology, Oceanography, Paleontology

GOVERNMENT DOCUMENTS & INFORMATION CENTER, 38 Mansfield St, PO Box 208294, 06520-8294. SAN 336-433X. Tel: 203-432-3209. FAX: 203-432-3214. Web Site: www.library.yale.edu/govdocs/gdchome.html. *Librn*, Sandra K Peterson
Subject Interests: American history, Economics, U.S. Congress
Special Collections: Canadian Research Index, Congressional Masterfile I; CDs: Access UN; CIS Unpublished US House of Representatives Hearings, 1833-1958, index & microfiche; CIS US Congressional Committee Prints, through 1969; CIS US Senate Executive Documents; CIS US Senate Unpublished Hearings, 1824-1972 Index Coll, micro; CIS US Serial Set Index; Congressional Universe; CRS Major Studies; Declassified Documents Reference System, micro; FAO Comprehensive Coll, 1978-1996, micro; FAO, European Union; Foreign Broadcast Information Service Daily Reports, 1946-1996; Index & Microfiche Coll; Index to Foreign Broadcast Information Service Daily Reports, StatCAN &Statistical Masterfile; Index to International Statistics, 1986-present, microfiche; Issue Briefs, micro; Joint Publications Research Services Translations, 1953-1996; Microfiche Coll; Nondepository Coll from the American Statistics Index & CIS Index to Publications of the US Congress; Presidential Executive Orders; Proclamations 1789-1983 Index; Readex United Nations Documents & Publications, microfiche, 1946-present; Reports 1817-1969 (not in serial set); World News Connection (online)

HUMAN RELATIONS AREA FILES, INC, 755 Prospect St, 06511. SAN 326-9922. Tel: 203-764-9401. FAX: 203-764-9404. E-Mail: hrafmem@minerva.cis.yale.edu. *Librn*, Marlene Martin
Library Holdings: Bk Vols 5,000; Per Subs 30
Special Collections: Human Relations Area Files Archive
Open Mon-Fri 8:30-5

KLINE SCIENCE LIBRARY, 219 Prospect St, PO Box 208111, 06520-8111. SAN 336-4208. Tel: 203-432-3439. FAX: 203-432-3441. E-Mail: science.reference@yale.edu. Web Site: www.library.yale.edu/scilib/top.html. *Dir*, David Stern; *Ref*, Lori Bronars; *Science*, Jennifer Kostelnik; *Tech Servs*, Carol L Jones
Founded 1966
Library Holdings: Bk Vols 346,611
Subject Interests: Chemistry, Conservation, Oceanography, Physics
Special Collections: Bryology & Lichenology (Evans Coll); Early Science Classics; Various 19th Century Expeditions Reports
Automation Activity & Vendor Info: (Circulation) NOTIS
Publications: Science Imprint (newsletter)
Partic in RLIN

LAW LIBRARY, 127 Wall St, PO Box 208215, 06520-8215. SAN 336-4232. Tel: 203-432-1600. Interlibrary Loan Service Tel: 203-432-1640. FAX: 203-432-9692. *Librn*, S Blair Kauffman; *Tech Servs*, Mary Jane Kelsey; *Ref*, Laura Orr-Waters; *Ref*, Lisa Fitzgerald; *Acq*, Jo-Anne Giammattei; *Cat*, Frances Woods; *Circ*, Martha Clark; *ILL*, Barbara Amato; *Publ Servs*, Fred Shapiro; *Ref*, Kenneth Rudolf
Founded 1834. Enrl 600; Fac 50; Highest Degree: Doctorate
Library Holdings: Bk Vols 744,868
Special Collections: American Statute Law (Cole Coll); Blackstone Coll; International Law; Italian Medieval Statutes; Roman Law (Wheeler Coll)
Partic in RLIN

LEWIS WALPOLE LIBRARY, 154 Main St, Farmington, 06032. SAN 336-4526. Tel: 860-677-2140. FAX: 860-677-6369. Web Site: www.library.yale.edu/walpole. *Curator*, Joan Sussler; E-Mail: joan.sussler@yale.edu; *Librn*, Margaret Powell
Library Holdings: Bk Vols 32,000; Bk Titles 16,500; Per Subs 32
Special Collections: British 18th Century Satirical Prints; Charles Hanbury Williams Coll; Horace Walpole (1717-1797) Coll; William Hogarth (1696-1764) Coll
Function: Archival collection

MATHEMATICS, Leet Memorial, Rm 224, 10 Hillhouse Ave, PO Box 208283, 06520-8283. SAN 336-4267. Tel: 203-432-4179. FAX: 203-432-7316.
Library Holdings: Bk Vols 25,112
Subject Interests: Mathematics
Library is housed in Rooms 223, 226 & 227 in Leet Memorial Hall at 12 Hillhouse Avenue

CM MEDICAL LIBRARY, 333 Cedar St, 06520. (Mail add: PO Box 208014, 06520-8014), SAN 336-4291. Tel: 203-785-5352. FAX: 203-785-4369. Web Site: www.med.yale.edu/library. *Dir*, R Kenny Marone; E-Mail: regina.marone@yale.edu; *Publ Servs*, Charles Greenberg; Tel: 203-737-2960, E-Mail: charles.greenberg@yale.edu; *Coll Develop, Tech Servs*, Cynthia Crooker; Tel: 203-785-4346, E-Mail: cynthia.crooker@yale.edu; *Coll Develop*, Naomi Ikeda; *ILL*, Mary Angelotti; Tel: 203-785-4359, E-Mail: mary.angelotti@yale.edu; *ILL*, Carissa DeLizio; *Rare Bks, Spec Coll*, Toby Appel; Tel: 203-785-4354, E-Mail: toby.appel@yale.edu; *Circ*, Vivian Bordeaux; Staff 38 (MLS 17, Non-MLS 21)
Founded 1814. Enrl 975; Fac 1,304; Highest Degree: Doctorate
Library Holdings: Bk Vols 416,697; Per Subs 1,668
Subject Interests: Medicine, Nursing
Special Collections: Early Ichthyology (George Milton Smith Coll), bks & per; History of Medicine, Medical Prints & Drawings (Clements C Fry Coll); Weights & Measures (Edward Clark Streeter Coll), artifacts
Database Vendor: Ebsco - EbscoHost, OVID Technologies, Wilson - Wilson Web
Publications: Connections
Partic in Nat Libr of Med; RLIN
Friends of the Library Group

SEELEY G MUDD LIBRARY, 38 Mansfield St, PO Box 208294, 06520-8294. SAN 336-4313. Tel: 203-432-3203. FAX: 203-432-3214.
Library Holdings: Bk Vols 1,347,635

MUSIC, 98 Wall St, 06520-8320. SAN 336-4321. Tel: 203-432-0492. FAX: 203-432-7339. *Librn*, Kendall L Crilly; *Publ Servs*, Suzanne Eggleston
Library Holdings: Bk Vols 139,606
Special Collections: Alec Templeton Coll; American Hymn Tunes-19th Century; Benny Goodman Coll; Carl Ruggles Coll; Charles Ives Coll; Deems Taylor Coll; E Robert Schmitz/Pro Musica Society Coll; German Theoretical Literature 16th-18th Centuries; Harold Rome Coll; Henry Gilbert Coll; Horatio Parker Coll; J Rosamund Johnson Coll; Kay Swift Coll; Kurt Weill Coll; Lehman Engel Coll; Leo Ornstein Coll; Leroy Anderson Coll; Lowell Mason Coll; Miscellaneous Manuscripts; Paul Bekker Coll; Paul Hindemith Coll; Quincy Porter Coll; Ralph Kirkpatrick Coll; Seymour Shifrin Coll; Stanley Dance Coll; Thomas de Hartmann Coll; Virgil Thomson Coll; Vladimir Horowitz Coll
Partic in RLIN
Friends of the Library Group

ORNITHOLOGY, 301 Bingham Lab, 41 Sachem St, PO Box 208109, 06520-8109. SAN 336-4380. Tel: 203-432-3797. FAX: 203-432-9816.
Library Holdings: Bk Vols 7,776
Subject Interests: Ornithology
Special Collections: William R Coe Coll

SOCIAL SCIENCE LIBRARIES & INFORMATION SERVICES, 140 Prospect St, 06520-8263. SAN 336-447X. Tel: 203-432-3300. FAX: 203-432-8979. E-Mail: ssda@yalevm. Web Site: www.library.yale.edu/socsci. *Librn*, Nancy Roderer
Library Holdings: Bk Vols 85,000
Subject Interests: Finance, International relations, Political science, Sociology
Special Collections: Economic Growth Center Coll; Roper Center Archive; Social Science Data Archive

STATISTICS, Dana House, 24 Hillhouse Ave, PO Box 2179 Yale Sta, 06520. SAN 336-450X. Tel: 203-432-0666. FAX: 203-432-0633. *Librn*, Jocelyn Tipton
Library Holdings: Bk Vols 4,536
Subject Interests: Statistics
Function: Archival collection

STERLING MEMORIAL LIBRARY, 120 High St, 06520-8240. SAN 336-3600. Tel: 203-432-1775. FAX: 203-432-7231. *Cat, Chief Librn*, Joan Swanekamp; *Curator*, Tatjana Lorkovic; *Curator*, Richie Rich; *Curator*, Cesar Rodriguez; *Curator*, Simon Samoeil; *Curator*, Nanette Stahl; *Curator*, Dorothy Woodson; *Acq*, Marcia Romanansky; *ILL*, Marlayne Gates
Library Holdings: Bk Vols 4,357,191
Special Collections: American Musical Theater, Civic Repertory Theater & Theater Guild; Antebellum American South & Civil War; Babylonian Tablets; Bibliography; Bookplates; British Economic Tracts; Canadian History & Literature (including French Canadian literature); Classical

Archaeology; Coins; Congregationalism; Connecticut & New England History; Contemporary Medical & Health Care Policy; Economic History; Ethnic (Black) Arts & Letters; Family History; Forestry & Ecology; Futurism; German Literature; Greek & Latin Classics; Historical Sound Recordings; Historiography; Individuals: Henry Ward Beecher Family, Berkeley, Chester Bowles, Edmund Burke, Aaron Burr Family, John Collier (1884-1968), Jerome Frank, Franklin, Gay, Goldsmith, Heine, Edward M House, Ellsworth Huntington, Josephus Flavius, Juvenal, Lafayette, Max Lerner, Lincoln, Lindbergh Family (restricted), Walter Lippman, Malinowski, Marcus Aurelius, O C Marsh, J S Mill, Jedediah & Samuel F B Morse Family, Napoleon, Ouspensky, Philo Judaeus, C Rhodes, Richelieu, Shaw, Silliman Family, Henry L Stimson, Anson Phelps Stokes, Harold Phelps Stokes, Rose Pastor Stokes, William Graham Sumner, Tacitus, Mabel Loomis Todd, Ernst Toller, John Trumbull, Twain, Eli Whitney. SUBJECTS OF SPECIAL STRENGTH - American & English Literature & History; Italian Literature & Travel; Journalism & Political Writing, 20th Century; Judaica; Latin America; Legal Thought; Maps & Atlases; Modern African History; Naval History; Near East, including Arabic & Sanskrit; Newspapers; Oxford; Printing History; Scandinavia; Science & Technology, 19th Century; Slavic; Social Sciences; Southeast Asia; Sporting Books; United States Colonial & Progressive Period, Religious History & Contemporary Reform Movements; Urban & Regional Planning; World War I & II Diplomacy; Yale University
Function: Archival collection
Partic in OCLC Online Computer Library Center, Inc

S YOUNG MEN'S INSTITUTE LIBRARY, 847 Chapel St, 06510. SAN 302-2633. Tel: 203-562-4045. *Librn*, Edythe McEwen; *Asst Librn*, Becky McGaffin
Founded 1826
Library Holdings: Bk Vols 28,500
Restriction: Private library

NEW LONDON

C CONNECTICUT COLLEGE LIBRARY, 270 Mohegan Ave, 06320-4196. SAN 336-4534. Tel: 860-439-2650. Circulation Tel: 860-439-5033. Reference Tel: 860-439-2655. FAX: 860-439-2871. E-Mail: libref@conncoll.edu. Web Site: www.conncoll.edu/is/info-resources/. *VPres*, Lee Hisle; E-Mail: wlhis@conncoll.edu; *Assoc Dean*, Robert Renaud; Tel: 860-439-5145, E-Mail: rren@conncoll.edu; *ILL*, Bridget Pupillo; Tel: 860-439-2658, E-Mail: bjpup@conncoll.edu; *ILL*, Erie Taniuchi; *Cat*, Laurie Deredita; *Acq, Ser*, Melodie Hamilton; *Ref*, W James MacDonald; *Circ*, Lori Blados; *Online Servs*, Ashley Hanson; *Spec Coll*, Brian Rogers; *AV*, Peter Berris; *Archivist*, Catherine Phinizy; *Coll Develop*, Marian Shilstone; Staff 29 (MLS 11, Non-MLS 18)
Founded 1911. Enrl 1,641; Fac 158; Highest Degree: Master
Library Holdings: Bk Vols 530,766; Bk Titles 445,537; Per Subs 2,355
Subject Interests: Art, Chinese Language, Dance, History, Humanities, Japanese (Language), Judaica (lit or hist of Jews), Natural science, Social sciences and issues
Special Collections: 19th & 20th Century Children's Literature (Helen O Gildersleeve Coll); Charles H Simmons Coll of John Masefield; Linda Lear & Rachel Carson Coll; Louis Schaeffer-Eugene O'Neill Coll; New London County History; Poetry (William Meredith Coll); Printing History (Carl & Alma Weiss Coll); Susanne K Langer Coll; William Meredith & Blanche McCrary Boyd Papers; Wyman Ballad Coll
Automation Activity & Vendor Info: (Cataloging) SIRSI; (OPAC) SIRSI
Database Vendor: OCLC - First Search, OVID Technologies
Publications: Friends Newsletter
Mem of Nelinet
Partic in CTW Library Consortium; Eastern Connecticut Libraries; Nelinet, Inc; OCLC Online Computer Library Center, Inc
Friends of the Library Group
Departmental Libraries:
GREER MUSIC, 270 Mohegan Ave, Box 5234, 06320-4196. Tel: 860-439-2711. FAX: 860-439-2871. Web Site: shain.lib.conncoll.edu/greer/greer.html. *Librn*, Carolyn A Johnson; *Asst Librn*, June Ingram
Library Holdings: Bk Vols 10,000
Subject Interests: Music
Special Collections: Jazz (McVitty & Shelley Colls), LP; Opera & Operetta (Hilliar Coll), LP; Roberta Bitgood Archive (Sheet Music Coll); Wymah Sheet Music Coll
Publications: Greer Music Library (informational brochure)
Partic in OCLC Online Computer Library Center, Inc
Friends of the Library Group

S THE DAY LIBRARY, 47 Eugene O'Neil Dr, 06320. Tel: 860-442-2200, Ext 385. FAX: 860-442-5599. Web Site: www.theday.com. *Librn*, Tammy Ferdula; E-Mail: tferdula@theday.com
Library Holdings: Bk Vols 250; Bk Titles 200; Per Subs 10

M LAWRENCE & MEMORIAL HOSPITALS, Health Sciences Library,* 365 Montauk Ave, 06320. SAN 302-265X. Tel: 860-442-0711, Ext 2238. FAX: 860-437-8001. *Librn*, Kerry Dennigan
Founded 1972
Library Holdings: Bk Vols 1,600; Per Subs 350
Subject Interests: Medicine, Nursing
Special Collections: 19th Century Coll of Medical Treatises
Partic in Basic Health Sciences Library Network; Conn Asn of Health Scis Librs; Docline; Greater NE Regional Med Libr Program; Nat Libr of Med

S LYMAN ALLYN ART MUSEUM LIBRARY, 625 Williams St, 06320-4199. SAN 302-2641. Tel: 860-443-2545. FAX: 860-442-1280. *Librn*, Lissa Van Dyke
Founded 1931
Library Holdings: Bk Vols 4,500; Per Subs 32
Subject Interests: Art history, Decorative arts, Fine arts, Local history
Special Collections: Art Exhibition Catalogs

J MITCHELL COLLEGE LIBRARY,* 437 Pequot Ave, 06320-4498. SAN 302-2668. Tel: 860-701-5156. FAX: 860-701-5099. *Dir*, Phyllis Leonardi; Tel: 860-701-5155; *Cat*, Betty Page; *Circ, ILL*, Alice G Shephard; *Acq*, Catherine Bill; *Ref*, Mildred Hodge; Staff 6 (MLS 3, Non-MLS 3)
Founded 1939. Enrl 500
Library Holdings: Bk Vols 42,000; Per Subs 90
Subject Interests: Art, Art history
Special Collections: Robert Penn Warren Letters
Automation Activity & Vendor Info: (Circulation) epixtech, inc.
Partic in Eastern Connecticut Libraries; Libraries Online, Inc

S NEW LONDON COUNTY HISTORICAL SOCIETY LIBRARY,* 11 Blinman St, 06320. SAN 302-2676. Tel: 860-443-1209. FAX: 860-443-1209. *Dir*, Alice D Sheriff
Founded 1872
Sep 1998-Aug 1999 Income $56,000. Mats Exp $19,150, Books $250, Presv $200, AV Equip $200, Other Print Mats $18,500. Sal $30,000
Library Holdings: Bk Titles 5,000
Subject Interests: Genealogy, Local history
Special Collections: Whaling, mss
Publications: A History of New London; Bulletin (quarterly); Connecticut's Naval Office at New London (during Revolution); Diary of Joshua Hempsted; Greetings from New London; Tapestry (History of Blacks in Southeastern Connecticut); The Whaling City, A History of New London
Restriction: By appointment only
Function: Reference only

P PUBLIC LIBRARY OF NEW LONDON, 63 Huntington St, 06320. SAN 302-2684. Tel: 860-447-1411. FAX: 860-443-2083. Web Site: lioninc.org/newlondon. *Dir*, Edward Murray; E-Mail: emurray@biblio-org; *Tech Servs*, Lee Clapp; E-Mail: lclapp@biblio.org; *Ch Servs*, Kim Balentine; E-Mail: kimbal@biblio.org; *Ad Servs*, Marcia Stuart; E-Mail: mstuart@biblio.org; *Coll Develop*, Victoria Connor; E-Mail: vconnor@biblio.org; Staff 22 (MLS 4, Non-MLS 18)
Founded 1891. Pop 28,540; Circ 147,118
Jul 1998-Jun 1999 Income $664,343, State $5,281, City $575,500, Locally Generated Income $39,924, Other $43,638. Mats Exp $102,561, Books $70,382, Per/Ser (Incl. Access Fees) $10,084. Sal $307,000 (Prof $160,100)
Library Holdings: Bk Vols 85,563; Per Subs 169
Subject Interests: Genealogy, Local history
Automation Activity & Vendor Info: (Acquisitions) epixtech, inc.; (Cataloging) epixtech, inc.; (Circulation) epixtech, inc.; (ILL) epixtech, inc.; (OPAC) epixtech, inc.; (Serials) epixtech, inc.
Database Vendor: Ebsco - EbscoHost, OCLC - First Search
Publications: Loomings (quarterly newsletter)
Mem of Eastern Conn Librs, Inc
Partic in Libraries Online, Inc
Special Services for the Blind - Kurzweil Reader
Friends of the Library Group

C UNITED STATES COAST GUARD ACADEMY LIBRARY, 35 Mohegan Ave, 06320-8105. SAN 302-2692. Tel: 860-444-8510. Interlibrary Loan Service Tel: 860-444-8516. FAX: 860-444-8263. *Dir*, Patricia Daragan; Tel: 860-444-8553, Fax: 860-444-8516, E-Mail: pdaragan@exmail.uscga.edu; *Ref*, Nijole Crane; Tel: 860-444-8514, Fax: 860-444-8516, E-Mail: ncrane@exmail.uscga.edu; *Cat*, Sheila Lamb; Tel: 860-444-8519, Fax: 860-444-8516, E-Mail: slamb@exmail.uscga.edu; *Syst Coordr*, Andrew Gardner; Tel: 860-444-8517, Fax: 860-444-8516, E-Mail: angardner@exmail.uscga.edu; Staff 10 (MLS 5, Non-MLS 5)
Founded 1876. Enrl 800; Fac 119; Highest Degree: Bachelor
Oct 1999-Sep 2000 Income $381,400. Mats Exp $279,300, Books $25,000, Per/Ser (Incl. Access Fees) $254,300
Library Holdings: Bk Vols 150,000; Per Subs 710
Subject Interests: Civil engineering, Electrical engineering, Mechanical engineering
Automation Activity & Vendor Info: (Acquisitions) SIRSI; (Cataloging) SIRSI; (Circulation) SIRSI; (OPAC) SIRSI; (Serials) SIRSI
Database Vendor: Dialog, OCLC - First Search
Partic in Fed Libr & Info Network

S WOMEN'S CENTER OF SOUTHEASTERN CONNECTICUT LIBRARY, 16 Jay St, 06320. SAN 326-9612. Tel: 860-447-0366. FAX: 860-440-3327. E-Mail: w.ctr@snet.net. Web Site: www.womenscenterofsect.com. *Actg Dir*, Michael Stramiello
Library Holdings: Bk Vols 500; Bk Titles 50

NEW MILFORD

S NESTLE PTC INFORMATION CENTER LIBRARY, (Formerly Nestle R&D Center Library), 201 Housatonic Ave, 06776. SAN 303-9439. Tel: 860-355-6213. FAX: 860-355-6367. *Info Specialist*, Martha Osborn; E-Mail: martha.osborn@rdct.nestle.com
Founded 1981
Library Holdings: Bk Vols 8,000; Bk Titles 7,000; Per Subs 300
Subject Interests: Analytical chemistry, Food sci, Nutrition
Special Collections: Nestle Nutrition Workshop Series
Automation Activity & Vendor Info: (Cataloging) EOS; (Serials) EOS
Database Vendor: Dialog, Silverplatter Information Inc.
Publications: Patent Bulletin; Periodicals list
Restriction: Lending to staff only, Private library
Function: For research purposes
Partic in Dialog Corporation; Nelinet, Inc; OCLC Online Computer Library Center, Inc

M NEW MILFORD HOSPITAL, Health Sciences Library,* 21 Elm St, 06776. SAN 324-3567. Tel: 860-350-7219. FAX: 860-350-7297. *Dir*, Diana L St Jean; Staff 1 (MLS 1)
Founded 1951
Library Holdings: Bk Titles 1,500; Per Subs 100
Subject Interests: Medicine, Nursing
Partic in Conn Asn of Health Scis Librs; Greater NE Regional Med Libr Program
Special Services for the Deaf - TTY machine

P NEW MILFORD PUBLIC LIBRARY, 24 Main St, 06776. SAN 302-2706. Tel: 860-354-0493, 860-355-1191. FAX: 860-350-9579. Web Site: www.biblio.org/newmilford/. *Dir*, Barbara J Ostertag-Holtkamp; E-Mail: bostertag-holtkamp@biblio.org; *Ch Servs*, Sue Ford; *Ad Servs, Ref*, Carl DeMilia; *ILL*, Sue Buckley; *Circ*, Laurie Putnam; Staff 6 (MLS 5, Non-MLS 1)
Founded 1898. Pop 25,512
Library Holdings: Bk Titles 88,210; Per Subs 231
Subject Interests: Connecticut, History, Local history, Medicine
Special Collections: Original Lithographs (Newton Coll); Pepper Coll
Publications: Newsletter

NEWINGTON

G CONNDOT LIBRARY & INFORMATION CENTER, 2800 Berlin Tpk, 06111-4116. SAN 302-4474. Tel: 860-594-3035. FAX: 860-594-3039. *Coll Develop, Librn*, Betty Ambler; E-Mail: betty.ambler@po.state.ct.us
Founded 1984
Library Holdings: Bk Vols 16,000; Bk Titles 15,000

GM DEPARTMENT OF VETERANS AFFAIRS, Hospital Health Sciences Library,* 555 Willard Ave, 06111. SAN 302-2730. Tel: 860-667-6702. FAX: 860-667-6767. *Librn*, Lynn Lloyd
Founded 1930
Library Holdings: Bk Vols 3,810
Subject Interests: Medicine, Nursing, Psychiatry, Surgery
Publications: Learning Resources News (annual public w/research bibliography)
Partic in Conn Asn of Health Scis Librs; Veterans Affairs Library Network
Friends of the Library Group

M JEFFERSON HOUSE, Gerontology Resource Center,* One John H Stewart Dr, 06111. SAN 328-4190. Tel: 860-667-4453. FAX: 860-667-4459. *Dir*, Barbara Plante; Tel: 860-570-5009, Fax: 860-570-5036, E-Mail: bplante@law.uconn.edu
Library Holdings: Bk Vols 1,000; Bk Titles 50; Per Subs 50
Special Collections: Geriatrics; Gerontology
Publications: GER: Source

P LUCY ROBBINS WELLES LIBRARY,* 95 Cedar St, 06111-2645. SAN 302-2749. Tel: 860-665-8730 (Admin). Reference Tel: 860-665-8700. FAX: 860-667-1255. E-Mail: newtref@newington.lib.ct.us. Web Site: www.newington.lib.ct.us. *Dir*, Marian Amodeo; *Asst Dir*, Lisa Masten; *Ref*, Diane Durette; *Commun Servs*, Shirlee-Ann Kober; *Circ*, Nancy Turek; *Ch Servs*, Helen Malinka; Tel: 860-665-8720; *Coll Develop*, Victoria Chase
Founded 1752. Pop 28,680; Circ 431,863
Jul 1997-Jun 1998 Income $1,197,651, State $34,086, City $116,705. Mats Exp $170,541. Sal $800,151
Library Holdings: Bk Vols 103,933; Per Subs 217
Special Collections: Index of Local Newspaper; Local History Coll
Automation Activity & Vendor Info: (Circulation) CARL
Publications: Index of Local Newspaper; Newington Business Directory; Newington Information Packet
Partic in Capitol Region Library Council; OCLC Online Computer Library Center, Inc
Friends of the Library Group

NEWTOWN

P CYRENIUS H BOOTH LIBRARY, 25 Main St, 06470. SAN 302-2757. Tel: 203-426-4533. Reference Tel: 203-426-8552. FAX: 203-426-2196. E-Mail: chbooth@biblio.org. Web Site: www.biblio.org/chbooth/chbooth.htm. *Dir*, Janet Woycik; Tel: 203-426-1561, E-Mail: jwoycik@biblio.org; *Ch Servs*, Alana Meloni; Tel: 203-426-3851, Fax: 203-270-4534; *Ref*, Beryl Harrison; Fax: 203-270-4536
Founded 1932. Pop 21,000; Circ 140,000
1999-2000 Income $829,568, State $3,534, City $642,300, Locally Generated Income $110,513, Other $73,221. Mats Exp $144,500, Books $68,300, Per/Ser (Incl. Access Fees) $8,000, Presv $200, AV Equip $5,000, Electronic Ref Mat (Incl. Access Fees) $63,000. Sal $422,170 (Prof $34,000)
Library Holdings: Bk Vols 100,000; Per Subs 507; High Interest/Low Vocabulary Bk Vols 25; Spec Interest Per Sub 36; Bks on Deafness & Sign Lang 15
Subject Interests: Art and architecture, History
Special Collections: Arts (Jack Landau Coll); Genealogy (Julia Brush Coll); Sculpture (John Angel Coll)
Automation Activity & Vendor Info: (Cataloging) CARL; (Circulation) CARL; (ILL) CARL; (OPAC) CARL
Database Vendor: CARL
Publications: Booth Bylines (Newsletter)
Partic in Housatonic Valley Libr Asn
Friends of the Library Group

R TRINITY EPISCOPAL CHURCH LIBRARY,* 36 Main St, 06470. SAN 302-2781. Tel: 203-426-9070. E-Mail: trin@36main.aol.com.
Founded 1971
Library Holdings: Bk Titles 5,000; Per Subs 15
Special Collections: C S Lewis Coll
Open 9-2, Mon until 5

NIANTIC

P EAST LYME PUBLIC LIBRARY, INC, 39 Society Rd, 06357-1100. SAN 302-279X. Tel: 860-739-6926. FAX: 860-691-0020. E-Mail: elpl@ely.lioninc.org. Web Site: www.lioninc.org/eastlyme. *Coll Develop, Dir*, William Deakyne; *Assoc Dir, ILL*, Lou Ann Wilson; *Ch Servs*, Randy Haines; *Cat*, Lydia Main; *Circ*, Billie Morrill; *Circ*, Patricia Reynolds; *Asst Dir, Per*, Athena Cone
Founded 1868. Pop 15,800
Jul 2000-Jun 2001 Income $745,779, State $4,365, City $674,005, Locally Generated Income $67,409. Mats Exp $123,232, Books $86,571, Per/Ser (Incl. Access Fees) $13,259, Presv $1,500, Micro $6,805, AV Equip $2,203. Sal $431,990
Library Holdings: Bk Vols 92,000; Per Subs 218
Subject Interests: American Indians, Cookbooks, Gardening, Genealogy, Local history
Special Collections: Victor Frank Ridder & Marie Thompson Ridder Music Coll
Automation Activity & Vendor Info: (Acquisitions) epixtech, inc.; (Cataloging) epixtech, inc.; (Circulation) epixtech, inc.
Publications: Annual report; bibliographic & program brochures
Mem of Eastern Conn Librs, Inc
Partic in Eastern Connecticut Libraries; Libraries Online, Inc
Friends of the Library Group

S J B GATES CORRECTIONAL INSTITUTION LIBRARY, 131 N Bridebrook Rd, 06357. Tel: 860-691-4781. *Media Spec*, Barbara Williams
Library Holdings: Bk Vols 16,000; Bk Titles 15,000; Per Subs 22

S YORK CORRECTIONAL INSTITUTION LIBRARY,* 201 W Main St, 06357. SAN 371-7984. Tel: 860-691-6810, 860-691-6888. FAX: 860-691-6864. E-Mail: york.corr.inst@snet.net. *Librn*, Margery A Cohen
Library Holdings: Bk Vols 20,000; Bk Titles 15,000; Per Subs 20
Special Collections: Law
Publications: The Niantic Voice (newspaper)

NORFOLK

P NORFOLK LIBRARY, 9 Greenwoods Rd E, 06058-1320. (Mail add: PO Box 605, 06058-0605), SAN 302-2811. Tel: 860-542-5075. FAX: 860-542-1795. Web Site: www.norfolklibrary.org. *Dir*, Mary Lou Wigley; E-Mail: mwigley@biblio.org; *Ch Servs*, Eileen Fitzgibbons; E-Mail: efitzgibbons@biblio.org; *Circ*, Mary Ann Anderson; E-Mail: manderson@biblio.org; *Circ*, Marilyn Davidson; E-Mail: mdavidson@biblio.org; *Circ*, Robin Yuran; E-Mail: ryuran@biblio.org; Staff 5 (MLS 1, Non-MLS 4)
Founded 1889. Pop 1,800; Circ 27,000

Library Holdings: Bk Titles 27,000; Per Subs 96
Special Collections: Fishing & Hunting (Barbour Coll)
Publications: The Owl (newsletter)
Friends of the Library Group

NORTH BRANFORD

P NORTH BRANFORD LIBRARY DEPARTMENT, Atwater Memorial, 1720 Foxon Rd, PO Box 258, 06471. SAN 336-4623. Tel: 203-315-6020. FAX: 203-315-6021. *Dir*, Robert V Hull; E-Mail: nbrdir@leaplibraries.org
Library Holdings: Bk Vols 57,720; Per Subs 216
Automation Activity & Vendor Info: (Circulation) GEAC
Friends of the Library Group
Branches: 1
EDWARD SMITH BRANCH, Old Post Rd, PO Box 130, Northford, 06472. SAN 336-4682. Tel: 203-484-0469. FAX: 203-315-6021. *Dir*, Robert Hull; E-Mail: nbrdir@leaplibraries.org
Friends of the Library Group

NORTH GROSVENORDALE

P THOMPSON PUBLIC LIBRARY, 934 Riverside Dr, 06255. SAN 336-5131. Tel: 860-923-9779. FAX: 860-923-3705.; Staff 13 (MLS 1, Non-MLS 12)
Founded 1902. Pop 9,014; Circ 71,496
Jul 1999-Jun 2000 Income $244,406. Mats Exp $42,972, Books $36,000, Per/Ser (Incl. Access Fees) $3,472, AV Equip $3,500. Sal $142,235 (Prof $39,975)
Library Holdings: Bk Vols 41,805; Per Subs 138
Subject Interests: Local history
Automation Activity & Vendor Info: (Circulation) CARL; (OPAC) CARL; (Serials) CARL
Database Vendor: CARL, Ebsco - EbscoHost, GaleNet
Partic in Bibliomation, Inc; Eastern Connecticut Libraries
Friends of the Library Group

NORTH HAVEN

P NORTH HAVEN MEMORIAL LIBRARY, 17 Elm St, 06473. SAN 302-2838. Tel: 203-239-5803. FAX: 203-234-2130. Web Site: www.leaplibraries.org/nhaven. *Dir Libr Serv*, Lois D Baldini; E-Mail: lbaldini@leaplibraries.org; *Asst Dir*, Patricia A Dortenzio; E-Mail: pdortenzio@leaplibraries.org; *Ref*, Nancy Haag; E-Mail: nhaag@leaplibraries.org; *Ch Servs*, Patricia Laterza; E-Mail: platerza@leaplibraries.org; Staff 20 (MLS 7, Non-MLS 13)
Founded 1894. Pop 21,080; Circ 146,622
Jul 2000-Jun 2001 Income City $690,832. Mats Exp Books $75,259. Sal $480,952
Library Holdings: Bk Vols 94,539; Per Subs 217
Special Collections: Rotary Job & Career Corner, AV sets, cassettes, CD's, DVD's, talking books, videos
Automation Activity & Vendor Info: (Circulation) GEAC; (OPAC) GEAC
Database Vendor: Ebsco - EbscoHost, GaleNet
Function: ILL available
Partic in Library Exchange Aids Patrons
Special Services for the Blind - Kurzweil Personal Reader; Large print & cassettes
Friends of the Library Group

NORTH STONINGTON

P WHEELER LIBRARY,* 101 Main St, 06359. (Mail add: PO Box 217, 06359), SAN 302-2862. Tel: 860-535-0383. Web Site: www.wheelerlibrary.org. *Dir*, Amy Kennedy
Founded 1900. Pop 111,489
Library Holdings: Bk Vols 32,000; Per Subs 84
Subject Interests: Local history, World War II
Friends of the Library Group
Bookmobiles: 1

NORTHFIELD

P GILBERT LIBRARY, INC,* 38 Main St, 06778. SAN 302-2870. Tel: 860-283-8176. E-Mail: gilbert.library@snet.com. *Librn*, Nancy Gnitzcavich
Founded 1892. Pop 1,000; Circ 8,675
Library Holdings: Bk Titles 8,385; Per Subs 50
Special Collections: Local History, scrapbks

NORWALK

S ARCH CHEMICALS INC, Business Information Center, 501 Merritt St, PO Box 5204, 06851-5204. SAN 302-3796. Tel: 203-229-2900. FAX: 203-229-3565. *Mgr*, K Stanyon; E-Mail: kkstanyon@archchemicals.com
Founded 1974
Library Holdings: Bk Titles 2,000; Per Subs 400
Subject Interests: Business and management, Finance
Special Collections: Business International; Conference Board; SR II
Publications: Over seven hundred & fifty publications including statistical series
Restriction: Private library

S BUSINESS COMMUNICATIONS COMPANY, INC LIBRARY,* 25 Van Zant St, 06855. SAN 324-6442. Tel: 203-853-4266. FAX: 203-853-0348. E-Mail: buscom2@aol.com. Web Site: www.buscom.com.
Library Holdings: Bk Vols 2,000; Per Subs 30
Restriction: Not open to public

P EAST NORWALK IMPROVEMENT ASSOCIATION LIBRARY,* 51 Van Zant St, 06855. SAN 302-2900. Tel: 203-838-0408. *Librn*, Eunice Van Zilen
Pop 6,540; Circ 50,941
Library Holdings: Bk Vols 75,000; Per Subs 200

S FINANCIAL ACCOUNTING FOUNDATION LIBRARY, 401 Merritt 7, PO Box 5116, 06856-5116. SAN 320-619X. Tel: 203-847-0700, Ext 238. FAX: 203-849-9714. E-Mail: library@f-a-f.org. Web Site: www.fasb.org, www.gasb.org. *Librn*, Charry D Boris; *Asst Librn*, Miriam A Solomon
Founded 1973
Library Holdings: Bk Vols 5,000; Per Subs 300
Subject Interests: Accounting, Finance
Automation Activity & Vendor Info: (Cataloging) EOS; (Serials) EOS
Restriction: Not open to public
Partic in Western Connecticut Library Council, Inc

§J GIBBS COLLEGE LIBRARY, 142 East Ave, 06851. Tel: 203-838-4173. FAX: 203-838-1501. *Librn*, John Shoup
Library Holdings: Bk Vols 3,000; Per Subs 40

S NORTHROP GRUMMAN NORDEN SYSTEMS, Library & Information Services,* Norden Pl, PO Box 5300, 06856-5300. SAN 302-2986. Tel: 203-852-5886. FAX: 203-852-4579. *Mgr*, Carol L Sloan
Founded 1943
Library Holdings: Bk Vols 5,000; Per Subs 111
Subject Interests: Business and management, Electrical engineering, Electronics, Mathematics
Restriction: Not open to public
Partic in Dialog Corporation
Friends of the Library Group

J NORWALK COMMUNITY COLLEGE BAKER LIBRARY, 188 Richards Ave, 06854. SAN 302-2935. Tel: 203-857-7200. Reference Tel: 203-857-7379. FAX: 203-857-7380. Web Site: www.nctc.commnet.edu/library. *Dir Libr Serv*, Donald Gilstrap; E-Mail: nk_gilstrap@commnet.edu; *Tech Servs*, Ann Tran; *Publ Servs*, Linda Petersen; *Cat*, Barbara Baken; *Ref*, Gunnar Sahlin; Staff 11 (MLS 6, Non-MLS 5)
Library Holdings: Bk Vols 55,000; Bk Titles 53,000; Per Subs 225
Special Collections: American Civilization, microfiche; English Literature, microfiche; Human Relations Area Files, microfiche
Database Vendor: Ebsco - EbscoHost, GaleNet, Lexis-Nexis, OCLC - First Search
Publications: Librations (newsletter)
Partic in Nelinet, Inc; OCLC Online Computer Library Center, Inc

M NORWALK HOSPITAL, Wiggans Health Sciences Library, Maple St, 06856. SAN 336-4712. Tel: 203-852-2793. FAX: 203-855-3575. *Dir*, Jill Golrick; Staff 2 (MLS 1, Non-MLS 1)
Founded 1950
Library Holdings: Bk Vols 2,500; Bk Titles 1,800; Per Subs 210
Subject Interests: Medicine
Partic in Conn Asn of Health Scis Librs; Health Info Librs of Westchester; Western Connecticut Library Council, Inc

S NORWALK MUSEUM, Norwalk Historical Reference Library,* 41 N Main St, 06854-2702. SAN 302-2927. Tel: 203-866-0202. *Dir*, Ralph Bloom
Founded 1972
Library Holdings: Bk Vols 1,850
Subject Interests: Art and architecture
Special Collections: Local History Coll; Names & Places of Old Norwalk (Malcolm P Hunt Coll); Norwalk Gazette 1818-1900; Norwalk Historical Records; Social History Coll (Lockwood & Beard Families), mss, So Norwalk Sentinel mircofilm 1873-1900
Friends of the Library Group

P NORWALK PUBLIC LIBRARY, One Belden Ave, 06850. SAN 336-4771. Tel: 203-899-2780. FAX: 203-857-4410. *Dir*, Les Kozerowitz; Tel: 203-899-2780, Ext 123, E-Mail: leskoz@yahoo.com; *Asst Dir*, Frank Ferro; *Ch Servs*, Ann Tomlinson; *Tech Servs*, William Jacob; Staff 60 (MLS 20, Non-MLS 40)
Founded 1895
Library Holdings: Bk Titles 140,000; Per Subs 410
Automation Activity & Vendor Info: (Circulation) GEAC
Database Vendor: Innovative Interfaces INN - View
Partic in Western Connecticut Library Council, Inc

Branches: 1
SOUTH NORWALK LIBRARY, 10 Washington St, South Norwalk, 06854. SAN 336-4801. Tel: 203-899-2790.
Library Holdings: Bk Vols 71,654
Subject Interests: Hispanic

S PERKIN-ELMER CORP, Corporate Library,* 761 Main Ave, 06859-0249. SAN 302-2951. Tel: 203-761-2798. FAX: 203-761-2750. *Mgr*, Debra Kaufman; E-Mail: kaufmadr@perkin-elmer.com
Founded 1958
Library Holdings: Bk Titles 10,000; Per Subs 150
Subject Interests: Business and management, Mathematics
Mem of Western Conn Libr Coun
Partic in Dialog Corporation; Dow Jones News Retrieval; Nelinet, Inc; STN

S R T VANDERBILT CO, INC, Corporate Library,* 30 Winfield St, 06855. SAN 302-3001. Tel: 203-853-1400, Ext 566. FAX: 203-831-0648. Web Site: www.rtvander.com.
Founded 1956
Library Holdings: Bk Titles 10,600; Per Subs 130
Subject Interests: Ceramics, Mineralogy
Publications: Monthly accessions list
Restriction: Staff use only

S STEVEN WINTER ASSOCIATES INC LIBRARY,* 50 Washington St, 06854. SAN 375-0957. Tel: 203-852-0110. FAX: 203-852-0741. *Librn*, Marie Starnes
Library Holdings: Bk Vols 1,500; Per Subs 25

S YANKELOVICH PARTNERS INC, Information Center,* 101 Merrit, 7 Corporate Park, 06851. SAN 375-2003. Tel: 203-846-0100. FAX: 203-845-8200. Web Site: www.yankelovich.com. *Librn*, Holly Riehl
Library Holdings: Bk Titles 100

NORWICH

R BETH JACOB SYNAGOGUE LIBRARY,* 400 New London Tpk, 06360-5388. SAN 302-301X. Tel: 860-886-2459. FAX: 860-859-9626. *Librn*, Candace Laney
Founded 1954
Library Holdings: Bk Vols 1,200

§GL CONNECTICUT JUDICIAL BRANCH, Law Library at Norwich, One Court House Square, 06360. Tel: 860-887-2398. FAX: 860-823-1752. *Librn*, Barbara J Bradley; E-Mail: barbara.bradley@jud.state.ct.us
Special Collections: American Jurisprudence; Connecticut & Federal Law; Corpus Juris Secundum; Emphasis on litigation in Connecticut Courts, Family Law in Connecticut, Will Drafting, etc, audiotapes; Legal treaties & form books & selected law reviews; New York, Massachusetts & Rhode Island Statues; Regional Reporters
Open Mon-Fri 9-5

P OTIS LIBRARY, 261 Main St, 06360. SAN 302-3044. Tel: 860-889-2365. FAX: 860-886-4744. Web Site: www.lionhinc.org/norwich. *Dir*, Elsie L Jenkins; Tel: 860-889-2365, Ext 15, E-Mail: ejenkins@otis.lioninc.org; *Ref Serv Ad*, Diane Norman; Tel: 860-889-2365, Ext 13, E-Mail: dnorman@otis.lioninc.org; *Cat*, Hannah Estra; *Ch Servs*, Laurie Emerson. Subject Specialists: *Local history*, Diane Norman; Staff 30 (MLS 3, Non-MLS 27)
Founded 1850. Pop 38,000; Circ 200,000
Jul 1999-Jun 2000 Income $950,996, State $13,421, City $790,300, Locally Generated Income $147,275. Mats Exp $80,445, Books $53,613, Per/Ser (Incl. Access Fees) $15,000. Sal $589,272
Library Holdings: Bk Vols 99,000; Per Subs 183
Subject Interests: Business and management, Careers
Special Collections: Genealogy & Local Hist; Large Print
Automation Activity & Vendor Info: (Cataloging) epixtech, inc.; (Circulation) epixtech, inc.; (OPAC) epixtech, inc.
Database Vendor: Ebsco - EbscoHost, epixtech, inc.
Publications: Monthly activities calendar
Function: ILL available
Partic in Eastern Connecticut Libraries; Libraries Online, Inc
Friends of the Library Group

S SOCIETY OF THE FOUNDERS OF NORWICH CONNECTICUT, Leffingwell House Library, 348 Washington St, PO Box 13, 06360. SAN 328-3321. Tel: 860-889-5990, 860-889-9440. *Librn*, Linda Kate Edgerton
Library Holdings: Bk Titles 402
Subject Interests: Local history

S SOUTHEASTERN CONNECTICUT COUNCIL OF GOVERNMENTS LIBRARY, 5 Connecticut Ave, 06360-1501. Tel: 860-889-2324. FAX: 860-889-1222. E-Mail: seccog@snet.net. *Head of Libr*, Wendy Leclair
Library Holdings: Bk Vols 1,000; Bk Titles 1,000

THREE RIVERS COMMUNITY TECHNICAL COLLEGE
J MOHEGAN CAMPUS LEARNING RESOURCE CENTER, Mahan Dr, 06360. SAN 302-3028. Tel: 860-823-2910. FAX: 860-886-0691. E-Mail: mo_library@commnet.edu. *Actg Dir*, Gaye Hoffman; *Librn*, Amy Orlomoski; *Librn*, Mildred Hodge; *Circ*, Janice DeWolf; Staff 7 (MLS 3, Non-MLS 4)
Founded 1970. Enrl 3,500; Highest Degree: Associate
Jul 2000-Jun 2001 Income $57,867. Mats Exp $51,395, Books $17,823, Per/Ser (Incl. Access Fees) $25,501, Micro $8,071. Sal $204,030 (Prof $128,742)
Library Holdings: Bk Vols 37,000; Per Subs 317
Subject Interests: Ireland, Nursing
Partic in Libraries Online, Inc; OCLC Online Computer Library Center, Inc

J THAMES VALLEY CAMPUS LIBRARY, 574 New London Tpk, 06360. SAN 302-3060. Tel: 860-885-2346. FAX: 860-886-4960. E-Mail: tv_library@trctc.commnet.edu. *Librn*, Gaye Hoffmen; *Librn*, Norma Nevers
Founded 1964
Library Holdings: Bk Vols 17,000; Per Subs 250
Special Collections: Local Public Records Room; Nuclear Regulatory Commission Documents
Partic in Ameritech; Libraries Online, Inc

M WILLIAM W BACKUS HOSPITAL, Medical-Nursing Library,* 326 Washington St, 06360-2733. SAN 325-884X. Tel: 860-823-6327. FAX: 860-823-6373. *Librn*, Sheila Hayes
Library Holdings: Bk Titles 850
Subject Interests: Allied health
Partic in Conn Asn of Health Scis Librs

OAKDALE

P RAYMOND LIBRARY,* 832 Raymond Hill Rd, 06370. SAN 376-2637. Tel: 860-848-9943. *Dir*, Elizabeth Dutka
Library Holdings: Bk Vols 23,000; Bk Titles 21,000; Per Subs 34
Partic in Eastern Connecticut Libraries
Open Wed 12-8, Thurs 10-5, Fri 2-5 & Sat 10-2

OLD GREENWICH

P PERROT MEMORIAL LIBRARY, 90 Sound Beach Ave, 06870. SAN 302-3095. Tel: 203-637-1066. Reference Tel: 203-637-3870. FAX: 203-698-2620. Web Site: www.perrotlibrary.org. *Dir*, Kevin McCarthy; *Asst Dir, Ch Servs*, Kate McClelland; *Ref*, Linda White; *Tech Servs*, Sheila Floer
Founded 1905. Pop 15,000; Circ 179,554
Jul 1999-Jun 2000 Income $940,441. Mats Exp $123,000, Books $85,000, Per/Ser (Incl. Access Fees) $8,000, Other Print Mats $12,100, Electronic Ref Mat (Incl. Access Fees) $17,900. Sal $683,241 (Prof $315,851)
Library Holdings: Bk Vols 51,000; Per Subs 100
Subject Interests: Gardening, Sailing
Automation Activity & Vendor Info: (Circulation) Innovative Interfaces Inc.
Partic in New England Libr Info Network; OCLC Online Computer Library Center, Inc; Western Connecticut Library Council, Inc

OLD LYME

S LEARN REGIONAL EDUCATIONAL SERVICE, Media Library, 44 Hatchetts Hill Rd, 06371-1512. Tel: 860-434-4800, Ext 157. Web Site: www.learn.k12.ct.us. *Librn*, Dorothy B Dugas

§C LYME ACADEMY OF FINE ARTS, Krieble Library, 84 Lyme St, 06371-2333. Tel: 860-434-5232, Ext 130. FAX: 860-434-8725. E-Mail: library@lymeacademy.edu. Web Site: www.lymeacademy.edu/library.htm. *Dir*, Loree Bourgoin; Tel: 860-434-5232, E-Mail: lbourgoin@lymeacademy.edu; *Cat*, Beth Rumery; *Publ Servs*, Brenda Heldreth; Staff 3 (MLS 1, Non-MLS 2)
Founded 1991. Enrl 92; Fac 13; Highest Degree: Bachelor
Library Holdings: Bk Vols 8,640; Bk Titles 7,563; Per Subs 46
Subject Interests: Fine arts, Painting, Sculpture
Automation Activity & Vendor Info: (Cataloging) Follett; (Circulation) Follett; (OPAC) Follett
Partic in Eastern Connecticut Libraries

S LYME HISTORICAL SOCIETY LIBRARY, 96 Lyme St, 06371. SAN 302-3109. Tel: 860-434-5542. FAX: 860-434-6259. Web Site: www.flogris.org. *Dir*, Jeff Andersen; *Curator*, Jack Becker
Founded 1956
Library Holdings: Bk Titles 600
Subject Interests: Connecticut, Genealogy, Local history
Special Collections: Art Colony at Old Lyme Archives; History of Lyme & Old Lyme Conn; Papers of Local Families
Restriction: By appointment only
The Lyme Historical Society is the governing organization for the Florence Griswold Museum where the library is located

P OLD LYME, Phoebe Griffin Noyes Library, 2 Library Lane, 06371. SAN 302-3117. Tel: 860-434-1684. FAX: 860-434-9547. E-Mail: pgn-library@lionine.org. Web Site: www.olpgnlib.org. *Dir*, Mary Fiorelli; *Asst Dir*, Maureen Kindilien; *Ch Servs*, Ronna Johnson; *Cat*, Karen Guigno; *Circ*, Anne Lise Vogel; Staff 13 (MLS 7, Non-MLS 6)
Founded 1898. Pop 6,670; Circ 76,894

Jul 1999-Jun 2000 Income $462,780, State $2,806, City $140,000, Locally Generated Income $57,545, Parent Institution $213,007, Other $11,499, Other $25,228. Mats Exp $46,370, Books $40,288, Electronic Ref Mat (Incl. Access Fees) $6,082. Sal $217,253
Library Holdings: Bk Vols 39,700; Bk Titles 37,755; Per Subs 130
Subject Interests: Genealogy, Local history
Automation Activity & Vendor Info: (Acquisitions) epixtech, inc.; (Cataloging) epixtech, inc.; (Circulation) epixtech, inc.; (OPAC) epixtech, inc.; (Serials) epixtech, inc.
Database Vendor: Ebsco - EbscoHost, GaleNet, OCLC - First Search
Publications: Phoebe News (Newsletter)
Mem of Eastern Conn Librs, Inc
Partic in Libraries Online, Inc
Open Mon & Wed 10-8, Tues, Thurs, Fri & Sat 10-5, Sun 1-4
Friends of the Library Group

OLD MYSTIC

S INDIAN & COLONIAL RESEARCH CENTER, INC, Butler Library, 39 Main St Rte 27, 06372. (Mail add: PO Box 525, 06372), SAN 302-3125. Tel: 860-536-9771. *Pres*, Joan Cohn
Founded 1965
Library Holdings: Bk Vols 3,500
Subject Interests: American Indians, Genealogy
Special Collections: Glass Plate negatives & prints 1890-1920; Local Genealogy; Rare American School Books
Publications: Our Woodland Indians (coloring-history book); Tasteful Treasures Cookbook

OLD SAYBROOK

P ACTON PUBLIC LIBRARY, 60 Old Boston Post Rd, 06475-2200. SAN 302-3133. Tel: 860-395-3184. FAX: 860-395-2462. Web Site: www.oldsaybrookct.com/library. *Dir*, Janet Crozier; E-Mail: jcrozier@oldsaybrooklibct.org; Staff 14 (MLS 2, Non-MLS 12)
Founded 1873. Pop 10,000; Circ 170,000
Jul 2000-Jun 2001 Income $421,698, State $4,600, City $417,098. Mats Exp $69,689, Books $64,072, Per/Ser (Incl. Access Fees) $5,617. Sal $253,425 (Prof $55,480)
Library Holdings: Bk Vols 59,604
Subject Interests: Large type print, Local history
Automation Activity & Vendor Info: (Cataloging) Follett
Open Mon-Thurs 12-8:30, Fri & Sat 9-5, Sun 1-5 (Sept-June)
Friends of the Library Group

ONECO

P STERLING PUBLIC LIBRARY,* 1110 Plainfield Pike, PO Box 158, 06373. SAN 323-6226. Tel: 860-564-2692. FAX: 860-564-1660. *Librn*, Rachel Vincent
Founded 1928. Pop 2,000; Circ 11,400
Library Holdings: Bk Titles 10,252

ORANGE

P CASE MEMORIAL LIBRARY, 176 Tyler City Rd, 06477-2498. SAN 302-315X. Tel: 203-891-2170. FAX: 203-891-2190. Web Site: www.leaplibraries.org/orange. *Librn*, Meryl S Farber; E-Mail: mfarber@leaplibraries.org; *ILL*, Marie Miller; *Ref*, Laura Hagendoorn; Staff 18 (MLS 4, Non-MLS 14)
Founded 1956. Pop 12,800; Circ 175,020
Jul 1999-Jun 2000 Income $477,571. Mats Exp $76,378. Sal $245,740
Library Holdings: Bk Vols 76,191; Per Subs 175
Subject Interests: Large type print, Local history
Special Collections: Large Type Coll
Automation Activity & Vendor Info: (Acquisitions) TLC; (Circulation) CLSI LIBS
Database Vendor: Ebsco - EbscoHost
Partic in CSLI Consortium; Library Exchange Aids Patrons
Friends of the Library Group

R TEMPLE EMANUEL LIBRARY,* 150 Derby Ave, PO Box 897, 06477. SAN 302-3168. Tel: 203-397-3000. *Librn*, Barbara Pivawer
Founded 1972
Library Holdings: Bk Vols 1,100; Bk Titles 1,050; Per Subs 8
Subject Interests: Judaica (lit or hist of Jews)

OXFORD

P OXFORD PUBLIC LIBRARY,* 486 Oxford Rd, 06478. SAN 302-3176. Tel: 203-888-6944. FAX: 203-888-2666. *Dir*, Pat DeAngelis; *Asst Librn*, Sandra Davis
Founded 1883. Pop 8,000; Circ 30,495
Library Holdings: Bk Vols 35,000; Per Subs 50
Subject Interests: History
Open Mon-Fri 9-8
Friends of the Library Group

PAWCATUCK

S YARDNEY TECH PRODUCTS INC,* 82 Mechanic St, 06379. SAN 302-3184. Tel: 860-599-1100, Ext 400. FAX: 860-599-3903.
Library Holdings: Bk Vols 500; Per Subs 10
Subject Interests: Chemistry, Electrical engineering, Metallurgy

PLAINFIELD

P PLAINFIELD PUBLIC LIBRARY,* 39 Railroad Ave, PO Box 286, 06374. SAN 302-3192. Tel: 860-564-4407. *Librn*, Nancy Wilcox
Pop 12,774
Library Holdings: Bk Vols 14,600
Partic in Eastern Connecticut Libraries
Friends of the Library Group

PLAINVILLE

S CONNECTICUT CLEARING HOUSE LIBRARY, 334 Farmington Ave, 06062-1321. SAN 378-3723. Tel: 800-232-4424. FAX: 860-793-9813. E-Mail: info@ctclearinghouse.org. Web Site: www.ctclearinghouse.org. *Librn*, Kathryn Goodman
Library Holdings: Bk Vols 2,050; Bk Titles 2,000

P PLAINVILLE PUBLIC LIBRARY, 56 E Main St, 06062. SAN 302-3206. Tel: 860-793-1446. FAX: 860-793-1450. Web Site: www.munic.state.ct.us/plainville/plaineville.htm. *Dir*, Pete F Chase; E-Mail: pchase@crlc.org; Staff 5 (MLS 4, Non-MLS 1)
Founded 1894. Pop 16,770; Circ 153,239
1999-2000 Income $477,571, State $6,297, City $425,841, Locally Generated Income $33,047. Mats Exp $106,194, Books $74,904, Per/Ser (Incl. Access Fees) $14,585, Other Print Mats $9,138, Electronic Ref Mat (Incl. Access Fees) $7,567. Sal $303,188
Library Holdings: Bk Vols 90,000; Per Subs 164
Automation Activity & Vendor Info: (Circulation) CARL
Partic in Capitol Region Library Council
Friends of the Library Group

PLYMOUTH

P PLYMOUTH LIBRARY ASSOCIATION,* 692 E Main St, 06782. SAN 302-3222. Tel: 860-283-5977. *Librn*, Johannah Maxwell
Founded 1871. Pop 3,500
1997-1998 Mats Exp $24,043, Books $3,001, Per/Ser (Incl. Access Fees) $650. Sal $14,759
Library Holdings: Bk Titles 9,521; Per Subs 28
Special Collections: Local History (Plymouth Coll)
Partic in Region I Coop Libr Servs Unit

POMFRET

R THE CHRIST CHURCH LIBRARY, 527 Pomfret St, PO Box 21, 06258. Tel: 860-928-7026. *In Charge*, Carole Gooder; Staff 1 (Non-MLS 1)
Founded 1988. Pop 300; Circ 300
Jan 1999-Dec 1999 Income $4,000, Locally Generated Income $3,000, Parent Institution $1,000. Mats Exp $600, Books $400, AV Equip $200. Sal $4,000
Library Holdings: Bk Titles 2,000; Per Subs 10
Function: Professional lending library
Friends of the Library Group

P POMFRET FREE PUBLIC LIBRARY,* 449 Pomfret St, 06258-0091. SAN 302-3230. Tel: 860-928-3475. FAX: 860-928-3475. *Dir*, Marjorie S Sirrine; *Asst Dir*, M Elizabeth Rollinson
Founded 1713. Pop 2,800; Circ 12,600
Library Holdings: Bk Vols 21,000; Per Subs 40
Special Collections: Pomfret & Windham County Historical Coll
Publications: Newsletter
Partic in Eastern Connecticut Libraries
Open Tues-Thurs & Sat 2-5, Fri 10-8

PORTLAND

P PORTLAND LIBRARY, 20 Freestone Ave, 06480. SAN 302-3257. Tel: 860-342-6770. FAX: 860-342-6778. Web Site: www.portland.lib.ct.us. *Dir*, Laurel Goodgion; E-Mail: goodgion@portland.lib.ct.us; *Asst Dir*, Anne Calvert; E-Mail: acalvert@portland.lib.ct.us; *Ch Servs*, Coral Lindenfelser
Founded 1895. Pop 8,652; Circ 165,199
Jul 1999-Jun 2000 Income $558,324, State $10,138, City $538,778, Other $9,408. Mats Exp $71,345. Sal $366,899

Library Holdings: Bk Vols 55,652; Per Subs 256
Subject Interests: Local history, Videos
Mem of Capitol Regional Libr Council; Southern Conn Libr Coun
Partic in Connect
Open Mon-Thurs 10-9, Fri & Sat 10-5
Friends of the Library Group

PRESTON

P PRESTON PUBLIC LIBRARY, 389 Rte 2, 06365. SAN 376-3242. Tel: 860-886-1010. FAX: 860-886-4952. E-Mail: prestonl@neca.com. *Dir*, Elizabeth A Monahan; E-Mail: preston.library@snet.net; *ILL*, Susan Brosnan. Subject Specialists: *Local genealogy*, Susan Brosnan; Staff 8 (MLS 1, Non-MLS 7)
Founded 1898. Pop 5,000
1998-1999 Income $118,476, State $4,858, City $105,185, Locally Generated Income $5,100, Other $3,333. Mats Exp $12,380, Books $11,000, Per/Ser (Incl. Access Fees) $1,200, Electronic Ref Mat (Incl. Access Fees) $180. Sal $60,995 (Prof $23,400)
Library Holdings: Bk Vols 17,995; Per Subs 44
Subject Interests: Genealogy
Special Collections: Preston Historical Society
Automation Activity & Vendor Info: (Cataloging) Sagebrush Corporation; (Circulation) Sagebrush Corporation; (OPAC) Sagebrush Corporation
Database Vendor: GaleNet
Function: ILL available
Partic in Eastern Connecticut Libraries
Friends of the Library Group

PROSPECT

SR PROSPECT CONGREGATIONAL CHURCH, UCC Library,* On the Green, 25 Center St, 06712. SAN 375-6467. Tel: 203-758-4872. *Librn*, Mary M Hinman
Library Holdings: Bk Vols 800; Bk Titles 650

P PROSPECT PUBLIC LIBRARY,* 17 Center St, 06712. SAN 302-3273. Tel: 203-758-3001. FAX: 203-758-0080. *Librn*, Barbara Peterson
Founded 1904. Pop 8,500; Circ 65,000
Library Holdings: Bk Vols 28,000; Per Subs 42
Special Collections: Large Print-Mysteries
Partic in Region I Coop Libr Servs Unit; Southern Connecticut Library Council
Friends of the Library Group

PUTNAM

GL CONNECTICUT JUDICIAL BRANCH, Putnam Law Library, Court House, 155 Church St, 06260. SAN 336-1985. Tel: 860-928-3716. FAX: 860-963-7531. Web Site: www.jud.state.ct.us/lawlib/index.html. *Librn*, Donna R Izbicki; E-Mail: donna.izbicki@jud.state.ct.us
Library Holdings: Bk Vols 17,000
Open Mon-Thurs 9-5, Fri 9-4

M LAPALME HEALTH SCIENCES LIBRARY, 320 Pomfret St, 06260. SAN 302-329X. Tel: 860-928-6541, Ext 2596. FAX: 860-928-1398. *Mgr*, Elaine Davis; E-Mail: edavis@hnne.org; Staff 1 (Non-MLS 1)
Founded 1973
Library Holdings: Bk Titles 500; Per Subs 65
Database Vendor: OCLC - First Search
Partic in Conn Asn of Health Scis Librs

P PUTNAM PUBLIC LIBRARY, 225 Kennedy Dr, 06260-1691. SAN 302-3303. Tel: 860-963-6826. FAX: 860-963-6828. E-Mail: ppl225@necca.com. *Dir*, Mary C Brumbaugh; *Asst Dir, Ch Servs*, Tina Aubin; *Coll Develop*, Patricia Jensen
Founded 1884. Pop 8,971; Circ 50,344
Jul 1998-Jun 1999 Income $261,893, State $4,768, City $256,875, Other $250. Mats Exp $16,189, Books $12,782, Per/Ser (Incl. Access Fees) $3,100, Manuscripts & Archives $307. Sal $151,521
Library Holdings: Bk Vols 38,628; Per Subs 73
Subject Interests: French lang, Genealogy
Mem of Conn Libr Asn; Eastern Conn Librs, Inc; New England Libr Asn
Partic in Auto-Graphics; Necanet; Nelinet, Inc; News Bank; OCLC Online Computer Library Center, Inc; ReQuest OPAC Catalog

SR SISTERS OF THE IMMACULATE CONCEPTION CONVENT LIBRARY, 600 Liberty Hwy, 06260. SAN 302-3311. Tel: 860-928-7955. FAX: 860-928-1930. *Librn*, Ona Strimaitis
Founded 1944
Library Holdings: Bk Vols 13,000; Bk Titles 12,000; Per Subs 30
Subject Interests: Linguistics
Special Collections: Lithuanian Art, paintings, ceramics, wood-carvings, amber & woven art

REDDING

P MARK TWAIN LIBRARY,* Rte 53 & Diamond Hill Rd, 06896. (Mail add: PO Box 1009, 06875), SAN 302-332X. Tel: 203-938-2545. FAX: 203-938-4026. E-Mail: mrk.twain.library@snet.net. *Dir*, Helen Stauderman; *Ch Servs*, Donna Bielaczyc
Founded 1908. Circ 70,082
Library Holdings: Bk Vols 37,000
Special Collections: Civil War (Massie Coll); Mark Twain Coll; Religion & Mysticism (Hutchinson Coll)
Founded by Mark Twain shortly after he moved to Redding in 1908

RIDGEFIELD

S ALDRICH MUSEUM OF CONTEMPORARY ARTS LIBRARY, 258 Main St, 06877. Tel: 203-438-4519. Web Site: www.aldrichart.org. *Dir*, Harry Philbrick; *Curator*, Nina Carlson; Fax: 203-438-0198
Library Holdings: Bk Titles 200; Per Subs 20

S BOEHRINGER INGELHEIM PHARMACEUTICALS, INC, Scientific & Corporate Information Services,* PO Box 368, 06877. SAN 321-5385. Tel: 203-798-5156. FAX: 203-791-6172. *Mgr, Tech Servs*, Myra Sterrett; *Coll Develop*, Helen Oen; Staff 10 (MLS 7, Non-MLS 3)
Founded 1971
Library Holdings: Bk Titles 10,000; Per Subs 1,400
Publications: Journals Holdings List user guide; Product Bibliography
Restriction: By appointment only
Partic in Univ Halifax
Friends of the Library Group

S THE MARLEY ORGANIZATION, INC LIBRARY, 412 Main St, Ste 3, 06877-4532. SAN 328-4026. Tel: 203-438-3801. FAX: 203-438-2313. E-Mail: chyer@tmoinc.com. Web Site: www.tmoinc.com. *Librn*, Beverly Brando
Library Holdings: Per Subs 30
Subject Interests: Govt standards, US voluntary
Special Collections: North American ISO9000 Registrars Compilation; US & European Product Certification Programs; US Laboratory Accreditation Systems (compilations); US Quality Assessment & Registration Systems; US State, Local & Municipal Product Approval Systems
Partic in Dialog Corporation

P RIDGEFIELD LIBRARY & HISTORICAL ASSOCIATION, 472 Main St, 06877-4585. SAN 302-3346. Tel: 203-438-2282. FAX: 203-438-4558. E-Mail: rdginfsv@biblio.org. Web Site: www.ridgefieldlibrary.org. *Dir*, Christina B Nolan; E-Mail: nolanc@biblio.org; *Ch Servs*, Marie Hasskarl; E-Mail: rdgchild@biblio.org; *Ref*, Victoria Carlquist; E-Mail: rdginfsv@biblio.org; *ILL*, Karen Kazzi; E-Mail: kkazzi@biblio.org; Staff 5 (MLS 5)
Founded 1901. Pop 22,000; Circ 308,422
Jul 1999-Jun 2000 Income $1,350,920, State $4,087, City $1,100,004, Other $246,829. Mats Exp $204,964, Books $152,109, Per/Ser (Incl. Access Fees) $12,337, Micro $5,000, AV Equip $20,000, Electronic Ref Mat (Incl. Access Fees) $15,518. Sal $695,116 (Prof $248,812)
Library Holdings: Bk Vols 121,386; Bk Titles 95,636; Per Subs 240; Bks on Deafness & Sign Lang 108
Subject Interests: Genealogy
Special Collections: Ridgefield History, bks, monographs
Automation Activity & Vendor Info: (Circulation) CARL
Database Vendor: CARL
Publications: Newsletter
Partic in Bibliomation
Special Services for the Blind - Kurzweil Reading Machine
Friends of the Library Group

S SCHLUMBERGER-DOLL, Research Library,* Old Quarry Rd, 06877-4108. SAN 302-3354. Tel: 203-431-5600. Interlibrary Loan Service Tel: 203-431-5604. FAX: 203-431-5625. E-Mail: banks@ridgefield.sdr.slb.com. *Librn*, Mary Ellen Banks; *Cat, ILL*, Maureen Jones
Founded 1947
Library Holdings: Bk Vols 15,000; Bk Titles 12,000; Per Subs 210
Subject Interests: Geochemistry, Geophysics, Mathematics, Nuclear science, Petroleum, Physics
Automation Activity & Vendor Info: (Cataloging) epixtech, inc.; (Circulation) epixtech, inc.; (Serials) epixtech, inc.
Publications: SDR Library Newsletter
Mem of Western Conn Libr Coun
Partic in Nelinet, Inc; OCLC Online Computer Library Center, Inc; Orbit

ROCKVILLE

L CONNECTICUT JUDICIAL BRANCH, Law Library at Rockville, 69 Brooklyn St, 06066. SAN 336-2019. Tel: 860-872-3824. FAX: 860-875-3213. *In Charge*, Larry Cheeseman; *Librn*, Christopher Roy; E-Mail: Christopher.Roy@jud.state.ct.us
Library Holdings: Bk Vols 15,000

ROCKY HILL

S CONNECTICUT HORTICULTURAL SOCIETY LIBRARY, 2433 Main St, 06067-2539. SAN 321-6748. Tel: 860-529-8713. FAX: 860-563-2217. E-Mail: cthort@connix.com. Web Site: www.cthort.org. *Librn*, Michael Polasko
Founded 1960
Library Holdings: Bk Titles 2,000
Subject Interests: Horticulture

P CONNECTICUT STATE LIBRARY, Library for the Blind & Physically Handicapped, 198 West St, 06067-3545. SAN 302-1750. Tel: 860-566-2151. Toll Free Tel: 800-842-4516. FAX: 860-566-6669. Web Site: www.cslib.org/lbph.htm. *Librn for Blind*, Carol Taylor; E-Mail: ctaylor@cslib.org; Staff 2 (MLS 2)
Founded 1968. Pop 10,000
Library Holdings: Bk Vols 216,437; Bk Titles 50,000
Special Collections: Connecticut & New England cassette books
Automation Activity & Vendor Info: (Circulation) DRA
Partic in NLSNET
Special Services for the Blind - Reading machine
Connecticut's regional library in Library of Congress's National Library Service for the Blind & Physically Handicapped Network; Open Mon-Fri 10-3
Branches: 1
STATE RECORDS CENTER Tel: 860-529-8684. Web Site: www.cslnet.ctstateu.edu/records.htm. *Dir*, LeAnne Johnson

P CORA J BELDEN LIBRARY, 33 Church St, 06067-1568. SAN 302-3370. Tel: 860-258-7621. Reference Tel: 860-258-7623. FAX: 860-258-7624. E-Mail: cora@ci.rocky-hill.ct.us. Web Site: www.rockyhill.lib.ct.us. *Dir*, Betsy Bray; E-Mail: bbray@ci.rocky-hill.ct.us; *Asst Dir, Ref*, John P Crowe; E-Mail: jcrowe@ci.rocky-hill.ct.us; *Ref*, Terri Corry; *Ref*, Patricia Miles; *Ch Servs*, Carole Fisher; *Ch Servs*, Barbara Wysocki; Staff 15 (MLS 5, Non-MLS 10)
Founded 1794. Pop 16,554; Circ 216,282
Jul 1999-Jun 2000 Income $748,154, State $30,708, City $717,446. Mats Exp $119,645, Books $130,659, Electronic Ref Mat (Incl. Access Fees) $11,164. Sal $512,138
Library Holdings: Bk Vols 74,061; Bk Titles 70,718; Per Subs 200
Automation Activity & Vendor Info: (Acquisitions) SIRSI; (Circulation) CARL
Database Vendor: Ebsco - EbscoHost, GaleNet
Function: ILL available
Partic in Capitol Region Library Council
Friends of the Library Group

GM DEPARTMENT OF VETERANS AFFAIRS VETERANS HOME & HOSPITAL, Medical Library,* 287 West St, 06067. SAN 302-3389. Tel: 860-529-2571, Ext 2261. FAX: 860-721-5954. *Librn*, Charlotte Storey
Library Holdings: Bk Titles 350; Per Subs 65
Subject Interests: Medicine, Nursing
Restriction: Staff use only

S LOCTITE CORPORATION LIBRARY,* 1001 Trout Brook Crossing, 06067-3910. SAN 326-9809. Tel: 860-571-5280. FAX: 860-571-5296. *Mgr*, Margaret Orszak
Library Holdings: Bk Titles 2,000; Per Subs 200
Special Collections: Adhesive and Sealant Technology

S ROCKY HILL HISTORICAL SOCIETY, Ethel Miner Cooke Historical Library, Old Main St, 06067-0185. SAN 302-3397. Tel: 203-563-6704, 860-563-6704. *Librn*, Mrs John A Sword
Founded 1969
Library Holdings: Bk Titles 700
Subject Interests: Local history
Restriction: By appointment only

ROGERS

S ROGERS CORP, Lurie Library, One Technology Dr, 06263-0188. (Mail add: PO Box 157, 06263-0157), SAN 302-3400. Tel: 860-779-5726. Interlibrary Loan Service Tel: 860-779-5749. FAX: 860-779-5760. *Ref*, Emily Westbrook; E-Mail: emily.westbrook@rogers-corp.com; *ILL*, Joseph Gannon; E-Mail: joseph.gannon@rogers-corp.com; Staff 2 (Non-MLS 2)
Founded 1962
Jan 1999-Dec 1999 Mats Exp $152,000, Books $8,000, Per/Ser (Incl. Access Fees) $37,000, Presv $1,000, Other Print Mats $12,000, Manuscripts & Archives $6,000, Electronic Ref Mat (Incl. Access Fees) $88,000. Sal $79,000 (Prof $48,000)
Library Holdings: Bk Titles 7,000; Per Subs 350; Spec Interest Per Sub 250
Subject Interests: Chemical engineering, Electronics, Polymer chemistry, Statistics
Automation Activity & Vendor Info: (Cataloging) EOS; (Circulation) EOS; (OPAC) EOS; (Serials) EOS
Function: Research library
Partic in Eastern Connecticut Libraries; Nelinet, Inc

ROWAYTON

P ROWAYTON LIBRARY, 33 Highland Ave, 06853. SAN 302-3419. Tel: 203-838-5038. E-Mail: rowlib@rowayton.com. Web Site: www.rowayton.org. *Dir*, Kathleen Gordon; Staff 4 (MLS 1, Non-MLS 3)
Founded 1903. Pop 5,000; Circ 23,473
Library Holdings: Bk Vols 33,000; Per Subs 88
Partic in Univ Halifax
Open Mon-Thurs 2-6 & 7-8:30, Fri 10-6, Sat 10-1

ROXBURY

P MINOR MEMORIAL LIBRARY, 23 South St, PO Box 249, 06783-0249. SAN 374-5791. Tel: 860-350-2181. FAX: 860-350-6882. *Dir*, Claudia Cayne; Staff 5 (MLS 1, Non-MLS 4)
Founded 1896. Pop 1,900
Jul 1999-Jun 2000 Income $140,661, State $1,334, City $86,000, Locally Generated Income $45,927, Other $7,400. Mats Exp $17,883, Books $16,427, Per/Ser (Incl. Access Fees) $956, Electronic Ref Mat (Incl. Access Fees) $500. Sal $53,747 (Prof $35,000)
Library Holdings: Bk Titles 40,000; Per Subs 36
Subject Interests: World War I
Special Collections: Hanson Baldwin Coll
Publications: Bookmark (Friends)
Friends of the Library Group

SALEM

P SALEM FREE PUBLIC LIBRARY,* 216 Hartford Rd, 06420. SAN 376-2645. Tel: 860-859-1130. FAX: 860-859-1130. E-Mail: slmpl@nai.net. *Dir*, Margaret B Leary; E-Mail: learmoak@aol.com
Library Holdings: Bk Vols 12,500; Bk Titles 12,000; Per Subs 30
Automation Activity & Vendor Info: (Cataloging) Follett; (Circulation) Follett
Database Vendor: GaleNet
Partic in Eastern Connecticut Libraries
Friends of the Library Group

SALISBURY

P SCOVILLE MEMORIAL LIBRARY,* 38 Main St, 06068. SAN 302-3443. Tel: 860-435-2838. FAX: 860-435-8136. *Dir*, Martha R Darcy
Pop 4,100; Circ 51,000
Jul 1997-Jun 1998 Income $254,000, State $2,550, City $45,000, Locally Generated Income $6,500, Other $198,000. Mats Exp $33,000, Books $22,000, Per/Ser (Incl. Access Fees) $3,300. Sal $134,000
Library Holdings: Bk Vols 35,000; Per Subs 70
Special Collections: Local History (Smith & Bingham Coll)
Partic in Region I Coop Libr Servs Unit

SCOTLAND

P SCOTLAND PUBLIC LIBRARY,* 9 Devotion Rd, PO Box 286, 06264. SAN 302-3451. Tel: 860-456-8627. FAX: 860-423-3666. E-Mail: scotland.lib@snet.net. *Dir*, Elizabeth Doucet
Pop 1,100
Library Holdings: Bk Vols 10,500
Partic in Eastern Connecticut Libraries

SEYMOUR

P SEYMOUR PUBLIC LIBRARY, 46 Church St, 06483-2698. SAN 302-346X. Tel: 203-888-3903. FAX: 203-888-4099. Web Site: www.invalley.org/seymour/lib/seymour/htm. *Asst Librn*, Diane Sosnovich; *Ad Servs*, Charlotte Rowell; *Ad Servs*, Mary Ann Magda; *Ch Servs*, Ann Mirisola; Staff 5 (MLS 3, Non-MLS 2)
Founded 1892. Pop 14,500; Circ 81,188
Jul 1998-Jun 1999 Income $362,861, City $298,161, Other $64,700. Mats Exp $33,200, Books $27,500, Per/Ser (Incl. Access Fees) $4,800, Presv $400, Micro $500. Sal $197,738
Library Holdings: Bk Vols 48,500; Bk Titles 47,000; Per Subs 101; Bks on Deafness & Sign Lang 20
Special Collections: Historical Reference Coll
Automation Activity & Vendor Info: (Circulation) CARL; (OPAC) CARL
Publications: Voices (the newsletter of the Seymour Public Library)
Partic in Southern Connecticut Library Council
Friends of the Library Group

SHARON

P HOTCHKISS LIBRARY OF SHARON, INC,* 10 Upper Main St, 06069. SAN 302-3478. Tel: 860-364-5041. FAX: 860-364-5041. *Librn*, Gail Mirabile
Founded 1893. Pop 2,900; Circ 29,645

Library Holdings: Bk Vols 23,608; Per Subs 55
Special Collections: Connecticut Historical Room
Partic in Region I Coop Libr Servs Unit

M SHARON HOSPITAL, Health Science Library, 50 Hospital Hill Rd, 06069. SAN 302-3486. Tel: 860-364-4095. FAX: 860-364-4465.
Library Holdings: Bk Vols 400; Per Subs 90
Restriction: Staff use only
Partic in Conn Asn of Health Scis Librs; North Atlantic Health Sciences Libraries, Inc; NW Conn Health Sci Libr

SHELTON

S BARNES ENGINEERING CO LIBRARY, Div of BF Goodrich, 88 Long Hill Cross Rds, PO Box 867, 06484-0867. SAN 302-3710. Tel: 203-926-1777, 203-926-4127. FAX: 203-926-5540. *Head Librn*, Joyce Rehling
Founded 1962
Library Holdings: Bk Titles 1,000; Per Subs 10
Subject Interests: Electronics, Physics

S PITNEY BOWES, Corporate Information Center, 35 Waterview Dr, 26-33, 06484-8000. SAN 302-3818. Tel: 203-924-3235. FAX: 203-924-3637. *Mgr*, Jack Stevens; Tel: 203-924-3559, E-Mail: stevenja@pb.com; Staff 2 (MLS 2)
Founded 1953
Library Holdings: Bk Titles 5,000; Per Subs 325
Subject Interests: Chemistry, Electronics, Mech eng, Printing
Special Collections: USPS Coll, office equipment
Publications: Now Available (newsletter)
Partic in Nelinet, Inc

P PLUMB MEMORIAL LIBRARY,* 65 Wooster St, 06484. SAN 302-3516. Tel: 203-924-1580. FAX: 203-924-8422. *Dir*, Doris Buchheit; *Asst Librn*, C Elspeth Lydon; *Ch Servs*, Phyllis Walsh; *Circ*, Morris Wolf; *Br Coordr*, Geralyn Z Roberts
Founded 1896. Pop 36,500
Library Holdings: Bk Vols 136,132; Per Subs 331
Subject Interests: Connecticut, Local history
Partic in Dialog Corporation; Southern Connecticut Library Council
Branches: 1
HUNTINGTON, 41 Church St, 06484-5804. SAN 375-5940. Tel: 203-926-0111. FAX: 203-926-0181. *Br Coordr*, Geralyn Z Roberts; *Tech Servs*, Susanne Alcutt; *Ch Servs*, Debra DuBois; Staff 6 (MLS 1, Non-MLS 5)
Founded 1991. Pop 15,000; Circ 88,000
Jul 1999-Jun 2000 Income City $205,914. Mats Exp $33,700, Books $30,600, Per/Ser (Incl. Access Fees) $3,100. Sal $139,634 (Prof $100,310)
Library Holdings: Bk Vols 32,000; Per Subs 25
Automation Activity & Vendor Info: (Cataloging) CARL; (Circulation) CARL; (OPAC) CARL
Database Vendor: CARL
Partic in Bibliomation
Special Services for the Deaf - Books on deafness & sign language; Special interest periodicals; Staff with knowledge of sign language

SHERMAN

P SHERMAN LIBRARY,* Rte 37 & 39, 06784. (Mail add: PO Box 40, 06784), SAN 302-3524. Tel: 860-354-2455. FAX: 860-354-7215. *Dir*, Millie Loeb
Founded 1926. Pop 3,084; Circ 42,000
Library Holdings: Bk Vols 20,000; Per Subs 40
Special Collections: Sherman Authors
Partic in Region I Coop Libr Servs Unit

SIMSBURY

S SIMSBURY HISTORICAL SOCIETY, Blanche C Skoglund Library,* 800 Hopmeadow St, PO Box 2, 06070. SAN 302-3532. Tel: 860-658-2500. FAX: 860-651-4354. E-Mail: simsburyhistorical@juno.com. *Librn*, Stephen E Simon; *Pres*, Dawn H Bobryk; Staff 2 (MLS 1, Non-MLS 1)
Founded 1978. Pop 22,000
Jul 1998-Jun 1999 Mats Exp $2,000. Sal $5,000
Library Holdings: Bk Vols 3,000
Subject Interests: Genealogy, Local history
Restriction: Non-circulating to the public, Reference only to non-staff
Open Mon-Fri 1-4

P SIMSBURY PUBLIC LIBRARY,* 725 Hopmeadow St, 06070. SAN 302-3540. Tel: 860-658-7663. FAX: 860-658-6732. Web Site: www.simsbury.lib.ct.us. *Dir*, Susan Bullock; E-Mail: sbullock@simsbury.lib.ct.us; *Ch Servs*, Jan Madrak; *Ref*, Jackie Hemond; *Ref*, Susan Ray; *Ref*, Celia Roberts; *Ad Servs*, Anne-Marie Kaminsky; Staff 6 (MLS 6)
Founded 1890. Pop 23,050; Circ 399,485
Library Holdings: Bk Vols 127,128
Subject Interests: Genealogy
Automation Activity & Vendor Info: (Circulation) CARL
Partic in Capitol Region Library Council; Dialog Corporation
Friends of the Library Group

SOMERS

S OSBORN CORRECTIONAL INSTITUTION, Somers Library,* 100 Bilton Rd, PO Box 100, 06071. SAN 302-3559. Tel: 860-749-8391, Ext 5483 or 5478. *Librn*, Dorothy Daboul
Library Holdings: Bk Titles 12,500; Per Subs 65
Subject Interests: Law

P SOMERS PUBLIC LIBRARY, 51 Ninth District Rd, 06071-0368. SAN 302-3567. Tel: 860-763-3501. FAX: 860-763-1718. E-Mail: somerspl@biblio.org. Web Site: www.qwd.com/spl. *Dir*, Francine A Aloisa; *Ch Servs*, Annette Ouellet; *Ref*, Cecelia Becker; Staff 6 (MLS 5, Non-MLS 1)
Founded 1887. Pop 9,414; Circ 85,292
Jul 1999-Jun 2000 Income $302,764, State $4,550, City $276,303, Locally Generated Income $8,672, Other $13,239. Mats Exp $42,958. Sal $159,488 (Prof $96,250)
Library Holdings: Bk Vols 41,948; Per Subs 171
Subject Interests: Local history
Automation Activity & Vendor Info: (Acquisitions) CARL; (Circulation) CARL; (OPAC) CARL; (Serials) CARL
Partic in Bibliomation
Friends of the Library Group

SOUTH GLASTONBURY

P SOUTH GLASTONBURY PUBLIC LIBRARY,* 80 High St, 06073. SAN 302-3575. Tel: 860-633-4793. *Librn*, Cheryl Thompson
Founded 1926. Pop 800
Library Holdings: Bk Vols 14,000; Per Subs 30
Subject Interests: Fiction, Large type print, Nonfiction
Special Collections: Antique books (Kinne Memorial Coll); Hodge Nature Science

SOUTH WINDHAM

P GUILFORD SMITH MEMORIAL LIBRARY, 17 Main St, 06266-1121. (Mail add: PO Box 159, 06266-0159), SAN 302-3583. Tel: 860-423-5159. FAX: 860-423-5159. *Dir*, Julie Culp; E-Mail: julie.culp@biblio.org; Staff 4 (MLS 1, Non-MLS 3)
Founded 1930. Pop 3,000; Circ 8,000
Library Holdings: Bk Titles 9,969; Per Subs 59
Bookmobiles: 1

SOUTH WINDSOR

P SOUTH WINDSOR PUBLIC LIBRARY,* 1550 Sullivan Ave, 06074. SAN 302-3605. Tel: 860-644-1541. TDD: 860-644-7645. FAX: 860-644-7645. Web Site: www.ctconnect.com/swlibrary. *Dir*, Mary J Etter; E-Mail: metter@connect.crlc.ort; *Ad Servs*, Joe Pava; *Ch Servs, YA Servs*, Maria Ecke; *Circ*, Linda Clark; *Commun Relations, Ref*, Sandy Westbrook; *Coll Develop*, Joseph Pava; Staff 28 (MLS 5, Non-MLS 23)
Founded 1898. Pop 22,325
Jul 1999-Jun 2000 Income $938,087, City $899,421, Locally Generated Income $20,538, Other $18,128. Mats Exp $134,496, Books $73,430, AV Equip $2,400, Electronic Ref Mat (Incl. Access Fees) $58,666. Sal $462,203 (Prof $201,749)
Library Holdings: Bk Vols 100,139; Per Subs 481
Subject Interests: Local history
Automation Activity & Vendor Info: (Cataloging) CARL; (Circulation) CARL; (ILL) CARL
Database Vendor: CARL, Ebsco - EbscoHost, GaleNet, OCLC - First Search
Partic in Capitol Region Library Council
Open Mon-Thurs 9-9, Fri-Sat 9-4:30 & Sun 1-4:30
Friends of the Library Group

P WOOD MEMORIAL LIBRARY, 783 Main St, 06074. SAN 376-2807. Tel: 860-289-1783. FAX: 860-289-4178. E-Mail: wood.memorial.lib@snet.net. Web Site: pages.cthome.net/wood.memorial.lib. *Dir*, Virginia Macro; *Librn*, Ann Masi
Jul 1998-Jun 1999 Income $74,000. Mats Exp $5,600. Sal $34,000
Library Holdings: Bk Vols 15,000; Bk Titles 10,000
Subject Interests: Birding, Birds, Local history, Native Americans
Partic in Capitol Region Library Council
Friends of the Library Group

SOUTHBURY

P SOUTHBURY PUBLIC LIBRARY, 561 Main St S, 06488. SAN 302-3613. Tel: 203-262-0626. FAX: 203-262-6734. *Dir*, Shirley Thorson; E-Mail: sthorson@biblio.org; *Ch Servs*, Joan Stokes; *Tech Servs*, Judy Von Holtz;

Ref, Valerie Oakley; *Circ*, Jacqueline Hoffman; Staff 5 (MLS 5)
Founded 1969. Pop 16,568; Circ 206,236
Jul 1999-Jun 2000 Income $512,479, State $6,702, City $460,363, Locally Generated Income $41,643, Other $3,771. Mats Exp $106,890. Sal $296,968
Library Holdings: Bk Vols 80,702; Per Subs 180
Subject Interests: Large type print
Automation Activity & Vendor Info: (Cataloging) CARL; (Circulation) CARL; (ILL) CARL; (OPAC) CARL
Database Vendor: Ebsco - EbscoHost
Publications: Monthly calendar
Partic in Bibliomation, Inc; Western Connecticut Library Council, Inc
Special Services for the Blind - Brailling & large print projects
Infrared listening system in community forum
Friends of the Library Group

M SOUTHBURY TRAINING SCHOOL, Medical Library,* Rte 172, Box 872, 06488. SAN 302-3621. Tel: 203-586-2000. FAX: 203-586-2701. *In Charge*, Dr Robert McDonald
Library Holdings: Bk Vols 650
Subject Interests: Mentally retarded

SOUTHINGTON

J BRIARWOOD COLLEGE LIBRARY,* 2279 Mount Vernon Rd, 06489-1057. SAN 324-282X. Tel: 860-628-4751, Ext 27. FAX: 860-628-6444. E-Mail: lib4@erols.com. Web Site: www.briarwood.edu. *Dir*, Carol Flood; Staff 1 (MLS 1)
Founded 1966. Enrl 300; Fac 50
Library Holdings: Bk Vols 10,000; Per Subs 140
Subject Interests: Vocational education
Partic in Capitol Region Library Council

P SOUTHINGTON PUBLIC LIBRARY,* 255 Main St, 06489. SAN 302-363X. Tel: 860-628-0940, 860-628-0947. FAX: 860-628-0488. E-Mail: sp/reference@megahits.com. Web Site: www.connect.crlc.org. *Dir*, Audrey Brown; *Ad Servs*, Billie Witkovic; *Ch Servs*, Daria Cesario; *Cat*, Ludmila Fidi; *Ref*, Gene Grass; *ILL*, Michelle Lord
Founded 1902. Pop 38,590; Circ 318,991
Library Holdings: Bk Vols 130,000; Per Subs 494
Subject Interests: Arts and crafts
Automation Activity & Vendor Info: (Circulation) CARL
Partic in Capitol Region Library Council
Friends of the Library Group

SOUTHPORT

P PEQUOT LIBRARY, 720 Pequot Ave, 06490-1496. SAN 302-3648. Tel: 203-259-0346. FAX: 203-259-5602. Web Site: www.biblio.org/pequot/pequot.htm. *Dir*, Mary Freedman; Tel: 203-259-0346, Ext 11, E-Mail: freedman@biblio.org; *Asst Dir*, Sally Ijams; Tel: 203-259-0346, Ext 10, E-Mail: sijams@biblio.org; *ILL*, David Cappiello; Tel: 203-259-0346, Ext 23, E-Mail: dbc@biblio.org; *Spec Coll*, Danielle Carriera; Tel: 203-259-0346, Ext 17, E-Mail: carriera@biblio.org; *Ch Servs*, Carolyn Kost; Tel: 203-259-0346, Ext 18, E-Mail: ckost@biblio.org
Founded 1887. Circ 59,352
Jul 1999-Jun 2000 Income $780,150, State $5,500, City $260,000, Locally Generated Income $514,650. Mats Exp $86,000, Books $67,000, Per/Ser (Incl. Access Fees) $9,000, Electronic Ref Mat (Incl. Access Fees) $10,000. Sal $300,500
Library Holdings: Bk Vols 132,827; Per Subs 141
Subject Interests: Am archit, Am art, Am hist, Americana, Biography, Genealogy, Local history
Special Collections: 19th Century Periodicals; Art of the Book
Automation Activity & Vendor Info: (Circulation) CARL; (OPAC) CARL
Database Vendor: CARL, Ebsco - EbscoHost, GaleNet, OCLC - First Search
Publications: Bookmark (quarterly newsletter); Catalogue of the Monroe, Wakeman & Holman Collection of the Pequot Library Southport, Connecticut Deposited in the Yale University Library (New Haven, Yale UP, 1960, 522 pgs); The Kelscott Press
Partic in Bibliomation

STAFFORD SPRINGS

M JOHNSON MEMORIAL HOSPITAL MEDICAL LIBRARY, 201 Chestnut Hill Rd, PO Box 860, 06076-0860. Tel: 860-684-8166. *Librn*, Stephanie Shippey; E-Mail: sshippey@jmhosp.org
Library Holdings: Per Subs 170

P STAFFORD LIBRARY, 5 Spring St, 06076. SAN 302-3672. Tel: 860-684-2852. FAX: 860-684-2128. Web Site: www.biblio.org/stafford. *Dir*, Barbara Butler; E-Mail: bbutler@biblio.org; Staff 4 (MLS 1, Non-MLS 3)
Founded 1876. Pop 12,000; Circ 50,020
Library Holdings: Bk Vols 36,000; Per Subs 83
Automation Activity & Vendor Info: (Cataloging) CARL; (Circulation) CARL; (OPAC) CARL
Database Vendor: GaleNet
Publications: Library Journal; School Library Journal
Partic in Eastern Connecticut Libraries
Friends of the Library Group

STAMFORD

S BARTLETT ARBORETUM LIBRARY,* 151 Brookdale Rd, 06903-4199. SAN 326-2588. Tel: 203-322-6971. FAX: 203-595-9168.
Library Holdings: Bk Titles 2,500; Per Subs 25
Special Collections: Horticulture & Plant Science (Bartlett Arboretum Library), bks, per, brochures

S BRAKELEY, JOHN, PRICE & JONES, INC LIBRARY,* 86 Porspect St, 06901. SAN 311-6514. Tel: 203-348-8100. FAX: 203-978-0114. E-Mail: brakeleyct@aol.com.
Founded 1919
Library Holdings: Bk Vols 1,500; Per Subs 25
Subject Interests: Fund-raising, Philanthropy, Pub relations

S CLAIROL RESEARCH LIBRARY,* 2 Blachley Rd, 06922. SAN 302-3745. Tel: 203-357-5001. FAX: 203-969-2577. *Librn*, Linda Massoni
Founded 1968
Library Holdings: Bk Vols 14,175; Bk Titles 9,660; Per Subs 315
Restriction: Staff use only
Partic in Dialog Corporation; Nat Libr of Med; SDC Info Servs

GL CONNECTICUT JUDICIAL BRANCH, Law Library at Stamford,* Court House, 123 Hoyt St, 06905. SAN 336-2043. Tel: 203-359-1114. FAX: 203-324-2418. *In Charge*, Jonathan C Stock; E-Mail: jonathan.stock@jud.state.ct.us
Jun 1998-May 1999 Income $134,000
Library Holdings: Bk Vols 34,186; Per Subs 38

S CONNECTICUT STATE BOARD OF EDUCATION LIBRARY, J M Wright Technical School,* Scalzi Park, 06904. (Mail add: PO Box 1416, 06904), SAN 326-971X. Tel: 203-324-7363. FAX: 203-324-1196. *Dir*, Diane Bauby; *Librn*, Pat Paktinat; *Coll Develop*, Patricia Paktinat
Library Holdings: Bk Titles 5,000
Subject Interests: Electronics

L CUMMINGS & LOCKWOOD, Law Library, 4 Stamford Plaza, PO Box 120, 06904. SAN 372-3399. Tel: 203-351-4466. FAX: 203-351-4534. Web Site: www.cl-law.com. *Dir*, Roseanne M Shea; Staff 2 (MLS 2)
Library Holdings: Bk Vols 20,000
Automation Activity & Vendor Info: (Acquisitions) Inmagic, Inc.; (Cataloging) Inmagic, Inc.; (OPAC) Inmagic, Inc.; (Serials) Inmagic, Inc.
Partic in Western Connecticut Library Council, Inc

S CYTEC INDUSTRIES, Technical Information Services,* 1937 W Main St, 06904-0060. (Mail add: PO Box 60, 06904-0060), SAN 302-3699. Tel: 203-321-2445. FAX: 203-321-2985. *Tech Servs*, Eve Mountford
Founded 1936
Library Holdings: Bk Vols 12,000; Per Subs 250
Subject Interests: Chemical engineering, Chemistry, Technology

L DAY, BERRY & HOWARD, Law Library,* One Canterbury Green, 06901. SAN 373-6741. Tel: 203-977-7300, Ext 559. FAX: 203-977-7301. *Librn*, Lisa Bologna; E-Mail: bolognl@dbn.com; Staff 2 (MLS 1, Non-MLS 1)
Restriction: Staff use only

R FIRST CONGREGATIONAL CHURCH LIBRARY, Walton Pl, 06901. SAN 302-3761. Tel: 203-323-0200. FAX: 203-348-2270. Web Site: www.fccstamford.org. *Chairperson*, Barbara Arata; Tel: 203-323-6511
Founded 1956
Library Holdings: Bk Vols 3,000
Subject Interests: Biblical studies, Children's literature, Church history, Religion

S GARTNER GROUP, INC, Information Resource Center, 56 Top Gallant Rd, 06904. SAN 374-8588. Tel: 203-316-6749, 203-316-6858. FAX: 203-316-6480. *Mgr*, Sandra Lahtinen; E-Mail: sandra.lahtinen@gartner.com; *Mgr*, Karen Laughlin; E-Mail: karen.laughlin@gartner.com
Library Holdings: Bk Vols 2,000; Per Subs 200
Database Vendor: Dialog, Ebsco - EbscoHost, GaleNet, Lexis-Nexis, OCLC - First Search
Restriction: Company library, Not open to public
Function: Business archives, Document delivery services, For research purposes

S GE ASSET MANAGEMENT, Information Center, 3003 Summer St, 06904. SAN 336-0547. Tel: 203-326-2404. FAX: 203-326-4026. *Mgr*, Mildred Lorenti
Founded 1987
Library Holdings: Bk Titles 2,000; Per Subs 100
Subject Interests: Finance, Real estate
Special Collections: Specialized Brokerage Reports
Partic in Dialog Corporation; Dow Jones News Retrieval

S INTERNATIONAL PAPER, (Formerly Champion International Corp), Business Information Center, 400 Atlantic St, 06921. SAN 302-3737. Tel: 203-358-7497. FAX: 203-358-7968. *Mgr*, William Langham; E-Mail: bill.langham@ipaper.com; Staff 2 (MLS 1, Non-MLS 1)
Founded 1975
Library Holdings: Bk Vols 500; Per Subs 180
Subject Interests: Business and management, Forestry, Pulp and paper
Restriction: Employees & their associates
Partic in Western Connecticut Library Council, Inc

L KELLEY DRYE & WARREN, Connecticut Library,* 2 Stamford Plaza, 281 Tresser Blvd, 06901. SAN 374-4671. Tel: 203-351-8068. FAX: 203-327-2669. *Librn*, Mary A McPherson; E-Mail: mmcpherson@kelleydrye.com; Staff 1 (MLS 1)
Library Holdings: Bk Titles 7,000; Per Subs 1,000
Subject Interests: Corporate law
Restriction: Staff use only
Partic in Dialog Corporation; Westlaw

S MARAKON ASSOCIATES LIBRARY, 300 Atlantic St, 12th Flr, 06901. SAN 374-5929. Tel: 203-978-6840. FAX: 203-978-6686. *Info Res*, Letty Nardone; E-Mail: lnardone@marakon.com. Subject Specialists: *Business*, Letty Nardone; Staff 2 (MLS 1, Non-MLS 1)
Founded 1988
2000-2001 Mats Exp $77,000, Books $2,000, Per/Ser (Incl. Access Fees) $35,000, Other Print Mats $40,000
Library Holdings: Bk Titles 3,000; Per Subs 150
Subject Interests: Business, Economics, Management, Marketing
Automation Activity & Vendor Info: (Cataloging) CASPR
Restriction: Staff use only
Mem of Western Conn Libr Coun
Partic in Nelinet, Inc

S NAC REINSURANCE CORPORATE LIBRARY, 70 Seaview Ave, 06902-6036. SAN 323-5823. Tel: 203-964-5216. FAX: 203-964-0763. *Librn*, Diane Fischer
Library Holdings: Bk Vols 500; Bk Titles 300; Per Subs 250
Mem of SW Conn Libr Coun, Inc
Partic in Dialog Corporation; Dow Jones News Retrieval; Westlaw

L PAUL, HASTINGS, JANOFSKY & WALKER LIBRARY,* 1055 Washington Blvd Ninth Flr, 06901. Tel: 203-961-7400.

M PURDUE PHARMA LP & ASSOCIATED COMPANIES, Purdue Library, 201 Tresser Blvd, 06901. SAN 302-296X. Tel: 203-588-7265. Interlibrary Loan Service Tel: 203-588-7268. Circulation Tel: 203-588-8500. Reference Tel: 203-588-8500. FAX: 203-588-6212. *Dir*, Kathryn Walsh; E-Mail: kathy.walsh@pharma.com; Staff 12 (MLS 7, Non-MLS 5)
Founded 1970
Library Holdings: Bk Vols 3,000; Per Subs 400
Subject Interests: Business, Medicine, Pharmaceuticals
Automation Activity & Vendor Info: (Acquisitions) EOS; (Cataloging) EOS; (Circulation) EOS; (Serials) EOS
Partic in Nat Libr of Med

S REEBIE ASSOCIATES LIBRARY, 2777 Summer St, Ste 401, 06905. SAN 370-6893. Tel: 203-705-0455. FAX: 203-705-0456. *In Charge*, J R Thomson; Staff 1 (MLS 1)
Founded 1975
Library Holdings: Bk Titles 2,500; Per Subs 33
Subject Interests: Freight
Restriction: Staff use only

S REHABILITATION CENTER OF SOUTHWESTERN CONNECTICUT, INC, (Formerly Easter Seal Rehabilitation Center Of Southwestern Connecticut, Inc), Resource Room, 26 Palmer's Hill Rd, 06902. SAN 302-3788. Tel: 203-325-1544. FAX: 203-978-1437.
Founded 1961
Library Holdings: Bk Vols 100
Subject Interests: Rehabilitation, physical, Speech and hearing
Partic in Nat Libr of Med

C SAINT BASIL COLLEGE LIBRARY, 195 Glenbrook Rd, 06902. Tel: 203-964-8003. FAX: 203-967-9948. *Librn*, Msgr. John Terlecky
Founded 1901
Library Holdings: Bk Vols 27,000; Bk Titles 25,000; Per Subs 108
Database Vendor: OCLC - First Search

S SOUTHERN CONNECTICUT NEWSPAPERS, INC, Advocate,* 75 Tresser Blvd, 06904-9301. SAN 375-0930. Tel: 203-964-3709. FAX: 203-964-2345. *Librn*, Leigh Baker Michels
Library Holdings: Bk Vols 200; Per Subs 15

SR STAMFORD CATHOLIC LIBRARY, INC,* 566 Elm St, 06902. SAN 302-3834. Tel: 203-348-4422. *In Charge*, Marylou Flowers; Staff 1 (Non-MLS 1)
Founded 1948. Circ 200
Library Holdings: Bk Titles 5,000; Per Subs 10
Subject Interests: Catholicism
Publications: Catholic Transcript; Fairfield County Catholic (newspaper)

S STAMFORD HISTORICAL SOCIETY LIBRARY,* 1508 High Ridge Rd, 06903-4107. SAN 302-3842. Tel: 203-329-1183. FAX: 203-322-1607. E-Mail: archivist@flvax.ferg.lib.ct.us. Web Site: www.stamfordhistory.org. *Exec Dir*, Linda Baulsir; *Librn*, Ronald Marcus; *Curator*, Joshua Lane; Staff 3 (MLS 3)
Founded 1901
Library Holdings: Bk Vols 10,000; Per Subs 10
Subject Interests: Local history
Special Collections: 17th-20th Century Americana, Maps & Atlases of Stamford & Fairfield County, Photographic Coll, Stamford Business & Industry, Stamford Government, Stamford Postcard

M STAMFORD HOSPITAL, Health Sciences Library,* Shelborne Rd at W Broad, PO Box 9317, 06901. SAN 324-4202. Tel: 203-325-7523. FAX: 203-325-7109. *Librn*, Katalin Gyorgyey
Founded 1963
Library Holdings: Bk Vols 1,276; Per Subs 167
Special Collections: Medicine, Allied Health & Nursing Coll
Partic in Conn Asn of Health Scis Librs; North Atlantic Health Sciences Libraries, Inc

P STAMFORD'S PUBLIC LIBRARY, Ferguson Library, 96 Broad Street, One Public Library Plaza, 06904. SAN 336-4925. Tel: 203-964-1000. FAX: 203-357-9098. E-Mail: comments@fergusonlibrary.org. Web Site: www.fergusonlibrary.org. *Pres*, Ernest A DiMattia, Jr; Tel: 203-964-1000, Ext 200, E-Mail: dimattia@fergusonlibrary.org; *Admin Dir*, Thomas H Blair, III; Tel: 203-357-9098, Ext 203, E-Mail: tblair@fergusonlibrary.org; *Admin Dir*, Nicholas A Bochicchio, Jr; Tel: 203-964-1000, Ext 202, E-Mail: nboch@fergusonlibrary.org; *Admin Assoc*, Melanie Keiffer; Tel: 203-964-1000, Ext 206, E-Mail: mkeiffer@fergusonlibrary.org; *Admin Dir*, Alice Knapp; Tel: 203-964-1000, Ext 201, E-Mail: aknpp@fergusonlibrary.org; *Publ Servs*, Katherine Griffith; Tel: 203-964-1000, Ext 207, E-Mail: kgriffith@ferg.lib.ct.us; *Publ Servs*, Kitty Griffith; *Head, Cat*, Michael Sweeney; *Head, Circ*, Alex Lee; Tel: 203-964-1000, Ext 260, E-Mail: alee@fergusonlibrary.org; *Head, Info Serv*, Michell Hackwelder; Tel: 203-964-1000, Ext 230, Fax: 203-357-0660, E-Mail: michell@fergusonlibrary.org; *Dir, Tech Serv*, Gary Giannelli; Tel: 203-964-1000, Ext 270, E-Mail: gary@fergusonlibrary.org; *Ad Servs*, Leeann Jaworski; Tel: 203-964-1000, Ext 220, Fax: 203-357-0660, E-Mail: ljaworski@ferg.lib.ct.us; *Ad Servs*, Carolyn Karwoski; Tel: 203-964-1000, Ext 220, Fax: 203-357-0660, E-Mail: ckarwoski@fergusonlibrary.org; *Ch Servs*, Caroline Ward; Tel: 203-964-1000, Ext 240, Fax: 203-359-6750, E-Mail: cward@fergusonlibrary.org; *Br Coordr*, Susan Baldwin; Tel: 203-964-1000, Ext 290, Fax: 203-968-2728, E-Mail: sbaldwin@fergusonlibrary.org; *Br Coordr*, Josephine Fulcher-Anderson; Tel: 203-964-1000, Ext 281, Fax: 203-969-0797, E-Mail: janderson@fergusonlibrary.org; *Bkmobile Coordr, Br Coordr*, Marilee Tremlett; Tel: 203-964-1000, Ext 284, Fax: 203-322-9110, 968-2728, E-Mail: mtrem@fergusonlibrary.org; *Business*, Marie Giuliano; Tel: 203-964-1000, Ext 210, E-Mail: marieg@fergusonlibrary.org; *Commun Relations*, Lisa Wyllie; Tel: 203-964-1000, Ext 207, E-Mail: lisa@fergusonlibrary.org; Staff 145 (MLS 35, Non-MLS 110)
Founded 1880. Pop 110,689; Circ 798,690
Jul 1999-Jun 2000 Income (Main Library and Branch Library) $6,320,363, State $10,712, City $5,927,492, Federal $14,168, Locally Generated Income $195,859, Other $172,131. Mats Exp $805,526, Books $549,691, AV Equip $95,999, Electronic Ref Mat (Incl. Access Fees) $159,836. Sal $3,607,599
Library Holdings: Bk Titles 395,799; Per Subs 656
Subject Interests: Business and management, Genealogy, Local history
Automation Activity & Vendor Info: (Circulation) DRA
Database Vendor: Dialog, DRA, Ebsco - EbscoHost, GaleNet, IAC - Info Trac, ProQuest
Publications: Ferguson Focus (Newsletter)
Partic in Dialog Corporation; Nelinet, Inc; OCLC Online Computer Library Center, Inc; Western Connecticut Library Council, Inc
Friends of the Library Group
Branches: 3
SOUTH END COMMUNITY CENTER, 34 Woodland Ave, 06902. SAN 336-4941. Tel: 203-964-1000. FAX: 203-357-9098. Web Site: www.ferglib.org/ferg. *Librn*, Josephine Fulcher-Anderson
Library Holdings: Bk Vols 11,986
Friends of the Library Group
TURN OF RIVER, 115 Vine Rd, 06905. SAN 336-495X. Tel: 203-964-1000. FAX: 203-357-9098. Web Site: www.ferglib.org/ferg. *Librn*, Susan Baldwin
Library Holdings: Bk Vols 64,778
Friends of the Library Group
WEED MEMORIAL, 1143 Hope St, 06907. SAN 336-4984. Tel: 203-964-1000. FAX: 203-357-9098. *Librn*, Marie Hoehn
Library Holdings: Bk Vols 31,296
Bookmobiles: 1

C UNIVERSITY OF CONNECTICUT AT STAMFORD, Jeremy Richard Library, One University Pl, 06901-2315. SAN 302-3877. Tel: 203-251-8500. Circulation Tel: 203-251-9599. FAX: 203-251-8501. E-Mail: stladm03@uconnvm_uconn.edu. Web Site: www.lib.uconn.edu/stamford/. *Dir*, Nancy Gillies; Tel: 203-251-8439, Fax: 203-251-8436, E-Mail: nancy.gillies@uconn.edu; *Circ*, Jane Lawless; Tel: 203-251-8519, E-Mail: jane.lawless@uconn.edu; *Ref*, Shelley Cudiner; Tel: 203-251-8521, E-Mail:

shelley.cudiner@uconn.edu; *Ref*, Shelley Roseman; Tel: 203-251-8522, E-Mail: shelley.roseman@uconn.edu. Subject Specialists: *Business*, Shelley Cudiner; *English literature*, Jane Lawless; *History*, Shelley Roseman; *Info*, Shelley Cudiner; *Literacy*, Shelley Cudiner; *Political science*, Shelley Roseman; Staff 7 (MLS 4, Non-MLS 3)
Founded 1962. Enrl 1,600; Fac 33; Highest Degree: Master
Jul 1999-Jun 2000 Mats Exp $214,200, Books $66,400, Per/Ser (Incl. Access Fees) $144,500. Sal $253,034 (Prof $163,222)
Library Holdings: Bk Vols 80,000; Per Subs 618
Subject Interests: Business and management, Economics, Literature, Social sciences and issues
Automation Activity & Vendor Info: (Cataloging) Endeavor; (Circulation) Endeavor; (OPAC) Endeavor
Database Vendor: CARL, Dialog, IAC - Info Trac, IAC - SearchBank, Lexis-Nexis, OCLC - First Search, OVID Technologies, Silverplatter Information Inc., Wilson - Wilson Web
Partic in Nelinet, Inc; Nerl

L XEROX CORP, Law Library, 800 Long Ridge Rd, 06904. SAN 302-3885. Tel: 203-968-3420. *Mgr*, Adriana Younskevicius
Founded 1969
Restriction: Staff use only
Partic in Southwestern Conn Libr Coun

STONINGTON

P STONINGTON FREE LIBRARY, 20 High St, PO Box 232, 06378. SAN 302-3907. Tel: 860-535-0658. FAX: 860-535-3945. E-Mail: stonington.free.lib@snet.net. Web Site: www.stoningtonfreelibrary.org. *Dir*, Nancy Z Young; Tel: 860-535-0268, E-Mail: nyoung@stoningtonpl.libct.org; *Ch Servs*, Natalie J Hinshaw; E-Mail: nhinshaw@stoningtonpl.libct.org; Staff 8 (MLS 1, Non-MLS 7)
Founded 1898. Pop 16,353
Jul 1999-Jun 2000 Income $197,998, State $1,923, City $74,925, Locally Generated Income $90,301. Mats Exp $29,417, Books $28,757, Electronic Ref Mat (Incl. Access Fees) $660. Sal $106,890 (Prof $35,302)
Library Holdings: Bk Vols 33,755; Bk Titles 31,247; Per Subs 58
Subject Interests: Genealogy, Local history
Database Vendor: GaleNet
Function: ILL limited
Open Mon, Tues, Thurs & Fri 10-5, Wed 10-8, Sat 10-3

S STONINGTON HISTORICAL SOCIETY LIBRARY, 40 Palmer St, PO Box 103, 06378. SAN 326-7989. Tel: 860-535-1131. *Dir*, Mary M Thacher; Staff 7 (Non-MLS 7)
Founded 1965
Library Holdings: Bk Vols 1,000
Subject Interests: Genealogy, Local history
Special Collections: Stonington Banks
Open Wed 1-5

STONY CREEK

P WILLOUGHBY WALLACE MEMORIAL LIBRARY,* 146 Thimble Islands Rd, 06405. SAN 302-3915. Tel: 203-488-8702. FAX: 203-315-3347. Web Site: www.lioninc.org/stonycreek/. *Dir*, Susan Donovan; E-Mail: sdonovan@connix.com
Founded 1958. Pop 3,000; Circ 45,000
Library Holdings: Bk Vols 23,000; Per Subs 70
Subject Interests: Art
Friends of the Library Group

STORRS

SR EDWINA WHITNEY LIBRARY OF THE STORRS CONGREGATIONAL CHURCH, 2 N Eagleville Rd, 06268. Tel: 860-429-9382. FAX: 860-429-9693. E-Mail: scchurch@uconn.edu. Web Site: www.storrscongo.uconn.edu. *Librn*, Janet Atkins; Tel: 860-423-5930
Library Holdings: Bk Titles 4,000

S MANSFIELD HISTORICAL SOCIETY, Edith Mason Library, c/o Richard Schimmelpfeng, 103 Courtyard Lane, 06268. (Mail add: PO Box 145, 06268), SAN 328-1663. Tel: 860-429-6575. E-Mail: webmaster@mansfield-history.org. Web Site: www.mansfield-history.org. *Librn*, Richard H Schimmelpfeng; Staff 1 (MLS 1)
Library Holdings: Bk Vols 2,804; Bk Titles 815
Subject Interests: Genealogy, Local history
Special Collections: Photograph Coll
Publications: Local History Pamphlets (annual)
Restriction: Non-circulating to the public

C UNIVERSITY OF CONNECTICUT LIBRARY, 369 Fairfield Rd, 06069-1005. SAN 336-5042. Tel: 860-486-2219. FAX: 860-486-0584. E-Mail: hblad125@uconnvm.uconn.edu. Web Site: www.lib.uconn.edu. *Dir Libr Serv*, Brinley Franklin; *Adminr*, Deborah Stansburg-Sunday; *Bibliogr*, Peter Allison; *Info Tech*, Fritzi Batchelor; *Archivist*, Betty Pittman; Staff 114 (MLS 44, Non-MLS 70)
Founded 1881. Enrl 25,374; Fac 1,103; Highest Degree: Doctorate
Library Holdings: Bk Titles 2,885,664; Per Subs 15,560
Special Collections: Alternative Press; American Socialism & Communism; Belgium History (Revolution, 1830-1839); Black Mountain Poets; Bookplates; Charles Olson Coll; Children's Literature; Chilean History & Literature; Conneticut History (primarily 1850-, emphasis on business, labor, ethnicity, public affairs); French History (including Paris Commune 1871); French Language & Linguistics; French Renaissance Literature; French Restoration Pamphlets; French Satirical Magazines, 19th Century; Italian History (including Italian Risorgimento, 1815-1870); Italian Risorgionento, 1815-1870; Labor History; Latin America; Little Magazines; Luis Camoens Coll; Madrid History; Maps; Medina; Medina Coll; Modern German Drama; Napoleonic Period; Paris Commune, 1871; Powys Brothers Coll; Sermons (Connecticut); Spanish Periodicals & Newspapers; University & Historical Archives; Videocassettes; William Berkson
Publications: Harvest; Journal of the Charles Olson Bibliography Series; University of Connecticut Libraries
Partic in Asn of Research Libraries; Nelinet, Inc; OCLC Online Computer Library Center, Inc
Special Services for the Deaf - Special interest periodicals; Staff with knowledge of sign language
Friends of the Library Group
Departmental Libraries:
COOKSON MUSIC LIBRARY Tel: 860-486-2502. *Librn*, Tracey Rudnick
Library Holdings: Bk Vols 23,968
PHARMACY Tel: 860-486-2218. *Librn*, Sharon Giovenale
Library Holdings: Bk Vols 18,587; Per Subs 300
Friends of the Library Group

STRATFORD

S SIKORSKY AIRCRAFT CORP, UTC Information Network,* 6900 Main St, S339A, PO Box 9729, 06615. SAN 302-394X. Tel: 203-386-4945. FAX: 203-386-7300. Web Site: www.sikorsky.com.; Staff 3 (MLS 2, Non-MLS 1)
Founded 1950
Library Holdings: Bk Titles 5,000; Per Subs 170
Publications: Library Bulletin
Restriction: Staff use only
Partic in Dialog Corporation; DROLS; SDC Info Servs; Wilsonline

S STRATFORD HISTORICAL SOCIETY LIBRARY,* 967 Academy Hill, 06615. (Mail add: PO Box 382, 06497), SAN 325-657X. Tel: 203-378-0630.
Library Holdings: Bk Titles 600
Subject Interests: Local history
Restriction: By appointment only
Open Tues & Thurs 9-2:30

P STRATFORD LIBRARY ASSOCIATION,* 2203 Main St, 06615. SAN 302-3931. Tel: 203-385-4161. FAX: 203-381-2079. E-Mail: kb@stratford@lib.ct.us. Web Site: www.stratford.lib.ct.us. *Dir*, Karen S Bowles; *Ref*, Gerry Gillespie; *Tech Servs*, Jane Murphy; *Ch Servs*, Martha Simpson; *Circ*, Claudia McCoach; *YA Servs*, Barbara Blosveren; *Publ Servs*, Tom Holehan; Staff 51 (MLS 18, Non-MLS 33)
Founded 1886. Pop 47,500; Circ 312,000
Jul 1998-Jun 1999 Income $1,942,417. Mats Exp $154,337. Sal $1,260,160
Library Holdings: Bk Vols 120,000; Per Subs 450
Subject Interests: Local history
Special Collections: Careers; Local History
Automation Activity & Vendor Info: (Acquisitions) epixtech, inc.; (Circulation) epixtech, inc.; (Serials) epixtech, inc.
Publications: Monthly calendar
Partic in Nelinet, Inc
Readers Theatre; Young Adult Homework Desk; Literacy Volunteers Programming

SUFFIELD

P KENT MEMORIAL LIBRARY, 50 N Main St (Junction of Rtes 75 & 168), 06078-2117. SAN 302-3958. Tel: 860-668-3896. Circulation Tel: 860-668-3897. Reference Tel: 860-668-3938. FAX: 860-668-3895. E-Mail: director@suffield-library.org. Web Site: www.suffield-library.org. *Dir*, Tony Bernardo; *Asst Dir, Coll Develop*, Kim Lord; E-Mail: kimlord@suffield-library.org; *Ch Servs*, Wendy Taylor; *ILL*, Anne Borg; *Circ*, Lois Hayes; *Cat*, Dorian Taylor; Staff 15 (MLS 3, Non-MLS 12)
Founded 1884. Pop 11,400
Jul 1998-Jun 1999 Income $409,718, State $4,140, City $341,465, Locally Generated Income $64,113. Mats Exp Books $52,589. Sal $211,785
Library Holdings: Bk Vols 92,000; Bk Titles 73,569; Per Subs 148
Special Collections: Local Suffield History, bks, doc
Automation Activity & Vendor Info: (Acquisitions) SIRSI; (Cataloging) SIRSI; (Circulation) SIRSI; (OPAC) SIRSI; (Serials) SIRSI
Database Vendor: Ebsco - EbscoHost
Publications: Directory of Suffield Clubs and Organizations
Partic in Capitol Region Library Council
Friends of the Library Group

TERRYVILLE

S LOCK MUSEUM OF AMERICA, INC LIBRARY, 230 Main St, PO Box 104, 06786. SAN 326-2537. Tel: 860-589-6359. FAX: 860-589-6359. Web Site: www.lockmuseum.com/. *Curator*, Thomas Hennessy
Founded 1972
Library Holdings: Bk Titles 100; Per Subs 500

P TERRYVILLE PUBLIC LIBRARY, 238 Main St, 06786. SAN 302-3974. Tel: 860-582-3121. Reference Tel: 860-583-4467. FAX: 860-585-4068. E-Mail: tplib@connix.com. Web Site: www.terryvillepl.lib.ct.us. *Dir*, Sharon LaCourse; E-Mail: lacourse@biblio.org; Staff 12 (MLS 1, Non-MLS 11)
Founded 1895. Pop 11,800; Circ 60,000
Jul 2000-Jun 2001 Income $325,068, State $4,000, City $303,369, Locally Generated Income $7,000, Other $10,699. Mats Exp $54,965, Books $41,000, Per/Ser (Incl. Access Fees) $4,400, Presv $100, Micro $400, AV Equip $5,665, Other Print Mats $400, Electronic Ref Mat (Incl. Access Fees) $3,000. Sal $193,199 (Prof $41,700)
Library Holdings: Bk Vols 51,000; Bk Titles 39,374; Per Subs 101; High Interest/Low Vocabulary Bk Vols 250; Bks on Deafness & Sign Lang 15
Subject Interests: Large type print, Literacy
Special Collections: Career Corner; Terryville-Plymouth Room
Automation Activity & Vendor Info: (Cataloging) CARL; (Circulation) CARL; (OPAC) CARL
Database Vendor: CARL
Publications: The Footnote (monthly) (Newsletter)
Partic in Bibliomation Inc; Region I Coop Libr Servs Unit
Friends of the Library Group

THOMASTON

P THOMASTON PUBLIC LIBRARY,* 248 Main St, 06787. SAN 302-3990. Tel: 860-283-4339. FAX: 860-283-4330. Web Site: www.biblio.org/thomaston. *Dir*, Jane T Kendrick; E-Mail: jkendrick@biblio.org; *Asst Librn*, Gloria Abbott
Founded 1898. Pop 6,276; Circ 70,000
Library Holdings: Bk Vols 50,000; Per Subs 115
Special Collections: Art Techniques (Bradshaw Coll); Career Information; Conklin Coll of the Arts, bks, fs; Connecticut History (Allan C Innes Coll); Innes Coll (J P Seth) Thomaston Centennial (Seth Thomas Clock Company & Family Coll)
Publications: Thomaston Public Library Gazette
Mem of Region One Coop Libr Servs Unit
Friends of the Library Group

TOLLAND

S FRENCH-CANADIAN GENEALOGICAL SOCIETY OF CONNECTICUT, INC LIBRARY, 53 Tolland Green, PO Box 928, 06084. SAN 326-9698. Tel: 860-872-2597. Web Site: home.att.net/~rich.carpenter/fcgsc/. *Pres*, Ivan Robinson; Tel: 860-875-8097; *Dir*, Maryanne Roy LeGrow
Founded 1981
Sep 2000-Aug 2001 Income $21,699. Mats Exp $13,508
Library Holdings: Bk Vols 3,000
Special Collections: Brown New England Coll; Hebert Acadian Coll; Tolland Libr Association Genealogical Coll
Publications: Connecticut Maple Leaf (semi annual)
Partic in Area Libr Serv Authority
Open Mon 1-8, Wed 4-8, Sat 9-4 & Sun 1-4

P TOLLAND PUBLIC LIBRARY, 21 Tolland Green, 06084. SAN 302-4008. Tel: 203-871-3620. FAX: 203-871-3626. *Dir*, Kay Mahoney; E-Mail: kmahoney@biblio.org; Staff 9 (MLS 2, Non-MLS 7)
Founded 1899. Pop 12,036; Circ 134,969
Jul 1999-Jun 2000 Income $347,176. Mats Exp $41,372, Per/Ser (Incl. Access Fees) $36,000, AV Equip $3,000. Sal $184,646
Library Holdings: Bk Titles 52,000; Per Subs 80
Automation Activity & Vendor Info: (Circulation) CARL
Database Vendor: Ebsco - EbscoHost, GaleNet
Function: ILL available, Photocopies available
Partic in Eastern Connecticut Libraries
Friends of the Library Group

TORRINGTON

M CHARLOTTE HUNGERFORD HOSPITAL, Health Sciences Library,* 540 Litchfield, 06790. Tel: 860-496-6689. FAX: 860-496-6631. *Librn*, Jackie Rorke; E-Mail: jrorke@hungerford.org
Library Holdings: Bk Vols 450; Bk Titles 350

S THE TORRINGTON COMPANY TECHNICAL INFORMATION CENTER, 59 Field St, 06790-1008. (Mail add: PO Box 1008, 06790-1008), Tel: 860-626-3290. *Dir*, Linda Senkus
Founded 1990
Library Holdings: Bk Vols 30,000; Bk Titles 30,000; Per Subs 100

S TORRINGTON HISTORICAL SOCIETY LIBRARY, John Thompson Memorial Library, 192 Main St, 06790. SAN 302-4016. Tel: 860-482-8260. E-Mail: torringtonhistorical@snet.net. *Dir*, Mark McEachern
Founded 1944
Library Holdings: Bk Titles 2,000
Subject Interests: Genealogy, Local history
Special Collections: CT Journal (1782-1813), newsp; General Archives; Litchfield Enquirer (1842-1941), newsp; Litchfield Monitor (1791-1795), newsp; Torrington Building Co, 800 sets of blueprints; Torrington History; Torrington Register (1874-present)

P TORRINGTON LIBRARY,* 12 Daycoeton Pl, 06790-6399. SAN 302-4024. Tel: 860-489-6684. FAX: 860-482-4664. *Dir*, Karen Worrall
Founded 1864. Pop 31,000; Circ 133,000
Library Holdings: Bk Vols 70,000; Per Subs 80
Special Collections: Large Print Coll
Partic in Region I Coop Libr Servs Unit

C UNIVERSITY OF CONNECTICUT - TORRINGTON REGIONAL CAMPUS LIBRARY, 855 University Dr, 06790. SAN 302-4032. Tel: 860-626-6820. FAX: 860-626-6817. E-Mail: torrrcl@lib.uconn.edu. Web Site: www.lib.uconn.edu/torrington. *In Charge*, Susan Thebarge; E-Mail: sue.thebarge@uconn.edu; Staff 2 (MLS 1, Non-MLS 1)
Founded 1965
Library Holdings: Bk Vols 15,000; Per Subs 85
Automation Activity & Vendor Info: (Circulation) Endeavor
Publications: INFOLINES (newsletter)
Mem of Region One Coop Libr Servs Unit

TRUMBULL

P TRUMBULL LIBRARY, 33 Quality St, 06611. SAN 336-5190. Tel: 203-452-5197. FAX: 203-452-5125. E-Mail: trumbull.library04@snet.net. Web Site: www.trumbullcc-library.org. *Dir*, Grace M Birch; *Asst Dir*, Louis G Sheehy; *Circ, Reader Servs*, Arlene Pellegrino; *Ch Servs, YA Servs*, Cathy Mauro; *Media Spec*, Paulette Bunco; *Tech Servs*, Sheri Szymanski; Staff 34 (MLS 5, Non-MLS 29)
Founded 1975. Pop 32,600; Circ 334,137
Jul 1999-Jun 2000 Income (Main Library and Branch Library) $1,035,424. Mats Exp $267,950, Books $139,000, Per/Ser (Incl. Access Fees) $15,000, AV Equip $34,000. Sal $647,727 (Prof $278,680)
Library Holdings: Bk Vols 139,866; Per Subs 176
Special Collections: Framed art & photos; Records; Sculpture
Automation Activity & Vendor Info: (Acquisitions) epixtech, inc.; (Circulation) epixtech, inc.
Partic in Univ Halifax
Friends of the Library Group
Branches: 1
FAIRCHILD NICHOLS MEMORIAL, 1718 Huntington Turnpike, 06611. SAN 336-5220. Tel: 203-452-5196. FAX: 203-452-5178. Web Site: www.trumbullct-library.org. *Librn*, Lisa Pichnarcik; Staff 6 (MLS 1, Non-MLS 5)
Library Holdings: Bk Vols 33,328
Friends of the Library Group

S UNILEVER HPC USA, Research Laboratories Library, Trumbull Corporate Park, 40 Merrit Blvd, 06611. SAN 302-4059. Tel: 203-381-4312. FAX: 203-381-4212. *Librn*, Mary Davis; E-Mail: mary.m.davis@unilever.com
Founded 1959
Library Holdings: Bk Vols 5,000; Per Subs 249
Subject Interests: Chemistry, Dentistry, Dermatology, Pharmacology
Partic in Data Star; Dialog Corporation

UNION

P UNION FREE PUBLIC LIBRARY, 979 Buckley Hwy, 06076. SAN 302-3680. Tel: 860-684-4913. FAX: 860-684-4913. E-Mail: union_free_pl@bigfoot.com. Web Site: www.ctschools.org/Union_Free_Pl/. *Librn*, Brigitte Botnick
Founded 1894. Pop 640; Circ 4,600
Library Holdings: Bk Vols 10,000; Bk Titles 9,500
Open Mon 1-4, Wed 5-8pm & Sat 9-1

VERNON

P ROCKVILLE PUBLIC LIBRARY, INC, George Maxwell Memorial Library,* 52 Union St, PO Box 1320, 06066. SAN 302-4067. Tel: 860-875-5892. FAX: 860-875-9795. E-Mail: rockville.publ.lib@snet.net. Web Site: www.state.ct.us/. *Dir*, Peter F Ciparelli; *Ch Servs*, Shahla Zarinejad; *Cat*, Eva Avery; *Circ*, D Anderson; *Ref*, Denise J Stankovics; *ILL*, J Smith; Staff 4 (MLS 4)
Founded 1896. Pop 29,811; Circ 121,781
Library Holdings: Bk Vols 51,559; Bk Titles 46,006; Per Subs 116
Subject Interests: Local history
Automation Activity & Vendor Info: (Cataloging) CARL; (Circulation)

CARL
Mem of Eastern Conn Librs, Inc
Partic in Bibliomation
Friends of the Library Group

VOLUNTOWN

P VOLUNTOWN PUBLIC LIBRARY,* 115 Main St, PO Box 26, 06384. SAN 302-4075. Tel: 860-376-0485. *Dir*, Barbara F Ayrton
Pop 2,268; Circ 3,811
Library Holdings: Bk Vols 5,000
Open Mon-Thurs 12-2, Tues 6:30-8:30 pm, Sat 10-1
Friends of the Library Group

WALLINGFORD

§S BRISTOL-MYERS SQUIBB CO, Scientific Information Resources, 5 Research Pkwy, 06492-1996. (Mail add: PO Box 5103, 06492-7663), SAN 378-388X. Tel: 203-284-6000. FAX: 203-677-6006. *Head, Info Serv*, Gina Addona; Tel: 203-284-6229
Library Holdings: Bk Vols 30,000; Per Subs 650
Automation Activity & Vendor Info: (Acquisitions) epixtech, inc.; (Cataloging) epixtech, inc.; (Circulation) epixtech, inc.

M GAYLORD HOSPITAL, Tremaine Library & Resource Center,* PO Box 400, 06492. SAN 328-4697. Tel: 203-284-2800, Ext 3328. FAX: 203-284-2892. Web Site: www.gaylord.org. *Librn*, Lyn Crispino; E-Mail: lcrispino@gaylord.org
Library Holdings: Bk Vols 1,500; Per Subs 120
Publications: Newsletter
Partic in Conn Asn of Health Scis Librs

S WALLINGFORD HISTORICAL SOCIETY INC, LIBRARY, 180 S Main St, 06492. (Mail add: PO Box 73, 06492-0073), SAN 326-9981. Tel: 203-294-1996. *Pres*, Robert N Beaumont; Tel: 203-269-9988, Fax: 203-296-5300, E-Mail: robert.n.beaumont@snet.net
Founded 1916
Library Holdings: Bk Vols 500
Subject Interests: Local genealogy, Local history
Publications: Wallingford - Images of America Series
Function: Research library

P WALLINGFORD PUBLIC LIBRARY, 200 N Main St, 06492-3791. SAN 336-5255. Tel: 203-265-6754. FAX: 203-269-5698. Web Site: www.wallingford.lioninc.org. *Dir*, Karen Roesler; E-Mail: kroesler@lioninc.org; *Dir*, Leslie Scherer; E-Mail: lscherer@lioninc.org; *Asst Dir*, Amy Humphries; *Head Tech Servs*, Patricia Johnson; *Head, Circ, ILL*, Kathleen Campion; *Ch Servs*, Ruth Gaffey; *Ref Serv Ad*, David Andrews; *Ref Servs YA*, Bobbie Borne; *Ref Serv, Tech Coordr*, Robert Nankin; *Commun Relations, Ref Serv Ad*, Susan Smayda; *Ref Servs Ch*, Susan Stewart; *Ref Servs Ch*, Bonnie Strickland-Naczi; Staff 51 (MLS 11, Non-MLS 40)
Founded 1881. Pop 40,998; Circ 490,599
Jul 1999-Jun 2000 Income (Main Library and Branch Library) $1,760,740, State $26,064, City $1,644,432, Locally Generated Income $62,970, Other $27,274. Mats Exp $234,897, Books $221,676, Electronic Ref Mat (Incl. Access Fees) $13,221. Sal $978,813 (Prof $493,062)
Library Holdings: Bk Vols 189,312; Per Subs 437
Subject Interests: Local history
Special Collections: Oneida Community, Holocaust
Automation Activity & Vendor Info: (Acquisitions) epixtech, inc.; (Cataloging) epixtech, inc.; (Circulation) epixtech, inc.; (ILL) epixtech, inc.; (OPAC) epixtech, inc.; (Serials) epixtech, inc.
Database Vendor: Ebsco - EbscoHost, epixtech, inc., GaleNet, IAC - SearchBank
Publications: WORDS (Newsletter)
Function: ILL available, Photocopies available
Partic in Libraries Online, Inc
Friends of the Library Group
Branches: 1
YALESVILLE BRANCH, 400 Church St, Yalesville, 06492. SAN 336-528X. Tel: 203-269-3688. Web Site: www.wallingford.lioninc.org.
Library Holdings: Bk Vols 5,000
Friends of the Library Group

WARREN

P WARREN PUBLIC LIBRARY,* Sackett Hill Rd, No 15, 06754. SAN 302-4105. Tel: 860-868-2195. *Librn*, Barbara Henry; Tel: 202-319-5091, Fax: 202-319-4735
Pop 1,200; Circ 7,000
Library Holdings: Bk Vols 10,000

WASHINGTON

S AMERICAN BOOK PRICES CURRENT LIBRARY,* PO Box 1236, 06793. Tel: 203-868-7408. *Dir*, Katharine Kyes Leab
Library Holdings: Bk Vols 6,000; Bk Titles 4,000

P GUNN MEMORIAL LIBRARY INC, 5 Wykeham Rd, 06793-1308. (Mail add: PO Box 1273, 06793-0273), SAN 302-4113. Tel: 860-868-7586. FAX: 860-868-7247. E-Mail: gunnlib@biblio.org. Web Site: www.biblio.org/gunn. *Dir*, Jean Chapin; *Ad Servs*, Kristine Dyson; *Ch Servs*, Martie Smolka; *Tech Servs*, Jennifer McKenzie
Founded 1908. Pop 4,000; Circ 46,388
Library Holdings: Bk Vols 39,408
Subject Interests: Connecticut

S THE GUNNERY, INC, The Tisch Family Library,* 99 Green Hill Rd, 06793. SAN 326-0054. Tel: 860-868-7334, Ext 224. FAX: 860-868-1614. *Dir*, William Chase; E-Mail: chasew@gunnery.crec.org
Enrl 256; Fac 41
1998-1999 Income $20,000. Mats Exp $10,000, Books $6,000, Per/Ser (Incl. Access Fees) $3,000, Micro $1,000
Library Holdings: Bk Vols 15,000; Per Subs 90
Special Collections: Alumni bks & publications
Partic in Western Connecticut Library Council, Inc

S THE INSTITUTE FOR AMERICAN INDIAN STUDIES, Research & Education Libraries,* 38 Curtiss Rd, 06793-0260. SAN 321-0359. Tel: 860-868-0518. FAX: 860-868-1649. *Exec Dir*, Alberto C Meloni
Founded 1975
Library Holdings: Bk Titles 2,400; Per Subs 1,000
Subject Interests: Am Indians, Archaeology, Ethnobotany

C INTERNATIONAL COLLEGE OF HOSPITALITY MANAGEMENT, 101 Wykeham Rd, 06793. Tel: 860-868-9555, Ext 128. Toll Free Tel: 800-955-0809. Web Site: www.ichm.cc.ct.us. *Librn*, Eugenie Rebres; E-Mail: eugenier@ichm.cc.ct.us
Library Holdings: Bk Vols 10,000; Bk Titles 10,000; Per Subs 50

WASHINGTON DEPOT

S WASHINGTON ART ASSOCIATION LIBRARY, 4 Bryan Plaza, 06794. Tel: 860-868-2878. Web Site: washingtonart.org. *In Charge*, Materne Delancey
Founded 1952
Library Holdings: Bk Titles 1,600

WATERBURY

P SILAS BRONSON LIBRARY,* 267 Grand St, 06702-1981. SAN 336-531X. Tel: 203-574-8222. FAX: 203-574-8055. Web Site: www.biblio.org/bronson/silas.htm. *Dir*, Leo N Flanagan; Tel: 203-574-8221, E-Mail: lflanagan@bronsonlibrary.org; *Ref Servs YA*, Ellen Gambini; Tel: 203-574-8248, E-Mail: egambini@bronsonlibrary.org; *Circ*, Emmett J McSweeney; Tel: 203-574-8205, E-Mail: emcsweeney@bronsonlibrary.org; *Ch Servs*, Joan B Rossi; Tel: 203-574-8214, E-Mail: jrossi@bronsonlibrary.org; *Tech Servs*, Marianne Young; Tel: 203-574-8218, E-Mail: myoung@bronsonlibrary.org; Staff 45 (MLS 24, Non-MLS 21)
Founded 1869. Pop 106,082; Circ 199,348
Jul 1998-Jun 1999 Income (Main Library and Branch Library) $2,188,540. Mats Exp $165,908. Sal $1,589,733
Library Holdings: Bk Vols 225,213; Per Subs 562
Subject Interests: Genealogy, Local history
Automation Activity & Vendor Info: (Cataloging) CARL; (Circulation) CARL
Database Vendor: Dialog, IAC - SearchBank
Publications: Books & Happenings (monthly newsletter)
Function: ILL available
Special Services for the Deaf - TDD
Friends of the Library Group
Branches: 1
BUNKER HILL, 192 Bunker Hill Ave, 06708. SAN 336-5344. Tel: 203-574-8240. *Librn*, David Landry
Library Holdings: Bk Vols 7,000

L CARMODY & TORRANCE, Law Library,* 50 Leavenworth St, 06702. SAN 372-3402. Tel: 203-573-1200. FAX: 203-575-2600. E-Mail: ahodges@carmodylaw.com. *Librn*, Ann C Hodges
Library Holdings: Bk Vols 12,000; Per Subs 100

L CONNECTICUT STATE JUDICIAL DEPARTMENT, Law Library at Waterbury,* Court House, 300 Grand St, 06702. SAN 375-7528. Tel: 203-596-4044. FAX: 203-596-4137. *Librn*, Mary Fuller; E-Mail: mary.fuller@jud.state.ct.us
Jul 1998-Jun 1999 Mats Exp $82,000. Sal $54,000
Library Holdings: Bk Vols 40,000; Per Subs 35

S COUNCIL OF GOVERNMENTS OF THE CENTRAL NAUGATUCK VALLEY LIBRARY, 20 E Main St, Ste 303, 06702-2399. SAN 373-0948. Tel: 203-757-0535. FAX: 203-756-7688. *Exec Dir*, Peter Dorpalen
Subject Interests: Transportation
Special Collections: US Census Data

L GAGER & PETERSON, Law Library,* One Exchange Pl, 06722. SAN 372-4840. Tel: 203-597-5100. FAX: 203-757-7888. E-Mail: library@gplaw.com. *Librn*, Ann Ferraro; *Librn*, Candace Majewski
Library Holdings: Bk Vols 5,000

S MACDERMID, INC LIBRARY,* 245 Freight St, 06702. SAN 302-4156. Tel: 203-575-5700. FAX: 203-575-5630. *Librn*, Eleanor Borkauskas
Library Holdings: Bk Vols 1,500; Per Subs 50

S MATTATUCK HISTORICAL SOCIETY LIBRARY,* 144 W Main St, 06702. SAN 302-4172. Tel: 203-753-0381. FAX: 203-756-6283. E-Mail: info@mattatuckmuseum.org. Web Site: www.mattatuckmuseum.org. *Exec Dir*, Marie Galbraith
Founded 1877
Library Holdings: Bk Vols 3,000; Per Subs 10
Subject Interests: Local history
Special Collections: Brass Workers History Project Archives; Connecticut Artists Coll; Decorative Arts; Pictorial History of Waterbury, 1674-1974; Platt Brothers Archives; Waterbury Industrial History Archives

M SAINT MARY'S HOSPITAL HEALTH SCIENCE LIBRARY,* 56 Franklin St, 06706. Tel: 203-574-6408. *Librn*, Ellen Sheehan
Library Holdings: Bk Titles 4,000; Per Subs 350

C TEIKYO POST UNIVERSITY, Traurig Library & Learning Resources Center, 800 Country Club Rd, 06723-2540. SAN 302-4180. Tel: 203-596-4560. FAX: 203-575-9691. E-Mail: library@teikyopost.edu. Web Site: www.teikyopost.edu/academics. *Mgr*, Tracy Ralston; Tel: 203-596-4564, E-Mail: tralston@teikyopost.edu; *Ref Serv, Tech Servs*, Joan Arnold; E-Mail: jarnold@teikyopost.edu; Staff 5 (MLS 2, Non-MLS 3)
Founded 1890. Enrl 1,400; Fac 25; Highest Degree: Bachelor
Jul 2000-Jun 2001 Mats Exp $86,000, Books $39,000, Per/Ser (Incl. Access Fees) $47,000. Sal $35,000
Library Holdings: Bk Vols 43,723; Bk Titles 39,108; Per Subs 565
Special Collections: Fed; University Archival Coll; Zwicker Tax Institute Coll
Database Vendor: Ebsco - EbscoHost, OCLC - First Search
Function: ILL available
Mem of Conn Libr Asn
Partic in Nelinet, Inc; OCLC Online Computer Library Center, Inc

J MAX R TRAURIG LEARNING RESOURCE CENTER LIBRARY,* 750 Chase Pkwy, 06708. SAN 302-4229. Tel: 203-575-8024. FAX: 203-575-8062. Web Site: www.nvctc.commnet.edu.library. *Dir*, Rosalie C Levinson; *Coll Develop*, Alison Wang
Founded 1964. Enrl 4,000; Fac 120
Jul 1996-Jun 1997 Income $500,000
Library Holdings: Bk Titles 38,000; Per Subs 518
Subject Interests: Chemical engineering, Data processing, Mechanical engineering

C UNIVERSITY OF CONNECTICUT - WATERBURY REGIONAL CAMPUS, Edward H Kirschbaum Library, 32 Hillside Ave, 06710-2288. SAN 302-4202. Tel: 203-236-9900. FAX: 203-236-9905. Web Site: www.lib.uconn.edu/waterbury. *Librn*, Janet M Swift; Tel: 203-236-9902, E-Mail: wbladm01@uconnvm.uconn.edu; *Librn*, Sheila A Lafferty; Tel: 203-236-9904, E-Mail: wbladm03@uconnvm.uconn.edu; *Librn*, Deborah Stansbury Sunday; Tel: 860-486-4481; Staff 2 (MLS 2)
Founded 1946
Library Holdings: Bk Vols 40,000; Per Subs 100
Subject Interests: Art
Special Collections: Philemon J Hewitt Jr Apicultural Coll
Automation Activity & Vendor Info: (Circulation) Endeavor; (Course Reserve) Endeavor; (OPAC) Endeavor; (Serials) Endeavor
Database Vendor: GaleNet, IAC - Info Trac, OCLC - First Search
Function: ILL available
Partic in Nelinet, Inc; OCLC Online Computer Library Center, Inc; Western Connecticut Library Council, Inc

S VOLTARC TECH, INC LIBRARY,* 400 Captain Neville Dr, 06705. SAN 324-4679. Tel: 203-578-4600. FAX: 203-575-3460. *Librn*, Evlyn Lafferty
Library Holdings: Bk Titles 700; Per Subs 60
Special Collections: Lamp Manufacturing & Related Subjects, bks, periodicals, patents

M WATERBURY HOSPITAL, Health Center Library,* 64 Robbins St, 06721. SAN 302-4210. Tel: 203-573-6136. FAX: 203-573-6706.; Staff 3 (MLS 1, Non-MLS 2)
Library Holdings: Bk Vols 8,800; Per Subs 290
Subject Interests: Medicine, Nursing
Partic in Conn Asn of Health Scis Librs; Coop Libr Agency for Syst & Servs; Nat Libr of Med

S WATERBURY REPUBLICAN & AMERICAN LIBRARY, 389 Meadow St, 06702. SAN 324-3583. Tel: 203-574-3636, Ext 346. FAX: 203-596-9277. *Librn*, Carol Ann Brown
Library Holdings: Bk Vols 2,000; Bk Titles 800; Per Subs 20
Subject Interests: NW Conn
Special Collections: Local History Books; Local Newspaper Clippings
Restriction: By appointment only

WATERFORD

S EUGENE O'NEILL THEATER CENTER'S, Liebling-Wood Library, 305 Great Neck Rd, 06385. SAN 302-4237. Tel: 860-443-0051, 860-443-5378. FAX: 860-443-9653. E-Mail: hummany@mindport.com. Web Site: www.ourworld.compuserve.com/homepage/o'neilltheater/. *Curator*, Sally Thomas Pavetti; *Curator*, Lois Erickson McDonald; Staff 2 (MLS 2)
Founded 1966
Library Holdings: Bk Titles 4,000
Special Collections: Eugene O'Neill Coll; National Critics Institute; National Playwrights Conference (1966-85); National Theatre Institute Library
Friends of the Library Group

P WATERFORD PUBLIC LIBRARY, 49 Rope Ferry Rd, 06385. SAN 302-4245. Tel: 860-444-5805. Web Site: www.waterfordpubliclibrary.org. *Dir*, Vincent Juliano; *Ad Servs*, Judith L Liskov; *ILL*, Sandra Joncus; *Tech Servs*, Margaret Rothen
Founded 1923. Pop 18,000; Circ 262,378
Jul 1998-Jun 1999 Income $1,126,724. Mats Exp $133,115. Sal $707,278
Library Holdings: Bk Vols 103,087; Per Subs 278
Automation Activity & Vendor Info: (Cataloging) TLC; (Circulation) GEAC; (OPAC) GEAC

WATERTOWN

S WATERTOWN HISTORICAL SOCIETY LIBRARY,* 22 De Forest St, 06795. SAN 302-4253. Tel: 860-274-1634. *In Charge*, Florence Crowell
Founded 1947
Library Holdings: Bk Vols 1,000
Subject Interests: Genealogy, Local history

P WATERTOWN LIBRARY ASSOCIATION,* 470 Main St, 06795. SAN 336-5409. Tel: 860-945-5360. FAX: 860-945-5367. E-Mail: wtnlib@watertownlibrary.org. Web Site: www.watertownlibrary.org. *Dir*, Joan K Rintelman; *Asst Dir*, Dona L Rintelman
Founded 1865. Pop 20,000; Circ 113,657
Library Holdings: Bk Vols 105,000; Per Subs 180
Partic in Bibliomation; Region I Coop Libr Servs Unit
Friends of the Library Group
Branches: 1
OAKVILLE BRANCH, 55 Davis St, Oakville, 06779. SAN 336-5433. Tel: 860-945-5368. E-Mail: wtnlib@watertownlibrary.org. Web Site: www.watertownlibrary.org. *Branch Mgr*, Donald Stepanek
Friends of the Library Group

WEST CORNWALL

P THE HUGHES MEMORIAL PUBLIC LIBRARY,* 35 Lower River Rd, 06796. SAN 324-3753. Tel: 860-672-6374. FAX: 860-672-6374. *Librn*, Estelle Stetson
Circ 5,000
Library Holdings: Bk Vols 15,000; Bk Titles 3,000
Open Tues 2-4:30 & Sat 9-12:30

S OPTIKON RESEARCH LABORATORIES LIBRARY,* 62 River Rd, 06796. SAN 302-4261. Tel: 860-672-6614. FAX: 860-672-6615. E-Mail: wwcovington@sprynet.com. *Librn*, William Covington
Library Holdings: Bk Titles 10,700

WEST HARTFORD

R CONGREGATION BETH ISRAEL, Deborah Library, 701 Farmington Ave, 06119. SAN 372-5820. Tel: 860-233-8215. FAX: 860-523-0223.
Founded 1934
Library Holdings: Bk Titles 14,200; Per Subs 40
Friends of the Library Group

R EMANUEL SYNAGOGUE LIBRARY, 160 Mohegan Dr, 06117. SAN 302-4288. Tel: 860-233-2774, 860-236-1275. *Librn*, Carolyn Topol
Library Holdings: Bk Vols 5,200

R FIRST CHURCH OF CHRIST CONGREGATIONAL, John P Webster Library, 12 S Main St, 06107. SAN 370-0305. Tel: 860-232-3893. FAX: 860-232-8183. Web Site: www.jpwlib.org. *Librn*, Lee K Ellenwood; Staff 2 (MLS 1, Non-MLS 1)
Library Holdings: Bk Vols 10,000; Per Subs 50
Special Collections: Religion; Social Issues; The Practice of Parish Ministry

C SAINT JOSEPH COLLEGE, Pope Pius XII Library, 1678 Asylum Ave, 06117. SAN 302-430X. Tel: 860-232-4571, Ext 5208. Circulation Tel: 860-232-4571, Ext 5209. Reference Tel: 860-232-4571, Ext 5435. FAX: 860-523-4356. Web Site: www.sjc.edu/index2.html. *Dir*, Linda Geffner; *Head, Circ*, Sheila Ward; Tel: 860-232-4571, Ext 5586; *ILL*, Kathleen Kelley; Tel: 860-232-4571, Ext 5750; *Cat*, Ann Williams; Tel: 860-232-4571, Ext 5207; *Archivist*, Diana Barnard; Tel: 860-232-4571, Ext 5740; *Archivist*, Sister Consolata O'Connor; Tel: 860-232-4571, Ext 5374; *Instrul Serv, Ref Serv*, Antoinette Collins; *Ref Serv*, Diane LeMay; *Instrul Serv, Ref Serv*, Lynne Piacentini; Tel: 860-232-4571, Ext 5751; *Circ*, Elizabeth Lesso; Tel: 860-232-4571, Ext 5209; *Circ*, Tanya Robbilard; Tel: 860-232-4571, Ext 5209; Staff 5 (MLS 5)
Founded 1932. Enrl 1,189
Jul 1999-Jun 2000 Income $606,729. Mats Exp $240,450, Books $70,000, Per/Ser (Incl. Access Fees) $163,500, Presv $6,950. Sal $318,339 (Prof $264,723)
Subject Interests: Catholicism, Child studies, Childrens educ, Counseling, Gerontology, Nursing, Womens' studies
Publications: Assistant Handbook; Newsletter; Student Handouts
Partic in Capitol Region Library Council; Dialog Corporation; Hartford Consortium For Higher Education; Nelinet, Inc; OCLC Online Computer Library Center, Inc

UNIVERSITY OF CONNECTICUT, GREATER HARTFORD CAMPUS
C HARLEIGH B TRECKER LIBRARY, University of Connecticut, Greater Hartford Campus, 1800 Asylum Ave, 06117. SAN 336-5506. Tel: 860-570-9024. Reference Tel: 860-570-9032. FAX: 860-570-9027. E-Mail: treckref@lib.uconn.edu. Web Site: www.lib.uconn.edu/WestHartford. *Admin Dir*, William Uricchio; Tel: 860-570-9028, E-Mail: william.uricchio@uconn.edu; *Info Res*, Barbara Lott; Tel: 860-570-9105, E-Mail: barbara.lott@uconn.edu; *Ref*, Norma Holmquist; Tel: 860-570-9043, E-Mail: norma.holmquist@uconn.edu; *Coll Develop*, Beverley Manning; Tel: 860-570-9031, E-Mail: beverley.manning@uconn.edu; *Circ*, Elizabeth Dzurnak; Tel: 860-570-9034, E-Mail: elizabeth.dzurnak@uconn.edu; *Doc Delivery*, Erika McNeil; Tel: 860-570-9040, E-Mail: libadm57@uconnvm.uconn.edu; *Per*, Iris King; Tel: 860-570-9030, E-Mail: iris.king@uconn.edu. Subject Specialists: *Business and management*, Norma Holmquist; *Humanities*, Beverley Manning; *Sciences*, Barbara Lott; *Social sciences*, Beverley Manning; *Social work*, Janice Lambert; *Urban studies*, Barbara Lott; Staff 8 (MLS 5, Non-MLS 3)
Founded 1985. Enrl 2,100; Fac 120; Highest Degree: Master
Jul 1999-Jun 2000 Income Parent Institution $889,000. Mats Exp $214,000, Books $115,900, Per/Ser (Incl. Access Fees) $88,700, AV Equip $4,600. (Prof $611,000)
Library Holdings: Bk Vols 85,000; Bk Titles 68,000; Per Subs 500; Spec Interest Per Sub 400; Bks on Deafness & Sign Lang 20
Subject Interests: Business and management, Social sciences, Social service (social work)
Special Collections: Social Work Theses
Automation Activity & Vendor Info: (Acquisitions) Endeavor; (Cataloging) Endeavor; (Circulation) Endeavor; (Course Reserve) Endeavor; (ILL) Endeavor; (OPAC) Endeavor; (Serials) Endeavor
Database Vendor: Dialog, GaleNet, IAC - Info Trac, Lexis-Nexis, OCLC - First Search, Silverplatter Information Inc., Wilson - Wilson Web
Publications: Guide to Services (Library handbook)
Partic in Greater Hartford Consortium for Higher Educ; Nelinet, Inc; OCLC Online Computer Library Center, Inc
Special Services for the Blind - Low vision aids & talking readers

C UNIVERSITY OF HARTFORD, Grant Resource Center,* S Cottage, 200 Bloomfield Ave, 06117. SAN 329-238X. Tel: 860-768-4849. FAX: 860-768-5220. *In Charge*, Mr Greenan; E-Mail: greenan@mail.hartford.edu; Staff 3 (MLS 2, Non-MLS 1)
Founded 1980
Library Holdings: Bk Vols 100; Bk Titles 100; Per Subs 5
Subject Interests: Engineering
Restriction: Staff use only

C UNIVERSITY OF HARTFORD LIBRARIES & LEARNING RESOURCES, W H Mortensen Library, 200 Bloomfield Ave, 06117. SAN 302-4318. Tel: 860-768-4264. Interlibrary Loan Service Tel: 860-768-4364. FAX: 860-768-5165. E-Mail: epp@mail.hartford.edu. Web Site: library.hartford.edu. *Dir*, Ronald Epp; *Acq, Asst Dir*, Randi Ashton-Pritting; *Circ*, Mariellen Baxter; *Tech Servs*, Deborah Herman; *Ref*, Kathryn Tynan; *ILL*, Kim Farrington
Founded 1957. Enrl 7,695; Fac 325; Highest Degree: Doctorate
Jul 1998-Jul 1999 Income $1,253,700. Mats Exp $526,700, Books $120,000, Per/Ser (Incl. Access Fees) $329,460, Presv $3,240, AV Equip $3,000, Manuscripts & Archives $1,000, Electronic Ref Mat (Incl. Access Fees) $73,000. Sal $727,000 (Prof $409,000)
Library Holdings: Bk Vols 561,500; Per Subs 2,089
Subject Interests: Art, Education, Music
Special Collections: Black Literature; Judaica (Millie & Irving Bercowetz Family Coll)
Automation Activity & Vendor Info: (Cataloging) DRA; (Circulation) DRA
Publications: Resources
Partic in Assoc New Am Coll; Coun of Conn Acad Libr Dirs; Greater Hartford Consortium for Higher Educ; Nelinet, Inc; OCLC Online Computer Library Center, Inc
Friends of the Library Group
Departmental Libraries:
MILDRED P ALLEN MEMORIAL, Hartt School-Gray Ctr, 200 Bloomfield Ave, 06117-0395. SAN 324-3060. Tel: 860-768-4491. FAX: 860-768-5295. Web Site: www.hartford.edu/llr/uofh_music.html. *Librn*, Linda Solow Blotner; E-Mail: blotner@mail.hartford.edu; *Asst Librn*, Deborah Herman-Morgan; E-Mail: dherman@mail.hartford.edu; *Publ Servs*, Amy Dankowski; *Tech Servs*, Ron Caldwell-Andrews; Staff 5 (MLS 2, Non-MLS 3)
Founded 1938. Circ 49,605; Enrl 650; Fac 125; Highest Degree: Doctorate
Library Holdings: Bk Vols 84,560; Per Subs 190
Subject Interests: Music, Performing arts
Special Collections: Kalmen Opperman Clarinet Coll; Stuart Smith Coll, mss, writings & published works
Automation Activity & Vendor Info: (Acquisitions) DRA; (Cataloging) DRA; (Circulation) DRA; (Course Reserve) DRA; (ILL) DRA; (OPAC) DRA
Database Vendor: DRA
Partic in Nelinet, Inc; OCLC Online Computer Library Center, Inc

S NOAH WEBSTER FOUNDATION & HISTORICAL SOCIETY OF WEST HARTFORD LIBRARY, 227 S Main St, 06107-3430. SAN 329-160X. Tel: 860-521-5362. FAX: 860-521-4036.
Founded 1974
2000-2001 Mats Exp $1,200, Books $200, Presv $1,000
Library Holdings: Bk Vols 300; Per Subs 10
Special Collections: 18th Century History, lifestyle, gardening; Lexicography
Restriction: Non-circulating
Function: Research library
Partic in W Hartford Libr Syst

P WEST HARTFORD PUBLIC LIBRARY, Noah Webster Memorial Library, 20 S Main St, 06107-2432. SAN 336-5522. Tel: 860-523-3277. Reference Tel: 860-523-3275. FAX: 860-523-3236. Web Site: www.west-hartford.com. *Dir*, Denis M Lorenz; Tel: 860-523-3279; *ILL*, Susan Potashner; *Ch Servs*, Carol Waxman; *Media Spec*, Gerard Molyneaux; *Ref*, Thomas F Kilfoil; *Online Servs*, Judy Eisenberg; *Coll Develop*, Susan Brewer; Staff 29 (MLS 10, Non-MLS 19)
Founded 1897. Pop 60,000; Circ 854,049
Jul 1998-Jun 1999 Income $2,897,050. Mats Exp $349,298, Books $319,574, Per/Ser (Incl. Access Fees) $29,724. Sal $1,766,740
Library Holdings: Bk Vols 237,320; Per Subs 701
Special Collections: Connecticut Reference Coll; Local History Coll; Noah Webster Coll; West Hartford News, micro
Automation Activity & Vendor Info: (Circulation) SIRSI; (OPAC) SIRSI
Partic in Cap Region Libr Coun; Nelinet, Inc
Special Services for the Deaf - Captioned media; Special interest periodicals; TTY machine
Friends of the Library Group
Branches: 2
BISHOP'S CORNER, 15 Starkel Rd, 06117. SAN 336-5581. Tel: 860-236-5446. Web Site: www.west-hartford.com/library. *Librn*, Nancy Pedersen; Tel: 860-523-3279, Fax: 860-523-3236, E-Mail: webwh@cric.org; *Librn*, John G Sturtevant
Library Holdings: Bk Vols 59,547
Friends of the Library Group
JULIA FAXON BRANCH, 1073 New Britain Ave, 06110. SAN 336-5557. Tel: 860-523-5545. Circulation Tel: 860-523-3277. TDD: 860-523-3246. Web Site: www.west-hartford.com/library. *Librn*, Eileen King; *Librn*, Nancy Pedersen; Tel: 860-523-3279, Fax: 860-523-3236, E-Mail: webwh@cric.org; *Automation Syst Coordr*, Glenn Grube; *Coll Develop*, Susan Brewer
Pop 56,349; Circ 843,695
Jul 1999-Jun 2000 Income $3,046,426. Mats Exp $412,815, Books $346,152, Per/Ser (Incl. Access Fees) $31,209, AV Equip $35,454. Sal $1,872,733
Library Holdings: Bk Vols 238,168
Automation Activity & Vendor Info: (Circulation) SIRSI; (OPAC) SIRSI
Friends of the Library Group

WEST HARTLAND

P HARTLAND PUBLIC LIBRARY,* 61 Center St, 06091. SAN 302-4326. Tel: 860-379-0048. *Chairperson*, Penelope Ziarnik; *Librn*, Dennis Bourque; *Librn*, Peggy Lutz
Founded 1965. Circ 3,483
Library Holdings: Bk Vols 8,000
Partic in Region I Coop Libr Servs Unit
Open Tues 3-5, Sat 10-12

WEST HAVEN

S BAYER CORP, Pharmaceutical Division Library, 400 Morgan Lane, 06516. SAN 304-8616. Tel: 203-812-2843. FAX: 203-812-3041, 203-812-3044.; Staff 9 (MLS 5, Non-MLS 4)
Library Holdings: Bk Titles 6,379; Per Subs 565
Subject Interests: Medicine, Pharmaceutical, Science/technology
Automation Activity & Vendor Info: (Acquisitions) EX Libris; (Cataloging) EX Libris; (Circulation) EX Libris; (OPAC) EX Libris; (Serials) EX Libris
Database Vendor: Dialog, Lexis-Nexis, OVID Technologies
Restriction: By appointment only
Partic in Nelinet, Inc

C UNIVERSITY OF NEW HAVEN, Marvin K Peterson Library, 300 Orange Ave, 06516. SAN 302-4342. Tel: 203-932-7190. Interlibrary Loan Service Tel: 203-932-7194. Circulation Tel: 203-932-7197. Reference Tel: 203-932-7189. FAX: 203-932-1469. Web Site: library.newhaven.edu. *Librn*, Hanko H Dobi; Tel: 203-932-7191; *Mgr*, Mildred Hodge; *Doc, Ref*, June Cheng; Tel: 203-932-7194; *Circ*, Steven Chaput; Tel: 203-932-7194; *Acq*, Amy Stevens; Tel: 203-932-7193; *Ser, Tech Servs*, Marion Sachdeva; Tel: 203-932-7193; Staff 6 (MLS 6)
Founded 1920. Enrl 3,140; Fac 232; Highest Degree: Master
Library Holdings: Per Subs 1,673
Subject Interests: Criminal law and justice, Engineering
Publications: Friends Newsletter; Library Guides; Library Newsletter
Partic in Dialog Corporation; Nelinet, Inc; OCLC Online Computer Library Center, Inc
Friends of the Library Group

GM VA CONNECTICUT HEALTH CARE SYSTEM, Library Service, 950 Campbell Ave, 06516-5247. SAN 302-4350. Tel: 203-932-5711, Ext 2898. FAX: 203-937-3822. *Librn*, Gail Lascola
Founded 1953
Library Holdings: Bk Titles 5,000; Per Subs 298
Partic in Conn Asn of Health Scis Librs; Medical Library Center Of New York; Valnet

P WEST HAVEN PUBLIC LIBRARY, 300 Elm St, 06516-4692. SAN 336-5611. Tel: 203-931-1136. Reference Tel: 203-931-1164. FAX: 203-931-1760. Web Site: www.leaplibraries.org. *Dir*, Bradley A Green; *Asst Dir*, Richard Thau; *Ad Servs, ILL*, Jane Dexter; *Tech Servs*, Linda Mattei; *Ref*, Margaret Dolan; Staff 36 (MLS 7, Non-MLS 29)
Founded 1906. Pop 51,477; Circ 267,580
Jul 1999-Jun 2000 Income (Main Library and Branch Library) City $1,207,623
Library Holdings: Bk Vols 153,649; Per Subs 303
Subject Interests: Connecticut, History
Automation Activity & Vendor Info: (Circulation) GEAC
Partic in Leap; Southern Connecticut Library Council
Friends of the Library Group
Branches: 2
LOUIS J PIANTINO BRANCH, Allington Commun Ctr, One Forest Rd, 06516-1698. SAN 336-5670. Tel: 203-933-9335. FAX: 203-931-7827. Web Site: www.leaplibraries.org. *Librn*, Raymond Woollett
Library Holdings: Bk Vols 30,655
Friends of the Library Group
ORA B MASON BRANCH, 260 Benham Hill Rd, 06516-6541. SAN 336-5646. Tel: 203-933-9381. FAX: 203-931-7149. Web Site: www.leaplibraries.org. *Librn*, H Joy Beringer
Library Holdings: Bk Vols 24,829
Friends of the Library Group
Bookmobiles: 1

WESTBROOK

P WESTBROOK PUBLIC LIBRARY, 61 Goodspeed Dr, 06498. SAN 302-4369. Tel: 860-399-6422. FAX: 860-399-8551. E-Mail: westbrook.public.lib@snet.net. *Librn*, Lewis B Daniels, III
Founded 1895. Pop 5,617; Circ 61,365
Jul 1999-Jun 2000 Income City $225,645. Mats Exp $32,400, Books $25,500, Per/Ser (Incl. Access Fees) $4,000. Sal $152,585
Library Holdings: Bk Vols 35,300
Special Collections: Literacy Volunteers Coll; Natural Resources Information Center
Automation Activity & Vendor Info: (Circulation) epixtech, inc.
Publications: Friends of the Library Monthly (newsletter)
Partic in Libraries Online, Inc; Southern Connecticut Library Council
Friends of the Library Group

WESTON

P WESTON PUBLIC LIBRARY,* 56 Norfield Rd, PO Box 1146, 06883-2225. SAN 302-4385. Tel: 203-222-BOOK. FAX: 203-222-2560. *Dir*, Jane Atkinson; *ILL*, Karen Bennett
Founded 1963. Pop 9,000; Circ 115,000
Library Holdings: Bk Titles 48,500
Partic in Western Connecticut Library Council, Inc
Open Mon, Tues, Thurs & Fri 9-5, Wed 9-8, Sat 10-4, Sun noon-4
Friends of the Library Group

WESTPORT

S WESTPORT HISTORICAL SOCIETY LIBRARY, 25 Avery Pl, 06880-3215. SAN 302-4458. Tel: 203-222-1424. FAX: 203-221-0981. *Dir*, Sheila O'Neill
Special Collections: Historical Items from 1783 to present
Restriction: Open to public for reference only

P WESTPORT LIBRARY ASSOCIATION, Westport Public Library, Arnold Bernhard Plaza, PO Box 5020, 06881-5020. SAN 302-4466. Circulation Tel: 203-227-8411. Reference Tel: 203-291-4840. E-Mail: mbleiweis@westport.lib.ct.us. Web Site: www.westportlibrary.org. *Dir*, Maxine Bleiweis; Tel: 203-291-4801, E-Mail: mbleiweis@westport.lib.ct.us; *Asst Dir*, George Wagner; Tel: 203-291-4802, Fax: 203-227-3829, E-Mail: gwagner@westport.lib.ct.us; *Ch Servs*, Kitty Lyons; Tel: 203-291-4811, E-Mail: klyons@westport.lib.ct.us; *Ref*, Kathy Breidenbach; Tel: 203-291-4841, Fax: 203-291-4850, E-Mail: kbreidenbach@westport.lib.ct.us
Founded 1907. Pop 24,221; Circ 648,415
Jul 1999-Jun 2000 Income $3,021,418, City $2,593,673, Locally Generated Income $376,307. Mats Exp $312,359, Books $202,439, Per/Ser (Incl. Access Fees) $40,384, AV Equip $42,012, Electronic Ref Mat (Incl. Access Fees) $27,524. Sal $1,810,688
Library Holdings: Bk Vols 180,260; Per Subs 464
Subject Interests: Performing arts, Visual arts
Special Collections: Lucille Lortel Theatre Coll; Picture File, clippings, photos
Automation Activity & Vendor Info: (Acquisitions) epixtech, inc.; (Cataloging) epixtech, inc.; (Circulation) epixtech, inc.; (OPAC) epixtech, inc.
Database Vendor: Dialog, epixtech, inc., GaleNet, IAC - Info Trac, OCLC - First Search
Publications: Westport Public Library Newsletter/Calendar (5 per yr)
Mem of Western Conn Libr Coun
Partic in Nelinet, Inc
Friends of the Library Group

WETHERSFIELD

S WETHERSFIELD HISTORICAL SOCIETY, Old Academy Library, 150 Main St, 06109. SAN 302-4482. Tel: 860-529-7656. FAX: 860-529-1905. E-Mail: weth.hist.society@snet.net. Web Site: www.wethhist.org. *Dir*, Brenda Milkofsky
Founded 1932
Library Holdings: Bk Vols 2,000; Bk Titles 1,500
Subject Interests: Architecture, Genealogy, Local history
Special Collections: Connecticut Horticultural Society Coll; Old manuscripts, deeds, letters, log books, maps, bibles, textbooks & account books; Pamphlet Coll; Photograph Coll
Special Services - Handicapped accessible

P WETHERSFIELD PUBLIC LIBRARY,* 515 Silas Deane Hwy, 06109. SAN 302-4490. Tel: 860-721-2985. FAX: 860-721-2991. Web Site: www.wethersfieldlibrary.org. *Dir*, Suzanne Elliot; *Asst Dir*, Elizabeth Kirkpatrick; *Ch Servs*, Regina Alexsandravicius; *Ref*, Sue Winne; *Tech Servs*, Dolores Mittica; Staff 8 (MLS 6, Non-MLS 2)
Founded 1893. Pop 25,651; Circ 210,712
Library Holdings: Bk Vols 131,640; Per Subs 138
Special Collections: Art
Automation Activity & Vendor Info: (Circulation) CARL
Database Vendor: CARL
Partic in Capitol Region Library Council
Friends of the Library Group

WILLIMANTIC

C EASTERN CONNECTICUT STATE UNIVERSITY, J Eugene Smith Library, 83 Windham St, 06226-2295. SAN 302-4512. Tel: 860-465-4466. Circulation Tel: 860-465-4506. Reference Tel: 860-465-4699. Toll Free Tel: 877-587-8693. FAX: 860-465-4355. Web Site: www.ecsu.ctstateu.edu/library. *Dir Libr Serv*, Tina C Fu; Fax: 860-465-5522, E-Mail: fut@easternct.edu; *Head, Cat*, Kristin M Jacobi; Tel: 860-465-4508, E-Mail: jacobikr@easternct.edu; *Head, Circ*, Greg Robinson; Tel: 860-465-5553, Fax: 860-465-5521, E-Mail: robinsong@easternct.edu; *Coll Develop, Head Tech Servs*, Marianne Hebert; Tel: 860-465-4464, Fax: 860-465-5523, E-Mail: hebertma@easternct.edu; *Ser*, Leonardi Phyllis; Tel: 860-465-5562, Fax: 860-465-5517, E-Mail: leonardip@easternct.edu; *Acq*, Patricia Mulhall; *Bibliog Instr*, Nicholas Welchman; Tel: 860-465-4699, Fax: 860-465-5521, E-Mail: welchman@easternct.edu; *Syst Coordr*, Mary Anne Doyle; *Govt Doc*, William Gamzon; Tel: 860-465-5551, E-Mail: gamzonw@easternct.edu; Staff 27 (MLS 10, Non-MLS 17)
Founded 1889. Enrl 3,463; Fac 205; Highest Degree: Master

Jul 1997-Jun 1998 Mats Exp $461,490, Books $190,181, Per/Ser (Incl. Access Fees) $243,609, Presv $21,000, Micro $2,500. Sal $1,120,580 (Prof $491,937)
Library Holdings: Bk Vols 235,368; Bk Titles 201,869; Per Subs 2,260
Special Collections: Connecticut History, bks, per, slides, prints, pamphlets; Vocational (Career Information Ctr), bks, per, microfiche
Automation Activity & Vendor Info: (Acquisitions) Innovative Interfaces Inc.; (Circulation) Innovative Interfaces Inc.; (Serials) Innovative Interfaces Inc.
Database Vendor: Ebsco - EbscoHost, OCLC - First Search, OVID Technologies
Publications: ECSU Library Newsletter
Partic in Conn State Univ Libr Syst; Eastern Connecticut Libraries; Nelinet, Inc; OCLC Online Computer Library Center, Inc
Friends of the Library Group

P WILLIMANTIC PUBLIC LIBRARY,* 905 Main St, 06226. (Mail add: PO Box 218, 06226), SAN 302-4520. Tel: 860-465-3079. FAX: 860-465-3083. *Coll Develop, Dir*, Ted Perch; *Ad Servs*, Tammis Fulton; *Ch Servs*, Mary Schweitzer; Staff 8 (MLS 3, Non-MLS 5)
Founded 1854. Pop 22,000; Circ 88,000
Library Holdings: Bk Vols 54,000
Partic in Colorado Alliance Of Research Libraries; Eastern Connecticut Libraries; OCLC Online Computer Library Center, Inc

M WINDHAM COMMUNITY MEMORIAL HOSPITAL, Grant Health Sciences Library, 112 Mansfield Ave, 06226. SAN 325-2809. Tel: 860-456-9116. FAX: 860-456-6883. *Coordr*, Mark Patros; E-Mail: mpatros@wcmh.org
Founded 1959
Library Holdings: Bk Vols 600

S WINDHAM TEXTILE & HISTORY MUSEUM, Dunham Hall Library, 157 Union & Main St, 06226. SAN 375-1856. Tel: 860-456-2178. *Dir*, Beverly York; *Librn*, Wunderly Sauder; Staff 2 (MLS 1, Non-MLS 1)
Founded 1989
1999-2000 Income $40,000
Library Holdings: Bk Titles 2,000
Subject Interests: Immigration, Textile
Publications: Willimantic, Industry & Community
Restriction: By appointment only, Open to public for reference only
Function: Research fees apply

WILLINGTON

P THE MARY D EDWARDS PUBLIC LIBRARY,* c/o Hall Memorial School, 111 River Rd Rte 32, 06279. SAN 302-4547. Tel: 860-429-3854. FAX: 860-429-2136. E-Mail: m.edwards.pub.libr@snet.net. Web Site: users.cyberzone.net/willington/index.htm. *Dir*, Roberta S Passardi
Founded 1923. Pop 5,100; Circ 17,379
Library Holdings: Bk Vols 11,000
Friends of the Library Group

WILTON

§S CSC WESTON GROUP, Research Network Library, 10 Westport Rd, 06897. (Mail add: PO Box 590, 06897-0590), Tel: 203-761-7500. FAX: 203-762-9955. *Librn*, Shira Honingstein
Library Holdings: Bk Vols 200; Per Subs 17
Restriction: Not open to public

S WILTON HISTORICAL SOCIETY INC LIBRARY,* 249 Danbury Rd, 06897. SAN 376-1908. Tel: 203-762-7257. FAX: 203-762-3297. *Dir*, Marilyn Gould

P WILTON LIBRARY ASSOCIATION,* 137 Old Ridgefield Rd, 06897-3019. SAN 302-4563. Tel: 203-762-3950. FAX: 203-834-1166. E-Mail: wla@ct2.nai.net. Web Site: www.wiltonlibrary.org. *Dir*, Karen Ronald; *Ch Servs*, Sharrie Alechman; *Circ*, Sue King; *Coll Develop*, Elizabeth Mason; *ILL*, Lynne Swanson; *Tech Servs*, David Ostergren; Staff 24 (MLS 8, Non-MLS 16)
Founded 1895
Jul 1997-Jun 1998 Income $1,227,098, State $2,420, City $934,813, Locally Generated Income $289,865. Mats Exp $1,224,764, Books $130,000, Per/Ser (Incl. Access Fees) $8,500, Micro $8,700. Sal $639,600 (Prof $400,920)
Library Holdings: Bk Vols 123,000; Per Subs 200
Special Collections: Brubeck Jazz Coll; Richard Gilmore Knott Memorial Record Coll; Wilton Historical Coll
Automation Activity & Vendor Info: (Circulation) epixtech, inc.
Publications: Annual Report; Newsletter (quarterly); Wilton Bulletin Index; Wilton Business Directory
Friends of the Library Group

WINDHAM

P WINDHAM FREE LIBRARY ASSOCIATION,* On the Green, PO Box 168, 06280. SAN 302-4571. Tel: 860-423-0636. *Chief Librn*, Margaret Frank
Founded 1897. Pop 4,300
Jul 1997-Jun 1998 Income $30,162, City $23,278, Locally Generated Income $6,884. Mats Exp $30,162, Books $3,500, Per/Ser (Incl. Access Fees) $1,500. Sal $15,700 (Prof $9,900)
Library Holdings: Bk Vols 8,462; Per Subs 50
Subject Interests: Connecticut, Local history
Partic in ALA; CLA; Eastern Connecticut Libraries

WINDSOR

S ALSTOM POWER, INC, (Formerly ABB Combustion Engineering, Inc Library), 2000 Day Hill Rd, 06095. SAN 302-458X. Tel: 860-285-3287. FAX: 860-285-5606. Web Site: www.power.alstom.com. *Mgr*, James Howarth; *Librn*, Catherine Fischer; *Librn*, Eun Joo Lee
Founded 1956
Library Holdings: Bk Vols 5,000; Bk Titles 4,000; Per Subs 100
Subject Interests: Engineering, Marketing, Metallurgy, Nuclear engineering
Special Collections: Federal & Association Codes & Standards; Government Research & Development Reports, micro paper
Publications: Business Digest
Restriction: Staff use only
Partic in Dialog Corporation; Dow Jones News Retrieval

S LIMRA INTERNATIONAL INFOCENTER, William J Mortimer Library, 300 Day Hill Rd, 06095-4761. (Mail add: PO Box 208, 06141-0208), SAN 374-468X. Tel: 860-688-3358. FAX: 860-298-9555. E-Mail: infocenter@limra.com. Web Site: www.limra.com. *Dir*, Gail W Buchholz; Staff 9 (MLS 6, Non-MLS 3)
Founded 1926
Library Holdings: Bk Vols 8,000; Per Subs 300
Automation Activity & Vendor Info: (Acquisitions) Inmagic, Inc.; (Cataloging) Inmagic, Inc.; (Circulation) Inmagic, Inc.; (Serials) Inmagic, Inc.
Restriction: By appointment only
Partic in Nelinet, Inc

S MORSE SCHOOL OF BUSINESS LIBRARY,* PO Box 837, 06095-0837. SAN 302-1882. Tel: 860-522-2261, Ext 162. FAX: 860-525-4504. *Librn*, Stephen R Corbeil
Library Holdings: Bk Vols 6,300; Per Subs 40
Subject Interests: Law, Nursing
Restriction: Not open to public

S WINDSOR HISTORICAL SOCIETY LIBRARY,* 96 Palisado Ave, 06095. SAN 302-4628. Tel: 860-688-3813. FAX: 860-687-1633. E-Mail: windsor@ntplx.net. *Coll Develop*, Kathryn L Earnest; Tel: 703-695-5346; *Actg Dir*, Cherie Sweeney; Staff 1 (MLS 1)
Founded 1925
Sep 1999-Aug 2000 Income $1,000. Mats Exp Books $1,000
Library Holdings: Bk Titles 2,000
Special Collections: Church & School Records & Newspapers; Local History, family papers, genealogies, photogs, slides, town histories; Manuscripts & Deeds

P WINDSOR PUBLIC LIBRARY,* 323 Broad St, 06095. SAN 336-5700. Tel: 860-285-1910. FAX: 860-285-1889. Web Site: www.crlc.org/windsor, www.townofwindsorct.com/library.htm. *Dir*, Laura Kahkonen; E-Mail: kahkonen@windsor.lib.ct.us; *Acq, Ref, Spec Coll*, Mary Ellen Johnson; *Cat, Circ, Tech Servs*, Sharron Eukers; *Ch Servs*, Barbara Tolvesilver; *ILL*, Gail Mannion; *Media Spec, Ref*, Leanne Costello; *Ref, YA Servs*, Marina Verhoeven; Staff 7 (MLS 7)
Founded 1888. Pop 28,350; Circ 303,288
Library Holdings: Bk Vols 100,537; Per Subs 200
Special Collections: Career Center; Health Info Ctr; Parenting Ctr; Travel Ctr
Automation Activity & Vendor Info: (Circulation) CARL
Database Vendor: CARL
Partic in Capitol Region Library Council
Branches: 1
WILSON, 365 Windsor Ave, 06095-4550. SAN 336-576X. Tel: 860-247-8960. *Librn*, Gaye Rizzo

WINDSOR LOCKS

S CONNECTICUT AERONAUTICAL HISTORICAL ASSOCIATION, INC, John W Ramsay Research Library, Bradley Int Airport, 06096. SAN 302-4636. Tel: 860-623-3305. FAX: 860-627-2820. Web Site: www.neam.org. *Dir*, Robert Foster; *Archivist*, William Hooper
Founded 1960
Library Holdings: Bk Titles 20,000; Per Subs 105,000
Special Collections: Burnelli Aircraft Coll; Igor Sikorsky Coll
Publications: Newsletter (quarterly)
Open Tues 10-2, 2nd & 4th Sat of month 10-2

S DEXTER NONWOVENS DIVISION, Technical Information Center,* 2 Elm St, 06096. SAN 302-4644. Tel: 860-654-8414. FAX: 860-654-8301. *Librn*, Joan Knight; Staff 2 (MLS 1, Non-MLS 1)
Founded 1965
Library Holdings: Bk Vols 2,000; Per Subs 60
Restriction: By appointment only

§S NEW ENGLAND AIR MUSEUM, Research Library, Bradley International Airport, 06096. Tel: 860-623-3305. FAX: 860-627-2820. Web Site: www.neam.org. *Librn*, Robert Foster; *Res*, William Hooper
Library Holdings: Bk Vols 100
Restriction: By appointment only

S UNITED TECHNOLOGIES CORP, Information Network, Hamilton Sundstrand, One Hamilton Rd, MS 1-3-BC52, 06096-1010. SAN 302-4652. Tel: 860-654-4352. FAX: 860-654-3689.
Founded 1957
Subject Interests: Aerospace science, Electronics
Restriction: Not open to public

P WINDSOR LOCKS PUBLIC LIBRARY,* 28 Main St, 06096. SAN 302-4660. Tel: 860-627-1495. FAX: 860-627-1496. Web Site: www.tiac.net/users/wlocks/library/library.htm. *Dir*, Terry Crescimanno; *Cat, Ref*, Carol Weidemier; *Circ*, Christopher Frank
Founded 1907. Pop 12,600; Circ 50,391
Library Holdings: Bk Vols 48,000; Per Subs 65
Subject Interests: Arts and crafts
Partic in Capitol Region Library Council

WINSTED

P BEARDSLEY MEMORIAL LIBRARY, 40 Munro Pl, 06098. SAN 302-4679. Tel: 860-379-6043. FAX: 860-379-3621. E-Mail: bmlstaff@globalinterplex.com. Web Site: www.beardsleyandmemorial.org. *Dir*, Mary Lee Bulat; *Circ*, Patricia Valsecchi; *Ch Servs*, Ruth Amutice; Staff 4 (MLS 3, Non-MLS 1)
Founded 1898. Pop 16,045; Circ 68,870
Library Holdings: Bk Vols 49,371; Per Subs 95
Subject Interests: Antiques, Economics, Genealogy, History, Humanities, Large type print, Science fiction
Automation Activity & Vendor Info: (Cataloging) Follett; (Circulation) Follett; (OPAC) Follett
Publications: Quarterly Book Review
Partic in Western Connecticut Library Council, Inc
Friends of the Library Group

J NORTHWESTERN CONNECTICUT COMMUNITY COLLEGE LIBRARY, 100 S Main St, 06098. SAN 302-4687. Tel: 860-738-6480. TDD: 860-738-6480. FAX: 860-379-4995. E-Mail: nw_dlibrary@commnet.edu. Web Site: www.commnet.edu/nwctc. *Dir*, Anne Dodge; Tel: 860-738-6482, E-Mail: nw_dodge@commnet.edu; *Bibliog Instr, Online Servs, Publ Servs*, Pamela Bellows; Tel: 860-738-6481, E-Mail: nw_bellows@commnet.edu; *Circ, ILL*, Andrea Dombrowski; Tel: 860-738-6481, E-Mail: nw_dombrowsk@commnet.edu; *Tech Servs*, Diane Hagymasi; Tel: 860-738-6481, E-Mail: nw_hagymasi@commnet.edu; Staff 4 (MLS 2, Non-MLS 2)
Founded 1965. Enrl 1,620; Fac 30; Highest Degree: Associate
Jul 1998-Jun 1999 Income $295,637. Mats Exp $59,709, Books $26,739, Per/Ser (Incl. Access Fees) $15,445, Micro $6,948, Electronic Ref Mat (Incl. Access Fees) $10,577. Sal $195,637 (Prof $173,421)
Library Holdings: Bk Vols 41,494; Per Subs 269
Subject Interests: Art, Deaf, Recreation
Special Collections: Deaf Education; Historical Jazz, compact discs; World War I & II
Automation Activity & Vendor Info: (Circulation) CARL; (Course Reserve) CARL; (OPAC) CARL; (Serials) CARL
Database Vendor: Lexis-Nexis, OCLC - First Search
Publications: Periodical List
Partic in Bibliomation, Inc; OCLC Online Computer Library Center, Inc; Western Connecticut Library Council, Inc
Special Services for the Deaf - TDD

S WINCHESTER HISTORICAL SOCIETY LIBRARY,* 225 Prospect St, PO Box 206, 06098. SAN 370-3029. Tel: 860-379-8433.
Subject Interests: Local genealogy, Local history
Restriction: By appointment only
Open June 15th-Oct 15th

WOLCOTT

P WOLCOTT PUBLIC LIBRARY, 469 Bound Line Rd, 06716. SAN 302-4695. Tel: 203-879-8110. FAX: 203-879-8109. Web Site: www.wolcottwebs.com. *Dir*, Ed Stubbs; *Ch Servs*, Joy Ann Hornby; *Circ, ILL*, Lillian Grant
Founded 1916. Pop 14,900; Circ 89,469
Jul 1999-Jun 2000 Income $300,571. Mats Exp $48,000. Sal $159,101
Library Holdings: Bk Vols 48,914; Per Subs 72
Special Collections: Foreign Language Cassettes; Job Resource Center; Large Print Books; New Adult Readers
Automation Activity & Vendor Info: (Circulation) CARL
Partic in Bibliomation
Summer reading program; pre-school storytimes; internet for public
Friends of the Library Group

WOODBRIDGE

P WOODBRIDGE TOWN LIBRARY,* 10 Newton Rd, 06525. SAN 302-4709. Tel: 203-389-3433. FAX: 203-389-3457. *Dir*, Janet Vaill Day; *Coll Develop*, Mary G Kelley; Staff 22 (MLS 8, Non-MLS 14)
Founded 1940. Pop 9,240
Jul 1999-Jun 2000 Income $126,924. Mats Exp $66,250, Books $52,670, Per/Ser (Incl. Access Fees) $13,580. Sal $376,254 (Prof $162,032)
Library Holdings: Bk Titles 75,743
Subject Interests: Travel
Automation Activity & Vendor Info: (Acquisitions) epixtech, inc.; (Cataloging) epixtech, inc.; (Circulation) epixtech, inc.; (OPAC) epixtech, inc.; (Serials) epixtech, inc.
Database Vendor: epixtech, inc.
Publications: Library Lines
Partic in Libraries Online, Inc
Friends of the Library Group

WOODBURY

S GLEBE HOUSE MUSEUM LIBRARY, Hollow Rd, PO Box 245, 06798. SAN 374-8618. Tel: 203-263-2855. FAX: 203-263-6726. E-Mail: ghmgjg@wtco.net. *Dir*, Frank Coburn
Library Holdings: Bk Vols 200
Special Collections: Museum Archives

S OLD WOODBURY HISTORICAL SOCIETY ARCHIVES, Hollow Rd, 06798. (Mail add: PO Box 705, 06798), SAN 374-8758. Tel: 203-263-2696. *In Charge*, Mary Tyrrell
Founded 1964
Library Holdings: Bk Titles 50
Subject Interests: Local history
Restriction: By appointment only

P WOODBURY PUBLIC LIBRARY,* 269 Main St S, 06798-3408. SAN 302-4717. Tel: 203-263-3502. FAX: 203-263-0571. Web Site: www.biblio.org/woodbury/WPLHome.htm. *Dir*, Elaine Seaton Wyden; E-Mail: ewyden@biblio.org
Pop 8,800; Circ 104,743
Jul 1999-Jun 2000 Income $456,319, City $444,024, Other $12,295. Mats Exp $55,383. Sal $274,399 (Prof $190,129)
Library Holdings: Bk Vols 65,000
Subject Interests: Local history
Automation Activity & Vendor Info: (Circulation) CARL; (OPAC) CARL
Partic in Bibliomation Network; Region I Coop Libr Servs Unit
Friends of the Library Group

WOODSTOCK

P BRACKEN MEMORIAL LIBRARY,* Academy Rd, 06281. SAN 302-4725. Tel: 860-928-0046. FAX: 860-928-2117. E-Mail: bracken@neca.com. Web Site: www.woodstockacademy.org/library.htm. *Librn*, Walter J Izbicki; *Tech Servs*, Amand Harrington; Staff 1 (MLS 1)
Founded 1926. Pop 5,000; Circ 10,000
Library Holdings: Bk Titles 18,000; Per Subs 80
Partic in Eastern Connecticut Libraries

SR FIRST CONGREGATIONAL CHURCH OF WOODSTOCK, John Eliot Library, PO Box 147, 06281. SAN 371-8360. Tel: 860-928-7405. FAX: 860-928-6795.
Library Holdings: Bk Titles 1,900
Subject Interests: Philosophy, Religion, Sociology
Special Collections: Church Archives
Publications: John Eliot Newsletter
Partic in Eastern Connecticut Libraries
Friends of the Library Group

P NORTH WOODSTOCK LIBRARY, 1286 Rte 169, 06281. Tel: 860-928-2629. *Librn*, Priscilla C Cady
Library Holdings: Bk Vols 10,000
Partic in Eastern Connecticut Libraries

P WEST WOODSTOCK LIBRARY,* 5 Bungay Hill Connector, 06281. SAN 320-6211. Tel: 860-974-0376, 860-974-1058. *Dir*, Lorraine Waldo
Pop 5,200
Library Holdings: Bk Vols 20,000
Partic in Eastern Connecticut Libraries
Open Tues, Wed & Sun 1-4

DELAWARE

Date of Statistics: Fiscal 1999
Population, 1990 Census: 666,168
Population Served by Public Libraries: 753,538
Total Materials in Public Libraries: 1,840,789
Materials Per Capita: 2.45
Total Public Library Circulation: 3,765,134
Circulation Per Capita: 5.00
Total Public Library Income: $1,115,579 (including State & Federal Grants-in-Aid)
Number of County Systems: 3
Number of Library Outlets: 34
Number of Bookmobiles in State: 2
Grants-in-Aid to Public Libraries:
Federal (Library Services & Technology Act): $655,667
State Aid: $1,621,600

BEAR

P BEAR LIBRARY, 101 Governors Pl, 19701. Tel: 302-838-3300. FAX: 302-838-3307. Web Site: www.lib.de.us. *Mgr*, Susan Menson; *Librn*, Renee Schmidt; E-Mail: rschmidt@co.new-castle.de.us; Staff 28 (MLS 3, Non-MLS 25)
Founded 1998. Pop 53,989; Circ 540,786
Jul 1999-Jun 2000 Income $663,773, State $58,340, County $604,925, Other $508. Mats Exp $132,400, Books $95,888, Per/Ser (Incl. Access Fees) $15,790, AV Equip $15,300, Electronic Ref Mat (Incl. Access Fees) $5,422
Library Holdings: Bk Vols 77,481; Bk Titles 69,337; Per Subs 214
Special Collections: Delawareana
Automation Activity & Vendor Info: (Cataloging) epixtech, inc.
Database Vendor: Ebsco - EbscoHost, ProQuest
Mem of New Castle County Public Library System
Friends of the Library Group

BRIDGEVILLE

P BRIDGEVILLE PUBLIC LIBRARY,* 210 Market St, 19933-1126. SAN 302-4733. Tel: 302-337-7401. FAX: 302-337-3270. *Dir*, Carol Gasior; E-Mail: cgasior@hollinet.lib.de.us; *Assoc Dir*, Karen J Johnson; *Ch Servs*, Arlene K Peterson; *Circ*, Joan Taylor; *ILL*, Alice DuBois Min; Staff 5 (Non-MLS 5)
Founded 1919. Pop 5,148; Circ 79,348
Jul 1998-Jun 1999 Income $133,000, State $16,246, County $111,546, Locally Generated Income $31,877. Mats Exp $19,481, Books $17,441, Per/Ser (Incl. Access Fees) $2,040. Sal $87,734
Library Holdings: Bk Vols 16,449; Per Subs 60
Special Collections: Delaware & Eastern Shore
Automation Activity & Vendor Info: (Circulation) epixtech, inc.
Database Vendor: epixtech, inc.
Mem of Sussex County Department Of Libraries
Open Mon-Thurs 11-8 & Fri-Sat 11-5

CLAYMONT

P CLAYMONT PUBLIC LIBRARY, 3303 Green St, 19703. SAN 302-4741. Tel: 302-798-4164. FAX: 302-798-6329. *Mgr*, Thomas Weaver; E-Mail: tweaver@co.new-castle.de.us; *Librn*, Shelley Lynn Stein; E-Mail: sstein@co.new-castle.de.us; *Ch Servs*, Ali Leeds; E-Mail: aleeds@tipcat.lib.de.us; Staff 8 (MLS 3, Non-MLS 5)
Founded 1929. Pop 39,000; Circ 115,000
Library Holdings: Bk Vols 32,953; Per Subs 111
Automation Activity & Vendor Info: (Circulation) epixtech, inc.
Database Vendor: Ebsco - EbscoHost, ProQuest
Function: ILL available
Mem of New Castle County Public Library System
Friends of the Library Group

DELAWARE CITY

P DELAWARE CITY PUBLIC LIBRARY,* 407 Clinton St, 19706. SAN 302-475X. Tel: 302-834-4148. FAX: 302-834-1305. *Dir*, Kevin R Swed; *Librn*, Kevin K Swed; E-Mail: swedk@tipcat.dtcc.edu; *Ch Servs*, Lynn B Williams; *Asst Librn*, Denise Cayz; Staff 1 (MLS 1)
Founded 1973
Jul 1998-Jun 1999 Income $89,000, State $10,000, County $79,000. Mats Exp $14,750, Books $13,000, Per/Ser (Incl. Access Fees) $1,750. Sal $56,000 (Prof $30,000)
Library Holdings: Bk Vols 23,000; Per Subs 62
Mem of New Castle County Public Library System
Friends of the Library Group

DELMAR

P DELMAR PUBLIC LIBRARY, 101 N Bi-State Blvd, 19940. SAN 302-4784. Tel: 302-846-9894. FAX: 302-846-3408. *Dir*, John N Philos; E-Mail: jphilos@hollinet.lib.de.us; *Asst Dir*, Sandra Scott; *Circ*, Brenda Davis; *Ch Servs*, Pam Schell; *Circ*, Betty Myers; *Cat*, Corretta Lowe; Staff 6 (MLS 1, Non-MLS 5)
Founded 1940. Pop 4,100; Circ 37,254
Jul 1999-Jun 2000 Income $144,764. Mats Exp $29,925, Books $25,925, Per/Ser (Incl. Access Fees) $4,000. Sal $77,224 (Prof $25,000)
Library Holdings: Bk Vols 24,000; Per Subs 50
Subject Interests: Railroad
Special Collections: Braille Coll
Mem of Sussex County Department Of Libraries
Special Services for the Deaf - TTY machine

DOVER

SR CHRIST EPISCOPAL CHURCH LIBRARY,* PO Box 1374, 19903. SAN 375-2801. Tel: 302-734-5731. FAX: 302-734-7702. *Actg Dir*, Rev Priss R Nickerbocker
Library Holdings: Bk Vols 450

S DELAWARE AGRICULTURAL MUSEUM & VILLAGE LIBRARY-ARCHIVES, 866 N Du Pont Hwy, 19901. SAN 377-5100. Tel: 302-734-1618. FAX: 302-734-0457. E-Mail: damv@dol.net. Web Site: www.agriculturalmuseum.org. *Curator*, Jennifer C Griffin
Founded 1980
Jan 1999-Dec 1999 Income $300. Mats Exp $300, Books $20, Per/Ser (Incl. Access Fees) $30, Presv $250. Sal $25,000
Library Holdings: Bk Titles 3,000; Per Subs 36
Subject Interests: Agriculture, Archives, Photos
Restriction: Not a lending library
Function: Research library

S DELAWARE DEPARTMENT OF TRANSPORTATION LIBRARY, 800 Bay Rd, PO Box 778, 19903. SAN 326-9868. Tel: 302-760-2104. FAX: 302-739-6371. *Librn*, Julianna Cheng; E-Mail: jcheng@mail.dot.state.de.us

Library Holdings: Bk Vols 10,000; Per Subs 15
Subject Interests: Transportation
Partic in Networks in Delaware

P DELAWARE DIVISION OF LIBRARIES-STATE LIBRARY, Department of State,* 43 S Dupont Hwy, 19901. SAN 336-5859. Tel: 302-739-4748. FAX: 302-739-6787. Web Site: www.lib.de.us. *Dir*, Mary Chute; *Automation Syst Coordr*, James Cayz; *Tech Servs*, Jane Tupin; Staff 11 (MLS 11)
Founded 1901. Pop 666,168
Library Holdings: Bk Vols 99,750; Bk Titles 63,800; Per Subs 1,740
Automation Activity & Vendor Info: (Cataloging) epixtech, inc.
Publications: An Action Agenda for Delaware Libraries; Delaware Public Library Statistics; Delaware Union List of Serials
Partic in OCLC Online Computer Library Center, Inc; PALINET & Union Library Catalogue of Pennsylvania
Provider of Delaware ™: The Digital Library of the First State
Friends of the Library Group
Branches: 1

P DELAWARE LIBRARY FOR THE BLIND & PHYSICALLY HANDICAPPED, 43 S Dupont Hwy, 19901-7430. Tel: 302-739-4748, Ext 125. Toll Free Tel: 800-282-8676. FAX: 302-739-6787. E-Mail: depbh@lib.de.us. *Librn*, Beth Landon
Sep 2000-Aug 2001 Income $817,000
Library Holdings: Bk Titles 39,000; Per Subs 25

S DELAWARE PUBLIC ARCHIVES, 121 Duke of York St, 19901. SAN 328-3917. Tel: 302-739-5318. FAX: 302-739-2578. E-Mail: archives@state.de.us. Web Site: www.archives.lib.de.us. *Archivist*, Joanne A Mattern; *Archivist*, Timothy Slavin
Library Holdings: Bk Titles 3,000; Per Subs 12
Subject Interests: Genealogy, Manuscripts
Partic in Kentucky Library Network, Inc
Friends of the Library Group

GL DELAWARE STATE LAW LIBRARY IN KENT COUNTY, (Formerly Delaware State Law Library In Kent County), 414 Federal St, Rm 100, 19901-3615. SAN 302-4857. Tel: 302-739-5467. FAX: 302-739-6721. *Librn*, Karen Parrott
Library Holdings: Bk Vols 30,000; Per Subs 30
Special Collections: Early & Unusual Law Books
Special Services for the Blind - CCTV (VisualTex); Kurzweil Reader

S DELAWARE STATE MUSEUMS, Johnson Victrola Museum Library, 102 S State St, 19901. SAN 375-1414. Tel: 302-739-3262, 302-739-5316. FAX: 302-739-6712. *Curator*, Ann Baker Horsey
Library Holdings: Bk Titles 100
Subject Interests: Opera
Special Collections: Caruso Memorabilia; EMI papers on Victor Talking Machine Co; Johnson Memorabilia & Papers
Publications: The Recordings of Enrico Caurso

C DELAWARE STATE UNIVERSITY, William C Jason Library-Learning Center, 1200 N Dupont Hwy, 19901-2277. SAN 302-4814. Tel: 302-857-6176. FAX: 302-857-6177. Web Site: www.dsc.edu. *Head Librn*, Gertrude Jackson; Tel: 302-857-6175; *Per, Ser*, Susan Hall; *Cat, Tech Servs*, Barbara Qaissaunee; *Bibliog Instr*, Rosamond Panda; *Reader Servs*, Rebecca Batson; *Reader Servs*, Carol Weber
Founded 1891
Library Holdings: Bk Vols 234,000
Subject Interests: Education, Nursing
Special Collections: Black Studies; Delaware Coll; Historical Resource Coll; Select Government Depository
Automation Activity & Vendor Info: (Circulation) NOTIS
Publications: Check It Out
Partic in OCLC Online Computer Library Center, Inc; PALINET & Union Library Catalogue of Pennsylvania

J DELAWARE TECHNICAL & COMMUNITY COLLEGE, Terry Campus Library,* 1832 N DuPont Pkwy, 19901. SAN 302-4822. Tel: 302-741-2740. FAX: 302-741-2739. Web Site: www.library.dtcc.edu. *Bibliog Instr, Chief Librn, Online Servs*, Carolyn W Davis; *Tech Servs*, Linda Helm; Staff 5 (MLS 5)
Founded 1974. Enrl 1,572
Library Holdings: Bk Vols 9,663; Bk Titles 8,890; Per Subs 245
Partic in Dialog Corporation; OCLC Online Computer Library Center, Inc

P DOVER PUBLIC LIBRARY,* 45 S State St, 19901-3526. SAN 302-4830. Tel: 302-736-7030. FAX: 302-736-5087. Web Site: www.kentnet.dtcc.edu. *Dir*, Robert S Wetherall; E-Mail: wetheral@kentnet.dtcc.edu; *Tech Servs*, Sue Parker; *Circ*, Linda Edwards; *Ch Servs*, Hilary Welliver; *Ad Servs*, Paula Davino
Founded 1885. Pop 60,786; Circ 247,540
Jul 1997-Jun 1998 Income $750,000, State $103,375, City $470,245, County $170,625. Mats Exp $20,045, Books $145, Per/Ser (Incl. Access Fees) $11,000. Sal $458,030 (Prof $268,750)
Library Holdings: Bk Vols 87,450; Per Subs 310
Special Collections: Delaware & Delmarva Peninsula (Delawareana)
Publications: booklets plus slide-tape history shows on selected towns; Six Tricentennial Views of Kent County
Partic in KentNet; OCLC Online Computer Library Center, Inc; PALINET & Union Library Catalogue of Pennsylvania
Friends of the Library Group

M KENT GENERAL HOSPITAL, Health Science Library,* 640 S State St, 19901. SAN 302-4849. Tel: 302-674-7421. FAX: 302-674-7460. *Librn*, Nadine Pieniaszek
Library Holdings: Bk Vols 750; Per Subs 90
Subject Interests: Clinical medicine, Nursing
Restriction: Staff use only
Partic in Kentucky Library Network, Inc

G LEGISLATIVE COUNCIL LIBRARY,* Legislative Hall, PO Box 1401, 19903. SAN 326-9825. Tel: 302-739-5808. FAX: 302-739-7322.
Library Holdings: Bk Titles 9,000; Per Subs 25

DOVER AFB

UNITED STATES AIR FORCE

A DOVER AIR FORCE BASE LIBRARY, 436 SVS/SVMG, 262 Chad St, 19902-7235. SAN 336-5913. Tel: 302-677-3992. FAX: 302-677-5490. *Dir*, Pamela Medolo
Library Holdings: Bk Vols 31,000; Per Subs 255
Special Collections: Quality Air Force; Transition Assistance

FRANKFORD

P FRANKFORD PUBLIC LIBRARY,* 8 Main St, PO Box 610, 19945-0610. SAN 302-4873. Tel: 302-732-9351. Interlibrary Loan Service Tel: 302-855-7890. FAX: 302-732-3353. *Librn*, Joan Loewenstein
Founded 1930. Circ 26,790
Library Holdings: Bk Vols 15,000; Per Subs 50
Subject Interests: Civil War, Delaware
Special Collections: Delaware
Mem of Sussex County Department Of Libraries

FREDERICA

SR UNITED METHODIST CHURCH, PENINSULA-DELAWARE ANNUAL CONFERENCE, Barratt's Chapel Museum Library, Commission on Archives & History, 6362 Bay Rd, 19946. SAN 375-0655. Tel: 302-335-5544. Web Site: users.aol.com/barratts/home.html. *Curator*, Lynn Hobbs
Library Holdings: Bk Vols 2,500
Special Collections: Rare Book Coll

GEORGETOWN

J DELAWARE TECHNICAL & COMMUNITY COLLEGE, Stephen J Betze Library, Rte 18, PO Box 630, 19947. SAN 302-4881. Tel: 302-856-9033. FAX: 302-858-5462. Web Site: www.library.dtcc.edu. *Dir*, John C Painter; E-Mail: jpainter@outland.dtcc.edu; *Cat, Tech Servs*, Aleta Esham; *Online Servs, Ref*, Mary Sue Drugash; Staff 9 (MLS 6, Non-MLS 3)
Founded 1967. Enrl 3,808; Fac 250; Highest Degree: Associate
2000-2001 Mats Exp $160,000
Library Holdings: Bk Vols 53,569; Bk Titles 46,270; Per Subs 541
Special Collections: Delaware Coll
Database Vendor: Ebsco - EbscoHost, OCLC - First Search, ProQuest
Partic in PALINET & Union Library Catalogue of Pennsylvania

P GEORGETOWN PUBLIC LIBRARY, 10 W Pine St, 19947. SAN 302-489X. Tel: 302-856-7958. FAX: 302-856-9234. Web Site: www.lib.de.us. *Dir*, Marti DeChene; E-Mail: mdechene@hollinet.lib.de.us; *Asst Dir*, Colleen Martin; *YA Servs*, Elaine Fike
Pop 9,266; Circ 41,791
1999-2000 Income $118,000, State $18,000, County $100,000. Mats Exp $15,300, Books $12,000, Per/Ser (Incl. Access Fees) $2,300, AV Equip $1,000
Library Holdings: Bk Vols 24,000
Subject Interests: Antiques, Delaware, Genealogy
Special Collections: Delawareana
Mem of Sussex County Department Of Libraries
Friends of the Library Group

P SUSSEX COUNTY DEPARTMENT OF LIBRARIES, 9 S DuPont Hwy, 19947-2809. (Mail add: PO Box 589, 19947-0589), SAN 302-4903. Tel: 302-855-7890. FAX: 302-855-7895. *Dir*, C Fitzgerald; E-Mail: cfitzger@hollinet.lib.de.us; *Bkmobile Coordr*, Faith Drummond; E-Mail: fdrummon@hollinet.lib.de.us
Founded 1975
Jul 1998-Jun 1999 Income (Main Library Only) $412,728, State $34,913, Federal $11,877, County $364,650, Other $1,288. Mats Exp $14,714, Books $2,998, Per/Ser (Incl. Access Fees) $7,700, Other Print Mats $4,016. Sal $245,400 (Prof $40,581)
Library Holdings: Bk Vols 4,910; Per Subs 42
Subject Interests: Library and information science

Special Collections: Eastern Shore Coll
Automation Activity & Vendor Info: (Acquisitions) epixtech, inc.; (Cataloging) epixtech, inc.; (Circulation) epixtech, inc.; (OPAC) epixtech, inc.; (Serials) epixtech, inc.
Member Libraries: Bridgeville Public Library; Delmar Public Library; Frankford Public Library; Georgetown Public Library; Laurel Public Library; Lewes Public Library; Milford Public Library; Millsboro Public Library; Rehoboth Beach Public Library; Seaford District Library; Selbyville Public Library; Sussex County Department Of Libraries
Branches: 4
GREENWOOD PUBLIC, Mill St, PO Box 839, Greenwood, 19950. SAN 320-085X. Tel: 302-349-5309. FAX: 302-349-5284. *Dir*, Pat Brown; E-Mail: pbrown@hollinet.lib.de.us
Library Holdings: Bk Titles 15,000; Per Subs 200
Friends of the Library Group
MILTON PUBLIC, 121 Union St, Milton, 19968. SAN 321-1312. Tel: 302-684-8856. FAX: 302-684-8956. *Dir*, Mary Catherine Hopkins; E-Mail: mhopkins@hollinet.lib.de.us
1996-1997 Income $166,613, State $18,027, County $148,459, Other $127. Mats Exp $20,212, Books $15,068, Per/Ser (Incl. Access Fees) $2,479. Sal $66,153 (Prof $23,174)
Library Holdings: Bk Vols 20,243; Bk Titles 16,610; Per Subs 123
Friends of the Library Group
SOUTH COASTAL, 43 Kent Ave, Bethany Beach, 19930. SAN 320-0841. Tel: 302-539-5231. FAX: 302-539-9108. *Dir*, Pamella Russell; E-Mail: prussell@hollinet.lib.de.us
Founded 1978
1996-1997 Income $252,681, State $19,184, County $207,070, Other $26,427. Mats Exp $38,416, Books $23,776, Per/Ser (Incl. Access Fees) $6,582. Sal $102,507 (Prof $25,841)
Library Holdings: Bk Vols 15,458; Per Subs 90
Friends of the Library Group
SUSSEX COUNTY BOOKMOBILE, PO Box 589, 19947. Tel: 302-855-7890, Ext 20. FAX: 302-855-7895. *Dir*, Faith Drummond; E-Mail: fdrummon@hollinet.lib.de.us; Staff 1 (Non-MLS 1)
Jul 1998-Jun 1999 Income $86,670, State $11,918, County $74,707, Locally Generated Income $45. Mats Exp $15,832. Sal $46,634 (Prof $25,592)
Library Holdings: Bk Vols 10,898; Bk Titles 10,479; Per Subs 84
Automation Activity & Vendor Info: (Acquisitions) epixtech, inc.; (Cataloging) epixtech, inc.; (Circulation) epixtech, inc.; (OPAC) epixtech, inc.; (Serials) epixtech, inc.
Mem of Sussex County Department Of Libraries

GL SUSSEX COUNTY SUPERIOR COURT, Law Library,* Court House, PO Box 717, 19947. SAN 302-4911. Tel: 302-856-5483. *Librn*, Mary Dickson
Library Holdings: Bk Titles 17,891; Per Subs 26
Partic in Am Asn of Law Librs; Greater Philadelphia Law Library Association
Friends of the Library Group

GREENVILLE

S MT CUBA ASTRONOMICAL OBSERVATORY MEMORIAL LIBRARY,* Hillside Mill Rd, PO Box 3915, 19807. SAN 326-9787. Tel: 302-654-6407. E-Mail: mtcuba@udell.edu. *Librn*, Mary Williams
Library Holdings: Bk Titles 608
Subject Interests: Astronomy

HARRINGTON

§P HARRINGTON PUBLIC LIBRARY, 110 Center St, 19952. Tel: 302-398-4647. FAX: 302-398-3847. *Dir*, Betty Van Vessen; E-Mail: bettyann@kentnet.dtcc.edu; *Asst Dir*, Christine Howard
Jan 2000-Dec 2000 Income $135,000
Library Holdings: Bk Titles 15,000; Per Subs 35
Automation Activity & Vendor Info: (Acquisitions) epixtech, inc.; (Cataloging) epixtech, inc.; (Circulation) epixtech, inc.; (Course Reserve) epixtech, inc.; (ILL) epixtech, inc.; (ILL) epixtech, inc.; (Media Booking) epixtech, inc.; (OPAC) epixtech, inc.; (Serials) epixtech, inc.

HOCKESSIN

P HOCKESSIN PUBLIC LIBRARY,* 1023 Valley Rd, 19707. SAN 302-4946. Tel: 302-239-5160. FAX: 302-239-1519. *Dir*, Janet M Chin; E-Mail: chin@tipcat.lib.de.us; *Ref Servs YA*, Joseph Tierney; E-Mail: tierney@tipcat.lib.de.us; *Ch Servs*, Youngkee Shin; E-Mail: youngkee@tipcat.lib.de.us; Staff 12 (MLS 3, Non-MLS 9)
Founded 1977. Pop 21,872; Circ 443,423
Jul 1998-Jun 1999 Income $618,889, County $617,505, Locally Generated Income $2,342, Other $30,893. Mats Exp $102,807, Books $91,917, Per/Ser (Incl. Access Fees) $8,000, Micro $660, Electronic Ref Mat (Incl. Access Fees) $2,230. Sal $373,656 (Prof $129,733)
Library Holdings: Bk Vols 67,610; Per Subs 136
Subject Interests: Delaware
Database Vendor: Ebsco - EbscoHost, epixtech, inc., ProQuest
Mem of New Castle County Public Library System
Partic in LINCS; OCLC Online Computer Library Center, Inc
Friends of the Library Group

LAUREL

S EPWORTH FELLOWSHIP CHURCH INC LIBRARY,* RD 1, Box 65 1/2, 19956. SAN 375-1198. Tel: 302-875-4488. FAX: 302-875-7207. *Librn*, Linda Marvin
Library Holdings: Bk Titles 5,000; Per Subs 6
Restriction: Restricted access

P LAUREL PUBLIC LIBRARY, 101 E Fourth St, 19956-1547. SAN 302-4954. Tel: 302-875-3184. FAX: 302-875-4519. *Dir*, Kristen Gramer; E-Mail: kgramer@hollinet.lib.de.us
Founded 1909. Pop 9,500; Circ 86,000
Library Holdings: Bk Vols 34,000; Per Subs 130
Special Collections: Local History (Delaware Coll)
Mem of Sussex County Department Of Libraries
Friends of the Library Group

LEWES

M BEEBE MEDICAL CENTER, Health Sciences Library, 424 Savannah Rd, 19958. SAN 336-5948. Tel: 302-645-3283. FAX: 302-645-2319. *Librn*, Gafvert Jane; E-Mail: jgafvert@bbmc.org. Subject Specialists: *Health sciences*, Gafvert Jane; Staff 1 (MLS 1)
Founded 1921
Library Holdings: Bk Vols 300; Per Subs 97
Subject Interests: Medicine, Nursing
Partic in BHSL; Nat Libr of Med
Branches:
NURSING SCHOOL LIBRARY, 424 Savannah Rd, 19958. SAN 336-5972. Tel: 302-644-1935. FAX: 302-645-3488. *Librn*, Eileen Vaughn; Tel: 302-644-1935, E-Mail: evaughn@bbmc.org; Staff 1 (MLS 1)
Founded 1921
Library Holdings: Bk Vols 2,135; Per Subs 45
Subject Interests: Nursing
Mem of Sussex Help Orgn for Res Exchange
Partic in BHSL; Mideastern Regional Med Libr Serv

P LEWES PUBLIC LIBRARY,* 111 Adams Ave, 19958. SAN 302-4962. Tel: 302-645-2733. FAX: 302-645-6235. *Dir*, Jane Pheiffer
Pop 3,000; Circ 15,533
Library Holdings: Bk Vols 27,325; Bk Titles 26,528; Per Subs 60
Mem of Sussex County Department Of Libraries
Partic in ALA; OLA

C UNIVERSITY OF DELAWARE, Marine Studies Library,* 700 Pilottown Rd, PO Box 700, 19958. SAN 302-4970. Tel: 302-645-4290. FAX: 302-645-4293. Web Site: www.udel.edu/lib. *Coordr*, Dorothy Allen; *Coordr*, Winifred Erbe; E-Mail: winifred.erbe@mvs.udel.edu
Founded 1973
Library Holdings: Bk Vols 7,088; Per Subs 136
Subject Interests: Marine biology
Special Collections: Sea Grant materials
Partic in Center For Research Libraries; OCLC Online Computer Library Center, Inc; PALINET & Union Library Catalogue of Pennsylvania

MIDDLETOWN

P APPOQUINIMINK COMMUNITY LIBRARY,* 118 Silver Lake Rd, 19709. SAN 302-4989. Tel: 302-376-4190. FAX: 302-378-5293. *Mgr*, Martha P Birchenall; E-Mail: birchena@tipcat.dtcc.edu; *Media Spec*, Margaret Brinkley
Pop 8,602; Circ 93,237
Library Holdings: Bk Vols 34,154; Per Subs 106
Automation Activity & Vendor Info: (Cataloging) epixtech, inc.; (Circulation) epixtech, inc.; (OPAC) epixtech, inc.
Mem of New Castle County Public Library System
Partic in Libraries In The New Castle County System
Friends of the Library Group

MILFORD

S FIRST CHURCH OF CHRIST SCIENTIST, Christian Science Reading Room Library,* 901 S Walnut St, 19963. SAN 374-8707. Tel: 302-422-3475. *Dir*, Mary Anderson
Library Holdings: Bk Vols 90

P MILFORD PUBLIC LIBRARY,* 11 SE Front St, 19963. SAN 302-4997. Tel: 302-422-8996. FAX: 302-422-9269. *Dir*, Kay Hudson; Staff 9 (MLS 1, Non-MLS 8)
Founded 1882. Pop 18,112; Circ 113,111
Jul 1997-Jun 1998 Income $279,423, State $33,494, City $4,000, County

$200,018, Locally Generated Income $15,409, Other $9,381. Mats Exp $46,000. Sal $113,714
Library Holdings: Bk Titles 42,000; Per Subs 116
Subject Interests: Delaware, Large type print
Mem of Sussex County Department Of Libraries
Open Mon, Wed & Fri 9-8, Tues & Thurs 9-6, Sat 9-2
Friends of the Library Group

MILLSBORO

S AKZO NOBEL, Intervet Inc Library,* 405 State St, 19966-0318. SAN 374-6216. Tel: 302-934-4364. Toll Free Tel: 800-922-8051, Ext 4364. FAX: 302-934-4204.
Founded 1990
Partic in Dialog Corporation

P MILLSBORO PUBLIC LIBRARY,* 217 W State St, PO Box 458, 19966. SAN 302-5012. Tel: 302-934-8743. FAX: 302-934-8623. *Dir*, Judy Murry; *Ch Servs*, Carolyn Hitchens
Pop 7,518; Circ 38,013
Library Holdings: Bk Vols 15,000; Per Subs 55
Special Collections: Delaware Coll
Mem of Sussex County Department Of Libraries
Friends of the Library Group

NEW CASTLE

M DELAWARE PSYCHIATRIC CENTER, Medical Library, 1901 N Dupont Hwy, 19720. SAN 302-5039. Tel: 302-577-4323. FAX: 302-577-4935. *Librn*, Janis Hunter; E-Mail: jhunter@state.de.us; Staff 1 (MLS 1)
2000-2001 Mats Exp $32,000, Books $2,000, Per/Ser (Incl. Access Fees) $30,000
Library Holdings: Bk Vols 3,000; Per Subs 200
Subject Interests: Nursing, Psychiatry, Psychology, Social service (social work)
Special Collections: Hospital Archives
Publications: Library Current
Partic in New Castle County Public Libr Syst; Wilmington Area Biomedical Library Consortium

P NEW CASTLE COUNTY PUBLIC LIBRARY SYSTEM,* 187A Old Churchman's Rd, 19720-3115. SAN 302-5314. Tel: 302-323-6480. FAX: 302-323-6490.; Staff 110 (MLS 30, Non-MLS 80)
Founded 1975. Pop 441,946; Circ 1,788,889
Library Holdings: Bk Vols 893,120; Per Subs 2,568
Member Libraries: Apollo Memorial Library; Appoquinimink Community Library; Bear Library; Claymont Public Library; Corbit-Calloway Memorial Library; Delaware City Public Library; Delaware Technical & Community College; Elsmere Public Library; Greenville Area Public Library; Hercules Incorporated; Hockessin Public Library; Kirkwood Highway Library; Kittanning Public Library; New Castle Public Library; Newark Free Library; Wilmington Institute Library
Partic in OCLC Online Computer Library Center, Inc
Friends of the Library Group

P NEW CASTLE PUBLIC LIBRARY,* 424 Delaware St, 19720-5099. SAN 302-5047. Tel: 302-328-1995. FAX: 302-328-4412. *Dir*, Sarah C Brown; *Asst Dir*, Sally L Hatton; Staff 9 (MLS 2, Non-MLS 7)
Founded 1811. Pop 35,726; Circ 109,629
Jul 1996-Jun 1997 Income $303,660. Mats Exp $43,477. Sal $257,291
Library Holdings: Bk Vols 39,505; Per Subs 67
Special Collections: Delawareana, Original New Castle Library Company Collection
Mem of New Castle County Public Library System
Friends of the Library Group

C WILMINGTON COLLEGE LIBRARY, 320 DuPont Hwy, 19720. SAN 302-5055. Tel: 302-328-9401, Ext 122. Toll Free Tel: 800-451-5724. FAX: 302-328-0914. Web Site: wilmcoll.edu/library. *Dir*, D Jane Bruton; E-Mail: jbrut@wilmcoll.edu; *Bibliog Instr*, Edwina Travers; E-Mail: etrav@wilmcoll.edu; *ILL*, Milo H Gibbons; E-Mail: mgibb@wilmcoll.edu; *Ser*, Jacqueline Correia; E-Mail: jcorr@wilmcoll.edu; *Ref*, Patti Poplos; E-Mail: ppopl@wilmcoll.edu; *Coll Develop, Tech Servs*, Pamela Shukitt; E-Mail: pshuk@wilmcoll.edu; *Ref*, Larry L Manuel; *Publ Servs*, William L Smith; E-Mail: wsmit@wilmcoll.edu; Staff 9 (MLS 3, Non-MLS 6)
Founded 1968. Highest Degree: Doctorate
Jul 1999-Jun 2000 Mats Exp $178,000, Books $74,000, Per/Ser (Incl. Access Fees) $50,000, Micro $12,000, Other Print Mats $16,000, Electronic Ref Mat (Incl. Access Fees) $26,000
Library Holdings: Bk Vols 89,427; Per Subs 468
Subject Interests: Aviation, Business and management, Education, Nursing
Automation Activity & Vendor Info: (Acquisitions) SIRSI; (Cataloging) SIRSI; (Circulation) SIRSI; (Course Reserve) SIRSI; (ILL) SIRSI; (OPAC) SIRSI; (Serials) SIRSI
Database Vendor: Ebsco - EbscoHost, IAC - Info Trac, OCLC - First Search, ProQuest, Silverplatter Information Inc.
Restriction: Non-circulating to the public
Partic in OCLC Online Computer Library Center, Inc; PALINET & Union Library Catalogue of Pennsylvania; Tri-State College Library Cooperative (TCLC)
Open Mon-Thurs 9am-10pm, Fri 9-8, Sat 9-5 & Sun 1-8

S ZENECA, INC, Process Technology Library,* 233 Cherry Ln, 19720. SAN 323-5076. Tel: 302-574-1017. FAX: 302-574-1029. *In Charge*, John Meyers
Library Holdings: Bk Vols 500; Per Subs 18
Subject Interests: Chemistry
Open Mon-Fri 8-4:30

NEWARK

M CHRISTIANA CARE HEALTH SYSTEM, Christiana Hospital Library, Christiana Hospital, 4755 Ogletown-Stanton Rd, 19718. (Mail add: PO Box 6001, 19718), SAN 302-539x. Tel: 302-733-1115. FAX: 302-733-1365. Web Site: www.christianacare.org. *Dir*, Christine Chastain-Warheit; Tel: 302-733-1116, E-Mail: ccw@christianacare.org; *Assoc Dir*, Diane Wolf; E-Mail: dwolf@christianacare.org; *Commun Servs*, Barbara Henry; E-Mail: bhenry@christianacare.org; *Syst Coordr*, Sharon Easterby-Gannett; Staff 9 (MLS 5, Non-MLS 4)
Founded 1965
Jul 2000-Jun 2001 Income $657,000. Mats Exp $280,000. Sal $325,000
Library Holdings: Bk Titles 4,500; Per Subs 520
Subject Interests: Clinical medicine, Consumer health, Preventive med
Automation Activity & Vendor Info: (Acquisitions) epixtech, inc.; (Cataloging) epixtech, inc.; (Circulation) epixtech, inc.; (OPAC) epixtech, inc.; (Serials) epixtech, inc.
Database Vendor: epixtech, inc.
Publications: Library Newsletter
Restriction: Circulates for staff only, Non-circulating to the public
Partic in Community Health Science Library; Delaware Library Consortium; Dialog Corporation; OCLC Online Computer Library Center, Inc; PALINET & Union Library Catalogue of Pennsylvania; Wilmington Area Biomedical Library Consortium
Information includes Library of Wilmington Hospital

S DELAWARE GEOLOGICAL SURVEY LIBRARY, University of Delaware, Delaware Geological Survey Bldg, 19716-7501. SAN 370-2081. Tel: 302-831-2833. FAX: 302-831-3579. Web Site: www.udel.edu/dgs/dgs.html.
Subject Interests: Cartography, Geology, Mineral res, Seismology, Water resources, Well sampling

J DELAWARE TECHNICAL & COMMUNITY COLLEGE, Stanton Campus Library, 400 Stanton-Christiana Rd, 19713-2197. SAN 302-5063. Tel: 302-454-3939. FAX: 302-453-3079. Web Site: www.dtcc.edu/stanton/library/station/. *Dir*, Regina Wells; *Ref, Ser*, Lynne Masters; *Bibliog Instr, Ref*, Dorri Holstein; *ILL*, Rebecca Murphy; Staff 4 (MLS 4)
Founded 1968. Enrl 1,800; Fac 106
Library Holdings: Bk Vols 32,000; Per Subs 364
Subject Interests: Careers, Fire science, Nursing, Social sciences and issues
Mem of New Castle County Public Library System
Partic in Tri-State College Library Cooperative (TCLC); Wilmington Area Biomedical Library Consortium

E I DU PONT DE NEMOURS & CO, INC

M HASKELL LABORATORY FOR TOXICOLOGY & INDUSTRIAL MEDICINE LIBRARY, Elkton Rd, PO Box 50, 19714. SAN 336-6065. Tel: 302-366-5268. FAX: 302-366-5732. *Librn*, Kathy McGowen; E-Mail: kathy.m.mcgowen@usa.dupont.com; Staff 1 (MLS 1)
Founded 1935
Library Holdings: Per Subs 241
Subject Interests: Industrial medicine, Toxicology
Restriction: Staff use only
Partic in Regional Med Libr - Region 1; Wilmington Area Biomedical Library Consortium

S STINE LABORATORY LIBRARY-200, Elkton Rd, PO Box 30, 19714. SAN 336-6030. Tel: 302-366-5353. FAX: 302-366-5739.
Founded 1947
Library Holdings: Bk Vols 5,950; Bk Titles 2,149; Per Subs 280
Subject Interests: Agriculture, Biochemistry, Plant sci
Restriction: Open to public for reference only

DUPONT COMPANY

S HASKELL TOXICOLOGY LIBRARY, Stine-Haskell Research Center, PO Box 50, 19714. SAN 377-0222. Tel: 302-366-5232. FAX: 302-366-5732. *Librn*, Scott Johnson

R FIRST CHURCH OF CHRIST SCIENTIST, Christian Science Reading Room Library,* 48 W Park Pl, 19711. SAN 374-8340. Tel: 302-366-9598. *Librn*, Mary Anderson
Library Holdings: Bk Vols 100

S W L GORE & ASSOCIATES, INC, Information Services Library,* 551 Paper Mill Rd, PO Box 9206, 19714-9206. SAN 325-8947. Tel: 302-738-4880. FAX: 302-292-4153. *In Charge*, Jamie Zingaro
Library Holdings: Bk Vols 10,000
Subject Interests: Chemistry, Electronics, Engineering, Textiles

S INTERNATIONAL READING ASSOCIATION LIBRARY, Ralph C Staiger Library, 800 Barksdale Rd, 19711. SAN 302-5071. Tel: 302-731-1600, Ext 217. FAX: 302-731-1057. E-Mail: library@read.org. Web Site: www.reading.org.; Staff 1 (Non-MLS 1)
Founded 1974
Library Holdings: Bk Titles 6,000; Per Subs 60
Subject Interests: Children's literature, Language arts, Learning disabilities, Reading
Special Collections: Children's Choices Coll; IRA Past President & Historical Readers Coll; Research in Reading (William S Gray Coll)
Partic in Delaware Library Consortium

S MAAR ASSOCIATES INC, Cultural Resource Management Library,* PO Box 655, 19715. SAN 372-5634. Tel: 302-368-5777. FAX: 302-999-1687. E-Mail: maarassoc@aol.com. *Tech Servs, VPres*, Ronald A Thomas
Library Holdings: Bk Titles 1,100; Per Subs 20
Special Collections: Cultural Resource Management

S MARGARET STERCK SCHOOL FOR THE DEAF LIBRARY,* 620 E Chestnut Hill Rd, 19713. SAN 302-5098. Tel: 302-454-2301. FAX: 302-454-3493. Web Site: www.dvdd.com/nec/sterck_school. *Librn*, Arden Lantz
Library Holdings: Bk Vols 10,000
Subject Interests: Deaf
Special Collections: Captioned Filmstrip Coll; Large Print Books for the Visually Impaired; Professional Library of materials on deafness, deaf culture & visual impairment
Special Services for the Deaf - Staff with knowledge of sign language

P NEWARK FREE LIBRARY, 750 Library Ave, 19711-7146. SAN 302-508X. Tel: 302-731-7550. Reference Tel: 302-731-7847. FAX: 302-731-4019. Web Site: www.lib.de.us. *Dir*, Charlesa Lowell; E-Mail: clowell@co.new-castle.de.us; *Ad Servs*, Margaret Darby; E-Mail: mdarby@co.new-castle.de.us; *Ch Servs*, Lisa Beamer; E-Mail: lbeamer@new-castle.de.us; Staff 15 (MLS 3, Non-MLS 12)
Founded 1897. Pop 62,777; Circ 437,238
Library Holdings: Bk Vols 135,839; Bk Titles 130,605; Per Subs 281
Automation Activity & Vendor Info: (Cataloging) epixtech, inc.
Function: Some telephone reference
Mem of New Castle County Public Library System
Special Services for the Deaf - High interest/low vocabulary books; Special interest periodicals
Friends of the Library Group

R NEWARK UNITED METHODIST CHURCH, Bunting Library, 69 E Main St, 19715-0595. SAN 326-2235. Tel: 302-368-8774. *Librn*, Marietta J Garrett; Tel: 302-738-6741, E-Mail: cgarr13@aol.com
Founded 1955
1999-2000 Income $800, Locally Generated Income $500, Parent Institution $300. Mats Exp $600
Library Holdings: Bk Vols 2,000
Subject Interests: Children's literature, Religion

S PRODUCE MARKETING ASSOCIATION, PMA Information Center, 1500 Casho Mill Rd, 19711-3598. (Mail add: PO Box 6036, 19714-6036), SAN 371-4020. Tel: 302-738-7100. FAX: 302-731-2409. E-Mail: infoctr@mail.pma.com. Web Site: www.aboutproduce.com, www.pma.com.
Library Holdings: Bk Vols 2,000; Per Subs 49

C UNIVERSITY OF DELAWARE LIBRARY,* 181 S College Ave, 19717-5267. SAN 336-609X. Tel: 302-831-2231. Interlibrary Loan Service Tel: 302-831-2236. FAX: 302-831-1046. Web Site: www.lib.udel.edu. *Dir*, Susan Brynteson; *Publ Servs*, Sandra Millard; *Tech Servs*, M Dina Giambi; *Coll Develop*, Craig Wilson; *Acq*, Josephine Williamson; *Assoc Librn, Br Coordr*, Margaret Welshmer; *Bibliog Instr*, Deborah Rae; *Coll Develop*, Susan Davi; Staff 54 (MLS 54)
Founded 1834. Enrl 21,380; Fac 920; Highest Degree: Doctorate
Jul 1996-Jun 1997 Income $11,324,763. Mats Exp $5,024,000, Books $1,865,101, Per/Ser (Incl. Access Fees) $3,046,725. Sal $5,313,355 (Prof $2,402,577)
Library Holdings: Bk Vols 2,259,121; Per Subs 12,034
Special Collections: Delaware History & Politics (James C Booth Papers, Senator John Williams Papers, Senator J Allen Frear, Jr Papers); History of Papermaking & Contemporary Fine Printing (Bird & Bull Press Archives, Plough Press Archives); Irish Literature; Twentieth-Century American Literature (Alice Dunbar-Nelson Papers, Emily Coleman Papers, Louis Untermeyer Papers, John Malcolm Brinnin Papers, Ishmael Reed Papers, Paul Bowles Papers, Donald Justice Papers, Tennessee Williams Collection, Marguerite & Captain Louis Henry Cohn Ernest Hemingway Collection, Archives of Pagany); Unidel History of Chemistry Coll; Unidel History of Horticulture & Landscape Architecture Coll; US Patent
Publications: Collections; Exhibition catalogs; University of Delaware Library Associates Newsletter
Mem of Asn of Research Libraries; Center for Res Librs
Partic in Chesapeake Info & Res Libr Alliance; OCLC Online Computer Library Center, Inc; PALINET & Union Library Catalogue of Pennsylvania
Friends of the Library Group
Departmental Libraries:
AGRICULTURAL, 002 Townsend Hall, 19717. SAN 336-612X. Tel: 302-831-2530. *Assoc Librn*, Frederick B Getze
CHEMISTRY, Brown Laboratory, Rm 202, 181 S College Ave, 19717. SAN 336-6154. Tel: 302-831-2993. *In Charge*, Barbara Vaughn; E-Mail: bvaughn@udel.edu
Pop 77,095; Circ 220,000
Library Holdings: Bk Vols 28,000; Per Subs 230
Subject Interests: Analytical chemistry, Biochemistry, Inorganic chemistry, Organic chemistry, Physical chemistry
Open Mon-Thurs 8am-10pm, Fri 8-5, Sat 1-5, Sun 2pm-10pm
Friends of the Library Group
MARINE STUDIES, 700 Pilottown Rd, Lewes, 19958. SAN 377-0745. Tel: 302-831-4290. *Coordr*, Ellen Erbe
PHYSICS, 221 Sharp Laboratory, 19717. SAN 336-6189. Tel: 302-831-2323.

ODESSA

P CORBIT-CALLOWAY MEMORIAL LIBRARY,* 115 High St, PO Box 128, 19730. SAN 302-511X. Tel: 302-378-8838. FAX: 302-378-7803. E-Mail: corbit@delaware.infi.net. *Dir*, Steven Welch; *Ch Servs*, Karen Quinn; *Doc*, Lynda Whitehead
Founded 1847. Circ 28,502
1997-1998 Income $160,000, State $30,000, Federal $17,557, County $85,069, Locally Generated Income $22,531. Mats Exp $16,000, Books $13,000, Per/Ser (Incl. Access Fees) $2,000, Micro $983. Sal $98,000 (Prof $31,000)
Library Holdings: Bk Vols 24,000
Special Collections: 19th Century History & Literature of Delaware, bks, photos
Publications: The Face of a Town: The Corbit-Calloway Memorial Library; Yesterday & Today (histories of eight towns)
Mem of New Castle County Public Library System
Open Mon & Thurs 1-9, Tues & Fri 10-5, Wed 10-9 & Sat 9-1; First free public library in Delaware (established 1847)
Friends of the Library Group

REHOBOTH BEACH

P REHOBOTH BEACH PUBLIC LIBRARY,* 226 Rehoboth Ave, 19971-2141. SAN 302-5128. Tel: 302-227-8044. FAX: 302-227-0597. *Dir*, Margaret LaFond; Staff 5 (MLS 5)
Circ 58,239
Library Holdings: Bk Vols 21,191; Per Subs 73
Subject Interests: Delaware
Special Collections: Bolton Bird Coll; Parks Wedgewood Coll; Quigg Sea Coll; Sussex Gardener's Coll
Automation Activity & Vendor Info: (Cataloging) epixtech, inc.; (Circulation) epixtech, inc.
Database Vendor: Ebsco - EbscoHost, ProQuest
Mem of Sussex County Department Of Libraries
Open Mon & Wed 10-8, Fri 10-5, Tues & Thurs 12-8, Sat 10-3
Friends of the Library Group

SEAFORD

P SEAFORD DISTRICT LIBRARY, 402 N Porter St, 19973. SAN 302-5136. Tel: 302-629-2524. FAX: 302-629-9181. *Dir*, Diana McDonnell
Founded 1902. Pop 16,935; Circ 99,978
Jul 1999-Jun 2000 Income $243,752, State $40,466, City $2,000, County $136,728, Locally Generated Income $64,558. Mats Exp $36,761. Sal $124,381 (Prof $28,200)
Library Holdings: Bk Vols 55,324; Per Subs 101
Special Collections: Classic Cars; Delaware History (Delawareana)
Mem of Sussex County Department Of Libraries
Friends of the Library Group

SELBYVILLE

P SELBYVILLE PUBLIC LIBRARY,* 11 Main & McCabe Sts, PO Box 739, 19975. SAN 302-5144. Tel: 302-436-8195. FAX: 302-436-1508. *Dir*, Lynn Massey; *Assoc Dir*, Karrie Lubiniecki
Pop 3,000
Library Holdings: Bk Vols 25,000; Per Subs 20
Mem of Sussex County Department Of Libraries
Friends of the Library Group

SMYRNA

S DELAWARE CORRECTIONAL CENTER LAW LIBRARY,* Smyrna Landing Rd, PO Box 500, 19977. SAN 302-5152. Tel: 302-653-9261, Ext 303. FAX: 302-653-5023. *Librn*, Edward Johnson
Founded 1971. Enrl 925
Library Holdings: Bk Titles 4,000

P SMYRNA PUBLIC LIBRARY,* 107 S Main St, 19977. SAN 302-5160. Tel: 302-653-4579. FAX: 302-653-2650. *Dir*, Beverly Hirt
Founded 1858. Circ 27,000
Library Holdings: Bk Vols 13,000; Per Subs 55
Subject Interests: Delaware, Genealogy
Partic in OCLC Online Computer Library Center, Inc; PALINET & Union Library Catalogue of Pennsylvania
Open Mon-Wed & Fri 9-6, Tues & Thurs 2-9, Sat 9-1
Friends of the Library Group

WILLIMINGTON

S NEWS JOURNAL LIBRARY,* 950 W Basin Rd, PO Box 15505, 19720. SAN 302-5330. Tel: 302-324-2896, 302-324-2897. FAX: 302-324-2390. *Librn*, Charlotte J Walker; Staff 8 (MLS 3, Non-MLS 5)
Founded 1955
Library Holdings: Bk Vols 3,000; Bk Titles 1,500; Per Subs 84
Restriction: By appointment only

WILMINGTON

S AMERICAN INSTITUTE OF PARLIAMENTARIANS LIBRARY, PO Box 2173, 19899. SAN 326-1689. Tel: 302-762-1811. Toll Free Tel: 888-644-0428. FAX: 302-762-2170. E-Mail: aip@aipparlipro.org. Web Site: www.aipparlipro.org. *Exec Dir*, A I Warner
Founded 1958
Library Holdings: Bk Titles 300
Publications: Parliamentary Journal (quarterly); Parliamentary Law & Procedures with Instructor's Manual & Student Workbook; Parliamentary Opinions

L BAYARD FIRM, Law Library, 222 Delaware Ave, Ste 900, 19801. (Mail add: PO Box 25130, 19899), SAN 372-3275. Tel: 302-655-5000. FAX: 302-658-6395. Web Site: www.bayardfirm.com. *Coordr*, Joanne Owens; E-Mail: jowens@bayardfirm.com; Staff 2 (Non-MLS 2)
Library Holdings: Bk Vols 1,000

M CHRISTIANA CARE HEALTH SYSTEM, Wilmington Hospital Library, PO Box 1668, 19899. SAN 374-4973. Tel: 302-428-2911. FAX: 302-428-2101. *Librn*, Diane Wolf; Tel: 302-428-2966, E-Mail: dwolf@christianacare.org; Staff 2 (MLS 1, Non-MLS 1)
Library Holdings: Bk Titles 1,000; Per Subs 115
Automation Activity & Vendor Info: (Circulation) epixtech, inc.; (OPAC) epixtech, inc.
Branches:
CHRISTIANA HOSPITAL, PO Box 6001, Newark, 19718. SAN 377-7804. Tel: 302-733-1115. FAX: 302-733-1365. *Librn*, Christine Chastain-Warheit
COMMUNITY HEALTH LIBRARY, 3506 Kennett Pike, 19807. Tel: 302-661-3471. FAX: 302-661-3465. *Librn*, Barbara Henry
Library Holdings: Bk Titles 1,000; Per Subs 80
Subject Interests: Chronic disease, Wellness

P CONCORD PIKE LIBRARY,* 3406 Concord Pike, 19803. SAN 302-5217. Tel: 302-478-7961. FAX: 302-478-2461. Web Site: www.lib.de.us. *Ref*, Brenda Ferris; *Dir*, Thomas Weaver; Staff 16 (MLS 4, Non-MLS 12)
Founded 1959. Pop 30,678; Circ 450,000
Jul 1997-Jun 1998 Income (Main Library Only) $836,211, State $77,930, County $744,708, Other $13,573. Mats Exp $196,162. Sal $471,281
Library Holdings: Bk Vols 130,726; Per Subs 312
Subject Interests: Coin collecting, Holocaust
Special Collections: Delawareana Coll
Publications: Friends of the Concord Pike Library Newsletter
Friends of the Library Group

R CONGREGATION BETH EMETH, William, Vitellia & Topkis Library,* 300 W Lea Blvd, 19802. SAN 302-5365. Tel: 302-764-2393. FAX: 302-764-2395. *Chairperson*, Barry Wexler
Pop 1,000
Library Holdings: Bk Vols 3,000
Subject Interests: Judaica (lit or hist of Jews)

M DELAWARE ACADEMY OF MEDICINE, INC, Lewis B Flinn Library, 1925 Lovering Ave, 19806. SAN 302-5225. Tel: 302-656-1629, 302-656-6398. FAX: 302-656-0470. E-Mail: library@delamed.org. Web Site: www.delamed.org. *Librn*, Gail P Gill; Staff 8 (MLS 6, Non-MLS 2)
Founded 1930
Library Holdings: Bk Vols 20,000; Per Subs 265
Subject Interests: Consumer health, History, Medicine
Special Collections: State Journals
Partic in Delaware Library Consortium; Health Sci Libr Info Consortium; National Network Of Libraries Of Medicine - South Central Region; PALINET & Union Library Catalogue of Pennsylvania; Wilmington Area Biomedical Library Consortium

S DELAWARE ART MUSEUM, Helen Farr Sloan Library, 2301 Kentmere Pkwy, 19806-2096. SAN 302-5233. Tel: 302-571-9590, Ext 529. FAX: 302-571-0220. Web Site: www.delart.org. *Head Librn*, Kraig A Binkowski; E-Mail: kbinkowski@delart.org; *Chief Librn*, Harriet Memeger; E-Mail: hmemeger@delart.mus.de.us; *Archivist*, Eileen Sklar-Sloan; Staff 3 (MLS 2, Non-MLS 1)
Founded 1912
Library Holdings: Bk Vols 40,000; Per Subs 50
Special Collections: Bancroft Pre-Raphaelite Library, archival records, bks, cat, mss; Everett Shinn Archives; Frank Schoonover Coll, archives, bks, illus, photog; Gayle Hoskins Coll, memorabilia, photog, complete published works; Howard Pyle Library & Archives, illus, photographs, complete published works; Jerome Myers Coll, archival rec, memorabilia; John Sloan Coll, bks, cat, personal papers, photographs; N C Wyeth Coll, bks, illus, per; Stanley Arthurs Coll, bks, illus, clippings
Database Vendor: Wilson - Wilson Web
Restriction: Non-circulating to the public, Public use on premises
Function: Research library

S DELAWARE MUSEUM OF NATURAL HISTORY LIBRARY, 4840 Kennett Pike, PO Box 3937, 19807-0937. SAN 302-492X. Tel: 302-658-9111. FAX: 302-658-2610. Web Site: www.delmnh.org. *Curator*, Timothy Pearce; Tel: 302-658-9111, Ext 319, E-Mail: tpearce@delmnh.org
Founded 1972
1998-1999 Mats Exp Presv $3,600
Library Holdings: Bk Vols 10,000
Subject Interests: Birds
Special Collections: Linne Coll; Old Zoology Periodicals (Wagner Coll)
Publications: Nemouria

J DELAWARE TECHNICAL & COMMUNITY COLLEGE, WILMINGTON CAMPUS, John Eugene Derrickson Memorial Library, 333 Shipley St, 19801. SAN 302-525X. Tel: 302-573-5432. Interlibrary Loan Service Tel: 302-573-5431. FAX: 302-577-2038. Web Site: www.dtcc.edu/wilmington/library/station.html. *Dir*, Donna M Abed; *Cat, Tech Servs*, Mary Anne Farrell; *Bibliog Instr, Ref*, Verlie A Gaither; *Electronic Resources*, Aurelia Mulch; Staff 4 (MLS 4)
Founded 1973. Enrl 3,000; Fac 125; Highest Degree: Associate
Jul 1999-Jun 2000 Income $453,368. Mats Exp $96,827, Books $55,000, Per/Ser (Incl. Access Fees) $26,255, Micro $8,072, Electronic Ref Mat (Incl. Access Fees) $7,500. Sal $345,816 (Prof $228,185)
Library Holdings: Bk Vols 31,738; Per Subs 372
Subject Interests: Allied health, Business and management
Automation Activity & Vendor Info: (Acquisitions) epixtech, inc.; (Cataloging) epixtech, inc.; (Circulation) epixtech, inc.; (Course Reserve) epixtech, inc.; (ILL) epixtech, inc.; (Media Booking) epixtech, inc.; (OPAC) epixtech, inc.; (Serials) epixtech, inc.
Database Vendor: Ebsco - EbscoHost, OCLC - First Search
Partic in Libraries In The New Castle County System; OCLC Online Computer Library Center, Inc; Tri-State College Library Cooperative (TCLC); Wilmington Area Biomedical Library Consortium

GM DEPARTMENT OF VETERANS AFFAIRS, Medical Library,* 1601 Kirkwood Hwy, 19805-4988. SAN 302-5381. Tel: 302-633-5354. FAX: 302-633-5540. *Dir*, Don Passidomo
Founded 1949
Library Holdings: Bk Vols 6,000; Bk Titles 5,500; Per Subs 200
Subject Interests: Allied health, Dentistry, Medicine, Nursing, Surgery
Publications: Acquisition Listings (quarterly); Extensive Current Awareness; Journal Holdings Listing (annually); Library Statistical Studies; Resources Services; SDI; Selected Audiovisual Subject Listings
Partic in BRS; Dialog Corporation; Medline; Vets Admin Libr Network; Wilmington Area Biomedical Library Consortium

SR DIOCESE OF WILMINGTON, Resource Center Library, 1626 N Union St, 19806. SAN 326-9728. Tel: 302-573-3136. Toll Free Tel: 800-756-3136. FAX: 302-573-2393. E-Mail: sgierk@cdow.org.
Library Holdings: Bk Titles 7,000

L DU PONT COMPANY, Legal Law Library,* 1007 Market St, 19898. SAN 336-6243. Tel: 302-774-3307. FAX: 302-773-0059. *Librn*, M Jane DiCecco
Founded 1935
Library Holdings: Bk Vols 18,000; Per Subs 214
Restriction: Private library

DUPONT COMPANY

S BRANDYWINE BUSINESS & ENGINEERING LIBRARY, Brandywine Bldg BG 368, 19898. SAN 371-0009. Tel: 302-774-9738. FAX: 302-774-2832.
Subject Interests: Marketing

S CHESTNUT RUN LIBRARY, Chestnut Run Plaza, Bldg 700, Center Rd, 19880-0700. SAN 336-6332. Tel: 302-999-4168. FAX: 302-999-4351. *Librn*, Rita Fisk; Tel: 302-999-3473; Staff 3 (MLS 2, Non-MLS 1)

Founded 1958
Library Holdings: Bk Vols 4,450; Per Subs 371
Restriction: Not open to public

S DUPONT CORPORATE INFORMATION SCIENCE LIBRARIES, Rte 141, 19880-0301. SAN 336-6308. Tel: 302-695-3200. FAX: 302-695-7731. *Mgr*, Evelyn Brownlee; E-Mail: evelyn.l.brownlee@usa.dupont.com; *Cat*, Catherine E Brown; Staff 68 (MLS 68)
Library Holdings: Bk Vols 55,000; Per Subs 3,200
Subject Interests: Agriculture, Bioengineering, Biology, Chemical engineering, Computer science, Electronics, Engineering, Inorganic chemistry, Marketing, Medicine, Organic chemistry, Petroleum, Toxicology
Publications: Coming Events at the Experimental Station (weekly); New Book List (monthly)
Restriction: Private library
Member Libraries: Dade Behring

S PIONEERING RESEARCH CENTER LIBRARY, DuPont Experimental Sta, Bldg 302, PO Box 80302, 19880-0302. Tel: 302-695-3451. FAX: 302-695-9843. *Librn*, John W Carter; Staff 4 (MLS 2, Non-MLS 2)
Founded 1928. Enrl 250
Library Holdings: Bk Vols 2,729
Subject Interests: Analytical chemistry, Chemical engineering, Organic chemistry, Polymer chemistry
Restriction: Not open to public

S POLYMER INFORMATION CENTER, DuPont Experimental Sta, PO Box 80323, 19880-0323. SAN 371-0017. Tel: 302-695-7606. FAX: 302-695-1513.
Library Holdings: Bk Vols 2,600
Subject Interests: Chemical engineering, Polymer chemistry
Restriction: Staff use only

M ALFRED I DUPONT HOSPITAL FOR CHILDREN, 1600 Rockland Rd, 19803. SAN 302-5306. Tel: 302-651-5820. FAX: 302-651-5823. *Librn*, Karene Chester; Tel: 302-651-5820, Fax: 302-651-5823, E-Mail: kjules@nemours.org; Staff 3 (MLS 2, Non-MLS 1)
Founded 1940
Library Holdings: Bk Vols 5,200; Bk Titles 5,200; Per Subs 330
Subject Interests: Biochemistry, Genetics, Orthopedics, Pediatrics
Special Collections: Older Orthopedic Texts
Database Vendor: OCLC - First Search, OVID Technologies
Restriction: Open to public for reference only
Partic in Delaware Library Consortium; NY Acad of Med; PALINET & Union Library Catalogue of Pennsylvania; Wilmington Area Biomedical Library Consortium

M DUPONT PHARMACEUTICALS COMPANY, Information Services Center,* Maple Run Bldg, PO Box 80721, 19880-0721. SAN 321-9879. Tel: 302-892-7337. FAX: 302-892-1686. *Dir*, Claudia Powers; Tel: 302-992-6485; *Mgr*, Patricia M Insetta-Rath; Tel: 302-992-4021, E-Mail: patricia.m.insetta-rath@dupontpharma.com; *Mgr*, Suzanne Tracy; *Librn*, Diana Kerestan; *Librn*, Nancy Loescher; *Automation Syst Coordr*, June F O'Brien; Tel: 302-892-1715; *Online Servs*, Karen Stesis; *Online Servs*, Karen Krasznavolgyi; *Online Servs*, Monica Weiss; *Online Servs*, Mary Skousen; *Online Servs*, Randall Ward; *Online Servs*, Peter Mattei; *Online Servs*, Cynthia Yang; *Online Servs*, Barbara Burg; *Online Servs*, Jing Belfield; *Tech Servs*, Jones Victoria; Staff 23 (MLS 6, Non-MLS 17)
Founded 1976
Library Holdings: Bk Vols 35,000; Bk Titles 13,000; Per Subs 800
Subject Interests: Bus, Chemistry, Life sciences, Medicine, Pharmaceuticals
Special Collections: Beilstein; Chemical Abstracts, 1907 to present; Corporate Annual Reports from Pharmaceutical Industry; Derwent World Patent Index Farmdoc, (micro film), 1963 to present; Index Medicus, 1920 to present; Off Patent Gazette (micro film), 1960 to present; pharm PDRs, 1950 to present
Automation Activity & Vendor Info: (Circulation) SIRSI; (Serials) SIRSI
Database Vendor: Dialog, Lexis-Nexis, OCLC - First Search, OVID Technologies
Restriction: Company staff only
Function: Research library
Information Services Department has five information centers at four company sites. Corporate archive for proprietary documents is also part of the department

P ELSMERE PUBLIC LIBRARY,* 30 Spruce Ave, 19805. SAN 377-0974. Tel: 302-892-9814. FAX: 302-892-9834. *Librn*, Margaret W Darby
Jul 1996-Jun 1997 Income $241,171
Library Holdings: Bk Vols 27,184; Bk Titles 25,142; Per Subs 87
Mem of New Castle County Public Library System
Partic in Libraries In The New Castle County System; OCLC Online Computer Library Center, Inc; Tipcat
Friends of the Library Group

C GOLDEY BEACOM COLLEGE, J Wilbur Hirons Library, 4701 Limestone Rd, 19808. SAN 302-5268. Tel: 302-225-6247. FAX: 302-998-6189. Web Site: hirons.gbc.edu. *Per*, Penny Brodigan; *Acq*, Pamela Stewart; Staff 3 (MLS 2, Non-MLS 1)
Founded 1969. Enrl 1,800; Fac 85; Highest Degree: Master
Library Holdings: Bk Vols 38,462; Bk Titles 30,970; Per Subs 884
Subject Interests: Business and management
Special Collections: College Archives; Delaware Business
Automation Activity & Vendor Info: (OPAC) SIRSI
Publications: Hirons Update
Partic in Libraries In The New Castle County System; PALINET & Union Library Catalogue of Pennsylvania

S HAGLEY MUSEUM & LIBRARY,* 298 Buck Rd E, PO Box 3630, 19807-0630. SAN 302-4938. Tel: 302-658-2400. FAX: 302-658-0568. E-Mail: 73116@udel.edu. Web Site: www.hagley.lib.de.us. *Dir*, Glenn Porter; *AV*, Jon Williams; E-Mail: jwilliam@udel.edu
Founded 1955
Library Holdings: Bk Vols 205,000; Per Subs 289
Subject Interests: Business and management, Consumerism, Economics, Hist of tech, History, Indust design, Indust hist
Special Collections: Chemical, bks, flm, mss; Dupont Company & Family Papers; Iron & Steel, bks & mss; Pennsylvania Power & Light Coll; Petroleum Bks & mss; Railroad Firms; Reading Railroad Coll, mss; Textile Bks & mss
Automation Activity & Vendor Info: (OPAC) Endeavor
Publications: A Guide to the Manuscripts in the Eleutherian Mills Historical Library (1970) & Supplement (1978); Pennsylvania Power & Light: A Guide to the Records (1985)
Restriction: Non-circulating to the public
Function: Research library
Partic in Independent Res Libr Asn; PALINET & Union Library Catalogue of Pennsylvania; Philadelphia Area Consortium Of Special Collections Libraries; Research Libraries Group, Inc

HERCULES INCORPORATED

L LAW DEPARTMENT LIBRARY, Hercules Plaza 8330 SE, 1313 N Market St, 19894. SAN 329-4188. Tel: 302-594-5678. FAX: 302-594-7038.
Library Holdings: Bk Vols 21,000; Per Subs 30
Restriction: Staff use only

S RESEARCH CENTER LIBRARY, 500 Hercules Rd, 19808-1599. SAN 336-6456. Tel: 302-995-3483. Interlibrary Loan Service Tel: 302-995-3455. FAX: 302-995-4101. *In Charge*, Wayne Messer; Tel: 302-995-3543, E-Mail: wmesser@herc.com; *Bibliog Instr, Online Servs*, Elizabeth Hunt; Staff 3 (MLS 1, Non-MLS 2)
Founded 1913
Library Holdings: Per Subs 400
Subject Interests: Chemical technology, Chemistry
Publications: Library Bulletin; List of Journal Holdings; List of Journals currently received
Mem of New Castle County Public Library System
Partic in Dialog Corporation; OCLC Online Computer Library Center, Inc

S HISTORICAL SOCIETY OF DELAWARE LIBRARY, 505 Market St, 19801. SAN 302-5276. Tel: 302-655-7161. FAX: 302-655-7844. E-Mail: hsd@dca.net. Web Site: www.hsd.org. *Exec Dir*, Dr Barbara E Benson; *Curator*, Ellen Rendle; *Ref*, Edward Chichirichi; *Curator*, Constance Cooper; Staff 4 (MLS 4)
Founded 1864
Library Holdings: Bk Vols 32,000; Per Subs 73
Subject Interests: American history, Delaware, Genealogy
Special Collections: Bayard Coll; Bird-Bancroft Coll; Civil War Coll; George Gray Coll; George Read Coll; Revolutionary War Coll; Rodney Coll; Wilmington Businesses Coll
Friends of the Library Group

S HOLY TRINITY (OLD SWEDES) CHURCH FOUNDATION, INC, Hendrickson House Library, 606 Church St, 19801-4421. SAN 325-4941. Tel: 302-652-5629. FAX: 302-652-8615. E-Mail: oldswedes@aol.com. Web Site: www.oldswedes.org. *Exec Dir*, Johelene (Jo) W Thompson; *Archivist*, Raymond (Ray) A Nichols. Subject Specialists: *Delaware*, Johelene (Jo) W Thompson; *Genealogy*, Johelene (Jo) W Thompson; Staff 3 (MLS 1, Non-MLS 2)
Founded 1947
Library Holdings: Bk Vols 250
Subject Interests: Del hist, Genealogy, Swedish colonial hist
Special Collections: Holy Trinity (Old Swedes) Church Records: Birth/Baptisms, Marriages, Burials from 1713 to present

S IFI CLAIMS PATENT SERVICE LIBRARY, 3202 Kirkwood Hwy Ste 203, 19808. SAN 329-9899. Tel: 302-998-0478. FAX: 302-998-0733. E-Mail: claims@ifiplenum.com. *VPres*, Harry Allcock; *Mgr*, Rick Myrick
Library Holdings: Bk Vols 1,200; Per Subs 40
Subject Interests: Patents

P KIRKWOOD HIGHWAY LIBRARY,* 6000 Kirkwood Hwy, 19808-4817. SAN 302-5284. Tel: 302-995-7663. FAX: 302-995-7687. *Dir*, Jeffrey Ferris; *Ch Servs*, Elizabeth M Simmons; *Ad Servs*, David Hamilton; Staff 14 (MLS 3, Non-MLS 11)
Founded 1967. Pop 94,376; Circ 332,059
Library Holdings: Bk Vols 85,725; Bk Titles 84,000; Per Subs 300
Mem of New Castle County Public Library System
Friends of the Library Group

S LOMBARDY HALL FOUNDATION LIBRARY, 1611 Concord Pike, PO Box 7036, 19803-7036. SAN 302-5292. Tel: 302-655-5254. *Archivist*, Harold J Littleton
Founded 1976
Library Holdings: Bk Vols 1,200; Bk Titles 1,000
Special Collections: Delaware History; Freemasonry (Gunning Bedford, Jr Coll)
Restriction: Staff use only

L MORRIS, JAMES, HITCHENS & WILLIAMS LAW LIBRARY, 222 Delaware Ave, 10th flr, 19801. (Mail add: PO Box 2306, 19899-2306), SAN 370-6672. Tel: 302-888-6863. FAX: 302-571-1750. Web Site: www.morrisjames.com. *Librn*, Sandra J Proctor; E-Mail: sproctor@morrisjames.com; Staff 2 (MLS 1, Non-MLS 1)
Subject Interests: Antitrust law, Corp law, Estate planning, Real estate law, Tax info
Automation Activity & Vendor Info: (Serials) Inmagic, Inc.

GL NEW CASTLE COUNTY LAW LIBRARY, Daniel L Herrmann Court House, 1020 N King St, 19801. SAN 302-5322. Tel: 302-577-2437. FAX: 302-577-2813. *Librn*, Jean Winstead; E-Mail: jwinstead@state.de.us; *Asst Librn*, Alda Monsen
Founded 1911
Library Holdings: Bk Vols 27,200; Per Subs 35

L PRICKETT, JONES, ELLIOTT, KRISTOL & SCHNEE, Law Library,* 1310 King St, 19899. (Mail add: PO Box 1328, 19899), SAN 328-2589. Tel: 302-888-6500, Ext 4105. FAX: 302-658-8111. *Librn*, Pam Reed
Library Holdings: Bk Vols 10,000; Per Subs 32
Partic in Greater Philadelphia Law Library Association

S RICHARDS, LAYTON & FINGER LIBRARY,* One Rodney Sq, 10th flr, PO Box 551, 19899. SAN 326-9744. Tel: 302-651-7782. FAX: 302-658-6548.
Library Holdings: Bk Vols 12,000
Subject Interests: Law
Partic in Dow Jones News Retrieval; Westlaw

M SAINT FRANCIS HOSPITAL, INC, Medical Library,* Seventh & Clayton St, 19805-0500. (Mail add: PO Box 2500, 19805-0500), SAN 371-1242. Tel: 302-421-4834, 302-656-6398. FAX: 302-421-4838.
Library Holdings: Bk Vols 1,540; Per Subs 95

SR SECOND BAPTIST CHURCH LIBRARY,* 2800 Silverside Rd, 19810. SAN 371-1323. Tel: 302-478-5921. FAX: 302-478-5995. E-Mail: sbcwilm@juno.com. *Librn*, Trina Gardner
Library Holdings: Bk Vols 1,400

L SKADDEN, ARPS, SLATE, MEAGHER & FLOM LLP LIBRARY,* One Rodney Sq, 7th flr, 19801. SAN 329-1073. Tel: 302-651-3000, Ext 3224. FAX: 302-651-3001. Web Site: www.skad-lib.com. *Librn*, Leslie Corey Leach; Staff 2 (MLS 1, Non-MLS 1)
Founded 1979
Library Holdings: Bk Vols 9,000; Bk Titles 850; Per Subs 45
Subject Interests: Law
Restriction: Staff use only

GL UNITED STATES COURT OF APPEALS, Branch Library,* 844 King St. (Mail add: US Courthouse, Lock Box 43, 19801), SAN 302-5373. Tel: 302-573-6178. FAX: 302-573-6430. *Librn*, Lesley Lawrence
Founded 1974
Library Holdings: Bk Vols 14,000; Per Subs 25

SR WESTMINSTER PRESBYTERIAN CHURCH, Juanita J Johnson Memorial Library, 1502 W 13th St, 19806. SAN 376-155X. Tel: 302-654-5214. FAX: 302-654-5706. *Dir*, Nook Edgell
Library Holdings: Bk Vols 3,000

WIDENER UNIVERSITY

CL HARRISBURG CAMPUS BRANCH LAW LIBRARY, 3800 Vartan Way, PO Box 69380, Harrisburg, 17106-9380. SAN 370-3517. Tel: 717-541-3932. FAX: 717-541-3998. *Dir*, Eileen B Cooper; *Assoc Dir*, Patricia Fox; E-Mail: patricia.fox@law.widener.edu
Founded 1989
Library Holdings: Bk Vols 180,000; Per Subs 643
Subject Interests: Pa law, Pub law

CL SCHOOL OF LAW LIBRARY, 4601 Concord Pike, 19803. SAN 302-5241. Tel: 302-477-2244, Ext 2111. FAX: 302-477-2240. E-Mail: law.libref@law.widener.edu. *Dir*, Eileen B Cooper; Tel: 302-477-2113; *Cat*, Susana De Checco; *Govt Doc, Ref*, Mary Jane Mallonee; *Tech Servs*, Mary Alice Peeling; *Publ Servs*, Mary Marzolla; *ILL*, Enza Klotzbucher; *Acq*, Ann Kolodzey; *Coll Develop*, Sandra P Sadow; Staff 12 (MLS 12)
Founded 1973. Enrl 2,200; Fac 80; Highest Degree: Doctorate
Library Holdings: Bk Vols 570,000; Per Subs 1,250
Subject Interests: Corp, Delaware, Health law, Tax law
Restriction: Open to faculty, students & qualified researchers
Partic in Dialog Corporation; OCLC Online Computer Library Center, Inc; Westlaw

P WILMINGTON INSTITUTE LIBRARY, Tenth & Market St, 19801. SAN 336-6480. Tel: 302-571-7400. Interlibrary Loan Service Tel: 302-571-7421. Reference Tel: 302-571-7416. FAX: 302-654-9132. Web Site: www.wilmlib.org. *Dir*, David H Burdash; Tel: 302-571-7402, E-Mail: dburdash@wilmnet.dtcc.edu; *Asst Dir*, Larry Manuel; *AV*, Tom Martin; *Ch Servs*, Daphne Santosa; *Acq, Ref*, Benedict Prestianni. Subject Specialists: *Classical languages*, David H Burdash; Staff 36 (MLS 9, Non-MLS 27)
Founded 1788. Pop 131,000
Jul 1999-Jun 2000 Income (Main Library and Branch Library) $2,925,658, State $314,100, City $63,000, Federal $74,500, County $1,533,255, Locally Generated Income $90,884, Parent Institution $849,919. Mats Exp $474,537, Books $398,037, Per/Ser (Incl. Access Fees) $32,000, Micro $12,500, AV Equip $25,000, Electronic Ref Mat (Incl. Access Fees) $7,000. Sal $1,317,116 (Prof $412,362)
Library Holdings: Bk Vols 324,000; Bk Titles 210,000; Per Subs 700
Special Collections: Delawareana; Periodicals
Automation Activity & Vendor Info: (Acquisitions) epixtech, inc.; (Circulation) epixtech, inc.; (Media Booking) epixtech, inc.
Publications: Institute of the Colonies; So Laudable An Undertaking: Grapevine; Wilmington Library
Mem of New Castle County Public Library System
Partic in PALINET & Union Library Catalogue of Pennsylvania
Friends of the Library Group
Branches: 3
LA BIBLIOTECA DEL PUEBLO, 403 N Van Buren St, 19805. SAN 336-6502. Tel: 302-571-7422. FAX: 302-571-7422. *Librn*, Tina White
Friends of the Library Group
NORTH WILMINGTON, 3400 N Market St, 19802. SAN 377-7383. Tel: 302-761-4290. Reference Tel: 302-761-4292. FAX: 302-761-4291. Web Site: www.wilmlib.org. *Librn*, Cathy Hall; E-Mail: cjh1@tfn.edu
Friends of the Library Group
WOODLAWN, 601 N Van Crost Pkwy, 19805. SAN 336-6545. Tel: 302-571-7425. FAX: 302-571-7425. *In Charge*, Sarah Cruz
Friends of the Library Group

L YOUNG, CONAWAY, STARGATT & TAYLOR LIBRARY,* Rodney Sq N, 11th flr, PO Box 391, 19899-0391. SAN 323-7265. Tel: 302-571-6600. Toll Free Tel: 800-255-2234. FAX: 302-571-1253. *Librn*, Gary Ireland; Staff 1 (MLS 1)
Restriction: Staff use only
Partic in Dialog Corporation; Westlaw

S ZENECA, INC, Zeneca Library,* PO Box 15365, 19850. SAN 320-4480. Tel: 302-886-8232. FAX: 302-886-5369. *Assoc Dir*, Claudia C Powers; Staff 21 (MLS 16, Non-MLS 5)
Founded 1918
Library Holdings: Bk Vols 30,000; Bk Titles 25,000; Per Subs 1,200
Subject Interests: Chemistry, Medicine, Pharmacology
Restriction: Company library

WINTERTHUR

S THE WINTERTHUR LIBRARY, Rte 52, 19735. SAN 302-5411. Tel: 302-888-4701. FAX: 302-888-4870. Web Site: www.winterthur.org. *Dir*, Gary Kulik; E-Mail: gkulik@winterthur.org; *Librn*, Bert Denker; E-Mail: bdenker@winterthur.org; *Librn*, Richard McKinstry; E-Mail: rmckinstry@winterthur.org; *Librn*, Neville Thompson; E-Mail: nthompson@winterthur.org. Subject Specialists: *Manuscripts*, Richard McKinstry; *Rare books*, Neville Thompson; *Visual*, Bert Denker; Staff 13 (MLS 6, Non-MLS 7)
Founded 1951
Library Holdings: Bk Vols 82,104; Per Subs 300
Special Collections: Auction Catalogs; Decorative Arts Photographic Coll, VF; Edward Deming Andrews Memorial Shaker Coll, mss, bks & photog; Joseph Downs Coll of Manuscripts & Printed Ephemera, mss, photostats & microfiche; Maxine Waldron Coll; Thelma S Mendsen Coll; Waldron Phoenix Belknap, Jr Research Library of American Painting; Winterthur Archives
Publications: American Cornucopia; Personal Accounts of Events, Travels & Everyday Life in America: An Annotated Bibliography; The Edward Deming Andrews Memorial Shaker Collection; The Winterthur Museum Library Collection of Printed Books & Periodicals (9 Vol); Trade Catalogues at Winterthur; Treasures From the Winterthur Library
Restriction: Open to public for reference only
Partic in Independent Res Libr Asn; Philadelphia Area Consortium Of Special Collections Libraries; RLIN

DISTRICT OF COLUMBIA

WASHINGTON

S ACADEMY FOR EDUCATIONAL DEVELOPMENT, Information Center, 1825 Connecticut Ave NW, 20009. SAN 328-5480. Tel: 202-884-8000, Ext 8064. FAX: 202-884-8491. E-Mail: admindc@aed.org. Web Site: www.aed.org. *Librn*, Eileen D'Andrea; Staff 2 (MLS 1, Non-MLS 1)
Founded 1961
2000-2000 Mats Exp $100,000,000
Library Holdings: Bk Vols 6,000
Database Vendor: Dialog

L ADMINISTRATIVE OFFICE OF THE UNITED STATES COURTS LIBRARY, Thurgood Marshall Federal Judiciary Bldg, One Columbus Circle NE, 20544. SAN 372-1108. Tel: 202-502-1237. *Actg Librn*, Jonathan B Chiza
Library Holdings: Bk Vols 10,000; Per Subs 60
Partic in Fedlink

S ADVOCATES FOR YOUTH, Resource Center,* 1025 Vermont Ave NW, Ste 200, 20005. SAN 375-0566. Tel: 202-347-5700. FAX: 202-347-2263. E-Mail: info@advocatesforyouth.org. Web Site: www.advocatesforyouth.org. *Dir*, Sue Alford
Library Holdings: Bk Vols 3,000; Per Subs 150

SR AHMADIYYA MOVEMENT IN ISLAM, Muslim Library,* 2141 Leroy Pl NW, 20008. SAN 326-9272. Tel: 202-232-3737. FAX: 202-232-8181. *Librn*, Zaheer Bajwa
Library Holdings: Bk Titles 1,100

S AIR TRANSPORT ASSOCIATION OF AMERICA LIBRARY,* 1301 Pennsylvania Ave NW, Ste 1100, 20004-1707. SAN 302-5527. Tel: 202-626-4184. FAX: 202-626-4181. E-Mail: mmistrik@air-transport.org. Web Site: www.air-transport.org. *Librn*, Marion Mistrik
Founded 1944
Library Holdings: Bk Titles 12,000; Per Subs 150
Subject Interests: Aviation, Law, Statistics
Special Collections: Official Airline Guides, 1929-present
Restriction: Open to public for reference only
Partic in Dialog Corporation; TRIS File; Westlaw

S AIRPORTS COUNCIL INTERNATIONAL LIBRARY,* 1775 K St NW, Ste 500, 20006. SAN 371-2885. Tel: 202-293-8500. FAX: 202-331-1362. *Publ Servs*, Evangeline PremDas
Library Holdings: Bk Vols 250; Per Subs 10

L AKIN, GUMP, STRAUSS, HAUER & FELD LLP, 1333 New Hampshire Ave NW, 20036-1511. SAN 377-3787. Tel: 202-887-4079. FAX: 202-887-4288. Web Site: www.akingump.com. *Librn*, Helen Wall
Library Holdings: Bk Vols 30,000
Partic in Am Asn of Law Librs; DC Soc of Law Librs

S ALEXANDER GRAHAM BELL ASSOCIATION FOR THE DEAF & HARD OF HEARING, Volta Bureau Library, 2000 M St NW, Ste 310, 20036. SAN 302-5969. Tel: 202-337-5220. FAX: 202-337-8314. E-Mail: agbell2@aol.com. *In Charge*, Carol Feaser Fisk
Founded 1887
Library Holdings: Bk Vols 30,500; Bk Titles 29,500; Per Subs 120
Subject Interests: Deaf, Speech and hearing
Special Collections: Hearing (Alexander Graham Bell Coll), mss, correspondence

S AMERICA'S COMMUNITY BANKERS LIBRARY,* 900 19th St NW Ste 400, 20006. SAN 302-8127. Tel: 202-857-3100. FAX: 202-296-8716. *In Charge*, Katherine Harahan
Founded 1972
Library Holdings: Bk Vols 10,000; Per Subs 111

S AMERICAN ASSOCIATION OF HEALTH PLANS, Information Center, 1129 20th St NW, Ste 600, 20036. SAN 302-6655. Tel: 202-778-3268. FAX: 202-778-8466. Web Site: www.aahp.org. *Dir*, Erin Carlson; E-Mail: ecarlson@aahp.org; Staff 3 (MLS 1, Non-MLS 2)
Founded 1972
Library Holdings: Bk Vols 3,000; Per Subs 75
Restriction: Members only
Partic in District Of Columbia Health Sciences Information Network; Nat Libr of Med

S AMERICAN ASSOCIATION OF HOMES & SERVICES FOR THE AGING LIBRARY, (AAHSA), 2519 Connecticut Ave NW, 20008-1520. SAN 377-1687. Tel: 202-783-2242. FAX: 202-783-2255. E-Mail: info@aahsa.org. Web Site: www.aahsa.org. *In Charge*, Gary Marshall
Library Holdings: Bk Vols 1,000; Per Subs 105

S AMERICAN ASSOCIATION OF RETIRED PERSONS, Research Information Center,* Bldg B, 3rd flr, 601 E St NW, 20049. SAN 302-7244. Tel: 202-434-6220, 202-434-6240. Interlibrary Loan Service Tel: 202-434-6234. FAX: 202-434-6408. Web Site: www.aarp.org. *Dir*, Hugh O'Connor; *Ref*, Jo-Ellen Vernali-Knoerl; *Doc Delivery*, Betty Landesman; Staff 23 (MLS 15, Non-MLS 8)
Founded 1964
Library Holdings: Bk Vols 30,000; Bk Titles 18,000; Per Subs 350
Subject Interests: Aging
Special Collections: 1981, 1971 & 1961 White House Conference on Aging), doc; Aging (Senate Special Committee on Aging; House of Representatives Select Committee on Aging; Statewide Teacher Histories (Bicentennial Pride-in-America)
Publications: Acronyms in Aging
Producer of "Age Line" online bibliographic database

S AMERICAN ASSOCIATION OF STATE HIGHWAY & TRANSPORTATION OFFICIALS LIBRARY,* 444 N Capitol St NW, Ste 249, 20001. SAN 377-1326. Tel: 202-624-8918. FAX: 202-624-5469. Web Site: www.aashto.org. *In Charge*, Kyung Kyu Lim
Library Holdings: Bk Vols 5,000; Per Subs 60
Partic in Spec Libr Asn

S AMERICAN ASSOCIATION OF UNIVERSITY WOMEN, Educational Foundation Library,* 1111 16th St NW, 20036-4873. SAN 302-5551. Tel: 202-785-7763. FAX: 202-872-1425. E-Mail: library@aauw.org.
Founded 1960
Library Holdings: Bk Titles 4,700; Per Subs 152
Special Collections: Archives of the Association & Foundation

S AMERICAN BANKERS ASSOCIATION, Center for Banking Information, 1120 Connecticut Ave NW, 20036. SAN 302-556X. Tel: 202-663-5040. FAX: 202-828-4535. E-Mail: reflib@aba.com. Web Site: www.aba.com. *Dir*, Joan Gervino; *Automation Syst Coordr*, Dachun Bao; *Tech Servs*, Elinor Dumont; Staff 8 (MLS 5, Non-MLS 3)
Founded 1907
Library Holdings: Bk Vols 75,000; Bk Titles 22,000; Per Subs 700
Subject Interests: Banks and banking, Business and management, Economics, Finance, Law, Marketing
Special Collections: Bank Marketing Association; MICR Archives; Stonier School Theses
Automation Activity & Vendor Info: (Acquisitions) Endeavor; (Cataloging) Endeavor; (Circulation) Endeavor; (OPAC) Endeavor; (Serials) Endeavor
Database Vendor: Lexis-Nexis
Publications: FYI Kits; Internet Sources for Bankers; School of Bank Marketing Papers; Stonier Theses
Partic in Capcon Library Network; Dialog Corporation; Dow Jones News Retrieval; OCLC Online Computer Library Center, Inc

L AMERICAN BAR ASSOCIATION, Law Library,* 740 15th St NW, 9th flr, 20005. SAN 326-9116. Tel: 202-662-1010. FAX: 202-662-1032. *Librn*, Nancy Matthews; *Librn*, Sharon Greene
Library Holdings: Bk Titles 4,000

S AMERICAN CHEMICAL SOCIETY LIBRARY,* 1155 16th St NW, 20036. SAN 302-5578. Tel: 202-872-4509. FAX: 202-872-6257.; Staff 2 (MLS 2)
Library Holdings: Bk Vols 16,000; Per Subs 600
Subject Interests: Chemistry, Mathematics
Special Collections: ACS materials
Publications: acquisitions list (monthly); Chemical & Engineering News Index
Restriction: Open to public for reference only
Function: ILL available
Partic in OCLC Online Computer Library Center, Inc
A chemical health & safety referral service is offered by mail or phone (800-227-5558, Ext 4511)

M AMERICAN COLLEGE OF OBSTETRICIANS & GYNECOLOGISTS, Resource Center,* 409 12th St SW, Box 96920, 20090-6920. SAN 303-8068. Tel: 202-863-2518. FAX: 202-484-1595. *Syst Coordr, Tech Servs*, Mary Glass; *Spec Coll*, Susan Rishworth; *Publ Servs*, Mary Hyde; *Publ Servs*, Susan Driscoll; Staff 8 (MLS 5, Non-MLS 3)
Founded 1969
Library Holdings: Bk Vols 10,000; Per Subs 450
Subject Interests: Obstetrics and gynecology
Publications: Bibliographies
Partic in BRS; Dialog Corporation; Mid-Atlantic Regional Med Libr Prog

S AMERICAN COUNCIL OF LIFE LIBRARY, (Formerly American Council of Life Insurance Library), 1001 Pennsylvania Ave NW, 20004-2599. SAN 302-5586. Tel: 202-624-2465. FAX: 202-624-2319. Web Site: www.acli.com. *Mgr*, Patrick Lyons
Library Holdings: Bk Titles 5,000; Per Subs 300
Subject Interests: Benefits (Labor), Economics
Publications: Acquisitions List; Daily Electronic Newsletter
Partic in Capcon Library Network

S AMERICAN COUNCIL ON EDUCATION, Library & Information Service, One Dupont Circle, Ste 1B-20, 20036-1193. SAN 302-5594. Tel: 202-939-9405. FAX: 202-833-4730. Web Site: www.acenet.edu. *Dir*, Jill Bogard; Staff 2 (MLS 1, Non-MLS 1)
Founded 1956
Oct 1998-Sep 1999 Mats Exp $7,754, Books $2,709, Per/Ser (Incl. Access Fees) $5,045
Library Holdings: Bk Titles 7,000; Per Subs 100; Spec Interest Per Sub 75
Subject Interests: Higher educ
Special Collections: American Council on Education Publications; Carnegie Commission on Higher Education Reports; Carnegie Council on Policy Studies Report; Carnegie Foundation for the Advancement of Teaching Reports; College catalogs (microfiche); Institutional Histories; National Commission on Excellence Reports; National Commission on Student Financial Assistance Reports; Sloan Commission on Government & Higher Education Reports
Publications: Informational Brochure; New Acquisitions List (monthly)
Partic in Educ Resources Info Ctr
American Council on Education archives housed at Hoover Institution, Stanford University, Stanford, CA

S AMERICAN ENTERPRISE INSTITUTE FOR PUBLIC POLICY RESEARCH LIBRARY,* 1150 17th St NW, 10th flr, 20036. SAN 302-5608. Tel: 202-862-5800. FAX: 202-862-7178. *Librn*, Gene A Hosey; E-Mail: ghosey@aei.org
Founded 1972
Library Holdings: Bk Titles 5,000; Per Subs 180
Subject Interests: Economics, Political science, Social sciences and issues
Restriction: Open to public with supervision only

S AMERICAN FEDERATION OF STATE, COUNTY & MUNICIPAL EMPLOYEES INFORMATION CENTER,* 1625 L St NW, 20036. SAN 328-6460. Tel: 202-429-1060. FAX: 202-223-3255. *Librn*, William Wilkinson
Library Holdings: Bk Vols 7,000; Per Subs 615
Partic in BRS; Datatyme; Dialog Corporation; Human Res Info Network; Newsnet; Statenet; Vutext; Wilsonline

S AMERICAN FEDERATION OF TEACHERS LIBRARY, 555 New Jersey Ave NW, 20001-2079. SAN 371-8840. Tel: 202-879-4481. FAX: 202-879-4406. Web Site: www.aft.org. *In Charge*, Paula O'Connor; *Asst Librn*, Bernadette Bailey; Staff 2 (MLS 1, Non-MLS 1)
Founded 1916
Library Holdings: Bk Vols 2,300; Bk Titles 2,000; Per Subs 500
Subject Interests: Education, Labor
Special Collections: AFT Conventions & Executive Council Minutes, 1916-1990

M AMERICAN HEALTH CARE ASSOCIATION, Information Resource Center,* 1201 L St NW, 20005. SAN 377-497X. Tel: 202-842-4444. FAX: 202-842-3860. *Dir*, Ann Williams; *Librn*, Karen Mark
Library Holdings: Bk Titles 54,000; Per Subs 100
Partic in Dialog Corporation; Medline

S AMERICAN HOTEL & MOTEL ASSOCIATION, Information Center, 1201 New York Ave NW, Ste 600, 20005-3931. SAN 377-2950. Tel: 202-289-3193. FAX: 202-289-3186. E-Mail: infoctr@ahma.com. Web Site: www.ahma.com. *Dir*, Daille Pettit
Founded 1988
Jan 1999-Dec 1999 Mats Exp $21,300, Books $5,200, Per/Ser (Incl. Access Fees) $15,400, Electronic Ref Mat (Incl. Access Fees) $700. Sal $189,000 (Prof $85,000)
Library Holdings: Bk Vols 3,000; Per Subs 300
Subject Interests: Hospitality, Lodging indust, Travel
Special Collections: AH&MA Archives
Automation Activity & Vendor Info: (Acquisitions) Inmagic, Inc.; (Cataloging) Inmagic, Inc.; (Circulation) Inmagic, Inc.; (Course Reserve) Inmagic, Inc.; (ILL) Inmagic, Inc.; (Media Booking) Inmagic, Inc.; (OPAC) Inmagic, Inc.; (Serials) Inmagic, Inc.
Database Vendor: Dialog
Restriction: By appointment only
Function: Research fees apply

M AMERICAN INSTITUTE FOR CANCER RESEARCH LIBRARY,* 1759 R St NW, 20009. SAN 377-3043. Tel: 202-328-7744. FAX: 202-328-7226. Web Site: www.aicr.org. *Librn*, Beverly Westermeyer; E-Mail: bwestermeyer@aicr.org
Library Holdings: Bk Vols 600; Per Subs 75
Partic in Medical Libr Asn; Spec Libr Asn

S AMERICAN INSTITUTE FOR CONTEMPORARY GERMAN STUDIES LIBRARY, 1400 16th St NW, Ste 420, 20036-2217. SAN 377-0710. Tel: 202-332-9312. FAX: 202-265-9531. Web Site: www.aicgs.org. *Asst Librn*, Joni Forster
Library Holdings: Bk Vols 250; Per Subs 80

S AMERICAN INSTITUTE OF ARCHITECTS LIBRARY & ARCHIVES,* 1735 New York Ave NW, 20006. SAN 302-5659. Tel: 202-626-7492. FAX: 202-626-7587. E-Mail: library@aiamail.aia.org. *Archivist*, Sarah Turner; *Info Res*, Maureen Booth; Staff 6 (MLS 6)
Library Holdings: Bk Titles 31,500; Per Subs 450
Subject Interests: Art and architecture, Urban planning
Special Collections: Architectural Archives; Rare Bk Coll
Publications: Acquisitions List (quarterly)
Restriction: Circulation limited, Open to public for reference only
Partic in AARCS

S AMERICAN INSTITUTES FOR RESEARCH, Washington Library,* 3333 K St NW, 20007. SAN 329-9058. Tel: 202-342-5034. FAX: 202-342-5033. *Actg Librn*, Pat Shettel; E-Mail: pshettel@air-dc.org; *Actg Librn*, Ruth Patapis
Founded 1946
Library Holdings: Bk Vols 2,500; Per Subs 54
Subject Interests: Criminal law and justice, Education, Psychology
Restriction: By appointment only
Partic in Dialog Corporation

L AMERICAN INSURANCE ASSOCIATION, Law Library,* 1130 Connecticut Ave NW, Ste 1000, 20036. SAN 311-5852. Tel: 202-828-7183. FAX: 202-293-1219. Web Site: www.aiadc.org. *Librn*, Allen Haddox; E-Mail: ahaddox@aiadc.org

Library Holdings: Bk Vols 30,000; Per Subs 150
Subject Interests: Auto liability, Environ, Health care, Property-casualty, Superfund, Workmen's comp ins

S AMERICAN LEGION NATIONAL HEADQUARTERS, National Security-Foreign Relations Div Library,* 1608 K St NW, 20006. SAN 302-5667. Tel: 202-861-2700, Ext 1504. FAX: 202-861-2728, 861-2786. *Dep Dir*, Dennis M Duggan
Library Holdings: Bk Vols 100
Subject Interests: National security
For primary library, see Indianapolis, Ind

S AMERICAN NURSES ASSOCIATION, Library Information Center,* 600 Maryland Ave SW, Ste 100 W, 20024-2571. SAN 374-5163. Tel: 202-651-7142. FAX: 202-651-7008. Web Site: www.nursingworld.org. *Librn*, Richard Barry; E-Mail: rbarry@ana.org; Staff 1 (MLS 1)
Library Holdings: Bk Titles 1,000; Per Subs 180
Subject Interests: Nursing
Partic in NNLM/SCR, OCLC Online Computer Libr Ctr, Inc

S AMERICAN PHARMACEUTICAL ASSOCIATION FOUNDATION LIBRARY,* 2215 Constitution Ave NW, 20037. SAN 302-5721. Tel: 202-429-7524. FAX: 202-783-2351. E-Mail: gen@mail.aphanet.org.
Founded 1934
Library Holdings: Bk Vols 6,000; Per Subs 119
Restriction: By appointment only

S AMERICAN POSTAL WORKERS UNION, APWU Library Information Center,* 1300 L St NW, Ste 407, 20005. SAN 370-5617. Tel: 202-842-4278. TDD: 202-408-5339. FAX: 202-842-4297. *Dir*, Evelyn E Johnson; *Asst Librn*, Valerie Foster
Library Holdings: Bk Titles 5,000; Per Subs 150
Publications: Annual Report, Handbook, Newsletter, Periodical Holdings
Partic in Capcon Library Network
Special Services for the Deaf - Books on deafness & sign language; Staff with knowledge of sign language; TDD

S AMERICAN PSYCHIATRIC ASSOCIATION LIBRARY & ARCHIVES,* 1400 K St NW, 20005-2492. SAN 302-5748. Tel: 202-682-6080. FAX: 202-682-6248. E-Mail: library_tech/apa@apa. Web Site: www.psych.org. *Asst Dir*, Soo Kim
Founded 1961
Library Holdings: Bk Vols 9,750; Per Subs 328
Subject Interests: Psychiatry
Special Collections: History of Psychiatry, rare bks, archives & mss
Publications: Acquisitions List (monthly); Audiovisual List; Journal Table of Contents Lists (weekly); Periodical List
Restriction: Staff use only, Use of others with permission of librarian
Partic in Dialog Corporation; Nat Libr of Med

M AMERICAN PSYCHOLOGICAL ASSOCIATION, Arthur W Melton Library, 750 First St NE, Rm 3012, 20002-4242. SAN 302-5756. Tel: 202-336-5640. FAX: 202-336-5643. E-Mail: libstaff@apa.org. Web Site: www.apa.org. *Librn*, Katherine Boyd
Founded 1970
Subject Interests: Allied disciplines, Mental health, Psychology
Special Collections: American Psychological Association Archives; American Psychological Association Central Office, Division & State Association Publications; Classic Books in Psychology
Publications: APA Convention Directory; Biography Index
The library also coordinates the APA Archives with the Library of Congress

S AMERICAN PUBLIC POWER ASSOCIATION LIBRARY,* 2301 M St NW, 20037. SAN 302-5764. Tel: 202-467-2957. FAX: 202-467-2910. Web Site: www.appanet.org. *Librn*, Mary Rufe
Founded 1973
Library Holdings: Bk Titles 6,000; Per Subs 200
Subject Interests: Electrical utilities, Energy
Restriction: By appointment only

S AMERICAN PUBLIC TRANSPORTATION, (Formerly American Public Transit Association), Information Center, 1666 K St, 20006. SAN 371-8654. Tel: 202-496-4800. FAX: 202-496-4324. E-Mail: info@apta.com. Web Site: www.apta.com. *Mgr*, Jim Olivetti; Staff 2 (MLS 1, Non-MLS 1)
Founded 1915
1999-2000 Mats Exp $51,000
Library Holdings: Bk Vols 10,000; Per Subs 125
Subject Interests: Pub transportation
Special Collections: APTA Publications; Fed Transit Agency
Automation Activity & Vendor Info: (OPAC) Inmagic, Inc.
Database Vendor: OCLC - First Search, Silverplatter Information Inc.
Publications: Catalog of Member Products & Services (COMPS); Index to weekly newspaper; Information Center brochure; Passenger Transport; Publication Catalog
Restriction: By appointment only

S AMERICAN SOCIETY OF ASSOCIATION EXECUTIVES, Research & Information Central Services,* 1575 I St NW, 12th flr, 20005-1168. SAN 302-5799. Tel: 202-626-2742, 202-626-2749. FAX: 202-842-1109. E-Mail: infocentral@asaenet.org. Web Site: www.asaenet.org. *Dir, Res*, Eve Shepard
Founded 1920
Library Holdings: Bk Vols 1,525; Per Subs 50
Subject Interests: Education, Finance
Special Collections: Association Management Coll
Publications: Association Management publications

L AMERICAN SOCIETY OF INTERNATIONAL LAW LIBRARY,* 2223 Massachusetts Ave NW, 20008-2864. SAN 302-5802. Tel: 202-939-6005. FAX: 202-319-1670. Web Site: www.asil.org/info.htm. *Librn*, Jill Watson; E-Mail: jwatson@asil.org; *Asst Librn*, Barbara Higdon; *Asst Librn*, Kuldip Dosanjh
Founded 1960
Library Holdings: Bk Vols 25,000; Per Subs 150
Subject Interests: International law, International trade, Intl orgn, Intl relations
Publications: Guide to Electronic Resources for International Lal (www.asil.org/resource/home.htm)
Friends of the Library Group

S AMERICAN SOCIETY OF LANDSCAPE ARCHITECTS, Information Resource Center,* 636 I St NW, 20001-3736. SAN 372-6142. Tel: 202-216-2320. FAX: 202-898-1185. Web Site: www.asla.org. *Librn*, Susan Cahill-Aylward; E-Mail: scahill@asla.org
Library Holdings: Bk Titles 2,100; Per Subs 150
Subject Interests: Historic preservation, Landscape architecture, Planning
Automation Activity & Vendor Info: (Acquisitions) Inmagic, Inc.; (Cataloging) Inmagic, Inc.; (Circulation) Inmagic, Inc.; (Serials) Inmagic, Inc.
Restriction: By appointment only

S AMERICAN SYMPHONY ORCHESTRA LEAGUE, Resources Center,* 1156 15th St NW Ste 800, 20005. SAN 329-2975. Tel: 202-776-0212. FAX: 202-776-0224. E-Mail: league@symphony.org. Web Site: www.symphony.org.
Library Holdings: Bk Titles 1,000
Subject Interests: Am orchestras, Orchestra mgt
Special Collections: League Publications; Orchestra Program, bks, season brochures

S AMERICAN TEXTILE MANUFACTURERS INSTITUTE LIBRARY,* 1130 Connecticut Ave, Ste 1200, 20036-3954. SAN 326-9175. Tel: 202-862-0500. FAX: 202-862-0570. *Librn*, Carolyn Vincent
Library Holdings: Bk Titles 1,600

AMERICAN UNIVERSITY
CL WASHINGTON COLLEGE OF LAW LIBRARY, 4801 Massachusetts Ave NW, 20016-8182. SAN 336-660X. Tel: 202-274-4350. Interlibrary Loan Service Tel: 202-274-4327. FAX: 202-274-4365. E-Mail: lawlibrary@wcl.american.edu. Web Site: library.wcl.american.edu. *Dir*, Patrick E Kehoe; Tel: 202-274-4374, E-Mail: pkehoe@wcl.american.edu; *Assoc Dir*, Margaret Milam; Tel: 202-274-4376, E-Mail: mmilam@wcl.american.edu; *Dep Dir*, Gary McCann; Tel: 202-274-4377, E-Mail: gmccann@wcl.american.edu; *Tech Servs*, Marla Schwartz; Tel: 202-274-4346, E-Mail: mschwar@wcl.american.edu; *Tech Coordr*, John Heywood; Tel: 202-274-4329, E-Mail: heywood@american.edu; *Reader Servs*, William Ryan; Tel: 202-274-4331, E-Mail: wryan@wcl.american.edu; *Reader Servs*, Susan Lewis-Somers; Tel: 202-274-4330, E-Mail: slewis@wcl.american.edu; *Cat*, Raymond VanDe Moortell; Tel: 617-353-1321; *Cat*, Stephen Pentek; E-Mail: spentek@bu.edu; *Cat*, Ann Marie Crossed; Tel: 202-274-4344, E-Mail: crossed@wcl.american.edu; *Cat*, Michael Petit; Tel: 202-274-4345, E-Mail: mpetit@wcl.american.edu; *Archivist*, Robert Forman; Tel: 202-274-4320, E-Mail: rforman@wcl.american.edu. Subject Specialists: *Intl law*, William Ryan; *Intl law*, John Heywood; Staff 23 (MLS 10, Non-MLS 13)
Founded 1896. Enrl 1,200; Fac 50
May 1999-Apr 2000 Income $2,555,773. Mats Exp $1,408,724, Books $856,384, Per/Ser (Incl. Access Fees) $552,340. Sal $1,096,419 (Prof $628,030)
Library Holdings: Bk Vols 443,413; Bk Titles 175,024; Per Subs 6,346
Special Collections: Archives of Former Administrative Conference of the United States & National Bankruptcy Review Commission; Goodman Coll of Rare Law Books; National Equal Justice Library
Automation Activity & Vendor Info: (Cataloging) Innovative Interfaces Inc.; (Circulation) Innovative Interfaces Inc.; (Course Reserve) Innovative Interfaces Inc.; (OPAC) Innovative Interfaces Inc.; (Serials) Innovative Interfaces Inc.
Database Vendor: Dialog, IAC - Info Trac, Innovative Interfaces INN - View, Lexis-Nexis, OCLC - First Search
Function: ILL available
Partic in Dialog Corporation; OCLC Online Computer Library Center, Inc; Washington Research Library Consortium; Westlaw

C THE AMERICAN UNIVERSITY, Jack I & Dorothy G Bender Library & Learning Resources Center, 4400 Massachusetts Ave NW, 20016-8046. SAN 336-657X. Tel: 202-885-3237. Interlibrary Loan Service Tel: 202-885-3852. FAX: 202-885-3226. Web Site: www.library.american.edu. *Dir*, Patricia A Wand; E-Mail: patwand@american.edu; *Asst Dir*, Linda Chase; *Asst Dir*,

Diana Vogelsong; *Cat*, Sue Neilson; *Access Serv*, Helen Goldstein; *Acq*, Janice Flug; *Media Spec*, Christopher Lewis; *Coll Develop*, Martin Shapiro; Staff 74 (MLS 24, Non-MLS 50)
Founded 1904. Enrl 11,285; Fac 469; Highest Degree: Doctorate
May 1998-Apr 1999 Mats Exp $1,989,000. Sal $3,196,000
Library Holdings: Bk Vols 706,000; Per Subs 3,500
Subject Interests: Art, Business and management, Economics, History, Humanities
Special Collections: Asia & the East, Japanese Culture (Spinks Coll); Drew Pearson Coll; John Hickman Coll; Mathematics (Artemas Martin Coll); The Papers of the National Commission on the Public Service
Automation Activity & Vendor Info: (OPAC) Endeavor
Publications: BiblioNet
Partic in Capcon Library Network; OCLC Online Computer Library Center, Inc; Washington Research Library Consortium
Friends of the Library Group
Departmental Libraries:
MUSIC LIBRARY, . SAN 336-6634. Tel: 202-885-3264. FAX: 202-885-3226. Web Site: www.library.american.edu. *Librn*, James R Heintze
Founded 1966
Partic in Capcon Library Network; OCLC Online Computer Library Center, Inc; Washington Research Library Consortium

L ANDREWS & KURTH LLP LIBRARY, 1701 Pennsylvania Ave NW, Ste 300, 20006. SAN 377-2845. Tel: 202-662-2700. FAX: 202-662-2739. E-Mail: webmaster@andrews-kurth.com. *Librn*, Martha Birdseye
Library Holdings: Bk Vols 10,000; Per Subs 150
Partic in DC Soc of Law Librs

S ARENT, FOX, KINTNER, PLOTKIN & KAHN LIBRARY,* 1050 Connecticut Ave NW, 20036. SAN 326-9191. Tel: 202-857-6297. FAX: 202-857-6395. *Librn*, Jim Clark
Library Holdings: Bk Vols 60,000; Per Subs 400

G ARMED FORCES INSTITUTE OF PATHOLOGY, Ash Library,* Bldg 54, Rm 4077, WRAMC, 20306-6000. SAN 302-5861. Tel: 202-782-1830. FAX: 202-782-6403. E-Mail: ashlib@afip.osd.mil. *Chief Librn, Coll Develop*, Ruth Li
Founded 1951
Oct 1998-Sep 1999 Income $530,000. Mats Exp $291,600, Books $8,600, Per/Ser (Incl. Access Fees) $263,000. Sal $133,000 (Prof $43,000)
Library Holdings: Bk Vols 19,000
Subject Interests: Pathology
Partic in Fedlink; National Network Of Libraries Of Medicine - South Central Region; OCLC Online Computer Library Center, Inc

S ARMY & NAVY CLUB LIBRARY,* 901 17th St NW, 20006-2503. SAN 302-587X. Tel: 202-628-8400, Ext 386, 202-721-2096. FAX: 202-296-8787. E-Mail: anclibr@pop.dn.net. Web Site: www.armynavyclub.org. *Librn*, Aleksandra M Zajackowski
Founded 1885
Library Holdings: Bk Titles 20,000; Per Subs 40
Special Collections: Reginald W Oakie Coll of Civil War Stereographs; Writings of Club Members

L ARNOLD & PORTER LIBRARY,* 555 12th St NW, 20004-1202. SAN 302-5888. Tel: 202-942-5000. Interlibrary Loan Service Tel: 202-942-5370. FAX: 202-942-6024. *Librn*, James W Shelar; *Tech Servs*, Jean Altschuler; Staff 16 (MLS 7, Non-MLS 9)
Library Holdings: Bk Vols 70,000; Per Subs 350
Subject Interests: Law, Legislation
Publications: Miscellaneous Research Guides; Monthly Accessions List
Partic in Dialog Corporation; OCLC Online Computer Library Center, Inc; Westlaw

S ARTHUR D JENKINS LIBRARY, Textile Museum, 2320 S St NW, 20008. SAN 302-7880. Tel: 202-667-0441, Ext 31. FAX: 202-483-0994. Web Site: www.textilemuseum.org. *Librn*, Mary Mallia; E-Mail: mmallia@textilemuseum.org; Staff 1 (MLS 1)
Founded 1926
Library Holdings: Bk Titles 16,000; Per Subs 144
Subject Interests: Costume design, Textiles
Special Collections: Cultural History of the Americas, Asia, Africa, the Middle East & the Pacific Rim; History of Rugs, Textiles, Costume
Publications: A Periodical Index 1890-1982 of Rugs & Textile Arts (G K Hall & Co); Annual Bibliography of Textile Literature, 1993- (co-published with the Textile Society of America); Textile Museum Journal
Restriction: Not a lending library
Open Wed-Fri 10-2

S ASIA PACIFIC CENTER FOR JUSTICE & PEACE LIBRARY, Resource Center,* 110 Maryland Ave NE, 20002. (Mail add: Box 70, 20002), SAN 370-3460. Tel: 202-543-1094. FAX: 202-546-5103. *Exec Dir*, Miriam A Young
Library Holdings: Bk Vols 500; Per Subs 35

S ASPIRA ASSOCIATION LIBRARY,* 1444 I St NW 8th flr Ste 800, 20005. SAN 373-0379. Tel: 202-835-3600. FAX: 202-835-3613. E-Mail: aspirai@aol.com. Web Site: www.aspira.org. *Publ Servs, VPres*, Hilda Crespo
Library Holdings: Bk Vols 600
Open Mon-Fri 9-5

S ASSOCIATION FOR GERONTOLOGY IN HIGHER EDUCATION, Resource Library, 1030 15th St NW Ste 240, 20005. SAN 371-5620. Tel: 202-289-9806. FAX: 202-289-9824. Web Site: www.aghe.org. *Exec Dir*, Cathy Tompkins; *Dir*, Derek Stepp
Library Holdings: Bk Titles 2,500
Restriction: By appointment only

S ASSOCIATION OF AMERICAN RAILROADS, Information Resource Center,* 50 F St NW, 4th Flr, 20001. SAN 302-590X. Tel: 202-639-2334. FAX: 202-639-2986. Web Site: www.aar.org. *In Charge*, Joyce W Koeneman; Tel: 202-639-2333, E-Mail: jkoenema@aar.org; Staff 1 (MLS 1)
Founded 1910
Library Holdings: Bk Titles 5,000; Per Subs 200
Subject Interests: Railroads, Transportation
Restriction: By appointment only, Open to public for reference only, Staff & members only
Partic in Dialog Corporation

S ASSOCIATION OF GOVERNING BOARDS OF UNIVERSITIES & COLLEGES, Zwingle Resource Center,* One Dupont Circle, Ste 400, 20036. SAN 326-3193. Tel: 202-776-0818. FAX: 202-775-8790, 223-7053. E-Mail: zrc@agb.org. Web Site: www.agb.org. *Dir*, Barbara L Perkins
Founded 1975
Library Holdings: Bk Titles 1,500; Per Subs 25

S ASSOCIATION OF UNIVERSITY PROGRAMS IN HEALTH ADMINISTRATION LIBRARY,* 730 11th St NW, 20001. SAN 322-7979. Tel: www.aupha.org. FAX: 202-638-3429. E-Mail: aupha@aupha.org. Web Site: www.aupha.org.
Founded 1948
Library Holdings: Bk Titles 4,500; Per Subs 25
Subject Interests: Hospital administration
Special Collections: World Health Orgn
Partic in Nat Libr of Med

S AUSTRIAN PRESS & INFORMATION SERVICE, 3524 International Ct NW, 20008-3021. SAN 370-4033. Tel: 202-895-6775. FAX: 202-895-6772. E-Mail: austroinfo@austria.org. Web Site: www.austria.org/. *Dir*, Martin Weiss
Library Holdings: Bk Vols 300
Subject Interests: Austrian affairs

L BAACH, ROBINSON & LEWIS LIBRARY,* One Thomas Circle NW, Ste 200, 20005. SAN 377-4546. Tel: 202-833-8900. FAX: 202-466-5738. *Librn*, Mia Engle
Library Holdings: Bk Vols 5,000

L BAKER & BOTTS LLP, Law Library, 1299 Pennsylvania Ave NW, 20004. SAN 377-3604. Tel: 202-639-7700. FAX: 202-639-7980. Web Site: www.bakerbotts.com. *Librn*, Ed O'Rourke; E-Mail: edward_orourke@bakerbotts.com; *Librn*, Janet James
Library Holdings: Bk Vols 25,000; Per Subs 250
Partic in Am Asn of Law Librs; DC Soc of Law Librs

L BAKER & HOSTETLER, Law Library,* 1050 Connecticut Ave NW, Ste 1100, 20036. SAN 377-3019. Tel: 202-861-1500. FAX: 202-861-1783. *Librn*, Marjorie Leary
Library Holdings: Bk Vols 25,000; Per Subs 50
Partic in Am Asn of Law Librs; DC Law Librs Asn

L BAKER & MCKENZIE LIBRARY,* 815 Connecticut Ave NW, Ste 900, 20006-4078. SAN 326-2162. Tel: 202-452-7070. FAX: 202-452-7074. *Librn*, John Hoffman; *Asst Librn*, Leslee Budlong; Staff 2 (MLS 1, Non-MLS 1)
Library Holdings: Bk Vols 20,000; Bk Titles 5,000; Per Subs 107
Subject Interests: International law, International trade
Partic in Westlaw

L BAKER BOTTS, (Formerly Miller, Cassidy, Larroca & Lewin LLP), 1299 Pennsylvania Ave NW, 20004-2400. SAN 377-4333. Tel: 202-639-7958, 202-639-7965. FAX: 202-639-7890. *Librn*, James T Courtney; *Librn*, Janet James; *Librn*, Edward O'Rourke; Staff 2 (MLS 1, Non-MLS 1)
Library Holdings: Bk Vols 25,000; Per Subs 50
Partic in Law Libr Soc of DC

L BALLARD, SPAHR, ANDREWS & INGERSOLL, Law Library,* 601 13th St NW Ste 1000 South, 20005-3807. SAN 372-3887. Tel: 202-661-2200. FAX: 202-661-2299.
Library Holdings: Bk Vols 10,000
Subject Interests: Commercial law

S R L BANKS & ASSOCIATES INC LIBRARY,* 1717 K St NW, Ste 1010, 20036-5331. SAN 373-3475. Tel: 202-296-6700. FAX: 202-296-3700. *Librn*, Lorraine Hart
Library Holdings: Bk Vols 2,000; Per Subs 100
Subject Interests: Engineering, Technology

SR BAPTIST JOINT COMMITTEE LIBRARY,* 200 Maryland Ave NE, 20002. SAN 375-7145. Tel: 202-544-4226. FAX: 202-544-2094. *Librn*, Matt Anderson
Library Holdings: Bk Titles 2,000

S BATTELLE PACIFIC NORTHWEST NATIONAL LABORATORY, Reference Center,* 901 D St SW, Ste 900, 20024-2115. SAN 371-0076. Tel: 202-479-0500. FAX: 202-646-5233.
Library Holdings: Bk Vols 600; Per Subs 75
Open Mon-Fri 8am-6pm

L BEVERIDGE & DIAMOND, PC LIBRARY, 1350 I St NW, Ste 700, 20005-3311. SAN 377-2993. Tel: 202-789-6000, 202-789-6173. FAX: 202-789-6190. *Librn*, Scott Larson
Library Holdings: Bk Vols 10,000; Per Subs 300
Partic in Am Asn of Law Librs; Law Libr Soc of DC

BOARD OF GOVERNORS OF THE FEDERAL RESERVE SYSTEM

GL LAW LIBRARY, 20th St & Constitution Ave NW, 20551. SAN 336-6723. Tel: 202-452-3284. FAX: 202-452-3101.; Staff 4 (MLS 3, Non-MLS 1)
Founded 1975
JanDec
Library Holdings: Bk Vols 20,000; Per Subs 100
Subject Interests: Administrative law
Special Collections: Congressional (Legislative History Coll of Banking-Related Statutes of the US), micro
Publications: Current Legislative Activity; Law Library Bulletin; Textual Changes in the Federal Reserve Act

G RESEARCH LIBRARY, 20th St & Constitution Ave NW, 20551. SAN 336-6758. Tel: 202-452-3332. FAX: 202-452-3819. *Chief Librn*, Susan R Vincent; *Ref*, Krista Box; *Govt Doc*, Sian Seldin; *Tech Servs*, Ioana Ratesh; *Per*, Bernice B Coles; Staff 11 (MLS 6, Non-MLS 5)
Founded 1914
Library Holdings: Bk Vols 50,000; Per Subs 2,000
Subject Interests: Banks and banking, Economics, Finance, Monetary policy
Special Collections: Federal Reserve System; Foreign Central Bank Publications
Automation Activity & Vendor Info: (Acquisitions) Innovative Interfaces Inc.; (Cataloging) Innovative Interfaces Inc.; (Circulation) Innovative Interfaces Inc.; (OPAC) Innovative Interfaces Inc.
Publications: Recent Acquisitions
Partic in OCLC Online Computer Library Center, Inc
Open to the public on Thursday
Friends of the Library Group

SR BOARDMAN UNITED METHODIST CHURCH LIBRARY,* North Bldg, Ste 800, 601 Pennsylvania Ave, 20004. SAN 372-4859. Tel: 330-726-8571, 330-758-4527. FAX: 330-758-7348. *Librn*, Mary Lou Henneman
Library Holdings: Bk Vols 500

L BRACEWELL & PATTERSON LLP, Law Library, 2000 K St NW, Ste 500, 20006. SAN 372-1728. Tel: 202-828-5800. FAX: 202-223-1225. Web Site: www.bracepatt.com. *Librn*, Ruth Mendelson
Library Holdings: Bk Vols 10,000; Per Subs 25
Subject Interests: Corporate law, Environmental law
Partic in OCLC Online Computer Library Center, Inc

C BRAZILIAN-AMERICAN CULTURAL INSTITUTE, INC, Harold E Wibberley Jr Library, 4103 Connecticut Ave NW, 20008. SAN 326-4742. Tel: 202-362-8334. FAX: 202-362-8337. E-Mail: baci_us@worldnetatt.net. Web Site: www.bacidc.org. *Dir*, Jose Neistein
Library Holdings: Bk Vols 4,000; Bk Titles 3,500
Special Collections: Brazilian Art & Literature, bks

S BREAD FOR THE WORLD INSTITUTE LIBRARY, 50 F St NW, Ste 500, 20001-1530. SAN 329-0514. Tel: 202-639-9400. FAX: 202-639-9401. *Info Specialist, Librn*, Karin Lyttkens-Blake; E-Mail: klyttkens@bread.org; Staff 1 (MLS 1)
Founded 1990
Library Holdings: Bk Titles 5,000; Per Subs 90
Publications: Acquisition list (monthly) (Annual report)
Restriction: Non-circulating to the public, Open to department staff only
Function: For research purposes, ILL to other special libraries

S BROOKINGS INSTITUTION LIBRARY,* 1775 Massachusetts Ave NW, 20036. SAN 302-6019. Tel: 202-797-6240. FAX: 202-797-2970. Web Site: www.brook.edu/lib/lib_hp.htm. *Dir*, Eric J Eisinger; E-Mail: eeisinger@brook.edu; *Acq, Per*, James Collins; *Cat*, David Bair; *Ref*, Mary Fry; Staff 6 (MLS 5, Non-MLS 1)
Founded 1927
Library Holdings: Bk Vols 75,000; Per Subs 700
Subject Interests: Economics, International relations, Social sciences and issues, U.S. Government
Publications: Acquisitions List
Partic in Capcon Library Network

L BRYAN CAVE LIBRARY,* 700 13th St NW, Ste 700, 20005-3960. SAN 377-2977. Tel: 202-508-6058. FAX: 202-508-6200. E-Mail: llw@bryancavellp.com. *Librn*, Laura Whitbeck
Library Holdings: Bk Vols 10,000; Per Subs 100
Partic in Am Asn of Law Librs; Law Libr Soc of DC

S BUILDING OWNERS & MANAGERS ASSOCIATION INTERNATIONAL, Corporate Library,* 1201 New York Ave NW, Ste 300, 20005. SAN 375-2313. Tel: 202-408-2662. FAX: 202-371-0181.
Library Holdings: Bk Titles 1,000

G RALPH J BUNCHE LIBRARY OF THE UNITED STATES DEPARTMENT OF STATE,* 2201 C St NW, 20520. SAN 302-8038. Tel: 202-647-2458. FAX: 202-647-2971. Web Site: library.state.gov. *Librn*, Dan O Clemmer; *Coll Develop*, Liina Keerdoja
Founded 1789
1998-1999 Mats Exp $750,000. Sal $1,200,000
Library Holdings: Bk Vols 600,000; Per Subs 1,100
Subject Interests: International law
Special Collections: Department of State Publications; Diplomatic Lists
Automation Activity & Vendor Info: (Cataloging) TLC; (Circulation) TLC; (OPAC) TLC
Publications: Acquisitions List (monthly)
Partic in Dialog Corporation; Dow Jones News Retrieval; Fedlink; Nat Libr of Med; OCLC Online Computer Library Center, Inc
Friends of the Library Group

G BUREAU OF ALCOHOL, TOBACCO & FIREARMS, ATF Reference Library,* 20226. SAN 326-1263. Tel: 202-927-7890. FAX: 202-927-8883. *Librn*, Vicki R Herrmann
Founded 1979
Oct 1999-Sep 2000 Income $60,000. Mats Exp $18,450, Books $1,000, Per/Ser (Incl. Access Fees) $2,000, Presv $250, Micro $15,000, Manuscripts & Archives $200. Sal $42,000
Library Holdings: Bk Titles 920; Per Subs 55
Subject Interests: Alcohol, Explosives, Firearms, Tobacco products
Special Collections: Hearings resulting from the Repeal of Prohibition
Open Mon-Fri 7-3:30

GL BUREAU OF NATIONAL AFFAIRS, INC LIBRARY,* 1231 25th St NW, 20037-1197. SAN 326-9256. Tel: 202-452-4466. FAX: 202-452-4084. E-Mail: library@bna.com. *Mgr*, Marilyn M Bromley; Tel: 202-452-6380, E-Mail: mbromley@bna.com; *Librn*, Catherine A Kitchell; Tel: 202-452-4431, E-Mail: ckitchell@bna.com; *Librn*, Karen W Silber; Tel: 202-452-4631, E-Mail: ksilber@bna.com; *Librn*, Susan A Jones; Tel: 202-452-7883, E-Mail: sajones@bna.com; *Cat*, Le-Chi Gallagher; Tel: 202-452-4116, E-Mail: lgallagh@bna.com; *Tech Servs*, Clare Bailey; Tel: 202-452-4670, E-Mail: cbailey@bna.com; *ILL*, Le T Pham; Tel: 202-452-4115, E-Mail: lepham@bna.com; *Acq, Ser, Tech Servs*, Karen Cenon. Subject Specialists: *Competitive intelligence*, Marilyn M Bromley; *Reference*, Catherine A Kitchell; *Reference*, Karen W Silber; *Reference*, Susan A Jones; Staff 11 (MLS 7, Non-MLS 4)
Library Holdings: Bk Vols 20,000; Per Subs 900
Subject Interests: Health care, Labor, Law, Personnel management
Special Collections: State Regulatory Codes
Automation Activity & Vendor Info: (Cataloging) SIRSI; (Circulation) SIRSI; (OPAC) SIRSI; (Serials) SIRSI
Database Vendor: Dialog, Lexis-Nexis, OCLC - First Search
Publications: BNA's Directory of State & Federal Courts, Judges & Clerks
Function: ILL limited
Partic in Capcon Library Network

L CADWALADER, WICKERSHAM & TAFT, Law Library,* 1333 New Hampshire Ave NW, Ste 700, 20036-1574. SAN 372-1442. Tel: 202-862-2217. FAX: 202-862-2400. E-Mail: cwtlib@aol.com. Web Site: www.cwt.com. *Librn*, Jane Platt-Brown
Library Holdings: Bk Vols 9,000; Per Subs 45

L CAHILL, GORDON & REINDEL LIBRARY,* 1990 K St NW, Ste 1990, 20006. SAN 302-6043. Tel: 202-862-8960. FAX: 202-862-8958. *Librn*, Denise Brown
Library Holdings: Bk Vols 3,000; Per Subs 25
Partic in Westlaw

L CAPLIN & DRYSDALE LIBRARY,* One Thomas Circle, 20005. SAN 302-606X. Tel: 202-862-5073. FAX: 202-429-3301. E-Mail: em@capdale.com. *Librn*, Ellen Mahar
Founded 1969
Library Holdings: Bk Vols 15,010; Bk Titles 4,911; Per Subs 158

C CAPUCHIN COLLEGE LIBRARY,* 4121 Harewood Rd NE, 20017. SAN 302-6078. Tel: 202-529-2188. FAX: 202-526-6664. *In Charge*, Mike Letostak
Library Holdings: Bk Vols 25,000; Per Subs 50
Subject Interests: Catholicism, Theology

S CARNEGIE ENDOWMENT FOR INTERNATIONAL PEACE LIBRARY,* 1779 Massachusetts Ave NW, 20036. SAN 328-5189. Tel: 202-939-2255. FAX: 202-483-4462. Web Site: www.ceip.org/library/library.htm. *Librn*, Jennifer L Little; E-Mail: jlittle@ceip.org; *Asst Librn*, Kathleen A Daly
Library Holdings: Bk Vols 8,500; Per Subs 200
Subject Interests: Foreign policy
Automation Activity & Vendor Info: (OPAC) Inmagic, Inc.
Partic in Capcon Library Network

CARNEGIE INSTITUTION OF WASHINGTON

S DEPARTMENT OF TERRESTRIAL MAGNETISM & GEOPHYSICAL LABORATORY LIBRARY, 5241 Broad Branch Rd NW, 20015-1395. SAN 336-6847. Tel: 202-686-2410, 202-686-4370. FAX: 202-364-8726. E-Mail: library@dtm.ciw.edu. Web Site: www.ciw.edu/library. *Librn*, Shaun J Hardy; Tel: 202-686-4370, Ext 2562; Staff 2 (MLS 1, Non-MLS 1)
Founded 1904
Library Holdings: Bk Vols 40,000; Per Subs 275
Subject Interests: Astrophysics, Crystallography, Geochemistry, Geophysics, Mineralogy, Physical chemistry
Special Collections: History of Terrestrial Magnetism; History of Volcanology, Petrology & Physical Chemistry
Automation Activity & Vendor Info: (Cataloging) Inmagic, Inc.; (OPAC) Inmagic, Inc.
Publications: Carnegie Institution of Washington Year Book; Scientific staff reprints
Restriction: Open to others by appointment
Partic in Capcon Library Network; Interlibrary Users Association

S INSTITUTION LIBRARY, 1530 P St NW, 20005-1910. SAN 336-6782. Tel: 202-939-1120. FAX: 202-387-8092. Web Site: www.ciw.edu. *Actg Librn*, Pat Craig; E-Mail: pcraig@pst.ciw.edu
Founded 1903
Library Holdings: Bk Vols 2,040; Per Subs 20
Library contains primarily the publications of Carnegie Institution

C CATHOLIC UNIVERSITY OF AMERICA, John K Mullen of Denver Memorial Library, 620 Michigan Ave NE, 20017. (Mail add: 308 Mullen, 20064), SAN 336-6871. Tel: 202-319-5055. Interlibrary Loan Service Tel: 202-319-5063. FAX: 202-319-4735, 202-319-6101. Web Site: libraries.cua.edu/. *Dir*, Adele R Chwalek; E-Mail: chwalek@cua.edu; *Assoc Dir*, Thomas Marcum; Tel: 202-319-5073, E-Mail: marcum@cua.edu; *Curator*, Barbara Henry; Tel: 202-319-5091; *Archivist*, Dr Timothy Meagher; Tel: 202-319-5065, Fax: 202-319-6554, E-Mail: meagher@cua.edu. Subject Specialists: *Rare books*, Barbara Henry; Staff 27 (MLS 27)
Founded 1889. Enrl 5,600; Fac 360; Highest Degree: Doctorate
Sep 1999-Aug 2000 Income (Main and Other College/University Libraries) $4,262,200. Mats Exp $1,750,000, Books $500,000, Per/Ser (Incl. Access Fees) $1,200,000, Presv $50,000. Sal $2,036,215 (Prof $1,010,843)
Library Holdings: Bk Vols 1,540,078; Per Subs 5,499
Special Collections: Canon Law; Catholic Americana; Celtic; Church History; Greek & Latin; Knights of Malta; Labor & Immigration; Library of Pope Clement XI (Clementine Library); Luso-Brazilian Studies (Lima Library); Medieval Studies; Patristics; Semitic & Egyptian Languages & Literatures
Automation Activity & Vendor Info: (Cataloging) Endeavor; (Circulation) Endeavor; (Course Reserve) Endeavor; (ILL) Endeavor; (OPAC) Endeavor; (Serials) Endeavor
Database Vendor: Lexis-Nexis, OCLC - First Search, OVID Technologies, ProQuest
Partic in Capcon Library Network; Washington Research Library Consortium; Washington Theological Consortium
Friends of the Library Group
Departmental Libraries:
ARCHIVES & MANUSCRIPTS DIVISION, Mullen Library, Rm 33, 20064. SAN 336-6901. Tel: 202-319-5065. FAX: 202-319-4181. Web Site: www.cua.edu. *Archivist*, Dr Timothy Meagher
CHEMISTRY & PHYSICS Tel: 202-319-5389. FAX: 202-319-5381. Web Site: www.cua.edu. *Librn*, William Guy
1997-1998 Mats Exp $282,298, Books $10,935, Per/Ser (Incl. Access Fees) $271,363
Library Holdings: Bk Vols 36,762
ENGINEERING-ARCHITECTURE & MATH LIBRARY, 200 Pangborn Hall, 20064. SAN 336-7177. Tel: 202-319-5167. FAX: 202-319-4485. Web Site: libraries.cua.edu. *Librn*, William Guy; E-Mail: guy@cua.edu; Staff 3 (MLS 1, Non-MLS 2)
Sep 1998-Aug 1999 Mats Exp $194,962, Books $51,902, Per/Ser (Incl. Access Fees) $143,060. Sal $91,299 (Prof $33,623)
Library Holdings: Bk Vols 36,940
CL JUDGE KATHRYN J DUFOUR LAW LIBRARY, 3600 John McCormack Rd NE, 20064-8206. SAN 336-6995. Tel: 202-319-5155. FAX: 202-319-4447, 319-5581. Web Site: law.cua.edu/library/library.shth. *Dir*, Stephen Margeton; *Assoc Dir*, Patrick Petit; *Assoc Dir*, Mary Strouse; Staff 10 (MLS 10)
Founded 1898
Library Holdings: Bk Vols 307,000; Per Subs 5,473
Partic in Dialog Corporation
LIBRARY & INFORMATION SCIENCE LIBRARY, 132 Marist Hall, 20064. SAN 336-7029. Tel: 202-319-5092. FAX: 202-319-5574. Web Site: libraries.cua.edu. *Librn*, Patricia Klingshirn; E-Mail: klingshp@cua.edu; Staff 2 (MLS 1, Non-MLS 1)
Sep 1998-Aug 1999 Mats Exp $32,047, Books $11,938, Per/Ser (Incl. Access Fees) $20,109. Sal $45,327 (Prof $22,327)
Library Holdings: Bk Vols 18,749
OLIVEIRA LIMA LIBRARY, Mullen Library, Rm 6, 20064. SAN 336-7118. Tel: 202-319-5059. FAX: 202-319-4735. *Curator*, Dr Thomas Cohen; *Librn*, Maria Angela Leal; E-Mail: leal@cua.edu
Library Holdings: Bk Vols 57,008
CR MUSIC, 101 Ward Music Bldg, 20064. SAN 336-7053. Tel: 202-319-5424. FAX: 202-319-6280. Web Site: libraries.cua.edu. *Librn*, Henry Grossi; E-Mail: grossi@cua.edu; Staff 3 (MLS 1, Non-MLS 2)
Sep 1998-Aug 1999 Mats Exp $22,533, Books $16,238, Per/Ser (Incl. Access Fees) $6,295. Sal $73,848 (Prof $32,465)
Library Holdings: Bk Vols 25,318
CM NURSING-BIOLOGY, 212 Gowan Hall, 20064. SAN 336-7088. Tel: 202-319-5411. FAX: 202-319-5410. Web Site: www.libraries.cua.edu. *Librn*, N L Powell; Staff 3 (MLS 1, Non-MLS 2)
Founded 1932
Sep 1998-Aug 1999 Mats Exp $148,356, Books $23,463, Per/Ser (Incl. Access Fees) $124,893. Sal $90,514 (Prof $45,935)
Library Holdings: Bk Vols 56,252; Per Subs 435
Subject Interests: Biology, Botany, Nursing
Special Collections: Nursing Historical Coll
REFERENCE & INSTRUCTIONAL SERVICES DIVISION, 206 Mullen Library, 20064. SAN 336-7142. Tel: 202-319-5070. FAX: 202-319-6054. Web Site: www.libraries.cua.edu. *In Charge*, Deborah Ozga; Tel: 202-319-5078, E-Mail: ozga@cua.edu; Staff 7 (MLS 5, Non-MLS 2)
Sep 1998-Aug 1999 Mats Exp $105,827, Books $30,300, Per/Ser (Incl. Access Fees) $75,527
Library Holdings: Bk Vols 20,394
Friends of the Library Group
RELIGIOUS STUDIES-PHILOSOPHY-HUMANITIES DIVISION, 314 Mullen Library, Rm 300, 20064. SAN 336-7150. Tel: 202-319-5088. FAX: 202-319-4735. Web Site: www.cua.edu. *Coordr*, Bruce Miller. Subject Specialists: *Humanities*, Betty Gutekunst
1997-1998 Mats Exp $200,139, Books $137,835, Per/Ser (Incl. Access Fees) $62,304. Sal $127,972 (Prof $105,480)
Library Holdings: Bk Vols 41,510
SEMITICS, Mullen Library, Rm 18, 20064. SAN 336-7207. Tel: 202-319-5084. FAX: 202-319-4735. Web Site: www.cua.edu. *Curator*, Monica Blanchard
1997-1998 Mats Exp $8,754, Books $7,263, Per/Ser (Incl. Access Fees) $1,491. Sal $127,972 (Prof $105,480)
Library Holdings: Bk Vols 41,510
RARE BOOKS SPECIAL COLLECTIONS, 104 Mullen Library, 20064. SAN 336-6936. Tel: 202-319-5091. FAX: 202-319-4735. Web Site: www.cua.edu/www/mul. *Curator*, Barbara Henry
1996-1997 Mats Exp Books $1,000
Library Holdings: Bk Vols 40,000
Friends of the Library Group

S CENTER FOR DEFENSE INFORMATION LIBRARY,* 1779 Massachusetts Ave NW, Ste 615, 20036. SAN 322-6867. Tel: 202-332-0600, Ext 132. FAX: 202-462-4559. E-Mail: cdi@igc.apc.org, info@cdi.org. *Librn*, Jeffrey Mason; E-Mail: jmason@cdi.org
Founded 1972
Library Holdings: Bk Titles 6,000; Per Subs 160
Subject Interests: Foreign affairs, Mil affairs
Videotape Library supervised by Director of Television Mark Sugg at Email: msugg@cdi.org

M CENTER FOR MOLECULAR NUTRITION & SENSORY DISORDERS, Taste & Smell Clinic Library, 5125 MacArthur Blvd Ste 20, 20016. SAN 371-8255. Tel: 202-364-4180. FAX: 202-364-9727. Web Site: www.tasteandsmell.com. *Chief Librn*, Robert I Henkin
Founded 1975
Library Holdings: Bk Titles 1,000; Per Subs 30; Spec Interest Per Sub 28
Special Collections: R I Henkin Coll

S CENTER FOR NATIONAL SECURITY STUDIES,* 2130 H St NW, Ste 701, 20037. SAN 326-9337. Tel: 202-994-7060. FAX: 202-994-7005. E-Mail: cnss@nicom.com. Web Site: www.gwu.edu/cnss. *Dir*, Kate Martin
Library Holdings: Per Subs 50

S CENTER TO PREVENT HANDGUN VIOLENCE LIBRARY,* 1225 I St NW, Ste 1100, 20005. SAN 375-2674. Tel: 202-289-7319. FAX: 202-408-1851. Web Site: www.landguncontrol.org.
Library Holdings: Bk Vols 2,500; Per Subs 40

L CENTRAL INTELLIGENCE AGENCY, Office of General Counsel Law Library, NHB Rm 6U25, 20505. SAN 372-1523. Tel: 703-874-3187. FAX: 703-874-3208. *Librn*, Claudette McLeod
Library Holdings: Bk Vols 20,000

L CHADBOURNE & PARKE LLP, Law Library, 1200 New Hampshire Ave NW, Ste 300, 20036. SAN 377-3760. Tel: 202-974-5695. FAX: 202-974-5602. *Librn*, Joan M Dulin
Library Holdings: Bk Vols 10,000; Per Subs 250
Partic in Law Libr Soc of DC

S CHAMBER OF COMMERCE OF THE UNITED STATES LIBRARY,* 1615 H St NW, 20062-2000. SAN 302-6094. Tel: 202-463-5448. FAX: 202-463-3174. E-Mail: spugh@uschamber.com. Web Site: www.uschamber.com. *In Charge*, Sean Pugh
Founded 1917
Library Holdings: Bk Vols 5,000; Per Subs 500
Subject Interests: Business and management, Economics

R CHEVY CHASE PRESBYTERIAN CHURCH LIBRARY,* One Chevy Chase Circle, 20015-2976. SAN 302-6116. Tel: 202-363-2202. FAX: 202-537-2916. E-Mail: chevy_chase_pc@pcusa.org. *Librn*, Pauline Bringen; *Asst Librn*, Christine Metcalf; *Asst Librn*, Julia Roberts; *Asst Librn*, Mary Lee Maples
Founded 1959
Library Holdings: Bk Titles 3,400; Per Subs 11
Subject Interests: Religion

S CHILD WELFARE LEAGUE OF AMERICA, Dorothy L Bernhard Library, 440 First St NW Ste 310, 20001-2085. SAN 311-6832. Tel: 202-638-2952. FAX: 202-638-4004. Web Site: www.cwla.org. *Dir Libr Serv*, Wong Ming
Founded 1920
Library Holdings: Bk Vols 3,000; Per Subs 100
Subject Interests: Child develop, Child welfare, Soc case work, Soc welfare, Soc work
Restriction: Staff & members only

M CHILDREN'S NATIONAL MEDICAL CENTER, Medical Library, 111 Michigan Ave NW, 20010-2970. SAN 302-6132. Tel: 202-884-3195. FAX: 202-884-5318. E-Mail: mlibrary@cnmc.org. *Ref*, Carolyn Willard
Founded 1968
Library Holdings: Bk Vols 5,000; Per Subs 300
Subject Interests: Child psychology, Pediatrics
Special Collections: Subject Bibliography of Parent Resource Coll
Restriction: Circulation limited
Partic in Dialog Corporation

S CHRONICLE OF HIGHER EDUCATION LIBRARY,* 1255 23rd St NW, Ste 700, 20037. SAN 302-6418. Tel: 202-466-1099. FAX: 202-452-1033. Web Site: chronicle.com. *Coll Develop, Librn*, Joan Waynick
Founded 1966
Library Holdings: Bk Titles 500; Per Subs 67

G COALITION ON RESOURCE RECOVERY & THE ENVIRONMENT LIBRARY,* 1620 I St NW, 4th flr, 20006. SAN 375-801X. Tel: 202-293-7330. FAX: 202-293-2352. *Dir, Tech Servs*, David Gatton
Library Holdings: Bk Titles 150

CR COLLEGE OF PREACHERS LIBRARY,* 3510 Woodley Rd NW, 20016. SAN 371-2079. Tel: 202-537-6387. FAX: 202-537-5650. E-Mail: cop@cathedral.org. *Pres*, Dr Erica B Wood
Library Holdings: Bk Vols 45,000; Per Subs 50

L COLLIER, SHANNON, & SCOTT, PLLC LIBRARY, (Formerly Collier, Shannon, Rill & Scott Library), 3050 K St NW No 400, 20007. SAN 323-7230. Tel: 202-342-8675. FAX: 202-342-8452. Web Site: www.colliershannon.com. *Mgr*, John H Harbison; Tel: 202-342-8468, E-Mail: jharbiso@colshan.com; *Ref Serv*, Pauline Apling; Tel: 202-342-8575; *Cat, Ref Serv*, Gregory Bailey; Tel: 202-342-8424
Oct 1998-Oct 1999 Mats Exp $1,248,550, Books $408,000, Per/Ser (Incl. Access Fees) $56,000, AV Equip $550, Other Print Mats $268,000, Electronic Ref Mat (Incl. Access Fees) $516,000
Library Holdings: Bk Vols 20,000; Bk Titles 8,000; Per Subs 320
Subject Interests: Environmental law, Intellectual property, International trade, Labor, Litigation
Special Collections: Antitrust documents
Automation Activity & Vendor Info: (Cataloging) Inmagic, Inc.
Database Vendor: Dialog, Lexis-Nexis, OCLC - First Search
Publications: Harbour Bulletin
Partic in Law Libr Soc of DC

COLUMBIA HOSPITAL FOR WOMEN
M MEDICAL CENTER LIBRARY, 2425 L St NW, 20037. SAN 320-6246. Tel: 202-293-6560. FAX: 202-293-1446.; Staff 1 (MLS 1)
1998-1999 Income $100,000. Mats Exp $35,400, Books $7,000, Per/Ser (Incl. Access Fees) $28,000, Presv $400. Sal $21,000
Library Holdings: Bk Vols 1,500; Per Subs 210
Subject Interests: Obstetrics and gynecology
Restriction: Not open to public

M COMMISSION ON MENTAL HEALTH SERVICES, Health Sciences Library, Admin Bldg, Rm 100, 2700 Martin Luther King Jr Ave SE, 20032. SAN 373-0395. Tel: 202-645-7388. *Librn*, Dee Desardina
Library Holdings: Bk Vols 12,000; Per Subs 275
Subject Interests: Mental health, Psychiatry, Psychology
Restriction: By appointment only

S COMMODITY FUTURES TRADING COMMISSION LIBRARY,* 1155 21st St NW, 20581. SAN 302-6183. Tel: 202-418-5255. FAX: 202-418-5537. *Chief Librn, Tech Servs*, Wayne S Nuckols; Staff 5 (MLS 2, Non-MLS 3)
Founded 1976
Library Holdings: Bk Vols 15,000; Per Subs 300
Subject Interests: Economics, Law
Special Collections: Commodity Exchange Act Coll; Legislative History Coll; Trading Acts Coll
Automation Activity & Vendor Info: (Acquisitions) EOS; (Cataloging) EOS; (Circulation) EOS; (Serials) EOS
Partic in Capcon Library Network; Fed Libr & Info Network

S COMMUNICATIONS WORKERS OF AMERICA LIBRARY,* 501 Third St NW, 20001-2797. SAN 302-6191. Tel: 202-434-1199. FAX: 202-434-1201. *Res*, Barbara Rosen; E-Mail: brosen@cwa_union.org
Library Holdings: Bk Vols 3,100; Per Subs 200
Subject Interests: Economics, Labor, Telecommunications
Restriction: By appointment only

G CONGRESSIONAL BUDGET OFFICE LIBRARY,* Ford House Office Bldg, Second & D St SW, Rm 472, 20515. SAN 326-9418. Tel: 202-226-2635. FAX: 202-225-1484. *Chief Librn*, Dr Majid S Moghaddam
Library Holdings: Bk Titles 19,000; Per Subs 842
Partic in Dialog Corporation; Dow Jones News Retrieval

S CORCORAN GALLERY OF ART LIBRARY,* 1705 H St, NW, 20006-3908. SAN 302-6248. Tel: 202-822-1482, 202-822-1484. FAX: 202-822-1486. Web Site: www.corcoran.edu. *Tech Servs*, Pat Reid; Staff 1 (MLS 1)
Founded 1869. Enrl 1,350; Fac 120
Jul 1997-Jun 1998 Income $77,650. Mats Exp $56,250, Books $38,250, Per/Ser (Incl. Access Fees) $11,000, Presv $7,000
Library Holdings: Bk Vols 20,000; Per Subs 148
Subject Interests: Fine arts, Graphic arts, Humanities, Photography
Partic in OCLC Online Computer Library Center, Inc

S COSMOS CLUB LIBRARY,* 2121 Massachusetts Ave NW, 20008. SAN 377-2381. Tel: 202-387-7783. FAX: 202-234-6817. *Librn*, Lura A Young
Library Holdings: Bk Vols 7,500; Per Subs 168
Restriction: Not open to public
Partic in DC Libr Asn

L COUDERT BROTHERS, Law Library,* 1627 I St NW, Ste 1200, 20006. SAN 377-5143. Tel: 202-736-1830. FAX: 202-775-1168. *Librn*, Rosalyn S Alleman; E-Mail: allemanr@coudert.com; Staff 1 (MLS 1)
Library Holdings: Bk Vols 1,500; Per Subs 60
Database Vendor: Lexis-Nexis
Partic in Am Asn of Law Librs

S COUNCIL FOR ADVANCEMENT & SUPPORT OF EDUCATION, Case Information Center, 1307 New York Ave Ste 1000, 20005-4701. SAN 302-6256. Tel: 202-478-5642. FAX: 202-387-4973. E-Mail: infoctr@case.org. Web Site: www.case.org. *Dir*, Laurie Calhoun; *Librn*, Mary Smith
Founded 1974
Library Holdings: Bk Titles 600; Per Subs 60
Special Collections: Dissertations on Institutional Advancement
Restriction: Members only
Partic in Dialog Corporation

S COUNCIL ON FOUNDATIONS, Information Center,* 1828 L St NW, 20036. SAN 375-1031. Tel: 202-466-6512. FAX: 202-785-3926. E-Mail: infoserv@cof.org. Web Site: www.cof.org. *Dir*, Jamie Coniglio
Library Holdings: Bk Titles 1,000; Per Subs 20
Restriction: Not open to public

L COVINGTON & BURLING, Law Library,* 1201 Pennslyvania Ave NW, PO Box 7566, 20004-2494. SAN 302-6264. Tel: 202-662-6184. FAX: 202-662-6291. *Dir*, R I Shaffer; E-Mail: rshaffer@cov.com; *Coll Develop*, Daniel H Bearss; Staff 28 (MLS 14, Non-MLS 14)
Founded 1919
Subject Interests: Trade
Partic in Capcon Library Network; OCLC Online Computer Library Center, Inc

S CRAWFORD LIBRARY,* 1050 17th St NW, Ste 280, 20036. SAN 328-3682. Tel: 202-331-8105. FAX: 202-296-0378. E-Mail: vma@vma.org. *Pres*, William S Sandler
Library Holdings: Bk Titles 300
Publications: Valve Magazine; Valve World

L CROWELL & MORING, Law Library,* 1001 Pennsylvania Ave NW, 10th flr, 20004. SAN 326-9434. Tel: 202-624-2828. FAX: 202-628-5116. *Mgr*, Christine Chapdelaine; *Ref*, Dianne Lewis
Library Holdings: Bk Titles 25,000; Per Subs 25,000

Publications: C & M Hillights; Good News; Prospectus
Partic in Data Time; Dialog Corporation; Dow Jones News Retrieval; Vutext; Westlaw
Introduced attorney work product database in 1992

L DAVIS, POLK & WARDWELL, Washington Library,* 1300 I St NW Ste 1000E, 20005. SAN 325-4690. Tel: 202-962-7400. FAX: 202-962-7111. *Librn*, Margaret Conley; E-Mail: conley@dpw.com
Founded 1980
Subject Interests: Banking, Law, Legis-regulatory, Securities, Tax
Special Collections: Banking Agency Documents; Congressional Documents
Restriction: By appointment only
Partic in OCLC Online Computer Library Center, Inc
A branch of Davis Polk & Wardwell (New York)

L DEBEVOISE & PLIMPTON LIBRARY,* 555 13th St NW, Ste 1100 E, 20004. SAN 377-3523. Tel: 202-383-8055. FAX: 202-383-8118. *Librn*, Mari Ann Buckwalter; *Asst Librn*, Brent Burton
Library Holdings: Bk Vols 15,000; Bk Titles 10,000; Per Subs 100
Partic in Am Asn of Law Librs; Law Libr Soc of DC

L DECHERT, PRICE & RHOADS, Law Library,* 1775 Eye St, 20006. SAN 372-3445. Tel: 202-261-7764. FAX: 202-261-3333. *Librn*, Beth Matthews
Library Holdings: Bk Vols 10,000
Subject Interests: Securities

G DEFENSE INTELLIGENCE AGENCY, Classified Library,* SVI-4, 20340-3231. SAN 302-6272. Tel: 202-231-3831. FAX: 202-231-3231.
Founded 1963
Library Holdings: Bk Vols 500,000; Per Subs 1,181
Special Collections: Document Coll, micro
Restriction: Not open to public
Partic in Fedlink

G DEFENSE INTELLIGENCE AGENCY - JOINT MILITARY INTELLIGENCE COLLEGE, John T Hughes Library, The DIAC, D4-100, Bolling Air Force Base, 20340-5100. SAN 374-597X. Tel: 202-231-3777, 202-231-3836. FAX: 202-231-3838. *Dir*, George Jupin; Staff 9 (MLS 7, Non-MLS 2)
Library Holdings: Bk Vols 110,000; Bk Titles 85,000; Per Subs 1,500
Restriction: Restricted access
Partic in Fedlink

S DELOITTE & TOUCHE LIBRARY,* 555 12th St NW Ste 500, 20004. SAN 329-0212. Tel: 202-879-5633. FAX: 202-879-5309. *Librn*, Nour E Dich
Library Holdings: Bk Titles 500; Per Subs 100
Subject Interests: Accounting, Auditing
Restriction: Staff use only

S DEMOCRATIC NATIONAL COMMITTEE RESEARCH LIBRARY,* 430 S Capitol St SE, 20003. SAN 302-6299. Tel: 202-863-8000. FAX: 202-863-7149. Web Site: www.dnc.democrats.org. *Archivist*, Kathy Vick; E-Mail: kvick@dnc.democrats.org
Library Holdings: Bk Vols 150
Restriction: Not open to public

DEPARTMENT OF VETERANS AFFAIRS

G HEADQUARTERS LIBRARY, 810 Vermont Ave NW, 20420. SAN 337-2510. Tel: 202-273-8522. FAX: 202-273-9125. *Chief Librn*, Ginny DuPont; E-Mail: ginny.dupont@mail.va.gov; *ILL*, Anne Janney; Staff 2 (MLS 2)
Founded 1923
Oct 1998-Sep 1999 Income $220,000. Mats Exp $140,200, Books $30,000, Per/Ser (Incl. Access Fees) $100,000, Micro $10,000
Library Holdings: Bk Vols 15,000; Per Subs 500
Subject Interests: Medicine
Partic in Veterans Affairs Library Network

GM MEDICAL CENTER LIBRARY, 50 Irving St NW, 20422. SAN 337-260X. Tel: 202-745-8262. FAX: 202-745-8632. E-Mail: dcwas@forum.va.gov. *Chief Librn*, Iris Renner; *Librn*, Linda Howard
1998-1999 Mats Exp $100,000, Books $25,000, Per/Ser (Incl. Access Fees) $75,000. Sal $150,000
Library Holdings: Bk Vols 5,550; Per Subs 200
Subject Interests: Clinical medicine
Partic in BRS; Nat Libr of Med; Veterans Affairs Library Network

GM OFFICE OF THE GENERAL COUNSEL LAW LIBRARY, 810 Vermont Ave NW, 20420. SAN 337-257X. Tel: 202-273-6558. FAX: 202-273-6645. Web Site: ogccoweb1/law/. *Librn*, Jane Lehman; E-Mail: jane.lehman@mail.va.gov; *Coll Develop*, Mary Reiman; E-Mail: mary.reiman@mail.va.gov; Staff 4 (MLS 2, Non-MLS 2)
Oct 1996-Sep 1997 Income $575,000. Mats Exp $126,000, Books $80,000, Other Print Mats $46,000
Library Holdings: Bk Vols 25,120; Per Subs 21

L DEWEY & BALLANTINE LIBRARY,* 1775 Pennsylvania Ave, Ste 300, 20006. SAN 377-3035. Tel: 202-862-1055. FAX: 202-862-1093. *Mgr*, Daria A Proud; *Asst Librn*, Laura Ray
Library Holdings: Bk Vols 30,000; Per Subs 400
Partic in Am Asn of Law Librs; Law Libr Soc of DC

L DICKSTEIN, SHAPIRO, MORIN & O'SHINSKY LIBRARY,* 2101 L St NW, 7th flr, 20037. SAN 377-4783. Tel: 202-828-2261. FAX: 202-775-2593. Web Site: www.dsmo.com. *Dir*, Frances Durako; *Ref*, Lisa Walsh
Library Holdings: Bk Vols 45,000; Per Subs 400
Partic in Am Asn of Law Librs; DC Soc of Law Librs

S DISTANCE EDUCATION & TRAINING COUNCIL LIBRARY,* 1601 18th St NW, 20009. SAN 327-1293. Tel: 202-234-5100. FAX: 202-332-1386. E-Mail: detc@detc.org. Web Site: www.detc.org. *Exec Dir*, Michael Lambert
Library Holdings: Bk Titles 1,200
Restriction: Non-circulating to the public

G DC COURT OF APPEALS LIBRARY, 500 Indiana Ave NW, 6th flr, Rm 6000, 20001. SAN 374-6143. Tel: 202-879-2767. FAX: 202-626-8840. *Librn*, Letty Limbach
Founded 1977
Library Holdings: Bk Vols 20,000
Restriction: Staff use only
Partic in Lexus

S DISTRICT OF COLUMBIA DEPARTMENT OF CORRECTIONS, Correction Treatment Law Library,* 1901 E St SE, 20003. SAN 377-1229. Tel: 202-698-3000, 202-698-4007. FAX: 202-698-3200. *Librn*, Christopher Forney
Library Holdings: Bk Vols 5,000; Per Subs 15

M DISTRICT OF COLUMBIA GENERAL HOSPITAL, Medical Library,* 19th St & Massachusetts Ave SE, 20003. SAN 302-6337. Tel: 202-675-5348. *Chief Librn*, Katherine V Chew; *Tech Servs*, Sharon Jackson; Staff 3 (MLS 1, Non-MLS 2)
Founded 1954
1997-1998 Mats Exp $60,000, Books $15,000, Per/Ser (Incl. Access Fees) $45,000
Library Holdings: Bk Titles 6,000; Per Subs 200
Subject Interests: Medicine, Nursing
Partic in District Of Columbia Health Sciences Information Network; Medical Libr Asn; Nat Libr of Med

P DISTRICT OF COLUMBIA LIBRARY FOR THE BLIND & PHYSICALLY HANDICAPPED,* 901 G St NW, Rm 215, 20001. SAN 302-6345. Tel: 202-727-2142. FAX: 202-727-1129. Web Site: www.loc.gov. *Chief Librn*, Grace J Lyons; *Asst Librn*, Edith Lewis; Staff 3 (MLS 3)
Library Holdings: Bk Vols 400; Per Subs 45
Special Collections: Blindness & Other Disabilities (Reference Coll); Consumer Advisory Commission; Friends Group; Services & Agencies for the Handicapped (File Coll); Volunteer Tapists; Washington Volunteer Readers for the Blind
Publications: Newsletter
Special Services for the Deaf - Books on deafness & sign language; Special interest periodicals; Staff with knowledge of sign language; TTY machine
Friends of the Library Group

GL DISTRICT OF COLUMBIA OFFICE OF THE CORPORATION COUNSEL, Law Library, 1C-S010,* One Judiciary Sq, 441 Fourth St NW, 20001. SAN 320-6254. Tel: 202-727-6274. FAX: 202-347-8922. *Librn*, Anne Llewellyn Meglis
Founded 1932
Library Holdings: Bk Vols 30,000
Special Collections: District of Columbia Coll
Restriction: By appointment only
Partic in Vutext; Westlaw

P DISTRICT OF COLUMBIA PUBLIC LIBRARY, Martin Luther King Memorial, 901 G St NW, 20001-4599. SAN 336-9366. Tel: 202-727-0321, 202-727-1101. Interlibrary Loan Service Tel: 202-727-1304. TDD: 202-727-2255. FAX: 202-727-1129. Web Site: www.dclibrary.org. *Dir*, Mary E Raphael; *Asst Dir*, Brenda Vy Johnson; *Head Librn*, Jewel Ogonji; *Ad Servs*, Yema Tucker; *Ch Servs*, Maria B Salvadore; *Ref*, Alan Bobowski; *Tech Servs*, Carol Bradwell; *Acq*, Joanne Adetayo; *AV*, Eric White; *YA Servs*, Michael Wallace; *Librn for Deaf*, Janice Rosen; Staff 377 (MLS 118, Non-MLS 259)
Founded 1896. Pop 543,000; Circ 1,476,935 Sal $13,689,949
Library Holdings: Bk Vols 2,863,296; Per Subs 4,088
Subject Interests: Art and architecture, Business and management, Economics, Education, Ethnic studies, Humanities, Local history, Music, Natural science, Social sciences and issues, Technology
Special Collections: Adult Basic Education Books, bks, pamphlets; Black Studies for Adult & Juvenile; Books in Large Type; Georgetown Material (Peabody Coll); Illustrators of Early English & American Children's Books Coll; Library for the Blind, recordings & braille; Local History & Local Authors (Washingtoniana Div); Musical Scores (Kindler Coll); Washington Star Newspaper Coll

Automation Activity & Vendor Info: (Circulation) GEAC
Partic in Fedlink; National Library Service For The Blind & Physically Handicapped, Library Of Congress; OCLC Online Computer Library Center, Inc
Special Services for the Deaf - TDD
Special Services - Telephone Reference Service 202-727-1126, Dial-a-Story 202-638-5717, Kiosk: 1. Librn, Edith Davis. Tel: 202-724-4162
Friends of the Library Group
Branches: 26
ANACOSTIA, 1800 Good Hope Rd, 20020. SAN 336-9390. Tel: 202-727-1329. Web Site: www.dclibrary.org. *Librn*, Ruth Wilson
Library Holdings: Bk Vols 145,880
Subject Interests: African-American
Friends of the Library Group
BENNING, 3935 Benning Rd NE, 20019. SAN 336-9420. Tel: 202-724-4787. Web Site: www.dclibrary.org. *Librn*, Jo Ann Ellis
Library Holdings: Bk Vols 65,904
Special Collections: A V Howard Black Reference Coll
Friends of the Library Group
CAPITOL VIEW, 5001 Central Ave & 50th St SE, 20019. SAN 336-9455. Tel: 202-645-0755. Web Site: www.dclibrary.org. *Librn*, Gregory Bargeman
Library Holdings: Bk Vols 62,542; Bk Titles 32,000
Subject Interests: Adult basic educ
Friends of the Library Group
CHEVY CHASE REGIONAL, 5625 Connecticut Ave NW, 20015. SAN 336-948X. Tel: 202-282-0021. Web Site: www.dclibrary.org. *In Charge*, Karen Butler
Library Holdings: Bk Vols 162,000
Special Collections: Foreign Language Coll
Friends of the Library Group
CLEVELAND PARK, Connecticut Ave & Macomb St NW, 20008. SAN 336-9544. Tel: 202-727-1345. *Librn*, Brian Brown
Library Holdings: Bk Vols 72,186
Friends of the Library Group
FRANCIS A GREGORY REGIONAL, 3660 Alabama Ave SE, 20020. SAN 336-9609. Tel: 202-645-4297. Web Site: www.dclibrary.org. *In Charge*, Lessie Mtewa
Library Holdings: Bk Vols 67,553
Friends of the Library Group
GEORGETOWN (REGIONAL), Wisconsin Ave & R St NW, 20007. SAN 336-9633. Tel: 202-282-0220. Web Site: www.dclibrary.org.
Library Holdings: Bk Vols 76,483
Friends of the Library Group
JUANITA E THORNTON - SHEPHERD PARK, 7420 Georgia Ave NW, 20012. SAN 373-5745. Tel: 202-541-6100. Web Site: www.dclibrary.org. *Librn*, Winell Montague
Library Holdings: Bk Vols 43,226
Friends of the Library Group
LAMOND RIGGS, S Dakota Ave & Kennedy St NE, 20011. SAN 336-965X. Tel: 202-541-6255. Web Site: www.dclibrary.org. *Librn*, Major Shackleford
Library Holdings: Bk Vols 51,988
Friends of the Library Group
LANGSTON COMMUNITY, 650 26th St NE, 20002. SAN 336-9668. Tel: 202-724-8665. Web Site: www.dclibrary.org. *In Charge*, James Quinn
Library Holdings: Bk Vols 25,795; Bk Titles 11,000
Friends of the Library Group
LIBRARY FOR THE BLIND & PHYSICALLY HANDICAPPED
See Separate Entry
MOUNT PLEASANT, 16th & Lamont Sts NW, 20010. SAN 336-9692. Tel: 202-727-1361. Web Site: www.dclibrary.org. *Librn*, Ellen Kardy
Library Holdings: Bk Vols 59,837
Friends of the Library Group
NORTHEAST, 330 Seventh St NE, 20002. SAN 336-9722. Tel: 202-698-3320. Web Site: www.dclibrary.org. *Librn*, Patricia Sullivan; E-Mail: patsull@yahoo.com; Staff 8 (MLS 4, Non-MLS 4)
Library Holdings: Bk Vols 30,000
Special Collections: Adult Basic Education Coll; African-American Reference Coll
Friends of the Library Group
PALISADES, 49th & V Sts NW, 20007. SAN 336-9757. Tel: 202-282-3139. Web Site: www.dclibrary.org. *Librn*, Grace-Ellen McCrann
Library Holdings: Bk Vols 70,878
Friends of the Library Group
PARKLANDS-TURNER COMMUNITY, 1720 Alabama Ave SE, 20020. SAN 337-0178. Tel: 202-698-1103. *In Charge*, Rita Strange
Library Holdings: Bk Vols 18,080
Friends of the Library Group
PETWORTH, Georgia Ave & Upshur St NW, 20011. SAN 336-9781. Tel: 202-541-6300. Web Site: www.dclibrary.org. *Librn*, Anthony Porter
Library Holdings: Bk Vols 44,224
Friends of the Library Group
R L CHRISTIAN COMMUNITY, 1300 H St NW, 20002. SAN 336-951X. Tel: 202-724-8599. Web Site: www.dclibrary.org. *In Charge*, Larry Day
Library Holdings: Bk Vols 13,942; Bk Titles 6,500
Special Collections: Black Studies Coll; Career & College Guide Coll
SOUTHEAST, 403 Seventh St SE, 20003. SAN 336-9811. Tel: 202-698-3377. Web Site: www.dclibrary.org. *Librn*, Sheila Power
Library Holdings: Bk Vols 58,185
Special Collections: History of Eastern Market & Capital Hill Communities
Friends of the Library Group
SOUTHWEST, Wesley Pl & K St SW, 20024. SAN 336-9846. Tel: 202-724-4752. Web Site: www.dclibrary.org. *Librn*, Norberta Winborne
Library Holdings: Bk Vols 54,188
Friends of the Library Group
SURSUM CORDA (COMMUNITY LIBRARY), 135 New York Ave, 20001. SAN 336-9870. Tel: 202-724-4772. Web Site: www.dclibrary.org.
Library Holdings: Bk Vols 8,080
TAKOMA PARK, Fifth & Cedar Sts NW, 20001. SAN 336-9900. Tel: 202-576-7252. Web Site: www.dclibrary.org. *Librn*, Elizabeth Madero
Library Holdings: Bk Vols 43,094
Friends of the Library Group
TENLEY-FRIENDSHIP, 4450 Wisconsin Ave NW, 20016. SAN 336-9935. Tel: 202-282-3090. Web Site: www.dclibrary.org. *Librn*, Kathryn Ray
Library Holdings: Bk Vols 100,000
Friends of the Library Group
WASHINGTON HIGHLANDS, 115 Atlantic St SW, 20032. SAN 336-9994. Tel: 202-645-5880. Web Site: www.dclibrary.org. *Librn*, Maria Brooks
Library Holdings: Bk Vols 13,500
Friends of the Library Group
WATHA T DANIEL BRANCH, Eighth St & Rhode Island Ave NW, 20001. SAN 336-9579. Tel: 202-671-0212. Web Site: www.dclibrary.org. *Librn*, Mary Hernandez
Library Holdings: Bk Vols 60,262
Friends of the Library Group
WEST END, 24th & L Sts NW, 20037. SAN 337-0054. Tel: 202-724-8707. Web Site: www.dclibrary.org. *Librn*, Barbara Kubinski
Library Holdings: Bk Vols 60,633
Friends of the Library Group
WOODRIDGE (REGIONAL), Rhode Island Ave & 18th St NE, 20018. SAN 337-0089. Tel: 202-541-6226. Web Site: www.dclibrary.org.
Library Holdings: Bk Vols 52,386
Friends of the Library Group
Bookmobiles: 1

GL DISTRICT OF COLUMBIA SUPERIOR COURT JUDGES LIBRARY,* 500 Indiana Ave NW, Rm 5400, 20001-2131. SAN 302-6353. Tel: 202-879-1435. FAX: 202-393-5853. *Librn*, Letty A Limbach; Staff 2 (MLS 1, Non-MLS 1)
1997-1998 Mats Exp $200,000
Library Holdings: Bk Vols 25,000; Per Subs 60

R DOMINICAN COLLEGE LIBRARY,* 487 Michigan Ave NE, 20017-1584. SAN 302-752X. Tel: 202-529-5300. FAX: 202-636-4460. E-Mail: oplibrary@tidalwave.net. *Cat*, Clare Imholtz; Staff 3 (MLS 3)
Founded 1905. Enrl 30; Fac 14
Library Holdings: Bk Vols 70,000; Per Subs 401
Special Collections: Dissertations by Dominican Authors; Dominican History, Liturgy & Authors; St Thomas Aquinas
Partic in Washington Theological Consortium

L DORSEY & WHITNEY,* 1330 Connecticut Ave NW, Ste 200, 20036. SAN 377-4597. Tel: 202-452-6952. FAX: 202-857-0569. *Librn*, Elizabeth Simmons
Library Holdings: Bk Vols 3,000; Per Subs 30
Partic in Am Asn of Law Librs; Law Libr Soc of DC

L DOW, LOHNES & ALBERTSON, Law Library,* 1200 New Hampshire NW, 20036. SAN 325-643X. Tel: 202-776-2650. FAX: 202-776-2222. *In Charge*, Elinor Russell
Library Holdings: Bk Titles 15,000

L DYER ELLIS & JOSEPH LIBRARY,* 600 New Hampshire Ave NW, Ste 1000, 20037. SAN 377-1350. Tel: 202-944-3527. FAX: 202-944-3068. *Librn*, Adeen Postar; E-Mail: ajp@dejlaw.com
Library Holdings: Bk Vols 2,500; Per Subs 150
Subject Interests: Maritime law
Partic in AALL; Law Libr Soc of DC

S ECONOMIC POLICY INSTITUTE LIBRARY INFORMATION CENTER,* 1660 L St NW, Ste 1200, 20036. SAN 374-5481. Tel: 202-331-5516. FAX: 202-775-0819. E-Mail: library@epinet.org. *Librn*, Terrel D Hale; Staff 2 (MLS 1, Non-MLS 1)
Founded 1991
Library Holdings: Bk Titles 3,500; Per Subs 35
Restriction: By appointment only

S ECONOMIC STRATEGY INSTITUTE LIBRARY,* 1401 H St NW, Ste 750, 20005. SAN 375-1155. Tel: 202-289-1288. FAX: 202-289-1319. E-Mail: presto@econstrat.org. Web Site: www.econstrat.org. *Pres*, Clyde V Prestowitz, Jr; *Librn*, Cheryl Walker; *Mgr*, Lori Harman
Library Holdings: Bk Titles 300; Per Subs 180
Restriction: Open to public for reference only

S ECONOMICS RESEARCH ASSOCIATES LIBRARY,* 1101 Connecticut Ave NW Ste 750, 20036. SAN 377-1504. Tel: 202-496-9870. FAX: 202-496-9877. E-Mail: plp@dc.econres.com. *Pres*, Patrick L Phillips
Library Holdings: Bk Vols 500; Per Subs 100
Friends of the Library Group

S ECONOMISTS INCORPORATED LIBRARY,* 1200 New Hampshire Ave NW, Ste 400, 20036. SAN 376-3730. Tel: 202-223-4700. FAX: 202-296-7138. Web Site: www.ei.com. *Librn*, Zelda Schiffenbauer; E-Mail: schiffenbauer.z@ei.com; *Asst Librn*, Kimberly Moriarty; E-Mail: moriarty.k@ei.com; *Asst Librn*, Suzanne Routhier; E-Mail: routhier.s@ei.com; Staff 3 (MLS 3)
Founded 1981
Library Holdings: Bk Titles 4,836; Per Subs 180
Special Collections: Industrial Organization Coll, bks, per

S EDISON ELECTRIC INSTITUTE, Information Resources Center,* 701 Pennsylvania Ave NW, 4th flr, 20004-2696. SAN 302-640X. Tel: 202-508-5623. Interlibrary Loan Service Tel: 202-508-5604. FAX: 202-508-5794. *Dir*, Susan Farkas
Founded 1917
Library Holdings: Bk Vols 24,000; Per Subs 400
Subject Interests: Energy, Engineering, Environmental studies, Legislation
Special Collections: Edison Electric Institute Publications; Electrical World Directory of Electric Utilities (1912-present); Moody's Public Utility Manual (1928-present)
Publications: Bibliographies (irregular); Edison Electric Institute Library (irregular); EEI Library Highlights (bi-monthly); Periodicals in the EEI Library (annual); Recent Additions to the EEI Library (monthly); Recent EEI Publications & Reports (bi-monthly)
Partic in Capcon Library Network

L ELIAS, MATZ, TIERNAN & HERRICK LIBRARY,* 734 15th St NW, 11th flr, 20005. SAN 377-2284. Tel: 202-347-0300. FAX: 202-347-2172. Web Site: www.emth.com. *Librn*, Susan Hyps
Library Holdings: Bk Vols 1,000; Per Subs 150
Partic in DC Soc of Law Librs

S EMBASSY OF AUSTRALIA LIBRARY,* 1601 Massachusetts Ave NW, 20036. SAN 302-6426. Tel: 202-797-3126. FAX: 202-797-3155. E-Mail: library.washington@dfat.gov.au. Web Site: www.austemb.org/library. *Librn*, Sally Hand; Staff 2 (MLS 1, Non-MLS 1)
Founded 1969
Library Holdings: Bk Vols 6,000; Per Subs 250
Subject Interests: Australia, Travel
Database Vendor: OCLC - First Search
Partic in Capcon Library Network

S EMBASSY OF BELGIUM IN THE UNITED STATES LIBRARY,* 3330 Garfield St NW, 20008. SAN 375-7064. Tel: 202-333-6900. FAX: 202-333-3079. E-Mail: usa@belgium-emb.org. Web Site: www.belgium-emb.org. *Librn*, Marie-Elise Tanabe
Library Holdings: Bk Titles 500; Per Subs 10

S EMBASSY OF CANADA IN THE UNITED STATES, Information Center, 501 Pennsylvania Ave NW, 20001. SAN 302-6051. Tel: 202-682-7703. FAX: 202-682-7701. Web Site: www.canadianembassy.org. *Chief Librn*, Barbara Donohue
Founded 1947
Library Holdings: Bk Titles 20,000; Per Subs 2,000
Subject Interests: Economics, Government, History
Special Collections: Government Documents, Statistics Canada publications, Parliamentary Debates, Federal & Provincial statutes & regulations; treaties
Automation Activity & Vendor Info: (Acquisitions) Innovative Interfaces Inc.; (Serials) Innovative Interfaces Inc.
Open Mon-Thurs 10-4

S EMBASSY OF INDIA, Information Service Library,* 2107 Massachusetts Ave NW, 20008. SAN 325-6413. Tel: 202-939-7046. FAX: 202-462-7276. *Librn*, Sumitra Singh
Library Holdings: Bk Vols 7,000; Per Subs 144

S EMBASSY OF JAPAN, Japan Information & Culture Center Library, 1155 21st St NW, 20036. SAN 375-3689. Tel: 202-238-6900. FAX: 202-822-6524. E-Mail: eojjicc@erols.com. Web Site: www.embjapan.org/jicc.html. *Librn*, Susan Okamoto
Library Holdings: Bk Vols 4,000

S EMBASSY OF REPUBLIC OF ARMENIA LIBRARY, 2225 R St NW, 20008. SAN 377-1318. Tel: 202-319-1976. FAX: 202-319-2982. E-Mail: amembusadm@msn.com. Web Site: www.armeniaemb.org. *Librn*, Mihran Toumajan
Library Holdings: Bk Vols 300; Per Subs 25
Restriction: By appointment only

S EMBASSY OF SWEDEN LIBRARY,* 1501 M St NW, 20005-1702. SAN 372-7769. Tel: 202-467-2600. FAX: 202-467-2656. Web Site: www.swedenemb.org. *Librn*, Larilyn Andre; E-Mail: larilyn.andre@foreign.ministry.se
Publications: Monthly List of Acquisitions
Restriction: Staff use only

S EMBASSY OF THE REPUBLIC OF KOREA, Korean Cultural Service,* 2370 Massachusetts Ave NW, 20008. SAN 374-4639. Tel: 202-797-6343. FAX: 202-387-0413. E-Mail: korinfo@koreaemb.org. Web Site: korea.emb.org. *Librn*, Kit Miller
Founded 1993
Library Holdings: Bk Titles 3,000; Per Subs 30
Subject Interests: Literature
Special Collections: Korean Art & Culture, bks, film, reproductions, video; Korean Development, bks, papers
Publications: Korea Update Biweekly Newsletter
Special Services for the Deaf - Captioned film depository

G EMBASSY OF UKRAINE LIBRARY,* 3350 M St NW, 20007. SAN 376-0014. Tel: 202-333-0606. FAX: 202-333-0817. E-Mail: infolook@aol.com. *Librn*, Tatya Galaka
Library Holdings: Bk Titles 3,000

S EMBASSY OF ZIMBABWE LIBRARY,* 1608 New Hampshire Ave NW, 20009. SAN 370-2324. Tel: 202-332-7100. FAX: 202-483-9326. *In Charge*, Lloyd Sithole
Library Holdings: Bk Vols 500
Subject Interests: Econ, Government, Immigration laws, Tourism, Zimbabwe
Restriction: Not open to public

S EMPLOYEE BENEFIT RESEARCH INSTITUTE LIBRARY, 2121 K St NW, Ste 600, 20037-1896. SAN 371-1803. Tel: 202-775-6349. FAX: 202-775-6312. E-Mail: ebri_library@ebri.org. Web Site: www.ebri.org. *Coll Develop, Librn*, Jeanette B Hull; E-Mail: hull@ebri.org; Staff 2 (MLS 2)
Founded 1978
Library Holdings: Bk Vols 7,000; Per Subs 150
Subject Interests: Employee benefits, Health care, Pensions
Special Collections: Participant Education Materials (pension plans)
Restriction: Members only

S ENVIRONMENTAL LAW INSTITUTE LIBRARY,* 1616 P St NW, Ste 200, 20036. SAN 302-6442. Tel: 202-939-3242. FAX: 202-939-3868. Web Site: www.eli.org. *Librn*, Larry Ross
Founded 1971
Library Holdings: Bk Titles 9,000; Per Subs 350
Subject Interests: Environmental law
Special Collections: Wetlands
Automation Activity & Vendor Info: (Cataloging) Inmagic, Inc.

G ENVIRONMENTAL PROTECTION AGENCY, Info Resources Center,* 401 M St SW, Rm 2904, 3404, 20460. SAN 302-6450. Tel: 202-260-9152. Interlibrary Loan Service Tel: 202-260-5922. FAX: 202-260-5153. E-Mail: library-hq@epa.epa.gov. Web Site: www.epa.gov/natlibra/nqirc/index.html.; Staff 16 (MLS 12, Non-MLS 4)
Founded 1971
Library Holdings: Bk Titles 16,000; Per Subs 100
Special Collections: Hazardous Waste Coll; International
Partic in C15; Dialog Corporation; Medline; OCLC Online Computer Library Center, Inc

S ESPERANTIC STUDIES FOUNDATION LIBRARY, 3900 Northampton St NW, 20015-2951. SAN 326-2952. Tel: 202-362-3963. FAX: 202-363-6899. E-Mail: ejl@gwu.edu. Web Site: www.esperantic.org. *Librn*, E James Lieberman
Founded 1968
1998-1999 Mats Exp $500, Books $100, Per/Ser (Incl. Access Fees) $400
Library Holdings: Bk Titles 1,000
Special Collections: Esperantic & Related Interlinquistics Coll
Publications: bibliography (bi-annual); Esperantic Studies (newsletter); Esperanto & International Language Problems

S ETHICS & PUBLIC POLICY CENTER LIBRARY,* 1015 15th St NW, Ste 900, 20005. SAN 375-1236. Tel: 202-682-1200. FAX: 202-408-0632. E-Mail: ethics@eppc.org. Web Site: www.eppc.org. *Pres*, W Elliott Abrams
Library Holdings: Bk Vols 200; Per Subs 61
Restriction: Not open to public

S EUROPEAN UNION, Delegation of the European Commission Library, 2300 M St NW, 20037. SAN 302-6477. Tel: 202-862-9500, 202-862-9539. FAX: 202-429-1766. E-Mail: help@eurunion.org. Web Site: www.eurunion.org. *In Charge*, Barbara Sloan; Tel: 202-864-9542, E-Mail: barbara.sloan@delusw.cec.eu.int
Founded 1963
Library Holdings: Bk Titles 60,000; Per Subs 99
Subject Interests: European Union law
Special Collections: Community and European Union; European Atomic

Energy; European Coal and Steel Community Official Documents; European Community
Restriction: By appointment only
Function: For research purposes

G EXECUTIVE OFFICE OF THE PRESIDENT LIBRARIES,* New Exec Off Bldg, Rm G-007, 725 17th St NW, 20503. SAN 336-7266. Tel: 202-395-4690. FAX: 202-395-6137. *Dir*, Mary Ann Nowell; Staff 21 (MLS 15, Non-MLS 6)
Library Holdings: Bk Vols 65,000; Per Subs 830
Subject Interests: Economics, International trade, Presidents (US)
Special Collections: Congressional Appropriations Legislation Coll; Federal Budget Documents Coll; Legal Coll; Legislative Histories of Federal Government Reorganization Plans Coll; The Presidency
Automation Activity & Vendor Info: (Acquisitions) Innovative Interfaces Inc.; (Cataloging) Innovative Interfaces Inc.; (Circulation) Innovative Interfaces Inc.; (OPAC) Innovative Interfaces Inc.; (Serials) Innovative Interfaces Inc.
Database Vendor: Dialog, Lexis-Nexis
Partic in Fedlink; OCLC Online Computer Library Center, Inc
Branches:
GL EXECUTIVE OFFICE OF THE PRESIDENT LAW LIBRARY, Old Exec Off Bldg, Rm 528, 17th & Pennsylvania Ave NW, 20503. SAN 336-7282. Tel: 202-395-3397. FAX: 202-395-6125. *Librn*, Randall Snyder
Restriction: Not open to public
NEW EXECUTIVE OFFICE BUILDING LIBRARY, 725 17th St NW, Rm G-102, 20503. SAN 336-7320. Tel: 202-395-3654. FAX: 202-395-6137. *Librn*, Susan Hawthorne
Restriction: By appointment only
OLD EXECUTIVE OFFICE BUILDING LIBRARY, 17th & Pennsylvania Ave NW, Rm 308, 20503. SAN 336-7290. Tel: 202-395-7000. FAX: 202-456-6569. *Librn*, Martha Schiele
Restriction: Not open to public

S EXPORT-IMPORT BANK OF THE UNITED STATES, Ex-Im Bank Library & Archives, 811 Vermont Ave NW, Rm 966, 20571-0001. SAN 302-6485. Tel: 202-565-3980. FAX: 202-565-3985. E-Mail: research@exim.gov. Web Site: www.exim.gov/links.html. *Dir*, Eugene Hardin Ferguson; E-Mail: eugene.ferguson@exim.gov; *ILL*, Bang D Tran; *Ref*, Peggy Broly; Staff 5 (MLS 2, Non-MLS 3)
Founded 1946
Oct 1998-Sep 1999 Mats Exp $550,000, Books $110,000, Per/Ser (Incl. Access Fees) $120,000, AV Equip $5,000, Electronic Ref Mat (Incl. Access Fees) $315,000
Library Holdings: Bk Vols 25,000; Bk Titles 17,687; Per Subs 215
Subject Interests: Foreign law, International trade, Law
Special Collections: Congressional Materials, VF; Country Coll; Ex-Im Bank Archives; Export credit histories; Federal Financing Bank, VF; Law (General Counsel Coll); Leasing, VF; Legislative history from 1934; Merchant Banking, VF; OECD, Berne Union, PEFCO, IMF & World Bank documents
Automation Activity & Vendor Info: (Cataloging) CASPR; (OPAC) CASPR; (Serials) CASPR
Database Vendor: Lexis-Nexis
Publications: Daily Press Briefing; Monthly Acquisitions; Subject Guides

S FANNIE MAE, Research & Information Center,* 3900 Wisconsin Ave NW, 20016. SAN 377-1342. Tel: 202-752-7750. FAX: 202-752-6134. Web Site: www.fanniemae.com. *Dir*, Otto Schultz; E-Mail: otto-schultz@fanniemae.com; *Librn*, Irma Hunt
Library Holdings: Bk Vols 10,000; Per Subs 400
Partic in Am Libr Asn; Coun of Planning Librns; Spec Libr Asn

L FARR & TARANTO LIBRARY,* 1850 M St NW, Ste 1000, 20036. SAN 377-1156. Tel: 202-775-0184. FAX: 202-223-8679. *Librn*, Tammy Johnson
Library Holdings: Bk Vols 800; Per Subs 20
Partic in DC Soc of Law Librs

G FEDERAL BUREAU OF INVESTIGATION, Forensic Science Information Resource System,* 935 Pennsylvania Ave NW, Rm 3865, 20535-0001. SAN 372-6177. Tel: 202-324-4384. FAX: 202-324-4323. E-Mail: lab@fbi.gov. *Librn*, Colleen Wade; Staff 3 (MLS 1, Non-MLS 2)
Founded 1985
Library Holdings: Bk Titles 8,000; Per Subs 400
Special Collections: Forensic Sciences, bks, AV, fiche
Publications: Subject Bibliographies
Partic in Dialog Corporation; Fedlink; OCLC Online Computer Library Center, Inc

G FEDERAL BUREAU OF PRISONS LIBRARY, 500 First St NW 7th flr, 20534. SAN 302-6507. Tel: 202-307-3029. FAX: 202-307-5756. E-Mail: library@bop.gov. Web Site: www.bop.library.net. *Head of Libr*, Denise W Lomax; E-Mail: dlomax@bop.gov; *ILL*, Leonard B Broomfield; Tel: 202-307-2207, E-Mail: lbroomfield@bop.gov; Staff 4 (MLS 3, Non-MLS 1)
Founded 1960
Library Holdings: Bk Vols 5,000; Bk Titles 4,000; Per Subs 70
Subject Interests: Corrections, Criminal justice, Psychology, Sociology
Database Vendor: GaleNet, ProQuest, Wilson - Wilson Web
Publications: Periodical List
Function: Research library
Partic in Fedlink; OCLC Online Computer Library Center, Inc; World Criminal Justice Libr Network

G FEDERAL COMMUNICATIONS COMMISSION LIBRARY,* 20554. SAN 302-6515. Tel: 202-418-0450. FAX: 202-418-2805. *Dir*, Gloria Jean Thomas
Library Holdings: Bk Titles 32,000; Per Subs 432
Subject Interests: Computer science, Economics, Engineering, Law, Telecommunications
Special Collections: Legislative Histories: Communications Act of 1934 & subsequent Amendments
Publications: Acquisitions List; Periodicals Holdings List; Telecommunications Legal Research Manual
Partic in Fedlink

S FEDERAL DEPOSIT INSURANCE CORP LIBRARY,* 550 17th St NW, 20429. SAN 302-6523. Tel: 202-898-3631. FAX: 202-898-3984. *Chief Librn*, Diana Smith; *Coll Develop*, Ellin McNamara; Staff 9 (MLS 9)
Founded 1934
Library Holdings: Bk Vols 80,000; Per Subs 800
Subject Interests: Banks and banking, Economics, Law, Real estate
Special Collections: Bank Reports (State Bank Commissions Annual Reports); FDIC Archival Material
Publications: Information Bank, Bank Rating & Analytical Services
Restriction: By appointment only
Partic in Fedlink; OCLC Online Computer Library Center, Inc

G FEDERAL ELECTION COMMISSION, (Formerly National Clearinghouse Election Administration), Law Library, 999 E St NW, Rm 801, 20463. SAN 325-7975. Tel: 202-694-1600. FAX: 202-208-3579. *Dir*, Leta Holley
Library Holdings: Bk Vols 10,000; Per Subs 180
Partic in DC Soc of Law Librs

G FEDERAL EMERGENCY MANAGEMENT AGENCY LIBRARY,* 500 C St SW, Rm 123, 20472. SAN 328-0543. Tel: 202-646-3768. FAX: 202-646-4295. *Head of Libr*, Mercedes Lopez Emperado; Tel: 202-646-3771, E-Mail: mercedes.emperado@fema.gov; *ILL*, Arlett Hodges Leigh; Tel: 202-646-3769, E-Mail: arlett.leigh@fema.gov; Staff 2 (MLS 1, Non-MLS 1)
Founded 1980
Oct 1999-Sep 2000 Income Federal $250,000
Library Holdings: Bk Vols 100,000; Bk Titles 25,000; Per Subs 7,150
Special Collections: Emergency Preparedness Coll; Security Management Coll
Database Vendor: Dialog, Lexis-Nexis, OCLC - First Search
Publications: Quarterly accessions list
Function: Some telephone reference
Partic in Dialog Corporation; DROLS; Fedlink; OCLC Online Computer Library Center, Inc

G FEDERAL ENERGY REGULATORY COMMISSION LIBRARY,* 888 First St NE, Rm 95-01, 20426. SAN 326-4491. Tel: 202-208-2179. FAX: 202-501-2870. *Acq, Librn*, Robert F Kimberlin; *Circ, ILL*, Bonnie Dodson; *Tech Servs*, Irene Barlow
Library Holdings: Bk Titles 40,000; Per Subs 800
Subject Interests: Electric power, Natural gas
Special Collections: Federal Power Commission/FERC publications, Reports & case material
Partic in VA Tech Libr Syst

G FEDERAL HOUSING FINANCE BOARD, Research Library,* 1777 F St NW, 20006. SAN 377-1385. Tel: 202-408-2500. FAX: 202-408-2895. E-Mail: bakerel@fhfb.gov. *In Charge*, Elaine L Baker
Library Holdings: Bk Vols 500

G FEDERAL JUDICIAL CENTER, Information Services,* One Columbus Cir NE, 20002-8003. SAN 325-7991. Tel: 202-502-4153. FAX: 202-502-4077. Web Site: www.fjc.gov. *In Charge*, Roger N Karr
Oct 1996-Sep 1997 Mats Exp $59,000, Books $26,000, Per/Ser (Incl. Access Fees) $33,000
Library Holdings: Bk Vols 12,000; Per Subs 350
Partic in Fedlink; OCLC Online Computer Library Center, Inc

G FEDERAL MARITIME COMMISSION LIBRARY,* 800 N Capitol St NW, 20573. SAN 302-6531. Tel: 202-523-5762. FAX: 202-523-5738. *Librn*, David J Vespa
Founded 1961
Library Holdings: Bk Vols 11,300; Per Subs 88
Publications: Library Acquisitions List
Restriction: Open to public for reference only
Partic in Fedlink

G FEDERAL TRADE COMMISSION LIBRARY,* Sixth & Pennsylvania Ave NW, Rm 630, 20580. SAN 302-654X. Tel: 202-326-2395. FAX: 202-326-2732. *Dir*, Elaine Sullivan
Founded 1914
Library Holdings: Bk Vols 117,000; Per Subs 1,000

Subject Interests: Economics, Law
Special Collections: Archives; Legislative Histories
Publications: Bibliography series; Bulletin (monthly); Periodical holdings list

S FEDERATION OF AMERICAN SCIENTISTS LIBRARY,* 307 Massachusetts Ave NE, 20002. SAN 371-1412. Tel: 202-546-3300. FAX: 202-675-1010. E-Mail: fas@fas.org. *Mgr*, Karen Kelley
Library Holdings: Bk Vols 4,000; Per Subs 29
Restriction: By appointment only

S FEMINISTS FOR LIFE OF AMERICA,* 733 15th St NW, Ste 1100, 20005. SAN 373-4862. Tel: 202-737-3352. FAX: 202-737-0414. E-Mail: fems4life@aol.com. Web Site: www.feministsforlife.org. *Pres*, Serrin Foster
Library Holdings: Bk Vols 30; Per Subs 20
Subject Interests: Abortion, Feminism

L FINNEGAN, HENDERSON, FARABOW, GARRETT & DUNNER, Law Library,* 1300 I St NW, 20005-3315. SAN 370-1166. Tel: 202-408-4373. FAX: 202-408-4400. *Mgr*, Virginia A McNitt; E-Mail: mcnittv@finnegan.com; *Res*, Tina Kelley
Library Holdings: Bk Vols 11,600; Bk Titles 2,400
Subject Interests: Antitrust law

L FOLEY & LARDNER, Private Law Library,* 3000 K St NW, Ste 500, 20007. SAN 321-7639. Tel: 202-672-5315. FAX: 202-672-5399. *Dir Libr Serv*, Charles M Knuth; E-Mail: cknuth@foleylaw.com; *Ref*, Robin Evans; Staff 4 (MLS 2, Non-MLS 2)
Library Holdings: Bk Titles 10,000
Partic in Dialog Corporation; Westlaw

S FOLGER SHAKESPEARE LIBRARY,* 201 E Capitol St SE, 20003-1094. SAN 302-6558. Tel: 202-544-4600. FAX: 202-544-4623. Web Site: www.folger.edu. *Dir*, Werner Gundersheimer; *Librn*, Richard Kuhta; E-Mail: kuhta@folger.edu; *Ref*, Georgianna Ziegler; *Tech Servs*, Jim Kuhn; *Curator*, Rachel Doggett; *Curator*, Laetitia Yeandle; *Reader Servs*, Betsy Walsh; *Cat*, Deborah Leslie; *Acq*, Laura Cofield; *Curator*, Erin Blake; Staff 90 (MLS 43, Non-MLS 47)
Founded 1932
Jul 1999-Jun 2000 Mats Exp $395,000
Library Holdings: Bk Titles 250,000; Per Subs 200
Subject Interests: Drama, Early civilization, History, Literature, Renaissance, Theatre
Special Collections: Art, engravings, drawings, paintings, prints; English Renaissance (Short-Title Catalogue Coll), bks; Manuscripts, doc, letters, commonplace bks; Shakespeare, bks, playbills, art, promptbooks
Publications: Exhibition Catalogues; Folger Library Edition of the Complete Plays of William Shakespeare; Folger News; Shakespeare Quarterly
Partic in RLIN
Friends of the Library Group

S FOOD MARKETING INSTITUTE, Information Service, 655 15th St NW Ste 700, 20005. SAN 371-0300. Tel: 202-452-8444. FAX: 202-220-0875. E-Mail: fmi@fmi.org. Web Site: www.fmi.org. *In Charge*, Susan C Wilkinson; Staff 5 (MLS 3, Non-MLS 2)
Founded 1948
1998-1999 Mats Exp $140,603, Books $30,000, Per/Ser (Incl. Access Fees) $90,000, Presv $5,003, Micro $1,600, Electronic Ref Mat (Incl. Access Fees) $14,000
Library Holdings: Bk Vols 3,000; Per Subs 800
Database Vendor: Dialog, Lexis-Nexis

S FOOTWEAR INDUSTRIES OF AMERICA, INC LIBRARY,* 1420 K St NW, Ste 600, 20005. SAN 329-8531. Tel: 202-789-1420. FAX: 202-789-4058.
Library Holdings: Bk Titles 500; Per Subs 40
Restriction: By appointment only

L FOREIGN CLAIMS SETTLEMENT COMMISSION, Law Library,* 600 E St NW, 20579. SAN 302-6566. Tel: 202-616-6975. FAX: 202-616-6993.
Founded 1954
Library Holdings: Bk Vols 2,100

S FOREIGN SERVICES RESEARCH INSTITUTE, Whiteford Memorial Library, PO Box 6317, 20015-0317. SAN 322-6778. Tel: 202-362-1588. *Acq, Librn, Publ Servs*, Dorsey F Sheroan; *Dir*, John W Boyle; Staff 2 (MLS 1, Non-MLS 1)
Founded 1974
1999-2000 Mats Exp Books $525
Library Holdings: Bk Titles 2,760
Subject Interests: Analytical psychology, Cerebral functions analysis, Evolutionary biol, Inter-disciplinary, New Age philos, Quantum physics

S FOUNDATION CENTER, Washington Library,* 1001 Connecticut Ave NW, Ste 938, 20036. SAN 302-6582. Tel: 202-331-1400. FAX: 202-331-1739. Web Site: www.fdncenter.org. *Librn*, Janice Rosenberg; *Ref*, Caroline Herbert
Founded 1964
Library Holdings: Bk Vols 4,000; Per Subs 60
Subject Interests: Philanthropy
Special Collections: Foundation IRS Information Returns Coll, fiche; Foundation Published Reports
Publications: Newsletter
Friends of the Library Group

P FOUNDATION FOR PUBLIC AFFAIRS LIBRARY, 2033 K St NW Ste 700, 20006. SAN 325-8033. Tel: 202-872-1750. FAX: 202-835-8343. Web Site: www.pac.org. *Exec Dir*, Leslie Swift-Rosenzweig; *Res*, Tony Kramer
Library Holdings: Bk Titles 1,000; Per Subs 60
Subject Interests: Pub affairs
Publications: 1994-95 Compensation Survey of Public Affairs Positions (biennial survey); 1999-2000 Corporate Compensation Survey of Public Affairs Positions (biennial survey); 1999-2000 State of Corporate Public Affairs Survey; Creating a Digital Democracy

SR FOUNDING CHURCH OF SCIENTOLOGY, Library of Dianetics & Scientology,* 1701 20th St NW, 20009. SAN 302-6590. Tel: 202-797-9826. FAX: 202-797-9813.
Founded 1952
Library Holdings: Bk Vols 1,800

L FOX, BENNETT & TURNER LIBRARY,* 750 17th St NW, Ste 1100, 20006. SAN 377-2918. Tel: 202-778-2375. FAX: 202-778-2330.
Library Holdings: Bk Vols 9,500; Per Subs 150
Partic in Am Asn of Law Librs; DC Law Librs Asn

SR FRANCISCAN MONASTERY LIBRARY,* 1400 Quincy St NE, 20017. SAN 302-6604. Tel: 202-526-6800. FAX: 202-529-9889. *Librn*, Kevin Treston
Founded 1900

L FREEDMAN, LEVY, KRULL & SIMONDS LIBRARY,* 1050 Connecticut Ave NW, Ste 825, 20036. SAN 377-1490. Tel: 202-457-5129. FAX: 202-457-5151. Web Site: www.flks.com. *Librn*, Robin Sacher
Library Holdings: Bk Vols 4,000; Per Subs 100
Partic in DC Law Librs Soc

L FRIED, FRANK, HARRIS, SHRIVER & JACOBSON, Law Library,* 1001 Pennsylvania Ave NW Ste 900, 20004. Tel: 202-639-7102. FAX: 202-639-7008. E-Mail: sandfdi@ffhsj.com. *Dir*, G Diane Sandford; *ILL*, Arnicia Rice; Tel: 202-639-7105, E-Mail: ricear@ffhsj.com; *Ref*, Leigh Crowe Beatson; Tel: 202-639-7103, E-Mail: beatsle@ffhsj.com; *Tech Servs*, Jeffers John; Tel: 202-639-7106, E-Mail: jeffejo@ffhsj.com; Staff 6 (MLS 3, Non-MLS 3)
Mar 1999-Feb 2000 Income $460,000. Mats Exp $460,000, Books $275,000, Per/Ser (Incl. Access Fees) $90,000, Micro $1,000. Sal $250,000 (Prof $170,000)
Library Holdings: Bk Vols 25,000; Bk Titles 5,500; Per Subs 300
Automation Activity & Vendor Info: (Cataloging) epixtech, inc.; (Circulation) epixtech, inc.; (OPAC) epixtech, inc.
Database Vendor: Dialog, Lexis-Nexis, OCLC - First Search
Restriction: By appointment only
Partic in Dialog Corporation; Dow Jones News Retrieval; Dunslink; OCLC Online Computer Library Center, Inc; Westlaw

SR FRIENDS MEETING OF WASHINGTON LIBRARY,* 2111 Florida Ave NW, 20008. SAN 302-6612. Tel: 202-483-3310.
Founded 1934
Library Holdings: Bk Titles 5,000; Per Subs 10
Subject Interests: Quakers

L FULBRIGHT & JAWORSKI LLP LIBRARY, 801 Pennsylvania Ave NW, 20004-2604. SAN 371-8352. Tel: 202-662-0200, 202-662-4601. FAX: 202-662-4643. *Librn*, Judith M Weiss; E-Mail: jweiss@fulbright.com; *ILL*, Rebecca Furnia; Staff 3 (MLS 1, Non-MLS 2)
Library Holdings: Bk Vols 24,000; Per Subs 1,000

L GALLAND, KHARASCH, GREENBERG, FELLMAN & SWIRSKY, Law Library, 1054 31st St NW, 20007. SAN 373-6296. Tel: 202-342-5282. FAX: 202-342-5219. *Librn*, Janet G Baxter; E-Mail: jbaxter@gkglaw.com; Staff 1 (MLS 1)
Library Holdings: Bk Vols 6,000; Bk Titles 1,000; Per Subs 50
Database Vendor: Dialog, Lexis-Nexis
Partic in Dialog Corporation; Dow Jones News Retrieval; Pacer; Westlaw

C GALLAUDET UNIVERSITY LIBRARY,* 800 Florida Ave NE, 20002. SAN 302-6620. Tel: 202-651-5217. Interlibrary Loan Service Tel: 202-651-5684. TDD: 202-651-5216. FAX: 202-651-5213. E-Mail: lirary.reference@gallaudet.edu. Web Site: www.gallaudet.edu/~library. *Librn*, John M Day; *Coordr*, Susan Davis; *Cat, Coordr*, Linda Alexander; *Acq, Coordr*, Marilyn Estes; *Ref*, Laura Jacobi; *Coll Develop*, Theresa Chang; *Archivist*, Ulf Hedberg; *Ref*, Diane Gates; *Ref*, Jane Rutherford; *Ref*, Patrick Oberholtzer; *Ref*, Thomas R Harrington; *Ref*, Sarah Hamrick; *Coordr, Ser*, Ying Yu; Staff 22 (MLS 13, Non-MLS 9)
Founded 1876. Enrl 1,543; Fac 214; Highest Degree: Doctorate
Oct 1998-Sep 1999 Income $1,912,854. Mats Exp $283,324, Books $60,734, Per/Ser (Incl. Access Fees) $142,823, Presv $7,498, Micro $39,523, Other Print Mats $26,140, Manuscripts & Archives $1,613. Sal $1,471,914 (Prof $730,215)

Library Holdings: Bk Vols 230,529; Per Subs 1,646
Special Collections: Archival Materials; Deafness, Audiology & Hearing (Materials Relating to Deafness), bks, micro, flm, v-tapes
Partic in Fedlink; FLICC; OCLC Online Computer Library Center, Inc; Washington Research Library Consortium
Special Services for the Deaf - Books on deafness & sign language; Captioned media; High interest/low vocabulary books; Special interest periodicals; Staff with knowledge of sign language; TDD

L GARDNER, CARTON & DOUGLAS LIBRARY,* 1301 K St NW Ste 900E, 20005. SAN 371-7909. Tel: 202-408-7100, 202-408-7143. FAX: 202-289-1504. *Librn*, Michael L McDonald; E-Mail: mmcdonald@gcd.com; *Asst Librn*, Francesca O'Connor
Library Holdings: Bk Vols 4,000; Bk Titles 500; Per Subs 120
Subject Interests: Environmental law, Telecommunications law
Automation Activity & Vendor Info: (Cataloging) Inmagic, Inc.; (Serials) Inmagic, Inc.

S GENERAL FEDERATION OF WOMEN'S CLUBS, Women's History & Resource Center, 1734 N St NW, 20036-2990. SAN 371-8417. Tel: 202-347-3168. FAX: 202-835-0246. E-Mail: whrc@gfwc.org. Web Site: www.gfwc.org/whrc.htm. *Exec Dir*, Gabrielle Smith; Staff 2 (MLS 1, Non-MLS 1)
Founded 1984
Library Holdings: Bk Vols 1,050; Bk Titles 1,000
Special Collections: GH Coll on UN Decade for Women, bks, mss; Women's History & Volunteerism (General Federation of Women's Clubs Archives), doc
Publications: Annual Report
Partic in Capcon Library Network
Friends of the Library Group

G GENERAL SERVICES ADMINISTRATION LIBRARY,* 1800 F St NW, Rm 1033, 20405. SAN 302-6639. Tel: 202-501-0788. FAX: 202-501-4452. Web Site: www.gsa.gov. *Librn*, Helen T Bradley; E-Mail: helen.bradley@gsa.gov; *ILL, Online Servs*, Darwin Koester
Founded 1961
Library Holdings: Per Subs 375
Subject Interests: Architecture, Telecommunications
Special Collections: FAI Procurement Coll; GPO Depository; Karel Yasko Coll (historical docs on US public buildings); legislative History of Public Laws
Publications: Quarterly News
Partic in Dialog Corporation; Fedlink; Legislate; OCLC Online Computer Library Center, Inc; Westlaw
Friends of the Library Group

C GEORGE WASHINGTON UNIVERSITY, Melvin Gelman Library, 2130 H St NW, 20052. SAN 336-741X. Tel: 202-994-6455. Circulation Tel: 202-994-6840. Reference Tel: 202-994-6048. FAX: 202-463-6205. E-Mail: astewart@gwu.edu. Web Site: www.gwu.edu/gelman. *Librn*, Jack A Siggins; E-Mail: siggins@gwu.edu; *Asst Librn*, Andrea Stewart; E-Mail: astewart@gwu.edu; *Assoc Librn*, Caroline C Long; Tel: 202-994-1317, E-Mail: clong@gwu.edu; *Info Res*, David Nutty; Tel: 202-994-3582, E-Mail: nutty@gwu.edu; *Doc Delivery, Publ Servs*, Gale Etschmaier; Tel: 202-994-6924, Fax: 202-994-7548, E-Mail: gale@gwu.edu; *Media Spec*, Gerald Phillips; *Coll Develop*, Elizabeth Harter; Tel: 202-994-1356, E-Mail: iharter@gwu.edu; *Acq*, Marifran Bustion; Tel: 202-994-1321, E-Mail: marifran@gwu.edu; *Spec Coll*, Francine Henderson; Tel: 202-994-7549, E-Mail: francine@gwu.edu; *Circ*, Barbra Tschida; Tel: 202-994-1336, Fax: 202-994-2645, E-Mail: btschida@gwu.edu; *Info Tech*, Deborah Bezanson; Tel: 202-994-3582, E-Mail: bezanson@gwu.edu; *Cat*, Jean Pec; Tel: 202-994-8886, E-Mail: jpec@gwu.edu; *Info Tech*, Blaine D'Amico; Tel: 202-994-8278, E-Mail: damico@gwu.edu; *Business*, Crystal Belk; Tel: 202-994-6060, E-Mail: cbelk@gwu.edu; Staff 147 (MLS 35, Non-MLS 112)
Founded 1821. Enrl 19,356; Fac 1,373; Highest Degree: Doctorate
Jul 1999-Jun 2000 Income (Main and Other College/University Libraries) $8,993,075. Mats Exp $3,542,305, Books $549,333, Per/Ser (Incl. Access Fees) $2,067,584, Presv $50,644, Other Print Mats $925,388. Sal $4,403,364 (Prof $1,789,276)
Library Holdings: Bk Vols 1,559,643; Per Subs 8,478
Subject Interests: Art history, Asian studies, Business and management, Civil engineering, Education, European, Int affairs, Judaica (lit or hist of Jews), Political science, Public affairs, Slavic studies
Special Collections: American Association of University Professors; Dance Archives of the Greater Washington Region; Diplomacy & International Relations (Carnegie Endowment for International Peace); Economic, Social, Political & Cultural History of Washington DC including Archives of the Greater Washington Board of Trade; History of Printing & Typography; International Counter Culture Archives (1910-1950); Jewish Community Council of Greater Washington; Judaica (I Edward Kiev Coll); Lesbian & Gay History Archives; Local Public Transportation Papers; Other discipline-related collections, including Event Management & Marketing Archives; Papers of Chauncey Depew, Frederick Kuh & Samuel Shaffer; Private Papers of DC City Council Members; Rare Holy Land Maps Coll; The University Archives including University Presidential Papers, Board of Trustees Papers, Faculty & Alumni Papers, Oral History Tapes & Transcripts; Washington Theatre Club; Washington Writing Archive
Automation Activity & Vendor Info: (Acquisitions) Endeavor; (Cataloging) Endeavor; (Circulation) Endeavor; (OPAC) Endeavor; (Serials) Endeavor
Database Vendor: CARL, Dialog, GaleNet, Lexis-Nexis, OCLC - First Search, OVID Technologies, ProQuest, Silverplatter Information Inc.
Publications: CONNECT (newsletter); Friends of the Libraries (newsletter); The Renaissance Times (newsletter)
Restriction: Not open to public
Function: Document delivery services, ILL available, Photocopies available, Research fees apply
Partic in Asn of Research Libraries; Cap Area Libr Consortium; Chesapeake Info & Res Libr Alliance; Washington Research Library Consortium
Friends of the Library Group
Departmental Libraries:

C ECKLES LIBRARY, 2100 Foxhall Rd NW, 20007-1199. SAN 302-6973. Tel: 202-625-4588. Interlibrary Loan Service Tel: 202-625-4591. FAX: 202-337-0259.; Staff 5 (MLS 4, Non-MLS 1)
Founded 1875. Enrl 320; Fac 35; Highest Degree: Master
Library Holdings: Bk Vols 63,234
Subject Interests: Art, Art history, Interior design, Women's studies
Special Collections: Les Dames d'Escoffier Culinary Book Coll; Walter Beach Archives of the American Political Science Association
Partic in OCLC Online Computer Library Center, Inc; Washington Research Library Consortium

CL JACOB BURNS LAW LIBRARY, 716 20th St NW, 20052. SAN 336-7444. Tel: 202-994-6648, 202-994-7338. Interlibrary Loan Service Tel: 202-994-4156. Reference Tel: 202-994-6647. FAX: 202-994-2874. Web Site: www.law.gwu.edu/burns. *Dir*, Scott B Pagel; *Bibliogr, Rare Bks*, Jennie C Meade; *Publ Servs*, Michelle Wu; *Ref*, Leahy Germaine; *Tech Servs*, Virginia Bryant; *Adminr*, Lee Leslie
Founded 1865. Enrl 1,730; Fac 90; Highest Degree: Doctorate
Library Holdings: Bk Vols 542,674; Bk Titles 114,702; Per Subs 5,660
Publications: Guide to the Law Library

CM PAUL HIMMELFARB HEALTH SCIENCES LIBRARY, Medical Ctr, 2300 I St NW, 20037. SAN 336-7479. Tel: 202-994-2850. Interlibrary Loan Service Tel: 202-994-2860. FAX: 202-223-3691. E-Mail: library@gwumc.edu. Web Site: www.gwumc.edu/library. *Dir*, Anne Linton; *Coll Develop*, Susan Leister; Staff 14 (MLS 14)
Founded 1857. Enrl 1,000; Fac 400; Highest Degree: Doctorate
Library Holdings: Bk Titles 25,824; Per Subs 1,542
Special Collections: Interviews with George Washington University VIPs from 1930-50's
Automation Activity & Vendor Info: (Circulation) SIRSI; (Serials) SIRSI
Publications: Information Interface
Partic in National Network Of Libraries Of Medicine - South Central Region; OCLC Online Computer Library Center, Inc

VIRGINIA CAMPUS LIBRARY, 20101 Academic Way, Ashburn, 20147-2604. SAN 371-9642. Tel: 703-726-8230. FAX: 703-729-8237. E-Mail: virginia@gwu.edu. Web Site: www.gwvirginia.gwu.edu/library. *Coll Develop, Dir*, Douglas Carroll; E-Mail: dcarroll@gwu.edu; *Ref*, Gary D Price; E-Mail: gprice@gwu.edu; *Ref*, Laura T Kazmierczack; E-Mail: laurak@gwu.edu. Subject Specialists: *Bus admin*, Laura T Kazmierczack; *Computer science*, Gary D Price; *Engineering*, Gary D Price; *Internet*, Gary D Price; *Management*, Laura T Kazmierczack; *Organization*, Laura T Kazmierczack; Staff 10 (MLS 3, Non-MLS 7)
Founded 1991. Enrl 600
Jul 2000-Jun 2001 Mats Exp $68,750, Books $13,000, Per/Ser (Incl. Access Fees) $28,750, Micro $4,000, Other Print Mats $4,000, Manuscripts & Archives $2,000, Electronic Ref Mat (Incl. Access Fees) $17,000. Sal $223,146 (Prof $115,900)
Library Holdings: Bk Vols 2,150; Bk Titles 1,980; Per Subs 75
Subject Interests: Business and management, Computer science, Engineering, Organization
Automation Activity & Vendor Info: (Circulation) Endeavor
Database Vendor: Lexis-Nexis, OCLC - First Search, OVID Technologies, ProQuest
Partic in Washington Research Library Consortium

C GEORGETOWN UNIVERSITY, Joseph Mark Lauinger Library, 3700 O St NW, 20057-1174. SAN 336-7533. Tel: 202-687-7425. Interlibrary Loan Service Tel: 687-7428. FAX: 202-687-7501. Interlibrary Loan Service FAX: 202-687-1215. Web Site: www.library.georgetown.edu. *Asst Librn*, Teresa Liedtka; Tel: 202-687-6851, E-Mail: liedtkat@gunet.georgetown; *ILL*, Kathy Julien; E-Mail: julienk@gunet.georgetown.edu; *Media Spec*, Mark Cohen; Tel: 202-687-7610, E-Mail: cohenm@gunet.georgetown.edu; *Acq*, David Marshall; Tel: 202-687-7616, E-Mail: marshald@gunet.georgetown.edu; *Head Ref, Online Servs*, Pamela Noyes; Tel: 202-687-7595, E-Mail: noyespa@gunet.georgetown.edu; *Spec Coll*, George Barringer; Tel: 202-687-7475, E-Mail: barringg@gunet.georgetown.edu; *Bibliog Instr*, Sandra Hussey; Tel: 202-687-8689, E-Mail: husseys@gunet.georgetown.edu; *Publ Servs*, Mark Jacobs; Tel: 202-687-1085, E-Mail: jacobsm@gunet.georgetown.edu; *Syst Coordr*, Steven Jackson; Tel: 202-687-7540, E-Mail: jacksons@gunet.georgetown.edu; *Govt Doc*, Joan Cheverie; Tel: 202-687-1870, E-Mail: cheverij@gunet.georgetown.edu; *Science*, Gwen Owens; Tel: 202-687-5685, E-Mail: owensg@gunet.georgetown.edu; *Admin Assoc*, Phyllis Barrow; Tel: 202-687-7454, E-Mail: barrowp@gunet.georgetown.edu; Staff 96 (MLS 34, Non-MLS 62)
Founded 1789. Enrl 12,500; Fac 1,417; Highest Degree: Doctorate

Jul 1998-Jun 1999 Income (Main and Other College/University Libraries) $8,700,000. Mats Exp $2,908,171. Sal $3,933,219
Library Holdings: Bk Vols 1,695,187; Per Subs 13,357
Special Collections: Archives of Dag Hammarskjold College; Archives of Maryland Province, Society of Jesus; Archives of the American Political Science Association; Archives of Woodstock College; Catholic History; Diplomacy & Foreign Affairs; Political Science; United States-American & English Literature; University Archives; Woodstock Theological Library Coll
Automation Activity & Vendor Info: (Acquisitions) Innovative Interfaces Inc.; (Cataloging) Innovative Interfaces Inc.; (Circulation) Innovative Interfaces Inc.; (Course Reserve) Innovative Interfaces Inc.; (OPAC) Innovative Interfaces Inc.; (Serials) Innovative Interfaces Inc.
Publications: Faculty/Library Newsletter; Library Associates Newsletter; More Than Books; Special Collections at Georgetown, A Descriptive Catalog
Mem of Asn of Research Libraries
Partic in Capcon Library Network; Chesapeake Info & Res Libr Alliance; Dialog Corporation; OCLC Online Computer Library Center, Inc
Friends of the Library Group
Departmental Libraries:
BLOMMER SCIENCE LIBRARY, PO Box 571230, 20057-1230. Tel: 202-687-5651. Circulation Tel: 202-687-5687. *Head Librn*, Gwen Owens

CL EDWARD BENNETT WILLIAMS LAW LIBRARY, Georgetown University Law Ctr, 111 G St NW, 20001. SAN 336-7592. Tel: 202-662-9131. Interlibrary Loan Service Tel: 202-662-9152. FAX: 202-662-9168. Web Site: www.ll.georgetown.edu. *Librn*, Tracey Bridgman; *Librn*, Robert L Oakley; *Assoc Librn*, Margaret Fry; *Ref*, Meg Collins; *Ref*, Karen Summerhill; *Ref*, William Taylor; *Acq*, Craig Lelansky; *Acq*, Kristina Tryon; *Doc, Media Spec*, Gary Bravy; *Tech Servs*, Janice S Anderson; *Cat*, Yuan Yao; *Coll Develop*, Doug Lind; *Access Serv*, Barbara Des Rosier; *Automation Syst Coordr*, Jane Walsh; *Spec Coll*, Laura Bedard; *ILL, Ref*, Mabel Shaw; *Coll Develop*, Vivian Campbell; *Publ Servs*, Kris Knott. Subject Specialists: *International*, Marci Hoffman; *Preservation*, Hilary Seo; Staff 72 (MLS 22, Non-MLS 50)
Founded 1870. Enrl 2,590; Fac 85
Jul 1998-Jun 1999 Income $7,406,657. Mats Exp Presv $2,889,195. Sal $2,895,945 (Prof $1,324,628)
Library Holdings: Bk Vols 456,491; Bk Titles 157,955; Per Subs 12,441
Subject Interests: International law
Automation Activity & Vendor Info: (Acquisitions) Innovative Interfaces Inc.; (Cataloging) Innovative Interfaces Inc.; (Circulation) Innovative Interfaces Inc.; (Course Reserve) Innovative Interfaces Inc.; (ILL) Innovative Interfaces Inc.; (Media Booking) Innovative Interfaces Inc.; (OPAC) Innovative Interfaces Inc.; (Serials) Innovative Interfaces Inc.
Database Vendor: Lexis-Nexis, ProQuest
Publications: Guides, Headnotes, Research Register
Partic in OCLC Online Computer Library Center, Inc

CM JOHN VINTON DAHLGREN MEMORIAL LIBRARY, Medical Ctr, 3900 Reservoir Rd NW, GM7, 20007. SAN 336-7568. Tel: 202-687-1448. FAX: 202-687-1703. Web Site: www.dml.georgetown.edu/home. *Dir*, Jane Blumenthal; *Assoc Dir*, Terry Tobias; *Asst Dir*, Veronica Gornick; *Asst Dir*, Jeanne Larson; *Tech Servs*, Vani Murthy; *Ref*, Avril Cunningham-Stillion; *Ref*, Becky Fisher; *Ref*, Leah Pellegrino. Subject Specialists: *Education*, Veronica Gornick; Staff 10 (MLS 10)
Founded 1912
Library Holdings: Bk Vols 172,000; Per Subs 1,300
Publications: Library Guide; Log-In (newsletter)
Friends of the Library Group

NATIONAL CENTER FOR EDUCATION IN MATERNAL & CHILD HEALTH, 2000 15th St N Ste 701, Arlington, 22201-2617. SAN 371-7402. Tel: 703-524-7802. FAX: 703-524-9335. E-Mail: info@ncemch.org. Web Site: www.ncemch.org. *In Charge*, Olivia K Pickett; E-Mail: opickett@ncemch.org
Founded 1982
Library Holdings: Per Subs 235
Subject Interests: Child health, Nutrition, Public health
Special Collections: Final reports of projects funded by Maternal & Child Health Bureau; Maternal Health Reports of State Title V Collection

S GERMAN HISTORICAL INSTITUTE LIBRARY,* 1607 New Hampshire Ave NW, 20009. SAN 323-8350. Tel: 202-387-3355. FAX: 202-483-3430. Web Site: www.ghi-dc.org. *Librn*, Monika Hein; E-Mail: m.hein@ghi-dc.org
Founded 1987
Library Holdings: Bk Titles 22,000; Per Subs 230
Subject Interests: Germany, History
Open Mon-Fri 9-5

S THE GOLD INSTITUTE LIBRARY,* 1112 16th St NW Ste 240, 20036. SAN 377-1512. Tel: 202-835-0185. FAX: 202-835-0155. E-Mail: info@goldinstitute.org. Web Site: www.gold.institute.org. *Pres*, Paul Bateman
Library Holdings: Bk Vols 2,000; Per Subs 100

S GOVERNMENT EMPLOYEES INSURANCE CO (GEICO), GEICO Library-Learning Center,* GEICO Plaza, 20076. SAN 370-0275. Tel: 301-986-2754. *Tech Servs*, Karen Mannes
Founded 1978
Library Holdings: Bk Vols 3,195; Per Subs 131
Publications: Complete holding list for regional offices (annual); quarterly bulletins

GL GOVERNMENT PRINTING OFFICE, Office of General Counsel Law Library,* 732 N Capitol NW, Rm C-818, MS GC, 20401. SAN 377-2012. Tel: 202-512-0064. FAX: 202-512-0076. *Librn*, Suzanne Campbell
Library Holdings: Bk Vols 2,000

L GRAHAM & JAMES LIBRARY,* 2000 M St NW, Ste 700, 20036. SAN 377-2896. Tel: 202-833-0827. FAX: 202-463-0823.
Library Holdings: Bk Vols 5,000; Per Subs 20
Partic in Am Asn of Law Librs; Law Libr Soc of DC

S GRAY PANTHERS PROJECT FUND, National Gray Panthers Library, 733 15th St NW Ste 437, 20005. SAN 329-1391. Tel: 202-737-6637. Toll Free Tel: 800-280-5362. FAX: 202-737-1160. E-Mail: info@graypanthers.org. Web Site: www.graypanthers.org. *Exec Dir*, Tim Fuller
Founded 1974
Library Holdings: Bk Vols 30; Per Subs 150
Subject Interests: Affordable housing, Age discrimination, Health care
Special Collections: Gray Panthers & Maggie Kuhn, public relation clippings
The archives of the Gray Panthers & Maggie Kuhn are housed in the Presbyterian Historical Center, 425 Lombard St., Philadelphia, Pa, 215-627-1852; Archives also at Temple University, 215-204-8257

M GREATER SOUTHEAST COMMUNITY HOSPITAL, Lura Health Sciences Library, 1310 Southern Ave SE, 20032. SAN 325-8092. Tel: 202-574-6793. FAX: 202-574-5395. E-Mail: steveman@adams.patriot.net. *Librn*, Steven S Krompf
Library Holdings: Bk Vols 2,000; Per Subs 110
Subject Interests: Allied health, Medicine, Nursing
Partic in Medlars

S GREENPEACE USA INC LIBRARY, 702 H St NW, Ste 300, 20001. SAN 375-2089. Tel: 202-462-1177. FAX: 202-462-4507. Web Site: www.greenpeaceusa.org. *Dir*, John Passacantando
Library Holdings: Bk Vols 125

S HAITI-EMBASSY, Documentation & Archives,* 2311 Massachusetts Ave NW, 20008-2892. SAN 374-566X. Tel: 202-332-4090, Ext 17. FAX: 202-745-7215. E-Mail: embassy@haiti.org. Web Site: www.haiti.org/embassy. *Dir*, Louis Harold Joseph; Staff 2 (MLS 1, Non-MLS 1)
Library Holdings: Bk Vols 10; Bk Titles 50; Per Subs 4
Subject Interests: Education
Publications: Education System in Haiti

L HALE & DORR, Law Library,* 1455 Pennsylvania Ave NW, 20004-1008. SAN 373-613X. Tel: 202-942-8400, Ext 8341. FAX: 202-942-8484. *Librn*, Karen Hinson; E-Mail: karen.hinson@haledorr.com
Library Holdings: Bk Titles 990

L HALT - AN ORGANIZATION OF AMERICANS FOR LEGAL REFORM, Self-Help Law Library,* 1612 K St NW, Ste 510, 20006. SAN 377-4007. Tel: 202-887-8255. FAX: 202-887-9699. E-Mail: halt@halt.org. Web Site: www.halt.org.
Library Holdings: Bk Titles 1,000; Per Subs 5

G HEALTH & HUMAN SERVICES DEPARTMENT, Office of the General Counsel Library,* Cohen Bldg, G-400, 330 Independence Ave SW, 20201. SAN 377-399X. Tel: 202-619-0190. FAX: 202-619-3719. E-Mail: llibrary@os.dhhs.gov. *Librn*, Carl Reed Kessler; *Ref*, Daniel Beam
Oct 1998-Sep 1999 Income $500,000. Mats Exp $100,000, Books $10,000, Per/Ser (Incl. Access Fees) $90,000. Sal $140,000
Library Holdings: Bk Vols 25,000; Per Subs 190
Partic in Fedlink; Law Libr Soc of DC
Friends of the Library Group

S HILLWOOD MUSEUM, Art Research Library,* 4155 Linnean Ave NW, 20008. SAN 374-6011. Tel: 202-686-8500. FAX: 202-966-7846. E-Mail: hwdlibry@erols.com. Web Site: www.hillwoodmuseum.org/resources.html. *In Charge*, Kristen Regina; Staff 1 (MLS 1)
Founded 1973
Jan 1999-Dec 1999 Mats Exp $26,000, Books $20,000, Per/Ser (Incl. Access Fees) $6,000. Sal $29,000
Library Holdings: Bk Titles 7,500; Per Subs 47
Special Collections: French Decorative Arts; Imperial Russian Decorative Arts
Restriction: By appointment only

S HISTORICAL SOCIETY OF WASHINGTON, DC, Library of Washington History, 1307 New Hampshire Ave NW, 20036-1507. SAN 302-6175. Tel: 202-785-2068, Ext 111. FAX: 202-785-6605. E-Mail: hswlibrary@hswdc.org. Web Site: www.hswdc.org. *Dir*, Gail Redmann
Founded 1894
Library Holdings: Bk Vols 14,000
Subject Interests: District Of Columbia

Special Collections: James M Goode Manuscript & Photograph Coll; John Clagett Proctor Manuscript Coll; Machen Print Coll
Publications: Collection Guide
Open Wed-Sat 10-4

L HOGAN & HARTSON, Information Resource Center,* 555 13th St NW, Ste 10W-100, 20004-1109. SAN 302-6701. Tel: 202-637-8701. FAX: 202-637-5910. *Dir*, R Austin Doherty; Staff 19 (MLS 8, Non-MLS 11)
Founded 1968
Library Holdings: Bk Vols 110,000; Per Subs 820
Mem of Capcon

L HOLLAND & KNIGHT LAW LIBRARY,* 2100 Pennsylvania Ave NW Ste 300, 20037. SAN 370-7636. Tel: 202-457-7172. FAX: 202-955-5564. *Mgr*, C Cleverdon; Staff 3 (MLS 1, Non-MLS 2)
Library Holdings: Bk Vols 6,000; Bk Titles 1,350; Per Subs 90
Subject Interests: Aviation, Construction, Housing, Real estate, Securities, Telecommunications
Restriction: By appointment only
Partic in Capcon Library Network

L HOPKINS & SUTTER LIBRARY,* 888 16th St NW, Ste 700, 20006. SAN 325-4488. Tel: 202-835-8040. FAX: 202-835-8136. *Librn*, Patricia Schmidt
Library Holdings: Bk Vols 10,000; Bk Titles 5,000; Per Subs 75
Subject Interests: Law
Publications: Library News

S HOSPITALITY SALES & MARKETING ASSOCIATION INTERNATIONAL, Sales Research Library,* 1300 L St NW, Ste 1020, 20005. SAN 377-5186. Tel: 202-789-0089. FAX: 202-789-1725. Web Site: www.hsmai.org.
Library Holdings: Bk Titles 30

G HOUSE LIBRARY,* Cannon Bldg, B-106, Legislative Resource Ctr, 20515-6606. SAN 302-8100. Tel: 202-226-5200. FAX: 202-226-5204. *Librn, Mgr*, Lea J Uhre; Staff 2 (MLS 1, Non-MLS 1)
Founded 1792
Library Holdings: Bk Vols 100,000
Restriction: Open to public for reference only

C HOWARD UNIVERSITY LIBRARIES SYSTEM,* 500 Howard Pl NW, 20059. SAN 336-7657. Tel: 202-806-7234, 202-806-7926. FAX: 202-806-5903. Web Site: www.founders.howard.edu. *Dir*, Mohammed Mekkawi; E-Mail: mmekkawi@fac.howard.edu; *Info Res*, Dr Arthuree Wright; *Tech Servs*, James K Ho; *Coordr*, Clara Guyton; *Acq*, Bobby Player; *Per*, Audrey Thompson; *Cat*, Violet Lee
Founded 1867. Enrl 9,063; Highest Degree: Doctorate
Jul 1997-Jun 1998 Income $11,422,284. Mats Exp $4,801,554, Books $510,994, Per/Ser (Incl. Access Fees) $2,422,586. Sal $5,333,051
Library Holdings: Bk Vols 2,372,000; Per Subs 14,202
Subject Interests: Architecture, Health sciences, Humanities, Law, Social sciences and issues
Special Collections: Channing Pollock Theatre Coll
Automation Activity & Vendor Info: (Acquisitions) NOTIS; (Cataloging) NOTIS; (Serials) NOTIS
Partic in Capcon Library Network; Consortium of Univs of the Wash Metrop Area
Friends of the Library Group
Departmental Libraries:
ALLEN MERCER DANIEL LAW LIBRARY, 2900 Van Ness St, 20008. SAN 336-8106. Tel: 202-806-8045. FAX: 202-806-8400. Web Site: www.law.howard.edu/library/. *Actg Dir, Tech Servs*, Mary C Wilson; Tel: 202-806-8175, E-Mail: mwilson@law.howard.edu; *Ref*, Iris Lee; *Ref*, Valerie Railey; *ILL*, Felicia Ayanbiola; *Cat*, Mary Strouse; *Acq*, Kwei Hung; *Coll Develop*, Leah Chanin; *Publ Servs*, Helane Davis; *Res*, Stephanie Dyson; Staff 17 (MLS 9, Non-MLS 8)
Founded 1868. Enrl 450; Fac 36; Highest Degree: Doctorate
Jul 1998-Jun 1999 Income $1,977,303. Mats Exp $680,555, Books $53,130, Per/Ser (Incl. Access Fees) $627,425. Sal $971,310 (Prof $407,413)
Library Holdings: Bk Vols 286,649; Per Subs 1,541
Subject Interests: Civil rights, Constitutional law, International law
Automation Activity & Vendor Info: (Cataloging) Innovative Interfaces Inc.; (Circulation) Innovative Interfaces Inc.; (Course Reserve) Innovative Interfaces Inc.; (ILL) Innovative Interfaces Inc.; (OPAC) Innovative Interfaces Inc.; (Serials) Innovative Interfaces Inc.
Database Vendor: Lexis-Nexis
Partic in Capcon Library Network; Consortium Of South Eastern Law Libraries; OCLC Online Computer Library Center, Inc; Westlaw
ARCHITECTURE LIBRARY, 2366 Sixth St NW, 20059. SAN 336-7835. Tel: 202-806-7773. Web Site: www.founders.howard.edu. *Curator*, Alliah Humber; E-Mail: ahumber@howard.edu; Staff 3 (MLS 1, Non-MLS 2)
Library Holdings: Bk Vols 33,876; Per Subs 408
Subject Interests: Art and architecture, Historic preservation, Interior design
BUSINESS LIBRARY, 2600 Sixth St NW, 20059. SAN 336-786X. Tel: 202-806-1561. FAX: 202-797-6393. Web Site: www.founders.howard.edu. *Librn*, Lucille Smiley; E-Mail: lsmiley@bschool.howard.edu; Staff 5 (MLS 1, Non-MLS 4)
Library Holdings: Bk Vols 92,331; Per Subs 1,372
Subject Interests: Accounting, Finance, Housing, Marketing, Real estate
Special Collections: Microcard, fiche & microfilm Coll
DEPARTMENT OF AFRO-AMERICAN STUDIES RESOURCE CENTER, Founders Library, Rm 300, PO Box 746, 20059. SAN 336-8076. Tel: 202-806-7242, 202-806-7686. FAX: 202-986-0538. Web Site: www.founders.howard.edu. *Librn*, Ethelbert Miller; E-Mail: emiller@howard.edu
Founded 1969
Library Holdings: Bk Vols 32,000; Per Subs 20

CR DIVINITY LIBRARY, 1400 Shepherd St NE, 20017. SAN 336-7924. Tel: 202-806-0760. FAX: 202-806-0711. Web Site: www.founders.howard.edu. *Librn*, Carrie Hackney; E-Mail: chackney@howard.edu; Staff 3 (MLS 1, Non-MLS 2)
Highest Degree: Doctorate
Library Holdings: Bk Vols 114,746; Per Subs 240
Subject Interests: Biblical studies, Church history, World religion
Special Collections: Black Religious Coll
Partic in Washington Theological Consortium
Friends of the Library Group
FOUNDERS LIBRARY & UNDERGRADUATE LIBRARY, 500 Howard Pl NW, 20059. Tel: 202-806-7252. FAX: 202-806-5903. Web Site: www.founders.howard.edu. *Dir*, Mohammed Mekkawi; E-Mail: mmekkawi@fac.howard.edu; Staff 58 (MLS 14, Non-MLS 44)
Library Holdings: Bk Vols 1,172,753; Per Subs 6,994
Subject Interests: Humanities, Social sciences and issues
Special Collections: Channing Pollock Theatre Coll; micro card-, fiche- & film coll
Automation Activity & Vendor Info: (Acquisitions) NOTIS; (Cataloging) NOTIS; (Serials) NOTIS
Partic in Consortium of Univs of the Wash Metrop Area
Friends of the Library Group

CM HEALTH SCIENCES LIBRARY, 600 W St NW, 20059. SAN 336-7711. Tel: 202-806-6433. FAX: 202-806-4567. Web Site: www.founders.howard.edu. *Dir*, Sekum Boni-Awotwi; E-Mail: sboni-awotwi@howard.edu; *Coll Develop*, Bettifae E Fassler; Staff 17 (MLS 5, Non-MLS 12)
Founded 1927
Jul 1997-Jun 1998 Income $1,495,475. Mats Exp $845,988, Books $33,150. Sal $560,502
Library Holdings: Bk Vols 277,143; Per Subs 1,540
Special Collections: Biographical Files on Blacks in Medicine, Dentistry & Nursing; Local History (Howard University, Colleges of Medicine, Dentistry & Nursing)
Automation Activity & Vendor Info: (Acquisitions) NOTIS; (Cataloging) NOTIS; (Serials) NOTIS
Partic in Capcon Library Network; Consortium of Univs of the Wash Metrop Area; District Of Columbia Health Sciences Information Network; National Network of Libraries of Medicine - Southeastern Atlantic Region
MOORLAND-SPINGARN RESEARCH CENTER, 500 Howard Pl NW, 20059. SAN 336-8130. Tel: 202-806-7239. FAX: 202-806-6405. Web Site: www.founders.howard.edu. *Dir*, Dr Thomas C Battle; E-Mail: tbattle@howard.edu; *Archivist*, Dr Clifford L Muse; *Chief Librn*, Jean Currie-Church; *Curator*, Joellen El Bashir
Founded 1914
1998-1999 Income $1,048,518. Mats Exp $107,683. Sal $940,835
Library Holdings: Bk Vols 131,328; Per Subs 573
Subject Interests: Africa, Afro-American, Caribbean, South America
Special Collections: Africa; Afro-American & Afro-Latin Authors (Spingarn Coll); Arthur B Spingarn Music Coll, sheet music; Civil Rights (Ralph S Bunche Oral History Coll), tapes; Journalism (Documentary Series on the Black Press), tapes; Mary O'H Williamson Photograph Coll; Rose McClendon-Carl Van Vechten Photograph Coll
SOCIAL WORK LIBRARY, 601 Howard Pl NW, 20059. SAN 336-7959. Tel: 202-806-7316. Web Site: www.founders.howard.edu. *Librn*, Gary McMillan; E-Mail: gmcmillan@howard.edu; Staff 3 (MLS 1, Non-MLS 2)
Library Holdings: Bk Vols 45,785; Per Subs 344
Subject Interests: Criminal law and justice, Mental health, Social service (social work)
Partic in Consortium of Univs of the Wash Metrop Area

L HOWREY & SIMON, Law Library,* 1299 Pennsylvania Ave NW, 6th flr, 20004. SAN 302-6728. Tel: 202-783-0800. Interlibrary Loan Service Tel: 202-383-7149. FAX: 202-383-6827. *Dir*, Joan Marshman
Library Holdings: Bk Vols 60,000; Per Subs 1,500
Subject Interests: International trade, Patents, Trade

L HUGHES, HUBBARD & REED LIBRARY,* 1775 I St NW, Ste 600, 20006. SAN 375-0213. Tel: 202-721-4600. FAX: 202-721-4646. *Librn*, Tina Ramoy; E-Mail: tina@clark.net
Library Holdings: Bk Vols 5,000; Per Subs 15

S THE HUMANE SOCIETY OF THE UNITED STATES LIBRARY,* 2100 L St NW, 20037. SAN 376-1975. Tel: 202-452-1100. FAX: 202-258-3078. E-Mail: hsuslib@ix.netcom.com. Web Site: www.hsus.org. *Dir*, Sharon Geiger
Library Holdings: Bk Vols 3,000
Subject Interests: Zoology

S INSTITUTE FOR LOCAL SELF-RELIANCE LIBRARY,* 2425 18th St NW, 20009. SAN 325-8114. Tel: 202-232-4108. FAX: 202-332-0463. E-Mail: ilsr@igc.org. Web Site: www.ilsr.org. *In Charge*, Karen Szulgit
Library Holdings: Bk Vols 75; Per Subs 50
Subject Interests: Recycling
Restriction: Non-circulating to the public

S INSTITUTE OF INTERNATIONAL FINANCE LIBRARY,* 2000 Pennsylvania Ave NW Ste 8500, 20006. SAN 329-1634. Tel: 202-857-3642. FAX: 202-775-1430. *Librn*, Elaine Hatfield; E-Mail: ehatfield@iif.com
Library Holdings: Bk Titles 1,500; Per Subs 500
Restriction: Staff use only

S INSTITUTE OF TRANSPORTATION ENGINEERS LIBRARY,* 525 School St SW, Ste 410, 20024. SAN 377-4112. Tel: 202-554-8050. FAX: 202-863-5486. Web Site: www.ite.org. *Librn*, Laura Hazan
Library Holdings: Bk Titles 500

S INTELSAT LIBRARY, 3400 International Dr NW, 20008. SAN 371-4047. Tel: 202-944-6820. FAX: 202-944-7319. Web Site: www.intelsat.int. *Mgr*, Rosa Liu; E-Mail: rosa.liu@intelsat.int
Founded 1979
Library Holdings: Bk Vols 12,000; Per Subs 350
Special Collections: International Telecommunication Union Publication
Database Vendor: Dialog
Publications: Bibliography; journal holding list
Restriction: Not open to public, Staff use only
Partic in Interlibrary Users Association

C INTER-AMERICAN DEFENSE COLLEGE LIBRARY,* Fort McNair, Bldg 52, 20319-6100. SAN 302-6779. Tel: 202-646-1324, 202-646-1333. FAX: 202-685-6054. Web Site: www.jid.org. *Librn*, Helvecia Martell; Staff 1 (MLS 1)
Founded 1962. Enrl 60; Fac 22
Library Holdings: Bk Titles 25,000; Per Subs 207
Special Collections: Orgn Am States

S INTER-AMERICAN DEVELOPMENT BANK LIBRARY, Felipe Herrera Library, 1300 New York Ave NW, Stop W-0102, 20577. SAN 336-8165. Interlibrary Loan Service Tel: 202-623-3211. FAX: 202-623-3183. E-Mail: library@iadb.org. Web Site: www.iadb.org/lib. *Librn*, Benita Vassallo; Staff 12 (MLS 9, Non-MLS 3)
Founded 1960
Library Holdings: Bk Titles 100,000; Per Subs 1,500
Subject Interests: Caribbean, Economics, Latin America
Special Collections: International Documents Coll (UN, OECD, World Bank, FAO, etc); Latin American & Caribbean History, Literature
Restriction: Open to public for reference only
Partic in Capcon Library Network; OCLC Online Computer Library Center, Inc

G INTERNAL REVENUE SERVICE LIBRARY,* 1111 Constitution Ave NW, Rm 4324, 20224. SAN 302-6787. Tel: 202-622-8050. FAX: 202-622-5844. *Tech Servs*, Jill Klein; *Cat*, Susan N Cushing; *Ref*, Jule McCartney; *Ref*, Rosemary Coskey; Staff 20 (MLS 10, Non-MLS 10)
Founded 1917
Library Holdings: Bk Vols 105,000; Per Subs 800
Subject Interests: Business and management, Economics, Law
Publications: Bi-monthly Library Bulletin
Partic in Dialog Corporation; Dow Jones News Retrieval; Fedlink; OCLC Online Computer Library Center, Inc; Westlaw

S INTERNATIONAL BROTHERHOOD OF TEAMSTERS LIBRARY,* 25 Louisiana Ave NW, 20001. SAN 302-6795. Tel: 202-624-6927. FAX: 202-624-6910. *Librn*, Janet Wamsley
Library Holdings: Bk Vols 5,000; Bk Titles 4,000; Per Subs 200
Partic in Am Libr Asn; Spec Libr Asn

S INTERNATIONAL CATHOLIC STEWARDSHIP COUNCIL, INC LIBRARY, 1275 K St NW Ste 980, 20005. SAN 371-229X. Tel: 202-289-1093. FAX: 202-682-9018. E-Mail: ICSC@catholicstewardship.org. Web Site: www.catholicstewardship.org. *In Charge*, Matthew R Paratore
Library Holdings: Bk Vols 300

S INTERNATIONAL CENTER FOR RESEARCH ON WOMEN LIBRARY, 1717 Massachusetts Ave NW, Ste 302, 20036. SAN 326-2847. Tel: 202-797-0007. FAX: 202-797-0020. E-Mail: info@icrw.org. Web Site: www.icrw.org. *Librn*, Brij Mathur
Library Holdings: Bk Titles 15,000; Per Subs 60
Restriction: Open to others by appointment
Collection includes unpublished papers, works in progress, dissertations

S INTERNATIONAL CITY-COUNTY MANAGEMENT ASSOCIATION LIBRARY,* 777 N Capitol St NE Ste 500, 20002-4201. SAN 302-6809. Tel: 202-289-4262. FAX: 202-962-3500. Web Site: www.icma.org.
Library Holdings: Bk Vols 3,147; Per Subs 100

S INTERNATIONAL FINANCE CORPORATION LIBRARY,* 2121 Pennsylvania Ave, 20433. SAN 375-7838. Tel: 202-473-9533. FAX: 202-974-4345. E-Mail: ilibrary@ifc.org. Web Site: www.ifc.org/publicat/library/ifclib.htm. *Dir*, Susan Hunchar
Library Holdings: Bk Titles 4,500; Per Subs 800

S INTERNATIONAL FOOD POLICY RESEARCH INSTITUTE LIBRARY, (IFPRI), 2033 K St NW, 20006. SAN 302-6817. Tel: 202-862-5614. FAX: 202-467-4439. Web Site: www.ifpri.org. *Librn*, Luz Alvare; Staff 2 (MLS 2)
Founded 1975
Library Holdings: Bk Vols 7,000; Per Subs 160
Subject Interests: Developing countries, Environment, Food admin, International trade, Nutrition
Database Vendor: OCLC - First Search
Publications: New Acquisitions List

S INTERNATIONAL FRANCHISE ASSOCIATION, IFA World Resource Center,* 1350 New York Ave NW Ste 900, 20005. SAN 374-4795. Tel: 202-628-8000. FAX: 202-628-0812. E-Mail: ifa@franchise.org. Web Site: www.franchise.org. *Dir Info Resources & Res*, Marcel Postmann
Library Holdings: Bk Vols 100; Per Subs 50
Special Collections: Franchising, a-tapes, bks, v-tapes
Publications: Newsletter
Restriction: Non-circulating to the public

L INTERNATIONAL LAW STUDENTS ASSOCIATION, Information Center,* 2223 Massachusetts Ave NW, 20008-2864. SAN 373-3467. Tel: 202-939-6030, 202-939-6031. FAX: 202-265-0386. Web Site: www.kentlaw.edu/ilsa. *Exec Dir*, Elizabeth Atkins
Library Holdings: Bk Vols 115
Subject Interests: Education, International law

S INTERNATIONAL MUNICIPAL LAWYERS ASSOCIATION,* 1110 Vermont Ave NW, Ste 200, 20005. SAN 326-1980. Tel: 202-466-5424. FAX: 202-785-0152.
Special Collections: Municipal Ordinances

S INTERNATIONAL UNION OF OPERATING ENGINEERS, Research Department Library,* 1125 17th St NW, 20036. SAN 328-5170. Tel: 202-429-9100. FAX: 202-778-2691. *Dir*, Dave Treanor; *Res*, Mary Ellen Douglas
Library Holdings: Bk Titles 2,000

L IVINS, PHILIPS & BARKER LIBRARY, 1700 Pennsylvania Ave NW, 20006. SAN 377-4635. Tel: 202-393-7600. FAX: 202-347-4256. E-Mail: ipb@mindspring.com. *Librn*, Jeffrey Freilich
Library Holdings: Bk Vols 3,000; Per Subs 25
Partic in Am Asn of Law Librs; Law Libr Soc of DC

S JAPAN ECONOMIC INSTITUTE OF AMERICA LIBRARY, 1717 K St NW, Ste 211, 20036. (Mail add: c/o JEI Library, 1000 Connecticut Ave NW, Ste 211, 20036), Tel: 202-296-5633. FAX: 202-296-8333. E-Mail: jei@jei.org. Web Site: www.jei.org.; Staff 1 (Non-MLS 1)
Founded 1957
Library Holdings: Bk Titles 5,000
Subject Interests: Business, Economics, Japanese, Politics
Special Collections: Japanese Government Publications; Japanese Language Publications
Restriction: Open to public for reference only
Function: Research library

S JAPAN SOCIETY FOR THE PROMOTION OF SCIENCE LIBRARY,* 1800 K St NW, Ste 920, 20006. SAN 375-8303. Tel: 202-659-8190. FAX: 202-659-8199. E-Mail: webmaster@jsps.usa.org.
Library Holdings: Bk Titles 50
Special Collections: Japanese Journals

S JAPAN-AMERICAN SOCIETY OF WASHINGTON DC LIBRARY, 1020 19th St NW, Ste LL40, 20036. SAN 375-7773. Tel: 202-833-2210. FAX: 202-833-2456. E-Mail: jaswdc@intr.net. Web Site: www.us-japan.org/dc.
Library Holdings: Bk Vols 2,600; Bk Titles 2,500
Subject Interests: Japanese studies

C JOHNS HOPKINS UNIVERSITY SCHOOL OF ADVANCED INTERNATIONAL STUDIES, Sydney R & Elsa W Mason Library, 1740 Massachusetts Ave NW, 20036. SAN 302-6868. Tel: 202-663-5600, 202-663-5905. FAX: 202-663-5916. *Acq, Dir*, Peter J Promen; *ILL, Ref*, Linda Carlson; *Cat*, Jennifer Kusmik; Staff 5 (MLS 5)
Founded 1943. Enrl 430; Fac 60; Highest Degree: Doctorate
Library Holdings: Bk Vols 110,000; Per Subs 950
Partic in Dialog Corporation; OCLC Online Computer Library Center, Inc; PALINET & Union Library Catalogue of Pennsylvania

S JOINT BANK FUND LIBRARY,* 700 19th St NW, 20431. SAN 321-9062. Tel: 202-623-7054. FAX: 202-623-6128. E-Mail: jointlib@imf.org. Web Site: www.jolis.worldbank.imflib.org. *Chief Librn*, Barbara Perry; *Chief Librn*,

Sylvia Piggott; Staff 55 (MLS 24, Non-MLS 31)
Founded 1946
Library Holdings: Bk Titles 125,000; Per Subs 4,500
Subject Interests: Banking, Econ develop, Int econ, Int finance, Money
Special Collections: UN Documents Coll
Publications: A Basic Collection for Central Bank Libraries (1984); Blueprint: Bibliolist Updates in Print (monthly); Economics & Finance Indexes: Index to Periodical Articles, 1947-1971 (1972, 4 vol); First Supplement, 1972-1974; IntlEc: Index to International Economics, Development & Finance, 1981-1991; Second Supplement, 1975-1977; The Developing Areas, a Classified Bibliography of the Joint Bank-Fund Library (1975, 3 vol)
Restriction: Staff use only
Partic in Capcon Library Network; OCLC Online Computer Library Center, Inc
The Joint Library manages a network of 12 specialized libraries serving the sectoral & technical staff of the World Bank & the International Monetary Fund. Specialized Network subject interests represented include agriculture, cartography, construction, education, energy, environment & natural resources, health information technology, language services, law, personnel management, population, private sector finance & development, public finance, rural & urban development, transportation, & water supply; Open to the public: Thurs 10-4

S JOINT CENTER FOR POLITICAL & ECONOMICS STUDIES LIBRARY, 1090 Vermont Ave NW, Ste 1100, 20005. SAN 325-2647. Tel: 202-789-3500. FAX: 202-789-6390. Web Site: www.jointcenter.org.; Staff 3 (MLS 2, Non-MLS 1)
Founded 1979
Library Holdings: Bk Vols 6,500; Per Subs 230
Subject Interests: Black econ develop, Black politics, Black women, Blacks in the military, Civil rights, Voting rights
Special Collections: Black Politics Coll; Minority Issues Coll
Automation Activity & Vendor Info: (Cataloging) Inmagic, Inc.
Publications: Periodicals Table of Contents Bulletin
Partic in Dialog Corporation

L JONES, DAY, REAVIS & POGUE, Law Library, 51 Louisiana Ave NW, 20001-2113. SAN 372-3232. Tel: 202-879-3939. FAX: 202-626-1700. Web Site: www.jonesday.com. *Librn*, Harva L Sheeler; E-Mail: hsheeler@jonesday.com
Library Holdings: Bk Vols 45,000; Per Subs 300
Partic in OCLC Online Computer Library Center, Inc

L JORDAN, COYNE & SAVITS LLP, Law Library, 1100 Connecticut Ave NW, Ste 600, 20036. SAN 377-3329. Tel: 202-296-4747. E-Mail: jocs@idt.net. Web Site: www.jocs-law.com. *Librn*, Jennifer S Durkin
1998-1999 Income $50,000
Library Holdings: Bk Vols 6,000; Bk Titles 4,900; Per Subs 70
Partic in Am Asn of Law Librs; Law Libr Asn of DC

L KATTEN, MUCHIN & ZAVIS, Law Library,* E Lobby, 1025 Thomas Jefferson NW, Ste 700, 20007. SAN 372-3879. Tel: 202-625-3500. FAX: 202-298-7570. *Librn*, Lourie Russell
Library Holdings: Bk Vols 10,000
Subject Interests: Aviation, Energy
Partic in OCLC Online Computer Library Center, Inc

S HENRY J KAUFMAN & ASSOCIATES INFORMATION CENTER,* 2233 Wisconsin Ave NW, Ste 500, 20007. SAN 302-6876. Tel: 202-333-0700. FAX: 202-333-0671. E-Mail: hjka@pop.erols.com.
Library Holdings: Bk Vols 2,000; Per Subs 250
Subject Interests: Advertising

L KELLEY, DRYE & WARREN, (KDW-DC), Law Library, 1200 19th St NW, Ste 500, 20036. SAN 372-1086. Tel: 202-955-9601. FAX: 202-955-9792. Web Site: www.kelleydrye.com. *Dir Libr Serv*, Thomas B Pulver; E-Mail: tpulver@kelleydrye.com; Staff 2 (MLS 1, Non-MLS 1)
Founded 1853
Library Holdings: Bk Vols 10,000; Per Subs 100
Subject Interests: Corporate law, Real estate law
Partic in Capcon Library Network

L KILPATRICK & STOCKTON LIBRARY,* 700 13th St NW, Ste 800, 20005. SAN 323-8121. Tel: 202-508-5839. FAX: 202-508-5858. *Librn*, Kevin Morton
Library Holdings: Per Subs 100
Subject Interests: Law
Automation Activity & Vendor Info: (Cataloging) Inmagic, Inc.; (Serials) Inmagic, Inc.

L KING & SPALDING, Law Library,* 1730 Pennsylvania Ave NW, Ste 1000, 20006. SAN 320-4340. Tel: 202-737-0500. FAX: 202-626-3737.
Library Holdings: Bk Vols 10,000

L KIRKLAND & ELLIS LIBRARY,* 655 15th St NW, Ste 1200, 20005. SAN 302-6892. Tel: 202-879-5220. FAX: 202-879-5200. *Librn*, Ansley Calhoun; Staff 8 (MLS 5, Non-MLS 3)
Founded 1951
Library Holdings: Bk Vols 10,000; Bk Titles 6,500
Subject Interests: Law, Legislation
Publications: Washington Update (distributed in-house)

L KIRKPATRICK & LOCKHART, Law Library,* 1800 Massachusetts Ave NW 2nd flr, 20036-1800. SAN 371-0319. Tel: 202-778-9160. FAX: 202-778-9100. *Dir*, Patricia Keller; *Asst Dir*, Stacey Digan
Library Holdings: Bk Vols 10,000; Per Subs 300
Subject Interests: Securities

S KNIGHT RIDDER NEWSPAPERS, Washington Bureau Library, 700 National Press Bldg, 529 14th St NW, 20045. SAN 325-1616. Tel: 202-383-6032. FAX: 202-628-4175. Web Site: www.kri.com. *Librn*, Tish Wells; E-Mail: twells@krwashington.com
Founded 1977
Library Holdings: Bk Vols 1,027; Bk Titles 960; Per Subs 25
Subject Interests: Government, Polit

S KUTAK & ROCK LIBRARY,* 1101 Connecticut Ave NW Ste 1000, 20036. SAN 370-1476. Tel: 202-828-2497. FAX: 202-828-2488. Web Site: www.kutakrock.com. *In Charge*, Doris Nay; E-Mail: doris.nay@kutakrock.com
Library Holdings: Bk Vols 2,500; Per Subs 250
Special Collections: Security Exchange Commission (microfiche)
Restriction: By appointment only
Partic in Dialog Corporation; Westlaw

L LATHAM & WATKINS, Law Library, 1001 Pennsylvania Ave NW, Ste 1300, 20004. SAN 372-3224. Tel: 202-637-2200. FAX: 202-637-2201. Web Site: www.lw.com. *Librn*, J O Wallace; Staff 7 (MLS 5, Non-MLS 2)
Founded 1978
Library Holdings: Bk Vols 18,000; Per Subs 900
Database Vendor: Dialog, epixtech, inc., Lexis-Nexis
Restriction: By appointment only
Function: For research purposes

S LEAGUE OF ARAB STATES, Arab Information Center, 1100 17th St NW, Ste 602, 20036-3602. SAN 325-741X. Tel: 202-265-3210. FAX: 202-331-1525. E-Mail: arableague@aol.com. *In Charge*, Dr Hussein Hassouna
Library Holdings: Bk Vols 1,000; Per Subs 12

L LEBOEUF, LAMB, GREENE & MACRAE LIBRARY,* 1875 Connecticut Ave NW, No 1200, 20009. SAN 377-4953. Tel: 202-986-8225. FAX: 202-986-8102. *ILL*, Sue Anderson
Library Holdings: Bk Vols 14,000; Per Subs 400
Partic in Am Asn of Law Librs; Law Libr Soc of DC

L LEVENTHAL, SENTER & LERMAN LIBRARY,* 2000 K St NW, Ste 600, 20006. SAN 377-1482. Tel: 202-429-8970. FAX: 202-293-7783.
Library Holdings: Bk Vols 200; Per Subs 50

P LIBRARY OF CONGRESS, 101 Independence Ave at First St SE, 20540. SAN 336-8343. Tel: 202-707-5000. Interlibrary Loan Service Tel: 202-707-5444. FAX: 202-707-5844, 202-707-5986. Web Site: www.loc.gov. *Dir*, Dr James H Billington; *Librn*, Donald Scott; *Assoc Librn*, Diane Kresh; Fax: 202-707-6269; *Assoc Librn*, Winston Tabb; Tel: 202-707-6240, Fax: 202-707-6269; *Info Tech*, Judith Stork; *Cat*, Beacher Wiggins; Fax: 202-707-6269
Founded 1800
Oct 1999-Sep 2000 Income $417,457,611. Mats Exp $11,540,406. Sal $302,192,000
Library Holdings: Bk Vols 26,000,000
Special Collections: Gutenberg Bible; Manuscripts of Eminent Americans; Papers of the first 23 Presidents
Publications: Library of Congress Information Bulletin (biweekly); The Gazette (weekly staff newsp)
Partic in Asn of Research Libraries; OCLC Online Computer Library Center, Inc; Research Libraries Group, Inc
Special Services for the Deaf - Special interest periodicals; Staff with knowledge of sign language; TTY machine
Special Services for the Blind - Kurzweil Reading Machine
For further information, see such Library of Congress publications as the following: Annual Report of the Librarian of Congress; Calendar of Events in the Library of Congress; Catalog of Copyright Entries; Guide to the Library of Congress; Library of Congress Information Bulletin; Library of Congress Publications in Print (annual); National Register of Microform Masters; The National Union Catalog
Friends of the Library Group
Branches: 23
ACQUISITIONS *Dir*, Nancy A Davenport
AFRICAN & MIDDLE EASTERN DIVISION, Jefferson Bldg, Rm 220, 20540. SAN 336-870X. Tel: 202-707-7793. FAX: 202-252-3180. *Chief Librn*, Beverly A Gray
Special Collections: African - Most material relating to Sub-Saharan Africa dispersed by subject in the library's general collections; esp strong in Biblical subj, response lit & sociopolitical conditions in Israel; files maintained of pamphlets, unpubl res papers, current issues of major per & sample issues of works in African lang & lit; Hebraic - About 123,000 vols in Hebrew, Yiddish, Judeo-Arabic, Judeo-Persian, Ladino, Aramaic,

Syriac, Samaritan, Amharic & cognate langs; Near East - Over 125,000 vols in Arabic, Armenian, Persian, Turkish & related langs; spec subj strengths in theol, hist, polit & lit

AMERICAN FOLKLIFE CENTER, Thomas Jefferson Bldg, G08, 20540. SAN 336-8521. Tel: 202-707-6590. FAX: 202-707-2076. *Dir*, Alan Jabbour

Special Collections: California; Chicago, Illinois; Field Documentary Recordings Dating Back to 1890, cylinders, discs, wires & tapes; Field Projects in West Virginia; Folk Related Books & Periodicals, Dissertations, Field Notes, Tape Transcriptions, etc; Folk Song, Folk Music, Folk Tale, Oral History & Lore from the United States & Worldwide; Lowell, Massachusetts; Maine; Montana; Paradise Valley, Nevada; Pinelands, New Jersey; Rhode Island & Utah; South Georgia; The Blueridge Parkway & the Ethnic Heritage & Language Schools Project, field notes, negatives, photogs, sound rec & transparencies

AREA STUDIES COLLECTION *Dir*, Carolyn Brown

ASIAN DIVISION, Jefferson Bldg, Rm 150, 20540. SAN 336-8858. Tel: 202-707-5426. FAX: 202-707-1724. *Chief Librn*, Mya Thanda Poe

Special Collections: Chinese - More than 570,000 vols, especially strong in local histories, Ch'ing (1644-1911) Period materials & current People's Republic of China periodicals & local newspapers. Japanese - Over 716,000 vols, especially strong in economics, statistics, history, literature; some 16,000 government, learned society & university periodical titles, especially strong in science technology & social sciences. Korean - 95,000 vols, especially strong in social sciences & modern history. Southern Asia - 216,000 vols of literature from Pakistan to the Philippines, especially Bengali, Punjabi, Gujarati, Kashmiri, Marathi, Hindi, Tamil, Telugu, Malayalam, Oriya, Kannada, Urdu, Sindhi, Nepali, Assamese, Indonesian, Malaysian, Vietnamese, Thai, Burmese

Contains more than 1,598,181 volumes in Asian languages

CATALOGING Web Site: www.loc.gov/catdir. *Dir*, Beacher J E Wiggins; *Cat*, Judith Mansfield; *Cat*, Barbara B Tillett

CATALOGING DISTRIBUTION SERVICE Tel: 202-707-6120. FAX: 202-707-3959. *Chief Librn*, Peter Young

CATALOGING IN PUBLICATION DIVISION Tel: 202-707-9797. FAX: 202-707-9798. *Chief Librn*, John P Celli

Pop 58,066; Circ 174,876

Friends of the Library Group

GEOGRAPHY & MAP DIVISION, James Madison Memorial Bldg, LMB01, 20540. SAN 336-8629. Tel: 202-707-8530. FAX: 202-707-8531.

Special Collections: County Maps & Plans of Cities & Towns; Earliest Printed Editions of Ptolemy's Geography & Representative Volumes of Leading Atlas Publishers Over the Last Five Centuries; Hydrographic & Aeronautical Chart Colls; Maps from the 14th Century; Maps of the United States & the Separate States; Sanborn Fire Insurance Map Coll (dating back to 1866 for some 12,000 towns & cities in the United States & Canada); Special Subject Maps & Map Series of the World & Its Various Political Entities

Friends of the Library Group

INTEGRATED LIBRARY SYSTEM PROGRAM, 20540-4719. SAN 375-4103. Tel: 202-707-4760. FAX: 202-707-4719. *Dir*, Barbara B Tillett; *Mgr*, Lucinda E Leonard

MANUSCRIPT DIVISION, James Madison Memorial Bldg, Rms 101-102, 20540. SAN 336-8734. Tel: 202-707-5383. FAX: 202-707-6336. *Chief Librn*, James H Hutson

Special Collections: Harkness Coll (Mexican & Peruvian); Lincolniana (Herndon-Weik Coll); Papers of Henry H Arnold, Newton D Baker, Nathaniel P Banks, Clara Barton, Alexander Graham Bell, Albert J Beveridge, Nicholas Biddle, Gutzon Borglum, Huntington Cairns, Truman Capote, Andrew Carnegie, Caleb Cushing, Charlotte S Cushman, Jo Davidson, William O Douglas, Frederick Douglass, James A Farley, Peter Force, Felix Frankfurter, Benjamin Franklin, Daniel Chester French, Sigmund Freud, Arnold Gesell, Lillian Gish, Alexander Hamilton, John Hay, Benjamin W Huebsch, Henry Kissinger, Clare Boothe Luce, Archibald MacLeish, Thurgood Marshall, Margaret Mead, Edna St Vincent Millay, Ogden Mills, William (Billy) Mitchell, S F B Morse, Louise Chandler Moulton, Reinhold Niebuhr, J Robert Oppenheimer, George S Patton Jr, John J Pershing, Gifford Pinchot, Whitelaw Reid, Elihu Root, Carl Schurz, William T Sherman, Carl Spaatz, Arthur B Spingarn, Edwin M Stanton, Robert A Taft, Melvin Tolson, Joseph M Toner, Earl Warren, Booker T Washington, Daniel Webster, Caspar W Weinberger, Gideon Welles, James McNeill Whistler, William Allen White, Walt Whitman, Harvey W Wiley, Roy Wilkins, Owen Wister, Wilbur & Orville Wright; Records of the Virginia Company of London, the American Colonization Society, the League of Women Voters, American Council of Learned Societies, the National Association for the Advancement of Colored People, the National Urban League, Russian Orthodox-Greek Catholic Church in Alaska; Reproductions of Manuscripts in European Archives that Relate to American History

MICROFORM READING ROOM Tel: 202-707-5522. *In Charge*, Dennis Hawkes

Subject Interests: American Indians, Art, Biblical studies, Black people (ethnic), Economics, Genealogy, Government publications, Labor

Special Collections: Archives of the Japanese Ministry of Foreign Affairs & of Other Ministries (1868-1945); Declassified Documents; Early State Records; Human Relations Area Files; Index to Early American Periodicals; Modern Language Association Coll, reprod of mss & rare bks; Monographs & Serials from the Library's General Coll Copied for Preservation Purposes; Portuguese Pamphlets; POW/MIA Vietnam Era Documentation; Published Microform Coll; Records of the Subversive Activists Control Board, 1950-1972; Spanish Plays; Underground Newspapers; US City Directories, 1860-1935; World War II Combat Interviews

MOTION PICTURE, BROADCASTING & RECORDED SOUND Tel: 202-707-8572. FAX: 202-707-2371. *Chief Librn*, David Francis

Special Collections: Armed Forces Radio & Television Service Coll; Berliner Coll; Early Films Dating from 1894; Edison Laboratories Coll; emphasis on American films from 1912-1942); George Kleine Coll (1898-1926); German, Japanese & Italian Film (received through transfer from other government agencies); House of Representatives Debates; John Secrist Coll; Mary Pickford Coll (1909-1931); National Broadcasting Company Coll; OWI Coll; Paper Print Coll of Early Film (1894-1915), deposited for copyright, converted to projectable flm; Raymond Swing Coll; Retrospective Acquisition Program (in cooperation with the American Film Institute; Selected Films & Television Programs (1942-present); Theodore Roosevelt Memorial Association Coll; US Marine Corps Combat Records

MUSIC, James Madison Memorial Bldg, Rm 113, 20540. SAN 336-8823. Tel: 202-707-5507. FAX: 202-707-0621. *Chief Librn*, Jon W Newsom

Special Collections: Comprehensive Coll of Books in all Western Languages & Music; Dance (Gwen Verdon/Bob Fosse Coll); Dayton C Miller Flute Coll (more than 1600 instruments plus music & books); George Gershwin Coll; Gertrude Clarke Whittall Foundation; Includes Autograph Manuscripts & Letters of Bach, Barber, Bartok, Beethoven, Berg, Berlin, Bernstein, Bloch, Brahms, Britten, Carter, Copland, Cowell, Delibes, Gershwin, Harris, Haydn, Herbert, Hindemith, Korngold, Liszt, MacDowell, Mendelssohn, Mozart, Piston, Rachmaninoff, R Rogers, Romberg, Rubenstein, Schoenberg, Schubert, W Schuman, Schumann, Sousa, Stravinsky, Weber, Zemlinsky, & others; Leonard Bernstein Archives; Mollenhauer Archives in the Library of Congress; Rachmaninoff Archives; Schoenberg Coll; Separate & Distinct Manuscript Collections in the Field of Music of Great Value are Included in the Holdings of: Elizabeth Sprague Coolidge Foundation; Serbe Koussevitzky Music Foundation; Whittall Foundation Coll of Stradivari Instruments (3 violins, viola & cello); World's Largest Coll of Opera Full Scores, Piano-Vocal Scores & Librettos

Services - Coolidge, Kindler & Koussevitsky Foundations & the McKim Fund commission new works, thus forming the premier collection of modern holographs. These & other private sources sponsor chamber music concerts for the public; recordings of the concerts are distributed for radio broadcast. Reference services on all aspects & periods of Western music

NATIONAL LIBRARY SERVICE FOR THE BLIND & PHYSICALLY HANDICAPPED, 1291 Taylor St NW, 20542. SAN 336-8610. Tel: 202-707-5100. FAX: 202-707-0712. *Dir*, Frank Kurt Cylke

Library Holdings: Bk Vols 14,300,000

Special Services for the Blind - Books available with recordings; Braille & recorded books; Brailling & large print projects; Recordings of textbook material

NATIONAL SERVICES *Actg Dir*, Winston Tabb; *Cat*, Peter Young; *Dir*, Frank Kurt Cylke; *Dir, Publ Servs*, Ralph Eubanks

OPERATIONS *Dir*, Clifford Cohen; *Automation Syst Coordr*, Susan M Hayduchok

PRESERVATION *Actg Dir*, Diane Kresh

PRINTS & PHOTOGRAPHS DIVISION, James Madison Memorial Bldg, Rm LM339, 20540. SAN 336-8882. Tel: 202-707-6394 (Reading Rm). FAX: 202-707-6647. *Chief Librn*, Linda Ayres

Special Collections: 19th century American historical & popular prints especially from Currier & Ives; American, French & British Satirical Prints from the 18th & 19th Centuries; among the 80,000 American & Foreign Posters are the Art Nouveau Posters, German Posters from 1914-1945, the Yander Coll of Political Propaganda Posters, 1965-1989 & Fine Arts Posters from the 1860's to the present; Architectural Colls include the Historic American Buildings Survey; Captured World War II Photographs of the Third Reich; Carnegie Survey of the Architecture of the South, & original documentary drawings & photographs. Outstanding graphic art collections include fine prints from the 15th century to the present, especially chiaroscuro woodcuts, extensive holdings of the graphic art of Joseph Pennell & James McNeil Whistler, American fine prints from 1900 to the 1980s & contemporary graphics from Eastern Europe; Civil War drawings by Edwin Forbes, A R Waud & others; Civil War, Portraits, The American Scene (Mathew S Brady & the Brady-Handy Coll); Daguerreotypes; Detroit Publishing Company Archive of Views, Events & Americana, 1898-1914; Erwin Evans Smith Coll of the American Cowboy; Geographic Coll; George Grantham Bain Coll of News Photographs, 1898-1926; Herbert E French Coll, 1910-1935, news photogs; Historic Native American, US News & World Report News Photo Coll; Matson Coll of the Near East, 1898-1946; Photographic Survey of America by Farm Security Administration & the Office of War Information, 1935-1945; Pictorial Archives of Early American Architecture; Professional & Personal Coll of Alexander Graham Bell & His Family; the Cabinet of American Illustration; the Caroline & Erwin Swann Coll of Caricature & Cartoon; The Historic American Engineering Record; The Seagram County Courthouse Archives; Toni Frissell Coll of Personalities, Fashion & World War II; Uriah Hunt Painter Coll of Early Kodak snapshots;

Washingtoniana; Work of such noted photographers as Roger Fenton, Arnold Genthe, Frances Benjamin Johnston, F Holland Day, the Photo-Secessionist group & Lewis Hine

PUBLIC SERVICE COLLECTIONS *Dir*, Diane Kresh; *Ch Servs*, Sybille Jagusch; *Chief Librn*, Stephen James; *Chief Librn, Rare Bks, Spec Coll*, Mark G Dimunation; *Chief Librn, Govt Doc, Ser*, Karen Renninger

RARE BOOK & SPECIAL COLLECTIONS DIVISION, Thomas Jefferson Bldg, Deck B, 20540. SAN 336-8912. Tel: 202-707-5434. FAX: 202-707-4142. *Chief Librn*, Mark G Dimunation

Special Collections: Aeronautics & Ballooning; American Imprints, 1640-1800; Americana (Marian S Carson Coll); Americana Almanacs, 1646-1900; Americana Extremism; Anarchism; Bacon-Shakespeare Controversy & Cryptography (George Fabyan Coll); Benjamin Franklin, books by, about, printed by & part of personal library; Bibles; Books designed by Bruce Rogers; Books from Peter Force's Library; Bound Pamphlets Coll (including Colls formed in the 18th & 19th centuries by Ebenezer Hazard, William Duane, Jacob Bailey Moore, Oliver Wolcott & Israel Thorndike); Broadsides, 15th century to present; Bulgarian Renaissance Imprints; Children's Books (including Frank Hogan Coll); Colls of the Printed Output of Individual Publishers, some received as archival sets from the publishers (Armed Forces Editions, Big Little Books, Bollingen Coll, Franklin Book Program, Little Blue Books, Stone & Kimball, Dell Paperbacks); Confederate States of America Coll, 1860-65; Copyright Records, 1790-1870; Copyright Title-Pages; Daniel Murray Coll of Pamphlets by Negro Authors; Dime Novels, 1860-1910; Documents of the First 14 Congresses; Don Quixote (Leonard Kebler Coll); Early American Architecture; Early English Plays (Francis Longe Coll); Early Printing, 1501-1520; English Printing, 1478-1640; Frederic W Goudy's Library; Gastronomy & Cookery (Kathleen Golden Bitting & Elizabeth Pennell Colls); Genealogical Manuscripts of Charles Edward Banks; Hans & Hanni Kraus Sir Francis Drake Coll; Harrison Elliott Coll of Paperiana; Hawaiian Coll; Henry James Coll; Hunting Library of Theodore Roosevelt; Jean Hersholt Colls of Hans Christian Andersen, Sinclair Lewis & Hugh Walpole; John Boyd Thacher Coll (incunabula, discovery of the Americas, history of the French Revolution, autographs of European notables); John Davis Batchelder Coll of First Editions & Association Copies; Joseph Meredith Toner Coll of Medicine & 19th Century Local History; Justice Oliver Wendell Holmes' Library; Lessing J Rosenwald Coll of Incunabula, Illustrated Books & Rare Books; Lincolniana (Alfred Whital Stern Coll); Magic & the Occult (Harry Houdini & McManus-Young Colls); Manuscript Plays received as Copyright Deposits; Martin Luther Coll; Medieval & Renaissance Manuscripts; Miniature Books; Otto H Vollbehr Coll of Incunabula & 16th-18th Century Continental Title Pages & Printers' Marks; Personal Library of Henry Harrisse; Playbills; Private Press Books; Reformation Coll; Rudyard Kipling (Admiral Lloyd H Chandler, William M Carpenter & H Dunscombe Colt Colls); Russian Imperial Coll; Shakers; Sigmund Freud Coll, including books from Freud's library; Spanish-American Imprints, 1543-1820; Third Reich Coll; Thomas Jefferson's Library; Wagner-Camp Coll; Walt Whitman (Carolyn Wells Houghton, Charles Feinberg & Thomas B Harned Colls); Woman Suffrage (Susan B Anthony's Library, Carrie Chapman Catt & National American Woman Suffrage Association Coll); Woodrow Wilson's Library; Yudin Collection of Early Russian Books

SCIENCE & TECHNOLOGY DIVISION, Sci Reading Rm, John Adams Bldg, 5th flr, 20540. SAN 374-4329. Tel: 202-707-5522. FAX: 202-707-1925. *Chief Librn*, William J Sittig

Library Holdings: Bk Vols 4,000,000

Special Collections: American National Standards; British, Chinese, French, German & Japanese Colls; OSRD Reports on World War II Research & Development (Department of Energy, Department of Defense, National Aeronautics & Space Administration & National Technical Information Service)

Reference service is provided & reports are available for consultation & copying in the Science & Technology Division Reading Room. Subject access is provided through the various indexing media issued by the report origination agencies & in some instances through in-house finding aids

SERIALS & GOVERNMENT PUBLICATIONS DIVISION, James Madison Memorial Bldg, Rm LM-133, 20540. SAN 336-8947. Tel: 202-707-5522. FAX: 202-707-6128. *Chief Librn*, Karen Renninger

Library Holdings: Per Subs 70,000

Special Collections: Early American Newspapers (1704-1820), microprint cards; National Foreign Government Serials; United States Government Serials (federal, state, county & municipal)

A LIBRARY OF THE NATIONAL GUARD,* One Massachusetts Ave NW, 20001. SAN 326-1786. Tel: 202-789-0031. FAX: 202-682-9358.

Library Holdings: Bk Vols 32,000; Bk Titles 30,000; Per Subs 75

Special Collections: Aircraft, photogs; NGAUS; State Histories, bks, correspondence, clippings

L MANATT, PHELPS & PHILLIPS, Law Library,* 1501 M St NW, Ste 700, 20005-7702. SAN 377-287X. Tel: 202-463-4318. FAX: 202-463-4394. *Librn*, Margo M Gustely; E-Mail: mgustely@manatt.com

Library Holdings: Bk Vols 7,000; Per Subs 250

Partic in Am Asn of Law Librs; Law Librs of DC; Spec Libr Asn

SR MARIST COLLEGE LIBRARY,* 815 Varnum St NE, 20017-2199. SAN 302-6922. Tel: 202-529-2821. FAX: 202-635-4627. *Dir*, Edwin Keel; *Librn*, Paul Osmanski

Founded 1898. Enrl 15; Fac 4

Library Holdings: Bk Titles 8,000; Per Subs 30

Special Collections: Philosophy & Theology Coll

Restriction: Not open to public

S MATHEMATICA POLICY RESEARCH, INC LIBRARY, 600 Maryland Ave SW Ste 550, 20024. SAN 377-1210. Tel: 202-484-4692. FAX: 202-863-1763. Web Site: www.mathematica-mpr.com. *Librn*, Sally Henderson; E-Mail: shenderson@mathematica-mpr.com; Staff 2 (MLS 1, Non-MLS 1)

Library Holdings: Bk Vols 7,500; Per Subs 300

Subject Interests: Health sciences, Social sciences

Restriction: Open to others by appointment, Staff use only

S MAYER, BROWN & PLATT LIBRARY,* 1909 K Street NW Ste 1200, 20006. SAN 329-8868. Tel: 202-263-3000. FAX: 202-263-3300. *Librn*, Barbara Fisher; E-Mail: bjfisher@mayerbrown.com

Library Holdings: Bk Vols 10,000

Partic in Legislate; Westlaw

S MCI WORLDCOM, Network MCI Library, 1133 19th St NW, 20036. SAN 328-5472. Tel: 202-736-6009, 202-887-3000. FAX: 202-736-6176. Web Site: www.mciworldcom.com.; Staff 24 (MLS 18, Non-MLS 6)

Library Holdings: Bk Vols 10,000; Per Subs 1,000

Subject Interests: Technology, Telecommunications

Restriction: Not open to public

Partic in ASIS; OCLC Online Computer Library Center, Inc; Spec Libr Asn

L MCKENNA & CUNEO, Law Library, 1900 K St NW, 20006. SAN 372-137X. Tel: 202-496-7579. FAX: 202-496-7756. *Dir, Librn*, Kate Martin; *Ref*, Lois Steinberg

Library Holdings: Bk Vols 20,000; Per Subs 210

Subject Interests: Environmental law, International law

Partic in OCLC Online Computer Library Center, Inc

S MCKINSEY & CO, INC, Research & Information Service, 600 14th St NW, 20004. SAN 302-6906. Tel: 202-662-3100. FAX: 202-662-3202. *In Charge*, Ann Robertson; E-Mail: ann_robertson@mckinsey.com; Staff 9 (MLS 7, Non-MLS 2)

Library Holdings: Bk Vols 4,000; Per Subs 250

R METROPOLITAN MEMORIAL UNITED METHODIST CHURCH LIBRARY,* 3401 Nebraska Ave NW, 20016. SAN 302-6930. Tel: 202-363-4900. FAX: 202-686-2056. *Librn*, Alma Stewart

Jul 1996-Jun 1997 Income $1,000. Mats Exp $1,000, Books $930, Per/Ser (Incl. Access Fees) $50

Library Holdings: Bk Vols 3,850

S METROPOLITAN WASHINGTON COUNCIL OF GOVERNMENTS, Information Center, 777 N Capitol St NE Ste 300, 20002-4239. SAN 336-9005. Tel: 202-962-3256. FAX: 202-962-3308. E-Mail: infocntr@mwcog.org. Web Site: www.mwcog.org/. *Mgr*, Denise Pinchback; *Info Specialist*, Gloria Knight

Founded 1957

Library Holdings: Bk Vols 10,000; Per Subs 124

Subject Interests: Air pollution, Census, Housing, Maps, Planning, Transportation, Water pollution

Special Collections: 1990 Census Co State Data Center; Selected Local Documents of Counties & Cities Within Washington Region

Special Services for the Deaf - TTY machine

Open Mon-Fri 1-5

S MIDDLE EAST INSTITUTE, George Camp Keiser Library, 1761 N St NW, 20036. SAN 302-6949. Tel: 202-785-0183. FAX: 202-331-8861. E-Mail: library@mideasti.org. Web Site: www.mideasti.org/library. *Librn*, Ruth Van Laningham

Founded 1946

Library Holdings: Bk Vols 23,000; Per Subs 300

Subject Interests: Art, Islam

Special Collections: 18th & 19th Century travel accounts of the Middle East; Arabic, Persian & Turkish Coll

Partic in OCLC Online Computer Library Center, Inc

L MIGRANT LEGAL ACTION PROGRAM LIBRARY,* PO Box 53308, 20009. SAN 373-0980. Tel: 202-462-7744. E-Mail: hn1645@handsnet.org. *Dir*, Roger C Rosenthal

Library Holdings: Bk Vols 500

L MILBANK, TWEED, HADLEY & MCCLOY LIBRARY LLP, 1825 I St NW Ste 1100, 20006. SAN 374-5511. Tel: 202-835-7578. FAX: 202-835-7586. Web Site: www.milbank.com/library/library.html. *Librn*, Gabriele C Zsebi; E-Mail: gzsebi@milbank.com; Staff 1 (MLS 1)

Library Holdings: Bk Vols 20,000

Subject Interests: Law

Restriction: Staff use only

L MILLER & CHEVALIER, Law Library,* 655 15th St NW, 20005. SAN 372-1361. Tel: 202-626-6094. FAX: 202-628-0858. *Librn*, Carol Gruenburg; E-Mail: cgruenburg@milchev.com; *Asst Librn*, Karen Polk
Library Holdings: Per Subs 350
Partic in Capcon Library Network

L MORGAN, LEWIS & BOCKIUS LLP, Law Library, 1800 M St NW, 20036. SAN 302-6957. Tel: 202-467-7131. Interlibrary Loan Service Tel: 202-467-7136. FAX: 202-467-7522. Web Site: www.mlb.com. *Librn*, Barbara Folensbee; *Librn*, Martha Klein; Tel: 202-467-7372, E-Mail: mfklein@mlb.com; *Librn*, Susan Quillian; Staff 11 (MLS 5, Non-MLS 6)
Library Holdings: Bk Vols 60,000; Bk Titles 11,000; Per Subs 750
Subject Interests: Biotechnology, Employment, Environmental law, Finance, Intellectual property, Labor, Law, U.S. Congress
Special Collections: Legislative Histories, federal agency releases
Automation Activity & Vendor Info: (Cataloging) Innovative Interfaces Inc.
Database Vendor: Dialog, IAC - Info Trac, Innovative Interfaces INN - View, Lexis-Nexis, OCLC - First Search
Publications: ML&B Library Bulletin
Partic in Capcon Library Network; Dialog Corporation; Dow Jones News Retrieval; OCLC Online Computer Library Center, Inc

L MORRISON & FOERSTER, Law Library,* 2000 Pennsylvania Ave NW Ste 5500, 20006. SAN 372-1507. Tel: 202-887-1520. FAX: 202-887-0763. *Librn*, Elmo Dattalo
Library Holdings: Bk Vols 10,000; Per Subs 250

S MORTGAGE BANKERS ASSOCIATION LIBRARY,* 1125 15th St NW, 20005. SAN 302-6965. Tel: 202-861-6580. FAX: 202-861-0734. E-Mail: library@mb22.com. *Librn*, Kathryn Kupstas-Barnard
Library Holdings: Bk Titles 8,000; Per Subs 250
Subject Interests: Economics, Housing, Real estate, Statistics
Restriction: By appointment only

R MOUNT VERNON PLACE UNITED METHODIST CHURCH, Dessie M Hallett Library, 900 Massachusetts Ave NW, 20001-4396. SAN 302-6981. Tel: 202-347-9620. FAX: 202-347-9217.
Founded 1855
Library Holdings: Bk Titles 1,750
Subject Interests: Biblical studies, Drama, History, Poetry, Psychology, Recreation

S MUNICIPAL WASTE MANAGEMENT ASSOCIATION LIBRARY,* US Conference of Mayors, 1620 I St NW Ste 600, 20006. SAN 373-3483. Tel: 202-293-7330, 202-861-6783. FAX: 202-429-0422. Web Site: www.uscm/org, www.usmajors.org/uscm/mwma. *Dir*, Geraldine Powell
Library Holdings: Bk Vols 50; Per Subs 15

G NASA HEADQUARTERS LIBRARY,* 300 E St SW, Code CFS-3, 20546-0001. SAN 302-699X. Tel: 202-358-0168. FAX: 202-358-3469. E-Mail: library@hq.nasa.gov. Web Site: www.hq.nasa.gov/office/hqlibrary. *Dir*, Jannie Pratte; *Mgr*, Andrew Pedrick; *Ref*, Heather Crump; *Coll Develop*, Andrew Pedrich
Founded 1958
Library Holdings: Bk Titles 16,000; Per Subs 200
Subject Interests: Aerospace science
Special Collections: NACA Documents
Publications: Hot Picks (current awareness service)
Partic in OCLC Online Computer Library Center, Inc

S NATIONAL ABORTION FEDERATION, Resource Center,* 1755 Massachusetts Ave NW, Ste 600, 20036. SAN 374-9967. Tel: 202-667-5881. FAX: 202-667-5890. *Exec Dir*, Vicki Saporta
Library Holdings: Bk Titles 1,000; Per Subs 20

S NATIONAL ACADEMY OF SOCIAL INSURANCE LIBRARY,* 1776 Massachusetts Ave NW, Ste 615, 20036. SAN 374-9959. Tel: 202-452-8097. FAX: 202-452-8111. E-Mail: nasi@nasi.org. *Exec Dir*, Pamela Larson
Library Holdings: Bk Titles 3,000; Per Subs 5

S NATIONAL AGING INFORMATION CENTER LIBRARY,* 330 Independence Ave SW Rm 4656, 20201. SAN 377-1415. Tel: 202-619-7501. FAX: 202-401-7620. Web Site: www.aoa.gov/naic. *Actg Dir*, Bruce M Craig
1998-1999 Income $200,000. Mats Exp $1,000. Sal $175,000
Library Holdings: Bk Vols 500; Per Subs 25
Subject Interests: Aging, Policy, Statistics
Special Collections: Project Reports of Grants/Contracts Awarded by US Administration on Aging
The Center operates primarily as an information center responding to telephone, mail, e-mail, fax & visitors inquiries on caregiving, research, education, housing & community service issues related to older adults & aging

S NATIONAL ALLIANCE OF SENIOR CITIZENS LIBRARY,* 1744 Riggs Pl NW, 20009-2508. SAN 327-4748. Tel: 202-986-0117. FAX: 202-986-2974.
Library Holdings: Bk Vols 3,500

S NATIONAL ASSOCIATION OF BROADCASTERS, Information & Resource Center, 1771 N St NW, 20036. SAN 302-704X. Tel: 202-429-5490. FAX: 202-429-4199. Web Site: www.nab.org. *VPres*, Vivian Pollard; E-Mail: vpollard@nab.org; *Ref Serv*, Steven Mitchel; *Info Specialist*, Jessica Matthews; Staff 4 (MLS 1, Non-MLS 3)
Founded 1946
Library Holdings: Bk Vols 8,000; Bk Titles 6,500; Per Subs 150
Special Collections: Association Publications/Archives
Restriction: Members only

S NATIONAL ASSOCIATION OF CORPORATE DIRECTORS LIBRARY, 1707 L St NW, Ste 560, 20036. SAN 377-5321. Tel: 202-775-0509. FAX: 202-775-4857. E-Mail: info@nacdonline.org. Web Site: www.nacdonline.org. *Dir*, Shannon Savage
Founded 1977
Library Holdings: Bk Vols 450; Per Subs 44
Publications: Director's Monthly (Newsletter)

S NATIONAL ASSOCIATION OF LETTER CARRIERS, Information Center, 100 Indiana Ave NW, 20001. SAN 370-6869. Tel: 202-393-4695. FAX: 202-393-8584. E-Mail: nalcinf@nalc.org. Web Site: www.nalc.org. *In Charge*, Candace Main Rush; Staff 2 (MLS 1, Non-MLS 1)
Founded 1985
Library Holdings: Bk Titles 3,000; Per Subs 250
Special Collections: NALC Union Publications; National Association of Letter Carriers Union Publications; United States Postal Service Regulations
Publications: NALC Activist Index

S NATIONAL BIOMEDICAL RESEARCH FOUNDATION LIBRARY,* Georgetown University Medical Center, 3900 Reservoir Rd NW, 20007. SAN 302-7082. Tel: 202-687-2121. FAX: 202-687-1662. E-Mail: pirmail@nbrf.georgetown.edu. *Librn*, Joseph Janda
Founded 1960
Library Holdings: Bk Titles 3,000; Per Subs 95
Subject Interests: Biochemistry

S NATIONAL CHAMBER FOUNDATION LIBRARY,* 1615 H St NW, 20062. SAN 375-9091. Tel: 202-463-5552. FAX: 202-463-3174. *Librn*, Martin Lefkowitz
Library Holdings: Bk Vols 7,000

S NATIONAL CLEARINGHOUSE ON CHILD ABUSE & NEGLECT INFORMATION,* 330 C St SW, 20447. SAN 371-0084. Tel: 703-385-7565. Toll Free Tel: 800-394-3366. FAX: 703-385-3206. E-Mail: nccanch@calib.com. Web Site: www.calib.com/nccanch.
Library Holdings: Bk Vols 24,000; Per Subs 25

S NATIONAL COALITION AGAINST THE MISUSE OF PESTICIDES LIBRARY,* 701 E St SE, Ste 200, 20003. SAN 375-1546. Tel: 202-543-5450. FAX: 202-543-4791. E-Mail: info@beyondpesticides.org. Web Site: www.beyondpesticides.org. *Exec Dir*, Jay Feldman
Library Holdings: Bk Titles 200; Per Subs 30

SR NATIONAL CONFERENCE OF CATHOLIC BISHOPS, US Catholic Conference Library,* 3211 Fourth St NE, 20017. SAN 371-6341. Tel: 202-541-3193. FAX: 202-541-3322. Web Site: www.nccbuscc.org. *Asst Librn*, Nancy Patterson; Staff 3 (MLS 1, Non-MLS 2)
Founded 1989
Library Holdings: Bk Vols 12,000; Bk Titles 11,000; Per Subs 120
Subject Interests: Church history, Human rights, Theology
Special Collections: Latin American Bishops, bks & pamphlets; National Conference of Catholic Bishops-United States Catholic Conference Publications, bks & pamphlets
Publications: Newsletter (monthly)

C NATIONAL CONFERENCE OF STATE LEGISLATURES, Intergovernmental Health Policy Project Library,* 444 N Capitol St NW, Ste 515, 20001. SAN 328-3518. Tel: 202-624-5400. FAX: 202-737-1069. *Dir*, Richard Merritt
Library Holdings: Bk Vols 10,000
Subject Interests: State health policy legis

S NATIONAL CONFERENCE ON SOVIET JEWRY RESEARCH BUREAU, 1640 Rhode Island Ave NW, 20036-3278. SAN 376-0693. Tel: 202-898-2500. FAX: 202-898-0822. E-Mail: ncj@ncj.org. Web Site: www.ncj.org. *Exec Dir*, Mark Levin; *Commun Relations*, Leslie Weiss

S NATIONAL CORRUGATED STEEL PIPE ASSOCIATION, Technical Library,* 1255 23rd St NW, Ste 850, 20037-1174. SAN 375-4723. Tel: 202-452-1700. FAX: 202-833-3636. E-Mail: csp@ncspa.org. *Librn*, Becca Dietrich; Staff 1 (MLS 1)
Library Holdings: Bk Vols 200

S NATIONAL COUNCIL FOR ADOPTION LIBRARY, 1930 17th St NW, 20009-6207. SAN 375-1473. Tel: 202-328-1200. FAX: 202-332-0935. E-Mail: ncfadc@ibm.net. Web Site: www.ncfa-usa.org. *Pres*, Patrick Purtill
Library Holdings: Bk Titles 1,000

S NATIONAL COUNCIL OF FARMER COOPERATIVE,* 50 F St NW, Ste 900, 20001. SAN 371-0327. Tel: 202-626-8700. FAX: 202-626-8722. Web Site: www.ncfc.org. *Pres*, David Graves
Library Holdings: Bk Vols 2,000; Per Subs 33

S NATIONAL COUNCIL ON THE AGING, INC, Ollie A Randall Library, 409 Thrid St SW, Ste 200, 20024. SAN 302-7155. Tel: 202-479-6669. FAX: 202-479-0735. Web Site: www.ncoa.org. *Librn*, Janette Hoisington; E-Mail: janette.hoisington@ncoa.org
Founded 1950
Library Holdings: Bk Titles 7,000; Per Subs 180
Subject Interests: Gerontology
Special Collections: NCOA Publications Archives
Publications: Abstracts in Social Gerontology: Current Literature on Aging (quarterly)
Partic in Capcon Library Network

S NATIONAL ECONOMIC RESEARCH ASSOCIATES, INC LIBRARY,* 1255 23rd St NW, Ste 600, 20037. SAN 302-7171. Tel: 202-466-3510. FAX: 202-466-3605. *Dir*, Lisa Harrington; E-Mail: lisa-harrington@nera.com; *Asst Librn, Ref*, Michelle Duque
Founded 1965
Library Holdings: Bk Vols 6,000; Per Subs 100
Subject Interests: Economics, Energy
Special Collections: Wall Street Journal (1973-present), micro
Publications: Library Letter, monthly
Partic in Dialog Corporation; Dow Jones News Retrieval; Vutext

S NATIONAL EDUCATION ASSOCIATION ARCHIVES,* 1201 16th St NW, 20036. SAN 329-885X. Tel: 202-833-4000. FAX: 703-644-3505. *Archivist*, Olivia Aguilar Gattis; *Archivist, Asst Librn*, Odessa Jones
Founded 1857
Library Holdings: Bk Titles 5,100

S NATIONAL ENDOWMENT FOR DEMOCRACY, Democracy Resource Center, 1101 15th St NW, Ste 802, 20005. SAN 377-4554. Tel: 202-293-0300. FAX: 202-293-0258. E-Mail: drc@ned.org. Web Site: www.ned.org. *Head Librn*, Allen Overland; *Asst Librn*, Tim Myers; *Electronic Resources*, Kristina Lively
Library Holdings: Bk Vols 10,000; Per Subs 350
Partic in Spec Libr Asn

S NATIONAL ENDOWMENT FOR THE ARTS LIBRARY, 1100 Pennsylvania Ave NW, Rm 213, 20506. SAN 302-7198. Tel: 202-682-5485. FAX: 202-682-5651. Web Site: www.arts.endow.gov. *Librn*, Joy Kiser; E-Mail: kiserj@arts.endow.gov
Library Holdings: Bk Vols 10,000; Per Subs 160
Partic in Fed Libr & Info Network; OCLC Online Computer Library Center, Inc

G NATIONAL ENDOWMENT FOR THE HUMANITIES LIBRARY,* 1100 Pennsylvania Ave NW, 20506. SAN 325-9854. Tel: 202-606-8244. FAX: 202-606-8457. *Dir*, Enayet Rahim; E-Mail: erahim@neh.gov; Staff 2 (MLS 1, Non-MLS 1)
Library Holdings: Bk Vols 20,000; Per Subs 200
Subject Interests: Education, Humanities
Special Collections: Jefferson Lectures; NEH reports
Publications: Acquisitions List; Serial List; Special Bibliographies
Restriction: By appointment only
Partic in Dialog Corporation; Fedlink; OCLC Online Computer Library Center, Inc

S NATIONAL GALLERY OF ART LIBRARY,* Fourth St & Constitution Ave NW, 20565. SAN 302-7228. Tel: 202-842-6511. Interlibrary Loan Service Tel: 202-842-6512. FAX: 202-408-8530. Web Site: www.nga.gov. *Librn*, Neal Turtell; *Reader Servs*, Lamia Doumato; *Bibliog Instr, Online Servs, Ref*, Frances Lederer; *Tech Servs*, Anna Rachwald; *Admin Assoc*, Roger Lawson; *Automation Syst Coordr*, Karen Cassedy; Staff 37 (MLS 13, Non-MLS 24)
Founded 1941
Library Holdings: Bk Vols 225,000; Bk Titles 220,000; Per Subs 958
Subject Interests: Graphic arts, Paintings, Sculpture
Special Collections: Art Exhibition Catalog; Art Sales Records; Artists Book Coll; Leonardo da Vinci Coll; Museum & Private Art Coll; Photograph Archives of European & American Art
Publications: Annotated Bibliography of Microforms, Washington, DC 1991; Guide to the National Gallery of Art Library, Washington, DC, 1994
Partic in Artquest; Dialog Corporation; OCLC Online Computer Library Center, Inc; RLIN; Wilsonline
Branches:
DEPARTMENT OF EDUCATION RESOURCES, Fourth St & Constitution Ave NW, 20565. SAN 329-9686. Tel: 202-842-6273. FAX: 202-842-6935. E-Mail: extprg@nga.gov. Web Site: www.nga.gov. *Curator*, Ruth R Perlin
Special Services for the Deaf - Captioned media

S NATIONAL GEOGRAPHIC SOCIETY LIBRARY,* 1145 17th St NW, 20036. SAN 336-9129. Tel: 202-857-7787. Interlibrary Loan Service Tel: 202-857-7786. FAX: 202-429-5731. E-Mail: sfiferca@ngs.org. Web Site: www.nationalgeographic.com/library/. *Dir*, Susan Fifer Canby; Staff 17 (MLS 9, Non-MLS 8)
Founded 1920
Library Holdings: Per Subs 300
Subject Interests: Geography, Natural history, Travel, Voyages
Special Collections: General A W Greely's Polar Library, scrapbooks; Hakluyt Society Publications; Research reports resulting from Research & Exploration Grants of National Geographic Society
Publications: Research Guides to the Internet (pathfinders); Staff Brochure; Staff Searches on Demand; Visitor Brochure
Restriction: Staff use only
Partic in Dialog Corporation; Dow Jones News Retrieval; First Search
Branches:
FILM Tel: 202-857-7659. FAX: 202-429-5755. *Librn*, Patricia Gang; Staff 11 (MLS 4, Non-MLS 7)
Subject Interests: Animals, behavior of, Geography, Recreation, Transportation
Special Collections: National Geographic Television & Educational Films, approximately 12,000,000 ft of 16mm color out-takes
IMAGE COLLECTION Tel: 202-857-7493. FAX: 202-429-5776.; Staff 32 (MLS 26, Non-MLS 6)
Founded 1919
Subject Interests: Geography
Special Collections: (Space Coll), transparencies, prints & negatives; Antarctic (Herbert G Ponting Coll), photog; China (Joseph F Rock Coll), photog; Machu; Mount Katmai, Alaska (Robert F Griggs Coll), photog; NASA Space Probes; Picchu, Peru (Hiram Bingham Coll), photog; Polar Expeditions (Robert E Peary Coll), photog; Skylab Missions (Skylab Coll), color; transparencies, prints & negatives; Wildlife (Georg Shiras III Coll), photog; Yukon (Bradford Washburn Coll), photog

M NATIONAL HEALTH INFORMATION CENTER,* PO Box 1133, 20013-1133. SAN 328-5677. Tel: 800-336-4797. FAX: 301-984-4256. E-Mail: nhicinfo@health.org. Web Site: nhic-nt.health.org/. *Ref*, Mahshid Amini; E-Mail: mamini@health.org
Library Holdings: Bk Titles 800
Publications: Health Information Resources in the Federal Government; Healthfinder: National Health Observances for 1992; Healthfinder: Selected Federal Health Information Clearinghouses & Information Centers; Healthy People 2000; Toll Free Numbers for Health Information

S NATIONAL HIGHWAY TRAFFIC SAFETY ADMINISTRATION, Technical Information Services,* 400 Seventh St SW Rm 5110 NAD-40, 20590. SAN 302-7252. Tel: 202-366-4000, 800-445-0197. FAX: 202-493-2833. E-Mail: tis@nhtsa.dot.gov. Web Site: www.nhtsa.dot.gov/. *Info Specialist, Tech Servs*, Kim S Jackson; Staff 12 (MLS 8, Non-MLS 4)
Founded 1967
Library Holdings: Bk Vols 34,000; Bk Titles 20,500; Per Subs 11
Special Collections: Automotive Safety (Research & Test Reports of National Highway Traffic Safety Administration); Defect Investigation Files Coll; of Rulemaking Activity of National Highway Traffic Safety Administration; Record
Partic in Dialog Corporation; TRIS File

S NATIONAL HOUSING LIBRARY,* 1201 15th St NW, 20005. SAN 302-7066. Tel: 202-822-0203. FAX: 202-861-2153. E-Mail: nhl@nahb.com. Web Site: www.nahb.com. *Dir*, Nancy Hunn; *Librn*, Elizabeth Schilling; *Info Res*, Mehret Samuel; Staff 5 (MLS 2, Non-MLS 3)
Founded 1955
Library Holdings: Bk Titles 10,000; Per Subs 240
Subject Interests: Construction, Housing
Special Collections: NAHB Archives
Restriction: By appointment only
Partic in Dialog Corporation

G NATIONAL INFORMATION CENTER FOR CHILDREN & YOUTH WITH DISABILITIES LIBRARY,* 1825 Connecticut Ave 7th floor, 20009. (Mail add: PO Box 1492, 20013-1492), SAN 326-887X. Tel: 202-884-8200. Toll Free Tel: 800-695-0285. TDD: 202-884-8200, 800-695-0285. FAX: 202-884-8441. E-Mail: nichcy@aed.org. Web Site: www.nichcy.org.
Library Holdings: Bk Vols 1,000
Partic in BRS
Special Services for the Deaf - TTY machine

GL NATIONAL INSTITUTE OF JUSTICE, Online Research & Information Center,* 810 Seventh St NW Rm 3700, 20531. SAN 377-4228. Tel: 202-307-6742. FAX: 202-616-2056. Web Site: www.ojt.usdoj.gov. *Coordr*, James Fort; E-Mail: fortj@ojp.usdoj.gov
Library Holdings: Bk Vols 1,000; Per Subs 50

S NATIONAL INSTITUTE ON ALCOHOL ABUSE & ALCOHOLISM, Research Library, 1400 Eye St NW, Ste 200, 20005. SAN 371-2621. Tel: 202-842-7600, Ext 361. FAX: 202-842-0418. Web Site: www.niaaa.nih.gov. *Mgr*, Nancy Winstanley; *Librn*, Shawn Montgomery
Library Holdings: Bk Vols 3,100; Per Subs 200
Subject Interests: Alcoholism
Publications: Alcohol Alert; Alcohol Research & Health
Produce online database: ETOH, alcohol problems science database; available OVID Technologies, Inc

L NATIONAL INTERRELIGIOUS SERVICE BOARD FOR CONSCIENTIOUS OBJECTORS & THE CENTER ON CONSCIENCE & WAR, CCW Law Library, 1830 Connecticut Ave NW, 20009-5706. SAN 370-7547. Tel: 202-483-2220. FAX: 202-483-1246. E-Mail: nisbco@nisbco.org. Web Site: www.nisbco.org. *Exec Dir*, J E McNeil
Founded 1940
Library Holdings: Bk Vols 400; Bk Titles 350; Per Subs 15
Subject Interests: Military
Special Collections: Conscientious Objection; Military Service & Conscription; Selective Service System, bks, government publ
Restriction: Public use on premises

S NATIONAL JOURNAL LIBRARY,* 1501 M St NW, Ste 300, 20005. SAN 302-6647. Tel: 202-739-8400, Ext 520. FAX: 202-739-8519. *Librn*, Chase Remaly; Staff 2 (MLS 2)
Founded 1969
Library Holdings: Bk Titles 1,800; Per Subs 175
Subject Interests: Congress
Partic in Dialog Corporation

S NATIONAL LABOR RELATIONS BOARD LIBRARY,* 1099 14th St NW Ste 8000, 20570. SAN 302-7260. Tel: 202-273-3720. FAX: 202-273-2906. Web Site: www.nlrb.gov. *Chief Librn*, Kenneth Nero; E-Mail: knero@nlrb.gov; Staff 9 (MLS 3, Non-MLS 6)
Library Holdings: Bk Vols 40,000; Per Subs 50
Subject Interests: Employment law, Labor, Law
Special Collections: Publications By or About National Labor Relations Board, National Labor Relations Act, Labor; Relations Act of 1947 & Landrum-Griffin Act, Title VII
Publications: New Books & Current Labor Articles
Partic in OCLC Online Computer Library Center, Inc

S NATIONAL LEAGUE OF CITIES, Municipal Reference Service, 1301 Pennsylvania Ave NW, 20004. SAN 302-7279. Tel: 202-626-3130. FAX: 202-626-3043. Web Site: www.nlc.org. *Librn*, Cyrus Behroozi; *Librn*, Bruce Calvin; *Info Specialist*, Laura Varricchione; Staff 4 (MLS 3, Non-MLS 1)
Founded 1963
Library Holdings: Bk Vols 20,000; Per Subs 300
Special Collections: Census Reports; Federal Documents; Representative City Reports, State Municipal League Publications
Automation Activity & Vendor Info: (Cataloging) Inmagic, Inc.
Publications: Issues & Options
Restriction: By permission only

G NATIONAL LIBRARY OF EDUCATION,* 400 Maryland Ave SW, Rm 4W317, 20202-5523. SAN 336-9242. Tel: 202-401-2492. FAX: 202-205-6688, 202-205-7759. E-Mail: library@ed.gov or usnei@ed.gov. Web Site: www.ed.gov/nle/. *Exec Dir*, Sheila McGarr; *Coll Develop, Tech Servs*, Christina Dunn; *Coll Develop*, Ted Brandhorst; Staff 36 (MLS 23, Non-MLS 13)
Founded 1994
Oct 1998-Sep 1999 Mats Exp $238,000, Books $80,000, Per/Ser (Incl. Access Fees) $125,000, Micro $15,000, AV Equip $10,000
Library Holdings: Bk Vols 250,000; Per Subs 900
Subject Interests: Education, Educational psychology
Special Collections: Early American Textbook Coll; ERIC (Educational Resources Information Center) Database; Kraus Curriculum , Michigan, (micro); Kraus Currie Coll; National Institutes of Education (NIE) Archival Coll; National Institutes of Education Reports; Newsbank (Micro); Rare Books Coll; US Beurau/Office of Education Archival Coll, 1863-1979; US Bureau/Office of Education, 1863-1979; US Department of Education Archival Coll; Williams S Gray Reading Coll (Micro)
Publications: Periodicals Holdings List; Recent Acquisitions (monthly)
Partic in Dialog Corporation; Fedlink; OCLC Online Computer Library Center, Inc
Electronic Collections: Free direct access via Internet for online materials; hard copies of ERIC database documents available for fee from contractors. A virtual library & information center that manages US Department of Education Internet web sites & the ERIC database system in addition to a physical collection of resources

S NATIONAL MUSEUM OF AMERICAN JEWISH MILITARY HISTORY LIBRARY,* 1811 R St NW, 20009. SAN 377-1172. Tel: 202-265-6280. FAX: 202-265-3192. E-Mail: nmajmh@erols.com. Web Site: www.penfed.org/jwv/museum.htm. *Archivist*, Sandor Cohen
Library Holdings: Bk Vols 22,000

S THE NATIONAL MUSEUM OF WOMEN IN THE ARTS, (LRC), Library & Research Center, 1250 New York Ave NW, 20005-3920. Tel: 202-783-7365. FAX: 202-393-3234. Web Site: www.nmwa.org. *Dir*, Krystyna Wasserman; Tel: 202-783-7364, Fax: 202-393-3235; Staff 5 (MLS 3, Non-MLS 2)
Founded 1982
Library Holdings: Bk Vols 12,000; Bk Titles 11,000; Per Subs 70
Subject Interests: Woman artists
Special Collections: Archives of International Festivals of Women Artists; Archives on Women Artists, bk plates; Artists' Books Coll; Irene Rice Pereira Personal Library
Automation Activity & Vendor Info: (Acquisitions) Endeavor; (Cataloging) Endeavor; (Circulation) Endeavor; (OPAC) Endeavor; (Serials) Endeavor

S NATIONAL PARK SERVICE - ROCK CREEK PARK, Old Stone House Library, 3051 M St NW, 20007. SAN 372-5154. Tel: 202-426-6851. FAX: 202-426-0125. Web Site: www.nps.gov/rocr/oldstonehouse. *In Charge*, Dwight Madison
Library Holdings: Bk Titles 200
Special Collections: American History; Washington DC History
Special Services for the Deaf - TTY machine
Open Wed-Sun 12-5

R NATIONAL PRESBYTERIAN CHURCH & CENTER, William S Culbertson Library, Administration Bldg, 4101 Nebraska Ave NW, 20016. SAN 302-7317. Tel: 202-537-0800. FAX: 202-686-0031. Web Site: www.natpresch.org. *Librn*, Dr Elizabeth W Stone
Founded 1969
Library Holdings: Bk Vols 5,400; Per Subs 26
Subject Interests: Children's literature, History, Large type print, Religion
Publications: Current Awareness Bulletin; New Book Lists; Reading for Special Days
Open Mon-Fri 9-4, Sun 9-1

S NATIONAL PRESS CLUB, Eric Friedheim Library, 529 14th St NW, 13th Flr, 20045. SAN 326-128X. Tel: 202-662-7523. FAX: 202-879-6725. E-Mail: info@press.org. Web Site: www.mtc.press.org/lib/. *Dir*, Tom Glad; *Mgr*, Gini Blodgett; *Res*, Gini Blodgett; *Res*, Heather Crocetto; Staff 5 (MLS 4, Non-MLS 1)
Founded 1908
Library Holdings: Bk Vols 3,000; Per Subs 300
Special Collections: Hammond Photographs (John Hay Hammond Coll), photogs; NPC Cartoon Coll, original art & political cartoons; Sigma Delta Chi DC Chapter docs; Washington Press Club Archives
Publications: The Record
Partic in Dow Jones News Retrieval; Northern Lights Library Network
Open Mon-Fri 9-8
Friends of the Library Group

S NATIONAL PUBLIC RADIO BROADCAST LIBRARY, 635 Massachusetts Ave NW, 20001. SAN 326-2189. Tel: 202-513-2060. FAX: 202-513-3056. Web Site: www.npr.org. *Dir*, Robert C Robinson; E-Mail: rrobinson@npr.org; *Cat*, Bethany Howard; *Cat*, Denise Chen; *Cat*, Ian Fairclough; *Cat*, Giselle Foss; *Cat*, Sally Robertson; *Music*, Robert Goldstein; *Coll Develop*, Katherine Baer; Staff 7 (MLS 5, Non-MLS 2)
Founded 1971
Library Holdings: Bk Titles 100,000
Special Collections: Current Events, audiotape; Drama Performances, audiotape; Music Performances, audiotape
Automation Activity & Vendor Info: (Acquisitions) TechLIB; (Cataloging) TechLIB; (Circulation) TechLIB; (Course Reserve) TechLIB
Friends of the Library Group

NATIONAL REFERENCE CENTER FOR BIOETHICS LITERATURE
S KENNEDY INSTITUTE OF ETHICS, Georgetown University, PO Box 571212, 20057-1212. SAN 336-8289. Tel: 202-687-3885. FAX: 202-687-6770. Web Site: bioethicsgeorgetown.edu/. *Ref*, Martina Darragh; *Ref*, Patricia McCarrick; Staff 13 (MLS 9, Non-MLS 4)
Founded 1973
Library Holdings: Bk Vols 26,000; Per Subs 240
Special Collections: Archives Colls of Federal Bioethics & Human Experimentation Commissions; Curriculum Development Clearinghouse for Bioethics (Syllubus Exchange Coll); Kampelman Coll of Jewish Ethics; Shriver Coll of Christian Ethics
Publications: Bibliography of Bioethics (published by Kennedy Institute beginning with vol 10); Bioethics: A Guide to Information Sources; New Titles in Bioethics; Scope Notes
Restriction: Open to public for reference only
Partic in Capcon Library Network; Dialog Corporation; Nat Libr of Med; OCLC Online Computer Library Center, Inc
On-site photocopying; document delivery service; ILL

M NATIONAL REHABILITATION HOSPITAL, Learning Resource Center,* 102 Irving St NW, 20010. SAN 371-2362. Tel: 202-877-1995. FAX: 202-722-0020. *Tech Servs*, Sharon Williams
Library Holdings: Bk Vols 510
Restriction: Staff use only

S NATIONAL RESEARCH COUNCIL LIBRARY,* 2101 Constitution Ave NW, 20418. SAN 302-7023. Tel: 202-334-2125. FAX: 202-334-1651. Web Site: www.nas.edu. *Dir*, Leona Coffee; *Mgr*, Joe Price; E-Mail: jprice@nas.edu; *Res*, Jim Igoe; *Res*, Susan Fourt; Staff 6 (MLS 3, Non-MLS 3)
Founded 1947
Library Holdings: Bk Vols 80,000; Per Subs 500
Special Collections: National Academy of Sciences, National Academy of Engineering, National Research Council & Institute of Medicine, rpts
Partic in Capcon Library Network; Dialog Corporation; Interlibrary Users

Association
Primarily serves staffs of National Academy of Sciences, National Academy of Engineering, Institute of Medicine & members of respective committees
Branches:
TRANSPORTATION RESEARCH BOARD LIBRARY, 2101 Constitution Ave NW, 20418. SAN 302-7015. Tel: 202-334-2989. FAX: 202-334-2527. Web Site: www.4.nationalacademics.org/trb. *Assoc Librn*, Donald Martin; *Ref*, Barbara Post; E-Mail: bpost@nas.edu
Founded 1946
Library Holdings: Bk Titles 17,000; Per Subs 380
Subject Interests: Civil engineering, Transportation
Special Collections: Highway Research Board & Transportation Research Board Publications; Strategic Highway Research Board Publications
Automation Activity & Vendor Info: (Acquisitions) Inmagic, Inc.; (Cataloging) Inmagic, Inc.; (Circulation) Inmagic, Inc.; (ILL) Inmagic, Inc.; (OPAC) Inmagic, Inc.
Publications: Per Holding List (annually)
Restriction: By appointment only
Partic in Dialog Corporation; Fedlink; OCLC Online Computer Library Center, Inc

S NATIONAL RESTAURANT ASSOCIATION, Information Service & Library,* 1200 17th St NW, 20036. SAN 303-9862. Tel: 202-331-5960. Toll Free Tel: 800-424-5156. FAX: 202-331-5950. E-Mail: info@dineout.org. Web Site: www.restaurant.org. *Mgr*, Myra Engers Weinberg; E-Mail: mweinberg@dineout.org; *Tech Servs*, Laurence Himelfarb; Staff 7 (MLS 3, Non-MLS 4)
Founded 1975
Library Holdings: Bk Titles 5,500
Subject Interests: Food industry and trade
Special Collections: Association Archives; Menus
Publications: Restaurant Information Abstracts (biweekly)

S NATIONAL RIGHT TO LIFE LIBRARY,* 419 Seventh St NW Ste 500, 20004. SAN 371-8689. Tel: 202-626-8809. FAX: 202-393-0745. Web Site: www.nrlc.org. *Admin Assoc*, Joe Landrum
Library Holdings: Bk Titles 1,000; Per Subs 30
Special Collections: Abortion; Euthanasia; Infanticide

S NATIONAL SOCIAL WORK LIBRARY,* 750 First St NE Ste 700, 20002-4241. SAN 326-2200. Tel: 202-336-8207. Toll Free Tel: 800-638-8799. FAX: 202-336-8310. E-Mail: info@naswdc.org. Web Site: www.socialworkers.org. *Dir*, Alfredda Payne
Founded 1982
Library Holdings: Bk Titles 10,000; Per Subs 350
Special Collections: Children's Mental Health (Everett Woods Coll); Choice Coll & Data Base; International Innovations for Strengthening Families; Special Purpose Housing & Social Work (Carroll Kowal Coll)
Publications: Aids & Ethics (bibliography); Effectiveness in School Social Work Programs & Practices (bibliography)

NATIONAL SOCIETY OF THE DAUGHTERS OF THE AMERICAN REVOLUTION
S DAR LIBRARY, 1776 D St NW, 20006-5392. SAN 302-7368. Tel: 202-879-3229. FAX: 202-879-3227. Web Site: www.dar.org. *Coll Develop, Dir*, Eric G Grundset; *Asst Dir*, Steven B Rhodes; *Librn, Tech Servs*, Bertha Mutz; *Acq*, Sally G Gray; Staff 6 (MLS 6)
Founded 1896
Mar 1998-Feb 1999 Income $833,250, Locally Generated Income $275,000, Parent Institution $558,250. Mats Exp $118,500, Books $75,000, Per/Ser (Incl. Access Fees) $15,000, Presv $3,500, Micro $25,000. Sal $595,000 (Prof $216,000)
Library Holdings: Bk Titles 150,000; Per Subs 1,100
Subject Interests: Genealogy, Local history
Special Collections: American Indians
Publications: American Genealogical Research at the DAR
Friends of the Library Group
S MUSEUM REFERENCE LIBRARY, 1776 D St NW, 20006. SAN 321-2262. Tel: 202-879-3241. FAX: 202-628-0820. E-Mail: museum@dar.org. Web Site: www.dar.org/museum. *Dir*, Diane Dunkley; E-Mail: ddunkley@dar.org; Staff 10 (Non-MLS 10)
Founded 1970
Library Holdings: Bk Vols 3,000; Bk Titles 3,000; Per Subs 30
Subject Interests: Decorative arts
Function: For research purposes

S NATIONAL SPACE SOCIETY, Von Braun-Oberth Memorial Library, 600 Pennsylvania Ave SE, Ste 201, 20003. SAN 371-2656. Tel: 202-543-1900, Ext 175. FAX: 202-546-4189. Web Site: www.nss.org. *Exec Dir*, Pat Dasch
Library Holdings: Bk Vols 600; Per Subs 25
Subject Interests: Astronomy, Technology

S NATIONAL TREASURY EMPLOYEES UNION LIBRARY,* 901 E St NW Ste 600, 20004. SAN 328-1949. Tel: 202-783-4444. FAX: 202-783-4085. E-Mail: nteuinfo@nteu.org. *Librn*, Mark Faherty
Founded 1979
Library Holdings: Bk Vols 5,500; Bk Titles 3,000; Per Subs 65
Publications: Acquisitions Lists
Restriction: By appointment only

M NATIONAL WOMEN'S HEALTH NETWORK, Health Clearinghouse,* 514 Tenth St NW, Ste 400, 20004. SAN 373-3505. Tel: 202-347-1140. FAX: 202-347-1168. *Coordr*, Brooke Grandle
Library Holdings: Bk Vols 450
Women's health information packets on 70 topics available

S NAVAL RESEARCH LABORATORY, Ruth H Hooker Research Library & Technical Information Center,* 4555 Overlook Ave SW, 20375-5334. SAN 302-7392. Tel: 202-767-2357. FAX: 202-767-3352. E-Mail: ref@library.nrl.navy.mil. Web Site: infoweb.nrl.navy.mil. *Librn*, Laurie E Stackpole; *Assoc Librn*, Patricia A Ames; Tel: 202-767-2269, E-Mail: pata@library.nrl.navy.mil; Staff 28 (MLS 7, Non-MLS 21)
Library Holdings: Per Subs 1,000
Subject Interests: Chemistry, Computers, Electronics, Physics
Publications: Bibliography of NRL Publications; User's Guide
Partic in Consortium of Navy Librs; Fedlink; Nat Res Libr Alliance
Involved in implementing contractual arrangements with publishers to disseminate journal literature throughout NRL. Host for database storage for National Research Library Alliance (ISI's Web of Science)

S NEW YORK TIMES, Washington Bureau Library, 1627 I St NW, 20006. SAN 302-7422. Tel: 202-862-0300. FAX: 202-862-0340. *Librn*, Barclay Walsh
Founded 1932
Library Holdings: Bk Titles 2,500; Per Subs 30
Restriction: Staff use only
Partic in NY Times Info Bank
Friends of the Library Group

L NIXON PEABODY LLP, Law Library, 401 Ninth St NW, Ste 900, 20004. SAN 371-5582. Tel: 202-585-8000. FAX: 202-585-8080. *Info Res, Mgr*, Sara G Eakes; E-Mail: seakes@nixonpeabody.com; *Librn*, Jennifer Dollar; *Librn*, Beverly Miller
Library Holdings: Bk Vols 5,000; Bk Titles 1,500

R NORTHMINSTER PRESBYTERIAN CHURCH LIBRARY, 7720 Alaska Ave NW, 20012. SAN 374-8391. Tel: 202-829-5311. FAX: 202-726-6899. *Librn*, Fay C Acker
Library Holdings: Bk Titles 400

S NUCLEAR ENERGY INSTITUTE LIBRARY,* 1776 I St NW, Ste 300, 20006. SAN 302-5926. Tel: 202-739-8000. FAX: 202-785-4019. Web Site: www.nei.org. *Librn*, Martha Parks Jarry; Tel: 202-739-8135, E-Mail: mpj@nei.org; Staff 1 (MLS 1)
Founded 1954
1998-1999
Library Holdings: Bk Titles 12,000; Per Subs 280
Subject Interests: Energy, Environmental studies, Nuclear energy, Radiation
Automation Activity & Vendor Info: (Acquisitions) EOS; (Cataloging) EOS; (Circulation) EOS; (OPAC) EOS; (Serials) EOS
Restriction: Staff & members only
Partic in Capcon Library Network

L O'CONNOR & HANNAN, Law Library,* 1666 K Street NW Ste 500, 20006. SAN 372-1493. Tel: 202-887-1400. FAX: 202-466-2198. E-Mail: adj@o&h-mail. *Librn*, Jane M Towell; *Asst Librn*, Ashley D Johnson
Library Holdings: Bk Vols 5,000; Per Subs 300

L O'MELVENY & MYERS, Law Library, 555 13th St NW, Ste 500 W, 20004. SAN 372-3208. Tel: 202-383-5311. FAX: 202-383-5414. Web Site: www.omm.com. *Librn*, Debra Fisher; E-Mail: dfisher@onn.com; Staff 4 (MLS 3, Non-MLS 1)
Library Holdings: Bk Vols 25,000
Subject Interests: Administrative law

OFFICE OF THRIFT SUPERVISION
GL THE LIBRARY, 1700 G St NW, 20552. SAN 336-7355. Interlibrary Loan Service Tel: 202-906-6470. FAX: 202-906-7591. *ILL, Tech Coordr*, Joseph Thornton; E-Mail: joseph.thornton@ots.treas.gov; *Acq*, Cookie Forest; Staff 3 (MLS 3)
Founded 1935
Library Holdings: Bk Vols 84,000; Per Subs 300
Subject Interests: Administrative law, Banks and banking
Special Collections: Annotated Compilations of Court Decisions; Compiled Legislative Histories Coll; State Reports; United States Supreme Court Reports
Partic in OCLC Online Computer Library Center, Inc; Westlaw

S OPERA AMERICA, Information Service Library,* 1156 15th St NW Ste 810, 20005-1704. SAN 325-7495. Tel: 202-293-4466. FAX: 202-393-0735. E-Mail: frontdesk@operaam.org. Web Site: www.operaam.org. *Pres*, Marc Scorca
Library Holdings: Bk Vols 4,000; Per Subs 70
Subject Interests: Opera
Restriction: Not open to public

S ORGANIZATION FOR ECONOMIC COOPERATION & DEVELOPMENT, Washington Center, 2001 L St NW, Ste 650, 20036-4922. SAN 320-1341. Tel: 202-785-6323. FAX: 202-785-0350. E-Mail: washington.contact@oecd.org. Web Site: www.oecdwash.org. *Info Specialist*, Sandra Wilson; Tel: 202-822-3866, E-Mail: sandra.wilson@oecd.org
Founded 1966
Library Holdings: Bk Vols 3,800; Per Subs 22
Subject Interests: Agriculture, Economics, Education, Energy, Environment, Industry, International law, Pub mgt, Science/technology, Transportation
Special Collections: Economics (OECD), bks, doc, electronic publication (CD-Rom & diskettes)
Publications: OECD Recent Publications

S ORGANIZATION OF AMERICAN STATES, Columbus Memorial Library, 19th & Constitution Ave NW, 20006-4499. SAN 302-7465. Tel: 202-458-6041. Interlibrary Loan Service Tel: 202-458-6037. FAX: 202-458-3914. Web Site: tlc.library.net/columbus. *Dir*, Virginia Newton; Tel: 202-458-6040, E-Mail: newton_virginia@oas.org; *Ref*, Stella Villagran; Tel: 202-458-6037, E-Mail: svilligran@oas.org; *Archivist*, Beverly Wharton-Lake; Tel: 202-458-3849, E-Mail: bwhartonlake@oas.org; *Doc*, Rene L Gutierrez; Tel: 202-458-6233, E-Mail: rgutierrez@oas.org; *Cat*, Jean Craigwell; Tel: 202-458-6172, E-Mail: jcraigwell@oas.org; Staff 11 (MLS 6, Non-MLS 5)
Founded 1890
Library Holdings: Bk Vols 300,000; Per Subs 2,679
Special Collections: Democracy; Drugs; Historical Photographs; Human Rights; Inter-American System; International Orgns; Latin America, Caribbean, Canada & the US; Sustainable Development; Trade; Women in the Americas
Publications: Catalogo de Informes y Documentos Tecnicos; Guide to the Columbus Memorial Library; Hipolito Unanue Bibliographic Servs; Indice Analitico de Documentos Oficiales; Information & Documentation Series; List of Recently Catalogued Books; Lista General de Documentos Oficiales; OAS Records Management Handbook; Periodical Articles of Interest
Restriction: Non-circulating to the public
Partic in Capcon Library Network
Friends of the Library Group

G OSHA, Technical Data Center,* 200 Constitution Ave NW, Rm N-2625, 20210-2001. SAN 323-9233. Tel: 202-693-2350. FAX: 202-693-1648. *Dir*, Chris Aaron; *Tech Servs*, Denise Hayes; *Tech Servs*, Marija Hughes; *Tech Servs*, Robert Turnage; *Tech Servs*, Elaine Bynum; Staff 5 (MLS 5)
Library Holdings: Bk Vols 12,500; Bk Titles 6,000; Per Subs 206
Subject Interests: Engineering, Medicine
Special Collections: OSHA Rulemaking Records 1971-present
Publications: OSHA Journal Review (monthly); topical bibliographies (about 4 per month)
Partic in Fedlink; OCLC Online Computer Library Center, Inc
The Center serves as the central repository for all OSHA rulemaking & committee dockets

S OVERSEAS DEVELOPMENT COUNCIL LIBRARY,* 1875 Connecticut Ave NW, Ste 1012, 20009. SAN 327-1803. Tel: 202-234-8701. FAX: 202-745-0067. E-Mail: mansour@odc.org. Web Site: www.odc.org. *Librn*, Zeina Mansour
Library Holdings: Bk Vols 3,000; Per Subs 68
Restriction: By appointment only

G OVERSEAS PRIVATE INVESTMENT CORPORATION LIBRARY,* 1100 New York Ave NW 11th flr, 20527. SAN 302-7473. Tel: 202-336-8565. FAX: 202-408-9860. Web Site: www.opic.gov. *Mgr*, Lena Paulsen; E-Mail: lpaul@opic.gov; *Ref*, Marian Francois; Staff 4 (MLS 3, Non-MLS 1)
Founded 1974
Library Holdings: Bk Titles 10,000; Per Subs 150
Subject Interests: Economics, Finance
Special Collections: Country File; Foreign Assistance & International Development (Legislative History Coll)
Automation Activity & Vendor Info: (Acquisitions) epixtech, inc.; (Cataloging) epixtech, inc.; (Circulation) epixtech, inc.; (OPAC) epixtech, inc.; (Serials) epixtech, inc.
Publications: Management Services (monthly newsletter & new accessions list); User's Guide to Information Services
Restriction: By appointment only
Partic in Dialog Corporation; Dow Jones News Retrieval; Fedlink; OCLC Online Computer Library Center, Inc

S PADCO, INC, Planning & Development Collaborative International Library, 1025 Thomas Jefferson St NW, Ste 170, 20007. SAN 375-6483. Tel: 202-337-2326. FAX: 202-944-2350. E-Mail: padco@padcoinc.com.
Library Holdings: Bk Titles 2,000; Per Subs 10

S PAN AMERICAN HEALTH ORGANIZATION HEADQUARTERS LIBRARY,* 525 23rd St NW, 20037. SAN 302-749X. Tel: 202-974-3305. FAX: 202-974-3623. Web Site: www.ajp/prg. *Librn*, Maria Teresa Astroza; E-Mail: astrozam@paho.org; *Ref*, Magdalena Ziver
Founded 1943
Library Holdings: Bk Titles 50,000; Per Subs 35
Subject Interests: Nutrition, Public health
Special Collections: World Health Organization & Pan American Health Organization Documents

L PATTON & BOGGS LLP, Law Library, 2550 M St NW, 8th flr, 20037. SAN 376-0669. Tel: 202-457-6000. FAX: 202-457-6315. *Librn*, Kevin McCall
Library Holdings: Bk Titles 5,000

L PAUL, HASTINGS, JANOFSKY & WALKER, Law Library,* 1299 Pennsylvania Ave NW, 10th flr, 20004. SAN 323-6870. Tel: 202-508-9858. FAX: 202-508-9700. *Librn*, Bill Grady; Staff 2 (MLS 1, Non-MLS 1)
Library Holdings: Bk Vols 8,000
Subject Interests: Environmental law

L PAUL, WEISS, RIFKIND, WHARTON & GARRISON, Law Library,* 1615 L St NW, Ste 1300, 20036-5694. SAN 372-106X. Tel: 202-223-7400. FAX: 202-223-7420. *Librn*, Jennifer G Eckel; E-Mail: jeckel@paulweiss.com
Library Holdings: Bk Vols 10,000; Per Subs 75
Subject Interests: International trade
Partic in Capcon Library Network; OCLC Online Computer Library Center, Inc

S PEACE CORPS, ICE Resource Center,* 1111 20th St NW 5th flr, 20526. SAN 325-8785. Tel: 202-692-2640. FAX: 202-692-2641. *Librn*, Marc Lippman; *Tech Servs*, Douglas Moors; *Coll Develop*, Anne Latimer; *Tech Servs*, Bridget Fox
Library Holdings: Bk Vols 10,000; Per Subs 275
Publications: Country Bibliographies; Recent Arrivals
Restriction: By appointment only
Partic in Fedlink

S PENSION BENEFIT GUARANTY CORP LIBRARY,* 1200 K St NW, Ste 340, 20005-4026. SAN 320-135X. Tel: 202-326-4020. FAX: 202-326-4112. *Dir*, Felice Sacks
Founded 1976
Library Holdings: Bk Vols 12,000; Per Subs 65

L PEPPER & HAMILTON, Law Library, 600 14th St NW, 20005. SAN 372-1558. Tel: 202-220-1200. FAX: 202-220-1665. *Librn*, Laura Riley
Library Holdings: Bk Vols 10,000; Per Subs 40
Subject Interests: International trade, Transportation
Partic in OCLC Online Computer Library Center, Inc

S THE PHILLIPS COLLECTION LIBRARY,* 1600 21st St NW, 20009-1090. SAN 321-2297. Tel: 202-387-2151, Ext 212. FAX: 202-387-2436. *Librn*, Karen Schneider; E-Mail: kschneider@phillipscollection.org
Founded 1976
Library Holdings: Bk Vols 6,800; Bk Titles 7,000; Per Subs 10
Special Collections: 19th & 20th Century European & American Artists, monographs; Duncan Phillips Coll, mss; Exhibition Catalogues; Phillips Coll Artists, monographs

L PILLSBURY, MADISON & SUTRO LIBRARY,* East Tower, Ste 900, 1100 New York Ave NW, 20005. SAN 377-3906. Tel: 202-861-3081. FAX: 202-822-0944. *Librn*, Patsy Stann
Library Holdings: Bk Vols 17,000; Per Subs 200
Partic in Am Asn of Law Librs; Am Libr Asn; Law Libr Asn of DC

L PIPER, MARBURY, RUDNICK & WOLFE LLP, Law Library, 1200 19th St NW, 20036-2412. SAN 372-154X. Tel: 202-861-3910, 202-861-4171. FAX: 202-223-2085. Web Site: www.piperrudnick.com. *Librn*, John Gall; *Librn*, Thomas Hay; *Librn*, Patricia Gudas Mitchell; Tel: 202-689-7010, E-Mail: pat.gudasmitchell@piperrudnick.com; *ILL*, John L Leigh, Jr; Staff 3 (MLS 2, Non-MLS 1)
Library Holdings: Bk Vols 8,000; Per Subs 150
Subject Interests: Environmental law
Special Collections: Environmental Law Coll
Partic in Capcon Library Network

L PIPER, MARBURY, RUDNICK & WOLFE LLP, Law Library, 1201 New York Ave NW, Penthouse, 20005-3919. SAN 326-3134. Tel: 202-712-7200. FAX: 202-712-7222. *Head Librn*, Pat Gudas Mitchell
Library Holdings: Bk Vols 20,000
Partic in Westlaw

S POINT-OF-PURCHASE ADVERTISING INSTITUTE, INC, Information Center,* 1660 L St NW, 10th flr, 20036. SAN 312-0031. Tel: 202-530-3000. FAX: 202-530-3030. Web Site: www.popeai.com.
Library Holdings: Bk Vols 165; Per Subs 115
Publications: Information Center Brochure; Newsletter

S THE POINTS OF LIGHT FOUNDATION LIBRARY,* 1400 I St, 20005-2208. SAN 373-0360. Tel: 202-729-8000. FAX: 202-729-8105. Web Site: www.pointsoflight.org.
Library Holdings: Bk Vols 150

P POLISH LIBRARY,* 1503 21st St NW, 20036. SAN 375-9237. Tel: 202-466-2665. Web Site: www.polishworld.com/pwguests/pollibwdc/pollibwdc.htm. *Pres*, Tadeusz Walendowski
Jan 1999-Dec 1999 Income Locally Generated Income $10,900. Mats Exp $7,842, Books $1,582, Per/Ser (Incl. Access Fees) $466, Other Print Mats $1,539. Sal $1,375
Library Holdings: Bk Titles 6,000
Open Tues 7:30pm-9:30pm, Thurs 1-4, Sat 11-2
Friends of the Library Group

S POPULATION ACTION INTERNATIONAL LIBRARY,* 1120 19th St NW, Ste 550, 20036. SAN 320-1368. Tel: 202-659-1833. FAX: 202-293-1795. E-Mail: ama@popact.org.
Library Holdings: Bk Titles 5,000; Per Subs 500
Subject Interests: Ecology
Publications: Weekly Periodicals Acquisitions List (in-house only)

S POPULATION REFERENCE BUREAU LIBRARY,* 1875 Connecticut Ave NW Ste 520, 20009. SAN 302-7538. Tel: 202-483-1100. FAX: 202-328-3937. Web Site: www.prb.org. *Librn*, Zuali Malsawma; E-Mail: zuali@prb.org
Library Holdings: Bk Titles 13,000; Per Subs 300
Subject Interests: Aging, Food industry and trade, Population studies, Women's studies
Special Collections: International Statistical Publications; United Nations Publications; United States Census Materials; United States Vital Statistics; World Bank Publications; World Fertility Surveys, Contraceptive Prevalence Surveys, Demographic & Health Surveys
Partic in Dialog Corporation

L PORTER, WRIGHT, MORRIS & ARTHUR, Law Library,* 1667 K St NW, Ste 1100, 20006. SAN 377-4279. Tel: 202-778-3000. FAX: 202-778-3063.
Library Holdings: Bk Vols 2,000; Per Subs 15
Partic in Law Libr Soc of DC

G POSTAL RATE COMMISSION LIBRARY,* 1333 H St NW, Ste 300, 20268. SAN 377-4562. Tel: 202-789-6877. FAX: 202-789-6861. *Librn*, Leona Anasiewicz; E-Mail: leonaanasiewicz@pre.gov
Library Holdings: Bk Vols 2,500; Per Subs 60

L POWELL, GOLDSTEIN, FRAZER & MURPHY, Law Library,* 1001 Pennsylvania Ave NW, Ste 600 N, 20004. SAN 372-4832. Tel: 202-624-7253. FAX: 202-624-7222. *Librn*, Tracy Fritz; Staff 3 (MLS 2, Non-MLS 1)
Library Holdings: Bk Vols 9,000
Subject Interests: International trade, Real estate

L PRESTON, GATES, ELLIS & ROUVELAS MEEDS LLP, Law Library, 1735 New York Ave NW No 500, 20006. SAN 372-1485. Tel: 202-662-8415. FAX: 202-331-1024. Web Site: www.prestongates.com. *Librn*, Gretchen W Asmuth; E-Mail: gasmuth@prestongates.com
1998-1999 Mats Exp $325,000. Sal $140,000 (Prof $105,000)
Library Holdings: Bk Vols 8,000; Bk Titles 4,500; Per Subs 300
Subject Interests: Maritime law

L PRICE WATERHOUSE, Law Library,* 1301 K St NW, Ste 800, 20005. SAN 377-4570. Tel: 202-414-1452. FAX: 202-414-1590. *Librn*, Lorna Cowen
Partic in Law Libr Soc of DC

L PRICE WATERHOUSE COOPERS LIBRARY,* 1301 K St NW Ste 800W, 20005. SAN 328-4549. Tel: 202-822-2000. FAX: 202-822-5839. Web Site: www.colybrand.com. *Librn*, Lorna Cohen
Library Holdings: Bk Vols 4,000; Per Subs 100
Subject Interests: Accounting, Auditing
Mem of Law Libr Soc of Washington DC

SR PRISON FELLOWSHIP MINISTERIES, Information Center,* PO Box 17500, 20041-0500. SAN 321-401X. Tel: 703-478-0100. FAX: 703-318-4183.
Founded 1980
Library Holdings: Bk Titles 3,500; Per Subs 175
Subject Interests: Christianity
Mem of District of Columbia Libr Asn
Partic in Criminal Justice Info Exchange; Dialog Corporation

L PROSKAUER & ROSE LLP LIBRARY, 1233 20th St NW, Ste 800, 20036. SAN 377-4473. Tel: 202-416-6823. FAX: 202-416-6899. *Librn*, Carla Evans; E-Mail: cevans@proskauer.com
Partic in Am Asn of Law Librs; Law Libr Soc of DC

M PROVIDENCE HOSPITAL, Health Sciences Library,* 1150 Varnum St NE, 20017. SAN 302-7554. Tel: 202-269-7144. FAX: 202-269-7142. *Dir*, Rose Marie Leone Winiewicz; Staff 4 (MLS 1, Non-MLS 3)
Library Holdings: Bk Vols 3,500; Per Subs 200
Subject Interests: Hospital administration, Medicine, Nursing
Partic in Dialog Corporation; Hospital Coun of Nat Capital Area; Mid-Atlantic Chapter-Med Libr Asn; Nat Libr of Med; OCLC Online Computer Library Center, Inc; Regional Med Libr - Region 2

S PUBLIC CITIZEN LIBRARY,* 215 Pennsylvania Ave SE, 20003. SAN 325-8580. Tel: 202-546-4996. FAX: 202-547-7392. Web Site: www.citizen.org. *In Charge*, John Herman
Library Holdings: Bk Titles 1,000; Per Subs 11

S PUTNAM, HAYES & BARTLETT INC LIBRARY,* 1776 Eye St NW, Ste 600, 20006. SAN 373-692X. Tel: 202-223-6665. FAX: 202-296-3858. *Librn*, Michelle Reaux
Library Holdings: Bk Titles 300; Per Subs 325
Subject Interests: Energy
Publications: Newsletter
Partic in Capcon Library Network; Dialog Corporation

S RAND LIBRARY,* 1333 H St NW, Ste 800, 20005-4707. SAN 302-7589. Tel: 202-296-5000, Ext 5330. FAX: 202-842-5926. Web Site: www.rand.org. *Mgr*, Gail Kouril; E-Mail: gkouril@rand.org
Founded 1950
Library Holdings: Bk Titles 8,500; Per Subs 250
Subject Interests: Education, Energy, Political science
Restriction: Staff use only
Partic in Interlibrary Users Association

L REED, SMITH, SHAW & MCCLAY, Law Library,* 1301 K St NW, Ste 1100 E Tower, 20005-3317. SAN 325-8564. Tel: 202-414-9415. FAX: 202-414-9299. *Librn*, Lorraine DeSouza
Library Holdings: Bk Vols 21,041

S REPUBLICAN NATIONAL COMMITTEE LIBRARY,* 310 First St SE, 20003. SAN 302-7600. Tel: 202-863-8815. FAX: 202-863-8744. Web Site: www.rnc.org. *In Charge*, Tom Geoghegan
Library Holdings: Bk Titles 1,500; Per Subs 50
Subject Interests: Government
Special Collections: Convention Proceedings
Restriction: By appointment only

S RESOURCES FOR THE FUTURE INC LIBRARY,* 1616 P St NW, Rm B-6, 20036-1400. SAN 374-471X. Tel: 202-328-5089. FAX: 202-939-3460. Web Site: www.rff.org. *Librn*, Christopher B Clotworthy; E-Mail: clotwort@rff.org; Staff 2 (MLS 1, Non-MLS 1)
Founded 1985
Library Holdings: Bk Titles 6,000; Per Subs 130

L ROGERS & WELLS LIBRARY,* 607 14th St NW, 20005. SAN 325-8602. Tel: 202-434-0842. FAX: 202-434-0800. *Librn*, Beverly R Miller
Library Holdings: Bk Vols 3,500
Subject Interests: Law
Open Mon-Fri 9-5

L ROSS, DIXON & BELL, LLP, Law Library, 601 Pennsylvania Ave NW, North Bldg, No 800, 20004. Tel: 202-662-2142. FAX: 202-662-2190. *Librn*, Mary M Maguire; Tel: 202-662-2979, E-Mail: mmaguire@rdblaw.com; *Asst Librn*, Tracie Garner; E-Mail: tgarner@rdblaw.com; Staff 2 (MLS 1, Non-MLS 1)
Founded 1984
Library Holdings: Bk Vols 10,000
Automation Activity & Vendor Info: (Cataloging) Inmagic, Inc.; (ILL) Inmagic, Inc.; (Serials) Inmagic, Inc.
Database Vendor: Lexis-Nexis, OCLC - First Search
Function: Reference services available

S ROY A CHILDS, JR LIBRARY, The Cato Institute, 1000 Massachusetts Ave NW, 20001-5403. Tel: 202-789-5263. Web Site: www.cato.org. *Librn*, Leonard T Harris; Fax: 202-842-3490, E-Mail: lharris@cato.org
Jan 1999-Dec 1999 Income Parent Institution $150,000. Mats Exp $110,000, Books $20,000, Per/Ser (Incl. Access Fees) $30,000, Electronic Ref Mat (Incl. Access Fees) $30,000. Sal $25,000
Library Holdings: Bk Vols 30,000; Per Subs 200
Subject Interests: Public policy
Automation Activity & Vendor Info: (Cataloging) Inmagic, Inc.
Database Vendor: Lexis-Nexis

R SAINT JOSEPH'S SEMINARY LIBRARY,* 1200 Varnum St NE, 20017. SAN 302-7627. Tel: 202-526-4231. FAX: 202-526-7811. *Dir*, John Filippelli
Library Holdings: Bk Vols 30,000; Per Subs 46

C SAINT PAUL'S COLLEGE LIBRARY, 3015 Fourth St NE, 20017. SAN 302-7643. Tel: 202-832-6262. FAX: 202-269-2507. *Librn*, Denise Eggers; Tel: 202-269-2545; Staff 2 (MLS 1, Non-MLS 1)
Founded 1889. Enrl 30; Highest Degree: Doctorate
Library Holdings: Bk Vols 45,000; Bk Titles 40,000; Per Subs 89
Special Collections: 17th & 18th Century Works; Isaac T Hecker Archival Coll; Paulist Fathers Archive
Partic in Washington Theological Consortium

SR ST PAUL'S EPISCOPAL CHURCH, Thomas Bray Library, Rock Creek Church Rd & Webster St NW, 20011. SAN 372-591X. Tel: 202-726-2080. FAX: 202-726-1084. *Librn*, Anne Greenwood; *Asst Librn*, Eunice Tinsley
1998-1999 Income $900. Mats Exp $900, Books $600, Per/Ser (Incl. Access Fees) $300
Library Holdings: Bk Titles 700; Per Subs 13

L SANDERS, SCHNABEL & BRANDENBURG LIBRARY, 900 17th St NW, Ste 900, 20006. SAN 377-4287. Tel: 202-638-2241. FAX: 202-293-3419. Web Site: ssblegal.com. *Librn*, Carmen McDevitt; Staff 1 (Non-MLS 1)
Library Holdings: Bk Vols 1,500; Per Subs 35
Partic in Law Libr Soc of DC

L SCHIFF, HARDIN & WAITE LIBRARY, 1101 Connecticut Ave NW, Ste 600, 20036. SAN 377-418X. Tel: 202-778-6435. FAX: 202-778-6460. *Librn*, Rosalind Kelman; E-Mail: rkelman@schiffhardin.com
Library Holdings: Bk Vols 9,000
Partic in Am Asn of Law Librs; Law Libr Soc of DC

S SCOTTISH RITE SUPREME COUNCIL LIBRARY, 1733 16th St NW, 20009-3103. SAN 302-7686. Tel: 202-232-3579, Ext 39. FAX: 202-387-1843. Web Site: www.srmason-sj.org. *Librn*, Joan Sansbury; E-Mail: jsnasbury@srmason-sj.org
Founded 1881
Library Holdings: Bk Titles 200,000; Per Subs 25
Subject Interests: History
Special Collections: Abraham Lincoln Coll; Burnsiana; Goethe Coll; J Edgar Hoover Coll; Masonic Coll; Panama Canal (Thatcher Coll)
Friends of the Library Group

S SERVICE EMPLOYEES INTERNATIONAL UNION LIBRARY, 1313 L St NW, 20005. SAN 377-4325. Tel: 202-898-3200. FAX: 202-898-3309. *Res*, Aimie Anderson
Library Holdings: Bk Vols 3,000; Per Subs 250

S SEYFARTH & SHAW, (Formerly Seyfarth, Shaw, Fairweather & Geraldson), Washington Branch Office Library, 815 Connecticut Ave NW, Ste 500, 20006-4004. SAN 302-7694. Tel: 202-463-2400. FAX: 202-828-3561. *Librn*, Susan Quinn; E-Mail: quinnsu@dc.seyfarth.com; Staff 3 (MLS 2, Non-MLS 1)
Library Holdings: Bk Vols 11,000; Per Subs 150
Subject Interests: Employment, Labor, Law
Partic in OCLC Online Computer Library Center, Inc

L SHAW PITTMAN, (Formerly Fisher, Wayland, Cooper, Leader & Zaragoza LLP Library), Law Library, 2300 N St NW, 20037. SAN 377-2934. Tel: 202-454-7499, 202-663-9033. FAX: 202-663-8007. Web Site: www.shawpittman.com. *Librn*, Sue Mills
Library Holdings: Bk Vols 23,000; Per Subs 100
Partic in Law Libr Soc of DC

L SHAW, PITTMAN, POTTS & TROWBRIDGE LIBRARY,* 2300 N St NW, 20037. SAN 325-8629. Tel: 202-663-8889. FAX: 202-663-8007. *Librn*, Susan Mills
Library Holdings: Bk Vols 23,419; Per Subs 306
Partic in Am Asn of Law Librs

L SHEARMAN & STERLING LIBRARY,* 801 Pennsylvania Ave NW Ste 900, 20004. SAN 373-0972. Tel: 202-508-8055. FAX: 202-508-8100. *Librn*, Jill Sidford
Library Holdings: Bk Vols 10,000
Subject Interests: International trade

R SHILOH BAPTIST CHURCH, Susie E Miles Library, 1500 Ninth St NW, 20001. SAN 302-7716. Tel: 202-232-4200, 202-232-4288. FAX: 202-234-6235. Web Site: shilohbaptist.org. *Librn*, Vera Hunter; *Asst Librn*, Rosa Jeter
Founded 1959
Library Holdings: Bk Titles 4,000; Per Subs 17
Subject Interests: Religion

M SIBLEY MEMORIAL HOSPITAL, Medical Library, 5255 Loughboro Rd NW, 20016. SAN 329-5184. Tel: 202-537-4110. FAX: 202-364-7648. *Librn*, Diana J Fitzgerald; E-Mail: dfitzgerald@sibley.org; Staff 1 (MLS 1)
Library Holdings: Bk Titles 2,500; Per Subs 100
Subject Interests: Medicine, Nursing
Partic in District Of Columbia Health Sciences Information Network

L SIDLEY & AUSTIN, Law Library,* 1722 I St NW, 20006. SAN 371-6317. Tel: 202-736-8505. FAX: 202-736-8711. *Dir*, Sabrina I Pacifici; *Assoc Librn, Coll Develop*, Jeffrey V Bosh; E-Mail: jbosh@cais.com; *Tech Servs*, Wen-Ling Tseng; *Circ*, Hang Ngo; *Ref*, Anne Kane; *ILL*, Wyman L Colona Jr; Staff 4 (MLS 4)
Library Holdings: Bk Vols 40,000; Per Subs 300
Special Collections: Legislative Histories
Partic in Capcon Library Network; OCLC Online Computer Library Center, Inc

S SILVER INSTITUTE LIBRARY, 1112 16th St NW, Ste 240, 20036. SAN 371-4276. Tel: 202-835-0185. FAX: 202-835-0155. E-Mail: info@silverinstitute.org. Web Site: www.silverinstitute.org. *Exec Dir*, Paul Bateman; *Publ Servs, VPres*, Michael DiRienzo
Founded 1971
Library Holdings: Bk Titles 900; Per Subs 40
Subject Interests: Mining

L SILVERSTEIN & MULLENS PLLC, Law Library,* 1776 K St NW, 8th flr, Ste 700, 20006-2304. SAN 377-3957. Tel: 202-452-7938. FAX: 202-452-7989. *Librn*, Matthew Mahaffie
Library Holdings: Bk Titles 2,000; Per Subs 200
Partic in Am Asn of Law Librs; Law Libr Soc of DC

L SKADDEN, ARPS, SLATE, MEAGHER & FLOM, Law Library,* 1440 New York Ave NW, 20005. SAN 372-1434. Tel: 202-371-7760. FAX: 202-393-5760. *Librn*, Margaret M Heath
Library Holdings: Bk Vols 25,000; Per Subs 400
Subject Interests: Energy, Securities
Partic in Capcon Library Network

S SMALL BUSINESS ADMINISTRATION, Reference Library,* 409 Third St SW, 20416. SAN 302-7724. Tel: 202-205-7033. FAX: 202-205-7064. *Librn*, Margaret Hickey; Staff 1 (MLS 1)
Founded 1958
Library Holdings: Bk Titles 8,000; Per Subs 75
Subject Interests: Small bus
Restriction: Open to public for reference only

S SMITHSONIAN INSTITUTION, Archives of American Art, 901 D St SW, Ste 704, 20560. SAN 325-0504. Tel: 202-314-3900. FAX: 202-314-3987. Web Site: www.archivesofamericanart.si.edu. *Dir*, Dr Richard Wattenmaker; *Ref*, Judith Throm; Tel: 202-314-3919, E-Mail: thromj@aaa.si.edu
Subject Interests: Am art hist
Special Collections: Personal papers of American artists: letters, diaries, photographs, interviews, business records, working sketches & drawings

SMITHSONIAN INSTITUTION
S OFFICE OF ARCHIVES, A & I Bldg, Rm 2135, 900 Jefferson Dr SW, 20560. SAN 302-7740. Tel: 202-357-1420. FAX: 202-357-2395. E-Mail: osiaref@ic.si.edu. Web Site: www.siris.si.edu/. *Dir*, Edie Hedlin
Publications: Guide to Smithsonian Archives, 1996; Guides to Collections

S SMITHSONIAN INSTITUTION LIBRARIES, NHB 22, MRC 154, Constitution Ave at Tenth St NW, 20560-0154. SAN 337-0321. Tel: 202-357-2240. FAX: 202-786-2866. E-Mail: libmail@sil.si.edu. Web Site: www.sil.si.edu. *Dir*, Nancy E Gwinn; *Asst Dir*, Tom Garnett; *Asst Dir*, Bonita Perry; *Asst Dir*, Mary Augusta Thomas; Staff 112 (MLS 60, Non-MLS 52)
Founded 1846
Library Holdings: Bk Vols 1,200,000
Subject Interests: African art, Am art, Am cultural hist, Am hist, Asian art, Aviation hist, Decorative art, Ecol, Ethnology, Natural history, Science/technology, Trade
Special Collections: History of Science & Technology
Automation Activity & Vendor Info: (Acquisitions) epixtech, inc.
Publications: Information (Newsletter)
Partic in Asn of Research Libraries; Chesapeake Info & Res Libr Alliance; Fedlink; OCLC Online Computer Library Center, Inc; Research Libraries Group, Inc
Branches:

ANACOSTIA MUSEUM LIBRARY, 1901 Fort Pl SE, 20020-0520. SAN 302-5845. Tel: 202-287-3380. FAX: 202-287-3183. E-Mail: libmail@sil.si.edu. Web Site: www.sil.si.edu. *Librn*, Tracy-Ann Sulciman-Stewart
Library Holdings: Bk Vols 2,500
Subject Interests: Abolitionism, African, African Am, Local history, Slavery
Publications: Newsletter
Restriction: By appointment only

ANTHROPOLOGY LIBRARY, NHB 331, MRC 112, Constitution Ave at Tenth St NW, 20560-0112. SAN 374-8081. Tel: 202-357-1819. FAX: 202-357-1896. E-Mail: libmail@sil.si.edu. Web Site: www.sil.si.edu. *Librn*, Margaret R Dittemore; *Ref*, Jim Haug
Library Holdings: Bk Vols 75,000
Subject Interests: Anthropology, Archaeology
Special Collections: Asian Cultural History (Echols Coll); Bureau of American Ethnology Library Coll; Mesoamerican Codices; Native American Languages/Linguistics; Physical Anthropology (Hrdlicka Coll)

BOTANY LIBRARY, NHB W422, MRC 166, Constitution Ave at Tenth St NW, 20560-0166. SAN 374-8073. Tel: 202-357-2715. FAX: 202-357-1896. E-Mail: libmail@sil.si.edu. Web Site: www.sil.si.edu. *Librn*, Ruth F Schallert; Staff 1 (MLS 1)
Library Holdings: Bk Vols 42,000
Subject Interests: Botany
Special Collections: Agrostology (Hitchcock-Chase Coll); Algology (Dawson Coll); General Botany (John Donnell Smith Coll)

CENTRAL REFERENCE & LOAN SERVICES LIBRARY, NHB 27, MRC 154, Constitution Ave at Tenth St NW, 20560-0154. SAN 337-0356. Tel: 202-357-2139. Interlibrary Loan Service Tel: 202-357-2158. FAX: 202-786-2443. *Librn*, Martin Smith; *Ref Serv*, Amy Levin
Library Holdings: Bk Vols 30,200
Subject Interests: Biography, Library and information science, Management, Social sciences
Special Collections: Smithsoniana (publication by & about the Smithsonian Institution)

COOPER-HEWITT, NATIONAL DESIGN MUSEUM LIBRARY

See Separate Entry in New York, NY

DIBNER LIBRARY OF THE HISTORY OF SCIENCE & TECHNOLOGY, NMAH 1041, MRC 630, 14th St & Constitution Ave NW, 20560-0630. SAN 375-5266. Tel: 202-357-1568. FAX: 202-633-9102. E-Mail: libmail@sil.si.edu. Web Site: www.sil.si.edu. *Librn, Spec Coll*, William Baxter; *Curator, Ref*, Ronald S Brashear; *Curator, Ref*, Leslie K Overstreet.
Subject Specialists: *Science/technology*, Ronald S Brashear
Subject Interests: Applied arts, Natural history, Physical science, Technology
Special Collections: Burndy Library Donation; Comegys Library; Smithson Coll; Wetmore Bequest
Publications: Heralds of Science; Manuscripts of the Dibner Collection
Restriction: By appointment only

FREER GALLERY OF ART & ARTHUR M SACKLER GALLERY LIBRARY, 12th St & Jefferson Dr SW, 20560-0707. SAN 337-047X. Tel: 202-357-4880, Ext 342. FAX: 202-786-2936. E-Mail: libmail@sil.si.edu. Web Site: www.sackler-freer-library.si.edu, www.sil.si.edu. *Librn*, Lily Kecskes; E-Mail: kecskli@asia.si.edu; *Ref Serv*, Kathryn Phillips; *Ref Serv*, Reiko Yoshimura; *Archivist*, Colleen Hennessey; *Tech Servs*, Yue Shu; Staff 3 (MLS 3)
Founded 1923
Library Holdings: Bk Vols 70,705; Per Subs 746
Subject Interests: Arts, Asia, E Asian, Far East, Near East, South Asia, Southeast Asia
Special Collections: Charles Lang Freer Coll, archives; Herzfeld Coll, archives; James M Whistler & His Contemporaries
Automation Activity & Vendor Info: (OPAC) Innovative Interfaces Inc.
Restriction: Non-circulating to the public
Partic in Research Libraries Group, Inc; RLIN

HIRSHHORN MUSEUM & SCULPTURE GARDEN LIBRARY, Seventh St & Independence Ave SW, 20560-0350. SAN 337-050X. Tel: 202-357-3222. FAX: 202-786-2682. E-Mail: libmail@sil.si.edu. Web Site: www.sil.si.edu. *Librn*, Anna Brooke; E-Mail: brookea@hmsg.si.edu; Staff 3 (MLS 1, Non-MLS 2)
Founded 1969
Library Holdings: Bk Vols 54,000; Per Subs 50
Subject Interests: 19th Century, 20th Century, Memorabilia, Painting, Sculpture
Special Collections: Press Books, photogs, slides
Partic in RLIN

HORTICULTURE LIBRARY, A&I Bldg Rm 2282 - MRC 420, 900 Jefferson Dr SW, 20560-0420. SAN 375-5274. Tel: 202-357-1544. FAX: 202-786-2026. E-Mail: libmail@sil.si.edu. Web Site: www.sil.si.edu.; Staff 1 (MLS 1)
Founded 1983
Library Holdings: Bk Vols 7,000
Subject Interests: Gardening, Horticulture, Landscape architecture
Special Collections: History & Design in Late 19th & Early 20th Century; W Atlee Burpee Seed & Nursery Company Archives
Restriction: By appointment only

MUSEUM REFERENCE CENTER, Center for Museum Studies, Arts & Industries Bldg, Rm 2235, 900 Jefferson Dr SW, 20560-0427. SAN 337-0747. Tel: 202-786-2271. FAX: 202-357-2311. E-Mail: libmail@sil.si.edu. Web Site: www.sil.si.edu. *Librn*, Valerie Wheat
Library Holdings: Bk Vols 4,000; Per Subs 1,500
Subject Interests: Museology
Special Collections: American Asssociation of Museums Annual Meetings (AV-tapes 1984-Present); Special Documentary files of handbooks, educational materials, evaluation studies & museum related publications

MUSEUM SUPPORT CENTER LIBRARY
See Separate Entry in Suitland, MD

NATIONAL AIR & SPACE MUSEUM LIBRARY, NASM 3100, MRC 314, Sixth St & Independence Ave SW, 20560-0314. SAN 337-0534. Tel: 202-357-3133. FAX: 202-786-2835. E-Mail: libmail@sil.si.edu. Web Site: www.sil.si.edu. *Librn*, Elaine Cline; *Ref Serv*, Paul McCutcheon
Library Holdings: Bk Titles 41,000
Subject Interests: Aeronautics, Astronautics, Astronomy, Astrophysics, Earth science, Planetary sci
Special Collections: Aerospace (Bella Landauer Sheet Music & Children's Book Coll); Aerospace (Institute of Aeronautical Sciences Historical Coll), bk, per, photog; Ballooning (William A M Burden Coll), bks, per; Rare & Scarce Aeronautica & Astronautica (Ramsey Room)

NATIONAL MUSEUM OF AFRICAN ART LIBRARY, MRC 708, 950 Independence Ave SW, 20560-0708. SAN 302-637X. Tel: 202-357-4600, Ext 286. FAX: 202-357-4879. E-Mail: libmail@sil.si.edu. *Librn*, Janet L Stanley
Library Holdings: Bk Vols 20,000
Subject Interests: Africa, Archeology, Art, Folklore, History, Material culture, Music, Religion

NATIONAL MUSEUM OF AMERICAN ART & THE NATIONAL PORTRAIT GALLERY, Victor Bldg, 750 Ninth St NW, 20560-0215. SAN 337-0569. Tel: 202-357-1886. FAX: 202-786-2583. E-Mail: libmail@sil.si.edu. Web Site: www.sil.si.edu. *Librn*, Cecilia H Chin; E-Mail: cchin@nmaa.si.edu; *Ref Serv*, Patricia M Lynagh; *Ref Serv*, Stephanie Moye; *Cat*, Kent Boese; Staff 4 (MLS 4)
Founded 1964
Library Holdings: Bk Vols 135,000; Per Subs 900
Subject Interests: 20th Century art, Am art, Biog, History, Portraiture
Special Collections: California Art & Artists (Ferdinand Perret Art Reference Library), scrapbks; Mallet Library of Art Reproductions
Publications: Brochure
Partic in Dialog Corporation; OCLC Online Computer Library Center, Inc; RLIN; Wilsonline

NATIONAL MUSEUM OF AMERICAN HISTORY LIBRARY, NMAH 5016, MRC 630, 14th & Constitution Ave NW, 20560-0630. SAN 337-0593. Tel: 202-357-2414. FAX: 202-357-4256. E-Mail: libmail@sil.si.edu. Web Site: www.sil.si.edu. *Librn*, Rhoda Ratner; *Ref Serv*, Chris Cottrill; *Ref Serv*, Jim Roan
Founded 1958
Library Holdings: Bk Vols 165,000
Subject Interests: American history, Culture, Decorative arts, Graphic arts, Military history, Numismatics, Photography, Textiles
Special Collections: Exhibitions & Expositions; History of Science & Technology; Radioana; Trade Literature

NATIONAL MUSEUM OF NATURAL HISTORY LIBRARY, NHB 51, MRC 154, Constitution Ave at Tenth St NW, 20560-0154. SAN 337-0623. Tel: 202-357-1496. FAX: 202-357-1896. E-Mail: libmail@sil.si.edu. Web Site: www.sil.si.edu. *Librn*, Ann Juneau; *Ref Serv*, Courtney Shaw; *Ref Serv*, Robert Skarr; *Ref Serv*, David Steere
Library Holdings: Bk Vols 5,000
Subject Interests: Botany, Ecology, Entomology, Evolution, Geology, Oceanography, Zoology
Special Collections: Entomology (Casey Coleoptera Coll); Foraminifera (Cushman Coll); Invertebrate Zoology (Wilson Copepoda Coll); Meteorites (Paneth Coll)

NATIONAL POSTAL MUSEUM LIBRARY, 2 Massachusetts Ave NE, 20560-0570. SAN 375-5258. Tel: 202-633-9370. FAX: 202-633-9371. E-Mail: libmail@sil.si.edu. Web Site: www.sil.si.edu. *Librn*, Timothy Carr; Fax: 202-633-9371, E-Mail: carrt@npm.si.edu
Library Holdings: Bk Vols 18,000; Per Subs 114
Subject Interests: Philately
Special Collections: Postal History (Thaddeus Hyatt Postcard & Clipping Files); Sydnor Zip-Code File; US Post Office Department Files
Automation Activity & Vendor Info: (OPAC) NOTIS
Restriction: By appointment only

NATIONAL ZOOLOGICAL PARK LIBRARY, National Zoological Park Education Bldg, MRC 551, 3000 Block of Connecticut Ave NW, 20008-0551. SAN 337-0712. Tel: 202-673-4771. FAX: 202-673-4900. E-Mail: libmail@sil.si.edu. Web Site: www.sil.si.edu. *Librn*, Alvin Hutchinson; Staff 1 (MLS 1)
Library Holdings: Bk Vols 6,500; Per Subs 290
Subject Interests: Animal husbandry, Animals, behavior of, Clinical medicine, Pathology, Veterinary medicine, Wildlife

NATURAL HISTORY RARE BOOKS LIBRARY, NMAH 1041, MRC 672, Constitution Ave at Tenth St NW, 20560-0672. SAN 378-1763. Tel: 202-357-3161. FAX: 202-357-1896. E-Mail: libmail@sil.si.edu. Web Site: www.sil.si.edu. *Librn*, Leslie Overstreet
Subject Interests: Am Indian culture, Anthropology, Linguistics, Natural scis

SMITHSONIAN ENVIRONMENTAL RESEARCH CENTER LIBRARY
See Separate Entry in Edgewater, MD

SMITHSONIAN TROPICAL RESEARCH CENTER LIBRARY, MRC 580, 20560-0580. SAN 328-977X. Tel: 507-212-8000. FAX: 507-212-8147. E-Mail: libmail@sil.si.edu. Web Site: www.sil.si.edu. *Librn*, Vielka Chang-Yau
Library Holdings: Bk Vols 65,000
Subject Interests: Animals, Anthropology, Archaeology, Botany, Ecology, Geology, Molecular biology, Plants, Ttropical ecology
Located in the Republic of Panama

S SOAP & DETERGENT ASSOCIATION LIBRARY,* 1500 K St NW, No 300, 20005-1256. SAN 312-0678. Tel: 212-725-1262. FAX: 212-213-0685.
Library Holdings: Bk Vols 1,000; Per Subs 205

S SOCIETY OF THE CINCINNATI LIBRARY,* 2118 Massachusetts Ave NW, 20008. SAN 302-7767. Tel: 202-785-2040, Ext 426. FAX: 202-785-0729. *Dir*, Sandra L Powers; *Publ Servs*, Ellen McCallister Clark; Staff 4 (MLS 3, Non-MLS 1)
Founded 1783
Library Holdings: Bk Titles 42,000; Per Subs 100
Subject Interests: American revolution
Special Collections: Archives; Ms Coll
Publications: George Rogers Clark Lectures
Partic in OCLC Online Computer Library Center, Inc

L SONNENSCHEIN, NATH & ROSENTHAL LIBRARY,* 1301 K St NW, Ste 600E, 20005. SAN 370-5714. Tel: 202-408-6452. FAX: 202-408-6399. E-Mail: acg@sonnenschein.com. Web Site: www.sonnenschein.com. *Dir*, Ann Green; Staff 2 (MLS 1, Non-MLS 1)
Library Holdings: Bk Vols 15,000; Bk Titles 1,000; Per Subs 25
Restriction: Not open to public
Partic in Capcon Library Network

C SOUTHEASTERN UNIVERSITY LIBRARY,* 501 I St SW, 20024. SAN 302-7783. Tel: 202-488-8162. FAX: 202-488-8093. E-Mail: seu.edu@usa.pipeline.com. Web Site: www.seu.edu. *Dir*, Kathleen Swanson; *Media Spec*, Larry Williams; *Tech Servs*, Maryalls Bedford; Staff 5 (MLS 5)
Founded 1879. Enrl 600; Fac 150; Highest Degree: Master
1998-1999 Income $331,000. Mats Exp $104,000. Sal $210,000
Library Holdings: Bk Titles 36,000; Per Subs 250
Subject Interests: Business and management, Economics
Publications: New Arrivals in the Library

S SPECIAL LIBRARIES ASSOCIATION, Information Resources Center, 1700 18th St NW, 20009-2514. SAN 312-0716. Tel: 202-234-4700. FAX: 202-265-9317. E-Mail: irc@sla.org. Web Site: www.sla.org. *Dir*, John Latham; Staff 2 (MLS 2)
Founded 1909
Library Holdings: Bk Vols 3,200; Per Subs 140
Subject Interests: Info sci, Libr sci, Operation of special librs
Special Collections: SLA archives

L SPIEGEL & MCDIARMID, Law Library, 1350 New York Ave NW, Ste 1100, 20005. SAN 372-1744. Tel: 202-879-4090. FAX: 202-393-2866. *Librn*, Kristy J Yarnell; Tel: 202-879-4055, E-Mail: kristy.yarnell@spiegelmcd.com; *Info Res*, Eve Valdivia; Tel: 202-879-4054, E-Mail: eve.valdivia@spiegelmcd.com; Staff 2 (MLS 1, Non-MLS 1)
Library Holdings: Bk Vols 10,500; Per Subs 200
Subject Interests: Environmental law
Automation Activity & Vendor Info: (Cataloging) Inmagic, Inc.; (Circulation) Inmagic, Inc.; (OPAC) Inmagic, Inc.; (Serials) Inmagic, Inc.
Publications: Library Log-on
Partic in Capcon Library Network

L SQUIRE, SANDERS & DEMPSEY LIBRARY,* 1201 Pennsylvania Ave NW, PO Box 407, 20044-0407. SAN 377-3817. Tel: 202-626-6708. *Librn*, Jacqueline Simpson; E-Mail: jsimpson@ssd.com
Library Holdings: Bk Vols 15,000; Per Subs 60
Partic in Am Asn of Law Librs; Law Libr Soc of DC

S STATE SERVICES ORGANIZATION LIBRARY,* Hall of the States, Ste 337, 444 North Capital St NW, 20001. SAN 320-1376. Tel: 202-624-5485. Interlibrary Loan Service Tel: 202-624-5483. FAX: 202-434-4873. E-Mail: library@sso.org. Web Site: www.sso.org. *Librn*, Marianne Reiff; E-Mail: mreiff@sso.org; *ILL*, Jerry McCoy; E-Mail: jmccoy@sso.org; Staff 3 (MLS 2, Non-MLS 1)
Founded 1977
Jul 1998-Jun 1999 Income $496,000. Mats Exp $99,000, Books $80,000, Per/Ser (Incl. Access Fees) $15,000, Presv $500, Micro $3,500
Library Holdings: Bk Vols 14,000; Bk Titles 7,000; Per Subs 265
Subject Interests: State government
Automation Activity & Vendor Info: (Cataloging) Sydney; (Circulation) Sydney; (OPAC) Sydney; (Serials) Sydney
Publications: State-Federal Relations Index (weekly)
Restriction: Open to public for reference only
Partic in Capcon Library Network

L STEPTOE & JOHNSON LIBRARY,* 1330 Connecticut Ave NW, 20036. SAN 302-7805. Tel: 202-828-3620. FAX: 202-429-3902. *Dir*, Ellen Brondfield; Tel: 202-429-6429, E-Mail: ebrondfield@steptoe.com
Founded 1972
Library Holdings: Bk Vols 60,000
Subject Interests: Law, Legislation
Partic in Capcon Library Network; OCLC Online Computer Library Center, Inc

L STERNE, KESSLER, GOLDSTEIN & FOX LIBRARY,* 1100 New York Ave NW, Ste 600, 20005. SAN 371-7666. Tel: 202-371-2600, Ext 557. FAX: 202-371-2540. *Librn*, Kelley Hayes Martin; E-Mail: kmartin@skgf.com; Staff 1 (MLS 1)
1997-1998 Mats Exp $95,850, Books $4,000, Per/Ser (Incl. Access Fees) $36,700, Other Print Mats $55,150. Sal $35,000
Library Holdings: Bk Titles 10,000

C STRAYER UNIVERSITY, Wilkes Library, 1133 15th St NW, 20005. SAN 302-7813. Tel: 202-463-6477. FAX: 202-463-7573. E-Mail: dam@strayer.edu. Web Site: www.strayer.edu. *Coll Develop, Dir*, David Moulton; Staff 13 (MLS 2, Non-MLS 11)
Founded 1965. Enrl 6,974; Fac 528; Highest Degree: Master
Library Holdings: Bk Vols 33,000; Bk Titles 30,000; Per Subs 465
Subject Interests: Accounting, Bus admin, Data processing
Automation Activity & Vendor Info: (Cataloging) epixtech, inc.; (Circulation) epixtech, inc.; (OPAC) epixtech, inc.
The library information includes figures for the Wilkes Library, DC campus & eleven other satellite campus facilities

S SUGAR ASSOCIATION, INC LIBRARY,* 1101 15th St NW, No 600, 20005. SAN 302-7821. Tel: 202-785-1122. FAX: 202-785-5019. E-Mail: sugar@sugar.org. Web Site: www.sugar.org.
Founded 1943
Library Holdings: Bk Titles 2,141; Per Subs 176
Subject Interests: Nutrition
Special Collections: History of Sugar

L SULLIVAN & CROMWELL, Law Library,* 1701 Pennsylvania Ave NW, 20006. SAN 372-1477. Tel: 202-956-7538. FAX: 202-293-6330. *Librn*, Denise Noller
Library Holdings: Bk Vols 8,000; Per Subs 25

S SULPHUR INSTITUTE LIBRARY,* 1140 Connecticut Ave NW, Ste 612, 20036. SAN 302-783X. Tel: 202-331-9660. FAX: 202-293-2940. Web Site: www.sulphurinstitute.org. *In Charge*, Patricia Bradford
Founded 1960
Library Holdings: Bk Titles 1,800; Per Subs 80

GL SUPREME COURT OF THE UNITED STATES LIBRARY,* One First St NE, 20543. SAN 302-7848. Tel: 202-479-3177. FAX: 202-479-3477. *Librn*, Shelley L Dowling; *Circ*, Sally Miles; *Tech Servs*, Diane Simpson; *Online Servs*, Linda Maslow
Founded 1897
Library Holdings: Bk Vols 450,000
Subject Interests: Law
Special Collections: Supreme Court Legislative Coll
Partic in Capcon Library Network; Dialog Corporation; OCLC Online Computer Library Center, Inc; Westlaw

G SURFACE TRANSPORTATION BOARD LIBRARY,* 1925 K St NW, 20423-0001. SAN 302-6841. Tel: 202-565-1668. FAX: 202-565-9004.
Founded 1894
Library Holdings: Bk Vols 10,000; Per Subs 10
Subject Interests: Administrative law, Statistics, Transportation
Special Collections: bks & documents; Congressional Materials; Transportation in the US, rare; US & Canada Regulatory Commissions, rpts
Restriction: Open to public for reference only

L SUTHERLAND, ASBILL & BRENNAN LIBRARY,* 1275 Pennsylvania Ave NW, 9th flr, 20004. SAN 302-7856. Tel: 202-383-0100. Interlibrary Loan Service Tel: 202-383-0450. FAX: 202-637-3593. *Mgr Libr Serv*, S L Stephens; E-Mail: sstephens@sablaw.com; *Librn*, Janet Bailin; Staff 5 (MLS 1, Non-MLS 4)
Library Holdings: Bk Vols 30,000
Subject Interests: Corporate securities, Energy, Insurance, Intellectual property, Tax
Special Collections: Energy, Insurance, Patents, Tax & Trademarks Coll; Tax Legislative Histories Coll
Database Vendor: GaleNet, Lexis-Nexis, OCLC - First Search
Function: ILL limited
Partic in Dialog Corporation; OCLC Online Computer Library Center, Inc; Westlaw

L SWIDLER, BERLIN, SHEREFF & FRIEDMAN LIBRARY, 3000 K St NW, Ste 300, 20007-5116. SAN 371-8905. Tel: 202-424-7544. FAX: 202-424-7643. *Dir*, Laura Speer; *Librn, Ref Serv*, Sandy Fennell; Staff 3 (MLS 2, Non-MLS 1)
Jan 1999-Dec 1999 Mats Exp $1,000,000
Library Holdings: Bk Titles 10,000; Per Subs 100
Subject Interests: Legal

S TAX EXECUTIVES INSTITUTE, INC, TEI Information System Library, 1200 G St NW, Ste 300, 20005-3814. SAN 327-7879. Tel: 202-638-5601. FAX: 202-638-5607. Web Site: www.tei.org. *Exec Dir*, Michael Murphy
Library Holdings: Per Subs 17

R TEMPLE SINAI LIBRARY,* 3100 Military Rd NW, 20015. SAN 302-7872. Tel: 202-363-6394. FAX: 202-363-6396. *Librn*, Margaret Mallett Chachkin
Founded 1955
Library Holdings: Bk Vols 6,000; Per Subs 40
Subject Interests: Biblical studies, Holocaust, Jewish history and literature, Philosophy, Religion
Special Collections: Children's Literature (Lisa Sanders Ressell Coll); Comparative Religion (Celia Freedman Coll); Hebrew Texts
Publications: Selected bibliographies on Judaica

C THE GEORGE WASHINGTON UNIVERSITY, National Clearinghouse for Bilingual Education,* 2011 I St NW, 20006. SAN 371-0122. Tel: 202-467-0867. FAX: 202-467-4283, 800-531-9347. E-Mail: askncbe@ncbe.gwu.edu. *Dir*, Minerva Gorena
Library Holdings: Bk Titles 19,000; Per Subs 22
Subject Interests: Bilingual Education
Special Collections: Materials Produced by Title VII Programs
NCBE operates a computerized information system, available free-of-charge, which includes three searchable databases & an electronic bulletin board

S THE NEWSPAPERGUILD-CWA, Heywood Broun Memorial Library, 501 Third St, Ste 250, 20001. SAN 302-7430. Tel: 202-434-7177. FAX: 202-434-1472. Web Site: www.newsguild.org. *Librn*, Christina Harrison
Founded 1957
Library Holdings: Bk Vols 900; Per Subs 50
Special Collections: Works of Heywood Broun

L THOMPSON & COBURN LIBRARY,* 700 14th St NW, Ste 900, 20005. SAN 377-4449. Tel: 202-508-1000. FAX: 202-508-1010. *Librn*, Jo-Ann Turner
Library Holdings: Bk Vols 200
Partic in Law Libr Soc of DC

S TRANSAFRICA FORUM, Arthur R Ashe Jr Foreign Policy Library, 1744 R St NW, 20009. SAN 377-4600. Tel: 202-797-2301. FAX: 202-797-2382. E-Mail: info@transafricaforum.org. Web Site: www.transafricaforum.org. *In Charge*, Mwiza Munthali
Library Holdings: Bk Vols 4,000; Per Subs 100
Partic in Am Libr Asn; Spec Libr Asn

S TRAVEL INDUSTRY ASSOCIATION OF AMERICA LIBRARY,* 1100 New York Ave, Ste 450, 20005. SAN 375-2267. Tel: 202-408-8422. FAX: 202-408-1255.

C TRINITY COLLEGE LIBRARY,* Trinity College, 125 Michigan Ave NE, 20017-1094. SAN 302-7929. Tel: 202-884-9350. Interlibrary Loan Service Tel: 202-884-9357. FAX: 202-884-9362. Web Site: www.library.trinitydc.edu. *Dir*, Susan Craig; *Per*, Erin Doherty-Lucas
Founded 1897. Enrl 1,100; Fac 80; Highest Degree: Master
Library Holdings: Bk Vols 200,000; Per Subs 595
Subject Interests: History, Literature, Women's studies
Partic in Capcon Library Network; OCLC Online Computer Library Center, Inc; Washington Research Library Consortium

L TUCKER, FLYER & LEWIS, Law Library,* 1615 L St NW, Ste 400, 20036-5612. SAN 373-6083. Tel: 202-452-8600. FAX: 202-429-3231. E-Mail: library@tuckerflyer.com. *Librn*, Victoria Kahn; *Asst Librn*, M Nassim; Staff 2 (MLS 1, Non-MLS 1)
Library Holdings: Bk Vols 10,000; Bk Titles 500; Per Subs 50
Restriction: Staff use only
Partic in Capcon Library Network

S UKRAINIAN CONGRESS COMMITTEE OF AMERICA LIBRARY,* 311 Massachusetts Ave NE, 20002. SAN 375-6386. Tel: 202-547-0018. FAX: 202-543-5502. E-Mail: unis@worldnet.att.net. *Dir*, Michael Sawkiw
Library Holdings: Bk Titles 5,000

S UNITED FOOD & COMMERCIAL WORKERS INTERNATIONAL UNION LIBRARY,* 1775 K St NW, 20006. SAN 337-0208. Tel: 202-223-3111. FAX: 202-466-1562. *Librn*, Ellen Newton
Founded 1974
Library Holdings: Bk Vols 2,000; Per Subs 750
Subject Interests: Business and management, Economics, Retailing
Restriction: By appointment only
Partic in Dialog Corporation
Branches:
LAW LIBRARY, 1775 K St NW, 20006. Tel: 20-223-3111. FAX: 202-466-1562. *In Charge*, Connie Petrides

S UNITED NATIONS INFORMATION CENTER,* 1775 K St NW Ste 400, 20006. SAN 302-7937. Tel: 202-331-8670. FAX: 202-331-9191. Web Site: www.unicwash.org. *Librn*, Jeanne Dixon; E-Mail: jdixon@unicwash.org
Founded 1946
Library Holdings: Bk Vols 10,000; Bk Titles 1,500
Subject Interests: Economics, Energy, Finance, Human rights, International law, Social sciences and issues
Special Collections: Film Libr; United Nations Chronicles & Publication

G US AGENCY FOR INTERNATIONAL DEVELOPMENT, Research & Reference Services - Africa Bureau Information Center, 1331 Pennsylvania Ave NW, Ste 1425, 20004. SAN 374-7913. Tel: 202-661-5822, 202-661-5825. FAX: 202-661-5890. *Mgr*, Patricia Mantey
Library Holdings: Bk Titles 500; Per Subs 24

G US AID DEVELOPMENT, Information Center, US Agency for International Development, Rm M01-010, 1300 Pennsylvania Ave NW, 20523-1000. SAN 302-5497. Tel: 202-712-0578, Ext 2. Interlibrary Loan Service Tel: 202-712-4963. FAX: 202-216-3515. *Mgr*, David Wolfe; Tel: 202-661-5857; *Ref*, Ellis Beteck; Tel: 202-712-5217; *Ref*, Mary Gillespie; *ILL*, Patsy Lee
Founded 1967
Library Holdings: Bk Vols 10,000; Per Subs 400
Special Collections: Project Document Archive 1958-1974; US Agency for International Development Program Documentation, 1950's to present
Publications: New This Month (acquisitions list)
Partic in OCLC Online Computer Library Center, Inc

UNITED STATES AIR FORCE

A AIR FORCE LEGAL SERVICES AGENCY-JAC LIBRARY, 1501 Wilson Blvd, Ste 617, Arlington, 22209. SAN 373-1774. Tel: 703-696-9040. FAX: 703-696-9084. *Librn*, Doneva M Jones
Library Holdings: Bk Vols 30,000
Subject Interests: Law

A ANDREWS AIR FORCE BASE LIBRARY FL4425, 89 SVS/SVMG, Brookley at D St Bldg 1642, Andrews AFB, 20762. SAN 337-0836. Tel: 301-981-6454. FAX: 301-981-4231. Web Site: www.andrews.af.mil/89sptg/89svs/89_svs.htm. *Coll Develop, Librn*, Richard Von Schlicten; E-Mail: richard.vonschlicht@andrews.af.mil; Staff 6 (MLS 1, Non-MLS 5)
Library Holdings: Bk Vols 30,714; Per Subs 150
Subject Interests: Business and management, International relations, Political science
Special Collections: Air War College; Children's Coll
Partic in Fed Libr & Info Network
Friends of the Library Group

A BOLLING AIR FORCE BASE LIBRARY, FL 4400 HQ 11 SPTG-SVMG, 410 Tinker St Bolling AFB, 20332-0703. SAN 337-0895. Tel: 202-767-5578. FAX: 202-404-8526. E-Mail: bolllib@mail.bolling.af.mil. *Dir*, Kristen A Campbell; E-Mail: kristen.campbell@bolling.af.mil
Founded 1931
Library Holdings: Bk Vols 14,120; Per Subs 176
Subject Interests: Military history
Automation Activity & Vendor Info: (Circulation) epixtech, inc.; (OPAC) epixtech, inc.
Database Vendor: Ebsco - EbscoHost, epixtech, inc., OCLC - First Search
Restriction: Not open to public

S UNITED STATES BOTANIC GARDEN LIBRARY,* 245 First St SW, 20024. SAN 374-7689. Tel: 202-226-8333. FAX: 202-225-1561. Web Site: www.aoc.gov. *In Charge*, Christine Flanagan; E-Mail: cflanaga@aoc.gov
Library Holdings: Bk Vols 1,000; Per Subs 10

G UNITED STATES COMMISSION ON CIVIL RIGHTS, National Clearinghouse Library,* 624 Ninth St NW, Ste 600, 20425. SAN 302-7953. Tel: 202-376-8110. TDD: 202-376-8116. FAX: 202-376-7597. Web Site: www.usccr.gov. *Librn*, Barbara Fontana
Founded 1957
Oct 1998-Sep 1999 Income $230,000. Mats Exp $268,500, Books $5,000, Per/Ser (Incl. Access Fees) $50,000, Presv $1,500, Electronic Ref Mat (Incl. Access Fees) $212,000. Sal $98,000 (Prof $58,000)
Library Holdings: Per Subs 95
Subject Interests: Aging, Civil rights, Education, Handicaps
Special Collections: Black Law School Reviews; Census Materials; Civil Rights (US Commission on Civil Rights Coll); Federal Register, micro; Native American Law Reviews; Spanish Speaking Background Law Reviews; Women's Law Reviews
Database Vendor: OCLC - First Search
Publications: A Citizen's Guide to Understanding the Voting Rights Act; An Annotated Bibliography on Selected Fair Housing Issues; Constructing Denver's New Airport: Are Minorities & Women Benefitting?; Directory of Private Fair Housing Organizations; Directory of State & Local Fair Housing Agencies; Federal Enforcement of Equal Employment Requirements; Fifteen Years Ago...Rural Alabama Revisited; Funding Federal Civil Rights Enforcement; Health Insurance-Coverage & Employment Opportunities for Minorities & Women; Intimidation & Violence: Racial & Religious Bigotry in America; New Evidence on School Desegregation; Recent Activities Against Citizens & Residents of Asian Decent; Religion in the Constitution: A Delicate Balance; The Economic Progress of Black Men in America; The Economic Status of Americans of Asian Decent: An Exploratory Investigation; The Economic Status of Americans of Southern & Eastern European Ancestry; Toward an Understanding of Johnson
Restriction: Restricted public use
Partic in GENL; OCLC Online Computer Library Center, Inc
Special Services for the Deaf - TDD

S US COMMITTEE FOR REFUGEES LIBRARY, 1717 Massachusetts Ave NW, Ste 200, 20036. SAN 370-2502. Tel: 202-347-3507. FAX: 202-347-3418. Web Site: www.refugeesusa.org. *Dir*, Roger Winter; *Asst Dir*, John Fredricksson

GL UNITED STATES COURT OF APPEALS, District of Columbia Circuit Court, Judges' Library,* US Court House, 333 Constitution Ave NW, Rm 5518, 20001. SAN 302-7961. Tel: 202-216-7396. FAX: 202-273-0915. *Librn*, Nancy Padgett
Library Holdings: Bk Vols 90,000; Per Subs 160
Partic in Dialog Corporation; OCLC Online Computer Library Center, Inc; Westlaw

GL UNITED STATES COURT OF APPEALS FOR THE ARMED FORCES LIBRARY,* 450 E St NW, 20442-0001. SAN 302-7988. Tel: 202-761-1466. FAX: 202-761-4672. *Librn*, Agnes Kiang
Founded 1951
Library Holdings: Bk Vols 20,000; Per Subs 50
Subject Interests: Criminal law and justice
Publications: Lawyers Coop; National Reporters; Service Regulations

GL UNITED STATES COURT OF APPEALS FOR THE FEDERAL CIRCUIT LIBRARY, Howard T Markey National Courts Bldg, 717 Madison Pl NW, 20439. SAN 302-797X. Tel: 202-312-5500. FAX: 202-786-7015. *Dir*, Patricia M McDermott; *Dep Dir*, David J Lockwood; *Asst Librn*, John D Moore; *Tech Servs*, Rosa G Alicea; *Tech Servs*, Michele Sancilio
Founded 1967
Library Holdings: Bk Vols 49,800; Per Subs 100
Subject Interests: Am Indian law, Constitutional law, Customs law,

Intellectual property law, International trade
Special Collections: Selected legislative histories
Automation Activity & Vendor Info: (Acquisitions) SIRSI; (Cataloging) SIRSI; (Circulation) SIRSI; (ILL) SIRSI; (OPAC) SIRSI; (Serials) SIRSI
Database Vendor: Dialog, Lexis-Nexis, OCLC - First Search
Publications: From the Law Reviews; Guide to Library Resources; Notes from the Library; The Clipping File
Restriction: Restricted public use
Partic in Dialog Corporation; Fedlink; OCLC Online Computer Library Center, Inc; Westlaw
Photo ID required

G UNITED STATES CUSTOMS SERVICE, Library & Information Center,* Ronald Regan Bldg, 1300 Pennsylvania Ave NW 75B Mailstop, 20229. SAN 302-7996. Tel: 202-927-1350. FAX: 202-927-0374. *Dir*, Patricia M Dobrosky
Founded 1975
Library Holdings: Bk Vols 60,000; Per Subs 695
Subject Interests: Business and management, Drug abuse, Economics, International trade, Law enforcement, Physical science
Publications: Media Varia
Partic in BRS; Dialog Corporation; Dow Jones News Retrieval; Fedlink; Legislate; OCLC Online Computer Library Center, Inc; Vutext; Westlaw

G US DEPARTMENT OF AGRICULTURE, Office of the General Counsel Law Library, 1400 Independence Ave SW, Rm 0325-South, 20250-1400. SAN 377-3728. Tel: 202-720-7751. FAX: 202-690-0682. *Librn*, Peter MacHare; *Assoc Librn*, David Isenberg; E-Mail: david.isenbergh@usda.gov
Library Holdings: Bk Vols 90,000; Per Subs 50

G UNITED STATES DEPARTMENT OF AGRICULTURE, Economic Research Service Reference Center,* 1800 M St Rm 3050, 20036. SAN 321-270X. Tel: 202-694-5065. FAX: 202-694-5689. *Ref*, Marilynn Graham; E-Mail: mgraham@econ.ag.gov
Founded 1978
Library Holdings: Bk Vols 20,000; Per Subs 289
Subject Interests: Agr econ
Special Collections: ERS/ESCS Publications on micro, incl staff rpts
Restriction: By appointment only
Partic in Dialog Corporation; Fedlink; Lexis, OCLC Online Computer Libr Ctr, Inc

G UNITED STATES DEPARTMENT OF COMMERCE, Office of the Library & Information Services,* HCHB, Rm 7046, 14th St & Constitution Ave, NW, 20230. SAN 337-1042. Tel: 202-482-5511. FAX: 202-482-5685. Web Site: www.doc.gov/lib/. *Dir*, Vera Whisenton; *Chief Librn*, Clyrice Ackerman
Founded 1913
Library Holdings: Bk Vols 47,000; Per Subs 500
Automation Activity & Vendor Info: (Acquisitions) epixtech, inc.; (Cataloging) epixtech, inc.
Partic in Dialog Corporation; Dow Jones News Retrieval; OCLC Online Computer Library Center, Inc
Branches:
GL LAW LIBRARY, 14th & Constitution Ave NW, Rm 1894, 20230. SAN 323-925X. Tel: 202-482-5517. FAX: 202-482-0221. *Librn*, Jane Sessa; Staff 4 (MLS 2, Non-MLS 2)
Founded 1983
Library Holdings: Bk Vols 190,000; Per Subs 170
Subject Interests: International trade
Special Collections: Legislative, bks, micro
Restriction: Staff use only
Partic in Capcon Library Network; Fedlink; OCLC Online Computer Library Center, Inc

UNITED STATES DEPARTMENT OF DEFENSE
G NATIONAL IMAGERY MAPPING AGENCY LIBRARY, 4600 Sangamore Rd, Bethesda, 20816-5003. SAN 321-5830. Tel: 301-227-2108, 301-227-2284 (Office). FAX: 301-227-5059. *Dep Dir*, Peggy Tuten; *Coll Develop*, Marylynn Francisco
Special Collections: Bathymetric Surveys; Geodetic Control; Geographic Names
Publications: Map & Chart Accession List
Partic in Dialog Corporation; SDC Info Servs

S US DEPARTMENT OF DEFENSE ARMED FORCES PEST MANAGEMENT BOARD, (DPMIAC), Defense Pest Management Information Analysis Center (DPMIAC), Walter Reed Army Medical Ctr, Forest Glen Section, 20307-5001. SAN 370-2561. Tel: 301-295-7476, 301-295-7479. FAX: 301-295-7482. Web Site: www.afpmb.org. *Chief Librn*, Richard Robbins; E-Mail: robbinrg@acq.osd.mil; Staff 5 (MLS 5)
Library Holdings: Bk Vols 1,532; Per Subs 261
Subject Interests: Pest control
Publications: bimonthly newsletter on pest management; quarterly newsletter on pest management; Technical Information Bulletin (TIB)

G UNITED STATES DEPARTMENT OF ENERGY, Office of Scientific & Technical Information,* 175 Oak Ridge Tpk, 20585. SAN 315-9477. Tel: 423-576-8401. FAX: 202-586-8054. Web Site: www.osti.gov. *Dir*, Walter L Warnick; E-Mail: walter.warnick@oer.doe.gov; *Mgr*, R Charles Morgan
Library Holdings: Bk Vols 4,700,000; Per Subs 50
Special Collections: US Department of Energy Research & Development Reports and Monographs
Publications: Radio Active Waste Mgmt
Manages the Scientific & Technical Information Program of DOE. OSTI is the central processing & distribution point for scientific & technical reports generated by DOE programs, including those with classified & limited distribution. OSTI also developed & maintains the DOE Energy Science & Technology Database

UNITED STATES DEPARTMENT OF ENERGY
G ENERGY LIBRARY, FORRESTAL BRANCH, 1000 Independence Ave SW Rm IG-063, 20585. SAN 337-1107. Tel: 202-586-9534. FAX: 202-586-0573. E-Mail: forrestal.library@hq.doe.gov. Web Site: www.hr.doe.gov/library/. *Chief Librn*, Denise Diggin; *Ref*, Gail Leithauser; *Ref*, Karen Catlin; Staff 2 (MLS 2)
Founded 1948
Library Holdings: Bk Titles 22,155; Per Subs 500
Subject Interests: Bus, Bus conserv, Engineering, Gen law, Hist of energy, Mgt, Statistics energy
Special Collections: Atomic Energy Commission, Department of Energy, Energy Research & Development Administration, Federal Energy Administration Reports, Micro; International Atomic Energy Agency Publications; National Technical Information Services Selected Research in Microfiche Service for Energy, micro
Automation Activity & Vendor Info: (Circulation) TLC
Publications: Energy Library Guide to Services; New at the Energy Library
Partic in Dialog Corporation; Dow Jones News Retrieval; Nat Libr of Med; OCLC Online Computer Library Center, Inc
GL LAW LIBRARY, 1000 Independence Ave SW, Rm 6A-156, 20585-0103. SAN 337-1131. Tel: 202-586-4848. FAX: 202-586-0865. *Chief Librn*, Elizabeth T McNulty; Staff 3 (MLS 2, Non-MLS 1)
Founded 1942
Library Holdings: Bk Vols 30,000
Subject Interests: Administrative law, Congressional, Contract law, Energy, Legal encyclopedia, Looseleaf servs, Nuclear law, Procurement, State code
Automation Activity & Vendor Info: (Circulation) GEAC
Publications: Energy Library Guide to Services; New at the Energy Library

S US DEPARTMENT OF ENERGY-ENERGY INFORMATION ADMINISTRATION, National Energy Information Center, EI-231, Forrestal Bldg, Rm 1E-238, 20585. SAN 370-274X. Tel: 202-586-8800. FAX: 202-586-0727. E-Mail: infoctr@eia.doe.gov. Web Site: www.eia.doe.gov. *Dir*, John H Weiner
Library Holdings: Per Subs 30

UNITED STATES DEPARTMENT OF HOUSING & URBAN DEVELOPMENT
G HUD LIBRARY, 451 Seventh St SW, Rm 8141, 20410. SAN 302-802X. Tel: 202-708-2370. FAX: 202-708-1485. E-Mail: library_circulation_desk@hud.gov. Web Site: www.hud.gov.
Founded 1934
Library Holdings: Bk Vols 680,000; Per Subs 2,200
Subject Interests: Am housing, Architecture, Bldg construction, Bldg tech, Commun develop, County, Econ, Environ, Fed govt, Homelessness, Law, Local government, Metrop area problems, Regional data, Regional planning, Sociologic data, State government, Urban land use
Special Collections: Comprehensive Housing Affordability Strategy Reports; Housing in the 70's Background Papers; Management Evaluation Reports
Publications: Library Periodicals List: internal distribution; Recent Library Acquisitions
Partic in Fedlink
HUD Library is operated under contract for the Department

GL UNITED STATES DEPARTMENT OF JUSTICE, Library Staff, 601 D St NW, Rm 7527, 20530. SAN 337-1190. Tel: 202-514-2133. FAX: 202-514-3546. Web Site: www.usdoj.gov. *Dir*, Blane K Dessy; Staff 49 (MLS 30, Non-MLS 19)
Founded 1831
Oct 1998-Sep 1999 Mats Exp $1,608,000. Sal $2,939,000
Library Holdings: Bk Vols 215,437; Per Subs 1,400
Special Collections: American, Canadian & British Law; Department of Justice Publications; United States Supreme Court Records & Briefs
Automation Activity & Vendor Info: (Cataloging) epixtech, inc.; (Serials) epixtech, inc.
Restriction: By appointment only
Partic in Fedlink; OCLC Online Computer Library Center, Inc
Branches:
ANTITRUST, 600 E St NW, Rm 1070, 20530. SAN 337-1220. Tel: 202-514-5870. FAX: 202-514-9099. *Librn*, Mary Clarity; Staff 4 (MLS 2, Non-MLS 2)
Library Holdings: Bk Vols 33,000; Per Subs 300
Subject Interests: Economics, Law
Special Collections: Legislative Histories

Restriction: Not open to public
CRIMINAL, Bond Bldg, 1400 New York Ave, 20530. SAN 337-1271. Tel: 202-514-1141. FAX: 202-616-2015. *Librn*, Catherine Harman; Staff 4 (MLS 3, Non-MLS 1)
Library Holdings: Bk Vols 16,000; Per Subs 64
Subject Interests: Criminal law and justice
Restriction: Not open to public
Friends of the Library Group
NEW YORK AVENUE, 1425 New York Ave NW, Rm 9004, 20530. SAN 374-809X. Tel: 202-616-8942. FAX: 202-616-8718. *Librn*, Kendra Swe

G UNITED STATES DEPARTMENT OF LABOR, National Labor Library,* 200 Constitution Ave NW Rm N-2445, 20210-0002. SAN 337-1344. Tel: 202-219-6992. FAX: 202-219-4187. Web Site: library.dol.gov. *Dir*, Dorothy Fisher Weed; Staff 16 (MLS 10, Non-MLS 6)
Founded 1917
1998-1999 Income $1,009,000
Library Holdings: Per Subs 500
Subject Interests: Economics, Labor
Special Collections: Labor Unions, docs, mat
Partic in Dialog Corporation; Westlaw
Friends of the Library Group

UNITED STATES DEPARTMENT OF THE ARMY
G OFFICE OF THE CHIEF OF ENGINEERS LIBRARY, CEHEC-IM-LP Bldg 2950, 7701 Telegraph Rd, Alexandria, 22315-3860. SAN 337-1522. Tel: 703-428-6388. FAX: 703-428-6896. *Chief Librn*, Lee W Porter; Tel: 703-428-7430, E-Mail: lee.porter@usace.army.mil; *Cat*, Myra J Craig; *Online Servs*, Nancy Faget; *Publ Servs*, Steve J Balanda; *Spec Coll*, Renate A Craft; Tel: 703-428-6386; *ILL*, Barbara J Clark; *Acq*, Donna Dickerson; Tel: 703-428-7430; Staff 8 (MLS 6, Non-MLS 2)
Founded 1942
Library Holdings: Bk Vols 108,000; Bk Titles 73,000; Per Subs 413
Special Collections: Civil & Environmental Engineering; Congressional Materials; Corps of Engineers History & Activities, 1776-present; Management Coll
Database Vendor: Dialog, Ebsco - EbscoHost, Lexis-Nexis, OCLC - First Search
Partic in Fedlink
The Library is the headquarter's library for the Army Corps of Engineers
G THE PENTAGON LIBRARY, 6605 Army Pentagon, 20310-6605. SAN 337-1611. Tel: 703-697-4301, 703-697-4301. FAX: 703-698-3731. Web Site: www.hqda.army.mil/library. *Dir*, Kathryn L Earnest; Tel: 703-695-5346, Fax: 703-693-6543, E-Mail: kathy.earnest@hqda.army.mil; *Syst Coordr*, Carol Hyslop; Tel: 703-697-4658, Fax: 703-695-2034; *Acq*, Mena Whitmore; Staff 28 (MLS 14, Non-MLS 14)
Founded 1944
Library Holdings: Bk Vols 200,000; Bk Titles 80,000; Per Subs 975
Subject Interests: Foreign affairs, International relations, Mil hist (US), Mil sci
Special Collections: DoD/DA Regulatory Publications & Manuals; Law; Legislative Histories Relating to DoD issues; Military History; Regulatory Publications
Automation Activity & Vendor Info: (Cataloging) VTLS; (Circulation) VTLS; (OPAC) VTLS
Database Vendor: Dialog, Ebsco - EbscoHost, Lexis-Nexis, OCLC - First Search, ProQuest
Publications: Bibliographies; Periodical Holdings Lists; User's Guides
Function: Research library
Partic in Fedlink

G UNITED STATES DEPARTMENT OF THE INTERIOR LIBRARY,* 1849 C St NW, MS 1151, 20240. SAN 302-8046. Tel: 202-208-5815. FAX: 202-219-1434. *Mgr*, John Sherrod; *Bibliog Instr*, Mark Leech
Founded 1949
Library Holdings: Per Subs 2,000
Subject Interests: Energy, Mining, Natural resources
Special Collections: (Dissertations), flm, micro; Conservation & Natural Resources; Dept of the Interior
Automation Activity & Vendor Info: (Acquisitions) SIRSI; (Cataloging) SIRSI; (Circulation) SIRSI; (Serials) SIRSI
Partic in Dialog Corporation; Fedlink; OCLC Online Computer Library Center, Inc

UNITED STATES DEPARTMENT OF THE NAVY
G NAVAL COMPUTER & TELECOMMUNICATIONS TECHNICAL INFORMATION OFFICE, Washington Navy Yard, Bldg 196, 3rd flr, 20374-5069. SAN 337-1794. Tel: 202-685-1088. FAX: 202-433-0491. *Librn*, Octavia J Ross
Founded 1964
Library Holdings: Bk Vols 3,000; Per Subs 100
G NAVSEA TECHNICAL LIBRARY, 2531 Jeff Davis Hwy, Arlington, 22242-5160. SAN 337-1972. Tel: 703-602-3305. FAX: 703-602-2818. *Acq, Purchasing*, Marie Crawley; Staff 4 (MLS 1, Non-MLS 3)
Founded 1943
Library Holdings: Bk Vols 15,000; Bk Titles 16,500; Per Subs 130
Subject Interests: Computer science, Electrical engineering, Electronics, Mathematics, Mechanical engineering, Metallurgy
Special Collections: Acquisition Reform; TQL/TQM
Publications: Focus
Partic in Navy Libr Consortium
G NAVY DEPARTMENT LIBRARY, Washington Navy Yard Bldg 44, 805 Kidder-Breese St SE, 20374-5060. SAN 337-1670. Tel: 202-433-4132. FAX: 202-433-9553. E-Mail: navylibrary@nhc.navy.mil. Web Site: navylibrary.nhc.navy.mil. *Dir*, Jean Hort; *Tech Servs*, David C Brown; Staff 8 (MLS 4, Non-MLS 4)
Founded 1800
Oct 1998-Sep 1999 Mats Exp $203,702, Books $25,000, Per/Ser (Incl. Access Fees) $25,552, Presv $108,500, Micro $3,150, AV Equip $40,000, Electronic Ref Mat (Incl. Access Fees) $1,500. Sal $210,973 (Prof $91,395)
Library Holdings: Bk Vols 170,000; Per Subs 375
Subject Interests: Maritime history, Naval hist
Special Collections: Administrative Histories of World War II; Cruisebooks; Dissertations on Naval & Military History; Rare Books & Manuscripts; Ship Registers
Automation Activity & Vendor Info: (Cataloging) TLC; (OPAC) TechLIB
Database Vendor: OCLC - First Search
Publications: Accessions list; subject bibliographies
Restriction: Open to public for reference only
Partic in Defense Technical Information Center; Dialog Corporation; Fedlink; OCLC Online Computer Library Center, Inc
Open Mon, Tues, Thurs & Fri 9-4, closed for reference Wed
G OFFICE OF NAVAL INTELLIGENCE INFORMATION CENTER, 4251 Suitland Rd, 20395-5720. SAN 337-1859. Tel: 301-669-4386. FAX: 301-669-4282. *Head of Libr*, Erica Johns; Staff 12 (MLS 2, Non-MLS 10)
Library Holdings: Bk Vols 2,500; Per Subs 800
Subject Interests: Maritime
Special Collections: Russian Language Monographs of Naval Interest
Partic in Fedlink; OCLC Online Computer Library Center, Inc
AL OFFICE OF THE GENERAL COUNSEL, LAW LIBRARY, SE Bldg 36, Rm 213, 901 M St, 20374. SAN 337-1948. Tel: 202-685-6820. FAX: 202-685-6868. *Librn*, Mary E Williams; E-Mail: williams-mary@secnav.navy.mil; Staff 1 (MLS 1)
Founded 1949
Library Holdings: Bk Vols 25,950
Special Collections: Law & Legislation (Legislative Histories)

UNITED STATES DEPARTMENT OF THE NAVY
A OFFICE OF THE JUDGE ADVOCATE GENERAL LAW LIBRARY, Washington Navy Yard, 1322 Patterson Ave SE, Ste 3000, 20374-5066. SAN 337-1735. Tel: 202-685-5270. FAX: 202-685-5171. *Dir*, Sue Roach; E-Mail: roachss@jag.navy.mil; Staff 5 (MLS 3, Non-MLS 2)
Founded 1939
Library Holdings: Bk Vols 45,000
Subject Interests: Admiralty law, International law, Mil justice
Special Collections: Naval Legal Material, vf
Partic in OCLC Online Computer Library Center, Inc; Westlaw

UNITED STATES DEPARTMENT OF THE TREASURY
G COMPTROLLER OF THE CURRENCY, ADMINISTRATOR OF NATIONAL BANKS LIBRARY, 250 E St SW, 20219. SAN 337-212X. Tel: 202-874-4720. FAX: 202-874-5138. Web Site: www.occ.treas.gov. *Ref*, Elizabeth Gullotta; *Ref*, Laura Keen; Staff 8 (MLS 5, Non-MLS 3)
Founded 1974
Library Holdings: Bk Titles 13,500; Per Subs 500
Subject Interests: Economics, Law
Publications: Recent acquisitions & journal articles
Partic in Dialog Corporation; Dow Jones News Retrieval; OCLC Online Computer Library Center, Inc; Westlaw
G TREASURY LIBRARY, Main Treasury Bldg, 1500 Pennsylvania Ave NW, 20220. SAN 337-209X. Tel: 202-622-0990. FAX: 202-622-2611.; Staff 17 (MLS 8, Non-MLS 9)
Founded 1789
Subject Interests: Taxation (finance)
Special Collections: Administrative Histories of World War II Civilian Agencies; Congressional Record, Predecessors & Congressional Serial set from 1789-present; League of Nations Publications; Legislative Compilations Dealing with Federal Taxes; Treasury History
Automation Activity & Vendor Info: (Acquisitions) TechLIB; (Circulation) TechLIB; (Serials) TechLIB
Publications: Periodicals List; Treas Notes
Partic in Dialog Corporation; Dow Jones News Retrieval; Legislate; OCLC Online Computer Library Center, Inc
Friends of the Library Group

G UNITED STATES DEPARTMENT OF TRANSPORTATION, TASC Library, 400 Seventh St SW, 20590. SAN 302-8062. Tel: 202-366-0745, 202-366-0752. FAX: 202-366-3670. Web Site: www.isweb.tasc.dot.gov. *Dir*, Clara M Smith; *Acq*, Annette Ellis; Staff 28 (MLS 16, Non-MLS 12)
Founded 1969
Library Holdings: Bk Titles 315,000; Per Subs 2,000
Subject Interests: Transportation

Publications: Selected Library Acquisitions
Restriction: Open to public for reference only
Partic in Fedlink; OCLC Online Computer Library Center, Inc
Branches:

GL COAST GUARD LAW, Trans Point Bldg, 1st flr, 2100 Second St SW, 20593. SAN 321-1320. Tel: 202-267-2536. *In Charge*, Rowena P Robinson

FAA, Federal Office Bldg 10A, Rm 93, 800 Independence Ave SW, 20591. SAN 320-0868. Tel: 202-267-3117. FAX: 202-267-5951. *In Charge*, Annette Wilson
Subject Interests: Air transportation, Law

GL US DEPARTMENT OF TRANSPORTATION-FEDERAL HIGHWAY ADMINISTRATION, Chief Counsel's Law Library, 400 Seventh St SW, Rm 4232, 20590. SAN 323-8725. Tel: 202-366-1388. FAX: 202-366-1380. Web Site: www.fhwa.dot.gov. *Librn*, Sherie Ann Abbasi; E-Mail: sherie.abbasi@fhwa.dot.gov; Staff 4 (MLS 1, Non-MLS 3)
Library Holdings: Bk Vols 10,000
Special Collections: Highway Legislative Histories (1893-present)
Publications: Federal Laws & Materials Relating to the Federal Highway Administration
Partic in CQ Washington Alert; Legislate; Westlaw

S UNITED STATES EQUAL EMPLOYMENT OPPORTUNITY COMMISSION LIBRARY,* 1801 L St NW, Rm 6502, 20507. SAN 302-8070. Tel: 202-663-4630. TDD: 202-663-4641. FAX: 202-663-4629. *Dir*, Susan Taylor; *Res*, Holly Wilson; E-Mail: holly.wilson@eeoc.gov; Staff 8 (MLS 2, Non-MLS 6)
Founded 1966
Subject Interests: Civil rights, Employment, Labor
Special Collections: EEOC (agency) archives
Publications: What's New in the Library? (monthly newsletter)
Partic in Fedlink; OCLC Online Computer Library Center, Inc
Special Services for the Deaf - TDD

S UNITED STATES FISH & WILDLIFE SERVICE, Broadcasting & Audio Visual Library,* Dept of Interior, Rm 3444, 1849 C St NW, 20240. SAN 370-2707. Tel: 202-208-5611. FAX: 202-208-7409.

G UNITED STATES FOOD & DRUG ADMINISTRATION, CFSAN Library, 200 C St SW, HFS-678, 20204. SAN 374-4647. Tel: 202-205-4235. FAX: 202-205-4587. Web Site: updates.cfsan.fda.gov/oms/dirm/lirb.htm. *In Charge*, Lee S Bernstein; Staff 5 (MLS 3, Non-MLS 2)
Library Holdings: Bk Vols 12,000; Per Subs 450
Publications: Food for Thought (newsletter)
Partic in Fedlink; OCLC Online Computer Library Center, Inc
Special Services for the Deaf - Books on deafness & sign language; Staff with knowledge of sign language; TTY machine

P UNITED STATES GENERAL ACCOUNTING OFFICE, Information Services Center,* 441 G St NW, Rm 7438, 20548. SAN 337-2154. Reference Tel: 202-512-2585. Interlibrary Loan Service FAX: 202-512-3373. Reference FAX: 202-512-5417. *Dir*, Phyllis Christenson; Tel: 202-512-2647, Fax: 202-512-3366; *Res*, Ellen Swain; E-Mail: swaine.isc@gao.gov; Staff 24 (MLS 15, Non-MLS 9)
Founded 1972
Library Holdings: Bk Vols 130,000; Per Subs 1,100
Subject Interests: Accounting, Auditing, Economics, Law, Social service (social work)
Special Collections: Federal Military & Civilian Regulations; GAO History; Legislative Histories
Publications: Bibliographies; GAO Library Periodicals List; research guides
Restriction: Open to public for reference only
Partic in OCLC Online Computer Library Center, Inc

S US HOLOCAUST MEMORIAL MUSEUM LIBRARY, 100 Raoul Wallenberg Pl SW, 20024-2126. SAN 376-2009. Tel: 202-479-9717. FAX: 202-479-9726. E-Mail: library@ushmm.org. Web Site: library.ushmm.org. *Dir*, Mark Ziomek; *Senior Librn*, Mary Ann Leonard; *Cat*, Holly Vorhies; *Ref Serv*, Anatol Steck; *Ref*, Kelly Skovbjerg
1998-1999 Mats Exp $240,000
Library Holdings: Bk Vols 40,000; Bk Titles 35,000; Per Subs 100
Subject Interests: Holocaust
Special Collections: Memorial Books
Partic in Fed Libr & Info Network

UNITED STATES INFORMATION AGENCY

G INFORMATION RESOURCE CENTER, 301 Fourth St SW, Rm 130, 20547. SAN 336-822X. Tel: 202-260-1234. FAX: 202-619-6190. Web Site: www.usia.gov.html.
Library Holdings: Bk Vols 17,000; Per Subs 500
Subject Interests: Social sciences and issues
Special Collections: USIA Historical Coll

G UNITED STATES INSTITUTE OF PEACE, Jeannette Rankin Library Program,* 1200 17th St NW Ste 200, 20036-3011. SAN 370-9973. Tel: 202-457-1700. FAX: 202-429-6063. E-Mail: library@usip.org. Web Site: www.usip.org/library.html. *Dir*, Margarita Studemeister; Tel: 202-429-3850, E-Mail: mss@usip.org; *Info Res*, James Cornelius; Tel: 202-429-3851, E-Mail: james_cornelius@usip.org; *Automation Syst Coordr*, Ellen Ensel; Tel: 202-429-3895, E-Mail: ellen_ensel@usip.org; Staff 4 (MLS 3, Non-MLS 1)
Library Holdings: Bk Titles 7,000; Per Subs 150
Subject Interests: Diplomacy, Int political relations, Mediation
Partic in Capcon Library Network; Fedlink; OCLC Online Computer Library Center, Inc

UNITED STATES INTERNATIONAL TRADE ADMINISTRATION

GL LAW LIBRARY, 500 E St SW, Rm 614, 20436. SAN 337-2219. Tel: 202-205-3287. FAX: 202-205-3111. *Librn*, Steven J Kover; E-Mail: skover@usitc.gov; *Librn*, Maureen Bryant; Staff 3 (MLS 2, Non-MLS 1)
Founded 1972
Library Holdings: Bk Vols 100,000; Per Subs 75
Subject Interests: Antidumping, Countervailing duties, Imports, Intellectual property, Tariffs, US trade law
Special Collections: Legislative Histories dealing with Trade & Tariff Acts
Publications: Bibliography of Law Journal Articles on Statutes Administered by the United States International Trade Commission & Related Subjects

G NATIONAL LIBRARY OF INTERNATIONAL TRADE, 500 E St SW, Rm 300, 20436. SAN 337-2189. Tel: 202-205-2630. FAX: 202-205-2316. Web Site: www.usitc.gov. *Ref*, Janet R Damon; E-Mail: damon@usitc.gov; *Ref*, Wendy Willis; E-Mail: wwillis@usitc.gov; Staff 8 (MLS 5, Non-MLS 3)
Founded 1916
Library Holdings: Bk Vols 100,000; Per Subs 2,500
Subject Interests: Agr products, Chems, Econ, Electronics, Energy, Forest products, International trade, Machinery manufacturers, Minerals, Misc manufacturers, Textiles, Transportation
Restriction: Open to public for reference only
Partic in Fedlink; OCLC Online Computer Library Center, Inc
Open Mon-Fri 9-5 to the public
Friends of the Library Group

S UNITED STATES MARINE BAND, Music Library,* Marine Barracks, Eighth & I Sts SE, 20390-5000. SAN 302-8135. Tel: 202-433-4298. FAX: 202-433-4752. Web Site: www.marineband.hqmc.usmc.mil. *Chief Librn*, D Michael Ressler; E-Mail: resslerdm@mbw.usmc.mil
Founded 1798
Library Holdings: Bk Vols 1,000; Per Subs 25
Special Collections: Band Music; Dance Band; Historical & Program Files; Instrumental Ensembles; John Philip Sousa Coll; Marine Band Archives & Historical Coll, mss, photogs; Military & Wind Music; Orchestra Music; Piano Sheet Music; Reference Books & Scores

UNITED STATES MARINE CORPS

A MARINE CORPS HISTORICAL CENTER LIBRARY, Code HDS-3, Bldg 58, Washington Navy Yard, 901 M St SE, 20374-5040. SAN 337-2243. Tel: 202-433-3447. FAX: 202-433-7265. *Librn*, Evelyn A Englander; E-Mail: eengland@notes.hqi.usmc.mil
Founded 1843
1997-1998 Mats Exp $6,500, Books $4,000, Per/Ser (Incl. Access Fees) $1,500, Micro $500, Other Print Mats $500
Library Holdings: Bk Vols 41,000; Per Subs 12
Subject Interests: Military history
Special Collections: Biographies of United States Marines; Foreign Marine Corps; General Naval &; History of Marine Corps & Amphibious Warfare; Marine Corps Operational Documents & After Action Reports; Military History; Muster Rolls & Unit Diaries
Publications: Fortitudine
Partic in OCLC Online Computer Library Center, Inc

G UNITED STATES MERIT SYSTEMS PROTECTION BOARD LIBRARY,* 1120 Vermont Ave NW, Rm 828, 20419. SAN 328-3488. Tel: 202-653-7132. FAX: 202-653-6182. *Librn*, Kathleen O'Sullivan
Library Holdings: Per Subs 75
Partic in Fed Law Libr Asn; Metrop Libr Coun; OCLC Online Computer Library Center, Inc; Westlaw

G UNITED STATES NATIONAL ARBORETUM LIBRARY,* 3501 New York Ave NE, 20002-1958. SAN 326-6680. Tel: 202-245-4538. FAX: 202-245-4575. *Tech Servs*, Ann McIntire
Library Holdings: Bk Titles 9,000; Per Subs 88
Subject Interests: Botany, Gardening, Horticulture
Special Collections: Arie F den Boer mss on crabapples; floral prints; Mary Cokely Wood Ikebana Coll; Nursery & Seed Trade Coll, catalogs; photog; Salix (Carlton R Ball Coll); US Department of Agriculture Plant Exploration Trips; US Plant Patent File

S US NATIONAL PARK SERVICE FREDERICK DOUGLASS NHS LIBRARY, 1411 W St SE, 20020. SAN 370-291X. Tel: 202-426-5961. TDD: 202-426-1452. FAX: 202-426-0880. Web Site: www.cr.nps.gov/csd/exhibits/douglass. *Curator*, Cathy Ingram; Tel: 202-426-1452; *Mgr*, Lawrence Burguess
Founded 1962
Oct 1999-Sep 2000 Income $250,000. Mats Exp $1,900, Per/Ser (Incl. Access Fees) $100, Presv $1,000, AV Equip $500, Other Print Mats $100,

Manuscripts & Archives $200
Library Holdings: Bk Vols 2,000
Special Collections: Cartes-de-visite; lantern slides; photographic prints
Special Services for the Deaf - TTY machine

G UNITED STATES NAVAL OBSERVATORY, James Melville Gilliss Library, 3450 Massachusetts Ave NW, 20392-5420. SAN 302-8143. Tel: 202-762-1463. FAX: 202-762-1083. E-Mail: lib@sicon.usno.navy.mil. Web Site: www.usno.navy.mil/library. *Librn*, Brenda G Corbin
Founded 1830
Library Holdings: Bk Vols 85,000; Per Subs 200
Special Collections: Pre-19th Century Books Covering Subjects of Astronomy, Mathematics, Physics & Navigation
Partic in Fedlink; OCLC Online Computer Library Center, Inc

S US NEWS & WORLD REPORT LIBRARY & INFORMATION SERVICES, 1050 Thomas Jefferson St NW, 20007-1196. SAN 302-8224. Tel: 202-955-2350. FAX: 202-955-2506. Web Site: www.usnews.com. *Dir*, Sheryl Rosenthal; *Asst Dir*, Kate Forsyth; *Asst Librn*, Lisa Costello; *Coll Develop*, Judith Katzung; *Online Servs*, Anne Bradley; *Acq*, Judy Katzung; *ILL*, Elaine Kovard; *Ref*, Carol Hook
Library Holdings: Bk Vols 7,500; Per Subs 300
Subject Interests: Current events, Government, History, Political science
Special Collections: News clippings, vertical files, govt documents
Publications: library guide; U.S. News Index
Partic in Capcon Library Network; OCLC Online Computer Library Center, Inc

G UNITED STATES OFFICE OF PERSONNEL MANAGEMENT LIBRARY,* 1900 E St NW, 20415-7740. SAN 302-8151. Tel: 202-606-1381. FAX: 202-606-0909. Web Site: www.opm.gov.; Staff 2 (MLS 1, Non-MLS 1)
Founded 1941
Library Holdings: Bk Vols 15,000; Per Subs 30
Subject Interests: Civil serv
Automation Activity & Vendor Info: (OPAC) Sagebrush Corporation
Partic in Fedlink

G UNITED STATES POSTAL SERVICE LIBRARY,* 475 L'Enfant Plaza SW, Rm 11800, 20260-1540. SAN 302-816X. Tel: 202-268-2900. FAX: 202-268-6436. *Librn*, Robert F Gardner; *Ref*, Jerry Mansfield; *Cat*, Ernest W Ghee; *Acq*, Barbara Hyman; Staff 10 (MLS 4, Non-MLS 6)
Founded 1955
Library Holdings: Bk Vols 56,000; Per Subs 1,700
Subject Interests: Data processing, Economics, Law, Marketing
Special Collections: Congressional Reports (US Congressional Serial Document Set)
Partic in Dialog Corporation; Dow Jones News Retrieval; News Edge; OCLC Online Computer Library Center, Inc; Profound

G UNITED STATES SECURITIES & EXCHANGE COMMISSION LIBRARY,* 450 Fifth St NW, Rm 1C00, 20549-9998. SAN 302-8178. Tel: 202-942-7090. FAX: 202-942-9629. *Dir*, Myra Norton; Staff 11 (MLS 6, Non-MLS 5)
Founded 1934
Oct 1996-Sep 1997 Mats Exp $1,000,000
Library Holdings: Bk Vols 100,000; Per Subs 700
Subject Interests: Accounting, Business and management, Economics, Finance, Investing, Law, Securities
Special Collections: Legislative Histories of Statutes Administered by Agency
Publications: Library Information Bulletin; Periodical Holdings
Partic in OCLC Online Computer Library Center, Inc

G UNITED STATES SENATE LIBRARY, B-15 Senate Russell Bldg, 20510-7112. SAN 302-8186. Tel: 202-224-7106. TDD: 202-228-1269. FAX: 202-224-0879. *Librn*, Gregory C Harness; *Ref*, Jennifer Casey; *Ref*, Chris Cochran; *Ref*, Zoe Davis; *Ref*, Megan Dunn; *Ref*, Kimberly Edwards; *Ref*, Lauren Gluckman; *Ref*, Nancy Kervin; *Head Tech Servs*, Leona Faust; *Cat*, Carmelita de Castro; *Cat*, Betsy Moon; *Tech Servs*, Hannah Moyer; *Coll Develop*, Jean Keleher; Staff 19 (MLS 13, Non-MLS 6)
Founded 1871
Oct 1999-Sep 2000 Mats Exp $159,000, Books $52,000, Per/Ser (Incl. Access Fees) $5,000, Per/Ser (Incl. Access Fees) $20,000, Micro $35,000, Electronic Ref Mat (Incl. Access Fees) $47,000. Sal $862,882 (Prof $681,732)
Library Holdings: Bk Vols 150,000; Per Subs 200
Special Collections: Bills & Resolutions, bk, micro; Congressional Hearings, bk, micro; Congressional Record, bk, micro; Serial Set, bk, micro
Automation Activity & Vendor Info: (Acquisitions) TLC; (Cataloging) TLC; (Circulation) TLC; (OPAC) TLC; (Serials) TLC
Publications: Presidential Vetoes
Partic in Dialog Corporation; OCLC Online Computer Library Center, Inc; Westlaw
Special Services for the Deaf - TDD
Branches:

G UNITED STATES CAPITAL READING ROOM, The Capital Rm S-333, 20510-7112. Tel: 202-224-7106.
Library Holdings: Bk Vols 3,000

L UNITED STATES SENTENCING COMMISSION LIBRARY,* One Columbus Circle NE, Ste 2-500 S Lobby, 20002-8002. SAN 372-3097. Tel: 202-502-4500. FAX: 202-502-4699. E-Mail: librarian@ussc.gov. Web Site: www.ussc.gov.
Library Holdings: Bk Vols 10,000
Partic in OCLC Online Computer Library Center, Inc

S US SOLDIER'S & AIRMEN'S HOME LIBRARY, Scott Bldg, 3700 N Capitol St NW, 20317. SAN 302-7775. Tel: 202-730-3319. FAX: 202-730-3405. *Librn*, Edward M Underwood
Founded 1851
Library Holdings: Bk Vols 40,000; Per Subs 115
Friends of the Library Group

S UNITED STATES STUDENT ASSOCIATION, Information Services,* 1413 K St NW, 9th flr, 20005. SAN 325-9919. Tel: 202-347-8772. FAX: 202-393-5886. Web Site: www.usstudents.org. *Pres*, Kendra Fox-Davis; *VPres*, Ali Fischer; E-Mail: vp@usstudents.org

GL UNITED STATES TAX COURT LIBRARY,* 400 Second St NW, 20217. SAN 302-8194. Interlibrary Loan Service Tel: 202-606-8707. FAX: 202-219-3794. E-Mail: tclib@mindspring.com. *Librn*, Elsa B Silverman; *Asst Librn*, Tania Andreeff; Staff 6 (MLS 2, Non-MLS 4)
Founded 1924
Library Holdings: Bk Titles 36,000; Per Subs 1,500
Special Collections: Tax Laws
Database Vendor: Lexis-Nexis, OCLC - First Search
Publications: Monthly Bulletin
Restriction: Not open to public
Function: ILL available
Partic in Dow Jones News Retrieval; OCLC Online Computer Library Center, Inc; Westlaw

S UNIVERSAL PROUTIST YOUTH FEDERATION LIBRARY,* PO Box 56466, 20040. SAN 376-1991. Tel: 202-829-2278. FAX: 202-829-0462. Web Site: www.prout.org. *Exec Dir*, Clark Fordon
Library Holdings: Bk Vols 100

S UNIVERSITY CLUB LIBRARY,* 1135 16th St NW, 20036. SAN 377-3876. Tel: 202-862-8800. FAX: 202-296-2347. Web Site: www.universityclubdc.com. *Librn*, Peggy Hudgins
Library Holdings: Bk Vols 6,000; Per Subs 70
Partic in Spec Libr Asn

C UNIVERSITY OF THE DISTRICT OF COLUMBIA, Learning Resources Division, 4200 Connecticut Ave NW, 20008. SAN 337-2391. Tel: 202-274-6370. Interlibrary Loan Service Tel: 202-274-6011. FAX: 202-274-6012. Web Site: www.wrlc.org/~lrdudc. *Dir*, Albert J Casciero; *Dep Dir*, John Page; Staff 28 (MLS 10, Non-MLS 18)
Founded 1976
Library Holdings: Bk Vols 536,776; Per Subs 530
Subject Interests: Education, Health sciences, Humanities
Publications: Access; Learning Link; Learning Resources Division Annual Report
Partic in Capcon Library Network; Washington Research Library Consortium
Special Services for the Blind - Print scanner & software for conversion to speech

CL UNIVERSITY OF THE DISTRICT OF COLUMBIA SCHOOL OF LAW LIBRARY,* 4200 Conn Ave NW, 20008. SAN 371-9952. Tel: 202-274-7354. FAX: 202-274-7311. *Dir*, Brian Baker; *Acq, Circ*, Eddie Caparas; *Publ Servs*, Mildred Baily; Staff 3 (MLS 3)
Founded 1987. Enrl 280
Oct 1998-Sep 1999 Income $900,000. Mats Exp $120,000, Books $60,000, Per/Ser (Incl. Access Fees) $50,000, Micro $10,000. Sal $300,000 (Prof $125,000)
Publications: Guide

S URBAN INSTITUTE LIBRARY,* 2100 M St NW, 20037-1207. SAN 302-8208. Tel: 202-261-5688. FAX: 202-223-3043. *Dir*, Nancy L Minter; Tel: 202-261-5534, E-Mail: nminter@ui.urban.org; *Reader Servs, Senior Librn*, Hetty H Barthel; Tel: 202-261-5508, E-Mail: hbarthel@ui.urban.org; Staff 6 (MLS 3, Non-MLS 3)
Founded 1968
Library Holdings: Bk Vols 47,000; Per Subs 700
Subject Interests: Demography, Economics, Education, Employment, Housing, Local government, Sociology, State government
Special Collections: Urban Institute Archives
Database Vendor: Dialog, Ebsco - EbscoHost, GaleNet, Lexis-Nexis, ProQuest, Silverplatter Information Inc.
Restriction: By appointment only
Partic in Capcon Library Network; Interlibrary Users Association

S URBAN LAND INSTITUTE LIBRARY,* 1025 Thomas Jefferson St NW, Ste 500W, 20007. SAN 302-8216. Tel: 202-624-7116. FAX: 202-624-7140. Web Site: www.uli.org. *Librn*, Joan Campbell
Founded 1936
Library Holdings: Bk Vols 10,000; Per Subs 275
Subject Interests: Real estate
Restriction: By appointment only

G US ARCHITECTURAL & TRANSPORTATION BARRIERS COMPLIANCE BOARD (ATBCB), Technical Resources Library, 1331 F St NW, Ste 1000, 20004-1111. SAN 325-9811. Tel: 202-272-5434. Toll Free Tel: 800-872-2253. FAX: 202-272-5447. Web Site: www.access-board.gov. *Librn*, Forrest Pecht; *Dir, Tech Servs*, David Capozzi
Library Holdings: Bk Vols 5,000; Per Subs 50
Subject Interests: Architecture, Recreation
Special Collections: State, Local & Model Code on Accessibility
Restriction: Open to others by appointment
Special Services for the Deaf - TTY machine

G US BUREAU OF ENGRAVING & PRINTING, Office of Technical Support, 14th & C St SW, 20228. SAN 377-3477. Tel: 202-874-3101. FAX: 202-874-3964.
Library Holdings: Bk Vols 2,500; Per Subs 100

G US DEPARTMENT OF DEFENSE NATIONAL DEFENSE UNIVERSITY LIBRARY, Bldg 62 Marshall Hall, 300 Fifth Ave, 20319-5066. SAN 302-7163. Tel: 202-685-3952. Interlibrary Loan Service Tel: 202-685-3968. Reference Tel: 202-685-6100. FAX: 202-685-3733. Web Site: www.ndu.edu. *Dir*, Sarah A Mikel; Tel: 202-685-3948, E-Mail: mikels@ndu.edu; *Tech Servs*, Wynne Tysdal; Tel: 202-685-2386, E-Mail: tysdalw@ndu.edu; *Spec Coll*, Susan K Lemke; Tel: 202-685-3957, E-Mail: lemkes@ndu.edu; *Chief Librn, Ref*, Alta Linthicum; Tel: 202-685-3952, E-Mail: linthicuma@ndu.edu; *Ref*, Rosemary Marlow-Dzuik; Tel: 202-685-3954, E-Mail: marlowe-dziukr@ndu.edu; Staff 14 (MLS 14)
Founded 1976. Enrl 1,495; Fac 220; Highest Degree: Master
Oct 1998-Sep 1999 Income (Main and Other College/University Libraries) Federal $2,300,000. Mats Exp $900,000. Sal $1,400,000
Library Holdings: Bk Vols 500,000; Per Subs 1,500
Subject Interests: International relations, Military history, Political science
Special Collections: Archives of the Hudson Institute; Conduct of the Persian Gulf War; Correspondence of Bernard Baruch & Julius A Krug; Ft McNair History, including photographs & materials of the Lincoln assassination; Library & Papers of Dr Ralph L Powell (China); Library of Hoffman Nickerson (military history); Military Classics, including the early editions of Marshal de Saxe; NDU Academic & Institutional Archives; Personal Papers (Restricted) of Generals Frank S Besson Jr, John Galvin, Andreu J Goodpaster, George Joulwan, Lyman L Lemniitzer, Colin Powell, John Shalikashvili, Maxwell D Taylor; Speeches on Industrial Mobilization & Papers of J Carlton Ward Jr; Working Papers for the Presidential Commission on Women in the Combat
Database Vendor: epixtech, inc.
Publications: Current Journals Awareness; Library Handbooks
Restriction: Not open to public
Partic in Fed Libr & Info Network; Libr Working Group; MECC

G US DEPT OF COMMERCE, Census Bureau Library, FB 3, Rm 2456, 20233. SAN 307-0476. Tel: 301-457-2511. FAX: 301-457-2194. E-Mail: library@census.gov. *Head Librn*, Kelly Yuille; Tel: 301-457-2507; *Tech Servs*, Earnestine McCoy; Tel: 301-457-2514, E-Mail: earnestine.mccoy@ccmail.cenus.gov; *Publ Servs*, Tamsen H Allen; Tel: 301-457-2531; *Ref*, Hong Hu; Tel: 301-457-2511; *Cat*, Terezia Matus; Tel: 301-457-2518; Staff 14 (MLS 7, Non-MLS 7)
Founded 1952
Library Holdings: Bk Vols 350,000; Per Subs 675
Subject Interests: Agriculture, Business and management, Computer science, Economics, Finance, Government, Housing, Population studies, Statistics
Special Collections: Census Authors Papers; Foreign Statistics (International Statistical Coll); United States Census Coll, bks, micro
Publications: Information Exchange
Partic in Fedlink; OCLC Online Computer Library Center, Inc

S US ENGLISH, Mary Cavitt Memorial Library, 1747 Pennsylvania NW, Ste 1100, 20006-2712. SAN 328-6509. Tel: 202-833-0100. FAX: 202-833-0108. E-Mail: library@us-english.org. Web Site: www.us-english.org. *Chair*, Mauro E Mujica
Library Holdings: Bk Titles 300

S USDA OFFICE OF COMMUNICATION, Photograph Library, 14th & Independence Ave SW, 20250. SAN 370-257X. Tel: 202-720-6633. FAX: 202-720-0902. Web Site: www.usda.gov/oc/photo. *Dir*, Bill Tarpenning
Restriction: By appointment only

L VAN NESS FELDMAN LIBRARY,* 1050 Thomas Jefferson St NW, 20007. SAN 371-8948. Tel: 202-298-1901. FAX: 202-338-2416. E-Mail: gbk@vnf.com. *Librn*, George Bernard Kirlin; Staff 3 (MLS 2, Non-MLS 1)
Founded 1976
Library Holdings: Bk Vols 35,000; Bk Titles 12,000; Per Subs 250
Subject Interests: Energy
Automation Activity & Vendor Info: (Cataloging) TLC
Partic in Capcon Library Network

L VERNER, LIIPFERT, BERNARD, MCPHERSON & HAND, Law Library,* 901 15th St NW, Ste 700, 20005-2327. SAN 325-8742. Tel: 202-371-6068. FAX: 202-371-6279. *Librn*, Maureen Stellino
Library Holdings: Bk Vols 22,000; Per Subs 2,000

L VORYS, SATER, SEYMOUR & PEASE LIBRARY,* 1828 L St, Ste 1111, 20036. SAN 377-3930. Tel: 202-467-8800. FAX: 202-467-8900. Web Site: www.vssp.com. *Librn*, William D Sullivan
Library Holdings: Bk Titles 1,000; Per Subs 40
Partic in Am Asn of Law Librs; Law Libr Soc of DC

WALTER REED ARMY INSTITUTE OF RESEARCH
GM INFORMATION RESOURCES CENTER LIBRARY, 503 Robert Grant Ave, Silver Spring, 20970-7500. SAN 337-2634. Tel: 301-319-9555. FAX: 301-319-9402. Web Site: wrair-www.army.mil/. *Dir*, Judy Kessenich; E-Mail: judy.kessenich@na.amedd.army.mil; *Acq*, Andrew Rogalski; E-Mail: andrew.rogalski@na.amedd.army.mil; *Ref*, Al Reynolds; E-Mail: allen.reynolds@na.amedd.army.mil; Staff 7 (MLS 3, Non-MLS 4)
Founded 1943
Library Holdings: Bk Titles 14,000; Per Subs 450
Subject Interests: Biochemistry, Immunology, Internal medicine, Physiology, Psychiatry, Surgery, Veterinary medicine
Special Collections: Malaria Reprints; Military Medical History (Smadel)
Publications: Recent Additions; Services & News (quarterly); Union list of Biomedical Serials
Restriction: Open to others by appointment
Partic in Dialog Corporation; Docline; Fedlink; National Network of Libraries of Medicine - Greater Midwest Region; OCLC Online Computer Library Center, Inc

WALTER REED ARMY MEDICAL CENTER
AM MEDICAL LIBRARY SERVICE, Bldg 2, Rm 2G, 20307-5001. SAN 337-1018. Tel: 202-782-6238. FAX: 202-782-6803. Web Site: www.wramc.amedd.army.mil. *Dir*, Hoyt W Galloway; *Chief Librn, Publ Servs*, Robert Mohrman; *Chief Librn, Coll Develop, Tech Servs*, Ann Crozier; *ILL*, Kevin Canning
Founded 1909
Library Holdings: Per Subs 880
Subject Interests: Clinical medicine
Special Collections: History of Military Medicine (Fred C Ainsworth Endowment Library), patient education
Publications: Bibliography of Walter Reed Authors; Library Handbook; Quarterly Accessions List
Restriction: Not open to public
Partic in Fedlink; Nat Libr of Med; OCLC Online Computer Library Center, Inc

A POST & PATIENTS' LIBRARY, Bldg 11, Rm G92, 20307-5001. SAN 337-0984. Tel: 202-782-6314. FAX: 202-782-3036. *Librn*, Estella Cary; *Ref*, Kathryn Mayall
Founded 1920
Library Holdings: Bk Vols 38,000; Per Subs 240
Subject Interests: Education, Recreation
Special Collections: Health Topics
Partic in Fedlink; OCLC Online Computer Library Center, Inc

R WASHINGTON HEBREW CONGREGATION, Hurston Adult Library, 3935 Macomb St NW, 20016. SAN 302-8259. Tel: 202-362-7100. FAX: 202-537-1091. Web Site: www.whctemple.org. *Librn*, Ellen Share; Staff 2 (MLS 1, Non-MLS 1)
Library Holdings: Bk Titles 7,000; Per Subs 10
Subject Interests: Biblical studies, Holocaust, Jewish history and literature
Friends of the Library Group
Branches:
SELINGER LIBRARY FAX: 202-537-1091. *Librn*, Ellen Share
Subject Interests: Jewish history and literature, Religion
Friends of the Library Group
TAUBER LIBRARY, Julia Bindeman Suburban Ctr, 11810 Falls Rd, Potomac, 20854. SAN 306-9990. Tel: 301-279-7505. FAX: 301-279-7314. *Librn*, Ellen Share
Founded 1978
Library Holdings: Bk Vols 2,000
Subject Interests: Judaica (lit or hist of Jews)
Friends of the Library Group

M WASHINGTON HOSPITAL CENTER, William B Glew MD Health Sciences Library, 110 Irving St NW, Rm 2A-21, 20010-2975. SAN 302-8267. Tel: 202-877-6221. FAX: 202-877-6757. E-Mail: libr@mhg.edu. *Dir*, Lynne Siemers; Staff 9 (MLS 5, Non-MLS 4)
Founded 1958
Library Holdings: Bk Vols 29,800; Bk Titles 10,000; Per Subs 700
Subject Interests: Health care administration, Medicine, Nursing
Automation Activity & Vendor Info: (Cataloging) epixtech, inc.; (Circulation) epixtech, inc.; (OPAC) epixtech, inc.; (Serials) epixtech, inc.

Publications: Annual Report; Newsletter
Partic in Capcon Library Network; Nat Libr of Med; OCLC Online Computer Library Center, Inc
Friends of the Library Group

G WASHINGTON METROPOLITAN AREA TRANSIT AUTHORITY, General Counsel's Office Law Library,* 600 Fifth St NW, 20001. SAN 377-3914. Tel: 202-962-1012. *Librn*, Marlene McGuirl
Jul 1997-Jun 1998 Mats Exp $74,300
Library Holdings: Bk Vols 7,000; Per Subs 200
Partic in Am Asn of Law Librs; Law Libr Soc of DC

S WASHINGTON NATIONAL CATHEDRAL, Cathedral Rare Book Library,* Massachusetts & Wisconsin Aves NW, 20016-5098. SAN 371-1129. Tel: 202-537-6208. FAX: 202-364-6611.
Library Holdings: Bk Vols 45,000; Per Subs 21

S THE WASHINGTON POST, News Research Center,* 1150 15th St NW, 20071. SAN 302-8275. Tel: 202-334-7341. FAX: 202-334-5575. Web Site: www.washingtonpost.com. *Dir*, Jennifer Belton; E-Mail: belton@washpost.com; *Online Servs*, Paul McCarthy; *Res*, Bob Lyford
Founded 1933
Library Holdings: Bk Vols 5,000; Per Subs 85
Publications: News Research Bulletin; Reference Guides
Partic in Dialog Corporation
Friends of the Library Group

M WASHINGTON PSYCHOANALYTIC SOCIETY, Hadley Memorial Library, 4925 MacArthur Blvd NW, 20007. SAN 302-8283. Tel: 202-338-5453. FAX: 202-338-1521. E-Mail: wpsasoc@bellatlantic.net. *Dir*, Joyce P Burke
Founded 1936
1998-1999 Mats Exp $3,000, Books $2,000, Per/Ser (Incl. Access Fees) $1,000. Sal $45,000
Library Holdings: Bk Titles 5,000; Per Subs 12

S WASHINGTON SERVICE BUREAU, INC, Publications Department,* 655 15th St NW, Ste 275, 20005. SAN 373-3491. Tel: 202-508-0600. FAX: 202-508-0694.

SR WASHINGTON THEOLOGICAL UNION LIBRARY,* 6896 Laurel St NW, 20012-2016. SAN 307-0433. Tel: 202-726-8800. FAX: 202-726-1716. E-Mail: library@wtu.edu.
Founded 1968
Library Holdings: Bk Vols 100,000; Per Subs 450
Partic in Washington Theological Consortium
Open Mon-Fri 8am-10pm, Sat 9am-4pm & Sun 1-5pm

S WASHINGTON TIMES CORP, The World & I Magazine Library & Research Department, 3600 New York Ave NE, 20002-1947. SAN 323-6773. Tel: 202-635-4059. FAX: 202-269-9353. E-Mail: library@worldandimag.com. Web Site: www.worldandi.com. *Librn*, Diane M Falk; Staff 1 (MLS 1)
Founded 1986
Library Holdings: Bk Titles 500; Per Subs 125
Subject Interests: Art, Film, History, Literature, Music, Philosophy, Politics, Religion, Science
Special Collections: International Conference on the Unity of the Science Papers, bd docs; International Federation for World Peace; Literary Federation for World Peace; Professors World Peace Academy Conference Papers, bd docs; Summit Council for Former Heads of State; Unification Movement Archives & Current Information, bks, bulletins, journals, newsletters; Women's Federation for World Peace; World Media Conference; Youth Federation for World Peace
Publications: Newsletter
Friends of the Library Group

L WEIL, GOTSHAL & MANGES LLP, Law Library, 1615 L St NW, Ste 700, 20036. SAN 372-1132. Tel: 202-682-7117. FAX: 202-682-7297. *Librn*, Ann Sloane; E-Mail: ann.sloane@weil.com; *Asst Librn*, David Reith; E-Mail: david.reith@weil.com
Library Holdings: Bk Vols 30,000
Subject Interests: Environmental law, International trade

L WEINER, BRODSKY, SIDMAN & KIDER PC, Law Library, 1300 19th St NW, 5th Flr, 5th Fl, 20036. SAN 372-1736. Tel: 202-628-2000. FAX: 202-628-2011. *Govt Doc*, Lisa Noel; E-Mail: noel@WBSK.com; Staff 1 (Non-MLS 1)
Founded 1992
Library Holdings: Bk Vols 6,500; Per Subs 40
Function: ILL to other special libraries

R WESLEY THEOLOGICAL SEMINARY LIBRARY, 4500 Massachusetts Ave NW, 20016-5690. SAN 302-8313. Tel: 202-885-8695. Reference Tel: 202-885-8696. FAX: 202-885-8691. Web Site: www.wesleysem.edu/library. *Dir*, Andrew G Kadel; Tel: 202-885-8960, E-Mail: akadel@wesleysem.edu; *Head Tech Servs*, William Lash Gwynn; Tel: 202-885-8690, E-Mail: lgwynn@wesleysem.org; *Head Ref*, Howertine Duncan; E-Mail: hduncan@wesleysem.org; *Circ*, Kuruvillac Abraham; E-Mail: kabraham@wesleysem.edu; *Acq*, Jonathan Andrew Klenklen; Tel: 202-885-8692, E-Mail: aklenklen@wesleysem.edu; *Tech Servs*, Sean Boyd; Tel: 202-885-8658, E-Mail: sboyd@wesleysem.org; Staff 6 (MLS 5, Non-MLS 1)
Founded 1882. Enrl 634; Fac 38; Highest Degree: Doctorate
Jul 1999-Jun 2000 Income $330,346. Mats Exp $127,600, Books $83,500, Per/Ser (Incl. Access Fees) $31,049, Presv $7,600, Electronic Ref Mat (Incl. Access Fees) $3,200. Sal $155,733
Library Holdings: Bk Vols 139,539; Per Subs 578
Subject Interests: Religion, Theology
Special Collections: Early American Methodism; Methodist Protestant Church
Automation Activity & Vendor Info: (Cataloging) Gaylord; (Circulation) Gaylord; (OPAC) Gaylord
Database Vendor: OCLC - First Search
Partic in OCLC Online Computer Library Center, Inc; Washington Theological Consortium

L WHITE & CASE, Law Library,* 601 13th St NW, Ste 600 S, 20005. SAN 372-1469. Tel: 202-626-6476. FAX: 202-639-9355. *Librn*, Richard Cousins; *Asst Librn*, Roshni Santiago
Library Holdings: Bk Vols 11,000; Per Subs 40
Subject Interests: International law
Partic in Capcon Library Network; OCLC Online Computer Library Center, Inc

SR WHITEFRIARS HALL, Order of Carmelites Library,* 1600 Webster St NE, 20017. SAN 371-8662. Tel: 202-526-1221, Ext 203. *Librn*, George Kennedy; Staff 2 (MLS 1, Non-MLS 1)
Founded 1948
Library Holdings: Bk Vols 14,000; Per Subs 87
Special Collections: Carmelite Order
Branches:
CARMELITANA LIBRARY *Librn*, Patrick McMahon
Founded 1950
Library Holdings: Bk Vols 8,000
Publications: Bibliography of Teresa of Avila; Catalog of Carmelitana
Partic in Washington Theological Consortium

S WILDLIFE MANAGEMENT INSTITUTE LIBRARY,* 1101 14th St NW Ste 801, 20005. SAN 325-8807. Tel: 202-371-1808. FAX: 202-408-5059. Web Site: www.wildlifemil.wmi. *Pres*, Roland D Sparrowe
Library Holdings: Bk Titles 1,330; Per Subs 58

L WILEY, REIN & FIELDING LIBRARY,* 1776 K St NW, Ste 1000, 20006. SAN 377-3833. Tel: 202-429-7000. FAX: 202-429-7049. Web Site: www.wrf.com. *Librn*, Carolyn Ahearn; E-Mail: carolyn_ahearn@wrf.com
Library Holdings: Bk Vols 25,000; Per Subs 200
Partic in Am Asn of Law Librs; Law Libr Soc of DC; Spec Libr Asn

L WILKES, ARTIS, HEDRICK & LANE, Chartered Library,* 1666 K St NW, Ste 1100, 20006. SAN 302-8321. Interlibrary Loan Service Tel: 202-457-7344. FAX: 202-457-7814. *Librn*, Annette Erbrecht; *Res*, Jeff Stickle
Library Holdings: Bk Vols 20,000
Subject Interests: Law, Real estate
Partic in Dialog Corporation; Dow Jones News Retrieval; Westlaw

L WILLIAMS & CONNOLLY LIBRARY,* 725 12th St NW, 20005. SAN 302-833X. Tel: 202-434-5303. FAX: 202-434-5029. *Dir Libr Serv*, Ellen Feldman; Tel: 202-434-5301, E-Mail: ellen.feldman@williamsandconnolly.com; *Res*, Alicia Julian; Tel: 202-434-5312, E-Mail: alicia.julian@williamsandconnolly.com; *Res*, Caitlin Lietzan; Tel: 202-434-5306, E-Mail: caitlin.lietzan@williamsandconnolly.com; *Tech Servs*, Andrea Bender; Tel: 202-434-5319, E-Mail: andrea.bender@williamsandconnolly.com; *ILL*, Pete Vay; E-Mail: pete.vay@williamsandconnolly.com; *Tech Servs*, Tony Minerva; Tel: 202-434-5310, E-Mail: anthony.minerva@williamsandconnolly.com; *Tech Servs*, Charles Clairdy; Tel: 202-434-5308; Staff 13 (MLS 4, Non-MLS 9)
Founded 1970
Library Holdings: Bk Vols 30,000; Per Subs 300
Subject Interests: Administrative law, Criminal law and justice
Database Vendor: Dialog, Lexis-Nexis, OCLC - First Search
Partic in OCLC Online Computer Library Center, Inc

L WILMER, CUTLER & PICKERING LIBRARY,* 2445 M St NW, 20037. SAN 302-8348. Tel: 202-663-6771. FAX: 202-663-6363. *Doc, ILL*, Teresa Llewellyn; *Res*, Melissa Fast; *Ser*, Jeff Dillard; *Coll Develop*, Joan Sherer; Staff 12 (MLS 7, Non-MLS 5)
Founded 1963
Library Holdings: Bk Vols 55,750
Subject Interests: Antitrust law, Banks and banking, Legislation, Securities
Partic in Dialog Corporation; Dow Jones News Retrieval; Westlaw

S WOODROW WILSON INTERNATIONAL CENTER FOR SCHOLARS LIBRARY,* 1300 Pennsylvania Ave NW, 20523. SAN 302-7732. Tel: 202-691-4150. FAX: 202-691-4001. *Librn*, Zdenek V David; Staff 4 (MLS 2, Non-MLS 2)
Founded 1970
Oct 1999-Sep 2000 Income $150,000. Mats Exp $65,000, Books $10,000,

Per/Ser (Incl. Access Fees) $55,000
Library Holdings: Bk Vols 15,000; Bk Titles 8,000; Per Subs 250
Subject Interests: Reference, Russia
Restriction: By appointment only
Branches:
KENNAN INSTITUTE FOR ADVANCED RUSSIAN STUDIES LIBRARY Tel: 202-691-4150. *Librn*, Zdenek V David; *ILL*, Linda Warden; *Acq*, Georgann Juneau; Staff 4 (MLS 2, Non-MLS 2)
Founded 1975
Library Holdings: Bk Vols 10,000; Bk Titles 8,000; Per Subs 55
Subject Interests: Economics, Literary criticism, Russia
Restriction: By appointment only

L WINSTON & STRAWN, Law Library,* 1400 L St NW, No 800, 20005. SAN 372-3089. Tel: 202-371-5843. FAX: 202-371-5950. *Librn*, Deborah A Miller; E-Mail: dmiller@winston.com
Library Holdings: Bk Vols 10,000; Per Subs 300
Subject Interests: Energy
Partic in Illinois Library & Information Network

R WOODSTOCK THEOLOGICAL CENTER LIBRARY, Georgetown University, PO Box 571170, 20057-1170. SAN 322-8568. Tel: 202-687-7513. FAX: 202-687-7473. Web Site: www.georgetown.edu/centers/woodstock/lib.htm. *Librn*, Joseph Tylenda; E-Mail: tylendaj@gunet.georgetown.edu; *Asst Librn*, Paul S Osmanski; Staff 4 (MLS 2, Non-MLS 2)
Founded 1869
Jul 1999-Jun 2000 Income $367,581. Mats Exp $162,611. Sal $204,970 (Prof $133,512)
Library Holdings: Bk Vols 195,000; Per Subs 708
Subject Interests: Religion, Theology
Special Collections: Palestinian Antiquities (Halpern Coll), engravings; Theology & Jesuitica (Joques, Shrub Oak, & Parsons Coll), bks

S THE WORLD BANK, Sectoral & IT Resource Center, 1818 H St NW, Rm MC-C3-220, 20433. SAN 377-4619. Tel: 202-473-8670. FAX: 202-522-3560. E-Mail: slibrary@worldbank.org. Web Site: www.jolis.worldbankimslib.org/external.htm. *Mgr*, Pamela Tripp-Melby
Library Holdings: Bk Vols 75,000; Per Subs 1,000

S WORLD JURIST ASSOCIATION, Information Center, 1000 Connecticut Ave NW,Ste 202, 20036. SAN 375-2216. Tel: 202-466-5428. FAX: 202-452-8540. E-Mail: wja@worldjurist.org. Web Site: www.worldjurist.org. *Dir*, Margaret Henneberry
Library Holdings: Bk Titles 10; Per Subs 10

S WORLD RESOURCES INSTITUTE INFORMATION CENTER & RESEARCH SERVICES, 10 G St NW, Ste 800, 20002. Tel: 202-729-7603. Web Site: www.wri.org. *Dir*, Elizabeth A Behrendt; Tel: 202-729-7601; Staff 3 (MLS 2, Non-MLS 1)
Founded 1982
Database Vendor: Dialog, Ebsco - EbscoHost, Lexis-Nexis, OCLC - First Search
Restriction: By appointment only

S WORLD WILDLIFE FUND-US LIBRARY, 1250 24th St NW, 20037-1125. SAN 302-623X. Tel: 202-778-9636. FAX: 202-293-9211. E-Mail: library@wwfus.org.
Founded 1949
Library Holdings: Bk Vols 15,000; Per Subs 400
Partic in Capcon Library Network; OCLC Online Computer Library Center, Inc

L WRIGHT & TALISMAN, Law Library,* 1200 G St NW, Ste 600, 20005. SAN 370-1174. Tel: 202-393-1200. FAX: 202-393-1240.
Library Holdings: Per Subs 37

L ZUCKERT, SCOUTT & RASENBERGER LIBRARY,* 888 17th St NW, 20006. SAN 373-7500. Tel: 202-298-8660. FAX: 202-342-0683. *Librn*, Sally C Hand; E-Mail: schand@zselaw.com
Library Holdings: Bk Vols 10,000
Special Collections: Aviation Law (DOT Orders Coll, complete), bd vols

FLORIDA

Date of Statistics: 2000
Population, 1997: 15,322,040
Population Served by Public Libraries: 15,257,347
Total Public Library Circulation: 73,899,704
Total Public Library Income (incl. Grants-in-Aid): $324,038,247
Source of Income: Public funds (93.52%); Local (84.33%); State (9.89%); Federal (.99%); Other (4.79%)
Expenditures Per Capita: $19.03
Number of County Systems: 40
Regional Systems: 9 Multi-county Systems covering 27 counties
Counties Served: 67
Number of Bookmobiles in State: 29
Grants-in-Aid to Public Libraries:
Federal (Library Services & Construction Act): (FY 1999-00) $6,861,953
Formula for Apportionment: Legally established county or multi-county libraries receive grants based on local support; additional funds are provided to 34 poorest counties and to multi-county systems.
State Aid: (FY 2000-01) $33,400,000

ALTAMONTE SPRINGS

P ALTAMONTE SPRINGS CITY LIBRARY, 281 N Maitland Ave, 32701. SAN 302-8380. Tel: 407-830-3895. FAX: 407-263-3716. *Dir*, Richard A Miller; E-Mail: rmiller@cflc.net; *Asst Librn*, Judy Zahn; Staff 5 (MLS 1, Non-MLS 4)
Founded 1959. Pop 40,000; Circ 47,730
Library Holdings: Bk Vols 32,775; Per Subs 96
Subject Interests: Florida
Special Collections: Local Historical Coll
Publications: Local information brochures

S INSTITUTE OF INTERNAL AUDITORS LIBRARY, 249 Maitland Ave, 32701-4201. SAN 302-8399. Tel: 407-830-7600, Ext 205. FAX: 407-831-5171. *Dir*, Basil Pflumm
Founded 1941
Library Holdings: Bk Vols 5,000; Per Subs 52
Subject Interests: Accounting, Business and management, Data processing
Special Collections: Institute of Internal Auditors publications
Restriction: Staff use only

APALACHICOLA

P APALACHICOLA MUNICIPAL LIBRARY, 76 Sixth St, 32320. SAN 370-4610. Tel: 850-653-8436. *Librn*, Erma Barber
Library Holdings: Bk Titles 15,000

APOPKA

S LITTON LASER SYSTEMS, Research & Information Center, 2787 S Orange Blossom Trail, 32703. (Mail add: PO Box 547300, 32854), SAN 329-9880. Tel: 407-295-4010. FAX: 407-297-4895. E-Mail: litlaser@magicnet.net. *Librn*, Jaime Foote; Tel: 407-297-4478
Library Holdings: Bk Titles 1,500; Per Subs 114
Partic in Dialog Corporation

C MID FLORIDA RESEARCH & EDUCATION CENTER LIBRARY, 2725 Binion Rd, 32703. SAN 322-9009. Tel: 407-884-2034. FAX: 407-814-6186. E-Mail: rhs@gnv.ifas.ufl.edu. Web Site: www.mrec.ifas.ufl.edu. *Librn*, Kathy Phillips; *Asst Librn*, Barbara Hill
Library Holdings: Bk Vols 7,500

C UNIVERSITY OF FLORIDA, Mid-Florida Research & Education Center, 2725 Binion Rd, 32703-8504. SAN 323-715X. Tel: 407-884-2034. FAX: 407-814-6187. E-Mail: mrec@gnv.ifas.ufl.edu.; Staff 1 (MLS 1)
Fac 6
Library Holdings: Bk Vols 12,000; Per Subs 132

ARCADIA

P DESOTO COUNTY LIBRARY, 125 N Hillsborough Ave, 34266. SAN 302-8402. Tel: 863-993-4852. FAX: 863-491-4095. Web Site: www.heartlineweb.org/des. *Dir*, Elizabeth M Kenney; E-Mail: ekenney@heartland.lib.fl.us
Founded 1963. Pop 23,865; Circ 167,811
Library Holdings: Bk Vols 30,648; Per Subs 63
Friends of the Library Group

S FLORIDA DEPARTMENT OF CORRECTIONS, DeSoto Correctional Institution Library, PO Drawer 1072, 34265. SAN 302-8410. Tel: 863-494-3727. FAX: 863-494-1740.; Staff 1 (MLS 1)
Founded 1970
Library Holdings: Bk Vols 9,200; Per Subs 100
Special Collections: Law (Inmate Legal Coll)

M G PIERCE WOOD MEMORIAL HOSPITAL, Resident Library, 5847 SE Hwy 31, 34266. SAN 302-8429. Tel: 863-494-8249. FAX: 863-494-4273. *Librn*, Anson Raymond; Staff 1 (MLS 1)
Founded 1966
Library Holdings: Bk Titles 6,000; Per Subs 50
Subject Interests: Mental health

§R THE ANNE NEVINS DIOCESAN LIBRARY, 10299 SW Peace River St, 34266-4068. Tel: 941-766-7334. FAX: 941-629-8555. E-Mail: ricenevinslib@nut-n-but.net. Web Site: www.riceschool.org.

AUBURNDALE

P AUBURNDALE PUBLIC LIBRARY, 100 W Bridgers Ave, 33823. SAN 302-8437. Tel: 863-965-5548. FAX: 863-965-5554. *Dir*, Karen Pixley
Founded 1951. Pop 10,000; Circ 62,000
Library Holdings: Bk Titles 40,000; Per Subs 56
Open Mon & Thurs 9:30-8, Tues, Wed & Fri 9-6 & Sat 1-5

AVON PARK

S AVON PARK CORRECTIONAL LIBRARY, State Rd 64 E, 33825. SAN 302-8445. Tel: 941-453-3174. *Librn*, Colby Joyner; Staff 2 (MLS 1, Non-MLS 1)
Founded 1958
Library Holdings: Bk Vols 9,000; Per Subs 90
Subject Interests: Fiction
Special Collections: Spanish Coll, large print, easy
Publications: Hot Picks
Partic in Fla State Libr ILL Network
Also have Law Library which serves Region V of the Florida Dept of Corrections

P AVON PARK PUBLIC LIBRARY, 100 N Museum Ave, 33825. SAN 302-8453. Tel: 863-452-3803. FAX: 941-452-3804. Web Site: www.heartlineweb.org/apl/. *Librn*, Don Brusha; E-Mail: dbrusha@

heartland.lib.fl.us
Pop 8,200
Library Holdings: Bk Vols 40,000; Per Subs 54
Subject Interests: Florida
Friends of the Library Group

GM FLORIDA CENTER FOR ADDICTIONS & DUAL DISORDERS LIBRARY, 100 W College Dr, 33825. SAN 302-8461. Tel: 863-452-3858. FAX: 863-452-3863.
Library Holdings: Bk Vols 5,100

J SOUTH FLORIDA COMMUNITY COLLEGE LIBRARY, 600 W College Dr, 33825-9356. SAN 302-847X. Tel: 863-784-7306. Reference Tel: 863-784-7304. FAX: 863-452-6042. E-Mail: lrc@mail.sfcc.cc.fl.us. Web Site: www.sfcc.cc.fl.us. *Actg Dir*, Lena Phelps; Tel: 863-784-7303, E-Mail: phelle4543@sfcc.cc.fl.us; Staff 10 (MLS 2, Non-MLS 8)
Founded 1966. Enrl 3,000; Fac 60; Highest Degree: Associate
Library Holdings: Bk Vols 45,685; Bk Titles 40,869; Per Subs 100
Database Vendor: DRA
Publications: Guide to Library

BABSON PARK

J WEBBER COLLEGE, Grace & Roger Babson Learning Center, 1201 State Rd 17, 33827-0097. (Mail add: PO Box 97, 33827-0097), SAN 302-8496. Tel: 863-638-2937. FAX: 863-638-2778. E-Mail: webbercollegelib@hotmail.com. Web Site: www.webber.edu. *Dir*, Sue Ammons
Founded 1927. Enrl 473; Highest Degree: Master
Library Holdings: Bk Vols 36,000; Bk Titles 26,500
Subject Interests: Business and management, Economics
Special Collections: Civil War Coll

BAREFOOT BAY

P SOUTH MAINLAND LIBRARY, 7921 Ron Beatty Blvd, 32976. SAN 370-3592. Tel: 321-664-4066. FAX: 321-664-0534. Web Site: manatee.brev.lib.fl.us/locations/moa/moa.htm. *Dir*, Jim Wheeler
Library Holdings: Bk Vols 30,000; Per Subs 72
Mem of Brevard County Library System
Friends of the Library Group

BARTOW

P BARTOW PUBLIC LIBRARY, 2150 S Broadway Ave, 33830. SAN 302-850X. Tel: 863-534-0131. FAX: 863-534-0913. Web Site: www.pclc.lib.fl.us/bartow/. *Dir*, Linda Chancey; E-Mail: chancel@pclc.lib.fl.us; *Asst Dir*, Gladys Roberts; *Cat*, Paula Hielscher; Staff 2 (MLS 2)
Founded 1897. Pop 14,740; Circ 113,001
Library Holdings: Bk Titles 36,000; Per Subs 110
Special Collections: Civil War
Friends of the Library Group

S FLORIDA INSTITUTE OF PHOSPHATE RESEARCH, FIPR Library & Info Clearinghouse, 1855 W Main St, 33830-4338. SAN 324-5594. Tel: 863-534-7160. FAX: 863-534-7165. *Librn*, Gary R Albarelli; Staff 3 (MLS 2, Non-MLS 1)
Founded 1980
Library Holdings: Bk Titles 6,000; Per Subs 80
Subject Interests: Beneficiation, Environ including radon, Phosphate mining, Processing, Reclamation
Automation Activity & Vendor Info: (Circulation) Sagebrush Corporation; (OPAC) Sagebrush Corporation
Database Vendor: OCLC - First Search
Publications: Annual Report; Quarterly Newsletter
Partic in Dialog Corporation; OCLC Online Computer Library Center, Inc; SE Libr Network; STN; Tampa Bay Library Consortium, Inc

S POLK COUNTY HISTORICAL & GENEALOGICAL LIBRARY, Historic Courthouse, 100 E Main St, 33830. SAN 302-8526. Tel: 863-534-4380. FAX: 863-534-4382. Web Site: www.polk-county.net/library.html. *Librn*, Joseph E Spann, Jr; E-Mail: joe_spann@bocc.ci.polk.fl.us
Founded 1940
Library Holdings: Bk Titles 11,000; Per Subs 40
Special Collections: Genealogy & History of the Southeastern US
Restriction: Open to public for reference only

GL POLK COUNTY LAW LIBRARY, Courthouse, Rm 3076, 255 N Broadway, 33830. SAN 302-8534. Tel: 863-534-4013. FAX: 863-534-7443. *Actg Librn*, Irene Morris
Founded 1956
Library Holdings: Bk Titles 19,000; Per Subs 60
Special Collections: Legal Materials Coll
Partic in Westlaw; Wilsonline

BELLE GLADE

S FLORIDA DEPARTMENT OF CORRECTIONS, Glades Correctional Institution Library, 500 Orange Ave Circle, 33430-5222. SAN 302-8569. Tel: 561-996-5241, Ext 266. FAX: 561-992-1355.
Founded 1968
Library Holdings: Bk Vols 8,000; Bk Titles 3,000; Per Subs 52

J PALM BEACH COMMUNITY COLLEGE, Glades Campus Library Learning Resource Center, 1977 College Dr, 33430. SAN 302-8577. Tel: 561-992-6150, 561-992-6175. FAX: 561-992-6179. Web Site: www.pbcc.cc.fl.us/glades/llrcg.htm. *Librn*, Mohamed Mansour; E-Mail: mmansourm@pbcc.cc.fl.us
Library Holdings: Bk Vols 8,660; Bk Titles 8,451; Per Subs 87

C UNIVERSITY OF FLORIDA, Everglades Research & Education Center, 3200 E Palm Beach Rd, 33430-8003. (Mail add: PO Box 8003, 33430-8003), SAN 302-8585. Tel: 561-993-1500. FAX: 561-993-1582. E-Mail: bgl@gnu.ifas.ufl.edu, klkr@gnu.ifas.ufl.edu. Web Site: erec.ifas.ufl.edu/. *Librn*, Kathleen Krawchuk
Founded 1926
Library Holdings: Bk Titles 12,000; Per Subs 100
Subject Interests: Agriculture, Turf grass
Publications: Journal Series; Research Reports

BEVERLY HILLS

P CITRUS COUNTY LIBRARY SYSTEM, 425 W Roosevelt Blvd, 34465. SAN 328-8633. Tel: 352-746-9077. FAX: 352-746-9493. Web Site: www.cclib.org. *Dir*, Flossil Benton Rogers; *Syst Coordr*, Eric Head
Founded 1987. Pop 112,424; Circ 470,633
Special Collections: NRC Depository Coll; Nuclear Regulatory
Friends of the Library Group
Branches: 5
CENTRAL RIDGE, 425 W Roosevelt Blvd, 34465. SAN 337-8780. Tel: 352-746-6622. FAX: 352-746-4170. *Branch Mgr*, Lisa Ehlis
Friends of the Library Group
COASTAL REGION, 8619 W Crystal St, 34428. SAN 337-8608. Tel: 352-795-3716. FAX: 352-795-3103. *Branch Mgr*, Marilyn Nykiforuk
Friends of the Library Group
FLORAL CITY LIBRARY, 8360 E Orange Ave, Floral City, 34436. SAN 337-8667. Tel: 352-726-3671. *Branch Mgr*, Phyllis Mengler
Friends of the Library Group
HOMOSASSA LIBRARY, 5530 S Mason Creek Rd, Homosassa, 34448. SAN 337-8721. Tel: 352-628-5626. *Branch Mgr*, Wylene Head
Friends of the Library Group
LAKES REGION, 1511 Druid Rd, Inverness, 34452. SAN 337-8756. Tel: 352-726-2357. FAX: 352-726-2814. *Branch Mgr*, Karen Slaska
Friends of the Library Group

BLOUNTSTOWN

S CALHOUN CORRECTION INSTITUTION LIBRARY, Rte 1, Box 1, 32424. SAN 323-9152. Tel: 850-674-5901, Ext 173. *Librn*, Dan Nolen; Staff 1 (MLS 1)
Founded 1988
Library Holdings: Bk Titles 7,800; Per Subs 60
Special Services for the Deaf - Books on deafness & sign language; High interest/low vocabulary books

P CALHOUN COUNTY PUBLIC LIBRARY, 16908 NW Pear St, 32424. SAN 370-4688. Tel: 850-674-8773. FAX: 850-674-2843. *Dir*, Rita Maupin; E-Mail: rita@digitalexp.com; *Admin Assoc*, Joyce Thomas
Library Holdings: Bk Titles 20,000; Per Subs 10
Branches: 4
ALTHA BRANCH, PO Box 241, Altha, 32421. SAN 370-4696. Tel: 850-762-8280. FAX: 850-762-8280. *Librn*, Alice McCardle
HUGH CREEK, Rte 1, Box 320, 32424. Tel: 850-674-3334. FAX: 850-674-3334. *Librn*, Manuel Gatlin
KINARD BRANCH, Rte 1, Box 50, Kinard, 32449. SAN 370-470X. Tel: 850-639-5125. FAX: 850-639-5125. *Librn*, Zulma Crocker
SHELTON'S PARK, Rte 3 Box 224, Altma, 32421. SAN 377-8355. Tel: 850-762-3992. FAX: 850-762-3992 (call first). *Branch Mgr*, Pat Shelton

BOCA RATON

S AMERICAN MEDIA, INC, Star Magazine Photo Library, 5401 NW Broken Sound Blvd, 33487. SAN 328-3356. Toll Free Tel: 800-749-7733. FAX: 561-989-1158. *Chief Librn*, Maria Peters; *Librn*, Kathleen Cottay
Library Holdings: Bk Titles 1,100; Per Subs 125

M BOCA RATON COMMUNITY HOSPITAL, Medical Staff Library, 800 Meadows Rd, 33486. SAN 324-5632. Tel: 561-393-4070. FAX: 561-750-4825. *Librn*, Carolyn F Hill; Staff 1 (MLS 1)

Founded 1969
Library Holdings: Bk Titles 4,800; Per Subs 200
Publications: Newsletters
Partic in Nat Libr of Med

S BOCA RATON NEWS LIBRARY, 5801 N Congress Ave, 33487. SAN 375-4936. Tel: 561-893-6604. FAX: 561-338-4944. *Librn*, Sandra L Wesley
Founded 1985
Library Holdings: Bk Titles 50; Per Subs 10
Special Collections: Newspaper Clippings from 1985-1993; SAVE SYSTEM Electronic Library, 1994-present

P BOCA RATON PUBLIC LIBRARY, 200 NW Boca Raton Blvd, 33432-3706. SAN 302-8593. Tel: 561-393-7852. Circulation Tel: 561-393-7980. Reference Tel: 561-393-7906. TDD: 561-347-0149. FAX: 561-393-7823. Web Site: www.bocalibrary.org. *Dir*, Catherine A O'Connell; Tel: 561-393-7916, E-Mail: oconnell@bocalibrary.org; *Ad Servs*, Patricia Goner Michalski; Tel: 561-393-7905; *Coll Develop*, Mary Jane Beasley; Tel: 561-393-7962, E-Mail: mbeasley@bocalibrary.org; *Tech Servs*, Susan L Sloan; Tel: 561-393-7904, Fax: 561-347-5190, E-Mail: ssloan@bocalibrary.org; *Ad Servs*, Patricia Goner Michalski; Tel: 561-393-7905, E-Mail: pmichals@bocalibrary.org; *Ref Serv Ad*, Dwight Rodden; Tel: 561-393-7963, E-Mail: drodden@bocalibrary.org; *Media Spec*, Regina Wolkoff; Tel: 561-393-7962; *Ch Servs*, Rebecca Swensen; Tel: 561-393-7967, E-Mail: rswensen@bocalibrary.org; Staff 54 (MLS 4, Non-MLS 50)
Founded 1938. Pop 70,000; Circ 558,030
Library Holdings: Bk Vols 126,525; Bk Titles 103,369; Per Subs 220; High Interest/Low Vocabulary Bk Vols 747; Bks on Deafness & Sign Lang 110
Subject Interests: Interior design
Special Collections: Florida Coll, bks, flms; US Civil War
Automation Activity & Vendor Info: (Acquisitions) epixtech, inc.; (Cataloging) epixtech, inc.; (Circulation) epixtech, inc.; (OPAC) epixtech, inc.; (Serials) epixtech, inc.
Database Vendor: Ebsco - EbscoHost, epixtech, inc., GaleNet, IAC - Info Trac, OCLC - First Search
Function: ILL available
Special Services for the Deaf - TDD
Friends of the Library Group

S CRC PRESS INC LIBRARY, 2000 Corporate Blvd NW, 33431. SAN 302-8615. Tel: 561-994-0555. FAX: 561-998-9784. *In Charge*, Bill Pacheco
Founded 1967
Library Holdings: Bk Titles 9,200
Restriction: Staff use only

S DUNHILL BUSINESS, Research Library, 1951 NW 19th St, 33431-7344. SAN 311-7421. Tel: 561-347-0200. FAX: 561-347-0400. *Librn*, Valerie Schmidt
Founded 1938
Library Holdings: Bk Titles 2,000
Publications: Trade Directories

C FLORIDA ATLANTIC UNIVERSITY, S E Wimberly Library, 777 Glades Rd, 33431-0992. (Mail add: PO Box 3092, 33431-0992), SAN 337-2693. Tel: 561-297-3760. Interlibrary Loan Service Tel: 561-297-3769. FAX: 561-336-4169 (Treasure Coast Campus), 561-799-8587 (Jupiter Campus). Interlibrary Loan Service FAX: 561-394-8829. Web Site: www.fau.edu/library/homehome.htm. *Dir*, William Miller; E-Mail: miller@fau.edu; *Asst Dir*, Connor D Tjarks; *Assoc Dir, Coll Develop*, Rita Pellen; *Librn*, Carla Robinson; *Assoc Librn*, Patricia Roshaven; *Acq*, Diane Kachmar; *Archivist, Spec Coll*, Zita M Cael; *Coll Develop*, Carlos Nelson; *ILL*, Ken Frankel; *Ref*, Darlene Parrish; *Syst Coordr*, Elaine Hyman; *Tech Servs*, Janice Donahue; *Tech Servs*, Maria A Treadwell; Staff 30 (MLS 30)
Founded 1961. Enrl 19,699; Fac 712; Highest Degree: Doctorate
Library Holdings: Bk Vols 808,239; Per Subs 4,184
Subject Interests: Art, Education, Engineering, Ethnic studies, Nursing, Technology, Women's studies
Special Collections: Children's Literature; Curriculum/School Text Books; Floridiana, mss & bks; Judaica; Theodore Pratt
Automation Activity & Vendor Info: (Acquisitions) NOTIS; (Circulation) NOTIS
Publications: Index to Florida Documents
Partic in OCLC Online Computer Library Center, Inc
Friends of the Library Group
Departmental Libraries:

S INTERNATIONAL MUSEUM OF CARTOON ART LIBRARY, 201 Plaza Real, 33432. SAN 374-6666. Tel: 561-391-2200. FAX: 561-391-2721. Web Site: www.cartoon.org. *Curator*, Stephen Charla
Founded 1974
Library Holdings: Bk Titles 10,000

J LYNN UNIVERSITY LIBRARY, 3601 N Military Trail, 33431-5598. SAN 302-8607. Tel: 561-237-7054. FAX: 561-237-7074. Web Site: www.lynn.edu/library. *Dir*, Charles Kuhn; E-Mail: ckuhn@lynn.edu; *Cat*, Sally Seaman; Tel: 561-237-7073, E-Mail: sseaman@lynn.edu; *ILL*, Judy Alsdorf; Tel: 561-237-7056, E-Mail: jalsdorf@lynn.edu; *Ser*, Leecy Barnett; Staff 9 (MLS 5, Non-MLS 4)
Founded 1963. Enrl 1,900; Fac 75; Highest Degree: Doctorate
1999-2000 Income $730,610. Mats Exp $299,000, Books $150,000, Per/Ser (Incl. Access Fees) $73,000, Micro $38,000, AV Equip $18,000. Sal $230,700
Library Holdings: Bk Titles 79,000; Per Subs 700
Subject Interests: Business and management, Fashion, Geriatrics and gerontology, Humanities, Retailing
Automation Activity & Vendor Info: (Acquisitions) Endeavor; (Cataloging) Endeavor; (Circulation) Endeavor; (Course Reserve) Endeavor; (ILL) Endeavor; (Media Booking) Endeavor; (OPAC) Endeavor; (Serials) Endeavor
Partic in Southeast Florida Library Information Network, Inc

§J PALM BEACH COMMUNITY COLLEGE, Media Services-South, 3000 St Lucie Ave, 33431-6415. Tel: 561-367-4554. FAX: 561-367-4612. Web Site: www.pbcc.cc.fl.us/south/media. *Librn*, Willie Ford; E-Mail: fordw@pbcc.cc.fl.us
Library Holdings: Bk Vols 2,660

BONIFAY

§S FLORIDA DEPARTMENT OF CORRECTIONS, Holmes Correctional Institution Library, 3142 Thomas Dr, 32425. Tel: 850-547-2100. FAX: 850-547-0522. *Librn*, John Kilhefner
Library Holdings: Bk Titles 8,500; Per Subs 50

P HOLMES COUNTY LIBRARY, 301 N Etheridge, 32425. SAN 376-2718. Tel: 850-547-3573. FAX: 850-547-5306. E-Mail: hcpl@digitalexp.com. *Coll Develop, Dir, Librn*, Bernice Skinner; *Asst Dir, Cat*, Susan Harris; E-Mail: ssssfour@yahoo.com; Staff 4 (Non-MLS 4)
Founded 1973
Library Holdings: Bk Vols 12,000; Bk Titles 6,000; Per Subs 50
Mem of Panhandle Library System

BOWLING GREEN

S HARDEE CORRECTIONAL INSTITUTION LIBRARY, 6901 State Rd 62, 33834. SAN 377-2632. Tel: 863-773-2441. FAX: 863-773-4310.
Library Holdings: Bk Vols 17,000; Per Subs 85

BOYNTON BEACH

M BETHESDA MEMORIAL HOSPITAL, Medical Library, 2815 S Seacrest Blvd, 33435. SAN 302-864X. Tel: 561-737-7733, Ext 4439. FAX: 561-735-7080.
Founded 1967
Library Holdings: Bk Vols 5,000; Per Subs 200
Special Collections: NCME Tapes
Publications: Quarterly Report

P BOYNTON BEACH CITY LIBRARY, 208 S Seacrest Blvd, 33435. SAN 302-8658. Tel: 561-742-6390. FAX: 561-742-6381. Web Site: www.coala.org. *Dir*, Virginia K Farace; *Publ Servs*, Joyce Waters; *Ch Servs, YA Servs*, Patricia Mooar; *Ref*, William Coup; *Tech Servs*, Jane Northup
Founded 1961. Pop 45,418; Circ 409,294
Library Holdings: Bk Vols 120,000; Per Subs 500
Subject Interests: Gardening, Investing
Special Collections: Large Print Books; Local Hist, photog; New Reader's Series; Song Books; Telephone Books
Mem of Palm Beach County Library System
Partic in Coop Authority for Libr Automation
Friends of the Library Group

§S MOTOROLA, Technical Library-Boynton Beach, 1500 Gateway Blvd, 33426-8292. Tel: 561-739-3702. FAX: 561-739-8850. *Librn*, Joan Lange; E-Mail: ejl002@email.mot.com
Library Holdings: Bk Titles 2,800; Per Subs 150

R ST VINCENT DE PAUL REGIONAL SEMINARY LIBRARY, 10701 S Military Trail, 33436-4811. SAN 302-8666. Tel: 561-732-4424, Ext 174. FAX: 561-737-2205. Web Site: www.svdp.edu. *Dir Libr Serv*, Arthur G Quinn; E-Mail: aquinn@svdp.edu; *Ser*, Ana Lopez; Tel: 561-732-4424, Ext 153, E-Mail: amlopez@svdp.edu; *Tech Servs*, Marguerite Wolf; Tel: 561-732-4424, Ext 173, E-Mail: mwolf@svdp.edu. Subject Specialists: *Theology*, Arthur G Quinn; Staff 2 (MLS 2)
Founded 1963. Enrl 103; Fac 18; Highest Degree: Master
Jul 1999-Jun 2000 Income Parent Institution $181,668. Mats Exp $74,716, Books $36,366, Per/Ser (Incl. Access Fees) $22,424, Presv $4,170, Micro $236, AV Equip $2,128, Manuscripts & Archives $1,604, Electronic Ref Mat (Incl. Access Fees) $7,788. Sal $54,424
Library Holdings: Bk Vols 55,380; Bk Titles 45,500; Per Subs 441
Subject Interests: Latin America, Philosophy, Theology
Special Collections: Loeb Series; Sources Chretiennes Series
Automation Activity & Vendor Info: (Cataloging) Athena; (Circulation) Athena; (OPAC) Athena
Function: Research library

BRADENTON

S ART LEAGUE OF MANATEE COUNTY, McKelvey Memorial Library, 209 Ninth St W, 34205. SAN 302-8674. Tel: 941-746-2862. FAX: 941-746-2319. *Mgr*, Pat Richmond
Founded 1955
Library Holdings: Bk Vols 900

J MANATEE COMMUNITY COLLEGE LIBRARY, Sara Scott Harllee Library, 5840 26th St W, PO Box 1849, 34207. SAN 302-8690. Tel: 941-752-5305. Reference Tel: 941-752-5304. FAX: 941-753-7458. Web Site: www.bc.mcc.cc.fl.us. *Chair*, Sue Clayton; Tel: 941-752-5399, E-Mail: claytos@bc.mcc.cc.fl.us; *Coll Develop*, Judy Born; Tel: 941-752-5262, E-Mail: bornj@bc.mcc.cc.fl.us; *Br Coordr*, Aggie Balash; Tel: 941-493-3504, Ext 2309, Fax: 941-486-2449, E-Mail: balasha@bc.mcc.cc.fl.us; Staff 12 (MLS 5, Non-MLS 7)
Founded 1958. Enrl 3,500; Fac 154; Highest Degree: Associate
Jul 1999-Jun 2000 Income Parent Institution $255,119. Mats Exp $135,825, Books $82,000, Per/Ser (Incl. Access Fees) $37,825, Micro $12,000, AV Equip $4,000
Library Holdings: Bk Vols 55,160; Bk Titles 50,517; Per Subs 315
Subject Interests: Literature, Nursing, Paramedics
Automation Activity & Vendor Info: (Cataloging) DRA; (Circulation) DRA; (Serials) DRA
Database Vendor: DRA, Ebsco - EbscoHost, OCLC - First Search
Partic in Solinet; Tampa Bay Library Consortium, Inc
Departmental Libraries:
VENICE CAMPUS, 8000 S Tamiami Trail, Venice, 34293. SAN 371-3660. Tel: 941-493-3504, Ext 2312. FAX: 941-493-3504, Ext 2399. *Librn*, Aggie Balash; Tel: 941-408-1434, E-Mail: balasha@sc.mcc.cc.fl.us; Staff 4 (MLS 2, Non-MLS 2)

L MANATEE COUNTY, Law Library, County Court House, 3rd flr, Rm 329, 1115 Manatee Ave W, 34205. (Mail add: PO Box 25400, 34206), SAN 302-8682. Tel: 941-741-4090. FAX: 941-741-4085. *Librn*, Judy Brand; E-Mail: jbrand@clerkofcourts.com; Staff 1 (Non-MLS 1)
Oct 2000-Sep 2001 Income $136,575. Mats Exp $96,844. Sal $39,731
Library Holdings: Bk Vols 26,000

P MANATEE COUNTY PUBLIC LIBRARY SYSTEM, 1301 Barcarrota Blvd W, 34205. SAN 337-2723. Tel: 941-748-5555. TDD: 941-742-5951. FAX: 941-749-7191. *Dir*, John C Van Berkel; E-Mail: john.vanberkel@co.manatee.fl.us; *Dep Dir*, Linda O'Connor-Levy; E-Mail: linda.oconnorlevy@co.manatee.fl.us; *Ch Servs*, Elizabeth Rupert; *Ad Servs*, Carol O'Neill; *Circ*, Ivan Vlasic; *ILL*, Rose Taylor; *Govt Doc*, Susan Mason; *Coll Develop*, Kevin Beach; Staff 73 (MLS 31, Non-MLS 42)
Founded 1971. Pop 252,000; Circ 1,349,485
Oct 1999-Sep 2000 Income (Main Library and Branch Library) $5,058,291, State $385,113, County $4,319,241, Locally Generated Income $353,937. Mats Exp $660,585, Books $612,160, Electronic Ref Mat (Incl. Access Fees) $48,425. Sal $2,383,848
Library Holdings: Bk Vols 346,298; Bk Titles 143,681; Per Subs 890
Subject Interests: Florida, Genealogy, Local history
Special Collections: Archival negatives, Talking Books for the Blind & Physically handicapped, Oral History
Automation Activity & Vendor Info: (Cataloging) epixtech, inc.; (Circulation) epixtech, inc.
Publications: Friends & Foundation (newsletter)
Partic in Tampa Bay Library Consortium, Inc
Special Services for the Deaf - Special interest periodicals; TDD
Special Services for the Blind - Kurzweil Reading Machine
Adult Literacy & Learning Center
Friends of the Library Group
Branches: 5
BRADEN RIVER, 4915 53rd Ave E, 34203. SAN 371-3709. Tel: 941-727-6079. *Librn*, Cathryn Laird; Staff 8 (MLS 3, Non-MLS 5)
Friends of the Library Group
ISLAND BRANCH, 5701 Marina Dr, Holmes Beach, 34217. SAN 337-2758. Tel: 941-778-6341. FAX: 941-749-7184. E-Mail: lib.isl@co.manatee.fl.us. *Librn*, Sarah Bicknell; Staff 6 (MLS 1, Non-MLS 5)
Friends of the Library Group
PALMETTO BRANCH, 923 Sixth St W, Palmetto, 34221. SAN 337-2812. Tel: 941-722-3333. *Librn*, Dottie Julien; Staff 5 (MLS 1, Non-MLS 4)
Friends of the Library Group
ROCKY BLUFF, 7042 US Hwy 301 N, Ellenton, 34222. SAN 374-5244. Tel: 941-723-4821.; Staff 3 (MLS 1, Non-MLS 2)
Friends of the Library Group
SOUTH MANATEE COUNTY, 1506 Bayshore Gardens Pkwy, 34207. SAN 337-2847. Tel: 941-755-3892. *Librn*, Madelene Barnard; Staff 8 (MLS 3, Non-MLS 5)
Friends of the Library Group

M MANATEE MEMORIAL HOSPITAL, Wentzel Medical Library, 206 Second St E, 34208. SAN 302-8704. Tel: 941-746-5111, Ext 7121. FAX: 941-745-7279. *Librn*, Susan Sabbia
Library Holdings: Bk Vols 2,000
Subject Interests: Medicine, Nursing
Restriction: Restricted public use

C UNIVERSITY OF FLORIDA, Gulf Coast Research & Education Center Library, Institute of Food & Agricultural Sciences, 5007 60th St E, 34203. SAN 302-8712. Tel: 941-751-7636. FAX: 941-751-7639.
Library Holdings: Bk Vols 1,000; Per Subs 25

BRADENTON BEACH

P TINGLEY MEMORIAL LIBRARY, 111 Second St N, 34217-2465. SAN 375-3360. Tel: 941-779-1208. FAX: 941-778-7585. E-Mail: tinglib@altavista.com. *In Charge*, Carol Sandidge; E-Mail: tingcarol@altavista.com
Founded 1993
Oct 1999-Sep 2000 Income $40,000. Mats Exp $6,100, Books $6,000, Per/Ser (Incl. Access Fees) $100. Sal $12,000
Library Holdings: Bk Vols 6,600
Subject Interests: Florida

BRISTOL

S LIBERTY CORRECTIONAL INSTITUTION LIBRARY, HCR 2 Box 144, 32321-9711. SAN 377-2659. Tel: 850-643-2141, Ext 235. FAX: 850-643-3813. *Librn*, Fran Rigsby; Staff 2 (MLS 1, Non-MLS 1)
Founded 1990
Jul 1998-Jun 1999 Mats Exp $12,600, Books $7,500, Per/Ser (Incl. Access Fees) $3,500, AV Equip $600, Other Print Mats $1,000. Sal $48,000 (Prof $31,000)
Library Holdings: Bk Vols 13,000; Per Subs 90; High Interest/Low Vocabulary Bk Vols 500; Bks on Deafness & Sign Lang 10
Subject Interests: Addictions, Law, Popular fiction, Self help, Spanish lang mat, Substance abuse

BROOKSVILLE

S HERNANDO CORRECTIONAL INSTITUTION LIBRARY, 16415 Spring Hill Dr, 34609. SAN 377-0435. Tel: 352-754-6715.; Staff 1 (MLS 1)
Jul 1999-Jun 2000 Income $10,000. Mats Exp $9,000, Books $7,000, Per/Ser (Incl. Access Fees) $1,000, Other Print Mats $1,000. Sal $30,000
Library Holdings: Bk Vols 4,200; Per Subs 30

P HERNANDO COUNTY PUBLIC LIBRARY SYSTEM, 238 Howell Ave, 34601. SAN 337-2871. Tel: 352-754-4043. FAX: 352-754-4044. E-Mail: library@co.hernando.fl.us. Web Site: www.hernando.com/moton/brooksville/lib/library.html. *Dir*, Barbara Shiflett; E-Mail: shiflett@hcpl.lib.fl.us; *Tech Servs*, Margaret Golovey; *Coll Develop*, Bradley Volgler; *Info Specialist*, Dee Fields; Staff 39 (MLS 7, Non-MLS 32)
Founded 1926. Pop 127,400; Circ 630,463
Oct 1998-Sep 1999 Income (Main Library and Branch Library) $1,766,850, Federal $12,250, County $1,754,600. Sal $926,662
Library Holdings: Bk Vols 217,432; Bk Titles 105,752; Per Subs 427
Subject Interests: Florida
Automation Activity & Vendor Info: (Cataloging) DRA; (Circulation) DRA
Database Vendor: DRA, IAC - SearchBank, OVID Technologies
Partic in Florida Library Information Network; Tampa Bay Library Consortium, Inc
Friends of the Library Group
Branches: 3
EAST HERNANDO, Sunrise Plaza, 31170 Cortez Blvd, 34602. SAN 373-806X. Tel: 352-754-4443. FAX: 352-754-4445. Web Site: www.co.hernando.fl.us/lib/home.htm. *Branch Mgr*, Amanda Rochefort
Friends of the Library Group
LITTLE RED SCHOOLHOUSE, 1208 Kenlake Dr, Spring Hill, 34606. SAN 337-2995. Tel: 352-688-5037. FAX: 352-688-5038. Web Site: www.co.hernando.fl.us/lib/home.htm. *In Charge*, Colleen Rodriguez
Friends of the Library Group
WEST HERNANDO, 6335 Blackbird Ave, 34613. SAN 325-4429. Tel: 352-596-1077. FAX: 352-596-6100. Web Site: www.co.hernando.fl.us/lib/home.htm. *Branch Mgr*, Patrick Downs
Friends of the Library Group

J PASCO-HERNANDO COMMUNITY COLLEGE, Alfred A McKethan Library, 11415 Ponce de Leon Blvd, 34601-8698. SAN 302-8720. Tel: 352-796-6726. FAX: 352-796-2351. Web Site: www.pasco-hernando.com. *Dir*, Barbara Jameson; E-Mail: barbara_jameson@pasco-hernandocc.com
Founded 1974
Library Holdings: Bk Vols 15,000

S SOUTHWEST FLORIDA WATER MANAGEMENT DISTRICT LIBRARY, 2379 Broad St, 34609-6899. SAN 302-8739. Tel: 352-796-7211, Ext 4051. FAX: 352-554-2343. Web Site: www.swfwmd.state.fl.us. *Librn*, Charles Tornabene, Jr; Staff 2 (MLS 1, Non-MLS 1)
Founded 1961
Library Holdings: Bk Vols 7,500; Per Subs 150
Subject Interests: Ecology, Engineering
Publications: List of District Technical Reports; Monthly List of New Acquisitions
Partic in Dialog Corporation

BUNNELL

M MEMORIAL HOSPITAL - FLAGLER, Computer Library, Moody Blvd, 32110. (Mail add: HC1 Box 2, 32110-9701), SAN 328-4182. Tel: 904-437-2211, Ext 500. FAX: 904-437-2014. *Admin Assoc*, Carol Goewey
Library Holdings: Bk Vols 58

BUSHNELL

P BUSHNELL PUBLIC LIBRARY, 217 N Market St, 33513. SAN 376-2998. Tel: 352-793-8274. FAX: 352-793-1608. *Librn*, Kelli Barnes
Mem of Sumter County Library System; Sumter County Public Library System
Open Mon & Wed 9-12 & 1-4:30, Tues & Thurs 10-1 & 2-5:30, Fri & Sat 10-1
Branches: 1
COLEMAN BRANCH, 712 Central Ave, Coleman, 33521-0456. SAN 376-2793. Tel: 352-748-4598. FAX: 352-748-5384. *Librn*, Tena L Cremshaw
Open Mon-Thurs 1-6, Fri & Sat 10-2

§S FLORIDA DEPARTMENT OF CORRECTIONS, Sumter Correctional Institution Library, PO Box 667, 33513-0667. Tel: 352-793-2525, Ext 357. FAX: 352-793-3542. *Librn*, Jeannie Chancellor
Library Holdings: Bk Vols 16,800; Per Subs 98

S FLORIDA DIVISION OF ADULT CORRECTIONS, Sumter Correctional Institution Library, 9544 County Rd 476B, PO Box 667, 33513. SAN 302-8747. Tel: 352-793-2525, Ext 357. FAX: 352-793-3542. *Librn*, J Chancellor
Founded 1968. Pop 1,700; Circ 4,065
Library Holdings: Bk Vols 15,560; Per Subs 98
Subject Interests: Science fiction, Spanish (language)
Special Collections: Black Interests; Easy-Reading; Paperbacks
Sumter houses a major law library, employs 11 certified law clerks (inmates) & meets the legal reference needs of approximately 1700 inmates

CAPE CANAVERAL

P CAPE CANAVERAL PUBLIC LIBRARY, 201 Polk Ave, 32920-3067. SAN 302-8755. Tel: 321-868-1101. FAX: 321-868-1103. Web Site: www.sunplus.brev.lib.fl.us. *Dir*, Isabel M Escapa; *YA Servs*, Marice Scarborough; *Ref*, Dorothy Livingstone; E-Mail: dlivingstone@manatee.brev.lib.fl.us; Staff 3 (MLS 2, Non-MLS 1)
Founded 1966. Pop 9,500; Circ 73,555
Oct 2000-Sep 2001 Income $374,745, County $361,745, Locally Generated Income $13,000. Mats Exp $65,181, Books $57,000, Per/Ser (Incl. Access Fees) $6,181, AV Equip $2,000. Sal $159,404 (Prof $78,674)
Library Holdings: Bk Vols 59,234; Per Subs 125; Per Subs 125; Bks on Deafness & Sign Lang 50
Special Collections: Theater (Play Coll)
Automation Activity & Vendor Info: (Cataloging) GEAC; (Circulation) GEAC; (OPAC) GEAC
Database Vendor: IAC - Info Trac, OCLC - First Search
Mem of Brevard County Library System
Partic in OCLC Online Computer Library Center, Inc; SE Libr Network
Friends of the Library Group

CARRABELLE

P FRANKLIN COUNTY PUBLIC LIBRARY, Carrabelle Branch, PO Box 722, 32322. SAN 376-7604. Tel: 850-697-2366. FAX: 850-697-2366. E-Mail: fcpl9@gtcom.net. Web Site: www.wild.lib.fl.us. *Head Librn*, Eileen Annie Ball; *Asst Librn*, Carolyn Sparks
Library Holdings: Bk Vols 10,000
Mem of Wilderness Coast Public Libraries
Friends of the Library Group

CASSELBERRY

§J CITY COLLEGE - CASSELBERRY LIBRARY, 853 Semoran Blvd, 32707. Tel: 407-831-9816. FAX: 407-831-1147. *Librn*, Jacqueline Ryan; E-Mail: jkr@bellsouth.net
Library Holdings: Bk Vols 2,000; Per Subs 50; Spec Interest Per Sub 20

CENTURY

S CENTURY CORRECTIONAL INSTITUTION LIBRARY, 400 Tedder Rd, 32535. SAN 377-306X. Tel: 850-256-0701, Ext 295.
Library Holdings: Bk Vols 9,000; Bk Titles 7,700; Per Subs 87

CHATTAHOOCHEE

M FLORIDA STATE HOSPITAL, Library Services, Main Library Bldg 1049, PO Box 1000, 32324. SAN 302-881X. Tel: 850-663-7671. FAX: 850-663-7303. *Dir Libr Serv*, Jane Marie Hamilton; Staff 3 (MLS 3)
Library Holdings: Bk Titles 25,400; Per Subs 135
Subject Interests: Law, Music, Psychology, Religion
Mem of Highlands County Libr
Library Services is composed of four libraries and one bookmobile

CHIEFLAND

LEVY COUNTY PUBLIC LIBRARY SYSTEM, Luther Callaway Public Library, 104 NE Third St, 32626-0937. SAN 374-4523. Tel: 352-493-2758. FAX: 352-493-2758. *Librn*, Ruth Davis
Friends of the Library Group

CHIPLEY

§S FLORIDA DEPARTMENT OF CORRECTIONS, Washington Correctional Institution Library, 4455 Sam Mitchell Dr, 32428. Tel: 850-773-6100, Ext 148. FAX: 850-773-6252. *Librn*, Evelyn Coskey
Library Holdings: Bk Vols 6,000; Per Subs 66

S WASHINGTON CORRECTIONAL INSTITUTION LIBRARY, 4455 San Mitchell Dr, 32428. SAN 377-0826. Tel: 850-773-6100. FAX: 850-773-6252. *Actg Librn*, J Brown
Library Holdings: Bk Vols 3,500; Bk Titles 3,000; Per Subs 85

P WASHINGTON COUNTY LIBRARY, 672 Fifth St, 32428. SAN 376-5016. Tel: 850-638-1314. FAX: 850-638-9499. *Dir*, Linda Norton
Library Holdings: Bk Vols 24,000
Mem of Panhandle Library System
Friends of the Library Group
Branches: 2
SAM MITCHELL PUBLIC LIBRARY, 3731 Roche Ave, Vernon, 32462. SAN 376-8287. Tel: 850-535-1208. FAX: 850-535-1208. *Mgr*, Robert Partlow
WAUSAU PUBLIC LIBRARY, 1607 Second Ave, Wausau, 32463. SAN 376-8295. Tel: 850-638-2532. FAX: 850-638-2532. *Mgr*, Susan Cook

CITRUS SPRINGS

P CITRUS SPRINGS MEMORIAL LIBRARY, 1826 W Country Club Blvd, 34434. SAN 376-3005. Tel: 352-489-2313. *Dir*, Donette Bergeson; *Pres*, Virginia Duelke
Library Holdings: Bk Titles 2,000
Mem of Citrus County Libr

CLEARWATER

C CLEARWATER CHRISTIAN COLLEGE, Easter Library, 3400 Gulf-to-Bay Blvd, 33759-4595. SAN 302-8828. Tel: 727-726-1153, Ext 218. FAX: 727-726-8597. E-Mail: library@clearwater.edu. Web Site: www.clearwater.edu. *Dir*, Roger C Miller; *Cat*, Betty Knight; *Circ*, Sue Olsen; *Coll Develop, Tech Servs*, Elizabeth Werner; *Info Tech*, Debra Kemper; *Ref*, June Delnay; Staff 6 (MLS 4, Non-MLS 2)
Founded 1966. Enrl 650; Fac 42; Highest Degree: Bachelor
Jul 2000-Jun 2001 Income $246,698. Mats Exp $77,000, Books $28,000, Per/Ser (Incl. Access Fees) $17,500, Presv $5,000, AV Equip $5,000. Sal $134,000
Library Holdings: Bk Vols 106,500; Per Subs 2,400
Subject Interests: American history, British hist, Native Americans, Religion
Database Vendor: epixtech, inc., ProQuest
Mem of Tampa Bay Libr Consortium, Inc
Partic in Asn of Christian Librs; OCLC Online Computer Library Center, Inc; Solinet

S CLEARWATER MARINE AQUARIUM LIBRARY, 249 Windward Passage, 33767. SAN 377-3086. Tel: 727-441-1790, Ext 222. Toll Free Tel: 888-239-9414. FAX: 727-442-9466. E-Mail: cma@cmaquarium.org. Web Site: www.cmaquarium.org. *Asst Dir*, Teri Hepburn
Founded 1972
Library Holdings: Bk Vols 3,000
Subject Interests: Marine sciences
Restriction: Not a lending library

P CLEARWATER PUBLIC LIBRARY SYSTEM, Main Library, 100 N Osceola Ave, 33755. SAN 337-3053. Tel: 727-462-6800. Interlibrary Loan Service Tel: 727-462-6800, Ext 234. Circulation Tel: 727-462-6800, Ext 234. Reference Tel: 727-462-6800, Ext 257. FAX: 727-462-6420. Web Site: www.clearwater-fl.com/cpl. *Dir*, John F Szabo; Tel: 727-462-6800, Ext 227, E-Mail: jszabo@clearwater-fl.com; *Ref*, Eleanor Scharf; Tel: 727-462-6800, Ext 243, Fax: 727-462-6689, E-Mail: escharf@clearwater-fl.com; *Circ*, Jeffrey Gifford; Tel: 727-462-6800, Ext 236, Fax: 727-298-0095, E-Mail: jgifford@clearwater-fl.com; *Commun Relations*, Jan Nickols; Tel: 727-462-6800, Ext 245, E-Mail: jnickols@clearwater-fl.com; *Tech Servs*, Linda Lange; Tel: 727-462-6800, Ext 249, E-Mail: llange@clearwater-fl.com; *Ch Servs, YA Servs*, Jane Fine; Tel: 727-462-6800, Ext 242, E-Mail: jfine@clearwater-fl.com; *Coll Develop*, Marsha McGrath; Tel: 727-462-6800, Ext

246, E-Mail: mmcgrath@clearwater-fl.com; *Cat*, Holly May; Tel: 727-462-6800, Ext 248, E-Mail: hmay@clearwater-fl.com; *ILL*, Candace McDaniel; Tel: 727-462-6800, Ext 235, Fax: 727-298-0095, E-Mail: cmcdanie@clearwater-fl.com; *Automation Syst Coordr*, Kent Walker; Tel: 727-462-6800, Ext 250, E-Mail: kwalker@clearwater-fl.com; *Acq*, Laura Dann; Tel: 727-462-6800, Ext 238, E-Mail: ldann@clearwater-fl.com; Staff 22 (MLS 18, Non-MLS 4)
Founded 1915. Pop 104,000
Oct 1999-Sep 2000 Income (Main Library and Branch Library) $4,547,944, State $141,373, City $3,701,793, County $682,557, Other $22,221. Mats Exp $669,009, Books $485,165, Per/Ser (Incl. Access Fees) $19,975, Micro $27,528, AV Equip $129,432, Electronic Ref Mat (Incl. Access Fees) $6,909. Sal $2,326,380 (Prof $1,339,560)
Library Holdings: Bk Vols 219,963; Per Subs 900
Automation Activity & Vendor Info: (Cataloging) Gaylord; (Circulation) Gaylord; (OPAC) Gaylord; (Serials) Gaylord
Database Vendor: OCLC - First Search
Publications: FROG (Florida Resource & Opportunity Guide)
Mem of Pinellas County Public Libr Coop
Partic in OCLC Online Computer Library Center, Inc; Tampa Bay Library Consortium, Inc
Greater Clearwater Public Library Foundation, Inc
Friends of the Library Group
Branches: 4
BEACH, 483 Mandalay Ave Ste 106, Clearwater Beach, 33767. SAN 337-3088. Tel: 727-462-6890. FAX: 727-462-6472. Web Site: www.clearwater-fl.com/cpl. *Librn*, Linda Hamrell; E-Mail: lhamrell@clearwater-fl.com; Staff 1 (MLS 1)
Founded 1961
Library Holdings: Bk Vols 19,966
Special Collections: Books of the Sea; Wickman Coll
Friends of the Library Group
COUNTRYSIDE, 2741 State Rd 580, 33761. SAN 329-6741. Tel: 727-669-1290. Circulation Tel: 727-669-1295. Reference Tel: 727-669-1290. FAX: 727-669-1289. Web Site: www.clearwater-fl.com/cpl. *Mgr*, Lois Klein; E-Mail: lklein@clearwater-fl.com; *Ref Serv*, Rebecca Wogoman; E-Mail: rwogomon@clearwater-fl.com; *Ch Servs*, Julie Hudson; E-Mail: jhudson@clearwater-fl.com; *Circ*, Paul Ritz; E-Mail: pritz@clearwater-fl.com; Staff 5 (MLS 5)
Founded 1988
Library Holdings: Bk Vols 115,403
Friends of the Library Group
EAST, 2251 Drew St, 33765. SAN 326-8586. Tel: 727-669-1280. Circulation Tel: 727-669-1285. Reference Tel: 727-669-1280. FAX: 727-669-1281. Web Site: www.clearwater-fl.com/cpl. *Mgr*, Matthew Moore; E-Mail: mmoore@clearwater-fl.com; *Ref Serv*, Ann Scheffer; E-Mail: ascheffe@clearwater-fl.com; *Ch Servs*, Tereasa Roose; E-Mail: troose@clearwater-fl.com; *Circ*, Georgina Ata; E-Mail: gata@clearwater-fl.com; Staff 4 (MLS 4)
Founded 1985
Library Holdings: Bk Vols 114,348
Friends of the Library Group
NORTH GREENWOOD, 1250 Palmetto St, 33755. SAN 337-3142. Tel: 727-462-6895. FAX: 727-462-6473. Web Site: www.clearwater-fl.com/cpl. *Librn*, Marlene Mitchell; E-Mail: mmitchel@clearwater-fl.com; Staff 1 (Non-MLS 1)
Founded 1950
Library Holdings: Bk Vols 33,491
Special Collections: African-American Coll
Friends of the Library Group

S FIRST UNITED METHODIST CHURCH, Clearwater United Church Library, 411 Turner St, 33756. SAN 372-7955. Tel: 727-446-5955. FAX: 727-447-1308. *Acq, Librn*, Alice Degarmo; Staff 6 (MLS 1, Non-MLS 5)
1999-2000 Income $800. Mats Exp $1,800, Books $750, Per/Ser (Incl. Access Fees) $50, Micro $1,000
Library Holdings: Bk Vols 4,391; Bk Titles 3,000
Subject Interests: Church history, Fiction
Special Collections: John Wesley's Works & Books

S HONEYWELL, INC, Jack Fatz Information Center, 13350 US Hwy 19 N, M/S 830-4, 33764-7290. SAN 303-1535. Tel: 727-539-3256. E-Mail: libraryfl51@honeywell.com. *Librn*, Ellen Turner; Staff 1 (MLS 1)
Founded 1982
Library Holdings: Bk Vols 1,500; Bk Titles 1,000; Per Subs 80
Restriction: Not open to public
Function: ILL limited

M MORTON PLANT MEASE HEALTH CARE, Medical Library, 300 Pinellas St, PO Box 210, 33756-0210. SAN 322-7219. Tel: 727-462-7889. FAX: 727-461-8755. E-Mail: medical.library@baycare.org. *Librn*, Karen L Roth; Staff 2 (MLS 1, Non-MLS 1)
Founded 1955
Jan 1999-Dec 1999 Income $195,000, Parent Institution $125,000, Other $70,000. Mats Exp $80,000, Books $15,000, Per/Ser (Incl. Access Fees) $65,000. Sal $41,400
Library Holdings: Bk Vols 3,000; Per Subs 250
Subject Interests: Allied health, Medicine, Nursing
Automation Activity & Vendor Info: (Cataloging) EOS; (Circulation) EOS; (OPAC) EOS; (Serials) EOS
Mem of Tampa Bay Med Libr Network
Partic in Nat Libr of Med; Tampa Bay Library Consortium, Inc

GL PINELLAS COUNTY LAW LIBRARY, Clearwater, 324 S Ft Harrison Ave, 33756-5165. SAN 302-8852. Tel: 727-464-3411. FAX: 727-464-4571. Web Site: circuit6.co.pinellas.fl.us/lawlibs. *Dir*, Trudie Root; Tel: 727-464-6520, Fax: 727-464-6142, E-Mail: troot@jud6.org; *Mgr Libr*, Donna L Haverkamp; E-Mail: dhaverka@jud6.org; *Asst Librn*, Norman J Tanguay; E-Mail: ntanguay@jud6.org; Staff 4 (MLS 2, Non-MLS 2)
Founded 1950
Oct 1999-Sep 2000 Income $236,000, County $22,800, Locally Generated Income $8,000. Mats Exp $147,000. Sal $82,000
Library Holdings: Bk Vols 24,000
Special Collections: Laws of Florida

CLERMONT

P COOPER MEMORIAL LIBRARY, 620 Montrose St, 34711. SAN 302-8887. Tel: 352-394-4265. FAX: 352-394-6359. E-Mail: bray@lakeline.lib.fl.com. *Dir*, Bonnie Ray; Staff 3 (MLS 2, Non-MLS 1)
Founded 1914. Pop 9,000; Circ 75,000
Oct 1999-Sep 2000 Income $331,145, City $148,624, County $159,121, Locally Generated Income $8,000, Parent Institution $15,400. Mats Exp $25,000, Books $23,500, Per/Ser (Incl. Access Fees) $1,500. Sal $242,525 (Prof $33,000)
Library Holdings: Bk Titles 52,000; Per Subs 109
Subject Interests: Florida, Genealogy, Large type print, Local history
Database Vendor: epixtech, inc.
Mem of Lake County Library System
Open Mon-Thurs 10-7, Fri 10-5, Sat 10-2
Friends of the Library Group

G FLORIDA DEPARTMENT OF CORRECTIONS, Lake Correctional Institution Library, 19225 US Hwy 27, 34711. SAN 337-3207. Tel: 352-394-6146, Ext 295.; Staff 1 (MLS 1)
Founded 1974. Pop 1,094
Jan 1999-Dec 1999 Mats Exp Books $6,000
Library Holdings: Bk Titles 12,200; Per Subs 50
Subject Interests: Vocational education
Branches:
GL LAW LIBRARY, 19225 US Hwy 27, 34711. Tel: 352-394-6146. *Librn*, Gus Kovacs

CLEWISTON

P HENDRY COUNTY LIBRARY SYSTEM, Clewiston Public Library, 120 W Osceola Ave, 33440. SAN 302-8895. Tel: 863-983-1493. FAX: 863-983-9194. *Dir*, John Fraser
Founded 1962. Pop 10,000; Circ 39,366
Library Holdings: Bk Vols 60,000; Per Subs 165

COCOA

J BCC-UCF JOINT USE LIBRARY, (Formerly Brevard Community College-UCF Library), Learning Resources Center- Cocoa Campus, 1519 Clearlake Rd, 32922. SAN 337-3266. Tel: 321-632-1111, Ext 62950. Circulation Tel: 321-632-1111, Ext 62966. Reference Tel: 321-632-1111, Ext 64470. FAX: 321-634-3734. E-Mail: libraryb@brevard.cc.fl.us. Web Site: www.brevard.cc.fl.us/lrc. *VPres*, Mike Hutton; *Ref*, Karen Simpson; *Media Spec*, Lois Broyles; *Acq, Cat, Tech Servs*, Carol Marshall; *Circ*, Christal Wood; *Per*, Michelle Rezeau
Founded 1960
Library Holdings: Bk Vols 196,700; Per Subs 1,700; Spec Interest Per Sub 1,000
Subject Interests: Genealogy
Database Vendor: DRA
Partic in Cent Fla Libr Consortium; SE Libr Network

S BREVARD CORRECTIONAL INSTITUTION LIBRARY, 855 Camp Rd, 32927. SAN 371-828X. Tel: 407-634-6122. FAX: 407-634-6040. *Actg Librn*, Felipe Dones; Staff 3 (MLS 1, Non-MLS 2)
Library Holdings: Bk Vols 7,642; Bk Titles 7,549; Per Subs 72
Special Collections: Black History Coll, bks, per, videos; Cultures of Worlds (Lands & Peoples Coll), bks, videos
Publications: Bibliographies; Reports (monthly & yearly)
Special Services for the Deaf - High interest/low vocabulary books; Special interest periodicals

P BREVARD COUNTY LIBRARY SYSTEM, 219 Indian River Dr, 32922-7781. SAN 303-0393. Tel: 407-633-1801. FAX: 407-633-1798. Web Site: www.brev.lib.fl.us. *Dir Libr Serv*, Catherine Schweinsberg; E-Mail: cshwein@manatee.brev.lib.fl.us; *Asst Dir*, Karen Nelson; Fax: 321-633-1837, E-Mail: knelson@manatee.brev.lib.fl.us; *AV*, Trudy Martell; *Commun Servs*, Mary Ann Alderman; E-Mail: malderma@manatee.brev.lib.fl.us; *Tech Servs*, Becky Slack

Founded 1972. Pop 465,825; Circ 2,405,351
Oct 1998-Sep 1999 Income $12,583,386, State $1,078,054, County $10,759,723, Locally Generated Income $377,857, Other $367,752. Mats Exp $1,568,535, Books $1,371,626, Per/Ser (Incl. Access Fees) $131,548, Micro $65,361. Sal $5,023,255
Library Holdings: Bk Titles 1,072,701; Per Subs 3,869
Automation Activity & Vendor Info: (Circulation) GEAC
Member Libraries: Cape Canaveral Public Library; Central Brevard Library & Reference Center; Cocoa Beach Public Library; Eau Gallie Public Library; Franklin T Degroodt Library; Martin Luther King Jr Library; Melbourne Public Library; Merritt Island Public Library; Mims-Scottsmoor Public Library; North Brevard Public Library; Palm Bay Public Library; Port St John Public Library; Satellite Beach Public Library; South Mainland Library; West Melbourne Public Library
Partic in Cent Fla Libr Consortium
Special Services for the Blind - Talking book center
Friends of the Library Group

P CENTRAL BREVARD LIBRARY & REFERENCE CENTER, 308 Forrest Ave, 32922. SAN 302-8909. Tel: 321-633-1792. Circulation Tel: 321-633-1793. FAX: 321-633-1806. Web Site: www.brev.lib.fl.us/. *Dir*, Camille Watts Johnson; Tel: 321-635-7845, Fax: 321-633-1964, E-Mail: cjohnson@manatee.brev.lib.fl.us; *Head Ref*, Diane Vosatka; E-Mail: dvosatka@manatee.brev.lib.fl.us; *Ch Servs*, Cynthia Ridolf; Tel: 321-633-1795, E-Mail: cridolf@manatee.brev.lib.fl.us; Staff 39 (MLS 3, Non-MLS 36)
Founded 1895
Oct 1999-Sep 2000 Income $1,412,310, County $1,402,310, Locally Generated Income $10,000. Mats Exp $213,952, Books $185,933, Per/Ser (Incl. Access Fees) $15,150, Micro $12,869. Sal $852,847 (Prof $95,221)
Library Holdings: Bk Vols 160,116; Per Subs 549
Special Collections: Florida; Genealogy; Large Print
Automation Activity & Vendor Info: (OPAC) GEAC
Database Vendor: CARL, Ebsco - EbscoHost, GaleNet, IAC - Info Trac, IAC - SearchBank, OCLC - First Search, ProQuest
Mem of Brevard County Library System
Partic in Cent Fla Libr Consortium
Special Services for the Blind - CCTV (VisualTex); Reading edge system; Talking Books
Friends of the Library Group

§S FLORIDA DEPARTMENT OF CORRECTIONS, Brevard Correctional Institution Library, 855 Camp Rd, 32927-3709. Tel: 407-634-6000, Ext 122. FAX: 407-634-6040. *Librn*, Rebecca DiJerome
Library Holdings: Bk Vols 8,250; Per Subs 55

S FLORIDA SOLAR ENERGY CENTER, Research Library, University of Central Florida, 1679 Clearlake Rd, 32922-5703. SAN 302-8763. Tel: 321-638-1460. Interlibrary Loan Service Tel: 321-638-1461. Circulation Tel: 321-638-1462. FAX: 321-638-1010, 321-638-1463. Web Site: www.fsec.ucf.edu. *Head Librn*, Iraida B Rickling; E-Mail: rickling@fsec.ucf.edu; Staff 3 (MLS 1, Non-MLS 2)
Founded 1975
Jul 1999-Jun 2000 Income $21,600. Mats Exp $19,000, Books $8,000, Per/Ser (Incl. Access Fees) $10,000, Presv $1,000
Library Holdings: Bk Vols 11,371; Per Subs 209
Subject Interests: Building constr, Energy, Solar energy
Publications: Acquisitions Bulletin; Solar Alert (current awareness bulletin)
Partic in Cent Fla Libr Consortium; Florida Library Information Network; OCLC Online Computer Library Center, Inc; SE Libr Network
The Center is an energy research institute of the State University System. The Research Library is housed in the Joint-Use Library of Brevard Community College/University of Central Florida, Cocoa campus

P PORT ST JOHN PUBLIC LIBRARY, 6500 Carole Ave, 32927. SAN 376-5105. Tel: 321-633-1867. FAX: 321-633-1869. Web Site: manatee.brev.lib.fl.us. *Dir*, David McMurrin
Oct 1998-Sep 1999 Income $300,000. Mats Exp $54,700, Books $47,000, Per/Ser (Incl. Access Fees) $4,200, Micro $3,500. Sal $170,000
Library Holdings: Bk Vols 32,000; Per Subs 75
Mem of Brevard County Library System
Friends of the Library Group

S TEBEAU-FIELD LIBRARY OF FLORIDA HISTORY, 435 Brevard Ave, 32922. SAN 338-196X. Tel: 321-690-1971. FAX: 321-690-4388. E-Mail: tbeaulib@aol.com. Web Site: www.florida-historical-soc.org. *Exec Dir*, Lewis N Wynne
Founded 1856
Library Holdings: Bk Vols 7,000; Per Subs 75
Publications: The Florida Historical (quarterly); The Society Report
Friends of the Library Group

COCOA BEACH

P COCOA BEACH PUBLIC LIBRARY, 550 N Brevard Ave, 32931. SAN 302-8917. Tel: 321-868-1104. FAX: 321-868-1107. *Dir*, Ray Dickinson; *Ad Servs, Circ*, Teresa Boleman; *Ref*, Gwen Birck; Staff 3 (MLS 3)
Founded 1955. Pop 20,000; Circ 269,000
Oct 2000-Sep 2001 Income $703,831. Mats Exp $128,245, Books $102,200, Per/Ser (Incl. Access Fees) $15,125, Micro $10,920. Sal $556,566 (Prof $112,626)
Library Holdings: Bk Vols 97,350; Per Subs 271
Subject Interests: Fiction, Florida
Special Collections: Cocoa Beach Artists, oil, watercolor, batik & bronze
Publications: Footnotes (newsletter of Friends of the Library)
Mem of Brevard County Library System
Friends of the Library Group

CORAL GABLES

M HEALTHSOUTH DOCTOR'S HOSPITAL, Medical Library, 5000 University Dr, 33146. SAN 324-6388. Tel: 305-666-2111, Ext 2334. FAX: 305-669-2456. *Librn*, Sandra Poston
Founded 1954
Library Holdings: Bk Vols 1,038; Bk Titles 1,000
Partic in SE Libr Network

R TEMPLE JUDEA, Mel Harrison Memorial Library, 5500 Granada Blvd, 33146. SAN 302-8941. Tel: 305-667-5657. FAX: 305-665-5834. Web Site: www.judeagables.org. *Librn*, Phyllis Robarts; Staff 1 (MLS 1)
Library Holdings: Bk Vols 5,000
Special Collections: Judaica Coll & Holocaust Col
Automation Activity & Vendor Info: (Cataloging) Athena; (Circulation) Athena; (OPAC) Athena
Restriction: Company staff only, Members only

C UNIVERSITY OF MIAMI LIBRARIES, Otto G Richter Library, 1300 Memorial Dr, 33124-0320. (Mail add: PO Box 248214, 33124-0320), SAN 337-3290. Tel: 305-284-3551. Interlibrary Loan Service Tel: 305-284-6102. Circulation Tel: 305-284-3233. Reference Tel: 305-284-4722. FAX: 305-665-7352. E-Mail: richter.library@miami.edu. Web Site: www.library.miami.edu. *Librn*, Don L Bosseau; *Asst Librn, Info Tech*, Jeff Barry; *Asst Librn, Tech Servs*, Cheryl Gowing; *Head, Acq*, Lee Kreiger; *Asst Librn*, Pat Hawthorne; *Asst Librn, Publ Servs*, Sharyn Ladner; *Asst Librn*, Susi Seiler; *Head Ref, Instrul Serv*, Jane Schillie; *Access Serv, Head, Info Serv*, Cecilia Leathem. Subject Specialists: *Admin*, Pat Hawthorne; *Govt info*, Daniel Blazek; *Resources mgt*, Susi Seiler; *Servs*, Pat Hawthorne; Staff 38 (MLS 38)
Founded 1926. Enrl 11,956; Fac 1,865; Highest Degree: Doctorate
Special Collections: Amigos of the University of Miami Library Cuban Heritage Coll; Floridiana; Latin American (especially Cuban, Caribbean & Colombian); Marine & Atomospheric Sciences
Database Vendor: Ebsco - EbscoHost, Innovative Interfaces INN - View
Publications: Library Links (Newsletter)
Partic in ARL; Association Of Southeastern Research Libraries (ASERL); OCLC Online Computer Library Center, Inc
Friends of the Library Group
Departmental Libraries:

L LAW, 1311 Miller Dr, 33146. (Mail add: PO Box 248087, 33124-0247), SAN 337-338X. Tel: 305-284-2250. Circulation Tel: 305-284-3563. Reference Tel: 305-284-3585. FAX: 305-284-3554. Web Site: www.law.miami.edu. *Dir*, Sally H Wise; Tel: 305-284-2755, E-Mail: swise@law.miami.edu; *Cat*, Leila S Mestrits; *Head, Info Serv*, Robin Schard; *Circ*, William Latham; *Ref*, Anne Klinefelter; *Ser*, Leanne Hillery; *Head Tech Servs*, Martha Spring; *Ref*, Janet Reinke; *Ref*, Virginia Templeton; *Ref*, Helen Wohl; *Head Ref*, Ckare Membiela; *Ref*, Edgardo Rotman; *Coll Develop*, Tica Stanton; Staff 16 (MLS 16)
Enrl 1,410; Fac 51
Library Holdings: Bk Vols 533,178; Bk Titles 82,032; Per Subs 6,923
Database Vendor: Lexis-Nexis
Publications: Law Library Guide; Pathfinder Series
Partic in SE Automated Librs, Inc

MUSIC, PO Box 248165, 33124. Tel: 305-284-2429. FAX: 305-284-1041. Web Site: www.library.miami.edu/music/home. *Librn*, Nancy C Zavac; E-Mail: nzavac@miami.edu

CRAWFORDVILLE

P WAKULLA COUNTY PUBLIC LIBRARY, 4330 Crawfordville Hwy, 32327. (Mail add: PO Box 1300, 32326-1300), SAN 320-4685. Tel: 850-926-7415. FAX: 850-926-4513. *Dir*, Doug Jones; *Asst Librn*, Myrtle McKenzie; Staff 5 (MLS 1, Non-MLS 4)
Founded 1972. Pop 20,000; Circ 52,000
Library Holdings: Bk Titles 20,000; Per Subs 18
Special Collections: Florida & Local History (The Elizabeth Smith Coll), bks, publications; Hi Lo Literary Coll
Partic in Panhandle Library Access Network
Open Wed, Thurs & Fri 9-6, Tues 9-8, Sat 9-1
Friends of the Library Group

CRESTVIEW

S OKALOOSA CORRECTIONAL INSTITUTION LIBRARY, 3189 Little Silver Rd, 32539. SAN 377-2616. Tel: 850-682-0931, Ext 159. FAX: 850-689-7803. *Actg Librn*, Bruce Boughman
Library Holdings: Bk Vols 15,000; Per Subs 50

P ROBERT L F SIKES PUBLIC LIBRARY, 805 James Lee Blvd E, 32539. SAN 302-8976. Tel: 850-682-4432. FAX: 850-689-4788. *Dir*, Mike Wing; Staff 2 (MLS 1, Non-MLS 1)
Founded 1973. Pop 15,000; Circ 71,184
Library Holdings: Bk Titles 40,000; Per Subs 42; High Interest/Low Vocabulary Bk Vols 50; Bks on Deafness & Sign Lang 10
Database Vendor: epixtech, inc., OCLC - First Search
Friends of the Library Group

CROSS CITY

S CROSS CITY CORRECTIONAL INSTITUTION LIBRARY, Old Airforce Radar Rd, 32628. (Mail add: PO Box 1500, 32628-1500), SAN 302-8984. Tel: 352-498-5576, Ext 172. FAX: 352-498-1275. E-Mail: msggsaf@aol.com. Web Site: www.dc.state.fl.us.
Founded 1974
Jul 1998-Jun 1999 Income $46,000, State $32,000, Other $14,000. Mats Exp $8,809, Books $6,956, Per/Ser (Incl. Access Fees) $1,853. Sal $32,000 (Prof $32,000)
Library Holdings: Bk Vols 9,953; Per Subs 26
Subject Interests: Black, Hispanic, Mysteries, Science fiction, Western

DADE CITY

J PASCO-HERNANDO COMMUNITY COLLEGE, Charles E Conger Library, 36727 Blanton Rd, 33523-7599. SAN 302-900X. Tel: 352-567-6701, Ext 1007. FAX: 352-567-3064. *Dir*, Charles R Rodgers
Founded 1972. Enrl 2,800; Highest Degree: Associate
Library Holdings: Bk Vols 58,000; Bk Titles 53,000; Per Subs 292
Subject Interests: Agriculture, Data processing, Electronics, Nursing, Paramedics
Automation Activity & Vendor Info: (Acquisitions) DRA; (Cataloging) DRA; (Circulation) DRA; (Course Reserve) DRA; (ILL) DRA; (OPAC) DRA; (Serials) DRA
Database Vendor: DRA
Partic in Tampa Bay Library Consortium, Inc

DANIA BEACH

S E K HARRY LIBRARY OF FISHES, IGFA Fishing Hall of Fame & Museum, 300 Gulf Stream Way, 33004. SAN 325-8823. Tel: 954-927-2628. FAX: 954-924-4299. E-Mail: igfahq@aol.com. Web Site: www.igfa.org. *Librn*, G Morchower
Founded 1973
Library Holdings: Bk Vols 13,000; Per Subs 150
Special Collections: Art; Historical Photos; Stamps

DAVIE

J BROWARD COMMUNITY COLLEGE, University-College Library, 3501 SW Davie Rd, 33314. SAN 337-3959. Tel: 954-475-6648. FAX: 954-423-6490. Web Site: ucl.broward.cc.fl.us. *Librn*, Julia Woods; *Assoc Dir*, Lydia LaCava; *Ref*, Jennifer Madden; *ILL*, Miguelina Jimenez; *Cat*, Jan Rothhaar; *Coll Develop*, Mary Melby; *Publ Servs*, Sandra Block; Staff 11 (MLS 11)
Founded 1960. Enrl 20,000; Fac 375
Jul 1999-Jun 2000 Income (Main Library Only) $2,274,190. Mats Exp $830,323, Books $497,171, Per/Ser (Incl. Access Fees) $122,400, Micro $37,770, Other Print Mats $47,200, Electronic Ref Mat (Incl. Access Fees) $125,782. Sal $1,316,661 (Prof $558,268)
Library Holdings: Bk Vols 195,890; Bk Titles 158,165; Per Subs 1,030
Database Vendor: DRA
Partic in SE Libr Network
Joint use library with Florida Atlantic University
Departmental Libraries:
NORTH CAMPUS LIBRARY LRC, 1000 Coconut Creek Blvd, Pompano Beach, 33066. SAN 321-1878. Tel: 954-973-2250. FAX: 954-969-2650. *Dir*, Isaac Call
Joint use with Broward County Public Library
SOUTH CAMPUS LIBRARY LRC, 7200 Hollywood, Pembroke Pines, 33024. SAN 321-1886. Tel: 954-963-8827. *Dir*, Terri Justice; Tel: 954-963-8909; *Librn*, Chris Casper
Joint use with Broward County Public Library

DAYTONA BEACH

C BETHUNE-COOKMAN COLLEGE, Carl S Swisher Library & Learning Resource Center, 640 Mary McLeod Bethune Blvd, 32114. SAN 302-9018. Tel: 904-255-1401, Ext 321. FAX: 904-257-4832. Web Site: www.bethune.cookman.edu. *Dir*, Bobby C Henderson; E-Mail: hendersb@cookman.edu; *Acq*, Judith W Collier; *Circ*, Mary Graves; *Media Spec*, Ervin Ross; *Ref*, Joseph A Campbell
Founded 1904. Enrl 1,626; Fac 117; Highest Degree: Bachelor
Library Holdings: Bk Vols 160,000
Special Collections: Africa & the Negro, bk, micro; Archival (Mary McLeod Bethune and others); Art (Peter Turcheon); Children's Coll
Automation Activity & Vendor Info: (Circulation) TLC
Publications: Annual Library Report; Faculty Library Manual; Nonprint Media Newsletter
Partic in OCLC Online Computer Library Center, Inc; SE Libr Network

P BUREAU OF BRAILLE & TALKING BOOK LIBRARY SERVICES, 420 Platt St, 32114-2804. SAN 302-9042. Tel: 904-239-6000. Toll Free Tel: 800-226-6075. FAX: 904-239-6069. Web Site: www.klas.com/talkingbooks/florida. *Dir*, Michael G Gunde; Tel: 904-239-6000, Ext 6050; *Reader Servs*, Linda Hill; Tel: 904-239-6000, Ext 6080; *Tech Servs*, Shirley Van Deroef; Tel: 904-239-6000, Ext 6010; Staff 4 (MLS 4)
Founded 1950. Pop 45,000
Jul 2000-Jun 2001 Income State $1,025,000
Library Holdings: Bk Vols 2,100,000; Bk Titles 48,000
Special Collections: Florida, braille & cassettes
Publications: Quarterly Patron Oriented Newsletter for Adults, Children & Young Adults (in large print, braille & cassette, English/Spanish); Subject Bibliographies (in large print, braille & cassette)
Special Services for the Blind - Braille & recorded books
Friends of the Library Group

J DAYTONA BEACH COMMUNITY COLLEGE LIBRARY, 1200 International Speedway Blvd, 32114. (Mail add: PO Box 2811, 32120-2811), SAN 302-9026. Tel: 904-254-3055. FAX: 904-254-3008. Web Site: www.dbcc.cc.fl.us. *Dean*, Yvonne Newcomb-Doty; E-Mail: newcomy.da@dbcc.cc.fl.us; *Head Librn*, Dustin Weeks; *Librn*, Mary Kautz; *Circ*, Katheleene Bryan; *Ref*, Fred Harden; *Ref*, Ted Wygant; *Tech Servs*, Mercedes Clement
Enrl 3,785
Library Holdings: Bk Vols 90,000; Per Subs 450
Special Collections: Lapensohn Newspaper Coll
Partic in OCLC Online Computer Library Center, Inc; SE Libr Network
Open Mon-Thurs 7:30-10, Fri 7:30-5, Sat 9-3, Sun 1-9

C EMBRY-RIDDLE AERONAUTICAL UNIVERSITY, Jack R Hunt Memorial Library, 600 S Clyde Morris Blvd, 32114-3900. SAN 302-9034. Tel: 904-226-6595. Interlibrary Loan Service Tel: 904-226-6290. FAX: 904-226-6368. Web Site: www.amelia.db.erau.edu. *Dir*, Richard E Waddell; Tel: 904-226-6593, E-Mail: waddellr@cts.db.erau.edu; *ILL*, Kathy Chumley; Tel: 904-226-6947, Fax: 904-226-7040, E-Mail: chumleyk@db.erau.edu; *Ref*, Kathleen Citro; E-Mail: citrok@cts.db.erau.edu; *Circ, Media Spec*, Laura Quatrella; Tel: 904-226-6591, E-Mail: quatrell@db.erau.edu; *Syst Coordr, Tech Servs*, Jane Deighan; Tel: 904-226-6589, E-Mail: deighanj@db.erau.edu; Staff 28 (MLS 15, Non-MLS 13)
Founded 1965. Enrl 10,700; Fac 266; Highest Degree: Master
May 1998-Apr 1999 Income $2,352,000. Mats Exp $1,345,000, Books $119,000, Per/Ser (Incl. Access Fees) $200,000, Presv $3,000, Other Print Mats $4,000, Electronic Ref Mat (Incl. Access Fees) $129,000. Sal $699,000 (Prof $404,500)
Library Holdings: Bk Vols 116,500; Bk Titles 91,500; Per Subs 1,780
Subject Interests: Aeronautical eng, Aerospace eng, Aviation
Special Collections: Aviation History & Aeronautical Engineering Coll, bks, per & doc; FAA, NTSB & NASA Documents
Automation Activity & Vendor Info: (Cataloging) Endeavor; (Circulation) Endeavor; (Course Reserve) Endeavor; (ILL) Endeavor; (OPAC) Endeavor; (Serials) Endeavor
Database Vendor: ProQuest, Silverplatter Information Inc.
Publications: Media Catalog; Periodicals Holding List
Partic in Central Florida Library Cooperative (CFLC); FLIN; OCLC Online Computer Library Center, Inc; SE Libr Network

S HALIFAX HISTORICAL SOCIETY, Museum Library, 252 S Beach St, 32114. SAN 326-6370. Tel: 904-255-6976. FAX: 904-255-7605. E-Mail: mail@halifaxhistorical.org. Web Site: www.halifax.historical.org. *Dir*, Cheryl Atwell
Founded 1949
Library Holdings: Bk Titles 550
Special Collections: Photograph & Newspaper Coll
Partic in Felusia Cultural Affairs League; National Trust for Historic Preservation

M HALIFAX MEDICAL CENTER, Medical Library, 303 N Clyde Morris Blvd, 32114. SAN 302-9077. Tel: 386-254-4051. FAX: 386-254-4189. E-Mail: medical.library@hmc.halifax.org. Web Site: www.halifax.org. *Head Librn*, Addajane L Wallace; E-Mail: addajane.wallace@hmc.halifax.org; *Asst Librn*, Simone Brodeur
Founded 1963
Library Holdings: Bk Vols 1,068; Per Subs 220
Restriction: Medical staff only

S MUSEUM OF ARTS & SCIENCES, Margaret & John Wilkinson Library, 1040 Museum Blvd, 32114. SAN 302-9093. Tel: 904-255-0285. FAX: 904-255-5040. Web Site: www.moas.org. *Dir*, Gary Russell Libby; Tel: 904-255-0285, Ext 14; *Librn*, Marjorie Sigerson; Staff 46 (MLS 28, Non-MLS 18)
Founded 1956. Circ 3,000
Oct 1999-Sep 2000 Income Other $15,000. Mats Exp $15,000, Books $5,000, Per/Ser (Incl. Access Fees) $3,000, AV Equip $2,000, Other Print Mats $2,000, Manuscripts & Archives $3,000

Library Holdings: Bk Vols 5,000
Subject Interests: Art, Astronomy, Cuba, Florida, Natural history, Technology
Special Collections: American Art; Florida history books, periodicals & manuscripts; Lucy Shepard Bequest; Natural history; Ornithology Coll; Rare Cuban books (General Fulgencio Batista Coll); World Art
Function: Reference only
Partic in Lee County

S TOMOKA CORRECTIONAL INSTITUTION LIBRARY, 3950 Tiger Bay Rd, 32124-1098. SAN 375-4650. Tel: 904-323-1195. FAX: 904-323-1168. *Librn*, M Rogers; Staff 3 (MLS 1, Non-MLS 2)
Library Holdings: Bk Vols 15,000; Per Subs 93

GL VOLUSIA COUNTY LAW LIBRARY, Courthouse Annex, Rm 208, 125 E Orange Ave, 32114. SAN 302-9107. Tel: 904-257-6041. FAX: 904-257-6052. *Librn*, Deborah Patterson
Library Holdings: Bk Vols 25,000

P VOLUSIA COUNTY PUBLIC LIBRARY SYSTEM, 1290 Indian Lake Rd, 32124. SAN 337-3444. Tel: 904-248-1745. TDD: 904-255-3765. FAX: 904-248-1746. Web Site: www.merlin.vcpl.lib.fl.us. *Dir*, Michael J Knievel; *Tech Coordr*, Anne Powers; *ILL*, Anna Tate; *Tech Servs*, Judy Valk; *Coll Develop*, Alice Haldeman
Founded 1961. Pop 456,000; Circ 3,127,427
Oct 1998-Sep 1999 Income $10,867,140. Mats Exp $1,339,931, Books $140,911. Sal $5,178,988
Library Holdings: Bk Vols 835,071; Per Subs 1,704
Subject Interests: Genealogy
Special Collections: Genealogy Coll
Automation Activity & Vendor Info: (Circulation) GEAC; (OPAC) GEAC
Publications: Annual Report; Happenings (monthly calendar of events), staff newsletter
Partic in OCLC Online Computer Library Center, Inc; SE Libr Network
Special Services for the Deaf - Books on deafness & sign language; High interest/low vocabulary books; Staff with knowledge of sign language
Friends of the Library Group
Branches: 15
DE BARY BRANCH, 200 N Charles R Beall Blvd, De Bary, 32713-2834. SAN 337-3568. Tel: 407-668-3835. FAX: 407-668-3837. *Librn*, Wayne Matthews; Staff 4 (MLS 1, Non-MLS 3)
Pop 18,000; Circ 157,000
Library Holdings: Bk Vols 42,000; Bk Titles 40,000; Per Subs 110; High Interest/Low Vocabulary Bk Vols 150; Bks on Deafness & Sign Lang 10
Friends of the Library Group
DELAND BRANCH, 130 E Howry Ave, Deland, 32724. SAN 337-3592. Tel: 904-822-6430. TDD: 904-822-6430. FAX: 904-822-6435. *Librn*, Kathleen Mann; Staff 20 (MLS 10, Non-MLS 10)
Library Holdings: Bk Vols 89,679
Special Services for the Deaf - TDD
Friends of the Library Group
DELTONA BRANCH, 2150 Eustace Ave, Deltona, 32725-4928. SAN 337-3622. Tel: 904-789-7207. FAX: 904-789-7211. *Librn*, Bill Bowden; Staff 14 (MLS 6, Non-MLS 8)
Founded 1976. Circ 493,567
Library Holdings: Bk Vols 64,217
Friends of the Library Group
DICKERSON COMMUNITY CENTER, 308 Martin Luther King Blvd, 32114-4820. SAN 337-3509. Tel: 904-239-6478. *Librn*, Inez Jeffers; Staff 1 (MLS 1)
Founded 1977. Circ 3,758
Library Holdings: Bk Vols 3,005
Friends of the Library Group
EDGEWATER BRANCH, 103 Indian River Blvd, Edgewater, 32132-3538. SAN 337-3681. Tel: 904-424-2916. FAX: 904-424-2918. *Librn*, Gayle Harmon; Staff 7 (MLS 4, Non-MLS 3)
Circ 164,198
Library Holdings: Bk Vols 26,819
Friends of the Library Group
HOLLY HILL BRANCH, 1066 Ridgewood Ave, Holly Hill, 32117-2808. SAN 337-3711. Tel: 904-239-6454. FAX: 904-947-2951. *Librn*, Jane Wright; Staff 2 (MLS 1, Non-MLS 1)
Circ 56,086
Library Holdings: Bk Vols 22,021
Friends of the Library Group
LAKE HELEN BRANCH, 221 N Euclid Ave, Lake Helen, 32744-9998. SAN 337-3746. Tel: 904-228-1152. FAX: 904-228-1154. *Librn*, Pam Pape; Staff 2 (Non-MLS 2)
Circ 78,964
Library Holdings: Bk Vols 13,895
Friends of the Library Group
NEW SMYRNA BEACH REGIONAL LIBRARY, 1001 S Dixie Freeway, New Smyrna Beach, 32168. SAN 337-3479. Tel: 904-424-2910. FAX: 904-424-2913. *Librn*, Margaret Minter; Staff 14 (MLS 5, Non-MLS 9)
Circ 259,721
Library Holdings: Bk Vols 80,000
Friends of the Library Group
OAK HILL BRANCH, US Hwy 1, PO Box 179, Oak Hill, 32759. SAN 337-3770. Tel: 904-345-5510. *Librn*, Kate Gardiner; Staff 1 (Non-MLS 1)
Circ 4,000
Library Holdings: Bk Vols 3,500
Friends of the Library Group
ORANGE CITY DICKINSON MEMORIAL, 148 Albertus Way, Orange City, 32763-5966. SAN 337-3657. Tel: 904-775-5270. *Assoc Librn*, Rachael Bowers; Staff 2 (Non-MLS 2)
Circ 84,418
Library Holdings: Bk Vols 19,678
Friends of the Library Group
ORMOND BEACH BRANCH, 30 S Beach St, Ormond Beach, 32174-6342. SAN 337-3789. Tel: 904-676-4191. FAX: 904-676-4194. *Librn*, Walter Jubinsky; Staff 18 (MLS 7, Non-MLS 11)
Circ 468,743
Library Holdings: Bk Vols 92,400
Friends of the Library Group
PIERSON PUBLIC, 115 N Volusia Ave, Pierson, 32180. SAN 378-0090. Tel: 904-749-6930. *Librn*, Sean Hurley; Staff 2 (MLS 1, Non-MLS 1)
Circ 1,753
Library Holdings: Bk Vols 1,200
PORT ORANGE BRANCH, 1005 City Center Circle, Port Orange, 32119. SAN 322-6174. Tel: 904-322-5152. FAX: 904-322-5155. *Librn*, Jane Weimer; Staff 16 (MLS 7, Non-MLS 9)
Circ 426,395
Library Holdings: Bk Vols 80,000
Friends of the Library Group
S CORNELIA YOUNG MEMORIAL, 302 Vermont Ave, 32118-4643. SAN 337-3800. Tel: 904-239-6436. *Librn*, Renata Bradley; Staff 1 (MLS 1)
Circ 40,996
Library Holdings: Bk Vols 33,568
Friends of the Library Group
VOLUSIA COUNTY LIBRARY CENTER, City Island, 32114-4304. SAN 337-3533. Tel: 904-257-6036. FAX: 904-257-6026. *Librn*, Lucinda Colee; Staff 21 (MLS 8, Non-MLS 13)
Circ 335,450
Library Holdings: Bk Vols 120,000
Friends of the Library Group
Bookmobiles: 1

DE FUNIAK SPRINGS

S WALTON CORRECTIONAL INSTITUTION LIBRARY, 691 WWII Veterans Lane, 32433. SAN 377-5062. Tel: 850-892-6141, Ext 343. FAX: 850-892-3691. E-Mail: walton@mail.de.state.fl.us. *Librn*, Hubert Barge
Library Holdings: Bk Vols 9,000; Per Subs 75

DEERFIELD BEACH

S INSTITUTE FOR ECONOMETRIC RESEARCH LIBRARY, 2200 SW Tenth St, 33442. SAN 376-1622. Tel: 954-421-1000. FAX: 954-421-1500.
Restriction: By appointment only

DEFUNIAK SPRINGS

P WALTON-DE FUNIAK LIBRARY, 3 Circle Dr, 32435. SAN 302-9115. Tel: 850-892-3624. FAX: 850-892-4438. *Dir*, William Dan Owens, III; Tel: 850-267-2809, Fax: 850-267-9452; Staff 9 (MLS 2, Non-MLS 7)
Founded 1886. Pop 38,304; Circ 101,562
Sep 1998-Aug 1999 Income (Main Library and Branch Library) $361,118, State $66,883, City $30,000, Federal $30,700, County $231,535, Locally Generated Income $2,000. Mats Exp $53,711, Books $45,677, Per/Ser (Incl. Access Fees) $534, AV Equip $500, Electronic Ref Mat (Incl. Access Fees) $7,000. Sal $127,875 (Prof $101,296)
Library Holdings: Bk Vols 55,059; Per Subs 15
Special Collections: Antique Record player; Armor Coll; Shell Coll
Automation Activity & Vendor Info: (Cataloging) Sagebrush Corporation; (Circulation) VTLS; (OPAC) Sagebrush Corporation
Database Vendor: OCLC - First Search, ProQuest
Function: ILL limited
Friends of the Library Group
Branches: 3
COASTAL, 3906 Hwy 98 E, PO Box 3, Santa Rosa Beach, 32459. SAN 328-641X. Tel: 850-267-2809. FAX: 850-267-9452. *Branch Mgr*, Nona Smith
Friends of the Library Group
FREEPORT PUBLIC, Hwy 20, PO Box 398, Freeport, 32439. SAN 328-6436. Tel: 850-835-2040. *Mgr*, Joan Cibiras
NORTH WALTON COUNTY, 261 Flowersview Blvd, Laurel Hill, 32456. Tel: 850-834-5383. *Librn*, Francis Cooey
Bookmobiles: 1

DELAND

M MEMORIAL HOSPITAL WEST VOLUSIA, Medical Library, 701 W Plymouth Ave, 32720. (Mail add: PO Box 6509, 32721-0509), SAN 302-914X. Tel: 904-734-3320, Ext 1204. FAX: 904-943-3685. *In Charge*, Sandy Nickels
Library Holdings: Bk Vols 750; Bk Titles 570; Per Subs 50
Subject Interests: Medicine, Nursing, Surgery
Partic in Tampa Bay Medical Library Network

C STETSON UNIVERSITY, DuPont-Ball Library, 421 N Woodland Blvd, Unit 8418, 32720-3769. SAN 337-3835. Tel: 904-822-7175. Interlibrary Loan Service Tel: 904-822-7183. Circulation Tel: 904-822-7183. FAX: 904-740-3626, 904-822-7199. Web Site: www.stetson.edu/departments/library. *Dir*, Sims D Kline; Tel: 904-822-7176, Fax: 904-740-3626, E-Mail: skline@stetson.edu; *Assoc Dir, Tech Servs*, Betty D Johnson; Tel: 904-822-7178, Fax: 904-740-3626, E-Mail: bjohnson@stetson.edu; *Assoc Dir, Publ Servs*, Susan M Ryan; Tel: 904-822—7181, Fax: 904-740-3626, E-Mail: sryan@stetson.edu; *Coordr, ILL*, Susan Derryberry; Tel: 904-822-4034, Fax: 904-822-7199, E-Mail: sconnell@stetson.edu; *Govt Doc*, Barbara Costello; Tel: 904-822-7185, Fax: 904-740-3626, E-Mail: bcostell@stetson.edu; *Tech Servs*, Debora Dinkins; Fax: 904-740-3626, E-Mail: ddinkins@stetson.edu; *Music*, Jean Finks; Tel: 904-822-8958, E-Mail: jfinks@stetson.edu; *Cat*, Laura Kirkland; Tel: 904-822-4027, E-Mail: lkirkland@stetson.edu; *Instrul Serv*, Jane Bradford; Tel: 904-822-7190, E-Mail: jbradford@stetson.edu; *Circ, Coordr*, Catherine Ervin; Tel: 904-822-7187, Fax: 904-822-7199, E-Mail: cervin@stetson.edu; Staff 10 (MLS 9, Non-MLS 1)
Founded 1883. Enrl 2,217; Fac 170; Highest Degree: Master
Jun 1999-May 2000 Income $1,425,000, Parent Institution $1,400,000, Other $25,000. Mats Exp $590,000, Books $265,000, Per/Ser (Incl. Access Fees) $195,000, Micro $40,000, Electronic Ref Mat (Incl. Access Fees) $90,000. Sal $600,000 (Prof $350,000)
Library Holdings: Bk Vols 275,000; Bk Titles 210,000; Per Subs 1,388
Subject Interests: Chemistry, Education, Humanities, Literature, Music, Religion, Russia, Social sciences and issues
Special Collections: Religion (Garwood Baptist Historical Coll)
Automation Activity & Vendor Info: (Acquisitions) SIRSI; (Cataloging) SIRSI; (Circulation) SIRSI; (Course Reserve) SIRSI; (OPAC) SIRSI; (Serials) SIRSI
Publications: Internet guides; Library handbook; Reference guides; Research aids
Partic in Central Florida Library Cooperative (CFLC); Florida Library Information Network; SE Libr Network
Departmental Libraries:
MUSIC, Presser Hall, 2nd flr, 32720. Tel: 904-822-8958. FAX: 904-822-7199.
Library Holdings: Bk Titles 2,500

DELRAY BEACH

P DELRAY BEACH PUBLIC LIBRARY, 29 SE Fourth Ave, 33483. SAN 302-9174. Tel: 561-266-0194. FAX: 561-266-9757. Web Site: www.delraylibrary.org. *Dir*, J John Callahan, III; Tel: 561-266-9488, E-Mail: john.callahan@delraylibrary.org; *Asst Dir, Syst Coordr*, Mykal Banta; Tel: 561-266-0198, E-Mail: mykal.banta@delraylibrary.org; *Ref*, Kathleen Hensman; Tel: 561-266-0196, E-Mail: kathleen.hensman@delraylibrary.org; *Ch Servs*, Lynda Hunter; Tel: 561-266-0197, E-Mail: lynda.hunter@delraylibrary.org; *Tech Servs*, Linda Otis; E-Mail: linda.otis@delraylibrary.org; *Head, Circ*, Brian Coleman; E-Mail: brian.coleman@delraylibrary.org
Founded 1939. Pop 50,000
Oct 1998-Sep 1999 Income $1,033,090, State $106,677, City $800,000, Locally Generated Income $126,413. Mats Exp $174,977. Sal $645,075 (Prof $299,928)
Library Holdings: Bk Vols 89,244; Per Subs 399
Subject Interests: Florida, Large type print
Publications: Newsletter (bimonthly)
Mem of Palm Beach County Library System
Partic in Libr Coop Palm Beaches
Open Mon, Tues & Wed 9-8, Thurs-Sat 9-5 & Sun 1-5
Friends of the Library Group

S B KLEIN PUBLICATIONS LIBRARY, 5329 W Atlantic Ave, 33484. SAN 302-8968. Tel: 561-496-3316. FAX: 561-496-5546. *In Charge*, Bernard Klein
Library Holdings: Bk Vols 4,000; Per Subs 100
Subject Interests: Business and management

S MORIKAMI MUSEUM, Donald B Gordon Memorial Library, 4000 Morikami Park Rd, 33446. SAN 322-8770. Tel: 561-495-0233, Ext 217. FAX: 561-499-2557. Web Site: www.morikami.org. *Librn*, Annie Van Assche; *Coll Develop*, John C Seery; *Curator*, Noelle A Shuey; Tel: 561-495-0233, Ext 209, E-Mail: nshuey@co.palm-beach.fl.us
Library Holdings: Bk Vols 3,000; Per Subs 24
Subject Interests: Japanese, Japanese (Language), Japanese culture
Special Collections: Japanese culture, language, people
Restriction: Non-circulating to the public
Function: For research purposes
Open Tues-Sun 10-5

L SOUTH COUNTY LAW LIBRARY, 200 W Atlantic Ave, 33444. SAN 373-0409. Tel: 561-274-1440. *Librn*, Patricia Judge
Library Holdings: Bk Vols 4,500
Partic in Westlaw

DESTIN

P THE DESTIN LIBRARY, 8 Stahlman Ave, 32541. (Mail add: PO Box 473, 32540), Tel: 850-837-8572. FAX: 850-837-5248. *Dir*, Jurate Burns; Tel: 850-837-5200, E-Mail: jburns@okaloosa.lib.fl.us; Staff 4 (MLS 2, Non-MLS 2)
Founded 1940. Pop 11,800; Circ 36,057
Oct 1998-Sep 1999 Income City $148,000. Mats Exp $40,000, Books $35,000, Per/Ser (Incl. Access Fees) $250. Sal $105,000 (Prof $34,000)
Library Holdings: Bk Vols 32,000; Bk Titles 30,000; Per Subs 16
Special Collections: Florida Coll, art, artifacts, bks, mss; Library of America, large print, Rare Book Coll, Sea Life Coll, art, artifacts, bks, films, mss
Automation Activity & Vendor Info: (Cataloging) epixtech, inc.; (Circulation) epixtech, inc.; (Course Reserve) epixtech, inc.
Database Vendor: Ebsco - EbscoHost
Partic in Panhandle Library Access Network
Friends of the Library Group

DUNDEE

§P DUNDEE PUBLIC LIBRARY, 203 Center St, 33838. Tel: 863-419-3125. FAX: 863-419-3126. *Dir*, Thelma Jones
Library Holdings: Bk Titles 6,000; Per Subs 10; High Interest/Low Vocabulary Bk Vols 20

DUNEDIN

P DUNEDIN PUBLIC LIBRARY, 223 Douglas Ave, 34698. SAN 302-9182. Tel: 727-738-4489. FAX: 727-738-1926. Web Site: www.dunedin.fl.com. *Actg Dir*, Barbara Skubish; Tel: 727-738-4489, Ext 223, E-Mail: skubish@tblc.org; *Ad Servs*, Elizabeth White; Tel: 727-738-4489, Ext 224, E-Mail: whitenetblc.org; *Circ*, Sherry Arfa; Tel: 727-738-4489, Ext 248; *Tech Servs*, Jeanne Williams; Tel: 727-738-4489, Ext 237, E-Mail: williamsj@tblc.org; Staff 10 (MLS 10)
Founded 1895. Pop 35,104; Circ 427,298
Oct 1998-Sep 1999 Income $1,623,523, State $87,209, City $1,137,446, Federal $15,000, County $375,868, Other $8,000. Mats Exp $193,860, Books $176,286, Per/Ser (Incl. Access Fees) $12,074, Presv $4,500, AV Equip $5,000. Sal $905,983
Library Holdings: Bk Vols 101,984; Bk Titles 84,594; Per Subs 377
Automation Activity & Vendor Info: (Acquisitions) epixtech, inc.; (Cataloging) epixtech, inc.; (Circulation) epixtech, inc.; (ILL) epixtech, inc.; (OPAC) epixtech, inc.; (Serials) epixtech, inc.
Publications: Friends Newsletter
Mem of Pinellas County Public Libr Coop
Partic in Tampa Bay Library Consortium, Inc
Friends of the Library Group

§J SCHILLER INTERNATIONAL UNIVERSITY, Florida Campus Library, 453 Edgewater Dr, 34698. Tel: 727-736-5082, Ext 229. FAX: 727-736-6263. Web Site: www.schiller.edu. *Dir*, Susan Heath Ryan; E-Mail: susan_ryan@schiller.edu
Library Holdings: Bk Vols 10,500; Per Subs 86; High Interest/Low Vocabulary Bk Vols 1,300

EAGLE LAKE

P EAGLE LAKE PUBLIC LIBRARY, 75 N Seventh St, 33839-3430. (Mail add: PO Box 129, 33839-0129), SAN 370-4718. Tel: 863-292-0210. FAX: 941-294-3590. *Librn*, Wendy Smith
Library Holdings: Bk Vols 7,000

EAST PALATKA

S PUTNAM CORRECTIONAL INSTITUTION LIBRARY, 126 Yelvington Rd, PO Box 279, 32131. SAN 377-2861. Tel: 904-325-2857, Ext 245. FAX: 904-312-2219. *Librn*, Suzzette Burnney
Library Holdings: Bk Vols 2,000; Bk Titles 1,900; Per Subs 58

EASTPOINT

P FRANKLIN COUNTY PUBLIC LIBRARY, Eastpoint Branch, Point Mall, 29 Island Dr, 32328. (Mail add: PO Box 722, 32328), SAN 377-2888. Tel: 850-670-8151. FAX: 904-670-8151. E-Mail: fcpl9@gtcom.net. *Dir*, Eileen

Annie Ball; *Asst Librn*, Carolyn Sparks
Library Holdings: Bk Vols 20,500; Bk Titles 20,000; Per Subs 10
Mem of Wilderness Coast Public Libraries

EGLIN AFB

S TESCO INC, Munitions Directorate Technical Library, 203 W Eglin Blvd, Ste 300, 32542-6843. SAN 377-3108. Tel: 850-882-5586. FAX: 850-882-3214. *Info Specialist*, Cheryl Mack
Library Holdings: Bk Vols 12,000; Per Subs 200
Partic in Fedlink

UNITED STATES AIR FORCE

A EGLIN AIR FORCE BASE LIBRARY, 305 W F St, Bldg 278, 32542-6842. SAN 337-386X. Tel: 850-882-5088. FAX: 850-882-2621. *Mgr*, Patricia McPhillips; *Publ Servs*, Patricia Bauernfeind; Tel: 850-882-5016; *Tech Servs*, Linda Schritter; Tel: 850-882-3462
Founded 1942
Library Holdings: Bk Vols 59,559; Per Subs 285
Subject Interests: Aeronautics, Business and management, Military history
Automation Activity & Vendor Info: (Acquisitions) GEAC; (Cataloging) GEAC; (Circulation) GEAC; (OPAC) GEAC; (Serials) GEAC
Database Vendor: OCLC - First Search
Publications: Accessions List
Restriction: Not open to public
Partic in Fedlink; OCLC Online Computer Library Center, Inc

A HURLBURT BASE LIBRARY, 16 SVS/SVMG, 443 Cody Ave, Hurlburt Field, 32544-5417. SAN 337-3894. Tel: 850-884-6947. FAX: 850-884-6050. *Dir*, Gloria Miller; E-Mail: gloria.miller@hurlburt.af.mil; *Dep Dir*, Pamala Doffek; E-Mail: pam.doffek@hurlburt.af.mil; Staff 2 (MLS 2)
Founded 1955
Library Holdings: Bk Vols 35,000; Per Subs 170
Special Collections: Special Operations (Military)
Automation Activity & Vendor Info: (OPAC) SIRSI
Publications: Selected Resources on Special Operations
Restriction: Non-circulating to the public
Function: ILL available
Partic in Panhandle Library Access Network

S TECHNICAL LIBRARY, 203 W Eglin Blvd Ste 300, 32542-6843. SAN 337-3924. Tel: 850-882-3212, 850-882-5586. FAX: 850-882-3214. *Dir*, Jim Elkins; *Info Specialist*, Cheryl Mack
Founded 1955
Library Holdings: Bk Vols 13,000; Per Subs 450
Subject Interests: Aeronautics, Biology, Chemistry, Electronics, Mathematics, Physics
Publications: Annual Users Update; Stinfo Current Awareness (monthly)
Partic in Fedlink

ELLENTON

R DAYSPRING EPISCOPAL CONFERENCE CENTER, Brown Memorial Library, PO Box 661, 34222. SAN 373-4145. Tel: 941-776-1018. FAX: 941-776-2678. E-Mail: dysprng@aol.com.
Library Holdings: Bk Vols 500; Per Subs 20
Subject Interests: Philosophy, Theology

ENGLEWOOD

P ELSIE QUIRK PUBLIC LIBRARY, 100 W Dearborn St, 34223-2987. SAN 302-9190. Tel: 941-474-3515. FAX: 941-474-3840. Web Site: suncat.co.sarasota.fl.us. *Head Librn*, Helen Burns; E-Mail: hburns@sarasota.lib.fl.us; *Head Ref*, Pat Lewis; *Ref*, Lorraine Miller; *Ref*, Karen Willams; *Head, Circ*, Michele Strickland; *YA Servs*, Tony Hopper; *YA Servs*, Cris Walton; Staff 5 (MLS 5)
Founded 1962. Pop 28,000; Circ 198,330
Library Holdings: Bk Titles 65,000; Per Subs 2,500
Subject Interests: Art and architecture, Natural science
Special Collections: Carroll Coll
Publications: Newsletter (quarterly); Newspaper column (weekly); Radio (weekly)
Mem of Sarasota County Dept of Librs
Partic in CLSI
Special Services for the Deaf - TTY machine
Friends of the Library Group

ESTERO

S COLLEGE OF LIFE FOUNDATION LIBRARY, (Formerly Koreshan Unity Foundation Research Library), 8661 Corkscrew Rd, PO Box 97, 33928. SAN 302-9204. Tel: 941-992-2184. FAX: 941-495-0201. *Pres*, Charles Dauray
Subject Interests: Florida, Utopianism
Restriction: Private library

EUSTIS

P EUSTIS MEMORIAL LIBRARY, 120 N Center St, 32726-3512. SAN 302-9212. Tel: 352-357-5686. TDD: 352-357-2495. FAX: 352-357-5450. E-Mail: library@eustis.org. Web Site: www.eustismemoriallibrary.org. *Dir*, E Steven Benetz; *Ch Servs*, Emily E Gerry; *Circ*, Marlene V Blye; *Circ*, Celeste Bringard; Staff 13 (MLS 3, Non-MLS 10)
Founded 1902. Pop 14,889; Circ 133,305
Oct 1998-Sep 1999 Income $754,276, City $707,066, Locally Generated Income $26,282, Other $20,928. Mats Exp $71,500, Books $65,000, Per/Ser (Incl. Access Fees) $6,500. Sal $378,694 (Prof $140,304)
Library Holdings: Bk Vols 87,754; Per Subs 223
Special Collections: Circulating Art Prints; Florida Coll
Automation Activity & Vendor Info: (Cataloging) DRA; (Circulation) DRA; (OPAC) DRA
Partic in Central Florida Library Cooperative (CFLC)
Special Services for the Deaf - Staff with knowledge of sign language; TDD

FERNANDINA BEACH

§P NASSAU COUNTY PUBLIC LIBRARY SYSTEM, Fernandina Beach Library, 25 N Fourth St, 32034-4123. Tel: 904-277-7365. FAX: 904-277-7366. Web Site: sirsi.nassau.lib.fl.us. *Dir*, Dawn Bostwiek; E-Mail: dawnb@mail.itd.ci.jax.fl.us; *Asst Dir*, Janet Loveless; *Cat*, Alma Nagle; *Ch Servs*, Marlene Deutcher; *ILL*, Teor Peterson; *Syst Coordr*, Michael Kucsek
Automation Activity & Vendor Info: (Acquisitions) SIRSI; (Cataloging) SIRSI; (Circulation) SIRSI; (Course Reserve) SIRSI; (ILL) SIRSI; (Media Booking) SIRSI; (OPAC) SIRSI; (Serials) SIRSI
Branches: 2
CALLAHAN BRANCH, 5266 State Rd 200, Callahan, 32011. Tel: 904-879-3434. FAX: 904-879-3434. *Branch Mgr*, Anne Smith; *Asst Librn*, Pat Barnes
Automation Activity & Vendor Info: (Acquisitions) SIRSI; (Cataloging) SIRSI; (Circulation) SIRSI; (Course Reserve) SIRSI; (ILL) SIRSI; (Media Booking) SIRSI; (OPAC) SIRSI; (Serials) SIRSI
HILLARD BRANCH, 205 Pecan St, Hillard, 32046. Tel: 904-845-2495. *Branch Mgr*, Sally Batten; *Asst Librn*, Dianna Roberts
Automation Activity & Vendor Info: (Acquisitions) SIRSI; (Cataloging) SIRSI; (Circulation) SIRSI; (Course Reserve) SIRSI; (ILL) SIRSI; (Media Booking) SIRSI; (OPAC) SIRSI; (Serials) SIRSI

FLAGLER BEACH

P FLAGLER BEACH LIBRARY, 315 S Seventh St, 32136-3524. (Mail add: PO Box 449, 32136-0449), SAN 370-4629. Tel: 904-517-2030. FAX: 904-517-2234. *Librn*, Randa Adams; E-Mail: randa@pcfl.net; *Asst Librn*, Ruth Young; Staff 2 (Non-MLS 2)
Library Holdings: Bk Titles 19,500; Per Subs 25; Bks on Deafness & Sign Lang 15
Special Services for the Blind - Bks on tape

FLORIDA CITY

S STATE OF FLORIDA, DEPARTMENT OF CORRECTIONS, Dade Correctional Institution Library-North Annex Unit, 19000 SW 377th St, 33034-0530. SAN 326-6230. Tel: 305-242-1912. FAX: 305-242-1851. *Librn*, Rolando H Valdes; Staff 14 (MLS 1, Non-MLS 13)
Library Holdings: Bk Vols 5,766; Bk Titles 5,161; Per Subs 58
Subject Interests: Fiction
Special Collections: Black Heritage Coll; Opera Coll; Spanish Heritage Coll
Special Programs: Opera on Video; Italian Language

FORT LAUDERDALE

C ART INSTITUTE OF FORT LAUDERDALE LIBRARY, Nevin C Meinhardt Memorial Library, 1650 SE 17th St, 33316. (Mail add: 1799 SE 17th St, 33316), SAN 377-8053. Tel: 954-463-3000, Ext 751. Toll Free Tel: 800-275-7603. FAX: 954-463-3393. E-Mail: aifllibrary@hotmail.com. Web Site: www.seflin.org/aifl/. *Dir Libr Serv*, Heather Payne; *Ref*, Kristin Kroger; Staff 4 (MLS 3, Non-MLS 1)
Enrl 3,000; Highest Degree: Bachelor
Jul 1999-Jun 2000 Income $285,000. Mats Exp $130,500, Books $100,000, Per/Ser (Incl. Access Fees) $26,000, Presv $1,400, AV Equip $3,100. Sal $118,420
Library Holdings: Bk Vols 23,000; Bk Titles 22,000; Per Subs 265
Subject Interests: Architecture
Restriction: Non-circulating to the public
Function: ILL available
Partic in OCLC Online Computer Library Center, Inc; Solinet; Southeast Florida Library Information Network, Inc

S BROWARD CORRECTIONAL INSTITUTION LIBRARY, 20421 Sheridan St, 33332. SAN 371-795X. Tel: 954-252-6500. FAX: 954-680-4168.; Staff 2 (MLS 1, Non-MLS 1)
Library Holdings: Bk Vols 12,000; Per Subs 30
Special Collections: Law

P BROWARD COUNTY DIVISION OF LIBRARIES, Broward County Library, 100 S Andrews Ave, 33301. SAN 337-3983. Tel: 954-357-7444. Interlibrary Loan Service Tel: 954-357-7443. TDD: 954-357-7528. FAX: 954-357-7397. Interlibrary Loan Service FAX: 954-761-7240. E-Mail: answer@browardlibrary.org. Web Site: www.broward.org/library. *Exec Dir*, Jean Trebbi; Tel: 954-357-7404, Fax: 954-357-6122, E-Mail: jtrebbi@mail.bcl.lib.fl.us; *Exec Dir*, Kay Harvey; Tel: 954-357-7469, Fax: 954-357-7856, E-Mail: kharvey@browardlibrary.org; *Br Coordr, Exec Dir*, Arglenda Friday; Tel: 954-765-4544, Fax: 954-765-4546, E-Mail: afriday@browardlibrary.org; *Dir*, Samuel Morrison; Tel: 954-357-7376, Fax: 954-357-6542, E-Mail: morrison@browardlibrary.org; *Assoc Dir*, Kathleen Imhoff; E-Mail: kimhoff@browardlibrary.org; *Asst Dir*, Betty L Dejean; Tel: 954-357-6592, Fax: 954-357-8057, E-Mail: bdejean@browardlibrary.org; *Assoc Dir*, Harriet Buchbinder; Tel: 954-357-7417, Fax: 954-357-6122, E-Mail: hbuchbin@browardlibrary.org; *Assoc Dir*, Eileen Cobb; Tel: 954-357-7379, Fax: 954-357-5681, E-Mail: ecobb@browardlibrary.org; *Assoc Dir*, Jessica Roberts; Tel: 954-357-5480, Fax: 954-357-6542, E-Mail: jroberts@browardlibrary.org; *Asst Dir*, Valrie Simpson; Tel: 954-963-8825, Fax: 954-964-0280, E-Mail: vsimpson@mail.bcl.lib.fl.us; *Mgr*, Marie Moisdon; Tel: 954-357-7847, Fax: 954-357-6096, E-Mail: mmoisdon@browardlibrary.org; *Regional Librarian*, Cindy Genovese-Shulman; Tel: 954-538-9996, E-Mail: cshulman@browardlibrary.org; *Outreach Serv*, Tanya Simons-Oparah; Tel: 954-357-7514, E-Mail: tsimons@browardlibrary.org; *Coordr*, Eileen McNally; Tel: 954-357-5997, Fax: 954-357-5681, E-Mail: emcnally@browardlibrary.org; *Automation Syst Coordr, Librn*, Barbara Schumacher; Tel: 954-357-7435, Fax: 954-357-6113, E-Mail: bschumac@browardlibrary.org; *Mgr*, Doris Williams; Tel: 954-357-7570, Fax: 954-357-5548, E-Mail: dwilliam@mail.bcl.lib.fl.us; *Branch Mgr*, Mimi Hershenson; Tel: 954-357-7335, Fax: 954-357-5681, E-Mail: mhershen@browardlibrary.org; *Mgr, Ref Serv Ad*, Marty Onieal; Tel: 954-357-7385, Fax: 954-357-6122, E-Mail: monieal@browardlibrary.org; *Librn for Blind*, Joann Block; Tel: 954-357-8686, Fax: 954-357-7413, E-Mail: jblock@browardlibrary.org; *Librn*, Terry Kutolowski; Tel: 954-831-3300, Fax: 954-831-3344, E-Mail: tkutolow@browardlibrary.org; *Librn*, Deborah Passalacqua; Tel: 954-969-2600, Fax: 954-968-2475, E-Mail: dpassala@browardlibrary.org; *Librn*, Easter Wilcher; Tel: 954-357-7427, Fax: 954-357-7411, E-Mail: ewilcher@browardlibrary.org; *Ref Serv Ad*, Ann Williams; Tel: 954-357-5995, Fax: 954-357-6096, E-Mail: awilliam@mail.bcl.lib.fl.us; *Web Coordr*, Louise Lee; Tel: 954-357-7465, E-Mail: llee@browardlibrary.org; *Commun Relations*, Sherry Lynch; Tel: 954-357-7470, Fax: 954-357-6096, E-Mail: slynch@bcl.lib.fl.us; *Coll Develop, Planning Services*, Gianna Miles; Tel: 954-497-3675, Fax: 954-497-3657, E-Mail: gmiles@mail.bcl.lib.fl.us; *Coll Develop*, Christopher Murray; Tel: 954-497-3690, Fax: 954-497-3657, E-Mail: cmurray@browardlibrary.org. Subject Specialists: *African-American*, Kay Harvey; *Afro-American*, Arglenda Friday; *Bus*, Mimi Hershenson; *Cultural res*, Arglenda Friday; *Government*, Mimi Hershenson; *Law*, Mimi Hershenson; Staff 853 (MLS 174, Non-MLS 679)
Founded 1974. Pop 1,490,289; Circ 7,387,149
Oct 1999-Sep 2000 Income (Main Library and Branch Library) $35,296,420, State $3,156,000, City $388,477, County $31,136,873, Other $615,070. Mats Exp $6,087,865, Books $2,473,409, Per/Ser (Incl. Access Fees) $695,737, Presv $10,000, AV Equip $241,075, Electronic Ref Mat (Incl. Access Fees) $1,698,610. Sal $251,818,330
Library Holdings: Bk Vols 2,660,189; Per Subs 9,750
Subject Interests: Florida, Genealogy, International trade, Patents
Special Collections: Bienes Rare Books Coll; Florida Diagnostic & Learning Resource System; Judaica (Isaac Mayer Wise Coll); Music Scores; Small Business Resource Center
Automation Activity & Vendor Info: (Acquisitions) Brodart; (Circulation) CARL
Database Vendor: CARL, Ebsco - EbscoHost, GaleNet, IAC - SearchBank, Lexis-Nexis, OCLC - First Search
Publications: Annual Report; Bookings; Multiethnic Resources Directory
Restriction: Open to student, faculty & staff
Function: ILL available
Partic in OCLC Online Computer Library Center, Inc; SE Libr Network; Southeast Florida Library Information Network, Inc
Special Services for the Deaf - Books on deafness & sign language; Captioned media; Special interest periodicals; Staff with knowledge of sign language; TTY machine; Videos & decoder
Special Services for the Blind - Talking book center
Friends of the Library Group
Branches: 37

BEACH BRANCH, 221 Pompano Beach Blvd, Pompano Beach, 33062. SAN 373-5192. Tel: 954-786-2197. FAX: 954-786-2146. *Planning Services*, Eileen McNally; Tel: 954-357-5997, Fax: 954-357-5681, E-Mail: emcnally@browardlibrary.org; *Librn*, Christine Walsh; Staff 3 (MLS 1, Non-MLS 2)
Circ 46,974
Library Holdings: Bk Vols 10,937
Mem of Broward County Div of Librs
Friends of the Library Group

BOOKS BY MAIL, 1300 E Sunrise Blvd, 33304. SAN 378-0678. Tel: 954-765-4356. *Librn*, Elouise Player; *Planning Services*, Eileen McNally; Tel: 954-357-5997, Fax: 954-357-5681, E-Mail: emcnally@browardlibrary.org; Staff 3 (Non-MLS 3)
Circ 21,696
Library Holdings: Bk Vols 9,646

S BROWARD COMMUNITY TECHNOLOGY CENTER, 100 S Andrews Ave, 1st Flr, 33301. SAN 378-0988. Tel: 954-357-7485. FAX: 954-357-7792. *Head Librn*, Kathleen Eavenson; Staff 6 (MLS 1, Non-MLS 5)

CARVER RANCHES BRANCH, 4735 SW 18th St, Hollywood, 33023. SAN 337-4025. Tel: 954-985-1945. FAX: 954-985-1947. *Librn*, Helen Jean; Staff 4 (Non-MLS 4)
Circ 61,736
Library Holdings: Bk Vols 19,281
Friends of the Library Group

CENTURY PLAZA, 1856A W Hillsboro Blvd, Deerfield Beach, 33442. SAN 337-405X. Tel: 954-360-1330. FAX: 954-360-1332. *Librn*, Kathleen Haefliger; E-Mail: Khaeflig@mail.bcl.lib.fl.us; Staff 6 (MLS 2, Non-MLS 4)
Circ 138,008
Library Holdings: Bk Vols 23,534
Friends of the Library Group

COLLIER CITY BRANCH, 2800 NW Ninth Ct, Pompano Beach, 33069. SAN 337-4033. Tel: 954-968-3820. FAX: 954-968-3822. *Librn*, Candida Fermin; Staff 6 (MLS 2, Non-MLS 4)
Circ 20,786
Library Holdings: Bk Vols 21,318
Subject Interests: Family literacy
Friends of the Library Group

DANIA BEACH-PAUL DEMAIO LIBRARY, 485 S Federal Hwy, Dania, 33004. SAN 337-4076. Tel: 954-926-2420. FAX: 954-926-2422.; Staff 5 (Non-MLS 5)
Circ 57,322
Library Holdings: Bk Vols 22,148

DAVIE-COOPER CITY BRANCH, 4600 SW 82nd Ave, Davie, 33328. SAN 337-4068. Tel: 954-680-0050. FAX: 954-680-0052. *Librn*, Mary Pat McNulty; Staff 9 (MLS 3, Non-MLS 6)
Circ 225,965
Library Holdings: Bk Vols 43,872
Friends of the Library Group

DEERFIELD BEACH (PERCY WHITE BRANCH), 837 E Hillsboro Blvd, Deerfield Beach, 33441. SAN 337-4084. Tel: 954-360-1380. FAX: 954-360-1382. *Librn*, Linda Kamin; *Librn*, Jim Paul; Staff 9 (MLS 3, Non-MLS 6)
Circ 142,622
Library Holdings: Bk Vols 40,685
Friends of the Library Group

FORT LAUDERDALE BRANCH, 1300 E Sunrise Blvd, 33304. SAN 337-4106. Tel: 954-765-4263. FAX: 954-765-4932. *Librn*, Elaine Wise; Staff 13 (MLS 2, Non-MLS 11)
Circ 72,265
Library Holdings: Bk Vols 56,423
Headquarters for the Greater Fort Lauderdale Art Serve project
Friends of the Library Group

GALT OCEAN MILE READING CENTER, 3403 Galt Ocean Dr, 33008. SAN 373-5206. Tel: 954-537-2877. FAX: 954-537-2879.; Staff 3 (MLS 1, Non-MLS 2)
Circ 98,038
Library Holdings: Bk Vols 8,830
Friends of the Library Group

HALLANDALE BRANCH, 300 S Federal Hwy, Hallandale, 33309. SAN 337-4130. Tel: 954-457-1750. FAX: 954-457-1753. *Librn*, Carol French; Staff 11 (MLS 2, Non-MLS 9)
Circ 185,514
Library Holdings: Bk Vols 44,916
Friends of the Library Group

HOLLYWOOD BEACH BERNICE P OSTER READING CENTER, 1301 S Ocean Dr, Hollywood, 33019. SAN 374-8049. Tel: 954-926-2437. FAX: 954-926-2438. *Mgr*, Joan Graff; Staff 3 (MLS 1, Non-MLS 2)
Circ 57,028
Library Holdings: Bk Vols 5,915
Friends of the Library Group

HOLLYWOOD BRANCH, 2600 Hollywood Blvd, Hollywood, 33020. SAN 337-4165. Tel: 954-926-2430. FAX: 954-926-2433. *Librn*, Carol Russo; Staff 12 (MLS 3, Non-MLS 9)
Circ 196,269
Library Holdings: Bk Vols 55,613
Friends of the Library Group

IMPERIAL POINT, 5985 N Federal Hwy, 33308. SAN 328-9036. Tel: 954-492-1881. FAX: 954-492-1804. *Librn*, Becky Peters; Staff 13 (MLS 3, Non-MLS 10)
Circ 164,596
Library Holdings: Bk Vols 53,610
Friends of the Library Group

LAUDERDALE LAKES BRANCH, 3521 NW 43rd Ave, Lauderdale Lakes, 33319. SAN 337-419X. Tel: 954-497-3627. FAX: 954-497-3630. *Librn*, Donna Bachowski; Staff 7 (MLS 2, Non-MLS 5)
Circ 84,420
Library Holdings: Bk Vols 34,390

Friends of the Library Group
LAUDERHILL CITY HALL COMPLEX, 2100 NW 55th Ave, Lauderhill, 33313. SAN 337-4238. Tel: 954-497-1630. FAX: 954-497-1632.; Staff 6 (MLS 1, Non-MLS 5)
Circ 60,452
Library Holdings: Bk Vols 22,818
Friends of the Library Group
LAUDERHILL MALL BRANCH, 4257 NW 12th St, Lauderhill, 33313. SAN 337-422X. Tel: 954-791-1000. FAX: 954-791-1002. *Librn*, Mary-Alice Gage; Staff 4 (MLS 1, Non-MLS 3)
Circ 47,932
Library Holdings: Bk Vols 16,460
Friends of the Library Group
MARGATE (CATHERINE YOUNG BRANCH), 5810 Park Dr, Margate, 33063. SAN 337-4246. Tel: 954-968-3800. FAX: 954-968-3803. *Librn*, Susan Hodos; Staff 10 (MLS 3, Non-MLS 7)
Circ 183,442
Library Holdings: Bk Vols 36,879
NORTH LAUDERDALE BRANCH, 6601 Boulevard of Champions, North Lauderdale, 33068. SAN 337-4262. Tel: 954-968-3840. FAX: 954-968-3842. *Librn*, Joan Hinton; Staff 5 (MLS 1, Non-MLS 4)
Circ 96,439
Library Holdings: Bk Vols 23,116
Friends of the Library Group
NORTH REGIONAL-BCC, 1100 Coconut Creek Blvd, Coconut Creek, 33066. SAN 373-5214. Tel: 954-969-2600. FAX: 954-786-2178. *Librn*, Deborah Passalaqua; Staff 64 (MLS 20, Non-MLS 44)
Circ 730,661
Library Holdings: Bk Vols 205,148
Also serves as library for Broward County Community College, North Campus
Friends of the Library Group
NORTHWEST, 1580 NW Third Ave, Pompano Beach, 33060. SAN 373-5222. Tel: 954-786-2186. FAX: 954-786-2167. *Head of Libr*, Rhonda Walker; E-Mail: rwalker@mail.bcl.lib.fl.us; *Librn*, Faye Blake; Staff 4 (Non-MLS 4)
Circ 19,111
Library Holdings: Bk Vols 13,483
Friends of the Library Group
NORTHWEST REGIONAL, 3151 University Dr, Coral Springs, 33065. Tel: 904-341-3900. Web Site: www.broward.org/library.; Staff 75 (MLS 20, Non-MLS 55)
Special Collections: International Language Coll
Special Services for the Blind - Large print bks; Talking Books
Open Mon-Thurs 7:30am-9:00pm, Fri-Sat 9:00-5:00, Sun 1-5
Friends of the Library Group
PEMBROKE PINES BRANCH - WALTER C YOUNG RESOURCE CENTER, 955 NW 129th Ave, Pembroke Pines, 33028. Tel: 954-437-2642. FAX: 954-437-2624. *Head of Libr*, Essie DeNoms; Staff 21 (MLS 6, Non-MLS 15)
Circ 394,797
Library Holdings: Bk Vols 57,720
Subject Interests: Middle sch
Friends of the Library Group
POMPANO BEACH BRANCH, 1213 E Atlantic Blvd, Pompano Beach, 33060. SAN 373-5230. Tel: 954-786-2181. FAX: 954-786-2178. *Librn*, Janice Rolle; Staff 10 (Non-MLS 10)
Circ 160,152
Library Holdings: Bk Vols 66,825
Friends of the Library Group
RIVERLAND, 2710 W Davie Blvd, 33312. SAN 337-4319. Tel: 954-791-1085. FAX: 954-791-1087. *Librn*, Frances Addison; Staff 9 (MLS 1, Non-MLS 8)
Circ 95,359
Library Holdings: Bk Vols 43,079
Friends of the Library Group
SOUTH REGIONAL BCC, 7300 Pines Blvd, Pembroke Pines, 33024. SAN 337-4343. Tel: 954-963-8825. FAX: 954-964-0282, 964-0280. *Librn*, Valrie Simpson; E-Mail: vsimpson@mail.bcl.lib.fl.us; Staff 65 (MLS 16, Non-MLS 49)
Circ 684,426
Library Holdings: Bk Vols 191,289
Special Services for the Deaf - TDD
Also serves as library for Broward County Community College, South Campus
Friends of the Library Group
SUNRISE (DAN PEARL BRANCH), 10500 W Oakland Park Blvd, Sunrise, 33351. SAN 375-605X. Tel: 954-749-2521. FAX: 954-749-2524. *Librn*, Ann Miller; Staff 15 (MLS 5, Non-MLS 10)
Circ 352,577
Library Holdings: Bk Vols 63,018
Friends of the Library Group
SUNSET STRIP, 6600 Sunset Strip, Sunrise, 33313. SAN 337-4351. Tel: 954-749-2525. FAX: 954-749-2428. *Librn*, Theresa Salantrie; Staff 5 (MLS 1, Non-MLS 4)
Circ 82,752
Library Holdings: Bk Vols 16,825
Friends of the Library Group
P TALKING BOOK LIBRARY, 100 S Andrews Ave, 33301. SAN 337-4017. Tel: 954-357-7555. *Librn*, Joann Block; Staff 6 (MLS 1, Non-MLS 5)
Founded 1977
Library Holdings: Bk Vols 6,390
TAMARAC BRANCH, 8601 N McNab Rd, Tamarac, 33321. SAN 337-4424. Tel: 954-720-2200. FAX: 954-720-2203. *Librn*, Linda Kamin; Staff 13 (MLS 3, Non-MLS 10)
Circ 304,877
Library Holdings: Bk Vols 52,760
Friends of the Library Group
TAMARAC POPULAR, 10044 W McNab Rd, Tamarac, 33321. SAN 378-0651. Tel: 954-720-2273. FAX: 954-720-2272. *Librn*, Mary Roberts; Staff 4 (Non-MLS 4)
Circ 118,665
Library Holdings: Bk Vols 9,061
TYRONE BRYANT BRANCH, 2230 NW 21st Ave, 33311. SAN 337-4327. Tel: 954-497-1675. FAX: 954-497-1677. *Planning Services*, Eileen McNally; Tel: 954-357-5997, Fax: 954-357-5681, E-Mail: emcnally@browardlibrary.org; *Librn*, Florence Ravin; *Librn, YA Servs*, Cassandra Jones; Staff 4 (MLS 1, Non-MLS 3)
Circ 23,022
Library Holdings: Bk Vols 16,179
Friends of the Library Group
VON D MIZELL BRANCH, 1409 Sistrunk Blvd, 954, 33311. SAN 337-4378. Tel: 954-765-4269. FAX: 954-761-7160. *Librn*, Argusta Walker; Staff 5 (Non-MLS 5)
Circ 16,249
Library Holdings: Bk Vols 32,792
Special Collections: Black Heritage
Friends of the Library Group
WEST ATLANTIC, 10643 W Atlantic Blvd, Coral Springs, 33071. SAN 374-8057. Tel: 954-341-3912. FAX: 954-341-3914. *Librn*, Betsy Medina; Staff 6 (MLS 1, Non-MLS 5)
Circ 182,251
Library Holdings: Bk Vols 23,518
Friends of the Library Group
WEST REGIONAL, 8601 W Broward Blvd, Plantation, 33324. SAN 337-4416. Tel: 954-831-3300. TDD: 954-831-3317. FAX: 954-831-3326.; Staff 53 (MLS 18, Non-MLS 35)
Circ 715,751
Library Holdings: Bk Vols 157,267
Special Services for the Deaf - TDD
Friends of the Library Group
WESTON READING CENTER, 2505 Arvida Pkwy, 33326. SAN 374-8065. Tel: 954-389-2046. FAX: 954-389-2047. *Librn*, Ann Rosen; Staff 2 (Non-MLS 2)
Circ 36,990
Library Holdings: Bk Vols 13,178
Friends of the Library Group
Bookmobiles: 3. 1300 E Sunrise Blvd; Tel: 954-765-4265. Librn, Elaine Wise. Bk vols 34,857

S BROWARD COUNTY HISTORICAL COMMISSION LIBRARY, 151 SW Second St, 33301. SAN 302-9247. Tel: 954-765-4670. FAX: 954-765-4437. Web Site: www.co.broward.fl.us/history.htm. *In Charge*, Barbara Poleo
Library Holdings: Bk Titles 2,000; Per Subs 50
Subject Interests: History, Local history
Special Collections: Judge Nance Coll, rare bks; Kirk Cooper Coll

L ENGLISH, MCCAUGHAN & O'BRYAN PA, Law Library, 100 NE Third Ave, 33301. (Mail add: PO Box 14098, 33302), SAN 325-8459. Tel: 954-462-3300. FAX: 954-763-2439. *Librn*, Angela Stramiello; E-Mail: astramiell@emolaw.com
Library Holdings: Bk Vols 7,000
Restriction: Staff use only

R FIRST PRESBYTERIAN CHURCH LIBRARY, 401 SE 15th Ave, 33301-2397. SAN 302-9271. Tel: 954-462-6200. FAX: 954-764-1081. *Librn*, Melanie Leonard
Pop 2,500
Library Holdings: Bk Vols 2,000; Per Subs 15
Subject Interests: Religion

S FLORIDA DIAGNOSTIC & LEARNING RESOURCE SYSTEM, Media Center, 100 S Andrews Ave, 33301. SAN 377-354X. Tel: 954-765-6704. FAX: 954-765-6962. *Coordr*, Sandra Doubleday
Library Holdings: Bk Vols 4,500; Bk Titles 3,500; Per Subs 54
Mem of Broward County Div of Librs
Open Mon-Sat 9-5, Sun 12-5:30
Friends of the Library Group

C FORT LAUDERDALE COLLEGE LIBRARY, 1040 Bayview Dr, 33304-2522. SAN 375-3239. Tel: 954-568-1600, Ext 69. FAX: 954-568-2008. *Actg Dir*, Milton Camirand; Staff 2 (Non-MLS 2)

Founded 1940. Enrl 350; Fac 55; Highest Degree: Master
Library Holdings: Bk Titles 8,700; Per Subs 75
Special Services for the Deaf - Books on deafness & sign language; High interest/low vocabulary books; Special interest periodicals

P FORT LAUDERDALE HISTORICAL SOCIETY, Old Fort Lauderdale Research Archives, 219 SW Second Ave, 33301. SAN 325-853X. Tel: 954-463-4431. Reference Tel: 954-463-4431, Ext 11. FAX: 954-463-4434. E-Mail: mrathbun@hobbyline.com. Web Site: www.oldfortlauderdale.org. *Curator*, Susan Gillis; Staff 2 (Non-MLS 2)
Founded 1962
Library Holdings: Bk Vols 3,500; Bk Titles 3,000; Per Subs 100
Subject Interests: Local history, Maps
Special Collections: Architectural Drawings; Manuscript & Subject Coll; Photographs (250,000)
Publications: New River News (quarterly)
Partic in Broward County Libr Asn; Fla Soc of Archivists

S INTERNATIONAL SWIMMING HALL OF FAME, Henning Library, One Hall of Fame Dr, 33316. SAN 302-9301. Tel: 954-462-6536, Ext 204. FAX: 954-522-4521. E-Mail: library@ishof.org. Web Site: www.ishof.org. *Librn*, Preston Levi; Staff 4 (MLS 1, Non-MLS 3)
Founded 1965
Library Holdings: Bk Vols 9,812; Per Subs 51
Special Collections: Image Coll; Olympic Games Book Coll; Photo Coll; Swimming & Related Aquatic Sports Coll, particulary rare & out-of-print editions
Significant Archival holdings of major international & national aquatic sport assoc

J KEISER COLLEGE, Jim Bishop Memorial Library, 1500 NW 49th St, 33309. SAN 373-1294. Tel: 954-351-4035. FAX: 954-351-4051. Web Site: www.keiserlibrary.com. *Exec Dir*, Benjamin Williams; E-Mail: ben@keisercollege.cc.fl.us; *Asst Dir*, Jan Bammel; *Circ*, Jone Claybrook; Staff 2 (MLS 2)
Founded 1976. Enrl 1,500; Fac 90; Highest Degree: Associate
Library Holdings: Bk Vols 50,000; Bk Titles 39,000; Per Subs 125
Automation Activity & Vendor Info: (Acquisitions) Athena; (Cataloging) Athena; (Circulation) Athena; (OPAC) Athena
Publications: Bibliographies; New Books; Student Manuals; Style Sheets
Partic in Southeast Florida Library Information Network, Inc
Departmental Libraries:
DAYTONA BEACH CAMPUS, 1800 Business Park Blvd, Daytona Beach, 32114. Tel: 904-255-1707. FAX: 904-274-2725. *Librn*, Martha Scanlon; *Asst Librn*, Robin Henderson
Library Holdings: Bk Vols 4,000; Per Subs 40
Automation Activity & Vendor Info: (Acquisitions) Athena; (Cataloging) Athena; (Circulation) Athena
EVERGLADES COLLEGE LIBRARY, 1500 NW 49th St, 33309. Tel: 954-772-2655. FAX: 954-772-2695. E-Mail: admissions@evergladescollege.edu. Web Site: www.evergladescollege.edu. *Dir*, Gary Markowitz; *Librn*, Ben Williams
Automation Activity & Vendor Info: (Acquisitions) Athena; (Cataloging) Athena; (Circulation) Athena
KEISER CAREER INSTITUTE - COOPER CITY BRANCH, 8688 Griffin Rd, Cooper City, 33328. Tel: 954-252-0002. FAX: 954-252-0003. *Dir*, Ray Nunizata
KEISER CAREER INSTITUTE - LAKE WORTH BRANCH, 1926 Tenth Ave, Lake Worth, 33461. Tel: 561-547-5472. FAX: 561-567-6609. Web Site: www.keisercollege.edu. *Dir*, Colleen Rupp
KEISER CAREER INSTITUTE - PORT SAINT LUCIE BRANCH, 9468 S US 1, Port Saint Lucie, 34952. Tel: 561-398-9990. FAX: 561-335-9619. *Dir*, Marlene Sheridan
LAKELAND CAMPUS, 3515 Aviation Dr, Lakeland, 33811. Tel: 863-701-7789. FAX: 863-701-8758. *Dir*, Jim Wallis
Automation Activity & Vendor Info: (Acquisitions) Athena; (Cataloging) Athena; (Circulation) Athena
MELBOURNE CAMPUS, 900 S Babcock St, Melbourne, 32901-1461. SAN 373-1308. Tel: 321-255-2255. FAX: 321-725-3766. Web Site: www.keisercollege.cc.fl.us. *Librn*, Suzanne Bhatia; E-Mail: suzyb_99@yahoo.com
Founded 1989. Enrl 400; Fac 22
Library Holdings: Bk Vols 10,000; Bk Titles 9,000; Per Subs 42
Publications: Bibliographies; New Book List; Student Manual; Style Sheets
Partic in Cent Fla Libr Consortium; Westlaw
SARASOTA CAMPUS, 332 Sarasota Quay, Sarasota, 34236. Tel: 941-954-0954. FAX: 941-366-5545.
Library Holdings: Bk Titles 5,000; Per Subs 40
Automation Activity & Vendor Info: (Acquisitions) Athena; (Cataloging) Athena; (Circulation) Athena
TALLAHASSEE CAMPUS, Bldg 2, 1700 Halstead Blvd, Tallahassee, 32308-5327. Tel: 850-906-9494. FAX: 850-906-9497. *Librn*, Lifeng Yu; *Tech Servs*, Daniel Trescott
Library Holdings: Bk Titles 6,000; Per Subs 35
Automation Activity & Vendor Info: (Acquisitions) Athena; (Cataloging) Athena; (Circulation) Athena

GL LAMAR WARREN LAW LIBRARY OF BROWARD COUNTY, 1800 Broward County Judicial Complex, 201 SE Sixth St, 33301. SAN 302-9255. Tel: 954-831-6226. E-Mail: lawlibrary@broward.org. *Dir*, Jeanne Underhill; E-Mail: junderhill@broward.org
Library Holdings: Bk Vols 60,000; Per Subs 225

S MOTOROLA, Technical & Business Library-Fort Lauderdale, 8000 W Sunrise Blvd, 33322. SAN 328-5502. Tel: 954-723-5049. FAX: 954-723-4466. *Librn*, Kim Searer
Library Holdings: Bk Titles 2,200; Per Subs 200
Subject Interests: Engineering, Technology
Friends of the Library Group

M NORTH RIDGE MEDICAL CENTER, Medical Library, 5757 N Dixie Hwy, 33334. SAN 322-8940. Tel: 954-776-6000, Ext 4221. FAX: 954-202-4866. *Librn*, Jenny Garcia
Founded 1976
Library Holdings: Bk Vols 450; Bk Titles 400; Per Subs 130
Partic in BRS

CM NOVA SOUTHEASTERN UNIVERSITY, Health Professions Division Library, 3200 S University Dr, 33328. SAN 373-420X. Tel: 954-262-3106. FAX: 954-262-2265. Web Site: www.nova.edu/cwis/hpdlibrary/. *Dir, Librn*, Janice Gottlieb; E-Mail: gottlieb@hpd.acast.nova.edu; *Cat*, Todd Puccio; *Circ, Ref*, Hilary O'Sullivan; *Circ, Ref*, Mary Lawrence; *Ref*, Alex Wachsler
Jul 1998-Jun 1999 Income $1,131,808, Federal $23,471, Locally Generated Income $7,122, Parent Institution $1,101,215. Mats Exp $712,820, Books $117,662, Per/Ser (Incl. Access Fees) $545,759, Presv $20,760, AV Equip $28,639. Sal $308,928 (Prof $160,636)
Library Holdings: Bk Titles 22,000; Per Subs 1,450
Subject Interests: Dentistry, Optometry, Pharmacology
Publications: Optometric Library Highlights
Partic in Association of Vision Science Librarians (AVSL); Docline; Fla Health Sci Libr Asn; Miami Health Sciences Library Consortium; OCLC Online Computer Library Center, Inc; SE Libr Network

C NOVA SOUTHEASTERN UNIVERSITY LIBRARIES, Einstein Library, 3301 College Ave, 33314. SAN 337-4432. Tel: 954-262-4620. FAX: 954-262-3805. Web Site: www.nova.edu/library. *VPres*, Donald E Riggs; *Dir*, Harriett MacDougall; *Tech Servs*, Mary Paige Smith; *Ref*, Kathleen Dunleavy; *Circ*, Marty Mandt; *Coll Develop*, Lia Hemphill; Staff 20 (MLS 20)
Founded 1966. Enrl 16,000; Highest Degree: Doctorate
Library Holdings: Bk Vols 166,288; Bk Titles 121,108; Per Subs 1,844
Special Collections: Microforms (252,654)
Partic in Southeast Florida Library Information Network, Inc
Departmental Libraries:
CM HEALTH PROFESSIONS DIVISION LIBRARY, 3200 S University Dr, Ft Lauderdale, 33328. SAN 376-9887. Tel: 954-262-3106. FAX: 954-262-2265. Web Site: www.nova.edu/cwis/hpdlibrary/index.html. *Dir*, Janice Gottlieb
1998-1999 Mats Exp $671,724. Sal $305,414 (Prof $157,080)
Library Holdings: Bk Vols 50,000; Per Subs 1,400
OCEANOGRAPHY, 8000 Ocean Dr, Dania, 33004. SAN 337-4580. Tel: 954-262-3643. FAX: 954-262-4098. Web Site: www.nova.edu/ocean/library.html. *Mgr*, Kathleen Maxson; E-Mail: maxson@ocean.nova.edu
Library Holdings: Bk Vols 10,000; Per Subs 100
SHEPARD BROAD LAW CENTER LIBRARY, 3305 College Ave, 33314. SAN 337-4491. Tel: 954-262-7300, Ext 6211. FAX: 954-262-3839. Web Site: www.nova.edu/library, www.nsulaw.nova.edu. *Asst Prof, Dir*, Billie Jo Kaufman; E-Mail: kaufmanb@nsu.law.nova.edu; *Assoc Dir*, Lisa Smith-Butler; *Tech Servs*, Mary Paige-Smith; *Doc*, Sarah Tabor; *Coll Develop*, Carol Yecies; *Acq*, Diane Altimari
Founded 1974. Enrl 830
1998-1999 Mats Exp $799,411. Sal $801,556 (Prof $326,099)
Library Holdings: Bk Vols 308,000; Per Subs 5,534
Partic in Alanet; BRS; Dialog Corporation; OCLC Online Computer Library Center, Inc; SE Libr Network

L RUDEN, MCCLOSKY, SMITH, SCHUSTER & RUSSELL, Law Library, 200 E Broward Blvd, PO Box 1900, 33302. SAN 327-781X. Tel: 954-764-6660. FAX: 954-764-4996. E-Mail: sir@ruden.com. *Librn*, Sheryll I Rappaport
Library Holdings: Bk Vols 10,000; Per Subs 25
Partic in S Fla Law Libr Asn; Spec Libr Asn

S SUN-SENTINEL EDITORIAL RESEARCH CENTER, 200 E Las Olas Blvd, 9th Flr, 33301-2293. SAN 372-6533. Tel: 954-356-4741. FAX: 954-356-4748. Web Site: www.sun-sentinel.com. *Mgr*, Barbara Hijek; E-Mail: bhijek@sun-sentinel.com; *Tech Servs*, Dean Perry; Staff 12 (MLS 7, Non-MLS 5)
Founded 1940
Library Holdings: Bk Vols 3,000; Bk Titles 2,500; Per Subs 120

FORT MEADE

P FORT MEADE PUBLIC LIBRARY, 75 E Broadway, 33841-2998. SAN 302-9328. Tel: 941-285-8287. FAX: 941-285-9159. Web Site: www.pclc.lib.fl.us. *Librn*, Kareen Jackson; E-Mail: jacksok@pclc.lib.fl.us; *Asst Librn*, Lela Bass; E-Mail: bassl@pclc.lib.fl.us; *Asst Librn*, June Gillis; E-Mail: gillisj@pclc.lib.fl.us
Pop 5,680; Circ 18,583
Oct 1999-Sep 2000 Income $146,862. Mats Exp $27,410. Sal $85,433
Library Holdings: Bk Vols 28,176
Special Collections: Fort Meade History

FORT MYERS

J EDISON COMMUNITY COLLEGE, Lee County Campus Learning Resource Center, 8099 College Pkwy SW Bldg J, 33919. (Mail add: PO Box 60210, 33906-6210), SAN 302-9336. Tel: 941-489-9300. Circulation Tel: 941-489-9220. Reference Tel: 941-489-9279. FAX: 941-489-9095. Web Site: www.edison.edu, www.edison.edu/lr/index.htm. *Dir*, Estrella Iglesia; Tel: 941-489-9219, E-Mail: eiglesia@edison.edu; *Ref*, William Shulak; Staff 3 (MLS 3)
Founded 1962. Enrl 1,644; Fac 95; Highest Degree: Master
Library Holdings: Bk Titles 81,480; Per Subs 400
Publications: User's Brochure
Partic in Dialog Corporation; Florida Library Information Network; SE Libr Network
Open Mon-Thurs 8am-10pm, Fri 8-5, Sat 10-6
Departmental Libraries:
COLLIER COUNTY CAMPUS LEARNING RESOURCE CENTER
See Separate Entry in Naples

S EDISON-FORD WINTER ESTATES LIBRARY, 2350 McGregor Blvd, 33901. SAN 326-0763. Tel: 941-334-7419. FAX: 941-332-6684. Web Site: www.edison-ford-estate.com. *Dir*, Judy K Surprise
Library Holdings: Bk Vols 60
Restriction: By appointment only
Partic in Fla Attraction Asn; SW Fla Asn

C FLORIDA GULF COAST UNIVERSITY LIBRARY, 10501 FGCU Blvd S, 33965-6501. SAN 377-6719. Tel: 941-590-7600. Circulation Tel: 940-590-7610. Reference Tel: 941-590-7610. TDD: 941-590-7618. FAX: 941-590-7609. Web Site: library.fgcu.edu. *Dean of Libr*, Dr Carolyn M Gray; *Assoc Dean*, Kathleen Hoeth; Tel: 941-590-7605, E-Mail: khoeth@fgcu.edu; *Adminr*, Donna Vasquez; Tel: 941-590-7603, E-Mail: devazque@fgcu.edu; *Asst Librn*, Anjana Bhatt; Tel: 941-590-7634, E-Mail: abhatt@fgcu.edu; *Asst Librn*, Chuck Malenfant; Tel: 941-590-7606, E-Mail: cmalenfa@fgcu.edu; *Assoc Librn*, Pamela Sawallis; Tel: 941-590-7633, E-Mail: psawalli@fgcu.edu; *Circ*, John MacLeod; *Syst Coordr*, Georgia Allen; Tel: 941-590-7619, E-Mail: gallen@fgcu.edu; *Acq, Cat, Tech Servs*, Shixing Wen; *Assoc Librn*, Mary Kay Hartung; Tel: 941-590-7651, E-Mail: mhartung@fgcu.edu; *Head, Circ*, Lorrie Evans; Tel: 941-590-7612, E-Mail: levans@fgcu.edu; *Head Tech Servs*, Rebecca Donlan; Tel: 941-590-7602, E-Mail: rdonlan@fgcu.edu; *Head Ref*, Dr Linda Marie Golian; Tel: 941-590-7632, E-Mail: lgolian@fgcu.edu. Subject Specialists: *Arts*, Chuck Malenfant; *Budgeting*, Donna Vasquez; *Business*, Anjana Bhatt; *Education*, Dr Linda Marie Golian; *Health related professions*, Mary Kay Hartung; *History*, Pamela Sawallis; *Humanities*, Pamela Sawallis; *Public admin*, Anjana Bhatt; *Sciences*, Chuck Malenfant; *Social sciences*, Mary Kay Hartung; Staff 28 (MLS 9, Non-MLS 19)
Founded 1997. Enrl 4,000; Fac 166; Highest Degree: Master
Jul 1999-Jun 2000 Income $1,434,127. Sal $1,026,203
Library Holdings: Bk Vols 127,174; Bk Titles 94,564; Per Subs 1,400
Special Collections: Electronic Serial Subscription Coll
Automation Activity & Vendor Info: (Acquisitions) NOTIS; (Cataloging) NOTIS; (Circulation) NOTIS
Database Vendor: Dialog, Ebsco - EbscoHost, GaleNet, IAC - Info Trac, Lexis-Nexis, OCLC - First Search, OVID Technologies, ProQuest, Silverplatter Information Inc.
Partic in Fla Ctr for Libr Automation; Solinet; SW Fla Libr Network
Special Services for the Deaf - TTY machine

GL LEE COUNTY LAW LIBRARY, Lee County Justice Ctr, 1700 Monroe St, 33901. SAN 302-9352. Tel: 941-335-2230. FAX: 941-335-2598. *Librn*, Virginia Groth
Founded 1959
Library Holdings: Bk Vols 17,500

P LEE COUNTY LIBRARY SYSTEM, 2050 Central Ave, 33901-3917. SAN 337-4610. Tel: 941-479-4620. Interlibrary Loan Service Tel: 941-479-4648. FAX: 941-479-4631. Web Site: www.lee-county.com/library/. *Dir*, Cynthia N Cobb; E-Mail: ccobb@leegov.com; *Dep Dir*, Judith Ring; E-Mail: jring@leegov.com; *ILL*, Ann Clark; E-Mail: aclark@leegov.com; *YA Servs*, Marilyn Graham; E-Mail: mgraham@leegov.com; *Publ Servs*, Kathy Toon; E-Mail: ktoon@leegov.com; *Publ Servs*, Thom Cummins; E-Mail: tcummins@leegov.com; *Ref*, Amy Krueger; E-Mail: akrueger@leegov.com. Subject Specialists: *Telephone*, Amy Krueger; Staff 212 (MLS 64, Non-MLS 148)
Founded 1964. Pop 423,873; Circ 6,437,332
Oct 1999-Sep 2000 Income (Main Library and Branch Library) $24,688,925, State $1,000,502, Federal $73,760, County $22,031,234, Locally Generated Income $151,684, Other $1,431,745. Mats Exp $2,294,556, Books $1,870,651, Per/Ser (Incl. Access Fees) $212,247, Micro $9,065, AV Equip $9,614, Electronic Ref Mat (Incl. Access Fees) $192,979. Sal $6,090,065 (Prof $1,955,647)
Library Holdings: Bk Vols 915,199; Bk Titles 218,606; Per Subs 2,562; High Interest/Low Vocabulary Bk Vols 3,449; Bks on Deafness & Sign Lang 73
Special Services for the Deaf - TTY machine
Open Mon-Fri 8-5
Friends of the Library Group
Branches: 14
BONITA SPRINGS PUBLIC, 26876 Pine Ave, Bonita Springs, 34135-5000. SAN 302-8631. Tel: 941-992-0101, 941-992-2118, 941-992-7457. FAX: 941-992-6680. *Librn*, Maureen Pollack; E-Mail: mpollack@leegov.com; Staff 12 (MLS 2, Non-MLS 10)
Library Holdings: Bk Vols 67,786
Special Services for the Deaf - TTY machine
Open Mon, Wed & Fri 10-6, Tues & Thurs 10-8, Sat 9-5
Friends of the Library Group
BOOKS-BY-MAIL-BOOKMOBILE, 21100 Three Oaks Pkwy, Estero, 33928. SAN 374-406X. Tel: 941-390-3234. Toll Free Tel: 800-660-6420. TDD: 941-498-6425. FAX: 941-498-6424. *Access Serv*, Kathy Mayo; E-Mail: kmayo@leegov.com; Staff 4 (MLS 1, Non-MLS 3)
Library Holdings: Bk Vols 21,353
Publications: Books-By-Mail (Newsletter); The Mailbag
Special Services for the Deaf - TTY machine
Office open Mon-Fri 8:30-5
CAPE CORAL-LEE COUNTY PUBLIC, 921 SW 39th Terrace, Cape Coral, 33914-5721. SAN 337-467X. Tel: 941-542-3953, 941-549-1868. FAX: 941-542-2711. *Regional Librarian*, Anne M Shepherd; E-Mail: ashepher@leegov.com; Staff 24 (MLS 7, Non-MLS 17)
Library Holdings: Bk Vols 156,711
Special Services for the Deaf - TTY machine
Open Mon-Thurs 9-9, Fri & Sat 9-6
Friends of the Library Group
CAPTIVA MEMORIAL, 11560 Chapin Lane, PO Box 99, Captiva, 33924-0099. SAN 302-8801. Tel: 941-472-2133. FAX: 941-472-0272. *Librn*, Carolyn McKinney; Staff 2 (MLS 1, Non-MLS 1)
Library Holdings: Bk Vols 27,180
Special Services for the Deaf - TTY machine
Open Tues, Thurs, Fri & Sat 9-5, Wed 12-8, closed Mon
Friends of the Library Group
DUNBAR JUPITER HAMMON LIBRARY, 3095 Blount St, 33916-2032. SAN 337-4734. Tel: 941-334-3602, 941-334-7341. FAX: 941-334-7940. *Librn*, Fred Smiley; E-Mail: fsmiley@leegov.com; Staff 7 (MLS 1, Non-MLS 6)
Library Holdings: Bk Vols 38,108
Special Services for the Deaf - TTY machine
Open Tues & Thurs 12-8, Wed & Fri 10-6 & Sat 9-5
Friends of the Library Group
EAST COUNTY REGIONAL, 811 Gunnery Rd, Lehigh Acres, 33971. *Mgr*, Leta Hamm; *Head Ref*, Linda Precoda; *YA Servs*, Bonnie Ward; Staff 6 (MLS 6)
FORT MYERS-LEE COUNTY PUBLIC, 2050 Central Ave, 33901-3917. SAN 302-9344. Tel: 941-479-4635. Interlibrary Loan Service Tel: 941-479-4648. FAX: 941-479-4634. *Mgr Libr Serv*, Daria A Parry; Tel: 941-479-4632, E-Mail: dparry@leegov.com; Staff 32 (MLS 10, Non-MLS 22)
Library Holdings: Bk Vols 140,447
Special Services for the Deaf - TTY machine
Open Mon-Thurs 9-9, Fri & Sat 9-6
NORTH FORT MYERS PUBLIC, 2001 N Tamiami Trail NE, North Fort Myers, 33903-2802. SAN 337-4823. Tel: 941-997-0320. FAX: 941-656-7949. *Librn*, Sharon Myers; E-Mail: smyers@leegov.com; Staff 13 (MLS 3, Non-MLS 10)
Library Holdings: Bk Vols 65,658
Special Services for the Deaf - TTY machine
Open Mon, Wed & Fri 10-6, Tues & Thurs 10-8 & Sat 9-5
Friends of the Library Group
PINE ISLAND, 10700 Russell Rd NW, Bokeelia, 33922-3110. SAN 337-4858. Tel: 941-283-1154, 941-461-3188. FAX: 941-283-7711. *Librn*, Mike Dinkins; E-Mail: mdinkins@leegov.com; Staff 6 (MLS 1, Non-MLS 5)
Library Holdings: Bk Vols 39,368
Special Services for the Deaf - TTY machine
Open Tues, Thurs & Fri 10-6, Wed 12-8 & Sat 9-5
Friends of the Library Group
PROCESSING CENTER, 11220-6 Metro Pkwy, 33912-1246. SAN 372-0217. Tel: 941-277-5025. FAX: 941-277-5034. *Tech Servs*, Connie Haley; E-Mail: chaley@leegov.com; *Acq*, Diane Millott; *Coll Develop, YA Servs*, Diane Lettieri; E-Mail: dlellier@leegov.com; *Ad Servs, Coll Develop*, Sally Jane; E-Mail: sjane@leegov.com; *Automation Syst Coordr*, Mindi Simon; E-Mail: msimon@leegov.com; Staff 20 (MLS 6, Non-MLS 14)
Subject Interests: Florida, Genealogy
Automation Activity & Vendor Info: (Acquisitions) epixtech, inc.; (Cataloging) epixtech, inc.; (Circulation) epixtech, inc.; (OPAC) epixtech, inc.; (Serials) epixtech, inc.
Database Vendor: epixtech, inc., OCLC - First Search

Open Mon-Fri 7:30-5:30
RIVERDALE, 14561 State Rd 80, 33905-2345. SAN 372-0225. Tel: 941-461-3130. FAX: 941-694-6146. *Librn*, Sharon Hamman-Monaghan; E-Mail: shamman@leegov.com; Staff 7 (MLS 1, Non-MLS 6)
Library Holdings: Bk Vols 47,008
Special Services for the Deaf - TTY machine
Open Tues & Thurs 12-8, Wed & Fri 10-6, Sat 9-5, closed Mon
Friends of the Library Group
RUTENBERG, 6490 South Pointe Blvd, 33919-4954. SAN 372-0233. Tel: 941-433-5900. FAX: 941-433-3630. *Librn*, Lesa Holstine; E-Mail: lholstin@leegov.com; Staff 15 (MLS 3, Non-MLS 12)
Library Holdings: Bk Vols 70,714
Special Services for the Deaf - TTY machine
Open Mon, Wed & Fri 10-6, Tues & Thurs 10-8 & Sat 9-5
Friends of the Library Group
SOUTH COUNTY REGIONAL, 21100 Three Oaks Pkwy, Estero, 33928-3020. SAN 376-9453. Tel: 941-390-3200. Toll Free Tel: 800-660-6420. FAX: 941-498-6424. *Regional Librarian*, Linda Holland; E-Mail: lholland@leegov.com; Staff 22 (MLS 7, Non-MLS 15)
Library Holdings: Bk Vols 152,917
Partic in Southwest Florida Library Network
Special Services for the Deaf - TTY machine
Open Mon-Thurs 9-9, Fri & Sat 9-6
TALKING BOOKS, 13240 N Cleveland Ave, North Fort Myers, 33903-4855. SAN 372-0241. Tel: 941-995-2665. Toll Free Tel: 800-854-8195. FAX: 941-995-1681. *Librn*, Ann Bradley; E-Mail: abradley@leegov.com; Staff 4 (MLS 1, Non-MLS 3)
Library Holdings: Bk Vols 152
Special Services for the Deaf - TTY machine
Open Mon-Fri 8:30-5
Bookmobiles: 1. Vols 17,890

§M LEE MEMORIAL HEALTH SYSTEM LIBRARY, PO Box 2218, 33902-2218. Tel: 941-334-5410. FAX: 941-332-6422. *Librn*, Narges Ahmadi; E-Mail: narges.ahmadi@leememorial.org
Library Holdings: Bk Vols 30,000; Per Subs 200

§C SOUTHWEST FLORIDA COLLEGE, Library Resource Center, 1685 Medical Lane, 33907. Tel: 941-939-4766. FAX: 941-936-4040. *Dir*, Mary Faulkner; E-Mail: mfaulkner@swfc.edu
Library Holdings: Bk Vols 2,500; Per Subs 35
Automation Activity & Vendor Info: (Acquisitions) Endeavor; (Cataloging) Endeavor; (Circulation) Endeavor; (Serials) Endeavor

FORT MYERS BEACH

P FORT MYERS BEACH PUBLIC LIBRARY, 2755 Estero Blvd, 33931. SAN 302-9379. Tel: 941-463-9691. FAX: 941-463-8776. Web Site: www.fmb.lib.fl.us. *Dir*, Leroy Hommerding; E-Mail: lreoyh@fmb.lib.fl.us; *Cat*, Michael John Lukow, Jr; *Ref*, Linda Tafel; Staff 3 (MLS 3)
Founded 1955. Pop 12,900; Circ 99,200
Oct 1999-Sep 2000 Income $723,168, State $10,000, County $678,146, Locally Generated Income $35,022. Mats Exp $108,688, Books $89,000, Per/Ser (Incl. Access Fees) $9,688, AV Equip $10,000. Sal $247,229 (Prof $110,000)
Library Holdings: Bk Vols 89,090; Per Subs 142
Automation Activity & Vendor Info: (Cataloging) TLC
Partic in SWFLN
Open Mon & Wed 9-8, Tues, Thurs & Fri 9-5, Sat 9-1
Friends of the Library Group

FORT PIERCE

S HARBOR BRANCH OCEANOGRAPHIC INSTITUTION, INC LIBRARY, 5600 US 1 N, 34946. SAN 302-9387. Tel: 561-465-2400, Ext 201. FAX: 561-465-2446. Web Site: www.hboi.edu. *Librn*, Kristen L Metzger; E-Mail: metzger@hboi.edu; Staff 1 (MLS 1)
Founded 1975
Jan 2000-Dec 2000 Income $325,000. Mats Exp $245,000. Sal $80,000
Library Holdings: Bk Titles 6,000; Per Subs 230
Subject Interests: Botany, Chemistry, Ecology, Engineering, Marine biology, Oceanography, Pollution
Publications: Acquisitions list; publications list
Partic in Dialog Corporation; OCLC Online Computer Library Center, Inc

J INDIAN RIVER COMMUNITY COLLEGE, Charles S Miley Learning Resources Center, 3209 Virginia Ave, 34981-5599. SAN 302-9395. Tel: 561-462-4757. FAX: 561-462-4780. Web Site: www.ircc.cc.fl.us/. *Asst Dean*, Rudolph P Widman; E-Mail: rwidman@ircc.cc.fl.us; *Head Librn*, Pat Profeta; *Ref*, Ru Wang; *Spec Coll*, Linda Smith; *Tech Servs*, Francenia Mimms; Staff 3 (MLS 3)
Founded 1960. Fac 132
Library Holdings: Bk Vols 68,000; Per Subs 442
Special Collections: Area Historical Coll; Florida Power & Light Coll
Database Vendor: DRA
Publications: Electronic Access to Information
Partic in OCLC Online Computer Library Center, Inc; SE Libr Network
Open Mon-Thurs 7:45-9, Fri 7:45-5 & Sun 1-5

G SAINT LUCIE COUNTY HISTORICAL MUSEUM, Research Library, 414 Seaway Dr, 34949. SAN 327-3113. Tel: 561-462-1795. FAX: 561-462-1877. *In Charge*, DeeDee Roberts
Library Holdings: Bk Vols 2,500; Per Subs 13

L SAINT LUCIE COUNTY LAW LIBRARY, 218 S Second St, Rm 102, 34950. SAN 302-9409. Tel: 561-462-2370. FAX: 561-462-2145. *Librn*, Beverly Klemenc
Library Holdings: Bk Vols 15,000

P SAINT LUCIE COUNTY LIBRARY SYSTEM, 101 Melody Lane, 34950-4402. SAN 337-4912. Tel: 561-462-1615. TDD: 561-462-1428. FAX: 561-462-2750. Web Site: www.st-lucie.fl.lib.fl.us. *Dir*, Susan Kilmer; E-Mail: susank@stlucieco.gov; *Asst Dir*, Dr Edward Werner; Tel: 561-462-1802, E-Mail: ewerner@stlubieco.gov; *Acq, ILL*, Lisa O'Neil; Tel: 561-462-1964, E-Mail: lisao@stlucieco.gov; *Ch Servs*, Gicele Perna; Tel: 561-462-2812, E-Mail: gicele@stlucieco.gov; *Publ Servs*, Marilyn Mittleman; Tel: 561-462-1607, E-Mail: marilynn@stlucieco.gov; *Ref*, John Byrn; Tel: 561-462-2189, Fax: 561-462-1803, E-Mail: jbyrn@stlucieco.gov; Staff 12 (MLS 12)
Founded 1953. Pop 172,000; Circ 755,307
Oct 1998-Sep 1999 Income (Main Library and Branch Library) $3,495,163, State $268,295, Federal $250,000, County $2,940,232, Other $36,636. Mats Exp $485,959. Sal $1,865,235
Library Holdings: Bk Vols 309,000; Bk Titles 171,000; Per Subs 998
Subject Interests: Business and management, Genealogy, Local history, Social sciences and issues
Special Collections: Black History; Florida Coll, bks; Local History
Automation Activity & Vendor Info: (Acquisitions) SIRSI; (Circulation) SIRSI; (OPAC) SIRSI
Partic in Central Florida Library Cooperative (CFLC)
Friends of the Library Group
Branches: 4
ZORA NEALE HURSTON BRANCH, 3008 Avenue D, 34947. SAN 328-6398. Tel: 561-462-2154. FAX: 561-462-2844. Web Site: www.st-lucie.lib.fl.us. *Br Coordr*, Sandra Gebert; E-Mail: sandrag@stlucieco.gov
Founded 1991
1999-1999 Mats Exp $55,000, Books $45,000, Per/Ser (Incl. Access Fees) $10,000
Special Collections: Zora Neale Hurston Coll
Automation Activity & Vendor Info: (Circulation) SIRSI; (OPAC) SIRSI
Partic in Central Florida Library Cooperative (CFLC)
LAKEWOOD PARK, 7605 Santa Barbara Dr, 34951. SAN 322-6239. Tel: 561-462-6870. TDD: 561-462-1428. FAX: 561-462-6874. Web Site: www.st-lucie.lib.fl.us/lwp.htm. *Branch Mgr*, Carol Shroyer; Staff 7 (MLS 1, Non-MLS 6)
MORNINGSIDE BRANCH, 2410 Morningside Blvd, Port Saint Lucie, 34952. SAN 372-7904. Tel: 561-337-5632. FAX: 561-337-5631. Web Site: www.st-lucie.lib.fl.us. *Branch Mgr*, Margery Rennison; Staff 3 (MLS 1, Non-MLS 2)
Founded 1993
1999-2000 Mats Exp $65,000, Books $55,000, Per/Ser (Incl. Access Fees) $10,000
Automation Activity & Vendor Info: (Circulation) SIRSI; (ILL) SIRSI; (OPAC) SIRSI
Partic in Central Florida Library Cooperative (CFLC)
PORT SAINT LUCIE BRANCH, 180 SW Prima Vista Blvd, Port Saint Lucie, 34983. SAN 337-4947. Tel: 561-871-5450. FAX: 561-871-5454. Web Site: www.st-lucie.lib.fl.us. *Branch Mgr*, Karen Marlin; E-Mail: karenm@stlucieco.gov
Founded 1970 Mats Exp $41,500, Books $35,000, Per/Ser (Incl. Access Fees) $6,500
Automation Activity & Vendor Info: (Circulation) SIRSI; (OPAC) SIRSI
Partic in Central Florida Library Cooperative (CFLC)
Bookmobiles: 1

G UNITED STATES DEPARTMENT OF AGRICULTURE, Agricultural Research Service, Horticultural Research Laboratory Library, 2001 S Rock Rd, 34945. SAN 303-108X. Tel: 561-462-5800. FAX: 561-462-5986. *Dir*, Calvin E Arnold; *Librn*, Lorraine Sonoda; Tel: 561-462-5801
Founded 1970
Library Holdings: Bk Titles 1,500
Subject Interests: Biochemistry, Marketing
Special Collections: Citrus, bks & reprints

C UNIVERSITY OF FLORIDA, IFAS Indian River Research & Education Center, 2199 S Rock Rd, 34945. SAN 325-3503. Tel: 561-468-3922. FAX: 561-468-5668. E-Mail: cea@gnv.ifas.ufl.edu. Web Site: www.irrec.ifas.wfl.edu. *Dir*, Dr Calvin Arnold; *Librn*, Laura McKeon
Founded 1960
Library Holdings: Bk Vols 525; Bk Titles 500; Per Subs 20

FORT WALTON BEACH

P FORT WALTON BEACH LIBRARY, 105 Miracle Strip Pkwy SW, 32548-6614. SAN 302-9417. Tel: 850-833-9590. FAX: 850-833-9594. E-Mail: fwblibr@fwb.org. Web Site: www.fwb.org. *Dir*, Carol J Hill; *Asst Librn*, Renita Looze; *Asst Librn*, Patricia Miller; *Asst Librn*, Kathleen Dawson; *Asst Librn*, Mary Ellen Ricks; *Asst Librn*, Stephanie Galipeau; *Asst Librn*, Jackie Whitegon; *Ad Servs*, Valerie Phillips; *Ch Servs*, Rosemary McCown; Staff 9 (MLS 2, Non-MLS 7)
Founded 1954. Pop 30,500; Circ 105,204
Oct 1999-Sep 2000 Income City $310,687. Mats Exp $50,000, Books $40,000, Per/Ser (Incl. Access Fees) $7,000, Micro $1,000, Other Print Mats $2,000. Sal $221,100 (Prof $35,000)
Library Holdings: Bk Vols 47,560; Per Subs 184
Friends of the Library Group

S INDIAN TEMPLE MOUND MUSEUM LIBRARY, 139 Miracle Strip Pkwy, 32548. (Mail add: PO Box 4009, 32549), SAN 373-0417. Tel: 850-833-9595. FAX: 850-833-9675. Web Site: www.fwb.org. *Dir*, Anna Peele; *Coordr*, Gail Meyer
Founded 1970
Library Holdings: Bk Vols 2,500; Per Subs 25
Subject Interests: Archaeology, Local history, Native Americans
Restriction: Not a lending library

FROSTPROOF

P LATT MAXCY MEMORIAL LIBRARY, 15 N Magnolia Ave, 33843. SAN 329-143X. Tel: 863-635-7857. FAX: 863-635-8502. Web Site: www.pclc.lib.fl.us/frostproof.html. *Dir*, Melissa Dawn Hadden; E-Mail: haddenm@pclc.lib.fl.us; *Tech Servs*, Ellis Karen Conley-Hollis; E-Mail: hollisk@pclc.lib.fl.us; *Circ*, Angela Dawn Galati; E-Mail: galatia@pclc.lib.fl.us; *Circ*, Shirley Ann Richardson; E-Mail: richars@pclc.lib.fl.us; Staff 4 (Non-MLS 4)
Founded 1922. Pop 2,800; Circ 38,217
Library Holdings: Bk Vols 35,478; Bk Titles 30,418; Per Subs 41
Special Collections: Florida Coll, large print bks; Spanish Coll, vertical file
Automation Activity & Vendor Info: (Cataloging) TLC
Database Vendor: Ebsco - EbscoHost
Function: ILL available
Partic in Polk County Libr Coop; Tampa Bay Library Consortium, Inc
Special Services for the Deaf - Books on deafness & sign language
Special Services for the Blind - Bks on tape
Friends of the Library Group

FRUITLAND PARK

P FRUITLAND PARK LIBRARY, 205 W Berckman St, 34731. (Mail add: 506 W Berckman St, 34731), SAN 302-9433. Tel: 352-728-3387. FAX: 352-728-1612. Web Site: www.lakeline.lib.fl.us. *Dir*, Maria Schofield; E-Mail: mschofie@lakeline.lib.fl.us; Staff 5 (Non-MLS 5)
Founded 1936
Library Holdings: Bk Vols 21,787
Mem of Lake County Library System
Friends of the Library Group

FT LAUDERDALE

C CITY COLLEGE LIBRARY - FT LAUDERDALE, 1401 W Cypress Creek Rd, 33309. Tel: 954-492-5353, Ext 39. FAX: 954-491-1965. Web Site: www.citycollege.edu. *Dir*, Nancy Wynen
Library Holdings: Bk Titles 7,000; Per Subs 70

GAINESVILLE

S ALACHUA COUNTY HISTORIC TRUST - MATHESON MUSEUM, INC LIBRARY, 513 E University Ave, 32601. SAN 377-8185. Tel: 352-378-2280. FAX: 352-378-1246. E-Mail: mathesonmuseum@usa.net. *Dir*, Lisa Auel; Staff 1 (MLS 1)
Founded 1994
Jan 2000-Dec 2000 Income $4,000, Parent Institution $2,000, Other $2,000. Mats Exp $4,000, Books $1,500, Per/Ser (Incl. Access Fees) $500
Library Holdings: Bk Titles 2,900; Per Subs 40
Special Collections: Bone Photo Coll; Florida Postcard Coll; Florida Scenes; Stereocard Coll
Restriction: Not a lending library

P ALACHUA COUNTY LIBRARY DISTRICT HEADQUARTERS, 401 E University Ave, 32601. SAN 337-503X. Tel: 352-334-3900. Circulation Tel: 352-334-3950. Reference Tel: 352-334-3934. TDD: 352-334-3904. FAX: 352-334-3918. Web Site: www.acld.lib.fl.us. *Dir*, Ann W Williams; Tel: 352-334-3910, E-Mail: awilliams@exchange.acld.lib.fl.us; *Asst Dir*, Sharon Jackson; E-Mail: sjackson@exchange.acld.lib.fl.us; *Head Librn*, Linda K Boyles; E-Mail: lboyles@exchange.acld.lib.fl.us; *Head Tech Servs*, Linda Gardner; E-Mail: lgardner@exchange.acld.lib.fl.us; *Automation Syst Coordr*, Bruce Stewart; E-Mail: bstewart@exchange.acld.lib.fl.us; *Br Coordr*, Carol Hole; E-Mail: chole@exchange.acld.lib.fl.us; *Ad Servs*, Nance Lempinen-Leedy; E-Mail: nleedy@exchange.acld.lib.fl.us; *Circ*, Phillis Filer; E-Mail: pfiler@exchange.acld.lib.fl.us; *YA Servs*, Roseanne Russo; E-Mail: rrusso@exchange.acld.lib.fl.us; *Tech Servs*, Shu-Min Hsieh; E-Mail: shsieh@exchange.acld.lib.fl.us; Staff 155 (MLS 40, Non-MLS 115)
Founded 1906. Pop 211,403; Circ 2,198,104
Oct 1999-Sep 2000 Income (Main Library and Branch Library) $8,705,869, State $714,002, County $7,550,457, Locally Generated Income $406,792, Other $34,618. Mats Exp $1,533,031, Books $710,803, Per/Ser (Incl. Access Fees) $301,876, Presv $2,164, Micro $16,117, AV Equip $374,056, Electronic Ref Mat (Incl. Access Fees) $128,015. Sal $4,916,477 (Prof $2,114,085)
Library Holdings: Bk Vols 688,884; Bk Titles 194,685; Per Subs 1,012; High Interest/Low Vocabulary Bk Vols 1,767; Bks on Deafness & Sign Lang 905
Subject Interests: Genealogy, Local history
Special Collections: Genealogy Local History (Alachua County/Gainesville), a-tapes, index to local newsp mss, maps, pamphlets, photog & v-tapes; local government documents (Gainesville Alachua County, North Central Florida), bd doc, microfilm & minutes
Automation Activity & Vendor Info: (Acquisitions) SIRSI; (Cataloging) SIRSI; (Circulation) SIRSI; (ILL) SIRSI; (OPAC) SIRSI; (Serials) SIRSI
Database Vendor: GaleNet, IAC - Info Trac, OCLC - First Search, ProQuest
Partic in NE Fla Libr Info Network; SE Libr Network
Special Services for the Deaf - TDD
Special Services for the Blind - Braille; Large print bks; Talking Books
Friends of the Library Group
Branches: 10
ALACHUA BRANCH, 14913 NW 140 St, Alachua, 32615-0550. SAN 337-5048. Tel: 904-462-2592. Reference Tel: 352-334-3934. FAX: 904-462-5537. Web Site: www.acld.lib.fl.us. *Branch Mgr*, Caryl McKellar; E-Mail: cmckellar@exchange.acld.lib.fl.us
Friends of the Library Group
ALACHUA COUNTY CORRECTIONS CENTER, 3333 NE 39th Ave, 32609. SAN 328-9672. Tel: 352-491-4540. FAX: 352-376-5365. Web Site: www.acld.lib.fl.us. *Librn*, Michael Nassau; E-Mail: mnassau@exchange.acld.lib.fl.us
Friends of the Library Group
ARCHER BRANCH, 204 N University Ave, Archer, 32618. SAN 373-5680. Tel: 352-495-3367. Reference Tel: 352-334-3934. FAX: 352-495-3061. Web Site: www.acld.lib.fl.us. *Branch Mgr*, Guy Hudspeth; E-Mail: ghudspeth@exchange.acld.lib.fl.us
Friends of the Library Group
HAWTHORNE BRANCH, 104 N Johnson St, Hawthorne, 32640-1087. SAN 337-5064. Tel: 352-481-1920. Reference Tel: 352-334-3934. FAX: 352-334-1921. Web Site: www.acld.lib.fl.us. *Branch Mgr*, Memree Stuart; E-Mail: mstuart@exchange.acld.lib.fl.us
Friends of the Library Group
HIGH SPRINGS BRANCH, 135 NW First Ave, High Springs, 32655. (Mail add: PO Box 808, High Springs, 32655), SAN 337-5099. Tel: 904-454-2515. Reference Tel: 352-334-3934. FAX: 904-454-3439. Web Site: www.acld.lib.fl.us. *Branch Mgr*, Martha Roberts; E-Mail: mroberts@exchange.acld.lib.fl.us
Friends of the Library Group
MICANOPY BRANCH, 706 Cholokka Blvd, Micanopy, 32667. (Mail add: PO Box 200, Micanopy, 32667), SAN 337-5129. Tel: 352-466-3122. Reference Tel: 352-334-3934. FAX: 352-466-3124. Web Site: www.acld.lib.fl.us. *Branch Mgr*, Michael Kemp; E-Mail: mkemp@exchange.acld.lib.fl.us
Friends of the Library Group
MILLHOPPER BRANCH, 3145 NW 43rd St, 32606. SAN 373-5664. Tel: 352-334-1272. Reference Tel: 352-334-3934. FAX: 352-334-1280. Web Site: www.acld.lib.fl.us. *Branch Mgr*, Linda Luke; E-Mail: lluke@exchange.acld.lib.fl.us
Friends of the Library Group
NEWBERRY BRANCH, 110 S Seaboard Dr, Newberry, 32669-1288. SAN 373-5699. Tel: 352-472-1135. Reference Tel: 352-334-3934. FAX: 352-334-1136. Web Site: www.acld.lib.fl.us. *Branch Mgr*, Susan Morton; E-Mail: smorton@exchnage.acld.lib.fl.us
Friends of the Library Group
TOWER ROAD BRANCH, 3020 SW 75th St, 32607. SAN 373-5672. Tel: 352-333-2840. Reference Tel: 352-334-3934. FAX: 352-333-2846. Web Site: www.acld.lib.fl.us. *Branch Mgr*, Ike Welch; E-Mail: iwelch@exchange.acld.lib.fl.us
Friends of the Library Group
WALDO BRANCH, 150 SW Second Pl, Waldo, 32694. SAN 376-9178. Tel: 352-468-3298. Reference Tel: 352-334-3934. FAX: 352-468-3299. Web Site: www.acld.lib.fl.us. *Branch Mgr*, Michael Kemp; E-Mail: mkemp@exchange.acld.lib.fl.us
Friends of the Library Group
Bookmobiles: 1

S BIENTCO, INC LIBRARY, 5819 NW 57th Way, 32653-3257. SAN 306-8439. Tel: 352-373-7384. FAX: 352-377-4030. *Librn*, Dr Eugene J Gerberg
Founded 1946
Library Holdings: Bk Titles 3,000; Per Subs 35
Subject Interests: Biology, Entomology, Public health

S CH2M HILL, Technical Library, 3011 SW Williston Rd, PO Drawer 147009, 32614-7009. SAN 302-9441. Tel: 352-335-7991, Ext 225. FAX: 352-335-2959.
Founded 1968
Library Holdings: Bk Titles 6,200; Per Subs 100
Subject Interests: Energy, Industrial wastes, Water resources

M CENTER FOR APPLICATIONS OF PSYCHOLOGICAL TYPE, Isabel Briggs Myers Memorial Library, 2815 NW 13th St, Ste 401, 32609. SAN 325-1683. Tel: 352-375-0160. FAX: 352-378-0503. E-Mail: library@capt.org. Web Site: www.capt.org. *Librn*, Jamelyn R Johnson; E-Mail: jamie@capt.org
Founded 1976
Library Holdings: Bk Titles 2,750; Per Subs 10
Subject Interests: Jungian psychol

§J CITY COLLEGE - GAINSVILLE LIBRARY, 2400 SW 13th St, 32608. Tel: 352-335-4000, Ext 29. FAX: 352-335-4303. *Librn*, Tina Worthen; E-Mail: tworthen@citycollege.edu
Library Holdings: Bk Vols 6,600; Per Subs 45

R FIRST BAPTIST CHURCH LIBRARY, 425 W University Ave, 32601. SAN 302-9468. Tel: 352-376-4681. FAX: 352-374-7269. *Librn*, Carol Tu; Staff 4 (MLS 1, Non-MLS 3)
Founded 1953
Library Holdings: Bk Titles 9,000
Subject Interests: Children's literature, Christianity, Fiction, Parenting, Psychology, Religion
Special Collections: Archives of Church
Publications: AV Catalog of Holdings

FIRST UNITED METHODIST CHURCH

R EPWORTH LIBRARY, 419 NE First St, 32601. SAN 302-9476. Tel: 352-372-8523. FAX: 352-372-2524.
Founded 1950
Library Holdings: Bk Vols 3,250
Subject Interests: Theology

R LAURA KNIGHT CHILDREN'S LIBRARY, 419 NE First St, 32601. SAN 320-9628. Tel: 352-372-8523. FAX: 352-372-2524.
Founded 1978
Library Holdings: Bk Vols 630

G FLORIDA DEPARTMENT OF AGRICULTURE & CONSUMER SERVICES, Division of Plant Industry Library, 1911 SW 34th St, 32608. (Mail add: PO Box 147100, 32614-7100), SAN 302-9484. Tel: 352-372-3505, Ext 131. FAX: 352-955-2301. Web Site: www.neslin.org/dpi. *Librn*, Beverly Pope; E-Mail: dpilib@doacs.state.fl.us; *Asst Librn*, Alice Sanders
Founded 1915
Library Holdings: Bk Titles 17,000; Per Subs 590
Subject Interests: Entomology
Automation Activity & Vendor Info: (Cataloging) NOTIS

S GAINESVILLE CORRECTIONAL INSTITUTION LIBRARY, 2845 NE 39th Ave, 32609. SAN 377-2322. Tel: 352-955-2001, Ext 131. FAX: 352-334-1675. *Head Librn*, Elma Hernderson
Library Holdings: Bk Vols 6,000; Bk Titles 40

GM GAINESVILLE VA MEDICAL CENTER LIBRARY, Alachua VA Medical Center, 1601 SW Archer Rd, 32608-1197. SAN 302-9506. Tel: 352-376-1611, Ext 6313. FAX: 352-374-6148. *Chief Librn*, Marylyn Gresser; *Asst Librn*, Marsha White
Founded 1967
Library Holdings: Bk Titles 7,000; Per Subs 350
Restriction: Staff use only
Partic in Vets Admin Libr Network

M NORTH FLORIDA EVALUATION & TREATMENT CENTER LIBRARY, 1200 NE 55th Blvd, 32641. SAN 377-3752. Tel: 352-375-8484. FAX: 352-334-1610. *Librn*, Errol Campbell; E-Mail: errol_campbell@def.state.fl.us
Library Holdings: Bk Vols 8,000; Bk Titles 6,000; Per Subs 55

J SANTA FE COMMUNITY COLLEGE LIBRARY, 3000 NW 83rd St, 32606. SAN 337-4971. Tel: 352-395-5406. Interlibrary Loan Service Tel: 352-395-5771. Reference Tel: 352-395-5397. FAX: 352-395-5102. E-Mail: library@santafe.cc.fl.us. Web Site: www.cisit.santafe.cc.fl.us. *Dir Libr Serv*, Joanne Laipply; Tel: 352-395-5150, E-Mail: joanne.laipply@santafe.cc.fl.us; *Coordr*, Sherry Dupree; Tel: 352-395-5407, E-Mail: sherry.dupree@santafe.cc.fl.us; *Ref*, Kim Hankins; Tel: 352-395-5415; *Ref*, June Littler; *Ref*, Mary McCarty; E-Mail: mary.mccarty@santafe.cc.fl.us; *Ref*, Karen Moore; E-Mail: karen.moore@santafe.cc.fl.us; *Syst Coordr*, Lori Driscoll; E-Mail: lori.driscoll@santafe.cc.fl.us; *Head, Circ*, Debbie Kennedy; Tel: 352-395-5411, E-Mail: debbie.kennedy@santafe.cc.fl.us; *Ref Serv*, Ramona Miller; Tel: 352-381-3637, E-Mail: ramona.miller@santafe.cc.fl.us; *ILL, Ser*, Trenita White; E-Mail: trenita.white@santafe.cc.fl.us; Staff 15 (MLS 7, Non-MLS 8)
Founded 1966. Enrl 12,000; Fac 300; Highest Degree: Associate
Jul 1998-Jun 1999 Income $786,003. Mats Exp $133,000, Books $70,000, Per/Ser (Incl. Access Fees) $63,000. Sal $547,000 (Prof $322,385)
Library Holdings: Bk Vols 89,029; Per Subs 550
Automation Activity & Vendor Info: (Cataloging) DRA; (Circulation) DRA; (Course Reserve) DRA; (ILL) DRA; (OPAC) DRA; (Serials) DRA
Database Vendor: DRA, Ebsco - EbscoHost, GaleNet, OCLC - First Search, ProQuest
Publications: Handbook
Partic in Col Ctr for Libr Automation; FLIN; NEFLIN; Solinet

C UNIVERSITY OF FLORIDA LIBRARIES, George A Smathers Libraries, Library West, PO Box 117001, 32611-7001. SAN 337-5153. Tel: 352-392-0361. Interlibrary Loan Service Tel: 352-392-0311. FAX: 352-392-7251. Interlibrary Loan Service FAX: 352-392-7598. Web Site: www.uflib.ufl.edu/. *Dir*, Dale B Canelas; Tel: 352-392-0342, E-Mail: dcanelas@mail.uflib.ufl.edu; *Publ Servs*, Carol Turner; Tel: 352-392-0342, E-Mail: carturn@mail.uflib.ufl.edu; *Tech Servs*, Martha Hruska; Tel: 352-392-0342, E-Mail: mhruska@mail.uflib.ufl.edu; *ILL*, David Hickey; Tel: 352-392-0345, Fax: 352-392-6540, E-Mail: dhickey@mail.uflib.ufl.edu; *Res*, Dot Hope; Tel: 352-392-0355, Fax: 352-392-4788, E-Mail: dothope@mail.uflib.ufl.edu; *Govt Doc*, Jan Swanbeck; Tel: 352-392-0366, E-Mail: janswan@mail.uflib.ufl.edu; *Spec Coll*, John Ingram; Tel: 352-932-6547', Fax: 352-846-6547, E-Mail: jeingr@mail.uflib.ufl.edu; *Coll Develop*, Frank Di Trolio; Tel: 352-392-4919, E-Mail: frandit@mail.uflib.ufl.edu; *Syst Coordr*, William Covey; Tel: 352-392-0796, Fax: 352-392-2354, E-Mail: wcovey@mail.uflib.ufl.edu; *Librn*, Erich Kesse; Tel: 352-846-0129, Fax: 352-846-3702, E-Mail: erich@mail.uflib.ufl.edu; *Music*, Robena Cornwell; Tel: 352-392-6678, E-Mail: robcorn@mail.uflib.ufl.edu; Staff 316 (MLS 101, Non-MLS 215)
Founded 1853. Enrl 42,000; Fac 4,572; Highest Degree: Doctorate
Jun 1998-Jun 1999 Income State $21,432,347. Mats Exp $14,496,314, Books $2,044,623, Per/Ser (Incl. Access Fees) $4,923,941, Presv $63,153, Micro $6,302,371, AV Equip $23,366, Other Print Mats $1,130,695, Manuscripts & Archives $8,165. Sal $9,703,854 (Prof $4,881,826)
Library Holdings: Bk Vols 3,565,879; Per Subs 28,547
Subject Interests: Africana, Archives, Judaica, Latin American, Rare books
Special Collections: Baldwin-Children; Belknap-Performing Arts
Automation Activity & Vendor Info: (Acquisitions) NOTIS; (Cataloging) NOTIS; (Circulation) NOTIS; (Serials) NOTIS
Database Vendor: Dialog, Ebsco - EbscoHost, GaleNet, IAC - Info Trac, IAC - SearchBank, Innovative Interfaces INN - View, Lexis-Nexis, OCLC - First Search, OVID Technologies, ProQuest, Silverplatter Information Inc., Wilson - Wilson Web
Publications: Chapter One; Library News
Function: Research library
Mem of Cent Fla Regional Libr
Partic in SE Libr Network; SPARC
Departmental Libraries:
ARCHITECTURE & FINE ARTS, PO Box 117017, 32611. SAN 337-5218. Tel: 352-392-0222, 352-392-0361. Interlibrary Loan Service Tel: 352-392-0311. FAX: 352-846-2747. Web Site: www.uflib.ufl.edu:80/afa. *Librn*, Ann Lindell; Staff 21 (MLS 3, Non-MLS 18)
Library Holdings: Bk Vols 76,314; Per Subs 21,950
Subject Interests: Architecture, Art, Construction
Special Collections: Architectural Preservation, docs; John Simonds, Turpin C Bannister & Operation Breakthrough Archives; Rare Book Coll
Partic in Dialog Corporation; OCLC Online Computer Library Center, Inc
COASTAL ENGINEERING ARCHIVES, 433 Weil Hall, 32611. SAN 337-5277. Tel: 352-392-2710. FAX: 352-392-2710. *Archivist*, Helen Twedell; E-Mail: helen@coastal.usl.edu
Enrl 1,973
Library Holdings: Bk Titles 715; Per Subs 41
Subject Interests: Ocean engineering
Special Collections: Aerial Photographs Coll; Coastal Engineering & Tidal Hydraulics (US Army Beach Erosion Board & Coastal Engineering Research Center Reports); Coastal Engineering (University of Florida Coastal & Oceanographic Engineering Department Reports); Florida Coastal Changes, docs; Hydraulics Research (Reports of Various Hydraulics Laboratories)
Publications: Acquisitions lists; Lists of Reports of UF Coastal & Oceanographic Engineering Department; Monthly wave data
Partic in Defense Technical Information Center
Reading room & reference service, FAX & photocopying available to public
EDUCATION LIBRARY, 1500 Norman Hall, 32611. (Mail add: PO Box 117016, 32611-7016), SAN 337-5307. Tel: 352-392-0707. FAX: 352-392-4789. Web Site: www.web.uflib.ufl.edu/educ/. *Head of Libr*, M Suzanne Brown; E-Mail: msbrown@ulf.edu; *Circ*, Damon Austin; E-Mail: daustin@mail.uflib.ufl.edu; *Tech Servs*, Carrie Hunt; E-Mail: carhunt@mail.uflib.ufl.edu; *Tech Servs*, Carol Whitmer; E-Mail: carwhite@mail.uflib.ufl.edu; Staff 6 (MLS 2, Non-MLS 4)
Founded 1950
2000-2001 Mats Exp $146,952, Books $52,785, Per/Ser (Incl. Access Fees) $94,167
Library Holdings: Bk Vols 125,197; Per Subs 588
Subject Interests: Educ policy, Educ psychol, Special education

Special Collections: Complete History of Education Coll; ERIC microfiche coll, 558697 government & non-government microforms; William S Gray Reading Research Coll
Database Vendor: CARL, Ebsco - EbscoHost, GaleNet, IAC - Info Trac, Lexis-Nexis, OCLC - First Search, OVID Technologies, ProQuest, Silverplatter Information Inc.
Restriction: Open to faculty, students & qualified researchers
Function: Research library
Partic in Solinet
Public may purchase a card to check out materials

GOVERNMENTS DOCUMENTS DEPARTMENT, 241 Library W, PO Box 117001, 32611. SAN 329-0018. Tel: 352-392-0367. FAX: 352-392-3357. Web Site: docs.uflib.ufl.edu/l/pages/. *Chair*, Jan Swanbeck; Staff 11 (MLS 6, Non-MLS 5)

CM HEALTH SCIENCE LIBRARY, J Hillis Miller Health Ctr, PO Box 100206, 32610. SAN 372-5455. Tel: 352-392-4011. FAX: 352-392-2565. Web Site: www.library.health.ufl.edu/. *Dir*, Faith Meakin; *Cat*, Cecilia Botero; *Coll Develop*, Lenny Rhine; Staff 55 (MLS 42, Non-MLS 13)
Founded 1956. Enrl 5,000; Fac 1,100; Highest Degree: Doctorate
Subject Interests: Allied health, Dentistry, Medicine, Nursing, Veterinary medicine
Publications: Acquisitions List; Library Bulletin (quarterly)

ISSER & RAE PRICE LIBRARY OF JUDAICA, 1504 Norman Hall, PO Box 117051, 32611-7051. SAN 337-5390. Tel: 352-392-0308. FAX: 352-392-4789. Web Site: www.uflib.ufl.edu/cm/plj.html. *Librn*, Robert Singerman; E-Mail: singrob@mail.uflib.ufl.edu; Staff 2 (MLS 1, Non-MLS 1)
Library Holdings: Bk Vols 64,000; Per Subs 435
Subject Interests: Hebrew language, Hebrew lit, Holocaust, Judaica (lit or hist of Jews), Judaism, Rabbinics
Partic in OCLC Online Computer Library Center, Inc

LATIN AMERICAN COLLECTION, 412 Smathers Library, 32611. SAN 337-5366. Tel: 352-392-0360. Interlibrary Loan Service Tel: 352-392-0311. FAX: 352-392-4787. Web Site: www.uflib.ufl.edu/lac/lacf.html. *Librn*, Richard Phillips; Staff 5 (MLS 2, Non-MLS 3)
Founded 1967. Enrl 5,400; Fac 90; Highest Degree: Doctorate
Subject Interests: Caribbean, Humanities, Latin America, Social sciences and issues
Publications: Latin American Reference Series
Partic in Dialog Corporation; OCLC Online Computer Library Center, Inc

LEGAL INFORMATION CENTER, 161A Holland Hall, 32611. SAN 337-5420. Tel: 352-392-0417. FAX: 352-392-5093. E-Mail: referenc@law.ufl.edu. Web Site: nersp.nerdc.ufl.edu/~lawinfo/college/lic/. *Dir*, Betty W Taylor; *Assoc Dir*, Rick Donnelly; *Asst Dir*, Mae Clark; *Asst Dir*, Pam Williams; *Media Spec*, Brian Burns; *Media Spec*, Jim Flavin; *Cat*, Jean Bostwick; *Circ*, Susy Potter; *Ref*, Robert Munro; Staff 27 (MLS 11, Non-MLS 16)
Founded 1909. Enrl 1,196; Fac 87; Highest Degree: Doctorate
Library Holdings: Bk Vols 331,189
Special Collections: Brazilian Law Coll; Great Britain Law Coll
Publications: Legal Bibliography; Library Handbook
Partic in Dialog Corporation; NEFLIN; OCLC Online Computer Library Center, Inc; Westlaw

MAP COLLECTION, PO Box 117011, 32611. SAN 329-0034. Tel: 352-392-2825. FAX: 352-392-7251. Web Site: www.uflib.ufl.edu:80/maps/. *Librn*, Dr Helen Jane Armstrong; Staff 3 (MLS 1, Non-MLS 2)
Special Collections: NASA/Kennedy Space Center Aerial Photo Repository; Spot Imagery Coll of Florida; United States Department of Agriculture Aerial Photos of Florida Archives
Publications: Latin American Reference Series
Partic in OCLC Online Computer Library Center, Inc

MARSTON SCIENCE LIBRARY, PO Box 117011, 32604. SAN 329-028X. Tel: 352-392-2759. FAX: 352-392-4787. Web Site: www.web.uflib.ufl.edu/msl. *Chair*, Carol Drum; Staff 22 (MLS 10, Non-MLS 12)
Library Holdings: Bk Vols 231,935; Per Subs 379,300
Subject Interests: Agriculture, Astronomy, Chemistry, Engineering, Mathematics, Physics
Partic in OCLC Online Computer Library Center, Inc

MUSIC, 231 Music Bldg, PO Box 117900, 32611-7900. SAN 337-548X. Tel: 352-392-6678. FAX: 352-846-2748. Web Site: www.uflib.ufl.edu/hss/ref/musiclib.html. *Librn*, Robena Cornwell; Staff 3 (MLS 1, Non-MLS 2)
Library Holdings: Bk Vols 21,807; Per Subs 3,185
Special Collections: Didier Graeffe Manuscript Scores; Eugene Grissom Trombone Music Library
Partic in OCLC Online Computer Library Center, Inc

UNIVERSITY ARCHIVES, PO Box 117007, 32611. SAN 337-5250. Tel: 352-392-9075. FAX: 352-846-2746. Web Site: special.uflib.ufl.edu/univarch.html. *Archivist*, Carl Van Ness; Staff 3 (MLS 2, Non-MLS 1)
Library Holdings: Bk Vols 36,909

S US GEOLOGICAL SURVEY, BIOLOGICAL RESOURCE DIVISION, Florida Caribbean Science Center, 7920 NW 71st St, 32653-3071. SAN 322-6158. Tel: 352-378-8181. FAX: 352-378-4956. *In Charge*, Ann Foster; Tel: 352-372-2571

GONZALEZ

S SOLUTIA INC, (Formerly Monsanto - The Chemical Group), Library & Information Services, PO Box 97, 32560-0097. SAN 303-125X. Tel: 850-968-8249. FAX: 850-968-8248.; Staff 3 (MLS 1, Non-MLS 2)
Founded 1954
Library Holdings: Bk Vols 12,275; Bk Titles 6,000; Per Subs 250
Subject Interests: Polymer chemistry, Textiles
Restriction: Employees & their associates
Partic in Missouri Library Network Corporation; OCLC Online Computer Library Center, Inc
Support company information needs.

GRACEVILLE

CR FLORIDA BAPTIST THEOLOGICAL COLLEGE, Ida J McMillan Library, 5400 College Dr, 32440-1833. SAN 302-9514. Tel: 850-263-3261, Ext 424. FAX: 850-263-5704. *Dir*, Irvin Murrell; E-Mail: irvin725@freenet.fsu.edu; *Cat*, Rhonda Spears; Staff 1 (MLS 1)
Founded 1943. Highest Degree: Bachelor
Library Holdings: Bk Vols 75,000; Per Subs 946
Subject Interests: Humanities, Music, Religion, Social sciences and issues
Special Collections: College Archives
Partic in OCLC Online Computer Library Center, Inc; Panhandle Library Access Network

GREEN COVE SPRINGS

P GREEN COVE SPRINGS PUBLIC LIBRARY, 403 Ferris St, 32043. SAN 337-5544. Tel: 904-284-6315. FAX: 904-284-4053. *Branch Mgr*, Jennifer Parker
Founded 1961. Pop 104,000; Circ 317,670
Library Holdings: Bk Vols 143,000; Per Subs 189
Subject Interests: Florida, Genealogy, Large type print
Partic in Florida Library Information Network; SE Libr Network
Friends of the Library Group
Bookmobiles: 1. In-Charge, Lorene Thacker

P KEYSTONE PUBLIC LIBRARY, Oriole at Palmetto, PO Box 710, 32656. SAN 337-5579. Tel: 352-473-4286. FAX: 352-473-5123. *In Charge*, Ann Shields
Library Holdings: Bk Vols 20,000

P ORANGE PARK PUBLIC LIBRARY, 2054 Plainfield Ave, 32073. SAN 337-5609. Tel: 904-278-4750. FAX: 904-278-4747. Web Site: ccpl.lib.fl.us. *Dir*, Arnold Weeks; *Branch Mgr*, Walter Brown
Library Holdings: Bk Vols 48,000
Friends of the Library Group

GULF BREEZE

G UNITED STATES ENVIRONMENTAL PROTECTION AGENCY, Gulf Ecology Division Library, One Sabine Island Dr, 32561-5299. SAN 302-9530. Tel: 850-934-9218. FAX: 850-934-2409. Web Site: www.epa.gov/ged/bld42.htm. *Mgr Libr*, Elizabeth J Pinnell; E-Mail: pinnell.liz@epa.gov; *ILL*, Sonya M Doten; Tel: 850-934-9318, E-Mail: doten.sonya@epa.gov; Staff 2 (MLS 1, Non-MLS 1)
Founded 1967
Library Holdings: Bk Titles 5,500; Per Subs 300
Subject Interests: Environmental analysis (water), Estuarine biology, Water pollution
Special Collections: Environmental Issues-Northwest Florida
Automation Activity & Vendor Info: (ILL) TechLIB
Database Vendor: Dialog, OCLC - First Search
Publications: Laboratory Publications Bibliography; Periodicals List
Restriction: By appointment only
Function: ILL available
Partic in EPA; Fedlink; Florida Library Information Network; OCLC Online Computer Library Center, Inc; Panhandle Library Access Network

GULFPORT

P GULFPORT PUBLIC LIBRARY, 5501 28th Ave S, 33707. SAN 302-9549. Tel: 727-893-1074. Reference Tel: 727-893-1073. FAX: 727-893-1072. Web Site: www.tblc.org/gpl/. *Adminr*, Catherine Smith; Tel: 727-893-1075, E-Mail: smithki@tblc.org; *Tech Servs*, Carol Parker; Tel: 727-893-1076, E-Mail: parkerc@tblc.org; *YA Servs*, Anthony Salveggi; Tel: 727-893-1134, E-Mail: salveggiaj@splib.lib.fl.us; *Ref*, Karen Aust; E-Mail: austk@tblc.org; *Ref*, Martha Loyd; E-Mail: loydm@tblc.org; *Ad Servs*, Sarah Wittstruck; Tel: 727-893-1133, E-Mail: wittsts@tblc.org; Staff 15 (MLS 6, Non-MLS 9)
Founded 1935. Pop 12,000; Circ 115,894
Oct 1999-Sep 2000 Income $487,683, State $35,343, City $292,424, County $159,916. Mats Exp $47,724, Books $46,963, Presv $761. Sal $267,500
Library Holdings: Bk Vols 65,723; Per Subs 100
Special Collections: Russian Books (popular)
Automation Activity & Vendor Info: (Cataloging) DRA; (Circulation)

DRA; (OPAC) DRA
Database Vendor: DRA
Mem of Pinellas County Public Libr Coop
Partic in Florida Library Information Network; Tampa Bay Library Consortium, Inc
Friends of the Library Group

CL STETSON UNIVERSITY COLLEGE OF LAW LIBRARY, 1401 61st St S, 33707. SAN 338-0580. Tel: 727-562-7820. Reference Tel: 727-562-7821. FAX: 727-345-8973. Web Site: www.law.stetson.edu. *Dir, Prof*, J Lamar Woodard; Tel: 727-562-7833, E-Mail: woodard@law.stetson.edu; *Assoc Dir*, Madison Mosley; Tel: 727-562-7827, E-Mail: mosley@law.stetson.edu; *Ref*, Pamela Burdett; Tel: 727-562-7824, E-Mail: burdett@law.stetson.edu; *Ref*, Dorothy Clark; Tel: 727-562-7825, E-Mail: clark@law.stetson.edu; *Ref*, Sally Waters; Tel: 727-562-7828, E-Mail: waters@law.stetson.edu; *Acq, Doc, Ser*, Earlene Kuester; Tel: 727-562-7826, E-Mail: kuester@law.stetson.edu; *Cat*, Julie Crowley; Tel: 727-562-7829, E-Mail: crowley@law.stetson.edu; Staff 17 (MLS 7, Non-MLS 10)
Founded 1901. Enrl 681; Fac 29; Highest Degree: Master
Jun 1999-May 2000 Income Parent Institution $2,027,476. Mats Exp $1,204,102, Books $135,518, Per/Ser (Incl. Access Fees) $744,780, Presv $19,329, Micro $28,116, AV Equip $92,346, Electronic Ref Mat (Incl. Access Fees) $71,446. Sal $787,772 (Prof $431,343)
Library Holdings: Bk Vols 366,251; Bk Titles 106,603; Per Subs 5,583
Automation Activity & Vendor Info: (Acquisitions) Innovative Interfaces Inc.; (Cataloging) Innovative Interfaces Inc.; (Circulation) Innovative Interfaces Inc.; (OPAC) Innovative Interfaces Inc.; (Serials) Innovative Interfaces Inc.
Database Vendor: IAC - Info Trac, Lexis-Nexis, OCLC - First Search
Publications: Acquisitions; periodical holdings
Partic in Consortium Of South Eastern Law Libraries; OCLC Online Computer Library Center, Inc; Tampa Bay Library Consortium, Inc

HAINES CITY

P HAINES CITY PUBLIC LIBRARY, 303 Ledwith Ave, 33844. (Mail add: PO Box 1507, 33845), SAN 302-9557. Tel: 863-421-3633. FAX: 941-421-3635. *Dir*, Margaret Barthe; E-Mail: mar_barthe@juno.com; *Librn*, Polly Key; *Ch Servs*, Debra Howell; Staff 7 (MLS 1, Non-MLS 6)
Founded 1920. Pop 459,000
Library Holdings: Bk Vols 36,000; Per Subs 48
Special Collections: Florida Coll
Partic in Polk County Libr Coop; Tampa Bay Library Consortium, Inc

HAVANA

S NORTHWEST FLORIDA WATER MANAGEMENT DISTRICT, Library & Information Center, 81 Water Management Dr, 32333. SAN 374-8405. Tel: 850-539-5999. FAX: 850-539-4380. *Librn*, Lucinda Scott
Library Holdings: Bk Titles 100

HEATHROW

S AAA LIBRARY, 1000 AAA Dr, 32746-5063. SAN 317-2708. Tel: 407-444-7965. FAX: 407-444-7759. *Mgr*, Melissa Phillips; E-Mail: mphillips@national.aaa.com; Staff 4 (MLS 3, Non-MLS 1)
Founded 1955
Library Holdings: Bk Titles 14,000; Per Subs 250
Subject Interests: Automotive, Bus, Driver educ, Financial servs, Hwys, Info systs, Ins, Traffic safety, Travel
Special Collections: AAA Publications
Database Vendor: Dialog, Lexis-Nexis
Partic in Cent Fla Libr Consortium

HIALEAH

M HIALEAH HOSPITAL, George H Wessel Memorial Library, 651 E 25th St, 33013. SAN 324-5934. Tel: 305-693-6100, 305-835-4635.
Founded 1969
Library Holdings: Bk Vols 1,500; Bk Titles 1,000; Per Subs 120
Subject Interests: Allied health, Medicine, Nursing

P HIALEAH-JOHN F KENNEDY LIBRARY, 190 W 49th St, 33012-3798. SAN 337-5633. Tel: 305-821-2700. FAX: 305-818-9144. E-Mail: jfklib@ci.hialeah.fl.us. Web Site: www.ci.hialeah.fl.us/library. *Dir*, Marla Alpizar; Tel: 305-818-9140; *Coll Develop*, Esther Nibot; *Syst Coordr*, Jackie Vargo; *Cat*, Les Bowles; *Ref*, Mary Bishop; *YA Servs*, Terry Warner; Staff 15 (MLS 10, Non-MLS 5)
Founded 1928. Pop 210,000
Oct 2000-Sep 2001 Income (Main Library and Branch Library) $1,804,431, State $25,000, City $1,706,431, Federal $73,000. Mats Exp $215,000, Books $150,000, Per/Ser (Incl. Access Fees) $45,000, Electronic Ref Mat (Incl. Access Fees) $20,000. Sal $903,337 (Prof $500,922)
Library Holdings: Bk Vols 108,036; Bk Titles 95,000; Per Subs 413
Subject Interests: Art and architecture, Audio bks, Business and management, Florida, Music, Science/technology, Spanish, Videos
Automation Activity & Vendor Info: (Cataloging) Gaylord; (Circulation) Gaylord; (OPAC) Gaylord
Publications: Que Pasa Hialeah (Newsletter)
Branches: 1
LUA A CURTIS BRANCH, 501 E Fourth Ave, 33010. SAN 337-5668. Tel: 305-883-6950. *Librn*, Rosa Cortes

HIGHLAND BEACH

P HIGHLAND BEACH LIBRARY, 3614 S Ocean Blvd, 33487. SAN 376-4990. Tel: 561-278-5455. FAX: 561-278-0156. Web Site: www.ci.highland-beach.fl.us. *Dir*, Mari Suarez; E-Mail: msuarez@ci.highland-beach.fl.us; Staff 4 (MLS 1, Non-MLS 3)
Library Holdings: Bk Titles 14,000; Per Subs 60
Special Collections: Florida Coll
Automation Activity & Vendor Info: (Cataloging) SIRSI; (Circulation) SIRSI; (OPAC) SIRSI
Friends of the Library Group

HOBE SOUND

CR HOBE SOUND BIBLE COLLEGE LIBRARY, PO Box 1065, 33475-1065. SAN 302-9603. Tel: 561-546-5534. FAX: 561-545-1422. Web Site: www.hsbc.edu/lib.html. *Librn*, Bob Triplett; Staff 2 (MLS 1, Non-MLS 1)
Founded 1960
Library Holdings: Bk Vols 33,400; Per Subs 220
Subject Interests: Humanities, Music
Special Collections: Child Evangelism Coll

HOLLYWOOD

M MEMORIAL HEALTHCARE SYSTEM, Resource Library, 3501 Johnson St, 33021. SAN 302-962X. Tel: 954-985-5840. FAX: 954-967-2951. *Librn*, Sally E Haff; E-Mail: shaff@mhs-net.com; Staff 1 (MLS 1)
Founded 1963
Library Holdings: Bk Titles 300; Per Subs 206
Subject Interests: Allied health, Clinical medicine, Nursing
Publications: Newsletter
Restriction: Clients only, Medical staff only
Partic in Miami Health Sciences Library Consortium

S SOUTH FLORIDA REGIONAL PLANNING COUNCIL LIBRARY, 3440 Hollywood Blvd Ste 140, 33021. SAN 303-0695. Tel: 954-985-4416. FAX: 954-985-4417. Toll Free FAX: 800-985-4416. E-Mail: sfadmin@sfrpc. Web Site: www.sfrpc.com. *Librn*, Karen Chang
Founded 1971
Library Holdings: Bk Titles 5,000; Per Subs 100
Subject Interests: Economics, Energy, Environmental studies, Transportation, Urban planning

R TEMPLE BETH EL, Billie Davis Rodenberg Memorial Library, 1351 S 14th Ave, 33020-6499. SAN 302-9638. Tel: 954-920-8225. FAX: 954-920-7026. *Librn*, Roslyn Kurland; Staff 3 (MLS 1, Non-MLS 2)
Library Holdings: Bk Titles 9,000
Subject Interests: Judaica (lit or hist of Jews)

HOMESTEAD

§J MIAMI DADE COMMUNITY COLLEGE, Homestead Campus Library, Bldg D, 500 College Terrace, 33030. Tel: 305-237-5139. *Dir*, Rosemary Garcia-Pendleton; E-Mail: rpendleton@mdcc.edu

S NATIONAL PARK SERVICE, Everglades National Park Research Center Library, 40001 State Rd 9336, 33034-6733. SAN 302-9654. Tel: 305-242-7800. FAX: 305-242-7836.
Founded 1965
Library Holdings: Per Subs 136
Subject Interests: Biology, Botany, Hydrology (environment), Oceanography
Special Collections: History and Natural Resources of Everglades National Park and South Florida area

C UNIVERSITY OF FLORIDA, TROPICAL RESEARCH & EDUCATION CENTER, Institute of Food & Agricultural Sciences Library, 18905 SW 280th St, 33031. SAN 302-9662. Tel: 305-246-6340. FAX: 305-246-7003. Web Site: www.ifau.ufl.edu/trecweb/. *In Charge*, Kelly Sullivan
Library Holdings: Bk Vols 4,000; Per Subs 71

HUDSON

P PASCO COUNTY LIBRARY SYSTEM, 8012 Library Rd, 34667. SAN 324-8003. Tel: 727-861-3020. Interlibrary Loan Service Tel: 727-861-3040. Circulation Tel: 727-861-3040. Reference Tel: 727-861-3040. Toll Free Tel: 800-368-2411, Ext 3020. FAX: 727-861-3025. Web Site: power.pasco.lib.fl.us. *Publ Servs*, Patricia Owen; E-Mail: pattyo@

pasco.lib.fl.us; *Coll Develop, ILL*, Casey McPhee; *Cat*, Chris Chudy; E-Mail: chrismail@pasco.lib.fl.us; *Automation Syst Coordr*, Ruth Urbanski; E-Mail: ruth@pasco.lib.fl.us; *YA Servs*, Karen Correa; E-Mail: karenc@pasco.lib.fl.us; *Publ Servs*, Linda Bragg; E-Mail: lindab@pasco.lib.fl.us; *Circ*, Loraine Cors; E-Mail: lorainec@pasco.lib.fl.us; *Ref Serv*, Gale Vaccaro; E-Mail: galev@pasco.lib.fl.us; Staff 25 (MLS 25)
Founded 1980. Pop 326,494; Circ 1,961,818
Oct 1999-Sep 2000 Income (Main Library and Branch Library) $5,194,389, State $431,550, Federal $133,867, County $4,592,362, Locally Generated Income $36,610. Mats Exp $994,143, Books $647,763, Per/Ser (Incl. Access Fees) $219,783, Electronic Ref Mat (Incl. Access Fees) $126,597. Sal $2,086,524
Library Holdings: Bk Vols 524,598; Per Subs 1,841
Subject Interests: Florida, Genealogy
Automation Activity & Vendor Info: (Acquisitions) DRA; (Circulation) DRA; (OPAC) DRA
Publications: Friends of Pasco County Newsletter
Partic in Florida Library Information Network; SE Libr Network; Tampa Bay Library Consortium, Inc
Friends of the Library Group
Branches: 7
CENTENNIAL PARK, 5740 Moog Rd, Holiday, 34690. SAN 370-3622. Tel: 727-834-3204. TDD: 727-834-3224, Dial-up Access 727-834-3370. FAX: 727-834-3225. Web Site: power.pasco.lib.fl.us. *Mgr*, Margaret Griffith; E-Mail: margaretg@pasco.lib.fl.us
Circ 301,923
Special Services for the Deaf - TDD
Friends of the Library Group
HUGH EMBRY BRANCH, 14215 Fourth St, Dade City, 33525. SAN 302-8992. Tel: 352-567-3576. TDD: 352-523-0902, Dial-up Access 352-521-4117. FAX: 352-521-6670. Web Site: power.pasco.lib.fl.us. *Mgr*, Mary Anne Gallagher; E-Mail: maryanneg@pasco.lib.fl.us
Founded 1904. Pop 57,525; Circ 151,019
Special Services for the Deaf - TDD
Friends of the Library Group
HUDSON REGIONAL, 8012 Library Rd, 34667. SAN 370-6257. Tel: 727-861-3040. TDD: 727-861-3024, Dial-up Access 727-834-3370. FAX: 727-861-3025. Web Site: power.pasco.lib.fl.us. *Mgr*, Patricia Owen; E-Mail: pattyo@pasco.lib.fl.us
Special Services for the Deaf - TDD
Friends of the Library Group
LAND O' LAKES BRANCH, 2818 Collier Pkwy, Land O' Lakes, 34639. SAN 370-6265. Tel: 813-929-1214. TDD: 813-949-3796, Dial-up Access 727-834-3370. FAX: 813-929-1235. Web Site: power.pasco.lib.fl.us. *Mgr*, Stephen Baumgarner; E-Mail: steveb@pasco.lib.fl.us
Circ 219,474
Special Services for the Deaf - TDD
Friends of the Library Group
NEW RIVER, 34043 State Rd 54, Zephyrhills, 33543. SAN 371-3687. Tel: 813-788-6375. TDD: 813-780-8054, Dial-up Access 727-834-3370. FAX: 813-788-6977. Web Site: power.pasco.lib.fl.us.
Circ 189,378
Special Services for the Deaf - TDD
Friends of the Library Group
REGENCY PARK, 9701 Little Rd, New Port Richey, 34654. SAN 370-6273. Tel: 727-861-3049. TDD: 727-861-3031, Dial-up Access 727-834-3370. FAX: 727-861-3011. Web Site: power.pasco.lib.fl.us. *Mgr*, Julie Ventura; E-Mail: juliev@pasco.lib.fl.us
Special Services for the Deaf - TDD
Friends of the Library Group
SOUTH HOLIDAY BRANCH, 4649 Mile Stretch Dr, Holiday, 34690. SAN 371-3695. Tel: 727-834-3331. TDD: 727-946-8085, Dial-up Access 727-834-3370. FAX: 727-942-6740. Web Site: power.pasco.lib.fl.us.
Circ 178,830
Special Services for the Deaf - TDD
Friends of the Library Group

IMMOKALEE

S HENDRY CORRECTIONAL INSTITUTION LIBRARY, 12551 Wainwright Dr, 34142-9747. SAN 375-3247. Tel: 941-657-3654, Ext 188. FAX: 941-657-3020. *Tech Servs*, Bobbie Jo Clark; Staff 22 (MLS 1, Non-MLS 21)
Jul 1999-Jun 2000 Income $22,000. Mats Exp $20,000, Books $14,000, Per/Ser (Incl. Access Fees) $6,000. Sal $56,000 (Prof $38,000)
Library Holdings: Bk Vols 16,500; Per Subs 70; High Interest/Low Vocabulary Bk Vols 60

P IMMOKALEE RESERVATION LIBRARY, 303 Lena Frank Dr, 34142. SAN 376-6063. Tel: 941-657-3400. FAX: 941-657-9547. E-Mail: libim@semtribe.com. *Librn*, Chris Marrero
Library Holdings: Bk Vols 6,000
Open Mon-Fri 1-5

INDIALANTIC

S MODUS OPERANDI, Technical Information Center, 122 Fourth Ave, 32903-0003. SAN 323-8695. Tel: 321-984-3370. FAX: 321-728-3957. *Librn*, Rhonda Edwards
Founded 1987
Library Holdings: Bk Titles 725; Per Subs 132
Special Collections: Software Engineering, articles, bks, proceedings
Publications: TIC Talk
Partic in Cent Fla Libr Consortium; Dialog Corporation

INDIANTOWN

S MARTIN CORRECTIONAL INSTITUTION LIBRARY, 1150 SW Allapattah Rd, 34956-4397. SAN 377-290X. Tel: 561-597-3705. FAX: 561-597-4529. *Librn*, B McClanahan
Library Holdings: Bk Vols 10,000; Bk Titles 5,000; Per Subs 20

JACKSONVILLE

S BLUE CROSS & BLUE SHIELD OF FLORIDA, Business Research Information Center, 4800 Deerwood Campus Pkwy, 32246. SAN 323-4185. Tel: 904-905-5345. FAX: 904-905-5346. *Mgr*, Marjorie M Pace
Library Holdings: Bk Vols 3,500; Per Subs 175
Subject Interests: Delivery, Gen bus, Health care, Health ins, Managed care

S CHURCH OF JESUS CHRIST OF LATTER-DAY SAINTS, Florida Branch Family History Library, 7665 Ft Caroline Rd, 32277. SAN 302-9697. Tel: 904-743-0527. *Dir*, Henry Allen; *Librn*, Edith Nixon
Library Holdings: Bk Vols 1,300
Open Tues-Thurs 10-2 & 7-9, Sat 10-1

L CSX TRANSPORTATION, INC, Law Library, 500 Water St, J-150, 32202. SAN 302-9859. Tel: 904-359-1258. FAX: 904-359-1248. *Librn*, Ron Allen
Library Holdings: Bk Vols 10,000; Bk Titles 990; Per Subs 23

S CUMMER MUSEUM OF ART LIBRARY, 829 Riverside Ave, 32204. SAN 326-5846. Tel: 904-356-6857. FAX: 904-353-4101.
Library Holdings: Bk Vols 10,000; Per Subs 31
Subject Interests: Art history
Special Collections: European Porcelains
Restriction: Non-circulating to the public

GL DUVAL COUNTY LAW LIBRARY, 102 County Courthouse, 330 E Bay St, 32202. SAN 302-9719. Tel: 904-630-2560. FAX: 904-630-2979. *Librn*, Bud Mauer; Staff 8 (MLS 1, Non-MLS 7)
Founded 1939
Library Holdings: Bk Vols 47,000
Subject Interests: Florida, Law

C EDWARD WATERS COLLEGE, Centennial Library, 1658 Kings Rd, 32209. SAN 302-9727. Tel: 904-366-2510. *Dir*, Charles N King; *Info Specialist*, Roderick Williams; *Tech Servs*, Gwendolyn Gatson
Founded 1945. Enrl 792; Fac 49; Highest Degree: Bachelor
Library Holdings: Bk Vols 99,000; Bk Titles 77,616; Per Subs 150
Special Collections: Afro-American
Publications: Library Guide (campus wide); Library Newsletter (campus wide)
Mem of Florida Libr Asn

J FLORIDA COMMUNITY COLLEGE AT JACKSONVILLE, Kent Campus Library, 3939 Roosevelt Blvd, 32210. SAN 337-5846. Tel: 904-381-3522. Reference Tel: 904-381-3545. FAX: 904-381-3579. Web Site: www.fccj.org/lr. *Chair*, Michelle Apps; *Librn*, Art Chiang; *Librn*, Sheri Davis; *Librn*, Ken Puckett; *Tech Servs*, Alice E Jones; Staff 10 (MLS 5, Non-MLS 5)
Founded 1966. Enrl 49,452
Library Holdings: Bk Vols 86,000; Per Subs 453
Database Vendor: DRA, Ebsco - EbscoHost, OCLC - First Search
Partic in Florida Library Information Network; NEFLIN; SE Libr Network
Departmental Libraries:
DEERWOOD CENTER LIBRARY, 9911 Old Baymeadows Rd, 32256. Tel: 904-997-2562. FAX: 904-997-2571. Web Site: www.fccj.org/library/deerwood/. *Chief Librn*, Kristin L Kubly; Tel: 904-997-2563, E-Mail: kkubly@fccj.org; *Mgr*, Mary Dumbleton; Tel: 904-997-2572, E-Mail: mdumblet@fccj.org; Staff 2 (MLS 1, Non-MLS 1)
Founded 2000. Enrl 9,337; Highest Degree: Associate
Library Holdings: Bk Titles 2,825; Per Subs 102
Automation Activity & Vendor Info: (Circulation) DRA; (OPAC) DRA
Database Vendor: DRA, Ebsco - EbscoHost, GaleNet, OCLC - First Search
Function: ILL available
Partic in LINCC; NEFLIN; Solinet
DOWNTOWN CAMPUS, 101 W State St, 32202-3056. SAN 337-5811. Tel: 904-633-8368. FAX: 904-633-8328. Web Site: www.fccj.org/l. *Chair*, Gwen Chandler-Thompson; *Librn*, John Lucy; *Librn*, John Haas
Library Holdings: Bk Vols 48,792; Per Subs 367
NORTH CAMPUS, 4501 Capper Rd, 32218-4499. SAN 337-5870. Tel: 904-766-6711. FAX: 904-766-6640. Web Site: www.fccj.org/lr. *Chair*, Harry

Hodges; E-Mail: hhodges@fccj.org; *Librn*, Victoria Mary McGlone; Tel: 904-766-6714, E-Mail: vmcglone@fccj.org
Library Holdings: Bk Vols 69,423; Per Subs 325
SOUTH CAMPUS, 11901 Beach Blvd, 32246-6624. SAN 337-5781. Tel: 904-646-2173. FAX: 904-646-2155. *Chair*, Judith Johnson; *Librn*, Barbara Markham
Library Holdings: Bk Vols 59,557; Per Subs 500

S FLORIDA TIMES UNION, Editorial Library, One Riverside Ave, 32231. SAN 325-8882. Tel: 904-359-4237. FAX: 904-359-4478. *Librn*, Jennifer Ann O'Neil
Library Holdings: Bk Vols 1,500
Special Collections: Newspaper clippings (5 million)

S HERCULES, INC, Pulp & Paper Division Technical Library, 7510 Baymeadows Way, 32256-7591. SAN 370-5110. Tel: 904-733-7110. FAX: 904-448-4995. *Librn*, Margaret W Morford; Staff 1 (MLS 1)
Founded 1984
Library Holdings: Bk Titles 2,250; Per Subs 120
Subject Interests: Biology, Chemistry, Environment, Pulp and paper
Automation Activity & Vendor Info: (Acquisitions) EOS; (Cataloging) EOS; (Serials) EOS
Publications: Acquisitions list
Restriction: Staff use only
Partic in Dialog Corporation; NE Fla Libr Info Network; SE Libr Network; STN

P JACKSONVILLE PUBLIC LIBRARY, 122 N Ocean St, 32202-3374. SAN 337-5935. Tel: 904-630-1994. Interlibrary Loan Service Tel: 904-630-2985. TDD: 904-630-2740. FAX: 904-630-1313. Web Site: jpl.coj.net. *Dir*, Kenneth G Sivulich; Tel: 904-630-1996, Fax: 904-630-1343, E-Mail: sivulich@coj.net; *Asst Dir*, Sylvia Cornell; Tel: 904-630-1636, Fax: 904-630-1343, E-Mail: scornell@coj.net; *Coordr*, Tricia Egbert; Tel: 904-630-1968, Fax: 904-630-1343, E-Mail: tegbert@coj.net; *Coordr*, Stephen Ludwig; Tel: 904-630-2665, Fax: 904-630-2431, E-Mail: sludwig@coj.net; *Coordr*, Margaret Smith; Tel: 904-630-2665, Fax: 904-630-1343, E-Mail: mnsmith@coj.net; *Acq, Tech Servs*, Theresa Barmer; Tel: 904-630-2665, Fax: 904-630-2431, E-Mail: tbarmer@coj.net; *Automation Syst Coordr*, Carol Bailey; Tel: 904-630-2665, Fax: 904-630-2431, E-Mail: cbailey@coj.net; *Circ*, Carole Schwartz; Tel: 904-630-2665, Fax: 904-630-2431, E-Mail: cschwartz@coj.net; *Coll Develop*, Charlene Adkins; Tel: 904-630-2265, Fax: 904-630-2431, E-Mail: cadkins@coj.net; *Govt Doc*, Gretchen Mitchell; Tel: 904-630-2665, Fax: 904-630-2431, E-Mail: gmitch@coj.net; *Govt Doc*, Louis Zalenka; Tel: 904-630-2409, Fax: 904-630-2431, E-Mail: lzelenka@coj.net; *Media Spec*, Carol Smith; Tel: 904-630-2665, Fax: 904-630-2431, E-Mail: cosmithcoj.net; *ILL*, Laurie Baumgardner; Tel: 904-630-2665, Fax: 904-630-2431, E-Mail: laurieb@coj.net; *Per*, Julie McNeil; Tel: 904-630-2665, Fax: 904-630-2431, E-Mail: jmcneil@coj.net; *Pub Relations*, Stacie Bucher; Tel: 904-630-2665, Fax: 904-630-2431, E-Mail: sbucher@coj.net; *YA Servs*, Elizabeth Walters; Tel: 904-630-2665, Fax: 904-630-2431, E-Mail: ewalters@coj.net. Subject Specialists: *Fine arts*, Carole Schwartz; *Recreation*, Carole Schwartz; Staff 90 (MLS 90)
Founded 1903. Pop 716,912; Circ 3,577,969
1998-1999 Income $14,124,265. Mats Exp $3,207,317, Books $1,844,000, Per/Ser (Incl. Access Fees) $275,000, Micro $60,000, AV Equip $415,000, Other Print Mats $250,000, Electronic Ref Mat (Incl. Access Fees) $363,317. Sal $7,761,221
Library Holdings: Bk Vols 2,395,076; Bk Titles 571,615; Per Subs 2,673
Special Collections: Delius Music (Frederick Delius Memorial Fund); Floridiana, bks, per; Genealogy, bks, micro
Automation Activity & Vendor Info: (Acquisitions) DRA; (Cataloging) DRA; (Circulation) DRA; (OPAC) DRA; (Serials) DRA
Database Vendor: OCLC - First Search
Publications: Annual Report; At Your Service; Children's Program Flyer
Partic in Fla Computer Catalogue of Monographic Holdings; Florida Library Information Network; NE Fla Libr Info Network; OCLC Online Computer Library Center, Inc; Solinet
Special Services for the Deaf - Deaf publications; TDD
Special Services for the Blind - Closed circuit TV in Per; Kurzweil Reading Machine
Friends of the Library Group
Branches: 15
BEACHES, 600 Third St, Neptune Beach, 32266-5014. SAN 337-6087. Tel: 904-241-1141. FAX: 904-241-4965. *In Charge*, Elsie Oishi; E-Mail: eoishi@coj.net
2000-2001 Mats Exp $106,000, Books $91,000, AV Equip $15,000
Library Holdings: Bk Vols 165,860
Special Collections: Joe Gill Business Coll
Friends of the Library Group
BRADHAM BROOKS NORTHWEST, 1755 Edgewood Ave W, 32208-7206. SAN 371-4748. Tel: 904-765-5402. *In Charge*, Melonee Slocum; E-Mail: mslocum@coj.net
2000-2001 Mats Exp $60,000, Books $53,000, AV Equip $7,000
Library Holdings: Bk Vols 149,883
Participant in state summer library program; site of LEARN educational computer center for children ages 6-11
Friends of the Library Group
BRENTWOOD, 3725 Pearl St, 32206-6401. SAN 337-6141. Tel: 904-630-0924. FAX: 904-630-0441. *In Charge*, Marshelle Denson; E-Mail: mdenson@coj.net
2000-2001 Mats Exp $17,000, Books $14,500, AV Equip $2,500
Library Holdings: Bk Vols 31,225
Site of LEARN Center for school-age children; computers, educational games & other special after school activities available
BROWN EASTSIDE, 1390 Harrison St, 32206-5399. SAN 337-6028. Tel: 904-630-5466. FAX: 904-630-5466. *In Charge*, Evelyn Brown; E-Mail: evelynb@coj.net
2000-2001 Mats Exp $12,000, AV Equip $3,600
Library Holdings: Bk Vols 18,031
Site of LEARN educational computer center for children aged 6-11
DALLAS GRAHAM, 2304 N Myrtle Ave, 32209-5099. SAN 337-5994. Tel: 904-630-0922. FAX: 904-630-0439. *In Charge*, Nkoyo Ross; E-Mail: nross@coj.net
2000-2001 Mats Exp $18,000, AV Equip $4,000
Library Holdings: Bk Vols 37,626
Site of LEARN educational computer center for children ages 6-11
HIGHLANDS, 1826 Dunn Ave, 32218-4712. SAN 325-416X. Tel: 904-696-4305. FAX: 904-696-4328. *In Charge*, Pat Morrison; Tel: 904-757-7702, E-Mail: patm@coj.net
2000-2001 Mats Exp $71,000, AV Equip $8,000
Library Holdings: Bk Vols 167,327
Friends of the Library Group
MANDARIN, 3330 Kori Rd, 32257-5454. SAN 328-7254. Tel: 904-262-5203. FAX: 904-292-1029. *In Charge*, Nancy Devereux; E-Mail: nancyd@coj.net
2000-2001 Mats Exp $115,000
Library Holdings: Bk Vols 196,095
MURRAY HILL, 918 Edgewood Ave S, 32205-5341. SAN 337-6117. Tel: 904-384-2665. FAX: 904-381-1104. *In Charge*, Paul Stella; E-Mail: pstella@coj.net
2000-2001 Mats Exp $45,000, AV Equip $13,000
Library Holdings: Bk Vols 69,084
REGENCY SQUARE, 9900 Regency Square Blvd, 32225. Tel: 904-726-5142. TDD: 904-726-5152. FAX: 904-726-5153. *In Charge*, Carolyn Williams; E-Mail: cshehee@coj.net
2000-2001 Mats Exp $200,000, $200,000, AV Equip $40,000
Library Holdings: Bk Vols 138,659
SAN MARCO, 1565 Hendricks Ave, 32207-3107. SAN 337-6206. Tel: 904-858-2907. FAX: 904-858-2901. *In Charge*, Bridgid Broderick; E-Mail: bridgidb@coj.net
2000-2001 Mats Exp $49,000, AV Equip $6,500
Library Holdings: Bk Vols 71,185
SOUTHEAST, 10599 Deerwood Park Blvd, 32256. SAN 377-6204. Tel: 904-996-0325. *In Charge*, Susan Shami; E-Mail: sshami@coj.net
2000-2001 Mats Exp $119,000
Library Holdings: Bk Vols 225,032
TALKING BOOKS LIBRARY, 1755 Edgewood Ave W, Ste 1, 32208-7206. SAN 375-5770. Tel: 904-765-5588. FAX: 904-768-7404. *In Charge*, Laurie Baumgardner; E-Mail: laurieb@coj.net
Library Holdings: Bk Vols 24,544
Information & referral service on community resources for the handicapped; Reader's Advisory Service for the hadicapped users; recorded books on cassette; braille books; Kurzweil Personal Reader; two PC/CD-ROM workstations
WEBB WESCONNETT BRANCH, 6887 103rd St, 32210-6897. SAN 337-6230. Tel: 904-778-7306. FAX: 904-777-2262. *In Charge*, Jane Harris; Tel: 904-778-7305, E-Mail: jharris@coj.net
2000-2001 Mats Exp $100,000, AV Equip $20,000
Library Holdings: Bk Vols 171,787
WESTBROOK, 2809 Commonwealth Ave, 32205-2599. SAN 337-596X. Tel: 904-384-7424. FAX: 904-381-1107. *In Charge*, Madonna Green; E-Mail: mgreen@coj.net
Founded 1959
2000-2001 Mats Exp $33,000, AV Equip $5,000
Library Holdings: Bk Vols 29,736
Site of LEARN educational computer center for children aged 6-11
WILLOWBRANCH, 2875 Park St, 32205-8099. SAN 337-6265. Tel: 904-387-4668. FAX: 904-381-1109. *In Charge*, Laura Kline; Tel: 904-381-8490, Fax: 904-381-8495, E-Mail: lkline@coj.net
2000-2001 Mats Exp $33,000
Library Holdings: Bk Vols 47,158
Friends of the Library Group
Bookmobiles: 1

C JACKSONVILLE UNIVERSITY, Carl S Swisher Library, 2800 University Blvd N, Univ PO Box 21, 32211-3394. SAN 302-976X. Tel: 904-745-7267. FAX: 904-744-9930. Web Site: www.ju.edu/library. *Dir*, Thomas H Gunn; Tel: 904-745-7267, Ext 7278, E-Mail: tgunn@ju.edu; *Coll Develop, Tech Servs*, Paula McIntyre; Tel: 904-745-7267, Ext 7265, E-Mail: pmcinty@ju.edu; *Publ Servs*, David Jones; Tel: 904-745-7267, Ext. 7266, E-Mail: djones1@ju.edu; *Publ Servs, Tech Coordr*, Kathleen Shearin; Tel: 904-745-7267, Ext 5475, E-Mail: ksheari@ju.edu; *Govt Doc*, Courtenay Cooper; Tel: 904-745-7267, Ext 7269, E-Mail: dcooper@ju.edu; *Per*, Linda Matyas; Tel:

904-745-7267, Ext 7274, E-Mail: lmatyas@ju.edu; *Cat*, Lynnette Taylor; Tel: 904-745-7267, Ext 7464, E-Mail: ltaylor@ju.edu; *Selection of Gen Ref Mat, Spec Coll*, Anna Large; Tel: 904-745-7267, Ext 5476, E-Mail: alarge@ju.edu; Staff 8 (MLS 8)
Founded 1934. Enrl 2,118; Fac 251; Highest Degree: Master
Aug 1999-Jul 2000 Income $755,632, Locally Generated Income $6,000, Parent Institution $715,632, Other $34,000. Mats Exp $188,500, Books $71,500, Per/Ser (Incl. Access Fees) $60,000, Presv $1,500, Micro $15,000, AV Equip $500, Electronic Ref Mat (Incl. Access Fees) $40,000. Sal $521,532 (Prof $278,434)
Library Holdings: Bk Vols 275,211; Per Subs 782; Bks on Deafness & Sign Lang 47
Subject Interests: Business, Education, Fine arts, Liberal arts, Nursing
Special Collections: Delius Coll, bks, rec, mss, scores; Jacksonville Historical Society, bks, pamphlets, artifacts, clippings; Jacksonville University Archives, clippings, rec, bks, pamphlets; Rare Books
Automation Activity & Vendor Info: (Circulation) Endeavor; (Course Reserve) Endeavor; (OPAC) Endeavor
Database Vendor: Ebsco - EbscoHost, GaleNet, Lexis-Nexis, OCLC - First Search, ProQuest
Publications: Friends of the Library (Newsletter); Library Logon
Function: Reference only
Partic in Florida Library Information Network; Independent Cols & Univs of Fla; NE Fla Libr Info Network; OCLC Online Computer Library Center, Inc; SE Libr Network
Special Services for the Blind - DECTalk/JAWS for synthetic voice output of computer screen contents; Magnifiers; ZoomText software to enlarge computer screen
Friends of the Library Group

C JONES COLLEGE, James V Forrestal Library, 5353 Arlington Expressway, Rm 311, 32211. SAN 302-9778. Tel: 904-743-1122, Ext 101. FAX: 904-743-4446. Web Site: www.jones.edu. *Dir*, Carmella D Martin; E-Mail: cmartin@jones.edu; *Assoc Dir*, Dr Bob Farnsworth; Staff 7 (MLS 1, Non-MLS 6)
Founded 1967. Enrl 1,400
Library Holdings: Bk Vols 15,000; Per Subs 75
Subject Interests: Allied health, Business and management
Automation Activity & Vendor Info: (Cataloging) Sagebrush Corporation; (Circulation) Sagebrush Corporation
Database Vendor: OCLC - First Search
Partic in NE Fla Libr Info Network

R RIVERSIDE PRESBYTERIAN CHURCH, Jean Miller Memorial Library, 849 Park St, 32204. SAN 302-9816. Tel: 904-355-4585. FAX: 904-355-4508. *Librn*, Arden Brugger; Staff 1 (MLS 1)
Founded 1946
Library Holdings: Bk Vols 3,167
Restriction: In-house use for visitors, Members only
Function: Archival collection

M ST LUKE'S HOSPITAL LIBRARY, 4201 Belfort Rd, 32216. SAN 302-9824. Tel: 904-296-3735. FAX: 904-296-4644. *Librn*, Carole Saville; E-Mail: saville@mayo.edu
Founded 1958
Library Holdings: Bk Titles 1,000; Per Subs 204
Restriction: Staff use only

M SAINT VINCENT'S MEDICAL CENTER, Doctors Library, 1800 Barrs St, 32204. SAN 302-9832. Tel: 904-308-8165. FAX: 904-308-2976. *Librn*, Deborah Lawless; Staff 1 (MLS 1)
Library Holdings: Bk Vols 1,500; Bk Titles 1,000; Per Subs 125
Subject Interests: Obstetrics and gynecology, Surgery
Database Vendor: OVID Technologies
Restriction: Not open to public
Function: ILL to other special libraries

§CR TRINITY BAPTIST COLLEGE LIBRARY, 800 Hammond Blvd, 32221-1398. Tel: 904-596-2507. FAX: 904-596-2531. *Librn*, Marguerite Closs; E-Mail: mcloss@tbc.edu
Library Holdings: Bk Vols 36,000; Per Subs 200
Automation Activity & Vendor Info: (Acquisitions) Athena; (Cataloging) Athena; (Circulation) Athena

M UNITED MEDICAL TECHNOLOGIES CORP, (Formerly Medical Cybernetics Foundation Library), Medical Cybernetics Foundation Library, 3804 Arrow Lakes Dr S, 32257. SAN 372-6282. Tel: 904-288-8832. *Librn*, Bob Frost
Founded 1986
Library Holdings: Bk Titles 4,000; Per Subs 4,000

UNITED STATES ARMY
A CORPS OF ENGINEERS, TECHNICAL LIBRARY, 400 W Bay St, Rm G13D, PO Box 4970, 32232-0019. SAN 337-629X. Tel: 904-232-3643. FAX: 904-232-1838. *Librn*, Oriana Brown West; E-Mail: oriana.b.west@usace.army.mil
Founded 1978
Library Holdings: Bk Vols 27,000; Per Subs 400
Subject Interests: Civil engineering, Construction, Engineering, Recreation, Science/technology, Technology
Special Collections: Cross Florida Barge Canal Study
Partic in Dialog Corporation; Fedlink; Legislate; LePac; OCLC Online Computer Library Center, Inc

UNITED STATES NAVY
A MAYPORT NAVAL STATION LIBRARY, Naval Station Mayport, Mayport, 32228-0037. SAN 337-632X. Tel: 904-270-5393. FAX: 904-270-5547. *Mgr*, Brent Brown
Library Holdings: Bk Vols 13,400; Per Subs 60
Friends of the Library Group

A NAVAL AIR STATION LIBRARY, Bldg 460, Massey Ave, Mayport, 32228-0037. (Mail add: PO Box 280037, Mayport, 32228-0037), SAN 337-6419. Tel: 904-270-5393. *Librn*, Deborah Ewing; *Mgr*, Brent Brown; Staff 3 (Non-MLS 3)
Founded 1941
Library Holdings: Bk Vols 29; Bk Titles 9,900; Per Subs 30
Subject Interests: Aviation, Computer tech, Military hist, World War II
Function: Research library

AM NAVAL HOSPITAL LIBRARY, Naval Hospital, 2080 Child St, 32214. SAN 337-6389. Tel: 904-777-7583. FAX: 904-542-7093. *Librn*, Bettye W Stilley
Library Holdings: Bk Titles 834; Per Subs 207
Subject Interests: Medicine
Restriction: Staff use only

M UNIVERSITY OF FLORIDA HEALTH SCIENCE CENTER-JACKSONVILLE, Borland Health Sciences Library, 653-1 W Eighth St, PO Box 44226, 32231-4226. SAN 302-9751. Tel: 904-549-3240. FAX: 904-355-3310. *Librn*, Pam Neuman
Founded 1961
Library Holdings: Bk Vols 30,000; Per Subs 560
Subject Interests: Allied health, Dentistry, Medicine, Nursing
Special Collections: Florida Public Health History
The Borland Health Sciences Library is the resource library for the ten Jacksonville Area Health Information Libraries (JAHIL) member hospitals plus other affiliated libraries & organizations

C UNIVERSITY OF NORTH FLORIDA, Thomas G Carpenter Library, 4567 St John's Bluff Rd S, 32224. (Mail add: PO Box 17605, 32245), SAN 320-9385. Tel: 904-620-2553. Interlibrary Loan Service Tel: 904-620-2615. TDD: 904-620-2615. FAX: 904-620-2613. Web Site: www.unf.edu/library. *Dir*, Andrew Farkas; E-Mail: afarkas@unf.edu; *Asst Dir*, Kathleen F Cohen; Tel: 904-620-2599, Fax: 904-620-2719, E-Mail: kcohen@unf.edu; *Circ, ILL*, Geraldine Collins; *Tech Servs*, John M Hein; *Media Spec*, Diane Kazlauskas; *Cat*, Linda L Smith; *Ref*, Sarah M Philips; *Ser*, Victoria Stanton; *Doc*, Bruce T Latimer; *Acq*, Sheila Mangum; *Per, Spec Coll*, Eileen Brady; *Bibliog Instr*, Mary Davis; *Publ Servs, Syst Coordr*, Robert P Jones; Staff 46 (MLS 20, Non-MLS 26)
Founded 1970. Pop 12,000; Enrl 12,000; Highest Degree: Doctorate
Jul 1999-Jun 2000 Income $3,484,829. Mats Exp $1,607,200, Books $496,383, Per/Ser (Incl. Access Fees) $861,175, Presv $32,053, Electronic Ref Mat (Incl. Access Fees) $181,496. Sal $1,698,121 (Prof $834,404)
Library Holdings: Bk Vols 724,473; Bk Titles 417,010; Per Subs 2,578
Subject Interests: Business and management, Economics, Education, Nursing
Special Collections: Eartha White Memorial Coll, memorabilia, photogs, Arthur N Sollee Papers; Senator Jack E Mathews Papers; University Archives
Automation Activity & Vendor Info: (Cataloging) NOTIS; (Circulation) NOTIS; (Course Reserve) NOTIS; (OPAC) NOTIS
Database Vendor: CARL, GaleNet, IAC - Info Trac, Lexis-Nexis, OCLC - First Search, ProQuest, Silverplatter Information Inc., Wilson - Wilson Web
Publications: Annual Report; Books & Bytes
Restriction: Open to faculty, students & qualified researchers
Partic in Florida Library Information Network; NEFLIN; OCLC Online Computer Library Center, Inc; SE Libr Network
Special Services for the Deaf - TDD

JASPER

S HAMILTON CORRECTIONAL INSTITUTION LIBRARY, PO Box 1360, 32052. SAN 377-2926. Tel: 904-792-5151. *Librn*, James Doswell
Library Holdings: Bk Vols 7,500; Per Subs 141

JUPITER

C FLORIDA ATLANTIC UNIVERSITY, John D MacArthur Campus Library, 5353 Parkside Dr, 33458. SAN 371-375X. Tel: 561-799-8530. FAX: 561-799-8587. Web Site: www.fau.edu/library/npb/npb.htm. *Chief Librn*, Patricia Roshaven; Tel: 561-799-8030, E-Mail: roshaven@fau.edu; *Asst Librn*, Holly Coats; Tel: 561-799-8686, E-Mail: hcoats@fau.edu; *Computer Services*, Caroline Wertz; Tel: 561-799-8032, E-Mail: cwetz@fau.edu; Staff 8 (MLS 5, Non-MLS 3)
Founded 1972. Enrl 1,300; Fac 77; Highest Degree: Master
Jul 2000-Jun 2001 Mats Exp $240,000, Books $200,000, Per/Ser (Incl. Access Fees) $21,000, Micro $3,000, AV Equip $5,000, Electronic Ref Mat (Incl. Access Fees) $11,000. Sal $299,575 (Prof $180,828)

Library Holdings: Bk Vols 45,000
Automation Activity & Vendor Info: (Acquisitions) NOTIS; (Cataloging) NOTIS; (Circulation) NOTIS; (Course Reserve) NOTIS; (OPAC) NOTIS; (Serials) NOTIS
Database Vendor: OCLC - First Search
Restriction: Open to student, faculty & staff
Partic in Fla Ctr for Libr Automation; SE Libr Network; Southeast Florida Library Information Network, Inc
Special Services for the Blind - Reading edge system

KENANSVILLE

P KENANSVILLE LIBRARY, 1180 S Canoe Creek Rd, 34749. SAN 377-3531. Tel: 407-436-1970. FAX: 407-436-1970. *Actg Dir*, MaryJo Albers
Library Holdings: Bk Vols 5,000; Bk Titles 4,000
Mem of Osceola County Pub Libr Syst

KENNEDY SPACE CENTER

G NASA, John F Kennedy Space Center Library, 32899. SAN 302-9905. Tel: 321-867-3600. FAX: 321-867-4534. *Chief Librn*, William G Cooper; *Doc*, D Atkins; *Archivist*, Elaine Liston; *Acq*, D Guelzow; *Ref Serv*, Susan Byrd; Staff 14 (MLS 7, Non-MLS 7)
Founded 1962
Library Holdings: Bk Titles 18,000; Per Subs 3,200
Subject Interests: Aerospace science
Special Collections: Archives Coll; Kennedy Space Center History Coll, photog
Publications: Chronology of KSC & Related Events (yearly); Index for the Space Transportation System; Index of KSC Specifications & Standards; Index to Spaceport News (official Space Center newspaper)
Partic in Aerospace Res Info Network; Cent Fla Libr Consortium; Florida Library Information Network

KEY WEST

J FLORIDA KEYS COMMUNITY COLLEGE LIBRARY, 5901 College Rd, 33040. SAN 302-9913. Tel: 305-296-9081, Ext 494. FAX: 305-292-5162. Web Site: www.firn.edu/fkcc/library. *Librn*, Maria J Soule; Tel: 305-296-9081, Ext 322; *Asst Librn*, Jennifer Mitchell; Tel: 305-296-9081, Ext 401, E-Mail: mitchell_j4@firn.edu; *Asst Librn*, Cynthia Lawson; Tel: 305-296-9081, Ext 301; Staff 7 (MLS 3, Non-MLS 4)
Founded 1965. Enrl 259; Fac 36
Jul 2000-Jun 2001 Income $342,396. Mats Exp $47,175, Books $20,200, Per/Ser (Incl. Access Fees) $13,650, Micro $6,800, AV Equip $3,525, Electronic Ref Mat (Incl. Access Fees) $3,000. Sal $262,261
Library Holdings: Bk Vols 30,799; Bk Titles 28,497; Per Subs 257
Database Vendor: DRA
Partic in Col Ctr for Libr Automation; SE Libr Network; Southeast Florida Library Information Network, Inc
Friends of the Library Group

P MONROE COUNTY PUBLIC LIBRARY, 700 Fleming St, 33040. SAN 337-6443. Tel: 305-292-3595. FAX: 305-295-3626. *Dir*, Norma Kula; *Tech Servs*, John Brown; *Spec Coll*, Tom Hambright; *Ch Servs*, Kathy Toribio; Staff 13 (MLS 6, Non-MLS 7)
Founded 1892. Pop 78,024
Library Holdings: Bk Vols 148,923
Subject Interests: Local history
Friends of the Library Group
Branches: 4
BIG PINE KEY BRANCH, 213 Key Deer Blvd, Big Pine Key, 33043. SAN 376-9143. Tel: 305-289-6303. FAX: 305-289-6304. *Mgr*, Stephen Chambers
Friends of the Library Group
KEY LARGO BRANCH, Trade Winds Plaza, 101485 Overseas Hwy, Key Largo, 33037. SAN 337-6508. Tel: 305-451-2396. FAX: 305-853-7311. *Mgr*, Paulette Sullivan
Library Holdings: Bk Vols 27,972
Friends of the Library Group
MARATHON BRANCH, 3251 Overseas Hwy, Marathon, 33050. SAN 337-6532. Tel: 305-743-5156. FAX: 305-743-6093. *Mgr*, Gloria Goodman
Library Holdings: Bk Vols 30,438
Friends of the Library Group
HELEN WADLEY BRANCH, PO Box 1129, Islamorada, 33036. SAN 337-6478. Tel: 305-664-4645. FAX: 305-853-7312. *Mgr*, James Clupper
Library Holdings: Bk Vols 27,959
Bookmobiles: 1

KISSIMMEE

§SR FLORIDA CHRISTIAN COLLEGE LIBRARY, 1011 Bill Beck Blvd, 34744. Tel: 407-847-8966, Ext 318. *Dir*, Linda Stark; E-Mail: linda.stark@fcc.edu; *Asst Librn*, Debbie Jones; E-Mail: debbie.jones@fcc.edu
Library Holdings: Bk Vols 35,000; Per Subs 275
Automation Activity & Vendor Info: (Acquisitions) SIRSI; (Cataloging) SIRSI; (Circulation) SIRSI

P OSCEOLA COUNTY LIBRARY SYSTEM, Central Library, 211 E Dakin, 34741. SAN 323-5947. Tel: 407-935-0777. FAX: 407-935-0676. *Dir*, Bill Johnson; E-Mail: bjohnson@cflc.net; *Librn*, Jennifer Sargent; *Tech Servs*, Sharon Pesante; *Circ*, Joyce Perrilo; *Ref*, Margaret Parrara; *Asst Dir*, Michele Cummings; *Ad Servs*, Margaret Perrera; *YA Servs*, Neil Robinson; *Business*, Susan Lacey; Staff 55 (MLS 6, Non-MLS 49)
Founded 1989. Pop 112,000; Circ 578,639
Library Holdings: Bk Vols 160,000; Per Subs 150
Friends of the Library Group
Branches: 7
BUENAVENTURA LAKES, 405 Buenaventura Blvd, 34743. SAN 376-9224. Tel: 407-348-8767. FAX: 407-348-8113. *Librn*, Maryjo Albers
Library Holdings: Bk Vols 13,000; Bk Titles 10,000
CELEBRATION BRANCH, 851 Celebration Library, Celebration, 34747. Tel: 407-566-2300, Ext 234. *Branch Mgr*, Joyce Gipson
Library Holdings: Bk Vols 13,000; Bk Titles 10,000; Per Subs 15
KENANSVILLE LIBRARY CENTER, 1180 Canoe Creek Rd S, Kenansville, 34749. Tel: 407-436-1970. *Branch Mgr*, Joyce Gipson
Library Holdings: Bk Vols 13,000; Bk Titles 10,000; Per Subs 15
NARCOSSEE, 2700 N Narcossee Rd, Saint Cloud, 34771. Tel: 407-891-6600, Ext 210. *Branch Mgr*, Joyce Gipson
Library Holdings: Bk Vols 13,000; Bk Titles 10,000; Per Subs 15
OSCEOLA CORRECTIONAL FACILITY, 401 Simpson Rd, 34741. Tel: 407-935-0777. *Librn*, Becky Miller
POINCIANA, 101 N Doverplum Ave, 34758. Tel: 407-935-1177. TDD: 407-935-1196. FAX: 407-935-1198. *Branch Mgr*, Beth Lucas
Library Holdings: Bk Vols 13,000; Bk Titles 10,000; Per Subs 15
Special Services for the Deaf - TDD
SAINT CLOUD LIBRARY, 810 13th St, Saint Cloud, 34769. SAN 376-2688. Tel: 407-892-6910. TDD: 407-892-5553. FAX: 407-892-8551. *Branch Mgr*, Diana Hurt
Library Holdings: Bk Vols 20,000; Bk Titles 12,000; Per Subs 15
Mem of Osceola County Pub Libr Syst
Special Services for the Deaf - TDD

J VALENCIA COMMUNITY COLLEGE, Learning Resource Center Osceola Campus, 1800 Denn John Lane, 34744. SAN 376-8309. Tel: 407-847-9496. FAX: 407-932-0855. Web Site: www.osceola.valencia.cc.fl.us/lrc/. *Coordr, Librn*, Linda Swaine; E-Mail: lswaine@gw.mail; *Librn*, Blair Jackson; *Librn*, Claire LeBlanc; *Circ*, Carol Jones; *Publ Servs*, Marcie Rhoads; Staff 10 (MLS 3, Non-MLS 7)
Library Holdings: Bk Titles 13,224; Per Subs 80
Database Vendor: DRA
Partic in Cent Fla Libr Consortium

LABELLE

P BARRON LIBRARY, 461 N Main St, 33935. (Mail add: PO Box 785, 33975), SAN 302-9948. Tel: 863-675-0833. FAX: 863-675-7544. *Librn*, Doris Cutshall
Pop 8,000; Circ 40,000
Library Holdings: Bk Vols 20,000; Per Subs 25
Automation Activity & Vendor Info: (Circulation) Gaylord
Friends of the Library Group

LADY LAKE

P LADY LAKE PUBLIC LIBRARY, 225 W Guava St, 32159. SAN 376-2661. Tel: 352-753-2957. FAX: 352-753-3361. Web Site: ladylakelibrary.com. *Dir*, Marilynn Nesbitt; E-Mail: marilynn77@aol.com; *Asst Librn, Ref*, Dina Hitchcock; E-Mail: deehitchco@aol.com; *Circ*, Mary McIntyre; E-Mail: mmacfla@aol.com; *Cat*, Dallace Meehan; E-Mail: DalMeehan@aol.com; *Tech Servs*, Estelle Clark. Subject Specialists: *Civil War*, Dallace Meehan; *Fiction*, Mary McIntyre; Staff 4 (MLS 1, Non-MLS 3)
Founded 1992. Pop 25,000
Oct 1999-Sep 2000 Income $219,463, State $14,000, City $165,721, County $39,742. Mats Exp $39,220. Sal $94,557 (Prof $21,174)
Library Holdings: Bk Vols 19,760; Bk Titles 18,264; Per Subs 93
Subject Interests: Civil War, Florida, Genealogy
Database Vendor: epixtech, inc.
Mem of Lake County Library System
Partic in Central Florida Library Cooperative (CFLC)
Friends of the Library Group

LAKE ALFRED

S CITRUS RESEARCH & EDUCATION CENTER, (Formerly University Of Florida), 700 Experiment Station Rd, 33850-2299. SAN 302-9964. Tel: 863-956-1151, Ext 226. FAX: 863-956-4631. E-Mail: pkr@lal.ufl.edu. Web Site: www.lal.ufl.edu/library/library.htm. *Assoc Librn*, Pamela K Russ; E-Mail: pkr@lal.ufl.edu; Staff 1 (MLS 1)
Founded 1947
Jul 1999-Jun 2000 Income Parent Institution $81,600. Mats Exp $69,200, Books $2,200, Per/Ser (Incl. Access Fees) $65,000, Presv $2,000. Sal $39,400
Library Holdings: Bk Vols 7,580; Bk Titles 6,800; Per Subs 85
Database Vendor: OCLC - First Search
Function: For research purposes, Reference only, Research library

P LAKE ALFRED PUBLIC LIBRARY, 195 E Pomelo St, 33850. SAN 302-9956. Tel: 863-291-5378. *Dir*, Sally W Mueller; *Asst Dir*, Nancy Timmer; Tel: 863-291-5378, E-Mail: timmer@pclc.lib.fl; Staff 2 (Non-MLS 2)
Founded 1973. Pop 4,000; Circ 14,000
Library Holdings: Bk Titles 24,000; Per Subs 20
Subject Interests: Florida, Large type print
Partic in Polk County Libr Coop

LAKE BUENA VISTA

S WALT DISNEY ATTRACTIONS, Information Services Technical Resource Center, PO Box 10000, 32830-1000. SAN 373-4161. Tel: 407-828-4250. FAX: 407-827-8260. *Librn*, David Hartman; E-Mail: david.hartman@disney.com
Library Holdings: Bk Vols 2,000; Per Subs 350
Subject Interests: Computer science
Special Collections: Systems/Hardware Documentation
Restriction: Staff use only
Partic in Cent Fla Libr Consortium

LAKE BUTLER

S FLORIDA DEPARTMENT OF CORRECTIONS, North Florida Reception Center Library (Main Unit), State Rd 231, PO Box 628, 32054-0628. SAN 302-9972. Tel: 904-496-6000. FAX: 904-496-3287.
Jul 1998-Jun 1999 Income $16,800. Mats Exp $3,930, Per/Ser (Incl. Access Fees) $3,100. Sal $31,000
Library Holdings: Bk Vols 15,000
Subject Interests: Criminal law and justice, Large type print
Special Collections: Hi-Lo Coll
Branches:
WEST UNIT, State Rd 121, 32054. (Mail add: PO Box 628, 32054-0628), Tel: 904-496-6000, Ext 6044. FAX: 904-496-4689. *Librn*, Janet M Coggan; *Librn*, J Hemadani
Jul 1998-Jun 1999 Mats Exp Per/Ser (Incl. Access Fees) $2,505. Sal $34,810
Library Holdings: Bk Vols 4,910; Per Subs 85
Subject Interests: Criminal law and justice, Large type print
Special Collections: Hi-Lo Coll

P NEW RIVER PUBLIC LIBRARY COOPERATIVE, 103 N Lake Ave, 32054. SAN 377-8800. Tel: 904-496-2526. FAX: 904-496-3394. Web Site: www.newriver.lib.fl.us. *Dir*, Virginia K Bird; E-Mail: bird_g@popmail.firn.edu; Staff 4 (MLS 1, Non-MLS 3)
Founded 1996
Oct 1998-Sep 1999 Income $479,000. Mats Exp Books $85,000. Sal $75,920 (Prof $37,000)

P UNION COUNTY PUBLIC LIBRARY, 175 W Main St, 32054. SAN 323-7516. Tel: 386-496-3432. FAX: 386-496-1285. *Dir*, Mary C Brown
Founded 1989. Pop 12,500
Oct 1998-Sep 1999 Income $108,000, State $45,000, County $63,000. Mats Exp $24,340, Books $19,539, Per/Ser (Incl. Access Fees) $1,500. Sal $46,000
Library Holdings: Bk Vols 22,000
Subject Interests: Local history
Friends of the Library Group

LAKE CITY

S COLUMBIA CORRECTIONAL INSTITUTION LIBRARY, Rte 7 Box 376, 32055-8767. SAN 377-0494. Tel: 904-758-8090. FAX: 904-758-0509. *Head Tech Servs*, Terry Bryant
Library Holdings: Bk Vols 5,000; Bk Titles 4,500; Per Subs 70

P COLUMBIA COUNTY PUBLIC LIBRARY, 490 N Columbia St, 32055. SAN 323-7761. Tel: 904-758-2101. FAX: 904-758-2135. Web Site: columbia.lib.fl.us. *Dir*, Faye Roberts; E-Mail: froberts@neflln.org; Staff 6 (MLS 3, Non-MLS 3)
Circ 224,108
Oct 1998-Sep 1999 Income (Main Library and Branch Library) $916,146, State $410,843, Federal $8,087, County $448,213, Other $49,003. Mats Exp $109,133, Books $107,046, Per/Ser (Incl. Access Fees) $2,087. Sal $586,864
Library Holdings: Bk Vols 96,695; Bk Titles 74,327; Per Subs 187
Automation Activity & Vendor Info: (Acquisitions) DRA; (Cataloging) DRA; (Circulation) DRA; (OPAC) DRA; (Serials) DRA
Publications: Friends Newsletter; various bibliographies
Friends of the Library Group
Branches: 1
FORT WHITE BRANCH, Rte 1, Box 2, Fort White, 32038. SAN 376-821X. Tel: 904-497-1108. *Mgr*, Patti Street
Friends of the Library Group

GM DEPARTMENT OF VETERANS AFFAIRS, Medical Center Library, 801 S Marion St, 32025. SAN 302-9999. Tel: 904-755-3016, Ext 2232. Reference Tel: 904-755-3016, Ext 2234. FAX: 904-758-3218. *Chief Librn*, Marylyn Gresser; Staff 2 (Non-MLS 2)
Founded 1955
Library Holdings: Bk Vols 7,964
Subject Interests: Med sci, Patient health educ
Publications: Acquisitions Bulletin; periodical holdings
Function: ILL limited, Referrals accepted
Partic in NE Fla Libr Info Network; Veterans Affairs Library Network

J LAKE CITY COMMUNITY COLLEGE, G T Melton Learning Resources Center, Rte 19, Box 1030, 32025. SAN 302-9980. Tel: 904-752-1822, Ext 1337. FAX: 904-755-1521. *Dir*, Jim Morris; E-Mail: morrisjlc1@lincc.ccla.lib.fl.us; *Asst Dir*, Jo-Ann Bailey; *Circ*, Alice Thomas; *Ser*, Ginney Rankin; Staff 4 (MLS 1, Non-MLS 3)
Founded 1962. Enrl 2,884; Fac 112
1998-1999 Income $221,960. Mats Exp $32,526, Books $12,419, Per/Ser (Incl. Access Fees) $1,020, Presv $308, Micro $7,055. Sal $190,514 (Prof $51,941)
Library Holdings: Bk Titles 47,698; Per Subs 90
Subject Interests: Allied health, Art, Forestry
Database Vendor: DRA
Publications: Annual Report; Internal Operations Manual; Media Catalog; Student Handbook

LAKE PANASOFFKEE

P PANASOFFKEE COMMUNITY LIBRARY INC, 1500 County Rd 459, 33538. SAN 376-2742. Tel: 352-793-8608. FAX: 352-793-4665. *Librn*, Cecelia Brewer Gomez
Library Holdings: Bk Vols 20,125
Mem of Sumter County Library System; Sumter County Public Library System
Open Mon, Wed & Fri 10-4:30, Tues & Thurs 10-4:30 & 7-9, Sat 10-2
Friends of the Library Group

LAKE PARK

P LAKE PARK PUBLIC LIBRARY, 529 Park Ave, 33403. SAN 303-0008. Tel: 561-848-6070. FAX: 561-848-8633. Web Site: www.coala.org. *Dir*, Jane C Terwillegar; *Asst Dir*, Elena Romeo; *Ch Servs*, Carole Lameier; *Automation Syst Coordr*, Molly Phillips; Staff 6 (MLS 2, Non-MLS 4)
Pop 6,704; Circ 32,092
Oct 1998-Sep 1999 Income $228,427, City $204,820, Other $19,671. Mats Exp $29,829, Books $27,776, Per/Ser (Incl. Access Fees) $2,053. Sal $134,114 (Prof $71,518)
Library Holdings: Bk Titles 23,000; Per Subs 83
Subject Interests: Florida, Large print
Publications: Lake Park Library News
Mem of Palm Beach County Library System
Partic in Libr Coop Palm Beaches
Friends of the Library Group

LAKE PLACID

S ARCHBOLD BIOLOGICAL STATION LIBRARY, PO Box 2057, 33862. SAN 303-0024. Tel: 863-465-2571. FAX: 863-699-1927. Web Site: www.archbold-station.org. *Librn*, Fred E Lohrer; E-Mail: flohrer@archbold-station.org; Staff 1 (Non-MLS 1)
Founded 1941
Library Holdings: Bk Vols 6,000; Per Subs 250
Subject Interests: Entomology, Herpetology, Ichthyology, Mammalogy, Ornithology, Plant ecology
Special Collections: Biology of North American Land Tortoise-Gopherus, cataloged reprints; Fla Dept of Geology Publs; Florida Natural History, cataloged slides; US Geology Survey, Florida quad maps
Restriction: By appointment only

P LAKE PLACID MEMORIAL LIBRARY, 47 Park Dr, 33852. SAN 376-5008. Tel: 863-699-3705. FAX: 863-699-3713. *Librn*, Merry Cresswell
Library Holdings: Bk Vols 28,503
Mem of Heartland Libr Coop; Highlands County Libr
Friends of the Library Group

LAKE WALES

S BOK TOWER GARDENS, Anton Brees Carillon Library, 1151 Tower Blvd, 33853-3412. SAN 371-7933. Tel: 863-676-1154. FAX: 863-676-6770. E-Mail: bokbells@cs.com. *Librn*, William De Turk; Staff 1 (Non-MLS 1)
Founded 1968
1999-2000 Mats Exp $2,000
Library Holdings: Bk Titles 6,500; Per Subs 15
Special Collections: Personal Archives (20)
Restriction: Not a lending library

P LAKE WALES PUBLIC LIBRARY, 290 Cypress Garden Lane, 33853. SAN 303-0032. Tel: 863-678-4004. FAX: 863-678-4051. Web Site: www.cityoflakewales.com/lwplhome.htm. *Dir*, Tina M Peak; E-Mail: peakt@pclc.lib.fl.us; *Coll Develop, Ref*, Marcia Loveman; E-Mail: loveman@pclc.lib.fl.us; *Ch Servs*, Ann Thomas; E-Mail: thomasa@pclc.lib.fl.us; Staff 10 (MLS 3, Non-MLS 7)
Founded 1919. Pop 10,000; Circ 47,052
Oct 2000-Sep 2001 Income $385,000, State $20,000, City $285,000, County $37,000, Locally Generated Income $43,000. Mats Exp $45,850, Books $40,000, Per/Ser (Incl. Access Fees) $2,400, Presv $750, AV Equip $1,500, Other Print Mats $1,200. Sal $197,700 (Prof $93,000)
Library Holdings: Bk Titles 60,000; Per Subs 110; High Interest/Low Vocabulary Bk Vols 100; Spec Interest Per Sub 30; Bks on Deafness & Sign Lang 20
Subject Interests: Business, Careers, Florida, Genealogy, Large type print, Spanish (language)
Special Collections: Library of Congress Talking Books; Local History Archives
Automation Activity & Vendor Info: (Cataloging) epixtech, inc.; (OPAC) epixtech, inc.
Database Vendor: epixtech, inc.
Publications: America Libraries; Book Links; Booklist; Library journal
Partic in Am Libr Asn; Fla Libr Asn; Polk County Libr Coop
Friends of the Library Group
Bookmobiles: 1. Serves 2 outlying areas twice monthly

C WARNER SOUTHERN COLLEGE, Learning Resource Center, 5301 US Hwy 27 S, 2nd Flr, 33853. SAN 303-0040. Tel: 941-638-1426, Ext 7235. FAX: 941-638-1472. Web Site: www.warner.edu/lrc/. *Dir*, Arthur Tetrick
Founded 1967. Enrl 760; Fac 60; Highest Degree: Bachelor
1998-1999 Mats Exp $47,075, Books $34,750, Per/Ser (Incl. Access Fees) $8,000, Presv $1,975, Micro $850, AV Equip $1,500
Library Holdings: Bk Vols 86,097; Bk Titles 57,384; Per Subs 348
Subject Interests: Education, Liberal arts, Music, Recreation, Religion, Social sciences and issues
Publications: LRC Connection

LAKE WORTH

P LAKE WORTH PUBLIC LIBRARY, 15 North M St, 33460. SAN 303-0059. Tel: 561-533-7354. FAX: 561-586-1651. Web Site: www.flinet.com/~lwlibrary. *Dir*, Judy Reed; *Ch Servs*, Bea Purcell
Founded 1912. Pop 27,249; Circ 151,089
Library Holdings: Bk Vols 74,809; Per Subs 140
Special Collections: Lake Worth History (Florida Coll), clipping, micro; Large Print Books Coll
Mem of Palm Beach County Library System
Friends of the Library Group

J PALM BEACH COMMUNITY COLLEGE, Harold C Manor Library, 4200 Congress Ave, 33461. SAN 337-6591. Tel: 561-439-8114. Circulation Tel: 561-439-8116. FAX: 561-439-8304. Web Site: www.pbcc.cc.fl.us/llrc/. *Dir*, Brian C Kelley; *Dir*, Mohamed Mansour; *Asst Dir, Publ Servs*, Estaline Rogers; *Per*, Rob Krull; *Media Spec*, William Buntin; *Tech Servs*, Kenneth Myers; *Ref*, Rosemarie Lowrey; *Ref*, Mike Donnelly; *Publ Servs, Tech Servs*, Lisa Hogan; *Instr*, Doug Cornwell; Staff 9 (MLS 9)
Founded 1933. Enrl 16,016; Fac 247
Library Holdings: Bk Titles 101,786; Per Subs 1,474
Subject Interests: Civil War
Partic in SE Libr Network

LAKELAND

C FLORIDA SOUTHERN COLLEGE, Roux Library, 111 Lake Hollingsworth Dr, 33801-5698. SAN 303-0067. Tel: 863-680-4164. FAX: 863-680-4126. Web Site: snoopy.tblc.lib.fl.us/fsc/roux.html. *Dir*, Andrew Pearson; *Online Servs, Ref*, Mary M Flekke; *Cat*, Desiree Sladky; *Publ Servs*, Eridan McConnell; *Per*, Harry Roberts; *Access Serv*, Nora Galbreath; *Coll Develop*, Randall M MacDonald; Staff 6 (MLS 6)
Founded 1885. Enrl 1,696
Library Holdings: Bk Titles 141,000; Per Subs 710
Special Collections: Andy Ireland Coll; Florida United Methodist History Coll; James A Haley Coll
Partic in SE Libr Network; Tampa Bay Library Consortium, Inc

P LAKELAND PUBLIC LIBRARY, 100 Lake Morton Dr, 33801-5375. SAN 337-6621. Tel: 863-284-4280. FAX: 863-284-4293. Web Site: library.lakeland.net. *Coll Develop, Dir, Librn*, Lisa Broodhead; E-Mail: lbroa@city.lakeland.net; *Asst Dir*, Rivanne Chasteen-Futch; E-Mail: rjchas@city.lakeland.net; *Ref*, Averil Townsley; *YA Servs*, Jeannine McCarter; *Tech Servs*, Janice Crawford; *Circ*, Henry Simmons; Staff 13 (MLS 13)
Founded 1926. Pop 74,552; Circ 483,879
Oct 1999-Sep 2000 Income (Main Library and Branch Library) $1,815,023, City $1,541,315, County $273,708. Mats Exp $313,161. Sal $1,291,075 (Prof $28,475)
Library Holdings: Bk Vols 226,533; Per Subs 490
Subject Interests: Local history
Special Collections: Lakeland Chapter DAR; Lakeland Coll; Lakeland Photographs; Polk County Citrus Labels
Automation Activity & Vendor Info: (Cataloging) epixtech, inc.; (OPAC) epixtech, inc.
Database Vendor: Ebsco - EbscoHost, epixtech, inc., ProQuest
Publications: Friends of the Library Newsletter (quarterly)
Partic in OCLC Online Computer Library Center, Inc; Polk County Libr Coop; SE Libr Network; Tampa Bay Library Consortium, Inc
Friends of the Library Group
Branches: 1
LARRY R JACKSON BRANCH, 1700 N Florida Ave, 33805. SAN 337-6656. Tel: 863-284-4288. FAX: 863-284-4327. Web Site: library.lakeland.net/. *Librn*, Cindy Logan; *Ch Servs*, Elizabeth Wesley
Library Holdings: Bk Titles 28,582; Per Subs 94
Bookmobiles: 1

M LAKELAND REGIONAL MEDICAL CENTER, Medical Library, 1324 Lakeland Hills Blvd, PO Box 95448, 33804-5448. SAN 325-8920. Tel: 863-687-1176. FAX: 863-687-1488. *In Charge*, Jan Booker; E-Mail: janbook@lakeland.net; Staff 4 (Non-MLS 4)
Library Holdings: Bk Titles 1,000
Special Collections: Management library
Partic in CinaHL; Health Star; Medline

S THE LEDGER LIBRARY, 300 W Lime St, 33815. (Mail add: PO Box 408, 33802), SAN 325-075X. Tel: 863-802-7000. FAX: 863-802-7809. Web Site: www.theledger.com. *Librn*, Sandy Kline
Library Holdings: Per Subs 28

S POLK MUSEUM OF ART LIBRARY, 800 E Palmetto, 33801-5529. SAN 303-0075. Tel: 941-688-7743. FAX: 941-688-2611. E-Mail: AFortunas@PolkMuseumofArt.org. Web Site: www.polkmuseumofart.org. *Exec Dir*, Daniel E Stetson; E-Mail: destetson@polkmuseumofart.org; Staff 11 (Non-MLS 11)
Library Holdings: Bk Vols 2,000
Subject Interests: Architecture, Fine arts
Special Collections: Florida Contemporary Artists
Restriction: Non-circulating
Research only
Friends of the Library Group

L SECOND DISTRICT COURT OF APPEALS, Law Library, 1005 E Memorial Blvd, 33801. (Mail add: PO Box 327, 33802), SAN 325-8416. Tel: 863-499-2290. FAX: 863-499-2277. *Librn*, Helen Jensen
Library Holdings: Bk Vols 21,000
Branches:
TAMPA BRANCH HEADQUARTERS, 801 Twigg St, Ste 600, Tampa, 33602. SAN 325-8394. Tel: 813-272-3430. *Librn*, Sue Gibbson

CR SOUTHEASTERN COLLEGE, Steelman Media Center-Mary Stribling Library, 1000 Longfellow Blvd, 33801. SAN 303-0083. Tel: 863-667-5000, 863-667-5059. FAX: 863-666-8196. Web Site: www.secollege.edu/academics_library.html. *Dir*, Linda Jones; E-Mail: lljones@secollege.edu; Staff 3 (MLS 3)
Founded 1935. Enrl 1,100; Fac 40; Highest Degree: Master
1999-2000 Income $234,250. Mats Exp $122,778, Books $63,000, Per/Ser (Incl. Access Fees) $40,000, Presv $6,000, Micro $5,225, AV Equip $8,553. Sal $107,944 (Prof $53,076)
Library Holdings: Bk Vols 95,000; Per Subs 448
Subject Interests: Education, Psychology, Religion, Social work
Special Collections: Church Builders Alcove; Curriculum Lab
Automation Activity & Vendor Info: (Acquisitions) epixtech, inc.; (Cataloging) epixtech, inc.; (Circulation) epixtech, inc.; (Course Reserve) epixtech, inc.; (ILL) epixtech, inc.
Partic in SE Libr Network; Tampa Bay Library Consortium, Inc

R SOUTHSIDE BAPTIST CHURCH, Hollis-Hays Library, 310 McDonald St, 33803. SAN 303-0091. Tel: 863-682-8764. FAX: 863-682-5849. *In Charge*, Evelyn Winter; Staff 18 (MLS 1, Non-MLS 17)
Founded 1944
Jan 2000-Dec 2000 Income $24,425. Mats Exp $6,310, AV Equip $2,310, Other Print Mats $4,000. Sal $10,920
Library Holdings: Bk Vols 10,826
Subject Interests: Biblical studies, Children's literature, Parenting
Special Collections: Biblical Studies
Automation Activity & Vendor Info: (OPAC) Follett

LANTANA

S AMERICAN MEDIA, INC, National Enquirer Research Department Library, 600 S East Coast Ave, 33464. SAN 303-013X. Tel: 561-586-1111, Ext 2309. FAX: 561-540-1090. E-Mail: anwen@gate.net. *Chief Librn*, Martha Moffett
Founded 1976
Library Holdings: Bk Titles 2,000
Special Collections: Biographical Clip File; National & International Biographical Directories
Restriction: Not open to public
Function: Newspaper reference library

A G HOLLEY STATE HOSPITAL
M BENJAMIN L BROCK MEDICAL LIBRARY, 1199 W Lantana Rd, PO Box 3084, 33462. SAN 322-8215. Tel: 561-582-5666. FAX: 561-540-3788. *Librn*, Markesha Pierce
Library Holdings: Bk Titles 200; Per Subs 10
M PATIENTS LIBRARY, 1199 W Lantana Rd, 33465. SAN 303-0105. Tel: 561-582-5666, Ext 276. FAX: 561-540-3753.
Library Holdings: Bk Titles 9,800

P LANTANA PUBLIC LIBRARY, 205 W Ocean Ave, 33462. SAN 303-0113. Tel: 561-540-5740. FAX: 561-540-5742. *Dir*, Sidney A Patchett; E-Mail: sidpatchett@netscape.net; Staff 1 (MLS 1)
Founded 1947. Pop 8,900
Oct 2000-Sep 2001 Income City $140,710. Mats Exp $32,000, Books $28,000, Per/Ser (Incl. Access Fees) $4,000. Sal $51,120
Library Holdings: Bk Vols 10,500; Per Subs 40
Friends of the Library Group

LARGO

R CHRISTIAN FAITH COLLEGE LIBRARY, 6900 142nd Ave N, 33771. SAN 303-0148. Tel: 727-531-4498. FAX: 727-533-8408. E-Mail: beacon47@juno.com. *Librn*, Shirley West; E-Mail: shirley.west49@juno.com
Founded 1947. Enrl 65
Library Holdings: Bk Vols 10,000; Per Subs 65

S GULF COAST MUSEUM OF ART, 12211 Walsingham Rd, 33778. SAN 302-8844. Tel: 727-518-6833. FAX: 727-518-1852. Web Site: www.gulfcoastmuseum.org. *Exec Dir*, Ken Rollins
Founded 1946
Library Holdings: Bk Vols 2,165; Bk Titles 2,130
Subject Interests: Art, Art history

G HERITAGE VILLAGE-PINELLAS COUNTY HISTORICAL MUSEUM, Library & Archives, 11909 125th St N, 33774. SAN 371-7437. Tel: 727-582-2128. FAX: 727-582-2455. Web Site: www.co.pinellas.fl.us/bcc/heritag.htm. *Curator*, Donald J Ivey; *Asst Curator*, Robin Walker; Staff 2 (Non-MLS 2)
Founded 1961
Oct 2000-Sep 2001 Income $4,000. Mats Exp $4,000, Books $2,500, Presv $500, Manuscripts & Archives $1,000
Library Holdings: Bk Vols 3,500; Per Subs 500; Per Subs 12
Subject Interests: Antiques, Collectibles, County hist, Florida, Genealogy, Historic preserv
Friends of the Library Group

P LARGO LIBRARY, 351 E Bay Dr, 33770. SAN 303-0156. Tel: 727-587-6715. Interlibrary Loan Service Tel: 727-587-6748. FAX: 727-587-6738. *Dir*, Barbara A Murphey; *Tech Servs*, Adeline Collins; *Ref*, Olga Koz; *Ref*, Gail Sweet; *Ch Servs*, Janice Fletcher; *Ad Servs*, Kathleen Dort; *Spec Coll*, Carla Kerns; Staff 7 (MLS 7)
Founded 1916. Pop 66,869; Circ 600,276
Library Holdings: Bk Vols 195,612; Per Subs 198
Subject Interests: Arts and crafts, Genealogy, Large type print, Local history
Special Services for the Deaf - Books on deafness & sign language; High interest/low vocabulary books
Friends of the Library Group

G PINELLAS COUNTY GOVERNMENT, Heritage Village Library, 11909 125th St N, 33774. SAN 372-6053. Tel: 727-582-2123. FAX: 727-582-2455. *Curator*, Don Ivey
Founded 1961
Library Holdings: Bk Vols 3,500; Per Subs 10
Special Collections: Genealogy; Pinellas County History, photogs

LAWTEY

S LAWTEY CORRECTIONAL INSTITUTION LIBRARY, 22298 NE County Rd 200B, 32058. SAN 325-2574. Tel: 904-782-3811, Ext 378. FAX: 904-782-3157. *Librn*, Raleigh Crosby
Library Holdings: Bk Vols 9,900; Bk Titles 6,000; Per Subs 80
Subject Interests: Criminal law

LEESBURG

§J BEACON COLLEGE LIBRARY, 101 W Main St, 34748. Tel: 352-787-0735. FAX: 352-787-0721. Web Site: www.beaconcollege.edu. *Dir Libr Serv*, Barbara J Morse; E-Mail: bjmorse@beaconcollege.edu; *Coordr*, Dianna Wade
Library Holdings: Bk Vols 19,000; Per Subs 151; Spec Interest Per Sub 12; Bks on Deafness & Sign Lang 197
Automation Activity & Vendor Info: (Acquisitions) SIRSI; (Cataloging) SIRSI; (Circulation) SIRSI
Database Vendor: OCLC - First Search

J LAKE-SUMTER COMMUNITY COLLEGE LIBRARY, 9501 US Hwy 441, 34788-8751. SAN 303-0164. Tel: 352-365-3541. Reference Tel: 352-365-3563. FAX: 352-365-3590. Web Site: www.lscc.cc.fl.us/library. *Dir Libr Serv*, Denise K English; E-Mail: englishd@lscc.cc.fl.us; *Cat, ILL*, David Goff; Tel: 352-365-3527, E-Mail: goffd@lscc.cc.fl.us; *Govt Doc, Ref, Ser*, Nora Rackley; Tel: 352-365-3586, E-Mail: rackleyn@lscc.cc.fl.us; *Circ*, Suzanne Shaffer; Tel: 352-365-3563, E-Mail: shaffers@lscc.cc.fl.us; Staff 4 (MLS 4)
Founded 1962. Enrl 2,511; Fac 64
Library Holdings: Bk Vols 57,779; Per Subs 350
Automation Activity & Vendor Info: (Acquisitions) DRA
Mem of Cent Fla Libr Consortium
Partic in OCLC Online Computer Library Center, Inc; SE Libr Network

P LEESBURG PUBLIC LIBRARY, 204 N Fifth St, 34748. SAN 337-6680. Tel: 352-728-9790. TDD: 352-787-8881. FAX: 352-728-9794. Web Site: www.ci.leesburg.fl.us/library. *Dir*, Nancy Ellen Flint; *Asst Dir*, Cathy Haines; *Ad Servs*, JoAnn Crawford; *Ad Servs*, Robin Dombrowsky; *Ad Servs*, Wendy Farley; *Ad Servs*, Ann Florko; *Cat*, Carol Hubbard; *Ch Servs*, Amy Stultz; *Circ*, Cathy Mahoney; *YA Servs*, Barbara Linder; Staff 18 (MLS 7, Non-MLS 11)
Founded 1883. Pop 40,000; Circ 264,743
Library Holdings: Bk Vols 136,447; Per Subs 371
Subject Interests: Genealogy
Special Collections: Florida Coll; Genealogy; Large Print Book Coll
Automation Activity & Vendor Info: (Cataloging) epixtech, inc.
Friends of the Library Group

LIGHTHOUSE POINT

P LIGHTHOUSE POINT LIBRARY, 2200 NE 38th St, 33064. SAN 303-0180. Tel: 954-946-6398. FAX: 954-781-1950. *Librn*, Doreen A Gauthier; E-Mail: gauthid22@hotmail.com; Staff 6 (MLS 1, Non-MLS 5)
Founded 1965. Pop 10,400
Oct 1999-Sep 2000 Income City $325,781. Mats Exp $86,900, Books $64,900, Per/Ser (Incl. Access Fees) $11,000, Micro $1,000, AV Equip $10,000. Sal $181,700 (Prof $59,835)
Library Holdings: Bk Vols 42,000; Bk Titles 41,500; Per Subs 126
Subject Interests: Florida, Large type print
Automation Activity & Vendor Info: (Cataloging) Athena; (OPAC) Athena
Friends of the Library Group

LIVE OAK

P SUWANNEE RIVER REGIONAL LIBRARY, 1848 Ohio Ave, 32060. SAN 337-6745. Tel: 904-362-2317. TDD: 904-362-2317. FAX: 904-364-6071. Web Site: www.neflin.org/srrl. *Dir*, John D Hales, Jr; Tel: 904-362-5779; *Ch Servs*, Susan Johnson; *ILL*, Paulette Hankerson; Tel: 904-364-3480; *Publ Servs*, Linda Sanderson; Staff 1 (Non-MLS 1)
Founded 1958. Pop 84,000; Circ 293,102
Oct 1998-Sep 1999 Income (Main Library and Branch Library) $1,530,310, State $752,815, Federal $107,927, County $500,785, Other $168,783. Mats Exp $188,343, Books $126,343, Per/Ser (Incl. Access Fees) $33,000, Electronic Ref Mat (Incl. Access Fees) $29,000. Sal $692,677 (Prof $92,000)
Library Holdings: Bk Vols 156,150; Bk Titles 41,200; Per Subs 128
Automation Activity & Vendor Info: (Acquisitions) epixtech, inc.; (Cataloging) epixtech, inc.; (Circulation) epixtech, inc.; (OPAC) epixtech, inc.
Partic in NE Fla Libr Info Network; Solinet
Friends of the Library Group
Branches: 6
BRANFORD PUBLIC (SUWANNE COUNTY), 703 N Suwannee, PO Box Drawer G, Branford, 32008. SAN 337-677X. Tel: 904-935-1556. FAX: 904-935-6351. *Mgr*, Shirley Clark
Library Holdings: Bk Vols 8,750
Automation Activity & Vendor Info: (Acquisitions) epixtech, inc.; (Cataloging) epixtech, inc.; (Circulation) epixtech, inc.; (OPAC) epixtech, inc.
Partic in NEFLIN; Solinet
Friends of the Library Group
GREENVILLE PUBLIC (MADISON COUNTY), PO Box 278, Greenville, 32331. SAN 337-6834. Tel: 850-948-2529. FAX: 850-948-5220. *Mgr*, Nancy Scarboro
Library Holdings: Bk Vols 6,200

Automation Activity & Vendor Info: (Acquisitions) epixtech, inc.; (Cataloging) epixtech, inc.; (Circulation) epixtech, inc.; (OPAC) epixtech, inc.
Partic in NE Fla Libr Info Network; Solinet
HAMILTON COUNTY, Rte 4, Box 3, Jasper, 32052. SAN 337-6869. Tel: 904-792-2285. FAX: 904-792-1966. *Mgr*, Barbara Jones
Library Holdings: Bk Vols 19,200
Automation Activity & Vendor Info: (Acquisitions) epixtech, inc.; (Cataloging) epixtech, inc.; (Circulation) epixtech, inc.; (OPAC) epixtech, inc.
Partic in NE Fla Libr Info Network; Solinet
LEE LIBRARY (MADISON COUNTY), PO Box 35, Lee, 32059. SAN 377-0508. Tel: 850-971-5665. FAX: 850-971-5665. *Mgr*, Tonya Stafford
Library Holdings: Bk Vols 2,200
Automation Activity & Vendor Info: (Acquisitions) epixtech, inc.; (Cataloging) epixtech, inc.; (Circulation) epixtech, inc.; (OPAC) epixtech, inc.
Partic in NE Fla Libr Info Network; Solinet
MADISON (MADISON COUNTY), 1000 College Dr, Madison, 32340. SAN 337-6958. Tel: 850-973-6814. FAX: 850-973-8322. *Mgr*, Charlotte Cason
Library Holdings: Bk Vols 23,500
Automation Activity & Vendor Info: (Acquisitions) epixtech, inc.; (Cataloging) epixtech, inc.; (Circulation) epixtech, inc.; (OPAC) epixtech, inc.
Partic in NE Fla Libr Info Network; Solinet
WHITE SPRINGS PUBLIC (HAMILTON COUNTY), 12797 Roberts St, PO Box 660, White Springs, 32096. SAN 377-6689. Tel: 904-397-1389. FAX: 904-397-4460. *Mgr*, Tracy Woodard
Founded 1997
Library Holdings: Bk Vols 3,300
Automation Activity & Vendor Info: (Acquisitions) epixtech, inc.; (Cataloging) epixtech, inc.; (Circulation) epixtech, inc.; (OPAC) epixtech, inc.
Partic in NE Fla Libr Info Network; Solinet

LONGBOAT KEY

P LONGBOAT LIBRARY, INC, 555 Bay Isles Rd, 34228-3102. SAN 324-7104. Tel: 941-383-2011. *Pres*, Virginia Withington
Founded 1957. Pop 15,000
Library Holdings: Bk Vols 15,100
Restriction: Not open to public

LYNN HAVEN

P LYNN HAVEN PUBLIC LIBRARY, 901 Ohio Ave, 32444. SAN 376-2734. Tel: 850-265-2781. FAX: 850-265-7311. E-Mail: library@beaches.net. *Librn*, Rebecah Digerone
Oct 2000-Sep 2001 Income $5,000
Library Holdings: Bk Titles 16,840; Per Subs 25
Automation Activity & Vendor Info: (Acquisitions) TLC; (Cataloging) TLC; (Circulation) TLC

MACCLENNY

P EMILY TABER PUBLIC LIBRARY, 14 McIver Ave W, 32063. SAN 377-8789. Tel: 904-259-6464. FAX: 904-259-1683. E-Mail: taber@neflin.org. *Dir*, Peg McCollum
Partic in NEFLIN

M NORTHEAST FLORIDA STATE PROFESSIONAL MEDICAL LIBRARY, Rte 1, PO Box 519, 32063. SAN 303-0210. Tel: 904-259-6211, Ext 1447. *Tech Servs*, Shelia Phillips
Library Holdings: Bk Vols 2,000

MACDILL AFB

UNITED STATES AIR FORCE
A MACDILL AIR FORCE BASE LIBRARY FL4814, 6 SVS/SVMG, 5102 Condor St, 33621-5408. SAN 337-7105. Tel: 813-828-2349, 813-828-3607. FAX: 813-828-4416. *Dir*, William W Foster; E-Mail: william.foster@macdill.af.mil; *Ref*, Linda G Janable; Staff 7 (MLS 2, Non-MLS 5)
Founded 1940
Library Holdings: Bk Vols 60,642; Per Subs 1,483
Subject Interests: Middle East, Military history
Database Vendor: IAC - Info Trac, OCLC - First Search, ProQuest
Publications: Bibliographies; Literary Ledger (newsletter)
Restriction: Not open to public
Partic in Fedlink; OCLC Online Computer Library Center, Inc; Tampa Bay Library Consortium, Inc
Library purchases books & subscriptions for all offices on base

AM MEDICAL INFORMATION RESOURCE CENTER, 8415 Bayshore Blvd, Ste 108, 33621-1607. Tel: 813-828-5208. FAX: 813-828-5209. *Dir*, Pamela Edgemon; E-Mail: edgemopm@moed01.mednet.af.mil
Library Holdings: Bk Titles 4,500; Per Subs 138

MADEIRA BEACH

P GULF BEACHES PUBLIC LIBRARY, 200 Municipal Dr, 33708. SAN 303-0229. Tel: 727-391-2828. FAX: 727-399-2840. Web Site: www.tblc.org/sppl/gulfbeaches.html. *Dir*, Jan L Horah; *Asst Dir, Ref*, Mary Alice Dobson; *Ref Servs Ch*, Magg Cinnella; *Head, Circ*, Stanley Silverstine
Founded 1952. Pop 16,900; Circ 165,000
Oct 1999-Sep 2000 Income $454,430, State $36,430, City $244,000, County $159,000, Locally Generated Income $15,000. Mats Exp $70,500, Books $61,000, Per/Ser (Incl. Access Fees) $7,500, Presv $2,000. Sal $204,000
Library Holdings: Bk Vols 67,000; Per Subs 127
Special Collections: Florida Coll
Mem of Pinellas County Public Libr Coop
Partic in Tampa Bay Library Consortium, Inc
Friends of the Library Group

MADISON

S MADISON CORRECTIONAL INSTITUTION LIBRARY, County Rd 360, PO Box 692, 32340. SAN 377-3388. Tel: 850-973-5300. FAX: 850-973-5339. *Librn*, John Davis
1998-1999 Mats Exp $19,000, Books $12,000, Per/Ser (Incl. Access Fees) $4,000
Library Holdings: Bk Vols 12,600; Per Subs 55
Friends of the Library Group

J NORTH FLORIDA COMMUNITY COLLEGE, Marshall W Hamilton Library, 1000 Turner Davis Dr, 32340-1699. SAN 303-0237. Tel: 850-973-1624. FAX: 850-973-1698. Web Site: edtech.nflcc.cc.fl.us/library. *Dir*, Sheila Hiss; Tel: 850-973-1625; *Ref*, Kathy Sale; Tel: 850-973-9452; Staff 3 (MLS 3)
Founded 1958. Enrl 900; Fac 33; Highest Degree: Associate
Jul 1998-Jun 2000 Income State $207,990. Mats Exp $46,023, Books $23,627, Per/Ser (Incl. Access Fees) $6,597, Presv $340, Micro $632, AV Equip $4,270, Electronic Ref Mat (Incl. Access Fees) $3,160. Sal $106,088 (Prof $161,967)
Library Holdings: Bk Vols 30,000; Bk Titles 25,000; Per Subs 125; Bks on Deafness & Sign Lang 85
Special Collections: Deafness Coll, bks, videos; Florida Coll, bks, microfilm, opera, video; Madison History, bks, microfilm, video
Database Vendor: DRA
Partic in Florida Library Information Network; NE Fla Libr Info Network; SE Libr Network
Special Services for the Deaf - TDD
Special Services for the Blind - Magnifying glasses/lamps

MAITLAND

P MAITLAND PUBLIC LIBRARY, 501 S Maitland Ave, 32751-5672. SAN 303-0261. Tel: 407-647-7700. FAX: 407-647-8436. Web Site: www.maitlandpubliclibrary.org. *Dir*, Karen Potter; E-Mail: kpotter@cflc.net; *Automation Syst Coordr*, Thomas Reitz; E-Mail: treitz@cflc.net; *Publ Servs*, Joan Mansson; E-Mail: jmansson@cflc.net; *Tech Servs*, Nancy Dulniak; E-Mail: ndulniak@cflc.net; Staff 15 (MLS 4, Non-MLS 11)
Founded 1896. Pop 9,100; Circ 120,981
Oct 1999-Sep 2000 Income $447,047. Mats Exp $120,419, Books $92,954, Per/Ser (Incl. Access Fees) $12,543, AV Equip $7,729, Manuscripts & Archives $1,693, Electronic Ref Mat (Incl. Access Fees) $5,500. Sal $246,848
Library Holdings: Bk Vols 77,616; Per Subs 240
Special Collections: Natural History & Environment (Audubon Coll)
Database Vendor: epixtech, inc.
Publications: Best of Friends Cookbook; Friends of the Library Friendly Reader; Newsletter (semi-annual)
Partic in Cent Fla Libr Consortium
Friends of the Library Group

MALONE

S JACKSON CORRECTIONAL INSTITUTE LIBRARY, 5563 Tenth St, 32445. SAN 377-2942. Tel: 850-569-5260. *Librn*, Dianne P Garrison
Library Holdings: Bk Vols 14,000; Bk Titles 13,000; Per Subs 94

MARIANNA

J CHIPOLA JUNIOR COLLEGE LIBRARY, 3094 Indian Circle, 32446. SAN 303-0288. Tel: 850-718-2274. FAX: 850-718-2349. Web Site: www.chipola.cc.fl.us. *Dir Libr Serv*, Dr Carolyn E Poole; Tel: 850-718-2272, E-Mail: poolec@chipola.cc.fl.us; *Acq*, Nell Donaldson; Tel: 850-718-2273,

E-Mail: donaldn@chipola.cc.fl.us; *Cat*, Nancy Nobles-Dunkle; Tel: 850-718-2353, E-Mail: nobles-dunklen@chipola.cc.fl.us; *Ser*, Edna Long; Tel: 850-718-2374, E-Mail: longe@chipola.cc.fl.us; Staff 4 (MLS 2, Non-MLS 2)
Founded 1948. Enrl 1,300; Highest Degree: Associate
Jul 1998-Jun 1999 Mats Exp $52,000, Books $18,000, Per/Ser (Incl. Access Fees) $15,000, Micro $7,200, Electronic Ref Mat (Incl. Access Fees) $5,800. Sal $141,102
Library Holdings: Bk Vols 35,000; Bk Titles 33,500; Per Subs 220
Special Collections: Florida Coll
Automation Activity & Vendor Info: (Cataloging) DRA; (Circulation) DRA; (Course Reserve) DRA; (ILL) DRA; (OPAC) DRA; (Serials) DRA
Database Vendor: DRA, Ebsco - EbscoHost, GaleNet, IAC - Info Trac, OCLC - First Search, ProQuest
Function: ILL available
Partic in Col Ctr for Libr Automation; Florida Library Information Network; OCLC Online Computer Library Center, Inc; Panhandle Library Access Network; SE Libr Network

P JACKSON COUNTY PUBLIC LIBRARY SYSTEM, 2929 Green St, 32446. SAN 303-0296. Tel: 850-482-9631. FAX: 850-482-9632. *Dir*, Joanne Rountree; *Asst Librn*, Stanley Littleton; *Bkmobile Coordr*, Randall Hanson
Founded 1977. Pop 43,000
Library Holdings: Bk Vols 32,000
Subject Interests: Genealogy, Local history
Partic in Panhandle Library Access Network; SE Libr Network
Friends of the Library Group

S SUNLAND TRAINING CENTER, Ellen A Thiel Library, 3700 Williams Dr, 32446. SAN 303-030X. Tel: 850-482-9378. FAX: 850-482-9236. *Librn*, Clifford Butler
Founded 1962. Enrl 340
Library Holdings: Bk Vols 2,000; Bk Titles 1,975; Per Subs 11
Special Collections: Audio-Visual Coll of General Interest for the Mentally Retarded
Partic in Fla ILL Network
Special Services for the Deaf - High interest/low vocabulary books; Staff with knowledge of sign language

MARY ESTHER

P MARY ESTHER PUBLIC LIBRARY, 100 Hollywood Blvd W, 32569-1957. SAN 303-0318. Tel: 850-243-5731. FAX: 850-243-4931. *Librn*, Betty Robertson; E-Mail: robertbl@firnvx.firn.edu
Founded 1974. Pop 6,000
Library Holdings: Bk Vols 15,616; Per Subs 26
Friends of the Library Group

MAYO

P THREE RIVERS REGIONAL LIBRARY SYSTEM, 305 W Main St, PO Box 1340, 32066. SAN 376-236X. Tel: 904-294-3858. FAX: 904-294-3861. Web Site: www.neflin.org/neflin/members/3rivers.html. *Dir*, Mildred Galentine-Steis; *ILL*, Janice Miller
Founded 1995
Library Holdings: Bk Vols 40,000; Per Subs 82
Branches: 3
DIXIE COUNTY PUBLIC LIBRARY, Dixie Plaza, Hwy 19, PO Box 306, Cross City, 32628-0306. SAN 337-680X. Tel: 352-498-1219. FAX: 352-498-1408. Web Site: www.neflin.org/neflin/members/3rivers.html. *Mgr*, Inez Swafford
Library Holdings: Bk Vols 11,900
Friends of the Library Group
GILCHRIST COUNTY PUBLIC LIBRARY, 105 NE 11th St, PO Box 128, Trenton, 32693. Tel: 352-463-3176. FAX: 352-463-3164. Web Site: www.neflin.org/neflin/members/3rivers.html. *Mgr*, Wilma Mattucci
Library Holdings: Bk Vols 10,400
Friends of the Library Group
LAFAYETTE COUNTY PUBLIC LIBRARY, PO Box 418, 32066. SAN 337-6982. Tel: 904-294-1021. FAX: 904-294-3396. Web Site: www.neflin.org/neflin/members/3rivers.html. *Mgr*, Kay Green
Library Holdings: Bk Vols 10,200

MELBOURNE

J BREVARD COMMUNITY COLLEGE, Melbourne Campus Library, Philip F Nohrr Learning Resource Ctr, 3865 N Wickham Rd, 32935-2399. SAN 303-0326. Tel: 321-632-1111, Ext 32270. FAX: 321-634-3764. Web Site: www.brevard.cc.fl.us/lrc. *Acq*, Nina Regis; *Per*, Norma Rudmik; *Ref*, Ken Lemhouse; Staff 3 (MLS 3)
Founded 1968
Library Holdings: Bk Vols 43,380; Bk Titles 43,000; Per Subs 580

P EAU GALLIE PUBLIC LIBRARY, 1521 Pineapple Ave, 32935-6594. SAN 303-0342. Tel: 321-255-4304. FAX: 321-255-4323. Web Site: www.brev.lib.fl.us. *Dir*, Sharon K Dwyer; *Ch Servs*, Abi Vandervest; *ILL*, *Ref*, Elanya K Quick; *Tech Servs*, Sandra Johnson-Meelhan; Staff 16 (MLS 4, Non-MLS 12)
Founded 1939. Pop 47,000
Library Holdings: Bk Vols 71,364; Per Subs 199
Mem of Brevard County Library System
Friends of the Library Group

C FLORIDA INSTITUTE OF TECHNOLOGY, Evans Library, 150 W University Blvd, 32901-6988. SAN 337-713X. Tel: 321-674-8021. Interlibrary Loan Service Tel: 321-674-7539. FAX: 321-724-2559. Web Site: www.lib.fit.edu. *Coll Develop, Dir*, Celine Alvey; E-Mail: calvey@fit.edu; *Syst Coordr*, Rodd Newcombe; *Cat*, Susan Massey; *Doc*, Jean Sparks; *Per*, Suzanne Jones; *Media Spec*, Adam Beard; *Circ*, Rosemary Kean; *ILL*, Tori Smith; *Ref*, Wendy Helmstetter; *Bibliog Instr*, Kathy Turner; Staff 8 (MLS 8)
Founded 1958. Enrl 5,937; Fac 471; Highest Degree: Doctorate
Library Holdings: Bk Vols 383,000; Per Subs 5,325
Subject Interests: Aeronautics, Engineering, Mathematics, Science/technology, Technology
Special Collections: Botanical Coll; Edwin A Link Coll (ocean related personal papers); General John Bruce Medaris Coll (personal papers & memorabilia); Indian River Lagoon Coll
Automation Activity & Vendor Info: (Acquisitions) SIRSI; (Cataloging) SIRSI; (Circulation) SIRSI; (Serials) SIRSI
Partic in Cent Fla Libr Consortium; Dialog Corporation; OCLC Online Computer Library Center, Inc
Special Services for the Blind - VisualTek closed circuit TV reading aid
Friends of the Library Group

S FLORIDA TODAY NEWSPAPER LIBRARY, One US Hwy 1, 32935. SAN 324-4512. Tel: 321-242-3500. FAX: 321-242-6620. *Dir*, Belinda Kehoe; Staff 1 (MLS 1)
Founded 1966
Library Holdings: Bk Titles 200
Special Collections: Newspaper 1917-Present
Publications: Library Clips (quarterly)
Restriction: Staff use only

S INTERSIL CORPORATION LIBRARY, Harris GCSD, PO Box 883, 32902-0883. SAN 303-0350. Tel: 321-729-4016. FAX: 321-729-5372. E-Mail: library2@intersil.com. *Head Librn*, Mary B Briand; Tel: 321-724-7733; *Asst Librn*, Stephanie McKinnon; Staff 2 (MLS 1, Non-MLS 1)
Founded 1952
Library Holdings: Bk Vols 15,329; Per Subs 150
Subject Interests: Electronics, Engineering
Automation Activity & Vendor Info: (Acquisitions) SIRSI; (Cataloging) SIRSI; (Circulation) SIRSI; (Course Reserve) SIRSI; (ILL) SIRSI; (Media Booking) SIRSI; (OPAC) SIRSI; (Serials) SIRSI
Database Vendor: Dialog
Restriction: Company library
Function: Archival collection, Document delivery services, ILL available, Literary searches, Outside services via phone, cable & mail, Photocopies available, Reference services available, Some telephone reference

P MARTIN LUTHER KING JR LIBRARY, 955 University Blvd E, 32901. SAN 376-2750. Tel: 321-952-4511. FAX: 321-952-4512. Web Site: www.brev.lib.fl.us. *Dir*, Estella Edwards; *Librn*, Emily Derrough
Library Holdings: Bk Vols 21,769; Per Subs 44
Mem of Brevard County Library System
Friends of the Library Group

P MELBOURNE PUBLIC LIBRARY, 540 E Fee Ave, 32901. SAN 303-0377. Tel: 321-952-4514. FAX: 321-952-4518. Web Site: www.brev.lib.fl.us. *Dir*, Geraldine E Prieth; E-Mail: jprieth@manatee.brev.lib.fl.us; *Ref Serv Ad*, Mauri Bauman; *Ch Servs*, Cindy Dann; *Tech Servs*, Cindy Carson; Staff 5 (MLS 5)
Founded 1918. Pop 66,970; Circ 459,601
Oct 2000-Sep 2001 Income $978,390. Mats Exp $188,851, Books $148,570, Per/Ser (Incl. Access Fees) $12,115, Micro $10,866
Library Holdings: Bk Vols 127,000; Per Subs 298
Subject Interests: Florida, Genealogy, Investing
Automation Activity & Vendor Info: (Circulation) GEAC
Mem of Brevard County Library System
Friends of the Library Group

S NORTHROP GRUMMAN AGS & BMS, Melbourne Library, 2000 W NASA Blvd, PO Box 9650, 32902-9650. SAN 377-2969. Tel: 321-951-5385. FAX: 321-951-5551. *Mgr Libr Serv*, Mary I L Shiau; E-Mail: shiauia@mail.northgrum.com; Staff 2 (MLS 1, Non-MLS 1)
Founded 1992
Library Holdings: Bk Vols 3,600; Bk Titles 2,000; Per Subs 85
Database Vendor: Dialog, OCLC - First Search
Partic in Am Libr Asn; Central Florida Library Cooperative (CFLC); Fla Libr Asn; Florida Library Information Network; SE Libr Network; Spec Libr Asn

C ORLANDO COLLEGE LIBRARY, Florida Metropolitan University Melbourne Campus, 2401 N Harbor City Blvd, 32935. SAN 375-5371. Tel: 321-253-2929, Ext 16. FAX: 321-255-2017. *Librn*, Gloria Semeroz

Fac 300; Highest Degree: Bachelor
Library Holdings: Bk Titles 4,021; Per Subs 54
Partic in Cent Fla Libr Consortium

§P SUNTREE-VIERA PUBLIC LIBRARY, 335 Pineda Court, Unit 103, 32940. Tel: 407-255-4404. FAX: 407-255-4406. *Dir*, Mary Scholtz; E-Mail: mscholtz@sunplus.brer.lib.fl.us
Library Holdings: Bk Titles 25,000; Per Subs 30; Bks on Deafness & Sign Lang 10
Automation Activity & Vendor Info: (Cataloging) GEAC; (Circulation) GEAC

MERRITT ISLAND

P MERRITT ISLAND PUBLIC LIBRARY, 1195 N Courtenay Pkwy, 32953-4596. SAN 303-0407. Tel: 321-455-1369. FAX: 321-455-1372. *Dir*, Susan Hayes; E-Mail: shayes@manatee.brevard.lib.fl.us; *Ch Servs*, Virginia Yuhr; *Tech Servs*, Cathy Latham; *Ref*, Joan Dutczak; Staff 3 (MLS 3)
Founded 1965. Pop 48,000; Circ 216,978
Oct 1998-Sep 1999 Income $872,911, County $661,555, Locally Generated Income $211,356. Mats Exp $162,941, Books $128,941, Per/Ser (Incl. Access Fees) $19,000, Micro $15,000. Sal $520,244 (Prof $114,390)
Library Holdings: Bk Vols 92,807; Per Subs 170
Automation Activity & Vendor Info: (Circulation) GEAC; (OPAC) GEAC
Mem of Brevard County Library System
Open Mon-Thurs 9-9, Fri & Sat 9-5

MIAMI

C ALBIZU LIBRARY, (Formerly Miami Institute Of Psychology Of The Caribbean Center For Advanced Studies), 2173 NW 99 Ave, 33172. SAN 375-3565. Tel: 305-593-1223, Ext 131. FAX: 305-593-8318. Web Site: www.mip.ccas.edu/library. *Librn*, Schlomit Schwarzer; Tel: 305-593-1223, Ext 132, E-Mail: sschwarzer@mip.ccas.edu; *Asst Librn*, Jacquelin Ortiz; E-Mail: jortiz@mip.ccas.edu; *Asst Librn*, Juan Zaragoza; E-Mail: jzaragoza@mip.ccas.edu; Staff 4 (MLS 1, Non-MLS 3)
Enrl 700; Fac 80; Highest Degree: Doctorate
Library Holdings: Bk Vols 20,000; Bk Titles 13,500; Per Subs 215; Bks on Deafness & Sign Lang 21
Subject Interests: Cross-cultural studies, Psychology
Special Collections: Psychological Assessment Instruments
Publications: Library Report
Partic in Florida Library Information Network; SE Libr Network; Solinet

S AMERICAN FEDERATION OF POLICE RESEARCH CENTER LIBRARY, 3801 Biscayne Blvd, 33137. SAN 325-9978. Tel: 305-573-0070. FAX: 305-573-9819. Web Site: www.aphf.org. *Actg Dir*, Donna Shepherd; *Librn*, Jamie Shepherd
Library Holdings: Bk Vols 3,000; Per Subs 10
Restriction: By appointment only

S AMERICAN WELDING SOCIETY, American Council of the International Institute of Welding Library, 550 NW LeJeune Rd, 33126. SAN 373-4188. Tel: 305-443-9353, Ext 299. FAX: 305-443-5951.
Library Holdings: Bk Vols 2,000; Per Subs 200

L BAKER & MCKENZIE, Law Library, 1200 Brickell Ave, 19th flr, 33131. SAN 372-1337. Tel: 305-789-8951. FAX: 305-789-8953. *Librn*, Eddie Martinez
Library Holdings: Bk Vols 10,000; Per Subs 120
Special Collections: Florida Law

M BAPTIST HOSPITAL OF MIAMI, Jaffee Medical Library, 8900 N Kendall Dr, 33176. SAN 303-0423. Tel: 305-596-1960, Ext 6139. FAX: 305-598-5910. E-Mail: baptist@class.org. *Librn, Online Servs*, Diane Rourke; Staff 1 (MLS 1)
Founded 1966
Library Holdings: Bk Titles 1,000; Per Subs 60
Subject Interests: Allied health, Consumer health, Hospital administration, Medicine, Nursing
Special Collections: Antique Surgical Instruments
Publications: Newsletter
Partic in BRS; Miami Health Sciences Library Consortium; Nat Libr of Med; SE-Atlantic Regional Med Libr Servs

CR BARRY UNIVERSITY, Monsignor William Barry Memorial Library, 11300 NE Second Ave, 33161. SAN 303-0806. Tel: 305-899-3760. FAX: 305-899-4792. Web Site: www.barry.edu/library. *Dir Libr Serv*, Nancy K Maxwell; Tel: 305-899-3761, E-Mail: nmaxwell@mail.barry.edu; *Head Tech Servs*, Rita M Cauce; Tel: 305-899-4029, E-Mail: rcauce@mail.barry.edu; *Head Ref*, Ken Venet; Tel: 305-899-3773, Fax: 305-899-3771, E-Mail: kvenet@mail.barry.edu; *Ref Serv*, William Patrick Morrissey; Tel: 305-899-3773, Fax: 305-899-3771, E-Mail: wmorrissey@mail.barry.edu; *Ref Serv*, Frances O'Dell, Sr; Tel: 305-899-2977, Fax: 305-899-3771, E-Mail: fodell@mail.barry.edu; *Ref Serv*, Philip M O'Neill; Tel: 305-899-3773, Fax: 305-899-3771, E-Mail: poneill@mail.barry.edu; *Ref Serv*, Daniele Perez-Venero; Tel: 305-899-3773, Fax: 305-899-3771, E-Mail: dperezvenero@mail.barry.edu; *Ref Serv*, Anthony Valenti; Tel: 305-899-3477, Fax: 305-899-3771, E-Mail: avalenti@mail.barry.edu; *Automation Syst Coordr*, Richard J Bazile; Tel: 305-899-4062, E-Mail: rbazile@mail.barry.edu; *AV*, Lynch Hymn; Staff 9 (MLS 9)
Founded 1940. Enrl 8,112; Fac 255; Highest Degree: Doctorate
Library Holdings: Bk Vols 650,000
Subject Interests: Catholicism
Database Vendor: DRA, IAC - Info Trac, Lexis-Nexis, OCLC - First Search, OVID Technologies, ProQuest, Silverplatter Information Inc.
Publications: Bibliographies (in-house & public); handbooks; periodicals directory
Partic in Solinet; Southeast Florida Library Information Network, Inc

R BETH DAVID CONGREGATION, Harry Simons Library, 2625 SW Third Ave, 33129. SAN 303-0431. Tel: 305-854-3911. FAX: 305-285-5841. *Librn*, Sylvia Friedman; *Chairperson*, Lillian Beer
Founded 1962. Pop 1,500
Library Holdings: Bk Vols 7,000
Subject Interests: Biology, Children's literature, Fiction, History, Religion

M CEDARS MEDICAL CENTER LIBRARY, 1400 NW 12th Ave, 33136. SAN 377-2985. Tel: 305-325-5737. FAX: 305-325-5736. *Librn*, Yvonne Barkman
Library Holdings: Bk Vols 800; Bk Titles 750; Per Subs 52
Partic in Miami Health Sciences Library Consortium

R CENTRAL AGENCY FOR JEWISH EDUCATIONAL RESOURCE CENTER, Adler Shinensky Library, 4200 Biscayne Blvd, 33137. SAN 303-0458. Tel: 305-576-4030, Ext 44. FAX: 305-576-0307. *Dir, Librn, Online Servs*, Shirley Wolfe; E-Mail: shirleywolfe@caje-miami.org. Subject Specialists: *Hebrew*, Shirley Wolfe; Staff 4 (MLS 1, Non-MLS 3)
Founded 1948
1999-2000 Income $100,000, Locally Generated Income $25,000, Parent Institution $75,000. Mats Exp $35,000, Books $20,000, Per/Ser (Incl. Access Fees) $10,000, Presv $2,000, AV Equip $1,000, Manuscripts & Archives $2,000. Sal $90,000 (Prof $45,000)
Library Holdings: Bk Vols 50,000; Per Subs 70
Subject Interests: Archaeology, Biblical studies, Holocaust, Israel, Jewish history and literature
Special Collections: Hebrew Reference; Holocaust (Educational Resource Center Coll), bk, flm, fs, a-tapes, CD-ROM
Automation Activity & Vendor Info: (Acquisitions) Sagebrush Corporation; (Cataloging) Sagebrush Corporation; (Circulation) Sagebrush Corporation; (ILL) Sagebrush Corporation; (Serials) Sagebrush Corporation
Publications: Chanukah Rappings; Ecology in the Bible; Joy of the Shabbat; Soviet Russian Jewry; Wandering through Jewish Miami
Friends of the Library Group

SR CENTRAL PRESBYTERIAN CHURCH LIBRARY, 12455 SW 104th St, 33186. SAN 375-0558. Tel: 305-274-4007. FAX: 305-598-1239.
Library Holdings: Bk Vols 1,200

§J CITY COLLEGE - MIAMI LIBRARY, 5975 Sunset Dr, 33143-5166. Tel: 305-666-9242. FAX: 305-666-9243. *Exec Dir*, Robert Wurst
Library Holdings: Bk Vols 2,000; Per Subs 50; Spec Interest Per Sub 20

S COULTER TECHNOLOGY CENTER LIBRARY, 11800 SW 147th Ave, PO Box 169015, 33116-9015. SAN 377-3124. Tel: 305-380-4230. FAX: 305-380-4344. *Librn*, Dolores Farooqi
Partic in Miami Health Sciences Library Consortium

DEPARTMENT OF VETERANS AFFAIRS

GM KNOWLEDGE BASED INFO MEDICAL LIBRARY, 1201 NW 16th St, 33125-1673. SAN 337-8128. Tel: 305-324-3187. FAX: 305-324-3118. *Chief Librn*, Susan Harker; E-Mail: harker.susan@miami.va.gov; Staff 5 (MLS 2, Non-MLS 3)
Founded 1947
Library Holdings: Bk Vols 2,500; Per Subs 400
Publications: Audiovisual Holdings List; Current Acquisitions; Journal Holdings List
Restriction: Staff use only
Partic in BRS; Medline; Valnet

GM BAY PINES, 10000 Bay Pines Blvd, St Petersburg, 33708. (Mail add: PO Box 5005, Bay Pines, 33744), Tel: 727-398-9366. FAX: 727-398-9367. *Chief Librn*, Diana F Akins; E-Mail: akinsdbay@med.va.gov
Oct 1998-Sep 1999 Mats Exp $206,000, Books $50,000, Per/Ser (Incl. Access Fees) $120,000, Micro $14,000, Manuscripts & Archives $2,000
Library Holdings: Bk Vols 7,000; Bk Titles 6,000; Per Subs 414
Subject Interests: Allied health, Consumer health, Geriatrics and gerontology, Medicine, Nursing
Automation Activity & Vendor Info: (Circulation) Sagebrush Corporation
Publications: Newsletter
Partic in Tampa Bay Library Consortium, Inc; Tampa Bay Medical Library Network; Veterans Affairs Library Network

S EVERGLADES CORRECTIONAL INSTITUTION LIBRARY, 1601 SW 187th Ave, 33185. SAN 377-0842. Tel: 305-228-2000, 305-228-2161. FAX: 305-228-2037. E-Mail: everglades@mail.dc.state.fl.us. *Librn*, L Dominguez; *Librn*, J Brown
Library Holdings: Bk Vols 4,000; Per Subs 51

S FAIRCHILD TROPICAL GARDEN, Montgomery Library, 11935 Old Cutler Rd, 33156. SAN 303-0504. Tel: 305-665-2844, Ext 3424. FAX: 305-665-8032. *In Charge*, Dr Scott Zona; *Librn*, Thomas Rogero
Founded 1941
1998-1999 Income $9,325. Mats Exp $6,825, Books $3,325, Per/Ser (Incl. Access Fees) $3,500
Library Holdings: Bk Vols 16,000; Per Subs 100
Subject Interests: Botany, Horticulture
Special Collections: David Fairchild Coll, papers & photos; Florida Botanists (indexed on-line at: www.ftg.fiu.edu/map/archives.html)
Restriction: By appointment only, Not a lending library
Function: Research library

C FLORIDA INTERNATIONAL UNIVERSITY, Steven & Dorothea Green Library, 11200 SW Eighth St, 33199. SAN 337-7199. Tel: 305-348-2461. Circulation Tel: 305-348-2451. Reference Tel: 305-348-2470. TDD: 800-955-8771. FAX: 305-348-3408. Web Site: www.library.fiu.edu. *Exec Dir*, Dr Laurence Miller; E-Mail: millerl@fiu.edu; *Access Serv, Asst Dir*, Sherry Carrillo; Tel: 305-348-2463, E-Mail: carrillo@fiu.edu; *Asst Dir, Coll Develop*, Salvador Miranda; Tel: 305-348-2982, Fax: 305-348-1798, E-Mail: mirandas@fiu.edu; *Doc Delivery*, Douglas Hasty; Tel: 305-348-2459, Fax: 305-348-6055, E-Mail: hastyd@fiu.edu; *Doc*, Sherry Mosley; Tel: 305-348-3137, E-Mail: mosleys@fiu.edu; *AV*, Mayra Nemeth; Tel: 305-348-2817, Fax: 305-348-3010, E-Mail: nemethm@fiu.edu; *Spec Coll*, Vicki Silvera; Tel: 305-348-3136, E-Mail: silverav@fiu.edu; *Head Ref*, Edward Erazo; Tel: 305-348-3423, E-Mail: erazoe@fiu.edu; *Bibliog Instr*, Stephanie Brenenson; Tel: 305-348-1843, E-Mail: brenenso@fiu.edu; *Syst Coordr*, George Fray; Tel: 305-348-2488, E-Mail: frayg@fiu.edu; *Info Specialist*, Jennifer Fu; Tel: 305-348-3138, E-Mail: fujen@fiu.edu. Subject Specialists: *Administration*, Dr Laurence Miller; *Archives*, Vicki Silvera; *Caribbean area*, Vicki Silvera; *Fine arts*, Mayra Nemeth; *Gen ref*, Vicki Silvera; *Gen ref*, Jennifer Fu; *GIS*, Jennifer Fu; *Govt doc*, Sherry Mosley; *Govt docs*, Jennifer Fu; *Latin American*, Vicki Silvera; *Reference*, Sherry Carrillo; *Reference*, Stephanie Brenenson; *Reference*, Sherry Mosley; *Resource mgt*, Salvador Miranda; *Systs*, Sherry Carrillo; Staff 73 (MLS 28, Non-MLS 45)
Founded 1972. Enrl 25,374; Highest Degree: Doctorate
Jul 1999-Jun 2000 Income State $10,150,155. Mats Exp $3,210,969, Books $757,226, Per/Ser (Incl. Access Fees) $1,479,494, Presv $96,769, Micro $131,013, Other Print Mats $327,568, Electronic Ref Mat (Incl. Access Fees) $383,332. Sal $2,784,966 (Prof $1,173,284)
Library Holdings: Bk Vols 902,265; Bk Titles 790,878; Per Subs 7,149
Special Collections: Geological Survey Maps; Latin Am & Caribbean; Urban & Regional Documents
Automation Activity & Vendor Info: (Acquisitions) NOTIS; (Cataloging) NOTIS; (Circulation) NOTIS; (Course Reserve) NOTIS; (ILL) NOTIS; (Serials) NOTIS
Database Vendor: epixtech, inc., GaleNet, IAC - Info Trac, IAC - SearchBank, Lexis-Nexis, OCLC - First Search, Silverplatter Information Inc., Wilson - Wilson Web
Publications: Info (libr newsletter for university community); Top of the Stacks (in-house publication)
Function: Research library
Partic in Association Of Southeastern Research Libraries (ASERL); Florida Library Information Network; RLIN; Solinet; Southeast Florida Library Information Network, Inc
Special Services for the Deaf - TDD
Special Services for the Blind - ADA terminals for visually impaired

C FLORIDA MEMORIAL COLLEGE, Nathan W. Collier Library, 15800 NW 42nd Ave, 33054. SAN 303-0539. Tel: 305-626-3640. Reference Tel: 305-626-3647. FAX: 305-626-3625. Web Site: www.fmc.edu. *Dir*, Dr Rosie L Albritton; Tel: 305-626-3641, E-Mail: rlalbrit@fmc.edu; *Asst Dir*, Glenn E Pippenger; Tel: 305-626-3641, E-Mail: pippenge@fmc.edu; *Circ*, Jacquina Sturdivant; E-Mail: jsturdiv@fmc.edu; *Per*, Leroy Thompson; Tel: 305-626-3646, E-Mail: lthompso@fmc.edu; *Tech Servs*, Gloria Oswald; Tel: 305-626-3643, E-Mail: goswald@fmc.edu; *Ref*, Daniel Buggs; E-Mail: dbuggs@fmc.edu; *Ref*, Mrs W Ruth Sims; E-Mail: rsims@fmc.edu; *Archivist*, Isis Bermudez; *Ref*, Sadie B Smith; E-Mail: sbsmith@fmc.edu; *Coll Develop*, Lucy Osemota; Tel: 305-626-3642, E-Mail: losemota@fmc.edu. Subject Specialists: *Business*, Gloria Oswald; *Computer science*, Daniel Buggs; *Education*, Sadie B Smith; *Humanities*, Mrs W Ruth Sims; *Mathematics*, Lucy Osemota; *Natural science*, Lucy Osemota; *Social sciences*, Jacquina Sturdivant; Staff 18 (MLS 8, Non-MLS 10)
Founded 1879. Enrl 1,662; Fac 55; Highest Degree: Bachelor
Library Holdings: Bk Vols 114,000; Per Subs 715
Subject Interests: Religion, Social sciences and issues
Special Collections: Archives Coll; Black Coll
Automation Activity & Vendor Info: (Acquisitions) Gaylord; (Cataloging) Gaylord; (OPAC) Gaylord
Database Vendor: Ebsco - EbscoHost, GaleNet, OCLC - First Search, ProQuest, Silverplatter Information Inc., Wilson - Wilson Web
Publications: Handbook; newsletter
Function: Reference services available
Partic in Independent Cols & Univs of Fla; Southeast Florida Library Information Network, Inc

L GREENBERG & TRAURIG, Law Library, 1221 Brickell Ave, 33131. SAN 328-0705. Tel: 305-579-0835. FAX: 305-579-0717. *Dir*, Linda Will; *Assoc Librn*, Terry Seale; *Electronic Resources, Librn*, Julie Bozzell; *Ref*, William Stafford; Staff 8 (MLS 4, Non-MLS 4)
Founded 1975
Library Holdings: Bk Vols 30,500; Bk Titles 10,500; Per Subs 600
Publications: Library handbook (internal use)
Restriction: Staff use only

L GUNSTER, YOAKLEY, VALDES-FAULI & STEWART, PA, One Biscayne Tower, Ste 3400, 2 S Biscayne Blvd, 33131. SAN 326-372X. Tel: 305-376-6000. FAX: 305-376-6010. *Librn*, Sally Haff
Library Holdings: Bk Vols 8,000; Per Subs 100
Subject Interests: Law
Special Collections: Cuban Task Force Info-Bank; International Banking
Publications: Newsletter
Partic in Dialog Corporation; Westlaw

S HISTORICAL ASSOCIATION OF SOUTHERN FLORIDA, Charlton W Tebeau Library of Florida History, 101 W Flagler St, 33130. SAN 303-0563. Tel: 305-375-1492. FAX: 305-372-6313. E-Mail: archives@historical-museum.org. Web Site: www.historical-museum.org. *Librn, Ref*, Rebecca A Smith; Staff 1 (MLS 1)
Founded 1962
Library Holdings: Bk Vols 6,500; Bk Titles 5,000; Per Subs 75
Subject Interests: Florida

L HOLLAND & KNIGHT LLP, Law Library, 701 Brickell Ave, Ste 3000, 33131. SAN 372-1329. Tel: 305-789-7420. FAX: 305-789-7799. *Librn*, Elizabeth Chifari; E-Mail: echifari@hklaw.com; Staff 3 (MLS 2, Non-MLS 1)
Library Holdings: Bk Vols 10,000; Per Subs 75
Partic in CourtLink; Westlaw

C INTERNATIONAL FINE ARTS COLLEGE, Daniel M Stack Memorial Library, 1737 N Bayshore Dr, 33132. SAN 375-3220. Tel: 305-995-5011. FAX: 305-374-0190. Web Site: www.ifac.edu.com. *Librn*, Ida Tomshinsky; E-Mail: itomshinsky@ifac.edu; *Asst Librn*, Carlos Sebastian Baca; Staff 2 (MLS 1, Non-MLS 1)
Founded 1967. Enrl 997; Fac 105; Highest Degree: Master
Library Holdings: Bk Titles 17,839; Per Subs 200
Special Collections: Vogue Magazine, 1947-
Publications: Library Handbook; MLA Bibliography; New Books Bulletin; Orientational Program
Restriction: Open to student, faculty & staff
Mem of Miami-Dade Public Library System
Partic in Libr Info Res Network; Southeast Florida Library Information Network, Inc

S A T KEARNEY INC, Information Center, 200 S Biscayne Blvd Ste 3500, 33131. SAN 377-3582. Tel: 305-577-0046. FAX: 305-577-3837. Web Site: www.atkearney.com. *In Charge*, Rosemary Freeman
Library Holdings: Bk Vols 260; Per Subs 30

M MERCY HOSPITAL LIBRARY SERVICES, 3663 S Miami Ave, 33133. SAN 303-0601. Tel: 305-285-2160. FAX: 305-285-2128. *Librn*, Jean Garrison; E-Mail: jgarrison@mercymiami.org; Staff 1 (Non-MLS 1)
Founded 1951
Library Holdings: Bk Titles 1,300; Per Subs 140
Subject Interests: Cardiology, Internal medicine, Nursing
Partic in Miami Health Sciences Library Consortium

M MIAMI CHILDREN'S HOSPITAL MEDICAL LIBRARY, 3100 SW 62nd Ave, 33155-3009. SAN 328-1329. Tel: 305-666-6511, Ext 4470. FAX: 305-284-1145. *Coordr*, Richard Riera; Tel: 305-663-8543, E-Mail: richard.riera@mch.com; *ILL*, Gerardo Urriola; E-Mail: geraldo.urriola@mch.com. Subject Specialists: *Pediatrics*, Gerardo Urriola; *Pediatrics*, Richard Riera; Staff 4 (MLS 1, Non-MLS 3)
Library Holdings: Bk Vols 3,500; Per Subs 180
Database Vendor: Ebsco - EbscoHost, OVID Technologies
Publications: Newsletter
Mem of Miami Health Sci Libr Consortium

S MIAMI CHILDREN'S MUSEUM, Resource Area, 701 Arena Blvd, 33136. SAN 377-5291. Tel: 305-373-5439. FAX: 305-373-5431. *Assoc Dir*, Deborah Spiegelman
Library Holdings: Bk Titles 500

MIAMI DADE COMMUNITY COLLEGE

J MEDICAL CENTER CAMPUS LIBRARY & INFORMATION RESOURCE CENTER, 950 NW 20th St, 33127. SAN 337-7318. Tel: 305-237-4129. FAX: 305-237-4301. Web Site: www.mdcc.edu. *Dir*, Isabel Hernandez; *Librn*, Carol Zahniser; *Librn*, Elisa Abella; E-Mail: abellae@mdcc.edu; Staff 7 (MLS 3, Non-MLS 4)

Founded 1975. Enrl 2,000; Fac 100
Library Holdings: Bk Vols 12,000; Bk Titles 11,000; Per Subs 200
Subject Interests: Allied health, Nursing
Publications: On the Way to an A (research paper)
Partic in Miami Health Sciences Library Consortium; SE Fla Educ Consortium; Southeast Florida Library Information Network, Inc

J NILES TRAMMEL LEARNING RESOURCES CENTER, Kendall Campus, 11011 SW 104th St, 33176-3393. SAN 337-7253. Tel: 305-237-2074 (Admin). Circulation Tel: 305-237-2291. Reference Tel: 305-237-2292. FAX: 305-237-0302. Interlibrary Loan Service FAX: 305-237-2864. Reference FAX: 305-237-2923. Web Site: www.mdcc.edu. *Dir*, Janis Jordan; *ILL*, Vincent Paterson
Founded 1965. Enrl 15,711; Fac 210
Library Holdings: Bk Vols 143,651; Bk Titles 127,801; Per Subs 704
Special Collections: Archival Coll
Automation Activity & Vendor Info: (Circulation) DRA
Publications: Kendall Campus Library Fact Sheet
Partic in Southeast Florida Library Information Network, Inc

J NORTH CAMPUS LIBRARY, 11380 NW 27th Ave, 33167. SAN 337-7229. Tel: 305-237-1414. Interlibrary Loan Service Tel: 305-237-1138. Reference Tel: 305-237-1139. FAX: 305-237-8276. *Dir*, Dr Celia C Suarez; E-Mail: celsuare@mdcc.edu; *Bibliog Instr*, Suzanne Lynch; *ILL*, Devi Singh; Staff 9 (MLS 9)
Founded 1960. Enrl 14,000; Fac 350
Library Holdings: Bk Vols 144,608; Bk Titles 133,130; Per Subs 650
Partic in SE Libr Network; Southeast Florida Library Information Network, Inc
Initiates online bibliographic services (Knight-Ridder)

J MITCHELL WOLFSON NEW WORLD CENTER CAMPUS LEARNING RESOURCES, 300 NE Second Ave, 33132. SAN 337-7288. Tel: 305-237-3144. Interlibrary Loan Service Tel: 305-237-3454. FAX: 305-237-3707. *Dir Libr Serv*, Zenaida Fernandez; Tel: 305-237-3452, E-Mail: zenaida@mdcc.edu; *Assoc Dir*, Barbara Roberts; E-Mail: brobert@mdcc.edu; *Librn*, Winnie S Huang; E-Mail: whuang@mdcc.edu; *Librn*, Juanita B Johnson; E-Mail: jjohnso@mdcc.edu; *Ref*, Esperanza Garcia-Rubio; Staff 11 (MLS 5, Non-MLS 6)
Founded 1972
Jul 1998-Jun 1999 Income $362,000. Mats Exp $39,800, Books $3,800, Per/Ser (Incl. Access Fees) $15,000, Presv $3,000, Micro $18,000. Sal $226,000
Library Holdings: Bk Vols 42,000; Bk Titles 36,000; Per Subs 189; Bks on Deafness & Sign Lang 100
Automation Activity & Vendor Info: (Cataloging) DRA; (Circulation) DRA; (OPAC) DRA; (Serials) DRA
Database Vendor: OVID Technologies
Partic in Southeast Florida Library Information Network, Inc

L MIAMI-DADE COUNTY LAW LIBRARY, (Formerly Dade County Law Library System), County Courthouse, Rm 2001, 73 W Flagler St, 33130. SAN 303-0466. Tel: 305-375-5422. FAX: 305-375-5436. E-Mail: mdclawlib@jud11.flcourts.org. *Actg Dir*, Chris Carr; *Assoc Librn*, Barbara Hunt; *Ref*, Johanna Porpiglia; *Librn*, Jorge Michalc; Staff 16 (MLS 6, Non-MLS 10)
Founded 1937
Library Holdings: Bk Vols 127,270
Subject Interests: Florida, Law
Partic in Westlaw

P MIAMI-DADE PUBLIC LIBRARY SYSTEM, 101 W Flagler St, 33130-1523. SAN 337-7342. Tel: 305-375-2665. TDD: 305-375-2878. FAX: 305-372-6428. Web Site: www.mdpls.org. *Dir*, Raymond Santiago; *Assoc Dir*, Manny Lomba; Tel: 305-375-5501; *Assoc Dir*, Sylvia Mora; Tel: 305-375-5005; *Assoc Dir, Coll Develop*, Phyllis Sue Alpert; Tel: 305-375-5184; *Assoc Dir*, William Urbizu; Tel: 305-375-5016; *Librn*, Sam J Boldrick; *Librn*, Sue Cvejanovich; *Librn*, Dorothy Donio; *Librn*, Jorge Gonzalez; *Librn*, John Heim; *Librn*, Renee Pierce; *Librn*, Barbara Young; *Tech Servs*, Susan Mead-Donaldson; *Govt Doc*, Maria D Garcia; *ILL*, Diana De Hernandez; *Cat*, Lou McLean; *Circ*, Alice Dupuis. Subject Specialists: *Art*, Barbara Young; *Business and management*, John Heim; *Fine arts*, Dorothy Donio; *Florida*, Sam J Boldrick; *Foreign Language*, Jorge Gonzalez; *Genealogy*, Renee Pierce; *Marketing*, William Urbizu; *Support servs*, Manny Lomba; *Urban studies*, Sue Cvejanovich; Staff 540 (MLS 154, Non-MLS 386)
Founded 1937. Pop 1,626,510 Sal $20,083,500 (Prof $6,456,845)
Library Holdings: Bk Vols 3,886,852
Subject Interests: Florida, International, Latin America, Patents, Spanish (language)
Special Collections: Florida Room, bks, photogs, clippings & rare bks; Foundations Center Regional Coll; Patent
Automation Activity & Vendor Info: (Circulation) epixtech, inc.
Publications: Annual Report, Long Range Plan; Guide to Services (English & Spanish); Library Happenings (Newsletter of the Friends of the Miami-Dade Public Library, Inc); Quarterly Schedule of Programs
Member Libraries: International Fine Arts College
Partic in Southeast Florida Library Information Network, Inc
Special Services for the Deaf - Staff with knowledge of sign language; TDD
Friends of the Library Group

Branches: 32
ALLAPATTAH, 1799 NW 35th St, 33142-5421. SAN 337-7407. Tel: 305-638-6086. FAX: 305-638-6782. *Librn*, Daniel Buggs
Library Holdings: Bk Vols 29,783
Open Mon 1-5:30, Tues, Thurs, Fri & Sat 9-5:30, closed Wed
CIVIC CENTER PORTA KIOSK, Metrorail Civic Center Sta, 1501 12th Ave, 33136. SAN 377-7138. Tel: 305-324-0291. FAX: 305-324-0291. *Librn*, Janice Morris; *Librn*, Sandra Cotto
Library Holdings: Bk Vols 10,970
Open Mon-Fri 6-10 & 2-6
COCONUT GROVE, 2875 McFarlane Rd, 33133-6008. SAN 337-7431. Tel: 305-442-8695. FAX: 305-567-9421.
Library Holdings: Bk Vols 33,779
Open Mon, Wed, Thurs & Sat 9:30-6, Tues 12:30-9, closed Fri
CORAL GABLES SUBREGIONAL BRANCH, 3443 Segovia St, Coral Gables, 33134-7099. SAN 337-7466. Tel: 305-442-8706. FAX: 305-529-2763. *Librn*, Phyllis Alpert
Library Holdings: Bk Vols 114,308
Open Mon-Thurs 9:30-9, Fri & Sat 9:30-6
CORAL REEF, 9211 Coral Reef Dr, 33157-1822. SAN 337-7474. Tel: 305-233-8324. FAX: 305-378-1166. *Librn*, Barbara Roy
Library Holdings: Bk Vols 70,000
Open Tues & Wed 12:30-9, Mon, Fri & Sat 9:30-6, closed Thurs
EDISON CENTER, 531 NW 62nd St, 33150-4327. SAN 337-7520. Tel: 305-757-0668. FAX: 305-757-3975. *In Charge*, Lalisha Mack
Library Holdings: Bk Vols 23,384
Open Mon 1-6, Tues, Wed, Thurs & Sat 8:30-5, closed Fri
FAIRLAWN, 6869 SW Eighth St, 33144-4742. SAN 337-7555. Tel: 305-261-1571. FAX: 305-264-1716. *Librn*, Diane Kemmerling
Library Holdings: Bk Vols 30,193
Open Mon 1-6, Tues 11:30-8, Wed & Thurs 9:30-6, Sat 9-5, closed Fri
Friends of the Library Group
GRAPELAND HEIGHTS, 1400 NW 37th Ave, 33125-1738. SAN 337-758X. Tel: 305-638-5255. FAX: 305-638-6786. *Librn*, Bill Adkins
Library Holdings: Bk Vols 30,614
Open Mon 1-6, Tues 11:30-8, Thurs & Fri 9:30-6, Sat 9-5, closed Wed
HISPANIC, 2190 W Flagler St, 33135-1639. SAN 337-761X. Tel: 305-541-9444. FAX: 305-642-6814. *Librn*, Ondina Arrondo
Library Holdings: Bk Vols 51,043
Subject Interests: Latin America, Spanish (language)
Open Mon, Tues, Thurs & Sat 9-5, Wed 11-7, closed Fri
HOMESTEAD BRANCH, 700 N Homestead Blvd, Homestead, 33030. SAN 337-7644. Tel: 305-246-0168. FAX: 305-248-7817. *Librn*, Rosa Wang
Library Holdings: Bk Vols 50,000
Open Mon, Thurs, Fri & Sat 9:30-6, Tues 12:30-9, closed Wed
KENDALL, 9101 SW 97th Ave, 33176-1985. SAN 337-7679. Tel: 305-279-0520. FAX: 305-270-2983. *Librn*, Phyllis Levy
Library Holdings: Bk Vols 102,316
Open Mon, Thurs & Sat 9:30-6, Tues & Wed 12:30-9, closed Fri
KEY BISCAYNE, 299 Crandon Blvd, Key Biscayne, 33149-1503. SAN 322-5941. Tel: 305-361-6134. FAX: 305-365-0496. *Branch Mgr*, Wayne Powell; Staff 5 (MLS 1, Non-MLS 4)
Founded 1985. Pop 13,000
Library Holdings: Bk Vols 35,982
Automation Activity & Vendor Info: (Cataloging) epixtech, inc.
Database Vendor: epixtech, inc.
Open Mon 1-6, Tues-Wed 12:30-9, Thurs 9:30-6, Sat 8:30-5, closed Fri
Friends of the Library Group
LEMON CITY, 430 NE 61st St, 33137-2221. SAN 337-7709. Tel: 305-757-0662. FAX: 305-757-5747. *Librn*, Faye Finlay
Library Holdings: Bk Vols 25,407
Open Mon 12-5, Tues-Thurs & Sat 8:30-5, closed Fri
LITTLE RIVER, 160 NE 79th St, 33138-4890. SAN 337-7733. Tel: 305-751-8689. FAX: 305-757-5237. *Librn*, Rose Hepburn-Ballou
Library Holdings: Bk Vols 31,633
Open Mon 12-5, Tues, Wed, Fri & Sat 8:30-5, closed Thurs
MAIN LIBRARY, 101 W Flagler St, 33130. Tel: 305-375-2665. FAX: 305-375-3048. *Librn*, Alice Dupuis
Library Holdings: Bk Vols 999,743
Subject Interests: Florida, Genealogy
Special Collections: US Patents
Open Mon-Sat 9-6, Thurs 9-9, Sun 1-5, Oct-May only
MIAMI BEACH BRANCH, 2100 Collins Ave, Miami Beach, 33139-1708. SAN 328-6452. Tel: 305-535-4219. FAX: 305-535-4224. *Librn*, Donald Chauncey
Library Holdings: Bk Vols 101,577
Open Mon & Wed 10-8, Tues, Thurs, Fri & Sat 10-5:30, closed Sun
MIAMI LAKES-PALM SPRINGS NORTH BRANCH, 6699 Windmill Gate Rd, Miami Lakes, 33014. SAN 337-775X. Tel: 305-822-6520. FAX: 305-364-0802. *Librn*, Arthur Liebhaber
Library Holdings: Bk Vols 56,048
Open Mon & Thurs 9:30-6, Tues-Wed 12:30-9, Sat 8:30-5, closed Fri
MIAMI SPRINGS BRANCH, 401 Westward Dr, Miami Springs, 33166-5155. SAN 337-7768. Tel: 305-884-2575. FAX: 305-883-8634. *Librn*, Carol Davis
Library Holdings: Bk Vols 23,358

Open Mon 1-6, Tues 12:30-9, Wed-Thurs 9:30-6, Sat 9-5, closed Fri
MODEL CITY, 2211 NW 54th St, 33142-3067. SAN 337-7792. Tel: 305-636-2233. FAX: 305-638-6828. *Librn*, Zelda Symonette
Library Holdings: Bk Vols 31,206
Open Mon, Tues, Thurs & Fri 9-5:30, Wed 11:30-8, closed Sat
NORTH CENTRAL, 9590 NW 27th Ave, 33147. SAN 371-3431. Tel: 305-693-4541. FAX: 305-694-0315. *Librn*, Anita Cole
Library Holdings: Bk Vols 33,563
Open Mon 1-6, Tues & Wed 9:30-6, Thurs 11:30-8, Sat 8:30-5, closed Fri
NORTH DADE REGIONAL, 2455 NW 183rd St, 33056. SAN 337-7822. Tel: 305-625-6424. FAX: 305-628-3854. *Librn*, Alma Brown
Library Holdings: Bk Vols 172,630
Special Collections: Schomburg Clipping & Index File
Open Mon-Thurs 9:30-9, Fri & Sat 9:30-6, closed Sun
NORTH SHORE, 7501 Collins Ave, Miami Beach, 33141-2107. SAN 328-6479. Tel: 305-864-5392. FAX: 305-861-2032. *Librn*, Barbara Sims
Library Holdings: Bk Vols 30,531
Open Mon 12:30-5:30, Tues, Thurs & Sat 9-5:30, Wed 12-8:30, closed Fri
NORTHEAST, 2930 Aventura Blvd, 33180-3199. SAN 337-7857. Tel: 305-931-5512. FAX: 305-933-4564. *Librn*, Gia Thompson
Library Holdings: Bk Vols 113,375
Open Mon-Thurs 9-8:30, Fri & Sat 9-5:30, closed Sun
CULMER OVERTOWN, 350 NW 13th St, 33136-2598. SAN 337-7490. Tel: 305-579-5322. FAX: 305-372-7734. *Librn*, Sherrill Martin
Library Holdings: Bk Vols 22,020
Open Mon 1-6, Tues, Wed, Fri & Sat 8:30-5, closed Thurs
SHENANDOAH, 2111 SW 19th St, 33145-2129. SAN 337-7881. Tel: 305-854-5286. FAX: 305-854-6324. *Librn*, Shirley Brosch
Library Holdings: Bk Vols 34,975
Open Mon 1-6, Tues-Wed 9:30-6, Thurs 11:30-8, Sat 9-5, closed Fri
SOUTH DADE REGIONAL, 10750 SW 211 St, 33189-2898. SAN 337-7911. Tel: 305-233-8140. FAX: 305-233-4419. *Librn*, Elyse Levy Kennedy
Library Holdings: Bk Vols 160,000
Open Mon-Thurs 9:30-9, Fri & Sat 9:30-6, closed Sun
SOUTH MIAMI BRANCH, 6000 Sunset Dr, South Miami, 33143-5004. SAN 337-7946. Tel: 305-667-6121. FAX: 305-661-6558. *Librn*, Ellen Book
Library Holdings: Bk Vols 64,464
Open Mon, Tues, Fri & Sat 9:30-6, Wed 12:30-9, closed Thurs
SOUTH SHORE, 225 Washington Ave, Miami Beach, 33139-7115. SAN 328-6495. Tel: 305-535-4223. FAX: 305-535-4225. *In Charge*, Margaret Zebrowski
Library Holdings: Bk Vols 14,100
Open Mon 1-5:30, Tues, Wed, Thurs & Sat 10-5:30, closed Fri
TALKING BOOKS, 150 NE 79th St, 33138. SAN 337-7377. Tel: 305-751-8687. Toll Free Tel: 800-451-9544. FAX: 305-757-8401. *Librn*, Barbara Moyer
Founded 1976
Library Holdings: Bk Vols 42,029
Special Collections: Blindness & Other Handicaps Reference Material; Spanish Language Coll, cassettes
Open Mon-Fri 8:30-5
WEST DADE REGIONAL, 9445 Coral Way, 33165-8115. SAN 337-7970. Tel: 305-553-1134. FAX: 305-226-5343. *Librn*, Catherine Conduitte
Library Holdings: Bk Vols 246,746
Open Mon-Thurs 9:30-9, Fri & Sat 9:30-6, closed Sun
WEST FLAGLER, 5050 W Flagler St, 33134-1299. SAN 337-8004. Tel: 305-442-8710. FAX: 305-445-5495. *Librn*, Grace Armada
Library Holdings: Bk Vols 30,472
Open Mon 1-6, Tues 11:30-8, Wed & Fri 9-5:30, Sat 9-5, closed Thurs
WEST KENDALL REGIONAL, 10201 Hammocks Blvd, 33196. SAN 371-3016. Tel: 305-385-7135. FAX: 305-385-5285. *Librn*, Susan Stringfield
Library Holdings: Bk Vols 130,000
Open Mon-Thurs 9:30-9, Fri & Sat 9:30-6, closed Sun
Bookmobiles: 6

P MICCOSUKEE COMMUNITY LIBRARY, Tamiami Sta, 33144. (Mail add: PO Box 440021, 33144), SAN 377-3140. Tel: 305-223-8380. FAX: 305-223-1011. *Librn*, Sharon Logan
Library Holdings: Bk Vols 11,000; Bk Titles 5,000; Per Subs 50

L MORGAN, LEWIS & BOCKIUS, Law Library, 5300 First Union Financial Ctr, 200 S Biscayne Blvd, 33131. SAN 372-1310. Tel: 305-579-0353. FAX: 305-579-0321. *In Charge*, Sid Kaskey; E-Mail: skaskey@mlb.com
Library Holdings: Bk Vols 10,000; Per Subs 100
Partic in OCLC Online Computer Library Center, Inc

G NATIONAL MARINE FISHERIES SERVICE, Southeast Fisheries Science Center Library, 75 Virginia Beach Dr, 33149. SAN 303-0660. Tel: 305-361-4229. FAX: 305-361-4499.
Founded 1965
Library Holdings: Bk Titles 4,000; Per Subs 310
Subject Interests: Ecology, Environmental studies, Marine biology
Special Collections: Fish, Fish Eggs, Larvae, Systematics & Scallops, reprints & micro
Partic in Dialog Corporation; OCLC Online Computer Library Center, Inc

M NORTH SHORE MEDICAL CENTER, Medical Library, 1100 NW 95th St, 33150. SAN 375-1643. Tel: 305-835-6000, Ext 6530. FAX: 305-694-4837. *Librn*, Diana Cormier
Library Holdings: Bk Titles 350; Per Subs 85

R SAINT JOHN VIANNEY COLLEGE, Seminary Library, 2900 SW 87th Ave, 33165. SAN 303-0687. Tel: 305-223-4561, Ext 16. FAX: 305-223-0650. *Dir*, Maria Rodriguez
Founded 1960
Library Holdings: Bk Vols 50,364; Bk Titles 42,398; Per Subs 233
Subject Interests: Religion
Special Collections: Philosophy & Literature Bi-lingual Coll

SR SAINT LOUIS CATHOLIC LIBRARY & RESOURCE CENTER, 7270 SW 120 St, 33156. SAN 372-0004. Tel: 305-238-7562. FAX: 305-238-6844. *Librn*, Joella Foster
Founded 1979
Library Holdings: Bk Vols 6,182; Bk Titles 4,493; Per Subs 15

C ST THOMAS UNIVERSITY LIBRARY, 16400 NW 32nd Ave, 33054. SAN 321-5415. Tel: 305-628-6667. FAX: 305-628-6666. Web Site: www.stu.edu. *Actg Dir*, Bryan Cooper; Tel: 305-474-6814, E-Mail: bcooper@stu.edu; *Acq*, Marta Gutierrez; Tel: 305-628-6672, E-Mail: mgutierr@stu.edu; *ILL*, Mary Monaco; Tel: 305-628-6671, E-Mail: mmonaco@stu.edu; *Govt Doc, Ref*, Jeannette Neuschaefer; Tel: 305-628-6668, E-Mail: jneuscha@stu.edu; *Media Spec*, Wolfgang Reisterer; Tel: 305-628-6733, E-Mail: wolfgang@stu.edu; *Ser*, Rosario Cruz; *Cat*, Grisel Choter; Tel: 305-628-6671, E-Mail: gchoter@stu.edu; *Ser*, Olga Ozores; Tel: 305-628-6672; *Circ*, Isabel Medina; *Archivist*, Margaret Elliston; Tel: 305-648-6669, E-Mail: mellisto@stu.edu; Staff 9 (MLS 5, Non-MLS 4)
Founded 1962. Enrl 2,100; Fac 80; Highest Degree: Master
1999-2000 Income $761,892. Mats Exp $192,937, Books $54,466, Per/Ser (Incl. Access Fees) $89,488, Presv $2,974, Micro $15,164, AV Equip $3,855, Electronic Ref Mat (Incl. Access Fees) $26,990. Sal $298,630 (Prof $178,368)
Library Holdings: Bk Vols 128,357; Bk Titles 99,000; Per Subs 900
Special Collections: Black Catholic Archives; Dorothy Day Coll; Jackie Gleason Kinescope Archives; Walt Whitman Coll
Publications: Library Handbook; Library Newsletter
Partic in OCLC Online Computer Library Center, Inc

S SOUTH FLORIDA CORRECTIONAL CENTER LIBRARY, 14000 NW 41st, 33178. SAN 377-3515. Tel: 305-592-9567. FAX: 305-470-5628. *Librn*, Marc Nazon, Jr
Library Holdings: Bk Vols 3,500; Per Subs 60
Friends of the Library Group

GM SOUTH FLORIDA EVALUATION & TREATMENT CENTER LIBRARY, 2200 NW Seventh Ave, 33127. SAN 377-3167. Tel: 305-637-4605.
Library Holdings: Bk Vols 1,000; Per Subs 20
Partic in Fla Libr Asn

M SOUTH MIAMI HOSPITAL, Health Sciences Library, 6200 SW 73rd St, 33143. SAN 328-1035. Tel: 305-661-4611, Ext 8219. FAX: 305-662-5124. *Librn*, Diane Rourke; E-Mail: dianer@bhssf.org; Staff 2 (MLS 1, Non-MLS 1)
Founded 1977
Library Holdings: Bk Titles 800; Per Subs 160
Subject Interests: Allied health, Medicine, Nursing
Publications: Library Letter
Mem of Miami Health Sci Libr Consortium
Partic in Medline

L STEARNS, WEAVER, MILLER, WEISSLER, ALHADEFF & SITTERSON, Law Library, 2200 Museum Tower, 150 W Flagler St, 33130. SAN 372-1345. Tel: 305-789-3251. FAX: 305-789-3395. *Librn*, Barbara A Beall; E-Mail: bbeall@swmwas.com; *Asst Librn*, Steven Frishknecht; Tel: 305-789-3225; Staff 2 (MLS 1, Non-MLS 1)
Library Holdings: Bk Vols 15,000; Per Subs 186
Subject Interests: Banking, Corp law, Securities
Automation Activity & Vendor Info: (Acquisitions) EOS; (Cataloging) EOS; (Circulation) EOS; (Serials) EOS
Database Vendor: Lexis-Nexis

L STEEL, HECTOR & DAVIS LIBRARY, 200 S Biscayne Blvd, Ste 4000, 33131. SAN 327-0939. Tel: 305-577-2954. FAX: 305-577-7001. Web Site: www.steelhector.com/library_banner.htm. *Dir Libr Serv, Librn*, Monica Wilson
Library Holdings: Bk Vols 30,000; Per Subs 700
Publications: "SH & D NEWSLETTER" (newsletter)
Restriction: Not open to public

S SURVIVAL RESEARCH FOUNDATION LIBRARY, PO Box 63-0026, 33163-0026. SAN 329-1960. Tel: 305-936-1408. *Librn*, Joyce Berger
Founded 1980
Library Holdings: Bk Titles 50
Subject Interests: Religion
Special Collections: Aristocracy of the Dead; Encyclopedia of Parapsychology & Psychical Research; Evidence of Life After Death;

Journals of the American Society for Psychical Research; Journals of the Society for Psychical Research; Lives & Letters in American Parapsychology; Religion & Parapsychology
Special Services for the Blind - Talking book center

R TEMPLE ISRAEL OF GREATER MIAMI LIBRARY, 137 NE 19th St, 33132. SAN 303-0717. Tel: 305-573-5900. FAX: 305-573-5904. *Librn*, Linda Datko
Founded 1944
Library Holdings: Bk Vols 11,000; Bk Titles 9,000; Per Subs 15
Subject Interests: Archaeology, Biblical studies, Fiction, History, Israel, Nonfiction, Philosophy
Special Collections: Art Books; Haggadahs; Special Catalogs (500)

S THE MIAMI HERALD, Information Center, One Herald Plaza, 33132. SAN 303-0636. Tel: 305-376-3402, 305-376-3434. FAX: 305-376-4424, 305-995-8183. Web Site: www.herald.com. *Mgr*, Liz Donovan; *Mgr*, Gay Nameti; *Info Specialist*, Bill Whiting
Founded 1940
Library Holdings: Bk Vols 2,500; Per Subs 70
Special Collections: Newspaper clippings: Mia-Herald & News 1940-1982
Partic in Dialog Corporation; Dow Jones News Retrieval
Friends of the Library Group

GL THIRD DISTRICT COURT OF APPEALS, Law Library, 2001 SW 117th Ave, 33175. SAN 303-0555. Tel: 305-229-3200. FAX: 305-229-3206.
Founded 1957
Library Holdings: Bk Vols 25,000; Per Subs 65
Partic in Westlaw
Open Mon-Fri 8-5

C TRINITY INTERNATIONAL UNIVERSITY LIBRARY, 500 NE First Ave, 33132. SAN 303-0628. Tel: 305-577-4600, Ext 138. FAX: 305-577-4612. *Dir*, Valda Adeyiga
Founded 1949. Enrl 380; Fac 20; Highest Degree: Master
Library Holdings: Bk Titles 49,000; Per Subs 150
Subject Interests: Business, Education, Psychology, Religion
Partic in Southeast Florida Library Information Network, Inc

G UNITED STATES NATIONAL OCEANIC & ATMOSPHERIC ADMINISTRATION, Miami Regional Library at AOML, 4301 Rickenbacker Causeway, 33149. SAN 303-0679. Tel: 305-361-4428, 305-361-4429. FAX: 305-361-4429. Web Site: www.aoml.noaa.gov/general/lib. *Dir*, Linda L Pikula; E-Mail: pikula@aoml.noaa.gov
Founded 1972
Library Holdings: Bk Titles 20,000; Per Subs 200
Subject Interests: Mathematics, Ocean engineering, Oceanography
Special Collections: US Coast & Geodetic Survey Report 1851-1928
Publications: Acquisitions Monthly; Database listing; Serials catalog
Partic in BRS; Dialog Corporation; OCLC Online Computer Library Center, Inc
Branches:
NATIONAL HURRICANE CENTER LIBRARY, 11691 SW 17 St, 33165-2149. SAN 302-8933. Tel: 305-229-4406. FAX: 305-553-9879. Web Site: www.aoml.noaa.gov/general/lib/nhcinfo.html. *Dir*, Linda Pikula; *Asst Dir*, Robert Britter
Founded 1956
Library Holdings: Bk Vols 9,000; Per Subs 50
Subject Interests: Meteorology
Special Collections: Technical Reports Coll; Tropical Typhoons & Cyclones
Publications: Acquisitions; Database listing; Newsletter; Serials listing
Restriction: Open to public for reference only
Partic in BRS; Dialog Corporation; OCLC Online Computer Library Center, Inc

C UNIVERSITY OF MIAMI, Rosenstiel School of Marine & Atmospheric Science Library, 4600 Rickenbacker Causeway, 33149-1098. SAN 337-8039. Tel: 305-361-4060. Interlibrary Loan Service Tel: 305-361-4020. FAX: 305-361-9306. E-Mail: library@rsmas.miami.edu. Web Site: www.rsmas.miami.edu/support/lib.html. *Asst Librn*, Helen D Albertson; Tel: 305-361-4020, E-Mail: halbertson@rsmas.miami.edu; *Acq*, Guillermina Carrandi; Staff 5 (MLS 2, Non-MLS 3)
Founded 1943. Highest Degree: Doctorate
Jun 1998-May 1999 Income $448,341, Locally Generated Income $4,322, Parent Institution $444,019. Mats Exp $240,961, Books $51,490, Per/Ser (Incl. Access Fees) $182,958, Presv $6,468, Micro $45. Sal $192,030 (Prof $99,283)
Library Holdings: Bk Vols 70,151; Per Subs 765
Subject Interests: Atmospheric sci, Marine sci
Special Collections: Expedition reports; Marine & Atmospheric Atlases; Nautical Charts
Database Vendor: Dialog, Ebsco - EbscoHost, IAC - Info Trac, OCLC - First Search
Publications: Serials list
Restriction: Restricted borrowing privileges
Partic in FLIN; OCLC Online Computer Library Center, Inc; Southeast Florida Library Information Network, Inc

Departmental Libraries:
CM CANCER INFORMATION SERVICE, FL & GA, 1150 NW 14th St, Ste 207, 33136. SAN 326-680X. Tel: 305-548-4821. Toll Free Tel: 800-422-6237. FAX: 305-243-6678.; Staff 5 (MLS 5)
CM LOUIS CALDER MEMORIAL LIBRARY, School of Medicine, PO Box 016950, 33101. SAN 337-8063. Tel: 305-243-6441. Interlibrary Loan Service Tel: 305-243-6749. FAX: 305-324-4089. Web Site: calder.med.miami.edu. *Chair, Dir*, Henry L Lemkau, Jr; E-Mail: hlemkau@med.miami.edu; *Coll Develop*, Mary P Dillon; *ILL*, Peter Cruz; *Ref*, Joaquin Arriaga; *Acq, Ser*, Amalia De la Vega; *Circ*, Teresita Sayus; *Dir, Tech Servs*, Erica Powell; *Cat*, Doreen Crooks
Founded 1952. Enrl 871; Fac 1,007; Highest Degree: Doctorate
Jun 1998-May 1999 Income $2,538,558. Mats Exp $837,606, Books $72,059, Per/Ser (Incl. Access Fees) $725,562, Presv $39,985. Sal $1,373,907 (Prof $968,035)
Library Holdings: Bk Vols 198,255; Per Subs 1,787
Special Collections: Florida Coll; Floridiana, bks, pamphlets; History of Medicine Archives & Faculty Publications
Automation Activity & Vendor Info: (Acquisitions) Innovative Interfaces Inc.; (Cataloging) Innovative Interfaces Inc.; (Circulation) Innovative Interfaces Inc.; (OPAC) Innovative Interfaces Inc.; (Serials) Innovative Interfaces Inc.
Database Vendor: OVID Technologies
Publications: Bi-annual Report; Bulletin (bi-monthly)
Partic in Consortium Of Southern Biomedical Libraries (CONBLS); Miami Health Sciences Library Consortium; National Network Of Libraries Of Medicine - South Central Region; OCLC Online Computer Library Center, Inc
Friends of the Library Group
MARY & EDWARD NORTON LIBRARY OF OPHTHALMOLOGY, Bascom Palmer Eye Inst, 900 NW 17th St, 33101. (Mail add: PO Box 016880, 33101), SAN 337-8098. Tel: 305-326-6078. FAX: 305-326-6015. *Librn*, Reva Hurtes; E-Mail: rhurtes@bpei.med.miami.edu
Founded 1962
Library Holdings: Bk Vols 20,000; Per Subs 230
Subject Interests: Ophthalmology
Special Collections: AV Coll; Historical Coll

S UP FRONT, INC, Drug Information Library, 12360 SW 132nd St, Ste 215, 33186. SAN 324-637X. Tel: 786-242-8222. *Exec Dir*, James Hall
Founded 1973
Library Holdings: Bk Titles 2,500
Subject Interests: Drug info, Drug related topics
Publications: Street Pharmacologist; Up Front About... (drug info pamphlets)

S VIZCAYA GUIDES LIBRARY, 3251 S Miami Ave, 33129-2897. SAN 303-0733. Tel: 305-250-9133, Ext 2242. FAX: 305-285-2004. *Librn*, Don Gayer
Founded 1954
Library Holdings: Bk Titles 3,000
Subject Interests: Art and architecture, Renaissance
Special Collections: James Deering Coll

L WALTON LANTAFF SCHROEDER & CARSON, Law Library, 9350 Financial Ctr, 10th flr, 9350 S Dixie Hwy, 33156. SAN 325-8572. Tel: 305-671-1300, Ext 390. FAX: 305-670-7065. E-Mail: wlscmia@bellsouth.net.
Library Holdings: Bk Vols 30,000

MIAMI BEACH

M MOUNT SINAI MEDICAL CENTER, Medical Library, 4300 Alton Rd, 33140. SAN 303-0768. Tel: 305-674-2840. FAX: 305-674-2843. *Librn*, Irene Bohlmann; E-Mail: ibohlman@msmc.com; Staff 2 (MLS 1, Non-MLS 1)
Founded 1946
Library Holdings: Bk Titles 6,500; Per Subs 450
Restriction: Staff use only
Partic in Miami Health Sciences Library Consortium

S REED INSTITUTE LIBRARY, 1015 W 47th St, 33140. SAN 329-7284. Tel: 305-532-5456. *Librn*, Lillian Martin
Library Holdings: Bk Vols 2,980; Per Subs 38
Partic in FLIN

R TEMPLE BETH SHOLOM LIBRARY, 4144 Chase Ave, 33140. SAN 303-0784. Tel: 305-538-7231. FAX: 305-531-5428.
Founded 1949
Library Holdings: Bk Titles 5,049; Per Subs 63
Subject Interests: Current events, Holocaust, Judaica (lit or hist of Jews)
Special Collections: Holocaust Literature
Friends of the Library Group

MIAMI SHORES

P BROCKWAY MEMORIAL LIBRARY, 10021 NE Second Ave, 33138. SAN 303-0814. Tel: 305-758-8107. FAX: 305-754-7660. E-Mail: msbml@yahoo.com. *Acq, Cat, Dir*, Elizabeth Esper; *Ch Servs, YA Servs*, Anne Kelly; Staff 9 (MLS 2, Non-MLS 7)

Founded 1949. Pop 10,065; Circ 52,044
Library Holdings: Bk Titles 50,425; Per Subs 128
Automation Activity & Vendor Info: (Cataloging) Follett; (Circulation) Follett; (OPAC) Follett
Database Vendor: Ebsco - EbscoHost
Friends of the Library Group

MIDDLEBURG

P MIDDLEBURG PUBLIC LIBRARY, 2245 Aster St, 32068. SAN 322-5712. Tel: 904-282-2495. FAX: 904-282-0457. *In Charge*, Opal Miller
Library Holdings: Bk Vols 30,000
Friends of the Library Group

MILTON

§S FLORIDA DEPARTMENT OF CORRECTIONS, Santa Rosa Correctional Institution Library, 5850 E Milton Rd, 32583. Tel: 850-983-5800. FAX: 850-983-5907. *Librn*, Barry Rhodes
Library Holdings: Bk Vols 1,500; Per Subs 21

UNITED STATES NAVY
A NAVAL AIR STATION, WHITING FIELD LIBRARY, Bldg 1417, 7180 Langley St, 32570-5000. SAN 337-8276. Tel: 850-623-7274, 850-623-7502, Ext 28. FAX: 850-623-7561. *Librn*, Lisa J Erhardt
Founded 1969
Library Holdings: Bk Vols 13,500; Per Subs 36
Subject Interests: Aeronautics, Electronics, Mathematics, Meteorology

MIMS

§P MIMS-SCOTTSMOOR PUBLIC LIBRARY, 3615 Lionel Rd, 32754. Tel: 407-264-5080. FAX: 407-264-5081. Web Site: manatee.brev.lib.fl.us/locations/msa/msa.htm. *Dir*, Heather Lennon; E-Mail: hlennon@manatee.brev.lib.fl.us; *Ch Servs*, Vicki Kelley
Library Holdings: Bk Titles 20,000; Per Subs 22
Mem of Brevard County Library System
Open Mon 9-5, Tues & Wed 10-6, Thurs 10-8, Fri 10-5, Sat 9-1

MONTICELLO

S JEFFERSON CORRECTIONAL INSTITUTION LIBRARY, Rte 1 Box 225, 32344-0430. SAN 377-3000. Tel: 850-997-1987, Ext 236. *Librn*, Theresa Cournoyer
Library Holdings: Bk Vols 9,017; Per Subs 107

P JEFFERSON COUNTY PUBLIC LIBRARY, 260 N Cherry St, 32344. SAN 303-0830. Tel: 850-342-0205. FAX: 850-342-0207. *Dir*, Verna Brock; *Circ*, Saundra Weilbacher; *Tech Servs*, Angela Scott; *Ch Servs*, Debbie Craig
Library Holdings: Bk Vols 23,000; Bk Titles 21,000; Per Subs 50
Special Collections: Florida Coll; Literacy, Prof, Equipment
Publications: Cherry Street Rag (newsletter)
Partic in Panhandle Library Access Network
Literacy Volunteers of America Programs
Friends of the Library Group

MOORE HAVEN

S MOORE HAVEN CORRECTIONAL INSTITUTION LIBRARY, 1990 E State Rd 78 NW, 33471-8837. (Mail add: PO Box 718501, 33471-5501), SAN 377-1288. Tel: 941-946-2420. FAX: 863-946-2481. *Librn*, Sabrina Gadson
Library Holdings: Bk Vols 2,303; Per Subs 27

MOUNT DORA

P W T BLAND PUBLIC LIBRARY, 1995 N Donnelly St, 32757. SAN 303-0849. Tel: 352-735-7180. FAX: 352-735-0074. Web Site: ci.mount-dora.fl.us/departments/library.htm. *Dir*, Stephanie Haimes; E-Mail: haimess@ci.mt-doro.fl.us; *Ch Servs*, Rosalie Williams; E-Mail: williamss@ci.mount-dora.fl.us; *Ref Serv*, Robert Turkel; E-Mail: turkelr@ci.mount-dora.fl.us; Staff 3 (MLS 3)
Founded 1905. Pop 25,000; Circ 46,750
Library Holdings: Bk Vols 45,721; Bk Titles 41,678; Per Subs 150
Special Collections: Florida Coll; Large Print Coll
Mem of Lake County Library System
Partic in Central Florida Library Cooperative (CFLC)
Friends of the Library Group

MULBERRY

P DR C C PEARCE MUNICIPAL LIBRARY, 103 E Canal St, 33860. (Mail add: PO Box 707, 33860), Tel: 863-425-3246. FAX: 863-425-8818. *Dir*, Roxanna Tovrea; E-Mail: tovrear@pclc.lib.fl.us; Staff 2 (MLS 1, Non-MLS 1)
Founded 1949. Pop 3,384
Oct 1999-Sep 2000 Income $90,839, City $82,312, County $8,527. Sal $48,747 (Prof $33,000)
Library Holdings: Bk Vols 10,000; Bk Titles 13,000
Automation Activity & Vendor Info: (Cataloging) epixtech, inc.; (Circulation) epixtech, inc.
Function: Photocopies available
Partic in Polk County Libr Coop

§SR SPURGEON BAPTIST BIBLE COLLEGE, Oluf & Lois Jensen Library, 4440 Spurgeon Dr, 33860-9531. Tel: 863-425-3429. FAX: 863-425-3861. *Librn*, Mary Hobson

NAPLES

S AMERICAN FAMILY FOUNDATION, Resource Center, PMB 313, PO Box 413005, 34101-3005. SAN 375-7226. Tel: 941-514-3081. FAX: 732-352-6818. E-Mail: aff@csj.org. Web Site: www.csj.org. *Exec Dir*, Dr Michael Langone
Library Holdings: Bk Titles 75

S AMERICAN IVY SOCIETY LIBRARY, PO Box 2123, 34106-2123. SAN 326-5145. Tel: 937-862-4700. FAX: 937-862-4479. E-Mail: ivylady@erinet.com. Web Site: www.ivy.org. *Dir, Res*, Sabina Mueller Sulgrove
Founded 1973
Publications: Between the Vines; The Ivy Journal

P COLLIER COUNTY PUBLIC LIBRARY, 650 Central Ave, 34102. SAN 337-8306. Tel: 941-262-4130. Interlibrary Loan Service Tel: 941-261-8208. Reference Tel: 941-263-7768. FAX: 941-649-1293. Web Site: www.collier-lib.org. *Dir*, John W Jones; *Asst Dir*, Marilyn Matthes; E-Mail: matthes@collier-lib.org; *Ref*, Beth Nagengast; *Syst Coordr*, Michael Widner; *Ch Servs*, Pamela Moore; *ILL*, Carolann Adams; *Exten Serv*, Marilyn Norris; *Acq*, Carol Travis; *Tech Servs*, Robert Rodriguez; Staff 22 (MLS 22)
Founded 1957. Pop 210,000; Circ 2,100,000
Oct 1999-Sep 2000 Income (Main Library and Branch Library) $5,712,252, State $398,852, County $4,986,500, Locally Generated Income $326,900. Mats Exp $1,333,232, Books $1,033,632, Per/Ser (Incl. Access Fees) $59,000, Micro $5,000, AV Equip $100,000, Electronic Ref Mat (Incl. Access Fees) $135,600. Sal $2,480,057
Library Holdings: Bk Vols 333,705; Per Subs 935
Subject Interests: Florida
Automation Activity & Vendor Info: (Acquisitions) DRA; (Cataloging) DRA; (Circulation) DRA; (OPAC) DRA; (Serials) DRA
Database Vendor: DRA
Publications: Bibliographies; Calendar (monthly); Friends of Library (newsletter)
Mem of SW Fla Libr Network
Friends of the Library Group
Branches: 7
EAST NAPLES BRANCH, 8787 E Tamiami Trail, 34113. SAN 337-8322. Tel: 941-775-5592. FAX: 941-774-5148. Web Site: www.collier-lib.org. *Librn*, Marilyn McKay; Staff 1 (MLS 1)
Database Vendor: DRA
ESTATES, 1266 Golden Gate Blvd W, 34120. SAN 374-7514. Tel: 941-455-8088. FAX: 941-455-8113. Web Site: www.collier-lib.org. *Librn*, Carmen Ruiz; Staff 1 (MLS 1)
Database Vendor: DRA
EVERGLADES BRANCH, City Hall, Everglades City, 33929. SAN 375-0175. Tel: 941-695-2511. Web Site: www.collier-lib.org. Subject Specialists: *Customer serv*, Roberta Stone
Database Vendor: DRA
Open Mon-Thurs 9-5, Fri 1-5
GOLDEN GATE, 4898 Coronado Pkwy, 34116. SAN 337-8330. Tel: 941-455-1441. FAX: 941-455-8921. Web Site: www.collier-lib.org. *Librn*, Jane Martin; *Ch Servs*, Rebecca Lanham; Staff 2 (MLS 2)
Database Vendor: DRA
IMMOKALEE BRANCH, 417 N First St, Immokalee, 34142. SAN 337-8365. Tel: 941-657-2882. FAX: 941-657-4901. Web Site: www.collier-lib.org. *Librn*, Tanya Crump; Staff 1 (MLS 1)
Database Vendor: DRA
MARCO ISLAND BRANCH, 210 S Heathwood Dr, Marco Island, 34145. SAN 337-839X. Tel: 941-394-3272. FAX: 941-394-2383. Web Site: www.collier-lib.org. *Librn*, Denise McMahon; Staff 1 (MLS 1)
Database Vendor: DRA
Friends of the Library Group
VANDERBILT BEACH, 788 Vanderbilt Beach Rd, 34108. SAN 337-8314. Tel: 941-597-8444. FAX: 941-597-3653. Web Site: www.collier-lib.org. *Librn*, Alison Saba; Staff 1 (MLS 1)
Database Vendor: DRA

§J EDISON COMMUNITY COLLEGE, Collier County Campus Learning Resource Center, 7007 Lely Cultural Pkwy, 34113-8976. Circulation Tel: 941-732-3774. FAX: 941-732-3777. *Dir*, Russell Bailey; Tel: 941-732-3776, E-Mail: rbailey@edison.edu
Library Holdings: Bk Titles 10,000; Per Subs 60
Automation Activity & Vendor Info: (Acquisitions) DRA; (Cataloging)

DRA; (Circulation) DRA; (Course Reserve) DRA; (ILL) DRA; (OPAC) DRA; (Serials) DRA
Database Vendor: OCLC - First Search
Open Mon-Thurs 8am-9pm, Fri 8-4

C INTERNATIONAL COLLEGE LIBRARY, 2655 Northbrooke Dr, 34119. SAN 374-6240. Tel: 941-513-1122. E-Mail: library@internationalcollege.edu. Web Site: www.internationalcollege.edu/irc. *VPres*, Melody Hainsworth; *Senior Librn*, Jan Edwards; *Librn*, Akos Delneky; *Tech Servs*, Carolynn Volz; Staff 3 (MLS 3)
Founded 1990. Highest Degree: Master
Library Holdings: Bk Vols 20,000; Bk Titles 10,000; Per Subs 181
Special Collections: Rare Books College Archives
Publications: Bibliographies
Partic in FLIN; LIRN; SE Libr Network; SW Fla Libr Network

M NAPLES COMMUNITY HOSPITAL, William J Bailey Library, 350 Seventh St N, 34102-5730. (Mail add: PO Box 413029, 34101-3029), SAN 375-4863. Tel: 941-436-5384. FAX: 941-436-5058. E-Mail: nchlibry@mindspring.com. *Librn*, Annette Campbell; Staff 2 (MLS 1, Non-MLS 1)
Founded 1975
Library Holdings: Bk Vols 3,000; Bk Titles 2,250
Subject Interests: Clinical medicine
Partic in SEND Network; SWFLN; Tampa Bay Medical Library Network

S NAPLES DAILY NEWS LIBRARY, 1075 Central Ave, 34102. SAN 329-3289. Tel: 941-263-4796. FAX: 941-263-4816. *Librn*, Gerald B Johnson; E-Mail: gbjohnson@naplesnews.com
Founded 1970. Highest Degree: Master
1998-1999 Income $32,500. Mats Exp $5,000, Per/Ser (Incl. Access Fees) $1,500, Micro $3,600, Manuscripts & Archives $2,500. Sal $30,000
Library Holdings: Bk Titles 250
Special Collections: Naples Daily News 1923-1999 micro, newsclips, newsphotos
Database Vendor: Lexis-Nexis
Publications: Bonita Banner
Restriction: Staff use only

S THE CONSERVANCY OF SOUTHWEST FLORIDA, EPIC Resource Center, 1450 Merrihue Dr, 34102. SAN 327-1412. Tel: 941-262-0304, Ext 237. FAX: 941-263-3019. Web Site: www.conservancy.org.
Library Holdings: Bk Titles 2,500

NEW PORT RICHEY

P NEW PORT RICHEY PUBLIC LIBRARY, 5939 Main St, 34652. SAN 303-0865. Tel: 727-841-4547. FAX: 727-841-4559. Web Site: www.tblc.org/newport. *Dir*, Susan D Dillinger; E-Mail: dillins@tblc.org; *Asst Dir*, Thomas Keene; *Tech Servs*, Rachel Mattox; *Coll Develop, Ref*, Fran Dee; Staff 21 (MLS 4, Non-MLS 17)
Founded 1919. Pop 80,000; Circ 95,733
Library Holdings: Bk Vols 69,351; Per Subs 140
Subject Interests: Florida, Genealogy
Special Collections: Avery Coll
Database Vendor: epixtech, inc.
Publications: Friends of the New Port Richey Library (Newsletter)
Partic in Sunline; Tampa Bay Library Consortium, Inc
Independent, municipal library, now serving multi-county residents for free through a formal reciprocal borrowing agreement
Friends of the Library Group

J PASCO-HERNANDO COMMUNITY COLLEGE, Alric CT Pottberg Library - West Campus Library, 10230 Ridge Rd, 34654-5199. SAN 337-842X. Tel: 727-847-2727, Ext 3006. FAX: 727-816-3346. *Assoc Dir*, Douglas A Butler; E-Mail: doug_butler@pasco-hernandocc.com; *Asst Dir*, Sarah Peaden; Tel: 727-816-3411, E-Mail: sarah_peaden@pasco-hernandocc.com; Staff 4 (MLS 3, Non-MLS 1)
Founded 1972. Enrl 3,003; Fac 200
Library Holdings: Bk Titles 27,500; Per Subs 150
Partic in Col Ctr for Libr Automation; OCLC Online Computer Library Center, Inc; SE Libr Network

NEWBERRY

S ESE LIBRARY, 404 SW 140th Terrace, 32669-3000. (Mail add; PO Box 1703, 32602-1703), SAN 377-0478. Tel: 352-332-3318. FAX: 352-333-6622. Web Site: www.eseworld.com. *Librn*, Bobbi J Walton; E-Mail: bwalton@nervm.nerde.us.edu
Library Holdings: Bk Vols 7,200; Bk Titles 7,000; Per Subs 200
Partic in Asn of Rec Mgrs & Adminrs; NEFLIN; Spec Libr Asn

NICEVILLE

P NICEVILLE PUBLIC LIBRARY, 206 N Partin Dr, 32578. SAN 370-4661. Tel: 850-729-4070. Interlibrary Loan Service Tel: 850-729-4090. Circulation Tel: 850-729-4070. Reference Tel: 850-729-4090. FAX: 850-729-4053. Web Site: www.niceville.org. *Dir*, Sheila K Bishop; Fax: 850-729-4093, E-Mail: sbishop@okaloosa.lib.fl.us; *ILL, Ref*, Lora Glass; E-Mail: lglass@okaloosa.lib.fl.us; *Tech Servs*, Lee Luton; Staff 12 (MLS 1, Non-MLS 11)
Founded 1974
Library Holdings: Bk Vols 34,000; Per Subs 134
Automation Activity & Vendor Info: (Circulation) epixtech, inc.
Partic in Panhandle Library Access Network

J OKALOOSA-WALTON COMMUNITY COLLEGE, Learning Resources Center, 100 College Blvd, 32578. SAN 303-0873. Tel: 850-729-5392. FAX: 850-729-5295. Web Site: www.owcc.cc.fl.us./lrc. *Acq, Coll Develop, Per*, Margaret T Phillips; *AV*, Edward M Livingston; *Cat, Circ*, Janice W Henderson; *Instrul Serv*, Ronald G Walls; *Ref*, Owen E Adams, Jr. Subject Specialists: *Television*, Ronald G Walls; Staff 5 (MLS 5)
Founded 1964. Enrl 3,527; Fac 305
Jul 1999-Jun 2000 Income $888,707
Library Holdings: Bk Vols 86,772; Per Subs 564
Special Collections: Florida & Works of Floridians Coll, bks, tapes
Partic in Col Ctr for Libr Automation; Florida Library Information Network; OCLC Online Computer Library Center, Inc; Panhandle Library Access Network

NORTH MIAMI

C FLORIDA INTERNATIONAL UNIVERSITY, North Campus Library, 3000 NE 151st St, 33181-3600. SAN 303-089X. Tel: 305-919-5731. Circulation Tel: 305-919-5718. Reference Tel: 305-919-5726. TDD: 305-919-5718. FAX: 305-919-5914. Web Site: library.fiu.edu. *Exec Dir*, Dr Laurence Miller; Tel: 305-919-5714, E-Mail: millerl@fiu.edu; *Assoc Dir*, Antonie Baker Downs; Tel: 305-919-5730, E-Mail: downst@fiu.edu; *ILL*, Annya Polselli; Tel: 305-919-5715, Fax: 305-949-1591, E-Mail: polselli@fiu.edu; *Circ*, Steven Switzer; Tel: 305-919-5797, E-Mail: switzers@fiu.edu; *Govt Doc*, Elaine Winske; Tel: 305-919-5722, Fax: 305-940-6865, E-Mail: winskee@fiu.edu; *Head Ref*, Scott Kass; Tel: 305-919-5933, Fax: 305-940-6865, E-Mail: kasss@fiu.edu; *Circ*, Robert Capuano; Tel: 305-919-5797, E-Mail: capuanor@fiu.edu; *Head, Acq*, Jenny Saxton; Tel: 305-919-5716, E-Mail: saxtonj@fiu.edu; *Tech Servs*, Nancy Sun Hershoff; Tel: 305-919-5727, E-Mail: sunn@fiu.edu; Staff 27 (MLS 11, Non-MLS 16)
Founded 1977. Enrl 7,667; Highest Degree: Doctorate
Jul 1999-Jun 2000 Mats Exp $924,180, Books $236,466, Per/Ser (Incl. Access Fees) $450,661, Presv $42,785, Micro $53,732, Other Print Mats $74,660, Electronic Ref Mat (Incl. Access Fees) $58,953. Sal $1,227,588 (Prof $436,341)
Library Holdings: Bk Vols 354,559; Bk Titles 336,181; Per Subs 2,523
Special Collections: Holocause Oral History Video Coll
Automation Activity & Vendor Info: (Acquisitions) NOTIS; (Cataloging) NOTIS; (Circulation) NOTIS; (Course Reserve) NOTIS; (ILL) NOTIS; (OPAC) NOTIS; (Serials) NOTIS
Database Vendor: GaleNet, Lexis-Nexis, OCLC - First Search, ProQuest, Silverplatter Information Inc., Wilson - Wilson Web
Publications: INFO (Newsletter)
Function: ILL available, Research library
Partic in Association Of Southeastern Research Libraries (ASERL); Solinet; Southeast Florida Library Information Network, Inc
Special Services for the Deaf - TDD
Special Services for the Blind - Kurzweil Reader

P NORTH MIAMI PUBLIC LIBRARY, E May Avil Library, 835 NE 132nd St, 33161. SAN 303-0903. Tel: 305-891-5535. TDD: 305-899-9268. FAX: 305-892-0843. E-Mail: library@ci.north-miami.fl.us. *Dir*, Gloria Zavish; E-Mail: gzavish@ci.north-miami.fl.us; *Asst Dir*, Ilene Zaleski; E-Mail: izaleski@ci.north-miami.fl.us; *Ch Servs*, William Painter; E-Mail: wpainter@ci.north-miami.fl.us; *Tech Servs*, Mary Culhane; *Tech Coordr*, Robert Zambrano; E-Mail: rzambrano@ci.north-miami.fl.us; *Circ*, Marcelle Sainvil; Staff 9 (MLS 5, Non-MLS 4)
Founded 1949. Pop 50,308; Circ 96,810
Oct 1998-Sep 1999 Income $997,616, City $955,402, Locally Generated Income $42,214. Mats Exp $104,796, Books $79,287, Per/Ser (Incl. Access Fees) $12,946, Presv $764, Electronic Ref Mat (Incl. Access Fees) $2,196. Sal $487,246
Library Holdings: Bk Vols 98,780; Bk Titles 89,348; Per Subs 316; High Interest/Low Vocabulary Bk Vols 800
Subject Interests: Careers, Large type print, Parenting
Special Collections: Art (Smik Memorial Coll); Bicentennial of the Constitution Coll; Civil War Coll; Filipiniana Coll; Florida Coll; Literacy Coll; Stage & Studio Coll
Automation Activity & Vendor Info: (Cataloging) Gaylord; (Circulation) Gaylord; (OPAC) Gaylord
Special Services for the Deaf - TDD
Special Services for the Blind - Braille printer (Romeo), Braille translator (MEGA DOTS); Braille Writer
Friends of the Library Group

NORTH MIAMI BEACH

P NORTH MIAMI BEACH PUBLIC LIBRARY, 1601 NE 164th St, 33162. SAN 303-0911. Tel: 305-948-2970. FAX: 305-787-6007. *Dir*, Florence Simkins Brown; Staff 8 (MLS 7, Non-MLS 1)

Pop 38,057; Circ 129,051
Library Holdings: Bk Vols 51,473
Friends of the Library Group

TEMPLE SINAI OF NORTH DADE, Hollander-Rachleff Library, 18801 NE 22nd Ave, 33180. SAN 303-092X. Tel: 305-932-9010. FAX: 305-933-2443. *Dir*, Jan Goldmann; *Librn*, Sandra Hoffman
Founded 1967
Library Holdings: Bk Titles 7,000
Subject Interests: Children's literature, Jewish history and literature
Friends of the Library Group

NORTH PALM BEACH

P NORTH PALM BEACH PUBLIC LIBRARY, 303 Anchorage Dr, 33408. SAN 303-0938. Tel: 561-841-3383. FAX: 561-848-2874. E-Mail: library@village-npb.org, npblib@pb.seflin.org. Web Site: www.seflin.org/npblib. *Dir*, Nancy F Moore; *Ref*, Karen White; *Ch Servs*, Mary Anne Caruso; *Tech Servs*, Ann Burton; Staff 7 (MLS 1, Non-MLS 6)
Founded 1963. Pop 15,000; Circ 117,000
Oct 1999-Sep 2000 Income City $533,000. Mats Exp $533,000, Books $55,000, Per/Ser (Incl. Access Fees) $4,000, Presv $1,000, Micro $600, AV Equip $4,000, Other Print Mats $2,000. Sal $403,000
Library Holdings: Bk Vols 44,686; Bk Titles 44,000; Per Subs 119
Special Collections: CD Col; North Palm Beach History, audio bks; Video Coll
Publications: Newsletter (monthly)
Friends of the Library Group

NORTH PORT

P NORTH PORT PUBLIC LIBRARY, 13800 S Tamiami Trail, 34287-2030. SAN 370-3614. Tel: 941-426-4300. TDD: 941-423-2939. FAX: 941-426-6564. Web Site: www.suncat.co.sarasota.fl.us. *Head of Libr*, Alicia C McHugh; E-Mail: amchugh@sarasota.lib.fl.us; *Ad Servs*, Charles Grubbs; E-Mail: cgrubbs@sarasota.lib.fl.us; *Ad Servs*, Lisa Leverock; E-Mail: lleverock@sarasota.lib.fl.us; *Ch Servs*, Patricia Finch; E-Mail: tfinch@sarasota.lib.fl.us; *Circ*, Marcia Caldwell; E-Mail: mcaldwell@sarasota.lib.fl.us; Staff 5 (MLS 5)
Founded 1975
Database Vendor: Innovative Interfaces INN - View
Mem of Sarasota County Dept of Librs
Partic in Tampa Bay Library Consortium, Inc
Special Services for the Deaf - TDD
Friends of the Library Group

OAKLAND PARK

P OAKLAND PARK CITY LIBRARY, 1298 NE 37th St, 33334. SAN 303-0946. Tel: 954-561-6287. FAX: 954-561-6146. *Dir*, Alan Kornblau; *Asst Dir*, Joanne B Fischer; *Ref*, Brian Long
Founded 1963. Pop 30,000; Circ 100,000
1999-2000 Income $647,162. Mats Exp $61,000, Books $42,000, Per/Ser (Incl. Access Fees) $7,000, Electronic Ref Mat (Incl. Access Fees) $12,000. Sal $376,484
Library Holdings: Bk Vols 42,816; Per Subs 142
Subject Interests: Florida, Large type print, Spanish (language)
Partic in Solinet
Friends of the Library Group

OCALA

S APPLETON MUSEUM OF ART LIBRARY, 4333 NE Silver Springs Blvd, 34470. (Mail add: PO Box 3190, 34478-3190), SAN 373-4218. Tel: 352-236-7100. FAX: 352-236-7137.
Library Holdings: Bk Vols 950; Per Subs 200
Subject Interests: Art, Art history

J CENTRAL FLORIDA COMMUNITY COLLEGE, Learning Resources Center, 3001 SW College Rd, PO Box 1388, 34474. SAN 303-0954. Tel: 352-237-2111, Ext 1347. FAX: 352-237-7097. *Dir*, Albert V Tweedy; *Librn*, Susan Bradshaw; Staff 4 (MLS 4)
Founded 1958. Enrl 6,271; Fac 122
Library Holdings: Bk Vols 61,000; Per Subs 294
Special Collections: Equine; Wisdom Traditions; Women's History

G FLORIDA DEPARTMENT OF CORRECTIONS, Florida Correctional Institution Library, 11120 NW Gainesville Rd, 34482. (Mail add: PO Box 147, 32663), SAN 337-7040. Tel: 352-622-5151, Ext 379. FAX: 352-369-2159. *In Charge*, M Miller; Staff 1 (MLS 1)
Founded 1967
Library Holdings: Bk Vols 11,288; Per Subs 100
Subject Interests: Law
Partic in Fla State Libr ILL Network

G MARION CORRECTIONAL INSTITUTION LIBRARY, (Formerly Lowell Correctional Institution Men's Library), 3269 NW 105th St, 34482. (Mail add: PO Box 158, 32663-0158), SAN 322-6689. Tel: 352-401-6813. FAX: 352-840-5657. *Librn*, Ana J Beauchamp; Staff 23 (MLS 1, Non-MLS 22)
Founded 1977. Pop 1,370; Circ 80,000
Jul 1999-Jun 2000 Income $8,000. Mats Exp $8,000, Books $2,900, Per/Ser (Incl. Access Fees) $3,400, Micro $1,000, Other Print Mats $700
Library Holdings: Bk Vols 15,000; Bk Titles 14,000; Per Subs 52; High Interest/Low Vocabulary Bk Vols 200; Bks on Deafness & Sign Lang 12
Subject Interests: Gen ref
Special Collections: Major Law Library Coll
Special Services for the Blind - Books available with recordings

P MARION COUNTY PUBLIC LIBRARY SYSTEM, 15 SE Osceola Ave, 34471. SAN 337-8454. Tel: 352-629-8551. Interlibrary Loan Service Tel: 352-629-8597. FAX: 352-629-1649. *Dir*, Julia H Sieg; *Asst Dir*, Patsy Marsee; *YA Servs*, Roslyn Brown; *Circ*, Pat Borax; *Ad Servs*, David Worden; *Coll Develop*, Julia Beamguard
Founded 1961. Pop 225,000; Circ 667,000
Library Holdings: Bk Vols 257,000; Per Subs 440
Subject Interests: Florida
Special Collections: Genealogy (Southeastern US)
Automation Activity & Vendor Info: (Cataloging) Gaylord; (Circulation) DRA
This is a two-county system serving Marion & Levy counties
Friends of the Library Group
Branches: 13
AF KNOTTS BRANCH, PO Box 489, Yankeetown, 34498-0489. SAN 374-454X. Tel: 352-447-4212. *Librn*, Cherie Fischer-Bowers
Friends of the Library Group
BELLEVIEW BRANCH, 6007 SE Earp Rd, Belleview, 34421-0310. (Mail add: PO Box 310, Belleview, 34421-0310), SAN 337-8489. Tel: 352-245-5552. FAX: 352-245-3719. *Librn*, Rosalie Cauthen; E-Mail: rosaliecauthen@marioncountyfl.org
Automation Activity & Vendor Info: (Cataloging) epixtech, inc.
Function: Archival collection
Friends of the Library Group
BRONSON BRANCH, PO Box 796, Bronson, 32621-0796. SAN 337-8519. Tel: 352-486-2015. *Librn*, Norene Andrews
CEDAR KEY BRANCH, PO Box 550, Cedar Key, 32625. SAN 337-8543. Tel: 352-543-5132. *Librn*, Janice Coupe
Friends of the Library Group
DUNNELLON BRANCH, 20804 W Pennsylvania Ave, Dunnellon, 344301. (Mail add: PO Box 758, Dunnellon, 34430-0758), SAN 337-8632. Tel: 904-489-4196. FAX: 352-489-0569. *Librn*, Mary Merenda
Founded 1961
Friends of the Library Group
FOREST BRANCH, c/o Mid-State Federal, 777 S County 314A, Ocklawaha, 32179. SAN 374-4515. *Librn*, Nancy Stewart
Friends of the Library Group
FORT MCCOY BRANCH, 14660 NE Hwy 315, Fort McCoy, 32134. SAN 377-7618. Tel: 352-236-2937. *Librn*, Marilyn Jones
FREEDOM PUBLIC LIBRARY, 5870 SW 95 St, 34476. Tel: 352-291-6040. *Branch Mgr*, Norman Fitzpatrick
Open Mon, Wed, Thurs, Fri & Sat 10-5 & Tues 1-8
HERMAN B OBERMAN BRANCH, Rainbow Lakes Estates, 4040 Deep Water Ct, Dunnellon, 34431. SAN 337-8810. Tel: 352-489-4716. *Librn*, Susan White
MARION OAKS, 294 Marion Oaks Lane, 34473. SAN 377-7634. Tel: 352-347-2179. *In Charge*, Elizabeth Fant
OCALA PUBLIC LIBRARY, 15 SE Osceola Ave, 34471. Tel: 352-629-8551. *Dir*, Julia Sieg
Open Sun 1-5, Mon-Thurs 10-8, Fri & Sat 10-6
REDDICK BRANCH, PO Box 699, Reddick, 32686-0699. SAN 374-4531. Tel: 352-591-2698. *Librn*, Lee Fanelli
Friends of the Library Group
WILLISTON BRANCH, PO Box 373, Williston, 32696-0373. SAN 337-8845. Tel: 352-528-2313. *Librn*, Michelle Traylor
Bookmobiles: 2

S MARION COUNTY TEACHERS PROFESSIONAL LIBRARY, 406 SE Alvarez Ave, 34471. SAN 325-8467. Tel: 352-671-7759. FAX: 352-671-7757. *Coordr*, Vic Burke; *Librn*, Dorothy Weaver
Library Holdings: Bk Titles 11,750
Subject Interests: Education
Special Collections: ERIC Documents, Kraus Curriculum Development Library
Publications: Acquisition List (monthly); Film Catalog (District); Media Memo
Partic in Wilsonline

S WITHLACOOCHEE REGIONAL PLANNING COUNCIL, 1241 SW Tenth St, 34474. SAN 325-8440. Tel: 352-732-1315. FAX: 352-732-1319. E-Mail: wrpc@atlantic.net. Web Site: www.atlantic.net/~wrpc. *Librn*, Olivette Waddell
Library Holdings: Bk Titles 6,000; Per Subs 15

OCOEE

SR ST PAUL'S PRESBYTERIAN CHURCH LIBRARY, 9600 W Colonial Dr, 34761. SAN 373-4234. Tel: 407-293-3696. FAX: 407-299-2124.
Library Holdings: Bk Vols 2,200

OKEECHOBEE

S OKEECHOBEE CORRECTIONAL INSTITUTION LIBRARY, 3420 NE 168th St, 34972. SAN 377-2101. Tel: 863-462-5400. FAX: 863-462-5602. *Librn*, Connie Shoots
Library Holdings: Bk Vols 1,500

P OKEECHOBEE COUNTY PUBLIC LIBRARY, 206 SW 16th St, 34974. SAN 370-3789. Tel: 863-763-3536. FAX: 863-763-5368. Web Site: www.heartlineweb.org. *Dir*, Edward A Kilroy; E-Mail: ekilroy@heartland.lib.fl.us; *Asst Dir, Coll Develop*, Margo Taylor; E-Mail: mtaylor@heartland.lib.fl.us; *Tech Servs*, Marcia Thigpen; E-Mail: mthigpen@heartland.lib.fl.us; Staff 7 (MLS 2, Non-MLS 5)
Founded 1967. Pop 35,000; Circ 114,449
Oct 1999-Sep 2000 Income $752,576, State $151,412, County $553,523. Mats Exp $68,119, Books $50,000, Per/Ser (Incl. Access Fees) $4,166, Presv $400, Micro $250, AV Equip $13,553. Sal $194,231 (Prof $66,000)
Library Holdings: Bk Vols 39,725; Bk Titles 34,509; Per Subs 81; High Interest/Low Vocabulary Bk Vols 400
Special Collections: Florida History; Genealogy
Automation Activity & Vendor Info: (Acquisitions) Gaylord; (Cataloging) Gaylord; (Circulation) Gaylord; (OPAC) Gaylord
Database Vendor: IAC - Info Trac
Mem of Heartland Libr Coop
Partic in Tampa Bay Library Consortium, Inc
Friends of the Library Group

P SEMINOLE TRIBE OF FLORIDA, Tribal Library System, Rte 6 Box 668, 34974. SAN 323-7842. Tel: 863-763-4236, 863-763-5520. FAX: 863-763-0679. E-Mail: libbrsem@okeechobee.com, libho@semtribe.com. *Actg Librn*, Deborah Johns; Staff 12 (MLS 7, Non-MLS 5)
Library Holdings: Bk Titles 22,000; Per Subs 141
Special Collections: Seminole Indians of Florida
Partic in SW Fla Libr Network
Friends of the Library Group
Branches: 4
DOROTHY SCOTT OSCEOLA MEMORIAL, 3100 NW 63rd Ave, Hollywood, 33024. SAN 378-0139. Tel: 954-989-6840, Ext 1226. FAX: 954-967-2395. E-Mail: libho@semtribe.com. *In Charge*, Diane Diaz
Library Holdings: Bk Vols 6,500; Per Subs 70
IMMOKALEE RESERVATION, 303 Lena Frank Dr Ste 3, Immokalee, 33934. SAN 378-0112. Tel: 863-657-6567. FAX: 863-657-9547. *In Charge*, Chriselda Marrara
TAMPA RESERVATION, 5219 Orient Rd, No K, Tampa, 33610. SAN 378-0155. Tel: 813-626-5765. FAX: 813-626-4537. *In Charge*, Carol Foret
WILLIE FRANK LIBRARY, Big Cypress Reservation, HC 61, Box 46A, Clewiston, 33440. SAN 376-9577. Tel: 863-983-6724. FAX: 863-983-3539. *In Charge*, Claudia C Doctor
Library Holdings: Bk Titles 5,000

OLDSMAR

P OLDSMAR LIBRARY, 101 State St W, 34677. SAN 323-9454. Tel: 813-855-5940. FAX: 813-854-1881. Web Site: www.tblc.org/opl/. *Dir*, Roberta L Weber; E-Mail: weberr@tblc.org; *Head Tech Servs*, Jane Lingle; *Ad Servs*, Janet Bergeron; *Tech Servs*, Nancy Batto; *Ch Servs*, Kathleen Matheny; Staff 13 (MLS 3, Non-MLS 10)
Founded 1920. Pop 11,000; Circ 16,000
Oct 1999-Sep 2000 Income $759,000, State $134,000, City $400,000, County $225,000. Mats Exp $58,529, Books $55,000, Per/Ser (Incl. Access Fees) $3,529. Sal $300,000
Library Holdings: Bk Vols 38,000; Bk Titles 29,402; Per Subs 93
Automation Activity & Vendor Info: (Circulation) epixtech, inc.
Database Vendor: OCLC - First Search, OVID Technologies
Mem of Pinellas County Public Libr Coop
Partic in Tampa Bay Library Consortium, Inc
Friends of the Library Group

OPA LOCKA

G FLORIDA DEPARTMENT OF HEALTH & REHABILITATIVE SERVICES, Landmark Learning Center Library, 20,000 NW 47th Ave, 33055. SAN 303-0970. Tel: 305-626-6198. FAX: 305-626-6173. *In Charge*, William Janiak
Library Holdings: Bk Vols 250
Subject Interests: Mentally retarded

P OPA-LOCKA PUBLIC LIBRARY, 215 N Perviz Ave, 33054. SAN 370-3797. Tel: 305-953-2850. FAX: 305-953-2949. *Librn*, Edna Hardy
Library Holdings: Bk Vols 16,000; Per Subs 25

ORANGE CITY

M VOLUSIA MEDICAL CENTER, 1055 Saxon Blvd, 32763-8463. SAN 302-9131. Tel: 904-774-9192. *In Charge*, Cathy Lundberg
Founded 1952
Library Holdings: Bk Titles 240; Per Subs 22
Access to Florida Hospital Library

ORLANDO

L AKERMAN, SENTERFITT & EIDSON PA, Law Library, PO Box 231, 32802-0231. SAN 325-8432. Tel: 407-843-7861. FAX: 407-843-6610. *Dir*, Linda Fowlie; *Librn*, Mary Hess
Library Holdings: Bk Vols 20,000
Partic in Am Libr Asn; Fla Libr Convention

S CENTRAL FLORIDA RECEPTION CENTER LIBRARY, PO Box 628040, 32862-8040. SAN 377-340X. Tel: 407-207-7777. *Librn*, Sharon Wedel
Library Holdings: Bk Vols 8,800; Bk Titles 5,900; Per Subs 187

S CIRENT SEMICONDUCTOR, Technical Library, 9333 S John Young Pkwy, 32819. SAN 375-877X. Tel: 407-371-6000, Ext 9622. FAX: 407-345-7358. Web Site: www.cirent.com.
Founded 1996. Pop 1,400
Library Holdings: Bk Vols 60; Bk Titles 50; Per Subs 60
Partic in OCLC, Lucent Tecnologies Network Bell Labs

M FLORIDA HOSPITAL, Medical Library, 601 E Rollins St, 32803. SAN 337-890X. Tel: 407-303-1860. FAX: 407-303-1786. *Librn*, Ann McDonald; Staff 3 (MLS 2, Non-MLS 1)
Library Holdings: Bk Vols 1,500; Per Subs 258
Subject Interests: Clinical medicine
Special Collections: Nursing Coll
Partic in Nat Libr of Med

C FLORIDA HOSPITAL COLLEGE OF HEALTH SCIENCES LIBRARY, 800 Lake Estelle Dr, 32803. SAN 303-1063. Tel: 407-303-1851. FAX: 407-303-9622. Web Site: www.fhchs.edu. *Coll Develop, Dir*, Marley H Soper; E-Mail: marley_soper@mail.fhmis.net
Jul 1998-Jun 1999 Income $460,026. Mats Exp $45,000, Books $25,000, Per/Ser (Incl. Access Fees) $20,000. Sal $206,678 (Prof $90,000)
Library Holdings: Bk Vols 12,000; Per Subs 161
Subject Interests: Health sciences, Nursing
Publications: Infolink

§J FLORIDA TECHNICAL COLLEGE LIBRARY, 1819 N Semoran Blvd, 32807. Tel: 407-678-5600. FAX: 407-678-1149. Web Site: www.flatech.edu. *Dir*, Nancy Cadwallender; E-Mail: ncadwall@flatech.edu
Library Holdings: Bk Vols 7,000; Per Subs 100
Automation Activity & Vendor Info: (Acquisitions) Sagebrush Corporation; (Cataloging) Sagebrush Corporation; (Circulation) Sagebrush Corporation; (ILL) Sagebrush Corporation

S GAY & LESBIAN CENTER SERVICES, Central Florida Library, 946 N Mills Ave, 32803. Tel: 407-228-8272. FAX: 407-228-8230. E-Mail: info@galbcc.org. Web Site: www.galbcc.org.
Library Holdings: Bk Vols 1,100; Bk Titles 1,100

S HARCOURT INC, Resource & Information Center, 6277 Sea Harbor Dr, 32887. SAN 353-1007. Tel: 407-345-3113. Interlibrary Loan Service Tel: 407-345-3114. FAX: 407-351-9906. *Librn*, Peggy Bridges; *Asst Librn*, Davis Walker; Staff 8 (MLS 2, Non-MLS 6)
Founded 1963
Library Holdings: Bk Vols 6,000; Per Subs 1,400
Subject Interests: Education, Publishing
Special Collections: Archive Coll; Harcourt Brace Books
Partic in Dialog Corporation; Lexis, Solinet, Westlaw

L HOLLAND & KNIGHT, LLP ORLANDO LIBRARY, 200 S Orange Ave, Ste 2600, 32801. (Mail add: PO Box 1526, 32802-1586), SAN 327-2702. Tel: 407-244-1153, 407-425-8500. Web Site: www.hklaw.com. *Librn*, Margie Hawkins; E-Mail: mhawkins@hklaw.com; Staff 2 (MLS 1, Non-MLS 1)
Library Holdings: Bk Vols 16,000; Per Subs 92
Subject Interests: Law
Automation Activity & Vendor Info: (Acquisitions) Inmagic, Inc.; (Cataloging) Inmagic, Inc.; (Circulation) Inmagic, Inc.; (Serials) Inmagic, Inc.
Database Vendor: OCLC - First Search
Restriction: Staff use only
Partic in Central Florida Library Cooperative (CFLC); Solinet

S LAW ENGINEERING ENVIRONMENTAL SERVICES, 605 E Robinson St, Ste 230, 32801. SAN 375-8222. Tel: 407-246-0066. FAX: 407-246-1566. *In Charge*, David Bass
Library Holdings: Bk Vols 1,000

S LOCKHEED MARTIN CORP, Electronics & Missiles Technical Information Center, 5600 Sand Lake Rd, MP 30, 32819-8907. SAN 377-130X. Tel: 407-356-2051. FAX: 407-356-6648. *Librn*, Richard Steinmetz; E-Mail: richarde.steinmetz@lmco.com
Library Holdings: Bk Vols 50,000; Per Subs 150

G ORANGE COUNTY HISTORICAL MUSEUM LIBRARY, 65 E Central Blvd, 32801. SAN 326-1883. Tel: 407-897-6350. FAX: 407-897-6409. *Librn*, Frank Mendola
Library Holdings: Bk Vols 1,935; Bk Titles 1,368; Per Subs 11
Restriction: Non-circulating to the public
Function: For research purposes

GL ORANGE COUNTY LAW LIBRARY, 101 E Central Blvd, 32801. SAN 303-1039. Tel: 407-835-7323. Reference Tel: 407-835-7640. FAX: 407-835-7646. Web Site: www.ocls.lib.fl.us.; Staff 4 (MLS 1, Non-MLS 3)
Founded 1959
Library Holdings: Bk Vols 50,000; Per Subs 148
Restriction: Non-circulating
Courtesy overnight check out to local legal community

P ORANGE COUNTY LIBRARY SYSTEM, (OCLS), Orlando Public Library, 101 E Central Blvd, 32801. SAN 337-8969. Tel: 407-835-7323. Interlibrary Loan Service Tel: 407-835-7426. Reference Tel: 407-835-7640. TDD: 407-835-7641. FAX: 407-835-7649. Web Site: www.ocls.lib.fl.us/. *Dir*, Dorothy Field; *Asst Dir*, Debbie Moss; *Commun Relations*, Marilyn Hoffman; *ILL*, Linda Gabriel; *Coll Develop*, Wendi Bost
Founded 1923. Pop 811,305; Circ 4,140,589
Oct 1999-Sep 2000 Income $21,099,897, State $1,654,170, County $17,267,760, Other $2,177,967. Mats Exp $3,227,000. Sal $11,337,897
Library Holdings: Bk Vols 1,571,136; Per Subs 2,800
Special Collections: Florida Coll; Genealogy (Florida DAR); Walt Disney World Coll
Automation Activity & Vendor Info: (Acquisitions) DRA; (Cataloging) DRA
Partic in Florida Library Information Network; OCLC Online Computer Library Center, Inc; SE Libr Network
Friends of the Library Group
Branches: 13
ALAFAYA, 12000 E Colonial Dr, 32826. SAN 337-8993. Tel: 407-249-6180. FAX: 407-249-6182. *Branch Mgr*, Kathleen Meiners
Library Holdings: Bk Vols 109,189
Open Mon-Thurs 10-9, Fri & Sat 10-5
EDGEWATER, 5049 Edgewater Dr, 32810-4743. SAN 329-6210. Tel: 407-296-5153. FAX: 407-296-5155. *Branch Mgr*, Cynthia Willie
Library Holdings: Bk Vols 98,327
Open Mon-Thurs 10-9, Fri & Sat 10-5
HERNDON, 4324 E Colonial, 32803. SAN 378-0392. Tel: 407-228-1410. FAX: 407-228-1412. *Branch Mgr*, Antonia Ripley
Library Holdings: Bk Vols 58,381
Open Mon-Thurs 10-9, Fri & Sat 10-5
NORTH ORANGE, 1211 E Semoran Blvd, Apopka, 32703. SAN 337-9116. Tel: 407-814-6150. FAX: 407-814-6152. *Branch Mgr*, Carolyn Rosenblum
Library Holdings: Bk Vols 95,333
Open Mon-Thurs 10-9, Fri & Sat 10-5
SOUTH ORANGE, 11346 S Orange Blossom Trail, 32821. SAN 371-9847. Tel: 407-858-4779. FAX: 407-858-4779. *Branch Mgr*, Ann Fenton
Library Holdings: Bk Vols 90,238
Open Mon-Thurs 10-9, Fri & Sat 10-5
SOUTH TRAIL, 4600 S Orange Blossom Trail, 32839. SAN 337-9027. Tel: 407-858-4749. FAX: 407-858-4751. Web Site: www.ocls.lib.fl.us. *Branch Mgr*, Patsy Williams; Staff 8 (MLS 1, Non-MLS 7)
Library Holdings: Bk Vols 81,085
Function: ILL to other special libraries
Open Mon-Thurs 10-7, Fri & Sat 10-5
SOUTHEAST, 5575 S Semoran Blvd, 32822. SAN 328-6517. Tel: 407-249-6210. FAX: 407-249-6212. *Branch Mgr*, Elazer Lindsay
Library Holdings: Bk Vols 77,416
Open Mon-Thurs 10-9, Fri & Sat 10-5
SOUTHWEST, 7255 Della Dr, 32819. SAN 329-6253. Tel: 407-355-7400. FAX: 407-355-7402. *Branch Mgr*, Clara Magee
Library Holdings: Bk Vols 94,763
Open Mon-Thurs 10-9, Fri & Sat 10-5
Friends of the Library Group
TALKING BOOKS SECTION, 101 E Central Blvd, 32801. SAN 337-8977. TDD: 407-835-7641. FAX: 407-835-7645. *Coll Develop*, Wendi Bost
Special Services for the Deaf - TDD
WASHINGTON PARK, 5151 Raleigh St, 32811. SAN 337-923X. Tel: 407-521-2466. FAX: 407-521-2468. *Branch Mgr*, Ann Wiley
Library Holdings: Bk Vols 44,851
Open Tues 10-8:30, Wed-Sat 10-5:30
WEST COLONIAL, 2768 N Hiawassee Rd, 32818. SAN 371-9855. Tel: 407-521-2459. FAX: 407-521-2461. *Branch Mgr*, Jim Baker
Library Holdings: Bk Vols 99,889
Open Mon-Thurs 10-9, Fri & Sat 10-5
WEST ORANGE, One E Cypress St, Winter Garden, 34787. SAN 337-9264. Tel: 407-656-4582. FAX: 407-656-5616. *Branch Mgr*, Glenda Houck
Library Holdings: Bk Vols 58,913
Open Tues-Thurs 10-9, Fri & Sat 10-5
WINDERMERE BRANCH, 530 Main St, Windermere, 34786. SAN 371-9871. Tel: 407-876-7540. FAX: 407-876-7542. *Branch Mgr*, Ann Wiley
Library Holdings: Bk Vols 42,307
Open Tues-Thurs 10-9, Fri & Sat 10-5

ORLANDO COLLEGE LIBRARY
J FLORIDA METROPOLITAN UNIVERSITY ORLANDO NORTH CAMPUS, 5421 Diplomat Circle, 32810. SAN 303-0997. Tel: 407-628-5870, Ext 32. FAX: 407-628-1344. *Dir*, Debra Rodensky; *Librn*, Mitchell McClay; E-Mail: mmcclay@juno.com
Library Holdings: Bk Vols 6,200; Per Subs 57
J FLORIDA METROPOLITAN UNIVERSITY ORLANDO SOUTH CAMPUS, 2411 Sand Lake Rd, 32809. SAN 329-3483. Tel: 407-851-2525, Ext 52. FAX: 407-851-1477. *Dir*, Susan Bobo; *Ref*, Elizabeth Murphrey; Staff 3 (MLS 2, Non-MLS 1)
Founded 1991. Enrl 1,300; Highest Degree: Master
Library Holdings: Bk Vols 10,000; Per Subs 120
Subject Interests: Business, Computer science, Criminal justice, Info sci, Law, Legal assisting, Med assisting
Automation Activity & Vendor Info: (OPAC) Athena
Database Vendor: IAC - SearchBank, Innovative Interfaces INN - View, OVID Technologies, Wilson - Wilson Web
Restriction: Open to students
Function: For research purposes
Partic in Central Florida Library Cooperative (CFLC); Solinet

G ORLANDO MUNICIPAL REFERENCE SERVICE, One City Commons, 400 S Orange Ave, 32801. SAN 303-1047. Tel: 407-246-2371. FAX: 407-246-3010. *Librn*, Penn McBride
Founded 1973
Library Holdings: Per Subs 185
Subject Interests: Florida, Local government
Partic in Login

M ORLANDO REGIONAL HEALTHCARE SYSTEM, Health Sciences Library, 1414 S Orange Ave, 32806-2134. SAN 328-3895. Tel: 407-841-5111, Ext 5454. FAX: 407-237-6349. *Mgr*, Naomi F Elia; *Librn*, Deedra J Walton; *Librn*, Richard A Mercer; Staff 5 (MLS 3, Non-MLS 2)
Library Holdings: Bk Titles 2,000; Per Subs 375
Subject Interests: Allied health, Medicine, Nursing
Partic in Tampa Bay Medical Library Network

S ORLANDO MUSEUM OF ART, 2416 N Mills Ave, 32803. SAN 329-9708. Tel: 407-896-4231, Ext 245. FAX: 407-896-9920. *Librn*, Patricia Adkins
Library Holdings: Bk Vols 5,000; Per Subs 10
Subject Interests: Pre-Columbian art
Publications: Library Corner (bi-monthly column in newsletter)
Open Wed & Fri 1-4

L RUMBERGER, KIRK & CALDWELL, Law Library, 201 S Orange Ave, Ste 300, 32801. (Mail add: PO Box 1873, 32802), SAN 323-6838. Tel: 407-872-7300. FAX: 407-841-2133. Web Site: www.rumberger.com. *In Charge*, Dennis Herald; E-Mail: dherald@rumberger.com; Staff 4 (Non-MLS 4)
Founded 1978
Library Holdings: Bk Titles 710,000
Subject Interests: Law
Special Collections: Continuing Legal Education audiovisuals; Engineering & Automotive Technical publications; Florida Attorney & Judge vertical files; Florida Legislative Histories; Skeletons & Organ Models
Database Vendor: Dialog, OCLC - First Search, OVID Technologies
Publications: Library Topics (Newsletter)
Partic in Central Florida Library Cooperative (CFLC); OCLC Online Computer Library Center, Inc; Solinet

J SOUTHERN COLLEGE LIBRARY, 5600 Lake Underhill Rd, 32807. SAN 326-0828. Tel: 407-273-1000, Ext 1226. FAX: 407-273-0492. Web Site: www.southerncollege.org. *Librn*, Michael Schau; E-Mail: mschau@southerncollege.org; Staff 2 (MLS 1, Non-MLS 1)
Founded 1980. Fac 100; Highest Degree: Associate
Jul 1999-Jun 2000 Income $12,600. Mats Exp $2,900, Books $500, Per/Ser (Incl. Access Fees) $1,700, AV Equip $600. Sal $29,880 (Prof $13,000)
Library Holdings: Bk Vols 4,701; Bk Titles 4,381; Per Subs 28
Subject Interests: Accounting, Business, Computer science, Interior design, Law
Restriction: Open to students
Partic in Cent Fla Libr Consortium

S THE ORLANDO SENTINAL, Editorial Research Division, 633 N Orange Ave, MP 214, 32801. SAN 303-1055. Tel: 407-420-5510. FAX: 407-420-5350. E-Mail: editresearch@olandosentinel.com. *Mgr*, Judy Grimsley; Tel: 407-420-5511, E-Mail: jgrimsley@orlandosentinel.com
Founded 1950. Circ 250,000
Library Holdings: Bk Vols 1,500
Special Collections: Clippings Coll; Photo Colls
Database Vendor: Dialog, Lexis-Nexis, OCLC - First Search

C UNIVERSITY OF CENTRAL FLORIDA LIBRARY, 4000 Central Florida Blvd, 32816-2666. SAN 303-1098. Tel: 407-823-2564. Circulation Tel: 407-823-2580. Reference Tel: 407-823-5880. FAX: 407-823-2529. Web Site: library.ucf.edu. *Dir*, Barry B Baker; E-Mail: bbaker@mail.ucf.edu; *ILL*, Jennifer Block; Tel: 407-823-2383, Fax: 407-823-3047, E-Mail: jmblock@mail.ucf.edu; *Assoc Dir*, Frank R Allen; E-Mail: fallen@mail.ucf.edu; *Assoc Dir*, Margaret (Meg) Scharf; E-Mail: mscharf@mail.ucf.edu; *Br Coordr*, Gary Hyslop; Tel: 407-823-5488, Fax: 407-823-3084, E-Mail: ghyslop@mail.ucf.edu; *Head, Acq*, Jeannette Ward; Tel: 407-823-2521, E-Mail: jaward@mail.ucf.edu; *Syst Coordr*, Selma Jaskowski; E-Mail: selmaj@mail.ucf.edu; *Branch Mgr*, Mary Stahley; E-Mail: mstahley@mail.ucf.edu; *Head, Cat*, Linda Sutton; Tel: 407-823-2523, E-Mail: sutton@mail.ucf.edu; *Circ*, Roger Simmons; Tel: 407-823-5370, E-Mail: rsimmons@mail.ucf.edu; *Coll Develop*, Joseph Andrews; Tel: 407-823-5442, Fax: 407-823-6289, E-Mail: jandrews@mail.ucf.edu; *Head, Circ*, Roger Sutton; Tel: 407-823-5370; *Head Ref*, Carole Hinshaw; E-Mail: chinshaw@mail.ucf.edu; *Branch Mgr*, Penny Beile; Tel: 407-823-2791, E-Mail: pbeile@mail.ucf.edu; Staff 108 (MLS 40, Non-MLS 68)
Founded 1963. Enrl 33,291; Fac 877; Highest Degree: Doctorate
Jul 1999-Jun 2000 Mats Exp $5,173,357, Per/Ser (Incl. Access Fees) $1,992,230, Presv $186,075, AV Equip $199,540, Other Print Mats $2,358,222, Electronic Ref Mat (Incl. Access Fees) $437,290. Sal $3,201,074 (Prof $2,785,334)
Library Holdings: Bk Vols 1,314,938; Bk Titles 865,527; Per Subs 7,423
Subject Interests: Arts, Business, Computer science, Education, Engineering, Health, Laser tech, Optics, Public affairs, Sciences
Special Collections: Bryant West Indies coll; Howard Eves Mathematics coll; Mickler Floridana coll; Sol & Sadie Malkoff Book Arts coll; Van Sickle Leftist Pamphlet coll
Automation Activity & Vendor Info: (Acquisitions) Innovative Interfaces Inc.; (Serials) Innovative Interfaces Inc.
Database Vendor: CARL, Dialog, Ebsco - EbscoHost, GaleNet, Lexis-Nexis, OCLC - First Search, ProQuest, Silverplatter Information Inc.
Publications: Info-to-Go pathfinders; Library Guide; Remote Access to LUIS; Special Coll bibliographies (Eves, Bryant)
Function: Research library
Partic in Central Florida Library Cooperative (CFLC); SE Libr Network
Special Services for the Blind - Kurzweil Reader; VisualTek print magnifying machine
Friends of the Library Group

VALENCIA COMMUNITY COLLEGE
C LEARNING RESOURCES CENTER EAST CAMPUS, 701 N Econlockhatchee Trail, 32825. SAN 329-269X. Tel: 407-299-5000, Ext 2467. Interlibrary Loan Service Tel: 407-299-5000 Ext 2461. Circulation Tel: 407-299-5000 Ext 2459. Reference Tel: 407-299-5000 Ext 2456. FAX: 407-273-7382. Web Site: orion.valencia.cc.fl.us/lrc. *Ref*, Pat Henderson; Staff 6 (MLS 5, Non-MLS 1)
Founded 1975. Enrl 13,000; Fac 200; Highest Degree: Associate
Jul 1999-Jun 2000 Income (Main Library Only) Parent Institution $1,192,828. Mats Exp $1,192,828. Sal $922,854 (Prof $303,729)
Library Holdings: Bk Vols 57,734; Bk Titles 46,360; Per Subs 385
Special Collections: College Archives
Automation Activity & Vendor Info: (Acquisitions) DRA; (Cataloging) DRA; (Circulation) DRA; (Course Reserve) DRA; (ILL) DRA; (OPAC) DRA; (Serials) DRA
Partic in Cent Fla Libr Consortium; SE Libr Network
C RAYMER MAGUIRE JR LEARNING RESOURCES CENTER, WEST CAMPUS, 1800 S Kirkman Rd, PO Box 3028, 32811. SAN 303-1012. Tel: 407-299-5000, Ext 1210. FAX: 407-295-7529. Web Site: www.valencia.cc.fl.us/lrcwest/lrcwest.html. *Coordr*, Donna J Carver; E-Mail: dcarver@valencia.cc.fl.us; *Ref*, Judi Delisle; *Circ, Coll Develop, ILL*, Paulette Smith; *AV*, Dan Kimble; *Tech Servs*, Kusum Aneja; Staff 6 (MLS 6)
Founded 1967. Enrl 5,120
Library Holdings: Bk Vols 72,000; Bk Titles 36,982; Per Subs 347
Subject Interests: Education, Horticulture, Hotel administration, Nursing
Automation Activity & Vendor Info: (Cataloging) DRA
Publications: Handbook; instructional materials in various formats; LRC Alert (biannual); pathfinders
Partic in Cent Fla Libr Consortium; Florida Library Information Network; OCLC Online Computer Library Center, Inc; SE Libr Network

OVIEDO

SR REFORMED THEOLOGICAL SEMINARY LIBRARY, Orlando Campus, 1231 Reformation Dr, 32765. SAN 371-8921. Tel: 407-366-9493, Ext 234. FAX: 407-366-9425. *Dir Libr Serv*, Dr John R Muether; *Coll Develop*, Dr Roger Nicole; Tel: 407-366-9493, Ext 214; Staff 2 (MLS 1, Non-MLS 1)
Founded 1989. Enrl 220; Fac 10
Library Holdings: Bk Vols 45,000; Per Subs 300
Subject Interests: Biblical studies, Church history, Theology
Partic in SE Libr Network

PALATKA

P PUTNAM COUNTY LIBRARY SYSTEM, 601 College Rd, 32177-3873. SAN 303-1136. Tel: 904-329-0126. FAX: 904-329-1240. *Dir*, Stephen J Crowley; *Circ, Ref*, Janice Mahaffey; *ILL*, Robin Bellamy; Staff 13 (MLS 5, Non-MLS 8)
Founded 1895
Library Holdings: Bk Vols 85,000; Per Subs 275
Subject Interests: Genealogy
Branches: 4
BOSTWICK PUBLIC, 125 Tillman Rd, 32177-8148. (Mail add: PO Box 489, Bostwick, 32007-0489), Tel: 904-326-2750. FAX: 904-326-2733. *Branch Mgr*, Claudia Wilkinson
CRESCENT CITY PUBLIC LIBRARY, 610 N Summit, Crescent City, 32112-2148. SAN 328-9001. Tel: 904-698-2600. FAX: 904-698-4212. *Branch Mgr*, Ardeth Collett
Friends of the Library Group
INTERLACHEN PUBLIC, PO Box 260, Interlachen, 32148-0260. SAN 372-7882. Tel: 904-684-1600. FAX: 904-684-1601. *Branch Mgr*, M Meetz
Friends of the Library Group
MELROSE PUBLIC LIBRARY, PO Box 1048, Melrose, 32666-1048. SAN 324-2617. Tel: 352-475-1237. FAX: 352-475-5779. *Branch Mgr*, Stella Brown
Friends of the Library Group

J SAINT JOHN'S RIVER COMMUNITY COLLEGE, B C Pearce Learning Resources Center, 5001 St Johns Ave, 32177. SAN 303-1144. Tel: 904-312-4200. FAX: 904-325-4292. Web Site: www.sjrcc.cc.fl.us/libraries/libhome.htm. *Dir*, Carmen M Cummings; E-Mail: cummings_c@popmail.firn.edu; *Tech Servs*, Glenda Brown; *Publ Servs*, Ruth Benjamin; E-Mail: benjamin_r@popmail.firn.edu; Staff 7 (MLS 7)
Founded 1958. Fac 160
Library Holdings: Bk Vols 70,000; Bk Titles 40,728; Per Subs 421
Special Collections: Civil War Coll; Florida Coll
Publications: SJRCC Faculty Handbooks; SJRCC Library Handbook
Partic in Col Ctr for Libr Info
Departmental Libraries:
ORANGE PARK CENTER LIBRARY, 283 College Dr, Orange Park, 32065. SAN 374-4558. Tel: 904-276-6830. Web Site: www.sjrcc.cc.fl..us/libraries/libhome.htm. *Librn*, Jennifer Wasick; Tel: 904-276-6831, Fax: 904-276-6796, E-Mail: wasickjss2@lincc.ccla.lib.fl.us
SAINT AUGUSTINE CENTER LIBRARY, 2990 College Dr, Saint Augustine, 32095-1275. SAN 323-5440. Tel: 904-808-7482. FAX: 904-808-7478. Web Site: www.cjscc.cc.fl.us/library. *Librn*, Christina Will
Library Holdings: Bk Vols 10,000; Per Subs 95

G ST JOHN'S RIVER WATER MANAGEMENT, District Library, 4049 Reid St, 32177. (Mail add: PO Box 1429, 32178-1429), SAN 322-6654. Tel: 904-329-4132. FAX: 904-329-4508. *Head Librn*, Judith H Salyers; E-Mail: judith_salyers@district.sjrwmd.state.fl.us; Staff 1 (MLS 1)
Founded 1975
Oct 2000-Sep 2001 Mats Exp $145,000, Books $75,000, Per/Ser (Incl. Access Fees) $60,000, Electronic Ref Mat (Incl. Access Fees) $10,000. Sal $62,000 (Prof $38,000)
Library Holdings: Bk Titles 19,330; Per Subs 217
Subject Interests: Ecology, Engineering, Geology, Hydrol, Water resources
Automation Activity & Vendor Info: (Cataloging) EOS
Publications: Bibliography of Acquisitions (monthly)
Restriction: Public use on premises

PALM BAY

C BREVARD COMMUNITY COLLEGE, Palm Bay Campus Library, 250 Community College Pkwy, 32909. SAN 370-7822. Tel: 321-632-1111, Ext 22217. Interlibrary Loan Service Tel: 321-632-1111, Ext 22271. FAX: 321-634-3754. Web Site: www.brevard.cc.fl.us/lrc. *Librn*, Deborah F Anderson; Tel: 321-632-1111, Ext 22215, E-Mail: andersond@brevard.cc.fl.us; *Librn*, JoAn Mahaffey; Tel: 321-632-1111, Ext 22270, E-Mail: mahaffeyj@brevard.cc.fl.us; *Instrul Serv*, Jayne Salvo; Tel: 321-632-1111, Ext 2220, E-Mail: salvoj@brevard.cc.fl.us; Staff 3 (MLS 2, Non-MLS 1)
Founded 1989. Enrl 2,500; Fac 30; Highest Degree: Associate
Library Holdings: Bk Vols 12,000; Per Subs 225
Automation Activity & Vendor Info: (Circulation) DRA; (Course Reserve) DRA; (OPAC) DRA; (Serials) DRA
Database Vendor: DRA, OCLC - First Search
Partic in Central Florida Library Cooperative (CFLC); FLIN; OCLC Online Computer Library Center, Inc

P FRANKLIN T DEGROODT LIBRARY, 6475 Minton Rd SW, 32908. SAN 325-0768. Tel: 321-952-6317. FAX: 321-952-6320. *Dir*, Patricia A Portnowitz; E-Mail: pportnow@manatee.brev.lib.fl.us; *Tech Servs*, Paige Divers; *YA Servs*, Jessica Sibayan; Staff 23 (MLS 4, Non-MLS 19)
Founded 1980. Pop 77,000
Library Holdings: Bk Vols 69,147; Per Subs 238
Automation Activity & Vendor Info: (Circulation) CLSI LIBS

Mem of Brevard County Library System
Special Services for the Deaf - Books on deafness & sign language; High interest/low vocabulary books; TDD
Friends of the Library Group

P PALM BAY PUBLIC LIBRARY, 1520 Port Malabar Blvd NE, 32905. SAN 372-7572. Tel: 321-952-4519. FAX: 321-952-4543. Web Site: www.brev.lib.fl.us. *Dir*, Patricia A Portnowitz
Library Holdings: Bk Vols 37,000; Per Subs 60
Mem of Brevard County Library System
Friends of the Library Group

PALM BEACH

S SOCIETY OF THE FOUR ARTS LIBRARY, 3 Arts Plaza, 33480. SAN 303-1160. Tel: 561-655-2766. FAX: 561-659-8510. *Librn*, Joanne Rendon; Staff 3 (MLS 1, Non-MLS 2)
Founded 1936
1998-1999 Income $400,000, City $125,000, Parent Institution $250,000, Other $25,000. Sal $150,000 (Prof $70,000)
Library Holdings: Bk Vols 50,000; Per Subs 60
Subject Interests: Fine arts, Paintings
Special Collections: Addison Mizner Coll; Jessup Coll
Publications: Library Notes & Booklist
Function: Research library

PALM BEACH GARDENS

J PALM BEACH COMMUNITY COLLEGE, Eissey Campus Library Learning Resource Center, 3160 PGA Blvd, 33410. SAN 303-2396. Tel: 561-625-2564. FAX: 561-625-2359. Web Site: www.pbcc.cc.fl.us/eissey/llrc/. *Actg Dir*, Lisa Hogan; Tel: 561-625-2562, E-Mail: hoganl@pbcc.cc.fl.us; *Circ*, Kay Newkirk; Tel: 561-625-2565, E-Mail: newkirkk@pbcc.cc.fl.us; *ILL, Ref*, Mike Donnelly; E-Mail: donnellr@pbcc.cc.fl.us
Founded 1974
Library Holdings: Bk Vols 29,000; Per Subs 700
Partic in Libr Info Network for Commun Cols; OCLC Online Computer Library Center, Inc; SE Libr Network; Southeast Florida Library Information Network, Inc

PALM COAST

P FLAGLER COUNTY PUBLIC LIBRARY, 2500 Palm Coast Pkwy NW, 32137. SAN 323-7044. Tel: 904-446-6763. FAX: 904-446-6773. E-Mail: flagp1@mail.state.fl.us. Web Site: www.flaglercounty.org. *Dir*, Douglas Cisney; Tel: 904-446-6764, E-Mail: doug@flaglercounty.org; *Head, Circ*, Regina McManus; *Tech Servs*, Beverly Ingersoll; Tel: 904-446-6764, E-Mail: beverly@flaglercounty.org; *Ch Servs*, Theresa Owen; E-Mail: childrens@flaglercounty.org; *Outreach Serv*, Linda Crego; E-Mail: outreach@flaglercounty.org; *Ref Serv*, Patricia Eldridge; E-Mail: info@flaglercounty.org; Staff 14 (MLS 3, Non-MLS 11)
Circ 20,649
Oct 1999-Sep 2000 Income $984,540, State $201,672, County $782,868. Mats Exp $190,806, Books $147,080, Per/Ser (Incl. Access Fees) $8,000, Electronic Ref Mat (Incl. Access Fees) $9,670. Sal $350,543 (Prof $18,900)
Library Holdings: Bk Vols 60,128; Bk Titles 47,973; Per Subs 171; High Interest/Low Vocabulary Bk Vols 49; Bks on Deafness & Sign Lang 18
Special Collections: Flagler County Coll
Automation Activity & Vendor Info: (Cataloging) Athena; (Circulation) Athena; (OPAC) Athena
Database Vendor: IAC - Info Trac, OCLC - First Search
Publications: FOL Newsletter
Function: ILL available, Photocopies available, Some telephone reference
Partic in NEFLIN
Special Services for the Deaf - Books on deafness & sign language; High interest/low vocabulary books; Staff with knowledge of sign language
Friends of the Library Group
Bookmobiles: 1

PALM HARBOR

P PALM HARBOR LIBRARY, 2330 Nebraska Ave, 34683. SAN 323-9217. Tel: 727-784-3332. FAX: 727-785-6534. Web Site: snoopy.tblc.lib.fl.us/phlib/. *Dir*, Gene Coppola; *Automation Syst Coordr*, Dana Dockery; *Head, Circ*, Kathy Souers; *Head Tech Servs*, Judy Nobles; *Ch Servs*, Lois Eannel; Staff 22 (MLS 6, Non-MLS 16)
Founded 1978. Pop 56,000; Circ 371,156
Library Holdings: Bk Vols 135,000; Per Subs 112
Subject Interests: Bus, Genealogy, Handcrafts
Special Collections: Florida Coll; French; German; Literacy; New Readers; Plays
Publications: Annual Report; Find Your Roots Genealogy Guide; Friends of the Library Newsletter
Mem of Pinellas County Public Libr Coop
Partic in Tampa Bay Library Consortium, Inc
Closed Sun
Friends of the Library Group

PALM SPRINGS

P PALM SPRINGS PUBLIC LIBRARY, 217 Cypress Lane, 33461-1698. SAN 324-0274. Tel: 561-965-2204. FAX: 561-964-2803. *Dir*, Don A Daniels; E-Mail: pete.daniels@vpslibrary.org; *Asst Dir, Ch Servs*, Mary Helen Sakellarios; E-Mail: mhs@vpslibrary.org; *Admin Assoc*, Libby McIntyre; E-Mail: libby.mcintyre@vpslibrary.org; *Circ*, Patricia Rogers; E-Mail: patricia.rogers@vpslibrary.org; *Tech Servs*, Vicki Webber; E-Mail: vicki.webber@vpslibrary.org; Staff 2 (MLS 2)
Pop 10,000; Circ 70,000
Library Holdings: Bk Vols 30,791; Bk Titles 36,000; Per Subs 110
Special Collections: Books on writing for authors
Automation Activity & Vendor Info: (Acquisitions) SIRSI
Mem of Palm Beach County Library System
Friends of the Library Group

PANAMA CITY

S BAY CORRECTIONAL FACILITY LIBRARY, 5400 Bay Line Dr, 32404. SAN 377-1997. Tel: 850-769-1455. FAX: 850-769-1942. *Librn*, Lee Lapensohn
Founded 1995
Library Holdings: Bk Vols 5,500; Bk Titles 5,000; Per Subs 35; High Interest/Low Vocabulary Bk Vols 500
Restriction: Not a lending library, Not open to public

P BAY COUNTY PUBLIC LIBRARY ASSOCIATION, Northwest Regional Library System, 25 W Government St, 32401. (Mail add: PO Box 59625, 32412-0625), SAN 337-9353. Tel: 850-872-7500. TDD: 850-747-5748. FAX: 850-872-7507. Web Site: www.nwrls.lib.fl.us. *Dir*, George Vickery; *Asst Dir, Coll Develop*, Joyce Dannecker; *Admin Assoc*, Deanne Coffield; E-Mail: dcoff@nwrls.lib.fl.us; *Ch Servs*, Sandra Pierce; *Tech Servs*, Rebecca Saunders; *Ref*, Sheila Bankhead; Staff 45 (MLS 8, Non-MLS 37)
Founded 1942. Pop 172,570; Circ 430,127
Oct 1999-Sep 2000 Income (Main Library and Branch Library) $2,155,079, State $562,995, City $215,849, County $1,121,480, Locally Generated Income $63,127, Other $191,628. Mats Exp $279,441, Books $260,120, Electronic Ref Mat (Incl. Access Fees) $19,321. Sal $1,402,107
Library Holdings: Bk Vols 193,460; Bk Titles 158,455; Per Subs 388
Subject Interests: Local history, Local newsp, Local photogs
Automation Activity & Vendor Info: (Cataloging) TLC; (Circulation) TLC; (OPAC) TLC; (Serials) TLC
Database Vendor: Ebsco - EbscoHost, GaleNet, OCLC - First Search
Mem of Northwest Regional Library System
Partic in Panhandle Library Access Network
Friends of the Library Group
Branches: 6
GULF COUNTY PUBLIC, 71 North, Port Saint Joe, 32456. SAN 337-9531. Tel: 850-229-8879. FAX: 850-229-8313. Web Site: www.nwrls.fl.us. *Mgr*, Jean Faliski; E-Mail: jfaliski@nwrls.lib.fl.us
Founded 1965
Partic in Panhandle Library Access Network
Friends of the Library Group
HARRELL MEMORIAL LIBRARY OF LIBERTY COUNTY, 537 South 12, PO Box 697, Bristol, 32321. SAN 337-9477. Tel: 850-643-2247. FAX: 850-643-2208. Web Site: www.nwrls.lib.fl.us. *Mgr*, Darlene Severance
Friends of the Library Group
PARKER PUBLIC, 4710 Second St, Parker, 32404. SAN 370-9329. Tel: 850-871-3092. FAX: 850-874-8978. Web Site: www.nwrls.lib.fl.us. *Mgr*, Debbie Daniels
Friends of the Library Group
ROBERT L YOUNG PUBLIC, 116 Arnold Rd, Panama City Beach, 32413. SAN 337-9523. Tel: 850-233-5055. FAX: 850-233-5019. Web Site: www.nwrls.lib.fl.us. *Mgr*, Frances Williams
Friends of the Library Group
SPRINGFIELD PUBLIC, 408 School Ave, Springfield, 32401. SAN 337-9566. Tel: 850-872-7510. FAX: 850-747-5758. Web Site: www.nwrls.lib.fl.us. *Mgr*, Frances Wittkopf
Friends of the Library Group
WEWAHITCHKA PUBLIC, Old Country Courthouse, PO Box 647, Wewahitchka, 32465. SAN 337-9620. Tel: 850-639-2419. FAX: 850-639-3862. Web Site: www.nwrls.lib.fl.us. *Mgr*, Ann Matlock
Friends of the Library Group

J GULF COAST COMMUNITY COLLEGE LIBRARY, 5230 W Hwy 98, 32401. SAN 303-1195. Tel: 850-872-3893. FAX: 850-872-3861. Web Site: nt.gc.cc.fl.us/library/gccc/.htm. *Dir*, Sue Hatfield; E-Mail: shatfield@ccmail.gc.cc.fl.us; *AV*, James Baxley; *Circ*, Stacey Shoup; *Per*, Lynn Welch; *Ref*, Belinda Norman; *Tech Servs*, John Armstrong; Staff 7 (MLS 5, Non-MLS 2)
Founded 1957. Enrl 4,000; Highest Degree: Associate
Jul 1998-Jun 1999 Income $711,453

Library Holdings: Bk Titles 80,000; Per Subs 800
Special Collections: Bureau of Ethnology Annual Reports 1879-1931; Smithsonian Institution Annual Reports 1849-1964
Automation Activity & Vendor Info: (Cataloging) DRA; (Serials) DRA

G NATIONAL MARINE FISHERIES SERVICE, Panama City Laboratory Library, 3500 Delwood Beach Rd, 32408. SAN 303-1209. Tel: 850-234-6541, Ext 227. FAX: 850-235-3559. Web Site: www.sefscpanamalab.noaa.gov/lib.html. *Tech Servs*, Rosalie Shaffer; E-Mail: rosalie.shaffer@noaa.gov
Founded 1973
Library Holdings: Bk Vols 5,000; Bk Titles 4,000; Per Subs 250
Subject Interests: Marine biology, Oceanography
Special Collections: St Andrew Bay Research
Publications: Reprints list; serials list
Partic in Fedlink; Florida Library Information Network; OCLC Online Computer Library Center, Inc; Panhandle Library Access Network

UNITED STATES NAVY
A NAVAL COASTAL SYSTEMS STATION, Naval Surface Warfare Ctr, 6703 W Hwy 98, 32407-7001. SAN 337-9655. Tel: 850-234-4848. FAX: 850-234-4844. *Librn*, Angelia Whatley; *Cat, Ref*, Deborah Caldwell; Staff 5 (MLS 3, Non-MLS 2)
Founded 1948
Library Holdings: Bk Vols 16,000; Per Subs 350
Publications: Catalog of NCSC Publications; Diving; Hydrodynamics; Mine Warfare; Offline (new accessions, monthly); Periodicals Index; Underwater Acoustics
Partic in Defense Technical Information Center; Dialog Corporation; EasyNet

PATRICK AFB

UNITED STATES AIR FORCE
A 45TH SPACE WING TECHNICAL LIBRARY FL2513, 45 MXS/MXSL CSR 1255, 1030 S Hwy A1A Bldg 989 Rm A-1-S3 Box 4127, 32925-0127. SAN 337-968X. Tel: 321-494-6636, 321-494-6638. *Chief Librn*, Valerie Mutter; *Tech Servs*, Sue Kinaham; *Tech Servs*, Rene Stevens; Staff 2 (MLS 1, Non-MLS 1)
Founded 1952
Library Holdings: Bk Vols 10,362; Per Subs 864
Subject Interests: Aerospace science, Engineering, Mathematics, Science/technology, Technology
Publications: Contractor Bulletin; Notices published in Base newspaper
Partic in Defense Technical Information Center; Dialog Corporation; OCLC Online Computer Library Center, Inc
A PATRICK AIR FORCE BASE LIBRARY, Bldg 722B, 842 Falcon Ave, 32925-3439. SAN 337-971X. Tel: 321-494-6881. FAX: 321-494-4190. *Dir*, Marta Demopoulos; Staff 4 (MLS 2, Non-MLS 2)
Founded 1950
Library Holdings: Bk Vols 48,166; Per Subs 112
Subject Interests: Military history
Special Collections: Air War College; Quality Management Coll
Automation Activity & Vendor Info: (Acquisitions) EOS; (Cataloging) EOS; (Circulation) EOS; (OPAC) EOS; (Serials) EOS
Partic in Central Florida Library Cooperative (CFLC); Fedlink
Friends of the Library Group

PEMBROKE PINES

GM FLORIDA DEPARTMENT OF CHILDREN & FAMILIES, Atlantic Shores Healthcare Inc Library, 1000 SW 84th Ave, 33025-1499. SAN 377-3736. Tel: 954-967-7000. FAX: 954-985-4709. *Librn*, Michelle Skoine
Highest Degree: Master
Library Holdings: Bk Vols 1,600; Per Subs 10
Restriction: Not open to public
Special Services for the Blind - Bks on cassette

§S FLORIDA DEPARTMENT OF CORRECTIONS, Broward Correctional Institution Library, PO Box 829503, 33084. Tel: 954-252-6500, Ext 362. FAX: 954-680-4168. *Librn*, Martin Helo
Library Holdings: Bk Vols 16,748; Per Subs 67

PENSACOLA

M BAPTIST HOSPITAL, Medical Library, 1000 W Moreno St, 32501. SAN 337-9744. Tel: 850-434-4877. *Librn*, Elizabeth Richbourg
Founded 1951
Library Holdings: Bk Vols 500; Per Subs 180
Subject Interests: Clinical medicine

GL ESCAMBIA COUNTY LAW LIBRARY, 190 Governmental Ctr, 32501. SAN 303-1241. Tel: 850-595-4468. FAX: 850-595-4470. *Librn*, Susan Dobinson
Library Holdings: Bk Vols 27,000; Per Subs 10

G HISTORIC PENSACOLA PRESERVATION BOARD, Research Library, 120 E Church St, 32501. (Mail add: PO Box 12866, 32576-2866), SAN 322-9157. Tel: 850-595-5985. FAX: 850-595-5989. *Dir*, John Daniels
Library Holdings: Bk Titles 2,000; Per Subs 20
Special Collections: bks; bks, slides, folders; Museums Management Coll; Pensacola History Coll

G LAKEVIEW CENTER, INC LIBRARY, 1221 W Lakeview Ave, 32501. SAN 326-3177. Tel: 850-432-1222, Ext 3757. FAX: 850-433-1314. *Librn*, Dr Susan Smith
Founded 1981
Library Holdings: Bk Vols 2,000
Subject Interests: Alcoholism, Drug abuse, Psychiatry, Psychology
Special Collections: Archives
Restriction: Staff use only

S PENSACOLA HISTORICAL SOCIETY, Lelia Abercrombie Historical Resource Center, 117 E Government St, 32501. SAN 303-1284. Tel: 850-434-5455. E-Mail: phstaff@pcola.gulf.net. Web Site: www.pensacolahistory.org. *Curator, Dir*, Sandra L Johnson; *Coll Develop*, Gayle Sheckelford
Founded 1960
Library Holdings: Bk Vols 2,000
Special Collections: Cartography (Maps of Pensacola & West Florida from 1500 to present); Genealogy (Pensacola); History of Pensacola & Northwest Florida
Restriction: Non-circulating
Open Tues, Wed, Thurs & Sat 10-12 & 1-3

J PENSACOLA JUNIOR COLLEGE, Learning Resources Center, 1000 College Blvd, 32504-8998. SAN 337-9809. Tel: 850-484-2013. FAX: 850-484-2098. Web Site: www.lsc.pjc.cc.fl.us, www.pjc.cc.fl.us. *Dean*, Dr Lawrence D Yax; E-Mail: lyax@pjc.cc.fl.us; *Automation Syst Coordr*, Mike Whaley; *ILL, Ref*, Virginia Vail; *Cat*, Virginia Thomas; *Circ*, Charlotte Sweeny; *Coll Develop, Ref*, Barbara Bedell; *ILL*, Virginia Vail; *Reader Servs*, Dr Sandra Lockney-Davis; *Tech Servs*, Frances Carroll; Staff 15 (MLS 15)
Founded 1948. Enrl 35,000; Fac 261
Library Holdings: Bk Vols 151,493; Bk Titles 129,700; Per Subs 899
Publications: PJC LRC News (newsletter)
Partic in Col Ctr for Libr Automation; OCLC Online Computer Library Center, Inc; SE Libr Network
Special Services for the Deaf - TTY machine
Departmental Libraries:
MILTON CAMPUS, 5988 Hwy 90, Milton, 32504. SAN 337-9833. Tel: 904-484-4410. FAX: 904-484-4453. Web Site: www.pjc.cc.fl.us. *Librn*, Dorothy Abbott; E-Mail: doabbott@pjc.cc.fl.us
Library Holdings: Bk Vols 21,149; Bk Titles 17,902; Per Subs 130
WARRINGTON CAMPUS, 5555 W Hwy 98, 32504. SAN 337-9868. Tel: 904-484-2252. FAX: 904-484-2355. Web Site: www.pjc.cc.fl.us. *Librn*, Dorothy Moloney
Library Holdings: Bk Vols 28,091; Bk Titles 24,990; Per Subs 235

S PENSACOLA MUSEUM OF ART, Harry Thornton Library, 407 S Jefferson St, 32501-5997. SAN 303-1276. Tel: 850-432-6247. FAX: 850-469-1532. E-Mail: pma407@aol.com. *Curator*, Deborah Bond
Founded 1960
Library Holdings: Bk Titles 300
Subject Interests: Art history

M SACRED HEART HOSPITAL, Medical Library, 5151 N Ninth Ave, 32504. SAN 337-9892. Tel: 850-416-7110. FAX: 850-416-6864. *Librn*, Ann Phillips; E-Mail: aphillips@sacred-heart.org
Founded 1959
Library Holdings: Bk Vols 933; Per Subs 161
Partic in Docline; Medline; Send

UNITED STATES NAVY
A NAVAL AIR STATION LIBRARY, Commanding Officer Sta Libr, Bldg 624, 190 Radford Blvd, NAS Pensacola, 32508-5217. SAN 337-9981. Tel: 850-452-4362. FAX: 850-453-2028. *Librn*, Judy Walker
Founded 1914
Library Holdings: Bk Vols 28,000; Per Subs 150
Subject Interests: Aviation
Friends of the Library Group
A NAVAL GENERAL LIBRARY PROGRAM, Naval Educ & Training Prof Develop & Tech Ctr, 6490 Saufley Field Rd, 32509-5239. SAN 337-9957. Tel: 850-452-1380. FAX: 850-452-1738. *Dir*, Marjorie Homeyard; Tel: 850-452-1001, Ext 2188, E-Mail: marjorie.homeyard@cnet.navy.mil; *Acq*, C R Moreland; Tel: 850-452-1001, Ext 2187, E-Mail: ron.moreland@cnet.navy.mil; *Librn*, Rebecca Slingerland; Tel: 850-452-1001, Ext 2185, E-Mail: rebecca.slingerland@cnet.navy.mil; Staff 5 (MLS 4, Non-MLS 1)
Founded 1919
Oct 1999-Sep 2000 Income Federal $2,933,558. Mats Exp $2,568,984. Sal $316,300
Publications: Naval General Library Infogram (M)

Provides professional assistance & material & technology support to US Navy & Marine Corps installation libraries, shipboard multimedia resource centers & remote site reading collections

AM NAVAL HOSPITAL, MEDICAL LIBRARY, 6000 W Hwy 98, Code 185, 32512-0003. SAN 338-0025. Tel: 850-505-6402, 850-505-6635. FAX: 850-505-6774. E-Mail: psa1ccw@psa10.med.navy.mil. *Librn*, Connie C Walker
Library Holdings: Bk Vols 1,260; Per Subs 165

AM NAVAL OPERATIONAL MEDICINE INSTITUTE LIBRARY, Code 31, 220 Hovey Rd, 32508-1047. SAN 338-0017. Tel: 850-452-2256. FAX: 850-452-2304. Web Site: www.nomi.navy.mil/library.htm. *Librn*, Valerie S McCann; E-Mail: vmccann@namrl.navy.mil; Staff 2 (MLS 1, Non-MLS 1)
Library Holdings: Bk Vols 10,000; Bk Titles 8,000; Per Subs 98
Special Collections: Naval Aerospace Medical Research Laboratory Reports
Partic in Florida Library Information Network; Panhandle Library Access Network

C UNIVERSITY OF WEST FLORIDA, John C Pace Library, 11000 University Pkwy, 32514-5070. SAN 303-1306. Tel: 850-474-2492. FAX: 850-474-3338. *Dir*, Grady Morein; E-Mail: gmorein@uwf.edu; *Assoc Dir, Coll Develop*, Helen Wigersma; E-Mail: hwigersm@uwf.edu; *Acq*, Daniel L North; Tel: 850-474-2449, E-Mail: dnorth@uwf.edu; *Cat*, Bob H T Sun; Tel: 850-474-2454, E-Mail: rsun@uwf.edu; *ILL*, Robert Perdue; Tel: 850-474-2413, E-Mail: rperdue@uwf.edu; *Bibliog Instr*, Lauren Brosnihan; Tel: 850-474-2264, E-Mail: lbrosnih@uwf.edu; *Spec Coll*, Dean DeBolt; Tel: 850-474-2213, E-Mail: ddebolt@uwf.edu; *Circ*, Caroline Rowe; Tel: 850-474-2412, E-Mail: crowe@uwf.edu; *Govt Doc*, Peggy Toifal; Tel: 850-474-2711, E-Mail: ptoifal@uwf.edu; Staff 16 (MLS 16)
Founded 1966. Enrl 8,011; Fac 210; Highest Degree: Doctorate
Jul 1998-Jun 1999 Income $3,028,090. Mats Exp $1,056,909, Books $422,019, Per/Ser (Incl. Access Fees) $535,534, Presv $51,709, Electronic Ref Mat (Incl. Access Fees) $47,647. Sal $1,710,147
Library Holdings: Bk Vols 628,438; Per Subs 3,060
Special Collections: Childrens Books; Langston Hughes Collection; Panton Leslie & Company Papers; West Florida History, mss, bks, maps, photos
Automation Activity & Vendor Info: (Acquisitions) NOTIS; (Cataloging) NOTIS; (Circulation) NOTIS; (Course Reserve) NOTIS; (ILL) NOTIS; (Media Booking) NOTIS; (OPAC) NOTIS; (Serials) NOTIS
Partic in Florida Library Information Network; OCLC Online Computer Library Center, Inc; Panhandle Library Access Network

P WEST FLORIDA REGIONAL LIBRARY, 200 W Gregory, 32501-4878. SAN 338-0041. Tel: 850-435-1760. Reference Tel: 850-435-1763. FAX: 850-435-1739. E-Mail: wfrl04@pcola.gulf.net. Web Site: www.wfrl.lib.fl.us. *Dir*, Eugene T Fischer; Tel: 850-435-1782, E-Mail: gfischer@ci.pensacola.fl.us; *AV, Circ*, Bill Nelson; *Bkmobile Coordr*, Steve Cox; *Commun Relations*, Melissa Thacker; E-Mail: mthacker@ci.pensacola.fl.us; *ILL*, Erma Lookabaugh; *Tech Servs*, Eileen Burg; E-Mail: eburg@ci.pensacola.fl.us; *Ch Servs, YA Servs*, Cindy Birden; *Ref*, Bonnie Demars. Subject Specialists: *Genealogy*, Dolly Pollard; Staff 61 (MLS 13, Non-MLS 48)
Founded 1937. Pop 405,000; Circ 991,366
Oct 1999-Sep 2000 Income (Main Library and Branch Library) $3,362,682, State $511,499, City $705,992, County $2,145,191. Mats Exp $285,845, Books $256,912, Electronic Ref Mat (Incl. Access Fees) $28,933. Sal $1,565,744
Library Holdings: Bk Vols 316,997; Per Subs 797
Subject Interests: Genealogy, Local history
Automation Activity & Vendor Info: (Acquisitions) DRA; (Cataloging) DRA; (Circulation) DRA; (OPAC) DRA; (Serials) DRA
Database Vendor: Ebsco - EbscoHost, IAC - Info Trac
Publications: PPL Friends Newsletter
Partic in Panhandle Library Access Network
Special Services for the Blind - Talking Books
Friends of the Library Group
Branches: 6
GULF BREEZE BRANCH, 1060 Shoreline Dr, Gulf Breeze, 32561. SAN 338-0106. Tel: 850-932-5166. FAX: 850-932-4595.
Library Holdings: Bk Vols 35,902
Friends of the Library Group
JAY BRANCH, 5259 Booker Lane, Jay, 32565. SAN 338-0130. Tel: 850-675-6293.
Library Holdings: Bk Vols 2,798
LUCIA M TRYON BRANCH, 5740 N Ninth Ave, 32504. SAN 338-0076. Tel: 850-494-7373.
Friends of the Library Group
MILTON BRANCH, 805 Alabama Ave, Milton, 32570. SAN 338-0165. Tel: 904-623-5565, 904-626-8398.
Library Holdings: Bk Vols 29,760
Friends of the Library Group
NAVARRE BRANCH, 8484 James M Harvell Rd, Navarre, 32566. SAN 374-7204. Tel: 850-939-0679.
Library Holdings: Bk Vols 7,771
Friends of the Library Group
SOUTHWEST BRANCH, 12385 Sorrento Rd, 32507. SAN 378-1410. Tel: 850-453-7780.
Bookmobiles: 2

M WEST FLORIDA REGIONAL MEDICAL CENTER LIBRARY, 8383 N Davis Hwy, PO Box 18900, 32523-8900. SAN 322-726X. Tel: 850-494-4490. FAX: 850-494-6060. *Librn*, Kay Franklin; Staff 2 (MLS 2)
Founded 1954
Library Holdings: Bk Vols 1,500; Per Subs 244
Subject Interests: Oncology
Special Collections: Oncology (Chadbourne Coll), bks
Restriction: Staff use only

PERRY

S TAYLOR CORRECTIONAL INSTITUTION LIBRARY, Rte 1, Box 1086, 32347. SAN 377-0869. Tel: 850-838-4000. *Librn*, Gary Parkhouse
Library Holdings: Bk Vols 10,000; Per Subs 50

P TAYLOR COUNTY PUBLIC LIBRARY, 403 N Washington St, 32347-2791. SAN 303-1314. Tel: 850-838-3512. FAX: 850-838-3514. Web Site: taco.perryfl.com/library.html. *Dir*, Boyd Bruce; *Asst Dir*, Karen Freeman
Pop 17,150; Circ 53,923
Library Holdings: Bk Vols 40,000; Per Subs 60
Special Services for the Deaf - Books on deafness & sign language; Captioned film depository; High interest/low vocabulary books
Friends of the Library Group

PINELLAS PARK

SR GOOD SAMARITAN CHURCH, Adult Resource Center, 6085 Park Blvd, 33781. SAN 328-4638. Tel: 727-544-8558.
Library Holdings: Bk Vols 1,303

G JUVENILE WELFARE BOARD OF PINELLAS COUNTY, Mailande W Holland Library, 6698 68th Ave N, 33781. SAN 326-0801. Tel: 727-547-5670. FAX: 727-547-5610. Web Site: jwbpinellas.org. *Librn*, Joyce Sparrow; Tel: 727-547-5671, E-Mail: jsparrow@jwbpinellas.org; Staff 2 (MLS 1, Non-MLS 1)
Founded 1976
Library Holdings: Bk Vols 4,000; Per Subs 200
Subject Interests: Grantsmanship, Parenting
Automation Activity & Vendor Info: (Circulation) SIRSI
Database Vendor: Ebsco - EbscoHost
Partic in Tampa Bay Library Consortium, Inc
Specialized library which supports public & private agencies providing services to families & children

P PINELLAS PARK PUBLIC LIBRARY, 7770 52nd St, 33781-3498. SAN 303-1322. Tel: 727-541-0718. FAX: 727-541-0818. E-Mail: libref@pppl.tblc.lib.fl.us. Web Site: pppl.tblc.lib.fl.us/. *Dir*, Barbara Ponce; *Asst Dir*, Gary L Bogart; *Ch Servs*, Arline Hollingsworth; *Circ*, Jan Ingle; *Coll Develop*, Judy Frishett; *Ref*, Desiree Spano; Staff 5 (MLS 5)
Founded 1948. Pop 44,126; Circ 322,932
Oct 1998-Sep 1999 Income $1,234,446, State $46,511, City $955,724, County $232,211. Mats Exp $104,562, Books $71,078, Per/Ser (Incl. Access Fees) $10,078, AV Equip $15,602, Other Print Mats $1,430, Electronic Ref Mat (Incl. Access Fees) $6,374. Sal $753,585 (Prof $316,505)
Library Holdings: Bk Vols 90,121; Bk Titles 87,090; Per Subs 313
Automation Activity & Vendor Info: (Cataloging) epixtech, inc.; (Circulation) epixtech, inc.; (OPAC) epixtech, inc.
Publications: Newsletter
Mem of Pinellas County Public Libr Coop
Partic in Tampa Bay Library Consortium, Inc
Friends of the Library Group

PLANT CITY

P BRUTON MEMORIAL LIBRARY, 302 McLendon St, 33566. SAN 303-1349. Tel: 813-757-9215. FAX: 813-757-9217. Web Site: www.hcplc.org/hcplc/bru/. *Dir*, Anne T Haywood; *Ch Servs*, Carol M Lane; *Tech Servs*, Susan Ambrose Miles; *Circ*, Julie Robinson; Staff 14 (MLS 4, Non-MLS 10)
Founded 1960. Pop 27,000; Circ 254,898
Oct 1998-Sep 1999 Income $756,000, City $517,889, County $223,836, Locally Generated Income $14,275. Mats Exp $118,342, Books $98,342, Per/Ser (Incl. Access Fees) $10,000, Electronic Ref Mat (Incl. Access Fees) $10,000. Sal $282,641
Library Holdings: Bk Vols 90,074; Per Subs 175
Special Collections: Florida History Coll
Automation Activity & Vendor Info: (Cataloging) epixtech, inc.; (Circulation) epixtech, inc.
Database Vendor: epixtech, inc.
Publications: Between the Pages (Friends Newsletter)
Partic in Tampa Bay Library Consortium, Inc
Friends of the Library Group

PLANTATION

P HELEN B HOFFMAN PLANTATION LIBRARY, 501 N Fig Tree Lane, 33317. SAN 303-1357. Tel: 954-797-2140. FAX: 954-797-2767. E-Mail: planlib@mediaone.net. *Dir*, Dee Anne Merritt
Founded 1963
Library Holdings: Bk Vols 70,000; Per Subs 225
Subject Interests: Art and architecture, Sculpture
Special Collections: Florida Coll; Large Print Coll
Friends of the Library Group

S THE INSTITUTE OF BUSINESS APPRAISERS, INC LIBRARY, 7420 NW Fifth St Ste 103, 33317. (Mail add: PO Box 17410, 33318), Tel: 954-584-1144. Toll Free Tel: 800-299-4130. FAX: 954-584-1184. Web Site: www.go-iba.org. *Exec Dir*, Michele Miles; E-Mail: mgm@instbusapp.org
Founded 1978
Library Holdings: Bk Titles 17,000; Per Subs 10

POINCIANA

P POINCIANA LIBRARY, 101 N Doverplum Ave, 34759. SAN 376-2696. Tel: 407-935-1177. FAX: 407-935-1196. Web Site: www.osceola.lib.fl.us. *Mgr*, Beth Lucas
Library Holdings: Bk Vols 15,000; Bk Titles 10,000; Per Subs 19
Mem of Osceola County Pub Libr Syst
Friends of the Library Group

POLK CITY

P POLK CITY MUNICIPAL LIBRARY, 215 S Bougainvillea St, 33868-1139. (Mail add: PO Box 1139, 33868-1139), SAN 377-2705. Tel: 863-984-4340. FAX: 863-965-6385. Web Site: www.pclc.lib.fl.us/polkcity.html. *Dir*, Pamela Watkins Burton; E-Mail: pamela@pclc.lib.fl.us; Staff 1 (Non-MLS 1)
Library Holdings: Bk Vols 5,611; Bk Titles 5,323
Function: ILL available
Partic in Polk County Libr Coop

S POLK CORRECTIONAL INSTITUTION LIBRARY, 10800 Evans Rd, 33868. SAN 377-4791. Tel: 863-984-2273. *Librn*, Henry P Ziegler
Library Holdings: Bk Vols 15,460; Per Subs 265

PORT CHARLOTTE

P CHARLOTTE GLADES LIBRARY SYSTEM, 18400 Murdock Circle, 33948. SAN 338-019X. Tel: 941-743-1460. Interlibrary Loan Service Tel: 941-743-1608. FAX: 941-743-1464. *Dir*, Mary Ellen Fuller; E-Mail: mefuller@cgls.lib.fl.us; *Asst Dir, Coll Develop*, Kaye Beasley; *Cat, Tech Servs*, Ann Surrette; *Ch Servs, YA Servs*, Patty Raisch; *Ref*, Bill MacDonald; Staff 9 (MLS 9)
Founded 1963. Pop 136,046
Oct 1999-Sep 2000 Income (Main Library and Branch Library) $2,175,099, State $321,561, County $1,788,454, Other $65,084. Mats Exp $289,418, Books $255,031, Per/Ser (Incl. Access Fees) $17,487, Electronic Ref Mat (Incl. Access Fees) $16,900. Sal $834,689
Library Holdings: Bk Vols 146,620; Per Subs 398
Subject Interests: Florida, Genealogy
Special Collections: Large Print Book Coll; Local Author Coll
Automation Activity & Vendor Info: (Cataloging) DRA; (Circulation) DRA
Publications: Friend's Newsletters; Information pamphlets
Partic in SW Fla Libr Network
Special Services for the Deaf - Captioned media; TDD
Special Services for the Blind - Braille & talking book collections (print)
Friends of the Library Group
Branches: 5
ENGLEWOOD CHARLOTTE PUBLIC, 3450 McCall Rd, Englewood, 34224. SAN 338-022X. Tel: 941-474-1881. FAX: 941-474-3816. *Head Librn*, Mary Louise Rowe; E-Mail: mrowe@cgls.lib.fl.us; Staff 1 (MLS 1)
Library Holdings: Bk Vols 25,410; Per Subs 59
Automation Activity & Vendor Info: (Cataloging) DRA; (Circulation) DRA
Publications: Friend's Newsletters
Partic in Southwest Florida Library Network
Special Services for the Blind - Talking Books
Friends of the Library Group
GLADES COUNTY PUBLIC, Riverside Dr, PO Box 505, Moore Haven, 33471. SAN 338-0254. Tel: 941-946-0744. FAX: 914-946-1661. *Librn*, Mary Booher; E-Mail: mbooher@cgls.lib.fl.us; *Librn*, Pam Brown; E-Mail: pbrown@cgls.lib.fl.us; Staff 2 (Non-MLS 2)
Library Holdings: Bk Vols 12,019; Per Subs 42
Subject Interests: County hist
Automation Activity & Vendor Info: (Circulation) DRA
Partic in SWFLN
Friends of the Library Group
MURDOCK, 18400 Murdock Circle, 33948. SAN 326-7377. Tel: 941-743-1462. Interlibrary Loan Service Tel: 941-743-1608. Circulation Tel: 941-743-1465. FAX: 941-743-8922. *Librn*, Angelyn Patteson; E-Mail: apatteson@cgls.lib.fl.us; Staff 2 (MLS 2)
Library Holdings: Bk Vols 28,717; Per Subs 95
Subject Interests: Business
Automation Activity & Vendor Info: (Circulation) DRA
Publications: Newsletters
Special Services for the Deaf - Captioned media; TDD
Friends of the Library Group
PORT CHARLOTTE, 2280 Aaron St, 33952. SAN 338-0289. Tel: 941-625-6470. FAX: 941-743-4898. *Librn*, Bob Kelley; E-Mail: bkelley@cgls.lib.fl.us; Staff 1 (MLS 1)
Library Holdings: Bk Vols 42,456; Per Subs 96
Subject Interests: Genealogy
Automation Activity & Vendor Info: (Circulation) DRA
Publications: Newsletters
Partic in SWFLN
Special Services for the Deaf - Captioned media
Special Services for the Blind - Talking Books
Friends of the Library Group
PUNTA GORDA PUBLIC, 424 W Henry St, Punta Gorda, 33950. SAN 338-0319. Tel: 941-639-2049. FAX: 941-505-9494. *Librn*, Sandra Davis; E-Mail: sdavis@cgls.lib.fl.us; Staff 1 (MLS 1)
Library Holdings: Bk Vols 36,073; Per Subs 92
Subject Interests: Florida
Automation Activity & Vendor Info: (Circulation) DRA
Publications: Newsletters
Partic in SWFLN
Special Services for the Deaf - Captioned media
Special Services for the Blind - Talking Books
Friends of the Library Group
Bookmobiles: 1. Services for homebound & senior citizens

PORT SAINT LUCIE

§C FLORIDA ATLANTIC UNIVERSITY, Saint Lucie West Library, 520 NW California Blvd, 34986. Tel: 561-871-0050. *Librn*, Carla Robinson; Tel: 561-462-4623, E-Mail: crobins@fau.edu
Library Holdings: Bk Vols 20,000; Per Subs 36; Bks on Deafness & Sign Lang 15
Automation Activity & Vendor Info: (Acquisitions) DRA; (Circulation) SIRSI
Database Vendor: DRA

§J INDIAN RIVER COMMUNITY COLLEGE, Saint Lucie West Library, 520 NW California Blvd, 34986. Tel: 561-462-4693. FAX: 561-336-4169. *Librn*, Leslie Hoyt; *Librn*, Linda Lesperance; *Librn*, Mary Bell Pickny; *Librn*, Karla Robinson
Library Holdings: Bk Vols 12,000; Per Subs 50

PUNTA GORDA

S CHARLOTTE CORRECTIONAL INSTITUTION LIBRARY, 33123 Oil Well Rd, 33955. SAN 377-3183. Tel: 941-575-2828, Ext 680. *In Charge*, Jerome Fraser; Staff 2 (MLS 1, Non-MLS 1)
Founded 1988
Library Holdings: Bk Vols 13,500; Per Subs 98

§J EDISON COMMUNITY COLLEGE, Charlotte County Campus - Vernon Peoples Learning Resource Center, 26300 Airport Rd, 33950. Circulation Tel: 941-637-5620. FAX: 941-637-3501. *Dir*, Jamie Reynolds; Tel: 941-637-5644, E-Mail: jreynolds@edison.edu
Library Holdings: Bk Titles 10,000; Per Subs 60
Automation Activity & Vendor Info: (Acquisitions) DRA; (Cataloging) DRA; (Circulation) DRA; (Course Reserve) DRA; (ILL) DRA; (OPAC) DRA; (Serials) DRA
Open Mon-Thurs 8am-9pm, Fri 8-4, Sat 10-3

§S INTEGRATED CONTROL SYSTEMS, INC, IMPAC Library, 900 W Marion Ave, 33950. Tel: 941-639-6677. FAX: 941-639-7645. Web Site: www.impac-systems.com. *Dir Libr Serv*, Donna Smith
Library Holdings: Bk Titles 2,000; Per Subs 30
Automation Activity & Vendor Info: (Acquisitions) Inmagic, Inc.; (Cataloging) Inmagic, Inc.; (Circulation) Inmagic, Inc.

QUINCY

P GADSDEN COUNTY PUBLIC LIBRARY, 341 E Jefferson St, 32351. SAN 320-4715. Tel: 850-627-7106. FAX: 850-627-7775. *Dir, Librn*, Jane Mock; Staff 2 (MLS 2)
Founded 1979. Pop 45,000
Library Holdings: Bk Titles 83,559; Per Subs 209
Friends of the Library Group
Branches: 2
CHATTAHOOCHEE PUBLIC LIBRARY, 715 Main St, Chattahoochee, 32324. SAN 320-5088. Tel: 904-663-2707. *Librn*, Sonia Crawford
Library Holdings: Bk Vols 14,500

Friends of the Library Group
HAVANA PUBLIC, 116 E Seventh Ave, Havana, 32333. SAN 320-9954. Tel: 850-539-5579. *Librn*, Dorothy Griffin; *Asst Librn*, Amy Andrews
Library Holdings: Bk Vols 12,700
Automation Activity & Vendor Info: (Cataloging) LS 2000; (Circulation) LS 2000; (OPAC) LS 2000
Friends of the Library Group
Bookmobiles: 1

S GADSEN CORRECTIONAL INSTITUTION LIBRARY, Hwy 12, 32353. (Mail add: PO Box 390, 32353), SAN 377-0885. Tel: 850-875-9701, Ext 2261. *Librn*, Karen Rhynes; *Asst Librn*, Marilyn Byrd
Library Holdings: Bk Vols 12,000; Per Subs 50

S QUINCY CORRECTIONAL INSTITUTION LIBRARY, 2225 Pat Thomas Pkwy, 32351. SAN 377-0451. Tel: 850-627-5400, Ext 463. *Librn*, M Proctor
1998-1999 Mats Exp $5,000
Library Holdings: Bk Vols 3,000; Bk Titles 2,900; Per Subs 53

RAIFORD

S NEW RIVER CORRECTIONAL INSTITUTION LIBRARY, PO Box 333, 32083-0333. SAN 371-5493. Tel: 904-368-3000, Ext 3294. *In Charge*, Charles W Houston; Staff 2 (MLS 2)
Founded 1990. Circ 789
Jul 1998-Jun 1999 Income $24,160. Mats Exp $21,760, Books $16,750, Per/Ser (Incl. Access Fees) $5,010
Library Holdings: Bk Vols 19,000; Per Subs 138

S UNION CORRECTIONAL INSTITUTION LIBRARY, State Road 16, 32083-0221. (Mail add: PO Box 221, 32083-0221), SAN 303-139X. Tel: 904-431-2000, Ext 2173. FAX: 904-431-1023. *Librn*, Daniel Weine; Fax: 904-431-2010; Staff 4 (MLS 1, Non-MLS 3)
Founded 1968
1998-1999 Income $48,999. Mats Exp $39,994
Library Holdings: Bk Vols 10,000; Per Subs 85
Subject Interests: Afro-American, Hispanic, Literature, Science fiction
Special Collections: Law Coll
Partic in Florida Library Information Network

RIVERVIEW

S HILLSBOROUGH CORRECTIONAL INSTITUTION LIBRARY, 11150 Hwy 672, 33569-8402. SAN 321-1207. Tel: 813-671-5022. FAX: 813-671-5037.
Founded 1980
Library Holdings: Bk Vols 7,000; Per Subs 90

S MERYMAN LIBRARY OF AQUATIC RESEARCH, 10408 Bloomingdale Ave, 33569. SAN 320-4707. Tel: 813-626-9551. FAX: 813-623-6613. *Coordr*, Mona Francis; Staff 3 (MLS 2, Non-MLS 1)
Founded 1974
Library Holdings: Bk Vols 6,500; Bk Titles 6,000; Per Subs 42
Subject Interests: Animals, behavior of
Special Collections: Fish and Aquatic Life, periodicals; Fisheries (Assorted First Issues from 1700's), bks
Publications: Research papers

RIVIERA BEACH

P RIVIERA BEACH PUBLIC LIBRARY, 600 W Blue Heron Blvd, 33404-1132. (Mail add: PO Box 11329, 33419), SAN 303-1403. Tel: 561-845-4195. FAX: 561-881-7308. *Cat, Dir*, Anne Sutton; E-Mail: agsutton@bellsouth.net
Founded 1950. Pop 30,000; Circ 79,230
Library Holdings: Bk Vols 82,000; Bk Titles 49,498; Per Subs 126
Special Collections: Black Studies Coll; Florida Coll
Publications: Cornucopia
Mem of Palm Beach County Library System
Friends of the Library Group

ROCKLEDGE

M WUESTHOFF MEMORIAL HOSPITAL, Medical Library, 110 Longwood Ave, PO Box 5002, 32956. SAN 326-310X. Tel: 321-636-2211, Ext 1421. FAX: 321-690-6620. *Librn*, Carol Crawford
Library Holdings: Bk Vols 500; Bk Titles 500; Per Subs 60
Subject Interests: Allied health

SAFETY HARBOR

P SAFETY HARBOR PUBLIC LIBRARY, 101 Second St N, 34695. SAN 323-7575. Tel: 813-724-1525. TDD: 813-724-1529. FAX: 813-724-1533. Web Site: www.tblc.org/shpl/homepg.htm. *Dir*, Monica Reed; E-Mail: reedm@tblc.org; *Ref*, Stephanie Clark; E-Mail: clarks@tblc.org; *Ch Servs*, Shirley Wilder; E-Mail: wilders@tblc.org; *Tech Servs*, Mary Ann De Meo; E-Mail: demeom@tblc.org; *Circ*, Gail Geraci; E-Mail: geracig@tblc.org; Staff 4 (MLS 4)
Founded 1938. Pop 17,300; Circ 224,000
Oct 1999-Sep 2000 Income $670,288, State $35,343, City $473,910, County $161,035. Mats Exp $139,700, Books $80,000, Per/Ser (Incl. Access Fees) $5,200, AV Equip $39,500, Electronic Ref Mat (Incl. Access Fees) $15,000. Sal $390,961
Library Holdings: Bk Vols 69,000; Per Subs 100; Bks on Deafness & Sign Lang 900
Special Collections: Books & Videos on Deafness & Sign Language
Automation Activity & Vendor Info: (Acquisitions) epixtech, inc.; (Cataloging) epixtech, inc.; (Circulation) epixtech, inc.; (OPAC) epixtech, inc.; (Serials) epixtech, inc.
Database Vendor: IAC - Info Trac
Mem of Pinellas County Public Libr Coop
Partic in Tampa Bay Library Consortium, Inc
Special Services for the Deaf - Books on deafness & sign language; Captioned film depository; TDD
Friends of the Library Group

SAINT AUGUSTINE

S CASTILLO DE SAN MARCOS & FORT MATANZAS, National Monument Library, One S Castillo Dr, 32084-3699. SAN 370-288X. Tel: 904-829-6506, Ext 223. FAX: 904-823-9388. *In Charge*, Shirley Vellis
Library Holdings: Bk Vols 620
Special Collections: Military History; Stetson Coll

S DOLPHIN MARINE RESEARCH LIBRARY, 41 Dune St, 32080-7020. (Mail add: Overseas Hwy, PO Box 522875, 33052-2875), SAN 326-5927. Tel: 509-996-2103, 509-996-2286. E-Mail: drc@dolphins.org. Web Site: www.dolphins.org. *Dir*, Robert W Hult; *Librn*, Frances F Brewster; *Coordr*, DeVona Podruchny
Library Holdings: Bk Titles 7,500; Per Subs 10
Special Collections: National Fisheries Service

C FLAGLER COLLEGE, William L Proctor Library, 74 King St, 32084. (Mail add: PO Box 1027, 32085-1027), SAN 303-1411. Tel: 904-829-6481, Ext 206. FAX: 904-823-8511. E-Mail: library@flagler.edu. Web Site: www.flagler.edu/academics/library.html. *Dir*, Michael Gallen; E-Mail: gallenm@flagler.edu; *Cat*, Eleanor Schofield; *Ref*, Cynthia Barrancotto; *Ref*, John Daniels; *Ref*, Brian Nesselrode; *ILL*, Peggy Dyess; *Ser*, Catherine Norwood; *Circ*, Grace Engelstadter; Staff 5 (MLS 5)
Founded 1968. Enrl 1,806; Fac 62; Highest Degree: Bachelor
Library Holdings: Bk Titles 66,476; Per Subs 453
Automation Activity & Vendor Info: (Cataloging) Endeavor; (Circulation) Endeavor; (OPAC) Endeavor
Database Vendor: Ebsco - EbscoHost, GaleNet, Lexis-Nexis, OCLC - First Search, ProQuest, Silverplatter Information Inc., Wilson - Wilson Web
Partic in Florida Library Information Network; NE Fla Libr Info Network; SE Libr Network

FLORIDA SCHOOL FOR THE DEAF & BLIND
P LIBRARY FOR THE BLIND (K-12), 207 N San Marco Ave, 32084. SAN 338-0343. Tel: 904-827-2720. FAX: 904-827-2403. E-Mail: gatewoodw@mail.fsdb.k12.us.fl. *Librn for Blind*, Wynema Jean Gatewood; Staff 2 (MLS 1, Non-MLS 1)
Founded 1920. Enrl 129
Jul 1999-Jun 2000 Mats Exp $15,500. Sal $45,000
Library Holdings: Bk Vols 10,094; Bk Titles 8,500; Per Subs 40; Spec Interest Per Sub 10
Subject Interests: Blindness, Education
Special Collections: Education of the Blind Coll
Publications: Staff newsletter (bi-monthly)
Special Services for the Blind - Bks on cassette; Braille; Large print bks; Special videos for visually handicapped

S LINDHEIMER LIBRARY FOR THE DEAF, 207 N San Marco Ave, 32084. SAN 338-0378. Tel: 904-827-2670. TDD: 904-827-2670. Web Site: www.fsdb.k12.fl.us. *Dir*, Debie Schuler; *Librn*, Linda Zimmerman; E-Mail: zimmermanl@mail.fsdb.k12.fl.us; *Media Spec*, Diane Edwards; Staff 5 (MLS 2, Non-MLS 3)
Founded 1885. Enrl 80; Highest Degree: Doctorate
Library Holdings: Bk Vols 14,000; Per Subs 60
Special Collections: Deafness & Hearing Impaired
Restriction: Open to student, faculty & staff
Special Services for the Deaf - TDD

S SAINT AUGUSTINE HISTORICAL SOCIETY, Research Library, 6 Artillery Lane, 2nd flr, 32084. (Mail add: 271 Charlotte St, 32084-5099), SAN 303-1438. Tel: 904-825-2333. FAX: 904-824-2569. E-Mail: sahs@aug.com. *Asst Librn*, William Temme; *Mgr*, Charles Tingley
Founded 1883
Library Holdings: Bk Vols 12,000; Bk Titles 10,000; Per Subs 75
Special Collections: Card Calendar of Spanish Documents, 1512-1764; Card Index of St Augustine Residents; Cathedral Parish Records, 1594-1763 & 1784-1882, including Baptisms, Marriages & Burials; Ceiba Mocha Parish, Cuban Archives, 1797-1920, microfilm; Census Records for Northeast Florida, 1784-1920; Colonial Office Records, 1763-1784, British period,

microfilm; Court Records for St Johns County, 1812-1960; East Florida Papers on microfilm, 1783-1821; Florida Times Union Newspaper, 1881-1895, microfilm; over 1000 maps of Florida & St Augustine (copies), 16th Century to present; over 1000 photographs of the St Augustine Area, 19th Century to present; St Augustine Newspapers, 1821 to Present, with gaps; Stetson Coll, 1500's-1817; various Manuscript Coll
Publications: East Florida Gazette (tri-annual); El Escribano, St Augustine Journal of History (annual)
Restriction: Open to public for reference only
Friends of the Library Group

S SAINT AUGUSTINE PRESERVATION DEPARTMENT LIBRARY, Government House, PO Box 210, 32085-0210. SAN 303-142X. Tel: 904-825-5033. FAX: 904-825-5096. *Dir*, William R Adams
Founded 1963
Library Holdings: Bk Vols 2,000
Subject Interests: Archaeology, Local history
Special Collections: Architectural Survey Coll; Historical Maps Coll, copies; Saint Augustine Preservation Projects Coll, VF; Translations & Transcripts of 16th-18th Century Documents

P SAINT JOHNS COUNTY PUBLIC LIBRARY SYSTEM, 1960 N Ponce de Leon Blvd, 32084. SAN 338-0408. Tel: 904-823-2650. TDD: 904-823-2652. FAX: 904-823-2656. E-Mail: libm@co.st-johns.fl.us. Web Site: www.co.st-johns.fl.us/bcc/library-services/index.html. *Dir*, Mary Jane Little; Tel: 904-823-2651, E-Mail: mjlittle@co.st-johns.fl.us; *Asst Dir, Coll Develop*, Sol M Hirsch; Tel: 904-823-2651, E-Mail: shirsch@co.st-johns.fl.us; *Mgr*, Cheryl Hirschi; E-Mail: cherylh@neflin.org; *Ch Servs*, Janet Paparelli; E-Mail: janetp@neflin.org; *Ref*, Steven Stangle; E-Mail: sstangle@neflin.org; Staff 45 (MLS 14, Non-MLS 31)
Founded 1875. Pop 120,000; Circ 771,484
Oct 1999-Sep 2000 Income (Main Library and Branch Library) $2,380,772, State $214,145, Federal $43,600, County $1,976,212, Other $146,815. Mats Exp $683,723, Books $486,887, Per/Ser (Incl. Access Fees) $32,000, Presv $8,840, Electronic Ref Mat (Incl. Access Fees) $155,996. Sal $1,297,116
Library Holdings: Bk Vols 233,667; Bk Titles 113,069; Per Subs 100
Subject Interests: Florida
Automation Activity & Vendor Info: (Acquisitions) epixtech, inc.; (Cataloging) epixtech, inc.; (Circulation) epixtech, inc.; (OPAC) epixtech, inc.
Partic in NE Fla Libr Info Network; OCLC; Solinet
Special Services for the Deaf - TDD
Books-by-mail project
Friends of the Library Group
Branches: 3
BARTRAM TRIAL BRANCH, 60 Davis Pond Blvd, Fruit Cove, 32259-4390. SAN 325-4100. Tel: 904-287-4929. FAX: 904-287-9464. Web Site: www.co.st-johns.fl.us/bcc/library-services/index.htm. *Librn*, Dan Markus; E-Mail: danm@neflin.org; *Ch Servs*, Brad Powell; E-Mail: bradp@flin.org; *Ref*, Lisa McDaniels; E-Mail: lisam@neflin.org; Staff 6 (MLS 3, Non-MLS 3)
Pop 20,000
Library Holdings: Bk Vols 48,021; Per Subs 75
Automation Activity & Vendor Info: (Acquisitions) epixtech, inc.; (Cataloging) epixtech, inc.; (Circulation) epixtech, inc.; (OPAC) epixtech, inc.
Partic in NEFLIN
Friends of the Library Group
HASTINGS BRANCH, 6195 S Main St No B, Hastings, 32145. SAN 338-0416. Tel: 904-692-2841. FAX: 904-692-1255. Web Site: www.co.st-johns.fl.us/bcc/library-services/index.html. *Librn*, Valerie Peischel-Wilkinson; E-Mail: vjpeischel@neflin.org; Staff 5 (MLS 1, Non-MLS 4)
Founded 1928. Pop 7,000
Library Holdings: Bk Vols 30,020; Per Subs 50; Spec Interest Per Sub 10; Bks on Deafness & Sign Lang 300
Automation Activity & Vendor Info: (Acquisitions) epixtech, inc.; (Cataloging) epixtech, inc.; (Circulation) epixtech, inc.; (OPAC) epixtech, inc.
Partic in NEFLIN
Special Services for the Deaf - Staff with knowledge of sign language
Friends of the Library Group
PONTE VEDRA BEACH BRANCH, 101 Library Blvd, Ponte Vedra Beach, 32082. SAN 325-4127. Tel: 904-273-1145. FAX: 904-273-0685. Web Site: www.co.st-johns.fl.us/bcc/library-services/index.html. *Librn*, Betty Frederick; E-Mail: betty@neflin.org; *Ch Servs*, Helena Hayes; E-Mail: helena@neflin.org; *Ref*, Lorri Davis; E-Mail: ljm@neflin.org; Staff 10 (MLS 3, Non-MLS 7)
Pop 30,000
Library Holdings: Bk Vols 71,476
Automation Activity & Vendor Info: (Acquisitions) epixtech, inc.; (Cataloging) epixtech, inc.; (Circulation) epixtech, inc.; (OPAC) epixtech, inc.
Partic in NEFLIN
Friends of the Library Group

SAINT LEO

C SAINT LEO COLLEGE, Cannon Memorial Library, 33701 State Rd 52, PO Box 6665 MC2128, 33574-6665. SAN 303-1446. Tel: 352-588-8258. Reference Tel: 352-588-8477. FAX: 352-588-8484. E-Mail: refdesk@saintleo.edu. Web Site: www.saintleo.edu. *Archivist, Dir Libr Serv*, Sister Dorothy Neuhofer; Tel: 352-588-8260, E-Mail: dorothy.neuhofer@saintleo.edu; *Librn*, Melanie Cooksey; *Distance Educ*, Carla Martindale; Tel: 352-588-8262, E-Mail: carla.martindale@saintleo.edu; *Ref*, Merle Romain; Tel: 352-588-8496, E-Mail: merle.romain@saintleo.edu; *ILL*, Lynn Correia; Tel: 352-588-8261, E-Mail: lynn.correia@saintleo.edu; *Syst Coordr*, Doris Van Kampen; Tel: 352-588-8485; Staff 6 (MLS 6)
Founded 1959. Enrl 5,875; Fac 64; Highest Degree: Master
Jul 1998-Jun 1999 Income $837,339. Mats Exp $297,095, Books $48,595, Per/Ser (Incl. Access Fees) $54,350, Presv $1,628, Micro $13,111, AV Equip $5,115, Electronic Ref Mat (Incl. Access Fees) $29,731. Sal $435,643
Library Holdings: Bk Vols 143,667; Bk Titles 79,587; Per Subs 709
Subject Interests: Catholicism, Humanities, Theology
Automation Activity & Vendor Info: (Acquisitions) Endeavor; (Cataloging) Endeavor; (Circulation) Endeavor; (Course Reserve) Endeavor; (OPAC) Endeavor; (Serials) Endeavor
Database Vendor: Ebsco - EbscoHost, Lexis-Nexis, OCLC - First Search, ProQuest, Silverplatter Information Inc., Wilson - Wilson Web
Publications: Acquisitions List; Bibliographies; Fact Sheet; Handbook; Library Guides; Newsletter; Periodicals & Media Lists
Partic in Libr & Info Resources Network; OCLC Online Computer Library Center, Inc; Solinet; Tampa Bay Library Consortium, Inc
Computer Instruction Center in Library operated cooperatively with CIS department

SAINT PETERSBURG

M ALL CHILDRENS' HOSPITAL, Medical Library, PO Box 31020, 33731-8920. SAN 303-1454. Tel: 727-892-4278. FAX: 727-892-8557. *Dir*, Patricia E Clark
Library Holdings: Bk Titles 750
Subject Interests: Immunology, Nursing, Pediatrics
Partic in Dialog Corporation; Tampa Bay Medical Library Network

M BAYFRONT MEDICAL CENTER, INC, Aucremann Medical Library, 701 Sixth St S, 33701. SAN 303-1462. Tel: 727-893-6136. FAX: 727-893-6819.; Staff 1 (MLS 1)
Founded 1937
1998-1999 Income $100,000. Mats Exp $52,000, Books $20,000, Per/Ser (Incl. Access Fees) $30,000, Micro $2,000. Sal $32,000
Library Holdings: Bk Vols 1,350; Per Subs 185
Subject Interests: Clinical medicine, Obstetrics and gynecology
Restriction: Medical staff only
Partic in Medline; SE-Atlantic Regional Med Libr Servs; Tampa Bay Medical Library Network

C ECKERD COLLEGE, William Luther Cobb Library, 4200 54th Ave S, 33711. SAN 303-1489. Tel: 727-864-8336. FAX: 727-864-8997. Web Site: www.eckerd.edu/academics/library. *Dir*, Edward Stevens; E-Mail: stevenei@eckerd.edu; *Coll Develop*, David Henderson; *Tech Servs*, Jamie Hastreiter; *ILL*, Deidre Wright; *Electronic Resources*, Helene Gold; Staff 5 (MLS 4, Non-MLS 1)
Founded 1959. Enrl 1,558; Fac 96; Highest Degree: Bachelor
Jul 1999-Jun 2000 Income $888,331. Mats Exp $502,086, Books $131,383, Per/Ser (Incl. Access Fees) $302,340, Presv $4,681, Micro $22,219. Sal $361,820 (Prof $249,828)
Library Holdings: Bk Vols 157,733; Bk Titles 113,927; Per Subs 928
Automation Activity & Vendor Info: (Acquisitions) Endeavor; (Cataloging) Endeavor; (Circulation) Endeavor; (Course Reserve) Endeavor
Database Vendor: IAC - Info Trac, OCLC - First Search, ProQuest, Wilson - Wilson Web
Partic in Dialog Corporation; FLIN; Independent Cols & Univs of Fla; LIRN; OCLC Online Computer Library Center, Inc; Tampa Bay Library Consortium, Inc
Friends of the Library Group

G FLORIDA DEPARTMENT OF ENVIRONMENTAL PROTECTION, Marine Research Institute Library, 100 Eighth Ave SE, 33701-5095. SAN 303-1497. Tel: 727-896-8626. FAX: 727-823-0166. *Librn*, Jan Boyett; E-Mail: boyett_j@harpo.dep.state.fl.us; Staff 4 (MLS 1, Non-MLS 3)
Founded 1955
Library Holdings: Bk Titles 6,500; Per Subs 167
Subject Interests: Environmental studies, Ichthyology, Marine biology, Oceanography
Publications: Florida Marine Research Publications; Memoirs of the Hourglass Cruises; Reprints of Articles in Outside Journals

S MUSEUM OF FINE ARTS, Reference Library, 255 Beach Dr NE, 33701-3498. SAN 303-156X. Tel: 727-896-2667. FAX: 727-894-4638. Web Site: www.fine-arts.org. *Librn*, Jordana S Bernstein; Staff 1 (MLS 1)

Founded 1962
Library Holdings: Bk Titles 20,000; Per Subs 25
Subject Interests: Art and architecture, Decorative arts
Restriction: Non-circulating

SR PASADENA COMMUNITY UNITED METHODIST CHURCH LIBRARY, 112 70th St S, 33707. SAN 322-807X. Tel: 727-381-2499. FAX: 727-343-7783. *In Charge*, Bill Anderson
Library Holdings: Bk Vols 7,208
Subject Interests: Bio, Fiction, History, Religion

R PASADENA PRESBYTERIAN CHURCH LIBRARY, 100 Pasadena Ave N, 33710-8315. SAN 303-1578. Tel: 813-345-0148. FAX: 813-347-6836. *Librn*, Laurie Smith; Staff 1 (MLS 1)
Founded 1960
Library Holdings: Bk Titles 5,000
Subject Interests: Religion

GL PINELLAS COUNTY LAW LIBRARY, Saint Petersburg Branch, 545 First Ave N, Rm 500, 33701-3769. SAN 303-1586. Tel: 727-582-7875. FAX: 727-582-7874. E-Mail: pcll@intnet.net. *Mgr*, Rebecca Frank
Founded 1949
Oct 1998-Sep 1999 Income $239,960. Mats Exp Books $149,430. Sal $74,060
Library Holdings: Bk Titles 20,000; Per Subs 75

S POYNTER INSTITUTE FOR MEDIA STUDIES, Eugene Patterson Library, 801 Third St S, 33701. SAN 323-5661. Tel: 727-821-9494. FAX: 727-898-9201. Web Site: www.poynter.org. *Chief Librn*, Sandra Evon Allen; E-Mail: sallen@poynter.org; *Archivist*, David B Shedden; Tel: 727-821-9494, Ext 252; *Dir*, Nara Paul; Staff 4 (MLS 2, Non-MLS 2)
Founded 1985
Library Holdings: Bk Vols 12,400; Per Subs 300
Subject Interests: Journalism, Mass communications
Special Collections: Archive of the Ombudsmen; Don Murray Papers; Newsleaders; Oral History of News Professionals, videotapes; Organization of News Ombudsmen Archives, vertical files
Database Vendor: Dialog, GaleNet, Lexis-Nexis, OCLC - First Search, Wilson - Wilson Web
Publications: Bibliography series (20 bibliographies - selected topics in journalism)
Restriction: Not open to public
Function: Research library
Mem of Tampa Bay Libr Consortium, Inc
Partic in Data Time; Dialog Corporation

S RAYTHEON, Technical Information Center, 1501 72nd St N, 33710-4600. (Mail add: PO Box 12248 MS3, 33733-2248), SAN 303-1470. Tel: 727-302-2187. FAX: 727-302-4779. E-Mail: njsa@eci.esys.com.
Founded 1959
Library Holdings: Bk Vols 6,000; Per Subs 350
Subject Interests: Aerospace science, Business and management, Electrical engineering, Electronics
Automation Activity & Vendor Info: (Acquisitions) CASPR
Partic in Defense Technical Information Center; Dialog Corporation

M SAINT ANTHONY'S HOSPITAL, INC LIBRARY, 1200 Seventh Ave N, 33705. SAN 303-1594. Tel: 727-825-1286. FAX: 727-825-1667.
Library Holdings: Bk Vols 6,200; Per Subs 86
Partic in Tampa Bay Medical Library Network

J SAINT PETERSBURG JUNIOR COLLEGE, M M Bennett Libraries, PO Box 13489, 33733. SAN 337-3185. Tel: 727-341-3719. FAX: 727-341-3658. Web Site: www.spjc.edu/central/lib/. *Dir*, Dr Susan Anderson; E-Mail: andersons@spjc.edu; Staff 36 (MLS 12, Non-MLS 24)
Founded 1927. Enrl 16,933; Highest Degree: Associate
Jul 1998-Jun 1999 Mats Exp $346,748, Books $169,078, Per/Ser (Incl. Access Fees) $121,737, Micro $3,685, AV Equip $11,343, Other Print Mats $1,850, Electronic Ref Mat (Incl. Access Fees) $39,055
Library Holdings: Bk Vols 217,061; Bk Titles 147,771; Per Subs 937
Automation Activity & Vendor Info: (Circulation) DRA
Partic in Tampa Bay Library Consortium, Inc
Departmental Libraries:
CLEARWATER CAMPUS LIBRARY, 2465 Drew St, Clearwater, 33765. SAN 337-3177. Tel: 727-791-2617. FAX: 727-791-2601. *Head Librn*, Janice Hall; Tel: 727-791-2413, E-Mail: hallj@spjc.edu; *Librn*, Antoinette Caraway; Tel: 727-791-2416, E-Mail: carawaya@spjc.edu; *Librn*, Donna Kelly; Tel: 727-791-2415, E-Mail: kellyd@spjc.edu; *Librn*, Pat Barbier; Tel: 727-791-2603, E-Mail: barbierp@spjc.edu; Staff 3 (MLS 3)
M M BENNETT LIBRARY-HEALTH EDUCATION CENTER, 7200 66th St N, Pinellas Park, 33781. SAN 370-2014. Tel: 727-341-3657. FAX: 727-341-3658. Web Site: www.spjc.edu/central/lib. *Actg Librn*, Susan Fitzgerald; E-Mail: fitzgerald@spjc.edu; Staff 4 (MLS 1, Non-MLS 3)
Partic in Southeast Florida Library Information Network, Inc; Tampa Bay Medical Library Network; TBLC
PROCESSING CENTER, 7200 66th St N, 33781. SAN 370-2022. Tel: 727-341-3693. FAX: 727-341-3658. *Head Librn*, Mary Jane Marden; E-Mail: mardenm@spjc.edu; Staff 4 (MLS 1, Non-MLS 3)
SAINT PETERSBURG - GIBBS CAMPUS LIBRARY, 6605 Fifth Ave N, 33710. SAN 338-0432. Tel: 727-341-3515. FAX: 727-341-4654. *Head Librn*, Melisandre Hilliker; Tel: 727-341-3517, E-Mail: hillikerm@spjc.edu; *Librn*, Jayson Nestler; Tel: 727-341-4795, E-Mail: nestlerj@spjc.edu; *Librn*, Dorothy Bell; Tel: 727-841-4732, E-Mail: belld@spjc.edu; *Librn*, Carla Levesque; Tel: 727-341-4756, E-Mail: levesquec@spjc.edu; *AV*, Dave Zarr; Staff 3 (MLS 3)
TARPON SPRINGS CAMPUS LIBRARY, 600 Klosterman Rd, Palm Harbor, 34683. SAN 370-226X. Tel: 727-712-5718. FAX: 727-712-5706. *Head Librn*, Jim Moir; Tel: 727-712-5728, E-Mail: moirj@spjc.edu; *Librn*, Dave Lichtenfels; Tel: 727-712-5872, E-Mail: lichtenfelsd@spjc.edu; Staff 2 (MLS 2)

S ST PETERSBURG MUSEUM OF HISTORY, 335 Second Ave NE, 33701-3501. SAN 303-1608. Tel: 727-894-1052. FAX: 727-823-7276. E-Mail: spmh@ij.net. Web Site: www.ij.net/spmh/. *Dir*, Sam Bond Jr; *Archivist*, Jordana Bernstein; *Curator*, Rebecca Jacobsen Hagen
Founded 1922
Mar 1999-Feb 2000 Income $2,400. Mats Exp $1,500
Library Holdings: Bk Vols 1,020
Subject Interests: Aviation, Baseball, Hist of Fla
Special Collections: Baseball Coll 1930-60's; Florida Tourism materials; Railroad & Early Florida Settlement (Peter Demens Coll); Regional Photgraph Coll; Regional Postcard Coll; St. Petersburg Area History (Blocker Coll)

P SAINT PETERSBURG PUBLIC LIBRARY, 3745 Ninth Ave N, 33713. SAN 338-0467. Tel: 727-893-7724. FAX: 727-893-7348. E-Mail: homeke@splib.lib.fl.us. Web Site: st-petersburg-library.org. *Dir*, Mary A Brown; *Mgr*, Elaine Birkinshaw; *Br Coordr*, Mary Hall; *Ad Servs, Circ*, Kate Holmes
Founded 1910. Pop 240,318; Circ 1,051,108
Library Holdings: Bk Vols 441,735; Per Subs 886
Special Collections: Florida History
Friends of the Library Group
Branches: 5
AZALEA BRANCH LIBRARY & MEDIA CENTER, 7801 22nd Ave N, 33710. SAN 323-9195. Tel: 727-893-7930. FAX: 727-347-4351. *Branch Mgr*, Donarita Vocca
Library Holdings: Bk Vols 30,000
Friends of the Library Group
JAMES WELDON JOHNSON BRANCH, 1111 18th Ave S, 33705. SAN 338-0491. Tel: 727-893-7113. FAX: 727-821-4845.
Library Holdings: Bk Vols 10,400
Friends of the Library Group
MIRROR LAKE, 280 Fifth St N, 33701. SAN 338-0521. Tel: 727-893-7268. FAX: 727-821-4975.
Library Holdings: Bk Vols 57,000
Friends of the Library Group
NORTH, 861 70th Ave N, 33702. SAN 338-0556. Tel: 727-893-7214. FAX: 727-522-6902. *Branch Mgr*, Alisia Ellison; *Asst Librn*, Deborah Henry
Library Holdings: Bk Vols 24,000
Friends of the Library Group
SOUTH, 1201 Country Club Way S, 33705. SAN 338-0564. Tel: 727-893-7244. FAX: 727-864-2470. *Branch Mgr*, Barbara McGiffin
Library Holdings: Bk Vols 22,000
Friends of the Library Group
Bookmobiles: 1

C SALVADOR DALI FOUNDATION INC, Dali Museum Library, 1000 Third St S, 33701. SAN 322-7421. Tel: 727-823-3767. Toll Free Tel: 800-442-3254. FAX: 727-823-8532. E-Mail: jkropf@salvadordalimuseum.org. Web Site: www.salvadordalimuseum.org. *Librn*, Peter Tush; E-Mail: ptush@salvadordalimuseum.org
Founded 1982
Library Holdings: Bk Vols 5,500; Bk Titles 4,700
Subject Interests: Surrealism
Special Collections: Salvador Dali Coll
Publications: Books on Dali: Dali in the Nude; Dali the Passions; Dali, A Panorama; Exhibit Catalogs; Newsletter

S TAMPA BAY REGIONAL PLANNING COUNCIL, Research & Information Center, 9455 Koger Blvd, Ste 219, 33702-2491. SAN 303-1632. Tel: 727-570-5151. FAX: 727-570-5118. *Mgr*, Jessica White; E-Mail: jessica@tbrpc.org
Library Holdings: Bk Vols 3,000; Per Subs 90
Subject Interests: Housing, Planning, Transportation
Special Collections: Developments of Regional Impact for Pinellas, Hillsborough, Pasco, and Manatee Counties Coll

S TIMES PUBLISHING CO, St Petersburg Times, 490 First Ave S, 33701-4204. (Mail add: PO Box 1121, 33701-4204), SAN 303-1640. Tel: 727-893-8111. FAX: 727-893-8107. Web Site: www.sptimes.com, www.tampabay.com. *Res*, Barbara Oliver; E-Mail: oliver@sptimes.com; Staff 16 (MLS 4, Non-MLS 12)
Founded 1923
Library Holdings: Bk Titles 3,000
Special Collections: Florida Book Coll; Historic Local Photographs

Publications: Florida Trend; St Petersburg Times Governing Magazine
Restriction: Staff use only
Partic in Tampa Bay Library Consortium, Inc

C UNIVERSITY OF SOUTH FLORIDA-SAINT PETERSBURG, Nelson Poynter Memorial Library, 140 Seventh Ave S, 33701. SAN 303-1667. Tel: 727-553-3401. Interlibrary Loan Service Tel: 727-553-3585. Circulation Tel: 727-553-3405. Reference Tel: 727-553-1124. FAX: 727-553-1196. Web Site: www.nelson.usf.edu. *Tech Servs*, Signe Oberhofer; Tel: 727-553-3407, E-Mail: signe@nelson.usf.edu; *Media Spec*, Gerald Notaro; Tel: 727-553-3408, E-Mail: notaro@nelson.usf.edu; *ILL, Ref*, Tina Neville; Tel: 727-553-3582, E-Mail: neville@nelson.usf.edu; *Bibliog Instr, Circ*, Jackie Jackson; Tel: 727-553-3581, E-Mail: jackson@nelson.usf.edu; *Electronic Resources*, Ed Sanchez; Tel: 727-553-3402, E-Mail: sanchez@nelson.usf.edu; *Ref*, Karilyn Jaap; Tel: 727-553-3583, E-Mail: jaap@nelson.usf.edu; *Coll Develop*, Kathy Arsenault; E-Mail: arsenaul@nelson.usf.edu. Subject Specialists: *Marine sci*, Deb Henry; Staff 20 (MLS 8, Non-MLS 12)
Founded 1968. Enrl 3,407; Fac 59; Highest Degree: Doctorate
Jul 1999-Jun 2000 Income $1,220,856, State $1,207,556, Locally Generated Income $13,300. Mats Exp $345,751, Books $149,811, Per/Ser (Incl. Access Fees) $137,532, Presv $3,028, Micro $39,909, AV Equip $3,992, Electronic Ref Mat (Incl. Access Fees) $11,479. Sal $549,164 (Prof $289,998)
Library Holdings: Bk Vols 181,639; Bk Titles 1,962; Per Subs 1,851
Subject Interests: Business and management, Education, Humanities, Marine sci, Social sciences
Special Collections: Coll of Dr David Hubbell: Mark Twain; Coll of Dr John C Briggs: Ichthyology, Natural History & Zoology; Papers of Nelson Poynter, Publisher of the St Petersburg Times
Automation Activity & Vendor Info: (Acquisitions) NOTIS; (Cataloging) NOTIS; (Circulation) NOTIS; (Course Reserve) NOTIS; (OPAC) NOTIS; (Serials) NOTIS
Database Vendor: OCLC - First Search
Publications: Poynter bibliographies on numerous subjects; Source Book for Marine Science Dept; The Library Connection (newsletter of the Society for Advancement of Poynter Library); Walking Tour Guide to the Library
Partic in Solinet; Tampa Bay Library Consortium, Inc
Friends of the Library Group

SAINT PETERSBURG BEACH

P ST PETE BEACH PUBLIC LIBRARY, 365 73rd Ave, 33706. SAN 303-1683. Tel: 727-363-9238. FAX: 727-360-4914. E-Mail: lib@spb.org. Web Site: www.tblc.org/spb. *Dir*, Roberta L Whipple
Pop 9,200; Circ 110,000
Library Holdings: Bk Vols 45,000; Per Subs 60
Friends of the Library Group

SAINT TERESA

S FLORIDA STATE UNIVERSITY, Marine Lab Library, 3618 Hwy 98, 32358-2702. SAN 338-1331. Tel: 850-697-4095. FAX: 850-697-3822. Web Site: www.fsu.edu/~fsuml/library.html. *Asst Dir*, Dr John Hitron; E-Mail: jhitron@mailer.fsu.edu
Library Holdings: Bk Vols 1,000

SANDERSON

L FLORIDA DEPARTMENT OF CORRECTIONS, Baker Correctional Institution Library, PO Box 500, 32087. SAN 321-4451. Tel: 904-719-4500. FAX: 904-758-5759. *Librn*, Evan Brown; Staff 2 (MLS 1, Non-MLS 1)
Founded 1979
Library Holdings: Bk Vols 10,000; Per Subs 20
Restriction: Not open to public

SANFORD

J SEMINOLE COMMUNITY COLLEGE, LRC-Library, 100 Weldon Blvd, 32773-6199. SAN 303-1691. Interlibrary Loan Service Tel: 407-328-4722, Ext 3336. Circulation Tel: 407-328-2295. Reference Tel: 407-328-2305. FAX: 407-328-2233. *Dean*, Patricia DeSalvo; Tel: 407-328-2136, E-Mail: desalvop@mail.seminole.cc.fl.us; *Media Spec*, Michael Simpson; Tel: 407-328-4722, Ext 3380; *Ref*, Richard Young; Tel: 407-328-4722, Ext 3346; *Tech Servs*, Laurie Linsley; Tel: 407-328-4722, Ext 3335; *Circ*, Leona Jones; Tel: 407-328-4722, Ext 3338; Staff 30 (MLS 6, Non-MLS 24)
Founded 1966. Enrl 7,800; Fac 240; Highest Degree: Associate
1999-2000 Income $1,200,000. Mats Exp $276,000, Books $170,000, Per/Ser (Incl. Access Fees) $38,000, Micro $13,000, AV Equip $40,000, Electronic Ref Mat (Incl. Access Fees) $15,000. Sal $721,825 (Prof $297,270)
Library Holdings: Bk Vols 83,496; Bk Titles 68,121; Per Subs 500; High Interest/Low Vocabulary Bk Vols 346; Bks on Deafness & Sign Lang 20
Automation Activity & Vendor Info: (Acquisitions) DRA; (Cataloging) DRA; (Circulation) DRA; (OPAC) DRA; (Serials) DRA
Database Vendor: DRA, OCLC - First Search
Partic in Central Florida Library Cooperative (CFLC); OCLC Online Computer Library Center, Inc; SE Libr Network
Special Services for the Blind - Assistive Technology Center for Persons who are blind or physically handicapped

P SEMINOLE COUNTY PUBLIC LIBRARY SYSTEM, 1101 E First St, 32771. SAN 338-0645. Tel: 407-330-3737. Interlibrary Loan Service Tel: 407-330-2923. FAX: 407-330-3120. Web Site: www.scpl.lib.fl.us. *Dir*, J Suzy Goldman; E-Mail: sgoldman@co.seminole.fl.us; *Mgr Libr Serv*, Jane Peterson; Tel: 407-339-0140; *Coll Develop*, Denise Tate; *Business*, Stephanie Kobrin; E-Mail: skobrin@co.seminole.fl.us; Staff 103 (MLS 37, Non-MLS 66)
Founded 1987. Pop 350,000; Circ 2,000,000
Oct 1999-Sep 2000 Income (Main Library and Branch Library) $5,518,336, State $513,856, County $5,004,480. Mats Exp $1,352,973, Books $1,163,181, Per/Ser (Incl. Access Fees) $161,715, Electronic Ref Mat (Incl. Access Fees) $28,077. Sal $2,688,833 (Prof $1,618,762)
Library Holdings: Bk Vols 432,718; Bk Titles 136,087
Automation Activity & Vendor Info: (Cataloging) epixtech, inc.; (Circulation) epixtech, inc.; (OPAC) epixtech, inc.; (Serials) epixtech, inc.
Database Vendor: GaleNet, OCLC - First Search
Partic in Cent Fla Libr Consortium; Florida Library Information Network
Friends of the Library Group
Branches: 5
EAST, 310 Division St, Oviedo, 32765. SAN 328-8978. Tel: 407-366-8150. FAX: 407-366-7923. *Librn*, Jane Finkbeiner; *Branch Mgr*, Beverly McCormick; *Business*, Stephanie Kobrin; Tel: 407-330-3737, Fax: 407-330-3120, E-Mail: skobrin@co.seminole.fl.us
Founded 1987. Circ 342,474
Library Holdings: Bk Vols 83,130
Automation Activity & Vendor Info: (Cataloging) epixtech, inc.; (Circulation) epixtech, inc.; (OPAC) epixtech, inc.; (Serials) epixtech, inc.
Database Vendor: GaleNet, OCLC - First Search
JEAN RHEIN CENTRAL LIBRARY, 215 N Oxford Rd, Casselberry, 32707. SAN 338-070X. Tel: 407-339-4000. FAX: 407-339-7931. *Branch Mgr*, Christina Patten
Founded 1975. Circ 735,461
Library Holdings: Bk Vols 130,160
NORTH, 150 N Palmetto Ave, 32771. SAN 338-067X. Tel: 407-322-2182. FAX: 407-322-7298. *Branch Mgr*, Janean Campanaro; *Business*, Stephanie Kobrin; Tel: 407-330-3737, Fax: 407-330-3120, E-Mail: skobrin@co.seminole.fl.us
Founded 1925. Circ 189,147
Library Holdings: Bk Vols 62,380
NORTHWEST, 580 Greenway Blvd, Lake Mary, 32746. SAN 328-8994. FAX: 407-321-9557. *Branch Mgr*, Richard Gardiner
Founded 1988. Circ 314,152
Library Holdings: Bk Vols 67,240
WEST, 245 Hunt Club Blvd N, Longwood, 32779. SAN 328-901X. Tel: 407-862-2282. FAX: 404-862-2046. *Branch Mgr*, Mildred Carter
Founded 1988. Circ 342,496
Library Holdings: Bk Vols 75,450

SANIBEL

P SANIBEL PUBLIC LIBRARY, INC, 770 Dunlop Rd, 33957. SAN 303-1705. Tel: 941-472-2483. FAX: 941-472-9524. Web Site: www.sanlib.org. *Dir*, Patricia J Allen; E-Mail: pallen@sanlib.org; *Tech Servs*, Sandra A Ham; E-Mail: sham@sanlib.org; *YA Servs*, Pamela Simones; E-Mail: psimones@sanlib.org; *Circ*, Wendy Veltz; *Per*, Mary Mitchell; *Ref*, Laura Degenaro; E-Mail: reference@sanlib.org; Staff 9 (MLS 4, Non-MLS 5)
Founded 1962. Pop 5,975; Circ 125,428
Oct 1998-Sep 1999 Income $896,385, County $772,705, Locally Generated Income $84,843, Other $38,837. Mats Exp $141,143, Books $81,518, Per/Ser (Incl. Access Fees) $5,742, Presv $51, AV Equip $5,918, Electronic Ref Mat (Incl. Access Fees) $47,914. Sal $245,597 (Prof $144,246)
Library Holdings: Bk Vols 51,763; Bk Titles 48,684; Per Subs 222; High Interest/Low Vocabulary Bk Vols 10
Subject Interests: Florida, Local history, Paintings
Automation Activity & Vendor Info: (Cataloging) Innovative Interfaces Inc.; (Circulation) Innovative Interfaces Inc.; (OPAC) Innovative Interfaces Inc.
Publications: SPLash
Partic in OCLC Online Computer Library Center, Inc; SW Fla Libr Network
Friends of the Library Group

SARASOTA

P GULF GATE PUBLIC LIBRARY, 7112 Curtiss Ave, 34231. Tel: 941-316-1213. FAX: 941-316-1221. Web Site: www.suncat.co.sarasota.fl.us. *Librn*, Anne Currin; Staff 17 (MLS 7, Non-MLS 10)
Library Holdings: Bk Vols 75,000; Per Subs 195
Friends of the Library Group

S MARIE SELBY BOTANICAL GARDENS LIBRARY, 811 S Palm Ave, 34236. SAN 371-6457. Tel: 941-366-5731, Ext 248. FAX: 941-366-9807. Web Site: www.selby.org. *Dir*, Bruce Holst; Tel: 941-955-7553, Ext 12, Fax:

941-951-1474, E-Mail: bholst@selby.org
Founded 1975
Jul 1999-Jun 2000 Mats Exp $10,640, Books $4,000, Per/Ser (Incl. Access Fees) $5,000, Presv $300, Other Print Mats $400
Library Holdings: Bk Vols 8,000; Bk Titles 6,500; Per Subs 307
Subject Interests: Botany, Conservation, Ecology, Horticulture, Orchids
Special Collections: Early Botanical Reference Microfiche Collection; Rare Botanical Book Coll
Automation Activity & Vendor Info: (Cataloging) TLC
Publications: Field Guide to the Mangroves of Florida; Icones; Selbyana; The Nature Trail at Pine View School - Plants of Sarasota County, Florida, Part 1 (Research guide)
Restriction: Circulates for staff only

S MOTE MARINE LABORATORY LIBRARY, Arthur Vining Davis Library, 1600 Ken Thompson Pkwy, 34236-1096. SAN 303-173X. Tel: 941-388-4441. FAX: 941-388-4312. E-Mail: library@mote.org. Web Site: www.mote.org/code/1/4/. *Librn*, Susan M Stover
Founded 1978
Library Holdings: Bk Titles 6,000; Per Subs 425
Subject Interests: Aquaculture, Fisheries, Marine biology, Oceanography
Special Collections: Reprint Coll of 3000 Articles
Database Vendor: OCLC - First Search
Publications: Collected Papers; Mote News
Function: Reference only
Partic in Florida Library Information Network; Int Asn of Aquatic & Marine Sci Libr & Info Centers; TBLC
Open Mon-Fri 1-4
Friends of the Library Group

S JOHN & MABLE RINGLING MUSEUM OF ART LIBRARY, 5401 Bayshore Rd, 34243. SAN 303-1756. Tel: 941-359-5743. FAX: 941-359-5745. E-Mail: library@ringling.org. Web Site: www.ringling.org. *Librn*, Linda R McKee; E-Mail: lmckee@ringling.org; Staff 2 (MLS 1, Non-MLS 1)
Founded 1949
Jul 1999-Jun 2000 Mats Exp $25,000, Books $4,000, Per/Ser (Incl. Access Fees) $19,000, Electronic Ref Mat (Incl. Access Fees) $2,000. Sal $40,000
Library Holdings: Bk Vols 55,000; Bk Titles 40,000; Per Subs 100
Subject Interests: Art, Art history, Rare books
Special Collections: John Ringling Book Coll
Automation Activity & Vendor Info: (OPAC) Sagebrush Corporation
Database Vendor: OCLC - First Search
Publications: Rare Books from the Library of the Ringling Museum of Art Sarasota, Florida
Restriction: Open to public for reference only
Partic in FLIN; OCLC Online Computer Library Center, Inc; SE Libr Network; TBLC

C RINGLING SCHOOL OF ART & DESIGN, Verman Kimbrough Memorial Library, 2700 N Tamiami Trail, 34234. SAN 303-1764. Tel: 941-359-7587. Interlibrary Loan Service Tel: 941-359-7630. FAX: 941-359-7632. E-Mail: library@ringling.edu. Web Site: www.lib.rsad.edu. *Dir Libr Serv*, Kathleen L List; Tel: 941-359-7582, E-Mail: klist@ringling.edu; *AV*, Allen Novak; Tel: 941-359-7583, E-Mail: anovak@ringling.edu; *Tech Servs*, Janet K Thomas; Tel: 941-359-7586, E-Mail: jthomas@ringling.edu; Staff 12 (MLS 3, Non-MLS 9)
Founded 1931. Enrl 884; Fac 105; Highest Degree: Bachelor
Jun 1999-May 2000 Income $572,453, Federal $4,000, Locally Generated Income $76,215, Parent Institution $492,238. Mats Exp $123,870, Books $63,533, Per/Ser (Incl. Access Fees) $30,123, Presv $5,449, AV Equip $17,978, Electronic Ref Mat (Incl. Access Fees) $6,787. Sal $320,421
Library Holdings: Bk Vols 39,000; Bk Titles 35,454; Per Subs 320
Subject Interests: Art and architecture, Computer art, Fine arts, Illustration, Interior design, Photography
Special Collections: Slide library of 93,000 images
Automation Activity & Vendor Info: (Acquisitions) Endeavor; (Cataloging) Endeavor; (Circulation) Endeavor; (Course Reserve) Endeavor; (OPAC) Endeavor; (Serials) Endeavor
Database Vendor: ProQuest, Wilson - Wilson Web
Restriction: Open to student, faculty & staff
Function: ILL available
Partic in Florida Library Information Network; Independent Cols & Univs of Fla; Solinet; Tampa Bay Library Consortium, Inc
Friends of the Library Group

M SARASOTA MEMORIAL HOSPITAL, Medical Library, 1700 S Tamiami Trail, 34239. SAN 303-1721. Tel: 941-917-1730. FAX: 941-917-1646. *Librn*, Barbara Hartman; Tel: 941-917-1730, E-Mail: barbara-hartman@smh.com; *ILL*, Patti Reynolds
Founded 1956
Library Holdings: Bk Titles 2,000; Per Subs 200
Subject Interests: Medicine, Nursing
Partic in Nat Libr of Med; Tampa Bay Medical Library Network

P SELBY PUBLIC LIBRARY, 331 First St, 34236-4899. SAN 338-0734. Tel: 941-316-1181. TDD: 941-955-3426. FAX: 941-316-1188. Web Site: suncat.co.sarasota.fl.us. *Ch Servs*, Sarabeth Kalajian; *Media Spec*, Lee Robin Davis; *Circ*, Catherine Morrisey; *Tech Servs*, Diana McGarigle; *ILL*, Pamela Burch; Staff 48 (MLS 17, Non-MLS 31)
Founded 1907. Pop 371,155; Circ 1,922,992
Library Holdings: Bk Vols 192,747; Bk Titles 98,700; Per Subs 372
Subject Interests: Genealogy
Partic in OCLC Online Computer Library Center, Inc
Special Services for the Deaf - TDD
Friends of the Library Group

C UNIVERSITY OF SARASOTA LIBRARY, 5250 17th St, 34235. SAN 320-1384. Tel: 941-379-0404. Toll Free Tel: 800-331-5995. FAX: 941-379-9464. E-Mail: 102556.2652@compuserve.com, 72620.2307@compuserve.com. Web Site: www.sarasota.edu. *Coll Develop, Librn*, Patricia A Shelley; E-Mail: shellep@snoopy.tblc.lib.fl.us
Founded 1974. Enrl 1,200; Fac 60; Highest Degree: Doctorate
Library Holdings: Bk Vols 5,202
Subject Interests: Business and management, Education, Psychology

C UNIVERSITY OF SOUTH FLORIDA - NEW COLLEGE, Jane Bancroft Cook Library, 5700 N Tamiami Trail, 34243. SAN 303-1748. Tel: 941-359-4300. Circulation Tel: 941-359-4305. Reference Tel: 941-359-4301. FAX: 941-359-4307. Web Site: lib.sar.usf.edu. *Dir*, Joan M Pelland; Tel: 941-359-4401, E-Mail: pelland@sar.usf.edu; *Dir, Tech Serv*, Judy M Kelly; Tel: 941-359-4416, E-Mail: jkelly1@sar.usf.edu; *Syst Coordr*, Kate Lippincott; Tel: 931-359-4402, E-Mail: klippinoc@sar.usf.edu; *Dir Info Resources & Res*, Sara Barnett; Tel: 941-359-4409, E-Mail: sbarnett@sar.usf.edu; *Ref*, Nancy Allen; Tel: 931-359-4405, E-Mail: nallen@sar.usf.edu; *Ref*, Gail Novak; Tel: 941-359-4406, E-Mail: novak@sar.usf.edu; Staff 16 (MLS 6, Non-MLS 10)
Founded 1962. Enrl 2,000; Fac 67; Highest Degree: Doctorate
Jul 1998-Jun 1999 Income $1,043,363. Mats Exp $322,063, Books $81,479, Per/Ser (Incl. Access Fees) $217,463, Presv $20,779, Other Print Mats $2,342. Sal $590,487 (Prof $248,690)
Library Holdings: Bk Vols 254,889; Bk Titles 162,746; Per Subs 1,592
Subject Interests: Education, Humanities
Special Collections: Hagberg Manuscripts
Automation Activity & Vendor Info: (Acquisitions) NOTIS; (Cataloging) NOTIS; (Circulation) NOTIS; (Course Reserve) NOTIS; (ILL) NOTIS; (OPAC) NOTIS; (Serials) NOTIS
Database Vendor: CARL, Ebsco - EbscoHost, GaleNet, Lexis-Nexis, OCLC - First Search, OVID Technologies, ProQuest, Silverplatter Information Inc., Wilson - Wilson Web
Function: Research library
Partic in Tampa Bay Library Consortium, Inc
Special Services for the Blind - Print enlarger, reading machine & an adaptive terminal to enlarge screen information when using library catalog
Friends of the Library Group

SATELLITE BEACH

P SATELLITE BEACH PUBLIC LIBRARY, 751 Jamaica Blvd, 32937. SAN 303-1772. Tel: 321-779-4004. TDD: 321-779-4005. FAX: 321-779-4036. Web Site: www.brev.lib.fl.us. *Dir*, Nancy Grout; *Ch Servs*, Mary Friers; *Circ*, Ellen Noyd; *Ref*, Irene Misconi
Founded 1966. Circ 283,973
Library Holdings: Bk Titles 74,500; Per Subs 201
Special Collections: Florida
Automation Activity & Vendor Info: (Circulation) CLSI LIBS
Mem of Brevard County Library System
Special Services for the Deaf - High interest/low vocabulary books; TDD
Friends of the Library Group

SEBASTIAN

P NORTH INDIAN RIVER COUNTY LIBRARY, 1001 CR 512, 32958. SAN 370-3584. Tel: 561-589-1355. TDD: 561-589-8130. FAX: 561-388-3697. Web Site: www.sebastianlibrary.com. *Dir*, Lynn Walsh; E-Mail: lwalsh@indian-river.lib.fl.us; *Tech Servs*, Anne Moutenot; *Ref*, Judy Wray; *Circ*, Ramona Widman; *Electronic Resources*, Daniel Clark; Staff 6 (MLS 1, Non-MLS 5)
Founded 1983
Oct 1999-Sep 2000 Income $868,510, Federal $2,624, Other $3,771. Mats Exp $192,497, Books $131,823, Per/Ser (Incl. Access Fees) $9,634, Micro $2,598, AV Equip $24,164, Electronic Ref Mat (Incl. Access Fees) $11,853. Sal $548,218
Library Holdings: Bk Vols 78,799; Bk Titles 64,278; Per Subs 250
Special Collections: Florida Coll
Automation Activity & Vendor Info: (Cataloging) GEAC; (Circulation) GEAC; (OPAC) GEAC
Database Vendor: GaleNet, IAC - Info Trac
Mem of Indian River County Libr
Partic in Cent Fla Libr Consortium
Special Services for the Deaf - TDD
Friends of the Library Group

SEBRING

P HIGHLANDS COUNTY LIBRARY SYSTEM, Sebring Public Library Bldg, 319 W Center Ave, 33870-6396. SAN 303-1780. Tel: 863-402-6716. FAX: 863-402-6743. *Dir*, Mary Myers; Staff 5 (MLS 4, Non-MLS 1)
Founded 1926. Pop 80,000; Circ 345,362; Highest Degree: Master
Library Holdings: Bk Vols 112,388; Bk Titles 83,341; Per Subs 160
Special Collections: Florida Coll
Automation Activity & Vendor Info: (Circulation) Gaylord; (OPAC) Gaylord
Friends of the Library Group

SEMINOLE

P SEMINOLE COMMUNITY LIBRARY, 9199 113th St N, 33772-2806. SAN 323-7966. Tel: 727-397-2112. FAX: 727-398-3113. Web Site: www.tblc.org/spl. *Dir*, Michael Bryan; E-Mail: bryanm@tblc.org; *Coll Develop, Ref*, Ben Fiedler; Staff 7 (MLS 6, Non-MLS 1)
Founded 1959. Pop 9,000; Circ 252,549
Oct 1998-Sep 1999 Income $567,842, City $402,089, County $144,597, Locally Generated Income $20,133, Other $1,023. Mats Exp $77,500, Books $69,000, Per/Ser (Incl. Access Fees) $5,000, AV Equip $3,500. Sal $337,500 (Prof $200,000)
Library Holdings: Bk Vols 59,862; Per Subs 127
Special Collections: Parent-Teacher
Mem of Pinellas County Public Libr Coop
Partic in SE Libr Network; Tampa Bay Library Consortium, Inc
Special Services for the Deaf - Books on deafness & sign language; Captioned film depository
Friends of the Library Group

SNEADS

APALACHEE CORRECTIONAL INSTITUTION

S EAST UNIT LIBRARY, 35 Apalachee Dr, 32460. SAN 303-1799. Tel: 850-593-6431, Ext 177. FAX: 850-593-6445. *Librn*, Susan Hughs; Staff 12 (MLS 2, Non-MLS 10)
Founded 1968
Library Holdings: Bk Titles 11,058; Per Subs 50
Special Collections: Florida Legal Coll

S WEST UNIT LIBRARY, 52 West Unit Dr, 32460. Tel: 850-593-6431. FAX: 850-593-6445. *Librn*, Susan Hughes
Library Holdings: Bk Vols 11,000; Per Subs 50

SOUTH BAY

§S FLORIDA DEPARTMENT OF CORRECTIONS, South Bay Correctional Facility Library, 600 US 27 South, 33493. Tel: 561-992-9505, Ext 150. FAX: 561-992-9551. *Librn*, Elmira Ross
Library Holdings: Bk Vols 4,100; Per Subs 35

STARKE

P BRADFORD COUNTY PUBLIC LIBRARY, 105 E Jackson St, 32091-3396. SAN 303-1802. Tel: 904-964-6400. FAX: 904-964-9463. E-Mail: bradford@neflin.org. *Dir*, Phalbe Henriksen; Staff 8 (MLS 1, Non-MLS 7)
Founded 1935. Pop 25,245; Circ 120,000
Oct 1999-Sep 2000 Income $227,899. Mats Exp $26,989, Books $21,589, Per/Ser (Incl. Access Fees) $5,000, Presv $400. Sal $154,876
Library Holdings: Bk Titles 42,000; Per Subs 100
Subject Interests: Florida, Genealogy
Automation Activity & Vendor Info: (Circulation) SIRSI; (OPAC) SIRSI
Database Vendor: OCLC - First Search
Partic in Florida Library Information Network; NEFLIN
Friends of the Library Group
Bookmobiles: 1

S FLORIDA STATE PRISON LIBRARY, Main Unit, PO Box 747, 32091. SAN 303-1810. Tel: 904-368-2583. *Librn*, Simeon Cerdan
Founded 1968
Jul 1999-Jun 2000 Mats Exp $6,600, Books $3,500, Per/Ser (Incl. Access Fees) $3,100. Sal $37,050
Library Holdings: Bk Vols 12,909; Bk Titles 8,000; Per Subs 61
Provides reading materials to confinement inmates

STUART

P MARTIN COUNTY LIBRARY SYSTEM, 2351 SE Monterey Rd, 34996. SAN 303-1837. Tel: 561-221-1408. Interlibrary Loan Service Tel: 561-221-1402. Circulation Tel: 561-221-1411. Reference Tel: 561-221-1413. FAX: 561-221-1358. E-Mail: jbalis@martin.fl.us. Web Site: www.library.martin.fl.us. *Dir*, Donna M Tunsoy; Tel: 561-221-1410, Fax: 561-219-4959, E-Mail: dtunsoy@martin.fl.us; *Branch Mgr*, Judith Snyder; Tel: 561-221-4959, Fax: 561-219-4959, E-Mail: jsnyder@martin.fl.us; *Ch Servs*, June Level; Tel: 561-219-4975, Fax: 561-219-4959, E-Mail: jlevel@martin.fl.us; *Tech Servs*, Nicole Lebeau; Tel: 561-221-1404, E-Mail: nlebeau@martin.fl.us; *Ref*, Scott Tarbox; Tel: 561-219-4908, E-Mail: starbox@martin.fl.us; *Acq*, Alice Harris; Tel: 561-221-1401, E-Mail: aharris@martin.fl.us; Staff 16 (MLS 12, Non-MLS 4)
Founded 1957. Pop 136,143
Oct 1999-Sep 2000 Income $2,871,324, State $307,751, County $2,423,280, Locally Generated Income $51,985, Other $88,308. Mats Exp $641,522, Books $505,024, Micro $18,335, Electronic Ref Mat (Incl. Access Fees) $118,163. Sal $1,710,554
Library Holdings: Bk Vols 244,664; Bk Titles 98,024; Per Subs 890
Special Collections: Florida Coll; Maritime (McArthur Coll); Travel Essay
Automation Activity & Vendor Info: (Acquisitions) SIRSI; (Cataloging) SIRSI; (Circulation) SIRSI; (OPAC) SIRSI
Database Vendor: Ebsco - EbscoHost
Partic in Florida Library Information Network; OCLC Online Computer Library Center, Inc; Southeast Florida Library Information Network, Inc
Friends of the Library Group
Branches: 5
CUMMINGS-PALM CITY BRANCH, 2551 SW Matheson Ave, Palm City, 34990. SAN 375-5924. Tel: 561-288-2551. FAX: 561-288-5563. Web Site: www.library.martin.fl.us. *Branch Mgr*, Charlotte Jackson; E-Mail: cjackson@martin.fl.us
Founded 1995
Friends of the Library Group
HOBE SOUND BRANCH, 10595 SE Federal Hwy, Hobe Sound, 33455. SAN 328-6533. Tel: 561-546-2257. FAX: 561-546-3816. Web Site: www.library.martin.fl.us. *Branch Mgr*, Effie D Anderson; E-Mail: danderso@martin.fl.us
Founded 1985
INDIANTOWN BRANCH, 15200 S W Adams Ave, Indiantown, 34956. SAN 328-655X. Tel: 561-597-4200. FAX: 407-597-3637. Web Site: www.library.martin.fl.us. *Branch Mgr*, Lora Shelton; E-Mail: lshelton@martin.fl.us
Founded 1991
Friends of the Library Group
JENSEN BEACH BRANCH, 1900 NE Ricou Terrace, Jensen Beach, 34957. SAN 329-5915. Tel: 561-221-1390, 561-334-4488. FAX: 561-221-1426. Web Site: www.library.martin.fl.us. *Branch Mgr*, Sandra Hawken; E-Mail: shawken@martin.fl.us
Founded 1986
Friends of the Library Group
MARTIN COUNTY LAW LIBRARY, 100 E Ocean Blvd, Ste 138, 34994. SAN 371-9146. Tel: 561-221-1427. FAX: 561-221-2317. Web Site: www.library.martin.fl.us. *In Charge*, Terri Jackson; E-Mail: tjackson@martin.fl.us
Friends of the Library Group
Bookmobiles: 1

SUMTERVILLE

§P SUMTER COUNTY PUBLIC LIBRARY SYSTEM, 1405 County Rd, 526A, 33585. Tel: 352-568-3456. FAX: 352-568-3481. *Dir*, Debra Rhodes Gibson; E-Mail: drhodes@cflc.net
Library Holdings: Bk Titles 50,000
Member Libraries: Bushnell Public Library; E C Rowell Public Library; George Nichols Public Library; Panasoffkee Community Library Inc

SUNRISE

S MILGO SOLUTIONS, Information Resources, 1619 N Harrison Pkwy, 33323-2899. SAN 328-4808. Tel: 954-846-6100, Ext 6101. FAX: 954-846-3946.
Library Holdings: Bk Vols 7,000; Per Subs 460
Subject Interests: Computer science
Partic in Dialog Corporation; Orbit

SURFSIDE

P SURF-BAL-BAY LIBRARY, 9301 Collins Ave, 33154. SAN 303-1853. Tel: 305-865-2409. *Librn*, Suzanne McGlynn; Staff 1 (MLS 1)
Founded 1956. Pop 11,500; Circ 47,605
Library Holdings: Bk Vols 26,000; Per Subs 55
Subject Interests: Florida

TALLAHASSEE

S AMERICAN SOCIETY OF NOTARIES LIBRARY, 2722 Apalachee Pkwy, 32301. (Mail add: PO Box 5707, 32314), Tel: 850-671-5164. Toll Free Tel: 800-522-3392. FAX: 850-671-5165. E-Mail: mail@notaries.org. Web Site: www.notaries.org. *Exec Dir*, Lisa Fisher; *Dir*, Carla Connell; E-Mail: carla@notaries.org
Library Holdings: Bk Vols 400

§G AUDITOR GENERAL'S LIBRARY, Claude Pepper Bldg, Rm G-78, 111 W Madison St, 32399. Tel: 850-488-0962. FAX: 850-488-6975. *Dir*, Mary Williams; E-Mail: marywilliams@aud.state.fl.us
Library Holdings: Bk Vols 3,000; Per Subs 15

J JIM BISHOP MEMORIAL LIBRARY, Keiser College, 1700 Halstead Blvd, 32308. SAN 373-1286. Tel: 850-906-9494. FAX: 850-906-9497. Web Site: www.keisercollege.cc.fl.us/libftl.htm. *Librn*, Lifeng Yu
Founded 1992. Enrl 415; Fac 20
Library Holdings: Bk Vols 7,534; Bk Titles 5,936; Per Subs 40
Special Collections: Belen Mills Educational Theory Coll
Automation Activity & Vendor Info: (Cataloging) Athena
Publications: Bibliographies; Faculty Manual; Library Manual; New Book List
Partic in Panhandle Library Access Network; Westlaw

G DEPARTMENT OF BANKING & FINANCE, Legal Library, Fla Office of the Comptroller, Fletcher Bldg, 101 E Gaines St, Ste 526, 32399-0350. SAN 325-8548. Tel: 850-956-5952. Toll Free Tel: 800-848-3792. FAX: 850-922-6386. *Librn*, Mary Howell
Library Holdings: Bk Vols 4,000

G DEPARTMENT OF STATE LIBRARY OF FLORIDA, The Capitol, Rm 701, 32399-1400. SAN 303-1993. Tel: 850-488-2812. FAX: 850-488-9879. *Dir*, Joann Mrazek; *Archivist*, Delbra D McGriff; Staff 8 (MLS 4, Non-MLS 4)
Founded 1949
Library Holdings: Bk Vols 21,000; Bk Titles 10,000; Per Subs 654
Publications: Checklist of Recent Acquisitions (monthly); Checklist of Recent Legislative Publications (quarterly); The Florida Legislative Library: Functions, Scope, Procedures (revised as needed)
Partic in Dialog Corporation; Westlaw

S FEDERAL CORRECTIONAL INSTITUTION LIBRARY, 501 Capital Circle NE, 32301-3572. SAN 303-1861. Tel: 850-878-2173, Ext 464. FAX: 850-942-9668. *In Charge*, Lewis James
Founded 1947. Pop 1,000
Library Holdings: Bk Vols 11,000; Per Subs 90
Partic in Florida Library Information Network
Friends of the Library Group

GL FIRST DISTRICT COURT OF APPEAL LIBRARY, 301 Martin Luther King Jr Blvd, 32399. SAN 377-3221. Tel: 850-488-8136. FAX: 850-488-7989. *Librn*, Janet McPherson
Library Holdings: Bk Vols 25,000

C FLORIDA AGRICULTURAL & MECHANICAL UNIVERSITY, Samuel H Coleman Memorial Library, 1500 S Martin Luther King Blvd, 32307-4700. SAN 338-0793. Tel: 850-599-3370. Circulation Tel: 850-599-3376. Reference Tel: 850-599-3330. FAX: 850-561-2293. Web Site: www.famu.edu. *Dir*, Dr Lauren B Sapp; E-Mail: lauren.sapp@famu.edu; *Asst Dir*, Ann J Hinson; Tel: 850-599-8674, E-Mail: ann.hinson@famu.edu; *Assoc Dir*, Margaret B Jones; *Mgr*, Dr Julita C Awkard; Tel: 850-561-2005, Fax: 850-599-3422, E-Mail: julita.awkard@famu.edu; *Bibliogr*, Jeneice Smith Williams; Tel: 850-599-8770, Fax: 850-599-3436, E-Mail: jeneice.williamssmith@famu.edu; *Bibliogr*, Gloria T Woody; Tel: 850-599-3704, Fax: 850-561-2648, E-Mail: gloria.woody@famu.edu; *Circ*, Priscilla Henry; Tel: 850-599-3376, E-Mail: priscilla.henry@famu.edu; *Coll Develop*, Dr Vivian Hall Royster; Tel: 850-599-3314, E-Mail: vivian.royster@famu.edu; *Govt Doc*, Minnie B Crump; Tel: 850-599-3330, E-Mail: minnie.crump@famu.edu; *ILL*, Carolyn T Bivens; Tel: 850-599-3330, E-Mail: carolyn.bivens@famu.edu; *Spec Coll*, Cornelia A Taylor; Tel: 850-599-3330, E-Mail: cornelia.taylor@famu.edu; *Tech Servs*, Saiyed A Ahmad; Tel: 850-599-3926, E-Mail: saiyed.ahmad@famu.edu. Subject Specialists: *Afro-American*, Cornelia A Taylor; *Architecture*, Jeneice Smith Williams; *Health sciences*, Dr Julita C Awkard; *Journalism*, Gloria T Woody; *Libr sci*, Dr Lauren B Sapp; Staff 64 (MLS 22, Non-MLS 42)
Founded 1909. Enrl 12,082; Fac 483; Highest Degree: Doctorate
Jul 1999-Jun 2000 Income (Main Library and Branch Library) $3,600,473, State $3,558,463, Federal $42,010. Mats Exp $1,443,509, Books $404,765, Per/Ser (Incl. Access Fees) $717,047, Presv $26,299, Micro $47,047, Other Print Mats $9,884, Electronic Ref Mat (Incl. Access Fees) $238,467. Sal $2,196,971 (Prof $892,864)
Library Holdings: Bk Vols 704,894; Per Subs 6,017
Special Collections: Afro-American, bks, clippings, magazines; Materials About Florida A&M University (FAMUANA), fac pub minutes, programs, memorabilia, 1890-present clippings, newsp
Automation Activity & Vendor Info: (Acquisitions) NOTIS; (Cataloging) NOTIS; (Circulation) NOTIS; (Course Reserve) NOTIS; (ILL) NOTIS; (OPAC) NOTIS
Database Vendor: CARL, Dialog, Ebsco - EbscoHost, GaleNet, IAC - Info Trac, IAC - SearchBank, Lexis-Nexis, OCLC - First Search, ProQuest, Wilson - Wilson Web
Publications: A Classified Catalogue of the Negro Collection in the Samuel H Coleman Memorial Library, 1969; A National Network for the Acquisition, Organization, Processing & Dissemination of Materials By & About Blacks, 1974; Instructional Media Film & Video Catalog, 1993; Library Handbook, 1993
Partic in FLIN; OCLC Online Computer Library Center, Inc; Panhandle Library Access Network; Solinet

GL FLORIDA ATTORNEY GENERAL'S LAW LIBRARY, Colins Bldg, 107 W Gaines St, Rm 437, 32399-1050. (Mail add: PL-01 The Capitol, 32399-1050), SAN 303-1950. Tel: 850-414-3300. FAX: 850-921-5784. E-Mail: library@oag.state.fl.us. *Dir Libr Serv*, Betsy L Stupski; *Head Ref*, Thomas E Baxter; *Head Tech Servs*, Kim Yun; Staff 3 (MLS 3)
Library Holdings: Bk Vols 50,000; Bk Titles 2,000; Per Subs 20
Function: Reference services available
Partic in Westlaw

S FLORIDA BANKERS ASSOCIATION LIBRARY, 1001 Thomasville Rd, No 201, 32302-1360. (Mail add: PO Box 1360, 32302-1360), SAN 371-1404. Tel: 850-224-2265. FAX: 850-224-2423. Web Site: www.flbankers.com. *In Charge*, Alex Sanchez
Library Holdings: Bk Vols 600
Special Collections: Association Management; Banking

GL FLORIDA DEPARTMENT OF AGRICULTURE & CONSUMER SERVICES, Legal Section Library, Mayo Bldg, Rm 515, 407 S Calhoune St, 32399-0800. SAN 326-9396. Tel: 850-488-6853. FAX: 850-488-1766.
Library Holdings: Per Subs 400

G FLORIDA DEPARTMENT OF EDUCATION, Clearinghouse Information Center, 325 W Gaines St, 32399-0400. SAN 377-0907. Tel: 850-488-1879. FAX: 850-487-2679. Web Site: www.firn.edu/doe/commhome/. *Dir*, Arlene Duncan
Library Holdings: Bk Vols 7,000; Bk Titles 7,000

G FLORIDA DEPARTMENT OF ENVIRONMENTAL PROTECTION, Division of Resource Assessment & Management, Florida Geological Survey Library, 903 W Tennessee St, 32304-7700. SAN 303-1969. Tel: 850-488-9380. FAX: 850-488-8086.; Staff 1 (MLS 1)
Founded 1908
Library Holdings: Bk Vols 20,000; Per Subs 40
Subject Interests: Florida, Geology
Special Collections: Florida Aerial Photographs; Florida Sinkhole Research Institute Archives; Geology (R B Campbell Coll); Geology Rare Book Coll; Paleontology (H S Puri Ostracod & Foraminifera Coll), card files, reprints; Photo Archives Coll
Partic in Panhandle Library Access Network

G FLORIDA DEPARTMENT OF ENVIRONMENTAL PROTECTION LIBRARY, 2600 Blair Stone Rd, Rm 176, 32399-2400. SAN 303-1926. Tel: 850-488-0890. FAX: 850-922-6661. *In Charge*, B Betancourt
Founded 1973
Library Holdings: Bk Vols 18,000; Bk Titles 15,000; Per Subs 150
Subject Interests: Ecology, Natural resources, Pollution, Toxicology, Water resources
Publications: SIGNAL (internal only)
Partic in Panhandle Library Access Network

G FLORIDA DEPARTMENT OF HIGHWAY SAFETY & MOTOR VEHICLES, Management & Planning Services Library, Neil Kirkman Bldg, Rm A430, 32399-0505. SAN 377-3558. Tel: 850-488-4300. FAX: 850-414-7195. Web Site: www.hsmv.state.fl.us. *Asst Librn, Res*, Heather Zawacki
Library Holdings: Bk Vols 1,200; Bk Titles 750; Per Subs 100

G FLORIDA DEPARTMENT OF INSURANCE, Legal Division Law Library, 612 Larson Bldg, 200 E Gaines St, 32399-0333. SAN 377-3493. Tel: 850-413-3100. FAX: 850-488-0697. *Librn*, Elamir Ghattas
Library Holdings: Bk Vols 3,000; Bk Titles 3,000; Per Subs 20

G FLORIDA DEPARTMENT OF LABOR & EMPLOYMENT SECURITY, Division of Safety Library, 2002 St Augustine Rd, Bldg E, Ste 45, 32399-0663. SAN 377-0923. Tel: 820-922-8955, 850-922-8954. FAX: 850-922-4538. Web Site: www.safety.fdles.state.fl.us. *Coordr*, Colette Drouillard Harlene; E-Mail: charlene_vespi@safety.fdles.state.fl.us; *Librn*, Bethany Kemp
Library Holdings: Bk Vols 500; Per Subs 30

G FLORIDA DEPARTMENT OF LAW ENFORCEMENT OFFICE, Research & Planning Library, PO Box 1489, 32302-1489. Tel: 850-410-7140. FAX: 850-410-7150. E-Mail: fsac@fdle.state.fl.us. Web Site: www.fdle.state.fl.us/fsac. *Dir*, Sue Burton; E-Mail: sueburton@fdle.state.fl.us
Library Holdings: Bk Vols 290

G FLORIDA DEPARTMENT OF TRANSPORTATION, Research Management Library, Burns Bldg, 605 Suwannee St, Mail Sta 30, 32399. SAN 303-1985. Tel: 850-414-4615. FAX: 850-413-0657. *Dir*, Richard C Long
Founded 1967
Library Holdings: Bk Vols 15,000; Per Subs 20
Subject Interests: Air transportation
Special Collections: Historical DOT Coll; HRD Materials; Transportation Research-Related Reports

G FLORIDA PUBLIC SERVICE COMMISSION, Resource Center, Easley Bldg, Rm 204, 2540 Shumard Oak Blvd, 32399-0850. SAN 303-2019. Tel: 850-413-6860. FAX: 850-413-6861. *Librn*, Brenda B Monroe
Founded 1977
Library Holdings: Bk Vols 13,500; Per Subs 400
Subject Interests: Law
Partic in Westlaw

FLORIDA STATE UNIVERSITY

C CENTER FOR THE STUDY OF POPULATION, 654 Bellamy Bldg, 32306-2240. SAN 338-1218. Tel: 850-644-1762. FAX: 850-644-8818. E-Mail: popctr@mailer.fsu.edu. Web Site: www.fsu.edu/~popctr/. *Librn*, Judy Kirk
Library Holdings: Bk Vols 13,500; Per Subs 50
Special Collections: Charles M Grigg Memorial Coll; Soviet Population Materials (Galina Selegan Coll)
Member of the Association for Population/Family Planning Libraries & Information Centers-International

CURRICULUM RESOURCE CENTER, Coll of Educ, 2 Stone Bldg, 32306. SAN 338-1161. Tel: 850-644-1583.
Library Holdings: Bk Titles 1,000; Per Subs 50

GEOPHYSICAL FLUID DYNAMICS INSTITUTE, 18 Keen Bldg, 32306-4360. SAN 338-1188. Tel: 850-644-5594. FAX: 850-644-8972. Web Site: www.gfdi.fsu.edu. *In Charge*, Dr Robin Kung
Library Holdings: Bk Titles 8,200; Per Subs 12

HAROLD GOLDSTEIN LIBRARY, 106 Louis Shores Bldg, 1st Flr, 32306. Tel: 850-644-1803. FAX: 850-644-0460. Web Site: www.fsu.edu/~lsl. *Head Librn*, Aimee Reist
Library Holdings: Bk Vols 80,000; Per Subs 450
Friends of the Library Group

PAUL A M DIRAE SCIENCE LIBRARY, Paul A M Dirac Science Library, 32306-4140. Tel: 850-644-5534. FAX: 850-644-0025. Web Site: www.fsuedu/~library/. *Dir*, Sharon W Schwerzel; Staff 17 (MLS 3, Non-MLS 14)
Founded 1988
Library Holdings: Bk Vols 550,000; Per Subs 3,500
Friends of the Library Group

SCHOOL OF NURSING, LEARNING RESOURCE CENTER, School of Nursing Bldg, 3rd Flr, 32306-3051. SAN 338-1315. Tel: 850-644-1291. FAX: 850-644-7660. Web Site: www.fsu.edu/~nursing/nursing.html. *Mgr*, Leonard Barnes; *AV*, John Puckett
Library Holdings: Per Subs 425
Subject Interests: Nursing
Special Collections: Nursing History
Automation Activity & Vendor Info: (Circulation) Sagebrush Corporation

ROBERT MANNING STROZIER LIBRARY, Strozier Library Bldg, Tallahasse, 32306-2047. Tel: 850-644-5425. Interlibrary Loan Service Tel: 850-644-4466. FAX: 850-644-4702, 850-644-5016 (Admin). Web Site: www.fsu.edu/~library/. *Dir*, F William Summers; *Assoc Dir*, Jeannette Cox; *Publ Servs*, Alberto Herrera; *Spec Coll*, Lucia Patrick; *Tech Servs*, Sally Somers; *Cat*, Kathie Goldfarb; *Circ, ILL*, Lew Conerly; *Doc*, Judy Depew; Staff 57 (MLS 57)
Founded 1888. Enrl 30,268; Fac 1,256; Highest Degree: Doctorate
Library Holdings: Bk Vols 2,216,018; Per Subs 15,864
Special Collections: 15th & 18th Century Books; Carothers Memorial Coll of Bibles & Rare Books; Florida Coll; Governor Fuller Warren Scottish Coll; Herbal Coll; Lois Lenski Coll; Mildred & Claude Pepper Coll; Napoleon & French Revolution; Night Before Christmas Coll; Private Press Works (including Kelmscott Press); Shaw Poetry Coll
Automation Activity & Vendor Info: (Acquisitions) NOTIS; (Circulation) NOTIS; (Serials) NOTIS
Mem of Asn of Research Libraries
Partic in Center For Research Libraries; Florida Library Information Network; OCLC Online Computer Library Center, Inc; Research Libraries Group, Inc; SE Libr Network
Friends of the Library Group

WARREN D ALLEN MUSIC LIBRARY, Housewright Music Bldg, 32306. Tel: 850-644-5028. FAX: 850-644-3982. *Head of Libr*, Dan Clark

CL FLORIDA STATE UNIVERSITY, Law Library, 425 W Jefferson St, 32306-1600. SAN 338-1242. Tel: 850-644-4578. Circulation Tel: 850-644-3405. Reference Tel: 850-644-4095. FAX: 850-644-5216. Web Site: www.law.fsu.edu/library/. *Dir*, Edwin M Schroeder; E-Mail: eschroed@law.fsu.edu; *Assoc Dir*, Robin Gault; Tel: 850-644-7487, E-Mail: rgault@law.fsu.edu; *ILL, Ref*, Patricia Simonds; *Acq*, Anne D Bardolph; *Cat, Spec Coll*, Alva Stone; *AV*, Mark Evans; *Ser*, Janice Ross; *Publ Servs*, Mary McCormick; Tel: 850-664-3405; *Electronic Resources*, John Lutz; Tel: 850-644-7488, E-Mail: jlutz@low.fsu.edu; *Ref*, Margaret Clark; Tel: 850-644-9244, E-Mail: maclark@law.fsu.edu; Staff 18 (MLS 8, Non-MLS 10)
Founded 1966. Enrl 683; Fac 40; Highest Degree: Doctorate
Jul 1999-Jun 2000 Income $1,628,271. Mats Exp $773,247, Books $72,141, Per/Ser (Incl. Access Fees) $575,421, Presv $14,909, Micro $13,916, Electronic Ref Mat (Incl. Access Fees) $96,860. Sal $747,544 (Prof $465,520)
Library Holdings: Bk Vols 419,511; Bk Titles 151,559; Per Subs 4,512
Special Collections: Works by or about US Supreme Court Justices
Automation Activity & Vendor Info: (Cataloging) NOTIS; (Circulation) NOTIS; (Course Reserve) NOTIS; (OPAC) NOTIS; (Serials) NOTIS
Database Vendor: Lexis-Nexis
Partic in OCLC Online Computer Library Center, Inc; Research Libraries Group, Inc; SE Libr Network

§G FLORIDA STATE UNIVERSITY-FLORIDA CLEARINGHOUSE FOR APPLIED RESEARCH & PUBLIC SERVICE, Florida Educational Information Service Library, 210 Sliger Bldg, 2035 E Dirac Dr, 32306-2800. Tel: 850-644-5549. Toll Free Tel: 800-428-1194. FAX: 850-644-8257. E-Mail: expertnet@boone2.esp.fsu.edu. Web Site: expertnet.org. *Dir*, Rebecca Augustyniak; Staff 8 (MLS 8)
Special Collections: ExpertNet Web-Based Network

G FLORIDA STATE UNIVERSITY-FLORIDA TOBACCO CONTROL CLEARINGHOUSE, Florida Educational Information Service Library, 210 Sliger Bldg, 2035 E Dirac Dr, 32306-2800. SAN 303-1918. Tel: 850-644-0830. Toll Free Tel: 877-682-3822. FAX: 850-644-5849. E-Mail: ftcc@mailer.fsu.edu. Web Site: www.fltcc.fsu.edu. *Dir*, Rebecca Augustyniak; Staff 8 (MLS 8)
Founded 1973
Library Holdings: Bk Vols 1,600; Per Subs 10
Subject Interests: Smoking, Tobacco
Publications: FEIS Information Series; Information Request Response Packets; Special Bibliographies
Partic in BRS; Dialog Corporation

§G FLORIDA STATE UNIVERSITY-FLORIDA WORKFORCE DEVELOPMENT EDUCATION CLEARINGHOUSE, Florida Educational Information Service Library, 210 Sliger Bldg, 2035 E Dirac Dr, 32306-2800. Tel: 850-644-5549. Toll Free Tel: 800-428-1194. FAX: 850-644-8257. E-Mail: workforce@workforce.fsu.edu. Web Site: workforce.fsu.edu. *Dir*, Rebecca Augustyniak; Staff 8 (MLS 8)
Special Collections: TeachNET Professional Development Network

GL FLORIDA SUPREME COURT LIBRARY, 500 S Duval, 32399-1926. SAN 303-2027. Tel: 850-488-8919. FAX: 850-922-5219. *Librn*, Joan Cannon; *Asst Librn*, Teresa Farley
Founded 1845
Library Holdings: Bk Vols 105,405; Bk Titles 10,533; Per Subs 1,381
Special Collections: Florida Supreme Court Historical Society
Partic in Dialog Corporation; SE Libr Network; Westlaw

L HOPPING, GREEN, SAMS & SMITH, Law Library, 123 S Calhoun St, 32301. SAN 372-1795. Tel: 850-222-7500. FAX: 850-224-8551. *Librn*, Nancy M Mazek
Library Holdings: Bk Vols 8,000; Per Subs 40
Subject Interests: Administrative law, Environmental law

P LEROY COLLINS LEON COUNTY PUBLIC LIBRARY SYSTEM, 200 W Park Ave, 32301-7720. SAN 303-2035. Tel: 850-487-2665. TDD: 850-922-0096. FAX: 850-487-1793. Web Site: www.co.leon.fl.us/library/index.htm. *Dir*, Helen Moeller; E-Mail: helenm@mail.co.leon.fl.us; *Asst Dir*, Linda Barber; Fax: 850-922-9289, E-Mail: lindab@mail.co.leon.fl.us; *Asst Dir*, Sarah Johnson; E-Mail: sarahj@mail.co.leon.fl.us; *Asst Dir*, Linda McCarthy; E-Mail: lindam@mail.co.leon.fl.us; *Asst Dir*, Clinton P Taffe; E-Mail: clinton@mail.co.leon.fl.us; *Head Ref*, Carol Wade; E-Mail: carolw@mail.co.leon.fl.us; *Publ Servs*, Robert Visk; E-Mail: robertv@mail.co.leon.fl.us; *Circ*, David Farnan; E-Mail: farnand@mail.co.leon.fl.us; *ILL*, Tina Campbell; E-Mail: tinac@mail.co.leon.fl.us; *Media Spec*, Tracy Miller; E-Mail: millert@mail.co.leon.fl.us; *YA Servs*, Mary Jo Peltier; E-Mail: peltierm@mail.co.leon.fl.us; *Head Tech Servs*, Trudi Green; E-Mail: greent@mail.co.leon.fl.us; *Head, Circ*, Gabe Burke; E-Mail: burkeg@mail.co.leon.fl.us; *ILL*, Breet Castleberry; E-Mail: castlebb@mail.co.leon.fl.us. Subject Specialists: *Acquisitions*, Linda Barber; *Budgeting*, Clinton P Taffe; *Operations*, Clinton P Taffe; *Outreach*, Sarah Johnson; *Pub servs tech*, Linda McCarthy; Staff 95 (MLS 22, Non-MLS 73)
Founded 1955. Pop 24,300; Circ 1,582,417
Oct 1999-Sep 2000 Income (Main Library and Branch Library) $5,681,298, State $726,920, Federal $23,186, County $4,605,977, Locally Generated Income $243,977, Other $81,238. Mats Exp $859,229. Sal $2,702,383
Library Holdings: Bk Vols 477,998; Bk Titles 233,698
Special Collections: Grantsmanship Coll; Map Coll
Automation Activity & Vendor Info: (Acquisitions) DRA; (Cataloging) DRA; (Circulation) DRA; (Serials) DRA
Database Vendor: Dialog, DRA, Ebsco - EbscoHost, IAC - Info Trac, OCLC - First Search, ProQuest, Silverplatter Information Inc., Wilson - Wilson Web
Partic in Florida Library Information Network; Panhandle Library Access Network; SE Libr Network
Special Services for the Deaf - Deaf publications; TDD; Videos & decoder
Special Services - Computer & Typing Labs; Classes for Literacy & Adult Education; Public Meeting Rooms; Tallahassee Free-Net coordination, development & public training; access to Internet via Tallahassee Free-Net; Map Resource Center; Junior Friends Group
Friends of the Library Group

Branches: 4

DR B L PERRY JR, BRANCH, Smith-Williams Ctr, 2295 Pasco St, 32304. SAN 321-9119. Tel: 850-487-1815. FAX: 850-922-2518. Web Site: www.co.leon.fl.us/library/index.htm. *Librn*, Ann Parrish; E-Mail: parrishc@mail.co.leon.fl.us
Friends of the Library Group

LAKE JACKSON BRANCH, Huntington Oaks Plaza, 3840-302 N Monroe, 32303. SAN 371-3768. Tel: 850-488-2665. TDD: 850-922-7171. FAX: 850-922-7171. Web Site: www.co.leon.fl.us/library/index.htm. *Branch Mgr*, Lonnie Walsh; E-Mail: walshl@mail.co.leon.fl.us; *Mgr*, Clinton P Taffe; Tel: 850-487-2665, Fax: 850-487-1793, E-Mail: clinton@mail.co.leon.fl.us
Special Services for the Deaf - TDD

NORTHEAST BRANCH, 5513 Thomasville Rd, 32308. SAN 374-6844. Tel: 850-921-1776. FAX: 850-921-1775. Web Site: www.co.leon.fl.us/library/index.htm. *Branch Mgr*, Ellen Ontko; E-Mail: ontkoe@mail.co.leon.fl.us; *Mgr*, Clinton P Taffe; Tel: 850-487-2665, Fax: 850-487-1793, E-Mail: clinton@mail.co.leon.fl.us

PARKWAY BRANCH, Cross Creek Square, 1210 Capital Circle SE, 32301. SAN 321-9100. Tel: 850-487-1926. Web Site: www.co.leon.fl.us/library/index.htm. *Branch Mgr*, Gloria Brooks; E-Mail: brookg@mail.co.leon.fl.us; *Mgr*, Clinton P Taffe; Tel: 850-487-2665, Fax: 850-487-1793, E-Mail: clinton@mail.co.leon.fl.us

Bookmobiles: 1. Librn, Brett Castleberry

P STATE LIBRARY OF FLORIDA, Division of Library & Information Services, Department of State, R A Gray Bldg, 32399-0250. SAN 303-2051. Tel: 850-487-2651. TDD: 850-922-4085. FAX: 850-487-6242. Interlibrary Loan Service FAX: 850-922-3678. E-Mail: info@mail.dos.state.fl.us. Web Site: www.dlis.dos.state.fl.us. *Dir*, Barratt Wilkins; *Asst Dir*, Lorraine Summers; *Tech Servs*, Connie Garrett; *Doc*, Deborah Mekeel; *AV, Circ*, Patricia Sorrenti; *Ad Servs*, Sandra Newell; *Automation Syst Coordr*, Mark Flynn; *Publ Servs*, Cay Hohmeister; Staff 32 (MLS 32)
Founded 1845. Pop 14,931,700
Jul 1999-Jun 2000 Income $50,976,490, State $44,114,537, Federal $6,861,953. Mats Exp $436,386. Sal $4,597,113 (Prof $1,687,140)
Library Holdings: Bk Vols 675,212; Per Subs 1,404
Special Collections: Florida Coll; State Planning Coll
Automation Activity & Vendor Info: (Acquisitions) DRA; (Cataloging) DRA; (Circulation) DRA
Database Vendor: DRA
Publications: Florida Library Directory & Statistics; Florida Public Documents; Florida State Agency Libraries & Resource Centers in Tallahassee: Orange Seed
Partic in Florida Library Information Network; SE Libr Network

S TALL TIMBERS RESEARCH STATION LIBRARY, 13093 Henry Beadel Dr, 32312-0918. SAN 320-1392. Tel: 850-893-4153. FAX: 850-668-7781. Web Site: www.talltimbers.org. *Librn*, Ann M Bruce; E-Mail: brucea@ttrs.org
Library Holdings: Bk Vols 6,048; Bk Titles 3,700; Per Subs 120
Subject Interests: Botany, Conservation, Ecology, Forestry
Special Collections: Fire Ecology File Coll

J TALLAHASSEE COMMUNITY COLLEGE LIBRARY, 444 Appleyard Dr, 32304-2895. SAN 303-2078. Tel: 850-414-2477, 850-922-8131. FAX: 850-922-4356. E-Mail: library@mail.tallahassee.cc.fl.us. Web Site: www.tallahassee.cc.fl.us. *Dir*, Cherry Alexander; *Bibliog Instr*, Carol Chenoweth; *Media Spec*, Albert Spradley; *Tech Servs*, Colleen Thorburn; *Circ*, Emmett Denny; *Ref*, Janys Barnidge; *ILL*, Jacqueline Druash; Staff 8 (MLS 8)
Founded 1966. Fac 409
Library Holdings: Bk Vols 109,104; Bk Titles 87,183; Per Subs 695
Subject Interests: Paramedics
Special Collections: Florida (Beatrice Shaw Coll)
Publications: Acquisitions (newsletter); Library Handbook; Library Staff Newsletter
Partic in Panhandle Library Access Network

TAMPA

S BAE SYSTEMS, (Formerly Reflectone, Inc), Flight Simulation & Training Library, 4908 Tampa West Blvd, 33634. SAN 326-7865. Tel: 813-887-1658. FAX: 813-887-1420. *Librn*, Betsy King; E-Mail: betsy.king@baesystem.com; Staff 1 (MLS 1)
Library Holdings: Bk Vols 800
Subject Interests: Aeronautics, Engineering

L CARLTON FIELDS, Law Library, One Harbour Pl, 777 S Harbour Island Blvd, PO Box 3239, 33602. SAN 303-2086. Tel: 813-223-7000. FAX: 813-229-4133. Web Site: www.carltonfields.com. *Ref*, Terry Psarras
Founded 1915
Partic in Dialog Corporation; Westlaw

S CHURCH OF JESUS CHRIST OF LATTER-DAY SAINTS, Tampa Florida Family History Center Library, 14048 Trouville Dr No 4, 33624. SAN 303-2094. Tel: 813-971-2869. Web Site: www.familysearch.org. *Dir*, John Wells; *Dir*, Bette Wells; *Asst Dir*, Joe Groom
Founded 1968
Library Holdings: Bk Titles 2,220
Subject Interests: Genealogy
Special Collections: Coulter Coll, book & mss
Open Mon & Wed 9-5, Tues 9-5 & 7-9, Thurs 9-9 & Sat 9-1

S CUBAN HISTORICAL & CULTURAL CENTER LIBRARY, 10905 Memorial Hwy, 33615. (Mail add: PO Box 260065, 33685), SAN 377-4813. Tel: 813-855-5771. *Pres*, Mimi Albaro; Tel: 813-968-4660
Library Holdings: Bk Titles 7,500

J EDUCATION AMERICA, INC, Tampa Technical Institute Library, 2410 E Busch Blvd, 33612-8410. SAN 370-5013. Tel: 813-935-5700. FAX: 813-935-7415. *Dir Libr Serv*, Kathleen M H Brady; E-Mail: kmhb_1@yahoo.com; Staff 5 (MLS 1, Non-MLS 4)
Founded 1948. Pop 1,400; Circ 2,089; Enrl 1,400; Fac 41; Highest Degree: Master
Oct 1999-Sep 2000 Income Parent Institution $56,300. Mats Exp $5,400, Books $4,000, Per/Ser (Incl. Access Fees) $800, AV Equip $500, Electronic Ref Mat (Incl. Access Fees) $100. Sal $50,100 (Prof $34,000)
Library Holdings: Bk Vols 4,200; Bk Titles 4,000; Per Subs 141
Subject Interests: Business, Computer, Electronics
Restriction: Non-circulating to the public, Open to student, faculty & staff
Function: Photocopies available, Reference services available, Some telephone reference
Partic in Am Libr Asn; ASIS; Fla Libr Asn; SLA; Tampa Bay Library Consortium, Inc
Special Services for the Deaf - Special interest periodicals; Staff with knowledge of sign language

SR EVANGELICAL LUTHERAN CHURCH IN AMERICA, Florida-Bahamas Synod Multimedia Library, 3838 W Cypress St, 33607. SAN 329-9775. Tel: 813-876-7660. FAX: 813-870-0826. *Librn*, Irene Flynn
Library Holdings: Bk Titles 500

C FLORIDA METROPOLITAN UNIVERSITY, Tampa Campus Library-West Hillsborough, 3319 W Hillsborough Ave, 33614. SAN 302-8879. Tel: 813-879-6000. FAX: 813-875-7764. E-Mail: fmutampalibrary@hotmail.com. Web Site: www.tblc.org/tcw. *Librn*, Katherine Ann Kaldenberg; Tel: 813-879-6000, Ext 117; Staff 1 (MLS 1)
Enrl 1,350; Fac 50; Highest Degree: Master
Library Holdings: Bk Vols 5,000; Per Subs 100
Subject Interests: Allied health, Commercial art, Data processing
Publications: Bibliographies; Internal Acquisitions List; Newsletter
Partic in Tampa Bay Library Consortium, Inc
Departmental Libraries:

BRANDON CAMPUS LIBRARY, Sabal Business Ctr, 3924 Coconut Palm Dr, 33619. SAN 370-9256. Tel: 813-621-0041. FAX: 813-623-5769. Web Site: www.tblc.org/tcb. *Dir*, Madeline Lock; E-Mail: mlock@cci.edu; Staff 2 (MLS 1, Non-MLS 1)
Highest Degree: Master
Mem of Tampa Bay Libr Consortium, Inc

LAKELAND CAMPUS LIBRARY, 995 E Memorial Blvd, Ste 110, Lakeland, 33801. SAN 376-9615. Tel: 863-686-1444. FAX: 863-683-1077. *Dir*, Betty Martinez; Tel: 863-686-1444, Ext 112, E-Mail: bettym@cci.edu; *Tech Servs*, Jeff Tribby; Tel: 863-686-1444, Ext 131, E-Mail: jtribby@cci.edu; Staff 2 (MLS 1, Non-MLS 1)
Enrl 680; Highest Degree: Master
Library Holdings: Bk Vols 8,000; Bk Titles 7,100; Per Subs 120
Automation Activity & Vendor Info: (Circulation) Athena; (OPAC) Athena
Partic in Tampa Bay Library Consortium, Inc

PINELLAS CAMPUS LIBRARY, 2471 McMullen Booth Rd, Ste 200, Clearwater, 33759. SAN 324-7937. Tel: 727-725-2688. FAX: 727-796-3722. *Librn*, Glenn A Hall

L FOWLER, WHITE, GILLEN, BOGGS, VILLAREAL & BANKER, Law Library, 501 E Kennedy Blvd, Ste 1700, 33602. SAN 372-1779. Tel: 813-228-7411. FAX: 813-229-8313. *Librn*, Elenita Lopez
Library Holdings: Bk Vols 25,000; Per Subs 75
Subject Interests: Immigration, Real estate, Securities
Friends of the Library Group

§M H LEE MOFFITT CANCER CENTER & RESEARCH INSTITUTE, Medical Library, 12902 Magnolia Dr, 33612. Tel: 813-979-7295. FAX: 813-979-3084. *Librn*, Joan Miller; E-Mail: millerj@moffett.usf.edu; *Coordr*, Sue Felber; E-Mail: felbes@moffitt.usf.edu
Library Holdings: Bk Vols 425; Per Subs 180
Automation Activity & Vendor Info: (Acquisitions) SIRSI; (Cataloging) SIRSI; (Circulation) SIRSI

GM JAMES A HALEY VETERANS HOSPITAL LIBRARY, 13000 Bruce B Downs Blvd, 33612. SAN 303-2183. Tel: 813-972-2000, Ext 6570. FAX: 813-978-5917. *Chief Librn*, Nancy Bernal
Founded 1972
Library Holdings: Bk Vols 8,120; Per Subs 360
Subject Interests: Medicine, Nursing
Publications: Medical Library Newsletter
Partic in Tampa Bay Medical Library Network; Vets Admin Libr Network

J HILLSBOROUGH COMMUNITY COLLEGE, District Learning Resources Services, 4001 Tampa Bay Blvd, 33614. (Mail add: PO Box 30030, 33630-3030), SAN 338-1390. Tel: 813-259-6059. FAX: 813-253-7510. Web Site: www.hcc.cc.fl.us/services/. *Head Tech Servs*, Patricia Manack; *Automation Syst Coordr*, Viveca Yoshikawa; Staff 31 (MLS 10, Non-MLS 21)
Founded 1968. Enrl 4,124; Fac 232
Jul 2000-Jun 2001 Mats Exp $306,378, Books $237,378, Per/Ser (Incl. Access Fees) $69,000
Library Holdings: Bk Vols 106,726; Bk Titles 78,555; Per Subs 1,008
Subject Interests: Allied health, Music, Nursing
Special Collections: Art Slides; Literary Criticism File
Database Vendor: DRA
Partic in Florida Library Information Network; SE Libr Network; Tampa Bay Library Consortium, Inc
Departmental Libraries:
BRANDON CAMPUS LEARNING RESOURCES CENTER, 10414 E Columbus Dr, 33619-9640. SAN 322-8983. Tel: 813-253-7803, 813-253-7812. FAX: 813-253-7800. Web Site: www.hcc.fl.us/services/. *Librn*, Jim Wood; *AV*, Jackie del Val; Staff 2 (MLS 2)
Enrl 823
Publications: LRC Newsletter (internal)
Partic in OCLC Online Computer Library Center, Inc
DALE MABRY CAMPUS LEARNING RESOURCES CENTER, 4001 Tampa Bay Blvd, PO Box 30030, 33630-3030. SAN 338-1420. Tel: 813-253-7381. FAX: 813-253-7400. Web Site: www.hcc.cc.fl.us/services/departments/library/library.asp. *Librn*, Jacqueline Cress; *Librn*, Vic Harke; E-Mail: vharke@hcc.cc.fl.us; *Librn*, Terri Singer; *AV*, Milan Gumbarevic; Staff 10 (MLS 3, Non-MLS 7)
Founded 1968. Enrl 2,040
Special Collections: Literary Criticism File; Slide Library
Publications: LRC Newsletter (internal)
Partic in OCLC Online Computer Library Center, Inc
PLANT CITY CAMPUS LEARNING RESOURCES CENTER, 1206 N Park Rd, Plant City, 33566-2799. SAN 303-1330. Tel: 813-757-2109, 813-757-2121. FAX: 813-757-2167. Web Site: www.hcc.cc.fl.us/services/. *Librn*, Tammy Schofield; E-Mail: tschofield@hcc.cc.fl.us; *AV*, Sherrie Colgain; Staff 3 (MLS 1, Non-MLS 2)
Enrl 483
Partic in OCLC Online Computer Library Center, Inc
YBOR CITY CAMPUS LEARNING RESOURCES CENTER, 1502 E Ninth Ave, 33605. SAN 329-5729. Tel: 813-253-7645. FAX: 813-259-6070. Web Site: www.hcc.cc.fl.us/services/. *Librn*, Jeneice Sorrentino; E-Mail: jsorrentino@hcc.cc.fl.us; *Librn*, Ave Reagor; *AV*, Charles Bowen; Staff 6 (MLS 2, Non-MLS 4)
Enrl 779
Partic in OCLC Online Computer Library Center, Inc

GL HILLSBOROUGH COUNTY LAW LIBRARY, 501 E Kennedy Blvd, 33602. SAN 303-2132. Tel: 813-272-5818. FAX: 813-272-5226. *In Charge*, Norma Wise
Library Holdings: Bk Vols 40,000; Per Subs 75
Partic in Westlaw
Friends of the Library Group

L HOLLAND & KNIGHT LLP, Law Library, 400 N Ashley, Ste 2300, PO Box 1288, 33602. SAN 372-1396. Tel: 813-227-8500. FAX: 813-229-0134. Web Site: www.hklaw.com. *Dir Libr Serv*, Glenn Ross; Tel: 813-227-6629, Fax: 813-223-9240, E-Mail: gross@hklaw.com
Library Holdings: Bk Vols 30,000

S INTERNATIONAL ACADEMY OF MERCHANDISING & DESIGN LIBRARY, 5225 Memorial Hwy, 33634. SAN 377-3248. Tel: 813-881-0007. FAX: 813-881-0008. E-Mail: iamd@tpa.edu. *Dir*, Glenn Hall; *Asst Librn*, Giesla Wendt
Library Holdings: Bk Vols 6,000; Bk Titles 5,800; Per Subs 185
Partic in Tampa Bay Library Consortium, Inc

S LAMALIE AMROP INTERNATIONAL, INC, Research Department, Northdale Plaza, Ste 200 E, 3903 Northdale Blvd, 33624-1864. SAN 322-8126. Tel: 813-961-7494. FAX: 813-962-6127. *Asst Librn*, Nancy M Clausen; *Doc, Mgr*, Tamara J Costello; *Res*, Dorothy K Siani; *Res*, Paula A Asinof; Staff 8 (MLS 6, Non-MLS 2)
Founded 1967
Library Holdings: Bk Vols 2,100; Bk Titles 2,000; Per Subs 150
Subject Interests: Bus
Special Collections: Executive Search Coll, bks & articles
Partic in Dialog Corporation; Dow Jones News Retrieval; Tampa Bay Library Consortium, Inc

S MUSEUM OF SCIENCE & INDUSTRY, MOSI Science Library, 4801 E Fowler Ave, Ste L, 33617. SAN 377-0516. Tel: 813-987-6378. FAX: 813-987-6381. *Librn*, Lorri Robinson
Library Holdings: Bk Vols 11,251; Bk Titles 11,000; Per Subs 13
Mem of Tampa-Hillsborough County Public Library System

S NATIONAL HEALTH ASSOCIATION, (Formerly American Natural Hygiene Society, Inc), Herbert Shelton Library, 11816 Racetrack Rd, 33626. (Mail add: PO Box 30630, 33630), SAN 371-2753. Tel: 813-855-6607. FAX: 813-855-8052. E-Mail: anhs@anhs.org. Web Site: www.anhs.org. *Dir*, Timothy Michael Duszynski
Library Holdings: Bk Vols 2,500

L PRICE WATERHOUSE LIBRARY, 400 N Ashley St, Ste 2800, 33602. SAN 377-3566. Tel: 813-222-7115. FAX: 813-222-9439. *In Charge*, Toni Jaeschke; Tel: 813-222-7115, Fax: 813-222-9439
Library Holdings: Bk Vols 500

S PROVIDENCE HISTORICAL SOCIETY, 12712 DuPont Circle, 33626. SAN 300-1717. Tel: 813-855-4635. *Librn*, Jeanette Lorenzo
Library Holdings: Bk Vols 900; Bk Titles 12,000

S PSI GLOBAL, Information Center, 4301 Anchor Plaza Pkwy, No 300, 33634-7521. SAN 311-9920. Tel: 813-287-2774. FAX: 813-286-7377. Web Site: www.psi-global-info.com. *Librn*, James L Belcher; E-Mail: jbelcher@psi-global-info.com
Library Holdings: Bk Vols 10,000; Per Subs 150
Research on financial service industries

L SHACKLEFORD, FARRIOR, STALLINGS & EVANS, Law Library, 501 E Kennedy Blvd, Ste 1400, 33601. (Mail add: PO Box 3324, 33601-3324), SAN 373-6598. Tel: 813-273-5000. Reference Tel: 813-273-5256. FAX: 813-273-5145.
Library Holdings: Bk Vols 25,000; Bk Titles 3,500; Per Subs 75
Restriction: Staff use only

M SHRINERS' HOSPITAL FOR CHILDREN, Professional Library, 12502 N Pine Dr, 33612-9499. SAN 371-5728. Tel: 813-972-2250, Ext 7608. FAX: 813-978-9442. *Librn*, Clar Kanelly; Staff 1 (MLS 1)
Founded 1985
Library Holdings: Bk Vols 5,000; Bk Titles 1,500; Per Subs 120
Subject Interests: Orthopedics
Special Collections: Orthopedics, bks, v-tapes
Partic in BRS; Medline; Tampa Bay Medical Library Network

M ST JOSEPH'S HOSPITAL LIBRARY, PO Box 4227, 33677. SAN 322-8223. Tel: 813-870-4659. FAX: 813-870-4479.
Library Holdings: Bk Vols 1,700; Per Subs 135
Special Collections: Medical Management Coll; Nursing Management Coll
Database Vendor: OVID Technologies
Restriction: Lending to staff only, Member organizations only
Function: ILL available, Reference services available
Partic in BRS; Dialog Corporation

M SUNCOAST GERONTOLOGY CENTER, The Eastern Star Library on Alzheimer's Disease, 10770 N 46th St, Ste A1200, 33617. SAN 377-2349. Tel: 813-974-4355. FAX: 813-974-4251. Web Site: www.med.usf.edu/suncoast/alzheimer/.
Founded 1985
1998-1999 Income $50,000
Library Holdings: Bk Vols 1,350
Partic in Tampa Bay Medical Library Network

S TAMPA BAY HISTORY CENTER, Hillsborough County Historic Commission Library, 225 S Franklin St, 33602. (Mail add: PO Box 948, 33601-0948), SAN 303-2124. Tel: 813-228-0097. FAX: 813-223-7021. E-Mail: thistory@gte.net. Web Site: www.tampabayhistorycenter.org. *Archivist*, Barbara Ware. Subject Specialists: *Anthropology*, Barbara Ware; Staff 1 (Non-MLS 1)
Founded 1949
Sep 1999-Oct 2000 Income County $36,000. Mats Exp $8,300, Books $2,000, Per/Ser (Incl. Access Fees) $100, Presv $800, Micro $700, AV Equip $2,000, Other Print Mats $1,500, Manuscripts & Archives $1,200. Sal $18,000
Library Holdings: Bk Titles 3,892
Subject Interests: Florida
Special Collections: Spanish-American (Hatton & Memorabilia)
Restriction: Non-circulating
Function: Research library
Partic in Tampa Bay Library Consortium, Inc
All library & museum materials & artifacts are housed at the Tampa Bay History Center

M TAMPA GENERAL HOSPITAL, Medical Library, PO Box 1289, 33601. SAN 303-2159. Tel: 813-251-7328. FAX: 813-251-7325. *Librn*, Margaret H Henry; Staff 2 (MLS 1, Non-MLS 1)
Founded 1960
Library Holdings: Bk Titles 2,000; Per Subs 450
Subject Interests: Clinical medicine
Publications: TGH Library Letter, brochure
Partic in SE-Atlantic Regional Med Libr Servs; Tampa Bay Medical Library Network

S TAMPA MUSEUM OF ART, Judith Rozier Blanchard Library, 600 N Ashley Dr, 33602. SAN 303-2140. Tel: 813-274-8130. FAX: 813-274-8732.
Library Holdings: Bk Vols 3,500; Per Subs 25

Special Collections: Greek & Roman Antiquities (550 bks, corpus vasoreum, journals, offprints, rare bks & elephant folios)
Publications: Exhibition catalogs; monthly newsletter
Friends of the Library Group

S TAMPA RESERVATION LIBRARY, 5219 N Orient Rd Bldg K, 33610. SAN 377-2144. Tel: 813-626-5765. *Librn*, Carol Foret
Library Holdings: Bk Vols 6,500; Bk Titles 5,000; Per Subs 70
Partic in SW Fla Libr Network

P TAMPA-HILLSBOROUGH COUNTY PUBLIC LIBRARY SYSTEM, 900 N Ashley Dr, 33602-3704. SAN 338-1455. Tel: 813-273-3652. FAX: 813-273-3707. Web Site: thpl.org. *Chair*, Sandra Cameron; *Dir*, Joe Stines; E-Mail: stinesj@thpl.org; *Asst Dir*, Marcee Challener; E-Mail: marcee@thpl.org; *Pub Relations*, Patrice Koerper; E-Mail: koerpep@thpl.org; *Access Serv, Commun Servs*, Janet Lorenzo; E-Mail: lorenzj@thpl.org; *YA Servs*, Priscilla Lakus; E-Mail: lakus@thpl.org; *Ref*, Jean Peters; E-Mail: petersj@thpl.org; *Planning Services*, Maurice Site; E-Mail: site@thpl.org; Staff 117 (MLS 114, Non-MLS 3)
Founded 1915. Pop 967,511; Circ 3,974,071
Oct 1999-Sep 2000 Income (Main Library and Branch Library) $23,711,794. Mats Exp $3,573,347, Books $2,998,762, Electronic Ref Mat (Incl. Access Fees) $574,585. Sal $10,668,811
Library Holdings: Bk Vols 2,126,111; Per Subs 3,929
Subject Interests: Florida, Genealogy, Local history
Automation Activity & Vendor Info: (Circulation) epixtech, inc.
Publications: Monthly Activities & Events Calendar
Member Libraries: Museum of Science & Industry; Temple Terrace Public Library
Partic in Florida Library Information Network; SE Libr Network
Friends of the Library Group
Branches: 19
BRANDON REGIONAL BRANCH, 619 Vonderburg Dr, Brandon, 33511-5972. SAN 338-151X. Tel: 813-744-5630. FAX: 813-744-5632. *Librn*, Virginia Zurflich; *Ch Servs*, Carol Nenninger
Library Holdings: Bk Vols 149,847
COLLEGE HILL, 2607 E Martin Luther King Blvd, 33610. SAN 370-0917. Tel: 813-273-3681. FAX: 813-276-2989. *Librn*, Darlene Harris
Library Holdings: Bk Vols 34,482
AUSTIN DAVIS BRANCH, 17808 Wayne Rd, Odessa, 33556. SAN 338-1544. Tel: 813-264-3825. FAX: 813-264-3903. *Librn*, Lauren Levy
Library Holdings: Bk Vols 48,625
LUTZ BRANCH, 101 Lutz Lake Fern Rd W, Lutz, 33549. SAN 338-1609. Tel: 813-264-3800. FAX: 813-264-3907. *Librn*, Jodi Cohen; Tel: 813-264-3827; *Ch Servs*, Beth Dolson; Tel: 813-264-3827
Founded 1970
Library Holdings: Bk Vols 52,293
NEW TAMPA REGIONAL, 10001 Cross Creek Blvd, 33675-2575. SAN 377-5798. Tel: 813-903-2280. *Librn*, Judy McAfee; *Ch Servs*, Corey Bennett
Library Holdings: Bk Vols 110,084
NORTH TAMPA, 8916 North Blvd, 33604. SAN 338-1633. Tel: 813-975-2111. FAX: 813-975-2057. *Librn*, Susan Oliver; *Ch Servs*, Carolyn Dial
Library Holdings: Bk Vols 101,215
NORTHWEST REGIONAL, 15610 Premiere Dr, 33624. SAN 328-8927. Tel: 813-264-3831. FAX: 813-264-3834. *Head Librn*, Stephanie Losurdo; E-Mail: losurds@scfn.thpl.lib.fl.us; *YA Servs*, Donna Scott
Founded 1986
Library Holdings: Bk Vols 128,197
PENINSULAR, 3909 Neptune St, 33629. SAN 338-1668. Tel: 813-273-3680. FAX: 813-276-8561. *Librn*, Eloise Hurst; *Ch Servs*, Jamie Thomas
Library Holdings: Bk Vols 69,519
PORT TAMPA, 4902 Commerce St, 33616. SAN 338-1692. Tel: 813-301-7001. FAX: 813-301-7008. *Librn*, Julie Beamguard; *Ch Servs*, Martin Sicard
Library Holdings: Bk Vols 25,679
RIVERVIEW BRANCH, 10509 Riverview Dr, Riverview, 33569. SAN 338-1714. Tel: 813-671-7690. FAX: 813-671-7793. *Librn*, Doris Losey
Library Holdings: Bk Vols 45,427
RUSKIN BRANCH, One Dickman Dr SE, Ruskin, 33570. SAN 338-1722. Tel: 813-671-7638. FAX: 813-671-7698. *Librn*, Margaret Steinfurth; *Ch Servs*, Rodrigo Diaz
Library Holdings: Bk Vols 61,523
SEFFNER-MANGO BRANCH, 11724 Dr Martin Luther King Jr Blvd W, Seffner, 33584-4923. Tel: 813-276-2606. FAX: 813-276-2642. *Librn*, Alan Nichter; *Ch Servs*, Susan Sevighy
SEMINOLE HEIGHTS, 4711 Central Ave, 33603. SAN 338-1757. Tel: 813-273-3669. FAX: 813-273-3670. Web Site: www.scfn.thpl.lib.fl.us/thpl/thpl.htm. *Librn*, Victorene Jackson; E-Mail: jacksov@scfn.thpl.lib.fl.us; Staff 6 (MLS 2, Non-MLS 4)
Library Holdings: Bk Vols 50,047
SEVENTY-EIGHTH STREET COMMUNITY, 7625 Palm River Rd, 33619-4131. SAN 377-5771. Tel: 813-612-9123. FAX: 813-612-9125. *Librn*, Walter Cook
Library Holdings: Bk Vols 36,684
TALKING BOOKS LIBRARY, 900 N Ashley Dr, 33602-3788. SAN 338-148X. Tel: 813-273-3609. TDD: 813-273-3610. *Dir*, Joe Stines
Special Collections: Talking Books Coll
Special Services for the Deaf - TDD
THONOTOSASSA BRANCH, 10715 Main St, PO Box 1529, Thonotosassa, 33592-1406. SAN 370-0925. Tel: 813-987-6215. FAX: 813-987-6216. *Librn*, Patty Leifer
Library Holdings: Bk Vols 51,370
WEST GATE REGIONAL, 7606 Paula Dr, 33615. SAN 338-1811. Tel: 813-554-5031. FAX: 813-554-5121. *Librn*, Carolyn Rankin; *Ch Servs*, Beverly Hladkey
Library Holdings: Bk Vols 108,038
WEST TAMPA, 1718 N Howard Ave, 33607. SAN 338-1846. Tel: 813-273-3674. FAX: 813-276-8264. *Librn*, Maureen Baez
Library Holdings: Bk Vols 21,120
YBOR CITY, 1505 N Nebraska Ave, 33602. SAN 338-1870. Tel: 813-272-5547. FAX: 813-273-3667. *Librn*, Peggy Callahan
Library Holdings: Bk Vols 34,239
Bookmobiles: 1

S THE TAMPA TRIBUNE CO, Archives & Research Center, 200 S Parker St, 33606. SAN 303-2167. Tel: 813-259-7379. FAX: 813-259-8199. E-Mail: library@tampatrib.com. Web Site: www.archives.tampatrib.com. *Chief Librn, Mgr*, Jody Habayeb
Library Holdings: Bk Vols 1,200; Per Subs 40

L TRENAM, KEMKER, SCHARF, BARKIN, FRYE, O'NEILL & MULLIS, Law Library, 101 E Kennedy Blvd, Ste 2700, 33602. (Mail add: PO Box 619, 33601), SAN 372-1787. Tel: 813-223-7474. FAX: 813-229-6553. *Mgr Libr Serv*, Marcia Morelli; E-Mail: mamorelli@trenam.com
Founded 1970
Library Holdings: Bk Vols 30,000; Bk Titles 1,130; Per Subs 50
Subject Interests: Real estate
Restriction: Employees & their associates, In-house use for visitors
Function: Reference only

M UNIVERSITY COMMUNITY HOSPITAL, Medical Library, 3100 E Fletcher Ave, 33613-4688. SAN 324-5616. Tel: 813-971-6000, Ext 1046, 813-972-7236. FAX: 813-972-7854. *Mgr, Ref*, Sharon Henrich; E-Mail: sharonh@mail.uch.org; *Tech Servs*, Sandra Rodis; Staff 3 (MLS 2, Non-MLS 1)
Founded 1974
Library Holdings: Bk Vols 1,435; Bk Titles 2,000; Per Subs 596
Partic in Nat Libr of Med; Regional Med Libr - Region 2; Tampa Bay Library Consortium, Inc; Tampa Bay Medical Library Network

M UNIVERSITY COMMUNITY HOSPITAL OF CARROLLWOOD, Medical Library, 7171 N Dale Mabry Hwy, 33614. SAN 371-2451. Tel: 813-932-2222. FAX: 813-558-8002. *In Charge*, Linda Cox
Library Holdings: Bk Vols 1,000; Per Subs 50

UNIVERSITY OF SOUTH FLORIDA

CM HINKS & ELAINE SHIMBERG HEALTH SCIENCES LIBRARY, 12901 Bruce B Downs Blvd, MDC Box 31, 33612-4799. SAN 338-1900. Tel: 813-974-2399. Interlibrary Loan Service Tel: 813-974-2123. FAX: 813-974-4930. Web Site: www.med.usf.edu/hsc. *Dir*, Beverly A Shattuck; E-Mail: bshattuc@hsc.usf.edu; *Cat*, Allison Howard; *Acq*, Shirley Outen; *Syst Coordr*, Rose Bland; *Ref*, Danny O'Neal; *ILL*, Jo Ella Young; *Ser*, Lee Ann Howlett; Staff 19 (MLS 9, Non-MLS 10)
Founded 1971. Enrl 1,117; Fac 551; Highest Degree: Doctorate
Library Holdings: Bk Titles 29,863; Per Subs 1,373
Subject Interests: Medicine, Nursing, Public health
Automation Activity & Vendor Info: (Acquisitions) NOTIS; (Cataloging) NOTIS
Publications: HSC (newsletter); The Clue
Partic in Dialog Corporation; Fla Ctr for Libr Automation; Medline; SE-Atlantic Regional Med Libr Servs; Tampa Bay Medical Library Network
See also the following USF libraries: Lakeland: USF Library at Lakeland; Saint Petersburg: Nelson Poynter Memorial Library; Sarasota: Jane Bancroft Cook Library; Tampa: Tampa Campus Library, Florida Mental Health Institute Library

C TAMPA CAMPUS LIBRARY, 4202 E Fowler Ave, LIB 122, 33620. SAN 338-1935. Tel: 813-974-2721. Interlibrary Loan Service Tel: 813-974-2515. Circulation Tel: 813-974-1603. Reference Tel: 813-974-2729. FAX: 813-974-5153. Web Site: www.lib.usf.edu. *Actg Dean*, Derrie Perez; Tel: 813-974-1642, E-Mail: dperez@libusf.edu; *Dir*, Samuel Y Fustukjian; *Head, Acq*, John E Keeth; Tel: 813-974-2733, E-Mail: johkeeth@lib.usf.edu; *Head, Cat*, Susan Heron; Tel: 813-974-6725; *Head, Circ*, Merilyn Burke; Tel: 813-974-4561; *Head Ref*, Virginia Cunningham; *Media Spec*, Rue Herbert; Tel: 813-974-4182; *Syst Coordr*, Beverly Caggiano; *Coll Develop*, Larry Heilos; Tel: 813-974-4496; *Ref Serv Ad*, Mark Dibble; *Ref*, Joe Floyd; Staff 111 (MLS 36, Non-MLS 75)
Founded 1960. Enrl 28,442; Fac 1,815; Highest Degree: Doctorate
Jul 1998-Jun 1999 Income $8,176,099. Mats Exp $4,630,897. Sal $3,545,202 (Prof $1,637,995)
Library Holdings: Bk Vols 1,754,540; Bk Titles 971,507; Per Subs 4,977; Bks on Deafness & Sign Lang 1,269
Subject Interests: Business and management, Economics, Education, History, Music, Natural science, Science/technology, Technology

Special Collections: 19th Century American Playscript Coll; 19th Century American Printed Ephemera Coll, advertising & greeting cards, rewards of merit; 19th Century American Songbook Coll; American Almanac Coll; American Juvenile Series Book Coll (boys', girls' & animal series); American Toybook Coll; Archives & Manuscripts Coll (Piers Anthony Papers, Dion Boucicault Theatre Coll, Florida Federal Writers Project Papers, Congressman Sam M Gibbons Papers, Miles Hanley Papers, Papers of Governor LeRoy Collins, Records of Tampa Ethnic Mutual Aid Societies, Robert W & Helen Saunders Papers); Cigar Art Coll, cigar labels & bands, cigar industry memorabilia & artifacts; Cigar Label Progressive Proof Books (Kane-Greenberg Lithography Coll); Coll US Tobacco Museum; Dime Novel Coll; Dobkin Coll of 19th Century American Literature; Early American Textbook Coll; Florida Sheet Music Coll; George Alfred Henty Coll; Haldeman-Julius Coll; Hampton Dunn Coll (Floridiana); Mosher Press Coll; National Amateur Press Coll; NationsBank Black Musical Heritage Coll; Rare Books Coll; Rare Map Coll (primarily North America, 1524-1900); Regional History Coll (relating to Florida), bks, journals, maps, mss, photogs, postcards; Tony Pizzo Coll (Floridiana); Wollowick Coll of American Currency
Automation Activity & Vendor Info: (Acquisitions) NOTIS; (Cataloging) NOTIS; (Circulation) NOTIS; (Course Reserve) NOTIS; (OPAC) NOTIS; (Serials) NOTIS
Publications: Ex Libris; Library Link
Partic in Fla Ctr for Libr Automation; SE Libr Network; Tampa Bay Library Consortium, Inc
Special Services for the Deaf - TDD
See also the following USF Libr: Lakeland (USF Libr at Lakeland); Saint Petersburg (Nelson Poynter Memorial Libr); Sarasota (Jane Bancroft Cook Libr); Tampa (Florida Mental Health Institute Libr Health Sciences Libr)
Friends of the Library Group

GM UNIVERSITY OF SOUTH FLORIDA, Louis de la Parte Florida Mental Health Institute Library, 13301 Bruce B Downs Blvd, 33612-3899. SAN 303-2108. Tel: 813-974-4471. FAX: 813-974-7242. E-Mail: dnialaa@cfrvm.usf, library@fmhi.usf.edu. Web Site: www.fmhi.usf.edu. *Dir*, Ardis Hanson; E-Mail: hanson@fmhi.usf.edu; Staff 5 (MLS 2, Non-MLS 3)
Founded 1974
Library Holdings: Bk Vols 24,390; Bk Titles 21,000; Per Subs 210
Subject Interests: Aging, Autism, Health care, Mental health, Psychology, Social service (social work)
Special Collections: AIDS; Audio-Visual Coll; Epidemiology; Florida Mental Health Institute Archives
Automation Activity & Vendor Info: (Circulation) NOTIS; (OPAC) NOTIS; (Serials) NOTIS
Database Vendor: CARL, Lexis-Nexis, OCLC - First Search, OVID Technologies, ProQuest, Silverplatter Information Inc., Wilson - Wilson Web
Function: Research library
Partic in OCLC Online Computer Library Center, Inc; SE Libr Network

C UNIVERSITY OF TAMPA, Mcdonald-Kelce Library, 401 W Kennedy Blvd, 33606-1490. SAN 303-2175. Tel: 813-253-6231. FAX: 813-258-7426. Web Site: www.utampa.edu. *Dir, Online Servs, Ref*, Marlyn Pethe; *Librn*, Elizabeth Baron; *Acq*, Art Bagley; *Cat*, Pat Tolbert; *Online Servs, Ref*, Jeanne Vince; *Online Servs, Per, Ref*, Mickey Wells; Staff 6 (MLS 6)
Founded 1931. Enrl 2,377; Fac 145; Highest Degree: Master
Library Holdings: Bk Vols 238,355; Bk Titles 173,867; Per Subs 1,685
Subject Interests: Business and management, Computer science, Nursing
Special Collections: Drama (Blanche Yurka Coll), letters, res mat, scrapbks; Florida Military; John Wilkes Booth (Stanley Kimmel Coll), bks, photog, res mat; Local History; University Archives
Automation Activity & Vendor Info: (Circulation) Endeavor
Publications: Bibliographies; faculty library handbook, library guide, fact sheet
Partic in BRS; Dialog Corporation; Florida Library Information Network; OCLC Online Computer Library Center, Inc; SE Libr Network; Tampa Bay Library Consortium, Inc
Friends of the Library Group

S URS CORPORATION LIBRARY, (Formerly URS Greiner Woodward Clyde Library), 7650 W Courtney Campbell Causeway, 33607-1462. SAN 370-873X. Tel: 813-286-1711. FAX: 813-287-8591. *Librn*, Lexie W Schwabel; Staff 3 (MLS 1, Non-MLS 2)
Founded 1984
Library Holdings: Bk Titles 4,000; Per Subs 150
Subject Interests: Architecture, Civil engineering, Environ sci, Planning, Structural engineering

TARPON SPRINGS

P TARPON SPRINGS PUBLIC LIBRARY, 138 E Lemon St, 34689. SAN 303-2221. Tel: 727-943-4922. FAX: 727-943-4926. E-Mail: tslref@tblc.org. Web Site: www.tblc.org/tarpon/. *Dir*, Elizabeth O'Brien; E-Mail: obriene@tblc.org; *Circ*, Barbara Aglieri; Staff 21 (MLS 5, Non-MLS 16)
Founded 1916
Oct 1999-Sep 2000 Income $994,204, State $88,277, City $706,769, County $199,158. Mats Exp $199,299, Books $138,780, Per/Ser (Incl. Access Fees) $8,005, AV Equip $9,600, Electronic Ref Mat (Incl. Access Fees) $40,814. Sal $396,536 (Prof $225,108)
Library Holdings: Bk Vols 82,558; Per Subs 277
Subject Interests: Florida, Greek
Automation Activity & Vendor Info: (Acquisitions) epixtech, inc.; (Cataloging) epixtech, inc.; (Circulation) epixtech, inc.; (OPAC) epixtech, inc.
Database Vendor: Ebsco - EbscoHost, epixtech, inc., OCLC - First Search
Publications: Newsletter
Mem of Pinellas County Public Libr Coop
Partic in Tampa Bay Library Consortium, Inc
Friends of the Library Group

TAVARES

S LAKE COUNTY HISTORICAL SOCIETY LIBRARY, 317 W Main St. (Mail add: PO Box 7800, 32778-7800), SAN 325-1845. Tel: 352-343-9890. FAX: 352-343-9814.
Founded 1954
Oct 1998-Sep 1999 Income $22,900, County $14,504, Locally Generated Income $7,000. Mats Exp $1,150, Books $50, Per/Ser (Incl. Access Fees) $200, Presv $1,000, Manuscripts & Archives $50. Sal $15,700
Subject Interests: Maps, Rare books
Special Collections: Poll Tax Books, 1887-1937
Publications: Lake County Florida: A Pictorial History
Function: Research library
Open Mon-Thurs 9-4

L LAKE COUNTY LAW LIBRARY, 202 N Sinclair Ave, PO Box 7800, 32778. SAN 326-7075. Tel: 352-742-4161. FAX: 352-742-4190. E-Mail: lawlib@digital.net. *Librn*, Faye Osebold; *Asst Librn*, Tracie Sumersil
Library Holdings: Bk Vols 16,500; Bk Titles 455
Partic in State Asn of Law Librns

P LAKE COUNTY LIBRARY SYSTEM, 315 W Main St, PO Box 7800, 32778-7800. SAN 370-4653. Tel: 352-343-9402. Interlibrary Loan Service Tel: 352-253-6163. FAX: 352-343-9896. E-Mail: lcls@lakeline.lib.fl.us. Web Site: www.lakeline.lib.fl.us. *Dir*, Wendy R Breeden; E-Mail: wbreeden@lakeline.lib.fl.us; *Tech Servs*, Donna Gray-Williams; Tel: 352-253-6161, Fax: 352-253-6170, E-Mail: dgraywms@lakeline.lib.fl.us; *Publ Servs*, Judy Buckland; Tel: 352-343-9462, E-Mail: jbucklan@lakeline.lib.fl.us; Staff 75 (MLS 19, Non-MLS 56)
Founded 1982. Pop 203,863; Circ 612,085
Oct 1999-Sep 2000 Income $3,176,505, State $218,763, City $1,126,869, Federal $57,767, County $1,621,061, Locally Generated Income $152,045. Mats Exp $406,248, Books $343,650, Electronic Ref Mat (Incl. Access Fees) $62,598. Sal $1,665,805
Library Holdings: Bk Vols 204,769; Bk Titles 130,356; Per Subs 675
Subject Interests: Genealogy
Special Collections: Florida Environment Coll
Automation Activity & Vendor Info: (Acquisitions) epixtech, inc.; (Cataloging) epixtech, inc.; (Circulation) epixtech, inc.; (OPAC) epixtech, inc.
Database Vendor: epixtech, inc.
Member Libraries: Cooper Memorial Library; Fruitland Park Library; Lady Lake Public Library; Tavares Public Library; Umatilla Public Library; W T Bland Public Library
Partic in Central Florida Library Cooperative (CFLC); SE Libr Network; Southeast Florida Library Information Network, Inc
Friends of the Library Group
Branches: 3
CITRUS RIDGE COUNTY LIBRARY, 17445 Hwy 192, Ste 8, Clermont, 34711-7016. Tel: 352-243-1840. Toll Free Tel: 877-292-7930. FAX: 352-243-3230. *Branch Mgr*, Melissa McKie
EAST LAKE COUNTY LIBRARY, 31336 County Rd 437 S, Sorrento, 32776. Tel: 352-383-9980. FAX: 352-383-9982. *Branch Mgr*, George Dore
MARION BAYSINGER MEMORIAL COUNTY LIBRARY, 243 S Lake Ave, Groveland, 34736. SAN 370-4645. Tel: 352-429-5840. FAX: 352-429-3852. *Branch Mgr*, Kristen Wiley
Library Holdings: Bk Vols 7,000

P TAVARES PUBLIC LIBRARY, 314 N New Hampshire Ave, 32778. SAN 323-651X. Tel: 352-742-6204. FAX: 352-742-6472. Web Site: www.tavares.org/library.html. *Dir*, Harriet Schwanke; Tel: 352-742-6090, E-Mail: hschwanke@tavares.org; *Asst Dir*, Marli Lopez; *Ch Servs*, Zita Wenzel; *Publ Servs*, Carla Garnto; Staff 11 (MLS 2, Non-MLS 9)
Founded 1959. Pop 8,078; Circ 79,304
Oct 1999-Sep 2000 Income $343,726, City $265,000, County $78,726. Mats Exp $49,380, Books $35,000, Per/Ser (Incl. Access Fees) $11,100, Presv $700, Electronic Ref Mat (Incl. Access Fees) $2,580. Sal $136,040 (Prof $57,484)
Library Holdings: Bk Vols 37,286; Bk Titles 34,337; Per Subs 120
Special Collections: Dorothy Young Johnson Dance & Theater Coll; Florida Materials; Large Print
Database Vendor: epixtech, inc.
Function: Reference services available
Mem of Cent Fla Libr Consortium; Lake County Library System
Friends of the Library Group

TEMPLE TERRACE

J FLORIDA COLLEGE, Chatlos Library, 119 N Glen Arven Ave, 33617-5578. SAN 303-223X. Tel: 813-899-6777. FAX: 813-899-6828. Web Site: www.flcoll.edu/library/library.htm. *Dir*, James Hodges; E-Mail: jwhodges@juno.com; *Librn*, Wanda Dickey; Tel: 813-899-6776; *Librn*, Mary Ann Pope; *Librn*, Wanda Dickey; Tel: 899-6776; Staff 5 (MLS 3, Non-MLS 2)
Founded 1946. Pop 630; Enrl 530; Fac 37; Highest Degree: Bachelor
Jul 1999-Jun 2000 Mats Exp $71,200, Books $27,500, Per/Ser (Incl. Access Fees) $27,500, Presv $1,500, Micro $500, AV Equip $1,200, Electronic Ref Mat (Incl. Access Fees) $13,000. Sal $124,383
Library Holdings: Bk Vols 83,626; Per Subs 388
Subject Interests: History, Music, Religion
Automation Activity & Vendor Info: (Cataloging) Follett; (Circulation) Follett; (OPAC) Follett
Database Vendor: Ebsco - EbscoHost
Partic in Tampa Bay Library Consortium, Inc

P TEMPLE TERRACE PUBLIC LIBRARY, 202 Bullard Pkwy, 33617. SAN 303-2248. Tel: 813-989-7160. FAX: 813-989-7069. *Librn*, Mary H Satterwhite; *Asst Librn*, Robin D Dombrowsky; Staff 5 (MLS 5)
Founded 1960. Pop 75,000; Circ 238,492
Library Holdings: Bk Titles 54,653; Per Subs 139
Mem of Tampa-Hillsborough County Public Library System
Friends of the Library Group

TITUSVILLE

J BREVARD COMMUNITY COLLEGE, Titusville Campus Library, Dr Frank Elbert Williams Learning Resource Ctr, 1311 N US 1, 32796-2192. SAN 303-2256. Tel: 321-632-1111, Ext 43008. FAX: 321-634-3765. Web Site: www.brevard.cc.fl.us/lrc. *Librn*, Dan Henderson; Staff 2 (MLS 2)
Founded 1973. Enrl 2,000; Fac 18
Library Holdings: Bk Vols 22,000; Per Subs 200
Partic in LINCC

P NORTH BREVARD PUBLIC LIBRARY, 2121 S Hopkins Ave, 32780. SAN 303-2272. Tel: 321-264-5026. FAX: 321-264-5030. Web Site: www.brev.lib.fl.us. *Dir*, Pamela D Boddy
Founded 1906. Pop 45,000; Circ 397,098
Library Holdings: Bk Vols 80,064; Per Subs 307
Subject Interests: Genealogy
Automation Activity & Vendor Info: (Circulation) GEAC
Mem of Brevard County Library System; SE Libr Network
Special Services for the Deaf - TTY machine
Open Sun 1-5, Mon-Thurs 9-9, Fri-Sat 9-5
Friends of the Library Group

TRENTON

S LANCASTER CORRECTIONAL INSTITUTION LIBRARY, 3449 SW SR 26, 32693. SAN 377-4775. Tel: 352-463-4100. FAX: 352-463-3476. E-Mail: lancasterci@mail.dc.state.fl.us.
Library Holdings: Bk Vols 9,000; Per Subs 56

TYNDALL AFB

UNITED STATES AIR FORCE

A AIR BASE & ENVIRONMENTAL TECH LIBRARY FL7050, Technical Information Center AFRL/MLQ-TIC, 139 Barnes Dr, Ste 2, 32403-5323. SAN 324-5845. Tel: 850-283-6285. FAX: 850-283-6500. *Chief Librn*, Andrew Poulis; E-Mail: poulis@afcesa1.af.mil; *Cat, Syst Coordr*, Virginia Davis
Founded 1968
Library Holdings: Bk Titles 12,500; Per Subs 400
Subject Interests: Chemical engineering, Civil engineering, Energy, Environmental engineering, Structural engineering
Special Collections: Air-Bird Strikes; Geotechnical Centrifuges; Hazardous Materials; Rapid Runway Repair; Sonic Boom Research
Automation Activity & Vendor Info: (Acquisitions) TechLIB; (Cataloging) TechLIB; (Circulation) TechLIB
Publications: Periodicals Listing; Tic Talk
Partic in Dialog Corporation; Fedlink; OCLC Online Computer Library Center, Inc

A TYNDALL AIR FORCE BASE LIBRARY FL4819, 325 SVS/SVMG/45, 640 Suwanee Rd, Bldg 916, 32403-5531. SAN 338-1994. Tel: 850-283-4287. FAX: 850-283-4994. *Librn*, James Clark; E-Mail: james.clark@tyndall.af.mil; Staff 5 (Non-MLS 5)
2000-2001 Mats Exp $310,462. Sal $264,649 (Prof $56,000)
Library Holdings: Bk Vols 26,524; Per Subs 300
Subject Interests: Aeronautics, Military history
Automation Activity & Vendor Info: (Cataloging) GEAC; (Circulation) GEAC; (OPAC) GEAC
Publications: Substance (monthly in-house newsletter)
Partic in Fedlink; OCLC Online Computer Library Center, Inc; Panhandle Library Access Network

UMATILLA

P UMATILLA PUBLIC LIBRARY, 412 Hatfield Dr, 32784-8913. SAN 303-2280. Tel: 352-669-3284. FAX: 352-669-2927. *Dir*, MaryEllen C Babb; E-Mail: mbabb@cflc.net
Founded 1917. Circ 67,738
1998-1999 Income $252,611, City $100,263, County $152,348. Mats Exp $34,500, Books $32,000, Per/Ser (Incl. Access Fees) $2,500. Sal $185,000
Library Holdings: Bk Vols 23,000; Per Subs 40
Mem of Lake County Library System
Friends of the Library Group

VALPARAISO

P VALPARAISO COMMUNITY LIBRARY, 459 Valparaiso Pkwy, 32580. SAN 303-2299. Tel: 850-729-5406. FAX: 850-678-4553. *Dir*, Sue Martin; E-Mail: smartin@okaloosa.lib.fl.us; Staff 6 (MLS 2, Non-MLS 4)
Founded 1973. Pop 178,000
Library Holdings: Bk Vols 22,094; Per Subs 128
Subject Interests: Genealogy
Database Vendor: epixtech, inc., OCLC - First Search
Friends of the Library Group

VENICE

P FRANCES T BOURNE JACARANDA PUBLIC LIBRARY, 4143 Woodmere Park Blvd, 34293. SAN 376-267X. Tel: 941-486-2723. FAX: 941-486-2725. *Head Librn*, Cynthia Guest; Staff 12 (MLS 5, Non-MLS 7)
Founded 1994
Library Holdings: Bk Vols 47,502; Bk Titles 41,925; Per Subs 209
Automation Activity & Vendor Info: (Acquisitions) Innovative Interfaces Inc.; (Cataloging) Innovative Interfaces Inc.; (Circulation) Innovative Interfaces Inc.; (Course Reserve) Innovative Interfaces Inc.; (ILL) Innovative Interfaces Inc.; (Media Booking) Innovative Interfaces Inc.; (OPAC) Innovative Interfaces Inc.; (Serials) Innovative Interfaces Inc.
Mem of Sarasota County Dept of Librs
Friends of the Library Group

P VENICE PUBLIC LIBRARY, 300 S Nokomis Ave, 34285-2296. SAN 303-2302. Tel: 941-486-2338. Reference Tel: 941-486-2341. TDD: 941-486-2342. FAX: 941-486-2342, 941-486-2345. Web Site: www.suncat.co.sarasota.fl.us. *Dir*, Nancy M Pike; *Ref*, Lynn Thierry; *Ch Servs*, Joanne Lize; *Publ Servs*, Mary Waddell; Staff 23 (MLS 8, Non-MLS 15)
Founded 1964. Pop 46,441; Circ 465,486
Library Holdings: Bk Vols 93,300; Per Subs 230
Publications: Bookbits (reviews, occasionally); FOL Newsletter (quarterly)
Mem of Sarasota County Dept of Librs
Open Mon-Thurs 9-9, Fri & Sat 9-5, Sun 1-5
Friends of the Library Group

VERO BEACH

S INDIAN RIVER CORRECTIONAL INSTITUTION LIBRARY, 7625 17th St SW, 32968. SAN 372-543X. Tel: 561-564-2822. FAX: 561-564-2880. *Librn*, Frank Roberts
Library Holdings: Bk Titles 4,500; Per Subs 60

P INDIAN RIVER COUNTY MAIN LIBRARY, 1600 21st St, 32960. SAN 303-2329. Tel: 561-770-5060. FAX: 561-770-5066. Web Site: www.indian-river.lib.fl.us. *Dir*, Mary Powell; E-Mail: mpowell@indian-river.lib.fl.us; Staff 13 (MLS 4, Non-MLS 9)
Founded 1915. Pop 106,000; Circ 869,448
Oct 2000-Sep 2001 Income $3,098,414, State $264,720, Federal $10,712, County $2,822,982. Mats Exp $837,542, Books $596,000, Per/Ser (Incl. Access Fees) $61,810, Presv $6,000, Micro $93,203, Electronic Ref Mat (Incl. Access Fees) $80,529. Sal $1,659,047 (Prof $750,000)
Library Holdings: Bk Vols 303,472; Bk Titles 275,271; Per Subs 160
Subject Interests: Civil War, Florida, Genealogy
Special Collections: Florida Authors; Vero Beach Authors
Automation Activity & Vendor Info: (Acquisitions) GEAC; (Cataloging) GEAC; (Circulation) GEAC; (Course Reserve) GEAC; (Media Booking) GEAC; (OPAC) GEAC; (Serials) GEAC
Database Vendor: OCLC - First Search
Partic in Cent Fla Libr Consortium
Special Services for the Deaf - TDD
Special Services for the Blind - Bks on cassette
Friends of the Library Group
Branches: 1
LAW, 2000 16th Ave, Ste 119, 32960. Tel: 561-770-5157. FAX: 561-388-3697. *Librn*, Cindy Krupp; E-Mail: ckrupp@indian-river.lib.fl.us; *Librn*, Siglinde Preston
Library Holdings: Bk Titles 20,000

M INDIAN RIVER MEMORIAL HOSPITAL, J C Robertson Memorial Library, 1000 36th St, 32960. SAN 326-2103. Tel: 561-567-4311, Ext 5039. FAX: 561-563-4661.
Founded 1967
Library Holdings: Bk Titles 816; Per Subs 75

G UNIVERSITY OF FLORIDA, Florida Medical Entomology Laboratory Library, 200 Ninth St SE, 32962. SAN 303-2310. Tel: 561-778-7200. FAX: 561-778-7205. E-Mail: caz@icon.vero.ufl.edu. Web Site: www.ifas.ufl.edu/~veroweb/vero.htm. *Librn*, Lena Carolee Zimmerman
Library Holdings: Bk Titles 5,600; Per Subs 105
Subject Interests: Biochemistry, Biology, Ecology, Entomology, Ornithology, Virology
Restriction: Not open to public
Branch of the Institute of Food & Agriculture Sciences Marston Science Libr Univ of Florida, Gainesville, Florida

VIERA

L A MAX BREWER MEMORIAL LAW LIBRARY, Brevard County Law Library, Moore Justice Ctr, 2825 Judge Fran Jamieson Way, 32940. SAN 324-7627. Tel: 321-617-7295. FAX: 321-617-7301. Web Site: www.manatee.brev.lib.fl.us/locations/law/law.htm. *Coll Develop, Dir*, Susan E Szymula; E-Mail: sszymula@iu.net; *Librn*, Wendy Oliver
Founded 1955
Library Holdings: Bk Vols 22,000
Restriction: Non-circulating to the public
Partic in Cent Fla Libr Consortium

WAUCHULA

P HARDEE COUNTY PUBLIC LIBRARY, 315 N Sixth Ave, Ste 114, 33873. SAN 303-2337. Tel: 941-773-6438. FAX: 941-767-1091. Web Site: www.heartlineweb.org. *Dir*, Diane C Hunt
Circ 15,000
Library Holdings: Bk Vols 30,000; Per Subs 600
Mem of Heartland Libr Coop
Friends of the Library Group

WEBSTER

P E C ROWELL PUBLIC LIBRARY, 85 E Central Ave, PO Box 1044, 33597. Tel: 352-568-1600. FAX: 352-568-1399. *Librn*, Judy Lee
Library Holdings: Bk Vols 11,000; Bk Titles 10,000; Per Subs 10
Mem of Sumter County Public Library System
Open Mon, Wed & Fri 10-4, Tues 10-12 & 2-4, Thurs 10-12, 2-4 & 6:30-8:30, Sat 10-12

WELAKA

P WOMEN'S CLUB OF WELAKA LIBRARY, Hwy 309, PO Box 154, 32193-1016. SAN 320-4723. Tel: 904-467-9706. *Librn*, Willanelle Wilcox
Founded 1960. Pop 1,000; Circ 2,100
Library Holdings: Bk Vols 3,000
Subject Interests: Florida

WEST MELBOURNE

P WEST MELBOURNE PUBLIC LIBRARY, 2755 Wingate Blvd, 32904. SAN 303-0369. Tel: 321-952-4508. FAX: 321-952-4510. Web Site: www.brev.lib.fl.us. *Dir*, Marian H Griffin; E-Mail: mgriffin@manatee.brev.lib.fl.us; Staff 14 (MLS 3, Non-MLS 11)
Founded 1970. Circ 138,361
Oct 1998-Sep 1999 Income $382,760. Mats Exp $77,348, Books $73,200, Per/Ser (Incl. Access Fees) $4,148. Sal $246,813
Library Holdings: Bk Vols 44,515; Per Subs 104
Automation Activity & Vendor Info: (Circulation) GEAC; (OPAC) GEAC
Mem of Brevard County Library System
Partic in Cent Fla Libr Consortium
Friends of the Library Group

WEST PALM BEACH

S GEE & JENSON ENGINEERS ARCHITECTS-PLANNERS, INC LIBRARY, One Harvard Circle, 33401-4600. SAN 303-2353. Tel: 561-515-6500. FAX: 561-515-6502. Web Site: www.geejenson.com. *Bibliog Instr, Dir, Online Servs*, John Day; E-Mail: jday@geejenson.com
Founded 1953
1998-1999 Mats Exp $500, Books $350, Per/Ser (Incl. Access Fees) $100, Presv $50. Sal $25,000
Library Holdings: Bk Vols 13,500; Bk Titles 8,300; Per Subs 205
Subject Interests: Art and architecture, Engineering, Florida
Special Collections: Quality Improvement Program bks - 25 titles, 300 vol
Restriction: Private library

M GOOD SAMARITAN MEDICAL CENTER, Richard S Beinecke Medical Library, PO Box 3166, 33401. SAN 303-2361. Tel: 561-650-6315. FAX: 561-650-6417. *Dir*, Karen Bledsoe; *Coordr*, Barbara Burke
Founded 1953
Library Holdings: Bk Titles 3,000; Per Subs 225
Subject Interests: Hospital administration, Medicine, Nursing, Surgery
Special Collections: Medicine (Rare Book Coll)
Partic in Palm Beach Health Sciences Library Consortium; SE-Atlantic Regional Med Libr Servs

L GUNSTER, YOAKLEY, VALDES-FAULI & STEWART LIBRARY, Ste 500 East Tower, 777 S Flagler Dr, 33401. SAN 323-973X. Tel: 561-655-1980. Toll Free Tel: 800-749-1980. FAX: 561-655-5677. E-Mail: library@gunster.com. Web Site: www.gunster.com. *Librn*, Susan McEvoy; *Tech Servs*, Roxann Waggener; Tel: 561-655-1980, Ext 231
Library Holdings: Bk Vols 12,000; Bk Titles 1,800
Automation Activity & Vendor Info: (Acquisitions) Inmagic, Inc.; (Cataloging) Inmagic, Inc.
Partic in Dialog Corporation; Dow Jones News Retrieval; Westlaw

S HISTORICAL SOCIETY OF PALM BEACH COUNTY LIBRARY, 400 N Dixie Hwy, 33401-4210. SAN 303-1152. Tel: 561-832-4164. FAX: 561-832-7965. E-Mail: historicalsocietypbc@yahoo.com. *Exec Dir*, Cheryl Houghtelin; Staff 3 (Non-MLS 3)
Founded 1937
Library Holdings: Bk Vols 3,000; Per Subs 10
Special Collections: Architectural Plans by Architects Addison Mizner, Treanor & Fatio, Gustav Maas; John Volk Coll; Joseph Urban Coll; Marion Sims Wyeth Coll; Original Manuscripts; Pioneer Manuscripts
Publications: The Newsletter (six issues)
Restriction: Open to public for reference only

S LEVY, KNEEN, MARIANI, WEINER, CURTIN, KORNFELD & DELRUSO LIBRARY, 1400 Centre Park Blvd, Ste 1000, 33401. SAN 327-4756. Tel: 561-478-4700. FAX: 561-478-5811. *In Charge*, John Mariani
Library Holdings: Bk Vols 350

C NORTHWOOD UNIVERSITY, Dr & Mrs Peter C Cook Library, 2600 N Military Trail, 33409-2911. SAN 329-5648. Tel: 561-478-5536. FAX: 561-697-3138. Web Site: www.northwood.edu. *Dir*, Sue Ann Luebke; E-Mail: luebke@northwood.edu; *Cat*, Donna J Link; E-Mail: link@northwood.edu; Staff 3 (MLS 1, Non-MLS 2)
Founded 1984. Enrl 1,000; Fac 13; Highest Degree: Bachelor
Sep 1998-Aug 1999 Income Parent Institution $221,956. Mats Exp $76,000, Books $38,000, Per/Ser (Incl. Access Fees) $30,000, AV Equip $2,000, Electronic Ref Mat (Incl. Access Fees) $6,000. Sal $74,100 (Prof $29,000)
Library Holdings: Bk Vols 26,000; Bk Vols 31,000; Bk Titles 25,000; Per Subs 250; Spec Interest Per Sub 100
Subject Interests: Business
Automation Activity & Vendor Info: (Cataloging) Sagebrush Corporation; (Circulation) Sagebrush Corporation
Database Vendor: Ebsco - EbscoHost, Lexis-Nexis, OCLC - First Search
Function: Research library
Partic in OCLC Online Computer Library Center, Inc; Solinet; Southeast Florida Library Information Network, Inc
Friends of the Library Group

S NORTON MUSEUM OF ART LIBRARY, 1451 S Olive Ave, 33401. SAN 303-2345. Tel: 561-832-5194. FAX: 561-659-4689. *Dir*, Dr Christina Orr-Tahall
Founded 1941
Library Holdings: Bk Vols 4,000; Per Subs 30
Subject Interests: Art (20th Century), Paintings, Sculpture
Special Collections: European & American Museum Catalogues

C PALM BEACH ATLANTIC COLLEGE, E C Blomeyer Library, 1101 S Olive St, 33401-6503. (Mail add: 900 S Olive Ave, 33401-6514), SAN 303-237X. Tel: 561-803-2226. Reference Tel: 561-803-2227. FAX: 561-803-2235. E-Mail: library@pbac.edu. Web Site: library.pbac.edu. *Dir Libr Serv*, Edwin R Nordine; Tel: 561-803-2232, E-Mail: nordinee@pbac.edu; *Acq, Admin Assoc*, Barbara A Rugolo; Tel: 561-803-2233, E-Mail: rugolob@pbac.edu; *Ref*, Cheri L du Mee; Tel: 561-803-2230, E-Mail: dumeec@pbac.edu; *Ref*, Tom Huehn; Tel: 561-803-2231, E-Mail: huehnt@pbac.edu; *Ref*, Debora A Stewart; Tel: 561-803-2224, E-Mail: stewartd@pbac.edu; *Ref*, Robert K Triplett; Tel: 561-803-2234, E-Mail: triplett@pbac.edu; *ILL*, Julia A Pichette; Tel: 561-803-2225, E-Mail: pichette@pbac.edu; Staff 8 (MLS 5, Non-MLS 3)
Founded 1968. Enrl 2,396; Fac 90; Highest Degree: Master
Jun 1998-Jul 1999 Income Parent Institution $426,020. Mats Exp $183,849, Books $96,607, Per/Ser (Incl. Access Fees) $45,539, Presv $646, Micro $13,759, AV Equip $8,750, Electronic Ref Mat (Incl. Access Fees) $18,548. Sal $222,817 (Prof $143,226)
Library Holdings: Bk Vols 129,463; Per Subs 2,137
Automation Activity & Vendor Info: (Cataloging) Endeavor; (Circulation) Endeavor; (Course Reserve) Endeavor; (ILL) Endeavor; (Media Booking) Endeavor; (OPAC) Endeavor; (Serials) Endeavor

Database Vendor: OCLC - First Search, ProQuest, Silverplatter Information Inc.
Partic in Southeast Florida Library Information Network, Inc

S PALM BEACH COUNTY GENEALOGICAL SOCIETY LIBRARY, 100 Clematis St, 33401-5511. (Mail add: PO Box 1746, 33402-1746), SAN 325-0571. Tel: 561-832-3279. E-Mail: pbgenlib@juno.com. Web Site: www.community.gopbi.com/pbcgensoc. *Acq, Librn, Per*, Mrs Alvin L Lentsch; *Circ*, Jane Allen; *Cat*, Dahrl Moore; Staff 2 (MLS 2)
Founded 1964
Apr 1998-Mar 1999 Income $46,400. Mats Exp $27,800, Books $3,750, Presv $1,250
Library Holdings: Bk Vols 11,500; Per Subs 10
Subject Interests: Census, History, Vital records
Special Collections: Genealogy (Palm Beach County Genealogical Society Coll)
Publications: Ancestry (quarterly)
We are an all volunteer organization and rely on dues and donations.

GL PALM BEACH COUNTY LAW LIBRARY, County Courthouse, Rm 12200, 205 N Dixie Hwy, 33401. SAN 303-2388. Tel: 561-355-2928. FAX: 561-355-1654. *Mgr*, Linda Sims
Founded 1947
Library Holdings: Bk Vols 30,000; Per Subs 30

P PALM BEACH COUNTY LIBRARY SYSTEM, 3650 Summit Blvd, 33406-4198. SAN 338-2028. Tel: 561-233-2600. TDD: 561-233-2628. FAX: 561-233-2622, 561-233-2644. E-Mail: pbcls@seflin.org. Web Site: www.seflin.org/pbcls/. *Dir*, Jerry W Brownlee; *Asst Dir*, Kathleen Perinoff; *Publ Servs*, Gail Peterson; *Outreach Serv*, Gary Corrigan; *Publ Servs*, Sharon Hill; *Ref*, Jane Craig; *Tech Servs*, Ann Fleming; *Commun Relations*, Kathy Boyes; *ILL*, Libby Nemota; *Info Tech*, Jeanne Brodbeck; *Coll Develop*, Jane Blevins; Staff 355 (MLS 87, Non-MLS 268)
Founded 1967. Pop 685,116; Circ 5,085,750
Oct 1999-Sep 2000 Income (Main Library and Branch Library) $22,177,412, State $1,846,857, Federal $105,000, County $18,423,908, Other $944,594. Mats Exp $3,799,572. Sal $11,670,293
Library Holdings: Bk Vols 1,090,579; Bk Titles 235,273; Per Subs 2,653
Special Collections: Audubon Coll; Florida Coll Large Print Coll
Automation Activity & Vendor Info: (Circulation) DRA
Publications: Calendar of Events (newsletter); column for children-public TV periodical; newspaper question & answer column; staff newsletter
Member Libraries: Boynton Beach City Library; Delray Beach Public Library; Lake Park Public Library; Lake Worth Public Library; Palm Springs Public Library; Riviera Beach Public Library; West Palm Beach Public Library
Partic in OCLC Online Computer Library Center, Inc; SE Libr Network
Special Services for the Deaf - TDD
Special Services for the Blind - Talking Books
Extension Services: Service to Blind & Physically Handicapped - Books-by-Mail, Literacy Program
Friends of the Library Group
Branches: 14
BELLE GLADE BRANCH, 530 S Main St, Belle Glade, 33430. SAN 302-8550. Tel: 561-996-3453. FAX: 561-996-2304. *Librn*, Phyllis J Lilley
Library Holdings: Bk Vols 49,360
CLARENCE E ANTHONY BRANCH, 375 SW Second Ave, South Bay, 33493. SAN 375-5894. Tel: 561-992-8393. FAX: 561-996-5925. *Librn*, Phyllis Lilley
Library Holdings: Bk Vols 17,800
GREENACRES BRANCH, 3750 Jog Rd, Greenacres City, 33467. SAN 338-2117. Tel: 561-641-9100. FAX: 561-642-0823. *Librn*, David Scott
Library Holdings: Bk Vols 86,714; Per Subs 108
JUPITER BRANCH, 705 Military Trail, Jupiter, 33458. SAN 326-7598. Tel: 561-744-2301. FAX: 561-744-6297. *Librn*, Michael A White
Library Holdings: Bk Vols 66,779
LOULA V YORK BRANCH, 525 Bacom Point Rd, Pahokee, 33476. SAN 370-0186. Tel: 561-924-5928. FAX: 561-924-2271. *Librn*, Phyllis J Lilley
Library Holdings: Bk Titles 20,267
NORTH COUNTY REGIONAL, 11303 Campus Dr, Palm Beach Gardens, 33410. SAN 377-0486. Tel: 561-626-6133. FAX: 561-626-9864. *Librn*, Carol Roggenstein
Library Holdings: Bk Vols 124,470
OKEECHOBEE BOULEVARD, 5689 Okeechobee Blvd, 33417. SAN 338-2176. Tel: 561-233-1880. FAX: 561-233-1889. *Librn*, Charles Waugh
Library Holdings: Bk Vols 82,903
PALM BEACH COUNTY LIBRARY ANNEX, 7950 Central Industrial Dr, Riviera Beach, 33404. SAN 338-2052. Tel: 561-845-4600. *Tech Servs*, Ann Fleming
Library Holdings: Bk Vols 20,323
Special Services: Lighted magnifiers available; Visualtek magnifier for in-house use
ROYAL PALM BEACH BRANCH, 500 Civic Center Way, Royal Palm Beach, 33411. SAN 338-2249. Tel: 407-790-6030. FAX: 407-790-6037. *Mgr*, Martha Murray
Library Holdings: Bk Vols 58,628; Bk Titles 61,382
SOUTHWEST COUNTY REGIONAL, 20701 95th Ave S, Boca Raton, 33434. SAN 338-2230. Tel: 561-482-4554. FAX: 561-483-9679.
Library Holdings: Bk Vols 145,074
TEQUESTA BRANCH, 461 Old Dixie Hwy, Tequesta, 33469. SAN 338-2141. Tel: 561-746-5970. FAX: 561-744-7251. *Librn*, Andy White
Library Holdings: Bk Vols 25,281
WELLINGTON BRANCH, 1951 Royal Fern Dr, Wellington, 33414. SAN 377-6530. Tel: 561-790-6070. FAX: 561-790-6078. *Librn*, Connie Brain
Library Holdings: Bk Vols 52,322
WEST ATLANTIC AVENUE, 7777 W Atlantic Ave, Delray Beach, 33446. SAN 338-2087. Tel: 561-498-3110. FAX: 561-498-7739. *Librn*, Lynn Pinilla
Library Holdings: Bk Vols 76,199
WEST BOYNTON BRANCH, 9451 Jog Rd, Boynton Beach, 33437. SAN 375-5908. Tel: 561-734-5556. FAX: 561-734-5392. *Librn*, Nemoure Ahmed
Library Holdings: Bk Vols 59,418
Bookmobiles: 1

S THE PALM BEACH POST LIBRARY, 2751 S Dixie Hwy, 33405. SAN 374-7727. Tel: 561-820-4495. FAX: 561-837-8409. E-Mail: salzofon@pbpost.com. *Dir*, Sammy Alzofon
Library Holdings: Bk Vols 1,600; Per Subs 60

C SOUTH COLLEGE, West Palm Beach Campus Library, 1760 N Congress Ave, 33409-5178. SAN 375-3786. Tel: 561-697-9200. FAX: 561-697-9944. Web Site: www.southcollege.edu. *Head Librn*, David Bosca; E-Mail: dbosca@southcollege.edu; *Librn*, Jacqueline Taylor; Staff 4 (MLS 2, Non-MLS 2)
Circ 1,800; Enrl 400; Fac 50; Highest Degree: Bachelor
Library Holdings: Bk Vols 12,165; Bk Titles 9,719; Per Subs 100
Subject Interests: Allied health, Business, Computer science, Medical assistant, Nursing, Paralegal studies, Physical therapy
Database Vendor: IAC - SearchBank, OCLC - First Search, ProQuest

S SOUTH FLORIDA WATER MANAGEMENT DISTRICT, Reference Center Library, 3301 Gun Club Rd, 33406. (Mail add: PO Box 24680, 33416-4680), SAN 303-2418. Tel: 561-682-6076. FAX: 561-682-6442. *Dir*, Cynthia H Plockelman; E-Mail: cplocke@sfwmd.gov; Staff 2 (MLS 1, Non-MLS 1)
Founded 1949
Oct 1998-Sep 1999 Mats Exp $125,000, Books $30,000, Per/Ser (Incl. Access Fees) $75,000, Micro $5,000, Other Print Mats $15,000. Sal $85,000 (Prof $57,000)
Library Holdings: Per Subs 225
Subject Interests: Agriculture, Conservation, Environmental engineering, Water pollution, Water resources
Special Collections: Florida Environmental History Coll; Technical Reports & Documents
Restriction: Open to public for reference only
Partic in Dialog Corporation; OCLC Online Computer Library Center, Inc; SE Libr Network

R TEMPLE ISRAEL LIBRARY OF JUDAICA, 1901 N Flagler Dr, 33407. SAN 303-2434. Tel: 561-833-8421. FAX: 561-833-0571. *Dir*, Joanne Wilson; *Asst Librn*, Adele Sayles
Founded 1958. Enrl 150; Fac 10; Highest Degree: Master
Library Holdings: Bk Titles 8,000; Per Subs 20
Subject Interests: Israel, Jewish history and literature, Judaism (religion)
Special Collections: Children's Coll
Friends of the Library Group

P WEST PALM BEACH PUBLIC LIBRARY, 100 Clematis St, 33401. SAN 303-2469. Tel: 561-659-8010. FAX: 561-835-7020. *Dir*, Pamela Sandlian-Smith; Tel: 561-653-2601, E-Mail: smithp@wpbpl.com; *Circ*, Dorris Jefferson; E-Mail: jeffersond@wpbpl.com; *Publ Servs*, Marsha Warfield; E-Mail: warfieldm@wpbpl.com; *YA Servs*, Meredith Cotler; *Coll Develop*, Tina Maura Albee; *Tech Servs*, Barbara Storch; Staff 34 (MLS 13, Non-MLS 21)
Founded 1921. Pop 84,000; Circ 360,771
Oct 1999-Sep 2000 Income $1,792,843, State $129,947, City $1,607,896, Federal $55,000. Mats Exp $275,530, Books $216,734, Per/Ser (Incl. Access Fees) $31,536, Electronic Ref Mat (Incl. Access Fees) $27,260. Sal $1,020,600
Library Holdings: Bk Vols 91,357; Per Subs 300
Special Collections: Floridiana
Mem of Palm Beach County Library System
Partic in Coop Authority for Libr Automation; Libr Coop Palm Beaches; Southeast Florida Library Information Network, Inc; Treasure Coast Libr Coun
Friends of the Library Group
Bookmobiles: 1

WEWAHITCHKA

S GULF CORRECTIONAL INSTITUTION LIBRARY, 500 Steel Rd, PO Drawer 10, 32465-0010. SAN 377-2675. Tel: 850-639-1000. FAX: 850-639-1182. *Actg Librn*, Janet McMillion
Library Holdings: Bk Vols 7,000; Per Subs 72

WILDWOOD

P GEORGE NICHOLS PUBLIC LIBRARY, 702 Webster St, 34785. SAN 370-4637. Tel: 352-748-1158. FAX: 352-748-5342. *Librn*, Betty McKinney
Library Holdings: Bk Vols 16,000; Per Subs 20
Mem of Sumter County Library System, Sumter County Public Library System
Open Mon-Thurs 10-6, Fri & Sat 10-2
Friends of the Library Group

WILTON MANORS

P WILTON MANORS PUBLIC LIBRARY, 500 NE 26th St, 33305. SAN 303-2477. Tel: 954-390-2195. FAX: 954-390-2183. E-Mail: wmlibrary@aol.com. *Dir*, Marcia Ellington
Founded 1957. Pop 12,000; Circ 55,000
Library Holdings: Bk Vols 20,000; Per Subs 70
Subject Interests: Travel
Special Collections: Florida - 350
Publications: Friend's Newsletter
Friends of the Library Group

WINTER HAVEN

J POLK COMMUNITY COLLEGE, James W Dowdy Memorial Library, 999 Avenue H NE, 33881-4299. SAN 303-2485. Tel: 863-297-1040. Reference Tel: 863-297-2356. FAX: 863-297-1065. E-Mail: rdesk@mail.polk.cc.fl.us. Web Site: www.polk.cc.fl.us/it/library/index.html. *VPres*, James H Horton; Tel: 863-669-2341; *Dir*, William C Foege; E-Mail: wfoege@polk.cc.fl.us; *Dir*, Sarah H Johnson; E-Mail: sarah_johnson@polk.cc.fl.us; *Bibliog Instr*, Ivy L Prewitt; E-Mail: iprewitt@polk.cc.fl.us; *Publ Servs*, Christina Fullerton; E-Mail: cfullerton@polk.cc.fl.us; *Publ Servs*, Helen Schmidt; E-Mail: hschmidt@polk.cc.fl.us. Subject Specialists: *Develop*, Sarah H Johnson; *Info tech*, James H Horton; *Pub servs tech*, William C Foege; Staff 12 (MLS 5, Non-MLS 7)
Founded 1965. Enrl 6,600; Fac 125; Highest Degree: Associate
Jul 1999-Jun 2000 Income (Main and Other College/University Libraries) $773,000. Mats Exp $181,250, Books $108,000, Micro $16,250, Other Print Mats $42,000, Electronic Ref Mat (Incl. Access Fees) $15,000. Sal $550,000
Library Holdings: Bk Titles 87,000; Per Subs 415
Subject Interests: Florida, State hist
Automation Activity & Vendor Info: (Acquisitions) DRA; (Cataloging) DRA; (Circulation) DRA; (ILL) DRA; (OPAC) DRA; (Serials) DRA
Database Vendor: DRA, Ebsco - EbscoHost, GaleNet, Lexis-Nexis, OCLC - First Search, ProQuest, Wilson - Wilson Web
Publications: Film Catalog; Manual Catalog Non-Print
Partic in Col Ctr for Libr Automation; Libr Info Network for Commun Cols; Polk County Libr Coop; Solinet; Tampa Bay Library Consortium, Inc
Departmental Libraries:
LAKELAND, US 98 S, Lakeland, 33803. SAN 374-6771. Tel: 863-297-1042. Reference Tel: 863-297-1067. FAX: 863-297-1064. *Publ Servs*, Helen Schmidt; E-Mail: hschmidt@polk.cc.fl.us; Staff 3 (MLS 1, Non-MLS 2)
Founded 1988

S RIDGE TECHNICAL CENTER LIBRARY, 7700 State Rd 544, 33881. SAN 377-3264. Tel: 863-419-3060, Ext 266. FAX: 863-419-3062. Web Site: www.sunlink.ucf.edu. *Media Spec*, Ann K Walsh; E-Mail: walsh_al@firn.edu
Founded 1979. Enrl 500
Jul 1999-Jun 2000 Mats Exp $75,000, Books $7,000, Per/Ser (Incl. Access Fees) $1,000, Presv $1,000, Micro $2,500. Sal $62,000 (Prof $43,000)
Library Holdings: Bk Vols 7,413; High Interest/Low Vocabulary Bk Vols 2,000; Spec Interest Per Sub 35; Bks on Deafness & Sign Lang 10
Subject Interests: Career, Children's books, Vocational
Friends of the Library Group

M WINTER HAVEN HOSPITAL, J D Converse Memorial Medical Library, 200 Avenue F NE, 33881. SAN 338-2265. Tel: 941-291-6033. FAX: 941-291-6022. *Res*, Henry Hasse; E-Mail: hankav@aol.com; Staff 1 (Non-MLS 1)
Founded 1950
Library Holdings: Bk Titles 700; Per Subs 84
Subject Interests: Medicine, Mental health, Nursing
Partic in SE-Atlantic Regional Med Libr Servs

P WINTER HAVEN PUBLIC LIBRARY, One Library Lane SE, 33880. SAN 303-2493. Tel: 941-291-5880. FAX: 941-291-5889. *Dir*, Kathryn L Smith; E-Mail: smithk@pclc.lib.fl.us; *Ch Servs*, Debra Couture; *Cat*, Sara Hanks; *Ref*, Jan Pickos
Founded 1910. Pop 25,000; Circ 237,414
Library Holdings: Bk Vols 60,000; Per Subs 182
Open Mon & Thurs 10-8, Tues, Wed, Fri & Sat 10-5:30
Friends of the Library Group

WINTER PARK

R ALL SAINTS' EPISCOPAL CHURCH LIBRARY, 338 E Lyman Ave, 32789. SAN 303-2507. Tel: 407-647-3413. FAX: 407-647-2406. *Librn*, Carolyn Bird
Library Holdings: Bk Vols 5,000
Subject Interests: Religion

C ROLLINS COLLEGE, Olin Library, 1000 Holt Ave, PO Box 2744, 32792. SAN 338-232X. Tel: 407-646-2676. Circulation Tel: 407-646-2521. Reference Tel: 407-646-2507. FAX: 407-646-1515. Web Site: www.rollins.edu/olin/index.html. *Dir*, Donna K Cohen; E-Mail: dcohen@rollins.edu; *Acq*, Patricia Pettijohn; Tel: 407-975-6431, E-Mail: ppettijohn@rollins.edu; *Head, Cat*, Edna McClellan; Tel: 407-646-2148, E-Mail: cmcclellan@rollins.edu; *Archivist, Spec Coll*, Kathleen Reich; Tel: 407-646-2231, Fax: 407-646-2122, E-Mail: kreich@rollins.edu; *Publ Servs*, Wenxian Zhang; Tel: 407-646-1533, E-Mail: wzhang@rollins.edu; *Govt Doc*, Naomi Harrison; Tel: 407-646-2684, E-Mail: nharrison@rollins.edu; *Ref*, Ann Carolyn Carpan; Tel: 407-646-2683, E-Mail: acarpan@rollins.edu; *Ref*, William Svitavsky; Tel: 407-646-2679, E-Mail: wsvitavsky@rollins.edu; Staff 8 (MLS 8)
Founded 1885. Enrl 2,624; Fac 195; Highest Degree: Master
Jun 1999-May 2000 Income $1,481,554. Mats Exp $491,289, Books $185,560, Per/Ser (Incl. Access Fees) $220,678, Presv $12,464, Micro $21,983, Electronic Ref Mat (Incl. Access Fees) $33,801. Sal $820,840
Library Holdings: Bk Vols 282,713; Bk Titles 227,443; Per Subs 1,441
Special Collections: Constance F Woolson Coll; Floridiana; Hamilton Holt Papers; M P Shiel Coll; Poetry & Letters (Jessie B Rittenhouse Coll); Theatre (Annie Russell Coll); Walt Whitman Coll
Database Vendor: OCLC - First Search, ProQuest
Publications: Olin Info (newsletter)
Partic in Central Florida Library Cooperative (CFLC); Consortium Of Midwest Community Colleges, Colleges & Universities; Solinet

M WINTER PARK MEMORIAL HOSPITAL, Medical Library, 200 N Lakemont Ave, 32792. SAN 303-2515. Tel: 407-646-7049. FAX: 407-646-7990. *Librn*, Patricia N Cole
Founded 1964
Library Holdings: Bk Titles 3,100; Per Subs 249
Special Collections: Historical Coll

P WINTER PARK PUBLIC LIBRARY, 460 E New England Ave, 32789-4493. SAN 303-2523. Tel: 407-623-3300. FAX: 407-623-3489. Web Site: www.wppl.org. *Dir*, Robert G Melanson; Tel: 407-623-3490, E-Mail: rmelanso@cflc.net; *Dep Dir*, Mrs Carolyn M Jeffries; Tel: 407-623-3496, E-Mail: cjeffrie@fcflc.net; *Dep Dir*, Craig Stillings; Tel: 407-623-3458, E-Mail: cstilling@cflc.net; *Tech Servs*, Ronald Chapman; *Ref*, Joyce Ward; *Commun Servs*, Marygail Dufresne; *Ch Servs*, Shanna Kuster; *Ch Servs*, Evelyn Malles; *Archivist*, Dean Padgett; Staff 28 (MLS 11, Non-MLS 17)
Founded 1885. Pop 24,501; Circ 369,794
Oct 1999-Sep 2000 Income $1,616,496, City $864,689, Federal $15,400, Locally Generated Income $88,249, Other $648,158. Mats Exp $238,596, Books $226,196, Micro $2,500, Electronic Ref Mat (Incl. Access Fees) $9,900. Sal $716,776
Library Holdings: Bk Vols 113,932; Bk Titles 96,123; Per Subs 466
Special Collections: Winter Park History Archive
Automation Activity & Vendor Info: (Circulation) epixtech, inc.; (OPAC) epixtech, inc.
Publications: Newsletter (quarterly)
Partic in Central Florida Library Cooperative (CFLC)
The Library is a non-profit corporation administratively independent of city & county government
Friends of the Library Group

ZEPHYRHILLS

S ZEPHYRHILLS CORRECTIONAL INSTITUTION LIBRARY, 2739 Gall Blvd, 33541. SAN 377-3485. Tel: 813-782-5521. FAX: 813-782-4954.
Library Holdings: Bk Vols 8,000; Per Subs 50

P ZEPHYRHILLS PUBLIC LIBRARY, 5347 Eighth St, 33540. SAN 303-2531. Tel: 813-782-1451. FAX: 813-783-2394. E-Mail: library@zephyrhills.net. *Dir*, Kathleen D Burnside; Staff 2 (MLS 1, Non-MLS 1)
Founded 1912. Pop 30,000; Circ 75,925
Library Holdings: Bk Vols 25,000; Per Subs 40
Subject Interests: Civil War, Florida, Gardening
Special Collections: Civil War; World War II

GEORGIA

Date of Statistics: 1998
Population, OPB Census: 7,545,790
Population Served by Public Libraries: 7,545,790
Total Volumes in Public Libraries: 15,317,769
Volumes Per Capita: 2.03
Total Public Library Circulation: 34,027,292
Circulation Per Capita: 4.51
Total Public Library Income: $111,036,874
Source of Income: Public funds-Federal, State & Local
Expenditures Per Capita: $14.99
Number of County & Multi-County Libraries: 57 (24 single county; 33 regional)
Counties Served: 159
Number of Bookmobiles & Other Vehicles in State: 33
Grants-in-Aid to Public Libraries:
Federal LSTA: $769,895
State Service Grants: $39,956,044
Local: $93,025,674

ALBANY

S ALBANY HERALD LIBRARY, 126 N Washington St, 31702. SAN 374-8952. Tel: 229-888-9371. FAX: 229-888-9357. Web Site: www.albanyherald.com. *Librn*, Mary Braswell
Library Holdings: Bk Titles 200

C ALBANY STATE UNIVERSITY, James Pendergrast Memorial Library, 504 College Dr, 31705-2796. SAN 303-2558. Tel: 912-430-4799. FAX: 912-430-4803. *Dir*, LaVerne McLaughlin; E-Mail: llm@asurams.edu
Founded 1903. Enrl 1,917; Fac 144; Highest Degree: Master
Library Holdings: Bk Vols 170,822; Bk Titles 165,000; Per Subs 964
Special Collections: History & Literature (Black Studies); Library of American Civilization; US Govt Census Data
Automation Activity & Vendor Info: (Acquisitions) Endeavor; (Cataloging) Endeavor; (Circulation) Endeavor; (Course Reserve) Endeavor; (ILL) Endeavor; (Media Booking) Endeavor; (OPAC) Endeavor; (Serials) Endeavor
Publications: New Acquisitions List
Mem of Univ Syst of Ga
Partic in OCLC Online Computer Library Center, Inc; Solinet

J DARTON COLLEGE, Harold B Wetherbee Library, 2400 Gillionville Rd, 31707. SAN 303-254X. Tel: 229-430-6760. Interlibrary Loan Service Tel: 229-430-6764. Circulation Tel: 229-430-6766. FAX: 229-430-6794. Web Site: www.dartnet.peachnet.edu/student/library.htm. *Dir, ILL, Per, Ser*, Dr Kay Lowry; E-Mail: lowry@mail.dartnet.peachnet.edu; *Tech Servs*, Mary Washington; *Syst Coordr*, Caryl Nemajovsky; Staff 4 (MLS 4)
Founded 1966. Enrl 2,900; Fac 86
Library Holdings: Bk Vols 87,200; Bk Titles 81,015; Per Subs 583
Subject Interests: Allied health, Nursing
Special Collections: American Enterprise Institute Coll
Partic in Georgia Online Database; OCLC Online Computer Library Center, Inc; South Georgia Associated Libraries

P DOUGHERTY COUNTY PUBLIC LIBRARY, 300 Pine Ave, 31701-2533. SAN 338-2419. Tel: 229-420-3200. FAX: 229-420-3215. *Dir*, Mike P Dugan; E-Mail: mdugan@gcpl.net; *Asst Dir*, David Piper; *ILL*, Faye Lewis; *Ch Servs*, Selena Wingfield; *Ser*, Jimmy Bass; *Cat*, Julia Ann Slappey; *Acq, Circ*, Patricia Henson; *Ref*, Beverly Linton; *Librn for Blind*, Katy Sinquefield; Staff 46 (MLS 13, Non-MLS 33)
Founded 1905. Pop 99,880
Jul 1999-Jun 2000 Income (Main Library and Branch Library) $2,188,322, State $373,662, County $1,777,094, Other $37,566. Mats Exp $600,973, Books $534,934, Per/Ser (Incl. Access Fees) $19,848, Micro $5,286, Electronic Ref Mat (Incl. Access Fees) $40,905. Sal $1,039,113 (Prof $527,733)
Library Holdings: Bk Vols 347,940; Bk Titles 161,780; Per Subs 875
Subject Interests: Genealogy, Local history
Partic in Georgia Online Database; South Georgia Associated Libraries
Branches: 5
P ALBANY LIBRARY FOR THE BLIND & PHYSICALLY HANDICAPPED, 300 Pine Ave, 31701-2533. SAN 338-2443. Tel: 229-420-3220. FAX: 229-430-4020. *Librn*, Katy Sinquefield
TALLULAH MASSEY BRANCH, 2004 Stratford Dr, 31705. SAN 338-2532. Tel: 229-420-3250. *Mgr*, Helen Pettiford
Library Holdings: Bk Vols 40,660
NORTHWEST, 2215 Barnesdale Way, 31707-2403. SAN 322-7189. Tel: 229-420-3270. FAX: 229-420-3200. *Dir*, M P Dugan; Tel: 229-420-3200, E-Mail: mdugan@gcpl.net; *Mgr*, Gary Barton
Library Holdings: Bk Vols 57,099
SOUTHSIDE, 2114 Habersham Rd, 31701. SAN 370-1085. Tel: 229-420-3260. *Mgr*, Tricia Henson
Library Holdings: Bk Vols 33,085
WESTTOWN, 2124 Waddell Ave, 31707. SAN 371-2982. Tel: 229-420-3280. *Mgr*, Mary Neal
Library Holdings: Bk Vols 25,805
Friends of the Library Group

UNITED STATES NAVY
A MARINE CORPS LOGISTICS BASE LIBRARY, Bldg 7450, 814 Radford Blvd, 31704-1128. SAN 338-2591. Tel: 912-639-5242. FAX: 912-639-5197. *Librn*, Amos Tookes
Library Holdings: Bk Titles 25,384; Per Subs 39

AMERICUS

C GEORGIA SOUTHWESTERN STATE UNIVERSITY, James Earl Carter Library, 800 Wheatley St, 31709. SAN 303-2582. Tel: 229-931-2259. FAX: 229-931-2265. E-Mail: vjw@canes.gsw.peachnet.edu. Web Site: www.gsw.edu/~library/index.html. *Dir*, Vera J Weisskopf; Tel: 229-931-2260, E-Mail: vjw@canes.gsw.edu; *Ref*, C Diane Bradley; Tel: 229-931-2262, E-Mail: cbradley@canes.gsw.edu; *Coll Develop*, Thedis Washington; Tel: 229-931-2789, E-Mail: thedis@canes.gsw.edu; *Cat*, Lee Ann Dalzell; Tel: 229-931-2258, E-Mail: lad@canes.gsw.edu; Staff 6 (MLS 5, Non-MLS 1)
Founded 1928. Enrl 2,600; Fac 125; Highest Degree: Master
Library Holdings: Bk Vols 138,390; Per Subs 788
Subject Interests: Education
Special Collections: Third World Studies Coll
Automation Activity & Vendor Info: (Acquisitions) Endeavor; (Cataloging) Endeavor; (Circulation) Endeavor; (Course Reserve) Endeavor; (ILL) Endeavor; (OPAC) Endeavor
Partic in Galileo; GALILEO-Ga Libr Learning Online; Solinet; South Georgia Associated Libraries

P LAKE BLACKSHEAR REGIONAL LIBRARY, 307 E Lamar St, 31709-3699. SAN 338-2621. Tel: 229-924-8091. FAX: 229-928-4445. *Dir*, Jane B Hendrix; *Mgr*, Jean Deriso; Staff 7 (MLS 5, Non-MLS 2)
Founded 1878. Pop 66,309; Circ 258,000
Library Holdings: Per Subs 425
Special Collections: Andersonville Prison, pictures, bks; Carter Coll, multi-media; Genealogy, bks, microfiche, microfilm; Georgia History, pictures, bks
Publications: Index to the Roster of Confederate Soldiers
Partic in SE Libr Network; South Georgia Associated Libraries
Friends of the Library Group

Branches: 5
BYROMVILLE PUBLIC, Byromville, 31007. SAN 338-2656. Tel: 478-433-2002. *Mgr*, Mary Anna Ingram
CORDELE - CRISP CARNEGIE, 115 E 11th Ave, Cordele, 31015. SAN 338-2680. Tel: 229-276-1300. FAX: 229-276-1300. *Branch Mgr*, Debbie Brogdon
Friends of the Library Group
DOOLY COUNTY PUBLIC, 1200 E Union St, Vienna, 31092. SAN 338-2710. Tel: 229-268-4687. FAX: 229-268-4687. *Mgr*, Marcine Crozier
ELIZABETH HARRIS LIBRARY, PO Box 39, Unadilla, 31091. SAN 326-8411. Tel: 478-627-9303. FAX: 478-627-9303. *Branch Mgr*, Deidre Hibberd
SCHLEY COUNTY PUBLIC, PO Box 365, Ellaville, 31806. SAN 338-2745. Tel: 229-937-2004. *Branch Mgr*, Sara W Tondee; E-Mail: stondee@gpal.net
Bookmobiles: 1

M SUMTER REGIONAL HOSPITAL, Frederick H Thompson MD, Medical Library, 100 Wheatley Dr, 31709. SAN 373-4242. Tel: 912-931-1196. FAX: 912-931-1246.
Library Holdings: Bk Vols 200; Per Subs 58
Subject Interests: Medicine, Neurology, Orthopedics, Urology

ATHENS

SR ATHENS FIRST UNITED METHODIST CHURCH LIBRARY, 327 N Lumpkin St, 30601. SAN 303-2604. Tel: 706-543-1442. FAX: 706-546-4797. *Dir*, Sidney Kuhlman
Library Holdings: Bk Vols 2,166; Bk Titles 2,244
Special Collections: UMW Holdings

P ATHENS REGIONAL LIBRARY SYSTEM, (Formerly Athens Clarke County Library), 2025 Baxter St, 30606-6331. SAN 338-277X. Tel: 706-613-3650. FAX: 706-613-3660. Web Site: www.clarke.public.lib.ga.us. *Dir*, Kathryn S Ames; E-Mail: kames@gcpl.net; *Assoc Dir*, Julie Walker; E-Mail: jwalker@mail.clarke.public.lib.ga.us; *Asst Dir, Materials Manager*, Judy Atwood; *Asst Dir, Ref*, Clare Auwarter; *Asst Dir*, Gail Firestone; *Admin Assoc*, Pam Blake; Tel: 706-613-3650, Ext 331, E-Mail: blakep@mail.clarke.public.lib.ga.us; *Ch Servs*, Jacqueline Elsner; *YA Servs*, Mary Jean Hartell; *Tech Servs*, Holly Bowden; *Circ*, Maryanne Driver. Subject Specialists: *Youth programs*, Gail Firestone; Staff 14 (MLS 14)
Founded 1936. Pop 92,178; Circ 542,732
Library Holdings: Bk Vols 181,454; Per Subs 243
Subject Interests: Local history, State hist
Special Collections: County Library; Genealogy & Georgia, Ivy Coll in Oconee; Genealogy, Daughters of American Revolution
Automation Activity & Vendor Info: (Acquisitions) epixtech, inc.; (Cataloging) epixtech, inc.; (Circulation) epixtech, inc.; (ILL) epixtech, inc.
Database Vendor: Ebsco - EbscoHost, epixtech, inc., OCLC - First Search, ProQuest
Partic in Georgia Libr Info Network; OCLC Online Computer Library Center, Inc
Special Services for the Deaf - Books on deafness & sign language; High interest/low vocabulary books
Friends of the Library Group
Branches: 8
BOGART BRANCH, 200 S Burson, Box 218, Bogart, 30622. SAN 338-280X. Tel: 770-725-9443. FAX: 770-725-9443. Web Site: www.clarke.public.lib.ga.us. *Branch Mgr*, Debbie Thrasher
Pop 6,701; Circ 25,348
Library Holdings: Bk Titles 12,260; Per Subs 21
Automation Activity & Vendor Info: (Circulation) epixtech, inc.
Friends of the Library Group
LAVONIA-CARNEGIE BRANCH, 28 Hartwell Rd, PO Box 237, Lavonia, 30553. SAN 338-2869. Tel: 706-356-4307. FAX: 706-356-4307. Web Site: www.clarke.public.lib.ga.us. *Mgr*, Emma LeCroy; Staff 1 (Non-MLS 1)
Pop 9,105; Circ 18,310
Library Holdings: Bk Vols 13,049; Per Subs 27
Automation Activity & Vendor Info: (Circulation) epixtech, inc.
Friends of the Library Group
MADISON COUNTY, 1315 Hwy 98 W, PO Box 38, Danielsville, 30633. SAN 338-2893. Tel: 706-795-5597. FAX: 706-795-0830. E-Mail: madcolib@yahoo.com. Web Site: www.clarke.public.lib.ga.us. *Mgr*, Marsha Carlan; Staff 2 (MLS 2)
Pop 25,460; Circ 47,392
Jul 1999-Jun 2000 Income $141,510, County $131,400, Locally Generated Income $10,110. Mats Exp $13,763. Sal $98,727
Library Holdings: Bk Vols 30,653; Per Subs 75
Automation Activity & Vendor Info: (Circulation) epixtech, inc.
Friends of the Library Group
OCONEE COUNTY, 1080 Experiment Station Rd, Box 837, Watkinsville, 30677. SAN 338-2923. Tel: 706-769-3950. FAX: 706-769-3952. Web Site: www.clarke.public.lib.ga.us. *Branch Mgr*, Debbie Thrasher; Staff 2 (MLS 1, Non-MLS 1)
Pop 23,518; Circ 103,727
Library Holdings: Bk Vols 41,229; Per Subs 48
Special Collections: Ivy Coll (Genealogy & Georgiana)
Automation Activity & Vendor Info: (Circulation) epixtech, inc.
Friends of the Library Group
OGLETHORPE COUNTY, 858 Athens Rd, Box 100, Lexington, 30648. SAN 338-2958. Tel: 706-743-8817. FAX: 706-743-8817. Web Site: www.clarke.public.lib.ga.us. *Mgr*, Jan Burroughs
Pop 11,813; Circ 34,531
Jul 1999-Jun 2000 Income $63,878, City $500, County $53,745, Locally Generated Income $7,833, Other $1,800. Mats Exp $6,385. Sal $41,710
Library Holdings: Bk Vols 22,621; Per Subs 41
Automation Activity & Vendor Info: (Circulation) epixtech, inc.
Friends of the Library Group
ROYSTON BRANCH, 684 Franklin Springs St, Royston, 30662. SAN 338-2982. Tel: 706-245-6748. FAX: 706-245-6748. Web Site: www.clarke.public.lib.ga.us. *Mgr*, Rosie Chitwood; Staff 1 (Non-MLS 1)
Pop 9,105; Circ 27,386
Library Holdings: Bk Vols 16,593; Per Subs 21
Automation Activity & Vendor Info: (Circulation) epixtech, inc.
Friends of the Library Group
TALKING BOOK CENTER, 2025 Baxter St, 30606. SAN 338-2788. Tel: 706-613-3655. Toll Free Tel: 800-531-2063. FAX: 706-613-3660. Web Site: www.clarke.public.lib.ga.us. *Mgr*, Paige Burns; Staff 2 (Non-MLS 2)
Founded 1975. Circ 42,632
Special Collections: Reference Collection on Accessibility, Handicapping Conditions, Aids & Appliances for Handicapped, regular print bks
Automation Activity & Vendor Info: (Circulation) epixtech, inc.
Publications: Flash (newsletter); Insight Newsletter (quarterly)
WINTERVILLE BRANCH, 115 Marigold Lane, PO Box 89, Winterville, 30683. SAN 338-3016. Tel: 706-742-7735. FAX: 706-742-7735. E-Mail: littlelibrary@hotmail.com. *Mgr*, Suzanne DeGrasse; Staff 2 (Non-MLS 2)
Pop 2,178; Circ 7,519
Library Holdings: Bk Vols 9,422; Per Subs 11
Subject Interests: Local history, State hist
Automation Activity & Vendor Info: (Circulation) epixtech, inc.
Special Services for the Blind - Talking Books
Friends of the Library Group
Bookmobiles: 1

J ATHENS TECHNICAL COLLEGE LIBRARY, (Formerly Athens Area Technical Institute Library), 700 US Hwy 29 N, 30601-1500. SAN 323-5513. Tel: 706-355-5020. FAX: 706-355-5162. E-Mail: alibrary@admin1.athens.tec.ga.us. Web Site: www.athens.tec.ga.us/homepage/index800.html. *Dir Libr Serv*, Metta L Nicewarner; Tel: 706-355-5019, E-Mail: metta@admin1.athens.tec.ga.us; *Librn*, Qian (Jan) Fang; Tel: 706-355-5164, E-Mail: qianfang@admin1.athens.tec.ga.us; *Asst Librn*, Maria Bruce; E-Mail: marbruce@admin1.athens.tec.ga.us; Staff 4 (MLS 2, Non-MLS 2)
Founded 1984. Enrl 2,700; Fac 110; Highest Degree: Associate
Jul 1999-Jun 2000 Income Parent Institution $404,679. Mats Exp $185,330, Books $58,734, Per/Ser (Incl. Access Fees) $42,239, Electronic Ref Mat (Incl. Access Fees) $19,814. Sal $219,349 (Prof $147,581)
Library Holdings: Bk Vols 49,117; Bk Titles 28,575; Per Subs 453
Special Collections: Allied Health; Technical Education
Automation Activity & Vendor Info: (Acquisitions) SIRSI; (Cataloging) SIRSI; (Circulation) SIRSI; (OPAC) SIRSI; (Serials) SIRSI
Database Vendor: Ebsco - EbscoHost, Lexis-Nexis, OCLC - First Search, ProQuest, Wilson - Wilson Web
Function: Research library
Partic in Ga Libr Learning Online; Georgia Online Database; SE Libr Network
Departmental Libraries:
ELBERT COUNTY CAMPUS, 1317 Athens Hwy, Elberton, 30635. SAN 377-7863. Tel: 706-213-2116. FAX: 706-213-2149. E-Mail: elibrary@admin1.athens.tec.ga.us. Web Site: www.athens.tec.ga.us/homepage/index800.html. *Librn*, Carol Stanley; E-Mail: stanley@admin1.athens.tec.ga.us; Staff 1 (MLS 1)
Founded 1997
Function: Reference services available

G ENVIRONMENTAL PROTECTION AGENCY, Ecosystems Research Division - Athens Library, 960 College Station Rd, 30605-2700. SAN 303-2590. Tel: 706-355-8011. FAX: 706-355-8007. *Librn*, Janice Sims; E-Mail: sims.janice@etamail.epa.gov
Founded 1966
Library Holdings: Bk Vols 5,000; Per Subs 80
Subject Interests: Biology, Chemistry, Engineering, Microbiology, Spectroscopy
Partic in Fedlink; OCLC Online Computer Library Center, Inc

S STATE BOTANICAL GARDEN OF GEORGIA LIBRARY, 2450 S Milledge Ave, 30605. SAN 375-7080. Tel: 706-542-3977. FAX: 706-542-3091. *Dir Libr Serv*, R Lee Meinersmann; Staff 3 (MLS 1, Non-MLS 2)
Founded 1990
Library Holdings: Bk Titles 2,000; Per Subs 24
Subject Interests: Horticulture
Special Collections: Archives: History of the Garden
Restriction: Staff use only

UNITED STATES NAVY

A NAVY SUPPLY CORPS SCHOOL STATION LIBRARY, 1425 Prince Ave, Code 0333, 30606-2205. SAN 338-3040. Tel: 706-354-7183. FAX: 706-354-7318. *Librn*, Steve Toepper
Library Holdings: Bk Vols 14,000; Per Subs 50
Friends of the Library Group

CL UNIVERSITY OF GEORGIA, Alexander Campbell King Law Library, Herty Dr, 30602-6018. (Mail add: Law Library Annex, Rm A203, 30602-6018), SAN 338-3105. Tel: 706-542-1922. Reference Tel: 706-542-6581. FAX: 706-542-5001. Web Site: www.lawsch.uga.edu/lawlib. *Dir*, Elizabeth Ann Puckett; Tel: 706-542-8480, E-Mail: apuckett@arches.uga.edu; *Publ Servs*, Sally Curtis Askew; Tel: 706-542-5077, E-Mail: scaskew@arches.uga.edu; *Info Specialist*, Carol Watson; Tel: 706-542-7365, E-Mail: cwatson@arches.uga.edu; *Ref*, Anne Burnett; Tel: 706-542-5082, E-Mail: aburnett@arches.uga.edu; *Ref*, Jim Sherwood; Tel: 706-542-5083, E-Mail: jshrwood@arches.uga.edu; *Cat*, Diana Duderwicz; Tel: 706-542-5597, E-Mail: dduder@arches.uga.edu; *Cat*, Carol Ramsey; Tel: 706-542-5082, E-Mail: caramse@arches.uga.edu; *Coll Develop*, Maureen Cahill; Tel: 706-542-3825, E-Mail: mcahill@arches.uga.edu; *Coll Develop*, Jose R Pages; *Acq, Ser*, Wendy Moore; Tel: 706-542-5081, E-Mail: wemoore@arches.uga.edu; *Librn*, Francis X Norton, Jr; Tel: 706-583-0630, E-Mail: fnorton@arches.uga.edu. Subject Specialists: *Computing*, Carol Watson; *Disability*, Elizabeth Ann Puckett; *Foreign law*, Anne Burnett; *International law*, Anne Burnett; *Law*, Maureen Cahill; *Law*, Wendy Moore; *Law*, Jim Sherwood; *Law*, Elizabeth Ann Puckett; *Law*, Francis X Norton, Jr; *Law*, Sally Curtis Askew; Staff 25 (MLS 10, Non-MLS 15)
Founded 1860
Jul 1999-Jun 2000 Income $1,733,054. Mats Exp $941,037, Books $57,730, Per/Ser (Incl. Access Fees) $637,340, Presv $17,982, Micro $30,988, Electronic Ref Mat (Incl. Access Fees) $84,089. Sal $787,853 (Prof $513,208)
Library Holdings: Bk Vols 363,816; Bk Titles 123,835; Per Subs 7,097
Subject Interests: International law, State codes
Special Collections: The Louis B Sohn Library on International Studies
Automation Activity & Vendor Info: (Serials) Innovative Interfaces Inc.
Database Vendor: IAC - Info Trac, IAC - SearchBank, Innovative Interfaces INN - View, Lexis-Nexis, OCLC - First Search, OVID Technologies
Function: Research library
Partic in Galileo; Lexis, Solinet, Westlaw; OCLC Online Computer Library Center, Inc

C UNIVERSITY OF GEORGIA, H B Owens Resource Center, School of Environmental Design, 609 Caldwell Hall, 30602. SAN 377-6220. Tel: 706-542-8292. FAX: 706-542-4485. E-Mail: rds@arches.uga.edu. Web Site: www.sed.uga.edu/owens/hbowens.htm. *Librn*, Rene D Shoemaker
Aug 1998-Jul 1999 Income $6,000
Library Holdings: Bk Vols 5,000
Subject Interests: Historic preservation, Landscape architecture, Planning

C UNIVERSITY OF GEORGIA LIBRARIES, UGA, 30602-1641. SAN 338-3075. Tel: 706-542-0621. Interlibrary Loan Service Tel: 706-542-3274. Circulation Tel: 706-542-3256. Reference Tel: 706-542-8460. FAX: 706-542-4144. Web Site: www.libs.uga.edu. *Librn*, Mary Ellen Brooks; *Librn*, William Gray Potter; E-Mail: wpotter@arches.uga.edu; *Assoc Librn, Publ Servs*, Merryll Penson; *Assoc Librn*, Barbara Winters; *Asst Librn*, William Clayton; *Cat*, Ann Hope; *Doc*, Susan Field; *Online Servs*, John Campbell; *Bibliog Instr*, Anne Hurst; *Acq*, Caroline Killens; *Circ*, Claire Colombo; *ILL*, Susan Morris; *Adminr*, Margaret S Hale; E-Mail: mshale@arches.uga.edu; Staff 87 (MLS 87)
Founded 1800. Enrl 29,404; Fac 1,803; Highest Degree: Doctorate
Jul 1998-Jun 1999 Income $17,333,876. Mats Exp $8,390,844, Books $2,298,244, Per/Ser (Incl. Access Fees) $5,726,213, Micro $366,387. Sal $8,559,725
Library Holdings: Per Subs 45,258
Subject Interests: Ecology, International relations, Law, Mathematics, Medicine, Photography
Special Collections: 19th & 20th Century Politics (Richard B Russell Coll), papers; Confederate Imprints Coll; Georgia Authors (Erskine Caldwell, Margaret Mitchell, Marsh & Lillian Smith Colls), papers; Georgia Newspaper Coll; Georgiana (De Renne Coll); Music (Olin Downes & Guido Adler Colls), papers; Rare Book Coll; Records Management Department & University Archives; Selective Can; Theater (Charles Coburn Papers, Paris Music Hall Drawings)
Database Vendor: Ebsco - EbscoHost, Lexis-Nexis, OCLC - First Search, ProQuest, Silverplatter Information Inc., Wilson - Wilson Web
Function: Research library
Mem of Asn of Research Libraries
Partic in Aerospace Res Info Network; BRS; Center For Research Libraries; Dialog Corporation; SDC Info Servs; SE Libr Network; University Center In Georgia, Inc

ATLANTA

L ALSTON & BIRD, Law Library, One Atlantic Ctr, 1201 W Peachtree St, 30309-3424. SAN 303-2620. Tel: 404-881-7120. FAX: 404-881-7777. *Librn*, Frances Pughsley; Staff 8 (MLS 5, Non-MLS 3)
Founded 1893
Subject Interests: Antitrust law, Banks and banking, Finance, Labor, Securities
Publications: Monthly Newsletter; Pocket Part
Restriction: Private library
Partic in Dialog Corporation; Dow Jones News Retrieval; Dun & Bradstreet Info Servs; Newsnet; Vutext; Westlaw

S ARGOSY EDUCATION GROUP, Georgia School of Professional Psychology Library, Bldg 1, Ste 740, 990 Hammond Dr, 30328. SAN 378-1984. Tel: 770-671-1200, Ext 260. FAX: 770-671-0418. *Librn*, David McCullough; E-Mail: dmccullough@gspp.edu; Staff 1 (MLS 1)
Founded 1990. Enrl 400; Fac 20; Highest Degree: Doctorate
Sep 2000-Aug 2001 Income $142,000, Locally Generated Income $4,045, Parent Institution $137,955. Mats Exp $47,400, Books $12,000, Per/Ser (Incl. Access Fees) $25,000, AV Equip $400, Electronic Ref Mat (Incl. Access Fees) $10,000. Sal $40,692
Library Holdings: Bk Titles 2,000; Per Subs 80
Subject Interests: Clinical psychol, Counseling psychology
Automation Activity & Vendor Info: (Circulation) Sagebrush Corporation; (OPAC) Sagebrush Corporation
Database Vendor: Ebsco - EbscoHost, Silverplatter Information Inc.
Restriction: Non-circulating to the public
Function: ILL available, Literary searches, Photocopies available, Reference services available, Some telephone reference
Partic in AHSLG; Georgia Health Sciences Library Association; Georgia Online Database; SE Libr Network

L ARNALL, GOLDEN & GREGORY LLP, Law Library, 1201 W Peachtree St Ste 2800, 30309-3450. SAN 303-2639. Tel: 404-873-8500. FAX: 404-873-8501. *Librn*, Harriet Day; *Asst Librn*, Sybil Turner; Staff 4 (MLS 2, Non-MLS 2)
Library Holdings: Bk Vols 25,000
Restriction: Private library

L ARTHUR ANDERSEN BUSINESS RESEARCH CENTER, 133 Peachtree St NE, Ste 2500, 30303. SAN 372-140X. Tel: 404-223-7390. FAX: 404-221-8022. *Dir*, Susan Maureen Klopper; E-Mail: susan.m.klopper@us.arthurandersen.com; *Cat*, Jim W Braden, Jr; *Ref*, Elissa Checov; *Ref*, Tanya Moraco
Library Holdings: Bk Vols 8,000; Per Subs 1,600
Subject Interests: Accounting, Corp bus, Tax

S ATLANTA BOTANICAL GARDEN, Sheffield Botanical Library, 1345 Piedmont Ave NE, 30309-9975. SAN 374-5597. Tel: 404-876-5859, Ext 225. FAX: 404-876-7472. Web Site: www.atlantabotanicalgarden.org. *Librn*, Miriam Boland; Staff 2 (MLS 2)
Founded 1985
Library Holdings: Bk Titles 4,000; Per Subs 75

C ATLANTA COLLEGE OF ART LIBRARY, 1280 Peachtree St NE, 30309. SAN 303-2647. Tel: 404-733-5020. E-Mail: acalib@woodruffcenter.org. *Head of Libr*, Moira Steven; Tel: 404-733-5021, E-Mail: moira.steven@woodruffcenter.org; *Asst Librn*, Jozina Cappello; Tel: 404-733-5029, E-Mail: jody.fish@woodruffcenter.org; *Curator*, Kevin Fitzgerald; Tel: 404-733-5024, E-Mail: kevin.fitzgerald@woodruffcenter.org; *Circ*, Abbie Reid; Tel: 404-733-5031; *Circ*, Yolanda Travis; Tel: 404-733-5031; Staff 5 (MLS 2, Non-MLS 3)
Founded 1931. Enrl 400; Fac 48; Highest Degree: Bachelor
Library Holdings: Bk Vols 25,000; Bk Titles 18,100; Per Subs 250
Subject Interests: Art, Art history, Design, Drawing, Film, Liberal arts, Painting, Photography, Printmaking, Sculpture, Video
Special Collections: Artists' Books Coll; Rare Book Coll
Database Vendor: Silverplatter Information Inc.
Partic in Cooperative College Libr Center, Inc; University Center In Georgia, Inc

ATLANTA HISTORY CENTER

S JAMES G KENAN RESEARCH CENTER, 3101 Andrews Dr NW, 30305. (Mail add: 130 W Paces Ferry Rd, 30305), Tel: 404-814-4000. FAX: 404-814-4175. Web Site: www.atlantahistorycenter.com. *Librn*, Jennie Williams
Founded 1926
Library Holdings: Bk Vols 25,000; Per Subs 90
Subject Interests: Genealogy
Special Collections: Cookbooks; Decorative Art Books; Joel Chandler Harris Coll; Revolutionary War in Georgia; Shutze Architecture Coll
Publications: Atlanta History: A Journal of Georgia and the South
Restriction: Non-circulating
Function: Archival collection
Partic in SE Libr Network
Friends of the Library Group

S ATLANTA JOURNAL & CONSTITUTION, News Research Services; Stacks Information Service, 72 Marietta St NW, PO Box 4689, 30303. SAN 303-268X. Tel: 404-526-5420. FAX: 404-526-5840. *Dir*, Virginia Everett; *Dep Dir*, Kathleen Flynn
Founded 1945
Library Holdings: Bk Vols 3,000; Per Subs 72

J ATLANTA METROPOLITAN COLLEGE LIBRARY, 1630 Metropolitan Pkwy, 30310. SAN 303-2663. Tel: 404-756-4010. FAX: 404-756-5613. *Dir*, Wanda L Crenshaw; Staff 5 (MLS 2, Non-MLS 3)
Founded 1974. Enrl 2,000; Highest Degree: Doctorate
Library Holdings: Bk Vols 40,000; Bk Titles 38,500; Per Subs 320
Automation Activity & Vendor Info: (Circulation) DRA
Partic in Georgia Libr Info Network
Friends of the Library Group

G ATLANTA REGIONAL COMMISSION, Information Center, 40 Courtland St NE, 30303. SAN 303-2698. Tel: 404-463-3100. FAX: 404-463-3105. E-Mail: infocenter@atlantaregional.com. Web Site: www.atlreg.com. *Dir*, Phyllis Thigpen; Tel: 404-463-3102
Founded 1947
Library Holdings: Bk Titles 850
Subject Interests: Planning, Transportation
Special Collections: Atlanta Regional Commission Planning Reports

C ATLANTA UNIVERSITY CENTER INC, Robert W Woodruff Library, 111 James P Brawley Dr SW, 30314. SAN 303-2701. Tel: 404-522-8980, Ext 208. FAX: 404-577-5158. Web Site: www.auctr.edu. *Dir*, Ella Yates; *Tech Servs*, Hulda Wilson; *Acq*, Ruth McClure; *Cat*, Buddhwanti Masih; *Circ*, William Holt; *Govt Doc*, Daniel Veach; *Ser*, Argent Sue Gibson; *Ref*, Helen Threatt; *Archivist*, Karen Jefferson; Staff 24 (MLS 24)
Founded 1964. Enrl 12,422; Fac 881; Highest Degree: Doctorate
Library Holdings: Bk Vols 372,265; Per Subs 2,351
Subject Interests: Accounting, Afro-American, Art, Chemistry, Computer science, Criminal law and justice, Economics, English (language), English literature, History, Mass communications, Nursing, Physics, Political science, Religion, Social service (social work), Sociology, Theology, Zoology
Special Collections: Abraham Lincoln Coll, memorabilia; Black History & Literature (Cullen-Jackman, Henry P Slaughter & Hoytt Fuller Collections); Music (Cuney-Hare Coll); Southern Regional Council Archival Collection on Race Relations
Publications: Index to Theses
Partic in Cooperative College Libr Center, Inc; Dialog Corporation; University Center In Georgia, Inc
Library serves the following institutions: Clark Atlanta University, Morehouse, Morris Brown, Spelman Colleges & Interdenominational Theological Center

P ATLANTA-FULTON PUBLIC LIBRARY SYSTEM, One Margaret Mitchell Sq NW, 30303-1089. SAN 338-313X. Tel: 404-730-1700. Interlibrary Loan Service Tel: 404-730-1929. FAX: 404-730-1990. Web Site: af.public.lib.ga.us. *Dir*, Mary Kaye Hooker; Tel: 404-730-1972; *Dep Dir*, Carolyn Garnes; *Adminr*, William Munro; *Branch Mgr*, Anne Haimes; *Branch Mgr*, Valerie Jackson; *Tech Servs*, Ruby Jones; *Tech Servs*, Ted Koppel; *Acq*, Beth Oehlerts; *Planning Services*, Stephanie McIver; *Per*, John Hilinski; Staff 346 (MLS 144, Non-MLS 202)
Founded 1901. Pop 807,096; Circ 2,534,636
Jan 1999-Dec 1999 Income $31,927,995, State $1,123,266, City $794,077, County $29,787,909, Locally Generated Income $222,743. Mats Exp $3,251,397. Sal $19,700,385 (Prof $7,893,875)
Library Holdings: Bk Vols 2,750,000; Bk Titles 600,000; Per Subs 6,000
Special Collections: African American Culture & History; Childrens Literature (High Coll); City of Atlanta; Genealogy Coll; Georgia Coll; Margaret Mitchell Coll
Automation Activity & Vendor Info: (Acquisitions) CARL; (Cataloging) CARL; (Circulation) CARL; (OPAC) CARL; (Serials) CARL
Publications: ACCESS
Partic in Dialog Corporation; Georgia Libr Info Network; OCLC Online Computer Library Center, Inc; SE Libr Network; University Center In Georgia, Inc
Special Services for the Deaf - Books on deafness & sign language; Captioned film depository; High interest/low vocabulary books; Special interest periodicals; TTY machine
Special Services for the Blind - Kurzweil Reading Machine
Friends of the Library Group
Branches: 32
ADAMS PARK, 2231 Campbellton Rd SW, 30311. SAN 338-3164. Tel: 404-752-8763. FAX: 404-752-8765. *Branch Mgr*, Celeste Gibson
ADAMSVILLE-COLLIER HEIGHTS, 3424 Martin Luther King Dr, 30331. SAN 338-3288. Tel: 404-699-4206. FAX: 404-699-6380. *Branch Mgr*, Donnie Dixon
Friends of the Library Group
ALPHARETTA BRANCH, 238 Canton St, Alpharetta, 30004. SAN 338-3199. Tel: 770-740-2425. FAX: 770-740-2427. *Branch Mgr*, Leona Bolch
Friends of the Library Group
AUBURN AVENUE RESEARCH LIBRARY ON AFRICAN-AMERICAN CULTURE & HISTORY, 101 Auburn Ave NE, 30303. SAN 375-1465. Tel: 404-730-4001, Ext 102. Reference Tel: 404-730-4001, Ext 110. FAX: 404-730-5879. *Adminr*, Dr Joseph Jordan
Friends of the Library Group
BANKHEAD COURT, 1415 Maynard Rd NW, 30331. SAN 370-4726. Tel: 404-699-8959. FAX: 404-699-8961. *Branch Mgr*, Stephanie Morgan
BOWEN HOMES, 2880 Yates Dr NW, 30318. SAN 370-4742. Tel: 404-792-4950. FAX: 404-792-4952. *Branch Mgr*, Marie Lee
BUCKHEAD BRANCH, 269 Buckhead Ave NE, 30305. SAN 338-361X. Tel: 404-814-3500. FAX: 404-814-3503. *Librn*, Thomas Budlong
Friends of the Library Group
CAPITOL AREA INFORMATION CENTER, 341 Kelly St, 30312. Tel: 404-730-7386. FAX: 404-730-7389. *Librn*, Erica Burrell
CARVER HOMES BRANCH, 1654 Pryor Rd, 30315. SAN 372-5073. Tel: 404-624-0623. FAX: 404-624-0625. *Librn*, Beverly Hawes-Allen
CLEVELAND AVENUE BRANCH, 47 Cleveland Ave, 30315. SAN 373-9333. Tel: 404-762-4116. FAX: 404-762-4118. *Librn*, Gloria Dennis
COLLEGE PARK BRANCH, 3647 Main St, College Park, 30337. SAN 338-3253. Tel: 404-762-4060. FAX: 404-762-4062. *Branch Mgr*, Bonita McZorn
DOGWOOD BRANCH, 1838 Bankhead Hwy NW, 30318. SAN 338-3342. Tel: 404-792-4961. FAX: 404-792-4963. *Librn*, Debra Perry
Library Holdings: Bk Vols 16,831
DUNBAR, 477 Windsor St SW, Rm 304, 30312. SAN 338-3377. Tel: 404-730-4779. FAX: 404-730-4778. *Branch Mgr*, Linda Jordan
EAST ATLANTA BRANCH, 457 Flat Shoals Ave SE, 30316. SAN 338-3407. Tel: 404-730-5438. FAX: 404-730-5436. *Librn*, Gayle Holloman
Friends of the Library Group
EAST POINT BRANCH, 2757 Main St, East Point, 30344. SAN 376-8546. Tel: 404-762-4842. FAX: 404-762-4844. *Branch Mgr*, Michael Hickman
Friends of the Library Group
FAIRBURN HOBGOOD-PALMER, 60 Valley View Dr, Fairburn, 30213. SAN 338-358X. Tel: 770-306-3138. FAX: 770-306-3140. *Branch Mgr*, Janice Steingruber
GEORGIA-HILL BRANCH, 250 Georgia Ave SE, 30312. SAN 338-3466. Tel: 404-730-5427. FAX: 404-730-5429. *Librn*, Mary Hook
HAPEVILLE BRANCH, 525 King Arnold St, Hapeville, 30354. SAN 338-3520. Tel: 404-762-4065. FAX: 404-762-4067. *Branch Mgr*, Jean Hughes
KIRKWOOD, 11 Kirkwood Rd SE, 30317. SAN 338-3679. Tel: 404-377-6471. FAX: 404-373-5024. *Branch Mgr*, Louise Nails
Friends of the Library Group
MARTIN LUTHER KING JR BRANCH, 461 Edgewood Ave, 30312. SAN 338-3709. Tel: 404-730-5415. FAX: 404-730-5417. *Branch Mgr*, Marquita Washington
NORTHSIDE, 3295 Northside Pkwy NW, 30327. SAN 338-3768. Tel: 404-814-3508. FAX: 404-814-3511. *Branch Mgr*, Emma Stanley
Friends of the Library Group
PEACHTREE BRANCH, 1315 Peachtree St NE, 30309. SAN 329-7438. Tel: 404-885-7830. FAX: 404-855-7833. *Librn*, Linda Martin
Friends of the Library Group
PONCE DE LEON, 980 Ponce de Leon Ave NE, 30306. SAN 338-3555. Tel: 404-885-7820. FAX: 404-885-7822. *Branch Mgr*, Susan Earl
ROSWELL REGIONAL LIBRARY, 115 Norcross St, Roswell, 30075. SAN 338-3857. Tel: 770-640-3075. FAX: 770-640-3077. *Librn*, Louise Conti
Friends of the Library Group
SANDY SPRINGS REGIONAL, 395 Mount Vernon Hwy, 30328. SAN 338-3822. Tel: 404-303-6130. FAX: 404-303-6133. *Branch Mgr*, Dorothy Parker
Library Holdings: Bk Vols 136,867
Friends of the Library Group
SOUTH FULTON REGIONAL, 4055 Flatshoals SW, 30291. SAN 373-9341. Tel: 770-306-3092. FAX: 770-306-3127. *Branch Mgr*, Gladys Dennard
Friends of the Library Group
SOUTHWEST REGIONAL, 3665 Cascade Rd SW, 30331. SAN 370-4777. Tel: 404-699-6363. FAX: 404-699-6381. E-Mail: library@af.public.lib.ga.us. Web Site: www.af.public.lib.ga.us. *Branch Mgr*, Brenda Hunter
STEWART-LAKEWOOD, 2893 Lakewood Ave SW, 30315. SAN 338-3881. Tel: 404-762-4054. FAX: 404-762-4056. *Librn*, Cathy McCoy
THOMASVILLE HEIGHTS, 1700 Thomasville Dr SE, 30315. SAN 370-4785. Tel: 404-624-0620. FAX: 404-624-0622. *Branch Mgr*, Belinda Yellock
WASHINGTON PARK-ANNIE MCPHEETERS BRANCH, 1116 M L King Jr Dr, 30314. SAN 338-3946. Tel: 404-752-8760. FAX: 404-752-8762. *Branch Mgr*, M A Bennett
WEST END BRANCH, 525 Peeples St SW, 30310. SAN 338-3911. Tel: 404-752-8740. FAX: 404-752-8742. *Librn*, Rosie Meadows
Bookmobiles: 2. Librn, Doris Jackson. Bk vols 44561

BELL SOUTH CORPORATION
L LAW LIBRARY, 4300 Southern Bell Ctr, 675 W Peachtree St NE, 30375. SAN 371-1161. Tel: 404-335-0746. FAX: 404-688-3988. *Mgr*, Judith Krone
Library Holdings: Bk Vols 27,000; Per Subs 50
Restriction: Staff use only
L LAW LIBRARY, 1155 Peachtree St, Ste 1800, 30309-3610. SAN 326-9043. Tel: 404-249-2616. FAX: 404-249-2895. *Mgr*, Judith Krone
Library Holdings: Bk Vols 20,000

Subject Interests: Securities
Restriction: Not open to public
Partic in Dialog Corporation; Westlaw

CR BEULAH HEIGHTS BIBLE COLLEGE, Barth Memorial Library, 892 Berne St SE, 30316-1873. (Mail add: PO Box 18145, 30316-0145), SAN 303-2728. Tel: 404-627-2681. Toll Free Tel: 888-777-2422. FAX: 404-627-0702. E-Mail: bk1642@aol.com, pdas@beulah.org. Web Site: www.beulah.org.; Staff 4 (MLS 1, Non-MLS 3)
Founded 1918. Enrl 582; Fac 32; Highest Degree: Bachelor
Jul 2000-Jun 2001 Income $85,000. Mats Exp $9,000, Books $4,000, Per/Ser (Incl. Access Fees) $2,300, AV Equip $1,700, Other Print Mats $1,000. Sal $59,000 (Prof $35,000)
Library Holdings: Bk Vols 32,000; Bk Titles 32,000; Per Subs 300
Subject Interests: Biblical studies, Religion

S BLACK WOMEN IN CHURCH & SOCIETY, Research Resource Center, Interdenominational Theological Ctr, 700 Martin Luther King Jr Dr, 30314. SAN 375-2364. Tel: 404-527-7740. FAX: 404-527-5715. *Asst Librn, Res,* Mary Anne Bellinger; E-Mail: mbellinger@itc.edu
Library Holdings: Bk Vols 1,500; Per Subs 10

S JIMMY CARTER LIBRARY, 441 Freedom Pkwy, 30307-1498. SAN 328-5650. Tel: 404-331-3942. FAX: 404-730-2215. E-Mail: library@carter.nara.gov. Web Site: carterlibrary.galileo.peachnet.edu. *Dir,* Jay Hakes; *Asst Dir,* Martin Elzy; *Archivist,* Robert Bohanan; *Head Librn,* Polly Nodine; *Curator,* Sylvia Naguib
Founded 1986
Library Holdings: Bk Vols 6,419; Per Subs 53
Special Collections: Presidental Papers of Jimmy Carter
Publications: Historical Materials in the Jimmy Carter Library (Atlanta, 1998)
Partic in Fedlink
Friends of the Library Group

CR CARVER BIBLE COLLEGE LIBRARY, 437 Nelson St SW, 30313. SAN 303-2736. Tel: 404-527-4529. FAX: 404-527-4526. *Librn,* Tosha L Bussey; E-Mail: tbussey@hotmail.com; *Asst Librn,* Beverly Williams; Staff 5 (Non-MLS 5)
Founded 1943. Enrl 125; Fac 120; Highest Degree: Bachelor
Library Holdings: Bk Vols 15,812; Bk Titles 14,434; Per Subs 12

G CENTERS FOR DISEASE CONTROL & PREVENTION INFORMATION CENTER, Bldg 1, Rm 4105, MS C-04, 1600 Clifton Rd NE, 30333. SAN 303-2744. Tel: 404-639-3396, Ext 2485. FAX: 404-639-1160. *Head Librn,* Carlo Dean; Tel: 404-639-3396, Ext 3170
Founded 1947
Library Holdings: Bk Titles 14,192; Per Subs 414
Subject Interests: Biochemistry, Microbiology, Public health, Virology
Special Collections: CDC Publications; CDC Thesis Coll; PHS (HHS) Pamphlet Coll
Automation Activity & Vendor Info: (Cataloging) TechLIB; (Serials) TechLIB
Partic in Dialog Corporation
Friends of the Library Group
Branches:
CHAMBLEE INFORMATION CENTER, Bldg 102, Rm 1208, MS F-26, 4770 Buford Hwy, Chamblee, 30341-3724. SAN 324-2749. Tel: 770-488-7066, 770-488-7067. FAX: 770-488-7422. *Mgr,* Carlo Dean
Library Holdings: Bk Titles 3,289; Per Subs 205
Subject Interests: Toxicology
Partic in Dialog Corporation; Fedlink; OCLC Online Computer Library Center, Inc
Friends of the Library Group

S CNN LIBRARY, One CNN Ctr, Box 105573, 30348-5573. SAN 370-8950. Tel: 404-827-1125. FAX: 404-827-5283. *Dir, Online Servs,* Debra Bade; *Archivist, Dir,* Dina Gunderson; *Dir, Res,* Susan Bennett; *Archivist, Mgr,* Krista Kordt; *Archivist, Res, VPres,* Kathy D Christensen; *Librn,* Akua Abotare; *Librn,* William Allen; *Librn,* Claudia Brave; *Librn,* Sally Griffin; *Librn,* Michelle Hall; *Librn,* Jerry Hufford; *Librn,* Priya Kamat; *Librn,* Amy Roberts; *Librn,* Abby Krystel; *Librn,* Sunny McClendon; *Librn,* Hilary Rogers; *Librn,* Caitlin Stark; Staff 59 (MLS 17, Non-MLS 42)
Founded 1980
Library Holdings: Bk Vols 3,000; Per Subs 86
Automation Activity & Vendor Info: (Circulation) Follett
Restriction: Not open to public
Function: Archival collection, For research purposes
CNN transcripts available on the Nexis Service & from FDCH (Federal Documents Clearinghouse); CNN video & licensing services available via FDCH or through CNN Imagesource

COCA-COLA COMPANY
S KO INFORMATION CENTER, Tec 1, One Cola-Cola Plaza NW, 30313. (Mail add: Tec 1, PO Box 1734, 30301-1734), SAN 324-0185. Tel: 404-515-4636. FAX: 404-515-2572. E-Mail: koinfo@na.ko.com. *Mgr,* Peter Pearson; Staff 6 (MLS 4, Non-MLS 2)
Founded 1967
Library Holdings: Bk Titles 15,000; Per Subs 600
Subject Interests: Chemistry, Food sci, Food tech, Packaging
Database Vendor: Dialog, OCLC - First Search
Publications: Information Bulletin (monthly)
Restriction: Open to public for reference only
Function: Research library
Partic in Georgia Libr Info Network; OCLC Online Computer Library Center, Inc; SE Libr Network

L LAW LIBRARY NAT20, One Coca-Cola Plaza NW, PO Drawer 1734, 30301. SAN 338-4004. Tel: 404-676-2096. FAX: 404-515-2244.
Library Holdings: Bk Vols 25,000; Bk Titles 4,500; Per Subs 200
Subject Interests: Foreign law
Partic in Dow Jones News Retrieval; Georgia Libr Info Network; Westlaw

S MARKETING INFORMATION CENTER, One Coca-Cola Plaza, PO Box 1734, 30313. SAN 303-2760. Tel: 404-676-3314.; Staff 2 (MLS 1, Non-MLS 1)
Founded 1968
Library Holdings: Bk Vols 1,400; Per Subs 256
Subject Interests: Advertising, Marketing
Partic in Dialog Corporation; SE Libr Network

S COURT OF APPEALS ELEVENTH CIRCUIT LIBRARY, 56 Forsyth St NW, 30303. SAN 327-8107. Tel: 404-335-6500. FAX: 404-335-6510. Web Site: www.ca11.uscourts.gov/library. *Librn,* Elaine Fenton
Founded 1981
Library Holdings: Bk Vols 50,000; Per Subs 300
Subject Interests: Law
Automation Activity & Vendor Info: (Acquisitions) SIRSI; (Cataloging) SIRSI; (Circulation) SIRSI; (Course Reserve) SIRSI; (ILL) SIRSI; (Media Booking) SIRSI; (OPAC) SIRSI; (Serials) SIRSI
Partic in Fedlink; OCLC Online Computer Library Center, Inc

S COX ENTERPRISES, INC, Cox Research Library, 1400 Lake Hearn, 30319. SAN 303-2779. Tel: 404-843-5000, Ext 5886. *Librn,* James Henderson
Library Holdings: Bk Vols 2,700; Per Subs 100
Subject Interests: Advertising

M CRAWFORD LONG HOSPITAL - EMORY HEALTHCARE, (CML), Medical Library, 550 Peachtree St, 30308-2225. SAN 303-3082. Tel: 404-686-2678. Interlibrary Loan Service Tel: 404-686-1293. Circulation Tel: 404-686-1293. Reference Tel: 404-686-1291. FAX: 404-686-4974. Web Site: www.eushc.org/medlib/. *Dir,* Rosalind Lett; E-Mail: rosalind_lett@emory.org; Staff 3 (MLS 2, Non-MLS 1)
Founded 1942
Library Holdings: Bk Vols 4,811; Per Subs 387; High Interest/Low Vocabulary Bk Vols 300
Subject Interests: Allied health, Consumer health, Hospital administration, Medicine, Nursing, Surgery
Special Collections: Performance Improvement Management
Automation Activity & Vendor Info: (Acquisitions) SIRSI; (Cataloging) SIRSI; (Circulation) SIRSI; (Course Reserve) SIRSI; (OPAC) SIRSI; (Serials) SIRSI
Database Vendor: OVID Technologies
Publications: Annual Report
Partic in Atlantic Health Sci Librs Consortium; Send

EMORY UNIVERSITY LIBRARIES
HEALTH SCIENCES - GRADY BRANCH, Glenn Memorial Bldg, 69 Butler St, 30335. SAN 338-4209. Tel: 404-616-3531. FAX: 404-522-3799.
Library Holdings: Bk Vols 15,636; Per Subs 297

CM HEALTH SCIENCES CENTER LIBRARY, 1462 Clifton Rd NE, 30322. SAN 338-4187. Tel: 404-727-8727. FAX: 404-727-8469. E-Mail: libcb@emory.edu. Web Site: www.emory.edu/whscl/. *Dir,* Carol A Burns; *Assoc Dir,* Sandra Franklin; *Ref,* Carolyn M Brown; *Ref,* Ingrid Hendrix; *Ref,* Mia White; *Acq,* Barbara Ruelle; Staff 17 (MLS 17)
Founded 1923
Sep 1997-Aug 1998 Income $3,240,116, Locally Generated Income $602,821, Parent Institution $2,637,295. Mats Exp $1,096,694, Books $105,415, Per/Ser (Incl. Access Fees) $989,955. Sal $1,545,591 (Prof $846,145)
Special Collections: History of Medicine in Georgia
Publications: Bookends
Partic in Consortium Of Southern Biomedical Libraries (CONBLS); OCLC Online Computer Library Center, Inc

HOKE O'KELLY BRANCH, 100 Hamill St, Oxford, 30054. SAN 378-2220. Tel: 404-784-8380. Web Site: www.oxford.emory.edu/oxford/library/. *Librn,* Kitty McNeill

CR PITTS THEOLOGY LIBRARY, Candler School of Theology, 505 Kilgo Circle, 30322. SAN 338-4063. Tel: 404-727-4166. FAX: 404-727-1219. E-Mail: libmpg@emory.edu. Web Site: sys1.pitts.emory.edu, www.pitts.emory.edu. *Dir,* Matt Patrick Graham; *Publ Servs, Reader Servs,* Douglas Gragg; *Cat,* David Chen; *Cat, Rare Bks,* Daniel J Rettberg; *Archivist,* Joan S Clemens; *Automation Syst Coordr, Ref,* Richard Wright
Founded 1914
Sep 1997-Aug 1998 Income $1,039,588. Mats Exp $453,762, Books $362,863, Per/Ser (Incl. Access Fees) $62,075, Micro $28,824. Sal $539,638 (Prof $305,096)
Library Holdings: Bk Vols 486,802; Per Subs 1,746

Subject Interests: Religion, Theology
Special Collections: Archives & Manuscript Coll; Early Book Coll including pre-1750 Books published outside the United States, pre-1820 United States Imprints & Incunabula; European Theological Dissertations Printed in the 16th-19th Centuries; Richard C Kessler Reformation Coll, including 16th Century volumes by Martin Luther; Thomas Menton Coll; Warrington-Paine-Pratt Hymnology Coll; Wesleyana Coll, bks & pamphlets, including First Edition of the Works of John & Charles Wesley
Publications: A Christian Sermon; Early Reformation Imprints, A Selective Bibliography of Recent Acquisitions Spring 1984; Elisabeth Creutziger, the Magdeburg Enchiridion, 1536, & Reformation Theology; Kessler Collection Comes to Emory; Luther, Bach, & the Early Reformation Chorale; Preserving the Traditions of Faith: A History of the Pitts Theology Library; Richard C Kessler Reformation Collection: An Annotated Bibliograph; The Politics of Manning's Conversion
Partic in RLIN; SE Libr Network

C ROBERT W WOODRUFF LIBRARY, 540 Asbury Circle, 30322-2870. SAN 338-4039. Tel: 404-727-6861. TDD: 404-727-4122. FAX: 404-727-0805. E-Mail: libjig@emory.edu. Web Site: www.emory.edu/libraries/. *Dir*, Dr Joan I Gotwals; *Business*, Ruth Pagell; Tel: 404-727-1112, Fax: 404-727-1012, E-Mail: rpagell@emory.edu; *Adminr*, Dianne Smith; Tel: 404-727-0133, E-Mail: libdms@emory.edu; *ILL*, Margaret Ellingson; Tel: 404-727-6893, Fax: 404-727-0052, E-Mail: libmgw@emory.edu; *Ser*, Lola Halpin; *Cat*, Ann Vidor; *Spec Coll & Archives*, Linda Matthews; Tel: 404-727-0159, Fax: 404-727-0360, E-Mail: librlm@emory.edu; *Circ*, Frances Maloy; *Coll Develop*, Susan Peters; *Planning Services*, Charles Forrest; Tel: 404-727-0137, E-Mail: libcgf@emory.edu; *Tech Servs*, Susan Bailey; Tel: 404-727-1067, Fax: 404-727-6882, E-Mail: libsbb@emory.edu; *Info Res*, Tim Cherubini; Tel: 404-727-9039, Fax: 404-727-0408, E-Mail: tcherub@emory.edu; *Access Serv*, Frances Maloy; Tel: 404-727-0126, Fax: 404-727-1655, E-Mail: libfm@emory.edu; *Syst Coordr*, Martin Halbert; Tel: 404-727-2204, Fax: 404-727-0827, E-Mail: mhalber@emory.edu; *Music*, Joyce Clinkscales; Tel: 404-727-1066, Fax: 404-727-2257, E-Mail: libjm01@emory.edu; Staff 175 (MLS 44, Non-MLS 131)
Founded 1915. Enrl 11,398; Fac 730; Highest Degree: Doctorate
Sep 1998-Aug 1999 Income $17,315,706. Mats Exp $10,056,410, Books $2,353,635, Per/Ser (Incl. Access Fees) $2,263,623, Other Print Mats $1,377,153, Electronic Ref Mat (Incl. Access Fees) $291,045. Sal $5,924,192 (Prof $2,615,485)
Library Holdings: Bk Vols 1,520,921; Per Subs 12,513
Special Collections: 19th Century English Prose Fiction; African-American History & Culture (James Weldon Johnson Coll, Raymond Andrews Family Papers); American & Asian Communism (Theodore Draper & Philip Jaffe Coll), mss, printed mat; Antebellum, Civil War & Post Civil War (Alexander Stephens & Others), mss; British & Irish Literature (W B Yeats, Lady Gregory, Ted Hughes Colls); Confederate Imprints; Early American History (McGregor Coll); Southern Economic History (Charles Herty Papers & Harrold Coll of Business & Family Letters & Records, Georgia 1836-1953), mss; Southern Literary & Journalistic History (Joel Chandler Harris, Henry Grady, Ralph McGill Coll), mss; Wesleyana & Methodist History, mss & printed mat; Yeats & 20th Century Irish Literature
Automation Activity & Vendor Info: (Acquisitions) SIRSI; (Cataloging) SIRSI; (Circulation) SIRSI; (Course Reserve) SIRSI; (OPAC) SIRSI; (Serials) SIRSI
Database Vendor: Dialog, Ebsco - EbscoHost, Lexis-Nexis, OCLC - First Search, OVID Technologies, ProQuest
Publications: Imprint (Newsletter); Imprint; Library Directions; Lucy M Stanton, Artist
Partic in Asn of Research Libraries; Association Of Southeastern Research Libraries (ASERL); Atlanta Regional Consortium for Higher Educ; Center For Research Libraries; Coalition for Networked Info; GALILEO; Georgia Libr Info Network; Nat Digital Libr Fedn; Research Libraries Group, Inc; RLIN; SE Libr Network
Special Services for the Deaf - TDD
The General Libraries at Emory are comprised of the Robert W Woodruff Library, which provides resources primarily for researchers & students of Emory College, the Graduate School of Arts & Sciences, the School of Business Administration, the Marian K Heilbrun Music & Media Library, which provides music library & media collection services, the Asa G Candler Library, which provides collection storage, user space & general classrooms & academic offices, & the Samuel J Guy Chemistry Library. All information applies to the General Libraries only.
Friends of the Library Group

CL EMORY UNIVERSITY SCHOOL OF LAW, (Formerly Emory University Libraries), Hugh F MacMillan Law Library, 1301 Clifton Rd, 30322. SAN 338-4128. Tel: 404-727-6823. Reference Tel: 404-727-6826. FAX: 404-727-2202. Web Site: www.law.emory.edu/LAW/library.html. *Assoc Dean*, Robin K Mills; Tel: 404-727-6983, E-Mail: rmills@law.emory.edu; *Assoc Dir*, Deborah Keene; *Assoc Dir*, Rosalie Sanderson; Tel: 404-727-6720, E-Mail: rsander@law.emory.edu; *Tech Servs*, Cindy Y Wang; Tel: 404-727-6796, E-Mail: libcw@law.emory.edu; *Cat*, Pamela Deemer; Tel: 404-727-0850, E-Mail: libped@law.emory.edu; *Ref*, Erika Beck; Tel: 404-727-0321, E-Mail: ebeck@law.emory.edu; *Ref*, Holliday Osborne; *Automation Syst Coordr*, Terry Gordon; Tel: 404-727-6950, E-Mail: tgordon@law.emory.edu; *Mgr*, Elmer Masters; Tel: 404-727-6994, E-Mail: emasters@law.emory.edu; *Doc*, Amy Flick; Tel: 404-727-6797, E-Mail: aflick@law.emory.edu; *ILL*, William Haines; Tel: 404-727-4322, E-Mail: libwjh@law.emory.edu; Staff 20 (MLS 8, Non-MLS 12)
Founded 1916
Sep 1999-Aug 2000 Income $1,257,099, Parent Institution $1,212,102, Other $44,997. Mats Exp $981,408, Books $107,163, Per/Ser (Incl. Access Fees) $772,247, Presv $11,196, Micro $19,007, Electronic Ref Mat (Incl. Access Fees) $71,795. Sal $1,268,972 (Prof $580,997)
Library Holdings: Bk Vols 274,769; Bk Titles 98,076; Per Subs 5,555
Special Collections: European Union
Automation Activity & Vendor Info: (Acquisitions) SIRSI; (Cataloging) SIRSI; (Circulation) SIRSI; (OPAC) SIRSI
Database Vendor: IAC - Info Trac, Lexis-Nexis, OCLC - First Search
Function: ILL available
Mem of Asn of Research Libraries
Partic in OCLC Online Computer Library Center, Inc

S FEDERAL HOME LOAN BANK OF ATLANTA, Market Information Services, 1475 Peachtree St NE, PO Box 105565, 30348-5565. SAN 323-5971. Tel: 404-888-8000. FAX: 404-888-5618. E-Mail: alublink@fhlbatl.com. *Librn*, Anita Lublink
Library Holdings: Bk Vols 1,000; Per Subs 400
Subject Interests: Housing

S FEDERAL RESERVE BANK OF ATLANTA, Research Library, 104 Marietta St NW, 30303-2713. SAN 303-2841. Tel: 404-521-8867. Interlibrary Loan Service Tel: 404-521-8195. FAX: 404-521-8572. Web Site: www.frbatlanta.org. *In Charge*, Barbara F Frolik; E-Mail: barbara.frolik@att.frb.org; *Res*, Ernie Evangelista; Staff 6 (MLS 3, Non-MLS 3)
Founded 1938
Library Holdings: Bk Titles 8,000; Per Subs 1,500
Subject Interests: Banks and banking, Economics, Finance, Trade
Special Collections: Federal Reserve Bank & Federal Reserve Board Publications; Southeastern Regional Economics
Publications: Monthly accessions list
Restriction: By appointment only
Partic in Dialog Corporation; Dow Jones News Retrieval; Georgia Online Database

G FEDERAL TRADE COMMISSION, Atlanta Regional Office Library, 100 Alabama St SW, 30303. SAN 303-285X. Tel: 404-656-1399. FAX: 404-347-4725. *Dir*, Anthony DiResta
Library Holdings: Bk Vols 3,000
Special Collections: Legal Coll

S FERNBANK SCIENCE CENTER LIBRARY, 156 Heaton Park Dr NE, 30307-1398. SAN 303-2795. Tel: 404-378-4311, Ext 215. FAX: 404-370-1336. *Librn*, Mary Larsen; E-Mail: mary.larsen@fernbank.edu; *Bibliog Instr*, Marilyn Bell; E-Mail: marilyn.bell@fernbank.edu; Staff 3 (MLS 1, Non-MLS 2)
Founded 1967
Library Holdings: Bk Vols 24,193; Bk Titles 14,658; Per Subs 350
Subject Interests: Astronomy, Botany, Environmental studies, Horticulture, Science/technology, Technology
Database Vendor: OCLC - First Search
Partic in Atlanta Health Science Libraries Consortium; Dialog Corporation; Georgia Libr Info Network; SE Libr Network; Wilsonline
Fernbank Science Center is a unit of the DeKalb County School System

G FOOD & DRUG ADMINISTRATION, Southeast Regional Laboratory Library, 60 Eighth St NE, 30309. SAN 372-7149. Tel: 404-347-2131, Ext 5299. FAX: 404-347-4225. *Librn, Tech Servs*, Regina Arts
Founded 1991
Library Holdings: Bk Vols 345; Bk Titles 2,000; Per Subs 70
Special Collections: Laboratory Methods (Laboratory Information Bulletins (LIB)); Safety Sheets (Material Safety Data Sheets (MSOS))
Partic in Dialog Corporation; STN; WWW

S FRY CONSULTANTS INCORPORATED LIBRARY, 2100 Powers Ferry Rd, Ste 125, 30339. SAN 303-8998. Tel: 770-226-8888. FAX: 770-226-8899. E-Mail: mail@fryconsultants.com. Web Site: www.fryconsultants.com. *Dir*, Lyne Smith; *Coll Develop*, Judy Cone
Founded 1942
1998-1999 Mats Exp $25,000, Books $20,000, Per/Ser (Incl. Access Fees) $5,000
Library Holdings: Bk Vols 2,000; Bk Titles 500; Per Subs 50
Subject Interests: Compensation, Corp outplacement, Exec search, Gen mgt, Indust marketing, Mgt consulting, Salary admin, Wage
Special Collections: Fry Client Reports; Management Consulting
Affiliated with MacFarlane Management Services, Inc (marketing research directories & business reference information sources). Agent for BERI (Business Environment Risk Intelligence). Exclusive agent for IMRI (International Market Research Information)

S FULTON COUNTY JAIL LIBRARY, 901 Rice St, 30318. SAN 370-453X. Tel: 404-853-2103. FAX: 404-853-2200.
Jan 1997-Dec 1998 Income $200,000. Mats Exp Books $25,000. Sal $179,000 (Prof $152,000)
Library Holdings: Bk Vols 6,000
Partic in Westlaw

GL FULTON COUNTY LAW LIBRARY, Justice Center Tower, 7th flr, 185 Central Ave, 30303. SAN 303-2868. Tel: 404-730-4544. FAX: 404-730-4565. Web Site: www.fultonlawlibrary.org. *Mgr*, Sandra Howell; *Ref*, Jeannie Ashley
Library Holdings: Bk Vols 19,500; Per Subs 12

CM GEORGIA BAPTIST COLLEGE OF NURSING LIBRARY, 274 Boulevard NE, 30312. SAN 338-4241. Tel: 678-547-6750. FAX: 404-265-1027. E-Mail: gbcn@mercer.edu. Web Site: www.gben.edu. *Dir Libr Serv*, Lynette Ralph; Tel: 404-265-3994, E-Mail: lynette.ralph@gbhcs.org; *Asst Librn*, Arlene Desselles; E-Mail: arlene.desselles@gbhcs.org; *Asst Librn*, Debjani Mukhopadhyay; Staff 4 (MLS 3, Non-MLS 1)
Founded 1960. Enrl 500; Highest Degree: Bachelor
Jan 1999-Dec 1999 Income $229,790. Mats Exp $91,000, Books $68,000, Per/Ser (Incl. Access Fees) $22,000, Presv $1,000. Sal $139,725 (Prof $70,400)
Library Holdings: Bk Vols 12,552; Bk Titles 12,000; Per Subs 190
Subject Interests: Nursing, Women's studies
Special Collections: Nursing (Historical Coll)
Automation Activity & Vendor Info: (Acquisitions) EOS; (Cataloging) EOS; (Circulation) EOS; (OPAC) EOS
Partic in Atlanta Health Science Libraries Consortium; Docline; Ga Health Scis Libr Asn; Ga Pvt Acad Librs Consortium; Georgia Online Database; Nat Libr of Med; SE Libr Network

M GEORGIA BAPTIST MEDICAL CENTER-TENET, Medical Library, 303 Parkway Dr NE, 30312-1212. SAN 338-4217. Tel: 404-265-4603. FAX: 404-265-3559. *Mgr*, Fay E Evatt; E-Mail: fay.evatt@tenethealth.com; Staff 3 (MLS 1, Non-MLS 2)
Founded 1930
Library Holdings: Bk Titles 5,000; Per Subs 322
Special Collections: Archives
Partic in Atlanta Health Science Libraries Consortium; Nat Libr of Med Region 2

G GEORGIA DEPARTMENT OF ARCHIVES & HISTORY, Public Services Division Library, 330 Capitol Ave SE, 30334. SAN 303-2884. Tel: 404-656-2350. FAX: 404-651-8471.; Staff 9 (MLS 9)
Founded 1918
Library Holdings: Bk Vols 20,000; Bk Titles 16,426; Per Subs 193
Special Collections: County & Family Histories Coll; County Government; DAR Coll; Family Charts; Georgia & Eastern United States Genealogy; Georgia & Southeast United States Map Coll; Georgia History; Georgia Newspapers; Georgia Photographs; Micro; Official State Records; Originals; Photostats; Private Papers; Records Micro; Research Information Exchange File; Surname Card File
Publications: Georgia Official & Statistical Register; Newsletter
Partic in RLIN; SE Libr Network
Friends of the Library Group

G GEORGIA DEPARTMENT OF CORRECTIONS, Reference-Resource Center, East Tower, Rm 852, 2 Martin Luther King SE, 30334-4900. SAN 303-2914. Tel: 404-656-4593. FAX: 404-651-8335.; Staff 1 (MLS 1)
Founded 1974
Library Holdings: Bk Vols 4,000; Bk Titles 3,500; Per Subs 47
Subject Interests: Criminal law and justice
Special Collections: Annual Correctional Agencies Reports; Annual Government Reports (Some Georgia State Agencies), doc; Law (Georgia Laws, Annual, & Georgia State Rules & Regulations)
Publications: Reference-Resource Center News
Partic in Criminal Justice Info Exchange

P GEORGIA DEPARTMENT OF TECHNICAL & ADULT EDUCATION, Office of Public Library Services, 1800 Century Pl, Ste 150, 30345-4304. SAN 338-4306. Tel: 404-982-3560. FAX: 404-982-3563. Web Site: www.public.lib.ga.us. *Actg Dir*, Tom Ploeg; Tel: 404-982-3578; *Tech Coordr*, Bill Gray; Tel: 404-982-3579, E-Mail: bgray@dtae.org; *Librn*, Rosemary Dyer; Tel: 404-657-6220, E-Mail: rdyer@dtae.org; *Res*, Susan Roberts; Tel: 404-982-3566, E-Mail: sroberts@dtae.org; *Reader Servs*, Linda Koldenhoven; Tel: 404-756-4619, E-Mail: lkoldenhoven@dtae.org; *Coll Develop*, Robyn Hollar; Tel: 404-982-3533, E-Mail: rhollar@dtae.org; Staff 14 (MLS 14)
Founded 1897
Library Holdings: Bk Vols 27,000; Bk Titles 21,630; Per Subs 142
Subject Interests: Library and information science
Special Collections: Georgia History, bks, clippings
Automation Activity & Vendor Info: (Acquisitions) SIRSI; (Cataloging) SIRSI; (Circulation) SIRSI; (OPAC) SIRSI; (Serials) SIRSI
Publications: Collection Development Statement (irregular); Georgia Public Library Statistics (annual); Georgia Public Library Trustees Handbook; GOLD ILL Procedures Manual: GOLD Serials Manual (monograph, irregularly updated); Periodicals List (irregular)
Partic in Association Of Southeastern Research Libraries (ASERL); Georgia Online Database; OCLC Online Computer Library Center, Inc; SE Libr Network; Soline
Headquarters for Georgia Online Database (GOLD); maintain Reference Exchange (REX) Database & GOLD Job Bank Online.
Branches: 1
LIBRARY FOR THE BLIND & PHYSICALLY HANDICAPPED
See Georgia Regional Library for the Blind & Physically Handicapped

C GEORGIA INSTITUTE OF TECHNOLOGY, Library & Information Center, 30332-0900. SAN 303-2922. Tel: 404-894-4501. Interlibrary Loan Service Tel: 404-894-4511. FAX: 404-894-8190. Web Site: library.gatech.edu. *Dean of Libr*, Richard Meyer; *Acq*, M Williamson; *Circ*, Thomas Fischer; *Syst Coordr*, Grace Agnew; *Librn*, K Brackney; *Doc*, B Walker; *Archivist*, Anne Salter; Staff 110 (MLS 48, Non-MLS 62)
Founded 1901. Enrl 14,000; Fac 1,829; Highest Degree: Doctorate
Jul 1999-Jun 2000 Income (Main Library and Branch Library) $9,593,678
Library Holdings: Bk Vols 2,138,945; Per Subs 17,601
Subject Interests: Architecture, Business and management, Economics, Engineering, Environmental studies, Natural science, Physical science, Science/technology, Technology
Special Collections: Patents Coll, bks, micro; Technical Reports (National Technical Information Services, NASA, DOE), micro
Partic in Association Of Southeastern Research Libraries (ASERL); Solinet
Departmental Libraries:
COLLEGE OF ARCHITECTURE, 225 North Ave NW, 30332-0900. SAN 321-222X. Tel: 404-894-4877.; Staff 4 (MLS 1, Non-MLS 3)
Library Holdings: Per Subs 136
Subject Interests: Architecture, Construction

G STATE DATA & RESEARCH CENTER, 101 Marietta St, Ste 2500, 30303. SAN 325-5514. Tel: 404-463-1100, 404-463-1113. FAX: 404-894-9372. Web Site: www.gadata.org. *Dir, Res*, Robert Giacomini
Subject Interests: Census data, Ga state agency data
Special Collections: Census Computer Tapes

S GEORGIA POWER CO-SOUTHERN CO, Business Information Center-Research Library, 241 Ralph McGill Blvd NE, Bin 10181, 30308. SAN 303-2930. Tel: 404-506-6633. FAX: 404-506-2184. E-Mail: bic@southernco.com. *Librn*, Margo Surovik-Bohnert; Tel: 404-506-2484, E-Mail: msbohner@southern.co; *Librn*, Deirdra N Kumar; Staff 3 (MLS 2, Non-MLS 1)
Founded 1957. Pop 10,000; Circ 10,000
Library Holdings: Bk Vols 8,000; Per Subs 160
Subject Interests: Business and management, Energy
Special Collections: Annual Reports; Company History; Energy Materials
Restriction: Company library
Partic in Dialog Corporation; Dow Jones News Retrieval; Dun & Bradstreet Info Servs; Moody's

P GEORGIA REGIONAL LIBRARY FOR THE BLIND & PHYSICALLY HANDICAPPED, 1150 Murphy Ave SW, 30310-3399. SAN 303-2949. Tel: 404-756-4619. Toll Free Tel: 800-248-6701. FAX: 404-756-4618. E-Mail: lbph@mail.gls.public.lib.ga.us. Web Site: www.lbph.public.lib.ga.us/lbph. *Regional Librarian*, Linda B Stetson; E-Mail: lstetson@state.lib.ga.us; Staff 4 (MLS 1, Non-MLS 3)
Founded 1931. Pop 4,000; Circ 150,000
Library Holdings: Bk Vols 250,000; Bk Titles 49,000
Special Collections: Georgia Coll, tapes
Partic in Atlanta Health Science Libraries Consortium
Special Services for the Blind - Braille; Cassette bks; CCTV's for print disabled; DECTalk/JAWS for synthetic voice output of computer screen contents; Local magazines & books recorded; Photo duplicator for making large print

GL GEORGIA STATE LAW LIBRARY, Division of Georgia Department of Law, 40 Capitol Sq, 30334-1520. SAN 303-2906. Tel: 404-656-3468. FAX: 404-657-7283. *Librn*, Joelle Gresham; Staff 3 (MLS 2, Non-MLS 1)
Founded 1831
Library Holdings: Bk Titles 2,500
Subject Interests: Georgia
Restriction: Non-circulating to the public

GEORGIA STATE UNIVERSITY

CL COLLEGE OF LAW LIBRARY, 140 Decatur St, PO Box 4008, 30302-4008. SAN 324-2684. Tel: 404-651-4143. FAX: 404-651-1112. Web Site: law.gsu.edu/library/. *Librn*, Nancy P Johnson; *Assoc Librn*, Rhea Ballard-Thrower; Staff 18 (MLS 6, Non-MLS 12)
Founded 1982. Enrl 600; Fac 30; Highest Degree: Doctorate
Library Holdings: Bk Titles 44,500; Per Subs 3,500
Automation Activity & Vendor Info: (Acquisitions) PALS
Publications: Book Docket; Information Series; Legal Pursuits
Partic in Dialog Corporation; OCLC Online Computer Library Center, Inc; Westlaw

C WILLIAM RUSSELL PULLEN LIBRARY, 100 Decatur St SE, 30303-3202. SAN 303-2957. Tel: 404-651-2172. Circulation Tel: 404-651-2178. Reference Tel: 404-651-2185. FAX: 404-651-2476. E-Mail: librlp@langate.gsu.edu. Web Site: www.lib.gsu.edu. *Branch Mgr*, Barbara Patersohn; Tel: 678-566-2222, Fax: 678-566-2205, E-Mail: libbsp@

langate.gsu.edu; *Dir*, Charlene S Hurt; E-Mail: churt@gsu.edu; *Assoc Dir*, Roger L Presley; E-Mail: rpresley@gsu.edu; *Assoc Dir*, Phyllis Ruscella; E-Mail: pruscella@gsu.edu; *ILL*, Margie D Patterson; Tel: 404-651-2473, Fax: 404-651-2508, E-Mail: libmdp@langate.gsu.edu; *Head, Acq*, Joan M Stephens; Tel: 404-651-2149, Fax: 404-651-2148, E-Mail: libjms2@langate.gsu.edu; *Head, Cat*, David G Anderson; Tel: 404-463-9967, Fax: 404-651-2148, E-Mail: libdga@langate.gsu.edu; *Head, Info Serv*, Michael McDavid; Tel: 404-463-9932, Fax: 404-651-4315, E-Mail: libmwm@langate.gsu.edu; *Ref*, Bill Kinyon; *Spec Coll & Archives*, Julia M Young; Tel: 404-651-2477, Fax: 404-651-4314, E-Mail: libjmy@langate.gsu.edu; *Circ*, Pamela Cravey; *Online Servs*, Stan Verhoeven; *Bibliog Instr*, Caroline Blumenthal; *Circ*, Viki Timian; Tel: 404-651-4331, E-Mail: libvht@langate.gsu.edu; *Bibliog Instr*, Laura Burtle; Tel: 404-463-9945, Fax: 404-651-4315, E-Mail: liblgb@langate.gsu.edu; *Coll Develop*, Akilah S Nosakhere; Tel: 404-651-3801, Fax: 404-651-2508, E-Mail: libasn@langate.gsu.edu; Staff 130 (MLS 43, Non-MLS 87)
Founded 1931. Enrl 23,618; Fac 864; Highest Degree: Doctorate
Jul 1999-Jun 2000 Income $9,045,441, Parent Institution $8,931,971, Other $113,470. Mats Exp $3,840,945, Books $965,348, Per/Ser (Incl. Access Fees) $2,253,277, Presv $51,884, Micro $89,627, Electronic Ref Mat (Incl. Access Fees) $480,809. Sal $5,597,731 (Prof $1,960,069)
Library Holdings: Bk Vols 1,278,850; Bk Titles 829,626; Per Subs 5,296
Subject Interests: Media, Popular music, Rare
Special Collections: Georgia Government Documentation Project; Georgia Women's Coll; Johnny Mercer Coll; Labor History (Southern Labor Archives)
Automation Activity & Vendor Info: (Acquisitions) Endeavor; (Cataloging) Endeavor; (Circulation) Endeavor; (Course Reserve) Endeavor; (Media Booking) Endeavor; (OPAC) Endeavor; (Serials) Endeavor
Database Vendor: CARL, Dialog, Ebsco - EbscoHost, GaleNet, IAC - Info Trac, Lexis-Nexis, OCLC - First Search, ProQuest, Silverplatter Information Inc.
Function: Research library
Mem of Univ Syst of Ga
Partic in Association Of Southeastern Research Libraries (ASERL); Atlanta Regional Consortium for Higher Educ; GALILEO; OCLC Online Computer Library Center, Inc; SE Libr Network

GL GEORGIA SUPREME COURT LIBRARY, Judicial Bldg, 40 Capitol Sq SW, 5th flr, 30334. SAN 303-2965. Tel: 404-656-3470. FAX: 404-656-2253. *Librn*, Iletha Dobbs
Library Holdings: Bk Vols 5,000; Per Subs 10
Restriction: Not open to public

S GEORGIA-PACIFIC CORP, Law Library, 133 Peachtree St NE, 30303. SAN 328-638X. Tel: 404-652-4829. FAX: 404-584-1461. *Librn*, Marion Groover; E-Mail: mdgroove@gapac.com
Library Holdings: Bk Vols 3,000; Per Subs 150
Partic in Dialog Corporation

R GLENN MEMORIAL UNITED METHODIST CHURCH LIBRARY, 1660 N Decatur Rd NE, 30307-1010. SAN 303-2973. Tel: 404-634-3936. FAX: 404-634-1994. *Chairperson*, Kathy Brockman
Library Holdings: Bk Vols 3,000

S GOETHE INSTITUT, Goethe Institut Atlanta Library, Colony Sq, Plaza Level, 1197 Peachtree St NE, 30361-2401. SAN 324-136X. Tel: 404-892-2226. FAX: 404-892-3832. E-Mail: goetheatllibrary@mindspring.com. Web Site: www.goethe.de/uk/atl/. *Librn*, Rowena Griem
Founded 1977
Library Holdings: Bk Titles 8,500; Per Subs 35
Subject Interests: Geography, German affairs, German art, History, Literature
Special Collections: German Language Material
Friends of the Library Group

S HIGH MUSEUM OF ART LIBRARY, 1280 Peachtree St, 30309. SAN 323-8598. Tel: 404-733-4528. FAX: 404-733-4503. Web Site: www.high.org. *Librn*, Rachel Hodges; Staff 2 (MLS 1, Non-MLS 1)
Founded 1984
Aug 1998-Jul 1999 Income $38,000, Locally Generated Income $15,000, Parent Institution $23,000. Mats Exp $23,000, Books $12,000, Per/Ser (Incl. Access Fees) $3,000, AV Equip $3,000, Other Print Mats $1,000
Library Holdings: Bk Vols 14,000; Bk Titles 12,000; Per Subs 35
Subject Interests: Art, Art history, Decorative arts, Folk art, Photography
Special Collections: Artist Files; Auction Catalogs; Pendley Coll
Restriction: By appointment only
Partic in OCLC Online Computer Library Center, Inc; SE Libr Network

C INSTITUTE OF PAPER SCIENCE & TECHNOLOGY, William R Haselton Library, 500 Tenth St NW, 30318-5794. SAN 317-8781. Tel: 404-894-5728. FAX: 404-894-4778. Web Site: www.ipst.edu/library. *Mgr*, Tyler O Walters; Fax: 404-894-9596, E-Mail: tyler.walters@ipst.edu; *Ref*, Hartley K Phinney, Jr; Staff 10 (MLS 4, Non-MLS 6)
Founded 1930. Enrl 85; Fac 23; Highest Degree: Doctorate
Library Holdings: Bk Vols 80,000; Per Subs 500
Special Collections: Dard Hunter Coll; History of Papermaking; Specifications from the United States, Canada, England, France, Germany & Japan; Technical Articles Translated from Foreign Languages into English
Automation Activity & Vendor Info: (Serials) SIRSI
Publications: Forthcoming Meetings; Library Acquisitions; Paper CLIPP
Partic in OCLC Online Computer Library Center, Inc

L JONES, DAY, REAVIS & POGUE, Law Library, 303 Peachtree St NE, Ste 3500, 30308. SAN 303-299X. Tel: 404-581-8118. FAX: 404-581-8330. *Librn*, Jane Crawford
Library Holdings: Bk Vols 35,000

L KILPATRICK STOCKTON, Law Library, 1100 Peachtree St, Ste 2800, 30309. SAN 303-304X. Tel: 404-815-6261. FAX: 404-815-6555. *Dir*, Robert Stivers; E-Mail: bstivers@kilstock.com; *Ref*, Louise Adams; *Ref*, Kathy Crosslin; *Ref*, Rachel Fisher; *Ref*, Patricia Flynn
Founded 1904
Library Holdings: Bk Vols 45,000
Publications: Recent Acquisitions; Seminar list (monthly)
Partic in Dialog Corporation; Westlaw

L KING & SPALDING, Law Library, 191 Peachtree St, 30303. SAN 303-3058. Tel: 404-572-4600, Ext 3300. FAX: 404-572-5141. E-Mail: lib.helpdesk@kslaw.com. *Dir*, Mary Ann C Fry; *Librn*, Joan Houghton-Theall
Library Holdings: Bk Vols 50,000
Also three satellite branch libraries: Washington, DC, Houston, TX & NY

S KING LIBRARY & ARCHIVES, 449 Auburn Ave, 30312. SAN 303-3066. Tel: 404-526-8983. FAX: 404-526-8969. E-Mail: mlkctr@aol.com. Web Site: www.thekingcenter.org. *Archivist, Dir*, Cynthia Patterson Lewis; Tel: 404-526-8986; Staff 3 (MLS 1, Non-MLS 2)
Founded 1969
Library Holdings: Bk Vols 5,000; Per Subs 25
Subject Interests: Civil rights
Special Collections: Black American History; Civil Rights Movement, 1954-1968, Post 1968; Nonviolence

L KUTAK & ROCK, Law Library, 225 Peachtree St, Ste 2100, 30303. SAN 326-9051. Tel: 404-222-4628. FAX: 404-222-4654.
Library Holdings: Bk Vols 10,000

S LIFE OFFICE MANAGEMENT ASSOCIATION, Information Center, 2300 Windy Ridge Pkwy, Ste 600, 30339. SAN 303-3074. Tel: 770-984-3722. *Librn*, Patricia Toups
Founded 1924
Library Holdings: Bk Vols 1,200; Per Subs 300
Publications: Index to Information

S LONG, ALDRIDGE & NORMAN, Law Library, One Peachtree Ctr, 303 Peachtree St, Ste 5300, 30308. SAN 325-6456. Tel: 404-527-4057. FAX: 404-527-8474. *Librn*, Cindy Adams
Library Holdings: Bk Titles 10,000
Open Mon-Fri 8-5:30

L JOHN MARSHALL LAW SCHOOL, Law Library, 1422 W Peachtree St NW, 30309. SAN 303-3031. Tel: 404-872-3593. FAX: 404-873-3802. Web Site: www.johnmarshall.edu. *Chief Librn*, Michael Lynch; *Tech Servs*, Morteza Parvin; *Coll Develop*, Amanda Farahany
Founded 1935. Enrl 150; Fac 20; Highest Degree: Doctorate
Sep 1996-Aug 1997 Income $750,000. Mats Exp $200,000, Books $65,000, Per/Ser (Incl. Access Fees) $135,000. Sal $200,000 (Prof $120,000)
Library Holdings: Bk Titles 5,000; Per Subs 700

MERCER UNIVERSITY IN ATLANTA

C MONROE F SWILLEY JR, LIBRARY, 3001 Mercer University Dr, 30341-4115. SAN 303-3104. Tel: 678-547-6280. FAX: 678-547-6270. Web Site: swilley.mercer.edu. *Head of Libr*, Judith Davis Brook; E-Mail: brook_jd@mercer.edu; *Publ Servs*, Trudy Kelly; Staff 6 (MLS 6)
Founded 1968. Enrl 1,600; Fac 80; Highest Degree: Doctorate
Jul 1997-Jun 1998 Income $745,000. Mats Exp $90,000, Books $11,000, Per/Ser (Incl. Access Fees) $63,000, Presv $4,500, Micro $11,500. Sal $390,000
Library Holdings: Bk Vols 114,921; Per Subs 900
Subject Interests: Bus, Education, Pharm, Theology
Special Collections: British & American Literature Coll, 18th-19th Century, 1st ed
Automation Activity & Vendor Info: (Circulation) Innovative Interfaces Inc.
Publications: Swilley Information
Partic in Dialog Corporation; Nat Libr of Med; OCLC Online Computer Library Center, Inc; SE Libr Network

CM MOREHOUSE SCHOOL OF MEDICINE, Multi-Media Center, 720 Westview Dr SW, 30310-1495. SAN 320-1457. Tel: 404-752-1530. Circulation Tel: 404-752-1536. Reference Tel: 404-752-1533. FAX: 404-752-1049. Web Site: www.msm.edu. *Dir*, Beverly E Allen; E-Mail: beverly@msm.edu; *Dep Dir*, Cynthia L Henderson; Tel: 404-752-1535, E-Mail: henderc@msm.edu; *Head Tech Servs*, Xiomara Arango; Tel: 404-752-1532, E-Mail: arangox@msm.edu; *Archivist*, Rosa Dickens; Tel: 404-756-1648,

E-Mail: dickensr@msm.edu; *Acq*, Joia Ellis-Dinkins; Tel: 404-756-1528, E-Mail: eldinj@msm.edu; *Head, Info Serv*, Darlene P Kelly; E-Mail: kellydp@msm.edu; *Branch Mgr*, Beth Poisson; Tel: 404-756-1240, E-Mail: poissob@msm.edu; *Syst Coordr*, Joe Swanson, Jr; Tel: 404-756-1542, E-Mail: swanson@msm.edu; Staff 14 (MLS 8, Non-MLS 6)
Founded 1978. Enrl 128
Library Holdings: Bk Vols 65,000; Per Subs 1,638; Per Subs 1,250
Subject Interests: Health sciences
Automation Activity & Vendor Info: (Cataloging) Endeavor; (Circulation) Endeavor; (Course Reserve) Endeavor; (OPAC) Endeavor
Database Vendor: OCLC - First Search, OVID Technologies
Publications: Multi-Media Center Guide, Subj BIBLIOS-AIDS HYPERTENSION
Mem of Coop Libr Agency For Systs & Servs; Nat Network of Librs of Med
Partic in Atlanta Health Science Libraries Consortium; BRS; Consortium Of Southern Biomedical Libraries (CONBLS); Coop Libr Agency for Syst & Servs; Dialog Corporation; OCLC Online Computer Library Center, Inc; SE Libr Network

SR MOUNT PARAN CHURCH OF GOD, Ruth Holt Library, 2055 Mount Paran Rd NW, 30327. SAN 329-8361. Tel: 404-261-0720. FAX: 404-233-6335. *Dir*, Monica Reese
Library Holdings: Bk Vols 40,000; Per Subs 39
Open Sun 9-1, Wed 5-9

M NORTHSIDE HOSPITAL LIBRARY, 1000 Johnson Ferry Rd NE, 30042. SAN 303-3155. Tel: 404-851-6431. FAX: 404-851-6167. *Librn*, Brenda Curry-Wimberrly
Founded 1970
Library Holdings: Bk Vols 1,050; Bk Titles 1,200; Per Subs 210
Subject Interests: Medicine, Nursing, Obstetrics and gynecology
Partic in Atlanta Health Science Libraries Consortium
Friends of the Library Group

S OFFICE ON SMOKING & HEALTH, Technical Information Center, 4770 Buford Hwy, MS K-50, 30341-3724. SAN 325-8750. Tel: 770-488-5705. FAX: 770-488-5939. E-Mail: tobaccoinfo@cdc.gov. Web Site: www.cdc.gov/tobacco. *Mgr*, Paulette Murphy
Library Holdings: Bk Vols 50,000; Per Subs 100
Publications: bibliography; Surgeon General's Report

C OGLETHORPE UNIVERSITY LIBRARY, 4484 Peachtree Rd NE, 30319. SAN 303-3163. Tel: 404-364-8511. FAX: 404-364-8517. Web Site: www.oglethorpe.edu. *Dir*, John A Ryland; E-Mail: jryland@facstaff.oglethorpe.edu; *Cat*, David Stockton; *Ref*, Tricia Clayton; *Ref*, George Stewart; Staff 3 (MLS 3)
Founded 1916. Enrl 850; Fac 48; Highest Degree: Master
Library Holdings: Bk Vols 125,504; Per Subs 745
Special Collections: James E Oglethorpe Coll; Sidney Lanier Coll
Partic in University Center In Georgia, Inc

S PARENTS, FAMILIES & FRIENDS OF LESBIANS & GAYS, PFLAG Library, PO Box 8482, 31106. SAN 375-474X. Tel: 770-662-6475. *Librn*, John Sassany; *Asst Librn*, Sheryl Exley; *Online Servs*, John Meeks
Founded 1992
Library Holdings: Bk Titles 114

L PAUL, HASTINGS, JANOFSKY & WALKER, Law Library, 600 Peachtree St NE, Ste 2400, 30308. SAN 372-1388. Tel: 404-815-2143. FAX: 404-815-2424. *Librn*, Rachel Scultz
Library Holdings: Bk Vols 10,000; Per Subs 40

R PEACHTREE PRESBYTERIAN CHURCH, Pattillo Library, 3434 Roswell Rd NW, 30363. SAN 303-3171. Tel: 404-842-5800, 404-842-5813. FAX: 404-842-5858. Web Site: www.peachtreepresb.org. *In Charge*, Meryl Dilcher
Founded 1960
Library Holdings: Bk Vols 11,400

M PIEDMONT HOSPITAL, Sauls Memorial Library, 1968 Peachtree Rd NW, 30309. SAN 303-318X. Tel: 404-605-3305. FAX: 404-609-6641.; Staff 11 (MLS 5, Non-MLS 6)
Founded 1934
Library Holdings: Bk Titles 6,000; Per Subs 400
Subject Interests: History of medicine, Medicine, Nursing
Special Collections: Piedmont Authors Coll
Automation Activity & Vendor Info: (Cataloging) Sydney; (OPAC) Sydney
Partic in Atlanta Health Science Libraries Consortium; Nat Libr of Med

L POPE & MCGLAMRY, Law Library, 3455 Peachtree Rd NE, Ste 925, 30326-3243. SAN 372-1760. Tel: 404-523-7706. FAX: 404-524-1648. E-Mail: pmkm@mindspring.com. *Librn*, Angie Rosenberg
Library Holdings: Bk Vols 500; Per Subs 100
Partic in OCLC Online Computer Library Center, Inc

S JOHN PORTMAN & ASSOCIATES LIBRARY, 303 Peachtree St NE, Ste 4600, 30308. SAN 303-3198. Tel: 404-614-5555. FAX: 404-614-5553. Web Site: www.portmanusa. *Librn*, Marvin Brewer
Founded 1973
Library Holdings: Bk Titles 2,000; Per Subs 150
Subject Interests: Architecture, Art, Finance, Interior design, Law, Real estate, Structural engineering
Special Collections: Firm's Architectural Drawings from 1953

L POWELL, GOLDSTEIN, FRAZER & MURPHY LIBRARY, Law Library & Information Center, 191 Peachtree St, 16th flr, 30303. SAN 327-8980. Tel: 404-572-6600. FAX: 404-572-6999. E-Mail: library@pgfm.com. Web Site: www.pgfm.com. *Ref*, Grace Holloway; *Tech Servs*, Elizabeth Isabelle
Library Holdings: Bk Vols 20,000

M SAINT JOSEPH'S HOSPITAL OF ATLANTA, Russell Bellman Medical Library, 5665 Peachtree Dunwoody Rd NE, 30342. SAN 303-3201. Tel: 404-851-7039. FAX: 404-851-7869. *Librn*, Paula Christian
Founded 1965
Library Holdings: Bk Titles 2,500; Per Subs 326
Restriction: Medical staff only
Partic in Atlanta Health Science Libraries Consortium; Georgia Libr Info Network; Southeastern Regional Med Libr Program
Friends of the Library Group

L SCHREEDER, WHEELER & FLINT LLP, Law Library, The Candler Bldg, 16th flr, 127 Peachtree St NE, 30303-1845. SAN 372-1426. Tel: 404-681-3450. FAX: 404-681-1046. *Librn*, Nancy Adams Deel; *Librn*, Dionne Lyne
Library Holdings: Bk Vols 10,000; Per Subs 10
Subject Interests: Real estate

L SMITH, CURRIE & HANCOCK, Law Library, 233 Peachtree St NE Ste 2600, 30303-1530. SAN 328-1183. Tel: 404-582-8098. FAX: 404-688-0671. Web Site: www.smithcurrie.com. *Librn*, Jennifer Elrod; E-Mail: jelrod@smithcurrie.com
Library Holdings: Bk Vols 15,000; Per Subs 60
Subject Interests: Environmental law
Open Mon-Fri 8-4:30

L SMITH, GAMBRELL & RUSSELL, Law Library, Prominade II, 1230 Peachtree St NE, Ste 3100, 30309. SAN 303-3228. Tel: 404-815-3538. Interlibrary Loan Service Tel: 404-815-3618. FAX: 404-685-6838, 404-815-3509. *Dir*, Adrienne McElroy-Boone; E-Mail: aboone@sgrlaw.com; Staff 4 (MLS 1, Non-MLS 3)
Founded 1893
Jan 2000-Dec 2000 Mats Exp $500,000. Sal $150,000 (Prof $70,000)
Library Holdings: Bk Vols 45,000; Per Subs 40
Partic in CT Advantage; Dialog Corporation; Dow Jones News Retrieval; Dun & Bradstreet Info Servs; Pacer; Thompson Saegis; Westlaw

C SOUTHERN CENTER FOR STUDIES IN PUBLIC POLICY, Clark Atlanta University, 223 James P Brawley Dr, 30314. SAN 326-9078. Tel: 404-880-8085. FAX: 404-880-8090. E-Mail: scspp@cau.edu. Web Site: www.scspp.org. *Dir*, Dr Robert A Holmes
Founded 1963
Jul 1999-Jun 2000 Income Locally Generated Income $500,000
Library Holdings: Bk Titles 8,800; Per Subs 70

S SOUTHERN ENGINEERING CO, Library Services, 1800 Peachtree St NW, 30309-2518. SAN 370-7105. Tel: 404-352-9200, Ext 2222. FAX: 404-351-1196. E-Mail: library@soeng.com. Web Site: www.soeng.com. *Mgr*, Lisa Austin; Staff 1 (MLS 1)
Library Holdings: Bk Vols 7,000; Per Subs 297
Partic in Dialog Corporation; Dow Jones News Retrieval

S SOUTHERN REGIONAL COUNCIL, INC, Reference Library, 133 Carnegie Way NW, Ste 900, 30303. SAN 329-3785. Tel: 404-522-8764, Ext 47. FAX: 404-522-8791. E-Mail: info@southerncouncil.org. Web Site: www.southerncouncil.org. *Exec Dir*, Wendy S Johnson
Library Holdings: Bk Titles 1,000

S SOUTHERN REGIONAL EDUCATION BOARD LIBRARY, 592 Tenth St NW, 30318-5790. SAN 303-3236. Tel: 404-875-9211. FAX: 404-872-1477. Web Site: www.sreb.org. *Librn*, Jennifer D Burke; Tel: 404-875-9211, Ext 258, E-Mail: jburke@sreb.org; Staff 1 (MLS 1)
Founded 1949
Jul 1999-Jun 2000 Income Parent Institution $57,500. Mats Exp $18,500, Books $5,000, Electronic Ref Mat (Incl. Access Fees) $13,500. Sal $39,000
Library Holdings: Bk Vols 19,000; Per Subs 175
Subject Interests: Educ policy, Health educ, Regional studies
Special Collections: Archive of corporate materials (SREB-published) to 1948
Database Vendor: Ebsco - EbscoHost
Restriction: Staff use only
Partic in Galileo

L TROUTMAN SANDERS, Law Library, 600 Peachtree St NE, Ste 5200, 30308-2216. SAN 326-1719. Tel: 404-885-3775. FAX: 404-885-3952. *Librn*, Linda Dekle; E-Mail: linda.dekle@troutmansanders.com; *Asst Librn*, Tammy Shirley

S US BUREAU OF THE CENSUS, Atlanta Regional Office Library, 101 Marietta St NW, Ste 3200, 30303-2700. SAN 370-2537. Tel: 404-730-3833. FAX: 404-730-3964. *Info Specialist*, Bea Piddock; E-Mail: beatrice.f.piddock@census.gov; *Info Tech*, Mary Beth Vetter

G UNITED STATES ENVIRONMENTAL PROTECTION AGENCY, Region 4 EAD Law Library, 61 Forsyth, 30303-3104. SAN 374-7034. Tel: 404-562-9654. FAX: 404-562-9598.; Staff 2 (MLS 1, Non-MLS 1)
Founded 1992
Library Holdings: Bk Vols 6,000; Bk Titles 600; Per Subs 50
Subject Interests: Environmental law
Special Collections: EPA Guidances
Restriction: Circulates for staff only, Not open to public
Function: For research purposes, Reference services available, Some telephone reference

S USA TEAM HANDBALL, Administrative Office Library, 1903 Powers Ferry Rd, Ste 230, 30339. SAN 375-2127. Tel: 770-956-7660. FAX: 770-956-7976. E-Mail: info@usateamhandball.org. Web Site: www.usateamhandball.org. *Pres*, Robert Djokovich
Library Holdings: Bk Vols 30; Per Subs 50

S UNITED STATES PENITENTIARY LIBRARY, 601 McDonough Blvd SE, 30315. SAN 303-3309. Tel: 404-635-5100. FAX: 404-730-3316. *Librn*, Ron Streeter
Library Holdings: Bk Vols 3,000

G US ENVIRONMENTAL PROTECTION AGENCY, Region 4 Library, Atlanta Federal Center, 61 Forsyth St SW, 30303-3104. SAN 303-2809. Tel: 404-562-8190. FAX: 404-562-8114. E-Mail: r4-library@epa.gov. Web Site: www.epa.gov/region4/library/. *Senior Librn*, kathy Piselli; Tel: 404-562-8122; *ILL*, Joellen O'Neill; *Web Coordr*, Emily Gore; Staff 1 (Non-MLS 1)
Founded 1973
Library Holdings: Bk Titles 27,000; Per Subs 60
Subject Interests: Air pollution, Environmental law, Noise pollution, Water pollution
Special Collections: Docket; EPA Reports; Public Display USGS Reports
Publications: Guide to Library Services
Partic in OCLC Online Computer Library Center, Inc; OLS

AUGUSTA

S AUGUSTA CHRONICLE LIBRARY, News Bldg 725 Broad St, PO Box 1928, 30903. SAN 303-3325. Tel: 706-724-0851, Ext 229, 706-823-3229. FAX: 706-722-7403. Web Site: www.augustachronicle.com. *Chief Librn*, Rhonda Hollimon; *Asst Librn*, Amanda Jones; *Asst Librn*, Rebecca Cox
Founded 1785

C AUGUSTA STATE UNIVERSITY, Reese Library, 2500 Walton Way, 30904-2200. SAN 303-3333. Tel: 706-737-1745. Interlibrary Loan Service Tel: 706-737-1744. FAX: 706-667-4415. Web Site: www.aug.edu/library/. *Dir*, William N Nelson; E-Mail: wnelson@aug.edu; *Assoc Dir, Coll Develop*, Roxann Bustos; *Govt Doc*, Mellie Kerins; *Automation Syst Coordr*, Jeff Heck; *Tech Servs*, Diane Black; *ILL*, Fay Verburg; *Media Spec*, Rose Axton; Staff 29 (MLS 10, Non-MLS 19)
Founded 1957. Enrl 5,317; Fac 225; Highest Degree: Master
Library Holdings: Bk Vols 446,613; Per Subs 1,743
Special Collections: Cumming Family Papers; Edison Marshall Papers; Local History (Richmond County Historical Society)
Automation Activity & Vendor Info: (Cataloging) Endeavor; (Circulation) Endeavor; (Course Reserve) Endeavor; (ILL) Endeavor; (Media Booking) Endeavor; (OPAC) Endeavor; (Serials) Endeavor
Partic in GALILEO-Ga Libr Learning Online; OCLC Online Computer Library Center, Inc; SE Libr Network

S AUGUSTA TECHNICAL INSTITUTE, Jack B Patrick Info Tech Center, 3116 Deans Bridge Rd, 30906. SAN 326-6605. Tel: 706-771-4165. FAX: 706-771-4169. Web Site: www.augusta.tech.ga.us. *Dir*, Dr Robert W Duttweiler; E-Mail: bduttwei@augusta.tec.ga.us; *Librn*, Patricia Brucker; *Media Spec*, Ann Young; Staff 9 (MLS 5, Non-MLS 4)
Fac 100
Library Holdings: Bk Titles 100,000; Per Subs 500
Subject Interests: Electronics
Partic in Dialog Corporation; SE Libr Network

GM DEPARTMENT OF VETERANS AFFAIRS, Medical Center Library, One Freedom Way, 30904-6285. SAN 303-3384. Tel: 706-733-0188, Ext 2820. FAX: 706-823-3920. *Actg Mgr*, Anita Bell; Tel: 706-733-0188, Ext 7514
Founded 1937
Library Holdings: Bk Vols 5,226; Per Subs 321
Subject Interests: Medicine, Nursing, Psychiatry, Psychology, Social service (social work), Surgery
Restriction: Staff use only
Partic in BRS; Coop Libr Agency for Syst & Servs; Medline; Vets Admin Libr Network

P EAST CENTRAL GEORGIA REGIONAL LIBRARY, Augusta-Richmond County Public Library, 902 Greene St, 30901-2294. SAN 338-4519. Tel: 706-821-2600. FAX: 706-724-6762. Web Site: www.ecgrl.home.duesouth.net. *Asst Dir*, LeeAnn Fisher; *ILL*, Linda Beck; *Publ Servs*, Alice Walker; *Media Spec*, Gary Swint; *YA Servs*, Deborah Barron; *Circ*, Dorcas Bess; *Bkmobile Coordr, Br Coordr*, Mary Beachum; *Tech Coordr*, Roberta Wilder; Staff 63 (MLS 16, Non-MLS 47)
Founded 1848. Pop 333,918; Circ 1,046,386
Library Holdings: Bk Vols 482,856; Per Subs 867
Special Collections: Georgia
Member Libraries: The Warren C Gibbs Memorial Library
Friends of the Library Group
Branches: 13
APPLEBY BRANCH, 2260 Walton Way, 30904. SAN 338-4578. Tel: 706-736-6244. FAX: 706-481-0616. Web Site: www.duesouth.net/~ecgrl/. *Librn*, Nancy Morrison
AUDIO VISUAL & TALKING BOOK CENTER, 425 Ninth St, 30901. SAN 338-4543. Tel: 706-821-2625. FAX: 706-724-5403. Web Site: www.duesouth.net/~ecgrl/. *Librn*, Gary Swint; Staff 1 (MLS 1)
Founded 1973
Special Services for the Blind - Brailling & large print projects; Kurzweil Reading Machine
BURKE COUNTY, 412 Fourth St, Waynesboro, 30830. SAN 373-9422. Tel: 706-554-3277. FAX: 706-554-0313. Web Site: www.duesouth.net/~ecgrl/. *Mgr*, Velna Glisson
Friends of the Library Group
EUCHEE CREEK, 5907 Euchee Creek Dr, Grovetown, 30813. SAN 374-8162. Tel: 706-556-0594. FAX: 706-556-2585. Web Site: www.duesouth.net/~ecgrl/. *Librn*, John Welch
FRIEDMAN BRANCH, 1447 Jackson Rd, 30909. SAN 328-7882. Tel: 706-736-6758. FAX: 706-737-2034. Web Site: www.duesouth.net/~ecgrl/. *Librn*, Tina Bennett
GIBBS MEMORIAL, 326 N Belair Rd, Evans, 30809. SAN 373-9406. Tel: 706-863-1946. FAX: 706-868-3351. Web Site: www.duesouth.net/~ecgrl/. *Librn*, Christina Rice
Friends of the Library Group
HARLEM BRANCH, 375 N Louisville Rd, PO Box 129, Harlem, 30814. SAN 373-9414. Tel: 706-556-9795. FAX: 706-556-2576. Web Site: www.duesouth.net/~ecgrl/. *Librn*, Lenore Kueber
Friends of the Library Group
JEFF MAXWELL BRANCH, 1927 Lumpkin Rd, 30906. SAN 338-4608. Tel: 706-793-2020. FAX: 706-790-1025. Web Site: www.duesouth.net/~ecgrl/. *Librn*, Mashell Fashion
LINCOLN COUNTY, PO Box 310, Lincolnton, 30817. SAN 373-9392. Tel: 706-359-4014. FAX: 706-359-1105. Web Site: www.duesouth.net/~ecgrl/. *Librn*, Sherly Dawkins
Friends of the Library Group
MIDVILLE BRANCH, Trout St, PO Box 428, Midville, 30441. SAN 373-9449. Tel: 912-589-7825. FAX: 912-589-7825. Web Site: www.duesouth.net/~ecgrl/. *Librn*, Eugenia Sikes
Friends of the Library Group
SARDIS COUNTY, C H Perry Ave, PO Box 57, Sardis, 30456. SAN 373-9430. Tel: 912-569-4866. FAX: 912-569-9510. Web Site: www.duesouth.net/~ecgrl/. *Librn*, Meredith Chandler
WALLACE BRANCH, 1237 Laney-Walker Blvd, 30901. SAN 338-4632. Tel: 706-722-6275. FAX: 706-724-0715. Web Site: www.duesouth.net/~ecgrl/. *Librn*, Helen Singley
WARREN COUNTY, 101 Warren St, Warrenton, 30828. SAN 303-4348. Tel: 706-465-2656. FAX: 706-465-2656. Web Site: www.duesouth.net/~ecgrl/. *Librn*, Sandra Green
Friends of the Library Group
Bookmobiles: 1

CM MEDICAL COLLEGE OF GEORGIA, Robert B Greenblatt Library, Med Coll of Georgia Bldg AB, 30912-4400. SAN 303-3341. Tel: 706-721-3441. FAX: 706-721-2018. Web Site: www.mcg.edu/library/. *Dir*, Tamera P Lee; E-Mail: tlee@mail.mcg.edu; *Asst Dir*, Lyn Dennison; E-Mail: ldenniso@mail.mcg.edu; *Coll Develop*, Gail Anderson; E-Mail: ganderson@mail.mcg.edu; *ILL*, Mary K Mosner; *ILL*, Lisa Workman; E-Mail: lworkman@mail.mcg.edu; *Rare Bks, Spec Coll*, Donna J Trainor; *Spec Coll*, Susanna Weaver; E-Mail: suweaver@mail.mcg.edu; Staff 36 (MLS 13, Non-MLS 23)
Founded 1828. Enrl 2,394; Fac 866; Highest Degree: Doctorate
Jul 1999-Jun 2000 Income $2,358,937, State $2,250,069, Locally Generated Income $66,000, Other $42,868. Mats Exp $879,977, Books $86,950, Per/Ser (Incl. Access Fees) $688,983, AV Equip $11,600, Electronic Ref Mat (Incl. Access Fees) $92,444. Sal $1,028,565 (Prof $598,030)
Library Holdings: Bk Vols 202,255; Bk Titles 66,024; Per Subs 1,321
Subject Interests: Allied health, Dentistry, Medicine, Nursing
Special Collections: 19th century, landmark & medical artifacts/colls
Publications: library information sheets; newsletter (Bimonthly); newsletter (bi-monthly)
Partic in Consortium Of Southern Biomedical Libraries (CONBLS); National Network Of Libraries Of Medicine - South Central Region; OCLC Online Computer Library Center, Inc; Regents Acad Comt on Librs

C PAINE COLLEGE, Collins Callaway Library, 1235 15th St, 30901-2799. SAN 303-335X. Tel: 706-821-8308. FAX: 706-821-8698. *Dir Libr Serv*, Casandra Norman-Henry; E-Mail: normanc@mail.paine.edu; *Ref*, Tom Donahue; Staff 9 (MLS 3, Non-MLS 6)

Founded 1947. Enrl 582; Highest Degree: Bachelor
Library Holdings: Bk Vols 76,000; Per Subs 315
Special Collections: Black History (Martin Luther King, Jr Coll)
Partic in Dialog Corporation; Georgia Libr Info Network; OCLC Online Computer Library Center, Inc

S RICHMOND COUNTY HISTORICAL SOCIETY LIBRARY, c/o Reese Library, Augusta State University, 2500 Walton Way, 30904-2200. SAN 303-3368. Tel: 706-737-1532. Interlibrary Loan Service Tel: 706-737-1747. Reference Tel: 706-737-1748. FAX: 706-667-4415. *Dir*, Vicki Greene; E-Mail: vgreene@aug.edu; *Acq, Cat*, Diane Black
Founded 1946
Library Holdings: Bk Vols 3,072; Bk Titles 2,091
Subject Interests: Genealogy, Georgia
Publications: An Augusta Scrapbook - Twentieth Century Memories; Augusta: A Pictorial History; Confederate City, Augusta, Georgia; Historical Markers and monuments of Augusta, Richmond County; Journal of Archibald Campbell in His Majesty's Service, 1778; Reminiscences of Augusta Marines; Richmond County History, The Journal of the Society (annual); Summerville: A Pictorial History; The Story of Augusta; Touring Historic Augusta
Open Mon, Tues, Thurs & Fri 9:30-12:30

SR SAINT PAUL'S CHURCH ARCHIVES, 605 Reynolds St, 30901. SAN 375-1732. Tel: 706-724-2485. FAX: 706-724-0904.
Special Collections: Church History 1750 to present

M UNIVERSITY HOSPITAL, Health Sciences Library, 1350 Walton Way, 30901-2629. SAN 303-3376. Tel: 706-774-2944. FAX: 706-774-4370. *In Charge*, Marianne Adams; E-Mail: madams@uh.org; Staff 1 (Non-MLS 1)
Founded 1956
Library Holdings: Bk Titles 2,700; Per Subs 300
Subject Interests: Allied health, Medicine, Nursing
Automation Activity & Vendor Info: (Cataloging) EOS; (OPAC) EOS
Database Vendor: OCLC - First Search, OVID Technologies
Open Mon-Fri 8-5

BAINBRIDGE

J BAINBRIDGE COLLEGE LIBRARY, 2500 E Shotwell St, 31717-0953. SAN 303-3392. Tel: 229-248-2590. FAX: 229-248-2589. E-Mail: library@catfish.bbc.peachnet.edu. Web Site: gil.bbc.peachnet.edu, www.bbc.peachnet.edu. *Dir*, Thomas J Frieling; E-Mail: tfrielin@catfish.bbc.peachnet.edu; *Asst Librn*, Naomi Carter; E-Mail: ncarter@catfish.bbc.peachnet.edu; *Asst Librn*, Martha Mitchell; E-Mail: mmitchel@catfish.bbc.peachnet.edu; Staff 3 (MLS 3)
Founded 1973. Enrl 1,270; Fac 50; Highest Degree: Associate
Jul 1999-Jun 2000 Income $297,398. Mats Exp $88,540, Books $44,930, Per/Ser (Incl. Access Fees) $28,476, Micro $13,076, AV Equip $1,190. Sal $161,679 (Prof $136,930)
Library Holdings: Bk Vols 35,187; Bk Titles 27,305; Per Subs 428
Special Collections: Apollo Lunar Surface EVA Video Coll; Donalson Papers, Maston O'Neal Papers; Papers of former Ga Governor Marvin Griffin
Automation Activity & Vendor Info: (Acquisitions) Endeavor; (Cataloging) Endeavor; (Circulation) Endeavor; (Course Reserve) Endeavor; (OPAC) Endeavor; (Serials) Endeavor
Database Vendor: OCLC - First Search
Partic in Ga Libr Learning Online; Georgia Libr Info Network; Georgia Online Database; SE Libr Network; South Georgia Associated Libraries

P SOUTHWEST GEORGIA REGIONAL LIBRARY, Gilbert H Gragg Library, 301 S Monroe St, 31717. SAN 338-4667. Tel: 912-248-2665. FAX: 912-248-2670. Web Site: www.decatur.public.lib.ga.us. *Dir*, Susan Whittle; E-Mail: s_whittle@decatur.public.lib.ga.us; *Ch Servs, Publ Servs*, Tom Bush; *Ref Servs YA*, Teri Maggio; *Bkmobile Coordr*, Mack Willis; *AV*, Susan Ralph; *ILL*, Carolyn King; *Librn for Blind*, Kathy Hutchins; Staff 15 (MLS 4, Non-MLS 11)
Founded 1902. Pop 51,014; Circ 253,085
Jul 1998-Jun 1999 Income (Main Library and Branch Library) $853,336, State $389,283, County $464,053. Mats Exp $104,198, Books $100,000, Per/Ser (Incl. Access Fees) $3,048, Electronic Ref Mat (Incl. Access Fees) $1,150. Sal $423,386 (Prof $193,870)
Library Holdings: Bk Titles 101,000; Per Subs 153
Subject Interests: Genealogy, Local history
Special Collections: Georgia Author Coll; Jack Wingate Hunters & Anglers Coll
Publications: Talking Book Newsletter
Friends of the Library Group
Branches: 3
BAINBRIDGE SUBREGIONAL LIBRARY FOR THE BLIND & PHYSICALLY HANDICAPPED-TALKING BOOK CENTER, 301 S Monroe St, 31717. Tel: 912-248-2680. Toll Free Tel: 800-795-2680. FAX: 912-248-2670. *Librn*, Kathy Hutchins
Founded 1971
Publications: Talking Book Newsletter
MILLER COUNTY (JAMES W MERRITT MEMORIAL), 259 E Main St, Colquitt, 31737. SAN 338-4721. Tel: 912-758-3131. FAX: 912-758-3131. *Branch Mgr*, Susan Grimsley
1997-1998 Income $48,162. Mats Exp Books $205. Sal $20,363
Friends of the Library Group
SEMINOLE COUNTY, 104 W Fourth St, Donalsonville, 31745. SAN 338-4756. Tel: 912-524-2665. FAX: 912-524-8913. *Branch Mgr*, Judy Smith
1997-1998 Income $95,932. Mats Exp $4,754, Books $4,470, Per/Ser (Incl. Access Fees) $263. Sal $51,354
Subject Interests: Genealogy, Local history
Bookmobiles: 2

BARNESVILLE

J GORDON COLLEGE LIBRARY, 419 College Dr, 30204. SAN 303-3406. Tel: 770-358-5078. FAX: 770-358-5240. Web Site: www.peachnet.edu/inst/gordon.html. *Head Librn*, Nancy D Anderson; E-Mail: nancya@eagle.gdn.peachnet.edu; *Circ*, Beverly Eskridge; *Tech Servs*, Diane Hollingsworth; *Ref*, Beth Pye; Staff 3 (MLS 3)
Founded 1939. Enrl 2,900; Fac 75
Jul 1999-Jun 2000 Income $333,722. Mats Exp $78,088, Books $20,827, Per/Ser (Incl. Access Fees) $15,632, Presv $1,518, Micro $15,526, AV Equip $2,801, Electronic Ref Mat (Incl. Access Fees) $14,268. Sal $191,676 (Prof $125,170)
Library Holdings: Bk Vols 79,668; Bk Titles 72,010; Per Subs 216
Subject Interests: Georgia
Automation Activity & Vendor Info: (Acquisitions) Endeavor; (Cataloging) Endeavor; (Circulation) Endeavor; (Course Reserve) Endeavor; (ILL) Endeavor; (Media Booking) Endeavor; (OPAC) Endeavor; (Serials) Endeavor
Publications: Library Handbook; Subject Guide to AV Materials
Partic in GALILEO; Solinet

BLAIRSVILLE

§J NORTH GEORGIA TECHNICAL INSTITUTE LIBRARY, Blairsville Campus, 434 Meeks Ave, 30512. Tel: 706-781-2333. FAX: 706-781-2307. Web Site: www.clarks.tec.ga.us/library. *Librn*, Linda Johnston

BRUNSWICK

P BRUNSWICK-GLYNN COUNTY REGIONAL LIBRARY, 606 O St, 31520-7007. (Mail add: 208 Gloucester St, 31520-7007), SAN 338-4780. Tel: 912-267-1212. FAX: 912-267-9597. *Dir*, Jim L Darby; E-Mail: darbyj@mail.glynn.public.lib.ga.us; *Ref*, Sara Cody; *Asst Dir, Coll Develop*, Joe Shimnick; *Tech Servs*, Melissa Moore; *Ch Servs*, Kathleen A Powell; *Circ*, Mary McKie; *Ad Servs*, Carolyn Knapp; *Coordr*, Jane Hildebrand; Staff 10 (MLS 10)
Founded 1883. Pop 185,218
Special Collections: Brunswick & Glynn County History, Maps & Photographs; Genealogy, Georgia & Southeast United States; Georgia History
Friends of the Library Group
Branches: 8
BRANTLEY COUNTY, PO Box 1090, Nahunta, 31553-1090. SAN 338-4837. Tel: 912-462-5454. FAX: 912-462-5329. *Mgr*, Kathy Moody
Founded 1980
Subject Interests: Local history
Friends of the Library Group
CAMDEN PUBLIC LIBRARY, 1410 Hwy 40, Kingsland, 31548-9380. SAN 338-487X. Tel: 912-729-2040. FAX: 912-729-2039. *Mgr*, Connie Suffoletto
Friends of the Library Group
CHARLTON COUNTY, 701 N Cross St, Folkston, 31537. SAN 338-4845. Tel: 912-496-2041. FAX: 912-496-1144. *Mgr*, Barbara Parker
Subject Interests: Local history
IDA HILTON LIBRARY, PO Box 1227, Darien, 31305-1227. SAN 329-0077. Tel: 912-437-2124. FAX: 912-437-5113. *Mgr*, Martha Carney
Subject Interests: Genealogy
Special Collections: Fanny Kemble; Gullah; Sapelo Island
Friends of the Library Group
LONG COUNTY, PO Box 640, Ludowici, 31316-0640. SAN 338-490X. Tel: 912-545-2521. FAX: 912-545-9569. *Mgr*, Cindy Hall
Subject Interests: Local history
ST MARYS PUBLIC LIBRARY, 100 Herb Bauer Dr, Saint Marys, 31558-3300. SAN 338-4934. Tel: 912-882-4800. FAX: 912-882-2453. *Mgr*, William Blankenship
TALKING BOOK CENTER Tel: 912-267-1212, Ext 106. FAX: 912-267-9597. *Librn*, Betty Ransom; Staff 1 (MLS 1)
Founded 1977
Special Collections: Blindness & Other Handicaps Reference Material; Georgia History Coll
WAYNE COUNTY, 759 Sunset Blvd, Jesup, 34545-4409. SAN 338-4969. Tel: 912-427-2500. FAX: 912-427-0071. *Mgr*, Edna Williamson
Subject Interests: Gardening, Georgia, Local history
Friends of the Library Group
Bookmobiles: 1

J COASTAL GEORGIA COMMUNITY COLLEGE, Clara Wood Gould Memorial Library, 3700 Altama Ave, 31520-3644. SAN 303-3414. Tel: 912-264-7270. FAX: 912-264-7274. *Dir Libr Serv*, Raymond J Calvert; E-Mail: calverr@bc9000.bc.peachnet.edu; *ILL*, Michelle Peet; *Acq, Cat, Tech Servs*, Jennifer Codding; *Circ*, Carolyn McCarthy; *Ref*, John Kissinger; *Media Spec*, Christine Strickland; *Media Spec*, Calvin Deweese; Staff 5 (MLS 5)
Founded 1961. Fac 54
Library Holdings: Bk Vols 64,991
Special Collections: Coastal Georgia History
Partic in SE Libr Network; South Georgia Associated Libraries

BUFORD

L PHILLIPS STATE PRISON, Law & General Library, 2989 W Rock Quarry Rd, 30519-4198. SAN 371-0971. Tel: 770-932-4500. FAX: 770-932-4544. *Librn*, Beverly Adkins; *Asst Librn*, Shirley Alley; Staff 2 (MLS 1, Non-MLS 1)
Library Holdings: Bk Vols 8,000; Per Subs 45
Special Services for the Deaf - High interest/low vocabulary books

CAIRO

P RODDENBERY MEMORIAL LIBRARY, 320 N Broad St, 31728-2109. SAN 338-4993. Tel: 912-377-3632. FAX: 912-377-7204. E-Mail: librarr0@mail.grady.public.lib.ga.us. Web Site: www.grady.public.lib.ga.us. *Dir*, Alan L Kaye; *Assoc Dir*, Janet R Boudet; *Tech Coordr*, Ana West; *Ch Servs*, Teresa Groves; *Outreach Serv*, Teri Phillips; *Circ*, Cathy David; *Online Servs*, Barbara Causey
Founded 1939. Pop 22,339; Circ 62,334
Jul 1999-Jun 2000 Income $561,500, State $150,000, City $200,000, Federal $8,500, County $190,000, Locally Generated Income $10,000. Mats Exp $63,800, Books $50,000, Per/Ser (Incl. Access Fees) $7,000, Micro $300, AV Equip $500, Electronic Ref Mat (Incl. Access Fees) $6,000. Sal $296,000 (Prof $101,000)
Library Holdings: Bk Vols 54,142; Per Subs 187; Per Subs 200
Subject Interests: Gardening, Local authors
Automation Activity & Vendor Info: (Acquisitions) SIRSI; (Cataloging) SIRSI; (Circulation) SIRSI; (OPAC) SIRSI; (Serials) SIRSI
Database Vendor: GaleNet
Publications: Gleanings from Grady County; Grady County Directory; I Remember Wessie
Partic in Galileo; Georgia Online Database; South Georgia Associated Libraries
Friends of the Library Group

CAMILLA

P DE SOTO TRAIL REGIONAL LIBRARY, 145 E Broad St, 31730-1842. SAN 338-5051. Tel: 229-336-8372. FAX: 229-336-9353. *Dir*, George R Mitchell; Staff 5 (MLS 5)
Pop 52,915; Circ 220,000
Library Holdings: Bk Vols 103,000; Bk Titles 101,000; Per Subs 76
Branches: 6
BACONTON CITY LIBRARY, Railroad St, Baconton, 31716-9998. SAN 338-5086.
MADDOX MEMORIAL LIBRARY, 628 Columbia Rd, Blakely, 31723. SAN 338-5116. Tel: 229-723-3079. *Librn*, Brenda Wall
MARGARET JONES LIBRARY, 205 E Pope St, Sylvester, 31791. SAN 338-523X. Tel: 229-776-2096. FAX: 229-776-0079. *Librn*, Vicki Young
PELHAM CARNEGIE LIBRARY, 133 Hand Ave W, Pelham, 31779. SAN 338-5140. Tel: 229-294-6030. *Librn*, Nancy Wynn
Friends of the Library Group
POULAN CITY LIBRARY, Main St, Poulan, 31780. SAN 338-5175.
WARWICK CITY LIBRARY, Broad St, Warwick, 31796. SAN 338-5205.
Bookmobiles: 2

CANTON

P SEQUOYAH REGIONAL LIBRARY SYSTEM, R T Jones Memorial Library, 116 Brown Industrial Pkwy, 30114-2899. SAN 338-5264. Tel: 770-479-3090, Ext. 21. Circulation Tel: 770-479-3090, Ext 34. Reference Tel: 770-479-3090, Ext 28. FAX: 770-479-3069. Web Site: www.tlc.library.net/sequoyah. *Dir*, Joan H Adam; E-Mail: 73324.265@compuserve.com; *Asst Dir*, Nanette B Kicker; Tel: 770-479-3090, Ext 30, E-Mail: kickern@mail.cherokee.public.lib.ga.us; *Ref*, Mary Ellen Johnson; Tel: 770-479-3090, Ext 32, E-Mail: johnsonm@mail.pickens.public.lib.ga.us; *Ch Servs*, Linda Kilburn; Tel: 770-479-3090, Ext 33, E-Mail: kilburn1@mail.cherokee.public.lib.ga.us; *Tech Servs*, Christy Southard; Tel: 770-479-3090, Ext 25, E-Mail: southac0@mail.cherokee.public.lib.ga.us; Staff 28 (MLS 5, Non-MLS 23)
Founded 1956. Pop 146,347; Circ 904,386
Jul 1999-Jun 2000 Income (Main Library and Branch Library) $2,355,904, State $582,994, City $45,000, County $1,442,861, Locally Generated Income $186,630, Other $118,549. Mats Exp $2,226,498, Books $181,185, Per/Ser (Incl. Access Fees) $15,089, Electronic Ref Mat (Incl. Access Fees) $21,830. Sal $1,211,814 (Prof $210,871)
Library Holdings: Bk Vols 225,751; Per Subs 519
Special Collections: Books on Tape; Career Center; Georgia History; Homeschooling Center; Large Print Books
Database Vendor: Ebsco - EbscoHost, GaleNet, OCLC - First Search, Wilson - Wilson Web
Partic in Georgia Libr Info Network; Georgia Online Database; SE Libr Network
Friends of the Library Group
Branches: 7
BALL GROUND PUBLIC, 435 Old Canton Rd, Ball Ground, 30107. Tel: 770-735-2025. FAX: 770-735-6050. Web Site: www.tlc.library.net/sequoyah. *Mgr*, Peggy Blackwell; E-Mail: blackwep@mail.cherokee.public.lib.ga.us; Staff 7 (Non-MLS 7)
Founded 1997
2000-2001 Income Parent Institution $58,703. Mats Exp Books $28,753. Sal $28,624
Friends of the Library Group
CHEROKEE COUNTY LAW LIBRARY, Cherokee County Justice Ctr, 90 North St Ste 250, 30114. Tel: 770-720-6358. Web Site: www.tlc.library.net/sequoyah. *Mgr*, Mary Crowley; E-Mail: crowleym@mail.cherokee.public.lib.ga.us
Founded 1996
Jan 2000-Dec 2000 Income Parent Institution $58,703. Mats Exp Books $28,753. Sal $28,624
GILMER COUNTY PUBLIC, 103 Dalton St, Ellijay, 30540. SAN 338-5299. Tel: 706-635-4528. FAX: 706-635-3528. Web Site: tlc.library.net/sequoyah. *Librn*, Anita D Summers; E-Mail: summersa@mail.gilmer.public.lib.ga.us; Staff 7 (MLS 1, Non-MLS 6)
Founded 1958
1999-2000 Income $150,356, City $5,500, County $118,284, Locally Generated Income $19,072, Other $7,500. Mats Exp $148,130, Books $9,072. Sal $131,240 (Prof $49,699)
Library Holdings: Bk Vols 23,071
Friends of the Library Group
HICKORY FLAT, 2740 E Cherokee Dr, 30115. SAN 374-4108. Tel: 770-345-7565. FAX: 770-345-7660. Web Site: www.tlc.library.net/sequoyah. *Mgr*, Shirley Clayton; E-Mail: claytons@mail.cherokee.public.lib.ga.us; Staff 7 (Non-MLS 7)
Founded 1993
Library Holdings: Bk Vols 20,469
Friends of the Library Group
PICKENS COUNTY PUBLIC, 100 Library Lane, Jasper, 30143. SAN 338-5329. Tel: 706-692-5411. FAX: 706-692-9518. Web Site: www.tlc.library.net/sequoyah. *Mgr*, Susan White; E-Mail: whites@mail.cherokee.public.lib.ga.us; Staff 7 (MLS 1, Non-MLS 6)
Founded 1958
2000-2001 Income $157,902, City $1,074, County $133,348, Locally Generated Income $21,480, Other $2,000. Mats Exp Books $17,660. Sal $138,891 (Prof $52,727)
Library Holdings: Bk Vols 23,313
Friends of the Library Group
ROSE CREEK, 4476 Towne Lake Pkwy, Woodstock, 30189. SAN 371-3636. Tel: 770-591-1491. FAX: 770-591-1693. Web Site: www.tlc.library.net/sequoyah. *Mgr*, Sally Burton; E-Mail: burtons@mail.cherokee.public.lib.ga.us; Staff 7 (Non-MLS 7)
Founded 1964
Library Holdings: Bk Vols 23,384
Friends of the Library Group
WOODSTOCK PUBLIC, 7745 Main St, Woodstock, 30188. SAN 338-5353. Tel: 770-926-5859. FAX: 770-591-8476. Web Site: www.tlc.library.net/sequoyah. *Mgr*, Pat Bull; E-Mail: bullp@mail.cherokee.public.lib.ga.us; Staff 7 (Non-MLS 7)
Founded 1991
Library Holdings: Bk Vols 30,597
Friends of the Library Group
Bookmobiles: 1

CARROLLTON

R OAK GROVE BAPTIST CHURCH LIBRARY, 2829 Oak Grove Church Rd, 30117. SAN 303-3430. Tel: 770-834-7019. *Dir*, Rudene B Hollingsworth; *Asst Librn*, Zelda Loftin
Founded 1967
Library Holdings: Bk Vols 2,226
Subject Interests: Biblical studies, Religion

S SOUTHWIRE CO, Research & Development Library, PO Box 1000, 30119. SAN 303-3449. Tel: 770-832-4242, Ext 5099. FAX: 770-838-6600. Web Site: southwire.com. *Dir*, Neil Hurwitz
Founded 1953
Library Holdings: Bk Vols 1,500; Per Subs 150

C STATE UNIVERSITY OF WEST GEORGIA, Ingram Library, 1600 Maple St, 30118. SAN 303-3473. Tel: 770-836-6492. Circulation Tel: 770-836-6502. Reference Tel: 770-836-6495. FAX: 770-836-6626. Web Site: www.westga.edu/library. *Dir*, Charles E Beard; E-Mail: cbeard@westga.edu;

Assoc Dir, Mark McManus; E-Mail: mmcmanus@westga.edu; *Acq*, Susan A Smith; Tel: 770-836-6498, E-Mail: ssmith@westga.edu; *Cat*, Sara E Griffies; Tel: 770-830-2365, E-Mail: bgriff@westga.edu; *Spec Coll*, Myron W House; Tel: 770-830-2361, E-Mail: mhouse@westga.edu; *Govt Doc*, Michael Aldrich; Tel: 770-836-2357, E-Mail: maldrich@westga.edu; *Circ*, Carol Goodson; Tel: 770-836-6496, E-Mail: cgoodson@westga.edu; *Automation Syst Coordr*, Chris Huff; Tel: 770-830-2364, E-Mail: chuff@westga.edu; *Instrul Serv, Ref*, Shirley Lankford; Tel: 770-830-3154, E-Mail: slankfor@westga.edu; Staff 28 (MLS 14, Non-MLS 14)
Founded 1933. Enrl 8,670; Fac 323
Jul 1999-Jun 2000 Income Parent Institution $1,911,359. Mats Exp $685,469, Books $178,723, Per/Ser (Incl. Access Fees) $205,888, Presv $8,026, Micro $43,006, AV Equip $7,025, Electronic Ref Mat (Incl. Access Fees) $242,801. Sal $1,062,322 (Prof $699,325)
Library Holdings: Bk Vols 360,696; Bk Titles 292,883; Per Subs 1,352
Subject Interests: Education, Govt docs
Automation Activity & Vendor Info: (Acquisitions) Endeavor; (Cataloging) Endeavor
Publications: Collection Connection
Partic in Cent Ga Associated Librs; N Ga Associated Librs; SE Libr Network

R TABERNACLE BAPTIST CHURCH LIBRARY, 150 Tabernacle Dr, 30117. SAN 303-3457. Tel: 770-832-7063. FAX: 770-834-2777. *Librn*, Juanita Davis
Library Holdings: Bk Vols 8,500

M TANNER MEDICAL CENTER, Medical Library, 705 Dixie St, 30117. SAN 303-3465. Tel: 770-836-9540. FAX: 770-836-9870. *Mgr*, Carol Arrington; E-Mail: carrington@tanner.org
Founded 1972
Library Holdings: Bk Titles 400; Per Subs 50
Subject Interests: Allied health, Medicine, Nursing

P WEST GEORGIA REGIONAL LIBRARY, Neva Lomason Memorial Library, 710 Rome St, 30117. SAN 338-5388. Tel: 770-836-6711. FAX: 770-836-4787. *Dir*, James P Cooper; E-Mail: cooperj@mail.carroll.public.lib.ga.us; *Asst Dir*, Roni L Willis; E-Mail: willisr@mail.carroll.public.lib.ga.us; *Acq*, Carol S Brown; E-Mail: browncs@mail.carroll.public.lib.ga.us; *Coordr*, Kay Scoggins; E-Mail: scoggink@mail.carroll.public.lib.ga.us; *Ref*, Helen Pearson; E-Mail: refdesk@mail.carroll.public.lib.ga.us; *Coordr*, Laurie Eubanks; E-Mail: eubanks@mail.carroll.public.lib.ga.us; *Coordr*, Cary Dunmire; E-Mail: dunmirec@mail.carroll.public.lib.ga.us; Staff 65 (MLS 9, Non-MLS 56)
Founded 1944. Pop 276,441; Circ 794,522
Jul 1998-Jun 1999 Income (Main Library and Branch Library) $2,774,321, State $836,898, City $525,388, County $1,372,579, Locally Generated Income $39,456. Mats Exp $653,799, Books $639,645, Per/Ser (Incl. Access Fees) $12,000, Presv $2,000, Micro $154. Sal $1,745,573 (Prof $414,287)
Library Holdings: Bk Titles 485,949; Per Subs 450
Subject Interests: Decorative arts, Genealogy, Local history
Partic in N Ga Associated Librs; Solinet
Friends of the Library Group
Branches: 10
DOUGLAS COUNTY PUBLIC, 6810 Selman Dr, Douglasville, 30134. SAN 338-5418. Tel: 770-920-7125. FAX: 770-920-3121. *Mgr*, Charlotte Hurt
Friends of the Library Group
HEARD COUNTY PUBLIC, 564 Main St, Franklin, 30217. SAN 338-5477. Tel: 706-675-6501. FAX: 706-675-1065. *Mgr*, Machelle Hill
LITHIA SPRINGS PUBLIC, 7100 Junior High Dr, Lithia Springs, 30122. SAN 338-5507. Tel: 770-944-5931. FAX: 770-944-5932. *Branch Mgr*, Mary Coley
Friends of the Library Group
MAUDE P RAGSDALE PUBLIC, 1815 Hiram-Douglasville Hwy, Hiram, 30141. SAN 375-5134. Tel: 770-943-3964. FAX: 770-943-8720. *Branch Mgr*, Carla Treadaway
NEW GEORGIA PUBLIC, 94 Ridge Rd, Dallas, 30157. SAN 377-7278. Tel: 770-459-8163. FAX: 770-459-9343. *Branch Mgr*, Coleda Phillips
PAULDING COUNTY PUBLIC, 1010 E Memorial Dr, Dallas, 30132. SAN 338-5531. Tel: 770-445-5680. FAX: 770-443-7626. *Mgr*, Dee McChain
TALLAPOOSA PUBLIC, 388 Bowden St, Tallapoosa, 30176. SAN 338-5442. Tel: 770-574-3124. FAX: 770-574-3124. *Mgr*, Karen McWhorter
Friends of the Library Group
VILLA RICA PUBLIC, 70 Horace Luther Dr, Villa Rica, 30180. SAN 338-5566. Tel: 770-459-7012. FAX: 770-459-7960. *Mgr*, Suzanne Watson; E-Mail: watsons@mail.carroll.public.lib.ga.us; *Asst Librn*, Debbi Bailey; *Asst Librn*, Brenda Eidson; *Asst Librn*, Deborah Eidson; Staff 4 (Non-MLS 4)
Founded 1969. Pop 6,500
Apr 1998-Mar 1999 Income (Main Library Only) City $95,000. Mats Exp Books $23,000
Automation Activity & Vendor Info: (Circulation) SIRSI
Friends of the Library Group
WARREN P SEWELL MEMORIAL LIBRARY OF BOWDON, 450 West Ave, Bowdon, 30108. SAN 338-5590. Tel: 770-258-8991. FAX: 770-258-8990. *Mgr*, Barbara Bridwell
WARREN P SEWELL MEMORIAL LIBRARY OF BREMEN, 315 Hamilton Ave, Bremen, 30110. SAN 338-5620. Tel: 770-537-3937. FAX: 770-537-1660.
Bookmobiles: 1

CARTERSVILLE

P BARTOW COUNTY LIBRARY SYSTEM, 429 W Main St, 30120. SAN 324-0800. Tel: 770-382-4203. FAX: 770-386-3056. E-Mail: howingtl@mail.bartow.public.lib.ga.us. Web Site: www.innerx.net/~library/. *Dir*, Lee Howington; *Asst Dir*, Carmen Sims; Staff 2 (MLS 2)
Founded 1981. Pop 69,281; Circ 185,100
Jul 1999-Jun 2000 Income (Main Library and Branch Library) $646,364, State $200,562, City $180,000, County $239,895, Locally Generated Income $28,000. Mats Exp $76,737, Books $71,037, Per/Ser (Incl. Access Fees) $3,000, Presv $1,500, Micro $200, AV Equip $3,500, Other Print Mats $500. Sal $358,433 (Prof $102,812)
Library Holdings: Bk Vols 80,926; Bk Titles 55,935; Per Subs 102
Subject Interests: Local history
Automation Activity & Vendor Info: (Cataloging) SIRSI; (Circulation) SIRSI
Partic in Georgia Online Database; OCLC Online Computer Library Center, Inc
Friends of the Library Group
Branches: 3
ADAIRSVILLE BRANCH, 202 N Main St, Adairsville, 30103. (Mail add: 429 W Main St, 30120), SAN 324-0827. Tel: 770-769-9200. FAX: 770-769-9200. Web Site: www.innerx.net/~library/.
Library Holdings: Bk Vols 15,373
Friends of the Library Group
CARTERSVILLE MAIN STREET, 429 W Main St, 30120. SAN 324-0843. Tel: 770-382-4203. FAX: 770-386-3056. Web Site: www.innerx.net/~library/.
Library Holdings: Bk Vols 55,769
Friends of the Library Group
EMMIE NELSON LIBRARY, 108 Covered Bridge Rd, Rte 1, 30120. (Mail add: 429 W Main St, 30120), SAN 328-7467. Tel: 770-382-2057. FAX: 770-382-2057. Web Site: www.innerx.net/~library/.
Library Holdings: Bk Vols 9,784
Friends of the Library Group

CLARKESVILLE

J NORTH GEORGIA TECHNICAL INSTITUTE LIBRARY, Clarkesville Campus, Hwy 197 N, PO Box 65, 30523. SAN 303-349X. Tel: 706-754-7720. FAX: 706-754-7777. Web Site: www.clarkes.tec.ga.us/library. *Librn*, Dawn V Adams; E-Mail: dadams@clarkes.tec.ga.us; Staff 1 (MLS 1)
Founded 1976. Enrl 1,100; Fac 50
Jul 1997-Jun 1998 Income $172,569. Mats Exp $24,294, Books $18,075, Per/Ser (Incl. Access Fees) $5,308. Sal $106,649 (Prof $89,094)
Library Holdings: Bk Vols 14,000; Per Subs 133
Partic in Georgia Online Database

P NORTHEAST GEORGIA REGIONAL LIBRARY, Clarksville-Habersham County Library, 178 E Green St, PO Box 2020, 30523. SAN 338-5655. Tel: 706-754-0416. FAX: 706-754-0420. *Dir*, Emerson G Murphy; E-Mail: murphye@mail.habersham.public.lib.ga.us; *Asst Dir*, John Skinkle; *Branch Mgr*, Martha Richardson; *Tech Servs*, Lila Porterfield; *AV, Ch Servs*, Sally Vickery; Staff 5 (MLS 5)
Founded 1938. Pop 81,632; Circ 402,930
Library Holdings: Bk Vols 200,000; Per Subs 426
Subject Interests: Genealogy
Partic in N Ga Associated Librs
Friends of the Library Group
Branches: 5
CORNELIA-HABERSHAM COUNTY, 301 N Main, Cornelia, 30531. SAN 338-5744. Tel: 706-778-2635. *Mgr*, Wally Warren
Friends of the Library Group
RABUN COUNTY PUBLIC, 73 Library Circle, PO Box 330, Clayton, 30525. SAN 338-568X. Tel: 706-782-3731. *Mgr*, Jewell Eller
Friends of the Library Group
TOCCOA-STEPHENS COUNTY PUBLIC, 121 W Savannah St, PO Box Drawer L, Toccoa, 30577. SAN 338-5809. Tel: 706-886-6082. *Mgr*, June Mize
WHITE COUNTY LIBRARY-CLEVELAND BRANCH, 60 Bell St, PO Box 657, Cleveland, 30528. SAN 338-571X. Tel: 706-865-5572. *Mgr*, Miriam Hammond
Friends of the Library Group
WHITE COUNTY LIBRARY-HELEN BRANCH, 90 Petes Park Rd, PO Box 1088, Helen, 30545. SAN 338-5779. Tel: 706-878-2438. *Mgr*, Deborah Kelley
Friends of the Library Group
Bookmobiles: 1

CLARKSTON

J GEORGIA PERIMETER COLLEGE, Jim Cherry Learning Resource Center, 555 N Indian Creek Dr, 30021-2396. SAN 324-2560. Tel: 404-294-3890. FAX: 404-298-4919. *Dir*, Eva Lautemann; Tel: 404-294-3475; *Media Spec*, Ed Conway; *Tech Servs*, Kathy Gallo; Staff 21 (MLS 21)
Highest Degree: Associate
Jul 1998-Jun 1999 Income (Main Library and Branch Library) $1,850,138. Mats Exp $335,366, Books $191,527, Per/Ser (Incl. Access Fees) $94,339, Presv $5,000, Micro $44,500. Sal $770,241
Library Holdings: Bk Vols 232,671; Bk Titles 151,775; Per Subs 1,073
Partic in OCLC Online Computer Library Center, Inc; SE Libr Network
Departmental Libraries:
DECATUR CAMPUS LEARNING RESOURCES CENTER, 3251 Panthersville Rd, Decatur, 30034. SAN 338-6554. Tel: 404-244-5026. FAX: 404-244-2996. *Dir*, Julius Whitaker; *Media Spec*, Anthony Bush
Founded 1972
DUNWOODY CAMPUS LEARNING RESOURCE CENTER, 2101 Womack Rd, Dunwoody, 30338-4497. SAN 320-1465. Tel: 770-551-3046. FAX: 770-551-3201. *Librn*, Sylvia George-Williams; *Librn*, Barbara Petersohn; *Librn*, Melora Mirza; *Media Spec*, Greg LaHatte
Founded 1979

CLEVELAND

J TRUETT-MCCONNELL COLLEGE, Cofer Library, 100 Alumni Dr, 30528-9799. SAN 303-3511. Tel: 706-865-2134, Ext 153. Reference Tel: 706-865-2136, Ext 193. FAX: 706-865-5130. Web Site: www.truett.cc.ga.us/library/. *Head Librn*, Janice E Wilson; Tel: 706-865-2136, Ext 173, E-Mail: janice@truett.cc.ga.us; *Asst Librn*, Christa Poparad; E-Mail: cpoparad@truett.cc.ga.us; Staff 10 (MLS 2, Non-MLS 8)
Founded 1946. Enrl 1,800; Fac 65; Highest Degree: Associate
Library Holdings: Bk Vols 50,000; Bk Titles 40,000; Per Subs 450
Special Collections: Religion (George W Truett Coll)
Automation Activity & Vendor Info: (Cataloging) TLC; (Circulation) TLC; (Course Reserve) TLC; (OPAC) TLC
Database Vendor: Lexis-Nexis, OCLC - First Search, ProQuest, Wilson - Wilson Web
Partic in Ga Pvt Acad Librs Consortium

COCHRAN

J MIDDLE GEORGIA COLLEGE, Roberts Memorial Library, 1100 Second St SE, 31014. SAN 303-352X. Tel: 912-934-3074. FAX: 912-934-3378. Web Site: www.mgc.peachnet.edu. *Librn, Tech Servs*, Paul Robards; *Publ Servs, Ref*, Leslie C Rampey
Founded 1928. Enrl 1,400; Fac 75
1998-1999 Income $216,000. Mats Exp $47,000, Books $20,000, Per/Ser (Incl. Access Fees) $25,000, Micro $2,000. Sal $230,000 (Prof $139,000)
Library Holdings: Bk Vols 77,000; Bk Titles 68,000; Per Subs 428
Special Collections: County Histories; Georgianna Genealogy
Publications: Library Handbook
Partic in Cent Ga Associated Librs; OCLC Online Computer Library Center, Inc; SE Libr Network

COLUMBUS

P CHATTAHOOCHEE VALLEY REGIONAL LIBRARY, W C Bradley Memorial Library, Headquarters, 1120 Bradley Dr, 31906-2800. SAN 338-5868. Tel: 706-649-0780. FAX: 706-649-1914. *Dir*, William Kendall; *ILL*, Ann Blalock; *Media Spec*, Matilda Smith; *Cat, Tech Servs*, JoAnn Lessner; *Ch Servs*, Cora Fay; *Ch Servs*, Sarah Daniel; *Coordr*, Donna Osborne; *Ad Servs*, Connie Heller; *Publ Servs*, Jan Carter; Staff 18 (MLS 18)
Founded 1908. Pop 221,046; Circ 650,336
Library Holdings: Bk Vols 483,082; Bk Titles 210,000; Per Subs 1,483
Special Collections: Georgia Genealogical & Historical Coll
Partic in SE Libr Network
Friends of the Library Group
Branches: 9
CHATTAHOOCHEE COUNTY PUBLIC, Broad St, PO Box 539, Cusseta, 31805-0539. SAN 338-5957. Tel: 706-989-3700. FAX: 706-989-3700. *Librn*, Ruby Smith
Library Holdings: Bk Vols 5,000
LUMPKIN PUBLIC, Courthouse Sq, Lumpkin, 31815. (Mail add: PO 727, Lumpkin, 31815), SAN 338-604X. Tel: 912-838-6472. FAX: 706-649-1914. *Librn*, Martha Sue Harnson; *Librn*, Winnie Paterson
Library Holdings: Bk Vols 5,500
MARION COUNTY PUBLIC, 132 Fifth Ave, Buena Vista, 31803-0391. (Mail add: PO Box 12, Buena Vista, 31803-0391), SAN 338-6015. Tel: 229-649-6385. *Librn*, Ina Kazmin
Library Holdings: Bk Vols 7,500
MILDRED L TERRY LIBRARY, 640 Veterans Pkwy, 31901. SAN 338-5981. Tel: 706-649-0787. FAX: 706-649-1260. *Librn*, Sylvia Bunn
Library Holdings: Bk Vols 20,100
NORTH COLUMBUS BRANCH, 5689 Armour Rd, 31909-4513. SAN 373-9325. Tel: 706-649-1151. FAX: 706-649-1154. *Librn*, Dana Brumbelow
PARKS MEMORIAL, 112 Wall St, Richland, 31825-0112. SAN 338-6104. Tel: 229-887-2103. *Librn*, Barbara Overby
Library Holdings: Bk Vols 5,800
QUITMAN COUNTY, Hwy 82, Box 278, Georgetown, 31754-0278. SAN 338-6074. Tel: 229-334-8972. *Librn*, Leroy Gay
Library Holdings: Bk Vols 2,200
SOUTH COLUMBUS BRANCH, 2034 S Lumpkin Rd, 31903-2728. SAN 338-5922. Tel: 706-685-7701. FAX: 706-685-7706. *Branch Mgr*, Suzanne Barnes
Library Holdings: Bk Vols 13,800
12TH STREET, 111 12th St, 31901. SAN 338-6112. Tel: 706-649-0789. FAX: 706-649-1261. *Librn*, Teresa O'Donnell; E-Mail: teresablankenbeker@yahoo.com; Staff 6 (MLS 1, Non-MLS 5)
Founded 1979
Library Holdings: Bk Vols 9,000
Bookmobiles: 2

S COLUMBUS LEDGER-ENQUIRER, Newspaper Library, PO Box 711, 31902-0711. SAN 303-3546. Tel: 706-324-5526. FAX: 706-576-6290. E-Mail: leolib@leo.infi.net. *Librn*, Valerie McNeill
Founded 1945
Library Holdings: Bk Titles 5,000; Per Subs 25

M COLUMBUS REGIONAL, Simon Schwob Medical Library, 710 Center St, PO Box 951, 31902-0951. SAN 303-3562. Tel: 706-571-1178. FAX: 706-571-1779. *Librn*, Cathy Woolbright; E-Mail: woolbright.c@gain.mercer.edu; Staff 2 (MLS 1, Non-MLS 1)
Founded 1949
Library Holdings: Bk Titles 2,810; Per Subs 222
Subject Interests: Cancer, Geriatrics and gerontology, Medicine, Nursing, Pediatrics
Partic in Alabama Health Libraries Association, Inc; Atlantic Health Sci Librs Consortium; Docline; Ga Health Scis Libr Asn; Georgia Libr Info Network; Health Science Libraries Of Central Georgia; Medical Libr Asn; Medline
Satellite library at Phenix Regional Hospital in Phenix City Ala

C COLUMBUS STATE UNIVERSITY, Simon Schwob Memorial Library, 4225 University Ave, 31907-5645. SAN 303-3538. Tel: 706-568-2080. Interlibrary Loan Service Tel: 706-568-2451. FAX: 706-568-2084. Web Site: www.lib.colstate.edu. *Dir*, Callie McGinnis; E-Mail: mcginnis_callie@colstate.edu; *Info Res*, Erma Banks; *Instrul Serv, Media Spec*, Sandra Stratford; *Archivist*, Craig Lloyd; *Syst Coordr*, Diana Lomarcan; *Doc*, John Hoft; *Music*, Roberta Ford; *Cat*, Hunter Eck; Staff 8 (MLS 8)
Founded 1961. Enrl 4,000; Fac 200; Highest Degree: Master
Library Holdings: Bk Vols 258,000; Bk Titles 230,000; Per Subs 700
Special Collections: Chattahoochee Valley Historical Coll; Columbus College Archives; US Representative J Brinkley Coll
Publications: Simon Says (faculty newsletter)
Partic in Dialog Corporation; SE Libr Network; South Georgia Associated Libraries

M HUGHSTON SPORTS MEDICINE FOUNDATION LIBRARY, 6262 Veterans Pkwy, PO Box 9517, 31908-9517. SAN 370-6400. Tel: 706-576-3390. FAX: 706-576-3341. *Librn*, Elaine Powers; E-Mail: epowers@hughston.com; Staff 2 (MLS 1, Non-MLS 1)
Library Holdings: Bk Titles 1,200; Per Subs 37
Publications: New books
Partic in Georgia Health Sciences Library Association; Health Science Libraries Of Central Georgia; Nat Libr of Med

M WEST CENTRAL GEORGIA REGIONAL HOSPITAL LIBRARY, 3000 Schatulga Rd, 31907-1035. SAN 303-3570. Tel: 706-568-5307 706-568-5309. FAX: 706-569-3189. E-Mail: mentalhealth@mindspring.com. *In Charge*, Linda Ames; Staff 1 (Non-MLS 1)
Founded 1975
1997-1998 Income $20,000. Mats Exp $15,000, Books $5,000. Sal $27,000
Library Holdings: Bk Vols 5,800; Per Subs 110
Subject Interests: Alcohol and drugs, Counseling, Nursing, Psychiatry, Psychology, Social service (social work)
Special Collections: Georgia Authors
Publications: brochures; Library Manual; Patient's Basic Guide to Psychotropic Medication; policy statements
Partic in Dept of Human Resource Consortium; Health Science Libraries Of Central Georgia; Medline; SE-Atlantic Regional Med Libr Servs

CONYERS

P CONYERS-ROCKDALE LIBRARY SYSTEM, 864 Green St, 30012. SAN 372-5995. Tel: 770-388-5040. FAX: 770-388-5043. *Librn*, Deborah S Manget; *Asst Dir, Publ Servs*, Lynn Hunter; *Tech Servs*, Harriet Kersey; *Tech Servs*, Joseph Valles; *Circ*, Patricia Stephany; *Ch Servs*, Lori Hatfield; Staff 7 (MLS 3, Non-MLS 4)
Library Holdings: Per Subs 126
Subject Interests: Genealogy
Special Collections: Law, bks
Automation Activity & Vendor Info: (Acquisitions) SIRSI; (Cataloging)

SIRSI; (Circulation) SIRSI
Partic in Georgia Online Database; OCLC Online Computer Library Center, Inc; SE Libr Network
Special Services for the Deaf - Staff with knowledge of sign language; Videos & decoder
Staffed Law Library (separate collection); Adult Literacy Program
Friends of the Library Group

COVINGTON

P NEWTON COUNTY LIBRARY, 7116 Floyd St, 30014. SAN 338-6880. Tel: 770-787-3231. TDD: 770-784-2091. FAX: 770-784-2092. *Dir*, Greg Heid; E-Mail: gheid@mail.newton.public.lib.ga.us; *Asst Libr Dir*, Leslie St John; E-Mail: lstjohn@mail.newton.public.lib.g.us; *Ch Servs*, Carol Durusau; E-Mail: cdurusau@mail.newton.public.lib.ga.us; *ILL*, Carolyn Clodfelter; *ILL*, Bob Halcums; *Ref*, Bob Halcums; E-Mail: bhalcums@mail.newton.public.lib.ga.us; Staff 17 (MLS 4, Non-MLS 13)
Founded 1944. Pop 59,000; Circ 330,000
Jul 2000-Jun 2001 Income $1,104,265, State $206,377, City $6,000, County $857,000, Locally Generated Income $32,250, Other $2,400. Mats Exp $191,000, Books $185,000, Micro $6,000. Sal $32,000
Library Holdings: Bk Vols 90,000; Bk Titles 74,000; Per Subs 260; High Interest/Low Vocabulary Bk Vols 1,600; Spec Interest Per Sub 20
Special Collections: Local History; Porter Foundation Garden Coll
Automation Activity & Vendor Info: (Circulation) SIRSI; (Circulation) Tapestry
Publications: Bookworm Notes: Friends of the Library Newsletter
Function: ILL limited
Partic in Georgia Online Database; SE Libr Network
Special Services for the Blind - Computers with Voice Synthesizer
Friends of the Library Group

CUMMING

§P FORSYTH COUNTY PUBLIC LIBRARY, 585 Dahlonega Rd, 30040-2109. SAN 375-4162. Tel: 770-781-9840. FAX: 770-781-8089. Web Site: www.forsyth.public.lib.ga.us. *Dir*, Jon McDaniels; Tel: 770-781-9840, Ext 362, E-Mail: mcdaniej@mail.forsyth.public.lib.ga.us; *Publ Servs*, Liz Forster; Tel: 770-781-9840, Ext 376, E-Mail: forsterl@mail.forsyth.public.lib.ga.us; *Materials Manager*, Carla Beasley; Tel: 770-781-9840, Ext 350, E-Mail: beasleyc@mail.forsyth.public.lib.ga.us; *Info Tech*, Lewis Lucas; Tel: 770-781-9840, Ext 394, E-Mail: lewisl@mail.forsyth.public.lib.ga.us; *Purchasing*, Patsy Bennett; Tel: 770-781-9840, Ext 357, E-Mail: bennettp@mail.forsyth.public.lib.ga.us; Staff 81 (MLS 14, Non-MLS 67)
Founded 1956. Pop 90,000; Circ 682,000
Jul 2000-Jun 2001 Income $2,756,000, State $211,000, County $2,400,000, Locally Generated Income $145,000. Mats Exp $403,220, Books $275,300, Per/Ser (Incl. Access Fees) $14,920, Micro $1,000, AV Equip $82,000, Electronic Ref Mat (Incl. Access Fees) $30,000
Library Holdings: Bk Vols 180,000; Bk Titles 118,600; Per Subs 400
Automation Activity & Vendor Info: (Cataloging) epixtech, inc.; (Circulation) epixtech, inc.; (OPAC) epixtech, inc.
Database Vendor: Ebsco - EbscoHost, epixtech, inc., GaleNet, OCLC - First Search, Wilson - Wilson Web
Friends of the Library Group

CUTHBERT

J ANDREW COLLEGE, Pitts Library, 413 College St, 31740. SAN 303-3589. Tel: 229-732-5944. FAX: 229-732-5957. *Coll Develop, Dir Libr Serv*, Karan B Pittman; E-Mail: karanpittman@andrewcollege.edu; Staff 3 (MLS 1, Non-MLS 2)
Founded 1854. Enrl 329; Fac 30; Highest Degree: Doctorate
Library Holdings: Bk Vols 33,000; Per Subs 237
Special Collections: Andrew College Archives; Georgia & Genealogy Coll
Automation Activity & Vendor Info: (Acquisitions) Endeavor; (Cataloging) Endeavor; (Circulation) Endeavor; (Course Reserve) Endeavor; (ILL) Endeavor; (OPAC) Endeavor; (Serials) Endeavor
Database Vendor: Ebsco - EbscoHost
Partic in Ga Pvt Acad Libs Consortium; Georgia Online Database; OCLC Online Computer Library Center, Inc; SE Libr Network; South Georgia Associated Libraries

DAHLONEGA

P CHESTATEE REGIONAL LIBRARY SYSTEM, 342 Courthouse Hill, 30533. SAN 377-6859. Tel: 706-864-2590. Reference Tel: 706-864-3668. FAX: 706-864-4481. E-Mail: crls@mail.lumpkin.public.lib.ga.us. Web Site: www.chestatee.public.lib.ga.us. *Dir*, Lyn Hopper; Tel: 706-864-2590, Ext 229, E-Mail: hopperl@mail.lumpkin.public.lib.ga.us; *Assoc Dir*, Claudia Gibson; Tel: 706-864-2590, Ext 230, E-Mail: gibsonc@mail.lumpkin.public.lib.ga.us; *Tech Servs*, Laurie MacLeod Bennett; Tel: 706-864-2590, Ext 231, E-Mail: bennettl@mail.lumpkin.public.lib.ga.us; Staff 17 (MLS 3, Non-MLS 14)
Founded 1953. Pop 32,482
Jul 1999-Jun 2000 Income (Main Library Only) $294,014, State $181,706, Federal $4,418, County $67,293, Locally Generated Income $3,210, Other $37,387. Sal $176,099
Automation Activity & Vendor Info: (Cataloging) SIRSI; (Circulation) SIRSI; (OPAC) SIRSI
Partic in Georgia Online Database
Branches: 2
DAWSON COUNTY, 298 Academy Ave, Dawsonville, 30534. SAN 374-7336. Tel: 706-344-3690. FAX: 706-344-3691. E-Mail: libraryd@mail.dawson.public.lib.ga.us. Web Site: www.chestatee.public.lib.ga.us. *Mgr*, Rebecca Stuckey; E-Mail: stuckeyr@mail.dawson.public.lib.ga.us; Staff 6 (Non-MLS 6)
Founded 1958. Pop 13,809
Jul 1999-Jun 2000 Income $150,502, State $10,895, County $134,779, Locally Generated Income $3,438, Other $44. Mats Exp Books $29,228. Sal $70,172
Library Holdings: Bk Vols 20,983; Per Subs 69
Subject Interests: Local history
Automation Activity & Vendor Info: (Cataloging) SIRSI; (Circulation) SIRSI; (OPAC) SIRSI
Friends of the Library Group
LUMPKIN COUNTY, 342 Courthouse Hill, 30533. Tel: 706-864-3668. FAX: 706-864-3937. E-Mail: libraryl@mail.lumpkin.public.lib.ga.us. Web Site: www.chestatee.public.lib.ga.us. *Mgr*, Mary Gallant; E-Mail: gallantm@mail.lumpkin.public.lib.ga.us; Staff 6 (Non-MLS 6)
Founded 1917. Pop 18,673
Jul 1999-Jun 2000 Income $158,116, State $10,895, County $133,711, Locally Generated Income $8,221, Other $2,455. Mats Exp Books $32,511. Sal $72,564
Library Holdings: Bk Vols 37,057; Per Subs 68
Subject Interests: Genealogy, Local history
Automation Activity & Vendor Info: (Cataloging) SIRSI; (Circulation) SIRSI; (OPAC) SIRSI
Friends of the Library Group

C NORTH GEORGIA COLLEGE STATE UNIVERSITY, Stewart Library, 238 Georgia Circle, 30597-3001. SAN 303-3597. Tel: 706-864-1518. Reference Tel: 706-864-1520. FAX: 706-864-1867. Reference E-Mail: refdesk@ngcsu.edu. Web Site: www.ngcsu.edu. *Dir*, Dr Marilyn S Lary; Tel: 706-864-1525, E-Mail: mlary@ngcsu.edu; *ILL, Ref*, Willie H Gordon; *Ref*, Aaron Lu; *Circ, Ref*, Bonnie Morris; *Tech Servs*, Janet Burkett; *Electronic Resources, Govt Doc*, Mike Saunders; Staff 12 (MLS 6, Non-MLS 6)
Founded 1873. Enrl 3,700; Fac 110; Highest Degree: Master
Jul 1999-Jun 2000 Income State $1,000,421. Mats Exp $395,682, Books $158,000, Per/Ser (Incl. Access Fees) $165,000, Presv $850, Micro $49,476, AV Equip $3,000, Other Print Mats $18,156, Manuscripts & Archives $1,200. Sal $524,950 (Prof $287,600)
Library Holdings: Bk Vols 121,281; Per Subs 1,446
Subject Interests: Military history
Special Collections: Educational Resources Information Center Coll, microfiche; US Military History
Automation Activity & Vendor Info: (Acquisitions) Endeavor; (Cataloging) Endeavor; (Circulation) Endeavor; (Course Reserve) Endeavor; (OPAC) Endeavor; (Serials) Endeavor
Publications: DataBit
Partic in Galileo; SE Libr Network

DALTON

C DALTON STATE COLLEGE, Darrell C Roberts Library, 213 N College Dr, 30720-3797. SAN 303-3600. Tel: 706-272-4583. Reference Tel: 706-272-4575. FAX: 706-272-4511. Web Site: www.daltonstate.edu/library.htm. *Dir*, Harriett Mayo; E-Mail: hmayo@carpet.dalton.peachnet.edu; *Ser*, Judith Weber; *Doc*, Barbara Durham; *Doc*, Lydia Knight; Staff 10 (MLS 4, Non-MLS 6)
Founded 1967. Enrl 3,139; Highest Degree: Bachelor
Library Holdings: Bk Vols 111,584; Bk Titles 109,385; Per Subs 667
Special Collections: Archives (Dalton Room)
Automation Activity & Vendor Info: (Cataloging) Endeavor; (Circulation) Endeavor
Database Vendor: Ebsco - EbscoHost, GaleNet, Lexis-Nexis, OCLC - First Search, ProQuest, Wilson - Wilson Web
Publications: Library Resource Center Handbook; LRC Info Newsletter
Partic in GALILEO; Georgia Online Database; SE Libr Network; Solinet

M HAMILTON MEDICAL CENTER, Medical Library, 1200 Memorial Dr, 30720. (Mail add: PO Box 1168, 30720), SAN 374-8650. Tel: 706-272-6056. FAX: 706-272-6094. *Librn*, Sarah Russell; E-Mail: srussell@alltel.net; Staff 1 (Non-MLS 1)
Library Holdings: Bk Vols 2,000; Per Subs 90

P NORTHWEST GEORGIA REGIONAL LIBRARY SYSTEM, 310 Cappes St, 30720. SAN 338-6139. Tel: 706-272-2974, 706-272-2976. FAX: 706-272-2977. Web Site: www.whitfield.public.lib.ga.us. *Dir*, Joe B Forsee; E-Mail: forseej@mail.whitefield.public.lib.qa.us; *Asst Dir, Coll Develop*, Rita Linker; *Ch Servs*, Barbara Giberson; *Ref, Spec Coll*, Linda Litton; Staff 7

(MLS 7)
Founded 1924. Pop 197,000; Circ 320,000
Library Holdings: Bk Vols 193,295; Per Subs 116
Subject Interests: Genealogy
Special Collections: Georgia Coll; Newspapers, micro
Mem of NW Ga Regional Libr Syst
Partic in Georgia Libr Info Network
Friends of the Library Group
Branches: 4
CALHOUN-GORDON COUNTY, 100 Park Ave, Calhoun, 30701. SAN 338-6163. Tel: 706-624-1456. FAX: 706-624-1458. Web Site: www.whitefield.public.lib.ga.us. *Mgr*, Dianne Cronon
Special Collections: Dr Henry T Malone Coll
CATOOSA COUNTY, Benton Place, 108 Catoosa Circle, Ringgold, 30736. SAN 338-6198. Tel: 706-965-3600. FAX: 706-965-3608. Web Site: www.whitfield.public.lib.ga.us. *Mgr*, Hope Napier
CATOOSA COUNTY LIBRARY AT RINGGOLD, 15 Tiger Paw Trail, Ringgold, 30736. SAN 338-6228. Tel: 706-935-3800. FAX: 706-935-3800. *Mgr*, Nina Mattox
Friends of the Library Group
CHATSWORTH-MURRAY COUNTY, 706 Old Dalton-Ellijay Rd, Chatsworth, 30705. SAN 338-6287. Tel: 706-695-4200. FAX: 706-695-4200. Web Site: www.whitefield.public.lib.ga.us. *Mgr*, Pat Ausmus
Bookmobiles: 1

S WHITFIELD-MURRAY HISTORICAL SOCIETY, Crown Gardens & Archives, 715 Chattanooga Ave, 30720. SAN 373-4250. Tel: 706-278-0217. *Exec Dir*, Marcelle White
Library Holdings: Bk Vols 300
Subject Interests: Genealogy, Local history

DAWSON

P KINCHAFOONEE REGIONAL LIBRARY SYSTEM, 913 Forrester Dr SE, 31742-2106. SAN 338-6317. Tel: 229-995-6331. FAX: 229-995-3383. Web Site: www.terrell.public.lib.ga.us. *Admin Dir*, Frances P Messer; E-Mail: messerf@mail.terrell.public.lib.ga.us; *Asst Dir, Tech Servs*, Diane Meaders; *Admin Assoc*, Cassandra Powell; Staff 2 (MLS 2)
Founded 1908. Pop 29,845; Circ 100,205
Library Holdings: Bk Titles 110,956; Per Subs 173
Subject Interests: Georgia
Publications: History of Terrell County
Open Mon-Fri 8-5
Branches: 6
ARLINGTON BRANCH LIBRARY, 326 Martin Luther King Dr, Arlington, 31713-9736. Tel: 229-725-0044. Web Site: www.calhoun.public.lib.ga.us. *Head Librn*, Helen H Manry; *Branch Mgr*, Patsy Miliner; Staff 1 (MLS 1)
Pop 4,552
Open Mon-Fri 2:30-5:30
CALHOUN COUNTY LIBRARY, 227 E Hartford St, Edison, 31746-9302. (Mail add: PO Box 365, Edison, 31746-0365), SAN 338-6341. Tel: 229-835-2012. FAX: 229-835-2012. Web Site: www.calhoun.public.lib.ga.us. *Head Librn*, Helen H Manry; E-Mail: manryh@mail.calhoun.public.lib.ga.us; *Circ*, Lenan Fowlkes; *Circ*, Martha Jenkins; Staff 1 (MLS 1)
Pop 4,552; Circ 10,386
Library Holdings: Bk Titles 10,870; Per Subs 44
Open Mon-Fri 10-6, Sat 9-1
Friends of the Library Group
CLAY COUNTY, 208 S Hancock St, Fort Gaines, 31751-9506. (Mail add: PO Box 275, Fort Gaines, 31751-0275), SAN 338-6406. Tel: 229-768-2248. FAX: 229-768-2248. Web Site: www.terrell.public.lib.ga.us. *Head Librn*, Martin A Willitts; E-Mail: willittm@mail.clay.public.lib.ga.us; *Branch Mgr*, Teresa Reynolds; *Circ*, Stan Stanfield; Staff 1 (MLS 1)
Pop 3,594; Circ 22,669
Library Holdings: Bk Titles 11,992; Per Subs 47
Open Mon-Fri 9-5 & Sat 9-1
RANDOLPH COUNTY, 200 E Pearl St, Cuthbert, 31740-1474. SAN 338-649X. Tel: 229-732-2566. FAX: 229-732-6824. Web Site: www.terrell.public.lib.ga.us. *Head Librn*, Leigh Wiley; E-Mail: wileys@mail.randolph.public.lib.ga.us; *Branch Mgr*, Barbara Sealy; *Circ*, Lisa Brazeal; *Circ*, Margaret Bridges; *Circ*, Joanne Clarke; Staff 1 (MLS 1)
Pop 8,293; Circ 29,762
Library Holdings: Bk Titles 12,720; Per Subs 25
Open Mon-Fri 10-6 & Sat 10-2
TERRELL COUNTY, 913 Forrester Dr SE, 31742-2106. SAN 370-7865. Tel: 229-995-2902. FAX: 229-995-5989. Web Site: www.terrell.public.lib.ga.us. *Head Librn*, Claudia Copeland; E-Mail: coplac0@mail.terrell.public.lib.ga.us; *Circ*, Clara Aultman; *Circ*, Pearlie Bishop; *Circ*, Cassandra Powell; Staff 1 (Non-MLS 1)
Pop 11,173; Circ 33,566
Library Holdings: Bk Titles 67,823; Per Subs 34
Open Mon 10-8, Tues-Thurs 10-6 & Fri-Sat 10-5
Friends of the Library Group
WEBSTER COUNTY, 169 Washington St, Preston, 31824. (Mail add: PO Box 316-A, Preston, 31824-0316), SAN 338-652X. Tel: 229-828-5740. FAX: 229-828-5740. Web Site: www.terrell.public.lib.ga.us. *Branch Mgr*, Diane Holbrook; E-Mail: holbrood@mail.webster.public.lib.ga.us; *Circ*, Bridget Stewart
Pop 2,233; Circ 3,822
Library Holdings: Bk Titles 7,420; Per Subs 14
Open Mon-Fri 2:30-5:30

DECATUR

C AGNES SCOTT COLLEGE, McCain Library, 141 E College Ave, 30030. SAN 303-3619. Tel: 404-471-6339. Interlibrary Loan Service Tel: 404-471-6337. Reference Tel: 404-471-6343. FAX: 404-471-5037. E-Mail: library@agnesscott.edu. Web Site: library.agnesscott.edu. *Librn*, Virginia Moreland; Tel: 404-471-5277; *Publ Servs*, Sala Rhodes; *Tech Servs*, Resa Harney; Tel: 404-471-6141; *ILL*, Linda Gray; Staff 9 (MLS 4, Non-MLS 5)
Founded 1889. Enrl 869; Fac 73; Highest Degree: Master
Jul 1998-Jun 1999 Income $658,832. Mats Exp $350,599, Books $119,718, Per/Ser (Incl. Access Fees) $202,000, Presv $3,139, Micro $25,742. Sal $282,499 (Prof $178,484)
Library Holdings: Bk Vols 175,530; Bk Titles 153,150; Per Subs 819
Subject Interests: History, Women's studies
Special Collections: Catherine Marshall Papers; Faculty & Student Publications; Frontier Religion; Robert Frost Coll
Automation Activity & Vendor Info: (Acquisitions) Innovative Interfaces Inc.; (Cataloging) Innovative Interfaces Inc.; (Circulation) Innovative Interfaces Inc.; (Course Reserve) Innovative Interfaces Inc.; (ILL) Innovative Interfaces Inc.; (Media Booking) Innovative Interfaces Inc.; (OPAC) Innovative Interfaces Inc.; (Serials) Innovative Interfaces Inc.
Partic in Atlanta Regional Consortium for Higher Educ; Ga Learning Libr Online; GALILEO; Georgia Libr Info Network; SE Libr Network; Solinet

GM ATLANTA VA MEDICAL CENTER LIBRARY, 1670 Clairmont Rd, 30033. SAN 303-3678. Tel: 404-321-6111, Ext 7672. FAX: 404-728-7781. *Chief Librn*, Shirley Avin; *Tech Servs*, Keith Edmonds; *Tech Servs*, Joedda Pessima; Staff 5 (MLS 2, Non-MLS 3)
Founded 1945
Library Holdings: Bk Titles 8,003; Per Subs 482
Subject Interests: Health sciences, Medicine
Restriction: Open to public for reference only
Partic in Atlanta Health Science Libraries Consortium

R CLAIRMONT PRESBYTERIAN CHURCH LIBRARY, 1994 Clairmont Rd, 30033. SAN 303-3635. Tel: 404-634-3355. FAX: 404-321-5057. *Librn*, Peggy Lathom
Nov 1998-Oct 1999 Income $600. Mats Exp $600, Books $573, Per/Ser (Incl. Access Fees) $27
Library Holdings: Bk Vols 2,750
Subject Interests: Fiction, Religion

R COLUMBIA THEOLOGICAL SEMINARY, John Bulow Campbell Library, 701 Columbia Dr, 30031. SAN 303-3643. Tel: 404-687-4549, Ext 47. Interlibrary Loan Service Tel: 404-687-4548. FAX: 404-687-4687. *Dir*, Tim Browning; E-Mail: browingt@ctsnet.edu; *Assoc Dir, Ref*, Clay Hulet; *Tech Servs*, Tammy Johnson; *Circ*, Mary Martha Riviere; *Coll Develop*, Linda Davis
Founded 1828. Enrl 625
Library Holdings: Bk Vols 130,000
Subject Interests: Philosophy, Religion
Partic in OCLC Online Computer Library Center, Inc

P DEKALB COUNTY PUBLIC LIBRARY, 215 Sycamore St, 4th flr, 30030. SAN 338-6589. Tel: 404-370-8450. Interlibrary Loan Service Tel: 404-370-3088. FAX: 404-370-8469. Web Site: www.dekalb.public.lib.ga.us. *Dir*, Darro Willey; E-Mail: willeyd@mail.dekalb.public.lib.ga.us; *Asst Dir*, Magda Sossa; E-Mail: sossam@mail.dekalb.public.lib.ga.us; *Br Coordr*, David Tucker; E-Mail: tuckerd@mail.dekalb.public.lib.ga.us; *Br Coordr*, Nancy Wright; E-Mail: wrightn@mail.dekalb.public.lib.ga.us; *ILL*, Ann Mallard; E-Mail: mallarda@mail.dekalb.public.lib.ga.us; *Tech Servs*, Melinda Wolf; E-Mail: wolfm@mail.dekalb.public.lib.ga.us; Staff 182 (MLS 55, Non-MLS 127)
Founded 1925. Pop 610,655; Circ 2,619,144
Jul 1999-Jun 2000 Income (Main Library and Branch Library) $10,696,567, State $1,095,497, City $1,000, County $9,038,646, Locally Generated Income $561,424. Mats Exp $1,732,327, Books $1,243,956, Per/Ser (Incl. Access Fees) $93,320, Presv $8,451, Micro $22,000, AV Equip $129,600, Electronic Ref Mat (Incl. Access Fees) $235,000. Sal $7,561,604 (Prof $821,489)
Library Holdings: Bk Vols 827,623; Bk Titles 821,489; Per Subs 2,163
Subject Interests: Genealogy, Literature
Special Collections: Georgia County History; Global (International Trade) Research Center; Large Print Books; Mailbox Books; Outreach
Publications: GA Libr Assoc Information Freedom Handbook; GA Library & Friends Assoc Trustee Handbook
Partic in Ga Peachnet; SE Libr Network
Special Services for the Deaf - TTY machine
Friends of the Library Group
Branches: 24
AVIS WILLIAMS LIBRARY, 1282 McConnell Dr, 30033. SAN 338-6910. Tel: 404-679-4404. FAX: 404-679-4407. Web Site:

www.dekalb.public.lib.ga.us. *Librn*, Karen Skellie; E-Mail: skellie@mail.dekalb.public.lib.ga.us
Library Holdings: Bk Vols 58,945; Bk Titles 55,800; Per Subs 87
Open Mon-Wed 10-8, Thurs-Sat 10-5
Friends of the Library Group

BRIARCLIFF, 2775 Briarcliff Rd, Atlanta, 30329. SAN 370-7962. Tel: 404-679-4400. FAX: 404-679-4403. Web Site: www.dekalb.public.lib.ga.us.
Library Holdings: Bk Vols 7,666; Bk Titles 6,685; Per Subs 20
Open Mon & Tues 12-8, Wed & Thurs 12-6, Fri & Sat 1-5

BROOKHAVEN, 1242 N Druid Hills Rd NE, Atlanta, 30319. SAN 338-6619. Tel: 404-848-7140. FAX: 404-848-7142. Web Site: www.dekalb.public.lib.ga.us. *Librn*, Quattlebaum Catherine; E-Mail: quattlec@mail.dekalb.public.lib.ga.us
Library Holdings: Bk Vols 31,428; Bk Titles 29,761; Per Subs 56
Open Mon & Tues 11-8, Wed-Sat 11-5
Friends of the Library Group

BRUCE STREET HOMEWORK CENTER LIBRARY, 2484 Bruce St, Lithonia, 30058. SAN 328-8757. Tel: 770-482-0405. FAX: 770-482-0299. Web Site: www.dekalb.public.lib.ga.us.
Library Holdings: Bk Vols 3,530; Bk Titles 3,156; Per Subs 39
Open Mon-Thurs 2-7 Sept-May; Mon-Thurs 12-5

CHAMBLEE LIBRARY, 4115 Clairmont Rd, Chamblee, 30341. SAN 338-6678. Tel: 770-936-1380. FAX: 770-936-1385. Web Site: www.dekalb.public.lib.ga.us. *Librn*, Kristi Gregory; E-Mail: gregoryk@mail.dekalb.public.lib.ga.us
Library Holdings: Bk Vols 66,118; Bk Titles 67,119; Per Subs 151
Open Mon-Thurs 10-8, Fri & Sat 10-5, Sun 1-5 (Sept-May)
Friends of the Library Group

CLARKSTON BRANCH, 951 N Indian Creek Dr, Clarkston, 30021. SAN 372-0101. Tel: 404-508-7175. TDD: 404-508-7179. FAX: 404-508-7178. Web Site: www.dekalb.public.lib.ga.us. *Librn*, Alison Weissinger; E-Mail: weissina@mail.dekalb.public.lib.ga.us
Library Holdings: Bk Vols 44,055; Bk Titles 40,765; Per Subs 88
Special Services for the Deaf - TTY machine
Open Mon-Wed 10-8, Thurs-Sat 10-5
Friends of the Library Group

COVINGTON, 3500 Covington Hwy, 30032. SAN 372-0152. Tel: 404-508-7180. FAX: 404-508-7183. Web Site: www.dekalb.public.lib.ga.us. *Librn*, Gladys Hardcastle; E-Mail: hardcasg@mail.dekalb.public.lib.ga.us
Library Holdings: Bk Vols 7,378; Bk Titles 28,205; Per Subs 79
Open Mon 2-8, Tues-Thurs 11-8, Fri 11-5, Sat 10-5
Friends of the Library Group

DECATUR BRANCH, 215 Sycamore St, 30030. SAN 338-6597. Tel: 404-370-3070. FAX: 404-370-3073. Web Site: www.dekalb.public.lib.ga.us. *Librn*, Nancy Wright; E-Mail: wrightn@mail.dekalb.public.lib.ga.us
Library Holdings: Bk Vols 125,501; Bk Titles 106,179; Per Subs 398
Open Mon-Thurs 9-9, Fri & Sat 9-5, Sun 1-5
Friends of the Library Group

DORAVILLE LIBRARY, 3748 Central Ave, Doraville, 30340. SAN 338-6732. Tel: 770-936-3852. FAX: 770-936-3854. Web Site: www.dekalb.public.lib.ga.us. *Librn*, James Draper; E-Mail: draperj@mail.dekalb.public.lib.ga.us
Library Holdings: Bk Vols 32,454; Bk Titles 31,075; Per Subs 49
Open Mon-Thurs 10-8, Fri 10-5, Sat 10-4

DUNWOODY LIBRARY, 5339 Chamblee-Dunwoody Rd, Dunwoody, 30338. SAN 321-4605. Tel: 770-512-4640. FAX: 770-512-4644. Web Site: www.dekalb.public.lib.ga.us. *Librn*, Mary Kay Will; E-Mail: willm@mail.dekalb.public.lib.ga.us
Library Holdings: Bk Vols 70,805; Bk Titles 61,309; Per Subs 122
Open Mon-Wed 10-8, Thurs-Sat 10-5
Friends of the Library Group

EMBRY HILLS, 3733 Chamblee-Tucker Rd, Chamblee, 30341. SAN 370-7970. Tel: 770-270-8230. FAX: 770-270-8233. Web Site: www.dekalb.public.lib.ga.us. *Librn*, Kate McLean; E-Mail: mcleank@mail.dekalb.public.lib.ga.us
Library Holdings: Bk Vols 10,723; Bk Titles 7,077; Per Subs 47
Open Mon-Tues 2-8, Wed-Thurs 2-6

FLAT SHOALS, 4022 Flat Shoals Pkwy, 30034. SAN 372-011X. Tel: 404-244-4370. FAX: 404-244-4373. Web Site: www.dekalb.public.lib.ga.us. *Librn*, Kitty Wilson
Library Holdings: Bk Vols 39,201; Bk Titles 20,598; Per Subs 67
Open Mon-Wed 10-8, Thurs-Sat 10-5
Friends of the Library Group

TOBIE GRANT HOMEWORK LIBRARY, 644 Parkdale Dr, Scottdale, 30079. SAN 338-6767. Tel: 404-508-7174. FAX: 404-508-6904. Web Site: www.dekalb.public.lib.ga.us. *Librn*, Alison Weissinger; E-Mail: weissinga@mail.dekalb.public.lib.ga.us
Library Holdings: Bk Vols 4,639; Bk Titles 4,286; Per Subs 28
Open Mon-Thurs 2-7 (Sept-May); Mon-Thurs 12-5 (June-Aug)

GRESHAM, 2418 Gresham Rd, Atlanta, 30316. SAN 372-0128. Tel: 404-244-4374. FAX: 404-244-4376. Web Site: www.dekalb.public.lib.ga.us.
Library Holdings: Bk Vols 13,136; Bk Titles 6,722; Per Subs 39
Open Mon-Tues 12-8, Wed-Thurs 12-6, Fri-Sat 1-5
Friends of the Library Group

HAIRSTON CROSSING, 4911 Redan Rd, Stone Mountain, 30088. SAN 370-7989. Tel: 404-508-7170. FAX: 404-508-7173. Web Site: www.dekalb.public.lib.ga.us. *Librn*, Alison White; E-Mail: whitea@mail.dekalb.public.lib.ga.us
Library Holdings: Bk Vols 11,729; Bk Titles 11,136; Per Subs 41
Open Mon-Tues 2-8, Wed-Thurs 2-6

LITHONIA LIBRARY, 6821 Church St, Lithonia, 30058. SAN 338-6856. Tel: 770-482-3820. FAX: 770-482-3831. Web Site: www.dekalb.public.lib.ga.us.
Library Holdings: Bk Vols 21,871; Bk Titles 20,598; Per Subs 77
Open Mon-Tues 11-8, Wed-Sat 11-5
Friends of the Library Group

NORTHLAKE, 3772 La Vista Rd, Tucker, 30084. SAN 372-0136. Tel: 404-679-4408. FAX: 404-679-4411. Web Site: www.dekalb.public.lib.ga.us. *Librn*, Claudia Medori; E-Mail: medoric@mail.dekalb.public.lib.ga.us
Library Holdings: Bk Vols 45,107; Bk Titles 41,310; Per Subs 90
Open Mon-Wed 10-8, Thurs-Sat 10-5
Friends of the Library Group

PROCESSING CENTER & PATRON SERVICES, 3560 Kensington Rd, 30032. SAN 377-6921. Tel: 404-508-7190. FAX: 404-508-7184. Web Site: www.dekalb.public.lib.ga.us.
Open Mon-Fri 8:30-5

REDAN-TROTTI, 1569 Wellborn Rd, Redan, 30074. SAN 372-0144. Tel: 770-482-3821. FAX: 770-482-3825. Web Site: www.dekalb.pub.lib.ga.us. *Librn*, Alison White; E-Mail: whitea@mail.dekalb.public.lib.ga.us
Library Holdings: Bk Vols 67,282; Bk Titles 59,612; Per Subs 215
Open Mon-Wed 10-8, Thurs-Sat 10-5
Friends of the Library Group

REID COFER LIBRARY, 4316 Church St, Tucker, 30084. SAN 338-6708. Tel: 770-270-8234. FAX: 770-270-8237. Web Site: www.dekalb.public.lib.ga.us. *Librn*, Kate McLean; E-Mail: mcleank@mail.dekalb.public.lib.ga.us
Library Holdings: Bk Vols 58,708; Bk Titles 53,839; Per Subs 49
Open Mon-Wed 10-8, Thurs-Sat 10-5

SALEM PANOLA, 5137 Salem Rd, Lithonia, 30038. SAN 370-7997. Tel: 770-987-6900. FAX: 770-987-6903. Web Site: www.dekalb.public.lib.ga.us. *Librn*, Brenda Zehran; E-Mail: zehranb@mail.dekalb.public.lib.ga.us
Library Holdings: Bk Vols 10,578; Bk Titles 9,769; Per Subs 57
Open Mon-Tues 12-8, Wed-Thurs 12-6, Fri-Sat 1-5
Friends of the Library Group

SCOTT CANDLER LIBRARY, 2644 McAfee Rd, 30032. SAN 338-6643. Tel: 404-286-6986. FAX: 404-286-6989. *Librn*, Scott Smith; E-Mail: smiths@mail.dekalb.public.lib.ga.us
Library Holdings: Bk Vols 34,989; Bk Titles 32,279; Per Subs 71
Open Mon & Tues 11-8, Wed-Sat 11-5
Friends of the Library Group

SUE KELLOGG LIBRARY, 952 Leon St, Stone Mountain, 30083. SAN 338-6821. Tel: 770-413-2020. FAX: 770-413-2023. Web Site: www.dekalb.public.lib.ga.us. *Librn*, Mia Buggs; E-Mail: buggsm@mail.dekalb.public.lib.ga.us
Library Holdings: Bk Vols 50,165; Bk Titles 45,768; Per Subs 83
Open Mon-Wed 10-8, Thurs-Sat 10-5
Friends of the Library Group

WESLEY CHAPEL, 2861 Wesley Chapel Rd, 30034. SAN 370-8012. Tel: 404-286-6980. FAX: 404-286-6985. Web Site: www.dekalb.pub.lib.ga.us. *Librn*, Doris Wells; E-Mail: wellsd@mail.dekalb.public.lib.ga.us
Library Holdings: Bk Vols 60,142; Bk Titles 51,574; Per Subs 210
Open Mon-Thurs 10-8, Fri & Sat 10-5, Sun 1-5 (Sept-May)
Friends of the Library Group

M DEKALB MEDICAL CENTER, Health Sciences Library, 2701 N Decatur Rd, 30033. SAN 303-3651. Tel: 404-501-5638. FAX: 404-501-1052. *Dir*, Marilyn Barry; Staff 3 (MLS 2, Non-MLS 1)
Founded 1974
Jul 1998-Jun 1999 Income $185,000, Locally Generated Income $14,000, Parent Institution $170,000. Mats Exp $56,000, Books $5,000, Per/Ser (Incl. Access Fees) $48,000. Sal $73,000
Library Holdings: Bk Titles 1,200; Per Subs 300
Subject Interests: Allied health, Clinical medicine, Nursing
Restriction: Staff use only
Partic in Atlanta Health Science Libraries Consortium; BRS; Georgia Online Database; Medline

S DEVRY INSTITUTE OF TECHNOLOGY LIBRARY, 250 N Arcadia Ave, 30030. SAN 303-271X. Tel: 404-292-7900, Ext 2292. FAX: 404-299-1344. *Dir*, Shirley Chambers Reichard; E-Mail: schambers@admin.atl.devry.edu
Founded 1969. Enrl 3,882
Library Holdings: Bk Vols 20,000; Bk Titles 19,000; Per Subs 75
Automation Activity & Vendor Info: (Cataloging) Endeavor; (OPAC) Endeavor
Database Vendor: Lexis-Nexis, OCLC - First Search, ProQuest
Partic in GALILEO; Georgia Online Database; Solinet

S GEORGIA ASSOCIATION OF EDUCATORS, Research & Production, 3951 Snapfinger Pkwy Ste 400, 30035. SAN 303-366X. Tel: 404-289-5867. FAX: 404-289-5931. *Exec Dir*, Dr Drew Allbritten
Founded 1973
Library Holdings: Bk Vols 1,637; Per Subs 39
Partic in Nat Educ Asn Res Div

SR GREENFOREST COMMUNITY BAPTIST CHURCH-CHRISTIAN ACADEMIC CENTER LIBRARY, Beulah Bible College Extension, 3250 Rainbow Dr, 30034. SAN 328-4700. Tel: 404-289-9636, Ext 134. FAX: 289-1520, 404-286-0052. Web Site: www.greenforest.org. *Dir*, Dorothy T Lassiter; *Media Spec*, Sloane Clark; Tel: 404-286-0479; Staff 2 (MLS 2)
Enrl 428; Fac 41; Highest Degree: Doctorate
Jan 2000-Dec 2000 Income $59,500, Locally Generated Income $12,000, Parent Institution $47,500. Mats Exp $27,950. Sal $31,550
Library Holdings: Bk Vols 8,000
Special Collections: Seminary Coll
Automation Activity & Vendor Info: (Acquisitions) Sagebrush Corporation; (Cataloging) Sagebrush Corporation; (Circulation) Sagebrush Corporation
Database Vendor: Ebsco - EbscoHost
Restriction: Circulation limited
Function: Photocopies available
Partic in Church & Synagogue Libr Asn
Friends of the Library Group

DEMOREST

C PIEDMONT COLLEGE, Arrendale Library, PO Box 40, 30535. SAN 303-3686. Tel: 706-776-0111. FAX: 706-778-2811. Web Site: library.piedmont.edu. *Dir*, Bob Glass; E-Mail: bglass@piedmont.edu; *Publ Servs*, Jennifer Inglis; Staff 4 (MLS 2, Non-MLS 2)
Founded 1897. Enrl 1,700; Fac 85; Highest Degree: Master
Jul 1998-Jun 1999 Income $317,500. Mats Exp $87,550, Books $44,550, Per/Ser (Incl. Access Fees) $43,000. Sal $137,500
Library Holdings: Bk Vols 111,000; Per Subs 426
Partic in Georgia Libr Info Network; OCLC Online Computer Library Center, Inc; SE Libr Network
Open Mon-Thurs 8-11, Fri 8-4, Sat 10-4 & Sun 2-10
Friends of the Library Group

DOUGLAS

P SATILLA REGIONAL LIBRARY, 201 S Coffee Ave, 31533. SAN 338-6945. Tel: 912-384-4667. FAX: 912-389-4365. *Cat, Dir*, Emory Smith; E-Mail: andersj@svcc.edu; *Bkmobile Coordr*, Eleanor Sammons; *Ch Servs*, Ronalea Stark; Tel: 808-845-9198; *Ref*, Walter Mitchell. Subject Specialists: *Genealogy*, Winifred Gourley; Staff 4 (MLS 4)
Founded 1914. Circ 115,246
Library Holdings: Bk Titles 130,000; Per Subs 317
Subject Interests: Genealogy
Partic in Georgia Libr Info Network; Georgia Online Database; SE Libr Network
Branches: 6
AMBROSE PUBLIC LIBRARY, 1070 Cypress Ave, Ambrose, 31512. SAN 376-9550. Tel: 912-359-2536. FAX: 912-359-2536. *Mgr*, Evelyn Harper
BROXTON PUBLIC LIBRARY, Corner-Church & West, PO Box 513, Broxton, 31519. SAN 338-6953. FAX: 912-359-3887. *Mgr*, Lisa Washington
Library Holdings: Bk Vols 4,500
JEFF DAVIS PUBLIC LIBRARY, 86 Cromartie St, Hazlehurst, 31539. SAN 338-697X. Tel: 912-375-2386. FAX: 912-375-9507. *Mgr*, Louise Hand; *Asst Librn*, Edna Cothran; *Asst Librn*, Ettamae Swain
Library Holdings: Bk Titles 12,500
NICHOLLS PUBLIC LIBRARY, 108 N Liberty St, Nicholls, 31554. SAN 338-7011. Tel: 912-345-2534. FAX: 912-345-2534. *Mgr*, Jackie Gardner
Library Holdings: Bk Titles 4,000
PEARSON PUBLIC LIBRARY, 202 E Bullard Ave, PO Box 1240, Pearson, 31642. SAN 338-7038. Tel: 912-422-3500. FAX: 912-422-3500. *Mgr*, Jimmie Smith
Library Holdings: Bk Vols 7,500
WILLACOOCHEE PUBLIC LIBRARY, Railroad St, PO Box 588, Willacoochee, 31650. SAN 338-7062. Tel: 912-534-5252. FAX: 912-534-5252. *Mgr*, Mary Lou Lee
Library Holdings: Bk Vols 7,500
Bookmobiles: 1

J SOUTH GEORGIA COLLEGE, William S Smith Library, 100 W College Park Dr, 31533-5098. SAN 303-3694. Tel: 912-389-4510. FAX: 912-389-4469. Web Site: www.sgc.peachnet.edu/library.sgc.peachnet.edu. *Media Spec*, Sylvia Brown; Staff 7 (MLS 2, Non-MLS 5)
Founded 1906
Library Holdings: Bk Vols 80,294; Per Subs 334
Special Collections: US Geological Survey Maps
Partic in Galileo; Georgia Libr Info Network

DUBLIN

GM DEPARTMENT OF VETERANS AFFAIRS, Carl Vinson VA Medical Center Library, Vet Admin Med Ctr, 1826 Veterans Blvd, 31021. SAN 303-3708. Tel: 912-277-2759. FAX: 912-277-2771. *In Charge*, Sandra Clem; Staff 3 (MLS 1, Non-MLS 2)
Founded 1948
Library Holdings: Per Subs 379
Partic in Georgia Libr Info Network; Medline; Vets Admin Libr Network

P OCONEE REGIONAL LIBRARY, Laurens County Library, 801 Bellevue Ave, 31021. (Mail add: PO Box 100, 31040), SAN 338-7097. Tel: 478-272-5710. Toll Free Tel: 800-453-5447. TDD: 478-275-5382. FAX: 478-275-5381. Web Site: www.laurens.pub.lib.ga.us. *Dir*, Susan S Williams; Tel: 912-272-5712, E-Mail: williams@mail.laurens.public.lib.ga.us; *Asst Dir*, Abbie Dillard; *Automation Syst Coordr*, Chris C Woodburn; *Ch Servs*, Tish Schrader; *Coll Develop*, Virginia C Hogan; *Head Ref*, Gail Thomas; *Head Tech Servs*, Donna Coleman; *Ref*, Jane Summey; *Ref*, Tricia Hilliard; Staff 25 (MLS 6, Non-MLS 19)
Founded 1904. Pop 79,516; Circ 334,627
Jul 1999-Jun 2000 Income $1,188,486, State $534,047, City $202,432, County $378,307, Locally Generated Income $57,295, Parent Institution $16,405. Mats Exp $98,125, Books $91,700, Per/Ser (Incl. Access Fees) $6,425. Sal $589,980 (Prof $286,864)
Library Holdings: Bk Vols 67,499; Per Subs 184
Subject Interests: Local history
Special Collections: Georgia Coll
Database Vendor: Ebsco - EbscoHost, OCLC - First Search, ProQuest, Wilson - Wilson Web
Publications: Library News; Talking Book News
Function: ILL available
Partic in Georgia Online Database; SE Libr Network
Special Services for the Blind - Braille & talking book collections (print)
Friends of the Library Group
Branches: 4
HARLIE FULFORD MEMORIAL, 301 Elm St, Wrightsville, 31096. SAN 338-7127. Tel: 478-864-3940. FAX: 478-864-0626. *Mgr*, Susan Green
1996-1997 Income $20,628
Library Holdings: Bk Vols 10,000
TALKING BOOK CENTER Tel: 478-275-5382. Toll Free Tel: 800-453-5541. FAX: 912-275-5381. Web Site: www.laurens.pub.lib.ga.us. *Mgr*, Linda Williams; *Librn*, Susan Williams
1996-1997 Income $60,458. Mats Exp $10,294, Books $4,826, AV Equip $5,468
Friends of the Library Group
TREUTLEN COUNTY, Second & Alabama St, Soperton, 30457. SAN 338-7186. Tel: 912-529-6683. FAX: 912-529-6050. *Mgr*, Ina Kurr
Library Holdings: Bk Vols 9,000
WASHINGTON COUNTY, 314 S Harris St, PO Box 268, Sandersville, 31082. SAN 338-7240. Tel: 478-552-7466. FAX: 478-552-6064. *Mgr*, Diane Meeks
1996-1997 Income $60,340
Library Holdings: Bk Vols 17,153
Friends of the Library Group

DULUTH

S NATIONAL RAILWAY HISTORICAL SOCIETY, ATLANTA CHAPTER, Southeastern Railway Museum Library, 3595 Peach Tree Rd, 30096-1267. (Mail add: PO Box 1267, 30096-1267), SAN 375-0590. Tel: 770-723-0190. FAX: 770-908-8322. Web Site: www.mdtsoft.com/srm, www.srmduluth.org. *Curator*, Paul Grether
Library Holdings: Bk Vols 850; Per Subs 450
Friends of the Library Group

EAST POINT

C ATLANTA CHRISTIAN COLLEGE, James A Burns Memorial Library, 2605 Ben Hill Rd, 30344-1999. SAN 303-3716. Tel: 404-669-2097. FAX: 404-669-4009. *Dir*, Michael Bain; E-Mail: mbain@acc.edu; *Ref*, Jennifer Clotfelter; Staff 2 (MLS 2)
Founded 1937. Enrl 385; Fac 40; Highest Degree: Bachelor
Jul 1999-Jun 2000 Income $134,252. Mats Exp $50,275, Books $18,868, Per/Ser (Incl. Access Fees) $19,800, Presv $872, Micro $300, AV Equip $2,006, Electronic Ref Mat (Incl. Access Fees) $6,000. Sal $53,479 (Prof $44,272)
Library Holdings: Bk Vols 54,044; Bk Titles 43,562; Per Subs 256
Special Collections: Alumni Coll; Library of American Civilizatiion (Core Coll)
Automation Activity & Vendor Info: (Cataloging) Sagebrush Corporation; (Circulation) Sagebrush Corporation; (OPAC) Sagebrush Corporation
Open Mon-Thurs 8-5:30 & 6:30-10, Fri 8-5, Sat 12-5

P EAST POINT PUBLIC LIBRARY, 2757 Main St, 30344. SAN 303-3724. Tel: 404-762-4842. FAX: 404-762-4844. *Mgr*, Carolyn Garnes; Staff 1 (MLS 1)
Founded 1939. Pop 39,400; Circ 44,400
Library Holdings: Bk Vols 40,000; Per Subs 60
Subject Interests: Large type print
Open Mon & Tues 10-8, Wed, Thurs & Fri 10-6, Sat 10-2
Friends of the Library Group

G NATIONAL ARCHIVES & RECORDS ADMINISTRATION, Southeast Region, 1557 Saint Joseph Ave, 30344-2593. SAN 329-8280. Tel: 404-763-7383. FAX: 404-763-7059. E-Mail: archives@atlanta.nara.gov. Web Site: www.nara.gov/regional/atlanta.html. *Archivist*, Suzanne Dewberry; *Archivist*, Mary Ann Hawkins; Tel: 404-763-7732; *Archivist*, Richard Rayburn; *Archivist*, Charles Reeves; Tel: 404-763-7065
Special Collections: Archival records of Federal agencies & courts in Alabama, Florida, Georgia, Kentucky, Mississippi, North Carolina, South Carolina & Tennessee
Restriction: Reference only to non-staff
Friends of the Library Group

EASTMAN

P OCMULGEE REGIONAL LIBRARY SYSTEM, 505 Second Ave, PO Box 4369, 31023-4369. SAN 338-7275. Tel: 478-374-4711. FAX: 478-374-5646. Web Site: www.lightwood.com. *Dir*, David C Wilson; *Media Spec*, Lewis Harrell; *Online Servs*, Stephen Whigham; *Tech Servs*, Harris Morgan; *Bkmobile Coordr*, Jackie Holder; *Acq, Ref Serv*, Susan Williams; Staff 6 (MLS 4, Non-MLS 2)
Founded 1954. Pop 62,529; Circ 496,344
Jul 2000-Jun 2001 Income (Main Library and Branch Library) $738,825, State $468,022, City $60,208, County $94,658, Locally Generated Income $13,065, Other $102,872. Mats Exp $52,623. Sal $724,438 (Prof $358,467)
Library Holdings: Bk Vols 209,584; Per Subs 262
Subject Interests: Ethnic studies, Local history, Natural science, Religion, Science/technology, Technology
Special Collections: American Indian (Ethlyn P Rolfe Coll); Genealogy (Burch-Harrell-Smallwood Coll)
Automation Activity & Vendor Info: (Acquisitions) Brodart; (Circulation) Sagebrush Corporation
Partic in S & Cent Ga Associated Libr
Branches: 6
DODGE COUNTY (SYSTEM HEADQUARTERS) Tel: 912-374-4711. FAX: 912-374-5646. *Dir*, David Wilson
Library Holdings: Bk Vols 88,722
M E RODEN MEMORIAL, Commerce & Duley Sts, Hawkinsville, 31036. SAN 338-7364. Tel: 912-892-3155. FAX: 912-892-3155. *Branch Mgr*, Dot Baker
Library Holdings: Bk Vols 26,664
TELFAIR COUNTY, 815 College St, McRae, 31055. SAN 338-7399. Tel: 912-868-2978. FAX: 912-868-2978. *Branch Mgr*, Evelyn Kersey
Library Holdings: Bk Vols 24,508
TESSIE W NORRIS PUBLIC LIBRARY, Second St, Cochran, 31014. SAN 338-7305. Tel: 912-934-2904. FAX: 912-934-2904. *Branch Mgr*, Kathy Wright
Library Holdings: Bk Vols 22,479
WHEELER COUNTY, PO Box 428, Alamo, 30411. SAN 338-7216. Tel: 912-568-7321. FAX: 912-568-7116. *Branch Mgr*, Loretha Evans
Library Holdings: Bk Vols 5,000
WILCOX COUNTY, Courthouse Sq, Abbeville, 31001. SAN 338-7429. Tel: 912-467-2075. FAX: 912-467-2075. *Branch Mgr*, Marie Brown
Library Holdings: Bk Vols 22,696
Bookmobiles: 1

ELBERTON

P ELBERT COUNTY LIBRARY, 345 Heard St, 30635. SAN 338-7453. Tel: 706-283-5375. FAX: 706-283-5456. *Coll Develop, Dir*, Paula A Bullock; E-Mail: bullockp@mail.elbert.public.lib.ga.us; *Circ*, Valencia Thornton; *Acq, Media Spec*, Camilla Bailey; *Asst Dir, Cat, Ref*, Peggy Johnson; *Bkmobile Coordr*, Nancy McCall
Founded 1925. Pop 19,478; Circ 83,987
Library Holdings: Bk Vols 55,176
Mem of Elbert County Libr Syst
Friends of the Library Group
Bookmobiles: 1

EVANS

P THE WARREN C GIBBS MEMORIAL LIBRARY, 326 N Belair Rd, 30809. SAN 373-6407. Tel: 706-863-1946. FAX: 706-868-3351. *Librn*, Christina Rice; Staff 9 (MLS 1, Non-MLS 8)
Founded 1981. Pop 75,000; Circ 212,705
Jul 1996-Jun 1997 Income $429,403, County $350,224, Locally Generated Income $23,739. Mats Exp $101,873. Sal $261,170
Library Holdings: Bk Vols 81,930; Per Subs 122
Publications: Newsletter
Mem of East Central Georgia Regional Library
Friends of the Library Group

FAYETTEVILLE

S FAYETTE COUNTY HISTORICAL SOCIETY, INC LIBRARY, 195 Lee St, PO Box 421, 30214. SAN 371-6368. Tel: 770-716-6020. FAX: 770-716-9203. E-Mail: Fayhistsoc@aol.com. Web Site: www.HistoryFayetteCoGa.org. *In Charge*, Janet Mack
Library Holdings: Bk Vols 700; Bk Titles 1,000
Special Collections: Civil War (War of the Rebellion Records Coll & Confederate Veteran Coll); Genealogy (Family History Coll), bks, mss

FITZGERALD

P FITZGERALD-BEN HILL COUNTY LIBRARY, 123 N Main St, 31750-2591. SAN 303-3775. Tel: 912-426-5080. FAX: 912-426-5084. *Dir*, Julia Bailey Meredith; Staff 2 (MLS 2)
Founded 1915. Pop 18,305; Circ 105,610
Jul 1999-Jun 2000 Income $331,000, State $160,000, City $78,000, Federal $4,000, County $78,000, Locally Generated Income $11,000. Mats Exp $19,810. Sal $212,000 (Prof $108,000)
Library Holdings: Bk Vols 100,000; Bk Titles 80,000; Per Subs 200
Subject Interests: Georgia, Local history
Special Collections: Georgia Room
Automation Activity & Vendor Info: (Acquisitions) SIRSI; (Cataloging) SIRSI; (Circulation) SIRSI; (OPAC) SIRSI; (Serials) SIRSI
Partic in Georgia Online Database
Open Mon-Thurs 9-9, Fri & Sat 9-6
Friends of the Library Group

FOREST PARK

G GEORGIA STATE DEPARTMENT OF TRANSPORTATION, Roy A Flynt Memorial Library, 15 Kennedy Dr, 30297-1599. SAN 323-4134. Tel: 404-363-7540. FAX: 404-363-7684. *Librn*, Stardina Wyche; E-Mail: stardina.wyche@dot.state.ga.us
Library Holdings: Bk Vols 26,000
Special Collections: Government Publications; Hazardous Waste; TRB Coll
Publications: Annotated Research Bibliography

FORT BENNING

UNITED STATES ARMY

AM MARTIN ARMY COMMUNITY HOSPITAL PROFESSIONAL LIBRARY, Bldg 9200, Rm 10 MCXB-CSL, 31905-6100. SAN 338-7682. Tel: 706-544-2041. FAX: 706-544-3532.
Oct 1997-Sep 1998 Income $58,000. Mats Exp $78,000, Books $30,000, Per/Ser (Incl. Access Fees) $37,000
Library Holdings: Per Subs 85

A SAYERS MEMORIAL LIBRARY, Bldg 93, 31905. SAN 338-7518. Tel: 706-545-7141. FAX: 706-689-3973. Web Site: www.benning.army.mil. *Mgr*, John P Cook; Tel: 706-545-8932, E-Mail: cookjo@benning.army.mil; *Tech Servs*, Barbara M Jordan; Staff 6 (MLS 3, Non-MLS 3)
Founded 1942
Library Holdings: Bk Vols 54,900; Bk Titles 51,700; Per Subs 227
Subject Interests: Business and management, History, Music, Political science
Partic in Georgia Libr Info Network; Telecommunications Libr Info Network; Tralinet

A DONOVAN TECHNICAL LIBRARY, Fort Benning Infantry School, Bldg Four Rm 101, Columbus, 31905-5452. SAN 338-7666. Tel: 706-545-5661. FAX: 706-545-8590. Web Site: www.benning.army.mil/fbhome/library/donovan.htm. *In Charge*, Germaine Pavlova; E-Mail: pavlovag@benning.army.mil; Staff 2 (MLS 1, Non-MLS 1)
Founded 1919
1998-1999 Mats Exp $43,000, Books $15,000, Per/Ser (Incl. Access Fees) $15, Micro $9,000. Sal $120,000 (Prof $60,000)
Library Holdings: Bk Vols 250,000; Bk Titles 55,000; Per Subs 120
Subject Interests: Military history
Special Collections: After Action Reports; Army Unit Histories; Classified Documents; Rare Books; Staff Studies
Publications: Bibliographies; library handbook; periodical holdings list
Partic in Fedlink; United States Army Training & Doctrine Command (TRADOC)

A US ARMY SCHOOL OF THE AMERICAS, John B Amos Library, Bldg 35, Rm 257, 31905-6245. SAN 329-2150. Tel: 706-545-1826, 706-545-4631. FAX: 545-1064, 706-545-1827. *Tech Servs*, Yamill Collazo; E-Mail: collazoy@benning-emh2.army.mil
Library Holdings: Bk Vols 25,000; Bk Titles 12,629; Per Subs 75
Subject Interests: Latin America
Partic in Fedlink
Open Mon-Fri 8:30-5:30

FORT GORDON

UNITED STATES ARMY

A CONSUMER HEALTH LIBRARY, Eisenhower Army Medical Ctr, Rm 3-D-15, 30905. SAN 338-778X. Tel: 706-787-1252, 706-787-6763. FAX: 706-787-2327. *Librn*, David Conlin
Founded 1942
Library Holdings: Bk Vols 1,100; Per Subs 80
Partic in Dialog Corporation

AM EISENHOWER ARMY MEDICAL CENTER, Health Sciences Libr, DDEAMC, 30905-5650. SAN 338-7755. Tel: 706-787-6765. FAX: 706-787-2327. *Librn*, Judy M Krivanek; *Librn*, Shelley Davis-Patterson
Library Holdings: Bk Vols 16,000; Per Subs 550
Partic in BRS; Dialog Corporation; Medline; OCLC Online Computer Library Center, Inc

A WOODWORTH LIBRARY, Bldg 33500, 549 Rice Rd, 30905-5081. SAN 338-7720. Tel: 706-791-4605. Interlibrary Loan Service Tel: 706-791-3086. Circulation Tel: 706-791-7323. Reference Tel: 706-791-2449. FAX: 706-791-5652. *Dir*, Linda L Orne; Tel: 706-791-6993, E-Mail: ornel@emhl.gordon.army.mil; Staff 3 (MLS 2, Non-MLS 1)
Founded 1950
Library Holdings: Per Subs 214
Subject Interests: Computer science
Special Collections: US Army Signal Corps
Partic in Defense Technical Information Center; Dialog Corporation; Georgia Libr Info Network; OCLC Online Computer Library Center, Inc; United States Army Training & Doctrine Command (TRADOC)

FORT MCPHERSON

UNITED STATES ARMY

A FORT MCPHERSON LIBRARY, 1794 Walker Ave SW, 30330-1013. SAN 338-781X. Tel: 404-464-2665. FAX: 404-464-3801. *Chief Librn*, Clayton Edward Blackburn; Tel: 404-464-2645, E-Mail: blackburnc@forscom.army.mil; *Ref*, Allie McNeal; *Govt Doc*, Gail Bardis; Tel: 404-464-2644, E-Mail: bardisg@forscom.army.mil; *ILL*, Linda Sue Nix; Tel: 404-464-2642, E-Mail: nix12@forscom.army.mil; *Cat*, Veronica Davis; Staff 5 (MLS 2, Non-MLS 3)
Founded 1941
Oct 1999-Sep 2000 Income $362,000. Mats Exp $52,600, Books $22,600, Per/Ser (Incl. Access Fees) $23,000, Electronic Ref Mat (Incl. Access Fees) $7,000. Sal $237,000 (Prof $167,000)
Library Holdings: Bk Vols 40,000; Bk Titles 38,000; Per Subs 300; Spec Interest Per Sub 10
Subject Interests: Mil sci
Special Collections: Department of Army Publications
Database Vendor: Dialog, Ebsco - EbscoHost, ProQuest
Function: ILL available
Partic in Fedlink; Georgia Online Database

FORT OGLETHORPE

S NATIONAL PARK SERVICE, Chickamauga-Chattanooga National Military Park, Longstreet Thomas Library, 3370 Lafayette Rd, 30742. (Mail add: PO Box 2128, 30742), SAN 373-0425. Tel: 706-866-9241. *In Charge*, Patrick H Reed
Library Holdings: Bk Vols 5,000; Per Subs 15
Subject Interests: Civil War
Special Collections: Chattanooga Campaign, ms
Restriction: By appointment only
Friends of the Library Group

FORT STEWART

UNITED STATES ARMY

A FORT STEWART MAIN POST LIBRARY, 316 Lindquist Rd, 31314-5126. SAN 338-7879. Tel: 912-767-2828. FAX: 912-767-3794, Autovon 870-3794. Web Site: www.stewlib3.stewart.army.mil. *Dir*, M Malinda Johnson; E-Mail: johnsonm@emh5.stewart.army.mil; *Tech Servs*, Meriam D Simmons
Founded 1942
Library Holdings: Bk Vols 68,000; Bk Titles 55,000; Per Subs 250
Subject Interests: Military history
Automation Activity & Vendor Info: (Acquisitions) Endeavor; (Cataloging) Endeavor; (Circulation) Endeavor; (OPAC) Endeavor
Database Vendor: Ebsco - EbscoHost, OCLC - First Search
Partic in Fedlink; Georgia Libr Info Network; OCLC Online Computer Library Center, Inc

AM WINN ARMY COMMUNITY HOSPITAL, MEDICAL LIBRARY-INFORMATION CENTER, Bldg 302, Ste 2J 11B, 1061 Harman Ave, 31314. SAN 338-7895. Tel: 912-370-6542. FAX: 912-370-5480. *Librn*, Laura Harvell
Library Holdings: Bk Vols 1,200; Bk Titles 500; Per Subs 36
Subject Interests: Allied health

FORT VALLEY

S AMERICAN CAMELLIA SOCIETY LIBRARY, 100 Massee Lane, 31030. SAN 326-8578. Tel: 478-967-2358, 478-967-2722. FAX: 478-967-2083. E-Mail: acs@alltell.net. Web Site: www.camellias-acs.com. *Dir*, Ann Walton
Library Holdings: Bk Vols 500; Per Subs 10

C FORT VALLEY STATE UNIVERSITY, Henry Alexander Hunt Memorial Library, 1005 State University Dr, 31030-4313. SAN 303-3791. Tel: 912-825-6342. Interlibrary Loan Service Tel: 912-825-6762. Circulation Tel: 912-825-6753. Reference Tel: 912-825-6761. FAX: 912-825-6916. Web Site: www.gil.fusu.edu. *Dir*, Carole R Taylor; Tel: 912-825-6754, E-Mail: taylorc@mail.fvsu.edu; *Asst Librn*, Connie O Smith; Tel: 912-825-6281, E-Mail: smithc2@mail.fvsu.edu; *Publ Servs*, Doris Gosier; Tel: 912-825-6764, E-Mail: gosierd@mail.fvsu.edu; *Head Ref*, Frank Mahitab; Tel: 912-825-6761, E-Mail: mahitabf@mail.fvsu.edu. Subject Specialists: *Sciences*, Frank Mahitab; *Sociology*, Carole R Taylor; Staff 13 (MLS 5, Non-MLS 8)
Founded 1925. Enrl 2,558; Fac 161; Highest Degree: Master
Jul 1999-Jun 2000 Income $841,041, State $14,500, Federal $18,434, Parent Institution $808,107. Mats Exp $335,411, Books $146,756, Per/Ser (Incl. Access Fees) $126,625, Presv $5,076, Micro $34,259, AV Equip $1,502, Other Print Mats $8,235, Electronic Ref Mat (Incl. Access Fees) $12,958. Sal $442,567 (Prof $177,090)
Library Holdings: Bk Vols 187,895; Bk Titles 155,000; Per Subs 805
Subject Interests: Agriculture, Art, Economics, Education, Ethnic studies, Home economics, Science/technology, Technology
Special Collections: Materials and books by and about Blacks
Automation Activity & Vendor Info: (Acquisitions) Endeavor; (Cataloging) Endeavor; (Circulation) Endeavor; (ILL) Endeavor; (OPAC) Endeavor; (Serials) Endeavor
Publications: LRC Student Handbook; Newsletter; The Info
Partic in Galileol SE Libr Network
Open Mon-Thurs 8am-10pm, Fri 8am-5pm, Sat 1-5pm & Sun 3-10pm

P PEACH PUBLIC LIBRARIES, 315 Martin Luther King Dr, 31030-4196. SAN 338-7933. Tel: 912-825-1640. FAX: 912-825-2061. Web Site: www.peach.public.lib.ga.us. *Dir*, Gilda E Stanbery-Cotney; E-Mail: stanberg@mail.peach.public.lib.ga.us; *Circ, Publ Servs*, Jane Matthews; Staff 2 (MLS 2)
Founded 1915. Pop 22,881; Circ 85,849
Library Holdings: Per Subs 124
Subject Interests: Local history
Publications: Adult & Young Adult (newsletters)
Friends of the Library Group
Branches: 2
BYRON PUBLIC, 105 Church St, Byron, 31008. SAN 338-7968. Tel: 478-956-2200. FAX: 478-956-5688. *Branch Mgr*, Ginger Teague
Library Holdings: Bk Vols 8,100
Friends of the Library Group
THOMAS PUBLIC LIBRARY (HQ), 315 Martin Luther King Jr Dr, 31030. SAN 338-7976. Tel: 478-825-1640. FAX: 478-825-2061. *Dir*, Gilda E Stanbery-Cotney; *Publ Servs*, Ashley Moore; *Ch Servs, Tech Servs*, Nancy Rairdon
Friends of the Library Group

FRANKLIN SPRINGS

CR EMMANUEL COLLEGE LIBRARY, 181 Springs St, PO Box 69, 30639. SAN 303-3805. Tel: 706-245-7226, Ext 4144. FAX: 706-245-4424. Web Site: www.emmanuel-college.edu/library. *Head Librn*, Richard R Dupont; Tel: 706-245-7226, Ext 2847, E-Mail: rdupont@emmanuel-college.edu; *Assoc Librn*, Xiaohong Hart; Tel: 706-245-7226, Ext 2735, E-Mail: xhart@emmanuel-college.edu; Staff 4 (MLS 2, Non-MLS 2)
Founded 1935. Enrl 837; Highest Degree: Bachelor
Jul 1999-Jun 2000 Mats Exp $102,000, Books $75,000, Per/Ser (Incl. Access Fees) $15,000, Electronic Ref Mat (Incl. Access Fees) $12,000
Library Holdings: Bk Vols 55,000; Bk Titles 43,000; Per Subs 200
Special Collections: Pentecostal Holiness Archives
Automation Activity & Vendor Info: (Cataloging) Follett; (Circulation) Follett; (OPAC) Follett
Database Vendor: ProQuest
Restriction: Open to faculty, students & qualified researchers, Restricted public use
Partic in Christian Libr Network; Ga Pvt Acad Librs Consortium

GAINESVILLE

C BRENAU UNIVERSITY, Trustee Library, One Centennial Circle, 30501. SAN 303-3813. Tel: 770-534-6113. FAX: 770-534-6254. Web Site: www.brenau.edu. *Dir*, Michael Brasel; *Acq, ILL*, Ed Archer; *Ref*, Kathryn Eskew; Staff 4 (MLS 4)
Founded 1878. Enrl 1,950; Fac 85
Library Holdings: Bk Vols 80,000; Bk Titles 75,200; Per Subs 960
Subject Interests: Education, Music, Nursing
Special Collections: Elson Judaica Coll; Thomas E Watson Coll
Publications: Library Handbook
Partic in SE Libr Network

R FIRST PRESBYTERIAN WEBSTER CHURCH LIBRARY, 800 S Enota Dr NE, 30501. SAN 303-3821. Tel: 770-532-0136. FAX: 770-287-1397. *Librn*, Judyt Hartley

J GAINESVILLE COLLEGE, John Harrison Hosch Library, UPS 3820 Mundy's Mill Rd, PO Box 1358, 30503. SAN 303-383X. Tel: 770-718-3653. TDD: 770-718-3736. FAX: 770-718-3657. Web Site: www.gc.peachnet.edu/library/main, www.gc.peachnet.edu/library/main. *Dir*, Byron Drew; E-Mail: bdrew@gc.peachnet.edu; *Coordr, Tech Servs*, Rebecca Homan; *Coll Develop*, Priscilla Rankin; Staff 8 (MLS 5, Non-MLS 3)
Founded 1964. Enrl 2,642; Fac 93
Library Holdings: Bk Vols 70,000; Bk Titles 63,000; Per Subs 253
Special Collections: Ed Dodd Coll
Automation Activity & Vendor Info: (Serials) Endeavor
Partic in SE Libr Network
Special Services for the Deaf - TDD

P HALL COUNTY LIBRARY SYSTEM, 127 Main St NW, 30501-3614. SAN 338-8026. Tel: 770-532-3311. FAX: 770-532-4305. E-Mail: refdesk@mail.hall.public.lib.ga.us. Web Site: www.hall.public.lib.ga.us. *Dir*, Susan Stewart; E-Mail: sstewart@mail.hall.public.lib.ga.us; *Assoc Dir*, Adrian Mixson; E-Mail: amixson@mail.public.lib.ga.us; *Asst Dir*, Elaine McCracken; E-Mail: emccracken@mail.hall.public.lib.ga.us; Staff 3 (MLS 3)
Founded 1997. Pop 120,000; Circ 518,112
Jun 1999-Jul 2000 Income $1,838,450, State $433,376, County $1,182,943, Locally Generated Income $120,262, Other $101,869. Mats Exp $224,966, Books $212,966, Electronic Ref Mat (Incl. Access Fees) $12,000. Sal $970,954 (Prof $166,888)
Library Holdings: Bk Vols 186,087; Per Subs 355
Subject Interests: Genealogy, Local history, Spanish
Special Collections: James Longstreet Coll, papers
Automation Activity & Vendor Info: (Acquisitions) DRA; (Circulation) DRA; (OPAC) DRA; (Serials) DRA
Database Vendor: OCLC - First Search
Publications: Talking Book Times (Newsletter)
Partic in Galileo; OCLC Online Computer Library Center, Inc; Peachnet; SE Libr Network
Special Services for the Blind - Talking Books
Books by mail
Friends of the Library Group
Branches: 5
BLACKSHEAR PLACE, 2927 Atlanta Hwy, Oakwood, 30507. SAN 370-9264. Tel: 770-287-3654. FAX: 770-287-3653. *Mgr*, Barbara Perry; E-Mail: bperry@mail.hall/public.lib.ga.us
Circ 164,564
Library Holdings: Bk Vols 43,192; Per Subs 94
Friends of the Library Group
CLERMONT BRANCH, 117 King St, Clermont, 30527-1714. SAN 326-1670. Tel: 770-983-3196. FAX: 770-983-1469. *Mgr*, Nancy Loggins; E-Mail: nloggins@mail.hall.public.lib.ga.us
Circ 9,123
Library Holdings: Bk Vols 2,651; Per Subs 10
Friends of the Library Group
EAST HALL & SPECIAL NEEDS LIBRARY, 2434 Old Cornelia Hwy, 30507-7854. SAN 375-569X. Tel: 770-531-2500. Toll Free Tel: 800-260-1598. TDD: 770-531-2520. FAX: 770-531-2502. *Mgr*, Kathy Evans; E-Mail: kevans@mail.hall.public.ga.us
Circ 62,225
Library Holdings: Bk Vols 14,718; Per Subs 31
Subject Interests: Talking books
Special Services for the Blind - Talking Books
Friends of the Library Group
HEADQUARTERS, 127 Main St NW, 30501-3614. Tel: 770-532-3311. Web Site: www.hall.public.lib.ga.us. *Asst Dir*, Elaine McCracken
Circ 223,657
Library Holdings: Bk Vols 98,541; Per Subs 208
Subject Interests: Genealogy, Local history
Special Collections: James Longstreet Coll, papers
MURRAYVILLE BRANCH, 4796 Thompson Bridge Rd, Murrayville, 30506-5320. SAN 374-7352. Tel: 770-503-1055. FAX: 770-503-9298. *Mgr*, Rick Kiser; E-Mail: rkiser@mail.hall.public.lib.ga.us
Circ 36,497
Library Holdings: Bk Titles 14,045; Per Subs 30
Friends of the Library Group

M NORTHEAST GEORGIA MEDICAL CENTER LIBRARY, 743 Spring St NE, 30501-3899. SAN 320-9393. Tel: 770-535-3553, Ext 1152. FAX: 770-718-5473. *Librn*, Kathleen Savage
Founded 1963
Library Holdings: Bk Titles 1,300; Per Subs 60
Subject Interests: Medicine, Nursing
Partic in Southeastern Regional Med Libr Program

GLYNCO

G FEDERAL LAW ENFORCEMENT TRAINING CENTER LIBRARY, Bldg 262, 31524. SAN 303-3848. Tel: 912-267-2320. *Librn*, Ann Pierce; Tel: 912-280-5432, Fax: 912-267-2822, E-Mail: apierce@fletc.treas.gov; Staff 3 (MLS 1, Non-MLS 2)
Founded 1975
Library Holdings: Bk Vols 40,000; Bk Titles 4,000
Automation Activity & Vendor Info: (Cataloging) Sagebrush Corporation
Restriction: Open to student, faculty & staff

GRACEWOOD

M GRACEWOOD STATE SCHOOL & HOSPITAL, Hospital Library, 100 Myrtle Blvd, PO Box 1299, 30812-1299. SAN 303-3856. Tel: 706-790-2011. FAX: 706-790-2247. *Librn*, Linda D Lawal; Tel: 706-790-2011, Ext 2183, E-Mail: llawal@dhr.state.ga.us
Founded 1963
Library Holdings: Bk Titles 3,780; Per Subs 55
Subject Interests: Dentistry, Genetics, Internal medicine, Medicine, Psychology
Special Collections: Mental Retardation, flm; Pediatrics, Psychiatry & Family Practice (Audio Digest Foundation Coll), tapes
Partic in Georgia Libr Info Network; Southeastern Regional Med Libr Program

GRIFFIN

P FLINT RIVER REGIONAL LIBRARY, 800 Memorial Dr, 30223. SAN 338-8174. Tel: 770-412-4770. FAX: 770-412-4773. Web Site: www.spalding.public.lib.ga.us. *Exec Dir*, Walter H Murphy; E-Mail: murphyw@mail.spalding.public.lib.ga.us; *Coordr, Publ Servs*, James D Tingen; *Cat*, Jeanne J Farris; *Ch Servs*, Marsha Parham; *Publ Servs*, Jack Colbert; *ILL*, Vicki Marshall. Subject Specialists: *Teaching*, Jack Colbert; Staff 48 (MLS 14, Non-MLS 34)
Founded 1949. Pop 217,453; Circ 1,512,848
Jul 2000-Jun 2001 Income (Main Library and Branch Library) $2,977,000. Mats Exp $350,000. Sal $1,409,000
Library Holdings: Bk Vols 349,976; Bk Titles 140,465; Per Subs 642
Subject Interests: Georgia
Automation Activity & Vendor Info: (Cataloging) SIRSI; (Circulation) SIRSI; (OPAC) SIRSI
Function: ILL available
Partic in Georgia Online Database; Solinet
Educational Learning Laboratory (computerized 10-station Novell network platform. K-adult) provides computer assisted instruction (CAI); free internet access
Branches: 8
BARNESVILLE-LAMAR COUNTY, 401 Thomaston St, Barnesville, 30204. SAN 338-8239. Tel: 770-358-3270. FAX: 770-358-4267. Web Site: www.spalding.public.lib.ga.us. *Exec Dir*, Walter H Murphy; Tel: 770-412-4770, Fax: 770-412-4773, E-Mail: murphyw@mail.spalding.public.lib.ga.us
Library Holdings: Bk Vols 29,867; Bk Titles 24,474; Per Subs 47
Automation Activity & Vendor Info: (Circulation) SIRSI; (OPAC) SIRSI
Function: ILL available
Friends of the Library Group
J JOEL EDWARDS PUBLIC, 618 Hwy 19 S, PO Box 574, Zebulon, 30295. SAN 338-8573. Tel: 770-567-2014. FAX: 770-567-2016. Web Site: www.spalding.public.lib.us. *Exec Dir*, Walter H Murphy; Tel: 770-412-4770, Fax: 770-412-4773, E-Mail: murphy@mail.spalding.public.lib.ga.us
Circ 26,368
Library Holdings: Bk Vols 16,588; Bk Titles 13,201; Per Subs 31
Automation Activity & Vendor Info: (Circulation) SIRSI; (OPAC) SIRSI
FAYETTE COUNTY, 1821 Heritage Park Way, Fayetteville, 30214. SAN 338-8441. Tel: 770-461-8841. FAX: 770-719-9662. Web Site: www.admin.co.fayette.ga.us/faylib.htm. *Exec Dir*, Walter H Murphy; Tel: 770-412-4770, Fax: 770-412-4773, E-Mail: murphy@mail.spalding.public.lib.ga.us; *Dir*, Christeen Snell
Library Holdings: Bk Vols 41,836; Bk Titles 40,080
Subject Interests: Education
Special Collections: Margaret Mitchell
Automation Activity & Vendor Info: (Circulation) SIRSI; (OPAC) SIRSI
Friends of the Library Group
GRIFFIN-SPALDING COUNTY, 800 Memorial Dr, 30223. SAN 338-8352. Tel: 770-412-4770. FAX: 770-412-4773. Web Site: www.spalding.public.lib.us. *Exec Dir*, Walter H Murphy; E-Mail: murphy@mail.spalding.public.lib.ga.us
Circ 465,768
Library Holdings: Bk Vols 94,979; Bk Titles 85,336; Per Subs 150
Automation Activity & Vendor Info: (Circulation) SIRSI; (OPAC) SIRSI
JACKSON-BUTTS COUNTY, 436 E College St, Jackson, 30233. SAN 338-8387. Tel: 770-775-7524. FAX: 770-775-4251. Web Site: www.spalding.public.lib.ga.us. *Exec Dir*, Walter H Murphy; Tel: 770-412-4770, Fax: 770-412-4773, E-Mail: murphy@mail.spalding.public.lib.ga.us
Circ 61,570

Library Holdings: Bk Vols 34,326; Bk Titles 29,139; Per Subs 50
Subject Interests: Education
Automation Activity & Vendor Info: (Circulation) SIRSI; (OPAC) SIRSI
MONROE COUNTY, 62 W Main St, Forsyth, 31029. SAN 338-8476. Tel: 478-994-7025. FAX: 478-994-7289. Web Site: www.spalding.public.lib.ga.us. *Exec Dir*, Walter H Murphy; Tel: 770-412-4770, Fax: 770-412-4773, E-Mail: murphy@mail.spalding.public.lib.ga.us
Circ 74,990
Library Holdings: Bk Vols 35,641; Bk Titles 28,408; Per Subs 55
Automation Activity & Vendor Info: (Circulation) SIRSI; (OPAC) SIRSI
Friends of the Library Group
PEACHTREE CITY BRANCH, 201 Willowbend Rd, Peachtree City, 30269. SAN 338-8565. Tel: 770-631-2520. FAX: 770-631-2522. Web Site: www.peachtree-city.org. *Exec Dir*, Walter H Murphy; Tel: 770-412-4770, Fax: 770-412-4773, E-Mail: murphy@mail.spalding.public.lib.ga.us
Founded 1973. Circ 333,669
Library Holdings: Bk Vols 57,417; Bk Titles 42,397; Per Subs 140
Subject Interests: Education
Automation Activity & Vendor Info: (Circulation) SIRSI; (OPAC) SIRSI
Friends of the Library Group
TYRONE PUBLIC, 881 Senoia Rd, Tyrone, 30290. SAN 338-859X. Tel: 770-487-1565. FAX: 770-487-1091. Web Site: www.spalding.public.lib.ga.us. *Exec Dir*, Walter H Murphy; Tel: 770-412-4770, Fax: 770-412-4773, E-Mail: murphy@mail.spalding.public.lib.ga.us
Circ 38,248
Library Holdings: Bk Vols 15,265; Bk Titles 9,776; Per Subs 22
Automation Activity & Vendor Info: (Circulation) SIRSI; (OPAC) SIRSI

C UNIVERSITY OF GEORGIA LIBRARIES, Griffin Campus, 1109 Experiment St, 30223-1797. SAN 303-3759. Tel: 770-228-7238. FAX: 770-229-3213. E-Mail: Internet: librgrf@gaes.griffin.peachnet.edu. Web Site: www.griffin.peachnet.edu/libpage.html. *Librn*, M Kay Mowery; Staff 1 (MLS 1)
Founded 1888
Library Holdings: Bk Vols 10,000; Per Subs 300
Subject Interests: Agriculture
Restriction: Non-circulating to the public
Function: ILL available
Partic in OCLC Online Computer Library Center, Inc

HARTWELL

P HART COUNTY LIBRARY, 150 Benson St, 30643. SAN 303-3864. Tel: 706-376-4655. FAX: 706-376-1157. E-Mail: hart10@mail.hart.public.lib.ga.us. *Dir*, Richard Sanders; *Librn*, Pam Bagby; *Info Tech*, Lynn Roberts; *Circ*, Kimbla Rucker; Staff 5 (MLS 2, Non-MLS 3)
Founded 1936. Pop 21,500; Circ 162,000
1996-1997 Income $220,000, State $117,000, City $12,000, Federal $4,000, County $80,000. Mats Exp $25,500, Books $24,000, Per/Ser (Incl. Access Fees) $1,500. Sal $112,000 (Prof $86,000)
Library Holdings: Bk Vols 52,000; Per Subs 32
Special Collections: History of Hart County, A-tapes
Friends of the Library Group

HOMERVILLE

S HUXFORD GENEALOGICAL SOCIETY INC, Genealogical Library, Corner of Dame & College Sts, PO Box 595, 31634. SAN 375-7730. Tel: 912-487-2310. FAX: 912-487-3881. E-Mail: hgs@huxford.com. Web Site: www.huxford.com. *Librn*, Violet Bennett
Library Holdings: Bk Titles 4,000; Per Subs 1,000

JEKYLL ISLAND

S JEKYLL ISLAND AUTHORITY, Jekyll Island Museum Archives, 381 Riverview Dr, 31527. SAN 373-4269. Tel: 912-635-2119. FAX: 912-635-4420. Web Site: www.jekyllisland.com, www.jinews.com. *Dir*, Warren Murphy
Library Holdings: Bk Vols 500

JONESBORO

P CLAYTON COUNTY LIBRARY SYSTEM, 865 Battlecreek Rd, 30236-1919. SAN 338-8417. Tel: 770-473-3850. FAX: 770-473-3858. Web Site: www.clayton.public.lib.ga.us. *Dir Libr Serv*, Carol Johnson Stewart; E-Mail: stewartc@mail.clayton.public.lib.ga.us; *Asst Dir, Ch Servs*, Janice Arcuria; *Asst Dir, Tech Servs*, Cynthia Hunter; *Asst Dir, Commun Servs*, Jeanne Mino; *Acq, Asst Dir, Coll Develop*, Flora Walker; Staff 49 (MLS 7, Non-MLS 42)
Founded 1941. Pop 211,243; Circ 823,871
Jul 1998-Jun 1999 Income (Main Library and Branch Library) $2,115,136, State $560,587, County $1,554,549. Mats Exp $329,981, Books $285,699, Per/Ser (Incl. Access Fees) $25,812, Electronic Ref Mat (Incl. Access Fees) $18,470. Sal $1,417,095
Library Holdings: Bk Vols 333,328; Bk Titles 110,472; Per Subs 680
Subject Interests: Georgia
Special Collections: Clayton County History
Publications: Monthly Calendar of Events
Special Services for the Deaf - High interest/low vocabulary books
Library sponsors Tower - Together We Read - Literacy tutor training & tutoring
Friends of the Library Group
Branches: 4
FOREST PARK BRANCH, 696 Main St, Forest Park, 30297. SAN 338-8298. Tel: 404-366-0850. FAX: 404-366-0884. *Librn*, Donna Thoman
Library Holdings: Bk Vols 49,343
Friends of the Library Group
JONESBORO BRANCH, 124 Smith St, 30236-3539. SAN 328-8897. Tel: 770-478-7120. FAX: 770-473-3846. *Librn*, Phyllis Philmon
Library Holdings: Bk Vols 53,329
MORROW BRANCH, 6225 Maddox Rd, Morrow, 30260. SAN 338-8506. Tel: 404-366-7749. FAX: 770-363-4569. *Librn*, M Hall
Library Holdings: Bk Vols 38,809
RIVERDALE BRANCH, 420 Valley Hill Rd, Riverdale, 30274. SAN 324-086X. Tel: 770-472-8100. FAX: 770-472-8106. *Librn*, Mary J Gowing
Library Holdings: Bk Vols 53,871
Friends of the Library Group

KENNESAW

J KENNESAW STATE UNIVERSITY, Horace W Sturgis Library, 1000 Chastain Rd, 30144. SAN 303-3937. Tel: 770-423-6186. FAX: 770-423-6185. Web Site: www.kennesaw.edu/library/. *Dir*, Robert Williams; Fax: 770-499-3376, E-Mail: rwilliam@ksumail.kennesaw.edu; *Asst Dir*, Dr David Evans; Tel: 770-423-6194, Fax: 770-499-3376, E-Mail: devans@kennesaw.edu; *Tech Servs*, Alan Lebish; *Cat*, Barbara Milam; Tel: 770-423-6259, Fax: 770-423-6727, E-Mail: bmilam@kennesaw.edu; *Publ Servs*, Betty Childres; Tel: 770-423-6199, E-Mail: bchildre@kennesaw.edu; *Ser*, Olga Russov; Tel: 770-423-6189, Fax: 770-423-6727, E-Mail: orussov@kennesaw.edu; *Doc*, Jack Purkey; Tel: 770-423-6248, Fax: 770-423-6727, E-Mail: jpurkey@kennesaw.edu; *Online Servs*, Mary Platt; Tel: 770-423-6197, E-Mail: mplatt@kennesaw.edu; *Ref*, Dewi Wilson; Tel: 770-423-6661, E-Mail: dwilson@kennesaw.edu; *Circ*, Martha Henry-Croom; Tel: 770-423-6511, E-Mail: mcroom@kennesaw.edu; *Bibliog Instr*, Cheryl Stiles; Tel: 770-423-6003, E-Mail: cstiles@kennesaw.edu; Staff 15 (MLS 15)
Founded 1963. Enrl 12,500; Fac 570; Highest Degree: Master
Jul 1998-Jun 1999 Income $2,978,336. Mats Exp $1,390,000, Books $400,000, Per/Ser (Incl. Access Fees) $650,000, Presv $10,000, Micro $300,000, Manuscripts & Archives $30,000. Sal $1,699,410 (Prof $1,099,410)
Library Holdings: Bk Vols 558,000; Bk Titles 310,000; Per Subs 3,800
Special Collections: Bentley Rare Book Coll; Difazio Children's Literature Coll; Teen Literature Coll
Automation Activity & Vendor Info: (Acquisitions) Endeavor; (Cataloging) Endeavor; (Circulation) Endeavor; (Course Reserve) Endeavor; (OPAC) Endeavor; (Serials) Endeavor
Database Vendor: Lexis-Nexis, OCLC - First Search, OVID Technologies
Publications: Bookmark (magazine); Compass (newsletter); Endnotes (newsletter); Helpkey 101 & 102 (BI); Recent Acquisitions (newsletter)
Partic in Dialog Corporation; SE Libr Network

S NATIONAL PARK SERVICE, Kennesaw Mountain National Battlefield Park Library, 900 Kennesaw Mountain Dr, 30152. SAN 303-3953. Tel: 770-427-4686. FAX: 770-528-8399. *Librn*, Retha Stevens
Founded 1935
Library Holdings: Bk Titles 1,000
Special Collections: Atlanta Campaign-1864
Open Mon-Sun 8:30-5

LA GRANGE

C LA GRANGE COLLEGE, William & Evelyn Banks Library, 601 Broad St, 30240-2999. SAN 338-8743. Tel: 706-880-8312. Interlibrary Loan Service Tel: 706-880-8289. Circulation Tel: 706-880-8312. Reference Tel: 706-880-8289. FAX: 706-880-8040. Web Site: www.lgc.edu/library. *Dir*, Loren L Pinkerman; Tel: 706-880-8234, E-Mail: pinkerman@lgc.edu; *Acq, Ser*, Yvonne Mills; Tel: 706-812-7233; *Cat*, Lori Slay; Tel: 706-812-7233; *Circ*, Lisa Farrow; Tel: 706-812-7312; *Electronic Resources*, Mary Lou Dabbs; Tel: 706-880-8027; *Publ Servs, Tech Servs*, Charlene Adams Baxter; Tel: 706-812-7311; *Ref*, Dr Arthur Robinson. Subject Specialists: *Business*, Loren L Pinkerman; *History*, Loren L Pinkerman; *Music*, Loren L Pinkerman; Staff 7 (MLS 4, Non-MLS 3)
Founded 1836. Enrl 945; Fac 60; Highest Degree: Master
Jul 2000-Jun 2001 Mats Exp $182,900, Books $70,000, Per/Ser (Incl. Access Fees) $83,500, Micro $6,400, Electronic Ref Mat (Incl. Access Fees) $23,000
Library Holdings: Bk Vols 135,522; Bk Titles 120,124; Per Subs 490
Automation Activity & Vendor Info: (Cataloging) SIRSI; (Circulation) SIRSI; (OPAC) SIRSI

Publications: Banks News (newsletter)
Partic in Dialog Corporation; OCLC Online Computer Library Center, Inc; SE Libr Network; Solinet
Friends of the Library Group

P TROUP-HARRIS-COWETA REGIONAL LIBRARY, La Grange Memorial Library, 115 Alford St, 30240-3041. SAN 338-8808. Tel: 706-882-7784. FAX: 706-883-7342. Web Site: lagrange.troup.public.lib.ga.us. *Dir*, Joellen Ostendorf; E-Mail: jostendorf@thclibrary.net; *Asst Dir*, Frank Bennett; E-Mail: fbennett@thclibrary.net; *Tech Servs*, Clare Zens; E-Mail: zensc@mail.troup.public.lib.ga.us; *Asst Dir*, Pamela Huff; E-Mail: huffp@mail.troup.public.lib.ga.us; *Ch Servs*, Patricia Gay; E-Mail: gayp@mail.troup.public.lib.ga.us; *Ref*, Bill Skelton; Fax: 770-253-3625 (Newnan), E-Mail: wskelton@westga.edu; *Branch Mgr*, Carrie Zelger; Tel: 770-253-3625 (Newnan), E-Mail: czelger@westga.edu; Staff 9 (MLS 9)
Founded 1926. Pop 165,000; Circ 465,604
Jul 1999-Jun 2000 Income (Main Library and Branch Library) $1,509,237, State $602,918, City $450,529, County $444,800, Other $10,990. Mats Exp $146,633. Sal $889,260 (Prof $320,424)
Library Holdings: Bk Vols 194,000; Bk Titles 150,000; Per Subs 414; High Interest/Low Vocabulary Bk Vols 300
Subject Interests: Georgia
Automation Activity & Vendor Info: (Acquisitions) SIRSI; (Cataloging) SIRSI; (Circulation) SIRSI; (ILL) SIRSI; (OPAC) SIRSI
Partic in Cent Ga Associated Librs; Georgia Online Database
Friends of the Library Group
Branches: 5
GRANTVILLE PUBLIC, 123 LaGrange St, PO Box 340, Grantville, 30220. SAN 373-8752. Tel: 770-583-2565. FAX: 770-583-2565. *Mgr*, Nadine Schultz; E-Mail: nschultz@mail.$coweta.public.lib.ga.us
Pop 2,000; Circ 8,000
Jul 1999-Jun 2000 Income $10,820, State $2,100, City $8,720. Mats Exp $3,000
Library Holdings: Bk Vols 8,000
Automation Activity & Vendor Info: (Circulation) SIRSI; (ILL) SIRSI; (OPAC) SIRSI
Friends of the Library Group
HARRIS COUNTY, PO Box 266, Hamilton, 31811. SAN 338-8867. Tel: 706-628-4685. FAX: 706-628-4685. *Mgr*, Ann Graffagnino; E-Mail: graffaga@mail.harris.public.lib.ga.us
Pop 30,000; Circ 57,424
Jul 1999-Jun 2000 Income $133,285, State $10,985, County $122,300. Mats Exp $12,000. Sal $96,915
Library Holdings: Bk Titles 17,652; Per Subs 458
Automation Activity & Vendor Info: (Circulation) SIRSI; (ILL) SIRSI; (OPAC) SIRSI
HOGANSVILLE PUBLIC, 600 E Main St, Hogansville, 30230. SAN 338-8891. Tel: 706-637-6230. FAX: 706-637-6230. *Mgr*, Jane Gottshall; E-Mail: gottshalj@mail.troup.public.lib.ga.us
Jul 1999-Jun 2000 Income $51,530, State $3,300, City $32,180, County $16,050. Mats Exp $6,200, Books $3,300, Per/Ser (Incl. Access Fees) $1,400, AV Equip $1,500. Sal $32,085
Automation Activity & Vendor Info: (Circulation) SIRSI; (ILL) SIRSI; (OPAC) SIRSI
NEWNAN-COWETA PUBLIC LIBRARY, 25 Hospital Rd, Newnan, 30263. SAN 338-8921. Tel: 770-253-3625. TDD: 770-502-1917. FAX: 770-254-7262. E-Mail: ncplibry@westga.edu. Web Site: www.communitynow.com/library/. *Librn*, Carrie Zeiger; E-Mail: czeiger@westga.edu; Staff 4 (MLS 4)
Pop 75,000; Circ 287,576
Jul 1999-Jan 2000 Income $525,085, State $101,477, City $213,609, County $210,000. Mats Exp $33,170. Sal $331,711 (Prof $66,396)
Library Holdings: Bk Vols 64,216
Automation Activity & Vendor Info: (Circulation) SIRSI; (ILL) SIRSI; (OPAC) SIRSI
SENOIA AREA PUBLIC, 62 Main St, PO Box 406, Senoia, 30276. SAN 338-8832. Tel: 770-559-3537. FAX: 770-559-3537. *In Charge*, Saundra Frank; E-Mail: franks@mail.coweta.public.lib.ga.us
Pop 10,000; Circ 12,604
2000-2001 Income $36,150, State $3,650, City $30,000, County $2,500. Mats Exp $4,000
Library Holdings: Bk Vols 5,136
Automation Activity & Vendor Info: (Circulation) SIRSI; (ILL) SIRSI; (Serials) SIRSI
Bookmobiles: 2. Thomas Built (Chevrolet Chassis) - 1990 model

LAFAYETTE

P CHEROKEE REGIONAL LIBRARY SYSTEM, La Fayette-Walker County Library, 305 S Duke St, 30728-2936. SAN 338-8980. Tel: 706-638-2992. FAX: 706-638-4028. Web Site: www.walker.public.lib.ga.us. *Dir*, Diana Ray Tope; Tel: 706-638-8311, E-Mail: dtope@mail.walker.public.lib.ga.us; *Branch Mgr*, Valinda Oliver; E-Mail: oliverl@mail.walker.public.lib.ga.us; *Asst Dir, Syst Coordr*, Lecia Eubanks; Tel: 706-638-7557, E-Mail: leubanks@mail.walker.public.lib.ga.us; *Br Coordr, Tech Servs*, Gayla Brewer; Tel: 706-638-2064, E-Mail: brewerg@mail.walker.public.lib.ga.us; *Librn for Blind*, Charles Stubbefield; Tel: 706-638-1958, E-Mail: stubblec@mail.walker.public.lib.ga.us; Staff 3 (MLS 3)
Founded 1944. Pop 76,857; Circ 91,570
Jul 1999-Jun 2000 Income (Main Library Only) $487,927, State $252,227, City $49,000, Federal $27,964, County $77,569, Locally Generated Income $34,765, Other $46,402. Mats Exp $31,936, Books $30,047, Per/Ser (Incl. Access Fees) $1,135, Micro $754. Sal $244,432 (Prof $75,636)
Library Holdings: Bk Vols 56,666; Per Subs 38
Subject Interests: Genealogy, Georgia, Local history
Special Collections: Local History of Dade & Walker Counties (Georgia Room), bk, micro, CD
Automation Activity & Vendor Info: (Acquisitions) SIRSI; (Cataloging) SIRSI; (Circulation) SIRSI; (ILL) SIRSI; (OPAC) SIRSI; (Serials) SIRSI
Function: Document delivery services, ILL available, Literary searches, Outside services via phone, cable & mail, Photocopies available, Reference services available, Some telephone reference
Friends of the Library Group
Branches: 4
CHICKAMAUGA PUBLIC, 306 Cove Rd, Chickamauga, 30707-1410. SAN 338-9073. Tel: 706-375-3004. FAX: 706-375-7034. Web Site: www.walker.public.lib.ga.us/branches/chick.html. *Branch Mgr*, Deborah Goodson; E-Mail: dgoodson@mail.walker.public.lib.ga.us
Jul 1999-Jun 2000 Income $57,988, State $7,000, City $5,000, County $23,791, Locally Generated Income $2,197, Other $20,000. Mats Exp $8,220, Books $7,248, Per/Ser (Incl. Access Fees) $972. Sal $30,750
Library Holdings: Bk Vols 24; Bk Vols 23,312
Subject Interests: Civil War, Local history
Automation Activity & Vendor Info: (Acquisitions) SIRSI; (Cataloging) SIRSI; (Circulation) SIRSI; (ILL) SIRSI; (OPAC) SIRSI; (Serials) SIRSI
Function: ILL available, Literary searches, Photocopies available, Reference services available, Some telephone reference
Friends of the Library Group
DADE COUNTY, 102 Court St, PO Box 340, Trenton, 30752-0340. SAN 338-9103. Tel: 706-657-7857. FAX: 706-657-7860. Web Site: www.walker.public.lib.ga.us/branes/dade.html. *Branch Mgr*, Glenda Winans; E-Mail: winansg@mail.walker.public.lib.ga.us
Jul 1999-Jun 2000 Income (Main Library Only) $88,158, State $7,437, City $10,214, County $63,943, Locally Generated Income $6,564. Mats Exp $6,897, Books $5,933, Per/Ser (Incl. Access Fees) $964. Sal $43,734
Library Holdings: Bk Vols 27,967; Per Subs 25
Subject Interests: Local history
Automation Activity & Vendor Info: (Acquisitions) SIRSI; (Cataloging) SIRSI; (Circulation) SIRSI; (ILL) SIRSI; (OPAC) SIRSI; (Serials) SIRSI
Friends of the Library Group
LAFAYETTE SUBREGIONAL LIBRARY FOR THE BLIND & PHYSICALLY HANDICAPPED - TALKING BOOK CENTER, 305 S Duke St, 30728-2936. Toll Free Tel: 888-506-0509. FAX: 706-638-4028. Web Site: www.walker.public.lib.ga.us/tbc/. *Mgr*, Charles Stubblefield; Tel: 706-638-1958, E-Mail: stubblec@mail.walker.public.lib.ga.us
Founded 1975
1998-1999 Income State $64,384. Sal $47,152
Library Holdings: Bk Vols 22,624; Bk Titles 22,330
Publications: Newsletter
Function: ILL to other special libraries, Photocopies available, Reference services available
Special Services for the Blind - Bks/mag in Braille, on rec & on tape available by post-free mail to individuals living in New York City or on Long Island who cannot read regular print because of a visual or physical handicap; Newsletter in large print
ROSSVILLE PUBLIC, 504 McFarland Ave, Rossville, 30741. SAN 338-9162. Tel: 706-866-1368. FAX: 706-858-9251. Web Site: www.walker.public.lib.ga.us/branches/rossville.html. *Branch Mgr*, Michael Roach; E-Mail: roachm@mail.walker.public.lib.ga.us
Founded 1944
Jul 1999-Jun 2000 Income $114,469, State $9,605, City $53,750, County $47,034, Locally Generated Income $4,080. Mats Exp $10,406, Books $9,042, Per/Ser (Incl. Access Fees) $1,336, Micro $28. Sal $55,786
Library Holdings: Bk Vols 32,718; Per Subs 79
Subject Interests: Local history
Automation Activity & Vendor Info: (Acquisitions) SIRSI; (Cataloging) SIRSI; (Circulation) SIRSI; (ILL) SIRSI; (OPAC) SIRSI; (Serials) SIRSI
Function: ILL available, Literary searches, Photocopies available, Reference services available, Some telephone reference
Friends of the Library Group

LAWRENCEVILLE

L GWINNETT COUNTY LAW LIBRARY, 75 Langley Dr, 30245. SAN 372-1752. Tel: 770-822-8577. FAX: 770-822-8570. Web Site: www.courts.co.gwinnett.ga.us/aoc/lawlib.htm. *Librn*, Claudia Cook
Library Holdings: Bk Vols 13,000; Per Subs 25

P GWINNETT COUNTY PUBLIC LIBRARY, 1001 Lawrenceville Hwy, 30045. SAN 338-9197. Tel: 770-822-4522. TDD: 770-822-5377. FAX: 770-822-5379. Web Site: www.gwinnett.public.lib.ga.us. *Dir*, Jo Ann Pinder; Tel: 770-822-5321, E-Mail: jpinder@gwinnettpl.org; *Tech Servs*, Ed McCabe; E-Mail: emcc@gwinnettpl.org; Staff 233 (MLS 60, Non-MLS 173)
Founded 1935. Pop 540,590; Circ 5,158,149

Jul 1998-Jun 1999 Income $10,842,055, State $1,108,048, Federal $5,000, County $8,882,402, Locally Generated Income $846,605. Mats Exp $2,187,591, Books $2,074,400, Electronic Ref Mat (Incl. Access Fees) $113,191. Sal $5,453,157
Library Holdings: Bk Vols 682,598; Per Subs 2,009
Automation Activity & Vendor Info: (Acquisitions) epixtech, inc.; (Cataloging) epixtech, inc.; (Circulation) epixtech, inc.; (Media Booking) epixtech, inc.; (OPAC) epixtech, inc.; (Serials) epixtech, inc.
Database Vendor: GaleNet, Wilson - Wilson Web
Partic in Georgia Online Database
Friends of the Library Group
Branches: 10
BUFORD-SUGAR HILL BRANCH, 2100 Buford Hwy, Buford, 30518. SAN 338-9251. Tel: 770-945-4196. FAX: 770-271-6983. *Branch Mgr*, Sue Kelly
COLLINS HILL, 455 Camp Perrin Rd, 30043. Tel: 770-822-2040. FAX: 770-822-2052. *Branch Mgr*, Nancy Stanbery-Kellam
Library Holdings: Bk Vols 68,150; Per Subs 1,220
DULUTH BRANCH, 3480 Duluth Park Lane, Duluth, 30096. SAN 338-9316. Tel: 770-476-1992. FAX: 770-418-2933. *Mgr*, Deborah George
ELIZABETH H WILLIAMS BRANCH, 2740 Lenora Church Rd, Snellville, 30078. SAN 338-9464. Tel: 770-972-0988. FAX: 770-978-5143. *Branch Mgr*, Alan Harkness
FIVE FORKS BRANCH, 2780 Five Forks Trickum Rd, 30044. SAN 373-8736. Tel: 770-978-5600. FAX: 770-978-5609. *Branch Mgr*, Beth McIntyre
LAWRENCEVILLE BRANCH, 1001 Lawrenceville Hwy, 30045. SAN 338-9227. Tel: 770-822-5361. FAX: 770-822-5376. *Branch Mgr*, Pat Edwards
LILBURN BRANCH, 788 Hillcrest Rd, Lilburn, 30047. SAN 338-9375. Tel: 770-921-7346. FAX: 770-717-3173. *Branch Mgr*, Nancy Chilcoat
MOUNTAIN PARK BRANCH, 1210 Pounds Rd SW, Lilburn, 30047. SAN 338-9405. Tel: 770-921-1299. FAX: 770-717-3193. *Branch Mgr*, Whitney Halcomb
NORCROSS BRANCH, 6025 Buford Hwy, Norcross, 30071. SAN 338-943X. Tel: 770-448-4938. FAX: 770-903-1073. *Branch Mgr*, Sharon Jackson
PEACHTREE CORNERS BRANCH, 5570 Spalding Dr, Norcross, 30092. SAN 329-7039. Tel: 770-729-0931. FAX: 770-903-1043. *Branch Mgr*, Julie Hunter

LITHONIA

R LUTHER RICE SEMINARY, Bertha Smith Library, 3038 Evans Mill Rd, 30038. SAN 302-9786. Tel: 770-484-1204. FAX: 770-484-1155. E-Mail: library@lrs.edu. *Dir*, Hal Haller; Staff 1 (MLS 1)
Founded 1972. Enrl 1,800; Fac 15; Highest Degree: Doctorate
Library Holdings: Bk Vols 44,000; Bk Titles 41,000; Per Subs 100
Subject Interests: Biblical studies, Theology
Special Collections: Religion (Christian Ministry), dissertations

LOOKOUT MOUNTAIN

C COVENANT COLLEGE, Anna Emma Kresge Memorial Library, 14049 Scenic Hwy, 30750. SAN 315-8411. Tel: 706-820-1560, Ext 1432. FAX: 706-820-0672. Web Site: www.covenant.edu. *Dir*, Gary B Huisman; E-Mail: huisman@convent.edu; *Ref*, Ethan P Pettit; Staff 2 (MLS 2)
Founded 1955. Enrl 1,030; Fac 62; Highest Degree: Master
Jul 1999-Jun 2000 Income Federal $7,099. Mats Exp $334,942, Books $53,000, Per/Ser (Incl. Access Fees) $55,000, Micro $3,000, AV Equip $3,089, Electronic Ref Mat (Incl. Access Fees) $23,200. Sal $133,243
Library Holdings: Bk Vols 76,090; Per Subs 412
Special Collections: American History, microfiche; Christian Authors (Kresge Coll); John Bunyan
Automation Activity & Vendor Info: (Acquisitions) Gaylord; (Cataloging) Gaylord; (Circulation) Gaylord; (Course Reserve) Gaylord; (OPAC) Gaylord; (Serials) Gaylord
Publications: Student Handbook
Partic in SE Libr Network

LOUISVILLE

P JEFFERSON COUNTY LIBRARY SYSTEM, 306 E Broad St, 30434. SAN 338-9499. Tel: 912-625-3751. FAX: 912-625-7683. *Dir*, Charlotte Rogers; E-Mail: rogers@mail.jefferson.public.lib.ga.us; *Asst Dir*, Bonnie Boatright; Staff 2 (MLS 2)
Founded 1954. Pop 17,697; Circ 50,497
Jul 1996-Jun 1997 Income $256,978, State $98,720, City $38,801, County $100,000, Locally Generated Income $14,455. Mats Exp $25,564, Books $22,557, Per/Ser (Incl. Access Fees) $2,800, AV Equip $207. Sal $164,824 (Prof $77,220)
Library Holdings: Bk Vols 81,000; Per Subs 143
Subject Interests: Children's literature, Local history
Special Collections: Georgia History (A P Little Coll); Southern Literature Coll
Partic in Georgia Online Database
Friends of the Library Group
Branches: 2
MCCOLLUM PUBLIC, 405 N Main St, Wrens, 30833-1142. SAN 338-9529. Tel: 706-547-3484. FAX: 706-547-9358. *Mgr*, Wanda McGahee
Friends of the Library Group
WADLEY PUBLIC, 11 W College Ave, Wadley, 30477-0356. Tel: 912-252-1366. FAX: 912-252-1366. *Mgr*, Kathy Hudson
Friends of the Library Group
Bookmobiles: 1

LUMPKIN

S WESTVILLE HISTORIC HANDICRAFTS, INC LIBRARY, Martin Luther King Jr Dr, PO Box 1850, 31815. SAN 303-3880. Tel: 912-838-6310. FAX: 912-838-4000. Web Site: www.westville.org. *Dir*, Matthew Moye
Founded 1966
Library Holdings: Bk Titles 1,400
Subject Interests: Decorative arts, Georgia, Horticulture
Special Collections: African-American Architecture & History Survey of West Georgia; John West Coll; Pre-Columbian Seminars Transcripts
Restriction: Not a lending library

MACON

S BROWN & WILLIAMSON TOBACCO CORP, Research Department Library, 2600 Weaver Rd, 31217. SAN 306-3305. Tel: 478-464-3565. Interlibrary Loan Service Tel: 478-464-3565. FAX: 478-464-4016. *Librn*, Carol S Lincoln; Staff 2 (MLS 1, Non-MLS 1)
Founded 1958
Library Holdings: Bk Titles 9,000; Per Subs 225
Subject Interests: Agriculture, Chemistry, Engineering, Physics, Tobacco
Partic in CAS Online; Dialog Corporation

C CENTRAL GEORGIA TECHNICAL COLLEGE LIBRARY, (Formerly Macon Technical Institute Library), 3300 Macon Tech Dr, 31206-3628. SAN 375-4898. Tel: 478-757-3549. FAX: 478-757-3545. E-Mail: library@cgtcollege.org. Web Site: www.cgtcollege.org/library. *Dir Libr Serv*, W Neil McArthur; Tel: 478-757-3548, E-Mail: nmcarth@cgtcollege.org; *Branch Mgr*, Sarah Lockmiller; Tel: 478-445-2333, Fax: 478-445-2319, E-Mail: slockmil@cgtcollege.org; *Bibliog Instr*, Ellen Jolley; Tel: 478-757-3547, E-Mail: ejolly@cgtcollege.org; *Info Tech*, David Garrett; Tel: 478-757-3546, E-Mail: dgarrett@cgtcollege.org; *Librn*, Max Brown; E-Mail: mbrown@cgtcollege.org; *Librn*, Rose Lear; E-Mail: rlear@cgtcollege.org; Staff 8 (MLS 4, Non-MLS 4)
Founded 1993. Enrl 3,000; Fac 100; Highest Degree: Associate
Jul 2000-May 2001 Income Parent Institution $120,000
Library Holdings: Bk Vols 12,000; Per Subs 300
Subject Interests: Allied health, Business, Industry, Info tech, Tech info, Trade
Automation Activity & Vendor Info: (Cataloging) TLC; (Circulation) TLC; (ILL) TLC; (OPAC) TLC
Database Vendor: Ebsco - EbscoHost, Lexis-Nexis, OCLC - First Search, ProQuest, Wilson - Wilson Web
Function: Reference services available

S GEORGIA FORESTRY COMMISSION LIBRARY, 5645 Riggins Mill Rd, PO Box 819, 31202-0819. SAN 303-3899. Tel: 912-751-3482. FAX: 912-751-3465.
Founded 1956
Library Holdings: Bk Vols 2,240; Per Subs 100

J MACON STATE COLLEGE LIBRARY, 100 College Station Dr, 31206-5144. SAN 303-3902. Tel: 912-471-2709. FAX: 912-471-2869. Web Site: www.maconstate.edu/library/library1.htm. *Dir*, James R R Macklin; E-Mail: jmacklin@mail.maconstate.edu; *Asst Dir*, Patricia Borck; Tel: 912-471-2865, E-Mail: pborck@mail.maconstate.edu; *Circ*, Bonita Tharpe; E-Mail: btharpe@mail.maconstate.edu; *Bibliog Instr, Ref*, Mary Morris; E-Mail: mkmorris@mail.maconstate.edu; *Cat, Online Servs, Tech Servs*, Kathy Adams; Tel: 912-471-2042, E-Mail: kadams@mail.maconstate.edu; *Per*, Barbara Walker; E-Mail: bwalker@mail.maconstate.edu; *Media Spec*, Roy Harper; Tel: 912-471-2831, E-Mail: rharper@mail.maconstate.edu; *Coll Develop*, Ann Elder; E-Mail: aelder@cennet.mc.peachnet.edu; Staff 8 (MLS 4, Non-MLS 4)
Founded 1968. Enrl 3,500; Fac 135; Highest Degree: Bachelor
Jul 1999-Jun 2000 Income State $484,724. Mats Exp $110,250, Books $68,750, Per/Ser (Incl. Access Fees) $23,000, Micro $15,000, AV Equip $3,000, Other Print Mats $500. Sal $324,760 (Prof $162,072)
Library Holdings: Bk Vols 85,279; Bk Titles 83,175; Per Subs 327
Subject Interests: Info tech, Nursing
Special Collections: College Archives
Automation Activity & Vendor Info: (Acquisitions) Endeavor; (Cataloging) Endeavor; (Circulation) Endeavor; (Course Reserve) Endeavor; (OPAC) Endeavor; (Serials) Endeavor
Mem of Univ Syst of Ga
Partic in Cent Ga Associated Librs; SE Libr Network
Special Services for the Blind - ZoomText software to enlarge computer screen

S MACON TELEGRAPH LIBRARY, 120 Broadway, 31208. SAN 371-1390. Tel: 478-744-4509. FAX: 478-744-4385. Web Site: www.macontelegraph.com. *Mgr*, R J Petrovich; E-Mail: rpetrovich@macontel.com; Staff 2 (Non-MLS 2)
Library Holdings: Bk Titles 350; Per Subs 15
Database Vendor: Dialog, Lexis-Nexis
Friends of the Library Group

MERCER UNIVERSITY

CL WALTER F GEORGE SCHOOL OF LAW LIBRARY, 1021 Georgia Ave, 31201. SAN 338-9618. Tel: 478-301-2612. Circulation Tel: 478-301-2612. Reference Tel: 478-301-2334. FAX: 478-301-2284. Web Site: www.library.law.mercer.edu. *Dir*, Suzanne l Cassidy; Tel: 478-301-2665, Fax: 478-301-2284, E-Mail: cassidy_sl@mercer.edu; *Assoc Librn*, Billie J Olsen; *Ref*, Sybyl Marshall; *Head Tech Servs*, Ismael Gullon; *Assoc Librn*, Sheri H Lewis; *Ref*, Denise M Gibson; Staff 6 (MLS 6)
Founded 1850. Enrl 429; Fac 25; Highest Degree: Doctorate
Library Holdings: Bk Vols 298,000; Bk Titles 38,000; Per Subs 1,050
Subject Interests: Law, Literature
Special Collections: Griffin B Bell Papers
Partic in OCLC Online Computer Library Center, Inc; Westlaw

C JACK TARVER LIBRARY, 1300 Edgewood Ave, 31207. SAN 338-9588. Tel: 478-301-2960. Circulation Tel: 478-301-2961. Reference Tel: 478-301-2055. FAX: 478-301-2111. Interlibrary Loan Service FAX: 478-752-2252. Web Site: tarver.mercer.edu. *Dir Libr Serv*, Elizabeth D Hammond; *Assoc Dir, Dir, Tech Serv*, Jane G Richards; Tel: 478-301-2193; *Assoc Dir, Publ Servs*, David P Bunnell; Tel: 912-301-2031; *Bibliog Instr*, Valerie B Edmonds; Tel: 478-301-2965; *Circ*, Lisa K Koehler; Tel: 478-301-2962; *Spec Coll & Archives*, Susan G Broome; Tel: 478-301-2968; *Govt Doc*, Christine M Fischer; Tel: 478-301-2934; *ILL*, Russell Palmer; Tel: 478-301-2102; *Cat*, Dana L Kemp; Tel: 912-301-2027; *Acq*, Glenda Flowers; Tel: 478-301-2505; *Ser*, Rhonda M Adkins; Tel: 912-301-2966; *Coll Develop*, John Dye; Tel: 478-301-5334; *Exten Serv*, Karen Harrell; Tel: 678-986-6379; Staff 29 (MLS 12, Non-MLS 17)
Founded 1833. Enrl 6,800; Fac 210; Highest Degree: Doctorate
Jul 1999-Jun 2000 Income (Main Library Only) $1,900,068, Parent Institution $1,875,068, Other $25,000. Mats Exp $338,341, Books $148,519, Per/Ser (Incl. Access Fees) $132,822, Presv $12,000, Micro $12,000, AV Equip $2,000, Manuscripts & Archives $1,000, Electronic Ref Mat (Incl. Access Fees) $30,000. Sal $917,947 (Prof $518,065)
Library Holdings: Bk Vols 220,000; Bk Titles 190,000; Per Subs 950
Subject Interests: Baptist hist, Baptists, Civil War
Special Collections: Cooperative Baptist Fellowship Archives; Georgia Baptist History Coll; Mercer University Archives; Percy Shelley Coll; Robert Burns Coll
Automation Activity & Vendor Info: (Acquisitions) Innovative Interfaces Inc.; (Cataloging) Innovative Interfaces Inc.; (OPAC) Innovative Interfaces Inc.; (Serials) Innovative Interfaces Inc.
Database Vendor: Innovative Interfaces INN - View, Silverplatter Information Inc., Wilson - Wilson Web
Partic in Georgia Online Database; OCLC Online Computer Library Center, Inc; SE Libr Network; Solinet

CM SCHOOL OF MEDICINE, MEDICAL LIBRARY & LRC, 1550 College St, 31207. SAN 338-9626. Tel: 478-301-2515. Interlibrary Loan Service Tel: 478-301-2830. Circulation Tel: 478-301-4056. Reference Tel: 478-301-2830. Toll Free Tel: 800-425-4246. FAX: 478-301-2051. Web Site: gain.mercer.edu/library/. *Dir*, Jan H LaBeause; E-Mail: labeause.j@gain.mercer.edu; *ILL*, Roxanne Nelson; Tel: 912-301-4057; Staff 24 (MLS 9, Non-MLS 15)
Founded 1974. Enrl 270; Fac 1,020; Highest Degree: Doctorate
Library Holdings: Bk Vols 94,935; Bk Titles 35,598; Per Subs 853
Subject Interests: Medicine
Special Collections: Southern History of Medicine
Automation Activity & Vendor Info: (Acquisitions) Innovative Interfaces Inc.; (Cataloging) Innovative Interfaces Inc.; (Circulation) Innovative Interfaces Inc.; (Course Reserve) Innovative Interfaces Inc.; (OPAC) Innovative Interfaces Inc.; (Serials) Innovative Interfaces Inc.
Restriction: Restricted public use
Partic in Dialog Corporation; Docline; Georgia Interactive Network For Medical Information; National Network of Libraries of Medicine - Southeastern Atlantic Region; OCLC Online Computer Library Center, Inc

P MIDDLE GEORGIA REGIONAL LIBRARY, Washington Memorial Main Library, 1180 Washington Ave, 31201-1790. SAN 338-9642. Tel: 912-744-0841. Interlibrary Loan Service Tel: 912-744-0825. FAX: 912-744-0840. Web Site: www.co.bibb.ga.us/library/. *Dir*, Charles J Schmidt; E-Mail: schmidtc@mail.bibb.public.lib.ga.us; *Head of Libr*, Gail Moon; *Ch Servs*, Joanne Hinman; *Coll Develop, Ref*, Larry Caldwell; *Tech Servs*, Thomas Jones; *ILL*, Robin Hudgins. Subject Specialists: *Genealogy*, Willard Rocker; Staff 27 (MLS 27)
Founded 1889. Pop 257,687
Library Holdings: Bk Vols 531,369; Per Subs 660
Friends of the Library Group
Branches: 16
CRAWFORD COUNTY PUBLIC, 340 Mccrary Sr, Roberta, 31078-0580. (Mail add: PO Box 580A, Roberta, 31078-0580), SAN 338-9677. Tel: 478-836-4478. FAX: 478-836-4478. Web Site: www.co.bibb.ga.us/library. *Branch Mgr*, Leda Starnes
Library Holdings: Bk Vols 17,628
EAST WILKINSON COUNTY PUBLIC, 154 E Main St, Irwinton, 31042-9703. SAN 325-4437. Tel: 478-946-2778. FAX: 478-946-2778. *Mgr*, Arlene Bache
Library Holdings: Bk Vols 10,869
GORDON PUBLIC, PO Box 336, Gordon, 31041-0336. SAN 338-9707. Tel: 478-628-5352. FAX: 478-628-5352. *Mgr*, Elizabeth Proctor
Library Holdings: Bk Vols 8,148
IDEAL PUBLIC, 605 Tom Watson Ave, Ideal, 31041-0009. (Mail add: PO Box 9, Ideal, 31041-0009), SAN 325-4399. Tel: 478-949-2720. FAX: 478-949-2720. *Mgr*, Myrtice Jones
Library Holdings: Bk Vols 1,395
JONES COUNTY PUBLIC, Railroad Ave, PO Box 156, Gray, 31032-0156. SAN 338-9766. Tel: 478-986-6626. FAX: 478-986-6626. *Branch Mgr*, Carole Dye
Founded 1936
Library Holdings: Bk Vols 30,000
MACON LIBRARY FOR THE BLIND & PHYSICALLY HANDICAPPED, Washington Memorial Library, 1180 Washington Ave, 31201-1790. SAN 338-9650. Tel: 478-744-0877. Toll Free Tel: 800-805-7613. TDD: 912-744-0877. FAX: 478-744-0814. *Librn*, Rebecca M Sherrill; E-Mail: sherrilr@mail.bibb.public.lib.ga.us
Founded 1973. Circ 88,936
Library Holdings: Bk Vols 4,640
Subject Interests: Braille, Large type print
Publications: Home Talking News (weekly)
Special Services for the Deaf - TDD
Weekly cassette newspaper; puppet shows for handicapped patrons; in-house repair of machines
Friends of the Library Group
MARSHALLVILLE PUBLIC, PO Box 201, Marshallville, 31057-0201. SAN 338-9790. Tel: 478-967-2413. FAX: 478-967-2413. *Mgr*, Nellie Williamson
Library Holdings: Bk Vols 8,175
MARY VINSON MEMORIAL, 151 S Jefferson St SE, Milledgeville, 31061-3419. SAN 339-0004. Tel: 478-445-0677. FAX: 478-445-0679. E-Mail: mvml@hom.net. Web Site: www.ccmil.com/mvml/. *Dir*, Lillie Crowe; *Head, Circ*, Kell Carpenter
Library Holdings: Bk Vols 73,562
Friends of the Library Group
MONTEZUMA PUBLIC, 506 N Dooley St, Montezuma, 31063-1308. SAN 338-9820. Tel: 478-472-6095. FAX: 478-472-6095. *Mgr*, Lucy Warnock
Library Holdings: Bk Vols 14,050
OGLETHORPE PUBLIC, 115 Chatham St, Oglethorpe, 31068. (Mail add: PO Box 425, Oglethorpe, 31068-0425), SAN 338-9855. Tel: 478-472-6485. FAX: 478-472-6485. *Mgr*, Marie Meadows
Library Holdings: Bk Vols 4,828
RIVERSIDE, 110 Holiday Dr N, 31210. SAN 338-991X. Tel: 478-757-8900. FAX: 478-744-0872.
Library Holdings: Bk Vols 56,296
Friends of the Library Group
ROCKY CREEK, 1504 Rocky Creek Rd, South Macon Plaza, 31206-3550. SAN 338-9944. Tel: 478-744-0880. FAX: 478-744-0882. *Librn*, Catherine B Servais
Library Holdings: Bk Vols 53,489
Friends of the Library Group
SHURLING, 1765 Shurling Dr, 31211-2152. SAN 338-9979. Tel: 478-744-0875. FAX: 478-744-0876. *Branch Mgr*, Suzanne McCullough
Library Holdings: Bk Vols 40,937
Friends of the Library Group
TWIGGS COUNTY PUBLIC, 181 Ash St, PO Box 305, Jeffersonville, 31044-0305. (Mail add: 101 Ash St, Jeffersonville, 31044), SAN 338-9731. Tel: 478-945-3814. FAX: 478-945-3814. *Mgr*, Merle Arnold
Library Holdings: Bk Vols 14,255
WASHINGTON MEMORIAL, 751 S Bascom Ave, San Jose, 95128-2699. Tel: 912-744-0841. FAX: 912-744-0840. *Librn*, Gail Moon
Library Holdings: Bk Vols 112,448
Subject Interests: Business and management, Genealogy, Local history
Special Collections: African-American; Archives; Business Reference; Genealogy; Georgiana; Local Hist; Telephone indexes
Partic in Georgia Online Database
Friends of the Library Group
WEST BIBB, 5580 Thomaston Rd, 31210-8118. SAN 377-6514. Tel: 478-744-0818. FAX: 478-744-0819. *Branch Mgr*, Iona Foreman
Library Holdings: Bk Vols 34,722

S NATIONAL PARK SERVICE, Ocmulgee National Monument Library, 1207 Emery Hwy, 31217. SAN 303-3910. Tel: 478-752-8257. FAX: 478-752-8259. Web Site: www.nps.gov/ocmu. *In Charge*, James David; *Librn*, Sylvia Flowers
Founded 1936
Library Holdings: Bk Titles 700; Per Subs 15
Subject Interests: Anthropology, Archaeology, Environmental studies
Restriction: Staff use only
Special Services for the Deaf - Staff with knowledge of sign language

S TRIBBLE & RICHARDSON INC LIBRARY, PO Box 13147, 31208-3147. SAN 373-4277. Tel: 912-474-6100. FAX: 912-474-8933. *Librn*, Cathy Darley
Library Holdings: Bk Vols 450; Per Subs 70
Subject Interests: Civil engineering

S WASHINGTON MEMORIAL LIBRARY, Middle Georgia Archives, 1180 Washington Ave, 31201-1790. SAN 377-5720. Tel: 478-744-0851. FAX: 478-744-0893. *Archivist*, Peer Ravnan
Subject Interests: Local history
Function: Archival collection
Friends of the Library Group

C WESLEYAN COLLEGE, Willet Memorial Library, 4760 Forsyth Rd, 31210-4462. SAN 303-3929. Tel: 478-757-5200. FAX: 478-757-3898. *Coll Develop, Librn*, Catherine Lee; E-Mail: clee@wesleyancollege.edu; *Asst Librn*, Kimberly Buffington; E-Mail: kbuffington@wesleyancollege.edu; *Tech Servs*, Betty G Shewfelt; E-Mail: bshewfelt@wesleyancollege.edu; *Archivist*, Tena Roberts; E-Mail: troberts@wesleyancollege.edu; Staff 6 (MLS 4, Non-MLS 2)
Founded 1836. Enrl 520; Highest Degree: Master
Jul 1998-Jun 1999 Income $462,055. Mats Exp $183,000, Books $48,000, Per/Ser (Incl. Access Fees) $113,000, Presv $7,000, Micro $12,000, Manuscripts & Archives $3,000. Sal $167,000
Library Holdings: Bk Vols 140,923; Per Subs 610
Special Collections: Americana (McGregor Coll); Georgiana (Park Coll)
Automation Activity & Vendor Info: (Acquisitions) Innovative Interfaces Inc.; (Cataloging) Innovative Interfaces Inc.; (Circulation) Innovative Interfaces Inc.; (Course Reserve) Innovative Interfaces Inc.; (OPAC) Innovative Interfaces Inc.
Partic in Georgia Online Database; SE Libr Network; South Georgia Associated Libraries

MADISON

P UNCLE REMUS REGIONAL LIBRARY SYSTEM, 1131 East Ave, 30650. SAN 339-0063. Tel: 706-342-4974. FAX: 706-342-4510. Web Site: www.uncleremus.org. *Dir*, Steve W Schaefer; Tel: 706-342-4974, Ext 12, E-Mail: steve@uncleremus.org; *Acq, Asst Dir*, Suzanne Paul; Tel: 706-342-4974, Ext 13, E-Mail: suzanne@uncleremus.org; *Cat*, Holly Jarrell; Tel: 706-342-4974, Ext 18, E-Mail: holly@uncleremus.org; *Instrul Serv*, Tamela Thomas; Tel: 706-342-4974, Ext 14, E-Mail: tamela@uncleremus.org; *Ref*, Ana Kadhum; Tel: 706-342-4974, Ext 19, E-Mail: ana@uncleremus.org; *Tech Servs*, Lois Upham; Tel: 706-342-4974, Ext 15, E-Mail: lois@uncleremus.org; *Tech Coordr*, Charles May; Tel: 706-342-4974, Ext 20, E-Mail: charles@uncleremus.org; *Commun Servs*, Cherly Rogers; Staff 8 (MLS 8)
Founded 1952. Pop 118,305; Circ 301,051
Jul 1998-Jun 1999 Income (Main Library and Branch Library) $1,402,415, State $627,941, City $198,497, County $411,662, Other $164,315. Mats Exp $119,056. Sal $876,244 (Prof $478,475)
Library Holdings: Bk Vols 243,406; Bk Titles 85,000; Per Subs 253
Subject Interests: Genealogy, Georgia
Special Collections: Joel Chandler Harris Coll
Automation Activity & Vendor Info: (Cataloging) TLC; (Circulation) TLC; (OPAC) TLC
Database Vendor: OCLC - First Search
Partic in SE Libr Network
Friends of the Library Group
Branches: 8
GREENE COUNTY LIBRARY, 610 S Main St, Greensboro, 30642. SAN 339-3038. Tel: 706-453-7276. FAX: 706-453-0500. Web Site: www.uncleremus.org. *Branch Mgr*, Jackie Richardson
Subject Interests: Genealogy, Georgia
Friends of the Library Group
HANCOCK COUNTY LIBRARY, 403 E Broad St, Sparta, 31087. SAN 339-0128. Tel: 706-444-5389. FAX: 706-444-6056. Web Site: www.uncleremus.org. *Branch Mgr*, Karen Meeks
Subject Interests: Genealogy, Georgia
JASPER COUNTY LIBRARY, 319 E Green St, Monticello, 31064. SAN 339-0152. Tel: 706-468-6292. FAX: 706-468-2060. Web Site: www.uncleremus.org. *Branch Mgr*, Elizabeth Greer
Subject Interests: Genealogy, Georgia
Friends of the Library Group
MONROE - WALTON COUNTY LIBRARY, 217 W Spring St, Monroe, 30655. SAN 339-3577. Tel: 770-267-4630. FAX: 770-267-6682. Web Site: www.uncleremus.org. *Branch Mgr*, Melaine Correll
Subject Interests: Genealogy, Georgia
Friends of the Library Group
MORGAN COUNTY LIBRARY, 1131 East Ave, 30650. SAN 370-0178. Tel: 706-342-1206. FAX: 706-342-0883. Web Site: www.uncleremus.org. *Branch Mgr*, Mary Sue Alexander
Subject Interests: Genealogy, Georgia
Special Collections: Joel Chandler Harris Coll
Friends of the Library Group
O'KELLY MEMORIAL LIBRARY, 363 Conyers Rd, Loganville, 30052. SAN 339-3518. Tel: 770-466-2895. FAX: 770-466-3700. Web Site: www.uncleremus.org. *Branch Mgr*, Catherine Mason
Friends of the Library Group
PUTNAM COUNTY LIBRARY, 309 N Madison Ave, Eatonton, 31024. SAN 339-0098. Tel: 706-485-6768. FAX: 706-485-5896. Web Site: www.uncleremus.org. *Branch Mgr*, Patricia Mason
Subject Interests: Genealogy, Georgia
W H STANTON MEMORIAL LIBRARY, 1045 W Hightower Trail, PO Box 566, Social Circle, 30025. SAN 339-3631. Tel: 770-464-2444. FAX: 770-464-1596. Web Site: www.uncleremus.org. *Branch Mgr*, Janice McPherson
Subject Interests: Genealogy, Georgia
Friends of the Library Group

MANCHESTER

P PINE MOUNTAIN REGIONAL LIBRARY, 218 Perry St NW, PO Box 709, 31816-0709. SAN 339-0187. Tel: 706-846-2186. FAX: 706-846-8455. *Dir*, Charles B Gee; *Tech Servs*, Bonita Thomas; *Ch Servs*, Alice McCloud; Staff 22 (MLS 6, Non-MLS 16)
Founded 1938. Pop 65,712; Circ 157,728
Library Holdings: Bk Vols 20,000
Subject Interests: Genealogy, Local history
Branches: 6
BUTLER PUBLIC, 210 W Main St, Butler, 31006-0508. (Mail add: PO Box 508, Butler, 31006-0508), SAN 339-0217. Tel: 912-862-5428. FAX: 912-862-5428. *Mgr*, Johnnie Harris
Library Holdings: Bk Vols 7,092; Per Subs 27
GREENVILLE AREA PUBLIC, 10 Gilbert St, Greenville, 30222-0710. (Mail add: PO Box 710, Greenville, 30222-0710), SAN 339-0241. Tel: 706-672-4004. FAX: 706-672-4004. *Mgr*, Paul Jones
Library Holdings: Bk Vols 5,914; Per Subs 25
HIGHTOWER MEMORIAL, 800 W Garden St, Thomaston, 30286-0436. (Mail add: PO Box 631, Thomaston, 30286), SAN 339-0330. Tel: 706-647-8649. FAX: 706-647-3977. *Librn*, Lorraine Greathouse
Library Holdings: Bk Vols 19,934; Per Subs 78
Friends of the Library Group
MANCHESTER PUBLIC, 218 Perry St, 31816-0709. SAN 373-6229. Tel: 706-846-3851. FAX: 706-846-9632. *Mgr*, Geraldine Holmes
REYNOLDS COMMUNITY, 124 E Talbot St, Reynolds, 31076-0467. (Mail add: PO Box 467, Reynolds, 31076-0467), SAN 339-0276. Tel: 912-847-3468. FAX: 912-847-3468. *Mgr*, Virginia Young
Library Holdings: Bk Vols 8,117; Per Subs 25
TALBOT COUNTY, Jefferson & Harrison St, Talbotton, 31827-0477. (Mail add: PO Box 477, Talbotton, 31827-0477), SAN 339-0306. Tel: 706-665-3134. FAX: 706-665-8777. *Mgr*, Mary Holmes
Library Holdings: Bk Vols 13,005; Per Subs 50
Bookmobiles: 1

MARIETTA

§C CHATTAHOOCHEE TECHNICAL COLLEGE LIBRARY, 980 South Cobb Drive SE, 30060-3300. SAN 375-4154. Tel: 770-528-4536. FAX: 770-528-4454. Web Site: www.chat-tec.com/libhome.htm. *Head Librn*, Barbara N Moore; E-Mail: bmoore@chat-tec.com; Staff 4 (MLS 2, Non-MLS 2)
Jul 2000-Jun 2001 Mats Exp $60,000
Library Holdings: Bk Vols 16,000; Per Subs 160
Special Collections: Georgia topics & authors
Automation Activity & Vendor Info: (Cataloging) SIRSI; (Circulation) SIRSI

P COBB COUNTY PUBLIC LIBRARY SYSTEM, 266 Roswell St, 30060-2004. SAN 339-0365. Tel: 770-528-2320. Interlibrary Loan Service Tel: 770-528-2367. FAX: 770-528-2349. E-Mail: cobbcat@cobbcat.org. Web Site: www.cobbcat.org. *Dir*, Gail R Rogers; Tel: 770-528-2347; *Assoc Dir*, Cathy Caine; Tel: 770-528-2332; *Assoc Dir*, Donnie Griffin; Tel: 770-528-2330; *Assoc Dir*, Beverly Harris; Tel: 770-528-2335; *Coordr*, Patricia Latch; Tel: 770-528-2342; *Ad Servs*, Suzanne Kinser; *Cat*, Sandra Barclay; Tel: 770-528-2354; *Coll Develop*, Tamara George; Tel: 770-528-2141; *ILL*, Susan Buak; Staff 174 (MLS 42, Non-MLS 132)
Founded 1958. Pop 592,245; Circ 3,311,382
Jul 1999-Jun 2000 Income (Main Library and Branch Library) $8,364,082, State $961,582, County $6,923,949, Locally Generated Income $478,551. Mats Exp $8,364,082, Books $1,428,864, Presv $8,836, Micro $22,817, Manuscripts & Archives $720. Sal $5,361,720
Library Holdings: Bk Vols 692,782; Per Subs 1,927
Special Collections: Georgia Room
Automation Activity & Vendor Info: (Acquisitions) DRA
Database Vendor: DRA
Friends of the Library Group
Branches: 15
ACWORTH BRANCH, 4569 Dallas St, Acworth, 30101. SAN 339-039X. Tel: 770-917-5168. FAX: 770-917-5177. E-Mail: cobbcat@cobbcat.org. Web Site: www.cobbcat.org. *Mgr*, Susan Harper
Founded 1958. Pop 96,175
Library Holdings: Bk Vols 22,145
Database Vendor: DRA

Friends of the Library Group
EAST MARIETTA, 2051 Lower Roswell Rd, 30068. SAN 339-042X. Tel: 770-509-2711. FAX: 770-509-2714. E-Mail: cobbcat@cobbcat.org. Web Site: www.cobbcat.org. *Mgr*, Virginia Hale
Founded 1958. Circ 211,595
Library Holdings: Bk Vols 45,361
Database Vendor: DRA
Friends of the Library Group
GRITTERS, 880 Shaw Pk Rd, 30066. SAN 339-0489. Tel: 770-528-2524. FAX: 770-528-2533. E-Mail: cobbcat@cobbcat.org. Web Site: www.cobbcat.org. *Mgr*, Jonathan McKeown
Founded 1958. Circ 172,631
Library Holdings: Bk Vols 35,916
Database Vendor: DRA
Friends of the Library Group
HATTIE G WILSON BRANCH, 350 Lemon St, 30060. SAN 339-0454. Tel: 770-528-2526. FAX: 770-528-2591. *Mgr*, Rachell Heard
Circ 42,921
Library Holdings: Bk Vols 14,371
Database Vendor: DRA
KEMP MEMORIAL, 4029 Due West Rd, 30064. SAN 370-8039. Tel: 770-528-2527. FAX: 770-528-2592. *Mgr*, Sherry Blomely
Founded 1958. Circ 249,131
Library Holdings: Bk Vols 37,539
Database Vendor: DRA
Friends of the Library Group
KENNESAW BRANCH, 2250 Lewis St, Kennesaw, 30144. SAN 339-0519. Tel: 770-528-2529. FAX: 770-528-2593. *Mgr*, Elizabeth McGuire
Founded 1958. Circ 237,503
Library Holdings: Bk Vols 32,139
Database Vendor: DRA
Friends of the Library Group
LEWIS A RAY BRANCH, 4500 Oakdale Rd, Smyrna, 30080. SAN 339-0608. Tel: 770-801-5335. FAX: 770-801-5316. *Mgr*, Steven Powell
Founded 1958. Circ 55,056
Library Holdings: Bk Vols 18,366
Database Vendor: DRA
Friends of the Library Group
MERCHANT'S WALK BRANCH, 1315 Johnson Ferry Rd, 30068. SAN 339-0551. Tel: 770-509-2730. FAX: 770-509-2733. *Mgr*, Colleen Harris
Founded 1958. Circ 383,601
Library Holdings: Bk Vols 49,694
Database Vendor: DRA
Friends of the Library Group
MOUNTAIN VIEW, 3320 Sandy Plains Rd, 30066. SAN 370-8047. Tel: 770-509-2725. FAX: 770-509-2726. *Mgr*, Suzanne Hoss
Founded 1958. Circ 540,940
Library Holdings: Bk Vols 90,617
Database Vendor: DRA
Friends of the Library Group
POWDER SPRINGS BRANCH, 4262 Marietta St, Powder Springs, 30073. SAN 339-0578. Tel: 770-439-3600. FAX: 770-439-3620. *Mgr*, Marcy Nader
Founded 1958. Circ 133,823
Library Holdings: Bk Vols 29,689
Database Vendor: DRA
Friends of the Library Group
SIBLEY BRANCH LIBRARY, 1539 S Cobb Dr, 30060. SAN 339-0632. Tel: 770-528-2520. FAX: 770-528-2594. *Mgr*, Bruce Thompson
Founded 1958. Circ 66,314
Library Holdings: Bk Vols 21,369
Database Vendor: DRA
Friends of the Library Group
SOUTH COBB BRANCH, 5801 Mableton Pkwy, Mableton, 30059. SAN 339-0667. Tel: 770-528-3280. FAX: 770-528-3283. *Mgr*, Jane G Sullivan
Founded 1958. Circ 42,859
Library Holdings: Bk Vols 29,175
Database Vendor: DRA
Friends of the Library Group
STRATTON BRANCH, 1100 Powder Springs Rd, 30064. SAN 339-0691. Tel: 770-528-2522. FAX: 770-528-2595. *Mgr*, Patricia Ball
Founded 1958. Circ 128,309
Library Holdings: Bk Vols 32,427
Database Vendor: DRA
Friends of the Library Group
SWEETWATER VALLEY, 2773 Sweetwater St, Austell, 30001. SAN 339-0721. Tel: 770-819-3290. FAX: 770-819-3293. *Mgr*, Rhonda Lane
Founded 1958. Circ 78,054
Library Holdings: Bk Vols 19,272
Database Vendor: DRA
Friends of the Library Group
VININGS, 4290 Paces Ferry Rd, Atlanta, 30339. SAN 370-8055. Tel: 770-801-5330. FAX: 770-801-5319. *Mgr*, Susan Kendall
Founded 1958. Circ 132,246
Library Holdings: Bk Vols 34,623
Friends of the Library Group

S GENEALOGICAL CENTER LIBRARY, PO Box 71343, 30007-1343. SAN 320-2194. Web Site: homepages.rootsweb.com/~gencenlb/index.html. *Dir*, Barbara A Geisert
Founded 1975
Library Holdings: Bk Titles 14,000; Per Subs 25
Subject Interests: Genealogy

M KENNESTONE HOSPITAL WELLSTAR, Health Sciences Library, 677 Church St, 30060. SAN 329-1715. Tel: 770-793-7178. FAX: 770-793-7956. E-Mail: medical.library@wellstar.org. Web Site: www.wellstar.org. *Librn*, Linda Venis; E-Mail: venis_linda@wellstar.org
Library Holdings: Bk Vols 1,500; Per Subs 190
Subject Interests: Allied health, Medicine, Nursing
Partic in Atlanta Health Science Libraries Consortium; Nat Libr of Med
Open Mon-Fri 8:30am-5pm

CM LIFE UNIVERSITY, Nell K Williams Learning Resource Center, 1269 Barclay Circle, 30060. SAN 370-5730. Tel: 770-426-2688. FAX: 770-421-1066. Web Site: www.life.edu. *Dean of Libr*, Nancy R Hill; E-Mail: nhill@life.edu; *Dir*, Terry K Selfe; *ILL*, David Free; *Media Spec*, Carla Williams; *Ref*, Danielle Knowles; Staff 10 (MLS 10)
Founded 1975. Enrl 3,428; Fac 254; Highest Degree: Master
Library Holdings: Bk Vols 54,000; Bk Titles 52,000; Per Subs 1,300
Subject Interests: Chiropractic, Health sciences
Automation Activity & Vendor Info: (Acquisitions) SIRSI; (Cataloging) SIRSI; (Circulation) SIRSI; (OPAC) SIRSI; (Serials) SIRSI
Database Vendor: Ebsco - EbscoHost, Lexis-Nexis, OCLC - First Search, ProQuest
Restriction: In-house use for visitors, Open to students
Function: Archival collection, Document delivery services, For research purposes, ILL available, ILL to other special libraries, Literary searches, Outside services via phone, cable & mail, Photocopies available, Reference services available, Some telephone reference
Partic in Atlanta Health Science Libraries Consortium; Chiropractic Libr Consortium; OCLC Online Computer Library Center, Inc
Special Services for the Blind - Large print bks

S LOCKHEED MARTIN AERONAUTICAL SYSTEMS, Tech Information Center, Dept 82-13, Zone 0681, 86 S Cobb Dr, 30063-0681. SAN 303-3945. Tel: 770-494-2522. FAX: 770-494-0732. *Mgr*, D Ellis; *Librn*, L W Kimbro; Staff 4 (MLS 1, Non-MLS 3)
Founded 1955
Library Holdings: Bk Titles 50,000; Per Subs 900
Subject Interests: Aeronautics, Economics, Electronics, Engineering, Marketing
Special Collections: Foreign Country Data; Recreation Coll
Publications: Abbreviation List; Accession List; Lockheed Style Manual
Partic in Defense Technical Information Center; Georgia Libr Info Network; Nasa Libraries Information System - Nasa Galaxie; OCLC Online Computer Library Center, Inc; SE-Atlantic Regional Med Libr Servs
Open Mon-Fri 9am-5pm

S SOLVAY PHARMACEUTICALS, Research Information Center, 901 Sawyer Rd, Rm 247, 30062. SAN 371-5450. Tel: 770-578-5648. FAX: 770-578-5635. *Librn*, Ellen Cooper; *Asst Librn*, Lauren Benevich; Staff 3 (MLS 2, Non-MLS 1)
Founded 1989
Library Holdings: Bk Titles 2,000; Per Subs 350
Subject Interests: Pharmaceuticals
Restriction: Employees & their associates
Partic in Atlanta Health Science Libraries Consortium

C SOUTHERN POLYTECHNIC STATE UNIVERSITY, Lawrence V Johnson Library, 1100 S Marietta Pkwy, 30060-2896. SAN 303-3961. Tel: 770-528-7275. Reference Tel: 770-528-7471. FAX: 770-528-4944. Web Site: www.spsu.edu/library/library.html. *Dir*, Dr Joyce W Mills; Tel: 770-528-7306, E-Mail: jmills0@spsu.edu; *Publ Servs*, Barbara Moore; *Head Ref*, Steven Vincent; E-Mail: svincen1@spsu.edu; *Archivist*, Leigh McNichols Hall; E-Mail: lhall@spsu.edu; *ILL*, David Rife; Tel: 770-528-7466; *Acq*, Yongli Ma; Tel: 770-528-7473, E-Mail: yma@spsu.edu; *Cat*, Wanda Jacak; *Cat*, Cheryl Karr; Tel: 770-528-7465, E-Mail: ckarr@spsu.edu; *Syst Coordr*, Li Chen; Tel: 770-528-7467, E-Mail: lchen@spsu.edu; Staff 12 (MLS 7, Non-MLS 5)
Founded 1948. Enrl 4,000; Fac 120; Highest Degree: Master
Jul 1999-Jun 2000 Income $806,417. Mats Exp $273,000, Books $79,000, Per/Ser (Incl. Access Fees) $168,500, Presv $500, Micro $4,000, Electronic Ref Mat (Incl. Access Fees) $21,000. Sal $480,217 (Prof $290,242)
Library Holdings: Bk Vols 117,963; Bk Titles 116,487; Per Subs 1,320
Subject Interests: Art and architecture, Business and management, Science/technology, Technology
Special Collections: American Architectural History; Architectural drawings; Geological Survey; Surveying maps; University archives
Automation Activity & Vendor Info: (Cataloging) Endeavor; (Circulation) Endeavor; (Course Reserve) Endeavor; (ILL) Endeavor; (OPAC) Endeavor; (Serials) Endeavor
Database Vendor: Ebsco - EbscoHost, GaleNet, Lexis-Nexis, OCLC - First Search, ProQuest, Silverplatter Information Inc., Wilson - Wilson Web

Partic in Ga Libr Learning Online; Georgia Libr Info Network; Georgia Online Database; SOQUIJ
Open Mon-Thurs 8-10, Fri 8-6, Sat 11-6, Sun 2-9
Friends of the Library Group

MILLEDGEVILLE

M CENTRAL STATE HOSPITAL, Medical, Staff & Clients' Libraries,* 31062-9989. SAN 303-397X. Tel: 912-445-5412. FAX: 912-445-6699. Web Site: accucom.net/~cshispe/. *Librn*, Katherine J Warner; E-Mail: warner.k@gain.mercer.edu
Jul 1997-Jun 1998 Income $100,000. Mats Exp $22,000, Books $6,000, Per/Ser (Incl. Access Fees) $16,000. Sal $70,000 (Prof $36,000)
Library Holdings: Bk Vols 15,600; Per Subs 180
Subject Interests: Medicine, Nursing, Psychiatry, Psychology
Partic in Georgia Health Sciences Library Association; Georgia Interactive Network For Medical Information; Health Science Libraries Of Central Georgia; SE-Atlantic Regional Med Libr Servs; Southern Chapter of Med Libr Asn

C GEORGIA COLLEGE & STATE UNIVERSITY, Ina Dillard Russell Library, 231 W Hancock St, 31061-3397. SAN 339-0780. Tel: 478-445-4047, 478-445-5573. FAX: 445-445-6847. Web Site: library.gcsu.edu. *Librn*, Bill Richards; *Dir*, R Neil Scott; E-Mail: nscott@mail.gac.peachnet.edu; *Asst Dir*, Lorene Flanders; *Spec Coll*, Nancy Davis Bray; Staff 25 (MLS 13, Non-MLS 12)
Founded 1889. Enrl 5,300; Fac 195; Highest Degree: Master
Jul 1998-Jun 1999 Income Parent Institution $1,406,635. Mats Exp $408,420, Books $93,870, Per/Ser (Incl. Access Fees) $178,423, Presv $10,000, Micro $30,000. Sal $960,451 (Prof $485,695)
Library Holdings: Bk Vols 182,085; Bk Titles 141,358; Per Subs 983
Subject Interests: Education, Nursing, Psychology
Special Collections: Branham Cookbook Coll; Flannery O'Conner Coll, bks, mss, per; Georgia College Archives Coll; Georgia College Horology Coll, clocks, watches; Georgia History Coll, bks, mss; Middle Georgia Towns & Cities Coll; US Senator Paul Coverdell Paners Coll
Partic in Dialog Corporation; Ga Libr Learning Online; Georgia Online Database; Health Science Libraries Of Central Georgia; OCLC Online Computer Library Center, Inc; SE Libr Network; Ser Holdings Network

J GEORGIA MILITARY COLLEGE, Sibley-Cone Memorial Library, 201 E Greene St, 31061. SAN 303-3988. Tel: 478-445-2718. Circulation Tel: 478-445-1422. Reference Tel: 478-445-1422. FAX: 478-445-5592. Web Site: www.launchpad.gmc.cc.ga.us/library/. *Dir*, Jane Simpson; E-Mail: jsimpson@gmc.cc.ga.us; *Media Spec*, Robbie F Jones; E-Mail: rjones@gmc.cc.ga.us; *Ref*, Sharron Lacy; E-Mail: slacy@gmc.cc.ga.us; Staff 3 (MLS 2, Non-MLS 1)
Founded 1879. Enrl 2,773; Fac 75; Highest Degree: Associate
Jul 1999-Jun 2000 Income Parent Institution $241,117. Mats Exp $85,439, Books $20,398, Per/Ser (Incl. Access Fees) $22,589, Micro $2,000, AV Equip $2,191, Electronic Ref Mat (Incl. Access Fees) $18,613. Sal $157,368 (Prof $128,513)
Library Holdings: Bk Vols 28,000; Bk Titles 25,000; Per Subs 423
Subject Interests: Georgia, History, Local history
Database Vendor: ProQuest
Function: Archival collection, ILL available, Photocopies available
Partic in Cent Ga Associated Librs; Georgia Online Database

MOODY AFB

UNITED STATES AIR FORCE
A MOODY AIR FORCE BASE LIBRARY FL4830, 347 SVS/SVMG, 5107 Austin Ellipse Ste A Bldg 103, 31699-1594. SAN 339-0845. Tel: 912-257-3018, 912-257-3539. FAX: 912-257-4119. *Dir*, Saundra Scanlon; *Syst Coordr*, Terri Perkins; *Ref*, Michaell P Fitzpatrick; *Tech Servs*, Debbie Cafferey; Staff 8 (MLS 4, Non-MLS 4)
Founded 1952
Library Holdings: Bk Vols 28,000; Per Subs 250
Subject Interests: Military history
Partic in OCLC Online Computer Library Center, Inc

MORROW

C CLAYTON COLLEGE & STATE UNIVERSITY LIBRARY, 5900 N Lee St, 30260. SAN 303-3996. Tel: 770-961-3520. FAX: 770-961-3712. Web Site: www.adminservices.clayton.edu/library/. *Dir*, Robert Fox; E-Mail: bobfox@mail.clayton.edu; *Publ Servs*, Gwen Bell; *Cat*, Cathy Jeffrey; *Tech Servs*, Debbie Meyer; *Bibliog Instr*, Jonathan Jay; Staff 15 (MLS 7, Non-MLS 8)
Founded 1969. Enrl 5,000; Fac 125; Highest Degree: Bachelor
Jul 1998-Jun 1999 Income $873,000. Mats Exp $248,000, Books $141,320, Per/Ser (Incl. Access Fees) $81,874, Micro $24,684. Sal $444,080 (Prof $251,240)
Library Holdings: Bk Vols 90,000; Bk Titles 80,000; Per Subs 750
Subject Interests: Business, Education, Music, Nursing, Technology
Special Collections: Civil War (War of the Rebellion); Georgia (Southern History)
Automation Activity & Vendor Info: (Acquisitions) Endeavor; (Cataloging) Endeavor; (Circulation) Endeavor; (Course Reserve) Endeavor; (OPAC) Endeavor; (Serials) Endeavor
Publications: Library Source
Partic in N Ga Associated Librs; OCLC Online Computer Library Center, Inc; SE Libr Network

MOULTRIE

M COLQUITT REGIONAL MEDICAL CENTER, Health Sciences Library, 3131 S Main St, 31768-6925. (Mail add: PO Box 40, 31776-0040), SAN 372-5936. Tel: 912-890-3460. FAX: 912-891-9345. *Librn*, Susan Leik; E-Mail: statom.s@gain.mercer.edu
Founded 1979
Library Holdings: Bk Vols 350; Bk Titles 400; Per Subs 63
Partic in Georgia Interactive Network For Medical Information

P MOULTRIE-COLQUITT COUNTY LIBRARY, 204 Fifth St SE, PO Box 2828, 31768. SAN 339-087X. Tel: 229-985-6540. FAX: 229-985-0936. *Dir*, Melody S Jenkins; *Ch Servs*, Norma S McKellar; *Cat*, Betty P Cooper; *Ref*, Elois Matthews; *YA Servs*, Ladonna Funderburk; *Tech Servs*, Carolyn Clark; Staff 2 (MLS 2)
Founded 1907. Pop 36,899; Circ 142,126
Jul 1998-Jun 1999 Income $483,638, State $146,656, City $5,000, Federal $4,000, County $264,554. Mats Exp $40,358, Books $30,138, Per/Ser (Incl. Access Fees) $4,700, Micro $800, Other Print Mats $800. Sal $283,901 (Prof $102,872)
Library Holdings: Bk Vols 135,702; Per Subs 144
Special Collections: Genealogy (Odom Genealogy Library), bks, per, micro
Publications: The Family Tree (bi-monthly genealogical newsletter)
Partic in Georgia Libr Info Network
Branches: 2
BERLIN COMMUNITY, PO Box 189, Berlin, 31722. SAN 339-090X. Tel: 229-324-2425. *Branch Mgr*, Tammi Gremm
MONROE MEMORIAL (Mail add: PO Box 427, Doerun, 31744), Tel: 229-782-5507. *Branch Mgr*, Odelle Cato
Bookmobiles: 2

MOUNT BERRY

C BERRY COLLEGE, Memorial Library, 30149. SAN 339-1086. Tel: 706-232-5374, Ext 2221. Interlibrary Loan Service Tel: 706-232-4056. FAX: 238-7814, 706-238-7937. E-Mail: library@berry.edu. Web Site: www.berry.edu/library. *Dir*, Lance J Foldes; Tel: 706-236-2285, E-Mail: lfoldes@berry.edu; *ILL, Ref*, Johnathan Harwell; Tel: jharwell@berry.edu; *Ref*, Judith Thompson; Tel: 706-233-4057, E-Mail: jthompson@berry.edu; *Tech Servs*, Jim Bunnelle; Tel: 706-233-4093, E-Mail: jbunnelle@berry.edu; *Publ Servs*, Martha Reynolds; Tel: 706-236-1705; *Doc, Ser*, Maureen Morgan; Tel: 706-233-4094, E-Mail: mmorgan@berry.edu; *Archivist*, Ruth D Ash; Tel: 706-233-4095, E-Mail: rash@berry.edu; Staff 12 (MLS 7, Non-MLS 5)
Founded 1936. Enrl 1,984; Fac 144; Highest Degree: Master
Jul 1998-Jun 1999 Income $1,349,318. Mats Exp $729,788, Books $289,000, Per/Ser (Incl. Access Fees) $320,788, Presv $15,000, Micro $22,000. Sal $424,667 (Prof $248,902)
Library Holdings: Bk Vols 161,719; Per Subs 1,424
Special Collections: Berry College Archives; Educational Resources Info Center, fiche
Publications: Library Lines (newsletter)
Partic in SE Libr Network

MOUNT VERNON

J BREWTON-PARKER COLLEGE, Fountain-New Library, Hwy 280, 30445-0197. SAN 303-4003. Tel: 912-583-3235. FAX: 912-583-3236. E-Mail: bpclibrary@bpc.edu. Web Site: www.bpc.edu/library. *Dir*, Ann C Turner; Tel: 912-583-3230, E-Mail: aturner@bpc.edu; Staff 5 (MLS 1, Non-MLS 4)
Founded 1904. Enrl 929; Fac 61; Highest Degree: Bachelor
Jul 1998-Jun 1999 Income $221,532. Mats Exp $53,000, Books $25,500, Per/Ser (Incl. Access Fees) $20,000, AV Equip $2,500, Electronic Ref Mat (Incl. Access Fees) $5,000. Sal $110,750 (Prof $40,250)
Library Holdings: Bk Vols 63,457; Bk Titles 55,412; Per Subs 400
Subject Interests: Christianity, Education, Music
Special Collections: Brewton-Parker College historical materials
Automation Activity & Vendor Info: (Cataloging) epixtech, inc.; (Circulation) epixtech, inc.; (OPAC) epixtech, inc.
Database Vendor: Ebsco - EbscoHost, Lexis-Nexis, OCLC - First Search, ProQuest
Publications: Handbook
Partic in Ga Pvt Libr Asn; OCLC Online Computer Library Center, Inc

NEWNAN

S COWETA COUNTY GENEALOGICAL SOCIETY LIBRARY, PO Box 1014, 30264. SAN 326-5455. Tel: 770-251-2877. *Acq*, Norma Gunby; *Publ Servs*, Frances Christopher
Founded 1980
Library Holdings: Bk Titles 2,500; Per Subs 100
Publications: Coweta County Cemeteries; Coweta County Census; Coweta County Genealogical Society Magazine

NORCROSS

S CONWAY DATA, INC LIBRARY, 35 Technology Park Atlanta, Ste 150, 30092-9934. SAN 320-1406. Tel: 770-446-6996. FAX: 770-263-8825. E-Mail: infomgr@conway.com. Web Site: www.sitemat.com. *Mgr*, James Cummins; *Asst Librn*, Julie Clark
Founded 1954
Library Holdings: Bk Vols 2,100; Bk Titles 2,100; Per Subs 45
Subject Interests: Construction
Publications: Industrial Development; Site Selection Magazine

S INSTITUTE OF INDUSTRIAL ENGINEERS, F & L Gilbreth Memorial Library, 25 Technology Park/Atlanta, 30092. SAN 324-5624. Tel: 770-449-0460. FAX: 770-441-3295. *Librn*, Donna Calvert
Library Holdings: Bk Titles 2,500; Per Subs 125
Subject Interests: Industrial eng, Industrial mgt
Special Collections: Industrial Engineering & Management Press publications

G SOUTHERN STATES ENERGY BOARD, Information Center, 6325 Amherst Ct, 30092. SAN 321-5652. Tel: 770-242-7712. FAX: 770-242-0421. Web Site: www.sseb.org. *Dir*, Kathryn A Baskin; E-Mail: baskin@sseb.org; *Info Specialist*, Maria I Betancourt; E-Mail: betancourt@sseb.org
Founded 1978
Library Holdings: Bk Titles 6,000; Per Subs 102
Subject Interests: Energy, Environmental studies
Publications: Nuclear Waste Articles; Publications; Southern Energy Report; Southern Sources; Southern Utility News Briefs

OXFORD

J OXFORD COLLEGE OF EMORY UNIVERSITY, Hoke O'Kelley Memorial Library, 100 Hammil St, 30054. (Mail add: PO Box 1448, 30054-1448), SAN 303-4038. Tel: 770-784-8380. FAX: 770-784-8408. E-Mail: libkmn@emory.edu. Web Site: www.emory.edu/OXFORD/library.html. *Dir*, Kitty McNeill; *Asst Dir*, Beth Matthews Haines; *Publ Servs*, Jennifer Howard; *Cat*, Barbara Williams; *Tech Servs*, Robin Fay; Staff 8 (MLS 3, Non-MLS 5)
Founded 1897. Enrl 575; Highest Degree: Associate
Library Holdings: Bk Vols 74,000; Per Subs 330
Special Collections: Confederate History (Lasseter Coll); Emoryana Coll; Methodism Coll; Robert Frost, Byron Herbert Reece, Jesse Stuart (Ogletree-Lewis Coll)
Automation Activity & Vendor Info: (Acquisitions) SIRSI
Publications: Guide to Library Resources
Partic in OCLC Online Computer Library Center, Inc; Research Libraries Group, Inc; Solinet

PERRY

P HOUSTON COUNTY PUBLIC LIBRARY SYSTEM, 1201 Washington Ave, 31069. SAN 339-1140. Tel: 912-987-3050. FAX: 912-987-4572. *Dir*, Judith A Golden; *Head Librn*, Nancy Granger; *Cat, Tech Servs*, Janet Sayre; Staff 4 (MLS 4)
Founded 1974. Pop 100,398; Circ 325,081
Jul 1998-Jun 1999 Income $709,653. Mats Exp $83,000. Sal $407,552
Library Holdings: Per Subs 251
Friends of the Library Group
Branches: 3
NOLA BRANTLEY MEMORIAL LIBRARY, 721 Watson Blvd, Warner Robins, 31093. SAN 339-123X. Tel: 912-923-0128. FAX: 912-929-8611. E-Mail: librarn0@mail.houston.public.lib.ga.us. *Librn*, Evelyn Merk; E-Mail: merk@mail.houston.public.lib.ga.us; *Ref*, Belle Bush; E-Mail: bushi@mail.houston.public.lib.ga.us; Staff 3 (MLS 2, Non-MLS 1)
Founded 1948. Pop 100,000
Library Holdings: Bk Titles 90,000; Per Subs 400
Automation Activity & Vendor Info: (Acquisitions) SIRSI; (Cataloging) SIRSI; (Circulation) SIRSI; (Media Booking) SIRSI; (OPAC) SIRSI; (Serials) SIRSI
Friends of the Library Group
CENTERVILLE BRANCH, Church St, Centerville, 31028. SAN 339-1175. Tel: 912-953-4500. FAX: 912-953-7850. *Head of Libr*, Ruth Faircloth
Library Holdings: Bk Vols 20,000
Friends of the Library Group
PERRY BRANCH, 1201 Washington Ave, 31069. SAN 339-1205. Tel: 912-987-3050. FAX: 912-987-4572. *Head Librn*, Nancy Granger
Library Holdings: Bk Vols 60,000
Friends of the Library Group
Bookmobiles: 1

R PERRY UNITED METHODIST CHURCH LIBRARY, 1001 Carrol St, PO Box 73, 31069. SAN 303-4046. Tel: 912-987-1852. FAX: 912-988-1428.
Founded 1967
Library Holdings: Bk Vols 4,500
Subject Interests: History

QUITMAN

P BROOKS COUNTY PUBLIC LIBRARY, 404 Tallokas Rd, 31643. SAN 303-4062. Tel: 912-263-4412. FAX: 912-263-8002. *Dir*, Laura Harrison
Pop 17,000; Circ 108,000
Library Holdings: Bk Vols 40,000; Per Subs 60
Subject Interests: Afro-American, Genealogy
Publications: Library Edition (Friends)
Friends of the Library Group

RIVERDALE

M SOUTHERN REGIONAL MEDICAL CENTER, Health Sciences Library, 11 Upper Riverdale Rd SW, 30274. SAN 320-6343. Tel: 770-991-8177. FAX: 770-991-8379. *Librn*, Ricky S Gibson; E-Mail: rsgibson@promina.org
Subject Interests: Allied health, Clinical medicine, Nursing
Partic in Atlanta Health Science Libraries Consortium; Docline

ROME

J FLOYD COLLEGE LIBRARY, 3175 Cedartown Hwy SE, 30161. SAN 303-4089. Tel: 706-295-6318. FAX: 706-295-6365. Web Site: www.fc.peachnet.edu/academics/lrnres/library/index.htm. *Dir*, Debbie Holmes; E-Mail: dholmes@mail.fc.peachnet.edu; *Tech Servs*, Jeannie Blakely; *Coll Develop*, Russell Fulmer; Staff 3 (MLS 3)
Founded 1970
1998-1999 Mats Exp $14,402, Books $13,235, Presv $371. Sal $287,266
Library Holdings: Bk Vols 61,712; Bk Titles 50,813; Per Subs 288
Subject Interests: Paramedics
Partic in Georgia Online Database

M FLOYD MEDICAL CENTER LIBRARY, 304 Turner McCall Blvd, PO Box 233, 30162. SAN 303-4097. Tel: 706-802-2171. FAX: 706-802-2656. *Librn*, Erin Hernandez
Library Holdings: Bk Titles 825; Per Subs 98
Subject Interests: Medicine, Nursing
Partic in Mercer Univ; Southeastern Regional Med Libr Program

P SARA HIGHTOWER REGIONAL LIBRARY, 205 Riverside Pkwy, 30161-2913. SAN 339-1264. Tel: 706-236-4611. TDD: 404-236-4621. FAX: 706-236-4631. Web Site: www.floyd.public.lib.ga.us. *Dir*, Susan Sexton Cooley; Tel: 706-236-4609, E-Mail: cooleys@mail.floyd.public.lib.ga.us; *Asst Dir*, Linda Floyd; Tel: 706-236-4612, E-Mail: floydl@mail.floyd.public.lib.ga.us; *ILL*, David Evans; *AV*, Diane Lackey; *Spec Coll*, Teresa Gentry; *Ref*, Jim Doyle; *Librn for Blind*, Diana Mills; *Ch Servs*, Barbara Evans; *Coll Develop*, Melanie Caldwell
Founded 1911. Pop 118,512; Circ 862,021
Jul 1999-Jun 2000 Income (Main Library and Branch Library) $1,996,545, State $515,450, City $552,665, Federal $53,954, County $819,476, Locally Generated Income $55,000. Mats Exp $208,132, Books $165,000, Per/Ser (Incl. Access Fees) $35,095, Micro $5,072, Other Print Mats $2,965. Sal $1,414,205 (Prof $182,032)
Library Holdings: Bk Vols 350,000; Per Subs 453
Special Collections: Audio-Visual Materials; Cherokee Indians; Genealogy & Local History; Library for the Blind & Physically Handicapped; Marshall Forest Collection; Video Studio Coll
Automation Activity & Vendor Info: (Acquisitions) epixtech, inc.
Database Vendor: epixtech, inc., OVID Technologies
Mem of N Georgia Affiliated Librs
Partic in Georgia Online Database
Special Services for the Deaf - Books on deafness & sign language; Captioned media; Special interest periodicals; Staff with knowledge of sign language; TDD
Video Services - Library Literacy Channel 24/hr Day Learn to Read GED/ other info; department includes two fully equipped fixed studios & one mobile studio as well as post-production facilities
Friends of the Library Group
Branches: 4
CAVE SPRING BRANCH, 10-B Cedartown St, Cave Spring, 30124. (Mail add: PO Box 329, Cave Spring, 30124), SAN 339-1418. Tel: 706-777-3346. FAX: 706-236-4611. E-Mail: floyd@mail.floyd.public.lib.ga.us. Web Site: www.floyd.public.lib.ga.us. *Mgr*, Patricia A Johnston
CEDARTOWN BRANCH, City Complex, 245 East Ave, Cedartown, 30125. SAN 339-1442. Tel: 770-748-5644. FAX: 770-748-4399. Web Site:

www.floyd.public.lib.ga.us. *Mgr*, Sharon Cleveland
Friends of the Library Group
LIBRARY FOR THE BLIND & PHYSICALLY HANDICAPPED - TBC, 206 Riverside Pkwy, 30161. SAN 339-1299. Tel: 706-236-4618. TDD: 706-236-4621. FAX: 706-236-4605. *Librn*, Diana Mills; Staff 1 (MLS 1)
Founded 1975
1997-1998 Income $99,863. Sal $84,178 (Prof $25,767)
Special Collections: Juvenile Books in Print & Braille
Publications: Monthly newsletter
Special Services for the Deaf - TDD; TTY machine
Special Services for the Blind - Kurzweil Reader; Newspapers on cassette; Production of talking books; Recordings of textbook material
Friends of the Library Group
ROCKMART BRANCH, 134 W Elm St, Rockmart, 30153. SAN 339-1477. Tel: 770-684-3022. FAX: 770-684-7876. Web Site: www.floyd.public.lib.ga.us. *Mgr*, Joann Davidson
Friends of the Library Group
Bookmobiles: 2

M NORTHWEST GEORGIA REGIONAL HOSPITAL, Health Science Library, 1305 Redmond Circle, 30165. SAN 303-4119. Tel: 706-295-6060. FAX: 706-295-6320. *Librn*, James Fletcher
Founded 1947
Library Holdings: Bk Vols 916; Per Subs 20
Subject Interests: Alcoholism, Mental health, Mentally retarded

C SHORTER COLLEGE, Livingston Library, 315 Shorter Ave, 30165. SAN 303-4127. Tel: 706-291-2121, Ext 7296. Interlibrary Loan Service Tel: 706-233-7298. Circulation Tel: 706-233-7296. Reference Tel: 706-233-7296. Toll Free Tel: 800-868-6980. FAX: 706-291-6630. Web Site: www.shorter.edu/academ/library/intro2.htm. *Dir*, Kimmetha Herndon; *Asst Dir, Cat, Tech Servs*, Bettie Sumner; *AV, ILL*, Karen Simpkins; *Music*, John Rivest. Subject Specialists: *Music*, John Rivest; Staff 5 (MLS 5)
Founded 1873. Enrl 1,826; Fac 62; Highest Degree: Master
Jun 1999-May 2000 Income $258,300. Mats Exp $258,300, Books $94,400, Per/Ser (Incl. Access Fees) $58,900, Micro $4,900, AV Equip $6,600, Electronic Ref Mat (Incl. Access Fees) $48,500
Library Holdings: Bk Vols 128,400; Per Subs 832
Subject Interests: Music, Religion
Special Collections: Baptist Convention & Association Minutes; Georgia Baptist History
Automation Activity & Vendor Info: (Cataloging) TLC; (Circulation) TLC; (OPAC) TLC
Publications: Livingston Library Handbook
Partic in Dialog Corporation; Ga Pvt Acad Librs Consortium; Galileo; OCLC Online Computer Library Center, Inc; SE Libr Network

ROSWELL

S KIMBERLY-CLARK CORP LIBRARY, Bldg 400-2, 1400 Holcomb Bridge Rd, 30076-9704. SAN 321-6322. Tel: 770-587-7905. FAX: 770-587-7228.; Staff 4 (MLS 2, Non-MLS 2)
Founded 1981
Library Holdings: Bk Titles 4,500; Per Subs 450
Subject Interests: Business, Consumer products testing, Medicine
Restriction: Company staff only
Partic in Dialog Corporation; Georgia Libr Info Network; STN

SAINT SIMONS ISLAND

G FORT FREDERICA NATIONAL MONUMENT LIBRARY, Rte 9, Box 286-C, 31522. SAN 373-4285. Tel: 912-638-3639. FAX: 912-638-3639. *Librn*, Patricia Barefoot
Library Holdings: Bk Vols 300

P SAINT SIMONS PUBLIC LIBRARY, 530A Beachview Dr, 31522. SAN 303-4143. Tel: 912-638-8234. *Librn*, Maureen Hersey
Pop 14,000; Circ 26,000
Library Holdings: Bk Vols 47,000
Friends of the Library Group

SR UNITED METHODIST CHURCH - SOUTH GEORGIA CONFERENCE - COMMISSION ON ARCHIVES & HISTORY, Arthur J Moore Methodist Library, Epworth-by-the-Sea, 31522. (Mail add: PO Box 20407, 31522), SAN 373-0433. Tel: 912-638-4050. FAX: 912-634-6042. E-Mail: methmuse@darientel.net. Web Site: methmuse.darientel.net. *Dir*, Mary L Vice
Library Holdings: Bk Vols 6,000

SANDERSVILLE

S THIELE KAOLIN, CO, Research & Development Library, 520 Kaolin Rd, 31082. SAN 303-4151. Tel: 912-552-3951. FAX: 912-552-4138. *Librn*, Brenda L Miller; E-Mail: brenda.miller@theielkaolin.com
Founded 1965
Library Holdings: Bk Vols 1,500; Per Subs 44

SAPELO ISLAND

C UNIVERSITY OF GEORGIA, Marine Institute Library, 31327. SAN 325-0210. Tel: 912-485-2276. FAX: 912-485-2133. *Librn*, Laura W Cammon; E-Mail: lcammon@arches.uga.edu
Founded 1953
Library Holdings: Bk Vols 5,000; Per Subs 85
Publications: Collected Reprint Series

SAVANNAH

C ARMSTRONG ATLANTIC STATE UNIVERSITY, Lane Library, 11935 Abercorn St, 31419-1997. SAN 303-416X. Tel: 912-927-5332. FAX: 912-927-5387. Web Site: www.library.armstrong.edu. *Dir*, Byung Moo Lee; E-Mail: leeben@mail.armstrong.edu; *Asst Dir*, Doug Frazier; Tel: 912-927-5485, E-Mail: fraziedo@mail.armstrong.edu; *Tech Servs*, Aran West; *Media Spec*, Ann Fuller; *Ref*, Beth Dinnebeil; *Ref*, Laura Greene; *ILL*, Caroline Hopkinson; *ILL*, Melissa Jackson; *Per*, Bea Taylor; Staff 19 (MLS 10, Non-MLS 9)
Founded 1935. Enrl 2,876; Fac 164; Highest Degree: Master
Jul 1998-Jun 1999 Income $1,041,464. Mats Exp $1,300,000, Books $350,000, Per/Ser (Incl. Access Fees) $180,000, Presv $10,000, Micro $10,000, AV Equip $5,000. Sal $517,000 (Prof $390,000)
Library Holdings: Bk Vols 183,000; Bk Titles 153,000; Per Subs 1,043
Subject Interests: Georgia
Special Collections: Educational Resources Information Center Coll, fiche; First Editions of Conrad Aiken & other Savannah authors; Library of American Civilization, fiche; Library of English Literature, fiche
Automation Activity & Vendor Info: (Cataloging) Endeavor; (Circulation) Endeavor; (OPAC) Endeavor
Database Vendor: Ebsco - EbscoHost, Lexis-Nexis, OCLC - First Search, OVID Technologies, ProQuest, Silverplatter Information Inc.
Publications: Annual Report; Faculty Guide to Lane Library; Library Guides
Partic in Dialog Corporation
Open Mon-Thurs 7:30am-11pm, Fri 7:30am-5pm, Sat 10am-5pm & Sun 2-11pm

P CHATHAM-EFFINGHAM-LIBERTY REGIONAL LIBRARY, 2002 Bull St, 31401-9180. SAN 339-1655. Tel: 912-652-3600. TDD: 912-652-3635. FAX: 912-652-3638. E-Mail: systems@cel.co.chatham.ga.us. Web Site: www.celrl.org. *Dir*, William Johnson; *Head Tech Servs*, Judy Nichols; *YA Servs*, Judy Strong; *Ref*, Barry Stokes; *Coordr, Publ Servs*, Diane Wilhelm; *Acq*, Diane Bronson; Staff 28 (MLS 28)
Founded 1903. Pop 325,811; Circ 1,084,212
Library Holdings: Bk Vols 572,434; Per Subs 1,476
Subject Interests: Genealogy
Special Collections: Local History (Gamble Coll); Municipal
Automation Activity & Vendor Info: (Acquisitions) SIRSI; (Circulation) SIRSI
Publications: CEL Regional Library: What's in it for you? (quarterly newsletter)
Partic in OCLC Online Computer Library Center, Inc; SE Libr Network
Special Services for the Deaf - TDD; Videos & decoder
Branches: 19
CARNEGIE, 537 E Henry St, 31401. SAN 339-168X. Tel: 912-232-1420. Web Site: www.celrl.org. *Branch Mgr*, Mark Darby
Library Holdings: Bk Vols 1,284
Subject Interests: Afro-American
EFFINGHAM COUNTY, PO Box 189, Springfield, 31329. SAN 339-171X. Tel: 912-754-3003. FAX: 912-754-9494. Web Site: www.celrl.org. *Br Coordr*, Carlos Egan
Library Holdings: Bk Vols 26,509
FOREST CITY, 1501 Stiles Ave, 31401. SAN 339-1701. Tel: 912-238-0614. FAX: 912-236-8879. *Coordr*, Kathleen Robertson
Library Holdings: Bk Vols 21,192
HITCH, 840 Hitch Dr, 31401. SAN 339-1744. Tel: 912-238-3210. FAX: 912-238-3210. *Coordr*, Ann Gloyd
Library Holdings: Bk Vols 539
ISLANDS, 125 Wilmington Island Rd, 31410. SAN 339-1752. Tel: 912-897-6233. FAX: 912-897-1496. Web Site: www.celrl.org. *Br Coordr*, Mary Beetle
Library Holdings: Bk Vols 34,948
KAYTON, 624 W Gwinnett St, 31401. SAN 339-1779. Tel: 912-238-3661. *Coordr*, Ann Gloyd
Library Holdings: Bk Vols 566
W W LAW LIBRARY, 909 E Bolton St, 31401. SAN 339-1809. Tel: 912-236-8040. FAX: 912-236-8040. *Coordr*, Ann Gloyd
Library Holdings: Bk Vols 405
LIBERTY COUNTY, 236 Memorial Dr, Hinesville, 31313. SAN 339-1833. Tel: 912-368-4003. FAX: 912-369-7148. *Br Coordr*, Carlos Egan
Library Holdings: Bk Vols 49,567
LIBRARY FOR THE BLIND & PHYSICALLY HANDICAPPED, . SAN 339-1663. Tel: 912-354-5864. Toll Free FAX: 800-342-4455. *Librn*, Linda Stokes

Library Holdings: Bk Vols 17,768
MIDWAY-RICEBORO BRANCH, 1165 Bill Martin Rd, Midway, 31320. SAN 375-5479. Tel: 912-884-5742. FAX: 912-884-5742. *Br Coordr*, Carlos Egan
Library Holdings: Bk Vols 1,500
OGEECHEE, 1820 Ogeechee Rd, 31401. SAN 339-1868. Tel: 912-232-1339. *Coordr*, Ann Gloyd
Library Holdings: Bk Vols 544
OGLETHORPE MALL, 7 Mall Annex, 31406. SAN 339-1892. Tel: 912-925-5432. FAX: 912-925-2031. *Branch Mgr*, Michael Hill
Library Holdings: Bk Vols 76,160
OLA WYETH, 4 E Bay St, 31401. SAN 339-204X. Tel: 912-232-5488. FAX: 912-232-5488. *Coordr*, Ann Gloyd
Library Holdings: Bk Vols 10,998
PORT CITY, 3501 Houlihan Ave, 31408. SAN 339-1949. Tel: 912-964-8013. FAX: 912-966-5142. *Coordr*, Kathleen Robertson
Library Holdings: Bk Vols 28,684
PORT WENTWORTH BRANCH, 102 Aberfeldy St, Port Wentworth, 31408. SAN 339-1957. Tel: 912-964-0371. FAX: 912-964-0371. *Coordr*, Kathleen Robertson
Library Holdings: Bk Vols 103
SOUTH EFFINGHAM, PO Box 468, 17th St & Hwy 21, Rincon, 31326. SAN 329-6059. Tel: 912-826-2222. FAX: 912-826-6304. *Coordr*, Richard Leach
Library Holdings: Bk Vols 23,077
THUNDERBOLT BRANCH, 2708 Mechanics Ave, Thunderbolt, 31404. SAN 339-1981. Tel: 912-354-5864. FAX: 912-354-5534. *Coordr*, Coni Coleman
Library Holdings: Bk Vols 14,350
TYBEE ISLAND BRANCH, 403 Butler Ave, Tybee Island, 31328. SAN 339-2015. Tel: 912-786-7733. FAX: 912-786-7734. *Coordr*, Coni Coleman
Library Holdings: Bk Vols 12,118
WEST CHATHAM, 216 S Rogers St, Pooler, 31322. SAN 339-1922. Tel: 912-748-0471. FAX: 912-748-4947. *Coordr*, Kathleen Robertson
Library Holdings: Bk Vols 29,589
Bookmobiles: 2

CITY OF SAVANNAH
G MUNICIPAL RESEARCH LIBRARY, City Hall, Rm 103, PO Box 1027, 31402. SAN 339-2139. Tel: 912-651-6412. FAX: 912-233-1992. Web Site: www.ci.savannah.ga.us. *Dir Libr Serv*, Glenda E Anderson; E-Mail: ganderson@milkyway.ci.savannah.ga.us
Founded 1974
Library Holdings: Bk Vols 30,000; Per Subs 125
Special Collections: Savannah Area Local Documents, including City of Savannah, Chatham County, Chatham County-Savannah Metropolitan Planning Commission & Coastal Area Planning and Development Commission
Publications: Bibliography & Indexes of Savannah Area Local Documents 1960-1979
Restriction: Non-circulating to the public
Partic in Georgia Libr Info Network; Local Govt Info Network; Local Info Network for Universal Serv; Pub Tech Inc

S GEORGIA HISTORICAL SOCIETY LIBRARY, 501 Whitaker St, 31401. SAN 303-4186. Tel: 912-651-2128. FAX: 912-651-2831. E-Mail: ghslib@georgiahistory.com. Web Site: www.georgiahistory.com. *Archivist, Dir*, Susan E Dick
Founded 1839
Library Holdings: Bk Vols 20,000; Per Subs 50
Subject Interests: Civil War, Genealogy, Georgia
Special Collections: Central of Georgia Railway
Publications: Georgia Historical Quarterly; Georgia Historical Society Collections; Georgia Historical Society Footnotes
Restriction: Non-circulating to the public
Partic in OCLC Online Computer Library Center, Inc; RLIN

S GIRL SCOUTS OF THE USA, Juliette Gordon Low Girl Scout National Center Library, 10 E Oglethorpe Ave, 31401. SAN 377-3965. Tel: 912-233-4501. FAX: 912-233-4659. E-Mail: kkeena@girlscouts.org. Web Site: www.girlscouts.org. *Dir*, Fran Harold
Library Holdings: Bk Vols 550
Restriction: By appointment only

S HERTY FOUNDATION LIBRARY, 110 Brampton Rd, PO Box 7798, 31418. SAN 323-4665. Tel: 912-963-2600. FAX: 912-963-2614. *Dir*, Dr Carl Counts
Library Holdings: Bk Vols 2,600
Subject Interests: Chemical engineering, Forest product, Paper product, Pulp product

M MEMORIAL HEALTH UNIVERSITY MEDICAL CENTER, Health Sciences Library, 4700 Waters Ave, PO Box 23089, 31403-3089. SAN 323-7370. Tel: 912-350-8345. FAX: 912-350-8685. *Tech Servs*, Vanessa Lonon; Staff 2 (MLS 1, Non-MLS 1)
Library Holdings: Bk Titles 4,200; Per Subs 400
Special Collections: Allied Health, Quality, bks; Medicine, Nursing, bks, videotapes

SR ROMAN CATHOLIC DIOCESE OF SAVANNAH ARCHIVES, Catholic Pastoral Ctr, 601 E Liberty St, 31401-5196. SAN 371-9499. Tel: 912-238-2320. FAX: 912-238-2339. E-Mail: diosav@sava.gulfnet.com, savarch@aol.com. *Librn*, Sarah Lloyd; *Archivist*, Gillian Brown
Founded 1850
Special Collections: Roman Catholic Sacramental Records, bks, flm

M SAINT JOSEPH'S-CANDLER HEALTH SYSTEM, (Formerly Saint Joseph's Hospital), Health Sciences Library, 11705 Mercy Blvd, 31419-1791. SAN 303-4194. Tel: 912-925-4100, Ext 4472. FAX: 912-921-3390. *Librn*, Maxine G Blair
Founded 1905
Library Holdings: Bk Titles 850; Per Subs 60
Subject Interests: Hospital administration, Medicine, Nursing
Partic in Southeastern Regional Med Libr Program
Open Mon-Fri 7am-3:30pm

M SAINT JOSEPH'S-CANDLER HEALTH SYSTEM, Candler Campus Professional Library, 5353 Reynolds St, 31405. SAN 326-9086. Tel: 912-692-6011. FAX: 912-692-6031. Web Site: www.stjosephs-candler.org. *Librn*, Annette Sheppard; E-Mail: sheppard.aj@gain.mercer.edu
Library Holdings: Bk Titles 1,000; Per Subs 150

S SAVANNAH MORNING NEWS, Research Hub, 111 Bay St W, PO Box 1088, 31402. SAN 303-4208. Tel: 912-652-0319, 912-652-0320. FAX: 912-234-6522. *Res*, Julia C Muller; Tel: 912-652-0819; *Res*, Sara Wright
Library Holdings: Bk Vols 350
Restriction: Not open to public

C SAVANNAH STATE UNIVERSITY, Asa H Gordon Library, PO Box 20394, 31404. SAN 303-4216. Tel: 912-356-2183. FAX: 912-356-2874. Web Site: www.168.20.205.158.; Staff 3 (MLS 3)
Founded 1891. Enrl 1,932; Highest Degree: Master
Library Holdings: Bk Vols 165,000; Per Subs 828
Subject Interests: Black people (ethnic)
Special Collections: Educational Resources Information Center
Publications: Bibliographies; Library Handbook
Partic in Dialog Corporation; SE Libr Network

S SKIDAWAY INSTITUTE OF OCEANOGRAPHY LIBRARY, 10 Ocean Science Circle, 31411-1011. SAN 303-4224. Tel: 912-598-2474. FAX: 912-598-2391. E-Mail: library@skio.peachnet.edu. Web Site: www.skio.peachnet.edu. *Branch Mgr*, Elizabeth B Cooksey; E-Mail: liz@skio.peachnet.edu; Staff 1 (MLS 1)
Founded 1970
Jul 2000-Jun 2001 Mats Exp $86,000, Books $8,000, Per/Ser (Incl. Access Fees) $75,000, Other Print Mats $3,000
Library Holdings: Bk Vols 8,000; Bk Titles 4,000; Per Subs 125
Subject Interests: Ecology, Geochemistry, Geology, Marine biology, Oceanography
Publications: Serials Holdings List
Partic in GALILEO

C SOUTH COLLEGE LIBRARY, 709 Mall Blvd, 31406. SAN 322-8800. Tel: 912-691-6000. FAX: 912-691-6070. *Librn*, Valerie E Yaughn; Staff 3 (MLS 2, Non-MLS 1)
Founded 1975. Enrl 400; Fac 50; Highest Degree: Bachelor
Library Holdings: Bk Vols 15,500; Bk Titles 10,500; Per Subs 65
Subject Interests: Allied health, Bus, Computer science, Hospitality, Paralegal
Automation Activity & Vendor Info: (Cataloging) Sagebrush Corporation; (OPAC) Sagebrush Corporation
Partic in Ga Pvt Libr Asn; South Georgia Associated Libraries

S TELFAIR MUSEUM OF ART LIBRARY, 121 Barnard St, 31401. SAN 371-1196. Tel: 912-232-1177. FAX: 912-232-6954.; Staff 10 (Non-MLS 10)
Founded 1886
Jan 2000-Dec 2000 Mats Exp $3,600, Books $2,400, Per/Ser (Incl. Access Fees) $1,200
Library Holdings: Bk Titles 2,480; Per Subs 25
Subject Interests: 18th Century decorative arts, 19th Century Am lit, 20th Century art
Restriction: Staff use only

SR ABE & ESTHER TENENBAUM LIBRARY, 9 Lee Blvd, 31405. SAN 329-7365. Tel: 912-352-4737. FAX: 912-352-3477.; Staff 1 (Non-MLS 1)
Library Holdings: Bk Vols 2,000
Special Collections: Judaica, bks

UNITED STATES ARMY
A CORPS OF ENGINEERS, SAVANNAH DISTRICT TECHNICAL LIBRARY (IM-PL), 100 W Oglethrope Ave, PO Box 889, 31402-0889. SAN 339-2163. Tel: 912-652-5462. FAX: 912-652-6070. *Chief Librn*, Joseph Taggart Page; E-Mail: joseph.t.page@sas02.usace.army.mil; Staff 1 (MLS 1)
Founded 1968
1999-2000 Income Federal $20,756. Mats Exp $11,048, Books $5,000, Per/Ser (Incl. Access Fees) $5,648, Micro $400
Library Holdings: Bk Vols 3,700; Bk Titles 3,200; Per Subs 286

Subject Interests: Architecture, Ecology, Engineering, Geology
Special Collections: Federal Register 1975 to Present
Automation Activity & Vendor Info: (Cataloging) Brodart
Database Vendor: Dialog, Lexis-Nexis, OCLC - First Search
Function: Research library
Partic in Fedlink; Solinet

S US NATIONAL PARK SERVICE, Fort Pulaski Monument Library, PO Box 30757, 31410-0757. SAN 370-2901. Tel: 912-786-5787. FAX: 912-786-6023. *Librn*, Kimberly Cunningham
Library Holdings: Bk Vols 800; Per Subs 10
Subject Interests: Natural history

SMYRNA

P SMYRNA PUBLIC LIBRARY, 100 Village Green Circle, 30080-3478. SAN 303-4232. Tel: 770-431-2860. FAX: 770-431-2862. E-Mail: slibrary@bellsouth.net. *Dir*, Michael E Seigler; E-Mail: mjseigler@msn.com; *Coordr, Tech Servs*, Rick Wright; *Tech Servs*, Guy Leach; *Ch Servs*, Tonda Morris; *ILL*, Rita Davis; *Govt Doc*, Derrick L Flood; *Coll Develop*, Pat Hawes; Staff 14 (MLS 4, Non-MLS 10)
Founded 1936. Pop 37,268; Circ 149,012
Jul 1999-Jun 2000 Income City $528,454. Mats Exp $90,667, Books $74,030, Per/Ser (Incl. Access Fees) $4,175, Presv $1,430, Micro $96, AV Equip $1,171, Electronic Ref Mat (Incl. Access Fees) $9,765. Sal $366,261 (Prof $121,488)
Library Holdings: Bk Vols 75,177; Per Subs 102
Subject Interests: Children's literature, Genealogy, Georgia, Law
Special Collections: Antique bks; Fed depository
Automation Activity & Vendor Info: (OPAC) Sagebrush Corporation
Database Vendor: IAC - Info Trac, ProQuest
Publications: Libr Link (Newsletter)
Partic in Georgia Online Database; N Ga Associated Librs; SE Libr Network
Friends of the Library Group

STATESBORO

C GEORGIA SOUTHERN UNIVERSITY, Zach S Henderson Library, PO Box 8074, 30460-8074. SAN 303-4240. Tel: 912-681-5114. FAX: 912-681-0289. Web Site: www.2.gasou.edu/library. *Acq, Coll Develop*, Charles A Skewis; E-Mail: cskewis@gasou.edu; *Librn*, Lora Davidson; *Assoc Dir*, Ann Hamilton; *Info Res*, Laura Davidson; *AV, Circ*, Fred Smith; *Syst Coordr*, David Lowder; Staff 16 (MLS 16)
Founded 1906. Enrl 14,000; Fac 550
Library Holdings: Bk Vols 517,575; Per Subs 3,520
Special Collections: Commander William M Rigdon Coll, 1940-1950 (correspondence of the Commander as Naval Aide to Presidents' Roosevelt & Truman); Congressman Ronald "Bo" Ginn Coll; Geer Coll; Gulver Kidd Coll; Zachert Coll of Private Press Books
Publications: Current Issues Only (newsletter)
Partic in Cent Ga Associated Libro; Dialog Corporation; E Ga Libr Triangle; Georgia Libr Info Network; SE Libr Network; South Georgia Associated Libraries

P STATESBORO REGIONAL LIBRARY, 124 S Main St, 30458. SAN 339-2198. Tel: 912-764-1341. FAX: 912-764-1348. Web Site: www.lcomcorp.com/library/. *Dir*, Peter G Sullivan; E-Mail: peters@srls.public.lib.sa.us; *Publ Servs*, Gretchen Dombrock; *Tech Servs*, Judy Glisson; *Ref*, Jim Rickerson; *Ch Servs*, Mary Matuszewski; *Ref*, Janice Waters. Subject Specialists: *Genealogy*, Pat Hutcheson; *Local history*, Pat Hutcheson; Staff 47 (MLS 7, Non-MLS 40)
Founded 1937. Pop 121,000; Circ 377,000
Jul 1999-Jun 2000 Income (Main Library and Branch Library) $1,600,000, State $475,114, City $229,676, Federal $16,723, County $511,157, Locally Generated Income $166,572, Other $95,461. Mats Exp $145,352. Sal $941,548 (Prof $388,419)
Library Holdings: Bk Vols 171,759; Per Subs 307
Special Collections: Genealogy Coll, bks, micro
Automation Activity & Vendor Info: (Cataloging) Gaylord
Publications: 1909 Map (Bulloch County Georgia); genealogy (incl cemetary rec, census, newsp abstracts); Regional Cooking (cookbook)
Partic in Georgia Libr Info Network
Friends of the Library Group
Branches: 5
EVANS COUNTY, 701 W Main, Claxton, 30417. SAN 339-2252. Tel: 912-739-1801. FAX: 912-739-0522. *Mgr*, Nancy B Odom
Circ 20,086
1999-2000 Mats Exp Electronic Ref Mat (Incl. Access Fees) $1,067
Library Holdings: Bk Titles 17,514; Per Subs 3,246
FRANKLIN MEMORIAL, 331 W Main, Swainsboro, 30401. SAN 339-2287. Tel: 912-237-7791. FAX: 912-237-3553. *Mgr*, Darryl Gray
Friends of the Library Group
L C ANDERSON MEMORIAL LIBRARY, PO Box 268, Metter, 30439. SAN 339-2228. Tel: 912-685-2455. FAX: 912-685-4462. *Mgr*, Leslie Massey
Friends of the Library Group
PEMBROKE PUBLIC, PO Box 7, Pembroke, 31321. SAN 339-2317. Tel: 912-653-2822. FAX: 912-653-2802. *Mgr*, Paul Weinberger
RICHMOND HILL PUBLIC, PO Box 939, Richmond Hill, 31324. SAN 339-2341. Tel: 912-756-3580. FAX: 912-756-2976. *Mgr*, Kate Barker
Friends of the Library Group

SUMMERVILLE

P CHATTOOGA COUNTY LIBRARY, 360 Farrar Dr, 30747-2016. SAN 338-9049. Tel: 706-857-2553. FAX: 706-857-7841. *Dir*, Barbara Hutsell; *Asst Dir*, Susan Stephens; Staff 11 (MLS 2, Non-MLS 9)
Founded 1941. Pop 22,321; Circ 85,005
Library Holdings: Bk Titles 52,006; Per Subs 91
Partic in Georgia Libr Info Network
Friends of the Library Group

SWAINSBORO

J EAST GEORGIA COLLEGE LIBRARY, 131 College Circle, 30401. SAN 303-4259. Tel: 478-289-2083. FAX: 478-289-2089. *Asst Librn*, Carol L Bray; Staff 2 (MLS 2)
Founded 1973. Enrl 1,350; Fac 24; Highest Degree: Associate
Library Holdings: Bk Vols 39,000; Bk Titles 33,500; Per Subs 125
Special Collections: Ehrlich Military History Coll; Southeast Georgia Archives Coll
Automation Activity & Vendor Info: (Acquisitions) Endeavor; (Cataloging) Endeavor; (Circulation) Endeavor; (Course Reserve) Endeavor; (ILL) Endeavor; (Media Booking) Endeavor; (OPAC) Endeavor; (Serials) Endeavor
Partic in Cent Ga Associated Libro; GALILEO; Georgia Online Database

SYLVANIA

P SCREVEN-JENKINS REGIONAL LIBRARY, 106 S Community Dr, 30467. SAN 339-2376. Tel: 912-564-7526. FAX: 912-564-7580. Web Site: www.tlc.library.net/screven. *Dir*, Sandra L Lively; E-Mail: slively@mail.screven.pub.lib.ga.us; *Asst Dir*, Kathyrn Youles; Staff 10 (MLS 3, Non-MLS 7)
Founded 1951. Pop 24,713; Circ 153,163
Library Holdings: Bk Vols 144,000; Per Subs 86
Subject Interests: Genealogy, Georgia, Local history
Partic in SE Libr Network
Friends of the Library Group
Branches: 1
JENKINS COUNTY MEMORIAL LIBRARY, 223 Daniel St, Millen, 30442. SAN 339-2406. Tel: 912-982-4244. FAX: 912-982-2192. *Mgr*, Wilma Gainey
Bookmobiles: 1

THOMASVILLE

M JOHN D ARCHBOLD MEMORIAL HOSPITAL, Ralph Perkins Memorial Library, PO Box 1018, 31799-1018. SAN 303-4267. Tel: 912-228-2063. FAX: 912-228-8584. *Librn*, Susan T Leik; E-Mail: statom.s@gain.mercer.edu
Library Holdings: Bk Titles 150; Per Subs 65
Restriction: Staff use only

P THOMAS COUNTY PUBLIC LIBRARY SYSTEM, 201 N Madison St, 31792-5414. SAN 373-2967. Tel: 229-225-5252. TDD: 229-225-5252. FAX: 229-225-5258. Web Site: home.rose.net/~tcpls. *Coll Develop, Dir*, Nancy Tillinghast; E-Mail: nancy@tcpls.org; *Asst Dir*, Carol Armstrong; *Tech Servs*, Lara Vowell; *Circ*, Becky Floyd; *Ref*, Perida Mitchell; *Ch Servs*, Deanna Ramsey; *ILL*, Angela Byrd; *Automation Syst Coordr*, Andy Kirkland; Staff 15 (MLS 1, Non-MLS 14)
Founded 1988. Pop 42,000; Circ 510,018
Jul 1998-Jun 1999 Income (Main Library and Branch Library) $626,247. Mats Exp $71,190, Books $54,440, Per/Ser (Incl. Access Fees) $6,500, Micro $250. Sal $440,703 (Prof $102,547)
Library Holdings: Bk Vols 73,000; Bk Titles 95,000; Per Subs 183
Subject Interests: Art
Special Collections: Black Culture/History (Flipper Coll); Plantation Project for South Georgia; Thomas County, Georgia a History (Heritage Room Coll), bks, microfilm & oral hist
Automation Activity & Vendor Info: (Acquisitions) SIRSI; (Cataloging) SIRSI; (Circulation) SIRSI
Publications: Friends Newsletter
Partic in Georgia Online Database; SE Libr Network
Special Services for the Deaf - Books on deafness & sign language; High interest/low vocabulary books; Special interest periodicals; TDD
Friends of the Library Group
Branches: 5
BOSTON CARNEGIE PUBLIC LIBRARY, 250 S Main St, PO Box 310, Boston, 31626-0310. SAN 373-2975. Tel: 229-498-5101. FAX: 229-498-5101. *Mgr*, Dolly Brooks; E-Mail: dolly@tcpls.org; Staff 2 (Non-MLS 2)
Library Holdings: Bk Vols 9,315
Automation Activity & Vendor Info: (Circulation) SIRSI

Friends of the Library Group
COOLIDGE PUBLIC LIBRARY, Verbena St, PO Box 429, Coolidge, 31738-0429. SAN 373-2983. Tel: 229-346-3463. FAX: 229-346-3463. *Mgr*, Kari Johnson; E-Mail: kari@tcpls.org; Staff 2 (Non-MLS 2)
Library Holdings: Bk Vols 8,717
Automation Activity & Vendor Info: (Circulation) SIRSI
Friends of the Library Group
GLADYS M CLARK PUBLIC LIBRARY, E Railroad St, PO Box 89, Ochlocknee, 31773. SAN 373-5966. Tel: 229-574-5884. FAX: 229-574-5884. *Mgr*, Mildred Welch; E-Mail: mildred@tcpls.org; Staff 2 (Non-MLS 2)
Library Holdings: Bk Vols 6,311
Automation Activity & Vendor Info: (Cataloging) SIRSI; (Circulation) SIRSI
Friends of the Library Group
MEIGS PUBLIC LIBRARY, Railroad St, PO Box 176, Meigs, 31765-0176. SAN 373-2991. Tel: 229-683-3853. FAX: 229-683-3853. *Mgr*, Donna Williams; E-Mail: donna@tcpls.org; Staff 2 (Non-MLS 2)
Library Holdings: Bk Vols 8,117
Automation Activity & Vendor Info: (Circulation) SIRSI
Friends of the Library Group
PAVO PUBLIC LIBRARY, 219 E Harris St, PO Box 396, Pavo, 31778-0396. SAN 373-5974. Tel: 229-859-2697. FAX: 229-859-2697. *Mgr*, Trish McCoy; E-Mail: trish@tcpls.org
Library Holdings: Bk Vols 7,555
Automation Activity & Vendor Info: (Circulation) SIRSI
Friends of the Library Group

C THOMAS UNIVERSITY LIBRARY, 1501 Millpond Rd, 31792. SAN 303-4275. Tel: 912-226-1621. FAX: 912-226-1679. *Dir*, Don Nickerson
Founded 1950. Enrl 800
Jul 1998-Jun 1999 Income $100,000. Mats Exp $80,000, Books $50,000, Per/Ser (Incl. Access Fees) $30,000
Library Holdings: Bk Vols 38,400; Per Subs 409
Partic in Georgia Online Database; SE Libr Network

TIFTON

J ABRAHAM BALDWIN AGRICULTURAL COLLEGE, Baldwin Library, Dormitory Dr, 2802 Moore Hwy, 31794. SAN 303-4283. Tel: 229-386-3223. FAX: 229-386-7471. Web Site: stallion.abac.peachnet.edu/library.htm. *Dir*, Brenda A Sellers; Tel: 229-386-3934, E-Mail: bsellers@abac.peachnet.edu; *Asst Librn*, Sharon Lynn Kelly; Tel: 229-386-7160, E-Mail: skelly@abac.peachnet.edu; *Asst Librn*, Mary J Rootes; E-Mail: mrootes@abac.peachnet.edu; Staff 3 (MLS 3)
Founded 1933. Enrl 2,700; Fac 158; Highest Degree: Associate
Jul 1999-Jun 2000 Income $474,019, State $427,873, Federal $24,720, Locally Generated Income $4,926, Parent Institution $8,000, Other $8,500. Mats Exp $96,889, Books $43,736, Per/Ser (Incl. Access Fees) $25,182, Presv $3,108, Micro $13,305, AV Equip $6,986, Other Print Mats $2,263, Electronic Ref Mat (Incl. Access Fees) $2,309. Sal $258,187 (Prof $90,293)
Library Holdings: Bk Vols 67,597; Bk Titles 59,900; Per Subs 513
Special Collections: Dorothy King & Betty King Carr Children's Classic Coll; Georgiana Coll
Automation Activity & Vendor Info: (Cataloging) Endeavor; (Circulation) Endeavor
Database Vendor: Ebsco - EbscoHost, Lexis-Nexis, OCLC - First Search, ProQuest
Publications: Library + (campus) (Newsletter)
Restriction: Circulation limited
Function: ILL available
Partic in Georgia Libr Info Network; SE Libr Network; Solinet; South Georgia Associated Libraries

P COASTAL PLAIN REGIONAL LIBRARY, Headquarters, 2014 Chestnut Ave, 31794. SAN 339-2430. Tel: 229-386-3400. TDD: 912-386-7148. FAX: 229-386-3400. Web Site: www.members.surfsouth.com/~spaulk/Home.htm. *Dir*, Gary F Frizzell; E-Mail: frizzelg@mail.tift.public.lib.ga.us; *Asst Dir, Ch Servs*, Kathy E Griffis; E-Mail: griffik0@mail.tift.public.lib.ga.us; *Asst Dir*, Sara J Paulk; *Head Tech Servs*, Jennifer lawley; *ILL*, Joan W Newberry; E-Mail: newberrj@mail.tift.public.lib.ga.us; *Cat*, D Yvonne Cooper; E-Mail: coopery@mail.tift.public.lib.ga.us; Staff 28 (MLS 6, Non-MLS 22)
Founded 1956. Pop 85,039; Circ 328,979
Jul 1998-Jun 1999 Income (Main Library and Branch Library) $1,213,400, State $440,320, City $183,812, County $427,151, Locally Generated Income $162,117. Mats Exp $154,570. Sal $296,989 (Prof $641,678)
Library Holdings: Bk Vols 287,101; Per Subs 340
Publications: Between the Bookends (newsletter)
Partic in Georgia Online Database; South Georgia Associated Libraries
Special Services for the Deaf - TDD
Special Services for the Blind - Large print bks; Magnifiers; Talking bk serv referral
Branches: 5
BERRIEN COUNTY-CARRIE DORSEY PERRY MEMORIAL, 315 W Marion Ave, Nashville, 31639. SAN 339-2465. Tel: 912-686-2782. FAX: 912-686-2782. *Branch Mgr*, Catherine Tucker
COOK COUNTY, 213 E Second St, Adel, 31620. SAN 339-249X. Tel: 912-896-3652. FAX: 912-896-3652. *Branch Mgr*, Janice Dobransky
IRWIN COUNTY, 213 E Second St, Ocilla, 31774. SAN 339-2554. Tel: 912-468-5456. FAX: 912-468-5456. *Branch Mgr*, DeLois Handley
Friends of the Library Group
TIFTON-TIFT COUNTY PUBLIC, One Library Lane, 31794. SAN 339-2619. Tel: 229-386-7205. FAX: 229-386-7205. *Head Librn*, J Sara Paulk; E-Mail: paulkj@mail.tift.public.lib.ga.us; *Ch Servs*, Patricia Tolar; *Head, Circ*, Sheila Peacock; *Head Ref*, Sandy Hester; *Admin Assoc*, Debbie Moorman
Friends of the Library Group
TURNER COUNTY-VICTORIA EVANS MEMORIAL, 605 North St, Ashburn, 31774. SAN 339-252X. Tel: 912-567-4027. FAX: 912-567-4027. *Branch Mgr*, Joanne F Brown
Bookmobiles: 1

C UNIVERSITY OF GEORGIA COLLEGE OF AGRICULTURAL & ENVIRONMENTAL SCIENCES, Tifton Campus Library, 4601 Research Way, PO Box 748, 31793-0748. (Mail add: PO Box 748, 31793), SAN 303-4291. Tel: 912-386-3447. FAX: 912-386-7005. E-Mail: librtif@tifton.cpes.peachnet.edu. *Librn*, Duncan McClusky; E-Mail: mcclusky@tifton.cpes.peachnet.edu; Staff 2 (MLS 1, Non-MLS 1)
Founded 1924
Library Holdings: Bk Titles 5,100; Per Subs 200
Subject Interests: Agriculture, Biology

TOCCOA FALLS

C TOCCOA FALLS COLLEGE, Seby Jones Library, PO Box 800749, 30598. SAN 303-4305. Tel: 706-886-6831, Ext 5300. FAX: 706-282-6010. Web Site: www.toccoafalls.edu. *Dir*, Patricia Fisher; E-Mail: pfisher@toccoafalls.edu; *Ref*, Sara Dodge; *Tech Servs*, Stephen Robbins; *Music*, Jamey Wilkes; *Acq*, Selina Slate
Founded 1911. Enrl 920; Fac 50; Highest Degree: Master
Library Holdings: Bk Vols 105,539; Per Subs 299
Subject Interests: Education, Music, Religion
Special Collections: Religion (R A Forrest Coll-Founder & First President of College)
Partic in Galileo; Georgia Online Database; OCLC Online Computer Library Center, Inc

TUCKER

M NORTHLAKE REGIONAL MEDICAL CENTER LIBRARY, 1455 Montreal Rd, 30084. SAN 370-6699. Tel: 770-270-3000. FAX: 770-270-3190. *Librn*, Angie Goss
Founded 1980
1997-1998 Mats Exp $10,000, Books $1,500, Per/Ser (Incl. Access Fees) $7,000, Other Print Mats $1,000
Library Holdings: Bk Titles 860; Per Subs 76
Subject Interests: Orthopedics, Podiatry
Partic in Atlanta Health Science Libraries Consortium

VALDOSTA

S GS CLUB OF AMERICA LIBRARY, 625 Pine Point Circle, 31602. SAN 374-8634. Tel: 912-244-0577. *Pres*, Richard Lassater
Library Holdings: Bk Vols 300

P LOWNDES COUNTY HISTORICAL SOCIETY & MUSEUM, 305 W Central Ave. (Mail add: PO Box 434, 31603), SAN 370-520X. Tel: 912-247-4780. FAX: 912-247-2840. E-Mail: lownhist@surfsouth.com. Web Site: www.surfsouth.com/lownhist. *Dir*, Allan Morgan; *Archivist*, Albert S Pendleton
Founded 1967. Pop 55,000
Library Holdings: Bk Vols 600; Bk Titles 600

M SOUTH GEORGIA MEDICAL, Medical Center Library, PO Box 1727, 31603-1727. SAN 325-0474. Tel: 912-259-4178. FAX: 912-245-6139. *Librn*, Susan T Leik; E-Mail: statom.s@gain.mercer.edu
Library Holdings: Bk Titles 250; Per Subs 70

P SOUTH GEORGIA REGIONAL LIBRARY SYSTEM, Valdosta-Lowndes County Public Library, 300 Woodrow Wilson Dr, 31602-2592. SAN 339-2643. Tel: 912-333-0086. Reference Tel: 912-333-0086, Ext 20. FAX: 912-333-7669. Web Site: www.sgrl.org. *Dir*, Liza C Newsom; E-Mail: lnewsom@sgrl.org; *Asst Dir*, Phyllis Love; *Ref*, Sharon Bernstein; *Ch Servs*, Gladys Seaman; *Librn for Deaf*, Beverly Peters; Staff 36 (MLS 5, Non-MLS 31)
Founded 1876. Pop 100,000; Circ 500,000
Jul 2000-Jun 2001 Income (Main Library and Branch Library) $1,293,638, State $473,583, City $10,000, Federal $15,000, County $730,455, Locally Generated Income $29,600, Other $50,000. Mats Exp $94,110. Sal $495,906 (Prof $223,000)
Library Holdings: Bk Vols 201,600; Per Subs 282
Special Collections: Birds

Special Services for the Deaf - Books on deafness & sign language; Captioned media; High interest/low vocabulary books; Special interest periodicals
Friends of the Library Group
Branches: 6
EDITH G JOHNSTON LAKES BRANCH, 720 Lakes Blvd, Lake Park, 31636. SAN 372-0063. Tel: 912-559-0360. *Mgr*, Maggie Castor
Library Holdings: Bk Vols 5,800
HAHIRA BRANCH, 220 E Main St, Hahira, 31632. SAN 339-2732. Tel: 912-794-3063. *Librn*, Janet Register
Library Holdings: Bk Vols 5,000
LAKELAND BRANCH, 124 S Valdosta Rd, Lakeland, 31635. SAN 339-2767. Tel: 912-482-2904. *Librn*, Betty Bradford
Library Holdings: Bk Vols 25,500
MAE WISENBAKER MEMORIAL MCMULLEN LIBRARY, 527 Griffin Ave, 31601-6343. SAN 373-7128. Tel: 229-253-8313. *Mgr*, Beverly Sanders
STATENVILLE BRANCH, US Hwy 129 & Jackson St, Statenville, 31648. SAN 339-2791. Tel: 912-559-8182. *Mgr*, Jackie Culpepper
Library Holdings: Bk Vols 3,000
Special Collections: Echols County History
TALKING BOOK CENTER, 300 Woodrow Wilson, 31602. SAN 339-2678. Tel: 229-333-7658. Toll Free Tel: 800-246-6515. FAX: 912-333-0774. *Librn*, Beverly Peters
Founded 1974
Bookmobiles: 1

C VALDOSTA STATE UNIVERSITY, Odum Library, 1500 N Patterson St, 31698. SAN 303-4313. Tel: 229-333-5860. Interlibrary Loan Service Tel: 229-333-5867. FAX: 229-259-5055. Web Site: books.valdosta.del.edu. *Librn*, George R Gaumond; E-Mail: ggaumond@valdosta.edu; *Assoc Librn*, Betty D Paulk; *Cat*, Katharine Johnson; *Automation Syst Coordr*, Sherrida Crawford; *ILL*, Denise Montgomery; *Coll Develop*, Tamiko Lawrence; Staff 16 (MLS 16)
Founded 1913. Enrl 9,780; Fac 478; Highest Degree: Doctorate
Library Holdings: Bk Vols 422,059; Per Subs 3,072
Special Collections: Archives of contemporary South Georgia History; Georgia History & Culture (Emily Hendree Park Memorial Coll). US Doc Dep, US Maps
Automation Activity & Vendor Info: (Acquisitions) Endeavor; (Circulation) Endeavor
Partic in GALILEO; OCLC Online Computer Library Center, Inc; Peachnet; SE Libr Network; South Georgia Associated Libraries

VIDALIA

P OHOOPEE REGIONAL LIBRARY SYSTEM, Vidalia-Toombs County Library Headquarters, 610 Jackson St, 30474-2835. SAN 339-2821. Tel: 912-537-9283. FAX: 912-537-3735. E-Mail: vidalial@mail.toombs.public.lib.ga.us. Web Site: www.toombs.public.lib.ga.us. *Dir*, Dusty Gres; E-Mail: gresd@mail.toombs.public.lib.ga.us; *Admin Assoc*, Waltine Moxley; *Bkmobile Coordr*, Melba Trull; E-Mail: trullm@mail.toombs.public.lib.ga.us; *Tech Servs*, Guogia Jin; E-Mail: jing@mail.toombs.public.lib.ga.us; *Exten Serv*, Beth Shoemaker; E-Mail: shoemakb@mail.toombs.public.lib.ga.us; *Publ Servs*, Dana Peller; E-Mail: peelerd@mail.toombs.public.lib.ga.us; *Circ*, Sally Jo Thompson; E-Mail: thompsos@mail.toombs.public.lib.ga.us; Staff 9 (MLS 4, Non-MLS 5)
Founded 1938. Pop 52,000; Circ 150,000
Library Holdings: Bk Vols 130,000; Per Subs 110
Special Collections: Genealogy Coll; Local Newspaper (Vidalia Advance Coll, 1920 to date), micro
Automation Activity & Vendor Info: (Cataloging) SIRSI; (Circulation) SIRSI
Database Vendor: Ebsco - EbscoHost, OCLC - First Search, ProQuest
Branches: 5
GLENNVILLE PUBLIC, 408 E Barnard St, Glennville, 30427. SAN 339-2856. Tel: 912-654-3812. FAX: 912-654-3812. Web Site: www.vidaliaga.com/library/index.html. *Branch Mgr*, Patty R Wilson; Staff 2 (Non-MLS 2)
Automation Activity & Vendor Info: (Circulation) SIRSI
Database Vendor: Ebsco - EbscoHost, OCLC - First Search, ProQuest
JOHN E LADSON JR HISTORICAL & GENEALOGICAL, 119 Church St, 30474. SAN 339-2880. Tel: 912-537-8186. FAX: 912-537-8186. Web Site: www.vidaliaga.com/library/index.html. *Branch Mgr*, Emillie Hartz; Staff 2 (Non-MLS 2)
MONTGOMERY COUNTY PUBLIC, 215 Railroad St, Mt Vernon, 30445. (Mail add: PO Box 242, Mt Vernon, 30445-0242), SAN 339-2945. Tel: 912-583-2780. FAX: 912-583-2780. Web Site: www.vidaliaga.com/library/index.html. *Branch Mgr*, Debra Fennell; Staff 1 (Non-MLS 1)
Founded 1976
NELLE BROWN MEMORIAL, 166 W Liberty Ave, Lyons, 30436. SAN 339-2910. Tel: 912-526-6511. FAX: 912-526-6511. Web Site: www.vidaliaga.com/library/index.html. *Branch Mgr*, Carolyn Thompson; Staff 1 (Non-MLS 1)
Automation Activity & Vendor Info: (Circulation) SIRSI
Database Vendor: Ebsco - EbscoHost, OCLC - First Search, ProQuest
TATTNALL COUNTY PUBLIC, 129 Tattnall St, Reidsville, 30453. (Mail add: PO Box 338, Reidsville, 30453-0338), SAN 339-297X. Tel: 912-557-6247. FAX: 912-557-6247. Web Site: www.vidaliaga.com/library/index.html. *Branch Mgr*, India K Sandford; Staff 1 (Non-MLS 1)
Bookmobiles: 1

WALESKA

C REINHARDT COLLEGE, Hill Freeman Library, 7300 Reinhardt College Circle, 30183. SAN 303-4321. Tel: 770-720-5587. Interlibrary Loan Service Tel: 770-720-5590. Circulation Tel: 770-720-5584. FAX: 770-720-5944. E-Mail: jcl@mail.reinhardt.edu. Web Site: www.reinhardt.edu. *Dir*, Joel C Langford; Staff 3 (MLS 2, Non-MLS 1)
Founded 1883. Enrl 1,200; Fac 45; Highest Degree: Bachelor
Jul 2000-Jun 2001 Income $358,985. Mats Exp $155,860, Books $65,400, Per/Ser (Incl. Access Fees) $37,000, Presv $1,500, AV Equip $3,200, Electronic Ref Mat (Incl. Access Fees) $19,100. Sal $100,000 (Prof $159,719)
Library Holdings: Bk Vols 41,570; Bk Titles 34,456; Per Subs 360
Automation Activity & Vendor Info: (Acquisitions) EOS; (Cataloging) EOS; (Circulation) EOS; (OPAC) EOS; (Serials) EOS

WARM SPRINGS

M ROOSEVELT WARM SPRINGS INSTITUTE FOR REHABILITATION, Professional Library, 6391 Roosevelt Hwy, PO Box 1000, 31830-1000. SAN 370-7180. Tel: 706-655-5616. FAX: 706-655-5630. *Librn*, Michael D Shadix; E-Mail: mdshadix@dhr.state.ga.us
Jul 1998-Jun 1999 Income $14,000
Library Holdings: Bk Titles 1,500; Per Subs 50
Partic in Georgia Interactive Network For Medical Information

WARNER ROBINS

§J MIDDLE GEORGIA TECHNICAL COLLEGE, 80 Cohen Walker Dr, 31088-2730. SAN 378-3901. Tel: 478-988-6863. FAX: 478-988-6813. *Librn*, Merele Daffer; E-Mail: mdaffer@mgtc.org
Library Holdings: Bk Vols 1,800; Bk Titles 1,681; Per Subs 72

WASHINGTON

P BARTRAM TRAIL REGIONAL LIBRARY, Mary Willis Library Headquarters, 204 E Liberty St, 30673. SAN 339-3003. Tel: 706-678-7736. FAX: 706-678-1474. *Librn*, Celeste Stover; *Tech Servs*, Patty Harber; E-Mail: harberp@mail.wilkes.pub.lib.ga.us
Founded 1888. Pop 32,962; Circ 131,073
Library Holdings: Bk Titles 104,670
Subject Interests: Georgia, Local history
Special Services for the Deaf - High interest/low vocabulary books
Friends of the Library Group
Branches: 2
TALIAFERRO COUNTY, Askin St, Crawfordville, 30631. SAN 339-3097. Tel: 706-456-2531. FAX: 706-456-2531. *Mgr*, Sharon DuBois
Friends of the Library Group
THOMSON-MCDUFFIE COUNTY, 338 Main St, Thomson, 30824. SAN 339-3062. Tel: 706-595-1341. FAX: 706-597-9458. *Librn*, Suzan Harris
Friends of the Library Group
Bookmobiles: 1

WAYCROSS

P OKEFENOKEE REGIONAL LIBRARY, 401 Lee Ave, 31501. SAN 339-3127. Tel: 912-287-4978. FAX: 912-287-4981. *Dir*, Charles B Eames; *Ch Servs*, Max Stock; *Ref*, James Britton III; *Tech Servs*, Linda K Lightfoot; *Tech Coordr*, Eric Mathis; Staff 6 (MLS 6)
Founded 1955. Pop 81,345
Library Holdings: Bk Vols 220,000; Per Subs 225
Subject Interests: Genealogy, Georgia
Publications: Newsletter
Partic in South Georgia Associated Libraries
Friends of the Library Group
Branches: 5
ALMA-BACON COUNTY PUBLIC, 201 N Pierce St, Alma, 31510. SAN 339-3216. Tel: 912-632-4710. FAX: 912-632-4512. *Mgr*, Fredda Ann Taylor
Friends of the Library Group
APPLING COUNTY PUBLIC, 301 City Hall Dr, Baxley, 31513. SAN 339-3186. Tel: 912-367-8103. FAX: 912-367-8104.
Friends of the Library Group
BLACKSHEAR MEMORIAL LIBRARY, 600 S Main St, Blackshear, 31516. SAN 339-3240. Tel: 912-449-7040. FAX: 912-449-2265. *Mgr*, Juanita Bryson

Friends of the Library Group
CLINCH COUNTY PUBLIC, PO Box 363, Homerville, 31634. SAN 339-3275. Tel: 912-487-3200. FAX: 912-487-3304. *Mgr*, Jane Welch
Friends of the Library Group
MARIAN ANDERSON BRANCH, 646 Lee St, Blackshear, 31516. SAN 339-3151. Tel: 912-449-7041.
Bookmobiles: 1

J WAYCROSS COLLEGE LIBRARY, 2001 S Georgia Pkwy, 31503. SAN 303-4356. Tel: 912-285-6136. FAX: 912-284-2990. Web Site: www.way.peachnet.edu/library/. *Dir*, Mary Jo Fayoyin; *Ref*, Gayle Everett; E-Mail: melissa@mail.way.peachnet.edu; *Circ*, Hannah Pratt; E-Mail: melissa@mail.way.peachnet.edu; Staff 7 (MLS 4, Non-MLS 3)
Founded 1976. Enrl 778; Fac 26; Highest Degree: Associate
Jun 1998-Jul 1999 Mats Exp $50,000, Books $6,032, Per/Ser (Incl. Access Fees) $27,205, Presv $215, Micro $8,262, Other Print Mats $759, Electronic Ref Mat (Incl. Access Fees) $7,527. Sal $195,574 (Prof $152,532)
Library Holdings: Bk Vols 34,457; Bk Titles 31,918; Per Subs 252
Special Collections: Okefenokee Swamp
Automation Activity & Vendor Info: (Acquisitions) Endeavor; (Cataloging) Endeavor; (Circulation) Endeavor; (Course Reserve) Endeavor; (ILL) Endeavor; (Media Booking) Endeavor; (OPAC) Endeavor; (Serials) DRA
Mem of Univ Syst of Ga
Partic in Georgia Libr Info Network; South Georgia Associated Libraries

WEST POINT

P HAWKES LIBRARY, W Eighth St, 31833. SAN 303-4364. Tel: 706-645-1549. *Librn*, Rebecca Cotney; *Asst Librn*, Florine Henderson
Pop 40,000
Library Holdings: Bk Vols 21,500; Per Subs 14
Subject Interests: Local history
Special Collections: Confederate Memorabilia; Georgia Culture Coll
Open Mon, Tues, Thurs & Fri 1-5pm
Friends of the Library Group

WINDER

P PIEDMONT REGIONAL LIBRARY, 189 Bellview, 30680-9998. SAN 339-3399. Tel: 770-867-2762. FAX: 770-867-7483. Web Site: library.barrow.public.lib.ga.us/. *Dir*, Nancy C Ray; E-Mail: rayn@mail.barrow.public.lib.qa.us; *Ch Servs, ILL*, Anna R Hoover; *Circ*, Vickie Braselton; *Cat*, Sandra R Holliday; *Bkmobile Coordr*, Nancy Holmes; Staff 4 (MLS 3, Non-MLS 1)
Founded 1954. Pop 89,581; Circ 210,231
Jul 1999-Jun 2000 Income (Main Library and Branch Library) $1,124,200, State $407,360, City $375,319, Federal $20,222, County $172,956, Locally Generated Income $32,002, Other $116,341. Mats Exp $984,748, Books $62,131, Per/Ser (Incl. Access Fees) $5,334, Presv $974, Electronic Ref Mat (Incl. Access Fees) $2,990. Sal $508,254 (Prof $214,193)
Library Holdings: Bk Vols 174,953; Per Subs 216
Friends of the Library Group
Branches: 5
BANKS COUNTY PUBLIC LIBRARY, 226 Hwy 51 W, PO Box 27, Homer, 30547. SAN 339-3429. Tel: 706-677-3164. *Branch Mgr*, Mrs Stacy G Krumnow; E-Mail: skrumnow@mail.com; Staff 3 (Non-MLS 3)
Friends of the Library Group
COMMERCE BRANCH, 1344 S Broad St, Commerce, 30529-1567. SAN 339-3453. Tel: 706-335-5946. *Branch Mgr*, Susan Harper
Friends of the Library Group
HAROLD S SWINDLE PUBLIC LIBRARY, 5466 US Hwy 441 S, Nicholson, 30565. SAN 339-3607. Tel: 706-757-3577. *Branch Mgr*, Betty Brock
JEFFERSON BRANCH, 379 Old Pindergrass Rd, Jefferson, 30549-9764. SAN 339-3488. Tel: 706-367-8012. *Branch Mgr*, Donna Butler
Friends of the Library Group
MAYSVILLE BRANCH, 9247 Gillsville Rd, Maysville, 30558-0086. (Mail add: PO Box 430, Maysville, 30558), SAN 374-6534. Tel: 706-652-2323. *Branch Mgr*, Sue Mealor
Bookmobiles: 1

WOODBINE

S BRYAN-LANG HISTORICAL LIBRARY, Fourth St at Camden Ave, PO Box 725, 31569. SAN 371-5337. Tel: 912-576-5841. *Librn*, Darren Harper; Staff 1 (MLS 1)
Founded 1984
Jul 1998-Jun 1999 Income $55,000. Mats Exp $500. Sal $42,000
Library Holdings: Bk Titles 3,000
Special Collections: Berrie Coll; Lang Coll
Restriction: Open to researchers by request

YOUNG HARRIS

P MOUNTAIN REGIONAL LIBRARY, 698 Miller St, PO Box 159, 30582. SAN 339-3720. Tel: 706-379-3732. FAX: 706-379-2047. *Dir*, Teresa Haymore; E-Mail: haymoret@mail.towns.public.lib.ga.us; *Asst Dir*, Donna Howell
Founded 1946. Pop 38,479; Circ 203,510
Library Holdings: Bk Vols 101,535
Special Collections: Appalachian Coll; Rare & Special Local Coll
Partic in Georgia Online Database; OCLC Online Computer Library Center, Inc; SE Libr Network
Friends of the Library Group
Branches: 3
FANNIN COUNTY, PO Box 1250, Blue Ridge, 30513. SAN 339-378X. Tel: 706-632-5263. FAX: 706-632-7719. *Head Librn*, Dorothea Sutphin
Friends of the Library Group
TOWNS COUNTY, 99 S Berrong St, Hiawassee, 30546. SAN 328-8951. Tel: 706-896-6169. FAX: 706-896-6169. *Branch Mgr*, Deborah Phillips
Friends of the Library Group
UNION COUNTY, PO Box 1029, Blairsville, 30512. SAN 339-3755. Tel: 706-745-7491. FAX: 706-745-7491. *Librn*, Wilma Ash
Friends of the Library Group
Bookmobiles: 1

J YOUNG HARRIS COLLEGE, Henry & J Lon Duckworth Memorial Libraries, One College St, PO Box 39, 30582. SAN 303-4372. Tel: 706-379-4313. FAX: 706-379-4314. Web Site: www.yhc.edu. *Dir*, Dawn A Lamade; E-Mail: dlamade@yhc.edu; *Tech Servs*, Judith Lee; E-Mail: jlee@yhc.edu; *Circ, ILL*, Joy Day; E-Mail: joyday@yhc.edu; *Ref, Spec Coll*, Debra March; E-Mail: dbmarch@yhc.edu
Founded 1886. Enrl 550; Fac 36; Highest Degree: Associate
Jul 1998-Jun 1999 Mats Exp $57,200, Books $32,200, Per/Ser (Incl. Access Fees) $15,000, Micro $5,000, Electronic Ref Mat (Incl. Access Fees) $5,000. Sal $100,875
Library Holdings: Bk Vols 60,000; Per Subs 237
Subject Interests: Humanities, Music, Religion
Special Collections: Byron Herbert Reece & J A Sharp Coll; Merle Mann Indian Artifacts
Partic in Ga Libr Net; Solinet

HAWAII

Date of Statistics: 1999-2000
Population, 2000: 1,193,001
Population Served by Public Libraries Statewide: 1,193,001
Total Volumes in Public Libraries (including State Library): 3,044,296 (FY 2000 statistics)
Volumes Per Capita: 2.55
Total Public Library Circulation: 6,912,342 (Includes Library for the Blind and Physically Handicapped)
Total Public Library Income: $22,789,160
Source of Income: State Legislative Appropriation, Federal LSTA Funds, and Special and Trust LSTA Funds: $861,635
Expenditures Per Capita: $18.63
Number of County Libraries: All public libraries are in one integrated statewide system
Number of Bookmobiles in State: 6
Grants-in-Aid to Public Libraries:
Federal (LSTA): $861,635
State Aid: State funded

AIEA

S HAWAII AGRICULTURE RESEARCH CENTER, Experiment Station Library, 99-193 Aiea Heights Dr, Ste 300, 96701-3911. SAN 303-4380. Tel: 808-486-5370. FAX: 808-486-5020. *Librn*, Ann L Marsteller; E-Mail: amarsteller@harc-hspa.com; Staff 1 (MLS 1)
Founded 1895
Jul 1999-Jun 2000 Income Parent Institution $104,000. Mats Exp $60,000, Books $3,500, Per/Ser (Incl. Access Fees) $54,000, Other Print Mats $2,500. Sal $43,000
Library Holdings: Bk Vols 87,000; Per Subs 100
Subject Interests: Agriculture, Plant sci
Restriction: Private library, Staff & members only
Function: Research fees apply

CAMP H M SMITH

UNITED STATES NAVY
A UNITED STATES MARINE CORPS, CAMP SMITH LIBRARY, MWR, Box 64123, 96861-4123. SAN 339-6061. Tel: 808-477-6348. FAX: 808-477-2452. *Librn*, Jan Steele; E-Mail: steelej@mfp.usmc.mil
Library Holdings: Bk Vols 20,000; Per Subs 85
Special Collections: Commandants Reading List

HAWAII NATIONAL PARK

S NATIONAL PARK SERVICE, Hawaii Volcanoes National Park Library, PO Box 52, 96718-0052. SAN 303-4402. Tel: 808-985-6130. FAX: 808-967-8186. Web Site: www.nps.gov/navo.
Founded 1925
Library Holdings: Bk Vols 3,550; Bk Titles 2,800; Per Subs 13
Special Collections: Hawaiiana; Volcano House Register, 1865-1926

HICKAM AFB

UNITED STATES AIR FORCE
A HICKAM AIR FORCE BASE LIBRARY FL5260, 15 SVS/SVMG, 990 Mills Blvd, Bldg 595, 96853-5316. SAN 339-3844. Tel: 808-449-7167. Circulation Tel: 808-449-7164. FAX: 808-449-7166. Web Site: www.hickam.af.mil/library. *Librn*, Joseph Barry; Tel: 808-449-7163; *Ref Serv*, Tina Grice; Staff 7 (MLS 2, Non-MLS 5)
Founded 1957
Library Holdings: Bk Vols 51,000; Per Subs 98
Subject Interests: Hawaii
Automation Activity & Vendor Info: (Acquisitions) SIRSI; (Cataloging) SIRSI; (Circulation) SIRSI
Database Vendor: Ebsco - EbscoHost, OCLC - First Search, ProQuest
Partic in Fedlink
Friends of the Library Group

HILO

HILO HOSPITAL
M MEDICAL LIBRARY, 1190 Waianuenue Ave, 96720. SAN 339-3879. Tel: 808-974-4795. FAX: 808-974-4746. E-Mail: hmclink@ilhawaii.net. *Librn*, Lorna Nekoba
Founded 1920
Library Holdings: Bk Titles 800; Per Subs 100
Partic in Med Libr Group of Hawaii; Pacific SW Regional Med Libr Serv

GL STATE SUPREME COURT, Third Circuit Court-Law Library, 75 Aupuni St, 96720. SAN 303-4429. Tel: 808-961-7438. FAX: 808-961-7416. *In Charge*, Margie Hanselman
Library Holdings: Bk Vols 30,000

C UNIVERSITY OF HAWAII AT HILO LIBRARIES,* 200 W Kawili St, 96720-4091. SAN 339-3933. Tel: 808-974-7346. Interlibrary Loan Service Tel: 808-974-7599. FAX: 808-974-7329. Web Site: www.uhh.hawaii.edu/~mookini. *Dir*, Kenneth R Herrick; Tel: 808-974-7507, E-Mail: herrick@hawaii.edu; *Assoc Dir*, Patricia N Okamura; Tel: 808-974-7575, E-Mail: pokamura@hawaii.edu; *Bibliog Instr*, Kevin M Roddy; Tel: 808-974-7577, E-Mail: kroddy@hawaii.edu; *Cat*, Coreen Ishimaru; Tel: 808-974-7345, E-Mail: ishimaru@hawaii.edu; *Publ Servs*, Susan F Maesato; Tel: 808-974-7577, E-Mail: maesato@hawaii.edu; *Ref, Spec Coll*, Junko I Nowaki; Tel: 808-974-7577, E-Mail: nowaki@hawaii.edu; *ILL*, Cyntha Reis; Tel: 808-974-7577, E-Mail: reis@hawaii.edu; *Coll Develop*, Helen Rogers; Tel: 808-974-7579, E-Mail: hrogers@hawaii.edu; *Publ Servs*, Thora Abarca; Tel: 808-974-7577, E-Mail: tconner@hawaii.edu; Staff 19 (MLS 8, Non-MLS 11)
Founded 1947. Enrl 2,700; Fac 145; Highest Degree: Master
Jul 1999-Jun 2000 Income State $1,270,724. Mats Exp $475,000, Books $130,000, Per/Ser (Incl. Access Fees) $109,500, Presv $20,000, Micro $14,000, AV Equip $14,000, Electronic Ref Mat (Incl. Access Fees) $15,000. Sal $795,724 (Prof $437,904)
Library Holdings: Bk Vols 257,688; Per Subs 1,100
Subject Interests: East Asia
Special Collections: Hawaiiana, bks & per
Automation Activity & Vendor Info: (Cataloging) CARL; (Circulation) CARL; (OPAC) CARL
Database Vendor: CARL, IAC - Info Trac, OCLC - First Search
Publications: Faculty Guide; Hawaii Island Newspaper Index; Student Guide, Libr Instr Workbook
Partic in Colorado Alliance Of Research Libraries; Dialog Corporation; OCLC Online Computer Library Center, Inc
Library also serves Hawaii Community College (2200 enrollment)
Friends of the Library Group

HONAUNAU

S US NATIONAL PARK SERVICE, Pu'uhonua o Honaunau National Historical Park Library, PO Box 129, 96726. SAN 376-1657. Tel: 808-328-2288. FAX: 808-328-9485. *Librn*, Blossom Sapp
Library Holdings: Bk Vols 1,300
Friends of the Library Group

HONOLULU

M AMERICAN LUNG ASSOCIATION OF HAWAII, Learning Center for Lung Health,* 245 N Kukui St, Ste 100, 96817. SAN 373-4307. Tel: 808-537-5966. FAX: 808-537-5971. *Exec Dir*, Mary Miller
Library Holdings: Bk Vols 200; Per Subs 12
Special Collections: American Review of Respiratory Diseases Coll

S BANK OF HAWAII, Information & Reference Center,* Financial Plaza, Bancorp Tower, 11th flr, Ste 1170, 131 Merchante St, PO Box 2900, 96846. SAN 303-4453. Tel: 808-537-8375. FAX: 808-536-9433. E-Mail: bhirc@pixi.comm. *Librn*, Martha B Laxson; Staff 1 (MLS 1)
Founded 1968
Library Holdings: Bk Titles 1,500; Per Subs 1,300
Subject Interests: Banks and banking, Economics, Finance, Hawaii, Pacific Islands

S BELT COLLINS HAWAII, Information Center, 680 Ala Moana Blvd, 96813-5406. SAN 370-6850. Tel: 808-521-5361. FAX: 808-538-7819. E-Mail: hawaii@beltcollins.com. Web Site: www.beltcollins.com. *Info Res*, Lisa Minato; E-Mail: lisam@beltcollins.com
Library Holdings: Bk Vols 4,000; Bk Titles 3,500; Per Subs 100
Subject Interests: Engineering, Environment, Landscape architecture, Landscape design
Publications: Acquisition List; Departmental Catalogs of Holdings
Open to staff only

S BERNICE P BISHOP MUSEUM LIBRARY, 1525 Bernice St, 96817-2704. SAN 303-447X. Tel: 808-848-4148. FAX: 808-847-8241. E-Mail: library@bishopmuseum.org. Web Site: www.bishopmuseum.org/bishop/library/library.html. *Chairperson*, Duane Wenzel; Tel: 808-848-4152, Fax: 808-847-8241, E-Mail: dwenzel@bishopmuseum.org; Staff 8 (MLS 5, Non-MLS 3)
Founded 1889
Jul 2000-Jun 2001 Income $360,000, Locally Generated Income $130,000, Parent Institution $230,000. Mats Exp $36,000, Books $6,000, Per/Ser (Incl. Access Fees) $30,000. Sal $242,000 (Prof $215,000)
Library Holdings: Bk Vols 115,000; Per Subs 1,100
Subject Interests: Anthropology, Archaeology, Botany, Ethnology, Geography, Hawaii, Museology, Pacific, Photography, Zoology
Special Collections: Hawaii Maritime Center Coll; Hawaiian Language Newspapers; Hawaiiana (Carter Coll); Japanese Hawaii Imprints; Pacific Island Languages; Pacificana (Fuller Coll); United States Geological Survey & South Pacific Commission
Automation Activity & Vendor Info: (Cataloging) Endeavor; (OPAC) Endeavor
Database Vendor: OCLC - First Search
Publications: Catalog of B P Bishop Museum Library (quarterly update)
Partic in Colorado Alliance Of Research Libraries; OCLC Online Computer Library Center, Inc
Open Tues-Fri 12-3 & Sat 9-12; $3.00 access fee to non-members & those without museum ticket purchase

L CADES, SCHUTTE, FLEMING & WRIGHT, Law Library, 1000 Bishop St, 14th Flr, 96813. (Mail add: PO Box 939, 96813), SAN 303-4488. Tel: 808-521-9366. FAX: 808-540-5078. E-Mail: cades@cades.com. Web Site: www.cades.com. *Librn*, Elizabeth Ann Weaver; Tel: 808-521-9264, E-Mail: bweaver@cades.com; *Asst Librn*, Renee Akita; Tel: 808-544-9881, E-Mail: rakita@cades.com; *Asst Librn*, Debra Anne Oandasan; E-Mail: dnagatani@cades.com; Staff 3 (Non-MLS 3)
Founded 1922
Library Holdings: Bk Vols 15,000; Bk Titles 5,000; Per Subs 215
Subject Interests: Corporate law, Medicine, Real estate, Securities
Special Collections: Ecology (Hawaiian Water Rights); Hawaii Legislative Reports
Restriction: Private library
Function: Research library

L CARLSMITH & BALL LIBRARY,* 2200 Pacific Tower, Ste 2200, 1001 Bishop St, 96813. SAN 303-4496. Tel: 808-523-2500. FAX: 808-523-0842. E-Mail: lgsh@carlsmith.com. *Asst Librn*, Grace Haitsuka
Library Holdings: Bk Vols 20,000; Per Subs 150
Partic in Westlaw

SR CELTIC EVANGELICAL CHURCH, Community of Saint Columba Library, PO Box 90880, 96835-0880. SAN 370-694X. *Librn*, Wayne W Gau
Library Holdings: Bk Titles 400
Special Collections: Early Celtic Church-History, liturgy, theology & modern revivals; Gallican-type Liturgy & Anglican Rites
Publications: The Celtic Evangelist (semi-annually)
All services to the public done by correspondence

C CHAMINADE UNIVERSITY OF HONOLULU, Sullivan Library, 3140 Waialae Ave, 96816-1578. SAN 303-4518. Tel: 808-735-4725. FAX: 808-735-4891. *Ref*, Valerie Coleman; *Tech Servs*, Kevin Allen; Staff 3 (MLS 2, Non-MLS 1)
Founded 1955. Enrl 2,000
Library Holdings: Bk Vols 74,000; Per Subs 902
Special Collections: Catholic Authors; Hawaiiana; Intergenerational; Judaica.
Partic in Dialog Corporation; OCLC Online Computer Library Center, Inc

G CITY & COUNTY OF HONOLULU, Department of Customer Services-Library, Records Management & Bookstore Section, City Hall Annex, 558 S King St, 96813-3006. SAN 303-4895. Tel: 808-527-5672. FAX: 808-523-4985. Web Site: www.state.hi.us/lrb/card/. *Librn*, Kathleen S Kudo; E-Mail: kkudo@co.honolulu.hi.us; *Librn*, Verna M Lee; Tel: 808-523-4578, E-Mail: vlee1@co.honolulu.hi.us; *Archivist*, Anne K Pulfrey; Tel: 808-523-4044, E-Mail: apulfrey@co.honolulu.hi.us; Staff 6 (MLS 3, Non-MLS 3)
Founded 1929
Jul 1999-Jun 2000 Mats Exp $27,716, Books $14,961, Per/Ser (Incl. Access Fees) $12,495, Presv $260. Sal $239,990
Library Holdings: Bk Vols 34,265; Per Subs 301
Subject Interests: Local government, Recreation, Transportation
Special Collections: Ordinances & Repository for Publications of the City & County of Honolulu; Selective US Fed Depository Libr Prog
Publications: Bookshelf (bimonthly acquisitions list)
Function: ILL available
Library responsible for management of city records & archives

S EAST-WEST CENTER, Research Information Services, 1601 East-West Rd, 96848-1601. SAN 326-7520. Tel: 808-944-7345. FAX: 808-944-7600. Web Site: www.ewc.hawaii.edu/. *Head Librn*, Phyllis Tabusa; E-Mail: tabusap@eastwestcenter.org; *Head, Cat*, Jerilyn Sumida; Tel: 808-944-7379, E-Mail: sumidaj@eastwestcenter.org; *Syst Coordr*, Terese Leber; E-Mail: lebert@eastwestcenter.org; *Tech Servs*, Audrey Minei; Tel: 808-944-7554, E-Mail: mineia@eastwestcenter.org; Staff 4 (MLS 4)
Founded 1971
Library Holdings: Bk Vols 66,000; Bk Titles 50,000; Per Subs 910
Subject Interests: Energy, International relations
Special Collections: Asian & Pacific Census; US Bureau of the Census (Hawaii Census mats in print form); World Fertility Survey
Automation Activity & Vendor Info: (Cataloging) EOS; (Circulation) EOS
Database Vendor: Dialog, ProQuest
Publications: Acquisitions Lists
Partic in OCLC Online Computer Library Center, Inc

S HAWAII CENTER FOR THE DEAF & BLIND LIBRARY,* 3440 Leahi Ave, 96815. SAN 303-4690. Tel: 808-733-4831. FAX: 808-733-4824. *Librn*, Laurianne Chun; E-Mail: laurianne@hcdb.k12.hi.us
Library Holdings: Bk Vols 7,000; Per Subs 30

S HAWAII CHINESE HISTORY CENTER LIBRARY,* 111 N King St, Ste 410, 96817-4703. SAN 303-4593. Tel: 808-521-5948. *Asst Librn*, Margaret A Wong
Founded 1970
Library Holdings: Bk Vols 850
Subject Interests: Chinese Language, Chinese-American, Genealogy, Hawaii
Publications: Books & Papers (some with the cooperation of University Press of Hawaii); Hawaii Chinese History Center Newsletter

P HAWAII CORRECTIONAL LIBRARY SYSTEM, Dept of Public Safety,* 919 Ala Moana, Rm 405, 96814. SAN 303-4720. Tel: 808-587-1273. FAX: 808-587-1280.; Staff 4 (MLS 1, Non-MLS 3)
Founded 1970
1997-1998 Income $626,000. Mats Exp $221,796. Sal $404,204

S HAWAII EMPLOYERS COUNCIL LIBRARY,* 1221 Kapio Lani Blvd Ste 900, 96820. (Mail add: PO Box 29699, 96820), SAN 303-4615. Tel: 808-836-1511. FAX: 808-836-1649. E-Mail: heclib@hecounbil.org. *Librn*, Sonja O Tyau
Founded 1943
Library Holdings: Bk Titles 6,000; Per Subs 144
Subject Interests: Benefits (Labor), Compensation (labor), Employment, Labor
Special Collections: Arbitration Decisions; Hawaii Revised Statistics; Session Law of Hawaii

M HAWAII MEDICAL LIBRARY, INC, 1221 Punchbowl St, 96813. SAN 303-4658. Tel: 808-536-9302. FAX: 808-524-6956. Web Site: hml.org. *Dir*, John A Breinich; Staff 19 (MLS 8, Non-MLS 11)
Founded 1913
Library Holdings: Bk Titles 30,000; Per Subs 2,100
Subject Interests: Clinical medicine
Special Collections: Medical Hawaiiana, bks, photogs, doc, clippings
Partic in Medline; OCLC Online Computer Library Center, Inc
Open Mon-Thurs 8-8, Fri 8-5 & Sat 9-5

S HAWAII NEWSPAPER AGENCY, INC LIBRARY,* 605 Kapiolani Blvd, PO Box 3350, 96813. SAN 303-4666. Tel: 808-525-7669. *Asst Librn*, Deanne Norton
Founded 1930
Library Holdings: Bk Vols 3,000
Special Collections: Hawaiiana

C HAWAII PACIFIC UNIVERSITY LIBRARIES, Meader Library, 1060 Bishop St, 96813-3192. SAN 303-4674. Tel: 808-544-0210. Reference Tel: 808-544-1133. FAX: 808-521-7998. E-Mail: lib@hpu.edu. Web Site: www.hpu.edu/index.cfm?section=llss. *VPres*, Stephen R Simpson; Tel: 808-544-0209, Fax: 808-544-0877, E-Mail: ssimpson@hpu.edu; *Assoc Librn*, Kathleen A Chee; Tel: 808-544-0292, Fax: 808-544-0880, E-Mail: kchee@hpu.edu; *Ser*, Patricia Martin; Tel: 808-544-0261, Fax: 808-521-7998, E-Mail: pmartin@hpu.edu; *Head, Circ*, Wayne Oshiro; Tel: 808-544-1110, Fax: 808-521-7998, E-Mail: woshiro@hpu.edu; *Head Ref*, Marilyn DeMattos; Tel: 808-544-9333, Fax: 808-521-7998, E-Mail: mdematto@hpu.edu; *Head Tech Servs*, Catherine Thomas; Tel: 808-544-9388, Fax: 808-544-0880, E-Mail: cthomas@hpu.edu; Staff 27 (MLS 14, Non-MLS 13)
Founded 1965. Enrl 8,400; Fac 405; Highest Degree: Master
Jun 1999-May 2000 Mats Exp $452,774, Books $123,253, Per/Ser (Incl. Access Fees) $300,578, Electronic Ref Mat (Incl. Access Fees) $28,943. Sal $452,774
Library Holdings: Bk Vols 156,554; Bk Titles 130,170; Per Subs 2,015
Special Collections: Atlas Coll; Closed Coll; Co-operative Education Coll; Corporation Information Coll; English Foundations Program Paperback Coll; Foreign Language Coll; Graduate Professional Paper Coll; Hawaiian-Pacific Coll; Index Center Coll; Topic Assistance Center Coll
Automation Activity & Vendor Info: (Cataloging) TLC; (Serials) TLC
Publications: curriculum materials (subject bibliographies); University Libraries Periodical List
All info includes Atherton Library, Kaneohe

C HAWAII RESEARCH CENTER FOR FUTURES STUDIES, University of Hawaii at Manoa,* 2424 Maile Way, Rm 720, 96822. SAN 328-3607. Tel: 808-956-2888. FAX: 808-956-2889. *Dir*, Jim Dator; E-Mail: dator@hawaii.edu
Library Holdings: Bk Titles 1,000
Subject Interests: Communication, Education, Law, Media, Politics, Sci, Technology
Special Collections: Futures Oriented Coll, bks, articles, periodicals

S HAWAII STATE ARCHIVES, Iolani Palace Grounds, 96813. SAN 303-4704. Tel: 808-586-0329. FAX: 808-586-0330. *Archivist*, Jolyn Tamura; Staff 7 (MLS 4, Non-MLS 3)
Founded 1905
Library Holdings: Bk Vols 9,000
Special Collections: 19th Century Hawaiian Newspapers; Captain James Cook Memorial Coll; Hawaiian Government Publications Coll; Immigration Records to 1900; National Territorial & State Archives, 1790 to date; Paul M Kahn Coll
Restriction: Non-circulating

P HAWAII STATE PUBLIC LIBRARY SYSTEM,* Office of the State Librarian, 465 S King St Rm B-1, 96813. SAN 339-3992. Tel: 808-586-3704. Interlibrary Loan Service Tel: 808-586-3549. TDD: 808-732-7767. FAX: 808-586-3715. E-Mail: stlib@lib.state.hi.us. Web Site: url: www.hcc.hawaii.edu/hspls/hsplshp.html. *State Librn*, Virginia Lowell; Staff 512 (MLS 146, Non-MLS 366)
Founded 1852. Pop 1,186,000; Circ 7,750,733
Jul 1997-Jun 1998 Income $21,122,887, State $18,345,872, Federal $856,655, Locally Generated Income $1,920,360. Mats Exp $2,178,733, Books $1,749,579, Per/Ser (Incl. Access Fees) $429,154. Sal $14,823,340 (Prof $6,358,682)
Library Holdings: Bk Vols 3,201,000
Subject Interests: Hawaii
Special Collections: Pacific Coll
Automation Activity & Vendor Info: (Acquisitions) epixtech, inc.; (Cataloging) epixtech, inc.; (Circulation) epixtech, inc.
Publications: Hawaii Documents; Honolulu Advertiser (index); Honolulu Star Bulletin (index)
Member Libraries: Hawaii State Public Library System
Special Services for the Deaf - Books on deafness & sign language; Captioned media; High interest/low vocabulary books; Special interest periodicals; Staff with knowledge of sign language; TDD
Friends of the Library Group
Branches: 49

AIEA PUBLIC, 99-143 Moanalua Rd, Aiea, 96701. SAN 339-4654. Tel: 808-483-7333. FAX: 808-483-7336. Web Site: www.hcc.hawaii.edu/hspls/hsplshp.html. *Librn*, Earline Funakoshi
Circ 251,084
Library Holdings: Bk Vols 72,000
Friends of the Library Group

AINA HAINA PUBLIC, 5246 Kalanianaole Hwy, 96821. SAN 339-4263. Tel: 808-377-2456. FAX: 808-377-2455. Web Site: www.hcc.hawaii.edu/hspls/hsplshp.html. *Librn*, Lynne Kobayashi
Circ 180,287
Library Holdings: Bk Vols 49,888
Friends of the Library Group

BOND MEMORIAL PUBLIC, Akoni Pule Hwy, Kapaau, 96755-0248. (Mail add: PO Box 248, Kapaau, 96755-0248), SAN 339-4921. Tel: 808-889-6729. FAX: 808-889-5997. E-Mail: hbmcirc@lib.state.hi.us. Web Site: www.hcc.hawaii.edu/hspls/hsplshp.html. *Librn*, Dawn Shibano
Circ 40,713
Library Holdings: Bk Vols 16,500
Friends of the Library Group

EWA BEACH PUBLIC & SCHOOL, 91-950 North Rd, Ewa Beach, 96706. SAN 339-4689. Tel: 808-689-1204. FAX: 808-689-8393. Web Site: www.hcc.hawaii.edu/hspls/hsplshp.html. *Librn*, Beryl Goo; E-Mail: berylg@lib.state.hi.us; Staff 10 (MLS 3, Non-MLS 7)
Founded 1971. Pop 42,967; Circ 155,846
Jul 1997-Jun 1998 Mats Exp $34,467, Books $26,500, Per/Ser (Incl. Access Fees) $5,169, Micro $2,798
Library Holdings: Bk Vols 80,464; Per Subs 40
Friends of the Library Group

HANA PUBLIC & SCHOOL, Hana Hwy, Hana, 96713. (Mail add: PO Box 490, Hana, 96713), SAN 339-5480. Tel: 808-248-7714. FAX: 808-248-7438. Web Site: www.hcc.hawaii.edu/hspls/hsplshp.html. *Librn*, Irene Pavao; E-Mail: irenep@lib.state.hi.us
Circ 19,984
Library Holdings: Bk Vols 27,897
Friends of the Library Group

HANAPEPE PUBLIC, 4490 Kona Rd, Hanapepe, 96716. (Mail add: PO Box B, Hanapepe, 96716), SAN 339-5316. Tel: 808-335-5811. FAX: 808-335-3560. Web Site: www.hcc.hawaii.edu/hspls/hsplshp.html. *Librn*, Karen Ikemoto
Circ 70,589
Library Holdings: Bk Vols 27,880
Friends of the Library Group

HAWAII STATE LIBRARY, 478 S King St, 96813. SAN 339-4050. Tel: 808-586-3500. FAX: 808-586-3584. Web Site: www.hcc.hawaii.edu/hspls/hsplshp.html. *Dir*, Caroline Spencer
Circ 717,539
Library Holdings: Bk Vols 546,247
Subject Interests: Art, History, Literature, Music, Philosophy, Recreation, Science/technology, Social sciences and issues, Technology
Special Collections: Asian Language Materials; Federal Documents; Hawaii & Pacific Coll; Patent & Trademark Depository; Telephone References
Publications: Hawaii Documents; Index to the Honolulu Advertiser; Star Bulletin
Friends of the Library Group

HAWAII-KAI PUBLIC, 249 Lunalilo Home Rd, 96825. SAN 339-4298. Tel: 808-397-5833. FAX: 808-397-5832. Web Site: www.hcc.hawaii.edu/hspls/hsplshp.html. *Librn*, Gail Urago
Circ 209,119
Library Holdings: Bk Vols 77,738
Friends of the Library Group

HILO PUBLIC, 300 Waianuenue Ave, Hilo, 96720. SAN 339-4891. Tel: 808-933-8888. FAX: 808-933-8895. Web Site: www.hcc.hawaii.edu/hspls/hsplshp.html. *Librn*, Wilma Matsumura
Circ 420,473
Library Holdings: Bk Vols 201,594
Friends of the Library Group

HOLUALOA PUBLIC, PO Box 214, Holualoa, 96725-0214. SAN 339-4956. Tel: 808-324-1233. FAX: 808-322-0664. Web Site: www.hcc.hawaii.edu/hspls/hsplshp.html. *Librn*, Barbara Bosz-Burczyk
Circ 15,254
Library Holdings: Bk Vols 6,521
Friends of the Library Group

HONOKAA PUBLIC, 45-3380 Mamane St, PO Box 236, Honokaa, 96727. SAN 339-4980. Tel: 808-775-7497. FAX: 808-775-7798. Web Site: www.hcc.hawaii.edu/hspls/hsplshp.html. *Librn*, Tahirih Foster; Staff 2 (MLS 1, Non-MLS 1)
Circ 34,371
Library Holdings: Bk Vols 14,384
Friends of the Library Group

KAHUKU PUBLIC & SCHOOL, 56-490 Kamehameha Hwy, Kahuku, 96731. SAN 339-4328. Tel: 808-293-8935. FAX: 808-293-8937. Web Site: www.hcc.hawaii.edu/hspls/hsplshp.html. *Librn*, Jean Okimoto; E-Mail: jeano@lib.state.hi.us
Founded 1968. Pop 15,000; Circ 65,108
Library Holdings: Bk Vols 44,211; Bk Titles 48
Friends of the Library Group

KAHULUI PUBLIC, 90 School St, Kahului, 96732. SAN 339-5499. Tel: 808-873-3097. FAX: 808-873-3094. Web Site: www.hcc.hawaii.edu/hspls/hsplshp.html. *Librn*, Lani P Scott
Circ 282,016
Library Holdings: Bk Vols 89,507
Friends of the Library Group

KAILUA PUBLIC, 239 Kuulei Rd, Kailua, 96734. SAN 339-4352. Tel: 808-266-9911. FAX: 808-266-9915. Web Site: www.hcc.hawaii.edu/hspls/hsplshp.html. *Librn*, Sandra Akana
Circ 307,473
Library Holdings: Bk Vols 78,094
Friends of the Library Group

KAILUA-KONA PUBLIC, 75-138 Hualalai Rd, Kailua-Kona, 96740. SAN 339-5014. Tel: 808-327-4327. FAX: 808-327-4326. Web Site: www.hcc.hawaii.edu/hspls/hsplshp.html. *Librn*, Irene Horvath
Circ 194,806
Library Holdings: Bk Vols 48,269

Friends of the Library Group

KAIMUKI PUBLIC, 1041 Koko Head Ave, 96816. SAN 339-4387. Tel: 808-733-8422. FAX: 808-733-8426. Web Site: www.hcc.hawaii.edu/hspls/hsplshp.html. *Librn*, Florence Yee
Circ 362,932
Library Holdings: Bk Vols 128,273
Friends of the Library Group

KALIHI-PALAMA PUBLIC, 1325 Kalihi St, 96819. SAN 339-4417. Tel: 808-832-3466. FAX: 808-832-3469. Web Site: www.hcc.hawaii.edu/hspls/hsplshp.html. *Librn*, Marcia Nakama; Staff 7 (MLS 3, Non-MLS 4)
Founded 1949. Circ 169,714
Library Holdings: Bk Vols 63,873
Friends of the Library Group

KANEOHE PUBLIC, 45-829 Kamehameha, Kaneohe, 96744. SAN 339-4441. Tel: 808-233-5676. FAX: 808-233-5672. Web Site: www.hcc.hawaii.edu/hspls/hsplshp.html. *Librn*, Tom Churma
Circ 305,463
Library Holdings: Bk Vols 124,595
Friends of the Library Group

KAPAA PUBLIC, 1464 Kuhio Hwy, Kapaa, 96746. SAN 339-5340. Tel: 808-821-4422. FAX: 808-821-4423. Web Site: www.hcc.hawaii.edu/hspls/hsplshp.html. *Librn*, Dale R Huber
Circ 113,990
Library Holdings: Bk Vols 42,356
Friends of the Library Group

KEAAU PUBLIC & SCHOOL, 16-571 Keaau-Pahoa Rd, Keaau, 96749-8106. SAN 339-5049. Tel: 808-966-8181. FAX: 808-966-7083. Web Site: www.hcc.hawaii.edu/hspls/hsplshp.html. *Librn*, Maxine Aki
Circ 95,457
Library Holdings: Bk Vols 22,459

KEALAKEKUA PUBLIC, Mamalahoa Hwy, PO Box 768, Kealakekua, 96750-0768. SAN 339-5073. Tel: 808-323-3653. FAX: 808-323-3354. Web Site: www.hcc.hawaii.edu/hspls/hsplshp.html. *Branch Mgr*, Mara Tepper
Circ 63,664
Library Holdings: Bk Vols 28,083
Friends of the Library Group

KIHEI PUBLIC, 35 Waimahaihai St, Kihei, 96753. SAN 326-8667. Tel: 808-875-6833. FAX: 808-875-6834. Web Site: www.hcc.hawaii.edu/hspls/hsplshp.html. *Librn*, Janet Fehr
Circ 100,258
Library Holdings: Bk Vols 48,000
Friends of the Library Group

KOLOA PUBLIC & SCHOOL, 3451 Poipu Rd, Koloa, 96756. (Mail add: PO Box 9, Koloa, 96756), SAN 339-5375. Tel: 808-742-1635. FAX: 808-742-6684. Web Site: www.aloha.net/~davidht/koloa.html. *Librn*, David Thorp
Circ 102,145
Library Holdings: Bk Vols 36,244; Per Subs 101
Special Collections: Koloa, Kauai history materials
Automation Activity & Vendor Info: (Circulation) epixtech, inc.
Database Vendor: epixtech, inc.
Friends of the Library Group

LAHAINA PUBLIC, 680 Wharf St, Lahaina, 96761. SAN 339-5529. Tel: 808-662-3950. FAX: 808-662-3951. Web Site: www.hcc.hawaii.edu/hspls/hsplshp.html. *Librn*, Carolyn Nuyen
Circ 43,216
Library Holdings: Bk Vols 26,000
Friends of the Library Group

LANAI PUBLIC & SCHOOL, Fraser & Sixth Aves, Lanai City, 96763. (Mail add: PO Box 630550, Lanai City, 96763-0550), SAN 339-5553. Tel: 808-565-6996. Web Site: www.hcc.hawaii.edu/hspls/hsplshp.html. *Librn*, Peggy Fink
Circ 54,435
Library Holdings: Bk Vols 33,000
Friends of the Library Group

LAUPAHOEHOE PUBLIC & SCHOOL, Mamalahoa Hwy, Laupahoehoe, 96764. (Mail add: PO Box 249, Laupahoehoe, 96764), SAN 339-5103. Tel: 808-962-6911. FAX: 808-962-6543. Web Site: www.hcc.hawaii.edu/hspls/hsplshp.html. *Librn*, Gabrielle Casart
Circ 20,082
Library Holdings: Bk Vols 20,000
Friends of the Library Group

LIBRARY FOR THE BLIND & PHYSICALLY HANDICAPPED
See separate entry , .

LIHUE PUBLIC, 4344 Hardy St, Lihue, 96766. SAN 339-5286. Tel: 808-241-3222. FAX: 808-241-3225. Web Site: www.hcc.hawaii.edu/hspls/hspls.html. *Librn*, Carol White
Circ 166,662
Library Holdings: Bk Vols 79,000
Friends of the Library Group

LILIHA PUBLIC, 1515 Liliha St, 96817. SAN 339-4476. Tel: 808-587-7577. FAX: 808-587-7579. Web Site: www.hcc.hawaii.edu/hspls/hsplshp.html. *Librn*, Sylvia Mitchell; E-Mail: sylvia@netra.lib.state.hi.us; Staff 9 (MLS 3, Non-MLS 6)
Circ 231,111
Library Holdings: Bk Vols 72,511
Friends of the Library Group

MAKAWAO PUBLIC, 1159 Makawao Ave, Makawao, 96768. SAN 339-5588. Tel: 808-572-8094. FAX: 808-572-1507. Web Site: www.hcc.hawaii.edu/hspls/hsplshp.html. *Librn*, Carla Mauri; Tel: 808-572-6665; Staff 5 (MLS 2, Non-MLS 3)
Pop 21,186; Circ 113,156
Library Holdings: Bk Vols 44,508
Automation Activity & Vendor Info: (Circulation) epixtech, inc.
Database Vendor: epixtech, inc.
Friends of the Library Group

MANOA PUBLIC, 2716 Woodlawn Dr, 96822. SAN 339-4506. Tel: 808-988-0459. FAX: 808-988-0458. Web Site: www.hcc.hawaii.edu/hspls/hsplshp.html. *Librn*, Lynn Masumoto
Circ 191,935
Library Holdings: Bk Vols 62,394
Automation Activity & Vendor Info: (Circulation) epixtech, inc.
Friends of the Library Group

MCCULLY-MOILIILI PUBLIC, 2211 S King St, 96826. SAN 339-4530. Tel: 808-973-1099. FAX: 808-973-1095. E-Mail: omccirc@lib.state.hi.us. Web Site: www.hcc.hawaii.edu/hspls/hsplshp.html. *Branch Mgr*, Christel Olson; Staff 15 (MLS 3, Non-MLS 12)
Founded 1969. Circ 356,358
Library Holdings: Bk Vols 85,000; Per Subs 75
Friends of the Library Group

MILILANI PUBLIC, 95-450 Makaimoimo St, Mililani, 96789. SAN 339-4700. Tel: 808-627-7470. FAX: 808-627-7309. Web Site: www.hcc.hawaii.edu/hspls/hsplshp.html. *Librn*, Wendi Woodstrup
Circ 372,844
Library Holdings: Bk Vols 76,869
Friends of the Library Group

MOLOKAI PUBLIC, 15 Ala Malama St, Kaunakakai, 96748. (Mail add: PO Box 395, Kaunakakai, 96748), SAN 339-5618. Tel: 808-553-5483. FAX: 808-553-5958. Web Site: www.hcc.hawaii.edu/hspls/hsplshp.html. *Librn*, Sri P TenCate; Staff 4 (MLS 1, Non-MLS 3)
Pop 6,900; Circ 48,006
Library Holdings: Bk Vols 22,704
Friends of the Library Group

MOUNTAIN VIEW PUBLIC & SCHOOL, Volcano Hwy, Mount View, 96771. (Mail add: PO Box 380, Mount View, 96771), SAN 339-5138. Tel: 808-968-6300. FAX: 808-968-6056. Web Site: www.hcc.hawaii.edu/hspls/hsplshp.html. *Librn*, Laura Ashton
Circ 47,942
Library Holdings: Bk Vols 16,407
Friends of the Library Group

NAALEHU PUBLIC, PO Box 653, Naalehu, 96772. SAN 339-5146. Tel: 808-929-7564. FAX: 808-929-9534. Web Site: www.hcc.hawaii.edu/hsplshp.html. *Librn*, Lisa Cabudol
Circ 23,659
Library Holdings: Bk Vols 7,000
Friends of the Library Group

PAHALA PUBLIC, 96-3150 Pikake St, PO Box 400, Pahala, 96777. SAN 339-5162. Tel: 808-928-2015. FAX: 808-928-6199. Web Site: www.hcc.hawaii.edu/hspls/hsplshp.html. *Librn*, Martha Hoverson
Circ 20,740
Library Holdings: Bk Vols 19,061
Friends of the Library Group

PAHOA PUBLIC & SCHOOL, Kalapana Rd, 15-3070 Pahoa-Kalapana Rd, Pahoa, 96778-0016. SAN 339-5197. Tel: 808-965-8574. FAX: 808-965-7170. Web Site: www.hcc.hawaii.edu/hspls/hsplshp.html. *Librn*, Maile Williams
Circ 110,839
Library Holdings: Bk Vols 31,362
Friends of the Library Group

PEARL CITY PUBLIC, 1138 Waimano Home Rd, Pearl City, 96782. SAN 339-4719. Tel: 808-453-6566. FAX: 808-453-6570. Web Site: www.hcc.hawaii.edu/hspls/hsplshp.html. *Librn*, Floriana Cofman
Circ 404,100
Library Holdings: Bk Vols 151,232
Friends of the Library Group

SALT LAKE-MOANALUA PUBLIC, 3225 Salt Lake Blvd, 96818. SAN 326-7393. Tel: 808-831-6831. FAX: 808-831-6834. Web Site: www.hcc.hawaii.edu/hspls/hsplshp.html. *Librn*, Claire Ikehara
Circ 291,290
Library Holdings: Bk Vols 55,232
Friends of the Library Group

THELMA PARKER MEMORIAL PUBLIC & SCHOOL, Mamalahoa Hwy, Kamuela, 96743. (Mail add: PO Box 698, Kamuela, 96743), SAN 339-5227. Tel: 808-887-6067. FAX: 808-887-6066. Web Site: www.hcc.hawaii.edu/hspls/hsplshp.html. *Librn*, Bruce Van Brocklin
Circ 127,260
Library Holdings: Bk Vols 43,000
Friends of the Library Group

WAHIAWA PUBLIC, 820 California Ave, Wahiawa, 96786. SAN 339-4743. Tel: 808-622-6345. FAX: 808-621-1121. Web Site: www.hcc.hawaii.edu/hspls/hsplshp.html. *Librn*, Patricia Lognion
Circ 107,912
Library Holdings: Bk Vols 58,199

Friends of the Library Group
WAIALUA PUBLIC, 67-068 Kealohanui St, Waialua, 96791. SAN 339-4778. Tel: 808-637-4876. FAX: 808-637-6212. E-Mail: owl.circ@lib.state.hi.us. Web Site: www.hcc.hawaii.edu/hspls/hsplshp.html. *Librn*, Timothy Littlejohn
Circ 65,894
Library Holdings: Bk Vols 37,535
Friends of the Library Group
WAIANAE PUBLIC, 85-625 Farrington Hwy, Waianae, 96792. SAN 339-4808. Tel: 808-696-4257. FAX: 808-696-4313. Web Site: www.hcc.hawaii.edu/hspls/hsplshp.html. *Librn*, Faith Arakawa
Circ 141,386
Library Holdings: Bk Vols 52,603
Friends of the Library Group
WAIKIKI-KAPAHULU PUBLIC, 400 Kapahulu Ave, 96815. SAN 339-4565. Tel: 808-733-8488. FAX: 808-733-8490. Web Site: www.hcc.hawaii.edu/hspls/hsplshp.html. *Librn*, Stephanie Strickland
Circ 156,541
Library Holdings: Bk Vols 52,351
Friends of the Library Group
WAILUKU PUBLIC, 251 High St, Wailuku, 96793. SAN 339-5464. Tel: 808-243-5766. FAX: 808-243-5768. Web Site: www.hcc.hawaii.edu/hspls/hsplshp.html. *Mgr*, Susan Werner; E-Mail: susanw@lib.state.hi.us; Staff 8 (MLS 2, Non-MLS 6)
Founded 1929. Pop 103,482
Library Holdings: Bk Vols 67,090; Per Subs 60
Automation Activity & Vendor Info: (Circulation) epixtech, inc.; (OPAC) epixtech, inc.
Database Vendor: epixtech, inc., IAC - Info Trac, IAC - SearchBank
Function: ILL available
Mem of Hawaii State Public Library System
Friends of the Library Group
WAIMANALO PUBLIC, 41-1320 Kalanianaole Hwy, Waimanalo, 96795. SAN 339-459X. Tel: 808-259-9925. FAX: 808-259-8209. Web Site: www.hcc.hawaii.edu/hspls/hsplshp.html. *Librn*, Richard Burns
Founded 1978. Circ 49,284
Library Holdings: Bk Vols 46,000; Per Subs 45
Friends of the Library Group
WAIMEA PUBLIC, 9750 Kaumuali Hwy, Waimea, 96796. (Mail add: PO Box 397, Waimea, 96796), SAN 339-5405. Tel: 808-338-6848. FAX: 808-338-6847. Web Site: www.hcc.hawaii.edu/hspls/hsplshp.html. *Mgr*, Susan C Remoaldo
Circ 40,505
Library Holdings: Bk Vols 25,437
WAIPAHU PUBLIC, 94-275 Mokuola St, Waipahu, 96797. SAN 339-4832. Tel: 808-675-0358. FAX: 808-675-0360. Web Site: www.hcc.hawaii.edu/hspls/hsplshp.html. *Librn*, Lorna Miyasaki
Circ 178,428
Library Holdings: Bk Vols 61,554
Friends of the Library Group
Bookmobiles: 7

P HAWAII STATE PUBLIC LIBRARY SYSTEM, Library for the Blind & Physically Handicapped, 402 Kapahulu Ave, 96815-3894. SAN 303-4712. Tel: 808-733-8444. FAX: 808-733-8449. *Dir*, Fusako Miyashiro; *Publ Servs*, Sue S Sugimura; Staff 13 (MLS 3, Non-MLS 10)
Founded 1931. Circ 41,539
Library Holdings: Bk Titles 141,834
Subject Interests: Braille, Large type print
Special Collections: Educational Games, multi-media; Filipino & Japanese Stories, cassettes; Hawaiiana Titles, braille & records; Reference Material on Various Handicaps; Textbooks in Math, Science & English, braille, large print, cassettes & tapes
Publications: News is Getting Around the Pacific (quarterly)
Partic in National Library Service For The Blind & Physically Handicapped, Library Of Congress
Special Services - Library service to the institutionalized; transcribing & machine lending services
Friends of the Library Group

HAWAIIAN ELECTRIC CO, INC
S ENGINEERING LIBRARY, 820 Ward Ave, 96814-2109. SAN 303-4755. Tel: 808-543-7915. FAX: 808-543-7720. *Librn*, Annette K Summerlin; E-Mail: asummerl@hei.com
Founded 1965
Library Holdings: Bk Vols 5,000; Per Subs 140
Special Collections: Engineering Society Transactions & Proceedings Coll; Engineering Standards & Codes Coll
Publications: Library Highlights

S HAWAIIAN HISTORICAL SOCIETY LIBRARY,* 560 Kawaiahao St, 96813. SAN 303-4763. Tel: 808-537-6271. FAX: 808-537-6271. Web Site: www.hawaiianhistory.org. *Librn*, Barbara E Dunn; E-Mail: bedunn@lava.net
Founded 1892
1997-1998 Income $100,000. Mats Exp $100,000
Library Holdings: Bk Titles 14,000
Special Collections: History of Hawaii & Pacific Coll (late 18th & 19th century)
Publications: The Hawaiian Historical Society, A Guide to the Library Collections, 1991
Restriction: Open to public for reference only

S HAWAIIAN MISSION CHILDREN'S SOCIETY, Mission Houses Museum, 553 S King St, 96813. SAN 303-4771. Tel: 808-531-0481. FAX: 808-545-2280. E-Mail: mhm@lava.net. Web Site: www.lava.net/~mhm/main.htm. *Chief Librn*, Marilyn L Reppun
Founded 1908
Library Holdings: Bk Vols 12,000; Bk Titles 10,000; Per Subs 6
Subject Interests: Hawaii
Special Collections: American Board of; Commissioners for Foreign Missions, letters, ledgers, reports; Hawaiian Evangelical Association Archives, church records; Hawaiian Language Imprints; Marquesan Language; Micronesian Language; Missionary Manuscripts, letters, reports, journals
Publications: A Guide to the Holdings of the Mission Houses Museum Library; Grapes of Canaan; Hawaiian Language Imprints, 1822-1899; Ka Pai Palapala: Early Printing in Hawaii; Missionary Album: Biographical Sketches & Portraits of the American Protestant Missionaries to Hawaii, HMCS, 1969, Voyages to Hawaii Before 1860; The Hawaii Journals of the New England Missionaries, 1813-1894; The Journals of Cochran Forbes

S HONOLULU ACADEMY OF ARTS, Robert C Allerton Library, 900 S Beretania St, 96814-1429. SAN 303-4798. Tel: 808-532-8754. FAX: 808-532-3668. *Head Librn*, Dr Ronald F Chapman; Staff 1 (MLS 1)
Founded 1927
Library Holdings: Bk Vols 37,000; Bk Titles 32,000; Per Subs 38
Special Collections: Chinese Art (Chinese National Palace & Central Museums Photographic Archives), photogs, slides, micro
Automation Activity & Vendor Info: (Acquisitions) Brodart; (Cataloging) Brodart
Restriction: Non-circulating to the public

C HONOLULU COMMUNITY COLLEGE LIBRARY, 874 Dillingham Blvd, 96817-4598. SAN 303-4801. Tel: 808-845-9199. FAX: 808-845-3618. Web Site: www.hcc.hawaii.edu/library. *Chief Librn*, Irene Mesina; Tel: 808-845-9195, E-Mail: irene@hcc.hawaii.edu; *Circ*, Janet Garcia; Tel: 808-845-9194; *Cat*, Nadine Leong-Kurio; Tel: 808-845-9198; *Bibliog Instr*, Eric Holmberg; Tel: 808-845-9463; *Bibliog Instr*, Xin Li; Tel: 808-845-9196; Staff 11 (MLS 5, Non-MLS 6)
Founded 1965. Enrl 4,524; Fac 215
Jul 1999-Jun 2000 Income State $75,000
Library Holdings: Bk Vols 54,505; Bk Titles 44,349; Per Subs 230
Subject Interests: Liberal arts, Occupational
Special Collections: Automotive Technical Coll; Hawaii/Pacific Coll
Automation Activity & Vendor Info: (Cataloging) CARL; (Circulation) CARL
Database Vendor: CARL, GaleNet

CR INTERNATIONAL COLLEGE LIBRARY, J W Cook Memorial Library, 20 Dowsett Ave, 96817. SAN 303-4844. Tel: 808-595-4247. FAX: 808-595-4779. *Dir Libr Serv*, Carol R White; E-Mail: cwhite@lava.net. Subject Specialists: *Religion*, Carol R White; Staff 1 (MLS 1)
Founded 1971. Enrl 56; Fac 6; Highest Degree: Doctorate
Library Holdings: Bk Vols 17,776; Bk Titles 13,751; Per Subs 65
Subject Interests: Ethics, Humanities, Missiology, Philosophy, Religion, Theology
Special Collections: Anthropology & Missiology Coll; Facsimiles of Hanoi POW's Bible; Theology Coll
Partic in Hawaii State Pub Libr Syst

CM JOHN A BURNS SCHOOL OF MEDICINE, (Formerly University Of Hawaii), Library Resource Center, 1960 East-West Rd, D-206, 96822. SAN 303-500X. Tel: 808-956-8666. FAX: 808-956-9093. E-Mail: sphlib@hawaii.edu. Web Site: www.hawaii.edu/sphlib. *Librn*, Virginia M Tanji; Staff 1 (MLS 1)
Founded 1964. Enrl 151; Fac 18; Highest Degree: Doctorate
Library Holdings: Bk Vols 14,500; Bk Titles 10,750; Per Subs 150
Subject Interests: Public health
Partic in OCLC Online Computer Library Center, Inc; Pac SW Regional Med Libr

J KAPIOLANI COMMUNITY COLLEGE LIBRARY,* 4303 Diamond Head Rd, 96816. SAN 303-4852. Tel: 808-734-9111, 808-734-9259. FAX: 808-734-9453. Web Site: library.kcc.hawaii.edu. *Dir*, Dr Terry D Webb; *Ref*, Mary Marko; *Ref*, Shirley Vashishta; *Circ*, Genny Mero; *Tech Servs*, Michelle Sturges; *Ref*, Bin Zhang; Staff 21 (MLS 13, Non-MLS 8)
Founded 1966. Enrl 7,400; Fac 360
Jul 1998-Jun 1999 Income $910,000, State $870,000, Locally Generated Income $40,000. Sal $667,000 (Prof $410,000)
Library Holdings: Bk Vols 75,000; Per Subs 800
Special Collections: Chinese History & Culture (Char Coll); Hawaii; Japan; Read (Developmental)
Automation Activity & Vendor Info: (Circulation) CARL
Mem of Univ of Hawaii Libr Syst

M KAPIOLANI MEDICAL CENTER LIBRARY,* 1319 Punahou St, Rm 611, 96826. SAN 370-1433. Tel: 808-983-8332. FAX: 808-983-6585. *Librn*, Pamela Shigezawa; E-Mail: pshigeza@hawaii.edu
Library Holdings: Bk Titles 5,000; Per Subs 120
Partic in Medline

S LEGAL AID SOCIETY OF HAWAII LIBRARY,* 924 Bethel St, 96813. SAN 323-4770. Tel: 808-536-4302. FAX: 808-527-8088. *In Charge*, Mikel Young
Library Holdings: Bk Vols 5,000; Per Subs 30

GL LEGISLATIVE REFERENCE BUREAU LIBRARY, (LRB), State Capitol, Rm 005, 96813. SAN 303-4879. Tel: 808-587-0690. FAX: 808-587-0699. Web Site: www.state.hi.us/lrb. *Coll Develop, Res*, Karen Mau; E-Mail: mau@capitol.hawaii.gov; *Res*, Clair Marumoto; *Res*, Carole Tanaka; Staff 6 (MLS 5, Non-MLS 1)
Founded 1943
Library Holdings: Bk Vols 55,000; Bk Titles 40,000; Per Subs 300
Subject Interests: Legislation, State government
Publications: Selected Recent Acquisitions (bimonthly)

S LEO A DALY CO LIBRARY,* America Saving Bldg, 1357 Kapiolani Blvd Ste 1230, 96814. SAN 303-5018. Tel: 808-521-8889. FAX: 808-521-3757. E-Mail: ladhnl@pixi.com. Web Site: www.leodaly.com. *In Charge*, Gary Koyama
Founded 1960
Library Holdings: Bk Vols 1,500; Per Subs 40
Subject Interests: Art and architecture, Structural engineering
Restriction: Staff use only

M MEDICAL LIBRARY AT KAISER MOA,* 3288 Moanalua Rd, 96819. SAN 325-7142. Tel: 808-834-9423. FAX: 808-834-9010.; Staff 3 (MLS 1, Non-MLS 2)
Library Holdings: Bk Titles 1,200; Per Subs 135
Subject Interests: Medicine, Nursing
Special Collections: Archives
Publications: Newsletter
Partic in Med Libr Group of Hawaii; Medline; TSRMLS

G NATIONAL MARINE FISHERIES SERVICE, Honolulu Laboratory Library,* 2570 Dole St, 96822-2396. SAN 303-4909. Tel: 808-983-5300. FAX: 808-983-2920. Web Site: www.lib.noaa.gov. *Librn*, Sandra L Abbott-Stout; E-Mail: sstout@honlab.nmfs.hawaii.edu
1997-1998 Income $30,000. Mats Exp $30,000
Library Holdings: Bk Vols 11,000; Per Subs 60
Subject Interests: Marine biology, Oceanography
Partic in OCLC Online Computer Library Center, Inc

M SAINT FRANCIS MEDICAL CENTER, Medical Library, 2230 Liliha St, 96817. SAN 303-4925. Tel: 808-547-6481. FAX: 808-545-5818. *Librn*, Laura Gerwitz; Staff 2 (MLS 1, Non-MLS 1)
Founded 1927
Library Holdings: Bk Titles 1,100; Per Subs 145
Subject Interests: Cancer, Diabetes, Transplantation
Partic in Health Info Network of the Pac; Medline

C SCHOOL OF OCEAN & EARTH SCIENCE & TECHNOLOGY LIBRARY, 2525 Correa Rd, 96822. SAN 303-464X. Tel: 808-956-7040. FAX: 808-956-2538. E-Mail: pubslib@soest.hawaii.edu. Web Site: www.soest.hawaii.edu/library/soestlibrary.html. *Mgr*, Diane J Henderson; Staff 1 (MLS 1)
Founded 1963. Enrl 300; Fac 70; Highest Degree: Doctorate
1998-1999 Income $60,000. Mats Exp Per/Ser (Incl. Access Fees) $60,000
Library Holdings: Bk Titles 3,800; Per Subs 83
Subject Interests: Geology, Meteorology, Oceanography
Special Collections: Hawaiian Earth Science Coll; HIG Reports
Restriction: Staff use only, Students only

M SHRINERS' HOSPITAL LIBRARY,* 1310 Punahou St, 96826. SAN 303-4941. Tel: 808-941-4466, Ext 638. FAX: 808-942-8573. *Librn*, Mae Matsumoto
Founded 1923
1997-1998 Income $8,700. Mats Exp $8,700
Library Holdings: Bk Vols 650; Per Subs 13

G STATE OF HAWAII DEPARTMENT OF BUSINESS ECONOMIC DEVELOPMENT & TOURISM, (DBEDT), 250 S Hotel St, 4th flr, 96813. (Mail add: PO Box 2359, 96804), SAN 303-4607. Tel: 808-586-2424. FAX: 808-587-2790. E-Mail: library@dbedt.hawaii.gov. Web Site: www.state.hi.us/dbedt. *Librn*, Debra Miyashiro; Staff 3 (MLS 2, Non-MLS 1)
Founded 1962
Library Holdings: Bk Titles 14,000; Per Subs 150
Subject Interests: Economics, Energy, Recreation, Statistics, Tourism
Publications: Acquistions List
Partic in Dow Jones News Retrieval

G STATE OF HAWAII DEPARTMENT OF LAND & NATURAL RESOURCES, DIVISION OF AQUATIC RESOURCES, Anuenue Fisheries Research Center Library, 1039 Sand Island Pkwy, 96819-4347. SAN 371-5744. Tel: 808-832-5002. FAX: 808-832-5012. *Librn*, Janet Yasumatsu
Library Holdings: Bk Titles 1,000; Per Subs 30

M STRAUB CLINIC & HOSPITAL, INC, Arnold Library, 888 S King St, 96813. SAN 303-495X. Tel: 808-522-4471. FAX: 808-522-3472. E-Mail: alss@aloha.net, deskim@aloha.net. Web Site: www.geoc.ties.com/~straub. *Librn, Online Servs*, Fran Smith
Founded 1922
Library Holdings: Bk Titles 4,500; Per Subs 200
Subject Interests: Medicine
Special Collections: Physicians' Articles Coll
Partic in Dialog Corporation; Nat Libr of Med

GL SUPREME COURT LAW LIBRARY, 417 S King St, Rm 115, 96813. SAN 303-4739. Tel: 808-539-4964. FAX: 808-539-4974. Web Site: www.state.hi.us/jud/library.htm. *Librn*, Ann S Koto; E-Mail: akoto@hotmail.com; *Tech Servs*, Sandra Okubo; *Publ Servs*, Irene Wong; Staff 8 (MLS 3, Non-MLS 5)
Founded 1851
Jul 1999-Jun 2000 Income (Main Library Only) $1,212,497, State $1,137,497, Locally Generated Income $75,000. Mats Exp $864,423, Books $260,375, Per/Ser (Incl. Access Fees) $578,908, Micro $3,300, Electronic Ref Mat (Incl. Access Fees) $21,840. Sal $296,189 (Prof $151,140)
Library Holdings: Bk Vols 128,009; Per Subs 290
Restriction: Open to public for reference only

S TENNENT ART FOUNDATION GALLERY LIBRARY,* 203 Prospect St, 96813. SAN 303-4976. Tel: 808-531-1987. *Curator*, Elaine Tennent
Library Holdings: Bk Vols 300

G UNESCO-INTERGOVERNMENTAL OCEANOGRAPHIC COMMISSION, International Tsunami Information Center Library, 737 Bishop St Ste 2200, 96813. SAN 326-3436. Tel: 808-532-6422. FAX: 808-532-5576. E-Mail: itic@moana.noaa.gov. *Actg Dir*, Michael Blackford; Staff 2 (MLS 1, Non-MLS 1)
Founded 1965
Library Holdings: Bk Titles 4,000; Per Subs 10
Subject Interests: Earthquakes, Geophysics, Oceanography
Special Collections: Catalog of Tsunamis in Pacific, bks; Marigrams 2/65-present, microfiche
Publications: Tsunami Newsletter; Tsunami Reports
Restriction: In-house use for visitors
Function: Reference only

UNITED STATES ARMY

A ALIAMANU LIBRARY, Aliamanu Military Reservation, 1782 Bougainvillea Loop, 96818-1311. SAN 371-3067. Tel: 808-833-4851. FAX: 808-833-3714. *Librn*, Walter Benavitz; E-Mail: benavitziii@hotmail.com; Staff 2 (MLS 1, Non-MLS 1)
Founded 1979
Library Holdings: Bk Titles 89,000; Per Subs 30
Subject Interests: Children's literature, Juv lit
Open Mon-Sat

A FORT SHAFTER LIBRARY, Bldg 650, Fort Shafter, 96858-5005. SAN 339-5677. Tel: 808-438-9521. FAX: 808-438-3100. *Tech Servs*, Donna Burkeen; *Tech Servs*, Donna Sviantek; Staff 3 (MLS 1, Non-MLS 2)
Founded 1943
Library Holdings: Bk Vols 18,000; Per Subs 65
Subject Interests: Hawaii
Partic in Fedlink

AM MEDICAL LIBRARY, Tripler Army Medical Ctr, One Jarrett White Rd, Tripler AMC, 96859-5000. SAN 339-5790. Tel: 808-433-6391. FAX: 808-433-4892. *Librn*, Linda Requena; E-Mail: marilyn_a.requena@tamc.chcs.amedd.army.mil; Staff 4 (MLS 2, Non-MLS 2)
Founded 1946
Library Holdings: Bk Vols 11,500; Per Subs 750
Partic in Docline; Medline; OCLC Online Computer Library Center, Inc

A PACIFIC, HQ & 25TH INFANTRY DIV, USAG-HI DCA, Library Activities Br, Schofield Barracks, 96857-5000. SAN 339-5642. Tel: 808-655-9269. FAX: 808-655-6375. *Acq*, Janet Howard; *Acq*, Amy Nogami
Subject Interests: Hawaii
Partic in Fedlink

AM PATIENT LIBRARY, Tripler Army Medical Ctr, Schofield Barracks, 96859-5000. SAN 377-8746. Tel: 808-433-6745, 808-433-6968. *Librn*, James Shepard; *Tech Servs*, Mary Jane Tiedemann
Founded 1944
Library Holdings: Bk Vols 4,000; Per Subs 91

A SERGEANT RODNEY J YANO MAIN LIBRARY, Bldg 560, Schofield Barracks, 96857-5000. SAN 339-5707. Tel: 808-655-8002. FAX: 808-655-6375. E-Mail: dcasblib@schofield-emh1.army.mil. *Dir*, Charles Walton; *Ref*, Samuel DiLucia; Tel: 808-655-8001; *Coll Develop, Publ Servs*, Christen Kobayashi; *Ref*, Bonnie Dong; Staff 10 (MLS 4, Non-MLS 6)
Founded 1915
Library Holdings: Bk Vols 89,560; Per Subs 335

Subject Interests: Military history
Special Collections: Hawaiian Islands (Hawaiiana)
Partic in Fedlink; Oahu Corporate Mil Database; OCLC Online Computer Library Center, Inc

AM TRIPLER COMMUNITY LIBRARY, Tripler AMC-HI, One Jarrett White Rd, Tripler Army Medical Center, 96859-5000. SAN 339-5766. Tel: 808-433-6869. FAX: 808-433-6745. *Librn*, James Shepherd; E-Mail: james.shepherd@shafter.army.mil; Staff 2 (MLS 1, Non-MLS 1)
Founded 1944
Library Holdings: Bk Vols 8,000; Per Subs 75
Special Collections: Hawaiiana, Health Education
Publications: Bibliographies; series on health education
Friends of the Library Group

GL UNITED STATES COURTS LIBRARY,* 300 Ala Moana Blvd C-341, 96850. SAN 303-4992. Tel: 808-541-1797. FAX: 808-541-3667. *Librn*, Patricia L Butson
1997-1998 Income $130,000
Library Holdings: Bk Vols 33,000; Per Subs 50

S US NATIONAL PARK SERVICE, USS Arizona Memorial Library, One Arizona Memorial Pl, 96818. SAN 375-6637. Tel: 808-422-2771. FAX: 808-541-3168. *In Charge*, Daniel Martinez
Library Holdings: Bk Titles 2,000; Per Subs 40
Restriction: By appointment only
Open Mon-Fri 8-12

C UNIVERSITY OF HAWAII, Thomas Hale Hamilton Library, 2550 The Mall, 96822. SAN 339-6096. Tel: 808-956-7203. Interlibrary Loan Service Tel: 808-956-7205. FAX: 808-956-5968. Web Site: www.hawaii.edu/lib. *Actg Librn*, Jean H Ehrhorn; E-Mail: ehrhorn@hawaii.edu; *Acq of Monographs, Coll Develop*, Thelma Diercks; *Coordr, Publ Servs*, Randy B Hensley; *Ref*, Ross Christensen; *Science*, Paul Wermager; *Access Serv, Circ*, Susan Murata. Subject Specialists: *Southeast Asia*, Lan Hiang Char; Staff 56 (MLS 56)
Founded 1907. Enrl 18,918; Fac 1,125; Highest Degree: Doctorate
Jul 1999-Jun 2000 Income $12,206,073. Mats Exp $4,731,061, Books $1,447,246, Per/Ser (Incl. Access Fees) $3,283,815. Sal $6,027,330 (Prof $1,919,590)
Library Holdings: Bk Vols 3,122,781; Per Subs 26,767
Special Collections: Asia; Book Arts; European Communities; Hawaii; Jean Charlot Coll; Pacific; Tsuzaki Reinecke Creole Coll; University Archives
Publications: Acquisitions List of the Pacific Coll, University of Hawaii; Current Hawaiiana; Selected Acquisitions of the Asia Coll
Mem of Asn of Research Libraries
Partic in OCLC Online Computer Library Center, Inc; Research Libraries Group, Inc; SDC
Friends of the Library Group
Departmental Libraries:
GREGG M SINCLAIR LIBRARY, 2425 Campus Rd, 96822. (Mail add: 2550 the Mall, 96822), SAN 339-6126. Tel: 808-956-8308. FAX: 808-956-5952. E-Mail: sinc@hawaii.edu. Web Site: www.sinclair.hawaii.edu. *Librn*, Gregg Geary
Library Holdings: Bk Vols 153,582
MONOGRAPH RECEIVING, 2550 The Mall, 96822. Tel: 808-956-8692. FAX: 808-956-5968. *Librn*, Thelma Diercks
SERIAL RECEIVING Tel: 808-956-6639. FAX: 808-956-5968. *Ser*, Amy Carlson

CL UNIVERSITY OF HAWAII, William S Richardson School of Law Library, 2525 Dole St, 96822-2369. SAN 326-5188. Tel: 808-956-7583. FAX: 808-956-4615. *Librn*, Leinaala Seeger; E-Mail: seegerl@hawaii.edu; *Tech Servs*, Nancy Westcott; *Circ, Ref*, Swee Berkey; Staff 9 (MLS 5, Non-MLS 4)
Enrl 240; Fac 18
Library Holdings: Bk Titles 28,904; Per Subs 2,896
Subject Interests: Environmental law
Partic in OCLC Online Computer Library Center, Inc

S UNIVERSITY OF HAWAII-COLLEGE OF EDUCATION, Western Curriculum Coordination Center,* 1776 University Ave UA2-5, 96822. SAN 324-3451. Tel: 808-956-6496, 808-956-7834. FAX: 808-956-3374. E-Mail: wccc@hawaii.edu. Web Site: www2.hawaii.edu/wccc/wccc.html. *Dir*, Lawrence Zane; Staff 1 (MLS 1)
1997-1998 Income $25,000
Library Holdings: Bk Vols 40,000
Subject Interests: Curriculum mat, Vocational education
Publications: Curriculum Materials (subject bibliographies)

S USS BOWFIN SUBMARINE MUSEUM & PARK LIBRARY, 11 Arizona Memorial Dr, 96818-3145. SAN 371-8395. Tel: 808-423-1341. FAX: 808-422-5201. E-Mail: bowfin@aloha.net. Web Site: www.aloha.net/~bowfin. *Res*, Charles R Hinman. Subject Specialists: *Submarines*, Charles R Hinman; Staff 3 (Non-MLS 3)
Founded 1981
Library Holdings: Bk Vols 4,500; Bk Titles 2,000
Subject Interests: Military hist, Naval hist, Submarines, World War II
Special Collections: Oral Histories of World War II Submariners; Photo Archives Submarines; U.S. Navy Training manuals for submariners; War Patrol Reports of U.S. submarines in World War II; USS Bowfin; WWII Crew '35
Publications: On Eternal Patrol
Restriction: Not a lending library
Function: Research library

KAHULUI

J MAUI COMMUNITY COLLEGE LIBRARY, 310 Kaahumanu Ave, 96732. SAN 303-5026. Tel: 808-984-3233. FAX: 808-244-9644. E-Mail: library.office@mauicc.hawaii.edu. Web Site: mauicc.hawaii.edu/unit/library/welcome.html. *Head Librn*, Dorothy Tolliver; E-Mail: Dorothy.Tolliver@mavicc.hawaii.edu; *Librn*, Lillian Mangum; *Tech Servs*, Lisa Sepa; *Publ Servs*, Gail Ainsworth; Staff 7 (MLS 4, Non-MLS 3)
Founded 1970. Enrl 2,300; Fac 67
Jul 1999-Jun 2000 Income State $410,738. Mats Exp $91,547, Books $40,968, Per/Ser (Incl. Access Fees) $26,865, Micro $11,714, Electronic Ref Mat (Incl. Access Fees) $12,000. Sal $261,785 (Prof $222,953)
Library Holdings: Bk Vols 49,812; Bk Titles 39,443; Per Subs 631
Subject Interests: Hawaii
Automation Activity & Vendor Info: (Cataloging) CARL; (Circulation) CARL; (OPAC) CARL
Database Vendor: CARL, IAC - Info Trac, Wilson - Wilson Web
Partic in Colorado Alliance Of Research Libraries; Dialog Corporation

KAILUA

R SAINT CHRISTOPHER'S EPISCOPAL CHURCH LIBRARY, 93 N Kainalu Dr, PO Box 456, 96734. SAN 303-5034. Tel: 808-262-8176. FAX: 808-262-1053. E-Mail: stchristopher@aloha.net. Web Site: www.oahu.net/saint-c. *In Charge*, Mrs Richard Lindsay; *Adminr*, Jane Sholes
Library Holdings: Bk Vols 700; Per Subs 20
Subject Interests: Christianity, Theology

KALAHEO

S NATIONAL TROPICAL BOTANICAL GARDEN LIBRARY, 3530 Papalina Rd, 96741. SAN 371-7852. Tel: 808-332-7324, Ext 118. FAX: 808-332-9765. Web Site: www.ntbg.org. *Librn*, Richard E Hanna; E-Mail: rhanna@ntbg.org; Staff 1 (MLS 1)
Founded 1971
Library Holdings: Bk Vols 16,800; Bk Titles 15,500; Per Subs 800
Subject Interests: Botany, Horticulture
Special Collections: Tropical Botany, bks, journals
Friends of the Library Group

KANEOHE

C HAWAII PACIFIC UNIVERSITY LIBRARIES, Atherton Library, 45-045 Kamehameha Hwy, 96744-5297. SAN 303-5050. Tel: 808-236-3505. FAX: 808-236-5806. *VPres*, Stephen R Simpson; Tel: 808-544-0209, Fax: 808-544-0877, E-Mail: ssimpson@hpu.edu; *Assoc Librn*, Kathlee A Chee; Tel: 808-544-0292, Fax: 808-544-0880, E-Mail: kchee@hpu.edu; Staff 5 (MLS 4, Non-MLS 1)
Founded 1967. Highest Degree: Master
Library Holdings: Bk Vols 57,987; Bk Titles 57,611; Per Subs 257
For financial info, see entry for Meader Library, Honolulu

M HAWAII STATE HOSPITAL, Medical Library, 45-710 Keaahala Rd, 96744-3597. SAN 303-5069. Tel: 808-236-8201, 808-236-8225. FAX: 808-235-5038. *Librn*, Lisa Anne Matsumoto; E-Mail: lymatsum@hsh.health.state.hi.us; Staff 2 (MLS 1, Non-MLS 1)
Founded 1950
1996-1997 Income $40,000. Mats Exp $40,000, Books $6,000, Per/Ser (Incl. Access Fees) $20,000
Library Holdings: Bk Titles 5,500; Per Subs 90
Subject Interests: Mental health, Neuropsychology, Psychiatry, Psychology
Publications: HSH Bulletin; List of Recent Acquisitions (for Hawaii distribution only)
Partic in Pacific SW Regional Med Libr Serv

UNITED STATES MARINE CORPS
A COMMUNITY SERVICES BASE LIBRARY, PO Box 63073, 96863-3073. SAN 339-6037. Tel: 808-254-7624. FAX: 808-254-7622. Web Site: www.10.1.1220/kaneohe/index.htm. *In Charge*, Murray R Visser; Tel: 808-254-7623, E-Mail: murray.visser@usmc_mccs.org; *Tech Servs*, Kerstin S Ehn; Staff 1 (MLS 1)
Founded 1953
Oct 1999-Sep 2000 Mats Exp $36,773, Books $27,771, Per/Ser (Incl. Access Fees) $8,715, Micro $200. Sal $119,059 (Prof $58,797)
Library Holdings: Bk Vols 46,515; Bk Titles 33,251; Per Subs 182
Special Collections: Children's Coll; Hawaiiana; MCI Courses; US Marine Corps Coll; US Marine Reading List
Automation Activity & Vendor Info: (Cataloging) SIRSI; (Circulation) SIRSI; (ILL) SIRSI; (OPAC) SIRSI
Database Vendor: ProQuest
Restriction: Private library

J WINDWARD COMMUNITY COLLEGE LIBRARY, 45-720 Keaahala Rd, 96744. SAN 303-5077. Tel: 808-235-7436. Circulation Tel: 808-235-7441. Reference Tel: 808-235-7338. FAX: 808-235-7344. Web Site: www.library.wcc.hawaii.edu. *Publ Servs*, Tiffany Severns; *Dir*, Nancy Heu; *Tech Servs*, Elizabeth Ashley; Staff 3 (MLS 3)
Founded 1972. Enrl 905; Fac 55; Highest Degree: Associate
Jul 1999-Jun 2000 Income $362,359, Federal $29,497, Locally Generated Income $4,499, Parent Institution $43,112, Other $1,755. Mats Exp $42,831, Books $22,279, Per/Ser (Incl. Access Fees) $12,608, Presv $385, Micro $5,795, AV Equip $1,764. Sal $262,433 (Prof $159,043)
Library Holdings: Bk Vols 46,330; Bk Titles 38,968; Per Subs 197
Special Collections: Hawaiian Coll
Automation Activity & Vendor Info: (Cataloging) CARL; (Circulation) CARL; (OPAC) CARL
Database Vendor: IAC - Info Trac
Publications: Audiovisual Materials in the WCC Library; Guide to the Library; Periodicals in the WCC Library
Mem of Univ of Hawaii Libr Syst
Friends of the Library Group

KEALAKEKUA

C UNIVERSITY OF HAWAII, West Hawaii Center,* PO Box 2059, 96750. SAN 370-3800. Tel: 808-322-4858. FAX: 808-322-4859. *Dir*, Laurel Gregory; E-Mail: lgregory@hawaii.edu; *ILL*, Karen Au; E-Mail: karenau@hawaii.edu; Staff 2 (MLS 1, Non-MLS 1)
Founded 1989. Enrl 375; Highest Degree: Master
Library Holdings: Bk Vols 5,500
Subject Interests: Hawaii
Automation Activity & Vendor Info: (Circulation) CARL
Database Vendor: CARL, IAC - Info Trac
Mem of Univ of Hawaii Libr Syst

KIHEI

S PACIFIC WHALE FOUNDATION LIBRARY,* 101 N Kihei Rd, 96753. SAN 373-4315. Tel: 808-879-8860. FAX: 808-879-2615. *Publ Servs*, Anne Rillero
Library Holdings: Bk Vols 500; Per Subs 150

LAIE

C BRIGHAM YOUNG UNIVERSITY-HAWAII, Joseph F Smith Library, 55-220 Kulanui St, BYU-H Box 1966, 96762-1294. SAN 303-5123. Tel: 808-293-3850. Interlibrary Loan Service Tel: 808-293-3878. FAX: 808-293-3877. E-Mail: frandser@byuh.edu. Web Site: www.library.byuh.edu. *Dir*, Rex Frandsen; Tel: 808-293-3850, E-Mail: frandser@byuh.edu; *Publ Servs*, Jocelyn Perriton; Tel: 808-293-3850, E-Mail: perritoj@byuh.edu; *Tech Servs*, Anita Henry; Tel: 808-293-3863, E-Mail: henrya@byuh.edu; *Cat*, Rose Ram; Tel: 808-293-3882, E-Mail: ramr@byuh.edu; *Cat*, Marynelle Chew; Tel: 808-293-3880, E-Mail: chewm@byuh.edu; *Automation Syst Coordr*, Tony Castillo; Tel: 808-293-3898, E-Mail: castillt@byuh.edu; *Ref*, Betty Versteeg; Tel: 808-293-3854, E-Mail: versteeb@byuh.edu; *Ref*, Riley Moffat; Tel: 808-293-3884, E-Mail: moffatr@byuh.edu; *Ref*, Gerald Bohnet; Tel: 808-293-3866, E-Mail: bohnetg@byuh.edu; *Ref*, Phil Smith; Tel: 808-293-3852, E-Mail: smithp@byuh.edu; *Archivist*, Greg Gubler; Tel: 808-293-3869, E-Mail: gublerg@byuh.edu; *Instrul Serv*, Dwight Miller; Tel: 808-293-3871, E-Mail: millerd@byuh.edu; Staff 22 (MLS 11, Non-MLS 11)
Founded 1955. Enrl 2,000; Fac 109; Highest Degree: Bachelor
Library Holdings: Bk Vols 192,500; Per Subs 1,300
Subject Interests: Pacific Islands
Special Collections: Children's Coll; Mormonism; Pacific Islands
Automation Activity & Vendor Info: (Acquisitions) SIRSI; (Cataloging) SIRSI; (Circulation) SIRSI; (Course Reserve) SIRSI; (Media Booking) SIRSI; (OPAC) SIRSI; (Serials) SIRSI
Publications: Library Newsgram
Partic in OCLC Online Computer Library Center, Inc

LIHUE

J KAUAI COMMUNITY COLLEGE, Learning Resource Center,* 3-1901 Kaumualii Hwy, 96766. SAN 303-5131. Tel: 808-245-8233. FAX: 808-245-8294. Web Site: www.kauaicc.hawaii.edu/library.lib.htm. *Head of Libr*, Robert M Kajiwara; Tel: 808-245-8236, E-Mail: kajiwara@hawaii.edu; *Librn*, Anne McKenna; Tel: 808-245-8374, E-Mail: annm@mail.kauaicc.hawaii.edu; *Cat*, Diane M Johnson; Tel: 808-245-8240, E-Mail: diane@mail.kauaicc.hawaii.edu; *Publ Servs*, Ramona Kincaid; Tel: 808-245-8253, E-Mail: rkincaid@mail.kauaicc.hawaii.edu. Subject Specialists: *Business*, Anne McKenna; *Fiction*, Diane M Johnson; *Health*, Anne McKenna; *Medicine*, Anne McKenna; *Reference*, Ramona Kincaid; *Science*, Ramona Kincaid; *Social sciences*, Diane M Johnson; *Sports*, Diane M Johnson; *Technology*, Ramona Kincaid; Staff 7 (MLS 4, Non-MLS 3)
Founded 1967. Enrl 1,200; Fac 78; Highest Degree: Associate
Jul 1998-Jun 1999 Income (Main Library Only) $50,559, State $41,000, Locally Generated Income $8,559, Other $1,000. Mats Exp $82,847, Books $30,000, Per/Ser (Incl. Access Fees) $14,588, Presv $500, Micro $9,464, AV Equip $795. Sal $253,138 (Prof $148,500)
Library Holdings: Bk Vols 49,939; Bk Titles 41,346; Per Subs 180
Subject Interests: Allied health, Nursing
Special Collections: Hawaii & the Pacific, v-tapes
Database Vendor: CARL, IAC - SearchBank
Publications: Circulation Policies; How to Locate Library Resources; Magazine Journal Microfilm Listing; Quick Reference
Mem of Univ of Hawaii Libr Syst

M WILCOX MEMORIAL HOSPITAL, Robert J Emrick MD Medical Library, 3420 Kuhio Hwy, 96766. SAN 303-5158. Tel: 808-245-1173. FAX: 808-246-2918.
Founded 1939
Library Holdings: Per Subs 20
Partic in Pacific SW Regional Med Libr Serv

PEARL CITY

J LEEWARD COMMUNITY COLLEGE LIBRARY,* 96-045 Ala Ike, 96782-3393. SAN 303-5182. Tel: 808-455-0379. FAX: 808-453-6729. Web Site: www.lcc.hawaii.edu/lib/library.html. *Dir*, Diane Sakai; E-Mail: dsakai@hawaii.edu; *Automation Syst Coordr*, Ralph Toyama; *Circ, Spec Coll*, Larry Goldstein; *Cat, Tech Servs*, Lenore Maruyama; *Bibliog Instr*, Janet Black; Staff 5 (MLS 5)
Founded 1968. Enrl 3,875; Fac 222
Jul 1997-Jun 1998 Income $460,375. Mats Exp $79,667, Books $50,892, Per/Ser (Incl. Access Fees) $18,103, Presv $50, Micro $8,533. Sal $438,129 (Prof $227,988)
Library Holdings: Bk Vols 76,169; Bk Titles 61,051; Per Subs 249
Special Collections: Fed Govt; Hawaiiana
Automation Activity & Vendor Info: (Cataloging) CARL; (Circulation) CARL
Publications: LCC Periodicals List

C UNIVERSITY OF HAWAII - WEST OAHU,* 96-129 Ala Ike, 96782. SAN 303-4399. Interlibrary Loan Service Tel: 808-455-0497. FAX: 808-453-6176. E-Mail: flower@hawaii.edu. *Dir*, Eric Flower; Staff 3 (MLS 2, Non-MLS 1)
Founded 1976. Enrl 744; Highest Degree: Bachelor
Library Holdings: Bk Titles 25,000; Per Subs 132
Automation Activity & Vendor Info: (Acquisitions) Brodart
Publications: Hawaii Herald Index

PEARL HARBOR

UNITED STATES NAVY
A NAVAL STATION LIBRARY PEARL HARBOR, Bldg 679, 850 Ticonderaga St, Ste 300, Honolulu, 96860-5100. SAN 339-5944. Tel: 808-471-8238. FAX: 808-423-4047. E-Mail: phlib@aloha.net. *Librn*, Terri Sato
Library Holdings: Bk Vols 30,000; Per Subs 55
Special Collections: Auxiliary Library Service Coll; China Coll; Hawaiiana; James E Wise Room of Naval History

A UNITED STATES NAVY - NAVAL SHIPYARD, Technical Library,* Code 244-52, 667 Safeguard St Ste 100, 96860-5033. SAN 371-1269. Tel: 808-474-0001, 808-474-0204. FAX: 808-474-0042. E-Mail: ls_c24@parts.navy.mil. *Dir*, Willie Ho
Library Holdings: Bk Vols 30,000

WAILUKU

GL HAWAII STATE CIRCUIT COURT-SECOND CIRCUIT, Law Library,* 2145 Main St, 96793. SAN 303-5212. Tel: 808-244-2959. FAX: 808-244-2932. *Librn*, Morris Haole
Library Holdings: Bk Vols 17,963

S MAUI HISTORICAL SOCIETY, Archival Resource Center,* 2375 A Main St, 96793. SAN 326-3118. Tel: 808-244-3326. FAX: 808-244-3920. Web Site: www.mauimuseum.org. *Exec Dir*, Cathy F Riley
Founded 1957
Library Holdings: Bk Titles 7,650
Special Collections: Photographs
Publications: Index to the Maui News, 1900-1932; Island of Maui cemetery directories

M MAUI MEMORIAL MEDICAL CENTER, Biomedical Library,* 221 Mahalani St, 96793. SAN 303-5204. Tel: 808-242-2337. FAX: 808-242-7472. E-Mail: mmhlib@mauigateway.com. *Librn*, Marilynn M L Wong
Founded 1967
Jul 1999-Jun 2000 Mats Exp $85,000, Books $10,000, Per/Ser (Incl. Access Fees) $30,000, AV Equip $2,000. Sal $37,464
Library Holdings: Bk Vols 7,000; Per Subs 270
Subject Interests: Medical
Special Collections: Partial Federal Depository for medical government documents for Maui County
Partic in Medical Libr Asn

WAIMANALO

S OCEANIC INSTITUTE LIBRARY, 41-202 Kalanianeole Hwy, 96795. SAN 303-5220. Tel: 808-259-3123, 808-259-3140, 808-259-7951. FAX: 808-259-5971. Web Site: www.oceanicinstitute.org. *Librn*, Esma Harper; E-Mail: esmaharper@compuserve.com
Founded 1964
Library Holdings: Per Subs 20
Subject Interests: Environmental studies, Ichthyology, Ocean engineering
Open Mon-Fri 8-4:30

IDAHO

Date of Statistics: Fiscal Year 1999
Population, 1998 Census: 1,251,700
Population Served by Public Libraries: 1,054,374
Unserved: 197,326
Total Volumes in Public Libraries: 3,636,309
Volumes Per Capita: 3.44
Circulation Per Capita: 7.7
Total Public Library Income: $21,370,413
Local Taxes: $187,372,400
Local Taxes (ad valorem): 86.0%
State Sales Tax: 3.2%
Federal (LSTA): 0.8%
Other: 10%
Total Expenditures: $21,325,736
Expenditures Per Capita: $20.23 (total operating)
Number of County or District Libraries: 52 (Includes 4 school/community and administrative)
Number of Public Libraries: 105 (including District/County Libraries)
Number of Bookmobiles in State: 6 local

ABERDEEN

P ABERDEEN PUBLIC LIBRARY,* 76 E Central, PO Box 207, 83210-0207. SAN 303-5247. Tel: 208-397-4427. E-Mail: aberdeenlib@hotmail.com. *Dir*, Bonnie Oldfield; *Librn*, Margaret Hoffman; *Asst Librn*, Kambrea Klassen
Circ 14,844
Library Holdings: Bk Vols 15,000

AMERICAN FALLS

P AMERICAN FALLS DISTRICT LIBRARY,* 308 Roosevelt St, 83211-1219. SAN 303-5255. Tel: 208-226-2335. FAX: 208-226-2303. E-Mail: amlib@directinter.net. *Dir*, Margaret McNamara; *ILL*, Ilene Haskell; Staff 1 (MLS 1)
Circ 37,500
Oct 1996-Sep 1997 Income $218,363. Mats Exp $36,140. Sal $115,225
Library Holdings: Bk Vols 29,000; Per Subs 100
Special Collections: Idaho Coll; Large Print Coll; Spanish Lang Coll, bks on tape; Young Adult Coll
Mem of Gateway Regional Libr Syst

ARCO

P LOST RIVERS DISTRICT LIBRARY, 126 S Front St, PO Box 170, 83213-0170. SAN 303-5263. Tel: 208-527-8511. *Dir*, Bettina Blattner; E-Mail: bettina_b@hotmail.com; *Asst Librn*, Krickett Merrill; *YA Servs*, Kami Freeman
Pop 2,907; Circ 15,716
Library Holdings: Bk Vols 13,000; Per Subs 50
Special Collections: American Classics; Antique Book Coll
Publications: Library Journal

ASHTON

P ASHTON PUBLIC LIBRARY,* 925 Main, PO Box 854, 83420-0854. SAN 303-5271. Tel: 208-652-7280. FAX: 208-652-7280. E-Mail: ashlib@nstep.net. *Ch Servs, Dir*, Kathy Henderson; *Ch Servs*, Barbara Moon
Pop 11,719; Circ 16,658
Library Holdings: Bk Vols 17,000; Per Subs 26
Subject Interests: Rare books

BELLEVUE

§P BELLEVUE PUBLIC LIBRARY, 115 E Pine, PO Box 449, 83313-0268. Tel: 208-788-2128. Circulation Tel: 208-788-2128. FAX: 208-788-2128. *Dir*, Wynn Bird
Library Holdings: Bk Vols 7,000
Automation Activity & Vendor Info: (Acquisitions) Follett; (Cataloging) Follett; (Circulation) Follett

BLACKFOOT

M BINGHAM MEMORIAL HOSPITAL, Medical Library,* 98 Poplar St, 83221. SAN 371-2052. Tel: 208-785-4100. *Librn*, Margaret Davis; Tel: 208-785-3858
Library Holdings: Bk Vols 500; Per Subs 50

P LUCY BOYLE PUBLIC LIBRARY,* 129 N Broadway, PO Box 610, 83221-0610. SAN 303-5298. Tel: 208-785-8628. FAX: 208-785-8602. E-Mail: blackft@micron.net. *Dir*, Robert K Wright; *Librn*, Brenda K Wilcox; *Librn*, Lisa Jensen Harral
Founded 1916. Pop 20,000; Circ 110,005
Oct 1999-Sep 2000 Income $483,718, State $20,000, City $120,206, Locally Generated Income $120,206, Other $223,306. Mats Exp $54,770, Books $48,270, Per/Ser (Incl. Access Fees) $5,500, Electronic Ref Mat (Incl. Access Fees) $1,000. Sal $136,233 (Prof $91,200)
Library Holdings: Bk Vols 37,000; Bk Titles 33,000; Per Subs 125
Special Collections: Local Newspaper Coll 1880 to present, micro
Database Vendor: Ebsco - EbscoHost, IAC - Info Trac
Partic in Idaho Libr Asn

P SNAKE RIVER SCHOOL COMMUNITY LIBRARY,* 924 W Hwy 39, 83221. SAN 303-5301. Tel: 208-684-3063. FAX: 208-684-3141. E-Mail: srscl@micron.net. Web Site: www.netnow.micron.net/~srscl. *Dir*, Sherian Abercrombie; *Asst Librn*, Susan Anderson; *Asst Librn*, Pat Kauer; *Asst Librn*, Renee White
Pop 7,700; Circ 90,473
Library Holdings: Bk Vols 34,000; Per Subs 600
Mem of Gateway Regional Libr Syst
Partic in OCLC

BOISE

P ADA COMMUNITY LIBRARY,* 10664 W Victory Rd, 83709. SAN 323-9756. Tel: 208-362-0181. FAX: 208-362-0303. Web Site: www.ala.libid.us. *Dir*, Dian Hoffpauir; Tel: 208-362-0181 Ext 23, E-Mail: dianh@ada.lib.id.us; *Ref*, Terri Wear; Tel: 208-362-0181 Ext 25, E-Mail: twear@ada.lib.id.us; *YA Servs*, Beth Short; Tel: 208-362-0181 Ext 31, E-Mail: beths@ada.lib.id.us; *Syst Coordr*, Robin Ballentyne; Tel: 208-362-0181 Ext 32, E-Mail: robin@ada.lib.id.us; *ILL*, Laura McNew; Tel: 208-362-0181 Ext 22, E-Mail: laura@ada.lib.id.us; *Circ*, Vicky Rae; Tel: 208-362-0181 Ext 28, E-Mail: vicki@ada.lib.id.us; Staff 7 (MLS 3, Non-MLS 4)
Founded 1984. Pop 47,400
Oct 1996-Sep 1997 Income $1,017,195. Mats Exp $110,373. Sal $549,075
Library Holdings: Bk Vols 77,445; Bk Titles 74,097; Per Subs 1,260
Subject Interests: Horses
Publications: Facts from the Stacks (newsletter)
Partic in OCLC
Friends of the Library Group
Branches: 2
HIDDEN SPRINGS BRANCH, 5892 W Hidden Springs Dr, Hidden Springs, 83703. Tel: 208-229-2265. *Librn*, Beth McGovey
Library Holdings: Bk Vols 2,000; Per Subs 500

Automation Activity & Vendor Info: (Acquisitions) epixtech, inc.; (Cataloging) epixtech, inc.; (Circulation) epixtech, inc.; (ILL) epixtech, inc.; (OPAC) epixtech, inc.; (Serials) epixtech, inc.
STAR BRANCH, PO Box 397, Star, 83669. Tel: 208-286-9755. FAX: 208-286-9755. *Librn*, Cheryl Parris
Library Holdings: Bk Vols 16,000; Per Subs 500
Automation Activity & Vendor Info: (Acquisitions) epixtech, inc.; (Cataloging) epixtech, inc.; (Circulation) epixtech, inc.; (ILL) epixtech, inc.; (OPAC) epixtech, inc.; (Serials) epixtech, inc.

S BOISE ART MUSEUM LIBRARY,* 670 S Julia Davis Dr, 83702. SAN 320-149X. Tel: 208-345-8330. FAX: 208-345-2247. Web Site: www.boiseartmuseum.org. *Curator*, Sandy Harthorn
Library Holdings: Bk Titles 2,500; Per Subs 10
Subject Interests: Art history

R BOISE BIBLE COLLEGE LIBRARY, 8695 W Marigold St, 83714-1220. SAN 303-5328. Tel: 208-376-7731. FAX: 208-376-7743. E-Mail: boisebible@boisebible.edu. Web Site: www.boisebible.edu. *Librn*, Glennis Thomas; Staff 1 (Non-MLS 1)
Founded 1945. Enrl 131; Fac 8; Highest Degree: Bachelor
Jul 1998-Jun 1999 Income $46,920. Mats Exp $10,500, Books $7,000, Per/Ser (Incl. Access Fees) $3,500. Sal $34,158 (Prof $26,333)
Library Holdings: Bk Vols 30,877; Bk Titles 25,747; Per Subs 109
Subject Interests: Biblical studies, Church history, Missions and missionaries
Special Collections: Restoration Movement materials
Automation Activity & Vendor Info: (Circulation) Sagebrush Corporation

P BOISE PUBLIC LIBRARY, 715 S Capitol Blvd, 83702-7195. SAN 303-5344. Tel: 208-384-4238. FAX: 208-384-4025. E-Mail: lynx@cityofboise.org. Web Site: www.boisepubliclibrary.org. *Dir*, Marilyn Poertner; Tel: 208-384-4210, E-Mail: mpoertner@cityofboise.org; *Asst Dir*, Kevin Booe; Tel: 208-384-4029, E-Mail: kbooe@cityofboise.org; *Ad Servs*, Grove Koger; Tel: 208-384-4076, E-Mail: gkoger@pobox.ci.boise.id.us; *Ad Servs*, Vicki Kreimeyer Brown; Tel: 208-384-4341, E-Mail: vkreimeyer@cityofboise.org; *YA Servs*, Susannah Price; Tel: 208-384-4026, E-Mail: sprice@cityofboise.org; *Automation Syst Coordr*, Dena Duncan; Tel: 208-384-4464, E-Mail: dduncan@pobox.ci.boise.id.us; *Ad Servs*, Julie Davis; Tel: 208-384-4023, E-Mail: jdavis@pobox.ci.boise.id.us; *Circ*, Laurel White; Tel: 208-384-4485, E-Mail: lwhite@cityofboise.org; *Admin Assoc*, Toni Hansen; Tel: 208-384-4237, E-Mail: thansen@cityofboise.org; Staff 129 (MLS 15, Non-MLS 114)
Founded 1895. Pop 170,327; Circ 1,309,287
Oct 1998-Sep 1999 Income $3,952,614. Mats Exp $577,281, Books $389,753, Electronic Ref Mat (Incl. Access Fees) $187,528. Sal $2,165,176
Library Holdings: Bk Titles 353,186
Special Collections: Newspaper (Idaho Stateman), micro; Northwest & Idaho History
Database Vendor: Ebsco - EbscoHost, epixtech, inc., IAC - Info Trac, Lexis-Nexis
Publications: Community Calendar
Special Services for the Deaf - TTY machine
Friends of the Library Group
Branches: 1
TOWNE SQUARE, 350 N Milwaukee, 83788. SAN 370-3649. Tel: 208-375-5020. FAX: 208-658-0781. *In Charge*, Marcia Courtney; *In Charge*, Anne Jennings
Friends of the Library Group

C BOISE STATE UNIVERSITY ALBERTSONS LIBRARY, 1865 Campus Lane, 83725-1430. (Mail add: 1910 University Dr, 83725-1430), SAN 339-624X. Tel: 208-426-4321. Interlibrary Loan Service Tel: 208-426-3756. TDD: 208-426-4286. FAX: 208-426-1885. Interlibrary Loan Service FAX: 208-426-1394. Web Site: library.boisestate.edu. *Dir*, Timothy A Brown; E-Mail: tbrown@boisestate.edu; *Head Tech Servs*, Gloria Ostrander-Dykstra; Tel: 208-426-3650, E-Mail: gostrand@boisestate.edu; *Head Ref*, Adrien Taylor; Tel: 208-426-1261, E-Mail: ataylor@boisestate.edu; *Ref*, Nick Bazemore; Tel: 208-426-1264, E-Mail: nbazemor@boisestate.edu; *Ref*, Larry Kincaid; Tel: 208-426-1584, E-Mail: lkincaid@boisestate.edu; *Ref*, Terry Madden; Tel: 208-426-3581, E-Mail: tmadden@boisestate.edu; *Ref*, Anne Matjeka; Tel: 208-426-1270, E-Mail: amatjeka@boisestate.edu; *Doc*, Elaine Watson; Tel: 208-426-1737, E-Mail: ewatson@boisestate.edu; *Archivist*, Alan Virta; Tel: 208-426-3958, E-Mail: avirta@boisestate.edu; *ILL*, Beverly Miller; Tel: 208-426-1626, E-Mail: bmiller@boisestate.edu; *Head, Cat*, Kai Stoeckenius; Tel: 208-426-3238, E-Mail: kstoecke@boisestate.edu; *Cat*, Mark Crotteau; Tel: 208-426-1082, E-Mail: mcrottea@boisestate.edu; *Head, Acq*, Nancy Rosenheim; Tel: 208-426-1660, E-Mail: nrosenhe@boisestate.edu; *Head, Ser Acq*, Jill Collins; Tel: 208-426-3175, E-Mail: jcollins@boisestate.edu; *Circ*, Mario Briseno; Tel: 208-426-4025, E-Mail: mbriseno@boisestate.edu; *Coll Develop*, Peggy Cooper; Tel: 208-426-2311, E-Mail: pcooper@boisestate.edu; *Automation Syst Coordr*, Dan Lester; Tel: 208-426-1235, E-Mail: dlester@boisestate.edu; *Publ Servs*, Janet Strong; E-Mail: jstrong@boisestate.edu; *Bibliog Instr*, Beth Brin; Tel: 208-426-3136, E-Mail: bbrin@boisestate.edu. Subject Specialists: *Accounting*, Peggy Cooper; *Applied tech*, Janet Strong; *Biology*, Mark Crotteau; *Canadian studies*, Adrien Taylor; *Chemistry*, Dan Lester; *Children's literature*, Anne Matjeka; *Communication*, Janet Strong; *Construction*, Beth Brin; *Counseling*, Anne Matjeka; *Criminal justice*, Janet Strong; *Economics*, Peggy Cooper; *Engineering*, Beth Brin; *English*, Kai Stoeckenius; *Finance*, Elaine Watson; *Geosciences*, Alan Virta; *Health sci*, Terry Madden; *History*, Larry Kincaid; *Libr sci*, Gloria Ostrander-Dykstra; *Management*, Elaine Watson; *Maps*, Nick Bazemore; *Marketing*, Elaine Watson; *Mathematics*, Beverly Miller; *Music*, Nick Bazemore; *Philosophy*, Larry Kincaid; *Physics*, Dan Lester; *Political science*, Nick Bazemore; *Psychology*, Mark Crotteau; *Reference*, Adrien Taylor; *Social work*, Peggy Cooper; *Teacher educ*, Anne Matjeka; Staff 61 (MLS 15, Non-MLS 46)
Founded 1932. Enrl 11,330; Fac 542; Highest Degree: Doctorate
Jul 1999-Jun 2000 Income $5,604,212, State $5,042,082, Federal $185,000, Locally Generated Income $146,720, Other $230,410. Mats Exp $1,981,128, Books $556,528, Per/Ser (Incl. Access Fees) $1,374,600, Presv $50,000. Sal $2,937,406 (Prof $1,194,628)
Library Holdings: Bk Vols 540,974; Bk Titles 448,467; Per Subs 3,684
Subject Interests: Business and management, Education
Special Collections: Idaho Historical Manuscripts & Photos; Idaho Writers Archive (literary mss); Papers of Governor Cecil Andrus; Rare Books Coll; Senatorial Papers of Frank Church & Len B Jordan
Automation Activity & Vendor Info: (Acquisitions) GEAC; (Cataloging) GEAC; (Circulation) GEAC; (Course Reserve) GEAC; (OPAC) GEAC; (Serials) GEAC
Publications: Guide to the Frank Church Papers; Hemingway Exhibit Catalog; Information Series
Special Services for the Deaf - Staff with knowledge of sign language

S CENTER FOR THE STUDY OF MARKET ALTERNATIVES LIBRARY, 11409 W Hickory Hill, 83713. SAN 370-9582. Tel: 208-376-6801. FAX: 208-376-6801. E-Mail: csma@micron.net. *Dir*, Barbara Sall; *Librn*, Jan Vincent
Founded 1972
Jan 1999-Dec 1999 Mats Exp $2,250, Books $2,000, Per/Ser (Incl. Access Fees) $250
Library Holdings: Bk Titles 6,000; Per Subs 15

GM DEPARTMENT OF VETERANS AFFAIRS, Medical Center Library-142D, 500 W Fort St, 83702-4598. SAN 303-545X. Tel: 208-422-1306. FAX: 208-422-1390. *Chief Librn, Online Servs*, Gordon Carlson; *Tech Servs*, Jean Stubbs; Staff 2 (MLS 1, Non-MLS 1)
Founded 1930
Oct 2000-Sep 2001 Income Federal $60,000. Mats Exp $60,000, Books $4,000, Per/Ser (Incl. Access Fees) $36,000
Library Holdings: Bk Vols 2,000; Per Subs 200
Special Collections: Clinical Medicine, bks, AV; Patient Education, bks, AV
Automation Activity & Vendor Info: (Acquisitions) Athena; (Cataloging) Athena; (Circulation) Athena; (Course Reserve) Athena; (OPAC) Athena
Partic in Nat Libr of Med; Pacific NW Regional Health Sci Libr; Vets Admin Libr Network

SR DIOCESE OF BOISE, Resource Center Library,* 303 Federal Way, 83705. SAN 328-2074. Tel: 208-342-1311. FAX: 208-342-0224. *Librn*, Gloria Pettinger
Library Holdings: Bk Titles 3,200; Per Subs 18
Open Mon-Fri 9-5

L ELAM & BURKE PA, Law Library,* PO Box 1539, 83701-1539. SAN 372-1124. Tel: 208-343-5454. FAX: 208-384-5844. *Librn*, Rochelle Edvalson
Library Holdings: Bk Vols 10,000; Per Subs 70
Subject Interests: Aviation

L HAWLEY TROXELL ENNIS & HAWLEY, 877 Main St, Ste 1000, 83701-1617. Tel: 208-344-6000. *Librn*, Dan Rutledge; E-Mail: ddr@hteh.com
Library Holdings: Bk Vols 12,000; Per Subs 50

S HEALTHWISE INCORPORATED RESEARCH LIBRARY, 2601 N Bogus Basin Rd, PO Box 1989, 83702. SAN 377-2276. Tel: 208-331-6957. FAX: 208-345-1897. *Dir*, Mary Ellen Lemon; E-Mail: mlemon@healthwise.org. Subject Specialists: *Medical*, Mary Ellen Lemon; *Research*, Mary Ellen Lemon; Staff 1 (MLS 1)
Library Holdings: Bk Titles 650; Per Subs 50
Database Vendor: Dialog, OVID Technologies
Function: Research library

S HEWLETT-PACKARD CO, Boise Site Library,* Mail Stop 0234, 83707. SAN 328-0667. Tel: 208-396-2911. FAX: 208-396-5205. E-Mail: gail_lester@hp.com. *Librn*, Gail Lester
Library Holdings: Bk Titles 3,500; Per Subs 140
Partic in HP Library Network; OCLC

G IDAHO LEGISLATIVE REFERENCE LIBRARY, State Capitol, 700 W Jefferson, 83702. (Mail add: PO Box 83720, 83720-0054), SAN 320-1759. Tel: 208-334-4822. FAX: 208-334-4860. E-Mail: kford@lso.state.id.us. Web Site: www2.state.id.us/legislat/legislat.html. *Librn*, Kristin M Ford; Staff 1 (MLS 1)
Founded 1978
Library Holdings: Bk Vols 3,100; Bk Titles 2,500; Per Subs 40
Automation Activity & Vendor Info: (Cataloging) Sagebrush Corporation; (Cataloging) Athena; (Circulation) Athena; (Circulation) Sagebrush

Corporation
Database Vendor: Ebsco - EbscoHost, GaleNet
Restriction: Circulates for staff only
Function: Photocopies available, Research fees apply, Some telephone reference

S IDAHO POWER COMPANY, Corporate Library, PO Box 70, 83707. SAN 328-7890. Tel: 208-388-2316. Interlibrary Loan Service Tel: 208-388-2238. FAX: 208-388-5884.
Library Holdings: Bk Titles 4,045; Per Subs 250

S IDAHO STATE HISTORICAL SOCIETY LIBRARY & ARCHIVES, 450 N Fourth St, 83702. SAN 339-6304. Tel: 208-334-3356. FAX: 208-334-3198. Web Site: www.state.id.us/ishs/index.htm.; Staff 10 (MLS 4, Non-MLS 6)
Founded 1907
Subject Interests: Genealogy, Local history
Special Collections: Idaho & Pacific Northwest History; Idaho Manuscripts including State & Local Governmental Records; Idaho Newspapers, microfilm, Idaho Photographs; Map Coll
Restriction: Non-circulating to the public
Open Tues-Sat 9-5

L IDAHO STATE LAW LIBRARY, 451 W State St, PO Box 83720, 83720. SAN 303-5395. Tel: 208-334-3316. Toll Free Tel: 877-345-8236. FAX: 208-334-4019. E-Mail: lawlibrary@isc.state.id.us. Web Site: www2.state.id.us/lawlib/lawlib.html. *Librn*, Rick Visser; *Ref*, Carol Marsh; Staff 12 (MLS 3, Non-MLS 9)
Founded 1869
Jul 1996-Jun 1997 Income $637,403. Mats Exp $244,000. Sal $337,903
Library Holdings: Bk Vols 180,530; Bk Titles 21,224; Per Subs 200
Subject Interests: Law, Legislation
Special Collections: Idaho Appellate Court briefs
Automation Activity & Vendor Info: (Cataloging) Innovative Interfaces Inc.
Database Vendor: Innovative Interfaces INN - View, Lexis-Nexis
Partic in Westlaw

P IDAHO STATE LIBRARY, 325 W State St, 83702-6072. SAN 339-6363. Tel: 208-334-2150. FAX: 208-334-4016. Web Site: www.lili.org/isl. *State Librn*, Dr Charles A Bolles; E-Mail: cbolles@isl.state.id.us; *Assoc Dir*, Ann Joslin; E-Mail: ajoslin@isl.state.id.us; *Ref*, Jane Houston; E-Mail: jhouston@isl.state.id.us; *Assoc Dir*, Richard Wilson; E-Mail: rwilson@isl.state.id.us; *Publ Servs*, Sue Walker; E-Mail: swalker@isl.state.id.us; Staff 46 (MLS 14, Non-MLS 32)
Founded 1901. Pop 1,200,000
Jul 1999-Jun 2000 Income $4,010,100, State $2,517,300, Federal $1,089,700, Other $403,100. Mats Exp $516,500, Books $49,000, Presv $2,500, Electronic Ref Mat (Incl. Access Fees) $465,000. Sal $1,804,000
Library Holdings: Bk Vols 98,000; Bk Titles 93,500; Per Subs 400
Subject Interests: Government, Idaho, Library and information science, Northwest
Automation Activity & Vendor Info: (Acquisitions) GEAC; (Cataloging) GEAC; (Circulation) GEAC; (Media Booking) GEAC; (Serials) GEAC
Database Vendor: Dialog, Ebsco - EbscoHost, IAC - Info Trac, OCLC - First Search, ProQuest
Publications: Newsletter (monthly); Public Library Statistics
Partic in OCLC Online Computer Library Center, Inc; Western Council Of State Libraries, Inc
Special Services for the Blind - Talking Books
Branches: 1

P IDAHO STATE TALKING BOOK LIBRARY, 325 W State St, 83702-6072. SAN 303-5379. Tel: 208-334-2117. Toll Free Tel: 800-233-4931. FAX: 208-334-2194. E-Mail: tblbrooks@isl.state.id.us. Web Site: www.lili.org/isl.; Staff 1 (MLS 1)
Founded 1973. Pop 2,808; Circ 159,279
Special Collections: Idaho & Pacific Northwest Recorded Books; Twin Vision Coll
Publications: large print calendar; Patron newsletter (large print & cassettes)
Partic in BRS; Ontyme; Washington Libr Network

S IDAHO STATESMAN LIBRARY, 1200 N Curtis Rd, 83706. (Mail add: PO Box 40, 83707), SAN 303-5387. Tel: 208-377-6435. Circulation Tel: 208-377-6370. Toll Free Tel: 800-635-8934. FAX: 208-377-6449. E-Mail: library@idstates.com. Web Site: www.idahostatesman.com. *In Charge*, Marsha MacLean; Staff 2 (MLS 1, Non-MLS 1)
Founded 1972
Special Collections: Idaho, newspapers
Partic in Dialog Corporation; Vutext

S MAXIM TECHNOLOGIES INC LIBRARY,* 3380 Americana Terrace, Ste 201, PO Box 7777, 83707. SAN 373-4323. Tel: 208-389-1030. FAX: 208-389-1183.
Library Holdings: Bk Vols 20,000; Per Subs 10
Subject Interests: Chemistry
Restriction: Staff use only

S REAL ESTATE COMMISSION LIBRARY, 633 N Fourth St, 83702-4510. (Mail add: PO Box 83720, 83720-0077), SAN 328-2236. Tel: 208-334-3285. FAX: 208-334-2050. Web Site: www2.state.id.us/irec. *Librn*, Pat Zaske; Tel: 208-334-3285, Ext 223, E-Mail: pzaske@irec.state.id.us
Open Mon-Fri 8-5

M SAINT ALPHONSUS REGIONAL MEDICAL CENTER, Kissler Family Health Sciences Library, 1055 N Curtis Rd, 83706. SAN 303-5417. Tel: 208-367-3993. FAX: 208-367-2702. Web Site: www.sarmc.org. *Librn*, Sandy Hight; *Librn*, Dot Dreyer
Founded 1970
Library Holdings: Bk Titles 1,200; Per Subs 265

M SAINT LUKE'S REGIONAL MEDICAL CENTER, Medical Library, 190 E Bannock St, 83712-6297. SAN 303-5425. Tel: 208-381-2277. Interlibrary Loan Service Tel: 208-381-2276. FAX: 208-381-4317. *Mgr*, Pamela Spickelmier; E-Mail: spickelp@slrmc.org; *Coll Develop*, Amy Claybaugh
Founded 1971
Oct 1996-Sep 1997 Income $191,073. Mats Exp $94,000
Library Holdings: Bk Vols 15,000; Bk Titles 1,300; Per Subs 300
Subject Interests: Cardiology, Internal medicine, Obstetrics and gynecology, Pediatrics
Partic in BRS; Medline; OCLC

G UNITED STATES GEOLOGICAL SURVEY, Water Resources Div Library Idaho Dist,* 230 Collins Rd, 83702. SAN 303-5441. Tel: 208-387-1300. FAX: 208-387-1372.
Library Holdings: Bk Vols 5,000; Per Subs 10

P WASHINGTON GROUP INTERNATIONAL INC, (Formerly Morrison Knudsen Corporation), 720 Park Blvd, 83712. Tel: 208-386-7154. FAX: 208-386-5000. *Asst Librn*, Dawn Yantek; E-Mail: dawn.yantek@wgint.com
Library Holdings: Bk Vols 1,000; Bk Titles 1,000; Per Subs 200

BONNERS FERRY

P BOUNDARY COUNTY DISTRICT LIBRARY,* 6370 Kootenal St, PO Box Y, 83805. SAN 303-5468. Tel: 208-267-3750. FAX: 208-267-5231. E-Mail: bcl@dmi.net. *Dir*, Sandra Ashworth; *Asst Librn*, Glenda McCalmant; *Ch Servs*, Beth Byars
Founded 1914. Pop 9,050; Circ 81,814
Oct 1996-Sep 1997 Income $180,930. Mats Exp $28,529. Sal $79,171
Library Holdings: Bk Vols 31,831; Bk Titles 27,978; Per Subs 130
Subject Interests: Environmental studies, Forestry
Partic in OCLC

BUHL

P BUHL PUBLIC LIBRARY,* 215 Broadway N, 83316-1624. SAN 303-5476. Tel: 208-543-6500. E-Mail: buhllib@hotmail.com. *Dir*, Fay A Parrott; *YA Servs*, Louise Nofziger
Pop 3,516; Circ 38,744
Library Holdings: Bk Vols 22,000; Per Subs 87
Special Collections: Idaho Coll; Quilting
Partic in OCLC

BURLEY

P BURLEY PUBLIC LIBRARY,* 1300 Miller Ave, 83318-1729. SAN 303-5492. Tel: 208-678-7708. *Dir*, Julie Woodford; *Asst Dir*, Mona Kenner
Founded 1922. Pop 9,578; Circ 70,524
Oct 1997-Sep 1998 Income $93,830. Mats Exp $25,000, Books $15,900. Sal $81,000
Library Holdings: Bk Vols 54,228
Special Collections: Idaho Coll
Mem of Magic Valley Libr Syst
Friends of the Library Group

S CASSIA COUNTY HISTORICAL SOCIETY, Reference Room, PO Box 331, E Main & Highland Ave, 83318. SAN 375-4677. Tel: 208-678-7172. *Curator*, Joy Young
Library Holdings: Bk Titles 100
Restriction: Open to public for reference only

CALDWELL

C ALBERTSON COLLEGE OF IDAHO, NL Terteling Library, 2112 Cleveland Blvd, 83605. SAN 303-5514. Tel: 208-459-5505. FAX: 208-459-5299. Web Site: www.albertson.edu/~library/. *Librn*, Dale Corning; E-Mail: dcorning@acofi.edu
Founded 1891. Highest Degree: Bachelor
Jul 1998-Jun 1999 Income $525,444. Mats Exp $218,647, Books $147,395, Per/Ser (Incl. Access Fees) $61,310, Presv $7,442, AV Equip $2,500. Sal $218,000
Library Holdings: Bk Vols 178,885; Per Subs 820

Subject Interests: Humanities
Special Collections: Children's Literature
Partic in OCLC
Curriculum Resource Center
Friends of the Library Group

P CALDWELL PUBLIC LIBRARY, 1010 Dearborn, 83605-4195. SAN 303-5506. Tel: 208-459-3242. FAX: 208-459-7344. *Dir*, Elaine Leppert; E-Mail: eleppert@yahoo.com; *Ref*, Linda Hieb; *Ch Servs*, Candi Ciscell; Staff 10 (MLS 3, Non-MLS 7)
Founded 1887. Pop 23,970; Circ 138,395
Oct 1998-Sep 1999 Income $557,173, State $66,092, City $357,699, Locally Generated Income $69,540, Other $63,842. Mats Exp $92,077, Books $81,234, Per/Ser (Incl. Access Fees) $10,000, Presv $543, Micro $300. Sal $287,817
Library Holdings: Bk Titles 97,800; Per Subs 217
Special Collections: Foundation Center Library Regional Coll; Historical Photographs
Automation Activity & Vendor Info: (Acquisitions) epixtech, inc.; (Cataloging) epixtech, inc.; (Circulation) epixtech, inc.
Publications: Directory of Idaho Foundations
Partic in Lynx; OCLC Online Computer Library Center, Inc
Friends of the Library Group

M COLUMBIA WEST VALLEY MEDICAL CENTER,* 1717 Arlington, 83605. SAN 320-6351. Tel: 208-455-4003. FAX: 208-455-3717. *In Charge*, Sandy Jenkins
Library Holdings: Bk Vols 220
Publications: Health Information Newsletter
Partic in Boise Valley Health Sciences Library Consortium

CAMBRIDGE

P CAMBRIDGE COMMUNITY LIBRARY, Superior St, PO Box 10, 83610. SAN 303-5522. Tel: 208-257-3434. E-Mail: cambplib@ctcweb.net. *Librn*, Nina Hawkins; *Asst Librn*, Tammy Holman; *Ch Servs*, Janet Bunker
Founded 1973. Pop 1,700; Circ 8,500
Library Holdings: Bk Vols 15,000

CAREY

P LITTLE WOOD RIVER DISTRICT LIBRARY, 16 Panther Ave, PO Box 218, 83320-0093. SAN 303-5530. Tel: 208-823-4510. *Librn*, Mary Bowman
Founded 1976. Circ 12,034
Library Holdings: Bk Titles 5,700; Per Subs 4
Open Mon 11-5, Wed 2-8, Fri 11-4

CASCADE

P CASCADE PUBLIC LIBRARY,* 105 Front St, PO Box 10, 83611-0010. SAN 303-5549. Tel: 208-382-4757. FAX: 208-382-4757. E-Mail: casclib@cyberhighway.net. *Librn*, Alyce Kelley
Founded 1955. Pop 1,020; Circ 6,726
Oct 1997-Sep 1998 Income $40,000
Library Holdings: Bk Vols 17,351; Per Subs 18
Special Collections: National Geographic Coll, 1936-82; Old West Coll

CHALLIS

P CHALLIS PUBLIC LIBRARY,* 501 Sixth St, PO Box 186, 83226-0186. SAN 303-5557. Tel: 208-879-4267. FAX: 208-879-5288. E-Mail: cpl@cyberhighway.net. *Librn*, Linda Hesse; *Asst Librn*, Joyce Renteria; Staff 1 (MLS 1)
Founded 1935. Pop 1,990; Circ 9,291
Library Holdings: Bk Titles 13,000
Partic in OCLC
Friends of the Library Group

CHUBBUCK

P PORTNEUF DISTRICT LIBRARY, 5210 Stuart, 83202-2214. SAN 303-6308. Tel: 208-237-2192. FAX: 208-237-2194. E-Mail: pdlib@dcdi.net. *Dir*, Karen Tate; *Librn*, Susan Marple
Founded 1958. Pop 15,000; Circ 50,000
Library Holdings: Bk Titles 47,000; Per Subs 305
Open Mon-Thurs 12-8, Fri 12-6, Sat 10-6 (winter), Mon-Sat 10-6, (summer)

COEUR D' ALENE

S HECLA MINING COMPANY LIBRARY, 6500 Mineral Dr, 83815-8788. Tel: 208-769-4132. FAX: 208-769-4122. Web Site: www.hecla-mining.com. *Librn*, Linda A Koep; E-Mail: lkoep@heclamining.com

COEUR D'ALENE

G BUREAU OF LAND MANAGEMENT, Coeur d'Alene District Office Library,* 1808 N Third St, 83814. SAN 303-5565. Tel: 208-769-5000. FAX: 208-769-5050.
Library Holdings: Bk Vols 250

P COEUR D'ALENE PUBLIC LIBRARY, 201 E Harrison Ave, 83814-2373. SAN 303-5573. Tel: 208-769-2315. FAX: 208-769-2381. E-Mail: cdapl@dmi.net. Web Site: www.dmi.net/cdalibrary. *Dir*, Julie Meier; *Tech Servs*, Alicia Clark; *Ch Servs*, Cathy Comfort; Staff 6 (MLS 2, Non-MLS 4)
Founded 1904. Pop 32,171; Circ 194,678
Oct 1999-Sep 2000 Income $563,777. Mats Exp $43,588, Books $32,787, Per/Ser (Incl. Access Fees) $7,269, Micro $300, Electronic Ref Mat (Incl. Access Fees) $3,232. Sal $361,611
Library Holdings: Bk Titles 67,763; Per Subs 143; Bks on Deafness & Sign Lang 301
Subject Interests: Local history
Special Collections: Human Rights Coll; Idaho Coll; Northwest Coll
Automation Activity & Vendor Info: (Circulation) Athena
Publications: Blind Club Newsletter; Deaf Club Newsletter; Foundation Letters; Friends of the Library Newsletter
Special Services for the Deaf - Deaf publications; Staff with knowledge of sign language
Special Services for the Blind - Blind Club (monthly newsletter); Club for the blind
Friends of the Library Group

M KOOTENAI MEDICAL CENTER, William T Wood Medical Library, 2003 Lincoln Way, 83814. SAN 328-0608. Tel: 208-666-2480. FAX: 208-666-2854. Web Site: www.kmc.org (clinical), www.nicon.org/dearmond/index.htm (consumer). *Librn*, Marcy Horner; E-Mail: hornerm@kmc.org
Founded 1984
Library Holdings: Bk Titles 1,300; Per Subs 320
Automation Activity & Vendor Info: (Acquisitions) SIRSI
Publications: NIHIN (newsletter)
Partic in Cooperative Information Network; Dialog Corporation; IHIN; ILCN; Nat Libr of Med; NIHIN

S MUSEUM OF NORTH IDAHO INCORPORATED ARCHIVES, 115 Northwest Blvd, PO Box 812, 83816-0812. SAN 371-2966. Tel: 208-664-3448. E-Mail: museumni@nidlink.com. *Dir*, Dorothy Dahlgren
Library Holdings: Bk Vols 750
Publications: Newsletter (quarterly)

C NORTH IDAHO COLLEGE LIBRARY, 1000 W Garden Ave, 83814-2199. SAN 303-5581. Tel: 208-769-3355. FAX: 208-769-3428. Web Site: www.nic.edu. *Cat*, Ann T Johnston; *Ref*, David Remington; *Publ Servs*, Denise Clark; E-Mail: denise_clark@nic.edu; *Acq, Coll Develop*, Jill Jascha; Staff 6 (MLS 6)
Founded 1933. Enrl 3,500
Library Holdings: Bk Titles 60,000; Per Subs 500
Special Collections: Pacific Northwest History & Indian Affairs (Special Coll & Veeder Coll)
Automation Activity & Vendor Info: (Acquisitions) CARL; (Circulation) CARL; (Serials) CARL
Partic in Coop Libr Agency for Syst & Servs; OCLC; OCLC Online Computer Library Center, Inc

COTTONWOOD

S NORTH IDAHO CORRECTIONAL INSTITUTION LIBRARY, Star Rte 3, Box 147, 83522. Tel: 208-962-3276, Ext 358. *Librn*, Patty Green
Library Holdings: Bk Vols 1,000; Bk Titles 500; Per Subs 50

COUNCIL

P COUNCIL DISTRICT LIBRARY, 104 California, PO Box E, 83612-0804. SAN 303-5611. Tel: 208-253-6004. E-Mail: cvfl@ctcweb.net. Web Site: wwwcvfl.cyberhighway.net. *Librn*, Patty Gross
Circ 36,000
Library Holdings: Bk Vols 20,000
Special Services for the Blind - Bks on tape
Friends of the Library Group

DOWNEY

P DOWNEY PUBLIC LIBRARY,* 18 N Main St, PO Box D, 83234. SAN 303-562X. Tel: 208-897-5270. FAX: 208-897-5270. *Dir*, Marcy Price; *Bkmobile Coordr*, Trudy Fullmer
Library Holdings: Bk Titles 32,000; Per Subs 70
Open Mon 10-2, Tues-Fri 1-5 & Sat 10-2
Friends of the Library Group

DUBOIS

P CLARK COUNTY DISTRICT LIBRARY, 160 Main St, PO Box 67, 83423-0067. SAN 303-5638. Tel: 208-374-5267. E-Mail: iddu@dcdi.net. *Librn*, Norma Jorgensen
Pop 979; Circ 4,969
Library Holdings: Bk Titles 9,000
Open 3:30-5:30, summer 2-6

G UNITED STATES DEPARTMENT OF AGRICULTURE, Sheep Experiment Station Library, HC 62 Box 2010, 83423. SAN 373-0441. Tel: 208-374-5306. FAX: 208-374-5582. Web Site: pwa.ars.usda.gov/usses. *In Charge*, Mary Edwards; E-Mail: medwards@pwa.ars.usda.gov

EAGLE

P EAGLE PUBLIC LIBRARY,* 100 N Stierman Way, 83616-5162. SAN 303-5646. Tel: 208-939-6814. FAX: 208-939-1359. E-Mail: eaglib@hotmail.com. *Dir*, Ann Gallinger
Founded 1969. Pop 3,360; Circ 19,228
Oct 1998-Sep 1999 Income $429,044. Mats Exp $153,000. Sal $203,019
Library Holdings: Bk Titles 16,000; Per Subs 40
Friends of the Library Group

ELK CITY

§P ELK CITY COMMUNITY LIBRARY, PO Box 419, 83525. Tel: 208-842-2218. FAX: 208-842-2218. *Librn*, Renny Parker
Library Holdings: Bk Vols 1,000
Automation Activity & Vendor Info: (Acquisitions) Follett; (Cataloging) Follett; (Circulation) Follett

ELK RIVER

P ELK RIVER FREE LIBRARY DISTRICT,* 203 Main St, PO Box 187, 83827-0187. SAN 321-0294. Tel: 208-826-3539. E-Mail: elkr.library@turbonet.com. *Librn*, Sue Ellison
Pop 265; Circ 2,872
Library Holdings: Bk Vols 8,000
Mem of N Cent Idaho Regional Libr Syst

EMMETT

P EMMETT PUBLIC LIBRARY,* 275 S Hayes, 83617-2972. SAN 303-5654. Tel: 208-365-6057. FAX: 208-365-6057. *Librn*, Marsha Werle
Founded 1924. Pop 4,556; Circ 53,178
Library Holdings: Bk Vols 55,000; Per Subs 39
Friends of the Library Group

FAIRFIELD

P CAMAS COUNTY DISTRICT LIBRARY, Camas Ave, PO Box 292, 83327. SAN 303-5662. Tel: 208-764-2553. E-Mail: camaslib@aol.com. *Librn*, Marilyn Ballard; *Asst Librn*, Faye Butler
Pop 859
Library Holdings: Bk Titles 7,182; Per Subs 30
Mem of Magic Valley Libr Syst

FERNWOOD

P BENEWAH COUNTY DISTRICT LIBRARY, Tri Community Branch, 46 Isaacson St, PO Box 157, 83830-0157. SAN 377-4104. Tel: 208-245-4883. FAX: 208-245-0129. E-Mail: readers@nidlink.com. *Librn*, JoAnne O'Dwyer
Library Holdings: Bk Vols 18,500
Partic in Am Libr Asn

FILER

P FILER PUBLIC LIBRARY,* 219 Main St, PO Box 52, 83328-0052. SAN 303-5670. Tel: 208-326-4143. *Librn*, Margaret Holley
Pop 1,850; Circ 13,567
Library Holdings: Bk Vols 11,351
Subject Interests: Idaho
Special Collections: Local History Archives
Open Mon-Tues & Thurs 3:30-6:30pm & Wed & Fri 2:30-6:30pm

FORT HALL

P SHOSHONE-BANNOCK LIBRARY, Fort Hall Library, PO Box 306, 83203-0306. SAN 303-5689. Tel: 208-238-3700. *Dir*, Ardith Peyope
Circ 18,169
Library Holdings: Bk Titles 6,000
Subject Interests: Indians
Mem of Gateway Regional Libr Syst

GARDEN CITY

P GARDEN CITY LIBRARY, 201 E 50th, 83714-1429. SAN 303-5360. Tel: 208-472-2940, 208-472-2999. E-Mail: gclnet@primenet.com. Web Site: www.gardencitylibrary.org. *Dir*, Heather Clark; Staff 8 (Non-MLS 8)
Founded 1962. Pop 9,000
Library Holdings: Bk Titles 27,000
Subject Interests: Children's literature, Fiction, Idaho, Large type print, Nonfiction
Database Vendor: Ebsco - EbscoHost, GaleNet
Partic in OCLC
Special Services - Preschool storytimes birth-K; summer reading programs; family literacy pilot project; 2 GED classes; adult book discussions; Host: IRS help; homework help

GARDEN VALLEY

P GARDEN VALLEY DISTRICT LIBRARY,* 342 Village Circle, 83622-8040. SAN 303-5697. Tel: 208-462-3317. FAX: 208-462-3758. E-Mail: grdnvaly@micron.net. Web Site: www.lili.org/gardenvalley. *Dir*, Stephaney Williamson; E-Mail: swgvlib@micron.net; *Ch Servs*, Kathy Smith; *Circ*, Marian Edinger; *Circ*, Mary Powell; Staff 5 (Non-MLS 5)
Pop 1,600; Circ 4,200
Oct 1999-Sep 2000 Income (Main Library Only) $74,915, County $50,880, Other $24,035. Mats Exp Books $5,000. Sal $39,028
Library Holdings: Bk Titles 14,300; Bks on Deafness & Sign Lang 10
Special Collections: Idaho History
Database Vendor: Ebsco - EbscoHost, IAC - Info Trac
Friends of the Library Group

GLENNS FERRY

P GLENNS FERRY PUBLIC LIBRARY, 204 E Second, PO Box 910, 83623-0910. SAN 303-5719. Tel: 208-366-7418. FAX: 208-366-2238. E-Mail: libraryg@cyberhighway.net. *Dir*, Pat Morris; Staff 1 (Non-MLS 1)
Founded 1930. Pop 1,500; Circ 13,000
Library Holdings: Bk Vols 11,000
Subject Interests: Large print
Special Collections: Christian Fiction
Function: ILL available
Mem of Gateway Regional Libr Syst

GOODING

P GOODING PUBLIC LIBRARY, 306 Fifth Ave W, 83330-1205. SAN 303-5727. Tel: 208-934-4089. FAX: 208-934-4089. *Dir*, Pat A Hamilton; *Ch Servs*, Carolyn DeWitt
Founded 1910. Pop 3,230; Circ 24,100
Sep 1999-Aug 2000 Income $60,200. Mats Exp $8,900, Books $6,500, Per/Ser (Incl. Access Fees) $900, AV Equip $800, Electronic Ref Mat (Incl. Access Fees) $700. Sal $34,800
Library Holdings: Bk Vols 20,680; Per Subs 66
Subject Interests: Idaho
Automation Activity & Vendor Info: (Circulation) Sagebrush Corporation

§P IDAHO SCHOOL FOR THE DEAF & BLIND LIBRARY, 1450 Main St, 83330. Tel: 208-934-4457. FAX: 208-934-8352. *Librn*, Shirley Cobble; Tel: 208-934-4457, Ext 341, E-Mail: scobble@isdh.state.id.us
Library Holdings: Bk Vols 30,000; Bks on Deafness & Sign Lang 2,000
Automation Activity & Vendor Info: (Acquisitions) Follett; (Cataloging) Follett; (Circulation) Follett

GRACE

P GRACE DISTRICT LIBRARY, 204 S Main, PO Box B, 83241-0200. SAN 303-5735. Tel: 208-425-3695. FAX: 208-425-3695. E-Mail: gracelib@hotmail.com. *Librn*, Linda Rasmussen; *Asst Librn*, Margo May
Founded 1941. Pop 2,436; Circ 45,402
1999-2000 Income $42,222, County $38,222, Locally Generated Income $4,000. Mats Exp $9,000, Books $8,540, Per/Ser (Incl. Access Fees) $460. Sal $19,875
Library Holdings: Bk Titles 18,000; Per Subs 26
Partic in OCLC

GRAND VIEW

P EAST OWYHEE COUNTY LIBRARY DISTRICT,* 520 Boise Ave, PO Box 100, 83624. SAN 303-5743. Tel: 208-834-2785. FAX: 208-834-2785. *Asst Dir*, Carol Anselment; *Librn*, Kathy Chick
Founded 1974. Pop 5,000
Library Holdings: Bk Vols 12,000; Per Subs 30

GRANGEVILLE

P GRANGEVILLE CENTENNIAL LIBRARY, 215 W North, 83530-1729. SAN 303-5751. Tel: 208-983-0951. FAX: 208-983-2336. E-Mail: granglib@camasnet.com. *Dir*, Linda Ruthruff; E-Mail: llruthruff@yahoo.com; *Acq*, Marge Pelham; E-Mail: margyp@hotmail.com
Founded 1899. Pop 3,200; Circ 32,328
Oct 1998-Sep 1999 Income $52,557, State $10,351, City $30,339, Locally Generated Income $3,805, Other $8,062. Mats Exp $39,412, Books $7,255, Per/Ser (Incl. Access Fees) $790. Sal $19,690
Library Holdings: Bk Titles 13,530; Per Subs 28
Subject Interests: Genealogy
Automation Activity & Vendor Info: (Circulation) Sagebrush Corporation
Database Vendor: Ebsco - EbscoHost, IAC - Info Trac

HAILEY

P HAILEY PUBLIC LIBRARY,* 7 W Croy St, 83333. SAN 303-5778. Tel: 208-788-2036. FAX: 208-788-2924. E-Mail: hplib@micron.net. *Dir*, Ann Tabler; Staff 6 (Non-MLS 6)
Founded 1919. Pop 5,500; Circ 50,500
Oct 1999-Sep 2000 Income $221,172. Sal $180,677
Library Holdings: Bk Vols 23,232; Bk Titles 22,454; Per Subs 50
Subject Interests: Idaho
Special Collections: Mallory Photo Coll - Historical Photographs of Wood River Valley
Database Vendor: Ebsco - EbscoHost, epixtech, inc., IAC - Info Trac, OCLC - First Search
Mem of Magic Valley Libr Syst
Partic in Lynx
Friends of the Library Group

HAMER

P HAMER BRANCH, Jefferson County District Library, 2450 E 2100 North, PO Box 240, 83425-9999. SAN 303-5786. Tel: 208-662-5275. FAX: 208-662-5213. E-Mail: jldham@dcd.net, jldham@directinter.net. *Coll Develop, Dir*, Ethel R Vadnais; *Asst Librn*, Rose Dixon
Founded 1972. Pop 800
Library Holdings: Bk Titles 15,000; Per Subs 20
Publications: Sands of Time - Desert in Bloom
Mem of Eastern Idaho Regional Libr Syst
Partic in OCLC
Friends of the Library Group

HANSEN

P HANSEN DISTRICT LIBRARY, 120 Maple Ave W, 83334-4975. (Mail add: PO Box 150, 83334-0150), SAN 303-5794. Tel: 208-423-4122. E-Mail: hanlib@micron.net. *Dir*, Linda Oatman; *Dep Dir*, Helen McCord
Founded 1975. Pop 2,600
Oct 1999-Sep 2000 Income $32,731, County $25,614, Locally Generated Income $7,117. Mats Exp $7,315, Books $7,080, Electronic Ref Mat (Incl. Access Fees) $235. Sal $11,414
Library Holdings: Bk Vols 11,058; Per Subs 21
Mem of Magic Valley Libr Syst

HAYDEN

P KOOTENAI-SHOSHONE AREAS LIBRARY, Hayden Branch, 8385 N Government Way, 83835-9280. SAN 303-5816. Tel: 208-772-5612. FAX: 208-772-2498. E-Mail: hay@cin.kcl.org. Web Site: www.nicon.org/ksal. *Dir*, John Hartung; Tel: 208-772-5612, Ext 16, E-Mail: jhartung@cin.kcl.org; *Dir*, Lee Starr
Founded 1976. Pop 63,700; Circ 400,000
Oct 2000-Sep 2001 Income (Main Library and Branch Library) $1,459,990, State $41,200, Federal $8,721, Locally Generated Income $1,410,069. Mats Exp Books $104,858. Sal $627,482
Library Holdings: Bk Vols 103,400; Per Subs 175
Special Collections: North Idaho Genealogical Materials; North Idaho Land Surveyors Materials
Automation Activity & Vendor Info: (Cataloging) SIRSI
Database Vendor: Ebsco - EbscoHost, IAC - Info Trac
Partic in Cooperative Information Network
Friends of the Library Group
Branches: 5
ATHOL BRANCH, PO Box 70, Athol, 83801. SAN 328-2228. Tel: 208-683-2979. FAX: 208-683-2979. E-Mail: abook@cin.kcl.org. *Mgr*, Sue Wagner
Friends of the Library Group
HARRISON PUBLIC, PO Box 169, Harrison, 83833-0169. SAN 303-5808. Tel: 208-689-3976. FAX: 208-689-3976. *Mgr*, Elaine DeSautel
Pop 305; Circ 6,873
Library Holdings: Bk Vols 5,400
Mem of Panhandle Library System
PINEHURST-KINGSTON BRANCH, PO Box 634, Pinehurst, 83850-0634. SAN 303-6251. Tel: 208-682-3483. FAX: 208-682-3483. E-Mail: pklib@cin.kcl.org. *Mgr*, Cheri Breidt
RATHDRUM BRANCH, PO Box 7, Rathdrum, 83858-0007. SAN 303-6359. Tel: 208-687-1029. FAX: 208-687-1029. E-Mail: bookstop@cin.kcl.org. *Mgr*, Sandy Burnett
Friends of the Library Group
SPIRIT LAKE BRANCH, PO Box 186, Spirit Lake, 83869-0186. SAN 328-2260. Tel: 208-623-5353. FAX: 208-623-5353. E-Mail: spirit@cin.kcl.org. *Mgr*, Karen Flohr
Friends of the Library Group
Bookmobiles: 1. Mgr, Twylla Rehder. Tel: 208-772-7648; Fax: 208-772-2498; Elec Mail: mobile@cin.kcl.org

HOMEDALE

P HOMEDALE PUBLIC LIBRARY,* 125 W Owyhee, PO Box 1087, 83628-1087. SAN 303-5824. Tel: 208-337-4228. FAX: 208-337-4228. *Dir*, Margaret Fujishin
Pop 1,963; Circ 12,504
Library Holdings: Bk Vols 9,065; Per Subs 13

HORSESHOE BEND

P HORSESHOE BEND DISTRICT LIBRARY, 392 Hwy 55, 83629-9701. SAN 303-5832. Tel: 208-793-2460. *Librn*, June Brown; *Asst Librn*, Teresa Cooper
Founded 1917
Library Holdings: Bk Vols 10,463; Per Subs 37
Special Collections: Idaho History Coll
Open Mon-Fri 10-5, Sat 10-12

IDAHO CITY

P BOISE BASIN LIBRARY DISTRICT, 404 Montgomery St, PO Box BL, 83631. SAN 303-5840. Tel: 208-392-4558. FAX: 208-392-4974. Web Site: boisebasin.lib.id.us. *Dir*, Erin McCusker; E-Mail: erinm@boisebasin.lib.id.us; Staff 5 (Non-MLS 5)
Founded 1962. Pop 3,000; Circ 21,009
Sep 1999-Oct 2000 Income $116,912, State $8,812, Federal $2,898, Locally Generated Income $102,680, Other $2,522. Mats Exp Books $7,145. Sal $45,759
Library Holdings: Bk Titles 11,806; Per Subs 48
Special Collections: Boise Basin History Room; History of Idaho City Coll; The Idaho World Coll, photo & micro
Open Tues, Wed & Fri 12-6, Thurs 12-8 & Sat 11-5
Friends of the Library Group
Bookmobiles: 1

IDAHO FALLS

S ARGONNE NATIONAL LABORATORY, Argonne-West Technical Library, PO Box 2528, 83403-2528. SAN 303-5859. Tel: 208-533-7237. FAX: 208-533-7656. *Librn*, Judy Krieger; E-Mail: judy.krieger@anl.gov; Staff 2 (MLS 1, Non-MLS 1)
Founded 1960
Library Holdings: Per Subs 85
Subject Interests: Chemistry, Metallurgy, Nuclear engineering, Nuclear science, Physics
Publications: New Materials List
Partic in Dialog Corporation; OCLC Online Computer Library Center, Inc

S BECHTEL BWXT IDAHO, (Formerly Lockheed Martin Idaho Technologies Company), LLC/INEEL Technical Library & Information Center, 1776 Science Center Dr, MS 2300, 83402. (Mail add: PO Box 1625, 83415-2300), SAN 303-5875. Tel: 208-526-1194. Circulation Tel: 208-526-1185. Reference Tel: 208-526-1682. FAX: 208-526-0211. E-Mail: lib@inel.gov. Web Site: www.inel.gov/resources/library/techlib.htm. *Mgr*, Brent N Jacobsen; Tel: 208-526-1144, E-Mail: bnj@inel.gov; *Ref*, Dave Klepich; *Web Coordr*, Jackie Loop; *Coll Develop*, Sandy Biermann; *ILL*, Tam Ellingford; *Cat*, Heather Redding; *Info Specialist*, Marie Suhre; E-Mail: mhs@inel.gov; *ILL*, Tamera Waldron; *Cat*, Gail Willmore; Staff 17 (MLS 11, Non-MLS 6)
Founded 1951
Library Holdings: Bk Vols 46,600; Bk Titles 38,000; Per Subs 700
Subject Interests: Business and management, Chemistry, Computer science, Electronics, Energy, Engineering, Geosciences, Mathematics, Metallurgy, Nuclear engineering, Nuclear physics, Nuclear science, Occupational safety, Optics, Physics
Special Collections: AEC, ERDA & DOE Reports; DOE Public Reading Room; Standards & Compliance Information; TMI-2 Research & Development Program Files
Database Vendor: CARL, Dialog, Lexis-Nexis, OCLC - First Search
Publications: INEEL Technical Library Journal Holdings (Serials catalog)

M EASTERN IDAHO REGIONAL MEDICAL CENTER, Medical Library,* PO Box 2077, 83403-2077. SAN 320-636X. Tel: 208-529-6077. FAX: 208-529-7014. E-Mail: library@eirmc.org. Web Site: www.eirmc.org. *Dir*, Kathy Nelson
Founded 1950
Library Holdings: Bk Vols 500; Per Subs 140
Subject Interests: Medicine
Special Collections: History of Medicine
Publications: Library News

J EASTERN IDAHO TECHNICAL COLLEGE LIBRARY,* 1600 S 25th E, 83404. SAN 371-8247. Tel: 208-524-3000, Ext 3312. FAX: 208-524-3007. *Librn*, E Suzanne Ricks; E-Mail: suzanner@admin.eitc.edu; Staff 3 (MLS 1, Non-MLS 2)
Founded 1989. Enrl 3,072; Fac 43
Jul 1997-Jun 1998 Income $51,586. Mats Exp $51,000, Books $42,900, Per/Ser (Incl. Access Fees) $8,100. Sal $27,500
Library Holdings: Bk Vols 10,000; Bk Titles 6,000; Per Subs 50; Spec Interest Per Sub 10
Automation Activity & Vendor Info: (Cataloging) Follett; (Circulation) Follett; (OPAC) Follett
Database Vendor: Ebsco - EbscoHost, IAC - Info Trac, Lexis-Nexis
Function: ILL available
Partic in Eastern Idaho Library System

P IDAHO FALLS PUBLIC LIBRARY, 457 Broadway, 83402. SAN 303-5891. Tel: 208-529-1450. Interlibrary Loan Service Tel: 208-529-1467. FAX: 208-529-1467. E-Mail: lfpl@mail.eils.lib.id.us. Web Site: www.eilsls.lib.id.us. *Dir*, Paul Holland; *Asst Dir, Tech Servs*, Rena Ferguson; *Ch Servs*, Brooke Snyder; *Circ*, Esther Schmuland; *ILL*, Madelaine Love; *Ref*, Carol Forker; Staff 5 (MLS 5)
Founded 1909. Pop 79,780; Circ 714,620
Oct 1998-Sep 1999 Income $1,568,050, City $916,750, Federal $7,000, County $325,500, Locally Generated Income $318,800. Mats Exp $257,024, Books $183,396, Per/Ser (Incl. Access Fees) $26,764, Micro $5,400, AV Equip $41,464. Sal $657,466 (Prof $208,208)
Library Holdings: Bk Vols 214,672; Per Subs 301
Special Collections: Local; Vardis Fisher Coll
Automation Activity & Vendor Info: (Circulation) epixtech, inc.
Partic in Eastern Idaho Library System; OCLC Online Computer Library Center, Inc
Open Mon-Thurs 9-9, Fri-Sat 9-5:30 & Sun 1:30-5:30
Friends of the Library Group

JEROME

P JEROME PUBLIC LIBRARY,* 100 First Ave E, 83338-2302. SAN 303-5921. Tel: 208-324-5427. FAX: 208-324-6426. E-Mail: jerpl@magiclink.com. *Librn*, Susan Jacobsen
Founded 1921. Circ 58,083
Library Holdings: Per Subs 31
Special Collections: Idaho History Coll; Large Print Coll
Mem of Magic Valley Libr Syst
Friends of the Library Group

M SAINT BENEDICTS FAMILY MEDICAL CENTER LIBRARY,* 709 N Lincoln Ave, 83338. SAN 371-4292. Tel: 208-324-4301. FAX: 208-324-3878. *Librn*, Karen Fjeld
Library Holdings: Bk Titles 25; Per Subs 10

KELLOGG

P KELLOGG PUBLIC LIBRARY,* 16 W Market Ave, 83837-2499. SAN 303-593X. Tel: 208-786-7231. FAX: 208-784-1100. E-Mail: kpl-ref@rand.nidlink.com. *Dir*, Karen Rumpel; *Asst Librn*, Donna Rude
Pop 2,491; Circ 14,533
Library Holdings: Bk Titles 15,746; Per Subs 31
Open Tues-Sat 12:30-5:30

KETCHUM

P COMMUNITY LIBRARY ASSOCIATION, 415 Spruce Ave N, PO Box 2168, 83340-2168. SAN 303-5948. Tel: 208-726-3493. FAX: 208-726-0756. E-Mail: webspinner@thecommunitylibrary.org. Web Site: www.thecommunitylibrary.org. *Dir*, Ollie Cossman
Founded 1955. Pop 25,000; Circ 110,000
Jan 1999-Dec 1999 Income $1,200,000. Mats Exp $110,500, Books $80,000, Per/Ser (Incl. Access Fees) $8,000, Micro $500, Other Print Mats $22,000. Sal $600,000
Library Holdings: Bk Titles 76,000; Per Subs 175
Special Collections: John Lister Coll of Astrology & Occult Sciences; Sun Valley Ski Coll
Friends of the Library Group
Branches: 2
CHILDREN'S LIBRARY Tel: 208-726-3493. Web Site: www.ketchum.lib.id.us. *Dir*, Ollie Cossman; *Librn*, Sheila Hall
REGIONAL HISTORY DEPARTMENT Tel: 208-726-3493. Web Site: www.ketchum.lib.id.us. *Librn*, Wendy Warren
Founded 1982
Special Collections: Wood River Valley Coll, letters, diaries & docs

KIMBERLY

P KIMBERLY PUBLIC LIBRARY, 120 Madison St W, 83341. (Mail add: PO Box 369, 83341), SAN 303-5956. Tel: 208-423-4556. E-Mail: kimblib@magiclink.com. *Dir*, Helen McCord; Tel: 208-423-4262; Staff 1 (Non-MLS 1)
Founded 1978. Pop 2,500; Circ 13,263
Oct 1999-Sep 2000 Income City $17,000. Mats Exp Books $4,592. Sal $9,571
Library Holdings: Bk Vols 14,040
Special Collections: Idaho Coll; Kipling's Works; Mark Twain Coll; O'Henry Coll; Writings of Abraham Lincoln
Open Mon & Thurs 1-6, Tues 3-8, Sat 10-2

G UNITED STATES DEPARTMENT OF AGRICULTURE, Agricultural Research Service, Northwest Irrigation & Soils Research Lab,* 3793 N 3600 E, 83341. SAN 321-771X. Tel: 208-423-5582. FAX: 208-423-6555.
Library Holdings: Bk Titles 1,800
Subject Interests: Agricultural engineering, Gen agr, Irrigation, Plants, Pollution, Soils, Water

KUNA

P KUNA SCHOOL COMMUNITY LIBRARY,* 457 N Locust, PO Box 129, 83634. SAN 303-5964. Tel: 208-922-1025. FAX: 208-922-1026. *Dir*, Anne Hankins
Founded 1964. Pop 12,000; Circ 101,960
Library Holdings: Bk Vols 40,867; Per Subs 85
Subject Interests: Idaho
Mem of Southwest Regional Library Service System
Friends of the Library Group

LAPWAI

P PRAIRIE-RIVER LIBRARY DISTRICT,* 103 N Main St, PO Box 1200, 83540. SAN 339-6517. Tel: 208-843-7254. FAX: 208-843-7254. *Dir*, Constance I Pentzer; Staff 1 (Non-MLS 1)
Founded 1959. Pop 14,904; Circ 79,641
Oct 1998-Sep 1999 Income County $323,227. Mats Exp $36,150, Books $34,150, Per/Ser (Incl. Access Fees) $2,000. Sal $169,000 (Prof $26,000)
Library Holdings: Bk Vols 76,361; Per Subs 75
Partic in Valnet
Branches: 7
CRAIGMONT COMMUNITY, 112 W Main, Craigmont, 83523-9999. SAN 339-6533. Tel: 208-924-5510. FAX: 208-924-5510. *Librn*, Sandra Riggers
CULDESAC COMMUNITY, 608 Main, Culdesac, 83524-9999. SAN 339-6525. Tel: 208-843-5215. FAX: 208-843-5215. *Librn*, Beverly Gilliam
KAMIAH COMMUNITY, 507 Main, PO Box 846, Kamiah, 83536-0846. SAN 339-6541. Tel: 208-935-0428. FAX: 208-935-0428. *Librn*, Frances A Woods
KOOSKIA COMMUNITY, PO Box 146, Kooskia, 83539. SAN 377-8495. Tel: 208-926-4539. FAX: 208-926-4539. *Librn*, Andrea Busse; *Librn*, Lois Leman
NEZPERCE COMMUNITY, 502 Oak, PO Box 124, Nezperce, 83543. SAN 321-8902. Tel: 208-937-2458. FAX: 208-937-2458. *Librn*, Holly Kraus; Staff 1 (Non-MLS 1)
PECK COMMUNITY, 217 N Main, PO Box 112, Peck, 83545-0112. SAN 339-655X. Tel: 208-486-6161. FAX: 208-486-6161. *Librn*, Virginia North
WINCHESTER COMMUNITY, 413-1/2 Nezperce, Winchester, 83555-0275. (Mail add: PO Box 275, Winchester, 83555-0275), SAN 339-6568. Tel: 208-924-5164. FAX: 208-924-5164. *Librn*, Rosemary McLeod; E-Mail: winclib@cammasnet.com; Staff 1 (MLS 1)
Friends of the Library Group

LEADORE

P LEADORE COMMUNITY LIBRARY, 202 S Railroad St, 83464-5022. (Mail add: PO Box 106, 83464-0106), SAN 303-5972. Tel: 208-768-2640, 208-768-2646. E-Mail: leadorelibrary@salmoninternet.com. *Librn*, Karen Slagg
Founded 1961. Pop 114
Library Holdings: Bk Vols 4,800
Mem of Eastern Regional Libr Syst
Friends of the Library Group

LEWISTON

C LEWIS-CLARK STATE COLLEGE LIBRARY, 500 Eighth Ave, 83501. SAN 303-5980. Tel: 208-792-2236. Circulation Tel: 208-792-2396. FAX: 208-792-2831. Web Site: www.lcsc.edu/library. *Dir*, Paul Krause; E-Mail: pkrause@lcsc.edu; *Coll Develop, Librn*, Chris Ashby; *Librn, Publ Servs*, Susan Niewenhous; *Instrul Serv*, Jennifer Ashby; *ILL, Ser*, Becky Grinolds; *Circ*, Sara Huffman; *Cat*, Shannon Casteel; *Electronic Resources*, Lynne Bidwell; *Ref*, Pam Howard; *Syst Coordr*, David Miyatake; Staff 12 (MLS 6, Non-MLS 6)
Founded 1893. Enrl 2,300; Fac 130; Highest Degree: Bachelor
Jul 1999-Jun 2000 Income $847,262, State $811,548, Locally Generated Income $35,714. Mats Exp $254,561, Books $81,180, Per/Ser (Incl. Access Fees) $145,998, Presv $6,200, Micro $15,600, AV Equip $5,583
Library Holdings: Bk Vols 236,736
Special Collections: Audio-Visual Coll; Children's Literature; Curriculum Library; Pacific Northwest Coll
Automation Activity & Vendor Info: (Acquisitions) Endeavor; (Cataloging) Endeavor; (Circulation) Endeavor; (Course Reserve) Endeavor; (OPAC) Endeavor
Partic in Dialog Corporation; OCLC Online Computer Library Center, Inc; Valnet; Westlaw
Open Mon-Thurs 8-11, Fri 8-7, Sat 9-5 & Sun 1-11

P LEWISTON CITY LIBRARY,* 428 Thain Rd, 83501-5399. SAN 339-6428. Tel: 208-743-6519. FAX: 208-743-6510. E-Mail: lewcitlib@ci.lewiston.id.us. *Dir*, Dawn Hampton; *Tech Servs*, Peggy McElfish; *ILL*, Rose M Hatke; *YA Servs*, Kathy Kestner; Staff 7 (MLS 3, Non-MLS 4)
Founded 1901. Pop 35,000; Circ 120,000
Library Holdings: Bk Vols 75,000; Per Subs 168
Subject Interests: Genealogy, Idaho
Friends of the Library Group
Branches: 1
TSCEMINICUM, 428 Thain Rd, 83501. SAN 339-6487. Tel: 208-743-6519. FAX: 208-743-4446. E-Mail: cityflewiston@ci.lewiston.id.us. *Dir*, Dawn Wittman
Library Holdings: Bk Vols 75,000; Bk Titles 43,500; Per Subs 168
Special Collections: Idaho and Genealogy
Mem of Valnet
Partic in Lewis & Clark Libr Syst; Prairie Libr Network Consortium
Friends of the Library Group

S LEWISTON MORNING TRIBUNE LIBRARY, 505 C St, PO Box 957, 83501. SAN 370-5544. Tel: 208-743-9411, Ext 292. FAX: 208-746-1185. Web Site: www.lmtribune.com. *Librn*, Phyllis Collins; E-Mail: pcollins@lmtribune

L NEZ PERCE COUNTY LAW LIBRARY, Courthouse, 1230 Main, PO Box 896, 83501. SAN 303-5999. Tel: 208-799-3040. FAX: 208-799-3058. E-Mail: lawclerk@co.nezperce.id.us.
Library Holdings: Bk Vols 10,000

MALAD CITY

P ONEIDA COUNTY FREE LIBRARY, 31 N 100 W, PO Box 185, 83252-0194. SAN 303-6049. Tel: 208-766-2229. FAX: 208-766-2229. *Dir*, Yvonne Jensen; E-Mail: jensyvon@m.sd351.k12.id.us; Staff 3 (Non-MLS 3)
Founded 1954. Pop 3,246; Circ 42,407
Oct 1999-Sep 2000 Income County $93,000. Mats Exp $14,000. Sal $98,000
Library Holdings: Bk Titles 24,000; Per Subs 50
Subject Interests: Local history
Open Mon 12-7, Tues & Fri 12-6, Sat 11-2

MARSING

P LIZARD BUTTE DISTRICT LIBRARY,* Owyhee Plaza, Ste 105. (Mail add: PO Box 60, 83639-0060), SAN 325-3058. Tel: 208-896-4690. FAX: 208-896-4472. E-Mail: butte@cyberhighway.net. *Dir, YA Servs*, Tresa Huntley; *Tech Servs, YA Servs*, Olida Poe
Founded 1982. Circ 5,000
Library Holdings: Bk Titles 9,500; Per Subs 18
Open Mon-Fri 12-6

MC CALL

P MCCALL PUBLIC LIBRARY, 218 Park St, PO Box 848, 83638-0848. SAN 303-6030. Tel: 208-634-5522. FAX: 208-634-3038. E-Mail: mccint@ctcweb.com. Web Site: www.mccint@ctcweb.net. *Chief Librn*, Gloria Cantrell; *Asst Librn*, Mary Jane Liberty
Founded 1930. Pop 2,520
Oct 1998-Sep 1999 Income $134,245. Mats Exp $13,000, Books $10,050. Sal $130,325
Library Holdings: Bk Titles 41,000; Per Subs 33
Special Collections: building trades; Idaho History; Nature Studies; Valley County Historical Coll
Mem of Idaho Region 3
Friends of the Library Group

MENAN

P JEFFERSON COUNTY DISTRICT LIBRARY, Menan-Annis Branch, 623 N 3500 E, PO Box 159, 83434-9999. SAN 377-4988. Tel: 208-754-0021. FAX: 208-754-4155. E-Mail: jclmen@srv.net. *Librn*, Norma Eames
Library Holdings: Bk Titles 60,695; Per Subs 50

MERIDIAN

P MERIDIAN DISTRICT LIBRARY,* 1326 W Cherry Lane, 83642. SAN 303-6057. Tel: 208-888-4451. FAX: 208-884-0745. Web Site: www.mld.org. *Dir*, Patricia Younger; E-Mail: director@mld.org; *Circ*, Gayla Pace; *Ch Servs*, Laura Oberbillig; *Ch Servs*, Mae Rodes
Founded 1924. Pop 39,465; Circ 237,880
Library Holdings: Bk Vols 63,665; Per Subs 175
Open Mon-Thurs 9-7:30, Fri 9-6, Sat 10-5
Friends of the Library Group
Branches: 1
OLD TOWN, 18 E Idaho Ave, 83642. Tel: 208-888-3828. FAX: 208-888-3828. *Branch Mgr*, Liz Doe
Automation Activity & Vendor Info: (Acquisitions) epixtech, inc.; (Cataloging) epixtech, inc.; (Circulation) epixtech, inc.; (Course Reserve) epixtech, inc.; (ILL) epixtech, inc.; (Serials) epixtech, inc.

MIDDLETON

P MIDDLETON PUBLIC LIBRARY,* 307 E Main St, PO Box 519, 83644-0519. SAN 303-6065. Tel: 208-585-3931. E-Mail: midlib@micron.net. *Librn*, Elaine Mathiasen
Founded 1960. Pop 2,000

MIDVALE

P MIDVALE DISTRICT LIBRARY, 70 E Bridge St, PO Box 127, 83645-0127. SAN 303-6073. Tel: 208-355-2213. E-Mail: midvlib@ruralnetwork.net. *Dir*, Kay Bonner
Founded 1959. Pop 800; Circ 10,606
Library Holdings: Bk Titles 12,038
Special Collections: Idaho Authors & History, bks & pamphlets
Open Mon-Fri 1-5

MONTPELIER

P BEAR LAKE COUNTY FREE LIBRARY,* 138 N Sixth St, 83254-1556. SAN 303-609X. Tel: 208-847-1664. FAX: 208-847-1664. E-Mail: blkcolib@directinter.net. *Librn*, Mary Nate
Founded 1959. Pop 7,250
Library Holdings: Bk Vols 43,000; Per Subs 153
Automation Activity & Vendor Info: (Circulation) Sagebrush Corporation
Partic in OCLC

MOSCOW

S APPALOOSA MUSEUM LIBRARY, 2720 W Pullman Rd, 83843. SAN 376-0820. Tel: 208-882-5578, Ext 279. FAX: 208-882-8150. E-Mail: director@appaloosamuseum.org. Web Site: www.appaloosamuseum.org. *Curator*, Stacey Garretson
Library Holdings: Bk Titles 400

S LATAH COUNTY HISTORICAL SOCIETY LIBRARY, 327 E Second St, 83843. SAN 303-6103. Tel: 208-882-1004. FAX: 208-882-0759. E-Mail: lchlibrary@moscow.com, lchs@moscow.com. Web Site: www.moscow.com/resources/museums. *Dir*, Mary Reed; *Librn*, Joann Jones
Founded 1968
1998-1999 Income $82,444, State $2,050, City $4,500, Federal $9,867, County $25,000. Mats Exp $213. Sal $27,607
Library Holdings: Bk Titles 450; Per Subs 500
Special Collections: Carol Ryrie Brink Coll (letters, interviews, photos, mss); Historic Preservation Coll; Psychiana Papers; Washington, Idaho & Montana Railroad Paper
Publications: Guide to Historical & Genealogical Records in Latah County; Guide to the Latah County Oral History Collection; Guide to the Local History Library at the Latah County Historical Society; Latah Legacy (quarterly journal of local history); newsletter (quarterly)
Restriction: Not a lending library
Open Tues-Fri 9-5

P LATAH COUNTY LIBRARY DISTRICT, (LCLD), 110 S Jefferson, 83843-2833. SAN 339-6576. Tel: 208-882-3925. FAX: 208-882-5098. Web Site: norby.latah.lib.id.us. *Ad Servs, Dir*, Chris Sokol; *YA Servs*, Janice Wall; *Tech Servs*, Jeannie Haag; *Br Coordr*, Betsy Bybell; *Circ*, Anne Cheadle; Staff 42 (MLS 3, Non-MLS 39)
Founded 1901. Pop 33,500; Circ 340,095
Oct 1998-Sep 1999 Income $682,881, County $613,977, Other $68,904.

Mats Exp $57,588, Books $51,605, Per/Ser (Incl. Access Fees) $5,983. Sal $546,320 (Prof $148,963)
Library Holdings: Bk Vols 99,500; Per Subs 215
Subject Interests: Local history, Science fiction
Friends of the Library Group
Branches: 6
BOVILL BRANCH, PO Box 795, Bovill, 83806-0795. SAN 371-3644. Tel: 208-826-3451. FAX: 208-826-3451. Web Site: drseuss.lib.uidaho.edu/~mpl/bovill.htm. *Librn*, Susan Hotinger
Library Holdings: Bk Vols 2,500
Friends of the Library Group
DEARY BRANCH, PO Box 213, Deary, 83823-0213. SAN 339-6592. Tel: 208-877-1664. FAX: 208-877-1664. Web Site: drseuss.uidaho.lib/~mpl/deary.htm. *Librn*, Susan Hotinger
Library Holdings: Bk Vols 5,000
Friends of the Library Group
GENESEE BRANCH, PO Box 278, Genesee, 83832-0278. SAN 339-6606. Tel: 208-285-1398. FAX: 208-285-1398. Web Site: drseuss.uidaho.edu/~mpl/genesee.htm. *Librn*, Sharon Steiger
Library Holdings: Bk Vols 5,000
Friends of the Library Group
JULIAETTA BRANCH, PO Box 470, Juliaetta, 83535-9999. SAN 339-6630. Tel: 208-276-7071. FAX: 208-276-7071. Web Site: drseuss.lib.uidaho.edu/~mpl/juliaett.htm. *Librn*, Janice Welles
Library Holdings: Bk Vols 5,000
Friends of the Library Group
POTLATCH BRANCH, Pine St, PO Box 335, Potlatch, 83855-0335. SAN 339-6665. Tel: 208-875-1036. FAX: 208-875-1036. Web Site: drseuss.lib.uidaho.edu/~mpl/potlatch.htm. *Librn*, Donna Quiring
Library Holdings: Bk Vols 5,000
Friends of the Library Group
TROY BRANCH, PO Box 477, Troy, 83871-0477. SAN 339-669X. Tel: 208-835-4311. FAX: 208-835-4311. Web Site: drseuss.lib.uidaho.edu/~mpl/troy.htm. *Librn*, Sandy Taylor
Library Holdings: Bk Vols 5,000
Friends of the Library Group

C UNIVERSITY OF IDAHO LIBRARY, Rayburn St, PO Box 442350, 83844-2350. SAN 339-672X. Tel: 208-885-6534. Circulation Tel: 208-885-6559. Reference Tel: 208-885-6584. FAX: 208-885-6817. E-Mail: liberdean@belle.lib.uidaho.edu. Web Site: www.lib.uidaho.edu. *Dean of Libr*, Ronald W Force; E-Mail: rforce@uidaho.edu; *Assoc Dean*, Monte L Steiger; *Circ, ILL*, Lynn Baird; *Acq, Cat, Ser*, Mary K Bolin; *Archivist, Spec Coll*, Terry Abraham; *Head Ref*, Dennis Baird; *Bibliog Instr*, Diane Prorak; *Govt Doc*, Lily Wai; Staff 53 (MLS 20, Non-MLS 33)
Founded 1889. Enrl 11,133; Fac 665; Highest Degree: Doctorate
Jul 1999-Jun 2000 Income (Main Library Only) $4,866,377, State $4,748,761, Other $117,616. Mats Exp $1,946,078, Books $354,071, Per/Ser (Incl. Access Fees) $1,505,699, Presv $55,545, Electronic Ref Mat (Incl. Access Fees) $30,763. Sal $2,296,015 (Prof $840,985)
Library Holdings: Bk Vols 1,092,084; Per Subs 4,380
Special Collections: Ezra Pound Coll; Idaho History, (Day-Northwest); Idaho State Publications; Imprints (Caxton Printers, Idaho); Sir Walter Scott Coll
Database Vendor: CARL, Ebsco - EbscoHost, IAC - Info Trac, Lexis-Nexis, OCLC - First Search, Silverplatter Information Inc.
Publications: Bookmark; Towers
Partic in Inland Northwest Library Automation Network
Special Services for the Blind - Kurzweil Reading Machine
Friends of the Library Group
Departmental Libraries:
CL COLLEGE OF LAW LIBRARY Tel: 208-885-6521. FAX: 208-885-2743. Web Site: www.uidaho.edu/law/library/. *Dir*, John Hasko; *Tech Servs*, Ruth Patterson Funabiki; *Reader Servs*, Joan Pilgram; *AV*, Robert Pikowsky
Founded 1914. Enrl 300; Fac 21; Highest Degree: Doctorate
Jul 1998-Jun 1999 Income $803,385, Federal $21,410, Locally Generated Income $6,314, Parent Institution $775,661. Mats Exp $333,101, Books $22,281, Per/Ser (Incl. Access Fees) $299,425, Presv $5,412, Micro $5,787. Sal $309,750 (Prof $165,375)
Library Holdings: Bk Vols 174,435; Per Subs 2,758
Subject Interests: Natural resources
Special Collections: Idaho Briefs, rec; Selected GPO Documents
Publications: Ad Lib
Partic in Colorado Alliance Of Research Libraries; Dialog Corporation; Westlaw

MOUNTAIN HOME

P MOUNTAIN HOME PUBLIC LIBRARY,* 790 N Tenth E, 83647-2830. SAN 303-6111. Tel: 208-587-4716. E-Mail: lhouse@micron.net. *Dir*, Luise House
Pop 8,533; Circ 39,518
Library Holdings: Bk Vols 32,480; Per Subs 70

MOUNTAIN HOME AFB

UNITED STATES AIR FORCE
A MOUNTAIN HOME AIR FORCE BASE LIBRARY FL4897, 366 SVS/SVMG, 520 Phantom Ave Bldg 2427, 83648-5000. SAN 339-6789. Tel: 208-828-2326. FAX: 208-832-9840. *Librn*, Kim Durr
Founded 1952
Oct 1997-Sep 1998 Income $215,340. Mats Exp $71,090, Books $8,300, Per/Ser (Incl. Access Fees) $20,400, Micro $26,800
Library Holdings: Bk Vols 39,540
Subject Interests: Aeronautics, Idaho, Military history
Publications: Newsletter (quarterly)
Partic in OCLC Online Computer Library Center, Inc
Open Mon-Thurs 9-9, Fri 9-5, Sat & Sun 10-4

MULLAN

P MULLAN PUBLIC LIBRARY,* 117 Hunter Ave, PO Box 479, 83846. SAN 303-612X. Tel: 208-744-1717. FAX: 208-744-1717. E-Mail: mplib@rand.nidlink.com. *Librn*, Kathleen Shook
Founded 1950. Pop 860; Circ 3,207
Library Holdings: Bk Vols 8,000
Open Mon 3-8, Wed & Fri 10-5
Friends of the Library Group

MURPHY

S OWYHEE COUNTY HISTORICAL SOCIETY, Museum & Library Complex,* PO Box 67, 83650-0067. SAN 303-6138. Tel: 208-495-2319. *Dir*, Byron Johnson
Founded 1964
Library Holdings: Bk Titles 1,000; Per Subs 13
Subject Interests: Archaeology, Genealogy, Geology, History, Mining
Special Collections: Newspaper (Owyhee Avalanche, Silver City), micro
Publications: Owyhee Outpost (annual historical book)
Restriction: Open to public for reference only
Friends of the Library Group

NAMPA

M IDAHO STATE SCHOOL & HOSPITAL, Resource Staff Library,* 3100 11th Ave N, 83687-3199. SAN 323-472X. Tel: 208-466-9255. FAX: 208-467-1929. *Dir*, Oscar Morgan
Library Holdings: Bk Vols 250; Per Subs 15
Subject Interests: Education, Pharmacology, Psychology

P NAMPA PUBLIC LIBRARY, 101 11th Ave S, 83651. SAN 303-6146. Tel: 208-465-2263. FAX: 208-465-2277. E-Mail: nampa@mailhost.idaho-lynx.org. Web Site: www.lili.org/nampa. *Dir*, Karen Ganske; *Asst Dir*, Camille Wood; *Ch Servs*, Katy Curl; *Tech Servs*, Marie Kindberg; *Circ*, Jana Brickey; *Ref Serv Ad*, Tammy LeBeau; Staff 4 (MLS 3, Non-MLS 1)
Founded 1904. Pop 50,000; Circ 333,818
Oct 1999-Sep 2000 Income (Main Library Only) $857,000, City $759,000, Locally Generated Income $58,000, Other $40,000. Mats Exp $118,000. Sal $407,000
Library Holdings: Bk Vols 87,280; Per Subs 204
Special Collections: Local History (Northwest Coll), bks, photogs, pamphlets
Automation Activity & Vendor Info: (Acquisitions) epixtech, inc.
Database Vendor: epixtech, inc.
Function: ILL available
Mem of Linx
Partic in Lynx
Friends of the Library Group

NEW MEADOWS

P MEADOWS VALLEY DISTRICT LIBRARY, 400 Virginia St, PO Box 436, 83654-5057. SAN 303-6162. Tel: 208-347-3147. FAX: 208-347-4121. *Dir*, Cheryl Bruce; *Asst Dir*, Deborah Hulse
Founded 1960. Pop 579; Circ 2,225
Library Holdings: Bk Vols 5,000
Partic in Idaho State Libr
Friends of the Library Group

NEW PLYMOUTH

P ARMORAL TUTTLE PUBLIC LIBRARY,* PO Box 158, 83655-0146. SAN 303-6170. Tel: 208-278-5338. FAX: 208-278-5330. *Librn*, Tammy Schlett
Founded 1916. Pop 1,186; Circ 11,810
Library Holdings: Bk Vols 40,000

NOTUS

§P NOTUS PUBLIC LIBRARY, 352 Elgin, PO Box 169, 83656-0169. Tel: 208-454-9097. *Dir*, Renee Taylor
Library Holdings: Bk Vols 12,000

OAKLEY

P OAKLEY LIBRARY DISTRICT,* 125 E Main, 83346. SAN 303-6197. Tel: 208-862-3434. *Librn*, Lynne Boren; *Asst Librn*, Pam Jenks
Founded 1973. Pop 1,800; Circ 8,085
Library Holdings: Bk Vols 9,884
Special Collections: Idaho History
Publications: Dusty Memories; History of the Latter Day Saints Community of Oakley; My Book and Me; The Twin Falls-Oakley Irrigation Project
Mem of Magic Valley Libr Syst

OROFINO

P CLEARWATER MEMORIAL PUBLIC LIBRARY, 402 Michigan Ave, PO Box 471, 83544-0471. SAN 303-6200. Tel: 208-476-3411. FAX: 208-476-4527. *Dir*, Pam McBride; *Asst Dir*, Virginia Rowland; *Ch Servs*, Jennifer Dunaway
Founded 1949. Pop 6,501; Circ 47,371
Library Holdings: Bk Titles 24,000; Per Subs 60
Partic in OCLC
Friends of the Library Group

OSBURN

P OSBURN PUBLIC LIBRARY, 921 E Mullan, PO Box 809, 83849-0809. SAN 303-6219. Tel: 208-752-9711. FAX: 208-753-8585. E-Mail: osburnpubliclibrary@home.com. Web Site: www.osburnlibrary.com. *Librn*, Judy Patrick; *Asst Librn*, Cindy Bachman
Founded 1960. Pop 1,750; Circ 12,331
Oct 1999-Sep 2000 Income $36,000. Mats Exp $4,500. Sal $19,200
Library Holdings: Bk Vols 9,000; Per Subs 35
Special Collections: Newspaper Coll, micro
Open Mon & Wed 12-8, Tues, Thurs & Fri 12-5

PARMA

P PATRICIA ROMANKO PUBLIC LIBRARY,* 121 N Third St, PO Box 309, 83660-0309. SAN 303-6227. Tel: 208-722-6605. E-Mail: patparma@w-idaho.net. *Librn*, Ann Nelson-Adamson
Pop 3,138; Circ 9,614
Library Holdings: Bk Titles 16,405
Subject Interests: Idaho
Partic in Idaho Libr Asn
Open Wed & Fri 12:30-5:30

PAYETTE

P PAYETTE PUBLIC LIBRARY, 24 S Tenth St, 83661-2861. SAN 303-6235. Tel: 208-642-6029. FAX: 208-642-6046. E-Mail: payetlib@primenet.com. *Librn*, Jeannette M Gatchel; Staff 3 (MLS 1, Non-MLS 2)
Founded 1920. Pop 6,170; Circ 36,755
Oct 1999-Sep 2000 Income (Main Library Only) $153,000. Mats Exp $27,500, Books $23,500, Per/Ser (Incl. Access Fees) $4,000. Sal $71,700
Library Holdings: Bk Vols 38,964; Per Subs 93

PIERCE

P PIERCE DISTRICT LIBRARY, 208 S Main St, PO Box 386, 83546-0386. SAN 303-6243. Tel: 208-464-2823. FAX: 208-464-2823. E-Mail: piercepl@clearwater.net. *Dir*, Kim Ward
Founded 1919. Pop 1,000; Circ 13,899
Library Holdings: Bk Titles 14,945; Per Subs 51
Special Collections: Local History Artifacts
Partic in OCLC
Open Mon-Thurs 11am-8pm & Fri 11am-5pm

PLUMMER

§P PLUMMER PUBLIC LIBRARY, 800 D St, 83851. (Mail add: PO Box 309, 83851-0309), Tel: 208-686-1812. FAX: 208-686-1089. *Librn*, Pauline Freeburg
Library Holdings: Bk Vols 13,500; Per Subs 12
Automation Activity & Vendor Info: (Acquisitions) Athena; (Cataloging) Athena; (Circulation) Athena; (ILL) Athena; (OPAC) Athena; (Serials) Athena

POCATELLO

S AMERICAN MICROSYSTEMS INC, Technical Library, 2300 Buckskin Rd, 83201. SAN 373-434X. Tel: 208-233-4690, Ext 6398. FAX: 208-234-6857. *Librn*, Cathy McPherson; E-Mail: cmcphers@amis.com; Staff 1 (Non-MLS 1)
Founded 1975
Jan 2000-Dec 2000 Income Parent Institution $600,000. Mats Exp $580,000, Books $350,000, Per/Ser (Incl. Access Fees) $150,000, Other Print Mats $30,000, Electronic Ref Mat (Incl. Access Fees) $50,000. Sal $35,000
Library Holdings: Bk Vols 4,000; Per Subs 290
Restriction: By appointment only
Partic in Coop Libr Agency for Syst & Servs

S IDAHO MUSEUM OF NATURAL HISTORY LIBRARY, Idaho State Univ, Campus Box 8096, 83209-0009. SAN 303-6286. Tel: 208-282-3168. FAX: 208-282-5893. *Dir*, Dr Skip Lohse
Founded 1934
Library Holdings: Bk Vols 600; Per Subs 275
Subject Interests: Anthropology, Biology
Publications: Tebiwa (Journal of the Idaho Museum of Natural History)

C IDAHO STATE UNIVERSITY, Idaho Health Science Library, 850 S Ninth St, 83209-8089. Tel: 208-282-3104. FAX: 208-282-4895. Web Site: www.isu.edu/Library/ihsl/. *Dir*, Nancy Griffin; E-Mail: griffnanc@isu.edu
Library Holdings: Bk Vols 1,700; Bk Titles 1,500; Per Subs 600

C IDAHO STATE UNIVERSITY, E M Oboler Library, Idaho State University, 850 S Ninth Ave, 83201-5314. (Mail add: PO Box 8089, 83209-8089), SAN 303-6294. Tel: 208-282-2997. Interlibrary Loan Service Tel: 208-282-3127. Circulation Tel: 208-282-5248. FAX: 208-282-4295. Web Site: www.isu.edu/library/. *Librn*, Kay A Flowers; Tel: 208-282-2997, E-Mail: flowkay@isu.edu; *Tech Servs*, Sandra Shropshire; Tel: 208-282-2671, E-Mail: shrosand@isu.edu; *Branch Mgr*, Nancy Griffin; Tel: 208-282-3104, E-Mail: grifnanc@isu.edu; *Spec Coll*, Gary Domitz; Tel: 208-282-3608, E-Mail: domigary@isu.edu; *Coll Develop*, Leonard Hitchcock; Tel: 208-282-3100, E-Mail: hitcleon@isu.edu; *Head Ref*, Jim Jatkevicius; Tel: 208-282-4073, E-Mail: jatkjim@isu.edu; *Instrul Serv*, Rosemarie Fouad; Tel: 208-282-3047, E-Mail: fouarom@isu.edu; *Syst Coordr*, Janet Higgins; Tel: 208-282-2697, E-Mail: higgjane@isu.edu; *Access Serv, Publ Servs*, Larry Murdock; Tel: 208-282-3045, E-Mail: murdlarr@isu.edu; Staff 40 (MLS 15, Non-MLS 25)
Founded 1902. Enrl 13,000; Fac 396; Highest Degree: Doctorate
Jul 1999-Jun 2000 Income $3,968,957, State $3,857,124, Locally Generated Income $111,833. Mats Exp $1,380,220, Books $302,805, Per/Ser (Incl. Access Fees) $986,215, Presv $76,700, Micro $8,000, AV Equip $6,000, Manuscripts & Archives $500. Sal $1,532,950
Library Holdings: Bk Vols 902,932; Per Subs 3,336
Subject Interests: Health sciences
Automation Activity & Vendor Info: (Acquisitions) Endeavor; (Cataloging) Endeavor; (Circulation) Endeavor; (Course Reserve) Endeavor; (ILL) Endeavor; (Media Booking) Endeavor; (OPAC) Endeavor; (Serials) Endeavor
Publications: Between-the-Lines (Newsletter)
Special Services for the Blind - Assistive Technology Center for Persons who are blind or physically handicapped
Friends of the Library Group

P MARSHALL PUBLIC LIBRARY, 113 S Garfield, 83204-5722. SAN 339-6819. Tel: 208-232-1263. FAX: 208-232-9266. Web Site: www.lili.org/marshall. *Ch Servs*, Betty J Holbrook; Tel: 208-232-1263, E-Mail: betty@spidaweb.eils.lib.id.us; *Circ*, Lou Chavers; Tel: 208-232-1263, Ext 30, E-Mail: chavers@spidaweb.eirls.lib.id.us; *ILL*, Kris Castro; Tel: 208-232-1263, Ext 25, E-Mail: kris@spidaweb.eils.lib.id.us; *Head Ref*, Joan Juskie; Tel: 208-232-1263, Ext 25; *Tech Servs*, Joan Shurtliff; Tel: 208-232-1263, Ext 24, E-Mail: ljs@spidaweb.eils.lib.id.us; *YA Servs*, Tammy Bartlett; Tel: 208-232-1263, Ext 28; Staff 10 (MLS 10)
Founded 1905. Pop 50,600; Circ 466,318
Oct 1999-Sep 2000 Income $1,190,276, City $1,155,276, Locally Generated Income $35,000. Mats Exp $141,000, Books $131,000, Per/Ser (Incl. Access Fees) $10,000. Sal $650,397 (Prof $208,000)
Library Holdings: Bk Vols 127,064; Bk Titles 111,984; Per Subs 233
Subject Interests: Idaho
Special Collections: Idaho Coll
Automation Activity & Vendor Info: (Circulation) epixtech, inc.
Mem of Eastern Idaho Regional Libr Syst
Friends of the Library Group

POST FALLS

P POST FALLS PUBLIC LIBRARY, 821 N Spokane St, 83854-9315. SAN 303-6316. Tel: 208-773-1506. FAX: 208-773-1507. E-Mail: pfalls@cin.kcl.org. *Dir*, Joe Reiss; E-Mail: jreiss@cin.kcl.org; Staff 10 (MLS 2, Non-MLS 8)
Founded 1915. Pop 30,000; Circ 170,000
Oct 2000-Sep 2001 Income $352,000, City $300,000, Other $52,000. Mats Exp $60,400, Books $45,000, Per/Ser (Incl. Access Fees) $3,400, Electronic Ref Mat (Incl. Access Fees) $12,000
Library Holdings: Bk Titles 28,000; Per Subs 110

Special Collections: Library of America; Northwest Coll
Automation Activity & Vendor Info: (Circulation) SIRSI
Database Vendor: OCLC - First Search
Open Mon-Thurs 10-8, Fri 10-6, Sat 10-5 & Sun 12-5
Friends of the Library Group

PRESTON

P PRESTON CARNEGIE LIBRARY, 28 E Oneida, 83263-1398. SAN 303-6324. Tel: 208-852-0175. FAX: 208-852-0175. E-Mail: preslib@idacom.net. *Librn*, Cloteele Dahle
Pop 11,000; Circ 90,000
Library Holdings: Bk Vols 36,000; Per Subs 52
Friends of the Library Group

PRIEST RIVER

P PRIEST LAKE LIBRARY,* HCR5 Box 161, 83856. SAN 303-6332. Tel: 208-443-2454. *Librn*, Marcella A Cooper
Founded 1974. Pop 500; Circ 3,628
Library Holdings: Bk Titles 6,000; Per Subs 22
Special Collections: History of Priest Lake
Open Wed 12-5:30, Sat 9-12

P PRIEST RIVER PUBLIC LIBRARY,* 209 High St, PO Box 1047, 83856-1047. SAN 303-6340. Tel: 208-448-2207. FAX: 208-448-0443. E-Mail: prpl@ebcl.lib.id.us. *Librn*, Kathryn Crill
Founded 1927. Pop 1,493; Circ 2,966
Library Holdings: Bk Vols 8,000
Friends of the Library Group

REXBURG

P MADISON DISTRICT LIBRARY, 73 N Center, 83440-1539. SAN 303-6367. Tel: 208-356-3461. FAX: 208-356-6344. *Dir*, Cathleen Peterson; E-Mail: cpete@mail.eils.lib.id.us; *Asst Dir, Cat*, Sharon Nielson; *Ch Servs*, Elaine McFerrin; *Circ, Ref*, Colleen Brewerton; *Tech Servs*, Valerie Stohl; *YA Servs*, Lorna Smith; Staff 6 (MLS 1, Non-MLS 5)
Founded 1920. Pop 15,000; Circ 133,468
Library Holdings: Bk Titles 45,000; Per Subs 115
Subject Interests: Idaho

M MADISON MEMORIAL HOSPITAL, Medical Library, 450 E Main St, 83440-2048. (Mail add: PO Box 310, 83440-0310), SAN 328-4069. Tel: 208-356-3691. FAX: 208-359-6454. Web Site: www.madisonhospital.org. *Dir*, Robert A Tietjen; E-Mail: rtietjen@madisonhospital.org; *Librn*, Teresa Murdock; E-Mail: tmurdock@madisonhospital.org
Library Holdings: Bk Titles 200; Per Subs 50
Partic in Idaho Health Information Association; SE Idaho Health Info Consortium

C RICKS COLLEGE LIBRARY, 525 S Center St, 83460-0405. SAN 303-6375. Tel: 208-356-2354. Interlibrary Loan Service Tel: 208-356-2357. Circulation Tel: 208-356-2360. Reference Tel: 208-356-2351. FAX: 208-356-2390. E-Mail: liaut@ricks.edu. Web Site: www.ricks.edu. *Dir*, Thomas Liau; *Circ*, Sam Nielson; *Govt Doc, Ref*, Shane Cole; *ILL*, Shirley Calder; *Online Servs*, Mathew Miles; *Publ Servs*, David Butler; *Ref*, Marcia Alldredge; *Ref*, Carolyn Roberts; *Spec Coll*, Blaine Bake; *Syst Coordr*, Bruce Bills; *Head Tech Servs*, Brooks Haderie; *Tech Servs*, Gale Reeser
Founded 1888. Enrl 8,600; Fac 370; Highest Degree: Associate
Jan 2000-Dec 2000 Income $2,200,000. Mats Exp $709,623, Books $286,000, Per/Ser (Incl. Access Fees) $87,661, Presv $5,962, Micro $20,000, AV Equip $250,000, Electronic Ref Mat (Incl. Access Fees) $60,000. Sal $1,081,202
Library Holdings: Bk Vols 185,500; Bk Titles 174,243; Per Subs 847
Subject Interests: Genealogy
Special Collections: Idaho History; Mormon Church Coll
Automation Activity & Vendor Info: (Acquisitions) epixtech, inc.; (Cataloging) epixtech, inc.; (Circulation) epixtech, inc.; (Course Reserve) epixtech, inc.; (Media Booking) epixtech, inc.; (OPAC) epixtech, inc.; (Serials) epixtech, inc.
Partic in Dialog Corporation; Medline; OCLC Online Computer Library Center, Inc

S UPPER SNAKE RIVER HISTORICAL SOCIETY LIBRARY, 51 N Center, 83440. (Mail add: PO Box 244, 83440), SAN 329-0174. Tel: 208-356-9101. E-Mail: dhc@srv.net. *Librn*, Bonnie Curtis; *Cat*, Louis Clements
Founded 1964
Library Holdings: Bk Titles 1,361; Per Subs 27
Subject Interests: Local history
Open winter Mon, Wed & Fri 11-2, summer (May-Sept) Mon-Fri 10-5, Sat 10-5 (June, July & Aug)

RICHFIELD

P RICHFIELD DISTRICT LIBRARY,* PO Box 146, 83349-0146. SAN 303-6383. Tel: 208-487-1242. *Librn*, Mary Luff
Pop 735; Circ 3,373
Library Holdings: Bk Vols 6,763
Mem of Magic Valley Libr Syst

RIGBY

P RIGBY PUBLIC LIBRARY, 110 N State St, PO Box 328, 83442-1313. SAN 303-6391. Tel: 208-745-8231. FAX: 208-745-8231. E-Mail: rcity1@ida.net. *Librn*, Marilynn Kamoe; *Asst Dir*, Bari Trost
Founded 1948. Pop 3,000; Circ 25,419
Library Holdings: Bk Vols 22,000; Per Subs 23
Partic in ILA
Open Mon-Fri 1-5, Wed 1-7, Sat 2-5

RIGGINS

§P SALMON RIVER PUBLIC LIBRARY, 236 N Main, 83549. (Mail add: PO Box 249, 83549-0249), Tel: 208-628-3394. FAX: 208-628-3792. E-Mail: srplinfo@cyberhighway.net. Web Site: www.salmonriverlibrary.tripod.com/home.html. *Librn*, Sue Logue; *Librn*, Georgia Slichter
Library Holdings: Bk Vols 11,000

ROBERTS

§P ROBERTS PUBLIC LIBRARY, 659 N 2870 East, PO Box 305, 83444-0305. Tel: 208-228-2210. FAX: 208-228-2585. *Librn*, Lee Karlinsey
Library Holdings: Bk Vols 4,000
Automation Activity & Vendor Info: (Acquisitions) Sagebrush Corporation; (Cataloging) Sagebrush Corporation; (Circulation) Sagebrush Corporation

ROCKLAND

P ROCKLAND SCHOOL COMMUNITY LIBRARY,* E Fork Rd, PO Box 119, 83271-0119. SAN 303-6405. Tel: 208-548-2222. FAX: 208-548-2549. *Librn*, Margene Tomkinson; E-Mail: margenet@rbulldogs.org
Founded 1974. Pop 650; Circ 13,400
Sep 1997-Aug 1998 Income $30,299. Mats Exp $2,455. Sal $20,920 (Prof $10,222)
Library Holdings: Bk Vols 11,000; Per Subs 33
Mem of Gateway Regional Libr Syst

RUPERT

P DEMARY MEMORIAL LIBRARY,* 417 Seventh St, 83350-1692. SAN 303-6413. Tel: 208-436-3874. *Librn*, Joan Falkner; *Cat*, Miriam Becker; *Circ*, Tessie Fowler
Pop 5,000; Circ 47,218
Library Holdings: Bk Vols 41,000; Per Subs 47
Special Collections: Idaho Coll; Large Print; Local Archives
Mem of Magic Valley Libr Syst
Open Mon, Tues, Thurs & Fri 11-7, Sat 12-4

SAINT ANTHONY

P SAINT ANTHONY PUBLIC LIBRARY,* 110 W Main, 83445-2115. SAN 303-6421. Tel: 208-624-3192. FAX: 208-624-3192. E-Mail: library@fretel.com. *Dir, YA Servs*, Brian Stanton, Jr
Founded 1920. Pop 3,182; Circ 47,924
Library Holdings: Bk Vols 29,000; Per Subs 38

SAINT MARIES

P SAINT MARIES PUBLIC LIBRARY,* 822 College, 83861-1720. SAN 303-643X. Tel: 208-245-3732. FAX: 208-245-7102. E-Mail: smlibrary@stmaries.com. *Librn*, Mikell Mowreader; *Asst Librn*, Leslee Adams
Pop 2,872; Circ 23,811
Library Holdings: Bk Vols 24,000; Per Subs 26

SALMON

G BUREAU OF LAND MANAGEMENT, Salmon District Office Library,* RR 2, Box 610, 83467. SAN 303-6448. Tel: 208-756-5400. FAX: 208-756-5436. *Librn*, Lori Bjorklund
Library Holdings: Bk Vols 374; Per Subs 32
Open Mon-Fri 7:45-4:15

P SALMON PUBLIC LIBRARY, 204 Main St, 83467-4111. SAN 303-6456. Tel: 208-756-2311. *Librn*, Ramona Stauffer; Staff 1 (Non-MLS 1)
Founded 1916. Pop 8,081; Circ 52,020

1999-2000 Income $126,101. Mats Exp $19,400, Books $17,000, Per/Ser (Incl. Access Fees) $2,400. Sal $48,000 (Prof $22,000)
Library Holdings: Bk Vols 22,151; Per Subs 50
Special Collections: Idaho Territorial & State Census Coll (1870-1910), microfilm; Lemhi Indian Agency Records, microfilm; Local Newspaper Coll (1882-1994), microfilm
Automation Activity & Vendor Info: (Circulation) Sagebrush Corporation
Publications: History of Lemhi County
Partic in OCLC; OCLC Online Computer Library Center, Inc

M STEELE MEMORIAL HOSPITAL, Medical Library,* PO Box 700, 83467. SAN 328-7475. Tel: 208-756-4291. FAX: 208-756-4169. *Librn*, Irene U Reinhold
Library Holdings: Bk Vols 400; Per Subs 780
Partic in Health Info Retrieval Servs

SANDPOINT

S BONNER COUNTY HISTORICAL SOCIETY, Research Library, 611 S Ella St, 83864. SAN 323-5378. Tel: 208-263-2344. *Pres*, John Hunt; Tel: 208-265-9102
Founded 1972
Library Holdings: Bk Titles 500
Subject Interests: Family hist, Idaho
Special Collections: Bonner County newspapers, 1891-present; Bonner County School Records, historic photos
Publications: "Beautiful Bonner," History of Bonner County, Idaho; "Morton Memories," History of Morton Community, Bonner County, Idaho
Open to the general public Tues & Thurs only (or by appointment)

-§M BONNER GENERAL HOSPITAL, Medical Library, PO Box 1448, 83864. Tel: 208-263-1441. FAX: 208-265-1266. E-Mail: bghhealthinfo@bonnergen.org. *Librn*, Katie Stevens
Library Holdings: Bk Vols 200; Bk Titles 50

P EAST BONNER COUNTY FREE LIBRARY DISTRICT,* 419 N Second Ave, 83864-1590. SAN 303-6464. Tel: 208-263-6930. FAX: 208-263-8320. *Coll Develop, Dir*, Wayne Gunter; Tel: 208-263-6930, Ext 208, E-Mail: wayne@ebcl.lib.id.us; *Tech Servs*, Gloria Ray; Tel: 208-263-6930, Ext 204, E-Mail: gloria@ebcl.lib.id.us; *YA Servs*, Tria Titus; Tel: 208-263-6930, Ext 211, E-Mail: tria@ebcl.lib.id.us; *Cat*, Kate Walton; Tel: 208-263-6930, Ext 502, E-Mail: kate@ebcl.lib.id.us; *Circ*, Susan McNutt; Tel: 208-263-6930, E-Mail: sue@ebcl.lib.id.us; Staff 3 (MLS 3)
Founded 1912. Pop 28,500; Circ 281,119
Oct 1998-Sep 1999 Income $1,593,416. Mats Exp $114,229. Sal $727,317
Library Holdings: Bk Vols 69,583; Per Subs 175
Special Collections: Pacific Northwest (Northwest Coll)
Publications: Newsletter
Partic in OCLC
Branches: 2
CLARK FORK BRANCH, 601 Main St, Clark Fork, 83811. SAN 328-6991. Tel: 208-266-1321. FAX: 208-266-1663. Web Site: ebcl.lib.id.us/ebcl/. *Br Coordr*, Diane Newcomer
Library Holdings: Bk Vols 8,000; Bks on Deafness & Sign Lang 20
Automation Activity & Vendor Info: (Cataloging) Bestseller
Function: Internet access
Friends of the Library Group
EDGEMERE, Edgemere Grange, No 355, 3273 Brancy Rd, Priest River, 83856. SAN 378-2069. Tel: 208-255-4830. FAX: 208-263-9312. *Dir*, Wayne Gunter; *Branch Mgr*, Robyn Ward
Library Holdings: Bk Vols 900
Open Fri 11-7 only
Friends of the Library Group

SHELLEY

P NORTH BINGHAM COUNTY DISTRICT LIBRARY, 197 W Locust St, 83274-1139. SAN 303-6472. Tel: 208-357-7801. FAX: 208-357-2272. Web Site: www.lili.org. *Librn*, Heidi Riddoch; E-Mail: heidir@ida.net; Staff 1 (Non-MLS 1)
Pop 9,438; Circ 150,000
2000-2000 Income (Main Library Only) $185,700, City $156,780. Mats Exp $27,000. Sal $70,000
Library Holdings: Bk Vols 34,000
Subject Interests: Local history
Automation Activity & Vendor Info: (Cataloging) Sagebrush Corporation
Friends of the Library Group

SHOSHONE

G BUREAU OF LAND MANAGEMENT, Shoshone District Library,* 400 West F St, PO Box 2B, 83352. SAN 303-6480. Tel: 208-886-2206. FAX: 208-886-7317. *Librn*, Kimberly Salvador
Library Holdings: Bk Titles 116; Per Subs 7

P SHOSHONE PUBLIC LIBRARY, (SPL), 211 S Rail St, 83352-0236. (Mail add: PO Box 236, 83352-0236), SAN 303-6499. Tel: 208-886-2426. FAX: 208-886-2426. E-Mail: sholib@magiclink.com. *Dir, Librn*, Pat Hamilton; *Asst Librn*, Laurie Cole; Staff 3 (MLS 1, Non-MLS 2)
Pop 2,312; Circ 22,678
Library Holdings: Bk Vols 15,000; Bk Titles 12,000; Per Subs 34; Bks on Deafness & Sign Lang 10
Subject Interests: Popular mat
Special Collections: Idaho History
Mem of Magic Valley Libr Syst
Open Mon, Tues & Fri 12-5, Wed 12-8, Thurs 11-4

SODA SPRINGS

P SODA SPRINGS PUBLIC LIBRARY, 149 S Main, 83276-1496. SAN 303-6502. Tel: 208-547-2606. E-Mail: sspl@cyberhighway.net. Web Site: www.sspl@dcdi.net. *Librn*, Val Ahmann; Staff 2 (Non-MLS 2)
Founded 1951. Pop 3,600; Circ 51,000
Oct 1999-Sep 2000 Income (Main Library Only) City $130,000. Mats Exp $20,200, Books $17,000, Per/Ser (Incl. Access Fees) $1,200, Electronic Ref Mat (Incl. Access Fees) $2,000. Sal $50,000
Library Holdings: Bk Vols 25,908; Per Subs 70; High Interest/Low Vocabulary Bk Vols 25; Bks on Deafness & Sign Lang 12
Subject Interests: Idaho
Special Collections: Idaho History (Southeast Idaho-especially Caribou County); Literature (Vardis Fisher Coll); Oregon Trail Newspapers (Caribou County Sun)
Automation Activity & Vendor Info: (Cataloging) Sagebrush Corporation; (Circulation) Sagebrush Corporation
Mem of Gateway Region V; WLN
Partic in Eastern Idaho Library System
Open Mon-Wed 11-8:30 & Thurs & Fri 11-5

SPALDING

S NEZ PERCE NATIONAL HISTORICAL PARK, (Formerly US National Park Service Nez Perce Park Library), Research Center, Rte 1 Box 100, 83540. SAN 370-307X. Tel: 208-843-2261, Ext 142. FAX: 208-843-2124. *Archivist, Librn*, Robert Applegate; E-Mail: robert_applegate@nps.gov; *Curator*, Robert Chenoweth
Library Holdings: Bk Vols 3,000; Per Subs 20
Subject Interests: Culture, History, Nez Perce Indians
Special Collections: Historical Photo Coll
Restriction: By appointment only

SUGAR CITY

P SUGAR-SALEM SCHOOL COMMUNITY LIBRARY, One Digger Dr, 83448-9999. SAN 303-6529. Tel: 208-356-0271. FAX: 208-359-3167. *Media Spec*, Sheila Jeppson; E-Mail: sheilaj@mail.sd322.k12.id.us
Library Holdings: Bk Vols 21,257; Per Subs 67
Mem of Eastern Idaho Regional Libr Syst
Friends of the Library Group

TERRETON

P JEFFERSON COUNTY DISTRICT LIBRARY, Heart of Valley Branch, PO Box 45, 83450. SAN 377-5429. Tel: 208-663-4834. FAX: 208-663-4834. E-Mail: hvpl@directinter.net. *Librn*, Elaine Davies
Library Holdings: Bk Vols 19,000; Per Subs 27
Friends of the Library Group

TWIN FALLS

C COLLEGE OF SOUTHERN IDAHO LIBRARY, 315 Falls Ave, 83303-3367. SAN 303-6545. Tel: 208-733-9554, Ext 2500. FAX: 208-736-3087. Web Site: www.library.csi.edu. *Dir*, William Beale; *Online Servs, Ref*, Stephen Poppino; Tel: 208-733-9554, Ext 2504, E-Mail: spoppino@csi.edu; Staff 2 (MLS 2)
Founded 1965. Enrl 3,066; Fac 144; Highest Degree: Associate
Jul 1998-Jun 1999 Income $522,145
Library Holdings: Bk Vols 60,692; Bk Titles 53,209; Per Subs 277
Automation Activity & Vendor Info: (Cataloging) epixtech, inc.; (Circulation) epixtech, inc.; (Course Reserve) epixtech, inc.; (OPAC) epixtech, inc.; (Serials) epixtech, inc.
Database Vendor: Ebsco - EbscoHost, IAC - Info Trac

M MAGIC VALLEY REGIONAL MEDICAL CENTER LIBRARY, 650 Addison Ave W, PO Box 409, 83301. SAN 320-6424. Tel: 208-737-2133. FAX: 208-737-2769.; Staff 1 (MLS 1)
Oct 1998-Sep 1999 Mats Exp $42,000, Books $1,000, Per/Ser (Incl. Access Fees) $22,000. Sal $41,000 (Prof $34,000)
Library Holdings: Bk Vols 600; Per Subs 120
Subject Interests: Allied health, Medicine, Nursing
Partic in Idaho Health Information Association

P TWIN FALLS PUBLIC LIBRARY, 434 Second St E, 83301-6397. SAN 303-6561. Tel: 208-733-2964. FAX: 208-733-2965. Web Site: www.lili.org/tfpl. *Dir*, Arlan Call; *Asst Dir*, Linda Parkinson; *Tech Servs*, Mareda Wright; *Ad Servs*, Susan Ash; *Ch Servs*, Annie-Laurie Burton; *Acq*, Jacqueline Smith; *Coll Develop*, Joshua Ghan; *Circ*, Barbara Ames; Staff 2 (MLS 2)
Founded 1908. Pop 84,000; Circ 269,501
Oct 1999-Sep 2000 Income $860,976, City $798,048, Locally Generated Income $62,928. Mats Exp $149,409, Books $106,037, Per/Ser (Incl. Access Fees) $17,262, Presv $329, Micro $1,856, Other Print Mats $10,212, Electronic Ref Mat (Incl. Access Fees) $13,713. Sal $528,924
Library Holdings: Bk Titles 153,648; Per Subs 359
Subject Interests: Agriculture, Business and management, History, Music, Travel
Special Collections: Early Local Photography (Bisbee Coll); Idaho History Coll; Large Print Coll; Musical Scores Coll; Pacific Northwest Americana Coll
Automation Activity & Vendor Info: (Acquisitions) epixtech, inc.; (Cataloging) epixtech, inc.; (Circulation) epixtech, inc.; (OPAC) epixtech, inc.; (Serials) epixtech, inc.
Partic in Lynx

VICTOR

P VALLEY OF THE TETONS DISTRICT LIBRARY, 56 N Main, PO Box 37, 83455-0037. (Mail add: PO Box 37, 83455-0037), SAN 303-657X. Tel: 208-787-2201. FAX: 208-787-2201. E-Mail: vallib@pdt.net. *Dir*, Carla Sherman; Staff 3 (Non-MLS 3)
Founded 1965. Pop 5,250; Circ 27,668
Oct 1998-Sep 1999 Income $70,548, State $10,096, County $49,619, Other $10,833. Mats Exp Books $10,583. Sal $34,724
Library Holdings: Bk Titles 15,777; Per Subs 13
Automation Activity & Vendor Info: (Cataloging) Follett; (Circulation) Follett
Database Vendor: Ebsco - EbscoHost
Mem of Eastern Idaho Regional Libr Syst
Friends of the Library Group

WALLACE

P WALLACE PUBLIC LIBRARY,* 415 River St, 83873-2260. SAN 303-6596. Tel: 208-752-4571. FAX: 208-752-4571. *Librn*, Bernie Ludwick; *Asst Librn*, Betty Wise
Founded 1902. Pop 1,010; Circ 14,154
Library Holdings: Bk Titles 16,367
Special Collections: Idaho & Pacific Northwestern History, bks, microfiche, microfilm, slides; Large Print Coll; Scandinavian History & Literature
Publications: Booklist

WEISER

P WEISER PUBLIC LIBRARY, 628 E First St, 83672-2241. SAN 303-660X. Tel: 208-549-1243. E-Mail: wpublib@ruralnetwork.net. *Dir*, Pat Hamilton
Founded 1890. Pop 4,900; Circ 40,000
Oct 1998-Sep 1999 Income $84,300. Mats Exp $22,800, Books $15,030, Per/Ser (Incl. Access Fees) $2,000. Sal $48,700 (Prof $24,253)
Library Holdings: Bk Titles 26,000; Per Subs 70
Automation Activity & Vendor Info: (Acquisitions) Athena; (Cataloging) Athena; (Circulation) Athena; (Course Reserve) Athena
Friends of the Library Group

WENDELL

P WENDELL PUBLIC LIBRARY,* 157 W Main, PO Box 208, 83355-0208. SAN 303-6618. Tel: 208-536-6195. *Dir*, Vivian Maltz
Pop 2,100; Circ 37,342
Library Holdings: Bk Vols 35,750
Mem of Magic Valley Libr Syst

WILDER

P WILDER DISTRICT LIBRARY, 207 Avenue A, PO Box 128, 83676-0128. SAN 303-6626. Tel: 208-482-7880. *Librn*, Susan Waldemer
Pop 3,120; Circ 6,100
Library Holdings: Bk Vols 7,500; Bk Titles 6,000

ILLINOIS

Date of Statistics: Fiscal Year 1999
Population, 1990 Census: 11,430,602
Population Served by Tax-Supported Public Libraries: 10,722,185
Total Volumes in Public Libraries:40,655,527 (books plus serials)
  Volumes Per Capita: 3.6
  Volumes Per Capita Served: 3.8
Total Non-book Resources Held:2,831,320 (audio plus video)
Total Public Library Circulation Transactions: 83,505,105
  Circulation Transactions Per Capita: 7.3
  Circulation Transactions Per Capita Served:7.8
Total Public Library Income (including some State & Federal Grants & Capital Income) : $442,744,536
  Source of Income: Primarily property tax
  Total Operating Expenditures: $388,208,115
  Expenditures Per Capita: $33.96
  Expenditures Per Capita Served: $36.21
Number of System (Regional Libraries): 12 multi-type
Number of Central Public Libraries: 628
  Counties Served: 102 whole or partial
  Grants, awarded & monitored (includes competitive grants, Live & Learn, systems funding, school per capita, and public library capita): 7,000 for $50,000,000

ABBOTT PARK

S ABBOTT LABORATORIES, Library Information Resources,* 100 Abbott Park Dr, 60064-3500. SAN 304-4815. Tel: 847-937-4600. FAX: 847-937-6333. *Dir*, Margaret Norman; E-Mail: margaret.norman@abbott.com; Staff 37 (MLS 24, Non-MLS 13)
Founded 1888
Library Holdings: Bk Vols 20,000; Per Subs 1,300
Special Collections: US, EPO & PCT Patents/Applications
Automation Activity & Vendor Info: (Acquisitions) SIRSI; (Cataloging) SIRSI; (Circulation) SIRSI; (Serials) SIRSI
Publications: Intranet; The Gateway (quarterly newsletter)
Mem of North Suburban Library System
Partic in OCLC Online Computer Library Center, Inc
Open Mon-Fri 8-5

ABINGDON

P JOHN MOSSER PUBLIC LIBRARY DISTRICT, 106 W Meek St, 61410. SAN 303-6634. Tel: 309-462-3129. FAX: 309-462-3129. E-Mail: j_mosser_pld@hotmail.com. *Dir*, Elizabeth Ann Kisler; *Asst Librn*, Karen Ann Yocum; *Asst Librn*, Jeanne Marie Neerdaels; *Ch Servs*, Linda Evelyn Crandall; Staff 4 (Non-MLS 4)
Founded 1895. Pop 3,600; Circ 20,131
Library Holdings: Bk Vols 23,966; Bk Titles 22,618; Per Subs 43
Subject Interests: Genealogy
Special Collections: Abingdon Pottery Coll; County Histories; Cramer Coll, 400 miniature vases; DAR Lineages from 1900; Hedding Coll Memorabilia; Hedding College Memorabilia; Mosser Coll
Mem of Alliance Library System
Special Services for the Blind - Bks on cassette
Friends of the Library Group

ADDISON

P ADDISON PUBLIC LIBRARY,* 235 N Kennedy Dr, 60101-2499. SAN 303-6642. Tel: 630-458-3338 (children's service), 630-543-3617. Reference Tel: 630-458-3318. FAX: 630-543-7275. E-Mail: adultref@addison.lib.il.us. Web Site: www.addison.lib.il.us. *Dir*, Sharon Hoffman; Tel: 630-458-3300, E-Mail: hoffman@addison.lib.il.us; *Asst Dir*, Edna Kaempfer; Tel: 630-458-3302, E-Mail: kaempfer@addison.lib.il.us; *Ad Servs*, Mary M Medjomzengue; Tel: 630-438-3314, E-Mail: medjomezengue@addison.lib.il.us; *Ch Servs*, Mary Marshall; Tel: 630-458-3332, E-Mail: marshall@addison.lib.il.us; *Circ, Tech Servs*, Tracey Collison; Tel: 630-458-3328, E-Mail: collison@addison.lib.il.us; *Reader Servs*, Karen Dini; Tel: 630-458-3347, E-Mail: dini@addison.lib.il.us; *Web Coordr*, Liu Yabin; Tel: 630-458-3316, E-Mail: liu@addison.lib.il.us
Founded 1962. Pop 33,175; Circ 263,738
May 1998-Apr 1999 Income $2,215,436, State $41,087, Locally Generated Income $242,114. Mats Exp $2,109,088, Books $226,288, Per/Ser (Incl. Access Fees) $67,210, Micro $9,788, AV Equip $47,890, Electronic Ref Mat (Incl. Access Fees) $31,580. Sal $869,814 (Prof $530,580)
Library Holdings: Bk Vols 88,020; Per Subs 165
Subject Interests: Careers, Genealogy, Italian (language), Large type print, Parenting, Polish (language), Spanish (language)
Automation Activity & Vendor Info: (Acquisitions) DRA; (Cataloging) DRA; (Circulation) DRA; (OPAC) DRA
Database Vendor: DRA
Publications: "Check It Out" (newsletter) & "Open Doors" (cable TV)
Mem of DuPage Library System
Special Services for the Deaf - TDD
Open Mon-Thurs 9-9, Fri 9-6, Sat 9-5 & Sun 1-5

P TECHNOLOGY CENTER OF DUPAGE, (Formerly Technology Center Of Du Page), Learning Resource Center, 301 S Swift Rd, 60101. SAN 376-1282. Tel: 630-620-8770. FAX: 630-691-7592. *Coordr*, Barbara Beck; *Coordr*, Jim Dildine
Library Holdings: Bk Titles 1,000; Per Subs 12

ALBANY

P ALBANY PUBLIC LIBRARY DISTRICT,* 302 S Main St, PO Box 516, 61230. SAN 376-0952. Tel: 309-887-4396. *Librn*, Mary K Hanson
Library Holdings: Bk Titles 6,000; Per Subs 15
Friends of the Library Group

ALBION

P ALBION PUBLIC LIBRARY,* 6 N Fourth St, 62806. SAN 303-6669. Tel: 618-445-3314. *Librn*, Carole L Shaw; *Asst Librn*, Rita Hortin
Founded 1818. Pop 2,290; Circ 19,044
Library Holdings: Bk Vols 14,000; Per Subs 60
Mem of Shawnee Library System
Open Mon-Fri 1:30-4:30, Tues & Wed 1:30-7:30, Sat 9-12 & 1-5
Friends of the Library Group

ALEDO

P MERCER CARNEGIE LIBRARY,* 200 N College Ave, 61231. SAN 303-6677. Tel: 309-582-2032. FAX: 309-582-5155. *Dir*, Daniel Chapman; Staff 2 (MLS 2)
Founded 1915. Pop 5,075; Circ 44,281
Library Holdings: Bk Titles 16,000; Per Subs 60
Subject Interests: Local history
Mem of Western Ill Libr Syst

ALGONQUIN

P ALGONQUIN AREA PUBLIC LIBRARY DISTRICT,* 115 Eastgate Dr, 60102-3097. SAN 303-6685. Tel: 847-658-4343. FAX: 847-658-0179. E-Mail: referenc@nsilsus.org. Web Site: www.nslsilus.org/alkhome. *Dir*, Randall Vlcek; *Circ*, Gary Christopherson; *Ref*, Vicky Tobias; *Ch Servs*, Joe Davis; *Tech Servs*, Patrice Pearsall

Founded 1921. Pop 23,664; Circ 366,509
Jul 1997-Jun 1998 Income $1,628,175, State $56,121, County $1,458,894, Locally Generated Income $113,160. Mats Exp $227,160, Books $164,684, Micro $62,476. Sal $779,923
Library Holdings: Bk Titles 92,159; Per Subs 277
Subject Interests: Local history
Publications: Library Leaves (newsletter)
Mem of North Suburban Library System
Friends of the Library Group

ALSIP

P ALSIP-MERRIONETTE PARK LIBRARY, 11960 S Pulaski Rd, 60803-1197. SAN 303-6693. Tel: 708-371-5666. FAX: 708-371-5672. E-Mail: ampl@sslic.net. Web Site: www.alsip-mp.lib.il.us. *Dir*, Pamela Nelson; E-Mail: pnelson@sslic.net; *Ch Servs*, Lisa Palombi; *Ref*, Ruthann Swanson; Staff 32 (MLS 8, Non-MLS 24)
Founded 1973. Pop 21,445
Jul 1998-Jun 1999 Income (Main Library Only) $1,100,790, State $120,270, Federal $1,605, Locally Generated Income $886,644, Other $92,271. Mats Exp $214,744, Books $180,642, Per/Ser (Incl. Access Fees) $11,835, Micro $5,267, Electronic Ref Mat (Incl. Access Fees) $17,000. Sal $493,432 (Prof $228,569)
Library Holdings: Bk Vols 117,070; Per Subs 284
Automation Activity & Vendor Info: (Cataloging) Innovative Interfaces Inc.; (Circulation) Innovative Interfaces Inc.; (OPAC) Innovative Interfaces Inc.
Publications: Newsampler (quarterly newsletter)
Mem of Suburban Library System
Friends of the Library Group

ALTAMONT

P ALTAMONT PUBLIC LIBRARY,* 121 W Washington St, 62411. SAN 303-6707. Tel: 618-483-5457. FAX: 618-483-5457. *Librn*, Patti Niehaus
Founded 1908. Pop 2,296; Circ 25,689
Library Holdings: Bk Vols 17,000; Per Subs 505
Mem of Shawnee Library System
Open Mon-Wed 2-7, Thurs 6-9, Fri 2-6, Sat 12-4

ALTON

M ALTON MENTAL HEALTH CENTER, Professional Library, 4500 College Ave, 62002. SAN 325-6162. Tel: 618-474-3368, Ext 3368. FAX: 618-474-3941. E-Mail: dhsmhsb@dhs.state.il.us.
Library Holdings: Bk Titles 3,082; Per Subs 20
Subject Interests: Nursing, Psychiatry, Psychology
Partic in Areawide Hospital Consortium
Open Mon-Fri 8-4:30

P HAYNER PUBLIC LIBRARY DISTRICT, 401 State St, 62002. SAN 303-6723. Tel: 618-462-0651. FAX: 618-462-0665. Web Site: www.altonweb.com/hayner/index.html. *Dir*, Joyce A Reid; Tel: 618-462-0677, Fax: 618-462-4919, E-Mail: joycer@lcls.org; *Mgr*, Beverly Schoeberle; Tel: 618-463-1276, Fax: 618-463-1277, E-Mail: beverlys@lcls.org; *Ch Servs, YA Servs*, Carol Brockmeyer; Tel: 618-462-0652, Fax: 618-462-4919, E-Mail: carolbr@lcls.org; *Ref Serv*, Susan L Kulasekara; E-Mail: susank@lcls.org; *Cat, Tech Servs*, Barbara B Ulffers; Tel: 618-462-0677, Fax: 618-462-4919, E-Mail: barbarau@lcls.org; *Pub Relations*, Bernadette Duvernoy; Tel: 618-462-0677, Fax: 618-462-4919, E-Mail: bernadetted@lcls.org; *Ad Servs*, Catherine Schrimpf; E-Mail: katies@lcls.org; Staff 4 (MLS 4)
Founded 1891. Pop 52,567
Jul 1998-Jun 1999 Income $1,673,767, State $182,322, County $1,338,612, Other $152,833. Mats Exp $1,193,873. Sal $630,000 (Prof $147,862)
Library Holdings: Bk Vols 167,979; Per Subs 323
Subject Interests: History
Special Collections: Illinois History (Illinois Room Coll), bks, microfilm & vertical file
Database Vendor: DRA
Publications: The Hayner Public Library District (quarterly newsletter)
Mem of Lewis & Clark Library System
Branch library in Alton Square Mall
Friends of the Library Group

CM SOUTHERN ILLINOIS UNIVERSITY, School of Dental Medicine Biomedical Library,* 2800 College Ave, 62002. SAN 303-674X. Tel: 618-474-7277. FAX: 618-474-7270. Web Site: www.siue.edu. *Dir*, Gloria Kharibian; E-Mail: gkharib@siue.edu; *Circ*, Mike Daech
Founded 1970
Library Holdings: Bk Vols 57,000; Per Subs 200
Mem of Lewis & Clark Library System
Partic in ILLINET

S THE TELEGRAPH LIBRARY, 111 E Broadway, 62002. (Mail add: PO Box 278, 62002), SAN 303-6715. Tel: 618-463-2573. Toll Free Tel: 800-477-1447. FAX: 618-463-2578. E-Mail: telegraph@primary.net. Web Site: www.thetelegraph.com. *Librn*, Barbara McLemore
Subject Interests: Newsp clipping files
Publications: The Telegraph

ALTONA

P RANSOM MEMORIAL PUBLIC LIBRARY, 110 E Main St, 61414-9998. SAN 303-6758. Tel: 309-484-6193. FAX: 309-484-6193. *Librn*, Janice Larson; E-Mail: larson2@winco.net; Staff 1 (Non-MLS 1)
Founded 1889. Pop 823; Circ 14,227
Library Holdings: Bk Vols 21,000; Per Subs 40
Mem of Alliance Library System
Open Mon & Thurs 7-9, Wed 2-5, Sat 10-12 & 2-4

AMBOY

P PANKHURST MEMORIAL LIBRARY, 3 S Jefferson Ave, 61310-1400. SAN 303-6766. Tel: 815-857-3925. FAX: 815-857-3065. E-Mail: pmlamboy@essex1.com. Web Site: nils.lib.il.us. *Dir*, Carol M Hanson; *Ad Servs*, Joan Kessel; *Ch Servs*, Ginger Daniels; Staff 3 (Non-MLS 3)
Founded 1928. Pop 2,377
2000-2001 Mats Exp Books $12,500
Library Holdings: Bk Vols 20,000; Bk Titles 19,280; Per Subs 25; High Interest/Low Vocabulary Bk Vols 60
Database Vendor: CARL, Innovative Interfaces INN - View, OCLC - First Search, Wilson - Wilson Web
Mem of Northern Illinois Library System
Partic in OWLSnet
Open Mon - Thurs 1-7 pm, Fri 9-5, Sat 9-3; closed Sun
Friends of the Library Group

ANDALUSIA

P ANDALUSIA TOWNSHIP LIBRARY,* 503 W Second St, PO Box 319, 61232. SAN 303-6774. Tel: 309-798-2542. FAX: 309-798-2542, 309-798-2567. E-Mail: and@libby.rbls.lib.il.us. *Librn*, Mary Casey
Pop 2,261; Circ 12,041
Library Holdings: Bk Vols 7,500; Per Subs 15
Mem of River Bend Library System
Open Mon, Tues & Thurs 12-9, Wed & Sat 9-1

ANNA

M CHOATE MENTAL HEALTH & DEVELOPMENT CENTER, Staff Library,* 1000 N Main St, 62906. SAN 303-6782. Tel: 618-833-5161, Ext 478. FAX: 618-833-4191. E-Mail: choate@midwest.net.
Founded 1930
Library Holdings: Bk Titles 5,694; Per Subs 87
Subject Interests: Mental health
Partic in Ill Dept of Mental Health Libr Servs
Open Mon-Fri 4-8:30
Friends of the Library Group

P STINSON MEMORIAL LIBRARY,* 409 S Main St, 62906. SAN 303-6790. Tel: 618-833-2521. FAX: 618-833-3560. *Dir*, Robert E Hafeman; *Ch Servs*, Gladas Freeze
Founded 1914. Pop 5,408; Circ 28,631
Library Holdings: Bk Vols 18,850; Per Subs 44
Mem of Shawnee Library System
Open Mon-Fri 9-8, Sat 10-5

ANNAWAN

P ANNAWAN-ALBA TOWNSHIP LIBRARY,* 320 W Front St, PO Box 298, 61234. SAN 303-6804. Tel: 309-935-6483. FAX: 309-935-6483. *Librn*, Carole Stern; E-Mail: cstern@libby.rbls.lib.il.us; *Assoc Librn*, Nancy Dynes
Founded 1930. Pop 1,649; Circ 21,702
1998-1999 Income $32,075, State $1,790, Other $7,073. Mats Exp $5,930, Books $4,890, Per/Ser (Incl. Access Fees) $750. Sal $24,179
Library Holdings: Bk Vols 16,739; Per Subs 44
Mem of River Bend Library System
Open Mon 1-5, Tues & Fri 9-12 & 1-5, Wed 1-7, Sat 9-4
Friends of the Library Group

ANTIOCH

P ANTIOCH DISTRICT LIBRARY, 757 Main St, 60002. SAN 303-6812. Tel: 847-395-0874. FAX: 847-395-9518. *Dir*, Kathy LaBuda; *Asst Dir, Ch Servs*, Joan Padbury; *Tech Servs*, Carol Weberg; *Circ*, Lynn Floyd; *Ref*, Amy Blue; Staff 5 (MLS 5)
Founded 1921. Pop 18,275; Circ 220,000
Jul 2000-Jun 2001 Income (Main Library Only) $1,227,000, State $27,000,

County $1,200,000. Mats Exp $1,300,000. Sal $430,000
Library Holdings: Bk Vols 84,000; Bk Titles 80,000; Per Subs 138
Special Collections: Antioch Hist, Cooking, Crafts, Developmental Games & Parenting
Automation Activity & Vendor Info: (Cataloging) TLC; (Circulation) TLC; (OPAC) TLC
Mem of North Suburban Library System
Open Mon-Thurs 9-9, Fri & Sat 9-5, Sun 1-5
Friends of the Library Group

ARCOLA

P ARCOLA PUBLIC LIBRARY DISTRICT, 407 E Main St, 61910-1513. SAN 303-6820. Tel: 217-268-4477. FAX: 217-268-4478. E-Mail: arcolapl@arcola-il.com. *Dir*, Jantha C Rollings; Staff 4 (Non-MLS 4)
Founded 1904. Pop 4,072; Circ 26,947
Library Holdings: Bk Titles 19,247; Per Subs 50
Database Vendor: OCLC - First Search, Wilson - Wilson Web
Mem of Lincoln Trail Libraries System
Friends of the Library Group

ARGENTA

P ARGENTA-OREANA PUBLIC LIBRARY DISTRICT, Argenta Public Library, 100 E Water, 62501. (Mail add: PO Box 350, 62501-0350), SAN 303-6839. Tel: 217-795-2144. FAX: 217-795-4763. E-Mail: cyndib@rpls.lib.il.us. *Dir*, Cyndi Bowman
Library Holdings: Bk Titles 30,000; Per Subs 200
Automation Activity & Vendor Info: (Acquisitions) DRA; (Cataloging) DRA; (Circulation) DRA; (ILL) DRA; (OPAC) DRA
Database Vendor: DRA
Mem of Rolling Prairie Library System

ARGONNE

S ARGONNE NATIONAL LABORATORY, Technical Information Services Department,* Bldg 203-D140, 9700 S Cass Ave, 60439-4801. SAN 339-6878. Tel: 630-252-4221. Interlibrary Loan Service Tel: 630-252-4223. FAX: 630-252-5886. Web Site: www.library.anl.gov/. *In Charge*, Shannon Savage; Staff 30 (MLS 15, Non-MLS 15)
Founded 1946
1998-1999 Mats Exp $1,700,000
Library Holdings: Bk Titles 65,000; Per Subs 1,400
Subject Interests: Chemical engineering, Inorganic chemistry, Mathematics, Nuclear science, Physics
Special Collections: DOE/ERDA/AEC Technical Report
Automation Activity & Vendor Info: (Acquisitions) TechLIB; (Cataloging) TechLIB; (Circulation) TechLIB; (Serials) TechLIB
Partic in OCLC Online Computer Library Center, Inc
Branches:
BIOMEDICAL Tel: 630-252-3876. *Librn*, Carol Lepzelter
CHEMICAL ENGINEERING Tel: 630-252-4481. *Librn*, Sharon Clark
CHEMISTRY Tel: 630-252-3566. *Librn*, Susan Pepalis
ENGINEERING & REACTOR SCIENCE Tel: 630-252-4825. *Librn*, Elizabeth Ybarra
ENVIRONMENTAL ASSESSMENT Tel: 630-252-7274. *Librn*, Swati Wagh
HIGH ENERGY PHYSICS-ENERGY SCIENCES Tel: 630-252-6203.
INTERLIBRARY LOAN Tel: 630-252-4223. FAX: 708-252-3609. *Librn*, Yvette Woell
MATERIALS SCIENCE Tel: 630-252-4936. *Librn*, Robert Noel
MATHEMATICS, PHYSICS & COMPUTER SCIENCE Tel: 630-252-4224. *Librn*, Gary Davidoff
SOLID STATE PHYSICS Tel: 630-252-5558. *Librn*, Lisha Li
SYCHROTRON RESEARCH Tel: 630-252-7770. *Librn*, Mary Pietryga

ARLINGTON HEIGHTS

P ARLINGTON HEIGHTS MEMORIAL LIBRARY,* 500 N Dunton Ave, 60004-5966. SAN 303-6863. Tel: 847-392-0100. Interlibrary Loan Service FAX: 847-392-0136. Web Site: www.ahml.lib.il.us. *Librn*, Kathleen M Balcom; *Admin Assoc*, Chris Meier; *Publ Servs*, Paula Moore; *Coll Develop*, Diane Brodson; *Coll Develop*, Abby Schor; *Coll Develop*, Harvey Barfield; *Coll Develop*, Jon Kadus; *Tech Servs*, Harvey Hahn; *Ch Servs*, Tina Hubert; *Ch Servs*, Deanna Hanson; *Ch Servs*, Jennifer Kaempfe; *Ch Servs*, Judy Moskal; *Ref*, Carol Blohm; *Ad Servs*, Caryl Mobley; *Commun Servs*, Joyce Voss; *Pub Relations*, Debora Meskauskas; *Circ*, Richard Hanrath; *Info Res*, Margaret Heraty; *Publ Servs*, Marcia Rogers; *Electronic Resources*, Bill Pardue; Staff 33 (MLS 33)
Founded 1926. Pop 75,462; Circ 1,559,438
May 1997-Apr 1998 Income $8,113,306, State $94,328, City $7,391,317, Federal $20,615, Locally Generated Income $607,046. Mats Exp $978,316, Books $644,779, Per/Ser (Incl. Access Fees) $106,272, Presv $9,888, Micro $51,226. Sal $4,081,313
Library Holdings: Bk Titles 399,239; Per Subs 1,113
Subject Interests: American literature, Education, Fiction, Genealogy, Illinois, Large type print, Law, Local history, Paintings
Automation Activity & Vendor Info: (Acquisitions) Innovative Interfaces Inc.; (Cataloging) Innovative Interfaces Inc.; (Circulation) Innovative Interfaces Inc.; (Serials) Innovative Interfaces Inc.
Publications: Read Out (monthly newsletter)
Mem of North Suburban Library System
Partic in OCLC Online Computer Library Center, Inc; SILO
Friends of the Library Group
Bookmobiles: 1

S MOTOROLA, INC, CNSS CIG Technical Information Resource Center,* 1501 W Shure Dr IL27/1300, 60004. SAN 374-5058. Tel: 847-632-5329. FAX: 847-632-5861. E-Mail: al0853@cemail.mot.com. Web Site: www.mot.com. *Mgr*, Grazyna T Langguth; E-Mail: langguth@cig.mot.com; Staff 2 (MLS 1, Non-MLS 1)
Founded 1989
Library Holdings: Bk Titles 3,500; Per Subs 135
Subject Interests: Regulations, Standards, Telecommunications
Special Collections: Telecommunications, Cellular, Standard Coll
Database Vendor: OCLC - First Search, ProQuest
Restriction: Staff use only
Function: For research purposes
Mem of North Suburban Library System
Friends of the Library Group

M NORTHWEST COMMUNITY HOSPITAL, Health Resource Library, 800 W Central Rd, 60005-2392. SAN 303-6871. Tel: 847-618-5180. FAX: 847-618-5189. Web Site: www.nch.org. *Chief Librn, Coll Develop*, Joy Kennedy; Tel: 847-618-5181, E-Mail: j1kennedy@nch.org
Founded 1963
Library Holdings: Bk Titles 5,577; Per Subs 298
Subject Interests: Medicine, Nursing, Oncology
Mem of North Suburban Library System
Partic in Metrop Consortium of Healthcare Librs

ARLIUTOU HEIGHTS

S TETRA-TECH EM INC,* 3550 SaH Creek Dr Ste 105, 60005. SAN 375-9717. Tel: 847-818-7193. FAX: 847-342-9733.
Library Holdings: Bk Titles 5,592

ARTHUR

P ARTHUR PUBLIC LIBRARY,* 225 S Walnut, 61911. SAN 303-6898. Tel: 217-543-2037. FAX: 217-543-2037. *Librn*, Alice Cisna; E-Mail: acisna@ltnet.ltis.org
Pop 4,709; Circ 60,000
Jul 1997-Jun 1998 Income $90,000. Mats Exp $16,200, Books $15,000, Per/Ser (Incl. Access Fees) $1,200. Sal $42,000 (Prof $25,000)
Library Holdings: Bk Vols 17,000; Per Subs 53
Subject Interests: Amish
Mem of Lincoln Trail Libraries System
Open Mon-Thurs 10-8, Fri & Sat 10-5
Friends of the Library Group

ASHLAND

P ASHLAND PUBLIC LIBRARY DISTRICT,* 125 W Editor St, PO Box 498, 62612. SAN 303-6901. Tel: 217-476-3417. FAX: 217-476-8076. *Dir*, Deborah Aggertt
Pop 1,351; Circ 6,355
Library Holdings: Bk Vols 22,000; Per Subs 80
Mem of Alliance Library System
Open Mon & Wed 9-7, Tues, Thurs & Fri 9-5, Sat 9-3

ASHLEY

P ASHLEY PUBLIC LIBRARY,* 68 NE Railroad St, PO Box 246, 62808. SAN 303-691X. Tel: 618-485-2295. *Librn*, Chris Newcomb
Pop 655; Circ 5,441
Library Holdings: Bk Vols 6,000; Per Subs 14
Mem of Kaskaskia Libr Syst
Open Mon 6-8, Tues & Fri 1-4:30

ASHTON

P MILLS-PETRIE MEMORIAL LIBRARY,* 704 N First St, PO Box 308, 61006. SAN 303-6928. Tel: 815-453-2213. FAX: 815-453-2723. *Librn*, Marie McCannon
Pop 1,143; Circ 13,282
Library Holdings: Bk Vols 10,000; Per Subs 32
Mem of Northern Illinois Library System
Open Mon 10-11:30, 1-5:30 & 6-8, Tues-Thurs 1-5:30, Sat 9-12

ASSUMPTION

P ASSUMPTION PUBLIC LIBRARY DISTRICT,* 205 N Oak St, 62510. SAN 303-6936. Tel: 217-226-3915. FAX: 217-226-4492. *Dir*, Cindy Jeppson
Founded 1903. Pop 2,101; Circ 12,637
1998-1999 Income $59,666, State $2,628, City $1,457, County $50,712, Other $4,869. Mats Exp $6,844, Books $5,000, Per/Ser (Incl. Access Fees) $994. Sal $19,880
Library Holdings: Bk Titles 14,000
Mem of Rolling Prairie Library System
Open Tues-Fri 9-5, Sat 9-3

ASTORIA

P ASTORIA PUBLIC LIBRARY DISTRICT LIBRARY, 220 W Broadway, PO Box 650, 61501-0650. SAN 376-091X. Tel: 309-329-2423. FAX: 309-329-2423. E-Mail: astorlib@netins.net. *Librn*, Eileen Rohman; E-Mail: erohman@hotmail.com; Staff 1 (Non-MLS 1)
Pop 2,506
Library Holdings: Bk Titles 40,000; Per Subs 25; Spec Interest Per Sub 10
Mem of Alliance Library System
Special Services for the Blind - Large print bks
Friends of the Library Group

ATKINSON

P ATKINSON PUBLIC LIBRARY DISTRICT,* 119 W Main, PO Box 633, 61235-0633. SAN 303-6944. Tel: 309-936-7606. FAX: 309-936-7857. E-Mail: apld@geneseo.net. *Dir*, Ninette Carton; *Asst Dir*, Ruthann Carton
Founded 1920. Pop 1,539; Circ 10,179
Library Holdings: Bk Vols 13,302; Per Subs 45
Special Collections: Bound local newspapers - 70 volumes (yearly)
Mem of Alliance Library System
Special Services for the Blind - Talking Books

ATLANTA

P ATLANTA PUBLIC LIBRARY DISTRICT, 100 NW Race St, 61723. (Mail add: PO Box 568, 61723), SAN 303-6952. Tel: 217-648-2112. FAX: 217-648-5269. E-Mail: apl@abelink.com. *Librn*, Sheila L Cotton; *Librn*, Ruth Ann Hieronymus; *Asst Librn*, Carol Begolka; *Curator*, Lucille Pech. Subject Specialists: *Genealogy*, Lucille Pech; *Libr sci*, Carol Begolka; *Technology*, Sheila L Cotton; Staff 4 (Non-MLS 4)
Founded 1873. Pop 2,390; Circ 6,116
Jul 2000-Jun 2001 Income $62,500. Mats Exp $7,650, Books $7,000, Per/Ser (Incl. Access Fees) $150, Micro $250, Manuscripts & Archives $250. Sal $30,000
Library Holdings: Bk Vols 13,468; Per Subs 6; Bks on Deafness & Sign Lang 4
Special Collections: Lincoln; Local Newspaper Coll, micro
Database Vendor: CARL, OCLC - First Search
Mem of Alliance Library System
Open Tues & Thurs 12:30-8, Wed & Fri 12:30-4:30, Sat 9-3
Friends of the Library Group

ATWOOD

P ATWOOD-HAMMOND PUBLIC LIBRARY, (A-HPLD), 123 N Main St, PO Box 440, 61913-0440. SAN 303-6960. Tel: 217-578-2727. FAX: 217-578-2727. *Librn*, Marsha Burgener
Pop 2,876; Circ 23,000
Jul 1999-Jun 2000 Income $95,348, State $3,548, County $91,800. Mats Exp $19,690, Books $15,000, Per/Ser (Incl. Access Fees) $1,340, Micro $350, AV Equip $3,000. Sal $32,949
Subject Interests: Local history
Database Vendor: DRA
Mem of Rolling Prairie Library System
Open Mon & Fri 9-5, Tues-Thurs 12-8, Sat 9-1
Friends of the Library Group

AUBURN

P AUBURN PUBLIC LIBRARY, 118 N Fifth St, 62615. SAN 303-6979. Tel: 217-438-6211. FAX: 217-438-9317. Web Site: www.ctnet.net/auburnlibrary. *Librn*, Betty Ludek; *Asst Librn*, Laura Carter
Founded 1932. Pop 3,603; Circ 27,084
Library Holdings: Bk Vols 19,000; Per Subs 30
Mem of Lewis & Clark Library System
Open Mon 1-7, Tues 2-7, Wed 10-7, Thurs 2-5, Fri 10-5 & Sat 10-2
Friends of the Library Group

AUGUSTA

P GREATER WEST CENTRAL PUBLIC LIBRARY DISTRICT, (GWC), Augusta Branch, 202 Center St, 62311. (Mail add: PO Box 235, 62311), SAN 303-6987. Tel: 217-392-2211. FAX: 217-392-2211. E-Mail: gwc@darkstar.rsa.lib.il.us. *Dir*, Dorothy Wessel; E-Mail: gwodie@hotmail.com; *Librn*, Wanda Eddington
Founded 1915. Pop 4,859; Circ 35,130
Library Holdings: Bk Titles 32,025; Per Subs 135
Subject Interests: Education, History
Special Collections: Local history (Augusta Township & Hancock County Coll), bks & microfilm
Mem of Alliance Library System
Open Tues & Thurs 1-6, Wed & Sat 9-12
Friends of the Library Group
Branches: 4
BOWEN BRANCH, 111 Fifth St, PO Box 246, Bowen, 62316. SAN 303-7436. Tel: 217-842-5573. FAX: 217-842-5573. *Librn*, Janis Vollbracht
Founded 1972. Pop 1,348; Circ 11,220
Library Holdings: Bk Vols 20,000; Per Subs 25
Mem of Alliance Library System
Open Tues & Sat 9-12, Wed 2-6, Thurs 9-12 & 2-5
GOLDEN BRANCH, 303 Quincy St, PO Box 87, Golden, 62339. SAN 372-5235. Tel: 217-696-2428. FAX: 217-696-2428. *Librn*, Sheila Leenerts
Library Holdings: Bk Titles 10,000; Per Subs 30
Mem of Alliance Library System
Open Tues 9-12 & 2-5, Wed 2-6, Thurs & Sat 9-12
Friends of the Library Group
LITTLETON BRANCH, 210 S Center, PO Box 207, Littleton, 61452. SAN 372-5243. Tel: 309-257-2202. *Librn*, Waynette Caldwell
Library Holdings: Bk Titles 7,000; Per Subs 13
Mem of Alliance Library System
Open Wed 12-7, Sun 1-5
PLYMOUTH BRANCH, 103 W Side Sq, PO Box 251, Plymouth, 62367. SAN 325-3929. Tel: 309-458-6616. FAX: 309-458-6616. *Librn*, Linda Switzer
Mem of Alliance Library System
Open Tues, Thurs & Sat 9-12, Wed 1-6

AURORA

P AURORA PUBLIC LIBRARY,* One E Benton St, 60505-4299. SAN 303-7002. Tel: 630-264-4100. TDD: 630-264-4108. FAX: 630-896-3209. E-Mail: apl-ill@dupagels.lib.il.u.s.. Web Site: www.aurora.lib.il.u.s. *Exec Dir*, Eva Luckinbill; *Mgr*, Donna Andrews; *Br Coordr*, Elizabeth Bumgarner; Tel: 630-264-3600, Fax: 630-844-8695; *Br Coordr*, Pamela Truemper; Tel: 630-264-3500, Fax: 630-898-5220; *Coll Develop*, Mary Ann Pirone; *Ch Servs*, Diane Christian; *Tech Servs*, Linda Whitmill; Staff 100 (MLS 20, Non-MLS 80)
Founded 1881. Pop 122,271; Circ 860,500
Jan 1998-Dec 1998 Income $4,524,189, State $170,257, City $4,102,215, Locally Generated Income $145,381, Other $106,336. Mats Exp $468,600, Books $409,000, Per/Ser (Incl. Access Fees) $39,600, Micro $20,000. Sal $2,145,239
Library Holdings: Bk Vols 397,133; Per Subs 8,891
Subject Interests: Local history
Automation Activity & Vendor Info: (Circulation) epixtech, inc.; (OPAC) epixtech, inc.
Database Vendor: epixtech, inc., GaleNet, IAC - Info Trac, IAC - SearchBank, OCLC - First Search
Function: ILL available
Mem of DuPage Library System
Partic in ILLINET; LVIS; OCLC Online Computer Library Center, Inc
Open Mon-Fri 9-9, Sat 9-6, Sun 1-5 (school year Sept-May)
Friends of the Library Group

C AURORA UNIVERSITY, Charles B Phillips Library, 347 S Gladstone, 60506. SAN 303-6995. Tel: 630-844-5437. FAX: 630-844-3848. Web Site: www.aurora.edu/library/. *Dir*, Dorman Smith; *Archivist, Per*, Ken Van Andel; *Cat, Ref*, Anne McKearn; *Acq*, Andrea Seifrid; Staff 9 (MLS 4, Non-MLS 5)
Founded 1893. Enrl 1,940; Highest Degree: Master
Library Holdings: Bk Vols 103,544; Bk Titles 94,391; Per Subs 707
Subject Interests: American Indians, English literature, Nursing, Social service (social work)
Special Collections: Adventism (Jenks Coll), bks, per; American History (Ritzman Coll), bks, per; Elizabethan History & Theatre (Prouty & Perry Memorial Colls), bks, per
Automation Activity & Vendor Info: (Cataloging) DRA; (Circulation) DRA; (OPAC) DRA
Mem of DuPage Library System
Partic in Libras, Inc; OCLC Online Computer Library Center, Inc; Private Academic Libraries Of Illinois

S ENGINEERING SYSTEMS INC LIBRARY, 3851 Exchange Ave, 60504-7900. SAN 375-3298. Tel: 630-851-4566, Ext 238. FAX: 630-851-4870. *Librn*, Cheryl A Hansen; E-Mail: cahansen@esi-il.com; Staff 1 (MLS 1)
Founded 1990

Library Holdings: Bk Titles 2,000
Mem of DuPage Library System
Partic in Illinois Library & Information Network

S ILLINOIS MATHEMATICS & SCIENCE ACADEMY, Leto M Furnas Information Resource Center,* 1500 W Sullivan Rd, 60506-1000. SAN 375-9539. Tel: 630-907-5920. Interlibrary Loan Service Tel: 630-907-5075. Reference Tel: 630-907-5972. FAX: 630-907-5004. E-Mail: irc@imsa.edu. Web Site: www.imsa.edu/team/irc. *Dir*, Sandra R Donahue; *Coll Develop, Ref*, Christopher Jocius; *Cat*, Sally Bailey; *Circ, ILL*, Angela Richardson; *Circ*, Carol Hirsch; *Circ*, Jessica Salgado; *Archivist, Ref*, Marti Guarin; *Syst Coordr, Tech Servs*, Jean Bigger; Staff 5 (MLS 5)
Founded 1986. Enrl 659; Fac 65
Jul 1997-Jun 1998 Income $389,200, State $375,500, Other $13,700. Mats Exp $55,300, Books $40,600, Per/Ser (Incl. Access Fees) $11,700. Sal $236,933 (Prof $215,022)
Library Holdings: Bk Titles 42,000; Per Subs 120
Special Collections: IMSA Archives; Western Electric Library Coll, management & technical materials
Automation Activity & Vendor Info: (Cataloging) DRA; (Circulation) DRA
Publications: bibliographies; broadsides; Connections (newsletter); Information Resource Center (brochure)
Partic in ILA; Illinois Library & Information Network; IOUG; LOEX; OCLC Online Computer Library Center, Inc
Open (Regular Session) - Mon & Thurs 7am-7:30pm, Tues & Fri 7-5, Wed 9-7:30, Sunday 3:30-7:30 (last 2 Sundays of each quarter), (summer) Mon-Fri 8-4:30

S MARMION ACADEMY LIBRARY,* 1000 Butterfield Rd, 60504-9742. SAN 375-9806. Tel: 630-897-6936. FAX: 630-897-7086. *Librn*, Mario Pedi
Library Holdings: Bk Titles 10,316

M PROVENA MERCY CENTER, Medical Library,* 1325 N Highland Ave, 60506. SAN 303-7010. Tel: 630-801-2686, 630-859-2222. FAX: 630-801-2687. *Librn*, Mary Howrey; Staff 2 (MLS 1, Non-MLS 1)
Founded 1965
Library Holdings: Bk Titles 5,600; Per Subs 190
Subject Interests: Hospital administration, Medicine, Nursing, Psychiatry
Special Collections: Gerontology
Publications: Periodicals Directory, HSN Video Guide
Partic in Fox Valley Health Science Library Consortium; Illinois Library & Information Network; OCLC Online Computer Library Center, Inc
Open Mon-Thurs 8-4:30

M RUSH-COPLEY MEDICAL CENTER, Health Science Library,* 2000 Ogden Ave, 60504. SAN 376-0065. Tel: 630-978-4917, 630-978-6200. FAX: 630-978-6854. *Librn*, Joyce Pallinger
Library Holdings: Bk Vols 500; Per Subs 85
Special Collections: Medical Records Coll
Restriction: Not open to public

AVON

P VILLAGE OF AVON PUBLIC LIBRARY,* 105 S Main St, PO Box 598, 61415-0598. SAN 303-7037. Tel: 309-465-3933. FAX: 309-465-3933. *Librn*, Linda Williams
Pop 1,019; Circ 6,631
Library Holdings: Bk Vols 11,000; Per Subs 42
Publications: Library Journal
Mem of Alliance Library System
Open Mon, Thurs & Fri 1:30-5, Wed 1:30-5 & 6:30-8:30, Sat 9-noon

BARRINGTON

P BARRINGTON PUBLIC LIBRARY DISTRICT, 505 N Northwest Hwy, 60010. SAN 303-7053. Tel: 847-382-1300. TDD: 847-382-1301. FAX: 847-382-1261. Web Site: www.bal.alibrary.com. *Librn*, Barbara L Sugden; E-Mail: bsugden@bal.alibrary.com; *Ad Servs*, Rose M Faber; E-Mail: rfaber@bal.alibrary.com; *Ch Servs*, Catherine Mau; E-Mail: cmau@bal.alibrary.com; *Circ*, Marie Thomas; E-Mail: mthomas@bal.alibrary.com; *Tech Servs*, Maripat Olson; E-Mail: molson@bal.alibrary.com; Staff 30 (MLS 30)
Founded 1913. Pop 39,925; Circ 570,903
Jul 1999-Jun 2000 Income $4,299,654, State $69,056, Locally Generated Income $404,003, Parent Institution $3,826,595. Mats Exp $526,666, Books $386,823, Per/Ser (Incl. Access Fees) $38,286, Presv $403, AV Equip $73,661, Electronic Ref Mat (Incl. Access Fees) $27,486. Sal $1,740,074 (Prof $1,017,024)
Library Holdings: Bk Vols 217,480; Per Subs 516
Automation Activity & Vendor Info: (Acquisitions) epixtech, inc.; (Cataloging) epixtech, inc.; (Circulation) epixtech, inc.; (OPAC) epixtech, inc.; (Serials) epixtech, inc.
Publications: Check It Out (newsletter)
Mem of North Suburban Library System
Special Services for the Deaf - TTY machine
Friends of the Library Group

S QUAKER OATS CO, John Stuart Research Laboratories Library, 617 W Main St, 60010-4199. SAN 303-707X. Tel: 847-304-2064. FAX: 847-304-2062. *Senior Info Specialist*, Sharon Lazzara; Staff 2 (MLS 1, Non-MLS 1)
Founded 1956
Library Holdings: Bk Vols 7,000; Bk Titles 5,500; Per Subs 250
Subject Interests: Nutrition
Publications: Current Research Awareness Bulletin
Mem of North Suburban Library System

S WIGHT CONSULTING ENGINEERS, INC, Technical Library,* 127 S Northwest Hwy, 60010. SAN 370-3010. Tel: 847-381-1800. FAX: 847-381-1875. *Librn*, Connie Schmidt
Library Holdings: Bk Vols 2,500; Per Subs 40
Restriction: Staff use only
Open Mon-Fri 8-5

BARRY

P BARRY PUBLIC LIBRARY, 880 Bainbridge St, 62312. SAN 303-7096. Tel: 217-335-2149. FAX: 217-335-2149. E-Mail: books@adams.net. *Librn*, Margaret L Rawlings
Founded 1876. Pop 1,391; Circ 17,492
Library Holdings: Bk Vols 12,000; Per Subs 100
Mem of Alliance Library System

BARTLETT

P BARTLETT PUBLIC LIBRARY DISTRICT,* 800 S Bartlett Rd, 60103. SAN 303-710X. Tel: 630-837-2855. TDD: 630-837-2922. FAX: 630-837-3167. E-Mail: bpldref@bartlett.lib.il.us. Web Site: www.bartlett.lib.il.us. *Dir*, Yvonne Beechler; *Coll Develop*, Judith Limon; Staff 11 (MLS 11)
Founded 1972. Pop 31,628; Circ 403,000
Jul 1998-Jun 1999 Income (Main Library Only) $2,048,446, State $46,052, Federal $1,393, Locally Generated Income $1,834,755, Other $166,246. Mats Exp $237,810, Books $158,990, Per/Ser (Incl. Access Fees) $20,000, AV Equip $27,920, Other Print Mats $900, Electronic Ref Mat (Incl. Access Fees) $30,000. Sal $904,070
Library Holdings: Bk Vols 135,012; Bk Titles 99,554; Per Subs 575
Publications: Newsletter (bi-monthly); Subject Bibliographics
Mem of DuPage Library System
Special Services for the Deaf - TDD
Friends of the Library Group

BARTONVILLE

P ALPHA PARK PUBLIC LIBRARY DISTRICT, 3527 S Airport Rd, 61607-1799. SAN 303-7118. Tel: 309-697-3822. Reference Tel: 309-697-3822, Ext 13. TDD: 309-697-9470. FAX: 309-697-9681. E-Mail: alpha@alphapark.org. Web Site: www.alphapark.org. *Dir*, Jo K Potter; Tel: 309-697-3822, Ext 12, E-Mail: jpotter@alphapark.org; *Ch Servs*, Marcia Brandenberg; *Publ Servs*, Julia Niemeier; Tel: 309-697-3822, Ext 17, E-Mail: jniemeier@alphapark.org; *Publ Servs*, Jason Zimmerman; Tel: 309-697-3822, Ext 25, E-Mail: jzimmerman@alphapark.org; *Tech Servs*, Debbie Wenzel; Tel: 309-697-3822, Ext 16, E-Mail: dwenzel@alphapark.org; Staff 7 (MLS 3, Non-MLS 4)
Founded 1972. Pop 24,275; Circ 184,298
Jul 1999-Jun 2000 Income $863,802, State $172,329, Federal $7,630, Locally Generated Income $683,843. Mats Exp $97,891, Books $67,421, Per/Ser (Incl. Access Fees) $8,000, Electronic Ref Mat (Incl. Access Fees) $22,470. Sal $372,290
Library Holdings: Bk Vols 69,363; Per Subs 355
Special Collections: Peoria State Hospital
Automation Activity & Vendor Info: (Circulation) CARL; (ILL) CARL; (OPAC) CARL
Database Vendor: CARL, OCLC - First Search
Publications: Library Times (bimonthly newsletter)
Mem of Alliance Library System
Partic in RSA
Special Services for the Deaf - TDD

BATAVIA

P BATAVIA PUBLIC LIBRARY DISTRICT,* 335 W Wilson St, 60510. SAN 303-7126. Tel: 630-879-1393. FAX: 630-879-9118. Web Site: www.batavia.lib.il.us. *Dir*, Margaret E Cooper
Founded 1873. Pop 23,855 Sal $307,456 (Prof $144,300)
Library Holdings: Bk Vols 115,000; Per Subs 127
Subject Interests: Local history
Mem of DuPage Library System
Friends of the Library Group

S FERMI NATIONAL ACCELERATOR LABORATORY LIBRARY, PO Box 500, MS 109, 60510-0500. SAN 303-7134. Tel: 630-840-3401. FAX: 630-840-4636. E-Mail: library@fnal.gov. Web Site: www-lib.fnal.gov. *Cat, Coll Develop*, Robert Atkinson; *ILL*, Celina Paul; Staff 6 (MLS 3, Non-MLS 3)

Founded 1967
Library Holdings: Bk Titles 15,000; Per Subs 180
Special Collections: Preprints
Mem of DuPage Library System
Open Mon-Fri 8:30am-5pm

S KANE COUNTY ADULT CORRECTIONS LIBRARY,* 777 E Fabyan Pkwy, 60510-1499. SAN 376-124X. Tel: 630-232-6677. *Librn*, Kathy Steberl
Library Holdings: Bk Titles 2,500; Per Subs 52

BEARDSTOWN

P BEARDSTOWN HOUSTON MEMORIAL LIBRARY, 13 Boulevard Rd, 62618-8119. SAN 303-7142. Tel: 217-323-4204. FAX: 217-323-4217. E-Mail: beardlib@motion.net. *Dir*, Alice Lou Schnake; Staff 1 (Non-MLS 1)
Founded 1904. Pop 6,000; Circ 21,000
May 2000-Apr 2001 Income $79,000. Mats Exp $17,500. Sal $45,000 (Prof $20,800)
Library Holdings: Bk Vols 21,000; Per Subs 60; High Interest/Low Vocabulary Bk Vols 25
Automation Activity & Vendor Info: (Circulation) Sagebrush Corporation
Mem of Alliance Library System
Partic in Resource Sharing Alliance
Open Sept 1-May 31: Mon-Thurs 10-7, Fri 12-4 & Sat 10-12; June 1-Aug 31: Mon & Thurs 10-7, Tues, Wed & Fri 10-4 & Sat 10-12

BEDFORD PARK

P BEDFORD PARK PUBLIC LIBRARY DISTRICT,* 7816 W 65th Pl, 60501. SAN 303-6847. Tel: 708-458-6826. FAX: 708-458-9827. *Dir*, Anne Murphy; *Circ*, Deborah Kalfut; *YA Servs*, Karen Sutherland
Founded 1963. Pop 988; Circ 89,000
Library Holdings: Bk Vols 88,000; Per Subs 223
Special Collections: Can
Publications: Calendar & booklist (monthly); newsletter (quarterly)
Mem of Suburban Library System
Open Mon-Thurs 9-8, Fri 9-5, Sat 9-4

BELLEVILLE

P BELLEVILLE PUBLIC LIBRARY,* 121 E Washington St, 62220. SAN 339-7203. Tel: 618-234-0441. TDD: 618-234-1496. FAX: 618-234-9474. E-Mail: baa@lcls.org. *Dir*, Mary Agnes Schlather; E-Mail: maryagness@lcls.org; *Archivist*, Lou-Ann James; Tel: 618-234-0441, Ext 22, E-Mail: louannj@lcls.org; *ILL*, Karen Beiter; Tel: 618-234-0441, Ext 20, E-Mail: karenb@lcls.org; *Ch Servs*, Terri Bassler; Tel: 618-234-0441, Ext 17, E-Mail: terrib@lcls.org; *Ad Servs*, Michele Bruce; Tel: 618-234-0441, Ext 19, E-Mail: micheleb@lcls.org; *Circ*, Pat Miller; Tel: 618-234-0441, Ext 15, E-Mail: patm@lcls.org; Staff 26 (MLS 1, Non-MLS 25)
Founded 1836. Pop 44,165; Circ 221,203
May 1999-Apr 2000 Income (Main Library and Branch Library) $910,025, State $53,508, City $814,517, Locally Generated Income $42,000. Mats Exp $152,000, Books $115,000, Per/Ser (Incl. Access Fees) $15,000, Micro $2,000, AV Equip $15,000, Manuscripts & Archives $5,000. Sal $442,914 (Prof $44,000)
Library Holdings: Bk Vols 103,935; Per Subs 443
Subject Interests: Area hist, Local history
Special Collections: Geneology
Automation Activity & Vendor Info: (Acquisitions) DRA; (Cataloging) DRA; (Circulation) DRA; (OPAC) DRA
Database Vendor: DRA, Ebsco - EbscoHost, OCLC - First Search
Publications: Anniversary booklet, Walking Tour Guide & Archives Bibliography
Function: ILL available
Mem of Lewis & Clark Library System
Friends of the Library Group
Branches: 1
WEST BRANCH, 3414 W Main St, 62226. SAN 339-7238. Tel: 618-233-4366. FAX: 618-233-1482. E-Mail: baabr@lcls.org. *Librn*, Mary Agnes Schlather; Tel: 618-234-0441, Fax: 618-234-9474; *Br Coordr*, Pat Feldt; E-Mail: patf.lcls.org
Automation Activity & Vendor Info: (Circulation) DRA
Database Vendor: DRA, Ebsco - EbscoHost, GaleNet, OCLC - First Search
Friends of the Library Group

SR LUTHERAN CHURCH-MISSOURI SYNOD, Southern Illinois District Archives,* 2408 Lebanon Ave, 62221. SAN 371-1595. Tel: 618-234-4767. FAX: 618-234-4830. *Exec Dir*, Daniel C Roth
Library Holdings: Bk Vols 60

M MEMORIAL HOSPITAL LIBRARY,* 4500 Memorial Dr, 62226. SAN 321-6594. Tel: 618-233-7750, Ext 5343. FAX: 618-257-5658. *Dir*, Barbara Grout; *Asst Librn*, Ruby Buettner; Staff 2 (MLS 1, Non-MLS 1)
Founded 1974
Library Holdings: Bk Titles 5,000; Per Subs 430
Publications: library infobooklet; Newsletter
Mem of Kaskaskia Libr Syst
Partic in Areawide Hospital Library Consortium Of Southwestern Illinois; BRS; Dialog Corporation; Nat Libr of Med; Regional Med Libr - Region 3
Open Mon-Fri 8-4:30
Friends of the Library Group

M SAINT ELIZABETH'S HOSPITAL, Health Science Library, 211 S Third St, 62222. SAN 303-7169. Tel: 618-234-2120, Ext 1181. FAX: 618-222-4620. Web Site: www.steliz.org. *Dir*, Michael A Campese; E-Mail: michaelc@lcls.org
Founded 1956
Library Holdings: Bk Titles 2,500; Per Subs 323
Subject Interests: Medicine
Mem of Lewis & Clark Library System
Partic in Areawide Hospital Consortium; Dialog Corporation; Med Libr Network; Nat Libr of Med; Regional Med Libr - Region 3

J SOUTHWESTERN ILLINOIS COLLEGE LIBRARY, 2500 Carlyle Ave, 62221. SAN 303-7150. Tel: 618-235-2700, Ext 5341. FAX: 618-235-1578. Web Site: www.bacnet.edu/library. *Dean*, Philip D Carlock; E-Mail: philip.carlock@southwestern.cc.il.us
Founded 1946. Enrl 6,788; Fac 128; Highest Degree: Associate
Jul 1999-Jun 2000 Income $504,642. Mats Exp $85,875, Books $42,000, Per/Ser (Incl. Access Fees) $15,112, Presv $614, Micro $2,037
Library Holdings: Bk Vols 60,433; Bk Titles 58,788; Per Subs 412
Database Vendor: epixtech, inc.
Mem of Shawnee Library System
Partic in NILRC; Saint Louis Regional Library Network; Southern Ill Learning Resources Coop

BELLWOOD

P BELLWOOD PUBLIC LIBRARY, 600 Bohland Ave, 60104-1896. SAN 303-7177. Tel: 708-547-7393. TDD: 708-547-7475. FAX: 708-547-9352. E-Mail: hoags@sls.lib.il.us. Web Site: www.bellwoodlibrary.org. *Admin Dir, Librn*, Jimmi Wooten; E-Mail: wootenj@sls.lib.il.us; *Ad Servs*, Kristin Schultz; E-Mail: schultzk@sls.lib.il.us; *Ref Servs YA*, Karen Fredrickson; *Ch Servs*, Barbara Devereaux; *Circ*, Jackie Spratt; *Assoc Librn*, Audrey Campbell; Staff 27 (MLS 5, Non-MLS 22)
Founded 1932. Pop 20,241; Circ 79,419
May 1997-Apr 1998 Income $963,879, State $25,301, Locally Generated Income $64,525. Mats Exp $103,130, Books $71,889, Per/Ser (Incl. Access Fees) $8,957, Micro $7,678. Sal $310,954 (Prof $125,693)
Library Holdings: Bk Vols 96,789; Per Subs 279
Subject Interests: Illinois
Publications: Bellwood, 1900-1975 (history)
Mem of Suburban Library System
Open Mon-Thu 9:30-9, Fri 9:30-6 & Sat 9:30-4

BELVIDERE

P IDA PUBLIC LIBRARY, 320 N State St, 61008-3299. SAN 303-7193. Tel: 815-544-3838. FAX: 815-544-8909. *Dir, Ref*, Connie Harrison; E-Mail: connieh@nils.lib.il.us; *AV*, Marjorie Hinrichs; *Tech Servs*, June Ottman; *Ch Servs*, Pat Walter; Staff 3 (MLS 3)
Founded 1885. Pop 17,722; Circ 158,873
May 1999-Apr 2000 Income $513,400, State $37,339, City $337,328, Locally Generated Income $138,733. Mats Exp $64,411, Books $42,037, Per/Ser (Incl. Access Fees) $7,556, Micro $150, AV Equip $12,218, Electronic Ref Mat (Incl. Access Fees) $2,450. Sal $246,052
Library Holdings: Bk Vols 70,000; Per Subs 195
Subject Interests: Local history
Automation Activity & Vendor Info: (Cataloging) Innovative Interfaces Inc.; (Circulation) Innovative Interfaces Inc.; (ILL) Innovative Interfaces Inc.; (OPAC) Innovative Interfaces Inc.; (Serials) Innovative Interfaces Inc.
Publications: Ida-Lites (Newsletter)
Mem of Northern Illinois Library System
Open Mon-Fri 9:30-9 & Sat 9:30-5
Friends of the Library Group

BEMENT

P BEMENT PUBLIC LIBRARY DISTRICT,* 349 S Macon, 61813-1412. SAN 303-7207. Tel: 217-678-7101. FAX: 217-678-7034. E-Mail: library@bement.net. *Dir*, Carol Bowen
Pop 2,400; Circ 22,679 Sal $22,000 (Prof $13,000)
Library Holdings: Bk Vols 16,667; Per Subs 75
Subject Interests: Local history
Mem of Lincoln Trail Libraries System
Friends of the Library Group

BENSENVILLE

P BENSENVILLE COMMUNITY PUBLIC LIBRARY, 200 S Church Rd, 60106. SAN 303-7215. Tel: 630-766-4642. FAX: 630-595-9171. E-Mail: library@bensenville.lib.il.us. Web Site: www.bensenville.lib.il.us. *Dir*, Jill

Rodriguez; E-Mail: jill@clearnet.org; *Asst Dir*, Bill Erbes; E-Mail: bill@clearnet.org; *Ch Servs*, Julia Brady; *Circ*, Joan Baader; *Commun Servs*, Jennie Cisna; Staff 8 (MLS 8)
Founded 1960. Pop 22,192; Circ 130,000
Jul 2000-Jun 2001 Income $1,050,000, County $900,000, Locally Generated Income $150,000. Mats Exp $165,000, Books $120,000, Per/Ser (Incl. Access Fees) $25,000, Electronic Ref Mat (Incl. Access Fees) $20,000. Sal $575,000
Library Holdings: Bk Vols 87,000; Bk Titles 80,000; Per Subs 358
Special Collections: Large Print Books; Local History
Automation Activity & Vendor Info: (Acquisitions) epixtech, inc.; (Cataloging) epixtech, inc.; (Circulation) epixtech, inc.; (Course Reserve) epixtech, inc.
Publications: Community News (monthly)
Mem of DuPage Library System

BENTON

P BENTON PUBLIC LIBRARY DISTRICT,* 502 S Main, 62812. SAN 303-7223. Tel: 618-438-7511. FAX: 618-435-2150. Web Site: www.sirin.lib.il.us. *Dir*, Molly Scanlan; Staff 3 (MLS 1, Non-MLS 2)
Founded 1916. Pop 10,452; Circ 60,000
1996-1997 Income $133,762, State $21,780, Locally Generated Income $10,604, Other $1,594. Mats Exp $21,169. Sal $77,375
Library Holdings: Bk Vols 42,000; Per Subs 120
Subject Interests: Fiction, Genealogy, Local history
Special Collections: Southern Illinois History
Automation Activity & Vendor Info: (Circulation) Follett
Mem of Shawnee Library System
Partic in Illinois Library & Information Network
Open Mon-Thurs 10-8, Fri & Sat 10-5:30, Sun 1-5

BERKELEY

P BERKELEY PUBLIC LIBRARY,* 1637 Taft Ave, 60163-1499. SAN 303-7231. Tel: 708-544-6017. FAX: 708-544-7551. *Coll Develop*, Kristen Nimmo
Founded 1946. Pop 5,137; Circ 35,244
Library Holdings: Bk Vols 33,200; Per Subs 82
Special Collections: Local History (Village of Berkeley Historical Coll), bks, doc & artifacts
Automation Activity & Vendor Info: (Cataloging) CLSI LIBS
Mem of Suburban Library System
Friends of the Library Group

BERWYN

P BERWYN PUBLIC LIBRARY,* 2701 Harlem Ave, 60402. SAN 339-7262. Tel: 708-795-8000. FAX: 708-795-8101. *Librn*, Gail Lofgren
Pop 45,426; Circ 211,812
Jan 1998-Dec 1999 Income $1,356,182. Mats Exp $225,310. Sal $771,105
Library Holdings: Bk Vols 156,161; Per Subs 494
Special Collections: Czechoslovakian Language Coll
Publications: Newsletter (quarterly)
Mem of Suburban Library System
Open Mon-Fri 9-9 & Sat 9-5
Friends of the Library Group

M VANGARD HEALTH, (Formerly Macneal Hospital), Macneal Hospital Health Sciences Resource Center, 3249 S Oak Park Ave, 60402. SAN 303-724X. Tel: 708-783-3089. FAX: 708-783-3369. *Mgr*, Andrea Oliver; E-Mail: aoliver@macneal.com
Founded 1950
1998-1999 Income $420,000. Mats Exp $73,100, Books $25,000, Per/Ser (Incl. Access Fees) $35,000, Presv $3,000, Micro $4,000, Other Print Mats $4,000. Sal $160,000 (Prof $120,000)
Library Holdings: Per Subs 250
Subject Interests: Medicine, Nursing
Special Collections: Consumer Health
Automation Activity & Vendor Info: (Circulation) Inmagic, Inc.; (ILL) Inmagic, Inc.
Database Vendor: OCLC - First Search, OVID Technologies
Mem of Suburban Library System
Partic in Illinois Library & Information Network; Metrop Consortium

BETHALTO

P BETHALTO PUBLIC LIBRARY DISTRICT, 321 S Prairie, 62010-1525. SAN 303-7266. Tel: 618-377-8141. FAX: 618-377-3520. E-Mail: bee@lcls.org. Web Site: www.bethaltolibrary.org. *Dir*, Mary Brewster
Founded 1947. Pop 15,280; Circ 95,000
Library Holdings: Bk Vols 30,000; Per Subs 155
Publications: Busy Bee (child newsletter); Prairie Homes (adult newsletter)
Mem of Lewis & Clark Library System

BETHANY

P MARROWBONE PUBLIC LIBRARY DISTRICT,* 216 W Main St, PO Box 246, 61914-0246. SAN 303-7274. Tel: 217-665-3014. FAX: 217-665-3246. *Librn*, Jane Hill; *Asst Librn*, Sally Ascenzo
Founded 1939. Pop 1,973; Circ 34,512
Library Holdings: Bk Vols 20,000; Bk Titles 16,450; Per Subs 63
Automation Activity & Vendor Info: (Circulation) CLSI LIBS
Mem of Rolling Prairie Library System
Open Mon-Sat 10-12, Mon 1-8, Tues-Fri 1-6, Sat 1-4 closed Sun

BIGGSVILLE

P HENDERSON COUNTY DISTRICT LIBRARY,* E Main St, PO Box 159, 61418-0159. SAN 303-7282. Tel: 309-627-2450. FAX: 309-627-2450. E-Mail: hcpl@darkstar.rsa.lib.il.us. Web Site: www.hendersoncounty.lib.il.us. *Librn*, Carolyn Fry; *Asst Librn*, Anita Smith; *Bkmobile Coordr*, Mary Lynn Weibel
Founded 1959. Pop 9,114; Circ 36,065
Library Holdings: Bk Vols 29,161
Mem of Alliance Library System; Western Ill Libr Syst
Open Mon-Sat 10-5

BLANDINSVILLE

P BLANDINSVILLE-HIRE DISTRICT LIBRARY, 130 S Main St, PO Box 50, 61420-0050. SAN 303-7290. Tel: 309-652-3166. FAX: 309-652-3166. E-Mail: blanhire@winco.net. *Librn*, Diana Curtis; *Asst Librn*, Pat Hainline
Founded 1953. Pop 2,864; Circ 27,382
Jul 1999-Jun 2000 Income $66,870, State $4,324, County $60,896, Locally Generated Income $1,650. Mats Exp $61,958, Books $10,104, Per/Ser (Incl. Access Fees) $1,486, AV Equip $265, Electronic Ref Mat (Incl. Access Fees) $800. Sal $31,396 (Prof $18,304)
Library Holdings: Bk Vols 23,000; Per Subs 91
Subject Interests: Antiques, Genealogy, History, Local history
Mem of Alliance Library System
Open Mon & Wed 8:30-8, Tues & Sat 8:30-5, Fri 12:30-5

BLOOMINGDALE

P BLOOMINGDALE PUBLIC LIBRARY, 101 Fairfield Way, 60108-1579. SAN 303-7304. Tel: 630-529-3120. TDD: 630-529-9841. FAX: 630-529-3243. E-Mail: bdref@linc.lib.il.us. Web Site: www.bloomingdale.lib.il.us. *Dir*, Mary E Rodne; E-Mail: mrodne@linc.lib.il.us; *Ad Servs*, Peggy Carlson; E-Mail: pcarlson@linc.lib.il.us; *Ch Servs*, Rosemary Lukas; E-Mail: rlukas@linc.lib.il.us; *Tech Servs*, Sally Mee; E-Mail: smee@linc.lib.il.us; *Tech Coordr*, Brian Meyer; E-Mail: bmeyer@linc.lib.il.us; *Business*, Peg Hartnett; E-Mail: phartnett@linc.lib.il.us; Staff 46 (MLS 11, Non-MLS 35)
Founded 1974. Pop 21,024; Circ 232,034
May 1999-Apr 2000 Income $2,049,467, State $25,936, City $1,865,246, Other $158,285. Mats Exp $1,536,854. Sal $924,866
Library Holdings: Bk Vols 90,302; Per Subs 150
Automation Activity & Vendor Info: (Circulation) DRA
Database Vendor: DRA
Publications: Off the Shelf (newsletter)
Mem of DuPage Library System
Open Mon-Thurs 9-9, Fri & Sat 9-5 & Sun 1-5
Friends of the Library Group

BLOOMINGTON

P BLOOMINGTON PUBLIC LIBRARY, 205 E Olive St, PO Box 3308, 61702-3308. SAN 303-7312. Tel: 309-828-6091. TDD: 309-828-6091. FAX: 309-828-7312. E-Mail: info@bloomingtonlibrary.org. Web Site: www.bloomingtonlibrary.org. *Dir*, Matthew C Kubiak; E-Mail: mattk@bloomingtonlibrary.org; *Mgr*, Gayle Tucker; E-Mail: gayletbpl@yahoo.com; *Ad Servs*, Jane Chamberlain; E-Mail: jchamber@bloomingtonlibrary.org; *Head, Circ*, Linda Hawkins; E-Mail: lindahbpl@yahoo.com; *Ch Servs*, Phyllis Wallace; E-Mail: phyllisw@bloomingtonlibrary.org; *YA Servs*, Carol Reid; E-Mail: go2yourlibrary@angelfire.com; *Per*, Karen Moen; E-Mail: bibliotecha@yahoo.com; *Business*, Kathy Perkins; E-Mail: kperkinsbpl@yahoo.com; *Commun Relations*, Krysta A Tepper; E-Mail: ktepper@bloomingtonlibrary.org; *Electronic Resources, Web Coordr*, Matt Gullett; E-Mail: mattg@bloomingtonlibrary.org; *Outreach Serv*, Carol Torrens; E-Mail: carolt@bloomingtonlibrary.org; *Commun Servs*, Sylvia Brandow; E-Mail: sylviab@bloomingtonlibrary.org; *Bkmobile Coordr*, Laura Kracher; E-Mail: laurakbpl@yahoo.com; Staff 48 (MLS 11, Non-MLS 37)
Founded 1867. Pop 66,000
May 1999-Apr 2000 Income $2,613,768, City $2,242,588, Other $371,180. Mats Exp $273,256, Books $216,932, Per/Ser (Incl. Access Fees) $31,793, AV Equip $8,532, Electronic Ref Mat (Incl. Access Fees) $15,999. Sal $1,353,750 (Prof $345,625)
Library Holdings: Bk Titles 209,570; Per Subs 653
Subject Interests: Genealogy, Illinois
Special Collections: Illinois Coll
Publications: Business Connection, News & Reviews

Mem of Alliance Library System
Partic in Colo Asn of Res Librs; Illinois Library & Information Network; OCLC Online Computer Library Center, Inc
Open Mon-Thurs 9-9, Fri & Sat 9-5, Sun 1-5
Friends of the Library Group
Bookmobiles: 1

S ILLINOIS AGRICULTURAL ASSOCIATION, (IRC), Information Research Center, 1701 Towanda Ave, 61701-2901. (Mail add: PO Box 2901, 61701-2901), SAN 303-7339. Tel: 309-557-2552. FAX: 309-557-3185. *Mgr*, Vince L Sampson; E-Mail: vsampson@davesworld.net; Staff 2 (MLS 1, Non-MLS 1)
Founded 1960
Sep 2000-Aug 2001 Income $400,000. Mats Exp $154,000, Books $21,250, Per/Ser (Incl. Access Fees) $31,200, Micro $2,500, Electronic Ref Mat (Incl. Access Fees) $51,000
Library Holdings: Bk Titles 15,000; Per Subs 500
Subject Interests: Agricultural economics
Automation Activity & Vendor Info: (Cataloging) Sydney; (Circulation) Sydney
Publications: Farm Facts
Mem of Alliance Library System
Partic in Dialog Corporation; Dow Jones Interactive; Illinois Library & Information Network; Libr User Info Syst

C ILLINOIS WESLEYAN UNIVERSITY, Sheean Library, PO Box 2899, 61702-2899. SAN 339-7351. Tel: 309-556-3053. Interlibrary Loan Service Tel: 309-556-3018. FAX: 309-556-3261. E-Mail: ask_us@titan.iwu.edu. Web Site: www.iwu.edu/library. *Dir*, Sue Stroyan; E-Mail: sstroyan@titan.iwu.edu; *Assoc Dir*, Kris Vogel; *Info Res*, Steve Witt; *Cat*, Gloria Redinger; *Acq*, Beth Kraft; *Circ*, Bruce Chamberlain; *ILL*, Tony Heaton; *Archivist, Spec Coll*, Anke Voss-Hubbard; *Per*, Crystal Goshay; *Ser*, Sarah George; *AV*, Mike Limacher; Staff 6 (MLS 6)
Founded 1850. Enrl 1,843; Fac 175; Highest Degree: Bachelor
Library Holdings: Bk Vols 250,000; Per Subs 1,023
Subject Interests: Music, Nursing
Special Collections: 20th Century Literature (Gernon Coll); Political Science & Government (Leslie Arends Coll), flm, memorabilia
Automation Activity & Vendor Info: (Cataloging) DRA; (Circulation) DRA; (OPAC) DRA; (Serials) DRA
Publications: Newsletter (quarterly)
Mem of Alliance Library System
Partic in Ill Libr Computer Systs Org; Illinois Library & Information Network; OCLC Online Computer Library Center, Inc
Departmental Libraries:
MUSIC Tel: 309-556-3003. *Librn*, Robert Delvin

S MCLEAN COUNTY HISTORICAL SOCIETY, Stevenson-Ives Library, 200 N Main, 61701. SAN 303-7347. Tel: 309-827-0428. FAX: 309-827-0100. E-Mail: mch@darkstar.rsa.lib.il.us. Web Site: www.mchistory.org. *Dir*, Greg Koos; *Archivist, Librn*, Patricia A Hamilton; Staff 2 (MLS 1, Non-MLS 1)
Founded 1892
Apr 1999-Mar 2000 Income $42,900
Library Holdings: Bk Titles 7,000
Subject Interests: Genealogy, Local history, Material culture
Special Collections: Adlai Stevenson Lectures on International Affairs, papers; Childrens Home Papers; Edward J Lewis Diaries & Civil War Correspondence; Ensenberger Furniture; Ezra M Prince Manuscripts & Correspondence; History (McLean County, Civil War & Illinois); Hutton Family Coll; Illinois Soldiers & Sailors; McLean County Home Bureau Papers; McLean County Photographs (1850 to present); Milo Cluster Manuscripts; Minnie Salzman Stevens Papers; Moon Family Coll; Phoenix Nursery; Political & Social History of McLean County, archives; Sons of Union Veterans'; William Brigham Papers; William Wantling Papers, poetry mss & correspondence
Automation Activity & Vendor Info: (Cataloging) Follett; (OPAC) TLC
Publications: Archive index with unpublished calendar; Indexes
Restriction: Non-circulating to the public
Mem of Alliance Library System
Partic in RSA
Library collections belong to Historical Society, McLean County Genealogical Society, Letitia Green Stevenson Chapter NSDAR

S PANTAGRAPH-NEWSPAPER LIBRARY, 301 W Washington, 61702-2907. (Mail add: PO Box 2907, 61702-2907), SAN 303-7320. Tel: 309-829-9411, Ext 247. FAX: 309-829-7000. E-Mail: library@pantagraph.com. *Chief Librn*, Diane Logsdon
Founded 1933
Library Holdings: Bk Vols 648; Bk Titles 500
Database Vendor: Lexis-Nexis
Mem of Alliance Library System

SR ST JOHN'S LUTHERAN CHURCH LIBRARY, 1617 E Emerson St, 61701. SAN 371-9987. Tel: 309-827-6121. FAX: 309-829-3866. *Librn*, Marge Mehlberg
Founded 1970
Library Holdings: Bk Titles 600

SR SECOND PRESBYTERIAN CHURCH, Capen Memorial Library, 313 N East St, 61701. SAN 303-7355. Tel: 309-828-6297. FAX: 309-828-7038. E-Mail: secondpres@hotmail.com. Web Site: www.secondpres.com. *Dir*, Carl Lauer
Library Holdings: Bk Vols 3,000
Open Mon-Fri 8:30-4:30, Sun 8:30-11, closed Sat

R UNITED METHODIST CHURCH ILLINOIS GREAT RIVERS CONFERENCE, Peter Cartwright Memorial Library, 1211 N Park St, PO Box 515, 61702-0515. SAN 303-7371. Tel: 309-828-5092. FAX: 309-829-4820. *In Charge*, Richard Chrisman
Founded 1886
Library Holdings: Bk Titles 5,000
Subject Interests: Evangelicalism
Special Collections: Conference Records; Local Church Records & Papers of Some Ministers; Peter Cartwright Material
Publications: Illinois Great Rivers Historical Messenger

BLUE ISLAND

P CITY OF BLUE ISLAND PUBLIC LIBRARY, 2433 York St, 60406-2011. SAN 303-738X. Tel: 708-388-1078. FAX: 708-388-1143. E-Mail: bis@sls.lib.il.us. Web Site: www.blueisland.org/bipl/library.html. *Dir*, David J Seleb; Tel: 708-388-1097, E-Mail: seleb@sis.lib.il.us; *Asst Dir*, Barbara Aron; *ILL*, Ann Jarret; *Ch Servs*, Deborah Beasley-Myers; E-Mail: beasleyd@sis.lib.il.us; *Tech Servs*, Julie Mueller; *Head Ref*, Lynne Ingersoll; E-Mail: ingersol@sis.lib.il.us; *Head, Circ*, David Boras; E-Mail: borasd@sis.lib.il.us; *YA Servs*, Julie Weber; E-Mail: weberj@sis.lib.il.us; Staff 5 (MLS 5)
Founded 1897. Pop 21,000; Circ 100,310
May 2000-Apr 2001 Income $681,408, State $33,178, Locally Generated Income $614,600, Other $33,630. Mats Exp $97,700, Books $91,500, Per/Ser (Incl. Access Fees) $23,250, AV Equip $6,200. Sal $392,730
Library Holdings: Bk Vols 81,683; Bk Titles 72,811; Per Subs 315
Special Collections: Blue Island Area History
Automation Activity & Vendor Info: (Circulation) Innovative Interfaces Inc.; (OPAC) Innovative Interfaces Inc.
Database Vendor: Ebsco - EbscoHost, Innovative Interfaces INN - View, OCLC - First Search
Publications: Library Guide; The Bookworm (Newsletter)
Mem of Suburban Library System
Museum Room houses permanent exhibit: "Blue Island, 1835-1985"
Friends of the Library Group

M SAINT FRANCIS HOSPITAL & HEALTH CENTER, Medical Library, 12935 S Gregory St, 60406. SAN 375-9431. Tel: 708-597-2000, Ext 5388. FAX: 708-824-4494. *Librn*, Kathy Tobar
Library Holdings: Bk Titles 800; Per Subs 85
Restriction: Not open to public
Mem of Suburban Library System
Partic in Chicago & South Consortium

BLUE MOUND

P BLUE MOUND MEMORIAL LIBRARY DISTRICT, 213 N St Marie St, PO Box 317, 62513. SAN 303-7401. Tel: 217-692-2774. FAX: 217-692-2191. *Head Librn*, Linda Perona; *Assoc Librn*, Alice Reed
Founded 1948. Pop 2,554; Circ 24,872
Library Holdings: Per Subs 46
Mem of Rolling Prairie Library System
Partic in Heartland Consortia; Illinois Library & Information Network
Open Mon, Tues, Wed & Fri 10-6, Thurs 10-8, Sat 10-2, closed Sun

BLUFFS

P BLUFFS PUBLIC LIBRARY,* Bluffs St, PO Box 177, 62621. SAN 303-741X. Tel: 217-754-3804. FAX: 217-754-3804. *Librn*, Ellen Graves
Pop 821; Circ 2,793
Library Holdings: Bk Vols 3,730; Per Subs 12
Mem of Alliance Library System
Open Tues, Thurs & Fri 1-5, Wed 1-7, Sat 9-12 & 1-5 closed Sun & Mon

BOLINGBROOK

P FOUNTAINDALE PUBLIC LIBRARY DISTRICT,* 300 W Briarcliff Rd, 60440-2894. SAN 339-7475. Tel: 630-759-2102. TDD: 630-759-0408. FAX: 630-759-6180, 630-759-9519. Web Site: www.fountaindale.lib.il.us. *Dir*, Lydia M Acosta; Tel: 630-759-2102, Ext 33, E-Mail: lmacosta@htls.lib.il.us; *Dep Dir*, Karen T Anderson; Tel: 630-759-2102, Ext 21, E-Mail: ktanderson@htls.lib.il.us; *Librn*, Nancy J Hackett; Tel: 815-886-2030, Ext 29, E-Mail: njhackett@htls.lib.il.us; *Coll Develop*, Jane M Whiteside; Tel: 630-759-2102, Ext 12, E-Mail: jmwhiteside@htls.lib.il.us; *Res*, Marianne M Thompson; Tel: 630-759-2102, Ext 36, E-Mail: mmthompson@htls.lib.il.us; *Circ*, Yvonne M McCurrie; Tel: 815-886-2030, Ext 30, E-Mail: ymccurrie@htls.lib.il.us; *Circ*, Cynthia E Palermo; Tel: 630-759-2102, Ext 19, E-Mail: cpalermo@htls.lib.il.us; *Tech Servs*, Pat J Auriene; Tel: 630-759-2102, Ext

25, E-Mail: pjauriene@htls.lib.il.us; *Automation Syst Coordr*, Sue Furman; Tel: 630-759-2102, Ext 20, E-Mail: slfurman@htls.lib.il.us; *Ch Servs*, Carol M Ellman; Tel: 815-886-2030, Ext 26, E-Mail: cmellman@htls.lib.il.us; *Ad Servs*, Helen Valantinas; Tel: 815-886-2030, Ext 20, E-Mail: hvalantinas@htls.lib.il.us; Staff 96 (MLS 18, Non-MLS 78)
Founded 1970. Pop 66,858; Circ 673,221
Jul 1998-Jun 1999 Income $4,567,419, State $176,748, County $3,842,230, Locally Generated Income $318,441. Mats Exp $403,459, Books $365,316, Per/Ser (Incl. Access Fees) $23,998, Micro $14,145. Sal $2,212,852 (Prof $997,518)
Library Holdings: Bk Vols 230,633; Per Subs 651
Automation Activity & Vendor Info: (Circulation) Gaylord
Database Vendor: Dialog, IAC - SearchBank, OCLC - First Search
Mem of Heritage Trail Library System
Friends of the Library Group
Branches: 1
ROMEOVILLE BRANCH, 201 Normantown Rd, Romeoville, 60446-1261. SAN 339-7505. Tel: 815-886-2030. FAX: 815-886-0686. Web Site: www.htls.lib.il.us/bbb/. *Librn*, N J Hackett; *Ch Servs*, C M Breska; *Circ*, Y M McCurrie
Library Holdings: Bk Vols 90,083
Subject Interests: Medicine
Friends of the Library Group

BOURBONNAIS

P BOURBONNAIS PUBLIC LIBRARY DISTRICT, 250 John Casey Rd, 60914. SAN 324-5713. Tel: 815-933-1727. FAX: 815-933-1961.; Staff 1 (MLS 1)
Founded 1982. Pop 18,337; Circ 106,000 Sal $95,168
Library Holdings: Bk Titles 45,000; Per Subs 126
Automation Activity & Vendor Info: (Circulation) GEAC
Mem of Heritage Trail Library System
Friends of the Library Group

CR OLIVET NAZARENE UNIVERSITY, Benner Library & Resource Center, 1 University Ave, 60914-2271. SAN 303-7428. Tel: 815-939-5354. Reference Tel: 815-939-5355. FAX: 815-939-5170. Web Site: www.library.olivet.edu. *Dir*, Kathryn R Boyens; Tel: 815-939-5211, E-Mail: kboyens@olivet.edu; *Cat*, Mary Ada Dillinger; Tel: 815-939-5144, E-Mail: mdilling@olivet.edu; *Info Tech*, Craighton T Hippenhammer; Tel: 815-939-5145, E-Mail: chhammer@olivet.edu; *Ref*, Diane Fox; Tel: 815-928-5438, E-Mail: dfox@olivet.edu; *Spec Coll*, Elesha A Keen; Tel: 815-939-5061, E-Mail: ekeen@olivet.edu. Subject Specialists: *Creative writing*, Craighton T Hippenhammer; *Education*, Elesha A Keen; *Education*, Mary Ada Dillinger; *Education*, Diane Fox; *General*, Kathryn R Boyens; *General*, Elesha A Keen; *General*, Craighton T Hippenhammer; *General*, Mary Ada Dillinger; *General*, Diane Fox; *Health*, Elesha A Keen; *Music*, Kathryn R Boyens; *Technology*, Craighton T Hippenhammer; Staff 11 (MLS 5, Non-MLS 6)
Founded 1909. Enrl 2,180; Fac 105; Highest Degree: Master
Jul 1999-Jun 2000 Income Parent Institution $930,816. Mats Exp $218,767, Books $83,982, Per/Ser (Incl. Access Fees) $79,033, Presv $1,800, Micro $10,540, Electronic Ref Mat (Incl. Access Fees) $45,212. Sal $498,146 (Prof $198,495)
Library Holdings: Bk Vols 166,500; Bk Titles 152,500; Per Subs 925
Subject Interests: Education, Nursing, Theology
Special Collections: Jacob Arminus Coll, bks, microflm; John Wesley Coll; Olivet Nazarene Univ Archives
Automation Activity & Vendor Info: (Acquisitions) GEAC; (Cataloging) GEAC; (Circulation) GEAC; (ILL) GEAC; (OPAC) GEAC
Database Vendor: Ebsco - EbscoHost, GaleNet, Lexis-Nexis, OCLC - First Search, Silverplatter Information Inc.
Publications: The Resource (Newsletter)
Mem of Heritage Trail Library System
Partic in Ill Coop Coll Mgt Prog; ILLINET
Special Services for the Blind - Kurzweil Reading Machine

BRADFORD

P BRADFORD PUBLIC LIBRARY DISTRICT,* 111 S Peoria St, 61421. SAN 303-7444. Tel: 309-897-8400. FAX: 309-897-8400. E-Mail: brpl@darkstar.rsa.lib.il.us. *Librn*, Mary Jason; *Asst Librn*, Cinda Scott
Founded 1924. Pop 678; Circ 6,198
Jul 1998-Jun 1999 Income (Main Library Only) $34,832, State $2,315, County $31,643, Other $874. Mats Exp $6,479, Books $3,795, Per/Ser (Incl. Access Fees) $798, AV Equip $1,025, Electronic Ref Mat (Incl. Access Fees) $861. Sal $13,173
Library Holdings: Bk Vols 8,459; Per Subs 20
Mem of Alliance Library System
Open Mon, Tues & Thurs 2-8, Wed 10-12 & 2-6, Fri 2-6, Sat 9-12

BRADLEY

M AVENTIS BEHRING LLC LIBRARY, (Formerly Centeon LLC Library), Rte 50, Armour Rd, 60915. (Mail add: PO Box 511, 60901), SAN 304-3037. Tel: 815-929-4343. FAX: 815-936-6610. *Librn*, Mary Blunk; Staff 1 (MLS 1)
Founded 1954
Library Holdings: Bk Vols 1,000; Per Subs 120
Subject Interests: Biochemistry, Engineering, Hematology, Pharmaceutical science
Restriction: Not open to public

P BRADLEY PUBLIC LIBRARY DISTRICT,* 296 N Fulton, 60915. SAN 303-7452. Tel: 815-932-6245. FAX: 815-932-6278. *Dir*, Renee Gorham
Founded 1944. Pop 11,152; Circ 94,508
Library Holdings: Bk Vols 33,438; Per Subs 167
Mem of Bur Oak Libr Syst
Open Mon, Wed & Fri 9:30-6, Tues & Thurs 9:30-8, Sat 9-5, closed Sun
Friends of the Library Group

BRAIDWOOD

P FOSSIL RIDGE PUBLIC LIBRARY, 386 Kennedy Rd, 60408. SAN 303-7460. Tel: 815-458-2187. FAX: 815-458-2042. *Dir*, Janie Votta
Founded 1970. Pop 11,350; Circ 131,488
Jul 1999-Jun 2000 Income $702,388, State $2,000, County $659,087, Other $32,278. Mats Exp $110,000, Books $92,932. Sal $264,237
Library Holdings: Bk Vols 50,000; Bk Titles 47,396; Per Subs 160
Mem of Heritage Trail Library System
Open Mon-Thurs 9-9, Fri 9-6, Sat 9-3, Sun 1-5 (Oct 1-May 31)
Friends of the Library Group
Bookmobiles: 1

BREESE

P BREESE PUBLIC LIBRARY, 530 N Third St, 62230. SAN 303-7479. Tel: 618-526-7361. FAX: 618-526-0143. E-Mail: bra@lcls.org. *Dir*, Jan Thomas; *Asst Librn*, Diane Holtgrave
Founded 1962. Pop 3,567; Circ 31,686
May 1998-Apr 1999 Income $90,506, State $4,418, City $78,522, Locally Generated Income $6,726, Other $840. Mats Exp $16,466, Books $8,000, Per/Ser (Incl. Access Fees) $1,200, Other Print Mats $500, Electronic Ref Mat (Incl. Access Fees) $6,766. Sal $40,678
Library Holdings: Bk Vols 23,000; Bk Titles 20,000; Per Subs 75
Automation Activity & Vendor Info: (Acquisitions) DRA; (Cataloging) DRA; (Circulation) DRA
Mem of Lewis & Clark Library System
Open Mon-Fri 10-8, Sat 10-3, closed Sun

BRIDGEVIEW

P BRIDGEVIEW PUBLIC LIBRARY, 7840 W 79th St, 60455. SAN 303-7487. Tel: 708-458-2880. FAX: 708-458-3553. E-Mail: bvs@sls.lib.il.us. Web Site: www.bridgeviewlibrary.org. *Dir*, Kari Hanson
Founded 1966. Pop 14,402
Mem of Suburban Library System

BRIGHTON

P BRIGHTON MEMORIAL PUBLIC LIBRARY,* 106 North St, 62012. SAN 375-9911. Tel: 618-372-8450. FAX: 618-372-7450. *Librn*, Lillian Bennet; *Librn*, Virginia Dawdy
Library Holdings: Bk Titles 11,000

BRIMFIELD

P BRIMFIELD PUBLIC LIBRARY,* 111 S Galena St, PO Box 207, 61517. SAN 303-7495. Tel: 309-446-9575. FAX: 309-446-9357. E-Mail: bipl@darkstar.rsq.lib.il.us. *Librn*, Patricia Smith; *Asst Dir*, Glenda Wilson
Founded 1924. Circ 17,373
Library Holdings: Bk Vols 22,000; Per Subs 39
Mem of Alliance Library System
Open Tues & Fri 3-6, Wed 9-12 & 3-7, Thurs 3-7, Sat 9-12

BROADVIEW

P BROADVIEW PUBLIC LIBRARY DISTRICT,* 2226 S 16th Ave, 60156. SAN 303-7509. Tel: 708-345-1325. FAX: 708-345-5024. E-Mail: brs@sos.lib.il.us. Web Site: www.sos.lib.il.us/brs. *Dir*, Carl J Caruso; *Tech Servs*, Robert Lafferty; *Publ Servs*, Joseph Bondi; *Ref*, John Flanagan
Founded 1955. Pop 8,713; Circ 68,922 Sal $279,000
Library Holdings: Bk Vols 65,658; Per Subs 120
Mem of Suburban Library System
Open Mon-Thurs 10-9, Fri & Sat 10-5

BROOKFIELD

P BROOKFIELD FREE PUBLIC LIBRARY,* 3609 Grand Blvd, 60513. SAN 303-7525. Tel: 708-485-6917. FAX: 708-485-5172. E-Mail: bfs@sls.lib.il.us. *Librn*, Mark A West; E-Mail: markwest@brookfield-pl.org; *Circ*, Antonia

Hergenrother; *Ad Servs, Ref*, John Krause
Founded 1913. Pop 18,876; Circ 132,008 Sal $215,266
Library Holdings: Bk Vols 63,383; Per Subs 191
Mem of Suburban Library System
Friends of the Library Group

S CHICAGO ZOOLOGICAL SOCIETY LIBRARY,* Brookfield Zoo, 8400 W 31st St, 60513. SAN 303-7533. Tel: 708-485-0263, Ext 580. FAX: 708-485-3532. *Librn*, Mary Rabb
Library Holdings: Bk Vols 10,000; Per Subs 250
Subject Interests: Animals, behavior of, Natural history, Veterinary medicine, Zoology

BRUSSELS

P SOUTH COUNTY PUBLIC LIBRARY DISTRICT,* PO Box 93, 62013. SAN 303-7541. Tel: 618-883-2522. *Librn*, Nancy Moennig
Pop 1,249; Circ 4,012
Library Holdings: Bk Vols 5,000
Mem of Lewis & Clark Library System
Open Mon, Tues, Wed & Fri 9:30-4, closed Thurs, Sat & Sun

BUDA

P MASON MEMORIAL PUBLIC LIBRARY,* 104 W Main St, PO Box 55, 61314. SAN 303-755X. Tel: 309-895-7701. FAX: 309-895-7701. *In Charge*, Jeannie Jarigese
Pop 563; Circ 6,848
Library Holdings: Bk Vols 10,325; Per Subs 48
Subject Interests: Genealogy, Local history
Mem of Alliance Library System; Ill Valley Libr Syst
Open Mon & Fri 1-5, Tues & Sat 11-5, Wed 1-8

BUNKER HILL

P BUNKER HILL PUBLIC LIBRARY, 220 E Warren St, PO Box P, 62014. SAN 303-7568. Tel: 618-585-4736. E-Mail: bhe@lcls.org. Web Site: bhil.com/~bhlibrary/. *Librn*, Carol Weindel
Pop 1,722; Circ 8,390
May 1999-Apr 2000 Income $38,934, State $2,303, City $13,475, Locally Generated Income $23,156. Mats Exp $2,070, Books $1,580, Per/Ser (Incl. Access Fees) $462, Micro $28. Sal $14,353
Library Holdings: Bk Vols 16,089; Per Subs 46
Mem of Lewis & Clark Library System

BURBANK

P PRAIRIE TRAILS PUBLIC LIBRARY DISTRICT, 8449 S Moody, 60459-2525. SAN 303-7576. Tel: 708-430-3688. FAX: 708-430-5596. Web Site: www.sls.lib.il.us/PTS. *Dir*, Ruth E Faklis; *Asst Librn*, Sarah Horn; *Ref*, Nicki Seidl; Staff 18 (MLS 4, Non-MLS 14)
Founded 1969. Pop 28,602; Circ 108,244
Library Holdings: Bk Titles 48,117; Per Subs 154
Subject Interests: Adult fiction, Audio bks, Large print
Database Vendor: Innovative Interfaces INN - View
Publications: Newsletter (quarterly)
Mem of Suburban Library System

BUREAU

P LEEPERTOWN TOWNSHIP PUBLIC LIBRARY, 201 E Nebraska, 61315. (Mail add: PO Box 80, 61315), SAN 303-7584. Tel: 815-659-3283. FAX: 815-659-3363. E-Mail: ltlibrary@netscape.net. *Librn*, Marilyn Dovcette
Founded 1976. Pop 518
Library Holdings: Bk Titles 3,000; Per Subs 12
Special Collections: Spanish language
Mem of Heritage Trail Library System
Open Mon, Wed & Fri 1-4, Sat 10-12

BURR RIDGE

P SUBURBAN LIBRARY SYSTEM, 125 Tower Dr, 60521. SAN 339-753X. Tel: 630-734-5000. Toll Free Tel: 800-310-5509. FAX: 630-734-5050. E-Mail: sls@sls.lib.il.us. Web Site: www.sls.lib.il.us. *Exec Dir*, Louise McAulay; Tel: 630-734-5146, E-Mail: mcaulayl@sls.lib.il.us; Staff 19 (MLS 15, Non-MLS 4)
Founded 1965
Jul 1999-Jun 2000 Income $2,672,992, State $2,526,534, Other $146,458. Mats Exp $80,729, Books $47,679, Per/Ser (Incl. Access Fees) $33,050. Sal $1,483,678 (Prof $906,368)
Library Holdings: Bk Vols 13,755; Per Subs 486
Automation Activity & Vendor Info: (Acquisitions) Innovative Interfaces Inc.; (Cataloging) Innovative Interfaces Inc.; (Circulation) Innovative Interfaces Inc.; (ILL) Innovative Interfaces Inc.; (OPAC) Innovative Interfaces Inc.; (Serials) Innovative Interfaces Inc.
Database Vendor: DRA, Ebsco - EbscoHost, Innovative Interfaces INN - View, OCLC - First Search
Publications: Insurance Manual for Illinois Public Library; SLS Directory; SLS Union List of Serials
Member Libraries: Acorn Public Library District; Adventist Health System, Midwest Region - Hinsdale Hospital; Alberto-Culver Co; Alliance of American Insurers; Alsip-Merrionette Park Library; Anderson-Oglesby Public Library; Bedford Park Public Library District; Bellwood Public Library; Benedictine University; Berkeley Public Library; Berwyn Public Library; Bridgeview Public Library; Broadview Public Library District; Brookfield Free Public Library; Calumet City Public Library; Calumet Park Public Library; Chicago Heights Free Public Library; Chicago Ridge Public Library; Christ Hospital & Medical Center; Cicero Public Library; City of Blue Island Public Library; Clarendon Hills Public Library; Clinton-Macomb Public Library; Columbia-La Grange Memorial Hospital; Concordia University; Crestwood Public Library District; Crete Public Library District; Dolton Public Library District; Dominican University; Eisenhower Public Library District; Elmhurst College; Elmhurst Public Library; Elmwood Park Public Library; Evergreen Park Public Library; Flossmoor Public Library; Forest Park Public Library; Frankfort Public Library District; Glenwood-Lynwood Public Library District; Governors State University; Grande Prairie Public Library District; Green Hills Public Library District; Harvey Public Library District; Hillside Public Library; Hinsdale Public Library; Hodgkins Public Library District; Hometown Public Library; Homewood Public Library District; Illinois Institute Of Technology; Indian Prairie Public Library District; Ingalls Hospital; Justice Public Library District; La Grange Park Public Library District; La Grange Public Library; Lansing Public Library; Lisle Library District; Lyons Public Library; Matteson Public Library; Maywood Public Library; Melrose Park Public Library; Midlothian Public Library; Moraine Valley Community College; Morton Arboretum; Morton College; Nancy L Mcconathy Public Library; Navistar International Transportation Corp; North Riverside Public Library District; Northlake Public Library District; Oak Forest Hospital; Oak Lawn Public Library; Oak Park Public Library; Orland Park Public Library; Palos Community Hospital; Palos Heights Public Library; Palos Park Public Library; Park Forest Public Library; Prairie Trails Public Library District; R R Donnelley & Sons Company; Richton Park Public Library District; River Forest Public Library; River Grove Public Library District; Riverdale Public Library District; Riverside Public Library; Saint Francis Hospital & Health Center; Schiller Park Public Library; South Cook ISC4 Library; South Holland Public Library; South Suburban College Library; Steger-South Chicago Heights Public Library District; Sterling Heights Public Library; Stickney-Forest View Public Library District; Summit Public Library District; Thomas Ford Memorial Library; Thornton Public Library; Tinley Park Public Library; Triton College Library; University Park Public Library District; Vangard Health; West Suburban Hospital Medical Center; Westchester Public Library; Westmont Public Library; William Leonard Public Library District; Woodridge Public Library; Woodridge School District No 68; Worth Public Library District
Partic in Illinois Library & Information Network

BUSHNELL

P BUSHNELL PUBLIC LIBRARY,* 455 N Dean, 61422-1299. SAN 303-7592. Tel: 309-772-2060. FAX: 309-772-2060. E-Mail: bush@darkstar.rsa.lib.il.us, plibrary@Bushnell.net. Web Site: www.homepage.Bushnell.net/~plib. *Dir*, Marcia Broady; *Asst Dir*, Wendy Preisoner
Pop 4,706; Circ 25,639
Library Holdings: Bk Vols 25,620; Bk Titles 24,895; Per Subs 77
Special Collections: Peter Newell Coll
Mem of Alliance Library System

BYRON

P BYRON PUBLIC LIBRARY DISTRICT, 109 N Franklin St, PO Box 434, 61010-0434. SAN 303-7606. Tel: 815-234-5107. FAX: 815-234-5582. E-Mail: byronlibrary@mwci.net. Web Site: www.byron.lib.il.us. *Dir*, Penny O'Rourke
Founded 1916. Pop 5,847; Circ 75,569
Jul 1999-Jun 2000 Income $565,773, County $306,137, Locally Generated Income $251,156. Mats Exp $43,739, Books $39,739, Per/Ser (Incl. Access Fees) $4,000. Sal $103,608 (Prof $47,000)
Library Holdings: Bk Titles 42,745; Per Subs 90
Special Collections: Commonwealth Edison
Automation Activity & Vendor Info: (Cataloging) TLC; (Circulation) TLC; (OPAC) TLC
Mem of Northern Illinois Library System

CAHOKIA

P CAHOKIA PUBLIC LIBRARY DISTRICT,* 140 Cahokia Park Dr, 62206-2129. SAN 303-7614. Tel: 618-332-1491. FAX: 618-332-1104. E-Mail: cha@lcls.org. Web Site: gatenet.lcls.lib.il.us/cha/library.htm. *Dir*, M Loretta Lopinot
Founded 1963. Pop 17,550; Circ 70,453

1999-2000 Income $289,603. Sal $111,708
Library Holdings: Bk Vols 29,588; Per Subs 79
Automation Activity & Vendor Info: (Circulation) DRA
Mem of Lewis & Clark Library System
Friends of the Library Group

CAIRO

P CAIRO PUBLIC LIBRARY, 1609 Washington Ave, 62914-1862. (Mail add: PO Box 151, 62914-0151), SAN 303-7630. Tel: 618-734-1840. FAX: 618-734-9346. *Librn*, Monica L Smith
Founded 1884. Pop 4,846; Circ 32,800
Library Holdings: Bk Vols 48,546; Per Subs 60
Special Collections: Army & Navy Records; Census Microfilm for 16 Southern Illinois Counties; Civil War Coll; Jesuit Relations; Local Newspapers on Microfilm from 1848; WPA Art
Mem of Shawnee Library System

CALUMET CITY

P CALUMET CITY PUBLIC LIBRARY, 660 Manistee Ave, 60409. SAN 303-7649. Tel: 708-862-6220. Circulation Tel: 708-862-6220, Ext 245. Reference Tel: 708-862-6220, Ext 248. FAX: 708-862-0872. E-Mail: ccs@sls.lib.il.us. Web Site: www.calumetcitypl.org. *Dir*, Vickie L Novak; Tel: 708-862-6220, Ext 244, E-Mail: vnovak@calumetcitypl.org; *YA Servs*, Gale Edgren-Krekovich; *Ad Servs*, William Pixley; E-Mail: wpixley@calumetcitypl.org; *Tech Servs*, Marilyn Okaiteye; *Ref*, Patrick Coffey; *Ref*, Lola Porter; *Circ*, Linda Castaing; E-Mail: lcastaing@calumetcitypl.org; Staff 7 (MLS 5, Non-MLS 2)
Founded 1927. Pop 37,840; Circ 268,196
May 1998-Apr 1999 Income $820,029. Mats Exp $165,961, Books $125,000, Per/Ser (Incl. Access Fees) $15,260, Presv $968, Micro $8,488, AV Equip $16,245. Sal $532,283 (Prof $186,752)
Library Holdings: Bk Vols 123,957; Per Subs 396
Automation Activity & Vendor Info: (Circulation) Innovative Interfaces Inc.
Publications: Library Links (quarterly newsletter)
Mem of Suburban Library System

CALUMET PARK

P CALUMET PARK PUBLIC LIBRARY,* 1500 W 127th St, 60827. SAN 303-7657. Tel: 708-385-5768. FAX: 708-385-8816. *Dir*, Melody E Coleman
Pop 8,788; Circ 15,770
Library Holdings: Bk Vols 20,000; Per Subs 90
Special Collections: Lupus
Mem of Suburban Library System

CAMBRIDGE

P CAMBRIDGE PUBLIC LIBRARY DISTRICT,* 212 W Center St, 61238-1239. SAN 303-7665. Tel: 309-937-2233. FAX: 309-937-2873. E-Mail: camblib@geneseo.net. *Librn*, Eleanor Sponsel
Pop 3,394
Library Holdings: Bk Vols 23,000; Per Subs 65
Subject Interests: Local history
Mem of Alliance Library System

CAMP POINT

P CAMP POINT PUBLIC LIBRARY DISTICT,* 206 E State St, PO Box 377, 62320. SAN 303-7673. Tel: 217-593-7021. FAX: 217-593-6121. E-Mail: cplibrary@adams.net. *Dir, Librn*, Ellen Scheuermann; *Librn*, Debra Rossiter
Founded 1906. Pop 3,138; Circ 12,648
Jul 1998-Jun 1999 Income $41,000. Mats Exp $5,000. Sal $19,000
Library Holdings: Bk Vols 10,650; Per Subs 38
Mem of Alliance Library System
Open Mon & Thurs 2-6, Tues 10-12 & 2-6, Wed & Fri 2-8, Sat 10-2

CANTON

M GRAHAM HOSPITAL ASSOCIATION, Medical Staff Library - School of Nursing Library, 210 W Walnut St, 61520. SAN 303-7681. Tel: 309-647-5240, Ext 2343. FAX: 309-649-5105. E-Mail: ghsn@darkstar.rsa.lib.il.us. Web Site: www.rsa.lib.il.us/~ghsn/home.htm. *Dir Libr Serv*, Michelle Quinones; *Ref*, Darleen Richardson
Jul 1999-Jun 2000 Mats Exp $23,500, Books $2,700, Per/Ser (Incl. Access Fees) $18,000, AV Equip $2,800. Sal $34,008
Library Holdings: Bk Vols 1,715; Per Subs 107
Subject Interests: Medicine, Nursing
Database Vendor: OCLC - First Search
Mem of Alliance Library System
Partic in Health Sci Librns of Ill; Heart Of Illinois Library Consortium

S ILLINOIS DEPARTMENT OF CORRECTIONS, Illinois River Correctional Center Library, PO Box 999, 61520. SAN 371-6600. Tel: 309-647-7030, Ext 549, 309-647-7030, Ext 550. *Librn*, Don Burkhart; *Asst Librn*, Roberta Fairburn; Staff 12 (MLS 2, Non-MLS 10)
Library Holdings: Bk Vols 17,778; Per Subs 27
Mem of Alliance Library System
Partic in Ill Valley Libr Syst

P PARLIN INGERSOLL PUBLIC LIBRARY,* 205 W Chestnut St, 61520. SAN 303-769X. Tel: 309-647-0064, 309-647-0328. FAX: 309-647-8117. *Dir*, Randy Wilson; *Ch Servs*, Linda Schultz; *Ref*, Kim Bunner
Pop 14,652; Circ 212,829
Library Holdings: Bk Titles 63,913; Per Subs 204
Special Collections: Fulton County History Coll
Automation Activity & Vendor Info: (Circulation) epixtech, inc.
Mem of Alliance Library System; Ill Valley Libr Syst
Partic in OCLC Online Computer Library Center, Inc
Open Mon-Thurs 9-8, Fri 9-6, Sat 9-4 & Sun 12-5

J SPOON RIVER COLLEGE, Learning Resource Center, 23235 N County Rte 22, 61520. SAN 303-7703. Tel: 309-647-4645. Circulation Tel: 309-649-6313. Reference Tel: 309-649-6222. FAX: 309-649-6235. Web Site: www.rsa.lib.il.us/~lbell/src/welcome.html. *Dir Libr Serv*, Lori Bell; E-Mail: lbell@src.cc.il.us; *Head, Circ*, Michelle Florea; E-Mail: mflorea@src.cc.il.us; *Head Tech Servs*, Monica Clark; Tel: 309-649-6208, E-Mail: mclark@src.cc.il.us; *Circ*, Lisa Brown; Tel: 309-833-6035, Fax: 309-833-6062, E-Mail: lbrown@src.cc.il.us; *Circ*, Barb Ferguson; Tel: 309-833-6035; *Circ*, Sara Hirz; Tel: 309-649-6219, E-Mail: saraann3@yahoo.com; *Circ*, Maribeth Nolan; Tel: 309-649-6219, E-Mail: mbnolan2000@yahoo.com; Staff 5 (MLS 1, Non-MLS 4)
Founded 1951. Enrl 1,100; Fac 32; Highest Degree: Associate
Jul 1999-Jun 2000 Income $195,000. Mats Exp $55,980, Books $24,180, Per/Ser (Incl. Access Fees) $11,000, Micro $3,857, AV Equip $9,800, Electronic Ref Mat (Incl. Access Fees) $8,000. Sal $98,924 (Prof $50,882)
Library Holdings: Bk Vols 38,331; Bk Titles 35,183; Per Subs 129
Subject Interests: Agriculture, General, Nursing, Vocational-technical
Automation Activity & Vendor Info: (OPAC) CARL
Database Vendor: Ebsco - EbscoHost, IAC - Info Trac, IAC - SearchBank, Lexis-Nexis, OCLC - First Search, ProQuest
Function: Document delivery services
Mem of Alliance Library System
Partic in Alliance Library System; CCMP; ILLINET; Northern Ill Learning Resources Coop; Resource Sharing Alliance
Special Services for the Blind - Electronic readers

CARBONDALE

P CARBONDALE PUBLIC LIBRARY, 405 W Main St, 62901-2995. SAN 303-7711. Tel: 618-457-0354. TDD: 618-457-0354. FAX: 618-457-0353. Web Site: www.public.lib.carbondale.il.us. *Dir*, Connie Steudel; *Tech Servs*, Karalyn Norris; *Ad Servs, YA Servs*, Frances Fanning; *Ref*, Jan Miller; Staff 4 (MLS 4)
Founded 1923. Pop 27,033; Circ 185,822
May 1999-Apr 2000 Income $513,716, State $67,030, City $402,229, Locally Generated Income $44,457. Mats Exp $114,343, Books $94,181, Per/Ser (Incl. Access Fees) $6,197, AV Equip $8,337, Electronic Ref Mat (Incl. Access Fees) $5,628. Sal $270,200 (Prof $105,068)
Library Holdings: Bk Vols 82,771; Per Subs 100
Automation Activity & Vendor Info: (Acquisitions) epixtech, inc.; (Cataloging) epixtech, inc.; (Circulation) epixtech, inc.
Mem of Shawnee Library System
Friends of the Library Group

S GREATER EGYPT REGIONAL PLANNING & DEVELOPMENT COMMISSION, Library Research Center, PO Box 3160, 62902-3160. SAN 326-9124. Tel: 618-549-3306. FAX: 618-549-3309. E-Mail: gerpdc@midwest.net. *Adminr*, Margie Mitchell
Library Holdings: Bk Vols 1,325; Per Subs 30
Restriction: Staff & professional research

C SOUTHERN ILLINOIS UNIVERSITY, CARBONDALE, Delyte W Morris Library, 555 W Grand Ave, 62901-6632. SAN 339-7599. Tel: 618-453-2522. Interlibrary Loan Service Tel: 618-453-3374. Interlibrary Loan Service FAX: 618-453-8109. Web Site: www.lib.siu.edu. *Actg Dean*, James W Fox; E-Mail: jfox@lib.siu.edu; *Prof*, John Y Simon; *Tech Servs*, Thyra Russell; Tel: 618-453-2681, E-Mail: trussell@lib.siu.edu; *Coll Develop, Publ Servs*, Philip Howze; Tel: 618-453-2681, E-Mail: phowze@lib.siu.edu; *Doc*, Susan Tulis; Tel: 618-453-2708, E-Mail: stulis@lib.siu.edu; *Doc*, Todd Spires; Tel: 618-453-2755, E-Mail: tspires@lib.siu.edu; *Cat*, Daren Callahan; Tel: 618-453-7681, E-Mail: dcallaha@lib.siu.edu; *Instrul Serv*, Susan Logue; Tel: 618-453-1028, E-Mail: slogue@lib.siu.edu; Staff 41 (MLS 31, Non-MLS 10)
Founded 1869. Highest Degree: Doctorate
Jul 1999-Jun 2000 Mats Exp $4,294,150, Books $893,520, Per/Ser (Incl. Access Fees) $3,400,630. Sal $4,821,194 (Prof $1,735,584)
Library Holdings: Bk Vols 2,233,752; Per Subs 16,400
Special Collections: American Philosophy; Expatriates; Grant, Robert Graves, James Joyce, D H Lawrence & Henry Miller, bks & mss; Irish Literary Renaissance; John Dewey; Lawrence Durrell; Private Presses;

Ulysses S; US Geol Surv & Food & Agr Orgn
Automation Activity & Vendor Info: (Cataloging) DRA; (Circulation) DRA; (OPAC) DRA
Database Vendor: IAC - Info Trac, OCLC - First Search, OVID Technologies, ProQuest, Silverplatter Information Inc.
Publications: Bibliographic Contributions (irregular)
Mem of Shawnee Library System
Partic in Big Twelve Plus Libr Consortium; Center For Research Libraries; Ill Libr Computer Systs Org; OCLC Online Computer Library Center, Inc
Friends of the Library Group
Departmental Libraries:
EDUCATION-PSYCHOLOGY Tel: 618-453-2274. *Librn*, Roland Person; E-Mail: rperson@lib.siu.edu
HUMANITIES Tel: 618-536-3391. *Librn*, Loretta Koch; E-Mail: lkoch@lib.siu.edu

CL LAW LIBRARY, Lesar Law Bldg, 1150 Douglas Dr, 62901-6803. (Mail add: Mailcode 6803, 62901-6803), Tel: 618-453-8796. Circulation Tel: 618-453-8796. Reference Tel: 618-453-8708. FAX: 618-453-8728. Web Site: www.law.siu.edu/lawlib. *Dir*, Frank G Houdek; Tel: 618-453-8788, E-Mail: houdek@siu.edu; *Assoc Dir*, Laurel A Wendt; Tel: 618-453-8780, E-Mail: wendt@siu.edu; *Tech Coordr*, James E Duggan; Tel: 618-453-8791, E-Mail: duggan@siu.edu; *Tech Servs*, Heija B Ryoo; Tel: 618-453-8781, E-Mail: hryoo@siu.edu; *Tech Servs*, Kevin Butterfield; Tel: 618-453-8783, E-Mail: butterfield@siu.edu; Staff 18 (MLS 6, Non-MLS 12)
Founded 1973. Enrl 369; Fac 30; Highest Degree: Doctorate
Jul 1999-Jun 2000 Income $1,692,778, State $1,687,570, Locally Generated Income $3,010, Other $2,198. Mats Exp $646,582, Books $37,034, Per/Ser (Incl. Access Fees) $563,509, Presv $9,997, Micro $20,066, AV Equip $1,549, Electronic Ref Mat (Incl. Access Fees) $14,427. Sal $637,593 (Prof $351,946)
Library Holdings: Bk Vols 198,232; Bk Titles 70,230; Per Subs 3,976
Special Collections: Lincoln as a Lawyer; Self-Help Legal Coll
Automation Activity & Vendor Info: (Acquisitions) Innovative Interfaces Inc.; (Cataloging) Innovative Interfaces Inc.; (Circulation) Innovative Interfaces Inc.; (Course Reserve) Innovative Interfaces Inc.; (Serials) Innovative Interfaces Inc.
Publications: SIU School of Law Publication Series
Partic in Illinois Library & Information Network; Mid-Am Law Sch Libr Consortium; OCLC Online Computer Library Center, Inc
SCIENCE Tel: 618-453-2700. *Librn*, Kathleen Fahey; Tel: 618-453-2706, E-Mail: kfahey@lib.siu.edu
SOCIAL STUDIES Tel: 618-453-2708. *Librn*, Darrell Jenkins; E-Mail: djenkins@lib.siu.edu
UNDERGRADUATE Tel: 618-453-2818. *Librn*, Mark Watson; Tel: 618-453-2949, E-Mail: mwatson@lib.siu.edu

CARLINVILLE

C BLACKBURN COLLEGE, Lumpkin Library, 700 College Ave, 62626. SAN 303-772X. Tel: 217-854-3231, Ext 4220. FAX: 217-854-8564. Web Site: www.blackburn.edu. *Dir*, Carol Schaefer; E-Mail: cscha@gorilla.blackburn.edu; Staff 3 (MLS 2, Non-MLS 1)
Founded 1862. Enrl 500; Fac 35; Highest Degree: Bachelor
Library Holdings: Bk Vols 85,000; Per Subs 250
Mem of Lewis & Clark Library System
Partic in Ill Coop Coll Mgt Prog; Private Academic Libraries Of Illinois; Sangamon Valley Academic Library Consortium

P CARLINVILLE PUBLIC LIBRARY, 510 N Broad St, PO Box 17, 62626. SAN 303-7738. Tel: 217-854-3505. FAX: 217-854-5349. E-Mail: cae@lcls.org. *Dir*, Elizabeth Kaburick; E-Mail: bethk@lcls.org; *Ch Servs*, Janet Rawlings; E-Mail: janetr@lcls.org; Staff 1 (Non-MLS 1)
Founded 1927. Pop 5,416
Library Holdings: Bk Titles 24,000; Per Subs 120
Subject Interests: Genealogy
Mem of Lewis & Clark Library System

CARLOCK

P CAREY E BURDETTE MEMORIAL LIBRARY, 202 E Washington, PO Box 39, 61725. SAN 321-2718. Tel: 309-376-5651. FAX: 309-376-4027. E-Mail: wotd@darkstar.rsa.lib.il.us. *Dir*, Linda Spencer; Staff 3 (MLS 3)
Founded 1979. Pop 2,600; Circ 10,501
2000-2001 Mats Exp Books $11,000
Library Holdings: Bk Vols 9,500
Automation Activity & Vendor Info: (Circulation) Follett
Mem of Alliance Library System
Friends of the Library Group

CARLYLE

P CASE-HALSTEAD LIBRARY, 571 Franklin St, 62231. SAN 303-7746. Tel: 618-594-5210. FAX: 618-594-8415. E-Mail: cra@lcls.org. Web Site: case-halstead.hypermart.net. *Librn*, Jim Roeckeman; *Asst Librn*, Juanita Evans
Founded 1938. Pop 3,474; Circ 38,500
May 1998-Apr 1999 Income $34,200, State $4,200, City $12,000, Locally Generated Income $8,000, Other $10,000. Mats Exp $15,627, Books $13,627, Per/Ser (Incl. Access Fees) $2,000. Sal $44,636
Library Holdings: Bk Vols 24,000; Bk Titles 23,000; Per Subs 60
Subject Interests: Genealogy, Local history
Automation Activity & Vendor Info: (Cataloging) DRA; (Circulation) DRA; (OPAC) DRA
Mem of Lewis & Clark Library System

CARMI

P CARMI PUBLIC LIBRARY, 103 Slocumb St, 62821. SAN 303-7754. Tel: 618-382-5277. FAX: 618-384-3118. E-Mail: carmilib@midwest.net. *Librn*, Elaine Foster
Founded 1914. Pop 5,735; Circ 35,911
1999-2000 Income $69,194, State $7,075, City $41,764, Locally Generated Income $7,000, Other $13,355. Mats Exp $13,841, Books $12,061, Per/Ser (Incl. Access Fees) $1,780. Sal $35,984
Library Holdings: Bk Vols 29,966; Per Subs 90
Mem of Shawnee Library System
Friends of the Library Group

CAROL STREAM

S C BERGER & COMPANY LIBRARY,* 327 E Gundersen Dr, 60188-2421. SAN 373-4366. Tel: 630-653-1115. FAX: 630-653-1691. E-Mail: c-berg@dupagels.lib.il.us. Web Site: www.cberger.com. *Coll Develop, Librn, Tech Servs*, Carol A Berger
Library Holdings: Bk Vols 1,200; Bk Titles 950; Per Subs 75
Subject Interests: Personnel management
Publications: Library Lingo, 2nd edition; Your Buried Treasures
Mem of DuPage Library System
Partic in Illinois Library & Information Network; OCLC Online Computer Library Center, Inc

P CAROL STREAM PUBLIC LIBRARY,* 616 Hiawatha Dr, 60188. SAN 303-7762. Tel: 630-653-0755. FAX: 630-653-6809. *Dir*, Lynn M O'Dell
Founded 1962. Pop 31,716; Circ 270,978
Library Holdings: Bk Vols 98,000; Per Subs 232
Special Collections: Arts & Crafts Coll; Audiobooks; Careers & Self-Improvement (Vocational Advancement Coll); French Coll
Automation Activity & Vendor Info: (Circulation) CLSI LIBS
Publications: Newsletter (quarterly)
Mem of DuPage Library System
Friends of the Library Group

CARRIER MILLS

P CARRIER MILLS-STONEFORT PUBLIC LIBRARY DISTRICT, 109 W Oak St, 62917. (Mail add: PO Box 338, 62917-0338), Tel: 618-994-2011. FAX: 618-994-2303. *Librn*, Dimple Enz; *Asst Librn*, Louis Shaw
Founded 1962. Pop 1,991; Circ 8,953
May 1998-Apr 1999 Income (Main Library Only) $20,056, State $10,641, City $7,664, Locally Generated Income $1,751. Mats Exp $774, Books $589. Sal $10,879
Library Holdings: Bk Vols 21,851; Per Subs 25
Subject Interests: Genealogy, Local history
Mem of Shawnee Library System
Open Mon-Fri 9-11:30 & 1:30-5, Sat 9-12

CARROLLTON

P CARROLLTON PUBLIC LIBRARY, 509 S Main, 62016. SAN 303-7789. Tel: 217-942-6715. FAX: 217-942-6005. E-Mail: cte@lcls.org. Web Site: www.c-hawks.org/library/libabout. *Librn*, Donna Droste; *Asst Librn*, Jean McGuire
Founded 1901. Pop 2,507
Library Holdings: Bk Titles 18,000; Per Subs 50
Subject Interests: Genealogy, Illinois
Mem of Lewis & Clark Library System
Friends of the Library Group

CARTERVILLE

P CARTERVILLE PUBLIC LIBRARY, 117 S Division St, 62918. SAN 303-7797. Tel: 618-985-3298. FAX: 618-985-9474. *Dir, Librn*, Jane Robertson
Founded 1965. Pop 3,616; Circ 31,983
Library Holdings: Bk Vols 16,000; Per Subs 60
Subject Interests: History
Special Collections: National Geographic, 1942 to date
Mem of Shawnee Library System
Open Mon-Fri 10-5, Sat 9-1, closed Sun
Friends of the Library Group

J JOHN A LOGAN COLLEGE, Learning Resources Center,* 700 Logan College Rd, 62918. SAN 303-7800. Tel: 618-985-2828, Ext 8338. FAX: 618-985-3899, Ext 8338. Web Site: www.jal.cc.il.us.lrc. *Dean of Libr*, Dr Linda Barrette; E-Mail: linda.barrette@jal.cc.il.us; *Dir*, Judy Vineyard; *Ref*, Regina Rhodes; Staff 13 (MLS 4, Non-MLS 9)
Founded 1968. Enrl 5,000; Fac 92
Library Holdings: Bk Vols 69,866; Bk Titles 57,338; Per Subs 450
Subject Interests: Genealogy, Illinois, Nursing
Special Collections: John A Logan Memorial Coll
Mem of Shawnee Library System
Partic in Illinois Library & Information Network

P SHAWNEE LIBRARY SYSTEM, 607 S Greenbriar Rd, 62918-9502. SAN 339-7777. Tel: 618-985-3711. FAX: 618-985-4211. Web Site: www.shawls.lib.il.us. *Exec Dir*, Walter A Burkhalter; E-Mail: wburkh@.shawls.lib.il.us; *Asst Dir*, Jeanette M Halldorson; *Ref*, Thomas J Harris; *Tech Servs*, Steven Johnson; *Automation Syst Coordr*, Deborah Hickman; *Acq*, Sandra Waldrop; Staff 12 (MLS 12)
Founded 1966
Library Holdings: Bk Vols 3,000; Per Subs 20
Automation Activity & Vendor Info: (Acquisitions) epixtech, inc.; (Cataloging) epixtech, inc.; (Circulation) epixtech, inc.; (OPAC) epixtech, inc.; (Serials) epixtech, inc.
Member Libraries: Albion Public Library; Altamont Public Library; Benton Public Library District; Bryan-Bennett Library; Cairo Public Library; Carbondale Public Library; Carmi Public Library; Carrier Mills-Stonefort Public Library District; Carterville Public Library; CE Brehm Memorial Public Library District; Centralia Correctional Center Library; Centralia Regional Library District; Chester Mental Health Center; Chester Mental Health Center; Chester Public Library; Christopher Public Library; Coulterville Public Library; Department Of Veterans Affairs Medical Center; Du Quoin Public Library; East St Louis Community College Center; Eldorado Memorial Public Library District; Evans Public Library; Evansville Public Library; Fairfield Public Library; Flora Public Library; Frontier Community College; Golconda Public Library; Grayville Carnegie Public Library; Harrisburg Public Library District; Hecker Public Library; Herrin City Library; John A Logan College; Johnston City Public Library; Jonesboro Public Library; Kaskaskia College Library; Lawrence Public Library District; Lebanon Public Library; Lincoln Trail College; Marion Carnegie Library; Marissa Public Library; Mascoutah Public Library; McCoy Memorial Library; McKendree College; Metropolis Public Library; Mound City Public Library; Mounds Public Library; Mount Carmel Public Library; Nashville Public Library; New Athens District Library; Newton Public Library & Museum; Norris City Memorial Public Library District; Olney Central College; Olney Public Library; Palestine Public Library District; Patoka Public Library; Pinckneyville Public Library; Red Bud Public Library; Rend Lake College; Rick Warren Memorial Public Library District; Robinson Public Library District; Rosiclare Memorial Public Library; Saint Elmo Public Library District; Sallie Logan Public Library; Shawnee Correctional Center Library; Shawneetown Public Library; Southeastern Illinois College; Southern Illinois University, Carbondale; Southwestern Illinois College; Southwestern Illinois College Library; Sparta Public Library; Steeleville Area Library; Stinson Memorial Library; Trenton Public Library; United States Air Force; Vienna Public Library; Wabash Valley College; Wayne City Public Library; West Frankfort Public Library; Zeigler Public Library
Special Services for the Deaf - Books on deafness & sign language; Captioned media; High interest/low vocabulary books; Special interest periodicals
Branches: 1
SOUTHERN ILLINOIS TALKING BOOK CENTER Tel: 618-985-8375.; Staff 1 (MLS 1)
Founded 1969
Library Holdings: Bk Vols 28,500
Subject Interests: Local history

CARTHAGE

P CARTHAGE PUBLIC LIBRARY DISTRICT,* 538 Wabash, 62321. SAN 303-7827. Tel: 217-357-3232. FAX: 217-357-2392. E-Mail: cartlib@adams.net. Web Site: www.carthage.lib.il.us. *Dir, Librn*, Susan Hunt
Founded 1894. Pop 4,394; Circ 41,897
Jul 1998-Jun 1999 Income (Main Library Only) $130,377, State $6,417, City $1,404, Locally Generated Income $106,783, Other $15,773. Mats Exp $16,623, Books $14,763, Per/Ser (Incl. Access Fees) $1,860. Sal $61,051 (Prof $26,000)
Library Holdings: Bk Vols 25,138; Bk Titles 25,138; Per Subs 99
Special Collections: Local History and Genealogy
Automation Activity & Vendor Info: (Cataloging) Sagebrush Corporation
Mem of Alliance Library System
Open Mon-Thurs 12-9, Fri 12-5, Sat 9-5
Friends of the Library Group

M MEMORIAL HOSPITAL LIBRARY, PO Box 160, 62321. SAN 320-6432. Tel: 217-357-3131, Ext 2236. FAX: 217-357-3140. *Librn*, Joyce Buckert
Library Holdings: Bk Vols 150; Per Subs 15
Mem of Alliance Library System
Partic in Illinois Health Libraries Consortium

CARY

P CARY AREA PUBLIC LIBRARY DISTRICT, 1606 Three Oaks Rd, 60013-1637. SAN 303-7843. Tel: 847-639-4210. Circulation Tel: 847-639-4210, Ext 221. Reference Tel: 847-693-4210, Ext 227. FAX: 847-639-8890. E-Mail: librarybd@cary.lib.il.us. Web Site: www.cary.lib.il.us. *Dir*, Diane R McNulty; Tel: 847-639-4210, Ext 224, E-Mail: dmcnulty@cary.lib.il.us; Staff 33 (MLS 4, Non-MLS 29)
Founded 1951. Pop 21,378; Circ 211,419
Jul 2000-Jun 2001 Income $1,008,267, State $26,394, Locally Generated Income $925,873, Other $56,000. Mats Exp $145,150, Books $114,000, Per/Ser (Incl. Access Fees) $9,000, AV Equip $7,000, Electronic Ref Mat (Incl. Access Fees) $15,150. Sal $444,735 (Prof $161,137)
Library Holdings: Bk Vols 67,000; Bk Titles 65,000; Per Subs 170
Automation Activity & Vendor Info: (Cataloging) GEAC; (Circulation) GEAC; (OPAC) GEAC
Database Vendor: Ebsco - EbscoHost, OCLC - First Search
Function: Reference services available
Mem of North Suburban Library System
Partic in Coop Computer Servs
Open Mon-Thurs 9-9, Fri & Sat 9-5; Sept-May Sun 1-4
Friends of the Library Group

CASEY

P CASEY TOWNSHIP LIBRARY, 307 E Main St, 62420-1698. SAN 303-7851. Tel: 217-932-2105. Interlibrary Loan Service Tel: 217-352-0047. FAX: 217-932-2105. E-Mail: kzlib@rr1.net. *Head Librn*, Jan Ellen Hickox; E-Mail: jhicko@ltnet.ltls.org; *Asst Librn*, Vicki Zink; E-Mail: vzink@ltnet.ltls.org; Staff 3 (Non-MLS 3)
Founded 1938. Pop 4,021; Circ 34,149
Apr 1999-Mar 2000 Income (Main Library Only) $97,481, State $10,142, Federal $47,022, Locally Generated Income $40,317. Mats Exp $93,770, Books $14,000, Per/Ser (Incl. Access Fees) $1,600. Sal $45,664
Library Holdings: Bk Titles 21,775; Per Subs 51
Mem of Lincoln Trail Libraries System
Friends of the Library Group

CASEYVILLE

P CASEYVILLE PUBLIC LIBRARY DISTRICT, 419 S Second St, 62232. SAN 303-786X. Tel: 618-345-5848. FAX: 618-345-0081. *Dir, Head Librn*, Diana Stanford; *Asst Librn*, Christine Stewart
Founded 1962. Pop 4,419
1998-1999 Income $55,000. Mats Exp $4,000. Sal $25,000
Library Holdings: Bk Titles 20,000; Per Subs 52
Database Vendor: DRA
Mem of Lewis & Clark Library System

CATLIN

P CATLIN PUBLIC LIBRARY DISTRICT,* 109 S Sandusky St, PO Box 350, 61817. SAN 303-7878. Tel: 217-427-2550. FAX: 217-427-2550. *Chief Librn*, Janette Nash
Founded 1972. Pop 3,402; Circ 20,422
1998-1999 Income $55,223, State $5,380, County $45,126, Other $4,716. Mats Exp $10,087, Books $8,176, Per/Ser (Incl. Access Fees) $1,200, Other Print Mats $711. Sal $16,367
Library Holdings: Bk Vols 12,065; Per Subs 43
Mem of Lincoln Trail Libraries System
Open Mon & Thurs 9-5, Tues & Wed 9-8, Fri 3-7, Sat 9-2

CENTRALIA

S CENTRALIA CORRECTIONAL CENTER LIBRARY,* Shattuc Rd, PO Box 1266, 62801. SAN 371-5280. Tel: 618-533-4111, Ext 710. *Mgr*, Larry Taylor
Founded 1980. Pop 2,000
Library Holdings: Bk Vols 15,000; Per Subs 66
Mem of Shawnee Library System

P CENTRALIA REGIONAL LIBRARY DISTRICT,* 515 E Broadway, 62801. SAN 303-7886. Tel: 618-532-5222. FAX: 618-532-8578-. Web Site: www.sirin.lib.il.us/docs/cen/docs/lib/index.html. *Dir*, Barbara Peterson; *Ch Servs*, Jacqueline Holleman
Founded 1874. Pop 26,200; Circ 110,000
Jul 1996-Jun 1997 Income $302,771, State $32,750, City $25,603, County $197,734, Locally Generated Income $22,252, Other $24,432. Mats Exp $57,475, Books $49,882, Per/Ser (Incl. Access Fees) $4,458. Sal $128,740

(Prof $59,174)
Library Holdings: Bk Vols 104,884; Per Subs 203
Special Collections: Legislative Documents; State Daughters of the American Revolution Genealogy Coll
Mem of Shawnee Library System
Open Mon-Thurs 12-8, Fri & Sat 12-5, Sun 1:30-5
Friends of the Library Group

J KASKASKIA COLLEGE LIBRARY, 27210 College Rd, 62801. SAN 303-7894. Tel: 618-545-3130. TDD: 618-532-9241. FAX: 618-532-9241. E-Mail: library@kc.cc.il.us. Web Site: www.kc.cc.il.us. *Head Librn*, Diana Hudson; Tel: 618-545-3131; *Acq*, Linda K Wimberly; Tel: 618-545-3135, E-Mail: lkwimbwerly@kc.cc.il.us; Staff 3 (MLS 1, Non-MLS 2)
Founded 1940. Enrl 2,022; Highest Degree: Associate
Library Holdings: Bk Vols 29,082; Per Subs 125
Special Collections: Centralia Sentinel on microfilm 1863-current
Automation Activity & Vendor Info: (Acquisitions) epixtech, inc.; (Cataloging) epixtech, inc.; (Circulation) epixtech, inc.; (Serials) epixtech, inc.
Database Vendor: Ebsco - EbscoHost, GaleNet, Lexis-Nexis, OCLC - First Search, ProQuest, Wilson - Wilson Web
Function: ILL available
Mem of Shawnee Library System
Partic in NILRC

CERRO GORDO

P HOPE WELTY PUBLIC LIBRARY DISTRICT,* 100 S Madison, PO Box 260, 61818. SAN 303-7908. Tel: 217-763-5001. FAX: 217-763-5391. *Dir*, Theresa A Cripe; *Asst Librn*, Marsha Leach; *Asst Librn*, Carol Durbin; *Asst Librn*, Evelyn Williamson
Pop 3,624; Circ 41,279
1998-1999 Income $116,905, State $10,175, Federal $5,100, County $67,643, Other $33,987. Mats Exp $109,477, Other Print Mats $1,519. Sal $32,803
Library Holdings: Bk Vols 15,628; Per Subs 116
Mem of Rolling Prairie Library System
Open Tues 8-5, Wed & Fri 1-5, Thurs 8-8, Sat 8-2

CHADWICK

P CHADWICK PUBLIC LIBRARY DISTRICT, 110 Main St, PO Box 416, 61014-0416. SAN 375-9946. Tel: 815-684-5215. FAX: 815-684-5215. E-Mail: chadpub@internetni.com. Web Site: www.internetni.com/~chadpub. *Dir*, Arlene Johnson
Founded 1988. Pop 1,221
Jul 1999-Jun 2000 Income $44,065, State $3,860, Federal $6,600, Locally Generated Income $29,365, Other $4,240. Mats Exp $5,790, Books $4,440, Electronic Ref Mat (Incl. Access Fees) $1,350. Sal $15,700
Library Holdings: Bk Titles 8,296; Per Subs 25
Mem of Northern Illinois Library System

CHAMPAIGN

S CHAMPAIGN COUNTY HISTORICAL MUSEUM LIBRARY, 102 E University Ave, 61820-4111. SAN 373-4374. Tel: 217-356-1010. FAX: 217-356-1478. E-Mail: director@champaignmuseum.org. Web Site: www.champaignmuseum.org. *Pres*, Barbara Peckham; Tel: 217-344-3475; *Pres*, Dr Harold Balbach; Tel: 217-359-1113, E-Mail: hbalbach@soltec.net; Staff 1 (Non-MLS 1)
Founded 1974
Library Holdings: Bk Vols 1,000
Subject Interests: Historic preservation, Local history
Special Collections: History of the Champaign County II area, including historic preservation issues, memorabilia, volumes owned by historic figures, local histories & studies of local buildings of historic value
Function: Research library

P CHAMPAIGN PUBLIC LIBRARY, 505 S Randolph St, 61820-5193. SAN 339-7831. Tel: 217-356-8207. TDD: 217-356-9898. FAX: 217-356-1131. Web Site: www.champaign.org. *Dir*, George H Scheetz; E-Mail: gscheetz@champaign.org; *Asst Dir*, Cecelia K Gaines; E-Mail: cgaines@champaign.org; *Asst Dir*, Lisa M Ruch; E-Mail: lruch@champaign.org; *Ad Servs*, Charles B Teval; Tel: 217-356-7243, Fax: 217-356-5064, E-Mail: cteval@champaign.org; *Tech Coordr*, William P Taylor; E-Mail: wtaylor@champaign.org; *Ch Servs*, Janice N Harrington; Tel: 217-356-3980, E-Mail: jharrington@champaign.org; *Circ*, Sharon A Davis; Tel: 217-356-2072, E-Mail: sdavis@champaign.org; *Outreach Serv*, Kelly S Strom; Tel: 217-356-1542, E-Mail: kstrom@champaign.org; *Planning Services*, Judith A Blaford; E-Mail: jblaford@champaign.org; *Tech Servs*, Mary E Bissey; Tel: 217-356-1970, E-Mail: mbissey@champaign.org
Founded 1876. Pop 63,502; Circ 986,009
Jul 1999-Jun 2000 Income $5,047,806, State $160,836, City $4,572,884, Federal $6,500, Other $307,586. Mats Exp $395,385. Sal $2,186,848
Library Holdings: Bk Vols 180,510; Per Subs 800
Automation Activity & Vendor Info: (Acquisitions) epixtech, inc.; (Cataloging) epixtech, inc.; (Circulation) epixtech, inc.; (OPAC) epixtech, inc.
Database Vendor: OCLC - First Search
Publications: The Last Word (monthly newsletter)
Mem of Lincoln Trail Libraries System
Partic in Illinois Library & Information Network
Special Services for the Deaf - TDD
Open Mon-Fri 9-9, Sat 9-6, Sun 1-6
Friends of the Library Group
Branches: 1
DOUGLASS, 504 E Grove St, 61820. SAN 339-7866. Tel: 217-356-4455. FAX: 217-356-9561.
Library Holdings: Bk Vols 7,771
Open Mon, Wed & Fri 10-6, Tues & Thurs 10-8, Sat 10-2
Friends of the Library Group
Bookmobiles: 1

G ILLINOIS NATURAL HISTORY SURVEY LIBRARY, 607 E Peabody Dr, 61820-6970. SAN 326-4262. Tel: 217-333-6892. FAX: 217-333-4949. Web Site: www.library.uiuc.edu/nhx. *Head Librn*, Beth Wohlgemuth; Tel: 217-244-4907, E-Mail: wohlgemu@mail.inhs.uius.edu; *Asst Librn*, JoAnn Jacoby; Tel: 217-333-5856, E-Mail: jacoby@mail.inhs.uiuc.edu; Staff 4 (MLS 2, Non-MLS 2)
Founded 1858
Jul 1999-Jun 2000 Income Parent Institution $64,000. Mats Exp $64,000, Books $7,000, Per/Ser (Incl. Access Fees) $52,000, Electronic Ref Mat (Incl. Access Fees) $5,000
Library Holdings: Bk Vols 40,000; Per Subs 500
Subject Interests: Botany, Ecology, Entomology, Environmental studies, Herpetology, Ichthyology, Mammalogy, Ornithology, Wildlife management
Publications: Acquisitions List (monthly)
Mem of Lincoln Trail Libraries System
Partic in BRS; Dialog Corporation
Friends of the Library Group

G ILLINOIS STATE GEOLOGICAL SURVEY, 469 Natural Resources Bldg, 615 E Peabody, 61820-6964. SAN 340-806X. Tel: 217-333-5110. FAX: 217-244-0802, 217-333-2830. E-Mail: library@isgs.uicu.edu. Web Site: www.library.uiuc.edu/gsx. *Librn*, Mary Krick; E-Mail: krick@isgs.uiuc.edu; *Asst Librn*, Kristi Mercer; E-Mail: mercer@isgs.uiuc.edu; *Asst Librn*, Lynne Raymond; E-Mail: raymond@isgs.uiuc.edu; Staff 3 (MLS 2, Non-MLS 1)
Founded 1906
Library Holdings: Bk Vols 4,000; Per Subs 240
Subject Interests: Analytical chemistry, Coal, Coal mining hist, Gas, Geochemistry, Geology, Groundwater, Illinois, Oil, Paleontology, Petroleum
Special Collections: Geologist Field Notes; Illinois Geology Map Coll; State Geological Survey Publications; US Bureau of Mines Publications; US Geological Survey Publications
Publications: Monthly list of acquisitions
Mem of Lincoln Trail Libraries System
Partic in Dialog Corporation
Open Mon-Fri 8-12 & 1-5

G ILLINOIS STATE WATER SURVEY, Research Center Library,* 2204 Griffith Dr, 61820-7495. SAN 304-713X. Tel: 217-333-4956. FAX: 217-333-6540. E-Mail: library@sun.sws.uiuc.edu. Web Site: www.sws.uiuc.edu/chief/library. *Librn*, Patricia G Wasson; Staff 1 (MLS 1)
Founded 1896
Library Holdings: Bk Titles 29,540; Per Subs 171
Subject Interests: Analytical chemistry, Climatology, Meteorology, Water resources
Special Collections: Global Climate Change
Publications: Acquisitions List (bi-monthly)
Mem of Lincoln Trail Libraries System

P LINCOLN TRAIL LIBRARIES SYSTEM, 1704 W Interstate Dr, 61822-1068. SAN 303-7932. Tel: 217-352-0047. Toll Free Tel: 800-275-5857. FAX: 217-352-7153. E-Mail: ltls@ltnet.ltls.org. Web Site: www.ltls.org. *Exec Dir*, Jan Ison; E-Mail: jison@ltnet.ltls.org; *Assoc Dir*, Brenda Pacey; E-Mail: bpacey@ltnet.ltls.org; *Coordr*, Linda Bial; E-Mail: lbial@ltnet.ltls.org; *Coordr*, Pat Boze; E-Mail: pboze@ltnet.ltls.org; *Coordr*, David Dorman; E-Mail: ddorma@ltnet.ltls.org; *Coordr*, Elaine Hershbarger; E-Mail: ehersh@ltnet.ltls.org; *Coordr*, Donna Schaal; E-Mail: dschaa@ltnet.ltls.org; *Coordr*, Joe Sciacca; E-Mail: jsciac@ltnet.ltls.org; *Coordr*, Meridith Smith; E-Mail: msmith@ltnet.ltls.org; *Coordr*, Amy Weber; E-Mail: aweber@ltnet.ltls.org; Staff 28 (MLS 9, Non-MLS 19)
Founded 1965. Pop 424,216
Jul 1999-Jun 2000 Income (Main Library Only) $1,129,988, State $974,448, Other $155,540. Sal $556,051 (Prof $279,026)
Library Holdings: Bk Vols 1,100; Per Subs 80
Special Collections: Professional Library Literature
Automation Activity & Vendor Info: (Acquisitions) epixtech, inc.; (Cataloging) epixtech, inc.; (Circulation) epixtech, inc.; (Course Reserve) epixtech, inc.; (ILL) epixtech, inc.; (Media Booking) epixtech, inc.; (OPAC) epixtech, inc.; (Serials) epixtech, inc.
Database Vendor: epixtech, inc., OCLC - First Search
Publications: Children in Crisis: A Planning Manual for Cooperative Library & Community Agency Support for Abused & Neglected Youth;

Connections (newsletter); County-wide Rural Library District: A Cooperative Approach to Providing Library Service to Citizens in Unserved Areas; Fiction Collection Assessment Manual; Focus on Literacy (v-tapes); Library Data Communications Networks; Library Directory; Lincoln Trail Libraries System Untaxed Area Research Implementation Handbook; Literacy & Libraries: A Planning Manual; Managing Illinois Libraries Effectively (MILE) I-IV (a-tape, v-tape & workbk); Market Research Study on Economic Development & the Public Library; Materials for Small Libraries: A Selected Bibliography; Non-print Resources Catalog; Personnel Policy; Ready Reference Guide to System Services; Regional Library Service Panel Reports; Regional Library Service Planning Panel Reports; Seniors & Their Caregivers: A Planning Manual
Member Libraries: A Herr Smith & E E Smith Library; Allerton Public Library; Arcola Public Library District; Arthur Public Library; Bement Public Library District; Blue Ridge Township Public Library; Breckinridge County Public Library; Camargo Township District Library; Carle Foundation Hospital; Carnegie Public Library; Casey Township Library; Catlin Public Library District; Champaign Public Library; Chrisman Public Library; Cissna Park Community Library District; Danville Area Community College; Danville Public Library; Department Of Veterans Affairs; Eastern Illinois University; Elwood Township Carnegie Library; Georgetown Public Library; Gilman Area District Library; Goose Creek Township Carnegie Library; Hardin County Public Library; Homer Community Library; Hoopeston Public Library; Illinois Natural History Survey Library; Illinois State Geological Survey; Illinois State Water Survey; Kansas Community Memorial Library; Lake Land College; Larue County Public Library; Mahomet Public Library District; Marion County Public Library; Marshall Public Library; Martinsville Public Library District; Mattoon Public Library; Melvin Public Library; Milford District Library; Moyer Library; National Council Of Teachers Of English Library; Nelson County Public Library; Newman Township Library; News-Gazette Library; Oakwood Public Library District; Ogden Rose Public Library; Onarga Community Public Library District; Paris Carnegie Public Library; Parkland College Library; Paxton Carnegie Library; Philo Public Library District; Piper City Public Library District; Potomac Public Library; Provena Covenant Medical Center; Provena United Samaritans Medical Center Library; Rantoul Public Library; Sarah Bush Lincoln Health Center; Sheldon Public Library District; Sidell District Library; Sidney Community Library; St Joseph Township-Swearingen Memorial Library; The Urbana Free Library; Tolono Public Library; Tuscola Public Library; United States Army Corps of Engineers; University of Illinois at Chicago; University of Illinois Library at Urbana-Champaign; University of Illinois Library at Urbana-Champaign; Vance Township Library; Washington County Public Library; Watseka Public Library; West Union District Library; Westville Public Library; Willow Branch Township Library
Partic in Illinois Library & Information Network; Librs in Coop; OCLC Online Computer Library Center, Inc
Open Mon-Fri 7:30-9pm, Sat 8:30-5, Sun 12-6

S NEWS-GAZETTE LIBRARY, 15 Main St, 61820. (Mail add: PO Box 677, 61824-0677), Tel: 217-351-5228. FAX: 217-351-5374. E-Mail: library@news-gazette.com. *Librn*, Carolyn J Vance; E-Mail: library@news-gazette.com; *Asst Librn*, Judy Huss; Staff 2 (MLS 1, Non-MLS 1)
Founded 1946
Jan 1999-Dec 1999 Mats Exp $8,027, Books $443, Per/Ser (Incl. Access Fees) $1,704, Micro $5,822, Electronic Ref Mat (Incl. Access Fees) $59. Sal $61,313
Library Holdings: Bk Vols 687; Bk Titles 445; Per Subs 12
Subject Interests: Local history, Local news
Special Collections: Database of Local News Stories (7-27-94 to present); News-Gazette, microfilm (1953-present) & clippings (mid 1946-July 1994), photos, etc.
Restriction: Not open to public, Public access by telephone only
Mem of Lincoln Trail Libraries System
Serve reporters, editors information needs. Create database of local newspaper stories

J PARKLAND COLLEGE LIBRARY, 2400 W Bradley Ave, 61821-1899. SAN 303-7940. Tel: 217-351-2223. Reference Tel: 217-373-3839. FAX: 217-351-2581. Web Site: www.parkland.cc.il.us/library. *Dir*, Anna Maria Watkin; E-Mail: amwatkin@parkland.cc.il.us; *Tech Servs*, Cliff Bishop; E-Mail: clbishop@parkland.cc.il.us; *Ref*, Raymond Bial; E-Mail: rbial@parkland.cc.il.us; *Ref*, Frances Drone-Silvers; E-Mail: fdrone-silvers@parkland.cc.il.us; *Ref*, Julia Hough; E-Mail: jhough@parkland.cc.il.us; *Ref*, Ann Neely; E-Mail: aneely@parkland.cc.il.us. Subject Specialists: *Electronic resources*, Cliff Bishop; Staff 14 (MLS 6, Non-MLS 8)
Founded 1967. Enrl 9,000; Fac 359
Jul 1999-Jun 2000 Income Parent Institution $972,983. Mats Exp $156,631, Books $72,423, Per/Ser (Incl. Access Fees) $26,858, Micro $19,000, Other Print Mats $36,355, Manuscripts & Archives $1,995. Sal $590,645 (Prof $271,597)
Library Holdings: Bk Vols 127,325; Per Subs 500
Subject Interests: Nursing
Automation Activity & Vendor Info: (Acquisitions) EOS; (Cataloging) TLC; (Circulation) TLC; (OPAC) TLC
Database Vendor: Ebsco - EbscoHost, IAC - Info Trac, OCLC - First Search, ProQuest
Function: Reference services available
Mem of Lincoln Trail Libraries System
Partic in CCMP; NILRC

A UNITED STATES ARMY CONSTRUCTION ENGINEERING RESEARCH LABORATORIES, 2902 Newmark Dr, 61822. (Mail add: PO Box 9005, 61826-9005), Tel: 217-373-7217. FAX: 217-373-7222.; Staff 2 (Non-MLS 2)
Founded 1969
Library Holdings: Bk Titles 19,000; Per Subs 500
Subject Interests: Civil engineering, Construction, Environmental engineering
Automation Activity & Vendor Info: (Cataloging) SIRSI; (Circulation) SIRSI; (OPAC) SIRSI
Restriction: Staff use only
Mem of Lincoln Trail Libraries System
Partic in Fedlink; Illinois Library & Information Network; OCLC Online Computer Library Center, Inc

G WASTE MANAGEMENT & RESEARCH CENTER,* One E Hazelwood Dr, 61820-7465. SAN 329-0972. Tel: 217-333-8957. FAX: 217-333-8944. Web Site: www.wmrc.uiuc.edu/library. *Librn*, Laura Barnes; *Asst Librn*, Priscilla Smiley; E-Mail: psmiley@wmrc.uiuc.edu
Founded 1986
Library Holdings: Bk Titles 5,000; Per Subs 200
Publications: Acquisitions list; Clearinghouse Publications List

CHANNAHON

P THREE RIVERS PUBLIC LIBRARY DISTRICT, 25207 W Channon Dr, 60410-5028. (Mail add: PO Box 300, 60410-0300), SAN 321-0308. Tel: 815-467-6200. FAX: 815-467-4012. Web Site: htls.lib.il.us/trb/. *Dir*, Erik R Blomstedt; E-Mail: erblomstedt@htls.lib.il.us; *Ch Servs*, Sherri Gierman; *Ref*, Pamela Dube; *Tech Servs*, Nancy Anderson; Staff 2 (MLS 2)
Founded 1976. Pop 11,547; Circ 124,892
Jul 2000-Jun 2001 Income (Main Library and Branch Library) $834,562, State $33,000, Locally Generated Income $736,538, Other $93,433. Mats Exp $110,900, Books $82,000, Per/Ser (Incl. Access Fees) $6,000, Presv $1,200, Other Print Mats $1,700, Electronic Ref Mat (Incl. Access Fees) $20,000. Sal $220,000 (Prof $130,000)
Library Holdings: Bk Vols 64,990; Per Subs 174
Automation Activity & Vendor Info: (Circulation) GEAC
Database Vendor: IAC - Info Trac, OCLC - First Search
Publications: Newsletter (2 times a year)
Mem of Heritage Trail Library System
Open Mon-Thurs 9-9, Fri 9-6, Sat 10-5 & Sun 1-5
Branches: 1
MINOOKA BRANCH, 109 N Wabena, PO Box 370, Minooka, 60447-0370. SAN 372-6355. Tel: 815-467-1600. FAX: 815-467-1632. *Dir*, Herbert Kinder; Staff 1 (Non-MLS 1)
Founded 1992. Pop 11,547
Jul 2000-Jun 2001 Income Parent Institution $258,350. Mats Exp $32,500, Books $20,000, Per/Ser (Incl. Access Fees) $2,500, Electronic Ref Mat (Incl. Access Fees) $10,000. Sal $92,000 (Prof $39,000)
Library Holdings: Bk Vols 14,500; Per Subs 36
Special Collections: Local History Coll
Automation Activity & Vendor Info: (Circulation) GEAC
Database Vendor: Ebsco - EbscoHost, OCLC - First Search
Mem of Heritage Trail Library System
Open Mon-Thurs 10-8, Fri 1-6 & Sat 10-3

CHARLESTON

P CARNEGIE PUBLIC LIBRARY, Charleston Public Library,* 712 Sixth St, 61920. SAN 303-7967. Tel: 217-345-4913. FAX: 217-348-5616. *Librn*, Sheryl Snyder; *Cat*, Nancy Curran
Founded 1896. Pop 20,395; Circ 163,143
Library Holdings: Bk Titles 52,000; Per Subs 206
Subject Interests: Education, Medicine, Religion
Mem of Lincoln Trail Libraries System
Open Mon-Thurs 10-8, Fri & Sat 10-6

S COLES COUNTY HISTORICAL SOCIETY, Research Library & Museum,* 895 Seventh St, 61920. SAN 370-8969. Tel: 217-345-2934. FAX: 217-581-7233. *In Charge*, Robert E Hennings
Library Holdings: Bk Vols 2,000

C EASTERN ILLINOIS UNIVERSITY, Booth Library, 600 Lincoln Ave, 61920-3099. SAN 303-7975. Tel: 217-581-6061. TDD: 217-581-6065. FAX: 217-581-7534. Web Site: www.eiu.edu/~booth. *Dean of Libr*, Dr Allen Lanham; E-Mail: cfakl@eiu.edu; *Head, Acq*, Marlene Slough; Tel: 217-581-6021, Fax: 217-581-7379, E-Mail: cfmms@eiu.edu; *Head, Cat*, John Whisler; Tel: 217-581-6092, E-Mail: cfklw@eiu.edu; *Head Ref*, Carl Lorber; Tel: 217-581-6072, Fax: 217-581-6911, E-Mail: cfcll@eiu.edu; *Head, Circ*, Bradley Tolppanen; Tel: 217-581-6071, Fax: 217-581-6911, E-Mail: cfbpt@eiu.edu; *Head Tech Servs*, Nackil Sung; Tel: 217-581-6091, Fax: 217-581-6933, E-Mail: cfnks@eiu.edu; *ILL*, Betty Gillham; Tel: 217-581-6074, Fax:

217-581-6066, E-Mail: cfwbg@eiu.edu; *Coll Develop*, Karen Whisler; Tel: 217-581-6092, Fax: 217-581-6911, E-Mail: cfklw@eiu.edu; *Archivist*, Robert Hillman; Tel: 217-581-6093, Fax: 217-581-6066, E-Mail: cfrvh@eiu.edu; *Media Spec*, William Gibbs; Tel: 217-581-6011, Fax: 217-581-6911, E-Mail: cfwjg1@eiu.edu; *Govt Doc*, Jocelyn Tipton; Tel: 217-581-7542, Fax: 217-581-6066, E-Mail: cfjtt@eiu.edu; Staff 20 (MLS 17, Non-MLS 3)
Founded 1896. Enrl 10,200; Fac 665; Highest Degree: Master
Jul 1999-Jun 2000 Income State $3,823,819. Mats Exp $1,516,660, Books $628,231, Per/Ser (Incl. Access Fees) $534,784, Presv $37,500, AV Equip $191,145, Electronic Ref Mat (Incl. Access Fees) $125,000. Sal $2,225,357 (Prof $1,071,073)
Library Holdings: Bk Vols 888,704; Bk Titles 516,145; Per Subs 2,750
Subject Interests: Business, Education, Liberal arts
Special Collections: Dorothy Hansen Theatre Organ Coll; Remo Belli International Percussion Library; Univ & IL Regional Depository
Automation Activity & Vendor Info: (Cataloging) DRA; (Circulation) DRA; (Course Reserve) DRA; (OPAC) DRA; (Serials) DRA
Database Vendor: CARL, Ebsco - EbscoHost, GaleNet, IAC - Info Trac, Lexis-Nexis, OCLC - First Search, OVID Technologies, Wilson - Wilson Web
Publications: Annual Report; Information Booth: Library Handbook & Faculty supplement; Instruction Handouts; NoteBooth: Library news for faculty
Mem of Lincoln Trail Libraries System
Partic in ILCSO; Ill Coop Coll Mgt Prog; OCLC Online Computer Library Center, Inc
Special Services for the Deaf - TTY machine
Open Mon-Thurs 8-12am, Fri & Sat 9-5, Sun 12pm-12am

CHATHAM

P CHATHAM AREA PUBLIC LIBRARY DISTRICT,* 600 E Spruce St, 62629. SAN 376-0022. Tel: 217-483-2713. FAX: 217-483-2361. Web Site: ghs.bcsd.k12.il.us.library. *Librn*, Linda Meyer; E-Mail: lindam@alphal.rpls.lib.il.us
1997-1998 Income $307,377, State $15,214, Locally Generated Income $24,357. Mats Exp $48,313, Books $38,077. Sal $140,380
Library Holdings: Bk Titles 40,832; Per Subs 95
Mem of Rolling Prairie Library System
Open Mon-Thurs 9-8, Fri 9-5, Sat 10-4
Friends of the Library Group

CHATSWORTH

P CHATSWORTH TOWNSHIP LIBRARY,* 432 E Locust St, PO Box 638, 60921-0638. SAN 303-7983. Tel: 815-635-3004. FAX: 815-635-3004. *Actg Librn*, Donna Aberle
Pop 1,431; Circ 7,280
Library Holdings: Bk Vols 8,500; Per Subs 24
Mem of Alliance Library System
Open Tues-Thurs 9:30-5, Fri 1-5, Sat 9:30-12:30, closed Sun & Mon

CHENOA

P CHENOA FREE PUBLIC LIBRARY, 211 S Division, 61726. SAN 303-7991. Tel: 815-945-4253. FAX: 815-945-4203. *Chief Librn*, Mayreta Weber; E-Mail: chepublic@dave-world.net
Pop 2,280; Circ 19,981
Apr 1998-Mar 1999 Income $33,782, State $2,759, County $24,690, Locally Generated Income $6,333. Mats Exp $8,802, Books $7,107, Per/Ser (Incl. Access Fees) $1,436, AV Equip $259. Sal $14,427 (Prof $13,066)
Library Holdings: Bk Vols 12,991; Per Subs 85; Bks on Deafness & Sign Lang 10
Mem of Alliance Library System

CHERRY VALLEY

P CHERRY VALLEY PUBLIC DISTRICT LIBRARY, 755 E State St, PO Box 449, 61016. SAN 320-4731. Tel: 815-332-5161. FAX: 815-332-2441. E-Mail: cvplgeneral@nils.lib.il.us. Web Site: www.cherryvalley.lib.il.us. *Dir Libr Serv*, Eve G Kirk; Tel: 815-332-5385, E-Mail: evek@nils.lib.il.us; *Media Spec Ch*, Barbara Fisler; *Coll Develop*, Judy Rogers; *Tech Servs*, Fran Schaible; *Circ*, Sharon Welty; Staff 16 (MLS 3, Non-MLS 13)
Founded 1977. Pop 12,106; Circ 120,613
Jul 1999-Jun 2000 Income $699,328, State $16,985, City $4,337, Federal $44,520, Locally Generated Income $576,830, Other $56,656. Mats Exp $60,000, Books $41,638, Per/Ser (Incl. Access Fees) $7,779, AV Equip $9,233, Electronic Ref Mat (Incl. Access Fees) $1,350. Sal $211,972 (Prof $40,000)
Library Holdings: Bk Vols 40,044; Bk Titles 39,713; Per Subs 173
Automation Activity & Vendor Info: (Acquisitions) Innovative Interfaces Inc.; (Cataloging) Innovative Interfaces Inc.; (Circulation) Innovative Interfaces Inc.; (OPAC) Innovative Interfaces Inc.; (Serials) Innovative Interfaces Inc.
Database Vendor: Innovative Interfaces INN - View
Function: ILL available
Mem of Northern Illinois Library System
Special Services for the Deaf - TDD
Open Mon-Thurs 9-9, Fri 9-6, Sat 9-3, Sun 1-5 (Sept-May)
Friends of the Library Group

CHESTER

CHESTER MENTAL HEALTH CENTER

S RECIPIENT LIBRARY, 1315 Lehmen Rd, PO Box 31, 62233. SAN 339-7955. Tel: 618-826-4571. *Librn*, Collette B Powley
Founded 1968
Library Holdings: Bk Titles 8,500; Per Subs 43; High Interest/Low Vocabulary Bk Vols 150
Subject Interests: Large print
Mem of Shawnee Library System

M STAFF LIBRARY, 1315 Lehmen Rd, PO Box 31, 62233. SAN 339-798X. Tel: 618-826-4571. *Librn*, Collette B Powley
Founded 1968
Library Holdings: Bk Titles 1,200; Per Subs 60
Subject Interests: Forensic medicine, Nursing, Psychiatry, Psychology, Social service (social work)
Restriction: Staff use only
Mem of Shawnee Library System

P CHESTER PUBLIC LIBRARY,* 733 State St, 62233-9998. SAN 303-8009. Tel: 618-826-3711. FAX: 618-826-2733.
Founded 1928. Pop 8,194; Circ 71,424
May 1996-Apr 1997 Income $106,799. Mats Exp $112,057. Sal $55,073
Library Holdings: Bk Vols 39,606; Per Subs 80
Subject Interests: Environmental studies, Ethnic studies, Genealogy, Local history, Medicine, Religion, Science/technology, Technology
Special Collections: Rare Books (First Books Room)
Mem of Shawnee Library System
Open Mon-Thurs 10-7, Fri 10-5, Sat 10-3
Friends of the Library Group

CHICAGO

S ADAMS ADVERTISING AGENCY, INC LIBRARY,* 111 N Canal, Ste 399, 60606. SAN 303-8017. Tel: 312-930-9446. FAX: 312-930-5903. *In Charge*, A C Hibbs
Founded 1938
Library Holdings: Bk Titles 500
Subject Interests: Psychology
Special Collections: American Business; Commercial History; Sales & Advertising
Open Mon-Fri 8:15-4:30

S ADLER PLANETARIUM & ASTRONOMY MUSEUM, (APLRC), Library & Resource Center, 1300 S Lakeshore Dr, 60605. SAN 303-8033. Tel: 312-322-0304. FAX: 312-322-2257. Web Site: www.adlerplanetarium.org.
Founded 1930
Library Holdings: Bk Vols 6,600; Bk Titles 6,100; Per Subs 40
Subject Interests: Astronomy, Astrophysics, Space science
Special Collections: Adleriana; History of Astronomy Department History of Navigation & Scientific Instruments; Maps & Atlases in Astronomy; Rare books in astronomy
Publications: Adler Planetarium Library Info Brochure; Annual List; Bibliographies; Library Notice (quarterly)
Mem of Chicago Libr Syst
Partic in Consortium Of Museum Libraries In The Chicago Area; Illinois Library & Information Network; OCLC Online Computer Library Center, Inc

S ADLER SCHOOL OF PROFESSIONAL PSYCHOLOGY, Sol & Elaine Mosak Library, 65 E Wacker Pl, Ste 2100, 60601-7201. SAN 303-8025. Tel: 312-201-5900, Ext 234. FAX: 312-201-8756. Web Site: www.adler.edu. *Dir*, Karen Drescher; *Librn*, Arlene Krizanic; *Librn*, Michael Zellner; Staff 3 (MLS 3)
Founded 1952. Enrl 500; Highest Degree: Doctorate
Library Holdings: Bk Titles 10,000; Per Subs 165
Subject Interests: Art therapy, Counseling, Forensic psychol, Geriatrics and gerontology, Marriage, Psychiatry, Psychology, Psychotherapy, Substance abuse
Special Collections: Adlerian Athenaeum; Adlerian Psychology; Alfred Adler
Publications: Index to individual psychology
Restriction: Not open to public
Mem of Chicago Libr Syst
Partic in Illinois Library & Information Network; LVIS; National Library Of Medicine, Medlars; OCLC Online Computer Library Center, Inc; Private Academic Libraries Of Illinois

M ADVOCATE HEALTH CARE - TRINITY HOSPITAL, (Formerly E H S Trinity Hospital), Department of Library Services, 2320 E 93rd St, 60617. SAN 377-5348. Tel: 773-978-2000, Ext 5839. FAX: 773-978-7211. *Dir*,

Vicky Koren; *Mgr*, Candace Gwizdalski
Library Holdings: Bk Vols 7,000; Per Subs 50
Subject Interests: Medical, Nursing
Automation Activity & Vendor Info: (Cataloging) Endeavor; (Circulation) Endeavor; (OPAC) Endeavor; (Serials) Endeavor
Mem of Chicago Libr Syst

S ALTHEIMER & GRAY, Library Information Services, 10 S Wacker, Ste 4000, 60606. SAN 376-0928. Tel: 312-715-4000. Interlibrary Loan Service Tel: 312-715-4000, Ext 5596. FAX: 312-715-4800. E-Mail: library@altheimer.com. Web Site: www.altheimer.com. *Dir*, L Cochard; Staff 5 (MLS 3, Non-MLS 2)
Library Holdings: Bk Titles 20,000; Per Subs 600
Subject Interests: Law
Automation Activity & Vendor Info: (Acquisitions) SIRSI; (Cataloging) SIRSI; (Circulation) SIRSI; (OPAC) SIRSI; (Serials) SIRSI

M ALZHEIMER'S ASSOCIATION, Green-Field Library, 919 N Michigan Ave, Ste 1000, 60611-1676. SAN 371-9901. Tel: 312-335-9602. FAX: 312-335-0214. E-Mail: greenfld@alz.org. Web Site: www.alz.org. *Dir*, Patricia E Pinkowski; Tel: 312-335-5730, E-Mail: patricia.pinkowski@alz.org; *Ref*, Laura Simpkins; Tel: 312-335-5766, E-Mail: laura.simpkins@alz.org; *Tech Servs*, Marisol Rojas; E-Mail: marisol.rojas@alz.org; Staff 4 (MLS 3, Non-MLS 1)
Founded 1991
Jul 1998-Jun 1999 Income $299,702, Locally Generated Income $3,000, Parent Institution $296,702. Mats Exp $46,830, Books $16,000, Per/Ser (Incl. Access Fees) $27,830, Micro $3,000. Sal $232,500
Library Holdings: Bk Titles 4,500; Per Subs 120
Subject Interests: Aging, Alzheimer's Disease, Care
Automation Activity & Vendor Info: (Acquisitions) EOS; (Cataloging) EOS; (Circulation) EOS; (OPAC) EOS; (Serials) EOS
Database Vendor: OCLC - First Search
Publications: Acquisitions lists; brochure; rolodex card; subject bibliographies
Mem of Chicago Libr Syst
Partic in Metropolitan Consortium Of Chicago

S AMERICAN COLLEGE OF HEALTHCARE EXECUTIVES, Richard J Stull Memorial Learning Resources Center, One N Franklin St, 60606-3491. SAN 327-9995. Tel: 312-424-2800. FAX: 312-424-0023. Web Site: www.ache.org.; Staff 2 (MLS 1, Non-MLS 1)
Library Holdings: Bk Titles 1,200; Per Subs 100
Special Collections: Ray E Brown Management Coll, bks
Automation Activity & Vendor Info: (Cataloging) Inmagic, Inc.
Publications: Access to Information for Management series
Restriction: Staff use only

M AMERICAN COLLEGE OF SURGEONS LIBRARY, 633 N St Clair St, 60611. SAN 303-8084. Tel: 312-202-5239. FAX: 312-202-5001. Web Site: www.facs.org. *Librn*, Barbara Hone; Staff 1 (Non-MLS 1)
Founded 1913
Library Holdings: Bk Vols 500; Per Subs 100
Subject Interests: Surgery
Special Collections: History of Medicine; Surgical Artifacts Coll
Restriction: By appointment only
Mem of Chicago Libr Syst

M AMERICAN DENTAL ASSOCIATION, Department of Library Services,* 211 E Chicago Ave, 60611-2678. SAN 303-8106. Tel: 312-440-2653. FAX: 312-440-2774. Web Site: www.ada.org. *Dir*, Mary Kreinbring; Tel: 312-440-2642, E-Mail: kreinbringm@ada.org; *Publ Servs*, Ruth Schultz; *ILL*, Carolann Sansone; *Archivist*, Andrea Matlak; Staff 14 (MLS 6, Non-MLS 8)
Founded 1927. Pop 140,000
Library Holdings: Bk Vols 50,000
Subject Interests: Dentistry
Special Collections: Archives of American Dental Association
Publications: Index to Dental Literature
Restriction: Member organizations only
Function: ILL available
Mem of Chicago Libr Syst

M AMERICAN HEALTH INFORMATION MANAGEMENT ASSOCIATION, Fore Library, 233 N Michigan Ave, Suite 2150, 60601. SAN 303-8157. Tel: 312-233-1501. FAX: 312-233-1901. Web Site: www.ahima.org. *Mgr*, David A Sweet; E-Mail: david.sweet@ahima.org; Staff 1 (MLS 1)
Founded 1965
Library Holdings: Bk Vols 2,500; Per Subs 150
Automation Activity & Vendor Info: (Cataloging) Inmagic, Inc.
Database Vendor: Lexis-Nexis, OCLC - First Search
Restriction: By appointment only
Mem of Chicago Libr Syst
Partic in National Network Of Libraries Of Medicine - South Central Region

S AMERICAN HOSPITAL ASSOCIATION RESOURCE CENTER,* One N Franklin, 60606. SAN 303-9455. Tel: 312-422-2000. FAX: 312-422-4700. E-Mail: rc@aha.org. Web Site: www.aha.org. *Dir*, Eloise C Foster; Staff 13 (MLS 7, Non-MLS 6)
Founded 1920
Library Holdings: Bk Vols 64,000; Per Subs 250
Special Collections: Center for Hospital & Healthcare Administration History; Ray E Brown Management Coll
Publications: Hospital & Health Administration Index
Partic in Dialog Corporation; Illinois Library & Information Network; National Network Of Libraries Of Medicine - South Central Region; OCLC Online Computer Library Center, Inc

C AMERICAN ISLAMIC COLLEGE LIBRARY,* 640 W Irving Park Rd, 60613. SAN 375-989X. Tel: 773-281-4700. FAX: 773-281-8552. *Librn*, Asad Busool
Library Holdings: Bk Titles 17,000

S AMERICAN LIBRARY ASSOCIATION, Library & Research Center,* 50 E Huron St, 60611-2729. SAN 303-8122. Tel: 312-280-2153. FAX: 312-280-3255. E-Mail: larc@ala.org. *Dir*, Mary Jo Lynch; *Assoc Dir*, Carolyn Kubisz; Staff 5 (MLS 2, Non-MLS 3)
Founded 1924
Sep 1997-Aug 1998 Income $236,412. Mats Exp $46,917, Books $22,000, Per/Ser (Incl. Access Fees) $11,917, Presv $10,000. Sal $168,782
Library Holdings: Bk Vols 15,000; Per Subs 300
Subject Interests: Art and architecture, Library and information science
Special Collections: Dana Scrapbooks; Library Buildings (Lama/AIA Building Award Program); Library Manuals; Library Policies; Library Public Relations Materials
Partic in Dialog Corporation; Illinois Library & Information Network; OCLC Online Computer Library Center, Inc

S AMERICAN MARKETING ASSOCIATION, Information Center,* 311 S Wacker Dr, 58th Fl, 60606-5819. SAN 303-8130. Tel: 312-648-0536. FAX: 312-648-4619. E-Mail: library@ama.org. Web Site: www.ama.org. *Dir*, Lorraine Caliendo
Founded 1977
Library Holdings: Bk Vols 5,500; Per Subs 80
Subject Interests: Marketing
Special Collections: All American Marketing Association Published Literature; American Marketing Association Conference Proceedings, 1944 to present; Journal of Consumer Research, 1974 to present; Journal of Health Care Marketing Winter 1980-81 to present; Journal of International Marketing, 1993-present; Journal of Marketing Research, 1964 to present; Journal of Marketing, 1934 to present; Journal of Public Policy & Marketing Vol 1, 1982 to current; March 1989 to present; Marketing Management Magazine, Winter 1992 to present; Marketing News, 1967 to present; Marketing Research: A Magazine of Management & Application
Publications: bibliographies on selected subjects; Brochure of American Marketing Association In-Print Publications
Mem of Chicago Libr Syst

M AMERICAN MEDICAL ASSOCIATION, James S Todd Memorial Library, 515 N State St, 60610. SAN 303-8149. Tel: 312-464-4855. FAX: 312-464-5226. E-Mail: amalibrary@ama-assn.org. Web Site: www.ama-assn.org/physinfo/library/library.htm. *Dir*, Sandra R Schefris; *Asst Librn*, Yolanda D Ellis; Staff 3 (MLS 1, Non-MLS 2)
Founded 1911
2000-2001 Income $472,000. Mats Exp $200,000, Per/Ser (Incl. Access Fees) $160,000, Micro $30,000, Other Print Mats $10,000. Sal $230,000
Library Holdings: Bk Vols 17,000; Bk Titles 12,000; Per Subs 1,200
Subject Interests: Health sciences, Medicine
Special Collections: American Medical Association Publications; History of Medicine in the United States
Database Vendor: Ebsco - EbscoHost, OCLC - First Search
Mem of Chicago Libr Syst; ILL Libr & Info Network; Nat Network of Librs of Med
Partic in OCLC Online Computer Library Center, Inc

S AMERICAN PLANNING ASSOCIATION, Merriam Center Library, 122 S Michigan Ave, Ste 1600, 60603-6107. SAN 303-9714. Tel: 312-431-9100, Ext 6353. FAX: 312-431-9985. E-Mail: library@planning.org. Web Site: www.planning.org. *Librn*, Shannon Paul; E-Mail: spaul@planning.org
Founded 1932
Library Holdings: Bk Vols 7,000; Per Subs 180
Subject Interests: Urban planning
Special Collections: Ira Bach Coll
Restriction: By appointment only
Function: Reference only

M AMERICAN SOCIETY OF CLINICAL PATHOLOGISTS PRESS LIBRARY,* 2100 W Harrison St, 60612. SAN 303-8173. Tel: 312-738-1336, 312-738-4864. FAX: 312-850-8808. *In Charge*, Joshua Weikersheimer
Founded 1960
Library Holdings: Bk Vols 5,000
Subject Interests: Medicine, Publishing
Open Mon-Fri 8:30-4:30

L AMERICANS UNITED FOR LIFE, Information Center,* 310 S Peoria St, Ste 300, 60607-3534. SAN 370-9701. Tel: 312-492-7234. FAX: 312-492-7235. Web Site: www.unitedforlife.org. *Dir*, Margaret Connolly
Library Holdings: Bk Vols 300; Per Subs 15
Open Mon-Fri 9-5

S AMERITECH, Law Library,* 225 W Randolph St, HQ 27-A, 60606. SAN 371-1455. Tel: 312-727-8458. FAX: 312-845-8871. *Librn*, Evelyn Kasprak
Library Holdings: Bk Vols 5,000; Per Subs 2
Restriction: Staff use only
Open Mon-Fri 8-5

S ARTHUR ANDERSEN LLP, Knowledge Management Center, 33 W Monroe St, No 1000, 60603-5385. SAN 303-8181. Tel: 312-580-0033. FAX: 312-507-1765. *In Charge*, Mark Wysocki; Staff 9 (MLS 4, Non-MLS 5)
Founded 1959
Library Holdings: Bk Vols 4,000
Subject Interests: Accounting, Auditing, Economics, Finance, Statistics
Mem of Chicago Libr Syst
Open Mon-Fri 8:30-5

R ARCHBISHOP QUIGLEY PREPARATORY SEMINARY LIBRARY, 103 E Chestnut St, 60611-2093. SAN 375-9873. Tel: 312-787-9343. FAX: 312-787-9167. *Librn*, Sister Mary Inez Moch; *Librn*, Christine Grosch; Staff 2 (MLS 2)
Library Holdings: Bk Vols 11,193; Bk Titles 10,256; Per Subs 37
Partic in Chicago Library System; Illinois Library & Information Network

L ARNSTEIN & LEHR LIBRARY, 120 S Riverside Plaza, Ste 1200, 60606-3910. SAN 371-7623. Tel: 312-876-7170. FAX: 312-876-0288. E-Mail: arnstein@mcs.net. Web Site: www.arnstein.com. *Dir Libr Serv*, Frank Drake; E-Mail: fldrake@arnstein.com; Staff 2 (MLS 1, Non-MLS 1)
Library Holdings: Bk Vols 12,000; Bk Titles 1,700; Per Subs 400
Subject Interests: Law
Publications: Titles & locations; Titles by keyword
Mem of Chicago Libr Syst
Partic in Illinois Library & Information Network

ART INSTITUTE OF CHICAGO
S RYERSON & BURNHAM LIBRARIES, 111 S Michigan Ave, 60603. SAN 339-8013. Tel: 312-443-3671. FAX: 312-443-0849. Web Site: www.artic.edu. *Bibliogr, Dir*, Jack Perry Brown; *ILL*, Marcy Neth; *Tech Servs*, Anne Champagne; *Ser*, Ann Leslie Jones; *Archivist*, Bart Ryckbosch; Staff 28 (MLS 12, Non-MLS 16)
Founded 1879
Jul 1997-Jun 1998 Income $1,600,000. Mats Exp $732,000, Books $530,000, Per/Ser (Incl. Access Fees) $104,000, Presv $45,000. Sal $950,000
Library Holdings: Bk Vols 260,000; Per Subs 1,200
Special Collections: Architecture, 18th & 19th Century (Percier & Fontaine Coll), bk, drawings; Catalan Art & Architectural (George R Collins Coll); Chicago & Midwestern Architecture, Archives, photogs; Chicago Art & Artists Scrapbook, newsp 1890-to-date, micro: Russian Art (Ernest Hamill Coll); Surrealism (Mary Reynolds Coll); Whistler (Walter Brewster Coll)
Publications: Annual Exhibition Record of the Art Institute of Chicago 1888-1950 (1991); Architectural Records in Chicago (1981); Burnham Index to Architectural Literature (1990); Final Official Report of the Director of Works of the World's Columbian Exposition (1990); P B Wright (1980); Plan of Chicago (1909-1979); Ryerson Index to Art Periodicals; Surrealism & Its Affinities: The Mary Reynolds Coll; The Burnham Library of Architecture (1912-1987)
Mem of Chicago Libr Syst
Partic in RLIN
Friends of the Library Group

SR ASSYRIAN UNIVERSAL ALLIANCE FOUNDATION, Ashurbanipal Library, 7055 N Clark St, 60626. SAN 375-9903. Tel: 773-274-9262. FAX: 773-274-5866. E-Mail: libashur@aol.com. *Librn*, Vasili Shoumanov
Library Holdings: Bk Titles 5,000; Per Subs 20
Subject Interests: History, Linguistics, Literature
Restriction: Circulation limited
Function: Research library

L BAKER & MCKENZIE LAW LIBRARY,* One Purdential Plaza, 130 E Randolph St, Ste 3900, 60601. SAN 303-8211. Tel: 312-861-2915. FAX: 312-861-2899. *Dir*, Barbara Schmid; *ILL, Ref*, Susan Browning
Library Holdings: Bk Vols 47,000; Bk Titles 32,000; Per Subs 790
Subject Interests: Corporate law, Securities
Special Collections: Foreign & US Tax Law; Illinois; Intellectual Property
Partic in Illinois Library & Information Network

S BALZEKAS MUSEUM OF LITHUANIAN CULTURE, Reference & Research Library, 6500 S Pulaski Rd, 60629. SAN 303-822X. Tel: 773-582-6500. FAX: 773-582-5133. E-Mail: editor@lithuanian-museum.org. *Pres*, Stanley Balzekas, Jr; *Chief Librn*, Robert A Balzekas; *Asst Librn*, Dana Viktora; *Asst Librn*, Edvardas Pocius; *Asst Librn*, Val Martis
Founded 1966
Library Holdings: Bk Titles 40,000; Per Subs 1,700
Subject Interests: Heraldry
Special Collections: Art Archives; History (Rare Books Coll); Lithuanian Genealogy, Personality & Photography Archives; Manuscripts, Pamphlets, Periodicals, Records
Publications: Genealogija; Museum Review
Friends of the Library Group

S BANKERS LIFE & CASUALTY CO, Marketing Library,* 222 Merchandise Mart Plaza, 60654-2014. SAN 373-4412. Tel: 312-396-7299. FAX: 312-396-5920. *Librn*, Anthony Witt
Library Holdings: Bk Vols 750; Per Subs 50

S BANNER & WITCOFF, LTD LIBRARY,* 10 S Wacker Dr, Ste 3000, 60606. SAN 376-0944. Tel: 312-715-1000, Ext 3455. FAX: 312-715-1234. *Librn*, Peggy Lucero
1997-1998 Mats Exp $205,000. Sal $38,000
Library Holdings: Bk Titles 6,290; Per Subs 47
Subject Interests: Law

L BARACK, FERRAZZANO, KIRSHBAUM & PERLMAN LIBRARY, 333 W Wacker Dr, Ste 2700, 60606. SAN 376-1339. Tel: 312-984-3100. FAX: 312-984-3150. Web Site: www.bfkpn.com. *Librn*, Carol Brosk
Library Holdings: Bk Titles 3,200; Per Subs 50
Restriction: Staff use only

S BBDO-CHICAGO, Information Center, 410 N Michigan Ave, 60611. SAN 303-9730. Tel: 312-595-2702. FAX: 312-467-0977. *Dir*, Jerry Delaney; E-Mail: jerry.delaney@chicago.bbdo.com; *Info Specialist*, Cindy Sands Primeau; E-Mail: cindy.sands@chicago.bbdo.com
Founded 1960
Library Holdings: Per Subs 200
Subject Interests: Advertising, Marketing
Special Collections: Confectionery Coll
Publications: It's New
Restriction: Not open to public
Mem of Chicago Libr Syst
Partic in Ill Regional Libr Coun

L BELL, BOYD & LLOYD LIBRARY,* 3 First National Plaza, 70 W Madison, Ste 3200, 60602-4207. SAN 376-1320. Tel: 312-558-7373. FAX: 312-372-2098. *Dir*, Evelyn D Yonan
Library Holdings: Bk Vols 30,000; Bk Titles 3,500

S WILLIAM BLAIR & CO LLC, Business Information Center, 222 W Adams St, 60606. SAN 371-5221. Tel: 312-364-8220. FAX: 312-236-1673. *Mgr*, Carol Gates; E-Mail: cmg@wmblair.com; *Ref*, Janet Hartmann; *Ref*, Pam LaMarca; *Ref*, Liz Mordarski; *Ref*, Sharon Rhodes; Staff 9 (MLS 5, Non-MLS 4)
Founded 1988
Library Holdings: Bk Vols 250; Bk Titles 200; Per Subs 200
Subject Interests: Finance, Investment
Automation Activity & Vendor Info: (Acquisitions) Inmagic, Inc.; (Cataloging) Inmagic, Inc.; (Circulation) Inmagic, Inc.; (Serials) Inmagic, Inc.
Database Vendor: Dialog, Lexis-Nexis, OCLC - First Search
Restriction: Company library
Function: ILL limited
Mem of Chicago Libr Syst

M BLUE CROSS & BLUE SHIELD ASSOCIATION LIBRARY,* 225 N Michigan, 60601. SAN 303-8270. Tel: 312-297-5678, 312-297-5934. FAX: 312-297-5695. *In Charge*, Shirley Cunningham
Founded 1956
Library Holdings: Bk Vols 5,000; Per Subs 175
Mem of Chicago Libr Syst
Partic in Illinois Library & Information Network; Midwest Health Sci Libr Network
Open Mon-Fri 8:30-5

S BODINE ELECTRIC CO LIBRARY,* 2500 W Bradley Pl, 60618. SAN 303-8289. Tel: 773-478-3515, Ext 241. FAX: 773-478-3232. *Librn*, Kristine A Hack
Founded 1967
Library Holdings: Bk Vols 1,615; Bk Titles 1,440; Per Subs 80
Subject Interests: Electrical engineering, Mechanical engineering
Special Collections: IEEE Transactions & Proceedings
Open Mon-Fri 8:15am-5pm

S BOOZ, ALLEN & HAMILTON, INC LIBRARY,* 225 W Wacker Dr, Ste 1700, 60606. SAN 303-8297. Tel: 312-346-1900. FAX: 312-578-4615. Web Site: www.bah.com. *Ref*, Andrew Plaukovich; *Ref*, Charles Jordan; *Ref*, Henry Bolzan; *Ref*, Michael Mahaley; Staff 9 (MLS 7, Non-MLS 2)
Library Holdings: Bk Titles 3,000; Per Subs 300
Subject Interests: Finance, Marketing
Publications: Periodicals list
Restriction: Staff use only
Mem of Chicago Libr Syst
Partic in Illinois Library & Information Network

S BOSTON CONSULTING GROUP, Research Library, 200 S Wacker Dr, 60606. SAN 326-9183. Tel: 312-993-3300. FAX: 312-876-0771. *Adminr*, Sandi Masson; *Dir Info Resources & Res*, Carla Owens; *Coll Develop*, Pat Heidkamp; *Info Specialist*, William Hagedorn; *Info Specialist*, Jill Jaracz; *Info Specialist*, Vera Ward; Staff 9 (MLS 7, Non-MLS 2)
Library Holdings: Bk Titles 1,500; Per Subs 100
Subject Interests: Finance
Special Collections: Business Reference; Industry Data; Trade Journals
Mem of Chicago Libr Syst

S BOZELL WORLDWIDE, INC, Corporate Information Center,* 101 E Erie, 60611. SAN 375-9415. Tel: 312-988-2000. FAX: 312-425-6322. *Dir*, Eileen Pyne; E-Mail: epyne@costamesa.bozell.com
Library Holdings: Bk Titles 1,000; Per Subs 200
Mem of Chicago Libr Syst

L BRINKS, HOFER, GILSON & LIONE, Law Library,* NBC Tower, 455 N Cityfront Plaza Dr, Ste 3600, 60611-5599. SAN 371-8506. Tel: 312-321-4200. FAX: 312-321-4299. *Librn*, Julia Jackson; Staff 2 (MLS 1, Non-MLS 1)
Founded 1986
Library Holdings: Bk Vols 1,200; Per Subs 100
Special Collections: Patent Law
Mem of Chicago Libr Syst

L BURKE, WEAVER & PRELL, Law Library,* 55 W Monroe, Ste 800, 60603. SAN 372-1191. Tel: 312-263-3600. FAX: 312-578-6666. *Librn*, Maria Willmer
Library Holdings: Bk Vols 8,500; Per Subs 60
Partic in OCLC Online Computer Library Center, Inc
Open Mon-Fri 8:45-5

S BURRELL ADVERTISING, INC, Information Center,* 20 N Michigan Ave, 60602. SAN 375-992X. Tel: 312-443-8603. FAX: 312-443-0974. *Dir, VPres*, Leslie Cole
Library Holdings: Bk Titles 1,000; Per Subs 200

S BURSON-MARSTELLER, Knowledge Center,* One E Wacker Dr, 60601. SAN 303-965X. Tel: 312-329-7615. FAX: 312-329-7583. *Mgr*, Ellen Kuner; E-Mail: ellen_kuner@yr.com; Staff 4 (MLS 2, Non-MLS 2)
Founded 1968
Library Holdings: Bk Titles 5,000; Per Subs 800
Subject Interests: Advertising, Marketing
Mem of Chicago Libr Syst

SR CATHOLIC THEOLOGICAL UNION, Paul Bechtold Library, 5401 S Cornell Ave, 60615-5698. SAN 303-8335. Tel: 773-753-5321. Reference Tel: 773-753-5322. FAX: 773-753-5340. Web Site: www.ctu.lib.il.us. *Coll Develop, Dir*, Kenneth O'Malley; Staff 6 (MLS 3, Non-MLS 3)
Founded 1968. Enrl 375; Fac 32; Highest Degree: Doctorate
Jul 1999-Jun 2000 Income $378,571. Mats Exp $88,469, Books $55,275, Per/Ser (Incl. Access Fees) $30,800, Presv $200, Micro $1,359, AV Equip $633, Manuscripts & Archives $202. Sal $228,108 (Prof $96,295)
Library Holdings: Bk Vols 140,000; Bk Titles 126,000; Per Subs 480
Subject Interests: Franciscans, Roman Catholic theology
Special Collections: Canon Law; Christian Art; Missiology; Religious Communities; Scriptures
Automation Activity & Vendor Info: (Cataloging) DRA; (Circulation) DRA; (Course Reserve) DRA; (ILL) DRA; (Media Booking) DRA; (OPAC) DRA; (Serials) DRA
Publications: New Theology Review
Mem of Chicago Libr Syst
Partic in Association Of Chicago Theological Schools (ACTS); Illinois Library Computer Systems Office

S CENTER FOR RESEARCH LIBRARIES, 6050 S Kenwood Ave, 60637-2804. SAN 303-8378. Tel: 773-955-4545. Circulation Tel: 773-955-4545, Ext 321. Reference Tel: 773-955-4545, Ext 321. Toll Free Tel: 800-621-6044. FAX: 773-955-4339. Web Site: wwwcrl.uchicago.edu. *Pres*, Beverly Lynch; Tel: 773-955-4545, Ext 335, E-Mail: lynch@crlmail.uchicago.edu; *VPres*, Marjorie Bloss; *VPres*, James Green; Tel: 773-955-4545, Ext 350, E-Mail: green@crlmail.uchicago.edu; *Cat*, Adriana Pilecky-Bekajlo; *Circ*, Kevin Wilks; Tel: 773-955-4545, Ext 314, E-Mail: wilks@crlmail.uchicago.edu; *Acq*, Carol Stukey; Tel: 773-955-4545, Ext 332, E-Mail: stukey@crlmail.uchicago.edu; *Admin Assoc*, Mary Wilke; Tel: 773-955-4545, Ext 351, E-Mail: wilke@crlmail.uchicago.edu; Staff 44 (MLS 23, Non-MLS 21)
Founded 1949
Jul 1999-Jun 2000 Income $4,500,000. Mats Exp $950,400, Books $52,900, Per/Ser (Incl. Access Fees) $333,300, Presv $10,600. Sal $1,643,500
Library Holdings: Per Subs 13,548
Special Collections: Africana (Cooperative Africana Microform Project); Children's Books; College Catalogues, Current & Restrospective; Foreign Doctoral Dissertations; Foreign, Domestic & US Ethnic Newspapers; Latin America (LAMP); Middle East (MEMP); Print JSTOR Archive; Rarely Held Current Serials; Russian Academy of Sciences Publications; Slavic & Eastern Europe (SEEMP); South Asia; South Asia (SAMP); South East Asia (SEAMP); Superseded Reference; Textbooks; United States & Foreign Archives; United States Documents (Pre 1951); United States State Documents; US & Foreign College Catalogs; War Crimes Trials Documents
Automation Activity & Vendor Info: (Acquisitions) Innovative Interfaces Inc.; (Cataloging) Innovative Interfaces Inc.; (Circulation) Innovative Interfaces Inc.; (OPAC) Innovative Interfaces Inc.; (Serials) Innovative Interfaces Inc.
Publications: annual report; assorted holdings lists; Focus on The Center for Research Libraries (Bimonthly); handbook
Mem of Asn of Research Libraries
Partic in ARL

L CHAPMAN & CUTLER, Law Library, 111 W Monroe, 60603-4080. SAN 303-8416. Tel: 312-845-3749. FAX: 312-701-6620. *Head Librn*, Denis S Kowalewski; E-Mail: kowalews@chapman.com; *Asst Librn*, David P Fanta; Tel: 312-845-3450, E-Mail: fanta@chapman.com; *Asst Librn*, Robert Luberda; Tel: 312-845-3437, E-Mail: luberda@chapman.com; *Asst Librn*, Jamie Stewart; Tel: 312-845-3435, E-Mail: stewart@chapman.com; Staff 6 (MLS 4, Non-MLS 2)
Library Holdings: Bk Titles 5,000; Per Subs 50
Automation Activity & Vendor Info: (Cataloging) CASPR; (Circulation) CASPR; (OPAC) CASPR; (Serials) CASPR
Restriction: Private library
Partic in Illinois Library & Information Network

S CHICAGO ACADEMY OF SCIENCES, Memorial Library, Lincoln Park, 2060 N Clark St, 60614. SAN 303-8424. Tel: 773-549-0606. FAX: 773-549-5199. Web Site: www.chias.org. *Librn*, Louise T Lunak
Founded 1857 Sal $12,000
Library Holdings: Bk Vols 20,000
Subject Interests: Environmental studies, Geology, Natural history, Ornithology
Publications: Bulletin; Natural History Miscellania
Restriction: By appointment only, Not open to public
Open Mon-Fri 9-5

S CHICAGO BOARD OF TRADE LIBRARY,* 141 W Jackson Blvd, Rm 339A, 60604. SAN 303-8467. Tel: 312-435-3552. FAX: 312-341-3373. *Librn*, Rita Macellaio
Founded 1972
Library Holdings: Bk Vols 8,000; Per Subs 300
Subject Interests: Agricultural economics, Commodities
Publications: Commodity Futures Trading Bibliography (annual)
Partic in Illinois Library & Information Network; OCLC Online Computer Library Center, Inc
Open Mon-Fri 6:45-1:30 members only, 1:30-5 general public, closed Sat & Sun

S CHICAGO BOARD OPTIONS EXCHANGE, Member Library,* 400 S LaSalle St, 60605. SAN 376-0030. Tel: 312-786-7498. FAX: 312-786-7409. *Librn*, Cynthia K Green
Library Holdings: Bk Titles 1,000; Per Subs 25

S CHICAGO COMMUNITY TRUST LIBRARY, 222 N LaSalle St, Ste 1400, 60601. SAN 376-0049. Tel: 312-372-3356. TDD: 312-853-0394. FAX: 312-580-7411. Web Site: www.cct.org.; Staff 2 (MLS 1, Non-MLS 1)
Founded 1978
Library Holdings: Bk Vols 2,000; Per Subs 150; Spec Interest Per Sub 20
Subject Interests: Foundations, Nonprofit organization management, Philanthropy
Database Vendor: OCLC - First Search
Restriction: Not open to public
Function: Archival collection, ILL limited
Mem of Chicago Libr Syst
Partic in Consortium for Found Librs

S CHICAGO HISTORICAL SOCIETY, Research Collections,* 1601 N Clark St, 60614-6099. SAN 303-8483. Tel: 312-642-4600. FAX: 312-266-2077. Web Site: www.chicagohistory.org. *Dir*, Bernie Riley; *Librn*, Paula Murphy; *Archivist, Curator*, Archie Motley; Staff 15 (MLS 12, Non-MLS 3)
Founded 1856
Library Holdings: Bk Vols 150,000; Per Subs 175
Subject Interests: Civil War, Illinois
Partic in OCLC Online Computer Library Center, Inc
Open Tues-Sat 9:30-4:30

S CHICAGO INSTITUTE LIBRARY, Garfield Park Conservatory, Garfield Park Conservatory, 300 N Central Park Ave, 60624. SAN 321-8791. Tel: 312-746-5100. FAX: 312-638-1777. *Dep Dir*, Roberts Lisa
Library Holdings: Bk Vols 700
Subject Interests: Botany, Horticulture
Open Mon-Fri 9-5

S CHICAGO MERCANTILE EXCHANGE, Library-Resource Center,* 30 S Wacker Dr, 60606. SAN 321-2726. Tel: 312-930-8239. FAX: 312-466-7436. *Dir*, Bruce Q Frost; Staff 6 (MLS 2, Non-MLS 4)
Founded 1977
Library Holdings: Bk Titles 3,500; Per Subs 500
Subject Interests: Futures trading, Options trading

Publications: Bibliography & Information Source List (Futures & Options)
Mem of Chicago Libr Syst
Partic in Dialog Corporation; Illinois Library & Information Network

P CHICAGO PUBLIC LIBRARY, (CPL), 400 S State St, 60605. SAN 339-8102. Tel: 312-747-4999. Interlibrary Loan Service Tel: 312-747-4344. Circulation Tel: 312-747-4396. Reference Tel: 312-747-4300. TDD: 312-747-4066. Web Site: www.chicagopubliclibrary.org. *Head of Libr*, Mary A Dempsey; Tel: 312-747-4090, Fax: 312-747-4968, E-Mail: mdempsey@chicagopubliclibrary.org; *Head Ref*, Maira Liriano; Tel: 312-745-0568, Fax: 312-747-4667, E-Mail: mliriano@chicagopubliclibrary.org; *Head Tech Servs*, Laura Zupko; Tel: 312-745-0567, Fax: 312-747-4667, E-Mail: lzupko@chicagopubliclibrary.org; *Ch Servs, YA Servs*, Elizabeth Huntoon; Tel: 312-747-4780, Fax: 312-747-4077, E-Mail: ehuntoon@chicagopubliclibrary.org; *Ad Servs*, Jim Pletz; Tel: 312-747-4252, Fax: 312-747-4076, E-Mail: jpletz@chicagopubliclibrary.org; *Coll Develop*, Sheryl Nichin-Keith; Tel: 312-747-4662, Fax: 312-747-4667, E-Mail: snichin@chicagopubliclibrary.org; Staff 1,443 (MLS 468, Non-MLS 975)
Founded 1872. Pop 2,783,726; Circ 6,835,882
Jan 2000-Dec 2000 Income (Main Library and Branch Library) $94,687,683, State $9,088,715, Federal $943,000, Locally Generated Income $84,655,968. Mats Exp $11,000,000. Sal $47,101,793
Library Holdings: Bk Vols 5,794,051; Per Subs 21,300
Automation Activity & Vendor Info: (Acquisitions) CARL; (Cataloging) CARL; (Circulation) CARL; (OPAC) CARL; (Serials) CARL
Database Vendor: CARL, Ebsco - EbscoHost, GaleNet, OCLC - First Search
Mem of Chicago Libr Syst
Partic in Illinois Library & Information Network; OCLC Online Computer Library Center, Inc
Special Services for the Deaf - Books on deafness & sign language; High interest/low vocabulary books; Special interest periodicals; TDD; TTY machine; Videos & decoder
Special Services for the Blind - Adapted computers & special software with speech output to assist learning disabled, mentally retarded & uneducated; Bks on tape; Braille; Large print bks
Branches: 89
ALBANY PARK, 5150 N Kimball Ave, 60625. SAN 339-8374. Tel: 312-744-1933. FAX: 312-744-6266. *Librn*, Cha-Hee Stanfield
Library Holdings: Bk Vols 52,351
Friends of the Library Group
ALTGELD, 950 E 132nd Pl, 60827. SAN 339-8404. Tel: 312-747-5952. FAX: 312-747-5944. *Librn*, Ellen L Womack
Library Holdings: Bk Vols 30,036
Friends of the Library Group
ARCHER HEIGHTS, 5055 S Archer Ave, 60632. SAN 339-8439. Tel: 312-747-9241. FAX: 312-747-5861. *Librn*, Barbara Stefanck
Library Holdings: Bk Vols 18,908
AUSTIN, 5615 W Race Ave, 60644. SAN 339-8498. Tel: 312-746-5038. FAX: 312-746-5192. *Librn*, Elroy Christy
Library Holdings: Bk Vols 40,787
Friends of the Library Group
AUSTIN-IRVING, 6100 W Irving Park Rd, 60634. SAN 339-8528. Tel: 312-744-6222. FAX: 312-744-0059. *Librn*, Anthony E Powers
Library Holdings: Bk Vols 18,590
AVALON, 8828 S Stony Island, 60617. SAN 339-8552. Tel: 312-747-5234. FAX: 312-747-0590. *Librn*, Jerri L Conner
Library Holdings: Bk Vols 37,527
Friends of the Library Group
BACK OF THE YARDS, 4650 S Damen, 60609. SAN 339-8587. Tel: 312-747-8367. FAX: 312-747-7803. *Librn*, Michelle Roubal
Library Holdings: Bk Vols 28,599
BESSIE COLEMAN BRANCH, 731 E 63rd St, 60637. SAN 340-0689. Tel: 312-747-7760. FAX: 312-747-7768. *Librn*, Evelyn Stewart
Library Holdings: Bk Vols 57,228
Friends of the Library Group
BEVERLY, 2121 W 95th St, 60643. SAN 339-8617. Tel: 312-747-9673. FAX: 312-747-5062. *Librn*, Gregory Carr
Library Holdings: Bk Vols 54,026
Friends of the Library Group
BEZAZIAN, 1226 W Ainslie St, 60640. SAN 339-8641. Tel: 312-744-0019. FAX: 312-744-9881. *Librn*, Mary Clark
Library Holdings: Bk Vols 46,128
BLACKSTONE, 4904 S Lake Park Ave, 60615. SAN 339-8676. Tel: 312-747-0511. TDD: 312-747-3015. FAX: 312-747-5821. *Librn*, Cathryn Baker
Library Holdings: Bk Vols 44,500
Special Services for the Deaf - TDD
BRAINERD, 1350 W 89th St, 60620. SAN 339-8706. Tel: 312-747-6291. FAX: 312-747-1319. *Librn*, Mary L Jones
Library Holdings: Bk Vols 22,630
Friends of the Library Group
BRIGHTON PARK, 4314 S Archer Ave, 60632. SAN 339-8765. Tel: 312-747-0666. FAX: 312-747-0665. *Librn*, Miguel Garcia-Colon
Library Holdings: Bk Vols 51,953
BUSINESS-SCIENCE-TECHNOLOGY DIV, 400 S State St, 60605. Tel: 312-747-4400 (Business), 312-747-4450 (Science & Technology). FAX: 312-747-4975. *Online Servs*, Marcia Dellenbach; Tel: 312-747-4472, Fax: 312-747-4473, E-Mail: dellenba@chicagopubliclibrary.org; *Business, Science*, David Rouse; Tel: 312-747-4463, Fax: 312-747-4975, E-Mail: drouse@chicagopubliclibrary.org
Subject Interests: Advertising, Business and management, Careers, Computer science, Economics, Electronics, Marketing, Mathematics, Medicine, Real estate, Science
Special Collections: Auto repair manuals; Complete British Patents (1617-date); Complete US Patents (1790-date); corporate reports; Electrical Schematics; Industrial Standards & Specifications; Investment Services; Product Directories; State & Foreign Industrial Directories; vendor catalogs
Friends of the Library Group
CANARYVILLE, 642 W 43rd St, 60609. SAN 374-6542. Tel: 312-747-0644. FAX: 312-747-0653. *Librn*, Connie Gordon
Library Holdings: Bk Vols 6,558
CARTER G WOODSON REGIONAL, 9525 S Halsted St, 60628. SAN 340-0891. Tel: 312-747-6900. TDD: 312-747-0121. FAX: 312-747-6947. *Dir*, Emily Guss; Tel: 312-747-6905, E-Mail: eguss@chipublib.org
Library Holdings: Bk Vols 343,849
Special Collections: Afro-American Newspapers, 1927 to date, microfilm; Annual Reports of the National Association for the Advancement of Colored People, 1910-1970; Literary Manuscripts, such as Richard Wright & Langston Hughes; Papers of the American Missionary Association; tapes, rec, VF of pamphlets & newspaper clippings, & posters; Vivian G Harsh Coll of Afro-American History & Literature, 15,000 monographs representing every phase of Afro-American & African history & literature, with particular strength in hist, sociol, biog & per
Special Services for the Deaf - TDD
Friends of the Library Group
CHICAGO BEE, 3647 S State St, 60609. SAN 376-8902. Tel: 312-747-6872. FAX: 312-747-7095. *Head of Libr*, Mitchell Smith
Library Holdings: Bk Vols 42,258
CHICAGO LAWN, 6120 S Kedzie Ave, 60629. SAN 339-882X. Tel: 312-747-0639. FAX: 312-747-6182. *Librn*, John Telli
Library Holdings: Bk Vols 49,995
CHINATOWN, 2353 S Wentworth Ave, 60616. SAN 339-8854. Tel: 312-747-8013. FAX: 312-747-5820. *Librn*, Irene Huang
Library Holdings: Bk Vols 109,529
Friends of the Library Group
CLEARING, 6423 W 63rd Pl, 60638. SAN 339-8889. Tel: 312-747-5657. FAX: 312-747-7658. *Librn*, Linda Dougherty
Library Holdings: Bk Vols 71,579
Friends of the Library Group
CONRAD SULZER REGIONAL, 4455 N Lincoln Ave, 60625. SAN 339-9397. Tel: 312-744-7616. TDD: 773-728-2062. FAX: 312-744-2899. *Dir*, Leah Joyce Steele; *Asst Dir*, Cornelius O'Shea
Library Holdings: Bk Vols 293,002
Special Collections: Local History of Two Northeast Chicago Communities from 1880's to Present (Ravenswood-Lake View Historical Association Coll), artifacts, city directories, maps, memorabilia, newsclippings, sch year bks, transcribed interviews
Special Services for the Deaf - TDD
Friends of the Library Group
DAMEN AVENUE, 2056 N Damen Ave, 60647. SAN 339-8919. Tel: 312-744-6022. FAX: 312-744-5521. *Librn*, Nathan Parker
Library Holdings: Bk Vols 22,825
Friends of the Library Group
DOUGLASS, 3353 W 13th St, 60623. SAN 339-8943. Tel: 312-747-3725. FAX: 312-747-8861. *Librn*, Shirley Thornton
Library Holdings: Bk Vols 35,267
ECKHART PARK, 1371 W Chicago Ave, 60622. SAN 339-9001. Tel: 312-746-6069. FAX: 312-746-6552. *Librn*, Jane Reens
Library Holdings: Bk Vols 22,939
EDGEBROOK, 5331 W Devon Ave, 60646. SAN 339-9036. Tel: 312-744-8313. FAX: 312-744-6212. *Librn*, Kyosik Oh
Library Holdings: Bk Vols 33,969
Friends of the Library Group
EDGEWATER, 1210 W Elmdale Ave, 60660. SAN 339-9060. Tel: 312-744-0718. FAX: 312-744-7605. *Librn*, Laura Gonzalez
Library Holdings: Bk Vols 57,484
Friends of the Library Group
GAGE PARK, 2807 W 55th St, 60632. SAN 339-915X. Tel: 312-747-0032. FAX: 312-747-3191. *Librn*, Donna Williams
Library Holdings: Bk Vols 10,390
GALEWOOD-MONT CLARE, 6969 W Grand Ave, 60707. SAN 339-9184. Tel: 312-746-5032. FAX: 312-746-8432. *Librn*, Maria Hayley
Library Holdings: Bk Vols 27,645
GARFIELD RIDGE, 6348 S Archer Ave, 60638. SAN 339-9214. Tel: 312-747-6094. FAX: 312-747-9465. *Librn*, Carol Roza
Library Holdings: Bk Vols 29,626
GENERAL INFORMATION SERVICES DIV, 400 S State St, 60605. Tel: 312-747-4300. FAX: 312-747-4361. *Per*, Margaret Kier; Tel: 312-747-4363, E-Mail: mkier@chicagopubliclibrary.org; *Info Res*, Paula Saitis; Tel: 312-747-4382, E-Mail: psaitis@chicagopubliclibrary.org; *Head, Circ*, Vergenia Roshell; Tel: 312-747-4389; *ILL*, Valerie Samuelson; Tel: 312-747-4344, Fax: 312-747-4344, E-Mail: samuelso@chicagopubliclibrary.org
Special Collections: Chicago Biography Index File; Chicago Curio

Information; Early American Newspapers; National & International Telephone Directories & Newspapers; National, US, Foreign & Trade Bibliographies
Publications: Clubs Directory; CPL Serials List
Friends of the Library Group
GOVERNMENT PUBLICATIONS, 400 S State St, 60605. Tel: 312-747-4500. FAX: 312-747-4516. *Govt Doc*, Roberta Palen; Tel: 312-747-4510, E-Mail: rrpalen@chicagopubliclibrary.org; *Ref Serv*, Shah Tiwana; Tel: 312-747-4524, E-Mail: stiwana@chicagopubliclibrary.org
Special Collections: American Statistics Index Microfiche Library (1974 retrospective-current); Chicago Municipal Reference Coll; CIS-Microfiche Library (1970-present); Congressional Committee Hearings (prior to 1953), microfiche; Congressional Committee Prints (prior to 1970), microfiche; Declassified Documents Reference System; Serial Set (1st-91st Congresses), microfiche
HALL, 4801 S Michigan Ave, 60615. SAN 339-9249. Tel: 312-747-2541. FAX: 312-747-1374. *Librn*, Versie Barnes
Library Holdings: Bk Vols 34,652
Friends of the Library Group
HAROLD WASHINGTON LIBRARY CENTER, 400 S State St, 60605. Tel: 312-747-4999. FAX: 312-747-4077, 312-747-4918. *Dir Libr Serv*, Barbara Ford; Tel: 312-747-4070, E-Mail: bford@chicagopubliclibrary.org
Library Holdings: Bk Vols 1,975,546
Automation Activity & Vendor Info: (Acquisitions) CARL; (Circulation) CARL
Partic in Illinois Library & Information Network; OCLC Online Computer Library Center, Inc
Special Services for the Deaf - Books on deafness & sign language; High interest/low vocabulary books; Special interest periodicals; TDD; TTY machine; Videos & decoder
HEGEWISCH, 3048 E 130th St, 60633. SAN 339-9362. Tel: 312-747-0046. TDD: 773-646-8644. FAX: 312-747-8862. *Librn*, Paul Bollheimer
Library Holdings: Bk Vols 54,116
Special Services for the Deaf - TDD
Friends of the Library Group
HUMBOLDT PARK, 1605 N Troy St, 60647. SAN 339-9427. Tel: 312-744-2244. FAX: 312-742-5522. *Librn*, Stark Thomas
Library Holdings: Bk Vols 66,763
Friends of the Library Group
INDEPENDENCE, 3548 W Irving Park Rd, 60618. SAN 339-9540. Tel: 312-744-0900. FAX: 312-744-7420. *Librn*, Lucy Hill
Library Holdings: Bk Vols 50,356
Friends of the Library Group
JEFFERSON PARK, 5363 W Lawrence Ave, 60630. SAN 339-9575. Tel: 312-744-1998. FAX: 312-744-3811. *Librn*, Elizabeth Varela
Library Holdings: Bk Vols 44,977
JEFFERY MANOR, 2401 E 100th St, 60617. SAN 339-9605. Tel: 312-747-6479. FAX: 312-747-7679. *Librn*, Rosetta Coleman
Library Holdings: Bk Vols 19,630
Friends of the Library Group
JOHN MERLO BRANCH, 644 W Belmont Ave, 60657. SAN 339-9699. Tel: 312-744-1139. FAX: 312-744-0716. *Librn*, Cynthia Rodgers
Library Holdings: Bk Vols 46,787
KELLY, 6151 S Normal Blvd, 60621. SAN 339-963X. Tel: 312-747-8418. FAX: 312-747-8417. *Librn*, Linda Greene
Library Holdings: Bk Vols 22,204
Friends of the Library Group
LEGLER, 115 S Pulaski Rd, 60624. SAN 339-9729. Tel: 312-746-7730. FAX: 312-746-7750. *Librn*, Tyron Ward
Library Holdings: Bk Vols 47,772
Friends of the Library Group
LINCOLN BELMONT, 1659 W Melrose St, 60657. SAN 339-9303. Tel: 312-744-0166. FAX: 312-742-1633. *Librn*, Jill Weigel
Library Holdings: Bk Vols 51,951
Friends of the Library Group
LINCOLN PARK, 1150 W Fullerton Ave, 60614. SAN 339-9753. Tel: 312-744-1926. FAX: 312-744-5018. *Librn*, Barbara Rieffel
Library Holdings: Bk Vols 44,544
Friends of the Library Group
LITERATURE & LANGUAGE DIV, 400 S State St, 60605. Tel: 312-747-4700, 312-747-4750. Toll Free Tel: 800-757-4654. FAX: 312-747-4745. *In Charge*, Robert Bibbee; Tel: 312-747-4702, E-Mail: rbibbee@chicagopubliclibrary.org
Library Holdings: Bk Vols 669,375
Subject Interests: Drama, English second language, Fiction, Foreign lang materials, Foreign lit, Journalism, Large print, Linguistics, Literary criticism, Poetry, Publishing, Young adult literature
Special Collections: Books Indexed in the Essay & General Literature Index, micro; Foreign Language Book & Serials Collections at the popular level in many languages, with strong collections in Spanish, Polish, French, German, Italian, Russian, Chinese & Urdu; Foreign Language Telephone Book Coll; Language Learning Audio-Visual Materials Coll; Spanish Information Services Community Information & Referral Database & Files; Wright's American Fiction, 1774-1905, micro
Special Services for the Blind - Bks on tape; Braille; Talking book center
LOGAN SQUARE, 3255 W Altgeld St, 60647. SAN 339-9788. Tel: 312-744-5295. FAX: 312-744-5551. *Librn*, Helen R Goodman
Library Holdings: Bk Vols 44,979
MABEL MANNING BRANCH, 6 S Hoyne Ave, 60612. SAN 374-6550. Tel: 312-746-6800. FAX: 312-746-6806. *Librn*, Tommie Waters
Library Holdings: Bk Vols 52,481
Friends of the Library Group
THURGOOD MARSHALL BRANCH, 7506 S Racine Ave, 60620. SAN 374-6569. Tel: 312-747-5927. FAX: 312-747-0518. *Librn*, Donna Morris
Library Holdings: Bk Vols 87,776
MARSHALL SQUARE, 2724 W Cermak Rd, 60608. SAN 339-9842. Tel: 312-747-0061. FAX: 312-747-7942. *Librn*, Julie Lockwood
Library Holdings: Bk Vols 37,489
MARTIN LUTHER KING JR BRANCH, 3436 S King Dr, 60616. SAN 339-9664. Tel: 312-747-7543. FAX: 312-747-3160. *Librn*, Celene Cole
Library Holdings: Bk Vols 28,680
MAYFAIR, 4400 W Lawrence Ave, 60630. SAN 339-9877. Tel: 312-744-1254. FAX: 312-744-0609. *Librn*, Patricia A Centeno
Library Holdings: Bk Vols 36,007
MCKINLEY PARK, 1915 W 35th St, 60609. SAN 339-9818. Tel: 312-747-6082. FAX: 312-747-1982. *Librn*, Bruce Ziemer
Library Holdings: Bk Vols 50,956
Friends of the Library Group
MEDIA EXPRESS, 400 S State St, 60605. Tel: 312-747-4100. FAX: 312-747-4126. *Mgr*, Mary Bonhomme; Tel: 312-747-4103, E-Mail: bonhomme@chicagopubliclibrary.org
Subject Interests: Audio bks, Films and filmmaking, Television, Videos
Special Collections: Complete BBC Sound Effects Library; Foreign Film Video Coll
MIDWEST, 2335 W Chicago Ave, 60622. SAN 339-9907. Tel: 312-744-7788. FAX: 312-742-2399. *Librn*, Edith Thomas
Library Holdings: Bk Vols 24,761
MOUNT GREENWOOD, 11010 S Kedzie Ave, 60655. SAN 339-9931. Tel: 312-747-2805. FAX: 312-747-0148. *Librn*, Margaret E Crema
Library Holdings: Bk Vols 59,821
Friends of the Library Group
NEAR NORTH, 310 W Division, 60610. SAN 339-879X. Tel: 312-744-0991. FAX: 312-744-6221. *Librn*, Craig Davis
Library Holdings: Bk Vols 35,994
NORTH AUSTIN, 5724 W North Ave, 60639. SAN 339-9990. Tel: 312-746-4233. FAX: 312-746-9514. *Librn*, Donna Kanapes
Library Holdings: Bk Vols 46,771
NORTH PULASKI, 4300 W North Ave, 60639. SAN 340-0085. Tel: 312-744-9573. FAX: 312-744-7365. *Librn*, Alex Fraser
Library Holdings: Bk Vols 28,266
NORTHTOWN, 6435 N California Ave, 60645. SAN 340-0050. Tel: 312-744-2292. FAX: 312-744-8221. *Librn*, Charles Pace
Library Holdings: Bk Vols 42,011
Friends of the Library Group
ORIOLE PARK, 5201 N Oketo Ave, 60656. SAN 340-0115. Tel: 312-744-1965. FAX: 312-744-7853. *Librn*, Pamela M Weinberg
Library Holdings: Bk Vols 38,273
Friends of the Library Group
PORTAGE-CRAGIN, 5108 W Belmont Ave, 60641. SAN 340-0174. Tel: 312-744-0152, 312-744-2820 (Computer Center). FAX: 312-744-3776. *Librn*, Greta Bever
Library Holdings: Bk Vols 48,086
PULLMAN, 11001 S Indiana Ave, 60628. SAN 340-0204. Tel: 312-747-2033. FAX: 312-747-2031. *Librn*, Robin Smith
Library Holdings: Bk Vols 62,001
RICHARD J DALEY LIBRARY, 3400 S Halsted St, 60608. SAN 339-8730. Tel: 312-747-8990. FAX: 312-747-0939. *Librn*, James Hardt
Library Holdings: Bk Vols 66,742
ROBERT TAYLOR BRANCH, 5120 S Federal St, 60609. SAN 340-0565. Tel: 312-747-2828. FAX: 312-747-7653. *Head of Libr*, Charlotte Chatmon
Library Holdings: Bk Vols 10,437
RODEN, 6083 Northwest Hwy, 60631. SAN 340-0263. Tel: 312-744-1478. FAX: 312-744-4245. *Librn*, Bruce Fox
Library Holdings: Bk Vols 57,329
Friends of the Library Group
ROGERS PARK, 6907 N Clark St, 60626. SAN 340-0298. Tel: 312-744-0156. FAX: 312-744-7591. *Librn*, Jacqueline Hui
Library Holdings: Bk Vols 48,547
Friends of the Library Group
ROOSEVELT, 1101 W Taylor St, 60608. SAN 340-0328. Tel: 312-746-5656. FAX: 312-746-5667. *Librn*, Marita Chuang
Library Holdings: Bk Vols 33,266
Friends of the Library Group
RUDY LOZANO LIBRARY, 1805 S Loomis St, 60608. SAN 340-014X. Tel: 312-746-4329. FAX: 312-746-4324. *Librn*, Hector R Hernandez
Library Holdings: Bk Vols 77,453
SCOTTSDALE, 4101 W 79th St, 60652. SAN 340-0352. Tel: 312-747-0193. FAX: 312-747-0144. *Librn*, Janice Byrne
Library Holdings: Bk Vols 40,008
SHERMAN PARK, 5440 S Racine Ave, 60609. SAN 340-0387. Tel: 312-747-0477. FAX: 312-747-1474. *Librn*, Joyce Wiggins
Library Holdings: Bk Vols 39,120
SOCIAL SCIENCES & HISTORY DIV, 400 S State St, 60605. Tel: 312-747-4690. Reference Tel: 312-747-4600. FAX: 312-747-4646. *In Charge*,

Diane Purtill; Tel: 312-747-4608, E-Mail: dpurtill@chicagopubliclibrary.org
Subject Interests: Anthropology, Education, History, Law, Library and information science, Philosophy, Political science, Psychology, Religion, Sociology, Sports, Travel
Special Collections: Abraham Lincoln Papers, 1809-1865 (Robert Todd Lincoln Coll), microfilm; Crime & Juvenile Delinquency, microfiche; Educational Resources Information Center, microfiche; Illinois County & Regional Histories & Atlases; Library of American Civilization, microfiche; Migne's Patrologia Cursus Completus, microfiche; Newsbank-Urban Affairs Library, microfiche; Public & Private Papers of President John Adams, President John Quincy Adams & Charles Francis Adams, Papers of their Wives & Children, microfilm, Crime & Juvenile Delinquency

SOUTH CHICAGO, 9055 S Houston Ave, 60617. SAN 340-0441. Tel: 312-747-8065. FAX: 312-747-8491. *Librn*, Kim Catledge
Library Holdings: Bk Vols 53,365

SOUTH SHORE, 2505 E 73rd St, 60649. SAN 340-0476. Tel: 312-747-5281. FAX: 312-747-3612. *Librn*, Diana Brice
Library Holdings: Bk Vols 45,339

SOUTHEAST, 1934 E 79th St, 60649. SAN 340-0506. Tel: 312-747-7177. FAX: 312-747-7926. *Librn*, Irma Jean Patterson
Library Holdings: Bk Vols 21,373
Friends of the Library Group

SPECIAL COLLECTIONS & PRESERVATION DIV, 400 S State St, 60605. Tel: 312-747-4875, 312-747-4876. FAX: 312-747-4890. *In Charge*, Sophia Jordan; Tel: 312-747-4740, E-Mail: sjordan@chicagopubliclibrary.org
Founded 1975
Special Collections: Art & Artifacts from the Grand Army of the Republic; Chicago Authors Coll; Chicago Public Library Archives, 1871-present; Chicago Publishing & Book Arts, 1837-present; Chicago Theatre Coll, 1855-present; City of Chicago Public Art Coll; Civil War Coll; Harold Washington Archives & Colls, 1965-1989; Neighborhood History Research Coll documenting over 30 neighborhoods in the city; Rare Books from the 15th-17th Centuries & First Editions & Private Presses; World's Columbian Exposition, 1893

THOMAS HUGHES CHILDREN'S LIBRARY, 400 S State St, 60605. Tel: 312-747-4200. FAX: 312-747-4646. *Librn*, Laura Culberg; Tel: 312-747-4614, Fax: 312-747-4223, E-Mail: lculberg@chicagopubliclibrary.org
Subject Interests: Children's literature
Special Collections: Dissertations on Children's Literature, microfiche; Mother Goose Coll; Opie Coll, microfiche; Retrospective Children's Literature (mostly 1900-1950); Walt Disney Coll, bks

TOMAN, 4005 W 27th St, 60623. SAN 340-059X. Tel: 312-747-8114. FAX: 312-747-8116. *Librn*, James E Smith
Library Holdings: Bk Vols 30,385

TULEY PARK, 501 E 90th Pl, 60619. SAN 340-0611. Tel: 312-747-7608. FAX: 312-747-1255. *Head of Libr*, Stella Beck
Library Holdings: Bk Vols 12,597

UPTOWN, 929 W Buena Ave, 60613. SAN 374-6577. Tel: 312-744-8400. FAX: 312-744-8453. *Librn*, Mary Jo Godziela
Library Holdings: Bk Vols 44,086
Friends of the Library Group

VISUAL & PERFORMING ARTS DIV, 400 S State St, 60605. Tel: 312-747-4800, 312-747-4850. FAX: 312-747-4832. *In Charge*, Carole Medal; Tel: 312-747-4811, E-Mail: cmedal@chicagopubliclibrary.org
Subject Interests: Architecture, Fine arts, Music, Performing arts
Special Collections: Ann Barzel Dance Magazine Coll; Arnold Jacobsen Recorded Sound Coll; Balaban & Katz Theatre Orchestra Coll; Charles A Sengstock, Jr Coll; Chicago Architecture Pamphlet File; Chicago Artists' Archives; Chicago Blues Archives; Chicago Dance Vertical Files; Chicago Music Programs, 1873 to date; Chicago Opera Programs, 1910 to date; Chicago Stagebills; Chicago Symphony Orchestra Programs, 1885 to date; Dance Video Coll; Elisa Stigler Dance Coll; Folk Dance Instructions, looseleaf vols; Historic American Buildings Survey, microfiche; History of Photography, microfilm; Index of American Design, microfiche; Jubilee Showcase (Gospel Music Program Coll), v-tapes; Jussi Bjorling Archives; Martin & Morris Gospel Sheet Music Archives; Picture Coll; Ruth Page Dance Coll, memorabilia & scrapbk mat; Sears & Roebuck Catalogs, 1937 to date, microfilm; Sheet Music Coll; Stanley Paul Coll; Van Damm Coll of the New York Theatre Photographs, 1919-1961

VODAK EAST SIDE, 10542 S Ewing Ave, 60617. SAN 339-8978. Tel: 312-747-5500. FAX: 312-747-7841. *Librn*, Sheila Hanion
Library Holdings: Bk Vols 25,964
Friends of the Library Group

WALKER, 11071 S Hoyne Ave, 60643. SAN 340-0654. Tel: 312-747-1920. FAX: 312-747-2929. *Librn*, Cassandra Carr
Library Holdings: Bk Vols 56,594
Friends of the Library Group

WEST ADDISON, 7536 W Addison St, 60634. SAN 340-0719. Tel: 312-746-4704. FAX: 312-746-6232. *Librn*, Valerie James
Circ 554,989
Library Holdings: Bk Vols 24,810

WEST BELMONT, 3104 N Narragansett Ave, 60634. SAN 340-0743. Tel: 312-746-5142. FAX: 312-746-9477. *Librn*, Ann L Huntting
Library Holdings: Bk Vols 57,384
Friends of the Library Group

WEST LAWN, 4020 W 63rd St, 60629. SAN 340-0778. Tel: 312-747-7381. FAX: 312-747-9281. *Librn*, Alan Ziebarth
Library Holdings: Bk Vols 73,784
Friends of the Library Group

WEST TOWN, 1271 N Milwaukee Ave, 60622. SAN 376-8910. Tel: 312-744-1473. FAX: 312-742-1272. *Librn*, Kristy Kisler
Library Holdings: Bk Vols 35,204
Friends of the Library Group

WHITNEY M YOUNG JR BRANCH, 7901 S King Dr, 60619. SAN 340-0956. Tel: 312-747-0039. FAX: 312-747-1459. *Librn*, Eloise Smith
Library Holdings: Bk Vols 48,056
Friends of the Library Group

WRIGHTWOOD-ASHBURN, 8530 S Kedzie Ave, 60652. SAN 340-0921. Tel: 312-747-2696. FAX: 312-747-1937. *Librn*, Regina Johnson
Library Holdings: Bk Vols 37,285
Friends of the Library Group

Bookmobiles: 2

S THE CHICAGO SCHOOL OF PROFESSIONAL PSYCHOLOGY LIBRARY,* 806 S Plymouth Ct, 60605. SAN 329-7381. Tel: 312-786-9443, Ext 3002. FAX: 312-786-9611. E-Mail: library@csopp.edu. Web Site: www.csopp.edu. *Dir*, Margaret Burnett-White; E-Mail: msbwhite@csopp.edu; Staff 3 (MLS 2, Non-MLS 1)
Enrl 200; Fac 30
Library Holdings: Bk Vols 8,500; Bk Titles 7,800; Per Subs 170
Mem of Chicago Libr Syst
Partic in HSLI; Illinois Library & Information Network; LVIS; OCLC Online Computer Library Center, Inc; Private Academic Libraries Of Illinois

R CHICAGO SINAI CONGREGATION, James & Leah Davis Memorial Library, 15 W Delaware, 60611. SAN 303-8513. Tel: 312-867-7000. FAX: 312-867-7006. E-Mail: sinai@interaccess.com. *Dir, Librn*, Sally Barnum
Founded 1950
Library Holdings: Bk Titles 4,000; Per Subs 10
Subject Interests: Judaica (lit or hist of Jews)
Database Vendor: OCLC - First Search
Restriction: Members only
Function: Archival collection, ILL available
Mem of Chicago Libr Syst
Friends of the Library Group

C CHICAGO STATE UNIVERSITY, Paul & Emily Douglas Library & Instruction Services, 9501 S King Dr LIB-206, 60628. SAN 303-8521. Tel: 773-995-2251. Interlibrary Loan Service Tel: 773-995-2341. Circulation Tel: 773-995-2341. Reference Tel: 773-995-2235. FAX: 773-995-3772. Web Site: www.csu.edu. *Dean of Libr*, Dr Lawrence McCrank; *Dir, Media Spec*, Notre Chatman; *Acq, Coll Develop*, Ivo Miletich; *Ref*, Robert Meeker; *Cat*, Mary Nuby; *Doc*, Annie Moore; *Per*, Mariana Herrera; Staff 20 (MLS 20)
Founded 1867. Enrl 7,580; Fac 420
Jul 1999-Jun 2000 Mats Exp $444,933, Books $241,161, Per/Ser (Incl. Access Fees) $199,772, AV Equip $4,000. Sal $1,963,408 (Prof $1,286,589)
Library Holdings: Bk Vols 408,566; Bk Titles 262,913; Per Subs 1,691
Special Collections: Education (Learning Materials, Children's Books)
Partic in Center For Research Libraries; Chicago Academic Libr Coun; Ill Regional Libr Coun; Illinois Library & Information Network; Midwest Health Sci Libr Network; OCLC Online Computer Library Center, Inc
Friends of the Library Group

S CHICAGO SUN-TIMES, Editorial Library,* 401 N Wabash Ave, 60611. SAN 303-853X. Tel: 312-321-2593. FAX: 312-321-0311. Web Site: www.suntimes.com. *Dir*, Terri Golembiewski; *Ref*, Diana Boriss; *Ref*, Judith Halper; *Ref*, Virginia Davis
Founded 1876
Library Holdings: Bk Vols 3,500; Per Subs 15
Subject Interests: Current events, Government
Partic in Data Time

R CHICAGO THEOLOGICAL SEMINARY, Hammond Library, 5757 S University Ave, 60637-9990. SAN 303-8556. Tel: 773-752-5757, Ext 247. FAX: 773-752-7194. Web Site: www.chgosem.edu. *Dir*, Neil Gerdes; Tel: 773-752-5757, Ext 225, E-Mail: ngerdes@chgosem.edu; *Asst Dir*, Joan Blocher; Staff 3 (MLS 2, Non-MLS 1)
Founded 1855. Enrl 224; Fac 15; Highest Degree: Doctorate
Jul 1998-Jun 1999 Income $153,545. Mats Exp $40,162. Sal $105,626
Library Holdings: Bk Vols 115,000; Bk Titles 96,200; Per Subs 144
Subject Interests: Biblical studies, Counseling, Religion, Sexuality, Theology
Mem of Chicago Libr Syst
Partic in Association Of Chicago Theological Schools (ACTS); Illinois Library & Information Network; OCLC Online Computer Library Center, Inc

L CHICAGO TITLE INSURANCE CO, Law Library,* 171 N Clark St, 60601-3294. SAN 372-1094. Tel: 312-223-2458. FAX: 312-223-2960. *Librn*, John Kareken
Library Holdings: Bk Vols 15,000; Per Subs 25
Open Mon-Fri 9-5

S CHICAGO TRANSIT AUTHORITY-LAW LIBRARY, Law Library, CTA Merchandise Mart Plaza, 222 W Bank Dr, 60654. SAN 303-8572. Tel: 312-664-7200. FAX: 312-822-0746. *Ref*, Violette Brooks
Founded 1969
Library Holdings: Bk Vols 5,000; Per Subs 15
Restriction: Staff use only
Mem of Chicago Libr Syst
Partic in OCLC Online Computer Library Center, Inc

S CHICAGO TRIBUNE, Editorial Information Center, 435 N Michigan Ave Rm 529, 60611. SAN 303-8580. Tel: 312-222-4265. Web Site: www.chicagotribune.com. *In Charge*, John F Jansson; Staff 23 (MLS 22, Non-MLS 1)
Founded 1920
Library Holdings: Bk Vols 8,000; Per Subs 150
Subject Interests: Great Lakes, Illinois
Tribune database available online day of publication to subscribers of NewsBank, Inc; Dialog Information Services Inc, Dow Jones News Retrieval & Lexis-Nexis; available on CD-ROM from Newsbank, Inc; available on America Online & www.chicagotribune.com day of publication

S CHICAGO URBAN LEAGUE, Research & Planning Library, 4510 S Michigan Ave, 60653. SAN 320-6440. Tel: 773-451-3597. FAX: 773-285-7772. *Librn*, Mary Ann Ross; E-Mail: mross@cul-chicago.org; Staff 1 (MLS 1)
Library Holdings: Bk Titles 1,900; Per Subs 50
Subject Interests: Race relations
Database Vendor: OCLC - First Search
Restriction: Circulates for staff only, Open to others by appointment
Function: Research library
Mem of Chicago Libr Syst

CL CHICAGO-KENT COLLEGE OF LAW LIBRARY, 565 W Adams St, 60661. SAN 375-9792. Tel: 312-906-5610. FAX: 312-906-5685. E-Mail: chicago-kent@libraryadmin.edu. Web Site: www.infoctr.edu. *Dir*, Keith Ann Stiverson; Staff 9 (MLS 8, Non-MLS 1)
Founded 1886
Library Holdings: Bk Vols 535,000; Bk Titles 79,000; Per Subs 7,329
Special Collections: FAD, WHO, WTO & European Document Depository; Library of International Relations; Stuart Business Library
Automation Activity & Vendor Info: (Acquisitions) SIRSI; (Cataloging) SIRSI; (Circulation) SIRSI; (OPAC) SIRSI; (Serials) SIRSI
Database Vendor: Dialog, Ebsco - EbscoHost, Lexis-Nexis, OCLC - First Search, ProQuest

M CHILDREN'S MEMORIAL HOSPITAL, Joseph Brennemann Library, 2300 N Children's Plaza, Box 12, 60614. SAN 303-8599. Tel: 773-880-4505. FAX: 773-880-3833. Web Site: www.childrensmemorial.org. *Mgr*, Irene Wood
Founded 1935
Library Holdings: Bk Vols 6,000; Bk Titles 4,500; Per Subs 350
Subject Interests: Child psychology, Genetics, Pediatrics
Automation Activity & Vendor Info: (Cataloging) Endeavor; (Circulation) Endeavor
Publications: Acquisitions List; Journals List; Newsletter
Partic in Chicago Library System; Dialog Corporation; Illinois Library & Information Network; MLA; National Network of Libraries of Medicine - Greater Midwest Region; OCLC Online Computer Library Center, Inc

GL CITY OF CHICAGO, Department of Law Library,* 600 City Hall, 60602. SAN 373-6172. Tel: 312-744-0200, 312-744-7632. FAX: 312-744-3932. *Librn*, Scott G Burgh; Staff 3 (MLS 2, Non-MLS 1)
Library Holdings: Bk Vols 16,000; Bk Titles 700
Mem of Chicago Libr Syst
Open Mon-Fri 9-5

L CLAUSEN MILLER, PC LIBRARY, (Formerly Clausen & Miller PC Library), 10 S LaSalle St 16th flr, 60603-1098. SAN 371-635X. Tel: 312-606-7887. FAX: 312-606-7777. E-Mail: ntuohy@clausen.com. *Dir*, Nancy L Tuohy; Tel: 312-606-7535; *Asst Librn*, Laura Selke; *Asst Librn*, Christine Weber; *Asst Librn, Tech Servs*, Anton Kresich; *Circ*, Leila Voigts; *ILL*, George J Staudemeyer; Staff 7 (MLS 3, Non-MLS 4)
Founded 1936
Library Holdings: Bk Vols 30,000; Per Subs 300
Mem of Chicago Libr Syst
Partic in Illinois Library & Information Network; OCLC Online Computer Library Center, Inc

S COLLECTORS CLUB OF CHICAGO LIBRARY, 1029 N Dearborn St, 60610. SAN 372-574X. Tel: 312-642-7981. *Pres*, Lester Winick; Tel: 847-364-6868, Fax: 847-364-6889, E-Mail: les@winick.net; *Librn*, George Fabian; *Acq*, James Duffy
Founded 1928
Library Holdings: Bk Titles 10,000; Per Subs 40
Publications: Philatelic Hard Bound, bks
American Philatelic Research Library

C COLUMBIA COLLEGE LIBRARY,* 624 S Michigan Ave, 60605-1996. SAN 340-0980. Tel: 312-344-7906. FAX: 312-344-8062. E-Mail: library@mail.colum.edu. Web Site: www.lib.colum.edu/library. *Dir*, Mary Schellhorn; *Tech Servs*, Patricia Smith; *Circ*, Larry Oberc; *Publ Servs*, Ronald Rayman; *Coll Develop*, Kim Hale; Staff 32 (MLS 14, Non-MLS 18)
Founded 1890. Enrl 7,886; Fac 199; Highest Degree: Master
Library Holdings: Bk Vols 180,000; Per Subs 1,042
Subject Interests: Art, Dance, Films and filmmaking, Journalism, Photography, Radio, Television, Theater
Special Collections: Black Music Resource Coll; George Lurie Fine Arts Coll
Publications: Film/Videotape; Index to Filmscripts; Newsletter; Periodicals list
Mem of Chicago Libr Syst
Partic in Illinois Library & Information Network; Libras, Inc; OCLC Online Computer Library Center, Inc

G COMMISSION ON CHICAGO LANDMARKS LIBRARY, 33 N La Salle St, Suite 1600, 60602. SAN 373-3564. Tel: 312-744-3200. FAX: 312-744-9140.
Library Holdings: Bk Vols 2,500; Per Subs 10
Subject Interests: Architecture, Local history

S COMMODITY RESEARCH BUREAU LIBRARY,* 30 S Wacker Dr Ste 1810, 60606. SAN 375-1309. Tel: 312-454-1801, Ext 1613. Toll Free Tel: 800-621-5271. FAX: 312-454-0239. E-Mail: crbinfo@bridge.com. Web Site: www.crbindex.com. *Librn*, Christopher Lown
Library Holdings: Bk Vols 1,000; Bk Titles 200; Per Subs 27
Restriction: Not open to public

R CONGREGATION KINS OF WEST ROGERS PARK, Jordan E Feuer Library, 2800 W North Shore, 60645. SAN 303-8645. Tel: 773-761-4000. FAX: 773-761-4959. *Librn*, Thelma Weiss; Staff 3 (MLS 2, Non-MLS 1)
Founded 1961
Library Holdings: Bk Vols 3,900
Subject Interests: Judaica (lit or hist of Jews)

SR CONGREGATION RODFEI ZEDEK, Joseph & Dora Abbell Library, 5200 Hyde Park Blvd, 60615. SAN 303-8653. Tel: 773-752-2770, Ext 106. FAX: 773-752-0330. Web Site: www.rodfei.org. *Exec Dir*, Thea Cook
Founded 1950
Library Holdings: Bk Vols 8,000; Per Subs 30
Subject Interests: Americana, Judaica (lit or hist of Jews)
Open Mon & Sun 10-1. Library currently under reconstruction - will reopen fall 2000

S CONSOER TOWNSEND ENVIRODYNE ENGINEERS, Library & Information Center,* 303 E Wacker Dr, Ste 600, 60601. SAN 303-8661. Tel: 312-938-0300. FAX: 312-938-1109. *Librn*, Carol DeBiak
Library Holdings: Bk Vols 10,000; Bk Titles 8,000; Per Subs 26
Subject Interests: Construction, Engineering, Waste disposal, Water treatment
Restriction: Staff use only
Mem of Chicago Libr Syst

M COOK COUNTY HOSPITAL LIBRARIES,* 1900 W Polk St, 60612. SAN 340-1073. Tel: 312-633-7787. FAX: 312-633-8988. E-Mail: ticememo@dial.cic.net. *Librn*, Neera Kukreja; *Librn*, Darlene G Ward
Library Holdings: Bk Vols 4,150; Bk Titles 3,000; Per Subs 320
Subject Interests: Allied health, Medicine, Nursing
Special Collections: Rare Medical Books by Notable Physicians
Publications: Vanguard
Mem of Chicago Libr Syst

GL COOK COUNTY LAW LIBRARY,* 2900 Richard J Daley Ctr, 60602. SAN 303-8718. Tel: 312-603-2416, 312-603-5423. FAX: 312-603-4716. *Dir*, Bennie Martin; *Acq*, Thomas Brody; *Ref*, Montell Davenport; *Cat*, Camille C Dzija; *Dir Br Serv*, Mitchell L Johnson; Tel: 312-603-2436, Fax: 312-603-2072
Founded 1966
Dec 1997-Nov 1998 Income $5,077,582. Mats Exp $4,828,866
Library Holdings: Bk Vols 246,345; Per Subs 1,020
Subject Interests: Anglo-American law, Foreign law
Publications: Acquisitions List (bi-monthly)
Partic in RLIN
Branches:
BRIDGEVIEW, 10220 W 76th Ave, 60455. SAN 370-0313. Tel: 708-974-6201. FAX: 708-974-6053. *Branch Mgr*, Mary Gosewisch
CRIMINAL COURT, 2650 S California, 4th flr, 60608. SAN 320-9903. Tel: 773-869-5039. FAX: 773-869-3413. *Librn*, Johnnie Gill
MARKHAM BRANCH, 16501 S Kedzie Pkwy, Markham, 60426. SAN 321-3900. Tel: 708-210-4125. FAX: 708-210-4374. *Branch Mgr*, Neoma Violetto
MAYWOOD BRANCH, 1500 Maybrook Dr, Maywood, 60153. SAN 321-3919. Tel: 708-865-6020. FAX: 708-865-4938. *Librn*, Festus Olaworetan
MICHIGAN AVENUE, 1340 S Michigan Ave, 60605. SAN 320-9938. Tel: 312-341-2765. FAX: 312-341-2709. *Librn*, Eleshia Steele
ROLLING MEADOWS BRANCH, 2121 Euclid, Rolling Meadows, 60008.

SAN 370-0321. Tel: 847-818-2290. FAX: 847-818-2025. *Librn*, Judy Lam
SKOKIE BRANCH, 5600 W Old Orchard Rd, Skokie, 60077. SAN 321-8570. Tel: 847-470-7298. FAX: 847-470-7526. *Librn*, Jeffrey Meyerowitz

S COVENANT ARCHIVES & HISTORICAL LIBRARY, Archives of North Park University, 3225 W Foster Ave, 60625-4895. SAN 325-6731. Tel: 773-244-6224. FAX: 773-244-4891. Web Site: www.northpark.edu/library/archives. *Archivist, Spec Coll*, Ellen M Engseth; E-Mail: eengseth@northpark.edu; Staff 1 (MLS 1)
Library Holdings: Bk Vols 3,000; Bk Titles 3,000; Per Subs 15
Subject Interests: Evangelicalism
Restriction: By appointment only

S CRAIN COMMUNICATIONS INC, Information Center,* 740 N Rush St, 60611. SAN 303-8742. Tel: 312-649-5329. FAX: 312-649-5443. Web Site: adag.comm. *Chief Librn*, Mark Mandle
Founded 1930
Library Holdings: Bk Titles 2,000; Per Subs 100
Subject Interests: Advertising, Marketing
Publications: Newsletter
Restriction: Not open to public

S D'ANCONA & PFLAUM LIBRARY,* 111 East Walker Dr, 60610. SAN 376-0081. Tel: 312-580-2126. FAX: 312-580-0330. *Librn*, Gabrielle Lewis; E-Mail: glewis@dancon.com
Library Holdings: Bk Titles 7,000; Per Subs 400

S DAWSON TECHNICAL INSTITUTE, Learning Resource Center, 3901 S State St, 60609. SAN 325-6758. Tel: 773-451-2087. FAX: 773-451-2090, 773-451-2160. *Media Spec*, Effie B Tyler; E-Mail: etyler@ccc.edu
Library Holdings: Bk Vols 16,250; Bk Titles 15,200; Per Subs 120
Database Vendor: DRA, OCLC - First Search, ProQuest
Restriction: Non-circulating to the public, Not a lending library, Public use on premises
Function: Photocopies available
Open Mon-Fri 7:30-7

S DDB WORLDWIDE, INC, Information Center, 200 E Randolf, 60601. SAN 303-9889. Tel: 312-552-6000, Ext 6934. FAX: 312-552-2379. E-Mail: infocenter@ddb.com. Web Site: www.ddb.com. *Dir*, Laura DeGraff; Staff 6 (MLS 3, Non-MLS 3)
Founded 1948
Library Holdings: Bk Titles 5,000; Per Subs 350
Subject Interests: Advertising
Publications: Bookends; Reference Shelf
Restriction: Staff use only
Partic in Dialog Corporation; Dow Jones News Retrieval; Illinois Library & Information Network

S DELOITTE & TOUCHE, Research Center,* Two Prudental Plaza, 180 N Stetson, 19th flr, 60601. SAN 370-2073. Tel: 312-946-3616. FAX: 312-946-2663. *Mgr*, Barbara Dolmon; Tel: 312-946-3617, E-Mail: bdolmon@dttus.com
Library Holdings: Bk Vols 2,500; Per Subs 265

DEPARTMENT OF VETERANS AFFAIRS VA CHICAGO - HEALTH CARE SYSTEM
GM WEST SIDE DIVISION, 820 S Damen Ave, 60612. SAN 340-3084. Tel: 312-633-2116. FAX: 312-633-2110.; Staff 4 (MLS 1, Non-MLS 3)
Library Holdings: Bk Titles 5,500; Per Subs 290
Partic in Illinois Library & Information Network; Regional III Regional Med Libr Network; Vets Admin Libr Network

C DEPAUL UNIVERSITY LIBRARIES, 2350 N Kenmore, 60201. SAN 340-1103. Tel: 773-325-7862. FAX: 773-325-7870. Web Site: www.lib.depaul.edu. *Access Serv, Coll Develop, Dir*, Linda Morrissett; Tel: 773-325-7850, E-Mail: lmorriss@wppost.depaul.edu; *In Charge*, Doris R Brown; Tel: 773-325-7800, Fax: 773-323-7869, E-Mail: dbrown@wppost.depaul.edu; *Dir, Instrul Serv, Res*, Mickey Ann Hinojosa; Tel: 773-325-7852, Fax: 773-325-7869, E-Mail: mhinojos@wppost.depaul.edu; *Coordr*, Firouzeh Logan; Tel: 630-548-6555, E-Mail: flogan@wppost.depaul.edu; *Cat*, Lori Murphy; Tel: 773-325-2472, Fax: 773-325-7592, E-Mail: lmurphy@wppost.depaul.edu; *Archivist, Spec Coll*, Kathryn DeGraff; Tel: 773-325-2167, E-Mail: kdegraff@wppost.depaul.edu; *Access Serv*, Mirielle Kotoklo; Tel: 773-325-7772, E-Mail: mkotoklo@wppost.depaul.edu; *Ref*, Margaret Power; Tel: 773-325-7835, E-Mail: mpower@wppost.depaul.edu; *Ref*, Paula Dempsey; Tel: 312-362-5403, Fax: 312-362-6186, E-Mail: pdempsey@wppost.depaul.edu; *Coll Develop*, Christopher Hoeppner; Tel: 312-362-5425, Fax: 312-362-6186, E-Mail: choeppner@wppost.depaul.edu; *Coll Develop*, Roger Stelk; Tel: 773-325-7831, Fax: 773-325-7592, E-Mail: rstelk@wppost.depaul.edu; *Acq*, Peter Boll; Tel: 773-325-7855, Fax: 773-325-7592, E-Mail: pboll@wppost.depaul.edu; Staff 61 (MLS 27, Non-MLS 34)
Founded 1898. Enrl 20,500; Fac 1,327; Highest Degree: Doctorate
Jul 1999-Jun 2000 Mats Exp $2,156,080, Books $610,000, Per/Ser (Incl. Access Fees) $1,046,080, Electronic Ref Mat (Incl. Access Fees) $500,000. Sal $2,849,700 (Prof $1,568,396)
Library Holdings: Bk Vols 749,505; Per Subs 5,873
Special Collections: Art Books; Charles Dickens; Horace; Napoleon; Sports
Automation Activity & Vendor Info: (Acquisitions) Innovative Interfaces Inc.; (Cataloging) DRA; (Circulation) DRA; (Course Reserve) DRA; (ILL) DRA; (Media Booking) DRA; (Serials) Innovative Interfaces Inc.
Database Vendor: CARL, DRA, GaleNet, Lexis-Nexis, OCLC - First Search, OVID Technologies, ProQuest, Silverplatter Information Inc., Wilson - Wilson Web
Mem of Chicago Libr Syst
Partic in Ill Coop Coll Mgt Prog; Ill Libr Computer Systs Org; ILLINET
Friends of the Library Group
Departmental Libraries:
LAKE FOREST, 150 Field Dr, Lake Forest, 60045. Tel: 847-604-8220. *Coordr*, Firouzeh Logan
CL LAW LIBRARY, 25 E Jackson Blvd 5th flr, 60604-2287. SAN 340-1197. Tel: 312-362-8121. FAX: 312-362-6908. E-Mail: jgaskell@condor.depaul.edu. Web Site: www.law.depaul.edu/library/index.htm. *Dir*, Judith A Gaskell; Tel: 312-362-6893, E-Mail: jgaskell@wppost.depaul.edu; *Asst Dir, Tech Servs*, Mary Lu Linnane; *Asst Dir, Publ Servs*, Milta Hall; *Ref*, Mark Giangrande; *Ref*, Michael Schiffer; *Cat*, Denise Glynn; *Cat, Govt Doc*, Walter Baumann; *Circ*, Laura Birmingham; Staff 9 (MLS 9)
Founded 1920. Enrl 1,000; Fac 50; Highest Degree: Master
Jul 1998-Jun 1999 Income $1,941,848. Mats Exp $1,654,930, Books $96,051, Per/Ser (Incl. Access Fees) $609,689, Presv $7,799, Other Print Mats $941,391. Sal $1,000,457
Library Holdings: Bk Vols 346,097; Bk Titles 64,459; Per Subs 4,926
Special Collections: Constitutional Law (Jameson Coll); Environmental Law (Stuart A Weisler Coll); Graduate Health Law Coll; Graduate Taxation Law Coll; International Human Rights Law; Supreme Court Justices' Signatures (Nathan Schwartz Coll)
Partic in Chicago Legal Acad Syst; Chicago Library System; Illinois Library & Information Network; OCLC Online Computer Library Center, Inc
LOOP, One E Jackson, 60604. SAN 340-1138. Tel: 312-362-5403. Circulation Tel: 312-362-8433. Reference Tel: 312-362-8432. FAX: 312-362-6186. *Ref*, Paula Dempsey; E-Mail: pdempsey@wppost.depaul.edu; *Coll Develop*, Chris Hoeppner; Tel: 312-362-5425, E-Mail: choeppne@wppost.depaul.edu; *Access Serv*, Mirielle Kotoklo; Tel: 312-362-5400, E-Mail: mkotoklo@wppost.depaul.edu
NAPERVILLE, 150 W Warrenville Rd, Naperville, 60563-8473. Tel: 630-448-9378. FAX: 630-548-1963. *Coordr*, Firouzeh Logan; *Instrul Serv, Ref*, Christopher Holly; *Instrul Serv, Ref*, Erin McCaffrey
O'HARE, 3166 S River Rd, Des Plaines, 60018. SAN 329-000X. Tel: 312-362-7611. FAX: 773-296-4381. *Ref*, Holly Dankert; E-Mail: hdankert@wppost.depaul.edu; *Ref*, Kara Malenfant; E-Mail: kmalenfant@wppost.depaul.edu
OAK FOREST, 16333 S Kilbourn Ave, Ste 5032, Oak Forest, 60452. SAN 375-2895. Tel: 708-633-9096. FAX: 708-633-9095. *Ref*, Firouzeh Logan
ROLLING MEADOWS, Meadows Corporate Center, East Tower, 2550 W Golf Rd, Ste 255, Rolling Meadows, 60008. Tel: 847-437-9595. *Coordr*, Firouzeh Logan

J DEVRY INSTITUTE OF TECHNOLOGY LIBRARY, 3300 N Campbell Ave, 60618. SAN 303-8807. Tel: 773-929-8500, Ext 2214. FAX: 773-929-9433. Web Site: www.chi.devry.edu/library. *Dir*, Catherine J Carter; Tel: 773-929-8500, Ext 2215, Fax: 773-929-9433, E-Mail: cjcarter@chi.devry.edu; Staff 3 (MLS 1, Non-MLS 2)
Founded 1967. Enrl 4,000; Fac 65; Highest Degree: Bachelor
Library Holdings: Bk Vols 18,000; Per Subs 85
Subject Interests: Business and management, Computer science, Electronics, Telecommunications
Special Collections: Photo facts; Series of schematic drawings of circuitry
Automation Activity & Vendor Info: (Cataloging) Endeavor; (Circulation) Endeavor; (Course Reserve) Endeavor; (OPAC) Endeavor
Database Vendor: Dialog, OCLC - First Search, ProQuest
Function: ILL available
Partic in Chicago Library System; Dialog Corporation
Open Mon-Thurs 7am-10pm, Fri 7-5, Sat & Sun 8:30-4:30

S DONORS FORUM OF CHICAGO LIBRARY, 208 S La Salle St, Ste 735, 60604-1006. SAN 303-884X. Tel: 312-578-0175. TDD: 312-578-0159. FAX: 312-578-0158. E-Mail: info@donorsforum.org. Web Site: www.donorsforum.org. *Dir Libr Serv*, Barbara Kemmis; E-Mail: barbarak@donorsforum.org; Staff 4 (MLS 2, Non-MLS 2)
Founded 1974
Sep 1999-Aug 2000 Income (Main Library Only) $232,500, State $7,500, Locally Generated Income $175,000, Parent Institution $50,000. Mats Exp $26,800, Books $19,096, Per/Ser (Incl. Access Fees) $2,800, Micro $1,000, Electronic Ref Mat (Incl. Access Fees) $1,000. Sal $123,000 (Prof $80,000)
Library Holdings: Bk Vols 2,480; Bk Titles 2,100; Per Subs 105
Subject Interests: Philanthropy
Special Collections: Foundation Center Regional Coll
Database Vendor: Lexis-Nexis
Publications: A Guide to Funding Youth Development Programs; Chicago Area Grant Application; Chicago Area Grant Report; Donors Forum Members & Forum Partners Directory; Duties & Responsibilities of Directors & Trustees of Illinois Private Foundations; Giving in Illinois; Principles for Community Health Care; The Directory of Illinois Foundations

Mem of Chicago Libr Syst
Special Services for the Deaf - TDD
Special Services for the Blind - CCTV for print enlargement

CM DR WILLIAM M SCHOLL COLLEGE OF PODIATRIC MEDICINE LIBRARY, 1001 N Dearborn St, 60610. SAN 303-9145. Tel: 312-280-2891. FAX: 312-280-2495. Web Site: scholl.bdu/b/lib.htm. *Dir*, Richard S Klein; Tel: 312-280-2486, E-Mail: rklein@scholl.edu; *Assoc Dir*, Donald J Nagolski; Tel: 312-280-2493, E-Mail: dnagolsk@scholl.edu; *Circ*, Connie S Jeffrey; E-Mail: cjeffrey@scholl.edu; Staff 2 (MLS 2)
Enrl 321; Highest Degree: Doctorate
Library Holdings: Bk Vols 9,400; Per Subs 270
Subject Interests: Orthopedics, Podiatry
Publications: Acquisition list (quarterly); Bookmark; Current Podiatric Articles (bi-monthly); Journal Holdings List; Library Fact Sheets; Library Handbook; Medline Fact Sheets; Notification Form
Partic in Chicago Library System; Dialog Corporation; Greater Midwest Regional Medical Libr Network; Metropolitan Consortium Of Chicago; OCLC Online Computer Library Center, Inc

S DU SABLE MUSEUM OF AFRICAN-AMERICAN HISTORY LIBRARY,* 740 E 56th Pl, 60637. SAN 328-7858. Tel: 773-947-0600. FAX: 773-947-0677. *Curator*, Ramon B Price; *Pres*, Antoinette Wright
Partic in Afro-American Museums Assoc; Black Caucus of the Am Libr Assoc; Soc of Am Archivists
Open Winter: Mon-Sat 10am-4pm & Sun noon-4pm; Summer: Mon-Sun 10am-5pm; Thurs free day/no admission (10am-4pm winter, 10am-6pm summer)

S DUFF & PHELPS LLC, Research Library, 311 S Wacker Dr, Ste 4200, 60606. SAN 325-6367. Tel: 312-697-4600. FAX: 312-697-0112. *Mgr*, Ramona Howerton; Tel: 312-697-4672, E-Mail: rhowerton@duffllc.com
Library Holdings: Bk Vols 400; Per Subs 50
Subject Interests: Finance
Automation Activity & Vendor Info: (Acquisitions) Inmagic, Inc.; (Cataloging) Inmagic, Inc.; (Circulation) Inmagic, Inc.; (Serials) Inmagic, Inc.
Mem of Chicago Libr Syst

M EDGEWATER MEDICAL CENTER, Dr George Kroll Memorial Medical Library, 5700 N Ashland Ave, 60660-4086. SAN 303-8858. Tel: 773-878-6000, Ext 3170, 773-878-6000, Ext 3634. FAX: 773-878-4431. *In Charge*, Karen McCaro
Founded 1960
Library Holdings: Bk Titles 800; Per Subs 75
Subject Interests: Cardiology, Medicine, Nursing, Podiatry
Publications: Holding List (annual)
Mem of Chicago Libr Syst
Partic in Greater Midwest Regional Medical Libr Network; Illinois Library & Information Network; Metrop Consortium

§J EDWARD GEORGE SCHUMACHER MEMORIAL LIBRARY, 4811 N Milwaukee Ave, 60630. SAN 375-4405. Tel: 773-481-3755. FAX: 773-777-2861. Web Site: www.cl.ais.net/egsmlib. *Dir Libr Serv*, Leslie Ellen Gordon; E-Mail: lgordon@northwesternbc.edu; *Branch Mgr*, Susan Suhayda; Tel: 708-430-0990, Fax: 708-430-0995, E-Mail: ssuhayda@northwesternbc.edu; Staff 7 (MLS 2, Non-MLS 5)
Founded 1991
Library Holdings: Bk Vols 6,277; Bk Titles 2,982; Per Subs 114
Automation Activity & Vendor Info: (Cataloging) Sagebrush Corporation; (Circulation) Sagebrush Corporation; (Course Reserve) Sagebrush Corporation; (ILL) Sagebrush Corporation; (OPAC) Sagebrush Corporation
Database Vendor: OCLC - First Search, ProQuest
Function: Research library
Mem of Chicago Libr Syst
Partic in ILLINET; OCLC Online Computer Library Center, Inc

SR EMANUEL CONGREGATION, Joseph Taussig Memorial Library, 5959 N Sheridan Rd, 60660. SAN 371-6597. Tel: 773-561-5173. FAX: 773-561-5420. Web Site: www.emanuel-cong.com. *Librn*, Penny Aronson; Staff 1 (MLS 1)
Library Holdings: Bk Vols 6,000; Bk Titles 5,012; Per Subs 10
Special Collections: Judaica
Restriction: Open to public for reference only

S ENCYCLOPAEDIA BRITANNICA INC, Editorial Library,* 310 S Michigan Ave, 60604. SAN 303-8874. Tel: 312-347-7403. FAX: 312-294-2162. E-Mail: suddin@eb.com. *Librn*, Shantha Uddin; Staff 5 (MLS 2, Non-MLS 3)
Founded 1933
Library Holdings: Bk Titles 45,000; Per Subs 2,500
Subject Interests: Geography, Statistics
Restriction: Staff use only
Mem of Chicago Libr Syst
Partic in OCLC Online Computer Library Center, Inc

S ERIKSON INSTITUTE, Edward Neisser Library Learning Center, 420 N Wabash Ave, 60611. SAN 320-6459. Tel: 312-755-2250, Ext 2256. FAX: 312-755-2255. *Dir*, Janet Lynch Forde; E-Mail: jforde@erikson.edu; Staff 2 (MLS 1, Non-MLS 1)
Founded 1966. Enrl 160; Fac 12; Highest Degree: Doctorate
Jul 1998-Jun 1999 Income Parent Institution $70,000. Mats Exp $40,000, Books $9,000, Per/Ser (Incl. Access Fees) $6,000, AV Equip $7,000, Electronic Ref Mat (Incl. Access Fees) $18,000. Sal $40,000
Library Holdings: Bk Vols 5,100; Bk Titles 4,000; Per Subs 26
Subject Interests: Curriculum mat
Automation Activity & Vendor Info: (Circulation) TLC; (Course Reserve) TLC; (OPAC) TLC
Database Vendor: Ebsco - EbscoHost, OCLC - First Search
Publications: New Journal Contents
Function: For research purposes, Reference services available
Mem of Chicago Libr Syst
Friends of the Library Group

S ERNST & YOUNG COMPANY LIBRARY,* 233 S Wacker Dr, 60606. SAN 321-7809. Tel: 312-879-2661. FAX: 312-879-4035. *Librn*, Jo Cates
Founded 1930
Library Holdings: Bk Vols 11,000; Bk Titles 6,000; Per Subs 500
Subject Interests: Accounting, Consulting, Taxation
Restriction: By appointment only
Mem of Chicago Libr Syst

S EURO RSCG TATHAM KNOWLEDGE MANAGEMENT, 36 E Grand Ave, 60611-3506. SAN 373-3548. Tel: 312-337-4400. FAX: 312-337-5930. Web Site: www.eurorscg.com. *Dir*, Grace Villamora; E-Mail: grace.villamora.com. Subject Specialists: *Advertising*, Grace Villamora; *Marketing*, Grace Villamora
Founded 1986
Library Holdings: Bk Vols 1,000; Per Subs 200
Subject Interests: Advertising, Marketing

S FAMILY RESOURCES COALITION, National Resource Center,* 20 N Wacker Dr Ste 1100, 60606. SAN 328-6355. Tel: 312-338-0900. FAX: 312-338-1522. E-Mail: frca@frca.org. Web Site: www.frca.org. *In Charge*, Phyllis Schub
Library Holdings: Bk Vols 500
Subject Interests: Parenting
Mem of Chicago Libr Syst

S FEDERAL RESERVE BANK OF CHICAGO LIBRARY, 230 S LaSalle St, PO Box 834, 60690-0834. SAN 303-8912. Tel: 312-322-5826. Interlibrary Loan Service Tel: 312-322-4437. Reference Tel: 312-322-5824. FAX: 312-322-5091. *Mgr*, Melanie Ehrhart. Subject Specialists: *Bus finance*, Melanie Ehrhart; Staff 9 (MLS 6, Non-MLS 3)
Founded 1920
Library Holdings: Bk Titles 18,500; Per Subs 500
Subject Interests: Agricultural economics, Banks and banking, Economics, Finance, Monetary policy, Statistics
Automation Activity & Vendor Info: (Acquisitions) epixtech, inc.; (Circulation) epixtech, inc.; (Serials) epixtech, inc.
Mem of Chicago Libr Syst
Partic in Illinois Library & Information Network

S FERGUSON PUBLISHING CO, Editorial Library, 200 W Jackson Blvd, 7th Flr, 60606. SAN 304-0305. Tel: 312-692-1000, Ext 230. FAX: 312-692-0109. *In Charge*, Joyce M Lofton; E-Mail: jmloft@www.com; Staff 1 (Non-MLS 1)
Founded 1958
Library Holdings: Bk Titles 10,000; Per Subs 135
Partic in Illinois Library & Information Network

S FIELD MUSEUM OF NATURAL HISTORY LIBRARY, 1400 S Lake Shore Dr, 60605-2498. SAN 303-8955. Tel: 312-665-7887, 312-922-9410. FAX: 312-665-7893. Web Site: www.fmnh.org. *Librn*, Benjamin Williams; *Cat*, Michael Godow; *Ref*, Michele Calhoun; Staff 5 (MLS 5)
Founded 1893
Library Holdings: Bk Vols 250,000
Subject Interests: Anthropology, Archaeology, Botany, Geology, Museology, Paleontology, Zoology
Special Collections: Berthold Laufer Coll of Far Eastern Studies; Edward E Ayer Ornithology Library Coll; Karl P Schmidt Herpetology Library Coll, bks & reprints
Mem of Chicago Libr Syst
Partic in Illinois Library & Information Network; OCLC Online Computer Library Center, Inc
Open Mon-Fri 8:30-4:30
Friends of the Library Group

FIRST NATIONAL BANK OF CHICAGO

S CORPORATE LIBRARY SERVICES, One Bank One Plaza, Mail Code: IL1-0477, 60670. SAN 303-8963. Tel: 312-732-3532, 312-732-3591. FAX: 312-732-7895. *Mgr*, Barbara Allamian
Founded 1931
Library Holdings: Bk Titles 10,000; Per Subs 500
Restriction: Private library
Partic in Ill Regional Libr Coun; Illinois Library & Information Network

L LAW DEPARTMENT LIBRARY, One First National Plaza, Ste 0284, 60670. SAN 376-0383. Tel: 312-732-5274. FAX: 312-732-9753. *Librn*, Kathleen Ransdell
Library Holdings: Bk Titles 11,000; Per Subs 84

L FOLEY & LARDNER LIBRARY,* 330 N Wabash Ave, Ste 3300, 60611-3608. SAN 373-8019. Tel: 312-755-2552. FAX: 312-755-1925. *Librn*, Christina Wagner
Founded 1988
Library Holdings: Bk Vols 10,000
Subject Interests: Commodities, Real estate, Securities
Mem of Chicago Libr Syst

S FRANKEL & COMPANY, Information Center, 111 E Wacker Dr, 60601-4884. SAN 329-8205. Tel: 312-552-5197. FAX: 312-552-5400. *Mgr*, Lynn Leinartas; E-Mail: lynn_leinartas@frankel.com
Library Holdings: Bk Vols 3,000; Per Subs 250
Subject Interests: Marketing research
Special Collections: Sales Promotion
Publications: Marketing Servs Review (quarterly)
Mem of Chicago Libr Syst
Partic in Dialog Corporation; Dow Jones News Retrieval; Illinois Library & Information Network

S FREEBORN & PETERS LIBRARY,* 311 S Wacker Dr, Ste 3000, 60606-6677. SAN 376-1711. Tel: 312-360-6000. FAX: 312-360-6575. *Mgr*, Debra Mack
Library Holdings: Bk Titles 150
Subject Interests: Law

S GARDNER, CARTON & DOUGLAS, Library & Information Services,* Quaker Tower, 321 N Clark St, Ste 3200, 60610-4795. SAN 376-1428. Tel: 312-245-8544. FAX: 312-644-3381. *Dir*, Karin V Donahue; E-Mail: kdonahue@gcd.com
Library Holdings: Bk Titles 10,050; Per Subs 31

S GOETHE-INSTITUTE CHICAGO LIBRARY, 150 N Michigan Ave Ste 200, 60601. SAN 321-2963. Tel: 312-263-0475. FAX: 312-263-0476. E-Mail: gibibl@interaccess.com. Web Site: www.goethe.de/uk/chi. *Dir*, Constance Edwards; Staff 1 (MLS 1)
Founded 1979
Jan 2000-Dec 2000 Mats Exp $8,000, Books $4,000, Per/Ser (Incl. Access Fees) $4,000
Library Holdings: Bk Vols 7,000; Bk Titles 6,000; Per Subs 100
Subject Interests: Contemporary German lit, German lang, Music, Translation
Special Collections: Contemporary German Fiction & Non-Fiction in Original Language & in Translation
Database Vendor: OCLC - First Search
Publications: Bibliographies on various subjects; Library Guide; New Acquisition Listings; Video Catalog
Mem of Chicago Libr Syst
Partic in ILA
The Goethe-Institute was founded in 1951 to promote a wider knowledge of German language & to foster cultural cooperation with other countries. It is a non-profit making, public funded organization with its head office in Munich. It is represented worldwide with 157 institutes in 73 countries

S GRANT THORNTON LLP INFORMATION CENTER,* 700 One Prudential Plaza, 130 E Randolph, 60601-6145. SAN 340-1227. Tel: 312-856-0001. FAX: 312-565-4719. *Librn*, Otis Joseph; E-Mail: ojoseph@gt.com
Founded 1972
Library Holdings: Bk Titles 1,400; Per Subs 125
Subject Interests: Accounting, Auditing
Restriction: Staff use only
Mem of Chicago Libr Syst

S GREELEY & HANSEN ENGINEERING LIBRARY, 100 S Wacker Dr, Ste 1400, 60606. SAN 303-9005. Tel: 312-578-2380. FAX: 312-558-1986. *Librn*, Bonnie C Goeser; E-Mail: bgoeser@greeley-hansen.com; Staff 2 (Non-MLS 2)
Founded 1914
Library Holdings: Bk Titles 5,000; Per Subs 150
Subject Interests: Sewage, Water treatment
Database Vendor: Dialog, OCLC - First Search, OVID Technologies
Publications: Newsletter
Restriction: Employees & their associates
Function: Some telephone reference
Mem of Chicago Libr Syst

J HAROLD WASHINGTON COLLEGE, CITY COLLEGES OF CHICAGO LIBRARY,* 30 E Lake St, 60601-9996. SAN 303-9501. Tel: 312-553-5760. FAX: 312-553-5783. *Acq, Coll Develop, Librn, Per*, J William Locke; Tel: 312-553-5766, E-Mail: wlocke@ccc.edu; *AV*, Alan Kagan; Tel: 312-553-5775; *Circ*, Sherry Ledbetter; Tel: 312-553-5765; *Online Servs*, John Kieraldo; Tel: 312-553-5761; *Ref*, Salvatore Attinello; Tel: 312-553-5762; Staff 5 (MLS 5)
Founded 1962. Enrl 12,520; Highest Degree: Associate
Jul 1998-Jun 1999 Income Parent Institution $835,019. Mats Exp $195,451, Books $87,775, Per/Ser (Incl. Access Fees) $27,688, Micro $20,289, AV Equip $28,000, Electronic Ref Mat (Incl. Access Fees) $31,699. Sal $639,568 (Prof $337,099)
Library Holdings: Bk Vols 68,414; Bk Titles 62,960; Per Subs 390
Subject Interests: Ethnic studies
Automation Activity & Vendor Info: (Acquisitions) DRA; (Cataloging) DRA; (Circulation) DRA; (Course Reserve) DRA; (ILL) DRA; (Media Booking) DRA; (OPAC) DRA; (Serials) DRA
Database Vendor: GaleNet, IAC - Info Trac, ProQuest
Mem of Chicago Libr Syst
Partic in Ill Regional Libr Coun; Illinois Library & Information Network
Open Mon-Thurs 8-9, Fri 8-6, Sat 8:30-1:30, closed Sun academic year, summer hours posted

S HARRINGTON INSTITUTE OF INTERIOR DESIGN LIBRARY,* 410 S Michigan Ave, 60605. SAN 320-1767. Tel: 312-939-4975. FAX: 312-939-8005. E-Mail: library@interiordesign.edu. *Dir*, Elaine Lowenthal; *Cat*, Thomas Hartmann; Staff 4 (MLS 2, Non-MLS 2)
Founded 1975. Enrl 429
Aug 1997-Jul 1998 Mats Exp $131,500, Books $11,000, Per/Ser (Incl. Access Fees) $5,000, Presv $1,456, Micro $426. Sal $100,500 (Prof $70,000)
Library Holdings: Bk Titles 22,000; Per Subs 89
Subject Interests: Art and architecture, Furniture, Interior design
Special Collections: Furniture Manufacturers Current Catalogs (Product Library Coll), originals
Automation Activity & Vendor Info: (Acquisitions) epixtech, inc.; (Cataloging) epixtech, inc.; (Circulation) epixtech, inc.
Database Vendor: OCLC - First Search
Publications: Accessions lists; subject bibliographies
Mem of Chicago Libr Syst
Partic in Illinois Library & Information Network; LVIS; OCLC Online Computer Library Center, Inc

S HARZA ENGINEERING COMPANY LIBRARY,* 233 S Wacker Dr, 60606. SAN 329-8612. Tel: 312-831-3397. FAX: 312-831-3999.
Library Holdings: Bk Titles 11,500; Per Subs 300
Partic in Dialog Corporation; Illinois Library & Information Network; OCLC Online Computer Library Center, Inc

S HEARTLAND INSTITUTE LIBRARY, 19 S LaSalle No 903, 60603. SAN 377-5232. Tel: 312-377-4000. FAX: 312-377-5000. Web Site: www.heartland.org. *Librn*, John R La Plante; E-Mail: laplante@heartland.org; Staff 1 (Non-MLS 1)
Founded 1984
Library Holdings: Bk Titles 1,500; Per Subs 25
Subject Interests: Agriculture, Economics, Global climate change, Health care, Politics, Public policy, Welfare
Function: Research library

S HEIDRICK & STRUGGLES, INC, Library Research Center, Sears Tower, 233 S Wacker Dr Ste 4200, 60606. SAN 303-903X. Tel: 312-496-1765. FAX: 312-496-1294. *Res*, Brenda M Glenn; E-Mail: bglen@h-s.com
Founded 1953
1998-1999 Mats Exp $100,000, Books $36,000, Per/Ser (Incl. Access Fees) $5,000, Other Print Mats $4,000, Electronic Ref Mat (Incl. Access Fees) $55,000. Sal $120,000
Library Holdings: Bk Vols 2,500
Special Collections: Biographies; Business Directories
Mem of Chicago Libr Syst
Partic in Ill Regional Libr Coun

S HILL & KNOWLTON, INC, Information Center,* 900 N Michigan Ave, Ste 2100, 60611-1542. SAN 374-776X. Tel: 312-255-1200. FAX: 312-255-3030.
Library Holdings: Bk Vols 20; Per Subs 40
Restriction: Not open to public

L HINSHAW & CULBERTSON LIBRARY, 222 N LaSalle, Ste 300, 60601-1081. SAN 370-6052. Tel: 312-704-3422. FAX: 312-704-3422. *Mgr*, Victoria Boylan; *Asst Librn*, James Wiederkehr; Staff 4 (MLS 2, Non-MLS 2)
Library Holdings: Bk Vols 20,000; Bk Titles 800; Per Subs 100
Publications: In-house newsletter
Mem of ILL Libr & Info Network

L HOLLEB & COFF LIBRARY,* 55 E Monroe St, Ste 4100, 60603. SAN 326-3010. Tel: 312-807-4600. FAX: 312-807-3900. E-Mail: library@holleb-coff.com. *Mgr*, Mary Williamson; *Asst Librn*, Pam Dralle; Staff 3 (MLS 2, Non-MLS 1)
Library Holdings: Bk Vols 19,000; Bk Titles 17,000; Per Subs 3,000
Restriction: Staff use only
Mem of Chicago Libr Syst
Partic in Illinois Library & Information Network

M HOLY CROSS HOSPITAL, Health Sciences Library,* 2701 W 68th St, 60629-1882. SAN 303-9072. Tel: 773-471-5643. Interlibrary Loan Service Tel: 773-471-5645. FAX: 773-471-5646. E-Mail: holycros@class.org. *Librn*, Warren Albert
Founded 1962

Library Holdings: Bk Vols 2,000; Bk Titles 2,000; Per Subs 200
Subject Interests: Allied health, Medicine, Nursing
Special Collections: Ethics; Hospital Administration
Publications: Health Science Library News; Occasional Memorandum
Mem of Chicago Libr Syst
Partic in Chicago & South Consortium; Greater Midwest Regional Medical Libr Network; Illinois Library & Information Network

L HOPKINS & SUTTER, Law Library, 3 First National Plaza, Ste 4300, 70 W Madison St, 60602. SAN 303-9080. Tel: 312-558-6785. FAX: 312-558-3315. E-Mail: library@hopsut.com. Web Site: www.hopsut.com. *Librn*, Mary Williamson
Library Holdings: Bk Vols 35,000
Subject Interests: Fed law, Ill law, Law

S HYATT CORPORATION, Legal Library,* 200 W Madison Ave, 60606. SAN 326-0135. Tel: 312-750-8149. FAX: 312-750-8581.
Founded 1979
Subject Interests: Securities
Restriction: Staff use only
Open Mon-Fri 8:30-5

S J ALLEN HYNEK CENTER FOR UFO STUDIES, Information Center,* 2457 W Peterson Ave, 60659. SAN 370-615X. Tel: 773-271-3611. *Librn*, George M Eberhart
Founded 1973
Library Holdings: Bk Titles 5,000; Per Subs 50
Special Collections: UFO Case Files, 1947-present
Restriction: Non-circulating to the public

S IIT RESEARCH INSTITUTE, Manufacturing Technology Information Analysis Center Library, 10 W 35th St, 60616. SAN 326-3568. Tel: 312-567-4730. Toll Free Tel: 800-421-0586. FAX: 312-567-4736. E-Mail: mtiac@iitri.org. Web Site: mtiac.iitri.org. *Dir*, Therese Philippi; E-Mail: tphilippi@iitri.org; Staff 5 (MLS 3, Non-MLS 2)
Library Holdings: Bk Vols 858; Per Subs 100
Publications: Directory of Manufacturing Research Centers; MTIAC Current Awareness Bulletin; MTIAC Thesaurus; MTIAC User's Guide

C ILLINOIS COLLEGE OF OPTOMETRY, Carl F Shepard Memorial Library, 3241 S Michigan Ave, 60616. SAN 303-9137. Tel: 312-949-7150. Circulation Tel: 312-949-7158. Reference Tel: 312-949-7152. FAX: 312-949-7690. Web Site: www.ico.edu. *Dir*, Gerald Dujsik; E-Mail: gdujsik@eyecare.ico.edu; *Publ Servs*, Laurie Curtis; E-Mail: lcurtis@eyecare.ico.edu; *Publ Servs*, Sandra Engram; E-Mail: sengram@eyecare.ico.edu; Staff 7 (MLS 4, Non-MLS 3)
Founded 1955. Circ 1,000; Enrl 650; Fac 75; Highest Degree: Doctorate
Jul 2000-Jun 2001 Income Parent Institution $311,971. Mats Exp $80,700, Books $26,000, Per/Ser (Incl. Access Fees) $48,800, Presv $2,600, AV Equip $800, Electronic Ref Mat (Incl. Access Fees) $2,500. Sal $247,372 (Prof $183,931)
Library Holdings: Bk Vols 29,857; Bk Titles 14,929; Per Subs 242; Bks on Deafness & Sign Lang 33
Subject Interests: Health sciences, Medicine, Natural science, Ophthalmology, Optics, Optometry
Automation Activity & Vendor Info: (Cataloging) PALS; (OPAC) PALS
Publications: Acquisitions List (quarterly)
Restriction: Open to others by appointment
Function: Document delivery services, Photocopies available, Some telephone reference
Mem of Chicago Libr Syst
Partic in Illinois Library & Information Network; Metrop Consortium; OCLC Online Computer Library Center, Inc; Regional Med Libr - Region 3

S ILLINOIS CPA SOCIETY, Library Services,* 222 S Riverside Plaza, 16th flr, 60606-5808. SAN 375-9520. Tel: 312-993-0407. FAX: 312-993-9954. *Mgr*, Michelle Haryasz
Library Holdings: Bk Titles 5,000; Per Subs 120
Subject Interests: Accounting, Auditing
Open Mon-Fri 8-5

L ILLINOIS CRIMINAL JUSTICE INFORMATION AUTHORITY LIBRARY, 120 S Riverside Plaza, Ste 1016, 60606-3997. SAN 329-5222. Tel: 312-793-8550. Interlibrary Loan Service Tel: 312-793-8901. FAX: 312-793-8422.
Library Holdings: Bk Vols 6,000; Per Subs 100
Open Mon-Fri 8:30-5

G ILLINOIS DEPARTMENT OF EMPLOYMENT SECURITY, Law & Reference Library, 401 S State St, Rm 719, 60605-2280. SAN 303-9110. Tel: 312-793-6202. FAX: 312-793-6292. E-Mail: emiluti@ides.state.il.us. *Librn*, Eunice Choi; Staff 1 (MLS 1)
Founded 1976
Library Holdings: Bk Vols 4,000; Bk Titles 3,000; Per Subs 122
Subject Interests: Economics, Employment, Labor, Law
Mem of Chicago Libr Syst; ILL Libr & Info Network
Partic in Illinois Library & Information Network

G ILLINOIS HOUSING DEVELOPMENT AUTHORITY LIBRARY,* 401 N Michigan Ave, Ste 900, 60611. SAN 376-1401. Tel: 312-836-5262. FAX: 312-832-2178. *Librn*, Pearl Madlock
Library Holdings: Bk Titles 500; Per Subs 10

C ILLINOIS INSTITUTE OF ART - CHICAGO LIBRARY, 350 N Orleans St, 60654-1593. SAN 372-588X. Tel: 312-280-3500. FAX: 312-280-3528. Web Site: www.aii.edu. *Dir*, Juliet Teipel; E-Mail: teipelj@aii.edu. Subject Specialists: *Design*, Juliet Teipel; Staff 4 (MLS 3, Non-MLS 1)
Founded 1985. Enrl 1,000; Fac 80; Highest Degree: Bachelor
Jul 1999-Jun 2000 Income $252,000. Mats Exp $112,000, Books $66,000, Per/Ser (Incl. Access Fees) $30,000, Electronic Ref Mat (Incl. Access Fees) $16,000. Sal $123,000
Library Holdings: Bk Vols 10,280; Bk Titles 8,790; Per Subs 275
Subject Interests: Animation, Fashion design, Interior design
Automation Activity & Vendor Info: (Circulation) Sagebrush Corporation; (OPAC) Athena; (Serials) Athena
Database Vendor: OCLC - First Search
Mem of Chicago Libr Syst

C ILLINOIS INSTITUTE OF TECHNOLOGY, Paul V Galvin Library, 35 W 33rd St, 60616. SAN 340-1340. Tel: 312-567-3616, 312-567-6844. FAX: 312-567-5318. Web Site: www.gl.iit.edu. *Dean*, Dr Sohair Elbaz; E-Mail: elbaz@charlie.cns.iit.edu; *Assoc Dean*, Charles Wenger; Tel: 312-567-3374, E-Mail: wenger@iit.edu; Staff 30 (MLS 15, Non-MLS 15)
Founded 1891. Enrl 6,003; Fac 280; Highest Degree: Doctorate
Jun 2000-May 2001 Mats Exp $2,352,500, Books $100,000, Per/Ser (Incl. Access Fees) $361,000, Other Print Mats $22,700, Electronic Ref Mat (Incl. Access Fees) $255,840. Sal $1,059,000 (Prof $693,750)
Library Holdings: Bk Vols 582,151; Bk Titles 243,685; Per Subs 3,800
Subject Interests: Art and architecture, Computer science, Economics, Engineering, Environmental studies, Mathematics, Science/technology, Technology
Special Collections: IIT Archives; Marvin Camras Coll, papers, inventions
Database Vendor: CARL, Dialog, OCLC - First Search, Wilson - Wilson Web
Publications: Booklines (Newsletter)
Mem of Chicago Libr Syst
Partic in Chicago Academic Libr Coun; Illinois Library & Information Network; LCS; OCLC Online Computer Library Center, Inc
Special Services for the Deaf - TDD
Departmental Libraries:
CENTER FOR THE STUDY OF ETHICS IN THE PROFESSIONS, Hermann Union Bldg/Mezzanine, 3241 S Federal St, 60616. SAN 326-6842. Tel: 312-567-6913. FAX: 312-567-3016. E-Mail: csep@iit.edu. Web Site: www.iit.edu/departments/csep. *Info Res, Librn*, Elizabeth Quinlan; E-Mail: quinlan@lit.edu; Staff 1 (MLS 1)
Founded 1976. Enrl 7,000; Fac 200; Highest Degree: Doctorate
Library Holdings: Bk Titles 1,850; Per Subs 34
Subject Interests: Ethics
Special Collections: Codes of Ethics Coll; Referal Bank of National & Foreign Organization Concerned With Professional Ethics
Publications: Perspectives on the Professions (newsletter)
Function: Research library
Partic in ILCSO
DOWNTOWN CAMPUS LIBRARIES, 565 W Adams, 60661-3691. SAN 340-1375. Tel: 312-906-5600. Reference Tel: 312-906-5670. FAX: 312-906-5679. Web Site: www.infoctr.edu, www.lir.edu. *Assoc Dir*, Frederick D Barnhart; Tel: 312-906-5615, Fax: 312-906-5685, E-Mail: fbarnhar@kentlaw.edu; *Head Ref*, Spencer Simons; Tel: 312-906-5662, E-Mail: ssimons@kentlaw.edu; *Cat*, Nadine Hoffman; E-Mail: nhoffman@kentlaw.edu; *Ref*, Lenore Glanz; Tel: 312-906-5621, E-Mail: lglanz@kentlaw.edu; *Ref*, Amy Jarmon; E-Mail: ajarmon@kentlaw.edu; *Ref*, Joseph Mitzenmacher; Tel: 312-906-5612, E-Mail: jmitzenm@kentlaw.edu; *Ref*, Lucy Moss; Tel: 312-906-5676, E-Mail: lmoss@kentlaw.edu; Staff 35 (MLS 10, Non-MLS 25)
Enrl 1,260; Fac 70; Highest Degree: Doctorate
Library Holdings: Bk Vols 550,000; Per Subs 7,200
Subject Interests: Aging, International relations, Law
Special Collections: European Econ Comm Doc Dep; Library of International Relations; Stuart Bus Libr
Database Vendor: Dialog, Ebsco - EbscoHost, Lexis-Nexis, OCLC - First Search, ProQuest, Silverplatter Information Inc.

M ILLINOIS MASONIC MEDICAL CENTER, Medical Library, 836 W Wellington Ave, Rm 7501, 60657. SAN 320-4499. Tel: 773-296-5084. FAX: 773-296-7421. *In Charge*, Ann Markham; E-Mail: amarkham@immc.org; Staff 3 (MLS 2, Non-MLS 1)
Founded 1963
2000-2000 Mats Exp $123,200, Books $30,000, Per/Ser (Incl. Access Fees) $90,000, AV Equip $3,200
Library Holdings: Bk Vols 5,000; Per Subs 340
Subject Interests: Health sciences
Publications: Update (quarterly)
Mem of Chicago Libr Syst; Metrop Consortium of Chicago
Branches:
ANESTHESIOLOGY Tel: 773-296-5084. FAX: 773-296-7421. *In Charge*,

Ann Markham
PATHOLOGY Tel: 773-296-5084. FAX: 773-296-7421. *In Charge*, Ann Markham
RADIOLOGY *In Charge*, Ann Markham

C ILLINOIS SCHOOL OF PROFESSIONAL PSYCHOLOGY LIBRARY, 20 S Clark St, 60603. SAN 375-9601. Tel: 312-279-3950. FAX: 312-578-8291. Web Site: www.isppchicago.net. *Dir Libr Serv*, Qi Chen; E-Mail: qchen@ispp.edu; Staff 3 (MLS 1, Non-MLS 2)
Founded 1979. Enrl 500; Fac 30; Highest Degree: Doctorate
1998-1999 Mats Exp $232,842, Books $179,801, Per/Ser (Incl. Access Fees) $23,575, Micro $2,700, Other Print Mats $23,022. Sal $116,800
Library Holdings: Bk Titles 7,000; Per Subs 100
Automation Activity & Vendor Info: (Cataloging) Sagebrush Corporation; (Circulation) Sagebrush Corporation
Database Vendor: OCLC - First Search, OVID Technologies, ProQuest, Silverplatter Information Inc.
Partic in Chicago Library System

C INSTITUTE FOR CLINICAL SOCIAL WORK LIBRARY, (ICSW), 68 E Wacker Pl, Ste 1400, 60601. SAN 375-2046. Tel: 312-726-8480. FAX: 312-726-7216. E-Mail: icsw@icsw.com, icsw@mindspring.com. Web Site: www.icsw.com. *Librn*, Filippa Genovese; *Librn*, Steven Olderr; Staff 1 (MLS 1)
Founded 1981. Enrl 100; Fac 75; Highest Degree: Doctorate
Library Holdings: Bk Vols 3,000; Per Subs 45
Subject Interests: Psychology, Social work
Special Collections: Faculty publications; student dissertations
Mem of Chicago Libr Syst

M INSTITUTE FOR PSYCHOANALYSIS, CHICAGO, McLean Library, 122 S Michigan Ave, 60603-6107. SAN 320-3719. Tel: 312-922-7474. FAX: 312-922-5656. E-Mail: tn011927@psinet.com. Web Site: www.chianalysis.org. *Dir Libr Serv*, Jerome Kavka; E-Mail: jkavka21@hotmail.com; Staff 1 (MLS 1)
Founded 1932. Enrl 400
Library Holdings: Bk Titles 10,000; Per Subs 100
Subject Interests: Psychiatry, Psychoanalysis, Psychology
Special Collections: Gitelson Film Library Coll; Institute Archives; Kohut Archives
Publications: Chicago Psychoanalytic Index, 1920-1988
Mem of Chicago Libr Syst

C INTERNATIONAL ACADEMY OF MERCHANDISING & DESIGN, IAMD Library, One N State St, Ste 400, 60602. SAN 375-5339. Tel: 312-980-9200. FAX: 312-541-3929. Web Site: www.iamd.edu. *Dir*, Kevin Kaufmann; E-Mail: kkaufmann@iamd.edu; Staff 1 (Non-MLS 1)
Founded 1990. Enrl 1,400; Fac 80; Highest Degree: Bachelor
Library Holdings: Bk Titles 3,000; Per Subs 80
Publications: DNA
Partic in Illinois Library & Information Network

J INTERNATIONAL GRAPHOANALYSIS SOCIETY, IGAS Library, 111 N Canal St, Ste 399, 60606. SAN 321-1134. Tel: 312-930-9446. FAX: 312-930-5903. Web Site: www.igas.com. *Librn*, Anthony Hibbs; *Librn*, Richard Meade
Founded 1929. Enrl 12,000
Library Holdings: Bk Titles 25,000
Subject Interests: Behav sci, Soc sci

M INTERNATIONAL MUSEUM OF SURGICAL SCIENCE LIBRARY, 1524 N Lake Shore Dr, 60610. SAN 303-9269. Tel: 312-642-6502. FAX: 312-642-9516. *Curator*, Leonard Kliwinski; E-Mail: info@imss.org
Founded 1956
Library Holdings: Bk Vols 7,000
Subject Interests: Dentistry, History, Medicine, Surgery
Restriction: By appointment only, Non-circulating to the public
Function: Archival collection, For research purposes

M JACKSON PARK HOSPITAL LIBRARY, 7531 Stony Island Ave, 60649. SAN 303-9315. Tel: 773-947-7653. FAX: 773-947-7791. *Dir*, Andrew Paradise; E-Mail: andrewparadise@jacksonpark.com; *Librn*, Jennifer Peters; Staff 1 (MLS 1)
Founded 1960
Library Holdings: Bk Vols 2,250; Bk Titles 2,000; Per Subs 50
Subject Interests: Medical
Database Vendor: OCLC - First Search
Partic in Chicago & South Consortium; Chicago Library System

L JENNER & BLOCK LIBRARY,* One IBM Plaza, 60611. SAN 303-9323. Tel: 312-222-9350. FAX: 312-923-4550. *Dir*, Mitchell Klaich; *Ref*, Linnette Papagianis; Staff 3 (MLS 3)
Founded 1914
Library Holdings: Bk Vols 35,000
Subject Interests: Law
Publications: Library Newsletter (monthly)
Partic in Illinois Library & Information Network; Westlaw

S JEWISH VOCATIONAL SERVICES LIBRARY,* One S Franklin St, 60606. SAN 303-934X. Tel: 312-357-4512. FAX: 312-855-3282. *Librn*, Julie Rosenfeld
Founded 1934
Library Holdings: Bk Vols 2,500; Bk Titles 2,000; Per Subs 90
Subject Interests: Psychiatry, Psychology, Vocational education
Publications: Infoalert (newsletter); Infosource (newsletter); Pertinent Publication (newsletter)

S JOHNSON PUBLISHING CO LIBRARY,* 820 S Michigan Ave, 60605. SAN 303-9366. Tel: 312-322-9320. FAX: 312-322-0951. Web Site: www.ebonymag.com. *Librn*, Pamela J Cash
Founded 1949
Library Holdings: Bk Vols 17,000; Bk Titles 15,000; Per Subs 300
Subject Interests: Afro-American, History, Music
Restriction: Staff use only

L JONES, DAY, REAVIS & POGUE, Law Library, 77 W Wacker Dr, Ste 3500, 60601-1692. SAN 371-8611. Tel: 312-782-3939. FAX: 312-782-8585. *Librn*, Sandy Jacobson; Staff 3 (MLS 2, Non-MLS 1)

L KATTEN, MUCHIN & ZAVIS LIBRARY,* 525 W Monroe, Ste 1600, 60661-3693. SAN 321-3994. Tel: 312-902-5675. FAX: 312-577-8715. *Dir Libr Serv*, Susan P Siebers; Staff 4 (MLS 4)
Founded 1974
Library Holdings: Bk Vols 40,000; Per Subs 950
Mem of Chicago Libr Syst
Partic in OCLC Online Computer Library Center, Inc

S A T KEARNEY INC, Information Center,* 222 W Adams, 17th flr, 60606. SAN 303-9374. Tel: 312-648-0111. FAX: 312-223-6386. *Dir*, Deborah Hammond
Founded 1940
Library Holdings: Bk Titles 1,469; Per Subs 325
Subject Interests: Finance, Marketing, Technology, Transportation
Publications: Acquisition List (quarterly); Article Newsletter (monthly); Subscription Services/Periodicals (annual)
Mem of Chicago Libr Syst
Partic in Dialog Corporation; Dow Jones News Retrieval; Illinois Library & Information Network

J KENNEDY-KING COLLEGE, CITY COLLEGES OF CHICAGO LIBRARY,* 6800 S Wentworth Ave, 60621. SAN 303-9390. Tel: 773-602-5449. FAX: 773-602-5463. Web Site: www.ccc.edu. *Circ*, Linda King; *Ref*, Melanie Thompson
Founded 1934. Enrl 2,100
Library Holdings: Bk Vols 57,000; Bk Titles 50,000; Per Subs 191
Subject Interests: Nursing
Mem of Chicago Libr Syst
Partic in Illinois Library & Information Network; NILRC
Open Mon-Thur 8:30-8, Fri 8:30-3:30 & Sat 9-2

L KIRKLAND & ELLIS LIBRARY, 200 E Randolph Dr, 60601-6637. SAN 303-9412. Tel: 312-861-2304. Interlibrary Loan Service Tel: 312-861-3208. FAX: 312-861-2290. *Mgr*, Joan Batchen; Tel: 312-861-2399; *Res*, Mary Eggert; Tel: 312-649-3851; *Res*, Mindy Parker; Tel: 312-861-2492; *Res*, Stacey Trotter; Tel: 312-861-3148; *Res*, Anne Waldron; Tel: 312-861-2346; *Res*, Clara Mosquera; Tel: 312-861-3270; *Res*, Carole Dauer; Tel: 312-861-3189; *Res*, Steve Abelson; Tel: 312-861-3246; *Res*, Renita Miller; *Res*, Nancy McQueeny; Staff 15 (MLS 9, Non-MLS 6)
Founded 1918

S KORN FERRY INTERNATIONAL, Research Library,* 233 S Wacker Dr, Ste 3300, 60606. SAN 375-8117. Tel: 312-466-1834. FAX: 312-559-9027.
Library Holdings: Bk Titles 300; Per Subs 64

S KPMG PEAT MARWICK LIBRARY, 303 E Wacker Dr, 60601. SAN 372-4115. Tel: 312-665-5386. FAX: 312-665-6000. Web Site: www.kpmg.com. *Librn*, Pam Ragsdale; Staff 3 (MLS 2, Non-MLS 1)
Library Holdings: Bk Titles 100; Per Subs 38
Automation Activity & Vendor Info: (Cataloging) Sydney; (Serials) Sydney
Partic in Dialog Corporation; Dow Jones News Retrieval

M LA RARBIDA CHILDREN'S HOSPITAL & RESEARCH CENTER, Lawrence Mercer Pick Memorial Library, E 65th St at Lake Michigan, 60649. SAN 328-3852. Tel: 773-363-6700, Ext 471. FAX: 773-363-7143. *Librn*, Lynne Cunningham
Library Holdings: Bk Vols 500; Per Subs 70

G LAKE MICHIGAN FEDERATION LIBRARY,* 220 S State, Ste 2108, 60604. SAN 325-6324. Tel: 312-939-0838. FAX: 312-939-2708. *Exec Dir*, Cameron Davis
Special Collections: Lake Michigan Toxics & Erosion Studies

L LATHAM & WATKINS, Law Library, 5800 Sears Tower, 60606. SAN 371-4071. Tel: 312-876-7687. FAX: 312-993-9767. Web Site: www.lw.com. *Librn*, Genevieve Zook; E-Mail: genevieve.zook@lw.com; Staff 3 (MLS 2, Non-MLS 1)
Library Holdings: Bk Vols 12,000; Per Subs 142

L LEGAL ASSISTANCE FOUNDATION OF CHICAGO LIBRARY, 111 W Jackson, 3rd Flr, 60604. SAN 320-1775. Tel: 312-341-1070, Ext 337. FAX: 312-341-1041. *Librn*, John Ryden
Founded 1974
Library Holdings: Bk Vols 18,000; Bk Titles 13,000; Per Subs 160
Partic in Illinois Library & Information Network

S LEO BURNETT CO, INC LIBRARY, 35 W Wacker Dr, 60601. SAN 303-8300. Tel: 312-220-1090. FAX: 312-220-6517. *Dir*, Douglas Buffo; Tel: 312-220-4291, E-Mail: douglas_buffo@chi.leoburnett.com; *Assoc Dir*, Astrida Robeznieks; E-Mail: astrida_robeznieks@chi.leoburnett.com; *Info Specialist*, Scott Jenkins; Tel: 312-220-4293, E-Mail: scott_jenkins@chi.leoburnett.com; Staff 5 (MLS 2, Non-MLS 3)
Founded 1938
Library Holdings: Bk Vols 4,000
Subject Interests: Advertising, Marketing
Special Collections: Classified Picture Files
Database Vendor: Dialog, Lexis-Nexis, OCLC - First Search, Wilson - Wilson Web
Function: For research purposes
Partic in Chicago Library System

S LEXECON INC,* 332 S Michigan Ave, Ste 1300, 60604-4306. SAN 376-0111. Tel: 312-322-0622. FAX: 312-322-0218.
Library Holdings: Bk Titles 15,260; Per Subs 82

S LITHUANIAN RESEARCH & STUDIES CENTER, INC, 5620 S Claremont Ave, 60636-1039. SAN 325-2728. Tel: 773-434-4545. FAX: 773-434-9363. E-Mail: lithuanian@ameritech.net. Web Site: www.lithuanianresearch.org. *Pres*, Dr John A Rackauskas; *VPres*, Dr Robert A Vitas; *Tech Servs*, Thomas R Miglinas; *Per*, Richard Petersonas; *Ref*, Skirmante Jakstaite; *Bibliog Instr*, Jonas Dainauskas; *Coll Develop*, Robert A Vitas. Subject Specialists: *Art*, Halina Moliejus; *Art*, Magdalena Stankunas; Staff 10 (MLS 3, Non-MLS 7)
Founded 1982
Library Holdings: Bk Vols 102,000; Bk Titles 85,000; Per Subs 1,600
Subject Interests: Costume, Crafts, Culture, Customs, Dance, Economy, Education, Folklore, Geography, History, Immigration, Language, Literature, Lithuanian, Lithuanian-Am Art, Mil, Music, Politics, Sports, Theater, Traditions
Special Collections: Cartography Dept; Dainauskas History Library; Krupavicius Coll; Lithuanian Historical Society; Lithuanian Institute of Education; Marian Fathers Coll; Pakstas Coll; Rare Book Coll; World Lithuanian Archives; World Lithuanian Community Coll; Zilevicius-Kreivenas Lithuanian Musicology Archive
Open Mon-Fri 11-5

L LORD, BISSELL & BROOK, Law Library,* 115 S La Salle St, 60603. SAN 303-951X. Tel: 312-443-0646. FAX: 312-443-0336. *Librn*, Sandra Gold; Staff 11 (MLS 4, Non-MLS 7)
Library Holdings: Bk Vols 30,000
Partic in Illinois Library & Information Network

M LOUIS A WEISS MEMORIAL HOSPITAL, L Lewis Cohen Memorial Library,* 4646 N Marine Dr, 60640. SAN 304-0526. Tel: 773-564-5820. FAX: 773-564-5829. *Librn*, Syed A Maghrabi
Library Holdings: Bk Titles 2,000; Per Subs 175
Partic in Illinois Library & Information Network; Medlars; Metrop Consortium; Regional Med Libr - Region 3

CR LOYOLA UNIVERSITY CHICAGO LIBRARIES, 25 E Pearson St, 60611. SAN 340-143X. Tel: 312-915-6948. Interlibrary Loan Service Tel: 773-508-2636. Circulation Tel: 773-508-2632. Reference Tel: 773-508-2654. FAX: 773-508-2993. E-Mail: cud_ref@luc.edu. Web Site: www.libraries.luc.edu/. *Dean of Libr*, Edward A Warro; Fax: 312-915-6637, E-Mail: ewarro@luc.edu; *Asst Dean*, Stephen Macksey; Tel: 773-508-2644, Fax: 773-508-8497, E-Mail: smackse@luc.edu; *Asst Dean*, Karla D Petersen; Tel: 773-508-2657, E-Mail: kpeter1@luc.edu; *Assoc Dean*, Melissa Trevvett; Tel: 773-508-2623, Fax: 773-508-8691, E-Mail: mtrevve@luc.edu; *Head, Acq*, Ling-Li Chang; Tel: 773-508-2651, E-Mail: lchang@luc.edu; *Acq*, Steven Harsin; *Archivist*, Bro Michael Grace; Tel: 773-508-2661, E-Mail: mgrace1@luc.edu; *Head, Cat*, Joan Schuitema; Tel: 773-508-2656, E-Mail: jschuit@luc.edu; *Head, Circ*, Catherine Miesse; Tel: 773-508-2674, E-Mail: cmiesse@luc.edu; *Head Ref*, Kerry Cochrane; Tel: 773-508-2637, E-Mail: kcochra@luc.edu; Staff 117 (MLS 48, Non-MLS 69)
Founded 1870. Enrl 12,612; Fac 2,563; Highest Degree: Doctorate
Jul 1999-Jun 2000 Income (Main and Other College/University Libraries) Parent Institution $10,225,244. Mats Exp $4,947,327, Books $1,610,823, Per/Ser (Incl. Access Fees) $2,401,611, Presv $118,144, Micro $36,018, AV Equip $58,557, Other Print Mats $126,193, Electronic Ref Mat (Incl. Access Fees) $595,981. Sal $4,418,537 (Prof $2,494,515)
Library Holdings: Bk Vols 1,765,133; Bk Titles 1,027,185; Per Subs 10,644
Special Collections: Jesuitica; Paul Claudel Coll
Automation Activity & Vendor Info: (Acquisitions) Endeavor; (Cataloging) Endeavor; (Circulation) Endeavor; (Course Reserve) Endeavor; (OPAC) Endeavor; (Serials) Endeavor
Database Vendor: Ebsco - EbscoHost, GaleNet, IAC - Info Trac, IAC - SearchBank, Lexis-Nexis, OCLC - First Search, OVID Technologies, ProQuest, Silverplatter Information Inc.
Partic in Center For Research Libraries; Chicago Library System; Illinois Library & Information Network; OCLC Online Computer Library Center, Inc
Friends of the Library Group
Departmental Libraries:

CR ELIZABETH M CUDAHY MEMORIAL LIBRARY, 6525 N Sheridan Rd, 60626. SAN 340-1464. Tel: 773-508-2641. Circulation Tel: 773-508-2632. Reference Tel: 773-508-2654. FAX: 773-508-2993. E-Mail: cud_ref@luc.edu. Web Site: www.libraries.luc.edu/about/cudahy.shtml. *Asst Dean*, Karla D Petersen; Tel: 773-508-2657, Fax: 773-508-8691, E-Mail: kpeter1@luc.edu
Jul 1999-Jun 2000 Income (Main Library Only) Parent Institution $5,539,439. Mats Exp $3,035,200, Books $911,863, Per/Ser (Incl. Access Fees) $1,390,902, Presv $88,314, AV Equip $53,826, Other Print Mats $15,398, Electronic Ref Mat (Incl. Access Fees) $574,897. Sal $2,016,827 (Prof $1,169,988)
Library Holdings: Bk Vols 663,784; Bk Titles 458,202; Per Subs 3,336
Subject Interests: Humanities, Philosophy, Theology
Library materials expenditures for Cudahy Library also include Lewis Library, Science, Mallinckrodt & Rome Libraries

CM HEALTH SCIENCES LIBRARY, 2160 S First Ave, Maywood, 60153-5585. SAN 340-1529. Tel: 708-216-9192. FAX: 708-216-9192. *Dir*, Dr Logan Ludwig; Tel: 708-216-5301, Fax: 708-216-6772, E-Mail: lludwig@luc.edu; *Tech Servs*, Dianne Olson; Tel: 708-216-5311, Fax: 708-216-8115, E-Mail: dolson@luc.edu; *Ser*, Katherine Hughes; Tel: 708-216-5302, Fax: 708-216-8115, E-Mail: khughes@luc.edu; *Publ Servs*, Mary Klatt; Tel: 708-216-5305, Fax: 708-216-8115, E-Mail: mklatt@luc.edu; *Circ*, Jeanne Sadlik; Tel: 708-216-5304, Fax: 708-216-8115, E-Mail: jsadlik@luc.edu; *Publ Servs*, Laura Robbins; Tel: 708-216-5308, Fax: 708-216-8115, E-Mail: lrobbins@luc.edu; *AV*, Gary Dandurand; Tel: 708-216-4368, Fax: 708-216-8115, E-Mail: gdandurand@luc.edu; Staff 25 (MLS 8, Non-MLS 17)
Jul 1998-Jun 1999 Income (Main Library Only) $2,977,575, Locally Generated Income $95,677, Parent Institution $2,881,898. Mats Exp $2,977,575, Books $147,326, Per/Ser (Incl. Access Fees) $918,536, Presv $21,500, AV Equip $5,760, Electronic Ref Mat (Incl. Access Fees) $93,129. Sal $758,566 (Prof $458,673)
Library Holdings: Bk Vols 175,857; Bk Titles 64,578; Per Subs 2,400
Subject Interests: Health sciences, Medicine, Nursing
Special Collections: History of Medicine
Automation Activity & Vendor Info: (Cataloging) Endeavor; (Circulation) Endeavor; (Course Reserve) Endeavor; (ILL) Endeavor; (OPAC) Endeavor; (Serials) Endeavor
Database Vendor: Ebsco - EbscoHost, OVID Technologies
Publications: Circulation Manual; Collection Development Manual; Interlibrary Loan Manual
Partic in Illinois Library & Information Network

LAW SCHOOL LIBRARY, 25 E Pearson St, 60611. SAN 340-1553. Tel: 312-915-7131, 312-915-7200, 312-915-7202. Interlibrary Loan Service Tel: 312-915-6921. FAX: 312-915-6797. Web Site: www.luc.edu/libraries/law/home.htm. *Dir*, Francis Robert Doyle; Tel: 312-915-7197, E-Mail: fdoyle@luc.edu; *Assoc Dir*, Julia Wentz; Tel: 312-915-7199, E-Mail: jwentz@luc.edu; *Acq*, Cynthia Allen; Tel: 312-915-7190, E-Mail: callen3@luc.edu; *Acq*, Carol Klink; *Cat*, Jayne McQuoid; Tel: 312-915-7191, E-Mail: jmcquoi@luc.edu; *Cat*, Janet Miranda; *Ref*, Silas Anderson; Tel: 312-915-7311, E-Mail: sander2@luc.edu; *Ref*, Elizabeth Cooper; Tel: 312-915-8516, E-Mail: ecooper@luc.edu; *Ref*, Mary Kenny; Tel: 312-915-6844, E-Mail: mkenny@luc.edu; *Ref*, Sherman Lewis; Tel: 312-915-8517, E-Mail: slewis1@luc.edu; *Ref*, James McMasters; Tel: 312-915-6844, E-Mail: jmcmast@luc.edu; Staff 21 (MLS 10, Non-MLS 11)
Founded 1909. Enrl 739; Fac 30
Jul 1999-Jun 2000 Income (Main Library Only) $1,873,144. Mats Exp $1,066,953, Books $209,884, Per/Ser (Incl. Access Fees) $531,716, Presv $5,999, Micro $36,018, Electronic Ref Mat (Incl. Access Fees) $84,463. Sal $876,235 (Prof $554,560)
Library Holdings: Bk Vols 170,923; Bk Titles 57,226; Per Subs 2,808
Subject Interests: Antitrust law
Special Collections: GPO depository; Medical Jurisprudence
Database Vendor: Lexis-Nexis
Restriction: Circulation limited
Function: ILL available
Partic in Center For Research Libraries; Chicago Legal Acad Syst; Jesuit Law Libr Consortium; OCLC Online Computer Library Center, Inc

LEWIS LIBRARY, 25 E Pearson St, 60611. SAN 340-1499. Tel: 312-915-6622. Circulation Tel: 312-915-6625. FAX: 312-915-6637. Web Site: www.libraries.luc.edu/about/lewis.shtml. *Head of Libr*, Yolande Wersching; Tel: 312-915-6623, E-Mail: ywersch@luc.edu; *Ref*, Thad Dickinson; Tel: 312-915-7271, E-Mail: tdickin@luc.edu; *Ref*, Rebecca Graff; Tel: 312-915-6627, E-Mail: rgraff@luc.edu; *Ref*, Rebecca Sedam; Tel: 312-915-8693, E-Mail: rsedam@luc.edu; *Ref*, Susan Wardzala; Tel: 312-915-6635, E-Mail: swardza@luc.edu; Staff 11 (MLS 5, Non-MLS 6)
Jul 1999-Jun 2000 Income Parent Institution $476,281. Sal $464,108 (Prof $233,298)
Library Holdings: Bk Vols 206,965; Bk Titles 160,048; Per Subs 1,707
Subject Interests: Criminal law and justice, Economics, Social service

(social work)
MALLINCKRODT LIBRARY, 1041 Ridge Rd, Wilmette, 60091-1560. SAN 304-7652. Tel: 847-853-3040. FAX: 847-853-3203. E-Mail: ed-lib@luc.edu. Web Site: www.luc.edu/libraries/mallinckrodt/. *Head of Libr*, Anne Houston; Tel: 847-853-3050, E-Mail: ahousto@luc.edu; *Ref*, Cecile Maciulis; Tel: 847-853-3045, E-Mail: cmaciul@luc.edu; Staff 4 (MLS 2, Non-MLS 2)
Founded 1917
Jul 1999-Jun 2000 Income Parent Institution $127,280. Sal $107,294
Library Holdings: Bk Vols 45,393; Bk Titles 39,398; Per Subs 91
Subject Interests: Education
SCIENCE LIBRARY, 6525 N Sheridan Rd, 60626. SAN 303-9765. Tel: 773-508-8400. Reference Tel: 773-508-8411. FAX: 773-508-8497. E-Mail: sciencelib@luc.edu. Web Site: www.luc.edu/libraries/science/. *Asst Dean*, Karla D Petersen; Tel: 773-508-2657, E-Mail: kpeter1@luc.edu; *Head of Libr*, Carla Lee; Tel: 773-508-8460, E-Mail: clee@luc.edu; *Librn*, Sister Frances Berger; Tel: 773-508-8407, E-Mail: fberger@luc.edu; *Ref*, Hilary Leon; Tel: 773-508-8409, E-Mail: hleon1@luc.edu; Staff 7 (MLS 4, Non-MLS 3)
Jul 1999-Jun 2000 Income Parent Institution $288,017. Sal $276,630 (Prof $128,794)
Library Holdings: Bk Vols 213,295; Bk Titles 147,441; Per Subs 962
Subject Interests: Biology, Chemistry, Computer science, Mathematics, Natural science, Nursing, Physics, Psychology
Materials expenditures are included in Cudahy Library figures

S YT & LOUISE LEE LUM LIBRARY, Appraisal Institute,* 875 N Michigan Ave, Ste 2400, 60611-1980. SAN 370-999X. Tel: 312-335-4467. FAX: 312-335-4486. E-Mail: ailibrary@appraisalinstitute.org. Web Site: www.appraisalinstitute.org. *Dir*, Eric B Goodman
Founded 1992
Library Holdings: Bk Titles 1,600; Per Subs 40
Automation Activity & Vendor Info: (Acquisitions) epixtech, inc.; (Cataloging) epixtech, inc.; (Circulation) epixtech, inc.; (OPAC) epixtech, inc.; (Serials) epixtech, inc.
Database Vendor: OCLC - First Search
Mem of Chicago Libr Syst

S LURA LYNN RYAN PREVENTION RESEARCH LIBRARY, (Formerly Lura Lynn Ryan Research Library), 720 N Franklin, Ste 500, 60610. SAN 376-0367. Tel: 312-988-4646, Ext 234. FAX: 312-988-7096. Web Site: www.prevention.org. *Assoc Librn*, James Chlipala; *Librn, Ref Serv*, Joanie Sebastian; Tel: 312-988-4646, Ext 227, E-Mail: sebastj@prevention.org; Staff 3 (MLS 3)
Library Holdings: Bk Titles 20,000; Per Subs 50
Database Vendor: OCLC - First Search
Mem of Chicago Libr Syst
Sister library to Lura Lynn Ryan Research Library, Springfield

R LUTHERAN SCHOOL OF THEOLOGY AT CHICAGO & MCCORMICK THEOLOGICAL SEMINARY, Jesuit-Krauss-McCormick Library, 1100 E 55th St, 60615-5199. SAN 303-9331. Tel: 773-256-0739. Interlibrary Loan Service Tel: 773-256-0703. Reference Tel: 773-256-0703. FAX: 773-256-0737. Web Site: www.lstc.edu/library/library_index.html, www.mccormick.edu/library. *Dir*, Allen W Mueller; Tel: 773-256-0735, E-Mail: amueller@lstc.edu; *Admin Assoc*, Sandra Magee; Tel: 773-256-0734; *Automation Syst Coordr*, Yana Serdyuk; Tel: 773-256-0733; *Cat*, William Beerman; Tel: 773-256-0736; *Cat*, Emilie Pulver; Tel: 773-256-0730; *Circ*, Elaine D Bonner; Tel: 773-256-0732; *Publ Servs*, Barry C Hopkins; Tel: 773-256-0738; *Reader Servs*, Martin Breen; *Ser*, Christina Browne; Tel: 773-256-0720. Subject Specialists: *Curric*, Judy Evans; Staff 11 (MLS 7, Non-MLS 4)
Founded 1975. Enrl 759; Fac 60; Highest Degree: Doctorate
Jul 1999-Jun 2000 Income $1,123,482. Mats Exp $196,408, Books $142,183, Per/Ser (Incl. Access Fees) $42,884, Micro $3,836, Electronic Ref Mat (Incl. Access Fees) $4,520
Library Holdings: Bk Vols 346,165; Per Subs 980
Subject Interests: Biblical studies, Lutheranism, Patristics, Reformation hist
Special Collections: Ecumenical Parish Resource Center; Reformation Imprints (L Franklin Gruber Coll); Reformed Churches
Automation Activity & Vendor Info: (Acquisitions) epixtech, inc.; (Cataloging) epixtech, inc.; (Circulation) epixtech, inc.; (OPAC) epixtech, inc.; (Serials) epixtech, inc.
Database Vendor: epixtech, inc., OCLC - First Search
Function: Research library
Partic in Illinois Library & Information Network; OCLC Online Computer Library Center, Inc
Collection contains the merger of McCormick Theological Seminary & Lutheran School of Theology at Chicago

S JOHN D & CATHERINE T MACARTHUR FOUNDATION LIBRARY, 140 S Dearborn St, Ste 1100, 60603. SAN 375-8281. Tel: 312-726-8000. FAX: 312-917-3663. Web Site: www.macfound.org. *Librn*, Rebecca Komen
Library Holdings: Bk Titles 3,000; Per Subs 500

J MACCORMAC COLLEGE LIBRARY, 29 E Madison, 2nd Flr, 60602. SAN 303-9552. Tel: 312-922-1884. FAX: 312-922-3196. E-Mail: library@maccormac.edu. Web Site: www.maccormac.edu/library. *Dir*, Leslie Ann Warren; Tel: 319-922-1884, Ext 215, E-Mail: lwarren@maccormac.edu; Staff 2 (MLS 1, Non-MLS 1)
Founded 1904. Enrl 400; Highest Degree: Associate
Library Holdings: Bk Vols 4,000; Per Subs 85; High Interest/Low Vocabulary Bk Vols 30
Subject Interests: Business and management, Economics
Database Vendor: GaleNet, OCLC - First Search
Mem of Chicago Libr Syst

J MALCOLM X COLLEGE LIBRARY,* City Colleges of Chicago, 1900 W Van Buren St, 60612. SAN 303-9609. Tel: 312-850-7250. FAX: 312-850-7187. Web Site: www.xx.edu/malcolmx/malcolmxl/library. *Librn*, Willie E Johnson; Tel: 312-850-7247, E-Mail: wejohnson@ccc.edu; *Coll Develop*, Chung I Park; Tel: 312-850-7246, E-Mail: cpark@ccc.edu
Founded 1934. Enrl 2,200
Jul 1997-Jun 1998 Mats Exp $68,466, Books $34,000, Per/Ser (Incl. Access Fees) $27,000, Micro $7,466. Sal $467,134 (Prof $260,194)
Library Holdings: Bk Titles 45,200; Per Subs 350

L MARSHALL, O'TOOLE, GERSTEIN, MURRAY & BORUN, Law Library, 6300 Sears Tower, 233 S Wacker Dr, 60606-6402. SAN 372-1175. Tel: 312-474-6300. FAX: 312-474-0448. *Librn*, Bridget MacMillan
1999-2000 Income $500,000
Library Holdings: Bk Vols 9,250; Per Subs 30
Mem of Chicago Libr Syst

L MAYER, BROWN & PLATT, Law Library, 190 S LaSalle St, 60603. SAN 303-9668. Tel: 312-701-7922. FAX: 312-701-7711. *Dir Info Resources & Res*, Gail Munden; E-Mail: gmunden@mayerbrown.com; *Librn*, Bobby Towns; *Ref*, John Curry
Library Holdings: Per Subs 60
Mem of Chicago Libr Syst
Partic in Dialog Corporation; Westlaw

L MCBRIDE, BAKER & COLES, Law Library, 500 W Madison, 40th flr, 60661. SAN 325-6200. Tel: 312-715-5700. FAX: 312-993-1103. Web Site: www.mbc.com. *Librn*, Elizabeth Robertson; E-Mail: robertson@mbc.com
Library Holdings: Bk Vols 8,000
Automation Activity & Vendor Info: (Cataloging) Inmagic, Inc.

L MCDERMOTT, WILL & EMERY LAW LIBRARY, 227 W Monroe St, 46th flr, 60606-5096. SAN 303-9587. Tel: 312-984-7650. FAX: 312-984-2094. *Mgr*, Jerry Trenholm; E-Mail: jtrenholm@mwe.com
Library Holdings: Bk Titles 50,000; Per Subs 500
Partic in ILLINET

S MCKINSEY & COMPANY, INC, Research & Information Services-Chicago, 21 S Clark St, Ste 2900, 60603. SAN 370-1743. Tel: 312-551-3500. FAX: 312-551-4222. Web Site: www.mckinsey.com. *Info Res*, Judith Bender
Library Holdings: Bk Titles 750; Per Subs 300
Restriction: Staff use only

CR MEADVILLE-LOMBARD THEOLOGICAL SCHOOL LIBRARY, 5701 S Woodlawn Ave, 60637. SAN 303-9684. Tel: 773-256-3000, Ext 225. FAX: 773-256-3008. Web Site: www.meadville.edu. *Dir*, Neil W Gerdes; E-Mail: ngerdes@meadville.edu; *Asst Librn*, Jennifer Satterfield; Tel: 773-256-3000, Ext 248, E-Mail: jsatterfield@meadville.edu
Founded 1844. Enrl 71; Fac 7; Highest Degree: Doctorate
Jul 1998-Jun 1999 Income $99,850
Library Holdings: Bk Titles 102,000; Per Subs 130
Special Collections: English Philosophy; Ethics & Society; Unitarian-Universalist History & Liberal Religion; World Religion
Partic in Assoc of Chicago Theological Sch; Illinois Library & Information Network; OCLC Online Computer Library Center, Inc
Open Mon-Fri 9-5

M MERCY HEALTH SYSTEM OF CHICAGO, Medical Library,* 2525 S Michigan Ave, 60616-2477. SAN 303-9706. Tel: 312-567-2363. FAX: 312-567-7086. *Librn, Online Servs*, Timothy Oh; Staff 1 (MLS 1)
Founded 1950
Jul 1998-Jun 1999 Mats Exp $87,000
Library Holdings: Bk Vols 5,150; Per Subs 380
Special Collections: John B Murphy, MD Coll
Mem of Chicago Libr Syst
Partic in Greater Midwest Regional Medical Libr Network; Medical Libr Asn; Midwest Health Sci Libr Network
Friends of the Library Group

G METROPOLITAN WATER RECLAMATION DISTRICT OF GREATER CHICAGO LIBRARY, 100 E Erie St, 60611. SAN 303-9722. Tel: 312-751-6658, 312-751-6659. FAX: 312-751-6635. Web Site: www.mwrdgc.dst.il.us. *Librn*, Gerald Austiff; E-Mail: gaustiff@mwrdgc.dst.il.us; Staff 2 (MLS 1, Non-MLS 1)
Founded 1966
Library Holdings: Bk Titles 3,000
Subject Interests: Environmental studies

Special Collections: Archives; Internal Reports & Proceedings of Metropolitan Sanitary District & Predecessors
Partic in Ill Regional Libr Coun

CR MOODY BIBLE INSTITUTE, Crowell Library, 820 N La Salle Blvd, 60610-3284. SAN 340-1618. Tel: 312-329-4136. Interlibrary Loan Service Tel: 312-329-4175. Reference Tel: 312-329-4175. FAX: 312-329-8959. Web Site: www.moody.edu. *Dir*, Roger A vanOosten; Tel: 312-329-4138, E-Mail: rvanoost@moody.edu; *Ref, Spec Coll*, Walter Osborn; Tel: 312-329-3574, E-Mail: wosborn@moody.edu; *Circ*, Mark King; Tel: 312-329-3571, E-Mail: mking@moody.edu; *Cat, Per, Tech Servs*, Lori Johnson; Tel: 312-329-4102, E-Mail: ljohnson@moody.edu; *Acq, Archivist*, Joe Cataio; Tel: 312-329-4880, E-Mail: archives@moody.edu; *ILL*, John Komaravalli; Tel: 312-329-3572; *Automation Syst Coordr*, Jeremy Peterson; Tel: 312-329-8081, E-Mail: jpeterso@moody.edu; Staff 9 (MLS 5, Non-MLS 4)
Founded 1889. Enrl 1,665; Fac 90; Highest Degree: Master
Jul 1999-Jun 2000 Income $843,571. Mats Exp $120,588, Books $57,164, Per/Ser (Incl. Access Fees) $28,869, Presv $3,029, AV Equip $4,979, Electronic Ref Mat (Incl. Access Fees) $26,547. Sal $406,394
Library Holdings: Bk Vols 138,292; Bk Titles 111,790; Per Subs 882
Subject Interests: Religion
Special Collections: D L Moody (Moodyana Coll), artifacts & bks; Moody Bible Institute Archives, docs, letters, newsp & photos
Automation Activity & Vendor Info: (Cataloging) epixtech, inc.; (Circulation) epixtech, inc.; (OPAC) epixtech, inc.; (Serials) epixtech, inc.
Database Vendor: epixtech, inc.
Restriction: Restricted public use
Function: Archival collection, ILL available, Photocopies available
Mem of Chicago Libr Syst
Partic in Illinois Library & Information Network; OCLC Online Computer Library Center, Inc
Special Services for the Blind - Braille
Departmental Libraries:

MOUNT SINAI HOSPITAL MEDICAL CENTER
M LEWISON MEMORIAL LIBRARY, California Ave at 15th St, 60608. SAN 340-1677. Tel: 773-257-6281. FAX: 773-257-6135. *Librn*, Estella B Escudero
Founded 1942
Library Holdings: Bk Vols 3,000; Per Subs 268
Subject Interests: Medicine, Nursing
Publications: Medical Library News
Partic in Medline; Midwest Libr Consortium
Friends of the Library Group

S MURPHY-JAHN LIBRARY, 35 E Wacker Dr, 60601. SAN 373-045X. Tel: 312-427-7300. FAX: 312-332-0274. *In Charge*, Joseph A Stypka
Library Holdings: Bk Titles 20,000; Per Subs 210; Spec Interest Per Sub 210
Subject Interests: Architecture, Planning, Products

S MUSEUM OF CONTEMPORARY ART LIBRARY, 220 E Chicago Ave, 60611-2604. SAN 303-9773. Tel: 312-397-3894. FAX: 312-397-4099. *Librn*, Dennis McGuire; E-Mail: dmcguire@mcachicago.org; Staff 1 (MLS 1)
Founded 1981
Library Holdings: Bk Vols 17,000; Per Subs 85
Subject Interests: Art
Special Collections: Artist & Gallery Files; Artists' books; MCA Exhibition Catalogs
Automation Activity & Vendor Info: (Acquisitions) Endeavor; (Cataloging) Endeavor; (Circulation) Endeavor; (OPAC) Endeavor; (Serials) Endeavor
Database Vendor: Ebsco - EbscoHost, OCLC - First Search, Wilson - Wilson Web
Partic in Illinois Library & Information Network; OCLC Online Computer Library Center, Inc; RLIN

S MUSEUM OF SCIENCE & INDUSTRY LIBRARY,* 57th St & Lake Shore Dr, 60637-2093. SAN 303-9781. Tel: 773-684-1414, Ext 2296. FAX: 773-684-7141. E-Mail: pnsmsi@mcsnet. *Librn*, Mike Sarna
Founded 1933
Library Holdings: Bk Vols 3,000
Subject Interests: Children's literature, Museology, Science/technology, Technology, Transportation
Publications: annual bibliography; Children's Science Books
Mem of Chicago Libr Syst
Partic in Illinois Library & Information Network
Historical documents housed in Collections Department

C NAES COLLEGE LIBRARY & RESOURCE CENTER, 2838 W Peterson, 60659. SAN 326-1913. Tel: 773-761-5000. FAX: 773-761-3808. E-Mail: naeschi@hotmail.com. *Head Librn*, Natalia Wilson. Subject Specialists: *Native Am hist*, Natalia Wilson; *Policy*, Natalia Wilson; Staff 2 (Non-MLS 2)
Founded 1975. Enrl 40; Fac 7; Highest Degree: Bachelor
Library Holdings: Bk Titles 10,000; Spec Interest Per Sub 13
Special Collections: American Indian Federal Indian Law; American Indians Tribal History
Database Vendor: epixtech, inc.
Restriction: Non-circulating
Function: Research library
Mem of Chicago Libr Syst
Friends of the Library Group

G NATIONAL ARCHIVES & RECORDS ADMINISTRATION, Great Lakes Region (Chicago), 7358 S Pulaski Rd, 60629-5898. Tel: 773-581-7816. FAX: 312-353-1294. E-Mail: archives@chicago.nara.gov. Web Site: www.nara.gov/regional/chicago.html. *Archivist*, Peter Bunce
Special Collections: Archival Records of Federal Agencies & Courts in Illinois, Indiana, Michigan, Minnesota, Ohio & Wisconsin; Indian Affairs Records, microfilm; Passenger Arrival & Naturalization Records, microfilm; Population Censuses for All States, 1790-1920, microfilm; Pre-Federal & Early Federal History Records, microfilm; Pre-World War I Military Service Records, microfilm; US Diplomacy Records, microfilm
Restriction: Reference only to non-staff
Open for public services: Mon-Fri 8-4:15, federal agency services: 7-4:30

S NATIONAL ASSOCIATION OF REALTORS, Information Central, 430 N Michigan Ave, 60611-4087. SAN 303-982X. Toll Free Tel: 800-874-6500. FAX: 312-329-5960. *Dir*, John Krukoff; Staff 6 (MLS 4, Non-MLS 2)
Founded 1923
Library Holdings: Bk Vols 15,000; Per Subs 500
Subject Interests: Real estate
Publications: Bibliographies, series; Real estate index
Mem of Chicago Libr Syst
Friends of the Library Group

L NATIONAL CLEARINGHOUSE FOR LEGAL SERVICES LIBRARY,* 205 W Monroe, 2nd flr, 60606. SAN 326-9574. Tel: 312-263-3830. FAX: 312-263-3846.
Library Holdings: Bk Titles 5,000; Per Subs 150

S NATIONAL OPINION RESEARCH CENTER LIBRARY (NORC), Paul B Sheatsley Library, 1155 E 60th St, Rm 281, 60637-2667. SAN 303-9854. Tel: 773-256-6204. FAX: 773-753-7886. Web Site: www.norc.uchicago.edu. *Librn*, Patricia Cloud; E-Mail: cloud@norcmail.uchicago.edu; Staff 3 (MLS 2, Non-MLS 1)
Founded 1941
Library Holdings: Bk Titles 8,700
Subject Interests: Population studies
Publications: NORC Bibliography of Publications, 1941-1991
Mem of Chicago Libr Syst

S NATIONAL PTA, Information Resource Center, 330 N Wabash Ave, Ste 2100, 60611-3690. SAN 373-353X. Tel: 312-670-6782. Toll Free Tel: 800-304-4782. FAX: 312-670-6783. Web Site: www.pta.org/apta/archive.htm. *Coordr*, Vannessa Powell; Tel: 312-670-6782, Ext 374, E-Mail: v_powell@pta.org; Staff 1 (MLS 1)
Founded 1897
2000-2001 Mats Exp $14,000, Books $2,500, Per/Ser (Incl. Access Fees) $5,500, Presv $500, Electronic Ref Mat (Incl. Access Fees) $5,500
Library Holdings: Bk Titles 2,000; Per Subs 50
Subject Interests: Education, Parent educ
Special Collections: National PTA Archives (1897-present)
Automation Activity & Vendor Info: (Cataloging) Inmagic, Inc.
Database Vendor: OCLC - First Search
Publications: Our Children (National PTA magazine)
Restriction: By appointment only
Function: Archival collection
Partic in Chicago Library System

L NEAL, GERBER & EISENBERG, Law Library, 2 N La Salle St, Ste 2300, 60602. SAN 323-8458. Tel: 312-269-8435. Interlibrary Loan Service Tel: 312-269-5220. Reference Tel: 312-269-8445. FAX: 312-269-1747. *Librn*, Robert Winger; E-Mail: rwinger@ngelaw.com; Staff 4 (MLS 2, Non-MLS 2)
Founded 1986
Library Holdings: Bk Vols 30,000; Bk Titles 3,000; Per Subs 175
Subject Interests: Securities
Partic in Illinois Library & Information Network
Friends of the Library Group

R NER TAMID CONGREGATION OF NORTH TOWN LIBRARY, 2754 W Rosemont Ave, 60659. SAN 303-9897. Tel: 773-465-6090. FAX: 773-465-6008. *Librn*, Judith Weintraub
Founded 1955
Library Holdings: Bk Vols 4,800
Subject Interests: Judaica (lit or hist of Jews)
Partic in Judaica Library Network Of Metropolitan Chicago

S NEWBERRY LIBRARY,* 60 W Walton St, 60610-3394. SAN 303-9900. Tel: 312-943-9090. Web Site: www.newberry.org. *Librn, Pres*, Charles T Cullen; *Assoc Librn*, Mary Wyly; *Reader Servs*, Hjordis Halvorson; *Curator*, Robert Karrow; *Res*, James Grossman; Staff 105 (MLS 46, Non-MLS 59)
Founded 1887
Library Holdings: Bk Vols 1,500,000; Per Subs 1,021
Subject Interests: American history, Calligraphy, Civil War, English literature, European history, Genealogy, Ireland, Latin America, Philippines, Travel, Utopianism, Voyages

Special Collections: Americana & American Indians (Edward E Ayer & Frank C Deering Coll); Americana (Everett D Graff Coll); Ben Hecht Papers Coll; Card Calendar of Spanish Documents, 1512-1764; Henry Blake Fuller; Herman Melville Coll; History of Printing (John M Wing Coll); Malcolm Cowley Papers; Midwest Dance Archive; Music (Jane Oakley Fund Coll); Papers; Portuguese Discovery & Colonization (William B Greenlee Coll); Sherwood Anderson Papers; Western
Mem of Chicago Libr Syst
Partic in Illinois Library & Information Network; OCLC Online Computer Library Center, Inc
Chicago Metro History Fair administered & housed here
Friends of the Library Group

NORTH PARK UNIVERSITY
C CONSOLIDATED LIBRARIES, 3225 W Foster Ave, 60625. SAN 340-1855. Tel: 773-244-5580, 773-244-6200. Interlibrary Loan Service Tel: 773-244-5588. Circulation Tel: 773-244-5580. Reference Tel: 773-244-5584. FAX: 773-244-4891. Web Site: www.northpark.edu/library. *Dir*, Sonia Bodi; Tel: 773-244-5587, E-Mail: sbodi@northpark.edu; *Ref, Ser*, Katie Maier; Tel: 773-244-5582, E-Mail: kmaier@northpark.edu; *Cat, Coll Develop, Tech Servs*, Eileen Karsten; Tel: 773-244-5585, E-Mail: ekarsten@northpark.edu; *Media Spec*, Bill Hartley; Tel: 773-244-5579, E-Mail: whartley@northpark.edu; *Bibliog Instr, Ref*, Sarah Anderson; Tel: 773-244-5584, E-Mail: saanderson@northpark.edu; *Circ, ILL*, Ann Briody; Tel: 773-244-5586, E-Mail: abriody@northpark.edu; *Syst Coordr*, H Dayle Zelenka; Tel: 773-244-6240, E-Mail: hzelenka@northpark.edu; Staff 10 (MLS 8, Non-MLS 2)
Founded 1891. Enrl 2,600; Fac 103; Highest Degree: Doctorate
Jul 1999-Jun 2000 Income $1,267,875. Mats Exp $506,674, Books $237,470, Per/Ser (Incl. Access Fees) $160,000, Presv $14,500, Micro $17,191, AV Equip $22,190, Manuscripts & Archives $13,323, Electronic Ref Mat (Incl. Access Fees) $42,000. Sal $553,859 (Prof $270,410)
Library Holdings: Bk Vols 250,000; Bk Titles 240,000; Per Subs 1,197
Subject Interests: Music, Nursing, Religion, Scandinavia, Theology
Special Collections: Bound Scores; China (Harold W Jacobson Coll); G Anderson Coll; Jenny Lind, bks, coins, glass objects, letters, medals, music; Karl A Olsson Coll; Paul L Homer Coll; Scandinavian Coll; Scandinavian Literature (Nils William Olsson Coll); Walter Johnson Coll
Automation Activity & Vendor Info: (Acquisitions) epixtech, inc.; (Circulation) epixtech, inc.; (OPAC) epixtech, inc.; (Serials) epixtech, inc.
Database Vendor: Ebsco - EbscoHost, Lexis-Nexis, OCLC - First Search, Wilson - Wilson Web
Publications: Library Guide; Library Instruction for First Year Students; North Park Faculty Publications & Creative Works (1992 & 1997)
Mem of Chicago Libr Syst
Partic in Association Of Chicago Theological Schools (ACTS); Illinois Library & Information Network; Libras, Inc
S SWEDISH-AMERICAN ARCHIVES OF GREATER CHICAGO, 5125 N Spaulding Ave, 60625. (Mail add: 3225 W Foster Ave, 60625), SAN 304-0348. Tel: 773-244-5594.; Staff 1 (MLS 1)
Founded 1968
Library Holdings: Bk Titles 3,000; Per Subs 20
Special Collections: Bengtson Coll, doc; Chicago Swedes (C M Lundquist Coll), doc; Chicago Swedes, newsp, orgn rec
Publications: Swedish American Historical Quarterly
Restriction: Open to public for reference only
Friends of the Library Group

S NORTHEASTERN ILLINOIS PLANNING COMMISSION LIBRARY, 222 S Riverside Plaza, Ste 1800, 60606-2642. SAN 303-9927. Tel: 312-454-0400, Ext 610. FAX: 312-454-0411. *Planning Services*, Marc Thomas; Tel: 312-454-0400, E-Mail: tomasso@nipc.org. Subject Specialists: *Demographics*, Marc Thomas; Staff 1 (Non-MLS 1)
Founded 1958
Library Holdings: Bk Vols 9,000; Per Subs 50
Subject Interests: Environmental studies
Special Collections: County; Northeastern Illinois Planning Commission Publications: Data bulletins, energy data, forecasts, housing reports, local assistance, planning aids, policy plans, recreation information, staffpapers, transportation reports, water quality; Selected Print-Outs of Census Summary Tapes; Small Area Socio-Econ Data for Northeastern Illinois; US Census
Restriction: By appointment only
Partic in Ill Regional Libr Coun

C NORTHEASTERN ILLINOIS UNIVERSITY, Ronald Williams Library, 5500 N Saint Louis Ave, 60625-4699. SAN 340-191X. Tel: 773-442-4535. Circulation Tel: 773-442-4400. Reference Tel: 773-442-4417. FAX: 773-442-4531. Web Site: www.neiu.edu/~neiulib. *Librn*, Bradley F Baker; Tel: 773-442-4534, E-Mail: b-baker@neiu.edu; *Assoc Librn*, Mary Jane Hilburger; Tel: 773-442-4414, E-Mail: m-hilburger@neiu.edu; *Ref*, Jill Althage; Tel: 773-442-4415, E-Mail: j-althage@neiu.edu; *Tech Servs*, Georgine Brabec; Tel: 773-442-4438, E-Mail: g-brabec@neiu.edu; *Circ, ILL*, James Olson; Tel: 773-442-4525, E-Mail: j-olson@neiu.edu; *Archivist*, Sara Lifson; *Archivist*, Dario Villa; Tel: 773-442-4416, E-Mail: d-villa@neiu.edu; *Govt Doc*, Patrice Stearley; Tel: 773-442-4474, E-Mail: p-stearley@neiu.edu; Staff 51 (MLS 17, Non-MLS 34)
Founded 1961. Enrl 10,200; Fac 525; Highest Degree: Master
Jul 1999-Jun 2000 Income (Main and Other College/University Libraries) $3,390,253. Mats Exp $1,059,214, Books $297,168, Per/Ser (Incl. Access Fees) $544,342, Presv $20,920, Micro $33,412, AV Equip $19,898, Other Print Mats $3,990, Electronic Ref Mat (Incl. Access Fees) $139,484. Sal $2,207,262 (Prof $996,321)
Library Holdings: Bk Vols 612,834; Per Subs 2,382
Subject Interests: Education, Ethnic studies, Psychology
Special Collections: American Prose Fiction 1774-1900, micro; American Radical Periodicals Series I, bk; Author-Title Catalog, bk; Chicago & Cook County Archives (1831- 1955); Chicago & Cook County Archives (1831-1955); Documents, micro; Educational Resources Information Center, micro; League of Nations; Little Magazines, American & English Languages, bks; London Times 1785-present; Parliamentary Debates: Hansard 1803-1899; Parliamentary Debates: Hansard 1803-1899, micro
Database Vendor: DRA, Innovative Interfaces INN - View, OCLC - First Search
Mem of Chicago Libr Syst
Partic in Chicago Library System; Illinois Library & Information Network; Illinois Library Computer Systems Office
Departmental Libraries:
CENTER FOR INNER CITY STUDIES, 700 E Oakwood Blvd, 60653-2395. SAN 340-1944. Tel: 773-268-7500, Ext 165. FAX: 773-294-1956. Web Site: www.neiu.edu/~neiulib. *Librn*, Sharon Scott
Subject Interests: Afro-American
Partic in Chicago Library System; Illinois Library & Information Network; Illinois Library Computer Systems Office

S NORTHERN TRUST CO LIBRARY,* 50 S La Salle St, L-10, 60675. SAN 303-9935. Tel: 312-630-6000. *Librn*, Cathy A Porter; *Res*, Jim Peterson; Tel: 312-444-4794, Fax: 312-444-4132, E-Mail: jvp1@notes.ntrs.com
Library Holdings: Bk Vols 3,500; Per Subs 300
Subject Interests: Accounting, Banks and banking, Finance, Investing
Mem of Chicago Libr Syst
Partic in Dialog Corporation; Dow Jones News Retrieval

M NORTHWESTERN MEMORIAL HOSPITAL, Alberto Culver Women's Health Center,* 333 E Superior St, Rm 161, 60611. SAN 373-3556. Tel: 312-908-9971, Ext 0565. FAX: 312-503-0804. *Mgr*, Sharon Perry
Library Holdings: Bk Vols 1,400; Per Subs 20
Subject Interests: Cancer, Nutrition

NORTHWESTERN UNIVERSITY, CHICAGO
CM GALTER HEALTH SCIENCES LIBRARY, 303 E Chicago Ave, 60611. SAN 340-2061. Tel: 312-503-8133. Circulation Tel: 312-503-8127. Reference Tel: 312-503-8109. FAX: 312-503-1204. E-Mail: j-shedlock@nwu.edu. Web Site: www.galter.northwestern.edu. *Dir*, James Shedlock; E-Mail: j-shedlock@northwestern.edu; *Asst Dir, Coll Develop*, Linda Walton; *Ref*, Ramon Kubilius; Staff 30 (MLS 12, Non-MLS 18)
Sep 1999-Aug 2000 Income $2,039,074. Mats Exp $821,546, Books $70,335, Per/Ser (Incl. Access Fees) $751,211. Sal $972,487
Library Holdings: Bk Vols 283,107; Bk Titles 133,414; Per Subs 2,095
Subject Interests: Clinical medicine, Dentistry, Health econ, Physical therapy
Special Collections: Dental History; Medical Classics; Medical History; Rare Books
Database Vendor: OVID Technologies
Publications: Guide Series; Library Guide; Library Notes
Restriction: Not open to public
Mem of Asn of Research Libraries
Partic in CIC; ILLINET; National Network of Libraries of Medicine - Greater Midwest Region
Friends of the Library Group
C JOSEPH SCHAFFNER LIBRARY, 339 E Chicago Ave, 60611. SAN 340-2002. Tel: 312-503-8422. FAX: 312-503-8930. *Head of Libr*, Joan Reyes; *Librn*, Jerilyn Marshall; *Librn*, Leslie LaPlante; Staff 6 (MLS 4, Non-MLS 2)
Founded 1908
Library Holdings: Bk Vols 60,500; Per Subs 110
Subject Interests: Humanities, Social sciences and issues
Mem of Asn of Research Libraries
Partic in Illinois Library & Information Network
CL SCHOOL OF LAW LIBRARY, 357 E Chicago Ave, 60611. SAN 340-2037. Tel: 312-503-8451. FAX: 312-503-9230. Web Site: www.library.nwu.edu/law/. *Assoc Dean*, Christopher Simoni; Tel: 312-503-0295, E-Mail: csimoni@nwu.edu; *Assoc Dir, Publ Servs*, Nancy A Armstrong; Tel: 312-503-8449, E-Mail: n-armstrong@nwu.edu; *Assoc Dir*, Eloise Vondruska; Tel: 312-503-7369, E-Mail: e-vondruska@nwu.edu; *Circ*, David D Daskal; Tel: 312-503-0314, E-Mail: d-daskal@nwu.edu; *Acq*, JoAnn Hounshell; Tel: 312-503-7920, E-Mail: jhoundshell@nwu.edu; *Ref*, Marcia Lehr; Tel: 312-503-4356, E-Mail: mglehr@nwu.edu; *Ref*, Steven R Miller; Tel: 312-503-7310, E-Mail: s-miller@nwu.edu; *Doc*, Pegeen Bassett; Tel: 312-503-7344, E-Mail: p-bassett@nwu.edu; *Cat*, Eric C Parker; Tel: 312-503-8476, E-Mail: ecp278@nwu.edu; *Cat*, Terence O'Connell; Tel: 312-503-7364, E-Mail: t-oconnell@nwu.edu; Staff 12 (MLS 12)
Founded 1859. Enrl 600; Fac 45; Highest Degree: Doctorate
Sep 1998-Aug 1999 Mats Exp $929,881. Sal $1,427,512 (Prof $713,486)
Library Holdings: Bk Vols 656,275; Bk Titles 195,648; Per Subs 8,258

Special Collections: Foreign & International Law
Publications: Recent acquisitions
Partic in Illinois Library & Information Network; OCLC Online Computer Library Center, Inc

M NORWEGIAN AMERICAN HOSPITAL, Seufert Memorial Library, 1044 N Francisco Ave, 60622. SAN 303-996X. Tel: 773-292-8200, Ext 4670. FAX: 773-292-5954. Web Site: www.n-ahs.org. *In Charge*, Janethe Polo
Founded 1922
Library Holdings: Bk Titles 800; Per Subs 45

S OGILVY & MATHER, INC, Chicago Library, 111 E Wacker Dr, 60601. SAN 320-3743. Tel: 312-856-8368. FAX: 312-856-8491. *Mgr*, Eric Halvorson; E-Mail: eric.halvorson@ogilvy.com
Founded 1978
Library Holdings: Bk Titles 5,000; Per Subs 200
Subject Interests: Advertising, Marketing
Publications: Acquisitions list; Reference shelf list
Restriction: Not open to public
Mem of Chicago Libr Syst
Partic in Data Time; Dialog Corporation

J OLIVE-HARVEY COLLEGE, CITY COLLEGES OF CHICAGO, (OH-LRC), Learning Resource Center, 10001 S Woodlawn Ave, 60628. SAN 303-9978. Tel: 773-291-6354, 773-291-6477. Circulation Tel: 773-291-6477. FAX: 773-291-6463. *Chairperson*, Dr Romeo Munoz; Tel: 723-291-6479, E-Mail: rmunoz@ccc.edu; *Librn*, Willa Lyn Fox
Founded 1957. Enrl 7,000; Fac 123; Highest Degree: Doctorate
Jul 1999-Jun 2000 Mats Exp $95,000, Books $8,500, AV Equip $9,000. Sal $323,550 (Prof $172,650)
Library Holdings: Bk Vols 57,095; Bk Titles 47,601; Per Subs 260
Subject Interests: Spanish (language)
Automation Activity & Vendor Info: (OPAC) DRA
Partic in Illinois Library & Information Network
Special Services for the Blind - Braille Webster's Dictionary
Learning Resources Center consists of the Library & audio visual service. Added services: Center for Open Learning/Institutional Video Programs for credit courses.

SR ORDER OF SERVANTS OF MARY, Eastern Province Library Morini Memorial Collection,* 3121 W Jackson Blvd, 60612. SAN 328-3461. Tel: 773-533-0360. FAX: 773-533-8307. *Archivist*, Conrad Borntrager
Library Holdings: Bk Vols 2,500; Per Subs 20

SR OUR LADY OF SORROWS BASILICA, Archives Library,* 3121 W Jackson Blvd, 60612. SAN 323-4703. Tel: 773-638-5800, Ext 31. *Archivist*, Conrad Borntrager
Library Holdings: Bk Vols 2,300

M OUR LADY OF THE RESURRECTION MEDICAL CENTER LIBRARY,* 5645 W Addison, 60634-4455. SAN 303-9943. Tel: 773-282-7000, Ext 3354. FAX: 773-794-8353. *Librn*, Sr Joan McGovern
Founded 1972
Library Holdings: Bk Titles 900; Per Subs 100
Publications: Acquisitions lists; library brochure
Mem of Chicago Libr Syst
Partic in Metropolitan Consortium Of Chicago; Regional Med Libr - Region 3

SR PASSIONIST ACADEMIC INSTITUTE LIBRARY, 5700 N Harlem Ave, 60631. SAN 373-0468. Tel: 773-631-1686, Ext 237. FAX: 773-631-8059. *Librn*, Irene Horst; E-Mail: irenebh@juno.com
Library Holdings: Bk Vols 16,000; Per Subs 35
Subject Interests: Philosophy, Theology

L PEDERSEN & HOUPT LIBRARY, 161 N Clark St, Ste 3100, 60601. SAN 373-6997. Tel: 312-641-6888. FAX: 312-641-6895. *Librn*, Jean Godwin; Staff 1 (MLS 1)
Library Holdings: Bk Vols 10,000; Bk Titles 2,000
Subject Interests: Law
Mem of Chicago Libr Syst
Partic in Illinois Library & Information Network

S PERKINS & WILL ARCHITECTS, INC, Resource Center,* 330 N Wabash Ave, Ste 3600, 60611-3608. SAN 373-3572. Tel: 312-755-0770. FAX: 312-755-0775. Web Site: www.perkinswill.com. *Librn*, Nicolette Daly; E-Mail: nicolette.daly@perkinswill.com
Library Holdings: Bk Vols 1,000; Per Subs 100
Subject Interests: Manufacturers' catalogs

L PETERSON & ROSS LIBRARY,* 200 E Randolph Dr, Ste 7300, 60601-6969. SAN 321-7531. Tel: 312-861-1400, Ext 4479. FAX: 312-861-1053. E-Mail: peteross@class.org.; Staff 4 (MLS 2, Non-MLS 2)
Library Holdings: Bk Vols 10,000
Subject Interests: Am law
Publications: Newsletter
Restriction: Staff use only
Mem of Chicago Libr Syst
Partic in Dialog Corporation; Dow Jones News Retrieval; Illinois Library & Information Network; OCLC Online Computer Library Center, Inc; Westlaw

L PIPER, MARBURY, RUDNICK & WOLFE LLP, Law Library, 203 N LaSalle St, Ste 1800, 60601. SAN 372-1116. Tel: 312-984-5651. Reference Tel: 312-849-3841. FAX: 312-236-7516. *Head Librn*, John M Klasey; Tel: 312-984-5222, Fax: 312-251-5727, E-Mail: john.klasey@piperrudnick.com; *Res*, Sally Baker; Tel: 312-984-2615, E-Mail: sally.baker@piperrudnick.com; *Res*, Joanne Brady; Tel: 312-984-5703, E-Mail: joanne.brady@piperrudnick.com; *Res*, Julie Magana; Tel: 312-849-8639, E-Mail: julie.magana@piperrudnick.com; Staff 7 (MLS 4, Non-MLS 3)
Library Holdings: Bk Vols 13,000; Bk Titles 4,000; Per Subs 300
Subject Interests: Real estate law
Special Collections: Illinois Municipalities Zoning Ordinances Coll
Database Vendor: Dialog, Lexis-Nexis, OCLC - First Search
Mem of Chicago Libr Syst
Partic in OCLC Online Computer Library Center, Inc

S PLAYBOY ENTERPRISES, INC, Editorial Research Library,* 680 N Lake Shore Dr, 60611. SAN 340-2096. Tel: 312-751-8000, Ext 2260. FAX: 312-751-2818.
Library Holdings: Bk Titles 10,000; Per Subs 75
Subject Interests: Civil rights, Films and filmmaking, Music, Sexuality, Sports
Branches:
PHOTO, 680 N Lake Shore Dr, 60611. SAN 340-2126. Tel: 312-751-8000, Ext 2808. FAX: 312-751-2818. *Librn*, Elizabeth Georgiou
Restriction: Staff use only

S POLISH MUSEUM OF AMERICA LIBRARY,* 984 N Milwaukee Ave, 60622-4101. SAN 303-9994. Tel: 773-384-3352. FAX: 773-384-3799. *Dir*, Jan Lorys; *Librn*, Malgorzata Kot; Staff 5 (MLS 4, Non-MLS 1)
Founded 1913
Library Holdings: Bk Vols 100,000; Bk Titles 38,716; Per Subs 143
Subject Interests: Art, Poland
Special Collections: 19th Century Polish Emigre Coll; Old Manuscripts; Paderewski Coll; Polish Publishers in the US Coll
Publications: Polish Past of America
Function: Research library
Friends of the Library Group

S PREVENTION FIRST INC, Lura Lynn Ryan Prevention Research Library, 720 N Franklin St, Ste 500, 60610. SAN 376-0375. Tel: 312-988-4646. Toll Free Tel: 800-572-5385. TDD: 312-988-7097. FAX: 312-988-7096. Web Site: www.prevention.org. *Dir*, Thomas A Mikolyzk; E-Mail: mikolyt@prevention.org; Staff 6 (MLS 1, Non-MLS 5)
Founded 1980
Library Holdings: Bk Titles 25,000; Per Subs 110
Subject Interests: Gambling, Preventive health, Substance abuse issues, Violence against women
Automation Activity & Vendor Info: (Cataloging) epixtech, inc.; (Circulation) epixtech, inc.; (OPAC) epixtech, inc.
Database Vendor: OCLC - First Search
Function: Research library
Mem of Chicago Libr Syst

S PRICE WATERHOUSE COOPERS HEALTH CARE LIBRARY,* 203 N La Salle, 60601. SAN 326-9663. Tel: 312-701-6412. FAX: 312-701-6558. *Librn*, Kim Garber
Library Holdings: Bk Vols 1,000
Publications: Library Bulletin

S PRICE WATERHOUSE COOPERS LIBRARY, 200 E Randolph Dr, Ste 7423C, 60601. SAN 304-0011. Tel: 312-540-2442. FAX: 312-856-1916. *Librn*, Susan Chenoweth
Library Holdings: Bk Titles 4,000; Per Subs 350
Automation Activity & Vendor Info: (Cataloging) Inmagic, Inc.
Partic in Price Waterhouse LLP

S PRO-LIFE ACTION LEAGUE LIBRARY,* 6160 N Cicero, No 600, 60646. SAN 373-3688. Tel: 773-777-2900. FAX: 773-777-3061. Web Site: www.prolifeaction.org. *Mgr*, Ann Scheidler; E-Mail: scheidl@ibm.net
Founded 1976
Library Holdings: Bk Vols 500; Per Subs 10
Subject Interests: Abortion, Medicine
Special Collections: Articles on Pro Life
Publications: Pro Life Action League (quarterly)

M PSYCHIATRIC INSTITUTE UIC, Professional Library, 1601 W Taylor St, 60612. SAN 303-917X. Tel: 312-413-4548. FAX: 312-413-4556. *Chief Librn*, Margo McClelland; E-Mail: margo@psych.uic.edu
Founded 1959
Library Holdings: Bk Vols 15,000; Per Subs 40
Subject Interests: Psychiatry, Psychopharmacology, Video
Special Collections: Psychiatry & Abnormal Psychology Video Coll
Publications: Newsletter, Video Listing; Subject Bibliographies
Partic in Chicago Library System; Illinois Health Libraries Consortium; Midwest Health Sci Libr Network

S QUAKER OATS CO, Business Information Center,* PO Box 049001, 60604-9001. SAN 375-9725. Tel: 312-222-7029. FAX: 312-222-2732. *Mgr*, Duncan McKenzie

M RAVENSWOOD HOSPITAL MEDICAL CENTER, Medical-Nursing Library,* 4550 N Winchester at Wilson, 60640. SAN 304-0046. Tel: 773-878-4300, Ext 1378. FAX: 773-279-4140. *Librn*, Zia Solomon Gilliana
Founded 1907
Library Holdings: Per Subs 258
Subject Interests: Medicine, Nursing
Publications: Guide to Librn

S REAL ESTATE ANALYSIS CORP LIBRARY,* 180 N LaSalle St, Ste 1718, 60601. SAN 376-0391. Tel: 312-346-1020. FAX: 312-346-1042. E-Mail: cal@interacceff.com.
Library Holdings: Bk Titles 2,040; Per Subs 230
Subject Interests: Geography, Real estate

S REAL ESTATE RESEARCH CORP LIBRARY,* 980 N Michigan St, Ste 1675, 60611. SAN 304-0054. Tel: 312-346-5885. FAX: 312-587-0357. *Librn*, Jasmine Hirst
Library Holdings: Bk Titles 650; Per Subs 70
Subject Interests: Real estate
Publications: RERC Reality Report & American Trends in Real Estate
Restriction: Staff use only
Mem of Chicago Libr Syst
Partic in Spec Libr Asn

M MICHAEL REESE HOSPITAL & MEDICAL CENTER, Florsheim Medical Library,* 2908 S Ellis Ave, 60616. SAN 340-2150. Tel: 312-791-3411. FAX: 312-791-4490. E-Mail: E Net: florlibr@class.org. *Librn*, Constance M Gibbon; Staff 3 (MLS 1, Non-MLS 2)
Founded 1935
Library Holdings: Bk Vols 5,500; Per Subs 445
Open Mon-Fri 8:30-8 & Sat-Sun 10-4

S REGIONAL TRANSPORTATION AUTHORITY,* 181 W Madison, Ste 1900, 60602. SAN 325-6774. Tel: 312-917-1416. FAX: 312-917-1344. *In Charge*, Hershell Scott
Restriction: Staff use only

M REHABILITATION INSTITUTE OF CHICAGO, Learning Resources Center,* 345 E Superior St, Rm 1671, 60611. SAN 324-7317. Tel: 312-908-2859. FAX: 312-908-4451. *Librn*, Elizabeth De La Hunt; E-Mail: bdelahunt@rehabchicago.org
Founded 1979
Library Holdings: Bk Titles 1,000; Per Subs 110
Subject Interests: Phys rehabilitation
Restriction: By appointment only
Affiliated with Northwestern University's Galter Health Sciences Library - Eric D Albright, Liaison

M RESURRECTION HEALTH CARE - ST JOSEPH HOSPITAL LIBRARY, (Formerly Saint Joseph Resurrection Health Care Centers Hospital Library), 2900 N Lake Shore Dr, 60657. SAN 304-016X. Tel: 773-665-3038. FAX: 773-665-3416. *Dir Libr Serv*, Gwendolyn Jones; E-Mail: gjones@cath-health.org; Staff 1 (MLS 1)
Library Holdings: Bk Vols 13,000; Bk Titles 3,865; Per Subs 130
Subject Interests: Medicine, Nursing
Mem of Chicago Libr Syst
Partic in Greater Midwest Regional Medical Libr Network; ILLINET; Metrop Consortium; SILO

M RESURRECTION MEDICAL CENTER LIBRARY,* 7435 W Talcott Ave, 60631-3746. SAN 304-0062. Tel: 773-792-9938. FAX: 773-594-7974. *Librn*, Laura Wimmer; E-Mail: lwimmer@interaccess.com; *Asst Librn*, Anne Hogan
Founded 1953
Library Holdings: Bk Vols 130; Per Subs 964
Mem of Chicago Libr Syst
Partic in Illinois Library & Information Network; Metro Consortium of Chicago; Nat Libr of Med

RICHARD J DALEY COLLEGE
C KELLY MEMORIAL LIBRARY, 7500 S Pulaski Rd, 60652-1200. SAN 376-2564. Tel: 773-838-7667. Circulation Tel: 773-838-7668. Reference Tel: 773-838-7669. FAX: 773-838-7670. *Coll Develop, Librn, Ref*, Ashok K Chawla; Tel: 773-838-7674, E-Mail: achawla@ccc.edu; *Ref*, Donald Koss; Tel: 773-838-7949, E-Mail: dkoss@ccc.edu; *Tech Servs*, Siew-Ben Chin; Tel: 773-838-7979, E-Mail: schin@ccc.edu; Staff 10 (MLS 6, Non-MLS 4)
Founded 1965. Enrl 4,900; Fac 112; Highest Degree: Doctorate
2000-2001 Income $415,000. Mats Exp $75,000, Books $40,000, Per/Ser (Incl. Access Fees) $20,000, Micro $7,000, Other Print Mats $3,000. Sal $295,000 (Prof $190,000)
Library Holdings: Bk Titles 63,830; Per Subs 225
Subject Interests: Local history
Database Vendor: DRA
Restriction: Circulation limited
Mem of Chicago Libr Syst
Partic in NILRC

S THE RJS GROUP, INC, 549 W Randolph St, 60661. SAN 326-5293. Tel: 312-831-8200. FAX: 312-831-8201. *Librn*, Andrea Kiene
Library Holdings: Bk Titles 15,000; Per Subs 120
Special Collections: City & State Building Codes; NFPA Fire Codes
Mem of North Suburban Library System

C ROBERT MORRIS COLLEGE LIBRARY, 401 S State St, 60605. SAN 303-7835. Tel: 312-935-4810. Circulation Tel: 312-935-6050. Reference Tel: 312-935-4812. FAX: 312-935-6253. Web Site: www.rmcil.edu. *In Charge*, Sue Dutler; Staff 11 (MLS 6, Non-MLS 5)
Founded 1913. Enrl 4,200
Jul 2000-Jun 2001 Mats Exp $688,143, Books $390,000, Per/Ser (Incl. Access Fees) $60,000, Electronic Ref Mat (Incl. Access Fees) $238,143. Sal $375,447
Library Holdings: Bk Titles 103,000; Per Subs 500
Automation Activity & Vendor Info: (Cataloging) Sagebrush Corporation; (Circulation) Sagebrush Corporation; (OPAC) Sagebrush Corporation
Mem of Chicago Libr Syst; DuPage Library System; Rolling Prairie Library System
Partic in Ill Coordinated Coll Mgt Prog

L ROOKS, PITTS & POUST LIBRARY, Information Center, 10 S Wacker Dr, Ste 2300, 60606. SAN 304-0097. Tel: 312-876-1700. FAX: 312-876-1155. E-Mail: mwmsn@rookspitts.com. *Dir Libr Serv*, Elaine Billingslea Dockens; E-Mail: edockens@rookspitts.com; *Librn*, Serpil Emre. Subject Specialists: *Ill law*, Elaine Billingslea Dockens; Staff 3 (MLS 1, Non-MLS 2)
Library Holdings: Bk Vols 16,000
Special Collections: Federal & Illinois & Ind Law
Database Vendor: Lexis-Nexis, OCLC - First Search
Restriction: Company library
Mem of Chicago Libr Syst

C ROOSEVELT UNIVERSITY, Murray-Green Library, 430 S Michigan Ave, 60605. SAN 340-224X. Tel: 312-341-3640. FAX: 312-341-2425. Web Site: www.roosevelt.edu/library. *Librn*, Mary Beth Riedner; E-Mail: mriedner@roosevelt.edu; *Circ*, Colm Hennessy; *Acq*, Scott Klink; *Ref, Ser*, Promilla Bansal; *ILL*, Diane Madrid; Tel: 312-341-3638, E-Mail: dmadrid@roosevelt.edu; *Cat*, David Pribyl; Staff 28 (MLS 8, Non-MLS 20)
Founded 1945. Enrl 3,769; Fac 237; Highest Degree: Doctorate
May 2000-Apr 2001 Mats Exp $556,181. Sal $812,204
Library Holdings: Bk Vols 163,345; Bk Titles 148,607; Per Subs 1,000
Special Collections: American Civilization & English Literature (Library Resources Microbook Coll), microfiche; Children's Books; Music Coll, bks, sheet music, recordings
Database Vendor: DRA, Ebsco - EbscoHost, GaleNet, IAC - Info Trac, IAC - SearchBank, Lexis-Nexis, OCLC - First Search, OVID Technologies, Wilson - Wilson Web
Publications: Bibliographies
Mem of Chicago Libr Syst
Partic in ILLINET
Departmental Libraries:
MUSIC Tel: 312-341-3651. FAX: 312-341-2425. Web Site: www.roosevelt.edu/library. *Librn*, Mary Beth Riedner; Tel: 312-341-3640, E-Mail: mriedner@roosevelt.edu; Staff 7 (MLS 1, Non-MLS 6)
May 2000-Apr 2001 Mats Exp $34,148
Library Holdings: Bk Vols 38,452; Bk Titles 32,592; Per Subs 100
ROBERT R MCCORMICK TRIBUNE FOUNDATION LIBRARY, 1400 N Roosevelt Blvd, Schaumburg, 60173. SAN 376-9771. Tel: 847-619-7980. FAX: 847-619-7983. Web Site: www.roosevelt.edu/library. *Branch Mgr*, Barbara Schoenfield; Tel: 847-619-7924, E-Mail: bschoenf@roosevelt.edu; Staff 8 (MLS 3, Non-MLS 5)
May 2000-Apr 2001 Mats Exp $17,250. Sal $104,135
Library Holdings: Bk Titles 2,316; Per Subs 250
Mem of North Suburban Library System

M ROSELAND COMMUNITY HOSPITAL, Health Science Library,* 45 W 111th St, 60628. SAN 304-0100. Tel: 773-995-3191. FAX: 773-995-5863. *Librn*, Donna Morris
Founded 1956
Library Holdings: Bk Vols 600; Per Subs 39
Subject Interests: Medicine, Nursing
Mem of Chicago Libr Syst
Partic in Chicago & South Consortium; Illinois Library & Information Network; Regional Med Libr - Region 3

L ROSENTHAL & SCHANFIELD, Law Library,* 55 E Monroe Ste 4620, 60603. SAN 372-1167. Tel: 312-236-5622. FAX: 312-236-7274.
Library Holdings: Bk Vols 15,000; Per Subs 20

L ROSS & HARDIES LIBRARY, 150 N Michigan Ave, 24th flr, 60601. SAN 304-0119. Tel: 312-750-3500. FAX: 312-750-8600. E-Mail: library@rosshardies.com. Web Site: www.rosshardies.com. *Tech Servs*, Jennifer Jacobson; Tel: 312-750-3526, E-Mail: jennifer.jacobson@rosshardies.com; *Asst Librn*, Jennifer Kiszka; Tel: 312-750-5764, Fax: 312-920-6196, E-Mail:

jennifer.kiszka@rosshardies.com. Subject Specialists: *Health care*, Jennifer Kiszka; *Intellectual property*, Jennifer Kiszka; *Law*, Jennifer Kiszka; Staff 2 (MLS 1, Non-MLS 1)
Library Holdings: Bk Vols 50,000; Per Subs 525
Subject Interests: Health care, Law
Special Collections: Rare Late 19th-Early 20th Century Law Books
Database Vendor: Dialog, Lexis-Nexis, OCLC - First Search
Publications: Library Litany
Function: ILL available
Partic in Chicago Library System; OCLC Online Computer Library Center, Inc

RUSH-PRESBYTERIAN-SAINT LUKE'S MEDICAL CENTER
M PATIENT'S LIBRARY, 1653 W Congress Pkwy, 60612. SAN 340-2339. Tel: 312-942-5691. *Librn*, Midge Adam Cogan
Founded 1884
Library Holdings: Bk Vols 11,000; Per Subs 60
Subject Interests: Talking books

C RUSH-PRESBYTERIAN-ST LUKE'S MEDICAL CENTER LIBRARY, 600 S Paulina St, 60612-3874. SAN 340-2304. Tel: 312-942-5950. Interlibrary Loan Service Tel: 312-942-2275. Reference Tel: 312-942-5952. FAX: 312-942-3143. E-Mail: libref@rushu.rush.edu. Web Site: www.lib.rush.edu/library. *Asst Dean*, Trudy A Gardner; Tel: 312-942-2270; *Assoc Dir*, Christine Frank; *Ref*, Toby Gibson; *Ref*, Karl Cremieux; *Ref*, Marianne Doherty; *Circ*, Bill Fleming; *Tech Servs*, Phillip Adrian; *Cat*, Judith Dzierba; *Media Spec*, Bill Karnoscak; *Coll Develop*, Elizabeth Lorbeer; *Archivist*, Ken Hernden; Staff 29 (MLS 12, Non-MLS 17)
Founded 1899. Enrl 1,348; Highest Degree: Doctorate
Library Holdings: Bk Vols 53,551; Bk Titles 46,065; Per Subs 1,800
Subject Interests: Health sciences
Special Collections: Cholera Coll; Dr Benjamin Rush Coll; Local & Regional Medical Imprints; Medical Americana; Rare Books in Medicine
Publications: InfoLINE
Partic in Docline; Greater Midwest Regional Medical Libr Network; OCLC Online Computer Library Center, Inc; SILO

C SAINT AUGUSTINE COLLEGE, Learning Resources Center, 1345 W Argyle, 60640. SAN 375-9423. Tel: 773-878-8756. FAX: 773-878-0937. E-Mail: staugustinec@yahoo.com. Web Site: www.staug.edu. *Dir*, Steven A Balcken
Library Holdings: Bk Titles 9,000; Per Subs 50
Automation Activity & Vendor Info: (Cataloging) Sagebrush Corporation; (Circulation) Sagebrush Corporation; (OPAC) Sagebrush Corporation

M SAINT ELIZABETH HOSPITAL, Luken Health Science Library,* 1431 N Claremont Ave, 60622. SAN 304-0151. Tel: 773-278-2000, Ext 4178. FAX: 312-850-5983. *Librn*, Olivija Fistrovic; E-Mail: ofistrovic@ancilla.org; Staff 2 (MLS 1, Non-MLS 1)
Founded 1956
Library Holdings: Per Subs 86

M SAINT MARY OF NAZARETH HOSPITAL, Sister Stella Louise Health Science Library, 2233 W Division, 60622. SAN 340-2363. Tel: 312-770-2219. FAX: 312-770-2221. E-Mail: smnlib@yahoo.com.; Staff 2 (MLS 1, Non-MLS 1)
Founded 1949
Library Holdings: Bk Vols 2,250; Per Subs 120
Subject Interests: Internal medicine, Surgery
Publications: Acquisition List; Annual Report; Journal List
Mem of Chicago Libr Syst
Partic in Illinois Library & Information Network; Metropolitan Consortium Of Chicago

C SAINT XAVIER UNIVERSITY, Byrne Memorial Library, 3700 W 103rd St, 60655-9989. SAN 304-0178. Tel: 773-298-3352. FAX: 773-779-5231. Web Site: www.sxu.edu/libr/library. *Dir, Online Servs*, Ursula Zyzik; E-Mail: zyzik@sxu.edu; *ILL*, Margaret Hofferle
Founded 1916. Enrl 4,100; Fac 168; Highest Degree: Master
Library Holdings: Bk Vols 172,104; Per Subs 1,607
Subject Interests: Education, Nursing, Religion
Automation Activity & Vendor Info: (Acquisitions) DRA; (Cataloging) DRA; (Circulation) DRA; (ILL) DRA; (OPAC) DRA
Partic in CCMP; Chicago Library System; Libras, Inc; OCLC Online Computer Library Center, Inc

S SARA LEE BAKERY, Research & Development Library,* 900 N Branch St, 60622-4230. SAN 304-1077. Tel: 847-342-5116, 847-342-9430 (Main). FAX: 847-342-5181. *Librn*, Carol Milzer
Founded 1964
Library Holdings: Bk Vols 900; Per Subs 15

S SARGENT & LUNDY, LLC, Resource Center, 55 E Monroe St, 24F60, 60603. SAN 340-2428. Tel: 312-269-3525. FAX: 312-269-3757. *Dir*, Dorothy Dryden; E-Mail: dorothy.l.dryden@slchicago.infonet.com; *Librn*, Gerard P Kenny; Staff 3 (MLS 2, Non-MLS 1)
Founded 1969
Library Holdings: Bk Titles 2,000; Per Subs 240
Subject Interests: Architecture, Civil engineering, Electrical engineering, Energy, Mechanical engineering
Automation Activity & Vendor Info: (Cataloging) Sydney
Restriction: Staff use only
Mem of Chicago Libr Syst
Partic in Illinois Library & Information Network
Branches:
COMPUTER SOFTWARE, 55 E Monroe St, 27th flr, 60603. SAN 340-2452. Tel: 312-269-3657. *Librn*, Ann Robinson

L SCHIFF, HARDIN & WAITE LIBRARY, 7300 Sears Tower, 60606. SAN 304-0186. Tel: 312-258-4701, 312-876-1000. FAX: 312-258-5600. *Dir*, Rebecca Corliss; Staff 5 (MLS 5)
Library Holdings: Bk Vols 35,000

SCHOOL OF THE ART INSTITUTE OF CHICAGO
S JOHN M FLAXMAN LIBRARY, 37 S Wabash Ave, 6th Flr, 60603-3103. SAN 339-8048. Tel: 312-899-5097. Reference Tel: 312-899-5096. FAX: 312-899-1465, 312-899-1851. E-Mail: flaxman.refdesk@artic.edu. Web Site: www.artic.edu/saic/library/. *Dir*, Claire Eike; E-Mail: ceike@artic.edu; *Bibliogr*, Henrietta Zielinski; Tel: 312-899-5099, E-Mail: hzielinski@artic.edu; *Cat*, Sylvia Choi; Tel: 312-899-2029, E-Mail: schoi2@artic.edu; *Circ*, Josh Berta; E-Mail: jberta@artic.edu; *Circ*, Eileen Black; *Circ*, John Pommerich; E-Mail: jpommerich@artic.edu; *ILL*, Alexis Petroff; E-Mail: apetroff@artic.edu; *Reader Servs*, Roland Hansen; E-Mail: rhansen@artic.edu; *Ref*, Kate Jarboe; Tel: 312-899-5096, E-Mail: kjarbo@artic.edu; *Spec Coll*, Doro Boehme; Tel: 312-899-5098, E-Mail: aboehme@artic.edu; *Tech Servs*, Fred Hillbruner; Tel: 312-899-5101, E-Mail: fhillbruner@artic.edu; *Acq*, Lorell Butler; Tel: 312-899-5144, E-Mail: lbutler@artic.edu. Subject Specialists: *Art*, Doro Boehme; *Art*, Fred Hillbruner; *Art*, Henrietta Zielinski; *Art*, Roland Hansen; *Art*, Kate Jarboe; *Art*, Claire Eike; *Artists bks*, Doro Boehme; Staff 11 (MLS 7, Non-MLS 4)
Founded 1968. Enrl 2,141; Highest Degree: Master
Jul 1999-Jun 2000 Income Parent Institution $701,445. Sal $373,800
Library Holdings: Bk Vols 66,325; Bk Titles 56,464; Per Subs 345
Subject Interests: Art
Special Collections: Film Study Coll (16mm film); Joan Flasch Artists' Books Coll; Randolph Street Gallery Archives; Tony Zwicker Archives
Automation Activity & Vendor Info: (Cataloging) DRA; (Circulation) DRA; (ILL) DRA; (OPAC) DRA
Database Vendor: DRA, Ebsco - EbscoHost, GaleNet, Lexis-Nexis, OCLC - First Search, OVID Technologies, Wilson - Wilson Web
Publications: Ferret; Library guides; Library Handbook
Restriction: Private library
Mem of Chicago Libr Syst
Partic in CLS; ILCSO; ILLINET; OCLC Online Computer Library Center, Inc

P SECURITIES & EXCHANGE COMMISSION, Public Reference Library,* 500 W Madison St, Ste 1440, 60661. SAN 329-4498. Tel: 312-353-7433. FAX: 312-353-7398. *Librn*, Bernard Krawczyk
Subject Interests: Securities

SR SEMINARY CONSORTIUM FOR URBAN PASTORAL EDUCATION, Resource Center,* 200 N Michigan Ave, Ste 502, 60601. SAN 376-0340. Tel: 312-726-1200. FAX: 312-726-0425. *Pres*, David J Frenchak; *Librn*, Mark Walden
Library Holdings: Bk Titles 3,500

S SEYFARTH SHAW, 55 E Monroe St, Ste 4200, 60603-5803. SAN 304-0224. Tel: 312-346-8000. FAX: 312-739-6226. *Librn*, Carolyn Hayes; E-Mail: hayesca@seyfarth.com; *Ref*, Nancy Faust; *Tech Servs*, Karen Tschanz; Staff 9 (MLS 3, Non-MLS 6)
Founded 1945
Library Holdings: Bk Vols 36,950; Per Subs 484
Subject Interests: Employment law, Environmental law, Labor law, Securities law
Special Collections: Arbitration Awards & Legal Memoranda (Seyfarth Shaw Coll), bd vols
Restriction: Company library
Function: ILL limited
Mem of Chicago Libr Syst
Partic in Illinois Library & Information Network; OCLC Online Computer Library Center, Inc

S JOHN G SHEDD AQUARIUM, Information Services, 1200 S Lake Shore Dr, 60605. SAN 320-1791. Tel: 312-939-2438. FAX: 312-939-8069. E-Mail: info@sheddaquarium.org. *Mgr Libr Serv*, Carolyn Kubisz; Tel: 312-692-3217, Fax: 312-939-3430; Staff 4 (MLS 2, Non-MLS 2)
Founded 1975
Jan 2000-Dec 2000 Mats Exp $18,000
Library Holdings: Bk Titles 10,000; Per Subs 200
Subject Interests: Animals, behavior of, Great Lakes
Publications: Bibliographies; monthly acquisitions
Restriction: Not open to public, Staff use only
Function: ILL available
Mem of Chicago Libr Syst

Partic in Illinois Library & Information Network
Internet access; services for youth & adults including teachers, home aquarium keepers & students interested in careers in aquatic sciences

S SHRINERS' HOSPITAL FOR CHILDREN, Professional Library,* 2211 N Oak Park Ave, 60707. SAN 323-7400. Tel: 773-385-5479. FAX: 773-385-5488. *Librn*, Laura Mueller; E-Mail: lmueller@shrinenet.org; Staff 2 (MLS 1, Non-MLS 1)
Founded 1981
Library Holdings: Bk Titles 1,055; Per Subs 100
Subject Interests: Orthopedics, Pediatrics
Partic in Metropolitan Consortium Of Chicago

L SIDLEY & AUSTIN LIBRARY, Bank One Plaza, 60603. SAN 304-0259. Tel: 312-853-7475. Interlibrary Loan Service Tel: 312-853-7087. FAX: 312-853-7036. *Dir Libr Serv*, Allyson D Withers
Library Holdings: Bk Vols 45,000
Subject Interests: Law
Partic in Illinois Library & Information Network; OCLC Online Computer Library Center, Inc

L SKADDEN, ARPS, SLATE, MEAGHER & FLOM (ILLINOIS) LIBRARY, 333 W Wacker Dr, 60606. SAN 375-9652. Tel: 312-407-0941. FAX: 312-407-0924. Web Site: www.skad-lib.com, www.skadden.com. *Librn*, Ann Morris; E-Mail: amorris@skadden.com; Staff 6 (MLS 4, Non-MLS 2)
Library Holdings: Bk Vols 20,000
Automation Activity & Vendor Info: (Cataloging) Innovative Interfaces Inc.; (Circulation) Innovative Interfaces Inc.; (OPAC) Innovative Interfaces Inc.; (Serials) Innovative Interfaces Inc.
Partic in Chicago Library System

S SKIDMORE, OWINGS & MERRILL LIBRARY, 224 S Michigan Ave, Ste 1000, 60604. SAN 304-0267. Tel: 312-554-9090. FAX: 312-360-4545.
Founded 1972
Library Holdings: Bk Titles 7,000; Per Subs 50
Subject Interests: Art and architecture, Engineering
Restriction: Staff use only
Partic in Chicago Library System; Illinois Library & Information Network

L SONNENSCHEIN, NATH & ROSENTHAL, Law Library, 8000 Sears Tower, 233 S Wacker Dr, 60606-6404. SAN 304-0275. Tel: 312-876-8000. Interlibrary Loan Service Tel: 312-876-8001. Reference Tel: 312-876-7906. FAX: 312-876-7934. E-Mail: njh@sonnenschein.com. Web Site: www.sonnenschein.com. *Head Ref*, Nancy Henry; *Ref*, Chris Morong; *Tech Servs*, Linda Devaun
Library Holdings: Bk Vols 30,000; Bk Titles 2,300; Per Subs 400
Subject Interests: US law
Automation Activity & Vendor Info: (Acquisitions) epixtech, inc.; (Cataloging) epixtech, inc.; (Circulation) epixtech, inc.; (Course Reserve) epixtech, inc.; (ILL) epixtech, inc.; (Media Booking) epixtech, inc.; (OPAC) epixtech, inc.; (Serials) epixtech, inc.
Database Vendor: Dialog, Lexis-Nexis, OCLC - First Search
Mem of Chicago Libr Syst
Partic in AALL; Call; CLS; OCLC Online Computer Library Center, Inc

S SPENCER STUART LIBRARY, 401 N Michigan Ave, Ste 3300, 60611. SAN 304-0283. Tel: 312-822-0088. FAX: 312-822-0117. E-Mail: shedrick@spencerstuart.com. *Dir Libr Serv, Librn*, Stacy Hedrick; Staff 7 (MLS 6, Non-MLS 1)
Library Holdings: Per Subs 50
Subject Interests: Exec search
Partic in Chicago Library System

CR SPERTUS INSTITUTE OF JEWISH STUDIES, Norman & Helen Asher Library, 618 S Michigan Ave, 60605. SAN 304-0291. Tel: 312-322-1749. TDD: 312-922-4950. FAX: 312-922-0455. E-Mail: asherlib@spertus.edu. Web Site: www.spertus.edu. *Dir*, Glenn Ferdman; Tel: 312-322-1759, E-Mail: gferdman@spertus.edu; *Assoc Dir*, Kathleen Bloch; Tel: 312-322-1745, E-Mail: kbloch@spertus.edu; *Archivist*, Joy Kingsolver; Tel: 312-322-1741, E-Mail: jkingsol@spertus.edu; *Per*, Katherine Breslow; Tel: 312-322-1751, E-Mail: kbreslow@spertus.edu; *Reader Servs*, Dan Sharon; E-Mail: dsharon@spertus.edu; *ILL*, Rivka Schiller; Tel: 312-322-1752, E-Mail: rschiller@spertus.edu. Subject Specialists: *Music*, Katherine Breslow; Staff 9 (MLS 4, Non-MLS 5)
Founded 1925. Enrl 900; Highest Degree: Doctorate
Jul 2000-Jun 2001 Income $703,740. Mats Exp $70,975, Books $37,175, Per/Ser (Incl. Access Fees) $24,500, Presv $4,800, Micro $3,000, Electronic Ref Mat (Incl. Access Fees) $1,500. Sal $396,293
Library Holdings: Bk Vols 100,000; Bk Titles 75,000; Per Subs 550
Subject Interests: Jewish hist, Jewish holocaust, Judaica, Judaism (religion)
Special Collections: Chicago Jewish Archives; Chicago Jewish History; Jewish Art (Badona Spertus Library of Art in Judaica); Jewish Music (Targ Center for Jewish Music); Non-Profit Management (Lewis Sulkin Human Services Coll)
Automation Activity & Vendor Info: (Acquisitions) EX Libris; (Cataloging) EX Libris; (Circulation) EX Libris; (OPAC) EX Libris; (Serials) EX Libris
Database Vendor: Ebsco - EbscoHost, OCLC - First Search
Function: ILL available
Mem of Chicago Libr Syst
Partic in Ill Regional Libr Coun; Judaica Library Network Of Metropolitan Chicago
Special Services for the Deaf - TTY machine

S STEIN, ROE & FARNHAM LIBRARY, One S Wacker Dr, 31st flr, 60606. SAN 304-0321. Tel: 312-368-5689. FAX: 312-368-6845, 368-8074. *Mgr, Ref*, Joanell C Breen; E-Mail: jbreen@steinroe.com; Staff 2 (MLS 1, Non-MLS 1)
Founded 1945
Library Holdings: Bk Vols 1,200; Bk Titles 1,100; Per Subs 170
Subject Interests: Business and management, Finance
Special Collections: Stein Roe & Farnham Archives; US & Foreign Government Publications
Publications: Library Resource Guide; Periodical Holdings
Mem of Chicago Libr Syst
Partic in Illinois Library & Information Network

M SWEDISH COVENANT HOSPITAL, Joseph G Stromberg Library of the Health Sciences, 5145 N California Ave, 60625. SAN 304-033X. Tel: 773-878-8200, Ext 5312. FAX: 773-878-1624. *Librn*, Dale Austin; E-Mail: daustin@schosp.org; Staff 1 (MLS 1)
Founded 1930
Library Holdings: Bk Titles 1,600; Per Subs 125
Subject Interests: Medicine
Mem of Chicago Libr Syst
Partic in Metropolitan Consortium Of Chicago

S TECHNOMIC, INC, Information Services, 300 S Riverside Plaza, Ste 1940 S, 60606. SAN 326-3584. Tel: 312-876-0004. FAX: 312-876-1158. E-Mail: foodinfo@technomic.com.; Staff 3 (MLS 2, Non-MLS 1)
Library Holdings: Bk Vols 2,000
Publications: TRA Food Service Digest & TRA Restaurant Info Service

S TELEPHONE & DATA SYSTEMS, INC LIBRARY,* 30 N LaSalle St, 40th flr, 60603. SAN 375-9687. Tel: 312-630-1900. FAX: 312-630-1908.
Library Holdings: Bk Titles 800; Per Subs 300

S TERRA MUSEUM OF AMERICAN ART LIBRARY, 664 N Michigan Ave, 60611. SAN 372-6797. Tel: 312-654-2260. FAX: 312-664-2052. E-Mail: terra@terramuseum.org. *Librn*, Janice McNeill; E-Mail: mcneill@terramuseum.org; Staff 1 (MLS 1)
Founded 1980
Library Holdings: Bk Titles 7,000; Per Subs 17
Restriction: Non-circulating, Staff & members only
Function: Research library
Mem of Chicago Libr Syst

S THE INTERNATIONAL ASSOCIATION OF ASSESSING OFFICERS, Paul V Corusy Memorial Library, 130 E Randolph, Ste 850, 60601. SAN 303-9250. Tel: 312-819-6117. FAX: 312-819-6149. Web Site: www.iaao.org. *Librn*, Mary Kay Siebert
Founded 1934
Library Holdings: Bk Titles 14,000
Subject Interests: Local government, State government
Automation Activity & Vendor Info: (Cataloging) CASPR; (OPAC) CASPR
Restriction: Members only
Partic in Illinois Library & Information Network; OCLC Online Computer Library Center, Inc
Friends of the Library Group

L THE JOHN MARSHALL LAW SCHOOL LIBRARY, 315 S Plymouth Ct, 60604. SAN 303-9358. Tel: 312-427-2737. Circulation Tel: 312-987-1413. FAX: 312-427-8307. E-Mail: 8li@jmls.edu. Web Site: www.jmls.edu. *Dir*, Dorothy Wang Li; E-Mail: 8li@jmls.edu; *Assoc Dir*, Kym Ogden; E-Mail: 8ogden@jmls.edu; *Assoc Dir*, William Wleklinski; E-Mail: 8wleklin@jmls.edu; *Ref*, Anne Abramson; E-Mail: 8abrams@jmls.edu; *Ref*, Claire Toomey Durkin; E-Mail: 8durkin@jmls.edu; *Ref*, Jason Levine; E-Mail: 8levine@jmls.edu; *Ref*, Elizabeth Larson; E-Mail: 8larson@jmls.edu; *Cat*, David Guion; E-Mail: 8guion@jmls.edu; Staff 23 (MLS 8, Non-MLS 15)
Founded 1899
Library Holdings: Bk Vols 361,778; Bk Titles 88,681; Per Subs 5,737
Subject Interests: Anglo-American law
Special Collections: CCH Tax Library Coll, ultrafiche; Chicago Bar Association Core Coll; IHS Legislative Histories; Illinois Appellate Court Unpublished Opinions; Illinois Supreme Court Briefs; National Reporter System Coll, First Series, ultrafiche; United States Circuit Court of Appeals 7th Circuit Briefs; United States Congressional Publications, 1970-date, micro; United States Supreme Court Records & Briefs, 1930-date
Database Vendor: Innovative Interfaces INN - View
Publications: The John Marshall Law School Publication Series
Partic in Chicago Legal Acad Syst; Illinois Library & Information Network; OCLC Online Computer Library Center, Inc
Also serves as the headquarters library of the Chicago Bar Association

S J WALTER THOMPSON CO, Information Center,* 900 N Michigan Ave, 60611. SAN 304-0372. Tel: 312-951-4071. FAX: 312-951-4199. *Dir*, Roberta Piccoli; Staff 4 (MLS 2, Non-MLS 2)

Founded 1921
Library Holdings: Bk Titles 5,000; Per Subs 400
Subject Interests: Advertising, Business and management, Marketing
Partic in Data Time; Dialog Corporation; Dun & Bradstreet Info Servs; Illinois Library & Information Network; Marketing Intelligence; Mead Data Cent; Newsnet; Vutext

P TOWERS PERRIN LIBRARY, 200 W Madison, Ste 3100, 60606-3414. SAN 375-9695. Tel: 312-609-9303. FAX: 312-609-9833. Web Site: www.towers.com. *In Charge*, Mary Ann Reandeau; E-Mail: reandem@towers.com
Library Holdings: Bk Titles 9,000; Per Subs 100
Database Vendor: Ebsco - EbscoHost
Restriction: Not open to public

S TRUE NORTH COMMUNICATIONS, INC, Corporate Information Center,* 676 N Saint Clair 12th flr, 60611. SAN 303-898X. Tel: 312-425-6600. FAX: 312-425-6322. E-Mail: infocenter@truenorth.com. *Dir*, John Kok; Tel: 312-425-6601, E-Mail: jkok@truenorth.com; *Online Servs*, Joanne Humphreville; Staff 14 (MLS 11, Non-MLS 3)
Founded 1943
Library Holdings: Bk Titles 3,000; Per Subs 400
Subject Interests: Advertising, Marketing
Partic in Chicago Library System; OCLC Online Computer Library Center, Inc

J TRUMAN COLLEGE, Cosgrove Library,* 1145 W Wilson Ave, 60640-5691. SAN 304-0380. Tel: 773-907-4865. FAX: 773-907-6803. Web Site: www.ccc.edu/truman/home.htm. *AV*, Leone McDermot; *Chairperson, Publ Servs*, Janis Marley; *Publ Servs*, Kwan-Yau Lam; *Tech Servs*, Susan Korn; Staff 4 (MLS 4)
Founded 1956. Enrl 4,900; Fac 180; Highest Degree: Associate
Jul 1997-Jun 1998 Income $500,000. Mats Exp $100,000. Sal $400,000
Library Holdings: Bk Vols 66,800; Bk Titles 63,000; Per Subs 251
Partic in Illinois Library & Information Network; OCLC Online Computer Library Center, Inc

M UKRAINIAN MEDICAL ASSOCIATION, Medical Archives & Library,* 2247 W Chicago Ave, 60622. SAN 325-7185. Tel: 773-278-6262. FAX: www.umana.goy. *Dir*, Roman Goy
Library Holdings: Bk Vols 18,000

S UNGARETTI & HARRIS LIBRARY, 3500 Three First National Plaza, 60602. SAN 325-5131. Tel: 312-977-4888. FAX: 312-977-4405. *Dir Libr Serv*, Michael Lamott Mason; E-Mail: mmason@uhlaw.com; Staff 1 (MLS 1)
Founded 1981
Library Holdings: Bk Vols 10,000; Bk Titles 3,500; Per Subs 134
Subject Interests: Corp law, Gen bus, Healthcare, Securities, Taxation
Database Vendor: CARL, OCLC - First Search, ProQuest
Mem of Chicago Libr Syst
Partic in Chicago Asn of Law Librs; Chicago Library System; ILLINET

S UNICOM CORPORATE LIBRARY,* 227 W Monroe, 60606. SAN 303-8637. Tel: 312-394-3066. FAX: 312-394-7336. *Librn*, Roberta J Goering; Tel: 312-394-3064, E-Mail: roberta.j.goering@ucm.com; Staff 4 (MLS 2, Non-MLS 2)
Founded 1902
1998-1999 Income $500,000. Mats Exp $400,000. Sal $100,000 (Prof $60,000)
Library Holdings: Per Subs 502
Subject Interests: Engineering
Database Vendor: Dialog, Lexis-Nexis
Mem of Chicago Libr Syst

S UNION LEAGUE CLUB LIBRARY,* 65 W Jackson Blvd, 60604. SAN 304-0399. Tel: 312-427-7800. FAX: 312-692-2322. *Librn*, Jill Postma
Library Holdings: Bk Vols 8,000
Subject Interests: American history, Art and architecture, Biology, Business and management, History
Restriction: Private library
Friends of the Library Group

G UNITED STATES DEPARTMENT OF JUSTICE, Antitrust Division Library,* 209 S LaSalle, Ste 600, 60604. SAN 304-0445. Tel: 312-353-7530. FAX: 312-353-1046. *Librn*, Christina Van Horn
Library Holdings: Bk Vols 3,800; Per Subs 20

G UNITED STATES ENVIRONMENTAL PROTECTION AGENCY, Region 5 Library, 77 W Jackson Blvd, PL-12J, 60604-3590. SAN 303-8882. Tel: 312-353-2022. FAX: 312-353-2001. Web Site: www.epa.gov/region5/library. *Mgr*, Patricia Krause; E-Mail: krause.patricia@epa.gov; Staff 3 (MLS 2, Non-MLS 1)
Founded 1972
Library Holdings: Bk Titles 17,500; Per Subs 300
Subject Interests: Air pollution, Environmental law, Great Lakes, Radiation
Special Collections: EPA Reports; Microfiche Federal Registers
Database Vendor: OCLC - First Search
Partic in Dialog Corporation; Illinois Library & Information Network; Nat Libr of Med; OCLC Online Computer Library Center, Inc

S UNITED STATES RAILROAD RETIREMENT BOARD LIBRARY,* 844 N Rush St, 60611-2031. SAN 304-0461. Tel: 312-751-4927. FAX: 312-751-4924. E-Mail: library@rrb.gov. *Head Librn*, Kay Collins; *Asst Librn*, Katherine M Tsang; Staff 2 (MLS 2)
Founded 1940
Library Holdings: Bk Vols 45,000; Per Subs 162
Subject Interests: Law
Publications: Quarterly Accessions list
Mem of Chicago Libr Syst
Partic in Fedlink

C UNIVERSITY OF CHICAGO, 1100 E 57th St, 60637-1502. SAN 340-2630. Tel: 773-702-8740. Interlibrary Loan Service Tel: 773-702-7031. Circulation Tel: 773-702-8782. Reference Tel: 773-702-7874. FAX: 773-702-6623. E-Mail: Ref: reg-reference@lib.uchicago.edu. Interlibrary Loan Service E-Mail: ill-lending@lib.uchicago.edu. Web Site: www.lib.uchicago.edu/. *Dir*, Martin D Runkle; Tel: 773-702-8744, E-Mail: maru@midway.uchicago.edu; *Assoc Dir*, Judith Nadler; Tel: 773-702-8743, E-Mail: judi@midway.uchicago.edu; *Cat*, Jane Ciacci; Tel: 773-702-8739, E-Mail: kjc2@midway.uchicago.edu; *ILL*, Sandra Applegate; Tel: 773-834-0198, Fax: 773-834-2598, E-Mail: illr@midway.uchicago.edu; *Business*, Denise Weintraub; Tel: 773-702-8752, Fax: 773-702-7730, E-Mail: dead@midway.uchicago.edu; *Spec Coll*, Alice D Schreyer; Tel: 773-702-0095, Fax: 773-702-3728, E-Mail: schreyer@midway.uchicago.edu; *Ref*, Katherine Haskins; Tel: 773-702-8708, E-Mail: kwh2@midway.uchicago.edu; *Admin Assoc*, Catherine Hardy; Tel: 773-702-8745, E-Mail: cshardy@midway.uchicago.edu. Subject Specialists: *Films and filmmaking*, Katherine Haskins; *Theater*, Katherine Haskins; Staff 68 (MLS 68)
Founded 1891. Enrl 12,788; Fac 2,287; Highest Degree: Doctorate
Jul 1999-Jun 2000 Mats Exp $22,315,487. Sal $9,708,152 (Prof $3,419,235)
Library Holdings: Bk Vols 6,557,970; Per Subs 38,669
Special Collections: American Drama (Atkinson & Morton Colls); Anatomical Illustration (Frank Coll); Balzac's Works (Croue Coll); Children's books, primarily 19th Century (Encyclopaedia Britannica Coll); Continental Literature (Hirsch-Bernays Coll); Cromwelliana (George Morris Eckels Coll); Dramatic Criticism (Briggs Coll); Early American School Books (Littlefield Coll); Early Theology & Biblical Criticism (American Bible Union & Hengstenberg Colls); English Bibles (Grant Coll); English Drama to 1800 (Celia & Delia Austrian Coll); Files of Poetry, a Magazine of Verse including the personal papers of Harriet Monroe; Fine Printing (Donnelley Coll); German Fiction, 1790-1850 (Lincke Coll); Goethe's works (Heinemann Coll); History of Kentucky & Ohio River Valley (Durrett Coll); History of Science & Medicine (Crerar Coll); Judaica (Rosenberger Coll); Life Records of Geoffrey Chaucer & Canterbury Tales in Transcripts & Photostat; Lincolniana (Barton Coll); Manuscript Coll of Manorial Records regarding Estates in Norfolk & Suffolk (Bacon Coll); Modern Poetry (Harriet Monroe Coll); New Testament Mss (Edgar J Goodspeed Coll); Notarial Documents of Northern Italy (Rosenthal Coll); Personal papers of: William Beaumont, Stephen A Douglas, William H English (History of Indiana), Frank O Lowden, Ida B Wells; Photostats of German Folksongs (Wieboldt-Rosenwald Coll); Source Material regarding first contact of Whites & Indians in Mississippi Valley (Ethno-History Coll); Taschenbuecher; The John Crerar Library Rare Book Coll; University Archives, contains the university's official records & papers of prominent members of the university's faculties including Edith & Grace Abbott, Thomas C Chamberlin, Enrico Fermi, James Franck, Samuel N Harper, William Rainey Harper, Robert Herrick, George Herbert Mead, William Vaughn Moody, Howard Taylor Ricketts, Marion Talbot, Herman Eduard von Holst
Database Vendor: epixtech, inc.
Publications: Internal staff newsletter; LIBRA (library reports & announcements); library society newsletter; special exhibit catalogs
Mem of Asn of Research Libraries
Partic in Center For Research Libraries; Illinois Library & Information Network; OCLC Online Computer Library Center, Inc; Research Libraries Group, Inc
Friends of the Library Group
Departmental Libraries:
CHEMISTRY LIBRARY, GHJ 204, 5745 S Ellis Ave, 60637-1499. SAN 340-269X. Tel: 773-702-8775. FAX: 773-702-7429. E-Mail: chemistry-library@lib.uchicago.edu. Web Site: www.lib.uchicago.edu/e/chem/. *Assoc Dir*, Catherine Hardy; Tel: 773-702-8745, Fax: 773-702-6623, E-Mail: cshardy@midway.uchicago.edu; *Br Coordr*, Torsten Schweickart; E-Mail: jtschwei@midway.uchicago.edu; *Bibliogr*, Andrea Twiss-Brooks; Tel: 773-702-8777, E-Mail: atbrooks@midway.uchicago.edu; Staff 2 (MLS 1, Non-MLS 1)
Library Holdings: Bk Vols 30,000; Per Subs 250
Subject Interests: Chemistry
Database Vendor: epixtech, inc.
CL D'ANGELO LAW LIBRARY, 1121 E 60th St, 60637-2786. SAN 340-2789. Tel: 773-702-9615. FAX: 773-702-2889. E-Mail: law@uchicago.edu. Web Site: www.lib.uchicago.edu/e/law. *Dir*, Judith Wright; *Assoc Dir*, Catherine Hardy; Tel: 773-702-8745, Fax: 773-702-6623, E-Mail: cshardy@

midway.uchicago.edu; *Publ Servs*, Charles Ten Brink; *Doc*, Constance Fleischer; *Tech Servs*, Lorna Tang; Staff 10 (MLS 10)
Founded 1902. Enrl 603; Fac 33; Highest Degree: Doctorate
Library Holdings: Bk Vols 651,882; Bk Titles 257,701; Per Subs 8,429
Subject Interests: Anglo-American law, International law
Special Collections: Henry Simons Papers Coll; Karl Llewelyn Papers Coll; US Supreme Court Briefs & Records Depository
Automation Activity & Vendor Info: (Acquisitions) Innovative Interfaces Inc.; (Cataloging) epixtech, inc.; (Circulation) epixtech, inc.; (Course Reserve) epixtech, inc.; (OPAC) epixtech, inc.; (Serials) epixtech, inc.
Mem of Chicago Libr Syst
Partic in OCLC Online Computer Library Center, Inc

ECKHART LIBRARY, 1118 E 58th St, 60637-1538. SAN 340-272X. Tel: 773-702-8778. FAX: 773-702-7535. Web Site: www.lib.uchicago.edu/e/eck/. *Librn*, Brenda Rice; Tel: 773-702-8774, E-Mail: bsr2@midway.uchicago.edu; *Admin Assoc*, Catherine Hardy; Tel: 773-702-8745, Fax: 773-702-6623, E-Mail: cshardy@midway.uchicago.edu
Library Holdings: Bk Vols 55,000; Per Subs 520
Subject Interests: Computer science, Mathematics, Statistics

HARPER LIBRARY, 1116 E 59th St, 60637-1592. SAN 340-2754. Tel: 773-702-7959. E-Mail: harper-library@lib.uchicago.edu. Web Site: www.lib.uchicago.edu/libinfo/libraries/harper/. *Librn*, Eileen Libby; Tel: 773-702-7960, E-Mail: lib3@midway.uchicago.edu; *Admin Assoc*, Catherine Hardy; Tel: 773-702-8745, Fax: 773-702-6623, E-Mail: cshardy@midway.uchicago.edu
Library Holdings: Bk Vols 68,497

JOHN CRERAR LIBRARY, 5730 S Ellis Ave, 60637-1434. SAN 303-8750. Tel: 773-702-7715. Interlibrary Loan Service Tel: 773-702-7031. Circulation Tel: 773-702-7409. Interlibrary Loan Service E-Mail: interlibrary-loan@lib.uchicago.edu. Reference E-Mail: crerar-reference@lib.uchicago.edu. Web Site: www.lib.uchicago.edu/lib/e/libraries/crerar. *Librn*, Kathleen A Zar; Tel: 773-702-7469, E-Mail: kzar@midway.uchicago.edu; *Ref*, Barbara Kern; Tel: 773-702-8717, E-Mail: bkern@midway.uchicago.edu; *Ref*, Rebecca Woolbert; Tel: 773-702-7569, E-Mail: rwoolber@midway.uchicago.edu. Subject Specialists: *Astronomy*, Fritz Whitcomb; *Biomedical*, Christa Modschiedler; *Chemical*, Andrea Twiss-Brooks; *Computer science*, Brenda Rice; *Geophysics*, Andrea Twiss-Brooks; *Mathematics*, Brenda Rice; *Physics*, Fritz Whitcomb; *Science*, Kathleen A Zar; *Statistics*, Brenda Rice; *Technology*, Fritz Whitcomb; Staff 7 (MLS 7)
Founded 1891
Library Holdings: Bk Vols 1,200,000
Subject Interests: Astrophysics, Biomedical, Botany, Clinical medicine, Earth scis, History of medicine, History of science, Oceanography, Physics, Technology, Zoology
Special Collections: Department of Special Coll; Incunabula; Joseph Regenstein Library; Manuscripts: See University of Chicago
Publications: At Your Service (Newsletter)
Partic in Center For Research Libraries; Comt for Institutional Coop; Illinois Library & Information Network; Nat Libr of Med; OCLC Online Computer Library Center, Inc; Research Libraries Group, Inc
Friends of the Library Group

SOCIAL SERVICE ADMINISTRATION, 969 E 60th St, 60637-2627. SAN 340-2819. Tel: 773-702-1199. FAX: 773-702-0874. Web Site: www.lib.uchicago.edu/libinfo/libraries/ssad/. *Librn*, Eileen Libby; Tel: 773-702-1100, E-Mail: lib3@midway.chicago.edu. Subject Specialists: *Social service (social work)*, Eileen Libby; Staff 1 (MLS 1)
Library Holdings: Bk Vols 36,424
Subject Interests: Social service (social work)

YERKES OBSERVATORY
See Separate Entry in Williams Bay, WI

C UNIVERSITY OF ILLINOIS AT CHICAGO, Richard J Daley Library, 801 S Morgan St (m/c 234), 60607. (Mail add: PO Box 8198, 60680-8198), SAN 340-2932. Tel: 312-996-2716. Interlibrary Loan Service Tel: 312-996-4886. Circulation Tel: 312-996-2724. Reference Tel: 312-996-2726. FAX: 312-413-0424. Web Site: www.uic.edu/depts/lib/. *Librn*, Sharon A Hogan; E-Mail: sahogan@uic.edu; *Asst Librn*, Susan Jacobson; *Acq*, Alex Bloss; E-Mail: abloss@uic.edu; *Cat*, Jay Lambrecht; Tel: 312-996-2736, E-Mail: jaylamb@uic.edu; *Circ*, Robert A Daugherty; Tel: 312-996-2734, E-Mail: rad@uic.edu; *Doc*, John Shuler; Tel: 312-996-2738, E-Mail: alfred@uic.edu; *Spec Coll*, Gretchen L Lagana; Tel: 312-996-2756, E-Mail: glagana@uic.edu; *Bibliogr*, Deborah Blecic; *Bibliogr*, John Cullars; *Bibliogr*, Joan Fiscella; *Bibliogr, Ref*, H Robert Malinowsky; Tel: 312-996-2730, E-Mail: hrm@uic.edu; *Bibliogr*, Stephen Wiberley, Jr; *Syst Coordr*, Nancy R. John; E-Mail: nrj@uic.edu. Subject Specialists: *Health sciences*, Susan Jacobson; Staff 241 (MLS 78, Non-MLS 163)
Founded 1946. Enrl 24,610; Fac 1,714; Highest Degree: Doctorate
Jul 1999-Jun 2000 Income (Main and Other College/University Libraries) $17,011,016. Mats Exp $6,545,146. Sal $8,095,512
Library Holdings: Bk Vols 2,072,288; Per Subs 17,465
Special Collections: 17th Century French Political & Intellectual History; Architecture (Mies van der Rohe, Charles Genther, Burnham & Hammond Colls); Archives of the Chicago Rock Island & Pacific Railroad Company; Chicago Design Archive (contains business & organizational records & personal papers, including Institute of Design, Chicago Book Clinic, IDCA, 27 Chicago Designers, R Hunter Middleton, Robert Vogele, Bruce Beck, Gordon Monsen, Phillip Reed & William Stone Colls); Chicago Fairs & Expositions (A Century of Progress World's Fair archives); Chicago Literature & Literary Societies (Chicago literature to the present & Society of Midland Authors, Indiana Society, Boswell Club of Chicago Colls); Chicago Photographic Archive (Phillips, Italian-American Colls); Chicago Railroad Fair, archives; Chicagoana (Lawrence J Gutter Coll), contains pre-fire imprints, maps, lit, literary mss, hist, politics, transportation, archit, crime, prints; Corporate Archives of the Chicago Board of Trade; Franklin Roosevelt (Joseph M Jacob Coll); Jane Adams Memorial Coll (contains Hull-House Association records, papers of individuals & organizations associated with Hull-House such as: Immigrants Protective League, Travelers Aid Society, Juvenile Protective Association & Wallace Kirkland photographs); Midwest Women's Historical Coll (contains personal & organizational records, including Mary Hastings Bradley, Neva Leona Boyd, Haldeman-Julius Family, Adena-Miller Rich & Esther Saperstein); Papers of Lenox Riley Lohr & Helen Tieken Garaghty; Records of the Chicago Urban League; Sheet Music (American popular music, 1900-1945); Slavery & Anti-Slavery (Sierra Leone Coll); University Archives (contains the University's official records & papers of prominent members of the university's faculties)
Automation Activity & Vendor Info: (Acquisitions) NOTIS; (Circulation) NOTIS; (OPAC) NOTIS
Publications: ShelfLife
Mem of Chicago Libr Syst
Partic in ARL; CIC; CRL; Ill Coop Coll Mgt Prog; Illinois Library Computer Systems Office; National Network of Libraries of Medicine - Greater Midwest Region; OCLC Online Computer Library Center, Inc
Departmental Libraries:

ARCHITECTURE & ART, Douglas Hall, 3rd flr, 60608. Tel: 312-996-4588. *Librn*, David Austin; Tel: 312-413-2965, Fax: 312-413-0424, E-Mail: daustin@uic.edu

LIBRARY OF THE HEALTH SCIENCES, CHICAGO, 1750 W Polk St, 60612. SAN 340-3025. Tel: 312-996-8974. Interlibrary Loan Service Tel: 312-996-8991. Circulation Tel: 312-996-8966. Reference Tel: 312-996-8993. FAX: 312-996-9584. *Librn*, Susan Jacobson; E-Mail: sjake@uic.edu
Subject Interests: Allied health, Dentistry, Environmental studies, Medicine, Nursing
Special Collections: Neurology & Psychiatry (Percival Bailey Coll); Pharmacopoeias, Herbals, Formularies, Dispensatories & History of the Health Sciences (Rare & Early Volumes); Urology & Anomalies (Joseph Kiefer Coll)

LIBRARY OF THE HEALTH SCIENCES, PEORIA, One Illini Dr, PO Box 1649, Peoria, 61656. SAN 304-5536. Tel: 309-671-8490. FAX: 309-671-8495. *Librn*, Josephine Dorsch; Tel: 309-671-8488, E-Mail: jod@uic.edu

LIBRARY OF THE HEALTH SCIENCES, ROCKFORD, 1601 Parkview Ave, Rockford, 61107. SAN 327-9987. Tel: 815-395-5650. FAX: 815-395-5655. *Librn*, Sue Hollander; Tel: 815-395-5658, E-Mail: sholland@uic.edu

LIBRARY OF THE HEALTH SCIENCES, URBANA, 102 Medical Sciences Bldg, 506 S Mathews Ave, Urbana, 61801. SAN 340-8604. Tel: 217-333-4893. FAX: 217-333-9559. *Librn*, Victoria Pifalo; Tel: 217-244-2259, E-Mail: vgp@uic.edu
Mem of Lincoln Trail Libraries System
Resources shared by the University of Illinois at Urbana-Champaign; see that entry

MATHEMATICS, PO Box 8198, m/c 234, 60680-8198. SAN 340-2967. Tel: 312-996-3024. *Librn*, Robert A Daugherty; Tel: 312-996-2734, Fax: 312-413-0424, E-Mail: rad@uic.edu

SCIENCE, PO Box 8198, m/c 234, 60680-8198. SAN 340-2991. Tel: 312-996-5396. FAX: 312-996-7822. *Librn*, Julie Hurd; E-Mail: jhurd@uic.edu

G US BUREAU OF THE CENSUS PARTNERSHIP & DATA SERVICES, (Formerly US Bureau of The Census Information Service Program), Chicago Regional Office Reference Center, 200 W Adams, 24th flr, 60604. SAN 325-6871. Tel: 312-353-9747. FAX: 312-353-8950. Web Site: www.census.gov. *Info Specialist*, Marilyn Stephens; E-Mail: marilyn.e.stephens@census.gov
Special Collections: Census Publications; Historical US Census Data 1970

C VANDERCOOK COLLEGE OF MUSIC, Harry Ruppel Memorial Library, 3140 S Federal St, 60616-3731. SAN 304-050X. Tel: 312-225-6288, Ext 226. FAX: 312-225-5211. Web Site: www.vandercook.edu/library/index.html. *Librn*, Don L Widmer; E-Mail: widmer@vandercook.edu; Staff 1 (MLS 1)
Founded 1967. Enrl 180; Fac 25; Highest Degree: Master
Aug 1999-Jul 2000 Income Parent Institution $49,609. Mats Exp $15,820, Books $7,770, Per/Ser (Incl. Access Fees) $4,230, Presv $1,500, AV Equip $600, Manuscripts & Archives $600, Electronic Ref Mat (Incl. Access Fees) $1,120. (Prof $33,000)
Library Holdings: Bk Vols 11,000; Per Subs 68
Subject Interests: Music, Music educ, Psychology
Special Collections: Choral Coll (Artman Coll); College Archive (Nutt Coll); Jazz Recordings (Williamson Coll); Rare Book Coll
Automation Activity & Vendor Info: (Acquisitions) epixtech, inc.; (Cataloging) epixtech, inc.; (Circulation) epixtech, inc.; (OPAC) epixtech, inc.
Database Vendor: epixtech, inc., OCLC - First Search
Function: Research library
Partic in Chicago Library System; Illinois Library & Information Network
Open Mon-Thurs 8:30am-10pm, Fri 8:30-6, Sat 9-5, Sun 1-9

L VEDDER, PRICE, KAUFMAN & KAMMHOLZ, Law Library, 222 N LaSalle, 60601. SAN 304-0518. Tel: 312-609-7500. FAX: 312-609-5005. *Librn*, Kenneth Halicki
Library Holdings: Bk Vols 22,000
Subject Interests: Corporate law

M VA CHICAGO HEALTH CARE SYSTEM - LAKESIDE DIVISION, Library Services (142D), 333 E Huron St, 60611. SAN 375-961X. Tel: 312-943-6600, Ext 3528. Interlibrary Loan Service Tel: 312-943-6600, Ext 3531. Reference Tel: 312-943-6600, Ext 3531. FAX: 312-640-2252. *Chief Librn*, Lydia Tkaczuk; E-Mail: lydia.tkaczuk@med.va.gov; Staff 2 (MLS 2)
Library Holdings: Bk Titles 5,600; Per Subs 170
Partic in Metropolitan Consortium Of Chicago

S VISKASE CORP LIBRARY,* 6855 W 65th St, 60638. SAN 340-2576. Tel: 708-496-4200, Ext 4286. FAX: 708-496-4698. *Librn*, Myron Nicholson
Founded 1945
Library Holdings: Bk Titles 4,100; Per Subs 100
Subject Interests: Chemistry

J WILBUR WRIGHT COLLEGE NORTH, City College of Chicago Library, 4300 N Narragansett, 60634. SAN 304-0542. Tel: 773-481-8400. FAX: 773-481-8407. Web Site: www.ccc.edu. *Dir*, Thomas Bauhs; E-Mail: tbauhs@ccc.edu; *Acq*, Linda Neil; *Ref*, Norma Lugo-Gulyas; Staff 3 (MLS 3)
Founded 1934. Enrl 6,250
1999-2000 Income $725,000. Mats Exp $62,000, Books $10,000, Per/Ser (Incl. Access Fees) $37,000, AV Equip $10,000
Library Holdings: Bk Vols 52,000; Bk Titles 48,000; Per Subs 245
Automation Activity & Vendor Info: (Cataloging) DRA; (Circulation) DRA; (OPAC) DRA
Database Vendor: Ebsco - EbscoHost, OCLC - First Search
Mem of Chicago Libr Syst

L WILDMAN, HARROLD, ALLEN & DIXON LIBRARY, 225 W Wacker Dr, Ste 3000, 60606. SAN 375-9199. Tel: 312-201-2000. FAX: 312-201-2555. Web Site: www.whad.com. *Dir Libr Serv*, Cristina Eckl; Tel: 312-201-2838, E-Mail: eckl@wildmanharrold.com; *Ref*, Karen Krupka; Tel: 312-201-2395, E-Mail: krupka@wildmanharrold.com; Staff 4 (MLS 1, Non-MLS 3)
Library Holdings: Bk Vols 30,000
Automation Activity & Vendor Info: (Cataloging) Inmagic, Inc.; (ILL) Inmagic, Inc.; (Serials) Inmagic, Inc.
Database Vendor: Dialog, Lexis-Nexis, OCLC - First Search
Mem of Chicago Libr Syst
Partic in ILLINET

GL WILLIAM J CAMPBELL LIBRARY OF THE US COURTS, 219 S Dearborn St, Rm 1637, 60604-1769. SAN 304-0410. Tel: 312-435-5660. FAX: 312-408-5031. *Librn*, Janet Wishinsky; *Acq*, Siew Kie Walsch; *Cat*, Kathleen Powers Goodridge; *Doc, Per*, John Klaus; *Librn*, Barry Herbert; *Librn*, Gretchen Van Dam; Tel: 312-435-5560, Ext 2643, E-Mail: Gretchen_VanDam@ib7.uscourts.gov
Library Holdings: Bk Vols 30,000
Subject Interests: Government publications
Partic in Fed Libr & Info Network; OCLC Online Computer Library Center, Inc; Westlaw

L WINSTON & STRAWN LIBRARY, 35 W Wacker Dr, Ste 4700, 60601. SAN 304-0550. Tel: 312-558-5813. Reference Tel: 312-558-5740. FAX: 312-558-5700. Web Site: www.winston.com.; Staff 9 (MLS 4, Non-MLS 5)
Library Holdings: Per Subs 750
Subject Interests: Law
Publications: Not Just Books (Newsletter)
Partic in Illinois Library & Information Network; OCLC Online Computer Library Center, Inc

S WORLD ASSOCIATION OF DOCUMENT EXAMINERS, Wade Library,* 111 N Canal, Ste 399, 60606. SAN 321-9704. Tel: 312-930-9446. FAX: 312-930-5903. *Librn*, Kathleen Kusta
Founded 1970
Library Holdings: Bk Titles 2,000
Subject Interests: Handwriting examination, Questioned document analysis
Restriction: Open to public for reference only

S WORLD BOOK PUBLISHING, Research Library, 233 N Michigan Ave, 20th Flr, 60601. SAN 304-0577. Tel: 312-729-5581. FAX: 312-729-5600. *Librn*, Jon Fjortoft; Staff 2 (MLS 1, Non-MLS 1)
Founded 1920
Library Holdings: Bk Vols 16,000; Per Subs 300
Special Collections: Archives of company products
Publications: Quarterly accessions list
Partic in Illinois Library & Information Network; OCLC Online Computer Library Center, Inc

W M WRIGLEY JR CO
S CORPORATE LIBRARY, 410 N Michigan Ave, 60611. SAN 340-3203. Tel: 312-645-3921. FAX: 312-644-0081. *Librn*, Linda Hanrath; E-Mail: lhanrath@wrigley.com; Staff 2 (MLS 1, Non-MLS 1)
Founded 1978
Library Holdings: Bk Titles 1,500; Per Subs 120
Special Collections: Corporate archives
Publications: Internal Holdings List (quarterly); Internal Serials List (annual)
Mem of Chicago Libr Syst

S RESEARCH & DEVELOPMENT LIBRARY, 3535 S Ashland Ave, 60609. SAN 340-3173. Tel: 773-523-4040, Ext 2671. FAX: 773-847-2335. *Librn*, K T Nelson; *Bibliog Instr, Librn, Online Servs*, Lynn Biline
Founded 1972
Library Holdings: Bk Titles 4,500; Per Subs 300
Subject Interests: Chemical engineering, Chemistry
Special Collections: Chewing Gum Patent File (from 19th century to present)
Restriction: Staff use only
Mem of Chicago Libr Syst
Partic in Dialog Corporation

M Y-ME NATIONAL BREAST CANCER ORGANIZATION LIBRARY,* 212 W Van Buren, 60607. SAN 373-4390. Tel: 312-294-8513. FAX: 312-294-8598. *Mgr*, June Adler
Library Holdings: Bk Vols 425; Per Subs 25
Subject Interests: Biology, Psychology

S YOUTH NETWORK COUNCIL LIBRARY,* 200 N Michigan Ste 400, 60605-1212. SAN 326-968X. Tel: 312-704-1257. E-Mail: yncicoy@aol.com. *In Charge*, Denis Murstein
Library Holdings: Bk Titles 1,000
Branches:

CHICAGO HEIGHTS

P CHICAGO HEIGHTS FREE PUBLIC LIBRARY, 25 W 15th St, 60411-3488. SAN 304-0585. Tel: 708-754-0323. TDD: 708-754-0328. FAX: 708-754-0325. E-Mail: chs@sls.lib.il.us. Web Site: www.chicagoheightslibrary.org, www.sls.lib.il.us/chs/. *Dir*, Barbara Paul; *Asst Dir*, Carolyn Wagner; *Ref*, Beth Faulkner; *Ad Servs*, Surekha Pal; Staff 30 (MLS 6, Non-MLS 24)
Founded 1901. Pop 33,072; Circ 158,671
May 2000-Apr 2001 Income $1,014,174. Mats Exp $118,852, Books $96,022, Per/Ser (Incl. Access Fees) $15,830, AV Equip $7,000. Sal $557,339
Library Holdings: Bk Vols 115,398; Per Subs 294
Subject Interests: Local history, Spanish (language)
Publications: Newsletter
Mem of Suburban Library System
Special Services for the Deaf - TDD

J PRAIRIE STATE COLLEGE LIBRARY, 202 S Halsted, 60411. SAN 304-0593. Tel: 708-709-3552. FAX: 708-709-3940. E-Mail: pgaitskill@prairie.cc.il.us. Web Site: www.prairie.cc.il.us/lrc. *Dir*, Pamela Gaitskill; *Ref*, Susan Bayer
Founded 1958
Jul 1999-Jun 2000 Income $509,920. Mats Exp $73,000, Books $42,000, Per/Ser (Incl. Access Fees) $31,000. Sal $318,000 (Prof $130,000)
Library Holdings: Bk Vols 50,000; Per Subs 505
Automation Activity & Vendor Info: (Circulation) Innovative Interfaces Inc.; (OPAC) Innovative Interfaces Inc.
Partic in NILRC; Suburban Libr Syst

S SOUTH COOK ISC4 LIBRARY, 253 W Joe Orr Rd, 60411. SAN 320-8559. Tel: 708-754-6600. FAX: 708-754-8687. Web Site: www.s-cook.org. *Librn*, Cathy Johnson
Subject Interests: Education
Special Collections: ERIC microfiche indexed by Council of Exceptional Children
Automation Activity & Vendor Info: (Cataloging) Sagebrush Corporation; (Circulation) Sagebrush Corporation; (OPAC) Sagebrush Corporation
Mem of Suburban Library System
Open 8-4:30

M ST JAMES HOSPITAL & HEALTH CENTERS, Dr Hugo Long Library, 1423 Chicago Rd, 60411-3483. SAN 304-0607. Tel: 708-756-1000, Ext 6150. FAX: 708-709-2193. *Coordr, Librn*, Linda L Fennema
Founded 1956
Library Holdings: Bk Vols 500; Per Subs 70
Partic in Chicago & South Consortium

CHICAGO RIDGE

P CHICAGO RIDGE PUBLIC LIBRARY, 6301 W Birmingham, 60415. SAN 304-0615. Tel: 708-423-7753. TDD: 708-423-2510. FAX: 708-423-2758. E-Mail: crs@sls.lib.il.us. *Dir*, Kathleen McSwain; *Ad Servs*, Kathryn Sofianos; *Ch Servs*, Constance Van Swol; *Tech Servs*, Mary Ann Azukas; *Ref*, Stephen Zumbo; Staff 18 (MLS 4, Non-MLS 14)
Founded 1966. Pop 13,643; Circ 101,376
Jan 2000-Dec 2000 Income $547,867, State $16,897, City $479,029, Locally Generated Income $51,941. Mats Exp $85,911, Books $76,592, AV Equip

$1,892. Sal $219,883
Library Holdings: Bk Titles 51,879; Per Subs 456
Publications: CR Library Lines (newsletter)
Mem of Suburban Library System
Friends of the Library Group

CHILLICOTHE

P CHILLICOTHE PUBLIC LIBRARY DISTRICT, (CPLD), 822 N Second St, 61523-1822. SAN 304-0623. Tel: 309-274-2719. TDD: 309-374-3650. FAX: 309-274-3000. E-Mail: cpld@darkstar.rsa.lib.il.us. Web Site: www.chillicothe.lib.il.us. *Ch Servs, Coll Develop*, Shari Wilson
Founded 1916. Pop 11,927; Circ 60,000
Jul 1999-Jun 2000 Income $411,060. Mats Exp $42,000, Books $23,000, Per/Ser (Incl. Access Fees) $4,000, AV Equip $5,000, Electronic Ref Mat (Incl. Access Fees) $10,000. Sal $117,000 (Prof $53,000)
Library Holdings: Bk Vols 26,300; Per Subs 88
Automation Activity & Vendor Info: (Cataloging) CARL; (Circulation) CARL; (OPAC) CARL
Mem of Alliance Library System
Partic in Resource Sharing Alliance

CHRISMAN

P CHRISMAN PUBLIC LIBRARY, 112 S Illinois, 61924. SAN 304-0631. Tel: 217-269-3011. Interlibrary Loan Service Tel: 800-275-5857. FAX: 217-269-3011. *Librn*, Mary Marvin; E-Mail: mmarvi@ltnet.ltls.org; *Asst Librn*, Mary E Galway
Founded 1932. Pop 1,136
May 1999-Apr 2000 Income $15,190, State $1,401, City $1,571, County $8,670, Other $3,548. Mats Exp $3,225, Books $3,052, Electronic Ref Mat (Incl. Access Fees) $173. Sal $10,939
Library Holdings: Bk Vols 9,029
Mem of Lincoln Trail Libraries System

CHRISTOPHER

P CHRISTOPHER PUBLIC LIBRARY,* 202 E Market St, PO Box 131, 62822. SAN 304-064X. Tel: 618-724-7534. FAX: 618-724-7534. *Librn*, Patricia Brown; *Ch Servs*, Jane Brayfield; *Asst Librn*, Irene Toiqo
Pop 3,086; Circ 18,117
Library Holdings: Bk Vols 18,976; Per Subs 20
Mem of Shawnee Library System

CICERO

P CICERO PUBLIC LIBRARY, 5225 W Cermak Rd, 60804. SAN 304-0658. Tel: 708-652-8084. FAX: 708-652-8095. Web Site: www.sls.lib.il.us/cis. *Asst Dir*, Patricia Terracino; *Head Librn*, Janice Mather; *Head Ref*, Ellen Lempera; Staff 32 (MLS 4, Non-MLS 28)
Founded 1921. Pop 67,436; Circ 219,688
Library Holdings: Bk Vols 106,778; Per Subs 384; Spec Interest Per Sub 12
Subject Interests: Polish (language), Spanish (language)
Database Vendor: IAC - Info Trac, Innovative Interfaces INN - View, OCLC - First Search
Publications: Cicero Public Library News (newsletter)
Mem of Suburban Library System

J MORTON COLLEGE, Learning Resources Center, 3801 S Central Ave, 60804. SAN 304-0666. Tel: 708-656-8000, Ext 321. Reference Tel: 708-656-8000, Ext 429. FAX: 708-656-3297. Web Site: www.morton.cc.il.us. *Dir*, Joyce Bennett VanCura
Founded 1924. Enrl 5,005; Fac 205
Library Holdings: Bk Titles 50,000; Per Subs 585; High Interest/Low Vocabulary Bk Vols 518; Bks on Deafness & Sign Lang 12
Subject Interests: Compact discs, Spanish (language), Videos
Publications: Learning Resources Chronicle (Newsletter); Subject Specific Pathfinders
Mem of NILRC; Suburban Library System
Partic in Dialog Corporation; Illinois Library & Information Network

CISCO

P WILLOW BRANCH TOWNSHIP LIBRARY,* Cisco Center, 61830-0039. (Mail add: PO Box 39, 61830-0039), SAN 304-0674. Tel: 217-669-2312. FAX: 217-669-2312. *Coll Develop, Librn*, Mary K Heidkamp; E-Mail: mkheidk@ltnet.ltls.org
Pop 728; Circ 4,900
Jan 1999-Dec 1999 Income $35,412, Other $5,194. Mats Exp $6,724, Books $5,836, Per/Ser (Incl. Access Fees) $888. Sal $15,600 (Prof $10,500)
Library Holdings: Bk Vols 6,165; Per Subs 27
Special Collections: Juvenile Coll
Mem of Lincoln Trail Libraries System

CISSNA PARK

P CISSNA PARK COMMUNITY LIBRARY DISTRICT,* 511 N Second St, PO Box 254, 60924. SAN 376-1304. Tel: 815-457-2452. FAX: 815-457-2452. *Librn*, Richard Dulaney
Library Holdings: Bk Titles 35,000; Per Subs 30
Mem of Lincoln Trail Libraries System

CLARENDON HILLS

P CLARENDON HILLS PUBLIC LIBRARY, 7 N Prospect Ave, 60514. SAN 304-0682. Tel: 630-323-8188. FAX: 630-323-8189. E-Mail: cns@sls.lib.ill.us. *Ch Servs*, Krista Devlin; *Ad Servs*, Barbara Stepina; *Ref*, Kathleen Strange; Staff 5 (MLS 3, Non-MLS 2)
Founded 1963. Pop 6,994; Circ 88,123
Library Holdings: Bk Vols 46,712; Per Subs 71
Subject Interests: Local history, Travel
Automation Activity & Vendor Info: (Circulation) Innovative Interfaces Inc.
Mem of Suburban Library System
Open Mon-Tues 9:30-9, Wed 9:30-5, Thurs 1-9, Fri 9:30-5, Sat 9:30-4
Friends of the Library Group

CLAYTON

P CLAYTON PUBLIC LIBRARY DISTRICT,* 102 E Maine St, PO Box 318, 62324-0318. SAN 304-0690. Tel: 217-894-6519. FAX: 217-894-6519. E-Mail: clay@darkstar.rsa.lib.il.us. *Librn*, Esther Carstens; *Asst Librn*, Jill Hapke
Pop 1,303; Circ 8,059
Library Holdings: Bk Vols 6,861; Per Subs 13
Mem of Alliance Library System

CLINTON

P VESPASIAN WARNER PUBLIC LIBRARY DISTRICT,* 310 N Quincy, 61727. SAN 304-0704. Tel: 217-935-5174. FAX: 217-935-4425. *Dir*, Malinda Evans
Founded 1901. Pop 10,250; Circ 66,391
Library Holdings: Bk Vols 47,000; Per Subs 200
Special Collections: Early Illinois History & Geography (C H Moore Coll)
Automation Activity & Vendor Info: (Circulation) CLSI LIBS
Mem of Rolling Prairie Library System
Friends of the Library Group

COAL CITY

P COAL CITY DISTRICT PUBLIC LIBRARY, 85 N Garfield St, 60416. SAN 304-0712. Tel: 815-634-4552. FAX: 815-634-2950. Web Site: www.coalcity.lib.il.us. *Dir*, Jolene Franciskovich; E-Mail: jfranciskovich@htls.lib.il.us; *Chief Librn*, Sharon Smith; *Ch Servs*, Chris Reigh; E-Mail: creigh@htls.lib.it.us; *Tech Servs*, Linda Smith; Staff 20 (Non-MLS 20)
Founded 1886. Pop 9,204; Circ 149,268
Jul 1999-Jun 2000 Income $816,867. Mats Exp $196,470, Books $73,198, Per/Ser (Incl. Access Fees) $7,170, Electronic Ref Mat (Incl. Access Fees) $43,698. Sal $265,426 (Prof $169,363)
Library Holdings: Bk Titles 47,973; Per Subs 240
Automation Activity & Vendor Info: (Circulation) GEAC; (OPAC) GEAC
Database Vendor: Ebsco - EbscoHost, GaleNet, IAC - Info Trac, OCLC - First Search, ProQuest, Wilson - Wilson Web
Function: ILL available
Mem of Heritage Trail Library System

COAL VALLEY

P RIVER BEND LIBRARY SYSTEM, 220 W 23rd Ave, 61240. (Mail add: PO Box 125, 61240-0125), SAN 340-3238. Tel: 309-799-3155. Interlibrary Loan Service FAX: 309-799-7916. Web Site: www.rbls.lib.il.us. *Dir*, Robert W McKay; E-Mail: rmckay@libby.rbls.lib.il.us; *Mgr*, Karen O'Dean; E-Mail: kodean@libby.rbls.lib.il.us; *Mgr, Publ Servs*, Judith Hutchinson; E-Mail: jhutchin@libby.rbls.lib.il.us; *Mgr, Tech Servs*, Mary Anne Stewart; E-Mail: mstewart@libby.rbls.lib.il.us; Staff 6 (MLS 4, Non-MLS 2)
Founded 1966. Pop 200,812
Jul 2000-Jun 2001 Income $1,230,931, State $542,107, Federal $1,600, Other $687,224. Mats Exp $3,665. Sal $387,200 (Prof $196,905)
Library Holdings: Bk Vols 13,000; Bk Titles 12,000; Per Subs 24
Automation Activity & Vendor Info: (Circulation) GEAC
Publications: Current Comment (weekly member newsletter); Directory of Libraries; Library Policies (quarterly); RBLS Service Manual (quarterly); Union List of Periodicals (annual)
Member Libraries: Andalusia Township Library; Annawan-Alba Township Library; Augustana College Library; Black Hawk College; Cordova District Library; Deere & Co Library; East Moline Public Library; Erie Public Library District; Geneseo Public Library District; Genesis Medical Center; Henry C Adams Memorial Library; Illini Hospital; Marycrest International

University; Moline Public Library; Moore Memorial Library District; Odell Public Library; Palmer College Of Chiropractic; River Valley District Library; Robert R Jones Public Library; Rock Island Public Library; Saint Ambrose University; Schmaling Memorial Public Library District; Sheffield Public Library; Silvis Public Library; Swenson Swedish Immigration Research Center; Trinity Medical Center; Twin Rivers District Public Library; Walnut Public Library District; Western District Library
Partic in Illinois Library & Information Network; Libr User Info Syst; OCLC Online Computer Library Center, Inc
Branches: 1

P TALKING BOOK CENTER OF NORTHWEST ILLINOIS, 220 W 23rd Ave, 61240. (Mail add: PO Box 125, 61240-0125), SAN 340-3262. Tel: 309-799-3137. FAX: 309-799-7916. *Mgr*, Karen O'Dean; E-Mail: kodean@libby.rbls.lib.il.us; Staff 1 (MLS 1)
Founded 1968
Jul 1999-Jun 2000 Income $171,936, State $166,499, Other $5,437. Mats Exp $1,020. Sal $102,081 (Prof $39,312)
Special Services for the Blind - Low vision aids for lending; Newsletter in large print; Newsletter on cassette
Talking Book Center of NW Illinois

P ROBERT R JONES PUBLIC LIBRARY,* PO Box 190, 61240-0190. SAN 304-0720. Tel: 309-799-3047. FAX: 309-799-5528. *Dir*, Jeffrey Stafford; *Asst Librn*, Phyllis Webb
Founded 1967. Pop 5,175; Circ 37,973
Library Holdings: Bk Titles 30,000; Per Subs 85
Subject Interests: Coal
Automation Activity & Vendor Info: (Circulation) CLSI LIBS
Mem of River Bend Library System

COLCHESTER

P COLCHESTER DISTRICT LIBRARY,* PO Box 237, 62326-0237. SAN 304-0739. Tel: 309-776-4861. FAX: 309-776-4099. E-Mail: copl@darkstar.lib.il.us. *Dir*, Susan Hunt
Founded 1974. Pop 1,645; Circ 12,191
Library Holdings: Bk Vols 10,000; Per Subs 83
Mem of Alliance Library System
Open Mon 1-5, Wed 9-11, 1-5 & 7-9, Fri 1-5, Sat 9-1

COLFAX

P MARTIN TOWNSHIP PUBLIC LIBRARY, 103 S Center St, PO Box 376, 61728. SAN 304-0747. Tel: 309-723-2541. FAX: 309-723-5037. E-Mail: mart@darkstar.rsa.lib.il.us. Web Site: www.mtpl.lib.il.us. *Librn*, Joyce Carmack; *Asst Librn*, Phyllis Towner
Founded 1942. Pop 1,154; Circ 20,401
Apr 1998-Mar 1999 Income (Main Library Only) $25,000, State $2,700, County $19,000, Locally Generated Income $1,650, Other $1,600. Mats Exp $4,525, Books $4,000, Per/Ser (Incl. Access Fees) $500, Micro $25. Sal $10,200
Library Holdings: Bk Vols 14,000; Per Subs 30
Special Collections: Colfax Press Coll (1896-1992), micro; Cooksville Interprise Coll (1879-1921), micro; Octavia Yearbooks; Ridgeview Review (1992-present)
Mem of Alliance Library System
Special Services for the Deaf - Books on deafness & sign language; High interest/low vocabulary books

COLLINSVILLE

P COLLINSVILLE MEMORIAL PUBLIC LIBRARY,* 408 W Main St, 62234. SAN 304-0755. Tel: 618-344-1112. FAX: 618-345-6401. E-Mail: cve@lcls.org. Web Site: gatenet.lcls.lib.il.us/cve/cmpl.htm. *Librn*, Barbara Rhodes; *Ch Servs*, Terry Rankin
Founded 1915. Pop 23,286; Circ 197,280
Jan 1998-Dec 1998 Income $456,882. Mats Exp $440,968. Sal $180,044
Library Holdings: Bk Vols 69,686; Per Subs 250
Subject Interests: Programming
Database Vendor: DRA
Mem of Lewis & Clark Library System
Friends of the Library Group

S ILLINOIS HISTORIC PRESERVATION AGENCY, Cahokia Mounds State Historic Site Library, 30 Ramey St, 62234. SAN 374-759X. Tel: 618-346-5160. FAX: 618-346-5162. Web Site: www.cahokiamounds.com. *In Charge*, Matt Migalla
Library Holdings: Bk Vols 2,000; Per Subs 2
Restriction: Internal circulation only

S SOUTHWESTERN ILLINOIS METROPOLITAN & REGIONAL PLANNING COMMISSION, Technical Library,* 203 W Main St, 62234. SAN 326-9558. Tel: 618-344-4250. FAX: 618-344-4253.
Publications: Grants & Miscellaneous Municality

COLONA

P TWIN RIVERS DISTRICT PUBLIC LIBRARY,* 911 First St, 61241. SAN 304-2405. Tel: 309-792-0548. FAX: 309-792-2143. *Librn*, Barbara Bennett; E-Mail: bbennett@libby.rbls.lib.il.us; *Asst Librn*, Paula Else; *Ch Servs*, Jackie Shattuck
Pop 6,728; Circ 24,646
Jul 1999-Jun 2000 Income $337,581, State $72,827, Federal $279, Locally Generated Income $252,836, Other $11,639. Mats Exp $7,638, AV Equip $663, Other Print Mats $6,975. Sal $36,919
Library Holdings: Bk Vols 12,770; Per Subs 66
Subject Interests: Local history
Publications: The Twin Rivers LINK (newsletter)
Mem of River Bend Library System
Special Services for the Blind - Talking Books
Open Mon-Fri 10-8 & Sat 10-3

COLUMBIA

P COLUMBIA PUBLIC LIBRARY, 106 N Metter, 62236-2299. SAN 304-0771. Tel: 618-281-4237. FAX: 618-281-6977. E-Mail: cla@lcls.org. *Dir*, Linda L Maus; *Asst Librn*, Annette Bland; *Asst Librn*, Deborah Huggins
Founded 1958. Pop 7,003; Circ 53,354
Library Holdings: Bk Vols 39,000; Per Subs 128
Subject Interests: Education, Genealogy, Investing
Publications: Monthly Newsletter
Mem of Lewis & Clark Library System
Friends of the Library Group

CORDOVA

P CORDOVA DISTRICT LIBRARY, 402 Main Ave, 61242=9790. (Mail add: PO Box 247, 61242-0247), SAN 304-078X. Tel: 309-654-2330. FAX: 309-654-2290. E-Mail: cor@libby.rbls.lib.il.us. Web Site: www.rbls.lib.il.us/cor/index.html. *Dir*, Sue Hebel; E-Mail: shebel@libby.rbls.lib.il.us; *Librn*, Cheryl Sasko; E-Mail: csasko@libby.rbls.lib.il.us; Staff 2 (Non-MLS 2)
Founded 1876. Pop 1,031; Circ 31,625
Jul 1998-Jun 1999 Income (Main Library Only) $131,251, State $9,845, County $119,285. Mats Exp $109,550, Books $12,344, AV Equip $1,836, Electronic Ref Mat (Incl. Access Fees) $11,679. Sal $38,067
Library Holdings: Bk Vols 13,500; Per Subs 35
Subject Interests: Mississippi River
Automation Activity & Vendor Info: (Cataloging) GEAC; (Circulation) GEAC; (OPAC) GEAC
Mem of River Bend Library System
Open Mon, Wed & Fri 9-5, Tues 12-8, Thurs 9-12 & 1-8, Sat 9-1pm

CORNELL

P AMITY TOWNSHIP PUBLIC LIBRARY,* 604 E Main St, PO Box 243, 61319. SAN 376-1355. Tel: 815-358-2231. FAX: 815-358-2217. *Librn*, Judy Pharis
Library Holdings: Bk Titles 1,100; Per Subs 18
Mem of Alliance Library System

COULTERVILLE

P COULTERVILLE PUBLIC LIBRARY,* 103 S Fourth St, PO Box 373, 62237. SAN 304-0798. Tel: 618-758-3013. *Librn*, Melissa Jarrett
Founded 1956. Pop 1,118; Circ 15,951
Library Holdings: Bk Vols 9,173
Subject Interests: Education, Genealogy, History, Religion
Mem of Shawnee Library System
Open Tues-Sat 1-6, Wed 9-6, Thurs 1-8

COWDEN

P DRY POINT TOWNSHIP LIBRARY, S Rte 128 & County Hwy 651, PO Box 275, 62422-0275. SAN 376-1479. Tel: 217-783-2616. *Librn*, Charlene Taylor
Founded 1972
Library Holdings: Bk Titles 11,000; Per Subs 15
Mem of Rolling Prairie Library System
Friends of the Library Group

CRESTWOOD

P CRESTWOOD PUBLIC LIBRARY DISTRICT,* 4955 W 135th St, 60445. SAN 304-0801. Tel: 708-371-4090. FAX: 708-371-4127. *Chief Librn*, Sue Bleskin
Founded 1973. Circ 36,640
Library Holdings: Bk Vols 33,000; Per Subs 100
Mem of Suburban Library System

CRETE

P CRETE PUBLIC LIBRARY DISTRICT, 1177 N Main St, 60417. SAN 304-081X. Tel: 708-672-8017. FAX: 708-672-3529. E-Mail: cts@sslic.net. *Librn*, Jane Schulten; *Ch Servs*, Martha Schlagel; *Ref*, Ellen Herrmann
Pop 15,248; Circ 97,842
Jul 1999-Jun 2000 Income $447,553, County $390,000, Locally Generated Income $76,300. Mats Exp $64,000, Books $50,000, Per/Ser (Incl. Access Fees) $7,000, AV Equip $4,000, Electronic Ref Mat (Incl. Access Fees) $3,000. Sal $270,000 (Prof $120,000)
Library Holdings: Bk Vols 47,900; Per Subs 105
Subject Interests: Antiques, Collectibles
Mem of Suburban Library System
Friends of the Library Group

CREVE COEUR

P CREVE COEUR PUBLIC LIBRARY DISTRICT,* 311 N Highland Ave, 61610. SAN 304-0828. Tel: 309-699-7921. FAX: 309-699-0949. E-Mail: crco@darkstar.rsa.lib.il.us. *Acq, Cat, Dir*, Vera Ingles
Founded 1945. Circ 23,147
Library Holdings: Bk Titles 20,000; Per Subs 60
Mem of Alliance Library System

CRYSTAL LAKE

P CRYSTAL LAKE PUBLIC LIBRARY, 126 Paddock St, 60014. SAN 304-0836. Tel: 815-459-1687. FAX: 815-459-9581. Web Site: www.crystallakelibrary.org. *Dir*, Kathryn I Martens; *Asst Dir*, Louise Nee; *Tech Servs*, Mary Van Sickle; *Ad Servs*, Janet Polep; *Ch Servs*, Nancy Myers; *Ad Servs*, Karen Migaldi; *Circ*, Pamela Miller; Staff 69 (MLS 10, Non-MLS 59)
Founded 1926. Pop 34,401; Circ 541,000
May 1999-Apr 2000 Income $2,006,004, State $59,577, City $1,719,841, Locally Generated Income $226,586. Mats Exp $316,145, Books $160,633, Per/Ser (Incl. Access Fees) $22,822, AV Equip $35,350, Electronic Ref Mat (Incl. Access Fees) $40,422. Sal $1,048,746
Library Holdings: Bk Vols 149,337; Per Subs 458
Automation Activity & Vendor Info: (Acquisitions) DRA
Database Vendor: DRA, IAC - SearchBank, OCLC - First Search
Publications: Beacon (quarterly newsletter)
Mem of North Suburban Library System

J MCHENRY COUNTY COLLEGE LIBRARY, 8900 US Hwy 14, 60012. SAN 304-0852. Tel: 815-455-8533. Reference Tel: 815-455-8762. FAX: 815-455-3999. Web Site: www.mchenry.cc.il.us/library/library.html. *Dir*, Amy E Faubl; Tel: 815-479-7545, E-Mail: afaubl@pobox.mchenry.cc.il.us; Staff 11 (MLS 5, Non-MLS 6)
Founded 1968. Pop 32,000; Circ 156,585; Enrl 1,850; Fac 84
Library Holdings: Bk Vols 36,885; Bk Titles 30,914; Per Subs 341
Subject Interests: Agriculture, Horticulture
Automation Activity & Vendor Info: (Cataloging) SIRSI; (Circulation) SIRSI; (Course Reserve) SIRSI; (OPAC) SIRSI; (Serials) SIRSI
Database Vendor: Ebsco - EbscoHost, Lexis-Nexis, OCLC - First Search, ProQuest
Function: ILL available
Mem of North Suburban Library System
Partic in N Suburban Libr Syst; NILRC
Learning Resource Center includes AV production, graphics & printing areas
Bookmobiles: 1

CUBA

P SPOON RIVER PUBLIC LIBRARY DISTRICT, 201 S Third St, 61427-0140. (Mail add: PO Box 140, 61427-0140), SAN 304-0860. Tel: 309-785-5496. Interlibrary Loan Service Tel: 309-343-2380. FAX: 309-785-5439. E-Mail: spoon_river_61427@yahoo.com. *Dir Libr Serv*, Betsy Evans; E-Mail: beevans37@yahoo.com; *Ch Servs*, Amy Diane Lowry; Tel: 309-785-3001; Staff 9 (Non-MLS 9)
Founded 1912. Pop 3,402; Circ 27,164
Library Holdings: Bk Vols 23,425; Per Subs 47; High Interest/Low Vocabulary Bk Vols 50; Bks on Deafness & Sign Lang 12
Special Collections: Census on microfilm, Fulton County bks; Cuba High School Yearbook, microfilm; Cuba Journal, microfilm; Genealogy (family history files, obituaries, cemetery plot bks, etc)
Database Vendor: CARL, OCLC - First Search, Wilson - Wilson Web
Mem of Alliance Library System
Open June 1-Aug 31, Mon-Fri 9-5 & Sat 9-12; Sept 1-May 30, Mon-Fri 9-5:30 & Sat 9-12

CUTLER

P CUTLER PUBLIC LIBRARY,* Civic Ctr, 409 S Main, 62238. SAN 376-1290. Tel: 618-497-2961. FAX: 618-497-8818. E-Mail: cutlib@egyptian.net. *Librn*, Jackie Carrothers
Library Holdings: Bk Titles 2,569

DANVERS

P DANVERS TOWNSHIP LIBRARY,* 105 S West St, PO Box 376, 61732. SAN 304-0879. Tel: 309-963-4269. FAX: 309-963-4269. *Librn*, Sharon Smith
Pop 1,692; Circ 12,000
Library Holdings: Bk Vols 19,000; Per Subs 54
Special Collections: Easy Reader
Mem of Alliance Library System
Open Mon, Wed & Thurs 1-5, Tues & Fri 9-5, Thurs 7-9, Sat 9-12

DANVILLE

J DANVILLE AREA COMMUNITY COLLEGE, Learning Resources Center, 2000 E Main St, 61832. SAN 304-0887. Tel: 217.443-8734. Circulation Tel: 217-443-8733. Reference Tel: 217-443-8739. FAX: 217-443-8147. E-Mail: library@dacc.cc.il.us. Web Site: www.dacc.cc.il.us/library. *Dir*, Sally M Duchow; E-Mail: smduchow@dacc.cc.il.us; *Head Tech Servs*, Holly Nordheden; Tel: 217-443-8852, E-Mail: hnordhed@dacc.cc.il.us; *Librn*, Harriet Whiteman; E-Mail: whiteman@dacc.cc.il.us; *Ref*, Ruth B Lindemann; Tel: 217-443-8735, E-Mail: rlinde@dacc.cc.il.us; *ILL*, Pam McCoy; E-Mail: pmccoy@dacc.cc.il.us; Staff 7 (MLS 4, Non-MLS 3)
Founded 1962. Enrl 1,600; Highest Degree: Associate
Jul 2000-Jun 2001 Income $388,263, State $5,505, Federal $11,173, Parent Institution $371,585. Mats Exp $70,705, Books $21,705, Per/Ser (Incl. Access Fees) $31,713, Micro $15,230, Electronic Ref Mat (Incl. Access Fees) $2,057. Sal $200,446 (Prof $147,404)
Library Holdings: Bk Vols 45,500; Per Subs 196
Automation Activity & Vendor Info: (Acquisitions) epixtech, inc.; (Cataloging) epixtech, inc.; (Circulation) epixtech, inc.; (ILL) epixtech, inc.
Database Vendor: Ebsco - EbscoHost, IAC - Info Trac, Lexis-Nexis, OCLC - First Search, ProQuest
Function: ILL available
Mem of Lincoln Trail Libraries System
Partic in Ill Coop Coll Mgt Prog; Illinois Library & Information Network; NILRC

P DANVILLE PUBLIC LIBRARY,* 319 N Vermilion St, 61832. SAN 304-0895. Tel: 217-477-5220. FAX: 217-477-5230. Web Site: www.danville.lib.il.us. *Dir*, Barbara J Nolan; *Ad Servs*, Phillip Cohee; *Ch Servs*, Vonna Bley; *Archivist, Ref*, Roberta Allen; *Outreach Serv*, Robert Jackson; *AV*, Michael Boedicker; *Circ*, Deborah Sebright; Staff 7 (MLS 7)
Founded 1883. Pop 33,828; Circ 389,147
May 1998-Apr 1999 Income $1,029,830, State $44,486, City $884,591, Locally Generated Income $100,753. Mats Exp $118,438, Books $101,231, Per/Ser (Incl. Access Fees) $15,402, Micro $1,805. Sal $528,313 (Prof $223,540)
Library Holdings: Bk Vols 152,360; Per Subs 501
Subject Interests: Gardening, Genealogy
Publications: Newsletter (quarterly)
Mem of Lincoln Trail Libraries System
Open Mon-Thurs 9-8, Fri & Sat 9-5:30 (closed Memorial Day & Labor Day)
Friends of the Library Group

GM DEPARTMENT OF VETERANS AFFAIRS, Medical Center Library Service,* 1900 E Main St, 61832. SAN 304-0925. Tel: 217-442-8000, Ext 5607. FAX: 217-431-6571. *Chief Librn*, Edward J Poletti; Staff 4 (MLS 1, Non-MLS 3)
Founded 1905. Circ 53,139
Library Holdings: Bk Titles 4,067; Per Subs 261
Subject Interests: Paramedics, Psychiatry, Psychology
Mem of Lincoln Trail Libraries System
Partic in Valnet

M PROVENA UNITED SAMARITANS MEDICAL CENTER LIBRARY, 812 N Logan Ave, 61832. SAN 304-0917. Tel: 217-443-5270. FAX: 217-431-4097. *Librn*, Lucy Webb; E-Mail: luciarwebb@provenahealth.com; *Asst Librn*, Sandy Cosat; Staff 2 (MLS 1, Non-MLS 1)
Library Holdings: Bk Vols 2,000; Per Subs 150
Database Vendor: Silverplatter Information Inc.
Mem of Lincoln Trail Libraries System

DARIEN

P INDIAN PRAIRIE PUBLIC LIBRARY DISTRICT, 401 Plainfield Rd, 60561-4207. SAN 324-1262. Tel: 630-887-8760. FAX: 630-887-8801. E-Mail: ins@sls.lib.il.us. Web Site: www.indianprairie.lib.il.us. *Dir*, Lenore A Schacht; E-Mail: schachtl@sls.lib.il.us; *Asst Dir*, Laura Birmingham; E-Mail: birmingl@sls.lib.il.us; *Tech Servs*, Ann Stovall; E-Mail: stovall@sls.lib.il.us; *Ad Servs*, Debra Wordinger; *Circ*, Bayneeta Freeland; E-Mail: freeland@sls.lib.il.us; *Ch Servs*, Suzanne Lippencott; E-Mail: lippenco@sls.lib.il.us; Staff 74 (MLS 12, Non-MLS 62)
Founded 1988. Pop 43,867; Circ 619,091
Jul 1999-Jun 2000 Income $2,615,577, State $82,045, City $10,050, Locally Generated Income $2,521,982, Other $1,500. Mats Exp $397,365, Books $238,289, Per/Ser (Incl. Access Fees) $54,863, AV Equip $49,213,

Electronic Ref Mat (Incl. Access Fees) $25,660. Sal $1,107,658
Library Holdings: Bk Vols 118,752; Per Subs 953
Automation Activity & Vendor Info: (Circulation) Innovative Interfaces Inc.
Database Vendor: OCLC - First Search
Publications: Guide to Organizations in Indian Prairie; Insider (staff newsletter) (Newsletter); Insider (staff) (Newsletter); Volunteer Handbook
Mem of Suburban Library System
Friends of the Library Group

DE KALB

P DE KALB PUBLIC LIBRARY, Haish Memorial Library, 309 Oak St, 60115-3369. SAN 304-0941. Tel: 815-756-9568. TDD: 815-756-6553. FAX: 815-756-7837. E-Mail: dekpgeneral@nilslib.il.us. Web Site: www.dkpl.org. *Dir*, Linda R Chesser; E-Mail: lindac@nils.lib.il.us; *Ch Servs*, Theresa Winterbauer; *Tech Servs*, Pat Adams; *Ad Servs*, Elaine Fulton; *Ref*, Joanne West; *Per*, Dee Coorer; Staff 5 (MLS 5)
Founded 1893. Pop 35,076; Circ 291,494
Jul 1999-Jun 2000 Income $827,500. Sal $442,800
Library Holdings: Bk Titles 118,486; Per Subs 329
Subject Interests: Local history
Automation Activity & Vendor Info: (Cataloging) Innovative Interfaces Inc.; (Circulation) Innovative Interfaces Inc.; (ILL) Innovative Interfaces Inc.; (OPAC) Innovative Interfaces Inc.; (Serials) Innovative Interfaces Inc.
Database Vendor: Innovative Interfaces INN - View
Mem of Northern Illinois Library System

S DEKALB GENETICS CORP, Research Library,* 3100 Sycamore Rd, 60115. SAN 304-0933. Tel: 815-756-7333, Ext 133. FAX: 815-758-4106.
Founded 1965
Library Holdings: Bk Titles 775
Restriction: Not open to public

C NORTHERN ILLINOIS UNIVERSITY, University Libraries, 413 Founders Memorial Library, 60115-2868. SAN 340-3297. Tel: 815-753-9806. Interlibrary Loan Service Tel: 815-753-9842. Circulation Tel: 815-753-9844. Reference Tel: 815-753-9851. TDD: 815-753-0150. Interlibrary Loan Service FAX: 815-753-2003. E-Mail: lib-admin@wpo.cso.niu.edu. Web Site: libws66.lib.niu.edu. *Dean*, Arthur Young; Tel: 815-753-9801, E-Mail: ayoung@niu.edu; *Asst Dean, Publ Servs*, Lorraine J Haricombe; Tel: 815-753-9804, E-Mail: ljharicombe@niu.edu; *Asst Dean, Syst Coordr*, T J Lusher; E-Mail: tlusher@niu.edu; *Asst Dean, Cat*, Mary Munroe; Tel: 815-753-9805, E-Mail: mmunroe@niu.edu; *Head of Libr, Music*, H Stephen Wright; *Access Serv*, Rebecca Martin; Tel: 815-753-9896; *Humanities and Soc Sci*, William Baker; Tel: 815-753-1857, E-Mail: bbaker@niu.edu; *Humanities and Soc Sci*, Charles Larry; Tel: 815-753-1634, E-Mail: clarry@niu.edu; *Humanities and Soc Sci*, Leanne Lauer; Tel: 815-753-4025, E-Mail: llauer@niu.edu; *Humanities and Soc Sci*, Jennie Ver Steeg; Tel: 815-753-1351, E-Mail: jversteeg@niu.edu; *Electronic Resources*, Robert Ridinger; *Govt Doc*, Earl Shumaker; *Science*, Jitka Hurych; Tel: 815-753-1947, E-Mail: jitka@niu.edu; *Archivist*, Glen Gildemeister; *Acq*, James Millhorn; *Ref*, Byron Anderson; *Cat*, Chalermsee Olson. Subject Specialists: *Business*, Ann Glenn; *Business*, Mary Grosch; *Business*, Nestor Osorio; *Business*, Jitka Hurych; *Engineering*, Ann Glenn; *Engineering*, Mary Grosch; *Engineering*, Nestor Osorio; *Engineering*, Jitka Hurych; *Science*, Ann Glenn; *Science*, Mary Grosch; *Science*, Nestor Osorio; *Southeast Asia*, May Kyi Win; Staff 136 (MLS 45, Non-MLS 91)
Founded 1899. Enrl 18,603; Fac 1,200; Highest Degree: Doctorate
Jul 2000-Jun 2001 Income State $8,935,546. Mats Exp $4,115,514, Books $1,164,059, Per/Ser (Incl. Access Fees) $2,662,402, Presv $89,847, AV Equip $46,813, Electronic Ref Mat (Incl. Access Fees) $152,393. Sal $4,532,996 (Prof $1,916,024)
Library Holdings: Bk Vols 1,719,217; Bk Titles 1,246,453; Per Subs 17,507
Subject Interests: Business and management, Economics, Education, History, Natural science, Science/technology, Technology
Special Collections: African-American Coll; American Popular Literature Coll; Angus Wilson Coll; Archives; Book Arts Coll; Burns Coll; Byron Coll; Chess Magazines; Chicago Lyrie Opera Coll; Colorado-Henkle Coll; Comic Book Coll; Denson Coll; Dos Passos Coll; Drama Coll (includes University & Nisbett-Snydere Colls); Edward Ardizzone Coll; Fine Arts Coll; Gay & Lesbian Press Coll; Graham Greene Coll; Hanley Manuscript Coll; Horatia Alger Coll; Imprint Society; James D Tobin Coll; Jeremy Taylor Coll; Johannsen Coll; Lovecraft Coll; Motley Coll; Music (Skinner Coll), mss; Private Press; Science Fiction Coll (includes Science Fiction Writers of America & the Science Fiction Magazine Coll); Southeast Asia Coll; Vincent Starrett Coll; Western Fiction Writers of America (WFMWA) Magazine Coll; Whitman Coll; Wordsworth Coll
Automation Activity & Vendor Info: (Acquisitions) Innovative Interfaces Inc.; (Cataloging) DRA; (Circulation) DRA; (OPAC) DRA; (Serials) Innovative Interfaces Inc.
Database Vendor: CARL, Dialog, DRA, Ebsco - EbscoHost, GaleNet, IAC - Info Trac, Lexis-Nexis, OCLC - First Search, ProQuest, Silverplatter Information Inc.
Mem of Northern Illinois Library System
Partic in CCMP; Conference of Dirs of State Univ Librns of Ill; ILCSO
Friends of the Library Group
Departmental Libraries:
FARADAY LIBRARY, Faraday Hall, 60115. SAN 340-3386. Tel: 815-753-1257. FAX: 815-753-1850.
Subject Interests: Chemistry, Physics
EARL W HAYTER REGIONAL HISTORY CENTER Tel: 815-753-1779. *Dir*, Glen Gildemeister
Special Collections: University Archives Coll
HOFFMAN ESTATES EDUCATION CENTER, NIU HEEC, 5555 Trillium Blvd, Hoffman Estates, 60192. SAN 373-5702. Tel: 815-753-8830. FAX: 815-753-8838.
MAP Tel: 815-753-1813. FAX: 815-753-4999.
Subject Interests: Geography, Geology, Maps
Special Collections: Rare Southeast Asian Maps
MUSIC Tel: 815-753-1426. *Librn*, Stephen Wright
Special Collections: Jazz Recordings & Musical Scores Coll
ROCKFORD EDUCATION CENTER, NIU REC, 8500 E State St, Rockford, 61108. SAN 377-0192. Tel: 815-753-8761. FAX: 815-753-8769.

CL NORTHERN ILLINOIS UNIVERSITY, David C Shapiro Memorial Law Library, 60115-2890. SAN 304-2227. Tel: 815-753-0505. Interlibrary Loan Service Tel: 815-753-9601. Circulation Tel: 815-753-0507. Reference Tel: 815-753-0519. FAX: 815-753-9499. Web Site: www.niu.edu/col/library/library2.htm. *Dir*, John Austin; Tel: 815-753-9493, E-Mail: jaustin@niu.edu; *Assoc Dir, Tech Servs*, Gary L Vander Meer; Tel: 815-753-9495, E-Mail: gvandermeer@niu.edu; *Computer Services, Ref*, Charles J Condon; Tel: 815-753-9495, E-Mail: ccondon@niu.edu; *Instrul Serv, Res*, Susan Boland; Tel: 815-753-9492, E-Mail: sboland@niu.edu; *Instrul Serv*, Therese Clarke; Tel: 815-753-9497, E-Mail: tclarke@niu.edu; Staff 12 (MLS 5, Non-MLS 7)
Founded 1974. Enrl 300; Fac 24; Highest Degree: Doctorate
Jul 1999-Jun 2000 Mats Exp $677,242, Per/Ser (Incl. Access Fees) $575,453, Presv $8,633, Other Print Mats $61,067, Electronic Ref Mat (Incl. Access Fees) $32,089. Sal $439,376 (Prof $238,537)
Library Holdings: Bk Vols 130,289; Bk Titles 34,544; Per Subs 3,305
Subject Interests: Law
Automation Activity & Vendor Info: (Cataloging) DRA; (Circulation) DRA; (ILL) DRA; (OPAC) DRA
Database Vendor: DRA, OCLC - First Search
Publications: Bibliographies of library's holdings
Mem of Northern Illinois Library System
Partic in Chicago Legal Acad Syst; ILLINET; Mid-Am Law Sch Libr Consortium; OCLC Online Computer Library Center, Inc

DE LAND

P GOOSE CREEK TOWNSHIP CARNEGIE LIBRARY,* 130 N Highway Ave, PO Box 237, 61839-0237. SAN 304-095X. Tel: 217-664-3572. FAX: 217-664-3624. *Librn*, Terri Wikoff
Pop 985; Circ 6,383
Mem of Lincoln Trail Libraries System
Friends of the Library Group

DE PUE

P SELBY TOWNSHIP LIBRARY DISTRICT, 101 Depot, PO Box 49, 61322. SAN 304-0968. Tel: 815-447-2660. FAX: 815-447-2598. E-Mail: rhotl@starbasel.lib.htls.il.us. *Librn*, Rita Holt; *Librn*, Ann Rodriguez
Founded 1937. Pop 2,460; Circ 19,288
Library Holdings: Bk Vols 12,500; Per Subs 21
Special Collections: Hist of De Pue Coll, A-tapes
Mem of Heritage Trail Library System
Open Mon, Tues & Fri 11-5, Wed 10-8, Sat 8-12
Friends of the Library Group

DECATUR

S ADM DESIGN SERVICES LIBRARY, 1900 E Eldorado, 62521. SAN 376-0227. Tel: 217-429-4412. FAX: 217-429-4416. *Librn*, Nancy Ryder
Library Holdings: Bk Titles 1,000; Per Subs 20
Restriction: Staff use only

S ARCHER DANIELS MIDLAND CO, ADM Research Library, 1001 Brush College Rd, 62521. SAN 305-2958. Tel: 217-424-4249. FAX: 217-424-4253. *Librn*, Sean Gaffney; E-Mail: gaffney@admworld.com; Staff 1 (MLS 1)
Founded 1957
Library Holdings: Bk Vols 3,000; Per Subs 70
Subject Interests: Biotechnology, Chemistry, Food sci, Microbiology, Nutrition
Automation Activity & Vendor Info: (Cataloging) Inmagic, Inc.; (Circulation) Inmagic, Inc.
Database Vendor: Dialog
Restriction: Staff use only
Mem of Rolling Prairie Library System

S ARCHER DANIELS MIDLAND CO LIBRARY,* 4666 Faries Pkwy, 62526. SAN 304-0976. Tel: 217-424-5398. FAX: 217-362-3965. *Asst Librn*, Alissa T Henkel; Tel: 217-424-6107, E-Mail: a_henkel@corp.admworld.com; *Dir*, Teresa Lanun; *Head of Libr, Librn*, Linda D Mills; E-Mail: l_mills@corp.admworld.com; Staff 2 (MLS 1, Non-MLS 1)
Founded 1970
Library Holdings: Bk Vols 9,400; Bk Titles 8,300; Per Subs 675
Subject Interests: Agricultural economics, Nutrition
Database Vendor: Dialog, Ebsco - EbscoHost, Lexis-Nexis, OCLC - First Search
Function: Research library
Mem of Rolling Prairie Library System
Partic in Data Star; Data Time; Dialog Corporation; Dow Jones News Retrieval

S DECATUR DEPARTMENT OF COMMUNITY DEVELOPMENT, Planning Library,* One Gary K Anderson Plaza, 62523. SAN 370-2154. Tel: 217-424-2793. FAX: 217-424-2728.
Library Holdings: Bk Vols 100
Subject Interests: Community facilities studies, Demographics, Econ, Housing, Land use planning, Natural resources, Transportation

S DECATUR GENEALOGICAL SOCIETY LIBRARY, 356 N Main St, PO Box 1548, 62525-1548. SAN 323-827X. Tel: 217-429-0135. E-Mail: dgs@dell.net. *Pres*, Sue Bergandine; *Librn*, Cheri J Hunter
Founded 1964
Library Holdings: Bk Vols 30,000; Bk Titles 20,000; Per Subs 14
Subject Interests: Bibles, Genealogy
Special Collections: County
Publications: Central Illinois Genealogical Quarterly

S DECATUR HERALD & REVIEW LIBRARY,* 601 E William St, PO Box 311, 62525. SAN 304-0984. Tel: 217-421-6979. FAX: 217-421-7965. E-Mail: hrnews@webmart.net. Web Site: www.herald-review.com. *Librn*, Lisa Morrison
Founded 1890
Library Holdings: Bk Vols 500; Per Subs 15

M DECATUR MEMORIAL HOSPITAL, Dean F Stanley, MD Memorial Library, 2300 N Edward St, 62526. SAN 304-0992. Tel: 217-876-2940. FAX: 217-876-2945. *Librn*, Karen J Stoner; E-Mail: karens@dmhhs.org
Founded 1970
Library Holdings: Bk Vols 2,145; Per Subs 80
Automation Activity & Vendor Info: (Cataloging) Inmagic, Inc.; (Circulation) Inmagic, Inc.
Publications: Newsletter
Restriction: Staff use only
Mem of Rolling Prairie Library System
Partic in Capital Area Health Consortium; Illinois Library & Information Network; Midwest Health Sci Libr Network

P DECATUR PUBLIC LIBRARY, 130 N Franklin St, 62523. SAN 340-3440. Tel: 217-424-2900. Interlibrary Loan Service Tel: 217-421-9747. Circulation Tel: 217-421-9728. Reference Tel: 217-421-9732. TDD: 217-421-9729. FAX: 217-233-4071. Web Site: www.decatur.lib.il.us. *Ad Servs*, Bev Hackney; Tel: 217-421-9771, E-Mail: bhackney@decaturnet.org; *Ch Servs*, Catherine Gross; E-Mail: kgross@decaturnet.org; *Circ*, Robyn Hendricks; E-Mail: rhendricks@decaturnet.org; *Exten Serv*, Karen Anderson; E-Mail: kanderson@decaturnet.org; *Tech Servs*, Grace Veach; E-Mail: gveach@decaturnet.org; Staff 67 (MLS 9, Non-MLS 58)
Founded 1876. Pop 85,306
May 2000-Apr 2001 Income $3,766,331, State $376,628, City $2,380,137, Locally Generated Income $1,009,566. Mats Exp $368,212, Books $264,215, AV Equip $95,882, Electronic Ref Mat (Incl. Access Fees) $8,115. Sal $1,577,573 (Prof $435,391)
Library Holdings: Bk Vols 254,051; Bk Titles 168,188; Per Subs 839
Automation Activity & Vendor Info: (Acquisitions) GEAC; (Cataloging) GEAC; (Circulation) GEAC; (OPAC) GEAC
Publications: Decatur Public Library Connections
Mem of Rolling Prairie Library System
Partic in Illinois Library & Information Network
Friends of the Library Group
Bookmobiles: 2

S ILLINOIS POWER CO, Info-Source,* Illinois Power Co C-21, 500 S 27th St, 62525. SAN 375-9598. Tel: 217-362-7685. FAX: 217-362-7977.
Library Holdings: Bk Titles 1,000

S MACON COUNTY COOPERATIVE FILM LIBRARY,* 1690 Huston Dr, 62526. SAN 376-0138. Tel: 217-872-3723. FAX: 217-872-0239. *Librn*, Nancy Hunter

L MACON COUNTY LAW LIBRARY,* 253 E Wood St Rm 303, 62523. SAN 326-9531. Tel: 217-424-1372. *Librn*, Donna I Mundy

C MILLIKIN UNIVERSITY, Staley Library, 1184 W Main, 62522. SAN 304-1018. Tel: 217-424-6214. Interlibrary Loan Service Tel: 217-424-6215. FAX: 217-424-3992. Web Site: www.millikin.edu/staley/. *Coll Develop, Dir*, Karin Borei; E-Mail: kborei@mail.millikin.edu; *Bibliog Instr, Ref*, Susan Avery; E-Mail: savery@mail.millikin.edu; *Tech Servs*, Cynthia Fuller; E-Mail: cfuller@mail.millikin.edu; Staff 4 (MLS 4)
Founded 1902. Enrl 2,200; Fac 175; Highest Degree: Bachelor
Jul 1999-Jun 2000 Income Parent Institution $670,361. Mats Exp $303,242, Books $81,369, Per/Ser (Incl. Access Fees) $146,393, Presv $3,400, Micro $25,972, Electronic Ref Mat (Incl. Access Fees) $46,108. Sal $310,232 (Prof $162,984)
Library Holdings: Bk Vols 183,000; Per Subs 965
Subject Interests: American literature, English literature, History, Music, Religion
Special Collections: Alice in Wonderland; Stephen Decatur; World War I Pamphlets
Automation Activity & Vendor Info: (Acquisitions) DRA; (Cataloging) DRA; (Circulation) DRA; (ILL) DRA; (OPAC) DRA; (Serials) DRA
Database Vendor: Ebsco - EbscoHost, GaleNet, Lexis-Nexis, OCLC - First Search, OVID Technologies, Wilson - Wilson Web
Mem of Rolling Prairie Library System
Partic in Ill Coop Coll Mgt Prog; Illinois Library & Information Network; Illinois Library Computer Systems Office; Private Academic Libraries Of Illinois; Sangamon Valley Academic Library Consortium

J RICHLAND COMMUNITY COLLEGE, Kitty Lindsay Learning Resources Center,* One College Park, 62521. SAN 304-1026. Tel: 217-875-7200, Ext 296. FAX: 217-875-6961. Web Site: www.richland.cc.il.us. *Dean of Libr*, David Zindel; E-Mail: dzindel@richland.cc.ll.us; *Librn*, John Law; Staff 2 (MLS 2)
Founded 1972. Enrl 3,500; Fac 60
Library Holdings: Bk Vols 38,000; Bk Titles 35,389; Per Subs 281
Publications: Media Index; Periodical Holdings List
Mem of Rolling Prairie Library System

P ROLLING PRAIRIE LIBRARY SYSTEM,* 345 W Eldorado St, 62522. SAN 340-3564. Tel: 217-429-2586. FAX: 217-428-1852. *Dir*, Robert F Plotzke; *Asst Dir*, Paul Johnson; *Tech Coordr*, Matt Wilkerson
Founded 1965. Pop 436,100
Jul 1998-Jun 1999 Income $1,423,844. Mats Exp $3,715. Sal $556,968
Library Holdings: Bk Titles 2,000; Per Subs 52
Special Collections: Library Science Coll
Automation Activity & Vendor Info: (Cataloging) DRA; (Circulation) DRA; (Course Reserve) DRA; (ILL) DRA; (OPAC) DRA
Publications: Let's Get It All Together; Prairie Schooner (newsletter); system directory
Member Libraries: A E Staley Manufacturing Co; Archer Daniels Midland Co; Archer Daniels Midland Co Library; Argenta-Oreana Public Library District; Argenta-Oreana Public Library District; Assumption Public Library District; Atwood-Hammond Public Library; Barclay Public Library District; Blue Mound Memorial Library District; Carnegie-Schuyler Library; Chatham Area Public Library District; Decatur Memorial Hospital; Decatur Public Library; Divernon Township Library; Dry Point Township Library; Elkhart Public Library District; Forsyth Public Library; Greenup Township Carnegie Library; Hanson Engineers, Inc; Helen Matthes Library; Herrick Township Public Library; Hope Welty Public Library District; Illinois Department Of Human Services-The Office Of Rehabilitation Services; Illinois Early Childhood Intervention Clearinghouse Library; Illinois Environmental Protection Agency Library; Illinois State Department of Transport; Illinois State Historical Library; Illinois State Museum Library; Illiopolis-Niantic Public Library District; Kitchell Memorial Library; Lincoln Christian College & Seminary; Lincoln College; Lincoln Correctional Center Library; Lincoln Land Community College; Lincoln Library; Lincoln Public Library District; Logan Correctional Center Library; Lovington Public Library District; Maroa Public Library District; Marrowbone Public Library District; Mason City Public Library; McFarland Mental Health Center; Memorial Medical Center; Millikin University; Mount Pulaski Public Library District; Moweaqua Public Library; Mt Zion District Library; Neoga Public Library District; Office of the Auditor General Library; Pawnee Public Library; Petersburg Public Library; Richland Community College; Robert Morris College Library; Rochester Public Library District; Saint Mary's Hospital; Shelbyville Free Public Library; South Macon Public Library District; Southern Illinois University School Of Medicine Library; Springfield Art Association; Springfield College In Illinois; St John's Hospital; Stonington Township Public Library; Sullivan City Public Library; Sumpter Township Library; Supreme Court Of Illinois Library; Taylorville Correctional Center Library; Taylorville Public Library; University Of Illinois At Springfield; Vespasian Warner Public Library District; Weldon Public Library District; Williamsville Public Library; Windsor Storm Memorial Public Library District
Partic in Illinois Library & Information Network; OCLC Online Computer Library Center, Inc

M SAINT MARY'S HOSPITAL, Health Science Library, 1800 E Lake Shore Dr, 62521-3883. SAN 304-1034. Tel: 217-464-2182. FAX: 217-464-1694. E-Mail: lbrosamer@smd.hshs.org. Web Site: www.StMARYS-hospital.com. *Librn*, Laura Brosamer; Staff 2 (MLS 1, Non-MLS 1)
Founded 1976
Library Holdings: Bk Titles 2,000; Per Subs 300
Subject Interests: Hospital administration, Medicine, Nursing
Automation Activity & Vendor Info: (Cataloging) DRA; (Circulation)

DRA
Mem of Rolling Prairie Library System
Partic in Capital Area Consortium; Regional Med Libr - Region 3

S A E STALEY MANUFACTURING CO, Technical Information Center, 2200 E Eldorado St, 62525-1801. SAN 304-1042. Tel: 217-421-2543. FAX: 217-421-2519. *Mgr*, Richard E Wallace; E-Mail: rewallace@tlna.com; Staff 1 (MLS 1)
Founded 1958
Library Holdings: Bk Titles 8,500; Per Subs 50
Subject Interests: Nutrition
Special Collections: Company Internal Documents; Patents Coll
Mem of Rolling Prairie Library System
Partic in OCLC Online Computer Library Center, Inc

DEER CREEK

P DEER CREEK DISTRICT LIBRARY,* 201 First St, PO Box 347, 61733-0347. SAN 304-1050. Tel: 309-447-6724. FAX: 309-447-6724. E-Mail: dclib1@yahoo.com. *Librn*, Carlene Mathis-Kull
Founded 1965. Pop 1,247; Circ 9,221
Library Holdings: Bk Vols 19,000; Per Subs 41
Mem of Alliance Library System
Open Mon 1-5:30 & 7-9pm, Tues, Wed & Fri 1-5:30, Thurs 7-9 & Sat 9-1

DEERFIELD

P DEERFIELD PUBLIC LIBRARY, 920 Waukegan Rd, 60015. SAN 304-1069. Tel: 708-945-3311. FAX: 708-945-3402. E-Mail: deerfield.library@usa.net. Web Site: www.deerfield.il.org. *Librn*, Jack Alan Hicks; E-Mail: jhicks@nslsilus.org; *Dep Dir*, Sally Seifert; *Ch Servs*, Chris Kopeck; *Tech Servs*, Glenn Poch; *Ref*, Judith Hortin; *Circ*, Joanne Bairstow; *Coll Develop*, Karen Kleckner; Staff 46 (MLS 8, Non-MLS 38)
Founded 1927. Pop 17,432; Circ 366,274
May 2000-Apr 2001 Income $1,889,000
Library Holdings: Bk Vols 180,000; Bk Titles 108,000; Per Subs 531
Subject Interests: Art
Special Collections: Deerfield Local History
Automation Activity & Vendor Info: (Acquisitions) epixtech, inc.; (Cataloging) epixtech, inc.; (Circulation) epixtech, inc.; (Course Reserve) epixtech, inc.; (ILL) epixtech, inc.; (Media Booking) epixtech, inc.; (OPAC) epixtech, inc.; (Serials) epixtech, inc.
Publications: Browsing
Mem of North Suburban Library System
Friends of the Library Group

M FUJISAWA HEALTHCARE CORPORATE LIBRARY, 3 Parkway North Ctr, 60015-2548. SAN 375-3417. Tel: 847-317-1083. FAX: 708-317-5975. Web Site: www.fujisawa.com. *Librn*, Barbara Petersen; E-Mail: barbara_petersen@fujisawa.com; Staff 1 (MLS 1)
Founded 1990
Library Holdings: Bk Titles 1,800; Per Subs 200
Mem of North Suburban Library System

S MMI COMPANIES, INC, Resource Center,* 540 Lake Cook Rd, 60015. SAN 375-1511. Tel: 847-940-7550. FAX: 847-940-7489. *Dir*, Brenda E Stenger
Library Holdings: Bk Vols 2,000; Per Subs 250

S NESTLE CLINICAL NUTRITION, Information Resource Center,* 3 Parkway N, Ste 500, 60015-0760. SAN 374-5066. Tel: 847-317-3024. FAX: 847-317-3090.
Founded 1990
Library Holdings: Bk Vols 750; Per Subs 60
Restriction: By appointment only
Mem of North Suburban Library System

G RYERSON NATURE LIBRARY, 21950 N Riverwoods Rd, 60015. SAN 304-3495. Tel: 847-968-3321. FAX: 847-948-7712. E-Mail: ryersonwoods@co.lake.il.us. Web Site: www.co.lake.il.us/forest. *Mgr*, Nan Buckardt
Founded 1974
Jul 1999-Jun 2000 Income $300
Library Holdings: Bk Titles 2,500
Subject Interests: Biology, Botany, Ecology, Entomology, Environmental studies, Forestry, Illinois, Landscape architecture, Zoology
Special Collections: Botany (Wildflower Coll), pressed plants; Herbarium
Mem of North Suburban Library System

S SCHIRMER ENGINEERING CORP LIBRARY, 707 Lake Cook Rd, 60203. SAN 375-1880. Tel: 847-272-8340. FAX: 847-272-2639. *Chief Librn*, Gayl A Liebman; Tel: 847-272-8340, Ext 233, E-Mail: gliebman@schirmerengineering.com; Staff 1 (MLS 1)
Library Holdings: Bk Vols 3,000; Per Subs 113
Function: Professional lending library
Mem of North Suburban Library System

S SHAND, MORAHAN & CO, INC LIBRARY, Ten Pkwy N, 60015. SAN 324-3621. Tel: 847-572-6080. FAX: 847-572-6098.
Founded 1980
Subject Interests: Casualty ins, Property ins
Restriction: Staff use only
Mem of North Suburban Library System
Partic in ILLINET

CR TRINITY INTERNATIONAL UNIVERSITY, James E Rolfing Memorial Library, 2065 Half Day Rd, 60015-1241. SAN 320-1805. Tel: 847-317-4000. Circulation Tel: 847-317-4000. Reference Tel: 847-317-4001. FAX: 847-317-4012. E-Mail: library@tiu.edu. Web Site: www.tiu.edu/library. *Dir*, Dr Robert H Krapohl; Tel: 847-317-4004, E-Mail: rkrapohl@tiu.edu; *Ref*, Roy Fry; Tel: 847-317-4001, E-Mail: rfry@tiu.edu; *Ref*, Gail Heideman; Tel: 847-317-4011, E-Mail: gheidema@tiu.edu; *Ref*, Keith Wells; Tel: 847-317-4010, E-Mail: kwells@tiu.edu; *Circ*, Mary Ditthardt; Tel: 847-317-4003, E-Mail: mditthar@tiu.edu; *Circ*, Linda Fratt; Tel: 847-317-4003, E-Mail: lfratt@tiu.edu; *Circ*, Kristin Howk; Tel: 847-317-4002, E-Mail: khowk@tiu.edu; *Acq, Ser*, Cathy Hanson; Tel: 847-317-4006, E-Mail: chanson@tiu.edu; *Acq*, Matt Ostercamp; Tel: 847-317-4005, E-Mail: mosterca@tiu.edu; *Acq of New Ser*, Laura Soppa; Tel: 847-317-4018, E-Mail: lsoppa@tiu.edu; *Cat*, Jennine Goodart; Tel: 847-317-4017, E-Mail: jgoodart@tiu.edu; *Cat*, Everett Meadors; Tel: 847-317-4016, E-Mail: emeadors@tiu.edu; *Cat*, Cindee Phillips; Tel: 847-317-4009, E-Mail: cphillip@tiu.edu; *Automation Syst Coordr*, Robert Fox; Tel: 847-317-4007, E-Mail: rfox@tiu.edu; *Tech Servs*, Howard Johnson; Tel: 847-317-4014, E-Mail: hjohnson@tiu.edu; *Tech Servs*, Blake Walter; Tel: 847-317-4006, E-Mail: bwalter@tiu.edu; *ILL*, Jackie Pointer; Tel: 847-317-4008, E-Mail: jpointer@tiu.edu. Subject Specialists: *Arts*, Linda Fratt; *Biblical studies*, Keith Wells; *Sciences*, Linda Fratt; *Theology*, Matt Ostercamp; *Theology*, Keith Wells; Staff 14 (MLS 6, Non-MLS 8)
Founded 1970. Enrl 4,132; Fac 168; Highest Degree: Doctorate
Jul 1999-Jun 2000 Income Parent Institution $791,562. Mats Exp $183,679, Books $57,876, Per/Ser (Incl. Access Fees) $94,777, Presv $5,331, Electronic Ref Mat (Incl. Access Fees) $25,695. Sal $586,568 (Prof $229,674)
Library Holdings: Bk Vols 200,307; Bk Titles 154,037; Per Subs 1,332
Subject Interests: Biblical studies, Church history, Missions and missionaries, Theology
Special Collections: Evangelical Free Church of America Archives, bks, per & files; Papers of Wilbur Smith, Carl F H Henry; Trinity International University Archives
Automation Activity & Vendor Info: (Acquisitions) Endeavor; (Cataloging) Endeavor; (Circulation) Endeavor; (Course Reserve) Endeavor; (OPAC) Endeavor; (Serials) Endeavor
Database Vendor: Dialog, Ebsco - EbscoHost, OCLC - First Search
Function: ILL available
Mem of North Suburban Library System
Partic in Association Of Chicago Theological Schools (ACTS); ILLINET; Libras, Inc; OCLC Online Computer Library Center, Inc

S WALGREEN CO, Employee Development Library,* 200 Wilmot Rd, 60015. SAN 373-4382. Tel: 847-914-2598. FAX: 847-914-3611. *Librn*, Norma Leonard
Library Holdings: Bk Vols 870; Per Subs 75
Subject Interests: Personnel management
Partic in Illinois Library & Information Network

C WEBSTER UNIVERSITY CHICAGO GRADUATE CENTER,* 570 Lake Cook Rd Ste 106, 60015. SAN 375-7781. Tel: 847-940-4556. FAX: 847-940-0364. E-Mail: chicago@webster.edu. Web Site: www.webster.edu. *In Charge*, Sandra J Ramey

DELAVAN

P AYER PUBLIC LIBRARY DISTRICT,* 208 Locust St, PO Box 500, 61734-0500. SAN 304-1107. Tel: 309-244-8236. FAX: 309-244-8237. E-Mail: ayerplb@yahoo.com. *Librn*, Lori Walsh
Pop 2,634; Circ 19,270
Jul 1997-Jun 1998 Income $89,000, County $47,400, Other $6,600. Mats Exp $8,500, Books $5,000, Per/Ser (Incl. Access Fees) $1,000, Other Print Mats $2,000. Sal $24,000
Library Holdings: Bk Vols 15,000; Per Subs 35
Special Collections: Delavan Times 1874-present, microfilm
Mem of Alliance Library System

DES PLAINES

S AMERICAN FOUNDRY SOCIETY INC LIBRARY, Butch Peters Memorial Library, 505 State St, 60016-8399. SAN 304-1115. Tel: 847-824-0181, Ext 254. FAX: 847-824-7848. E-Mail: library@afsinc.org. Web Site: www.afsinc.org, www.afslibrary.com. *Librn*, Virginia Khatib
Founded 1953
Library Holdings: Bk Vols 3,000; Per Subs 80
Special Collections: History of Cast Metals
Publications: Metalcasting Abstract Service
Mem of North Suburban Library System

S DES PLAINES HISTORICAL SOCIETY LIBRARY, 789 Pearson St, 60016. SAN 304-1158. Tel: 847-391-5399. FAX: 847-297-1710. E-Mail: dphslibrary@juno.com. *Dir*, Joy Matthiessen; Staff 6 (MLS 4, Non-MLS 2)
Founded 1969
Library Holdings: Bk Vols 500; Per Subs 10
Special Collections: Dr C A Earle Coll

P DES PLAINES PUBLIC LIBRARY, 1501 Ellinwood St, 60016-4553. SAN 304-1166. Tel: 847-827-5551. TDD: 847-827-0515. FAX: 847-376-2837. E-Mail: dpplinfo@desplaines.lib.il.us. Web Site: www.desplaines.lib.il.us. *Dir*, Sandra K Norlin; E-Mail: snorlin@desplaines.lib.il.us; *ILL*, Paul Audino; *Ad Servs*, Holly Richards Sorensen; *Ch Servs*, Mary Ann Brown; *Tech Servs*, Hector Marino; *Publ Servs*, Leslie Steiner; *Commun Servs*, Robert Blanchard; *Coll Develop, Publ Servs*, Martha Sloan; *Circ*, Susan Farid; Staff 130 (MLS 25, Non-MLS 105)
Founded 1906. Pop 53,414; Circ 776,872
Jan 2000-Dec 2000 Income $3,189,628. Mats Exp $621,101. Sal $1,973,271
Library Holdings: Bk Vols 180,894; Per Subs 535
Automation Activity & Vendor Info: (Circulation) GEAC
Database Vendor: IAC - Info Trac, IAC - SearchBank, OCLC - First Search, ProQuest
Publications: Foreword (newsletter)
Mem of North Suburban Library System
Partic in Coop Computer Servs
Special Services for the Deaf - TTY machine
Special Services for the Blind - Adapted computers & special software with speech output to assist learning disabled, mentally retarded & uneducated; Low vision aids & talking readers
Friends of the Library Group
Bookmobiles: 1

S GAS TECHNOLOGY INSTITUTE, Technical Information Center, 1700 S Mount Prospect Rd, 60018-1804. SAN 303-9226. Tel: 847-768-0664. FAX: 847-768-0669. Web Site: www.igt.org. *Librn*, Marianna Rozenfeld; Tel: 847-768-0662; Staff 2 (MLS 2)
Founded 1941
Library Holdings: Bk Vols 36,000; Per Subs 400
Subject Interests: Natural gas
Special Collections: American Chemical Society Division of Fuel Chemistry, Preprints 1957 to present; Energy Reports (DOE, EPRI, GRI); Pipeline Simulation Interest Group, Proc
Restriction: By appointment only
Mem of North Suburban Library System
Partic in Illinois Library & Information Network; OCLC Online Computer Library Center, Inc

M HOLY FAMILY HOSPITAL, Health Science Library,* 100 N River Rd, 60016. SAN 329-4951. Tel: 847-297-1800, Ext 1055. FAX: 847-297-7924. *Librn*, Halina E Maj
Library Holdings: Bk Vols 6,000; Per Subs 300

S NATIONAL ASSOCIATION OF INDEPENDENT INSURERS, Insurance Library,* 2600 River Rd, 60018-3286. SAN 373-0476. Tel: 847-297-7800. FAX: 847-297-5064. *In Charge*, Holly Grossman; Staff 2 (MLS 1, Non-MLS 1)
Library Holdings: Bk Vols 5,000; Per Subs 250
Subject Interests: Insurance
Restriction: Not open to public
Mem of North Suburban Library System
Partic in OCLC Online Computer Library Center, Inc

J OAKTON COMMUNITY COLLEGE LIBRARY, 1600 E Golf Rd, 60016. SAN 304-436X. Tel: 847-635-1642, 847-635-1644. FAX: 847-635-1987. Web Site: www.oakton.edu/resource/libmedia/library. *Dir*, Gary Newhouse; Tel: 847-635-1640, E-Mail: garyn@oakton.edu; *Librn*, Sandra Wittman; *Cat*, Susan Miller Maltese; *Chair*, Barbara Keeley; E-Mail: barbk@oakton.edu; *Acq*, Beverly Drick; *Ref*, Joan Cichon; *Bibliog Instr, Doc, ILL*, Judith Mayzel
Founded 1970
Library Holdings: Bk Vols 92,000; Per Subs 586
Automation Activity & Vendor Info: (Cataloging) DRA; (Circulation) DRA; (OPAC) DRA
Partic in Illinois Library & Information Network; OCLC Online Computer Library Center, Inc

G OSHA-US DEPARTMENT OF LABOR, H Lee Saltsgaver Library, 1555 Times Dr, 60018. SAN 375-9857. Tel: 847-759-7736. FAX: 847-297-4874. Web Site: www.osha.gov. *Librn*, Linda Vosburgh
Library Holdings: Bk Titles 2,920; Per Subs 30

S REFRIGERATION SERVICE ENGINEERS SOCIETY LIBRARY,* 1666 Rand Rd, 60016-3552. SAN 375-6491. Tel: 847-297-6464. FAX: 847-297-5038.
Library Holdings: Bk Titles 500
Restriction: Not open to public

S THE CENTER LIBRARY, 1855 Mount Prospect Rd, 60018. SAN 324-3370. Tel: 847-803-3535, Ext 308. FAX: 847-803-2828. Web Site: www.thecenterweb.org. *Librn*, Michelle Meyer-Edley; Tel: 847-803-3535, Ext 308, E-Mail: mmeyer@irc-desplaines.org; *Online Servs*, Rodrigo Garreton; Staff 3 (MLS 1, Non-MLS 2)
Founded 1974
Library Holdings: Bk Vols 26,388; Per Subs 60
Subject Interests: Bilingual Education, Early childhood educ, Educ improvements, English as second lang, Literacy, Refugee assistance, Special educ, Vocational education
Publications: Cataloguing Scheme; Documents on Specialized Catalogue
Function: ILL by photocopy only
Mem of North Suburban Library System
Special Services for the Deaf - High interest/low vocabulary books

UOP RESEARCH CENTER

S LIBRARY & INFORMATION SERVICES, 50 E Algonquin Rd, PO Box 5016, 60017-5016. SAN 340-3653. Tel: 847-391-3109. FAX: 847-391-3330. *Mgr*, Susan E Litka; Staff 11 (MLS 5, Non-MLS 6)
Founded 1926
Library Holdings: Bk Titles 20,000; Per Subs 700
Subject Interests: Alternative sources (energy), Chemical engineering
Special Collections: Petroleum Industry; Petroleum Products (American Petroleum Institute's Project Publications)
Publications: CAR (current awareness report); What's New (current reading list)

DIVERNON

P DIVERNON TOWNSHIP LIBRARY,* 221 S Second St, 62530. SAN 304-1204. Tel: 217-628-3813. *Librn*, Dorla Reavis
Founded 1967. Pop 1,303; Circ 6,113
Library Holdings: Bk Vols 1,700
Mem of Rolling Prairie Library System

DIXON

M KATHERINE SHAW BETHEA HOSPITAL, Medical Library,* 403 E First St, 61021. SAN 377-225X. Tel: 815-288-5531. FAX: 815-288-3789.
Library Holdings: Bk Vols 158; Bk Titles 158
Partic in Health Sci Librns of Ill

S DIXON CORRECTIONAL CENTER LIBRARY,* 2600 N Brinton Ave, PO Box 1200, 61021. SAN 371-7208. Tel: 815-288-5561, Ext 3041. *Librn*, Linda Morrissey; Staff 3 (MLS 1, Non-MLS 2)
Library Holdings: Bk Vols 10,000; Bk Titles 9,000
Special Collections: Federal & Illinois Law

P DIXON PUBLIC LIBRARY, (DPL), 221 S Hennepin Ave, 61021-3093. SAN 304-1212. Tel: 815-284-7261. TDD: 815-284-7261. FAX: 815-288-7323. Web Site: iisweb1.svcc.edu/dixonlibrary. *Dir*, Nancy Gillfillan; E-Mail: ngillfil@essex1.com; Staff 7 (MLS 1, Non-MLS 6)
Founded 1872. Pop 15,134; Circ 119,836
May 1999-Apr 2000 Income $308,631, State $74,122, City $177,149, Federal $13,557, Other $43,803. Mats Exp $32,370, Books $21,920, Per/Ser (Incl. Access Fees) $3,000, Micro $450, Electronic Ref Mat (Incl. Access Fees) $7,000. Sal $177,204 (Prof $41,000)
Library Holdings: Bk Vols 95,786; Bk Titles 79,000; Per Subs 314; Bks on Deafness & Sign Lang 12
Special Collections: Lincoln Coll; Local History-Genealogy Coll; Local Newspaper (Dixon Evening Telegraph) on microfilm from 1851
Automation Activity & Vendor Info: (Cataloging) TLC; (Circulation) TLC; (OPAC) TLC
Publications: 1942-1945 (history book); Library Lines (newsletter); Lincoln in Dixon (history book); Memories of the Green River Ordinance Plant
Mem of Northern Illinois Library System
Friends of the Library Group

J SAUK VALLEY COMMUNITY COLLEGE, Learning Resources Center, 173 IL Rte 2, 61021-9112. SAN 304-1239. Tel: 815-288-5511, Ext 306. FAX: 815-288-5651. Web Site: www.svcc.edu/services1/lrc/. *Coordr*, Robert D Thomas, Sr; E-Mail: thomasr@svcc.edu; *Publ Servs, Tech Servs*, Judy Anderson
Founded 1966
Library Holdings: Bk Vols 56,000; Per Subs 275
Special Collections: Illinois & Local History; Popular Culture (film, music & television)
Automation Activity & Vendor Info: (Cataloging) TLC; (Circulation) TLC; (OPAC) TLC
Partic in Northern Ill Learning Resources Coop; Northern Ill Libr Syst

DOLTON

P DOLTON PUBLIC LIBRARY DISTRICT, 14037 Lincoln, 60419-1091. SAN 304-1247. Tel: 708-849-2385. FAX: 708-841-2725. E-Mail: dos@sls.lib.il.us. Web Site: www.sis.lib.il.us/dos. *Adminr*, Renata Ochsner; E-Mail: ochsnerr@sls.lib.il.us; *Ad Servs*, Kris Mogle; E-Mail: moglek@sls.lib.il.us; *Ch Servs*, Shannon Morgan; E-Mail: morgans@sls.lib.il.us; *Circ*, Nancy Sannito; E-Mail: sanniton@sls.lib.il.us; *Tech Servs*, Laura Fazio; E-Mail: faziol@sls.lib.il.us; Staff 6 (MLS 3, Non-MLS 3)

Founded 1963. Pop 23,956; Circ 112,063
Jul 1999-Jun 2000 Income $1,099,671, State $181,970, Federal $47,700, Locally Generated Income $61,086, Other $808,915. Mats Exp $151,745, Books $74,007, Per/Ser (Incl. Access Fees) $8,397, Micro $4,144, Other Print Mats $30,939, Electronic Ref Mat (Incl. Access Fees) $34,258. Sal $495,780 (Prof $168,524)
Library Holdings: Bk Vols 104,839; Per Subs 1,807
Subject Interests: African-Am hist, Local history
Special Collections: Adult New Readers Coll
Automation Activity & Vendor Info: (Cataloging) Innovative Interfaces Inc.; (Circulation) Innovative Interfaces Inc.; (ILL) Innovative Interfaces Inc.; (OPAC) Innovative Interfaces Inc.
Database Vendor: OCLC - First Search
Publications: Dolton Notes (quarterly) (Newsletter)
Function: ILL available, Internet access, Photocopies available, Reference services available
Mem of Suburban Library System
Headquarters for South Area Literacy Council

DONGOLA

P DONGOLA PUBLIC LIBRARY DISTRICT,* PO Box 113, 62926. SAN 376-1487. Tel: 618-827-3622. *Librn*, Alison Holderfield
Library Holdings: Bk Titles 5,000; Per Subs 10

DOWNERS GROVE

S ALLIANCE OF AMERICAN INSURERS, Library Information Services, 3025 Highland Pkwy, Ste 800, 60515. SAN 376-0243. Tel: 630-724-2100. FAX: 630-724-2190. E-Mail: library@allianceai.org. Web Site: www.alliancai.org. *In Charge*, Jean M Demas; Staff 7 (MLS 1, Non-MLS 6)
Founded 1925
1999-2000 Mats Exp $210,500, Books $30,000, Per/Ser (Incl. Access Fees) $50,000, AV Equip $500, Other Print Mats $10,000, Electronic Ref Mat (Incl. Access Fees) $120,000. (Prof $300,000)
Library Holdings: Bk Titles 12,000; Per Subs 320
Subject Interests: Casualty ins, Property ins, Regulatory law, Safety, Workers comp
Automation Activity & Vendor Info: (Acquisitions) Inmagic, Inc.; (Cataloging) Inmagic, Inc.; (OPAC) Inmagic, Inc.; (Serials) Inmagic, Inc.
Database Vendor: Lexis-Nexis, OCLC - First Search
Publications: Policy Kit; Sample Insurance Forms; Your Information Experience Newsletter
Restriction: Access for corporate affiliates, Not open to public
Function: Research library
Mem of Suburban Library System

S ARMOUR SWIFT-ECKRICH, Research Library,* 3131 Woodcreek Dr, 60515-5429. SAN 304-4947. Tel: 630-512-1084. FAX: 630-512-1125. *Dir*, Eileen Breen
Founded 1905
1998-1999 Income $45,000. Mats Exp $26,200, Books $1,800, Per/Ser (Incl. Access Fees) $11,000. Sal $18,000
Library Holdings: Bk Titles 4,000; Per Subs 95
Subject Interests: Biochemistry, Chemistry, Food industry and trade, Microbiology, Nutrition

P DOWNERS GROVE PUBLIC LIBRARY, 1050 Curtiss St, 60515. SAN 304-1255. Tel: 630-960-1200. TDD: 630-960-1345. FAX: 630-960-9374. E-Mail: dgs@downersgrovelibrary.org. Web Site: www.downersgrovelibrary.org. *Dir*, Christopher Bowen; E-Mail: bowenc@downersgrovelibrary.org; *Asst Dir*, Jamie Bukovac; *Ref*, Bonnie Reid; *Ch Servs*, Sara Pemberton; *Reader Servs*, Joyce Saricks; *Acq, Cat*, Amy Ruyle; *Circ*, Nadine Walsh; Staff 19 (MLS 19)
Founded 1891. Pop 46,845; Circ 867,224
May 1999-Apr 2000 Income $2,767,993, State $105,870, City $2,355,621, Locally Generated Income $304,845. Mats Exp $426,558, Books $321,037, AV Equip $75,521, Electronic Ref Mat (Incl. Access Fees) $30,000. Sal $1,458,465
Library Holdings: Bk Vols 218,685; Per Subs 568
Subject Interests: Art and architecture, Education, Humanities, Local history
Publications: Discoveries (Newsletter)
Partic in Suburban Libr Syst
Friends of the Library Group

M MIDWESTERN UNIVERSITY, Alumni Memorial Library, 555 31st St, 60515. SAN 339-8072. Tel: 630-515-6200. FAX: 630-515-6195. *Librn*, Faith Ross; Tel: 630-515-6185, Fax: 630-515-7144, E-Mail: frossx@midwestern.edu; *Head Tech Servs*, Pui Wong; E-Mail: pwongx@midwestern.edu; *Ref*, Sallie Klipp; E-Mail: sklipp@midwestern.edu; *Ref*, Teresa McClow; E-Mail: tmcclo@midwestern.edu; Staff 12 (MLS 4, Non-MLS 8)
Founded 1913. Enrl 1,305; Fac 258; Highest Degree: Doctorate
Jul 1999-Jun 2000 Mats Exp $444,267, Books $20,000, Per/Ser (Incl. Access Fees) $424,267. Sal $507,482 (Prof $195,843)
Library Holdings: Bk Vols 14,747; Bk Titles 11,626; Per Subs 858
Subject Interests: Allied health, Medicine, Science/technology, Technology
Database Vendor: Dialog, epixtech, inc., OCLC - First Search, OVID Technologies
Publications: Newsletter (quarterly)
Mem of Chicago Libr Syst
Partic in Chicago Library System; Metropolitan Consortium Of Chicago; Nat Libr of Med; Regional Med Libr - Region 3

S R R DONNELLEY & SONS COMPANY, Corporate Library, 3075 Highland Pkwy, 60515. SAN 371-5612. Tel: 630-322-6242. FAX: 630-322-6733. *Chief Librn*, Nichole A Novak; E-Mail: nichole.novak@rrd.com; *Asst Librn*, Patricia Genardo; Tel: 630-322-6628, E-Mail: patricia.genardo@rrd.com; Staff 2 (MLS 1, Non-MLS 1)
Founded 1989
Jan 2000-Dec 2000 Mats Exp $72,000, Books $22,000, Per/Ser (Incl. Access Fees) $50,000. Sal $104,400
Library Holdings: Bk Titles 3,600; Per Subs 190
Database Vendor: Dialog, Lexis-Nexis
Publications: Current Awareness Bulletin
Restriction: Staff use only
Function: Research library
Mem of Suburban Library System

S VYSIS INC, Information Services Library, 3100 Woodcreek Dr, 60515. SAN 375-9148. Tel: 630-271-7173. FAX: 630-271-7048. *Librn*, Andrea Garren
Library Holdings: Bk Vols 400

DU QUOIN

P DU QUOIN PUBLIC LIBRARY,* 28 S Washington St, 62832. SAN 304-128X. Tel: 618-542-5045. *Librn*, Donna Campenella
Founded 1934. Circ 16,638
1997-1998 Income $67,070, State $6,549, City $60,521. Mats Exp $20,343, Books $18,343, Per/Ser (Incl. Access Fees) $2,000. Sal $22,000
Library Holdings: Bk Vols 15,074; Per Subs 60
Special Collections: Genealogy
Mem of Shawnee Library System
Friends of the Library Group

DUNDEE

P DUNDEE TOWNSHIP PUBLIC LIBRARY DISTRICT,* 555 Barrington Ave, 60118-1496. SAN 304-1336. Tel: 847-428-3661. FAX: 847-428-0521. Web Site: www.northstarnet.org/dukhome/dundeep/. *Dir*, Sylvia Murphy Williams; E-Mail: smwill@nslsilus.org; *Ad Servs*, Carolyn Friedlund; *Ch Servs*, Ruthann Heidgerken; *Tech Servs*, Karin Nelson; *Circ*, Cheryl Sarto; Staff 3 (MLS 3)
Founded 1879. Pop 40,076; Circ 254,402
Jul 1997-Jun 1998 Income $1,111,048, State $48,959, County $953,199, Locally Generated Income $108,890. Mats Exp $130,776, Books $113,126, Per/Ser (Incl. Access Fees) $17,650. Sal $653,624 (Prof $163,179)
Library Holdings: Bk Vols 112,988; Per Subs 402
Automation Activity & Vendor Info: (Circulation) GEAC
Publications: Newsletter
Mem of North Suburban Library System
Partic in Coop Computer Servs
Friends of the Library Group

DUNLAP

P DUNLAP PUBLIC LIBRARY DISTRICT,* 13918 Cedar Hill Dr, 61525. SAN 304-1301. Tel: 309-243-5716. FAX: 309-243-5874. E-Mail: dunlap@darkstar.rsa.lib.il.us. Web Site: www.ws.npoint.net/dunlap1. *Dir, Librn*, Jane Sieck; Staff 8 (MLS 2, Non-MLS 6)
Founded 1954. Pop 5,184; Circ 59,115
Library Holdings: Bk Titles 30,698; Per Subs 88
Publications: The Library Connection (District newsletter)
Mem of Alliance Library System

DUPO

P DAUGHERTY PUBLIC LIBRARY DISTRICT,* 220 S Fifth St, 62239. SAN 304-131X. Tel: 618-286-4444. FAX: 618-286-3636. *Librn*, Rosemary Barnett
Founded 1971. Pop 7,700; Circ 40,529
Library Holdings: Bk Vols 28,000; Per Subs 53
Mem of Lewis & Clark Library System
Friends of the Library Group

DWIGHT

P PRAIRIE CREEK PUBLIC LIBRARY DISTRICT, 501 Carriage House Lane, 60420-1399. SAN 304-1328. Tel: 815-584-3061. FAX: 815-584-3120. E-Mail: pcpldist@fcg.net. Web Site: www.fcg.net/~pcpldist. *Dir*, John Bryce Rumbles. Subject Specialists: *Creative writing*, John Bryce Rumbles;

Entertainment, John Bryce Rumbles; Staff 6 (MLS 1, Non-MLS 5)
Founded 1926. Pop 6,100; Circ 39,053
Jul 1998-Jun 1999 Income $198,000, State $7,552, Locally Generated Income $1,665, Other $24,693. Mats Exp $33,881, Books $27,645, Per/Ser (Incl. Access Fees) $2,806, Presv $150, AV Equip $2,000, Electronic Ref Mat (Incl. Access Fees) $1,280. Sal $62,000 (Prof $33,000)
Library Holdings: Bk Vols 20,000; Bk Titles 16,000; Per Subs 88; High Interest/Low Vocabulary Bk Vols 100; Bks on Deafness & Sign Lang 10
Subject Interests: Am Civil War, Local history
Automation Activity & Vendor Info: (Circulation) Follett; (OPAC) TLC
Database Vendor: OCLC - First Search
Publications: American Libraries (Annual report); Public Libraries (Annual report)
Mem of Alliance Library System
Open Mon-Thurs 10-8, Fri 1-5, Sat 10-3

EARLVILLE

P EARL TOWNSHIP PUBLIC LIBRARY,* 205 Winthrop St, PO Box 420, 60518. SAN 304-1336. Tel: 815-246-9543. FAX: 815-246-9543. *Librn*, Maureen Corrigan; *Tech Servs*, Pat Foster
Pop 2,305; Circ 21,350
Library Holdings: Bk Vols 20,000; Per Subs 52
Special Collections: Local Weekly Newspaper, 1868-present, micro
Mem of Heritage Trail Library System
Open Mon-Wed 1-8, Tues, Thurs & Fri 1-5, Sat 9-1
Friends of the Library Group

EAST ALTON

P EAST ALTON PUBLIC LIBRARY DISTRICT,* 250 Washington, 62024-1547. SAN 304-1344. Tel: 618-259-0787. FAX: 618-259-0788. E-Mail: eae@lcls.org, eae_ill@lcls.lib.il.us. *Dir*, Richard Chartrand; Staff 10 (MLS 1, Non-MLS 9)
Founded 1936. Pop 14,882; Circ 200,000 Sal $149,000 (Prof $42,000)
Library Holdings: Bk Vols 56,000; Per Subs 180
Automation Activity & Vendor Info: (Acquisitions) DRA
Mem of Lewis & Clark Library System

EAST DUBUQUE

P EAST DUBUQUE DISTRICT LIBRARY,* 301 Sinsinawa Ave, 61025-1222. SAN 304-1352. Tel: 815-747-3052. FAX: 815-747-6062. E-Mail: edpl@mwci.net. Web Site: users.mwci.net/edpl/~home.htm. *Librn*, Michelle Wessels; *Asst Librn*, Lorri Regan; *Ch Servs*, Kathy Williams
Pop 4,514; Circ 18,011
Library Holdings: Bk Vols 13,644; Per Subs 33
Publications: Booklist; Illinois Libraries
Mem of Northern Illinois Library System

EAST MOLINE

S EAST MOLINE CORRECTIONAL CENTER LIBRARY,* 100 Hillcrest Rd, 61244. SAN 376-088X. Tel: 309-755-4511, Ext 393. *Librn*, Jennie Dedmon
Library Holdings: Bk Titles 4,437; Per Subs 15

P EAST MOLINE PUBLIC LIBRARY, 740 16th Ave, 61244-2122. SAN 304-1379. Tel: 309-755-9614. FAX: 309-755-3901. E-Mail: emp@libby.rbls.lib.il.us. Web Site: www.rbls.lib.il.us/emp/index.html. *Dir*, Cynthia K Coe; E-Mail: ccoe@libby.rbls.lib.il.us; *Mgr*, Tami Cox; Staff 13 (MLS 1, Non-MLS 12)
Founded 1917. Pop 20,147; Circ 102,355
May 1999-Apr 2000 Income $503,388, State $130,643, City $321,775, Locally Generated Income $46,110, Other $4,860. Mats Exp $78,430, Books $66,930, Per/Ser (Incl. Access Fees) $11,500. Sal $250,676
Library Holdings: Bk Vols 49,355; Per Subs 154
Automation Activity & Vendor Info: (Circulation) GEAC
Database Vendor: OCLC - First Search
Publications: Newsletter
Mem of River Bend Library System
Friends of the Library Group

EAST PEORIA

P FONDULAC PUBLIC LIBRARY DISTRICT, 140 E Washington St, 61611-2598. SAN 304-1395. Tel: 309-699-3917. FAX: 309-699-7851. E-Mail: fond@darkstar.rsa.lib.il.us. Web Site: www.fondulac.lib.il.us.
Founded 1935. Pop 22,478; Circ 209,343
Library Holdings: Bk Titles 80,000; Per Subs 132
Subject Interests: Local history
Special Collections: East Peoria & Tazewell County History
Mem of Alliance Library System
Friends of the Library Group

J ILLINOIS CENTRAL COLLEGE, Learning Resources Center, One College Dr, 61635-0001. SAN 304-1409. Tel: 309-694-5461. FAX: 309-694-5473. Web Site: www.icc.cc.il.us. *Bibliog Instr, Librn, Ref*, Becky Houghton; Tel: 309-694-8504, E-Mail: bhoughton@icc.cc.il.us; *Media Spec*, Ed Smith; *Cat*, Joann Foster; *Bibliog Instr, Ref*, Tom Eertmoed; *ILL, Ref*, William Crawley; Staff 4 (MLS 4)
Founded 1967. Enrl 6,068
Library Holdings: Bk Vols 90,000; Per Subs 3,500
Automation Activity & Vendor Info: (Circulation) CARL
Database Vendor: Ebsco - EbscoHost, GaleNet, IAC - SearchBank, Lexis-Nexis, OCLC - First Search, ProQuest, Wilson - Wilson Web
Publications: Audio-Visual Software Bibliography List; Recent Additions List; Serials Holding List
Mem of Alliance Library System
Partic in Illinois Library & Information Network; OCLC Online Computer Library Center, Inc; Resource Sharing Alliance

EAST SAINT LOUIS

J EAST ST LOUIS COMMUNITY COLLEGE CENTER, Kenneth Hall Learning Resource Center, 601 J R Thompson Blvd, 62201. SAN 304-1441. Tel: 618-874-8718. Reference Tel: 618-874-8719. FAX: 618-874-8734. *Coordr, Librn*, Cynthia E Jones; E-Mail: cjones@shawls.lib.il.us; Staff 1 (MLS 1)
Founded 1969. Enrl 1,000; Fac 47; Highest Degree: Associate
Library Holdings: Bk Vols 31,205; Bk Titles 3,000; Per Subs 85
Subject Interests: African-American, Transportation
Database Vendor: Innovative Interfaces INN - View, OCLC - First Search, OVID Technologies, Wilson - Wilson Web
Function: For research purposes, Reference only
Mem of Shawnee Library System
Partic in Illinois Library & Information Network

P EAST SAINT LOUIS PUBLIC LIBRARY,* 405 N Ninth St, 62201. SAN 304-1417. Tel: 618-271-3875. FAX: 618-874-0418. E-Mail: browva@vax.lcls.il.us. Web Site: gatenet.lcls.il.us/publics.htm. *Dir*, Vandella Brown; *Cat*, Jean Brezger; *Ch Servs*, Pamela Jennings; *Circ, ILL*, Madie Dowell; *Ref*, Regina Agnew
Founded 1872. Pop 46,000; Circ 175,000
1998-1999 Income $550,000, State $167,000, City $141,000, Other $5,000. Mats Exp $53,000, Books $41,000, Per/Ser (Incl. Access Fees) $12,000. Sal $252,000 (Prof $54,500)
Library Holdings: Bk Vols 63,000; Per Subs 80
Special Collections: Metro-East Journal since 1889, micro
Partic in Lewis & Clark Libr Syst
Friends of the Library Group

M SAINT MARY'S HOSPITAL, Doctors Library, 129 N Eighth, 62201. SAN 304-1425. Tel: 618-274-1900, Ext 7178. FAX: 618-482-7015. *In Charge*, Nancy Clemons
Founded 1930
Library Holdings: Bk Vols 100; Per Subs 10
Partic in Regional Med Libr - Region 3

EDWARDSVILLE

P EDWARDSVILLE PUBLIC LIBRARY, 112 S Kansas St, 62025. SAN 304-145X. Tel: 618-692-7556. FAX: 618-692-9566. E-Mail: ede@lcls.org. Web Site: www.lcls.lib.il.us/ede/. *Dir*, Deanne W Holshouser; E-Mail: deanneh@lcls.org; *Asst Dir*, Susan Philp; *Ch Servs*, Barbara Driesner; *Ref*, Judy Thompson; Staff 33 (MLS 6, Non-MLS 27)
Founded 1818. Pop 20,243; Circ 241,143 Sal $235,000
Library Holdings: Bk Vols 86,164
Special Collections: Madison Cty Genealogical Soc Libr Coll
Database Vendor: DRA
Function: ILL available
Mem of Lewis & Clark Library System
Partic in Coop Libr Agency for Syst & Servs
Friends of the Library Group

P LEWIS & CLARK LIBRARY SYSTEM, 425 Goshen Rd, 62025. SAN 340-3688. Tel: 618-656-3216. Toll Free Tel: 800-642-9545. FAX: 618-656-9401. Web Site: www.lcls.lib.il.us. *Exec Dir*, Susan Lucco; E-Mail: susanl@lcls.org; Staff 9 (MLS 7, Non-MLS 2)
Founded 1966. Pop 391,368
Jul 2000-Jun 2001 Income (Main Library Only) $1,800,000. Mats Exp Books $5,000. Sal $965,000 (Prof $322,000)
Library Holdings: Bk Vols 200
Database Vendor: DRA
Publications: Expedition newsletter; Extra (weekly updates); System Directory
Member Libraries: Auburn Public Library; Belleville Public Library; Bethalto Public Library District; Blackburn College; Breese Public Library; Bunker Hill Public Library; Cahokia Public Library District; Carlinville Public Library; Carrollton Public Library; Case-Halstead Library; Caseyville Public Library District; Collinsville Memorial Public Library; Columbia Public Library; Daugherty Public Library District; East Alton Public Library

District; East St Louis Public Library; Edwardsville Public Library; Fairview Heights Public Library; Farmersville-Waggoner Public Library District; Gillespie Public Library; Girard Township Library; Graham Correctional Center Library; Grand Prairie Of The West Public Library District; Granite City Public Library District; Greenfield Public Library; Greenville College; Greenville Public Library; Hartford Public Library District; Hayner Public Library District; Hillsboro Public Library; Jerseyville Public Library; Lewis & Clark Community College; Litchfield Carnegie Public Library; Louis Latzer Memorial Public Library; Madison Public Library; Millstadt Library; Morrison-Talbott Library; Mount Olive Public Library; Nokomis Public Library; O'Fallon Public Library; Principia College; Roodhouse Public Library; Roxana Public Library District; Saint Anthony's Health Center; Saint Elizabeth's Hospital; Smithton Public Library District; South County Public Library District; Southern Illinois University; Southern Illinois University Edwardsville; Staunton Public Library; Tri-Township Public Library District; Valmeyer Public Library District; Venice Public Library; White Hall Township Library; Witt Memorial Public Library; Wood River Public Library
Partic in Illinois Library & Information Network; OCLC Online Computer Library Center, Inc

S MADISON COUNTY HISTORICAL SOCIETY MUSEUM LIBRARY, 715 N Main St, 62025-1111. SAN 326-601X. Tel: 618-656-7562. Web Site: www.plantnet.com/~museum. *Dir*, Suzanne Dietrich; *Librn*, Marion Sperling; *Asst Librn*, Leah Deem
Dec 1999-Nov 2000 Income $85,945, County $75,200, Parent Institution $10,745. Mats Exp $2,985, Books $98, Per/Ser (Incl. Access Fees) $50, Presv $569, Micro $789, Other Print Mats $504, Electronic Ref Mat (Incl. Access Fees) $975. Sal $58,000
Library Holdings: Bk Vols 4,500; Bk Titles 4,300; Spec Interest Per Sub 10
Subject Interests: Genealogy, Local history
Special Collections: Edwardsville Street Index & Housing Inventory (beginning 1894); Index to First Sales of Land in Illinois; Madison County Poor Farm Records; N O Nelson - Village of Leclaire papers; WPA Index to Alton Telegraph 1836-1940; WPA Index to Edwardsville Intelligencer 1862-1937
Publications: General Index for Brink's History of Madison County, Ill 1882; Madison County Poor Farm Index; Military Index for Brink's History of Madison County, Ill; Republication of Brink's History of Madison County Ill 1882
Restriction: Non-circulating to the public
Income, salaries & plant operation/maintenance figures represent that of both Museum & Library combined
Friends of the Library Group

C SOUTHERN ILLINOIS UNIVERSITY EDWARDSVILLE, Elijah P Lovejoy Library, Campus Box 1063, 62026-1063. SAN 340-3777. Tel: 618-650-2711. Interlibrary Loan Service Tel: 618-650-2174. FAX: 618-650-2381, 618-650-2717. Web Site: www.library.siue.edu/. *Dean of Libr, Ref*, Jay Starratt; Tel: 618-650-2712, E-Mail: jstarra@siue.edu; *Assoc Dean*, Regina McBride; Tel: 618-650-5198, E-Mail: rmcbrid@sieu.edu; *AV*, Fred J Noel; Tel: 618-650-3050, E-Mail: fnoel@siue.edu; *Access Serv*, Claudia Davidage; Tel: 618-650-2277, E-Mail: cdavida@siue.edu; *Doc*, Gary Denue; Tel: 618-650-2632, E-Mail: gdenue@siue.edu; *ILL*, Hope Myers; E-Mail: hmyers@siue.edu; *Archivist, Spec Coll*, Stephen Kerber; Tel: 618-650-2665, E-Mail: skerber@siue.edu; *Access Serv, Dir, Tech Serv*, Linda Hulbert; Tel: 618-650-2779, E-Mail: lhulber@sieu.edu
Founded 1957. Enrl 11,520; Fac 540; Highest Degree: Master
Jul 1998-Jun 1999 Mats Exp $1,167,022, Books $233,087, Per/Ser (Incl. Access Fees) $846,287, Presv $28,084. Sal $2,361,497 (Prof $1,198,367)
Library Holdings: Bk Vols 763,443; Bk Titles 516,873; Per Subs 5,048
Subject Interests: Business, Education, Engineering, Illinois, Nursing
Special Collections: Illinois Coll; Illinois, Missouri, & Regional Maps; Mormons in Illinois; Music Coll, sheet music, piano rolls, records, mss, cinema music, hymnals, song bks, instruments, photogs; Slavic-American Imprints Coll
Automation Activity & Vendor Info: (Acquisitions) DRA; (Cataloging) DRA; (Circulation) DRA; (Course Reserve) DRA; (ILL) DRA; (OPAC) DRA; (Serials) DRA
Publications: Lovejoy Imprints
Mem of Lewis & Clark Library System
Partic in Conference of Dirs of State Univ Librns of Ill; ILCSO; Ill Coordinated Coll Mgt Prog; Ill Libr Computer Systs Org; Illinois Library & Information Network; OCLC Online Computer Library Center, Inc; Saint Louis Regional Library Network
Friends of the Library Group

EFFINGHAM

P HELEN MATTHES LIBRARY, 100 E Market Ave, 62401. SAN 304-1476. Tel: 217-342-2464. FAX: 217-342-2413. E-Mail: hmlib@effinghamlibrary.org. Web Site: www.effinghamlibrary.org. *Dir*, Normalie Strickland; E-Mail: nstrickl@effinghamlibrary.org; *Tech Servs*, Karla Johnson; E-Mail: karlaj@effinghamlibrary.org; *Ch Servs*, Teresa Beltz; Staff 13 (MLS 1, Non-MLS 12)
Founded 1942. Pop 12,000; Circ 110,000
May 1998-Apr 1999 Income $336,554, State $44,323, City $238,491, Locally Generated Income $41,090. Mats Exp $140,148, Books $33,852, Per/Ser (Incl. Access Fees) $7,077, Micro $1,460. Sal $170,170 (Prof $91,595)
Library Holdings: Bk Vols 69,000; Per Subs 183
Subject Interests: Genealogy, World War II
Automation Activity & Vendor Info: (Cataloging) DRA; (Circulation) DRA; (OPAC) DRA
Database Vendor: DRA, OCLC - First Search
Function: Reference services available
Mem of Rolling Prairie Library System
Friends of the Library Group

EL PASO

P EL PASO PUBLIC LIBRARY,* 149 W First St, 61738. SAN 304-1484. Tel: 309-527-4360. FAX: 309-527-7100. E-Mail: eppl@darkstar.rsa.lib.il.us. Web Site: www.rsa.lib.il.us. *Librn*, Mary Byerly
Founded 1873
Library Holdings: Bk Vols 19,100; Bk Titles 19,000; Per Subs 50
Subject Interests: Agriculture, Business and management, Education, Natural science, Science/technology, Technology
Special Collections: Art (Time-Life Coll)
Mem of Alliance Library System

ELBURN

P TOWN & COUNTRY PUBLIC LIBRARY DISTRICT, 320 E North St, 60119. SAN 304-1492. Tel: 630-365-2244. FAX: 630-365-2358. *Librn*, Mary Lynn Alms; Staff 2 (MLS 1, Non-MLS 1)
Founded 1929. Pop 6,080; Circ 44,172
Jul 1999-Jun 2000 Income $260,036, State $214,874, Locally Generated Income $20,000. Mats Exp $40,000, Books $26,000, Per/Ser (Incl. Access Fees) $4,000, AV Equip $8,000, Electronic Ref Mat (Incl. Access Fees) $2,000. Sal $100,000
Library Holdings: Bk Vols 26,000; Per Subs 75
Automation Activity & Vendor Info: (Cataloging) epixtech, inc.; (Circulation) epixtech, inc.
Mem of DuPage Library System
Friends of the Library Group

ELDORADO

P ELDORADO MEMORIAL PUBLIC LIBRARY DISTRICT, 1001 Grant St, 62930-1714. (Mail add: PO Box 426, 62930-0426), SAN 304-1506. Tel: 618-273-7922. FAX: 618-273-4402. Web Site: www.sirin.lib.il.us/docs/eml/docs/lib/index.html. *Librn*, Brenda Funkhouser; E-Mail: brendaf@shawnet.shawls.lib.il.us; *Asst Librn*, Miriam Richardson; Staff 3 (Non-MLS 3)
Founded 1987. Pop 8,000; Circ 58,000
1999-2000 Mats Exp $9,366, Books $7,416, Per/Ser (Incl. Access Fees) $1,700, AV Equip $250. Sal $66,000
Library Holdings: Bk Vols 27,000; Per Subs 47
Mem of Shawnee Library System
Friends of the Library Group

ELGIN

SR CHURCH OF THE BRETHREN GENERAL BOARD, (BHLA), Brethren Historical Library & Archives, 1451 Dundee Ave, 60120-1694. SAN 304-1522. Tel: 847-742-5100, Ext 294. FAX: 847-742-6103. Web Site: www.brethren.org/genbd/bhla/. *Archivist, Librn*, Kenneth M Shaffer, Jr; E-Mail: kshaffer_gb@brethren.org; Staff 1 (MLS 1)
Founded 1936
Jan 2000-Dec 2000 Income $76,900. Mats Exp $76,900
Library Holdings: Bk Vols 8,997
Special Collections: Archives & Manuscripts Coll; Church of the Brethren history & doctrines
Publications: Guide for Local Church Historians; Guide to Research in Brethren Family History; Guide to Research in Brethren History; Guide to the Brethren in Europe
Restriction: Non-circulating to the public, Open to others by appointment
Function: Archival collection, ILL by photocopy only
Mem of North Suburban Library System
Partic in OCLC Online Computer Library Center, Inc

J ELGIN COMMUNITY COLLEGE, Renner Learning Resources Center,* 1700 Spartan Dr, 60123. SAN 304-1530. Tel: 847-214-7337, 847-697-1000. FAX: 847-888-7995. Web Site: www.elgin.cc.il.us. *Dean*, Jack Weiss; E-Mail: jweiss@mail.elgin.cc.il.us; *Coll Develop, Tech Servs*, Linda McEwan; *Bibliog Instr, Ref*, Gretl Kramer; Staff 20 (MLS 7, Non-MLS 13)
Founded 1949. Enrl 3,500; Fac 120
Jul 1998-Jun 1999 Income $792,000. Mats Exp $156,232, Books $102,866, Per/Ser (Incl. Access Fees) $53,366. Sal $523,000 (Prof $367,000)
Library Holdings: Bk Vols 70,000; Per Subs 425
Database Vendor: Ebsco - EbscoHost, IAC - Info Trac, IAC - SearchBank,

OCLC - First Search, ProQuest
Mem of North Suburban Library System
Partic in Illinois Library & Information Network; Northern Ill Learning Resources Coop; OCLC Online Computer Library Center, Inc

M ELGIN MENTAL HEALTH CENTER LIBRARY, (ABPL), Anton Boison Professional Library, 750 S State St, 60123-7692. SAN 340-3807. Tel: 847-742-1040, Ext 2660. FAX: 847-429-4931. E-Mail: dhs599c@dhs.state.il.us. *Librn*, Jennifer Ford; *Librn*, David Hagerman; Tel: 847-742-1040, Est 3537; Staff 2 (MLS 2)
2000-2001 Mats Exp $17,500, Books $2,000, Per/Ser (Incl. Access Fees) $15,000, Presv $500. Sal $70,000
Library Holdings: Bk Titles 15,000; Per Subs 240
Subject Interests: Psychiatry, Psychology, Recreation
Mem of DuPage Library System
Partic in Fox Valley Health Science Library Consortium

SR FOX VALLEY LUTHERAN ACADEMY, Resource Center,* 220 Division St, 60120. SAN 376-1703. Tel: 847-468-8207. FAX: 847-742-2930. *Librn*, Hannibal Frederich
Library Holdings: Bk Titles 2,100; Per Subs 24

P GAIL BORDEN PUBLIC LIBRARY DISTRICT, 200 N Grove Ave, 60120-5596. SAN 304-1514. Tel: 847-742-2411. TDD: 847-742-2455. FAX: 847-742-0485. E-Mail: admin@nslsilus.org. Web Site: www.elgin.lib.il.us. *Dir*, Daniel Zack; E-Mail: dzack@nslsilus.org; *Asst Dir*, Karen E Maki; E-Mail: maki@nslsilus.org; *Head Tech Servs*, Patricia K Noonan; E-Mail: pnoonan@nslsilus.org; *Head, Circ*, Eileen Sant; E-Mail: esant@nslsilus.org; *Ad Servs*, Patricia V Gebhardt; E-Mail: pgebhard@nslsilus.org; *Ch Servs*, Faith Brautigam; E-Mail: fbrautig@nslsilus.org; *ILL*, Nancy Hunt; *Automation Syst Coordr*, Betsy O'Connell; E-Mail: oconnell@nslsilus.org; Staff 98 (MLS 21, Non-MLS 77)
Founded 1873. Pop 110,314
Jul 1999-Jun 2000 Income $4,878,764, State $251,928, City $52,274, County $4,201,579, Locally Generated Income $372,983. Mats Exp $699,127, Books $549,500, Per/Ser (Incl. Access Fees) $31,253, Micro $30,183, Electronic Ref Mat (Incl. Access Fees) $98,191. Sal $2,275,395 (Prof $1,094,178)
Library Holdings: Bk Vols 245,951; Bk Titles 222,057; Per Subs 723; High Interest/Low Vocabulary Bk Vols 300; Bks on Deafness & Sign Lang 210
Special Collections: Genealogy Coll; Local History Coll (Elgin & Kane County); Spanish language materials for adults & children
Automation Activity & Vendor Info: (Acquisitions) epixtech, inc.; (Cataloging) epixtech, inc.; (Circulation) epixtech, inc.; (OPAC) epixtech, inc.; (Serials) epixtech, inc.
Database Vendor: GaleNet, IAC - Info Trac, IAC - SearchBank, OCLC - First Search
Publications: Newsletter (quarterly)
Mem of North Suburban Library System

CR JUDSON COLLEGE, Benjamin P Browne Library, 1151 N State St, 60123. SAN 304-1549. Tel: 847-695-2500, Ext 3000. FAX: 847-695-0407. Web Site: www.judson-il.edu/library/. *Dir*, Larry C Wild; Tel: 847-695-2500, Ext 3040, E-Mail: lwild@judson-il.edu; *Tech Servs*, Lynn Hammerlund; Tel: 847-695-2500, Ext 3030, E-Mail: lhammerlund@judson-il.edu; *Ser*, Brad Seeman; Tel: 847-695-2500, Ext 3050, E-Mail: bseeman@judson-il.edu; *Librn*, Kirsten Wenzel Butterworth; Tel: 847-695-2500, Ext 3011, E-Mail: kbutterworth@judson-il.edu; *Circ*, Carol Warner; Tel: 847-695-2500, Ext 3020, E-Mail: cwarner@judson-il.edu; *Ref*, Karen Johnson; Tel: 847-692-2500, Ext 3022, E-Mail: kjohnson@judson-il.edu; *Ref*, Brian Smith; Tel: 847-695-2500, Ext 3011, E-Mail: bsmith@judson-il.edu; Staff 6 (MLS 4, Non-MLS 2)
Founded 1963. Enrl 1,100; Highest Degree: Master
Jul 1998-Jun 1999 Income $487,168. Mats Exp $245,500, Books $154,391, Per/Ser (Incl. Access Fees) $52,600, Micro $550, AV Equip $561, Other Print Mats $500, Electronic Ref Mat (Incl. Access Fees) $9,000. Sal $241,293 (Prof $138,256)
Library Holdings: Bk Vols 100,000; Bk Titles 95,000; Per Subs 550
Subject Interests: Architecture, Music, Religion
Special Collections: Baptist History & Missons; Edmundson Contemporary Christian Music Coll; Library of American Civilization, ultrafiche, micro
Automation Activity & Vendor Info: (Cataloging) DRA; (Circulation) DRA
Database Vendor: DRA, Ebsco - EbscoHost, IAC - Info Trac, IAC - SearchBank, Lexis-Nexis, OCLC - First Search, OVID Technologies, Silverplatter Information Inc.
Publications: Browne Bugle
Mem of North Suburban Library System
Partic in CCMP; Illinois Library Computer Systems Office; Libras, Inc; OCLC Online Computer Library Center, Inc
Friends of the Library Group

M PROVENA SAINT JOSEPH HOSPITAL, Health Science Library,* 77 N Airlite St, 60123. SAN 375-9458. Tel: 847-695-3200, Ext 5385. FAX: 847-622-2059. *Librn*, Susan Anderson
Library Holdings: Bk Titles 600; Per Subs 60

ELIZABETH

P ELIZABETH TOWNSHIP LIBRARY,* 210 E Myrtle St, PO Box 243, 61028. SAN 304-1565. Tel: 815-858-2212. FAX: 815-858-3475. *Librn*, Gereldine L Hatfield
Founded 1943. Pop 1,202; Circ 9,352
Library Holdings: Bk Vols 10,000; Per Subs 35
Mem of Northern Illinois Library System
Open Mon & Wed 10-11:30 & 12:30-5, Tues & Sat 9-5, Fri 1-6

ELK GROVE VILLAGE

M ALEXIAN BROTHERS MEDICAL CENTER, Medical Library, 800 Biesterfield Rd, 60007-3397. SAN 320-3751. Tel: 847-437-5500, Ext 4756. FAX: 847-981-5922. *Librn*, Sarah Stannard; E-Mail: stannars@abeg.hbocvan.com; Staff 1 (MLS 1)
Founded 1967
Library Holdings: Bk Titles 2,634; Per Subs 165
Subject Interests: Medicine, Nursing
Publications: New Books & Audiovisuals List (quarterly)
Mem of North Suburban Library System
Partic in Fox Valley Consortium; Greater Midwest Regional Medical Libr Network; Illinois Library & Information Network; Metropolitan Consortium Of Chicago

M AMERICAN ACADEMY OF PEDIATRICS, Bakwin Library, 141 NW Point Blvd, 60007. SAN 304-1689. Tel: 847-434-7635. FAX: 847-434-4993. Web Site: www.aap.org. *Dir*, Susan Bolda Marshall; Tel: 847-434-4722, E-Mail: smarshall@aap.org; *Librn*, Chris Kwiat; E-Mail: ckwiat@aap.org; Staff 3 (MLS 2, Non-MLS 1)
Founded 1965
Library Holdings: Bk Titles 1,000; Per Subs 150
Subject Interests: Child health
Special Collections: Pediatric History Center
Automation Activity & Vendor Info: (Cataloging) EOS; (Circulation) EOS; (OPAC) EOS
Database Vendor: Dialog, Lexis-Nexis, OVID Technologies
Mem of ILL Libr & Info Network
Partic in Illinois Library & Information Network; Metropolitan Consortium Of Chicago; OCLC Online Computer Library Center, Inc

SR ARCHIVES OF THE EVANGELICAL LUTHERAN CHURCH IN AMERICA, 321 Bonnie Lane, 60007. SAN 329-9074. Tel: 847-690-9410. FAX: 847-690-9502. E-Mail: archives@elca.org. Web Site: www.elca.org/os/archives/intro.html. *Dir*, Elisabeth Wittman; E-Mail: ewittman@elca.org; Staff 7 (MLS 5, Non-MLS 2)
Founded 1988
Subject Interests: Lutheran Church, Religion
Publications: ELCA Archives Network News
Partic in Illinois Library & Information Network

P ELK GROVE VILLAGE PUBLIC LIBRARY, 1001 Wellington Ave, 60007. SAN 304-1573. Tel: 847-439-0447. FAX: 847-439-0475. Web Site: www.egvpl.org. *Dir*, Lee Maternowski; E-Mail: leem@egvpl.org; *Tech Servs*, Donna Hudson; *Circ*, Patricia Hertzberg; *Ref*, Minni Sood; *YA Servs*, Adelaide Rowe; *Ad Servs*, Lisa Malinowski; *Network Services*, Judy Kennedy; Staff 15 (MLS 8, Non-MLS 7)
Founded 1959. Pop 33,429; Circ 600,000
May 2000-Apr 2001 Income $3,093,909, State $41,240, City $2,555,208, Locally Generated Income $497,461. Mats Exp $489,700, Books $290,000, Per/Ser (Incl. Access Fees) $32,750, Micro $16,000, AV Equip $80,000, Other Print Mats $15,950, Electronic Ref Mat (Incl. Access Fees) $55,000. Sal $1,254,924 (Prof $350,000)
Library Holdings: Bk Vols 290,000; Per Subs 425; High Interest/Low Vocabulary Bk Vols 300; Spec Interest Per Sub 50; Bks on Deafness & Sign Lang 50
Subject Interests: Civil War, World War II
Automation Activity & Vendor Info: (Acquisitions) epixtech, inc.; (Cataloging) epixtech, inc.; (Circulation) epixtech, inc.; (OPAC) epixtech, inc.; (Serials) epixtech, inc.
Publications: Bookworm Express; Elk Grove-The Peony Village; Highlights
Mem of North Suburban Library System
Special Services for the Deaf - TDD
Special Services for the Blind - Homebound services
Friends of the Library Group

S SAFETY-KLEEN CORP, Technical Center Library, 12555 W Old Higgins Rd, 60007. (Mail add: PO Box 92050, 60009-2050), SAN 375-2119. Tel: 773-825-7320. FAX: 773-825-7850. *Dir*, Sharo Meyer Lazzara; E-Mail: sharon.lazzara@safety-kleen.com; *Info Res*, Pamela J Teliszczak; E-Mail: pteliszczak@safety-kleen.com; Staff 2 (Non-MLS 2)
Founded 1987. Pop 5,600
Library Holdings: Bk Vols 7,500; Per Subs 161
Function: Research library
Mem of North Suburban Library System

ELKHART

P ELKHART PUBLIC LIBRARY DISTRICT, 121 E Bonhan, PO Box 170, 62634-0170. SAN 376-1460. Tel: 217-947-2313. FAX: 217-947-2313. E-Mail: library@ccaonline.com. *Librn*, Donna Cunningham
Founded 1893. Pop 913
Jul 1999-Jun 2000 Mats Exp Books $5,200
Library Holdings: Bk Titles 10,000
Automation Activity & Vendor Info: (Cataloging) Follett; (Circulation) Follett
Mem of Rolling Prairie Library System

ELKVILLE

P RICK WARREN MEMORIAL PUBLIC LIBRARY DISTRICT, (Formerly Elkville District Library), Community Bldg, Fourth & Board St, PO Box 128, 62932. SAN 376-1681. Tel: 618-568-1843. FAX: 618-568-1843. E-Mail: rwmplibrary@hotmail.com. *Librn*, Janet Eisenhauer
Library Holdings: Bk Titles 5,160; High Interest/Low Vocabulary Bk Vols 100
Mem of Shawnee Library System
Open Mon, Wed & Fri 2-5, Tues & Thurs 9-12

ELLIS GROVE

P CENTRAL PUBLIC LIBRARY DISTRICT,* 6102 Walsh Rd, 62241-9742. SAN 370-7237. Tel: 618-774-2516. TDD: 618-774-2516. FAX: 618-774-2516. E-Mail: books@egyptian.net. *Librn*, June Runge; *Asst Librn*, Bonnie Breithaupt
Founded 1985. Pop 1,300
Library Holdings: Bk Titles 7,245
Partic in Illinois Library & Information Network
Special Services for the Deaf - TDD

ELMHURST

C ELMHURST COLLEGE, AC Buehler Library, 190 Prospect St, 60126-3271. SAN 304-159X. Tel: 630-617-3160. FAX: 630-617-3332. Web Site: www.elmhurst.edu/~/library. *Dir*, Susan Swords Steffen; E-Mail: susanss@elmhurst.edu; *Ref*, Anne Jordan-Baker; *Media Spec*, Bonnie Torres; *Tech Servs*, Elaine Page; *Bibliog Instr, Online Servs, Ref*, Donna Goodwyn; Staff 4 (MLS 4)
Founded 1871. Enrl 2,775; Fac 93; Highest Degree: Bachelor
Library Holdings: Bk Vols 221,463; Per Subs 770
Subject Interests: Nursing
Automation Activity & Vendor Info: (Cataloging) DRA; (Circulation) DRA; (OPAC) DRA; (Serials) DRA
Mem of Suburban Library System
Partic in ELVIS; Illinois Library Computer Systems Office; Libras, Inc; OCLC Online Computer Library Center, Inc

S ELMHURST HISTORICAL MUSEUM LIBRARY, 120 E Park Ave, 60126. SAN 326-0364. Tel: 630-833-1457. FAX: 630-833-1326. *Dir*, Brian F Bergheger; *Archivist*, Nancy Wilson
Founded 1974. Pop 43,000
Library Holdings: Bk Titles 577
Subject Interests: Local history, Museology

M ELMHURST MEMORIAL HOSPITAL, Marquardt Memorial Library, 200 Berteau Ave, 60126. SAN 304-1611. Tel: 630-833-1400, Ext 42712. FAX: 630-782-7834. E-Mail: png@emhc.org.; Staff 2 (MLS 1, Non-MLS 1)
1999-2000 Income $193,000
Library Holdings: Bk Titles 8,000; Per Subs 240
Subject Interests: Medicine
Publications: Acquisition List (monthly)
Restriction: Medical staff only
Mem of Surburban Libr Syst
Partic in Fox Valley Health Science Library Consortium; Illinois Health Libraries Consortium; Illinois Library & Information Network

P ELMHURST PUBLIC LIBRARY, 211 Prospect, 60126-3298. SAN 304-1603. Tel: 630-279-8696. TDD: 630-832-1252. FAX: 630-279-0636. Web Site: www.elmhurstpubliclibrary.org. *Dir*, Marilyn Boria; *Asst Librn*, Raita Vilnins; *Ch Servs*, Sharon Karpiel; *Tech Servs*, Kathleen Murphy; *Circ*, Shirley Hammond; *Ad Servs*, Sarah Caltvedt; Staff 15 (MLS 15)
Founded 1916. Pop 42,680; Circ 794,777
May 1999-Apr 2000 Income $3,316,900. Mats Exp $3,133,521, Books $514,059, Per/Ser (Incl. Access Fees) $55,681, Presv $3,527. Sal $1,650,388
Library Holdings: Bk Vols 246,069; Per Subs 1,023
Subject Interests: Art and architecture, Business and management
Automation Activity & Vendor Info: (Acquisitions) Innovative Interfaces Inc.; (Circulation) Innovative Interfaces Inc.; (ILL) Innovative Interfaces Inc.; (OPAC) Innovative Interfaces Inc.
Publications: Newsletter - Fine Print
Mem of Suburban Library System
Partic in OCLC Online Computer Library Center, Inc
Special Services for the Deaf - Books on deafness & sign language; High interest/low vocabulary books; Special interest periodicals; TTY machine
Friends of the Library Group

S LIZZADRO MUSEUM OF LAPIDARY ART LIBRARY,* 220 Cottage Hill Ave, 60126. SAN 326-9493. Tel: 630-833-1616. FAX: 630-833-1225. *Asst Dir*, Dorothy Asher
Subject Interests: Geology

S THEATRE HISTORICAL SOCIETY OF AMERICA, Archive & Research Center, York Theatre Bldg, 2nd flr, Ste 200, 152 N York Rd, 60126-2806. SAN 371-5256. Tel: 630-782-1800. FAX: 630-782-1802. Web Site: www.historictheatres.org. *Archivist*, Richard Sklenar
Library Holdings: Bk Titles 500
Special Collections: Ben Hall Coll, memorabilia & photogs; Bill Clifford Coll, drawings & sketches; Bill Peterson Coll, photogs; Blueprint Coll; Michael Miller Coll; Postcard Coll; Slide Coll; Terry Helgesen Coll, negatives; The Chicago Architectural Photographing Company Coll, negatives

ELMWOOD

P MORRISON-MARY WILEY LIBRARY DISTRICT,* 206 W Main, PO Box 467, 61529. SAN 304-162X. Tel: 309-742-2431. FAX: 309-742-8298. E-Mail: elmlib@elmnet.net. *Librn*, Karen Miles; *Asst Librn*, Lynne Cafferty; *Asst Librn*, Mary Stenwall
Pop 2,284; Circ 18,878
Library Holdings: Bk Vols 19,000; Per Subs 35
Mem of Alliance Library System

ELMWOOD PARK

P ELMWOOD PARK PUBLIC LIBRARY, 4 Conti Pkwy, 60707. SAN 304-1638. Tel: 708-453-7645. FAX: 708-453-4671. E-Mail: eps@sls.lib.il.us. Web Site: www.epeusd.w-cook.k12.il.us/eppl. *Coordr*, Mary Moss; *Ref*, Russell N Parker; *Ch Servs*, Dorothy Holland; *Tech Servs*, Marcy Campagna; *Head, Circ*, Edlyn Le Fevour; Staff 9 (MLS 4, Non-MLS 5)
Founded 1936. Pop 23,206; Circ 117,649
May 1999-Apr 2000 Income $915,490, State $54,179, City $797,111, Federal $6,853, Other $57,347. Mats Exp Books $124,176. Sal $347,615
Library Holdings: Bk Vols 91,670; Per Subs 503
Subject Interests: Italian (language), Literature, Local history, Polish (language), Spanish (language)
Automation Activity & Vendor Info: (Circulation) Innovative Interfaces Inc.
Publications: Off the Shelves (quarterly newsletter)
Mem of Suburban Library System
Friends of the Library Group

ELSAH

C PRINCIPIA COLLEGE, Marshall Brooks Library, 62028-9799. SAN 304-1646. Tel: 618-374-5235. FAX: 618-374-5107. *Dir, Ser*, Carol Stookey; E-Mail: cds@prin.edu; *Tech Servs*, David Haslam; *Govt Doc*, Lisa Roberts; Staff 7 (MLS 4, Non-MLS 3)
Founded 1898. Enrl 550; Fac 62; Highest Degree: Bachelor
Library Holdings: Bk Vols 205,000; Bk Titles 174,000; Per Subs 800
Subject Interests: Art history, Biblical studies, Christian Scientists, Rare books
Special Collections: Curriculum; US Govt Documents (Selective Depository)
Mem of Lewis & Clark Library System
Partic in IAC Expanded Acad, Inc; Illinois Library & Information Network; OCLC Online Computer Library Center, Inc; Saint Louis Regional Library Network

ERIE

P ERIE PUBLIC LIBRARY DISTRICT, Eighth St & Eighth Ave, PO Box 436, 61250-0436. SAN 304-1654. Tel: 309-659-2707. FAX: 309-659-2707. *Dir*, Laurel M Reiss; E-Mail: lreiss@libby.rbls.lib.il.us
Founded 1964. Pop 3,458
Library Holdings: Bk Vols 20,000; Per Subs 71
Mem of River Bend Library System
Friends of the Library Group

EUREKA

C EUREKA COLLEGE, Melick Library, 301 College Ave, 61530-1563. SAN 304-1662. Tel: 309-467-6380. Reference Tel: 309-467-6892. FAX: 309-467-6386. E-Mail: library@eureka.edu. Web Site: www.eureka.edu/support/library. *Dir*, Virginia McCoy; Tel: 309-467-6382, E-Mail: vmccoy@eureka.edu; *AV*, James M Perry; Tel: 309-467-6390, E-Mail: jperry@eureka.edu; *Circ*, Ann L Shoemaker; Tel: 309-467-6381, E-Mail: ashoemaker@eureka.edu; *Publ Servs*, Brent Etzel; E-Mail: betzel@

eureka.edu; *Ref*, Dana Dempsey; *Tech Servs*, Anthony R Glass; Tel: 309-467-6383, E-Mail: arglass@eureka.edu; Staff 11 (MLS 3, Non-MLS 8)
Founded 1855. Enrl 475; Fac 41; Highest Degree: Bachelor
Jul 1999-Jun 2000 Income $315,775, State $2,400, Parent Institution $313,375. Mats Exp $97,750, Books $35,850, Per/Ser (Incl. Access Fees) $38,500, Presv $2,750, Micro $11,200, AV Equip $1,100, Electronic Ref Mat (Incl. Access Fees) $8,350. Sal $226,000 (Prof $143,550)
Library Holdings: Bk Vols 74,870; Bk Titles 60,755; Per Subs 320
Special Collections: Christian Church (Disciples of Christ Coll), archives; Eureka College Archives; History of Eureka Archives
Automation Activity & Vendor Info: (Cataloging) CARL; (Circulation) CARL; (OPAC) CARL
Database Vendor: CARL, Ebsco - EbscoHost, Lexis-Nexis, OCLC - First Search
Mem of Alliance Library System
Partic in Illinois Library & Information Network; RSA

P EUREKA PUBLIC LIBRARY DISTRICT, 202 S Main St, 61530. SAN 304-1670. Tel: 309-467-2922. FAX: 309-467-3527. E-Mail: eure@mtco.com. Web Site: www.eureka.lib.il.us. *Librn*, Nancy H Scott; E-Mail: nscott@mtco.com; Staff 6 (MLS 1, Non-MLS 5)
Founded 1930. Pop 5,755; Circ 90,090
Jul 1999-Jun 2000 Income $250,729, State $1,540, City $216,282, Federal $7,375, Locally Generated Income $18,409, Other $2,300. Mats Exp $33,737, Books $20,479, Per/Ser (Incl. Access Fees) $6,737, AV Equip $3,535, Electronic Ref Mat (Incl. Access Fees) $2,986. Sal $104,143 (Prof $48,278)
Library Holdings: Bk Vols 31,590; Per Subs 251
Special Collections: Local History
Automation Activity & Vendor Info: (Circulation) CARL; (OPAC) CARL
Mem of Alliance Library System

EVANSTON

SR BETH EMET SYNAGOGUE, Bruce Gordon Memorial Library, 1224 Dempster St, 60202. SAN 325-6596. Tel: 847-869-4230. FAX: 847-869-7830. E-Mail: office@bethemet.org. Web Site: www.bethemet.org. *Librn*, Rosalind Shlaes
Library Holdings: Bk Titles 8,000; Per Subs 40
Restriction: Not open to public

S EVANSTON HISTORICAL SOCIETY LIBRARY, Charles Gates Dawes House Library, 225 Greenwood St, 60201. SAN 304-1719. Tel: 847-475-3410. FAX: 847-475-3599. Web Site: www.evanstonhistorical.org. *Curator*, Eden Pearlman; E-Mail: e-pearlman@nwu.edu; *Archivist*, Teresa Yoder
Founded 1898
Library Holdings: Bk Titles 2,500; Per Subs 10
Special Collections: Life of Charles Gates Dawes, Vice President of the United States of America 1925-29
Publications: Newsletters: "TimeLines" (quarterly)
Restriction: Non-circulating to the public

M EVANSTON NORTHWESTERN HEALTHCARE-EVANSTON HOSPITAL, Webster Library, 2650 Ridge Ave, 60201-1781. SAN 304-1727. Tel: 847-570-2665. FAX: 708-570-2926. E-Mail: webster@nslsilus.org. Web Site: www.enh.org. *Dir*, Dalia S Kleinmuntz; *Librn*, Julaine McLemore; *Automation Syst Coordr*, Linda Feinberg; Staff 6 (MLS 3, Non-MLS 3)
Founded 1906
Oct 1999-Sep 2000 Income $348,000, Locally Generated Income $22,000, Parent Institution $330,000. Mats Exp $175,000, Books $34,000, Per/Ser (Incl. Access Fees) $78,000. Sal $155,000 (Prof $114,000)
Library Holdings: Bk Titles 4,000
Subject Interests: Health sciences
Automation Activity & Vendor Info: (Cataloging) EOS; (Circulation) EOS
Database Vendor: OVID Technologies
Publications: Brochure; Newsletter (quarterly); Serial Lists
Mem of North Suburban Library System
Partic in Health Sci Librns of Ill; Metropolitan Consortium Of Chicago; Nat Libr of Med

P EVANSTON PUBLIC LIBRARY, 1703 Orrington, 60201. SAN 304-1735. Tel: 847-866-0300. Circulation Tel: 847-866-0304. Reference Tel: 847-866-0305. FAX: 847-866-0313. Web Site: www.epl.org. *Dir*, Neal J Ney; *Tech Servs*, Laura Shea-Clark; *AV*, Laura Hirshfield; *Ch Servs*, Jan Bojda; *Coll Develop*, Susan Robertson
Founded 1873. Pop 73,233; Circ 858,343
Mar 1999-Feb 2000 Income $4,310,611, State $142,774, City $2,775,060, Federal $35,000, Locally Generated Income $135,777. Mats Exp $568,831, Books $480,295, AV Equip $88,536. Sal $2,171,826
Library Holdings: Bk Vols 411,671; Per Subs 1,072
Subject Interests: Art
Special Collections: Antique Silver (Berg Coll); Music (Sadie Coe Coll)
Mem of North Suburban Library System
Partic in Dialog Corporation; OCLC Online Computer Library Center, Inc
Friends of the Library Group

S FAMILY INSTITUTE, Kramer Resource Center,* 618 Library Pl, 60201. SAN 325-6715. Tel: 847-733-4300. FAX: 847-733-0390. *Librn*, Katie Stonebraker
Library Holdings: Bk Vols 3,000; Per Subs 25
Subject Interests: Psychology
Non-profit

SR FIRST PRESBYTERIAN CHURCH, Thomas E Boswell Memorial Library, 1427 Chicago Ave, 60201. SAN 304-1743. Tel: 847-864-1472. FAX: 847-864-1494. *Dir*, Judith Akers; Staff 3 (MLS 2, Non-MLS 1)
Founded 1962
1998-1999 Income $900. Mats Exp $900, Books $700, Per/Ser (Incl. Access Fees) $200
Library Holdings: Bk Titles 4,000; Per Subs 13
Subject Interests: Church history, Fiction, Theology

S FRANCES E WILLARD MEMORIAL LIBRARY, National Woman's Christian Temperance Union,* 1730 Chicago Ave, 60201-4585. SAN 304-1786. Tel: 847-864-1397. FAX: 847-864-9497. Web Site: www.wctu.org. *Librn*, William K Beatty; *Archivist*, Virginia L Beatty; Staff 2 (MLS 2)
Founded 1940
Library Holdings: Bk Titles 5,000
Subject Interests: Alcohol and drugs, Economics, Tobacco, Women's studies
Special Collections: Frances E Willard Papers; WCTU Presidential Papers (eg, Anna Gordon, Lillian Stevens); WCTU Records

R GARRETT-EVANGELICAL & SEABURY-WESTERN THEOLOGICAL SEMINARIES, The United Library,* 21-22 Sheridan Rd, 60201. SAN 304-1751. Tel: 847-328-9300, 847-866-3911. FAX: 847-866-3957. *Dir*, Alva R Caldwell; *Dir*, Newland Smith; E-Mail: nsmith@nwu.edu; *Reader Servs*, David K Himrod; *Tech Servs*, Colleen O'Connor; *Cat*, Loren Hagen; Staff 5 (MLS 5)
1996-1997 Income $595,247. Mats Exp $166,067, Books $116,192, Per/Ser (Incl. Access Fees) $36,433, Presv $9,368, Micro $3,009. Sal $345,995 (Prof $236,481)
Library Holdings: Bk Vols 299,724; Bk Titles 225,000; Per Subs 1,869
Subject Interests: Biblical studies, Church history, Religion, Theology
Special Collections: Egyptology (Hibbard Egyptian Coll); Keen Bible Coll
Mem of North Suburban Library System
Partic in Association Of Chicago Theological Schools (ACTS); OCLC Online Computer Library Center, Inc

J KENDALL COLLEGE LIBRARY, 2408 Orrington Ave, 60201. SAN 304-1778. Tel: 847-866-1322. FAX: 847-866-1320. Web Site: www.kendall.edu. *Dir*, Iva M Freeman; E-Mail: Ifreeman@kendall.edu; *Cat*, Andrea Leftwich; Staff 3 (MLS 2, Non-MLS 1)
Founded 1934. Enrl 600; Fac 23; Highest Degree: Bachelor
Library Holdings: Bk Titles 35,000; Per Subs 210
Subject Interests: Americana
Mem of North Suburban Library System
Partic in Libras, Inc; OCLC Online Computer Library Center, Inc

S NATIONAL LEKOTEK CENTER,* 2100 Ridge Ave, 60201-2796. SAN 329-7896. Tel: 847-328-0001. FAX: 847-328-5514. E-Mail: lekotek@lekotek.org. *Exec Dir*, Beth Boosalis Davis
Special Collections: Parent Resource Information; Videos
Special Services for the Deaf - TTY machine

C NATIONAL-LOUIS UNIVERSITY LIBRARY,* 2840 Sheridan Rd, 60201-1796. SAN 340-3866. Tel: 847-475-1100. FAX: 847-465-5659. Web Site: nlu.nl.edu/ulibrary. *Dir*, Roxy Zimmerman; E-Mail: rzim@wheeling1.nl.edu; *Cat, Coordr*, David Hoogakker; *Coordr*, Sara McLaughlin; *Publ Servs*, Rose Novil; E-Mail: rnov@evan1.nl.edu; *ILL*, Mark Burnett; E-Mail: mbur@evan1.nl.edu; Staff 13 (MLS 13)
Founded 1920. Enrl 5,370; Fac 274; Highest Degree: Doctorate
Jul 1998-Jun 1999 Income $2,202,014. Mats Exp $461,715, Books $135,485, Per/Ser (Incl. Access Fees) $314,610, Presv $620, Micro $11,000. Sal $1,525,730 (Prof $436,555)
Library Holdings: Bk Vols 272,919; Bk Titles 128,121; Per Subs 1,266
Subject Interests: Business and management, Education, Psychology
Special Collections: Elizabeth Harrison Early Childhood Education Archives
Automation Activity & Vendor Info: (Cataloging) DRA
Publications: Film & Video Catalog; Library Research Manual; List of Journals
Mem of North Suburban Library System
Partic in Coop Coll Mgt Prog; Ill Libr Computer Systs Org; N Suburban Higher Educ Consortium; Regional Educ Alliance of the Fox Valley; W Suburban Post-Secondary Consortia
Friends of the Library Group
Departmental Libraries:
CHICAGO, 122 S Michigan Ave, Chicago, 60603. SAN 340-1820. Tel: 312-621-9650, Ext 3376. FAX: 312-621-1205. E-Mail: ckab@chicago1.nl.edu. *Coordr*, Carole Kabel
WHEATON, 200 S Naperville Rd, Wheaton, 60187. SAN 321-5695. Tel: 630-668-3838, Ext 4530. FAX: 630-668-5883. *Librn*, Kathleen Jordan-Baker; *Coordr*, Sherrill Weaver; Tel: 630-668-3838, Ext 4531, E-Mail:

swea@evan1.nl.edu
WHEELING, 1000 Capital Dr, Wheeling, 60090. SAN 378-0732. Tel: 847-465-0575, Ext 5503. Toll Free Tel: 800-443-5522. FAX: 847-465-5669. E-Mail: libcirc@evan1.nl.edu. Web Site: www.nl.edu/ulibrary. *Dir*, Roxy Zimmerman; Tel: 847-465-0575, Ext 5501, Fax: 847-465-5659, E-Mail: rzim@wheeling1.nl.edu; *Br Coordr*, Carol Moulden; Tel: 847-465-0575, Ext 5242, E-Mail: cmou@wheeling1.nl.edu; *Cat*, David Hoogakker; Tel: 847-465-5501, Ext 4608, E-Mail: dhoo@whe2.nl.edu; *Ch Servs*, Sara McLaughlin; Tel: 847-465-0575, Ext 2522, E-Mail: smcl@evan1.nl.edu; *Coll Develop*, Kathleen Walsh; Tel: 847-465-0575, Ext 4610, E-Mail: kwals@whe2.nl.edu; *Publ Servs*, Victoria West-Pawl; Tel: 847-465-0575, Ext 2852, E-Mail: vwes@evan1.nl.edu; Staff 63 (MLS 22, Non-MLS 41)
Founded 1920. Enrl 5,216; Highest Degree: Doctorate
Jul 1999-Jun 2000 Income Parent Institution $2,267,906. Mats Exp $490,731, Books $116,648, Per/Ser (Incl. Access Fees) $207,067, Micro $10,107, AV Equip $39,665, Electronic Ref Mat (Incl. Access Fees) $117,244. Sal $1,366,036 (Prof $585,947)
Library Holdings: Bk Vols 278,341; Bk Titles 131,287; Per Subs 1,083
Subject Interests: Business and management, Education, Psychology
Special Collections: Elizabeth Harrison Early Childhood Education Archives
Automation Activity & Vendor Info: (Cataloging) DRA; (Circulation) DRA; (OPAC) DRA
Database Vendor: Ebsco - EbscoHost, IAC - SearchBank, OCLC - First Search, OVID Technologies, ProQuest
Function: ILL available
Mem of North Suburban Library System
Partic in ILCSO

C NORTHWESTERN UNIVERSITY LIBRARY, 1935 Sheridan Rd, 60208-2300. SAN 340-3920. Tel: 847-491-7658. Interlibrary Loan Service Tel: 847-491-7630. Circulation Tel: 847-491-7633. Reference Tel: 847-491-7656. TDD: 847-467-5188. FAX: 847-491-8306. Interlibrary Loan Service FAX: 847-491-5685. E-Mail: refdept@northwestern.edu. Web Site: www.library.northwestern.edu. *Librn*, David F Bishop; *Publ Servs*, Laurel Minott; *Coll Develop*, Diane Perushek; *Tech Servs*, Roxanne Sellberg; *Info Tech*, Harry Samuels; *Archivist*, Patrick Quinn; *Curator*, David Easterbrook. Subject Specialists: *Africana*, David Easterbrook; *Art*, Russell Clement; Staff 85 (MLS 66, Non-MLS 19)
Founded 1851. Enrl 13,547; Fac 2,143; Highest Degree: Doctorate
Sep 1998-Aug 1999 Income (Main Library and Branch Library) $20,271,953. Mats Exp $8,075,665. Sal $9,652,811 (Prof $5,363,751)
Library Holdings: Bk Vols 4,014,312; Per Subs 40,008
Special Collections: Africana; Architecture (Frank Lloyd Wright); Contemporary Music Scores; Descriptions can be obtained from special collections librarian; Dublin Gate Theatre; European Union, Orgn of Am States, World Trade Orgn; Manuscripts; Modern Movements In Art & Literature (German Expressionism, Italian Futurism, Dadaism, Surrealism, Concrete Poetry); Printing (Graphic Arts, Private Presses); Rare Books (Aldines, Deism, Elzeviers, Fichte, German Classics, Grundtvig, Ibsen, Kant, Kierkegaard, Little Magazines, Twain, Whitman); Women's Liberation Movement, 1960 to date
Automation Activity & Vendor Info: (Acquisitions) Endeavor; (Cataloging) Endeavor; (Circulation) Endeavor; (Course Reserve) Endeavor; (Media Booking) Endeavor; (OPAC) Endeavor; (Serials) Endeavor
Publications: Footnotes; Joint Acquisitions List of Africana (JALA); The Lantern's Core
Mem of North Suburban Library System
Partic in Asn of Research Libraries; Center For Research Libraries; Comt for Institutional Coop; Illinois Library & Information Network; OCLC Online Computer Library Center, Inc
Special Services for the Deaf - Captioned media; TDD
Current Northwestern identification must be presented after 5pm Mon-Fri, after noon on Sat & all day Sun for admittance.
Departmental Libraries:
GEOLOGY, Locy Hall, Rm 101, 1847 Sheridan Rd, 60208. SAN 340-398X. Tel: 847-491-5525. Web Site: www.library.northwestern.edu/geology/. *Librn*, Anna Ren
Library Holdings: Bk Vols 26,400
Subject Interests: Geochemistry, Geophysics, Oceanography
MATHEMATICS, Lunt Bldg, Rm 111, 2033 Sheridan Rd, 60208. SAN 340-4013. Tel: 847-491-7627. Web Site: www.library.northwestern.edu/math/. *In Charge*, Bob Ren
Library Holdings: Bk Vols 34,600
Subject Interests: Mathematics, Statistics
MUSIC Tel: 847-491-3434. FAX: 847-467-7574. E-Mail: musiclib@northwestern.edu. Web Site: www.library.northwestern.edu/music. *Librn*, Don L Roberts
Founded 1945
Library Holdings: Bk Vols 33,300
Special Collections: Ben Johnston Coll; Early Editions & Rare Publications of Treatises, Libretti & Scores; Foundation for Contemporary Performing Arts Coll, mss; Fritz Reiner Library; John Cage Archive; Moldenhauer Archives (partial coll); Scores & Correspondence from the Ricordi Publishing House
Publications: Quarter Notes
SEELEY G MUDD LIBRARY FOR SCIENCE & ENGINEERING, 2233 N Campus Dr, 60208. SAN 340-4072. Tel: 847-491-3362. FAX: 847-491-4655. Web Site: www.library.northwestern.edu/sel. *Librn*, Robert Michaelson
Library Holdings: Bk Vols 275,000
Subject Interests: Applied math, Astronomy, Chemistry, Computer science, Engineering, Life sci, Physics
TRANSPORTATION Tel: 847-491-5273. FAX: 847-491-8601. E-Mail: trans@northwestern.edu. Web Site: www.library.northwestern.edu/transportation. *Librn*, Roberto A Sarmiento
Library Holdings: Bk Vols 232,892
Subject Interests: Environ impact, Law enforcement, Transportation
Publications: Current Literature in Traffic & Transportation

S ROTARY INTERNATIONAL, Slide Library,* 1560 Sherman Ave, 60201. SAN 375-9768. Tel: 847-866-3230. FAX: 847-866-8215. *AV*, Janet Zupko

SAINT FRANCIS HOSPITAL
M MEMORIAL MEDICAL LIBRARY, 355 Ridge Ave, 60202. SAN 340-4137. Tel: 847-316-2456, 847-316-2460. FAX: 847-316-5816. *Librn*, Helene Gottesmann; *Asst Librn*, Pat Pearson
Founded 1919
Library Holdings: Bk Vols 3,000; Per Subs 300
Publications: Newsletter
Mem of North Suburban Library System
Partic in Illinois Library & Information Network; Metropolitan Consortium Of Chicago

S THE SHAKESPEARE DATA BANK, INC LIBRARY, 1217 Ashland Av, 60202-1103. SAN 329-5168. Tel: 847-475-7550. E-Mail: avon4@juno.com. *Pres*, Louis Marder
Founded 1981
Library Holdings: Bk Vols 9,000; Bk Titles 10,000
Subject Interests: Drama, Shakespeare, Theatre
Special Collections: Shakespeare Coll
Restriction: Open to researchers by request

S SIGMA ALPHA EPSILON FRATERNITY, Levere Memorial Foundation Library, 1856 Sheridan Rd, 60201-3837. (Mail add: PO Box 1856, 60204-1856), SAN 304-1808. Tel: 847-475-1856. FAX: 847-475-2250. Web Site: www.saefraternity.net. *Exec Dir*, Thomas Goodale
Founded 1930
Library Holdings: Bk Titles 2,000; Per Subs 75
Special Collections: Books By & About Members of Sigma Alpha Epsilon; Histories & Journals of Fraternities & Sororities

EVANSVILLE

P EVANSVILLE PUBLIC LIBRARY,* 602 Public, PO Box 299, 62242. SAN 304-1824. Tel: 618-853-2613, 618-853-4067. FAX: 618-853-2342. *Librn*, Roberta Huff
Founded 1965. Pop 844; Circ 2,051
Library Holdings: Bk Vols 6,165; Per Subs 12
Subject Interests: History, Religion
Mem of Shawnee Library System
Open Tues 4-7, Thurs 8-4 & Sat 10-1

EVERGREEN PARK

P EVERGREEN PARK PUBLIC LIBRARY,* 9400 S Troy Ave, 60642-2383. SAN 304-1832. Tel: 708-422-8522. FAX: 708-422-8665. *Dir*, Nicolette Seidl; *Librn*, Margaret Smith; *Ch Servs*, Lori Lurquin; *Tech Servs*, Connie Evans; *Ad Servs, Ref*, Christine Raap; Staff 13 (MLS 5, Non-MLS 8)
Founded 1944. Pop 20,860; Circ 125,000
Library Holdings: Bk Vols 62,000
Mem of Suburban Library System

M LITTLE COMPANY OF MARY HOSPITAL, Medical Library,* 2800 W 95th St, 60805. SAN 304-1840. Tel: 708-229-5299. *Librn*, Therese Montgomery
Library Holdings: Bk Vols 3,000; Per Subs 100

FAIRBURY

P DOMINY MEMORIAL LIBRARY, 201 S Third St, 61739. SAN 304-1859. Tel: 815-692-3231. FAX: 815-692-3503. E-Mail: dominy@dave-world.net. Web Site: www.fairbury.lib.il.us. *Head of Libr*, Margie Hedrick; *Assoc Librn*, Marlene Walter; *Ch Servs*, Nancy Ifft; *Circ Media*, Linda Michou
Founded 1904. Pop 3,643; Circ 34,266
Apr 1998-Mar 1999 Income $111,091, State $5,012, City $64,528, Other $41,551. Mats Exp $68,318, Books $8,756, Per/Ser (Incl. Access Fees) $1,261. Sal $42,758
Library Holdings: Bk Vols 19,327; Per Subs 15; High Interest/Low Vocabulary Bk Vols 20
Automation Activity & Vendor Info: (Circulation) Follett

Database Vendor: CARL, Ebsco - EbscoHost, OCLC - First Search, ProQuest, Wilson - Wilson Web
Mem of Alliance Library System
Friends of the Library Group

FAIRFIELD

P FAIRFIELD PUBLIC LIBRARY, 300 SE Second St, 62837. SAN 304-1867. Tel: 618-842-4516. FAX: 618-842-6708. Web Site: www.sirin.lib.il.us. *Librn*, Barbara DeWitt; E-Mail: bdewitt@shaw.net.shawlib.il.us; Staff 2 (Non-MLS 2)
Founded 1923. Pop 5,442; Circ 57,496
May 1999-Apr 2000 Income $657,964, State $122,690, City $91,112, Federal $4,500, Other $239,662. Mats Exp $7,290, Books $5,496, Per/Ser (Incl. Access Fees) $992, Micro $189, AV Equip $38, Other Print Mats $27, Electronic Ref Mat (Incl. Access Fees) $548. Sal $48,023 (Prof $22,881)
Library Holdings: Bk Vols 32,197; Per Subs 64
Database Vendor: epixtech, inc.
Mem of Shawnee Library System
Friends of the Library Group

J FRONTIER COMMUNITY COLLEGE, Learning Resource Center, 2 Frontier Dr, 62837-9705. SAN 325-1810. Tel: 618-842-3711. Toll Free Tel: 877-464-3687. FAX: 618-842-4425. Web Site: www.iecc.cc.il.us. *Librn*, Ted Davis; E-Mail: davist@iecc.cc.il.us; Staff 1 (MLS 1)
Founded 1976. Enrl 700; Fac 425; Highest Degree: Associate
Jul 2000-Jun 2001 Income State $102,000. Mats Exp $18,500, Books $10,000, Per/Ser (Incl. Access Fees) $5,000, AV Equip $1,500, Electronic Ref Mat (Incl. Access Fees) $2,000. Sal $52,400 (Prof $37,000)
Library Holdings: Bk Titles 13,000; Per Subs 125; High Interest/Low Vocabulary Bk Vols 1,300
Subject Interests: Nursing
Automation Activity & Vendor Info: (Cataloging) epixtech, inc.; (Circulation) epixtech, inc.; (OPAC) epixtech, inc.
Mem of Shawnee Library System

FAIRMOUNT

P VANCE TOWNSHIP LIBRARY,* 107 S Main St, PO Box 230, 61841. SAN 304-1875. Tel: 217-733-2164. FAX: 217-733-2164. *In Charge*, Barbara B Biggerstaff; Staff 2 (Non-MLS 2)
Founded 1941. Pop 1,088
Apr 1997-Mar 1998 Income $16,403, State $1,360, Locally Generated Income $14,100, Other $943. Mats Exp $19,923, Books $4,338, Per/Ser (Incl. Access Fees) $300. Sal $9,298
Library Holdings: Bk Vols 9,289; Per Subs 30
Special Collections: History of Fairmount Coll; Jamaica Area; Senior Citizen Info; State of Illinois
Mem of Lincoln Trail Libraries System
Special Services for the Blind - Talking book & recordings for the blind catalogs

FAIRVIEW

P VALLEY PUBLIC LIBRARY DISTRICT,* 515 Carter St, PO Box 200, 61432-0248. SAN 376-1215. Tel: 309-778-2240. FAX: 309-778-2240. E-Mail: valley1@netins.net. *Librn*, Carol Baxter
Library Holdings: Bk Titles 4,000; Per Subs 26

FAIRVIEW HEIGHTS

P FAIRVIEW HEIGHTS PUBLIC LIBRARY, 10017 Bunkum Rd, 62208-1703. SAN 321-8961. Tel: 618-489-2070. FAX: 618-489-2079. E-Mail: fha@lcls.org. *Librn*, Deborah Owen; Tel: 618-489-2071, E-Mail: debbieo@lcls.org; Staff 10 (MLS 1, Non-MLS 9)
Founded 1972. Pop 15,745
May 2000-Apr 2001 Income $378,780, State $29,424, City $325,356, Locally Generated Income $24,000. Mats Exp $66,050, Books $61,500, Per/Ser (Incl. Access Fees) $4,550. Sal $183,105 (Prof $52,924)
Library Holdings: Bk Vols 50,000; Per Subs 156
Subject Interests: Cookbooks, How-to videos
Automation Activity & Vendor Info: (Cataloging) DRA; (Circulation) DRA; (ILL) DRA; (OPAC) DRA; (Serials) DRA
Database Vendor: DRA
Mem of Lewis & Clark Library System
Partic in Illinois Library & Information Network
Friends of the Library Group

FARMER CITY

P FARMER CITY PUBLIC LIBRARY,* 105 E Green St, PO Box 201, 61842. SAN 304-1883. Tel: 309-928-9532. FAX: 309-928-2540. E-Mail: scpl@darkstar.rsa.lib.il.us. *Librn*, Catherine Hoffman
Pop 2,252; Circ 14,504
Library Holdings: Bk Vols 15,000; Per Subs 28
Subject Interests: Local history
Mem of Alliance Library System
Open Mon & Wed 1-8, Fri & Sat 9-1

FARMERSVILLE

P FARMERSVILLE-WAGGONER PUBLIC LIBRARY DISTRICT,* 210 S Cleveland St, PO Box 12, 62533. SAN 376-1444. Tel: 217-227-3711. *Librn*, Barbara Gentry
Library Holdings: Bk Titles 12,500; Per Subs 10
Mem of Lewis & Clark Library System

FARMINGTON

P FARMINGTON PUBLIC LIBRARY DISTRICT, 266 E Fort St, 61531-1276. SAN 304-1891. Tel: 309-245-2175. FAX: 309-245-2175. E-Mail: farm@darkstar.rsa.lib.il.us. Web Site: www.rsa.lib.il.us/~farm. *Dir*, Barbara Love; Staff 8 (Non-MLS 8)
Founded 1901. Pop 7,839; Circ 17,000
Library Holdings: Bk Titles 25,000; Per Subs 89
Database Vendor: CARL
Mem of Alliance Library System

M FRANKLIN MEMORIAL HOSPITAL, Turner Memorial Library, 111 Franklin Health Commons, 04938. SAN 325-7525. Tel: 207-779-2554. FAX: 207-779-2548. *Librn*, Emily Scribner; E-Mail: escribner@fchn.org; Staff 2 (MLS 1, Non-MLS 1)
Library Holdings: Bk Vols 700; Per Subs 75
Subject Interests: Child care, Health care, Medicine, Nursing
Partic in Health Science Library Information Consortium; Medline; North Atlantic Health Sciences Libraries, Inc
Open Mon-Fri 9:30-4

FLORA

P FLORA PUBLIC LIBRARY,* 216 N Main, 62839-1510. SAN 304-1905. Tel: 618-662-6553. FAX: 618-662-5007. Web Site: www.sirin.lib.il.us/docs/flo/docs/lib/index.html. *Dir*, Donna Corry; E-Mail: donna7@www.wworld.com
Pop 5,093; Circ 48,793
1997-1998 Income $133,059, State $6,816, City $96,402, Federal $4,860, Other $24,981. Mats Exp $21,089, Books $16,488, Per/Ser (Incl. Access Fees) $2,202, Micro $50. Sal $48,400
Library Holdings: Bk Vols 31,717; Per Subs 97
Mem of Shawnee Library System
Friends of the Library Group

FLOSSMOOR

P FLOSSMOOR PUBLIC LIBRARY, 1000 Sterling Ave, 60422-1295. SAN 304-1913. Tel: 708-798-4006. FAX: 708-798-3585. E-Mail: flossref@sslic.net. *Dir*, Dee Canfield; E-Mail: canfield@sslic.net; *Ad Servs*, Karen Bala; E-Mail: balak@sslic.net; *Ch Servs*, Margie Wegrzyn; E-Mail: wegrzynm@sslic.net; *Head Tech Servs*, Deborah Majka; E-Mail: majkad@sslic.net
Founded 1953. Pop 8,651; Circ 125,023
May 1999-Apr 2000 Income $636,048, State $20,200, Federal $9,208, County $558,845, Locally Generated Income $37,323. Mats Exp $96,378, Books $69,541, Micro $739, AV Equip $8,893, Electronic Ref Mat (Incl. Access Fees) $6,023. Sal $379,730 (Prof $153,625)
Library Holdings: Bk Vols 50,685; Per Subs 211
Special Collections: Helen Tenenbaum Women's Studies
Automation Activity & Vendor Info: (Circulation) Innovative Interfaces Inc.
Database Vendor: Ebsco - EbscoHost, Innovative Interfaces INN - View
Mem of Suburban Library System
Partic in Illinois Library & Information Network
Friends of the Library Group

FOREST PARK

P FOREST PARK PUBLIC LIBRARY, 7555 Jackson Blvd, 60130. SAN 304-1921. Tel: 708-366-7171. FAX: 708-366-7293. Web Site: www.sls.lib/il/us/FPS. *Dir*, Krista Kloepper; Tel: 708-366-7171, Ext 306, E-Mail: kloeppek@sls.lib.il.us; *Ch Servs*, Elizabeth Drennan; *Ad Servs*, Cynthia Maroon; *Tech Servs*, Deb Harris; *Circ*, Sandy Heitzman; Staff 32 (MLS 5, Non-MLS 27)
Founded 1906. Pop 14,918; Circ 112,798
May 2000-Apr 2001 Mats Exp $108,400, Books $72,000, Per/Ser (Incl. Access Fees) $10,500, AV Equip $15,000, Other Print Mats $8,900, Manuscripts & Archives $2,000, Electronic Ref Mat (Incl. Access Fees) $9,100. Sal $408,000
Library Holdings: Bk Vols 82,000; Per Subs 210
Automation Activity & Vendor Info: (Circulation) Innovative Interfaces Inc.; (OPAC) Innovative Interfaces Inc.

Database Vendor: IAC - Info Trac, Innovative Interfaces INN - View, OCLC - First Search, OVID Technologies, ProQuest
Mem of Suburban Library System
Partic in Suburban Libr Syst
Friends of the Library Group

FORREST

P FORREST PUBLIC LIBRARY DISTRICT,* 301 W James, 61741. SAN 304-193X. Tel: 815-657-8805. FAX: 815-657-8837. E-Mail: forrest@davesworld.net. Web Site: www.forrest.lib.il.us. *Dir*, Carol Nelson
Founded 1939. Pop 2,131; Circ 20,158
Library Holdings: Bk Vols 15,000; Per Subs 52
Subject Interests: Agriculture, Australia
Special Collections: Louis L'Amour Westerns, large print bks
Publications: Monthly Calendar
Mem of Alliance Library System

FORRESTON

P FORRESTON PUBLIC LIBRARY,* 204 First Ave, PO Box 606, 61030. SAN 304-1948. Tel: 815-938-2624. FAX: 815-938-2624. E-Mail: forrestonlib@mucl.net. *In Charge*, Cindy Bahr
Pop 1,364; Circ 10,000
Library Holdings: Bk Vols 8,000; Per Subs 24
Mem of Northern Illinois Library System

FORSYTH

P FORSYTH PUBLIC LIBRARY,* 268 S Elwood, PO Box 20, 62535-0020. SAN 324-6124. Tel: 217-877-8174. FAX: 217-877-3533. *Dir*, Andrea L Johnson; E-Mail: andrea@alpha1.rpls.lib.il.us; *Librn*, Jeannie L Alexander; Staff 5 (MLS 1, Non-MLS 4)
Founded 1981
May 1998-Apr 1999 Income $230,550. Mats Exp $52,000, Books $30,000, Per/Ser (Incl. Access Fees) $8,000, Other Print Mats $7,000. Sal $63,000 (Prof $25,000)
Library Holdings: Bk Vols 21,171; Per Subs 71
Mem of Rolling Prairie Library System

FOX LAKE

P FOX LAKE DISTRICT LIBRARY,* 255 E Grand Ave, 60020-1697. SAN 304-1956. Tel: 847-587-0198. FAX: 847-587-9493. Web Site: www.fllib.org. *Dir*, Harry J Bork; *Asst Librn*, Cynthia Lobaza; *YA Servs*, Therese Johnson; *Tech Servs*, Violet Lojdl; Staff 1 (MLS 1)
Founded 1939
Library Holdings: Bk Titles 64,137; Per Subs 179
Publications: Footnotes; Newsletter (bi-monthly)
Mem of North Suburban Library System
Friends of the Library Group

FOX RIVER GROVE

P FOX RIVER GROVE PUBLIC LIBRARY DISTRICT,* 306 Lincoln Ave, 60021-1093. SAN 304-1964. Tel: 847-639-2274. FAX: 847-639-0300. *Librn*, Merle D Gunderman; E-Mail: mdgunder@juno.com; Staff 9 (MLS 2, Non-MLS 7)
Founded 1954. Pop 4,082; Circ 37,477
Library Holdings: Bk Vols 18,214; Per Subs 117
Automation Activity & Vendor Info: (Circulation) Brodart; (OPAC) Brodart
Publications: Newsletter (quarterly)
Mem of North Suburban Library System
Friends of the Library Group

FRANKFORT

P FRANKFORT PUBLIC LIBRARY DISTRICT,* 21119 S Pfeiffer Rd, 60423-9302. SAN 304-1972. Tel: 815-469-2423. FAX: 815-469-9307. E-Mail: frs@sls.lib.il.us. *Dir*, Detlev Pansch; Staff 5 (MLS 5)
Founded 1966. Pop 19,000; Circ 195,397
Library Holdings: Bk Titles 87,000; Per Subs 218
Publications: Quarterly newsletter
Mem of Suburban Library System
Open Mon-Thurs 10-9, Fri & Sat 9-5; Sept-May Sun 1-5
Friends of the Library Group

FRANKLIN GROVE

P FRANKLIN GROVE PUBLIC LIBRARY,* N 223 Elm St, PO Box 326, 61031. SAN 304-1980. Tel: 815-456-2823. FAX: 815-456-2619. E-Mail: fgrvlib@essex1.com. Web Site: www.fvonline.net/~fgrulib/. *Librn*, Ellie Brauhn
Founded 1916. Pop 968; Circ 5,175
Library Holdings: Bk Titles 11,500; Per Subs 30
Mem of Northern Illinois Library System
Open Mon & Wed 1-8, Tues & Fri 1-5, Sat 9-2

FRANKLIN PARK

P FRANKLIN PARK PUBLIC LIBRARY DISTRICT,* 10311 Grand Ave, 60131. SAN 304-1999. Tel: 847-455-6016. FAX: 847-455-6299. *Exec Dir*, Robert E Watson; E-Mail: bwatson@linc.lib.il.us; *Dep Dir*, George Barr; *Tech Servs*, Jean Erickson; *Ref*, Lawrence Boyle; *Ch Servs*, Roberta Morrison. Subject Specialists: *Local history*, Mark Johnson; Staff 6 (MLS 6)
Founded 1962
Jul 1997-Jun 1998 Income $1,341,520, State $23,106. Mats Exp $130,500, Books $110,000, Per/Ser (Incl. Access Fees) $15,000, Micro $5,500. Sal $594,000
Library Holdings: Bk Vols 160,500; Per Subs 382
Subject Interests: Business and management, Local history, Science/technology, Technology
Automation Activity & Vendor Info: (Serials) DRA
Publications: Newsletter (monthly)
Mem of DuPage Library System
Partic in Libr Integrated Network Consortium

FREEPORT

M FREEPORT HEALTH NETWORK, (Formerly Freeport Memorial Hospital), Health Science Library, 1045 W Stephenson St, 61032. SAN 371-6333. Tel: 815-599-6132. Toll Free Tel: 800-747-4131. FAX: 815-599-6858. *Librn*, Mary Pat Gordon; E-Mail: mgordon@fhn.org; Staff 2 (MLS 1, Non-MLS 1)
Library Holdings: Bk Titles 750; Per Subs 70
Database Vendor: OCLC - First Search
Mem of Northern Illinois Library System
Partic in ILLINET; Upstate Consortium

P FREEPORT PUBLIC LIBRARY, 314 W Stephenson St, 61032. SAN 304-2022. Tel: 815-233-3000. FAX: 815-233-1099. E-Mail: librarian@freeportpub.lib.il.us. Web Site: www.freeportpub.lib.il.us. *Dir*, Frank Novak; *ILL*, Chad Daws; *Tech Servs*, Margaret Morgan; *Ad Servs*, Christena Barratt; *Ch Servs*, Barbara Sowers; Staff 32 (MLS 3, Non-MLS 29)
Founded 1874. Pop 25,840; Circ 310,324
May 1998-Apr 1999 Income $937,945, State $66,197, City $770,471, Other $101,277. Mats Exp $115,027, Books $103,848, Per/Ser (Incl. Access Fees) $11,077, Presv $102. Sal $445,586 (Prof $146,965)
Library Holdings: Bk Vols 119,688; Per Subs 396
Special Collections: Freeport & Stephenson County History, bks & pamphlet files; Local Newspapers, microfilm; Louis Sullivan Coll, pamphlet file
Mem of Northern Illinois Library System

J HIGHLAND COMMUNITY COLLEGE LIBRARY, 2998 W Pearl City Rd, 61032-9341. SAN 304-2030. Tel: 815-235-6121, Ext 3539. Interlibrary Loan Service Tel: 815-235-6121, Ext 3608. Reference Tel: 815-235-6121, Ext 3613. FAX: 815-235-1366. Web Site: www.highland.userworld.com. *Instrul Serv*, Eric C Welch; E-Mail: ewelch@admin.highland.cc.il.us
Founded 1962
Library Holdings: Bk Vols 45,000; Per Subs 250
Special Collections: Local authors
Publications: Welch's Rarebits (newsletter)
Mem of Northern Illinois Library System
Partic in BRS; Dialog Corporation; Northern Ill Learning Resources Coop; Wilsonline

S HONEYWELL SENSING & CONTROL, (BTIC), Business & Technical Information Center, 11 W Spring St, 61032. SAN 304-2049. Tel: 815-235-5609. FAX: 815-235-5580. E-Mail: mary.schneider@honeywell.com.; Staff 2 (MLS 2)
Founded 1960
Library Holdings: Bk Vols 2,600; Per Subs 300
Subject Interests: Business and management, Chemistry, Electrical engineering, Engineering
Mem of Northern Illinois Library System
Partic in Dialog Corporation; Illinois Library & Information Network

FULTON

P SCHMALING MEMORIAL PUBLIC LIBRARY DISTRICT, Fulton Public Library, 501 Tenth Ave, PO Box 125, 61252. SAN 304-2057. Tel: 815-589-2045. FAX: 815-589-2045. E-Mail: fulpublib@home.com. *Dir*, Debra Duhr; Staff 4 (MLS 1, Non-MLS 3)
Founded 1909. Pop 3,768; Circ 32,445
Library Holdings: Bk Vols 15,000; Per Subs 70
Special Collections: Dutch Costumes & Books in Dutch Language
Mem of River Bend Library System
Partic in Docline

GALENA

P GALENA PUBLIC LIBRARY DISTRICT, 601 S Bench St, 61036-2320. SAN 304-2065. Tel: 815-777-0200. FAX: 815-777-0219. *Dir*, Maren Coates; E-Mail: coatesm@galenalink.com; Staff 1 (Non-MLS 1)
Founded 1894. Pop 4,425; Circ 27,264
Jul 1999-Jun 2000 Income $213,601, State $11,286, Federal $3,750, Locally Generated Income $154,801, Other $43,764. Mats Exp Books $21,401. Sal $82,477
Library Holdings: Bk Vols 21,777; Per Subs 117
Special Collections: Historical Coll, bks, rec, micro
Publications: The Galena Library Letter (newsletter)
Mem of Northern Illinois Library System
Open Mon & Wed 1-8:30, Tues & Fri 1-6, Thurs 9-6, Sat 10-5
Friends of the Library Group

S ILLINOIS HISTORIC PRESERVATION AGENCY, Division of Historic Sites-US Grant's Home State Historic Site Library, 307 Decatur St, PO Box 333, 61036. SAN 325-6839. Tel: 815-777-0248, 815-777-3310. FAX: 815-777-3310. *Mgr*, Terry J Miller
Library Holdings: Bk Titles 1,500
Special Collections: E B Washburne Coll; Regional History, decorative arts, architecture, historic sites, local newspapers 1828-1930, historic photographs, 19th century artifacts; U S Grant Coll

GALESBURG

J CARL SANDBURG COLLEGE, Learning Resources Center, 2232 S Lake Storey Rd, 61401. SAN 340-4285. Tel: 309-341-5290. FAX: 309-344-3526. E-Mail: sand@darkstar.rsa.lib.il.us. Web Site: www.csc.cc.il.us. *Dean of Libr*, Michael Eugene Walters; E-Mail: mwalters@csc.cc.il.us; *ILL*, Lou Coatney; Tel: 309-341-5206, E-Mail: lcoatey@csc.cc.il.us; *Media Spec*, Fritz Archer; *Tech Servs*, Joyce Nelson; *Bibliog Instr, Coll Develop*, Sandy Wallace; Tel: 309-341-5207, E-Mail: swallace@csc.cc.il.us; Staff 5 (MLS 2, Non-MLS 3)
Founded 1967. Enrl 4,014; Fac 54; Highest Degree: Associate
Jul 2000-Jun 2001 Income (Main Library and Branch Library) $366,510. Mats Exp $152,370, Books $33,080, Per/Ser (Incl. Access Fees) $32,000, Presv $100, Micro $28,000, AV Equip $7,570. Sal $214,140 (Prof $96,440)
Library Holdings: Bk Vols 46,599; Bk Titles 37,617; Per Subs 417
Subject Interests: Vocational education
Special Collections: Bill Campbell Cartoon Art Coll, original graphic art; Carl Sandburg & Institutional Archives
Automation Activity & Vendor Info: (Circulation) CARL
Publications: Serendipity Bibliography Series
Function: Research library
Mem of Alliance Library System
Partic in ALS Interlibr Servs; Illinois Library & Information Network; OCLC Online Computer Library Center, Inc
Departmental Libraries:
ATTENDANCE CENTER, Carthage, 62321. SAN 340-4293. Tel: 217-357-3129. FAX: 217-357-3512. *In Charge*, Dana Dunham

P GALESBURG PUBLIC LIBRARY, 40 E Simmons St, 61401-4591. SAN 340-4315. Tel: 309-343-6118. FAX: 309-343-4877. E-Mail: gplibrary@misslink.net. Web Site: www.gplibrary.net. *Dir*, Pamela Van Kirk; E-Mail: pam@galesburg.lib.il.us; *YA Servs*, Jan La Roche; E-Mail: jan@galesburg.lib.il.us; *Ch Servs*, Karen Marple; E-Mail: karen@galesburg.lib.il.us; *Spec Coll*, Patty Mosher; E-Mail: patty@galesburg.lib.il.us; *Govt Doc*, Robert Conklin; E-Mail: bob@galesburg.lib.il.us; *Circ*, Sue Steller; E-Mail: sue@galesburg.lib.il.us; *Tech Servs*, Nancy Terpening; E-Mail: nancy@galesburg.lib.il.us; Staff 4 (MLS 4)
Founded 1874. Pop 35,305; Circ 317,792
Apr 1998-Mar 1999 Income $1,150,453, State $75,000, City $1,025,753, Locally Generated Income $49,700. Mats Exp $194,200, Books $157,500, Per/Ser (Incl. Access Fees) $16,000, Presv $8,000, Micro $7,700, AV Equip $3,000, Electronic Ref Mat (Incl. Access Fees) $2,000. Sal $627,454
Library Holdings: Bk Vols 209,743; Bk Titles 207,946; Per Subs 350
Subject Interests: Humanities, Local history
Database Vendor: CARL, IAC - Info Trac
Function: Archival collection, ILL available, Photocopies available, Reference services available, Some telephone reference
Mem of Alliance Library System
Partic in Resource Sharing Alliance
Friends of the Library Group

S HILL CORRECTIONAL CENTER LIBRARY,* 600 Linwood Rd, PO Box 1327, 61401. SAN 371-6449. Tel: 309-343-4212, Ext 360. FAX: 309-343-4212, Ext 123. *Librn*, Camilla A Willmart; *Asst Librn, Tech Servs*, Lenard E Palmer; Staff 2 (MLS 1, Non-MLS 1)
Founded 1986
Jul 1997-Jun 1998 Income $30,000
Library Holdings: Bk Titles 12,000; Per Subs 10
Special Collections: Law Library Coll (7000 vol)
Mem of Alliance Library System

C KNOX COLLEGE, Henry W Seymour Library, 2 S Cedar St, 61401-4425. (Mail add: PO Box 500X, 61402-0500), SAN 340-4404. Tel: 309-341-7248. Interlibrary Loan Service Tel: 309-341-7244. Circulation Tel: 309-341-7246. Reference Tel: 309-341-7228. FAX: 309-341-7799. Web Site: www.library.knox.edu. *Dir*, Jeffrey A Douglas; Tel: 309-341-7491, E-Mail: jdouglas@knox.edu; *Archivist*, Carley Robison; Tel: 309-341-7392, E-Mail: crobison@knox.edu; *Assoc Librn*, Sharon Clayton; Tel: 309-341-7249, E-Mail: sclayton@knox.edu; *Info Tech*, Laurie Sauer; Tel: 309-341-7788, E-Mail: lsauer@knox.edu; *Publ Servs*, Anne Giffey; Tel: 309-341-7483, E-Mail: agiffey@knox.edu
Founded 1837. Fac 95; Highest Degree: Bachelor
Jul 1999-Jun 2000 Income $1,073,280. Mats Exp $328,416, Books $70,187, Per/Ser (Incl. Access Fees) $206,211, Presv $10,415, Micro $8,321, AV Equip $5,684, Electronic Ref Mat (Incl. Access Fees) $27,598. Sal $367,109
Library Holdings: Bk Vols 29,394; Bk Titles 196,000; Per Subs 668
Special Collections: American Civil War (Smith Coll), bks, mss, maps & photos; Ernest Hemingway & the Lost Generation (Hughes Coll), bks, mss, (non-print & per; Old Northwest Territory (Finley Coll), bks & maps; Upper Mississippi River Valley (Player Coll), bks, maps & prints
Automation Activity & Vendor Info: (Acquisitions) epixtech, inc.; (Cataloging) epixtech, inc.; (Circulation) epixtech, inc.; (Course Reserve) epixtech, inc.; (OPAC) epixtech, inc.; (Serials) epixtech, inc.
Mem of Alliance Library System
Partic in LVIS; OCLC Online Computer Library Center, Inc; Private Academic Libraries Of Illinois

GALVA

P GALVA PUBLIC LIBRARY DISTRICT, 120 NW Third Ave, 61434. SAN 304-2103. Tel: 309-932-2180. FAX: 309-932-2280. E-Mail: galvalib@cin.net. Web Site: users.cin.net/~galvalib/index.html. *Admin Dir*, Melody Heck; Staff 1 (Non-MLS 1)
Founded 1909. Pop 3,926; Circ 34,460
1998-1999 Income $153,186, State $4,843, County $2,266, Locally Generated Income $135,286, Other $10,791. Mats Exp $14,611, Books $12,014, Per/Ser (Incl. Access Fees) $2,597. Sal $45,866 (Prof $18,500)
Library Holdings: Bk Vols 20,767; Bk Titles 18,512; Per Subs 97
Special Collections: Galva News, 1879-present on microfilm; Swedish & Local History
Automation Activity & Vendor Info: (OPAC) CARL
Mem of Alliance Library System
Open Mon-Thurs 9:30-8, Fri 1-5, Sat 9-1

GENESEO

P GENESEO PUBLIC LIBRARY DISTRICT, (GPLD), 218 S State St, 61254. SAN 304-2111. Tel: 309-944-6452. FAX: 309-944-6721. E-Mail: gpl@libby.rbls.lib.il.us. Web Site: www.rbls.lib.il.us/gpl. *Dir*, Brenda J Fowler
Founded 1855. Pop 12,112; Circ 125,000
Jul 1998-Jun 1999 Income $401,549, State $27,120, County $217,258, Other $157,171. Mats Exp $60,230, Books $51,108, Per/Ser (Incl. Access Fees) $800. Sal $142,003
Library Holdings: Bk Titles 45,900; Per Subs 223
Subject Interests: Compact discs, Large print
Special Collections: Early Geneseo Historical Material 1836-to-1920, including oral hist tapes
Publications: Library Events (Newsletter)
Mem of River Bend Library System
Special Services for the Blind - Talking Books
Open Mon-Thurs 9-8, Fri & Sat 9-5
Friends of the Library Group

GENEVA

M DELNOR COMMUNITY HOSPITAL, Health Science Library, 300 Randall Rd, 60134. SAN 325-0776. Tel: 630-208-4299. FAX: 630-208-3479.
Library Holdings: Bk Titles 1,000
Subject Interests: Medicine
Restriction: Staff use only
Partic in Dialog Corporation; Fox Valley Health Science Library Consortium; Illinois Library & Information Network

P DUPAGE LIBRARY SYSTEM, 127 S First St, PO Box 268, 60134. SAN 340-4463. Tel: 630-232-8457. FAX: 630-232-0699. Web Site: www.dupagels.lib.il.us. *Dir*, Pamela P Feather; *Exec Dir*, Shirley May Byrnes; *Asst Dir*, Sharon Ruda; Staff 8 (MLS 8)
Founded 1966. Pop 781,439
Special Collections: Library Science, bks, micro
Automation Activity & Vendor Info: (Circulation) CLSI LIBS
Publications: DL Essence (newsletter); Miscellany
Member Libraries: Addison Public Library; Aurora Public Library; Aurora University; Bartlett Public Library District; Batavia Public Library District; Bensenville Community Public Library; Bloomingdale Public Library; C Berger & Company Library; Carol Stream Public Library; Central Dupage Hospital; Colonel Robert Mccormick Research Center; DuPage County Health Department; Edward Hospital Library; Elgin Mental Health Center

Library; Engineering Systems Inc Library; Fermi National Accelerator Laboratory Library; Franklin Park Public Library District; Geneva Public Library District; Glen Ellyn Public Library; Glen Oaks Hospital; Glenside Public Library District; Hanley-Wood LLC Library; Helen M Plum Memorial Library; Illinois Youth Center - Warrenville Library; Itasca Community Library; Joint Commission on Accreditation of Healthcare Organizations; Kaneville Public Library; Marianjoy Rehabilitation Hospital; Masonite Corp; Messenger Public Library Of North Aurora; Nalco Chemical Company; Naperville Public Libraries; Naperville Sun News Library; National Safety Council Library; National University of Health Sciences; Nicor Gas; North Central College; North Central Regional Educational Laboratory; North East Multi-Regional Training; Northern Baptist Theological Seminary; Oak Brook Public Library; Packer Engineering Inc; Poplar Creek Public Library District; Robert Morris College Library; Roselle Public Library District; St Charles Public Library District; Sugar Grove Public Library District; Theosophical Society In America; Town & Country Public Library District; Van Kampen Funds; Van Kampen Funds Library; Villa Park Public Library; Warrenville Public Library District; Waubonsee Community College; West Chicago Public Library District; Wheaton Public Library; Winfield Public Library; Wood Dale Public Library District

P GENEVA PUBLIC LIBRARY DISTRICT, 127 James St, 60134. SAN 304-212X. Tel: 630-232-0780. TDD: 630-232-0780. FAX: 630-232-0881. E-Mail: genevapl@dupagels.lib.il.us. Web Site: www.geneva.lib.il.us. *Dir*, Jeanne Hintz; Tel: 630-232-0780, Ext 224, E-Mail: jhintz@dupagels.lib.il.us; Staff 60 (MLS 9, Non-MLS 51)
Founded 1894. Pop 21,310; Circ 320,137
Jul 1999-Jun 2000 Income $2,370,598, State $86,304, County $2,100,673, Locally Generated Income $167,821. Mats Exp $250,782, Books $185,840, Per/Ser (Incl. Access Fees) $18,106, Micro $1,000, AV Equip $24,140, Electronic Ref Mat (Incl. Access Fees) $21,696. Sal $977,018 (Prof $377,278)
Library Holdings: Bk Vols 120,299; Bk Titles 108,268; Per Subs 269
Subject Interests: Art and architecture, Folklore, Local history
Automation Activity & Vendor Info: (Cataloging) epixtech, inc.; (Circulation) epixtech, inc.; (OPAC) epixtech, inc.
Database Vendor: IAC - Info Trac, OCLC - First Search
Publications: Library Link (Newsletter)
Mem of DuPage Library System
Friends of the Library Group

S MANUFACTURERS REPRESENTATIVES EDUCATIONAL RESEARCH FOUNDATION LIBRARY,* 339 Stevens, Unit K, PO Box 247, 60134. SAN 328-3798. Tel: 630-208-1466. FAX: 630-208-1475. E-Mail: info@mrerf.org. *VPres*, Dr Marilyn Friesen; Staff 2 (MLS 1, Non-MLS 1)
Library Holdings: Bk Vols 150

GENOA

P GENOA PUBLIC LIBRARY DISTRICT,* 232 W Main St, 60135. SAN 304-2138. Tel: 815-784-2627. FAX: 815-784-2627. E-Mail: genoalbry@tbcnet.com. *Librn*, Susan Walker
Pop 3,200; Circ 27,153
Jul 1997-Jun 1998 Income $87,000. Mats Exp $10,600. Sal $30,300
Library Holdings: Bk Vols 19,000; Per Subs 44
Mem of Northern Illinois Library System
Open Mon-Thurs 10-8, Sat 10-2
Friends of the Library Group

GEORGETOWN

P GEORGETOWN PUBLIC LIBRARY, 107 E West St, 61846. SAN 304-2146. Tel: 217-662-2164. FAX: 217-662-6790. E-Mail: lddd97@aol.com. *Librn*, Linda Davidson; E-Mail: lddd97@advancenet.net; *Assoc Librn*, Mary Pearman; *Assoc Librn*, Ruth Bonebrake
Founded 1936. Pop 3,678; Circ 19,000
Library Holdings: Bk Vols 17,468; Per Subs 30
Automation Activity & Vendor Info: (Acquisitions) epixtech, inc.; (Cataloging) epixtech, inc.; (Circulation) epixtech, inc.
Mem of Lincoln Trail Libraries System
Open Mon, Wed & Thurs 12:30-5:30, Tues & Fri 9-5:30, Sat 9-2
Friends of the Library Group

GIBSON CITY

SR GIBSON CITY UNITED METHODIST CHURCH LIBRARY,* 206 E Tenth, 60936. SAN 328-4670. Tel: 217-784-5452.
Library Holdings: Bk Vols 1,300
Subject Interests: Religion

P MOYER LIBRARY, 307 N Sangamon, 60936. SAN 304-2154. Tel: 217-784-5343. FAX: 217-784-5373. Web Site: www.gibsoncityillinois.org/moyer. *Dir*, Sharon Craig; E-Mail: scraig@ltnet.ltls.org
Founded 1876. Pop 3,500; Circ 23,668
May 1999-Apr 2000 Income $66,200, City $25,000, Federal $4,200, County $37,000. Mats Exp $12,400, Books $9,000, Per/Ser (Incl. Access Fees) $2,200, AV Equip $1,200. Sal $50,000
Library Holdings: Bk Vols 30,000; Per Subs 65
Automation Activity & Vendor Info: (Acquisitions) epixtech, inc.; (Cataloging) epixtech, inc.; (Circulation) epixtech, inc.; (Course Reserve) epixtech, inc.
Publications: Booklist; Illinois Libraries; Wilson Library Bulletin
Mem of Lincoln Trail Libraries System
Special Services for the Deaf - TTY machine
Friends of the Library Group

GILLESPIE

P GILLESPIE PUBLIC LIBRARY,* 201 W Chestnut, 62033. SAN 304-2162. Tel: 217-839-3614. FAX: 217-839-3614. *Librn*, Helen T Bauer
Founded 1944. Pop 3,740; Circ 25,005
Library Holdings: Bk Vols 18,865; Per Subs 49
Subject Interests: Education, Feminism, Medicine
Mem of Lewis & Clark Library System
Friends of the Library Group

GILMAN

P GILMAN AREA DISTRICT LIBRARY,* 117 E Second St, PO Box 335, 60938. SAN 304-2170. Tel: 815-265-7522. FAX: 815-265-4599. *Librn*, Doris Miller
Pop 3,084; Circ 13,351
Library Holdings: Bk Vols 14,020
Mem of Lincoln Trail Libraries System

GIRARD

P GIRARD TOWNSHIP LIBRARY, 201 W Madison, 62640-1550. SAN 304-2189. Tel: 217-627-2414. FAX: 217-627-2093. E-Mail: gre@lcls.org. *Librn*, Joan Ekiss; *Asst Librn*, Linda Peper; Staff 2 (MLS 1, Non-MLS 1)
Founded 1947. Pop 2,454; Circ 16,933; Highest Degree: Master
Apr 1999-Mar 2000 Income $33,300. Mats Exp $7,498, Books $5,700, Per/Ser (Incl. Access Fees) $1,328, Presv $40, AV Equip $430. Sal $16,978
Library Holdings: Bk Titles 20,000; Per Subs 76
Special Collections: City Ord/genealogy
Mem of Lewis & Clark Library System
Friends of the Library Group

GLEN ELLYN

J COLLEGE OF DUPAGE LIBRARY, 425 22nd St, 60137-6599. SAN 304-2197. Tel: 630-942-2351. FAX: 630-858-8757. Web Site: www.cod.edu/library/. *Dean of Libr*, Bernard Fradkin; E-Mail: fradkin@cdnet.cod.edu; *Assoc Dean*, Ellen Sutton; *Tech Servs*, Harold Temple; *Ref*, James Belz; *Ref*, Marianne Berger; *Ref*, Diana Fitzwater; *Ref*, Marjorie Peters; *Ref*, Linda Slusar; *Ref*, Nancy Thomas; *Ref*, Judy Wagner; Staff 45 (MLS 14, Non-MLS 31)
Founded 1967. Enrl 34,000; Fac 293
Library Holdings: Bk Vols 159,209; Per Subs 1,057
Special Collections: Art, Vocational & Technical Coll; College & Career Information
Automation Activity & Vendor Info: (Acquisitions) Innovative Interfaces Inc.; (Cataloging) Innovative Interfaces Inc.; (Circulation) Innovative Interfaces Inc.; (OPAC) Innovative Interfaces Inc.; (Serials) Innovative Interfaces Inc.
Partic in ELVIS; Illinois Library & Information Network; NLRC; OCLC Online Computer Library Center, Inc

R FIRST UNITED METHODIST CHURCH LIBRARY, 424 Forest Ave, 60137. SAN 304-2200. Tel: 630-469-3510. FAX: 630-469-2041. *Librn*, Kathryn E Collord
Founded 1954
1999-2000 Income $700. Mats Exp $600, Books $500, AV Equip $100
Library Holdings: Bk Vols 5,500
Special Collections: New Media Bible Coll (29 Books)

P GLEN ELLYN PUBLIC LIBRARY,* 400 Duane St, 60137-4508. SAN 304-2219. Tel: 630-469-0879. FAX: 630-469-1086. E-Mail: glenref@linc.lib.il.us. Web Site: www.gepl.org. *Actg Dir, Ad Servs, Coll Develop*, Nancy Zander; *Circ*, Nancy Peterson; *Ch Servs*, Amy Teske; Staff 10 (MLS 10)
Founded 1907. Pop 26,093; Circ 425,219
May 1997-Apr 1998 Income $1,518,010, State $53,546, City $1,205,535, Federal $38,317, Locally Generated Income $220,612. Mats Exp $195,450, Other Print Mats $152,512. Sal $729,015
Library Holdings: Bk Vols 138,881; Per Subs 775
Automation Activity & Vendor Info: (Circulation) DRA
Publications: Newsletter
Mem of DuPage Library System
Partic in OCLC Online Computer Library Center, Inc
Friends of the Library Group

GLENCOE

S CHICAGO BOTANIC GARDEN, June Price Reedy Horticultural Library, 1000 Lake-Cook Rd, 60022. SAN 304-2235. Tel: 847-835-8200. FAX: 847-835-6885. E-Mail: cbglib@nslsilus.org. Web Site: www.chicago-botanic.org. *Librn*, Edward J Valauskas; Staff 3 (MLS 3)
Founded 1958
Library Holdings: Bk Vols 17,000; Per Subs 200
Subject Interests: Botany, Gardening, Horticulture

P GLENCOE PUBLIC LIBRARY, 320 Park Ave, 60022-1597. SAN 304-2243. Tel: 847-835-5056. FAX: 847-835-5648. Web Site: www.glencoe.lib.il.us. *Dir*, Margaret M Hamil; *Circ, ILL*, Danny Burdett; *Ch Servs*, Janet M Hauser; *Coll Develop, Ref Serv Ad*, Teri Hennes; *Tech Servs*, Rebecca Halcli; Staff 32 (MLS 10, Non-MLS 22)
Founded 1909. Pop 8,499; Circ 155,795
Mar 2000-Feb 2001 Income $1,313,500, State $15,000, County $1,213,500, Locally Generated Income $85,000. Mats Exp $176,500, Books $102,000, Per/Ser (Incl. Access Fees) $17,000, Micro $1,000, AV Equip $19,500, Electronic Ref Mat (Incl. Access Fees) $37,000. Sal $650,000
Library Holdings: Bk Vols 76,419; Per Subs 235
Automation Activity & Vendor Info: (Circulation) GEAC; (ILL) GEAC; (OPAC) GEAC
Database Vendor: OCLC - First Search
Publications: Excerpts (newsletter)
Mem of North Suburban Library System
Partic in Coop Computer Servs
Special Services for the Blind - Talking book center
Friends of the Library Group

SR NORTH SHORE CONGREGATION ISRAEL, Romanek Library, 1185 Sheridan Rd, 60022. SAN 325-7010. Tel: 847-835-0724. FAX: 847-835-5613. *Librn*, Janice B Footlik
Library Holdings: Bk Vols 20,000; Per Subs 24
Subject Interests: Archaeology
Mem of North Suburban Library System
Partic in Nonpub Bk Asn

GLENDALE HEIGHTS

M GLEN OAKS HOSPITAL, Medical Library, 701 Winthrop Ave, 60139. SAN 376-172X. Tel: 630-545-5450. FAX: 630-545-3920. *Librn*, Sophia S Apostolopoulos; E-Mail: sapostolopoulos@ahss.org; Staff 1 (MLS 1)
Library Holdings: Bk Titles 200; Per Subs 24
Mem of DuPage Library System
Partic in Fox Valley Health Science Library Consortium

P GLENSIDE PUBLIC LIBRARY DISTRICT, 25 E Fullerton Ave, 60139-2697. SAN 304-2251. Tel: 630-260-1550. TDD: 630-260-1566. FAX: 630-260-1433. E-Mail: ghdadmin@glensidepld.org. Web Site: glensidepld.org/gpld.htm. *Dir*, Liz Fitzgerald; *Ad Servs*, Michael Moulds; *Ch Servs*, Vincent Sovanski; *Automation Syst Coordr*, Jean Johnson; *Circ*, Peggy Tomzik; *Circ*, Penny Roche; Staff 14 (MLS 14)
Founded 1974. Pop 30,032; Circ 116,496
Jul 1999-Jun 2000 Income $5,791,836, State $43,146, Federal $4,400, Locally Generated Income $801,343, Other $167,947. Mats Exp $91,695, Books $85,349, AV Equip $6,346. Sal $495,975 (Prof $325,039)
Library Holdings: Bk Vols 64,859; Per Subs 809
Subject Interests: Deaf
Special Collections: Learning Games; Signed English Children's Books
Automation Activity & Vendor Info: (Circulation) Innovative Interfaces Inc.; (OPAC) Innovative Interfaces Inc.
Database Vendor: Innovative Interfaces INN - View, OCLC - First Search
Mem of DuPage Library System
Special Services for the Deaf - TDD
Special Services for the Blind - VisualTek equipment
Friends of the Library Group

GLENVIEW

M EVANSTON NORTHWESTERN HEALTHCARE-GLENBROOK HOSPITAL, (Formerly Glenbrook Hospital), Medical Library, 2100 Pfingsten Rd, 60025. SAN 374-8308. Tel: 847-657-5618. FAX: 847-657-5995. E-Mail: wanngh@enh.org. *Librn*, Hailan Wang; E-Mail: wangh@enh.org; Staff 1 (MLS 1)
Founded 1970
Library Holdings: Bk Vols 1,000; Per Subs 115
Mem of North Suburban Library System
Partic in ILLINET; Northeastern Ill Libr Consortia

P GLENVIEW PUBLIC LIBRARY, 1930 Glenview Rd, 60025-2899. SAN 304-226X. Tel: 847-729-7500. FAX: 847-729-7682. E-Mail: info@glenview.lib.il.us. Web Site: www.glenview.lib.il.us. *Dir*, John Blegen; E-Mail: blegen@clsn3046.glenview.lib.il.us; *Ad Servs, Asst Dir*, Jane Berry; *Ch Servs*, Anne Dierbeck; *Cat*, Muffet Schroer; *ILL*, Elisabeth Bogucki; *Acq*, Gordon Field
Founded 1930. Pop 38,073; Circ 725,591
Library Holdings: Bk Vols 250,000; Per Subs 605
Subject Interests: Medicine
Special Collections: Genealogy (Lundberg Coll)
Automation Activity & Vendor Info: (Circulation) CLSI LIBS
Publications: Newsletter (quarterly)
Mem of North Suburban Library System
Friends of the Library Group

SR IMMANUEL CHURCH LIBRARY,* 74 Park Dr, 60025. SAN 304-2278. Tel: 847-724-1080. FAX: 847-724-3042. *Librn*, Connie Smith
Library Holdings: Bk Vols 25,000; Per Subs 10

KRAFT GENERAL FOODS, INC
S TECHNICAL INFORMATION GROUP, 801 Waukegan Rd, 60025-4312. SAN 340-4552. Tel: 847-646-3753. FAX: 847-646-5150. *Acq*, Jolinda Pacay; *Online Servs*, David Jourdan; Staff 5 (MLS 4, Non-MLS 1)
Founded 1938. Pop 650
Library Holdings: Bk Vols 13,000; Per Subs 600
Subject Interests: Food sci, Nutrition
Mem of North Suburban Library System

S SCOTT FORESMAN LIBRARY, 1900 E Lake Ave, 60025-2086. SAN 304-2286. Tel: 847-486-2617. FAX: 847-486-3948. Web Site: www.nslsilus.org/scott-foresman. *Mgr Libr Serv*, Judith L Besterfeldt; E-Mail: judy.besterfeldt@scottforesman.com; *Asst Librn*, Jenny Forbes; Staff 1 (MLS 1)
Founded 1942
Library Holdings: Bk Titles 35,000; Per Subs 250
Subject Interests: Children's literature
Special Collections: Addison-Wesley Archives; Scott, Foresman Archives
Database Vendor: OCLC - First Search
Mem of North Suburban Library System

S ZENITH ELECTRONICS CORP, Technical Library,* 1000 N Milwaukee Ave, 60025. SAN 304-2294. Tel: 847-391-8452. FAX: 847-391-8555. *Dir*, Toni Mix; E-Mail: toni.mix@zenith.com; Staff 1 (Non-MLS 1)
Founded 1956
Library Holdings: Bk Titles 5,000; Per Subs 46
Subject Interests: Business, Engineering, Mathematics
Database Vendor: OCLC - First Search
Restriction: Not open to public
Function: Research library
Mem of North Suburban Library System
Partic in Illinois Library & Information Network
Friends of the Library Group

GLENWOOD

P GLENWOOD-LYNWOOD PUBLIC LIBRARY DISTRICT, 320 Glenwood-Lansing Rd, 60425. SAN 304-2308. Tel: 708-758-0090. FAX: 708-758-0106. E-Mail: gws@sls.lib.il.us. *Dir*, Maryjeanne Crowe-Crawford; *Ref*, Laura Gaughan; *Ch Servs*, Julie Yekel; Staff 5 (MLS 3, Non-MLS 2)
Founded 1974. Pop 17,148; Circ 66,000
Library Holdings: Bk Vols 27,000; Per Subs 111
Publications: Newsletter
Mem of Suburban Library System

GODFREY

J LEWIS & CLARK COMMUNITY COLLEGE, Reid Memorial Library, 5800 Godfrey Rd, 62035. SAN 304-2316. Tel: 618-466-3411. Circulation Tel: 618-468-4301. FAX: 618-466-1294. E-Mail: lce.lxe@lcls.lib.il.us. Web Site: www.lc.cc.il.us/libweb.nsf. *Dir*, Brett Reinert; Tel: 618-466-3411, Ext 4300, E-Mail: breinert@lc.cc.il.us; *Assoc Dir*, Elizabeth Burns; Tel: 618-466-3411, Ext 4310, E-Mail: lburns@lc.cc.il.us; *Assoc Dir*, Dennis Krieb; Tel: 618-466-3411, Ext 4312, E-Mail: dkrieb@lc.cc.il.us; *Cat*, Reva Van Hoose; Tel: 618-466-3411, Ext 4306, E-Mail: rvanhoose@lc.cc.il.us; *Circ*, Debra Gipson; Tel: 618-466-3411, Ext 4301, E-Mail: dgipson@lc.cc.il.us; *ILL*, Paula Seaman; Tel: 618-466-3411, Ext 4304, E-Mail: pseaman@lc.cc.il.us; Staff 6 (MLS 3, Non-MLS 3)
Founded 1970. Enrl 4,500; Fac 100
1999-2000 Income $170,000. Mats Exp $37,000, Books $20,000, Per/Ser (Incl. Access Fees) $17,000. Sal $120,000 (Prof $60,000)
Library Holdings: Bk Titles 28,000; Per Subs 35
Special Collections: Monticello College History
Automation Activity & Vendor Info: (Cataloging) epixtech, inc.; (Circulation) epixtech, inc.; (Course Reserve) epixtech, inc.; (ILL) epixtech, inc.; (OPAC) epixtech, inc.
Database Vendor: epixtech, inc., OCLC - First Search, ProQuest, Silverplatter Information Inc.
Mem of Lewis & Clark Library System
Partic in Ill State Libr Network

GOLCONDA

P GOLCONDA PUBLIC LIBRARY, Main St, PO Box 523, 62938-0523. SAN 304-2324. Tel: 618-683-6531. *Librn*, Phyllis King
Founded 1915. Pop 823; Circ 12,450
Library Holdings: Bk Vols 18,267; Per Subs 20
Subject Interests: Genealogy, Local history
Mem of Shawnee Library System
Open Mon-Fri 1-9, Sat 9-12

GRAND TOWER

P GRAND TOWER PUBLIC LIBRARY,* 516 Front St, PO Box 287, 62942. SAN 376-141X. Tel: 618-565-2181. FAX: 618-565-2181. *Librn*, Wanda Nation
Library Holdings: Bk Titles 12,000; Per Subs 62

GRANITE CITY

P GRANITE CITY PUBLIC LIBRARY DISTRICT, 2001 Delmar St, 62040-4590. SAN 304-2332. Tel: 618-452-6238. FAX: 618-876-6317. Web Site: www.gatenet.lcls.lib.il.us/gce/index.htm. *Dir*, Lester McKiernan; *Asst Dir*, Jeanette Kampen; *Cat*, Lynda C Seegert; *Ref*, Michael Hillmer; Staff 5 (MLS 5)
Founded 1912. Pop 40,809; Circ 331,637
Library Holdings: Bk Vols 176,583; Per Subs 405
Mem of Lewis & Clark Library System
Friends of the Library Group
Branches: 1
DISTRICT BRANCH LIBRARY, 2145 Johnson Rd, 62040. SAN 376-2491. Tel: 618-452-6244. FAX: 618-452-6226. Web Site: www.gatenet.lclc.lib.il.us/gce/index.htm. *Librn*, Gregg McGee; Staff 1 (MLS 1)
Library Holdings: Bk Vols 25,000; Bk Titles 20,000
Friends of the Library Group

J SOUTHWESTERN ILLINOIS COLLEGE, Granite City Campus Library, 4950 Maryville Rd, 62040. SAN 371-9111. Tel: 618-931-0600, Ext 6654. FAX: 618-931-0523. Web Site: www.southwestern.cc.il.us/library/int_lib_home.htm. *Librn*, Janice Zuke; Tel: 618-931-0600, Ext 6653, E-Mail: jan.zuke@southwestern.cc.il.us; Staff 3 (MLS 3)
Founded 1983. Enrl 2,138; Fac 45
Library Holdings: Bk Vols 22,587; Per Subs 100
Automation Activity & Vendor Info: (Cataloging) epixtech, inc.; (Circulation) epixtech, inc.; (Course Reserve) epixtech, inc.; (OPAC) epixtech, inc.; (Serials) epixtech, inc.
Database Vendor: Ebsco - EbscoHost
Mem of Shawnee Library System

UNITED STATES ARMY

GRANT PARK

P GRANT PARK PUBLIC LIBRARY,* 107 W Taylor St, PO Box 392, 60940-0392. SAN 304-2359. Tel: 815-465-6047. FAX: 815-465-6575. *Librn*, Erma Mittag
Founded 1919. Pop 1,024; Circ 3,151
Library Holdings: Bk Vols 5,020
Special Collections: James Whitcomb Riley; Mark Twain; Zane Grey
Mem of Heritage Trail Library System

GRAYSLAKE

J COLLEGE OF LAKE COUNTY, Learning Resource Center, 19351 W Washington St, 60030. SAN 304-2367. Tel: 847-543-2619. Reference Tel: 847-543-2071. FAX: 847-223-7690. Web Site: www.clc.cc.il.us/dept/lrc/home.htm. *ILL*, Shirley Haslow; Tel: 847-543-2465; *Tech Servs*, Rayne Armour; Tel: 547-543-2461; *Circ*, Mary Byrne; *Ref*, Jo Beckwith; *Ref*, Michelle Carter; Tel: 847-543-2891; *Ref*, Cassandra McGovern; Tel: 847-543-2460; *Ref*, Norman Sage; Tel: 847-543-2469; Staff 8 (MLS 8)
Founded 1970. Fac 165; Highest Degree: Associate
Jul 2000-Jun 2001 Mats Exp $369,000, Books $165,000, Per/Ser (Incl. Access Fees) $81,000, Micro $55,000, AV Equip $31,000, Other Print Mats $5,000, Electronic Ref Mat (Incl. Access Fees) $32,000. Sal $881,000 (Prof $488,000)
Library Holdings: Bk Vols 121,968; Bk Titles 104,517; Per Subs 695
Special Collections: ERIC Documents, 1978
Automation Activity & Vendor Info: (Acquisitions) Innovative Interfaces Inc.; (Cataloging) Innovative Interfaces Inc.; (Circulation) Innovative Interfaces Inc.; (Media Booking) Innovative Interfaces Inc.; (OPAC) Innovative Interfaces Inc.; (Serials) Innovative Interfaces Inc.
Database Vendor: OCLC - First Search
Mem of North Suburban Library System
Partic in OCLC Online Computer Library Center, Inc
Open Mon-Thurs 8am-9:30pm, Fri 8-9, Sat 9-4:30 & Sun 1-5

P GRAYSLAKE AREA PUBLIC LIBRARY DISTRICT, 100 Library Lane, 60030-1684. SAN 304-2375. Tel: 847-223-5313. TDD: 847-223-5362. FAX: 847-223-6482. Web Site: www.grayslake.lib.il.us. *Librn*, Roberta Thomas; E-Mail: rthomas@grayslake.lib.il.us; *Tech Servs*, Joan Crilly; *Circ*, Diane Wagner; *Ad Servs*, Caroline Dolter; Staff 55 (MLS 9, Non-MLS 46)
Founded 1931. Pop 18,796; Circ 288,240
Jul 1999-Jun 2000 Income $1,853,634, State $29,938, Locally Generated Income $1,823,696. Mats Exp $251,709, Books $184,874, Per/Ser (Incl. Access Fees) $12,500, AV Equip $23,700, Electronic Ref Mat (Incl. Access Fees) $30,635. Sal $674,479 (Prof $185,223)
Library Holdings: Bk Vols 85,425; Per Subs 343
Automation Activity & Vendor Info: (Acquisitions) epixtech, inc.; (Cataloging) epixtech, inc.; (Circulation) epixtech, inc.; (OPAC) epixtech, inc.; (Serials) epixtech, inc.
Publications: Newsletter
Mem of North Suburban Library System
Friends of the Library Group

GRAYVILLE

P GRAYVILLE CARNEGIE PUBLIC LIBRARY, 110 W Mill St, 62844. SAN 304-2383. Tel: 618-375-7121. FAX: 618-375-7121. E-Mail: khjmst@hotmail.com. *Dir*, Mickie L Collard; Staff 2 (Non-MLS 2)
Founded 1909. Pop 2,043; Circ 8,630
Library Holdings: Bk Titles 12,825; Per Subs 50
Special Collections: Rear Admiral James M Helm Coll, memorables
Mem of Shawnee Library System

GREAT LAKES

M NAVAL DENTAL RESEARCH INSTITUTE, Thomas S Meyer Memorial Library, 310 A "B" St, Bldg 1-H, 60088-5259. SAN 376-0898. Tel: 847-688-5647, Ext 154. FAX: 847-688-4279. Web Site: navymedicine.med.navy.mil/ndri/. *In Charge*, Myra Portis; Tel: 847-688-5647, Ext 106, E-Mail: myra.portis@ndri.med.navy.mil
Library Holdings: Bk Titles 8,004; Per Subs 20

UNITED STATES NAVY

AM MEDICAL LIBRARY, Naval Hospital, 3001A Sixth St, 60088-5230. SAN 324-0231. Tel: 847-688-6969. FAX: 847-688-6701. E-Mail: grl1cjs@grl10.med.navy.mil. *Librn*, Carol Struck
Founded 1945
Oct 1998-Sep 1999 Income $108,000. Mats Exp $92,000, Books $30,000, Per/Ser (Incl. Access Fees) $60,000
Library Holdings: Bk Vols 12,000; Per Subs 250
Subject Interests: Clinical medicine, Health admin, Nursing
Mem of North Suburban Library System

A NAVAL TRAINING CENTER LIBRARY, MWR Library Bldg 160, 2601A Paul Jones St Bldg 3, 60088. SAN 304-2391. Tel: 847-688-4617. FAX: 847-688-3602. Web Site: www.ntcmwr.com/library.html. *Librn*, Wendy Moore; Staff 4 (MLS 1, Non-MLS 3)
Founded 1912. Pop 32,000; Circ 35,000
2000-2001 Mats Exp $150,000
Library Holdings: Bk Vols 18,000; Per Subs 170
Subject Interests: Naval art, Naval hist, Naval sci
Mem of North Suburban Library System

GREENFIELD

P GREENFIELD PUBLIC LIBRARY,* 515 Chestnut, PO Box 214, 62044-1305. SAN 304-2413. Tel: 217-368-2613. FAX: 217-368-2604. E-Mail: gpl1@midwest.com. *Librn*, Pat Theivagt; *Asst Librn*, Brenda Shipley
Founded 1914. Circ 6,000
Library Holdings: Bk Vols 5,000; Per Subs 18
Mem of Lewis & Clark Library System
Open Mon & Tues 3-5, Wed 2:30-7, Fri 9-11, Sat 9-12 (June-Aug); Mon 1-6, Tues 1-8, Wed 1-7, Fri 9-11, Sat 9-2, Thurs & Sun closed (Sept-May)
Friends of the Library Group

GREENUP

P GREENUP TOWNSHIP CARNEGIE LIBRARY,* 101 N Mill St, PO Box 275, 62428. SAN 304-2421. Tel: 217-923-3616. *Librn*, Gayle Carr
Pop 2,500; Circ 14,714
Apr 1997-Mar 1998 Income $33,000. Mats Exp $12,000. Sal $13,000
Library Holdings: Bk Vols 15,500; Per Subs 60
Special Collections: Genealogy Coll
Mem of Rolling Prairie Library System

GREENVILLE

C GREENVILLE COLLEGE, Ruby E Dare Library, 315 E College Ave, 62246. SAN 304-243X. Tel: 618-664-6603. FAX: 618-664-9578. E-Mail: genlib@greenville.edu. Web Site: www.greenville.edu/learningresources/library. *Dir*, Jane L Hopkins; E-Mail: jhopkins@greenville.edu; *Ref*, Jim

Butts; *Ref*, Georgann Kurtz Shaw; *AV*, Kenny Hampton; Staff 5 (MLS 3, Non-MLS 2)
Founded 1892. Enrl 900; Highest Degree: Bachelor Sal $195,687 (Prof $110,220)
Library Holdings: Bk Vols 128,000; Per Subs 494
Special Collections: Free Methodist Church History; Greenville College History
Automation Activity & Vendor Info: (Cataloging) DRA; (Circulation) DRA; (OPAC) DRA
Publications: Annual report; library orientation packet
Mem of Lewis & Clark Library System
Partic in Illinois Library & Information Network; OCLC Online Computer Library Center, Inc

P GREENVILLE PUBLIC LIBRARY,* 414 W Main, 62246-1615. SAN 304-2448. Tel: 618-664-3115. FAX: 618-664-9442. *Dir*, Ted Thies; *Librn*, Mary Hoiles; *Asst Librn*, Judy Huff
Founded 1856. Pop 6,438; Circ 40,000
Library Holdings: Bk Vols 25,000; Bk Titles 21,000; Per Subs 90
Subject Interests: Genealogy
Mem of Lewis & Clark Library System
Friends of the Library Group

GRIDLEY

P GRIDLEY PUBLIC LIBRARY DISTRICT, 320 Center St, PO Box 370, 61744. SAN 304-2456. Tel: 309-747-2284. FAX: 309-747-3195. E-Mail: gpld@gridley.org. *Librn*, Lynn McKinley
Founded 1916. Pop 2,045
Library Holdings: Bk Titles 16,000; Per Subs 55
Special Collections: Library of America Coll
Automation Activity & Vendor Info: (Circulation) Follett
Mem of Alliance Library System

GRIGGSVILLE

P GRIGGSVILLE PUBLIC LIBRARY,* 119 S Corey St, 62340. SAN 304-2464. Tel: 217-833-2633. FAX: 217-833-2633. E-Mail: grigglib@adams.net. Web Site: www.hccweb.com. *Librn*, Deborah Griggs
Founded 1887. Pop 1,301; Circ 24,862
Library Holdings: Bk Vols 13,000; Per Subs 58
Mem of Alliance Library System

GURNEE

P WARREN-NEWPORT PUBLIC LIBRARY DISTRICT, 224 N O'Plaine Rd, 60031. SAN 304-2472. Tel: 847-244-5150. TDD: 847-244-5195. FAX: 847-244-3499. E-Mail: webcontact@wnpl.alibrary.com. Web Site: www.wnpl.alibrary.com. *Dir*, Lynn Stainbrook; Tel: 847-244-5152, Ext 3101, E-Mail: lynn_stainbrook@wnpl.alibrary.com; *Asst Dir*, Lynne Jacobsen; Tel: 847-244-5150, Ext 3006, E-Mail: jacobsen@wnpl.alibrary.com; *Ch Servs*, Gail Dever; Tel: 847-244-5152, Ext 3040, E-Mail: gdever@wnpl.alibrary.com; *Tech Coordr*, Barb Brattin; Tel: 847-244-5152, Ext 3026, E-Mail: bbrattin@wnpl.alibrary.com; *Outreach Serv*, Noreen Reese; Tel: 847-244-5152, Ext 3015, E-Mail: nreese@wnpl.alibrary.com; *Publ Servs*, Thomas Rich; Tel: 847-244-5152, Ext 3025, E-Mail: trich@wnpl.alibrary.com; *Tech Servs*, Ruth Bogen; Tel: 847-244-5152, Ext 3030, E-Mail: rbogan@wnpl.alibrary.com; *Tech Servs*, Jeff Gilderson-Duwe; *Ad Servs*, Ken Draves; Tel: 847-244-5152, Ext 3002, E-Mail: kdraves@wnpl.alibrary.com; *Circ*, Carolyn Crabtree; Tel: 847-244-5152, Ext 3024, E-Mail: ccrabtree@wnpl.alibrary.com; Staff 89 (MLS 13, Non-MLS 76)
Founded 1973. Pop 48,777; Circ 914,738
Jul 1999-Jun 2000 Income $3,536,514, State $115,163, County $3,091,691, Locally Generated Income $291,604. Mats Exp $569,836, Books $343,424, Per/Ser (Incl. Access Fees) $75,405, Micro $10,074, AV Equip $70,725, Electronic Ref Mat (Incl. Access Fees) $70,208. Sal $1,438,947 (Prof $529,504)
Library Holdings: Bk Vols 164,197; Bk Titles 156,825; Per Subs 370; High Interest/Low Vocabulary Bk Vols 93; Spec Interest Per Sub 355; Bks on Deafness & Sign Lang 229
Subject Interests: Illinois
Automation Activity & Vendor Info: (Acquisitions) SIRSI; (Cataloging) SIRSI; (Circulation) SIRSI; (OPAC) SIRSI
Database Vendor: IAC - SearchBank, OCLC - First Search
Publications: Inside Angle (newsletter)
Function: Reference services available
Mem of North Suburban Library System
Partic in OCLC Online Computer Library Center, Inc
Special Services for the Deaf - TTY machine
Special Services for the Blind - Children's Braille, Books on Cassette; Closed circuit television; Screen enlargement software for people with visual disabilities; ZoomText software to enlarge computer screen
Friends of the Library Group
Bookmobiles: 14,781

HAMILTON

P HAMILTON PUBLIC LIBRARY, 861 Broadway St, 62341. SAN 304-2480. Tel: 217-847-2219. FAX: 217-847-2219. E-Mail: hamlib@adams.net. *Librn*, Barbara Breheny; Staff 4 (Non-MLS 4)
Founded 1902. Pop 3,281; Circ 18,650
1999-1999 Income $50,478, State $4,048, City $36,824, Locally Generated Income $6,335. Mats Exp Books $12,170. Sal $24,246
Library Holdings: Bk Vols 22,832; Per Subs 70
Mem of Alliance Library System
Friends of the Library Group

HAMPSHIRE

P ELLA JOHNSON MEMORIAL PUBLIC LIBRARY DISTRICT, 109 S State St, PO Box 429, 60140. SAN 304-2499. Tel: 847-683-4490. FAX: 847-683-4493. Web Site: www.ellajohnson.lib.il.us. *Dir*, Jerry MacKay; E-Mail: mackayj@ellajohnson.lib.il.us
Founded 1943. Pop 8,322; Circ 49,892
Jul 1999-Jun 2000 Income $286,364. Mats Exp $31,122. Sal $141,517
Library Holdings: Bk Vols 18,799; Per Subs 118
Subject Interests: Local history
Publications: Children Newsletter (monthly)
Mem of Northern Illinois Library System

HANOVER

P HANOVER TOWNSHIP LIBRARY,* 204 Jefferson St, PO Box 475, 61041. SAN 304-2510. Tel: 815-591-3517. FAX: 815-591-2174. E-Mail: hanoverlib@internetni.com. *Librn*, Frank McCann
Founded 1937. Pop 1,394; Circ 9,391
Library Holdings: Bk Titles 9,359; Per Subs 44
Subject Interests: Local history, Nutrition
Mem of Northern Illinois Library System

HARRISBURG

P HARRISBURG PUBLIC LIBRARY DISTRICT, 2 W Walnut St, 62946-1261. SAN 304-2529. Tel: 618-253-7455. FAX: 618-252-1239. E-Mail: hpld@shawls.lib.il.us. Web Site: www.sirin.lib.il.us. *Dir*, Ruth Miller
Founded 1909. Pop 10,410; Circ 45,000
Library Holdings: Bk Vols 33,000; Per Subs 89
Subject Interests: Genealogy
Automation Activity & Vendor Info: (Cataloging) epixtech, inc.; (Circulation) epixtech, inc.
Mem of Shawnee Library System
Friends of the Library Group

C SOUTHEASTERN ILLINOIS COLLEGE, Melba Patton Library, 3575 College Dr, 62946. SAN 304-2537. Tel: 618-252-5400, Ext 2260. FAX: 618-252-2713. Web Site: www.sic.cc.il.us. *Librn*, Lois Meldrum; E-Mail: lmeldrum@sic.cc.il.us; Staff 4 (MLS 1, Non-MLS 3)
Founded 1960. Enrl 2,300; Fac 85; Highest Degree: Associate
Jul 1999-Jun 2000 Income $280,822. Mats Exp $98,625, Books $31,890, Per/Ser (Incl. Access Fees) $16,100, Presv $500, Micro $2,000, Electronic Ref Mat (Incl. Access Fees) $11,000. Sal $85,255 (Prof $45,000)
Library Holdings: Bk Vols 40,000; Per Subs 250
Automation Activity & Vendor Info: (Acquisitions) epixtech, inc.; (Cataloging) epixtech, inc.; (Circulation) epixtech, inc.; (ILL) epixtech, inc.; (OPAC) epixtech, inc.; (Serials) epixtech, inc.
Mem of Shawnee Library System
Partic in MLNC; NILRC; SILRC

HARTFORD

P HARTFORD PUBLIC LIBRARY DISTRICT,* 143 W Hawthorne, 62048. SAN 304-2545. Tel: 618-254-9394. FAX: 618-254-6522. E-Mail: hae@lcls.org. *Dir*, Gloria Smith
Founded 1965. Pop 1,676; Circ 17,689
Library Holdings: Bk Vols 25,000; Per Subs 50
Special Collections: Lewis & Clark Reference Center
Publications: Newsletter
Mem of Lewis & Clark Library System
Open Mon-Thurs 10-7, Fri 11-4 & Sat 12-4

HARVARD

P HARVARD DIGGINS PUBLIC LIBRARY, (Formerly Delos F Diggins Public Library), 900 E McKinley St, 60033. SAN 304-2553. Tel: 815-943-4671. FAX: 815-943-2312. Web Site: www.harvard-diggins.org. *Dir*, Harriet Roll; E-Mail: harrietr@nils.lib.il.us
Founded 1908. Pop 6,567; Circ 34,000
May 1998-Apr 1999 Income $220,000, State $20,000, City $167,000, Locally Generated Income $20,000. Mats Exp $29,500, Books $25,000, Per/Ser (Incl. Access Fees) $2,500, Micro $2,000. Sal $89,000 (Prof $56,000)

Library Holdings: Bk Vols 26,000; Bk Titles 24,000; Per Subs 80; High Interest/Low Vocabulary Bk Vols 100; Bks on Deafness & Sign Lang 10
Special Collections: Butterfly Coll
Automation Activity & Vendor Info: (Cataloging) Innovative Interfaces Inc.; (Circulation) Innovative Interfaces Inc.; (OPAC) Innovative Interfaces Inc.; (Serials) Innovative Interfaces Inc.
Mem of Northern Illinois Library System
Open Mon-Wed 9:30-8, Fri & Sat 9:30-5:30
Friends of the Library Group

HARVEY

P HARVEY PUBLIC LIBRARY DISTRICT,* 15441 Turlington Ave, 60426-3683. SAN 304-257X. Tel: 708-331-0757. FAX: 708-331-2835. E-Mail: has@harvey.lib.il.us. Web Site: www.harvey.lib.il.us. *Dir*, Jay Kalman; *Publ Servs*, Jacqueline McDonald; *Ref*, Terry Vande Berg; Staff 4 (MLS 4)
Founded 1898. Pop 35,810; Circ 79,620
Library Holdings: Bk Vols 80,000; Per Subs 240
Subject Interests: Ethnic studies, Local history
Automation Activity & Vendor Info: (Circulation) CLSI LIBS
Publications: Internal & Patron Newsletters
Mem of Suburban Library System
Open Mon-Thurs 9-8, Fri & Sat 9-5

M INGALLS HOSPITAL, Medical Library,* One Ingalls Dr, 60426. SAN 304-2588. Tel: 708-915-6881. FAX: 708-915-3109. *Librn*, Donna Foley; E-Mail: foleyd@ingalls.org
Founded 1968
Library Holdings: Bk Vols 2,800; Per Subs 210
Subject Interests: Clinical medicine, Nursing
Mem of Suburban Library System
Partic in Chicago & South Consortium; Medline; Regional Med Libr - Region 3

HARWOOD HEIGHTS

P EISENHOWER PUBLIC LIBRARY DISTRICT,* 4652 N Olcott, 60706. SAN 304-2596. Tel: 708-452-8989, 708-867-7828. FAX: 708-867-1535. E-Mail: ess@sls.lib.il.us. *Dir*, Ronald V Stoch; *Asst Librn, Ref*, Leonora Leibik; *Ch Servs*, David Ziegler; *Librn*, Penny Blubaugh; Staff 16 (MLS 7, Non-MLS 9)
Founded 1972. Pop 22,139; Circ 275,442
Jul 1997-Jun 1998 Income $963,272, State $43,597. Mats Exp $186,643, Books $127,921, Per/Ser (Incl. Access Fees) $11,416, Micro $4,290. Sal $511,221
Library Holdings: Bk Titles 90,000; Per Subs 275
Automation Activity & Vendor Info: (Circulation) CLSI LIBS
Mem of Suburban Library System
Special Services for the Deaf - TTY machine
Friends of the Library Group

HAVANA

P HAVANA PUBLIC LIBRARY DISTRICT, 201 W Adams St, 62644-1321. SAN 304-260X. Tel: 309-543-4701. TDD: 309-543-4701. FAX: 309-543-2715. E-Mail: hava@darkstar.rsa.lib.il.us. Web Site: www.havana.lib.il.us. *Dir*, Nancy I Glick; Staff 11 (MLS 2, Non-MLS 9)
Founded 1896. Pop 8,313; Circ 30,000
Library Holdings: Bk Vols 30,000; Per Subs 184
Special Collections: Historic Photograph Coll; Mason County Genealogical & Historical Society Colls
Database Vendor: CARL
Mem of Alliance Library System
Partic in RSA
Special Services for the Blind - Talking Books
Friends of the Library Group

HAZEL CREST

P GRANDE PRAIRIE PUBLIC LIBRARY DISTRICT, 3479 W 183rd St, 60429. SAN 304-2618. Tel: 708-798-5563. FAX: 708-798-5874. E-Mail: gps@sslic.net. Web Site: www.grandeprairie.org. *Dir*, Susan K Roberts; E-Mail: robertss@sslic.net; *Ad Servs*, Linda Ameling; *Ch Servs*, Tracy Duckworth; *Circ*, Donna Scholz; Staff 18 (MLS 2, Non-MLS 16)
Founded 1960. Pop 29,583; Circ 120,485
Jul 1999-Jun 2000 Income $987,926, State $80,447, Locally Generated Income $850,411, Other $57,068. Mats Exp $120,706, Books $87,615, Per/Ser (Incl. Access Fees) $10,971, AV Equip $11,295, Electronic Ref Mat (Incl. Access Fees) $10,825. Sal $378,196
Library Holdings: Bk Vols 80,913; Per Subs 210
Special Collections: Fiction works by African American writers
Automation Activity & Vendor Info: (Cataloging) Innovative Interfaces Inc.; (Circulation) Innovative Interfaces Inc.; (ILL) Innovative Interfaces Inc.; (OPAC) Innovative Interfaces Inc.
Database Vendor: GaleNet, IAC - Info Trac, Innovative Interfaces INN - View, OCLC - First Search
Publications: Prairie Notes (Newsletter)
Mem of Suburban Library System

M SOUTH SUBURBAN HOSPITAL, Medical Library,* 178th & Kedzie Ave, 60429. SAN 375-9679. Tel: 708-799-8000, Ext 3067. FAX: 708-799-9772. Web Site: www.advocatehealth.com. *Librn*, Joanna Tsong; E-Mail: joanna.tsong@advocatehealth.com
Library Holdings: Bk Titles 1,000; Per Subs 80
Partic in Am Libr Asn; Health Sci Librns of Ill; ILLINET; Medical Libr Asn; Suburban Libr Syst

HECKER

P HECKER PUBLIC LIBRARY,* 1551 W Monroe, PO Box 119, 62248-0119. SAN 371-5159. Tel: 618-473-2957, 618-473-3022. *Librn*, Joan Powell
Founded 1983. Pop 534; Circ 3,900
Library Holdings: Bk Vols 5,070
Mem of Shawnee Library System

HENNEPIN

P PUTNAM COUNTY PUBLIC LIBRARY DISTRICT, 214 N Fourth St, PO Box 199, 61327. SAN 340-4641. Tel: 815-925-7020. FAX: 815-925-7020. *Dir*, Randie Dellatori; E-Mail: rdellatori@starbase1.hlts.lib.il.us; Staff 1 (Non-MLS 1)
Pop 5,730; Circ 38,000
Library Holdings: Bk Vols 30,000; Per Subs 40
Mem of Heritage Trail Library System
Partic in Illinois Library & Information Network
Branches: 5
GRANVILLE BRANCH, PO Box 495, Granville, 61326. SAN 340-4676. Tel: 815-339-2480. *Librn*, Ann Wink
MAGNOLIA BRANCH, PO Box 9, Magnolia, 61336. SAN 340-4765. Tel: 815-869-3038. *Librn*, Peggy Smith
MCNABB BRANCH, PO Box 135, McNabb, 61336. SAN 340-4730. Tel: 815-882-2278. *Librn*, Marilyn Calbow
PUTNAM COUNTY - CONDIT BRANCH, PO Box 4, Putnam, 61560. SAN 340-479X. Tel: 815-437-2811. *Librn*, Sandy Ziegler
STANDARD BRANCH, PO Box 114, Standard, 61363. SAN 340-482X. Tel: 815-339-2711. *Librn*, Darlene Scheri

HENRY

P HENRY PUBLIC LIBRARY,* 702 Front St, PO Box 183, 61537. SAN 304-2634. Tel: 309-364-2516. FAX: 309-364-2717. *Dir*, Jean Mitchell
Founded 1936. Pop 2,591; Circ 27,261
Library Holdings: Bk Vols 21,000; Per Subs 61
Subject Interests: Local history
Mem of Alliance Library System

HERRICK

P HERRICK TOWNSHIP PUBLIC LIBRARY,* RR1 Box 166B, 62431. SAN 375-9482. Tel: 618-428-5223. *Librn*, Becky Wilson
Library Holdings: Bk Titles 1,500
Subject Interests: Genealogy
Mem of Rolling Prairie Library System
Friends of the Library Group

HERRIN

P HERRIN CITY LIBRARY,* 120 N 13th St, 62948-3233. SAN 304-2642. Tel: 618-942-6109. FAX: 618-942-4165. *Dir*, Michael Keepper; E-Mail: mkeepper@shawnet.shawls.lib.il.us; *Asst Librn, Ch Servs*, Irena Just; *Circ*, Karla McCowen; Staff 4 (MLS 1, Non-MLS 3)
Pop 10,857; Circ 50,000
May 1997-Apr 1998 Income $135,800, State $13,500, City $90,000, Locally Generated Income $17,300, Other $15,000. Mats Exp $18,000, Books $15,000, Per/Ser (Incl. Access Fees) $3,000. Sal $50,000 (Prof $20,000)
Library Holdings: Bk Vols 35,000; Per Subs 50
Subject Interests: Local history
Mem of Shawnee Library System
Open Mon-Thurs 10-8, Fri 10-6 & Sat 12-6
Friends of the Library Group

HEYWORTH

P HEYWORTH PUBLIC LIBRARY DISTRICT,* 119 E Main, 61745. SAN 304-2650. Tel: 309-473-2313. FAX: 309-473-2313. *Librn*, Betty Zoerb
Pop 3,926; Circ 35,153
Library Holdings: Bk Titles 17,000; Per Subs 102
Mem of Alliance Library System
Friends of the Library Group

HIGHLAND

P LOUIS LATZER MEMORIAL PUBLIC LIBRARY,* 1001 Ninth St, PO Box 188, 62249. SAN 304-2669. Tel: 618-654-5066. FAX: 618-654-1324. E-Mail: hie@lcls.org. Web Site: www.lcls.lib.il.us/hie. *Librn*, Romy Schrage; E-Mail: romys@lcls.org
Founded 1929. Pop 8,011; Circ 110,000
Library Holdings: Bk Vols 40,000; Per Subs 110
Mem of Lewis & Clark Library System
Open Mon & Wed 9-6, Tue & Thurs 12-8, Fri 9-5, Sat 9-3
Friends of the Library Group

HIGHLAND PARK

R CONGREGATION SOLEL LIBRARY, 1301 Clavey Rd, 60035. SAN 304-2677. Tel: 847-433-3555. FAX: 847-433-3573. E-Mail: soleloffice@solel.org. *Librn*, M W Hanig; *Assoc Librn*, N Belrose
Founded 1963
Library Holdings: Bk Vols 12,000; Bk Titles 10,000; Per Subs 20
Subject Interests: Biblical studies, Holocaust, Israel, Jewish history and literature
Special Collections: Judaica (art, music)
Automation Activity & Vendor Info: (Cataloging) Follett

S HIGHLAND PARK HISTORICAL SOCIETY LIBRARY, 326 Central Ave, 60035. (Mail add: PO Box 56, 60035), SAN 325-6952. Tel: 847-432-7090. FAX: 847-432-7307. Web Site: www.highlandpark.org/histsoc/. *In Charge*, Ellsworth Mills II
Library Holdings: Bk Vols 300
Subject Interests: Local history
Special Collections: Ravinia Festival (Summer Home, Chicago Symphony Orchestra)
Handicapped accessible
Friends of the Library Group

M HIGHLAND PARK HOSPITAL, Medical Library,* 718 Glenview Ave, 60035. SAN 370-5455. Tel: 847-432-8000, Ext 4051. FAX: 847-480-3895. *Librn*, Nancy Petersen; E-Mail: npetersen@hphosp.org
Library Holdings: Bk Titles 1,900; Per Subs 146
Subject Interests: Medicine, Nursing
Mem of North Suburban Library System
Open Mon-Fri 7:30-4

P HIGHLAND PARK PUBLIC LIBRARY, 494 Laurel Ave, 60035-2690. SAN 304-2685. Tel: 847-432-0216. TDD: 847-432-7674. FAX: 847-432-9139. E-Mail: hpplweb@nslsilus.org. Web Site: hppl.lib.il.us. *Exec Dir*, Jane W Greenfield; *Ad Servs*, Julia Johnas; *Tech Servs*, Mercedes Mantilla; *Ch Servs*, Linda Wicher; Staff 41 (MLS 13, Non-MLS 28)
Founded 1887. Pop 30,575
May 1999-Apr 2000 Income $2,670,300, State $50,183, City $2,474,189, Locally Generated Income $145,928. Mats Exp $441,253, Electronic Ref Mat (Incl. Access Fees) $52,806. Sal $1,433,961
Library Holdings: Bk Vols 192,606; Per Subs 764
Subject Interests: Local history
Automation Activity & Vendor Info: (Cataloging) DRA; (Circulation) DRA; (OPAC) DRA
Database Vendor: OCLC - First Search
Publications: Bibliographies; Laurels (newsletter)
Mem of North Suburban Library System
Partic in OCLC Online Computer Library Center, Inc
Special Services for the Deaf - TDD
Friends of the Library Group

S NATIONAL ASSOCIATION OF ANOREXIA NERVOSA & ASSOCIATED DISORDERS, INC LIBRARY,* PO Box 7, 60035. SAN 375-149X. Tel: 847-831-3438. FAX: 847-433-4632. E-Mail: anad20@aol.com. Web Site: www.anad.org. *Pres*, Vivian Hanson Meehan
Library Holdings: Bk Titles 500

R NORTH SUBURBAN SYNAGOGUE BETH EL, Maxwell Abbell Library, 1175 Sheridan Rd, 60035. SAN 304-2693. Tel: 847-432-8900. FAX: 847-432-9242. E-Mail: nssbe@nssbethel.org. Web Site: www.nssbethel.org. *Librn*, Cheryl Banks; Staff 3 (MLS 1, Non-MLS 2)
Founded 1959
Library Holdings: Bk Titles 20,000; Per Subs 85
Subject Interests: Judaica (lit or hist of Jews)
Special Collections: 650 Judaica VHF Videos
Automation Activity & Vendor Info: (Cataloging) Sagebrush Corporation
Mem of North Suburban Library System

HIGHWOOD

P HIGHWOOD PUBLIC LIBRARY,* 102 Highwood Ave, 60040-1597. SAN 304-2707. Tel: 847-432-5404. FAX: 847-432-5806. E-Mail: highwoodlibrary@juno.com. *Dir*, Joan Retnauer; *Tech Servs*, Jill Doyle
Founded 1977. Pop 5,452; Circ 30,804
Library Holdings: Bk Vols 38,500; Per Subs 180
Special Collections: Italian Language Coll & Mozart
Mem of North Suburban Library System
Partic in Midwest Health Sci Libr Network

HILLSBORO

S GRAHAM CORRECTIONAL CENTER LIBRARY,* Rte 185 Box 499, 62049. SAN 376-0871. Tel: 217-532-6961, Ext 2705. *Librn*, Colleen Lindberg
Library Holdings: Bk Titles 4,075
Mem of Lewis & Clark Library System

P HILLSBORO PUBLIC LIBRARY,* 214 School St, 62049. SAN 304-2715. Tel: 217-532-3055. FAX: 217-532-6813. E-Mail: lib@cillnet.com. *Dir*, Cheryl J Sale; *Asst Dir*, Patty A Paden
Pop 4,400; Circ 35,000
Library Holdings: Bk Vols 20,000; Bk Titles 18,000; Per Subs 55
Subject Interests: Genealogy
Mem of Lewis & Clark Library System

HILLSDALE

P MOORE MEMORIAL LIBRARY DISTRICT, 509 Main St, 61257-9701. (Mail add: PO Box 325, 61257-0325), SAN 304-2723. Tel: 309-658-2666. FAX: 309-658-2666. *Librn*, Lois Black; E-Mail: lblack@libby.rbls.lib.il.us
Founded 1942. Pop 762; Circ 3,900
Library Holdings: Bk Vols 6,100; Per Subs 20
Mem of River Bend Library System
Open Mon 9-12 & 2-9, Tues 5-9, Wed 2-6, Thurs 9-12 & Sat 10-2

HILLSIDE

P HILLSIDE PUBLIC LIBRARY, 405 N Hillside Ave, 60162-1295. SAN 304-2731. Tel: 708-449-7510. FAX: 708-449-6119. E-Mail: hss@sls.lib.il.us. Web Site: www.hillsidelibrary.org. *Dir*, Pamela Streich Smith; E-Mail: smithp@sls.lib.il.us; *Ch Servs*, Vicki Schwartz; *Ref*, Jane Chesham; Staff 17 (MLS 5, Non-MLS 12)
Founded 1962. Pop 7,672; Circ 81,501
May 1999-Apr 2000 Income $489,221, State $45,722, City $372,320, Federal $9,065, Other $58,114. Mats Exp $79,000, Books $50,000, Per/Ser (Incl. Access Fees) $10,000, AV Equip $14,000, Electronic Ref Mat (Incl. Access Fees) $5,000. Sal $240,000 (Prof $108,008)
Library Holdings: Bk Vols 53,100; Bk Titles 51,291; Per Subs 192
Automation Activity & Vendor Info: (Cataloging) Innovative Interfaces Inc.; (Circulation) Innovative Interfaces Inc.; (ILL) Innovative Interfaces Inc.; (OPAC) Innovative Interfaces Inc.
Database Vendor: Ebsco - EbscoHost, GaleNet, IAC - Info Trac, Lexis-Nexis, OVID Technologies
Publications: Newsletter
Function: ILL available
Mem of Suburban Library System
Friends of the Library Group

HINCKLEY

P SQUAW GROVE PUBLIC LIBRARY DISTRICT,* 100 N Maple St, 60520. (Mail add: PO Box 865, 60520), SAN 304-2758. Tel: 815-286-3220. FAX: 815-286-3664. E-Mail: hinckleylibrary@thestix.net. *Dir*, Shirley Wilhelmsen
Pop 2,387; Circ 28,633
Jul 1998-Jun 1999 Income $83,434, State $11,527. Mats Exp $9,579. Sal $58,327
Library Holdings: Bk Vols 14,000
Mem of Northern Illinois Library System
Friends of the Library Group

HINES

GM DEPARTMENT OF VETERANS AFFAIRS, Library Service (142D),* PO Box 5000/142D, 60141-5142. SAN 304-2774. Tel: 708-202-2000. FAX: 708-202-2719. *Chief Librn*, John Cline; E-Mail: clinej@med.va.gov; Staff 6 (MLS 2, Non-MLS 4)
Library Holdings: Bk Vols 9,500; Per Subs 575
Subject Interests: Allied health
Automation Activity & Vendor Info: (Acquisitions) Sagebrush Corporation; (Cataloging) Sagebrush Corporation; (Circulation) Sagebrush Corporation
Database Vendor: Dialog, OVID Technologies
Partic in Docline; OCLC Online Computer Library Center, Inc; Vets Admin Libr Network

HINSDALE

M ADVENTIST HEALTH SYSTEM, MIDWEST REGION - HINSDALE HOSPITAL, (Formerly Hinsdale Hospital), Health Sciences Library & Information Center, 120 N Oak St, 60521. SAN 304-2790. Tel: 630-856-7230. FAX: 630-856-7239. E-Mail: pgrundke@ahss.org. Web Site: www.ahsmidwest.org. *Mgr*, Pat Grundke; Staff 2 (MLS 1, Non-MLS 1)
Library Holdings: Bk Vols 4,000; Per Subs 230; Spec Interest Per Sub 10
Subject Interests: Medicine, Nursing, Seventh-Day Adventists
Special Collections: E G White Coll
Publications: Newsletter
Mem of ILL Libr & Info Network; Suburban Library System
Partic in Chicago & South Consortium; Illinois Library & Information Network; LVIS

P HINSDALE PUBLIC LIBRARY,* 20 E Maple St, 60521. SAN 304-2782. Tel: 630-986-1976. FAX: 630-986-9720. E-Mail: reference@hinsdale.lib.il.us. Web Site: www.hinsdale.lib.il.us. *Librn*, Jack Hurwitz; E-Mail: jhurwitz@hinsdale.lib.il.us; *Asst Librn, Tech Servs*, Mary Beth Sharples; E-Mail: mbsharples@hinsdale.lib.il.us; *Ch Servs*, Jane Byczek; E-Mail: jbyczek@hinsdale.lib.il.us; *Ref*, Susan McNeil-Marshall; E-Mail: smmarshall@hinsdale.lib.il.us; *Circ*, JoAnn Schusterich; E-Mail: jschusterich@hinsdale.lib.il.us; Staff 50 (MLS 13, Non-MLS 37)
Founded 1892. Pop 17,498; Circ 265,591
May 1998-Apr 1999 Income $1,496,067, State $36,704, Federal $71,250, Locally Generated Income $1,198,572, Other $189,541. Mats Exp $204,600, Books $147,800, Per/Ser (Incl. Access Fees) $15,900, Presv $800, Micro $11,800, Electronic Ref Mat (Incl. Access Fees) $28,300. Sal $748,076 (Prof $390,200)
Library Holdings: Bk Vols 125,700; Per Subs 338
Automation Activity & Vendor Info: (Circulation) Innovative Interfaces Inc.; (ILL) Innovative Interfaces Inc.; (OPAC) Innovative Interfaces Inc.
Publications: Newsletter (4 times per yr)
Mem of Suburban Library System
Special Services for the Deaf - TTY machine
Friends of the Library Group

HODGKINS

P HODGKINS PUBLIC LIBRARY DISTRICT,* 6500 Wenz Ave, 60525. SAN 321-4613. Tel: 708-579-1844. FAX: 708-579-1896. E-Mail: hks@sls.lib.il.us. Web Site: www.northstarnet.org/hkshome. *Librn*, Judy Young; *Ch Servs*, Connie Grune; Staff 2 (MLS 2)
Founded 1975. Pop 1,963
Library Holdings: Bk Vols 32,320; Bk Titles 31,850; Per Subs 122
Mem of Suburban Library System

HOFFMAN ESTATES

M HOFFMAN ESTATES MEDICAL CENTER, Medical Library,* 1555 N Barrington Rd, 60194. SAN 375-9776. Tel: 847-843-2000, Ext 6213. FAX: 847-490-2548. *Librn*, Patricia Whelihan
Special Collections: Medical Records Coll (past & present subjects)

HOMER

P HOMER COMMUNITY LIBRARY, 101 N Main St, 61849. SAN 304-2812. Tel: 217-896-2121. Web Site: www.holbrook.net66.com/~homer/library.htm. *Librn*, Christina L Reel; E-Mail: creel@net66.com
Founded 1971. Pop 1,264; Circ 9,920
May 1999-Apr 2000 Income $20,135, State $1,659, City $11,860, Federal $5,965, Other $651. Mats Exp $2,300, Books $2,257, AV Equip $43. Sal $9,699
Library Holdings: Bk Titles 11,748; Per Subs 21
Mem of Lincoln Trail Libraries System
Friends of the Library Group

HOMETOWN

P HOMETOWN PUBLIC LIBRARY, Jack R Ladwig Memorial Library, 4331 Southwest Hwy, 60456. SAN 304-2820. Tel: 708-636-0997. FAX: 708-636-8127. E-Mail: hometownlibrary@home.com. *Librn*, Annette R Selmeister; Staff 1 (MLS 1)
Founded 1956. Pop 4,769; Circ 25,814
Library Holdings: Bk Vols 24,600; Per Subs 480
Subject Interests: History, Local history, Religion, Social sciences and issues
Mem of Suburban Library System

HOMEWOOD

P HOMEWOOD PUBLIC LIBRARY DISTRICT, 17917 Dixie Hwy, 60430. SAN 304-2839. Tel: 708-798-0121. FAX: 708-798-0662. E-Mail: hws@sls.lib.il.us. Web Site: www.homepage.interaccess.com/~homewood/. *Ad Servs, Mgr*, Judi Wolinsky; *Ch Servs*, Dee Skelton; *Cat, Tech Servs*, Joan Webb; *Circ*, Carol Candeloro; Staff 7 (MLS 7)
Founded 1927. Pop 19,724; Circ 315,265
Jul 1998-Jun 1999 Income $1,370,465, State $26,058, Locally Generated Income $140,029, Other $999,000. Mats Exp $147,902, Books $122,848, Per/Ser (Incl. Access Fees) $7,402. Sal $704,000
Library Holdings: Bk Vols 112,795; Per Subs 240
Automation Activity & Vendor Info: (Acquisitions) Innovative Interfaces Inc.; (Cataloging) Innovative Interfaces Inc.; (Circulation) Innovative Interfaces Inc.; (Course Reserve) Innovative Interfaces Inc.; (ILL) Innovative Interfaces Inc.; (Media Booking) Innovative Interfaces Inc.; (OPAC) Innovative Interfaces Inc.; (Serials) Innovative Interfaces Inc.
Database Vendor: Innovative Interfaces INN - View
Publications: Homewood Hi-Lites
Mem of Suburban Library System
Friends of the Library Group

HOOPESTON

P HOOPESTON PUBLIC LIBRARY,* 110 N Fourth St, 60942-1499. SAN 304-2847. Tel: 217-283-6711. FAX: 217-283-7077. *Dir*, Lou Graham
Founded 1898. Pop 10,838; Circ 55,412
Jul 1998-Jun 1999 Mats Exp $27,000. Sal $105,000
Library Holdings: Bk Vols 34,000; Per Subs 100
Mem of Lincoln Trail Libraries System
Open Mon-Thurs 9:30-8, Fri 9:30-6, Sat 9:30-3
Friends of the Library Group

HOPEDALE

M HOPEDALE MEDICAL COMPLEX LIBRARY,* 61747. SAN 304-2855. Tel: 309-449-3321, Ext 392. FAX: 309-449-5568. *Librn*, Joy Wiemer
Founded 1965
Library Holdings: Bk Vols 164; Per Subs 60
Subject Interests: Alcohol and drugs, Hospital administration, Medicine, Nursing, Podiatry
Mem of Ill Valley Libr Syst
Partic in Heart Of Illinois Library Consortium; Nat Libr of Med

HUDSON

P HUDSON AREA PUBLIC LIBRARY DISTRICT, 104 Pearl St, PO Box 461, 61748. SAN 375-9504. Tel: 309-726-1103. FAX: 309-726-1646. E-Mail: hpld@darkstar.rsa.lib.il.us. *Librn*, Dolores Bauman
Pop 2,770
Jul 1999-Jun 2000 Income $112,998. Mats Exp $108,435. Sal $44,747
Library Holdings: Bk Titles 18,000; Per Subs 40
Mem of Alliance Library System

HUNTLEY

P HUNTLEY AREA PUBLIC LIBRARY, 11000 Ruth Rd, 60142-7155. (Mail add: PO Box 898, 60142-0898), SAN 375-9512. Tel: 847-669-5386. FAX: 847-669-5439. E-Mail: main@huntleylibrary.org. Web Site: www.huntleylibrary.org. *Admin Assoc*, Connie Eskin; E-Mail: ceskin@huntleylibrary.org; Staff 26 (MLS 2, Non-MLS 24)
Founded 1989. Pop 10,730; Circ 15,000
Jul 1999-Jul 2000 Income $978,751, State $132,037, City $136,260, County $679,149, Locally Generated Income $20,467, Other $10,838. Mats Exp $142,557, Books $105,369, Per/Ser (Incl. Access Fees) $7,907, AV Equip $1,847, Other Print Mats $2,094, Electronic Ref Mat (Incl. Access Fees) $9,041. Sal $267,554 (Prof $55,501)
Library Holdings: Bk Vols 36,900; Bk Titles 33,000; Per Subs 194; High Interest/Low Vocabulary Bk Vols 400; Bks on Deafness & Sign Lang 50
Subject Interests: Illinois, Local history
Database Vendor: IAC - Info Trac, OCLC - First Search
Function: ILL available
Mem of North Suburban Library System
Open Mon-Thurs 9-8, Fri 9-5, Sat 9-3 & Sun 12-4
Friends of the Library Group

ILLIOPOLIS

P ILLIOPOLIS-NIANTIC PUBLIC LIBRARY DISTRICT,* Sixth & Mary Sts, 62539. SAN 304-2863. Tel: 217-486-5561. Interlibrary Loan Service Tel: 800-801-7757. FAX: 217-486-7811. *Librn*, Shelley Perry
Founded 1935. Pop 2,296; Circ 19,739
Library Holdings: Bk Vols 16,977; Per Subs 34
Special Collections: War Plants Located at Illiopolis During WWII
Mem of Rolling Prairie Library System
Open Mon & Fri 1-5, Tues & Thurs 1-8, Wed 10-5, Sat 10-4

INA

J REND LAKE COLLEGE, Learning Resource Center,* 468 N Ken Gray Pkwy, 62846. SAN 304-2871. Tel: 618-437-5321. FAX: 618-437-5598. E-Mail: reference@ric.cc.il.us. Web Site: www.rlc.cc.il.us/lrc/lrchome.htm. *In Charge*, Lisa Collier; E-Mail: collier@rlc.cc.il.us; *Circ*, Kim Davis; *AV*, Andrea Whitoff; Staff 6 (Non-MLS 6)
Founded 1956. Enrl 1,540; Fac 54
Jul 1997-Jun 1998 Income $351,000. Mats Exp $43,648, Books $27,745, Per/Ser (Incl. Access Fees) $15,903. Sal $205,652 (Prof $89,824)
Library Holdings: Bk Vols 35,072; Per Subs 278
Mem of Shawnee Library System
Partic in Ill Coop Coll Mgt Prog; NILRC; SILRC

ITASCA

P ITASCA COMMUNITY LIBRARY,* 500 W Irving Park Rd, 60143. SAN 304-288X. Tel: 630-773-1699. FAX: 630-773-1707. E-Mail: itascal@linc.lib.il.us. Web Site: www.itasca.com/library/itlib.htm. *Dir*, Ruth Sender; *Tech Servs*, Nancy McCabe; *YA Servs*, Elizabeth Adamowski; *Circ*, Peggy Rice; *Ad Servs*, Lawrence Zevnik
Founded 1957. Pop 7,585; Circ 114,945
Library Holdings: Bk Vols 69,900; Per Subs 180
Special Collections: Business Coll for DuPage Libr System; Learning Games Library; Parent Teacher Texts
Mem of DuPage Library System

S NATIONAL SAFETY COUNCIL LIBRARY, 1121 Spring Lake Dr, 60143. SAN 303-9870. Tel: 630-285-1121, Ext 2199. FAX: 630-285-0765. Web Site: www.nsc.org. *Mgr*, Robert J Marecek; E-Mail: bob-nsc@dupagels.lib.il.us, marecekr@nsc.org
Founded 1913
Jul 1999-Jun 2000 Mats Exp $41,000, Books $17,000, Per/Ser (Incl. Access Fees) $22,000, Presv $500, Micro $1,000, Manuscripts & Archives $500
Library Holdings: Bk Titles 150,000; Per Subs 150
Subject Interests: Accident prevention, Occupational safety, Traffic (safety)
Publications: Historical Index to the Industrial Data Sheets
Mem of DuPage Library System
Partic in Illinois Library & Information Network

JACKSONVILLE

C ILLINOIS COLLEGE, Schewe Library, 1101 W College Ave, 62650-2299. SAN 304-2898. Tel: 217-245-3020. Circulation Tel: 217-245-3021. Reference Tel: 217-245-3022. FAX: 217-245-3082. Web Site: www.ic.edu/library.htm. *Dir*, Martin H Gallas; E-Mail: gallas@hilltop.ic.edu; *Bibliog Instr*, W Michael Westbrook; Tel: 217-245-3022, E-Mail: mwestbro@hilltop.ic.edu; *Tech Servs*, A Stuart Gaetjens; Tel: 217-245-3023, E-Mail: gaetjens@hilltop.ic.edu; Staff 7 (MLS 3, Non-MLS 4)
Founded 1829. Enrl 890; Fac 65; Highest Degree: Bachelor
Jul 2000-Jun 2001 Income $424,578, State $2,000, Parent Institution $422,578. Mats Exp $153,703, Books $86,534, Per/Ser (Incl. Access Fees) $63,399, Presv $361, AV Equip $1,609, Electronic Ref Mat (Incl. Access Fees) $1,800. Sal $215,015 (Prof $127,449)
Library Holdings: Bk Vols 152,709; Bk Titles 98,773; Per Subs 625
Special Collections: Civil War Coll; Lincoln Coll; Local History
Database Vendor: epixtech, inc.
Mem of Alliance Library System
Partic in Illinois Library & Information Network; OCLC Online Computer Library Center, Inc; Sangamon Valley Academic Library Consortium

S ILLINOIS DEPARTMENT OF CORRECTIONS (IDOC), Jacksonville Correctional Center Library, 2268 E Morton Ave, 62650-9347. SAN 375-5347. Tel: 217-245-1481, Ext 334. FAX: 217-245-1481, Ext 324. *Librn*, Susan Crowfoot; Staff 2 (MLS 1, Non-MLS 1)
Founded 1984
Jul 1999-Jun 2000 Income $86,041. Mats Exp $19,600, Books $1,000, Per/Ser (Incl. Access Fees) $2,600, Other Print Mats $16,000. Sal $63,696 (Prof $33,696)
Library Holdings: Bk Vols 8,800; Per Subs 26
Special Collections: Federal/State Statutory & Case Law Coll; Self-Help Legal Books
Partic in ILLINET; Illinois Library & Information Network; Resource Sharing Alliance

S ILLINOIS SCHOOL FOR THE DEAF, Media Center, 125 Webster, 62650. SAN 326-9477. Tel: 217-479-4240. TDD: 217-479-4240. FAX: 217-479-4244. E-Mail: dhsrspg@dhs.state.il.us. *Dir*, Marybeth Heinemann; *Librn for Deaf*, Mary Jane Metcalf; *Tech Servs*, Sue Vedder; *Info Tech*, Lana Shea; *Info Tech*, Nancy Bradbury; *Librn*, William Patton; *Outreach Serv*, Terri Jones. Subject Specialists: *Computers*, Lana Shea; *Graphic art*, William Patton; *Outreach*, Terri Jones; Staff 7 (Non-MLS 7)
Jul 1999-Jun 2000 Income $403,100, State $400,600, Federal $2,500. Mats Exp $11,500, Books $9,000, Per/Ser (Incl. Access Fees) $1,500. Sal $271,900 (Prof $144,000)
Library Holdings: Bk Vols 15,100; Bk Titles 15,000; Per Subs 49; High Interest/Low Vocabulary Bk Vols 4,000; Spec Interest Per Sub 5; Bks on Deafness & Sign Lang 1,010
Subject Interests: Deaf educ, Deafness, Education, Sign lang
Special Collections: Deafness and related subjects, bks
Automation Activity & Vendor Info: (Cataloging) Follett; (Circulation) Follett
Database Vendor: CARL, OCLC - First Search
Publications: Sights & Sounds
Function: ILL available
Mem of Alliance Library System
Special Services for the Deaf - Captioned film depository; Captioned media; Staff with knowledge of sign language; TTY machine

C ILLINOIS SCHOOL FOR THE VISUALLY IMPAIRED LIBRARY,* 658 E State St, 62650-2184. SAN 326-9582. Tel: 217-479-4400, Ext 471. FAX: 217-479-4479. E-Mail: isvi@fgi.net. Web Site: www.morgan.k12.il.us/isvi. *Librn*, Beverly Sanderson
Library Holdings: Bk Titles 27,000; Per Subs 40
Subject Interests: Blindness, Special education
Mem of Alliance Library System

M JACKSONVILLE DEVELOPMENTAL CENTER LIBRARY,* 1201 S Main St, 62650-3396. SAN 304-2901. Tel: 217-479-2117 (Admin). FAX: 217-245-1165. *Librn*, Bill Curry
Library Holdings: Bk Vols 225; Per Subs 25

P JACKSONVILLE PUBLIC LIBRARY,* 201 W College, 62650-2497. SAN 304-291X. Tel: 217-243-5435. TDD: 217-245-5022. FAX: 217-243-2182. E-Mail: japl@csj.net. Web Site: japl.lib.il.us/library. *Dir*, Kathleen Roegge; *Outreach Serv*, Betty Pine; Staff 7 (MLS 4, Non-MLS 3)
Founded 1889. Pop 19,324; Circ 168,016
1997-1998 Income $350,000, State $24,000, City $250,000, Locally Generated Income $74,000. Mats Exp $56,550, Books $45,000, Per/Ser (Incl. Access Fees) $7,500, Other Print Mats $50. Sal $211,919 (Prof $150,780)
Library Holdings: Bk Vols 85,000; Per Subs 161
Special Collections: Morgan County History (Morgan County Historical Society)
Publications: J P L Pages (newsletter)
Mem of Alliance Library System
Friends of the Library Group

C MACMURRAY COLLEGE, Henry Pfeiffer Library, 447 E College Ave, 62650-2510. SAN 304-2928. Tel: 217-479-7110. FAX: 217-245-5214. Web Site: www.mac.edu/academic/lib. *Dir*, Mary Jo Thomas; E-Mail: mjthomas@mac.edu; *Publ Servs*, Penelope Mitchell; E-Mail: penmitch@mac.edu; *Circ*, Mary Ellen Blackston; Tel: 217-479-7111, E-Mail: meblack@mac.edu; *Tech Servs*, Susan Eilering; E-Mail: susane@mac.edu; Staff 5 (MLS 3, Non-MLS 2)
Founded 1846. Enrl 875; Fac 55; Highest Degree: Bachelor
Library Holdings: Bk Vols 120,000; Per Subs 300
Subject Interests: Deaf educ, Special education
Special Collections: Lincoln Coll; McMurray College Archives
Automation Activity & Vendor Info: (Cataloging) TLC; (Circulation) TLC; (OPAC) TLC
Database Vendor: Ebsco - EbscoHost, OCLC - First Search, ProQuest
Mem of Alliance Library System; Nat Network of Librs of Med
Partic in Alliance Library System; Illinois Library & Information Network
Open Mon-Thurs 7:45am-9:30pm, Fri 7:45pm-4pm, Sat 10am-2pm & Sun 3-9:30pm

M PASSAVANT AREA HOSPITAL, Sibert Library, 1600 W Walnut, 62650. SAN 304-2936. Tel: 217-245-9541, Ext 3534. FAX: 217-479-5639. Web Site: www.passavanthospital.com. *Dir*, Karen Douglas; E-Mail: kdouglas@csj.net
Founded 1902
Oct 1999-Sep 2000 Income $55,000. Mats Exp $30,000, Books $5,500, Per/Ser (Incl. Access Fees) $16,000, Other Print Mats $1,000. Sal $23,000
Library Holdings: Bk Vols 1,000; Per Subs 390
Subject Interests: Allied health, Medicine, Nursing
Special Collections: American Journal of Nursing (1902 to present)
Mem of Alliance Library System
Partic in Capital Area Consortium; Illinois Library & Information Network; LVIS
Accessible for the handicapped

JERSEYVILLE

P JERSEYVILLE PUBLIC LIBRARY,* 105 N Liberty St, 62052-1512. SAN 304-2944. Tel: 618-498-9514, Ext 9515. FAX: 618-498-3036. E-Mail: jee_ill@lcls.lib.il.us. *Librn*, Anita Driver
Founded 1894. Pop 7,382; Circ 107,723
Apr 1998-Mar 1999 Income $251,559. Mats Exp $32,336. Sal $112,520
Library Holdings: Bk Vols 49,817; Per Subs 144
Mem of Lewis & Clark Library System
Partic in Illinois Library & Information Network; OCLC Online Computer Library Center, Inc
Homebound Service
Friends of the Library Group

JOHNSBURG

P JOHNSBURG PUBLIC LIBRARY DISTRICT, 3000 W Johnsburg Rd, 60050. SAN 323-5491. Tel: 815-344-0077. FAX: 815-344-3524. Web Site: www.johnsburglibrary.org. *Dir*, Maria Zawacki; E-Mail: mariaz@nils.lib.il.us; *Circ*, Virginia Brya; *Ch Servs*, Paulette Babchak; E-Mail: pbabchak@jpld.org; Staff 9 (MLS 1, Non-MLS 8)
Founded 1982. Pop 10,697; Circ 92,980
Jul 1999-Jun 2000 Income $373,969, State $14,322, Federal $16,270, Locally Generated Income $310,242. Mats Exp $53,511, Books $48,168, AV Equip $5,343. Sal $108,972
Library Holdings: Bk Vols 33,523; Per Subs 293
Automation Activity & Vendor Info: (Cataloging) Follett; (Circulation) Follett; (OPAC) Follett
Database Vendor: OCLC - First Search
Publications: Quarterly newsletter
Mem of Northern Illinois Library System
Friends of the Library Group

JOHNSTON CITY

P JOHNSTON CITY PUBLIC LIBRARY,* 506 Washington Ave, 62951. SAN 304-2952. Tel: 618-983-6359. FAX: 618-983-3006. *Librn*, Brenda Gilpatrick
Pop 3,928; Circ 16,800
Library Holdings: Bk Vols 15,113; Per Subs 36
Mem of Shawnee Library System
Open Mon-Fri 2-7:30, Sat 11-3:30
Friends of the Library Group

JOLIET

S AMERICAN THEATRE ORGAN SOCIETY, INC, Archives & Library, 5 E Van Buren St, 60432-4223. SAN 325-5247. Tel: 708-562-8538. *Curator*, James Patak
Founded 1975
Library Holdings: Bk Titles 75
Subject Interests: Exhibition of theatre pipe organs, History, Maintenance of theatre pipe organs, Presv, Restoration
Special Collections: Glass Song Slides; Silent Motion Picture Cue Sheets & Scores; Wurlitzer Organ Rolls
Publications: Archives & Library catalogue; educator's guide; technical manual

S ILLINOIS YOUTH CENTER, Joliet Library, 2848 W McDonough St, 60436. SAN 375-9555. Tel: 815-725-1206. FAX: 815-725-9819. *Librn*, Alice Hopman
Library Holdings: Bk Titles 500; Per Subs 30

J JOLIET JUNIOR COLLEGE, Learning Resource Center,* 1215 Houbolt Rd, 60431. SAN 304-2987. Tel: 815-729-9020, Ext 2350. FAX: 815-744-2465. E-Mail: ganderso@jjc.cc.il.us. Web Site: www.jjc.cc.il.us/dept/library.html. *Dean of Libr*, Dr Denis Wright; *Acq, Coordr*, Gerald Anderson; *Circ, Ref*, Marvin Schumaker; *Tech Servs*, Judy Hansen; *Automation Syst Coordr*, Barbara Wilson; Staff 6 (MLS 3, Non-MLS 3)
Founded 1902. Enrl 5,000; Fac 150
1997-1998 Income $684,357. Mats Exp $147,725, Books $76,318, Per/Ser (Incl. Access Fees) $28,157, Micro $11,000. Sal $353,646 (Prof $192,165)
Library Holdings: Bk Vols 70,000; Bk Titles 53,000; Per Subs 675
Subject Interests: Education, Horticulture, Nursing
Special Collections: Children's books, soil surveys
Publications: Acquisitions report; film catalogue; video catalogue
Mem of Heritage Trail Library System
Partic in Ill Regional Libr Coun; Northern Ill Learning Resources Coop

P JOLIET PUBLIC LIBRARY, 150 N Ottawa St, 60432-4192. SAN 340-4854. Tel: 815-740-2660. Reference Tel: 815-740-2662. FAX: 815-740-6161. Web Site: www.joliet.lib.il.us. *Dir*, James R Johnston; E-Mail: jrjohnston@joliet.lib.il.us; *Assoc Dir*, Dianne Harmon; *Asst Dir*, John Mozga; *Ref*, Marcia Frowein; *Ch Servs*, Phyllis Davis; *Circ*, Chris Pesavento; Staff 12 (MLS 10, Non-MLS 2)
Founded 1875. Pop 94,000; Circ 500,000
Library Holdings: Bk Titles 367,614; Per Subs 595
Special Collections: Granger Poetry; Illinois History
Automation Activity & Vendor Info: (Circulation) CLSI LIBS
Publications: Public & Staff Newsletters
Friends of the Library Group

M PROVENA SAINT JOSEPH MEDICAL CENTER, Health Science Library, 333 N Madison St, 60435. SAN 304-2995. Tel: 815-725-7133, Ext 3530. FAX: 815-725-9459. Web Site: www.provenahealth.com. *Librn*, Virginia Gale; E-Mail: virginiagale@provenahealth.com
Founded 1975
Library Holdings: Bk Vols 2,000; Bk Titles 1,500; Per Subs 300
Subject Interests: Medicine, Nursing
Automation Activity & Vendor Info: (Cataloging) EOS; (OPAC) EOS
Database Vendor: OCLC - First Search, Silverplatter Information Inc.
Mem of Heritage Trail Library System
Partic in Chicago & South Consortium

M SILVER CROSS HOSPITAL, Lloyd W Jessen Health Science Library, 1200 Maple Rd, 60432-9988. SAN 304-3002. Tel: 815-740-1100, Ext 7477. FAX: 815-740-7024. Web Site: www.silvercross.org.
Founded 1956
Library Holdings: Bk Vols 600; Per Subs 200
Subject Interests: Education, Health sciences, Medicine
Restriction: Medical staff only
Mem of Heritage Trail Library System
Partic in Dialog Corporation

S STATEVILLE CORRECTIONAL CENTER LIBRARIES,* PO Box 112, 60434. SAN 340-4919. Tel: 815-727-3607, Ext 5550. *Dir*, Gary Wintersteen; *Asst Librn*, Phyllis Chapel; Staff 3 (MLS 3)
Founded 1936
Library Holdings: Bk Vols 39,000; Per Subs 140
Subject Interests: Criminal law and justice, Law, Recreation
Partic in Hertiage Trail Libr Syst

CR UNIVERSITY OF SAINT FRANCIS, Main Library, 600 Taylor St, 60435. SAN 304-2960. Tel: 815-740-3447. Circulation Tel: 815-740-3448. Reference Tel: 815-740-5041. FAX: 815-740-3364. Web Site: www.stfrancis.edu. *Dir*, Sister Carol Ann Novak; E-Mail: cnovak@stfrancis.edu; *Admin Dir*, Janet Gayle; Tel: 815-740-4292, E-Mail: jgayle@stfrancis.edu; *Head Ref*, Julie Dahl; E-Mail: jdahl@stfrancis.edu; *Ref, Tech Servs*, Barbara Predy; *AV*, Cheryl Basso; *ILL*, Joan Koren; E-Mail: jkoren@stfrancis.edu; *Cat, Tech Servs*, Judy Moroz; E-Mail: jmoroz@stfrancis.edu; *Per*, Michelle Caputo; E-Mail: mcaputo@stfrancis.edu. Subject Specialists: *Libr sci*, Sister Carol Ann Novak
Founded 1930. Enrl 3,718; Highest Degree: Master
Library Holdings: Bk Vols 110,000; Per Subs 700
Subject Interests: Franciscans
Special Collections: Business Ethics
Automation Activity & Vendor Info: (Cataloging) Innovative Interfaces Inc.; (Circulation) Innovative Interfaces Inc.; (OPAC) Innovative Interfaces Inc.; (Serials) Innovative Interfaces Inc.
Database Vendor: Ebsco - EbscoHost, IAC - SearchBank, OCLC - First Search, ProQuest
Publications: Faculty Library Handbook; Student Libarary Handbook
Mem of Heritage Trail Library System
Partic in Illinois Library & Information Network; Libras, Inc; LIRN; OCLC Online Computer Library Center, Inc; SMRHEC
Departmental Libraries:
JOHN & CICELY LEACH LIBRARY, Saint Joseph College of Nursing, 600 Taylor St, 60435. SAN 375-944X. Tel: 815-773-7823. FAX: 815-741-7243. Web Site: www.stfrancis.edu. *Admin Dir*, Janet Gayle; Tel: 815-740-3447, 740-4292, Fax: 815-740-3364, E-Mail: jgayle@stfrancis.edu; *Librn*, Gladys Hughes; E-Mail: ghughes@stfrancis.edu; *Cat*, Gail Gawlik; E-Mail: ggawlik@stfrancis.edu
Library Holdings: Bk Vols 2,000; Per Subs 80
Subject Interests: Nursing
Automation Activity & Vendor Info: (Cataloging) Innovative Interfaces Inc.; (Circulation) Innovative Interfaces Inc.; (OPAC) Innovative Interfaces Inc.; (Serials) Innovative Interfaces Inc.
Database Vendor: Ebsco - EbscoHost, IAC - SearchBank, OCLC - First Search, ProQuest
Mem of Heritage Trail Library System
Partic in Chicago & South Consortium; HSLI; Libras, Inc; LIRN; SMRHEC

L WILL COUNTY LAW LIBRARY,* 14 W Jefferson St Ste 453, 60432. SAN 373-0484. Tel: 815-727-8536. FAX: 815-727-8785. *Librn*, Jean Warner
Library Holdings: Bk Vols 3,000; Per Subs 15
Subject Interests: Compact discs
Special Collections: US Tax Reports
Partic in ILL State Syst

JONESBORO

P JONESBORO PUBLIC LIBRARY,* 412 S Main, PO Box AD, 62952. SAN 304-3010. Tel: 618-833-8121. FAX: 618-833-8121. *Librn*, Martha Davidson
Pop 1,786; Circ 4,269
Library Holdings: Bk Vols 6,221
Mem of Shawnee Library System

JUSTICE

P JUSTICE PUBLIC LIBRARY DISTRICT,* 7641 Oak Grove Ave, 60458-1397. SAN 320-474X. Tel: 708-496-1790. FAX: 708-496-1898. E-Mail: jplonline@yahoo.com. Web Site: www.justicepubliclibrary.com. *Dir*, Adrian Dalwood
Founded 1978. Pop 12,610; Circ 56,000
Jul 1996-Jun 1997 Income $289,752. Mats Exp $36,570, Books $26,000, Per/Ser (Incl. Access Fees) $3,000, AV Equip $2,000, Other Print Mats

$4,670. Sal $102,000
Library Holdings: Bk Vols 35,000; Per Subs 117
Publications: Cover to Cover Newsletter
Mem of Suburban Library System
Friends of the Library Group

KAMPSVILLE

S CENTER FOR AMERICAN ARCHEOLOGY, Research Library, PO Box 366, 62053. SAN 371-165X. Tel: 618-653-4316. FAX: 618-653-4232. E-Mail: caa@caa-archeology.org. Web Site: www.caa-archeology.org. *Librn*, Mary Gilman
Library Holdings: Bk Vols 1,000; Per Subs 5
Restriction: Not open to public

KANEVILLE

P KANEVILLE PUBLIC LIBRARY, 2 S 101 Harter Rd, PO Box 29, 60144-0029. SAN 304-3029. Tel: 630-557-2441. FAX: 630-557-2553. *Dir*, Judith Krajecki; Staff 4 (MLS 1, Non-MLS 3)
Founded 1934. Pop 1,367; Circ 10,800
Library Holdings: Bk Vols 20,000; Per Subs 62
Subject Interests: Fiction, Local history
Mem of DuPage Library System
Friends of the Library Group

KANKAKEE

J KANKAKEE COMMUNITY COLLEGE, Learning Resource Center, River Rd, PO Box 888, 60901. SAN 304-3045. Tel: 815-933-0260. FAX: 815-933-0217. Web Site: www.kcc.cc.il.us. *Dir*, Donna Smith; Tel: 815-933-0259, E-Mail: dsmith@kcc.cc.il.us; Staff 6 (MLS 1, Non-MLS 5)
Founded 1966. Enrl 3,800
1997-1998 Mats Exp $72,272, Books $40,500, Per/Ser (Incl. Access Fees) $31,772
Library Holdings: Bk Vols 45,151; Bk Titles 41,017; Per Subs 392
Special Collections: Gordon Graves Environmental Coll; Reece L Ayers Soil & Water Conservation Coll
Automation Activity & Vendor Info: (Cataloging) DRA
Mem of Heritage Trail Library System
Partic in Ill Libr Computer Systs Org

S KANKAKEE COUNTY HISTORICAL SOCIETY MUSEUM LIBRARY, 801 S Eighth Ave, 60901-4744. SAN 304-3053. Tel: 815-932-5279. FAX: 815-932-5204. E-Mail: museum@daily-journal.com. Web Site: www.kankakeecountymuseum.com. *Exec Dir*, Michael J Erickson
Founded 1906
Library Holdings: Bk Vols 3,500
Subject Interests: History
Special Collections: Adjutant's Records; Biographies; County History; Documents Coll; History of County Townships, bks, photog; Letters Coll; Manuscripts Coll
Publications: Newsletter (quarterly)
Restriction: By appointment only, In-house use for visitors

S KANKAKEE DAILY JOURNAL LIBRARY,* 8 Dearborn Sq, 60901. SAN 374-9568. Tel: 815-937-3378. FAX: 815-937-3876. *Chief Librn*, Glory Klasey
Special Collections: Microfilm, 1854 to present; Newspaper Clipping Files, 1967 to present

P KANKAKEE PUBLIC LIBRARY,* 304 S Indiana Ave, 60901. SAN 304-3061. Tel: 815-939-4564. FAX: 815-939-9057. Web Site: www.htls.lib.il.us/kkb. *Librn*, Cynthia Fuerst; E-Mail: cfuerst@starbase1.htls.lib.il.us; *Asst Dir*, Mary Costanza; *Ref*, Stephen Bertrand; *Ch Servs*, Carol O'Malley; *Tech Servs*, Cheryl Pankey-Hawkins; *Ad Servs*, Allison Toth
Founded 1899. Pop 27,575; Circ 134,895
Library Holdings: Bk Vols 104,102; Per Subs 250
Subject Interests: Genealogy
Special Collections: Art Books
Publications: Between the Lions Newsletter (bi-monthly)
Mem of Heritage Trail Library System
Partic in CLSI
Friends of the Library Group

M RIVERSIDE HEALTHCARE SYSTEMS, Department of Library Services,* 350 N Wall St, 60901. SAN 304-307X. Tel: 815-933-1671, Ext 4855. FAX: 815-935-7480. *In Charge*, Lou Miller
Library Holdings: Bk Vols 1,540; Bk Titles 330; Per Subs 84
Mem of Heritage Trail Library System
Partic in Chicago & South Consortium

M SAINT MARY'S HOSPITAL, Medical Library, 500 W Court St, 60901. SAN 375-9466. Tel: 815-937-2477. FAX: 815-937-8772. *Librn*, Sandy Kambic
Library Holdings: Bk Titles 200

M SHAPIRO DEVELOPMENTAL CENTER, Resident Library,* 100 E Jeffery, 60901. SAN 326-9973. Tel: 815-939-8011, 815-939-8505. FAX: 815-939-8414.
Library Holdings: Bk Titles 6,000; Per Subs 40
Mem of Corn Belt Library System
Open Mon-Fri 8-4:30

KANSAS

P KANSAS COMMUNITY MEMORIAL LIBRARY, (KCML), 107 N Front St, PO Box 319, 61933-0319. SAN 304-3096. Tel: 217-948-5484. FAX: 217-948-5484. E-Mail: rhelts@ltnet.ltls.org. *Librn*, Rebecca Heltsley; E-Mail: rhelts@ltnet.ltls.org
Founded 1932. Pop 1,114; Circ 9,173
Library Holdings: Bk Vols 9,200; Per Subs 16
Mem of Lincoln Trail Libraries System
Open Mon 10-5, Tues 10-5, Wed-Fri 1-5, Sat 10-3

KENILWORTH

S KENILWORTH HISTORICAL SOCIETY, Archives & Library, 415 Kenilworth Ave, 60043-1134. (Mail add: PO Box 181, 60043-0181), SAN 304-310X. Tel: 847-251-2565. FAX: 847-251-3908. *Pres*, Patricia M Babb; *Archivist, Curator*, Melinda Kwedar
Founded 1972
Library Holdings: Bk Vols 750
Special Collections: Photograph Coll
Restriction: Open to public for reference only
Open Mon 9-4:30, Thurs 9-12 or by appointment

P KENILWORTH PUBLIC LIBRARY DISTRICT,* 419 Richmond Rd, 60043. SAN 376-2785. Tel: 847-446-7220. FAX: 847-446-5084. *Librn*, Donna G Sundstrom
1998-1999 Income $189,192
Mem of North Suburban Library System
Partic in Wilmette Pub Libr District; Winnetka-Northfield Pub Libr District
Friends of the Library Group

KEWANEE

J BLACK HAWK COLLEGE-EAST CAMPUS, Lundberg Learning Resource Center,* 1501 State Hwy 78, 61443. SAN 304-3118. Tel: 309-852-5671, Ext 273 or 214. FAX: 309-852-0038. Web Site: www.bhc.edu. *Dir*, Ann Larson; E-Mail: larsona@eastadmin.bhc.edu; *AV*, Lavon Franklin; E-Mail: franklinl@eastadmin.bhc.edu
Founded 1967. Enrl 600
1997-1998 Income $28,500. Mats Exp Books $10,000
Library Holdings: Bk Vols 17,000; Per Subs 175
Subject Interests: Agriculture, Horses
Special Collections: Local Authors Coll
Mem of Alliance Library System

S KEWANEE HISTORICAL SOCIETY LIBRARY,* 211 N Chestnut St, 61443. SAN 374-9428. Tel: 309-854-9701. *Pres*, Robert Richards
Library Holdings: Bk Vols 400
Subject Interests: Local history
Special Collections: Corn Husking Hall of Fame

P KEWANEE PUBLIC LIBRARY DISTRICT, 102 S Tremont St, 61443. SAN 304-3126. Tel: 309-852-4505. FAX: 309-852-4466. E-Mail: kewaneelibrary@yahoo.com. *Dir*, John E Sayers; E-Mail: jesayers@yahoo.com; *Asst Dir*, Patricia Goffrier; *Head Ref*, Emily J Knott; *Head Tech Servs*, Jean Craig; *ILL, Tech Servs*, Patricia Lock; *Ad Servs*, Marcia Sunquist; *YA Servs*, Melanie Johnston; *Ch Servs*, Sara Marsh; Staff 17 (MLS 2, Non-MLS 15)
Founded 1875. Pop 14,671; Circ 110,636
Jul 1998-Jun 1999 Income $317,983. Mats Exp $53,900, Books $38,000, Per/Ser (Incl. Access Fees) $9,900, AV Equip $6,000. Sal $188,871
Library Holdings: Bk Vols 46,708; Per Subs 144
Subject Interests: Local history
Automation Activity & Vendor Info: (Circulation) CARL; (OPAC) CARL
Database Vendor: CARL, OCLC - First Search
Publications: Between the Lines (Newsletter)
Mem of Alliance Library System
Friends of the Library Group

KIRKLAND

P KIRKLAND PUBLIC LIBRARY, 513 W Main St, 60146. (Mail add: PO Box 189, 60146), SAN 304-3142. Tel: 815-522-6260. FAX: 815-522-6260. E-Mail: kirklandlib@tbcnet.com. Web Site: www.geocities.com/kirkland_lib/index.html. *Dir*, Cindy K Brown; *Asst Librn*, Dawn Cihlar; *Asst Librn*, Peggy Mowers; *Tech Servs*, David Mowers; Staff 1 (Non-MLS 1)
Founded 1920. Pop 1,014; Circ 9,424
May 1999-Apr 2000 Income $20,822, State $1,248, City $17,285, Locally Generated Income $2,289. Mats Exp $20,886, Books $1,423, Per/Ser (Incl.

Access Fees) $413, AV Equip $424. Sal $13,175
Library Holdings: Bk Vols 9,590; Per Subs 16; High Interest/Low Vocabulary Bk Vols 56; Bks on Deafness & Sign Lang 11
Automation Activity & Vendor Info: (Circulation) Sagebrush Corporation
Database Vendor: OCLC - First Search
Function: ILL available
Mem of Northern Illinois Library System
Partic in Northern Ill Libr Asn
Special Services for the Deaf - TDD
Open Mon & Thur 11-8, Tues 4-8, Sat 9-1
Friends of the Library Group

KNOXVILLE

P KNOXVILLE PUBLIC LIBRARY, 200 E Main St, 61448-1351. SAN 304-3150. Tel: 309-289-2113. FAX: 309-289-8063. E-Mail: kpl@galesburg.net. *Dir*, Patricia A Rose
Founded 1878. Pop 3,432; Circ 21,716
Library Holdings: Bk Vols 19,000; Per Subs 50
Mem of Alliance Library System

LA GRANGE

M COLUMBIA-LA GRANGE MEMORIAL HOSPITAL, Zitek Medical Library, 5101 Willow Springs Rd, 60525. SAN 304-3169. Tel: 708-579-4040. FAX: 708-352-6072.
Founded 1956
Library Holdings: Bk Vols 1,700; Bk Titles 600; Per Subs 225
Subject Interests: Medicine, Nursing
Mem of Suburban Library System
Partic in Chicago & South Consortium; Greater Midwest Regional Medical Libr Network; Illinois Library & Information Network; MLA

R GRACE LUTHERAN CHURCH LIBRARY, 200 N Catherine Ave, 60525-1826. (Mail add: PO Box 207, 60525-0207), SAN 304-3185. Tel: 708-352-0730. FAX: 708-352-0737. *Librn*, Grace Puls; E-Mail: gracielib@aol.com; *Librn*, Marilyn Burns; Staff 12 (MLS 1, Non-MLS 11)
Founded 1954
Library Holdings: Bk Vols 2,693
Subject Interests: Religion
Automation Activity & Vendor Info: (Cataloging) Sagebrush Corporation
Open Thurs & Sun 9-12 noon

P LA GRANGE PUBLIC LIBRARY,* 10 W Cossitt, 60525-2391. SAN 304-3193. Tel: 708-352-0576. TDD: 708-352-5339. FAX: 708-352-1620. E-Mail: lgs@lagrangelibrary.org. Web Site: www.lagrangelibrary.org. *Dir*, Stephen L Moskal, Sr; *Ref*, Debra Darwine; *Ch Servs*, Mary Forbes; *Ad Servs*, Delores Riccio; *Ref*, Victor Smith; *Tech Servs*, Nancy Hardisty; *ILL*, Pat Prohl; *Ref*, Gail Morrissey; Staff 30 (MLS 6, Non-MLS 24)
Founded 1903. Pop 15,362; Circ 163,568
May 1998-Apr 1999 Income $1,051,227, State $37,953, City $920,085, Other $93,189. Mats Exp $950,755, Books $107,712, Per/Ser (Incl. Access Fees) $6,000, Micro $3,000, Electronic Ref Mat (Incl. Access Fees) $4,000. Sal $528,215
Library Holdings: Bk Vols 84,002; Per Subs 200
Subject Interests: Genealogy, Local history
Special Collections: Business
Publications: The Book Report
Mem of Suburban Library System
Friends of the Library Group

LA GRANGE PARK

S AMERICAN NUCLEAR SOCIETY LIBRARY,* 555 N Kensington Ave, 60526. SAN 304-3207. Tel: 708-352-6611, Ext 292. FAX: 708-352-0499. *Librn*, Jeanette Gabrys
Founded 1973
Library Holdings: Bk Vols 4,000; Bk Titles 3,000; Per Subs 175
Subject Interests: Business and management, Government, Nuclear science
Restriction: By appointment only

P LA GRANGE PARK PUBLIC LIBRARY DISTRICT, 555 N LaGrange Rd, 60526-5644. SAN 304-3215. Tel: 708-352-0100. TDD: 708-352-1970. FAX: 708-352-1606. E-Mail: lps@sls.lib.il.us. Web Site: www.lplibrary.org. *Dir*, Dixie M Conkis; *Ad Servs*, Kate Zdenek; *Ch Servs*, Meb Ingold; Staff 6 (MLS 4, Non-MLS 2)
Founded 1975. Pop 12,861; Circ 129,650
Jul 1999-Jun 2000 Income $960,105. Mats Exp $89,747. Sal $325,873
Library Holdings: Bk Vols 59,595; Bk Titles 55,565; Per Subs 219
Publications: Quarterly newsletter
Mem of Suburban Library System
Friends of the Library Group

LA HARPE

P LA HARPE CARNEGIE PUBLIC LIBRARY DISTRICT,* 209 E Main St, PO Box 506, 61450. SAN 304-3223. Tel: 217-659-7729. FAX: 217-659-7735. E-Mail: lahalib@winco.net. *Dir*, Martha Miller; *Asst Librn*, Kate Harden
Founded 1890. Pop 2,700; Circ 15,280
Library Holdings: Bk Vols 18,000; Per Subs 32
Special Collections: Hancock Co Quill 1893-1982, (weekly newsp)
Mem of Alliance Library System
Open Mon & Tues 10-5, Wed 3-8, Thurs & Fri 10-12, Sat 10-5

LA MOILLE

P LA MOILLE CLARION DISTRICT PUBLIC LIBRARY, 81 Main St, PO Box 260, 61330. SAN 304-3231. Tel: 815-638-2356. FAX: 815-638-2356. *Chief Librn*, Barbara Bartoli; *Asst Librn*, Charlene McClain; *Asst Librn*, Miranda Wamhoff; Staff 3 (Non-MLS 3)
Founded 1973. Pop 2,020; Circ 11,555
Jul 1999-Jun 2000 Income $39,605. Sal $19,813
Library Holdings: Bk Titles 15,862; Per Subs 56
Mem of Heritage Trail Library System
Open Mon, Tues & Thurs 2-5, Wed 2-8, Fri & Sat 9-5

LA SALLE

S CARUS CHEMICAL CO, Research Library,* 1500 Eighth St, 61301-3500. SAN 375-9938. Tel: 815-224-6854. FAX: 815-224-6841. E-Mail: reslib@iunet.com. *Librn*, Joan Hlavin
Library Holdings: Bk Titles 1,400; Per Subs 45

P LA SALLE PUBLIC LIBRARY, 305 Marquette St, 61301. SAN 304-324X. Tel: 815-223-2341. TDD: 815-223-2341. FAX: 815-223-2353. E-Mail: lfrizol@htls.lib.il.us. Web Site: www.htls.lib.il.us/lsb. *Dir*, Laura Trower; E-Mail: lfrizol@htls.lib.il.us; *Asst Librn*, Denise Hodgett; Staff 5 (MLS 2, Non-MLS 3)
Founded 1907. Pop 9,717; Circ 62,040
May 2000-Apr 2001 Income $163,000, State $12,000, City $9,000, County $142,000. Mats Exp $27,000, Books $25,000, Per/Ser (Incl. Access Fees) $2,000. Sal $75,400 (Prof $48,207)
Library Holdings: Bk Vols 47,000; Per Subs 52
Special Collections: Local (La Salle-Peru) History materials & original documents regarding history of library
Automation Activity & Vendor Info: (Circulation) GEAC
Database Vendor: OCLC - First Search
Mem of Heritage Trail Library System
Open Mon & Wed 9-6, Tues & Thurs 9-8, Fri & Sat 9-5

LACON

P LACON PUBLIC LIBRARY DISTRICT, (Formerly Lacon Public Library), 205 Sixth St, 61540. SAN 304-3266. Tel: 309-246-2855. FAX: 309-246-4047. E-Mail: library3@lacon.net. *Librn*, Debra Pasdik
Founded 1839. Pop 2,132; Circ 21,098
Jul 1997-Jun 1998 Income $30,899, City $18,077, Other $7,482. Mats Exp $30,899, Books $4,031, Per/Ser (Incl. Access Fees) $1,100. Sal $10,422
Library Holdings: Bk Vols 11,556
Subject Interests: Antiques, Local history
Mem of Alliance Library System
Open Mon-Wed 1-7, Thurs-Fri 10-5, Sat 9-1

S MARSHALL COUNTY HISTORICAL SOCIETY LIBRARY,* 314 Fifth St, PO Box 123, 61540. SAN 374-9371. Tel: 309-246-2349. *Curator*, Eleanor Bussell
Library Holdings: Bk Vols 450
Subject Interests: Local history
Special Collections: Doll Coll; Lincoln Coll
Publications: Newsletter

LADD

P LADD PUBLIC LIBRARY DISTRICT, 125 N Main St, PO Box 307, 61329. SAN 304-3274. Tel: 815-894-3254. FAX: 815-894-3254. *Librn*, Nancy Hoxsey; *Asst Librn*, Ann King
Founded 1930. Pop 1,582; Circ 3,499
Library Holdings: Bk Vols 7,000
Subject Interests: Large type print
Special Collections: Library of America Coll
Mem of Heritage Trail Library System

LAFAYETTE

P IRA C REED PUBLIC LIBRARY,* PO Box 185, 61449. SAN 304-3282. Tel: 309-995-3042. FAX: 309-995-3042. *Librn*, Judy King
Pop 268; Circ 2,717
Library Holdings: Bk Vols 7,342

Subject Interests: Local history
Mem of Alliance Library System
Open Mon 6-8, Wed 4-7 & Sat 9-2

LAKE BLUFF

P LAKE BLUFF PUBLIC LIBRARY, 123 Scranton Ave, 60044. SAN 304-3290. Tel: 847-234-2540. FAX: 847-234-2649. Web Site: www.nslsilus.org/ibkhome. *Librn*, Sara Lamb; E-Mail: slamb@nslsilus.org; Staff 3 (MLS 3)
Founded 1926. Pop 5,486; Circ 70,201
May 1999-Apr 2000 Income $393,786, State $6,794, City $366,057, Locally Generated Income $20,935. Mats Exp $89,745, Books $60,000, Per/Ser (Incl. Access Fees) $6,376, Electronic Ref Mat (Incl. Access Fees) $23,369. Sal $220,692 (Prof $132,280)
Library Holdings: Bk Vols 65,512; Bk Titles 50,995; Per Subs 148
Automation Activity & Vendor Info: (Cataloging) TLC; (Circulation) TLC; (OPAC) TLC
Publications: Quarterly newsletter
Mem of North Suburban Library System
Friends of the Library Group

LAKE FOREST

C BARAT COLLEGE, Sister Madeleine Sophie Cooney Library, 700 Westleigh Rd, 60045. SAN 304-3304. Tel: 847-295-4488. FAX: 847-604-6255. E-Mail: library@barat.edu. Web Site: www.library.barat.edu. *Dir*, Lourdes Mordini; Tel: 847-604-6252, Fax: 847-604-6255, E-Mail: lmordini@barat.edu; *Ref*, Alice McNeil; *Circ, ILL*, Vicky Miksis; Staff 13 (MLS 4, Non-MLS 9)
Founded 1858. Enrl 820; Fac 121; Highest Degree: Master
Jul 1999-Jun 2000 Income Parent Institution $329,721. Mats Exp $91,500, Books $44,000, Per/Ser (Incl. Access Fees) $28,500, Electronic Ref Mat (Incl. Access Fees) $19,000. Sal $210,846 (Prof $109,180)
Library Holdings: Bk Vols 72,563; Per Subs 264
Subject Interests: Dance, Education, Literature, Psychology, Theater, Women's studies
Automation Activity & Vendor Info: (Acquisitions) DRA; (Cataloging) DRA; (Circulation) DRA; (Course Reserve) DRA; (ILL) DRA; (OPAC) DRA; (Serials) DRA
Database Vendor: Ebsco - EbscoHost, IAC - Info Trac, Lexis-Nexis, OCLC - First Search, OVID Technologies, ProQuest, Silverplatter Information Inc., Wilson - Wilson Web
Publications: Annual operating plan; Annual report; Library guides
Mem of North Suburban Library System
Partic in Ill Coop Coll Mgt Prog; Illinois Library Computer Systems Office; Libras, Inc; OCLC Online Computer Library Center, Inc; Private Academic Libraries Of Illinois

C LAKE FOREST COLLEGE, Donnelley Library, 555 N Sheridan, 60045. SAN 340-4978. Tel: 847-735-5056. FAX: 847-735-6296. Web Site: www.lib.lfc.edu. *Dir*, James Cubit; *Circ*, Karen Ludlow; *Syst Coordr*, David Levinson; *Spec Coll*, Arthur Miller, Jr; *Govt Doc*, John Brandt; *ILL*, Susan Cloud; *Publ Servs, Ref*, Cory Stevens; Staff 5 (MLS 5)
Founded 1857. Fac 91; Highest Degree: Master
Library Holdings: Bk Titles 268,760; Per Subs 5,839
Special Collections: Capt Joseph Medill Patterson Papers (NY Daily News Coll); Humanities, Rare Books (Hamill Coll); Library); Printing History, Western Americana (O'Kieffe); Railroad (Elliott Donnelley, Munson Paddock & James Sloss Coll); Scotland (Stuart Coll); Theatre (Garrett Leverton Memorial
Automation Activity & Vendor Info: (Acquisitions) DRA; (Cataloging) DRA; (Circulation) DRA; (OPAC) DRA
Mem of North Suburban Library System
Partic in Center For Research Libraries; Illinois Library & Information Network
Departmental Libraries:
FREEMAN SCIENCE Tel: 847-735-5085. *In Charge*, Cheryl Zobel

M LAKE FOREST HOSPITAL, Medical Staff Library,* 660 N Westmoreland Rd, 60045. SAN 370-1484. Tel: 847-234-5600, Ext 6847. FAX: 847-234-6552. *Librn*, Judy Curtis
Library Holdings: Bk Titles 1,250; Per Subs 41
Partic in Dialog Corporation; NLM; Northeastern Ill Libr Consortia

P LAKE FOREST LIBRARY, 360 E Deerpath Ave, 60045-2252. SAN 304-3312. Tel: 847-234-0636. FAX: 847-234-1453. Web Site: lfkhome.northstarnet.org/library.html. *Dir*, Kaye Grabbe; *AV*, Judy Gummere; *Ch Servs*, Lorie Rohrer; *Ch Servs*, Karen Fossell; *Ch Servs*, Mary Webber; *Head Ref*, Cynthia Infantino; *Ref Serv*, Judy Nickels; *Ref*, Felicia Song; *Ref*, Valerie Wolfgram; *Head Tech Servs*, Pat Gundrum; *Tech Servs*, Jian Tan; Staff 14 (MLS 14)
Founded 1898. Pop 18,606
May 1999-Apr 2000 Income $3,028,745, State $22,295, City $1,858,752, Locally Generated Income $170,886, Other $602,468. Mats Exp $307,944, Books $169,956, Per/Ser (Incl. Access Fees) $19,110, Presv $12,000, Micro $1,500, AV Equip $26,133, Electronic Ref Mat (Incl. Access Fees) $71,245. Sal $1,382,935
Library Holdings: Bk Vols 124,000; Per Subs 350
Subject Interests: Art and architecture, Gardening, Local history
Automation Activity & Vendor Info: (Circulation) GEAC
Publications: Info-Bytes (in library monthly newsletter); Open Book (quarterly community wide newsletter)
Mem of North Suburban Library System
Partic in OCLC Online Computer Library Center, Inc
Open Mon-Thurs 9-9, Fri 9-6, Sat 9-5 & Sun 1-5
Friends of the Library Group

LAKE VILLA

P LAKE VILLA DISTRICT LIBRARY, 1001 E Grand Ave, 60046. SAN 304-3320. Tel: 847-356-7711. FAX: 847-265-9595. Web Site: www.lvdl.org. *Dir*, Nann Blaine Hilyard; E-Mail: nhilyard@lvdl.org; *Ref Serv*, Jeremy Green; *Ch Servs*, Lynn Schofield-Dahl; E-Mail: slynn@lvdl.org; *Circ*, Debbie Rosen; E-Mail: debbie@lvdl.org; *Cat*, Lois Wessale; *Tech Servs*, Kim Rutter; E-Mail: kim@lvdl.org; *Coll Develop, Publ Servs*, Paul Kaplan; E-Mail: pkaplan@lvdl.org; *Commun Servs*, Liz Glazer; E-Mail: lglazer@lvdl.org; Staff 38 (MLS 10, Non-MLS 28)
Founded 1952. Pop 22,996; Circ 517,668
Jul 1999-Jun 2000 Income $2,839,914, State $42,021, Locally Generated Income $2,439,738, Other $345,052. Mats Exp $308,501, Books $178,180, Per/Ser (Incl. Access Fees) $15,000, AV Equip $80,421, Electronic Ref Mat (Incl. Access Fees) $34,900. Sal $959,624
Library Holdings: Bk Vols 111,321; Per Subs 351
Automation Activity & Vendor Info: (Circulation) GEAC; (OPAC) GEAC
Database Vendor: OCLC - First Search
Publications: Checking Out (Newsletter)
Mem of North Suburban Library System
Partic in Coop Computer Servs
Friends of the Library Group

LAKE ZURICH

P ELA AREA PUBLIC LIBRARY DISTRICT, 135 S Buesching Rd, 60047. SAN 304-3347. Tel: 847-438-3433. TDD: 847-438-3799. FAX: 847-438-9290. E-Mail: elaref@ela.alibrary.com. Web Site: www.ela.alibrary.com. *Dir*, Carol Larson; *Asst Dir*, Marian Milling; *Cat, Tech Servs*, Marlene Coleman; *Ch Servs*, Brenda Duff; *Commun Servs*, Liza Collins; Staff 17 (MLS 16, Non-MLS 1)
Founded 1972. Pop 34,000; Circ 659,000
Jul 1999-Jun 2000 Income $2,893,660, State $30,462, County $9,483, Locally Generated Income $2,494,210. Mats Exp $454,780, Books $300,000, Per/Ser (Incl. Access Fees) $15,000, Presv $350, Micro $1,000, AV Equip $69,920, Electronic Ref Mat (Incl. Access Fees) $68,510. Sal $1,366,029
Library Holdings: Bk Vols 150,000; Per Subs 150
Automation Activity & Vendor Info: (Acquisitions) GEAC; (Cataloging) GEAC; (Circulation) GEAC
Publications: Footnotes
Mem of North Suburban Library System
Special Services for the Deaf - TDD
Friends of the Library Group

LANARK

P LANARK PUBLIC LIBRARY, 110 W Carroll St, 61046. SAN 304-3355. Tel: 815-493-2166. FAX: 815-493-2166. E-Mail: lanarklib@internetni.com. Web Site: www.internetni.com/~lanarklib. *Librn*, Janie A Dollinger
Pop 1,382; Circ 16,500
1999-2000 Income $30,000, County $20,000, Locally Generated Income $10,000. Mats Exp Books $10,000. Sal $10,000
Library Holdings: Bk Vols 23,000; Per Subs 50
Subject Interests: Genealogy, Local history
Mem of Northern Illinois Library System

LANSING

P LANSING PUBLIC LIBRARY, (LSS), 2750 Indiana Ave, 60438. SAN 304-3363. Tel: 708-474-2447. FAX: 708-474-9466. E-Mail: library@lansing.lib.il.us. Web Site: www.lansing.lib.il.us. *Dir*, William D Babcock; E-Mail: wbabcock@lansing.lib.il.us; Staff 9 (MLS 3, Non-MLS 6)
Founded 1936. Pop 28,131; Circ 215,440
May 1999-Apr 2000 Income $1,129,163. Mats Exp $190,000, Books $145,000, Per/Ser (Incl. Access Fees) $20,000, Electronic Ref Mat (Incl. Access Fees) $25,000
Library Holdings: Bk Vols 99,636; Bk Titles 150,000; Per Subs 195
Automation Activity & Vendor Info: (Cataloging) epixtech, inc.; (Circulation) epixtech, inc.; (OPAC) epixtech, inc.
Mem of Suburban Library System
Open Mon-Thurs 9-8:30, Fri 9-6 & Sat 9-5

LAWRENCEVILLE

P LAWRENCE PUBLIC LIBRARY DISTRICT,* 814 12th St, 62439. SAN 304-3371. Tel: 618-943-3016. FAX: 618-943-3215. E-Mail: library@wworld.com. *Librn*, Linda Phillippe
Founded 1921. Pop 7,830; Circ 66,702
Library Holdings: Bk Vols 37,000; Per Subs 113
Mem of Shawnee Library System
Open Tues & Thurs 12-6, Mon, Wed & Fri 12-5, Sat 10-3
Friends of the Library Group

LE ROY

P J T & E J CRUMBAUGH MEMORIAL PUBLIC CHURCH LIBRARY, 405 E Center St, PO Box 129, 61752-0129. SAN 304-338X. Tel: 309-962-3911. E-Mail: jtejbe@leroy2.k12.il.us. Web Site: www.geocities.com/soho/square/3857. *Coll Develop, Dir*, Lois Evans; E-Mail: levans@crumbaughlibrary.org; *Asst Librn*, Fae Morris
Founded 1927. Circ 39,797
Library Holdings: Bk Titles 14,000; Per Subs 30; High Interest/Low Vocabulary Bk Vols 150
Subject Interests: Fine arts, Genealogy, History, Local history
Special Collections: Local Cemetery Records; Spiritualist Section
Publications: J T & E J Crumbaugh Spiritualist Church & Memorial Library (history booklet); Tracing Your Roots (genealogy booklet)
Function: Archival collection, Internet access, Research library

LEAF RIVER

P BERTOLET MEMORIAL LIBRARY DISTRICT, 705 Main, PO Box 339, 61047. SAN 324-5551. Tel: 815-738-2742. FAX: 815-738-2742. E-Mail: bertolib@lrnet1.com. *Librn*, Cheryl L Campbell; *Asst Librn*, JoAnne Badertscher; *Asst Librn*, Shirley Kruse; Staff 1 (Non-MLS 1)
Founded 1981. Pop 1,750; Circ 9,180
Jul 2000-Jun 2001 Income $54,000
Library Holdings: Bk Vols 8,178; Bk Titles 8,624; Per Subs 25
Special Collections: Local History Coll, bks, diaries, ledgers
Mem of Northern Illinois Library System
Open Mon, Wed & Fri 9-12, Mon, Tue, Wed & Thurs 3-8, Sat 8-12

LEBANON

P LEBANON PUBLIC LIBRARY,* 314 W Saint Louis St, 62254. SAN 304-3398. Tel: 618-537-4504. FAX: 618-537-4399. *Librn*, Margaret Whaley; E-Mail: mwhaley@shawls.lib.il.us
Founded 1946. Pop 3,688; Circ 13,655
Library Holdings: Bk Vols 15,000; Per Subs 35
Special Collections: Charles Dickens Coll
Mem of Shawnee Library System

C MCKENDREE COLLEGE, Holman Library, 701 College Rd, 62254-1299. SAN 304-3401. Tel: 618-537-6950. FAX: 618-537-8411. Web Site: www.mckendree.edu. *Dir*, Helen E Gilbert; E-Mail: hgilbert@atlas.mckendree.edu; Staff 3 (MLS 3)
Founded 1828. Highest Degree: Bachelor
Library Holdings: Bk Vols 84,362; Per Subs 473
Subject Interests: Computer science, Education, Humanities, Nursing, Social sciences and issues
Special Collections: Archives of the Southern Illinois Conference of the United Methodist Church
Automation Activity & Vendor Info: (Cataloging) DRA; (Circulation) DRA; (OPAC) DRA
Mem of Shawnee Library System
Partic in Ill Libr Computer Systs Org; Illinois Library & Information Network; OCLC Online Computer Library Center, Inc

LEMONT

P LEMONT PUBLIC LIBRARY DISTRICT,* 50 E Wend St, 60439. SAN 304-3428. Tel: 630-257-6541. FAX: 630-257-7737. Web Site: www.lemont.il.us/library1.htm. *Dir*, James L McGloin; *Ref, Tech Servs*, Maria Meachum; *Ch Servs*, Mary Inman
Founded 1943. Pop 14,614; Circ 102,699
Library Holdings: Bk Vols 51,612; Per Subs 142
Publications: Newsletter
Mem of Heritage Trail Library System
Friends of the Library Group

LENA

P LENA COMMUNITY DISTRICT LIBRARY,* 300 W Mason St, 61048. SAN 304-3444. Tel: 815-369-4211. FAX: 815-369-5288. *Librn*, Linda Benninger
Founded 1912. Pop 5,184; Circ 43,000
Jul 1996-Jun 1997 Income $93,931. Mats Exp $15,725, Books $10,634, Per/Ser (Incl. Access Fees) $1,401, AV Equip $3,690. Sal $55,223
Library Holdings: Bk Titles 20,000; Per Subs 92
Subject Interests: Child welfare, Health sciences, History, Religion
Special Collections: Lena Stars since 1871 (local newspapers for genealogy research)
Mem of Northern Illinois Library System

LEWISTOWN

S DICKSON MOUNDS MUSEUM LIBRARY,* 10956 N Dickson Mounds Rd, 61542. SAN 375-1279. Tel: 309-547-3721. FAX: 309-547-3189. *Dir*, Judith Franke
Library Holdings: Bk Titles 1,500; Per Subs 40
Publications: Illinois State Museum Scientific Reports; newsletter
Mem of Alliance Library System

P LEWISTOWN CARNEGIE PUBLIC LIBRARY DISTRICT,* 321 W Lincoln Ave, 61542. SAN 304-3452. Tel: 309-547-2860. FAX: 309-547-2865. *Librn*, Rebecca Shumaker
Founded 1985. Pop 5,762; Circ 26,842
Library Holdings: Bk Vols 19,000; Per Subs 60
Subject Interests: Local history
Mem of Alliance Library System
Open Mon, Tues, Thurs & Fri 9-5, Wed 12-8

LEXINGTON

P LEXINGTON PUBLIC LIBRARY DISTRICT, 207 S Cedar St, 61753. SAN 304-3460. Tel: 309-365-7801. FAX: 309-365-9028. E-Mail: lexingtonl@yahoo.com. Web Site: www.lexington.lib.il.us. *Dir*, Evelyn Homan; E-Mail: evelynhoman@yahoo.com
Founded 1896. Pop 3,000; Circ 26,000
Jul 1999-Jun 2000 Income $110,000, State $3,662, Other $4,000. Mats Exp $18,411, Books $16,000, Per/Ser (Incl. Access Fees) $1,511, Electronic Ref Mat (Incl. Access Fees) $900. Sal $45,900 (Prof $24,000)
Library Holdings: Bk Titles 21,519; Per Subs 86
Special Collections: Art prints, Library of America-Literacy Materials
Automation Activity & Vendor Info: (Circulation) Follett; (OPAC) Follett
Database Vendor: OCLC - First Search
Mem of Alliance Library System

LIBERTYVILLE

M CONDELL MEDICAL CENTER, Fohrman Library, 900 Garfield Ave, 60048. SAN 375-9385. Tel: 847-362-2900, Ext 5265. FAX: 847-362-5529. E-Mail: library@condell.org. Web Site: www.condell.org. *Dir*, Mary Ellen Jankowski
Jan 2000-Dec 2000 Mats Exp $16,000, Books $2,000, Per/Ser (Incl. Access Fees) $14,000. Sal $6,816
Library Holdings: Bk Titles 1,000; Per Subs 130
Database Vendor: OCLC - First Search
Restriction: Access at librarian's discretion, Company library, Employees & their associates, In-house use for visitors, Not a lending library
Function: ILL available, Photocopies available
Mem of North Suburban Library System

P COOK MEMORIAL PUBLIC LIBRARY DISTRICT,* 413 N Milwaukee Ave, 60048. SAN 304-3479. Tel: 847-362-2330. FAX: 847-362-2354. Web Site: www.cooklib.org. *Dir*, Frederick H Byergo; *Ad Servs, Ref*, Carol Hubert; *Tech Servs*, Mary Ellen Stembal; *Ch Servs*, Eileen Sullivan; *Circ*, John Matthews; Staff 53 (MLS 19, Non-MLS 34)
Founded 1921. Pop 47,500; Circ 732,500
Library Holdings: Bk Vols 218,365; Per Subs 555
Special Collections: Genealogy Reference Coll; Lake County History Coll
Automation Activity & Vendor Info: (Circulation) CLSI LIBS
Publications: INS and Outs
Mem of North Suburban Library System
Partic in Lake County Consortium; Midwest Health Sci Libr Network
Friends of the Library Group

S HOLLISTER INCORPORATED, Minnie Schneider Resource Center, 2000 Hollister Dr, 60048. SAN 326-9604. Tel: 847-918-3890. FAX: 847-918-3453. *Librn*, Elizabeth A Cunningham; E-Mail: ecunning@hollister.com; Staff 1 (Non-MLS 1)
Library Holdings: Bk Titles 4,000; Per Subs 250
Subject Interests: Medicine, Technology
Mem of North Suburban Library System

S USG RESEARCH & TECHNOLOGY CENTER LIBRARY, 700 N Hwy 45, 60046. SAN 304-1190. Tel: 847-970-5037. FAX: 847-970-5299. *Senior Librn*, Robyn E Petry; E-Mail: rpetry@usg.com. Subject Specialists: *Construction*, Robyn E Petry; Staff 2 (MLS 1, Non-MLS 1)
Founded 1961
Jan 1999-Dec 1999 Income Parent Institution $65,000. Mats Exp $65,000
Library Holdings: Bk Vols 6,155; Bk Titles 6,217; Per Subs 233
Subject Interests: Construction, Inorganic chemistry
Special Collections: Gypsum Rock Coll

Automation Activity & Vendor Info: (Cataloging) Inmagic, Inc.; (OPAC) Inmagic, Inc.; (Serials) Inmagic, Inc.
Database Vendor: Dialog, OCLC - First Search
Publications: Acquisitions List (new materials received in Library) (Monthly); International Patents Alert (Monthly); U.S. Patents Alert (Monthly)
Restriction: Company library
Function: For research purposes
Mem of North Suburban Library System

LINCOLN

CR LINCOLN CHRISTIAN COLLEGE & SEMINARY, Jessie C Eury Library, 100 Campus View Dr, 62656. SAN 304-3509. Tel: 217-732-3168, Ext 2234. FAX: 217-732-3785. Web Site: www.lccs.edu/library. *Dir*, Nancy J Olson; *Media Spec*, Ann Spellman; *Asst Librn*, Mike Reid; *Info Res*, Leslie Starasta
Founded 1944. Enrl 1,000; Fac 50; Highest Degree: Master
Library Holdings: Bk Vols 124,772; Bk Titles 99,496; Per Subs 459
Subject Interests: Biblical studies, Church history, Education, Occult, Theology
Special Collections: Restoration Movement, sermons, hymnals, mission materials
Automation Activity & Vendor Info: (Cataloging) DRA; (Circulation) DRA
Mem of Rolling Prairie Library System
Partic in Christian Libr Network; Illinois Library Computer Systems Office

J LINCOLN COLLEGE, McKinstry Library, 300 Keokuk, 62656. SAN 304-3517. Tel: 217-732-3155, Ext 290. FAX: 217-732-4465. Web Site: www.lincolncollege.com. *Dir*, June Burke; E-Mail: jburke@lincolncollege.com
Founded 1865. Enrl 642; Highest Degree: Doctorate
Library Holdings: Bk Vols 40,000; Per Subs 250
Special Collections: Lincoln
Mem of Rolling Prairie Library System
Partic in Sangamon Valley Academic Library Consortium

S LINCOLN CORRECTIONAL CENTER LIBRARY,* RR 3, Box 549, 62656. SAN 376-1231. Tel: 217-735-5411, Ext 368. FAX: 217-735-1361. *Librn*, Lana Wildman
Library Holdings: Bk Titles 8,500
Mem of Rolling Prairie Library System

S LINCOLN DEVELOPMENTAL CENTER LIBRARY,* 861 S State St, 62656. SAN 376-0987. Tel: 217-735-2361, Ext 310. FAX: 217-735-5283. *Librn*, Bob Gephart
Library Holdings: Bk Titles 5,910; Per Subs 12

P LINCOLN PUBLIC LIBRARY DISTRICT, 725 Pekin, 62656. SAN 304-3525. Tel: 217-732-5732, 217-732-8878. FAX: 217-732-6273. Web Site: www.lincolnpubliclibrary.org. *Coll Develop, Dir*, Richard Sumrall; E-Mail: richards@alpha1.rpls.lib.il.us; *Asst Dir*, Sue Rehtmeyer
Founded 1901. Pop 15,418
Jul 1999-Jun 2000 Income $530,829, Federal $10,451, Locally Generated Income $406,810, Other $24,019. Mats Exp $310,076. Sal $220,994
Library Holdings: Bk Titles 46,011; Per Subs 206
Special Collections: Lincoln; Logan County History & Genealogy
Automation Activity & Vendor Info: (Circulation) DRA; (OPAC) DRA
Publications: Human Services Directory
Mem of Rolling Prairie Library System
Partic in Dranet
Friends of the Library Group

S LOGAN CORRECTIONAL CENTER LIBRARY,* 1096 1350th St, 62656. SAN 376-0863. Tel: 217-735-5581. FAX: 217-735-4381. *Librn*, Kevin Britton
Library Holdings: Bk Titles 6,160
Mem of Rolling Prairie Library System

LINCOLNSHIRE

S HEWITT ASSOCIATES LIBRARY, 100 Half Day Rd, 60069. SAN 304-3533. Tel: 847-295-5000. FAX: 847-295-0016. *Mgr Libr Serv*, Patricia Ludwig Kuhl; E-Mail: plkuhl@hewitt.com; *Info Specialist*, Elaine Y Bao; *Info Specialist*, Dawn L Braun; *Info Specialist*, Linda Carpenter; *Info Specialist*, Michelle Jarzembski-Strauch; *Info Specialist*, Mike LaComb; *Info Specialist*, Sue B Poterek; *Info Specialist*, Kate Prentice; *Automation Syst Coordr*, Debbie Reeber; *Coll Develop*, Rachel R Mohr; Staff 10 (MLS 7, Non-MLS 3)
Founded 1946
Library Holdings: Bk Vols 40,000; Per Subs 4,000
Subject Interests: Benefits (Labor), Compensation (labor), Human resources
Automation Activity & Vendor Info: (Cataloging) EOS; (Circulation) EOS; (OPAC) EOS; (Serials) EOS
Database Vendor: Dialog, Ebsco - EbscoHost, Lexis-Nexis
Restriction: Company library
Function: ILL limited
Mem of North Suburban Library System

P VERNON AREA PUBLIC LIBRARY DISTRICT, 300 Olde Half Day Rd, 60069-2901. SAN 304-5722. Tel: 847-634-3650. TDD: 847-634-8875. FAX: 847-634-8449. Interlibrary Loan Service FAX: 847-634-8667. Web Site: www.vernon-area.lib.il.us. *Dir*, Allen Meyer; E-Mail: ameyer@nslsilus.org; *Head Ref*, Laurel Vlcek; *Head Tech Servs*, Caren Soltysiak; *Info Tech*, Reed Martin; *Ch Servs*, Colleen Costello; *Circ*, Dawn Miller; *Commun Relations*, Echo Morgan; *Materials Manager*, Loretta Foss; Staff 130 (MLS 24, Non-MLS 106)
Founded 1974. Pop 40,000; Circ 858,856
Jul 1999-Jun 2000 Income $5,050,684, State $58,270, Locally Generated Income $4,992,414. Mats Exp $658,811. Sal $2,062,930
Library Holdings: Bk Vols 194,030; Per Subs 522
Subject Interests: Local history
Automation Activity & Vendor Info: (Circulation) epixtech, inc.
Database Vendor: Dialog, epixtech, inc., IAC - Info Trac, IAC - SearchBank, OCLC - First Search, Wilson - Wilson Web
Publications: Columns (Newsletter)
Function: Some telephone reference
Mem of North Suburban Library System
Friends of the Library Group

LINCOLNWOOD

P LINCOLNWOOD PUBLIC LIBRARY DISTRICT, 4000 W Pratt Ave, 60712. SAN 320-1813. Tel: 847-677-5277. FAX: 847-677-1937. Web Site: nsls1.nslsilus.org/lnk/. *Dir*, Kellie J Flynn; E-Mail: cjosephs@nslsilus.org; *Ad Servs, Coll Develop*, Gail Inman; *Circ*, Janice Miller; *Ch Servs*, Sharon Levine; *Tech Servs*, Shao-Chen Lin
Founded 1978. Pop 11,365; Circ 148,000
Jul 1998-Jun 1999 Income $1,356,033, State $14,206, City $1,185,998, Locally Generated Income $155,829. Mats Exp $144,000. Sal $561,298 (Prof $368,000)
Library Holdings: Bk Vols 54,000; Per Subs 121
Special Collections: David Zemsky Low Vision Center; Lincolnwood Historical Coll; Literacy Coll
Automation Activity & Vendor Info: (Cataloging) GEAC; (Circulation) GEAC; (ILL) GEAC; (OPAC) GEAC
Publications: Lincolnwood Library; The Acorn (quarterly newsletter)
Mem of North Suburban Library System
Partic in Illinois Library & Information Network; OCLC Online Computer Library Center, Inc
Friends of the Library Group

LISLE

C BENEDICTINE UNIVERSITY, Theodore Lownik Library, 5700 College Rd, 60532-0900. SAN 304-355X. Tel: 630-829-6050. Reference Tel: 630-829-6057. FAX: 630-960-9451. Web Site: www.ben.edu. *Dir*, Mary Joyce Pickett; E-Mail: mpickett@ben.edu; *Ref*, Sharon Nelson; *Ref*, Luann DeGreve; *Bibliog Instr, Govt Doc*, Joan Hopkins; *Online Servs, Tech Servs*, Mark A Kroll; *Archivist*, Christian Ceplecha; Staff 7 (MLS 7)
Founded 1887. Enrl 2,842; Fac 127; Highest Degree: Doctorate
Library Holdings: Bk Vols 126,464; Per Subs 676
Subject Interests: Theology
Special Collections: Abraham Lincoln Coll; Autographed Coll; College Archives; Rare Books & Manuscripts
Automation Activity & Vendor Info: (Acquisitions) DRA; (Cataloging) DRA; (Circulation) DRA; (OPAC) DRA; (Serials) DRA
Mem of Suburban Library System
Partic in Dialog Corporation; Illinois Library Computer Systems Office; Libras, Inc; OCLC Online Computer Library Center, Inc

P LISLE LIBRARY DISTRICT,* 777 Front St, 60532-3599. SAN 304-3568. Tel: 630-971-1675. FAX: 630-971-1701. Web Site: www.lislelibrary.org. *Dir*, D Huslig; E-Mail: director@lislelibrary.org; *Asst Dir*, K Seelig; *Ch Servs*, A Krzak; *Ref*, C Kuhn; *Circ*, A Lin; *Tech Servs*, M Elgin; Staff 19 (MLS 19)
Founded 1967. Pop 27,817; Circ 429,092
Jul 1998-Jun 1999 Income $4,206,847, County $3,932,285, Locally Generated Income $274,562. Mats Exp $473,676, Books $252,840, Per/Ser (Incl. Access Fees) $220,836. Sal $1,744,258
Library Holdings: Bk Titles 109,061; Per Subs 800
Subject Interests: Local history, Oriental art
Automation Activity & Vendor Info: (Circulation) Gaylord
Publications: Newsletter (monthly)
Mem of Suburban Library System
Special Services for the Deaf - TTY machine; Videos & decoder
Friends of the Library Group

S MORTON ARBORETUM, Sterling Morton Library, 4100 Illinois Rte 53, 60532-1293. SAN 304-3576. Tel: 630-719-7932. Interlibrary Loan Service Tel: 630-719-2430. Circulation Tel: 630-719-2430. FAX: 630-719-7950. Web Site: www.mortonarb.org. *Adminr, Ref, Spec Coll*, Michael T Stieber;

E-Mail: mstieber@mortonarb.org; *Tech Servs*, Rita Hassert; Tel: 630-719-2430, E-Mail: rhassert@mortonarb.org; *Cat*, Peter Wang; Tel: 630-719-2429, E-Mail: pwang@mortonarb.org; Staff 4 (MLS 2, Non-MLS 2)
Founded 1922
Jan 1999-Dec 1999 Income $230,000. Mats Exp $34,500, Books $11,000, Per/Ser (Incl. Access Fees) $19,000, Presv $4,000, Manuscripts & Archives $500. Sal $177,000 (Prof $166,000)
Library Holdings: Bk Titles 26,500; Per Subs 300; Spec Interest Per Sub 150
Subject Interests: Botany, Environmental studies, History, Horticulture, Landscape architecture, Natural history
Special Collections: Botanical Art; History & topography maps of Arboretum & vicinity 1922-present; Landscape Architecture (Jens Jensen Archives), bks, plans, letters; May T Watts Coll, mss; Morton Arboretum Archives
Mem of Suburban Library System
Partic in Illinois Library & Information Network

S WATER QUALITY ASSOCIATION, Research Council Library,* 4151 Naperville Rd, 60532. SAN 326-9817. Tel: 630-505-0160. FAX: 630-505-9637. E-Mail: info@mail.wqa.org. Web Site: www.wqa.org. *Exec Dir*, Peter Censky; *Asst Dir*, Lynn Mathers; *Tech Servs*, Joe Harrison
Library Holdings: Bk Vols 300

LITCHFIELD

P LITCHFIELD CARNEGIE PUBLIC LIBRARY,* 400 N State St, 62056. SAN 304-3584. Tel: 217-324-3866. FAX: 217-324-3884. E-Mail: library@litchfieldil.com. *Librn*, Sara Zumwalt; Staff 5 (Non-MLS 5)
Founded 1872. Pop 6,883; Circ 67,348
Library Holdings: Bk Vols 37,000; Per Subs 136
Subject Interests: Genealogy
Special Collections: Genealogy & Local History
Automation Activity & Vendor Info: (Cataloging) Sagebrush Corporation; (Circulation) Sagebrush Corporation
Mem of Lewis & Clark Library System
Open Mon-Thurs 10-8, Fri 10-5, Sat 10-2
Friends of the Library Group

LOCKPORT

P DES PLAINES VALLEY PUBLIC LIBRARY DISTRICT, 121 E Eighth St, 60441. SAN 340-5036. Tel: 815-838-0755. FAX: 815-838-9131. Web Site: www.htls.lib.il.us/dpv/. *Dir*, Tina Bianco; *Asst Dir*, Debra Chapp
Founded 1921. Pop 40,170; Circ 228,427
Library Holdings: Bk Vols 155,367
Subject Interests: Genealogy, Local history
Publications: Check It Out]
Mem of Heritage Trail Library System
Branches: 1
DES PLAINES VALLEY LIBRARY-CREST HILL, 1298 Theodore St, Crest Hill, 60435. SAN 328-8692. Tel: 815-725-0234. FAX: 815-725-3786. E-Mail: dvp@starbase1.htls.lib.il.us. Web Site: www.htls.lib.il.us/dpv/. *Dir*, Christina Bianco; E-Mail: cmbianco@htls.lib.il.us; *Asst Librn*, Beverly Jean Krakovec; E-Mail: bkrakovec@@htls.lib.il.us; Staff 13 (Non-MLS 13)
Founded 1968. Pop 40,170
Library Holdings: Bk Vols 80,000; Per Subs 164
Automation Activity & Vendor Info: (Circulation) GEAC
Friends of the Library Group

P HOMER TOWNSHIP PUBLIC LIBRARY DISTRICT, 14320 151st St, 60441. SAN 375-9490. Tel: 708-301-7908. FAX: 708-301-4535. Web Site: www.homerlibrary.org. *Adminr*, Sheree Kozel-La Ha; E-Mail: skozel@homerlibrary.org; *Actg Dir*, Jody Studer; *Actg Dir*, Kathryn Mitchel; Staff 24 (MLS 1, Non-MLS 23)
Pop 30,000; Circ 200,000
Library Holdings: Bk Titles 100,000; Per Subs 200
Mem of Heritage Trail Library System

LODA

P A HERR SMITH & E E SMITH LIBRARY, Loda Township Library, 105 E Adams St, PO Box 247, 60948. SAN 304-3592. Tel: 217-386-2783. FAX: 217-386-2223. *Librn*, Nancy Seamands; E-Mail: nseama@ltnet.lits.org
Pop 1,306; Circ 5,010
Library Holdings: Bk Vols 4,600
Mem of Lincoln Trail Libraries System
Open Mon, Tues & Thurs 9-noon & 2-5, Sat 9-noon

LOMBARD

P HELEN M PLUM MEMORIAL LIBRARY, Lombard Public Library, 110 W Maple St, 60148-2594. SAN 304-3630. Tel: 630-627-0316. FAX: 630-627-0336. Web Site: www.plum.lib.il.us. *Dir*, Robert A Harris; E-Mail: b-harris@plum.lib.il.us; *Ad Servs*, Donna Slyfield; E-Mail: dslyfield@plum.lib.il.us; *Circ*, Karen Kee; E-Mail: kkee@plum.lib.il.us; *Tech Servs*, Mrs May Anstee; E-Mail: manstee@plum.lib.il.us; *Ch Servs*, Denise Zielinski; E-Mail: dzielinski@plum.lib.il.us; Staff 63 (MLS 13, Non-MLS 50)
Founded 1927. Pop 40,870
Jun 1999-May 2000 Income $2,047,423. Mats Exp $413,518, Books $320,614, Per/Ser (Incl. Access Fees) $27,059, Presv $3,505, Micro $12,633, Electronic Ref Mat (Incl. Access Fees) $49,707. Sal $1,137,241
Library Holdings: Bk Vols 200,023; Per Subs 447
Subject Interests: Art and architecture, Music
Automation Activity & Vendor Info: (Acquisitions) Innovative Interfaces Inc.; (Cataloging) Innovative Interfaces Inc.; (Circulation) Innovative Interfaces Inc.; (OPAC) Innovative Interfaces Inc.; (Serials) Innovative Interfaces Inc.
Database Vendor: GaleNet, OCLC - First Search, ProQuest
Publications: Plum Tree
Mem of DuPage Library System
Partic in Illinois Library & Information Network
Friends of the Library Group

S LOMBARD HISTORICAL SOCIETY LIBRARY,* 23 W Maple St, 60148. SAN 374-9193. Tel: 630-629-1885. FAX: 630-629-9927. *Dir*, Joel VanHaaften
Library Holdings: Bk Vols 350; Per Subs 20

S MACKAY & CO LIBRARY,* One Imperial Pl, 60148. SAN 376-012X. Tel: 630-916-6110. FAX: 630-916-4661. *Librn*, Gloria Manata
Library Holdings: Bk Titles 100,000; Per Subs 30

CM NATIONAL UNIVERSITY OF HEALTH SCIENCES, (Formerly National College Of Chiropractic), Sordoni-Burich Library, 200 E Roosevelt Rd, 60148-4583. SAN 304-3614. Tel: 630-889-6612. Circulation Tel: 630-889-6612. Reference Tel: 630-889-6616. FAX: 630-495-6658. Web Site: national.chiropractic.edu/lrc/lrc/html. *Dir*, Joyce Ellen Whitehead; Tel: 630-889-6610, E-Mail: joycew@national.chiropractic.edu; *Circ*, James Chlipala; Tel: 630-889-6597; *ILL*, Helen Wagner; Tel: 630-889-6613; *Ref*, Russell Iwami; Tel: 630-889-6616, E-Mail: russi@national.chiropractic.edu; *Ser*, Linnea Warda; Tel: 630-889-6611; *Tech Servs*, Anne Scott Hope; Tel: 630-889-6538, E-Mail: anneh@national.chiropractic.edu; Staff 7 (MLS 3, Non-MLS 4)
Founded 1920. Enrl 650; Fac 40; Highest Degree: Doctorate
Library Holdings: Bk Vols 15,700; Per Subs 445
Subject Interests: Alternative healing, Biomed sci
Special Collections: History of Chiropractic; Natural Healing
Automation Activity & Vendor Info: (Circulation) epixtech, inc.; (OPAC) epixtech, inc.
Database Vendor: OCLC - First Search, OVID Technologies
Mem of DuPage Library System
Partic in Chiropractic Libr Consortium; Fox Valley Health Science Library Consortium; Illinois Library & Information Network

CR NORTHERN BAPTIST THEOLOGICAL SEMINARY, Brimson Grow Library, 660 E Butterfield Rd, 60148. SAN 304-4904. Tel: 630-620-2104. FAX: 630-620-2170. E-Mail: library@northern.seminary.edu. Web Site: www.seminary.edu. *Dir, Librn*, Dr Helen Kenik Mainelli; Tel: 630-620-2115, E-Mail: mainelli@northern.seminary.edu; *Info Tech*, Dr James Nogalski; Tel: 630-620-2146, E-Mail: jnogalski@northern.seminary.edu; *Cat*, JoAnn Hrabak; Tel: 630-620-2153, E-Mail: jhrabak@northern.seminary.edu; *Circ*, Silvia Larrondo; Tel: 630-620-2116, E-Mail: slarrondo@northern.seminary.edu; *Acq*, Pat Ulery; Tel: 630-620-2142, E-Mail: pulery@northern.seminary.edu. Subject Specialists: *Bible*, Dr Helen Kenik Mainelli; *Theology*, Dr Helen Kenik Mainelli; Staff 5 (MLS 2, Non-MLS 3)
Founded 1913. Enrl 284; Highest Degree: Doctorate
Jul 1999-Jun 2000 Income Locally Generated Income $257,971. Mats Exp $67,791, Books $24,953, Per/Ser (Incl. Access Fees) $15,006, Presv $4,493, Micro $10, AV Equip $1,935, Electronic Ref Mat (Incl. Access Fees) $21,394. Sal $168,520 (Prof $148,240)
Library Holdings: Bk Vols 45,608; Bk Titles 39,000; Per Subs 290
Subject Interests: Bible, Christian hist, Relig in Am, Theology, Women's studies in relig
Special Collections: Baptist History & Heritage
Automation Activity & Vendor Info: (Serials) epixtech, inc.
Database Vendor: epixtech, inc., OCLC - First Search
Restriction: Non-circulating to the public
Function: ILL limited, Professional lending library
Mem of DuPage Library System
Partic in Association Of Chicago Theological Schools (ACTS); Ill Coop Coll Mgt Prog

LOSTANT

P LOSTANT COMMUNITY LIBRARY,* 102 W Third St, PO Box 189, 61334. SAN 304-3657. Tel: 815-368-3530. FAX: 815-368-3530. *Librn*, Jeanne Naggio
Founded 1961. Pop 1,400; Circ 1,843
Library Holdings: Bk Vols 3,775
Subject Interests: History
Mem of Heritage Trail Library System

LOVES PARK

P NORTH SUBURBAN LIBRARY-LOVES PARK, 6340 N Second St, 61111. SAN 304-3665. Tel: 815-633-4247. FAX: 815-633-4249. Web Site: www.northsuburbanlibrary.org. *Dir*, Ann Powell; E-Mail: annp@nils.lib.il.us; *ILL*, Mary Packer; *Acq, Coll Develop, Ref*, Denise Williams; *Circ*, Margaret Miller; *YA Servs*, Nicole Scorgie; *Ch Servs*, Gloria Ford; *Cat*, Kathryn M Rasch; Staff 7 (MLS 7)
Founded 1944. Pop 55,644; Circ 403,632
Library Holdings: Bk Vols 185,455; Per Subs 354
Subject Interests: Local history
Automation Activity & Vendor Info: (Acquisitions) Innovative Interfaces Inc.; (Cataloging) Innovative Interfaces Inc.; (Circulation) Innovative Interfaces Inc.; (OPAC) Innovative Interfaces Inc.; (Serials) Innovative Interfaces Inc.
Publications: Elementary Education Newsletter; North Suburban District Library Newsletter; Secondary Education Newsletter; Staff Notes; Young Adult Committee Newsletter
Mem of Northern Illinois Library System
Open Mon-Thurs 9-9, Fri & Sat 8:30-5, Sun 1-5
Friends of the Library Group
Branches: 1
ROSCOE BRANCH, 5562 Clayton Circle, Roscoe, 61073. SAN 329-2614. Tel: 815-623-6266. FAX: 815-623-8591. *Librn*, Sandra Arden; *Librn*, Nicole Scorgie
Friends of the Library Group

LOVINGTON

P LOVINGTON PUBLIC LIBRARY DISTRICT,* 110 W State St, PO Box 199, 61937. SAN 304-3673. Tel: 217-873-4468. FAX: 217-873-4468. *Librn*, Suzanne Saunders; E-Mail: suzsaunders@usa.net
Founded 1943. Pop 710; Circ 20,824
Library Holdings: Bk Vols 16,170; Per Subs 45
Mem of Rolling Prairie Library System

LYONS

P LYONS PUBLIC LIBRARY, 4209 Joliet Ave, 60534-1597. SAN 304-3681. Tel: 708-447-3577. TDD: 708-447-3577. FAX: 708-447-3589. E-Mail: lys@sls.lib.il.us. Web Site: www.lyons.lib.il.us. *Dir*, Denise E Ard; E-Mail: ardd@sls.lib.il.us; *Circ*, Pat Demco; *Tech Servs*, Pat Gore; Staff 8 (MLS 1, Non-MLS 7)
Founded 1938
Jan 1999-Dec 1999 Income $265,444, State $13,821, City $221,640, Locally Generated Income $23,562, Other $6,421. Mats Exp $47,230, Books $36,907, Per/Ser (Incl. Access Fees) $7,283, Electronic Ref Mat (Incl. Access Fees) $3,040. Sal $121,312
Library Holdings: Bk Vols 51,988; Bk Titles 49,660; Per Subs 151
Subject Interests: Genealogy, Illinois
Special Collections: 17th, 18th, 19th Century Passenger Lists; Chicago Metropolitan & Genealogy
Automation Activity & Vendor Info: (Cataloging) Innovative Interfaces Inc.; (Circulation) Innovative Interfaces Inc.; (ILL) Innovative Interfaces Inc.; (OPAC) Innovative Interfaces Inc.
Database Vendor: IAC - SearchBank, Innovative Interfaces INN - View, OCLC - First Search
Publications: Literally Lyons (irregularly)
Mem of Suburban Library System
Special Services for the Deaf - TDD

MACKINAW

P MACKINAW DISTRICT PUBLIC LIBRARY,* 117 S Main, PO Box 560, 61755-0560. SAN 304-372X. Tel: 309-359-8022. FAX: 309-359-8146. *Librn*, Vicky Dierker
Founded 1934. Pop 3,008; Circ 35,684
1998-1999 Income $85,347, State $3,725, County $71,770, Other $6,127. Mats Exp $13,925. Sal $32,046
Library Holdings: Bk Vols 20,862; Per Subs 76
Mem of Alliance Library System
Partic in Illinois Library & Information Network; RSA
Visiting Librarian Service to shut-ins (temporary or permanent)

MACOMB

P MACOMB PUBLIC LIBRARY DISTRICT, 235 S Lafayette St, PO Box 220, 61455-0220. SAN 304-3754. Tel: 309-833-2714. FAX: 309-833-2714. E-Mail: library@macomb.com, maco@darkstar.rsa.lib.il.us. Web Site: www.macomb.lib.il.us. *Dir*, Dennis Danowski; *Ch Servs*, Margaret Sowers; Staff 2 (MLS 1, Non-MLS 1)
Founded 1881. Pop 20,129; Circ 97,000
Jul 2000-Jun 2001 Income $310,000, State $40,000, Locally Generated Income $270,000. Mats Exp $53,000, Books $36,000, Per/Ser (Incl. Access Fees) $4,800, Micro $500
Library Holdings: Bk Vols 60,000; Per Subs 200
Special Collections: Illinois Local History Coll, bks & photog
Mem of Alliance Library System
Friends of the Library Group

C WESTERN ILLINOIS UNIVERSITY LIBRARIES,* 61455-1391. SAN 304-3762. Tel: 309-298-2762. FAX: 309-298-2791. Web Site: www.wlu.edu/library. *Ref*, Kate Joswick; E-Mail: kate_joswick@ccmail.wlu.edu; *Archivist*, Frank Goudy; *Circ*, Roderick Sharpe; *Cat*, Felix Chu; *Govt Doc*, Sheila Nollen; *Per*, Dean Howd; *Coll Develop*, Carol Covey; Staff 18 (MLS 18)
Founded 1903. Fac 650
Jul 1997-Jun 1998 Income $3,877,601. Mats Exp $1,192,485, Books $424,580, Per/Ser (Incl. Access Fees) $732,905, Presv $35,000. Sal $2,277,960 (Prof $1,020,690)
Library Holdings: Bk Vols 732,190; Bk Titles 636,687; Per Subs 3,225
Special Collections: Birds of Prey (Elton Fawks Coll); Center for Icarian Studies; Political Science (US Congressman Tom Railsback Coll); Theatre (Burl Ives Coll); West Central Illinois Local History Coll; Western Illinois University Theses; Wildlife Conservation (Virginia Eifert Coll)
Mem of Alliance Library System
Partic in OCLC Online Computer Library Center, Inc; Statewide LCS/FBR

MACON

P SOUTH MACON PUBLIC LIBRARY DISTRICT, 451 W Glenn, PO Box 288, 62544-0288. SAN 304-3770. Tel: 217-764-3356. FAX: 217-764-5490. *Librn*, Mary Lee Melhorn; E-Mail: maryleem@rpls.lib.il.us; *Asst Librn*, Carol Smith
Founded 1980. Pop 3,708; Circ 12,161
Jul 1999-Jun 2000 Income $79,133, State $6,499, Provincial $67,177, Other $5,457. Mats Exp Books $11,876. Sal $32,481
Library Holdings: Bk Titles 8,829; Per Subs 97
Subject Interests: Large type print
Mem of Rolling Prairie Library System
Partic in Data Res Assocs

MADISON

P MADISON PUBLIC LIBRARY,* 1700 Fifth St, 62060. SAN 304-3789. Tel: 618-876-8448. FAX: 618-876-8316. *Dir*, Dawn Leona Davis; Staff 2 (MLS 2)
Pop 7,042; Circ 123,982
Library Holdings: Bk Vols 26,000; Per Subs 100
Mem of Lewis & Clark Library System

MAHOMET

P MAHOMET PUBLIC LIBRARY DISTRICT, 512 E Main St, PO Box 829, 61853-0829. SAN 304-3797. Tel: 217-586-2611. FAX: 217-586-5710. *Librn*, Lynn Schmit; Staff 9 (MLS 1, Non-MLS 8)
Founded 1966. Pop 8,440; Circ 91,774
Library Holdings: Bk Vols 21,000; Per Subs 90
Automation Activity & Vendor Info: (Acquisitions) epixtech, inc.; (Cataloging) epixtech, inc.; (Circulation) epixtech, inc.; (Media Booking) epixtech, inc.; (OPAC) epixtech, inc.; (Serials) epixtech, inc.
Mem of Lincoln Trail Libraries System
Friends of the Library Group

MALTA

J KISHWAUKEE COLLEGE, Learning Resources Center, 21193 Malta Rd, 60150-9699. SAN 304-3800. Tel: 815-825-2086, Ext 225. FAX: 815-825-2072. Web Site: judie.kish.cc.il.us/. *Dir*, R H Gaylor; Tel: 815-825-2086, Ext 366, E-Mail: rgaylor@kougars.kish.cc.il.us; *Media Spec*, Bradley Lipman; Tel: 815-825-2086, Ext 562, E-Mail: blipman@kougars.kish.cc.il.us; *Bibliog Instr, Ref*, Jean Evans; E-Mail: jevans@kougars.kish.cc.il.us; *Bibliog Instr, Ref*, Carol Wubbena; E-Mail: cwubbena@kougars.kish.cc.il.us; Staff 13 (MLS 3, Non-MLS 10)
Founded 1968. Enrl 1,933; Fac 105; Highest Degree: Associate
Jul 1999-Jun 2000 Income Parent Institution $513,245. Mats Exp $95,500, Books $30,000, Per/Ser (Incl. Access Fees) $40,000, Presv $500, Micro $5,000, AV Equip $10,000, Electronic Ref Mat (Incl. Access Fees) $10,000. Sal $497,000 (Prof $170,000)
Library Holdings: Bk Vols 44,399; Bk Titles 38,966; Per Subs 248; High Interest/Low Vocabulary Bk Vols 815
Automation Activity & Vendor Info: (Acquisitions) Endeavor; (Cataloging) Endeavor; (Circulation) Endeavor; (Course Reserve) Endeavor; (Media Booking) Endeavor; (OPAC) Endeavor; (Serials) Endeavor
Database Vendor: Ebsco - EbscoHost, GaleNet, OCLC - First Search, ProQuest
Mem of Northern Illinois Library System
Partic in NILRC
Friends of the Library Group

P MALTA TOWNSHIP PUBLIC LIBRARY,* 101 S Second & Adams Sts, PO Box 54, 60150. SAN 304-3819. Tel: 815-825-2525. FAX: 815-825-2525. *Librn*, Donna Clark
Founded 1921. Pop 1,550; Circ 11,519
Library Holdings: Bk Vols 15,000; Per Subs 39
Subject Interests: Indians
Mem of Northern Illinois Library System

MANHATTAN

P MANHATTAN PUBLIC LIBRARY DISTRICT, 240 Whitson St, PO Box 53, 60442. SAN 304-3827. Tel: 815-478-3987. FAX: 815-478-3988. *Dir*, Judy Pet; E-Mail: jpet@htls.lib.il.us; *Asst Dir*, Barbara Hnetkovsky; E-Mail: bhnetkovsky@htls.lib.il.us; *Ch Servs*, Paula Basile
Founded 1909. Pop 6,178; Circ 55,001
Jul 1999-Jun 2000 Income $242,290, State $13,033, County $196,504, Other $32,753. Mats Exp $29,115. Sal $116,023
Library Holdings: Bk Vols 34,500; Per Subs 120
Subject Interests: Local history
Mem of Heritage Trail Library System
Friends of the Library Group

MANITO

P MANITO PUBLIC LIBRARY DISTRICT,* 308 Harrison St, PO Box 710, 61546. SAN 320-8230. Tel: 309-968-6093. FAX: 309-968-6093. *Librn*, Debbie Horchem; *Asst Librn*, Mary Livengood; *Asst Librn*, Michele Wyss
Pop 6,000
Library Holdings: Bk Vols 8,360; Per Subs 22

MANSFIELD

P BLUE RIDGE TOWNSHIP PUBLIC LIBRARY, Mansfield Public Library, 101 W Oliver, PO Box 459, 61854-0459. SAN 304-3835. Tel: 217-489-9033. FAX: 217-489-9320. E-Mail: library2@farmwagon.com. *Librn*, Dorothy M Eddings
Founded 1923. Pop 1,418; Circ 12,970
Library Holdings: Bk Vols 10,000; Per Subs 55
Mem of Lincoln Trail Libraries System
Open Mon, Wed & Fri 1-5, Tues & Thurs 4-7, Sat 8-12

MANTENO

P MANTENO PUBLIC LIBRARY DISTRICT,* 50 W Division St, 60950. SAN 304-3843. Tel: 815-468-3323. FAX: 815-468-3360. *Librn*, Jan Heppe; *Asst Librn*, Mary Ann Curl
Founded 1965. Pop 8,633; Circ 52,763
Jul 1997-Jun 1998 Income $188,227, State $13,506, County $149,525, Other $25,196. Mats Exp $30,483, Books $27,383. Sal $62,295
Library Holdings: Bk Vols 29,842; Per Subs 80
Mem of Heritage Trail Library System
Open Mon-Thurs 10-8, Fri 10-6, Sat 10-3

MAPLE PARK

P MAPLE PARK PUBLIC LIBRARY DISTRICT,* 302 Willow St, PO Box 159, 60151. SAN 304-386X. Tel: 815-827-3362. *Dir*, Karen Flowers
Founded 1963. Pop 651; Circ 1,069
Library Holdings: Bk Vols 6,943
Mem of Northern Illinois Library System

MAQUON

P MAQUON PUBLIC LIBRARY DISTRICT,* 210 Main St, 61458-0218. SAN 304-3878. Tel: 309-875-3573. FAX: 309-875-3295. E-Mail: maquon01@wins.net. *Dir*, Eileen Lemon; *Asst Librn*, Marcia Zimmerman
Founded 1943. Circ 10,215
Library Holdings: Bk Vols 14,300; Per Subs 24
Mem of Alliance Library System
Open Mon 9-12, Tues & Fri 1-5, Wed & Thurs 1-8, Sat 9-3
Branches: 1
GILSON BRANCH, 1261 Harding St, Gilson, 61436. SAN 378-1518. Tel: 309-876-2300. FAX: 309-876-2300. *Asst Librn*, Marcia Zimmerman

MARENGO

P MARENGO PUBLIC LIBRARY DISTRICT, 200 S State St, 60152. SAN 304-3886. Tel: 815-568-8236. FAX: 815-568-5209. E-Mail: marp3@mc.net. Web Site: www.marengolib.org. *Dir*, Elizabeth Riak; Tel: 815-568-8238; *Ch Servs*, Sondra Terry
Founded 1878. Pop 10,120; Circ 47,091
Jul 1998-Jun 1999 Income (Main Library Only) $357,383, State $21,220, Locally Generated Income $298,067, Other $38,096. Mats Exp $45,974, Books $39,508, Per/Ser (Incl. Access Fees) $1,920, Electronic Ref Mat (Incl. Access Fees) $4,546. Sal $133,562 (Prof $54,340)
Library Holdings: Bk Vols 42,591; Bk Titles 42,244; Per Subs 84
Automation Activity & Vendor Info: (Cataloging) Follett; (Circulation) Follett; (OPAC) Follett
Database Vendor: OCLC - First Search
Function: ILL available
Mem of Northern Illinois Library System
Friends of the Library Group

MARION

P CRAB ORCHARD LIBRARY DISTRICT,* 19229 Bailey St, 62959. SAN 376-0073. Tel: 618-982-2141. FAX: 618-982-9135. *Librn*, Lola Morris
Library Holdings: Bk Titles 15,000; Per Subs 55
Subject Interests: Genealogy

GM DEPARTMENT OF VETERANS AFFAIRS MEDICAL CENTER, Medical Library, 2401 W Main St, 62959. SAN 304-3908. Tel: 618-997-5311. FAX: 618-993-4176. *Mgr*, Debra Goddard
Library Holdings: Bk Vols 1,031; Per Subs 176
Mem of Shawnee Library System
Partic in BRS; Nat Libr of Med; Vets Admin Libr Network

P MARION CARNEGIE LIBRARY, 206 S Market St, 62959-2519. SAN 304-3894. Tel: 618-993-5935. FAX: 618-997-6485. E-Mail: mrncar@midwest.net. *Dir*, Linda J Mathias; E-Mail: lmathias@shawls.lib.il.us; Staff 13 (MLS 1, Non-MLS 12)
Founded 1912. Pop 14,545; Circ 93,939
May 1999-Apr 2000 Income $534,666, State $25,854, City $430,591, Locally Generated Income $24,221, Other $54,000. Mats Exp $493,955, Books $51,298, Per/Ser (Incl. Access Fees) $2,100, Presv $500, AV Equip $5,612, Electronic Ref Mat (Incl. Access Fees) $3,157. Sal $312,635 (Prof $63,294)
Library Holdings: Bk Vols 57,010; Per Subs 220
Subject Interests: Civil War, Genealogy, Local history, Small bus
Special Collections: Williamson County Local History Coll
Automation Activity & Vendor Info: (Circulation) epixtech, inc.
Database Vendor: epixtech, inc., OCLC - First Search
Publications: The Patron (newsletter)
Function: ILL available
Mem of Shawnee Library System
Partic in Illinois Library & Information Network; OCLC Online Computer Library Center, Inc
Open Mon-Thurs 9-8, Fri & Sat 9-5; Local Hist & Genealogy Mon-Thurs 1-8 & Fri & Sat 1-5
Friends of the Library Group

MARISSA

P MARISSA PUBLIC LIBRARY,* 212 N Main, 62257. SAN 304-3916. Tel: 618-295-2825. FAX: 618-295-2825. Web Site: www.egyptian.net/~reading. *Librn*, Winona Laumbattus; *Asst Librn*, Linda Smith
Founded 1959. Pop 3,590; Circ 13,859 Sal $14,071
Library Holdings: Bk Titles 14,148; Per Subs 38
Mem of Shawnee Library System
Friends of the Library Group

MARKHAM

P ANDERSON-OGLESBY PUBLIC LIBRARY,* 16640 S Kedzie Ave, 60426. SAN 304-3924. Tel: 708-331-0130. FAX: 708-331-0137. E-Mail: aoglesby@aol.com. *Pres*, Dorothy Bradford; Staff 1 (MLS 1)
Founded 1967. Pop 15,172; Circ 53,321
Library Holdings: Bk Vols 27,000; Bk Titles 21,000; Per Subs 35
Mem of Suburban Library System
Friends of the Library Group

MAROA

P MAROA PUBLIC LIBRARY DISTRICT, 305 E Garfield, PO Box 620, 61756-0620. SAN 304-3932. Tel: 217-794-5111. FAX: 217-794-3005. *Librn*, Marilyn Gentle; E-Mail: marilyngentle@hotmail.com; Staff 4 (Non-MLS 4)
Founded 1945. Pop 2,538
Jul 1999-Jun 2000 Income $91,000, County $70,820, Other $20,180. Mats Exp $6,724, Books $6,133, Per/Ser (Incl. Access Fees) $591. Sal $33,853
Library Holdings: Bk Titles 18,022; Per Subs 42
Automation Activity & Vendor Info: (Cataloging) DRA; (Circulation) DRA
Database Vendor: OCLC - First Search
Mem of Rolling Prairie Library System
Friends of the Library Group

MARQUETTE HEIGHTS

P MARQUETTE HEIGHTS PUBLIC LIBRARY,* 715 Lincoln Rd, 61554-1313. SAN 304-3940. Tel: 309-382-3778. FAX: 309-382-3791. *Librn*, Katie Sumner
Founded 1959. Pop 3,077; Circ 10,506
Library Holdings: Bk Vols 10,602; Per Subs 46
Mem of Alliance Library System
Open Mon & Wed 10-5, Tues & Thurs 2-9, Sat 10-2

MARSEILLES

P MARSEILLES PUBLIC LIBRARY, 155 E Bluff St, 61341. SAN 304-3959. Tel: 815-795-4437. FAX: 815-795-5137. *Head Librn*, Gloria Votava; E-Mail: gvotava@htls.lib.il.us
Founded 1904. Pop 4,811; Circ 21,914
Library Holdings: Bk Titles 19,435; Per Subs 70
Subject Interests: Local history
Automation Activity & Vendor Info: (Circulation) Athena
Mem of Heritage Trail Library System
Friends of the Library Group

MARSHALL

P MARSHALL PUBLIC LIBRARY, 612 Archer Ave, 62441. SAN 304-3967. Tel: 217-826-2535. FAX: 217-826-5529. *Librn*, Leanna Morris; *Asst Librn*, Carloyn Tinglay
Pop 3,379; Circ 26,000
Library Holdings: Bk Vols 19,000; Per Subs 70
Mem of Lincoln Trail Libraries System
Friends of the Library Group

MARTINSVILLE

P MARTINSVILLE PUBLIC LIBRARY DISTRICT,* 120 E Cumberland, PO Box 190, 62442. SAN 304-3975. Tel: 217-382-4113. FAX: 217-382-4113. *Librn*, Barbara Kannmacher
Library Holdings: Bk Vols 14,000; Per Subs 55
Mem of Lincoln Trail Libraries System

MASCOUTAH

P MASCOUTAH PUBLIC LIBRARY,* 3 W Church St, 62258. SAN 304-3983. Tel: 618-566-2562. FAX: 618-566-2563. *Dir*, Linda K Zacharski; E-Mail: lindaz@shawls.lib.il.us; *Asst Librn*, Kerry Fangmeyer; Staff 6 (MLS 2, Non-MLS 4)
Founded 1929. Pop 5,511; Circ 43,571
May 1998-Apr 1999 Income (Main Library Only) $159,826, State $6,825, City $137,225, Federal $15,776. Mats Exp $29,210, Books $26,061, AV Equip $3,149
Library Holdings: Bk Titles 39,065; Per Subs 108
Database Vendor: epixtech, inc., OVID Technologies
Mem of Shawnee Library System
Friends of the Library Group

MASON CITY

P MASON CITY PUBLIC LIBRARY,* 145 S Main St, 62664. SAN 304-3991. Tel: 217-482-3799. FAX: 217-482-3799. *Librn*, Gisa Power; E-Mail: gisap@alpha.rpls.lib.ilius
Pop 2,719; Circ 11,722
Library Holdings: Bk Vols 15,000; Per Subs 45
Mem of Rolling Prairie Library System
Open Mon 9-7, Tues & Thurs 12-5, Sat 9-12
Friends of the Library Group

MATTESON

P MATTESON PUBLIC LIBRARY,* 801 S School St, 60443-1897. SAN 304-4009. Tel: 708-748-4431. FAX: 708-748-0510. E-Mail: mts@sslic.net. *Dir*, Dean Bryan; *Asst Dir*, William W Madsen; *Ad Servs, Ref*, Bill Downs; *Ref*, Marsha Lotz; *Ch Servs*, Jean Day; Staff 6 (MLS 6)
Founded 1964. Pop 11,500; Circ 144,080
May 1997-Apr 1998 Income $754,383, State $14,909, City $697,668, Locally Generated Income $41,806. Mats Exp $150,729, Books $71,265, Per/Ser (Incl. Access Fees) $26,000, AV Equip $17,410, Other Print Mats $98. Sal $458,105
Library Holdings: Bk Vols 80,000; Per Subs 210
Automation Activity & Vendor Info: (Circulation) CLSI LIBS
Publications: Quarterly newsletter
Mem of Suburban Library System
Open Sat 10-5, Sun 1-5
Friends of the Library Group

MATTOON

J LAKE LAND COLLEGE, Virgil H Judge Learning Resource Center, 5001 Lakeland Blvd, 61938. SAN 304-4017. Tel: 217-234-5367. Circulation Tel: 217-234-5367. Reference Tel: 217-234-5440. Toll Free Tel: 800-252-4121 (Illinois only). FAX: 217-258-6459. Web Site: www.lakeland.cc.il.us/library/. *Dir*, Scott C Drone-Silvers; Tel: 217-234-5338, E-Mail: dsilvers@lakeland.cc.il.us; Staff 7 (MLS 2, Non-MLS 5)
Founded 1968. Enrl 3,612; Fac 101; Highest Degree: Associate
Jul 1999-Jun 2000 Income Parent Institution $427,180. Mats Exp $122,555, Books $59,165, Per/Ser (Incl. Access Fees) $14,600, Micro $2,320, Electronic Ref Mat (Incl. Access Fees) $46,470. Sal $183,176 (Prof $90,197)
Library Holdings: Bk Vols 35,775; Bk Titles 33,090; Per Subs 219
Automation Activity & Vendor Info: (Cataloging) epixtech, inc.; (Circulation) epixtech, inc.; (OPAC) epixtech, inc.
Database Vendor: Ebsco - EbscoHost, epixtech, inc., IAC - SearchBank, OCLC - First Search, ProQuest, Silverplatter Information Inc., Wilson - Wilson Web
Function: ILL available
Mem of Lincoln Trail Libraries System
Partic in ILLINET; MILRC; MLNC; NILRC

M SARAH BUSH LINCOLN HEALTH CENTER, Medical Library, PO Box 372, 61938. SAN 375-9474. Tel: 217-258-2262. FAX: 217-258-2288. *Librn*, Nina Pals
Library Holdings: Bk Titles 1,000; Per Subs 200
Mem of Lincoln Trail Libraries System

P MATTOON PUBLIC LIBRARY, 1600 Charleston Ave, 61938-3635. (Mail add: PO Box 809, 61938-0809), SAN 304-4025. Tel: 217-234-2621. FAX: 217-234-2660. *Dir*, Mona R Bays; E-Mail: mbays@ltnet.ltls.org; *Admin Assoc*, Larry E Oathout; E-Mail: loatho@ltnet.ltls.org; Staff 6 (MLS 1, Non-MLS 5)
Founded 1893. Pop 18,441; Circ 86,000
May 1999-Apr 2000 Income $416,808, State $48,324, City $320,591, Locally Generated Income $47,893, Other $76,053. Mats Exp $55,151, Books $39,269, Per/Ser (Incl. Access Fees) $4,409, Electronic Ref Mat (Incl. Access Fees) $11,473. Sal $165,787 (Prof $74,400)
Library Holdings: Bk Vols 58,278; Per Subs 140; Bks on Deafness & Sign Lang 10
Database Vendor: OCLC - First Search
Mem of Lincoln Trail Libraries System
Friends of the Library Group

MAYWOOD

P MAYWOOD PUBLIC LIBRARY, 121 S Fifth Ave, 60153. SAN 340-5095. Tel: 708-343-1847. FAX: 708-343-2115. Web Site: www.maywood.org. *Dir*, Stan Huntington; *Ch Servs*, Sheila Jones-Ferrari; *Tech Servs*, Marcia Burton; *Circ*, Cathy Schuemer; *Ref Serv*, Carol Clover; Staff 7 (MLS 4, Non-MLS 3)
Founded 1874. Pop 27,139
Jul 1998-Jun 1999 Income $1,647,132, State $718,154, Locally Generated Income $51,022. Mats Exp $87,617, Books $78,444, Presv $1,061, Other Print Mats $2,807, Electronic Ref Mat (Incl. Access Fees) $1,800. Sal $513,227
Library Holdings: Bk Titles 89,918; Per Subs 65; Bks on Deafness & Sign Lang 56
Subject Interests: Afro-American, History, Literature, Local history
Automation Activity & Vendor Info: (Circulation) Innovative Interfaces Inc.; (OPAC) Innovative Interfaces Inc.
Publications: WWW.MAYWOOD.ORG (quarterly) (Newsletter)
Mem of Suburban Library System

MC COOK

P MC COOK PUBLIC LIBRARY DISTRICT, 8419 W 50th St, PO Box 1553, 60525. SAN 376-0146. Tel: 708-442-1242. FAX: 708-442-0148. E-Mail: mcs@sls.lib.il.us. *Dir*, Allan Morrow; Staff 8 (MLS 1, Non-MLS 7)
Jul 1999-Jun 2000 Income $239,528, State $15,595, County $213,234, Locally Generated Income $10,699. Mats Exp $27,066. Sal $78,738
Library Holdings: Bk Titles 17,943; Per Subs 61
Automation Activity & Vendor Info: (Circulation) Innovative Interfaces Inc.
Partic in Suburban Libr Syst

MC HENRY

P MCHENRY NUNDA PUBLIC LIBRARY DISTRICT, 813 W Rte 120, 60050. SAN 304-3703. Tel: 815-385-6303. FAX: 815-385-6337. E-Mail: mnpublib@mc.net. *Dir*, Linda Burdette
Founded 1960. Pop 4,002
2000-2000 Mats Exp Books $10,662. Sal $44,520
Library Holdings: Bk Titles 13,317; Per Subs 46
Mem of North Suburban Library System

P MCHENRY PUBLIC LIBRARY DISTRICT, (MPLD), 809 N Front St, 60050. SAN 304-3711. Tel: 815-385-0036. FAX: 815-385-7085. E-Mail: mcpld@nslsilus.org. Web Site: www.nslsilus.org/mpld. *Dir*, Arlene M Kaspik; *Assoc Dir, Tech Servs*, R William Edminster; *ILL*, Sue Thompson; *Circ*, Kathy Milfajt; *Ad Servs*, Colette Myers; *Ch Servs*, Jane Halsall; Staff 30 (MLS 7, Non-MLS 23)
Founded 1943. Pop 33,225; Circ 202,692
Jul 2000-Jun 2001 Income $1,024,064, State $40,239, City $6,600, County $735,000, Locally Generated Income $32,000, Other $225,000. Mats Exp $68,024, Books $40,009, Per/Ser (Incl. Access Fees) $7,327. Sal $375,000
Library Holdings: Bk Vols 65,000; Per Subs 150
Subject Interests: Genealogy
Special Collections: Large-Type Books Coll
Automation Activity & Vendor Info: (Cataloging) GEAC; (Circulation) GEAC; (ILL) GEAC; (OPAC) GEAC
Database Vendor: OCLC - First Search
Publications: The Preface (newsletter)
Mem of North Suburban Library System
Partic in Coop Computer Servs
Friends of the Library Group

M NORTHERN ILLINOIS MEDICAL CENTER LIBRARY, 4201 Medical Center Dr, 60050-8499. SAN 375-9814. Tel: 815-759-4076. FAX: 815-759-8088. Web Site: www.centerga.com.
Library Holdings: Bk Titles 550

MC LEAN

P MOUNT HOPE-FUNKS GROVE TOWNSHIPS LIBRARY DISTRICT, Clinton & Morgan St, PO Box 320, 61754. SAN 304-3738. Tel: 309-874-2291. FAX: 309-874-2291. Web Site: library1@davesworld.net. *Dir*, Suzanne Kruger
Founded 1917. Pop 1,432
1998-1999 Income $21,243. Mats Exp $7,367, Books $7,000, Per/Ser (Incl. Access Fees) $367. Sal $6,916
Library Holdings: Bk Titles 12,740; Per Subs 35
Subject Interests: Antiques
Special Collections: McLeans Lens Micro Film Coll
Mem of Alliance Library System
Open Tues & Thurs 2-8, Wed 3:30-6:30, Sat 10-3

MC LEANSBORO

P MCCOY MEMORIAL LIBRARY, 118 S Washington St, 62859. SAN 304-3746. Tel: 618-643-2125. FAX: 618-643-2207. *Librn*, Eileen Drake
Founded 1921. Pop 2,677
Library Holdings: Bk Titles 10,451; Per Subs 101
Subject Interests: Genealogy
Mem of Shawnee Library System

MELROSE PARK

S ALBERTO-CULVER CO, Research Library, 2525 Armitage Ave, 60160. SAN 304-4033. Tel: 708-450-3155. FAX: 708-450-3067. *Res*, Mary Elaine Woolsey; E-Mail: mwoolsey@alberto.com; Staff 1 (MLS 1)
Founded 1964
Library Holdings: Bk Titles 2,264; Per Subs 195
Subject Interests: Cosmetics industry
Database Vendor: Dialog, OCLC - First Search
Publications: Industry Happenings Newsletter; Library Lites; Research Library Newsletter
Mem of Suburban Library System

M GOTTLIEB MEMORIAL HOSPITAL, Medical Library,* 701 W North Ave, 60160. SAN 375-9393. Tel: 708-681-3200, Ext 1173. FAX: 708-681-3973. *Librn*, Gloria Kroc
Library Holdings: Bk Titles 450

P MELROSE PARK PUBLIC LIBRARY, 801 N Broadway, 60160. SAN 304-405X. Tel: 708-343-3391. FAX: 708-531-5327. E-Mail: mps@sls.lib.il.us. *Dir*, Patrick Itiala; *Asst Librn*, Dolores Connelly; Staff 9 (MLS 3, Non-MLS 6)
Founded 1898. Pop 20,859; Circ 58,203
Jan 2000-Dec 2000 Income $705,000. Mats Exp $651,235
Library Holdings: Bk Vols 78,801
Special Collections: Cinema Coll
Database Vendor: Ebsco - EbscoHost, Innovative Interfaces INN - View, OCLC - First Search
Mem of Suburban Library System

S NAVISTAR INTERNATIONAL TRANSPORTATION CORP, Engine Engineering Information Center, 10400 W North Ave, 60160-1065. SAN 304-4041. Tel: 708-865-4004. FAX: 708-216-0696. *Librn*, Janet Hines; E-Mail: janet.hines@nav-international.com; *Mgr*, William Warren; Staff 1 (MLS 1)
Founded 1987
Library Holdings: Bk Vols 1,000; Per Subs 91; Per Subs 94
Subject Interests: Automotive engineering
Database Vendor: CARL, Dialog, OVID Technologies
Mem of Suburban Library System

M WESTLAKE COMMUNITY HOSPITAL LIBRARY,* 1225 Lake St, 60160. SAN 320-6572. Tel: 708-681-3000, Ext 3215. FAX: 708-681-0151. *Librn*, Christina E Rudawski
Library Holdings: Bk Vols 300; Per Subs 145
Partic in BRS; Metrop Consortium; Suburban Libr Syst

MELVIN

P MELVIN PUBLIC LIBRARY, (MMN), 102 S Center St, PO Box 184, 60952. SAN 304-4084. Tel: 217-388-2421. FAX: 217-388-2421. *Librn*, Jacqueline Allen; E-Mail: jallen@ltnet.ltls.org
Pop 654; Circ 7,739
Apr 1998-Mar 1999 Income $16,414. Mats Exp $16,202
Library Holdings: Bk Vols 8,417; Per Subs 36
Mem of Lincoln Trail Libraries System
Open Mon-Wed 12:30-6:30, Fri 12:30-5:00, Sat 10-3

MENDON

P FOUR STAR PUBLIC LIBRARY DISTRICT, 129 W South St, PO Box 169, 62351-0169. SAN 375-3271. Tel: 217-936-2131. FAX: 217-936-2132. E-Mail: fourstar@adams.net. Web Site: www.fourstar.lib.il.us. *Librn*, Jill Lucey; Staff 3 (MLS 1, Non-MLS 2)
Founded 1990. Pop 4,485
Jul 2000-Jun 2001 Income $83,833, State $5,400, Locally Generated Income $76,000, Other $2,433. Mats Exp $11,900, Books $10,000, Per/Ser (Incl. Access Fees) $1,400, Micro $500. Sal $34,000 (Prof $14,400)
Library Holdings: Bk Titles 8,950; Per Subs 45
Database Vendor: CARL, DRA, OCLC - First Search
Mem of Alliance Library System
Partic in Resource Sharing Alliance

MENDOTA

P GRAVES-HUME PUBLIC LIBRARY DISTRICT, 1401 W Main, 61342. SAN 304-4092. Tel: 815-538-5142. FAX: 815-538-3816. *Dir*, Loretta Causa; E-Mail: lcausa@htls.lib.il.us; *Ch Servs*, Connie Beetz; Staff 2 (Non-MLS 2)
Founded 1870. Pop 7,000; Circ 50,200
Jul 1999-Jun 2000 Income $199,329, State $9,657, City $4,000, Federal $10,440, County $116,241, Other $58,991. Mats Exp $32,538, Books $25,000, Per/Ser (Incl. Access Fees) $3,000, Micro $138, AV Equip $4,400. Sal $69,267 (Prof $28,000)
Library Holdings: Bk Vols 31,000
Mem of Heritage Trail Library System
Friends of the Library Group

MEREDOSIA

P M-C RIVER VALLEY PUBLIC LIBRARY DISTRICT, 304 Main St, 62665. (Mail add: PO Box 259, 62665-0259), SAN 304-4106. Tel: 217-584-1571. FAX: 217-584-1571. E-Mail: vrevircm@accessus.net. *Librn*, Janet Wells; *Asst Librn*, Debbie Sullivan
Circ 29,532
Library Holdings: Bk Vols 18,000; Per Subs 75
Automation Activity & Vendor Info: (Cataloging) Follett; (Circulation) Follett; (OPAC) Follett
Mem of Alliance Library System
Open Mon & Thurs 6-9, Tues 9-5, Wed 9-9, Fri & Sat 1-5

METAMORA

P ILLINOIS PRAIRIE DISTRICT PUBLIC LIBRARY, 208 E Partridge, PO Box 770, 61548-0770. SAN 340-515X. Tel: 309-367-4594. FAX: 309-367-2687. E-Mail: ipdp@darkstar.rsa.lib.il.us. *Dir*, Grant A Fredericksen; Staff 1 (MLS 1)
Founded 1950. Pop 17,749; Circ 139,977
Jul 1999-Jun 2000 Income $458,855, State $30,613, County $428,242. Mats Exp $87,803, Books $75,249, Per/Ser (Incl. Access Fees) $4,000, AV Equip $8,554. Sal $166,968 (Prof $32,000)
Library Holdings: Bk Vols 103,406; Per Subs 381
Subject Interests: Agriculture, Antiques, Education, History
Special Collections: Local Newspaper (Metamora Herald 1887-present & Washburn Leader 1963-present), micro
Automation Activity & Vendor Info: (Circulation) CARL
Database Vendor: OCLC - First Search
Mem of Alliance Library System
Partic in OCLC Online Computer Library Center, Inc
Branches: 6
BENSON BRANCH, 420 E Front, PO Box 58, Benson, 61516. SAN 340-5184. Tel: 309-394-2542. *Librn*, Diana Kolb

Library Holdings: Bk Titles 6,272
GERMANTOWN-HILLS BRANCH, 101 Warrior Way, Germantown-Hills, 61548. SAN 340-5214. Tel: 309-383-2263. *Librn*, Pat Staab
Library Holdings: Bk Titles 5,196
METAMORA, 208 E Partridge, PO Box 770, 61548. SAN 340-5249. Tel: 309-367-4594. FAX: 309-367-2687. *In Charge*, Mary Ann Spencer
Library Holdings: Bk Vols 52,746; Bk Titles 43,974
ROANOKE BRANCH, 311 N Main, PO Box 657, Roanoke, 61561. SAN 340-5273. Tel: 309-923-7686. *Librn*, Marge Braker
Library Holdings: Bk Titles 7,825
SPRINGBAY BRANCH, 406 Illinois St, Springbay, 61611. SAN 340-5303. Tel: 309-566-0444. *Librn*, Lyn Wiegand
Library Holdings: Bk Titles 5,723
WASHBURN BRANCH, 112 W Magnolia, PO Box 128, Washburn, 61570. SAN 340-5338. Tel: 309-248-7429. *Librn*, Phyllis Strauch
Library Holdings: Bk Titles 7,114

METROPOLIS

S FORT MASSAC STATE PARK & HISTORIC SITE, 1308 E Fifth St, 62960. SAN 329-7810. Tel: 618-524-4712. FAX: 618-524-9321. E-Mail: SMCCREE@dnrmail.state.illinois.us. *In Charge*, Terry Johnson
Subject Interests: Historic sites

P METROPOLIS PUBLIC LIBRARY,* 317 Metropolis St, 62960. SAN 304-4114. Tel: 618-524-4312. E-Mail: public@hcis.net. *Librn*, Joanne Dowing
Pop 7,171; Circ 51,066
Library Holdings: Bk Vols 25,690; Per Subs 150
Subject Interests: Genealogy
Mem of Shawnee Library System

MIDLOTHIAN

P MIDLOTHIAN PUBLIC LIBRARY, 14701 S Kenton Ave, 60445. SAN 304-4122. Tel: 708-535-2027. FAX: 708-535-2053. E-Mail: mds@sls-lib.il.us. *Librn*, Carolyn Peterson; Staff 3 (MLS 1, Non-MLS 2)
Founded 1931. Pop 14,374; Circ 125,984
May 1999-Apr 2000 Mats Exp $110,066, Books $83,737, AV Equip $26,329. Sal $215,885
Library Holdings: Bk Vols 49,950; Per Subs 127
Mem of Suburban Library System
Partic in Shared Library Services
Friends of the Library Group

MILFORD

P MILFORD DISTRICT LIBRARY,* 2 S Grant Ave, 60953-1399. SAN 304-4130. Tel: 815-889-4722. Interlibrary Loan Service Tel: 800-275-5857. FAX: 815-889-4171. *Librn*, Susan Moenck; E-Mail: smoenc@ltnet.hls.org
Founded 1896. Pop 3,415; Circ 23,284
Library Holdings: Bk Vols 23,000; Per Subs 32
Mem of Lincoln Trail Libraries System

MILLEDGEVILLE

P WYSOX TOWNSHIP LIBRARY, 8 W Fifth St, 61051. (Mail add: PO Box 545, 61051), SAN 304-4149. Tel: 815-225-7572. FAX: 815-225-7036. E-Mail: wysoxlib@essex1.com. *Librn*, Nancy Dittmar
Pop 3,000; Circ 8,968
Library Holdings: Bk Vols 9,300; Per Subs 17
Mem of Northern Illinois Library System

MILLSTADT

P MILLSTADT LIBRARY,* 115 W Laurel St, 62260. SAN 376-0901. Tel: 618-476-1887. FAX: 618-476-1887. *Librn*, Mary Eckert
Library Holdings: Bk Titles 18,050; Per Subs 46
Mem of Lewis & Clark Library System

MINERAL

P MINERAL-GOLD PUBLIC LIBRARY DISTRICT,* 120 E Main St, PO Box 87, 61344. SAN 304-4157. Tel: 309-288-3971. FAX: 309-288-3971. *Librn*, Susan Whitmore; *Asst Librn*, Linda Morey
Pop 951; Circ 15,425
Library Holdings: Bk Vols 14,638; Per Subs 35
Subject Interests: Gardening, Local history
Mem of River Valley Libr Syst

MINIER

P H A PEINE MEMORIAL LIBRARY,* 202 N Main Ave, 61759. SAN 304-4165. Tel: 309-392-3220. FAX: 309-392-2697. *Librn*, Denise Litwiller
Founded 1929. Pop 1,262; Circ 9,600
Library Holdings: Bk Vols 6,000; Per Subs 23
Mem of Alliance Library System

MINONK

P FILGER PUBLIC LIBRARY, 261 E Fifth St, 61760. SAN 304-4173. Tel: 309-432-2929. FAX: 309-432-2929. E-Mail: library@fieldcrest.k12.il.us. Web Site: www.minonk.lib.il.us. *Librn*, Karen Podzamsky; *Asst Librn*, Ethel Weakly
Founded 1915. Pop 1,984; Circ 25,412
Library Holdings: Bk Vols 23,000; Per Subs 65
Automation Activity & Vendor Info: (Cataloging) Follett
Publications: Filger News Dispatch (YA book reviews)
Mem of Alliance Library System

MOKENA

P MOKENA COMMUNITY PUBLIC LIBRARY DISTRICT, 11327 W 195th St, 60448-1399. SAN 304-4181. Tel: 708-479-9663. TDD: 708-479-9663. FAX: 708-479-9684. Web Site: www.htls.lib.il.us/mkb. *Coll Develop, Dir*, Phyllis A Jacobek; E-Mail: pjacobek@htls.lib.il.us; *Asst Dir, Circ*, Dawn Ellingham; E-Mail: dellingham@htls.lib.il.us; *Business*, Cathy Palmer; E-Mail: cpalmer@htls.lib.il.us; *Cat, Ref Serv, YA Servs*, Carol Tracy; E-Mail: ctracy@htls.lib.il.us; *Tech Servs*, Mrs Nelvie Fremel; E-Mail: nfremel@htls.lib.il.us; *Ch Servs, Coll Develop*, Kathy Wierzibicki; Staff 38 (Non-MLS 38)
Founded 1976. Pop 12,982; Circ 100,000
Jul 1999-Jun 2000 Income $560,000. Mats Exp $86,200, Books $50,000, Per/Ser (Incl. Access Fees) $9,200, Micro $1,000, AV Equip $6,000, Electronic Ref Mat (Incl. Access Fees) $20,000. Sal $282,000
Library Holdings: Bk Vols 75,000; Per Subs 300
Subject Interests: Large type print, Parenting
Database Vendor: Ebsco - EbscoHost, IAC - SearchBank, OCLC - First Search
Publications: Newsletter (in-house, monthly)
Mem of Heritage Trail Library System
Friends of the Library Group

MOLINE

J BLACK HAWK COLLEGE, (BHC), 6600 34th Ave, 61265. SAN 340-5362. Tel: 309-796-5700. FAX: 309-796-0393. Web Site: www.bhc.edu. *Dir*, Charlet Key; *Publ Servs*, Pat Beitel; *Tech Servs*, Caroline Barnes; Staff 9 (MLS 4, Non-MLS 5)
Founded 1946. Enrl 5,400; Fac 140; Highest Degree: Associate
Jul 1999-Jun 2000 Income $386,402. Mats Exp $95,000. Sal $256,908 (Prof $179,000)
Library Holdings: Bk Vols 51,200; Bk Titles 47,900; Per Subs 350
Automation Activity & Vendor Info: (Acquisitions) GEAC; (Cataloging) GEAC; (Circulation) GEAC; (OPAC) GEAC
Database Vendor: Ebsco - EbscoHost, IAC - Info Trac, Lexis-Nexis
Mem of River Bend Library System
Partic in Bi-State Academic Libraries; CCMP; NILRC

S DEERE & CO LIBRARY,* One John Deere Pl, 61265. SAN 340-5397. Tel: 309-765-4733. FAX: 309-765-4088. *Mgr*, Betty Hagberg; Tel: 309-765-4881; *Archivist*, Les Stegh; *Online Servs, Ref*, Diana Polk; *Ref*, Sean O'Hanlon; Staff 11 (MLS 5, Non-MLS 6)
Founded 1958
Library Holdings: Bk Vols 12,000; Bk Titles 10,000; Per Subs 800
Subject Interests: Agriculture, Business and management, Construction, Economics, Engineering, Finance, Forestry, Marketing
Special Collections: Deere & Company History
Automation Activity & Vendor Info: (Acquisitions) SIRSI; (Cataloging) GEAC; (Circulation) GEAC; (Serials) SIRSI
Database Vendor: Dialog
Mem of River Bend Library System
Partic in Illinois Library & Information Network; Nat Libr of Med; OCLC Online Computer Library Center, Inc
Branches:
TECHNICAL CENTER LIBRARY, 3300 River Dr, 61265. SAN 340-5427.

S MOLINE DISPATCH PUBLISHING CO, The Dispatch & The Rock Island Argus Library,* 1720 Fifth Ave, 61265. SAN 324-4008. Tel: 309-764-4344. FAX: 309-757-4992.
Subject Interests: Local history

P MOLINE PUBLIC LIBRARY,* 504 17th St, 61265. SAN 340-5451. Tel: 309-762-6883. TDD: 309-762-0239. FAX: 309-797-0484. E-Mail: refmpl@libby.rbls.lib.il.us. Web Site: www.rbls.lib.il.us/mpl/index.html. *Dir*, Phillis Wilson; *Ch Servs*, Shelli Fehr; *Tech Servs*, Leslie A Hood; *Circ*, Mary Coussens; *Commun Relations*, Judy Dusenberry; *YA Servs*, Lisa Powell

Williams; Staff 30 (MLS 9, Non-MLS 21)
Founded 1873. Pop 43,200; Circ 450,075
Apr 1999-Mar 2000 Income (Main Library and Branch Library) $1,854,890, State $53,355, City $1,705,560, Locally Generated Income $95,975. Mats Exp $178,600, Books $116,500, Per/Ser (Incl. Access Fees) $25,200, Micro $8,500, AV Equip $13,000, Electronic Ref Mat (Incl. Access Fees) $15,400. Sal $1,078,995
Library Holdings: Bk Vols 192,004; Per Subs 420
Subject Interests: Genealogy, Spanish (language)
Special Collections: Katherine Deere Butterworth Coll; Rehr Art Gallery
Database Vendor: OCLC - First Search
Publications: Literary Lines (newsletter)
Mem of River Bend Library System
Partic in OCLC Online Computer Library Center, Inc; Quad Cities Libraries In Cooperation
Special Services for the Deaf - TDD
Friends of the Library Group
Branches: 1
SOUTHEAST, 3130 41st St, 61265. SAN 340-5486. Tel: 309-797-4141. TDD: 309-762-0609. FAX: 309-797-0480. E-Mail: refmpl@libby.rbls.lib.il.us. Web Site: www.rbls.lib.il.us/mpl/index.html.
Special Services for the Deaf - TDD

MOMENCE

P EDWARD CHIPMAN PUBLIC LIBRARY, 126 N Locust St, 60954. SAN 304-4211. Tel: 815-472-2581. FAX: 815-472-2581. E-Mail: chipmunk@colinti.com. *Librn*, Linda Schultz
Pop 3,300; Circ 23,660
Library Holdings: Bk Vols 14,000; Per Subs 72
Mem of Heritage Trail Library System
Friends of the Library Group

MONMOUTH

S WYATT EARP BIRTHPLACE, INC, Museum Library, 406 S Third St. (Mail add: 1020 E Detroit Ave, 61462-1453), SAN 371-7488. Tel: 309-734-6419. FAX: 309-734-6419. E-Mail: wyattearpbirthp@webtv.net. Web Site: www.misslink.net/misslink/earp.htm. *Curator*, Melba Matson
Founded 1986
Library Holdings: Bk Titles 41
Special Collections: Wyatt Earp & Family Coll
Publications: The Birthplace of Wyatt Earp: A Review (parts 1 & 2); Wyatt Earp (brochure); Wyatt Earp, Native Son
Books & souvenirs on Wyatt Earp are sold; Productions: Wyatt Earp & OK Corral Reenactment on 1st Sunday in Aug; Open Sun (Memorial Day-Labor Day) 1-4 or by appt, group tours all year
Friends of the Library Group

C MONMOUTH COLLEGE, Hewes Library, 700 E Broadway, 61462-1963. SAN 304-422X. Tel: 309-457-2191. Circulation Tel: 309-457-2190. Reference Tel: 309-457-2301. FAX: 309-734-7500. E-Mail: library@monm.edu. Web Site: department.monm.edu/library. *Dir*, John Richard Sayre; Tel: 309-457-2192, E-Mail: rsayre@monm.edu; *Circ, ILL*, Patricia Mitchell; Tel: 309-457-2188, E-Mail: pepmeyer@monm.edu; *Publ Servs*, Matthew Antoline; Tel: 309-457-2303, E-Mail: rsayre@monm.edu; *Acq*, Anita Sue Stevenson; Tel: 309-457-2191, E-Mail: sue@monm.edu; *Tech Servs*, Lynn K Daw; Tel: 309-457-2187, E-Mail: ldaw@monm.edu; *Tech Servs*, Rita Schwass; Tel: 309-457-2334, E-Mail: rschwass@monm.edu; *AV*, Amanda Huxtable; Tel: 309-457-2193, E-Mail: ahetzel@monm.edu; Staff 7 (MLS 3, Non-MLS 4)
Founded 1853. Enrl 1,066; Fac 76; Highest Degree: Bachelor
Jul 2000-Jun 2001 Income $520,293, State $2,000, Federal $22,246, Parent Institution $496,047. Mats Exp $194,371, Books $89,413, Per/Ser (Incl. Access Fees) $60,007, Presv $3,994, Micro $6,323, Electronic Ref Mat (Incl. Access Fees) $31,038. Sal $194,430 (Prof $127,109)
Library Holdings: Bk Vols 296,598; Per Subs 514
Special Collections: Government Documents; James Christie Shields Collection of Ancient Art & Antiques; Monmouth College Archives
Automation Activity & Vendor Info: (Acquisitions) epixtech, inc.; (Cataloging) epixtech, inc.; (Circulation) epixtech, inc.; (OPAC) epixtech, inc.; (Serials) epixtech, inc.
Database Vendor: Dialog, Ebsco - EbscoHost, epixtech, inc., GaleNet, Lexis-Nexis, OCLC - First Search, ProQuest, Silverplatter Information Inc.
Function: ILL available
Partic in Alliance Library System; Associated Cols of the Midwest; Ill Coop Coll Mgt Prog; Illinois Library & Information Network; Private Academic Libraries Of Illinois

P WARREN COUNTY PUBLIC LIBRARY DISTRICT, 62 Public Square, 61462-1756. SAN 340-5516. Tel: 309-734-3166. FAX: 309-734-5955. E-Mail: wcpl@monmouth.net. Web Site: www.wcpl.monmouth.net. *Head Librn*, Julian C Bruening; *Ad Servs*, Karen Vandeveer; *Cat*, Donna Objartel; *Acq, Coll Develop*, Betty Loomis; *Ch Servs*, Genie Doty; Staff 2 (MLS 1, Non-MLS 1)
Founded 1868. Pop 19,181
Jul 2000-Jun 2001 Income $407,743, State $23,663, County $344,271, Other $39,809. Mats Exp $70,408, Books $49,500, Per/Ser (Incl. Access Fees) $4,908, Other Print Mats $16,000. Sal $165,356 (Prof $43,056)
Library Holdings: Bk Vols 87,643; Bk Titles 72,548; Per Subs 170
Subject Interests: Agriculture, Genealogy, Law
Special Collections: Lincoln Coll
Automation Activity & Vendor Info: (Acquisitions) Follett; (Cataloging) Follett; (Circulation) Follett
Mem of Alliance Library System
Special Services for the Blind - Audio-cassettes
Friends of the Library Group
Branches: 3
ALEXIS BRANCH, 102 W Broadway, Alexis, 61412. SAN 340-5540. Tel: 309-482-6109. *Librn*, Mary Richardson
Library Holdings: Bk Titles 3,106; Per Subs 15
Friends of the Library Group
KIRKWOOD BRANCH, 134 S Kirk, Kirkwood, 61447. SAN 340-5605. Tel: 309-768-2173. *Librn*, Linda Hollenberg
Library Holdings: Bk Titles 2,660; Per Subs 19
ROSEVILLE BRANCH, 145 W Penn Ave, Roseville, 61473. SAN 340-5664. Tel: 309-426-2336. *Librn*, Louise Rankin
Library Holdings: Bk Vols 3,923; Per Subs 22
Friends of the Library Group

MONTICELLO

P ALLERTON PUBLIC LIBRARY, 201 N State St, 61856. SAN 304-4238. Tel: 217-762-4676. FAX: 217-762-2021. Web Site: www.monticellolibrary.org. *Dir*, Lisa Winters; E-Mail: lwinte@ltnet.ltls.org; *Ch Servs*, Paula Valentine; *Circ*, Lorrie Taylor; *Tech Servs*, Lynn Richardson; Staff 4 (Non-MLS 4)
Founded 1897. Pop 5,300; Circ 117,658
Library Holdings: Bk Titles 33,000; Per Subs 97
Subject Interests: Interior design, Local history
Special Collections: Census (Piatt County Coll), micro; Piatt County Newspaper Coll, micro
Automation Activity & Vendor Info: (Circulation) epixtech, inc.
Publications: Monticello 150 Years Later
Mem of Lincoln Trail Libraries System

S PIATT COUNTY HISTORICAL & GENEALOGICAL SOCIETY LIBRARY, Courthouse Annex, 301 S Charter, 61856-1823. (Mail add: PO Box 111, 51856-0111), SAN 372-5642. *Pres*, Kay Gilbreath; *Librn*, Louise Primmer; E-Mail: primmer@pdnt.com
Founded 1980
Library Holdings: Bk Titles 500
Special Collections: Piatt County Illinois Local History (PGHGS Coll), bks & microflm
Publications: PCHGS (quarterly newsletter)
Publications for sale. Open Mon & Wed 1-4 or by appointment

MORRIS

S EQUISTAR CHEMICALS, LP LIBRARY,* 8935 N Tabler Rd, 60450-9988. SAN 304-4262. Tel: 815-942-7683. FAX: 815-942-7422. *Dir Libr Serv*, Mary Beth Dergo
Library Holdings: Bk Titles 1,800; Per Subs 50
Subject Interests: Chemical engineering, Physics
Special Collections: Polymer Information
Restriction: Non-circulating to the public

P MORRIS AREA PUBLIC LIBRARY DISTRICT,* 604 Liberty St, 60450. SAN 304-4254. Tel: 815-942-6880. FAX: 815-942-6415. *Dir*, Pamela J Wilson; *Ch Servs*, Carol Hutchings; *Spec Coll*, Debbie Steffes; Staff 16 (MLS 2, Non-MLS 14)
Founded 1913. Pop 14,769; Circ 213,704
Jul 1998-Jun 1999 Income $567,779, State $18,291, Federal $151, Locally Generated Income $101,131, Other $448,206. Mats Exp $74,906, Books $65,871, Per/Ser (Incl. Access Fees) $5,807, Electronic Ref Mat (Incl. Access Fees) $3,228. Sal $238,931 (Prof $70,502)
Library Holdings: Bk Vols 47,540; Per Subs 130
Special Collections: Local History (Morris-Grundy County Historical Coll), bks & photog
Mem of Heritage Trail Library System
Friends of the Library Group

MORRISON

P ODELL PUBLIC LIBRARY, 307 S Madison St, 61270. SAN 304-4270. Tel: 815-772-7323. FAX: 815-772-7323. *Librn*, Connie Boonstra; E-Mail: cboonstr@libby.rbls.lib.il.us
Founded 1877. Pop 4,600; Circ 47,653
Library Holdings: Bk Vols 29,390; Per Subs 100
Subject Interests: Genealogy
Mem of River Bend Library System

MORRISONVILLE

P KITCHELL MEMORIAL LIBRARY,* Fifth & Carlin St, PO Box 49, 62546. SAN 304-4289. Tel: 217-526-4553. FAX: 217-526-3695. E-Mail: mvillelibrary@chipsnet.com. *Librn*, Linda Sheedy; *Asst Librn*, Beckey Kramer
Founded 1964. Circ 5,700
Library Holdings: Bk Vols 5,339; Per Subs 11
Subject Interests: Large type print, Talking books
Special Collections: Historical Books of Christian Counties & Centennial Releases; Maps of Christian County, Morrisonville, Tounship & Illinois; Morrisonville Public School Mohawk & Tomahawk Year Books; National Geographic Magazine (1929 to present)
Publications: Morrisonville Times; Taylorville Breeze Courier
Mem of Rolling Prairie Library System

MORTON

P MORTON PUBLIC LIBRARY DISTRICT, 315 W Pershing St, 61550. SAN 304-4300. Tel: 309-263-2200. FAX: 309-266-9604. E-Mail: mortonpl@darkstar.rsa.lib.il.us. Web Site: www.morton.lib.il.us. *Dir*, Janice Sherman
Founded 1925. Pop 15,430; Circ 230,282
Jul 1999-Jun 2000 Income $535,704. Mats Exp $96,286, Books $72,600, Per/Ser (Incl. Access Fees) $4,300. Sal $199,000
Library Holdings: Bk Vols 65,900; Per Subs 192
Automation Activity & Vendor Info: (Circulation) CARL; (OPAC) CARL
Database Vendor: OCLC - First Search
Mem of Alliance Library System

MORTON GROVE

P MORTON GROVE PUBLIC LIBRARY, 6140 Lincoln Ave, 60053-2989. SAN 304-4351. Tel: 847-965-4220. TDD: 746-965-4236. FAX: 847-965-7903. E-Mail: refdesk@mgk.nslsilus.org. Web Site: www.webrary.org. *Dir*, Sharron L McCoy; *Assoc Dir, Tech Servs*, Kevin Justie; *Ref Serv*, Susan McGowan; *Ch Servs*, Joan Gross; *Assoc Dir, Publ Servs*, Eugenia Bryant; *Cat*, Edward Ashcroft; *Circ*, Virginia Castillo; Staff 43 (MLS 13, Non-MLS 30)
Founded 1938. Pop 22,373; Circ 238,993
Jan 1999-Dec 1999 Income $1,774,700, State $27,950, County $1,636,950, Locally Generated Income $20,000, Other $70,700. Mats Exp $1,774,700, Books $152,000, Per/Ser (Incl. Access Fees) $30,800, Micro $6,400, Electronic Ref Mat (Incl. Access Fees) $5,000. Sal $941,000 (Prof $495,000)
Library Holdings: Bk Vols 126,067; Per Subs 308
Special Collections: Morton Grove Village History (Local History Room)
Automation Activity & Vendor Info: (Cataloging) SIRSI; (Circulation) SIRSI; (OPAC) SIRSI
Publications: Books & Beyond
Mem of North Suburban Library System
Partic in OCLC Online Computer Library Center, Inc

MOUND CITY

P MOUND CITY PUBLIC LIBRARY,* 224 High St, 62963. SAN 304-4386. Tel: 618-748-9427. *Librn*, Shirley Douglas
Founded 1935. Pop 1,102; Circ 2,966
Library Holdings: Bk Vols 5,000
Special Collections: Gun Boats; Naval Hospital
Mem of Shawnee Library System
Friends of the Library Group

MOUNDS

P MOUNDS PUBLIC LIBRARY,* 130-132 S Blanche Ave, 62964. SAN 304-4394. Tel: 618-745-6610. *Librn*, Carol Eddleman
Pop 1,669; Circ 4,277
Library Holdings: Bk Vols 7,362; Per Subs 90
Mem of Shawnee Library System

MOUNT CARMEL

P MOUNT CARMEL PUBLIC LIBRARY,* 727 Mulberry St, 62863-2047. SAN 304-4408. Tel: 618-263-3531. FAX: 618-262-4243. Web Site: www.sirin.lib.il.us. *Dir*, Louise Taylor
Founded 1911. Pop 8,287; Circ 85,025
May 1997-Apr 1998 Income $207,582, State $54,150, City $117,121, Federal $17,280, Locally Generated Income $19,031. Mats Exp $19,586, Books $14,940, Per/Ser (Incl. Access Fees) $3,641. Sal $64,537 (Prof $30,500)
Library Holdings: Bk Vols 42,163; Per Subs 128
Special Collections: Daily Republican-Register Local Newspaper (1844 to present), microfilm
Automation Activity & Vendor Info: (Acquisitions) epixtech, inc.; (Cataloging) epixtech, inc.; (Circulation) epixtech, inc.
Mem of Shawnee Library System
Open Mon-Thurs 11-8, Fri-Sat 11-5:30

J WABASH VALLEY COLLEGE, Bauer Media Center, 2200 College Dr, 62863. SAN 304-4416. Tel: 618-262-8641, Ext 3400. FAX: 618-262-8962. *Dir*, Sandra Craig; Staff 1 (MLS 1)
Founded 1961. Enrl 1,396
Library Holdings: Bk Vols 32,000; Bk Titles 30,000; Per Subs 85
Subject Interests: Agriculture, Electronics, Environmental studies, Mining, Nursing, Social sciences and issues
Special Collections: Children's Book Coll
Publications: Academic periodical; Brochures for each special collection
Mem of Shawnee Library System

MOUNT CARROLL

P MOUNT CARROLL TOWNSHIP PUBLIC LIBRARY,* 208 N Main, 61053. SAN 304-4424. Tel: 815-244-1751. FAX: 815-244-1751. E-Mail: mtcpublib.@internetnl.com. *Librn*, Dorothy J Caldwell
Founded 1908. Pop 2,467; Circ 18,964
Mar 1998-Apr 1999 Mats Exp $4,987, Books $4,762, Per/Ser (Incl. Access Fees) $225. Sal $11,129
Library Holdings: Bk Vols 15,930; Bk Titles 15,820; Per Subs 40
Subject Interests: Local history
Mem of Northern Illinois Library System

MOUNT MORRIS

P MOUNT MORRIS PUBLIC LIBRARY, 101 E Front St, 61054. SAN 304-4440. Tel: 815-734-4927. FAX: 815-734-4927. E-Mail: mmlib@essex1.com. *Librn*, Rebecca McCanse
Founded 1931. Pop 2,919; Circ 26,400
May 2000-Apr 2001 Income $79,000. Sal $52,000
Library Holdings: Bk Vols 19,500; Per Subs 58
Subject Interests: Local history
Automation Activity & Vendor Info: (Circulation) Sagebrush Corporation
Mem of Northern Illinois Library System

MOUNT OLIVE

P MOUNT OLIVE PUBLIC LIBRARY,* 111 W Main St, 62069-1609. SAN 304-4459. Tel: 217-999-7311. FAX: 217-999-7311. *Librn*, Janice Thimsen; *Asst Librn*, Colleen Hood
Founded 1973. Pop 2,126; Circ 21,578
Jul 1998-Jun 1999 Income $23,000. Mats Exp $21,000
Library Holdings: Bk Vols 17,000; Bk Titles 20,000; Per Subs 30; Bks on Deafness & Sign Lang 10
Special Collections: Mount Olive Herald Newspaper, 1892-1998, micro
Mem of Lewis & Clark Library System

MOUNT PROSPECT

S GREAT LAKES CHEMICAL CORP, (Formerly NSC Technologies), Support Services Library, 601 E Kensington Rd, 60056. SAN 375-9822. Tel: 847-506-2889. FAX: 847-506-2825. *Mgr*, Mary Campbell
Library Holdings: Bk Titles 10,000; Per Subs 250

S INSTITUTE OF ENVIRONMENTAL SCIENCES LIBRARY,* 940 E Northwest Hwy, 60056. SAN 373-4404. Tel: 847-255-1561. FAX: 847-255-1699. E-Mail: publicationsales@iest.org. Web Site: instenvsci.org, www.iest.org. *Librn*, Liz Lockyer
Library Holdings: Bk Vols 230

P MOUNT PROSPECT PUBLIC LIBRARY, 10 S Emerson St, 60056. SAN 304-4475. Tel: 847-253-5675. FAX: 847-253-0642. Web Site: www.mppl.org. *Exec Dir*, Marilyn G Genther; *Dep Dir*, Catherine Deane; *Asst Dir*, John Bailie; *Cat*, Elizabeth Spaeth; *Ad Servs*, Lawrence D'Urso; *Ch Servs, YA Servs*, Carol Leeson; *ILL*, Virginia Schlachter; *Coll Develop*, Nancy Prichard; Staff 99 (MLS 19, Non-MLS 80)
Founded 1943. Pop 53,168; Circ 615,448
Jan 1999-Dec 1999 Income $4,197,485, State $65,849, City $4,026,466, Other $105,170. Mats Exp $438,908, Books $333,775, Per/Ser (Incl. Access Fees) $33,023, Micro $23,876, Electronic Ref Mat (Incl. Access Fees) $48,234. Sal $1,844,100 (Prof $629,505)
Library Holdings: Bk Vols 336,844; Per Subs 417
Subject Interests: Genealogy, Local history
Special Collections: Fed
Automation Activity & Vendor Info: (Acquisitions) GEAC; (Cataloging) GEAC; (Circulation) GEAC; (OPAC) GEAC
Database Vendor: Dialog, IAC - SearchBank, OCLC - First Search
Publications: Read On (newsletter, 6 per year)
Mem of North Suburban Library System
Special Services for the Deaf - TTY machine
Friends of the Library Group

S NUTRASWEET CO, Research Library,* 601 E Kensington Rd, 60050. SAN 376-0960. Tel: 847-506-2000. FAX: 847-506-2825. *Librn*, Alison Taylor
Library Holdings: Bk Titles 2,837

MOUNT PULASKI

P MOUNT PULASKI PUBLIC LIBRARY DISTRICT,* 320 N Washington St, 62548. SAN 304-4483. Tel: 217-792-5919. FAX: 217-792-3449. *Librn*, Carolyn Greger
Founded 1892. Pop 2,404; Circ 41,602
Library Holdings: Bk Titles 26,280; Per Subs 65
Subject Interests: Genealogy
Mem of Rolling Prairie Library System
Library Club

MOUNT STERLING

P BROWN COUNTY PUBLIC LIBRARY DISTRICT,* 143 W Main St, 62353. SAN 304-4491. Tel: 217-773-2013. FAX: 217-773-2013. E-Mail: browncty@adams.net. *Librn*, Sharon Hillyer; Staff 7 (Non-MLS 7)
Founded 1915. Pop 5,812; Circ 30,496
Library Holdings: Bk Vols 23,000
Special Collections: Best Seller & Popular Fiction
Mem of Alliance Library System

S WESTERN ILLINOIS CORRECTIONAL CENTER LIBRARY, Rte 99 S, PO Box 1000, 62353. SAN 376-1207. Tel: 217-773-4441, Ext 640. *Librn*, Janet Nicholas
Library Holdings: Bk Vols 6,000; Per Subs 40
Mem of Alliance Library System

MOUNT VERNON

P CE BREHM MEMORIAL PUBLIC LIBRARY DISTRICT, 101 S Seventh St, 62864. SAN 304-4521. Tel: 618-242-6322. Interlibrary Loan Service Tel: 618-242-6323. FAX: 618-242-0810. Web Site: www.sirin.lib.il.us/docs/bml/docs/lib/index.html. *Asst Librn, Cat, Ref*, Marilyn Konold; *Ch Servs*, Jacqueline Ross; *Circ*, Jan Kreher; Staff 3 (MLS 1, Non-MLS 2)
Founded 1899. Pop 23,938
Jul 1999-Jun 2000 Income $558,919. Mats Exp $49,050. Sal $270,110
Library Holdings: Bk Vols 59,550; Per Subs 208
Special Collections: Genealogy Coll; Southern Illinois History
Automation Activity & Vendor Info: (Acquisitions) epixtech, inc.; (Cataloging) epixtech, inc.; (Circulation) epixtech, inc.; (OPAC) epixtech, inc.; (Serials) epixtech, inc.
Mem of Shawnee Library System
Friends of the Library Group

M GOOD SAMARITAN REGIONAL HEALTH CENTER, Health Science Library,* 605 N 12th St, 62864. SAN 329-773X. Tel: 618-241-2062, 618-242-4600, Ext 2062. FAX: 618-242-9452. *Librn*, Coleen Saxe; E-Mail: csaxe@ssmhcs.com
Library Holdings: Bk Vols 2,000; Per Subs 45

GL ILLINOIS APPELLATE COURT, Fifth District, Law Library, 14th & Main Sts, 62864. (Mail add: PO Box 867, 62864-0018), SAN 304-4505. Tel: 618-242-6414. FAX: 618-242-9133. *Librn*, Janet Girvan; *Res*, James Sanders
Founded 1857
Library Holdings: Bk Vols 13,000; Per Subs 20
Subject Interests: Law

S MITCHELL MUSEUM LIBRARY, Richview Rd, 62864. (Mail add: PO Box 923, 62864-0019), SAN 304-4513. Tel: 618-242-1236. FAX: 618-242-9530. E-Mail: mitchell@midwest.net. Web Site: www.cedarhurst.org. *Librn*, Beth Brennan; Staff 1 (Non-MLS 1)
Founded 1973
Library Holdings: Bk Vols 2,000; Spec Interest Per Sub 15
Subject Interests: Americana, Art, Paintings, Sculpture
Restriction: By appointment only, Circulation limited, Open to public for reference only

MOUNT ZION

P MT ZION DISTRICT LIBRARY, 115 W Main, 62549. SAN 304-453X. Tel: 217-864-3622. FAX: 217-864-5708. *Dir*, Jennie Alexander; E-Mail: степ
jenniealexander@yahoo.com
Founded 1975. Pop 10,722; Circ 66,155
Library Holdings: Bk Vols 25,000; Per Subs 119
Automation Activity & Vendor Info: (Circulation) DRA
Publications: Newsletter (monthly)
Mem of Rolling Prairie Library System
Friends of the Library Group

MOWEAQUA

P MOWEAQUA PUBLIC LIBRARY,* 122 N Main St, 62550. SAN 304-4548. Tel: 217-768-4700. FAX: 217-768-9070. *Librn*, Barbara Collins
Founded 1893. Pop 2,000; Circ 14,164
Library Holdings: Bk Vols 12,600; Per Subs 32
Subject Interests: Genealogy
Mem of Rolling Prairie Library System
Friends of the Library Group

MUNDELEIN

P FREMONT PUBLIC LIBRARY DISTRICT,* 470 N Lake St, 60060. SAN 304-4556. Tel: 847-566-8702. TDD: 847-566-8722. FAX: 847-566-0204. Web Site: www.fpld.alibrary.com. *Dir*, Kelly Kreig-Sigman; *Business*, Roz Bonar; *Ref*, Rick Becker; *Circ*, Ruth Isaachsen; *Ref Serv Ad*, Jean Siddall; *Publ Servs*, Kathleen Callahan
Founded 1955
Jul 1998-Jun 1999 Income $1,522,832, State $28,043, County $1,232,534, Other $262,255. Mats Exp $181,550, Books $170,750, Per/Ser (Incl. Access Fees) $10,800. Sal $643,420
Library Holdings: Bk Vols 90,600; Per Subs 300
Subject Interests: American Indians, Local government
Special Collections: Local Newspaper, 1894-present, micro
Publications: Fremont (quarterly newsletter)
Mem of North Suburban Library System
Partic in Lake County Consortium
Special Services for the Deaf - TDD
Open Mon-Thurs 9-9, Fri & Sat 9-5, Sun 1-5 (Oct-Apr)
Friends of the Library Group

R UNIVERSITY OF SAINT MARY OF THE LAKE SEMINARY, Feehan Memorial Library, 1000 E Maple Ave, 60060. SAN 304-4572. Tel: 847-970-4820. FAX: 847-566-5229. *Librn*, Herman Peterson; E-Mail: hpeterson@usml.edu; Staff 4 (MLS 2, Non-MLS 2)
Founded 1929. Enrl 209; Fac 33; Highest Degree: Doctorate
Library Holdings: Bk Vols 180,000; Bk Titles 95,000; Per Subs 430
Subject Interests: Religion

MURPHYSBORO

P SALLIE LOGAN PUBLIC LIBRARY, 1808 Walnut St, 62966. SAN 304-4580. Tel: 618-684-3271. FAX: 618-684-2392. Web Site: www.sirin.lib.il.us/docs/salldocs/lib/index.html. *Head Librn*, Donella L Odum; E-Mail: donella@shwls.lib.il.us; *Asst Librn*, Sherry Carlock
Founded 1936. Pop 9,866; Circ 89,335
1999-2000 Income $209,767. Mats Exp $50,416, Books $41,809, Per/Ser (Incl. Access Fees) $4,000, Electronic Ref Mat (Incl. Access Fees) $4,607. Sal $77,871
Library Holdings: Bk Titles 47,585; Per Subs 52
Database Vendor: epixtech, inc.
Mem of Shawnee Library System
Friends of the Library Group

NAPERVILLE

S BP CORPORATION, Technical Information Center, 602 Main Library, 150 W Warrenville Rd, 60563. SAN 304-0313. Tel: 630-961-7634. FAX: 630-420-3697. *Librn*, Debbie Buschman; E-Mail: buschmdl@bp.com; Staff 11 (MLS 7, Non-MLS 4)
Founded 1972
Library Holdings: Bk Vols 60,000; Per Subs 1,500
Subject Interests: Business and management, Chemistry, Engineering, Environmental studies, Law, Petroleum
Automation Activity & Vendor Info: (Cataloging) EOS; (Circulation) EOS
Publications: New acquisitions bulletin (semi-monthly); quarterly newsletter
Restriction: Staff use only

SR COMMUNITY UNITED METHODIST CHURCH LIBRARY,* 20 N Center St, 60540-4611. SAN 372-641X. Tel: 630-355-1483. FAX: 630-778-2011. *Librn*, Forrest Rice; *Asst Librn*, Gertrude Brown; Staff 2 (MLS 1, Non-MLS 1)
Founded 1958
Library Holdings: Bk Titles 5,000; Per Subs 12
Special Collections: Illinois Evangelical Church 1850-1946, bks, papers, ledgers; Illinois Evangelical United Brethren Church 1946-1968, bks, papers, ledgers
Restriction: By appointment only

M EDWARD HOSPITAL LIBRARY,* 801 S Washington St, 60540. SAN 371-7240. Tel: 630-527-3937. FAX: 630-355-9703. E-Mail: d-edhos@dupagels.lib.il.us. *Dir*, Donna Roginski
Library Holdings: Bk Titles 2,500; Per Subs 253
Subject Interests: Consumer health, Medicine
Mem of DuPage Library System

Partic in Fox Valley Health Science Library Consortium; Greater Midwest Regional Medical Libr Network; Health Sci Libr Info Consortium; Illinois Library & Information Network

S NALCO CHEMICAL COMPANY, Information Services, One Nalco Ctr, 60563-1198. SAN 303-9803. Tel: 630-305-2402. FAX: 630-305-2876. E-Mail: nlibrary@nalco.com. *Coll Develop, Librn*, Nancy Maloney; Staff 6 (MLS 4, Non-MLS 2)
Founded 1928
Library Holdings: Bk Vols 25,000; Per Subs 400
Subject Interests: Chemistry, Water treatment
Automation Activity & Vendor Info: (Acquisitions) TechLIB; (Cataloging) TechLIB; (Circulation) TechLIB; (OPAC) TechLIB; (Serials) TechLIB
Publications: Library Bulletin (quarterly)
Restriction: Staff use only
Mem of DuPage Library System
Partic in Dialog Corporation; Dow Jones News Retrieval; Nat Libr of Med

P NAPERVILLE PUBLIC LIBRARIES,* Nichols Library, 200 W Jefferson Ave, 60540-5374. SAN 304-4602. Tel: 630-961-4100. Reference FAX: 630-961-4111. *Dir*, Donna Dziedzic; *Dir, Info Tech*, Mark West; *Mgr*, Olya Tymciurak; *ILL, Ref*, Sue Prindiville; *Ch Servs*, Julie Rothenfluh; *Ad Servs, Circ*, Betty Gillen; *Media Spec*, Susan Fielder; *Automation Syst Coordr*, Mary Juzenas; Staff 51 (MLS 30, Non-MLS 21)
Founded 1897. Pop 100,422; Circ 1,428,298
Library Holdings: Bk Titles 330,188
Automation Activity & Vendor Info: (Circulation) epixtech, inc.
Publications: Business Newsletter; Quarterly Newsletter
Mem of DuPage Library System
Partic in ILLINET; OCLC Online Computer Library Center, Inc
Branches: 1
NAPER BOULEVARD LIBRARY, 2035 S Naper Blvd, 60565-3353. SAN 372-4999. Tel: 630-961-4100. TDD: 630-355-1585. FAX: 630-961-4116. Web Site: www.naperville-lib.org. *In Charge*, Anna McElroy
Pop 120,000; Circ 500,000
Library Holdings: Bk Titles 125,000; Per Subs 204

S NAPERVILLE SUN NEWS LIBRARY, 1500 W Ogden Ave, 60566. SAN 371-2273. Tel: 630-416-5202. FAX: 630-416-5163. *In Charge*, Laurie K Kagann
Library Holdings: Bk Vols 658
Restriction: Staff use only
Mem of DuPage Library System

S NICOR GAS, Corporate Library, 1844 Ferry Rd, 60563-9600. (Mail add: PO Box 1690, 60507-1690), SAN 375-328X. Tel: 630-983-8676, Ext 2190. FAX: 630-983-4566. Web Site: www.nicor.com. *Info Specialist*, Mary M Howrey; E-Mail: mhowrey@nicor.com
Founded 1965
Library Holdings: Bk Vols 2,500; Per Subs 520
Subject Interests: Business and management, Energy, Natural gas
Automation Activity & Vendor Info: (Cataloging) EOS; (OPAC) EOS
Mem of DuPage Library System

C NORTH CENTRAL COLLEGE, Oesterle Library, 320 E School St, 60540. SAN 304-4610. Tel: 630-637-5700. Interlibrary Loan Service Tel: 630-637-5705. Reference Tel: 630-637-5715. TDD: 630-637-5719. FAX: 630-637-5716. E-Mail: cas@noctrl.edu. Web Site: www.noctrl.edu/library/library.htm. *Dir Libr Serv*, Carolyn A Sheehy; Tel: 630-637-5701; *Access Serv*, Belinda Cheek; Tel: 630-637-5703, E-Mail: bdc@noctrl.edu; *Ref*, Carol Murdoch; Tel: 630-637-5708; *Instrul Serv, Media Spec*, Tom Gill; Tel: 630-637-5723, E-Mail: thgill@noctrl.edu; *Archivist*, Kim Butler; Tel: 630-637-5714, E-Mail: kibutler@noctrl.edu; *Tech Servs*, Ted Schwitzner; Tel: 630-637-5709, E-Mail: tcs@noctrl.edu; *Instrul Serv*, Rosemary Henders; Tel: 630-637-5707, E-Mail: rohenders@noctrl.edu; Staff 7 (MLS 5, Non-MLS 2)
Founded 1861. Enrl 2,532; Fac 147; Highest Degree: Master
Jul 2000-Jun 2001 Income $820,629. Mats Exp $319,064, Books $162,510, Per/Ser (Incl. Access Fees) $149,802, Presv $2,415, AV Equip $4,337. Sal $471,157 (Prof $280,047)
Library Holdings: Bk Vols 132,322; Per Subs 736
Special Collections: History (Leffler Lincoln Coll); Literature (Sang Limited Edition Coll); Music (Sang Jazz Coll)
Database Vendor: DRA
Publications: EX LIBRIS (Newsletter)
Mem of DuPage Library System; Illinois Libr Computer Syst Orgn
Partic in Libras, Inc; OCLC Online Computer Library Center, Inc
Special Services for the Deaf - TDD

S PACKER ENGINEERING INC, Technical Information Services, 1950 N Washington St, 60563-1366. (Mail add: PO Box 353, 60566-0353), SAN 375-3530. Tel: 630-577-1963. FAX: 630-577-1989. E-Mail: library@packereng.com. *Dir*, Sara Tompson; E-Mail: srt@packereng.com; Staff 2 (MLS 1, Non-MLS 1)
Library Holdings: Bk Titles 4,500; Per Subs 300
Subject Interests: Fire, Forensic eng, Metallurgy
Mem of DuPage Library System

NASHVILLE

P NASHVILLE PUBLIC LIBRARY,* 219 E Elm St, 62263-1711. SAN 304-4629. Tel: 618-327-3827. FAX: 618-327-4820. *Librn*, Linda Summers; *Asst Librn*, Dorothy Bahr; *Asst Dir*, Vivian Wynn
Founded 1943. Pop 3,202; Circ 26,585 Sal $31,000
Library Holdings: Bk Vols 15,000
Subject Interests: Genealogy, Local history
Publications: Reading Lines (newsp article)
Mem of Shawnee Library System
Friends of the Library Group

NAUVOO

P NAUVOO PUBLIC LIBRARY,* 1270 Mulholland St, 62354. SAN 304-4637. Tel: 217-453-2707. FAX: 217-453-2707. *Librn*, Lois Crouse
Founded 1913. Pop 1,108; Circ 10,125
Library Holdings: Bk Vols 9,500; Per Subs 30
Subject Interests: Genealogy, Mormons
Mem of Alliance Library System

NEOGA

P NEOGA PUBLIC LIBRARY DISTRICT, 551 Chestnut St, PO Box 888, 62447. SAN 376-0154. Tel: 217-895-3944. FAX: 217-895-3944. E-Mail: neogalib@rrl.net. *Librn*, Melissa Coleman
Library Holdings: Bk Titles 11,000; Per Subs 25
Mem of Rolling Prairie Library System

NEPONSET

P NEPONSET PUBLIC LIBRARY,* 201 W Commercial St, PO Box 110, 61345. SAN 304-4645. Tel: 309-594-2204. FAX: 309-594-2204. *Librn*, Deborah L Cordrey; *Asst Librn, Ch Servs*, Nancy Hulslander
Founded 1875. Pop 819; Circ 13,758
Library Holdings: Bk Vols 16,817; Per Subs 24
Special Collections: Clippings File; Local History, bks, cassettes, flm, micro; School & Cemetary Records
Mem of Alliance Library System

NEW ATHENS

P NEW ATHENS DISTRICT LIBRARY, 201 N Van Buren St, 62264. SAN 304-4653. Tel: 618-475-3255. FAX: 618-475-9384. E-Mail: nadlib@icss.net. *Librn*, Charlotte M Main
Founded 1963. Pop 3,290; Circ 12,483
Mem of Shawnee Library System
Open Mon-Thurs 2-8, Fri 2-5, Sat 10-4

NEW BADEN

P NEW BADEN PUBLIC LIBRARY,* 210 N First St, 62265. SAN 376-2211. Tel: 618-588-4554. FAX: 618-588-4554. *Librn*, Judy Korte
Library Holdings: Bk Vols 14,000; Bk Titles 11,000; Per Subs 20
Friends of the Library Group

NEW LENOX

P NEW LENOX PUBLIC LIBRARY DISTRICT, 516 S Cedar Rd, 60451. SAN 304-4661. Tel: 815-485-2605. FAX: 815-485-2548. Web Site: newlenox.lib.il.us. *Dir*, JoAnn Potenziani; E-Mail: japotenziani@htls.lib.il.us; *Ad Servs*, Lauren Denney; E-Mail: ldenney@htls.lib.il.us; *Ch Servs*, Barbara Plautz; E-Mail: bplautz@htls.lib.il.us; *Tech Servs*, Georgia Madden; E-Mail: gmadden@htls.lib.il.us; Staff 21 (MLS 2, Non-MLS 19)
Founded 1936. Pop 25,809; Circ 235,978
Jul 1999-Jun 2000 Income $1,078,760, State $43,725, Federal $2,097, County $844,063, Locally Generated Income $188,875. Mats Exp $125,734, Books $78,946, Per/Ser (Incl. Access Fees) $25,312, Electronic Ref Mat (Incl. Access Fees) $21,476. Sal $420,265 (Prof $169,799)
Library Holdings: Bk Vols 90,875; Bk Titles 86,331; Per Subs 215
Automation Activity & Vendor Info: (Circulation) GEAC
Database Vendor: IAC - Info Trac, OCLC - First Search
Publications: The Lexicon (Newsletter)
Mem of Heritage Trail Library System
Open Mon-Thurs 9-9, Fri & Sat 9-5 & Sun 1-5 (Sept-May), Sat 9-1 (June-Aug), closed Sun (June-Aug)
Friends of the Library Group

NEW WINDSOR

P NEW WINDSOR PUBLIC LIBRARY DISTRICT,* 412 Main St, 61465. SAN 304-467X. Tel: 309-667-2515. FAX: 309-667-2515. *Librn*, David Kruse; E-Mail: dkruse@winco.net; *Asst Librn*, Katherine Lake; *Asst Librn*, Linda Spencer; Staff 3 (MLS 1, Non-MLS 2)

Founded 1959. Pop 1,335; Circ 14,772
Library Holdings: Bk Vols 10,700; Per Subs 22
Subject Interests: Agriculture, Local history
Mem of Alliance Library System
Friends of the Library Group

NEWMAN

P NEWMAN TOWNSHIP LIBRARY, 108 W Yates St, PO Box 118, 61942. SAN 304-4688. Tel: 217-837-2412. E-Mail: nlibrary@newman.net. *Librn*, Melissa Catron
Pop 1,248; Circ 6,399
Library Holdings: Bk Titles 10,603; Per Subs 20
Mem of Lincoln Trail Libraries System
Friends of the Library Group

NEWTON

P NEWTON PUBLIC LIBRARY & MUSEUM,* 100 S Van Buren St, 62448. SAN 304-4696. Tel: 618-783-8141. FAX: 618-783-8141. *Librn*, Barbara Swearingen
Founded 1927. Pop 3,186; Circ 20,677
Library Holdings: Bk Vols 18,500; Per Subs 45
Mem of Shawnee Library System

NILES

P NILES PUBLIC LIBRARY DISTRICT, 6960 Oakton St, 60714. SAN 340-5907. Tel: 847-663-1234. FAX: 847-663-1350. E-Mail: nileslib@ccs.nsls.org. Web Site: www.nileslibrary.org. *Dir*, Cary Czarnecki; *Tech Servs*, Ann Pasnick; *Mgr Libr Serv*, Linda Weiss; *AV, Reader Servs*, Barbara Kruser; *Ch Servs*, Susan Lempke; *Circ*, Kathy Pricone; *Ref*, Valerie Clark; *Business*, Joseph Vlach; Staff 102 (MLS 24, Non-MLS 78)
Founded 1958. Pop 54,338; Circ 804,102
Jul 1999-Jun 2000 Income $4,060,950, State $174,390, County $3,556,170, Other $330,390. Mats Exp $521,446. Sal $1,962,742
Library Holdings: Bk Vols 208,325; Per Subs 709
Publications: Chapter One (Newsletter)
Mem of North Suburban Library System
Partic in Coop Computer Servs; OCLC Online Computer Library Center, Inc
Open Mon-Thurs 9-9, Fri-Sat 9-5 & Sun hours Sept-May only 1-5
Friends of the Library Group

S TRIODYNE INC, Information Center, 5950 W Touhy Ave, 60714-4610. SAN 320-5819. Tel: 847-677-4730. FAX: 847-647-0743. E-Mail: infoserv@triodyne.com. Web Site: www.triodyne.com. *Mgr*, Marna S Sanders; *Librn*, Cathy Friedman; *Circ*, Jackie Schwartz; *Res*, John Kristelli; *ILL*, Donna Klick; Staff 5 (MLS 2, Non-MLS 3)
Founded 1979
Library Holdings: Bk Vols 10,500; Per Subs 200
Subject Interests: Accident prevention, Automotive engineering, Ergonomics, Forensic sci
Special Collections: Expert Transcript Center, Bibcat 2500 (bibliographies)
Database Vendor: Dialog, OCLC - First Search
Publications: BIBCAT 2500 (bibliography)
Mem of North Suburban Library System

NOKOMIS

P NOKOMIS PUBLIC LIBRARY, 22 S Cedar St, Rm 2, 62075. SAN 304-4742. Tel: 217-563-2734. FAX: 217-563-2740. E-Mail: noklibrary@ccipost.net. *Head Librn*, Debra A Lehman; *Asst Librn*, Regina Edrington; *Asst Librn*, Mindy Carroll
Pop 3,372; Circ 36,872
Apr 1999-Mar 2000 Income (Main Library Only) $42,104, State $6,403, Locally Generated Income $27,800, Other $7,901. Mats Exp $44,640, Books $4,000, Per/Ser (Incl. Access Fees) $1,230, AV Equip $2,941, Other Print Mats $500, Electronic Ref Mat (Incl. Access Fees) $1,773. Sal $24,809
Library Holdings: Bk Titles 18,007; Per Subs 45
Subject Interests: Local history
Mem of Lewis & Clark Library System

NORMAL

M BROMENN HEALTHCARE, AE Livingston Health Sciences Library, Virginia at Franklin, 61761. SAN 339-7416. Tel: 309-827-4321, Ext 5281. FAX: 309-888-0953. *Dir*, Molly Horio; *Librn*, Eleanore Brown; Staff 2 (MLS 2)
Founded 1973. Circ 2,500
Library Holdings: Bk Titles 4,500; Per Subs 300
Subject Interests: Medicine, Nursing
Mem of Alliance Library System
Partic in Heart Of Illinois Library Consortium

SR FIRST UNITED METHODIST CHURCH LIBRARY, 211 N School St, 61761. SAN 325-6936. Tel: 309-452-2096. FAX: 309-452-1327. *Librn*, Catherine Knight
Library Holdings: Bk Vols 1,000

C ILLINOIS STATE UNIVERSITY, (MLB), Milner Library, 201 N School, Campus Box 8900, 61791-8900. SAN 304-4777. Tel: 309-438-3451. Interlibrary Loan Service Tel: 309-438-3461. TDD: 309-438-5942. FAX: 309-438-3676. Web Site: www.mlb.ilstu.edu. *Dean of Libr*, Cheryl Elzy; *Assoc Dean*, Steve Meckstroth; *Cat*, Priscilla Matthews; *Syst Coordr*, Richard Christensen; *Coordr*, Cecile M Jagodzinski; Staff 117 (MLS 36, Non-MLS 81)
Founded 1890. Enrl 20,281; Fac 1,088; Highest Degree: Doctorate
Jul 1998-Jun 1999 Income $7,328,921, State $7,209,831, Parent Institution $23,900. Mats Exp $2,617,186, Books $745,930, Per/Ser (Incl. Access Fees) $1,576,226, Presv $74,795, AV Equip $26,953, Other Print Mats $3,940, Electronic Ref Mat (Incl. Access Fees) $189,342. Sal $3,696,419 (Prof $1,474,934)
Library Holdings: Bk Vols 1,451,195; Per Subs 8,915
Subject Interests: American history, Education, Mathematics, Psychology, Theater
Special Collections: 19th Century Elementary & Secondary School Textbooks; Children's Literature (Lenski, 19th Century); Circus & Allied Arts; Lincoln Coll
Automation Activity & Vendor Info: (Cataloging) DRA; (Circulation) DRA; (OPAC) DRA
Publications: Friends of Milner Library Newsletter; Milner Memos
Mem of Alliance Library System
Partic in Coop Coll Mgt Prog; Illinois Library Computer Systems Office
Friends of the Library Group

P NORMAL PUBLIC LIBRARY,* 206 W College Ave, PO Box 325, 61761. SAN 304-4785. Tel: 309-452-1757. FAX: 309-452-5312. *Dir*, Robert L Wegman; *ILL*, Brenda Peden; *Circ*, Ruth Reeves; *YA Servs*, Mary Williams; *Publ Servs*, Mari McKeeth; *Cat*, Norma Trumble; *Ch Servs*, Vivian Carter; *AV*, Jeanne Moonan; *Cat, Ch Servs*, Judy Poultney; *Coll Develop*, Lynn Freymann; Staff 3 (MLS 3)
Founded 1939. Pop 42,200; Circ 459,800
Library Holdings: Bk Vols 101,335; Per Subs 345
Publications: Monthly Newsletter
Mem of Alliance Library System
Open Mon-Thurs 9-9, Fri & Sat 9-5, Sun 1-5
Friends of the Library Group

NORRIS CITY

P NORRIS CITY MEMORIAL PUBLIC LIBRARY DISTRICT, 603 S Division St, PO Box 430, 62869. SAN 304-4793. Tel: 618-378-3713. FAX: 618-378-3713. E-Mail: ncmpld@shawnee.com. *Dir*, Mary McKenzie; *Asst Librn*, Judy Daubs
Founded 1945. Circ 37,182
Jul 1998-Jun 1999 Income $48,130, State $6,330, Federal $41,000, Other $800. Mats Exp $4,838, Books $4,000, Per/Ser (Incl. Access Fees) $600, Micro $238. Sal $20,000 (Prof $15,000)
Library Holdings: Bk Titles 19,000; Per Subs 35
Subject Interests: Gardening, Genealogy, History, Illinois, Nutrition
Special Collections: Cookbooks
Publications: Periodical Guide
Mem of Shawnee Library System

NORTH AURORA

P MESSENGER PUBLIC LIBRARY OF NORTH AURORA, 14 E State St, 60542. SAN 304-4807. Tel: 630-896-0240. FAX: 630-896-4654.; Staff 3 (MLS 1, Non-MLS 2)
Founded 1937. Pop 11,000; Circ 104,186
Jun 1999-May 2000 Income $353,087, State $11,307, City $330,231, Locally Generated Income $11,549. Mats Exp $47,500, Books $34,000, Per/Ser (Incl. Access Fees) $7,000, AV Equip $6,500. Sal $185,000 (Prof $85,000)
Library Holdings: Bk Vols 41,565; Per Subs 103
Automation Activity & Vendor Info: (Cataloging) epixtech, inc.; (Circulation) epixtech, inc.; (OPAC) epixtech, inc.
Publications: Newsletter (monthly)
Mem of DuPage Library System
Friends of the Library Group

S NORTH EAST MULTI-REGIONAL TRAINING, Instructors' Library, One Smoke Tree Plaza, Ste 111, 60542-1718. SAN 372-5782. Tel: 630-896-8860, Ext 108. FAX: 630-896-4422. Web Site: www.nemrt.com. *Librn*, Sarah Cole; E-Mail: sarah@nemrt.com; Staff 1 (MLS 1)
Founded 1990
2000-2000 Mats Exp $6,500, Books $1,000, Per/Ser (Incl. Access Fees) $2,200, Electronic Ref Mat (Incl. Access Fees) $2,500. Sal $38,000
Library Holdings: Bk Titles 5,000; Per Subs 30
Special Collections: Law Enforcement
Mem of DuPage Library System

NORTH CHICAGO

GM DEPARTMENT OF VETERANS AFFAIRS MEDICAL CENTER, Library Service,* 3001 Green Bay Rd, 60064. SAN 340-5966. Tel: 847-688-1900. FAX: 847-578-3819.; Staff 2 (Non-MLS 2)
Library Holdings: Bk Vols 20,000; Bk Titles 3,900; Per Subs 200
Subject Interests: Medicine, Psychiatry, Psychology, Social service (social work)
Partic in Medline; Midwest Health Sci Libr Network; N Suburban Libr Syst; Northeastern Ill Libr Consortia; Virginia Library & Network Information

CM FINCH UNIVERSITY OF HEALTH SCIENCES-CHICAGO MEDICAL SCHOOL, Boxer University Library, 3333 Green Bay Rd, 60064. SAN 340-2878. Tel: 847-578-3000. FAX: 847-578-3401. Web Site: www.finchcms.edu/lrc/lrc.html. *VPres*, Nancy W Garn; Tel: 847-578-3242, E-Mail: nancy.garn@finchcms.edu; *Assoc Dir, Online Servs, Ref*, Sharyn C Fradin; Tel: 847-578-8642, E-Mail: sharyn.fradin@finchcms.edu; *Web Coordr*, Ron Hunsberger; Tel: 847-578-3225, E-Mail: ron.hunsberger@finchcms.edu; *AV*, Peter Nierenberger; *ILL*, Kevin Robertson; *Ser*, Mark Russell; *Cat*, Afshan Hussanini; *Circ*, Heather Furtek
Founded 1912. Enrl 1,373; Fac 350; Highest Degree: Doctorate
Library Holdings: Bk Vols 95,000; Per Subs 1,084
Subject Interests: Health sciences, Medicine
Publications: audiovisual catalog; current monographs & serials, resources; LRC Guide
Partic in Data Star; Dialog Corporation; Nat Libr of Med; OCLC Online Computer Library Center, Inc; Regional Med Libr - Region 3

P NORTH CHICAGO PUBLIC LIBRARY, 2100 Argonne Dr, 60064. SAN 304-4831. Tel: 847-689-0125. Circulation Tel: 847-689-0125, Ext 100. Reference Tel: 847-689-0125, Ext 113. FAX: 847-689-9117. Web Site: www.ncpublib.org. *Dir*, Elizabeth Hoke; *Cat*, Suzanne Ginsparg; Tel: 847-689-0125; *Ch Servs*, Judi McFarlin; *Head Ref*, Linda A Krause; Tel: 847-689-0125, Ext 110, E-Mail: dlkraus@nslsilus.org. Subject Specialists: *African-American hist*, Linda A Krause; *Humanities*, Linda A Krause; *Technology*, Linda A Krause; Staff 6 (MLS 3, Non-MLS 3)
Founded 1916. Pop 34,978
Library Holdings: Bk Vols 48,000; Bk Titles 39,000; Per Subs 140
Special Collections: African American & Military Coll; North Chicago
Database Vendor: OCLC - First Search, Wilson - Wilson Web
Mem of North Suburban Library System
Friends of the Library Group

NORTH RIVERSIDE

P NORTH RIVERSIDE PUBLIC LIBRARY DISTRICT, 2400 S DesPlaines Ave, 60546-1520. SAN 376-0197. Tel: 708-447-0869. FAX: 708-447-0526. *Dir*, Paul Klain; Tel: 708-447-0869, Ext 225, E-Mail: pklain@interaccess.com; *Ch Servs*, Arlene Kurzawa; Tel: 708-447-0869, Ext 224, Fax: 708-442-6566; *Ref*, John F Zmola; Tel: 708-447-0869, Ext 227, E-Mail: zmola@sls.lib.il.us; Staff 18 (MLS 3, Non-MLS 15)
Founded 1983. Pop 6,180
Library Holdings: Bk Titles 25,000; Per Subs 97
Automation Activity & Vendor Info: (Circulation) Innovative Interfaces Inc.; (ILL) Innovative Interfaces Inc.; (OPAC) Innovative Interfaces Inc.
Database Vendor: Innovative Interfaces INN - View, OCLC - First Search
Mem of Suburban Library System
Friends of the Library Group

NORTHBROOK

L ALLSTATE INSURANCE COMPANY, (Formerly Allstate Insurance Company Library), Law Library, 2775 Sanders Rd, No A-5, 60062-6127. SAN 304-484X. Tel: 847-402-7267. Reference Tel: 847-402-8735. FAX: 847-402-9757.; Staff 2 (MLS 1, Non-MLS 1)
Founded 1973
Library Holdings: Bk Titles 3,000; Per Subs 300
Automation Activity & Vendor Info: (OPAC) Sydney
Mem of North Suburban Library System
Partic in Coop Libr Agency for Syst & Servs; Dialog Corporation; Dow Jones News Retrieval; Illinois Library & Information Network; News Edge; OCLC Online Computer Library Center, Inc
Branches:
SPECIALTY OPERATIONS LIBRARY, Allstate South Barrington Plaza, 51 W Higgins Rd, TIA, South Barrington, 60010. SAN 375-9377. Tel: 847-551-2079. FAX: 847-551-2080. *In Charge*, Janet Gustafson; E-Mail: jgustafs@allstate.com; Staff 1 (MLS 1)
Library Holdings: Bk Titles 500; Per Subs 40
Mem of North Suburban Library System

SR CONGREGATION BETH SHALOM, Irving Rubenstein Memorial Library, 3433 Walters Ave, 60062-3298. SAN 371-7690. Tel: 847-498-4100. FAX: 847-498-9160. *Librn*, Karen Wadler; *Librn*, Wynne Weiss
Founded 1969. Pop 5,000; Enrl 525; Fac 27
Library Holdings: Bk Vols 5,000; Per Subs 15
Subject Interests: Holocaust
Automation Activity & Vendor Info: (Cataloging) Follett; (Circulation) Follett
Mem of North Suburban Library System

S MCILVAINE CO, Technical Library, 2970 Maria Ave, 60062. SAN 373-4420. Tel: 847-272-0010. FAX: 847-272-9673. E-Mail: editor@mcilvainecompany.com. Web Site: www.mcilvainecompany.com. *Librn*, Francine Hakimian
Library Holdings: Per Subs 100
Subject Interests: Air pollution, Energy, Water pollution
Special Collections: Conference papers

S MOTOROLA, INC, AIEG Library,* 4000 Commercial Ave, 60062-1840. SAN 375-1554. Tel: 847-480-3581, 847-480-8000. FAX: 847-480-3597. *Librn*, Soon Ho Lee
Library Holdings: Bk Titles 1,000; Per Subs 180

P NORTHBROOK PUBLIC LIBRARY,* 1201 Cedar Lane, 60062-4581. SAN 304-4866. Tel: 847-272-6224. FAX: 847-498-0440. Web Site: nsn.nslsilus.org/nbkhome. *Dir*, Chadwick T Raymond; *Asst Dir*, Eric Robbins; *ILL*, Nancy Poch; *Acq*, Betty Wright; *Reader Servs*, Donna Hicks; *Tech Servs*, Joyce Horvath; *Ref*, Elaine Stenzel; *Circ*, Ann Weston; Staff 23 (MLS 23)
Founded 1952. Pop 33,476
May 1998-Apr 1999 Income $4,378,848, State $244,910, County $3,357,637, Locally Generated Income $776,301. Mats Exp $438,647. Sal $1,482,883
Library Holdings: Bk Vols 261,724; Per Subs 522
Subject Interests: Art and architecture, Landscape architecture, Science/technology, Technology
Publications: Newsletter
Mem of North Suburban Library System
Special Services for the Deaf - Staff with knowledge of sign language
Friends of the Library Group

R SAINT GILES' EPISCOPAL CHURCH, Saint Bede's Library, 3025 Walters Ave, 60062. SAN 304-4874. Tel: 847-272-6622. FAX: 847-272-7664. *Librn*, Doug Downey
Founded 1952
Library Holdings: Bk Vols 1,100
Subject Interests: Religion
Restriction: Members only, Open to others by appointment

S WISS JANNEY & ELSTNER ASSOCIATES, INC LIBRARY,* 330 Pfingsten Rd, 60062. SAN 373-0492. Tel: 847-272-7400, Ext 202. FAX: 847-291-9599. *Librn*, Natalie Blake; Fax: 847-753-7200, E-Mail: nblake@wje.com
Library Holdings: Bk Vols 8,000
Database Vendor: OCLC - First Search
Partic in OCLC Online Computer Library Center, Inc

NORTHFIELD

S BIOMEGA CORP LIBRARY,* 191 Waukegan Rd, Ste 206, 60093. SAN 374-9916. Tel: 847-446-5511. FAX: 847-446-5572. E-Mail: biomega@nslsilus.org.
Library Holdings: Bk Titles 300; Per Subs 24
Restriction: Staff use only

M JOSSELYN CENTER FOR MENTAL HEALTH LIBRARY,* 405 Central Ave, 60093. SAN 374-955X. Tel: 847-441-5600. FAX: 847-441-7968. *Librn*, Jean M Peterson
Library Holdings: Bk Vols 1,100; Per Subs 15

S STEPAN COMPANY, Information Research Center, 22 W Frontage Rd, 60093. SAN 326-9647. Tel: 847-501-2389. FAX: 847-501-2466. Web Site: www.stepan.com. *Mgr*, Marlene J Slifka; E-Mail: mslifka@stepan.com; *Coordr*, Dawn Stout; Tel: 847-501-2277, E-Mail: dstout@stepan.com; Staff 3 (MLS 1, Non-MLS 2)
Library Holdings: Bk Vols 3,899; Per Subs 155
Subject Interests: Chemistry
Database Vendor: Ebsco - EbscoHost
Mem of North Suburban Library System

SR TEMPLE JEREMIAH, Marshall B & Viola R Schwimmer Library, 937 Happ Rd, 60093. SAN 374-5716. Tel: 847-441-5760. FAX: 847-441-5765. Web Site: www.temple-jeremiah.org. *Librn*, Noni Dodge
Library Holdings: Bk Titles 4,500; Per Subs 32
Special Collections: Allan Tarshish Rabbinical Coll; Jewish Art
Restriction: By appointment only
Mem of North Suburban Library System

NORTHLAKE

P NORTHLAKE PUBLIC LIBRARY DISTRICT, 231 N Wolf Rd, 60164. SAN 304-4890. Tel: 708-562-2301. FAX: 708-562-8120. E-Mail: nls@sls.lib.il.us. Web Site: www.northlake.lib.il.us. *Dir*, Jan Schmudde; *Tech Servs*, Mary Jane Garrett; *Ch Servs*, Marianne Ryczek; *Ad Servs*, Emily

Meehan
Founded 1957. Pop 25,741; Circ 116,529
Jul 1999-Jun 2000 Income $1,411,025, State $110,605, Federal $1,600, Locally Generated Income $1,214,237, Other $84,583. Mats Exp $164,915, Books $122,648, Per/Ser (Incl. Access Fees) $14,013, AV Equip $15,972, Electronic Ref Mat (Incl. Access Fees) $12,282. Sal $453,749 (Prof $243,436)
Library Holdings: Bk Vols 66,656; Per Subs 238; High Interest/Low Vocabulary Bk Vols 50
Subject Interests: Spanish
Automation Activity & Vendor Info: (Circulation) Innovative Interfaces Inc.; (ILL) Innovative Interfaces Inc.; (OPAC) Innovative Interfaces Inc.
Database Vendor: Innovative Interfaces INN - View
Publications: Newsletter
Mem of Suburban Library System
Partic in Ill Regional Libr Coun

OAK BROOK

S AMERICAN SOKOL EDUCATIONAL & PHYSICAL CULTURE ORGANIZATION, Library-Archives, 122 W 22nd St, 60523-1557. SAN 326-7873. Tel: 708-795-6671. FAX: 708-795-0539. *Librn*, Annette B Schabowski; Staff 1 (Non-MLS 1)
Founded 1976
Library Holdings: Bk Titles 3,031

S CZECHOSLOVAK HERITAGE MUSEUM, Library & Archives, 122 W 22nd St, 60523. SAN 326-5250. Tel: 630-472-0500. Toll Free Tel: 800-543-3272. FAX: 630-472-1100. E-Mail: czslemuseum@aol.com. Web Site: www.csafraternallife.org. *Librn*, Jitka Vesel
Founded 1974
Library Holdings: Bk Vols 8,000

S ESM ASSOCIATION, Information Center, 2211 York Rd, Ste 207, 60523-2371. SAN 374-5813. Tel: 630-368-1280. FAX: 630-368-1286. E-Mail: esmahq@esmassn.org. Web Site: www.esmassn.org. *Exec Dir*, Patrick B Stinson; *Librn*, Cynthia M Helson
Library Holdings: Bk Vols 44
Publications: Employee Services Management (mag)

S NORTH CENTRAL REGIONAL EDUCATIONAL LABORATORY, Resource Center, 1900 Spring Rd, Ste 300, 60523-1480. SAN 371-2737. Tel: 630-571-4700. Toll Free Tel: 800-356-2735. FAX: 630-571-4716. E-Mail: info@ncrel.org. Web Site: www.ncrel.org/. *ILL, Ref*, Arlene Hough; E-Mail: hough@ncrel.org; *Tech Servs*, Lorraine Obert
Library Holdings: Bk Vols 6,000; Per Subs 130
Subject Interests: Education
Mem of DuPage Library System
Parent institution is federally-funded Regional Educational Laboratory; provides information services on educational topics to persons in Illinois, Iowa, Indiana, Michigan, Minnesota, Ohio & Wisconsin; parent institution also operates Midwest Consortium for Mathematics & Science Education & North Central Regional Technology in Education Consortium

P OAK BROOK PUBLIC LIBRARY, 1112 Oak Brook Rd, 60523-2272. SAN 304-4920. Tel: 630-990-2222. FAX: 630-990-0170. *Dir*, Ruth A Martin; *Circ*, Vernette R Richmond; *Ref*, Julia M Adamski; *Tech Servs*, Eileen M Nolan; *YA Servs*, Susan C Madorin
Founded 1960. Pop 9,178
Jan 1999-Dec 1999 Income Locally Generated Income $686,659. Mats Exp $127,000, Books $116,000, Per/Ser (Incl. Access Fees) $8,000, Micro $1,000, AV Equip $2,000, Electronic Ref Mat (Incl. Access Fees) $2,000. Sal $376,900 (Prof $281,000)
Library Holdings: Bk Titles 51,000; Per Subs 200
Automation Activity & Vendor Info: (Acquisitions) epixtech, inc.; (Cataloging) epixtech, inc.; (Circulation) epixtech, inc.; (OPAC) epixtech, inc.; (Serials) epixtech, inc.
Mem of DuPage Library System
Partic in Dynix Consortium
Friends of the Library Group

S RADIOLOGICAL SOCIETY OF NORTH AMERICA, 820 Jorie Blvd, 60523. SAN 371-4314. Tel: 630-571-2670. FAX: 630-571-7837. Web Site: www.rsna.org. *Dir*, Roberta Arnold
Library Holdings: Bk Vols 400; Per Subs 40

M UNIVERSITY HEALTH SYSTEM CONSORTIUM LIBRARY,* 2001 Spring Rd, Ste 700, 60523-1890. SAN 376-0359. Tel: 630-954-1700. FAX: 630-954-4730. Web Site: www.uhc.edu. *Librn*, Wendy Wagner
Library Holdings: Bk Titles 500
Partic in Nat Libr of Med

OAK FOREST

P ACORN PUBLIC LIBRARY DISTRICT, 15624 S Central Ave, 60452-3299. SAN 304-4955. Tel: 708-687-3700. FAX: 708-687-3712. Web Site: www.sls.lib.il.us/ads. *Dir*, Denise Webber; E-Mail: dwebber@sslic.net; *Ch Servs*, Julia Churchill; *Cat*, Patricia Sasveld; *Circ*, Donna Bos; *Ref*, Beth Lescak; Staff 16 (MLS 2, Non-MLS 14)
Founded 1966. Pop 31,697; Circ 168,414
Jul 1999-Jun 2000 Income $777,158, State $93,413, Federal $2,000, County $637,340, Other $44,405. Mats Exp $138,222, Books $92,445, Per/Ser (Incl. Access Fees) $21,000, AV Equip $20,277, Electronic Ref Mat (Incl. Access Fees) $4,500. Sal $324,898
Library Holdings: Bk Vols 61,054; Per Subs 192; High Interest/Low Vocabulary Bk Vols 132; Bks on Deafness & Sign Lang 42
Automation Activity & Vendor Info: (Cataloging) Innovative Interfaces Inc.; (Circulation) Innovative Interfaces Inc.; (OPAC) Innovative Interfaces Inc.
Database Vendor: IAC - Info Trac, OCLC - First Search
Publications: Community Awareness Brochures; newsletter (semi-annual)
Mem of Suburban Library System
Partic in Suburban Libr Syst
Special Services for the Blind - CCTV (VisualTex); Computers with Voice Synthesizer; Descriptive videos
Open Mon & Tues 9-9, Wed 1-9, Thurs, Fri & Sat 9-5, Sun 12-5
Friends of the Library Group

OAK FOREST HOSPITAL
M MEDICAL LIBRARY, 15900 S Cicero Ave, 60452. SAN 340-6083. Tel: 708-687-7200, Ext 3554. FAX: 708-633-3557. E-Mail: ofs@sos.lib.il.us. *Dir*, Cerrelda Jones; *Ref*, Hui Li Liu
Founded 1973
Library Holdings: Bk Vols 13,800; Per Subs 250
Subject Interests: Paramedics
Restriction: Staff use only
Mem of Suburban Library System
Partic in Illinois Health Libraries Consortium
Income statistics includes the Patient Library

S PATIENT LIBRARY, 15900 S Cicero Ave, 60452. SAN 340-6113. Tel: 708-687-7200, Ext 3550. FAX: 708-633-3557. *Dir*, Cerrelda Jones; *Asst Librn*, Hui Li Liu
Founded 1957
Library Holdings: Bk Vols 1,500; Per Subs 75
Special Collections: Books on Record; Braille books; Large-Print Books

SR SLOVAK CATHOLIC CULTURE CENTER LIBRARY,* 5900 W 147th St, 60452-1104. SAN 321-2289. Tel: 708-687-2877. *In Charge*, Sister Irene Sebo
Circ 3,000
Library Holdings: Bk Titles 3,500; Per Subs 40

OAK LAWN

M CHRIST HOSPITAL & MEDICAL CENTER, Advocate Health Sciences Library, 4440 W 95th St, 60453. SAN 304-4963. Tel: 708-346-5200. FAX: 708-346-5145.; Staff 5 (MLS 3, Non-MLS 2)
Library Holdings: Bk Titles 6,000; Per Subs 310
Subject Interests: Medicine
Automation Activity & Vendor Info: (Cataloging) Endeavor; (Circulation) Endeavor; (Media Booking) Endeavor; (OPAC) Endeavor
Database Vendor: OVID Technologies
Mem of Suburban Library System
Partic in Chicago & South Consortium

P OAK LAWN PUBLIC LIBRARY, 9427 S Raymond Ave, 60453-2434. SAN 304-498X. Tel: 708-422-4990. FAX: 708-422-5061. Web Site: www.lib.oak-lawn.il.us. *Dir*, James B Casey; E-Mail: jimcasey@lib.oak-lawn.il.us; *Ch Servs*, Judith McMahon; *Publ Servs*, Susan Baird; *Ref*, William D Goodfellow; *Tech Servs*, James E Baker; Staff 87 (MLS 20, Non-MLS 67)
Founded 1943. Pop 56,182; Circ 640,000
Jan 2000-Dec 2000 Income $3,346,389. Mats Exp $601,500, Books $365,000, Per/Ser (Incl. Access Fees) $79,500, Presv $28,300, Electronic Ref Mat (Incl. Access Fees) $57,000. Sal $1,804,592 (Prof $777,104)
Library Holdings: Bk Vols 220,000; Per Subs 735
Subject Interests: Careers, Law, Local history
Special Collections: Telephone Books on CD ROM & microfiche; US College Catalogs, microfiche
Automation Activity & Vendor Info: (Acquisitions) Brodart; (Circulation) Innovative Interfaces Inc.
Publications: Oak Lawn Public Library Newsletter
Mem of Suburban Library System
Partic in BRS; Dialog Corporation; Illinois Library & Information Network; OCLC Online Computer Library Center, Inc; Wilsonline
Special Services for the Deaf - Books on deafness & sign language; Captioned film depository
Special Services for the Blind - Talking Books
Friends of the Library Group

OAK PARK

S FRANK LLOYD WRIGHT PRESERVATION TRUST, 931 Chicago Ave, 60302. SAN 325-2949. Tel: 708-848-1976. FAX: 708-848-1248. Web Site: www.wrightplus.org. *Dir*, Joan Mercuri; E-Mail: mercuri@enteract.com
Founded 1974

Library Holdings: Bk Vols 2,000
Special Collections: Artifacts; Frank Lloyd Wright Coll; John L Wright Toy Coll; Large Drawings; Maginal Wright Barney Archive; Prairie School of Architecture, mat; William Drummond Coll
Publications: Frank Lloyd Wright Newsletter, Research Center Brochure, Wright Angles
Open Wed-Sat 1-4, closed in Aug

M OAK PARK HOSPITAL LIBRARY, 520 S Maple, 60304. SAN 375-9830. Tel: 708-660-2665. FAX: 708-383-8480. *Dir*, Wanda Mathews
Library Holdings: Bk Titles 200
Special Collections: Medical Reports; Survey Responses

P OAK PARK PUBLIC LIBRARY,* 834 Lake St, 60301. SAN 340-6148. Tel: 708-383-8200. FAX: 708-383-6384. Web Site: www.oppl.org. *Exec Dir*, Edward Byers; *Tech Servs*, Constance Strait; *Ch Servs*, Barbara Botham; *Automation Syst Coordr*, Kwang Kye; *Coll Develop*, Sheila Stevenson; Staff 26 (MLS 26)
Founded 1903. Pop 53,648; Circ 670,156
Library Holdings: Bk Vols 288,622; Per Subs 1,522
Subject Interests: Art and architecture, Local history
Special Collections: Frank Lloyd Wright & Ernest Hemingway (Local Authors), bks, pamphlets, papers; History, bks, photos, papers; Oak Park Local
Automation Activity & Vendor Info: (Circulation) epixtech, inc.
Mem of Suburban Library System
Open Mon-Thurs 9-9, Fri 9-6 & Sat 9-5; Sun 1-5 (Sept-May only)
Friends of the Library Group
Branches: 2
DOLE, 255 Augusta St, 60302. SAN 340-6202. Tel: 708-386-9032. FAX: 708-445-2385. *Librn*, Jeanne Friedell
Friends of the Library Group
MAZE, 845 Gunderson Ave, 60304. SAN 340-6172. Tel: 708-386-4751. FAX: 708-386-0023. *Librn*, Jim Przepasniak
Library Holdings: Bk Vols 30,333
Friends of the Library Group

M WEST SUBURBAN HOSPITAL MEDICAL CENTER, Professional Library, 3 Erie Court, 60302. SAN 304-5013. Tel: 708-763-6501. FAX: 708-383-8783. E-Mail: lib.jas@wshmc.org. *Dir Libr Serv*, Julie Stielstra; *Asst Librn*, Laura Swieck
Founded 1937
Library Holdings: Bk Vols 4,000; Per Subs 350
Subject Interests: Clinical medicine, Nursing
Database Vendor: OCLC - First Search
Publications: Acquisitions List; Annual Report; Journals Holdings
Mem of Suburban Library System
Partic in Greater MW Regional Med Libr Program; Illinois Library & Information Network; Metrop Consortium

OAKBROOK TERRACE

S JOINT COMMISSION ON ACCREDITATION OF HEALTHCARE ORGANIZATIONS, Resource Center, One Renaissance Blvd, 60181. SAN 375-9784. Tel: 630-792-5474. FAX: 630-792-4474. *In Charge*, Jan Aleccia; E-Mail: jaleccia@jcaho.org; Staff 2 (MLS 1, Non-MLS 1)
Library Holdings: Bk Titles 2,500; Per Subs 175
Subject Interests: Health care admin
Mem of DuPage Library System
Partic in Fox Valley Health Science Library Consortium; Nat Libr of Med

S VAN KAMPEN FUNDS, Corporate Information Center, One Parkview Plaza, 60181. Tel: 630-684-6365. FAX: 630-684-6378. *Mgr*, Rita McGreal; E-Mail: mcgrear@vankampen.com; *Librn*, Roberta Fox; Tel: 630-684-6480, E-Mail: foxr@vankampen.com; *Circ*, Macaluso Alex; Tel: 630-684-6612, E-Mail: macalua@vankampen.com; Staff 4 (MLS 2, Non-MLS 2)
Library Holdings: Bk Vols 1,000; Per Subs 100
Subject Interests: Finance
Special Collections: Collection of lipper materials; Municipal Bond Prospectuses from 1985
Database Vendor: Lexis-Nexis
Mem of DuPage Library System

OAKWOOD

P OAKWOOD PUBLIC LIBRARY DISTRICT, 110 E Finley, PO Box 99, 61858. SAN 376-0162. Tel: 217-354-4777. FAX: 217-354-4782. Web Site: www.ltls.org. *Dir*, Sue Fletcher
Founded 1987. Pop 7,409
Library Holdings: Bk Titles 14,000; Per Subs 62
Subject Interests: Large type print
Special Collections: Audio Coll; Local History Room
Automation Activity & Vendor Info: (Cataloging) epixtech, inc.; (Circulation) epixtech, inc.
Mem of Lincoln Trail Libraries System
Friends of the Library Group

ODELL

P ODELL PUBLIC LIBRARY DISTRICT,* 301 E Richard St, PO Box 347, 60460. SAN 304-5021. Tel: 815-998-2012. FAX: 815-998-2339. *Pres*, Dan Dixon; *Librn*, Sharon Stahler; *Asst Librn*, Rita Verdun
Pop 1,606; Circ 12,672
Library Holdings: Bk Vols 18,000; Per Subs 27
Mem of Alliance Library System
Friends of the Library Group

O'FALLON

P O'FALLON PUBLIC LIBRARY, 120 Civic Plaza, 62269-2692. SAN 304-503X. Tel: 618-632-3783. FAX: 618-632-3759. E-Mail: ofa@lcls.org. *Librn*, Mary L Smith; E-Mail: marys@lcls.org; *Asst Librn, YA Servs*, Anne Glasscock; *Ref, Tech Coordr*, James Doil; E-Mail: jamied@lcls.org; Staff 3 (MLS 2, Non-MLS 1)
Founded 1943. Pop 20,018; Circ 177,755
May 1999-Apr 2000 Income $683,751, State $28,695, City $377,126, Federal $300, Locally Generated Income $277,630. Mats Exp $49,487, Books $38,647, Per/Ser (Incl. Access Fees) $5,900, Micro $4,940. Sal $230,832 (Prof $110,000)
Library Holdings: Bk Titles 42,491; Per Subs 237
Subject Interests: Local history
Special Collections: Learning Activities Resource Center
Automation Activity & Vendor Info: (Cataloging) DRA; (OPAC) DRA
Database Vendor: OCLC - First Search
Mem of Lewis & Clark Library System
Partic in Ill Networking
Friends of the Library Group

OGDEN

P OGDEN ROSE PUBLIC LIBRARY,* 103 W Main, PO Box 297, 61859. SAN 304-5048. Tel: 217-582-2411. FAX: 217-582-2411. *Librn*, Anne Miller
Pop 800
Library Holdings: Bk Vols 7,000
Mem of Lincoln Trail Libraries System
Open Mon-Thurs 3:30-7:30, Sat 9-12
Friends of the Library Group

OGLESBY

J ILLINOIS VALLEY COMMUNITY COLLEGE, Jacobs Memorial Library, 815 Orlando Smith Ave, 61348-9692. SAN 304-5056. Tel: 815-224-0306. FAX: 815-224-9147. E-Mail: jacobs@waldo.ivcc.edu. Web Site: www.ivcc.edu/library. *Dir*, Carol S Bird; Tel: 815-224-0397, E-Mail: bird@ivcc.edu; *Per*, Frank Frostestad; Tel: 815-224-0263, E-Mail: ffrostes@ivcc.edu; *Doc*, Jeanne Struna; Tel: 815-224-0204, E-Mail: jstruna@ivcc.edu; Staff 9 (MLS 3, Non-MLS 6)
Founded 1968. Pop 145,000; Enrl 4,400; Fac 145; Highest Degree: Associate
Jul 1999-Jun 2000 Income $315,725. Mats Exp $112,023, Books $67,787, Per/Ser (Incl. Access Fees) $37,237, Presv $690, Other Print Mats $3,587, Electronic Ref Mat (Incl. Access Fees) $2,722. Sal $146,257 (Prof $73,200)
Library Holdings: Bk Vols 132,798; Bk Titles 121,294; Per Subs 967
Subject Interests: Local history, Nursing
Special Collections: NRC
Automation Activity & Vendor Info: (Cataloging) DRA; (Circulation) DRA; (OPAC) DRA
Database Vendor: DRA, Ebsco - EbscoHost, GaleNet, IAC - SearchBank, Lexis-Nexis, OVID Technologies, ProQuest
Publications: Handbook; newsletter
Restriction: Open to faculty, students & qualified researchers
Function: Research library
Mem of Heritage Trail Library System
Partic in Illinois Library Computer Systems Office; LVIS; Missouri Library Network Corporation; Northern Ill Learning Resources Coop; OCLC Online Computer Library Center, Inc; SILO

P OGLESBY PUBLIC LIBRARY,* 111 S Woodland St, 61348. SAN 304-5064. Tel: 815-883-3619. *Librn*, Irene Claudnic
Founded 1925. Pop 3,979; Circ 12,819
1999-1999 Mats Exp $12,500, Books $10,000, Per/Ser (Incl. Access Fees) $2,500
Library Holdings: Bk Vols 23,000; Per Subs 75
Mem of Heritage Trail Library System
Friends of the Library Group

OHIO

P OHIO PUBLIC LIBRARY DISTRICT, 112 N Main St, PO Box 187, 61349. SAN 304-5072. Tel: 815-376-5422. FAX: 815-376-5014. Web Site: ohiolib@ivnet.com. *Librn*, Mary Lou Clinton; E-Mail: mlclinton@

starbase1.htls.lib.il.us
Pop 1,122; Circ 5,364
Library Holdings: Bk Vols 8,942; Per Subs 42

OLIVE BRANCH

P DODGE MEMORIAL PUBLIC LIBRARY, South Rt 3, PO Box 65, 62969. SAN 376-6764. Tel: 618-776-5115. FAX: 618-776-5115. *Librn*, Charlotte Grant
Library Holdings: Bk Vols 4,600; Bk Titles 4,000
Friends of the Library Group

OLMSTED

P OLMSTED PUBLIC LIBRARY,* 160 N Front St, PO Box 157A, 62970. SAN 376-0170. Tel: 618-742-8296. FAX: 618-742-8296. *Librn*, Katherine Robertson
Library Holdings: Bk Titles 5,070; Per Subs 25

OLNEY

J OLNEY CENTRAL COLLEGE, Anderson Learning Resource Center,* 305 N West St, 62450. SAN 304-5080. Tel: 618-395-7777. FAX: 618-392-3293. E-Mail: stencelf@iecc.cc.il.us. Web Site: www.iecc.il.us.org. *Librn*, Fran Stencel
Founded 1963. Enrl 1,135
Library Holdings: Bk Titles 35,000; Per Subs 125
Mem of Shawnee Library System

P OLNEY PUBLIC LIBRARY, 400 W Main St, 62450. SAN 340-6237. Tel: 618-392-3711. FAX: 618-392-3139. *Chief Librn*, Ruth Childers; E-Mail: ruthchil@shawls.lib.il.us; *Asst Librn*, Roberta Eck
Founded 1872. Pop 8,895; Circ 80,000
May 2000-Apr 2001 Income $186,568, State $11,118, City $135,450, Locally Generated Income $26,500, Other $13,500. Mats Exp $29,500, Books $23,000, Per/Ser (Incl. Access Fees) $3,000, AV Equip $2,000, Other Print Mats $1,500. Sal $90,000 (Prof $31,500)
Library Holdings: Bk Titles 50,000; Per Subs 90
Special Collections: Antiques & Collectibles - Toys & Dolls; Civil War; Genealogy
Database Vendor: epixtech, inc.
Mem of Shawnee Library System

M RICHLAND MEMORIAL HOSPITAL STAFF LIBRARY,* 800 E Locust, 62450. SAN 375-6416. Tel: 618-395-2131. FAX: 618-392-3228.
Library Holdings: Per Subs 10

OLYMPIA FIELDS

CM MIDWESTERN UNIVERSITY, St. James Hospital & Medical Center Library, 20201 S Crawford, 60461. SAN 304-5099. Tel: 708-747-4000, Ext 1190. FAX: 708-747-0244. *Librn*, Vicki High
Founded 1978
Library Holdings: Bk Titles 2,907; Per Subs 229
Publications: Library Newsletter
Partic in Illinois Library & Information Network; Midwest Health Sci Libr Network

ONARGA

P ONARGA COMMUNITY PUBLIC LIBRARY DISTRICT,* 209 W Seminary Ave, 60955-1131. SAN 304-5102. Tel: 815-268-7626. FAX: 815-268-4635. E-Mail: library@coliut.com. Web Site: www.prairienet.org/fordiroq./library.htm. *Dir*, Mary Harroun
Pop 1,678; Circ 14,161
1997-1998 Income $50,000, County $40,000, Locally Generated Income $10,000. Mats Exp $10,000, Books $9,000, Per/Ser (Incl. Access Fees) $1,000. Sal $10,000
Library Holdings: Bk Vols 6,200; Per Subs 20
Mem of Lincoln Trail Libraries System

ONEIDA

P GREIG MEMORIAL LIBRARY,* 110 S Joy St, PO Box 446, 61467-0446. SAN 304-5110. Tel: 309-483-3482. FAX: 309-483-3482. E-Mail: gmpl@darkstar.rsa.lib.il.us. *Librn*, Sara Stotts
Founded 1916. Pop 728; Circ 4,638
Library Holdings: Bk Vols 11,899; Per Subs 19
Mem of Alliance Library System
Open Mon & Fri 10-12 & 3-5, Sat 9-1

OREANA

P ARGENTA-OREANA PUBLIC LIBRARY DISTRICT, Oreana Public Library, 214 W South St, PO Box 261, 62554-0261. SAN 304-5129. Tel: 217-468-2340. FAX: 217-468-2340. *Librn*, Cindy Bowman
Circ 5,080
Jul 1998-Jun 1999 Income $161,219, County $109,636, Other $51,583. Sal $61,017
Library Holdings: Bk Vols 1,200
Automation Activity & Vendor Info: (Acquisitions) DRA; (Cataloging) DRA; (Circulation) DRA; (ILL) DRA; (OPAC) DRA
Database Vendor: DRA
Mem of Rolling Prairie Library System
Open Mon & Wed 10-8, Tues & Thurs 1-5, Fri 10-5, Sat 10-12

OREGON

P OREGON PUBLIC LIBRARY DISTRICT,* 300 Jefferson St, 61061. SAN 304-5137. Tel: 815-732-2724. FAX: 815-732-6643. *Ch Servs*, Gladis Keebler
Pop 5,189; Circ 47,809
Library Holdings: Bk Vols 35,991; Per Subs 56
Subject Interests: Genealogy
Special Collections: Laredo Tast Eagles Nest Art Coll
Mem of Northern Illinois Library System

ORION

P WESTERN DISTRICT LIBRARY, 1111 Fourth St, PO Box 70, 61273-0070. SAN 304-5145. Tel: 309-526-8375. FAX: 309-526-8375. *Librn*, Shirley Carney; E-Mail: scarney@libby.rbls.lib.il.us; Staff 1 (Non-MLS 1)
Founded 1905. Pop 5,301; Circ 33,405
Jul 1999-Jun 2000 Income $178,562, State $6,540, Federal $3,398, County $111,121, Other $53,265. Mats Exp $21,250, Books $15,774, Per/Ser (Incl. Access Fees) $2,440, AV Equip $3,036. Sal $56,859 (Prof $19,281)
Library Holdings: Bk Vols 22,715; Per Subs 95; Bks on Deafness & Sign Lang 10
Mem of River Bend Library System
Partic in Quad-Link Libr Consortium

ORLAND HILLS

P ORLAND HILLS PUBLIC LIBRARY DISTRICT,* Orland Hills Village Hall, 60477. SAN 376-1363. Tel: 708-349-6666.

ORLAND PARK

P ORLAND PARK PUBLIC LIBRARY,* 14760 Park Lane, 60462. SAN 304-5153. Tel: 708-349-8138. FAX: 708-349-8196. E-Mail: ors@sls.lib. *Librn*, Sharon Wsol
Pop 44,628
Library Holdings: Bk Vols 110,943; Per Subs 353
Automation Activity & Vendor Info: (Circulation) GEAC
Publications: Newsletter (6 per year)
Mem of Suburban Library System
Friends of the Library Group

OSWEGO

P OSWEGO PUBLIC LIBRARY DISTRICT, 32 W Jefferson St, 60543. SAN 304-5161. Tel: 630-554-3150. FAX: 630-554-3150. *Dir*, Sarah Skilton; Fax: 630-554-8445, E-Mail: saskil@opld.org; *Ch Servs*, Patricia Cederoth; *Tech Servs*, John Fallmaier; *Ad Servs*, Carolyn Leifheit; *Ad Servs*, Peggy Tegel; Staff 33 (MLS 6, Non-MLS 27)
Founded 1964. Pop 29,179
Subject Interests: Antiques, Collectibles
Special Collections: Illinois Census (1820-1900), micro; Oswego Township Historical Records, micro
Automation Activity & Vendor Info: (Cataloging) Gaylord; (Circulation) epixtech, inc.
Publications: Library Lines; Off the Top Shelf
Mem of Happy Times Library System
Friends of the Library Group

OTTAWA

P REDDICK LIBRARY, 1010 Canal St, 61350. SAN 304-517X. Tel: 815-434-0509. FAX: 815-434-2634. Web Site: www.htls.lib.il.us/OTB. *Dir*, Kathy Berggren; E-Mail: kberggren@starbase1.htls.lib.il.us; *Asst Dir*, Tina Lantz; Staff 3 (MLS 1, Non-MLS 2)
Founded 1888. Pop 17,528; Circ 109,493
May 1999-Apr 2000 Income $442,635, State $70,155, City $268,144, Federal $20,385, Locally Generated Income $87,414. Mats Exp $71,896, Books $62,835, Per/Ser (Incl. Access Fees) $9,000, Micro $500, AV Equip $8,000, Electronic Ref Mat (Incl. Access Fees) $9,065. Sal $195,988 (Prof $77,000)

Library Holdings: Bk Vols 70,000; Per Subs 179; High Interest/Low Vocabulary Bk Vols 200
Special Collections: State & Local History (Illinois Coll)
Mem of Heritage Trail Library System
Friends of the Library Group

GL THIRD DISTRICT APPELLATE COURT LIBRARY,* 1004 Columbus St, 61350. SAN 304-5188. Tel: 815-434-5050. *Librn*, Sharon M Smith
Library Holdings: Bk Vols 15,000
Restriction: Open to public for reference only

PALATINE

S AMERICAN SOCIETY OF ARTISTS, INC, Resource Center, PO Box 1326, 60078. SAN 326-0100. Tel: 312-751-2500. E-Mail: asoa@webtv.net. Web Site: community.webtv.net/asoa/asa. *Librn*, Donald Metcoff

P PALATINE PUBLIC LIBRARY DISTRICT, 700 N Court, 60067-8159. SAN 304-5196. Tel: 847-358-5881. FAX: 847-358-7192. Web Site: www.ppld.alibrary.com. *Dir*, Daniel G Armstrong; *Publ Servs*, Judy Palmer; *AV, Tech Servs*, Marcia Getty; *Coll Develop, Mgr*, Jill Skwerski; *Circ*, Carol Haggerty
Founded 1923. Pop 89,943; Circ 1,557,843
Jul 1999-Jun 2000 Income $5,000,000, State $111,000. Mats Exp $750,000, Books $400,000, Per/Ser (Incl. Access Fees) $100,000, Other Print Mats $100,000, Electronic Ref Mat (Incl. Access Fees) $150,000. Sal $2,000,000 (Prof $700,000)
Library Holdings: Bk Vols 320,000; Bk Titles 250,000; Per Subs 1,000
Automation Activity & Vendor Info: (Circulation) epixtech, inc.; (OPAC) epixtech, inc.
Mem of North Suburban Library System
Partic in Ill Regional Libr Coun
Open Mon-Thurs 9-9, Fri 9-6, Sat 9-5 & Sun 12-5
Friends of the Library Group
Branches: 2
FREEMAN ROAD, 1262 Freeman Rd, Hoffman Estates, 60195. SAN 370-3657. Tel: 847-934-0220. TDD: 847-358-9106. FAX: 847-934-8624. Web Site: www.ppld.alibrary.com. *Branch Mgr*, Linda Zeilstra; Staff 8 (MLS 1, Non-MLS 7)
Founded 1981. Pop 11,000; Circ 160,000
Library Holdings: Bk Titles 23,000; Per Subs 40
Database Vendor: epixtech, inc., IAC - SearchBank
Function: Photocopies available
Friends of the Library Group
RAND ROAD, 1585 N Rand Rd, 60067. *Mgr*, Linda Zeilstra; Tel: 847-358-5881
Founded 2000
Library Holdings: Bk Vols 4,500; Bk Titles 4,000; Per Subs 20
Bookmobiles: 1

J WILLIAM RAINEY HARPER COLLEGE, Resources for Learning, 1200 W Algonguin Rd, 60067. SAN 304-520X. Tel: 847-925-6000, Ext 6584. FAX: 847-925-6164. Interlibrary Loan Service FAX: 847-925-6037. Web Site: www.harper.cc.il.us/lrc, www.harper.com. *Dean*, Joseph Accardi; *Tech Servs*, Jim Edstrom; Tel: 847-925-6763; *Instrul Serv*, Linda Glover; Tel: 847-925-6000, Ext 6770; *Circ*, Kim Heinz; *Circ*, Deb McManus; Tel: 847-925-6000, Ext 6767; *Ref Serv*, Tom Goetz; *Coll Develop*, Valerie Harley
Founded 1967
Library Holdings: Bk Vols 163,063; Per Subs 971
Automation Activity & Vendor Info: (Acquisitions) Endeavor; (Cataloging) Endeavor; (Circulation) Endeavor; (OPAC) Endeavor; (Serials) Endeavor
Mem of North Suburban Library System
Partic in Ill Regional Libr Coun; Ill State Libr Network; Northern Ill Learning Resources Coop; OCLC Online Computer Library Center, Inc
Open Mon-Thurs 8am-10pm, Fri 8am-4:30pm, Sat 9am-3:30pm & Sun 1-5pm

PALESTINE

P PALESTINE PUBLIC LIBRARY DISTRICT, 116 S Main St, 62451. SAN 320-4758. Tel: 618-586-5317. FAX: 618-586-9711. E-Mail: palestinelibrary@frsb.net. *Librn*, Susan Lockhart
Founded 1977. Pop 2,751
Library Holdings: Bk Vols 14,000; Per Subs 32
Mem of Shawnee Library System
Friends of the Library Group

PALOS HEIGHTS

M PALOS COMMUNITY HOSPITAL, Medical Library,* 80th Ave at McCarthy Rd, 60463. SAN 340-6415. Tel: 708-923-4640. FAX: 708-923-4674. *Librn*, Gail K Lahti; *Chair*, Kenneth Armbruster
Founded 1972
Library Holdings: Bk Titles 2,000; Per Subs 103
Restriction: Staff use only
Mem of Suburban Library System
Partic in Chicago & South Consortium
Branches:
NURSING LIBRARY

P PALOS HEIGHTS PUBLIC LIBRARY,* 12501 S 71st Ave, 60463. SAN 304-5226. Tel: 708-448-1473. FAX: 708-448-8950. E-Mail: phs@sls.lib.il.us. Web Site: www.sls.lib.il.us/phs/phs/phs.html. *Dir*, Elaine Savage
Founded 1944. Pop 12,188; Circ 155,380
Jan 1997-Dec 1998 Income $646,450, State $24,876, City $544,844, Locally Generated Income $69,252, Other $7,478. Mats Exp $109,495. Sal $313,001
Library Holdings: Bk Vols 52,623; Per Subs 223
Subject Interests: Local history
Mem of Suburban Library System
Special Services for the Deaf - TTY machine
Friends of the Library Group

J TRINITY CHRISTIAN COLLEGE, Jennie Huizenga Memorial Library, 6601 W College Dr, 60463. SAN 304-5234. Tel: 708-597-3000, Ext 4925. FAX: 708-385-5665. Web Site: www.trnty.edu/library. *Coll Develop, Dir*, Perry Recker; Tel: 708-597-3000, Ext 4794, E-Mail: perry.recker@trnty.edu
Founded 1959. Enrl 630
Library Holdings: Bk Vols 68,518; Bk Titles 56,186; Per Subs 400
Subject Interests: Humanities, Music, Natural science, Religion, Social sciences and issues
Special Collections: Dutch Heritage Center; Library of American Civilization
Automation Activity & Vendor Info: (Cataloging) DRA; (Circulation) DRA; (OPAC) DRA
Partic in Illinois Library & Information Network; Suburban Libr Syst

PALOS HILLS

P GREEN HILLS PUBLIC LIBRARY DISTRICT, 8611 W 103rd St, 60465-1698. SAN 304-5242. Tel: 708-598-8446. Circulation Tel: 708-598-8446, Ext 10. Reference Tel: 708-598-8446, Ext 20. FAX: 708-598-0856. E-Mail: ghs@greenhills.lib.il.us. Web Site: www.greenhills.lib.il.us. *Dir*, Annette T Armstrong; Tel: 708-598-8446, Ext 11, E-Mail: armstrong@greenhills.lib.il.us; *Asst Dir*, Megan Heligas; Tel: 708-598-8446, Ext 15, E-Mail: heligasm@greenhills.lib.il.us; *Asst Dir*, Nancy Kersten; Tel: 708-598-8446, Ext 14, E-Mail: kersten@greenhills.lib.il.us; *Circ*, Howard Griffin; E-Mail: griffin@greenhills.lib.il.us; *Ad Servs*, Mary Rogus; Tel: 708-598-8446, Ext 15, E-Mail: rogusm@greenhills.lib.il.us; Staff 24 (MLS 3, Non-MLS 21)
Founded 1962. Pop 30,824; Circ 213,993
Jul 1999-Jun 2000 Income $914,016, State $64,118, County $781,126, Other $68,772. Mats Exp $86,065, Books $47,873, Per/Ser (Incl. Access Fees) $12,030, Micro $41, AV Equip $12,975, Electronic Ref Mat (Incl. Access Fees) $13,146. Sal $333,206 (Prof $158,696)
Library Holdings: Bk Vols 77,009; Bk Titles 69,071; Per Subs 168; Bks on Deafness & Sign Lang 37
Subject Interests: Large-print bks, Literary criticism, Local history, Polish (language)
Automation Activity & Vendor Info: (Cataloging) epixtech, inc.; (Circulation) epixtech, inc.; (OPAC) epixtech, inc.
Database Vendor: GaleNet, IAC - Info Trac, IAC - SearchBank
Publications: The Biblio-Files (Newsletter)
Function: ILL available
Mem of Suburban Library System
Friends of the Library Group

J MORAINE VALLEY COMMUNITY COLLEGE, Robert E Turner Learning Resources Ctr,* 10900 S 88th Ave, 60465. SAN 304-5250. Tel: 708-974-5234. FAX: 708-974-1184. *In Charge*, Diane Grund; E-Mail: grund@moraine.cc.il.us; *Tech Servs*, Maria D'Aversa; E-Mail: d'aversa@moraine.cc.il.us; *Coll Develop, Ref*, Nancy Hessler; E-Mail: hessler@moraine.cc.il.us; Staff 36 (MLS 13, Non-MLS 23)
Founded 1967. Enrl 16,330; Fac 183; Highest Degree: Associate
Library Holdings: Bk Vols 79,696; Bk Titles 66,612; Per Subs 747
Subject Interests: Allied health, Nursing
Automation Activity & Vendor Info: (Acquisitions) Innovative Interfaces Inc.; (Cataloging) Innovative Interfaces Inc.; (Circulation) Innovative Interfaces Inc.; (Course Reserve) Innovative Interfaces Inc.; (ILL) Innovative Interfaces Inc.
Mem of Suburban Library System
Partic in Northern Ill Learning Resources Coop

PALOS PARK

P PALOS PARK PUBLIC LIBRARY, 12330 Forest Glen Blvd, 60464. SAN 304-5269. Tel: 708-448-1530. FAX: 708-448-1530. *Librn*, J Miller; E-Mail: millerj@sls.lib.il.us; Staff 3 (MLS 3)
Pop 4,162; Circ 37,182
May 1999-Apr 2000 Income $278,371, State $9,134, City $234,000, Federal $800, Locally Generated Income $34,437. Mats Exp $52,146, Books $41,408, Per/Ser (Incl. Access Fees) $4,838, Micro $2,299, AV Equip $2,272, Other Print Mats $500, Electronic Ref Mat (Incl. Access Fees) $829. Sal $134,912

Library Holdings: Bk Vols 37,182; Per Subs 130
Subject Interests: Local history
Mem of Suburban Library System
Open Mon-Thurs 10-8, Fri & Sat 10-5

PANA

P CARNEGIE-SCHUYLER LIBRARY, Pana Public Library, 303 E Second St, 62557. SAN 304-5277. Tel: 217-562-2326. FAX: 217-562-2343. E-Mail: panlibrary@chipsnet.com. *Librn*, Janet Hicks; *Asst Librn*, Cynthia Cothern; *Asst Librn*, Toni Nollman; *Asst Librn*, Cynthia Schmitz
Pop 5,796; Circ 67,631
Library Holdings: Bk Vols 28,000; Per Subs 111
Mem of Rolling Prairie Library System
Friends of the Library Group

PARIS

P PARIS CARNEGIE PUBLIC LIBRARY, 207 S Main St, 61944. SAN 304-5285. Tel: 217-463-3950. FAX: 217-463-1155. E-Mail: parislib@tigerpaw.com. *Dir*, Teresa Pennington; Staff 6 (MLS 1, Non-MLS 5)
Founded 1904. Pop 9,016; Circ 77,031
May 1999-Apr 2000 Mats Exp $23,509, Books $20,200, Per/Ser (Incl. Access Fees) $1,830, AV Equip $733, Electronic Ref Mat (Incl. Access Fees) $746. Sal $79,900
Library Holdings: Bk Vols 32,987; Per Subs 225
Mem of Lincoln Trail Libraries System

PARK FOREST

P PARK FOREST PUBLIC LIBRARY,* 400 Lakewood Blvd, 60466. SAN 304-5307. Tel: 708-748-3731. FAX: 708-748-8829. E-Mail: pfs@sls.lib.il.us. Web Site: www.sls.lib.il.us/pfs. *Tech Servs*, Marcella Lucas; *Ref*, Susan Woodbury; *Ch Servs*, Chrysantha Rudnik; Staff 7 (MLS 7)
Founded 1955. Pop 24,656; Circ 218,627
Jul 1997-Jun 1998 Income $1,139,359, State $66,980, Federal $16,123, Locally Generated Income $188,621. Mats Exp $145,344, Books $109,733, Per/Ser (Incl. Access Fees) $27,111, Micro $5,000, Other Print Mats $3,500. Sal $579,127 (Prof $293,699)
Library Holdings: Bk Vols 170,111; Per Subs 337
Subject Interests: Civil War, Drama, Local history
Automation Activity & Vendor Info: (Circulation) CLSI LIBS
Publications: Oh, Park Forest - Interpretation of Oral History Tapes
Mem of Suburban Library System
Partic in Illinois Library & Information Network; Metrop Chicago Libr Assembly
Friends of the Library Group

PARK RIDGE

M AMERICAN ASSOCIATION OF NURSE ANESTHETISTS LIBRARY-ARCHIVES, 222 S Prospect Ave, 60068-4001. SAN 374-6704. Tel: 847-692-7050, Ext 3006. FAX: 847-685-4570. Web Site: www.aana.com/archives/. *Archivist*, Kevin D Corbitt; E-Mail: kcorbitt@aana.com
Library Holdings: Bk Vols 2,000; Bk Titles 1,500; Per Subs 150
Special Collections: AANA Archives; Nurse Anesthesia History
Restriction: Use of others with permission of librarian
Mem of North Suburban Library System
Friends of the Library Group

S AMERICAN FARM BUREAU FEDERATION LIBRARY, 225 Touhy Ave, 60068. SAN 329-286X. Tel: 847-685-8781. FAX: 847-685-8969. Web Site: www.fb.org. *Asst Librn*, Susan Nolan; Staff 2 (MLS 1, Non-MLS 1)
Library Holdings: Bk Titles 8,000; Per Subs 150
Restriction: By appointment only
Mem of North Suburban Library System

M AMERICAN SOCIETY OF ANESTHESIOLOGISTS, Wood Library-Museum of Anesthesiology, 520 N Northwest Hwy, 60068-2573. SAN 304-5331. Tel: 847-825-5586. FAX: 847-825-1692. E-Mail: wlm@asahq.org. Web Site: www.asahq.org/wlm/homepage.html. *Librn*, Patrick Sim; *Asst Librn*, Karen Bieterman; Tel: 847-825-5586, Ext 58, E-Mail: k.bieterman@ASAhq.org; *Archivist*, Judith Robins; Staff 3 (MLS 3)
Founded 1929
Library Holdings: Bk Titles 8,500; Per Subs 100
Subject Interests: Anesthesiology
Special Collections: Curare (R Gill Coll), mss; History of Anesthesiology Coll; Mesmerism Coll
Automation Activity & Vendor Info: (Cataloging) Sydney
Publications: Historical Monographs; History of Anesthesiology Reprint Series (annual)
Friends of the Library Group

SR CATHOLIC CASSETTE LIBRARY,* 1420 Renaissance Dr, 60068-1330. SAN 376-2505. Tel: 847-827-4075. FAX: 847-825-5081. *Dir*, Patrick F O'Connor

M LUTHERAN GENERAL HOSPITAL, Advocate Health Sciences Library Network,* 1775 Dempster St, 60068. SAN 304-5366. Tel: 847-723-5494. FAX: 847-692-9576. *Dir*, Marie Burns; E-Mail: marie.burns@advocatehealth.com
Founded 1966
Library Holdings: Bk Vols 24,000; Per Subs 490
Subject Interests: Medicine, Nursing, Nutrition, Psychiatry
Mem of North Suburban Library System
Partic in Metropolitan Consortium Of Chicago; OCLC Online Computer Library Center, Inc

S MILLION DOLLAR ROUND TABLE, Information Services, 325 W Touhy, 60068. SAN 373-4439. Tel: 847-692-6378. FAX: 847-518-8921. *Dir*, John Prast; *In Charge*, William Jesse; *Coll Develop*, Sandee Zivin
Library Holdings: Bk Vols 150; Bk Titles 100; Per Subs 55

P PARK RIDGE PUBLIC LIBRARY, 20 S Prospect, 60068-4188. SAN 304-5374. Tel: 847-825-3123. TDD: 847-825-8219. FAX: 847-825-0001. Web Site: www.park-ridge.il.us/library. *Dir*, Janet Van De Carr; Tel: 847-720-3203, Ext 203, E-Mail: jvandcar@park-ridge.lib.il.us; *Ad Servs*, Gretchen Kottkamp; Tel: 847-720-3245, E-Mail: gkottkam@park-ridge.lib.il.us; *Reader Servs*, Vivian Mortensen; Tel: 847-720-3282, E-Mail: vmortens@park-ridge.lib.il.us; *Tech Servs*, Linda Egebrecht; Tel: 847-720-3221, E-Mail: legebrec@park-ridge.lib.il.us; Staff 117 (MLS 25, Non-MLS 92)
Founded 1910. Pop 37,075; Circ 652,474
May 1999-Apr 2000 Income $3,597,273, State $206,557, City $2,907,050, Locally Generated Income $149,464. Mats Exp $539,741, Books $365,691, Per/Ser (Incl. Access Fees) $19,091, Miero $10,437, AV Equip $44,155, Electronic Ref Mat (Incl. Access Fees) $100,367. Sal $1,890,079
Library Holdings: Bk Vols 232,547; Per Subs 450
Special Collections: Park Ridge History, newspapers
Database Vendor: IAC - Info Trac, IAC - SearchBank, OCLC - First Search
Publications: Advance Notice] (program bulletin); Spokesman (city newsletter); The Lightbulb (newsletter for teachers); Youthpack (young adult newsletter)
Mem of North Suburban Library System
Partic in Illinois Library & Information Network; OCLC Online Computer Library Center, Inc
Special Services for the Deaf - TDD
Friends of the Library Group

PATOKA

P PATOKA PUBLIC LIBRARY,* 210 W Bond St, PO Box 58, 62875. SAN 304-5382. Tel: 618-432-5519 (township), 618-432-7754. *Librn*, Lynn Eagleton
Founded 1934. Pop 662; Circ 5,694
Library Holdings: Bk Vols 4,000; Per Subs 10
Mem of Shawnee Library System

PAW PAW

P PAW PAW PUBLIC LIBRARY DISTRICT, 362 Chicago Rd, PO Box 60, 61353. SAN 304-5390. Tel: 815-627-9396. FAX: 815-627-3707. *Librn*, Mary Dodaro
Founded 1925. Pop 791; Circ 13,471
Library Holdings: Bk Vols 17,000; Per Subs 42
Special Collections: Lee & DeKalb Counties Local History, includes written materials, census, newspaper slides, photos, scrapbooks & memorabilia
Mem of Heritage Trail Library System

PAWNEE

P PAWNEE PUBLIC LIBRARY,* 704 Seventh St, PO Box 229, 62558. SAN 304-5404. Tel: 217-625-7716. FAX: 217-625-7716. *Librn*, Bennett A Bess
Founded 1951. Circ 10,135
Library Holdings: Bk Vols 15,000; Bk Titles 14,500
Subject Interests: History, Illinois
Mem of Rolling Prairie Library System

PAXTON

P PAXTON CARNEGIE LIBRARY,* 254 S Market St, 60957-1499. SAN 304-5412. Tel: 217-379-3431. FAX: 217-379-3431. E-Mail: read@illicom.net. *Librn*, Anne Newman
Founded 1903. Pop 4,289; Circ 36,886
May 1997-Apr 1998 Income $65,584, State $9,611, City $51,114. Mats Exp $30,984, Books $10,500, Per/Ser (Incl. Access Fees) $800, Micro $100, Manuscripts & Archives $18,984. Sal $25,511 (Prof $15,080)
Library Holdings: Bk Vols 26,800; Per Subs 115
Mem of Lincoln Trail Libraries System
Special Services for the Deaf - Books on deafness & sign language

PEARL CITY

P PEARL CITY PUBLIC LIBRARY DISTRICT,* 221 S Main St, PO Box 158, 61062. SAN 304-5420. Tel: 815-443-2832. FAX: 815-443-2832. *Chief Librn*, Mary Vivian; E-Mail: maryv@aeroine.net
Pop 1,338; Circ 12,912
Library Holdings: Bk Vols 9,000
Mem of Northern Illinois Library System
Open Mon, Thurs & Fri 3-7, Tues & Wed 3-9, Sat 10-4

PECATONICA

P PECATONICA PUBLIC LIBRARY DISTRICT, 403 Main St, PO Box 599, 61063-0599. SAN 304-5439. Tel: 815-239-2616. FAX: 815-239-2250. Web Site: www.peclib@aeroinc.net. *Dir*, Mickey Vipond; Staff 6 (Non-MLS 6)
Founded 1967. Pop 3,809; Circ 22,830
Jul 1999-Jun 2000 Income $92,147, State $9,590, County $62,635, Other $19,922. Mats Exp $12,652, Books $10,734, Per/Ser (Incl. Access Fees) $1,227, Electronic Ref Mat (Incl. Access Fees) $691. Sal $45,190
Library Holdings: Bk Titles 15,716; Per Subs 42; Bks on Deafness & Sign Lang 10
Subject Interests: Large type print
Automation Activity & Vendor Info: (Circulation) Sagebrush Corporation
Mem of Northern Illinois Library System

PEKIN

P ALLIANCE LIBRARY SYSTEM, 845 Brenkman Dr, 61554. SAN 340-6598. Tel: 309-353-4110. Toll Free Tel: 800-700-4857. FAX: 309-353-8281. E-Mail: alsp@darkstar.rsa.lib.il.us. Web Site: www.rsa.lib.il.us/. *Exec Dir*, Valerie J Wilford; E-Mail: vwilford@darkstar.rsa.lib.il.us; *Mgr*, Mary Whalen; E-Mail: mwhalen@darkstar.rsa.lib.il.us; *Ref*, Felicia Sworsky; Fax: 309-343-0150, E-Mail: fsworsky@darkstar.rsa.lib.il.us; *Ref*, Ron Winner; Fax: 309-343-0150, E-Mail: rwinner@darkstar.rsa.lib.il.us; *Coordr*, Angie Watson; E-Mail: awatson@darkstar.rsa.lib.il.us; *Automation Syst Coordr*, Lori Bell; E-Mail: lbell@darkstar.rsa.lib.il.us; *Network Services*, Ted Matheny; E-Mail: tmetheny@darkstar.rsa.lib.il.us
Founded 1994. Pop 928,677
Jul 1999-Jun 2000 Income $2,515,662. Sal $1,119,166 (Prof $589,927)
Library Holdings: Per Subs 110
Publications: At First Glance (newsletter)
Member Libraries: Allin Township Library; Alpha Park Public Library District; Amity Township Public Library; Ashland Public Library District; Astoria Public Library District Library; Atkinson Public Library District; Atlanta Public Library District; Ayer Public Library District; Barry Public Library; Beardstown Houston Memorial Library; Black Hawk College-East Campus; Blandinsville-Hire District Library; Blessing Health Professions Library; Bloomington Public Library; Bluffs Public Library; Bradford Public Library District; Bradley University; Brimfield Public Library; Bromenn Healthcare; Brown County Public Library District; Bushnell Public Library; Cambridge Public Library District; Camp Point Public Library Distict; Carey E Burdette Memorial Library; Carl Sandburg College; Carthage Public Library District; Caterpillar Inc; Caterpillar Inc; Chatsworth Township Library; Chenoa Free Public Library; Chillicothe Public Library District; Clayton Public Library District; Clover Library District; Colchester District Library; Creve Coeur Public Library District; Danvers Township Library; Deer Creek District Library; Department of Human Services; Dickson Mounds Museum Library; Dominy Memorial Library; Dunlap Public Library District; El Paso Public Library; Eureka College; Eureka Public Library District; Farmer City Public Library; Farmington Public Library District; Filger Public Library; Fondulac Public Library District; Forrest Public Library District; Four Star Public Library District; Galesburg Public Library; Galva Public Library District; Graham Hospital Association; Greater West Central Public Library District; Greater West Central Public Library District; Greater West Central Public Library District; Greater West Central Public Library District; Greater West Central Public Library District; Greig Memorial Library; Gridley Public Library District; Griggsville Public Library; H A Peine Memorial Library; Hamilton Public Library; Havana Public Library District; Henderson County District Library; Henry Public Library; Heyworth Public Library District; Hill Correctional Center Library; Historical Society Of Quincy & Adams County Library; Hudson Area Public Library District; Illinois Agricultural Association; Illinois Central College; Illinois College; Illinois Department of Corrections; Illinois Prairie District Public Library; Illinois School For The Deaf; Illinois School For The Visually Impaired Library; Illinois State University; Illinois Veteran's Home Library; Illinois Wesleyan University; Ira C Reed Public Library; Jacksonville Public Library; John Mosser Public Library District; John Wood Community College Library; Kewanee Public Library District; Knox College; Knoxville Public Library; Komatsu Mining Systems Inc; La Harpe Carnegie Public Library District; Lacon Public Library District; Lewistown Carnegie Public Library District; Lexington Public Library District; Lillie M Evans Library District; M-C River Valley Public Library District; Mackinaw District Public Library; MacMurray College; Macomb Public Library District; Maquon Public Library District; Marquette Heights Public Library; Martin Township Public Library; Mason Memorial Public Library; McLean County Historical Society; Memorial Hospital Library; Midstate College; Morrison-Mary Wiley Library District; Morton Public Library District; Mount Hope-Funks Grove Townships Library District; Nauvoo Public Library; Neponset Public Library; New Windsor Public Library District; Normal Public Library; Odell Public Library District; Pantagraph-Newspaper Library; Parlin Ingersoll Public Library; Passavant Area Hospital; Pekin Public Library; Peoria Heights Public Library; Peoria Public Library; Pittsfield Public Library; Pontiac Public Library; Prairie Creek Public Library District; Proctor Hospital; Quincy Public Library; Quincy University; Ransom Memorial Public Library; Rushville Public Library; Saint Francis Medical Center; Salem Township Public Library District; Sherrard Public Library District; South Pekin Public Library; Spoon River College; Spoon River Public Library District; State Farm Insurance Co; Toulon Public Library District; Towanda District Public Library; Tremont District Public Library; United States Department Of Agriculture; Vermont Public Library; Victoria Public Library District; Village Of Avon Public Library; Viola Public Library District; Virginia Memorial Public Library; Warren County Public Library District; Warsaw Public Library; Washington District Library; Waverly Public Library; Waynesville Township Library; Western Illinois Correctional Center Library; Western Illinois University Libraries; Williamsfield Public Library District; Winchester Public Library; Wyoming Public Library District
Partic in Illinois Library & Information Network
Branches: 5
BLOOMINGTON SERVICE CENTER, 2201 Eastland Dr, Ste 2, Bloomington, 61704. SAN 375-5622. Tel: 309-661-9556. Toll Free Tel: 800-700-4857. FAX: 309-661-9553. E-Mail: alsh@darkstar.rsa.lib.il.us. Web Site: www.rsa.lib.il.us/. *Mgr*, Leanne Welch; E-Mail: lwelch@darkstar.rsa.lib.il.us
GALESBURG SERVICE CENTER, 1518 S Henderson St, Galesburg, 61401-5708. SAN 340-5729. Tel: 309-343-2380. Toll Free Tel: 800-700-4857. FAX: 309-343-0150. E-Mail: alsg@darkstar.rsa.lib.il.us. Web Site: www.rsa.lib.il.us/. *Mgr*, Susan Laird; E-Mail: slaird@darkstar.rsa.lib.il.us
MID-ILLINOIS TALKING BOOK CENTER-PEKIN, 845 Brenkman Dr, 61554. SAN 340-6628. Tel: 309-353-4110. Toll Free Tel: 800-426-0709. FAX: 309-353-8281. Web Site: www.rsa.lib.il.us/~hitbc/heart.htm. *Dir*, Eileen Sheppard; E-Mail: esheppard@darkstar.rsa.lib.il.us; *Reader Servs*, Nancy Boucher; *Outreach Serv*, Linda Dahl; *Outreach Serv*, LaRae Muselman; E-Mail: mitbc@darkstar.rsa.lib.il.us
1999-2000 Income $431,633. Sal $364,637 (Prof $123,223)
Partic in Nat Libr of Med
MID-ILLINOIS TALKING BOOK CENTER-QUINCY, 515 York St, Quincy, 62301-3997. SAN 377-0184. Tel: 217-224-6619. Toll Free Tel: 800-537-1274. FAX: 217-224-9818. Web Site: www.rsa.lib.il.us/~hitbc/heart.htm. *Dir*, Eileen Sheppard; E-Mail: esheppard@darkstar.rsa.lib.il.us; *Reader Servs*, Charmaine Starman; *Outreach Serv*, Edwin Waters
QUINCY SERVICE CENTER, 515 York St, Quincy, 62301. SAN 375-5630. Tel: 217-223-2560. Toll Free Tel: 800-700-4857. FAX: 217-223-8647. E-Mail: alsg@darkstar.rsa.lib.il.us. Web Site: www.rsa.lib.il.us/. *Mgr*, Ann Schaller; E-Mail: aschaler@darkstar.rsa.lib.il.us

P PEKIN PUBLIC LIBRARY, 301 S Fourth St, 61554-4284. SAN 304-5455. Tel: 309-347-7111. FAX: 309-347-6587. E-Mail: library@pekin.net. Web Site: www.pekin.net/library. *Dir*, Paula Weiss; *Ref*, Laurie Hartshorn; *Publ Servs*, Emily Lambe; *Ch Servs*, Mary Alyce Hofsess; *Ad Servs*, Linda Mace; *Head Tech Servs*, Jeffrey Brooks; *Circ*, Betty Wethington; Staff 5 (MLS 3, Non-MLS 2)
Founded 1896. Pop 33,050; Circ 279,827
May 1999-Apr 2000 Income $873,807, State $124,440, City $574,964, Federal $30,499, Other $143,904. Mats Exp $124,836, Books $91,503, AV Equip $23,333, Electronic Ref Mat (Incl. Access Fees) $10,000. Sal $479,249
Library Holdings: Bk Vols 129,656; Per Subs 240
Special Collections: History of Pekin; Tazewell Co
Automation Activity & Vendor Info: (Circulation) CARL; (OPAC) CARL
Database Vendor: IAC - Info Trac, OCLC - First Search
Publications: Newsletter
Mem of Alliance Library System
Partic in Illinois Library & Information Network; OCLC Online Computer Library Center, Inc
Friends of the Library Group

PEORIA

SR BAHAI REFERENCE LIBRARY OF PEORIA, 5209 N University, 61614. SAN 304-5463. Tel: 309-691-9311. FAX: 309-691-4407. *Head Librn*, Juliette Whittaker
Founded 1928
Apr 1999-Mar 2000 Income $6,500, Parent Institution $4,000, Other $2,500. Mats Exp $4,010, Books $3,300, Per/Ser (Incl. Access Fees) $240, Presv $75, Other Print Mats $140, Manuscripts & Archives $185, Electronic Ref Mat (Incl. Access Fees) $60
Library Holdings: Bk Vols 4,778; Bk Titles 4,198; High Interest/Low Vocabulary Bk Vols 366
Subject Interests: Christianity, Education, Human rights, Islam, Philosophy, Sociology
Special Collections: Afro-American Coll, bks & videos; Baha'i (Star of the West, World Order Mag & Early United States Publications); Collection

Letters of Early Believers; Meso-America & South American Cultures; Native American
Restriction: Circulation limited, Open to others by appointment, Open to students
Function: Archival collection, For research purposes, Photocopies available, Research library

C BRADLEY UNIVERSITY, Cullom-Davis Library, 1511 W Bradley Ave, 61625. SAN 340-6474. Tel: 309-677-2850. Interlibrary Loan Service Tel: 309-677-2837. FAX: 309-677-2558. Web Site: www.bradley.edu/irt/lib/. *Exec Dir*, Barbara A Galik; *Tech Servs*, Deirdre Redington; *Govt Doc, Ref*, Denise Johnson; *Electronic Resources*, Hungyune Chao. Subject Specialists: *Business and management*, Denise Johnson; *Engineering*, Denise Johnson; Staff 11 (MLS 11)
Founded 1897. Enrl 5,882; Fac 305; Highest Degree: Master
Library Holdings: Bk Vols 524,945; Per Subs 1,965
Special Collections: Abraham Lincoln & Civil War (including Martin L Howser Coll); APCO (Public Safety Communications History Coll); Bradleyana; Industrial Arts History (Charles A Bennett Coll); Jubilee College (Philander Chase Coll & Citizens Committee to Preserve Jubilee College Coll); Peoria-Area History (Library of Peoria Historical Society)
Automation Activity & Vendor Info: (Cataloging) DRA; (Circulation) DRA; (OPAC) DRA
Publications: Access Guide
Mem of Alliance Library System
Partic in Heart of Ill Consortium; Ill Coop Coll Mgt Prog; Ill Libr Computer Systs Org; Illinois Library & Information Network
Friends of the Library Group
Departmental Libraries:
VIRGINIUS H CHASE SPECIAL COLLECTIONS CENTER Tel: 309-677-2822. FAX: 303-677-2558. *Librn*, Charles J Frey
Library Holdings: Bk Vols 17,000
MUSIC Tel: 309-677-2591. FAX: 309-677-2558. *Librn*, Eleonore Hansen

CATERPILLAR INC
S BUSINESS RESOURCE CENTER, 100 NE Adams St, 61629-7110. SAN 340-6539. Tel: 309-675-4003. FAX: 309-675-5948. *Mgr*, Lea McCall; E-Mail: mccall_lea@cat.com; Staff 3 (MLS 2, Non-MLS 1)
Founded 1949
Library Holdings: Bk Titles 3,500; Per Subs 275
Subject Interests: Business and management
Automation Activity & Vendor Info: (Circulation) Follett
Publications: Business Update
Mem of Alliance Library System
Partic in OCLC Online Computer Library Center, Inc
S TECHNICAL INFORMATION CENTER, 14009 Old Galena Rd, PO Box 225, Mossville, 61552. SAN 340-6563. Tel: 309-578-6118. FAX: 309-578-6733. Web Site: www.cat.com. *Dir*, Shirley Streib; Tel: 309-578-2992, E-Mail: streib_shirley_l@cat.com; Staff 7 (MLS 4, Non-MLS 3)
Founded 1939
Library Holdings: Bk Vols 16,000; Per Subs 500
Subject Interests: Mechanical engineering
Mem of Alliance Library System
Partic in OCLC Online Computer Library Center, Inc

S CENTRAL ILLINOIS LANDMARKS FOUNDATION, Architectural Archives,* Peoria Public Library, 107 NE Monroe St, 61602-1070. SAN 371-1986. Tel: 309-672-8663. FAX: 309-497-2007.
Library Holdings: Bk Vols 100

S CENTRAL ILLINOIS LIGHT CO, Resource Center,* 300 Liberty St, 61602. SAN 376-1347. Tel: 309-677-5289. FAX: 309-677-5282.
Library Holdings: Bk Titles 200

GM DEPARTMENT OF HUMAN SERVICES, George A Zeller Mental Health Center Professional Library, 5407 N University, 61614. SAN 304-5471. Tel: 309-693-5014. FAX: 309-693-5101. *Librn*, Arlene Parr
Founded 1967
1997-1998 Mats Exp $5,400, Books $1,949, Per/Ser (Incl. Access Fees) $3,451. Sal $28,500
Library Holdings: Bk Vols 2,500; Per Subs 25
Subject Interests: Psychiatry, Psychology
Special Collections: Walter Bear MD Coll
Mem of Alliance Library System
Partic in Heart Of Illinois Library Consortium; Illinois Library & Information Network; Midwest Health Sci Libr Network

S KOMATSU MINING SYSTEMS INC, Engineering Technical Library,* 2300 NE Adams St, 61650-0240. SAN 304-5544. Tel: 309-672-7132. FAX: 309-672-7753. E-Mail: koma@darkstar.rsa.lib.il.us. *Librn*, Marilyn Kopp
Founded 1965
Jan 1998-Dec 1999 Mats Exp $3,459, Books $2,042, Per/Ser (Incl. Access Fees) $1,319, Other Print Mats $98
Library Holdings: Bk Titles 3,888; Per Subs 38
Mem of Alliance Library System

METHODIST MEDICAL CENTER OF ILLINOIS
M HEALTH SCIENCE RESOURCES CENTER, 221 NE Glen Oak, 61636. SAN 340-6687. Tel: 309-672-4937. FAX: 309-672-3141. E-Mail: hsrc@mmci.org. *Coordr*, Royden R Jones
Library Holdings: Bk Titles 4,300; Per Subs 15
Partic in Heart Of Illinois Library Consortium; Nat Libr of Med; OCLC Online Computer Library Center, Inc; Regional Med Libr - Region 3
M SCHOOL OF NURSING-LRC, 415 Saint Mark's Court, 61636. (Mail add: 221 NE Glen Oak, 61636), SAN 340-6652. Tel: 309-671-2794. FAX: 309-671-8303. *Librn*, Leslie Menz; E-Mail: lmenz@mmci.org; Staff 1 (MLS 1)
Founded 1900. Enrl 210; Fac 32
Library Holdings: Bk Vols 5,000; Bk Titles 4,500; Per Subs 40
Subject Interests: Hist of nursing, Nursing
Restriction: In-house use for visitors
Function: ILL limited, Photocopies available, Reference only, Some telephone reference
Partic in Heart Of Illinois Library Consortium; Midwest Health Sci Libr Network

J MIDSTATE COLLEGE, Barbara Fields Memorial Library, 411 W Northmoor Rd, 61614. SAN 321-5032. Tel: 309-692-4092. FAX: 309-692-3918. E-Mail: library@midstate.edu. Web Site: www.midstate.edu. *Coll Develop, Dir*, D Colletti; Staff 6 (MLS 1, Non-MLS 5)
Founded 1965. Enrl 200; Fac 27; Highest Degree: Doctorate
Library Holdings: Bk Titles 8,150; Per Subs 100
Subject Interests: Bus
Automation Activity & Vendor Info: (Cataloging) DRA; (Circulation) DRA
Mem of Alliance Library System
Partic in RSA

L PEORIA COUNTY LAW LIBRARY, Peoria County Court House, 324 Main, Rm 211, 61602. SAN 375-9865. Tel: 309-672-6084. *Librn*, Vicky Mundwiler
Library Holdings: Bk Vols 14,000

P PEORIA PUBLIC LIBRARY, 107 NE Monroe St, 61602-1070. SAN 340-6741. Tel: 309-497-2000. Interlibrary Loan Service Tel: 309-497-2153. Circulation Tel: 309-497-2164. TDD: 309-497-2156. FAX: 309-674-0116. Web Site: www.peoria.lib.il.us. *Dir*, Susan Herring; Tel: 309-497-2140, Fax: 309-497-2007, E-Mail: sueherring@ppl.peoria.lib.il.us; *Asst Dir*, Leann Johnson; Tel: 309-497-2139, Fax: 309-497-2007, E-Mail: leannjohnson@ppl.peoria.lib.il.us; *Ch Servs*, Suellen Kirkwood; Tel: 309-497-2143, E-Mail: suellenkirkwood@ppl.peoria.lib.il.us; *Head Ref*, Jean Shrier; Tel: 309-497-2160, E-Mail: jeanshrier@ppl.peoria.lib.il.us; *Outreach Serv*, Teresa Miller; Tel: 309-497-2069, E-Mail: teriwiley@ppl.peoria.lib.il.us; *Head, Circ*, Cossandra Stokes; Tel: 309-497-2165, E-Mail: cossandrastokes@ppl.peoria.lib.il.us; *Music*, Elwanda Phillips; Tel: 309-497-2149, E-Mail: wandaphillips@ppl.peoria.lib.il.us; *Business, Science, Tech Coordr*, Jennifer Sevier; Tel: 309-497-2125, E-Mail: jennifersevier@ppl.peoria.lib.il.us. Subject Specialists: *Art*, Elwanda Phillips; Staff 39 (MLS 15, Non-MLS 24)
Founded 1880. Pop 119,227; Circ 691,281
Jan 1999-Dec 1999 Income (Main Library and Branch Library) $4,249,703, State $604,725, Federal $77,834, Locally Generated Income $3,356,662, Other $210,482. Mats Exp $462,818, Books $320,751, Per/Ser (Incl. Access Fees) $51,944, Micro $27,979, Other Print Mats $62,144. Sal $2,367,184 (Prof $561,233)
Library Holdings: Bk Vols 835,908; Per Subs 1,435
Subject Interests: Census, Genealogy, Local history
Special Collections: Genealogy, Local History, Government Documents
Automation Activity & Vendor Info: (Circulation) CARL; (OPAC) CARL
Database Vendor: OCLC - First Search
Publications: Passages (bi-weekly newsletter)
Mem of Alliance Library System
Partic in Illinois Library & Information Network
Friends of the Library Group
Branches: 4
LAKEVIEW, 1137 W Lake, 61614-5935. SAN 340-6776. Tel: 309-497-2200. FAX: 309-497-2211. Web Site: www.peoria.lib.il.us. *Branch Mgr*, Roberta Koscielski; Tel: 309-497-2204, E-Mail: robertakoscielski@ppi.peoria.lib.il.us; Staff 5 (MLS 2, Non-MLS 3)
Library Holdings: Bk Vols 59,423
Friends of the Library Group
LINCOLN, 1312 W Lincoln, 61605-1976. SAN 340-6806. Tel: 309-497-2600. FAX: 309-497-2611. Web Site: www.peoria.lib.il.us. *Branch Mgr*, Cynthia Smith; Tel: 309-497-2601, E-Mail: cynthiasmith@ppl.peoria.lib.il.us
Library Holdings: Bk Vols 15,876
MCCLURE, 315 W McClure Ave, 61604. SAN 340-6830. Tel: 309-497-2700. FAX: 309-497-2711. Web Site: www.peoria.lib.il.us. *Branch Mgr*, Patricia Pritchard; Tel: 309-497-2701, E-Mail: patriciapritchard@ppl.peoria.lib.il.us
Library Holdings: Bk Vols 21,200
Friends of the Library Group
SOUTH SIDE, 2605 W Krause, 61605-2977. Tel: 309-497-2300. FAX: 309-497-2311. Web Site: www.peoria.lib.il.us. *Branch Mgr*, Alyce Hutchison;

Tel: 309-497-2301, E-Mail: alycehutchison@ppl.peoria.lib.il.us
Founded 1999
Library Holdings: Bk Vols 6,655
Friends of the Library Group

M PROCTOR HOSPITAL, Medical Library,* 5409 N Knoxville Ave, 61614. SAN 320-6599. Tel: 309-691-1065. FAX: 309-691-4543. *Dir*, Janice Schoener; Staff 1 (MLS 1)
Publications: Library guide; serial holdings list
Mem of Alliance Library System
Partic in Greater Midwest Regional Medical Libr Network; Heart Of Illinois Library Consortium; Midwest Health Sci Libr Network

SAINT FRANCIS MEDICAL CENTER

CM COLLEGE OF NURSING LIBRARY, 511 NE Greenleaf St, 61603. SAN 340-692X. Tel: 309-655-2180. FAX: 309-655-3680. E-Mail: sfcn@darkstar.rsa.lib.il.us. *Librn*, Ann Phillips; Tel: 309-655-8120, Fax: 309-655-3648, E-Mail: ann.phillips@osfhealthcare.org. Subject Specialists: *Humanities*, Ann Phillips; Staff 3 (MLS 1, Non-MLS 2)
Founded 1936
Library Holdings: Bk Vols 5,300; Bk Titles 4,900; Per Subs 130
Subject Interests: Education
Database Vendor: CARL, GaleNet, IAC - Info Trac, OCLC - First Search, OVID Technologies
Mem of Alliance Library System
Partic in Heart Of Illinois Library Consortium; Illinois Library & Information Network

M LIBRARY & RESOURCE CENTER, 530 NE Glen Oak Ave, 61637. SAN 340-689X. Tel: 309-655-2210, 309-655-2268. FAX: 309-655-6997. *Dir*, Carol J Galganski; *Ref*, Carolann Purcell; *Ref*, Joanna Jordan
Library Holdings: Bk Vols 6,000; Per Subs 650
Subject Interests: Orthopedics, Pediatrics, Surgery
Publications: Newsletter (quarterly)
Partic in GMRMLN - Region 3 of NLM Network; Heart Of Illinois Library Consortium; Illinois Library & Information Network

S TRI COUNTY REGIONAL PLANNING COMMISSION LIBRARY,* 411 Hamilton Blvd Ste 2001, 61602. SAN 327-1447. Tel: 309-673-9330. FAX: 309-673-9802. E-Mail: tcrpc@umtech.com. *Dir*, Terry Kohlbuss
Library Holdings: Bk Vols 200; Per Subs 12

G UNITED STATES DEPARTMENT OF AGRICULTURE, Agricultural Research Service, National Center for Agricultural Utilization Research Library,* 1815 N University St, 61604. SAN 304-5528. Tel: 309-681-6526. FAX: 309-681-6681. *Librn*, Joyce Blumenshine; E-Mail: jblumen@mail.ncaur.usda.gov; Staff 2 (MLS 1, Non-MLS 1)
Founded 1941
Library Holdings: Bk Vols 6,000; Per Subs 218
Subject Interests: Biochemistry, Organic chemistry
Publications: New Book Lists
Restriction: Staff use only
Mem of Alliance Library System
Partic in Dialog Corporation; Fedlink; Heart of Ill Med Libr Consortia; OCLC Online Computer Library Center, Inc

PEORIA HEIGHTS

P PEORIA HEIGHTS PUBLIC LIBRARY,* 816 E Glen Ave, 61614-5206. SAN 304-5560. Tel: 309-682-5578. FAX: 309-682-4457. E-Mail: phpl@darkstar.rsa.lib.il.us. Web Site: darkstar.rsa.lib.il.us/~phpl/. *Dir*, Marsha Westfall; *Ch Servs*, Lorriane Stotts; Staff 2 (MLS 2)
Founded 1935. Pop 6,930; Circ 42,186
Library Holdings: Bk Vols 32,000; Per Subs 126
Subject Interests: Art, History
Publications: Newsletter: Check It Out
Mem of Alliance Library System
Partic in Illinois Library & Information Network

PEOTONE

P PEOTONE PUBLIC LIBRARY DISTRICT,* 213 W North St, 60468. SAN 304-5579. Tel: 708-258-3436. FAX: 708-258-9796. *Librn*, Cynthia Cooper; *Ch Servs*, Marie Christensen
Pop 6,500; Circ 28,412
Library Holdings: Bk Vols 37,000; Per Subs 78
Subject Interests: Genealogy
Mem of Heritage Trail Library System

PERU

M ILLINOIS VALLEY COMMUNITY HOSPITAL, Medical Library,* 925 West St, 61354. SAN 304-3258. Tel: 815-223-3300, Ext 502. FAX: 815-224-1747. *Librn*, Rene Rebles
Library Holdings: Bk Vols 506

P PERU PUBLIC LIBRARY, 1409 11th St, 61354. SAN 304-5587. Tel: 815-223-0229. FAX: 815-223-1559. Web Site: www.htls.lib.il.us/pub. *Dir*, Marydale Stewart; E-Mail: mstewart@starbase1.htls.lib.il.us; *Asst Dir*, Shirley Sharpe; *YA Servs*, Laurie A Moss; Staff 4 (MLS 1, Non-MLS 3)
Founded 1911. Pop 9,302; Circ 90,000
May 2000-Apr 2001 Income $258,900, State $11,600, City $124,000, Locally Generated Income $120,000, Other $3,300. Mats Exp $57,000, Books $28,000, Per/Ser (Incl. Access Fees) $7,000, AV Equip $2,000, Electronic Ref Mat (Incl. Access Fees) $20,000. Sal $152,000 (Prof $80,000)
Library Holdings: Bk Vols 48,007; Per Subs 155
Subject Interests: Local history
Automation Activity & Vendor Info: (Circulation) GEAC; (OPAC) GEAC
Mem of Heritage Trail Library System
Friends of the Library Group

PETERSBURG

P PETERSBURG PUBLIC LIBRARY,* 220 S Sixth St, 62675. SAN 304-5595. Tel: 217-632-2807. FAX: 217-632-2833. E-Mail: MKLIB@yahoo.com. *Librn*, Mary Kleinschmidt
Founded 1908. Pop 2,419; Circ 29,000
Library Holdings: Bk Vols 12,900; Per Subs 86
Special Collections: Abraham Lincoln & Edgar Lee Masters
Mem of Rolling Prairie Library System
Friends of the Library Group

S STARHILL FOREST ARBORETUM LIBRARY, Rte 1, Box 272, 62675-9736. SAN 371-5477. Tel: 217-632-3685. FAX: 217-632-3685.
Founded 1976
Library Holdings: Bk Vols 2,100; Bk Titles 2,000; Per Subs 10
Subject Interests: Horticulture, Natural history
Special Collections: Antiquarian Natural History; Modern Natural History, bks & slides
Restriction: Non-circulating, Private library, Staff use only
Function: Reference only

PHILO

P PHILO PUBLIC LIBRARY DISTRICT, 115 E Washington St, PO Box 199, 61864-0199. SAN 304-5609. Tel: 217-684-2896. FAX: 217-684-2719. *Librn*, June E Highsmith
Founded 1961. Pop 1,753; Circ 12,000
Library Holdings: Bk Vols 12,393; Bk Titles 12,000; Per Subs 75
Mem of Lincoln Trail Libraries System
Partic in Illinois Library & Information Network
Friends of the Library Group

PINCKNEYVILLE

P PINCKNEYVILLE PUBLIC LIBRARY, 312 S Walnut St, 62274. SAN 304-5617. Tel: 618-357-2410. FAX: 618-357-5101. E-Mail: pvillepl@midwest.net. *Librn*, Margaret Urbanek
Founded 1917. Pop 4,068; Circ 16,405
May 1998-Apr 1999 Income $36,854, State $7,217, City $26,474, Other $3,163. Mats Exp $4,738, Books $3,961, Per/Ser (Incl. Access Fees) $777. Sal $19,570
Library Holdings: Bk Vols 26,088; Per Subs 53
Mem of Shawnee Library System

PIPER CITY

P PIPER CITY PUBLIC LIBRARY DISTRICT, 39 W Main, PO Box 248, 60959. SAN 304-5625. Tel: 815-686-9234. FAX: 815-686-2007. *Librn*, Beth Thorndyke; *Asst Librn*, Julie Kurtenbach; *Asst Librn*, Beverly Richardson
Pop 1,200; Circ 6,866
Library Holdings: Bk Vols 7,110; Per Subs 37
Subject Interests: Local history
Mem of Lincoln Trail Libraries System

PITTSFIELD

P PITTSFIELD PUBLIC LIBRARY, 205 N Memorial, 62363-1406. SAN 304-5633. Tel: 217-285-2200. FAX: 217-285-9423. *Dir*, Rita Burbridge; *Asst Librn*, Sara Bernard; *Asst Librn*, Mary Welbourne; *Ch Servs*, Sandra Henry
Founded 1906. Pop 1,200
May 1999-Apr 2000 Income $136,390. Mats Exp $104,685. Sal $55,312
Library Holdings: Bk Vols 22,000; Per Subs 87
Subject Interests: History, Mississippi River
Special Collections: Pike County History
Mem of Alliance Library System

PLAINFIELD

P PLAINFIELD PUBLIC LIBRARY DISTRICT, 705 N Illinois St, 60544. SAN 304-565X. Tel: 815-436-6639. FAX: 815-439-2878. *Adminr*, Julie Milavec; Staff 2 (MLS 2)
Pop 18,885; Circ 181,277
Jul 1999-Jun 2000 Income $1,045,060. Mats Exp $108,079, Books $80,479, Per/Ser (Incl. Access Fees) $7,600, Electronic Ref Mat (Incl. Access Fees) $20,000
Library Holdings: Bk Titles 67,587; Per Subs 274
Special Collections: Local History (state, county & city); Local Newspaper & Obituary Index (The Enterprise Coll), micro; Tornado (August 28, 1990), newsp clippings & pictures
Automation Activity & Vendor Info: (Circulation) GEAC
Mem of Heritage Trail Library System

PLANO

P PLANO COMMUNITY LIBRARY DISTRICT, 15 N Center Ave, 60545. SAN 304-5668. Tel: 630-552-8003. FAX: 630-552-1008. *Dir*, Deanna Howard; E-Mail: dmhanson@htls.lib.il.us; *Librn*, Diana Hastings; E-Mail: dhastings@starbasel.htls.lib.il.us; *Ch Servs*, Pat Schwartz; *Tech Servs*, Alesia Hacker; Staff 9 (MLS 1, Non-MLS 8)
Founded 1905. Pop 7,081; Circ 59,652
Jul 1999-Jun 2000 Income $374,150, State $43,791, County $292,885, Other $37,474. Mats Exp $39,815. Sal $115,187 (Prof $42,000)
Library Holdings: Bk Vols 37,278; Per Subs 112
Subject Interests: Local history
Database Vendor: IAC - Info Trac, OCLC - First Search
Mem of Heritage Trail Library System
Friends of the Library Group

POLO

P POLO PUBLIC LIBRARY DISTRICT, 302 W Mason St, 61064. SAN 304-5676. Tel: 815-946-2713. FAX: 815-946-4127. *Dir*, Gail A Carrillo; *Ch Servs*, Phyllis Houck; *Cat*, Kris Schauff
Founded 1871. Pop 3,003; Circ 22,000
Jul 1999-Jun 2000 Income $68,499, State $3,700, County $56,000, Other $8,799. Mats Exp $9,500, Books $7,500, Per/Ser (Incl. Access Fees) $1,000, Micro $1,000. Sal $31,000 (Prof $21,000)
Library Holdings: Bk Vols 15,000; Per Subs 75
Special Collections: Indian Relic Coll
Mem of Northern Illinois Library System
Carnegie Library building (1904)

PONTIAC

S PONTIAC CORRECTIONAL CENTER LIBRARY,* 700 W Lincoln St, PO Box 99, 61764. SAN 304-5684. Tel: 815-842-2816, Ext 2406 & 2201. FAX: 815-842-3051. *Librn*, Malini Patel; Staff 4 (Non-MLS 4)
Library Holdings: Bk Vols 31,500; Per Subs 14
Subject Interests: Law
Partic in Corn Belt Libr Syst

P PONTIAC PUBLIC LIBRARY, 211 E Madison St, 61764. SAN 304-5692. Tel: 815-844-7229. FAX: 815-844-3475. E-Mail: pontiac@davesworld.net. Web Site: www.pontiac.lib.il.us. *Dir*, William Lamb; *Librn*, Carrie Goodrum; *Cat*, Levada Lee; *Circ*, Susan Strauch; *Ch Servs*, Kari Hennenfent; Staff 10 (MLS 1, Non-MLS 9)
Founded 1858. Pop 11,500; Circ 70,000
Apr 1999-Mar 2000 Income $243,000, State $28,000, City $138,000, Other $77,000. Mats Exp $47,500, Books $38,000, Per/Ser (Incl. Access Fees) $7,500, AV Equip $2,000. Sal $130,000 (Prof $32,000)
Library Holdings: Bk Vols 40,000; Per Subs 130
Subject Interests: Agriculture
Special Collections: Local History (Livingston County & Pontiac, Ill Coll)
Database Vendor: OCLC - First Search
Mem of Alliance Library System

M SAINT JAMES HOSPITAL, Medical Library,* 610 E Water St, 61764. SAN 322-6514. Tel: 815-842-2828, Ext 1128. FAX: 815-842-4911. *Librn*, Patty Wolf
Library Holdings: Bk Titles 168; Per Subs 20
Mem of Corn Belt Library System
Partic in Heart Of Illinois Library Consortium

PORT BYRON

P RIVER VALLEY DISTRICT LIBRARY,* 214 S Main St, PO Box 10, 61275. SAN 304-5706. Tel: 309-523-3440. FAX: 309-523-3516. *Dir*, Lisa Ford; Staff 8 (Non-MLS 8)
Pop 3,890; Circ 101,138
1998-1999 Income $195,000, State $3,600, City $2,000, County $185,000, Other $4,400. Mats Exp $29,100, Books $14,000, Per/Ser (Incl. Access Fees) $2,500, Micro $400, AV Equip $4,000, Other Print Mats $500, Manuscripts & Archives $400. Sal $54,610 (Prof $24,000)
Library Holdings: Per Subs 78; Spec Interest Per Sub 18,000
Special Collections: 1800's local paper on micro film Coll; Rock Island County History
Mem of River Bend Library System
Open Mon, Wed & Fri 1-8:30, Thurs 9-1:30 & 5:30-8:30 & Sat 1-5
Friends of the Library Group

POSEN

P POSEN PUBLIC LIBRARY DISTRICT,* Posen Village Hall, 2440 W Walter Zimny Dr, 60469. SAN 376-1371. Tel: 708-385-0139. FAX: 708-385-5107.
Library Holdings: Bk Titles 1,040

POTOMAC

P POTOMAC PUBLIC LIBRARY, 110 E State St, PO Box 171, 61865. SAN 304-5714. Tel: 217-987-6457. *Librn*, Dixie Howie
Pop 754; Circ 6,109
Library Holdings: Bk Vols 9,902
Special Collections: Large Print Coll
Mem of Lincoln Trail Libraries System

PRINCETON

S BUREAU COUNTY HISTORICAL SOCIETY MUSEUM & LIBRARY, 109 Park Ave W, 61356-1927. SAN 304-5730. Tel: 815-875-2184. *Actg Dir*, Barbara Hansen
Founded 1948
Library Holdings: Bk Titles 500
Subject Interests: Genealogy, Local history
Special Collections: Henry W Immke Photographic Coll
Open Feb 1-Dec 23, Sun, Mon & Wed-Sat 1-5

P MATSON PUBLIC LIBRARY, 15 Park Ave W, 61356. SAN 304-5749. Tel: 815-875-1331. FAX: 815-872-1376. *Librn*, Caryl M Harris; E-Mail: cmharris@htls.lib.il.us
Founded 1886. Pop 7,197; Circ 62,000
May 2000-Apr 2001 Income $287,000, State $9,000, City $232,000, Locally Generated Income $46,000. Mats Exp $49,400, Books $33,000, Per/Ser (Incl. Access Fees) $7,000, Micro $200, AV Equip $4,000, Manuscripts & Archives $200, Electronic Ref Mat (Incl. Access Fees) $5,000. Sal $133,000 (Prof $42,000)
Library Holdings: Bk Titles 38,500; Per Subs 110
Special Collections: Bureau County (Illinois) Farm Architecture Exhibit, photog; Local History Coll, art, bks, blueprints, cassettes, Indian artifacts, micro, pamphlets, photog; World War II Coll, posters
Automation Activity & Vendor Info: (Circulation) GEAC; (OPAC) GEAC
Database Vendor: Ebsco - EbscoHost, OCLC - First Search
Mem of Heritage Trail Library System
Friends of the Library Group

M PERRY MEMORIAL HOSPITAL, Kenneth O Nelson Library of the Health Sciences,* 530 Park Ave E, 61356. SAN 320-6602. Tel: 815-875-2811, Ext 4479. FAX: 815-872-1257. *Dir*, Linda Litherland
Founded 1954
Library Holdings: Bk Titles 421; Per Subs 15
Subject Interests: Nursing
Partic in Heart Of Illinois Library Consortium

PRINCEVILLE

P LILLIE M EVANS LIBRARY DISTRICT,* 207 N Walnut Ave, PO Box 349, 61559-0742. SAN 304-5757. Tel: 309-385-4540. FAX: 309-385-2661. E-Mail: lill@darkstar.rsa.lib.il.us. *Dir*, Joanne R Cox
Founded 1956. Pop 3,791; Circ 29,914
Library Holdings: Bk Vols 23,000; Per Subs 84
Subject Interests: Local history, Spanish (language)
Mem of Alliance Library System
Friends of the Library Group

PROPHETSTOWN

P HENRY C ADAMS MEMORIAL LIBRARY, 209 W Third St, 61277. SAN 304-5765. Tel: 815-537-5462. FAX: 815-537-5462. Web Site: www.rbls.lib.il.us/ptn/index.html. *Librn*, Pat Stewart; E-Mail: pstewart@libby.rbls.lib.il.us
Founded 1929. Pop 1,800; Circ 12,868
May 1999-Apr 2000 Income $38,160, State $2,220, City $22,840, Locally Generated Income $13,100. Mats Exp $13,840, Books $4,200, Per/Ser (Incl. Access Fees) $500, Micro $1,500, AV Equip $4,500, Other Print Mats $200, Electronic Ref Mat (Incl. Access Fees) $2,940. Sal $18,900
Library Holdings: Bk Vols 14,000; Per Subs 21
Special Collections: Civil War Records

Automation Activity & Vendor Info: (Acquisitions) GEAC; (Cataloging) GEAC; (Circulation) GEAC; (Course Reserve) GEAC; (ILL) GEAC; (Media Booking) GEAC; (OPAC) GEAC; (Serials) GEAC
Mem of River Bend Library System

PROSPECT HEIGHTS

S HOUSEHOLD INTERNATIONAL, Corporate Library, 2700 Sanders Rd, 60070. SAN 304-5773. Tel: 847-564-6211. FAX: 847-205-7526. *Librn*, Mollie R Brumbaugh
Library Holdings: Bk Vols 4,000
Subject Interests: Accounting
Mem of North Suburban Library System

P PROSPECT HEIGHTS PUBLIC LIBRARY DISTRICT, 12 N Elm St, 60070-1499. SAN 304-5781. Tel: 847-259-3500. FAX: 847-259-4602. E-Mail: phlib@phl.alibrary.com. Web Site: www.phl.alibrary.com. *Exec Dir*, William McCully; *Ch Servs*, Sue Seggeling; *Ad Servs*, Alexander Todd; *Online Servs*, Bin Zhao; Staff 24 (MLS 7, Non-MLS 17)
Founded 1955. Pop 12,022; Circ 153,025
Jul 1999-Jun 2000 Income $1,708,200, State $29,285, Federal $4,500, Locally Generated Income $1,551,132, Other $123,283. Mats Exp $224,389, Books $109,723, Per/Ser (Incl. Access Fees) $8,370, AV Equip $2,500, Electronic Ref Mat (Incl. Access Fees) $103,796. Sal $595,044 (Prof $241,620)
Library Holdings: Bk Vols 95,778; Bk Titles 77,100; Per Subs 248
Subject Interests: Landscape architecture
Automation Activity & Vendor Info: (Circulation) GEAC; (OPAC) GEAC
Database Vendor: OCLC - First Search
Publications: Elm Leaf (monthly bulletin)
Mem of North Suburban Library System
Partic in Coop Computer Servs
Friends of the Library Group

QUINCY

S ADAMS COUNTY YOUTH HOME LIBRARY,* 5200 Broadway, 62301. SAN 376-0235. Tel: 217-277-2233. FAX: 217-277-2241. *Librn*, Ray Davis
Library Holdings: Bk Titles 4,000; Per Subs 10

M BLESSING HEALTH PROFESSIONS LIBRARY, Broadway & 11th Sts, PO Box 7005, 62305-7005. SAN 304-579X. Tel: 217-228-5520, Ext 6970. FAX: 217-223-6400. Web Site: www.brcn.edu/library. *Dir*, Arlis D Dittmer; E-Mail: adittmer@blessinghospital.com; *Asst Librn*, Daria Mammel; Staff 3 (MLS 2, Non-MLS 1)
Founded 1891. Enrl 150; Fac 13; Highest Degree: Bachelor
1998-1999 Income $40,000. Mats Exp $39,000, Books $7,000, Per/Ser (Incl. Access Fees) $20,000, Micro $6,000, AV Equip $6,000. Sal $72,000 (Prof $60,000)
Library Holdings: Bk Titles 5,000; Per Subs 120
Subject Interests: Nursing
Automation Activity & Vendor Info: (Circulation) CARL; (OPAC) CARL
Database Vendor: OCLC - First Search, Silverplatter Information Inc.
Mem of Alliance Library System
Partic in HSLI; Illinois Library & Information Network; MCMLA; RSA

S HISTORICAL SOCIETY OF QUINCY & ADAMS COUNTY LIBRARY, 425 S 12th St, 62301. SAN 326-145X. Tel: 217-222-1835. *Librn*, Barbara Lieber
Founded 1896
Library Holdings: Bk Vols 1,100; Bk Titles 1,050
Special Collections: Civil War (Gen James D Morgan Coll), mss
Restriction: Non-circulating to the public
Mem of Alliance Library System

S ILLINOIS VETERAN'S HOME LIBRARY, 1707 N 12th St, 62301. SAN 375-9547. Tel: 217-222-8641, Ext 248. FAX: 217-222-0139. E-Mail: ivhqlib@rnet.com. *Librn*, Lynn Fleming
Library Holdings: Bk Titles 10,234; Per Subs 85
Automation Activity & Vendor Info: (Cataloging) CARL; (Circulation) CARL
Mem of Alliance Library System

J JOHN WOOD COMMUNITY COLLEGE LIBRARY, 150 S 48th St, 62301. SAN 320-1821. Tel: 217-224-6564, Ext 4537. FAX: 217-224-4746. Web Site: www.jwcc.edu/instruct/library/lib.htm. *Dir Libr Serv*, Patricia Woodworth; Tel: 217-224-6564, Ext 4535, E-Mail: woodworth@jwcc.edu; *Publ Servs*, Cheri Weyermann; Tel: 217-224-6564, Ext 4538, E-Mail: weyermann@jwcc.edu; Staff 5 (MLS 1, Non-MLS 4)
Founded 1974. Enrl 4,700; Fac 50; Highest Degree: Associate
Library Holdings: Bk Titles 14,500; Per Subs 190
Subject Interests: Agriculture, Local history, Nursing, Vocational education
Database Vendor: CARL, Ebsco - EbscoHost, IAC - Info Trac, OCLC - First Search, ProQuest
Mem of Alliance Library System
Partic in Alliance Library System; NILRC
Open Mon-Thurs 7:30-8 & Fri 7:30-4

S QUINCY MUSEUM, 1601 Maine St, 62301. SAN 328-3933. Tel: 217-224-7669. FAX: 217-224-9323. *Dir*, Steve Adams; E-Mail: quinmu@adams.net
Library Holdings: Bk Titles 500
Subject Interests: Natural history
Special Collections: Illinois Fossils, Rocks & Minerals

P QUINCY PUBLIC LIBRARY,* 526 Jersey St, 62301-3996. SAN 304-582X. Tel: 217-223-1309. FAX: 217-222-5672. E-Mail: reference@quincylibrary.org. Web Site: www.quincylibrary.org. *Dir*, Susan R Beach; Tel: 217-223-1309, Ext 204, E-Mail: sbeach@quincylibrary.org; *Tech Servs*, Donna Knodel; Tel: 217-223-1309, Ext 224, E-Mail: dknodel@quincylibrary.org; *Publ Servs*, Angela Laymon; *Circ*, Pamela Clow; Tel: 217-223-1309, Ext 243, E-Mail: pclow@quincylibrary.org; *Ch Servs*, Judy J Decker; Tel: 217-223-1309, Ext 219, E-Mail: jdecker@quincylibrary.org; *AV*, Mary B O'Brien; Tel: 217-223-1309, Ext 205, E-Mail: mobrien@quincylibrary.org; *Res*, Nancy J Dolan; Tel: 217-222-1309, Ext 211, Fax: 217-222-3052, E-Mail: ndolan@quincylibrary.org; *Bkmobile Coordr*, Patricia Woodworth; Tel: 217-223-1309, Ext 216, E-Mail: pwood@quincylibrary.org; Staff 49 (MLS 11, Non-MLS 38)
Founded 1888. Pop 51,000; Circ 684,915
Apr 1998-May 1999 Income $1,745,595, State $64,758, City $1,259,578, Federal $421,259. Mats Exp $287,061, Books $248,528, AV Equip $38,533. Sal $779,751
Library Holdings: Bk Vols 159,834; Bk Titles 228,875; Per Subs 376
Subject Interests: Genealogy
Special Collections: CD-ROMs
Automation Activity & Vendor Info: (Cataloging) epixtech, inc.; (Circulation) epixtech, inc.; (ILL) epixtech, inc.
Database Vendor: epixtech, inc., OCLC - First Search
Publications: Read All About It (Newsletter)
Mem of Alliance Library System
Special Services for the Blind - Closed circuit television; Large print bks; Talking Books
Open Mon-Thurs 9-9, Fri-Sat 9-6 & Sun 1-5
Friends of the Library Group

C QUINCY UNIVERSITY, Brenner Library, 1800 College Ave, 62301-2699. SAN 304-5811. Tel: 217-228-5345. Circulation Tel: 217-228-5346. FAX: 217-228-5354. Web Site: www.quincy.edu/library. *Coll Develop, Dean of Libr*, Patricia Tomczak; Tel: 217-228-5351, E-Mail: tomczpa@quincy.edu; *Ref*, Michelle Kaleck; Tel: 217-228-5347, 228-5350; *ILL, Ser*, Nancy Crow; Tel: 217-228-5348, E-Mail: crowna@quincy.edu; Staff 6 (MLS 3, Non-MLS 3)
Founded 1860. Enrl 1,200; Fac 85; Highest Degree: Master
Jun 1999-May 2000 Income $357,500. Mats Exp $171,000, Books $44,000, Per/Ser (Incl. Access Fees) $82,000, Presv $5,500, Micro $500, AV Equip $400, Manuscripts & Archives $400, Electronic Ref Mat (Incl. Access Fees) $38,200. Sal $177,000 (Prof $102,000)
Library Holdings: Bk Vols 239,983; Bk Titles 230,223; Per Subs 814
Subject Interests: Am hist, American literature, English literature, Theology
Special Collections: Early Christian & Medieval (Bonaventure Library), Local History (Quincyana; East Asian Coll; Rare Book Library; Spanish-American History (Biblioteca Fraborese)
Automation Activity & Vendor Info: (Cataloging) CARL; (Circulation) CARL; (Course Reserve) CARL; (ILL) CARL; (Media Booking) CARL; (OPAC) CARL
Database Vendor: CARL, Ebsco - EbscoHost, OCLC - First Search
Publications: Bibliographies; Bibliography of the Spanish Borderlands in the Fraborese Coll; Catalog of the Incunabula in the Quincy University Library; Rare Book Collection
Mem of Alliance Library System
Partic in Colorado Alliance Of Research Libraries; Illinois Library & Information Network; OCLC Online Computer Library Center, Inc; Resource Sharing Alliance

S SOCIETY FOR ACADEMIC ACHIEVEMENT LIBRARY,* WCU Bldg, 510 Maine St, 62301. SAN 326-9779. Tel: 217-224-0570. *Exec Dir*, Richard Heitholt; *Pres*, Wayne Nelson; *Librn*, Maxine Clement
Library Holdings: Bk Vols 2,000
Subject Interests: Education

RAMSEY

P RAMSEY PUBLIC LIBRARY,* 401 S Superior St, PO Box 128, 62080. SAN 375-9733. Tel: 618-423-2019. FAX: 618-423-2120. *Librn*, Shirley Whitten
Library Holdings: Bk Titles 3,000; Per Subs 15

RANTOUL

P RANTOUL PUBLIC LIBRARY,* 225 S Century Blvd, 61866. SAN 304-5838. Tel: 217-893-3955. FAX: 217-893-3961. *Dir*, Don Thorsen
Founded 1934. Pop 17,212; Circ 89,000
Library Holdings: Bk Vols 50,000; Per Subs 175

Special Collections: Aero-Space
Automation Activity & Vendor Info: (Circulation) epixtech, inc.
Mem of Lincoln Trail Libraries System
Friends of the Library Group

RED BUD

P RED BUD PUBLIC LIBRARY, 112 Bloom St, 62278. SAN 304-5846. Tel: 618-282-2255. FAX: 618-282-4055. *Dir*, Brenda Gilpatrick; E-Mail: brendag@htc.net; *Asst Librn*, Glenda Fricke
Founded 1945. Pop 3,007; Circ 28,627
Library Holdings: Bk Titles 12,000; Per Subs 90
Subject Interests: Illinois
Publications: Bookshelf (quarterly)
Mem of Shawnee Library System

RICHMOND

P NIPPERSINK DISTRICT LIBRARY, (NPLD), 5418 Hill Rd, 60071. SAN 304-5854. Tel: 815-678-4014. FAX: 815-678-4484. E-Mail: nippersink@nils.lib.il.us. Web Site: library.mbn.net. *Dir*, Kathryn Hausman; E-Mail: kathryn@nils.lib.il.us; *Librn*, Michael Champion
Founded 1972. Pop 5,430; Circ 64,000
Jul 1999-Jun 2000 Income $411,300, State $13,500, Federal $9,000, Locally Generated Income $365,400, Other $23,400. Mats Exp $36,700, Books $25,500, Per/Ser (Incl. Access Fees) $3,600, AV Equip $6,000, Other Print Mats $1,000, Electronic Ref Mat (Incl. Access Fees) $600. Sal $144,400 (Prof $77,500)
Library Holdings: Bk Vols 39,200; Per Subs 100
Automation Activity & Vendor Info: (Circulation) Innovative Interfaces Inc.; (OPAC) Innovative Interfaces Inc.
Publications: Library News (quarterly)
Mem of Northern Illinois Library System

RICHTON PARK

P RICHTON PARK PUBLIC LIBRARY DISTRICT, 4045 Sauk Trail, 60471. SAN 304-5862. Tel: 708-481-5333. FAX: 708-481-4343. E-Mail: rps@sls.lib.il.us. *Head Librn*, Patrick Nevins; E-Mail: nevinsp@sls.lib.il.us; *Ch Servs*, Sharon Dudeck; E-Mail: dudecks@sls.lib.il.us; Staff 9 (MLS 2, Non-MLS 7)
Founded 1974. Pop 12,013; Circ 80,499
Jul 1999-Jun 2000 Income $635,277, State $23,705, County $552,891, Locally Generated Income $58,681. Mats Exp $63,322, Books $48,615, Per/Ser (Incl. Access Fees) $4,000, Electronic Ref Mat (Incl. Access Fees) $1,844. Sal $157,635 (Prof $83,527)
Library Holdings: Bk Vols 33,488; Bk Titles 35,000; Per Subs 177
Automation Activity & Vendor Info: (Circulation) Innovative Interfaces Inc.; (OPAC) Innovative Interfaces Inc.
Database Vendor: Innovative Interfaces INN - View
Mem of Suburban Library System
Friends of the Library Group

RICHVIEW

P RICHVIEW TOWNSHIP LIBRARY,* PO Box 95, 62877. SAN 304-5870. Tel: 618-249-6751. *Librn*, Stacie Moss
Founded 1896. Pop 408; Circ 1,850
Library Holdings: Bk Vols 6,500
Mem of Kaskaskia Libr Syst

RIDGE FARM

P ELWOOD TOWNSHIP CARNEGIE LIBRARY, 104 N State St, PO Box 349, 61870-0349. SAN 304-5889. Tel: 217-247-2820. FAX: 217-247-2835. *Librn*, Lisa Davis
Founded 1909. Pop 1,773; Circ 10,404
Library Holdings: Bk Vols 9,800
Mem of Lincoln Trail Libraries System
Open Tues-Fri 2-7, Sat 9-2
Friends of the Library Group

RIVER FOREST

C CONCORDIA UNIVERSITY, Klinck Memorial Library,* 7400 Augusta St, 60305-1499. SAN 304-5897. Tel: 708-209-3050. FAX: 708-209-3175. E-Mail: crflibrary@curf.edu. Web Site: www.curf.edu/lib. *Dir*, Henry R Latzke; Tel: 708-209-3056, E-Mail: crflatzkehr@curf.edu; *Publ Servs*, Kristin Flanders; Tel: 708-209-3057, E-Mail: crfflandekn@curf.edu; *Tech Servs*, Lee Forrest; Tel: 708-209-3254, E-Mail: crfforreslm@curf.edu; *Media Spec*, Barb Peterson; Tel: 708-209-3055, E-Mail: crfpetersbl@curf.edu; *Media Spec*, Richard G Richter; Tel: 708-209-3029, E-Mail: crfrichterg@curf.edu; Staff 4 (MLS 4)
Founded 1864. Enrl 1,885; Fac 88; Highest Degree: Master
Jul 1998-Jun 1999 Income $547,493, State $8,112, Parent Institution $539,381. Mats Exp $166,828, Books $63,242, Per/Ser (Incl. Access Fees) $49,055, Presv $1,973, Micro $11,560, AV Equip $24,815, Other Print Mats $1,550, Electronic Ref Mat (Incl. Access Fees) $14,633. Sal $370,530 (Prof $135,355)
Library Holdings: Bk Vols 162,782; Bk Titles 121,500; Per Subs 534
Subject Interests: Education, Music, Religion
Special Collections: Curriculum Library; Educational Resources Info Center, micro; Test file
Automation Activity & Vendor Info: (Cataloging) DRA; (Circulation) DRA; (Course Reserve) DRA
Database Vendor: Ebsco - EbscoHost, OCLC - First Search
Mem of Suburban Library System
Partic in Ill Coop Coll Mgt Prog; Ill Libr Computer Systs Org; Illinois Library & Information Network; Libras, Inc

C DOMINICAN UNIVERSITY, Rebecca Crown Library, 7900 W Division St, 60305-1066. SAN 304-5927. Tel: 708-524-6875. FAX: 708-366-5360. Web Site: 207.56.177.198/library/index.htm. *Dir*, Dr Inez I Ringland; *Asst Dir*, Mary Pat Radke; *Ref*, Ben Weseloh; *Cat*, Mary Fisher; *Access Serv*, Heather Parisi; Staff 6 (MLS 6)
Founded 1918. Enrl 2,045; Fac 150; Highest Degree: Master
Jul 1999-Jun 2000 Income Parent Institution $932,120. Mats Exp $235,613, Books $95,000, Per/Ser (Incl. Access Fees) $120,500, Presv $6,000, Micro $14,100, AV Equip $13. Sal $548,165 (Prof $240,200)
Library Holdings: Bk Vols 292,000; Per Subs 850
Subject Interests: Library and information science
Special Collections: 18th & 19th Century British Culture (Harleian Miscellany, Parker Society, Somers Tracts), microcard; American Fiction 1774-1900, microcard; History (Anti-Slavery Propaganda in the Oberlin College Library), microcard; Small Press Coll, print, fiche & microfilm; Western Americana, microcard
Publications: Bibliographies; Handbooks
Mem of Suburban Library System
Partic in Dialog Corporation; ILCSO; Illinois Library & Information Network; Libras, Inc; OCLC Online Computer Library Center, Inc

P RIVER FOREST PUBLIC LIBRARY, 735 Lathrop Ave, 60305-1883. SAN 304-5919. Tel: 708-366-5205. FAX: 708-366-8699. E-Mail: rfs@sls.lib.il.us. Web Site: riverforestlib.org. *Dir*, Susan Hanes; *Tech Servs*, Joy Donahue; *Ad Servs, Ref*, Jeanne Walsh; *Ch Servs*, Lori Pulliam; Staff 7 (MLS 6, Non-MLS 1)
Founded 1899. Pop 11,669; Circ 145,319
Library Holdings: Bk Vols 66,904; Per Subs 247
Automation Activity & Vendor Info: (Circulation) Innovative Interfaces Inc.
Database Vendor: IAC - Info Trac
Publications: Newsletter (semi-annual)
Mem of Suburban Library System
Open Sept-May Mon-Thurs 9:30-9, Fri & Sat 9:30-5, Sun 1-5
Friends of the Library Group

RIVER GROVE

P RIVER GROVE PUBLIC LIBRARY DISTRICT, 8638 W Grand Ave, 60171. SAN 304-5935. Tel: 708-453-4484. FAX: 708-453-4517. E-Mail: rgs@sls.lib.il.us. *Dir*, Orion Jurkowski; *Ch Servs*, Sylvia Chavez; *Circ*, Darlene Zurek; Staff 11 (MLS 1, Non-MLS 10)
Founded 1963. Pop 9,961; Circ 27,000
Library Holdings: Bk Vols 30,000; Per Subs 121
Special Collections: Local History
Automation Activity & Vendor Info: (OPAC) Innovative Interfaces Inc.
Database Vendor: Innovative Interfaces INN - View
Publications: New Book List, Monthly calender of events
Mem of Suburban Library System
Friends of the Library Group

J TRITON COLLEGE LIBRARY,* 2000 N Fifth Ave, 60171. SAN 304-5943. Tel: 708-456-0300, Ext 3747. FAX: 708-583-3120. Web Site: www.triton.cc.il.us. *Dean of Libr*, Kathleen W Langston; *Dir*, Lucy Smith; *Librn*, Cynthia Lagon; *Tech Servs*, Linda Fairbanks; *Circ*, Jane Sorensen
Founded 1964
Jul 1997-Jun 1998 Income $653,569. Mats Exp $220,540, Books $100,000, Per/Ser (Incl. Access Fees) $50,540, Presv $500, Micro $6,500. Sal $412,529 (Prof $231,573)
Library Holdings: Bk Vols 76,646; Per Subs 515
Subject Interests: Nursing, Science/technology, Technology
Publications: LRC Update
Mem of Suburban Library System
Partic in Illinois Library Computer Systems Office; Northern Ill Learning Resources Coop; OCLC Online Computer Library Center, Inc

RIVERDALE

P RIVERDALE PUBLIC LIBRARY DISTRICT,* 208 W 144th St, 60827-2788. SAN 304-5951. Tel: 708-841-3311. FAX: 708-841-1805. Web Site: www.sls.lib.il.us/rds/. *Adminr, Head of Libr*, Adelle Swanson; E-Mail: rds@sls.lib.il.us; *Asst Dir*, Brett Shelton; *Publ Servs*, Arlene Mallek; *Tech Servs*,

Barbara Diehl; *Ref*, Judith Murphy; *Circ*, Sandy Schroeder; Staff 22 (MLS 6, Non-MLS 16)
Founded 1973. Pop 13,671; Circ 90,000
Jul 1998-Jun 1999 Income $672,038. Mats Exp $590,680
Library Holdings: Bk Vols 37,274; Bk Titles 25,757; Per Subs 113
Automation Activity & Vendor Info: (Circulation) Innovative Interfaces Inc.
Database Vendor: Ebsco - EbscoHost, Innovative Interfaces INN - View
Mem of Suburban Library System

RIVERSIDE

P RIVERSIDE PUBLIC LIBRARY, One Burling Rd, 60546. SAN 304-596X. Tel: 708-442-6366. FAX: 708-442-9462. E-Mail: rss@slslib.il.us. Web Site: www.riversidelibrary.org. *Dir*, Janice Fisher; E-Mail: fisherjanicelib@hotmail.com; Staff 34 (MLS 4, Non-MLS 30)
Founded 1930. Pop 8,774; Circ 134,000
Library Holdings: Bk Titles 67,000; Per Subs 125
Subject Interests: Landscape architecture, Local history
Special Collections: Frederick Law Olmsted
Automation Activity & Vendor Info: (Circulation) GEAC
Publications: Bibliography of Frederick Law Olmsted & Calvert Vaux; Local History Index; Local Newspaper Index 1912-39; Newsletter; Origins of Riverside Street Names
Mem of Suburban Library System
Friends of the Library Group

ROBBINS

P WILLIAM LEONARD PUBLIC LIBRARY DISTRICT,* 13822 Central Park Ave, 60472-1999. SAN 304-5978. Tel: 708-597-2760. FAX: 708-597-2778. E-Mail: williamleonard@rosslsil.us. *Librn*, Sharon L Highler; *Ref*, Willie Maude Johnson
Founded 1973. Pop 8,853
Library Holdings: Bk Vols 14,000; Per Subs 88
Mem of Suburban Library System
Friends of the Library Group

ROBINSON

J LINCOLN TRAIL COLLEGE, Eagleton Learning Resources Center, 11220 State Hwy 1, 62454-9524. SAN 304-5986. Tel: 618-544-8657, Ext 1460. FAX: 618-544-3957. Web Site: www.iecc.cc.il.us. *Dir*, Karen Coleman; *AV*, Paul Lange
Founded 1970. Enrl 1,025
Library Holdings: Bk Vols 26,181; Per Subs 89
Special Collections: AEI Coll; Reavis Coll
Automation Activity & Vendor Info: (Cataloging) epixtech, inc.; (Circulation) epixtech, inc.; (OPAC) epixtech, inc.
Mem of Shawnee Library System

P ROBINSON PUBLIC LIBRARY DISTRICT, 606 N Jefferson, 62454-2699. SAN 304-5994. Tel: 618-544-2917, 618-544-3273. TDD: 618-544-2917. FAX: 618-544-7172. E-Mail: rpladmin@shawls.lib.il.us. Web Site: www.sirin.lib.il.us/docs/rob/docs/lib. *Dir*, Dena Wilson; *Asst Dir*, Marilyn Manning; *ILL*, Joyce Marble; *Ch Servs*, Donna Atteberry; *Coll Develop*, Barbara Moody; *Admin Assoc*, Kara Catt; Staff 31 (MLS 2, Non-MLS 29)
Founded 1906. Pop 14,352; Circ 100,745
Jul 1999-Jun 2000 Income (Main Library and Branch Library) $605,735, State $81,523, Locally Generated Income $414,763, Other $109,450. Mats Exp $59,619, Books $30,239, Per/Ser (Incl. Access Fees) $5,824, AV Equip $20,657, Electronic Ref Mat (Incl. Access Fees) $2,899. Sal $200,094 (Prof $84,387)
Library Holdings: Bk Vols 70,400; Per Subs 142
Special Collections: Antiques & Collectibles; Crawford County History; Genealogy; Parenting
Automation Activity & Vendor Info: (Acquisitions) epixtech, inc.; (Cataloging) epixtech, inc.; (Circulation) epixtech, inc.; (ILL) epixtech, inc.; (OPAC) epixtech, inc.; (Serials) epixtech, inc.
Database Vendor: OCLC - First Search
Restriction: Non-circulating
Mem of Shawnee Library System
Special Services for the Deaf - Books on deafness & sign language; TDD
Special Services for the Blind - Kurzweil Reading Machine; Optelek 20/20 video magnification system
Open Fall through Spring: Mon-Thurs 10-7, Fri & Sat 10-5:30; Summer: Mon 10-7, Tues-Sat 10-5:30. Delivery of materials to the homebound
Branches: 3
HUTSONVILLE BRANCH, 104 S Main St, PO Box 158, Hutsonville, 62433-0158. Tel: 618-563-9603. FAX: 618-563-9603. E-Mail: hutsonville@frsb.net. Web Site: www.sirin.lib.il.us/docs/rob/docs/lib.; Staff 2 (Non-MLS 2)
Founded 1994. Pop 1,333
SUSIE WESLEY MEMORIAL, 105 S Main, PO Box 185, Flat Rock, 62427-0185. Tel: 618-584-3636. FAX: 618-584-3636. E-Mail: swlibrary@frsb.net. Web Site: www.sirin.lib.il.us/docs/rob/docs/lib.; Staff 2 (Non-MLS 2)
Founded 1988. Pop 1,296
OBLONG, 110 E Main St, Oblong, 62449. Tel: 618-592-3001. FAX: 618-592-3001. E-Mail: dpoblibrary2@hotmail.com. Web Site: www.sirin.lib.il.us/docs/rob/docs/lib.; Staff 2 (Non-MLS 2)
Founded 1968. Pop 2,547
Friends of the Library Group

ROCHELLE

P FLAGG-ROCHELLE PUBLIC LIBRARY DISTRICT, 619 Fourth Ave, 61068. SAN 304-6001. Tel: 815-562-3431. TDD: 815-562-3457. FAX: 815-562-3432. E-Mail: library@rochelle.net. *Dir*, Barbara A Kopplin; *Ch Servs*, Connie Avery
Founded 1889. Pop 12,338; Circ 91,304
Library Holdings: Bk Vols 40,400; Per Subs 162
Subject Interests: Genealogy, Local history
Mem of Northern Illinois Library System
Open Mon-Thurs 10-8:30, Fri & Sat 10-5

ROCHESTER

P ROCHESTER PUBLIC LIBRARY DISTRICT, One Community Dr, 62563. (Mail add: PO Box 617, 62563), SAN 376-1266. Tel: 217-498-8454. FAX: 217-498-8455. Web Site: www.rochesterlibrary.org. *Dir*, Linda K Shaw; E-Mail: lindas@rpls.lib.us; *Reader Servs*, Nancy F L Kruse; E-Mail: nancyk@rpls.lib.il.us; Staff 2 (MLS 2)
Founded 1985. Pop 8,094
Jul 1999-Jun 2000 Income $156,000, State $10,000, Locally Generated Income $5,000. Mats Exp $20,000, Books $14,000, Per/Ser (Incl. Access Fees) $2,500. Sal $60,200 (Prof $51,000)
Library Holdings: Bk Vols 256; Bk Titles 23,000
Automation Activity & Vendor Info: (Cataloging) DRA; (Circulation) DRA; (ILL) DRA; (OPAC) DRA
Publications: Bibliobits
Mem of Rolling Prairie Library System
Special Services for the Blind - Cassette bks; Magnifiers
Friends of the Library Group

ROCK FALLS

P ROCK FALLS PUBLIC LIBRARY DISTRICT, (Formerly Coloma Township - Rock Falls Public Library), 1007 Seventh Ave, 61071. SAN 304-601X. Tel: 815-626-3958. FAX: 815-626-8750. *Dir*, Eric S Tommerdahl; E-Mail: etommerdahl@hotmail.com; *Ch Servs*, Eva A Tetidrick; Staff 8 (MLS 1, Non-MLS 7)
Founded 1939. Pop 12,083; Circ 34,646
Library Holdings: Bk Vols 32,000; Per Subs 131
Automation Activity & Vendor Info: (Cataloging) TLC; (Circulation) TLC; (OPAC) TLC
Mem of Northern Illinois Library System

ROCK ISLAND

C AUGUSTANA COLLEGE LIBRARY, 3435 9 1/2 Ave, 61201-2296. SAN 304-6028. Tel: 309-794-7266. Interlibrary Loan Service Tel: 309-794-7585. FAX: 309-794-7640. Web Site: www.augustana.edu/library. *Dir*, Jonathan Miller; E-Mail: alijm@augustana.edu; *Ref*, Greg MacAyeal; *Ref*, Marian Miller; *Ref*, Sue O'Dell; *Spec Coll*, Jamie Nelson; *Coll Develop*, Carla Tracy; Staff 16 (MLS 6, Non-MLS 10)
Founded 1860. Enrl 2,219; Fac 173; Highest Degree: Bachelor
Jul 1999-Jun 2000 Income $1,253,349. Mats Exp $406,046, Books $170,134, Per/Ser (Incl. Access Fees) $208,157, Presv $3,316, Micro $11,830, AV Equip $12,609. Sal $512,988 (Prof $328,343)
Library Holdings: Bk Vols 270,691; Bk Titles 185,026; Per Subs 2,040
Special Collections: French Revolution (Charles XV Coll); Upper Mississippi Valley (Hauberg Coll)
Database Vendor: Ebsco - EbscoHost, Lexis-Nexis, OCLC - First Search, ProQuest, Wilson - Wilson Web
Publications: Augustana Library Publications; Occasional Papers
Mem of River Bend Library System
Partic in Bi-State Academic Libraries; Illinois Library & Information Network; OCLC Online Computer Library Center, Inc; Quad-Link Libr Consortium

S BLACKHAWK GENEALOGICAL SOCIETY OF ROCK ISLAND & MERCER COUNTIES LIBRARY, PO Box 3912, 61204-3912. SAN 370-8144. Tel: 309-786-3058, 309-786-5927, 786-3058. Web Site: www.geocities.com/hartland/plains/1507. *Librn, Pres*, Pamela M Langston; E-Mail: pamelang@revealed.net; Staff 1 (Non-MLS 1)
1999-1999 Mats Exp $850, Books $800, Per/Ser (Incl. Access Fees) $50, Micro $400
Library Holdings: Bk Vols 2,000; Spec Interest Per Sub 30
Subject Interests: Genealogy
Special Collections: Cemetery Records; County Records; Newspaper Abstracts

Publications: Blackhawk Genealogical Society of Rock Island & Mercer Counties (quarterly)
Restriction: Non-circulating to the public
The Blackhawk Genealogical Society Library is located in the Rock Island Public Library
Friends of the Library Group

L ROCK ISLAND COUNTY LAW LIBRARY,* Courthouse, 61201. SAN 375-975X. Tel: 309-786-4451, Ext 226. FAX: 309-786-9917. *Dir*, Evelyn Schafer
Library Holdings: Bk Titles 10,000
Special Collections: Legal Item Coll

P ROCK ISLAND PUBLIC LIBRARY,* 401 19th St, 61201-8143. SAN 340-7012. Tel: 309-732-7323. FAX: 309-732-7327. Web Site: www.rbls.lib.il.us/rip/index.html. *Dir*, Ava Ohrlund; *Asst Dir*, Amy Penry; *Ref*, Skip Burhans; *Circ*, Lisa M Davison; *ILL*, Alma Grimett; *Ch Servs*, Sue Foster; Staff 32 (MLS 7, Non-MLS 25)
Founded 1872. Pop 48,184; Circ 311,064
1997-1998 Mats Exp $243,319, Books $177,300, Per/Ser (Incl. Access Fees) $15,600, Micro $6,500, AV Equip $15,700
Library Holdings: Bk Vols 174,278; Bk Titles 124,399; Per Subs 382
Subject Interests: Literary criticism, Literature
Special Collections: Local History, Adults & Children's Large Print Bks
Automation Activity & Vendor Info: (Circulation) CLSI LIBS
Publications: Rock Island Library Lines
Mem of River Bend Library System
Contracted to serve: Blackhawk Township & Village of Milan, pop 7632; Edgington Township & Portions of Bowling Township
Friends of the Library Group
Branches: 2
SOUTHWEST, 9010 Ridgewood Rd, 61201. SAN 340-7071. Tel: 309-732-7338. FAX: 309-732-7337. Web Site: www.rbls.lib.il.ws/rip/branch.html. *Librn*, Kim Kirtzman
Library Holdings: Bk Vols 23,991; Bk Titles 22,806
THIRTY-THIRTY-ONE BRANCH, 3059 30th St, 61201. SAN 340-7101. Tel: 309-732-7369. FAX: 309-732-7371. Web Site: www.rbls.lib.il.us/rip/branch.html. *Librn*, Kim Kirtzman
Library Holdings: Bk Vols 18,322; Bk Titles 17,649
Bookmobiles: 1

S SRI, (ELLF), Elderly Living & Learning Facility, 729 34th Ave, 61201-5950. SAN 375-1775. Tel: 309-793-6800. FAX: 309-793-6807. *Info Res*, Joan Blaser
1999-2000 Income $5,000. Mats Exp $3,700, Books $1,500, Per/Ser (Incl. Access Fees) $1,200, Other Print Mats $1,000
Library Holdings: Bk Titles 1,000; Per Subs 15

S SWENSON SWEDISH IMMIGRATION RESEARCH CENTER, Augustana College, 3520 Seventh Ave, 61201. (Mail add: Augustana College, 639 38th St, 61201-2296), Tel: 309-794-7204. FAX: 309-794-7443. E-Mail: sag@augustana.edu, swseaholm@augustana.edu. Web Site: www.augustana.edu/administration/swenson/. *Dir*, Dag Blanck; *Archivist, Librn*, Christina Johansson; *Res*, Jill Seaholm
Founded 1981
Library Holdings: Bk Titles 17,000; Per Subs 30
Special Collections: Chicago City Directories (1838-1929); Kopparbergslan, Kronobergslan; Minneapolis & St Paul City Directories 1860-1900; Name Indexes to Swedish Embarkation Ports of Gothenburg (1869-1930) & Malmo (1874-1895); Swedish-American Churches-Societies-Organizations-Businesses-Personal Papers; Swedish-American Newspapers, microfilm
Publications: Guide to Resources & Holdings (1984); Occasional Papers (since 1991); Swedish-American Newspapers: A Guide to Microfilms (1981); Swenson Center News (since 1986)
Mem of River Bend Library System
Partic in OCLC Online Computer Library Center, Inc
Only microfilmed Swedish-American newspapers & periodicals circulate out-of-house on interlibrary loan; photocopying available at a nominal charge
Friends of the Library Group

R TRI-CITY JEWISH CENTER LIBRARY, 2715 30th St, 61201. SAN 373-0514. Tel: 309-788-3426. FAX: 309-788-3428. E-Mail: tcjc@qconline.com. *Librn*, Kristine Cawley; *Librn*, Bob Cawley
Library Holdings: Bk Vols 10,000
Special Collections: Coin Coll
Friends of the Library Group

M TRINITY MEDICAL CENTER, Health Sciences Library, 2701 17th St, 61201. SAN 304-419X. Tel: 309-779-2600. Interlibrary Loan Service Tel: 309-779-2603. FAX: 309-779-2601. Web Site: www.trinityqc.com. *Librn*, Jeanne Gittings; E-Mail: gittingsj@trinityqc.com; Staff 3 (MLS 1, Non-MLS 2)
Library Holdings: Bk Vols 4,000; Per Subs 160
Mem of River Bend Library System
Partic in Greater Midwest Regional Medical Libr Network; Illinois Library & Information Network; Quad City Area Biomedical Consortium
Branches:
COMMUNITY HEALTH RESOURCE CENTER Tel: 309-779-2069. *Librn*, Jeanne Gittings
Founded 1994
Library Holdings: Bk Vols 2,320; Bk Titles 2,254
Subject Interests: Consumer health

UNITED STATES ARMY
A CORPS OF ENGINEERS, ROCK ISLAND DISTRICT TECHNICAL LIBRARY, Clock Tower Bldg, PO Box 2004, 61204-2004. SAN 340-7160. Tel: 309-794-5576. FAX: 309-794-4201. Web Site: lepacl.brodart.com/search/um, www.mvr.usaze.army.mil/ncrim/imhp.htm. *Tech Servs*, Tricia L Kane; *Librn*, Bob Romic
Founded 1975
Library Holdings: Bk Vols 11,000; Per Subs 200
Subject Interests: Civil engineering, Soil mechanics
Special Collections: Civil Engineering; Corps of Engineers History Coll; Environmental Resources; Hydraulics (Locks & Dams)
Publications: Periodical Holding List
Partic in Defense Technical Information Center; Dialog Corporation; Fedlink; OCLC Online Computer Library Center, Inc; River Bend Library System

S UPPER MISSISSIPPI RIVER CONSERVATION COMMITTEE LIBRARY,* 4469 48th Ave Ct, 61201. SAN 371-7917. Tel: 309-793-5800. FAX: 309-793-5804. *Coordr*, Jon Duyvejonck; E-Mail: jon_duyvejonck@mail.fws.gov
Restriction: Non-circulating to the public

ROCKFORD

S FABRICATORS & MANUFACTURERS ASSOCIATION INTERNATIONAL, Technical Information Center, 833 Featherstone Rd, 61107-6302. SAN 370-6583. Tel: 815-399-8700. FAX: 815-484-7700. Web Site: www.fmametalfab.org. *Dir*, Nancy Olson; Staff 4 (MLS 2, Non-MLS 2)
Library Holdings: Bk Vols 500; Per Subs 200
Mem of Northern Illinois Library System

G H DOUGLAS SINGER MENTAL HEALTH CENTER, Northern Illinois Library for Mental Health, 4402 N Main St, 61103. SAN 322-8991. Tel: 815-987-7092. FAX: 815-987-7581. *Librn*, Pat E Ellison; E-Mail: pellison@uic.edu. Subject Specialists: *Psychiatry*, Pat E Ellison
Founded 1966
Library Holdings: Bk Titles 1,500; Per Subs 60
Database Vendor: OCLC - First Search
Restriction: Staff use only
Mem of Northern Illinois Library System
Partic in Northern Ill Libr Syst

P NORTHERN ILLINOIS LIBRARY SYSTEM,* 4034 E State St, 61108-2094. SAN 304-6044. Tel: 815-229-0330. *Exec Dir*, Jan Eakins Jones; *Coll Develop, Ref*, Christopher Anthon; *Automation Syst Coordr*, Linda Kautz; Staff 10 (MLS 10)
Founded 1965. Pop 671,656
Library Holdings: Bk Vols 29,229
Special Collections: Professional Coll for Librarians
Automation Activity & Vendor Info: (Circulation) Inlex
Publications: Board Bulletin; Board Links; Crayon Connection; Link Letter; Network News; Union List of Serials
Member Libraries: Alpena Community College; Beloit Corp Research Center; Bertolet Memorial Library District; Byron Public Library District; CGH Medical Center; Chadwick Public Library District; Cherry Valley Public District Library; Clinton Township Public Library; De Kalb Public Library; Dixon Public Library; East Dubuque District Library; Elizabeth Township Library; Ella Johnson Memorial Public Library District; Fabricators & Manufacturers Association International; Flagg-Rochelle Public Library District; Forreston Public Library; Franklin Grove Public Library; Freeport Health Network; Freeport Public Library; Galena Public Library District; Genoa Public Library District; H Douglas Singer Mental Health Center; Hanover Township Library; Harvard Diggins Public Library; Highland Community College Library; Honeywell Sensing & Control; Ida Public Library; Johnsburg Public Library District; Julia Hull District Library; Kirkland Public Library; Kishwaukee College; Lanark Public Library; Lena Community District Library; Malta Township Public Library; Maple Park Public Library District; Marengo Public Library District; Marengo Public Library District, Milledgeville; Mills-Petrie Memorial Library; Mount Carroll Township Public Library; Mount Morris Public Library; Nippersink District Library; North Suburban Library-Loves Park; Northern Illinois University; Northern Illinois University; Oregon Public Library District; OSF Saint Anthony Medical Center; Pankhurst Memorial Library; Pearl City Public Library District; Pecatonica Public Library District; Polo Public Library District; Rock Falls Public Library District; Rockford College; Rockford Public Library; Rohm & Haas; Savanna Public Library District; South Beloit Public Library; Squaw Grove Public Library District; Sterling Public Library; Stockton Township Public Library; Swedish American

Hospital; Sycamore Public Library; Talcott Free Public Library; Warren Township Public Library; Winnebago County Law Library; Winnebago Public Library; Woodstock Public Library; Wysox Township Library; York Township Public Library

M OSF SAINT ANTHONY MEDICAL CENTER, Medical Library, 5666 E State St, 61108-2472. SAN 324-5969. Tel: 815-395-5191. Circulation Tel: 815-227-2558. FAX: 815-395-5551. *Head of Libr*, Karen Wark; E-Mail: karen.wark@osfhealthcare.org. Subject Specialists: *Medical*, Karen Wark; Staff 2 (MLS 1, Non-MLS 1)
Library Holdings: Bk Titles 1,000; Per Subs 180
Subject Interests: Clinical medicine, Healthcare admin, Nursing
Database Vendor: OCLC - First Search, OVID Technologies
Mem of Northern Illinois Library System
Partic in Greater Midwest Regional Medical Libr Network

SR OUR SAVIOR'S LUTHERAN CHURCH LIBRARY, 3300 Rural St, 61107. SAN 374-8901. Tel: 815-399-0531. FAX: 815-399-8934. E-Mail: oslc.rock@worldnet.att.net, oslcoffice@aol.com. *Adminr*, Mimi Streed
Library Holdings: Bk Titles 1,000
Special Collections: Martin Luther King

J ROCK VALLEY COLLEGE LIBRARY, Educational Resources Center, 3301 N Mulford Rd, 61114. SAN 304-6052. Tel: 815-654-4432. Interlibrary Loan Service Tel: 815-654-4434. Circulation Tel: 815-654-4437. Reference Tel: 815-654-5241. FAX: 815-654-4339. E-Mail: libref@ednet.rvc.cc.il.us. Web Site: www.rvc.cc.il.us/services/library. *Dir*, Dr Hsiao-Hung Lee; *Tech Servs*, Patricia Farney; Tel: 815-654-4442; *Ref*, Maria Figiel-Krueger; *Automation Syst Coordr*, MaryRose Amidjaya; *Bibliog Instr*, Deborah Ebster; Tel: 815-654-4439; Staff 12 (MLS 5, Non-MLS 7)
Founded 1965. Enrl 3,800; Fac 123; Highest Degree: Associate
Jul 1999-Jun 2000 Mats Exp $265,000, Books $82,850, Per/Ser (Incl. Access Fees) $100,000, Presv $600, Micro $15,000, Electronic Ref Mat (Incl. Access Fees) $32,000. Sal $420,000 (Prof $275,000)
Library Holdings: Bk Vols 79,825; Per Subs 515
Automation Activity & Vendor Info: (Acquisitions) Endeavor; (Cataloging) Endeavor; (Circulation) Endeavor; (OPAC) Endeavor; (Serials) Endeavor
Database Vendor: Ebsco - EbscoHost, GaleNet, Lexis-Nexis, OCLC - First Search, ProQuest, Silverplatter Information Inc.
Restriction: Residents only, Students only
Function: ILL available
Partic in ILLINET; LVIS; Northern Ill Learning Resources Coop; Northern Ill Libr Syst; OCLC Online Computer Library Center, Inc

C ROCKFORD COLLEGE, Howard Colman Library, 5050 E State St, 61108-2393. SAN 304-6079. Tel: 815-226-4035. Interlibrary Loan Service Tel: 815-394-5042. FAX: 815-226-4084. Web Site: www.rockford.edu. *Dir*, Karen H Tibbetts; Tel: 815-394-5040, E-Mail: karen_tibbetts@rockford.edu; *Publ Servs*, Phil Hjemboe; Tel: 815-226-4165, E-Mail: phil_hjemboe@rockford.edu; *Tech Servs*, Margaret M Maiken; *Tech Servs*, Jenica Rogers; Tel: 815-394-5044, E-Mail: jenica_rogers@rockford.edu; Staff 7 (MLS 3, Non-MLS 4)
Founded 1847. Enrl 1,000; Fac 80; Highest Degree: Master
Jul 1999-Jun 2000 Income Parent Institution $510,760. Mats Exp $214,800, Books $82,000, Per/Ser (Incl. Access Fees) $95,000, Micro $10,100, Electronic Ref Mat (Incl. Access Fees) $40,955. Sal $275,161 (Prof $113,870)
Library Holdings: Bk Vols 138,732; Bk Titles 120,625; Per Subs 657
Special Collections: Holbrook ABC Coll; Jane Addams Coll, mss
Automation Activity & Vendor Info: (Acquisitions) Innovative Interfaces Inc.; (Circulation) Innovative Interfaces Inc.; (OPAC) Innovative Interfaces Inc.; (Serials) Innovative Interfaces Inc.
Database Vendor: Ebsco - EbscoHost, Lexis-Nexis, OCLC - First Search
Mem of Northern Illinois Library System
Partic in Ill Coop Coll Mgt Prog; Illinois Library & Information Network; OCLC Online Computer Library Center, Inc
Friends of the Library Group

S ROCKFORD INSTITUTE LIBRARY,* 928 N Main St, 61103. SAN 377-4309. Tel: 815-964-5053. FAX: 815-964-9403. *Assoc Dir*, Christopher Check
Library Holdings: Bk Vols 400; Per Subs 30

ROCKFORD MEMORIAL HOSPITAL
M HEALTH SCIENCE LIBRARY, 2400 N Rockton Ave, 61103. SAN 321-9402. Tel: 815-968-6861, Ext 5625. FAX: 815-968-7007. *Dir*, Phyllis Nathan; E-Mail: pnathan@rhsnet.org; *Assoc Librn*, Jan Asprooth; Staff 2 (MLS 1, Non-MLS 1)
Founded 1974
Library Holdings: Bk Titles 2,500; Per Subs 381
Subject Interests: Medicine
Special Collections: Pediatrics (Hunter Memorial Coll)
Publications: Library guide; new acquisitions; patient/consumer catalog

P ROCKFORD PUBLIC LIBRARY,* 215 N Wyman St, 61101-1061. SAN 340-7195. Tel: 815-965-6731. TDD: 815-965-3007. FAX: 815-965-0866. Web Site: www.rpl.rockford.org. *Exec Dir*, Joel C Rosenfeld; *Ad Servs*, Marie Phillips; *Circ, ILL*, Dawn Diventi; *Exten Serv*, Judith Long; *Tech Servs*, James Rentz. Subject Specialists: *Local history*, John Molyneaux; Staff 34 (MLS 19, Non-MLS 15)
Founded 1872. Pop 139,426; Circ 1,021,174
Library Holdings: Bk Vols 437,929; Bk Titles 229,205; Per Subs 928
Subject Interests: Art and architecture, Business and management, Economics
Special Collections: Genealogy & Local History, bks, cemetery census, microtext
Automation Activity & Vendor Info: (Circulation) Inlex
Publications: That Men Know So Little of Men (Local Black History)
Mem of Northern Illinois Library System
Special Services for the Deaf - Books on deafness & sign language; High interest/low vocabulary books; TDD
Extension services to County Jail, homebound & nursing homes; Assignment Alert Program with schools; Project Read Literacy collection & advisory service
Friends of the Library Group
Branches: 5
LEWIS LEMON BRANCH, 1988 Jefferson St, 61101. SAN 375-6106. Tel: 815-962-4767. FAX: 815-962-4863. *Exten Serv*, Judith Long
MONTAGUE, 1238 S Winnebago St, 61102. SAN 340-7284. Tel: 815-965-1912. FAX: 815-965-1922. *Exten Serv*, Judith Long
Library Holdings: Bk Vols 17,560
Outreach to Spanish-speaking community & elderly in SW city area
NORTH EAST, 320 N Alpine, 61107. SAN 340-7268. Tel: 815-226-1533. FAX: 815-226-1538. *Exten Serv*, Judith Long
Library Holdings: Bk Vols 27,773
ROCK RIVER, 3128 11th St, 61109. SAN 340-7314. Tel: 815-398-7514. FAX: 815-398-1345. *Exten Serv*, Judith Long
Library Holdings: Bk Vols 24,631
ROCKTON CENTRE, 3114 N Rockton Ave, 61103. SAN 340-7349. Tel: 815-963-5617. FAX: 815-963-8855. *Exten Serv*, Judith Long
Library Holdings: Bk Vols 26,554

S SUNDSTRAND AEROSPACE, Information Resource Center,* 4747 Harrison Ave, PO Box 7002, 61125-7002. SAN 304-6095. Tel: 815-226-6752. FAX: 815-226-5372.
Founded 1965
Library Holdings: Bk Vols 10,000; Per Subs 150
Subject Interests: Aerospace science
Special Collections: Military & Federal Specifications & Standards
Partic in Northern Ill Libr Syst

M SWEDISH AMERICAN HOSPITAL, Health Care Library,* 1400 Charles St, 61104. SAN 324-5365. Tel: 815-489-4556. FAX: 815-968-3713. *Dir*, Nancy Dale; E-Mail: ndale@uic.edu; Staff 2 (MLS 1, Non-MLS 1)
Library Holdings: Bk Vols 2,000; Bk Titles 2,000; Per Subs 250
Subject Interests: Clinical medicine, Clinical mgt, Clinical nursing
Publications: List of Current Serials
Restriction: Staff use only
Mem of Northern Illinois Library System
Partic in Upstate Consortium

S SWEDISH HISTORICAL SOCIETY OF ROCKFORD, Erlander Home Museum Library, 404 S Third St, 61104. SAN 375-0922. Tel: 815-963-5559. *Pres*, Franklin Johnson; Tel: 815-399-2342
Library Holdings: Bk Vols 2,000

GL WINNEBAGO COUNTY LAW LIBRARY, Courthouse Bldg, Ste 301, 61101-1221. SAN 304-6117. Tel: 815-987-2514. FAX: 815-987-3018.
Founded 1975
Library Holdings: Bk Vols 20,000; Per Subs 20
Special Collections: IICLE Handbooks; Illinois Law; Illinois Law School Law Reviews; ISBA Publications
Mem of Northern Illinois Library System

ROCKTON

P TALCOTT FREE PUBLIC LIBRARY,* 101 E Main St, 61072. SAN 304-6125. Tel: 815-624-7511. FAX: 815-624-1176. *Librn*, Bonnie Estrada
Founded 1888. Pop 12,500; Circ 100,000
Jul 1998-Jun 1999 Income $343,825, State $15,202, Federal $15,650, Locally Generated Income $295,753. Mats Exp $36,457, Books $26,391, Per/Ser (Incl. Access Fees) $650, AV Equip $4,879, Other Print Mats $3,037, Electronic Ref Mat (Incl. Access Fees) $1,500. Sal $130,339
Library Holdings: Bk Vols 42,000; Per Subs 117
Automation Activity & Vendor Info: (Cataloging) Inlex; (Circulation) Inlex; (OPAC) Inlex
Mem of Northern Illinois Library System
Friends of the Library Group

ROLLING MEADOWS

S NORTHROP GRUMMAN CORP, Technical - Business Library, 600 Hicks Rd M3300, 60008. SAN 376-0979. Tel: 847-259-9600, Ext 4590. FAX: 847-818-5756. *Librn*, Mary L Crompton; Tel: 847-259-9600, Ext 4592, E-Mail: crompma@mail.northgrum.com. Subject Specialists: *Engineering*, Mary L Crompton; Staff 1 (MLS 1)

Library Holdings: Bk Vols 7,000; Bk Titles 6,100; Per Subs 212
Subject Interests: Aeronautics, Aviation, Electronics, Engineering, Radar
Automation Activity & Vendor Info: (Cataloging) Athena; (Circulation) Athena; (OPAC) Sagebrush Corporation
Database Vendor: OCLC - First Search
Restriction: Company library
Mem of North Suburban Library System

P ROLLING MEADOWS LIBRARY, 3110 Martin Lane, 60008. SAN 304-615X. Tel: 847-259-6050. FAX: 847-259-5319. Web Site: www.rolling-meadoows.lib.il.us. *Exec Dir*, David Ruff; E-Mail: ruffda@rolling.meadows.lib.il.us; *Asst Dir*, Kenneth Gross; *Cat*, Joyce Schweda; *Ch Servs, YA Servs*, Charlene Peterson; *Ref*, Scott Davis; *ILL*, Arlene Sergot; *Coll Develop*, Marcia Bose
Founded 1959. Pop 23,140; Circ 380,000
Jan 1999-Dec 1999 Income $2,580,000, State $29,000, County $2,363,000, Locally Generated Income $129,000. Mats Exp $404,000, Books $206,000, Per/Ser (Incl. Access Fees) $19,000, Micro $2,000, Other Print Mats $36,000, Electronic Ref Mat (Incl. Access Fees) $70,000. Sal $1,389,000 (Prof $455,140)
Library Holdings: Bk Titles 160,000; Per Subs 250
Subject Interests: Careers, Spanish (language)
Special Collections: Rolling Meadows History, photog
Automation Activity & Vendor Info: (Circulation) epixtech, inc.
Publications: They Took the Challenge: The Story of Rolling Meadows
Mem of North Suburban Library System
Special Services for the Deaf - TTY machine
Friends of the Library Group

S UNILEVER HOME & PERSONAL CARE, Business & Technical Library, 3100 Golf Rd, 60008. SAN 303-8769. Tel: 847-734-3830. FAX: 847-734-3832. *Mgr*, Laura Claggett
Founded 1952
Library Holdings: Bk Titles 5,000; Per Subs 490
Subject Interests: Annual reports, Automation, Business and management, Chemistry, Cosmetics industry, Dermatology, Marketing, Textiles, Toxicology
Special Collections: Helene Curtis Archives
Publications: Journal List
Restriction: Staff use only
Mem of North Suburban Library System
Partic in ILLINET

ROMEOVILLE

C LEWIS UNIVERSITY LIBRARY, One University Pkwy, 60446. SAN 340-7403. Tel: 815-836-5300. Reference Tel: 815-838-0500, Ext 5307. FAX: 815-838-9456. Web Site: www.lewisu.edu/library/. *Dir*, Laura Patterson; Tel: 815-838-0500, Ext 5582, E-Mail: patterla@lewisu.edu; *Head Tech Servs*, Frederieke A Moskal; Tel: 815-838-0500, Ext 5302, E-Mail: moskalfr.lewisu.edu; *Coordr*, Bethany Jackson; Tel: 815-838-0500, Ext 5304, E-Mail: jacksobe@lewisu.edu; *Circ*, Merilee Buchar; Tel: 815-838-0500, Ext 5300; *Ref*, Ronald Noon; Tel: 815-838-0500, Ext 5307; *Govt Doc*, Bro Robert Wilsbach; Tel: 815-838-0500, Ext 5307, E-Mail: wilsbaro@lewisu.edu; *ILL*, Carrie Pollock; Tel: 815-838-0500, Ext 5300, E-Mail: pollocca@lewisu.edu; Staff 10 (MLS 4, Non-MLS 6)
Founded 1952. Enrl 2,892; Fac 138; Highest Degree: Master
Library Holdings: Bk Vols 176,000; Per Subs 716
Subject Interests: Business and management, Nursing, Religion
Special Collections: Contemporary Print Archives; Library of American Civilization, ultrafiche; Library of English Literatures, Part I & II, ultrafiche
Database Vendor: CARL, Dialog, DRA, Ebsco - EbscoHost, Lexis-Nexis, OCLC - First Search, OVID Technologies, ProQuest, Silverplatter Information Inc.
Mem of Heritage Trail Library System
Partic in Illinois Library & Information Network; Libras, Inc; OCLC Online Computer Library Center, Inc; Private Academic Libraries Of Illinois

ROODHOUSE

P ROODHOUSE PUBLIC LIBRARY, 220 W Franklin St, 62082-1412. SAN 304-6176. Tel: 217-589-5123. FAX: 217-589-5412. E-Mail: rhe@lcls.org. *Librn*, Sue Bradford
Founded 1926. Pop 9,988; Circ 10,169
May 1998-Apr 1999 Income (Main Library Only) $25,457, State $5,789, City $15,629, Other $4,039. Mats Exp $3,899. Sal $13,677
Library Holdings: Bk Vols 16,046; Per Subs 38
Mem of Lewis & Clark Library System
Open Mon-Thurs 2-7, Fri 9-11 & 2-5, Sat 9-12, June-Aug, Tues & Wed 2-5

ROSELLE

P ROSELLE PUBLIC LIBRARY DISTRICT,* 40 S Park St, 60172. SAN 304-6184. Tel: 630-529-1641. FAX: 630-529-7579. Web Site: www.roselle.lib.il.us. *Exec Dir*, Dianne Lueder; E-Mail: dlueder@roselle.lib.il.us; *Tech Servs*, Lynn Dennis; *Circ*, Rhonie Zymboly; *Ref*, Kara Giles; Staff 7 (MLS 7)
Founded 1940. Pop 24,710
Jul 1997-Jun 1998 Income $1,199,473, State $63,574, Locally Generated Income $118,883. Mats Exp $106,857, Books $79,199, Per/Ser (Incl. Access Fees) $7,200, Micro $3,439. Sal $445,586
Library Holdings: Bk Vols 79,000; Per Subs 374
Automation Activity & Vendor Info: (Circulation) TLC
Publications: Newsletter
Mem of DuPage Library System
Open Mon-Thurs 9:30-9, Fri & Sat 9:30-5, Sun 1-5
Friends of the Library Group

ROSEMONT

M AMERICAN SOCIETY FOR SURGERY OF THE HAND, Museum & Library,* 6300 N River Rd, Ste 600, 60018. SAN 329-1235. Tel: 847-384-8300. FAX: 847-384-1435. E-Mail: info@hand-surg.org. Web Site: www.hand-surg.org. *Exec Dir*, Mark Anderson
Founded 1983
Library Holdings: Bk Vols 284; Bk Titles 261; Per Subs 19
Publications: Catalog

S DAIRY MANAGEMENT INC, Information Resources, 10255 W Higgins Rd, Ste 900, 60018. SAN 304-6192. Tel: 847-803-2000. FAX: 847-803-2077. Web Site: www.dairyinfo.com. *Dir*, Ronald P Stoner; Staff 4 (MLS 3, Non-MLS 1)
Founded 1956
Library Holdings: Bk Vols 4,000; Bk Vols 11,272
Subject Interests: Nutrition
Database Vendor: Dialog, Ebsco - EbscoHost, Lexis-Nexis, OCLC - First Search
Mem of North Suburban Library System

ROSICLARE

P ROSICLARE MEMORIAL PUBLIC LIBRARY, Main St, 62982. (Mail add: PO Box 10, 62982), Tel: 618-285-6213. FAX: 618-285-6213. E-Mail: rosilib@shawneelink.com. *Head Librn*, Judy Largent; Staff 2 (Non-MLS 2)
Founded 1936. Pop 1,378; Circ 4,335
May 1999-Apr 2000 Income $20,586. Mats Exp $18,463. Sal $10,288
Library Holdings: Bk Vols 12,497; Per Subs 27
Mem of Shawnee Library System

ROUND LAKE

S BAXTER INTERNATIONAL, Information Management Center, Rte 120 & Wilson Rd - RLT-22, 60073. Tel: 847-270-5360. FAX: 847-270-5381. E-Mail: imc@baxter.com. *Dir*, Pam Fritz; *Mgr*, Deb Armer; *Mgr*, Ardys Chang; *Mgr*, James Johnson; *Mgr*, Steve Vaitonis; Staff 12 (MLS 9, Non-MLS 3)
Library Holdings: Bk Titles 6,000; Per Subs 325
Mem of North Suburban Library System
Partic in Illinois Library & Information Network

P ROUND LAKE AREA PUBLIC LIBRARY DISTRICT, 906 Hart Rd, 60073. SAN 304-6214. Tel: 847-546-7060. TDD: 847-546-7064. FAX: 847-546-7104. E-Mail: rlake@lib.il.us. Web Site: www.rlalibrary.org. *Dir*, Barbara Pfannkuche; *Ch Servs*, Madeline Reed; *Ad Servs*, Beth Nickels-Wisdom; *Tech Servs*, Paul Deane
Founded 1972. Pop 27,984; Circ 218,837
Jul 1999-Jun 2000 Income $1,360,188, State $43,901, Federal $7,000, Locally Generated Income $1,113,728, Other $195,559. Mats Exp $149,790, Books $104,296, Per/Ser (Incl. Access Fees) $10,939, AV Equip $23,265, Electronic Ref Mat (Incl. Access Fees) $11,290. Sal $449,580 (Prof $242,576)
Library Holdings: Bk Vols 89,674; Per Subs 294
Mem of North Suburban Library System
Partic in Coop Computer Servs
Friends of the Library Group

ROXANA

P ROXANA PUBLIC LIBRARY DISTRICT, 200 N Central Ave, 62084. SAN 304-6230. Tel: 618-254-6713. FAX: 618-254-6904. E-Mail: roe@lcls.org. Web Site: www.lcls.lib.il.us/roe. *Dir*, Rita L Hand; E-Mail: ritah@lcls.org; *Asst Librn*, Stacey L Haas; E-Mail: staceyh@lcls.org; Staff 8 (MLS 1, Non-MLS 7)
Founded 1941. Pop 1,562; Circ 31,306
Jul 1998-Jun 1999 Income $148,379, State $13,749, County $87,519, Locally Generated Income $14,570, Other $32,541. Mats Exp $15,102, Books $12,100, AV Equip $1,270, Other Print Mats $1,732. Sal $31,827 (Prof $31,494)
Library Holdings: Bk Vols 26,779; Per Subs 71; Bks on Deafness & Sign Lang 25
Special Collections: Newbery & Caldicott Award Books; Reading Rainbow
Automation Activity & Vendor Info: (Cataloging) DRA; (Circulation)

DRA; (OPAC) DRA
Database Vendor: Dialog, DRA, Ebsco - EbscoHost, OCLC - First Search
Publications: Newsletter (bi-annual)
Mem of Lewis & Clark Library System
Partic in Lewis & Clark Libr Syst
Open Mon-Thurs 10-8, Fri & Sat 10-5

RUSHVILLE

P RUSHVILLE PUBLIC LIBRARY, 104 N Monroe St, 62681. SAN 304-6249. Tel: 217-322-3030. FAX: 217-322-3030. E-Mail: library@inx.net. *Librn*, Charlene Copeland; *Asst Librn*, Sandy Bullard; Staff 3 (MLS 1, Non-MLS 2)
Founded 1878. Pop 3,229; Circ 30,646
Library Holdings: Bk Titles 20,000; Per Subs 74
Mem of Alliance Library System
Special Services for the Deaf - Books on deafness & sign language

SAINT CHARLES

R BETHLEHEM LUTHERAN CHURCH LIBRARY, 1145 N Fifth Ave, 60174-1230. (Mail add: PO Box 3850, 60174-9085), SAN 304-6265. Tel: 630-584-2199. FAX: 630-584-2674. E-Mail: office@bethlehemluth.org. Web Site: www.bethlehemluth.org. *Dir*, Donna Blomquist; *Librn*, Theresa Meyer
Founded 1957
Library Holdings: Bk Titles 2,000; Per Subs 20

ILLINOIS YOUTH CENTER

S SAINT CHARLES LIBRARY, 4450 Lincoln Hwy, 60175. SAN 376-0448. Tel: 630-584-0506, Ext 284. FAX: 630-584-1126.
Library Holdings: Bk Titles 12,000; Per Subs 14

S VALLEY VIEW LIBRARY, 34W826 Villa Maria Rd, 60174. SAN 376-0456. Tel: 847-695-6080, Ext 250. FAX: 847-695-6191. *Librn*, Shawnetta Graham
Library Holdings: Bk Titles 7,000; Per Subs 30
Subject Interests: Sociology

P ST CHARLES PUBLIC LIBRARY DISTRICT, One S Sixth Ave, 60174-2195. SAN 304-6281. Tel: 630-584-0076. TDD: 630-584-0961. FAX: 630-584-3448. E-Mail: library@linc.lib.il.us. Web Site: www.st-charles.lib.il.us. *Dir*, Diana M Brown; Tel: 630-584-0076, Ext 228, E-Mail: dbrown@linc.lib.il.us; *Asst Dir*, Bryan Wood; Tel: 630-584-0076, Ext 227, E-Mail: bwood@linc.lib.il.us; *Ad Servs, Ref*, Laura Haule; Tel: 630-584-0961, Ext 225, E-Mail: lhaule@linc.lib.il.us; *Ch Servs*, Denise Farrugia; Tel: 630-584-0076, Ext 236, E-Mail: dfarrugia@linc.lib.il.us; *Tech Servs*, Myung Sung; Tel: 630-584-0076, Ext 237, E-Mail: msung@linc.lib.il.us; *Coll Develop*, Sue Pfotenhauer; Tel: 630-584-0076, Ext 220, E-Mail: spfotenhauer@linc.lib.il.us; *Automation Syst Coordr*, Robin Boulton; Tel: 630-584-0076, Ext 258, E-Mail: rboulton@linc.lib.il.us; Staff 22 (MLS 22)
Founded 1906. Pop 37,662; Circ 704,668
Jul 1999-Jun 2000 Income $3,568,859, State $69,173, County $3,119,821, Locally Generated Income $337,429, Other $42,436. Mats Exp $566,888, Books $368,857, Per/Ser (Incl. Access Fees) $28,933, Micro $35,043, AV Equip $73,310, Electronic Ref Mat (Incl. Access Fees) $60,745. Sal $1,523,782
Library Holdings: Bk Vols 188,484; Bk Titles 169,636; Per Subs 1,446
Subject Interests: Genealogy
Special Collections: Adult New Reader Colls; Municipal
Database Vendor: DRA
Publications: A Step Up: From Readers to Chapter Books; Action Rhymes
Mem of DuPage Library System
Partic in Libr Integrated Network Consortium; OCLC Online Computer Library Center, Inc
Special Services for the Deaf - TDD
Special Services for the Blind - CCTV (VisualTex)
Friends of the Library Group

SAINT ELMO

P SAINT ELMO PUBLIC LIBRARY DISTRICT,* 502 N Main St, 62458. SAN 304-629X. Tel: 618-829-5544. FAX: 618-829-9104. E-Mail: elibrary@csuol.com. *Librn*, Terri Gillespie; *Asst Librn*, Lisa Newburn
Founded 1948. Pop 3,200
1997-1998 Income $91,984, State $4,552, County $43,420, Other $44,012. Mats Exp $9,000, Books $7,000, Per/Ser (Incl. Access Fees) $1,000, Other Print Mats $1,000. Sal $18,249 (Prof $11,849)
Library Holdings: Bk Vols 22,000; Per Subs 40
Mem of Shawnee Library System
Friends of the Library Group

SAINT JOSEPH

P ST JOSEPH TOWNSHIP-SWEARINGEN MEMORIAL LIBRARY, 201 N Third, 61873. (Mail add: PO Box 259, 61873), SAN 304-6303. Tel: 217-469-2159. FAX: 217-469-2159. E-Mail: sjlibray@prairienet.org. Web Site: www.prairienet.org/sjlibrary. *Dir*, Susan Dawn McKinney; E-Mail: smckin@ltnet.ltls.org; Staff 3 (MLS 1, Non-MLS 2)
Founded 1929. Pop 4,234; Circ 29,712
Apr 1999-Mar 2000 Income $89,220, State $5,223, Locally Generated Income $73,221, Other $10,776. Mats Exp $79,030, Books $12,426, Per/Ser (Incl. Access Fees) $1,500, AV Equip $1,017. Sal $35,539 (Prof $19,500)
Library Holdings: Bk Vols 23,579; Per Subs 69
Automation Activity & Vendor Info: (Acquisitions) epixtech, inc.; (Cataloging) epixtech, inc.; (Circulation) epixtech, inc.; (ILL) epixtech, inc.; (Serials) epixtech, inc.
Database Vendor: epixtech, inc., OCLC - First Search
Mem of Lincoln Trail Libraries System
Special Services for the Deaf - Deaf publications
Special Services for the Blind - Talking books for the Blind; Talking machines

SALEM

P BRYAN-BENNETT LIBRARY,* 217 W Main St, 62881. SAN 304-6311. Tel: 618-548-7784. FAX: 618-548-9593. Web Site: www.sirin.lib.il.us/docs/bbl/docs/lib/index.html. *Dir*, Theresa J Schaefer
Founded 1908. Pop 7,470; Circ 49,562
May 1998-Apr 1999 Income $138,648, State $13,553, City $80,947, Locally Generated Income $13,182, Other $30,966. Mats Exp $15,186, Books $13,285, Per/Ser (Incl. Access Fees) $1,901. Sal $65,416
Library Holdings: Bk Vols 27,374; Per Subs 79
Subject Interests: Genealogy, Illinois
Mem of Shawnee Library System
Open Mon-Thurs 12-8, Fri & Sat 9-2, closed Sun

SANDWICH

P SANDWICH DISTRICT LIBRARY, (SA), 107 E Center St, 60548-1603. SAN 304-632X. Tel: 815-786-8308. FAX: 815-786-9231. E-Mail: sandwiclib@prairicnet.com. Web Site: sab@htls.lib.il.us. *Dir*, Jennifer A Burke; *Asst Librn*, Donna Leonard; *YA Servs*, Debby Hill; Staff 13 (MLS 2, Non-MLS 11)
Founded 1915. Pop 6,783; Circ 44,235
Jul 2000-Jun 2001 Income $253,539. Mats Exp $201,300, Books $28,667, Per/Ser (Incl. Access Fees) $2,000, Micro $500, AV Equip $5,301, Other Print Mats $500, Electronic Ref Mat (Incl. Access Fees) $2,000. Sal $86,813 (Prof $32,000)
Library Holdings: Bk Titles 36,935; Per Subs 137; High Interest/Low Vocabulary Bk Vols 100
Mem of Heritage Trail Library System
Friends of the Library Group

SAUK VILLAGE

P NANCY L MCCONATHY PUBLIC LIBRARY,* 7 Surreybrook Plaza, 60411. SAN 304-6338. Tel: 708-757-4771. Interlibrary Loan Service Tel: 708-757-4788. FAX: 708-757-3580. *Dir*, Nanette Festa Wargo
Founded 1973. Pop 11,859; Circ 66,428
Library Holdings: Bk Vols 32,000; Per Subs 89
Special Collections: Cookbooks; Motion Picture Stars Biography
Mem of Suburban Library System

SAVANNA

P SAVANNA PUBLIC LIBRARY DISTRICT, 326 Third St, 61074. SAN 304-6346. Tel: 815-273-3714. FAX: 815-273-4634. E-Mail: savpublib@internetni.com. *Librn*, Katherina M Handel; Staff 4 (Non-MLS 4)
Founded 1896. Pop 4,483
Library Holdings: Bk Vols 15,581; Per Subs 74
Special Collections: Savanna Times Journal, microfilm
Mem of Northern Illinois Library System
Friends of the Library Group

SAYBROOK

P CHENEY'S GROVE TOWNSHIP LIBRARY, 204 S State St, PO Box 58, 61770. SAN 376-7817. Tel: 309-475-6131. FAX: 309-475-6131. *Pres*, Barbara Lewis
Library Holdings: Bk Vols 8,000; Per Subs 10
Open Tues 1-5, Wed 11-1, Thurs 1-5, 6:30-8:30 & Sat 9-12

SCHAUMBURG

M AMERICAN VETERINARY MEDICAL ASSOCIATION LIBRARY, 1931 N Meacham Rd, Ste 100, 60173-4360. SAN 371-0106. Tel: 847-925-8070, Ext 245. FAX: 847-925-9329. Web Site: www.avma.org. *Librn*, Diane A Fagen; E-Mail: dfagen@avma.org
Founded 1863
Library Holdings: Bk Vols 5,000; Bk Titles 4,960; Per Subs 400

C ILLINOIS INSTITUTE OF ART LIBRARY,* 1000 Plaza Dr, 60173. SAN 372-5898. Tel: 847-619-3450, Ext 153. FAX: 847-619-3064. Web Site: www.ilia.edu. *Head Librn*, Dennis McGuire; Tel: 847-619-3450, E-Mail: mcguired@aii.edu; *Librn*, Susan Kehrer; Staff 2 (MLS 1, Non-MLS 1)
Founded 1986. Enrl 275; Fac 25
Library Holdings: Bk Vols 5,200; Bk Titles 4,500; Per Subs 175
Automation Activity & Vendor Info: (OPAC) Athena
Mem of North Suburban Library System

C KELLER GRADUATE SCHOOL OF MANAGEMENT, Information Center In Schaumburg,* 1051 Perimeter Dr, No 900, 60173. SAN 376-0219. Tel: 847-330-0040. FAX: 847-330-0046. Web Site: www.keller.edu. *Dir*, Bob Trombetta
Library Holdings: Bk Titles 3,389; Per Subs 30

S LA LECHE LEAGUE INTERNATIONAL, Center for Breastfeeding Information,* PO Box 4079, 60168-4079. SAN 371-747X. Tel: 847-519-7730. FAX: 847-519-0035. E-Mail: cbi@llli.org. Web Site: www.lalecheleague.org/. *Ref*, Carol Huotari
Founded 1956

S PREVENT BLINDNESS AMERICA, Conrad Berens Library, 500 E Remington Rd, 60173. SAN 311-9270. Tel: 847-843-2020. Toll Free Tel: 800-331-2020. FAX: 847-843-8458. E-Mail: info@preventblindness.org. Web Site: www.preventblindness.org. *Librn*, Ann Horan
Founded 1944
Library Holdings: Bk Titles 3,000; Per Subs 60
Subject Interests: Eye health, Eye pathology, Industrial safety, Ophthalmology, Optics, Prevention of blindness, Preventive med, Public health, Vision, Vision screening, Vol agency
Special Collections: NSPB Archives
Restriction: By appointment only

P SCHAUMBURG TOWNSHIP DISTRICT LIBRARY, 130 S Roselle Rd, 60193. SAN 340-7438. Tel: 847-985-4000. Interlibrary Loan Service Tel: 847-923-3349. Circulation Tel: 847-923-3386. Reference Tel: 847-923-3322. TDD: 847-985-1462. FAX: 847-923-3207. Web Site: www.stdl.org. *Dir, Spec Coll*, Michael J Madden; Tel: 847-923-3200, E-Mail: mmadden@stdl.org; *Ad Servs*, Patricia Llerandi; Tel: 847-923-3215, Fax: 847-923-3428, E-Mail: pllerandi@stdl.org; *Bibliog Instr, Online Servs*, Tim Jarzemsky; Tel: 847-923-3356, Fax: 847-923-3355, E-Mail: tjarzemsky@stdl.org; *Ch Servs*, Todd Morning; Tel: 847-923-3426, Fax: 847-923-3426, E-Mail: tmorning@stdl.org; *Coll Develop*, Suzanne Boudreau; Tel: 847-923-3336, Fax: 847-923-3342, E-Mail: sboudreau@stdl.org; *ILL*, Barbara Nolan; Fax: 847-923-3342, E-Mail: lmerkel@stdl.org; *Media Spec*, Judy Napier; Tel: 847-923-3180, Fax: 847-923-3188, E-Mail: jnapier@stdl.org; *Ref*, Dawn Bussey; Tel: 847-923-3326, Fax: 847-923-3335, E-Mail: dbussey@stdl.org; Staff 37 (MLS 27, Non-MLS 10)
Founded 1963. Pop 124,773; Circ 2,008,010
Jul 2000-Jun 2001 Income $11,120,408, State $244,000, Locally Generated Income $9,896,121, Other $980,287. Mats Exp $1,537,800. Sal $6,259,300
Library Holdings: Bk Vols 477,407; Per Subs 2,274
Subject Interests: Business and management
Automation Activity & Vendor Info: (Circulation) SIRSI
Mem of North Suburban Library System
Special Services for the Deaf - Captioned media; High interest/low vocabulary books; Special interest periodicals
Friends of the Library Group
Branches: 2
HANOVER PARK BRANCH, 1570 Irving Park Rd, Hanover Park, 60103. SAN 373-7136. Tel: 630-372-7800. Web Site: www.stdl.org. *Dir*, Barbara Adrianopoli; Tel: 847-923-3386, E-Mail: badrianopoli@stdl.org; Staff 1 (MLS 1)
Library Holdings: Bk Titles 16,327
HOFFMAN ESTATES BRANCH, 1890 Hassell Rd, Hoffman Estates, 60195. SAN 340-7462. Tel: 847-885-3511. Web Site: www.stdl.org. *Dir*, Barbara Adrianopoli; Tel: 847-923-3460, Fax: 847-923-9973, E-Mail: badrianopoli@stdl.org; Staff 1 (MLS 1)
Library Holdings: Bk Titles 37,484
Friends of the Library Group

S SOCIETY OF ACTUARIES LIBRARY, 475 N Martingale Rd, Ste 800, 60173-2226. SAN 329-2266. Tel: 847-706-3575. FAX: 847-706-3599. Web Site: www.soa.org. *Librn*, Ellen Bull; Staff 1 (MLS 1)
Founded 1949
Jan 2000-Dec 2000 Mats Exp $57,010, Books $9,043, Per/Ser (Incl. Access Fees) $12,694, Electronic Ref Mat (Incl. Access Fees) $35,273. Sal $70,000 (Prof $55,750)
Library Holdings: Bk Titles 1,500; Per Subs 188
Subject Interests: Actuarial sci, Employee benefits, Health ins, Investments, Life ins, Mathematics
Mem of North Suburban Library System
Partic in Chicago Asn of Law Librs; OCLC Online Computer Library Center, Inc; SLA

SCHILLER PARK

P SCHILLER PARK PUBLIC LIBRARY,* 4200 Old River Rd, 60176-1699. SAN 304-6362. Tel: 847-678-0433. FAX: 847-678-0567. E-Mail: sps@sos.lib.il.us. *Dir*, Tina J Setzer
Founded 1962. Pop 11,189; Circ 59,594
Library Holdings: Bk Vols 80,000; Per Subs 184
Automation Activity & Vendor Info: (Circulation) CLSI LIBS
Publications: Schiller Park Library PEN
Mem of Suburban Library System

SCOTT AFB

UNITED STATES AIR FORCE
A SCOTT AIR FORCE BASE LIBRARY FL4407, 375 SVS/SVMG, 510 Ward Dr, 62225-5360. SAN 340-7551. Tel: 618-256-5100. Interlibrary Loan Service Tel: 618-256-3028. FAX: 618-256-4558. *Librn*, Cynthia Jones; *Acq, ILL*, Sandra Koontz; *Ref*, Lorene Simmons; Staff 2 (MLS 2)
Founded 1926
Library Holdings: Bk Vols 40,000; Per Subs 281
Subject Interests: Military history
Special Collections: TQM, Audio-visual, Education Office Coll
Mem of Shawnee Library System

GM US AIR FORCE, Medical Center Library, 310 W Losey St, Bldg 1530, 62225-5252. SAN 326-9876. Tel: 618-256-7437. FAX: 618-256-7244. *Librn*, Patricia L Schmidgall; E-Mail: patricia.schmidgall@medgrp.scott.af.mil. Subject Specialists: *Medical*, Patricia L Schmidgall; Staff 1 (MLS 1)
Oct 2000-Sep 2001 Income $55,000. Mats Exp Per/Ser (Incl. Access Fees) $43,000
Library Holdings: Bk Vols 9,500; Bk Titles 400; Per Subs 355
Subject Interests: Medicine
Partic in Fedlink; Illinois Library & Information Network; OCLC Online Computer Library Center, Inc

SENECA

P SENECA PUBLIC LIBRARY DISTRICT,* 210 N Main St, 61360-0980. (Mail add: PO Box 980, 61360-0980), SAN 304-6370. Tel: 815-357-6566. FAX: 815-357-6568. *Dir*, Susan Prokopeak
Founded 1938. Pop 3,304; Circ 41,088
Library Holdings: Bk Vols 32,480; Per Subs 145
Special Collections: Seneca LST Shipyard; WW II
Mem of Heritage Trail Library System

SESSER

P SESSER PUBLIC LIBRARY,* 303 W Franklin St, 62884. SAN 376-1274. Tel: 618-625-6566. FAX: 618-625-6566. *Librn*, Lowanda Johnson
Library Holdings: Bk Titles 9,207

SHABBONA

P FELWELLIN MEMORIAL LIBRARY,* 108 W Comanche Ave, PO Box 190, 60550-0190. SAN 304-6389. Tel: 815-824-2079. FAX: 815-824-2079. *Librn*, Ada Gallagher
Pop 750; Circ 15,473
Library Holdings: Bk Vols 10,000; Per Subs 50
Special Collections: Chief Shabbona Coll
Open Mon 5-8, Tues, Thurs & Fri 6-8, Wed 3-6, Sat 9-12

SHAWNEETOWN

P SHAWNEETOWN PUBLIC LIBRARY,* E Posey at E Lincoln, 62984-0972. SAN 304-6397. Tel: 618-269-3761. *Dir*, Cynthia Vickery
Founded 1968. Pop 1,575; Circ 10,000
Library Holdings: Bk Vols 3,500
Subject Interests: Genealogy
Mem of Shawnee Library System

SHEFFIELD

P SHEFFIELD PUBLIC LIBRARY,* 136 E Cook St, 61361-0608. SAN 304-6400. Tel: 815-454-2628. FAX: 815-454-2628. *Librn*, Tammy Criminger
Founded 1896. Pop 1,130; Circ 11,358
Library Holdings: Bk Vols 10,300; Per Subs 43
Subject Interests: History
Special Collections: Lincoln
Mem of River Bend Library System
Friends of the Library Group

SHELBYVILLE

P SHELBYVILLE FREE PUBLIC LIBRARY,* 154 N Broadway St, 62565-1698. SAN 304-6419. Tel: 217-774-4432. FAX: 217-774-2634. *Dir*, Shelley Koehler; *Asst Librn*, Nancy Wallace; *Asst Librn*, Pat Robertson
Founded 1902. Pop 5,259; Circ 68,219
Library Holdings: Bk Vols 28,000
Subject Interests: Annual reports, Genealogy, History, Rare books
Special Collections: 144 rolls of local & misc newspapers on microfilm dating 1812 to present
Mem of Rolling Prairie Library System
Partic in Illinois Library & Information Network
Art prints, cameras, projector, extensive film & record catalogues for loan to public; TV & video cassette recorder available by appointment; books distributed to five locations in city for disabled senior patrons. Also delivered to detention center. Mostly large print books which are rotated quarterly

SHELDON

P SHELDON PUBLIC LIBRARY DISTRICT,* 125 N Fifth, PO Box 370, 60966. SAN 304-6427. Tel: 815-429-3521. FAX: 815-429-3804. *Librn*, Kim Zumwalt
Founded 1917. Pop 1,542; Circ 6,373
Library Holdings: Bk Vols 11,288; Per Subs 30
Mem of Lincoln Trail Libraries System
Open Mon-Fri 1-6:30 & Sat 10-3

SHERIDAN

P ROBERT W ROWE PUBLIC LIBRARY DISTRICT, (ROB), 120 E Si Johnson Ave, PO Box 358, 60551. SAN 375-9741. Tel: 815-496-2031. FAX: 815-496-2067. Web Site: www.welcome.to/robertwrowe. *Librn*, Debby Smith; E-Mail: dsmith@htls.lib.il.us
Pop 3,678
Library Holdings: Bk Titles 16,000; Per Subs 40
Automation Activity & Vendor Info: (Cataloging) GEAC; (Circulation) GEAC; (OPAC) GEAC
Mem of Heritage Trail Library System
Friends of the Library Group

S SHERIDAN CORRECTIONAL CENTER LIBRARY,* 4017 E 2603 Rd, 60551. (Mail add: PO Box 38, 60551), SAN 376-1010. Tel: 815-496-2311. *Librn*, Ramona Witte
Library Holdings: Bk Titles 10,500; Per Subs 110

SHERRARD

P SHERRARD PUBLIC LIBRARY DISTRICT, 200 Fifth Ave, PO Box 345, 61281-0345. SAN 376-1223. Tel: 309-593-2178. FAX: 309-593-2179. E-Mail: sherrard.lib@reavealed.net. *Dir*, Nancy Mixdorf; Staff 1 (MLS 1)
Pop 5,770
Library Holdings: Bk Titles 14,900; Per Subs 66
Mem of Alliance Library System
Friends of the Library Group

SHOREWOOD

P HERITAGE TRAIL LIBRARY SYSTEM, 405 Earl Rd, 60431. SAN 304-6435. Tel: 815-729-3345. Circulation Tel: 815-729-3345, Ext 111. Reference Tel: 877-485-7733. Toll Free Tel: 800-206-3834. FAX: 815-725-0930. Toll Free FAX: 800-725-0930. Web Site: www.htls.lib.il.us. *Exec Dir*, Sandra Soderquist; E-Mail: ssoderqu@htls.lib.il.us; *Dir*, Joe McElroy; *Asst Dir*, Catherine Perry; Tel: 815-729-3345, Ext 106, E-Mail: cperry@htls.lib.il.us; *Librn*, Richard Gooch; Tel: 815-729-3345, Ext 107, E-Mail: rgooch@htls.lib.il.us; *Publ Servs*, Roger Brtva; *YA Servs*, Mary Soucie; *Info Tech*, Paul Mills; Tel: 815-729-3345, Ext 120, E-Mail: pmills@htls.lib.il.us; Staff 33 (MLS 5, Non-MLS 28)
Founded 1967. Pop 490,000
Library Holdings: Bk Vols 12,000; Per Subs 60
Special Collections: Library Science
Automation Activity & Vendor Info: (Circulation) GEAC
Publications: Along the Trail; Trail Mix
Member Libraries: Bourbonnais Public Library District; Coal City District Public Library; Des Plaines Valley Public Library District; Earl Township Public Library; Edward Chipman Public Library; Fossil Ridge Public Library; Fountaindale Public Library District; Grant Park Public Library; Graves-Hume Public Library District; Homer Township Public Library District; Illinois Valley Community College; Joliet Junior College; Kankakee Community College; Kankakee Public Library; La Moille Clarion District Public Library; La Salle Public Library; Ladd Public Library District; Leepertown Township Public Library; Lemont Public Library District; Lewis University Library; Lostant Community Library; Manhattan Public Library District; Manteno Public Library District; Marseilles Public Library; Matson Public Library; Mokena Community Public Library District; Morris Area Public Library District; New Lenox Public Library District; Oglesby Public Library; Olivet Nazarene University; Paw Paw Public Library District; Peotone Public Library District; Peru Public Library; Plainfield Public Library District; Plano Community Library District; Provena Saint Joseph Medical Center; Putnam County Public Library District; Raymond A Sapp Memorial Library; Reddick Library; Richard A Mautino Memorial Library; Riverside Healthcare Systems; Robert W Rowe Public Library District; Sandwich District Library; Selby Township Library District; Seneca Public Library District; Shorewood-Troy Public Library District; Silver Cross Hospital; Somonauk Public Library District; Streator Public Library; Three Rivers Public Library District; Three Rivers Public Library District; Tiskilwa Township Library; Toluca City Library; University Of Saint Francis; University of Saint Francis; Utica Public Library District; Wilmington Public Library District; Yorkville Public Library
Partic in Illinois Library & Information Network

P SHOREWOOD-TROY PUBLIC LIBRARY DISTRICT, 650 Deerwood Dr, 60431. SAN 321-0278. Tel: 815-725-1715. TDD: 815-725-2173. FAX: 815-725-1722. Web Site: www.htls.lib.il.us/stb/. *Dir*, Mary F Thomas; E-Mail: mfthomas@htls.lib.il.us; *Ch Servs*, Diana Hollingsworth; Tel: 815-725-4368; *Ad Servs*, Judith Finley; Staff 17 (MLS 2, Non-MLS 15)
Founded 1975. Pop 13,528; Circ 113,456
Jul 1999-Jun 2000 Income $487,301, State $35,250, Federal $24,798, County $386,537, Other $40,716. Mats Exp $66,807. Sal $198,427
Library Holdings: Bk Titles 53,861; Per Subs 129
Subject Interests: Audio bks, Cassette bks, Large-print bks, Local genealogy, Local history
Special Collections: Township Records
Database Vendor: Dialog, OVID Technologies
Mem of Heritage Trail Library System

SIDELL

P SIDELL DISTRICT LIBRARY,* 101 E Market St, PO Box 19, 61876-0019. SAN 304-6443. Tel: 217-288-9031. FAX: 217-288-9543. *Librn*, Mary Tate
Pop 1,950; Circ 18,435
1998-1999 Income $59,084, State $3,378, Federal $4,500, County $49,409. Mats Exp $17,477, Books $14,612, Per/Ser (Incl. Access Fees) $1,310. Sal $20,866
Library Holdings: Bk Vols 9,389; Per Subs 57
Subject Interests: Fiction, Large type print, Religion
Mem of Lincoln Trail Libraries System

SIDNEY

P SIDNEY COMMUNITY LIBRARY,* 205 S David, 61877. SAN 304-6451. Tel: 217-688-2332. FAX: 217-688-2332. *Librn*, Eleanor Fear; *Asst Librn*, Alberta West
Pop 886; Circ 10,000
Library Holdings: Bk Vols 6,500; Per Subs 20
Mem of Lincoln Trail Libraries System

SILVIS

M ILLINI HOSPITAL, Perlmutter Library of the Health Sciences, 855 Hospital Rd, Ste 102, 61282. SAN 329-2231. Tel: 309-792-4360. FAX: 309-792-4362. *Coordr*, Barb Tharp; E-Mail: btharp@libby.rbls.lib.il.us; *ILL*, Dee Vanscoy
Library Holdings: Bk Titles 2,800; Per Subs 185
Subject Interests: Consumer health, Nursing, Nutrition
Special Collections: Genontology/Elder Care, V-tapes; Respiratory therapy (Quad City Respiratory Care Consortium Coll), V-tapes
Publications: Acquisitions list
Mem of River Bend Library System
Partic in Illinois Library & Information Network; Quad City Area Biomedical Consortium; River Bend Library System
Open Mon-Fri 7:30-4

P SILVIS PUBLIC LIBRARY, 105 Eighth St, 61282-1199. SAN 304-6478. Tel: 309-755-3393. FAX: 309-755-3393. Web Site: www.rbls.lib.il.us/svp/index.html. *Librn*, Imogene Jensen
Founded 1912. Pop 11,168; Circ 32,908
May 1999-Apr 2000 Income $131,121, State $19,644, City $62,474, Other $49,003. Mats Exp $19,000, Books $17,000, AV Equip $2,000. Sal $59,874 (Prof $22,500)
Library Holdings: Bk Vols 36,092; Per Subs 89
Automation Activity & Vendor Info: (Circulation) GEAC
Mem of River Bend Library System

SKOKIE

R EZRA-HABONIM, THE NILES TOWNSHIP JEWISH CONGREGATION, Hillman Library, 4500 Dempster, 60076. SAN 324-363X. Tel: 847-675-4141. FAX: 847-675-0327. *Librn*, Janice B Footlik
Founded 1963

Library Holdings: Bk Vols 5,000; Per Subs 10
Subject Interests: Judaica
Partic in N Suburban Libr Syst

CR HEBREW THEOLOGICAL COLLEGE, (SSML), Saul Silber Memorial Library, 7135 N Carpenter Rd, 60077-3263. SAN 340-7640. Tel: 847-982-2500. FAX: 847-674-6381. E-Mail: ssmlhtc@htcnet.edu, ssmlhtc@nslsilus.org. Web Site: www.htcnet.edu. *Librn*, Elie Ginsparg. Subject Specialists: *Judaica*, Elie Ginsparg
Founded 1922. Enrl 275
Library Holdings: Bk Vols 70,000; Per Subs 182
Subject Interests: Biblical studies, Jewish history and literature
Special Collections: Bet Midrash Coll; Halakah (Rabbi Simon H Album Coll); Lazar Holocaust Coll; Rev M Newman Coll, per; Woman in Judaism (Moses Wolfe Coll)
Automation Activity & Vendor Info: (Cataloging) Follett; (Circulation) Follett; (OPAC) Follett
Mem of North Suburban Library System
Partic in Judaica Library Network Of Metropolitan Chicago
Friends of the Library Group
Branches:
ANNE BLITSTEIN TEACHERS INSTITUTE *Librn*, Daniel D Stuhlman
Subject Interests: Judaica (lit or hist of Jews)
Friends of the Library Group

S KNOWLEDGE SYSTEMS INSTITUTE GRADUATE SCHOOL, KSI Library,* 3420 Main St, 60076. SAN 376-0103. Tel: 847-679-3135. FAX: 847-679-3166. E-Mail: office@ksi.edu. *Dir*, Judy Pan; *Librn*, Margaret Price
Library Holdings: Bk Titles 1,955

S PHARMACIA CORP, (Formerly Searle Research Library), Searle Research Library, 4901 Searle Pkwy, 60077. SAN 304-6486. Tel: 847-982-4700. FAX: 847-982-4941. *Acq, Coll Develop, Mgr*, Linda Thomas; E-Mail: linda.a.thomas@pharmacia.com; *Ref Serv*, Sharon Duffy; *Doc, ILL*, Elaine Lehmann; *Ser*, Marie Lasquety
Founded 1952
Library Holdings: Bk Vols 40,000; Per Subs 550
Subject Interests: Biology, Chemistry, Obstetrics and gynecology, Pharmacology, Toxicology
Automation Activity & Vendor Info: (Cataloging) epixtech, inc.
Restriction: Not open to public
Mem of North Suburban Library System
Partic in Ill Regional Libr Coun; Illinois Library & Information Network

S PORTLAND CEMENT ASSOCIATION, Library Services,* 5420 Old Orchard Rd, 60077-1083. SAN 340-7705. Tel: 847-966-6200. FAX: 847-966-6221. Web Site: www.portcement.org. *Mgr*, Connie N Field; Tel: 847-966-6200, Ext 530, E-Mail: connie_field@portcement.org; *Tech Servs*, William J Burns; Tel: 847-966-6200, Ext 534, E-Mail: bill_burns@portcement.org; Staff 3 (MLS 2, Non-MLS 1)
Founded 1950
Jan 2000-Dec 2000 Mats Exp $100,000, Per/Ser (Incl. Access Fees) $20,000, Other Print Mats $30,000
Library Holdings: Bk Vols 105,000; Per Subs 200
Subject Interests: Cement, Concrete, Construction
Special Collections: ASTM Standards; Foreign Literature Studies; Limited Bibliographies; Occupational Health & Safety Coll; PCA Publications (out-of-print); Translations; TRB Coll
Automation Activity & Vendor Info: (Cataloging) Sydney; (Circulation) Sydney
Database Vendor: Dialog, OCLC - First Search
Publications: Library Update (bimonthly newsletter)
Mem of North Suburban Library System
Partic in Illinois Library & Information Network

S RAND MCNALLY, Map Library, 8255 N Central Park Ave, 60076-2970. SAN 304-6494. Tel: 847-329-6516. FAX: 847-329-1944. *Librn*, Aurora Cabiltes; E-Mail: acabilte@randmcnally.com; Staff 1 (Non-MLS 1)
Founded 1949
Jan 2000-Dec 2000 Mats Exp $20,000, Books $5,000, Per/Ser (Incl. Access Fees) $5,000, Other Print Mats $10,000. Sal $28,496
Library Holdings: Bk Vols 12,920; Bk Titles 12,500; Per Subs 65
Subject Interests: Cartography, Census, Geography, Railroads
Special Collections: Atlases, Maps
Partic in SLA
Friends of the Library Group

M RUSH NORTH SHORE MEDICAL CENTER, Carl Davis Jr, MD Medical Library, 9600 Gross Point Rd, 60076-1257. SAN 373-1952. Tel: 847-933-6236. FAX: 847-933-3830. *Dir*, Jennifer Diehl; E-Mail: jdiehl@rsh.net; Staff 2 (MLS 1, Non-MLS 1)
Founded 1970
Library Holdings: Bk Titles 1,500; Per Subs 200
Database Vendor: OCLC - First Search, OVID Technologies
Restriction: Staff use only
Mem of North Suburban Library System
Partic in Metro Consortium of Chicago

R SAINT PAUL LUTHERAN CHURCH & SCHOOL LIBRARY, 5201 Galitz, 60077. SAN 304-6508. Tel: 847-673-5030. FAX: 847-673-9828. *Librn*, Rosalie Croon
Library Holdings: Bk Vols 11,000; Per Subs 20
Friends of the Library Group

P SKOKIE PUBLIC LIBRARY, 5215 Oakton St, 60077-3680. SAN 304-6516. Tel: 847-673-7774. TDD: 847-673-8926. FAX: 847-673-7797. E-Mail: tellus@skokielibrary.org. Web Site: www.skokie.lib.il.us. *Dir*, Carolyn A Anthony; E-Mail: anthc@skokie.lib.il.us; *Tech Servs*, Camille Cleland; *Acq*, Melody Lucchesi; *Publ Servs*, Barbara A Kozlowski; *Doc*, Jane Hagedorn; *Ref*, Bruce Brigell; *Cat*, Earleen Myers Hickey; *Ad Servs*, Deborah Grodinsky; *Reader Servs*, Ricki Nordmeyer; *YA Servs*, Maryann Mondrus; *Bkmobile Coordr*, Philip Carlsen; *Commun Servs*, Patricia Groh; *Coll Develop*, Teri Room; *Ch Servs*, Jan Watkins; *Circ*, Tobi Oberman; Staff 31 (MLS 31)
Founded 1941. Pop 59,432; Circ 1,176,457
May 1999-Apr 2000 Income $6,438,293, State $348,316, City $5,679,637, Federal $5,500, Locally Generated Income $321,946. Mats Exp $942,858, Books $611,951, Per/Ser (Incl. Access Fees) $102,965, Micro $42,838, AV Equip $76,756, Electronic Ref Mat (Incl. Access Fees) $108,348. Sal $3,150,609
Library Holdings: Bk Vols 386,335; Per Subs 1,807
Subject Interests: American literature, Art and architecture, Business and management, English literature, Foreign Language, Holocaust
Special Collections: College Catalogs, micro; Local History (Cook County), bks & pamphlets; Organized File on Threat and Nazi March in Skokie, 1977
Automation Activity & Vendor Info: (Acquisitions) Innovative Interfaces Inc.; (Cataloging) Innovative Interfaces Inc.; (Circulation) Innovative Interfaces Inc.; (OPAC) Innovative Interfaces Inc.; (Serials) Innovative Interfaces Inc.
Database Vendor: OCLC - First Search
Publications: Skokie Public Library Update (quarterly)
Mem of North Suburban Library System
Special Services for the Deaf - TDD
Special Services for the Blind - Adapted computers & special software with speech output to assist learning disabled, mentally retarded & uneducated; Kurzweil Reading Machine; VisualTek closed circuit TV reading aid
Bookmobiles: 1

R TEMPLE JUDEA MIZPAH LIBRARY,* 8610 Niles Center Rd, 60077. SAN 304-6532. Tel: 847-676-1566. FAX: 847-676-1579. E-Mail: tjm@nics.com. *Librn*, Judy Duesenberg
Library Holdings: Bk Vols 4,000
Special Collections: Jewish Authors, bks, publications

SMITHTON

P SMITHTON PUBLIC LIBRARY DISTRICT, 109 S Main, 62285-1707. SAN 376-4958. Tel: 618-233-8057. FAX: 618-233-3670. E-Mail: sma@lcls.org. *Librn*, Marian Albers; Staff 3 (MLS 1, Non-MLS 2)
Founded 1988. Pop 2,850
Jul 1998-Jun 1999 Income $73,000, State $3,500, County $52,000, Locally Generated Income $2,500, Other $15,000. Mats Exp $11,400, Books $10,000, Per/Ser (Incl. Access Fees) $500, AV Equip $100, Other Print Mats $800. Sal $22,000
Library Holdings: Bk Titles 13,000; Per Subs 18
Special Collections: Automotive Coll, Repairs & Collectables
Automation Activity & Vendor Info: (Circulation) DRA
Database Vendor: OCLC - First Search
Mem of Lewis & Clark Library System

SOMONAUK

P SOMONAUK PUBLIC LIBRARY DISTRICT, 115 E Dekalb St, 60552-0307. (Mail add: PO Box 307, 60552-0307), SAN 304-6540. Tel: 815-498-2440. FAX: 815-498-2135. *Dir*, Julie Harte; E-Mail: jhbookwoman@yahoo.com; Staff 1 (Non-MLS 1)
Founded 1921. Pop 5,880
Jan 2000-Dec 2000 Income $247,728, State $7,254, City $828, Federal $4,500, County $212,885, Other $22,261. Mats Exp $35,179, Books $30,000, Per/Ser (Incl. Access Fees) $2,594, AV Equip $2,585. Sal $56,295
Library Holdings: Bk Vols 24,000; Bk Titles 18,381; Per Subs 3,958
Automation Activity & Vendor Info: (Circulation) GEAC
Database Vendor: IAC - Info Trac
Function: ILL available
Mem of Heritage Trail Library System
Friends of the Library Group

SOUTH BELOIT

P SOUTH BELOIT PUBLIC LIBRARY, 630 Blackhawk Blvd, 61080-1919. SAN 304-6559. Tel: 815-389-2495. FAX: 815-389-0871. E-Mail: sliblju1@net.com. *Librn*, Ortus Dunbar; *Asst Librn*, Kathleen Fago; Staff 1 (MLS 1)
Founded 1948. Pop 4,072; Circ 19,397
Jul 1999-Jun 2000 Income $155,236, City $105,851. Mats Exp $102,533,

Books $20,814, Per/Ser (Incl. Access Fees) $1,560. Sal $56,232 (Prof $26,014)
Library Holdings: Bk Titles 23,335; Per Subs 76
Special Collections: Newbery Award & Coretta Scott King Award Books
Mem of Northern Illinois Library System

SOUTH HOLLAND

P SOUTH HOLLAND PUBLIC LIBRARY,* 16250 Wausau Ave, 60473. SAN 304-6575. Tel: 708-331-5262. FAX: 708-331-6557. E-Mail: shs@sls.lib.il.us. *Librn*, Alma J DeYoung
Founded 1961. Pop 22,105; Circ 180,706
Library Holdings: Bk Vols 89,000
Mem of Suburban Library System

J SOUTH SUBURBAN COLLEGE LIBRARY,* 15800 S State, 60473-9998. SAN 304-6591. Tel: 708-596-2000, Ext 5751. FAX: 708-210-5755. Web Site: www.ssc.cc.il.us. *Actg Dir, Chair*, Marilyn Wells; *Govt Doc, Ref*, Carla Connolly; E-Mail: cconnolly@ssc.cc.il.us; Staff 3 (MLS 3)
Founded 1927. Fac 130
Library Holdings: Bk Titles 42,000; Per Subs 308
Subject Interests: Nursing
Special Collections: Local History Center
Publications: LRC Newsletter; LRC Pamphlet
Mem of Suburban Library System

S SOUTH SUBURBAN GENEALOGICAL & HISTORICAL SOCIETY LIBRARY, Roosevelt Community Center, 320 E 161st Pl, 60473. (Mail add: PO Box 96, 60473-0096), SAN 304-6583. Tel: 708-333-9474. E-Mail: ssghs@hotmail.com. Web Site: www.rootsweb.com/~ssghs/ssghs.htm. *Pres*, Marilea Zajec
Founded 1972
1998-1999 Income $2,500, Locally Generated Income $1,500, Parent Institution $1,000. Mats Exp $1,725, Books $1,000, Per/Ser (Incl. Access Fees) $50, Presv $50, Micro $50
Library Holdings: Bk Titles 9,500; Per Subs 500
Subject Interests: Genealogy, Local history
Special Collections: Cemetery Listings in Northern Illinois; Federal Population Census 1790-1920, bk, micro; Illinois - Cook & Will Counties; Naturalization Records for Calumet City; Obituary Files; Pullman Car Works, personnel rec; Roseland (Chicago) Church Hist; School rec; Township rec
Publications: Cemetery readings; monthly newsletter; research series; Where the Trails Cross (quarterly)
Restriction: Non-circulating to the public

SOUTH PEKIN

P SOUTH PEKIN PUBLIC LIBRARY,* 208 W Main St, PO Box 490, 61564. SAN 304-6605. Tel: 309-348-2446. *Librn*, Janet Switzer
Pop 1,243; Circ 3,195
Library Holdings: Bk Vols 2,621; Per Subs 11
Mem of Alliance Library System
Open Mon, Wed, Fri 3:30-5:30, Tues & Thurs 6-9

SPARTA

P SPARTA PUBLIC LIBRARY, 211 W Broadway, 62286. SAN 304-6613. Tel: 618-443-5014. FAX: 618-443-2952. E-Mail: sparta@egyptian.net. Web Site: sirin.lib.il.us. *Dir*, Carol Pirtle; *Asst Librn*, Lois Cunningham; *Asst Librn*, Dorothy Stephenson; Staff 6 (Non-MLS 6)
Founded 1944. Pop 4,853; Circ 45,240
Apr 1998-Mar 1999 Income $75,441, State $6,010, City $51,152, Other $18,279. Mats Exp $21,525, Books $11,837, Per/Ser (Incl. Access Fees) $150, Other Print Mats $9,538. Sal $43,894 (Prof $16,000)
Library Holdings: Bk Vols 39,506; Bk Titles 39,506; Per Subs 292; Bks on Deafness & Sign Lang 10
Subject Interests: Local history
Automation Activity & Vendor Info: (Cataloging) Athena; (Circulation) Athena
Database Vendor: Ebsco - EbscoHost, OVID Technologies
Function: Some telephone reference
Mem of Shawnee Library System
Friends of the Library Group

SPRING VALLEY

P RICHARD A MAUTINO MEMORIAL LIBRARY, 215 E Cleveland St, 61362. SAN 304-6621. Tel: 815-663-4741. *Librn*, Barbara White; *Ch Servs*, Mary Boehm
Founded 1912. Pop 5,822; Circ 18,726
Library Holdings: Bk Titles 19,533; Per Subs 90
Mem of Heritage Trail Library System

SPRINGFIELD

S AIRCHIVE, Historair File,* 428 W Vine St, 62704-2933. SAN 374-8960. Tel: 217-544-6122. E-Mail: writer@eosinc.com. *Exec Dir*, Job C Conger, IV
Library Holdings: Bk Titles 300

S HANSON ENGINEERS, INC, Technical Library, 1525 S Sixth St, 62703-2886. SAN 304-663X. Tel: 217-788-2450. FAX: 217-747-9416. Web Site: www.hansonengineers.com. *In Charge*, Betty Lou Hicks; E-Mail: bhicks@hansonengineers.com; Staff 1 (MLS 1)
Founded 1975
Library Holdings: Bk Titles 19,582
Subject Interests: Architecture, Civil engineering, Electrical engineering, Industrial hygiene, Mechanical engineering
Special Collections: Geology (Illinois Coll); Illinois Topo, maps; Walter E Hanson Coll
Automation Activity & Vendor Info: (Cataloging) DRA; (Circulation) DRA
Restriction: Staff use only
Mem of Rolling Prairie Library System
Partic in Capital Area Health Consortium; OCLC Online Computer Library Center, Inc

S ILLINOIS COMMERCE COMMISSION, Technical Information Center,* 527 E Capitol, 62701-1827. SAN 375-9571. Tel: 217-524-5054. FAX: 217-524-0674. *Librn*, Sandy Schmohe
Library Holdings: Bk Titles 1,200

G ILLINOIS DEPARTMENT OF HUMAN SERVICES-THE OFFICE OF REHABILITATION SERVICES, Resource Center,* 623 E Adams St, 62701. SAN 375-3875. Tel: 217-524-0706. FAX: 217-524-0707. *Librn*, Jan Perone; E-Mail: jperone@dors.state.il.us; *Tech Servs*, Kristi Ruppel; Staff 2 (Non-MLS 2)
Founded 1990
Jul 1996-Jun 1997 Mats Exp $6,000. Sal $79,000
Library Holdings: Bk Titles 2,000; Per Subs 200
Automation Activity & Vendor Info: (Acquisitions) Sagebrush Corporation; (Cataloging) Sagebrush Corporation; (Circulation) Sagebrush Corporation
Publications: News You Can Use
Mem of Rolling Prairie Library System
Partic in Capital Area Consortium; Illinois Library & Information Network
Special Services for the Deaf - Books on deafness & sign language; Captioned film depository; TTY machine

S ILLINOIS EARLY CHILDHOOD INTERVENTION CLEARINGHOUSE LIBRARY,* 830 S Spring St, 62704. SAN 371-523X. Tel: 217-785-1364. FAX: 217-524-5339. E-Mail: clearinghouse@eosinc.com. *Dir*, Chet Brandt; Staff 3 (MLS 1, Non-MLS 2)
Founded 1986
Jul 1998-Jun 1999 Income $196,250. Mats Exp $28,000, Books $10,000, Per/Ser (Incl. Access Fees) $13,000. Sal $77,000 (Prof $37,000)
Library Holdings: Bk Titles 6,000; Per Subs 150
Automation Activity & Vendor Info: (Cataloging) DRA; (Circulation) DRA
Publications: Bibliography Series; Early Intervention (free quarterly newsletter)
Mem of Rolling Prairie Library System
Partic in Capitol Area Health Consortium; Health Sci Libr Info Consortium; Illinois Library & Information Network
Special Services for the Deaf - Books on deafness & sign language; TDD; Videos & decoder

G ILLINOIS ENVIRONMENTAL PROTECTION AGENCY LIBRARY,* 1021 N Grand Ave E, PO Box 19276, 62794-9276. SAN 321-897X. Tel: 217-782-9691. FAX: 217-524-4916. E-Mail: epa7131@epa.state.il.us. Web Site: www.epa.state.il.us. *Librn*, Nancy R Simpson; Staff 1 (MLS 1)
Founded 1970
Library Holdings: Bk Titles 30,000; Per Subs 400
Subject Interests: Environ protection, Environmental engineering, Environmental law
Publications: Acquisitions List (monthly)
Mem of Rolling Prairie Library System
Partic in Capitol Area Health Consortium; Illinois Library & Information Network; Library Network; OCLC Online Computer Library Center, Inc
Open Mon-Fri 8:30-5

G ILLINOIS STATE ARCHIVES,* Margaret Cross Norton Bldg, 62756. SAN 304-6648. Tel: 217-782-1083, 217-782-4682. FAX: 217-524-3930. Web Site: www.sos.state.il.us. *Dir*, John Daly; E-Mail: jdaly@ccgate.sos.state.il.us; Staff 66 (MLS 31, Non-MLS 35)
Founded 1921
Publications: A Summary Guide to Local Government Records in the Illinois Regional Archives; Chicago City Council Proceedings Files, 1833-1871 (An Index); Chicago City Council Proceedings Files, 1833-1871 (An Inventory); Descriptive Inventory of the Archives of the State of Illinois; Guide to County Records in the Illinois Regional Archives; Illinois Public Domain Land Sales (1985)

G ILLINOIS STATE DATA CENTER COOPERATIVE, Illinois Department of Commerce & Community Affairs, 620 E Adams, 62701. Tel: 217-782-1381. FAX: 217-524-3701. *Coordr*, Sue Ebetsch; E-Mail: sebetsch@commerce.state.il.us
Library Holdings: Bk Titles 5,000; Per Subs 50
Special Collections: US Bureau of the Census, Bureau of Economic Analysis, Bureau of Labor Statistics, print & electronic data
Publications: Illinois Population Trends - 1990 to 2020

G ILLINOIS STATE DEPARTMENT OF TRANSPORT, Technical Reference Library, 320 Harry Hanley Bldg, 2300 S Dirksen Pkwy, 62764-0001. SAN 326-9957. Tel: 217-782-6680. FAX: 217-524-3834. *Librn*, Gisela Motzkus; E-Mail: motzkusgh@nt.dot.state.il.us
Library Holdings: Bk Vols 12,000; Per Subs 298
Automation Activity & Vendor Info: (OPAC) DRA
Database Vendor: OCLC - First Search
Publications: Recent Acquisitions
Restriction: Not open to public
Mem of Rolling Prairie Library System
Partic in Illinois Library & Information Network; OCLC Online Computer Library Center, Inc

S ILLINOIS STATE HISTORICAL LIBRARY, Old State Capitol, 62701. SAN 304-6656. Tel: 217-524-7216. Reference Tel: 217-524-6358. TDD: 217-524-7128. FAX: 217-785-6250. Web Site: www.state.il.us/hpa/lib. *Dir*, Kathryn M Harris; Tel: 217-524-7219; *Senior Librn*, Sandra Stark; Tel: 217-524-7238, E-Mail: sstark@hpa084r1.state.il.us; *Librn*, Bonnie Parr; Tel: 217-785-7934; *Librn*, Cheryl Pence; Tel: 217-785-7941; *Curator*, Cheryl Schnirring; Tel: 217-785-7942; *Acq*, Jill Blessman; Tel: 217-785-7943; *Acq*, Gary Stockton; Tel: 217-524-5939; *AV*, Mary Michals; Tel: 217-785-7955; *Res*, Kim Bauer; Tel: 217-785-7954; *Ref, Tech Servs*, Jane Ehrenhart; Tel: 217-785-7945. Subject Specialists: *Abraham Lincoln*, Kim Bauer; *Conservation*, Bonnie Parr; *Manuscripts*, Cheryl Schnirring; *Newspapers*, Cheryl Pence; Staff 27 (MLS 6, Non-MLS 21)
Founded 1889
Jul 1999-Jun 2000 Income $1,363,000. Mats Exp $113,500, Books $37,000, Per/Ser (Incl. Access Fees) $9,500, Presv $5,000, Micro $15,000, AV Equip $5,000, Other Print Mats $10,000, Manuscripts & Archives $7,000, Electronic Ref Mat (Incl. Access Fees) $25,000. Sal $1,097,457 (Prof $627,253)
Library Holdings: Bk Vols 190,000; Per Subs 1,200
Subject Interests: Civil War, Illinois, Mormons
Special Collections: Illinois Newspapers; Lincolniana
Automation Activity & Vendor Info: (Cataloging) DRA; (OPAC) DRA
Database Vendor: OCLC - First Search
Publications: Journal of Illinois History (quarterly)
Restriction: Non-circulating to the public
Function: Research library
Mem of Rolling Prairie Library System
Partic in Illinois Library & Information Network; OCLC Online Computer Library Center, Inc
Division of the Illinois Historic Preservation Agency

P ILLINOIS STATE LIBRARY,* 300 S Second St, 62701-1976. SAN 304-6672. Interlibrary Loan Service Tel: 217-782-7523. Reference Tel: 217-782-7596. Toll Free Tel: 800-665-5576. FAX: 217-785-4326. Web Site: www.library.sos.state.il.us. *Dir*, Jean Wilkins; Tel: 217-782-2994, E-Mail: jwilkins@il.sos.net; *Dep Dir*, Mike Ragen; Tel: 217-524-4200, E-Mail: mragen@il.sos.net; *Dep Dir*, Greg McCormick; Tel: 217-782-3504, E-Mail: gmccormick@il.sos.net; *Assoc Dir*, Kathleen Bloomberg; Tel: 217-785-0052, E-Mail: kbloomberg@il.sos.net; *Coll Develop*, Jane Rishel; Tel: 217-782-7791, E-Mail: jrishel@il.sos.net; *Automation Syst Coordr, Tech Coordr*, Anne Craig; Tel: 217-785-5607, E-Mail: acraig@il.sos.net; *Network Services*, Barbara B Alexander; Tel: 217-785-7334, E-Mail: balexander@il.sos.net; *Publ Servs*, Jim Bradley; Tel: 217-782-1890, E-Mail: jbradley@il.sos.net; *Info Tech*, Andrew Bullen; Tel: 773-291-0005, E-Mail: abullen@findit.sos.state.il.us; *Outreach Serv*, Jeanne Flynn; Tel: 217-785-0977, E-Mail: jflynn@il.sos.net; *YA Servs*, Karen Muskopf; Tel: 217-782-7749, E-Mail: kmuskopf@il.sos.net. Subject Specialists: *Maps*, Arlyn Sherwood Booth; *Patents-trademarks*, Jane Running
Founded 1839. Pop 47,000
Jul 1998-Jun 1999 Income (Main Library Only) $81,986,719, State $77,030,765, Federal $4,955,954. Mats Exp $577,965, Books $84,674, Per/Ser (Incl. Access Fees) $222,541, Presv $29,897, Micro $132,169, Other Print Mats $870, Electronic Ref Mat (Incl. Access Fees) $107,814. Sal $4,216,795 (Prof $2,479,668)
Library Holdings: Bk Vols 2,600,000; Per Subs 2,500
Subject Interests: Political science
Special Collections: Patent, Trademark & Maps
Automation Activity & Vendor Info: (Acquisitions) DRA; (Cataloging) DRA; (Circulation) DRA
Database Vendor: OCLC - First Search
Publications: Illinois Insight; Illinois Libraries; Illinois Literacy; Publications of the State of Illinois
Partic in Ill Libr Computer Systs Org; Illinois Library & Information Network; OCLC Online Computer Library Center, Inc
Special Services for the Deaf - Staff with knowledge of sign language; TDD
Special Services for the Blind - Kurzweil Reading Machine
Branches: 1

P ILLINOIS REGIONAL LIBRARY FOR THE BLIND & PHYSICALLY HANDICAPPED, 300 S Second St, 62701. Tel: 217-782-9434. Toll Free Tel: 800-665-5576. FAX: 217-782-8261. Web Site: www.cyberdriveillinois.com/library/isl/outreach.html. *Librn*, Sharon Ruda; E-Mail: sruda@ilsos.net

S ILLINOIS STATE MUSEUM LIBRARY, Spring & Edwards Sts, 62706-5000. SAN 304-6680. Tel: 217-782-6623. FAX: 217-782-1254. Web Site: www.museum.state.il.us. *Head Librn*, Patricia Burg; E-Mail: pburg@museum.state.il.us; *Assoc Librn*, Ronald Sauberli; Staff 2 (MLS 1, Non-MLS 1)
Founded 1877
Library Holdings: Bk Vols 23,200; Per Subs 283
Subject Interests: Anthropology, Art, Natural science
Special Collections: Anthropology (Thorne Deuel Coll); Art (Benjamin F Hunter Coll); Ornithology (R M Barnes Coll); Paleontology (Raymond E Janssen Coll); Zoology (Donald F Hoffmeister Coll)
Automation Activity & Vendor Info: (Cataloging) DRA; (Circulation) DRA; (OPAC) DRA
Database Vendor: OCLC - First Search
Mem of Rolling Prairie Library System
Partic in Data Res Assocs; Illinois Library & Information Network

S LEGISLATIVE REFERENCE BUREAU LAW LIBRARY,* State Capitol Rm 112, 62706. SAN 304-6702. Tel: 217-782-6625. FAX: 217-785-4583. Web Site: www.legis.state.il.us. *Librn*, Bernadine Gretzer
Founded 1913
Library Holdings: Bk Vols 20,000; Per Subs 29
Special Collections: Annotated Statutes for all Fifty States, Legislative Synopsis & Digests; Illinois Laws (since 1840)

J LINCOLN LAND COMMUNITY COLLEGE, Learning Resource Center,* 5250 Shepherd Rd, PO Box 19256, 62794-9256. SAN 304-6710. Tel: 217-786-2353. FAX: 217-786-2251. E-Mail: library@llcc.cc.il.us. Web Site: www.llcc.il.us. *In Charge*, Mike Miller; E-Mail: mike.miller@llcc.cc.il.us; *Automation Syst Coordr*, Cheryl Bushnell; *ILL*, Ann Hopkins; *Coll Develop, Online Servs, Publ Servs, Ref*, Elijah Singley; *Cat*, Mike Barnard; *Br Coordr*, Becky Parton; Staff 6 (MLS 6)
Founded 1968. Enrl 10,000; Fac 130
Jul 1998-Jun 1999 Income $786,960. Mats Exp $128,300, Books $39,460, Per/Ser (Incl. Access Fees) $51,340, Micro $2,000. Sal $595,200 (Prof $325,522)
Library Holdings: Bk Vols 64,000; Bk Titles 56,000; Per Subs 265
Subject Interests: Nursing
Mem of Rolling Prairie Library System
Partic in Cap Area Libr Consortium; NILRC; OCLC Online Computer Library Center, Inc; Sangamon Valley Academic Library Consortium
Special Services for the Deaf - Staff with knowledge of sign language

P LINCOLN LIBRARY, Springfield's Public Library, 326 S Seventh St, 62701. SAN 340-7853. Tel: 217-753-4900. Interlibrary Loan Service Tel: 217-753-4900, Ext 222. FAX: 217-753-5329. Web Site: lincolnlibrary.rpls.lib.il.us/llhome5.htm. *Dir*, Nancy Huntley; *Ch Servs*, Jean Jaderborg; *Coll Develop, Ref*, Pat Blinn; *Outreach Serv*, Jamie Wilcox; *Tech Servs*, Shirley Ackerman; Staff 57 (MLS 18, Non-MLS 39)
Founded 1886. Pop 105,227; Circ 950,342
Library Holdings: Bk Vols 504,327; Per Subs 873
Subject Interests: History, Music, Political science
Special Collections: Local History; Newspaper Index; Vachel Lindsay (Sangamon Valley Coll)
Automation Activity & Vendor Info: (Cataloging) DRA; (Circulation) DRA; (OPAC) DRA
Publications: Lincoln Library Bulletin
Mem of Rolling Prairie Library System
Partic in Illinois Library & Information Network; OCLC Online Computer Library Center, Inc
Special Services for the Deaf - Special interest periodicals; Staff with knowledge of sign language; TTY machine
Friends of the Library Group
Branches: 3
NORTH, 719 N Grand Ave E, 62702. SAN 340-7918. Tel: 217-753-4970. FAX: 217-753-4972. *Librn*, Jamie Wilcox
Library Holdings: Bk Vols 33,047
SOUTHEAST, 2500 S Grand Ave E, 62703. SAN 328-7491. Tel: 217-753-4980. FAX: 217-753-4982. *Librn*, Jamie Wilcox
Library Holdings: Bk Vols 27,801
WEST, 1251 W Washington, 62702. SAN 340-7977. Tel: 217-753-4985. FAX: 217-787-5987. *Librn*, Jamie Wilcox
Library Holdings: Bk Vols 44,534
Bookmobiles: 1

M MCFARLAND MENTAL HEALTH CENTER, Staff Library, 901 Southwind Rd, 62703. SAN 304-6729. Tel: 217-786-6851. FAX: 217-786-7167. *Librn*, Wanda Beck
Library Holdings: Bk Vols 12,500; Per Subs 49
Subject Interests: Psychiatry, Psychology
Mem of Rolling Prairie Library System

M MEMORIAL MEDICAL CENTER, Kenneth H Schnepp Professional Library, 701 N First St, 62781-0001. SAN 304-6737. Tel: 217-788-3331. FAX: 217-788-5540. *Mgr Libr Serv*, Lynne Ferrell; E-Mail: ferrell.lynne@mhsil.com
Founded 1943
Library Holdings: Bk Vols 5,000; Per Subs 165
Subject Interests: Health sciences
Automation Activity & Vendor Info: (Cataloging) DRA; (Circulation) DRA
Database Vendor: DRA, Ebsco - EbscoHost, OCLC - First Search
Restriction: Open to student, faculty & staff
Function: ILL available, Literary searches, Photocopies available, Professional lending library, Research library
Mem of Rolling Prairie Library System
Partic in Capitol Area Consortium; Greater Regional Med Libr-Region 3; Illinois Library & Information Network; LVIS; Nat Libr of Med; OCLC Online Computer Library Center, Inc

G OFFICE OF THE AUDITOR GENERAL LIBRARY, 740 E Ash St, 62703. SAN 326-9914. Tel: 217-782-1055. FAX: 217-785-8222. E-Mail: auditor@mail.state.il.us. Web Site: www.state.il.us/auditor. *Librn*, Barbara Gossrow
Library Holdings: Bk Titles 2,600
Special Collections: Financial-Compliance & Performance Audits 1974-present
Mem of Rolling Prairie Library System
Partic in ILLINET

ST JOHN'S HOSPITAL

M HEALTH SCIENCES LIBRARY, 800 E Carpenter, 62769. SAN 340-8000. Tel: 217-544-6464, Ext 44566. FAX: 217-525-2895. *Dir*, Kathryn Wrigley; E-Mail: kwrigley@st-johns.org; *Ref*, Roger Swartzbaugh; Staff 3 (MLS 2, Non-MLS 1)
Founded 1932
Library Holdings: Bk Titles 5,948; Per Subs 395
Subject Interests: Nursing, Orthopedics, Pediatrics, Surgery
Automation Activity & Vendor Info: (Acquisitions) epixtech, inc.; (Cataloging) epixtech, inc.; (Circulation) epixtech, inc.; (Media Booking) epixtech, inc.; (OPAC) epixtech, inc.; (Serials) epixtech, inc.
Database Vendor: OCLC - First Search, OVID Technologies
Mem of Rolling Prairie Library System
Partic in Capital Area Consortium; Nat Libr of Med; OCLC Online Computer Library Center, Inc

CM SOUTHERN ILLINOIS UNIVERSITY SCHOOL OF MEDICINE LIBRARY, 801 N Rutledge, PO Box 19625, 62794-9625. SAN 304-6761. Tel: 217-782-2658. Circulation Tel: 217-785-2122. Reference Tel: 217-785-2113. FAX: 217-782-0988, 217-782-7503. Web Site: www.siumed.edu/lib/. *Dir*, Connie Poole; E-Mail: cpoole@siumed.edu; *Head Ref*, Rhona Kelley; *Ref Serv Ad*, Fran Kovach; *Ref Serv Ad*, Carol Thornton; Staff 20 (MLS 4, Non-MLS 16)
Founded 1970. Enrl 300
Jul 1999-Jun 2000 Income $1,502,356, Locally Generated Income $67,460, Parent Institution $1,434,896. Mats Exp $730,867, Books $90,046, Per/Ser (Incl. Access Fees) $619,295, AV Equip $3,120, Electronic Ref Mat (Incl. Access Fees) $18,406. Sal $400,963 (Prof $242,212)
Library Holdings: Bk Vols 70,792; Bk Titles 55,256; Per Subs 1,207
Subject Interests: Medicine
Special Collections: History of Medicine
Database Vendor: Dialog, Ebsco - EbscoHost, OCLC - First Search, OVID Technologies
Publications: AV titles; Newsletter (quarterly); serials subjects; serials titles
Function: Reference services available
Mem of Rolling Prairie Library System
Partic in Illinois Library & Information Network

S SPRINGFIELD ART ASSOCIATION, Michael Victor II Art Library,* 700 N Fourth, 62702. SAN 304-677X. Tel: 217-523-3507. FAX: 217-523-3866. *Librn*, Mark Jenkins
Founded 1950
1997-1998 Income $13,890, Locally Generated Income $6,550, Parent Institution $7,340. Mats Exp $8,750, Books $8,250, Per/Ser (Incl. Access Fees) $500. Sal $10,140
Library Holdings: Bk Titles 5,000; Per Subs 16
Subject Interests: Art, Art history, Arts and crafts, Paintings, Photography, Prints
Mem of Rolling Prairie Library System

C SPRINGFIELD COLLEGE IN ILLINOIS, Charles E Becker Library, 1521 N Sixth St, 62702. SAN 304-6788. Tel: 217-525-1420, Ext 221. FAX: 217-525-2651. E-Mail: library@sci.edu. Web Site: www.sci.edu. *Librn*, Susan Full; E-Mail: full@sci.edu; Staff 2 (MLS 2)
Founded 1929. Enrl 462; Fac 45
Library Holdings: Bk Vols 20,000; Per Subs 146
Subject Interests: Humanities
Automation Activity & Vendor Info: (Cataloging) DRA; (Circulation) DRA; (OPAC) DRA
Mem of Rolling Prairie Library System
Partic in Capital Area Consortium; Private Academic Libraries Of Illinois; Sangamon Valley Academic Library Consortium

S THE STATE JOURNAL & REGISTER, Editorial Library,* Copley Plaza, PO Box 219, 62701. SAN 304-6664. Tel: 217-788-1504. FAX: 217-788-1551. E-Mail: sjr@sj-r.com. Web Site: www.sj-r.com. *Dir*, Lynda L Schmitz Fuhrig; Staff 2 (MLS 1, Non-MLS 1)
Founded 1930
Library Holdings: Bk Titles 500

GL SUPREME COURT OF ILLINOIS LIBRARY, Supreme Court Bldg, 200 E Capital Ave, 62701-1791. SAN 304-6699. Tel: 217-782-2424. FAX: 217-782-5287. *Dir*, Brenda Larison; E-Mail: blarison@mail.state.il.us; Staff 6 (MLS 3, Non-MLS 3)
Founded 1839
Library Holdings: Bk Vols 100,000; Bk Titles 6,000; Per Subs 500
Subject Interests: Illinois, Law
Special Collections: SJI Depository
Automation Activity & Vendor Info: (Cataloging) DRA
Database Vendor: DRA
Mem of Rolling Prairie Library System
Partic in OCLC Online Computer Library Center, Inc
Branches:
CHICAGO BRANCH, 160 N LaSalle S-1800, Chicago, 60601.; Staff 2 (MLS 1, Non-MLS 1)
Founded 1993

L UNITED STATES COURTS LIBRARY,* 600 E Monroe St, Rm 305, 62701. SAN 372-1159. Tel: 217-492-4191. FAX: 217-492-4192. *Librn*, Martha Doyle
Library Holdings: Bk Vols 8,000; Per Subs 35
Partic in OCLC Online Computer Library Center, Inc

C UNIVERSITY OF ILLINOIS AT SPRINGFIELD, Norris L Brookens Library,* PO Box 19243, 62794-9243. SAN 304-6753. Tel: 217-206-6597. Reference Tel: 217-206-6633. FAX: 217-206-7188. Web Site: www.uis.edu/library/. *Dean of Libr*, Edward Wass; E-Mail: wass.edward@uls.edu; *Tech Servs*, Barbara Klintworth; *Bibliog Instr*, Denise Green; *Doc*, Linda Kopecky; *Acq*, Ruth West; *Coll Develop*, Janis Peach; Staff 38 (MLS 13, Non-MLS 25)
Founded 1970. Enrl 2,574; Fac 184; Highest Degree: Doctorate
Jul 1997-Jun 1998 Income $2,297,033, State $2,170,490, Locally Generated Income $126,243. Mats Exp $686,018, Books $296,213, Per/Ser (Incl. Access Fees) $338,946, Presv $23,000, Micro $20,859, AV Equip $7,000. Sal $1,255,550 (Prof $548,936)
Library Holdings: Bk Vols 445,902; Per Subs 2,732
Subject Interests: Business and management, Economics, Education, Law
Special Collections: Handy Colony Coll; Illinois Regional Archives Depository
Publications: James Jones in Illinois: A Guide to the Handy Colony Collection, 1989.
Mem of Rolling Prairie Library System
Partic in Capital Area Consortium; Ill Libr Computer Systs Org; OCLC Online Computer Library Center, Inc; Sangamon Valley Academic Library Consortium
Friends of the Library Group

S YOUTH NETWORK COUNCIL, Illinois Youth Service Resource Center,* 321 1/2 S Sixth St Ste 200, 62701. SAN 375-1767. Tel: 217-522-2663. FAX: 217-522-2676. E-Mail: icoy-ync@springnet1.com. *In Charge*, Casey Custer
Library Holdings: Bk Titles 25

STANFORD

P ALLIN TOWNSHIP LIBRARY,* 101 S Armstrong St, PO Box 258, 61774. SAN 376-0936. Tel: 309-379-4631. FAX: 309-379-4631. E-Mail: allinlib@davesworld.net. *Librn*, Katie Larkin
Library Holdings: Bk Vols 2,500
Mem of Alliance Library System
Friends of the Library Group

STAUNTON

P STAUNTON PUBLIC LIBRARY,* 306 W Main St, 62088. SAN 304-6796. Tel: 618-635-3852. FAX: 618-635-2246. *Librn*, Oleta Massie
Founded 1912. Pop 4,806; Circ 35,466
Library Holdings: Bk Vols 17,328; Per Subs 72
Special Collections: House the Macoupin Company Genealogical Coll
Mem of Lewis & Clark Library System

STEELEVILLE

P STEELEVILLE AREA LIBRARY,* 107 W Broadway, 62288. SAN 376-494X. Tel: 618-965-9732. FAX: 618-965-2057. *Librn*, Eileen Tegtmeyer
Library Holdings: Bk Vols 15,000; Bk Titles 10,000; Per Subs 35
Mem of Shawnee Library System
Friends of the Library Group

STEGER

P STEGER-SOUTH CHICAGO HEIGHTS PUBLIC LIBRARY DISTRICT,* 54 E 31st St, 60475. SAN 304-6567. Tel: 708-755-5040. FAX: 708-755-2504. E-Mail: sts2@sslic.net. *Tech Servs*, Lori Williams; *Librn*, Barbara Byrne Osuch; *ILL*, Donna Bivona; *Ch Servs*, Katharin Kalweit
Founded 1975. Pop 12,955
Library Holdings: Bk Vols 37,393; Per Subs 97
Publications: Newsletter (quarterly)
Mem of Suburban Library System

STERLING

M CGH MEDICAL CENTER, Health Sciences Library, 100 E LeFevre Rd, 61081-1278. SAN 375-2739. Tel: 815-625-0400. FAX: 815-625-0203. E-Mail: medlib04@essex1.com. *Librn*, Dana Gerberi; Tel: 815-625-0400, Ext 4416; Staff 1 (Non-MLS 1)
Founded 1972
May 1999-Apr 2000 Income $5,000. Mats Exp $19,400, Per/Ser (Incl. Access Fees) $15,400, Other Print Mats $4,000. Sal $28,751
Library Holdings: Bk Vols 2,200; Bk Titles 850; Per Subs 110
Database Vendor: OCLC - First Search
Restriction: Staff use only
Function: Literary searches
Mem of Northern Illinois Library System
Partic in Upstate Consortium

P STERLING PUBLIC LIBRARY, 102 W Third St, 61081-3511. SAN 304-680X. Tel: 815-625-1370. FAX: 815-625-7037. E-Mail: director@sterlingpubliclibrary.org. Web Site: www.sterlingpubliclibrary.org. *Dir*, Jennifer Slaney; Staff 12 (MLS 2, Non-MLS 10)
Pop 15,132; Circ 161,986
May 1999-Apr 2000 Income $449,284. Sal $187,000 (Prof $55,000)
Library Holdings: Bk Vols 54,300; Per Subs 147
Subject Interests: Genealogy, Local history, Political science
Automation Activity & Vendor Info: (Cataloging) TLC; (Circulation) TLC
Mem of Northern Illinois Library System
Open Mon-Thurs 9-8, Fri 9-5, Sat 8-5 & Sun 1-4 (Sept-May)
Friends of the Library Group

STICKNEY

P STICKNEY-FOREST VIEW PUBLIC LIBRARY DISTRICT,* 6800 W 43rd St, 60402. SAN 304-6818. Tel: 708-749-1050. FAX: 708-749-1054. *Dir*, Elaine Swan; *Ch Servs*, Margaret Chervinko; *Cat, Tech Servs*, Ramona Wolf; Staff 1 (MLS 1)
Founded 1953. Pop 6,657; Circ 64,750
Library Holdings: Bk Vols 56,000; Per Subs 189
Special Collections: Czechoslovakian Language
Mem of Suburban Library System
Friends of the Library Group

STILLMAN VALLEY

P JULIA HULL DISTRICT LIBRARY, 122 S Walnut St, 61084-0340. SAN 304-6826. Tel: 815-645-8611. FAX: 815-645-8611. E-Mail: jhlibrary@rockford.com. *Librn*, Kimberly Eckert; Fax: 815-645-1341
Pop 961; Circ 12,647
1998-1999 Mats Exp $3,000
Library Holdings: Bk Vols 11,500
Special Collections: Blackhawk War & Local History Coll
Mem of Northern Illinois Library System
Open Mon & Thurs 9-8, Tues & Wed 9-5 & Sat 9-2
Friends of the Library Group

STOCKTON

P STOCKTON TOWNSHIP PUBLIC LIBRARY,* 140 W Benton St, 61085. SAN 304-6834. Tel: 815-947-2030. FAX: 815-947-2030. *Librn*, M J O'Boyle
Founded 1926. Pop 2,471; Circ 21,029
Library Holdings: Bk Vols 16,400; Per Subs 60
Subject Interests: Local history
Special Collections: Paintings (J Howard Smith Coll)
Mem of Northern Illinois Library System
Houses Heritage League of Northwest Illinois Museum Open Mon & Wed 2-8, Tues & Thurs 1-5, Fri 11-5 & Sat 10-4

STONINGTON

P STONINGTON TOWNSHIP PUBLIC LIBRARY, 500 E North St, 62567. SAN 304-6842. Tel: 217-325-3512. FAX: 217-325-3750. Web Site: stonlib@chipsnet.com. *Librn*, Nancy Moma; *Asst Librn*, Cheryl Connington
Founded 1982. Pop 1,480
Mar 1999-Feb 2000 Mats Exp $3,400, Books $3,000, AV Equip $400
Library Holdings: Bk Vols 22,000; Per Subs 16
Mem of Rolling Prairie Library System
Open Mon & Thurs 12-6:30, Tues, Wed & Fri 9-12 & 1-5, Sat 9-11
Friends of the Library Group

STREAMWOOD

P POPLAR CREEK PUBLIC LIBRARY DISTRICT,* 1405 S Park Ave, 60107-2997. SAN 304-6850. Tel: 630-837-6800. FAX: 630-837-6823. *Dir*, Patricia Hogan; *Asst Dir*, Betty Cress; *Tech Servs*, Julie Blackwell; *Ch Servs*, Carol Davis; *YA Servs*, Joyce Wagner; *Ad Servs*, Margery Kiefer Newman; *Doc*, Paulette Harding; Staff 13 (MLS 13)
Founded 1966. Pop 59,124
Library Holdings: Bk Titles 336,583; Per Subs 3,457
Automation Activity & Vendor Info: (Circulation) epixtech, inc.
Publications: Library Digest (newsletter, bimonthly)
Mem of DuPage Library System
Branches: 1
HANOVER PARK BRANCH, 4300 Audrey Lane, Hanover Park, 60103. SAN 374-3578. Tel: 630-372-0052. FAX: 630-372-0024.

STREATOR

M SAINT MARY'S HOSPITAL, Hengen Library, 111 E Spring St, 61364. SAN 320-6610. Tel: 815-673-2311, Ext 3390. FAX: 815-673-4541. *Librn*, Ann Jane Flanigan
Library Holdings: Bk Vols 350; Per Subs 12
Partic in Heart Of Illinois Library Consortium

P STREATOR PUBLIC LIBRARY, (SPL), 130 S Park St, 61364. SAN 304-6869. Tel: 815-672-2729. FAX: 815-672-2729. E-Mail: library@sainet.net. Web Site: www.udnet.net/~library. *Dir*, Leslie Dianne Poldek; *Cat*, Rose Ann Negray; Staff 5 (Non-MLS 5)
Founded 1903. Pop 14,121; Circ 20,000
May 1999-Apr 2000 Income $212,411, State $39,310, City $115,775, Locally Generated Income $21,056, Other $36,270. Mats Exp $30,575, Books $25,575, Per/Ser (Incl. Access Fees) $5,000. Sal $62,180 (Prof $14,900)
Library Holdings: Bk Vols 47,960; Per Subs 167; Bks on Deafness & Sign Lang 26
Special Collections: History of Streator & La Salle County
Mem of Heritage Trail Library System

SUGAR GROVE

P SUGAR GROVE PUBLIC LIBRARY DISTRICT, 54 Snow St, PO Box 1049, 60554-1049. SAN 304-6877. Tel: 630-466-4686. TDD: 800-526-0844 (relay). FAX: 630-466-4189. E-Mail: ill@sugargrove.lib.il.us. Web Site: www.sugargrove.lib.il.us. *Dir*, Beverly S Holmes; E-Mail: director@sugargrove.lib.il.us; Staff 9 (MLS 1, Non-MLS 8)
Founded 1962. Pop 6,747; Circ 45,617
Jul 1999-Jun 2000 Income $205,283, State $9,920, Locally Generated Income $195,909, Other $11,210. Mats Exp $39,519, Books $32,040, Per/Ser (Incl. Access Fees) $3,979, Electronic Ref Mat (Incl. Access Fees) $3,500. Sal $85,101 (Prof $34,350)
Library Holdings: Bk Vols 24,125; Bk Titles 22,380; Per Subs 142
Automation Activity & Vendor Info: (Cataloging) epixtech, inc.; (Circulation) epixtech, inc.; (OPAC) epixtech, inc.
Database Vendor: epixtech, inc.
Mem of DuPage Library System
Friends of the Library Group

J WAUBONSEE COMMUNITY COLLEGE, Todd Library, State Rte 47 & Waubonsee Dr, 60554. SAN 304-6885. Tel: 630-466-7900, Ext 2400. FAX: 630-466-7799. Web Site: wcc.cc.il.us. *Assoc Dean*, Jill Wold; *Librn*, Adam Burke; *Circ*, Rhea Hunter; E-Mail: rhunter@mail.wcc.cc.il.us; *Circ, Tech Servs*, Laura Michalek; *Ref*, Marilee Stach; Staff 5 (MLS 5)
Founded 1967. Enrl 10,000; Fac 266
Library Holdings: Bk Vols 57,204; Per Subs 530
Subject Interests: Deaf
Automation Activity & Vendor Info: (Cataloging) DRA; (Circulation) DRA; (OPAC) DRA
Mem of DuPage Library System
Partic in Northern Ill Learning Resources Coop

SULLIVAN

S MOULTRIE COUNTY HISTORICAL & GENEALOGICAL SOCIETY LIBRARY, 117 E Harrison St, PO Box 588, 61951-0588. SAN 327-7917. Tel: 217-728-4085. *Librn*, Mary Storm
Special Collections: Family Histories, County Newspapers on Film

P SULLIVAN CITY PUBLIC LIBRARY, Elizabeth Titus Memorial Library, 2 W Water St, 61951. SAN 304-6893. Tel: 217-728-7221. FAX: 217-728-2215. *Dir*, Colleen Mitchell; *Asst Librn*, Susan Wood; *Circ*, Marlene Jenkins
Founded 1915. Circ 35,880
Library Holdings: Bk Vols 41,000; Per Subs 80
Special Collections: Braille
Automation Activity & Vendor Info: (Cataloging) DRA; (Circulation) DRA; (OPAC) DRA
Mem of Rolling Prairie Library System
Open Mon-Thurs 9-8, Fri 9-5, Sat 9-2

SUMMIT

P SUMMIT PUBLIC LIBRARY DISTRICT,* 6209 S Archer Rd, 60501. SAN 304-6915. Tel: 708-458-1545. FAX: 708-458-1842. E-Mail: sas@sls.lib.il.us. Web Site: www.nsn.org/sashome/sas. *Dir*, Matthew Suddarth; Staff 8 (MLS 1, Non-MLS 7)
Founded 1917. Pop 9,971; Circ 28,000
Jul 1999-Jun 2000 Income (Main Library Only) $206,000, State $32,000. Mats Exp $36,000, Books $32,000, Per/Ser (Incl. Access Fees) $4,000. Sal $105,000 (Prof $29,400)
Library Holdings: Bk Vols 25,000
Subject Interests: Spanish (language)
Automation Activity & Vendor Info: (Circulation) Innovative Interfaces Inc.
Mem of Suburban Library System
Friends of the Library Group

SUMMIT ARGO

S ILLINOIS INSTITUTE OF TECHNOLOGY, National Center for Food Safety & Technology Library, 6502 S Archer Rd, 60501. SAN 375-5363. Tel: 708-563-8160, 708-563-8163. FAX: 708-563-8164. E-Mail: speakman@iit.edu. Web Site: www.ncfst.iit.edu. *Librn*, Carolyn Speakman; *ILL*, Pat O'Brien; Staff 2 (MLS 1, Non-MLS 1)
Founded 1993
Library Holdings: Bk Vols 6,800; Bk Titles 5,000; Per Subs 200
Automation Activity & Vendor Info: (Cataloging) EOS; (Serials) EOS
Mem of Suburban Library System
Partic in Illinois Library & Information Network; OCLC Online Computer Library Center, Inc

SYCAMORE

P SYCAMORE PUBLIC LIBRARY,* 103 E State St, 60178-1440. SAN 304-6923. Tel: 815-895-2500. TDD: 815-895-2500. FAX: 815-895-9816. *Dir*, Alexander C Todd; E-Mail: spldir@tbcnet.com; Staff 23 (MLS 1, Non-MLS 22)
Founded 1891. Pop 11,057; Circ 110,506
May 1999-Apr 2000 Income (Main Library Only) $551,334, State $32,000, City $437,734, Locally Generated Income $81,600. Mats Exp $90,100, Per/Ser (Incl. Access Fees) $7,200, Other Print Mats $82,900. Sal $251,685 (Prof $79,000)
Library Holdings: Bk Vols 674; Bk Titles 49,266; Per Subs 35
Subject Interests: Local history
Database Vendor: epixtech, inc., OCLC - First Search
Mem of Northern Illinois Library System
Special Services for the Deaf - TDD
Friends of the Library Group

TAYLORVILLE

S TAYLORVILLE CORRECTIONAL CENTER LIBRARY,* PO Box 1000, 62568. SAN 376-1185. Tel: 217-824-4004, Ext 5802. FAX: 217-824-4042. *Librn*, Jan Bloom
Library Holdings: Bk Vols 7,000; Bk Titles 4,000; Per Subs 40
Mem of Rolling Prairie Library System

P TAYLORVILLE PUBLIC LIBRARY,* 121 W Vine St, 62568. SAN 304-6931. Tel: 217-824-4736. FAX: 217-824-8921. *Librn*, Dorothy Siles
Founded 1899. Pop 11,113; Circ 79,653
Library Holdings: Bk Vols 35,000; Per Subs 120
Subject Interests: Antiques
Database Vendor: DRA
Mem of Rolling Prairie Library System

THOMSON

P YORK TOWNSHIP PUBLIC LIBRARY, 1005 W Main St, 61285. SAN 304-694X. Tel: 815-259-2480. FAX: 815-259-2194. E-Mail: thomsonlib@internetni.com. *Librn*, Deeann Kramer
Founded 1919. Pop 2,272; Circ 13,890
Library Holdings: Bk Vols 12,000; Per Subs 22
Subject Interests: Local history
Mem of Northern Illinois Library System

THORNTON

P THORNTON PUBLIC LIBRARY,* 115 E Margaret St, 60476. SAN 304-6958. Tel: 708-877-2579. Interlibrary Loan Service Tel: 708-325-6640. FAX: 708-877-2608. *Librn*, Kathy Vente
Founded 1940. Pop 2,778; Circ 15,729
Library Holdings: Bk Vols 20,000; Per Subs 75
Special Collections: American Indians
Publications: Bookends (newsletter)
Mem of Suburban Library System

TINLEY PARK

P TINLEY PARK PUBLIC LIBRARY,* 17101 S 71st Ave, 60477-3398. SAN 304-6974. Tel: 708-532-0160. FAX: 708-532-2981. E-Mail: tps@sls.lib.il.us. Web Site: www.tplibrary.org. *Mgr Libr*, Pamela J Deiters; *Admin Assoc*, Richard Wolfe; *Ad Servs*, Robin Lauren; *Ch Servs*, Karen Siwak; *Circ*, Nancy Hoffman; *Tech Servs*, Joy Anholt
Founded 1959. Pop 42,528; Circ 437,754
May 1997-Apr 1998 Income $1,552,415. Mats Exp $165,818. Sal $842,146
Library Holdings: Bk Vols 110,056; Per Subs 444
Special Collections: German Language Books Coll
Automation Activity & Vendor Info: (Circulation) CLSI LIBS
Mem of Suburban Library System
Open Mon-Fri 9-9, Sat 9-5, Sun 1-5
Friends of the Library Group
Bookmobiles: 1

TISKILWA

P TISKILWA TOWNSHIP LIBRARY,* 119 E Main St, PO Box 150, 61368. SAN 304-6982. Tel: 815-646-4511. FAX: 815-646-4247. E-Mail: tisklib@theramp.net. *Librn*, Nancy Harmon
Founded 1875. Pop 1,587; Circ 17,183
Library Holdings: Bk Vols 12,823; Per Subs 48
Mem of Heritage Trail Library System

TOLEDO

P SUMPTER TOWNSHIP LIBRARY,* 148 Courthouse Sq, PO Box 67, 62468. SAN 304-6990. Tel: 217-849-2072. FAX: 217-849-2072. *Librn*, Cassandra Stewart
Pop 1,970; Circ 19,371
Library Holdings: Bk Vols 20,000; Per Subs 84
Mem of Rolling Prairie Library System
Open Tues & Thurs 12-7, Wed 9-5, Fri 12-5, Sat 9-12

TOLONO

P TOLONO PUBLIC LIBRARY,* 111 Main St, 61880. (Mail add: PO Box 759, 61880), SAN 304-7008. Tel: 217-485-5558. FAX: 217-485-3088. *Librn*, Janet Sutherland; *Asst Librn*, Sandy Hettinger
Founded 1968. Pop 6,957; Circ 68,125
Library Holdings: Bk Vols 20,000
Special Collections: Local Archives
Mem of Lincoln Trail Libraries System
Friends of the Library Group

TOLUCA

P TOLUCA CITY LIBRARY,* 102 N Main St, 61369. SAN 304-7016. Tel: 815-452-2211. FAX: 815-452-2494. *Librn*, Janet Guaderrama; E-Mail: jguaderrama@starbase1.htls.lib.il.us
Founded 1974. Pop 1,400; Circ 5,030
Library Holdings: Bk Vols 8,079
Special Collections: National Geographic 1929-to-present
Mem of Heritage Trail Library System
Friends of the Library Group

TOULON

P TOULON PUBLIC LIBRARY DISTRICT, 306 W Jefferson, 61483. SAN 304-7024. Tel: 309-286-5791. FAX: 309-286-4481. E-Mail: staff@toulonlibrary.org. Web Site: users.cin.net/~toulonlib. *Dir*, Ann Turnbull; *Ch*

Servs, Crystal Donovan; Staff 9 (Non-MLS 9)
Pop 3,512; Circ 20,755
Jul 1999-Jun 2000 Income $136,398, State $6,183, City $202, Federal $4,550, County $122,515, Locally Generated Income $2,692, Other $256. Mats Exp $14,647, Books $13,587, Per/Ser (Incl. Access Fees) $910, Other Print Mats $150. Sal $52,005 (Prof $18,900)
Library Holdings: Bk Vols 13,862; Per Subs 61
Database Vendor: CARL
Publications: Newsletter (bi-annually)
Mem of Alliance Library System
Friends of the Library Group

TOWANDA

P TOWANDA DISTRICT PUBLIC LIBRARY, 301 S Taylor St, 61776-7582. (Mail add: PO Box 170, 61776-0170), SAN 304-7032. Tel: 309-728-2176. FAX: 309-728-2176. *Dir*, Mary Pasek Williams; *Asst Librn*, Shirley Porter; Staff 1 (MLS 1)
Founded 1939. Pop 1,394; Circ 6,091
Jul 1999-Jun 2000 Income $57,991, State $1,721, County $53,170, Locally Generated Income $800, Other $2,300. Mats Exp $7,461, Books $5,661, Per/Ser (Incl. Access Fees) $750, Electronic Ref Mat (Incl. Access Fees) $1,050. Sal $21,093
Library Holdings: Bk Vols 9,249; Per Subs 28
Special Collections: History Coll; Illinois Coll; National Geographic Coll, 1916-present
Database Vendor: Ebsco - EbscoHost
Mem of Alliance Library System

TREMONT

P TREMONT DISTRICT PUBLIC LIBRARY, (TRDL), 215 S Sampson St, 61568. (Mail add: PO Box 123, 61568), SAN 304-7040. Tel: 309-925-5432. FAX: 309-925-9953. E-Mail: trdl@darkstar.rsa.lib.il.us. Web Site: www.tremont.lib.il.us. *Librn*, Judith Scheirer; *Circ*, Dawn Boston; *Ch Servs*, Adele Pollock
Founded 1928. Pop 4,551; Circ 81,003
Jul 1998-Jun 1999 Income $156,749, State $7,870, Federal $658, County $132,182, Locally Generated Income $14,371, Other $1,668. Mats Exp $27,784, Books $20,850, Per/Ser (Incl. Access Fees) $2,000, AV Equip $4,934. Sal $44,003
Library Holdings: Bk Vols 24,809; Bk Titles 24,109; Per Subs 80; High Interest/Low Vocabulary Bk Vols 110; Bks on Deafness & Sign Lang 10
Subject Interests: Local history
Automation Activity & Vendor Info: (Circulation) Follett
Database Vendor: CARL
Mem of Alliance Library System
Partic in Resource Sharing Alliance

TRENTON

P TRENTON PUBLIC LIBRARY, 118 E Indiana St, 62293. SAN 304-7059. Tel: 618-224-7662. FAX: 618-224-7671. *Dir*, Linda Richter; E-Mail: lrichter@shawnet.shawls.lib.il.us
Founded 1974. Pop 2,504; Circ 12,116
Library Holdings: Bk Vols 11,114; Per Subs 75
Subject Interests: Genealogy
Database Vendor: OCLC - First Search, Wilson - Wilson Web
Mem of Shawnee Library System
Open Tues 9-8, Wed & Thurs 12-8, Fri 3-7, Sat 9-11

TROY

P TRI-TOWNSHIP PUBLIC LIBRARY DISTRICT, 209 S Main St, 62294. SAN 375-9709. Tel: 618-667-2133. FAX: 618-667-9866. E-Mail: tre@lcls.org. *Librn*, Karen Walker; E-Mail: karenw@lcls.org; *Cat*, Debra Sumner; E-Mail: debs@lcls.org
Library Holdings: Bk Titles 30,000; Per Subs 195
Special Collections: Local Area Parenting Coll
Mem of Lewis & Clark Library System
Friends of the Library Group

TUSCOLA

P TUSCOLA PUBLIC LIBRARY, 112 E Sale St, PO Box 56, 61953. SAN 304-7067. Tel: 217-253-3812. FAX: 217-253-4599. *Librn*, Bethany Bolduc; Staff 1 (MLS 1)
Founded 1898. Pop 4,327
Library Holdings: Bk Vols 15,140; Per Subs 30
Mem of Lincoln Trail Libraries System
Open Mon, Wed & Fri 10-6, Tue & Thurs 10-8, Sat 10-4
Friends of the Library Group

ULLIN

J SHAWNEE COLLEGE LIBRARY, 8364 College Rd, 62992. SAN 304-7083. Tel: 618-634-2242, Ext 271. FAX: 618-634-9711. Web Site: www.shawnee.cc.il.us. *Dir*, Julia Johnson; E-Mail: juliaj@shawnee.cc.il.us
Founded 1969
Library Holdings: Bk Vols 40,000; Per Subs 175
Automation Activity & Vendor Info: (Acquisitions) epixtech, inc.; (Cataloging) epixtech, inc.; (Circulation) epixtech, inc.; (OPAC) epixtech, inc.; (Serials) epixtech, inc.
Partic in Illinois Library & Information Network; Southern Ill Learning Resources Coop

UNION

S ILLINOIS RAILWAY MUSEUM, Pullman Technical Library, 7000 Olsen Rd, PO Box 427, 60180-0427. SAN 326-4009. Tel: 815-923-4391, 923-2020. FAX: 815-923-2006. *Librn*, Jim Kehrein; *Asst Librn*, Bruce Klapper
Founded 1974
Library Holdings: Bk Titles 5,000
Special Collections: Pullman Company Linen Tracings & Blueprints Coll; T-Z Company Coll (blue prints)

UNIVERSITY PARK

C GOVERNORS STATE UNIVERSITY, Library,* One University Park, 60466-0975. SAN 304-5315. Tel: 708-534-4111. FAX: 708-534-4564. Web Site: www.govst.edu/library. *Ref*, Beth Hansen-Shaw; *Dir*, Rebecca Bostian; *Ref*, Nancy Shales; *Acq*, Que Owens; *Circ*, Coleen Waltman; *Cat*, Diane Dates Casey; *Ref*, Mari Ellen Leverance; *Ser*, Lydia Rutten; *Doc*, Ann Glascoff; E-Mail: a-glasco@govst.edu; Staff 9 (MLS 9)
Founded 1970. Enrl 6,073; Fac 146; Highest Degree: Master
Jul 1997-Jun 1998 Income $1,632,611
Library Holdings: Bk Vols 330,000; Bk Titles 189,846; Per Subs 2,655
Subject Interests: Accounting, Biology, Business and management, Chemistry, Computer science, Criminal law and justice, Education, Finance, Humanities
Special Collections: Afro-American Literature (Schomberg Coll); Art Slides Coll; ERIC Documents Coll, microfiche; Materials Center Coll
Automation Activity & Vendor Info: (Acquisitions) DRA; (Cataloging) DRA; (Serials) DRA
Publications: Index to Non-print Materials; Information Please (newsletter); Media Holdings List; Periodicals Holding List; Subject Guide to Indexes & Abstracts
Mem of Suburban Library System
Partic in Chicago & South Consortium; Chicago Academic Libr Coun; Illinois Library Computer Systems Office; OCLC Online Computer Library Center, Inc; SMRHEC

P UNIVERSITY PARK PUBLIC LIBRARY DISTRICT,* 1100 Blackhawk Dr, 60466. SAN 304-5323. Tel: 708-534-2580. FAX: 708-534-2583. E-Mail: pss@sos.lib.il.us. Web Site: www.lincolnnet.net/users/llunvprk/uplib2.htm. *Dir*, Penny E McCreight
Founded 1974. Pop 6,245; Circ 16,314
1997-1998 Income $236,000
Library Holdings: Bk Vols 23,000; Per Subs 130
Mem of Suburban Library System
Friends of the Library Group

URBANA

M CARLE FOUNDATION HOSPITAL, Medical Library,* 611 W Park St, 61801. SAN 304-7091. Tel: 217-383-3011. FAX: 217-383-3452.; Staff 3 (MLS 2, Non-MLS 1)
Library Holdings: Bk Vols 1,500; Per Subs 200
Special Collections: Archives for Carle Clinic Association & Carle Foundation Hospital
Mem of Lincoln Trail Libraries System
Partic in East Central Illinois Consortium

R COUNTRYSIDE UNITED METHODIST CHURCH LIBRARY, 990 County Rd 1800 E, 61802. SAN 304-7121. Tel: 217-684-2422, 217-688-2422. FAX: 217-688-2422. E-Mail: boinhwang@hotmail.com. *In Charge*, In-Sook Hwang
Founded 1975
Library Holdings: Bk Vols 250
Subject Interests: Education, Evangelicalism
Partic in Media Resource Ctr

S NATIONAL COUNCIL OF TEACHERS OF ENGLISH LIBRARY, 1111 W Kenyon Rd, 61801. SAN 325-1535. Tel: 217-278-3639. FAX: 217-278-3761. Web Site: www.ncte.org. *Librn*, Cheri Cameron; E-Mail: ccameron@ncte.org
Founded 1959
Library Holdings: Bk Vols 4,800; Bk Titles 3,100
Special Collections: NCTE Monographs - English Language Arts (NCTE

Archives Coll), bks, microfiche, records, tapes
Publications: Bibliographies; New Book List; Staff Memos
Mem of Lincoln Trail Libraries System
Partic in Illinois Library & Information Network

M PROVENA COVENANT MEDICAL CENTER, 1400 W Park St, 61801. SAN 304-7148. Tel: 217-337-2283. FAX: 217-337-2299. E-Mail: pcmclib@pdnt.com. *Librn*, Gennye Varvel; *Asst Librn*, Carol Hutjens; Staff 2 (MLS 1, Non-MLS 1)
Founded 1931
Library Holdings: Bk Titles 1,000; Per Subs 100
Subject Interests: Medicine, Nursing
Database Vendor: OCLC - First Search
Mem of Lincoln Trail Libraries System
Partic in Illinois Library & Information Network; Regional Med Libr - Region 3

C UNIVERSITY OF ILLINOIS LIBRARY AT URBANA-CHAMPAIGN, 230 Main Library, 1408 W Gregory Dr, 61801. SAN 340-8124. Tel: 217-333-0790. Interlibrary Loan Service FAX: 217-244-0398. Web Site: www.library.uiuc.edu. *Librn*, Paula Kaufman; E-Mail: ptk@uiuc.edu; *Librn*, Barton M Clark; Tel: 217-333-0317, E-Mail: b-clark@uiuc.edu; *Spec Coll*, Barbara Jones; *ILL*, Lynn Wiley; *Ref*, Jo Kibbee; *Acq*, Lisa German; *Circ*, Betsy Kruger; *Coll Develop*, Karen Schmidt; Staff 163 (MLS 110, Non-MLS 53)
Founded 1868. Enrl 38,000; Highest Degree: Doctorate
Jul 1999-Jun 2000 Income (Main Library and Branch Library) $29,966,773, State $24,283,518, Locally Generated Income $4,248,638, Parent Institution $762,522, Other $672,095. Mats Exp $10,185,674, Books $2,887,005, Per/Ser (Incl. Access Fees) $5,832,463, Presv $415,303, Other Print Mats $1,050,903. Sal $14,916,188 (Prof $7,292,319)
Library Holdings: Bk Vols 9,469,620; Per Subs 90,962
Special Collections: 16th & 17th Century Italian Drama; 17th Century Coll; 17th Century Newsletters; 18th Century English Literature (Nickell Coll); 19th Century Publishing (William Bentley & Grant Richards Coll); Abraham Lincoln Coll; American Humor & Folklore (Franklin J Meine Coll); Aquinas; Baskette Coll on Freedom of Expression; Carl Sandburg Coll; Cobbett (Muierhead Coll); Confederate Imprints (Richard B Harwell Coll); H G Wells Coll; Hollander Library of Economic History; Incunabula including St Thomas; John Milton Coll; Political & Religious Pamphlets; Shakespeare (Ernest Ingold Coll); T W Baldwin Elizabethan Library; William Shakespeare Coll
Database Vendor: Dialog, DRA, Ebsco - EbscoHost, GaleNet, IAC - Info Trac, IAC - SearchBank, Innovative Interfaces INN - View, OCLC - First Search, OVID Technologies, ProQuest, Silverplatter Information Inc.
Publications: Friendscript
Mem of Asn of Research Libraries; Lincoln Trail Libraries System
Partic in Illinois Library & Information Network; Midwest Universities Consortium for Int Activities, Inc; OCLC Online Computer Library Center, Inc
Friends of the Library Group
Departmental Libraries:
AFRICANA, 328 Main Library, 1408 W Gregory Dr, 61801. SAN 340-8167. Tel: 217-244-1903. FAX: 217-333-2214. *Librn*, Alfred Kagan
Library Holdings: Bk Vols 180,000
AFRO-AMERICANA, 328 Main Library, 1408 W Gregory Dr, 61801. SAN 340-8175. Tel: 217-333-3006.
Library Holdings: Bk Vols 625
AGRICULTURAL, CONSUMER & ENVIRONMENTAL SCIENCES, 226 Mumford Hall, 1301 W Gregory Dr, 61801. SAN 340-8183. Tel: 217-333-2416. FAX: 217-333-0558. *Librn*, Robert Allen
Library Holdings: Bk Vols 119,815
APPLIED LIFE STUDIES, 146 Main Library, 1408 W Gregory Dr, 61801. SAN 340-8213. Tel: 217-333-3615. FAX: 217-333-8384. Web Site: www.library.uiuc.edu/alx/. *Librn*, Mary Beth Allen; Tel: 217-244-1870, E-Mail: m-allen3@uiuc.edu; Staff 3 (MLS 1, Non-MLS 2)
Library Holdings: Bk Vols 25,000
ARCHITECTURE, 208 Architecture, 608 E Lorado Taft Dr, 61801. SAN 340-8248. Tel: 217-333-0224. FAX: 217-244-5169. Web Site: www.library.uiuc.edu/arx. *Librn*, Jane Block
Library Holdings: Bk Vols 56,179
ASIAN (EAST ASIAN DIVISION), 325 Main Library, 1408 W Gregory Dr, 61801. SAN 340-8256. Tel: 217-333-1501. FAX: 217-333-2214. Web Site: www.gateway.library.uiuc.edu/asx. *Librn*, Fung-Yin Simpson; Tel: 217-244-2047, E-Mail: fyks@uiuc.edu; *Librn*, Karen Wei; Tel: 217-244-2046, E-Mail: k-wei@uiuc.edu
Library Holdings: Bk Vols 235,360
ASIAN (SOUTH & WEST ASIAN DIVISION), 1408 W Gregory Dr, 325 Main Library, 61801. SAN 340-8264. Tel: 217-333-2492. Circulation Tel: 217-333-1501. FAX: 217-333-2214. Web Site: www.gateway.library.uiuc.edu/asx. *Librn*, Karen Wei
Library Holdings: Bk Vols 139,528
BIOLOGY, 101 Burrill Hall, 407 S Goodwin Ave, 61801. SAN 340-8272. Tel: 217-333-3654. FAX: 217-333-3662. E-Mail: biolib@uiuc.edu. Web Site: www.library.uiuc.edu/bix. *Librn*, Diane Schmidt; Tel: 217-333-0281, E-Mail: dcschmid@uiuc.edu. Subject Specialists: *Classics*, Diane Schmidt
Library Holdings: Bk Vols 127,846
CHEMISTRY, 255 Noyes Lab, 505 S Matthews, 61801. SAN 340-8302. Tel: 217-333-3737. FAX: 217-333-9208. *Librn*, Tina Chrazstowski
Library Holdings: Bk Vols 70,000
CITY PLANNING & LANDSCAPE ARCHITECTURE, 203 Mumford Hall, 61801. SAN 340-8337. Tel: 217-333-0424. FAX: 217-333-0558. *Librn*, Priscilla Yu
Library Holdings: Bk Vols 23,074
CLASSICS, 1408 W Gregory Dr, 61801. SAN 340-8361. Tel: 217-244-1872. FAX: 217-333-2214. Web Site: www.library.uiuc.edu/clx. *Librn*, Bruce W Swann; E-Mail: b-swann@uiuc.edu. Subject Specialists: *Classics*, Bruce W Swann
Library Holdings: Bk Titles 54,000
COMMERCE, 101 Main Library, 1408 W Gregory, 61801. SAN 340-8396. Tel: 217-333-3619. Web Site: www.library.uiuc.edu/crx/. *Librn*, Beth Woodard; Tel: 217-244-0388, E-Mail: bswoodar@uiuc.edu; Staff 3 (MLS 3)
Library Holdings: Bk Vols 62,563
COMMUNICATIONS, 122 Gregory Hall, 61801. SAN 340-8426. Tel: 217-333-2216. FAX: 217-333-9882. *Librn*, Lisa Romero; Tel: 217-333-6348, E-Mail: l-romero@uiuc.edu
Library Holdings: Bk Vols 16,600
EDUCATION & SOCIAL SCIENCES, 1408 W Gregory Dr, 100 Library, 61801. SAN 340-8450. Tel: 217-333-2305. Reference Tel: 217-244-1864. FAX: 217-333-2214. E-Mail: educlib@library.uiuc.edu. Web Site: www.library.uiuc.edu/edx/. *Librn*, Nancy O'Brien; E-Mail: n-obrien@uiuc.edu. Subject Specialists: *Children's literature*, Nancy O'Brien; *Education*, Nancy O'Brien
Library Holdings: Bk Vols 316,000
ENGLISH, 321 Main Libr, 1408 W Gregory Dr, 61801. SAN 340-8515. Tel: 217-333-2220. Web Site: www.library.uiuc.edu/egx/. *Librn*, William Brockman; Tel: 217-333-6348, E-Mail: brockman@uiuc.edu. Subject Specialists: *Am lit*, William Brockman; *Cinema*, William Brockman; *Eng lit*, William Brockman; *Theater*, William Brockman
Library Holdings: Bk Vols 35,000
GEOLOGY, 223 Natural History, 1301 W Green St, 61801. SAN 340-8574. Tel: 217-333-1266. FAX: 217-244-4319. *Librn*, Lois Pausch; Tel: 217-333-2676, E-Mail: l-pausch@uiuc.edu; *Librn*, Gregory Youngen
Library Holdings: Bk Vols 100,359
GOVERNMENT DOCUMENTS, 200-D Main Libr, 1408 W Gregory Dr, 61801. SAN 340-8434. Tel: 217-244-6445. FAX: 217-333-2214. E-Mail: gdoclib@uiuc.edu. Web Site: www.library.uiuc.edu/doc/. *Librn*, Mary Mallory; Tel: 217-333-0317; Staff 7 (MLS 4, Non-MLS 3)
Library Holdings: Bk Vols 230,000
GRAINGER ENGINEERING LIBRARY INFO CENTER, 1301 W Springfield, 61801. SAN 340-8485. Tel: 217-333-3576. FAX: 217-244-7764. E-Mail: enginlib@uiuc.edu. Web Site: www.library.uiuc.educ/grainger/. *Librn*, William Mischo; E-Mail: w-mischo@uiuc.edu
Library Holdings: Bk Vols 271,625
HISTORY & PHILOSOPHY, 424 Main Libr, 61801. SAN 340-8639. Tel: 217-333-1091. Web Site: www.library.uiuc.edu/hix/. *Librn*, Martha Friedman; *Librn*, Mary Stuart; Tel: 214-244-0797, E-Mail: m-stuart@uiuc.edu; Staff 4 (MLS 1, Non-MLS 3)
Library Holdings: Bk Vols 40,944

C ILLINI UNION BROWSING ROOM, 133 Illini Union, 61801. SAN 340-8698. Tel: 217-333-2475. *Librn*, F Bennett-Hess; *Librn*, Joyce Wright
Library Holdings: Bk Vols 5,418
ILLINOIS HISTORICAL SURVEY, 346 Main Libr, 1408 W Gregory Dr, 61801. SAN 340-8728. Tel: 217-333-1777. *Librn*, John Hoffmann
Library Holdings: Bk Vols 18,000
LABOR & INDUSTRIAL RELATIONS, 147 ILIR, 504 E Armory Ave, Champaign, 61820. SAN 340-8752. Tel: 217-333-2380. FAX: 217-244-4091. Web Site: www.gateway.library.uiuc.edu. *Librn*, Margaret A Chaplan; Tel: 217-333-7993, E-Mail: chaplan@uiuc.edu
Library Holdings: Bk Vols 15,722
LATIN AMERICAN, 324 University of Illinois Library MC 522, 1408 W Gregory Dr, 61801. SAN 340-8779. Tel: 217-333-2786. FAX: 217-333-2214. Web Site: www.library.uiuc.edu/lat/. *Head Librn*, Nelly S Gonzalez; Tel: 217-244-1902, E-Mail: ngonzale@uiuc.edu; *Tech Servs*, Silda Andrick; E-Mail: sandrick@staff.uiuc.edu. Subject Specialists: *Humanities*, Nelly S Gonzalez; *Social sciences*, Nelly S Gonzalez; Staff 4 (MLS 1, Non-MLS 3)
Founded 1904
1999-2000 Mats Exp $114,783, Books $81,903, Per/Ser (Incl. Access Fees) $32,880. Sal $110,000 (Prof $85,908)
Library Holdings: Bk Titles 399,811; Per Subs 212
Subject Interests: Brazil, Humanities, Mexico, Social sciences
Special Collections: Gabriel Garcia Marquez Coll
Database Vendor: CARL, Dialog, DRA, Ebsco - EbscoHost, GaleNet, IAC - Info Trac, Innovative Interfaces INN - View, Lexis-Nexis, OCLC - First Search, OVID Technologies, Silverplatter Information Inc., Wilson - Wilson Web
Publications: ILLIPATHS Series (Bibliographies)
Function: Research library
Mem of Illinois Libr Computer Syst Orgn
Partic in CRL
Friends of the Library Group

CL LAW LIBRARY, 142 Law Bldg, 504 E Pennsylvania Ave, Champaign, 61820. SAN 340-8787. Tel: 217-333-2914. Interlibrary Loan Service Tel: 217-333-1958. FAX: 217-244-8500. *Librn*, Janis Johnston; E-Mail: jljohnst@law.uiuc.edu; Staff 6 (MLS 6)
Founded 1897
Library Holdings: Bk Vols 695,000; Per Subs 8,317
Subject Interests: Foreign law
Special Collections: European Economic Commun
Publications: Law Library Aids; Law Library Collection Information

LIBRARY SCIENCE & INFORMATION SCIENCE, 306 Main Library, 1408 W Gregory Dr, 61801. SAN 340-8817. Tel: 217-333-3804. E-Mail: lislib@library@uiuc.edu. Web Site: www.library.uiuc.edu/lsx. *Librn*, Susan Searing; Staff 4 (MLS 1, Non-MLS 3)
Library Holdings: Bk Vols 25,353

MAP & GEOGRAPHY, 1408 W Gregory Dr, 418 Main Library, Mc-522, 61801. SAN 340-8841. Tel: 217-333-0827. FAX: 217-333-2214. E-Mail: mapgeog@cliff.library.uiuc.edu. Web Site: www.libray.uiuc.edu/max/. *Librn*, Jenny Johnson; Staff 2 (MLS 1, Non-MLS 1)
Library Holdings: Bk Vols 582,405

MATHEMATICS, 1409 W Green St, 216 Altgeld Hall, 61801. SAN 340-8876. Tel: 217-333-0258. FAX: 217-244-4362. Web Site: www.gateway.library.uiuc.edu/mtx/. *Librn*, Timothy Cole; Tel: 217-244-7837, E-Mail: t-cole3@uiuc.edu
Library Holdings: Bk Vols 96,019

MODERN LANGUAGES & LINGUISTICS, 425 Main Library, 1408 W Gregory Dr, 61801. SAN 340-8906. Tel: 217-333-0076. FAX: 217-333-2214. Web Site: www.library.uiuc.edu/mdx. *Librn*, Tom Kilton; Staff 6 (MLS 3, Non-MLS 3)
Library Holdings: Bk Vols 24,000

MUSIC, 2146 Music Bldg, 1114 W Nevada St, 61801. SAN 340-8930. Tel: 217-333-1173. FAX: 217-244-9097. *Librn*, Richard Griscom
Library Holdings: Bk Vols 301,277

NATURAL HISTORY SURVEY-STATE, 196 Natural Resources Bldg, 607 E Peabody Dr, Champaign, 61820. Tel: 217-333-6892. FAX: 217-333-4949. Web Site: www.library.uiuc.edu/nhx. *Head of Libr*, Elizabeth Rose Wohlgemuth; Tel: 217-244-4907, E-Mail: wohlgemu@mail.inhs.uiuc.edu; *Librn*, JoAnn Jacoby; Tel: 217-333-5856, E-Mail: jacoby@mail.inhs.uiuc.edu; Staff 4 (MLS 2, Non-MLS 2)
Founded 1858
1998-1999 Income (Main Library Only) Parent Institution $59,000. Mats Exp $59,000, Books $7,000, Per/Ser (Incl. Access Fees) $47,000, Electronic Ref Mat (Incl. Access Fees) $5,000
Library Holdings: Bk Vols 40,000; Bk Titles 900; Per Subs 180
Subject Interests: Aquatic biol, Biodiversity, Botany, Ecology, Entomology, Environmental studies, Ichthyology, Mammalogy, Wetlands, Wildlife
Automation Activity & Vendor Info: (Cataloging) DRA
Database Vendor: DRA, Ebsco - EbscoHost, OCLC - First Search, OVID Technologies, Silverplatter Information Inc., Wilson - Wilson Web
Function: ILL limited
Mem of Lincoln Trail Libraries System
Friends of the Library Group

NEWSPAPER, One Main Library, 1408 W Gregory Dr, 61856. SAN 340-899X. Tel: 217-333-1509. FAX: 217-333-2214. Web Site: www.library.uiuc.edu/nex/default.asp. *Librn*, Sharon Clark; Tel: 217-333-2579, E-Mail: s-clar3@uiuc.edu; *Librn*, Gregg Hamerding; Tel: 217-333-9046, E-Mail: greggh@uiuc.edu; *Librn*, Glen Martin; Tel: 217-244-2050, E-Mail: gmartin@uiuc.edu
Library Holdings: Bk Vols 20,000
Special Collections: English Language-Foreign Coll

PHYSICS-ASTRONOMY, 204 Loomis Lab, 61801. SAN 340-9023. Tel: 217-333-2101. FAX: 217-333-3207. Web Site: gateway.library.uiuc.edu/phx. *Librn*, Gregory Youngen; E-Mail: youngen@uiuc.edu
Library Holdings: Bk Vols 45,690

RARE BOOK ROOM, 346 Main Libr, 1408 W Gregory Dr, 61801. SAN 340-9058. Tel: 217-333-3777. Toll Free FAX: 217-333-2214. *Librn*, Barbara Jones
Library Holdings: Bk Vols 172,983

SLAVIC & EAST EUROPEAN, 225 Main Libr, 1408 W Gregory Dr, 61801. SAN 340-9066. Tel: 217-333-1349. FAX: 217-244-8976. E-Mail: srscite@cliff.library.uiuc.edu. Web Site: www.library.uiuc.edu/spx/. *Librn*, Robert Burger; Tel: 217-333-1340, E-Mail: r-burger@uiuc.edu
Library Holdings: Bk Vols 17,140

UNDERGRADUATE, 1402 W Gregory Dr, 61801. Tel: 217-333-1031. TDD: 217-265-0967. FAX: 217-265-0936. Web Site: www.library.uiuc.edu/ugl/default.asp. *Librn*, Joyce Wright; Tel: 217-333-3489, E-Mail: jcwright@uiuc.edu; Staff 20 (MLS 5, Non-MLS 15)
Library Holdings: Bk Vols 252,011

UNIVERSITY ARCHIVES, 19 Main Libr, 1408 W Gregory Dr, 61801. SAN 340-9082. Tel: 217-333-0798. FAX: 217-333-2868. E-Mail: illiarch@uiuc.edu. Web Site: www.library.uiuc.edu/ahx. *Archivist*, William Maher; Fax: 217-333-2808, E-Mail: w-maher@uiuc.edu; *Archivist*, Christopher Prom; Tel: 217-333-0798, E-Mail: prom@uiuc.edu; *Archivist*, Ellen Swain; Tel: 217-333-7841, E-Mail: eswain@uiuc.edu

UNIVERSITY HIGH SCHOOL, 1212 W Springfield Ave, Rm 201, 61801. SAN 340-9112. Tel: 217-333-1589. FAX: 217-333-4064. Web Site: www.uni.uiuc.edu/library. *Librn*, Frances Jacobsen Harris; E-Mail: francey@uiuc.edu
Library Holdings: Bk Vols 13,182

CM VETERINARY MEDICINE LIBRARY, 1257 Veterinary Med Basic Science Bldg, 2001 S Lincoln Ave, 61802. SAN 340-9147. Tel: 217-333-2193. FAX: 217-333-2286. Web Site: www.library.uiuc.edu/vex. *Librn*, Mitsuko Williams; Staff 5 (MLS 2, Non-MLS 3)
Library Holdings: Bk Vols 48,971

P THE URBANA FREE LIBRARY,* 201 S Race St, 61801-3283. SAN 304-7164. Tel: 217-367-4057. FAX: 217-367-4061. Web Site: www.prairienet.org/ufl. *Exec Dir*, Frederick A Schlipf; *Ad Servs, Assoc Dir*, Debra Booth; *Ch Servs*, Barbara Lintner; *Archivist, Doc*, Jean Koch; Staff 13 (MLS 13)
Founded 1874. Pop 36,383; Circ 765,579
Library Holdings: Bk Vols 191,009; Per Subs 673
Subject Interests: Folklore
Special Collections: City of Urbana Document & Records (Urbana Municipal Documents Center); Genealogy & Champaign County History (Champaign County Historical Archives)
Publications: Champaign County Historical Archives; Historical Publications Series (9 bks, 3 maps); The Urbana Municipal Documents Center Manual
Mem of Lincoln Trail Libraries System
Partic in CCNet; CRL; Illinois Library & Information Network; OCLC Online Computer Library Center, Inc; Prairienet
Special Services for the Deaf - TTY machine
Friends of the Library Group

UTICA

P UTICA PUBLIC LIBRARY DISTRICT, Mill & Grove Sts, 61373. SAN 304-7172. Tel: 815-667-4509. *Librn*, Marlene Ernat; *Asst Librn*, Beverly Pleskovitch; *Asst Librn*, Gloria Alvarado
Founded 1956. Circ 1,962
Library Holdings: Bk Vols 34,000; Per Subs 17
Special Collections: LaSalle County History
Mem of Heritage Trail Library System
Friends of the Library Group

VALMEYER

P VALMEYER PUBLIC LIBRARY DISTRICT, 300 S Cedar Bluff, 62295. SAN 323-4495. Tel: 618-935-2626. FAX: 618-935-2622. Web Site: www.schools.lth5.k12.il.us/valmeyer. *Pres*, Pam Roever; *Librn*, Portia Stueve; Staff 3 (MLS 1, Non-MLS 2)
Founded 1984. Pop 2,319
Library Holdings: Bk Vols 20,000; Bk Titles 17,000; Per Subs 101
Database Vendor: DRA
Mem of Lewis & Clark Library System
Open Mon & Thurs 8-7:30, Tues, Wed & Fri 8-4

VANDALIA

P EVANS PUBLIC LIBRARY, 215 S Fifth St, 62471. SAN 304-7180. Tel: 618-283-2824. FAX: 618-283-4705. E-Mail: evanspl@shawls.lib.il.us. Web Site: www.sirin.lib.il.us/docs/epl/. *Librn*, Candy Zeman; E-Mail: czeman@shawnet.shawls.lib.il.us; *Asst Librn*, Fran Rickman; Staff 1 (MLS 1)
Founded 1921. Pop 6,568; Circ 55,467
May 1999-Apr 2000 Income $237,190, State $31,464, City $119,083, Federal $9,820, Locally Generated Income $76,823. Mats Exp $23,222, Books $21,694, AV Equip $1,528. Sal $97,719
Library Holdings: Bk Vols 31,106; Per Subs 120
Special Collections: James Hall Coll; Lincoln (Rankin Coll); Local History & Genealogy; Vandalia Authors
Automation Activity & Vendor Info: (Circulation) epixtech, inc.
Mem of Shawnee Library System
Partic in Illinois Library & Information Network
Open Mon-Thurs 10-7, Fri & Sat 10-5
Friends of the Library Group

S VANDALIA CORRECTIONAL CENTER LIBRARY,* PO Box 500, 62471. SAN 376-1193. Tel: 618-283-4170. *Librn*, Bruce Griggs
Library Holdings: Bk Vols 11,000; Per Subs 31

VENICE

P VENICE PUBLIC LIBRARY, 325 Broadway, 62090. SAN 304-7199. Tel: 618-877-1330. FAX: 618-877-0633. *Dir*, Muriel Shackelford
Founded 1953. Pop 3,500; Circ 10,000
Library Holdings: Bk Vols 5,000; Per Subs 10
Mem of Lewis & Clark Library System

VERMONT

P VERMONT PUBLIC LIBRARY,* 101 N Main St, PO Box 199, 61484. SAN 304-7202. Tel: 309-784-6291. FAX: 309-784-6291. *Librn*, Ann Patridge
Pop 806; Circ 5,676
Library Holdings: Bk Vols 3,000
Mem of Alliance Library System
Open Mon-Fri 10-12 & 1-4, Sat 10-4

VERNON HILLS

S STS CONSULTANTS LTD LIBRARY, 750 Corporate Woods Pkwy, 60061. SAN 370-5390. Tel: 847-279-2500, Ext 2426. *Librn*, Marilyn Cichon; Fax: 847-279-2510, E-Mail: cichon@stsltd.com; Staff 1 (MLS 1)
Founded 1983. Pop 360
Library Holdings: Bk Vols 5,344; Bk Titles 10,000
Automation Activity & Vendor Info: (OPAC) Inmagic, Inc.
Database Vendor: Dialog, Lexis-Nexis, OCLC - First Search
Restriction: Open to others by appointment
Mem of North Suburban Library System
Partic in Illinois Library & Information Network

VICTORIA

P VICTORIA PUBLIC LIBRARY DISTRICT,* 227 E Main St, PO Box 212, 61485-0216. SAN 375-9628. Tel: 309-879-2295. FAX: 309-879-2295. *Librn*, Carol Weedman
Library Holdings: Bk Titles 30,000; Per Subs 15
Mem of Alliance Library System

VIENNA

S SHAWNEE CORRECTIONAL CENTER LIBRARY, Rte 146E, Box 400, 62995. SAN 371-7429. Tel: 618-658-8331, Ext 2120. *Librn*, Leanne Pate; *Tech Servs*, Theresa Casteel; Staff 3 (Non-MLS 3)
Founded 1985. Circ 15,500
Jul 2000-Jun 2001 Income State $41,000. Mats Exp $41,100, Books $37,000, Per/Ser (Incl. Access Fees) $1,800, Presv $500, Other Print Mats $1,800. Sal $98,000
Library Holdings: Bk Titles 15,000; Per Subs 45
Special Collections: Federal & Illinois Law
Mem of Shawnee Library System
Special Services for the Blind - Talking Books
Library employs 4 inmate law clerks, 4 inmate library clerks & 1 inmate porter

S VIENNA CORRECTIONAL CENTER LIBRARY,* PO Box 200, 62995. SAN 304-7210. Tel: 618-658-8371, Ext 470. *Librn*, Suzanne Kerley; *Asst Librn*, Karen Elder; Staff 2 (MLS 1, Non-MLS 1)
Founded 1972
Library Holdings: Bk Titles 17,000; Per Subs 40
Subject Interests: Law
Special Collections: Criminology Coll; Law Library; SW Reporter
Partic in Shawnee Libr Syst
Also serves center at Hardin County Work Camp which has 1000 vols & assists at Tamms Work Camp

P VIENNA PUBLIC LIBRARY,* 401 Poplar St, PO Box 616, 62995. SAN 304-7229. Tel: 618-658-5051. FAX: 618-658-2027. *Librn*, Margaret Mathis
Founded 1910. Pop 1,420; Circ 6,000
Library Holdings: Bk Vols 9,553
Special Collections: Old books & literature
Mem of Shawnee Library System

VILLA GROVE

P CAMARGO TOWNSHIP DISTRICT LIBRARY, 14 N Main St, 61956. SAN 304-7237. Tel: 217-832-5211. FAX: 217-832-7203. Web Site: www.villagrove.com/~clibrary. *Dir*, Jan Johnson; E-Mail: jjohns@ltnet.ltls.org
Founded 1919. Pop 4,216; Circ 32,784
1998-1999 Income $88,318, County $71,780, Locally Generated Income $11,268, Other $5,270. Mats Exp $6,359, Books $5,041, Per/Ser (Incl. Access Fees) $1,318. Sal $46,791
Library Holdings: Bk Vols 25,000; Per Subs 106
Automation Activity & Vendor Info: (Cataloging) epixtech, inc.; (Circulation) epixtech, inc.
Mem of Lincoln Trail Libraries System
Special Services for the Blind - Talking Books
Open Tues, Wed & Fri 11-5, Mon & Thurs 11-8, Sat 9-12 & 1-5
Friends of the Library Group

VILLA PARK

P VILLA PARK PUBLIC LIBRARY, 305 S Ardmore Ave, 60181-2698. SAN 304-7245. Tel: 630-834-1164. TDD: 630-834-1165. FAX: 630-834-0489. E-Mail: vppladmin@linc.lib.il.us. Web Site: www.villapark.lib.il.us. *Dir*, Barbara L Flynn; E-Mail: bflynn@linc.lib.il.us; *Asst Dir*, Sandra Hill; E-Mail: shill@linc.lib.il.us; *Head, Circ*, Martha Bledsoe; E-Mail: mbledsoe@linc.lib.il.us; *Head Ref*, Sean Birmingham; E-Mail: sbirmingham@linc.lib.il.us; *Acq*, Linda Sherman; *Ad Servs*, Candace Smith; E-Mail: csmith@linc.lib.il.us; *Ch Servs*, Tiffany Auxier; E-Mail: tauxier@linc.lib.il.us; *Circ*, Joan Kodanko; *Ad Servs*, Brian Smith; E-Mail: bsmith@linc.lib.il.us; Staff 45 (MLS 9, Non-MLS 36)
Founded 1928. Pop 22,279; Circ 233,147
May 1999-Apr 2000 Income $1,553,650, State $72,312, City $1,318,250, Federal $2,325, Locally Generated Income $140,763. Mats Exp $1,388,207. Sal $754,106
Library Holdings: Bk Vols 99,267; Per Subs 278
Special Collections: Local History (Early History of Villa Park), bks, clippings, microfilm, slides, tapes
Automation Activity & Vendor Info: (Acquisitions) DRA; (Circulation) DRA
Database Vendor: DRA
Publications: The Resource (Newsletter)
Mem of DuPage Library System
Partic in LINCC
Friends of the Library Group

VIOLA

P VIOLA PUBLIC LIBRARY DISTRICT, 1705 14th St, PO Box 479, 61486. SAN 304-7253. Tel: 309-596-2620. FAX: 309-596-2822. E-Mail: violapid@winco.net. *Librn*, Linda Mixson; Staff 1 (Non-MLS 1)
Founded 1948. Pop 2,443; Circ 17,150
Jul 1999-Jun 2000 Mats Exp Books $8,277. Sal $20,828
Library Holdings: Bk Titles 12,678; Per Subs 28
Mem of Alliance Library System
Friends of the Library Group

VIRDEN

P GRAND PRAIRIE OF THE WEST PUBLIC LIBRARY DISTRICT,* 142 W Jackson St, 62690-1257. SAN 304-7261. Tel: 217-965-3015. Interlibrary Loan Service Tel: 618-656-3216. FAX: 217-965-3801. *Librn*, Wanda Lake; *Ch Servs*, Margaret Hendricks
Pop 5,665; Circ 28,853
Jul 1998-Jun 1999 Income $142,416, State $7,000, County $78,616, Locally Generated Income $5,800, Other $51,000. Mats Exp Books $13,250. Sal $52,400 (Prof $25,000)
Library Holdings: Bk Vols 20,000; Per Subs 55
Subject Interests: Large type print
Mem of Lewis & Clark Library System
Open Mon-Fri 10-4:50 & Sat 10-12

VIRGINIA

P VIRGINIA MEMORIAL PUBLIC LIBRARY,* 100 N Main St, 62691-1364. SAN 304-727X. Tel: 217-452-3846. FAX: 217-452-3846. *Librn*, Linda Mae Phillips
Pop 1,824; Circ 13,711
Library Holdings: Bk Vols 15,200; Bk Titles 15,000; Per Subs 35
Subject Interests: Local history
Special Collections: Genealogy
Publications: Illinois Libraries
Mem of Alliance Library System
Friends of the Library Group

WALNUT

P WALNUT PUBLIC LIBRARY DISTRICT, Heaton & Main Sts, PO Box 728, 61376-0728. SAN 304-7288. Tel: 815-379-2159. FAX: 815-379-2159. Web Site: www.rbls.lib.il.us/wal/index.html. *Librn*, Jill Van Acker; E-Mail: jillmva@yahoo.com
Founded 1939. Pop 1,894; Circ 28,700
Jul 1999-Jun 2000 Income $65,166, State $12,125, City $36,966, Federal $5,122, Other $10,953. Mats Exp $13,907, Books $12,253, Per/Ser (Incl. Access Fees) $1,354, Micro $25, AV Equip $275. Sal $32,213 (Prof $23,653)
Library Holdings: Bk Vols 22,330; Per Subs 61; Bks on Deafness & Sign Lang 10
Subject Interests: Local history
Special Collections: Don Marquis
Mem of River Bend Library System

WARREN

P WARREN TOWNSHIP PUBLIC LIBRARY, 210 Burnett Ave, PO Box 427, 61087. SAN 304-7296. Tel: 815-745-2076. FAX: 815-745-2076. *Dir*, Karen Graves; *Ch Servs*, Deborah Blair
Founded 1886. Pop 2,000
Library Holdings: Bk Vols 7,800; Per Subs 50
Subject Interests: Local history
Mem of Northern Illinois Library System

WARRENSBURG

P BARCLAY PUBLIC LIBRARY DISTRICT, 220 S Main St, 62573-9657. (Mail add: PO Box 349, 62573-0349), SAN 304-730X. Tel: 217-672-3621. FAX: 217-672-8404. E-Mail: libriann@yahoo.com. Web Site: www.decaturnet.org/barclaypubliclibrary. *Librn*, Ann Adkesson; Staff 1 (Non-MLS 1)
Founded 1942. Pop 7,600; Circ 48,000
Jul 1999-Jun 2000 Income $174,173, State $12,600, Federal $8,135, Locally Generated Income $153,438. Mats Exp $160,305, Books $15,333, Per/Ser (Incl. Access Fees) $3,600, AV Equip $11,894, Electronic Ref Mat (Incl. Access Fees) $9,700. Sal $72,130 (Prof $28,800)
Library Holdings: Bk Vols 29,000; Bk Titles 28,145; Per Subs 135
Automation Activity & Vendor Info: (Cataloging) DRA; (Circulation) DRA; (ILL) DRA; (OPAC) DRA
Database Vendor: OCLC - First Search
Mem of Rolling Prairie Library System
Open Mon, Wed & Fri 9-5, Tues & Thurs 9-8, Sat 9-12
Friends of the Library Group

WARRENVILLE

S ILLINOIS YOUTH CENTER - WARRENVILLE LIBRARY, Warrenville Public,* 30 W 200 Ferry Rd, PO Box 828, 60555. SAN 324-0045. Tel: 630-983-6231. FAX: 630-983-6213. *Mgr*, Mary Rodgers; Staff 2 (MLS 1, Non-MLS 1)
Founded 1973
Library Holdings: Bk Vols 5,032; Bk Titles 4,675; Per Subs 25
Mem of DuPage Library System
Partic in Illinois Library & Information Network

S RAILWAY SUPPLY ASSOCIATION INC,* 29 W 140 Butterfield Rd, Ste 103A, 60555. SAN 370-9736. Tel: 630-393-0106. FAX: 630-393-0108. *Exec Dir*, Howard Tonn
Library Holdings: Bk Vols 130

P WARRENVILLE PUBLIC LIBRARY DISTRICT, 28 W 751 Stafford Pl, 60555. SAN 324-5144. Tel: 630-393-1171. TDD: 630-393-1171. FAX: 630-393-1688. E-Mail: wville@anet-chi.com. Web Site: www.warrenville.com. *Actg Dir*, Barbara G West; E-Mail: bwest@warrenville.com; *Ad Servs*, Lisa Pappas; Fax: 630-393-2577, E-Mail: lisa@warrenville.com; *Ch Servs*, Sue Larson; E-Mail: sue@warrenville.com; *Circ*, Maureen Coleman; E-Mail: maureen@warrenville.com; *Tech Servs*, Barbara Heilenbach; E-Mail: barb@warrenville.com; Staff 22 (MLS 5, Non-MLS 17)
Founded 1979. Pop 12,640; Circ 155,782
Jul 1999-Jun 2000 Income $932,201, State $20,764, Locally Generated Income $831,649, Other $79,788. Mats Exp $175,989, Books $100,446, AV Equip $28,062, Electronic Ref Mat (Incl. Access Fees) $45,866. Sal $357,466 (Prof $171,478)
Library Holdings: Bk Titles 71,085; Per Subs 200; High Interest/Low Vocabulary Bk Vols 118
Subject Interests: Local history, Visual arts
Special Collections: Local Artist (Albright Coll), original art; Original Fine Arts Coll
Automation Activity & Vendor Info: (Cataloging) Gaylord; (Circulation) Gaylord; (OPAC) Gaylord
Database Vendor: Ebsco - EbscoHost, GaleNet, IAC - Info Trac, OCLC - First Search
Publications: Adult Services (quarterly); Youth Services (quarterly)
Function: ILL available
Mem of DuPage Library System
Special Services for the Deaf - Books on deafness & sign language; High interest/low vocabulary books
Friends of the Library Group

WARSAW

P WARSAW PUBLIC LIBRARY,* 210 N Fourth St, 62379-1050. SAN 304-7326. Tel: 217-256-3417. FAX: 217-256-3154. *Librn*, Sue Cunningham
Pop 1,882; Circ 23,658
Library Holdings: Bk Vols 13,555; Per Subs 68
Special Collections: Local History; Local Newspapers (on film from 1840-1973)
Mem of Alliance Library System

WASHINGTON

P WASHINGTON DISTRICT LIBRARY, 301 Walnut St, 61571. SAN 304-7334. Tel: 309-444-2241. FAX: 309-444-4711. *Dir*, Pamela Tomka; *Ch Servs, Ref*, Veronica Walker; *Tech Servs*, Sally Hackney; Staff 5 (MLS 2, Non-MLS 3)
Founded 1937. Pop 19,955; Circ 128,136
Jul 1999-Jun 2000 Mats Exp $55,000, Books $40,000, Per/Ser (Incl. Access Fees) $15,000
Library Holdings: Bk Vols 65,000; Bk Titles 43,000; Per Subs 150
Database Vendor: CARL
Mem of Alliance Library System
Partic in OCLC Online Computer Library Center, Inc
Open Mon, Tues, Wed & Thurs 9-8, Fri & Sat 9-5
Friends of the Library Group

WATERLOO

P MORRISON-TALBOTT LIBRARY,* 215 Park St, 62298-1305. SAN 304-7342. Tel: 618-939-6232. FAX: 618-939-4974. E-Mail: waa@lcls.org. Web Site: www.gatenet.lcls.lib.il.us/waa/. *Dir*, Elaine L Steingrubey; E-Mail: elaines@lcls.org; Staff 7 (Non-MLS 7)
Founded 1892. Pop 6,579; Circ 82,889
May 1998-Apr 1999 Income (Main Library Only) $217,672, State $51,213, City $131,803, Other $34,656
Library Holdings: Bk Vols 24,926; Per Subs 141
Special Collections: History & Genealogy of Monroe County, Ill
Database Vendor: DRA, Ebsco - EbscoHost, OCLC - First Search
Mem of Lewis & Clark Library System
Friends of the Library Group

WATERMAN

P CLINTON TOWNSHIP PUBLIC LIBRARY,* 110 S Elm St, PO Box 368, 60556. SAN 304-7350. Tel: 815-264-3339. *Librn*, Dorothy L Baie; *Asst Librn*, Millie Gordon
Founded 1905. Circ 9,490
Library Holdings: Bk Vols 9,984; Per Subs 62
Subject Interests: Genealogy
Mem of Northern Illinois Library System

WATSEKA

S IROQUOIS COUNTY GENEALOGICAL SOCIETY LIBRARY, Old Courthouse Museum, 103 W Cherry St, 60970-1524. SAN 326-3916. Tel: 815-432-3730. FAX: 815-432-3732. E-Mail: iroqgene@techinter.com. Web Site: www.rootsweb.com/~ilicgs/index.htm. *Dir, Publ Servs*, Cheryl Gocken; *Publ Servs*, Verna Drake
Founded 1969
Jan 1999-Dec 1999 Mats Exp $4,700, Books $600, Per/Ser (Incl. Access Fees) $150
Library Holdings: Bk Vols 800; Bk Titles 800; Per Subs 20
Subject Interests: Census, Marriage
Special Collections: County; Iroquois County Census (1790-1920), micro; Iroquois County Newspapers (1850-1959), micro
Publications: Stalker (quarterly)

P WATSEKA PUBLIC LIBRARY,* 201 S Fourth St, 60970. SAN 304-7369. Tel: 815-432-4544. FAX: 815-432-4545. *Librn*, Diann Peabody
Founded 1904. Pop 5,543; Circ 49,293
Library Holdings: Bk Vols 26,000; Per Subs 100
Mem of Lincoln Trail Libraries System
Friends of the Library Group

WAUCONDA

S LAKE COUNTY DISCOVERY MUSEUM, Curt Teich Postcard Archives & Lake County History Archives, 27277 Forest Preserve Dr, 60084. SAN 376-1258. Tel: 847-968-3381. FAX: 847-526-1545. E-Mail: teicharchives@co.lake.il.us. Web Site: www.co.lake.il.us/forest/educate.htm. *Archivist*, Christine A Pyle; E-Mail: cpyle@co.lake.il.us
Library Holdings: Bk Titles 2,000; Per Subs 40
Special Collections: Curt Teich Postcard Archives; Lake County History Archives
Database Vendor: OCLC - First Search
Publications: Historian; Image File
Friends of the Library Group

P WAUCONDA AREA PUBLIC LIBRARY,* 801 N Main St, 60084. SAN 304-7377. Tel: 847-526-6225. FAX: 847-526-6244. *Dir*, Thomas D Kern; E-Mail: tkern@wauclib.org
Founded 1939. Pop 16,528; Circ 160,000
Library Holdings: Bk Vols 87,000; Per Subs 500
Publications: Newsletter
Mem of North Suburban Library System
Friends of the Library Group

WAUKEGAN

GL WILLIAM D BLOCK MEMORIAL LAW LIBRARY, Lake County Law Library, 18 N County St, 60085-4339. SAN 304-7385. Tel: 847-360-6654. Web Site: 19thcircuitcourt.state.il.us/library/libr_toc.htm. *Librn*, David Bender; E-Mail: dbender@co.lake.il.us; Staff 4 (MLS 1, Non-MLS 3)
Founded 1845
Library Holdings: Bk Vols 25,000; Per Subs 60
Special Collections: Illinois Appellate Court Briefs of the Second Judicial District, 1964-present; Law Books on the State of Illinois

S DEXTER CORP, Information Resource Center,* One E Water St, 60085. SAN 374-5856. Tel: 847-625-4438. FAX: 847-625-4482. *Librn*, Robyn Petry; E-Mail: robyn.petry@internetmci.com
Founded 1984
Jan 1997-Dec 1998 Income $45,500. Mats Exp $20,200, Books $3,400, Per/Ser (Incl. Access Fees) $12,800, AV Equip $4,000
Library Holdings: Bk Vols 5,046; Bk Titles 4,921; Per Subs 72
Publications: New materials list; Waukegan Information Resource Center World
Restriction: Staff use only
Mem of North Suburban Library System
Partic in Dialog Corporation; STN

G LAKE COUNTY PLANNING RESOURCE CENTER, (LCPRC), Research Library, 18 N County St, 6th Flr, 60085. SAN 329-952X. Tel: 847-360-6350. Reference Tel: 847-360-6368. FAX: 847-360-6734. E-Mail: planning@co.lake.il.us. Web Site: www.co.lake.us. *Librn*, Barbara Decker; E-Mail: bdecker@co.lake.il.us; Staff 1 (MLS 1)
Founded 1977
Jan 2000-Dec 2000 Mats Exp $3,600. Sal $36,000
Library Holdings: Bk Vols 5,000
Subject Interests: Census data, Land use, Maps, Municipal info, Natural environ, Planning, Planning law
Special Collections: Lake County Aerial Maps, 1939-present
Automation Activity & Vendor Info: (OPAC) Inmagic, Inc.
Restriction: Open to public for reference only
Mem of North Suburban Library System

S NEWS SUN LIBRARY, 1615 Lakeside Dr, Ste 100, 60085. SAN 304-7393. Tel: 847-249-7228, 847-249-7239 (Library No.), 847-336-7000 (Main No.). FAX: 847-249-7202. *Librn*, Julie Crye; E-Mail: julie.crye@copleypress.com
Founded 1950
Library Holdings: Bk Titles 1,100
Subject Interests: Graphic arts, Photography
Partic in Spec Libr Asn

M PROVENA SAINT THERESE MEDICAL CENTER LIBRARY,* 2615 Washington St, 60085. SAN 304-7407. Tel: 847-360-2671. FAX: 847-625-6222. *Librn*, Nellie E Dorsey
Founded 1969
Library Holdings: Bk Titles 1,000; Per Subs 64
Restriction: Staff use only
Partic in Lake County Consortium; Medline

C SHIMER COLLEGE LIBRARY,* 438 Sheridan Rd, 60079. SAN 304-4432. Tel: 847-249-7192, 847-623-8400. FAX: 847-249-7171. *In Charge*, Barbara S Stone; E-Mail: barbara@shimer.edu
Founded 1904

M VICTORY MEMORIAL HOSPITAL, Medical Library,* 1324 N Sheridan Rd, 60085. SAN 325-6995. Tel: 847-360-3000, Ext 5144. FAX: 847-360-4143. *In Charge*, Inka Alasade
Library Holdings: Bk Vols 300; Per Subs 40
Mem of North Suburban Library System
Partic in BRS; Med Libr Asn, Midwest Chapter; Northeastern Ill Libr Consortia
Open Mon-Fri 8-12

P WAUKEGAN PUBLIC LIBRARY,* 128 N County St, 60085. SAN 304-7415. Tel: 847-623-2041. FAX: 847-623-2092, 847-623-2094. *Dir*, Andrew Stimson; *Asst Dir*, Grace Li; *Ch Servs*, Delfina Laffler; *Bkmobile Coordr*, Robert Blanchard; *Ad Servs*, Sandra Carnelli
Founded 1898. Pop 67,392; Circ 476,267
Library Holdings: Bk Vols 276,000; Per Subs 395
Special Collections: Current Social Problems; Lake County History; US Census; Waukegan Authors
Mem of North Suburban Library System
Open Mon-Thurs 9-9, Fri 9-6, Sat 9-5, Sun 1-5
Friends of the Library Group

WAVERLY

P WAVERLY PUBLIC LIBRARY, 291 N Pearl St, 62692. SAN 304-7423. Tel: 217-435-2051. FAX: 217-435-2051. E-Mail: wavp@darkstar.rsa.lib.il.us. Web Site: www.waverly.lib.il.us. *Librn*, Julie Samaras
Pop 1,402; Circ 11,000
Library Holdings: Bk Vols 11,000; Per Subs 29
Mem of Alliance Library System
Friends of the Library Group

WAYNE CITY

P WAYNE CITY PUBLIC LIBRARY,* 103 E Mill St, 62895. SAN 304-7431. Tel: 618-895-2661. FAX: 618-895-2241. *Librn*, Sue Musgrave; *Asst Librn*, Phyllis Clark
Founded 1971. Pop 1,135; Circ 6,710
Library Holdings: Bk Vols 12,000; Per Subs 25
Subject Interests: Illinois
Mem of Shawnee Library System

WAYNESVILLE

P WAYNESVILLE TOWNSHIP LIBRARY, 303 E Second St, PO Box 59, 61778. SAN 304-744X. Tel: 217-949-5111. FAX: 217-949-5111. E-Mail: waytlib@hotmail.com. *Librn*, Margie Rich; *Asst Librn*, Margie Craig
Founded 1938. Pop 768; Circ 5,191
Apr 1999-Mar 2000 Income $38,048, State $960, County $334, Other $679. Mats Exp Books $2,803. Sal $11,558
Library Holdings: Bk Vols 12,372
Mem of Alliance Library System

WELDON

P WELDON PUBLIC LIBRARY DISTRICT,* PO Box 248, 61882-0248. SAN 304-7458. Tel: 217-736-2215. FAX: 217-736-2215. *Librn*, Stephanie Edwards
Pop 867; Circ 9,801
Library Holdings: Bk Vols 9,784; Per Subs 44
Mem of Rolling Prairie Library System

WENONA

P BOND LIBRARY,* 208 S Chestnut St, 61377. SAN 304-7466. Tel: 815-853-4665. *Librn*, Pauline Harsted; *Pres*, Alan Beckmann
Founded 1896. Pop 1,250; Circ 6,728
1997-1998 Income $20,681, State $2,375, City $13,699, Other $4,607. Mats Exp $2,808. Sal $5,294
Library Holdings: Bk Titles 18,568; Per Subs 45
Special Collections: County History (Marshall, La Salle, Tazewell, Putnam, Livingston, McLean, Upper Ohio Valley, Logan); Local Newspapers, micro
Mem of Starved Rock Libr Syst
Open Tues 7-9, Wed & Fri 2-5, Sat 9-5
Friends of the Library Group

WEST CHICAGO

S MASONITE CORP, Masonite Research Center Library,* 1955 Powis Rd, 60185. SAN 304-6273. Tel: 630-584-6330. FAX: 630-584-1139.
Founded 1963
Library Holdings: Bk Vols 1,600; Per Subs 100
Subject Interests: Forestry
Mem of DuPage Library System

P WEST CHICAGO PUBLIC LIBRARY DISTRICT, 118 W Washington St, 60185-2803. SAN 304-7474. Tel: 630-231-1552. FAX: 630-231-1709. Web Site: www.westchicago.lib.il.us. *Admin Assoc*, Julie Milavec; *YA Servs*, Chris Waite; *Ad Servs*, Lisa Pappas; Staff 27 (MLS 7, Non-MLS 20)
Founded 1927. Pop 22,337; Circ 146,219
Jul 1998-Jun 1999 Income $1,183,148. Mats Exp $109,294. Sal $374,774
Library Holdings: Bk Vols 81,851; Per Subs 238
Subject Interests: Railroads
Special Collections: Book-plates Coll
Automation Activity & Vendor Info: (Acquisitions) DRA; (Cataloging) DRA; (Circulation) DRA; (Course Reserve) DRA; (ILL) DRA; (Media Booking) DRA; (OPAC) DRA; (Serials) DRA
Publications: Biblio News (quarterly newsletter)
Mem of DuPage Library System
Friends of the Library Group

WEST FRANKFORT

P WEST FRANKFORT PUBLIC LIBRARY, 402 E Poplar St, 62896. SAN 304-7482. Tel: 618-932-3313. FAX: 618-932-3313. *Librn*, Sarah-Jane Alexander; Staff 1 (Non-MLS 1)
Founded 1927. Pop 8,526; Circ 50,000
May 1999-Apr 2000 Income $87,227, State $12,420, City $74,807. Mats Exp $87,228, Books $12,169, Per/Ser (Incl. Access Fees) $2,964, Electronic Ref Mat (Incl. Access Fees) $5,286. Sal $45,484
Library Holdings: Bk Vols 32,726; Per Subs 80; High Interest/Low Vocabulary Bk Vols 75

Subject Interests: Antiques, Art, Fine arts, Furniture, Genealogy, Indians
Automation Activity & Vendor Info: (Cataloging) epixtech, inc.; (Circulation) epixtech, inc.; (ILL) epixtech, inc.; (OPAC) epixtech, inc.
Mem of Shawnee Library System
Special Services for the Blind - Talking Books

WEST SALEM

P WEST SALEM PUBLIC LIBRARY,* 112 W South St, PO Box 128, 62476-0128. SAN 304-7490. Tel: 618-456-8970. FAX: 618-456-8970. *Librn*, Mary Jane McKinney
Founded 1966. Pop 1,145
Library Holdings: Bk Vols 7,000; Per Subs 15
Mem of Cumberland Trail Libr Syst

WEST UNION

P WEST UNION DISTRICT LIBRARY, 209 W Union St, PO Box 138, 62477. SAN 376-2769. Tel: 217-279-3556. FAX: 217-279-3556. *Librn*, Anita Dolson; Staff 1 (Non-MLS 1)
Founded 1986. Pop 851
Library Holdings: Bk Vols 15,500; Bk Titles 12,000; Per Subs 15
Mem of Lincoln Trail Libraries System
Friends of the Library Group

WESTCHESTER

S ELRICK & LAVIDGE INC LIBRARY,* 3 Westbrook Corporate Ctr, Ste 600, 60154. SAN 375-1171. Tel: 708-449-5300. FAX: 708-449-4498. *Mgr*, Theresa Litoborski
Library Holdings: Bk Titles 300
Restriction: Not open to public

P WESTCHESTER PUBLIC LIBRARY, 10700 Canterbury St, 60154. SAN 304-7504. Tel: 708-562-3573. TDD: 708-562-9364. FAX: 708-562-1298. E-Mail: wcs@sublibsy.sls.lib.il.us. Web Site: www.sls.lib.il.us/wcs. *Dir*, Mary K Graham; *Asst Dir*, Bonnie Schwanz; *Ref*, Ann Weaver; *Ref Servs Ch*, Kristen Jacobson; Staff 6 (MLS 6)
Founded 1956. Pop 17,301; Circ 189,000
May 1999-Apr 2000 Income $884,700, State $22,000, Locally Generated Income $862,700. Mats Exp $105,000, Books $95,000, Per/Ser (Incl. Access Fees) $10,000. Sal $440,000
Library Holdings: Bk Vols 99,000; Per Subs 342
Automation Activity & Vendor Info: (Circulation) Innovative Interfaces Inc.; (OPAC) Innovative Interfaces Inc.
Database Vendor: IAC - Info Trac
Mem of Suburban Library System
Open Mon-Fri 9:30-9, Sat 9:30-4, Sun 1-5
Friends of the Library Group

WESTERN SPRINGS

P THOMAS FORD MEMORIAL LIBRARY, Western Springs Library, 800 Chestnut Ave, 60558. SAN 304-7520. Tel: 708-246-0520. FAX: 708-246-0403. E-Mail: tfs@sls.lib.il.us. Web Site: www.sls.lib.il.us/tfs/. *Dir*, Anne Kozak; *Circ*, Sandy Frank; *Ch Servs*, Richard Roche; *Ad Servs*, Anne Vandeven; *YA Servs*, Nancy Smith; *YA Servs*, Susan Westgate; Staff 6 (MLS 6)
Founded 1932. Pop 12,876; Circ 170,108
Library Holdings: Bk Vols 71,828; Per Subs 382
Special Collections: Play & Theatre Coll
Automation Activity & Vendor Info: (Cataloging) CLSI LIBS; (Circulation) CLSI LIBS; (OPAC) CLSI LIBS
Publications: Quarterly Newsletter
Mem of Suburban Library System
Open Mon-Thurs 10-9, Fri & Sat 10-5, Sun 1-5
Friends of the Library Group

WESTMONT

S MCCRONE ASSOCIATES INC LIBRARY, 850 Pasquinelli Dr, 60559. SAN 303-9579. Tel: 630-887-7100. FAX: 630-887-7417. Web Site: www.mccrone.com.
Founded 1956
Library Holdings: Bk Titles 3,300; Per Subs 125
Subject Interests: Chemistry, Crystallography, Microscopy

S TRI BROOK GROUP, INC LIBRARY,* 999 Oakmont Plaza Dr, Ste 600, 60559-5504. SAN 326-9620. Tel: 630-990-8070. FAX: 630-325-0337.
Library Holdings: Bk Titles 4,000; Per Subs 60
Partic in Fox Valley Health Science Library Consortium

P WESTMONT PUBLIC LIBRARY, 428 N Cass, 60559-1502. SAN 304-7539. Tel: 630-969-5625. FAX: 630-969-6490. E-Mail: wms@sls.lib.il.us. *Dir*, Charlene R Sanders; *Ad Servs*, Mitch Flesner; *Ch Servs*, Marcy Simpson; Staff 7 (MLS 7)
Founded 1943. Pop 23,029; Circ 138,700
May 1999-Apr 2000 Income $939,633. Mats Exp $99,830. Sal $325,014
Library Holdings: Bk Vols 76,868; Per Subs 275
Automation Activity & Vendor Info: (Cataloging) Innovative Interfaces Inc.; (Circulation) Innovative Interfaces Inc.; (ILL) Innovative Interfaces Inc.; (OPAC) Innovative Interfaces Inc.
Mem of Suburban Library System
Friends of the Library Group

WESTVILLE

P WESTVILLE PUBLIC LIBRARY,* 149 N State St, PO Box 97, 61883. SAN 304-7547. Tel: 217-267-3170. FAX: 217-267-3468. *Dir*, Mae Thompson; *Asst Dir*, Cherrie Burke; *Asst Dir*, Laura Gondry
Founded 1937. Pop 3,573
Library Holdings: Bk Titles 17,780
Special Collections: Antique & Collectibles Coll
Mem of Lincoln Trail Libraries System

WHEATON

SR COLLEGE CHURCH IN WHEATON LIBRARY, 330 E Union, 60187. SAN 304-7555. Tel: 630-668-0878. FAX: 630-668-0984. E-Mail: library@college-church.org. Web Site: www.college-church.org. *Librn*, John Wickberg
Library Holdings: Bk Vols 12,000
Subject Interests: Biblical studies, Missions and missionaries
Publications: New in the Church Library (monthly)

GM DUPAGE COUNTY HEALTH DEPARTMENT, John P Case Library, 111 N County Farm Rd, 60187-3988. SAN 304-7563. Tel: 630-682-7400, Ext 7372. FAX: 630-462-9249. Web Site: www.dupagehealth.org. *Librn*, Paula Salvadore; Tel: 630-682-7400, Ext 7667; Staff 4 (MLS 1, Non-MLS 3)
Founded 1973
Library Holdings: Bk Titles 3,000; Per Subs 160
Subject Interests: Mental health
Restriction: Open to public for reference only
Mem of DuPage Library System
Partic in BRS; Fox Valley Health Science Library Consortium

L DUPAGE COUNTY LAW LIBRARY,* DuPage County Law Library-Judicial Ctr, 505 N County Farm Rd, 60187-3907. SAN 326-0860. Tel: 630-682-7337. FAX: 630-682-6794.

M MARIANJOY REHABILITATION HOSPITAL, Medical Library,* 26 W 171 Roosevelt Rd, PO Box 795, 60189. SAN 324-4903. Tel: 630-462-4104. Interlibrary Loan Service Tel: 630-462-4270. FAX: 630-260-0143. *Librn*, Nalini Mahajan; E-Mail: m-nalini@dupagels.lib.il.us; Staff 1 (MLS 1)
Founded 1974
Library Holdings: Bk Titles 2,875; Per Subs 273
Special Collections: Rehabilitation Medicine
Mem of DuPage Library System
Partic in BRS; Dialog Corporation; Fox Valley Health Science Library Consortium; Illinois Library & Information Network
Open Mon-Fri 8-4:30

S COLONEL ROBERT MCCORMICK RESEARCH CENTER, First Division Museum at Cantigny, One S 151 Winfield Rd, 60187-6097. SAN 375-1333. Tel: 630-260-8186. Interlibrary Loan Service Tel: 630-260-8211. Reference Tel: 630-260-8223. FAX: 630-260-9298. E-Mail: fdmuseum@tribune.com. Web Site: www.rrmtf.org/firstdivision. *Dir*, John F Votaw; *Assoc Dir*, Eric Gillespie; *Tech Servs*, Tracy Crockett; *Ref*, Andrew Woods
Library Holdings: Bk Vols 10,000; Per Subs 75
Database Vendor: OCLC - First Search
Restriction: Non-circulating to the public, Open to public with supervision only
Function: Archival collection, Research fees apply, Research library
Mem of DuPage Library System

S THEOSOPHICAL SOCIETY IN AMERICA, Henry S Olcott Memorial Library, 1926 N Main St, 60187. (Mail add: PO Box 270, 60189-0270), SAN 304-758X. Tel: 630-668-1571, Ext 304. FAX: 630-668-4976. E-Mail: library@theosmail.net. Web Site: www.theosophical.org. *Librn*, Elisabeth Trumpler; Staff 1 (MLS 1)
Founded 1926
Apr 2000-Mar 2001 Income $180,000
Library Holdings: Bk Vols 18,000; Per Subs 100
Subject Interests: Eastern philosophy, Mythology, Philosophy, Theosophy
Special Collections: Boris de Zirkoff Coll; Mary K Neff Coll; Rare Theosophical Journals Coll, micro
Automation Activity & Vendor Info: (Cataloging) SIRSI; (Circulation) SIRSI
Database Vendor: OCLC - First Search
Publications: Annotated Book List 1990; Audio-Video Guide (1997 with annual updates); New Accessions Lists
Mem of DuPage Library System
Partic in OCLC Online Computer Library Center, Inc

C WHEATON COLLEGE, Buswell Memorial Library, 510 Irving Ave, 60187-5593. (Mail add: 501 College Ave, 60187-5535), SAN 304-7598. Tel: 630-752-5102. Interlibrary Loan Service Tel: 630-752-5843. Reference Tel: 630-752-5169. FAX: 630-752-5855. Web Site: www.wheaton.edu/learnres/library. *Dir*, P Paul Snezek; Tel: 630-752-5101, E-Mail: p.p.snezek@wheaton.edu; *Tech Coordr*, Terry Huttenlock; *Tech Servs*, Mary Sue Preisler; *Publ Servs*, Gregory Morrison; *Publ Servs*, Maggie Noll; *Head, Info Serv*, John Fawcett; *Archivist, Spec Coll*, David Malone; *Head Tech Servs*, Stewart McElroy. Subject Specialists: *Arts*, Keith Eiten; *Communication*, Keith Eiten; *Media*, Keith Eiten; *Music*, Stewart McElroy; Staff 14 (MLS 8, Non-MLS 6)
Founded 1860. Enrl 2,600; Fac 135; Highest Degree: Doctorate
1999-2000 Income $1,256,000. Mats Exp $642,326, Books $222,221, Per/Ser (Incl. Access Fees) $311,321, Presv $26,305, Micro $47,701, Other Print Mats $3,827, Manuscripts & Archives $8,000, Electronic Ref Mat (Incl. Access Fees) $22,951. Sal $673,531 (Prof $287,571)
Library Holdings: Bk Vols 311,105; Bk Titles 217,032; Per Subs 1,713
Subject Interests: American literature, Anthropology, English literature, History, Music, Philosophy, Political science, Religion
Special Collections: David Aikman, Frederick Buechner, John Bunyan, Anita & Peter Deyneka, Charles Dickens, Jaque Ellul, Samuel Johnson, Kenneth & Margaret Landon, Madeline L'Engle, Coleman Luck, Calvin Miller, Malcolm Muggeridge, Hans Rookmaaker, Luci Shaw, Norman Stone, Angela Tilloy; Jonathan & Charles Blanchard Papers & Publications
Automation Activity & Vendor Info: (Acquisitions) epixtech, inc.; (Cataloging) epixtech, inc.; (Circulation) epixtech, inc.; (Course Reserve) epixtech, inc.; (OPAC) epixtech, inc.; (Serials) epixtech, inc.
Publications: Bibliotheca Colleggii
Partic in Libras, Inc; OCLC Online Computer Library Center, Inc
Departmental Libraries:
BILLY GRAHAM CENTER LIBRARY, 500 E College Ave, 60187-5534. SAN 321-4060. Tel: 630-752-5194. FAX: 630-752-5532. E-Mail: bgclibr@wheaton.edu. Web Site: www.wheaton.edu/bgc/library. *Dir*, Ferne Weimer; *Acq*, Marsha Schuppner; *Publ Servs*, Jan Verdsema; Staff 3 (MLS 1, Non-MLS 2)
Jul 1999-Jun 2000 Income $163,113. Mats Exp $20,691, Books $12,850, Per/Ser (Incl. Access Fees) $5,741, Presv $2,100. Sal $102,310
Library Holdings: Bk Vols 72,540; Bk Titles 59,334; Per Subs 610
Subject Interests: Evangelicalism, Missions and missionaries
Special Collections: Billy Graham Coll; M K Coll (Children of Missionaries); Prison Ministries; Theological Education by Extension Curriculum
Automation Activity & Vendor Info: (Acquisitions) epixtech, inc.; (Cataloging) epixtech, inc.; (Circulation) epixtech, inc.; (OPAC) epixtech, inc.; (Serials) epixtech, inc.
Partic in OCLC Online Computer Library Center, Inc
MARION E WADE CENTER, 501 College Ave, 60187. Tel: 630-752-5908. FAX: 630-752-5855. E-Mail: wade@wheaton.edu. *Dir*, Dr Christopher Mitchell; *Assoc Dir*, Marjorie L Mead; *Archivist*, Alicia Pearson; *Archivist*, Pam Schwartz; Staff 4 (MLS 2, Non-MLS 2)
Founded 1965
Library Holdings: Bk Titles 13,000; Per Subs 42
Subject Interests: Children's literature, Fantasy, Science fiction, Theology
Special Collections: C S Lewis Coll; Charles Williams Coll; Dorothy L Sayers Coll; G K Chesterton Coll; George MacDonald Coll; J R R Tolkien Coll; Owen Barfield Coll
Publications: Seven: An Anglo-American Literary Review

P WHEATON PUBLIC LIBRARY,* 225 N Cross St, 60187-5376. SAN 304-7601. Tel: 630-668-1374. TDD: 630-668-0256. FAX: 630-668-1465. Web Site: www.wheaton.lib.il.us/library/. *Dir*, Sarah Meisels; Tel: 630-668-3097, E-Mail: s-meisels@mail.wheaton.lib.il.us; *Tech Servs*, Dawn Kovacs; E-Mail: d-kovacs@mail.wheaton.lib.il.us; *Ch Servs*, Janet Dumas; Fax: 630-668-8950, E-Mail: j-dumas@mail.wheaton.lib.il.us; *Per*, Bev Jirsa; Fax: 630-668-8950, E-Mail: b-jirsa@mail.wheaton.lib.il.us; *Ref*, Carolyn Deare; Fax: 630-668-8950, E-Mail: c-deare@mail.wheaton.lib.il.us; *Circ*, Ann Barnfield; E-Mail: barnfield@mail.wheaton.lib.il.us; *Circ*, Kay Beranis; E-Mail: k-beranis@mail.wheaton.lib.il.us
Founded 1891. Pop 55,755; Circ 916,416
May 1998-Apr 1999 Income (Main Library Only) $2,709,188, State $69,053, City $2,395,540, Federal $12,000, Locally Generated Income $218,862, Other $13,733. Mats Exp $461,225, Books $330,767, Per/Ser (Incl. Access Fees) $30,779, Presv $6,679, Micro $8,000, AV Equip $4,000, Electronic Ref Mat (Incl. Access Fees) $81,000. Sal $1,399,340 (Prof $562,718)
Library Holdings: Bk Vols 328,561; Per Subs 570
Subject Interests: Genealogy
Special Collections: DuPage County History Coll
Automation Activity & Vendor Info: (Cataloging) Innovative Interfaces Inc.; (Circulation) Innovative Interfaces Inc.; (ILL) Innovative Interfaces Inc.; (OPAC) Innovative Interfaces Inc.; (Serials) Innovative Interfaces Inc.
Database Vendor: OCLC - First Search
Publications: Adult & Children's newsletters; bibliographies
Mem of DuPage Library System
Partic in OCLC Online Computer Library Center, Inc
Special Services for the Deaf - TDD
Open Mon-Fri 9-9, Sat 9-5 & Sun 1-5

WHEELING

P INDIAN TRAILS PUBLIC LIBRARY DISTRICT,* 355 S Schoenbeck Rd, 60090. SAN 304-761X. Tel: 847-459-4100. FAX: 847-459-4760. E-Mail: wgkadmin@ccs.nslsilus.org. Web Site: www.itpld.lib.il.us. *Dir*, Tamiye Meehan; E-Mail: tmeehan@itpld.lib.il.us; *Ad Servs*, Sally Decker Smith; E-Mail: ssmith@itpld.lib.il.us; *Tech Servs*, Wei Jeng-Chu; *Ch Servs*, Kathleen Simonetta; *Commun Relations*, Chris Gibson Reading; *Tech Coordr*, Michael Jackiw; *Circ*, Barbara Czechorski; Staff 92 (MLS 14, Non-MLS 78)
Founded 1959. Pop 58,789; Circ 600,000
Jul 1998-Jun 1999 Income $3,082,863. Mats Exp $3,033,857. Sal $1,620,203
Library Holdings: Bk Vols 209,044; Bk Titles 146,405
Database Vendor: IAC - Info Trac, OCLC - First Search
Publications: Children's newsletter; general library newsletter
Mem of North Suburban Library System
Special Services for the Deaf - TTY machine
Friends of the Library Group

P NORTH SUBURBAN LIBRARY SYSTEM,* 200 W Dundee Rd, 60090-2799. SAN 304-7628. Tel: 847-459-1300. FAX: 847-459-0380. Web Site: nslsilus.org. *Dir*, Sarah A Long; *Coordr, Tech Servs*, David Green
Founded 1966
Jul 1998-Jun 1999 Income $2,819,900
Publications: Legislative Notes (Legislative updates issued irregularly); NSLS Directory; The Blue Sheets (weekly information sheet distributed on electronic bulletin boards)
Member Libraries: Abbott Laboratories; Alexian Brothers Medical Center; Algonquin Area Public Library District; Allstate Insurance Company; Allstate Insurance Company; American Association of Nurse Anesthetists Library-Archives; American Farm Bureau Federation Library; American Foundry Society Inc Library; Antioch District Library; Arlington Heights Memorial Library; Barat College; Barrington Public Library District; Baxter International; Beth Hillel Congregation Library; Cary Area Public Library District; Church of The Brethren General Board; College Of Lake County; Condell Medical Center; Congregation Beth Shalom; Cook Memorial Public Library District; Crystal Lake Public Library; Dairy Management Inc; Deerfield Public Library; Des Plaines Public Library; Dexter Corp; Dundee Township Public Library District; Ela Area Public Library District; Elgin Community College; Elk Grove Village Public Library; Evanston Northwestern Healthcare-Evanston Hospital; Evanston Northwestern Healthcare-Glenbrook Hospital; Evanston Public Library; Fox Lake District Library; Fox River Grove Public Library District; Fremont Public Library District; Fujisawa Healthcare Corporate Library; Gail Borden Public Library District; Garrett-Evangelical & Seabury-Western Theological Seminaries; Gas Technology Institute; Glencoe Public Library; Glenview Public Library; Grayslake Area Public Library District; Hebrew Theological College; Hewitt Associates Library; Highland Park Hospital; Highland Park Public Library; Highwood Public Library; Hollister Incorporated; Household International; Huntley Area Public Library; Illinois Institute Of Art Library; Indian Trails Public Library District; Judson College; Kendall College Library; Kenilworth Public Library District; Kraft General Foods, Inc; Lake Bluff Public Library; Lake County Planning Resource Center; Lake Forest College; Lake Forest Library; Lake Villa District Library; Lincolnwood Public Library District; Lutheran General Hospital; McHenry County College Library; McHenry Nunda Public Library District; McHenry Public Library District; Morton Grove Public Library; Motorola, Inc; Motorola, Inc; Mount Prospect Public Library; National Association Of Independent Insurers; National-Louis University Library; National-Louis University Library; Nestle Clinical Nutrition; Niles Public Library District; North Chicago Public Library; North Shore Congregation Israel; North Suburban Synagogue Beth El; Northbrook Public Library; Northrop Grumman Corp; Northwest Community Hospital; Northwestern University Library; Pactive Corp; Palatine Public Library District; Park Ridge Public Library; Pharmacia Corp; Portland Cement Association; Prospect Heights Public Library District; Quaker Oats Co; Rolling Meadows Library; Roosevelt University; Round Lake Area Public Library District; Rush North Shore Medical Center; Ryerson Nature Library; Safety-Kleen Corp; Saint Francis Hospital; Schaumburg Township District Library; Schirmer Engineering Corp Library; Scott Foresman Library; Shand, Morahan & Co, Inc Library; Skokie Public Library; Society Of Actuaries Library; Stepan Company; STS Consultants Ltd Library; Temple Jeremiah; The Center Library; The Nutrasweet Kelko Co; The RJS Group, Inc; Trinity International University; Triodyne Inc; Unilever Home & Personal Care; United States Navy; United States Navy; USG Research & Technology Center Library; Vernon Area Public Library District; Victory Memorial Hospital; Warren-Newport Public Library District; Wauconda Area Public Library; Waukegan Public Library; William Rainey Harper College; Wilmette Public Library District; Winnetka-Northfield Public Library District; Zenith Electronics Corp; Zion-Benton Public Library District
Partic in OCLC Online Computer Library Center, Inc

WHITE HALL

P WHITE HALL TOWNSHIP LIBRARY, 119 E Sherman St, 62092. SAN 304-7636. Tel: 217-374-6014. E-Mail: whlib@irtc.net. *Head Librn*, Alice Ford; *Asst Librn*, Janis Chapman; *Asst Librn*, Joyce Coates; Staff 3 (Non-MLS 3)
Founded 1876. Pop 3,296; Circ 13,289
Apr 1999-Mar 2000 Income $37,768, State $4,066, County $652, Locally Generated Income $27,050, Other $6,000. Mats Exp $16,000, Books $8,000, Per/Ser (Incl. Access Fees) $1,100, Micro $63, Other Print Mats $405, Electronic Ref Mat (Incl. Access Fees) $532. Sal $20,000
Library Holdings: Bk Vols 14,774; Per Subs 42
Special Collections: County Histories, White Hall Register - Republican Paper on Microfilm 1869 to 1985 - Green Prairie Press 1985 to present
Mem of Lewis & Clark Library System
Special Services for the Blind - Cassette bks
Open Mon-Thurs 2-8, Fri & Sat 9-5

WILLIAMSFIELD

P WILLIAMSFIELD PUBLIC LIBRARY DISTRICT,* 111 W Gale St, PO Box 268, 61489-0268. SAN 376-1398. Tel: 309-639-2630. FAX: 309-639-2611. *Librn*, Gayla Karrick
Library Holdings: Bk Titles 5,984; Per Subs 29
Mem of Alliance Library System
Friends of the Library Group

WILLIAMSVILLE

P WILLIAMSVILLE PUBLIC LIBRARY,* 141 W Main, 62693-9999. SAN 304-7644. Tel: 217-566-3520. *Librn*, Hugh Moore
Founded 1980. Pop 996; Circ 5,147
Library Holdings: Bk Titles 12,000
Subject Interests: Children's literature
Mem of Rolling Prairie Library System
Friends of the Library Group

WILLOWBROOK

S VIBRATION INSTITUTE LIBRARY,* 6262 S Kingery Hwy, Ste 212, 60514. SAN 373-4447. Tel: 630-654-2254. FAX: 630-654-2271. E-Mail: vibinst@anet-chi.com. *Dir*, Ronald L Eshleman
Library Holdings: Bk Vols 200; Per Subs 150

WILMETTE

SR BETH HILLEL CONGREGATION LIBRARY, 3220 Big Tree Lane, 60091. SAN 376-0057. Tel: 847-256-1213, Ext 29. *Librn*, Marcie Eskin; *Librn*, Sandra Helman; Staff 1 (MLS 1)
Library Holdings: Bk Titles 2,000
Mem of North Suburban Library System

S WILMETTE HISTORICAL MUSEUM, Research Library, 609 Ridge Rd, 60091-2721. SAN 329-1154. Tel: 847-853-7666. FAX: 847-853-7706. Web Site: wilmete.com. *Dir*, K Hussey Arntson
Founded 1951
Library Holdings: Bk Vols 500; Bk Titles 400
Subject Interests: Local history
Special Collections: Village of Wilmette
Restriction: Non-circulating to the public

P WILMETTE PUBLIC LIBRARY DISTRICT, 1242 Wilmette Ave, 60091-2558. SAN 304-7660. Tel: 847-256-5025. FAX: 847-256-6911. Reference FAX: 847-256-6933. E-Mail: wilref@wilmette.lib.il.us. Web Site: www.wilmette.lib.il.us. *Dir*, Richard E Thompson; Tel: 847-256-6915, Fax: 847-256-6911; *Ad Servs*, Ellen Clark; Tel: 847-256-6936, Fax: 847-256-6933; *Ch Servs*, Lyn Persson; Tel: 847-256-6940; *Commun Servs*, Bonnie Forkosh; Tel: 847-256-6925; *ILL*, Louise Neidorf; Tel: 847-256-6955, Fax: 847-256-6933; *ILL*, Shirley Pearsall; Tel: 847-256-6955, Fax: 847-256-6933; *Tech Servs*, Gayle Rosenberg; Tel: 847-256-6920, Fax: 847-256-6944; Staff 96 (MLS 29, Non-MLS 67)
Founded 1901. Pop 26,694; Circ 529,774
Jul 1999-Jun 2000 Income $3,681,307, State $72,618, Other $601,001. Mats Exp $543,441, Books $369,876, Per/Ser (Incl. Access Fees) $46,684, Presv $1,450, AV Equip $60,744, Electronic Ref Mat (Incl. Access Fees) $64,697. Sal $1,559,876 (Prof $545,096)
Library Holdings: Bk Vols 223,490; Bk Titles 187,080; Per Subs 665
Subject Interests: Art, Local history, Travel
Special Collections: Annual Reports of Corporations
Publications: Off The Shelf
Mem of North Suburban Library System
Friends of the Library Group

WILMINGTON

S COMMONWEALTH EDISON LIBRARY, Learning Resource Center,* 36400 S Essex Rd, 60481. SAN 329-1022. Tel: 815-458-3411, Ext 2261. FAX: 815-458-3688.
Library Holdings: Bk Titles 100; Per Subs 15
Subject Interests: Nuclear energy
Restriction: Staff use only
Mem of Bur Oak Libr Syst

P WILMINGTON PUBLIC LIBRARY DISTRICT, 201 S Kankakee St, 60481-1338. SAN 304-7679. Tel: 815-476-2834. FAX: 815-476-7805.; Staff 2 (Non-MLS 2)
Founded 1909. Pop 8,966; Circ 52,421
Jul 1999-Jun 2000 Income $394,310, State $25,382, City $14,375, Federal $145, County $339,632, Locally Generated Income $14,776. Mats Exp $38,022, Books $30,548, Per/Ser (Incl. Access Fees) $1,402, AV Equip $4,695, Electronic Ref Mat (Incl. Access Fees) $1,377. Sal $135,112 (Prof $53,040)
Library Holdings: Bk Titles 30,008
Subject Interests: Antiques, Genealogy, Local history
Special Collections: Joliet Arsenal Redevelopment, papers
Mem of Heritage Trail Library System
Open Mon-Thurs 9-8, Fri & Sat 9-5

WINCHESTER

P WINCHESTER PUBLIC LIBRARY, 215 N Main St, 62694. SAN 304-7687. Tel: 217-742-3150. Interlibrary Loan Service Tel: 800-252-0889. FAX: 217-742-3150. E-Mail: wlibrary@irtc.net. *Librn*, Mary Cowhick
Founded 1907. Pop 1,769; Circ 11,911
May 1999-Apr 2000 Mats Exp $49,952
Library Holdings: Bk Vols 17,402
Subject Interests: Local history
Mem of Alliance Library System
Open Mon & Thurs 1-8, Tues 1-5, Wed 1-7, Fri 10-5, Sat 10-12

WINDSOR

P WINDSOR STORM MEMORIAL PUBLIC LIBRARY DISTRICT,* 102 S Maple, 61957. SAN 375-9342. Tel: 217-459-2498. FAX: 217-459-2498. *Librn*, Eileen Curry
Library Holdings: Bk Titles 10,000; Per Subs 59
Mem of Rolling Prairie Library System

WINFIELD

M CENTRAL DUPAGE HOSPITAL, Medical Library,* 25 N Winfield Rd, 60190. SAN 304-7695. Tel: 630-681-4535. FAX: 630-682-0028. *Librn*, Gloria Sullivan; E-Mail: gloria_sullivan@cdh.org
Founded 1974
Library Holdings: Bk Titles 4,000; Per Subs 283
Subject Interests: Medicine, Nursing
Mem of DuPage Library System
Partic in Illinois Library & Information Network; OCLC Online Computer Library Center, Inc; Regional Med Libr - Region 3

P WINFIELD PUBLIC LIBRARY,* OS-291 Winfield Rd, 60190. SAN 304-7709. Tel: 630-653-7599. FAX: 630-653-7781. Web Site: www.winfield.lib.il.us. *Librn*, Georgianna Pulver; E-Mail: gpulver@dupagels.lib.il.us; *YA Servs*, Joan Ranahan-Rader; E-Mail: jranahan@dupagels.lib.il.us; *Ref*, Leslie Brittain; E-Mail: brittain@dupagels.lib.il.us; Staff 3 (MLS 3)
Founded 1970. Pop 8,625; Circ 76,440
May 1998-Apr 1999 Income $403,415, State $9,505, County $333,709, Locally Generated Income $31,401, Other $28,800. Mats Exp $356,812, Books $50,016, Per/Ser (Incl. Access Fees) $9,943, Micro $385, Electronic Ref Mat (Incl. Access Fees) $10,000. Sal $152,014 (Prof $91,000)
Library Holdings: Bk Vols 37,631; Per Subs 168
Subject Interests: Local history
Automation Activity & Vendor Info: (Circulation) Follett; (OPAC) Follett
Mem of DuPage Library System
Open Mon-Thurs 9-9, Fri & Sat 9-5

WINNEBAGO

P WINNEBAGO PUBLIC LIBRARY, 210 N Elida St, 61088-0536. (Mail add: PO Box 536, 61088-0536), SAN 324-5756. Tel: 815-335-7050. FAX: 815-335-7049. *Librn*, Alice Rowley; Staff 2 (Non-MLS 2)
Founded 1983. Pop 5,072
Jul 1999-Jun 2000 Income $171,941, State $6,282, Locally Generated Income $152,958. Mats Exp $16,907, Books $15,087, Per/Ser (Incl. Access Fees) $1,820. Sal $54,765
Library Holdings: Bk Vols 24,455; Per Subs 102

Subject Interests: Illinois, Local history
Automation Activity & Vendor Info: (Circulation) Sagebrush Corporation
Mem of Northern Illinois Library System

WINNETKA

P WINNETKA-NORTHFIELD PUBLIC LIBRARY DISTRICT, 768 Oak St, 60093-2583. SAN 340-9171. Tel: 847-446-7220. FAX: 847-446-5085. Web Site: www.wpld.alibrary.com. *Dir*, Barbara J Aron; E-Mail: barbaron@wpld.alibrary.com; *ILL*, Carol Keenan; *Ch Servs*, Bronwyn Parhad; *Ref*, Juli Janovicz; *Tech Servs*, Jane Levine; Staff 12 (MLS 12)
Founded 1884. Pop 16,845; Circ 228,228
Jul 1999-Jun 2000 Income (Main Library and Branch Library) $2,162,007, State $47,373, Locally Generated Income $1,819,516, Other $295,118. Mats Exp Books $325,463. Sal $996,539
Library Holdings: Bk Vols 114,417; Per Subs 16,561
Subject Interests: Genealogy
Automation Activity & Vendor Info: (Circulation) GEAC; (ILL) GEAC; (OPAC) GEAC
Publications: Source (quarterly) (Newsletter)
Mem of North Suburban Library System
Friends of the Library Group
Branches: 1
NORTHFIELD, 1785 Orchard Ln, 60093. SAN 340-9201. Tel: 847-446-5990. FAX: 847-446-6586. Web Site: www.wpld.alibrary.com. *Librn*, Sara Milovanovic; Staff 3 (MLS 3)
Friends of the Library Group

WITT

P WITT MEMORIAL PUBLIC LIBRARY,* 18 N Second St, PO Box 442, 62094. SAN 304-7725. Tel: 217-594-7333. FAX: 217-594-7333. *Librn*, Sue VanOstran
Founded 1953. Pop 1,391; Circ 3,791
Library Holdings: Bk Vols 10,000
Subject Interests: Genealogy, History
Special Collections: County Genealogical Quarterlies Coll; Hist of Civil War Coll; Illinois & County History Coll; Semi Centennial Memorial Coll, photogs
Mem of Lewis & Clark Library System

WOOD DALE

P WOOD DALE PUBLIC LIBRARY DISTRICT, (WDD), 520 N Wood Dale Rd, 60191. SAN 304-7733. Tel: 630-766-6762. FAX: 630-766-5715. Web Site: www.wooddale.com. *Dir*, Larry E Parks; E-Mail: lparks@dupagels.lib.il.us; *Ch Servs*, Jenny Collier; *Ref*, Joanne Karss; Staff 24 (MLS 1, Non-MLS 23)
Founded 1958. Pop 13,173; Circ 75,000
Library Holdings: Bk Vols 87,000; Per Subs 221
Subject Interests: Large print, Local history
Automation Activity & Vendor Info: (Cataloging) epixtech, inc.; (Circulation) epixtech, inc.; (OPAC) epixtech, inc.
Mem of DuPage Library System

WOOD RIVER

P WOOD RIVER PUBLIC LIBRARY,* 326 E Ferguson Ave, 62095-2098. SAN 304-775X. Tel: 618-254-4832. FAX: 618-254-4836. E-Mail: wre_ill@lclc.lib.il.us. *Coll Develop, Dir*, Diane Steele; *Asst Dir*, Wanda Ringering
Founded 1920. Pop 11,490; Circ 129,980
Library Holdings: Bk Vols 65,316
Mem of Lewis & Clark Library System
Partic in Coop Libr Agency for Syst & Servs
Friends of the Library Group

WOODHULL

P CLOVER LIBRARY DISTRICT, 440 N Division St, PO Box 369, 61490. SAN 304-7768. Tel: 309-334-2680. FAX: 309-334-2378. *Librn*, Rene Bramlett
Founded 1965. Pop 3,054; Circ 21,000
Library Holdings: Bk Vols 22,000; Per Subs 54
Special Collections: Woodhull Hist Coll; World War II Coll
Mem of Alliance Library System
Open Mon, Wed-Thurs 9-12 & 2-8, Fri 9-12 & 2-5, Sat 9-2, Closed Tues

WOODRIDGE

P WOODRIDGE PUBLIC LIBRARY, 3 Plaza Dr, 60517-5014. SAN 304-7776. Tel: 630-964-7899. TDD: 630-964-7986. FAX: 630-964-0175. E-Mail: wrs@sls.lib.il.us. Web Site: www.woodridgelibrary.org. *Adminr*, Mary Sue Brown; E-Mail: brownm@sls.lib.il.us; *Ad Servs, YA Servs*, Victoria Trupiano; E-Mail: trupiano@sls.lib.il.us; *Ch Servs*, Sheri Daun-Bedford; E-Mail: bedfords@sls.lib.il.us; *Head Tech Servs*, Amy Weiss; E-Mail: weissa@sls.lib.il.us; *Head, Circ*, Julie Lombardo; E-Mail: lombardo@sls.lib.il.us; Staff 55 (MLS 14, Non-MLS 41)
Founded 1967. Pop 29,605
May 1999-Apr 2000 Income $2,414,002, State $37,666, County $2,220,070, Locally Generated Income $144,398, Other $11,868. Mats Exp $334,057, Books $225,041, Per/Ser (Incl. Access Fees) $24,624, AV Equip $51,722, Electronic Ref Mat (Incl. Access Fees) $32,670. Sal $913,923 (Prof $593,629)
Library Holdings: Bk Vols 118,008; Per Subs 458
Automation Activity & Vendor Info: (Cataloging) Innovative Interfaces Inc.; (Circulation) Innovative Interfaces Inc.; (Course Reserve) Innovative Interfaces Inc.; (ILL) Innovative Interfaces Inc.; (OPAC) Innovative Interfaces Inc.
Database Vendor: Innovative Interfaces INN - View
Mem of Suburban Library System
Partic in Suburban Libr Syst
Friends of the Library Group

P WOODRIDGE SCHOOL DISTRICT NO 68, Sipley School Library, 2806 83rd St, 60517. SAN 376-7973. Tel: 630-985-7150. FAX: 630-985-0064. Web Site: www.wdgdst68.dupage.k12.il.us. *Dir*, Rebecca Briskey; E-Mail: briskeyr@wdgdst68.dupage.k12.il.us; Staff 1 (MLS 1)
Founded 1973
Library Holdings: Bk Vols 13,000; Bk Titles 12,000; Per Subs 33
Automation Activity & Vendor Info: (Cataloging) Sagebrush Corporation; (Circulation) Sagebrush Corporation
Mem of Suburban Library System

WOODSTOCK

L MCHENRY COUNTY LAW LIBRARY, 2200 N Seminary Ave, 60098. SAN 372-1140. Tel: 815-334-4166. FAX: 815-334-1005. *Librn*, Betty Reffke
Library Holdings: Bk Vols 12,000

S ROHM & HAAS, Information Center, 1275 Lake Ave, 60098. SAN 304-7784. Tel: 815-337-5241. FAX: 815-337-5222. *Info Specialist*, Barbara Ober; E-Mail: bober@rohmhaas.com; Staff 2 (Non-MLS 2)
Founded 1954
Library Holdings: Bk Vols 4,000; Bk Titles 3,000; Per Subs 150
Subject Interests: Chemistry
Mem of Northern Illinois Library System

P WOODSTOCK PUBLIC LIBRARY,* 414 W Judd, 60098-3195. SAN 304-7792. Tel: 815-338-0542. FAX: 815-334-2296. *Dir*, Margaret E Crane; Staff 6 (MLS 6)
Founded 1890. Pop 24,600; Circ 203,492
Library Holdings: Bk Vols 90,000; Bk Titles 81,000; Per Subs 271
Special Collections: McHenry County History & Genealogy
Mem of Northern Illinois Library System
Friends of the Library Group

WORTH

P WORTH PUBLIC LIBRARY DISTRICT,* 6917 W 111th St, 60482. SAN 304-7806. Tel: 708-448-2855. FAX: 708-448-9174. E-Mail: wos@sls.lib.il.us. *Adminr*, Carol Hall; *Ad Servs*, Tim White; *YA Servs*, Jeannine Kelly
Founded 1963. Pop 11,467; Circ 79,410
Jul 1997-Jun 1998 Income $395,752, State $49,664. Mats Exp $60,438, Books $43,000, Per/Ser (Incl. Access Fees) $8,100. Sal $165,500 (Prof $83,700)
Library Holdings: Bk Titles 45,724; Per Subs 149
Automation Activity & Vendor Info: (Circulation) GEAC
Publications: Worth It] (triannual library newsletter)
Mem of Suburban Library System
Friends of the Library Group

WYANET

P RAYMOND A SAPP MEMORIAL LIBRARY, 103 E Main St, PO Box 23, 61379. SAN 304-7814. Tel: 815-699-2342. FAX: 815-699-2342. E-Mail: rasapp@theramp.net. *Librn*, Donna Dable; *Asst Librn*, Sheila Johnsen; Staff 2 (Non-MLS 2)
Founded 1915. Pop 1,483; Circ 4,710
1999-2000 Income $23,294, State $1,830, Federal $180, County $20,860, Other $424. Mats Exp $38,275, Books $3,312, Other Print Mats $1,492. Sal $10,073
Library Holdings: Bk Vols 12,103; Per Subs 23
Mem of Heritage Trail Library System
Friends of the Library Group

WYOMING

P WYOMING PUBLIC LIBRARY DISTRICT, 119 N Seventh St, 61491. SAN 304-7822. Tel: 309-695-2241. FAX: 309-695-2241. *Librn*, Jane Scholl; E-Mail: jkscholl@juno.com

Pop 2,367; Circ 11,890
Library Holdings: Bk Vols 8,228; Per Subs 23
Mem of Alliance Library System
Open Mon-Fri 2-5:30, Wed 2-9 & Sat 8-12

YATES CITY

P SALEM TOWNSHIP PUBLIC LIBRARY DISTRICT,* 115 W Main St, 61572. (Mail add: PO Box 217, 61572), SAN 304-7830. Tel: 309-358-1678. FAX: 309-358-1678. *Chief Librn*, Karen Siegel
Founded 1923. Pop 1,268; Circ 8,716
Library Holdings: Bk Titles 8,500; Per Subs 30
Mem of Alliance Library System

YORKVILLE

P YORKVILLE PUBLIC LIBRARY,* 902 Game Farm Rd, 60560. SAN 304-7849. Tel: 630-553-4354. FAX: 630-553-1504. *Dir*, Michelle Pfister
Founded 1915. Circ 35,900
Library Holdings: Bk Vols 25,000; Per Subs 55
Subject Interests: Art, Local history, Music
Special Collections: Irma Hardekopf Music Coll, bks, sheet music; Kendall County Record 1864-1978 Coll, microflm
Mem of Heritage Trail Library System
Telecourses from Waubonsee Community College
Friends of the Library Group

ZEIGLER

P ZEIGLER PUBLIC LIBRARY,* 111 S Main St, 62999. SAN 304-7857. Tel: 618-596-2041. FAX: 618-596-2041. *Librn*, Peggy Carpenter
Pop 1,748; Circ 7,500
Library Holdings: Bk Vols 9,000; Per Subs 37
Mem of Shawnee Library System

ZION

P ZION-BENTON PUBLIC LIBRARY DISTRICT, 2400 Gabriel Ave, 60099. SAN 304-7873. Tel: 847-872-4680. FAX: 847-872-4942. E-Mail: library@zblibrary.org. Web Site: www.zblibrary.org. *Dir*, Cheryl Nordlund Isom; Tel: 847-872-4680, Ext 110, E-Mail: cisom@zlibrary.org; *Ad Servs*, Susan Clark; Tel: 847-872-4680, Ext 111, E-Mail: sclark@zblibrary.org; *Ch Servs*, Stephanie Smith; Tel: 847-872-4680, Ext 116, E-Mail: smsmith@zblibrary.org; *Cat*, Diane Tarnowske; Tel: 847-872-4680, Ext 124, E-Mail: dtarno@zblibrary.org; *Circ*, Elaine Thomas; E-Mail: ethomas@zblibrary.org
Founded 1937. Pop 37,380; Circ 323,184
Jul 1999-Jun 2000 Income $2,592,764, State $223,670, Locally Generated Income $1,980,280, Other $388,814. Mats Exp $190,149. Sal $734,297
Library Holdings: Bk Vols 118,064; Per Subs 294
Subject Interests: Genealogy, Local history
Automation Activity & Vendor Info: (Circulation) GEAC; (ILL) GEAC; (OPAC) GEAC
Database Vendor: OCLC - First Search
Publications: Zion in Focus
Mem of North Suburban Library System
Partic in Coop Computer Servs; OCLC Online Computer Library Center, Inc
Special Services for the Deaf - TDD; TTY machine
Friends of the Library Group

INDIANA

Date of Statistics: FY 1999
Population, 1990 Census: 5,544,159
Total Volumes in Public Libraries: 22,566,649
Volumes Per Capita: (Statewide) 4.00
Total Public Library Income: $212,443,209
Average Income: $892,619
Source of Income: Local property tax, optional local income tax, contractual revenue received for service financial institution tax, private endorsements/grants, state grants-in-aid, intangibles tax, license excise, county option income tax
Number of County Libraries: 25
Counties Served: 92 (all) receive complete or partial service
Number of Bookmobiles in State: 40
Grants-in-Aid to Public Libraries:
Federal: $1,243,335
State: $2,107,936

AKRON

P AKRON CARNEGIE PUBLIC LIBRARY,* 205 E Rochester St, 46910. (Mail add: PO Box 428, 46910-0428), SAN 304-7881. Tel: 219-893-4113. FAX: 219-893-4113. *Dir*, Velma Bright
Founded 1912. Pop 2,615; Circ 27,436
1998-1999 Income $104,633, State $9,809. Mats Exp $12,037, Books $10,776, Per/Ser (Incl. Access Fees) $1,261. Sal $39,015 (Prof $22,235)
Library Holdings: Bk Vols 28,496; Per Subs 90
Special Collections: Local History, bks, microfilm
Partic in Indiana Cooperative Library Services Authority
Friends of the Library Group

ALBION

P NOBLE COUNTY PUBLIC LIBRARY, 813 E Main St, 46701. SAN 340-9236. Tel: 219-636-7197. FAX: 219-636-3321. E-Mail: ncpublib@noblecan.org. *Dir*, Alennea M Landis
Founded 1914
Library Holdings: Bk Vols 91,996; Per Subs 210
Special Collections: History & Genealogy (Noble County Coll); History (Albion Memories Coll)
Automation Activity & Vendor Info: (Cataloging) epixtech, inc.; (Circulation) epixtech, inc.
Database Vendor: epixtech, inc.
Partic in Indiana Cooperative Library Services Authority
Friends of the Library Group
Branches: 2
NOBLE COUNTY PUBLIC LIBRARY EAST, 116 Albion St, PO Box 699, Avilla, 46710. SAN 340-9260. Tel: 219-897-3900. FAX: 219-897-3900.
Library Holdings: Bk Vols 2,000; Per Subs 20
NOBLE COUNTY PUBLIC LIBRARY WEST, PO Box 555, Cromwell, 46732. SAN 328-6592. Tel: 219-856-2119. FAX: 219-856-2119.

ALEXANDRIA

P ALEXANDRIA-MONROE PUBLIC LIBRARY, 117 E Church St, 46001-2005. SAN 304-789X. Tel: 765-724-2196. Interlibrary Loan Service Tel: 800-662-8903. FAX: 765-724-2204. Web Site: www.alex.k12.in.us. *Librn*, Nancy Norris; E-Mail: nnorris@alex.k12.in.us; Staff 2 (MLS 1, Non-MLS 1)
Founded 1903. Pop 10,057; Circ 75,531
Library Holdings: Bk Vols 40,578; Per Subs 136
Automation Activity & Vendor Info: (Cataloging) Gaylord; (Circulation) Gaylord; (OPAC) Gaylord
Partic in Indiana Cooperative Library Services Authority

ANDERSON

P ANDERSON CITY, ANDERSON, STONY CREEK & UNION TOWNSHIPS PUBLIC LIBRARY, 111 E 12th St, 46016-2701. SAN 340-9295. Tel: 765-641-2451. Circulation Tel: 765-641-2440. Reference Tel: 765-641-2456. TDD: 765-641-2466. FAX: 765-641-2197 (Admin), 765-641-2468. E-Mail: sysadmin@and.lib.in.us. Web Site: www.and.lib.in.us. *Dir*, Marsha Grove; *Asst Dir*, Sarah Later; Tel: 765-641-2460, E-Mail: slater@and.lib.in.us; *Ref*, Kathy Closter; *Ref*, Elaine Mathews; *Ch Servs*, Marcia Murphy; *Tech Servs*, Alice Milley; *AV*, Carolyn Metz; *Ser*, Judith Murphy; Staff 85 (MLS 16, Non-MLS 69)
Founded 1891. Pop 74,072; Circ 870,092
Jan 1999-Dec 1999 Income (Main Library and Branch Library) $3,589,935. Mats Exp $777,160, Books $614,591, Per/Ser (Incl. Access Fees) $26,517, Micro $22,000, AV Equip $107,856, Electronic Ref Mat (Incl. Access Fees) $6,196. Sal $1,582,893
Library Holdings: Bk Vols 269,578; Bk Titles 177,746; Per Subs 775
Special Collections: Government Documents; Literacy; Local History & Genealogy (Indiana Room), bks & microfilm; Music (Wendell Hall Coll), sheet music; Popular Records, compact discs
Automation Activity & Vendor Info: (Acquisitions) epixtech, inc.; (Cataloging) epixtech, inc.; (Circulation) epixtech, inc.
Database Vendor: CARL, Ebsco - EbscoHost, epixtech, inc., OCLC - First Search
Partic in Indiana Cooperative Library Services Authority; OCLC Online Computer Library Center, Inc
Special Services for the Deaf - Books on deafness & sign language; High interest/low vocabulary books; Staff with knowledge of sign language; TTY machine
Open Mon-Thurs 9-9, Fri-Sat 9-5:30 & Sun 1-5
Friends of the Library Group
Branches: 1
LAPEL PUBLIC, 610 Main St, Lapel, 46051. (Mail add: PO Box 668, Lapel, 46051-0668), SAN 340-9325. Tel: 765-534-4654. FAX: 765-534-4654. Web Site: www.and.lib.in.us. *Asst Dir*, Sarah Later; Tel: 765-641-2460, E-Mail: slater@and.lib.in.us; *Librn*, Nancy Lee; Staff 6 (MLS 1, Non-MLS 5)
Founded 1972
Library Holdings: Bk Vols 22,888
Friends of the Library Group
Bookmobiles: 3

S ANDERSON FINE ARTS CARNEGIE CENTER LIBRARY,* 32 W Tenth St, 46016. SAN 304-7903. Tel: 765-649-1248. FAX: 765-649-0199. *Dir*, Deborah McBratney-Stapleton
Founded 1967
Library Holdings: Bk Titles 600; Per Subs 12
Subject Interests: Art history, Fine arts
Special Collections: Art Videos
Publications: Exhibition catalogues
Open Tues-Sat 10am-5pm & Sun 2-5pm

ANDERSON UNIVERSITY
C INSTRUCTIONAL MATERIALS CENTER, Decker Hall, 1100 E Fifth St, 46012-3495. SAN 340-9414. Tel: 765-641-4290. FAX: 765-641-3851. Web Site: bones.anderson.edu/. *Dir*, Shelby D Cantley; Staff 2 (MLS 2)
Founded 1962. Fac 109; Highest Degree: Master

1997-1998 Income $117,700. Mats Exp AV Equip $8,500. Sal $88,000
Library Holdings: Bk Vols 3,527
Special Collections: Fine Arts Photographic Slide Coll

C ROBERT A NICHOLSON UNIVERSITY LIBRARY, 1100 E Fifth St, 46012-3495. SAN 340-9384. Tel: 765-641-4280. FAX: 765-641-3850. Web Site: bones.anderson.edu/home.html. *Dir*, Richard E Snyder; E-Mail: resnyder@anderson.edu; *Archivist*, Douglas Welch; Staff 9 (MLS 6, Non-MLS 3)
Founded 1917. Enrl 2,065; Fac 155; Highest Degree: Master
Jun 1999-May 2000 Mats Exp $231,357, Books $88,644, Per/Ser (Incl. Access Fees) $83,270, Presv $3,791, Micro $27,591, AV Equip $394, Electronic Ref Mat (Incl. Access Fees) $27,667. Sal $386,558 (Prof $251,125)
Library Holdings: Bk Vols 296,946; Bk Titles 153,143; Per Subs 886
Subject Interests: Criminal law and justice, Nursing, Religion
Special Collections: Archives (Archival Material of Charles E Wilson), mementoes & personal & pub papers; Archives of Church of God (Anderson, Indiana)
Automation Activity & Vendor Info: (OPAC) SIRSI
Partic in Private Acad Libr Network of Ind

L EAST CENTRAL LEGAL SERVICES LIBRARY,* 1106 Meridian Plaza, Ste 215, 46016-1766. SAN 325-7193. Tel: 765-644-2816. FAX: 765-642-2473.
Library Holdings: Bk Vols 100; Per Subs 20
Special Collections: Federal Reports

J IVY TECH STATE COLLEGE,* 104 W 53rd St, 46013. SAN 372-493X. Tel: 765-643-7133. FAX: 765-643-3294. Web Site: www.ivy.tec.in.us. *Dir*, Joline Fuller
Enrl 392; Fac 9
Open Mon-Thurs 8am-10pm & Fri 8am-5pm

M SAINT JOHNS HEALTH SYSTEM, Health Science Library,* 2015 Jackson St, 46016-4339. SAN 304-792X. Tel: 765-646-8262. FAX: 765-646-8264. *Librn*, Scott Steven Loman; E-Mail: sslowman@sjhsnet.org
Founded 1970
1996-1997 Mats Exp $50,000
Library Holdings: Bk Vols 3,000; Bk Titles 2,500; Per Subs 165
Subject Interests: Medicine, Nursing
Partic in Medline; Midwest Health Sci Libr Network

ANDREWS

P ANDREWS DALLAS TOWNSHIP PUBLIC LIBRARY,* PO Box 367, 46702. SAN 321-0502. Tel: 219-786-3574. *Librn*, Susan Anderson; *Asst Librn*, Margaret Casey
Pop 1,982
Library Holdings: Bk Vols 12,000; Per Subs 44
Partic in Area 3 Libr Serv Authority
Friends of the Library Group

ANGOLA

P STEUBEN COUNTY LIBRARY, 322 S Wayne St, 46703. SAN 304-7938. Tel: 219-665-3362. FAX: 219-665-8958. E-Mail: scl@cnz.com. Web Site: www.scl.cnz.com. *Actg Dir*, Sonya Dintaman; E-Mail: sdintaman@scl.cnz.com; Staff 16 (MLS 1, Non-MLS 15)
Founded 1915. Pop 13,000; Circ 119,578
Library Holdings: Bk Vols 59,267; Bk Titles 48,350; Per Subs 116
Subject Interests: Genealogy, Local history
Special Collections: Juvenile Nature (Elizabeth Hanna Coll); Nature (Helen L Skelton Coll)
Automation Activity & Vendor Info: (Circulation) Sagebrush Corporation
Partic in Area Libr Servs Authority, Region 3; Indiana Cooperative Library Services Authority; OCLC Online Computer Library Center, Inc
Open Mon-Thurs 9-8, Fri 9-5 & Sat 9-3
Friends of the Library Group

C TRI-STATE UNIVERSITY, Perry T Ford Memorial Library, 300 S Darling St, 46703. (Mail add: One University Ave, 46703), SAN 304-7946. Tel: 219-665-4162. FAX: 219-665-4283. Web Site: www.tristate.edu/library/index.htm. *Dir*, Kristina Brewer; Tel: 219-665-4161, E-Mail: brewerk@tristate.edu; *Publ Servs*, Linda Sebring; E-Mail: sebringl@tristate.edu; *Electronic Resources, Tech Servs*, Anne Abernathey; Tel: 219-665-4164, E-Mail: abernatheya@tristate.edu; Staff 3 (MLS 2, Non-MLS 1)
Founded 1962. Enrl 1,267; Fac 56; Highest Degree: Bachelor
Jun 1999-May 2000 Income $179,121. Mats Exp $58,136, Books $12,273, Per/Ser (Incl. Access Fees) $16,895, Presv $1,294, Micro $5,617, AV Equip $1,292, Electronic Ref Mat (Incl. Access Fees) $20,765. Sal $97,840 (Prof $50,839)
Library Holdings: Bk Vols 123,338; Bk Titles 64,218; Per Subs 306
Subject Interests: Business, Education, Engineering
Special Collections: Elementary Curriculum & Textbooks (Kostyshak Education Coll); Kostyshak Educational Media & Learning Resources; NASA Publications; NATO Publications
Automation Activity & Vendor Info: (Acquisitions) DRA; (Cataloging) DRA; (Circulation) DRA; (Course Reserve) DRA; (OPAC) DRA; (Serials) DRA
Database Vendor: GaleNet, OCLC - First Search
Publications: Tri Status (staff & admin newsletter); Triangle (sch newsp)
Partic in Indiana Cooperative Library Services Authority; Private Acad Libr Network of Ind

ARGOS

P ARGOS PUBLIC LIBRARY,* 119 W Walnut St, 46501-1098. SAN 304-7954. Tel: 219-892-5818. FAX: 219-892-5818. E-Mail: argospublib@skyenet.net. *Coll Develop, Dir*, Jane Hall; *Asst Librn*, Jane Mechling
Founded 1936. Pop 3,500; Circ 42,710
Library Holdings: Bk Vols 26,125; Per Subs 147
Subject Interests: Art and architecture
Partic in Indiana Cooperative Library Services Authority
Open Mon-Fri 10-6, Sat 10-4

ATTICA

P ATTICA PUBLIC LIBRARY, 305 S Perry St, 47918-1494. SAN 304-7962. Tel: 765-764-4194. FAX: 765-764-0906. *Librn*, Norma Lee Fink; Staff 1 (MLS 1)
Founded 1902. Pop 4,429; Circ 35,920
Jan 1999-Dec 1999 Income $137,807, State $78,110, Federal $112, County $52,290, Locally Generated Income $6,589, Other $706. Mats Exp $18,433, Books $15,933, Per/Ser (Incl. Access Fees) $2,500. Sal $64,600 (Prof $21,649)
Library Holdings: Bk Vols 23,188; Per Subs 90
Partic in Wabash Valley Area Libr Servs Authority
Friends of the Library Group

AUBURN

S AUBURN CORD DUESENBERG MUSEUM, Automotive Literature Library, 1600 S Wayne St, PO Box 271, 46706-0271. SAN 321-9712. Tel: 219-925-1444. FAX: 219-925-6266. Web Site: www.welcome.to/acd.museum. *Archivist*, John Emery
Founded 1974
Library Holdings: Bk Vols 1,000; Bk Titles 600; Per Subs 50
Subject Interests: Automotive lit, Indiana-built automobiles, Transportation
Special Collections: Alan H Leamy Coll; Gordon Buehrig Coll; Herbert Newport Coll; Herbert Snow Coll; International Harvester Coll; Raymond A Wolff Coll; Walter Troemel Coll
Publications: The Accelerator (newsletter)

P ECKHART PUBLIC LIBRARY,* 603 S Jackson St, 46706-2298. SAN 304-7970. Tel: 219-925-2414. FAX: 219-925-9376. Web Site: www.epl.lib.in.us. *Dir*, Janelle Graber; *Ch Servs*, Deborah Argast; *Ad Servs*, Daryl Schrock
Founded 1910. Pop 12,000; Circ 180,000
Jan 1999-Dec 1999 Income $571,000
Library Holdings: Bk Vols 65,000
Special Collections: De Kalb County History Coll, bks & genealogy
Automation Activity & Vendor Info: (Cataloging) Gaylord; (Circulation) Gaylord
Partic in Indiana Cooperative Library Services Authority
Van delivery - Eckhart Mobile Outreach Services
Friends of the Library Group

AURORA

P AURORA PUBLIC LIBRARY DISTRICT, 414 Second St, 47001-1384. SAN 304-7989. Tel: 812-926-0646. FAX: 812-926-0665. E-Mail: aurplib@seidata.com. *Dir*, Mary Alice Horton; Staff 1 (MLS 1)
Founded 1901. Pop 15,000; Circ 53,794
Jan 1999-Dec 1999 Income (Main Library and Branch Library) $744,016. Mats Exp $52,439, Books $32,085, Per/Ser (Incl. Access Fees) $5,939, Electronic Ref Mat (Incl. Access Fees) $14,415. Sal $144,138 (Prof $43,000)
Library Holdings: Bk Titles 26,949; Per Subs 101
Partic in Indiana Cooperative Library Services Authority
Open Mon-Fri 10-6 & Sat 10-2
Branches: 1
DILLSBORO PUBLIC, 10151 Library Lane, PO Box 547, Dillsboro, 47018. SAN 377-7448. Tel: 812-432-5200. FAX: 812-432-3898. *Librn*, Mary Alice Horton; Staff 1 (MLS 1)
Founded 1997

AVON

P AVON-WASHINGTON TOWNSHIP PUBLIC LIBRARY,* 498 N State Rd 267, 46123. SAN 376-5385. Tel: 317-272-4818. FAX: 317-272-7302. E-Mail: wtpl@avonlibrary.org. Web Site: www.avonlibrary.org/books. *Dir*, Laurel Setser
Jan 1998-Dec 1998 Income $620,681, State $2,751, County $394,168,

Locally Generated Income $23,886, Other $13,556. Mats Exp $152,344, Books $109,293, Per/Ser (Incl. Access Fees) $8,604, Micro $34,447. Sal $201,400
Library Holdings: Bk Vols 86,228; Bk Titles 60,000; Per Subs 210
Friends of the Library Group

BATESVILLE

P BATESVILLE MEMORIAL PUBLIC LIBRARY, 131 N Walnut St, 47006-4897. SAN 304-7997. Tel: 812-934-4706. FAX: 812-934-6288. E-Mail: bmpl@cnz.com. Web Site: www.bmpl.cnz.com. *Dir*, Michael J Kruse; Staff 15 (MLS 1, Non-MLS 14)
Founded 1937. Pop 8,557; Circ 150,000
Library Holdings: Bk Vols 39,492; Per Subs 125
Subject Interests: Aviation, Entrepreneurship, Genealogy, Local history
Special Collections: 352nd Fighter Group Memorial Aviation Coll; Hillenbrand Family Coll; Mary Stewart Center for Entrepreneurship Coll; Miriam Mason Coll, bks, original ms
Automation Activity & Vendor Info: (Cataloging) Sagebrush Corporation; (Circulation) Sagebrush Corporation; (OPAC) Sagebrush Corporation
Database Vendor: ProQuest
Partic in Indiana Cooperative Library Services Authority
Open Mon-Thurs 10-9, Fri & Sat 10-5, Sun 1-5

BATTLE GROUND

S NORTH AMERICAN WILDLIFE PARK FOUNDATION-WOLF PARK, Institute of Ethology Library,* 47920. SAN 375-1597. Tel: 765-567-2265. FAX: 765-567-4299. E-Mail: wolfpark@aol.com. *Dir*, Erich Klinghammer
Library Holdings: Bk Titles 50

BEDFORD

P BEDFORD PUBLIC LIBRARY, 1323 K St, 47421. SAN 304-8004. Tel: 812-275-4471. Interlibrary Loan Service Tel: 812-278-5247. FAX: 812-277-1145. Web Site: www.bedlib.org. *Dir*, Susan A Miller; *Ch Servs*, Susan Smith; *Ad Servs*, Mary Hall; *Bkmobile Coordr*, Chris Kimmel; *Cat*, Sherri Alexander; *Tech Coordr*, Susan Breidenback; Staff 15 (MLS 6, Non-MLS 9)
Founded 1898. Pop 32,795
Jan 1999-Dec 1999 Income $1,133,154, State $25,242, County $1,063,027, Parent Institution $44,885. Mats Exp $139,430, Books $99,327, Per/Ser (Incl. Access Fees) $5,664, AV Equip $16,188, Electronic Ref Mat (Incl. Access Fees) $18,251. Sal $536,548 (Prof $314,717)
Library Holdings: Bk Vols 93,577; Per Subs 173
Special Collections: Genealogy Coll
Automation Activity & Vendor Info: (Acquisitions) epixtech, inc.; (Cataloging) epixtech, inc.; (Circulation) epixtech, inc.
Database Vendor: OCLC - First Search
Partic in Indiana Cooperative Library Services Authority
Bookmobiles: 1

S INDIANA LIMESTONE INSTITUTE OF AMERICA, INC, Library & Information Center,* Stone City Bank Bldg, Ste 400, 47421. SAN 371-1811. Tel: 812-275-4426. FAX: 812-279-8682. *Exec Dir*, Jim Owens
Library Holdings: Bk Vols 940; Per Subs 10
Restriction: Staff use only

BEECH GROVE

P BEECH GROVE PUBLIC LIBRARY,* 1102 Main St, 46107. SAN 304-8012. Tel: 317-788-4203. FAX: 317-788-0489. Web Site: www.bgpl.lib.in.us. *Dir*, Diane Burns; *Ch Servs*, Doriene Malloy; *Ref*, Michele Patterson
Founded 1949. Pop 13,383; Circ 112,000
Jan 1997-Dec 1998 Income $534,047, State $2,259. Mats Exp $117,986, Books $90,526, Per/Ser (Incl. Access Fees) $11,238, Other Print Mats $16,222. Sal $222,187 (Prof $93,645)
Library Holdings: Bk Vols 62,437; Per Subs 168
Partic in Cent Ind Area Libr Servs Authority
Open Mon-Thurs 9-8, Fri & Sat 9-5
Friends of the Library Group

M SAINT FRANCIS HOSPITAL, Medical Library,* 1600 Albany, 46107. SAN 304-8020. Tel: 317-783-8106. FAX: 317-782-6934. *Librn*, Jennifer Burford
Founded 1972
Library Holdings: Bk Vols 1,900; Per Subs 200
Subject Interests: Nursing
Publications: Bull of the Medical Library Association
Mem of Cent Indiana Area Libr Servs Authority
Partic in BRS; Cent Ind Health Sci Libr Asn; Ind Health Libr Asn; Ind State Libr Asn; MLA
Open Mon-Fri 8-4:30

BERNE

P BERNE PUBLIC LIBRARY, 166 N Sprunger St, 46711-1595. SAN 304-8039. Tel: 219-589-2809. FAX: 219-589-2940. E-Mail: bpl@bernepl.lib.in.us. *Librn*, Marvel Zuercher; Staff 11 (MLS 1, Non-MLS 10)
Founded 1935. Pop 3,559
Library Holdings: Bk Vols 50,000; Bk Titles 48,684; Per Subs 128
Special Collections: Berne and Adams County; Indiana history and genealogy; Mennonite History
Automation Activity & Vendor Info: (Cataloging) Brodart; (Circulation) Brodart; (OPAC) Brodart
Partic in Area 3 Libr Serv Authority
Open Mon-Wed & Fri 9-6, Thurs 12-8, Sat 10-4

BICKNELL

P BICKNELL-VIGO TOWNSHIP PUBLIC LIBRARY, 201 W Second St, 47512-2109. SAN 304-8047. Tel: 812-735-2317. FAX: 812-735-2018. *Dir*, Johnnie M Clark; E-Mail: clarkj@bicknell-vigo.lib.in.us
Founded 1926. Pop 8,000
Library Holdings: Bk Vols 23,650; Per Subs 50
Partic in Ind Libr Asn
Friends of the Library Group

BLOOMFIELD

P BLOOMFIELD - EASTERN GREENE COUNTY PUBLIC LIBRARY,* 125 S Franklin St, 47424-1406. SAN 304-8055. Tel: 812-384-4125. FAX: 812-384-0820. Web Site: www.bloomfield.lib.in.us. *Dir*, Carolyn Konnert; E-Mail: ckonnert@bloomfield.lib.in.us
Founded 1907. Pop 12,300
Jan 1997-Dec 1998 Income $350,838, State $69,060. Mats Exp $40,791, Books $36,790, Per/Ser (Incl. Access Fees) $4,001. Sal $131,866 (Prof $39,073)
Library Holdings: Bk Titles 24,811; Per Subs 99
Special Collections: Advertising Art; Humor (Don Herold Coll)
Friends of the Library Group
Branches: 2
EASTERN, RR 4, Box 388, 47424. SAN 373-8795. Tel: 812-825-2677. FAX: 812-825-2677. Web Site: www.bloomfield.lib.in.us. *Librn*, Karen Holz
Library Holdings: Bk Vols 4,382
Friends of the Library Group
HATFIELD MUSEUM, PO Box 7, Owensburg, 47453. SAN 373-8809. Tel: 812-863-2899. FAX: 863-2899. Web Site: www.bloomfield.lib.in.us. *Librn*, Martha Ashcraft
Library Holdings: Bk Vols 2,445
Friends of the Library Group

BLOOMINGTON

INDIANA UNIVERSITY
S RESEARCH INSTITUTE FOR INNER ASIAN STUDIES, Indiana University, Goodbody 344, 1011 E Third St, 47405-7005. SAN 324-3575. Tel: 812-855-1605. FAX: 812-855-7500. Web Site: www.indiana.edu/~rifias. *Dir*, Devin DeWeese
Founded 1963
Library Holdings: Bk Titles 8,000; Per Subs 18
Subject Interests: Cent Asia, Inner Asia, Mongol studies, Tibetan studies, Turkic studies, Uralic studies
Special Collections: Central Asian Archives/Tibetan Collection
Restriction: Open to public for reference only
Mem of Asn of Research Libraries
CL SCHOOL OF LAW LIBRARY, Law Bldg, 47405. SAN 304-8071. Tel: 812-855-9666. FAX: 812-855-7099. Web Site: www.law.indiana.edu/lawlib/. *Dir*, Colleen K Pauwels; *Assoc Dir*, Linda Fariss; *Ref*, Keith Buckley; *Acq, Ser*, Richard Vaughan; *Tech Servs*, Nona Watt; *Doc*, Marianne Mason; *Cat*, Michael Maben; *Selection of Elec Mat*, Juliet Smith; Staff 11 (MLS 9, Non-MLS 2)
Founded 1842. Enrl 645; Fac 34
Jul 1996-Jun 1997 Income $2,293,645. Mats Exp $1,116,165, Books $130,702, Per/Ser (Incl. Access Fees) $949,416, Presv $25,674. Sal $761,756 (Prof $516,236)
Library Holdings: Bk Vols 591,504; Bk Titles 143,836; Per Subs 7,584
Special Collections: 7th Circuit Records & Briefs; Indiana Court of Appeals Briefs; Indiana Supreme Court Records & Briefs; Rare Books & Archives; US Government Publications; US Supreme Court Records & Briefs
Publications: Res Ipsa Loquitur (inhouse newsletter)
Mem of Asn of Research Libraries
Partic in GPO Access, Ind Coop Libr Servs Authority; OCLC Online Computer Library Center, Inc; Westlaw

C INDIANA UNIVERSITY, Indiana Institute on Disability & Community, 2853 E Tenth St, 47408-2696. SAN 371-6953. Tel: 812-855-9396. TDD: 812-855-9396. FAX: 812-855-9630. E-Mail: cedir@indiana.edu. Web Site:

www.iiidc.indiana.edu/cedir. *Librn*, Marilyn Irwin; *Media Spec*, Melanie Hounshell; Staff 2 (MLS 2)
Library Holdings: Bk Vols 8,000; Bk Titles 8,000; Per Subs 30
Subject Interests: Aging
Special Collections: Autism; Early Childhood Special Needs
Publications: Library Access
Special Services for the Deaf - Books on deafness & sign language; High interest/low vocabulary books; Special interest periodicals; TDD

C INDIANA UNIVERSITY BLOOMINGTON, University Libraries, 1320 E Tenth St, 47405. SAN 340-9538. Tel: 812-855-0100. Circulation Tel: 812-855-4673. Reference Tel: 812-855-8028. FAX: 812-855-2576. E-Mail: libadmin@ucs.indiana.edu. Web Site: www.indiana.edu/~libweb. *Dean of Libr*, Suzanne E Thorin; E-Mail: thorin@indiana.edu; *Assoc Dean*, Martha Brogan; E-Mail: mbrogan@indiana.edu; *Assoc Dean*, Harriette Hemmas; E-Mail: hhemmasi@indiana.edu; *Media Spec*, Kris Brancolini; Staff 313 (MLS 101, Non-MLS 212)
Founded 1824. Enrl 34,017; Fac 1,531; Highest Degree: Doctorate
Jul 1999-Jun 2000 Mats Exp $8,586,366, Books $3,128,052, Per/Ser (Incl. Access Fees) $5,458,314. Sal $11,655,462 (Prof $6,283,537)
Library Holdings: Bk Vols 6,252,932; Per Subs 45,090
Special Collections: 19th Century British Plays; American Revolution; Aristotle; Austrian History, 1790-1843; English History (Civil War, Anglo-Dutch Relations during 17th Century, Glorious Revolution, Political & Economical Pamphlets through End of Walpole Administration); George Frederick Handel; History of Science & Medicine (Archives of Herman Muller - Genetics & V Hlavety - Mathematics); Indiana History; Lafayette; Latin Americana through the Independence Period; Lilly Rare Book Library: English & American Literature, 1640 to present (Milton, Defoe, John Gray, Sterne, Wordsworth, Coleridge, Byron, Tennyson, Henty, Andrew Lang, Yeats, Joseph Conrad, Upton Sinclair, Sylvia Plath); Lincoln; London Low Life during First Half of 19th Century (Sadleir Coll); Voyages & Explorations, especially Spanish, Portuguese & Dutch; War of 1812; Western Americana (Overland Travel from Lewis & Clark through Development of Railroads, Pacific Northwest & California Gold rush) newspapers
Automation Activity & Vendor Info: (Acquisitions) SIRSI; (Cataloging) SIRSI; (Circulation) SIRSI; (OPAC) SIRSI; (Serials) SIRSI
Database Vendor: CARL, Dialog, Ebsco - EbscoHost, GaleNet, IAC - Info Trac, Lexis-Nexis, OCLC - First Search, OVID Technologies, ProQuest, Silverplatter Information Inc., Wilson - Wilson Web
Publications: Indiana University Bookman (Journal of Lilly Library (Newsletter); IUL News (Newsletter); The Source (Newsletter)
Function: Research library
Partic in Area Libr Serv Authority; Center For Research Libraries; Digital Libr Fedn; Indiana Cooperative Library Services Authority; OCLC Online Computer Library Center, Inc
Friends of the Library Group
Departmental Libraries:
AFRICAN AMERICAN CULTURAL CENTER LIBRARY, 203 Coulter Hall, 1975 E Seventh St, 47405. SAN 373-5761. Tel: 812-855-3237. FAX: 812-855-4558. E-Mail: aaclib@indiana.edu. Web Site: www.indiana.edu/~libbcc. *Head of Libr*, Grace Jackson-Brown; E-Mail: jacksob@indiana.edu. Subject Specialists: *Afro-Am studies*, Grace Jackson-Brown
Library Holdings: Bk Vols 6,426; Per Subs 35
Friends of the Library Group
CHEMISTRY, Chemistry Bldg 003, 800 E Kirkwood Ave, 47405. SAN 340-9651. Tel: 812-855-9452. FAX: 812-855-6611. E-Mail: libchem@indiana.edu. Web Site: www.indiana.edu/~libchem. *Head of Libr*, Gary Wiggins; E-Mail: wiggins@indiana.edu. Subject Specialists: *Chemistry*, Gary Wiggins
Library Holdings: Bk Vols 44,134; Per Subs 225
DIGITAL LIBRARY PROGRAM, Main Library E170, 1320 E Tenth St, 47405-1801. Tel: 812-855-3710. FAX: 812-855-2062. E-Mail: diglib@indiana.edu. Web Site: www.dlib.indiana.edu. *Dir*, Kristine Brancolini; E-Mail: brancoli@indiana.edu
EDUCATION LIBRARY, Wright Education Bldg 1160, 201 N Rose St, 47405. SAN 340-9686. Tel: 812-856-8590. FAX: 812-856-8593. E-Mail: libeduc@indiana.edu. Web Site: www.indiana.edu/~libeduc. *Head of Libr*, Steven Sowell; E-Mail: sowell@indiana.edu; *Asst Dean*, P Douglas McKinney; Tel: 812-855-9280, Fax: 812-855-2576, E-Mail: pdmckinn@indiana.edu
Library Holdings: Bk Vols 82,670; Per Subs 450
Special Collections: Childrens Coll; ERIC Documentation Coll; Indiana Textbook Repository
FINE ARTS, Fine Arts Bldg, No 125, 1201 E Seventh St, 47405. SAN 340-9716. Tel: 812-855-3314. FAX: 812-855-3443. E-Mail: libart@indiana.edu. Web Site: www.indiana.edu/~/libfinea. *Head of Libr*, Betty Jo Irvine; E-Mail: irvine@indiana.edu
Library Holdings: Bk Vols 104,280; Per Subs 330
Friends of the Library Group
GEOGRAPHY & MAP, Student Bldg 015, 701 E Kirkwood Ave, 47405. SAN 340-9740. Tel: 812-855-1108. FAX: 812-855-4919. E-Mail: libgm@indiana.edu. Web Site: www.indiana.edu/~libgm. *Head Librn*, Louise Malcomb; E-Mail: malcomb@indiana.edu
Library Holdings: Bk Vols 17,990; Per Subs 137
Friends of the Library Group
GEOLOGY, Geology 601, 1001 E Tenth St, 47405. SAN 340-9775. Tel: 812-855-7170. FAX: 812-855-6614. E-Mail: libgeol@indiana.edu. Web Site: www.indiana.edu/~libgeol. *Head of Libr*, Lois Heiser; E-Mail: heiser@indiana.edu. Subject Specialists: *Geol*, Lois Heiser
Library Holdings: Bk Vols 118,667; Per Subs 236
Friends of the Library Group
HALLS OF RESIDENCE, Library W121, 1320 E Tenth St, 47405. SAN 340-983X. Tel: 812-855-9857. FAX: 812-855-1649. E-Mail: libugls@indiana.edu. Web Site: www.indiana.edu/~libugls/hrl.html. *Head of Libr*, Jo McClamroch; E-Mail: jmcclamr@indiana.edu
HEALTH, PHYSICAL EDUCATION & RECREATION, HPER 029, 1025 E Seventh St, 47405. SAN 340-9562. Tel: 812-855-4420. FAX: 812-855-6778. E-Mail: libhper@indiana.edu. Web Site: www.indiana.edu/~libhper. *Head of Libr*, Mary Strow; E-Mail: mstrow@indiana.edu
Library Holdings: Bk Vols 24,279; Per Subs 250
LIFE SCIENCES LIBRARY, Jordan Hall A304, 1001 E Third St, 47405. SAN 340-9597. Tel: 812-855-8947. FAX: 812-855-6612. E-Mail: liblife@indiana.edu. Web Site: www.indiana.edu/~liblife. *Head of Libr*, Roger Beckman; E-Mail: beckmanr@indiana.edu
Library Holdings: Bk Vols 121,052; Per Subs 667
LILLY RARE BOOKS, Lilly Library, 1200 E Seventh St, 47405. SAN 340-9899. Tel: 812-855-2452. FAX: 812-855-3143. E-Mail: liblilly@indiana.edu. Web Site: www.indiana.edu/~liblilly/text/lillyhome.html. *Actg Dir*, Joel Silver; E-Mail: silverj@indiana.edu. Subject Specialists: *Manuscripts*, Joel Silver; *Rare books*, Joel Silver
Library Holdings: Bk Vols 391,549; Per Subs 94
Friends of the Library Group
CM OPTOMETRY, Optometry Bldg, 800 E Atwater Ave, 47405. SAN 340-9988. Tel: 812-855-8629. FAX: 812-855-6616. E-Mail: libopt@indiana.edu. Web Site: www.opt.indiana.edu/optlib/optlib.html. *Head of Libr*, Douglas Freeman; *Asst Dean*, P Douglas McKinney; Tel: 812-855-9280, Fax: 812-855-2576, E-Mail: pdmckinn@indiana.edu
Founded 1968
Library Holdings: Bk Vols 21,014; Per Subs 114
BUSINESS SPEA, SPEA Bldg 150, 1309 E Tenth St, 47405. SAN 340-9627. Tel: 812-855-1957. FAX: 812-855-3398. E-Mail: libbus@indiana.edu. Web Site: www.indiana.edu/~bslib. *Head of Libr*, Michael Parrish; E-Mail: parrish1@indiana.edu; *Asst Dean*, P Douglas McKinney; Tel: 812-855-9280, Fax: 812-855-2576, E-Mail: pdmckinn@indiana.edu
Library Holdings: Bk Vols 211,587; Per Subs 1,700
SWAIN HALL LIBRARY, Swain Hall W208, 703 E Third St, 47405. SAN 341-0048. Tel: 812-855-2758. FAX: 812-855-6613. E-Mail: libswain@indiana.edu. Web Site: www.indiana.edu/~libswain. *Asst Dean*, P Douglas McKinney; Tel: 812-855-9280, Fax: 812-855-2576, E-Mail: pdmckinn@indiana.edu; *Head of Libr*, Robert Noel; E-Mail: rnoel@indiana.edu
Library Holdings: Bk Vols 99,341; Per Subs 756
Subject Interests: Astronomy, Computer science, Mathematics, Physics
UNIVERSITY ARCHIVES, Bryan Hall 201, 107 S Indiana Ave, 47405. SAN 373-577X. Tel: 812-855-1127. FAX: 812-855-8104. E-Mail: archives@indiana.edu. Web Site: www.indiana.edu/~libarch. *Asst Dean*, P Douglas McKinney; Tel: 812-855-9280, Fax: 812-855-2576, E-Mail: pdmckinn@indiana.edu; *Head of Libr*, Philip Bantin; E-Mail: bantin@indiana.edu
Library Holdings: Bk Vols 1,500
Special Collections: Archives of the official documentation & publications of Indiana University
WEIL JOURNALISM LIBRARY, Ernie Pyle Hall 102, 940 E Seventh St, 47405. SAN 340-9864. Tel: 812-855-3517. FAX: 812-855-0901. E-Mail: libjourn@indiana.edu. Web Site: www.indiana.edu/~llibjourn/home.html. *Br Coordr*, Linda Butler; Tel: 812-855-1726, E-Mail: libutler@indiana.edu; *Ser*, Edwin Cheek; Tel: 812-855-1726, E-Mail: edcheek@indiana.edu; *Asst Dean*, P Douglas McKinney; Tel: 812-855-9280, Fax: 812-855-2576, E-Mail: pdmckinn@indiana.edu; Staff 3 (MLS 1, Non-MLS 2)
Library Holdings: Bk Vols 28,413; Per Subs 219
Subject Interests: Communication, Culture, Journalism, Telecommunications
Special Collections: Roy Howard Archives
Database Vendor: CARL, Ebsco - EbscoHost, GaleNet, Lexis-Nexis, OCLC - First Search, OVID Technologies, ProQuest, Silverplatter Information Inc., Wilson - Wilson Web
WILLIAM & GAYLE COOK MUSIC LIBRARY, Simon Music Library & Recital Center, 200 S Jordan Ave, 47405. SAN 340-9953. Tel: 812-855-2970. FAX: 812-855-3843. E-Mail: libmus@indiana.edu. Web Site: www.music.indiana.edu/muslib.html. *Head of Libr*, Mary Wallace Davidson; E-Mail: mdavidson@indiana.edu. Subject Specialists: *Mus*, Mary Wallace Davidson
Library Holdings: Bk Vols 367,074; Per Subs 321
Subject Interests: Music

C IVY TECH STATE COLLEGE LIBARY, 3116 Canterbury Ct, Rm D133, 47404. SAN 374-5317. Tel: 812-332-1559, Ext 4464. FAX: 812-332-2852. E-Mail: library@bloom.ivy.tec.in.us. Web Site: www.ivy.tec.in.us/library/libr10/index.html. *Librn*, Susan Catt; E-Mail: scatt@ivy.tec.in.us; Staff 3 (MLS 2, Non-MLS 1)
Enrl 2,132; Highest Degree: Associate

Library Holdings: Bk Vols 2,072; Bk Titles 3,000; Per Subs 95
Special Collections: Nursing Coll, bks, per
Automation Activity & Vendor Info: (Cataloging) NOTIS
Database Vendor: Dialog, Ebsco - EbscoHost, GaleNet, Lexis-Nexis, OCLC - First Search, ProQuest, Wilson - Wilson Web
Restriction: Open to student, faculty & staff
Partic in Indiana Cooperative Library Services Authority

S THE KINSEY INSTITUTE FOR RESEARCH IN SEX, GENDER & REPRODUCTION, INC, Research Collections, Indiana University, 313 Morrison Hall, 47405. SAN 304-8098. Tel: 812-855-7686. FAX: 812-855-8277. E-Mail: libknsy@indiana.edu. Web Site: www.indiana.edu/~kinsey/.; Staff 3 (MLS 1, Non-MLS 2)
Founded 1947
Library Holdings: Bk Vols 90,000; Per Subs 85
Subject Interests: Archives, Art, Comic bks, Films, Mag publ, Newspapers, Photography, Rare books, Sexuality
Restriction: Non-circulating, Not a lending library, Private library

P MONROE COUNTY PUBLIC LIBRARY,* 303 E Kirkwood Ave, 47408-3534. SAN 341-0072. Tel: 812-349-3050. FAX: 812-349-3051. Web Site: www.monroe.lib.in.us. *Dir*, David Bucove; *Assoc Dir*, Cass Owens; *Circ*, John Anderson; *AV*, Donna Newman; *Ch Servs*, Ginny Richey; *Tech Servs*, Elaina Kintgen; *Ad Servs*, Susan Jackson
Founded 1821. Pop 108,978; Circ 1,169,029
Library Holdings: Per Subs 527
Special Collections: BCAT - Bloomington Community Access Television; Indiana & Monroe County History (Indiana Coll), bks, mag, microfilm, newsp, pamphlets, hist tapes, maps, video & audio cassettes; VITAL - Volunteers in Tutoring Adult Learners
Partic in Indiana Cooperative Library Services Authority; OCLC Online Computer Library Center, Inc
Friends of the Library Group
Branches: 1
ELLETTSVILLE BRANCH, 600 W Temperance, Ellettsville, 47429. SAN 341-0102. Tel: 812-876-1272. FAX: 812-876-2515. Web Site: www.monroe.lib.in.us. *Librn*, Michelle Needham
Library Holdings: Bk Titles 19,105
Friends of the Library Group
Bookmobiles: 1

C WALDEN UNIVERSITY, Library Liaison at Indiana University - Bloomington, IU Main Library E-164, 1320 E Tenth St, 47405-3907. SAN 303-0857. Tel: 812-855-6058. FAX: 812-855-6077. E-Mail: waldenlb@waldenu.edu. Web Site: www.lib.waldenu.edu/. *Librn*, Rita M Barsun; *Asst Librn*, Jay Edd Wilkerson; Staff 2 (MLS 2)
Founded 1992. Enrl 1,400; Fac 145; Highest Degree: Doctorate
Database Vendor: Silverplatter Information Inc.
Departmental Libraries:
INDIANA UNIVERSITY BRANCH, Main Libr E-164, 1320 E Tenth St, 47405. SAN 329-5451. Tel: 812-855-6058. FAX: 812-855-6077. Web Site: www.lib.waldenu.edu. *Asst Librn*, Rita M Barsun; E-Mail: rbarsun@indiana.edu; Staff 3 (MLS 2, Non-MLS 1)
Founded 1992
Database Vendor: CARL, Silverplatter Information Inc.
Function: Some telephone reference

BLUFFTON

M CAYLOR-NICKEL MEDICAL CENTER LIBRARY,* One Caylor-Nickel Sq, 46714. SAN 304-8128. Tel: 219-824-3500, Ext 7504. FAX: 219-824-8875. *Librn*, Pat Symon
Founded 1916
Library Holdings: Bk Vols 9,290; Per Subs 360
Partic in Midwest Health Sci Libr Network; Northeast Indiana Health Science Libraries Consortium

P WELLS COUNTY PUBLIC LIBRARY, 200 W Washington St, 46714-1999. SAN 304-811X. Tel: 219-824-1612. FAX: 219-824-3129. E-Mail: wcpldavis@parlorcity.com. Web Site: www.wellscolibrary.org. *Dir*, Stephanie D Davis; *Dir*, Sara Gartin; E-Mail: wcplsara@parlorcity.com; *Br Coordr*, Terry Burns; Tel: 765-728-8035, E-Mail: swbranch@wellscolibrary.org; *Br Coordr*, Susan M Dailey; Tel: 219-622-4691, Fax: 219-622-7030, E-Mail: obldailey@wellscolibrary.org; *Ch Servs*, Amy G Greiner; E-Mail: childserv@wellscolibrary.org; *Ref*, Vi Tester; E-Mail: reference@wellscolibary.org; *Ref Servs YA*, Jennifer Martin; E-Mail: youngadult@wellscolibrary.org; *Circ*, Nancy Lowe; E-Mail: circ@wellscolibrary.org; *AV*, Doris Hoffer; E-Mail: av@wellscolibrary.org; Staff 38 (MLS 4, Non-MLS 34)
Founded 1902. Pop 25,529; Circ 255,176
Jan 1999-Dec 1999 Income (Main Library and Branch Library) $1,246,783, State $94,030, Federal $13,943, Locally Generated Income $1,042,967, Other $95,843. Mats Exp $259,530, Books $163,406, Per/Ser (Incl. Access Fees) $12,770, Micro $1,589, AV Equip $30,400, Electronic Ref Mat (Incl. Access Fees) $17,418. Sal $620,571 (Prof $329,063)
Library Holdings: Bk Vols 85,000; Per Subs 308
Special Collections: Large Print Books; Literacy Coll; Wells County History Coll; Young Teen Fiction
Automation Activity & Vendor Info: (Circulation) MultiLIS
Database Vendor: Ebsco - EbscoHost
Publications: Librarian's Book Report (newsletter) (Newsletter)
Friends of the Library Group
Branches: 2
OSSIAN BRANCH, 207 N Jefferson, Ossian, 46777. SAN 320-0892. Tel: 219-824-1612. FAX: 219-824-3129. E-Mail: osslib@wellscolibrary.org. Web Site: www.wellscolibrary.org. *Librn*, Susan Dailey; E-Mail: obldailey@wellscolibrary.org
Library Holdings: Bk Vols 10,000
Friends of the Library Group
SOUTHERN WELLS, 9120 S 300 West, Poneto, 46781. SAN 377-7642. Tel: 765-728-8035. E-Mail: swbranch@wellscolibrary.org. Web Site: www.wellscolibrary.org. *Librn*, Terry Burns
Library Holdings: Bk Vols 2,000
Friends of the Library Group

BOONVILLE

P BOONVILLE-WARRICK COUNTY PUBLIC LIBRARY,* 611 W Main St, 47601-1544. SAN 304-8136. Tel: 812-897-1500. FAX: 812-897-1508. *Librn*, Lois A Aigner; Staff 6 (MLS 4, Non-MLS 2)
Founded 1911. Pop 193,151; Circ 154,041
Library Holdings: Bk Vols 95,000; Per Subs 200
Special Collections: Indiana Coll; Lincoln Coll
Publications: Between the Pages (patrons newsletter); Book Ends (staff newsletter)
Mem of Four Rivers Area Libr Servs Authority
Open Mon-Thurs 10-8, Fri 10-5 & Sat 12-5
Branches: 3
ELBERFELD BRANCH, 175 Sycamore, 47613. SAN 377-7596. Tel: 812-983-4029. *Librn*, Betty Grimes
LYNNVILLE BRANCH, 211 N Main, 47619. SAN 377-760X. Tel: 812-922-5409. *Librn*, Anice Howard
TENNYSON BRANCH, 114 E Oak St, 47637. SAN 377-7626. Tel: 812-567-8933. *Librn*, Sheila King
Bookmobiles: 2

BOSWELL

P BOSWELL & GRANT TOWNSHIP PUBLIC LIBRARY,* 101 Main St, PO Box 315, 47921-0315. SAN 304-8144. Tel: 765-869-5428. FAX: 765-869-5428. *Dir*, Marilyn Johnson; *Asst Librn*, Elizabeth Varner
Founded 1912. Pop 1,000; Circ 9,557
Library Holdings: Bk Vols 15,000; Per Subs 100

BOURBON

P BOURBON PUBLIC LIBRARY, 307 N Main St, 46504. SAN 304-8152. Tel: 219-342-5655. FAX: 219-342-5001. *Librn*, Ramona Baer
Founded 1940. Pop 3,899; Circ 39,425
Library Holdings: Bk Vols 25,000

BRAZIL

P BRAZIL PUBLIC LIBRARY,* 204 N Walnut St, 47834. SAN 304-8160. Tel: 812-448-1981. FAX: 812-446-3215.; Staff 1 (MLS 1)
Founded 1879. Circ 96,248
Library Holdings: Bk Titles 29,402; Per Subs 82
Friends of the Library Group

BREMEN

P BREMEN PUBLIC LIBRARY, (Formerly W E Walter Memorial Library), 304 N Jackson St, 46506. SAN 304-8179. Tel: 219-546-2849. FAX: 219-546-4938. E-Mail: bremenpl@breman.lib.in.us. Web Site: www.bremenlib.in.us. *Dir*, Marsha L Patterson; *Ad Servs*, Rose Humphries; *Ch Servs*, Sandra Krost; *Tech Servs*, Arlene Dettbrenner; Staff 2 (MLS 2)
Founded 1956. Pop 7,144; Circ 111,452
Library Holdings: Bk Vols 45,325; Bk Titles 45,000; Per Subs 220
Subject Interests: Art
Partic in Area Libr Servs Authority Region 2; Indiana Cooperative Library Services Authority; Indiana Libr Video Circuit
Open Mon-Thurs 9-8, Fri 9-5:30, Sat 9-5

BRISTOL

P BRISTOL-WASHINGTON TOWNSHIP PUBLIC LIBRARY, 505 W Vistula St, 46507-9464. SAN 304-8187. Tel: 219-848-7458. FAX: 219-848-4391. Web Site: www.bristol.lib.in.us. *Actg Dir*, Darlene Hauger; E-Mail: darlene@bristol.lib.in.us; Staff 1 (MLS 1)
Founded 1921. Pop 5,200
Jan 2000-Dec 2000 Income $261,075. Mats Exp $40,500, Books $35,000, Per/Ser (Incl. Access Fees) $5,500. Sal $91,000 (Prof $32,000)

Library Holdings: Bk Vols 42,000; Per Subs 80
Special Collections: Indiana Coll
Automation Activity & Vendor Info: (Acquisitions) epixtech, inc.; (Cataloging) epixtech, inc.; (Circulation) epixtech, inc.
Partic in Indiana Cooperative Library Services Authority

S ELKHART COUNTY HISTORICAL SOCIETY, INC, Winifred Cosbey Library, 304 W Vistula, PO Box 434, 46507. SAN 329-1286. Tel: 219-848-4322. FAX: 219-848-5703. E-Mail: echm@juno.com. Web Site: www.elkhartcountypark.org. *Curator, Dir*, Tina Mellott; *Asst Dir*, Diana Zornow; Staff 3 (MLS 3)
Founded 1968
Library Holdings: Bk Titles 1,610
Special Collections: Elkhart County from 1830, archives
Publications: Bibliographies

BROOK

P BROOK-IROQUOIS TOWNSHIP CARNEGIE PUBLIC LIBRARY, 100 W Main, PO Box 155, 47922-0155. SAN 304-8195. Tel: 219-275-2471. FAX: 219-275-8471. Web Site: www.midwest.prairienet.com. *Dir*, Joyce K Whaley
Founded 1910. Pop 1,389; Circ 14,123
Library Holdings: Bk Vols 22,000; Per Subs 35
Subject Interests: Indiana, Local history
Open Mon-Fri 9-5, Sat 9-12 (closed Thurs)

BROOKSTON

P BROOKSTON - PRAIRIE TOWNSHIP PUBLIC LIBRARY,* 111 W Second St, 47923. SAN 304-8209. Tel: 765-563-6511. FAX: 765-563-6833. E-Mail: bptpl@dcwi.com. Web Site: www.dcwi.com/bptpl welcome.html. *Dir*, Nancy H Hartman
Founded 1917. Pop 2,788; Circ 29,418
Library Holdings: Bk Vols 20,000; Per Subs 55
Special Collections: Cookbooks; Crafts, Indiana History, bks, pamphlets
Partic in Indiana Cooperative Library Services Authority
Friends of the Library Group

BROOKVILLE

P BROOKVILLE TOWN-TOWNSHIP LIBRARY,* 919 Main St, 47012-1498. SAN 304-8217. Tel: 765-647-4031. FAX: 765-647-0278. *Dir*, Karla R Ariens; E-Mail: kariens@cn2.com
Founded 1912. Pop 7,000; Circ 44,543
Library Holdings: Bk Vols 28,409; Per Subs 86
Special Collections: Family Histories; Genealogy Items; Local History
Partic in Eastern Ind Area Libr Servs Authority
Open Mon-Fri 10am-8pm & Sat 10am-1pm
Friends of the Library Group

BROWNSBURG

P BROWNSBURG PUBLIC LIBRARY,* 450 S Jefferson St, 46112-1310. SAN 304-8225. Tel: 317-852-3167, 317-852-9314 (Dial-in-access). TDD: 317-852-3168. FAX: 317-852-7734. E-Mail: brownsburg@iquest.net. Web Site: www.brownsburg.lib.in.us. *Dir*, Wanda Pearson; *Ref*, Kelly Hale; *Circ*, Ardith Peterson
Founded 1917. Pop 18,625; Circ 328,620
Jan 1998-Dec 1999 Income $675,395, State $43,857, Other $67,199. Mats Exp $99,636, Books $92,445, Per/Ser (Incl. Access Fees) $7,191. Sal $392,301
Library Holdings: Bk Titles 84,102; Per Subs 266
Special Collections: Audio Visual Coll; Large Print Coll
Automation Activity & Vendor Info: (Circulation) Gaylord
Partic in Indiana Cooperative Library Services Authority
Special Services for the Deaf - TDD; TTY machine; Videos & decoder
Open Mon-Thurs 9-8, Fri-Sat 9-5 & Sun 1-5
Friends of the Library Group

BROWNSTOWN

P BROWNSTOWN PUBLIC LIBRARY,* 120 E Spring St, 47220-1546. SAN 304-8233. Tel: 812-358-2853. FAX: 812-358-4116. *Librn*, Sherri May
Founded 1910. Pop 6,034; Circ 22,879
Library Holdings: Bk Vols 24,000; Per Subs 84
Subject Interests: Indiana

BUTLER

P BUTLER PUBLIC LIBRARY, 340 South Broadway, 46721. SAN 304-8241. Tel: 219-868-2351. FAX: 219-868-5491. Web Site: www.butler.lib.in.us. *Dir*, Ellen Stuckey; *Ch Servs*, Jerry Sargent; *Circ*, Patty McRobert; Staff 3 (MLS 1, Non-MLS 2)
Founded 1906. Pop 4,047; Circ 20,295
Library Holdings: Bk Vols 26,025; Bk Titles 22,710; Per Subs 110
Subject Interests: History
Partic in Area 3 Libr Serv Authority
Friends of the Library Group

BUTLERVILLE

M MUSCATATUCK STATE DEVELOPMENTAL CENTER, Resident & Staff Development Library,* PO Box 77, 47223. SAN 327-8840. Tel: 812-346-4401. FAX: 812-346-2854. *Dir*, Bonnie Miller; *Librn*, Barbara Carter
Library Holdings: Bk Vols 800

CAMBRIDGE CITY

P CAMBRIDGE CITY PUBLIC LIBRARY, 33 W Main St, 47327-1196. SAN 304-825X. Tel: 765-478-3335. FAX: 765-478-6144. E-Mail: cclib@infcom.com. *Librn*, Vicki Rivers; Tel: 765-478-6591; Staff 6 (MLS 1, Non-MLS 5)
Founded 1913. Pop 5,537; Circ 65,908
Library Holdings: Bk Vols 42,234; Per Subs 112
Special Collections: History (Western Wayne County); Overbeck Pottery Coll
Mem of Indiana Coop Libr Servs Authority

CAMDEN

P CAMDEN-JACKSON TOWNSHIP PUBLIC LIBRARY,* PO Box 24, 46917. SAN 304-8268. Tel: 219-686-2120. FAX: 219-686-2120. *Librn*, Shirley L Schock
Founded 1940. Pop 1,266; Circ 6,358
Library Holdings: Bk Vols 10,459; Per Subs 22
Partic in Wabash Valley Area Libr Servs Authority
Friends of the Library Group

CANNELTON

P CANNELTON PUBLIC LIBRARY,* 210 S Eighth, 47520. SAN 304-8276. Tel: 812-547-6028. FAX: 812-547-8590. E-Mail: canpub@psci.net. *Librn*, Douglas D Oleson
Founded 1893. Pop 2,280; Circ 7,550
Jan 1998-Nov 1999 Income $26,292. Mats Exp $8,452, Books $7,452, Per/Ser (Incl. Access Fees) $1,000. Sal $10,700 (Prof $4,800)
Library Holdings: Bk Vols 14,600; Per Subs 32
Subject Interests: Indiana
Partic in Indiana Cooperative Library Services Authority

CARLISLE

WABASH VALLEY CORRECTIONAL FACILITY

S LEVEL FOUR LIBRARY, 6908 S Old US Hwy 41, 47838. Tel: 812-398-5050, Ext 4573. *Librn*, Chris Stogsdill; E-Mail: stogsdill_@hotmail.com
Library Holdings: Bk Titles 1,500; Per Subs 4

S LEVEL THREE LIBRARY, PO Box 500, 47838. Tel: 812-398-5050, Ext 3271. *Librn*, Michele Lincoln
Library Holdings: Bk Vols 5,000; Per Subs 10

CARMEL

P CARMEL CLAY PUBLIC LIBRARY, 55 Fourth Ave SE, 46032-2297. SAN 304-8284. Tel: 317-814-3900. Circulation Tel: 317-844-3361. Reference Tel: 317-844-3362. TDD: 317-571-4294. FAX: 317-571-4285. Web Site: www.carmel.lib.in.us. *Dir*, Wendy A Phillips; Tel: 317-844-6711, E-Mail: wphillips@carmel.lib.in.us; *Head, Circ*, Kathy Ransom; *Head Tech Servs*, Nancy Newport; *Head Ref*, Christine Hintzman; *Tech Coordr*, Peter Konshak; *Ch Servs*, Chelsea Bayh; *ILL*, Bonnie Johnson; *AV*, Mark Freed; *AV*, Ann Heber; *Commun Relations*, Beth Smietana; *YA Servs*, Mari Hardacre; *YA Servs*, Renee Vaillancourt; Staff 160 (MLS 25, Non-MLS 135)
Founded 1904. Pop 60,000; Circ 1,007,933
Jan 2000-Dec 2000 Income $2,960,351. Mats Exp $573,200, Books $378,200, Per/Ser (Incl. Access Fees) $30,000, Electronic Ref Mat (Incl. Access Fees) $165,000. Sal $2,650,000
Library Holdings: Bk Vols 215,357; Bk Titles 158,172; Per Subs 450
Special Collections: Indiana Coll
Automation Activity & Vendor Info: (Acquisitions) GEAC; (Cataloging) GEAC; (Circulation) GEAC; (OPAC) GEAC
Publications: Happenings; Just Between Friends; Library News
Special Services for the Deaf - TDD
Friends of the Library Group

SR KING OF GLORY LUTHERAN CHURCH LIBRARY, 2201 E 106th St, 46032. SAN 328-5219. Tel: 317-846-1555. FAX: 317-846-1590.
Library Holdings: Bk Titles 3,000

CARTHAGE

P HENRY HENLEY PUBLIC LIBRARY,* 102 N Main St, PO Box 35, 46115-0035. SAN 373-8671. Tel: 765-565-6631. *Librn*, Denise Walker; *Asst Librn*, Betty Foster
Founded 1890. Pop 1,100
Library Holdings: Bk Vols 9,675
Friends of the Library Group

CENTERVILLE

P CENTERVILLE & CENTER TOWNSHIP PUBLIC LIBRARY, 126 E Main St, 47330-1206. SAN 304-8292. Tel: 765-855-5223. FAX: 765-855-2009. E-Mail: cctpl@gte.net. *Dir*, Marie Bunch; *Asst Dir*, Cynthia Wiggins; *ILL, Ref*, Margaret Malone; Staff 2 (MLS 2)
Pop 7,500; Circ 50,000
Jan 2000-Dec 2000 Income $193,861. Mats Exp $29,500, Books $27,000, Per/Ser (Incl. Access Fees) $2,700. Sal $148,643 (Prof $24,000)
Library Holdings: Bk Titles 29,500; Per Subs 116
Subject Interests: Antiques, Architecture, Art, Local history
Special Collections: Art History (Elmira Kempton Coll), slides; Paintings by Local Artists
Partic in Indiana Cooperative Library Services Authority
Friends of the Library Group

CHARLESTOWN

P CHARLESTOWN-CLARK COUNTY PUBLIC LIBRARY,* 51 Clark Rd, 47111-1997. SAN 304-8306. Tel: 812-256-3337. FAX: 812-256-3890. *Dir*, Tamsie Maurer; *Coll Develop*, Susan Mullins
Founded 1966. Pop 42,000; Circ 146,850
Library Holdings: Bk Vols 51,000; Per Subs 125
Subject Interests: Genealogy, Local history
Special Collections: Lexicography (J E Schmidt, MD Coll)
Publications: Monthly Calendar of Activities
Partic in Ind Area Libr Servs Authority; Indiana Cooperative Library Services Authority
Open Mon-Thurs 9-8, Fri & Sat 9-5

CHESTERTON

P WESTCHESTER PUBLIC LIBRARY, Thomas Library, 200 W Indiana, 46304-3122. SAN 341-0137. Tel: 219-926-7696. FAX: 219-926-6424. Web Site: www.wpl.lib.in.us. *Dir*, Phil Baugher; *Asst Dir*, Jane Walsh-Brown; *Ref*, Jessie Affelder; *Ch Servs*, Joyce Oury; *Circ*, Jeanette Burton; *Tech Servs*, Rosemary Canright; Staff 5 (MLS 5)
Founded 1972. Pop 15,500; Circ 262,804
Library Holdings: Bk Vols 210,100; Bk Titles 140,000; Per Subs 290
Subject Interests: Local history
Special Collections: Chesterton Tribune Photo Morgue; Prairie Club Archives
Publications: Calendar of Events (monthly)
Partic in Indiana Cooperative Library Services Authority; Northwest Indiana Health Science Library Consortium
Friends of the Library Group
Branches: 1
HAGEMAN, 100 Francis St, Porter, 46304. SAN 341-0161. Tel: 219-926-9080. FAX: 219-926-9081. *Librn*, Sue Enamorado
Library Holdings: Bk Titles 30,000
Friends of the Library Group

CHURUBUSCO

P CHURUBUSCO PUBLIC LIBRARY,* 116 N Mulberry St, 46723. SAN 304-8322. Tel: 219-577-3439. *Librn*, Carol Scherer; *Asst Librn*, Joanne Sattison; Staff 2 (MLS 1, Non-MLS 1)
Founded 1914. Pop 5,082; Circ 13,840
Jan 1997-Dec 1998 Income $59,367, County $54,181, Locally Generated Income $5,186. Mats Exp $7,863, Books $7,212, Per/Ser (Incl. Access Fees) $348. Sal $18,535
Library Holdings: Bk Vols 17,468; Per Subs 17
Friends of the Library Group

CICERO

P HAMILTON NORTH PUBLIC LIBRARY,* 209 W Brinton, 46034-0149. SAN 340-9503. Tel: 317-984-5623. FAX: 317-984-7505. *Dir*, Martha Collins
Jan 1997-Dec 1998 Income $247,924, State $30,863, Other $5,161. Mats Exp $32,709, Books $29,379, Per/Ser (Incl. Access Fees) $3,330. Sal $75,587
Library Holdings: Bk Titles 34,355
Partic in Indiana Cooperative Library Services Authority
Friends of the Library Group
Branches: 2
ARCADIA BRANCH, 107 W South St, Arcadia, 46030-0497. SAN 340-9473. Tel: 317-984-4115. *Librn*, Elaine Eastwood
Friends of the Library Group
ATLANTA BRANCH, 100 S Walnut St, Atlanta, 46031-0068. SAN 340-9449. Tel: 765-292-2521. FAX: 765-292-2249. *Librn*, Mary Palmiero
Founded 1916
Library Holdings: Bk Vols 10,000
Mem of Cent Indiana Area Libr Servs Authority
Friends of the Library Group

CLAYTON

P CLAYTON-LIBERTY TOWNSHIP PUBLIC LIBRARY, 5199 Iowa St, PO Box E, 46118. SAN 304-8330. Tel: 317-539-2991. FAX: 317-539-2050. E-Mail: cltpl@indy.tds.net. *Dir*, Jonnie Wallis; Staff 1 (MLS 1)
Founded 1929
Jan 1999-Dec 1999 Income $96,300. Mats Exp $9,900, Books $8,000, Per/Ser (Incl. Access Fees) $1,600. Sal $52,000 (Prof $25,000)
Library Holdings: Bk Vols 18,100; Per Subs 77
Subject Interests: American literature, Indiana, Local authors, Local history
Publications: The Ex Libris (quarterly)
Partic in Indiana Cooperative Library Services Authority
Special Services for the Deaf - High interest/low vocabulary books; Videos & decoder
Special Services - Summer Reading Program; pre-school story/time; peer tutoring program; homebound services; large print collection

CLINTON

P CLINTON PUBLIC LIBRARY, 313 S Fourth St, 47842-2398. SAN 304-8349. Tel: 765-832-8349. FAX: 765-832-3823. E-Mail: cpl@clintonpl.lib.in.us. Web Site: www.clintonpl.lib.in.us. *Dir*, Karen E Walker; E-Mail: karen@clintonpl.lib.in.us; *Ch Servs*, Stephanie Hoctor; E-Mail: steph@clintonpl.lib.in.us; *YA Servs*, Judy Karanovich; E-Mail: judy2clintonpl.lib.in.us; Staff 12 (MLS 1, Non-MLS 11)
Founded 1911. Pop 9,250; Circ 16,704
Jan 1998-Dec 1999 Income $57,047. Mats Exp $71,565. Sal $137,392
Library Holdings: Bk Vols 37,504; Per Subs 141
Subject Interests: Local history
Special Collections: Indiana Coll
Database Vendor: OCLC - First Search
Publications: Library Lines (6 times per yr); Pieces of Our Lives (booklet on local folkarts)
Partic in Stone Hills Area Libr Servs Authority
Open Mon-Thurs 9am-8pm, Fri 9am-5pm & Sat 9am-2pm
Friends of the Library Group

COATESVILLE

P COATESVILLE PUBLIC LIBRARY,* PO Box 147, 46121. SAN 304-8357. Tel: 765-386-2355. FAX: 765-386-2355. *Librn*, Cheryl Steinborn
Founded 1912. Pop 2,036
Library Holdings: Bk Vols 16,000
Special Collections: Coatesville Herald, 1910-1961, microfilm
Open Mon 1-6pm, Tues & Thurs 1-8pm, Wed 10am-6pm, Fri 1-5pm & Sat 10am-5pm
Friends of the Library Group

COLFAX

P COLFAX PUBLIC LIBRARY,* 207 S Clark St, 46035. SAN 304-8365. Tel: 765-324-2915. FAX: 765-324-2689. E-Mail: library@tctc.com. *Librn*, Judy Hemmerling
Founded 1917. Pop 1,397; Circ 19,853
Jul 1997-Jun 1998 Income $63,530, Locally Generated Income $35,000. Mats Exp $16,100, Books $6,500, Per/Ser (Incl. Access Fees) $2,300. Sal $30,175 (Prof $17,000)
Library Holdings: Bk Vols 12,500
Subject Interests: Genealogy, Local history
Publications: Periodic Newsletter
Friends of the Library Group

COLUMBIA CITY

P PEABODY PUBLIC LIBRARY, 1160 E Hwy 205, PO Box 406, 46725. SAN 304-8373. Tel: 219-244-5541. FAX: 219-244-5653. E-Mail: janet@peabody.whitleynet.org. Web Site: www.whitleynet.org/ppl. *Dir*, Janet M Scank; Staff 5 (MLS 4, Non-MLS 1)
Founded 1901. Pop 12,000; Circ 139,143
Jan 1999-Dec 1999 Income $547,240, State $47,940, Federal $8,500, County $474,333, Locally Generated Income $322,173, Other $172,729. Mats Exp $67,129, Books $56,468, Per/Ser (Incl. Access Fees) $5,030, Electronic Ref Mat (Incl. Access Fees) $5,631. Sal $269,452 (Prof $136,919)
Library Holdings: Bk Vols 69,528; Per Subs 164

Subject Interests: Large type print, Local history
Automation Activity & Vendor Info: (Cataloging) SIRSI; (Circulation) SIRSI; (OPAC) SIRSI
Partic in Indiana Cooperative Library Services Authority
Friends of the Library Group

COLUMBUS

S BARTHOLOMEW COUNTY HISTORICAL SOCIETY, Cline-Keller Library, 524 Third St, 47201. SAN 329-126X. Tel: 812-372-3541. FAX: 812-372-3113. E-Mail: bchs@hsonline.net. Web Site: www.bchs@hsonline.com. *Exec Dir*, Laura Moses; *Curator*, Sandy Greenlee
Founded 1921
Library Holdings: Bk Vols 1,310
Special Collections: Pence Coll

P BARTHOLOMEW COUNTY PUBLIC LIBRARY,* 536 Fifth St, 47201-6225. SAN 341-0196. Tel: 812-379-1255. Interlibrary Loan Service Tel: 812-379-1266. FAX: 812-379-1275. E-Mail: library@barth.lib.in.us. *Dir*, Stephen W Suckow; *Asst Dir*, Elizabeth Booth-Poor; *Tech Servs*, Teresa Rhoades; *Ref*, Susan Mercer; *Ch Servs*, Melessa Wiesehan; *Ad Servs, Circ*, Marilnn Rondot; *Bkmobile Coordr*, Regina Cummings; Staff 10 (MLS 10)
Founded 1899. Pop 65,088; Circ 699,235
1997-1998 Income $2,162,985, State $3,975, County $2,051,720, Locally Generated Income $98,000, Other $9,290. Mats Exp $240,000, Books $160,000, Per/Ser (Incl. Access Fees) $40,000. Sal $767,498 (Prof $271,870)
Library Holdings: Bk Vols 204,270; Bk Titles 147,179; Per Subs 400
Subject Interests: American history, Architecture, History, Indiana
Special Collections: Talking Books for Blind & Physically Handicapped, rec, cassettes, large print
Partic in Indiana Cooperative Library Services Authority
Open Mon-Thurs 8:30am-9pm & Fri-Sat 8:30am-6pm
Friends of the Library Group
Branches: 2
HOPE BRANCH, 638 Main St, Hope, 47246. SAN 341-0250. Tel: 812-546-5310. Web Site: www.library.barth.lib.in.us. *Mgr*, Karen Brown
Library Holdings: Bk Vols 11,000; Bk Titles 9,000
P SUBREGIONAL LIBRARY FOR THE BLIND & PHYSICALLY HANDICAPPED Tel: 812-379-1277. FAX: 812-379-1275. Web Site: www.library.barth.lib.in.us.
Oct 1996-Sep 1997 Income $47,310. Sal $46,675
Publications: Newsletter for Talking Books Users
Special Services - Birthday cards & newsletters for talking books patrons; Open Mon-Fri 8:30-5:30
Bookmobiles: 1

M COLUMBUS REGIONAL HOSPITAL LIBRARY,* 2400 E 17th St, 47201. SAN 375-1325. Tel: 812-376-5074. FAX: 812-376-5964. E-Mail: tashcraft@chr.com. *Librn*, Mary Clapp
Library Holdings: Bk Vols 670; Per Subs 80

S CUMMINS ENGINE CO, INC, Technical Library-50120,* PO Box 3005, 47202-3005. SAN 341-0285. Tel: 812-377-7201. FAX: 812-377-7032. *Librn*, William E Poor
Founded 1966
Library Holdings: Bk Vols 5,000; Per Subs 400
Subject Interests: Engineering

C INDIANA UNIVERSITY-PURDUE UNIVERSITY, Columbus Campus Library, 4601 Central Ave, 47203. SAN 341-2830. Tel: 812-348-7222. FAX: 812-348-7230. Web Site: www.columbus.iupui.edu/library. *Dir*, Janet Feldmann; Tel: 812-348-7204, E-Mail: feldmann@indiana.edu; *Asst Librn*, Amy Cavanaugh; *ILL*, Jo Davis; Staff 4 (MLS 2, Non-MLS 2)
Library Holdings: Bk Vols 37,500; Bk Titles 35,000; Per Subs 300
Partic in Indiana Cooperative Library Services Authority

J IVY TECH STATE COLLEGE LIBRARY,* 4475 Central, 47203. SAN 320-6629. Tel: 812-372-9925, Ext 160. FAX: 812-372-0311. Web Site: www.ivy.tec.in.us/library/librio/index.html. *Dir*, Karen Nissen; E-Mail: knissen@ivy.tec.in.us; Staff 2 (MLS 1, Non-MLS 1)
Library Holdings: Bk Vols 5,000; Per Subs 110
Open Mon-Thurs 8-9 & Fri 8-5

CONNERSVILLE

S BLOMMEL HISTORIC AUTOMOTIVE DATA COLLECTION LIBRARY, 427 E County Rd 215 S, 47331. SAN 326-0909. Tel: 765-825-9259. *Curator*, Henry H Blommel
Founded 1928
Library Holdings: Bk Vols 35; Bk Titles 5,000; Per Subs 15
Publications: Facts on US Auto Industry

P FAYETTE COUNTY PUBLIC LIBRARY, 828 Grand Ave, 47331. SAN 304-839X. Tel: 765-827-0883. FAX: 765-825-4592. E-Mail: fcplconnersville@yahoo.com. Web Site: www.fcplibrary.com. *Dir*, Connie Lake; Staff 16 (MLS 2, Non-MLS 14)
Pop 26,000; Circ 165,873
Library Holdings: Bk Vols 89,000; Per Subs 270
Database Vendor: Ebsco - EbscoHost
Friends of the Library Group

CONVERSE

P CONVERSE JACKSON TOWNSHIP PUBLIC LIBRARY,* PO Box 529, 46919-0529. SAN 304-8403. Tel: 765-395-3344. FAX: 765-395-3733. *Dir*, Coleen Carlson
Founded 1916. Pop 2,333; Circ 17,000
Library Holdings: Bk Titles 26,000; Per Subs 52
Friends of the Library Group

CORYDON

P CORYDON PUBLIC LIBRARY,* 105 N Capitol Ave, 47112. SAN 304-8411. Tel: 812-738-4110. FAX: 812-738-5408. *Dir*, Vi Eckart; *Asst Dir, Tech Servs*, Daniel Bays; *Ch Servs*, Alisa Busch
Pop 10,434; Circ 50,805
Library Holdings: Bk Vols 30,000; Per Subs 50
Subject Interests: Genealogy, Local history
Friends of the Library Group

GM HARRISON COUNTY HOSPITAL LIBRARY,* 245 Atwood St, 47112. SAN 320-6637. Tel: 812-738-4251. FAX: 812-738-7829.
Library Holdings: Bk Titles 137; Per Subs 14

COVINGTON

P COVINGTON & VEEDERSBURG PUBLIC LIBRARY,* 622 Fifth St, 47932. SAN 341-034X. Tel: 765-793-2572. FAX: 765-793-2572. *Dir, Librn*, Elaine Ramsey
Founded 1914. Pop 7,285; Circ 27,128
Library Holdings: Bk Vols 33,033; Per Subs 107
Subject Interests: Art
Publications: Newsletter
Partic in Wabash Valley Area Libr Servs Authority
Branches: 1
VEEDERSBURG PUBLIC, 408 N Main St, Veedersburg, 47987. SAN 341-0374. Tel: 765-294-2808. FAX: 765-294-2808. *Librn*, Christy Kruger
Library Holdings: Bk Vols 10,200
Friends of the Library Group

CRAWFORDSVILLE

P CRAWFORDSVILLE DISTRICT PUBLIC LIBRARY, 222 S Washington St, 47933-2444. SAN 304-842X. Tel: 765-362-2242. FAX: 765-362-7986. E-Mail: dir@cdpl.lib.in.us. Web Site: www.cdpl.lib.in.us. *Dir*, Laurence Hathaway; *Asst Dir, Cat*, Deatra Smith; *Ch Servs*, Angela Clements; *ILL, Media Spec*, Anna Pennington; *Head Ref*, Judith Spencer; Staff 6 (MLS 6)
Founded 1897. Pop 22,872; Circ 196,577
Library Holdings: Bk Vols 106,457; Per Subs 250
Special Collections: Crawfordsville History bks, microfilm, pamphlets
Automation Activity & Vendor Info: (Cataloging) Gaylord; (Circulation) Gaylord
Partic in Indiana Cooperative Library Services Authority; Wabash Valley Libr Network
Friends of the Library Group

C WABASH COLLEGE, Lilly Library, 301 W Wabash Ave, PO Box 352, 47933. SAN 304-8438. Tel: 765-361-6161. Circulation Tel: 765-361-6330. Reference Tel: 765-361-6443. FAX: 765-361-6295. Web Site: www.wabash.edu/library/. *Dir*, Larry J Frye; Tel: 765-361-6327, E-Mail: fryel@wabash.edu; *Bibliog Instr, Ref*, Jeff Beck; Tel: 765-361-6346, E-Mail: beckj@wabash.edu; *Archivist, Tech Servs*, Brian McCafferty; Tel: 765-361-6404, E-Mail: mccaffeb@wabash.edu; *Acq*, Susan Albrecht; Tel: 765-361-6216, E-Mail: albrechs@wabash.edu; *Spec Coll*, Johanna Herring; Tel: 765-361-6378, E-Mail: herringj@wabash.edu; *ILL*, Deborah Polley; Tel: 765-361-6376, E-Mail: polleyde@wabash.edu; *Doc*, Linda Petrie; Tel: 765-361-6361, E-Mail: petriel@wabash.edu; *Per*, Anne Sexton; Tel: 765-361-6215, E-Mail: sextona@wabash.edu; *Circ*, Diane Norton; E-Mail: nortond@wabash.edu; *Media Spec*, Garry Bohm; Tel: 765-361-6251, E-Mail: bohmg@wabash.edu; Staff 3 (MLS 3)
Founded 1832. Enrl 859; Fac 80; Highest Degree: Bachelor
Jul 1999-Jun 2000 Income Parent Institution $1,051,448. Mats Exp $451,751, Books $159,056, Per/Ser (Incl. Access Fees) $254,829, Presv $8,756, Micro $13,039, Electronic Ref Mat (Incl. Access Fees) $23,143. Sal $326,377 (Prof $220,969)
Library Holdings: Bk Vols 260,086; Bk Titles 182,371; Per Subs 1,402
Special Collections: College Archives
Automation Activity & Vendor Info: (Acquisitions) DRA; (Cataloging) DRA; (Circulation) DRA; (Course Reserve) DRA; (OPAC) DRA; (Serials) DRA

Database Vendor: DRA, OCLC - First Search
Partic in Indiana Cooperative Library Services Authority; OCLC Online Computer Library Center, Inc; Private Acad Libr Network of Ind

CROWN POINT

P CROWN POINT COMMUNITY LIBRARY, 214 S Court St, 46307-3975. SAN 304-8446. Tel: 219-663-0270, 219-663-0271. FAX: 219-663-0403. *Dir*, Lynn M Frank; *Ch Servs*, Faith Loane; *Tech Servs*, Michael Sheets; *Circ*, Laurie Kingery; *Ref Serv*, Mary Walsko; *Ad Servs*, Barb Houk; Staff 4 (MLS 4)
Founded 1906. Pop 29,356; Circ 233,451
Library Holdings: Bk Vols 119,563; Bk Titles 90,110; Per Subs 175
Database Vendor: Innovative Interfaces INN - View
Publications: Check It Out (Newsletter)
Partic in Indiana Cooperative Library Services Authority; Northwest Indiana Health Science Library Consortium
Open Mon-Thurs 9-8, Fri 9-6 & Sat 9-5, Sun 1-5 thru the school year
Friends of the Library Group

M SAINT ANTHONY MEDICAL CENTER, Health Sciences Library,* 1201 S Main St, 46307-8483. SAN 304-8462. Tel: 219-757-6345. FAX: 219-757-6161. E-Mail: mnowesn@samc.fscc.com. *In Charge*, Monica A Nowesnick
Library Holdings: Bk Vols 1,250; Per Subs 175
Partic in Northwest Indiana Health Science Library Consortium

CULVER

P CULVER-UNION TOWNSHIP PUBLIC LIBRARY,* 107 N Main St, 46511-1595. SAN 304-8470. Tel: 219-842-2701, 219-842-2941. FAX: 219-842-3441. *Dir*, Frederick R Harper
Pop 3,289; Circ 37,659
Jan 1998-Dec 1999 Income $262,803. Mats Exp $31,100. Sal $91,000
Library Holdings: Bk Vols 27,430; Per Subs 111
Mem of ALSA
Open Mon-Fri 10-7, Sat 10-4, Sun 12-4

DALE

P LINCOLN HERITAGE PUBLIC LIBRARY,* 106 N Wallace St, PO Box 564, 47523-0564. SAN 376-6802. Tel: 812-937-7170. FAX: 812-937-7102. Web Site: www.lincolnheritage.lib.in.us. *Dir*, Karen Moran; E-Mail: karen@lincolnheritage.lib.in.us; *Assoc Librn, Tech Servs*, Joyce Hopkins; *Assoc Librn, Ch Servs*, Nancy Jacobs; *Circ*, Diana Bockstahler; *Circ, Tech Servs*, Becky Hunter; *Circ, Tech Servs*, Jennifer Winkler
1998-1999 Income $165,591, State $622, County $143,801. Mats Exp $41,100, Books $30,100, Per/Ser (Incl. Access Fees) $5,000, Other Print Mats $6,000. Sal $60,559
Library Holdings: Bk Vols 25,000
Subject Interests: Genealogy, Local history
Friends of the Library Group

DANVILLE

P DANVILLE PUBLIC LIBRARY, 101 S Indiana St, 46122-1809. SAN 304-8489. Tel: 317-745-2604. FAX: 317-745-0756. E-Mail: dpldir@dpl.lib.in.us. Web Site: www.dpl.lib.in.us. *Dir*, Diana Lehr; *Ch Servs*, Golam Kibreah; *Ad Servs*, Janet Woodrum; Staff 15 (MLS 3, Non-MLS 12)
Founded 1903. Pop 9,827
Jan 1999-Dec 1999 Income $400,342, State $37,851, City $231,535, County $109,827, Locally Generated Income $21,129. Mats Exp $71,494, Books $62,096, Per/Ser (Incl. Access Fees) $3,994, Micro $2,926, Electronic Ref Mat (Incl. Access Fees) $2,478. Sal $227,322 (Prof $84,213)
Library Holdings: Bk Vols 56,406; Per Subs 149
Subject Interests: Genealogy
Automation Activity & Vendor Info: (Cataloging) Follett; (Circulation) Follett; (OPAC) Follett
Database Vendor: Ebsco - EbscoHost, GaleNet
Publications: "Spolight" newsletter (6 times yr)
Function: Archival collection, ILL available, Internet access, Photocopies available, Reference services available, Some telephone reference
Partic in Indiana Cooperative Library Services Authority
Open Mon-Thurs 9-8, Fri & Sat 9-5, Sun 2-5
Friends of the Library Group

DARLINGTON

P DARLINGTON PUBLIC LIBRARY,* Main St, PO Box 248, 47940-0248. SAN 304-8497. Tel: 765-794-4813. *Librn*, John Dale; *Asst Librn*, Mardelle Lehe; Staff 1 (MLS 1)
Founded 1915. Pop 2,052; Circ 8,804
Library Holdings: Bk Titles 12,000; Per Subs 45
Partic in Wabash Valley Area Libr Servs Authority
Friends of the Library Group

DECATUR

P DECATUR PUBLIC LIBRARY, 128 S Third St, 46733-1691. SAN 304-8500. Tel: 219-724-2605. FAX: 219-724-2877. *Dir*, Kelly A Ehinger; *Ch Servs*, Priscilla J Scott; *Ad Servs*, Gene Knoch; *Ad Servs*, Louise A Wolpert
Founded 1905. Pop 8,642; Circ 377,710
Jan 1999-Dec 1999 Income $486,945, State $30,011, City $304,034, Federal $6,000, County $107,356, Locally Generated Income $19,318, Other $20,226. Mats Exp $64,000, Books $56,000, Per/Ser (Incl. Access Fees) $6,000, Micro $2,000. Sal $259,025 (Prof $33,900)
Library Holdings: Bk Vols 58,944
Special Collections: Adams County Genealogy; Indiana Materials (Gene Stratton Porter Coll); Large Print
Open Mon-Thurs 9-8, Fri 9-6, Sat 9-5 & Sun 1-5
Friends of the Library Group

DELPHI

P DELPHI PUBLIC LIBRARY, 222 E Main St, 46923-1593. SAN 304-8519. Tel: 765-564-2929. FAX: 765-564-4746. E-Mail: dplibrar@carlnet.org. Web Site: www.carlnet.org/dpl. *Dir*, Kelly D Currie; E-Mail: kelly@carinet.org; *Ch Servs*, Marcia Sledd; *Ad Servs*, Sara Daly-Brosman; *Tech Servs*, Cathy Kesterson; *Ref Serv Ad*, Jane Cruz; Staff 12 (MLS 1, Non-MLS 11)
Founded 1904. Pop 7,065; Circ 105,000
Jan 1999-Dec 1999 Income $537,663. Mats Exp $533,593, Books $69,215, Per/Ser (Incl. Access Fees) $7,500, AV Equip $23,519. Sal $229,520 (Prof $40,816)
Library Holdings: Bk Vols 59,278; Per Subs 205
Subject Interests: Indiana, Local history
Automation Activity & Vendor Info: (Acquisitions) SIRSI; (Circulation) SIRSI
Partic in Indiana Cooperative Library Services Authority
Friends of the Library Group

DONALDSON

JR ANCILLA COLLEGE, Gerald J Ball Library, 9601 S Union Rd, PO Box 1, 46513. SAN 304-8527. Tel: 219-936-8898, Ext 323. FAX: 219-935-1773. *Librn*, Glenda Bockman; E-Mail: gbockma@ancilla.edu; Staff 1 (MLS 1)
Founded 1966. Enrl 445; Fac 21
Jul 1998-Jun 1999 Mats Exp $13,198, Books $6,294, Per/Ser (Incl. Access Fees) $6,282, Electronic Ref Mat (Incl. Access Fees) $622. Sal $32,370
Library Holdings: Bk Vols 28,300; Per Subs 200
Subject Interests: Art, Computer science, Education, Energy, History, Indiana, Library and information science, Religion
Special Collections: History of the Poor Handmaids of Jesus Christ, bks, slides, photos; Old & Rare Book Coll
Partic in PALNI

DUBLIN

P DUBLIN PUBLIC LIBRARY,* 2249 E Cumberland, PO Box 188, 47335-0188. SAN 304-8535. Tel: 765-478-6206. *Librn*, Diane Lawrence
Founded 1886. Pop 1,003; Circ 4,146
Library Holdings: Bk Titles 9,000; Per Subs 17
Special Collections: Dublin History

DUNKIRK

P DUNKIRK CITY PUBLIC LIBRARY, 127 W Washington St, 47336-1218. SAN 376-5393. Tel: 765-768-6872. FAX: 765-768-6872. E-Mail: dunkirklibrary@netscape.net. Web Site: www.dunkirkpubliclibrary.com. *Dir*, Gay Rife
Founded 1917. Pop 2,739
Library Holdings: Bk Vols 13,000; Bk Titles 10,000; Per Subs 80
Automation Activity & Vendor Info: (Circulation) Sagebrush Corporation

DYER

§R MID-AMERICA REFORMED SEMINARY LIBRARY, 229 Seminary Dr, 46311. Tel: 219-864-2400, Ext 216. FAX: 219-864-2409. Web Site: www.midamerica.edu. *Asst Librn*, Stan Riecken
Library Holdings: Bk Titles 35,000; Per Subs 200
Automation Activity & Vendor Info: (Acquisitions) Sagebrush Corporation; (Cataloging) Sagebrush Corporation

M ST MARGARET MERCY HEALTHCARE CENTERS-SOUTH CAMPUS, Health Sciences Library,* 24 Joliet St, 46311-1799. SAN 304-8543. Tel: 219-865-2141, Ext 42133. FAX: 219-864-2146. *Librn*, Carol L Yancich
Library Holdings: Bk Vols 2,000; Per Subs 100
Partic in Northwest Indiana Health Science Library Consortium

EARL PARK

P EARL PARK PUBLIC LIBRARY,* 102 E Fifth St, PO Box 97, 47942-0097. SAN 304-8551. Tel: 219-474-6932. FAX: 219-474-6932. *Librn*, Terry Hoover
Founded 1914. Pop 679; Circ 7,721
Library Holdings: Bk Vols 17,000
Partic in Wabash Valley Libr Network
Open Mon, Wed & Fri 1-5:30, Tues 1-8 & Sat 11-3:30

P YORK TOWNSHIP PUBLIC LIBRARY,* 8475 N 885 West, Ste 1, 47942-8701. SAN 377-5690. Tel: 219-474-9669. *Librn*, Karen Kain
Library Holdings: Bk Vols 5,500

EAST CHICAGO

P EAST CHICAGO PUBLIC LIBRARY,* 2401 E Columbus Dr, 46312-2998. SAN 341-0439. Tel: 219-397-2453. FAX: 219-397-6715. *Dir*, Dr Theodore Mason; *Assoc Dir, Publ Servs*, Pearlie Eatman; Staff 12 (MLS 12)
Founded 1909. Pop 33,892; Circ 128,103
Library Holdings: Bk Vols 181,573; Bk Titles 113,781; Per Subs 560
Subject Interests: Ethnic studies
Special Collections: History of East Chicago
Publications: Bibliographies; Historical booklets
Partic in OCLC Online Computer Library Center, Inc
Friends of the Library Group
Branches: 1
ROBERT A PASTRICK BRANCH, 1008 W Chicago Ave, 46312. SAN 341-0463. Tel: 219-397-5505. FAX: 219-398-2827. *Librn*, Leticia Jones
Library Holdings: Bk Vols 83,254
Friends of the Library Group

S ISPAT INLAND INC, Research Library, 3001 E Columbus Dr, 46312. SAN 304-856X. Tel: 219-399-6120. FAX: 219-399-6562. *Librn*, Barbara Minne Banek; E-Mail: bmbane@inland.com
Founded 1954
Library Holdings: Bk Titles 10,000; Per Subs 325
Partic in Indiana Cooperative Library Services Authority

M SAINT CATHERINE HOSPITAL, McGuire Memorial Library, 4321 Fir St, 46312. SAN 304-8578. Tel: 219-392-7230. FAX: 219-392-7231. *Librn*, Susan Miller; E-Mail: smiller@ancilla.org
Founded 1946
Library Holdings: Bk Titles 1,600; Per Subs 90
Subject Interests: Allied health
Partic in Midwest Health Sci Libr Network; Northwest Indiana Health Science Library Consortium

EDINBURG

P EDINBURGH WRIGHT-HAGEMAN PUBLIC LIBRARY,* 119 W Main Cross, 46124-1499. SAN 304-8594. Tel: 812-526-5487. FAX: 812-526-7057. *Librn*, Cathy Hamm
Founded 1921. Pop 4,800; Circ 32,468
Library Holdings: Bk Vols 17,003; Bk Titles 17,001; Per Subs 75
Subject Interests: Genealogy
Open Mon-Thurs 9:30-8, Fri 9:30-5 & Sat 9:30-1

G UNITED STATES DEPARTMENT OF LABOR, Atterbury Job Corps Center Library,* Job Corps Ctr, PO Box 187, 46124. SAN 304-8586. Tel: 812-526-5581. FAX: 812-526-9551.
Library Holdings: Bk Titles 5,000; Per Subs 12
Subject Interests: Chicano studies, Vocational education
Open Mon-Fri 8am-5pm

ELKHART

R ASSOCIATED MENNONITE BIBLICAL SEMINARY LIBRARY, 3003 Benham, 46517. SAN 304-8608. Tel: 219-296-6253. FAX: 219-295-0092. Web Site: www.ambs.edu/library. *Dir*, Eileen K Saner; E-Mail: esaner@ambs.edu; Staff 2 (MLS 2)
Founded 1945. Enrl 180; Highest Degree: Master
1999-2000 Mats Exp $57,861, Books $33,031, Per/Ser (Incl. Access Fees) $16,989, Presv $1,420, Micro $45, Electronic Ref Mat (Incl. Access Fees) $3,590. Sal $99,500 (Prof $59,588)
Library Holdings: Bk Vols 107,936; Per Subs 523
Subject Interests: Mennonites, Religion
Special Collections: Studer Bible Coll
Database Vendor: DRA
Partic in Indiana Cooperative Library Services Authority; OCLC Online Computer Library Center, Inc; Private Acad Libr Network of Ind

P ELKHART PUBLIC LIBRARY, 300 S Second St, 46516-3184. SAN 341-0587. Tel: 219-522-3333. Interlibrary Loan Service Tel: 219-522-5669. Circulation Tel: 219-522-2665. Reference Tel: 219-522-5669. FAX: 219-293-9213, 219-522-2174. Web Site: www.elkhart.lib.in.us. *Dir*, Connie Jo Ozinga; E-Mail: cjo@elkhart.lib.in.us; *Assoc Dir, ILL*, Marsha J Eilers; E-Mail: meilers@elkhart.lib.in.us; *Ad Servs, Assoc Dir*, Patricia McClure; E-Mail: pmcclure@elkhart.lib.in.us; *Assoc Dir, AV*, Jeanne Glanders; E-Mail: jglander@elkhart.lib.in.us; Staff 111 (MLS 19, Non-MLS 92)
Founded 1903. Pop 79,074; Circ 800,825
Jan 1999-Dec 1999 Income (Main Library Only) $3,947,863. Mats Exp $3,582,080
Library Holdings: Bk Vols 236,671; Per Subs 1,334
Subject Interests: Local history
Publications: Montage (newsletter); Monthly calendar of programs
Partic in Ind Area Libr Servs Authority 2; Indiana Cooperative Library Services Authority
Open (Main Library) Mon-Thurs 9-9 & Fri-Sat 9-6, closed Sun; (Branches) Mon-Thurs 9-8, Fri-Sat 9-6 & Sun 1-5
Branches: 4
P BLIND & PHYSICALLY HANDICAPPED SERVICES, 300 S Second St, 46516. Tel: 219-522-2665, Ext 46. *In Charge*, Patricia Ciancio
Founded 1968
Oct 1999-Sep 2000 Income $61,938
Open Mon-Fri 9am-5pm
DUNLAP, 58485 E County Rd 13, 46516. SAN 373-9066. Tel: 219-875-3100. FAX: 219-875-5512. *Assoc Dir*, Beth Pomeroy; E-Mail: bpomeroy@elkhart.lib.in.us
Library Holdings: Bk Vols 27,277
OSOLO, 3429 E Bristol St, 46514. SAN 328-9133. Tel: 219-264-7234. FAX: 219-264-7343. *Assoc Dir*, Deborah Stewart; E-Mail: dstewart@elkhart.lib.in.us
Library Holdings: Bk Vols 26,653
PIERRE MORAN BRANCH, 2400 Benham Ave, 46517. SAN 341-0641. Tel: 219-294-6418. FAX: 219-294-6419. *Assoc Dir*, Marcia Vierck; E-Mail: mvierck@elkhart.lib.in.us
Library Holdings: Bk Vols 29,372
Bookmobiles: 2. 1999 Blue Birds

M OAKLAWN PSYCHIATRIC CENTER & OAKLAWN HOSPITAL, Staff Library, 2600 Oakland Ave, 46517. SAN 304-8624. Tel: 219-537-2690. FAX: 219-537-2605. *Librn*, Nancy P Price; E-Mail: pricenp@oaklawn.org
Founded 1966
Jan 2000-Dec 2000 Income $20,676. Mats Exp $6,984, Books $207, Per/Ser (Incl. Access Fees) $6,767, Electronic Ref Mat (Incl. Access Fees) $10. Sal $11,376
Library Holdings: Bk Titles 2,764; Per Subs 96
Subject Interests: Alcohol and drugs, Mental health, Psychiatry, Psychology, Social service (social work)
Restriction: Staff use only
Partic in Indiana Cooperative Library Services Authority

S RUTHMERE, Robert B Beardsley Arts Reference Library, 302 E Beardsley Ave, 46514. SAN 374-6275. Tel: 219-264-0330. FAX: 219-266-0474. *Librn*, Marilou C Ritchie
Founded 1980
Library Holdings: Bk Vols 1,803; Bk Titles 1,750; Per Subs 23
Subject Interests: Architecture, Art, Decorative arts
Restriction: Open to public for reference only
Partic in Indiana Cooperative Library Services Authority

ELWOOD

P NORTH MADISON COUNTY PUBLIC LIBRARY SYSTEM, 1600 Main St, 46036-1598. SAN 304-8632. Tel: 765-552-5001. FAX: 765-552-0955. *Librn*, Beverly J Austin; *Tech Servs*, Glenna Stewart; *Ch Servs*, Sharon Fouts; *Ad Servs*, E Davidson; Staff 1 (MLS 1)
Founded 1898. Pop 23,400; Circ 150,000
Library Holdings: Bk Vols 63,439; Per Subs 109
Special Collections: Local History (Indiana Coll); Wendell L Willkie Coll
Partic in Eastern Ind Area Libr Servs Authority
Friends of the Library Group
Branches: 2
FRANKTON COMMUNITY LIBRARY, 111 Sigler St, Frankton, 46044. SAN 323-536X. Tel: 765-754-7116. FAX: 765-754-3312. *Librn*, Barbara McAdams
RALPH E HAZELBAKER LIBRARY, 1013 W Church St, Summitville, 46070. SAN 323-5386. Tel: 765-536-2335. FAX: 765-536-9050. *Librn*, Carolyn Lambertson

ENGLISH

P CRAWFORD COUNTY PUBLIC LIBRARY,* PO Box 159, 47118-0159. SAN 304-8640. Tel: 812-338-2606. FAX: 812-338-3034. E-Mail: libstaff@cccn.net. Web Site: www.cccn.net. *Librn*, Janet LaBreche
Founded 1954. Pop 9,699; Circ 69,556
Jan 1997-Dec 1998 Income $125,653. Mats Exp $18,295, Books $12,997, Per/Ser (Incl. Access Fees) $2,473. Sal $63,752
Library Holdings: Bk Vols 35,000; Per Subs 123

EVANSVILLE

S ANGEL MOUNDS STATE HISTORIC SITE LIBRARY,* 8215 Pollack Ave, 47715. SAN 373-4471. Tel: 812-853-3956. FAX: 812-853-6271. *Curator*, Mary Alexander
Library Holdings: Bk Vols 250; Per Subs 4
Subject Interests: Archaeology

M DEACONESS HOSPITAL, Grace O Hahn Health Science Library, 600 Mary St, 47747. SAN 304-8659. Tel: 812-450-3385. FAX: 812-450-7255. Web Site: www.deaconess.com. *Mgr Libr Serv*, Marina Will; E-Mail: marina_will@deaconess.com; Staff 2 (MLS 1, Non-MLS 1)
Founded 1970
1999-2000 Mats Exp $47,000, Books $4,000, Per/Ser (Incl. Access Fees) $33,000, Electronic Ref Mat (Incl. Access Fees) $10,000
Library Holdings: Bk Vols 5,000; Bk Titles 3,000; Per Subs 200
Subject Interests: Allied health, Hospital administration, Medicine, Nursing
Automation Activity & Vendor Info: (Cataloging) Sydney; (Circulation) Sydney; (OPAC) Sydney; (Serials) Sydney
Partic in Evansville Area Library Consortium; Medline; Midwest Health Sci Libr Network

S EVANSVILLE MUSEUM OF ARTS & SCIENCE LIBRARY, 411 SE Riverside Dr, 47713. SAN 304-8675. Tel: 812-425-2406. FAX: 812-421-7509. Web Site: www.emuseum.org. *Curator*, Mary McNamee Schnepper; *Curator*, Thomas R Lonnberg
Founded 1904
Library Holdings: Bk Vols 5,000; Per Subs 28
Subject Interests: Anthropology, Antiques, Art and architecture, Astronomy, History, Natural history
Special Collections: Henry B Walker Jr Memorial Art Books Coll; Vanderburgh County History
Restriction: Non-circulating to the public
Open Tues-Sat 10-5

M EVANSVILLE PSYCHIATRIC CHILDREN'S CENTER LIBRARY, 3300 E Morgan Ave, 47715. SAN 304-8691. Tel: 812-477-6436. FAX: 812-474-4248. *Librn*, Emilee Burnett
Founded 1966
Library Holdings: Bk Vols 300
Partic in Evansville Area Library Consortium

M EVANSVILLE STATE HOSPITAL, Staff Library,* 3400 Lincoln Ave, 47714. SAN 341-0919. Tel: 812-473-2261. FAX: 812-473-2109. *Librn*, Carol Huffman
Founded 1944
Jul 1996-Jun 1997 Mats Exp $14,077. Sal $8,225
Library Holdings: Bk Vols 2,410; Per Subs 45
Subject Interests: Nursing, Psychiatry, Psychology, Social service (social work)
Partic in Evansville Area Library Consortium
Friends of the Library Group
Branches:
PATIENTS LIBRARY Tel: 812-473-2222, Ext 237. FAX: 812-473-2109. *Librn*, Cindy Gehlhausen
Friends of the Library Group

P EVANSVILLE-VANDERBURGH PUBLIC LIBRARY, 22 SE Fifth St, 47708-1604. SAN 341-0676. Tel: 812-428-8200. FAX: 812-428-8397. E-Mail: comments@evans.evcpl.lib.in.us. Web Site: www.evcpl.lib.in.us. *Dir*, Marcia Learned-Au; *YA Servs*, Lola Teuber; *Assoc Dir, Publ Servs*, Evelyn Walker; *ILL*, Janice Reitz; *ILL*, Katherine Sherrill; *Ch Servs*, Linda Hahus; *Media Spec*, Scott Lehman; *Spec Coll*, Judith Harp; *Bibliog Instr, Online Servs*, Andrea Kappler; Staff 160 (MLS 24, Non-MLS 136)
Founded 1911. Pop 165,058
Library Holdings: Bk Vols 801,901; Per Subs 2,116
Subject Interests: Agriculture, Business and management, Economics, Education, Religion
Special Collections: Judaica (Marcus & Mina Ravdin Memorial Coll); Library Science
Automation Activity & Vendor Info: (Acquisitions) Innovative Interfaces Inc.; (Cataloging) Innovative Interfaces Inc.; (Circulation) Innovative Interfaces Inc.; (Media Booking) Innovative Interfaces Inc.; (OPAC) Innovative Interfaces Inc.; (Serials) Innovative Interfaces Inc.
Publications: River City Library Times
Partic in OCLC Online Computer Library Center, Inc
Special Services for the Deaf - High interest/low vocabulary books
Friends of the Library Group
Branches: 8
EAST, 840 E Chandler, 47713. SAN 341-0706. Tel: 812-428-8231. FAX: 812-436-7320. *Librn*, Nancy Higgs; Staff 5 (MLS 1, Non-MLS 4)
Library Holdings: Bk Vols 47,807; Bk Titles 31,252
MCCOLLOUGH, 5115 Washington Ave, 47715. SAN 341-0765. Tel: 812-428-8236. FAX: 812-473-0877. *Librn*, Glynis Rosendall
Library Holdings: Bk Vols 91,327; Bk Titles 69,048
NORTH PARK, 750 N Park Dr, 47710. SAN 341-079X. Tel: 812-428-8237. FAX: 812-428-8243. *Librn*, Donna Yuschak
Library Holdings: Bk Vols 84,193; Bk Titles 61,915
OAKLYN, 3820 Oak Hill Rd, 47711. SAN 341-0854. Tel: 812-428-8234. FAX: 812-428-8234. *Librn*, Mollie Pharo
Library Holdings: Bk Vols 62,110; Bk Titles 44,735
RED BANK, 120 S Red Bank Rd, 47712. SAN 371-9774. Tel: 812-428-8205. FAX: 812-428-8240. *Librn*, Pamela Locker
Library Holdings: Bk Vols 79,090; Bk Titles 51,146
STRINGTOWN, 2100 Stringtown Rd, 47711. SAN 341-082X. Tel: 812-428-8233. FAX: 812-428-8233.
Library Holdings: Bk Vols 32,388; Bk Titles 23,512
TALKING BOOKS SERVICE Tel: 812-428-8235. FAX: 812-428-8215. *Librn*, Barbara Shanks
Founded 1977. Circ 32,276
WEST, 2000 W Franklin St, 47712. SAN 341-0889. Tel: 812-428-8232. FAX: 812-428-8232. *Librn*, Ron Henze
Library Holdings: Bk Vols 51,783; Bk Titles 36,337
Bookmobiles: 1. Bk titles 838, vols 1695

J IVY TECH STATE COLLEGE, Carter Library, 3501 First Ave, 47710. SAN 304-8713. Tel: 812-429-1412. FAX: 812-429-9802. *Librn*, Saundra Voegel; Staff 1 (MLS 1)
Founded 1969. Enrl 1,895; Fac 49
Jul 1999-Jun 2000 Income $75,000. Mats Exp $49,000, Books $19,000, Per/Ser (Incl. Access Fees) $22,000, AV Equip $8,000
Library Holdings: Bk Vols 3,472; Bk Titles 3,432; Per Subs 163
Subject Interests: Science/technology, Technology
Hours: Mon-Thurs 8-9, Fri 8-5

S LEGAL SERVICE ORGANIZATION OF INDIANA, INC LIBRARY,* 101 Court St, Ste 101, 47708. SAN 325-7460. Tel: 812-426-1295. FAX: 812-422-7332.
Library Holdings: Bk Vols 800
Restriction: Staff use only

S PLANNED PARENTHOOD OF CENTRAL & SOUTHERN INDIANA LIBRARY,* 125 N Weinbach Center Pointe, Ste 120, 47711. SAN 329-7985. Tel: 812-473-4990. Toll Free Tel: 800-230-7526. FAX: 812-473-4992.
Library Holdings: Bk Titles 472
Subject Interests: Family planning, Sexuality, Women's health
Partic in Evansville Area Library Consortium

M SAINT MARY'S MEDICAL CENTER, INC, Library Services, 3700 Washington Ave, 47750-0000. SAN 304-8748. Tel: 812-485-4151. FAX: 812-485-7564. *Mgr*, Jane Saltzman; E-Mail: jsaltzman@stmarys.org; Staff 2 (MLS 1, Non-MLS 1)
Founded 1969
Library Holdings: Bk Vols 3,000; Per Subs 150
Subject Interests: Medicine, Nursing
Partic in Evansville Area Library Consortium; Greater Midwest Regional Medical Libr Network

SAINT PAUL'S UNITED CHURCH OF CHRIST LIBRARY, 2227 W Michigan St, 47712. SAN 304-8756. Tel: 812-425-1522. FAX: 812-425-2145.
Founded 1956
Library Holdings: Bk Vols 760; Per Subs 10

M SOUTHWESTERN INDIANA MENTAL HEALTH CENTER LIBRARY,* 415 Mulberry St, 47713-1298. SAN 341-0978. Tel: 812-423-7791, Ext 251. FAX: 812-422-7558. *Librn*, A Brinkman
Founded 1974
Jul 1998-Jun 1999 Income $23,000. Mats Exp $12,000. Sal $11,000
Library Holdings: Bk Vols 1,791; Per Subs 68
Subject Interests: Psychiatry, Psychology, Psychotherapy, Sexuality, Social service (social work), Substance abuse
Partic in Indiana Cooperative Library Services Authority

C UNIVERSITY OF EVANSVILLE, University Libraries,* 1800 Lincoln Ave, 47722. SAN 341-1036. Tel: 812-479-2482. Interlibrary Loan Service Tel: 812-488-1062. FAX: 812-471-6996. E-Mail: kb4@evansville.edu, libweb@evansville.edu. Web Site: www.evansville.edu, www.evansville.edu/libweb. *Dir*, William F Louden; *Acq*, Marvin Guilfoyle; *Ref*, Randy Abbott; *Cat*, Steve Mussett; *Circ, ILL*, Kathryn R Bartelt; Staff 8 (MLS 8)
Founded 1872. Highest Degree: Master
Jun 1997-May 1998 Income $1,185,000. Mats Exp $556,000, Presv $10,000. Sal $461,000 (Prof $292,970)
Library Holdings: Bk Vols 260,000; Per Subs 1,350
Special Collections: James L Clifford, 18th Century Materials; Knecht Cartoons Coll; Law (Kiltz Coll)
Partic in Evansville Area Library Consortium; Indiana Cooperative Library Services Authority; OCLC Online Computer Library Center, Inc; State Univ Libr Automation Network

C UNIVERSITY OF SOUTHERN INDIANA, David L Rice Library, 8600 University Blvd, 47712-3595. SAN 304-8705. Tel: 812-464-1824. Interlibrary Loan Service Tel: 812-464-1683. Circulation Tel: 812-464-1913. Reference Tel: 812-464-1907. FAX: 812-465-1693. Web Site: www.usi.edu/library/library.htm. *Dir*, Ruth H Miller; E-Mail: rhmiller@usi.edu; *Assoc Dir, Coll Develop*, Martha Niemeier; Tel: 812-464-1834, E-Mail: mniemeier@

usi.edu; *Access Serv*, Ruth N Hahn; Tel: 812-464-1912, E-Mail: rnhan@usi.edu; *Govt Doc*, Mona Meyer; Tel: 812-464-1920, E-Mail: mmeyer@usi.edu; *Instrul Serv*, Carrie Donovan; Tel: 812-465-1277, E-Mail: cdonovan@usi.edu; *Ref*, Joanne Artz; Tel: 812-465-1056, E-Mail: jartz@usi.edu; *Ser*, Peter Whiting; Tel: 812-465-1280, E-Mail: pwhiting@usi.edu; *Spec Coll & Archives*, Gina Walker; Tel: 812-464-1896, E-Mail: gwalker@usi.edu; *Tech Servs*, Dianne Grayson; Tel: 812-464-1905, E-Mail: dgrayson@usi.edu; Staff 8 (MLS 8)
Founded 1965. Enrl 8,695; Fac 253; Highest Degree: Master
Jul 1999-Jun 2000 Income $1,463,852. Mats Exp $515,598, Books $119,588, Per/Ser (Incl. Access Fees) $176,313, Presv $439, Micro $32,490, Other Print Mats $93,384, Electronic Ref Mat (Incl. Access Fees) $93,384. Sal $669,336 (Prof $327,832)
Library Holdings: Bk Vols 200,503; Bk Titles 169,283; Per Subs 928
Subject Interests: Business and management, Education, History, Liberal arts, Natural science, Nursing, Science/technology, Social service (social work), Technology
Special Collections: Center for Communal Studies; Indiana Labor History Coll; Local Government Coll; Mead Johnson Coll; Movie Press Kits
Automation Activity & Vendor Info: (Acquisitions) Endeavor; (Cataloging) Endeavor; (Circulation) Endeavor; (Course Reserve) Endeavor; (OPAC) Endeavor; (Serials) Endeavor
Partic in Evansville Area Library Consortium; Four Rivers Area Libr Serv Authority; Indiana Cooperative Library Services Authority
Open Mon-Thurs 7:45am-12, Fri 7:45am-4:30pm, Sat 9-5 & Sun 1-11pm

M VISITING NURSE ASSOCIATION LIBRARY,* 610 E Walnut St, 47713. SAN 327-8735. Tel: 812-425-3561. FAX: 812-463-4600. *In Charge*, John Welcher
Library Holdings: Bk Vols 50

P WILLARD LIBRARY OF EVANSVILLE, 21 First Ave, 47710-1294. SAN 304-8772. Tel: 812-425-4309. FAX: 812-421-9742. E-Mail: willard@willard.lib.in.us. Web Site: www.willard.lib.in.us. *Dir*, Gregory M Hager; E-Mail: ghager@willard.lib.in.us; *Ad Servs*, Brian Rhoden; E-Mail: brhoden@willard.lib.in.us; *Spec Coll*, Lyn Martin; Fax: 812-425-4303, E-Mail: lmartin@willard.lib.in.us; *Tech Servs*, John Scheer; E-Mail: jscheer@willard.lib.in.us; *Mgr*, Kathy Simpson; E-Mail: ksimpson@willard.lib.in.us; Staff 22 (MLS 7, Non-MLS 15)
Founded 1885. Pop 126,272; Circ 446,539
Jan 2000-Dec 2000 Income $611,486, City $495,324, County $61,712, Other $54,450. Mats Exp $99,439, Books $44,439, Per/Ser (Incl. Access Fees) $4,561, Electronic Ref Mat (Incl. Access Fees) $50,439. Sal $239,442 (Prof $367,941)
Library Holdings: Bk Vols 130,000; Per Subs 379
Subject Interests: Arts, Humanities, Nonfiction, Popular fiction
Special Collections: Architecture (Thrall Art Book Coll); Arts &; Local History & Genealogy (Regional & Family History Center), bks, microfilm, mss; Nineteenth Century Periodical Lit, bd per
Automation Activity & Vendor Info: (Cataloging) EOS; (Circulation) EOS; (OPAC) EOS
Database Vendor: Ebsco - EbscoHost
Partic in Indiana Cooperative Library Services Authority
Friends of the Library Group

GL WILLIAM H MILLER LAW LIBRARY, 207 City-County Courts Bldg, 825 Sycamore, 47708-1828. SAN 304-8764. Tel: 812-435-5175. FAX: 812-426-1091. E-Mail: evvlaw@evansville.net. Web Site: www.evansville.net/~evvlaw. *Librn*, Helen S Reed
1999-2000 Income $49,000. Mats Exp Per/Ser (Incl. Access Fees) $49,000. Sal $25,100
Library Holdings: Bk Vols 18,200
Restriction: Restricted access
Partic in Evansville Area Library Consortium; Indiana Cooperative Library Services Authority

FAIRMOUNT

P FAIRMOUNT PUBLIC LIBRARY,* 205 S Main St, PO Box 27, 46928-0027. SAN 304-8780. Tel: 765-948-3177. Toll Free Tel: 800-662-8903. *Librn*, Linda Magers
Founded 1922. Pop 3,300; Circ 9,000
Library Holdings: Bk Vols 13,999; Per Subs 48
Subject Interests: Local history
Special Collections: James Deal Coll, bks, mag & newsp articles
Mem of Eastern Ind Area Libr Servs Authority
Open Mon-Wed, Fri & Sat 9:30am-5:30pm; closed Sun, Thurs & major holidays

FARMLAND

P FARMLAND PUBLIC LIBRARY,* 116 S Main St, PO Box 189, 47340-0189. SAN 376-6772. Tel: 765-468-7292. FAX: 765-468-7067. *Dir*, Iraida Davis
Library Holdings: Bk Vols 10,000
Mem of Indiana Coop Libr Servs Authority

FERDINAND

SR SISTERS OF ST BENEDICT, St Benedict Library, 802 E Tenth St, 47532-9154. SAN 374-7425. Tel: 812-367-1411, Ext 2110. FAX: 812-367-2313. *Archivist*, Sister Mary Dominic Frederick
Founded 1890
Library Holdings: Bk Titles 30,000; Per Subs 75

FISHERS

S CONNER PRAIRIE, Research Department Library,* 13400 Allisonville Rd, 46038-4499. SAN 325-6693. Tel: 317-776-6000. FAX: 317-776-6014. *Archivist*, Timothy Crumrin; E-Mail: tcrumrin@connerprairie.org
Jan 1997-Dec 1998 Mats Exp $2,850
Library Holdings: Bk Vols 5,000; Per Subs 20
Special Collections: 19th century newsp, microfilm; Eli Lilly Papers, re: restoration of Conner house & creation of Conner Prairie Museum; William Conner Papers

FLORA

P FLORA-MONROE PUBLIC LIBRARY, 109 N Center St, 46929-1004. SAN 304-8799. Tel: 219-967-3912. FAX: 219-967-3671. E-Mail: floralib@carlnet.org. *Dir*, Melissa Bishop; Staff 2 (MLS 2)
Founded 1918. Pop 2,916; Circ 30,474
Jan 1999-Dec 1999 Income $137,222, State $67,789, Locally Generated Income $67,444, Other $1,989. Mats Exp $26,207, Books $19,580, Per/Ser (Incl. Access Fees) $3,730, AV Equip $2,897. Sal $70,110
Library Holdings: Bk Vols 30,102; Per Subs 150
Partic in Indiana Cooperative Library Services Authority
The library is handicapped accessible
Friends of the Library Group

FORT WAYNE

§S LINCOLN RE LIBRARY, 1700 Magnavox Way, 46801-7808. SAN 375-4189. Tel: 219-455-5002. FAX: 219-455-9050. E-Mail: taderbyshire@lnc.com. *In Charge*, Tracie Derbyshire; Staff 1 (Non-MLS 1)
Library Holdings: Bk Vols 1,100; Per Subs 31
Subject Interests: Business, Fiction, Wellness
Automation Activity & Vendor Info: (Cataloging) CASPR; (Circulation) CASPR
Restriction: Staff use only

FORT BRANCH

P FORT BRANCH-JOHNSON TOWNSHIP PUBLIC LIBRARY,* 107 E Locust St, 47648. SAN 304-8802. Tel: 812-753-4212. *Librn*, Lois Kissel
Founded 1916. Pop 6,479; Circ 104,000
Library Holdings: Bk Vols 27,705

FORT WAYNE

L ALLEN COUNTY LAW LIBRARY ASSOCIATION, INC, Court House, Rm 105, 46802. SAN 304-8829. Tel: 219-449-7638.
Founded 1910
Oct 1999-Sep 2000 Income $68,257. Mats Exp $65,193, Books $64,985, Electronic Ref Mat (Incl. Access Fees) $208. Sal $23,288
Library Holdings: Bk Vols 17,500
Subject Interests: Law
Special Collections: Supreme Ct reporter, regional reporters, ALR, Amjur, Ind Statutes, misc servs
Restriction: Members only
Partic in Westlaw

P ALLEN COUNTY PUBLIC LIBRARY, 900 Webster St, 46801-3699. (Mail add: PO Box 2270, 46801-2270), SAN 341-1338. Tel: 219-421-1200. Circulation Tel: 219-421-2727, 219-421-2728, 219-421-2729. Reference Tel: 219-421-1235. FAX: 219-422-9688. Web Site: www.acpl.lib.in.us. *Dir*, Jeffrey R Krull; Tel: 219-421-1201, E-Mail: jkrull@acpl.lib.in.us; *Assoc Dir*, Steven Fortriede; Tel: 219-421-1205, E-Mail: sfortriede@acpl.lib.in.us; *Acq*, Suzanne Druehl; Tel: 219-421-1291, E-Mail: sdruehl@acpl.lib.in.us; *Br Coordr*, Michael Clegg; Tel: 219-421-1301, E-Mail: mclegg@acpl.lib.in.us; *Business*, Susan Riehm Goshorn; Tel: 219-421-1216, E-Mail: sgoshorn@acpl.lib.in.us; *Ch Servs*, Mary Voors; Tel: 219-421-1221, E-Mail: mvoors@acpl.lib.in.us; *Coll Develop*, Joyce Misner; Tel: 219-421-1207, E-Mail: jmisner@acpl.lib.in.us; *Commun Relations*, Cheryl Hackworth; Tel: 219-421-1266, E-Mail: chackworth@acpl.lib.in.us; *Media Spec*, Stacy Huxhold; Tel: 219-421-1211, E-Mail: shuxhold@acpl.lib.in.us; *Reader Servs*, Carol Nahrwold; Tel: 219-421-1236, E-Mail: cnahrwold@acpl.lib.in.us; *Syst Coordr*, Luana Stanley; Tel: 219-421-1290, E-Mail: lstanley@acpl.lib.in.us; *Tech Servs*, Janet Hartzell; Tel: 219-421-1290, E-Mail: jharzell@acpl.lib.in.us; *YA Servs*, Sheila Anderson; Tel: 219-421-1256, E-Mail: sanderson@acpl.lib.in.us. Subject Specialists: *Finance*, Dave Sedestrom; *Genealogy*, Curt Witcher; *Properties*, Eugene Johnson; *Television*, Norm

Compton; Staff 396 (MLS 74, Non-MLS 322)
Founded 1895. Pop 300,836; Circ 3,835,302
Jan 1999-Dec 1999 Income (Main Library and Branch Library) $18,708,376, State $72,553, City $280,472. Mats Exp $2,716,086, Books $2,093,583, Per/Ser (Incl. Access Fees) $358,362, Presv $59,035, Micro $93,695, Electronic Ref Mat (Incl. Access Fees) $111,411. Sal $7,310,148 (Prof $3,025,984)
Library Holdings: Bk Vols 2,869,276; Bk Titles 870,244; Per Subs 7,708
Special Collections: Fine Arts (Art & Music), bks & slides; Genealogy, Local History & Heraldry (Reynolds Historical Genealogy Coll), bks, film & micro
Automation Activity & Vendor Info: (Cataloging) SIRSI; (Circulation) SIRSI; (OPAC) SIRSI; (Serials) SIRSI
Publications: Bookfriends; Legacy; What's Happening (calendar)
Partic in Indiana Cooperative Library Services Authority; OCLC Online Computer Library Center, Inc
Friends of the Library Group
Branches: 13
ABOITE, 5630 Coventry Lane, 46804. SAN 370-0941. Tel: 219-421-1310. FAX: 219-432-2394. *Librn*, Susan Hunt; E-Mail: shunt@acpl.lib.in.us
DUPONT, 536 E Dupont Rd, 46825. SAN 370-095X. Tel: 219-421-1315. FAX: 219-489-7756. *Librn*, Deborah Zumbrun; E-Mail: dzumbrun@acpl.lib.in.us
GEORGETOWN, 6600 E State Blvd, 46815. SAN 341-1397. Tel: 219-421-1320. FAX: 219-749-8513. *Librn*, Kathryn Witwer; E-Mail: kawitwer@acpl.lib.in.us
Library Holdings: Bk Vols 66,544
HARLAN BRANCH, State Rd 37, Harlan, 46743. SAN 341-1427. Tel: 219-421-1325. FAX: 219-657-3482. *Librn*, Melissa Kiser; E-Mail: mkiser@acpl.lib.in.us
Library Holdings: Bk Vols 10,000
HESSEN CASSEL, 3030 E Paulding Rd, 46816. SAN 341-1451. Tel: 219-421-1330. FAX: 219-447-5978. *Librn*, Lynn Hoffman; E-Mail: lhoffman@acpl.lib.in.us
Library Holdings: Bk Vols 43,601
LITTLE TURTLE, 2201 Sherman Blvd, 46808. SAN 341-1486. Tel: 219-421-1335. FAX: 219-424-5170. *Librn*, Rosie Stier; E-Mail: rstier@acpl.lib.in.us
Library Holdings: Bk Vols 43,844
MONROEVILLE BRANCH, 104 Allen St, Monroeville, 46773. SAN 341-1516. Tel: 219-421-1340. FAX: 219-623-6321. *Librn*, Christopher Wiljer; E-Mail: cwiljer@acpl.lib.in.us
Library Holdings: Bk Vols 10,000
NEW HAVEN BRANCH, 435 Ann St, New Haven, 46774. SAN 341-1540. Tel: 219-421-1345. FAX: 219-493-0130. *Librn*, Linda Jeffrey; E-Mail: ljeffrey@acpl.lib.in.us
Library Holdings: Bk Vols 18,000
PONTIAC, 3304 Warsaw St, 46806. SAN 341-1575. Tel: 219-421-1350. FAX: 219-744-5372.
Library Holdings: Bk Vols 15,000
SHAWNEE, 5600 Noll Ave, 46806. SAN 341-1605. Tel: 219-421-1355. FAX: 219-456-1871. *Librn*, Pamela Martin-Diaz; E-Mail: pmartin@acpl.lib.in.us
Library Holdings: Bk Vols 50,133
TECUMSEH, 1411 E State Blvd, 46805. SAN 341-163X. Tel: 219-421-1360. FAX: 219-482-5236. *Librn*, Lisa Costich; E-Mail: lcostich@acpl.lib.in.us
Library Holdings: Bk Vols 31,948
WAYNEDALE, 2200 Lower Huntington Rd, 46819. SAN 341-1664. Tel: 219-421-1365. FAX: 219-747-4123. *Librn*, Don Fisher; Tel: 219-421-1370, E-Mail: dfisher@acpl.lib.in.us
Library Holdings: Bk Vols 39,022
WOODBURN BRANCH, 22735 Main St, Woodburn, 46797. SAN 341-1699. Tel: 219-421-1370. FAX: 219-632-0101. *Librn*, Genie Bishop; E-Mail: gbishop@acpl.lib.in.us
Library Holdings: Bk Vols 6,000
Bookmobiles: 1

S CENTRAL SOYA COMPANY, INC, Research Library, 1946 W Cook Rd, 46818-1100. SAN 304-8837. Tel: 219-425-5901. FAX: 219-425-5936. *Res*, Denise Buhr; E-Mail: dbuhr@us.ebsworld.com; Staff 1 (MLS 1)
Founded 1940
Library Holdings: Bk Titles 3,000; Per Subs 50
Subject Interests: Nutrition
Restriction: Company library, Not open to public
Function: Business archives
Partic in Indiana Cooperative Library Services Authority
Open Mon-Fri 8-4:30

R CONCORDIA THEOLOGICAL SEMINARY, Walther Library,* 6600 N Clinton St, 46825. SAN 304-8845. Tel: 219-452-2145. FAX: 219-452-2126. E-Mail: library@ctsfw.edu. Web Site: www.ctsfw.edu. *Dir Libr Serv*, Robert Roethemeyer; *Publ Servs*, Richard Lammert; *Tech Servs*, Lois Guebert
Founded 1846. Highest Degree: Doctorate
Jul 1997-Jun 1998 Income $369,766. Mats Exp $100,800, Books $53,298, Per/Ser (Incl. Access Fees) $41,340, Micro $5,028. Sal $150,523 (Prof $100,637)
Library Holdings: Bk Vols 152,674; Bk Titles 150,637; Per Subs 825
Subject Interests: Theology
Special Collections: 16th & 17th Century Lutheran Orthodoxy; Hermann Sasse; Missions
Partic in Area Libr Servs Authority, Region 3; Indiana Cooperative Library Services Authority; OCLC Online Computer Library Center, Inc

GM DEPARTMENT OF VETERANS AFFAIRS, Medical Center Library,* 2121 Lake Ave, 142D, 46805. SAN 304-8969. Tel: 219-460-1490. FAX: 219-460-1364. *Librn*, Laveta Diem
Founded 1950
1997-1998 Income $123,662. Mats Exp $43,000, Per/Ser (Incl. Access Fees) $28,000
Library Holdings: Bk Vols 765; Per Subs 190
Subject Interests: Allied health, Nursing
Partic in Veterans Affairs Library Network
Friends of the Library Group

G FORT WAYNE DEPARTMENT OF COMMUNITY & ECONOMIC DEVELOPMENT LIBRARY,* One Main St, Rm 800, 46802. SAN 325-6960. Tel: 219-427-1140. FAX: 219-427-1132.
Library Holdings: Bk Vols 4,000; Per Subs 10
Subject Interests: Historic preservation, Housing

S FORT WAYNE MUSEUM OF ART, Auer Library, 311 E Main St, 46802, SAN 328-6312. Tel: 219-422-6467. FAX: 219-422-1374. E-Mail: fwma@art-museum-ftwayne.org. *Librn*, Joyce L Leckrone
Library Holdings: Bk Titles 5,325; Per Subs 20
Subject Interests: American art
Special Collections: Art Exhibition Catalogs

S FORT WAYNE NEWS-SENTINEL LIBRARY,* 600 W Main St, 46802. SAN 374-8367. Tel: 219-461-8468. FAX: 219-461-8817. *Mgr*, Laura Weston-Elchert; E-Mail: lweston@news-sentinel.com
Library Holdings: Bk Vols 100; Per Subs 500

GM FORT WAYNE STATE DEVELOPMENTAL CENTER, Staff Library, 4900 Saint Joe Rd, 46835-3299. SAN 320-6653. Tel: 219-485-7554, Ext 2764. FAX: 219-485-2863. *Librn*, Judith Smith-Lantz
Library Holdings: Bk Vols 1,100; Per Subs 12
Subject Interests: Mentally retarded
Partic in Northeast Indiana Health Science Libraries Consortium

S FRIENDS OF THE THIRD WORLD, INC, Whole World Books,* 611 W Wayne St, 46802-2167. SAN 326-7369. Tel: 219-422-6821. FAX: 219-422-1650. E-Mail: fotw@igc.org. Web Site: www.parlorcity.com/secop/fotw. *Librn*, Marian Waltz; *Ref*, Jim Goetsch; Staff 1 (MLS 1)
1999-2000 Mats Exp $5,000
Library Holdings: Bk Vols 800; Bk Titles 600; Per Subs 50
Publications: Alternative Trading News (quarterly); Catalogue of Books for sale
Open Tues-Sat 10-6

S HUGHES DEFENSE COMMUNICATIONS, Engineering Library,* 1010 Production Rd, 46808-4106. SAN 304-8926. Tel: 219-429-5313. FAX: 219-429-4534. *Actg Librn*, Jill Rose
Founded 1957
Library Holdings: Bk Titles 6,000; Per Subs 50
Subject Interests: Optics
Restriction: Staff use only

C INDIANA INSTITUTE OF TECHNOLOGY, McMillen Library, 1600 E Washington Blvd, 46803. SAN 304-8896. Tel: 219-422-5561, Ext 2215. FAX: 219-422-3189. Web Site: www.indtech.edu. *Dir*, Joan Hartranft; Tel: 219-422-5561, Ext 2224, E-Mail: hartranft@indtech.edu; *Ref*, Linda Paul; E-Mail: paul@indtech.edu; *Ref*, Daryl Shrock; E-Mail: shrock@indtech.edu; Staff 4 (MLS 4)
Founded 1932. Highest Degree: Master
1999-2000 Mats Exp $30,000, Books $10,000, Per/Ser (Incl. Access Fees) $15,000, AV Equip $1,000, Electronic Ref Mat (Incl. Access Fees) $4,000
Library Holdings: Bk Vols 33,000; Per Subs 250
Subject Interests: Business, Engineering, Science/technology, Technology
Automation Activity & Vendor Info: (Cataloging) Athena; (Circulation) Athena
Partic in Indiana Cooperative Library Services Authority
Open Mon-Thurs 8-9:30, Fri 8-4:30, Sat 10-4 & Sun 2:30-9:30

C INDIANA UNIVERSITY-PURDUE UNIVERSITY FORT WAYNE, Walter E Helmke Library, 2101 E Coliseum Blvd, 46805-1499. SAN 341-1214. Tel: 219-481-6512. Reference Tel: 219-481-6505. FAX: 219-481-6509. Web Site: www.lib.ipfw.edu. *Dir*, Judith Violette; E-Mail: violette@ipfw.edu; *Asst Dir, Doc, Govt Doc*, Cheryl Truesdell; Tel: 219-481-6508; *Librn*, Ken Balthafer; *Circ*, Joyce Saltsman; *Acq, Cat*, Margit Codispoti; *Archivist, Coll Develop*, Larry Griffin; Tel: 219-237-4433; *Ref*, Feng Shan; Tel: 219-237-4421, E-Mail: fshan@iusb.edu; *Ser*, Marla Baden; *Science*, Deloice Holliday; Staff 9 (MLS 9)
Founded 1964. Enrl 6,451; Fac 648; Highest Degree: Master
Library Holdings: Bk Vols 333,323; Per Subs 1,439
Subject Interests: Business and management, Health sciences, Science/technology, Technology

Special Collections: Bob Englehart Cartoons; Fort Wayne Government; Sylvia Bowman Papers; University Archives
Publications: More Than Books (newsletter); Self-Guided Tour, guides
Partic in Indiana Cooperative Library Services Authority
Open Mon-Thurs 8-11, Fri 8-6, Sat 9-6 & Sun 12-11

C INTERNATIONAL BUSINESS COLLEGE LIBRARY, 3811 Illinois Rd, 46804. SAN 375-4340. Tel: 219-459-4500.
Library Holdings: Bk Vols 2,500; Bk Titles 2,000; Per Subs 45
Database Vendor: Dialog, Ebsco - EbscoHost, Lexis-Nexis, OCLC - First Search, Silverplatter Information Inc.

S ITT INDUSTRIES-DEFENSE & ELECTRONICS DIVISION, Technical Information Center, 1919 W Cook Rd, PO Box 3700, 46801. SAN 325-7150. Tel: 219-451-6298. FAX: 219-451-6269. *Librn*, Carol Hilkey; E-Mail: clhilkey@itt.com
Library Holdings: Bk Vols 5,000; Per Subs 100
Subject Interests: Electronics
Partic in Dialog Corporation
Open Mon-Fri 7:30am-4:30pm

§C ITT TECHNICAL INSTITUTE, Fort Wayne Library, 4919 Coldwater Rd, 46825. Tel: 219-484-4107. Toll Free Tel: 800-866-4488. FAX: 219-484-0860. *Dir*, Jack Cozad
Library Holdings: Bk Vols 5,000; Per Subs 40

J IVY TECH STATE COLLEGE, 3800 N Anthony Blvd, 46805-1430. SAN 304-890X. Tel: 219-480-4172, 219-482-9171. Interlibrary Loan Service Tel: 219-480-2032. Circulation Tel: 219-480-4172. FAX: 219-480-4121. Web Site: www.ivy.tec.in.us/library/libR3/libR3.htm. *Dir*, Sharon Shurtz Hultquist; Tel: 219-480-4280, E-Mail: shultqui@ivy.tec.in.us; *Circ*, Barbara Bailey; Tel: 219-480-4246, E-Mail: bbailey@ivy.tec.in.us; *Asst Librn*, Connie Freeman; Tel: 219-480-2032, E-Mail: cfreeman@ivy.tec.in.us; *Materials Manager*, Sarah Berndt; Tel: 219-480-2033, E-Mail: sberndt@ivy.tec.in.us; Staff 6 (MLS 2, Non-MLS 4)
Founded 1976. Pop 2,000; Circ 13,148; Enrl 4,000; Fac 130; Highest Degree: Associate
Jul 1998-Jun 1999 Income $265,762, Parent Institution $265,762. Mats Exp $234,363, Books $33,273, Per/Ser (Incl. Access Fees) $4,187, Presv $1,564, Electronic Ref Mat (Incl. Access Fees) $7,354. Sal $126,211 (Prof $36,882)
Library Holdings: Bk Titles 12,221; Per Subs 2,148; High Interest/Low Vocabulary Bk Vols 125; Spec Interest Per Sub 100
Subject Interests: Child care, Children's fiction, Parenting, Puppets
Special Collections: Family Reading Center, children's bks, per, parenting bks; Practical Nursing, bks, per; Respiratory Therapy, bks, per
Automation Activity & Vendor Info: (Circulation) Endeavor; (ILL) Endeavor; (OPAC) Endeavor
Database Vendor: Ebsco - EbscoHost, Lexis-Nexis, OCLC - First Search, ProQuest, Wilson - Wilson Web
Publications: Bibliographies; Flow Chart; Guide to the Library; OPAC Guide; Union List of Serials
Function: Reference services available
Partic in Northeast Indiana Health Science Libraries Consortium

S JOURNAL GAZETTE LIBRARY, 600 W Main St, 46802. SAN 320-6661. Tel: 219-461-8377. FAX: 219-461-8648. E-Mail: jgnews@jg.net. Web Site: www.journalgazette.net. *Dir*, Tom Pellegrene; E-Mail: tpellegrene@jg.net; *Asst Librn*, Kara Whiting; Tel: 219-461-8456, E-Mail: kwhiting@jg.net; *Asst Librn*, Lyn Windell; Tel: 219-461-8258, E-Mail: lwindel@jg.net. Subject Specialists: *Photos*, Kara Whiting; *Texts*, Lyn Windell; Staff 4 (Non-MLS 4)
Founded 1977
Library Holdings: Bk Vols 1,000; Per Subs 20
Special Collections: Journal-Gazette-1885 to Present, microfilm
Restriction: Private library
Partic in Area Libr Servs Authority, Region 3; Dialog Corporation; Vutext

L LINCOLN NATIONAL CORPORATION, Law Library, 7C,* 1300 S Clinton St, PO Box 1110, 46801. SAN 341-1273. Tel: 219-455-3870. FAX: 219-455-5135. *Librn*, Pam Thornton
Founded 1923
Library Holdings: Bk Vols 10,000; Per Subs 45
Special Collections: 50 State Statutes & Complete National Reporter System
Publications: Information Services Newsletter (in-house)
Partic in Area Libr Servs Authority, Region 3; Dialog Corporation; Indiana Cooperative Library Services Authority

S LINCOLN NATIONAL FOUNDATION, Lincoln Museum,* 200 E Berry, PO Box 7838, 46801. SAN 341-1303. Tel: 219-455-3031. Interlibrary Loan Service Tel: 219-455-5590. FAX: 219-455-6922. Web Site: www.thelincolnmuseum.org. *Dir*, Joan L Flinspach
Founded 1928
Library Holdings: Bk Vols 18,000; Bk Titles 16,000; Per Subs 50
Special Collections: Abraham Lincoln & Contemporaries, broadsides, engravings, lithographs, mss, photogs, sheet music; Civil War, paintings & pamphlets; Richard W Thompson & Others, mss, newsp
Publications: Lincoln Lore (bulletin); R Gerald McMurtry Lecture

M LUTHERAN COLLEGE OF HEALTH PROFESSIONS, Health Sciences Library,* 2701 Spring St, 46808. SAN 304-8918. Tel: 219-434-7691. FAX: 219-434-7695. Web Site: www.sfc.edu/~library. *Librn*, Lauralee Aven; E-Mail: avenk@cris.com; *Librn*, Marla Baden; Staff 3 (MLS 3)
Founded 1978
Library Holdings: Bk Vols 4,100; Bk Titles 3,700; Per Subs 225
Subject Interests: Allied health, Medicine, Nursing
Restriction: Open to public for reference only
Partic in Northeast Indiana Health Science Libraries Consortium

S NORTHEAST JUVENILE CORRECTIONAL FACILITY LIBRARY, 315 W Washington Blvd, PO Box 13069, 46867. Tel: 219-422-8223. *Librn*, Beatty Donald
Library Holdings: Bk Titles 200; Per Subs 25

M PARK CENTER, INC LIBRARY,* Corporate Services, 909 E State Blvd, 46805. SAN 320-183X. Tel: 219-481-2700, Ext 2185. FAX: 219-481-2810. *In Charge*, Roxsandra McClemons-McFerthing
Library Holdings: Bk Titles 900
Subject Interests: Psychiatry, Psychology, Social service (social work)
Restriction: Staff use only
Partic in Area Libr Serv Authority; Northwest Indiana Health Science Library Consortium; Region 3

M PARKVIEW HOSPITAL, Ridderheim Health Science Library,* 2200 Randallia Dr, 46805. SAN 304-8934. Tel: 219-484-6636, Ext 22400. FAX: 219-480-5961. E-Mail: parkview@cris.com. *Librn*, Shannon Clever; Staff 3 (MLS 2, Non-MLS 1)
1997-1998 Income $188,000. Mats Exp $55,000, Books $16,000, Per/Ser (Incl. Access Fees) $26,000, Micro $13,000. Sal $85,000
Library Holdings: Bk Vols 8,000; Per Subs 499
Subject Interests: Allied health, Medicine, Nursing
Special Collections: Patient Information
Partic in Indiana Cooperative Library Services Authority; Midwest Health Sci Libr Network; Northeast Indiana Health Science Libraries Consortium

M ST JOSEPH MEDICAL CENTER, Medical Information Resource Center,* 700 Broadway, 46802. SAN 304-8950. Tel: 219-425-3094. FAX: 219-425-3093.
Founded 1945
Subject Interests: Cardiology, Geriatrics and gerontology, Orthopedics
Partic in Indiana Cooperative Library Services Authority

CR TAYLOR UNIVERSITY - FORT WAYNE, S A Lehman Memorial Library, 919 W Rudisill Blvd, 46807. SAN 304-887X. Tel: 219-744-8625. Interlibrary Loan Service Tel: 219-744-8664. FAX: 219-744-8631. Web Site: www.tayloru.edu//fw/departments/library/. *Dir*, Mary Jean Johnson; E-Mail: mrjohnson@tayloru.edu; *Ref*, Michael Van Huisen; *Instrul Serv*, Miriam Rose; *Tech Servs*, Ruth Elder; Staff 5 (MLS 3, Non-MLS 2)
Founded 1904. Enrl 400; Fac 28; Highest Degree: Bachelor
Jul 1998-Jun 1999 Mats Exp $131,845, Books $87,647, Per/Ser (Incl. Access Fees) $43,319, Presv $879. Sal $166,462 (Prof $110,769)
Library Holdings: Bk Vols 75,603; Per Subs 520
Special Collections: Instructional Materials Center
Automation Activity & Vendor Info: (Acquisitions) DRA; (Cataloging) DRA; (Circulation) DRA; (Serials) DRA
Database Vendor: DRA, Ebsco - EbscoHost, Lexis-Nexis, OCLC - First Search, Silverplatter Information Inc., Wilson - Wilson Web
Publications: Library Handbook; Library Workbook
Partic in Indiana Cooperative Library Services Authority; OCLC Online Computer Library Center, Inc; Private Acad Libr Network of Ind

S TOKHEIM CORPORATION, Engineering Lab Library,* 10501 Corporate Dr, PO Box 360, 46801. SAN 328-2503. Tel: 219-470-4600, Ext 4766. FAX: 219-470-4719. *Mgr*, Wm G Goggin
Library Holdings: Bk Vols 500

C UNIVERSITY OF SAINT FRANCIS LIBRARY, 2701 Spring St, 46808. SAN 304-8942. Tel: 219-434-7455. FAX: 219-434-3194. Web Site: www.sf.edu/library. *Publ Servs, Ref*, Laura Lee Aven; Tel: 219-434-7691; *Tech Servs*, Maureen McMahan; Staff 3 (MLS 3)
Founded 1890. Fac 37; Highest Degree: Master
Library Holdings: Bk Titles 60,000; Per Subs 480
Subject Interests: Art, Counseling, Education, Nursing, Psychology, Special education
Special Collections: ERIC Document Coll
Open Mon-Thurs 8:30am-9pm, Fri 8:30-5, Sat 9-5, Sun 1-9

FORTVILLE

P FORTVILLE-VERNON TOWNSHIP PUBLIC LIBRARY,* 625 E Broadway, 46040. SAN 304-8977. Tel: 317-485-6402. FAX: 317-485-4084. *Dir*, Richard Bell; *Ch Servs*, Marian Taulman; Staff 1 (MLS 1)
Founded 1917. Pop 5,883; Circ 131,673
Jan 1999-Dec 2000 Income $282,000. Mats Exp $40,000. Sal $125,000
Library Holdings: Bk Vols 34,547; Per Subs 130
Partic in Cent Ind Area Libr Servs Authority

FOWLER

P BENTON COUNTY PUBLIC LIBRARY,* 102 N Van Buren Ave, 47944-1299. SAN 304-8985. Tel: 765-884-1720. FAX: 765-884-1720. *Dir*, Kay Rickard; Staff 2 (MLS 2)
Founded 1906. Pop 5,059; Circ 42,960
Jan 1997-Dec 1998 Income $228,000
Library Holdings: Bk Titles 30,000; Per Subs 80
Subject Interests: Agriculture, Art and architecture, Environmental studies, Genealogy
Special Collections: Louis L'Amour Westerns

FRANCESVILLE

P FRANCESVILLE-SALEM TOWNSHIP PUBLIC LIBRARY,* PO Box 577, 47946-0577. SAN 304-8993. Tel: 219-567-9433. FAX: 219-567-9433. *Librn*, Helen Vollmer
Founded 1916. Pop 1,898; Circ 40,824
Library Holdings: Bk Titles 18,000; Per Subs 95

FRANKFORT

P FRANKFORT COMMUNITY PUBLIC LIBRARY, 208 W Clinton St, 46041. SAN 304-9000. Tel: 765-654-8746. TDD: 765-659-3047. FAX: 765-654-8747. E-Mail: fcpl@accs.net. Web Site: www.accs.net/fcpl/. *Dir*, Claude W Caddell; E-Mail: bcaddell@accs.net; *Asst Dir*, Sheryl Sollars; E-Mail: ssollars@accs.net; *Ch Servs*, Margaret Williams; E-Mail: peggy@accs.net; *AV*, Marian Coapstick; *Circ*, Carol Scott; *Ref*, Libby Kreisher; *Bkmobile Coordr*, Kathy Johnson; *Acq*, Barbara Goodnight; Staff 13 (MLS 4, Non-MLS 9)
Founded 1880. Pop 32,000; Circ 270,154
Jan 1999-Dec 1999 Income (Main Library and Branch Library) $1,165,991, State $68,756, City $608,095, County $425,000, Locally Generated Income $43,289, Other $20,851. Mats Exp $1,160,515, Books $124,012, Per/Ser (Incl. Access Fees) $10,217, Presv $831, Micro $231, Electronic Ref Mat (Incl. Access Fees) $5,551. Sal $553,248 (Prof $174,303)
Library Holdings: Bk Vols 141,819; Per Subs 379
Subject Interests: Agriculture, Civil War, Gardening, Nuclear energy
Special Collections: Genealogy (Fugate & Culver Coll)
Automation Activity & Vendor Info: (Acquisitions) Gaylord; (Cataloging) Gaylord; (Circulation) Gaylord; (OPAC) Gaylord
Publications: Library Lines
Partic in Indiana Cooperative Library Services Authority
Special Services for the Deaf - TDD
Friends of the Library Group
Branches: 3
MICHIGANTOWN COMMUNITY, 702 N Main, Michigantown, 46057. SAN 376-8384. FAX: 765-249-2303. Web Site: www.accs.net/fcpl/. *Branch Mgr*, Rosie McKinney; Tel: 765-249-2303; Staff 1 (Non-MLS 1)
Founded 1984
Jan 1999-Dec 1999 Mats Exp $8,400
Library Holdings: Bk Vols 13,544
Automation Activity & Vendor Info: (Circulation) Gaylord; (OPAC) Gaylord
Friends of the Library Group
MULBERRY COMMUNITY, 143 S Glick St, PO Box 489, Mulberry, 46058. SAN 376-8392. Tel: 765-296-2604. FAX: 765-296-2604. E-Mail: furgs@ecn.purdue.edu. Web Site: www.accs.net/fcpl/. *Branch Mgr*, Sharon Furgason; Staff 1 (MLS 1)
Jan 1999-Dec 1999 Mats Exp Books $8,400
Library Holdings: Bk Vols 13,190
Automation Activity & Vendor Info: (Circulation) Gaylord; (OPAC) Gaylord
Friends of the Library Group
ROSSVILLE COMMUNITY, 400 W Main, Rossville, 46065. SAN 376-8406. FAX: 765-379-2246. Web Site: www.accs.net/fcpl/. *Branch Mgr*, Kathy Scircle; Staff 1 (Non-MLS 1)
Jan 1999-Dec 1999 Mats Exp Books $10,500
Library Holdings: Bk Vols 24,023
Automation Activity & Vendor Info: (Circulation) Gaylord; (OPAC) Gaylord
Friends of the Library Group
Bookmobiles: 1

FRANKLIN

S ARAC, INTERNATIONAL TECHNOLOGY KNOWLEDGE CO, 604 E Davis Dr, 46131. SAN 329-4536. Tel: 317-738-3886. FAX: 317-738-3980. E-Mail: arac@iquest.net. Web Site: www.aracin.com. *Pres*, Dr F Timothy Janis
Library Holdings: Per Subs 100

C FRANKLIN COLLEGE LIBRARY,* 501 E Monroe St, 46131. SAN 304-9019. Tel: 317-738-8164. FAX: 317-738-8787. Web Site: www.franklincol.edu/library. *Dir*, Carla Jacobs; *Bibliog Instr, Online Servs, Ref*, Ronald L Schuetz; E-Mail: schuetr@franklincoll.edu; *Archivist, Spec Coll*, Mary Alice Medlicott; *Cat, Tech Servs*, Emilio Martinez Jr; Staff 5 (MLS 5)
Founded 1888. Enrl 864; Fac 69; Highest Degree: Bachelor
Library Holdings: Bk Vols 113,100; Bk Titles 88,652; Per Subs 375
Subject Interests: Art and architecture, Business and management, Economics, Education, History, Natural science, Religion, Science/technology, Social sciences and issues, Technology
Special Collections: Indiana (David Demaree Banta Coll); Indiana Baptist Coll; Roger D Branigan Papers Coll
Publications: Catalog of the David Demaree Banta Coll
Partic in Cent Ind Area Libr Servs Authority; Indiana Cooperative Library Services Authority; OCLC Online Computer Library Center, Inc

P JOHNSON COUNTY PUBLIC LIBRARY,* 401 S State St, 46131-2545. SAN 304-9027. Tel: 317-738-2833. FAX: 317-738-9635. Web Site: www.jcpl.lib.in.us. *Dir*, Beverly Martin; E-Mail: bmartin@infodepo.jcpl.lib.in.us; *Asst Dir*, Rod Burkett; *Tech Servs*, Jill Wright; *Ad Servs*, Walt Owens; *AV*, Catherine McKenzie; *Info Tech*, Hassan Dwehji; *Commun Relations*, Mike Aldrich; *YA Servs*, Julie Bascum; Staff 34 (MLS 14, Non-MLS 20)
Founded 1911. Pop 85,000
Jan 1999-Dec 1999 Income (Main Library and Branch Library) $3,730,120. Mats Exp $436,750, Books $350,000, Per/Ser (Incl. Access Fees) $29,000, Presv $5,800, Micro $1,950, Electronic Ref Mat (Incl. Access Fees) $50,000. Sal $1,739,350
Library Holdings: Bk Vols 325,340; Bk Titles 200,000; Per Subs 550
Subject Interests: Careers, Consumer, Travel
Special Collections: Johnson County History
Automation Activity & Vendor Info: (Acquisitions) SIRSI; (Cataloging) SIRSI; (Circulation) SIRSI; (ILL) SIRSI; (Media Booking) SIRSI; (OPAC) SIRSI; (Serials) SIRSI
Publications: Connections
Partic in Indiana Cooperative Library Services Authority; Johnson County Commun Network; OCLC Online Computer Library Center, Inc
Open Mon-Thurs 9-8, Fri 9-6, Sat 9-5 & Sun 1-5 (sch yr only)
Friends of the Library Group
Branches: 2
BREAK-O-DAY, 700 Sawmill Rd, New Whiteland, 46184. SAN 376-9445. Tel: 317-535-6206. FAX: 317-535-6018. Web Site: www.jcpl.lib.in.us. *AV, Librn*, Linda Oldham; *Ad Servs*, Liz Schoettle
Friends of the Library Group
WHITE RIVER LIBRARY, 1664 Library Blvd, Greenwood, 46142. SAN 320-9539. Tel: 317-885-1330. FAX: 317-882-4117. Web Site: www.jcpl.lib.in.us. *Librn*, Annette Demaree; *Ad Servs*, Sylvia Rule; *YA Servs*, Rachel Bowell; Staff 16 (MLS 10, Non-MLS 6)
Automation Activity & Vendor Info: (Acquisitions) SIRSI; (Cataloging) SIRSI; (ILL) SIRSI; (Media Booking) SIRSI; (OPAC) PALS; (Serials) SIRSI
Open Mon-Thurs 10-9, Fri 10-6, Sat 10-5 & Sun 1-5 (during sch yr)
Friends of the Library Group

S MASONIC LIBRARY & MUSEUM OF INDIANA, INC, 690 State St, 46131. SAN 371-148X. Tel: 317-736-5741. *Dir*, James W Prairie
Special Collections: Dwight Louis Smith, bks, papers

FREMONT

P FREMONT PUBLIC LIBRARY,* PO Box 7, 46737-0007. SAN 376-2653. Tel: 219-495-7157. *Dir*, Gerallee Baker
Library Holdings: Bk Vols 12,000; Bk Titles 7,500

FRENCH LICK

P MELTON PUBLIC LIBRARY,* 8496 W College St, 47432-1026. SAN 304-9035. Tel: 812-936-2177. FAX: 812-936-2177. E-Mail: meltonpublib@smithville.net. Web Site: www.smithville.net/~meltonpublib/inex/htm. *Librn*, Hillary Campbell; *Asst Librn*, Katherine Beaty; *Asst Librn*, Robin Coulter; *Asst Librn*, Maxine Parks; *YA Servs*, Carol Anderson Sal $79,000
Library Holdings: Bk Vols 25,188; Per Subs 46
Database Vendor: DRA

GARRETT

P GARRETT PUBLIC LIBRARY, 107 W Houston St, 46738. SAN 304-9043. Tel: 219-357-5485. FAX: 219-357-5170. Web Site: www.gpl.lib.in.us. *Dir*, Kate Birdseye; E-Mail: kbirdseye@gpl.lib.in.us; Staff 4 (MLS 2, Non-MLS 2)
Founded 1914. Pop 8,065; Circ 34,365
Jan 1999-Dec 1999 Income $415,000. Mats Exp $400,000
Library Holdings: Bk Vols 32,263; Bk Titles 29,900; Per Subs 109
Special Collections: Cameron Park Indian Relics Coll
Automation Activity & Vendor Info: (Cataloging) Brodart; (Circulation) Brodart; (ILL) Brodart; (OPAC) Brodart

Publications: Baker & Taylor
Partic in Area 3 Libr Serv Authority; Indiana Cooperative Library Services Authority
Friends of the Library Group

GARY

P GARY PUBLIC LIBRARY, 220 W Fifth Ave, 46402-1215. SAN 341-1729. Tel: 219-886-2484. Interlibrary Loan Service Tel: 219-886-2484, Ext 336. FAX: 219-886-6829. Web Site: www.gary.lib.in.us. *Dir*, Marcia King; *Asst Libr Dir*, Janet Hawkins Guydon; Tel: 219-886-2484, Ext 321, Fax: 219-882-9528, E-Mail: janet@gary.lib.in.us; *Tech Servs*, Pamela Vance; Tel: 219-886-2484, Ext 335, Fax: 219-882-9528, E-Mail: pam@gary.lib.in.us; *Ch Servs*, Mary Ann Mrozosko; Tel: 219-886-2484, Ext 331, Fax: 219-882-9528, E-Mail: maryann@gary.lib.in.us; *AV, Circ*, Roma Ivey; Tel: 219-886-2484, Ext 334, Fax: 219-882-9528, E-Mail: roma@gary.lib.in.us; *ILL*, Kenneth Green; Fax: 219-882-9528, E-Mail: kenneth@gary.lib.in.us; *Bkmobile Coordr*, Karen Blocker; Tel: 219-886-2484, Ext 329, Fax: 219-882-9528, E-Mail: karen@gary.lib.in.us; *Coll Develop*, Samuel Custard. Subject Specialists: *Art*, Maria Strimbu; *Public affairs*, Maria Strimbu; *Videos*, Roma Ivey; Staff 21 (MLS 14, Non-MLS 7)
Founded 1908. Pop 116,646; Circ 998,361
Jan 2000-Dec 2000 Income (Main Library and Branch Library) $7,255,021. Mats Exp $750,000. Sal $2,000,000
Library Holdings: Bk Vols 650,000; Bk Titles 475,000
Special Collections: Gary & Indiana History Coll
Automation Activity & Vendor Info: (Circulation) DRA
Database Vendor: DRA, OCLC - First Search
Publications: Bibliographies; Calendar of Events; Staff Newsletter
Partic in Indiana Cooperative Library Services Authority; OCLC Online Computer Library Center, Inc
Friends of the Library Group
Branches: 4
WEB DU BOIS BRANCH, 1835 Broadway, 46407-2298. SAN 341-1753. Tel: 219-886-9120. FAX: 219-886-9391. *Head Librn*, Kokuleeba S Lwanga; E-Mail: koku@gary.lib.in.us; Staff 2 (MLS 1, Non-MLS 1)
Library Holdings: Bk Vols 57,861
Special Collections: Afro-American Rare Book Coll, micro-fiche
Friends of the Library Group
JOHN F KENNEDY BRANCH, 3953 Broadway, 46408-1799. SAN 341-1818. Tel: 219-887-8112. FAX: 219-887-5967. *Head Librn*, Dorothy Swain; E-Mail: dorothy@gary.lib.in.us; Staff 2 (Non-MLS 2)
Library Holdings: Bk Vols 43,864
Friends of the Library Group
ORA L WILDERMUTH BRANCH, 501 S Lake, 46403-2408. SAN 341-1907. Tel: 219-938-3941. FAX: 219-938-8759. *Head Librn*, Patience Ojomo; E-Mail: patience@gary.lib.in.us; Staff 2 (MLS 1, Non-MLS 1)
Library Holdings: Bk Vols 31,791
Friends of the Library Group
TOLLESTON, 1113 Taft St, 46404-2297. SAN 341-1877. Tel: 219-944-2795. FAX: 219-944-9255. *Head Librn*, Diana Morrow; E-Mail: dianam@gary.lib.in.us; Staff 2 (MLS 1, Non-MLS 1)
Library Holdings: Bk Vols 59,283
Friends of the Library Group
Bookmobiles: 1

S HOLLINGER INTERNATIONAL INC, Post Tribune Library,* 1065 Broadway, 46402. SAN 329-0190. Tel: 219-881-3134. FAX: 219-881-3026. Web Site: www.post-trib.com. *Chief Librn*, Linda Krueger; Staff 3 (MLS 1, Non-MLS 2)
Founded 1935
Library Holdings: Bk Titles 795
Special Collections: Golden Jubilee Edition, films & bound
Restriction: Staff use only

C INDIANA UNIVERSITY NORTHWEST LIBRARY, 3400 Broadway, 46408. SAN 304-9051. Tel: 219-980-6580. Interlibrary Loan Service Tel: 219-980-6933. Reference Tel: 219-980-6582. FAX: 219-980-6558. Web Site: www.lib.iun.edu/. *Librn*, Robert F Moran, Jr; Tel: 219-980-6928, E-Mail: moranr@iun.edu; *Syst Coordr*, Nicholas Rosselli; Tel: 219-980-6929, E-Mail: rosselli@iun.edu; *Bibliog Instr, Ref*, Arena Stevens; Tel: 219-980-6625, E-Mail: astevens@iun.edu; *ILL*, Cynthia Szymanski; Tel: 219-980-6521, E-Mail: cszymans@iun.edu; *Govt Doc*, Tim Sutherland; Tel: 219-980-6946, E-Mail: sutherla@iun.edu; *Archivist*, Stephen McShane; Tel: 219-980-6628, E-Mail: smcshane@iun.edu; *Tech Servs*, Ellen Bosman; Tel: 219-980-6947, E-Mail: ebosman@iun.edu; *Ref*, Carol Rusinek; Tel: 219-980-6547, E-Mail: crusin@iun.edu; Staff 16 (MLS 8, Non-MLS 8)
Founded 1940. Enrl 4,900; Fac 175; Highest Degree: Master
Jul 1999-Jun 2000 Income $1,219,163, State $1,215,152, Federal $2,311, Other $1,700. Mats Exp $374,389, Books $118,416, Per/Ser (Incl. Access Fees) $255,973. Sal $599,011 (Prof $363,075)
Library Holdings: Bk Vols 237,293
Special Collections: Calumet Regional Archives
Automation Activity & Vendor Info: (Acquisitions) SIRSI; (Cataloging) SIRSI; (Circulation) SIRSI; (Course Reserve) SIRSI; (ILL) SIRSI; (Media Booking) SIRSI; (OPAC) SIRSI; (Serials) SIRSI
Partic in Northwest Indiana Health Science Library Consortium; OCLC Online Computer Library Center, Inc

M INDIANA UNIVERSITY SCHOOL OF MEDICINE - NORTHWEST CENTER FOR MEDICAL EDUCATION, Steven C Beering Medical Library, 3400 Broadway, 46408-1197. SAN 320-1848. Tel: 219-980-6852. Interlibrary Loan Service Tel: 219-980-6852. Reference Tel: 219-980-6709. Toll Free Tel: 800-437-5409, Ext 6852. FAX: 219-980-6566. Web Site: www.medlib.iupui.edu/nwcme/library.html. *Librn*, Felicia Young; Tel: 219-980-6709, E-Mail: fyoung@iunhaw1.iun.indiana.edu; Staff 3 (MLS 1, Non-MLS 2)
Library Holdings: Bk Titles 1,800; Per Subs 80
Partic in Northwest Indiana Health Science Library Consortium

J IVY TECH STATE COLLEGE-NORTHWEST REGION, Gary Campus Library,* 1440 E 35th Ave, 46409-1499. SAN 304-906X. Tel: 219-981-1111, Ext 218. FAX: 219-981-4415. Web Site: www.gar.in.tec. *Dir Libr Serv*, Barbara Burns; *Ref, Tech Servs*, Nick Vasil; Staff 4 (MLS 1, Non-MLS 3)
Founded 1972. Enrl 5,000
Jul 1997-Jun 1998 Mats Exp $71,348, Books $27,414, Per/Ser (Incl. Access Fees) $6,909, Micro $12,500, AV Equip $4,047. Sal $169,108 (Prof $42,399)
Library Holdings: Bk Vols 10,105; Bk Titles 7,356; Per Subs 228
Partic in Duplicate Exchange Union; Indiana Cooperative Library Services Authority
Service rendered to three satellite campuses: Gary, Valaraiso & East Chicago. Figures reported include these 3 libraries. Hours: Mon-Thurs 8-9, Fri 8-6 & Sat 8-1

GL LAKE COUNTY LAW LIBRARY, 3400 Broadway, 46408. SAN 304-9078. Tel: 219-980-6797. FAX: 219-980-6558. *Dir*, Robert Moran
1998-1999 Income $150,000. Mats Exp $150,000
Library Holdings: Bk Vols 19,600
Special Collections: Indiana Law; Pre-National Reporter Coll of State Reports
Publications: Access to Calumet Regional Archive (housed@IUN Libr); Access to Online Catalogs used by Indiana University Northwest Library; Access to research materials (non-circulating) & Government Depository at Indiana University Northwest Library

M METHODIST HOSPITAL, Health Science Libraries,* 600 Grant St, 46402. SAN 304-9086. Tel: 219-886-4554. FAX: 219-886-4271. E-Mail: mathlib@mail.netnitco.net.; Staff 2 (MLS 1, Non-MLS 1)
Founded 1950
Library Holdings: Bk Titles 3,000; Per Subs 323
Subject Interests: Cardiology, Internal medicine, Oncology
Restriction: Staff use only
Friends of the Library Group

GAS CITY

P GAS CITY-MILL TOWNSHIP PUBLIC LIBRARY, 135 E Main St, 46933-1433. SAN 304-9108. Tel: 765-674-4718. FAX: 765-674-5176. Web Site: www.gascity.com. *Admin Dir*, Mary Helen Stigall; E-Mail: mary_stigall@yahoo.com; *Ch Servs*, Nancy Bryant; E-Mail: nlb723@yahoo.com; Staff 11 (MLS 1, Non-MLS 10)
Founded 1913. Pop 9,685; Circ 62,574
Jan 1999-Dec 1999 Income $422,833, State $41,797, County $356,426, Locally Generated Income $24,610. Mats Exp $85,486, Books $62,883, Per/Ser (Incl. Access Fees) $12,603, AV Equip $10,000. Sal $174,145 (Prof $33,500)
Library Holdings: Bk Vols 34,633; Bk Titles 33,000; Per Subs 108
Automation Activity & Vendor Info: (Cataloging) Gaylord; (Circulation) Gaylord; (OPAC) Gaylord
Partic in Indiana Cooperative Library Services Authority
Open Mon-Thurs 10-8, Fri-Sat 10-5; Closed Sun; Closed Sat during summer

GENEVA

P GENEVA PUBLIC LIBRARY,* 307 E Line, PO Box 189, 46740. SAN 304-9116. Tel: 219-368-7270. FAX: 219-368-9776. *Librn*, Rose Bryan
Founded 1945. Pop 1,430; Circ 15,316
Library Holdings: Bk Vols 27,000; Per Subs 80
Special Collections: Gene Stratton Porter Coll
Partic in Ind Libr Asn; Ind Trustee Asn
Open Mon-Fri 1-5, Sat 9-12:30
Friends of the Library Group

GOODLAND

P GOODLAND & GRANT TOWNSHIP PUBLIC LIBRARY,* 111 S Newton St, 47948. (Mail add: PO Box 405, 47948-0405), SAN 304-9124. Tel: 219-297-4431. FAX: 219-297-4431. *Dir*, Velora Miller; *Librn*, Mary Anne Templin; *Asst Librn*, Caryl Keeney
Founded 1907. Pop 1,570

Library Holdings: Bk Vols 12,500; Per Subs 40
Subject Interests: Indiana
Open Mon, Tues, Wed & Fri 12-5, Thurs 12-8, Sat 9-12

GOSHEN

GOSHEN COLLEGE
C HAROLD & WILMA GOOD LIBRARY, 1700 S Main, 46526-4794. SAN 341-1931. Tel: 219-535-7427. Interlibrary Loan Service Tel: 219-535-7430. Reference Tel: 219-535-7431. FAX: 219-535-7438. Web Site: www.goshen.edu/library. *Dir*, Lisa Guedea Carreno; E-Mail: lisagc@goshen.edu; *Asst Librn*, Yvonne Ransel; E-Mail: yvonnemr@goshen.edu; *Assoc Librn, Tech Servs*, Kathy Kauffman; E-Mail: kathyak@goshen.edu; *Assoc Librn, ILL*, Sally Jo Milne; E-Mail: sallyjm@goshen.edu; Staff 4 (MLS 4)
Founded 1894. Enrl 945; Highest Degree: Bachelor
Jul 1999-Jun 2000 Income $598,000. Mats Exp $211,556, Books $92,411, Per/Ser (Incl. Access Fees) $85,882, Presv $670, Micro $32,593. Sal $297,814 (Prof $120,205)
Library Holdings: Bk Vols 122,980; Per Subs 716
Subject Interests: Peace, Religion
Special Collections: Early American Hymnody (Jesse Hartzler Coll)
Database Vendor: DRA, Ebsco - EbscoHost, Lexis-Nexis, OCLC - First Search
Function: ILL available
Partic in Indiana Cooperative Library Services Authority; OCLC Online Computer Library Center, Inc; Private Acad Libr Network of Ind

CR MENNONITE HISTORICAL LIBRARY, 1700 S Main, 46526. SAN 341-1966. Tel: 219-535-7418. FAX: 219-535-7438. E-Mail: mhl@goshen.edu. Web Site: www.goshen.edu/mhl/. *Dir*, Dr John D Roth; *Librn, Online Servs*, Joe A Springer; Staff 5 (MLS 3, Non-MLS 2)
Founded 1907
1998-1999 Mats Exp $24,000
Library Holdings: Bk Vols 53,000; Per Subs 450
Subject Interests: Amish, Genealogy
Publications: Mennonite Quarterly Review
Partic in Indiana Cooperative Library Services Authority; OCLC Online Computer Library Center, Inc

P GOSHEN PUBLIC LIBRARY, 601 S Fifth St, 46526-3994. SAN 304-9132. Tel: 219-533-9531. FAX: 219-533-5211. *Dir*, Valerie Gross; *Asst Dir*, Susanne Friesen; *Ch Servs*, Mary Ann Hunsberger; *Ref*, Ann Kauffman; *AV*, Marcy Gerig; *Ad Servs, YA Servs*, Ann-Margaret Rice; *Automation Syst Coordr*, Ross Riker; Staff 11 (MLS 6, Non-MLS 5)
Founded 1897. Pop 28,342; Circ 35,168
Jan 1999-Dec 1999 Income $1,506,699. Mats Exp $835,699. Sal $785,574
Library Holdings: Bk Vols 140,000; Bk Titles 90,000; Per Subs 325
Special Collections: Indiana History & Local Genealogy Coll; Large Print Coll
Automation Activity & Vendor Info: (Acquisitions) epixtech, inc.; (Cataloging) epixtech, inc.; (Circulation) epixtech, inc.; (OPAC) epixtech, inc.; (Serials) epixtech, inc.
Partic in Indiana Cooperative Library Services Authority
Special Services for the Blind - ADA terminals for visually impaired
Open Mon-Fri 9:30-9, Sat 9:30-3, Sun 1:30-5
Friends of the Library Group

GRANGER

§C DAVENPORT UNIVERSITY, Granger Library, 7121 Granger Rd, 46530. Tel: 219-272-4413, 219-277-8447. Toll Free Tel: 800-277-8447. FAX: 219-272-2967. *Asst Librn*, Patricia A Rea; E-Mail: sbprea@davenport.edu
Library Holdings: Bk Titles 4,000
Open Mon-Thurs 9-9, Fri 9-4, Sat 9-3

GREENCASTLE

C DEPAUW UNIVERSITY, Roy O West Library, 400 S College, 46135. SAN 341-1990. Tel: 765-658-4434. FAX: 765-658-4017. Web Site: www.depauw.edu/lib/homepg.htm. *Dir*, Dr Kathy Davis; E-Mail: kdavis@depauw.edu; *Asst Dir*, Pei-Ling Wu; *Archivist, Spec Coll*, Wesley Wilson; *Cat*, Bruce Sanders; *Coll Develop*, Joyce Dixon-Fyle; Staff 10 (MLS 10)
Founded 1837. Enrl 2,334; Fac 184; Highest Degree: Bachelor
Library Holdings: Bk Vols 254,806; Per Subs 1,481
Subject Interests: Business and management, Economics, Music
Special Collections: Archives of DePauw University & Indiana United Methodism, doc, flm, ms; Bret Harte Library of First Editions; German (Bence Coll); Latin (Simison Coll); Pre-Law (Williams Coll), bks, per
Publications: Bibliographies; Information Series; Instructional Media Services Brochures; Library Service Brochures; Update (acquisitions list)
Partic in Dialog Corporation; Indiana Cooperative Library Services Authority; OCLC Online Computer Library Center, Inc
Departmental Libraries:
CURRICULUM, 18 Asbury Hall, 46135. SAN 370-1131. Tel: 765-658-4795. *Mgr*, Marjorie Smith
MUSIC, Performing Arts Ctr, 46135. SAN 341-2024. Tel: 765-658-4442. *Librn*, Holling Smith-Borne
PREVO CENTER, Julian Science & Mathematics Ctr, 46135. SAN 341-2059. Tel: 765-658-4309. *Mgr*, Pam Smith

P PUTNAM COUNTY PUBLIC LIBRARY,* 103 E Poplar St, PO Box 116, 46135-0116. SAN 304-9159. Tel: 765-653-2755. FAX: 765-653-2756. E-Mail: pcpl@ccrtc.com. *Dir*, Ellen M Sedlack; *Ref*, Lynne Tweedie; *Ref*, Margot Payne; *Bkmobile Coordr*, Jane Glier; *Ch Servs*, Kim Tesmer
Founded 1902. Pop 28,820; Circ 145,241
Library Holdings: Bk Vols 46,783; Per Subs 219
Publications: New Books List (monthly); subject bibliographies
Mem of Indiana Coop Libr Servs Authority
Friends of the Library Group
Bookmobiles: 1

S PUTNAMVILLE CORRECTIONAL FACILITY, Learning Resource Center, 1946 W US 40, 46135-9275. SAN 304-9140. Tel: 765-653-8441. FAX: 765-653-7461. *Media Spec*, Brent Roark
Founded 1954
Library Holdings: Bk Titles 4,000; Per Subs 50

GREENFIELD

P HANCOCK COUNTY PUBLIC LIBRARY, 700 N Broadway, 46140-1741. SAN 304-9167. Tel: 317-462-5141. FAX: 317-462-5711. E-Mail: hcpl@hancockpub.lib.in.us. Web Site: www.hancockpub.lib.in.us. *Dir*, Dianne Osborne; Tel: 317-467-6663, Fax: 317-462-5141, E-Mail: dianneo@hancockpub.lib.in.us; Staff 34 (MLS 6, Non-MLS 28)
Founded 1898. Pop 39,799; Circ 382,647
Jan 1999-Dec 1999 Income $989,596, State $71,558, Federal $23,342, County $429,775, Locally Generated Income $797,266. Mats Exp $202,715, Books $125,617, Per/Ser (Incl. Access Fees) $17,500. Sal $469,209 (Prof $160,000)
Library Holdings: Bk Vols 111,133; Bk Titles 100,000; Per Subs 295
Subject Interests: Genealogy, Indiana
Automation Activity & Vendor Info: (Circulation) Gaylord; (OPAC) Gaylord
Database Vendor: GaleNet, OCLC - First Search
Partic in Indiana Cooperative Library Services Authority
Open Mon-Thurs 10-9, Fri 10-6 & Sat 10-5
Friends of the Library Group

S ELI LILLY & CO, Greenfield Intelligence Center,* 2001 W Main, PO Box 708, 46140-0704. SAN 304-9175. Tel: 317-277-4000. FAX: 317-277-4783.
Founded 1957
Library Holdings: Bk Vols 1,500; Per Subs 250
Subject Interests: Agriculture, Toxicology
Restriction: By appointment only
Partic in Dialog Corporation; Medline; OCLC Online Computer Library Center, Inc; Orbit Info Serv

GREENSBURG

P GREENSBURG-DECATUR COUNTY PUBLIC LIBRARY,* 1110 E Main St, 47240. SAN 304-9183. Tel: 812-663-2826. FAX: 812-663-5617. Web Site: www.treecity.com/library. *Dir*, Kim Porter; E-Mail: kport00@hsonline.net; *Ch Servs*, Doris Adams; Staff 6 (MLS 6)
Founded 1903. Pop 23,841; Circ 213,650
Library Holdings: Bk Vols 59,833; Bk Titles 57,833; Per Subs 204
Subject Interests: Local history
Partic in SE Ind Area Libr Servs Authority
Friends of the Library Group
Branches: 1
WESTPORT BRANCH, 205 W Main St, Westport, 47283. SAN 371-3830. Tel: 812-591-2330. FAX: 812-591-2330. Web Site: www.treecity.com/library. *Librn*, Martha Hershauer
Friends of the Library Group
Bookmobiles: 1

GREENTOWN

P GREENTOWN & EASTERN HOWARD SCHOOL & PUBLIC LIBRARY, 421 S Harrison St, 46936-1496. SAN 304-9191. Tel: 765-628-3534. FAX: 765-628-3759. *Dir*, Margi Bontrager; E-Mail: mbontrager@eastern.k12.in.us; Staff 5 (MLS 1, Non-MLS 4)
Founded 1919. Pop 6,000; Circ 119,847
Jan 1999-Dec 1999 Income $192,151, State $31,219, County $154,141, Locally Generated Income $6,791. Mats Exp $51,080, Books $32,065, Per/Ser (Incl. Access Fees) $4,723, Micro $8,670, Electronic Ref Mat (Incl. Access Fees) $5,622. Sal $133,831 (Prof $35,000)
Library Holdings: Bk Vols 48,181; Per Subs 161
Special Collections: Civil War Coll; Large Print Books Coll
Automation Activity & Vendor Info: (Circulation) Follett; (OPAC) Follett
Database Vendor: Ebsco - EbscoHost
Open Mon, Wed & Fri 8am-4pm, Tues & Thurs 8am-8pm & Sat 9-1

GREENWOOD

P GREENWOOD PUBLIC LIBRARY, 310 S Meridian, 46143-3135. SAN 304-9205. Tel: 317-881-1953. Reference Tel: 317-885-5036. FAX: 317-881-1963. Web Site: www.greenwood.lib.in.us. *Dir*, Margaret L Hamilton; E-Mail: mhamilton@mail.greenwood.lib.in.us; *Asst Dir*, Janine Orr; E-Mail: jorr@mail.greenwood.lib.in.us; *Ad Servs*, Georgia Ellars; E-Mail: gellars@mail.greenwood.lib.in.us; Staff 39 (MLS 12, Non-MLS 27)
Founded 1917. Pop 26,409; Circ 207,325
Jan 1999-Dec 1999 Income $1,083,005, State $2,717, County $383,698, Locally Generated Income $21,111, Other $21,071. Mats Exp $156,321, Books $157,548, Per/Ser (Incl. Access Fees) $15,821. Sal $547,231 (Prof $268,547)
Library Holdings: Bk Vols 80,000; Per Subs 270
Partic in ALA; Cent Ind Area Libr Servs Authority; Ind Libr Asn
Friends of the Library Group

CR HERITAGE BAPTIST UNIVERSITY LIBRARY,* 1301 W County Line Rd, 46142. SAN 304-9612. Tel: 317-882-2327. FAX: 317-885-2950. *In Charge*, Russell Dennis Jr
Founded 1954. Enrl 178
Library Holdings: Bk Vols 10,000
Open Mon-Fri 8:30-5 for students

HAGERSTOWN

P HAGERSTOWN-JEFFERSON TOWNSHIP PUBLIC LIBRARY,* 10 W College St, 47346-1295. SAN 304-9213. Tel: 765-489-5632. FAX: 765-489-5808. Web Site: www.hagerstown.lib.in.us. *Librn*, Nancy Grimes
Founded 1929. Pop 3,501; Circ 79,584
Library Holdings: Bk Vols 32,500; Per Subs 90
Partic in E Ind Area Libr State Asn

HAMMOND

S AMERICAN CONSERVATORY OF MUSIC, Robert R McCormick Memorial Library, 252 Wildwood Rd, 46324. SAN 303-8092. Tel: 219-931-6000. FAX: 219-931-6089. E-Mail: amerconsmu@home.com. Web Site: www.americanconservatory.edu. *Pres*, Theodora Schulze
Founded 1962. Enrl 123
Library Holdings: Bk Vols 20,000
Subject Interests: Music
Special Collections: Bach, Neue Ausgabe; Bach-Gesellshaft; Beethoven, Werke; Choral Music, Mini Scores, Orch Scor/pts; Haydn, Werke; International Library Piano Music; Mozart, Neue Ausgabe; Musik in Geschichte und Gegenwart; New Grove Dict Music & Musicians; New Oxford HM; NG Dict American Music
Restriction: Not open to public
Mem of Chicago Libr Syst
Special Services - Listening stations

S CERESTAR USA, INC, Corn Processing Division Research Department Library, 1100 Indianapolis Blvd, 46320. SAN 304-923X. Tel: 219-659-2000. FAX: 219-473-6607. *In Charge*, Danita Stringer; Tel: 219-659-2260
Library Holdings: Bk Vols 3,000; Per Subs 100

R CONGREGATION BETH ISRAEL LIBRARY, 7105 Hohman Ave, 46324. SAN 321-8260. Tel: 219-931-1312. FAX: 219-931-1379. E-Mail: cbischool@aol.com. Web Site: www.cbisynagogue.org. *Librn*, Kelly Farkas
Library Holdings: Bk Vols 3,000; Bk Titles 2,100
Subject Interests: English lang Judaica for laypersons
Publications: Monthly bulletin
Open Mon-Thurs 8:30am-5pm & Fri 9am-noon

P HAMMOND PUBLIC LIBRARY, 564 State St, 46320-1532. SAN 341-2113. Tel: 219-931-5100. FAX: 219-931-3474. Web Site: www.hammond.lib.in.us. *Dir*, Margaret Evans; Tel: 219-852-2230, E-Mail: evansm@hammond.lib.in.us; *ILL*, Herbertine Peck; *Ad Servs*, Rosalie Ruff; *Ch Servs*, Jacqueline Ruman; *Tech Servs*, Jennifer Bull; Staff 23 (MLS 9, Non-MLS 14)
Founded 1902. Pop 84,000; Circ 341,449
Jan 1999-Dec 1999 Income $3,085,072, State $10,057, City $2,835,371, Locally Generated Income $239,644. Mats Exp $412,280, Books $315,953, Per/Ser (Incl. Access Fees) $17,579, Micro $23,075, AV Equip $55,673. Sal $1,381,910 (Prof $657,515)
Library Holdings: Bk Vols 282,148
Special Collections: Hammond Area History (Calumet Room), bks, pictures, maps, A-tapes, photog, monographs, videos
Automation Activity & Vendor Info: (Acquisitions) Innovative Interfaces Inc.; (Cataloging) Innovative Interfaces Inc.; (Circulation) Innovative Interfaces Inc.; (OPAC) Innovative Interfaces Inc.
Publications: Bookends
Partic in Indiana Cooperative Library Services Authority
Friends of the Library Group
Branches: 2
E B HAYWARD BRANCH, 1212 172nd St, 46324. SAN 328-6614. Tel: 219-844-2668. FAX: 219-844-0834. Web Site: www.hammond.lib.in.us. *Librn*, Elaine Hunt; E-Mail: huntel@hammond.lib.in.us; Staff 2 (MLS 1, Non-MLS 1)
Library Holdings: Bk Vols 30,292
HOWARD, 7047 Grand, 46323. SAN 341-2237. Tel: 219-844-1622. FAX: 219-844-3986. Web Site: www.hammond.lib.in.us. *Librn*, Alice Comstock; E-Mail: comsta@hammond.lib.in.us; Staff 2 (MLS 1, Non-MLS 1)
Library Holdings: Bk Vols 31,943

C PURDUE UNIVERSITY CALUMET LIBRARY, 169th & Wicker, 46323-2590. (Mail add: PO Box 2590, 46323-2590), Tel: 219-989-2224, 219-989-2430 (Acquisitions). Interlibrary Loan Service Tel: 219-989-2676. Reference Tel: 219-989-2676. FAX: 219-989-2070. Web Site: library.calumet.purdue.edu. *Dir*, Kathryn H Carpenter; Tel: 219-989-2249, E-Mail: carpent@calumet.purdue.edu; *ILL*, Sheila A Rezak; Tel: 219-989-2677, E-Mail: rezak@calumet.purdue.edu; *Reader Servs*, Karen M Corey; Tel: 219-989-2674, E-Mail: corey@calumet.purdue.edu; *Tech Servs*, Rebecca H Stankowski; Tel: 219-989-2435, E-Mail: rhs@calumet.purdue.edu; *Online Servs, Ref*, Peter P Chojenski; Tel: 219-989-2676, E-Mail: chojenpp@calumet.purdue.edu; Staff 17 (MLS 6, Non-MLS 11)
Founded 1947. Fac 258; Highest Degree: Master
Jul 1999-Jun 2000 Income $1,246,635. Mats Exp $464,156, Books $112,299, Per/Ser (Incl. Access Fees) $287,775, Presv $17,681, Electronic Ref Mat (Incl. Access Fees) $33,063. Sal $609,248 (Prof $305,525)
Library Holdings: Bk Vols 253,574; Bk Titles 207,237; Per Subs 1,440
Special Collections: Archives, Collects non-current university records; Northwest Indiana materials
Automation Activity & Vendor Info: (Acquisitions) Endeavor; (Circulation) Endeavor
Publications: New Book List (monthly)
Partic in Dialog Corporation; Indiana Cooperative Library Services Authority; OCLC Online Computer Library Center, Inc

M SAINT MARGARET MERCY HEALTHCARE CENTERS-NORTH CAMPUS, Sallie M Tyrrell MD Memorial,* 5454 Hohman Ave, 46320. SAN 304-9280. Tel: 219-932-2300, Ext 34633, 219-933-2133. FAX: 219-933-2146. *Coordr*, Carol Yancich
Founded 1937
Library Holdings: Bk Titles 2,500; Per Subs 150
Subject Interests: Medicine, Nursing
Publications: Newsletter
Partic in Docline; Northwest Indiana Health Science Library Consortium

HANOVER

C HANOVER COLLEGE, Duggan Library, 121 Scenic Dr, 47243-0287. (Mail add: PO Box 287, 47243-0287), SAN 304-9302. Tel: 812-866-7165. FAX: 812-866-7172. Web Site: www.hanover.edu/library. *Dir*, Chris Hanson; Tel: 812-866-7160, E-Mail: hanson@hanover.edu; *Acq*, Bernice Hatton; Tel: 812-866-7161; *Archivist, Govt Doc*, Judith Nagata; Tel: 812-866-7164, E-Mail: nagata@hanover.edu; *Cat*, Shannon Doll; *Circ*, Victoria Bramwell; Tel: 812-866-7169, E-Mail: bramwell@hanover.edu; *Electronic Resources*, Heather Bennett; Tel: 812-866-7170, E-Mail: bennetth@hanover.edu; *ILL*, Lori Ferguson; *Per*, Grace Ireland; *Ref*, Ken Gibson; Tel: 812-866-7166, E-Mail: gibson@hanover.edu; *Tech Servs*, Patty Glasson; Tel: 812-866-7162, E-Mail: glassonp@hanover.edu
Founded 1827. Enrl 1,123; Fac 104; Highest Degree: Bachelor
Jul 1998-Jun 1999 Income $932,623. Mats Exp $379,297, Books $114,173, Per/Ser (Incl. Access Fees) $219,670, Presv $6,740, Micro $14,697, AV Equip $24,017. Sal $262,244 (Prof $168,769)
Library Holdings: Bk Vols 544,970; Bk Titles 192,188; Per Subs 1,140
Special Collections: Church History (Archives of the Presbyterian Church of Indiana) bks, micro; Civil War (Daugherty Coll); Hanover College Archives; Indiana History (I M Bridgman Coll); Senator William E Jenner Papers
Automation Activity & Vendor Info: (Acquisitions) DRA; (Cataloging) DRA; (Circulation) DRA; (Course Reserve) DRA; (OPAC) DRA; (Serials) DRA
Database Vendor: DRA
Partic in Indiana Cooperative Library Services Authority; OCLC Online Computer Library Center, Inc; Private Acad Libr Network of Ind

HARTFORD CITY

S BLACKFORD COUNTY HISTORICAL SOCIETY LIBRARY, 321 N High, PO Box 264, 47348. SAN 371-2044. *Pres*, Sinuard Castelo; E-Mail: sacastelo@hotmail.com; *Coll Develop*, Dealie Dodds; E-Mail: ronndee@voyager.net
Library Holdings: Bk Vols 750

P HARTFORD CITY PUBLIC LIBRARY,* 314 N High St, 47348-2143. SAN 304-9310. Tel: 765-348-1720. FAX: 765-348-5090. *Dir*, Vicki Cecil; *Ch Servs*, Jeff Kieffer; *Ref*, Marion Boots; Staff 5 (MLS 1, Non-MLS 4)
Founded 1903. Pop 9,670; Circ 64,902
Library Holdings: Bk Vols 45,000; Per Subs 200
Subject Interests: History, Indiana
Special Collections: Music (George Leonard Fulton Memorial Record

Library)
Partic in Eastern Ind Area Libr Servs Authority
Open Mon-Thurs 10am-8pm, Fri 10am-5:30pm & Sat 10am-5pm
Friends of the Library Group

HENRYVILLE

S HENRYVILLE CORRECTIONAL FACILITY LIBRARY, PO Box 148, 47126. Tel: 812-294-4372. *Librn*, Steve Bonsett
Library Holdings: Bk Titles 500; Per Subs 12

HOBART

S HOBART HISTORICAL SOCIETY, INC, Mariam Pleak Library, 706 E Fourth St, PO Box 24, 46342-0024. SAN 304-9337. Tel: 219-942-0970. *Archivist, Curator*, Elin Christianson
Founded 1973
Library Holdings: Bk Titles 500; Per Subs 10
Subject Interests: History, Indiana, Local history
Special Collections: Genealogy; Local Newspapers; Photographs

M SAINT MARY MEDICAL CENTER, Reference Library, 1500 S Lake Park Ave, 46342. SAN 304-9094. Tel: 219-947-6230. FAX: 219-947-6331. *Librn*, Lucinda Macko
Library Holdings: Bk Titles 268; Per Subs 80
Subject Interests: Hospital administration, Medicine, Nursing
Partic in National Network of Libraries of Medicine - Greater Midwest Region; Northwest Indiana Health Science Library Consortium

HUNTINGBURG

P HUNTINGBURG PUBLIC LIBRARY,* 419 Jackson St, 47542. SAN 304-9345. Tel: 812-683-2052. FAX: 812-683-2056. *Librn*, Kathie Lett
Founded 1922. Pop 6,213; Circ 65,000
1997-1998 Income $130,502, State $13,802, County $29,134, Locally Generated Income $5,698, Other $71,868. Mats Exp $20,314, Books $13,934, Per/Ser (Incl. Access Fees) $2,730. Sal $70,864
Library Holdings: Bk Vols 31,500
Partic in Indiana Cooperative Library Services Authority
Open Mon & Wed 9-8, Tues, Thurs, Fri, & Sat 9-5

HUNTINGTON

P HUNTINGTON CITY TOWNSHIP PUBLIC LIBRARY,* 200 W Market St, 46750-2655. SAN 304-9353. Tel: 219-356-0824. FAX: 219-356-3073. Web Site: huntingtonpub.lib.in.us. *Dir*, Kathryn Holst; *Ad Servs, Cat, Tech Servs*, Sue Strass; *Ch Servs*, Kay Stine; *Spec Coll*, Joan Keefer
Founded 1874. Pop 20,236; Circ 180,889
1998-1999 Mats Exp $800,090. Sal $260,000
Library Holdings: Bk Vols 86,000
Special Collections: Genealogy; Local & State History; Trains Coll
Partic in Area 3 Libr Serv Authority
Friends of the Library Group

C HUNTINGTON COLLEGE, RichLyn Library, 2303 College Ave, 46750. SAN 304-9361. Tel: 219-359-4063. FAX: 219-358-3698. Web Site: www.huntington.edu/library. *Dir*, Robert E Kaehr; E-Mail: rkaehr@huntington.edu; *Assoc Dir*, Randy Neuman; E-Mail: rneuman@huntington.edu
Founded 1897. Enrl 780; Fac 46; Highest Degree: Master
Library Holdings: Bk Vols 180,000; Per Subs 570
Special Collections: Archives of Huntington College; Curriculum Materials Center; United Brethren In Christ Church
Automation Activity & Vendor Info: (Acquisitions) epixtech, inc.; (Cataloging) epixtech, inc.; (Circulation) epixtech, inc.; (Course Reserve) epixtech, inc.; (OPAC) epixtech, inc.; (Serials) epixtech, inc.
Partic in Indiana Cooperative Library Services Authority; OCLC Online Computer Library Center, Inc; PALNI

INDIANAPOLIS

SR ALL SOULS UNITARIAN CHURCH, E Burdette Backus Memorial Library, 5805 E 56th St, 46226-1526. SAN 304-937X. Tel: 317-545-6005. FAX: 317-545-4662. E-Mail: allsouls@iserve.net. Web Site: www.iserve.net/~allsouls. *Librn*, Valarie Elliot
Library Holdings: Bk Vols 1,000
Subject Interests: Economics, Fiction, Philosophy, Poetry, Political science, Psychology, Social sciences and issues, Unitarianism
Restriction: Not open to public
Open 9-4

S AMERICAN LEGION NATIONAL HEADQUARTERS LIBRARY, 700 N Pennsylvania St, 46206-1055. (Mail add: PO Box 1055, 46206-1055), SAN 304-9388. Tel: 317-630-1366. FAX: 317-630-1241. E-Mail: library@legion.org. Web Site: www.legion.org. *Curator, Librn*, Joseph J Hovish; E-Mail: jhovish@legion.org; *Dep Dir*, Kevin Flanagan; Staff 6 (MLS 2, Non-MLS 4)
Founded 1923
Jan 2001-Dec 2001 Income $315,174. Mats Exp $28,925, Books $26,000, Micro $2,925. Sal $207,055
Library Holdings: Bk Vols 10,000; Per Subs 375
Subject Interests: Military history
Special Collections: Archives of the American Legion, (including national organization, state organization & posts); National Defense; Patriotism (1919-date); Veterans' Affairs; World War I & II Posters
Automation Activity & Vendor Info: (Cataloging) Inmagic, Inc.; (Circulation) Inmagic, Inc.; (Serials) Inmagic, Inc.
Partic in Indiana Cooperative Library Services Authority

S AMERICAN STATES BUSINESS INSURANCE LIBRARY,* 500 N Meridian St, 46204. SAN 304-9396. Tel: 317-262-6560. FAX: 317-262-6392. *Librn*, Linda Wombles; E-Mail: llwombles@americanstates.com
Founded 1973
Library Holdings: Bk Vols 10,000
Subject Interests: Business and management, Finance, Law
Special Collections: Family Resource Center; Individual Development Plan

S AMERICAN UNITED LIFE INSURANCE CO LIBRARY,* One American Sq, PO Box 368, 46206. SAN 304-940X. Tel: 317-263-1877. Interlibrary Loan Service Tel: 317-263-1709. FAX: 317-285-1470, 317-285-1709. *Librn*, Debbie Howell; E-Mail: deborahhowell@aul.com
Special Collections: Company Archives

L BAKER & DANIELS LIBRARY, 300 N Meridian St, Ste 2700, 46204. SAN 304-9418. Tel: 317-237-0300. Interlibrary Loan Service Tel: 317-237-1353. FAX: 317-237-1000. *Dir Libr Serv*, Constance Matts; E-Mail: cmatts@bakerd.com; *Ref*, Zoya Golban; E-Mail: zgolbang@bakerd.com; *Ref*, Howard Trivers; E-Mail: hetriver@bakerd.com; Staff 8 (MLS 3, Non-MLS 5)
Founded 1952
Library Holdings: Bk Vols 70,000; Bk Titles 35,000; Per Subs 324
Restriction: Staff use only
Partic in OCLC Online Computer Library Center, Inc

CR BAPTIST BIBLE COLLEGE OF INDIANAPOLIS LIBRARY,* 601 N Shortridge Rd, 46219-4912. SAN 327-974X. Tel: 317-352-8736. FAX: 317-352-9145. Web Site: www.bbci.edu. *Coll Develop, Librn*, Liz Le Mond; E-Mail: llemond@bbci.edu; Staff 2 (MLS 1, Non-MLS 1)
Founded 1980. Enrl 189; Fac 12; Highest Degree: Bachelor
1997-1998 Income $22,300. Mats Exp $11,220, Books $6,200, Per/Ser (Incl. Access Fees) $4,920, Micro $100. Sal $19,000 (Prof $18,000)
Library Holdings: Bk Vols 34,000; Per Subs 170
Subject Interests: Theology
Special Collections: Afro-American History & the Black Church Coll

L BINGHAM, SUMMERS, WELSH & SPILMAN, Law Library, 2700 Market Tower, 10 W Market St, 46204-4900. SAN 374-4760. Tel: 317-635-8901, Ext 289. FAX: 317-236-9907. E-Mail: dbh@bsws.com. Web Site: www.bsws.com. *Librn*, Nikki Schofield; E-Mail: nls@bsws.com
Founded 1917
Library Holdings: Bk Vols 15,000; Per Subs 70
Automation Activity & Vendor Info: (Cataloging) CASPR

L BOSE, MCKINNEY & EVANS, Law Library,* 2700 First Indiana Plaza, 135 N Pennsylvania, Ste 2700, 46204. SAN 372-1213. Tel: 317-684-5000. FAX: 317-684-5173. *Librn*, Trudy Timkovich
Library Holdings: Bk Vols 27,000; Per Subs 150
Subject Interests: Civil rights, Labor, Securities

C BUTLER UNIVERSITY LIBRARIES, Irwin Library, 4600 Sunset Ave, 46208. SAN 341-2474. Tel: 317-940-9227. Interlibrary Loan Service Tel: 317-940-9677. Reference Tel: 317-940-9235. FAX: 317-940-9711. Web Site: www.butler.edu/www/library. *Dean of Libr*, Lewis R Miller; Tel: 317-940-9714, E-Mail: lmiller@butler.edu; *Doc, ILL*, Tim Zou; *Acq*, Dan Roose; *Spec Coll & Archives*, Sally Childs-Helton; Tel: 317-940-9265, E-Mail: schildsh@butler.edu; *Automation Syst Coordr*, Samantha Skutnik; Tel: 317-940-9949, E-Mail: sskutnik@butler.edu. Subject Specialists: *Fine arts*, Sheridan Stormes; *Music*, Sheridan Stormes; Staff 24 (MLS 12, Non-MLS 12)
Founded 1855. Enrl 3,819; Fac 305; Highest Degree: Master
Jun 1999-May 2000 Income $1,800,088. Mats Exp $743,809, Books $118,559, Per/Ser (Incl. Access Fees) $466,932, Presv $19,300, Micro $22,187, AV Equip $8,399, Electronic Ref Mat (Incl. Access Fees) $108,432. Sal $682,945 (Prof $490,263)
Library Holdings: Bk Vols 313,397; Bk Titles 204,831; Per Subs 1,254
Special Collections: 19th Century American sheet music; 20th century American poetry, bks, mss; Abraham Lincoln, bks, pamphlets, mss, prints; Botanical & Zoological prints 16th-19th century; Jean Sibelius, publ & unpubl scores, recordings, & secondary sources; Kin Hubbard-Gaar Williams Coll of original cartoons, bks, mss, memorabilia; Mme de Stael Research Coll; National Track & Field Historical Research Library; Pacific Islands 16th-20th century; Rare Books Coll, bks, prints, mss; USABA Archives
Automation Activity & Vendor Info: (Acquisitions) DRA; (Cataloging) DRA; (Circulation) DRA; (Serials) DRA

Database Vendor: Ebsco - EbscoHost, Lexis-Nexis, OCLC - First Search
Publications: Catalogues of Special Collections; Information packets & handouts; New Acquisitions List
Partic in Indiana Cooperative Library Services Authority; PALNI
Departmental Libraries:
SCIENCE LIBRARY Tel: 317-940-9401. FAX: 317-940-9519. *Dean of Libr*, Lewis R Miller; Tel: 317-940-9714, Fax: 317-940-9711, E-Mail: lmiller@butler.edu; *Librn*, Barbara Howes
Subject Interests: Chemistry, Mathematics

LARUE D CARTER MEMORIAL HOSPITAL
S PATIENT LIBRARY, 2601 Cold Spring Rd, 46222-2202. SAN 341-2598. Tel: 317-941-4183. FAX: 317-941-4085. *Actg Librn*, Glenda Rutan
Founded 1953
Jul 2000-Jun 2001 Mats Exp $750
Library Holdings: Bk Titles 3,360; Per Subs 23
Restriction: Circulation limited
M PROFESSIONAL LIBRARY, 2601 Cold Spring Rd, 46222-2202. SAN 341-2563. Tel: 317-941-4154. FAX: 317-941-4085. *Librn*, Judith K Smith; E-Mail: jsmith5@fssa.state.in.us
Founded 1952
Jul 2000-Jun 2001 Mats Exp $32,500, Books $2,500, Per/Ser (Incl. Access Fees) $30,000
Library Holdings: Bk Titles 9,800; Per Subs 103
Subject Interests: Mental health, Psychiatry
Special Collections: Murray Coll; Psychiatry & Mental Health (Hahn Coll, McMahan Coll, Barrows Coll, Reed Coll)
Restriction: Circulation limited

S CHILDREN'S MUSEUM OF INDIANAPOLIS, Rauh Memorial Library, 3000 N Meridian St, PO Box 3000, 46206. SAN 304-9477. Tel: 317-924-5431. FAX: 317-921-4019.
Founded 1925
Library Holdings: Bk Titles 6,000; Per Subs 65
Subject Interests: Antiques, Art, Education, History
Restriction: Staff use only
Partic in OCLC Online Computer Library Center, Inc

R CHRIST CHURCH CATHEDRAL, Margaret Ridgely Memorial Library, 125 Monument Circle, 46204-2993. SAN 304-9485. Tel: 317-636-4577. FAX: 317-635-1040. *Librn*, Cornell Lumpkin
Founded 1928
Library Holdings: Bk Vols 2,600; Bk Titles 2,575; Per Subs 14
Subject Interests: Religion
Publications: Acquisitions list (quarterly)
Friends of the Library Group

R CHRISTIAN THEOLOGICAL SEMINARY LIBRARY, 1000 W 42nd St, 46208. SAN 304-9507. Tel: 317-924-1331. FAX: 317-923-1961. Web Site: www.cts.edu. *Dir*, David Bundy; E-Mail: dbundy@cts.edu; *Asst Librn, Tech Servs*, Jeff Siemon; *Circ*, Laura Isenthal; Staff 6 (MLS 3, Non-MLS 3)
Founded 1942. Enrl 320; Fac 21; Highest Degree: Doctorate
Library Holdings: Bk Vols 200,000; Per Subs 1,420
Subject Interests: History, Music, Religion, Social sciences and issues
Special Collections: Disciples of Christ History (Literature of the Restoration Movement), bks, per, mss
Automation Activity & Vendor Info: (Acquisitions) DRA; (Cataloging) DRA; (Circulation) DRA; (Course Reserve) DRA; (ILL) DRA; (Media Booking) DRA; (OPAC) DRA; (Serials) DRA
Partic in Indiana Cooperative Library Services Authority; OCLC Online Computer Library Center, Inc

M CLARIAN HEALTH PARTNERS, Medical Library,* 1701 N Senate Blvd, Rm D1422, 46206-1367. SAN 304-9760. Tel: 317-929-8021. Interlibrary Loan Service Tel: 317-929-2979. FAX: 317-929-8397. Web Site: www.clarian.com/library. *Librn*, Christine Bockrath; E-Mail: cbockrath@clarion.com; Staff 6 (MLS 1, Non-MLS 5)
Founded 1947
Library Holdings: Bk Vols 4,000; Per Subs 500
Subject Interests: Medicine, Nursing
Special Collections: Audiovisuals; Health Education
Partic in Bibliog Retrieval Servs Inc; Cent Ind Area Libr Servs Authority; Central Indiana Health Science Libraries Consortium; Dialog Corporation; Indiana Cooperative Library Services Authority; Medline; Midwest Health Sci Libr Network

M COMMUNITY HOSPITAL LIBRARY, The Library Network & Satellites,* 1500 N Ritter Ave, 46219. SAN 304-9515. Tel: 317-355-5591. Interlibrary Loan Service Tel: 317-355-5504. FAX: 317-351-7736. *Mgr*, Sheila Hofstetter
Founded 1960
Library Holdings: Bk Titles 2,500; Per Subs 350
Subject Interests: Business and management, Medicine, Nursing
Partic in Cent Ind Area Libr Servs Authority; Central Indiana Health Science Libraries Consortium; Health Sci Libr Network; Indiana Cooperative Library Services Authority

R CONGREGATION BETH-EL ZEDECK, Religious School Library, 600 W 70th St, 46260-4194. SAN 329-2762. Tel: 317-253-3441. FAX: 317-259-6849. *Librn*, Ann T Lieber
Founded 1964. Circ 500
Library Holdings: Bk Vols 2,800; Bk Titles 2,700; Per Subs 15
Subject Interests: Judaica

GM DEPARTMENT OF VETERANS AFFAIRS, Health Science Library,* 1481 W Tenth St, 46202. SAN 304-985X. Tel: 317-554-0000. FAX: 317-269-6376. *Chief Librn*, Linda J Bennet
Founded 1952
Library Holdings: Bk Vols 6,050; Per Subs 700
Subject Interests: Allied health, Medicine, Nursing
Publications: Audiovisual list; new acquisitions list
Partic in Cent Ind Area Libr Servs Authority; Central Indiana Health Science Libraries Consortium; Veterans Affairs Library Network

R DOWNEY AVENUE CHRISTIAN CHURCH LIBRARY,* 111 S Downey Ave, 46219. SAN 328-2015. Tel: 317-359-0836, 317-359-5304. *Librn*, Lois Leamon
Library Holdings: Bk Titles 700

S EITELJORG MUSEUM OF AMERICAN INDIANS & WESTERN ART,* 500 W Washington St, 46204-2707. SAN 325-6820. Tel: 317-636-9378. FAX: 317-264-1724. E-Mail: museum@eiteljorg.org. Web Site: www.eiteljorg.org. *In Charge*, Kitty Jansen
Library Holdings: Bk Vols 4,000
Subject Interests: Contemporary art, Native Am art, Western American art
Partic in Indiana Cooperative Library Services Authority; OCLC Online Computer Library Center, Inc

R ENGLEWOOD CHRISTIAN CHURCH LIBRARY, 57 N Rural St, 46201. SAN 304-9566. Tel: 317-639-1541. FAX: 317-639-3447. *Librn*, Norene Martin
Founded 1961
Library Holdings: Bk Titles 7,000
Subject Interests: Biblical studies, Christianity, Missions and missionaries, Philosophy, Religion
Special Collections: Children's Library (980 vols)
Open Sun 8-9 & 11:30-12:15

S FEDERAL HOME LOAN BANK OF INDIANAPOLIS LIBRARY,* 8250 Woodfield Crossing Blvd, PO Box 60, 46240. SAN 375-0493. Tel: 317-465-0438. FAX: 317-465-0397. *Librn*, Miriam Lemen; E-Mail: mlemen@fhlbi.com
Library Holdings: Bk Titles 1,704; Per Subs 75
Special Collections: Thrift Industry, bks, per, printouts
Publications: Current Library Selections
Partic in Indiana Cooperative Library Services Authority

M FOUNDATION FOR HAND RESEARCH & EDUCATION, Ruth Lilly Hand Surgery Library, 8501 Harcourt Rd, 46260. (Mail add: PO Box 80434, 46280-0434), SAN 372-6436. Tel: 317-471-4340. Toll Free Tel: 800-888-4263. FAX: 317-876-0462. E-Mail: fdnhand@inetdirect.net. Web Site: www.indianahandcenter.com. *Head Librn*, Elaine Skopelja; Staff 2 (MLS 1, Non-MLS 1)
Founded 1980
Library Holdings: Bk Vols 1,100; Bk Titles 1,000; Per Subs 22
Subject Interests: Orthopedics
Special Collections: Hand, Shoulder & Elbow Diseases; Surgery, Rehabilitation, bks, videotapes
Automation Activity & Vendor Info: (OPAC) Inmagic, Inc.
Database Vendor: OCLC - First Search
Restriction: By appointment only
Function: ILL available, Literary searches
Partic in Central Indiana Health Science Libraries Consortium; Indiana Cooperative Library Services Authority; National Network Of Libraries Of Medicine; OCLC Online Computer Library Center, Inc

SR FREE METHODIST CHURCH OF NORTH AMERICA, Marston Memorial Historical Center-White Memorial Library, 770 N High School Rd, PO Box 535002, 46253. SAN 326-5552. Tel: 317-244-3660. Toll Free Tel: 800-342-5531. FAX: 317-244-1247. E-Mail: history@FMCNA.org. *Dir*, Cathy Fortner
Founded 1969
Jan 2000-Dec 2000 Income $15,620, Locally Generated Income $2,120, Parent Institution $7,500, Other $6,000. Mats Exp $450, Books $150, Other Print Mats $300. Sal $13,718
Library Holdings: Bk Vols 7,000; Bk Titles 12,000
Special Collections: Methodism (John Wesley Coll), Wesleyana Material, Free Methodist Memoribilia
Restriction: Not a lending library

S GENERAL MOTORS CORP, Allison Transmission Divisional Library, 4700 W Tenth St, 46222-5200. (Mail add: PO Box 894 m/c K09, 46206-0894), SAN 377-8207. Tel: 317-242-0470. FAX: 317-242-3626. *Librn*, Barbara McCall; E-Mail: barbara.mccall@gm.com; Staff 1 (MLS 1)
Founded 1991
Library Holdings: Bk Vols 4,580; Bk Titles 4,482; Per Subs 70

Subject Interests: Quality control, Statistics
Database Vendor: Dialog, OCLC - First Search
Restriction: Company library
Partic in Dow Jones News Retrieval; Indiana Cooperative Library Services Authority; OCLC Online Computer Library Center, Inc

S GIRLS INC, National Resource Center Library,* 441 W Michigan St, 46202. SAN 326-422X. Tel: 317-634-7546. FAX: 317-634-3024. *Librn*, Mary Maschino; E-Mail: mmaschino@girls-inc.org
Founded 1981
Library Holdings: Bk Titles 4,000; Per Subs 50
Special Collections: Organizational archives
Partic in Indiana Cooperative Library Services Authority

S GOLDEN RULE INSURANCE CO, Archives-Library, 7440 Woodland Dr, 46278-1719. SAN 373-6350. Tel: 317-290-8100, Ext 7456. FAX: 317-298-4139. E-Mail: library@goldenrule.com. *Dir*, Madge Engle; Staff 4 (MLS 1, Non-MLS 3)
Founded 1981
Library Holdings: Bk Titles 700; Per Subs 110
Subject Interests: Education, Health care, Ins
Restriction: Not open to public
Function: Archival collection, ILL to other special libraries, Research library
Partic in Indiana Cooperative Library Services Authority

S PRESIDENT BENJAMIN HARRISON HOME RESEARCH LIBRARY,* 1230 N Delaware St, 46202. SAN 326-5064. Tel: 317-631-1898. FAX: 317-236-1688. Web Site: www.surs-ici.com/harrison. *Librn*, Ann Moore
Library Holdings: Bk Titles 2,700
Open Mon-Fri 10-3:30

S HISTORIC LANDMARKS FOUNDATION OF INDIANA, Information Center Library, 340 W Michigan St, 46202-3204. SAN 326-8896. Tel: 317-639-4534. Toll Free Tel: 800-450-4534. FAX: 317-639-6734. Web Site: www.historiclandmarks.org. *In Charge*, Suzanne Stanis; E-Mail: stanis@historiclandmarks.org; Staff 1 (MLS 1)
Library Holdings: Bk Titles 3,000; Per Subs 90
Subject Interests: Architecture, Historic preservation
Automation Activity & Vendor Info: (Acquisitions) CASPR; (Cataloging) CASPR; (Circulation) CASPR
Publications: The Indiana Preservationist
Partic in Indiana Cooperative Library Services Authority

S HUDSON INSTITUTE LIBRARY,* 5395 Emerson Way, PO Box 26-919, 46226. SAN 311-1059. Tel: 317-549-4130. FAX: 317-545-9639. *Mgr, Res*, Rebecca A Cline; *Asst Librn*, Gayle Crouse; Tel: 317-549-4101; Staff 2 (MLS 1, Non-MLS 1)
Founded 1962
Library Holdings: Bk Titles 5,000; Per Subs 200
Subject Interests: Crime, Economics, Educ policy, Education, Environmental studies, Foreign policy, Race relations, Statistics, Welfare
Special Collections: area studies; Hudson Studies & Reports; statistics
Database Vendor: Ebsco - EbscoHost, Lexis-Nexis, OCLC - First Search
Restriction: Non-circulating to the public
Function: For research purposes
Partic in Indiana Cooperative Library Services Authority
Open Mon-Fri 8:30-5

L ICE, MILLER, DONADIO & RYAN, Law Library,* One American Sq, PO Box 82001, 46282-0002. SAN 321-7698. Tel: 317-236-2335. FAX: 317-592-4791. *Ref*, Melanie A Kelley; *Ref*, Debra A DeFouw; E-Mail: defouw@imdr.com; Staff 5 (MLS 2, Non-MLS 3)
Founded 1923
Library Holdings: Bk Vols 35,000; Bk Titles 2,600; Per Subs 62
Partic in ABA/NET; BRS; Dialog Corporation; Dow Jones News Retrieval; Indiana Cooperative Library Services Authority; OCLC Online Computer Library Center, Inc; Westlaw

S INDIANA ACADEMY OF SCIENCE, John Shepard Wright Memorial Library, Indiana State Library, 140 N Senate Ave, 46204-2296. SAN 373-0530. Tel: 317-232-3686. FAX: 317-232-3728. *Librn*, J Holly Oster; E-Mail: hoster@statelib.lib.in.us
Founded 1885
Library Holdings: Bk Vols 13,000
Subject Interests: Natural history, Science

S INDIANA CHAMBER OF COMMERCE, Business Research & Information Center, 115 W Washington St S Ste 850, 46204-3497. SAN 329-1162. Tel: 317-264-3110. FAX: 317-264-6855. Web Site: www.indianachamber.com. *Dir*, Cynthia Monnier; E-Mail: cmonnier@indianachamber.com; Staff 2 (MLS 1, Non-MLS 1)
Library Holdings: Bk Vols 3,000; Bk Titles 200; Per Subs 100
Subject Interests: Bus, Econ, Employee benefits, Employee relations, Labor laws, Marketing, Mgt, Unions
Special Collections: Indiana Companies & Unions
Publications: Top 200 Indiana Employers
Restriction: Members only, Staff use only

S INDIANA DEPARTMENT OF EDUCATION, Professional Library, 231 E Ohio St, 46204-2118. (Mail add: 229 State House, 46204-2798), SAN 325-6847. Tel: 317-232-9129. FAX: 317-232-9121. *Librn*, Dorothy Everett; E-Mail: deverett@doe.state.in.us
Jan 1999-Dec 1999 Mats Exp $42,901, Books $10,000, Per/Ser (Incl. Access Fees) $20,901, Micro $1,000, Other Print Mats $9,000, Electronic Ref Mat (Incl. Access Fees) $2,000. Sal $25,000
Library Holdings: Bk Titles 4,000; Per Subs 272
Subject Interests: Education
Special Collections: Department publications, legislative information

S INDIANA DEPARTMENT OF ENVIRONMENTAL MANAGEMENT, Office of Legal Counsel Library,* IGCN-100 N Senate Ave, PO Box 6015, 46206-6015. SAN 329-4897. Tel: 317-232-8493. FAX: 317-233-5517.
Library Holdings: Bk Vols 1,000

S INDIANA HISTORICAL SOCIETY LIBRARY, William Henry Smith Memorial Library, 450 W Ohio St, 46202-3269. SAN 304-9639. Tel: 317-232-1879. FAX: 317-234-0168. Web Site: www.indianahistory.org. *Dir*, Bruce L Johnson; Tel: 317-234-0034, E-Mail: bjohnson@indianahistory.org; *Ref*, Eric Mundell; Tel: 317-234-0037, E-Mail: emundell@indianahistory.org; *Cat*, Ellen Crosby; Tel: 317-234-0043, E-Mail: ecrosby@indianahistory.org; *Curator*, Leigh Darbee; Tel: 317-234-0051, E-Mail: ldarbee@indianahistory.org; *Curator*, Stephen J Fletcher; Tel: 317-234-0040, E-Mail: sfletcher@indianahistory.org; *Archivist*, Glenn McMullen; Tel: 317-234-0037, E-Mail: gmcmullen@indianahistory.org; Staff 32 (MLS 20, Non-MLS 12)
Founded 1934
Library Holdings: Bk Titles 67,862
Subject Interests: Civil War, Indiana
Special Collections: 19th-Century Indiana Politics, papers, pictures; Agricultural History, bks, papers, photogs; Architectural History, papers; Black History, papers, pictures; Charitable Organizations, papers; Ethnic History, papers, pictures; Indiana Covered Bridges, papers, pictures; Indiana Mills, papers, pictures; Medical History, bks, papers; Midwestern Railroads, bks, mss; Northwest Territory, papers; Transportation, papers, pictures; William Henry Harrison & Indiana Territory History, papers
Publications: Black History News & Notes; Indiana Historical Society (Annual Report)
Restriction: Non-circulating
Partic in Indiana Cooperative Library Services Authority; OCLC Online Computer Library Center, Inc

M INDIANA MEDICAL HISTORY MUSEUM LIBRARY,* 3045 W Vermont St, 46222-4943. SAN 373-3653. Tel: 317-635-7329. FAX: 317-635-7349. *Dir*, Oren S Cooley
Library Holdings: Bk Vols 4,000
Subject Interests: Bacteriology, Neurology, Pathology, Psychology
Special Collections: Personal & Professional Papers of Dr Walter L Bruetsch
Publications: Snakeroot Extract

G INDIANA STATE ARCHIVES,* 140 N Senate Ave, 46204-2296. SAN 371-9189. Tel: 317-232-3660. FAX: 317-233-1085. E-Mail: arc@icprlan.state.in.us. Web Site: www.ai.org/icpr/webfile/archives/homepage.html. *Archivist, Coll Develop*, Alan F January; *Archivist*, F Gerald Handfield Jr; *Archivist*, Geof Scott; *Archivist*, Stephen E Towne; *Archivist*, Kelly Jones; *Archivist*, Vicki Casteel; Staff 10 (MLS 9, Non-MLS 1)
Founded 1913
Special Collections: Aerial Photographs; Indian Public Land Records; Ku Klux Klan; Military Records (1811-1987); Official Indiana State Records (1790-present)
Publications: Descriptive handouts; Finding aids; Inventories
Friends of the Library Group

P INDIANA STATE LIBRARY, 140 N Senate Ave, 46204-2296. SAN 341-2628. Tel: 317-232-3675. Interlibrary Loan Service Tel: 317-232-3727. FAX: 317-232-3728. Web Site: www.statelib.lib.in.us. *Dir*, Charles Ray Ewick; Tel: 317-232-3692, Fax: 317-232-0002, E-Mail: ewick@statelib.lib.in.us; *Assoc Dir, Publ Servs*, Barney R Mc Ewen; Tel: 317-232-3693, Fax: 317-232-0002, E-Mail: bmcewen@statelib.lib.in.us; *Assoc Dir*, Robert Logsdon; Tel: 317-232-3569, Fax: 317-232-0002, E-Mail: rlogsdon@statelib.lib.in.us; *Assoc Dir*, Martha Roblee; Tel: 312-232-3715, Fax: 312-232-0002, E-Mail: mroblee@statelib.lib.in.us; *Ref*, Cynthia St Martin; E-Mail: cstmartin@statelib.lib.in.us. Subject Specialists: *Blindness*, Lissa Shanahan; *Genealogy*, Diane Sharp; *Physically handicapped*, Lissa Shanahan; Staff 76 (MLS 37, Non-MLS 39)
Founded 1825. Pop 5,200,000
Jul 1999-Jun 2000 Income State $3,175,416. Mats Exp $541,747. Sal $2,346,382
Library Holdings: Bk Vols 2,102,471; Per Subs 16,908
Subject Interests: Genealogy, History, Indiana, Library and information science
Special Collections: Americana (Holliday Coll); Genealogy (Darrach Coll of Indianapolis Pub Libr); Hymn Books (Levering Sunday School); Indiana Academy of Science; Library; Shorthand & Typewriting (Strachan Coll)
Automation Activity & Vendor Info: (Acquisitions) DRA; (Cataloging) DRA; (Circulation) DRA; (Serials) DRA
Publications: Focus on Indiana Libraries; Hoosier Highlights; Indiana

Libraries
Partic in Coop Libr Servs Authority; OCLC Online Computer Library Center, Inc
Special Services for the Deaf - Books on deafness & sign language
Branches: 1

P INDIANA STATE LIBRARY, Special Services Division,* 140 N Senate Ave, 46204-2296. SAN 304-9655. Tel: 317-232-3684. Toll Free Tel: 800-622-4970. FAX: 317-232-3728. Web Site: www.statelib.lib.in.us.; Staff 2 (MLS 2)
Founded 1934. Circ 315,935
Jul 1996-Jun 1997 Income $504,000, State $155,000, Federal $349,000. Mats Exp $25,000. Sal $147,000
Library Holdings: Bk Vols 192,909; Per Subs 11
Special Collections: Indiana History & Literature, cassettes
Automation Activity & Vendor Info: (Circulation) DRA
Publications: Hoosier Highlights (newsletter); In Touch (newsletter)
Special Services for the Blind - Braille Embosser; Reading aids - Oscar with DEC Talk

GL INDIANA SUPREME COURT LAW LIBRARY, 316 State House, 46204-2788. SAN 304-968X. Tel: 317-232-2557. FAX: 317-232-2557. *Librn*, Rebecca M Bethel; Staff 3 (MLS 2, Non-MLS 1)
Founded 1867
Library Holdings: Bk Vols 77,000; Per Subs 170
Subject Interests: State law
Special Collections: Selective Government & State Justice Institute
Partic in Indiana Cooperative Library Services Authority; OCLC Online Computer Library Center, Inc; Westlaw

INDIANA UNIVERSITY

CM RUTH LILLY MEDICAL LIBRARY, Medical Research & Library Bldg 100, 975 W Walnut, 46202. SAN 341-2741. Tel: 317-274-7182. FAX: 317-278-2349. E-Mail: rlmllib@ind/cms.iupui.edu. Web Site: www.medlib.iupui.edu. *Dir Libr Serv*, Fran Brahmi; *Automation Syst Coordr*, James J Morgan; *Ser*, Rick Ralston; *Spec Coll*, Nancy Eckerman; *Ref*, Allan Barclay; *Ref*, Kellie Kaneshiro; Staff 12 (MLS 12)
Founded 1908. Enrl 3,428; Fac 1,002; Highest Degree: Doctorate
Jul 1998-Jun 1999 Income (Main Library Only) $3,105,423, Locally Generated Income $40,008. Mats Exp $1,378,964, Books $185,000, Per/Ser (Incl. Access Fees) $1,193,964. Sal $1,042,214
Library Holdings: Bk Vols 232,128
Subject Interests: Allied health, Medicine, Nursing
Special Collections: History of Medicine
Automation Activity & Vendor Info: (Cataloging) NOTIS
Mem of Asn of Research Libraries
Partic in Dialog Corporation; Indiana Cooperative Library Services Authority; Nat Libr of Med; OCLC Online Computer Library Center, Inc

CM SCHOOL OF DENTISTRY LIBRARY, 1121 W Michigan St, 46202-5186. SAN 341-2687. Tel: 317-274-7204. Interlibrary Loan Service Tel: 317-274-5203. FAX: 317-278-1256. Web Site: www.iupui.edu/~dentlib/. *Actg Librn*, Jan Cox; Tel: 317-274-5207, E-Mail: jcox@iupui.edu
Founded 1927. Enrl 569; Fac 129; Highest Degree: Doctorate
Jul 1999-Jun 2000 Income $373,154. Mats Exp $139,916. Sal $204,972
Library Holdings: Bk Vols 56,658; Per Subs 599
Subject Interests: Dentistry, Medicine
Special Collections: Archives Coll
Automation Activity & Vendor Info: (Acquisitions) SIRSI; (Cataloging) SIRSI; (Circulation) SIRSI; (Course Reserve) SIRSI; (OPAC) SIRSI; (Serials) SIRSI
Database Vendor: OCLC - First Search, OVID Technologies
Function: ILL available
Partic in Central Indiana Health Science Libraries Consortium; Dialog Corporation; Indiana Cooperative Library Services Authority; OCLC Online Computer Library Center, Inc

JL SCHOOL OF LAW LIBRARY, 735 W New York St, 46202-5194. SAN 341-2717. Tel: 317-274-3884, 317-274-4028. FAX: 317-274-8825. Web Site: www.iulaw.indy.indiana.edu. *Dir*, James F Bailey, III; E-Mail: jbailey1@iupui.edu; *Reader Servs*, Minde Browning; *Acq*, Mahnaz Moshsegh; *Ref*, Bruce Kleinschmidt; *Ref*, Richard Humphrey; *Cat*, Chris Evan Long; *Tech Servs*, Wendell Johnting
Founded 1944. Highest Degree: Doctorate
Library Holdings: Bk Vols 308,222; Per Subs 6,226
Special Collections: Commonwealth Coll; Council of Europe; European Communities, law & law-related publications; International & Comparative Materials; OAS Official Records; Rare Book Coll (especially in legal history)
Publications: Bibliography of Indiana Legal Materials; recent monthly acquisitions lists for internal use only
Mem of Asn of Research Libraries
Partic in Dialog Corporation; ELSS; Indiana Cooperative Library Services Authority; Vutext; Westlaw

C INDIANA UNIVERSITY-PURDUE UNIVERSITY INDIANAPOLIS, University Libraries,* 755 W Michigan St, 46202. SAN 341-2776. Tel: 317-274-0462, 317-274-0500 (Borrowing). Interlibrary Loan Service Tel: 317-278-2595. Interlibrary Loan Service FAX: 317-274-0492. Web Site: www.lib.iupul.edu. *Actg Librn, Exec Dir*, David Lewis; E-Mail: dlewis@iupui.edu; *Assoc Dir*, Dolores J Hoyt; *Acq*, Vania Goodwin; *Cat*, Joseph Harmon; *Res*, Mary Beth Minick; *Spec Coll*, Todd Daniels-Howell; *Ref, Res*, Randi Stocker. Subject Specialists: *Afro-American*, Marie Wright; *Am sign lang*, Steven J Schmidt; *Americana*, Janet Huettner; *Anthropology*, Anthony Stamatoplos; *Art*, Sonja Staum-Kuniej; *Biology*, Randall Halverson; *Business*, Polly Boruff-Jones; *Business and management*, Shirley Yegerlehner; *Chemistry*, Randi Stocker; *Classics*, Jennifer Hehman; *Communications*, Steven J Schmidt; *Computer science*, Randi Stocker; *Computer science*, Randall Halverson; *Economics*, Cindi Stokes; *Education*, Carol Withers; *Education*, Mary Beth Minick; *Engineering*, May Jafari; *English (language)*, Marie Wright; *Environment*, Robert Hinton; *Film*, Cindi Stokes; *French*, James Baldwin; *Geography*, James Baldwin; *German*, Dolores J Hoyt; *History*, Todd Daniels-Howell; *Japanese studies*, Brenda Burk; *Journalism*, Steven J Schmidt; *Labor*, Shirley Yegerlehner; *Labour studies*, Polly Boruff-Jones; *Languages*, Brenda Burk; *Library and information science*, Vania Goodwin; *Mass communications*, Jennifer Hehman; *Mathematics*, Randall Halverson; *Media*, Renee Jackson; *Mil sci*, Jonathan Makepeace; *Museology*, Anthony Stamatoplos; *Music*, Jay Fern; *Music*, Jennifer Hehman; *Newsmedia*, Robin Crumrin; *Nursing*, Martha McCormick; *Nursing*, Susan Schlag; *Philanthropy*, Frances Huehls; *Philanthropy*, Janet Huettner; *Philosophy*, Michelle Fiander; *Phys educ*, Jonathan Makepeace; *Political science*, William Orme; *Psychology*, Randi Stocker; *Public affairs*, Robert Hinton; *Religious studies*, Joseph Harmon; *Social work*, Mary J Stanley; *Sociology*, Marie Wright; *Southeast Asia*, Anthony Stamatoplos; *Spanish*, James Baldwin; *Technology*, May Jafari; *Tourism mgt*, Jonathan Makepeace; *Womens' studies*, May Jafari; Staff 40 (MLS 40)
Founded 1939. Enrl 27,587; Highest Degree: Doctorate
1997-1998 Income $6,257,967. Mats Exp $2,182,657, Presv $46,629, Manuscripts & Archives $720. Sal $2,816,422 (Prof $1,548,823)
Library Holdings: Bk Vols 681,385; Per Subs 4,701
Subject Interests: Business and management, Education, Engineering, Humanities, Science/technology, Social sciences and issues, Technology
Special Collections: Archives Coll; German Americana; Philanthropy
Automation Activity & Vendor Info: (Cataloging) NOTIS
Partic in Cent Ind Libr Servs Authority; Dialog Corporation; Indiana Cooperative Library Services Authority; OCLC Online Computer Library Center, Inc
Departmental Libraries:
HERRON SCHOOL OF ART, 1701 N Pennsylvania Ave, 46202. SAN 341-2806. Tel: 317-920-2432. FAX: 317-920-2430. Web Site: www.lib.iupui.edu/herron. *Librn*, Sonya Staum-Kuniej; E-Mail: sstaumku@iupui.edu
Founded 1970
Library Holdings: Bk Vols 26,500; Per Subs 144

S INDIANA WOMEN'S PRISON LIBRARY, 401 N Randolph St, 46201. SAN 304-9701. Tel: 317-639-2671, Ext 242. FAX: 317-684-9643. *Librn, Media Spec*, Sandra Marksberry
Founded 1932. Pop 330
Library Holdings: Bk Vols 11,000
Mem of Cent Indiana Area Libr Servs Authority

S INDIANAPOLIS MOTOR SPEEDWAY HALL OF FAME MUSEUM LIBRARY,* 4790 W 16th St, 46222. SAN 329-5125. Tel: 317-484-6744. FAX: 317-484-6449. *Librn*, Donald Davidson
Library Holdings: Bk Vols 600
Restriction: By appointment only

S INDIANAPOLIS MUSEUM OF ART, Reference Library,* 1200 W 38th St, 46208. SAN 304-9728. Tel: 317-920-2647. FAX: 317-926-8931. Web Site: web.ima-art.org/. *Chief Librn*, Ursula Kolmstetter; *Ref*, Diane S Krall; *Cat*, Christopher Handy; Staff 3 (MLS 2, Non-MLS 1)
Founded 1908
Library Holdings: Bk Vols 40,000; Per Subs 159
Subject Interests: Africa, Art, Asia, Decorative arts, Paintings, Prints, Sculpture, Textiles
Special Collections: Indiana Artists; Museum Exhibition Catalogs; Sales & Auction Catalogs
Partic in Cent Ind Area Libr Servs Authority
Open Tues, Wed, Fri & Sat 10-5, Thurs 10-8

S INDIANAPOLIS PUBLIC SCHOOLS, Karl R Kalp Library, 120 E Walnut St, 46204. SAN 328-3496. Tel: 317-226-4499. FAX: 317-226-4848. Web Site: www.ipsk12in.us.
Library Holdings: Bk Titles 10,597; Per Subs 1,400
Publications: Bookmark

S INDIANAPOLIS STAR LIBRARY, 307 N Pennsylvania St, PO Box 145, 46206-0145. SAN 304-9736. Tel: 317-444-6496 (Pub Serv). FAX: 317-444-6150. E-Mail: informationdesk@starnews.com. Web Site: www.indystar.com/library. *Dir*, Michael Jesse; Tel: 317-444-6293, E-Mail: michael.jesse@starnews.com
Founded 1912
Subject Interests: History, Indiana
Special Collections: Articles from the Indianapolis Star & the Indianapolis

News, 1912-present
Articles available commercially on Dow Jones, Inc & Lexis-Nexis, also CD-ROM from Newsbank, Inc

S INDIANAPOLIS ZOO LIBRARY,* 1200 W Washington St, 46222. SAN 325-6863. Tel: 317-630-5110. FAX: 317-630-5114. *Librn*, Suzanne K Braun; E-Mail: sbraun@mail.indyzoo.com
Library Holdings: Bk Vols 2,000; Per Subs 100

P INDIANAPOLIS-MARION COUNTY PUBLIC LIBRARY,* 40 E St Clair, PO Box 211, 46206-0211. SAN 341-289X. Tel: 317-269-1700. Interlibrary Loan Service Tel: 317-269-1719. FAX: 317-269-5220. Web Site: www.imcpl.lib.in.us. *Dir*, Edward M Szynaka; *Assoc Dir, Publ Servs*, Laura Johnson; *Ad Servs, Librn*, Catherine Gibson; *Ch Servs*, Christine Cairo; *Automation Syst Coordr*, Brian Stone; *Assoc Dir, Tech Servs*, Colleen Obergfell; *Tech Servs*, Laura Bramble; *Circ*, Stephanie Whitmore; *Coll Develop*, Theresa Butler. Subject Specialists: *Art*, Penny Pace- Cannon; *Business and management*, Mark Leggett; *Science/technology*, Mark Leggett; *Social sciences and issues*, Lois Laube; *Technology*, Mark Leggett; Staff 162 (MLS 162)
Founded 1873. Circ 8,391,727
Jan 1997-Dec 1998 Income $27,153,160, State $2,832,907, Federal $132,103, Locally Generated Income $1,323,324, Other $88,202. Mats Exp $4,927,195, Books $3,481,744, Per/Ser (Incl. Access Fees) $303,030, Presv $32,871, Micro $58,000. Sal $15,582,581 (Prof $5,783,275)
Library Holdings: Bk Vols 1,748,670
Subject Interests: Art and architecture, Business and management, History, Music, Science/technology, Technology
Special Collections: Books on the Home (Julia Connor Thompson); Early Children's Lit; Early Text Books; First Editions of Indiana Authors; Foundation Coll; Illustrated Children's; James Whitcomb Riley; Old Cook Books; Storytelling
Automation Activity & Vendor Info: (Acquisitions) GEAC; (Circulation) GEAC
Publications: A Live Thing in the Whole Town; Indianapolis in the World of Books; Reading in Indianapolis
Partic in Indiana Cooperative Library Services Authority; OCLC Online Computer Library Center, Inc
Friends of the Library Group
Branches: 21
BRIGHTWOOD, 2435 N Sherman Dr, 46218-3852. SAN 341-292X. Tel: 317-269-1860. *Librn*, Ruby Anderson
Library Holdings: Bk Vols 21,329
BROAD RIPPLE, 1550 Broad Ripple Ave, 46220-1928. SAN 341-2954. Tel: 317-269-1791. *Librn*, William Liles
Library Holdings: Bk Vols 87,306
BROADWAY, 4186 Broadway, 46205-2733. SAN 341-2989. Tel: 317-269-1863. *Librn*, Reta Rutledge
Library Holdings: Bk Vols 24,362
BROWN, 5427 E Washington St, 46219-6411. SAN 341-3012. Tel: 317-269-1864. Web Site: www.imcpl.org. *Branch Mgr*, Cheryl Wright; E-Mail: cwright@imcpl.lib.in.us; Staff 11 (MLS 4, Non-MLS 7)
Founded 1903
Library Holdings: Bk Vols 40,115
Friends of the Library Group
DECATUR, 5301 Kentucky Ave, 46241-6540. SAN 341-3195. Tel: 317-269-1872. *Librn*, Kathleen Chudyk
Library Holdings: Bk Vols 37,240
EAGLE, 3325 Lowry Rd, 46222-1240. SAN 341-3047. Tel: 317-269-1788. *Librn*, Carol Blake-Henshaw
Library Holdings: Bk Vols 74,799
EAST WASHINGTON, 2822 E Washington St, 46201-4215. SAN 341-3071. Tel: 317-269-1867. *Librn*, Karen Cohen
Library Holdings: Bk Vols 20,413
EMERSON, 3642 N Emerson, 46218-1736. SAN 341-3101. Tel: 317-269-1868. *Librn*, Sharon Smith
Library Holdings: Bk Vols 34,021
FLANNER HOUSE, 2424 Dr Martin Luther King Jr St, 46208-5598. SAN 341-311X. Tel: 317-269-1869. *Librn*, Carla Gregory
Library Holdings: Bk Vols 20,417
FOUNTAIN SQUARE, 1066 Virginia Ave, 46203. SAN 341-3284. Tel: 317-269-1877. *Librn*, Tia Jah Wynne
Library Holdings: Bk Vols 24,423
FRANKLIN BRANCH, 5500 S Franklin Rd, 46239. SAN 341-3403. Tel: 317-269-1883. *Librn*, Ruth Hans; E-Mail: rhans@imcpl.lib.in.us
Library Holdings: Bk Vols 24,426
HAUGHVILLE, 3805 W Michigan St, 46222-3321. SAN 341-3136. Tel: 317-269-1870. Web Site: www.imcpl.org. *Librn*, David Vaprin; E-Mail: dvaprin@imcpl.lib.in.us; Staff 6 (MLS 2, Non-MLS 4)
Library Holdings: Bk Vols 22,516
LAWRENCE, 7898 N Hague Rd, 46256-1754. SAN 341-3160. Tel: 317-269-1884. *Librn*, Marian Miller
Library Holdings: Bk Vols 97,578
NORA, 8625 Guilford, 46240-1835. SAN 341-3225. Tel: 317-269-1830. *Librn*, Sharon Bernhardt
Library Holdings: Bk Vols 113,192
Friends of the Library Group
PIKE, 6525 Zionsville Rd, 46268-2352. SAN 341-3527. Tel: 317-269-1889. *Librn*, Carol Schlake
Library Holdings: Bk Vols 67,917
SHELBY, 2502 Shelby St, 46203-4236. SAN 341-3314. Tel: 317-269-1878. *Librn*, Laurence Whitmore
Library Holdings: Bk Vols 40,322
SOUTHPORT, 2630 E Stop 11 Rd, 46227-8899. SAN 341-3349. Tel: 317-269-1873. *Librn*, Cheryl McCulley
Library Holdings: Bk Vols 104,998
SPADES PARK, 1801 Nowland Ave, 46201-1158. SAN 341-3373. Tel: 317-269-1882. *Mgr*, Susan Heilman
Founded 1912. Pop 12,000; Circ 90,000
Library Holdings: Bk Vols 17,635
WARREN, 9701 E 21st St, 46229-1707. SAN 341-3438. Tel: 317-269-1890. *Librn*, Alice Greenburg
Library Holdings: Bk Vols 101,623
WAYNE, 198 S Girls School Rd, 46231-1120. SAN 341-3462. Tel: 317-269-1847. *Librn*, Joyce Karns
Library Holdings: Bk Vols 74,859
WEST INDIANAPOLIS, 1216 Kappes St, 46221-1540. SAN 341-3497. Tel: 317-269-1888. *Librn*, Michael Williams
Library Holdings: Bk Vols 23,517
Bookmobiles: 2

C INTERNATIONAL BUSINESS COLLEGE LIBRARY, 7205 Shadeland Station, 46256. SAN 375-4456. Tel: 317-841-6400, Ext 194. FAX: 317-841-6419. Web Site: www.intlbusinesscollege.com. *Librn*, Karen Ainslie; E-Mail: k_ainslie@yahoo.com; Staff 1 (MLS 1)
Founded 2000. Enrl 200; Fac 8; Highest Degree: Associate
Library Holdings: Bk Vols 720; Bk Titles 180; Per Subs 30
Partic in Indiana Cooperative Library Services Authority

J IVY TECHNICAL STATE COLLEGE LIBRARY, (Formerly Indiana Vocational Technical College, Indianapolis (IVY Tech) Library), One W 26th St, PO Box 1763, 46206-1763. SAN 304-9698. Tel: 317-921-4882, 317-921-4916. FAX: 317-921-4355. Web Site: www.ivy.tec.in.us. *Coordr*, Susan Mannan; E-Mail: smannan@ivy.tec.in.us; *Tech Servs*, Michelle Shaw; *Coll Develop, ILL, Publ Servs, Ref*, Sue Gulesian; *Ref*, Donna Funk; *AV*, Mary Burris; Staff 6 (MLS 1, Non-MLS 5)
Founded 1969. Pop 6,038; Circ 7,125; Enrl 3,268; Fac 390
Library Holdings: Bk Vols 18,062; Per Subs 374
Subject Interests: Allied health, Business and management, Education, Science/technology, Technology, Vocational education
Publications: Annual serials list; bibliographies; LRC newsletter; Periodical Holdings (annual); reading lists
Partic in Indiana Cooperative Library Services Authority; OCLC Online Computer Library Center, Inc
Open Mon-Thurs 8-9, Fri 9-4:30 & Sat 9-2

L KRIEG, DEVAULT, ALEXANDER & CAPEHART LIBRARY,* One Indiana Sq, Ste 2800, 46204-2017. SAN 323-5920. Tel: 317-636-4341. FAX: 317-636-1507. Web Site: www.kdac.com. *Librn*, Julia Rhyne; Staff 2 (MLS 1, Non-MLS 1)
Library Holdings: Bk Vols 17,500
Restriction: Staff use only
Mem of Cent Indiana Area Libr Servs Authority

L LEGAL SERVICES ORGANIZATION OF INDIANA INC LIBRARY,* 151 N Delaware St, Ste 1800, 46204. SAN 329-9600. Tel: 317-631-9410. FAX: 317-631-9775. *Librn*, Ida Hayes
Library Holdings: Bk Vols 10; Per Subs 69
Partic in Westlaw
Open Mon-Fri 8:30-5

ELI LILLY & CO
S KM LIBRARY & INFORMATION SERVICES, Lilly Corporate Ctr, Drop Code 0737, 46285. SAN 341-3551. Tel: 317-277-4225, 317-433-0936. FAX: 317-276-4418. *Librn*, Paula O Schmidt; Tel: 317-276-7748, E-Mail: pos@lilly.com; *Instrul Serv*, Sandra Stauffer; Tel: 317-276-0300, E-Mail: stauffer_sandra_l@lilly.com; *Ref Serv*, Nola Heyns; E-Mail: heyns_nola@lilly.com; Staff 40 (MLS 8, Non-MLS 32)
Founded 1890
Library Holdings: Bk Titles 5,700; Per Subs 1,650
Subject Interests: Biology, Bus and mgt, Chemistry, Economics, Law, Medicine, Toxicology
Special Collections: Domestic & Foreign Drug Encyclopedias Coll; Drug Product Information, cards; Foreign Pharmacopeias Coll
Automation Activity & Vendor Info: (Cataloging) SIRSI; (Circulation) SIRSI; (OPAC) SIRSI; (Serials) SIRSI
Partic in Indiana Cooperative Library Services Authority; Midwest Health Sci Libr Network; OCLC Online Computer Library Center, Inc
S BUSINESS-LAW LIBRARY, Lilly Corporate Ctr, 46285. SAN 341-3616. Tel: 317-276-7748. FAX: 317-276-9607.; Staff 6 (MLS 1, Non-MLS 5)
Founded 1949
Library Holdings: Bk Titles 3,500

Subject Interests: Business and management, Economics, Finance, Law
Restriction: By appointment only
Partic in Indiana Cooperative Library Services Authority

S LILLY ENDOWMENT LIBRARY, 2801 N Meridian St, 46208. SAN 304-9744. Tel: 317-924-5471. FAX: 317-926-4431. *Librn*, Elizabeth Hansen; E-Mail: hansenb@lei.org; Staff 1 (MLS 1)
Founded 1974
Library Holdings: Bk Titles 3,000; Per Subs 130
Subject Interests: Higher educ, Philanthropy, Religion
Partic in Consortium Of Foundation Libraries; Indiana Cooperative Library Services Authority

L LOCKE, REYNOLDS, BOYD & WEISELL LIBRARY,* 1000 Capital Center S, 201 N Illinois St, 46204. SAN 323-7397. Tel: 317-237-3945. FAX: 317-237-3900. *Librn*, Randy Thompson; E-Mail: rthompson@locke.com; *Asst Librn*, Elizabeth Belew
Founded 1913
Jan 1997-Dec 1998 Income $401,000. Mats Exp $153,500, Books $33,000, Per/Ser (Incl. Access Fees) $118,000, AV Equip $2,500. Sal $108,000 (Prof $64,000)
Library Holdings: Bk Vols 14,500; Bk Titles 100; Per Subs 180
Partic in Dialog Corporation; Indiana Cooperative Library Services Authority; OCLC Online Computer Library Center, Inc; Westlaw

C MARIAN COLLEGE, Hackelmeier Memorial Library, 3200 Cold Spring Rd, 46222. SAN 304-9752. Tel: 317-955-6090. Interlibrary Loan Service Tel: 317-955-6008. FAX: 317-955-6418. Web Site: www.marian.edu. *Librn*, Kelley Griffith; *Asst Librn*, Sister Patricia Connor; *Asst Librn*, Mary Hougland; Staff 5 (MLS 3, Non-MLS 2)
Founded 1937. Enrl 1,325; Fac 96; Highest Degree: Bachelor
Library Holdings: Bk Vols 140,295; Per Subs 384
Subject Interests: Education, Nursing, Roman Catholic Church
Special Collections: Am far west; Archbishop Paul C Schulte, bks, papers; Monsignor Doyle Coll
Database Vendor: DRA
Publications: Annual Report; Marian Coll Libr Guide
Partic in Indiana Cooperative Library Services Authority; OCLC Online Computer Library Center, Inc; Private Acad Libr Network of Ind

GL MARION COUNTY LAW LIBRARY,* 200 E Washington St, Ste T-360, 46204. SAN 321-9976. Tel: 317-327-5499. FAX: 317-327-3298. *Librn*, Terri Lea Ross; *Asst Librn*, Libby Schilling
Library Holdings: Bk Vols 14,500; Per Subs 15
Subject Interests: Ind law
Partic in Cent Ind Area Libr Servs Authority; Westlaw

C MARTIN UNIVERSITY LIBRARY,* 2171 Avondale Pl, PO Box 18567, 46218. SAN 373-6490. Tel: 317-543-3260. FAX: 317-543-4790. *Librn*, David Wilhelmus
Founded 1991. Fac 50
Library Holdings: Bk Titles 10,947
Special Collections: Black History, bks & v-tapes; Religion

M ORTHOPAEDICS INDIANAPOLIS INC LIBRARY,* 8450 Northwest Blvd, 46278. SAN 373-367X. Tel: 317-923-5352. FAX: 317-929-6751.
Library Holdings: Bk Vols 4,500; Per Subs 40

S PLANNED PARENTHOOD OF GREATER INDIANA, (Formerly Planned Parenthood Of Central & Southern Indiana), Resource Center, 3209 N Meridian St, 46208. SAN 326-0887. Tel: 317-927-3644, Ext 142. FAX: 317-927-3663. Web Site: www.ppcsi.org. *Info Res, Mgr*, Betsy Lambie; E-Mail: betsy@ppcsi.org
Founded 1980
Jan 1998-Dec 1998 Income $26,736, Locally Generated Income $2,117, Parent Institution $24,619. Mats Exp $5,000, Books $2,000, Per/Ser (Incl. Access Fees) $1,000. Sal $13,936
Library Holdings: Bk Titles 1,721; Per Subs 66
Subject Interests: Abortion, Birth control, Teen sexuality

S PRAXAIR SURFACE TECHNOLOGIES, INC LIBRARY,* 1500 Polco St, PO Box 24166, 46224-0166. SAN 304-9833. Tel: 317-240-2514, 317-240-2520. FAX: 317-240-2426.
Founded 1956
Library Holdings: Bk Titles 7,500; Per Subs 225
Friends of the Library Group

RAYTHEON TECHNICAL SERVICES CO
A TECHNICAL LIBRARY, 6125 E 21st St, 46219-2058. SAN 341-3640. Tel: 317-306-3232. FAX: 317-306-3122. *Cat*, Toni O'Connor
Founded 1945
Library Holdings: Bk Vols 25,150; Per Subs 653
Subject Interests: Computer science, Electronics, Engineering, Mathematics, Metallurgy, Physics, Safety
Special Collections: DOD, DESC Drawings, Instructions & Specifications; Magazine Subscriptions; Manuals; NA Air Manuals; Qualified Parts Lists (QPLS); Technical Reports; Vendor Product Catalog

S REILLY INDUSTRIES, INC, Laboratory Library, 1500 S Tibbs Ave, PO Box 42912, 46242-0912. SAN 328-2376. Tel: 317-247-8141. FAX: 317-248-6528. *Dir*, Eric Scriven
Library Holdings: Bk Vols 4,000; Per Subs 100

M RILEY HOSPITAL, Riley Family Library,* 702 Barnhill Dr, Rm 4560, 46202-5200. SAN 304-9809. Tel: 317-274-1149. FAX: 317-278-4588.
Founded 1922
Library Holdings: Bk Vols 4,300; Per Subs 16
Special Collections: Lay Medical Information Coll
Publications: Lay Medical Bibliography; Riley Family Library
Partic in Indiana Cooperative Library Services Authority

S ROLLS-ROYCE, Library Information Resource Services,* Mail Code S5, 2001 S Tibbs Ave, 46241. (Mail add: Mail Code 55, PO Box 420, 46206-0420), SAN 304-9590. Tel: 317-230-5651. FAX: 317-230-8901. *Librn*, Melanie S Johnson; E-Mail: melanie.s.johnson@allison.com
Founded 1941
Library Holdings: Bk Titles 10,000; Per Subs 350
Subject Interests: Metallurgy
Special Collections: Aeronautical Research Council Reports; Allison Archives; Partial Federal Depository for medical government documents for Maui County
Database Vendor: Dialog, OCLC - First Search
Partic in Indiana Cooperative Library Services Authority

M SAINT VINCENT HOSPITAL & HEALTH SERVICES, Garceau Library, 2001 W 86th St, 46260. SAN 304-9825. Tel: 317-338-2095. FAX: 317-338-6516. E-Mail: library@stvincent.org. *Mgr Libr Serv*, Louise S Hass; Tel: 317-338-9717, E-Mail: lshass@stvincent.org; *Librn*, Denise Rumschlag; *Librn*, Barbara Gushrowski; Staff 3 (MLS 3)
Founded 1935
Jul 1999-Jun 2000 Mats Exp $365,644
Library Holdings: Bk Vols 5,000; Per Subs 346
Subject Interests: Hospital administration, Medicine, Nursing, Spirituality
Special Collections: Hospital Archives Coll
Automation Activity & Vendor Info: (OPAC) Inmagic, Inc.
Database Vendor: OVID Technologies
Partic in Cent Ind Area Libr Servs Authority; Central Indiana Health Science Libraries Consortium; Indiana Cooperative Library Services Authority

S SATURDAY EVENING POST ARCHIVES,* 1100 Waterway Blvd, 46202. SAN 304-9523. Tel: 317-636-8881. FAX: 317-637-0126. *Archivist*, Steve Pettinga
Library Holdings: Per Subs 100
Subject Interests: Fiction
Special Collections: Country Gentleman Archives, 1914-date; Joseph Lyndecker; Norman Rockwell; Saturday Evening Post, 1820-date

M SIGMA THETA TAU INTERNATIONAL, Virginia Henderson International Nursing Library, 550 W North St, 46202. SAN 329-1367. Tel: 317-634-8171. Toll Free Tel: 888-634-7575. FAX: 317-634-8188. Web Site: www.nursingsociety.org. *Coordr*, Margaret Wilson; E-Mail: margie@stti.iupui.edu
Founded 1987
1999-2000 Mats Exp $8,000, Books $2,000, Per/Ser (Incl. Access Fees) $2,000, Presv $2,000, Electronic Ref Mat (Incl. Access Fees) $2,000
Library Holdings: Bk Titles 2,460; Per Subs 19
Subject Interests: Nursing
Special Collections: Sigma Theta Tau International Honor Society of Nursing
Publications: Directory of Nurse Researchers
Partic in Central Indiana Health Science Libraries Consortium; Indiana Cooperative Library Services Authority; Medical Libr Asn
Special Services for the Deaf - Staff with knowledge of sign language
Friends of the Library Group

THOMSON CONSUMER ELECTRONICS
S ENGINEERING LIBRARY, 101 W 103rd St, 46290-1102. SAN 304-9787. Tel: 317-587-4340. FAX: 317-587-9340. E-Mail: libtec@indy.tce.com.
Founded 1956
Library Holdings: Bk Vols 4,000; Per Subs 200
Subject Interests: Electrical engineering, Electronics, Mathematics, Mechanical engineering
Partic in Cent Ind Area Libr Servs Authority; Dialog Corporation; Indiana Cooperative Library Services Authority; OCLC Online Computer Library Center, Inc

R UNITED PRESBYTERIAN CHURCH, First Meridian Heights Library, 4701 N Central Ave, 46205. SAN 304-9841. Tel: 317-283-1305. FAX: 317-921-2266. E-Mail: fmhpc@aol.com. *Adminr*, Pat Perkins
Founded 1964
Library Holdings: Bk Vols 2,000
Subject Interests: Religion

S UNITED STATES GEOLOGICAL SURVEY - WATER RESOURCES DIVISION, Information Resource Center, 5957 Lakeside Blvd, 46278-1996. SAN 373-0522. Tel: 317-290-3333, Ext 183. FAX: 317-290-3313. *Librn*,

Sonja Sanders
Library Holdings: Bk Vols 6,000; Per Subs 23
Subject Interests: Geology, Pollution, Water resources

C UNIVERSITY OF INDIANAPOLIS, Krannert Memorial Library, 1400 E Hanna Ave, 46227-3697. SAN 304-9620. Tel: 317-788-3399. Toll Free Tel: 120-1670. FAX: 317-788-3275. Web Site: www.kml.uindy.edu. *Dir*, Philip Young; E-Mail: pyoung@uindy.edu; *Asst Dir*, Shirley Bigna; Tel: 317-788-3402, E-Mail: bigna@uindy.edu; *Cat*, Linda Shaw; Tel: 317-788-3398, E-Mail: lshaw@uindy.edu; *Ref*, Daniel Schuetz; Tel: 317-788-6180, E-Mail: dschuetz@uindy.edu; *Circ*, Kim Wenning; E-Mail: kwenning@uindy.edu; *Ref, Res*, Christine Guyonneau; Tel: 317-788-6106, E-Mail: guyonneau@uindy.edu; Staff 13 (MLS 6, Non-MLS 7)
Founded 1902. Enrl 2,850; Fac 154; Highest Degree: Doctorate
Jul 1999-Jun 2000 Income $974,737. Mats Exp $470,514, Books $207,451, Per/Ser (Incl. Access Fees) $190,500, Presv $10,450, Electronic Ref Mat (Incl. Access Fees) $62,113. Sal $376,353 (Prof $226,171)
Library Holdings: Bk Vols 151,000; Bk Titles 130,000; Per Subs 1,000
Subject Interests: Education, History, Nursing, Physical therapy, Psychology, Religion
Special Collections: Evangelical United Brethren Coll; Krannert Coll (specially bd limited editions)
Automation Activity & Vendor Info: (Acquisitions) DRA; (Cataloging) DRA; (Circulation) DRA
Partic in Indiana Cooperative Library Services Authority; Private Acad Libr Network of Ind

R WESLEYAN CHURCH, Archives & Historical Library, 6060 Castleway W Dr, PO Box 50434, 46250-0434. SAN 305-0262. Tel: 317-570-5145. FAX: 317-594-8309. *Dir*, Craig A Dunn; *Archivist*, Wayne Keller
Founded 1968
1998-1999 Income $2,000. Mats Exp $2,000, Books $1,800, Per/Ser (Incl. Access Fees) $200
Library Holdings: Bk Vols 6,200; Bk Titles 5,000; Per Subs 60

M WINONA HOSPITAL, Health Sciences Library,* 3232 N Meridian St, 46208. SAN 304-9868. Tel: 317-927-2219, 317-927-3392. FAX: 317-927-2951. *Dir*, Ellen Gilbert
Founded 1956
Library Holdings: Bk Vols 1,000; Bk Titles 500; Per Subs 75
Partic in Cent Ind Area Libr Servs Authority; Central Indiana Health Science Libraries Consortium; Indiana Cooperative Library Services Authority; Midwest Health Sci Libr Network

M WISHARD HEALTH SERVICES, Library & Media Services, 1001 W Tenth St, 46202. SAN 304-9876. Tel: 317-630-7028. FAX: 317-656-4149. Web Site: www.wishard.edu. *Coordr*, Lydia Chuang; Tel: 317-630-6160, E-Mail: chuangl@wishard.edu; *Media Spec*, Janet Walls; Tel: 317-630-6166, E-Mail: wallsj@wishard.edu; Staff 3 (MLS 1, Non-MLS 2)
Library Holdings: Bk Titles 6,000; Per Subs 125
Subject Interests: Clinical medicine, Hospital administration, Nursing
Partic in Cent Ind Area Libr Servs Authority; Central Indiana Health Science Libraries Consortium; Greater Midwest Regional Medical Libr Network; Indiana Cooperative Library Services Authority; OCLC Online Computer Library Center, Inc

JASONVILLE

P JASONVILLE PUBLIC LIBRARY,* 380 E Main St, 47438. SAN 304-9884. Tel: 812-665-2025. *Librn*, Judy Fougerousse; *Asst Librn*, Lori Caddell
Founded 1924. Pop 2,384; Circ 12,010
Library Holdings: Bk Vols 14,291; Per Subs 22
Subject Interests: Genealogy
Special Collections: Indiana History Holdings

JASPER

P JASPER PUBLIC LIBRARY, 1116 Main St, 47546-2899. SAN 304-9892. Tel: 812-482-2712. FAX: 812-482-7123.; Staff 2 (Non-MLS 2)
Founded 1934. Pop 29,869; Circ 184,085
Library Holdings: Bk Vols 52,000; Per Subs 155
Subject Interests: Genealogy, History, Indiana, Large type print
Mem of Area 2 Libr Servs Authority; Four Rivers Area Libr Servs Authority
Partic in Indiana Cooperative Library Services Authority
Open Mon-Thurs 9-8, Fri & Sat 9-5
Branches: 1
FERDINAND BRANCH, Ferdinand, 47542. SAN 371-3717. Tel: 812-367-1671. FAX: 812-367-1063. *Librn*, Diana Melton; Staff 1 (MLS 1)
Library Holdings: Bk Vols 21,000
Open Mon-Thurs 10-7, Sat 10-3
Bookmobiles: 1. Librn, Pat Riley. Bk vols 33,000

JEFFERSONVILLE

M CLARK MEMORIAL HOSPITAL, Health Science Library, 1220 Missouri Ave, 47130-3743. (Mail add: PO Box 69, 47130-0069), SAN 320-6688. Tel: 812-283-2358. FAX: 812-283-2688. *Librn*, Kathleen Lynn; E-Mail: klynn@cmh1.com; Staff 1 (MLS 1)
Founded 1971
Library Holdings: Bk Vols 600; Per Subs 59
Restriction: Employees & their associates, Medical staff only
Partic in Bluegrass Med Librns; Kentucky Health Science Libraries Consortium; SE Ind Area Libr Servs Authority

P JEFFERSONVILLE TOWNSHIP PUBLIC LIBRARY, 211 E Court Ave, 47130. (Mail add: PO Box 1548, 47131-1548), SAN 304-9906. Tel: 812-282-7765. Circulation Tel: 812-285-5631. Reference Tel: 812-285-5634. FAX: 812-282-1264. Web Site: jefferson.lib.in.us. *Dir*, William F Bolte; Tel: 812-285-5633, E-Mail: bbolte@jefferson.lib.in.us; *Circ*, Brenda Redd; Tel: 812-285-5630; *Ad Servs*, Ilona Franck; E-Mail: ifranck@jefferson.lib.in.us; *Ad Servs*, Becky Kelien; E-Mail: bkelien@jefferson.lib.in.us; *Cat*, Gary J Stengel; Tel: 812-285-5630; *Coll Develop*, Harriet Goldberg; Tel: 812-285-5634, E-Mail: hgoldberg@jefferson.lib.in.us; *Branch Mgr*, Kathleen Rosga; Tel: 812-285-5647, Fax: 812-285-5642, E-Mail: krosga@jefferson.lib.in.us; Staff 46 (MLS 10, Non-MLS 36)
Founded 1900. Pop 53,449; Circ 543,859
Jan 1999-Dec 1999 Income (Main Library and Branch Library) $1,307,723, State $132,000, Locally Generated Income $1,105,419, Other $70,304. Mats Exp $205,031, Books $137,535, Per/Ser (Incl. Access Fees) $11,243, Micro $40,210, Electronic Ref Mat (Incl. Access Fees) $16,043. Sal $648,751 (Prof $264,850)
Library Holdings: Bk Vols 202,726; Bk Titles 169,405; Per Subs 446
Special Collections: Local & Indiana History (Indiana Coll), bk, microfilm, slides, photogs
Automation Activity & Vendor Info: (Cataloging) GEAC; (Circulation) GEAC; (OPAC) GEAC
Database Vendor: Ebsco - EbscoHost, ProQuest
Partic in Indiana Cooperative Library Services Authority; OCLC Online Computer Library Center, Inc
Open Mon-Thurs 9-9, Fri 9-5:30 & Sat 9-5
Friends of the Library Group
Branches: 1
CLARKSVILLE BRANCH, 1312 Eastern Blvd, Clarksville, 47129-1704. Tel: 812-285-5647. FAX: 812-285-5642. *Branch Mgr*, Kathleen Rosga; E-Mail: krosga@jefferson.lib.in.us

C MID AMERICA COLLEGE OF FUNERAL SERVICE LIBRARY, 3111 Hambury Pike, 47130. Tel: 812-288-8878. Toll Free Tel: 800-221-6158. Web Site: www.midamerical.edu. *Branch Mgr*, Gary Bridgewater
Library Holdings: Bk Titles 550; Per Subs 15

JONESBORO

P JONESBORO PUBLIC LIBRARY,* 124 E Fourth St, 46938-1105. SAN 304-9914. Tel: 765-677-9080. *Librn*, Carol Jones
Founded 1941. Pop 2,466; Circ 8,600
Library Holdings: Bk Vols 10,000; Per Subs 55

KENDALLVILLE

P KENDALLVILLE PUBLIC LIBRARY, 126 W Rush St, 46755-1740. SAN 341-3675. Tel: 219-347-2768. FAX: 219-347-5314. E-Mail: kpldir@noble.cioe.com. Web Site: www.noblecan.org/~super/kpl/. *Head Librn*, Jenny Draper; *Commun Servs*, Nancy Leighty; *Ad Servs*, Paul Beck; *Tech Servs*, Barb Huth; *Ch Servs*, Ellie Teaford; Staff 5 (MLS 3, Non-MLS 2)
Founded 1913. Pop 14,111; Circ 158,206
Jan 1999-Dec 1999 Income (Main Library and Branch Library) $715,000. Mats Exp $99,300, Books $64,000, Per/Ser (Incl. Access Fees) $7,800. Sal $388,000 (Prof $171,000)
Library Holdings: Bk Vols 61,500; Per Subs 214
Subject Interests: Local history
Special Collections: Gene Stratton-Porter Coll; M F Owen Scrapbook
Database Vendor: Ebsco - EbscoHost
Publications: Annual Report; Newsletter (monthly)
Partic in Indiana Cooperative Library Services Authority
Friends of the Library Group
Branches: 1
LIMBERLOST PUBLIC, 164 Kelly St, PO Box 368, Rome City, 46784. SAN 341-3705. Tel: 219-854-2775. Web Site: www.noblecan.org/~super/kpl/. *Librn*, Linda Leighty
Library Holdings: Bk Vols 11,000

KENTLAND

P KENTLAND - JEFFERSON TOWNSHIP PUBLIC LIBRARY,* 201 E Graham St, 47951-1233. SAN 304-9922. Tel: 219-474-5044. FAX: 219-474-5351. *Dir*, Roberta Dewing; E-Mail: robdew@kentland.ffni.com
Pop 2,384; Circ 24,535
Library Holdings: Bk Vols 20,000; Per Subs 33
Open Mon 9-8, Tues & Thurs 1-5, Wed 1-8, Fri 9-5 & Sat 8-12
Friends of the Library Group

KEWANNA

P KEWANNA PUBLIC LIBRARY,* 210 E Main St, 46939-9529. (Mail add: PO Box 365, 46939-0365), SAN 304-9930. Tel: 219-653-2011. Interlibrary Loan Service Tel: 800-844-5081. *Dir*, Linda Hawkey; *Asst Librn*, Carol Bauman
Founded 1914. Pop 1,000; Circ 7,278
Library Holdings: Bk Vols 17,000; Per Subs 300
Subject Interests: Antiques, Arts and crafts
Special Collections: Fulton County; Indiana

KINGMAN

P KINGMAN PUBLIC LIBRARY, State St, PO Box 116, 47952-0116. SAN 304-9949. Tel: 765-397-3138. FAX: 765-397-3138. *Librn*, Delores A Sunderman; *Asst Librn*, Catherine Ratcliff; Staff 2 (Non-MLS 2)
Founded 1916. Pop 1,475; Circ 3,849
Library Holdings: Bk Vols 14,000; Bk Titles 13,900; Per Subs 30
Subject Interests: Local history
Partic in Area Libr Serv Authority; Indiana Cooperative Library Services Authority
Special Services for the Blind - Talking Books

KIRKLIN

P KIRKLIN PUBLIC LIBRARY, 115 N Main, PO Box 8, 46050-0008. SAN 304-9957. Tel: 765-279-8308. FAX: 765-279-8258. Web Site: www.accs.net/kirklinpl/kirklin.htm. *Librn*, Nancy Rogers; *YA Servs*, Beth Sillars; Staff 1 (MLS 1)
Founded 1913. Pop 1,275; Circ 14,764
Library Holdings: Bk Vols 18,000; Per Subs 48
Special Collections: Archives on Kirklin History
Partic in Wabash Valley Area Libr Servs Authority
Library offers free tutorial reading service to school age children, summer reading program
Friends of the Library Group

KNIGHTSTOWN

P KNIGHTSTOWN PUBLIC LIBRARY,* 5 E Main St, 46148-1248. SAN 304-9965. Tel: 765-345-5095. FAX: 765-345-5377. *Librn*, Marjorie Wilkinson
Founded 1906. Pop 2,325; Circ 18,436
Jan 1997-Dec 1998 Income $73,881. Mats Exp $5,550. Sal $32,147
Library Holdings: Bk Vols 16,597; Bk Titles 15,356; Per Subs 50
Special Collections: Knightstown, Henry County & Indiana History
Mem of Eastern Ind Area Libr Servs Authority
Friends of the Library Group

KNOX

P STARKE COUNTY PUBLIC LIBRARY SYSTEM, Henry F Schricker Main Library, 152 W Culver Rd, 46534-2220. SAN 304-9973. Tel: 219-772-7323. FAX: 219-772-4207. Web Site: www.scpl.lib.in.us. *Dir*, John Brock; *Circ*, Mary Wharton; *Ref*, Ellen Dodge; Staff 2 (MLS 2)
Founded 1919. Pop 18,094; Circ 179,250
Jan 1999-Dec 1999 Income (Main Library and Branch Library) $679,658, State $60,528, Locally Generated Income $560,170, Other $58,960. Mats Exp $661,946, Books $95,418, Per/Ser (Incl. Access Fees) $10,219. Sal $303,853
Library Holdings: Bk Vols 81,821; Per Subs 240
Subject Interests: Genealogy, Local history
Automation Activity & Vendor Info: (Cataloging) epixtech, inc.; (Circulation) epixtech, inc.; (OPAC) epixtech, inc.
Database Vendor: Ebsco - EbscoHost
Partic in Indiana Cooperative Library Services Authority
Branches: 3
HAMLET BRANCH, 4 N Starke St, Hamlet, 46532. SAN 324-2498. Tel: 219-867-6033. FAX: 219-867-6033. Web Site: www.scpl.lib.in.us. *Branch Mgr*, Barbara Pilger
Circ 10,427
Library Holdings: Bk Vols 9,019
Automation Activity & Vendor Info: (Circulation) epixtech, inc.; (OPAC) epixtech, inc.
KOONTZ LAKE, 7954 N Hwy 23, Walkerton, 46574. SAN 321-415X. Tel: 219-586-3353. FAX: 219-586-3353. Web Site: www.scpl.lib.in.us. *Branch Mgr*, Bonita Davis
Circ 15,336
Library Holdings: Bk Vols 10,289
Automation Activity & Vendor Info: (Circulation) epixtech, inc.; (OPAC) epixtech, inc.
SAN PIERRE BRANCH, 103 Broadway, PO Box 218, San Pierre, 46374. SAN 321-4168. Tel: 219-828-4352. FAX: 219-828-4352. Web Site: www.scpl.lib.in.us. *Branch Mgr*, Nancy Capouch
Circ 9,289
Library Holdings: Bk Vols 9,729
Automation Activity & Vendor Info: (Circulation) epixtech, inc.; (OPAC) epixtech, inc.

KOKOMO

S DELPHI DELCO ELECTRONIC SYSTEMS, Technical Library, PO Box 9005, CT 1 TL, 46904-9005. SAN 304-999X. Tel: 765-451-0268. FAX: 765-451-0295. *In Charge*, Deborah Russell; E-Mail: deborah.s.russell@delphiauto.com; Staff 1 (MLS 1)
Founded 1962
Library Holdings: Bk Titles 3,500; Per Subs 300
Subject Interests: Automotive engineering, Electrical engineering
Special Collections: Conference Board Reports Coll; SAE Report Coll
Database Vendor: Dialog, Ebsco - EbscoHost, Lexis-Nexis, OCLC - First Search
Publications: IRC catalog update
Partic in Dialog Corporation; Indiana Cooperative Library Services Authority

S HAYNES INTERNATIONAL, Technical Library, 1020 W Park Ave, PO Box 9013, 46904-9013. SAN 304-9981. Tel: 765-456-6140. FAX: 765-456-6905. Web Site: www.haynesintl.com. *Librn*, Amy Russell; E-Mail: arussell@haynesintl.com; Staff 1 (MLS 1)
Founded 1952
Library Holdings: Bk Titles 7,500; Per Subs 150
Subject Interests: Business and management, Metallurgy
Database Vendor: Dialog, Ebsco - EbscoHost, OCLC - First Search
Restriction: Company library, Open to others by appointment
Partic in Indiana Cooperative Library Services Authority; OCLC Online Computer Library Center, Inc

C INDIANA UNIVERSITY KOKOMO LIBRARY, 2300 S Washington, PO Box 9003, 46904-9003. SAN 305-0009. Tel: 765-455-9265. Reference Tel: 765-455-9521. FAX: 765-455-9276. E-Mail: iuklib@iuk.edu. Web Site: www.iuk.edu/library/index.html. *Dir*, Richard L Ardrey; *Circ, ILL*, Garry Hancock; *Acq, Ser*, Janine Stanley; *Publ Servs*, Diane Bever; *Bibliog Instr*, Gail MacKay; *Tech Servs*, Ria Lukes; *Govt Doc*, Joyce Eikenberry; Staff 5 (MLS 5)
Founded 1945. Enrl 1,622; Fac 89; Highest Degree: Master
Jul 1999-Jun 2000 Income $828,942. Mats Exp $808,570, Books $75,651, Per/Ser (Incl. Access Fees) $231,507, Presv $3,542, AV Equip $45,082. Sal $333,160 (Prof $199,814)
Library Holdings: Bk Vols 114,109; Per Subs 1,707
Automation Activity & Vendor Info: (Acquisitions) SIRSI; (Cataloging) SIRSI; (Circulation) SIRSI; (Course Reserve) SIRSI; (ILL) SIRSI; (Media Booking) SIRSI; (OPAC) SIRSI; (Serials) SIRSI
Database Vendor: CARL, Dialog, Ebsco - EbscoHost, GaleNet, Lexis-Nexis, OCLC - First Search, ProQuest, Silverplatter Information Inc.
Publications: Check It Out (newsletter)
Partic in Greater Midwest Regional Medical Libr Network; Indiana Cooperative Library Services Authority
Open Mon-Thurs 8:15-9pm, Fri 8:15-5, Sat 12-5 & Sun 1-5

P KOKOMO HOWARD COUNTY PUBLIC LIBRARY, 220 N Union St, 46901-4614. SAN 305-0017. Tel: 765-457-3242. Reference Tel: 765-454-4710. FAX: 765-457-3683. E-Mail: khcpl@kokomo.lib.in.us. Web Site: www.kokomo.lib.in.us. *Dir*, Charles Joray; E-Mail: cjoray@kokomo.lib.in.us; *Asst Dir*, Peg Harmon; E-Mail: pharmon@kokomo.lib.in.us; *YA Servs*, Jerry Henry; *Coll Develop*, Diane Chladil; E-Mail: dchladil@kokomo.lib.in.us; *Bkmobile Coordr*, Doug Workinger; *Ch Servs*, Beth Werking; E-Mail: bwerking@kokomo.lib.in.us; *Head Tech Servs*, Janice Weaver; E-Mail: jweaver@kokomo.lib.in.us; *Ad Servs*, Tammy Keith; E-Mail: tkeith@kokomo.lib.in.us; *Archivist*, Michele McNabb; Staff 79 (MLS 15, Non-MLS 64)
Founded 1885. Pop 74,891; Circ 716,839
Jan 2000-Dec 2000 Mats Exp $471,644, Books $352,295, Per/Ser (Incl. Access Fees) $37,029. Sal $1,493,399
Library Holdings: Bk Titles 357,854
Subject Interests: Genealogy, Local history
Special Collections: Hoosier Art
Automation Activity & Vendor Info: (Acquisitions) Nicholas; (Cataloging) Nicholas; (Circulation) Innovative Interfaces Inc.; (OPAC) PALS
Database Vendor: Ebsco - EbscoHost, Innovative Interfaces INN - View, OCLC - First Search
Publications: Books Along the Wildcat: The History of the Kokomo-Howard County Public Library by Leonard B Felkey; Hoosier Art Collection of the Kokomo-Howard County Public Library; Old Richardville Publications (desktop publishing of local history information); Preface newsletter
Function: Some telephone reference
Partic in Indiana Cooperative Library Services Authority
Friends of the Library Group
Branches: 2
RUSSIAVILLE BRANCH, 315 Mesa Dr, Russiaville, 46979. SAN 370-0054. Tel: 765-883-5112. *Librn*, Kathy Newby

Library Holdings: Bk Vols 7,000
SOUTH, 423 E Center Rd, 46902-5322. SAN 321-8589. Tel: 765-453-4150. FAX: 765-453-6677. *Librn*, Lori Hugley
Library Holdings: Bk Vols 11,220
Bookmobiles: 2

M SAINT JOSEPH HOSPITAL & HEALTH CENTER, Health Science Library, 1907 W Sycamore St, 46901. SAN 305-0025. Tel: 765-452-5611. FAX: 765-456-5603. *Chief Librn*, Clarene Junker; E-Mail: junkerc@st.jhhc.org
Founded 1970
Library Holdings: Bk Vols 500; Per Subs 200
Subject Interests: Allied health, Nursing

LA CROSSE

P LA CROSSE PUBLIC LIBRARY,* 16 E Main, PO Box 300, 46348-0300. SAN 376-5369. Tel: 219-754-2606. FAX: 219-754-2606. *Dir*, Patricia Spiess
1997-1998 Income $50,150, State $672, County $16,930, Other $3,548. Mats Exp $11,174, Books $5,259, Per/Ser (Incl. Access Fees) $638. Sal $24,804 (Prof $19,804)
Library Holdings: Bk Vols 12,000; Bk Titles 10,000; Per Subs 30

LA PORTE

P LA PORTE COUNTY PUBLIC LIBRARY, 904 Indiana Ave, 46350-3407. SAN 305-0033. Tel: 219-362-6156. FAX: 219-362-6158. Web Site: www.lcpl2.lpco.lib.in.us. *Dir*, Judy R Hamilton; *Ad Servs*, Jennifer McFerron; *Ch Servs*, Lori Richardson; *AV*, Vicki Dwyer; *Tech Servs*, Doris Logan; *Commun Servs*, Mary Hedge; Staff 16 (MLS 13, Non-MLS 3)
Founded 1897. Pop 59,125; Circ 650,000
Jan 2000-Dec 2000 Income $2,900,000, State $100,000, County $2,100,000, Locally Generated Income $100,000. Sal $1,304,000 (Prof $630,000)
Library Holdings: Bk Vols 257,000; Bk Titles 180,000; Per Subs 55; High Interest/Low Vocabulary Bk Vols 2,000; Bks on Deafness & Sign Lang 50
Special Collections: History of La Porte County, City of La Porte & State of Indiana
Automation Activity & Vendor Info: (Acquisitions) DRA
Partic in Indiana Cooperative Library Services Authority; OCLC Online Computer Library Center, Inc
Friends of the Library Group
Branches: 6
COOLSPRING BRANCH, 7089 W 400 N, Michigan City, 46360. SAN 322-5798. Tel: 219-879-3272. FAX: 219-879-3272. *Librn*, Marge Berry
Library Holdings: Bk Titles 20,000
FISH LAKE, 7981 E SR 4, PO Box 125, Walkerton, 46574. SAN 341-3764. Tel: 219-369-1337. FAX: 219-369-1337. *Librn*, Carolyn Shaffer
Library Holdings: Bk Vols 9,250
HANNA BRANCH, 202 N Thompson, PO Box 78, Hanna, 46340. SAN 341-3799. Tel: 219-797-4735. FAX: 219-797-4735. *Librn*, Anna Arnett
Library Holdings: Bk Vols 7,720
KINGSFORD HEIGHTS BRANCH, 436 Evanston, PO Box 219, Kingsford Heights, 46346. SAN 341-3829. Tel: 219-393-3280. FAX: 219-393-3280. *Librn*, Maria Posey
Library Holdings: Bk Vols 8,825
ROLLING PRAIRIE BRANCH, One E Michigan Ave, PO Box 157, Rolling Prairie, 46371. SAN 341-3853. Tel: 219-778-2390. FAX: 219-778-2390. *Librn*, Linda Shortt
Library Holdings: Bk Vols 16,000
UNION MILLS BRANCH, 3727 W 800 South, PO Box 98, Union Mills, 46382. SAN 341-3888. Tel: 219-767-2604. FAX: 219-767-2604. *Librn*, Geraldine Grott
Library Holdings: Bk Vols 8,725
Friends of the Library Group
Bookmobiles: 1

LADOGA

P LADOGA-CLARK TOWNSHIP PUBLIC LIBRARY,* 128 E Main St, PO Box 248, 47954-0248. SAN 373-8965. Tel: 765-942-2456. *Dir*, Wanda Bennett
Founded 1919. Pop 3,283
Library Holdings: Bk Titles 20,000; Per Subs 64
Special Collections: Local History & Genealogy (Maude Long Neff Coll), bks, newsps on microfilm
Publications: Newsletter (quarterly)
Open Tues 1-7, Wed & Fri 10-5, Thurs 10-7 & Sat 10-3
Friends of the Library Group

LAFAYETTE

J IVY TECH STATE COLLEGE, REGION 4, LAFAYETTE LIBRARY, Ninth & Brown Sts, PO Box 6299, 47903. SAN 305-0041. Tel: 765-772-9172. FAX: 765-772-9161. Web Site: www.ivy.tec.in.us/library. *Librn*, Dennis Lawson; E-Mail: dlawson@ivy.tec.in.us; *Asst Librn*, Evelyn Samad; Tel: 765-772-9152, E-Mail: esamad@ivy.tec.in.us; Staff 3 (MLS 2, Non-MLS 1)
Founded 1973. Enrl 1,419; Fac 40; Highest Degree: Associate
1998-1999 Income $172,163. Mats Exp $39,631, Books $30,537, Per/Ser (Incl. Access Fees) $3,752, AV Equip $3,468, Electronic Ref Mat (Incl. Access Fees) $1,874. Sal $120,000 (Prof $69,368)
Library Holdings: Bk Vols 10,748; Bk Titles 10,618; Per Subs 165
Subject Interests: Business and management, Medicine, Science/technology, Technology
Automation Activity & Vendor Info: (Cataloging) Endeavor; (Circulation) Endeavor; (Course Reserve) Endeavor; (ILL) Endeavor; (OPAC) Endeavor; (Serials) Endeavor
Database Vendor: Ebsco - EbscoHost, ProQuest
Partic in Indiana Cooperative Library Services Authority
Open Mon-Thurs 8-7, Fri 8-5

S JOURNAL & COURIER NEWSPAPER LIBRARY,* 217 N Sixth St, 47901-1448. SAN 305-005X. Tel: 765-420-5204. FAX: 765-420-5246. Web Site: www.jconline.com (newspaper).
Founded 1964. Circ 43,000
Special Collections: Microfilm, newsp clippings, ref bks
Restriction: Staff use only

SAINT ELIZABETH MEDICAL CENTER
M BANNON HEALTH SCIENCE LIBRARY, 1501 Hartford St, PO Box 7501, 47903-7901. SAN 341-3918. Tel: 765-423-6143. FAX: 765-742-5764. *Librn*, Patty Matkovic; E-Mail: pmatkovic@glhsi.org; Staff 1 (MLS 1)
Founded 1919
Library Holdings: Bk Vols 7,200; Per Subs 250
Subject Interests: Clinical medicine, Hospital administration
Special Collections: Bioethics Coll
Partic in Greater Midwest Regional Medical Libr Network
M SCHOOL OF NURSING LIBRARY, 1508 Tippecanoe St, 47904. SAN 341-3942. Tel: 765-423-6125. FAX: 765-423-6385. *Librn*, Jenne McMillin; Tel: 765-423-6347; Staff 1 (Non-MLS 1)
Sep 1998-Aug 1999 Mats Exp $32,000, Books $10,000, Per/Ser (Incl. Access Fees) $12,000, AV Equip $10,000. Sal $11,000
Library Holdings: Bk Titles 2,200; Per Subs 125
Subject Interests: Consumer health, Nursing
Publications: Annual report; bibliographies

S TIPPECANOE COUNTY HISTORICAL ASSOCIATION, Alameda McCollough Library, 1001 South St, 47901. SAN 305-0068. Tel: 765-476-8407. FAX: 765-476-8414. E-Mail: library@tcha.mus.in.us. Web Site: www.tcha.mus.in.us. *Mgr*, Paul J Schueler; Staff 2 (MLS 1, Non-MLS 1)
Founded 1925. Pop 150,000
Library Holdings: Bk Vols 20,000; Bk Titles 7,000; Per Subs 40
Subject Interests: Genealogy, Local history
Special Collections: Archives Coll, diaries, letters, photos; Local History Coll; Marriage & Local Court Records
Automation Activity & Vendor Info: (Cataloging) Inmagic, Inc.
Publications: 100 Years of the TC Courthouse; Grist Mills of Tippecanoe County, Indiana; Indians & A Changing Frontier, The Art of George Winter; Lafayette Newspapers, 150 years; Old Lafayette 1811-1853; Old Lafayette 1854-1875; Recollections of the Early Settlement of the Wabash Valley; Sandford Cox, Tippecanoe Tales (pamphlets on various local subjects); The House That Moses Fowler Built
Restriction: Non-circulating to the public
Function: Research library
Partic in Indiana Cooperative Library Services Authority
Friends of the Library Group

P TIPPECANOE COUNTY PUBLIC LIBRARY, 627 South St, 47901-1470. SAN 305-0076. Tel: 765-429-0100. FAX: 765-429-0150. Web Site: www.tcpl.lib.in.us. *Dir*, Joel Robinson; E-Mail: jrobinsn@tcpl.lib.in.us; *Asst Dir*, Scottie Patterson; E-Mail: scottie@tcpl.lib.in.us; *Ref*, Bradley Bradley; E-Mail: mbradley@tcpl.lib.in.us; *Tech Servs*, Terry Travis; E-Mail: tmtravis@tcpl.lib.in.us; *Circ*, Carin Schleicher; E-Mail: cschleic@tcpl.lib.in.us; *Ch Servs*, Amy Paget; E-Mail: amypaget@tcpl.lib.in.us; *YA Servs*, Ian McKinney; E-Mail: ianmck@tcpl.lib.in.us; *Outreach Serv*, Kirsten Serrano; E-Mail: kserrano@tcpl.lib.in.us; Staff 22 (MLS 20, Non-MLS 2)
Founded 1882. Pop 104,310; Circ 1,122,635
Jan 1999-Dec 1999 Income $3,004,874, State $124,836, County $2,713,313, Other $166,725. Mats Exp $2,798,183, Books $381,176, Per/Ser (Incl. Access Fees) $44,993, Micro $5,384, AV Equip $32,475, Electronic Ref Mat (Incl. Access Fees) $13,904. Sal $1,517,554 (Prof $531,648)
Library Holdings: Bk Vols 297,091; Per Subs 1,947
Subject Interests: Mental health
Special Collections: Indiana; Large Print Books; Local Newspaper Coll, 1831-date, micro; New Reader's Coll
Automation Activity & Vendor Info: (Acquisitions) SIRSI; (Circulation) SIRSI
Publications: Notes & Quotes (friends newsletter); The Pocket Edition (newsletter)
Partic in Indiana Cooperative Library Services Authority

Special Services for the Blind - ADA terminals for visually impaired
Open Mon-Thurs 9-9, Fri & Sat 9-6 & Sun 1-6
Friends of the Library Group
Bookmobiles: 1

LAGRANGE

P LAGRANGE COUNTY LIBRARY,* 203 W Spring St, 46761. SAN 341-3977. Tel: 219-463-2841. FAX: 219-463-2841. E-Mail: info@lagrange.lib.in.us. *Dir*, Mary Ball; *Bkmobile Coordr*, Jackie Oliver; Staff 24 (MLS 2, Non-MLS 22)
Founded 1919. Pop 30,000; Circ 200,000
Jan 1999-Dec 1999 Income $608,781. Mats Exp $115,700, Books $90,000, Per/Ser (Incl. Access Fees) $8,000, Micro $2,000, AV Equip $1,500, Other Print Mats $14,200. Sal $237,638
Library Holdings: Bk Titles 87,500; Per Subs 150
Subject Interests: Large type print
Publications: Newsletter
Branches: 3
HOWE BRANCH, Howe, 46746. SAN 341-4000. *Librn*, Marie Prendergast; *Librn*, Sharon Yoder
SHIPSHEWANA BRANCH, Shipshewana, 46565. SAN 323-5602. *Librn*, Salina Yoder; *Librn*, Sharon Yoder
TOPEKA BRANCH, Topeka, 46571. SAN 341-406X. *Librn*, Salina Yoder; *Librn*, Sharon Yoder; *Librn*, Vera Miller
Bookmobiles: 1

LAKE VILLAGE

P NEWTON COUNTY PUBLIC LIBRARY, Lake Village Memorial Township Public Library, 9458 N 315 West, 46349. (Mail add: PO Box 206, 46349), SAN 305-0084. Tel: 219-992-3490. FAX: 219-992-3490. E-Mail: lakevil@netnitco.net. *Dir*, Mary K Emmrich; Staff 6 (MLS 1, Non-MLS 5)
Founded 1947. Pop 8,260; Circ 73,654
Jan 1999-Dec 1999 Income (Main Library and Branch Library) $337,100. Mats Exp $64,195, Books $41,995, Per/Ser (Incl. Access Fees) $1,300. Sal $96,000 (Prof $32,000)
Library Holdings: Bk Vols 50,000; Bk Titles 49,500; Per Subs 12
Subject Interests: Fiction, Local history
Special Collections: Kankakee River, Bogus Island & Beaver Lake Info
Automation Activity & Vendor Info: (Circulation) Follett
Function: ILL available
Partic in Indiana Cooperative Library Services Authority
Merger of Lake Village Memorial Township Public Library & Newton County Contractual Library - 1996
Friends of the Library Group
Branches: 2
MOROCCO COMMUNITY LIBRARY, 120 E State, Morocco, 47963. (Mail add: PO Box 57, Morocco, 47963), SAN 375-9008. Tel: 219-285-2664. FAX: 219-285-2664. E-Mail: morocco@netnitco.net. *In Charge*, Jane T Gulley; Staff 2 (Non-MLS 2)
Founded 1963
Library Holdings: Bk Titles 15,000
Automation Activity & Vendor Info: (Circulation) Follett
Partic in Indiana Cooperative Library Services Authority
Friends of the Library Group
ROSELAWN LIBRARY, 4077 Kellar, Roselawn, 46372. (Mail add: PO Box 87, Roselawn, 46372), SAN 375-9016. Tel: 219-992-2010. FAX: 219-345-2010. E-Mail: rlswn@netnitco.net. *Dir*, Mary K Emmrich; Tel: 219-992-3490, Fax: 219-992-3490, E-Mail: lakvil@netnitco.net; *In Charge*, Leposave Tepavcevich; *Br Coordr*, T Jane Gulley. Subject Specialists: *Fiction*, T Jane Gulley; *Reference*, T Jane Gulley; Staff 4 (Non-MLS 4)
Founded 1962. Pop 8,645; Circ 73,654
Jan 1999-Dec 1999 Income (Main Library and Branch Library) $140,400, County $131,400, Locally Generated Income $9,000. Mats Exp $32,700, Books $25,000, Per/Ser (Incl. Access Fees) $700, Electronic Ref Mat (Incl. Access Fees) $7,000. Sal $86,400 (Prof $32,000)
Library Holdings: Bk Vols 44,000; Bk Titles 32,000; Per Subs 12; Bks on Deafness & Sign Lang 50
Subject Interests: Classical literature, Crafts, Local history, North American Indians in all aspects, Popular fiction
Special Collections: Beaver Lake History Coll; Bogus Island History Coll; Kankakee River History Coll
Automation Activity & Vendor Info: (Circulation) Follett
Function: ILL available
Partic in Indiana Cooperative Library Services Authority
Special Services for the Blind - Homebound services; Talking Books
Friends of the Library Group

LAWRENCEBURG

M DEARBORN COUNTY HOSPITAL, Medical Library, 600 Wilson Creek, 47025. SAN 375-1058. Tel: 812-537-1010. FAX: 812-537-2833. *Librn*, Carol Gillespie
Library Holdings: Bk Titles 180; Per Subs 30
Restriction: Not open to public

P LAWRENCEBURG PUBLIC LIBRARY DISTRICT, 123 W High St, 47025. SAN 305-0092. Tel: 812-537-2775. FAX: 812-537-2810. E-Mail: lawplib@seidata.com. Web Site: www.birch.palmi.edu/-lawpublib/, www.lpld.lib.in.us. *Dir*, Eleanor Ewbank; *Cat*, Sally Ann Stegner; *Ch Servs*, Jody Maples; *Circ*, Debra Beckett; Staff 17 (MLS 3, Non-MLS 14)
Founded 1910. Pop 23,105; Circ 148,000
Jan 2000-Dec 2000 Income $762,158, State $2,158, Locally Generated Income $750,000, Other $10,000. Mats Exp $135,000, Books $85,000, Per/Ser (Incl. Access Fees) $12,000, AV Equip $30,000, Electronic Ref Mat (Incl. Access Fees) $8,000. Sal $200,000 (Prof $126,000)
Library Holdings: Bk Vols 70,000; Per Subs 170
Subject Interests: Genealogy, Local history
Special Collections: Dearborn County Indiana cemetary records
Automation Activity & Vendor Info: (Cataloging) Gaylord; (Circulation) Gaylord
Partic in Indiana Cooperative Library Services Authority
Friends of the Library Group

S SURVEYORS HISTORICAL SOCIETY LIBRARY, 300 W High St, Ste 2, 47025-1912. SAN 373-2134. Tel: 812-537-2000. FAX: 812-537-2000.

LEBANON

P LEBANON PUBLIC LIBRARY, 104 E Washington St, 46052-2298. SAN 305-1684. Tel: 765-482-3460. FAX: 317-873-5059. Web Site: www.bccn.boone.in.us. *Dir*, Kay K Martin; *Ad Servs*, Yvonne Welty; *Ch Servs*, Christina Johnson; *Circ*, Cheryl Walden; *Ref*, Donna Boone; *Tech Servs*, Marcy Tranbarger; Staff 4 (MLS 1, Non-MLS 3)
Founded 1905. Pop 14,376
Jan 2000-Dec 2000 Income $735,323. Mats Exp $101,522, Books $83,618, Per/Ser (Incl. Access Fees) $4,500, Other Print Mats $8,892, Electronic Ref Mat (Incl. Access Fees) $4,512. Sal $357,791 (Prof $228,158)
Library Holdings: Bk Vols 60,479; Per Subs 176; High Interest/Low Vocabulary Bk Vols 200; Bks on Deafness & Sign Lang 100
Subject Interests: Local genealogy
Special Collections: Abraham Lincoln; Indiana Coll
Automation Activity & Vendor Info: (Acquisitions) Gaylord; (Cataloging) TLC
Partic in Indiana Cooperative Library Services Authority
Friends of the Library Group

LIBERTY

P UNION COUNTY PUBLIC LIBRARY, 2 E Seminary St, 47353-1398. SAN 305-0114. Tel: 765-458-5355. Toll Free Tel: 800-694-6300. FAX: 765-458-9375. E-Mail: ucpubliclibrary@usa.net. Web Site: ucpl.cnz.com. *Dir*, Karen Kahl; E-Mail: kkahl@usa.net; Staff 2 (MLS 1, Non-MLS 1)
Founded 1913. Pop 6,970; Circ 60,000
1999-2000 Income $247,387, State $833, City $172,366, Federal $22,249, County $51,939. Mats Exp $53,000, Books $35,000, Per/Ser (Incl. Access Fees) $6,000, AV Equip $12,000. Sal $135,400 (Prof $29,200)
Library Holdings: Bk Vols 25,000; Per Subs 106
Subject Interests: Genealogy, Indiana
Automation Activity & Vendor Info: (Cataloging) epixtech, inc.; (Circulation) epixtech, inc.
Partic in Eastern Ind Area Libr Servs Authority
Friends of the Library Group

LIGONIER

P LIGONIER PUBLIC LIBRARY,* 300 S Main St, 46767-1812. SAN 305-0122. Tel: 219-894-4511. FAX: 219-894-4509. *Dir*, Jerry L Nesbitt
Founded 1907. Pop 4,100; Circ 25,000
Jan 1997-Dec 1998 Income $160,000
Library Holdings: Bk Vols 22,000; Per Subs 91
Special Collections: Jewish Culture (Jewish Historical)
Partic in Area Libr Servs Authority, Region 3

LINCOLN CITY

S US NATIONAL PARK SERVICE, Lincoln Boyhood National Memorial, PO Box 1816, 47552. SAN 323-8652. Tel: 812-937-4541. FAX: 812-937-9929. Web Site: www.nps.gov/libo. *In Charge*, Dusty Shultz
Library Holdings: Bk Vols 1,100; Bk Titles 940
Special Collections: Abraham Lincoln
Restriction: Open to public for reference only

LINDEN

P LINDEN-CARNEGIE PUBLIC LIBRARY, 102 South Main St, 47955. (Mail add: PO Box 10, 47955), Tel: 765-339-4239. FAX: 765-339-4239. E-Mail: lindenlib@yahoo.com. *Admin Dir*, Lisa J Whipple; E-Mail: lwhipplelpl@yahoo.com; *Asst Librn*, Ruth Evans; *Asst Librn*, Delta Owens; Staff 3 (MLS 1, Non-MLS 2)

Founded 1915. Pop 1,154; Circ 18,000
Library Holdings: Bk Titles 17,322; Per Subs 116
Partic in Wabash Valley Area Libr Servs Authority
Open Mon, Wed, Fri 1-5, Tues & Thurs 1-8 & Sat 8:30am-12:30pm

LINTON

P MARGARET COOPER PUBLIC LIBRARY,* 110 E Vincenne St, PO Box 613, 47441. SAN 305-0149. Tel: 812-847-7802. FAX: 812-847-4695. Web Site: www.margaret-cooper.lib.in.us/. *Librn*, Ann Wright Gainey; *Ch Servs*, Phyllis Franklin
Founded 1907. Pop 7,883; Circ 60,000
Library Holdings: Bk Vols 19,000; Per Subs 90
Special Collections: Phil & Alice Faye Harris Coll (open by reservation & during Phil Harris Festival)
Publications: Friends of the Library Newsletter
Open Mon-Thurs 10-8, Fri & Sat 10-5
Friends of the Library Group

LOGANSPORT

S CASS COUNTY HISTORICAL SOCIETY & MUSEUM LIBRARY,* 1004 E Market St, 46947. SAN 373-0549. Tel: 219-753-3866. FAX: 219-753-3866. *Curator*, Bruce Stuart
Library Holdings: Bk Vols 1,500; Per Subs 10
Subject Interests: Genealogy
Open Tues-Sat 1-5

LOGANSPORT STATE HOSPITAL
M STAFF LIBRARY, 1098 South State Rd 25, 46947-9699. Tel: 219-722-4141, Ext 4002. FAX: 219-735-3414. *Librn*, Brian Newell
Founded 1938
Library Holdings: Bk Titles 2,000; Per Subs 60
Subject Interests: Alcoholism, Geriatrics and gerontology, Nursing, Psychiatry, Psychology, Social service (social work)
Partic in Indiana Cooperative Library Services Authority

P LOGANSPORT-CASS COUNTY PUBLIC LIBRARY,* 616 E Broadway, 46947-3187. SAN 341-4124. Tel: 219-753-6383. FAX: 219-722-5889. *Dir*, Philip C Shih; *Publ Servs*, Mary Jane Guise; *Acq, ILL, Tech Servs*, John Brock; *Ref*, Mary Snider; *Per*, Judith A Long; *Br Coordr*, Patricia Hamilton; *Cat*, Anita Harman; *Ref*, Mary Snyder; *Bkmobile Coordr*, Susan Brock; *Bibliog Instr*, Sandra Noakes; *Ch Servs*, Patricia Moore; Staff 29 (MLS 5, Non-MLS 24)
Founded 1894. Pop 348,749; Circ 278,750
Jan 1997-Dec 1998 Income $1,073,447
Library Holdings: Bk Titles 236,000; Per Subs 355
Subject Interests: Genealogy, Local history
Branches: 1
GALVESTON BRANCH, 304 E Jackson, Galveston, 46932. SAN 341-4159. Tel: 219-699-6170. *Librn*, Patricia Hamilton
Library Holdings: Bk Vols 6,000
Bookmobiles: 1

LOOGOOTEE

P FRANCES L FOLKS MEMORIAL LIBRARY, Loogootee Public Library, 410 N Line St, 47553-1263. SAN 305-0165. Tel: 812-295-3713. FAX: 812-295-3713. *Asst Librn*, Mary Ringwald; Staff 2 (MLS 2)
Founded 1939. Pop 2,958; Circ 15,318
Library Holdings: Bk Vols 18,289; Per Subs 52
Subject Interests: Business and management, Economics, History, Science/technology, Technology
Partic in Four Rivers Area Libr Serv Authority

LOWELL

P LOWELL PUBLIC LIBRARY,* 1505 E Commercial Ave, 46356-1899. SAN 305-0173. Tel: 219-696-7704. FAX: 219-696-5280. Web Site: birch.palni.edu/~drigg/. *Dir*, Michael Furl; *Asst Dir*, Phyllis Nelson; *Ref*, Darlene Rigg. Subject Specialists: *Indiana*, Doreen Anglis
Pop 15,000; Circ 250,000
Jan 1998-Dec 1999 Income $1,097,492, State $66,300, Locally Generated Income $122,752. Mats Exp $156,540, Books $122,646, Per/Ser (Incl. Access Fees) $17,800. Sal $391,600 (Prof $127,600)
Library Holdings: Bk Vols 86,000
Subject Interests: Genealogy, Indiana, Large type print, Local history
Publications: Two Newsletters
Partic in Indiana Cooperative Library Services Authority
Open Mon-Thurs 9-8 & Fri-Sat 9-5
Friends of the Library Group

LYNN

P WASHINGTON TOWNSHIP PUBLIC LIBRARY,* PO Box 127, 47355-0127. SAN 305-0181. Tel: 765-874-1488. FAX: 765-874-1427. *Librn*, Suzanne Robinson
Founded 1942. Pop 3,929; Circ 93,029
Jan 1998-Dec 1999 Income $45,708. Mats Exp $8,055. Sal $26,141
Library Holdings: Bk Vols 25,216; Bk Titles 15,634; Per Subs 60
Partic in Cent Ind Area Libr Servs Authority

MADISON

J IVY TECH STATE COLLEGE - SOUTHEAST, 590 Ivy Tech Dr, 47250. SAN 372-4077. Tel: 812-265-2580, Ext 4106. FAX: 265-4028, 812-265-2579. Web Site: www.ivy.tec.in.us. *Dir*, Margaret Seifert; E-Mail: mseifert@ivy.tec.in.us
Enrl 1,200; Fac 30; Highest Degree: Associate
Library Holdings: Bk Vols 8,500; Bk Titles 8,000; Per Subs 95
Subject Interests: Business, Computer, Electronics, Nursing
Database Vendor: Ebsco - EbscoHost, GaleNet, Lexis-Nexis, ProQuest
Function: ILL available, Internet access
Partic in Indiana Cooperative Library Services Authority; Jefferson County Libr Coop; SE Ind Area Libr Servs Authority
Special Services for the Deaf - High interest/low vocabulary books
Special Services for the Blind - Kurzweil Reader

M MADISON STATE HOSPITAL, Cragmont Professional Library, 711 Green Rd, 47250. SAN 341-4272. Tel: 812-265-2611, 812-265-7236. FAX: 812-265-7227. *Dir*, Wilma Bishop
Founded 1956
Library Holdings: Bk Vols 3,824; Per Subs 50
Partic in SE Ind Area Libr Servs Authority
Branches:
PATIENTS' LIBRARY Tel: 812-265-7406. FAX: 812-265-7227. *In Charge*, Cheryl Adams
Library Holdings: Bk Vols 4,000; Per Subs 15

P MADISON-JEFFERSON COUNTY PUBLIC LIBRARY, 420 W Main St, 47250-3796. SAN 305-019X. Tel: 812-265-2744. FAX: 812-265-2217. E-Mail: mjcplib@seidata.com. Web Site: www.seidata.com/~mjcplib/. *Dir*, Dianne Hill; *Bkmobile Coordr*, Cheryl Marriage; *Ch Servs*, Brenda Evans; *Cat, Tech Servs*, Julie Rubio; *ILL, Ref*, Charlene Peters; *Media Spec*, Charlene Abel; Staff 5 (MLS 5)
Founded 1818. Pop 29,800; Circ 200,074
Library Holdings: Bk Titles 106,636; Per Subs 230
Subject Interests: Historic preservation, Local history
Special Collections: Genealogy, bk & micro; Lemen Photog Coll; Local Newspapers 1840-date (Courier Coll), micro, bd; Local Newspapers, 1840-present (Courier Coll), Micro
Publications: Monthly calendar of events
Partic in Ind Video & Audio Network; Indiana Cooperative Library Services Authority
Special Services for the Blind - ADA terminals for visually impaired
Open Mon-Thurs 9-9, Fri 9-6, Sat 9-5 & Sun 1-5
Friends of the Library Group
Bookmobiles: 1

MARION

GM DEPARTMENT OF VETERANS AFFAIRS, Hospital Medical Library,* 1700 E 38th St, 46953. SAN 305-0254. Tel: 765-677-3110. FAX: 765-677-3111.
Library Holdings: Bk Vols 4,236; Per Subs 100
Subject Interests: Geriatrics and gerontology, Medicine, Nursing, Psychiatry, Psychology
Publications: AV catalog; newsletter
Partic in Eastern Ind Area Libr Servs Authority; Greater Midwest Regional Medical Libr Network; Indiana Cooperative Library Services Authority; Vets Admin Libr Network
Branches:
S PATIENT SERVICES Tel: 765-674-3321, Ext 3569. FAX: 765-677-3111. *Librn*, Karen A Davis
Library Holdings: Bk Vols 4,435
Subject Interests: Consumer health
Publications: AV catalog
Partic in Eastern Ind Area Libr Servs Authority; Indiana Cooperative Library Services Authority; Valnet
Special Services for the Deaf - Captioned film depository; High interest/low vocabulary books

C INDIANA WESLEYAN UNIVERSITY LIBRARY,* 4201 S Washington St, 46953. SAN 305-022X. Tel: 765-677-2184. FAX: 765-677-2767. Web Site: www.indwes.edu/academics/library/. *Dir*, Sheila O Carlblom; E-Mail: scarlblom@indwes.edu; *ILL*, Patti Ashby; *Ref*, Bruce Brinkley; *Circ*, Janice E Hanes; *Media Spec*, Wenda Clement; *Tech Servs*, Stephen Brown; *Acq, Per*, Cheri Colter; *Dir Libr Serv*, Jule Kind
Founded 1920. Highest Degree: Master

Jul 1998-Jun 1999 Income Parent Institution $612,493. Mats Exp $315,248, Books $148,767, Per/Ser (Incl. Access Fees) $152,391, Presv $6,232, Micro $6,673, Electronic Ref Mat (Incl. Access Fees) $1,185. Sal $495,731 (Prof $360,971)
Library Holdings: Bk Vols 103,536; Per Subs 663
Subject Interests: Counseling, Education, Nursing, Religion
Special Collections: Holiness; Wesleyan Church History
Database Vendor: Ebsco - EbscoHost
Partic in OCLC Online Computer Library Center, Inc; Private Acad Libr Network of Ind

M MARION GENERAL HOSPITAL, Medical Library, 441 N Wabash Ave, 46952. SAN 328-381X. Tel: 765-662-4760. FAX: 765-662-4523. E-Mail: tdoyle@mgh.net. Web Site: www.mgh.net. *Dir*, Dr Steven D Poe; *Coll Develop*, Theresa Doyle; Staff 1 (Non-MLS 1)
Jul 1999-Jun 2000 Mats Exp $31,089, Books $4,962, Per/Ser (Incl. Access Fees) $26,127
Library Holdings: Bk Vols 1,120; Per Subs 150
Subject Interests: Medicine
Partic in Nat Libr of Med
Open Mon-Fri 7:30-4:00

P MARION PUBLIC LIBRARY,* 600 S Washington St, 46953-1992. SAN 305-0238. Tel: 765-668-2900. TDD: 765-668-2907. FAX: 765-668-2911. E-Mail: mpl@comteck.com. Web Site: www.marion.lib.in.us. *Dir*, Sue Ann Israel; *Curator*, Barbara Love; *Ad Servs*, Mary Leffler; *AV*, Michelle Morgan; *Ch Servs*, Mary Eckerle; *Tech Servs*, Karen E Blinn; Staff 46 (MLS 3, Non-MLS 43)
Founded 1884. Pop 1,603; Circ 4,000
Jan 1999-Dec 1999 Income $1,612,857. Mats Exp $220,093. Sal $676,201
Library Holdings: Bk Vols 125,392; Per Subs 373
Subject Interests: Local history, Mus
Special Collections: Genealogy (Margaret Weesner Haram Coll)
Automation Activity & Vendor Info: (Cataloging) epixtech, inc.; (Circulation) epixtech, inc.; (OPAC) epixtech, inc.
Database Vendor: epixtech, inc., IAC - Info Trac
Publications: Special Edition (newsletter)
Partic in Indiana Cooperative Library Services Authority
Open Winter hrs (after Labor Day) Mon-Fri 9-9, Sat 9-5 & Sun 1-5; Summer hrs (after Memorial Day) Mon-Fri 9-8 & Sat 9-5

MARKLE

P MARKLE PUBLIC LIBRARY,* 155 W Sparks, PO Box 366, 46770-0519. SAN 376-5342. Tel: 219-758-3332. FAX: 219-758-2005. E-Mail: marklelibrary@coolsky.com. *Dir*, Rhonda Hamilton; Staff 4 (Non-MLS 4)
Pop 1,200
Jan 1999-Dec 1999 Income $53,600. Mats Exp $9,000, Books $3,500, AV Equip $3,500. Sal $35,600
Library Holdings: Bk Vols 10,000; Bk Titles 8,500; Per Subs 46
Open Mon-Fri 1-7, Sat & Sun 9-12

MARTINSVILLE

P MORGAN COUNTY PUBLIC LIBRARY,* 110 S Jefferson St, 46151. SAN 305-0270. Tel: 765-342-3451. FAX: 765-342-9992.
Founded 1906. Pop 44,321; Circ 178,000
Library Holdings: Bk Vols 80,000; Bk Titles 62,000; Per Subs 140
Subject Interests: Genealogy
Publications: Audio cassettes list; Children's Calendar (monthly); guide to services; irregular bookmark & handouts for special programs; new book list (monthly); newspaper column (weekly); video list
Partic in Central Ind Area Libr Servs; Ind Libr Film Serv; Indiana Cooperative Library Services Authority

MENTONE

P BELL MEMORIAL PUBLIC LIBRARY,* 306 N Broadway, 46539. (Mail add: PO Box 368, 46539-0368), SAN 305-0289. Tel: 219-353-7234. FAX: 219-353-1307. E-Mail: bellibl@medt.com. *Dir*, Madeleine Fisher; *Asst Dir*, Eileen Bowser; Staff 1 (MLS 1)
Founded 1916. Pop 4,001; Circ 57,507
Jan 1997-Dec 1998 Income $167,576, State $14,872, County $50,163, Parent Institution $6,019. Mats Exp $32,000, Books $15,000, Per/Ser (Incl. Access Fees) $5,000, Micro $12,000. Sal $87,800 (Prof $39,000)
Library Holdings: Bk Titles 33,000
Subject Interests: Agriculture, Arts and crafts, Genealogy, History, Indiana, Medicine, Natural science, Religion, Science/technology, Technology
Partic in Indiana Cooperative Library Services Authority
Friends of the Library Group

MERRILLVILLE

§C DAVENPORT UNIVERSITY, Merrillville Library, 8200 Georgia St, 46410. Tel: 219-769-5556. Circulation Tel: 219-650-5224. Toll Free Tel: 800-748-7880. FAX: 219-745-8911. E-Mail: mvlibrary@davenport.edu. Web Site: davenport.edu. *Asst Librn*, Marlene Adams; Tel: 219-650-5235
Library Holdings: Bk Titles 5,800
Open Mon-Thurs 7:30am-9:30pm, Fri 8-4, Sat 8-4:30

P LAKE COUNTY PUBLIC LIBRARY, 1919 W 81st Ave, 46410-5382. SAN 341-4337. Tel: 219-769-3541. FAX: 219-756-9358. E-Mail: webmaster@lakeco.lib.in.us. Web Site: www.lakeco.lib.in.us. *Dir*, Lawrence Acheff; *Asst Dir*, Ana Grandfield; *Head Tech Servs*, David Swinehart; *Ch Servs*, Denise Swinehart; *Bkmobile Coordr*, Janet Kotarski; *Publ Servs*, Kathleen Berda; *Head Ref*, Carolyn Strickland; *AV*, Dawn Mogle; *Per*, Christine Rettig; Staff 37 (MLS 37)
Founded 1959. Pop 200,064; Circ 1,255,115
Library Holdings: Bk Vols 1,029,171; Bk Titles 458,809; Per Subs 2,398
Special Collections: Indiana Coll, bks, pamphlets
Automation Activity & Vendor Info: (Acquisitions) epixtech, inc.; (Circulation) epixtech, inc.
Database Vendor: epixtech, inc.
Publications: business directory; directory of organizations; Happenings (Newsletter); media catalogs; newsletter for the deaf & hearing impaired
Partic in Northwest Indiana Health Science Library Consortium; OCLC Online Computer Library Center, Inc
Special Services for the Deaf - Books on deafness & sign language; Captioned film depository; High interest/low vocabulary books; Special interest periodicals; Videos & decoder
Participate in Northwest Indiana Literacy Coalition
Friends of the Library Group
Branches: 12

BLACK OAK, 5921 W 25th Ave, Gary, 46406-3024. SAN 341-4396. Tel: 219-844-8809. FAX: 219-844-5824. *Librn*, Kathy Deal
Library Holdings: Bk Vols 36,040
Open Mon & Wed-Fri 10-6, Tues 12:30-8:30, Sat 9-5

CEDAR LAKE BRANCH, 13330 Parrish St, Cedar Lake, 46303-9201. SAN 341-4426. Tel: 219-374-7121. FAX: 219-374-6333. *Librn*, Jeannine Furukawa
Library Holdings: Bk Vols 45,677
Open Mon-Thurs 12:30-8:30, Fri 10-6 & Sat 9-5

DYER-SCHERERVILLE BRANCH, 1001 W Lincoln Hwy, Schererville, 46375-1552. SAN 341-4450. Tel: 219-322-4731. FAX: 219-865-5478. *Librn*, Pam Maud
Library Holdings: Bk Vols 92,673
Open Mon-Thurs 10-8:30, Fri 10-6 & Sat 9-5

FORTY-FIRST AVENUE, 3491 W 41st Ave, Gary, 46408-3007. SAN 341-4485. Tel: 219-980-5180. FAX: 219-985-8057. *Librn*, Kathy Deal
Library Holdings: Bk Vols 37,977
Open Mon, Wed & Thurs 12:30-8:30, Tues & Fri 10-6, Sat 9-5

GRIFFITH BRANCH, 940 N Broad St, Griffith, 46319-1528. SAN 341-4515. Tel: 219-838-2825. FAX: 219-923-5772. *Librn*, Kathy Deal
Library Holdings: Bk Vols 62,935
Open Mon-Thurs 10-8:30, Fri 10-6 & Sat 9-5

HIGHLAND BRANCH, 2841 Jewett St, Highland, 46322-1617. SAN 341-454X. Tel: 219-838-2394. FAX: 219-923-5886. *Librn*, Ingrid Norris
Library Holdings: Bk Vols 76,407
Open Mon-Thurs 10-8:30, Fri 10-6 & Sat 9-5

HOBART BRANCH, 100 Main St, Hobart, 46342-4391. SAN 341-4574. Tel: 219-942-2243. FAX: 219-947-1823. Web Site: www.lakeco.libin.us/htwppage.htm. *Librn*, Mark Furukawa
Pop 25,000
Library Holdings: Bk Vols 72,751; Per Subs 100
Subject Interests: Investing
Open Mon-Thurs 10-8:30, Fri 10-6 & Sat 9-5
Friends of the Library Group

LAKE STATION BRANCH, 2400 Central Ave, Lake Station, 46405-2122. SAN 341-4604. Tel: 219-962-2409. FAX: 219-962-8460. Web Site: www.lakeco.lib.in.us/htwppage.htm. *Librn*, Mark Furukawa
Library Holdings: Bk Vols 34,209
Open Mon-Thurs 12:30-8:30, Fri 10-6 & Sat 9-5

MUNSTER BRANCH, 8701 Calumet Ave, Munster, 46321-2526. SAN 341-4663. Tel: 219-836-8450. FAX: 219-836-5694. *Librn*, Linda Dunn
Library Holdings: Bk Vols 70,651
Open Mon-Thurs 10-8:30, Fri 10-6 & Sat 9-5

NEW CHICAGO BRANCH, 3250 Michigan Ave, New Chicago, 46342-1172. SAN 341-4698. Tel: 219-962-2421. FAX: 219-962-4150. *Librn*, Mark Furukawa
Library Holdings: Bk Vols 28,378
Open Mon-Thurs 12:30-8:30, Fri 10-6 & Sat 9-5

SAINT JOHN BRANCH, 9450 Wicker Dr, Saint John, 46373-9646. SAN 341-4728. Tel: 219-365-5379. FAX: 219-365-5963. *Librn*, Pam Maud
Library Holdings: Bk Vols 29,174
Open Mon-Thurs 12:30-8:30, Fri 10-6 & Sat 9-5

TALKING BOOK SERVICE Tel: 219-769-3541, Ext 323. *Librn*, Dawn Mogle; *Circ*, Sharon Adley
Founded 1970
Special Collections: Descriptive videos

S NORTHERN INDIANA PUBLIC SERVICE CO, Corporate Reference Library,* 801 E 86th Ave, 46410. SAN 377-5674. Tel: 219-647-4011. FAX: 219-647-4007. *Asst Librn*, Cheryl Weaver
Library Holdings: Bk Vols 7,500; Per Subs 175

MICHIGAN CITY

C COMMONWEALTH BUSINESS COLLEGE, 325 E US Hwy 20, 46360. Tel: 219-877-3100. Web Site: www.cbcaec.com. *Librn*, Barbara Case
Library Holdings: Bk Vols 800; Bk Titles 900; Per Subs 30

S INDIANA STATE PRISON, Michael S Thomas Learning Resource Center, PO Box 41, 46360. SAN 341-4787. Tel: 219-874-7256, Ext 6100. FAX: 219-878-5825. *Dir Libr Serv*, Kenneth J Boyle; Staff 11 (MLS 1, Non-MLS 10)
Founded 1969
Library Holdings: Bk Vols 14,000; Per Subs 68
Subject Interests: Careers, Current events, Fiction
Restriction: Internal circulation only, Non-circulating to the public, Not open to public, Open to students, Private library
Function: Document delivery services, For research purposes, Newspaper reference library, Photocopies available, Research library
Partic in N Ind Asn Libr Servs Auth

P MICHIGAN CITY PUBLIC LIBRARY,* 100 E Fourth St, 46360-3393. SAN 341-4906. Tel: 219-873-3040. FAX: 219-873-3067. Web Site: www.mclib.org. *Dir*, Rose Chenoweth; E-Mail: rchenoweth@mclib.org; *Asst Dir, Circ, Publ Servs*, Don Glossinger; *Asst Dir, Publ Servs*, Lynn Lada; *AV*, Blane Halliday; *Acq*, Beth Jarnutowski; *Tech Servs*, Andrew Smith; *Ref*, Ronald B Hageman; *Publ Servs*, Martin Buechley; Staff 16 (MLS 16)
Founded 1897. Pop 42,250; Circ 285,126
Jan 1999-Dec 1999 Income $2,060,038, State $4,562, County $1,841,506, Locally Generated Income $213,970. Mats Exp $1,111,987, Books $154,838, Per/Ser (Incl. Access Fees) $20,380, AV Equip $33,355, Other Print Mats $79,636, Electronic Ref Mat (Incl. Access Fees) $972
Library Holdings: Bk Vols 184,660; Bk Titles 153,386; Per Subs 625
Special Collections: Genealogy Coll; Indiana Coll
Automation Activity & Vendor Info: (Cataloging) DRA; (Circulation) DRA; (OPAC) DRA
Open Mon-Thurs 9-8, Fri & Sat 9-6, Sun 1-5 (Sept-May)
Friends of the Library Group

M NORTHERN INDIANA EDUCATION FOUNDATION LIBRARY, 402 Michigan, 46360. SAN 378-1801. Tel: 219-872-7032. FAX: 219-872-1453. *Dir, Librn*, Mark Plaiss; E-Mail: markp@niefonline.org
Library Holdings: Bk Titles 400
Subject Interests: Medicine

MIDDLEBURY

P MIDDLEBURY COMMUNITY LIBRARY,* 101 E Winslow St, PO Box 192, 46540-0192. SAN 375-2860. Tel: 219-825-5601. FAX: 219-825-5150. E-Mail: mclib@pln.net. *Librn*, Teresa Rheinheimer; *Ch Servs*, Lori Nykiel; *Tech Servs*, Barbara Luebke; *AV*, Effie Bertolino; Staff 13 (MLS 3, Non-MLS 10)
Founded 1978. Pop 13,321; Circ 120,000
Library Holdings: Bk Vols 26,294; Per Subs 72
Special Services for the Deaf - Books on deafness & sign language
Friends of the Library Group

MIDDLETOWN

P MIDDLETOWN FALLCREEK TOWNSHIP PUBLIC LIBRARY,* 780 High St, 47356-1399. SAN 305-0351. Tel: 765-354-4071. FAX: 765-354-4071. Web Site: www.member.aol.mplib.org. *Dir*, Jana Whitesel; E-Mail: whitesel@ecicnet.org; *Ch Servs*, Tricia Jessup
Founded 1929. Pop 5,500; Circ 83,272
1997-1998 Income $143,050, State $500, County $142,450. Mats Exp $37,500, Books $27,000, Per/Ser (Incl. Access Fees) $3,000, AV Equip $2,000, Other Print Mats $3,000. Sal $91,500
Library Holdings: Bk Titles 29,432; Per Subs 62
Special Collections: Local Genealogy; Local Paper 1885-present (micro)
Friends of the Library Group

MILFORD

P MILFORD PUBLIC LIBRARY,* 101 Main St, PO Box 269, 46542-0269. SAN 305-036X. Tel: 219-658-4312. FAX: 219-658-9454. *Dir*, Lissa Krull; E-Mail: lkrull@fourway.net; *Ch Servs*, Donna G Angle
Founded 1907. Circ 34,558
Library Holdings: Bk Titles 35,000; Per Subs 75
Special Collections: PBS video collection; Town of Milford & Van Buren & East Jefferson Townships History
Partic in Area Libr Servs Authority Region 2

MISHAWAKA

C BETHEL COLLEGE, Bowen Library, 1001 W McKinley Ave, 46545. SAN 305-0386. Tel: 219-257-3347. FAX: 219-257-3499. Web Site: www.bethel-in.edu. *Dir*, Dr Clyde Root; E-Mail: rootc@bethel-in.edu; *ILL, Per, Ref*, Mark Root; Tel: 219-257-3504; *Cat*, Wendy Adams; *Ref*, Esther Matteson; Tel: 219-257-3283; *Archivist*, Tim Erdel; *Circ*, Kevin Blower; Tel: 219-257-3329. Subject Specialists: *Adult education*, Wendy Adams; *Business and management*, Wendy Adams; *Education*, Wendy Adams; *Fine arts*, Esther Matteson; *Language arts*, Esther Matteson; *Literature*, Esther Matteson; *Nursing*, Dr Clyde Root; *Philosophy*, Tim Erdel; *Religion*, Tim Erdel; *Science/technology*, Dr Clyde Root; Staff 7 (MLS 4, Non-MLS 3)
Founded 1947. Enrl 1,725; Fac 81; Highest Degree: Master
Jul 1999-Jun 2000 Income Parent Institution $431,111. Mats Exp $168,292, Books $68,036, Per/Ser (Incl. Access Fees) $52,841, Presv $10,664, Micro $7,972, Manuscripts & Archives $8,000, Electronic Ref Mat (Incl. Access Fees) $20,779. Sal $181,124 (Prof $111,314)
Library Holdings: Bk Vols 99,381; Per Subs 450; Bks on Deafness & Sign Lang 250
Subject Interests: Education, Nursing, Religion
Special Collections: Bethel College Archives; Dr Otis Bowen Museum & Archives; Missionary Church Archives & Historical Coll
Mem of Area Libr Servs Authority Region 2
Partic in Dialog Corporation; MALC Consortium; OCLC Online Computer Library Center, Inc

P MISHAWAKA-PENN PUBLIC LIBRARY, 209 Lincoln Way E, 46544-2084. SAN 341-4965. Tel: 219-259-5277. Interlibrary Loan Service Tel: 219-259-5277, Ext 218. Circulation Tel: 219-259-5277, Ext 214. Reference Tel: 219-259-5277, Ext 218. TDD: 219-254-5585. FAX: 219-255-8489. Web Site: www.mppl.lib.in.us. *Dir*, David J Eisen; Tel: 219-259-5585, Ext 300, E-Mail: d.eisen@mppl.lib.in.us; *Asst Dir, Coll Develop*, Gail Marti; E-Mail: g.marti@mppl.lib.in.us; *ILL*, Pamela Mims; E-Mail: pmims@mppl.lib.in.us; *Ch Servs*, Wava Furlong; E-Mail: w.furlong@mppl.lib.in.us; *YA Servs*, Constance Behrens-Hoffstetter; *AV*, Marsha Loyer; E-Mail: m.loyer@mppl.lib.in.us; *Cat, Tech Servs*, Florence Klecka; *Ref*, Anita Lutz; E-Mail: a.lutz@mppl.lib.in.us; Staff 67 (MLS 19, Non-MLS 48)
Founded 1907. Pop 60,869; Circ 487,336
Jan 1999-Dec 1999 Income (Main Library and Branch Library) $1,930,672, State $182,089, County $1,579,743, Locally Generated Income $168,840. Mats Exp $280,273, Books $192,784, Per/Ser (Incl. Access Fees) $47,789, Presv $5,200, Micro $15,000, AV Equip $2,500, Other Print Mats $2,000, Electronic Ref Mat (Incl. Access Fees) $15,000. Sal $1,002,222 (Prof $511,133)
Library Holdings: Bk Vols 190,385; Per Subs 632
Subject Interests: Local history
Special Collections: Heritage Center Coll
Automation Activity & Vendor Info: (Acquisitions) Innovative Interfaces Inc.; (Cataloging) Innovative Interfaces Inc.; (Circulation) Innovative Interfaces Inc.; (Course Reserve) Innovative Interfaces Inc.; (ILL) Innovative Interfaces Inc.; (Media Booking) Innovative Interfaces Inc.; (OPAC) Innovative Interfaces Inc.; (Serials) Innovative Interfaces Inc.
Database Vendor: Innovative Interfaces INN - View
Publications: Hi-Lites (monthly newsletter of Friends of Library) (Monthly)
Partic in Indiana Cooperative Library Services Authority; OCLC Online Computer Library Center, Inc
Friends of the Library Group
Branches: 1
BITTERSWEET, 602 Bittersweet Rd, 46544-4155. SAN 322-5887. Tel: 219-259-0392. FAX: 219-259-0399. Web Site: www.mppl.lib.in.us. *Librn*, Linda Sears; E-Mail: l.sears@mppl.lib.in.us; Staff 17 (MLS 6, Non-MLS 11)
Library Holdings: Bk Vols 56,846
Automation Activity & Vendor Info: (Acquisitions) Innovative Interfaces Inc.; (Cataloging) Innovative Interfaces Inc.; (Circulation) Innovative Interfaces Inc.; (Course Reserve) Innovative Interfaces Inc.; (ILL) Innovative Interfaces Inc.; (Media Booking) Innovative Interfaces Inc.; (OPAC) Innovative Interfaces Inc.; (Serials) Innovative Interfaces Inc.
Database Vendor: Innovative Interfaces INN - View
Friends of the Library Group

M ST JOSEPH COMMUNITY HOSPITAL LIBRARY, 215 W Fourth St, 46544. SAN 325-6766. Tel: 219-258-1354. FAX: 219-254-5318. *Head Librn*, Kristina Flora; Staff 1 (MLS 1)
Library Holdings: Bk Titles 800; Per Subs 33
Subject Interests: Podiatry
Partic in Indiana Cooperative Library Services Authority

MITCHELL

P MITCHELL COMMUNITY PUBLIC LIBRARY,* 804 Main St, 47446. SAN 305-0394. Tel: 812-849-2412. FAX: 812-849-2665. *Dir*, Sue Medland
Pop 11,050; Circ 109,767
Jan 1997-Dec 1998 Income $301,594, State $27,815, County $255,360, Locally Generated Income $18,419. Mats Exp $43,465, Books $33,893, Per/Ser (Incl. Access Fees) $3,554. Sal $154,424 (Prof $64,424)
Library Holdings: Bk Titles 39,000

Special Collections: Local History; Virgil "Gus" Grissom
Publications: Newsletter (monthly)
Partic in Indiana Cooperative Library Services Authority
Friends of the Library Group

MONON

P MONON TOWN & TOWNSHIP PUBLIC LIBRARY, 427 N Market, PO Box 305, 47959-0305. SAN 305-0408. Tel: 219-253-6517. FAX: 219-253-8373. *Dir*, Jo Minnick; E-Mail: jminnick@urhere.net
Founded 1914. Pop 3,140; Circ 25,744
Jan 1999-Dec 1999 Income $185,434, State $6,938, Federal $9,196, Locally Generated Income $165,100, Other $4,200. Mats Exp $24,155, Books $15,952, Per/Ser (Incl. Access Fees) $2,389, AV Equip $5,814. Sal $67,158
Library Holdings: Bk Vols 26,229; Per Subs 104
Automation Activity & Vendor Info: (Cataloging) Brodart; (Circulation) Brodart; (OPAC) Brodart
Partic in Indiana Cooperative Library Services Authority

MONTEREY

P MONTEREY-TIPPECANOE TOWNSHIP PUBLIC LIBRARY,* PO Box 38, 46960-0038. SAN 305-0416. Tel: 219-542-2171. FAX: 219-542-2171. *Librn*, Renita Potthoff; *Asst Librn*, Toni Mersch
Founded 1918. Pop 1,000; Circ 10,000
Jan 1997-Dec 1998 Income $67,000. Mats Exp $15,889. Sal $27,800
Library Holdings: Bk Vols 14,400; Per Subs 30
Special Collections: Indiana Coll
Partic in Northwest Indiana Health Science Library Consortium

MONTEZUMA

P MONTEZUMA PUBLIC LIBRARY, 212 Crawford St, 47862. (Mail add: PO Box 70, 47862), SAN 305-0424. Tel: 765-245-2772, 765-245-2782. FAX: 765-245-2772. *Dir*, Nancy Mattson
Pop 1,597; Circ 12,370
Library Holdings: Bk Vols 14,580; Per Subs 44
Partic in Indiana Cooperative Library Services Authority
Open Tues & Wed 12-5, Thurs 12-7 & Sat 9-12

MONTICELLO

S ANTIQUE STOVE ASSOCIATION LIBRARY,* 421 N Main St, 47960-1932. SAN 328-090X. Tel: 219-583-6465. *Librn*, Clifford Boram
Founded 1985
Library Holdings: Bk Vols 25
Special Collections: Stove Manufacturers Catalogs 1860-1935
Publications: Periodical (quarterly)
Have access to the archives of the Antique Stove Information Clearinghouse, which include over 2000 stove manufacturers' catalogs

P MONTICELLO UNION TOWNSHIP PUBLIC LIBRARY,* 321 W Broadway, 47960-2047. SAN 305-0432. Tel: 219-583-5643. FAX: 219-583-2782. Web Site: birch.palni.edu/~mutpl. *Dir*, Margaret I Hirschy; *Ad Servs*, Kathy Cotner; *Circ*, Mary Kestle; *Ch Servs*, Sandy Wagner; Staff 4 (Non-MLS 4)
Founded 1903. Pop 10,010; Circ 111,401
Jan 1998-Dec 1998 Income $345,769, State $1,117, Locally Generated Income $306,039, Other $38,613. Mats Exp $339,831, Books $39,453, Per/Ser (Incl. Access Fees) $2,535. Sal $191,285 (Prof $25,867)
Library Holdings: Bk Titles 45,801; Per Subs 133
Subject Interests: Genealogy, Local history
Automation Activity & Vendor Info: (Cataloging) SIRSI; (Circulation) SIRSI; (OPAC) SIRSI
Database Vendor: Ebsco - EbscoHost
Mem of Indiana Coop Libr Servs Authority
Friends of the Library Group

MONTPELIER

P MONTPELIER PUBLIC LIBRARY,* 301 S Main St, 47359. SAN 305-0440. Tel: 765-728-5969. FAX: 765-728-5969. E-Mail: mhtpl@netusa1.net. *Librn*, Laura Lee
Pop 2,911; Circ 42,936
Library Holdings: Bk Vols 16,790; Per Subs 66

MOORESVILLE

P MOORESVILLE PUBLIC LIBRARY,* 220 W Harrison St, 46158-1633. SAN 305-0459. Tel: 317-831-7323. FAX: 317-831-7383. *Librn*, Lynn Jurewicz; *Asst Librn*, Patricia Overmyer; *Ch Servs*, Sarah Kearns
Founded 1912. Pop 10,040; Circ 78,000
Jan 1997-Dec 1998 Income $307,130, State $300. Mats Exp $54,191, Books $20,000, Per/Ser (Incl. Access Fees) $10,000, Other Print Mats $5,000. Sal $151,703
Library Holdings: Bk Vols 44,063; Per Subs 127
Subject Interests: Local history
Special Collections: Local History Coll (Clifford C Furnas, John Dillinger & Paul Hadley)
Publications: Monthly newsletter
Partic in Indiana Cooperative Library Services Authority
Friends of the Library Group

MOUNT VERNON

P ALEXANDRIAN PUBLIC LIBRARY, 115 W Fifth St, 47620-1869. SAN 305-0467. Tel: 812-838-3286. FAX: 812-838-9639. E-Mail: alexpl@evansville.net. Web Site: www.apl.lib.in.us. *Dir*, Jos N Holman; *Asst Dir, Tech Servs*, Stephen Cochran; *Ch Servs*, Anne Cottrell; *Bkmobile Coordr*, LeAnn Seifert; *Ref*, Leanne York; *Circ*, Brian Winterman. Subject Specialists: *Servs*, Brian Winterman; Staff 6 (MLS 6)
Founded 1895. Pop 21,250
Jan 1999-Dec 1999 Income $1,026,000, State $2,500, County $1,023,500. Mats Exp $183,000, Books $170,000, Per/Ser (Incl. Access Fees) $13,000. Sal $525,000 (Prof $198,000)
Library Holdings: Bk Vols 85,000; Per Subs 114
Subject Interests: Genealogy, Indiana, Local history
Special Collections: Curriculum Enrichment
Publications: APL Core (quarterly) (Newsletter)
Partic in Indiana Cooperative Library Services Authority; OCLC Online Computer Library Center, Inc
Friends of the Library Group
Bookmobiles: 1

MUNCIE

M BALL MEMORIAL HOSPITAL, Medical Library & Information Center, 2401 W University Ave, 47303-3499. SAN 305-0491. Tel: 765-747-3204. Circulation Tel: 765-747-1959. FAX: 765-747-0137. *Dir Libr Serv*, Lorna Springston; Tel: 765-747-4229, E-Mail: lsprings@cami3.com; Staff 4 (MLS 1, Non-MLS 3)
Founded 1931
Library Holdings: Bk Vols 2,700; Per Subs 430
Subject Interests: Allied health, Commun health, Medicine, Nursing
Special Collections: Clinical, Medical & Nursing Journals & Textbooks; Consumer Health Information
Function: Reference services available
Partic in BRS; Dialog Corporation; Medline; Northeast Indiana Health Science Libraries Consortium

C BALL STATE UNIVERSITY, Alexander M Bracken Library, 2000 University Ave, 47306-1099. SAN 341-5023. Tel: 765-285-5277. Circulation Tel: 765-285-5143. Reference Tel: 765-285-1101. FAX: 765-285-2008. Web Site: www.library.bsu.edu. *Head Librn*, Hilde Calvert; *Dean of Libr*, Michael B Wood; *Asst Dean, Tech Servs*, Sharon Roberts; *Asst Dean, Publ Servs*, Judy Koor; *Archivist, Librn, Spec Coll*, John Straw; *Info Res*, Suzanne Rice; *Instrul Serv*, Melissa Muth; *Govt Doc, Ref*, Diane Calvin; *Cat*, Vanda Carnes; *Acq*, Rebecca Sheffield; *Music*, Keith Cochran; Staff 119 (MLS 40, Non-MLS 79)
Founded 1918. Enrl 16,745; Highest Degree: Doctorate
Jul 1999-Jun 2000 Income (Main Library and Branch Library) $6,897,418. Mats Exp $2,010,489, Books $559,379, Per/Ser (Incl. Access Fees) $1,102,602, Presv $65,447, AV Equip $53,022, Electronic Ref Mat (Incl. Access Fees) $177,017. Sal $4,132,255 (Prof $1,665,563)
Library Holdings: Bk Vols 1,114,321; Bk Titles 756,733; Per Subs 3,060
Special Collections: Althea L Stoeckel Delaware County Archives & Local History Coll; Elisabeth Ball World War I Coll, posters; Frederic W Goudy Coll; John Steinbeck Coll; Middletown Studies Coll; Modern American Poetry Coll; Nazi Coll; Richard Roller Coll (glass industry); Sir Norman Angell Coll; University Archives
Automation Activity & Vendor Info: (Cataloging) SIRSI; (Circulation) SIRSI
Function: Document delivery services, ILL available, Photocopies available
Partic in Indiana Cooperative Library Services Authority; OCLC Online Computer Library Center, Inc
Friends of the Library Group
Departmental Libraries:
ARCHITECTURE, Architecture Bldg Rm 116, 47306. SAN 341-5058. Tel: 765-285-5857. FAX: 765-285-2644. *Librn*, Wayne Meyer
Founded 1966
Subject Interests: Architecture, Historic preservation, Landscape architecture, Urban planning
ARCHIVES & SPECIAL COLLECTIONS, Rm BL 210, 47306. SAN 373-532X. Tel: 765-285-5078. FAX: 765-285-2644. *Archivist, Librn, Spec Coll*, John Straw
MUSIC, Bracken Library, Rm 106, 47306. SAN 341-5112. Tel: 765-285-5065. FAX: 765-285-2644. *Music*, Keith Cochran
Founded 1975
Special Collections: Tubists Universal Brotherhood Association

Resources, scores
SCIENCE-HEALTH SCIENCE, Cooper Science Bldg, CN16, 47306. SAN 341-5147. Tel: 765-285-5079. FAX: 765-285-2644. *Science*, Christy Groves

P CARNEGIE LIBRARY,* 301 E Jackson St, 47305-1878. SAN 341-5171. Tel: 765-747-8200. FAX: 765-747-8221. Web Site: www.munpl.org. *Dir*, Virginia Nilles; *Asst Dir*, John Drumm; *Tech Servs*, Iris Grieswell; *Ad Servs*, Mary Lou Gentis; *Ch Servs, Coll Develop*, Valerie Thompson; *Doc*, Donna Catron; *Coll Develop*, Jeff Weiss; Staff 27 (MLS 17, Non-MLS 10)
Founded 1874. Pop 74,656
Library Holdings: Bk Vols 264,020; Per Subs 805
Special Collections: Indiana Authors (Goddard Memorial Coll)
Publications: Just for Kids; LIBwire; Little Bits; MPLnow
Partic in Eastern Ind Area Libr Servs Authority; Indiana Cooperative Library Services Authority
Open Mon-Thurs 8-8, Fri 8-6 & Sat 9-6
Friends of the Library Group
Branches: 4
GRACE MARING BRANCH, 1808 S Madison St, 47302. SAN 341-535X. Tel: 765-747-8217. FAX: 765-747-8217. *Librn*, Cecelia Howard
Library Holdings: Bk Vols 22,125
WEBB HUNT BRANCH, 1110 W Memorial Dr, 47302. SAN 341-5295. Tel: 765-747-8218. FAX: 765-741-7336. *Librn*, Charlotte McNally
Library Holdings: Bk Vols 35,779
JOHN F KENNEDY BRANCH, 1700 W McGalliard Rd, 47304. SAN 341-5325. Tel: 765-747-8212. FAX: 765-747-8213. *Librn*, Barbara Baker
Library Holdings: Bk Vols 60,369
VIVIAN CONLEY BRANCH, 1824 E Centennial Ave, 47303. SAN 341-5260. Tel: 765-747-8216. FAX: 765-747-8216. *Librn*, Cecelia Howard
Library Holdings: Bk Vols 20,807
Bookmobiles: 1

P MUNCIE CENTER TOWNSHIP PUBLIC LIBRARY, 301 E Jackson St, 47305-2304. Tel: 765-747-8209. Web Site: www.munpl.org/. *Dir*, Virginia Nilles; E-Mail: mpladmin@ecic.cioe.com
Library Holdings: Bk Titles 352,063

S PLANNED PARENTHOOD OF EAST CENTRAL INDIANA LIBRARY,* 424 W Main St, 47305-1599. SAN 374-6739. Tel: 765-282-3546. FAX: 765-286-3701. *Librn*, Mridula Jarial
Founded 1965
Restriction: Non-circulating to the public
Mem of Eastern Ind Area Libr Servs Authority

NAPPANEE

P NAPPANEE PUBLIC LIBRARY,* 157 N Main St, 46550-1956. SAN 305-0513. Tel: 219-773-7919. FAX: 219-773-7910. *Dir*, Linda Yoder
Founded 1921. Pop 5,510; Circ 115,373
Library Holdings: Bk Vols 47,232; Per Subs 231
Special Collections: Heritage Center
Mem of Area Libr Servs Authority Region 2
Partic in Ind Libr Asn
Friends of the Library Group

NASHVILLE

S BROWN COUNTY HISTORICAL SOCIETY, Genealogy Collection,* PO Box 668, 47448. SAN 373-448X. Tel: 812-988-4297.
Library Holdings: Bk Vols 100; Per Subs 3
Subject Interests: Genealogy

P BROWN COUNTY PUBLIC LIBRARY, 205 Locust Lane, PO Box 8, 47448-0008. SAN 305-0521. Tel: 812-988-2850. FAX: 812-988-8119. Web Site: www.browncounty.lib.in.us. *Dir*, Yvonne Oliger; E-Mail: yoliger@browncounty.lib.in.us
Founded 1919. Pop 14,000; Circ 56,300
Jan 1998-Dec 1999 Income $231,050. Mats Exp $61,000. Sal $110,750
Library Holdings: Bk Vols 40,000; Per Subs 100
Special Collections: Brown County Artists & Authors
Publications: Annual Report
Mem of SE Ind Area Libr Servs Authority
Partic in Indiana Cooperative Library Services Authority
Friends of the Library Group

NEW ALBANY

C INDIANA UNIVERSITY SOUTHEAST LIBRARY, 4201 Grant Line Rd, 47150. SAN 305-053X. Tel: 812-941-2262. Circulation Tel: 812-941-2485. FAX: 812-941-2493. Web Site: www.ius.edu/library. *Dir Libr Serv*, C Martin Rosen; E-Mail: crosen@ius.edu; *Electronic Resources*, Dennis Kreps; E-Mail: dkreps@ius.edu; *Coll Develop, Spec Coll*, Jacqueline Johnson; E-Mail: jfjohnso@ius.edu; *Instrul Serv, Publ Servs*, Nancy Totten; E-Mail: ntotten@ius.edu; *Access Serv*, Gabrielle M Carr; E-Mail: gcarr@ius.edu; Staff 16 (MLS 6, Non-MLS 10)
Founded 1941. Enrl 6,400; Fac 241; Highest Degree: Master
Jul 1999-Jul 2000 Mats Exp $425,000. Sal $530,000 (Prof $262,000)
Library Holdings: Bk Vols 150,000; Per Subs 1,035
Subject Interests: Music
Special Collections: Ars Femina Archives; Education (Curriculum Laboratory), bks, media kit, Center for Cultural Resources; IUS Archives
Automation Activity & Vendor Info: (Acquisitions) SIRSI; (Cataloging) SIRSI; (Circulation) SIRSI; (Course Reserve) SIRSI; (OPAC) SIRSI; (Serials) SIRSI
Database Vendor: Ebsco - EbscoHost, GaleNet, Lexis-Nexis, OCLC - First Search, OVID Technologies, Silverplatter Information Inc.
Partic in Indiana Cooperative Library Services Authority; Kentuckiana Metroversity, Inc; OCLC Online Computer Library Center, Inc
Special Services for the Blind - Adapted computers & special software with speech output to assist learning disabled, mentally retarded & uneducated

P NEW ALBANY-FLOYD COUNTY PUBLIC LIBRARY,* 180 W Spring St, 47150-3692. SAN 305-0548. Tel: 812-944-8464. FAX: 812-949-3532. *Dir*, Stephen T Day; *Tech Servs*, Cyndi Kepley; *ILL, Ref*, Carla Baldwin; *Circ*, Martha Stubbins; *Ch Servs*, Ruth Houghton; *AV*, Edward Eggenspiller; Staff 47 (MLS 7, Non-MLS 40)
Founded 1884. Pop 64,400; Circ 470,521
Jan 1999-Dec 1999 Income $1,834,950
Library Holdings: Bk Vols 197,256; Per Subs 381
Subject Interests: Genealogy, Local history
Automation Activity & Vendor Info: (Cataloging) epixtech, inc.; (Circulation) epixtech, inc.; (Media Booking) epixtech, inc.; (OPAC) epixtech, inc.
Partic in Indiana Cooperative Library Services Authority
Open Mon-Thurs 9-8:30, Fri & Sat 9-5:30
Friends of the Library Group

NEW CARLISLE

P NEW CARLISLE & OLIVE TOWNSHIP PUBLIC LIBRARY, 124 E Michigan St, PO Box Q, 46552-0837. SAN 305-0556. Tel: 219-654-3046. FAX: 219-654-8260. Web Site: ncpl.lib.in.us. *Dir*, Stephen J Boggs; E-Mail: stephen@ncpl.lib.in.us; *Asst Dir*, Amy Schrock; *Ch Servs*, Sara Smigielski; Staff 1 (MLS 1)
Founded 1894. Pop 5,019
Jan 1999-Dec 2000 Income $258,000, State $30,000, City $200,000, Other $28,000. Mats Exp $43,403, Books $17,748, Per/Ser (Incl. Access Fees) $3,990, AV Equip $12,000, Electronic Ref Mat (Incl. Access Fees) $1,000. Sal $119,966 (Prof $33,184)
Library Holdings: Bk Vols 35,000; Per Subs 105
Subject Interests: Arts and crafts, Fiction, Local history
Automation Activity & Vendor Info: (OPAC) Follett
Partic in Indiana Cooperative Library Services Authority
Open Mon-Thurs 9-7, Fri 9-5 & Sat 9-3

NEW CASTLE

S HENRY COUNTY HISTORICAL SOCIETY, Reference Room, 614 S 14th St, 47362. SAN 305-0564. Tel: 765-529-4028. E-Mail: hchisoc@kiva.net. Web Site: www.kiva.net/~hchisoc/museum.htm. *Curator*, Marianne Hughes
Founded 1887
Library Holdings: Bk Vols 1,360; Bk Titles 821
Subject Interests: Indiana, Local history
Special Collections: Genealogy
Publications: Historicalog (newsletter)

P NEW CASTLE-HENRY COUNTY PUBLIC LIBRARY, 376 S 15th St, PO Box J, 47362-1050. SAN 305-0572. Tel: 765-529-0362. FAX: 765-521-3581. Web Site: www.nchcpl.lib.in.us. *Dir*, Jan Preusz; E-Mail: janp@nchcpl.lib.in.us; *Ch Servs*, Celesta Dudley; E-Mail: celestad@nchcpl.lib.in.us; Staff 32 (MLS 5, Non-MLS 27)
Founded 1913. Pop 39,208; Circ 374,222
Library Holdings: Bk Vols 160,248; Bk Titles 149,000; Per Subs 278; High Interest/Low Vocabulary Bk Vols 300
Special Collections: Indiana History; New Castle & Henry County
Automation Activity & Vendor Info: (Cataloging) DRA; (Circulation) DRA; (Serials) DRA
Database Vendor: Ebsco - EbscoHost
Partic in Indiana Cooperative Library Services Authority
Open Mon-Thurs 9-9, Fri 9-6, Sat 9-5 & Sun 1-5
Friends of the Library Group
Bookmobiles: 1

NEW HARMONY

S WORKINGMEN'S INSTITUTE LIBRARY, 407 W Tavern St, PO Box 368, 47631-0368. SAN 305-0599. Tel: 812-682-4806. FAX: 812-682-4806. Web Site: www.newharmonywmi.lib.in.us. *Dir*, Sherry Graves; Staff 1 (MLS 1)
Founded 1838
Library Holdings: Bk Vols 32,000; Per Subs 36

Subject Interests: Education, Theater
Special Collections: 19th Century Women's Rights (Workingmen's Institute), mss; New Harmony History Manuscript Coll
Friends of the Library Group

NEWBURGH

C ITT TECHNICAL INSTITUTE, Newburgh Learning Resource Center, 10999 Stahl Rd, 47630. Tel: 812-858-1600. Toll Free Tel: 800-832-4488. Web Site: www.itttech.edu. *Dir*, Diana Hamer; E-Mail: dhamer@ittesi.com
Library Holdings: Bk Vols 2,250; Bk Titles 3,000; Per Subs 50

P OHIO TOWNSHIP PUBLIC LIBRARY SYSTEM, 23 W Jennings St, 47630-1408. SAN 305-0602. Tel: 812-853-5468. FAX: 812-853-0509. Web Site: www.ohio.lib.in.us. *Dir*, Stephen Thomas; E-Mail: sthomas@ohio.lib.in.us; *Asst Dir*, Margaret Hill; *Ch Servs*, Linda Spillman Bruns; *Circ*, Bob Tremper; *Ref Servs YA*, Jacalin Downs; *Tech Servs*, Joan Elliott Parker; Staff 37 (MLS 4, Non-MLS 33)
Founded 1897. Pop 25,420; Circ 483,559
Jan 1999-Dec 1999 Income (Main Library and Branch Library) $978,082. Mats Exp $128,405. Sal $633,761
Library Holdings: Bk Vols 109,365; Per Subs 225
Subject Interests: Local history
Special Collections: Warrick County Families Genealogy; Warrick County History
Automation Activity & Vendor Info: (Circulation) Gaylord; (OPAC) Gaylord
Partic in Four Rivers Area Libr Serv Authority; Indiana Cooperative Library Services Authority
Friends of the Library Group
Branches: 2
CHANDLER LIBRARY, 402 S Jaycee St, Chandler, 47610. SAN 324-3079. Tel: 812-925-7179. FAX: 812-925-7192. *In Charge*, Joan Parker; Staff 13 (MLS 1, Non-MLS 12)
Library Holdings: Bk Titles 20,000
Friends of the Library Group
NEWBURGH LIBRARY, 23 W Jennings St, 47630. SAN 370-1069. Tel: 812-853-5468. FAX: 812-853-6377. Web Site: www.ohio.lib.in.us. *In Charge*, Margaret Hill
Library Holdings: Bk Titles 50,000
Friends of the Library Group

NEWPORT

P NEWPORT-VERMILLION COUNTY LIBRARY, 385 E Market St, PO Box 100, 47966. SAN 341-5384. Tel: 765-492-3555. FAX: 765-492-4553. *Librn*, Rebecca Gosnell; E-Mail: rgosnell@usa.net; Staff 1 (MLS 1)
Founded 1929. Pop 7,523; Circ 32,948
Jan 1999-Dec 2000 Income $204,489. Mats Exp $25,000. Sal $86,451 (Prof $24,204)
Library Holdings: Bk Vols 33,840; Per Subs 143
Subject Interests: Cooking, Genealogy
Partic in Indiana Cooperative Library Services Authority

NOBLESVILLE

S INDIANA TRANSPORTATION MUSEUM LIBRARY,* PO Box 83, 46061. SAN 325-7258. Tel: 317-773-6000. FAX: 317-773-5530. *Librn*, Jerry Marlette
Subject Interests: Aviation, Transportation
Special Collections: Aviation Timetables; Railroad Engineering Drawings; Railroad Public & Employee Timetables

P NOBLESVILLE-SOUTHEASTERN PUBLIC LIBRARY, One Library Plaza, Cumberland Rd, 46060-5639. SAN 305-0610. Tel: 317-773-1384. FAX: 317-776-6936. Web Site: www.nspl.lib.in.us/nspl.html. *Dir*, David L Cooper; Tel: 317-770-3203, E-Mail: cooperd@nspl.lib.in.us; *Asst Dir*, Gail A Winsmore; Tel: 317-770-3202, E-Mail: winsmoreg@nspl.lib.in.us; *Tech Servs*, Holly Kennerly; Tel: 317-770-3220, E-Mail: kennerlyh@nspl.lib.in.us; *Ch Servs*, Ann Marie Short; Tel: 317-770-3218, E-Mail: heroldsam@nspl.lib.in.us; *AV*, Melissa Stewart; Tel: 317-770-3235, E-Mail: stewartm@nspl.lib.in.us; *Ref*, Linda Shaw; Tel: 317-770-3207, E-Mail: shawl@nspl.lib.in.us; *Circ*, Mary Kay Patterson; Tel: 317-770-3226, E-Mail: pattersonm@nspl.lib.in.us; *Syst Coordr*, Rob Brown; Tel: 317-770-3231, E-Mail: brownr@nspl.lib.in.us
Founded 1909. Pop 66,420; Circ 954,640
Jan 1999-Dec 1999 Income $4,266,496, State $232,176, County $3,763,176, Locally Generated Income $271,144. Mats Exp $860,857, Books $431,044, Per/Ser (Incl. Access Fees) $157,255, AV Equip $134,818, Electronic Ref Mat (Incl. Access Fees) $137,740. Sal $1,799,400
Library Holdings: Bk Vols 278,988; Bk Titles 260,074; Per Subs 636
Special Collections: Hamilton County History & Genealogy, bk & microfilm
Automation Activity & Vendor Info: (Acquisitions) SIRSI; (Cataloging) SIRSI; (Circulation) SIRSI; (OPAC) SIRSI
Database Vendor: GaleNet
Publications: Abstracts of the Will Records of Hamilton County, Indiana 1824-1901
Partic in Indiana Cooperative Library Services Authority
Special Services for the Deaf - Books on deafness & sign language; TDD; Videos & decoder
Operates van in four townships
Friends of the Library Group
Bookmobiles: 1

NORTH JUDSON

P NORTH JUDSON-WAYNE TOWNSHIP PUBLIC LIBRARY, 208 Keller Ave, 46366. SAN 305-0629. Tel: 219-896-2841. FAX: 219-896-2892. Web Site: www.njwt.lib.in.us. *Dir*, Jane Ellen Felchuk; Staff 1 (MLS 1)
Founded 1921. Pop 4,653; Circ 34,982
Jan 1999-Dec 1999 Income $131,667, State $701, County $110,271, Locally Generated Income $20,695. Mats Exp $34,803, Books $29,711, Per/Ser (Incl. Access Fees) $2,262. Sal $67,363 (Prof $22,000)
Library Holdings: Bk Titles 22,000; Per Subs 101
Special Collections: Excalibur Coll; Mint Growing
Automation Activity & Vendor Info: (Acquisitions) Sagebrush Corporation; (Cataloging) Sagebrush Corporation; (Circulation) Sagebrush Corporation; (OPAC) Sagebrush Corporation
Partic in Indiana Cooperative Library Services Authority
Open Mon-Thurs 11-8, Fri 11-6 & Sat 10-3
Friends of the Library Group

NORTH MANCHESTER

C MANCHESTER COLLEGE, Funderburg Library, College Ave, 46962. SAN 305-0637. Tel: 219-982-5063. FAX: 219-982-5362. Web Site: www.manchester.edu/library. *Coll Develop, Dir*, Robin J Gratz; E-Mail: rjgratz@manchester.edu; *Tech Servs*, Darla Vornberger; *Archivist*, Sara Smith; *Ref*, Jill Lichtsinn; *ILL*, Doris Stephenson; Staff 6 (MLS 4, Non-MLS 2)
Founded 1889. Enrl 1,132; Highest Degree: Master
Jul 1999-Jun 2000 Income $478,884. Mats Exp $160,512, Books $61,052, Per/Ser (Incl. Access Fees) $66,067, Presv $4,191, Micro $5,446, AV Equip $193, Electronic Ref Mat (Incl. Access Fees) $23,563. Sal $236,787
Library Holdings: Bk Vols 172,822; Per Subs 733
Special Collections: Church of the Brethren Coll; College Archives; Peace Studies
Database Vendor: DRA
Publications: Periodicals Holdings List
Partic in Indiana Cooperative Library Services Authority; OCLC Online Computer Library Center, Inc; Private Acad Libr Network of Ind

P NORTH MANCHESTER PUBLIC LIBRARY, 405 N Market St, 46962. SAN 305-0645. Tel: 219-982-4773. FAX: 219-982-6342. E-Mail: nmpl@nman.lib.in.us. Web Site: www.nman.lib.in.us. *Dir*, Davonne Rogers; *Ch Servs*, Nancy Lance; Staff 4 (MLS 1, Non-MLS 3)
Founded 1912. Pop 6,300; Circ 114,335
Jan 1999-Dec 1999 Income $301,458. Mats Exp $39,700, Books $33,000, Per/Ser (Incl. Access Fees) $4,700, AV Equip $2,000. Sal $144,320
Library Holdings: Bk Vols 48,860; Per Subs 140
Subject Interests: Genealogy, Large type print, Local history
Special Collections: North Manchester News-Journal, 1882-present
Automation Activity & Vendor Info: (Cataloging) Follett; (Circulation) Follett; (OPAC) Follett
Partic in Indiana Cooperative Library Services Authority
Friends of the Library Group

NORTH VERNON

P JENNINGS COUNTY PUBLIC LIBRARY,* 2375 N Hwy 3, 47265-1596. SAN 305-0653. Tel: 812-346-2091. FAX: 812-346-2127. E-Mail: jlibrary@seidata.com. Web Site: www.seidata.com/~jlibrary/jcplhome.html. *Dir*, Larry Cunningham; *Publ Servs*, Joyce Null; *Tech Servs*, Illah Allsop; Staff 9 (MLS 2, Non-MLS 7)
Founded 1813. Pop 27,210; Circ 100,000
Jan 1998-Dec 1999 Income $606,000. Mats Exp $113,000, Books $65,000, Per/Ser (Incl. Access Fees) $24,000. Sal $309,485
Library Holdings: Bk Vols 90,000; Per Subs 236
Subject Interests: Genealogy, Local history
Special Collections: Local History
Partic in Indiana Cooperative Library Services Authority; SE Ind Area Libr Servs Authority
Friends of the Library Group

NOTRE DAME

J HOLY CROSS COLLEGE LIBRARY, 54515 SR 933 N, Box 308, 46556-0308. SAN 305-0661. Tel: 219-239-8391. FAX: 219-245-5772. *Dir*, Bro Charles Gregg; E-Mail: cgregg@hcc-nd.edu; *Assoc Librn*, Thomas Cashore; E-Mail: tcashore@hcc-nd.edu; Staff 3 (MLS 1, Non-MLS 2)
Founded 1966. Fac 41; Highest Degree: Associate

Library Holdings: Bk Vols 15,200; Bk Titles 14,123; Per Subs 165
Automation Activity & Vendor Info: (Circulation) EX Libris; (Course Reserve) EX Libris; (ILL) EX Libris; (OPAC) EX Libris
Database Vendor: OCLC - First Search
Mem of Indiana Coop Libr Servs Authority
Partic in Michiana Acad Libr Consortium

SR MOREAU SEMINARY LIBRARY, 107 Moreau, PO Box 668, 46556. SAN 325-6707. Tel: 219-631-5046. FAX: 219-631-6813, 631-9233. E-Mail: morsmlib.morsmlib.l@nd.edu. *Dir*, Sr Elizabeth Panero; *Ser*, Barbara Varda
Library Holdings: Bk Titles 47,500
Subject Interests: Theology

C SAINT MARY'S COLLEGE, Cushwa-Leighton Library, 46556. SAN 305-067X. Tel: 219-284-5280. Interlibrary Loan Service Tel: 219-284-4804. Circulation Tel: 219-284-5278. Reference Tel: 219-284-5288. FAX: 219-284-4791. Web Site: www.saintmarys.edu/. *Dir*, Sister Bernice Hollenhorst; E-Mail: bernice@saintmarys.edu; *ILL, Ref*, Jill Hobgood; E-Mail: jhobgood@saintmarys.edu; *Cat*, Katherine Marschall; Tel: 219-284-5638, E-Mail: marschal@saintmarys.edu; *Bibliog Instr, Ref*, Robert Hohl; Tel: 219-284-5287, E-Mail: rhohl@saintmarys.edu; *Per*, Susan Wiegand; Tel: 219-284-4789, E-Mail: swiegand@saintmarys.edu; *Acq, Coll Develop*, Marcia Burns; Tel: 219-284-5285, E-Mail: mburns@saintmarys.edu; *Archivist*, John Kovach; Tel: 219-284-5282, E-Mail: jkovach@saintmarys.edu; *Online Servs, Ref*, Julia Long; Tel: 219-284-5289, E-Mail: jlong@saintmarys.edu; Staff 13 (MLS 6, Non-MLS 7)
Founded 1855. Enrl 1,604; Fac 128; Highest Degree: Bachelor
Jun 1999-May 2000 Income Parent Institution $885,770. Mats Exp $187,080, Books $68,686, Per/Ser (Incl. Access Fees) $98,201, Presv $6,604, Micro $3,841, AV Equip $2,135, Electronic Ref Mat (Incl. Access Fees) $7,613. Sal $461,982 (Prof $294,811)
Library Holdings: Bk Vols 209,375; Bk Titles 157,557; Per Subs 776
Special Collections: Dante
Automation Activity & Vendor Info: (Acquisitions) EX Libris; (Cataloging) EX Libris; (Circulation) EX Libris; (OPAC) EX Libris; (Serials) EX Libris
Database Vendor: Dialog, Ebsco - EbscoHost, IAC - Info Trac, OCLC - First Search, Wilson - Wilson Web
Partic in Indiana Cooperative Library Services Authority; Michiana Acad Libr Consortium; OCLC Online Computer Library Center, Inc

C UNIVERSITY LIBRARIES OF NOTRE DAME, 221 Hesburgh Library, 46556. SAN 341-5414. Tel: 219-631-5252. FAX: 219-631-6772. Web Site: www.md.edu:80/~ndlibs/. *Dir*, Jennifer A Younger; *Acq*, Lorenzo A Zeugner; *Ref*, Marsha Stevenson; *Spec Coll*, Louis Jordan; *Doc*, Michael A Lutes; *Circ*, Sue Dietl; Staff 204 (MLS 44, Non-MLS 160)
Founded 1873. Enrl 10,087; Fac 706; Highest Degree: Doctorate
1998-1999 Mats Exp $6,863,380, Books $2,281,522, Per/Ser (Incl. Access Fees) $3,546,272, Other Print Mats $804,530. Sal $6,752,889 (Prof $2,614,997)
Library Holdings: Bk Vols 2,705,052; Bk Titles 1,281,484; Per Subs 24,435
Special Collections: 1798 Irish Rebellion Coll; 17th-Early 19th Century Books from Religious Libraries Near Olmutz (Olmutz Coll); Anastos Byzantine Coll; Armed Services Editions Coll; Autographed Books (Theodore M Hesburgh Coll); Catholic Americana Coll; Chesterton (John Bennett Shaw Coll); Dante (John A Zahm Coll); Descartes (Denisoff Coll); Early American Newspapers (Thackenbruch Coll); Early Editions of the Works of Edmund Burke (William Todd Coll); Early Printed Books (Astrik L Gabriel Coll); Early Printed Maps of Ireland Coll; Edward Gorey Coll; Eric Gill Coll; European Communities; Fundamentalist/Evangelical Magazines (Adam L Lutzweiler Coll); Garcilaso de la Vega & the History of Peru (Durand Coll); George Berkeley (A A Luce Coll); Historical Botany (Edward Greene Coll); Irish Music (Captain Francis O'Neill Coll); Jacques Maritain Coll; Jorge Luis Borges Coll; McDevitt Inquisition Coll; Medieval & Renaissance Manuscripts; Modern Manuscript Coll; Notre Dame Coll; Penguin Paperbacks, 1935-1965; R H Gore, Sr Orchid Coll; Robert H Gore Numismatic Coll; Sports (Edmund Joyce Coll); Vatican II Documents Coll; Wolf Irish Stamp Coll
Automation Activity & Vendor Info: (Acquisitions) EX Libris; (Cataloging) EX Libris; (Serials) EX Libris
Publications: Access
Mem of Asn of Research Libraries
Partic in Center For Research Libraries; Indiana Cooperative Library Services Authority; Nerl; OCLC Online Computer Library Center, Inc; RLIN
Departmental Libraries:
ARCHITECTURE, 117 Bond Hall, 46556-5652. SAN 341-5449. Tel: 219-631-6654. FAX: 219-631-9662. E-Mail: library.archlib.l@nd.edu. Web Site: www.nd.edu/~archlib/. *Librn*, Jane A Devine; Tel: 219-631-9401; *Branch Mgr*, Deborah Webb; Staff 4 (MLS 1, Non-MLS 3)
Founded 1931. Enrl 250; Fac 20; Highest Degree: Master
Library Holdings: Bk Vols 23,000; Spec Interest Per Sub 125
Subject Interests: Architecture, Interior design, Landscape architecture, Rare books, Urban planning
Publications: New Acquisitions
Restriction: Circulation limited
CHEMISTRY-PHYSICS, 231 Nieuwland Science Hall, 46556. SAN 341-5473. Tel: 219-631-7203. FAX: 219-631-9661. E-Mail: chphlibr@vma.cc.nd.edu. Web Site: www.nd.edu/~chemlib/. *Librn*, Thurston Miller
Library Holdings: Bk Vols 39,336
Subject Interests: Astronomy, Chemistry, Physics
Publications: New Acquisitions
ENGINEERING, 149 Fitzpatrick Hall, 46556. SAN 341-5503. Tel: 219-631-6665. FAX: 219-631-9208. E-Mail: library.engrlib.1@nd.edu. Web Site: www.nd.edu/~engrlib. *Librn*, Carol A Szambelan; E-Mail: szambelan.1@nd.edu; Staff 4 (MLS 1, Non-MLS 3)
Library Holdings: Bk Vols 40,941; Per Subs 800
Publications: New Book List (Accession list)
KELLOGG/KROC INFORMATION CENTER, Hesburgh Ctr International Studies, 46556. SAN 378-0430. Tel: 219-631-8534. FAX: 219-631-6717. Web Site: www.nd.edu/~kic/. *Librn*, Scott Van Jacob
LIFE SCIENCES, B149 Paul V Galvin Life Sci Ctr, 46556. SAN 341-5597. Tel: 219-631-7209. FAX: 219-631-9207. Web Site: www.nd.edu/~lifeslib/. *Librn*, Sherri Edwards; Tel: 219-631-4034, E-Mail: edwards.49@nd.edu; Staff 4 (MLS 1, Non-MLS 3)
Library Holdings: Bk Vols 27,000; Per Subs 575
Subject Interests: Biology, Ecology, Genetics, Microbiology, Molecular biology
Publications: New Book List
Partic in Greater Midwest Regional Medical Libr Network
MATHEMATICS, 200 Computing Center & Mathematics Bldg, 46556. SAN 341-5627. Tel: 219-631-7278. FAX: 219-631-9660. E-Mail: library.mathlib.1@nd.edu. Web Site: www.nd.edu/~mathlib. *Librn*, Parker Ladwig; E-Mail: ladwig.1@nd.edu. Subject Specialists: *Mathematics*, Parker Ladwig; Staff 3 (MLS 1, Non-MLS 2)
Library Holdings: Bk Vols 35,000; Per Subs 287
Subject Interests: Computer science, Mathematics
Special Collections: Marston Morse
Publications: Acquisitions List
Friends of the Library Group
MEDIEVAL INSTITUTE, 715 Hesburgh Library, 46556. SAN 341-5651. Tel: 219-5724, 219-631-7420. FAX: 219-631-8644. Web Site: www.nd.edu/~medvlib/. *Librn*, Louis Jordan; *Bibliogr*, Marina Smyth; Staff 6 (MLS 3, Non-MLS 3)
Founded 1948
1999-2000 Mats Exp $150,000
Library Holdings: Bk Vols 75,000
Subject Interests: Byzantine studies, Medieval studies
Special Collections: Ambrosiana microfilm & photographic (Frank M Folsom Coll); History of Medieval Universities
RADIATION CHEMISTRY DATA CENTER Tel: 219-631-6527. E-Mail: Internet: chphlibr@vma.cc.nd.edu. Web Site: www.nd.edu/~radlab/. *Librn*, Thurston Miller
Library Holdings: Bk Vols 6,800
THOMAS J MAHAFFEY JR BUSINESS INFORMATION CENTER, University of Notre Dame, L001 Mendoza College of Business, 46556. SAN 378-0414. Tel: 219-631-9098. FAX: 219-631-6367. E-Mail: library.bic.1@nd.edu. Web Site: www.nd.edu/~bic. *Branch Mgr*, Christian H Poehlmann; Tel: 219-631-9099, E-Mail: cpoehlma@nd.edu; *Librn*, Stephen M Hayes; Tel: 219-631-5268, E-Mail: shayes1@nd.edu; *Info Tech*, Sandi Collins; Tel: 219-631-9097, E-Mail: collins.96@nd.edu; *Info Tech*, Scott Gaglio; Tel: 219-631-9097, E-Mail: scott.s.gaglio.4@nd.edu; *Ref*, Cameron Tuai; Tel: 219-631-6977, E-Mail: ctua@nd.edu; *Tech Coordr*, Andy Boze; Tel: 219-631-8708, E-Mail: fboze@nd.edu; Staff 5 (MLS 3, Non-MLS 2)
Founded 1995. Highest Degree: Master
Jul 1998-Jul 1999 Income (Main Library Only) $238,564. Mats Exp Electronic Ref Mat (Incl. Access Fees) $71,998. Sal $180,000
Library Holdings: Per Subs 35
Database Vendor: CARL, Ebsco - EbscoHost, IAC - Info Trac, Lexis-Nexis, OCLC - First Search, ProQuest, Silverplatter Information Inc.
Function: Research library

L UNIVERSITY OF NOTRE DAME, Kresge Law Library, Notre Dame Law School, PO Box 535, 46556. SAN 341-5562. Tel: 219-631-7024. FAX: 219-631-6371. Web Site: www.nd.edu/~lawlib. *Assoc Dean, Dir*, Roger Jacobs; Tel: 219-631-5868; Staff 16 (MLS 7, Non-MLS 9)
Founded 1869
Library Holdings: Bk Vols 519,477; Bk Titles 97,947

OAKLAND CITY

C OAKLAND CITY UNIVERSITY, Founders Memorial Library, 710 W Columbia St, 47660. SAN 305-0688. Tel: 812-749-1269. FAX: 812-749-1268. Web Site: www.oak.oak.edu. *Dir*, Denise J Pinnick; Tel: 812-749-1267, E-Mail: dpinnick@oak.edu; *Asst Dir*, Stephanie Frederick; Tel: 812-749-1268; Staff 2 (MLS 1, Non-MLS 1)
Founded 1890. Enrl 1,668; Fac 37; Highest Degree: Master
Jun 1999-May 2000 Income $161,983
Library Holdings: Bk Vols 81,389; Per Subs 218
Special Collections: General Baptist Denomination Materials
Automation Activity & Vendor Info: (Cataloging) DRA; (Circulation) DRA; (Course Reserve) DRA; (OPAC) DRA; (Serials) DRA
Database Vendor: Ebsco - EbscoHost, epixtech, inc., IAC - SearchBank, OCLC - First Search, OVID Technologies

Function: Research library
Partic in PALNI
Open Mon-Thurs 8-10, Fri 8-5, Sat 10-2 & Sun 6-10 (winter hours)

P OAKLAND CITY-COLUMBIA TOWNSHIP PUBLIC LIBRARY,* 210 S Main, 47660. SAN 305-0696. Tel: 812-749-3559. FAX: 812-749-3559. *Dir*, Patsy Creasey; *Asst Librn*, Donna Phillips; *Asst Librn*, Kelly Rogers; Staff 3 (Non-MLS 3)
Founded 1917. Pop 4,600; Circ 33,401
Jan 1997-Dec 1998 Income $203,479. Mats Exp $53,848, Books $50,165, Per/Ser (Incl. Access Fees) $3,283, Electronic Ref Mat (Incl. Access Fees) $400. Sal $99,220
Library Holdings: Bk Titles 28,242; Per Subs 73
Automation Activity & Vendor Info: (Circulation) Sagebrush Corporation
Partic in Indiana Cooperative Library Services Authority

ODON

P ODON WINKELPLECK MEMORIAL LIBRARY, 202 W Main St, 47562. SAN 305-070X. Tel: 812-636-4949. FAX: 812-636-4949. E-Mail: library@rtccom.net, odonlibrarian@aol.com. Web Site: rtccom.net/~library. *Dir*, Marsha Lynn; *Asst Librn*, Sandra Armstrong; *Cat*, Marie Milton; Staff 4 (Non-MLS 4)
Founded 1906. Pop 2,570
Jan 1999-Dec 1999 Income $32,457, State $3,415, Other $2,943. Mats Exp $3,937, Books $2,817, Per/Ser (Incl. Access Fees) $765, AV Equip $355. Sal $9,427
Library Holdings: Bk Vols 14,057; Per Subs 35
Automation Activity & Vendor Info: (Circulation) Sagebrush Corporation
Function: Photocopies available

ORLAND

P JOYCE PUBLIC LIBRARY,* 6035 N State Rd 327, PO Box 240, 46776-6329. SAN 376-5350. Tel: 219-829-6329. *Librn*, Virginia Evens
Jan 1999-Dec 2000 Income $12,000. Mats Exp $5,000. Sal $3,000
Library Holdings: Bk Vols 6,000; Bk Titles 4,500; Per Subs 12

ORLEANS

P ORLEANS PUBLIC LIBRARY,* Maple St, PO Box 142, 47452. SAN 305-0718. Tel: 812-865-3270. FAX: 812-865-3270. *Actg Dir*, Rosalie Allen
Founded 1913. Pop 4,325; Circ 23,493
Library Holdings: Bk Vols 26,000; Per Subs 40

OSGOOD

P OSGOOD PUBLIC LIBRARY,* 136 W Ripley, 47037-0235. SAN 305-0726. Tel: 812-689-4011. FAX: 812-689-4016. E-Mail: osgoodpl@bugs.vemus.net. *Librn*, Don Rice
Founded 1912. Pop 2,048; Circ 22,120
Jan 1998-Dec 1999 Income $78,500
Library Holdings: Bk Vols 25,000; Bk Titles 23,000; Per Subs 42
Special Collections: Peoples History of Ripley County; Township Geneological Papers
Partic in SE Ind Area Libr Servs Authority
Friends of the Library Group

OTTERBEIN

P OTTERBEIN PUBLIC LIBRARY,* 29 S Main St, 47970. (Mail add: PO Box 550, 47970), SAN 305-0734. Tel: 765-583-2107. E-Mail: oplcrif@gte.net. *Librn*, Cynthia M Rifner
Founded 1919. Pop 2,029; Circ 28,305
Jan 1997-Dec 1998 Income $62,090, State $5,061, County $40,350, Locally Generated Income $4,895. Mats Exp $7,111, Books $4,619, Per/Ser (Incl. Access Fees) $881. Sal $64,274
Library Holdings: Bk Vols 12,000; Per Subs 63
Subject Interests: Local history
Special Collections: Adam Kennedy; Gene Stratton Porter
Mem of Wabash Valley Area Libr Servs Authority

OWENSVILLE

P OWENSVILLE CARNEGIE LIBRARY, 110 S Main St, PO Box 219, 47665-0219. SAN 305-0742. Tel: 812-724-3335. FAX: 812-724-3336. E-Mail: owenlib1@evansvillenet. *Librn*, Peggy Callis; *Asst Librn*, Betty Wade; *Ch Servs*, Donna Keller
Founded 1917. Pop 3,188
Jan 1999-Dec 1999 Income $157,866, State $384, County $151,056. Mats Exp $81,735, Books $38,658, Per/Ser (Incl. Access Fees) $6,140, AV Equip $9,051, Electronic Ref Mat (Incl. Access Fees) $4,960. Sal $60,869 (Prof $20,000)
Library Holdings: Bk Vols 27,500; Per Subs 140
Subject Interests: Local history
Automation Activity & Vendor Info: (Acquisitions) Brodart; (Cataloging) Brodart; (Circulation) Brodart
Partic in Indiana Cooperative Library Services Authority

OXFORD

P OXFORD PUBLIC LIBRARY,* PO Box 6, 47971. SAN 305-0750. Tel: 765-385-2177. FAX: 765-385-2177. *Dir*, Julie Frew
Founded 1917. Pop 1,629; Circ 12,500
Jan 1997-Dec 1998 Income $102,470. Mats Exp $18,469. Sal $51,455
Library Holdings: Bk Vols 17,000; Per Subs 76
Friends of the Library Group

PAOLI

P PAOLI PUBLIC LIBRARY,* 10 E Court, 47454. SAN 305-0769. Tel: 812-723-3841. FAX: 812-723-3841. *Dir*, Carole Vance; *Ch Servs*, Glenda Hess
Founded 1918. Pop 5,780; Circ 32,907
Jan 1997-Dec 1998 Income $67,640. Mats Exp $63,920
Library Holdings: Bk Vols 27,778; Per Subs 54
Subject Interests: Genealogy, Local history
Open Mon, Tues, Thurs & Fri 12:30-5:30 & Sat 9-1

PENDLETON

P PENDLETON COMMUNITY LIBRARY, 595 E Water St, 46064-1070. SAN 305-0777. Tel: 765-778-7527. FAX: 765-778-7529. Web Site: www.pendleton.lib.in.us. *Dir*, Dennis L Babbitt; E-Mail: dbabbitt@pendleton.lib.in.us; *Asst Dir, Ch Servs*, Alicia Pitman; E-Mail: jpitman@pendleton.lib.in.us; *Business*, Jo Ann Fryback; E-Mail: jfryback@pendleton.lib.in.us; Staff 2 (MLS 1, Non-MLS 1)
Founded 1912. Pop 14,917; Circ 125,874
Jan 1999-Dec 1999 Income $429,053, State $1,781, County $234,961, Locally Generated Income $16,000. Mats Exp $46,177, Books $33,270, Per/Ser (Incl. Access Fees) $4,959, AV Equip $6,948, Electronic Ref Mat (Incl. Access Fees) $1,000. Sal $216,425
Library Holdings: Bk Vols 50,000; Per Subs 151
Partic in Indiana Cooperative Library Services Authority
Open Mon-Thurs 9-8, Fri 9-6, Sat 9-5 & Sun 1-5
Friends of the Library Group

S PENDLETON CORRECTIONAL FACILITY, Fender Library, PO Box 28, 46064-0028. SAN 341-5716. Tel: 765-778-2107, Ext 1221. FAX: 765-778-8166. *Librn*, Joe Spegal
Founded 1897
Library Holdings: Bk Titles 13,000; Per Subs 48
Subject Interests: Science fiction
Branches:
L LAW, PO Box 28, 46064. SAN 341-5724. Tel: 765-778-2107. *In Charge*, Chuck Fowler; *In Charge*, Kelly Coombs

PENNVILLE

P PENNVILLE TOWNSHIP PUBLIC LIBRARY, 195 N Union, PO Box 206, 47369-0206. SAN 305-0785. Tel: 219-731-3333. FAX: 219-731-3333. E-Mail: pntnlb@jayco.net. *Dir*, Carla Wilson
Pop 1,236; Circ 7,045
Library Holdings: Bk Vols 12,000; Per Subs 35
Open Tues-Thurs 2-7, Sat 9-2

PERU

S MIAMI COUNTY MUSEUM, Hal C Phelps Archives,* 51 N Broadway, 46970. SAN 373-4498. Tel: 765-473-9183. FAX: 765-473-3880. E-Mail: mchs@netusa1.net. *Dir*, Catherine Powell; *Archivist*, Joyce Miller; *Curator*, Mildred Kopis
Library Holdings: Bk Vols 1,000
Subject Interests: Civil War, Genealogy, Railroads
Special Collections: Circus Town Information; Civil War Letters & Diaries; Local History; Old Rare Books & Newspapers; Railroad (C20, Wabash)

P PERU PUBLIC LIBRARY, 102 E Main St, 46970-2338. SAN 305-0793. Tel: 765-473-3069. FAX: 765-473-3060. E-Mail: peru@lib.in.us. Web Site: www.peru.lib.in.us. *Dir*, Charles A Wagner; *Asst Dir*, Maryanne Farnham; *Tech Servs*, Terri Hall; *Ad Servs*, Cheryl Mallow; *Ref*, Laura Spear; *Ch Servs*, Carla Murtha; Staff 7 (MLS 1, Non-MLS 6)
Founded 1902. Pop 17,000; Circ 158,000
Jan 2001-Dec 2001 Income $407,000, State $1,000, City $344,800, County $51,200, Locally Generated Income $10,000. Mats Exp $68,400, Books $57,000, Per/Ser (Incl. Access Fees) $10,000, Micro $800, Electronic Ref Mat (Incl. Access Fees) $600. Sal $198,000 (Prof $36,500)
Library Holdings: Bk Vols 49,000; Bk Titles 33,000; Per Subs 179
Subject Interests: Genealogy, Indiana

Publications: Miami County (encyclopedia 12 vols, genealogies 9 vols); Miami County Obituaries
Mem of Indiana Coop Libr Servs Authority
Friends of the Library Group

PETERSBURG

P PIKE COUNTY PUBLIC LIBRARY, 1104 Main St, 47567. SAN 305-0807. Tel: 812-354-6257. FAX: 812-354-6259. *Asst Dir*, Kevin Engel; Tel: 515-269-4234, E-Mail: engelk@grinnell.edu; Staff 1 (MLS 1)
Pop 12,509; Circ 71,000
Jan 2001-Dec 2001 Income (Main Library and Branch Library) $394,600, State $26,400, County $351,700, Other $16,500. Mats Exp $40,000, Books $22,500, Per/Ser (Incl. Access Fees) $4,000, AV Equip $8,000. Sal $225,000 (Prof $28,000)
Library Holdings: Bk Vols 40,000; Bk Titles 34,000; Per Subs 120
Subject Interests: Genealogy, Indiana, Local history
Automation Activity & Vendor Info: (Cataloging) Gaylord; (Circulation) Gaylord; (OPAC) Gaylord
Partic in Indiana Cooperative Library Services Authority
Open Mon & Thurs 9-8, Tues, Wed, Fri & Sat 9-5
Branches: 1
WINSLOW BRANCH, 105 E Center St, Winslow, 47598. SAN 376-818X. Tel: 812-789-5423. FAX: 812-789-9496.
Library Holdings: Bk Vols 8,000

PIERCETON

P PIERCETON & WASHINGTON TOWNSHIP LIBRARY,* PO Box 328, 46562. SAN 305-0815. Tel: 219-594-5474. *Librn*, R Cecilia Knight; Tel: 515-269-3368, E-Mail: knight@grinnell.edu
Founded 1915. Pop 4,729; Circ 5,545
Library Holdings: Bk Vols 21,000; Per Subs 37
Open Tues & Thurs 11:30-5, Wed & Fri 1-5, Sat 9-1

PLAINFIELD

G INDIANA LAW ENFORCEMENT ACADEMY, David F Allen Memorial Learning Resources Center, 5402 Sugar Grove Rd, PO Box 313, 46168. SAN 305-0823. Tel: 317-839-5191, Ext 236. Reference Tel: 317-837-3290. FAX: 317-839-9741. E-Mail: ilealrcdz@surf-ici.com. Web Site: www.state.in.us/ilea. *Librn*, Donna K Zimmerman
Founded 1975
Library Holdings: Bk Vols 5,000; Per Subs 100
Subject Interests: Law, Law enforcement, Photography
Database Vendor: Lexis-Nexis, ProQuest
Publications: AV catalog
Restriction: Open to others by appointment
Function: Reference services available
Partic in Indiana Cooperative Library Services Authority; Nat Criminal Justice Ref Serv

G INDIANA RECEPTION DIAGNOSTIC CENTER LIBRARY,* 737 Moon Rd, 46168. SAN 325-6723. Tel: 317-839-7727. FAX: 317-839-7727, Ext 1332. *Librn*, Errol Baker
Library Holdings: Bk Vols 150; Per Subs 25

SR THE ISLAMIC SOCIETY OF NORTH AMERICA,* PO Box 38, 46168. SAN 375-1686. Tel: 317-839-8157. FAX: 317-839-1840.
Library Holdings: Bk Vols 43,000; Per Subs 5

S PLAINFIELD JUVENILE CORRECTIONAL FACILITY LIBRARY, 501 W Main St, 46168. Tel: 317-839-7751, Ext 4312. *Asst Dir*, Stuart Sharp; *Media Spec*, Elizabeth Coffey
Library Holdings: Bk Vols 1,800; Bk Titles 1,500; Per Subs 26
Automation Activity & Vendor Info: (Cataloging) Follett

P PLAINFIELD PUBLIC LIBRARY,* 1120 Stafford Rd, 46168-2230. SAN 305-0831. Tel: 317-839-6602. FAX: 317-839-4044. Web Site: www.plainfield.lib.in.us. *Dir*, Charr Skirvin; E-Mail: cskirvin@plainfield.lib.in.us; *Admin Assoc, Info Res*, Susan Miller Carter; E-Mail: scarter@plainfield.lib.ln.us; *Ad Servs, YA Servs*, Debra Shaw; Tel: 317-839-6602, Ext 113, E-Mail: dshaw@plainfield.lib.in.us; *Ch Servs*, Jan Owens; *Circ*, Jo Sibley; E-Mail: jsibley@plainfield.lib.in.us; *Tech Servs*, Judy Hill; E-Mail: jhill@plainfield.lib.in.us; *YA Servs*, Kerry Green; Tel: 317-839-6602, Ext 113, E-Mail: kgreen@plainfield.lib.in.us; Staff 8 (MLS 8)
Founded 1901. Pop 19,468; Circ 267,321
Jan 1999-Dec 1999 Income $1,138,260, State $2,324, Locally Generated Income $168,902. Mats Exp $1,116,350, Books $135,000, Per/Ser (Incl. Access Fees) $10,000, Micro $2,000, AV Equip $15,000, Electronic Ref Mat (Incl. Access Fees) $10,000. Sal $552,700 (Prof $97,460)
Library Holdings: Bk Vols 127,004; Per Subs 371
Subject Interests: Indiana, Local history
Special Collections: Guilford Township Historical Coll
Automation Activity & Vendor Info: (Acquisitions) Gaylord; (Cataloging) Gaylord; (Circulation) Gaylord; (OPAC) Gaylord
Database Vendor: Ebsco - EbscoHost
Publications: Novel News (monthly); PPL News (semi-annual)
Partic in Indiana Cooperative Library Services Authority
Friends of the Library Group

SR WESTERN YEARLY MEETING OF FRIENDS, Lending Library, PO Box 70, 46168. SAN 305-084X. Tel: 317-839-2789. FAX: 317-839-2616. E-Mail: westernym@aol.com. *Librn*, Kay Record Carter
Library Holdings: Bk Vols 700
Subject Interests: Art, Biblical studies, Quakers

PLYMOUTH

S MARSHALL COUNTY HISTORICAL SOCIETY LIBRARY, 123 N Michigan St, 46563. SAN 305-0858. Tel: 219-936-2306. FAX: 219-936-9306. E-Mail: mchistmuseum@keonline.com. *Exec Dir*, Linda Rippy; *Librn*, Judy McCullough
Founded 1957
Library Holdings: Bk Titles 550
Subject Interests: Genealogy
Special Collections: Newpapers 1853-1988, micro

P PLYMOUTH PUBLIC LIBRARY,* 201 N Center St, 46563. SAN 305-0866. Tel: 219-936-2324. FAX: 219-936-7423. Web Site: www.plymouth.lib.in.us. *Dir*, Susie Reinholt; E-Mail: s.reinholt@gomail.sjcpl.lib.in.us; *Ch Servs*, Marie Dylag; *AV*, Betty Fish; *Ref*, Nancy Newton; *Circ*, Marilee Douglass
Founded 1910. Pop 13,617; Circ 195,000
Jan 1999-Dec 2000 Income $951,000. Mats Exp $205,000. Sal $394,000
Library Holdings: Bk Vols 82,470
Special Collections: Antiques; Dolls; Indiana History; Marshall County Authors
Partic in Area Libr Serv Authority; Dialog Corporation; Ind Info Retrieval Syst; Indiana Cooperative Library Services Authority
Friends of the Library Group

PORTLAND

P JAY COUNTY PUBLIC LIBRARY,* 315 N Ship St, 47371. SAN 305-0874. Tel: 219-726-7890. FAX: 219-726-7317. Web Site: www.jaycpl.lib.in.us. *Dir*, Rosalie Clamme; E-Mail: rclamme@jaycpl.lib.in.us
Founded 1898
Library Holdings: Per Subs 210
Publications: Library Newsnotes (newsletter)
Partic in Indiana Cooperative Library Services Authority
Bookmobiles: 1

POSEYVILLE

P POSEYVILLE CARNEGIE PUBLIC LIBRARY, PO Box 220, 47633. SAN 305-0882. Tel: 812-874-3418. FAX: 812-874-3418. E-Mail: library2@ccsi.tds.net. *Librn*, Stanley Campbell
Founded 1905. Pop 3,000; Circ 15,561
Library Holdings: Bk Vols 17,000; Per Subs 55

PRINCETON

P PRINCETON PUBLIC LIBRARY,* 124 S Hart St, 47670. SAN 305-0890. Tel: 812-385-4464. FAX: 812-385-4466. E-Mail: princepl@evansville.net. *Dir*, Sabrina Frederick; *Asst Dir*, Brenda Williams; *Ch Servs*, Judith Daniels
Founded 1883. Pop 12,000; Circ 119,046
Jul 2000-Jun 2001 Income $354,230. Mats Exp $49,000, Books $35,000, Per/Ser (Incl. Access Fees) $5,500. Sal $186,030
Library Holdings: Bk Titles 60,000; Per Subs 91
Subject Interests: Genealogy
Partic in Indiana Cooperative Library Services Authority
Open Mon-Fri 9-8, Sat 9-5, Sun 1-5 (during school year); Genealogy room hours Mon 9-8, Tues-Fri 9-5, 2nd & 4th Sat 9-5, closed Sun; Goodtimes Nursery Hour; Summer Reading Program; Library school

REMINGTON

P REMINGTON-CARPENTER TOWNSHIP PUBLIC LIBRARY,* PO Box 65, 47977-0065. SAN 305-0904. Tel: 219-261-2543. *Dir*, Nan E McGlynn; *Asst Librn*, Agnes J Dombrowski; Staff 1 (MLS 1)
Founded 1913. Pop 1,800
Library Holdings: Bk Titles 30,000; Per Subs 80
Special Collections: Geology Coll
Partic in Northwest Ind Area Libr Servs Authority

RENSSELAER

P JASPER COUNTY PUBLIC LIBRARY, Rensselaer Public Library, 208 W Susan St, 47978. SAN 341-5805. Tel: 219-866-5881. FAX: 219-866-7378. Web Site: www.jasperco.lib.in.us. *Dir*, Lynn E Daugherty; E-Mail: ldaugherty@jasperco.lib.in.us; *Librn*, Patty Stringfellow; E-Mail: pstringfellow@jasperco.lib.in.us; *Tech Coordr*, Sheila Maxwell; E-Mail: sheila@jasperco.lib.in.us; *Tech Servs*, Jennifer Evers; E-Mail: jevers@jasperco.lib.in.us; *Publ Servs*, Kathryn Weed; E-Mail: kweed@jasperco.lib.in.us; Staff 23 (MLS 4, Non-MLS 19)
Founded 1904. Pop 27,323; Circ 274,569
Jan 1999-Dec 1999 Income (Main Library and Branch Library) $1,236,006, State $76,919, Federal $4,229, County $1,079,515, Locally Generated Income $75,343. Mats Exp $210,309, Books $142,872, Per/Ser (Incl. Access Fees) $23,135. Sal $729,847
Library Holdings: Bk Vols 53,690; Per Subs 581
Subject Interests: Humanities, Natural science
Special Collections: Mementos of Civil War (Major General Robert H Milroy Coll)
Automation Activity & Vendor Info: (Cataloging) Gaylord; (Circulation) Gaylord; (OPAC) Gaylord
Publications: Community Connections Newsletter
Partic in Indiana Cooperative Library Services Authority
Friends of the Library Group
Branches: 2
DEMOTTE BRANCH, 901 Birch St SW, PO Box 16, DeMotte, 46310. SAN 341-583X. Tel: 219-987-2221. FAX: 219-987-2220. Web Site: www.jasperco.lib.in.us. *Br Coordr*, Rebecca Gibson; E-Mail: rgibson@jasperco.lib.in.us; Staff 10 (Non-MLS 10)
Library Holdings: Bk Vols 45,582
Friends of the Library Group
WHEATFIELD BRANCH, 170 S Grace St, Wheatfield, 46392. SAN 341-5864. Tel: 219-956-3774. FAX: 219-956-4808. Web Site: www.jasperco.lib.in.us. *Librn*, Diana Kooy; E-Mail: dkooy@jasperco.lib.in.us; Staff 6 (MLS 6)
Library Holdings: Bk Vols 23,541
Database Vendor: Ebsco - EbscoHost
Friends of the Library Group

C SAINT JOSEPH'S COLLEGE, Robinson Memorial Library, Hwy 231 S, PO Box 990, 47978-0410. SAN 305-0912. Tel: 219-866-6187. Interlibrary Loan Service Tel: 219-866-6213. FAX: 219-866-6135. Web Site: www.saintjoe.edu/~dept45. *Dir*, Catherine Salyers; Tel: 219-866-6209, E-Mail: cathys@mfldclin.edu; *Asst Dir, Online Servs, Ref*, Jody Taylor-Watkins; *Acq, ILL*, Carla Luzadder; Staff 3 (MLS 3)
Founded 1892. Enrl 1,037; Fac 63; Highest Degree: Master
Library Holdings: Bk Vols 132,000; Per Subs 585
Subject Interests: Latin America, Music, Religion, Women's studies
Partic in BRS; Indiana Cooperative Library Services Authority; Northwest Indiana Health Science Library Consortium; OCLC Online Computer Library Center, Inc

RICHMOND

C EARLHAM COLLEGE, Lilly Library, 801 National Rd W, 47374-4095. SAN 341-5899. Tel: 765-983-1360. Interlibrary Loan Service Tel: 765-983-1307. FAX: 765-983-1304. Web Site: www.earlham.edu/~libr. *Dir*, Thomas G Kirk, Jr; E-Mail: kirkto@earlham.edu; *Cat, Doc, Tech Servs*, Janet Wagner; *Acq*, Debbie Follis; *Online Servs, Ref*, Neal Baker; *Online Servs, Ref*, Christine Larson; *Online Servs, Ref*, Nancy Taylor; *Spec Coll*, Dr Thomas D Hamm; Staff 10 (MLS 6, Non-MLS 4)
Founded 1847. Enrl 1,111; Fac 95; Highest Degree: Master
Jul 1999-Jun 2000 Income $1,061,456. Mats Exp $402,246, Books $158,557, Per/Ser (Incl. Access Fees) $164,472, Presv $11,394, Electronic Ref Mat (Incl. Access Fees) $67,823. Sal $503,998 (Prof $295,392)
Library Holdings: Bk Vols 389,230; Per Subs 1,195
Special Collections: East Asian Materials, bks, micro; Society of Friends, bks, micro
Partic in Indiana Cooperative Library Services Authority; OCLC Online Computer Library Center, Inc; Private Acad Libr Network of Ind
Departmental Libraries:
CONNER PRAIRIE RESEARCH LIBRARY, 13400 Allisonville Rd, Fishers, 46038. SAN 326-0941. Tel: 317-776-6000, Ext 246. FAX: 317-776-6014. *Librn*, Tim Crumrin
Founded 1964
Library Holdings: Bk Vols 2,850; Per Subs 27
Subject Interests: American history, Indiana
Special Collections: William Conner (1777-1855) Papers Coll, docs
Restriction: Non-circulating to the public

S THE S W HAYES RESEARCH FOUNDATION, Regional Arboretum Library,* 801 Elks Rd, 47374. SAN 326-0925. Tel: 765-962-3745. FAX: 765-966-1931. Web Site: www.infocom.com/hayes/. *Dir*, Rodney Waltz
Library Holdings: Bk Vols 1,200; Bk Titles 1,000

C INDIANA UNIVERSITY EAST, Library & Media Services, 2325 Chester Blvd, 47374. SAN 320-9113. Tel: 765-973-8311. FAX: 765-973-8315. Web Site: www.iue.indiana.edu/library/index.html. *Dir*, Gordon Lynn Hufford; Tel: 765-973-8326, E-Mail: hufford@indiana.edu; *Publ Servs*, Sue A McFadden; Tel: 765-973-8325, E-Mail: mcfadde@indiana.edu; *Info Tech*, Lora Baldwin; Tel: 765-973-8226, E-Mail: mcclell@indiana.edu; *Acq*, Sherri Hamilton; Tel: 765-973-8465, E-Mail: sahamilt@indiana.edu; Staff 8 (MLS 4, Non-MLS 4)
Founded 1975
Jul 1999-Jun 2000 Income Parent Institution $479,468. Mats Exp $143,542, Books $57,831, Per/Ser (Incl. Access Fees) $85,711. Sal $247,435 (Prof $159,824)
Library Holdings: Bk Vols 65,888; Per Subs 433
Database Vendor: CARL, Ebsco - EbscoHost, Lexis-Nexis, OCLC - First Search, OVID Technologies, Silverplatter Information Inc.
Partic in OCLC Online Computer Library Center, Inc

S RICHMOND ART MUSEUM LIBRARY, 350 Hub Etchison Pkwy, 47374. SAN 305-0920. Tel: 765-966-0256. FAX: 765-973-3738. Web Site: www.richmondartmuseum.org. *Dir*, Shaun Dingwerth; E-Mail: sdingwerth@richmondartmuseum.org; Staff 3 (MLS 3)
Founded 1898
Library Holdings: Bk Vols 800
Subject Interests: Art

M RICHMOND STATE HOSPITAL LIBRARY,* 498 NW 18th St, 47374. SAN 305-0939. Tel: 765-966-0511. FAX: 765-966-4593. *Librn*, Dale Land
Founded 1968
Library Holdings: Bk Titles 7,000; Per Subs 25
Partic in Area VI Libr Servs Authority; Ind Libr Film Serv; Midwest Health Sci Libr Network

S WAYNE COUNTY, INDIANA, HISTORICAL MUSEUM LIBRARY, 1150 North A St, 47374. SAN 305-0947. Tel: 765-962-5756. FAX: 765-939-0909. *Dir*, Michele Bottorff; Staff 3 (MLS 2, Non-MLS 1)
Founded 1929
Library Holdings: Bk Vols 1,200; Bk Titles 1,000; Per Subs 15
Subject Interests: Genealogy, Local history
Special Collections: Cartoons (Gaar Williams Coll); Motion Pictures & Early Television (C Francis Jenkins Coll), doc
Publications: Newsletter (monthly)

P WAYNE TOWNSHIP LIBRARY, Morrisson-Reeves Library, 80 N Sixth St, 47374-3079. SAN 341-5988. Tel: 765-966-8291. TDD: 765-966-8291. FAX: 765-962-1318. Web Site: www.mrl.lib.in.us. *Librn*, Carol B Smyth; E-Mail: csmyth@mrl.lib.in.us; *AV*, Lou Spicer; *Cat*, Carol McCafferty; *Circ*, Mark Beals; *Ref*, Mary Thiedeman; Staff 64 (MLS 4, Non-MLS 60)
Founded 1864. Pop 54,920
Library Holdings: Bk Vols 216,020; Bk Titles 152,000; Per Subs 591
Special Collections: Cook Books; Large Print; Local Newspapers (1831 to date), indexed, microfilm; Popular & Semi-popular Music (Singin' Sam), sheet music
Automation Activity & Vendor Info: (Acquisitions) epixtech, inc.; (Cataloging) epixtech, inc.; (Circulation) epixtech, inc.; (ILL) epixtech, inc.; (Media Booking) epixtech, inc.; (OPAC) epixtech, inc.; (Serials) epixtech, inc.
Database Vendor: epixtech, inc.
Partic in Eialsa; Indiana Cooperative Library Services Authority
Special Services for the Deaf - Staff with knowledge of sign language; TDD
Friends of the Library Group
Branches: 2
RICHARDSON LIBRARY, Townsend Community Ctr, 855 N 12th St, 47374. SAN 341-6011. Tel: 765-962-7591. Web Site: www.mrl.lib.in.us. *Librn*, Judith Spicer
Library Holdings: Bk Vols 3,500
WAYNE COUNTY CONTRACTUAL LIBRARY, 80 N Sixth St, 47374. SAN 341-6070. Tel: 765-966-8291. FAX: 765-962-1318. Web Site: www.mrl.lib.in.us. *Librn*, Debra McClanahan
Library Holdings: Bk Vols 19,347
Bookmobiles: 1

RIDGEVILLE

P RIDGEVILLE PUBLIC LIBRARY, Walnut & Camden Sts, PO Box 63, 47380. SAN 305-0955. Tel: 765-857-2025. FAX: 765-857-2025. *Librn*, Marcella McCormick; Staff 2 (MLS 1, Non-MLS 1)
Founded 1912. Pop 1,539; Circ 5,000
Jan 1998-Dec 1999 Income $12,728. Mats Exp $4,617, Books $3,587, Per/Ser (Incl. Access Fees) $630. Sal $6,466 (Prof $3,876)
Library Holdings: Bk Vols 14,000; Per Subs 38
Partic in Indiana Cooperative Library Services Authority
Open Tues 12:30-8, Wed 1-5 & Thurs 12:30-7
Friends of the Library Group

RISING SUN

P OHIO COUNTY PUBLIC LIBRARY, 100 N High St, 47040-1022. SAN 305-0963. Tel: 812-438-2257. E-Mail: ohiopubl@seidata.com. *Dir*, Amy C Ketzer; *Chief Librn*, Helen Mason; Staff 4 (MLS 1, Non-MLS 3)
Founded 1916. Pop 5,114; Circ 32,000
Library Holdings: Bk Vols 25,000; Per Subs 42
Special Collections: Local News & History (Ohio County Newspapers, 1834-1970), microfilm (1970-present), loose files
Open Mon, Wed & Fri 9-5, Tues & Thurs 9-7:30, Sat 9-1

ROACHDALE

P ROACHDALE-FRANKLIN TOWNSHIP PUBLIC LIBRARY,* 100 E Washington, PO Box 399, 46172. SAN 305-0971. Tel: 765-522-1491. FAX: 765-522-1491. *Librn*, Debbie Sillery
Founded 1913. Pop 2,000; Circ 12,000
Jan 1998-Dec 1999 Income $43,480
Library Holdings: Bk Vols 15,000; Per Subs 26
Partic in Indiana Cooperative Library Services Authority

ROANN

P ROANN-PAW PAW PUBLIC LIBRARY, 240 S Chippewa Rd, PO Box 248, 46974. SAN 305-098X. Tel: 765-833-5231. FAX: 765-833-5231. E-Mail: robrary@netusa.net. *Librn*, Joy Harber; *Asst Librn*, Virginia Bozarth; *Asst Librn*, Jakae Francis; Staff 3 (Non-MLS 3)
Founded 1914. Pop 1,616; Circ 7,983
1998-1999 Mats Exp $6,200, Books $4,000, Per/Ser (Incl. Access Fees) $1,500. Sal $20,184 (Prof $17,614)
Library Holdings: Bk Titles 16,810; Per Subs 35
Subject Interests: Local genealogy
Special Services for the Blind - Bks on tape; Talking Books
Friends of the Library Group

ROANOKE

P ROANOKE PUBLIC LIBRARY, 126 N Main St, 46783-0249. (Mail add: PO Box 249, 46783-0249), SAN 305-0998. Tel: 219-672-3306. FAX: 219-672-3306. E-Mail: rpl@netusa1.net. *Librn*, Joyce Iliff
Founded 1910. Pop 1,287
Jan 1999-Dec 1999 Income $34,724, State $200, City $32,524, Locally Generated Income $2,000. Mats Exp $4,588, Books $3,200, Per/Ser (Incl. Access Fees) $200, Other Print Mats $1,008, Electronic Ref Mat (Incl. Access Fees) $180. Sal $18,900
Library Holdings: Bk Titles 15,000; Per Subs 11
Special Collections: Roanoke Review, 1919 to 1981, micro
Partic in Indiana Cooperative Library Services Authority
Open Mon Tues & Wed 9-1 & 2-7, Thurs 2-7, Sat 9-2
Friends of the Library Group

ROCHESTER

S FULTON COUNTY HISTORICAL SOCIETY, INC, Museum & Library, 37E 375 N, 46975-8384. SAN 371-9103. Tel: 219-223-4436. Web Site: www.icss.net/~fchs. *Pres*, Shirley Willard; E-Mail: wwillard@rtcol.com; *Publ Servs*, Melinda Clinger; Staff 3 (Non-MLS 3)
Founded 1963
Library Holdings: Bk Titles 10,000; Per Subs 100
Special Collections: Fulton County; Fulton County, Inc; Potawatomi Indians
Publications: FCHS Newsletter - Scrapbook; Fulton County Folk Finder; Fulton County Images; Indian Awareness Center Newsletter
Open Mon-Sat 9-5

P FULTON COUNTY PUBLIC LIBRARY,* 320 W Seventh St, 46975-1332. SAN 341-6100. Tel: 219-223-2713. FAX: 219-223-5102. *Dir*, David L Ewick; *Ad Servs*, Krystal K Smith; *Ch Servs*, Becky Williams; Staff 30 (MLS 2, Non-MLS 28)
Founded 1906. Pop 14,870; Circ 354,750
Jan 1998-Dec 1999 Income $719,965. Mats Exp $132,660, Books $82,911, Per/Ser (Incl. Access Fees) $9,653. Sal $401,760
Library Holdings: Bk Titles 97,277; Per Subs 190
Subject Interests: Agriculture, Business and management, History, Indiana
Special Collections: Indiana (Local & State History), bks
Publications: American Lib; Booklist; Focus; Library Admin Digest; Mosaic; Publishers Weekly
Mem of Indiana Coop Libr Servs Authority
Open Mon-Fri 9am-8pm, Sat 9-5, Sun 1-5 (Oct-May)
Friends of the Library Group
Branches: 2
AUBBEE, PO Box 566, Leiters Ford, 46945. SAN 341-6135. Tel: 219-542-4859. FAX: 219-542-4859. *Librn*, Carol Eismann
Friends of the Library Group
FULTON BRANCH, PO Box 206, Fulton, 46931. SAN 341-616X. Tel: 219-857-3895. FAX: 219-857-3895. *Librn*, Selena Rouch
Friends of the Library Group

ROCKPORT

P SPENCER COUNTY PUBLIC LIBRARY, 210 Walnut St, 47635-1398. SAN 305-1005. Tel: 812-649-4866. FAX: 812-649-4018. E-Mail: scpl@psci.net. Web Site: www.rockport-spco.lib.in.us. *Dir*, Beverly Symon; E-Mail: symonb@rockport-scpl.lib.in; Staff 2 (MLS 1, Non-MLS 1)
Founded 1917. Pop 9,378; Circ 177,631
Jan 1999-Dec 1999 Income $584,028, County $535,931, Other $48,097. Mats Exp $76,902, Books $71,027, Per/Ser (Incl. Access Fees) $5,875. Sal $283,567 (Prof $60,254)
Library Holdings: Bk Titles 73,752; Per Subs 154; Bks on Deafness & Sign Lang 51
Subject Interests: Genealogy, History, Large type print, Local history, Religion
Special Collections: Lincoln Coll, bks, pamphlets, pictures, vf
Automation Activity & Vendor Info: (Cataloging) Sagebrush Corporation; (Circulation) Sagebrush Corporation
Mem of Indiana Coop Libr Servs Authority

ROCKVILLE

P ROCKVILLE PUBLIC LIBRARY,* 106 N Market St, 47872. SAN 305-1013. Tel: 765-569-5544. FAX: 765-569-5546. *Dir*, Cindy Hein
Founded 1913. Pop 4,161; Circ 30,000
Library Holdings: Bk Vols 23,000; Per Subs 75
Special Collections: Census Records, including Illinois, Ohio & New York 1820-1900; County Newspapers 1871-1974, microfilm; Genealogy Coll; Indiana Coll
Open Mon-Fri 9-6 & Sat 9-2

ROYAL CENTER

P ROYAL CENTER-BOONE TOWNSHIP PUBLIC LIBRARY,* PO Box 459, 46978. SAN 305-1021. Tel: 219-643-3185. FAX: 219-643-5003. *Librn*, Phyllis J Gray
Founded 1915. Pop 1,500; Circ 16,031
Jan 1997-Dec 1998 Income $80,000. Mats Exp $17,329. Sal $15,252
Library Holdings: Bk Vols 26,978; Per Subs 15
Subject Interests: Ethnic studies, Religion, Social sciences and issues
Partic in Wabash Valley Area Libr Servs Authority
Open Mon-Wed 12:30-5, Thurs 12:30-6 & Sat 9-3

RUSHVILLE

P RUSHVILLE PUBLIC LIBRARY, 130 W Third St, 46173-1899. SAN 305-103X. Tel: 765-932-3496. FAX: 765-932-4528. E-Mail: rushlib@comsys.net. Web Site: www.rushcounty.com/library. *Dir*, Sue Prifogle Otte; Staff 1 (MLS 1)
Founded 1910. Pop 5,533; Circ 65,374
Jan 1999-Dec 1999 Income $286,622, State $600, City $238,490, Locally Generated Income $22,458. Mats Exp $36,500, Books $33,000, Per/Ser (Incl. Access Fees) $3,500. Sal $159,995 (Prof $33,228)
Library Holdings: Bk Titles 43,806; Per Subs 102
Special Collections: Indiana History Coll; Rush County History; Wendell Wilkie Coll
Partic in Indiana Cooperative Library Services Authority
Friends of the Library Group

SAINT MARY-OF-THE-WOODS

C SAINT MARY-OF-THE-WOODS COLLEGE LIBRARY, 47876. SAN 305-1048. Tel: 812-535-5223. FAX: 812-535-5127. Web Site: www.smwc.edu. *Coll Develop, Dir*, Regina Jannink; Tel: 812-535-5255, E-Mail: rjannink@smwc.edu; *Cat*, Sister Leona Walsh; Tel: 812-535-5252, E-Mail: lwalsh@smwc.edu; *Per*, Damita Lewis; Tel: 812-535-5128, E-Mail: dlewis@smwc.edu; *Ref*, Sister Emily Walsh; E-Mail: ewalsh@smwc.edu; Staff 4 (MLS 3, Non-MLS 1)
Founded 1841. Enrl 709; Fac 58; Highest Degree: Master
Jul 2000-Jun 2001 Mats Exp $34,500, Books $22,500, Per/Ser (Incl. Access Fees) $12,000
Library Holdings: Bk Vols 151,389; Per Subs 319
Special Collections: Catholic Americana; Fore-edge Painting Coll; Seventeenth & Eighteenth Century French Religious Books
Partic in Indiana Cooperative Library Services Authority; OCLC Online Computer Library Center, Inc

SAINT MEINRAD

CR SAINT MEINRAD SCHOOL OF THEOLOGY, Archabbey Library, One Hill Dr, 47577. SAN 305-1056. Tel: 812-357-6566. Interlibrary Loan Service Tel: 812-357-6746. Circulation Tel: 812-357-6401. FAX: 812-357-6398. *Dir*, Luba Zakharov; E-Mail: lzakharov@saintmeinrad.edu; Staff 7 (MLS 2, Non-MLS 5)
Founded 1854. Enrl 108; Fac 18; Highest Degree: Master
Jul 1998-Jun 1999 Income $513,525. Mats Exp $67,823, Books $56,837,

Per/Ser (Incl. Access Fees) $20,508, Presv $3,104, Micro $6,996. Sal $180,843 (Prof $57,167)
Library Holdings: Bk Vols 163,233; Bk Titles 130,091; Per Subs 480
Subject Interests: Art and architecture, Religion
Automation Activity & Vendor Info: (Cataloging) DRA; (Circulation) DRA; (Course Reserve) DRA; (ILL) DRA; (OPAC) DRA; (Serials) DRA
Partic in Indiana Cooperative Library Services Authority; PALNI

SALEM

P SALEM PUBLIC LIBRARY, 212 N Main St, 47167. SAN 305-1064. Tel: 812-883-5600. FAX: 812-883-1609. E-Mail: salemlib@blueriver.net. *Dir*, Eric Magness-Eubank
Founded 1903. Pop 9,000; Circ 36,000
2000-2001 Mats Exp $45,000, Books $30,000, Per/Ser (Incl. Access Fees) $5,000, AV Equip $10,000. Sal $31,000
Library Holdings: Bk Vols 30,000; Bk Titles 27,000; Per Subs 140
Subject Interests: Local history
Automation Activity & Vendor Info: (Cataloging) Athena; (Circulation) Athena; (OPAC) Athena
Mem of Indiana Coop Libr Servs Authority
Friends of the Library Group

S WASHINGTON COUNTY HISTORICAL SOCIETY LIBRARY, Stevens Museum - The John Hay Center, 307 E Market St, 47167. SAN 305-1072. Tel: 812-883-6495. *Librn*, Martha Bowers; *Asst Librn*, Rhodella Martin
Library Holdings: Bk Titles 5,000; Per Subs 10
Subject Interests: Genealogy
Open Tues-Sat 9-5

SCOTTSBURG

P SCOTT COUNTY PUBLIC LIBRARY, 108 S Main St, 47170. SAN 305-1080. Tel: 812-752-2751. FAX: 812-752-2878. E-Mail: librarys@hsonline.net. *Dir*, Andrew Rowden; *Ch Servs*, Martha Burns; *Publ Servs*, Vicki Bordner; *Computer Services, Tech Servs*, Lori Christie. Subject Specialists: *Military hist*, Andrew Rowden; Staff 4 (MLS 2, Non-MLS 2)
Founded 1921. Pop 22,000
Jan 2001-Dec 2001 Income $440,000. Mats Exp $32,000, Books $25,000, Per/Ser (Incl. Access Fees) $7,000. Sal $272,334 (Prof $35,000)
Library Holdings: Bk Vols 69,000; Per Subs 170; Spec Interest Per Sub 20
Subject Interests: Civil War, Genealogy, History, Indiana, Local history
Special Collections: Carl R Bogardus Sr, MD Coll
Automation Activity & Vendor Info: (Cataloging) Gaylord; (Circulation) Gaylord; (OPAC) Gaylord
Partic in Indiana Cooperative Library Services Authority
Friends of the Library Group

SELLERSBURG

J IVY TECH STATE COLLEGE, Library-Sellerburg,* 8204 Hwy 311, 47172-1897. SAN 320-6718. Tel: 812-246-3301, Ext 4225. FAX: 812-246-9905. Web Site: www.ivy.tec.in.us/library/libr13/libr13.htm. *Dir*, Gool B Randelia; *Librn*, Alexa Bartel; E-Mail: abartel@ny.tec.in.us; Staff 1 (MLS 1)
Founded 1974
Library Holdings: Bk Titles 3,703; Per Subs 140
Subject Interests: Medicine
Partic in Indiana Cooperative Library Services Authority

SEYMOUR

P JACKSON COUNTY PUBLIC LIBRARY, 303 W Second St, 47274-2147. SAN 341-6194. Tel: 812-522-3412. Circulation Tel: 812-522-3412, Ext 243. Reference Tel: 812-522-3412, Ext 240 (ILL). FAX: 812-522-5456. E-Mail: jaker@japl.lib.in.us. Web Site: www.seymour.org/mainlib/. *Dir*, Julia Aker; Tel: 812-522-3412, Ext 223, E-Mail: jaker@japl.lib.in.us; *Bkmobile Coordr*, Fay Gardner; Tel: 812-522-3412, Ext 234, E-Mail: fgardner@japl.lib.in.us; *Ad Servs*, Kelly Joyce; Tel: 812-522-3412, Ext 238, E-Mail: kjoyce@japl.lib.in.us; *YA Servs*, Melessa Wiesehan; Tel: 812-522-3412, Ext 231, E-Mail: melessa@japl.lib.in.us; Staff 34 (MLS 5, Non-MLS 29)
Founded 1904. Pop 31,076; Circ 308,047
Jan 1999-Dec 1999 Income (Main Library and Branch Library) $1,044,899, County $989,625, Locally Generated Income $37,251, Other $18,023. Mats Exp $112,001, Books $81,193, Per/Ser (Incl. Access Fees) $12,300, Presv $336, AV Equip $4,885. Sal $665,397
Library Holdings: Bk Vols 100,514; Per Subs 325
Subject Interests: Local history
Automation Activity & Vendor Info: (Acquisitions) DRA; (Cataloging) DRA; (Circulation) DRA; (OPAC) DRA; (Serials) DRA
Partic in Indiana Cooperative Library Services Authority
Special Services for the Deaf - TDD
Special Services for the Blind - ADA terminals for visually impaired; Descriptive videos
Friends of the Library Group
Branches: 2
CROTHERSVILLE BRANCH, 120 E Main, Crothersville, 47274. SAN 341-6224. Tel: 812-793-2927. FAX: 812-793-3721. Web Site: www.seymour.org/mainlib. *Librn*, Sharon Langdon; E-Mail: slangdon@japl.lib.in.us; Staff 3 (Non-MLS 3)
Friends of the Library Group
MEDORA BRANCH, 27 Main St, PO Box 400, Medora, 47260. SAN 371-3458. Tel: 812-966-2278. FAX: 812-966-2229. Web Site: www.seymour.org/mainlib. *Librn*, Alberta Wineinger; E-Mail: albertaw@japl.lib.in.us; Staff 2 (Non-MLS 2)
Friends of the Library Group
Bookmobiles: 1. Farber ELF

SHELBYVILLE

P SHELBYVILLE-SHELBY COUNTY PUBLIC LIBRARY, 57 W Broadway, 46176. SAN 305-1099. Tel: 317-398-7121, 317-835-2653. FAX: 317-398-4430. Web Site: www.sscpl.lib.in.us/library/. *Dir*, Cynthia Faunce; E-Mail: cfaunce@sscpl.lib.in.us; *Mgr*, Valerie Stevens; *Ad Servs*, Judy Cheatham; *Ch Servs*, Janet Wallace; *Ref*, Carol Antle; *Head Tech Servs*, Beverly Compton; *Spec Coll*, Maureen Sheehan; Staff 34 (MLS 1, Non-MLS 33)
Founded 1898. Pop 40,300; Circ 132,000
Jan 1999-Dec 1999 Income $651,918, State $1,084, County $650,834. Mats Exp $124,008, Books $111,973, Per/Ser (Incl. Access Fees) $9,705, Electronic Ref Mat (Incl. Access Fees) $2,330. Sal $389,536
Library Holdings: Bk Titles 90,000; Per Subs 240; High Interest/Low Vocabulary Bk Vols 50
Subject Interests: Local history
Partic in Indiana Cooperative Library Services Authority
Friends of the Library Group

SHERIDAN

P SHERIDAN PUBLIC LIBRARY, 214 Main St, 46069. SAN 305-1102. Tel: 317-758-5201. FAX: 317-758-5201. Web Site: www.sheridan.org/library. *Dir*, Ann Emery; E-Mail: ann@sheridan.lib.in.us; *Ch Servs*, Nancy Urban
Founded 1912. Pop 4,263; Circ 35,499
Jan 2001-Dec 2001 Income $149,000. Mats Exp $28,000, Books $20,000, Per/Ser (Incl. Access Fees) $2,000. Sal $81,000
Library Holdings: Bk Vols 35,000; Per Subs 57
Partic in Cent Ind Libr Asn
Friends of the Library Group

SHOALS

P SHOALS PUBLIC LIBRARY,* PO Box 909, 47581. SAN 305-1110. Tel: 812-247-3838. FAX: 812-247-3838. *Librn*, Linda Jones
Jan 1997-Dec 1998 Income $23,989. Mats Exp $7,019. Sal $13,246
Library Holdings: Bk Vols 9,688; Per Subs 38
Open Mon-Wed, Fri & Sat 12-5, Thurs 12-7

SOUTH BEND

S ALLIED-SIGNAL, Controls & Accessories Library 857-3,* 717 N Bendix Dr, 857-3, 46620. SAN 305-1137. Tel: 219-231-3290. FAX: 219-231-3283. *Librn*, Kari Ambler
Founded 1943
Library Holdings: Bk Vols 50; Per Subs 46
Special Collections: Air Force Materials Laboratories Coll
Publications: Aviation Week; Electronics Science News Rotor Wing

S ENVIRONIC FOUNDATION INTERNATIONAL, INC LIBRARY, 916 St Vincent St, 46617-1443. SAN 326-0968. Tel: 219-233-3357. FAX: 219-289-6716. E-Mail: environics@aol.com. *Librn*, Patrick Horsbrugh
Founded 1970
Library Holdings: Bk Vols 10,000
Subject Interests: Archaeology, Architecture, Biology, Ecology
Special Collections: Environic graduate program thesis
Additional location in Washington, DC; No original documents provided-copies only

C INDIANA CHRISTIAN UNIVERSITY LIBRARY, 530 E Ireland Rd, 46614. Tel: 219-291-3292, Ext 509. *Dean*, Steve Swihart
Enrl 100
Library Holdings: Bk Vols 10,000; Bk Titles 10,000; Per Subs 10

C INDIANA UNIVERSITY SOUTH BEND, Franklin D Schurz Library, 1700 Mishawaka Ave, 46614. (Mail add: PO Box 7111, 46634), SAN 305-1145. Tel: 219-237-4449. Circulation Tel: 219-237-4440. Reference Tel: 219-237-4441. FAX: 219-237-4472. Web Site: www.iusb.edu/~libg. *Dir Libr Serv*, Michele C Russo; Tel: 219-237-4448, E-Mail: mrusso@iusb.edu; *Head Ref*, Rosanne Cordell; Tel: 219-237-4209, E-Mail: rcordell@iusb.edu; *Ref*, Nancy Colborn; Tel: 219-237-4321, E-Mail: ncolborn@iusb.edu; *Head Tech Servs*, Judith Gottwald; Tel: 219-237-4444, E-Mail: jgottwald@iusb.edu; *Cat, Tech Servs*, Scott Opasik; Tel: 219-237-4446, E-Mail: sopasik@iusb.edu; *ILL*, Maureen Kennedy; Tel: 219-237-4433, E-Mail: maurkenn@iusb.edu; *Head*,

Circ, Katherin Plodowski; Tel: 219-237-4380, E-Mail: kplodows@iusb.edu; *Automation Syst Coordr*, Feng Shan; Tel: 219-237-4421, E-Mail: fshan@iusb.edu; *Branch Mgr*, Kim Parker; Tel: 219-237-4120, E-Mail: kparker@iusb.edu; *Coll Develop*, Ellen Maher; Tel: 219-237-6500, E-Mail: emaher@iusb.edu; *Govt Doc*, Linda Fisher; Tel: 219-237-4442, E-Mail: lfisher@iusb.edu; *Bibliog Instr*, Mark van Lummel; Tel: 219-237-4410, E-Mail: mvanlumm@iusb.edu; *Purchasing*, Rebecca Neiswender; Tel: 219-237-4404, E-Mail: rneiswen@iusb.edu; *Electronic Resources*, Joanne Evanoff; Tel: 219-237-4189, E-Mail: jevanoff@iusb.edu; Staff 20 (MLS 10, Non-MLS 10)
Founded 1940. Enrl 4,205; Fac 321; Highest Degree: Master
Jul 2000-Jun 2001 Income Parent Institution $1,763,779. Mats Exp $588,180, Books $123,212, Per/Ser (Incl. Access Fees) $361,468, Presv $18,500, Electronic Ref Mat (Incl. Access Fees) $85,000. Sal $717,969 (Prof $470,528)
Library Holdings: Bk Vols 208,442; Per Subs 2,116
Subject Interests: Art, Business and management, Education, Music, Theatre
Special Collections: James Lewis Casaday Theatre Coll; Lincoln Coll
Database Vendor: Dialog, Ebsco - EbscoHost, GaleNet, Lexis-Nexis, OCLC - First Search, OVID Technologies, ProQuest, Silverplatter Information Inc., Wilson - Wilson Web
Publications: Franklin D Schurz Library Newsletter (quarterly)
Function: Reference services available
Partic in Indiana Cooperative Library Services Authority; OCLC Online Computer Library Center, Inc
Friends of the Library Group

J IVY TECH STATE COLLEGE, South Bend Campus Library, 220 Dean Johnson Blvd, 46601. SAN 305-1153. Tel: 219-289-7001, Ext 5343. FAX: 219-236-7165. Web Site: www.ivy.tec.in.us/library/libr2. *Librn*, Allen McKiel; *Instr*, Kathy Peterson; Tel: 219-289-7001, Ext 5342, E-Mail: kpeterson@ivy.tec.in.us; Staff 3 (MLS 1, Non-MLS 2)
Founded 1968. Enrl 2,500; Highest Degree: Associate
Jul 1999-Jun 2000 Income State $154,000. Mats Exp $56,000. Sal $98,000
Library Holdings: Bk Vols 5,000; Bk Titles 4,800; Per Subs 70
Subject Interests: Art and architecture, Business and management, Medicine, Photography, Science/technology, Technology
Automation Activity & Vendor Info: (Acquisitions) Endeavor; (Cataloging) Endeavor; (Circulation) Endeavor; (OPAC) Endeavor
Database Vendor: epixtech, inc., IAC - SearchBank, OVID Technologies, Wilson - Wilson Web
Partic in Area 2 Libr Servs Authority; Indiana Cooperative Library Services Authority
Open Mon-Fri 8am-9pm & Sat 8-1

G LIBRARY OF THE US COURTS, (Formerly Federal Courts Library), Robert A Grant Courthouse, 204 S Main St, Rm 316, 46601. SAN 372-1183. Tel: 219-246-8050. FAX: 219-246-8002. Web Site: www.lb7.uscourts.gov. *Branch Mgr*, Patricia S Piasecki; E-Mail: pat_piasecki@ca7.uscourts.gov; *Tech Servs*, Karen M Shandor; E-Mail: karen_shandor@ca7.uscourts.gov. Subject Specialists: *Law*, Patricia S Piasecki; Staff 2 (Non-MLS 2)
Founded 1986
Library Holdings: Bk Vols 14,000; Per Subs 135
Automation Activity & Vendor Info: (Acquisitions) SIRSI; (Cataloging) SIRSI; (OPAC) SIRSI; (Serials) SIRSI
Database Vendor: Lexis-Nexis, OCLC - First Search

M MEMORIAL HOSPITAL OF SOUTH BEND, Library Services, 615 N Michigan, 46601. SAN 329-1316. Tel: 219-284-7491. Interlibrary Loan Service Tel: 219-284-7389. FAX: 219-284-3319. Web Site: Qualityoflife.org. *Coordr*, Charles A LeGuern; Tel: 219-284-7491, E-Mail: cleguern@memorialsb.org; Staff 2 (MLS 1, Non-MLS 1)
Founded 1978
Jan 2001-Dec 2001 Mats Exp $54,000, Books $6,000, Per/Ser (Incl. Access Fees) $45,000, Electronic Ref Mat (Incl. Access Fees) $8,000
Library Holdings: Bk Vols 2,000; Bk Titles 1,800; Per Subs 510
Subject Interests: Health care, Medicine, Nursing
Database Vendor: Dialog, Ebsco - EbscoHost, OCLC - First Search
Partic in Dialog Corporation; Indiana Cooperative Library Services Authority; National Network of Libraries of Medicine - Southeastern Atlantic Region; OCLC Online Computer Library Center, Inc

S NATIONAL FOOTBALL FOUNDATION'S COLLEGE, College Football Hall of Fame Library,* 111 S St Joseph St, 46601. SAN 313-5527. Tel: 219-235-5711, 219-235-9999. FAX: 219-235-5720. Web Site: collegefootball.org.
Library Holdings: Bk Vols 3,000
Subject Interests: Col football hist

S NORTHERN INDIANA CENTER FOR HISTORY, Vincent Bendix Library, 808 W Washington St, 46601. SAN 305-1161. Tel: 219-235-9064. FAX: 219-235-9059. E-Mail: archives@centerforhistory.org. Web Site: www.centerforhistory.org.
Library Holdings: Bk Vols 7,500; Per Subs 25
Subject Interests: Local history
Special Collections: All American Girls Professional Baseball League Repository; History of St Joseph River Valley Region of Northern Indiana & Southern Michigan
Restriction: Non-circulating to the public

GL SAINT JOSEPH COUNTY LAW LIBRARY, Court House, 101 S Main St, 46601. SAN 305-117X. Tel: 219-235-9657. FAX: 219-235-9905. *Librn*, Ford Diane
Library Holdings: Bk Vols 18,350
Special Collections: Law Books Coll; Reporters Coll; Statutes Coll

P SAINT JOSEPH COUNTY PUBLIC LIBRARY, 304 S Main, 46601-2125. SAN 341-6259. Tel: 219-282-4646. Interlibrary Loan Service Tel: 219-282-4671. Circulation Tel: 219-282-4617. Reference Tel: 219-282-4630. TDD: 219-235-4194. FAX: 219-280-2763. Web Site: sjcpl.lib.in.us. *Dir*, Donald J Napoli; E-Mail: donald.napoli@gomail.sjcpl.lib.in.us; *Asst Dir*, Debra Futa; E-Mail: debra.futa@gomail.sjcpl.lib.in.us; *Ref*, Julia Hill; E-Mail: j.hill@gomail.sjcpl.lib.in.us; *Automation Syst Coordr, Tech Servs*, Linda Broyles; E-Mail: l.broyles@gomail.sjcpl.lib.in.us; *Per*, Patricia Gable; E-Mail: p.gable@gomail.sjcpl.lib.in.us; *AV*, Judith Falzon; E-Mail: j.falzon@gomail.sjcpl.lib.in.us; *Ch Servs*, Frances Walters; E-Mail: f.walters@gomail.sjcpl.lib.in.us; *Ad Servs*, Nancy Korpal; E-Mail: n.korpal@gomail.sjcpl.lib.in.us; *Coll Develop*, Joseph Sipocz; E-Mail: j.sipocz@gomail.sjcpl.lib.in.us; Staff 73 (MLS 37, Non-MLS 36)
Founded 1888. Pop 167,477; Circ 2,258,267
Jan 1998-Dec 1999 Income $8,602,775, State $51,048, Locally Generated Income $7,004,560. Mats Exp $2,113,830, Books $1,528,396, Per/Ser (Incl. Access Fees) $232,321, AV Equip $373,113, Electronic Ref Mat (Incl. Access Fees) $354,736. Sal $3,481,973
Library Holdings: Bk Titles 538,927; Per Subs 1,842
Special Collections: Adult Reading Center; Genealogy (Local History/Gen), books, clippings, indexes; Large Type Books
Publications: Brief History of South Bend, Indiana 1820-1969
Special Services for the Deaf - Books on deafness & sign language; High interest/low vocabulary books; Special interest periodicals
Open Mon-Thurs 9-9, Fri-Sat 9-6 & Sun 1-5
Friends of the Library Group
Branches: 8
CENTRE TOWNSHIP, 1150 E Kern Rd, 46614. Tel: 219-251-3700. *Librn*, Dana Labrum
ROGER B FRANCIS BRANCH, 52655 N Ironwood Rd, 46635. SAN 341-6283. Tel: 219-282-4641. *Librn*, Linda Conyers; E-Mail: l.conyers@gomail.sjcpl.lib.in.us
Library Holdings: Bk Vols 98,191
LAKEVILLE BRANCH, 601 N Michigan, 46536. SAN 370-9248. Tel: 219-784-3446. *Head of Libr*, Amy Magiera; E-Mail: a.magiera@gomail.sjcpl.lib.in.us
Library Holdings: Bk Vols 11,170
LASALLE, 3232 W Ardmore, 46628-3232. SAN 341-6313. Tel: 219-282-4633. *Librn*, Dawn Matthews; E-Mail: d.matthews@gomail.sjcpl.lib.in.us
Library Holdings: Bk Vols 48,848
NORTH LIBERTY BRANCH, 105 W Center, North Liberty, 46554. SAN 329-6822. Tel: 219-656-3664. *Head of Libr*, Patty Fowler; E-Mail: p.fowler@gomail.sjcpl.lib.in.us
Library Holdings: Bk Vols 13,589
RIVER PARK, 2022 Mishawaka Ave, 46615. SAN 341-6348. Tel: 219-282-4635. *Librn*, Victoria Gutschenritter; E-Mail: v.ritter@gomail.sjcpl.lib.in.us
Library Holdings: Bk Vols 40,814
VIRGINIA M TUTT BRANCH, 2223 S Miami St, 46613. SAN 341-6372. Tel: 219-282-4637. *Librn*, Scott Sinnett; E-Mail: s.sinnett@gomail.sjcpl.lib.in.us
Library Holdings: Bk Vols 68,152
WESTERN, 611 S Lombardy Dr, 46619. SAN 341-6402. Tel: 219-282-4639. *Librn*, Paula Dale; E-Mail: p.dale@sjcpl.lib..in.us
Library Holdings: Bk Vols 32,529
Bookmobiles: 1. Serves at risk children grades 1-3. Bk vols 6086

M SAINT JOSEPH'S REGIONAL, Medical Center, 801 E LaSalle, 46617. SAN 325-7231. Tel: 219-237-7228. FAX: 219-280-7533. *Librn*, Jennifer Helmen
Library Holdings: Bk Vols 800; Per Subs 150

S SOUTH BEND JUVENILE FACILITY LIBRARY,* 52363 Laurel Rd, 46637. SAN 325-674X. Tel: 219-277-3070, Ext 25. FAX: 219-277-3072. *Dir*, Chuck Henry
Library Holdings: Bk Vols 2,500

S SOUTH BEND REGIONAL MUSEUM OF ART LIBRARY,* 120 S St Joseph St, 46601. SAN 305-1129. Tel: 219-235-9102. FAX: 219-235-5782. *Dir*, Susan Visser; *Curator*, Leisa Rundquist
Founded 1947
Library Holdings: Bk Vols 1,250; Per Subs 45
Special Collections: Art Books; Art Coll, sl, flm; Art Exhibition Catalogues; Carlotta Murray Banta Coll
Restriction: Non-circulating to the public

S STUDEBAKER NATIONAL MUSEUM ARCHIVES,* 525 S Main St, 46601. SAN 325-4526. Tel: 219-235-9714. FAX: 219-235-5522. E-Mail: stumuseum@michiana.net. Web Site: www.studebakermuseum.org. *Dir*, Ronald Radecki
Library Holdings: Bk Titles 400; Per Subs 20
Subject Interests: General indust hist, Local indust hist
Special Collections: Agricultrual History (Oliver Photograph Coll), prints

negatives; Labor History; South Bend area business, labor & industry, vertical files & photographs; South Bend Labor Oral History Project; transcriptions industrial history; Transportation History (Studebaker Coll), mss, flms, photogs, trade lit
Restriction: Non-circulating to the public

SOUTH WHITLEY

P SOUTH WHITLEY-CLEVELAND TOWNSHIP PUBLIC LIBRARY, 201 E Front St, PO Box 536, 46787-1315. SAN 305-1196. Tel: 219-723-5321. FAX: 219-723-5321. *Dir*, Marian E Bollinger
Founded 1913. Pop 3,215; Circ 51,932
Library Holdings: Bk Vols 40,057; Per Subs 140
Subject Interests: Local history

SPEEDWAY

S ANTIQUE DOORKNOB COLLECTORS OF AMERICA, Emil Miller Memorial Library, 5538 W 25th St, 46224. SAN 374-9045. Tel: 317-291-6043. *Archivist*, Barbara Menchhofer; *Archivist*, Stephen A Menchhofer
Library Holdings: Bk Titles 250

P SPEEDWAY PUBLIC LIBRARY,* 5633 W 25th St, 46224-3899. SAN 305-120X. Tel: 317-243-8959. FAX: 317-243-9373. Web Site: birch.palni.edu/~riggle/spdwx3.htm. *Dir*, Darsi Bohr; *Ch Servs*, Carol Lewis; *Ch Servs*, Toni Sekula; Staff 3 (MLS 3)
Founded 1965. Pop 13,092; Circ 115,752
Library Holdings: Bk Vols 62,491; Per Subs 14
Subject Interests: Genealogy
Publications: Speedreader (library newsletter)
Partic in Indiana Cooperative Library Services Authority
Friends of the Library Group

SPENCER

P OWEN COUNTY PUBLIC LIBRARY,* 10 S Montgomery St, 47460-1713. SAN 305-1218. Tel: 812-829-3392. FAX: 812-829-6165. *Dir*, Bickey Freeland; E-Mail: vfreeland@owenlib.org; *Dep Dir*, Debbie Campbell; Staff 2 (MLS 2)
Founded 1912. Pop 17,281; Circ 71,000
Jan 1997-Dec 1998 Income $297,981, State $262,342, Locally Generated Income $35,639. Mats Exp $47,968, Books $34,692, Per/Ser (Incl. Access Fees) $4,050, Micro $2,576. Sal $138,462 (Prof $49,000)
Library Holdings: Bk Vols 49,482; Bk Titles 50,938; Per Subs 174
Special Collections: Genealogy, V-tapes
Partic in Stone Hills Libr Network
Friends of the Library Group

SPICELAND

P SPICELAND TOWN-TOWNSHIP PUBLIC LIBRARY,* 106 W Main St, 47385. SAN 305-1226. Tel: 765-987-7472. FAX: 765-987-8840. *Librn*, Teresa Janney; *Asst Librn*, Lila Mondrush
Library Holdings: Bk Vols 19,000; Per Subs 45
Open Tues & Thurs 1-7, Wed 1-5 & Sat 10-2

SULLIVAN

P SULLIVAN COUNTY PUBLIC LIBRARY,* 100 S Crowder St, 47882-1750. SAN 341-6437. Tel: 812-268-4957. FAX: 812-268-5370. *Circ*, Mary Ann McCann; *Ch Servs*, Carol Swisher
Founded 1904. Pop 18,993; Circ 130,233
Jul 1996-Jun 1997 Income $625,000. Mats Exp $78,750. Sal $157,500
Library Holdings: Bk Vols 100,000; Per Subs 225
Subject Interests: Genealogy
Special Collections: Indiana Coll

SYRACUSE

P SYRACUSE TURKEY CREEK TOWNSHIP PUBLIC LIBRARY,* 115 E Main St, 46567. SAN 305-1242. Tel: 219-457-3022. FAX: 219-457-8971. *Dir, Librn*, Rosalyn Jones; E-Mail: rjones@fourway.net; *Ref*, Dee Stults; *Ref*, June Treka; *Ch Servs*, Ed Batesla
Founded 1909. Circ 39,000
Jan 1997-Dec 1998 Income $239,268, State $20,648, County $96,429, Other $11,256. Mats Exp $65,451, Books $47,444, Per/Ser (Incl. Access Fees) $4,075. Sal $140,004
Library Holdings: Bk Vols 43,000; Per Subs 70
Special Collections: Local Newspaper Coll, micro; Old historical photographs & slides
Partic in Area Libr Serv Authority
Open Mon, Tues & Wed 10-8, Thrus 12-7, Fri 10-6, Sat 10-5
Friends of the Library Group

TELL CITY

S BRANCHVILLE TRAINING CENTER LIBRARY,* PO Box 500, 47586. SAN 327-9006. Tel: 812-843-5921. FAX: 812-843-4262. *Librn*, Tammy Solomon
Library Holdings: Bk Titles 15,000; Per Subs 30
Open Thurs 8-4

P TELL CITY-PERRY COUNTY PUBLIC LIBRARY, 909 Franklin St, 47586-1717. SAN 305-1250. Tel: 812-547-2661. FAX: 812-547-3038. E-Mail: tcpublib@psci.net. Web Site: www.psci.net/~tcpublib. *Dir*, Judy Howe; *Asst Librn*, Paul Sanders; *Ch Servs*, Lisa Hammack; Staff 3 (MLS 1, Non-MLS 2)
Founded 1905. Pop 17,321; Circ 131,531
1999-2000 Income $458,796, State $57,318, Federal $9,949, County $377,231, Locally Generated Income $14,298. Mats Exp $76,418, Books $48,316, Per/Ser (Incl. Access Fees) $4,578, Micro $5,007, AV Equip $10,824, Electronic Ref Mat (Incl. Access Fees) $7,693. Sal $198,730 (Prof $32,000)
Library Holdings: Bk Vols 44,212; Bk Titles 39,790; Per Subs 172
Subject Interests: Genealogy, Local history
Automation Activity & Vendor Info: (Cataloging) Sagebrush Corporation; (Circulation) Sagebrush Corporation; (OPAC) Sagebrush Corporation
Partic in Indiana Cooperative Library Services Authority
Special Services for the Blind - ADA terminals for visually impaired
Friends of the Library Group
Bookmobiles: 1

TERRE HAUTE

R CENTRAL PRESBYTERIAN CHURCH LIBRARY,* 125 N Seventh St, 47807-3195. SAN 305-1269. Tel: 812-232-5049. *In Charge*, Alice Wert
Founded 1960 Income $100, Other $100. Mats Exp Per/Ser (Incl. Access Fees) $25
Library Holdings: Bk Vols 2,492
Subject Interests: Church history, Religion
Special Collections: Archives on Central Presbyterian Church & Presbyterian Church in the U S
Publications: CP Annual Report; Herald & Sunday Bulletin
Partic in Indiana Cooperative Library Services Authority

R FIRST BAPTIST CHURCH OF WEST TERRE HAUTE LIBRARY, 1920 College Ave, 47803. SAN 305-1293. Tel: 812-232-2772. FAX: 812-232-2772. *Librn*, Margaret Watson
Founded 1966
Library Holdings: Bk Titles 5,000; Per Subs 10
Subject Interests: Christianity, Fiction, Missions and missionaries, Music, Religion
AV equipment available

R IMMANUEL LUTHERAN CHURCH LIBRARY, 645 Poplar St, 47807. SAN 305-1331. Tel: 812-232-4972. *In Charge*, Kathy Tschudny
Founded 1973
Library Holdings: Bk Vols 7,000; Bk Titles 5,000
Subject Interests: Religion
Open Mon 8:30-4

C INDIANA STATE UNIVERSITY, Cunningham Memorial Library, 650 Sycamore, 47809. SAN 341-6496. Tel: 812-237-3700. Interlibrary Loan Service Tel: 812-237-2566. Toll Free Tel: 800-851-4279. TDD: 812-237-4450. FAX: 812-237-3376. Web Site: odin.indstate.edu. *Dean of Libr*, Ellen Watson; E-Mail: eiw@indstate.edu; *Asst Dean*, Joan Evans; *Asst Dean*, Michael Somers; *Info Res*, Judith T Scott; Tel: 812-237-8824, Fax: 812-237-3376; *Acq*, Elizabeth Lorenzen; Tel: 812-237-4397, Fax: 812-237-2567, E-Mail: liblore@isugw.indstate.edu; *Rare Bks, Spec Coll*, David Vancil; Tel: 812-237-2610, Fax: 812-237-2567, E-Mail: libvanc@isugw.indstate.edu; *Electronic Resources*, Ralph Gabbard; Tel: 812-237-2578, Fax: 812-237-2567, E-Mail: libgabb@isugw.indstate.edu; *Doc*, Penny Kyker; Tel: 812-237-2629, Fax: 812-237-2567, E-Mail: libkyker@isugw.indstate.edu; *Cat*, Sara B Hardin; Tel: 812-237-2572, Fax: 812-237-2567; *Coll Develop, Info Res*, Betz Herie; Tel: 812-237-2672, Fax: 812-237-3376; *Ser*, John Lunceford; Tel: 812-237-2621, Fax: 812-237-2567, E-Mail: liblunc@isugw.indstate.edu
Founded 1870. Enrl 10,985; Fac 560; Highest Degree: Doctorate
Jul 1998-Jun 1999 Income (Main Library Only) $4,133,343, State $4,080,882, Locally Generated Income $40,161, Other $12,300. Mats Exp $1,701,946, Books $400,100, Per/Ser (Incl. Access Fees) $962,728, Presv $48,050, Micro $46,215. Sal $2,189,575 (Prof $1,318,744)
Library Holdings: Bk Vols 1,275,966; Per Subs 22,023
Special Collections: American Education, classics (Cunningham Coll) & textbks (Walker Coll); American Labor Movement (Debs Coll); Indian Education (Floyd Family Coll); Indian History & Culture (Indiana Coll); Indiana Federal Writers' Materials (Indiana Federal Writers Project/Program Coll); Music, sheet & orchestra (Kirk Coll); Pre-1901 Dictionaries & other word books (Cordell Coll); Publishing History & Culture, local (Faculty Coll) & history, culture, travel & literature (Rare Books Coll)
Automation Activity & Vendor Info: (Acquisitions) Endeavor; (Cataloging) Endeavor; (Circulation) Endeavor; (Course Reserve) Endeavor; (ILL) Endeavor; (OPAC) Endeavor; (Serials) Endeavor

Publications: Floyd Family Collection: Catalog of Textbooks & Related Materials; Friends of Cunningham Memorial Library Newsletter; ISU Library Newsletter
Partic in Center For Research Libraries; Indiana Cooperative Library Services Authority; OCLC Online Computer Library Center, Inc
Special Services for the Deaf - Staff with knowledge of sign language; TDD
Special Services for the Blind - Braille; Closed circuit television magnifier; Large print bks; ZoomText software to enlarge computer screen
Friends of the Library Group
Departmental Libraries:
CAREER CENTER, Student Services Bldg, Rm 235, 47809. SAN 370-016X. Tel: 812-237-2812. FAX: 812-237-4392. *Librn*, Elizabeth Lorenzen

J IVY TECH STATE COLLEGE,* 7999 S US Hwy 41, 47802. SAN 341-6550. Tel: 812-299-1121. FAX: 812-299-5723. Web Site: ivytech7.cc.in.us. *Coordr*, David Barton; E-Mail: dbarton@ivy.tech.in.us
Founded 1967. Enrl 1,600; Fac 45
Library Holdings: Bk Titles 4,500; Per Subs 65
Subject Interests: Business and management, Health sciences, Vocational education
Open Mon-Thurs 8am-9pm & Fri 8-4

L NATIONAL LEGAL CENTER FOR THE MEDICALLY DEPENDENT & DISABLED, INC, Library,* 7 S Sixth St, Ste 208, 47807. SAN 372-7483. Tel: 812-238-0769. FAX: 812-232-0268.
Founded 1984
Library Holdings: Bk Titles 360
Special Collections: Medical Treatment Rights for Persons with Disabilities, bks, ref mat
Restriction: Staff use only

S PFIZER, INC, Animal Health Central Research Library,* PO Box 88, 47808. SAN 305-1366. Tel: 812-299-2121, Ext 465. FAX: 812-299-8120. *Librn*, Stacy Blake-Miller; E-Mail: blakes@pfizer.com
Founded 1952
Library Holdings: Bk Vols 800; Per Subs 75
Subject Interests: Veterinary medicine
Open Mon-Fri 8-4:30

C ROSE-HULMAN INSTITUTE OF TECHNOLOGY, John A Logan Library, 5500 Wabash Ave, 47803. SAN 305-1374. Tel: 812-877-8200. FAX: 812-877-8175. Web Site: www.rose-hulman.edu/library/. *Dir*, John M Robson; E-Mail: john.robson@rose-hulman.edu; Staff 2 (MLS 2)
Founded 1874. Enrl 1,300; Fac 101; Highest Degree: Master
Library Holdings: Bk Vols 74,000; Per Subs 480
Subject Interests: Science/technology, Technology
Special Collections: Institute Archives
Partic in OCLC Online Computer Library Center, Inc
Open Mon-Thurs 8am-11pm, Fri 8am-5pm, Sat 10am-5pm & Sun 2-10pm

S SHELDON SWOPE ART MUSEUM LIBRARY, 25 S Seventh St, 47807. SAN 305-1382. Tel: 812-238-1676. FAX: 812-238-1677. E-Mail: info@swope.org. Web Site: www.swope.org. *Librn*, Alice L Wert
Jan 1999-Dec 1999 Income Parent Institution $1,470. Mats Exp $1,500, Books $1,300, Per/Ser (Incl. Access Fees) $200
Library Holdings: Bk Vols 1,200; Bk Titles 1,000
Subject Interests: Am archit, Arts and crafts (American)
Special Collections: Rare Books
Restriction: Not a lending library

M UNION HOSPITAL, Medical Library,* 1606 N Seventh St, 47804-2789. SAN 305-1412. Tel: 812-238-7641. FAX: 812-238-7446. *Librn*, Ami Amerman
Founded 1976
Sep 1996-Aug 1997 Income $132,657. Mats Exp $25,459. Sal $63,000
Library Holdings: Bk Vols 500; Per Subs 150
Restriction: Staff use only
Partic in Greater Midwest Regional Medical Libr Network

S UNITED STATES PENITENTIARY, Independent Study Library,* PO Box 33, 47808. SAN 305-1439. Tel: 812-238-1531, Ext 289. *In Charge*, Larry McDaniel
Founded 1939. Pop 1,400
Library Holdings: Bk Titles 5,000; Per Subs 47
Mem of Stone Hills Area Library Services Authority

R UNITY PRESBYTERIAN CHURCH LIBRARY, (Formerly Washington Avenue Presbyterian Church Library), 619 Washington Ave, 47802. SAN 305-1447. Tel: 812-232-1638, 812-232-4057. E-Mail: linpaster@aol.com. *Librn*, Bess Enright
Library Holdings: Bk Vols 300

S VIGO COUNTY HISTORICAL MUSEUM LIBRARY,* 1411 S Sixth St, 47802. SAN 323-4398. Tel: 812-235-9717. FAX: 812-235-9717. E-Mail: vchs@holli.com. *Exec Dir*, Mary Lee Hagan; *Asst Dir*, Barbara Carney
Library Holdings: Bk Titles 1,500
Open Tues-Sun 1-4
Friends of the Library Group

P VIGO COUNTY PUBLIC LIBRARY, Seventh & Poplar St, One Library Square, 47807-3609. SAN 341-6615. Tel: 812-232-1113. Circulation Tel: 812-232-1113, Ext 250, 251, 252. Reference Tel: 812-232-1113, Ext 241, 242. TDD: 812-232-2055. FAX: 812-232-3208. Web Site: www.vigo.lib.in.us. *Dir*, Nancy E Dowell; Tel: 812-232-1113, Ext 202, Fax: 812-235-1439, E-Mail: ndowell@vigo.lib.in.us; *Ref*, Clarence Brink; Tel: 812-232-1113, Ext 214, E-Mail: cbrink@vigo.lib.in.us; *Circ*, Jeff Trinkle; Tel: 812-232-1113, Ext 285, E-Mail: jtrinkle@vigo.lib.in.us; *Ch Servs*, June Dunbar; Tel: 812-232-1113, Ext 222, E-Mail: jdunbar@vigo.lib.in.us; *ILL*, Brigitte Gardner; Tel: 812-232-1113, Ext 243, E-Mail: bgardner@vigo.lib.in.us; *Commun Servs*, Christine Schellenderg; Tel: 812-232-1113, Ext 281; *Ref*, Kathy Prothero-Wleklinski; *Head Tech Servs*, Libby Walker; Tel: 812-232-1113, Ext 203, E-Mail: lwalker@vigo.lib.in.us; *Archivist*, Susan Dehler; Tel: 812-232-1113, Ext 292, E-Mail: sdehler@vigo.lib.in.us; *Cat*, Judy Morge; *Tech Servs*, Elizabeth Walker; *Ref*, Jeanne Puacz; Tel: 812-232-1113, Ext 248; *Mgr*, Susan Jakaitis; Tel: 812-232-1113, Ext 290; *Outreach Serv*, Michael Konnert; E-Mail: mkonnert@vigo.lib.in.us; *Spec Coll*, Nancy Sherrill; Tel: 812-232-1113, Ext 212, E-Mail: nsherrill@vigo.lib.in.us. Subject Specialists: *English second language*, Susan Jakaitis; *Genealogy*, Nancy Sherrill; *Human res*, Libby Walker; *Marketing*, Christine Schellenderg; *Programming*, Christine Schellenderg; *Pub relations*, Christine Schellenderg; *Storytelling*, Michael Konnert; Staff 112 (MLS 27, Non-MLS 85)
Founded 1882. Pop 106,107; Circ 841,984
Jan 1999-Dec 1999 Income $4,196,079, State $452,542, Federal $11,900, County $3,677,050, Other $54,587. Sal $2,364,447
Library Holdings: Bk Vols 322,960; Bk Titles 133,374; Per Subs 850
Special Collections: Community Archives Coll; Eugene V Debs Coll; LifeLong Learning Center Literacy Materials; Max Ehrmann Coll
Automation Activity & Vendor Info: (Acquisitions) DRA; (Cataloging) DRA; (Circulation) DRA; (Course Reserve) DRA; (ILL) DRA; (Media Booking) DRA; (OPAC) DRA; (Serials) DRA
Database Vendor: DRA, Ebsco - EbscoHost, IAC - Info Trac, OCLC - First Search
Publications: Directory of Voluntary Clubs & Organizations; History of the Public Library in Vigo County, 1816-1975; Tutortalk (literacy newsletter)
Function: Archival collection
Partic in Econ Develop Info Network; Indiana Cooperative Library Services Authority; Stone Hills Libr Network
Monthly "Brown Bag" programs at noon featuring various speakers/performers on a variety of topics; legislative Crackerbarrel sessions January through April of each year; "Notes at Noon" presentations featuring musical performances
Friends of the Library Group
Branches: 4
MEADOWS, Meadows Shopping Ctr, 47803. SAN 341-6674. Tel: 812-232-1113, Ext 255. FAX: 812-232-3208. *Librn*, Charlene Pierard
Library Holdings: Bk Vols 16,838
Friends of the Library Group
PLAZA NORTH, Plaza North Shopping Ctr, 1800 E Ft Harrison Rd, No 5, 47804-1492. SAN 341-6704. Tel: 812-232-1113, Ext 206. FAX: 812-478-9504. Web Site: vax1.vigo.lib.in.us. *Librn*, Cheryl Blevens; Tel: 812-232-1113, Ext 302, E-Mail: cblevens@vigo.lib.in.us
Library Holdings: Bk Vols 35,502
Friends of the Library Group
SOUTHLAND, Southland Shopping Ctr, 47802. SAN 341-6739. Tel: 812-232-1113, Ext 223. FAX: 812-232-3208. *Librn*, Suzanne VanReed
Library Holdings: Bk Vols 26,341
Friends of the Library Group
WEST TERRE HAUTE BRANCH, 626 National Ave, West Terre Haute, 47885. SAN 341-6763. Tel: 812-232-1113, Ext 211. FAX: 812-478-9602. Web Site: www.vaxl.vigo.lib.in.us. *Branch Mgr*, Raina Konazeski; E-Mail: rkonazeski@vigo.lib.in.us; Staff 4 (Non-MLS 4)
Library Holdings: Bk Vols 17,877
Database Vendor: DRA
Friends of the Library Group
Bookmobiles: 1. Librn, Elaine Liveoak

C VIGO COUNTY SCHOOL CORP, Instructional Materials Center Library,* 3000 College Ave, 47803. SAN 325-6782. Tel: 812-462-4354. FAX: 812-462-4114. *Coordr*, Brenda Allen; *Circ*, Georgann Sandiford; *Circ*, Laura Callahan
Special Collections: Classroom Coll; Professional Coll
Partic in OCLC Online Computer Library Center, Inc

THORNTOWN

P THORNTOWN PUBLIC LIBRARY,* 124 N Market St, 46071-1144. SAN 305-1455. Tel: 765-436-7348. FAX: 765-436-7011. *Dir*, Karen Niemeyer; E-Mail: kniemey@n-motion.net; *Asst Librn*, Yvonne Welty; *Ch Servs*, Shirley Hodgen; *Circ*, Alma Smith
Pop 4,350; Circ 51,516
Library Holdings: Bk Vols 24,000
Subject Interests: Local history

Special Collections: Local Indian Coll
Mem of Cent Indiana Area Libr Servs Authority
Open Mon & Fri 10-6, Tues-Thurs 10-8, Sat 10-4
Friends of the Library Group

TIPTON

P TIPTON COUNTY PUBLIC LIBRARY, 127 E Madison St, 46072-1993. SAN 341-6798. Tel: 765-675-8761. FAX: 765-675-4475. E-Mail: tipton@tiptonpl.lib.in.us. Web Site: www.tiptonpl.lib.in.us. *Dir*, Linda Joines; *Asst Dir, AV, Coll Develop, Ref*, Renda Hurst; *Ch Servs*, Paris Head; *Circ*, Carl Watson; *Tech Servs*, Anita Gunning; Staff 26 (MLS 3, Non-MLS 23)
Founded 1902. Pop 16,532
Jan 1999-Dec 1999 Income (Main Library and Branch Library) $905,072, State $5,398, County $868,126, Locally Generated Income $31,548. Mats Exp $121,000, Books $92,000, Per/Ser (Incl. Access Fees) $11,000, AV Equip $18,000. Sal $243,488 (Prof $122,427)
Library Holdings: Bk Titles 89,000; Per Subs 318
Subject Interests: Indians
Special Collections: Tipton & Indiana, bks, clippings & newspapers
Automation Activity & Vendor Info: (Circulation) epixtech, inc.
Partic in Indiana Cooperative Library Services Authority
Friends of the Library Group
Branches: 1
WINDFALL BRANCH, PO Box 487, Windfall, 46076. SAN 341-6828. Tel: 765-945-7655. *Librn*, Donna Williams

UNION CITY

P UNION CITY PUBLIC LIBRARY, 408 N Columbia St, 47390-1404. SAN 305-1463. Tel: 765-964-4748. FAX: 765-964-4748.; Staff 1 (MLS 1)
Founded 1904. Pop 5,393; Circ 21,575
Jan 1999-Dec 1999 Income $125,799. Mats Exp $28,131, Books $22,084, Per/Ser (Incl. Access Fees) $3,111, Micro $941, Electronic Ref Mat (Incl. Access Fees) $1,995. Sal $39,202 (Prof $24,810)
Library Holdings: Bk Titles 25,886; Per Subs 88
Subject Interests: Genealogy, Local history
Special Collections: Local Newspapers, micro
Partic in Indiana Cooperative Library Services Authority
Friends of the Library Group

UPLAND

P BARTON REES POGUE MEMORIAL LIBRARY, Upland Public Library, 029 W Washington St, PO Box 488, 46989. SAN 305-1471. Tel: 765-998-2971. FAX: 765-998-2971. *Dir*, Valentina Hiatt; *Asst Librn*, Ellen Valliere; *Asst Librn*, Marilyn Bottoms
Founded 1934. Pop 3,295; Circ 11,506
Jan 1999-Dec 1999 Income $38,624, State $4,689, Other $393. Mats Exp $8,676, Books $7,125, Per/Ser (Incl. Access Fees) $1,145, Electronic Ref Mat (Incl. Access Fees) $406. Sal $16,890 (Prof $10,500)
Library Holdings: Bk Vols 16,449; Per Subs 36
Automation Activity & Vendor Info: (OPAC) Follett

C TAYLOR UNIVERSITY, Zondervan Library, 236 W Reade Ave, 46989-1001. SAN 305-148X. Tel: 765-998-5241. Interlibrary Loan Service Tel: 765-998-5530. Circulation Tel: 765-998-5522. Reference Tel: 765-998-5267. FAX: 765-998-5569. *Dir*, Daniel J Bowell; E-Mail: dnbowell@tayloru.edu; *Acq*, Paula Bremer; Tel: 765-998-5270, E-Mail: plbremer@tayloru.edu; *Ref*, Roger Phillips; E-Mail: rgphillip@tayloru.edu; *Archivist, Ref*, Bonnie Houser; Tel: 765-998-5220, E-Mail: bnhouser@tayloru.edu; *Tech Servs*, Laurie Wolcott; Tel: 765-998-5242, E-Mail: lrwolcott@tayloru.edu; Staff 5 (MLS 5)
Founded 1846. Enrl 1,913; Fac 120; Highest Degree: Bachelor
Jul 2000-Jun 2001 Income Parent Institution $679,695. Mats Exp $179,975, Books $48,208, Per/Ser (Incl. Access Fees) $74,648, Presv $3,778, Micro $10,298, AV Equip $14,543, Electronic Ref Mat (Incl. Access Fees) $28,500. Sal $265,374 (Prof $200,504)
Library Holdings: Bk Vols 195,343; Per Subs 704
Special Collections: Old & Scarce Books on all Subjects (Ayres Coll)
Automation Activity & Vendor Info: (Acquisitions) DRA; (Cataloging) DRA; (Circulation) DRA; (OPAC) DRA; (Serials) DRA
Database Vendor: CARL, Dialog, DRA, Ebsco - EbscoHost, Lexis-Nexis, OCLC - First Search, Silverplatter Information Inc.
Partic in Indiana Cooperative Library Services Authority; OCLC Online Computer Library Center, Inc; Private Acad Libr Network of Ind

VALPARAISO

S HISTORICAL SOCIETY OF PORTER COUNTY, Old Jail Museum Library,* 153 Franklin St, 46383. SAN 371-1587. Tel: 219-465-3595. *Curator*, Bonnie Cuson
Library Holdings: Bk Vols 4,000
Subject Interests: History
Open Tues, Wed & Fri 1-4

R LUTHERAN DEACONESS ASSOCIATION, Diaconal Center Library, 1304 La Porte Ave, 46383. SAN 325-5549. Tel: 219-464-6925. FAX: 219-464-6928. E-Mail: deacserv@valpo.edu. *Exec Dir*, Louise Williams
Founded 1943. Enrl 21; Fac 3
Library Holdings: Bk Vols 1,500; Per Subs 50
Special Collections: History of Diaconate; Spirituality; Women in Church

P PORTER COUNTY PUBLIC LIBRARY SYSTEM, 103 Jefferson St, 46383-4820. SAN 341-6852. Tel: 219-462-0524. TDD: 219-462-4948. FAX: 219-477-4866. *Dir*, Donald C Johnson; Tel: 219-462-0524, Ext 121, E-Mail: djohnson@pcpls.lib.in.us; *Asst Dir*, James D Cline; Tel: 219-462-0524, Ext 126, E-Mail: jcline@pcpls.lib.in.us; *Librn*, Phyllis Nelson; Tel: 219-462-0524, Ext 103, E-Mail: pnelson@pcpls.lib.in.us; *AV, Circ*, Dawn Myers; Tel: 219-462-0524, Ext 107, E-Mail: dmyers@pcpls.lib.in.us; *Automation Syst Coordr*, Judith Wilkin; Tel: 219-462-0524, Ext 120, E-Mail: jwilkin@pcpls.lib.in.us; *Bkmobile Coordr*, Shirley Gacsy; Tel: 219-462-0524, Ext 143; *Cat, Tech Servs*, Alice Gustin; Tel: 219-462-0524, Ext 129; *ILL*, Machelle Gold; *Ref*, Ken Hansen; Tel: 219-462-0524, Ext 110, E-Mail: khansen@pcpls.lib.in.us; *YA Servs*, Gail Komer; Tel: 219-462-0524, Ext 136, E-Mail: gkomer@pcpls.lib.in.us. Subject Specialists: *Genealogy*, Larry Clark; Staff 98 (MLS 10, Non-MLS 88)
Founded 1905. Pop 118,500; Circ 1,630,920
Jan 1999-Dec 1999 Income (Main Library and Branch Library) $2,899,124, State $13,505, County $2,707,041, Locally Generated Income $153,374. Mats Exp $712,098, Books $487,203, Per/Ser (Incl. Access Fees) $54,481, Presv $4,777, Micro $61,063, Other Print Mats $104,574. Sal $1,401,908 (Prof $563,264)
Library Holdings: Bk Vols 362,029; Per Subs 1,100; High Interest/Low Vocabulary Bk Vols 1,500
Subject Interests: Genealogy, Indiana
Automation Activity & Vendor Info: (Acquisitions) epixtech, inc.; (Cataloging) Gaylord; (Circulation) epixtech, inc.; (OPAC) epixtech, inc.
Publications: Between-the-Stacks (staff/public monthly newsletter); Calendar of Events (monthly); Summer Reading Booklet, Baby Talk Bibliography
Partic in Ind Video & Audio Network; Indiana Cooperative Library Services Authority
Special Services for the Deaf - High interest/low vocabulary books; TDD
Friends of the Library Group
Branches: 5
HEBRON PUBLIC, 201 W Sigler St, Hebron, 46341. SAN 371-9561. Tel: 219-996-3684. FAX: 219-996-3680. *Librn*, Pam Feber
Library Holdings: Bk Vols 34,276
Friends of the Library Group
KOUTS PUBLIC, PO Box 450, Kouts, 46347-0450. SAN 341-6917. Tel: 219-766-2271. FAX: 219-766-2273. *Librn*, Gladys Villars
Library Holdings: Bk Vols 32,251
Friends of the Library Group
PORTAGE PUBLIC, 2665 Irving St, Portage, 46368. SAN 341-6941. Tel: 219-763-1508. FAX: 219-762-0101. Web Site: www.pcpls.lib.in.us. *Librn*, Nancy Clark
Founded 1970
Library Holdings: Bk Vols 77,195
Subject Interests: Careers
Special Collections: Local History Coll (Portage, Portage Township & Ogden Dunes)
Database Vendor: epixtech, inc.
Friends of the Library Group
SOUTH HAVEN, 403 West, 700 North, 46385. SAN 341-6976. Tel: 219-759-4474. FAX: 219-759-4454. *Librn*, Judy Thomas
Library Holdings: Bk Vols 45,026
Friends of the Library Group
VALPARAISO PUBLIC (CENTRAL), 103 Jefferson St, 46383. SAN 341-6887. Tel: 219-462-0524. FAX: 219-477-4867. *Asst Dir*, James D Cline
Founded 1905
Library Holdings: Bk Vols 149,828
Subject Interests: Genealogy, Local history
Friends of the Library Group
Bookmobiles: 1. Head, Shirley Gacsy. Vols 23453

C VALPARAISO UNIVERSITY, Henry F Moellering Memorial Library, 46383-6493. SAN 341-700X. Tel: 219-464-5364. Interlibrary Loan Service Tel: 219-464-5363. FAX: 219-464-5792. Web Site: www.valpo.edu/library. *Dir Libr Serv*, Richard A AmRhein; E-Mail: rick.amrhein@valpo.edu; *AV*, Patricia Hogan-Vidal; Tel: 219-464-5774, E-Mail: pat.hoganvidal@valpo.edu; *Bibliog Instr*, Trisha Mileham; Tel: 219-464-5693, E-Mail: trisha.mileham@valpo.edu; *Cat*, Stephanie Umbach; Tel: 219-464-5397, E-Mail: stephanie.umbach@valpo.edu; *ILL*, Susan Wanat; E-Mail: susan.wanat@valpo.edu; *Selection of Gen Ref Mat*, Ruth Connell; Tel: 219-464-5360, E-Mail: ruth.connell@valpor.edu; *Govt Doc*, Rebecca Byrum; Tel: 219-464-5771, E-Mail: becky.byrum@valpo.edu; *Circ*, Donna R R Resetar; Tel: 219-464-6183, E-Mail: donna.resetar@valpo.edu; *Coll Develop*, Judith Miller; Tel: 219-464-5808, E-Mail: judith.miller@valpo.edu; Staff 21 (MLS 8, Non-MLS 13)
Founded 1859. Enrl 3,603; Fac 245; Highest Degree: Master
Library Holdings: Bk Vols 348,331; Per Subs 2,600
Subject Interests: Theology

Special Collections: University Archives Coll
Automation Activity & Vendor Info: (Cataloging) Innovative Interfaces Inc.; (Circulation) Innovative Interfaces Inc.
Database Vendor: Ebsco - EbscoHost, IAC - Info Trac, OCLC - First Search, ProQuest
Partic in CRL; Indiana Cooperative Library Services Authority; OCLC Online Computer Library Center, Inc; Private Acad Libr Network of Ind
Departmental Libraries:
SCHOOL OF LAW LIBRARY, Wesemann Hall, 46383-9978. SAN 341-7034. Tel: 219-465-7838. Interlibrary Loan Service Tel: 219-465-7876. FAX: 219-465-7917. Web Site: www.valpo.edu/law. *Librn*, Mary G Persyn; E-Mail: mary.persyn@valpo.edu; *Res*, Michael Bushbaum; *Tech Servs*, Naomi Goodman; *Publ Servs*, Troy Johnson; *Doc*, Sarah Holterhoff; *Acq*, Elaine Moore; Staff 6 (MLS 6)
Founded 1879. Enrl 400; Fac 23; Highest Degree: Doctorate
Jul 1997-Jun 1998 Income $990,824. Mats Exp $568,800, Books $75,000, Per/Ser (Incl. Access Fees) $412,910, Presv $8,075, Micro $9,500. Sal $353,803 (Prof $263,690)
Library Holdings: Bk Vols 275,392; Bk Titles 46,168; Per Subs 3,227
Subject Interests: Law
Special Collections: Supreme Court Records & Briefs Coll
Publications: Third World Legal Studies; Valparaiso University Law Review
Partic in Indiana Cooperative Library Services Authority; PALNI

VAN BUREN

P VAN BUREN PUBLIC LIBRARY, 115 S First, PO Box 405, 46991. SAN 305-151X. Tel: 765-934-2171. FAX: 765-934-2171. E-Mail: vbpl@comteck.com. Web Site: ww1.comteck.com/~vbpl. *Librn*, Cheryl Smith
Circ 18,641
Library Holdings: Bk Vols 21,000; Per Subs 30
Automation Activity & Vendor Info: (Cataloging) Nicholas; (Circulation) Nicholas

VERSAILLES

P TYSON LIBRARY ASSOCIATION, 325 W Tyson St, PO Box 769, 47042-0393. SAN 376-5326. Tel: 812-689-5894. FAX: 812-689-7401. *Dir*, Christy Russell; *Chief Librn*, Stephen M Richmond; Staff 6 (MLS 1, Non-MLS 5)
Founded 1942
Library Holdings: Bk Vols 20,000; Bk Titles 10,000; Per Subs 25
Subject Interests: Fiction, Geography, History, Literature, Religion
Special Collections: Indiana Coll; James Tyson Coll; Ripley Coll; Versailles Coll
Publications: Tyson Tomes (Collection catalog)
Friends of the Library Group

VEVAY

P SWITZERLAND COUNTY PUBLIC LIBRARY,* 205 Ferry St, PO Box 133, 47043-0133. SAN 305-1528. Tel: 812-427-3363. FAX: 812-427-3654. Web Site: switzcpl.lib.in.us, switzcpl.lib.in.us. *Dir*, Susan Nimrsheim; Staff 1 (Non-MLS 1)
Founded 1915. Pop 7,738; Circ 32,000
1999-2000 Income $150,000, State $1,000, County $99,000. Mats Exp $36,000, Books $24,000, Per/Ser (Incl. Access Fees) $3,000, Electronic Ref Mat (Incl. Access Fees) $9,000
Library Holdings: Bk Titles 32,425; Per Subs 63
Special Collections: Switzerland County History, bks, VF, microfilm, a-tapes
Partic in Indiana Cooperative Library Services Authority

VINCENNES

M GOOD SAMARITAN HOSPITAL LIBRARY, 520 S Seventh St, 47591. SAN 305-1536. Tel: 812-882-5220, 812-885-3228. FAX: 812-885-3089. Web Site: www.gshvin.org. *Librn*, Carmon Graves; E-Mail: cgraves@gshvin.org
Library Holdings: Bk Vols 350; Bk Titles 300; Per Subs 30
Partic in Evansville Area Library Consortium
Open Mon-Fri 8-4

P KNOX COUNTY PUBLIC LIBRARY,* 502 N Seventh St, 47591-2119. SAN 305-1544. Tel: 812-886-4380. FAX: 812-886-0342. Web Site: www.kcpls1.vinu.edu. *Dir*, Emily Cooper Bunyan; E-Mail: ebunyan@kcpls1.binu.edu; *Asst Dir*, Steven Smith; *Syst Coordr*, Rosalie Fleck; *Tech Servs*, Bernice Doades; *Circ*, Mary Studley
Founded 1889. Pop 35,114
Jan 1998-Dec 1999 Income $1,193,811. Mats Exp $81,904, Books $60,000, Per/Ser (Incl. Access Fees) $9,904, Micro $12,000. Sal $319,207 (Prof $97,375)
Library Holdings: Bk Vols 107,124; Bk Titles 83,965; Per Subs 205
Subject Interests: Genealogy, History
Special Collections: Northwest Territory History; Vincennes History
Publications: Friends newsletter
Partic in Indiana Cooperative Library Services Authority; OCLC Online Computer Library Center, Inc
Friends of the Library Group

SR OLD CATHEDRAL LIBRARY,* 205 Church St, 47591-1191. Tel: 812-882-5638. FAX: 812-882-4042. *In Charge*, Father John Schipp; Staff 1 (MLS 1)
Founded 1794
Library Holdings: Bk Titles 11,000
Subject Interests: History, Theology
Special Collections: Brute Coll

VINCENNES UNIVERSITY
C SHAKE LEARNING RESOURCES LIBRARY, 1002 N First St, 47591. SAN 341-7069. Tel: 812-888-4166. Circulation Tel: 812-888-4165. Reference Tel: 812-888-5810. FAX: 812-888-5471. Web Site: www.vinu.edu. *Dean*, Robert Allen Slayton; E-Mail: bslayton@indian.vinu.edu; *AV*, Jay Wolf; Tel: 812-888-4172, E-Mail: jwolf@indian.vinu.edu; *Head, Circ*, Bonnie B Riggins; Tel: 812-888-4427, E-Mail: briggins@indian.vinu.edu; *Head Ref*, Joseph H Helms; Tel: 812-888-5377, E-Mail: jhelms@indian.vinu.edu; *Ref*, Richard King; Tel: 812-888-5411, E-Mail: rking@indian.vinu.edu; *Head, Cat*, Michaela M Coffey; Tel: 812-888-5807, E-Mail: mcoffey@indian.vinu.edu. Subject Specialists: *Allied health*, Michaela M Coffey; *Humanities*, Bonnie B Riggins; *Humanities*, Richard King; *Literature*, Richard King; *Soc sci*, Joseph H Helms; *Technology*, Bonnie B Riggins; *Technology*, Richard King; Staff 28 (MLS 5, Non-MLS 23)
Founded 1801. Enrl 6,000; Fac 250; Highest Degree: Associate
Jul 2000-Jun 2001 Income State $1,379,500. Mats Exp $279,800, Books $113,300, Per/Ser (Incl. Access Fees) $61,000, Presv $12,000, Micro $7,000, AV Equip $39,000, Manuscripts & Archives $1,000, Electronic Ref Mat (Incl. Access Fees) $41,500. Sal $732,114 (Prof $449,547)
Library Holdings: Bk Vols 100,102; Bk Titles 95,306; Per Subs 528
Special Collections: Lewis Historical Library Coll
Automation Activity & Vendor Info: (Acquisitions) Endeavor; (Cataloging) Endeavor; (Circulation) Endeavor; (ILL) Endeavor
Database Vendor: Ebsco - EbscoHost, epixtech, inc., OCLC - First Search, ProQuest
Restriction: Residents only
Partic in Indiana Cooperative Library Services Authority

WABASH

P WABASH CARNEGIE PUBLIC LIBRARY, 188 W Hill St, 46992-3048. SAN 305-1560. Tel: 219-563-2972. FAX: 219-563-0222. E-Mail: general@wabash.lib.in.us. Web Site: www.wabash.lib.in.us. *Dir*, Joanna Strode; *Tech Servs*, Helen Bruss; *Ref*, Ann Unger; *Circ*, Sarah Sear; *Ch Servs*, Nancy Snyder; Staff 19 (MLS 1, Non-MLS 18)
Founded 1903. Pop 12,127; Circ 149,553
Library Holdings: Bk Vols 58,385; Per Subs 206
Subject Interests: Gardening, Genealogy, Local history
Special Collections: Gene Stratton-Porter Coll
Automation Activity & Vendor Info: (Circulation) Gaylord
Publications: oral history (local) transcripts; Volumes of local records
Open Mon-Thurs 9-8, Fri & Sat 9-5

S WABASH COUNTY HISTORICAL MUSEUM, Historical Library,* Memorial Hall, 46992. SAN 370-2987. Tel: 219-563-0661.
Library Holdings: Bk Vols 1,000
Subject Interests: Civil War, Genealogy

WAKARUSA

P WAKARUSA PUBLIC LIBRARY, 124 N Elkhart St, PO Box 485, 46573-0485. SAN 305-1579. Tel: 219-862-2465. FAX: 219-862-4156. *Dir*, Jody O'Neill; E-Mail: joneill@wakarusa.lib.in.us; *Ch Servs*, Matt Bowers; E-Mail: mbowers@wakarusa.lib.in.us
Founded 1945. Pop 6,539; Circ 91,702
Jan 1999-Dec 1999 Income $248,927, State $21,977, Locally Generated Income $13,327. Mats Exp $64,526, Books $44,554, Per/Ser (Incl. Access Fees) $6,472, AV Equip $13,500. Sal $174,577 (Prof $77,600)
Library Holdings: Bk Titles 40,000
Special Collections: Local History (Wakarusa, Indiana), pictures, clippings, oral, pamphlets
Partic in Indiana Cooperative Library Services Authority
Friends of the Library Group

WALKERTON

P WALKERTON-LINCOLN TOWNSHIP PUBLIC LIBRARY,* 300 Michigan St, 46574. SAN 305-1587. Tel: 219-586-2933. FAX: 219-586-2933. E-Mail: wnpl@dnsonline.net. *Librn*, Connie Jo Young
Founded 1913. Pop 2,000; Circ 24,000
Library Holdings: Bk Vols 20,000; Per Subs 37
Mem of Area Libr Servs Authority Region 2
Friends of the Library Group

WALTON

P WALTON-TIPTON TOWNSHIP PUBLIC LIBRARY,* 103 E Bishop, 46994. (Mail add: PO Box 406, 46994-0406), SAN 305-1595. Tel: 219-626-2234. FAX: 219-626-2234. E-Mail: waltontl@holli.com. Web Site: birch.palni.edu/~cmcclosk/index.htm. *Dir*, Robert O Moore
Founded 1914. Pop 2,439; Circ 25,169
Library Holdings: Bk Vols 19,500; Per Subs 58
Special Collections: Indiana
Open Tues-Fri 10-6, Sat 9-12
Friends of the Library Group

WANATAH

P WANATAH PUBLIC LIBRARY,* PO Box 299, 46390. SAN 305-1609. Tel: 219-733-9303. E-Mail: wanatahl@mail.netnitco.net. *Dir, Librn*, Anna Marie Shaver
Founded 1935. Pop 1,500; Circ 10,000
1997-1998 Income $45,202. Mats Exp $13,275, Books $11,275, Per/Ser (Incl. Access Fees) $1,000. Sal $22,272 (Prof $12,600)
Library Holdings: Bk Vols 15,898; Per Subs 50
Subject Interests: History
Open Mon-Fri 1:30-7 & Sat 9-12

WARREN

P WARREN PUBLIC LIBRARY,* PO Box 327, 46792. SAN 305-1617. Tel: 219-375-3450. FAX: 219-375-3450. E-Mail: warrenpublib@hotmail.com. *Dir*, Rosalie Walter
Founded 1916. Pop 2,513; Circ 14,619
Jan 1997-Dec 1998 Income $62,555, State $8,422, County $50,899, Locally Generated Income $3,234. Mats Exp $14,733, Books $11,549, Per/Ser (Incl. Access Fees) $1,967. Sal $27,181 (Prof $23,230)
Library Holdings: Bk Vols 16,000; Per Subs 90
Special Collections: Local Newspaper, micro
Partic in Area 3 Libr Serv Authority
Friends of the Library Group

WARSAW

S KOSCIUSKO COUNTY HISTORICAL SOCIETY, Research Library & Archives, 121 N Indiana St, 46581-2739. (Mail add: PO Box 1071, 45681-1071), SAN 373-4501. Tel: 219-269-1078. Web Site: culture.kconline.com/kchs. *Librn*, Caroline Fawley
Library Holdings: Bk Vols 30,000; Per Subs 100
Subject Interests: Genealogy, Local history
Special Collections: County Newspapers (except Warsaw); County Records, 1830-present
Located in Kosciusko County Historical Museum. Open Thurs - Sat 10-4, Sun 1-4 & closed major holidays
Friends of the Library Group

P WARSAW COMMUNITY PUBLIC LIBRARY, 310 E Main St, 46580-2882. SAN 305-1625. Tel: 219-267-6011. FAX: 219-269-7739. E-Mail: refdesk@wcpl.lib.in.us. Web Site: www.wcpl.lib.in.us. *Dir*, Ann M Zydek; E-Mail: azydek@wcpl.lib.in.us; *Asst Dir, Cat*, Joni L Brookins; *Ref*, Dana L Owen; Staff 50 (MLS 3, Non-MLS 47)
Founded 1885. Pop 22,465; Circ 409,118
Library Holdings: Bk Vols 91,241; Per Subs 361
Subject Interests: Genealogy, Local history
Special Collections: Old & Current Local Papers, microfilms
Publications: Check It Out
Mem of Indiana Coop Libr Servs Authority
Special Services for the Deaf - Captioned media; Videos & decoder
Special Services for the Blind - ADA terminals for visually impaired
Open Mon-Thurs 9-9, Fri & Sat 9-6, Closed Sun

WASHINGTON

P WASHINGTON-CARNEGIE PUBLIC LIBRARY,* 300 W Main St, 47501-2698. SAN 305-1633. Tel: 812-254-4586. FAX: 812-254-4585. *Dir*, Elizabeth Dowling; *Ch Servs, YA Servs*, Lori Osmon; Staff 2 (MLS 2)
Founded 1902. Pop 15,412; Circ 186,000
Jan 1998-Dec 1999 Income $272,042, City $124,475, Other $147,567. Mats Exp $46,500, Books $35,000, Per/Ser (Incl. Access Fees) $6,000. Sal $113,112 (Prof $47,565)
Library Holdings: Per Subs 125
Subject Interests: Local history
Partic in Four Rivers Area Libr Serv Authority
Open Mon-Thurs 10-8, Fri & Sat 10-5

WATERLOO

P WATERLOO-GRANT TOWNSHIP PUBLIC LIBRARY, 300 S Wayne St, 46793-0707. (Mail add: PO Box 707, 46793-0707), Tel: 219-837-4491. FAX: 219-837-9148. E-Mail: waterloo@cwaterloo.lib.in.us. Web Site: www.dekalbnet.org/waterloolib. *Dir*, Linda Dunn
Pop 3,800; Circ 26,295
Library Holdings: Bk Vols 25,301; Per Subs 80
Partic in Area 3 Libr Serv Authority
Open Mon-Thurs 9-8, Fri 9-5 & Sat 9-3

WAVELAND

P WAVELAND-BROWN TOWNSHIP PUBLIC LIBRARY, 115 E Green, 47989. (Mail add: PO Box 158, 47989-0158), SAN 305-165X. Tel: 765-435-2700. FAX: 765-435-2434. E-Mail: wavelib@wico.net. *Librn*, Karen D Moser; *Asst Librn*, Sandra L Greene; Staff 5 (MLS 3, Non-MLS 2)
Founded 1916. Pop 1,603; Circ 18,000
1999-2000 Income $87,000. Mats Exp $18,000, Books $9,000, Per/Ser (Incl. Access Fees) $2,000, Other Print Mats $3,000, Electronic Ref Mat (Incl. Access Fees) $4,000
Library Holdings: Bk Vols 14,000; Per Subs 50

WEST LAFAYETTE

S J C ALLEN & SON, INC, Photo Library,* PO Box 2061, 47906. SAN 323-4681. Tel: 765-463-9614. *In Charge*, John Allen
Library Holdings: Bk Vols 77,000

S GREAT LAKES CHEMICAL CORPORATION, Corporate & Research Library, 1801 Hwy 52 NW, PO Box 2200, 47906. SAN 305-1668. Tel: 765-497-6275. FAX: 765-497-6680. E-Mail: library@glcc.com. *Senior Info Specialist*, John Rubacha; Tel: 765-497-6353, E-Mail: jrubacha@glcc.com; *Librn*, Laura Harlow; E-Mail: lharlow@glcc.com; Staff 4 (MLS 2, Non-MLS 2)
Founded 1965
Library Holdings: Bk Titles 5,000; Per Subs 350
Subject Interests: Organic chemistry, Polymer chemistry, Water treatment
Special Collections: Entire US, EP, & WO Patents on CD from 1975-present
Restriction: Staff use only
Open Mon-Fri 8-5

S INDIANA VETERAN'S HOME, Lawrie Library, 3851 North River Rd, 47906. SAN 371-6384. Tel: 765-463-1502, Ext 8654. FAX: 765-497-8692. *Librn*, Gary Mounce
Library Holdings: Bk Titles 8,500; Per Subs 52

C PURDUE UNIVERSITY LIBRARIES, 1530 Stewart Ctr, 47907-1530. SAN 341-7158. Tel: 765-494-2900. Interlibrary Loan Service Tel: 765-494-2800. FAX: 765-494-9007. Web Site: www.lib.purdue.edu. *Dean of Libr*, Emily R Mobley; Fax: 765-494-0156, E-Mail: emobley@purdue.edu; *Info Tech*, William L Corya; Fax: 765-494-0156, E-Mail: wcorya@purdue.edu; *ILL*, Suzanne Ward; Tel: 765-494-2850, E-Mail: ward@purdue.edu; *Tech Servs*, Patricia Kantner; Tel: 765-494-2812; Staff 61 (MLS 61)
Founded 1874. Enrl 44,427; Fac 2,200; Highest Degree: Doctorate
Jul 1999-Jun 2000 Mats Exp $5,301,126, Per/Ser (Incl. Access Fees) $4,434,107, Manuscripts & Archives $867,019. Sal $6,244,273 (Prof $2,887,939)
Library Holdings: Bk Vols 2,343,268; Per Subs 18,635
Special Collections: (Krannert Special Coll); Bruce Rogers (Anna Embree Baker Rogers Coll); Economic History; English & American Literature (George Ade Coll, Charles Major Coll); History of Engineering (Goss Coll)
Database Vendor: Dialog, Ebsco - EbscoHost, GaleNet, IAC - SearchBank, Lexis-Nexis, OCLC - First Search, OVID Technologies, ProQuest, Silverplatter Information Inc., Wilson - Wilson Web
Mem of Asn of Research Libraries
Partic in Center For Research Libraries; Indiana Cooperative Library Services Authority; OCLC Online Computer Library Center, Inc
Departmental Libraries:
AVIATION TECHNOLOGY, Terminal Bldg 163, 47907-1322. SAN 341-7182. Tel: 765-494-7640. *Librn*, Sheila Curl
BIOCHEMISTRY, Biochemistry Bldg, 47907-1107. SAN 341-7212. Tel: 765-494-1621. *Librn*, Sarah Kelly
CONSUMER & FAMILY SCIENCES, Stone Hall, Rm 220, 47907-1002. SAN 341-7247. Tel: 765-494-2914. *Librn*, Priscilla C Geahigan
EARTH & ATMOSPHERIC SCIENCES, 2215 CIVL, 47907-1210. SAN 341-7360. Tel: 765-494-3264. FAX: 765-496-1210.
HUMANITIES, SOCIAL SCIENCE & EDUCATION, Stewart Ctr, 47907-1530. SAN 341-7336. Tel: 765-494-2831. FAX: 765-494-9007. *Librn*, Mark Tucker
JOHN W HICKS UNDERGRADUATE LIBRARY, Hicks Bldg, 47907-1531. SAN 341-7166. Tel: 765-494-6733. *Librn*, Judith Pask
LIFE SCIENCE, Lilly Hall of Life Sciences, Rm 2-400, 47907-1323. SAN 341-7425. Tel: 765-494-2910. *Librn*, Sarah Kelly
M G MELLON LIBRARY OF CHEMISTRY, Wetherill Lab of Chemistry

Bldg, 47907-1333. SAN 341-7484. Tel: 765-494-2862. *Librn*, Bartow Culp
MANAGEMENT & ECONOMICS, Krannert Bldg, Rm 226, 47907-1340. SAN 341-7395. Tel: 765-494-2920. *Librn*, Judith M Nixon
MATHEMATICAL SCIENCES, Mathematical Sciences Bldg, Rm 311, 47907-1385. SAN 341-745X. Tel: 765-494-2855. *Librn*, Richard Funkhouser
PHARMACY, NURSING & HEALTH SCIENCES, Heine Pharmacy Bldg, Rm 272, 47907-1324. SAN 341-7514. Tel: 765-494-1416. *Librn*, Vicki Killion
PHYSICS, Physics Bldg, Rm 290, 47907-1321. SAN 341-7549. Tel: 765-494-2858. *Librn*, Michael Fosmire; Tel: 765-494-2858
PSYCHOLOGICAL SCIENCES, Peirce Hall, Rm 290, 47907-1303. SAN 341-7573. Tel: 765-494-2968. *Librn*, Priscilla C Geahigan
SIEGESMUND ENGINEERING LIBRARY, Potter Ctr, Rm 160, 47907-1250. SAN 341-7301. Tel: 765-494-2873. *Librn*, Sheila Curl
CM VETERINARY MEDICAL, Lynn Hall of Veterinary Medicine, Rm 1133, 47907-1027. SAN 341-7603. Tel: 765-494-2853. *Librn*, Gretchen Stephens

P WEST LAFAYETTE PUBLIC LIBRARY, 208 W Columbia St, 47906. SAN 305-1676. Tel: 765-743-2261. TDD: 765-743-2515. FAX: 765-743-2063. E-Mail: refdesk@wlaf.lib.in.us. Web Site: www.wlaf.lib.in.us. *Librn*, Nick Schenkel; E-Mail: nschenkez@wlaflib.in.us; *Circ*, Ruth Cushman; *Circ*, Phyllis Heath; *Ch Servs*, Carol Abell; *Ch Servs*, Pam Koehler; *Ref*, William H Friday; *Cat*, Jane Dolan; Staff 12 (MLS 3, Non-MLS 9)
Founded 1922. Pop 22,000; Circ 209,048
Jan 1998-Dec 1999 Income $565,500. Mats Exp $87,100. Sal $227,700
Library Holdings: Bk Vols 112,000; Per Subs 325
Special Collections: Children's Literature Award Winners (Dickey Coll); Cookbooks (Reisner Coll); Large Print Books Coll; Literature Coll; Needlework & Crafts Coll; Play Coll
Publications: Friend's (newsletter)
Partic in Indiana Cooperative Library Services Authority; Wabash Valley Area Libr Servs Authority
Special Services for the Deaf - Staff with knowledge of sign language
Friends of the Library Group

WEST LEBANON

P WEST LEBANON-PIKE TOWNSHIP PUBLIC LIBRARY, 200 High St, PO Box 277, 47991-0277. SAN 376-5377. Tel: 765-893-4605. FAX: 765-893-4605. E-Mail: l6tlbook@tctc.com. Web Site: www.tctc.com/~16tlbook. *Dir*, Terri Wargo; Staff 1 (Non-MLS 1)
Founded 1916
Jan 1999-Dec 1999 Income $54,255, State $6,034, Locally Generated Income $45,670, Other $2,551. Mats Exp $44,519, Books $9,362, Per/Ser (Incl. Access Fees) $1,051. Sal $23,768
Library Holdings: Bk Vols 12,031; Per Subs 54
Open Mon 11-7, Tues-Fri 11-5 & Sat 8-2

WESTFIELD

SR UNION BIBLE COLLEGE LIBRARY,* 434 S Union St, PO Box 900, 46074. SAN 325-6650. Tel: 317-896-9324. FAX: 317-867-0784. *Dir*, James Ward; *Dean*, Wallace Thornton Jr
Open Mon-Fri 8-4:30

P WESTFIELD PUBLIC LIBRARY,* 333 W Hoover St, 46074. SAN 305-1692. Tel: 317-896-9391. FAX: 317-896-3702. *Dir*, Katherine Spurgeon; *Asst Dir, Ref*, Mary Decker; *Ch Servs*, Vicki Parker
Founded 1901. Pop 15,000
Jan 1998-Dec 1998 Income $885,000. Mats Exp $186,060, Books $120,000, Per/Ser (Incl. Access Fees) $8,400, Micro $2,000, Other Print Mats $25,500, Electronic Ref Mat (Incl. Access Fees) $30,160. Sal $303,200 (Prof $85,000)
Library Holdings: Bk Vols 77,300; Per Subs 330
Special Collections: American Quaker Genealogy Coll
Partic in Indiana Cooperative Library Services Authority
Friends of the Library Group

WESTVILLE

C PURDUE UNIVERSITY, North Central Campus Library, LSF Bldg, 1401 S US Hwy 421, 46391. SAN 305-1706. Tel: 219-785-5200, Ext 5248. FAX: 219-785-5501. Web Site: www.purduenc.edu/ls/index.html. *Dir*, Kent R Johnson; E-Mail: krj@purduenc.edu; *ILL, Ref*, Naomi Sutherland; *Cat, Coll Develop*, Tricia Wilke; Staff 3 (MLS 3)
Founded 1967. Enrl 3,500; Fac 65; Highest Degree: Master
Library Holdings: Bk Vols 88,800; Per Subs 348
Partic in Northwest Indiana Health Science Library Consortium

WESTVILLE CORRECTIONAL FACILITY
S RESIDENT LIBRARY, PO Box 473, 46391. SAN 341-7662. Tel: 219-785-2511, Ext 4672. FAX: 219-785-4864. *Dir Libr Serv*, Janice Scott
Founded 1951. Enrl 300; Fac 23; Highest Degree: Bachelor
Jul 1997-Jun 1998 Mats Exp $22,000. Sal $42,700 (Prof $40,000)
Library Holdings: Bk Titles 27,000; Per Subs 90
Automation Activity & Vendor Info: (Cataloging) Follett; (Circulation) Follett
Partic in Indiana Cooperative Library Services Authority

P WESTVILLE-NEW DURHAM TOWNSHIP PUBLIC LIBRARY,* PO Box 789, 46391-0789. SAN 305-1714. Tel: 219-785-2015. FAX: 219-785-2015. *Librn*, Sara Johnson
Pop 4,234; Circ 19,173
Jan 1997-Dec 1998 Income $60,053. Mats Exp $14,855. Sal $23,495
Library Holdings: Bk Titles 18,000; Per Subs 53
Open Mon-Thurs 1-6 & Sat 10-3

WHITING

C CALUMET COLLEGE OF SAINT JOSEPH, Mary Gorman Specker Memorial Library, 2400 New York Ave, 46394. SAN 304-9248. Tel: 219-473-4373. FAX: 219-473-4259. E-Mail: library@ccsj.edu. Web Site: www.ccsj.edu/specker.html. *Dir*, JoAnn Arnold; E-Mail: jarnold@ccsj.edu; *Circ*, Marsha Keith
Founded 1963. Enrl 597; Fac 33; Highest Degree: Bachelor
Library Holdings: Bk Vols 105,232; Per Subs 327
Subject Interests: Theology
Partic in Indiana Cooperative Library Services Authority; Northwest Indiana Health Science Library Consortium; OCLC Online Computer Library Center, Inc
Open Mon-Thurs 8:15am-10pm, Fri 8:15am-9:30pm & Sat 8:45am-12:15pm

P WHITING PUBLIC LIBRARY,* 1735 Oliver St, 46394-1794. SAN 305-1722. Tel: 219-659-0269. FAX: 219-659-5833. E-Mail: cyh@whiting.lib.in.us. Web Site: www.whiting.lib.in.us. *Dir*, Christina Y Hyun; *Tech Servs*, Linda Biagi; E-Mail: linda@whiting.lib.in.us; *Circ*, Rachel Deluna; E-Mail: rachael@whiting.lib.in.us; *Ch Servs*, Kelly Reed; E-Mail: kelly@whiting.lib.in.us; *Chair*, Lyle Warrick; E-Mail: lyle@whiting.lib.in.us
Founded 1906. Pop 5,155; Circ 132,336
Jan 1999-Dec 1999 Income $419,957. Mats Exp $69,945, Books $61,684, Per/Ser (Incl. Access Fees) $4,556, Micro $1,727, Electronic Ref Mat (Incl. Access Fees) $1,978. Sal $258,900 (Prof $49,096)
Library Holdings: Bk Vols 83,355; Per Subs 256
Special Collections: Books on Early Settlement of Lake County, Indiana (prehistoric period to 1800's); Local City Directory 1900's; Local History Room; Whiting, Indiana (early 1900's)
Automation Activity & Vendor Info: (Acquisitions) SIRSI; (Circulation) SIRSI; (OPAC) SIRSI; (Serials) SIRSI
Database Vendor: Ebsco - EbscoHost, OCLC - First Search
Publications: monthly bulletin; monthly calendar; The Communicator (quarterly newsletter)
Partic in Indiana Cooperative Library Services Authority
Friends of the Library Group

S WHITING-ROBERTSDALE HISTORICAL SOCIETY MUSEUM,* 1610 119th St, 46394. SAN 371-6570. Tel: 219-659-1432. *Curator*, Mary Skvara; *VPres*, Gertrude Sandrick
Subject Interests: Local history
Open Tues, Wed & Sat 1-4

WILLIAMSPORT

P WILLIAMSPORT-WASHINGTON TOWNSHIP PUBLIC LIBRARY, 9 Fall St, 47993-1299. SAN 305-1730. Tel: 765-762-6555. FAX: 765-762-6588. E-Mail: wmsptpl@ash.palni.edu. Web Site: www.tpl.lib.in.us. *Dir*, Christopher Brown; E-Mail: cbrown@ash.palni.edu
Founded 1917. Pop 2,075; Circ 19,000
Library Holdings: Bk Titles 17,000; Per Subs 70
Automation Activity & Vendor Info: (Cataloging) Follett; (Circulation) Follett; (Course Reserve) Follett; (Serials) Follett
Partic in Indiana Cooperative Library Services Authority
Open Mon, Tues, Thurs & Fri 10-5, Wed 10-8, Sat 9-2

WINAMAC

P PULASKI COUNTY PUBLIC LIBRARY, 121 S Riverside Dr, 46996-1596. SAN 341-7697. Tel: 219-946-3432. TDD: 219-946-6981. FAX: 219-946-6598.; Staff 1 (MLS 1)
Founded 1905. Pop 9,838; Circ 162,978
Jan 1999-Dec 1999 Income $551,000, State $1,186, County $400,825. Mats Exp $436,338, Books $40,879, Per/Ser (Incl. Access Fees) $5,971, Micro $16,391. Sal $213,356
Library Holdings: Bk Titles 59,662
Subject Interests: Genealogy, Indiana, Local history
Special Collections: Local Newspapers 1869-, micro
Partic in Indiana Cooperative Library Services Authority
Special Services for the Deaf - TDD
Branches: 1
MEDARYVILLE STATION, 515 Main St, Medaryville, 47957. SAN 341-7727. Tel: 219-843-4141. FAX: 219-843-4141. *Librn*, Lorna DePoy
Collection rotates from the main library

WINCHESTER

GL RANDOLPH CIRCUIT COURT, Law Library,* 100 S Main, 47394. SAN 305-1749. Tel: 765-584-7070, Ext 230. FAX: 765-584-2958. *Librn*, Mike O'Neal
Library Holdings: Bk Vols 14,000

P WINCHESTER COMMUNITY LIBRARY,* 125 N East St, 47394-1698. SAN 305-1757. Tel: 765-584-4824. FAX: 765-584-3624. *Actg Dir*, Jenny Stonerock; *Asst Dir, Ch Servs*, Bonnie Coffman; Staff 8 (MLS 2, Non-MLS 6)
Founded 1912. Pop 9,791; Circ 115,000
1997-1998 Income $141,500, State $1,500, City $140,000. Mats Exp $41,500, Books $31,000, Per/Ser (Incl. Access Fees) $3,500, Micro $4,500. Sal $135,000 (Prof $28,600)
Library Holdings: Bk Vols 31,558; Per Subs 72
Special Collections: Abraham Lincoln Coll; Large Print Books
Partic in Eastern Ind Area Libr Servs Authority; Indiana Cooperative Library Services Authority
Friends of the Library Group

WINONA LAKE

R GRACE COLLEGE & GRACE THEOLOGICAL SEMINARY, Morgan Library,* 200 Seminary Dr, 46590. SAN 305-1765. Interlibrary Loan Service Tel: 219-372-5100, Ext 6294. FAX: 219-372-5176. Web Site: www.grace.edu. *Dir*, William Darr; Tel: 219-372-5100, Ext 6291, E-Mail: wedarr@grace.edu; *Assoc Dir*, Anita Gray; Tel: 219-372-5100, Ext 6292, E-Mail: algray@grace.edu; *Publ Servs*, Rhoda Palmer; Tel: 219-372-5100, Ext 6293, E-Mail: rfpalmer@grace.edu; Staff 3 (MLS 3)
Founded 1939. Enrl 950; Fac 51; Highest Degree: Doctorate
Library Holdings: Bk Vols 147,449; Bk Titles 58,000; Per Subs 442
Subject Interests: Biblical studies
Special Collections: Billy Sunday Papers Coll
Automation Activity & Vendor Info: (Acquisitions) DRA; (Circulation) DRA; (OPAC) DRA; (Serials) DRA
Partic in Area Libr Servs Authority Region 2; Indiana Cooperative Library Services Authority; OCLC Online Computer Library Center, Inc

WOLCOTT

P WOLCOTT COMMUNITY PUBLIC LIBRARY,* 101 E North St, PO Box 376, 47995-0376. SAN 305-1773. Tel: 219-279-2695. *Librn*, Deanna Dreblow
Founded 1923. Pop 1,850; Circ 11,003
Jan 1997-Dec 1998 Income $52,138, State $4,372, County $46,803, Other $963. Mats Exp $10,005, Books $7,005, Per/Ser (Incl. Access Fees) $1,500. Sal $32,191 (Prof $21,736)
Library Holdings: Bk Vols 18,600

WORTHINGTON

P WORTHINGTON-JEFFERSON TOWNSHIP PUBLIC LIBRARY,* 26 N Commercial St, 47471-1415. SAN 305-1781. Tel: 812-875-3815. FAX: 812-875-3815. *Dir*, Lori Markle; E-Mail: markle@juno.com
Founded 1918. Pop 2,373; Circ 18,000
Library Holdings: Bk Titles 20,500; Per Subs 72
Partic in Stone Hills Area Libr Servs Authority
Open Mon & Wed 12-4, Tues & Thurs 12-8, Fri 9-4, Sat 10-2

YORKTOWN

§P YORKTOWN-MT PLEASANT TOWNSHIP COMMUNITY LIBRARY, 8920 W Adaline, 47396. Tel: 765-759-9723. *Pres*, Beverly LaVelle
Library Holdings: Bk Titles 6,200

ZIONSVILLE

P HUSSEY-MAYFIELD MEMORIAL PUBLIC LIBRARY, 250 N Fifth St, 46077-0840. (Mail add: PO Box 840, 46077-0840), SAN 305-179X. Tel: 317-873-3149. Circulation Tel: 317-873-3149, Ext 5102. Reference Tel: 317-873-3149, Ext 5203. FAX: 317-873-8339. Web Site: www.zionsville.lib.in.us. *Dir*, Martha Ellen Catt; Tel: 317-873-3149, Ext 5104, E-Mail: marthac@zionsville.lib.in.us; *Tech Servs*, Maxine Stover; Tel: 317-873-3149, Ext 5300, E-Mail: maxines@zionsville.lib.in.us; *Ad Servs*, Lee Greaves; Tel: 317-873-3149, Ext 5201, Fax: 317-873-3149, E-Mail: leeg@zionville.lib.in.us; *Ch Servs*, Maru Rueff; Tel: 317-873-3149, Ext 5109, E-Mail: maryr@zionsville.lib.in.us; *Circ*, Judy Bolinger; Tel: 317-873-3149, Ext 5102, E-Mail: jbolinger@zionsville.lib.in.us; *YA Servs*, Barbara Wright; Tel: 317-873-3149, Ext 5207, E-Mail: bwright@zionsville.lib.in.us; Staff 44 (MLS 3, Non-MLS 41)
Founded 1989. Pop 11,571; Circ 211,000
Jan 1999-Dec 1999 Income $1,361,981. Mats Exp $169,926, Books $114,064, Per/Ser (Incl. Access Fees) $6,410, AV Equip $39,688, Electronic Ref Mat (Incl. Access Fees) $9,764. Sal $553,251 (Prof $312,441)
Library Holdings: Bk Vols 71,033; Per Subs 223
Subject Interests: Arts and crafts, Business, Civil War, Gardening, Investment, Large type print
Automation Activity & Vendor Info: (Circulation) epixtech, inc.; (Media Booking) epixtech, inc.
Database Vendor: epixtech, inc.
Publications: Seasons (Newsletter)
Function: ILL available
Mem of Indiana Coop Libr Servs Authority
Open Mon-Thurs 9:30-8:30 & Fri-Sat 9:30-5
Friends of the Library Group

S PATRICK HENRY SULLIVAN FOUNDATION, Museum & Genealogy Library,* 225 W Hawthorne St, PO Box 182, 46077. SAN 373-4528. Tel: 317-873-4900. FAX: 317-873-4047. *Exec Dir*, Edie Kellar Mahaney; *Asst Librn*, Marianne Doyle
Library Holdings: Bk Vols 5,000
Subject Interests: Genealogy
Special Collections: Books Scripted by Indiana Authors; Early Photographs; Indiana Paintings including Portrait of William Zion

IOWA

Date of Statistics: 1997-98
Population, 1990 Census: 2,776,755
Total Titles in Public Libraries: 12,019,915
Titles Per Capita: 5.85
Total Public Library Circulation: 25,149,766
Circulation Per Capita: 12.2
Total Public Library Income (Including Grants-in-Aid): $74,902
Average Income: $143,768
Source of Income: Mainly public funds
Expenditures Per Capita: $28.50
Number of County & Regional Libraries: 7 regional, 3 county
State Aid:
Federal: (Library Services & Construction Actv FY 98)
Total LSTA: $1,584,711

ACKLEY

P ACKLEY PUBLIC LIBRARY,* 401 State St, 50601. SAN 305-1803. Tel: 515-847-2233. FAX: 515-847-2233. E-Mail: ackleypl@cnsinternet.com. *Librn*, Sharon Homan
Pop 1,900; Circ 19,643
Library Holdings: Bk Vols 13,468; Per Subs 51
Mem of N Iowa Libr Extension; North Central Regional Library System

ADAIR

P ADAIR PUBLIC LIBRARY,* 310 Audubon, PO Box 276, 50002. SAN 305-1811. Tel: 515-742-3323. FAX: 515-742-3323. *Dir*, Bertha Fagan; *Asst Librn*, Connie Scarlet
Founded 1936. Pop 883; Circ 6,231
Library Holdings: Bk Titles 9,000; Per Subs 25
Mem of Southwest Iowa Regional Library System

ADEL

P ADEL PUBLIC LIBRARY,* 820 Prairie St, 50003. SAN 305-182X. Tel: 515-993-3512. FAX: 515-993-3191. E-Mail: adelpl@netins.net. *Dir*, Jane Stine; *Librn*, Saundra Boots
Pop 3,400; Circ 46,000
Library Holdings: Bk Titles 22,154; Per Subs 64
Mem of Central Iowa Regional Library
Open Mon 10-8, Tues-Thurs 10-5:30, Sat 10-1
Friends of the Library Group

AGENCY

P AGENCY PUBLIC LIBRARY, 104 E Main St, PO Box 346, 52530. SAN 305-1838. Tel: 641-937-6002. E-Mail: agencylib@lisco.com. *Librn*, Marsha Hunter
Founded 1955. Pop 657; Circ 4,260
Library Holdings: Bk Vols 6,025; Per Subs 20
Special Collections: Iowa History
Mem of Southeastern Regional Libr Syst
Open Mon 2-8, Tues 2-5, Thurs 5-8, Sat 9-3 & Sun 2-5

AKRON

P AKRON PUBLIC LIBRARY,* 350 Reed St, PO Box 348, 51001. SAN 305-1846. Tel: 712-568-2601. FAX: 712-568-2601. *Librn*, Nadine Philips; *Asst Librn*, Pat Dennison; *Ch Servs*, Jeannie Frerichs
Pop 2,000; Circ 22,000
Library Holdings: Bk Vols 18,000; Bk Titles 12,471; Per Subs 55
Mem of Northwest Regional Library System

ALBERT CITY

P ALBERT CITY PUBLIC LIBRARY,* 106 S Second St, 50510-0368. SAN 305-1854. Tel: 712-843-2012. E-Mail: albeblib@rconnect.com. *Librn*, Nola Josephson
Pop 779; Circ 9,107
Jul 1998-Jun 1999 Income $14,438. Mats Exp $3,600. Sal $8,141
Library Holdings: Bk Vols 12,000; Bk Titles 11,614; Per Subs 46
Mem of Northwest Regional Library System
Open Mon 3:30-7:30, Wed 2-6, Fri 9:30-11:30 & 12-5, Sat 8:30-11:30
Friends of the Library Group

ALBIA

P CARNEGIE-EVANS PUBLIC LIBRARY,* 203 Benton Ave E, 52531-2036. SAN 305-1862. Tel: 515-932-2469. FAX: 515-932-2469. E-Mail: albiapl@se-iowa.net. *Dir*, Marilyn Woods; *Ch Servs*, Betty Reeves; *AV*, Linda Whitlock; *Ch Servs*, Ruth Raskie
Founded 1906. Pop 3,870; Circ 200,730
Library Holdings: Bk Titles 38,000; Per Subs 50
Mem of Southeastern Regional Libr Syst
Open Mon-Fri 12-6, Sat 10-3

S MONROE COUNTY GENEALOGICAL SOCIETY, c/o Carnegie-Evans Library, 203 Benton Ave E, 52531. SAN 374-9851. Tel: 515-932-2469, 515-932-2726. FAX: 515-932-2469. *Pres*, Helen Johnson; *Res*, Twila Chidester
Library Holdings: Bk Titles 2,000
Subject Interests: Genealogy, Local history, State hist
Open weekdays 12-6 & Sat 10-3
Friends of the Library Group

ALBION

P ALBION MUNICIPAL LIBRARY,* 107 S Main St, PO Box 118, 50005-0118. SAN 321-8295. Tel: 515-488-2226. *Librn*, Jan Borton
Founded 1982. Pop 1,500; Circ 15,000
Library Holdings: Bk Titles 13,000; Per Subs 50
Friends of the Library Group

ALDEN

P DR GRACE O DOANE ALDEN PUBLIC LIBRARY, 1012 Water St, PO Box 78, 50006. SAN 305-1870. Tel: 515-859-3820. FAX: 515-859-3919. E-Mail: aldenlibrary@iafalls.com. *Dir*, Janeice Murra
Pop 855; Circ 14,308
Jul 1998-Jun 1999 Income $58,997, City $46,472, County $12,525. Mats Exp $11,662, Books $10,162, Per/Ser (Incl. Access Fees) $1,500. Sal $20,177
Library Holdings: Bk Vols 6,600; Bk Titles 6,550; Per Subs 50
Mem of North Central Regional Library System
Partic in Hardin County Libr Asn
Friends of the Library Group

ALEXANDER

P ALEXANDER PUBLIC LIBRARY,* 409 Harriman St, PO Box 27, 50420-0027. SAN 305-1889. Tel: 515-692-3238. FAX: 515-692-3238. *Dir*, Ann Bonde
Founded 1962. Pop 190; Circ 6,950
Library Holdings: Bk Titles 8,000; Per Subs 30
Mem of North Central Regional Library System
Open Mon 9-5, Tues-Thurs 2:30-5, Fri 2:30-5:30 & Sat 8-12

ALGONA

P ALGONA PUBLIC LIBRARY, 210 N Phillips St, 50511. SAN 305-1897. Tel: 515-295-5476. FAX: 515-295-3307. E-Mail: algonapl@ncn.net. Web Site: www.algona.org. *Dir*, Claudia Warner; *Ch Servs*, Penny Rahm
Founded 1904. Pop 6,015; Circ 115,393
Jul 1999-Jun 2000 Income $239,635, State $4,543, City $186,539, County $23,278, Locally Generated Income $25,275. Mats Exp $39,004, Books $27,228, Per/Ser (Incl. Access Fees) $3,633, AV Equip $5,888. Sal $103,062 (Prof $64,175)
Library Holdings: Bk Titles 43,310; Per Subs 122; Bks on Deafness & Sign Lang 10
Subject Interests: History, Iowa, Local history
Automation Activity & Vendor Info: (Cataloging) Follett; (Circulation) Follett; (OPAC) Follett
Mem of North Central Regional Library System
Friends of the Library Group

ALLERTON

P ALLERTON PUBLIC LIBRARY,* S Central, Box 216, 50008. SAN 305-1900. Tel: 515-873-4575. *Librn*, Sharon Sinclair
1996-1997 Income $1,700
Library Holdings: Bk Titles 5,000
Mem of Southwest Regional Library Service System

ALLISON

P ALLISON PUBLIC LIBRARY, 410 N Main St, PO Box 605, 50602. SAN 305-1919. Tel: 319-267-2562. Interlibrary Loan Service Tel: 800-772-2023. FAX: 319-267-2562. E-Mail: allilib@netins.net. *Librn*, Roberta Wiegmann; *Asst Librn*, Rena Kruse
Founded 1929. Pop 1,132; Circ 30,027
Library Holdings: Bk Titles 13,643; Per Subs 76
Mem of Northeastern Iowa Regional Library System

ALTA

P ALTA PUBLIC LIBRARY,* 409 W Hwy No 7, 51002. SAN 305-1927. Tel: 712-284-1250. E-Mail: altapublib@ncn.net. *Dir*, Sue Pedersen
Founded 1911. Pop 1,823
Jul 1997-Jun 1998 Income $21,730. Mats Exp $7,000. Sal $8,000
Library Holdings: Bk Titles 10,300; Per Subs 35
Open Mon-Fri 3:30-7:30, Sat 9-1 (acad yr), Mon & Wed 3:30-7:30, Sat 9-1 (summer hrs)

ALTA VISTA

P ALTA VISTA PUBLIC LIBRARY,* PO Box 167, 50603. SAN 376-6551. Tel: 515-364-2975. *Librn*, Eileen Sweeney
Library Holdings: Bk Vols 7,700; Per Subs 30
Mem of Northeastern Iowa Regional Library System

ALTON

P ALTON PUBLIC LIBRARY, 905 Third Ave, PO Box 379, 51003. SAN 305-1943. Tel: 712-756-4516. *Librn*, Cheryl Hoekstra
Founded 1923. Pop 1,059; Circ 15,000
1998-1999 Income $50,020, State $43, City $31,600, County $18,377. Mats Exp $10,773, Books $7,000, Per/Ser (Incl. Access Fees) $2,500, Presv $250, Micro $200. Sal $22,427
Library Holdings: Bk Vols 9,376; Per Subs 77
Special Collections: Local newspaper (Alton Democrat, 1883-present), micro
Automation Activity & Vendor Info: (Circulation) Follett
Mem of Northwest Regional Library System

ALTOONA

P ALTOONA PUBLIC LIBRARY,* 700 First Ave S, 50009-1796. SAN 305-1951. Tel: 515-967-3881. FAX: 515-967-6934. *Dir*, Kim Smith; *Librn*, Carol Roovaart; *Librn*, Rosie Gaudette; *Librn*, Lisa Heffelfinger; *Librn*, Phyllis McCormack; *Librn*, Sheila Nelson
Founded 1971. Pop 7,000; Circ 46,503
Library Holdings: Bk Titles 24,000
Mem of Central Iowa Regional Library
Open Mon-Thurs 10-8, Fri & Sat 10-5, Sun 1-5
Friends of the Library Group

AMANA

S AMANA HERITAGE SOCIETY ARCHIVES, 705 44th Ave, 52203. (Mail add: PO Box 81, 52203-0081), SAN 328-0209. Tel: 319-622-3567. FAX: 319-622-6481. E-Mail: amherit@juno.com. *Curator*, Catherine Guerra; Staff 1 (Non-MLS 1)
Founded 1978
Apr 1998-Mar 1999 Income $800. Mats Exp $450, Books $100, Presv $350
Library Holdings: Bk Vols 2,000; Bk Titles 1,200
Subject Interests: Local history
Special Collections: Architectural Photography Libr; Local Genealogical Research File, 1690-present
Restriction: By appointment only
Open Mon-Fri 9-4

AMES

P AMES PUBLIC LIBRARY, 515 Douglas Ave, 50010. SAN 305-1978. Tel: 515-239-5630. Circulation Tel: 515-239-5646. Reference Tel: 515-239-5656. FAX: 515-233-1718. Web Site: www:ames.lib.ia.us. *Dir*, Gina Millsap; Tel: 515-239-5632; *Asst Dir*, Dawn Hayslett; Tel: 515-239-5633, E-Mail: dhayslet@ames.lib.ia.us; *Ref*, Evelyn Oltmanns; *Head, Info Serv*, Michael Quinn; Tel: 515-239-5660; *Automation Syst Coordr*, Scott Dermont; Tel: 515-239-5655; *Ch Servs*, Carol A Elbert; Tel: 515-239-5644; *Coll Develop*, Marianne Malinowski; Tel: 515-239-5652; *ILL*, Judith Hughes; Tel: 515-239-5659; *Circ*, Joyce A Fisher; Tel: 515-239-4646; *AV*, T J Larson; Tel: 515-239-5667; Staff 51 (MLS 12, Non-MLS 39)
Founded 1903. Pop 54,000; Circ 931,695
Jul 1999-Jun 2000 Income $2,407,837, State $70,000, City $1,985,022, Federal $7,000, County $115,278, Locally Generated Income $119,726, Other $26,607. Mats Exp $298,490, Books $207,251, Per/Ser (Incl. Access Fees) $25,965, AV Equip $51,274, Electronic Ref Mat (Incl. Access Fees) $14,000. Sal $1,626,725
Library Holdings: Bk Vols 180,092; Per Subs 420; Bks on Deafness & Sign Lang 20
Subject Interests: Photography
Special Collections: Farwell T Brown Photographic Archives; Local History Photographic Archive
Automation Activity & Vendor Info: (Acquisitions) epixtech, inc.; (Cataloging) epixtech, inc.
Database Vendor: epixtech, inc., OCLC - First Search
Publications: monthly calendar of events; Page One - Friends of the Ames Public Library New Book List & Newsletter
Friends of the Library Group

M MARY GREELEY MEDICAL CENTER LIBRARY, 1111 Duff Ave, 50010. SAN 377-5623. Tel: 515-239-2154. FAX: 515-239-2020. *Librn*, Lynn Cummings; E-Mail: cummings@mgmc.com
Library Holdings: Bk Vols 3,000; Per Subs 80
Partic in Polk County Biomedical Consortium

G IOWA DEPARTMENT OF TRANSPORTATION LIBRARY,* 800 Lincoln Way, 50010-6915. SAN 305-1994. Tel: 515-239-1200. FAX: 515-233-7840. *Librn*, Hank Zaletel; E-Mail: hzalete@iadot.e-mail.com
Founded 1970
Library Holdings: Bk Vols 20,000; Per Subs 340
Subject Interests: Air transportation, Business and management, Environmental studies, Iowa, Railroads, Transportation
Special Collections: Iowa Historic Road Files 1914-1930, photogs; Iowa State Parks 1920-1945, photogs; Rock Island Railroad, newsp & mag clippings 1958-, 5 vol Iowa coverage
Publications: Library Bulletin (recent acquisitions, semi-monthly)
Partic in BCR; Dialog Corporation; OCLC Online Computer Library Center, Inc

C IOWA STATE UNIVERSITY LIBRARY, 302 Parks Library, 50011-2140. SAN 341-7751. Tel: 515-294-1442. Interlibrary Loan Service Tel: 515-294-8073. FAX: 515-294-5525. Interlibrary Loan Service FAX: 515-294-1885. Web Site: www.lib.iastate.edu. *Dean of Libr*, Olivia M A Madison; *Br Coordr*, Mary Jo Bergmann; *Assoc Dir*, David Gregory; *Humanities and Soc Sci*, Rebecca Jackson; *Science*, Lorraine Knox; *Cat*, Collin Hobert; *Tech Servs*, Lori Osmus; *Access Serv, ILL*, Wayne Pedersen; *Acq*, Janet Arcand; *Spec Coll*, Tanya Zanish-Belcher; *Info Tech*, George Covert; *Electronic Resources*, David Fowler. Subject Specialists: *Presv*, Ivan Hanthorn; Staff 160 (MLS 49, Non-MLS 111)
Founded 1869. Enrl 26,110; Fac 1,781; Highest Degree: Doctorate
Jul 1999-Jun 2000 Income (Main and Other College/University Libraries) $16,269,590, State $14,975,595, Locally Generated Income $601,706, Other $692,289. Mats Exp $7,279,557, Books $1,550,483, Per/Ser (Incl. Access Fees) $4,355,733, Micro $676,735, Other Print Mats $161,330, Electronic Ref Mat (Incl. Access Fees) $535,276. Sal $6,051,741 (Prof $2,122,409)

Library Holdings: Bk Vols 2,266,061; Per Subs 21,239
Subject Interests: Agriculture, History of science, Labor relations, Regional hist, Soil conservation
Special Collections: American Archives of the Factual Film; American Archives of Veterinary Medicine; Archives of Women in Science & Engineering; Evolution/Creation Archives; Statistical Archive
Automation Activity & Vendor Info: (Acquisitions) epixtech, inc.; (Cataloging) epixtech, inc.; (Circulation) epixtech, inc.; (Course Reserve) epixtech, inc.; (ILL) epixtech, inc.; (Media Booking) epixtech, inc.; (OPAC) epixtech, inc.; (Serials) epixtech, inc.
Database Vendor: Ebsco - EbscoHost, epixtech, inc., IAC - SearchBank, Lexis-Nexis, OCLC - First Search, Silverplatter Information Inc.
Partic in BCR; Big Twelve Plus Libr Consortium; Center For Research Libraries; OCLC Online Computer Library Center, Inc
Special Services for the Blind - Arkenstone, a computer system for the visually handicapped; Braille printer & software
Friends of the Library Group
Departmental Libraries:

CM VETERINARY MEDICAL LIBRARY Tel: 515-294-2225. FAX: 515-294-1954. Web Site: www.lib.iastate.edu/library/vetlib/html. *Librn*, William Wiese; Staff 4 (MLS 2, Non-MLS 2)
Enrl 501; Fac 112; Highest Degree: Doctorate
Library Holdings: Bk Vols 31,593; Per Subs 570
Subject Interests: Biomedical engineering
Partic in Nat Libr of Med

SR SAINT THOMAS AQUINAS CHURCH, Barr Memorial Library, 2210 Lincoln Way, 50014. SAN 327-9081. Tel: 515-292-3810. FAX: 515-292-3841. Web Site: www.STAparish.net. *Librn*, Anne Recker
Library Holdings: Bk Vols 5,500

G UNITED STATES DEPARTMENT OF AGRICULTURE, National Animal Disease Center Library, 2300 Dayton Ave, 50010. (Mail add: PO Box 70, 50010), SAN 305-2001. Tel: 515-663-7271. FAX: 515-663-7458. Web Site: www.nadc.ars.usda.gov. *Librn*, Janice K Eifling; E-Mail: jeifling@nadc.ars.usda.gov; Staff 2 (MLS 1, Non-MLS 1)
Founded 1961
Library Holdings: Bk Vols 8,000; Per Subs 200
Subject Interests: Biochemistry, Microbiology, Physiology, Veterinary medicine

ANAMOSA

P ANAMOSA PUBLIC LIBRARY, 100 E First St, 52205. SAN 305-201X. Tel: 319-462-2183. FAX: 319-462-2183. E-Mail: anamosa@server.silo.lib.ia.us. *Dir*, Marg Folkerts
Founded 1902. Pop 5,594; Circ 30,518
Jul 1999-Jun 2000 Income $82,016, City $70,650, County $8,116, Locally Generated Income $3,250. Mats Exp $16,190. Sal $37,120
Library Holdings: Bk Vols 19,000; Per Subs 80
Mem of East Central Regional Library
Friends of the Library Group

J ANAMOSA STATE PENITENTIARY, Men's Reformatory Library,* 406 N High St, PO Box 10, 52205-0010. SAN 305-2028. Tel: 319-462-3504, Ext 283. *In Charge*, Jeffery J Ditch
Library Holdings: Bk Titles 12,000; Per Subs 102
Special Collections: Science Fiction Coll

ANITA

P ANITA PUBLIC LIBRARY, 812 Third St, PO Box 366, 50020-0366. SAN 305-2036. Tel: 712-762-3639. FAX: 712-762-3639. E-Mail: anitapl@nwidt.com. *Librn*, Sherry Waddell; Staff 2 (Non-MLS 2)
Pop 1,058; Circ 16,579
2000-2000 Income $32,000, City $25,100, County $6,900. Mats Exp $5,000
Library Holdings: Bk Vols 10,500; Per Subs 49
Mem of Southwest Regional Library Service System

ANKENY

J DES MOINES AREA COMMUNITY COLLEGE LIBRARY, Ankeny Campus, 2006 S Ankeny Blvd, 50021. SAN 305-2044. Tel: 515-964-6317. FAX: 515-965-7126. Web Site: www.dmacc.cc.ia.us. *Dir*, Lisa Stock; *ILL, Ref*, Diana Messersmith; *Tech Servs*, Shirley Peterson
Library Holdings: Bk Vols 55,000; Per Subs 600
Partic in BCR; OCLC Online Computer Library Center, Inc; Polk County Biomedical Consortium

CR FAITH BAPTIST BIBLE COLLEGE & THEOLOGICAL SEMINARY, John L Patten Library, 1900 NW Fourth St, 50021. SAN 305-2052. Tel: 515-964-0601. FAX: 515-964-1638. Web Site: www.faith.edu. *Head Librn*, Jeffery S Gates; E-Mail: gatesj@faith.edu; Staff 5 (MLS 1, Non-MLS 4)
Enrl 494; Highest Degree: Master
Jul 1999-Jun 2000 Income $97,797. Mats Exp $37,459, Books $10,529, Per/Ser (Incl. Access Fees) $16,568, Presv $4,763, Electronic Ref Mat (Incl. Access Fees) $2,910. Sal $63,710 (Prof $32,000)
Library Holdings: Bk Vols 60,728; Per Subs 424
Special Collections: Bible Coll; Theology Coll
Automation Activity & Vendor Info: (Cataloging) Sagebrush Corporation; (Circulation) Sagebrush Corporation; (OPAC) Sagebrush Corporation
Database Vendor: OCLC - First Search
Partic in SILO
Mon-Fri 8-4:30 (summer), Mon, Tues & Thurs 7-10, Wed 7-5:30, Fri 7-6 & Sat 9-5

P KIRKENDALL PUBLIC LIBRARY,* 1210 NW Prairie Ridge Dr, 50021. SAN 305-2060. Tel: 515-965-6460. FAX: 515-965-6474. *Dir*, Myrna Anderson
Founded 1960. Pop 18,482
Jul 1998-Jun 1999 Income $635,818, State $5,252, City $503,073, County $99,187, Other $28,306. Mats Exp $80,626, Books $68,326, Per/Ser (Incl. Access Fees) $8,877, AV Equip $2,133, Electronic Ref Mat (Incl. Access Fees) $1,290. Sal $383,875 (Prof $150,539)
Library Holdings: Bk Vols 56,577; Per Subs 235
Subject Interests: Large type print
Automation Activity & Vendor Info: (Acquisitions) epixtech, inc.; (Cataloging) epixtech, inc.; (Circulation) epixtech, inc.
Mem of Central Iowa Regional Library
Member of the Metropolitan Library Group including: Urbandale, West Des Moines & Des Moines. Also serves county residents under contract with the Polk County Board of Supervisors; allows walk-ins from any other participating library to check out materials through State funded open access program

ANTHON

P ANTHON PUBLIC LIBRARY,* 303 E Main, 51004-0293. SAN 305-2079. Tel: 712-373-5275. *Librn*, Helen Pulliam
Founded 1903. Pop 687; Circ 19,855
Library Holdings: Bk Vols 10,000; Per Subs 15
Mem of Northwest Regional Library System
Partic in Woodbury County Libr Syst
Open Mon-Wed & Fri 1-5, Sat 10-12

APLINGTON

P APLINGTON LEGION MEMORIAL LIBRARY,* Parrot St, 50604. SAN 305-2087. Tel: 319-347-2432. FAX: 319-347-6696. E-Mail: books@cnsinternet.com. *Librn*, Nancy Huisman; *Asst Librn*, Sharon Seehusen
Pop 1,000; Circ 12,500
1998-1999 Income $26,896, State $700, City $17,996, County $7,450, Locally Generated Income $600, Other $150. Mats Exp $10,000, Books $8,300, Per/Ser (Incl. Access Fees) $1,500, AV Equip $200. Sal $12,696 (Prof $125)
Library Holdings: Bk Vols 16,500; Per Subs 87
Mem of Northeastern Regional Libr Syst

ARCHER

P ARCHER PUBLIC LIBRARY, PO Box 165, 51231. SAN 376-5024. Tel: 712-723-5629. E-Mail: archerpl@netins.net. *Dir*, Marlys Wolthuizen
1998-1999 Income $6,700, City $1,200, County $5,500. Mats Exp $2,168, Books $1,952, Per/Ser (Incl. Access Fees) $216. Sal $2,164
Library Holdings: Bk Vols 5,500; Per Subs 17
Mem of Northwest Regional Library System
Open Tues 6-8, Thurs 4-7, Sat 9-12
Friends of the Library Group

ARLINGTON

P ARLINGTON PUBLIC LIBRARY,* 711 Main St, PO Box 176, 50606. SAN 305-2095. Tel: 319-633-3475. FAX: 319-633-3475. E-Mail: arlingtonlib@trxinc.com. *Dir*, Linda K Adams
Founded 1875. Pop 476; Circ 7,000
Jul 1997-Jun 1998 Income $11,019. Mats Exp $3,333. Sal $7,686
Library Holdings: Bk Vols 6,120; Per Subs 20
Mem of Northeastern Iowa Regional Library System

ARMSTRONG

P ARMSTRONG PUBLIC LIBRARY,* 308 Sixth St, PO Box 169, 50514-0169. SAN 305-2109. Tel: 712-868-3353. FAX: 712-868-3779. E-Mail: apl@ncn.net. *Dir*, Gertrude Jensen
Founded 1945. Pop 1,153; Circ 15,254
1998-1999 Income $18,178, State $262, City $9,950, County $4,450, Locally Generated Income $1,011, Other $2,505. Mats Exp $3,585, Books $2,922, Per/Ser (Incl. Access Fees) $663. Sal $5,651 (Prof $5,000)
Library Holdings: Bk Vols 18,000; Per Subs 37
Subject Interests: Art and architecture, Medicine, Natural science, Religion, Science/technology, Technology
Special Services for the Blind - Bks on cassette

ARNOLDS PARK

P ARNOLDS PARK PUBLIC LIBRARY,* Hwy 71, PO Box 556, 51331. SAN 305-2117. Tel: 712-332-2033. FAX: 712-332-9245. E-Mail: aparklib@rconnet.com. *Librn*, Susan Sup; *Asst Librn*, Wilma Lehnhoff; *Asst Librn*, Lorraine Little
Pop 1,051; Circ 25,043
Library Holdings: Bk Titles 10,000; Per Subs 50
Mem of Northwest Regional Library System
Friends of the Library Group

ARTHUR

P ARTHUR PUBLIC LIBRARY,* 224 S Main St, 51431. SAN 305-2125. Tel: 712-367-2240. FAX: 712-367-2240. E-Mail: arthurpl@netins.net. *Dir, Librn*, Pat Bell
Pop 288; Circ 3,185
Library Holdings: Bk Titles 3,428; Per Subs 15
Mem of Northwest Regional Library System
Open Mon 3:30-5, Wed 6:30-7:30, Thurs 6:30-8 & Sat 10-12

ASHTON

P ASHTON PUBLIC LIBRARY, 3029 Third St, 51232. (Mail add: PO Box 277, 51232-0277), SAN 305-2133. Tel: 712-724-6426. FAX: 712-724-6426. E-Mail: ashtlib@rconnect.com. *Head Librn*, Alfreda Verdoorn
Pop 462; Circ 14,400
Jul 1999-Jun 2000 Income $13,000. Mats Exp $4,000. Sal $8,000 (Prof $5,000)
Library Holdings: Bk Titles 10,900; Per Subs 55
Mem of Northwest Regional Library System

ATKINS

P ATKINS PUBLIC LIBRARY,* 84 Main Ave, 52206. SAN 305-2141. Tel: 319-446-7676. FAX: 319-446-7676. *Librn*, Cathy Becker
Pop 880; Circ 14,244
Jul 1997-Jun 1998 Income $26,000. Mats Exp $14,250. Sal $12,480
Library Holdings: Bk Titles 7,833; Per Subs 43
Open Mon & Tues 9-12 & 2-5:30, Wed 2-6, Thurs 2-5, Fri 2-5:30, Sat 9-12

ATLANTIC

P ATLANTIC PUBLIC LIBRARY,* 507 Poplar, 50022. SAN 305-215X. Tel: 712-243-5466. Interlibrary Loan Service Tel: 800-432-1045. FAX: 712-243-5466. E-Mail: helpublib@netins.net. *Dir*, Carole Stanger; *Ch Servs*, Julie Tjepkes
Pop 7,700; Circ 73,464
Jul 1997-Jun 1998 Mats Exp $114,000
Library Holdings: Bk Vols 36,000; Per Subs 99
Mem of Southwest Iowa Regional Library System
Friends of the Library Group

AUBURN

P AUBURN PUBLIC LIBARARY,* 209 Pine, PO Box B, 51433-0306. SAN 373-7586. Tel: 712-688-2264. FAX: 712-688-7704. E-Mail: auburnpl@netins.net. *Librn*, Kim Olson
Library Holdings: Bk Titles 8,000; Per Subs 42
Open Mon 4-8, Wed 4-6, Thurs 3-8, Sat 9:30-11:30

AUDUBON

P AUDUBON PUBLIC LIBRARY,* 401 N Park Pl, 50025-1258. SAN 305-2168. Tel: 712-563-3301. FAX: 712-563-2580. *Dir*, Gail Richardson
Founded 1893. Pop 5,100; Circ 31,000
Library Holdings: Bk Vols 23,000
Special Collections: Local History & Geneaology
Mem of Southwest Iowa Regional Library System
Open Mon 12-5, Tues-Fri 10-5, Sat 10-2, Mon-Thurs evenings 7-8:30
Friends of the Library Group

AURELIA

P AURELIA PUBLIC LIBRARY, 232 Main St, PO Box 188, 51005. SAN 305-2176. Tel: 712-434-5330. FAX: 712-434-5330. E-Mail: alibrary@netins.net. *Librn*, Debra Garman; *Circ*, Alissa Smith; Staff 2 (Non-MLS 2)
Founded 1917. Pop 2,000; Circ 15,000
Jul 1999-Jul 2000 Income $34,551, City $29,051, County $5,500. Sal $17,160
Library Holdings: Bk Titles 10,500; Per Subs 34
Subject Interests: History, Natural science, Religion
Special Collections: Iowa Coll
Function: Professional lending library
Mem of NW Iowa Regional Libr Syst
Partic in Iowa Libr Network
Friends of the Library Group

AURORA

P AURORA PUBLIC LIBRARY,* 301 Main St, PO Box 7, 50607-0007. SAN 376-7396. Tel: 319-634-3660. FAX: 319-634-3660. *Librn*, Eileen Knapp
Jul 1997-Jun 1998 Mats Exp $3,949
Library Holdings: Bk Vols 3,000
Mem of Northeastern Iowa Regional Library System

AVOCA

P EDWIN M DAVIS MEMORIAL LIBRARY,* 213 N Elm, PO Box 219, 51521. SAN 305-2184. Tel: 712-343-6358. FAX: 712-343-6358. E-Mail: avocaoo@iren.net, avocapl@fmctc.com. *Librn*, Sherry Jacobsen
Pop 1,650; Circ 20,000
Jul 1998-Jun 1999 Income $62,000. Mats Exp $9,900. Sal $26,500
Library Holdings: Bk Vols 19,568; Per Subs 51
Special Collections: Media: Video (500), Audio (400)
Mem of Southwest Regional Library Service System
Open Mon, Tue, Thur & Fri 10-5, Wed 10-8, Sat 9-12

BADGER

P BADGER PUBLIC LIBRARY, 211 First Ave SE, PO Box 255, 50516. SAN 376-5229. Tel: 515-545-4793. FAX: 515-545-4440. *Librn*, Michele L Boyd
Library Holdings: Bk Vols 9,000; Per Subs 25
Mem of North Central Regional Library System
Partic in Small Libr Asn
Friends of the Library Group

BAGLEY

P BAGLEY PUBLIC LIBRARY,* First & Main, PO Box 206, 50026. SAN 305-2192. Tel: 515-427-5214. Interlibrary Loan Service Tel: 800-432-1045. FAX: 515-427-5214. *Librn*, Denise Chapman
Founded 1976. Pop 600
Library Holdings: Bk Titles 7,500; Per Subs 20
Special Collections: Town
Mem of Southwest Iowa Regional Library System
Partic in Iowa Libr Information Teletype Exchange
Friends of the Library Group

BANCROFT

P BANCROFT PUBLIC LIBRARY,* 208 E Ramsey, PO Box 347, 50517. SAN 305-2206. Tel: 515-885-2753. FAX: 515-885-2753. *Dir*, Mary Richter
Founded 1961. Circ 21,500
Jul 1997-Jun 1998 Income $38,000
Library Holdings: Bk Titles 13,000; Per Subs 86
Mem of North Central Regional Library System
Open Mon & Fri 1-5, Tues 9-11 & 1-6, Wed & Thurs 1-6, Sat 9-12

BATAVIA

P BATAVIA PUBLIC LIBRARY,* Third St, PO Box 129, 52533. SAN 305-2214. Tel: 515-662-2317. *Librn*, Judy Dovico
Pop 525; Circ 2,761
Library Holdings: Bk Vols 5,400; Bk Titles 5,112; Per Subs 20
Mem of Southeastern Regional Libr Syst
Open Tues-Thurs 1-6, Fri 1:30-4:30, Sat 1-6

BATTLE CREEK

P BATTLE CREEK PUBLIC LIBRARY,* 115 Main St, PO Box 267, 51006. SAN 305-2222. Tel: 712-365-4912. FAX: 712-365-4912. *Librn*, Sheila Petersen
Pop 919; Circ 9,676
Library Holdings: Bk Titles 11,989; Per Subs 29
Mem of Northwest Regional Library System
Open Mon & Thurs 2-5:30, Tues, Wed & Fri 2-5, Sat 11-3

BAXTER

P BAXTER PUBLIC LIBRARY,* 202 E State, PO Box 586, 50028. SAN 376-5059. Tel: 515-227-3934. FAX: 515-227-3217.
1998-1999 Income $15,600
Library Holdings: Bk Vols 15,000; Per Subs 20
Mem of Central Iowa Regional Library
Friends of the Library Group

BAYARD

P BAYARD PUBLIC LIBRARY,* 315 Main St, PO Box 338, 50029-0338. SAN 305-2230. Tel: 712-651-2238. FAX: 712-651-2420. *Librn*, Jeannie Stone; *Asst Librn*, Joan Mantz
Founded 1936. Pop 511
Jul 1998-Jun 1999 Income $46,821, State $2,750, City $32,612, County $9,059, Other $2,400. Mats Exp $13,100, Books $10,800, Per/Ser (Incl. Access Fees) $1,400, AV Equip $900. Sal $26,182
Library Holdings: Bk Vols 14,720
Subject Interests: Antiques, Sports
Mem of Southwest Iowa Regional Library System

BEAMAN

P BEAMAN COMMUNITY MEMORIAL LIBRARY, 223 Main St, 50609-0135. (Mail add: PO Box 135, 50609-0135), SAN 305-2249. Tel: 641-366-2912. FAX: 641-366-2912. E-Mail: bcmlib@marshallnet.com. *Dir*, LaVonne Sternhagen; *Asst Librn*, JoAnn Spear; Staff 2 (Non-MLS 2)
Founded 1955. Pop 183; Circ 9,564
Jul 1999-Jun 2000 Income $24,831, City $7,823, County $14,259, Locally Generated Income $1,612, Other $1,137. Mats Exp $11,274, Books $4,500, Per/Ser (Incl. Access Fees) $850, Other Print Mats $755. Sal $13,190
Library Holdings: Bk Titles 7,345; Per Subs 55
Subject Interests: Local history
Mem of Northeastern Iowa Regional Library System

BEDFORD

P BEDFORD PUBLIC LIBRARY, Jefferson St, 50833-1312. SAN 305-2257. Tel: 712-523-2828. E-Mail: bedforl@bedford.heartland.net. *Librn*, Coryl Pace
Founded 1915. Pop 1,516; Circ 16,924
Jul 1999-Jun 2000 Income $33,489, State $447, City $27,723, County $2,327, Locally Generated Income $2,982. Mats Exp $5,229, Books $3,615, Per/Ser (Incl. Access Fees) $668, Other Print Mats $946. Sal $20,417 (Prof $15,033)
Library Holdings: Bk Titles 22,578; Per Subs 41
Subject Interests: Audio bks
Special Collections: Genealogical Coll, bks, prints; Local Newspapers; Taylor County Census, microfilm
Mem of Southwest Iowa Regional Library System

BELLE PLAINE

P BELLE PLAINE COMMUNITY LIBRARY,* 904 12th St, 52208-1711. SAN 305-2265. Tel: 319-444-2902. FAX: 319-444-2902. E-Mail: bpcl@kirkwood.cc.ia.us. *Dir*, Karen Bergan; *Asst Dir*, Loretta Posekany; *Asst Librn*, Dorothy Kalina; *Asst Librn*, Nadine Thomasson; *Asst Librn, Ch Servs*, Reda Prichard
Founded 1907. Pop 3,178; Circ 17,702
Library Holdings: Bk Vols 17,510; Per Subs 70
Subject Interests: Iowa

BELLEVUE

P BELLEVUE PUBLIC LIBRARY,* 106 N Third St, 52031. SAN 305-2273. Tel: 319-872-4991. FAX: 319-872-4094. *Librn*, Marian L Kieffer
Pop 2,475; Circ 33,000
Jul 1998-Jun 1999 Income $79,928. Mats Exp $10,000, Books $5,300. Sal $43,000
Library Holdings: Bk Vols 19,000; Per Subs 55
Friends of the Library Group

BELMOND

P BELMOND PUBLIC LIBRARY, 440 E Main St, 50421-1224. SAN 305-2281. Tel: 641-444-4160. FAX: 641-444-3457. E-Mail: belmondlibrary@belmond-klemme.k12.ia.us. *Dir*, Carol Bailey
Founded 1917. Pop 2,505; Circ 39,217
Jul 1999-June 2000 Income $90,696, State $3,958, City $57,507, County $23,957, Locally Generated Income $4,470, Other $804. Mats Exp $16,523, Books $13,350, Per/Ser (Incl. Access Fees) $2,497, Micro $62, AV Equip $542, Electronic Ref Mat (Incl. Access Fees) $72. Sal $61,217
Library Holdings: Bk Vols 16,754; Per Subs 94
Automation Activity & Vendor Info: (Cataloging) Follett; (Circulation) Follett; (OPAC) Follett
Mem of North Central Regional Library System
Open Mon & Thurs 10-7:30, Tues & Wed 10-5:30, Fri & Sat 10-3
Friends of the Library Group

BENNETT

P BENNETT PUBLIC LIBRARY, 203 Main St, PO Box 299, 52721. SAN 305-229X. Tel: 319-893-2238. FAX: 319-893-2358. E-Mail: benetlib@netins.net. *Dir*, Colette Seligman
Founded 1942. Pop 495; Circ 800
1998-1999 Income $4,100, City $300, County $3,800. Mats Exp $4,271, Books $1,794, Micro $256. Sal $5,460
Library Holdings: Bk Titles 5,543
Mem of East Central Regional Library

BETTENDORF

P BETTENDORF PUBLIC LIBRARY INFORMATION CENTER, 2950 Learning Campus Dr, PO Box 1330, 52722-1330. SAN 305-2311. Tel: 319-344-4175. Circulation Tel: 319-344-4195. Reference Tel: 319-344-4179. TDD: 319-344-4181. FAX: 319-344-4185. E-Mail: infobpl@libby.rbls.lib.il.us. Web Site: www.rbls.lib.il.us/bpl. *Dir*, Faye Clow; *Ad Servs*, Rita Rosauer; Tel: 319-344-4191; *Ch Servs*, Tami Chumbley; *Ref*, Barbara Reardon; *Tech Servs*, Marjorie Martin; *YA Servs*, Maria Wegscheid; Staff 24 (MLS 10, Non-MLS 14)
Founded 1957. Pop 30,874; Circ 485,000
Jul 1999-Jun 2000 Income $1,741,952, State $72,000, City $1,585,000, Locally Generated Income $84,952. Mats Exp $266,640, Books $192,850, Per/Ser (Incl. Access Fees) $38,790, Electronic Ref Mat (Incl. Access Fees) $35,000. Sal $1,212,494
Library Holdings: Bk Titles 124,133; Per Subs 348
Special Collections: Iowa Hist Coll
Automation Activity & Vendor Info: (Circulation) GEAC
Publications: Pages (Newsletter)
Mem of Southeastern Library Services
Special Services for the Deaf - TDD
Friends of the Library Group

J SCOTT COMMUNITY COLLEGE LIBRARY, 500 Belmont Rd, 52722. SAN 305-3253. Tel: 319-441-4150. FAX: 319-441-4154. E-Mail: scclibrary@eiccd.cc.ia.us. Web Site: www.bridges.eiccd.cc.ia.us/library/scc.html. *Librn*, Jane Campagna; E-Mail: jcampagna@eiccd.cc.ia.us
Founded 1968. Enrl 3,700; Fac 120
Library Holdings: Bk Titles 22,600; Per Subs 176
Automation Activity & Vendor Info: (Cataloging) GEAC; (Circulation) GEAC; (OPAC) GEAC
Publications: Infotrac
Partic in Bi-State Academic Libraries; River Bend Library System
Open Mon-Thurs 7:30-8:30, Fri 7:30-4:30 & Sat 9-1

BIRMINGHAM

P BIRMINGHAM PUBLIC LIBRARY,* Main St, PO Box 167, 52535. SAN 305-232X. Tel: 319-498-4296. FAX: 319-498-4298. *Librn, Pres*, Arlene Lyon
Pop 1,217; Circ 6,556
Library Holdings: Bk Vols 8,500; Bk Titles 7,215
Mem of Southeastern Library Services

BLAIRSTOWN

P BLAIRSTOWN PUBLIC LIBRARY,* 303 Locust St NW, PO Box 187, 52209-0187. SAN 305-2338. Tel: 319-454-6497. FAX: 319-454-6497. E-Mail: btown@netins.net. *Dir*, Melanie S Long; *Asst Dir*, Traci Kullmer; Staff 1 (MLS 1)
Founded 1930
Jul 1996-Jun 1997 Income $31,739, State $46, City $20,585, County $4,000, Locally Generated Income $1,697, Other $379. Mats Exp $8,387, Books $7,165, Per/Ser (Incl. Access Fees) $633, AV Equip $589. Sal $15,087
Library Holdings: Bk Titles 8,856

BLAKESBURG

P BLAKESBURG PUBLIC LIBRARY,* High St, PO Box 87, 52536. SAN 373-6954. Tel: 515-938-2894. *Librn*, Garland Seaba
Pop 333
Library Holdings: Bk Titles 5,398

BLOOMFIELD

P BLOOMFIELD PUBLIC LIBRARY,* 107 N Columbia St, 52537-1498. SAN 305-2354. Tel: 515-664-2209. FAX: 515-664-2209. *Dir*, Regina Gooden
Founded 1913. Pop 2,800; Circ 28,000
Library Holdings: Bk Titles 18,000; Per Subs 65
Subject Interests: Iowa, Local history
Special Collections: Davis County Genealogy Society
Mem of Southeastern Library Services

BODE

P BODE PUBLIC LIBRARY,* 114 Humboldt Ave, PO Box 122, 50519-0122. SAN 305-2362. Tel: 515-379-1258. FAX: 515-379-1486. *Librn*, Orlys Maassen
Pop 406; Circ 5,149
Library Holdings: Bk Vols 4,682; Per Subs 32
Mem of North Central Regional Library System
Open Mon & Fri 9-12 & 1-4, Wed 9-12, 1-4 & 6-8, Sat 9-12, closed Tues & Thurs

BONAPARTE

P BONAPARTE PUBLIC LIBRARY,* Second Washington, 52620. SAN 305-2370. Tel: 319-592-3677. *Librn*, Verna Coleman
Pop 465; Circ 5,026
1997-1998 Income $3,693, City $1,750, County $1,943. Mats Exp Books $2,011. Sal $92
Library Holdings: Bk Titles 10,618
Mem of Southeastern Library Services
Open Tues, Thurs & Sat 1-5

BONDURANT

P BONDURANT COMMUNITY LIBRARY,* 17 Main St SE, PO Box 160, 50035. SAN 320-4766. Tel: 515-967-4790. *Dir, Librn*, Dena Heilik
Founded 1977. Pop 1,560; Circ 11,961
1998-1999 Income $24,000. Mats Exp $6,500. Sal $13,000
Library Holdings: Bk Titles 9,541; Per Subs 30
Mem of Central Regional Libr Syst
Friends of the Library Group

BOONE

§J DES MOINES AREA COMMUNITY COLLEGE, Boone Campus Library, 1125 Hancock Dr, 50036. SAN 305-2389. Tel: 515-433-5043. FAX: 515-433-5044. *Dir*, Ann L Watts; Tel: 515-433-5040, E-Mail: alwatts@dmacc.cc.ia.us; Staff 3 (MLS 1, Non-MLS 2)
Founded 1966
Library Holdings: Bk Vols 20,000; Per Subs 170
Special Collections: Railroads & Iowa
Database Vendor: Ebsco - EbscoHost, OCLC - First Search
Partic in OCLC Online Computer Library Center, Inc

P ERICSON PUBLIC LIBRARY, 702 Greene St, 50036. SAN 341-7816. Tel: 515-432-3727. FAX: 515-432-1103. E-Mail: eplb@opencominc.com. *Dir*, Rosann M Sanders; *YA Servs*, Barbara Rardin; *ILL*, Cathy Cottrell; Staff 3 (MLS 1, Non-MLS 2)
Founded 1901. Pop 12,602; Circ 192,030
Jul 1999-Jun 2000 Income $506,101, City $460,277, County $28,000, Locally Generated Income $17,824. Mats Exp $87,427, Books $49,007, Per/Ser (Incl. Access Fees) $6,503, Micro $400, AV Equip $8,488, Other Print Mats $1,561, Electronic Ref Mat (Incl. Access Fees) $21,468. Sal $210,147 (Prof $43,000)
Library Holdings: Bk Titles 65,168; Per Subs 173
Subject Interests: Antiques, Genealogy, Iowa, Railroads
Automation Activity & Vendor Info: (Circulation) Gaylord
Mem of Central Iowa Regional Library
Partic in OCLC Online Computer Library Center, Inc
Friends of the Library Group

S MAMIE DOUD EISENHOWER BIRTHPLACE FOUNDATION, INC LIBRARY, 709 Carroll St, PO Box 55, 50036. SAN 325-4968. Tel: 515-432-1896. FAX: 515-432-2571. *Curator*, Larry Adams
Founded 1977
Library Holdings: Bk Titles 2,000; Per Subs 10
Special Collections: Boone County, Iowa History & Genealogy; Carlson & Doud Families Coll; Dwight D Eisenhower Coll, bks, photogs, letters; Mamie Doud Eisenhower Coll, bks, photogs, letters
Publications: Newsletter
Open Tues-Sun 1-5 (Apr-May), 10-5 daily (June-Oct) & open at other times by appointment
Friends of the Library Group

BOYDEN

P BOYDEN PUBLIC LIBRARY,* 905 Main St, PO Box 249, 51234-0905. SAN 305-2397. Tel: 712-725-2281. *Librn*, Clleon Stueven
Library Holdings: Bk Vols 25,260; Per Subs 15
Mem of Northwest Regional Library System

BREDA

P BREDA PUBLIC LIBRARY,* 208 Maple, 51436. SAN 376-6780. Tel: 712-673-2660 (City Clerk). *In Charge*, Sheri Dirkx
Library Holdings: Bk Vols 200
Mem of Northwest Regional Library System

BRITT

P BRITT PUBLIC LIBRARY, 132 S Main Ave, 50423-1628. SAN 305-2400. Tel: 515-843-4245. FAX: 515-843-4245. E-Mail: brittlib@ncn.net. *Librn*, Jo Lang; Staff 3 (Non-MLS 3)
Founded 1917. Pop 2,200; Circ 13,000
1999-2000 Income $59,100, State $2,000, City $41,000, County $15,400, Locally Generated Income $700. Mats Exp $9,200, Books $7,000, Per/Ser (Incl. Access Fees) $2,200. Sal $42,200
Library Holdings: Bk Vols 16,000; Per Subs 42
Mem of North Central Regional Library System
Open Mon-Fri 10-5, Thurs 5-8, Sat 9-12

BROOKLYN

P BROOKLYN PUBLIC LIBRARY,* 306 Jackson St, 52211. (Mail add: PO Box 515, 52211-0515), SAN 305-2419. Tel: 515-522-9272. FAX: 515-522-9272. E-Mail: brooklyn@netins.net. *Librn*, Lu Ann Jahlas
Library Holdings: Bk Titles 9,000; Per Subs 45
Database Vendor: OCLC - First Search

BUFFALO CENTER

P BUFFALO CENTER PUBLIC LIBRARY,* 113 First St NW, 50424. SAN 305-2427. Tel: 515-562-2546. FAX: 515-562-2546. *Librn*, Jean Breckunitch
Pop 1,250; Circ 8,063
Jul 1996-Jun 1997 Income $17,650, City $9,500, County $7,500, Locally Generated Income $650. Mats Exp Books $4,650. Sal $6,670
Library Holdings: Bk Vols 8,000
Mem of North Central Regional Library System

BURLINGTON

P BURLINGTON PUBLIC LIBRARY, 501 N Fourth St, 52601. SAN 305-2443. Tel: 319-753-1647. FAX: 319-753-5316. Web Site: www.burlington.lib.ia.us. *Dir*, Kay Weiss; E-Mail: kweiss@aea16.k12.ia.us; *Ch Servs*, Linda Fowler; E-Mail: lfowler@aea16.k12.ia.us; *Tech Servs*, Paula J Buhrow; E-Mail: pbuhrow@aea16.k12.ia.us; *Ad Servs*, Lois J Blythe; E-Mail: lblythe@aea16.k12.ia.us; Staff 4 (MLS 4)
Founded 1868. Pop 30,000; Circ 408,320
Jul 1998-Jun 1999 Income $840,000. Mats Exp $172,000, Books $142,000, Per/Ser (Incl. Access Fees) $27,000, Micro $3,000. Sal $555,000
Library Holdings: Bk Titles 85,000; Per Subs 400
Subject Interests: Genealogy, Local history
Automation Activity & Vendor Info: (Acquisitions) epixtech, inc.; (Cataloging) epixtech, inc.; (Circulation) epixtech, inc.; (Serials) epixtech, inc.
Mem of Southeastern Library Services
Friends of the Library Group

BURT

P BURT PUBLIC LIBRARY,* 119 Walnut St, PO Box 128, 50522-0128. SAN 305-2451. Tel: 515-924-3680. FAX: 515-924-3680. *Librn*, Sharon Kay Dykshoorn; E-Mail: dykshos@witcc.com; *Asst Librn*, Linda Bunkofske
Pop 689; Circ 4,474
Library Holdings: Bk Vols 6,000; Per Subs 25
Mem of North Central Regional Library System

BUSSEY

P BUSSEY PUBLIC LIBRARY,* 314 Fourth St, PO Box 29, 50044. SAN 376-5423. Tel: 515-944-5331.
Library Holdings: Bk Vols 11,000
Mem of Central Iowa Regional Library

CALAMUS

P CALAMUS PUBLIC LIBRARY,* Second & Main, PO Box 128, 52729. SAN 305-246X. Tel: 319-246-2755. *Librn*, Tammy Wiese
Pop 495; Circ 2,100
Library Holdings: Bk Vols 2,300
Open Mon 3-6 & Thurs 6-9

CALLENDER

P CALLENDER HERITAGE LIBRARY,* 505 Thomas St, PO Box 69, 50523. SAN 305-2478. Tel: 515-548-3803. FAX: 515-548-3801. Web Site: www.gowrie.k12.ia.us/community/call/library.htm. *Librn*, Robin Newell; E-Mail: robin@netins.net
Founded 1903. Pop 387; Circ 9,230
1998-1999 Income $21,500
Library Holdings: Bk Titles 6,500; Per Subs 34
Mem of North Central Regional Library System

CALMAR

P CALMAR PUBLIC LIBRARY,* 101 S Washington, PO Box 806, 52132. SAN 305-2486. Tel: 319-562-3010. FAX: 319-562-3010. *Librn*, Anna Houdek
Pop 1,053; Circ 6,948
Library Holdings: Bk Titles 10,000; Per Subs 50
Mem of Northeastern Regional Libr Syst

J NORTHEAST IOWA COMMUNITY COLLEGE, Wilder Library, 1625 Hwy 150, PO Box 400, 52132-0400. SAN 305-2494. Tel: 319-562-3263. Toll Free Tel: 800-728-2256. FAX: 319-562-4361. Web Site: www.nicc.edu. *Coordr*, Julie G Huiskamp; Tel: 319-562-3263, Ext 257, E-Mail: huiskamj@nicc.cc.ia.us; Staff 4 (MLS 1, Non-MLS 3)
Founded 1966. Enrl 1,200; Fac 120; Highest Degree: Associate
Jul 2000-Jun 2001 Mats Exp $119,000, Books $75,000, Per/Ser (Incl. Access Fees) $23,000, AV Equip $15,000, Electronic Ref Mat (Incl. Access Fees) $6,000. Sal $84,400 (Prof $34,400)
Library Holdings: Bk Vols 19,200; Per Subs 305
Subject Interests: Agriculture, Business and management, Nursing, Science/technology, Technology
Special Collections: Holocaust Coll
Automation Activity & Vendor Info: (Acquisitions) epixtech, inc.; (Cataloging) epixtech, inc.; (Circulation) epixtech, inc.
Database Vendor: Ebsco - EbscoHost, OCLC - First Search
Partic in BCR

CAMANCHE

P CAMANCHE PUBLIC LIBRARY,* 102 12th Ave, 52730. SAN 305-2508. Tel: 319-259-1106. FAX: 319-259-1106. E-Mail: library@jdv.net. *Dir*, Beth Thilmany; *Ch Servs*, Kris Cassaday; *Librn*, Marian Paasch; *Librn*, Sondra Taylor
Founded 1965. Pop 4,725; Circ 35,780
Library Holdings: Bk Titles 28,189; Per Subs 150
Special Collections: Iowa Coll; Mark Twain Coll; Mississippi River Coll
Mem of East Central Regional Library
Friends of the Library Group

CANTRIL

P CANTRIL PUBLIC LIBRARY, 104 W Third, PO Box 158, 52542-0158. SAN 376-5482. Tel: 319-397-2366. FAX: 319-397-2366. E-Mail: cantril@netins.net. *Librn*, Sherri Hamann
Library Holdings: Bk Vols 7,000
Mem of Southeastern Library Services
Open Mon, Wed & Fri 9-11, Thurs 3:30-5

CARLISLE

P CARLISLE PUBLIC LIBRARY,* 135 School St, PO Box S, 50047-0718. SAN 305-2532. Tel: 515-989-0909. FAX: 515-989-4328. E-Mail: carlpl@netins.net. *Dir*, Robert Berning
Pop 6,026; Circ 23,139
Jul 1998-Jun 1999 Income $92,056. Mats Exp $15,950, Books $14,650, Per/Ser (Incl. Access Fees) $1,300. Sal $49,254
Library Holdings: Bk Vols 26,532; Per Subs 62
Special Collections: Carlisle/Hartford Scrapbook Coll; Iowa Coll; Probate Records for Warren County Iowa (1915-1970)
Automation Activity & Vendor Info: (Cataloging) Follett; (Circulation) Follett
Mem of Central Iowa Regional Library
Open Mon & Thurs 10-9, Tues, Wed & Fri 10-5, Sat 10-5
Friends of the Library Group

CARROLL

P CARROLL PUBLIC LIBRARY, 118 E Fifth St, 51401. SAN 305-2540. Tel: 712-792-3432. *Bibliog Instr, Coll Develop, Dir, Online Servs*, Gordon S Wade; *Ad Servs, Tech Servs*, Judy Behm; *Ch Servs*, Nancy Pudenz; *Ad Servs*, Sharon Rogers; Staff 1 (MLS 1)
Founded 1893. Pop 18,911; Circ 108,076
Jul 2000-Jun 2001 Income $239,451, State $5,000, City $204,451, County $30,000. Mats Exp $55,000, Books $50,000, Per/Ser (Incl. Access Fees) $5,000. Sal $129,900
Library Holdings: Bk Vols 67,500; Bk Titles 62,000; Per Subs 250
Subject Interests: Genealogy, Large type print, Science fiction
Automation Activity & Vendor Info: (Cataloging) epixtech, inc.; (Circulation) epixtech, inc.
Mem of Northwest Regional Library System
Partic in Iowa Libr Information Teletype Exchange
Open Mon-Thurs 10-8:30, Fri 10-6, Sat 10-5
Friends of the Library Group

CARTER LAKE

P OWEN MEMORIAL LIBRARY, 1120 Willow Dr, 51510-1332. SAN 305-2559. Tel: 712-347-5492. FAX: 712-347-5013. E-Mail: owenlibrary@home.com. *Dir*, Theresa Hawkins; *Asst Dir*, Peggy Settles; *Ch Servs*, Shawna Hawkins
Founded 1977. Pop 3,438; Circ 13,292
Jul 1998-Jun 1999 Income $102,222. Mats Exp $10,000. Sal $39,953
Library Holdings: Bk Titles 13,666; Per Subs 75
Mem of Southwest Regional Library Service System
Open Mon & Wed 12-6, Tues & Thurs 10-7, Sat 10-2

CASCADE

P CASCADE PUBLIC LIBRARY,* 301 First Ave W, Box 117, 52033-0117. SAN 305-2567. Tel: 319-852-3222. FAX: 319-852-6011. E-Mail: cpl@bel-net.com. *Librn*, Nancy Pfab; *Ch Servs*, Sarah Zoller
Founded 1968. Pop 1,812; Circ 26,055
Jul 1998-Jun 1999 Income $36,508, State $4,000, City $31,308, Locally Generated Income $1,200. Mats Exp $7,000, Books $6,000, Per/Ser (Incl. Access Fees) $1,000. Sal $31,000
Library Holdings: Bk Vols 15,044; Per Subs 28
Mem of Northeastern Iowa Regional Library System
Open Tues 1-7, Wed 9:30-8:30, Thurs & Fri 1-5, Sat 9-12
Friends of the Library Group

CASEY

P DUNCAN MEMORIAL LIBRARY,* 610 Antique Country Dr, PO Box 178, 50048. SAN 305-2575. Tel: 515-746-2670. E-Mail: caseylib@netins.net. *Librn*, Maxine Stetzel
Founded 1941. Pop 500
Jul 1997-Jun 1998 Income $10,808, State $116, City $1,500, County $8,992. Mats Exp $3,450, Books $2,804, Per/Ser (Incl. Access Fees) $231, Presv $26, Micro $364, Electronic Ref Mat (Incl. Access Fees) $25. Sal $3,715
Library Holdings: Bk Titles 10,000; Per Subs 10; High Interest/Low Vocabulary Bk Vols 150
Special Collections: A-C Yearbooks; Adair news 1951-present; Casey Obituaries; Casey School Alumni Class Pictures; Casey Vindicator on microfilm 1878-1950
Mem of Southwest Iowa Regional Library System
Special Services for the Blind - Cassette bks; Large print bks
Open Mon & Wed 1-5:30pm & Sat 2-5, Fri 9-12
Friends of the Library Group

CEDAR FALLS

S CEDAR FALLS HISTORICAL SOCIETY ARCHIVES, (Formerly Cedar Falls Historical Society Library), 308 W Third St, 50613. (Mail add: 303 Franklin St, 56013), SAN 325-7282. Tel: 319-266-5149, 319-277-8817. Reference Tel: 319-266-5149. FAX: 319-268-1812. *Exec Dir*, Doris Schmitz; E-Mail: cfhs_schmitz@cfu.net; *Dir*, Erica Lee
Subject Interests: Local history
Special Collections: Local Authors

P CEDAR FALLS PUBLIC LIBRARY,* 524 Main St, 50613-2889. SAN 305-2583. Tel: 319-273-8643. FAX: 319-273-8648. E-Mail: cfpl@iren.net. Web Site: www.iren.net/cfpl. *Dir*, Carol Johnson; *ILL, Ref*, Jewel Devin; *Ad Servs, Ser*, Aleta Anderson; *Ch Servs*, Paige Nangle; *ILL*, Steve Sorenson; Staff 7 (MLS 7)
Founded 1865. Pop 34,600; Circ 295,985
Library Holdings: Bk Titles 94,017; Per Subs 248
Friends of the Library Group

C UNIVERSITY OF NORTHERN IOWA LIBRARY, Rod Library, 1227 W 27 St, 50613-3675. SAN 305-2605. Tel: 319-273-2737. FAX: 319-273-7182. Web Site: www.library.uni.edu. *Actg Dean*, Marilyn Mercado; *Coll Develop*, Katherine Martin; *Acq*, Cynthia Coulter; *YA Servs*, Lucille Lettow; *Archivist, Spec Coll*, Gerald Peterson; *Doc*, Becky Lutkenhaus; *Online Servs*, Stanley Lyle; *Info Tech*, Jerry Caswell; *Cat*, Colleen Valente; Staff 29 (MLS 23, Non-MLS 6)
Founded 1876. Enrl 13,700; Fac 830; Highest Degree: Doctorate
Jul 2000-Jun 2001 Income $5,860,370, State $16,000, Locally Generated Income $86,910, Parent Institution $5,757,460. Mats Exp $1,976,751. Sal $3,361,308 (Prof $1,470,331)
Library Holdings: Bk Vols 867,344; Bk Titles 593,159; Per Subs 3,268

Subject Interests: Art, Education, Music
Special Collections: American Fiction; Grassley Papers; University Archives
Automation Activity & Vendor Info: (Acquisitions) Innovative Interfaces Inc.; (Cataloging) Innovative Interfaces Inc.; (Circulation) Innovative Interfaces Inc.; (Course Reserve) Innovative Interfaces Inc.; (ILL) Innovative Interfaces Inc.; (Media Booking) Innovative Interfaces Inc.; (OPAC) Innovative Interfaces Inc.; (Serials) Innovative Interfaces Inc.
Publications: Guide to the Library; Library User's Guide Series
Partic in Bibliographical Center For Research, Rocky Mountain Region, Inc; Cedar Valley Libr Consortium; OCLC Online Computer Library Center, Inc

CEDAR RAPIDS

S ANCIENT FREE & ACCEPTED MASONS, Grand Lodge of Iowa Masonic Library, 813 First Ave SE, PO Box 279, 52406. SAN 305-2613. Tel: 319-365-1438. FAX: 319-365-1439. *Librn*, William Crawford; *Asst Librn*, William Kreuger; Staff 2 (MLS 1, Non-MLS 1)
Founded 1845
Library Holdings: Bk Titles 100,000
Subject Interests: History, Iowa, Poetry, Religion
Special Collections: Abraham Lincoln Coll; Arthur Edward Waite Coll; Cedar Rapids Gazette, micro; Dr Erskine Medical Coll; Early Cedar Rapids, paper, micro; Prince Hall Masonic Coll; Robert Burns Coll

S CEDAR RAPIDS GAZETTE LIBRARY,* 500 Third Ave SE, 52406. SAN 325-1284. Tel: 319-398-8328. FAX: 319-398-5846. *Librn*, Bridget Janus; Staff 2 (MLS 1, Non-MLS 1)
Restriction: Restricted public use

S CEDAR RAPIDS MUSEUM OF ART, Herbert S Stamats Library, 410 Third Ave SE, 52401. SAN 325-1438. Tel: 319-366-7503. FAX: 319-366-4111. E-Mail: crma@earthlink.net. Web Site: www.crma.org. *Exec Dir*, Terence Pitts; *Dir*, Tris Dows
Founded 1905
Subject Interests: Art
Special Collections: Grant Wood Art Coll; Marvin Cone Art Coll

P CEDAR RAPIDS PUBLIC LIBRARY, 500 First St SE, 52401-2095. SAN 341-7875. Tel: 319-398-5123. FAX: 319-398-0476. Web Site: www.cedar-rapids.lib.ia.us/crpl/home.html. *Dir*, Thomas Armitage; Tel: 319-398-5145, Ext 222; *Asst Dir*, Bryan Davis; *Ad Servs*, Stephnie Schulte; *Cat, Tech Servs*, Leon Green; *Circ*, Tamara Filbert; Staff 98 (MLS 17, Non-MLS 81)
Founded 1896. Pop 108,426; Circ 1,356,132
Jul 1999-Jun 2000 Income (Main Library and Branch Library) $4,244,595, State $136,891, City $3,055,555, Federal $421,716, County $113,089, Locally Generated Income $517,344. Mats Exp $4,244,595, Books $369,384, Per/Ser (Incl. Access Fees) $45,700, Micro $33,836, Other Print Mats $67,066, Electronic Ref Mat (Incl. Access Fees) $96,776. Sal $2,796,570
Library Holdings: Bk Vols 317,165; Per Subs 442
Special Collections: US Census
Automation Activity & Vendor Info: (Acquisitions) DRA; (Cataloging) DRA; (Circulation) DRA; (OPAC) DRA; (Serials) DRA
Database Vendor: Ebsco - EbscoHost, IAC - SearchBank, Innovative Interfaces INN - View
Publications: Shelf Life
Mem of East Central Regional Library
Friends of the Library Group
Branches: 2
WESTSIDE, Westdale Mall, 52404. SAN 329-7454. Tel: 319-390-7806. *Librn*, Tamara Filbert

C COE COLLEGE, Stewart Memorial Library, 1220 First Ave NE, 52402-5092. SAN 305-2621. Tel: 319-399-8023. Interlibrary Loan Service Tel: 319-399-8018. Circulation Tel: 319-399-8585. Reference Tel: 319-399-8586. FAX: 319-399-8019. Web Site: www.public.coe.edu/departments/library. *Dir*, Richard Doyle; E-Mail: rdoyle@coe.edu; *AV*, Cedra Williamson; Tel: 319-399-8211, E-Mail: cwilliam@coe.edu; *Cat, Tech Servs*, Randall Roeder; Tel: 319-399-8026, E-Mail: rroeder@coe.edu; *Circ*, Sandy Blanchard; Tel: 319-399-8595, E-Mail: sblancha@coe.edu; *Ref*, Betty J Rogers; Tel: 319-399-8017, E-Mail: brogers@coe.edu; Staff 4 (MLS 4)
Founded 1900. Enrl 1,192; Fac 105; Highest Degree: Master
Jul 1999-Jun 2000 Income (Main Library Only) $850,000, Locally Generated Income $50,000, Parent Institution $800,000. Mats Exp $285,603, Books $77,479, Per/Ser (Incl. Access Fees) $151,055, Presv $6,695, Micro $8,037, AV Equip $8,432, Electronic Ref Mat (Incl. Access Fees) $33,905. Sal $304,811 (Prof $179,450)
Library Holdings: Bk Vols 206,290; Bk Titles 156,066; Per Subs 818
Subject Interests: Art and architecture, History, Religion, Social sciences and issues
Special Collections: Wm Shirer Manuscripts; Works by Paul Engle
Automation Activity & Vendor Info: (Acquisitions) epixtech, inc.; (Cataloging) epixtech, inc.; (Circulation) epixtech, inc.; (Course Reserve) epixtech, inc.; (OPAC) epixtech, inc.; (Serials) epixtech, inc.
Database Vendor: epixtech, inc.
Publications: Coe College Library Association (newsletter)
Partic in Bibliographical Center For Research, Rocky Mountain Region, Inc; Iowa Res & Educ Network; Linn County Library Consortium; OCLC Online Computer Library Center, Inc
Friends of the Library Group

P EAST CENTRAL REGIONAL LIBRARY,* Guaranty Bldg, 222 Third St SE, Ste 402, 52401. SAN 305-2648. Tel: 319-365-0521. FAX: 319-365-0194. *Mgr*, Linda Lumsden; *ILL*, Mary Finch-Foghi; *Ref*, Georgia Heald; Staff 3 (MLS 3)
Founded 1973. Pop 448,070
Jul 1996-Jun 1997 Income $270,564, State $244,564, Locally Generated Income $500, Other $1,500. Mats Exp $2,900, Books $1,100, Per/Ser (Incl. Access Fees) $500, Other Print Mats $1,300. Sal $181,331 (Prof $114,946)
Library Holdings: Bk Vols 300; Per Subs 30
Special Collections: Bifolkal (multimedia) Kits Coll; Language Cassettes Coll; Large Print Books Coll; Professional Coll
Publications: Annual Statistical Summary; East Central News (newsletter); Subject Catalog of Professional Materials
Member Libraries: Amana School-Community Library; Anamosa Public Library; Bennett Public Library; Camanche Public Library; Cedar Rapids Public Library; Clutier Public Library; Coggon Public Library; Fairfax Public Library; Hinckley Public Library; Lost Nation Public Library; Marion Public Library; Monticello Public Library; Newhall Public Library; North Branch Area Library; Oxford Public Library; Schroeder Public Library; Williamsburg Public Library; Wyoming Public Library
Open Mon-Fri 8am-noon & 1-5pm; Serve ten counties; ILL available to other libraries

R FIRST LUTHERAN CHURCH LIBRARY,* 1000 Third Ave SE, 52403-2481. SAN 305-2656. Tel: 319-365-1494. FAX: 319-364-3962. *Librn*, Linda Corey; Staff 1 (MLS 1)
Founded 1959. Pop 2,000; Circ 4,500
Jan 1999-Dec 1999 Income $1,400. Mats Exp $1,370, Books $1,000, Per/Ser (Incl. Access Fees) $70, Other Print Mats $300
Library Holdings: Bk Vols 3,083; Per Subs 5
Subject Interests: Lutheranism, Martin Luther, Religion
Restriction: Members only, Open to public for reference only
Partic in Church & Synagogue Libr Asn
Special Services for the Blind - Large print bks

S GENEALOGICAL SOCIETY OF LINN COUNTY IOWA LIBRARY, 813 First Ave SE, 52402. (Mail add: PO Box 175, 52406-0175), SAN 370-1697. Tel: 319-369-0022. *Pres*, Ron Baty
Library Holdings: Bk Titles 3,500; Per Subs 20
Special Collections: Linn County Cemetery & Court House records
Publications: Linn County Heritage Hunter (quarterly newsletter)
Open Tues-Sat 10-4

J KIRKWOOD COMMUNITY COLLEGE LIBRARY, Benton Hall, 6301 Kirkwood Blvd SW, 52406-2068. (Mail add: PO Box 2068, 52406-2068), SAN 305-2664. Tel: 319-398-5553. Interlibrary Loan Service Tel: 319-398-1254. FAX: 319-398-4908. Web Site: www.kirkwood.cc.ia.us/library. *Dir*, Jerrie Bourgo; Tel: 319-398-5403, E-Mail: jbourgo@kirkwood.cc.ia.us; *Librn*, Gary Botos; Tel: 319-398-5887, E-Mail: gbotos@kirkwood.cc.ia.us; *Librn*, Annie Locher; Tel: 319-398-5697, E-Mail: alocher@kirkwood.cc.ia.us; *Librn*, Steve Sickels; Tel: 319-398-5605, E-Mail: ssickel@kirkwood.cc.ia.us; *Librn*, Nancy Sweet; Tel: 319-398-5697, E-Mail: nsweet@kirkwood.cc.ia.us; *Librn*, Julia Venzke; Tel: 319-398-5697, E-Mail: jvenzke@kirkwood.cc.ia.us; *Librn*, Kathy Wendling; Tel: 319-887-3619, Fax: 319-351-3895, E-Mail: kwendli@kirkwood.cc.ia.us; *Librn*, Arron Wings; Tel: 319-887-3612, Fax: 319-351-3895, E-Mail: awings@kirkwood.cc.ia.us; *Librn*, Genny Yarne; Tel: 319-398-5687, E-Mail: gyarne@kirkwood.cc.ia.us; Staff 23 (MLS 11, Non-MLS 12)
Founded 1967. Pop 11,321; Enrl 5,825
Jul 1999-Jun 2000 Income Parent Institution $545,107. Mats Exp $108,505, Books $57,392, Per/Ser (Incl. Access Fees) $30,753, Presv $703, Micro $6,148, Other Print Mats $3,921, Manuscripts & Archives $306, Electronic Ref Mat (Incl. Access Fees) $9,282. Sal $425,800 (Prof $260,572)
Library Holdings: Bk Vols 65,609; Bk Titles 60,622; Per Subs 565; Bks on Deafness & Sign Lang 209
Special Collections: Carl Van Vechten Coll
Automation Activity & Vendor Info: (Cataloging) TLC; (Circulation) VTLS; (OPAC) VTLS; (Serials) VTLS
Database Vendor: IAC - Info Trac, IAC - SearchBank, OCLC - First Search
Publications: Faculty handbook; Student handbook
Partic in Linn County Library Consortium; NILRC

GL LINN COUNTY LAW LIBRARY,* Linn County Courthouse, 52401. SAN 305-2672. Tel: 319-398-3449. *Librn*, Betty Dye
Founded 1925
Library Holdings: Bk Titles 16,000

M MERCY MEDICAL CENTER, Health Science Library, 701 Tenth St SE, 52403. SAN 305-2680. Tel: 319-398-6165. FAX: 319-369-4524. *Head of Libr*, Molaan K Mosell; Tel: 319-398-6166, E-Mail: mmosell@mercycare.org; Staff 2 (MLS 1, Non-MLS 1)
Founded 1970

Jul 2000-Jun 2001 Income Parent Institution $153,000. Mats Exp $56,235, Books $22,500, Per/Ser (Incl. Access Fees) $24,500, AV Equip $2,500, Electronic Ref Mat (Incl. Access Fees) $6,735. Sal $37,000 (Prof $31,000)
Library Holdings: Bk Titles 3,000; Per Subs 250
Subject Interests: Cancer treatment, Emergency med, Family med, Obstetrics and gynecology
Special Collections: Mercy Hospital Authors Coll
Automation Activity & Vendor Info: (Acquisitions) EOS; (Cataloging) EOS; (Circulation) EOS; (OPAC) EOS; (Serials) EOS
Database Vendor: OCLC - First Search, OVID Technologies
Partic in Greater Midwest Regional Medical Libr Network; Nat Libr of Med

C MOUNT MERCY COLLEGE, Busse Library,* 1330 Elmhurst Dr NE, 52402-4797. SAN 305-2699. Tel: 319-363-8213, Ext 244. FAX: 319-363-9060. Web Site: www.mtmercy.edu. *Librn*, Marilyn Murphy; E-Mail: marilyn@mmc.mtmercy.edu; *Cat, Tech Servs*, Janis Dickes; *Online Servs, Ref*, Linda Scarth; *Media Spec, Per*, Constance Walther; Staff 11 (MLS 6, Non-MLS 5)
Founded 1958. Enrl 1,008; Fac 84; Highest Degree: Bachelor
Jul 1997-Jun 1998 Mats Exp $178,000
Library Holdings: Bk Vols 114,000; Per Subs 716
Special Collections: National League for Nursing
Partic in Linn County Library Consortium; OCLC Online Computer Library Center, Inc
Friends of the Library Group

S ROCKWELL COLLINS, Information Center,* 400 Collins Rd NE, Mail Sta 124-203, 52498-1000. SAN 305-263X. Tel: 319-295-3070. FAX: 319-295-8417. *Librn*, Judith A Leavitt; E-Mail: jaleavit@collins.rockwell.com; Staff 9 (MLS 3, Non-MLS 6)
Founded 1942. Pop 14,000
Library Holdings: Bk Titles 8,000; Per Subs 300
Subject Interests: Business and management, Electronics, Telecommunications
Publications: Competitive Intelligence Alert (weekly)
Restriction: Not open to public

M SAINT LUKE'S HOSPITAL, Health Science Library, 1026 A Ave NE, 52402. SAN 305-2710. Tel: 319-369-7358. FAX: 319-369-8036. *Librn*, Donald Pohnl; E-Mail: pohnldr@crstlukes.com; Staff 3 (MLS 1, Non-MLS 2)
Founded 1969
Library Holdings: Bk Vols 4,500; Bk Titles 4,000; Per Subs 350
Subject Interests: Administrative law, Allied health, Child welfare
Automation Activity & Vendor Info: (Cataloging) EOS; (Circulation) EOS; (Serials) EOS
Partic in Linn County Library Consortium
Friends of the Library Group

R TEMPLE JUDAH LIBRARY,* 3221 Lindsay Lane SE, 52403. SAN 305-2729. Tel: 319-362-1261. FAX: 319-365-6276. *Librn*, Sue Reider
Founded 1950
Library Holdings: Bk Titles 1,850
Subject Interests: Judaica (lit or hist of Jews)

CENTER POINT

P CENTER POINT PUBLIC LIBRARY,* 1025 Franklin, 52213-0903. SAN 305-2737. Tel: 319-849-1509. FAX: 319-849-1509. E-Mail: cpulib@netins.net. *Librn*, Donna Turner
Pop 1,591; Circ 30,000
Library Holdings: Bk Titles 17,000; Per Subs 40
Open Mon, Wed & Fri 1-5:30, Tues 8:30-1, Thurs 1-8, Sat 10-4

CENTERVILLE

P DRAKE PUBLIC LIBRARY,* 115-117 Drake Ave, 52544. SAN 305-2745. Tel: 515-856-6676. FAX: 515-856-6135. E-Mail: drkpblib@se-iowa.net. *Dir*, Debra Eurom; *Asst Librn*, Barbara Skidmore; *Asst Librn*, Deborah Egeland; *Asst Librn*, Jamie Livingston; *Ch Servs*, Molly Williams
Founded 1903. Pop 5,936; Circ 108,138
Library Holdings: Bk Titles 30,478; Per Subs 105
Special Collections: Media: videos (325), ,audios (600)
Mem of Southeastern Library Services
Partic in Am Libr Asn; Iowa Libr Asn
Open Mon-Thurs 10-7, Fri, Sat 10-4

J INDIAN HILLS COMMUNITY COLLEGE, Centerville Center Library, 721 N First St, 52544. SAN 305-2753. Tel: 641-856-2143, Ext 237. Toll Free Tel: 800-670-3641, Ext 237. FAX: 515-856-5527. Web Site: www.ihcc.cc.ia.us/. *Dean of Libr*, Darlas Shockley; *Publ Servs*, Debra Sloan; E-Mail: dsloan@ihcc.cc.ia.us
Library Holdings: Bk Vols 24,000; Per Subs 98
Branch campus of Indian Hill Community College, Ottumwa, Iowa; Main facilities in Ottumwa

CENTRAL CITY

P JOHN C CLEGG PUBLIC LIBRARY,* 137 Fourth St N, 52214. SAN 305-2761. Tel: 319-438-6685. FAX: 319-438-6685. *Dir*, Denise Levenhagen
Founded 1895. Pop 1,063; Circ 6,793
1998-1999 Mats Exp $6,930, Books $6,000, Per/Ser (Incl. Access Fees) $930
Library Holdings: Bk Titles 10,000; Per Subs 34
Mem of E Cent Libr Syst
Open Mon 1-5, Tues 9-5, Wed 1-5, Thurs 1-7, Fri 12-4:30
Friends of the Library Group

CHARITON

P CHARITON FREE PUBLIC LIBRARY,* 803 Braden Ave, 50049. SAN 305-277X. Tel: 515-774-5514. FAX: 515-774-8695. E-Mail: library@lucasco.net. *Librn*, Roberta Reynolds; *Ch Servs*, Kristin Tyree
Founded 1898. Pop 5,163; Circ 40,517
Library Holdings: Bk Titles 35,000; Per Subs 135
Special Collections: Iowa Census Coll; Lucas County, Federal Census, micro; Newspapers (Chariton Coll)
Mem of Southwest Iowa Regional Library System
Open Mon-Thurs 12-8, Fri 10-6, Sat 10-4
Friends of the Library Group

CHARLES CITY

P CHARLES CITY PUBLIC LIBRARY, 106 Milwaukee Mall, 50616-2281. SAN 305-2788. Tel: 515-257-6319. FAX: 515-257-6325. *Librn*, Virginia Ruzicka; E-Mail: vruzicka@server.silo.lib.ia.us; *Ch Servs*, Marilyn Buttjer; Staff 2 (MLS 2)
Founded 1904. Pop 8,000; Circ 125,000
Library Holdings: Bk Titles 52,000; Per Subs 156
Subject Interests: Art, Genealogy
Special Collections: Iowa History; Media: videos (822), audios (666); Mooney Art Coll
Mem of North Central Regional Library System
Open Winter Mon-Thurs 10-9, Fri, Sat, Sun 1-4:45, Summer, Mon-Thurs 10-7, Fri, Sat 1-4:45
Friends of the Library Group

S FLOYD COUNTY HISTORICAL SOCIETY MUSEUM LIBRARY,* 500 Gilbert St, 50616-2738. SAN 373-4536. Tel: 515-228-1099. FAX: 515-228-1157. *Dir*, Frank McKennaly; *Coll Develop*, Mary Ann Townsend
Library Holdings: Bk Vols 1,000
Subject Interests: Genealogy
Special Collections: Oliver Hart Parr Coll
Publications: Floyd County Heritage Newsletter

CHARTER OAK

P CHARTER OAK PUBLIC LIBRARY,* 461 Railroad, 51439. SAN 320-8249. Tel: 712-678-3425. *Librn*, Carol Rosburg
Library Holdings: Bk Vols 5,000
Mem of Northwest Regional Library System
Friends of the Library Group

CHELSEA

P CHELSEA PUBLIC LIBRARY, 600 Station St, PO Box 187, 52215. SAN 305-280X. Tel: 515-489-2525. FAX: 515-489-2525. *Librn*, Beverly Kasal; E-Mail: bevkasal@pcpartner.net
Founded 1974. Circ 4,767
Library Holdings: Bk Vols 7,500; Per Subs 21
Open Mon-11:30-4:30, Tues & Wed 1:30-5:30, Thurs 2-7, Sat 9-12

CHEROKEE

M CHEROKEE MENTAL HEALTH INSTITUTE, Health Science Library,* 1251 W Cedar Loop, 51012. SAN 375-2747. Tel: 712-225-2594, Ext 2239. FAX: 712-225-6969. *Librn*, Laurel Armstrong; Staff 1 (Non-MLS 1)
Library Holdings: Bk Vols 750; Per Subs 35

P CHEROKEE PUBLIC LIBRARY,* 215 S Second St, 51012. SAN 305-2818. Tel: 712-225-3498. FAX: 712-225-4964. E-Mail: cherlib@ncn.net. *Librn*, Mary Jo Ruppert
Founded 1886. Pop 6,000; Circ 69,021
Jul 1998-Jun 1999 Income $135,000
Library Holdings: Bk Vols 23,625; Per Subs 86
Special Collections: Media: videos (200), audios (1100)
Mem of Northwest Regional Library System
Open Mon, Wed & Thurs 10-8, Tues & Fri 10-5, Sat 10-3
Friends of the Library Group

S SANFORD MUSEUM & PLANETARIUM, Reference Library,* 117 E Willow, 51012. SAN 305-2826. Tel: 712-225-3922. E-Mail: sanford@cherokee.k12.ia.us. *Dir*, Linda Burkhart
Founded 1951
Library Holdings: Bk Vols 5,000
Subject Interests: Anthropology, Archaeology, Astronomy, History, Museology, Paleontology

CHURDAN

P CHURDAN CITY LIBRARY, Sand St, PO Box 185, 50050. SAN 305-2834. Tel: 515-389-3423. FAX: 515-389-3401. E-Mail: smm@netins.net. *Librn*, Shirley Hamilton
Pop 435; Circ 25,016
Library Holdings: Bk Vols 9,806; Bk Titles 7,699; Per Subs 26
Mem of Central Iowa Regional Library
Friends of the Library Group

CLARE

P CLARE PUBLIC LIBRARY,* E Front St, PO Box 5, 50524. SAN 376-5164. Tel: 515-546-6222. FAX: 515-546-6222. E-Mail: clarepl@net.net. *Librn*, Kathy Allen
Library Holdings: Bk Vols 6,500; Per Subs 20
Special Collections: Media: videos (557)
Mem of North Central Regional Library System
Open MOn 5-8, Wed & Fri 1:30-5:30, Sat 9-1

CLARENCE

P EDNA ZYBELL MEMORIAL LIBRARY,* 309 Sixth Ave, 52216. SAN 305-2842. Tel: 319-452-3734. FAX: 319-452-3734. *Librn*, Deb Minar
Pop 1,001; Circ 7,590
Library Holdings: Bk Vols 8,843
Open Tues & Thurs 1-5, Wed 1-5 & 7-9, Fri 1-6, Sat 9-12

CLARINDA

P CLARINDA PUBLIC LIBRARY,* 300 N 16th St, 51632. SAN 305-2850. Tel: 712-542-2416. FAX: 712-542-3590. E-Mail: clarlib@clarinda.heartland.net. *Dir*, Gretchen Sump
Pop 5,104; Circ 58,886
Library Holdings: Bk Titles 43,158; Per Subs 96
Special Collections: Media: videos (321)
Mem of Southwest Iowa Regional Library System
Open Mon 10-8, Tues-Fri 10-6, Sat 10-4

CLARINDA TREATMENT COMPLEX

M CORRECTIONAL FACILITY LIBRARY, PO Box 338, 51632. SAN 329-3513. Tel: 712-542-5634, Ext 5527. FAX: 712-542-4844. *In Charge*, Richard Reilly
Library Holdings: Bk Vols 5,500; Per Subs 40
Partic in Midwest Health Sci Libr Network

M PROFESSIONAL LIBRARY, PO Box 338, 51632. SAN 341-7964. Tel: 712-542-2161, Ext 3304. FAX: 712-542-4844. *In Charge*, Jim Dunn
Library Holdings: Bk Vols 3,600
Subject Interests: Counseling, Medicine, Nursing, Psychiatry, Psychology
Partic in Midwest Health Sci Libr Network

S RESIDENT'S LIBRARY, PO Box 338, 51632. SAN 341-7999. Tel: 712-542-2161, Ext 3304. FAX: 712-542-4844. *In Charge*, Jim Dunn
Founded 1941
Library Holdings: Bk Titles 11,000; Per Subs 15
Special Collections: National Geographic 1915 to date
Mem of Southwest Iowa Regional Library System

J IOWA WESTERN COMMUNITY COLLEGE-CLARINDA CAMPUS, Edith Lisle Library, 923 E Washington, 51632. SAN 305-2869. Tel: 712-542-5117, Ext 234. FAX: 712-542-3604. Web Site: www.iwcc.cc.ia.us. *Coordr*, Shelly Anderson; E-Mail: sanderson@iwcc.cc.ia.us; Staff 1 (MLS 1)
Founded 1963. Enrl 427
1998-1999 Income $12,300. Mats Exp $10,730, Books $8,000, Per/Ser (Incl. Access Fees) $2,730
Library Holdings: Bk Titles 25,000; Per Subs 64
Automation Activity & Vendor Info: (Cataloging) epixtech, inc.; (Circulation) epixtech, inc.; (Serials) epixtech, inc.

CLARION

P CLARION PUBLIC LIBRARY,* 302 N Main St, 50525. SAN 305-2877. Tel: 515-532-3673. FAX: 515-532-6322. *Dir, Librn*, Nola Waddingham; *Ch Servs*, Joyce Eriksen
Pop 3,500; Circ 23,000
Library Holdings: Bk Titles 17,000; Per Subs 32
Mem of North Central Regional Library System
Open Mon-Wed 12-8, Thurs-Sat 10-5

CLARKSVILLE

P CLARKSVILLE PUBLIC LIBRARY,* 103 W Greene St, 50619-0039. SAN 305-2885. Tel: 319-278-1168. FAX: 319-278-1168. E-Mail: lcld@netins.net. *Librn*, Lola Clark; *Asst Librn*, Rebecca Forry
Founded 1929. Pop 5,400; Circ 23,810
Library Holdings: Bk Vols 17,119; Bk Titles 12,000; Per Subs 90
Special Collections: Media: Videos- 500; Audios- 45
Mem of Northeastern Regional Libr Syst
Open Tues & Thurs 10-5, Wed 10-8, Fri & Sat 10-4

CLEAR LAKE

P CLEAR LAKE PUBLIC LIBRARY,* 200 N Fourth St, 50428. SAN 305-2893. Tel: 515-357-6133, 515-357-6134. FAX: 515-357-4645. E-Mail: clplib@netins.net. *Librn*, Jean Casey
Founded 1889. Circ 130,762
Jul 1998-Jun 1999 Income $221,777. Mats Exp $42,384. Sal $116,838 (Prof $46,138)
Library Holdings: Bk Vols 49,718; Per Subs 169
Special Collections: Media: videos (1060), audios (1176)
Mem of North Central Regional Library System
Open Mon-Thurs 10-8, Fri, Sat 10-5
Friends of the Library Group

CLEARFIELD

P CLEARFIELD PUBLIC LIBRARY, 302 Broadway, PO Box 51, 50840. SAN 305-2907. Tel: 515-336-2944. *Librn*, Virginia Siverly; Tel: 641-336-2832
Founded 1916. Pop 433; Circ 2,168
Library Holdings: Bk Vols 4,611
Mem of Southwest Iowa Regional Library System
Special Services for the Blind - Books available with recordings; Large print bks
Open Wed & Fri 12-5
Bookmobiles: 1

CLEGHORN

P MC COMMUNITY LIBRARY, 200 W Grace St, PO Box 124, 51014-0124. SAN 305-2915. Tel: 712-436-2521. FAX: 712-436-2695. E-Mail: mclib@marcus-mer-cleg.k12.ia.us. *Librn*, Lois Alquist
Pop 250; Circ 6,000
Library Holdings: Bk Vols 15,151; Bk Titles 13,618; Per Subs 25
Mem of Northwest Regional Library System
Open Mon 8:15-5:30 & 7-9, Tues-Fri 8:15-5:30, Sat 9-11

CLERMONT

P CLERMONT PUBLIC LIBRARY,* 503 Larrabee St, PO Box 49, 52135. SAN 305-2923. Tel: 319-423-7286. FAX: 319-423-7286. E-Mail: clmtlib@means.net. *Dir, Librn*, Helena Zweibohmer
Pop 539; Circ 10,230
Library Holdings: Bk Titles 6,231; Per Subs 36
Special Collections: Media: Video (183), Audio (237)
Mem of Northeastern Regional Libr Syst
Open Mon & Wed 1-6, Fri 9:30-11:30 & 1-5, Sat 9-1

CLINTON

S BICKELHAUPT ARBORETUM LIBRARY, 340 S 14th St, 52732-5432. SAN 324-7813. Tel: 319-242-4771. FAX: 319-242-5128. E-Mail: bickarb@clinton.net. Web Site: www.bickarb.com. *Commun Relations*, Francie Hill; Staff 3 (MLS 3)
Founded 1970
2000-2001 Mats Exp $400, Books $250, Per/Ser (Incl. Access Fees) $150
Library Holdings: Bk Vols 845; Bk Titles 800; Per Subs 10
Subject Interests: Horticulture

J CLINTON COMMUNITY COLLEGE LIBRARY, 1000 Lincoln Blvd, 52732. SAN 305-2931. Tel: 319-244-7046. FAX: 319-244-7107. Web Site: www.eiccd.cc.ia.us/library/ccc.html. *Librn*, Cindy Hoogheem; Tel: 319-244-7106, E-Mail: choogheem@eiccd.cc.ia.us
Founded 1966. Enrl 1,100
Jul 2000-Jun 2001 Mats Exp $23,958, Books $11,398, Per/Ser (Incl. Access Fees) $12,560. Sal $78,092 (Prof $42,500)
Library Holdings: Bk Vols 18,000; Per Subs 140
Automation Activity & Vendor Info: (Circulation) GEAC; (OPAC) GEAC
Partic in Regional Med Libr - Region 3; River Bend Library System

P CLINTON PUBLIC LIBRARY, 306 Eighth Ave S, 52732. SAN 341-8022. Tel: 319-242-8441. TDD: 319-243-8879. FAX: 319-242-8162. E-Mail: library@sanasys.com. Web Site: www.sanasys.com/~patron/. *Dir*, Dan Horwath; E-Mail: danh@cis.net; *Ch Servs*, Kay Spittler; *Ref*, Kim Limond; *Purchasing*, Sherrianna McKenrick; *ILL*, Marilyn Pelisek; *Reader Servs*,

Beth Mosher; Staff 28 (MLS 3, Non-MLS 25)
Founded 1904. Pop 29,202; Circ 167,001
Jul 1999-Jun 2000 Income (Main Library and Branch Library) $851,532, State $10,963, City $798,400, County $12,392, Locally Generated Income $20,587, Other $9,190. Mats Exp $158,947, Books $95,291, Per/Ser (Incl. Access Fees) $18,095, Micro $939, Electronic Ref Mat (Incl. Access Fees) $2,210. Sal $407,811 (Prof $91,760)
Library Holdings: Bk Vols 94,044; Per Subs 313
Subject Interests: Genealogy
Special Collections: Clinton & Lyons Newspapers on Microfilm 1854 to date; Clinton Authors
Automation Activity & Vendor Info: (Cataloging) epixtech, inc.; (Circulation) epixtech, inc.
Database Vendor: epixtech, inc., ProQuest
Function: ILL available
Friends of the Library Group
Branches: 1
LYONS, 105 Main Ave, 52732. SAN 341-8057. Tel: 319-242-5355. FAX: 319-243-6553. *Dir*, Dan Horwath; Tel: 319-242-8441, Fax: 319-242-8162, E-Mail: danh@clinton.net; *Circ*, Mary Bertrand; Staff 5 (Non-MLS 5)
Jul 1999-Jun 2000 Mats Exp $11,500, Books $10,000, Per/Ser (Incl. Access Fees) $1,500. Sal $25,187
Library Holdings: Bk Vols 14,740; Per Subs 51
Automation Activity & Vendor Info: (Circulation) epixtech, inc.
Database Vendor: epixtech, inc., ProQuest
Function: ILL available
Friends of the Library Group

C MOUNT SAINT CLARE COLLEGE LIBRARY, 400 N Bluff Blvd, 52732. SAN 305-294X. Tel: 319-242-4023, Ext 3211. FAX: 319-242-2003. Web Site: www.clare.edu. *Dir*, Flora S Lowe; Tel: 319-242-4023, Ext 3210, E-Mail: flolow@clare.edu; Staff 2 (MLS 1, Non-MLS 1)
Founded 1918. Highest Degree: Bachelor
Library Holdings: Bk Vols 89,723; Per Subs 701
Special Collections: St Francis, St Clare & the Medieval Woman Autograph Coll
Automation Activity & Vendor Info: (Cataloging) GEAC; (Circulation) GEAC; (OPAC) GEAC
Database Vendor: Ebsco - EbscoHost, Lexis-Nexis, OCLC - First Search, ProQuest
Partic in Quad-Link Libr Consortium

M SAMARITAN HEALTH SYSTEM, INC LIBRARY,* 1410 N Fourth St, 52732. SAN 377-5445. Tel: 319-244-5555. FAX: 319-244-5592. *In Charge*, Donna Herkelman
Library Holdings: Bk Vols 300; Per Subs 80

CLIVE

P CENTRAL IOWA REGIONAL LIBRARY, 8345 University Blvd, Ste E-1, 50325-1168. SAN 305-3393. Tel: 515-223-7709. FAX: 515-223-7710. Web Site: www.cirls.lib.ia.us.; Staff 5 (MLS 3, Non-MLS 2)
Founded 1973. Pop 617,966
Jul 1999-Jun 2000 Income $325,951, State $312,151, Federal $8,468, Locally Generated Income $5,332. Mats Exp $723, Books $232, Per/Ser (Incl. Access Fees) $491. Sal $190,780 (Prof $141,257)
Subject Interests: Library and information science
Publications: Newsletter
Member Libraries: Adel Public Library; Altoona Public Library; Baxter Public Library; Bussey Public Library; Carlisle Public Library; Churdan City Library; Colfax Public Library; Collins Public Library; Colo Public Library; De Soto Public Library; Dexter Public Library; Earlham Public Library; Ericson Public Library; Grand Junction Public Library; Granger Public Library; Grimes Public Library; Gutekunst Public Library; Huxley Public Library; Indianola Public Library; Iowa Department Of Human Services Library; Jefferson Public Library; Johnston Public Library; Kirkendall Public Library; Knoxville Public Library; Lacona Public Library; Laurel Community Library; Leonard A Good Community Library; Linden Public Library; Lynnville Public Library; Madrid Public Library; Maxwell Public Library; Melbourne Public Library; Milo Public Library; Minburn Public Library; Mingo Public Library; Mitchellville Public Library; Monroe Public Library; Nevada Public Library; New Virginia Public Library; Norwalk Easter Public Library; Paton Public Library; Pella Public Library; Pioneer Heritage Library; Pleasant Hill Public Library; Polk City Community Library; Prairie City Public Library; Redfield Public Library; Rippey Public Library; Roland Public Library; Scranton Public Library; Slater Public Library; The Bertha Bartlett Public Library; Truro Public Library; Urbandale Public Library; Van Meter Public Library; Waukee Public Library; Webb Shadle Memorial Library; West Des Moines Public Library; Winterset Public Library; Woodward Public Library
Partic in OCLC Online Computer Library Center, Inc; State Of Iowa Libraries Online Interlibrary Loan

CLUTIER

P CLUTIER PUBLIC LIBRARY,* 404 Main St, PO Box 182, 52217-0182. SAN 376-7450. Tel: 319-479-2171. FAX: 319-479-2171. *Librn*, Michelle Patizek
Library Holdings: Bk Vols 5,000; Per Subs 18
Special Collections: Media: Video (238), Audio (31)
Mem of East Central Regional Library
Open Mon & Wed 9:15-12 & 2-6, Tues & Thurs 2-6, Sat 9:15-12
Friends of the Library Group

COGGON

P COGGON PUBLIC LIBRARY, 216 E Main St, 52218-0182. SAN 376-5407. Tel: 319-435-2542. FAX: 319-435-2542. E-Mail: coggon@server.silo.lib.ia.us. *Librn*, Diane Knott
Library Holdings: Bk Vols 10,000; Per Subs 15
Mem of East Central Regional Library
Friends of the Library Group

COIN

P COIN PUBLIC LIBRARY, 115 Main St, 51636. SAN 376-5202. Tel: 712-583-3684. *Librn*, Irma Sallee
Jul 1999-Jun 2000 Income $1,215, City $250, County $350, Other $615. Mats Exp Books $100
Library Holdings: Bk Vols 14,000
Mem of Southwest Iowa Regional Library System

COLESBURG

P COLESBURG PUBLIC LIBRARY, 220 Main St, PO Box 159, 52035-0159. SAN 376-5237. Tel: 319-856-5800. FAX: 319-856-5800. E-Mail: colepl@mwci.net. *Librn*, Jill Pasker
Founded 1983. Pop 430; Circ 5,150
Jul 1999-Jun 2000 Income $14,023, State $387, City $7,500, County $3,636, Locally Generated Income $2,500. Mats Exp $3,580. Sal $6,266
Library Holdings: Bk Vols 12,192; Bk Titles 12,192; Per Subs 26
Mem of Northeastern Iowa Regional Library System
Friends of the Library Group

COLFAX

P COLFAX PUBLIC LIBRARY,* 25 W Division St, 50054. SAN 305-2966. Tel: 515-674-3625. *Librn*, Kathy Lecnar
Pop 2,300; Circ 9,000
Library Holdings: Bk Vols 7,110; Per Subs 32
Special Collections: Media: Video (100), Audio (30)
Mem of Central Iowa Regional Library
Open Mon 2-8, Tues-Fri 2-6, Sat 9-12

COLLINS

P COLLINS PUBLIC LIBRARY,* 214 Main St, 50055. SAN 305-2974. Tel: 515-385-2464. FAX: 515-385-2205. E-Mail: collinsl@midiowa.net. *Dir*, Patricia Trowbridge
Founded 1936. Pop 451; Circ 4,393
Library Holdings: Bk Vols 6,580; Per Subs 15
Special Collections: Media: Video (600), Audio (50)
Mem of Central Iowa Regional Library
Open Tues, Wed & Fri 3-6, Thurs 6-9, Sat 9-12
Friends of the Library Group

COLO

P COLO PUBLIC LIBRARY,* 309 Main St, PO Box 324, 50056-0324. SAN 305-2982. Tel: 515-377-2900. FAX: 515-377-2900. E-Mail: colopl56@netins.net. *Asst Dean*, Wanda Carlson; *Librn*, Joanie Jamison; *Librn*, Jennifer Gogarty
Pop 808; Circ 21,786
Library Holdings: Bk Vols 15,000; Per Subs 40
Special Collections: Videos (1100)
Mem of Central Iowa Regional Library
Open Mon, Wed, Thurs & Fri 11-6, Sat 8-6

COLUMBUS JUNCTION

P COLUMBUS JUNCTION PUBLIC LIBRARY,* 122 E Maple St, PO Box 109, 52738-0109. SAN 305-2990. Tel: 319-728-7972. FAX: 319-728-2303. E-Mail: coljctpl@lisco.net. *Dir, Librn*, Ardith W Ostrem; *Asst Librn*, Barbara Stewart; *Asst Librn*, Beth Martin; *Asst Librn*, Helen Aringdale
Founded 1948. Pop 1,616; Circ 16,579

Jul 1999-Jun 2000 Mats Exp $36,000
Library Holdings: Bk Titles 13,000; Per Subs 45
Special Collections: Audio tapes; Large prints; videos
Mem of Southeastern Library Services
Friends of the Library Group

CONRAD

P CONRAD PUBLIC LIBRARY,* 102 E Grundy Ave, PO Box 189, 50621-0189. SAN 305-3008. Tel: 515-366-2583. FAX: 515-366-3105. E-Mail: conradlib@mtnia.com. *Dir*, Susan Blythe
Founded 1936. Pop 1,133
Jul 1998-Jun 1999 Income $76,446, State $4,600, City $49,254, County $15,359, Locally Generated Income $1,560, Other $5,673. Mats Exp $27,920, Books $15,217, Per/Ser (Incl. Access Fees) $2,201, AV Equip $5,352, Electronic Ref Mat (Incl. Access Fees) $2,038. Sal $28,937
Library Holdings: Bk Vols 17,885; Per Subs 132
Subject Interests: Genealogy
Automation Activity & Vendor Info: (Cataloging) Follett; (Circulation) Follett
Mem of Northeastern Iowa Regional Library System
Open Mon, Tues & Thurs 2-8, Wed 9-8, Fri 2-6, Sat 9-12

COON RAPIDS

P COON RAPIDS PUBLIC LIBRARY,* 123 Third Ave, 50058. SAN 305-3016. Tel: 712-684-5410. FAX: 712-684-5410. E-Mail: crlib@pionet.net. *Librn*, Cynthia K Golay
Pop 1,448; Circ 29,796
Library Holdings: Bk Vols 18,986; Bk Titles 18,014; Per Subs 65
Special Collections: Media: Video (472), Audio (756)
Mem of Northwest Regional Library System
Open Mon & Wed 11-8, Tues, Thurs & Fri 11-5:30, Sat 10-4

CORALVILLE

P CORALVILLE PUBLIC LIBRARY, 1401 Fifth St, 52241. SAN 305-3024. Tel: 319-351-2163. TDD: 319-351-1265. FAX: 319-351-1837. E-Mail: corallib@coralville.lib.ia.us. Web Site: www.coralvillepubliclibrary.org. *Dir*, Alison Ames Galstad; E-Mail: agalstad@coralville.lib.ia.us; *Asst Dir*, Ellen L Hample; E-Mail: ehampe@coralville.lib.ia.us; *Ad Servs*, Georgia L Heald; E-Mail: gheald@coralville.lib.ia.us; *Ch Servs*, Linda Parker; E-Mail: lparker@coralville.lib.ia.us; Staff 10 (MLS 4, Non-MLS 6)
Founded 1965. Pop 12,700; Circ 216,660
Jul 1999-Jun 2000 Income $572,136, State $26,958, City $469,333, County $47,655, Locally Generated Income $14,285, Other $13,905. Mats Exp $91,398, Books $63,904, Per/Ser (Incl. Access Fees) $6,943, Other Print Mats $2,727, Electronic Ref Mat (Incl. Access Fees) $17,824. Sal $367,100
Library Holdings: Bk Titles 66,726; Per Subs 169
Automation Activity & Vendor Info: (Cataloging) epixtech, inc.; (Circulation) epixtech, inc.
Database Vendor: epixtech, inc., OCLC - First Search
Special Services for the Deaf - TDD
Friends of the Library Group

CORNING

P CORNING PUBLIC LIBRARY,* 603 Ninth St, 50841-1304. SAN 305-3032. Tel: 515-322-3866. FAX: 515-322-3491. E-Mail: cornpl@mddc.com. *Librn*, Becky Rike; *Ch Servs*, Connie George; *Ad Servs*, Marsha Davis
Founded 1916. Pop 5,400; Circ 44,618
Jul 1998-Jun 1999 Income $80,974. Mats Exp $80,974. Sal $45,101
Library Holdings: Bk Vols 26,494; Per Subs 98
Special Collections: American Indian Literature; Media: Video (600), Audio (500)
Mem of Southwest Iowa Regional Library System
Partic in Am Libr Asn; Iowa Libr Asn
Open Mon, Tues, Thurs & Fri 9:30-5:30, Wed 9:30-8 & Sat 9:30-1

CORRECTIONVILLE

P CORRECTIONVILLE PUBLIC LIBRARY,* 532 Driftwood, 51016. SAN 305-3040. Tel: 712-372-4203. *Librn*, Heather Langschwager
Founded 1899. Circ 8,047
Library Holdings: Bk Vols 11,000
Mem of Northwest Regional Library System
Open Mon 1-5, Wed 4-8, Sat 9-2

CORWITH

P CORWITH PUBLIC LIBRARY,* 102 Elm St NW, PO Box 305, 50430-0305. SAN 305-3059. Tel: 515-583-2536. FAX: 515-583-2536. E-Mail: clibrary@trvnet.net. *Librn*, Phyllis Oxley; *Asst Librn*, Sylvia Poage
Pop 500; Circ 9,072
Library Holdings: Bk Vols 7,784; Per Subs 17
Mem of North Central Regional Library System
Partic in N Iowa Libr Exten
Special Services for the Blind - Large print bks
Open Mon & Fri 1-6, Wed 1-8, Thurs 6-8, Sat 9-12

CORYDON

P KARL MILES LECOMPTE MEMORIAL LIBRARY, 110 S Franklin, 50060-1518. SAN 305-3067. Tel: 641-872-1621. E-Mail: lecompte@grm.net. Web Site: www.swirls.lib.ia.us/libspages/Corydon/libhome.htm. *Librn*, Dianne Mitchell
Pop 1,818; Circ 30,192
Library Holdings: Bk Titles 16,000; Per Subs 30
Mem of Southwest Iowa Regional Library System
Open Mon-Wed & Fri 12:30-5, Thurs 12:30-5:30, Sat 10-2

S WAYNE COUNTY HISTORICAL SOCIETY, Prairie Trails Museum of Wayne County Iowa Library, Hwy 2, E Jefferson St, 50060. SAN 375-1783. Tel: 641-872-2211 (Museum), 641-872-2483. *In Charge*, Wilma West; Staff 8 (Non-MLS 8)
Founded 1975
Library Holdings: Bk Vols 150
Subject Interests: Obituary info
Special Collections: County Census Records 1850-1920; Doctor's Records; Early Wills & Birth Certificates; Obituaries; Old Newspapers & Newspaper Clippings
Open Apr 15-Oct 15

COULTER

P COULTER PUBLIC LIBRARY,* 111 Main St, PO Box 87, 50431-0087. SAN 305-3075. Tel: 515-866-6798. FAX: 515-866-6798. E-Mail: coullib@frontiernet.net. *Librn*, Barb Gardner
Founded 1971. Pop 264; Circ 4,391
Library Holdings: Bk Titles 7,081; Per Subs 12
Mem of North Central Regional Library System
Open Tues, Wed & Thurs 2-6, Fri 1-6, Sat 9-12

COUNCIL BLUFFS

P COUNCIL BLUFFS PUBLIC LIBRARY, (CBPL), 400 Willow Ave, 51503-4269. SAN 305-3091. Tel: 712-323-7553. Interlibrary Loan Service Tel: 712-327-7553, Ext 17. Circulation Tel: 712-323-7553, Ext 10. Reference Tel: 712-323-7553, Ext 32. TDD: 712-322-6338. FAX: 712-323-1269. Web Site: www.swirls.lib.ia.us/libspages/cbpl/home.htm. *Dir*, James Godsey; Tel: 712-323-7553, Ext 23, E-Mail: jgodsey@server.silo.lib.ia.us; *YA Servs*, Dianne Herzog; Tel: 712-323-7553, Ext 13; *Ad Servs*, Arlene Wright; Tel: 712-323-7553, Ext 18; *Ref*, Pam Collins; Tel: 712-323-7553, Ext 35; *Automation Syst Coordr*, Tom Ryan; Tel: 712-323-7553, Ext 11; *Tech Servs*, David Archer; Tel: 712-323-7553, Ext 27; Staff 8 (MLS 7, Non-MLS 1)
Founded 1866. Pop 78,290; Circ 391,735
Jul 1999-Jun 2000 Income $1,674,449, State $18,875, City $1,110,000, County $44,200, Locally Generated Income $56,500. Mats Exp $90,000, Books $30,000, Per/Ser (Incl. Access Fees) $25,000, Electronic Ref Mat (Incl. Access Fees) $15,000. Sal $686,138
Library Holdings: Bk Vols 133,827; Per Subs 346
Special Collections: Lewis Carroll Coll; Railroads (Grenville Mellen Dodge Coll); Woman Suffrage (Amelia Bloomer Coll)
Automation Activity & Vendor Info: (Acquisitions) Innovative Interfaces Inc.; (Cataloging) Innovative Interfaces Inc.; (Circulation) Innovative Interfaces Inc.; (ILL) Innovative Interfaces Inc.; (OPAC) Innovative Interfaces Inc.; (Serials) Innovative Interfaces Inc.
Database Vendor: OCLC - First Search
Publications: Friends FLYLEAF (Newsletter)
Mem of Southwest Iowa Regional Library System
Special Services for the Deaf - TTY machine
Special Services for the Blind - Printed text enlargers
Friends of the Library Group

S IOWA SCHOOL FOR THE DEAF LIBRARY,* 1600 S Hwy 275, 51503. SAN 320-6734. Tel: 712-366-0571, Ext 237. FAX: 712-366-3297. *Librn*, Lori Siefering; E-Mail: lsiefering@iadeaf.k12.ia.us
Library Holdings: Bk Vols 27,500; Per Subs 40
Subject Interests: Deaf
Special Collections: Books & Materials on Deafness Coll; Teacher Reference Coll

J IOWA WESTERN COMMUNITY COLLEGE, Learning Resource Center, 2700 College Rd, 51503. SAN 341-8081. Tel: 712-325-3247. FAX: 712-325-3244. Web Site: www.iwcc.cc.ia.us/library/. *Dir*, Pam Collins; E-Mail: pcollins@iwcc.cc.ia.us; *Librn*, Kyle Winward; Staff 4 (MLS 2, Non-MLS 2)
Founded 1966. Enrl 3,000; Fac 150
Library Holdings: Bk Titles 56,237
Subject Interests: Deaf, Nursing, Technology, Vocational education
Mem of Southwest Iowa Regional Library System

M JENNIE EDMUNDSON HOSPITAL LIBRARY, 933 E Pierce St, 51503. SAN 305-3083. Tel: 712-328-6130. FAX: 712-328-6203. *Librn*, Christine A Armstrong; Tel: 712-328-4499, E-Mail: ckirby@nmhs.org; *ILL*, Linda Black; E-Mail: lblack@nmhs.org; Staff 3 (MLS 1, Non-MLS 2)
Founded 1959
Jan 2000-Dec 2000 Income Parent Institution $45,796. Mats Exp $31,838, Books $7,200, Per/Ser (Incl. Access Fees) $24,638. Sal $59,791 (Prof $30,000)
Library Holdings: Bk Titles 2,000; Per Subs 124
Database Vendor: OCLC - First Search, OVID Technologies
Publications: Annual Report
Partic in Health Sci Libr Network; ICON

S SMITH PETERSON LAW LIBRARY, (Formerly Smith & Peterson Law Library), 35 Main Pl, Ste 300, PO Box 249, 51502. SAN 326-050X. Tel: 712-328-1833. FAX: 712-328-8320. E-Mail: email@smithpeterson.com. *Librn*, Beverly Hobbs
Jan 2000-Dec 2000 Income $60,000. Mats Exp $30,000. Sal $10,000
Library Holdings: Bk Titles 7,392

P SOUTHWEST IOWA REGIONAL LIBRARY SYSTEM,* 310 W Kanesville, M-4, 51503. SAN 305-5760. Tel: 712-328-9218. FAX: 712-328-9218. E-Mail: swirls@mail.swirls.lib.ia.us. Web Site: www.swirls.lib.ia.us.; Staff 1 (MLS 1)
Founded 1973. Pop 291,129
Jul 1998-Jun 1999 Income $194,763, State $185,000, Federal $4,642, Other $5,121. Mats Exp $16,191, Books $7,691. Sal $79,909
Library Holdings: Bk Titles 200; Per Subs 10
Special Collections: Bifolkal Kits; Professional
Publications: Directory of SW Region's Libraries; Southwest Iowa Regional Newsline (bi-monthly)
Member Libraries: Adair Public Library; Atlantic Public Library; Audubon Public Library; Bagley Public Library; Bayard Public Library; Bedford Public Library; Chariton Free Public Library; Clarinda Public Library; Clarinda Treatment Complex; Clearfield Public Library; Coin Public Library; Corning Public Library; Council Bluffs Public Library; Cumberland Public Library; Duncan Memorial Library; Dunlap Public Library; Eckels Memorial Library; Elliott Public Library; Essex Public Library; Fontanelle Public Library; Garden Grove Public Library; Glenwood Public Library; Greenfield Public Library; Griswold Public Library; Hamburg Public Library; Harlan Community Library; Humeston Public Library; Iowa Western Community College; Jamaica Public Library; Karl Miles Lecompte Memorial Library; Kimballton Public Library; Lamoni Public Library; Lenox Public Library; Leon Public Library; Lewis Public Library; Logan Public Library; Malvern Public Library; Mary Barnett Memorial Library; Massena Public Library; Matilda J Gibson Memorial Library; Menlo Public Library; Missouri Valley Public Library; Modale Public Library; Mondamin Public Library; Murray Public Library; New Market Public Library; Osceola Public Library; Panora Public Library; Prescott Public Library; Randolph Public Library; Red Oak Public Library; Seymour Community Library; Shenandoah Public Library; Sidney Public Library; Stanton Community Library; Stuart Public Library; Tabor Public Library; Villisca Public Library; Walnut Public Library; Woodbine Public Library
Partic in Iowa Computer Assisted Network

CRESCO

P CRESCO PUBLIC LIBRARY,* 320 N Elm St, 52136-1452. SAN 305-3105. Tel: 319-547-2540. FAX: 319-547-1769. E-Mail: creslib@powerbank.net, crestub@sbtek.net. Web Site: www.crescoia.com/library/. *Dir*, Paula Cummins
Founded 1905. Pop 5,000; Circ 121,238
Jul 1998-Jun 1999 Mats Exp $30,825. Sal $93,744
Library Holdings: Bk Titles 37,288; Per Subs 106
Special Collections: Media: Video (1500), Audio (1000)
Mem of Northeastern Regional Libr Syst
Open Mon-Thur 9-8, Fri & Sat 9-5
Friends of the Library Group

CRESTON

P MATILDA J GIBSON MEMORIAL LIBRARY, 200 W Howard, 50801-2339. SAN 305-3113. Tel: 641-782-2277. FAX: 641-782-4604. E-Mail: clibrary@aea14.k12.ia.us. Web Site: www.swirls.lib.ia.us/libspages/creston/home.htm. *Dir*, Diana Dillinger; *Asst Dir*, Charlene Hudson; *Ch Servs*, Sue Teutsch; Staff 6 (MLS 1, Non-MLS 5)
Founded 1932
Library Holdings: Bk Titles 27,800; Per Subs 100
Subject Interests: Genealogy
Automation Activity & Vendor Info: (Cataloging) Follett; (Circulation) Follett; (OPAC) Follett
Mem of Southwest Iowa Regional Library System
Open Mon-Wed 10-8, Thurs & Fri 10-6, Sat 10-2
Friends of the Library Group

J SOUTHWESTERN COMMUNITY COLLEGE, Learning Resource Center,* 1501 W Townline, 50801. SAN 305-3121. Tel: 515-782-1462. FAX: 515-782-1301. Web Site: www.swcc.cc.ia.us/lrc/lrc.htm. *Dir Libr Serv*, Ann Coulter; Tel: 515-782-1340, E-Mail: coulter@swcc.cc.ia.us; Staff 4 (MLS 1, Non-MLS 3)
Founded 1965. Enrl 1,200
Library Holdings: Bk Vols 15,194; Bk Titles 14,320; Per Subs 170
Automation Activity & Vendor Info: (Circulation) Gaylord; (OPAC) Gaylord
Database Vendor: OCLC - First Search

CRYSTAL LAKE

P JUANITA EARP MEDIA CENTER LIBRARY,* E Fifth & Summit, Box 130, 50432-0130. SAN 377-547X. Tel: 515-565-3211. FAX: 515-565-3320. E-Mail: jemcenter@netins.net. Web Site: www.netins.net/showcase/cryslake/education/htm. *Librn*, Brenda Steen
Library Holdings: Bk Titles 5,300; Per Subs 48
Mem of North Central Regional Library System
Open Mon, Wed, Fri 7:45-3:30, Tues, Thurs 7:45-7, Sat 9-11

CUMBERLAND

P CUMBERLAND PUBLIC LIBRARY,* 119 Main St, PO Box 150, 50843-0150. SAN 305-313X. Tel: 712-774-5614. E-Mail: cmblibry@netins.net. *Librn*, Cathy Jones
Pop 351; Circ 6,400
Library Holdings: Bk Vols 7,000; Bk Titles 6,800; Per Subs 25
Special Collections: Videos (300)
Mem of Southwest Iowa Regional Library System
Open Mon-Wed 9-11 & 3-6, Fri 5-6, Sat 2-5

DALLAS CENTER

P ROY R ESTLE MEMORIAL LIBRARY, 1308 Walnut St, 50063-0521. (Mail add: PO Box 521, 50063-0521), Tel: 515-992-3185. FAX: 515-992-3185. E-Mail: estledc@dwx.com. *Dir*, Mary Werch; Staff 4 (Non-MLS 4)
Founded 1945. Pop 1,454; Circ 30,991
Jul 1999-Jun 2000 Income $94,671, State $4,624, City $60,116, County $12,718, Locally Generated Income $2,669, Other $14,544. Mats Exp $15,133, Books $13,573, Per/Ser (Incl. Access Fees) $1,560. Sal $34,560
Library Holdings: Bk Titles 16,218; Per Subs 59
Subject Interests: Local history
Special Collections: Cemetery Records for Dallas County; Dallas County Genealogical Society Coll, microfilm of County Newspapers back to 1890
Automation Activity & Vendor Info: (Circulation) Follett; (OPAC) Follett
Database Vendor: OCLC - First Search

DAVENPORT

J AMERICAN INSTITUTE OF COMMERCE LIBRARY,* 1801 E Kimberly Rd, 52807. SAN 371-7062. Tel: 319-355-3500. Toll Free Tel: 800-747-1035. FAX: 319-355-0464. *Librn*, Marlene Metzgar; E-Mail: metzgarm@aicedu.com; Staff 1 (MLS 1)
Enrl 600
Library Holdings: Bk Vols 8,200; Per Subs 110
Subject Interests: Accounting, Medicine, Travel
Partic in River Bend Library System
Departmental Libraries:

J CEDAR FALLS BRANCH, 2302 W First St, Cedar Falls, 50613. SAN 371-7089. Tel: 319-277-0220. FAX: 319-268-0978. *Librn*, Judy Mitchell
Library Holdings: Bk Vols 5,500

M DAVENPORT MEDICAL CENTER, Medical Staff Library,* 1111 W Kimberly Rd, 52806. SAN 325-5700. Tel: 319-445-4295. FAX: 319-328-7586. *Mgr*, Julia Hopwell
Library Holdings: Bk Vols 600; Bk Titles 500
Partic in Quad City Area Biomedical Consortium

S DAVENPORT MUSEUM OF ART, Art Reference Library,* 1737 W 12th St, 52804. SAN 305-3164. Tel: 319-326-7804. FAX: 319-326-7876. *Librn*, Sheryl E Haut
Founded 1934
Library Holdings: Bk Vols 6,000; Per Subs 20
Subject Interests: Art history

P DAVENPORT PUBLIC LIBRARY, 321 Main St, 52801-1490. SAN 305-3172. Tel: 319-326-7832. Interlibrary Loan Service Tel: 319-326-6838. Reference Tel: 319-326-7844. TDD: 319-326-7843. FAX: 319-326-7809. Web Site: www.davenportlibrary.com. *Dir*, Kay K Runge; E-Mail: krunge@libby.rbls.lib.il.us; *Archivist, Spec Coll*, Amy Groskopf; *Ch Servs*, Rochelle Murray; *Circ*, Valerie Farrar; *Publ Servs*, Meg Sarff; *Ref*, Cathy Stone; *Tech Servs*, Connie Owings; Staff 14 (MLS 14)
Founded 1877. Pop 95,333; Circ 535,693
Jul 1999-Jun 2000 Income (Main Library and Branch Library) $2,798,567, State $55,123, City $2,566,802, Federal $20,000, Other $156,642. Mats Exp

$2,235,836, Books $214,733, Per/Ser (Incl. Access Fees) $42,614, Presv $1,400, Micro $12,921, Electronic Ref Mat (Incl. Access Fees) $191,712. Sal $1,740,127 (Prof $664,605)
Library Holdings: Bk Vols 253,268; Per Subs 707
Subject Interests: Business and management, Economics, Genealogy
Special Collections: Chess Coll; Iowa Authors Coll
Automation Activity & Vendor Info: (Acquisitions) GEAC; (Circulation) GEAC
Publications: Main Entries (newsletter)
Mem of Southeastern Library Services
Partic in OCLC Online Computer Library Center, Inc
Special Services for the Deaf - TDD
Friends of the Library Group
Branches: 1
ANNIE WITTENMYER BRANCH, 2804 Eastern Ave, 52803. SAN 324-2552. Tel: 319-326-7893. FAX: 319-326-7806. *Librn*, Ann Hetzler
Library Holdings: Bk Vols 31,000
Bookmobiles: 1

M GENESIS MEDICAL CENTER, Medical Library, 1227 E Rusholme St, 52803. SAN 375-9369. Tel: 319-421-2287, 319-421-7150. FAX: 319-421-2288, 319-421-7152. *Librn*, Syl Rex; Tel: 319-421-7150, Fax: 319-421-7152, E-Mail: rex@genesishealth.com; *Librn*, Mary Vickrey; Tel: 319-421-2287, Fax: 319-421-2288, E-Mail: vickrey@genesishealth.com; Staff 2 (MLS 2)
Library Holdings: Bk Titles 2,000; Per Subs 100
Database Vendor: Ebsco - EbscoHost, OCLC - First Search, OVID Technologies
Mem of River Bend Library System
Partic in Quad City Area Biomedical Consortium

L LANE & WATERMAN, Law Library,* 220 N Main St Ste 600, 52801. SAN 372-1221. Tel: 319-324-3246. FAX: 319-324-1616. Web Site: www.l-wlaw.com. *Librn*, James Thurow; E-Mail: jthurow@l-wlaw.com
Library Holdings: Bk Vols 10,000; Per Subs 30
Partic in Westlaw
Open Mon-Fri 8:30-5

S LITTON LIFE SUPPORT, Engineering Library,* 2734 Hickory Grove Rd, PO Box 4508, 52808-4508. SAN 305-3156. Tel: 319-383-6000. FAX: 319-383-6323. *Librn*, Sandy Meier
Library Holdings: Bk Titles 980; Per Subs 83
Subject Interests: Chemistry, Cryogenics, Electronics
Open Mon-Fri 7-3:30

C MARYCREST INTERNATIONAL UNIVERSITY, Cone Library, 1607 W 12th St, 52804. SAN 305-3199. Tel: 319-326-9254. FAX: 319-326-9250. Web Site: www.mcrest.edu. *Actg Dir*, Mary Edwards; E-Mail: medwards@mcrest.edu; *Circ*, Sister Carla Takes; *Per, Publ Servs*, Helen Lammers; Staff 4 (MLS 3, Non-MLS 1)
Founded 1939. Pop 70,000; Circ 280,754; Enrl 1,100; Fac 64; Highest Degree: Master
Library Holdings: Bk Vols 110,073; Bk Titles 100,000; Per Subs 425
Subject Interests: Computer science, Education, Law, Nursing, Social sciences and issues
Automation Activity & Vendor Info: (Circulation) GEAC
Database Vendor: Ebsco - EbscoHost, IAC - Info Trac, OCLC - First Search, Silverplatter Information Inc.
Mem of River Bend Library System
Partic in Bi-State Academic Libraries; Bibliographical Center For Research, Rocky Mountain Region, Inc; Iowa Private Academic Library Consortium; OCLC Online Computer Library Center, Inc; Quad Cities Libraries In Cooperation
Friends of the Library Group
Bookmobiles: 1

CM PALMER COLLEGE OF CHIROPRACTIC, David D Palmer Health Sciences Library, 1000 Brady St, 52803-5287. SAN 305-3202. Tel: 319-884-5896. Circulation Tel: 319-884-5641. FAX: 319-884-5897. Web Site: www.palmer.edu. *Dir*, Dennis Peterson; Tel: 319-884-5442, E-Mail: peterson_d@palmer.edu; *Archivist*, Glenda Wiese; Tel: 319-884-5894; *Acq*, Susan Burns; Tel: 319-884-5467, E-Mail: burns_s@palmer.edu; *Cat*, Ruth Hall; Tel: 319-884-5671, E-Mail: hall_r@palmer.edu; *Ser*, Phyllis Harvey; Tel: 319-884-5529, E-Mail: harvey_p@palmer.edu; Staff 6 (MLS 6)
Founded 1978. Enrl 1,900; Fac 130; Highest Degree: Doctorate
Jul 1999-Jun 2000 Income $821,420. Mats Exp $196,820, Books $40,369, Per/Ser (Incl. Access Fees) $134,725, Presv $8,510. Sal $425,352 (Prof $195,352)
Library Holdings: Bk Vols 29,158; Bk Titles 17,542; Per Subs 708
Subject Interests: Biology, Chiropractic medicine, Health sciences
Special Collections: BJ Palmer Osteological Coll; BJ Palmer Papers Coll; Lyndon Lee Papers Coll; Palmer College Archives Coll
Automation Activity & Vendor Info: (Circulation) epixtech, inc.
Database Vendor: Dialog, Ebsco - EbscoHost, epixtech, inc., OCLC - First Search, OVID Technologies
Publications: Recurring Bibliography for Chiropractic (National Library of Medicine); The Nexus
Mem of River Bend Library System
Partic in Bi-State Academic Libraries; Chiropractic Libr Consortium; Greater Midwest Regional Medical Libr Network; Iowa Private Academic Library Consortium; OCLC Online Computer Library Center, Inc; Quad City Area Biomedical Consortium
Chiropractic &/or Chiropractic Researching Information Services available upon request, fee charged

S PUTNAM MUSEUM OF HISTORY & NATURAL SCIENCE, 1717 W 12th St, 52804. SAN 305-3229. Tel: 319-324-1933. FAX: 319-324-6638. E-Mail: museum@putnam.org. *Dir*, Christopher J Reich; *Curator*, Eunice Schlichting; *Chief Librn, Curator*, Janice Hall
Founded 1867
Library Holdings: Bk Titles 30,000
Subject Interests: Art, History, Local history, Science/technology, Technology
Special Collections: Manuscripts (A LeClaire, I Hall, L Summers, I Wetherby, R Cram, Black Store, Putnam Family, James Grant); Steamboats, files, photog
Restriction: By appointment only

CR SAINT AMBROSE UNIVERSITY, O'Keefe Library, 518 W Locust St, 52803. SAN 305-3237. Tel: 563-333-6246. Reference Tel: 563-333-6245. FAX: 563-333-6248. Web Site: library.sau.edu/. *Dir*, John H Pollitz; Tel: 563-333-6241, E-Mail: jpollitz@sau.edu; *Head Ref*, Patricia Kranovich; Tel: 563-333-6472, E-Mail: pkranovh@sau.edu; *Head Tech Servs*, Jennifer J Davis; Tel: 563-333-6244, E-Mail: jdavis2@sau.edu; *Media Spec*, Harold Krubsack; Tel: 563-333-6242, E-Mail: hkrubsak@sau.edu; *Circ*, Carol Anne Chouteau; Tel: 563-333-6474, E-Mail: cachoutu@sau.edu; *ILL*, Susan Baumbach; Tel: 563-333-6467, E-Mail: sbaumbah@sau.edu; *Acq*, Nancy Johnson-Van Hecke; Tel: 319-333-6247, E-Mail: nvanhece@saunix.sau.edu; *Cat*, Susan Green; Tel: 319-333-6469, E-Mail: sgreen@saunix.sau.edu; *Ref*, Mary Heinzman; *Ref*, Stella Herzig; Tel: 573-333-6056, E-Mail: sherzig@sau.edu; *Ref*, Barbara Kuttler; Tel: 563-333-6473, E-Mail: bkuttler@sau.edu; *Ref*, Sylvia Rex; E-Mail: srex@sau.edu. Subject Specialists: *Business*, Mary Heinzman; *History*, John H Pollitz; *Medical*, Sylvia Rex; *Research*, Stella Herzig; Staff 16 (MLS 8, Non-MLS 8)
Founded 1882. Enrl 2,328; Highest Degree: Doctorate
Jul 1999-Jun 2000 Income Parent Institution $990,647. Mats Exp $331,136, Books $144,677, Per/Ser (Incl. Access Fees) $106,987, Presv $7,491, Micro $9,110, AV Equip $5,868, Other Print Mats $15,016, Electronic Ref Mat (Incl. Access Fees) $41,987. Sal $456,435 (Prof $250,123)
Library Holdings: Bk Vols 101,928; Bk Titles 86,233; Per Subs 642
Subject Interests: Business and management, Economics, Liberal arts, Occupational therapy, Physical therapy, Religion
Automation Activity & Vendor Info: (Circulation) GEAC
Database Vendor: Ebsco - EbscoHost, Lexis-Nexis, OCLC - First Search, Silverplatter Information Inc.
Function: Reference services available
Mem of River Bend Library System
Partic in Bi-State Academic Libraries; Bibliographical Center For Research, Rocky Mountain Region, Inc; Iowa Private Academic Library Consortium; OCLC Online Computer Library Center, Inc; Quad Cities Libraries In Cooperation; Rocky Mountain Region, Inc

S SCOTT COUNTY GENEALOGICAL SOCIETY LIBRARY,* PO Box 3132, 52808-3132. SAN 371-8646. Tel: 319-326-7902. *Librn*, Gaycha Mayhew
Library Holdings: Bk Titles 1,600; Per Subs 20
Society's holdings are housed at the Davenport Public Library, 351 Main St, Davenport, IA 52801
Friends of the Library Group

P SOUTHEASTERN LIBRARY SERVICES, Southeast Iowa Regional Library, 4209 1/2 W Locust, 52804. SAN 305-327X. Tel: 319-386-7848. FAX: 319-386-6843. Web Site: www.sls.lib.ia.us/sls/. *In Charge*, Emily L Navarre; E-Mail: enavarr@server.silo.lib.ia.us; Staff 2 (MLS 2)
Founded 1973. Pop 445,000
Jul 1999-Jun 2000 Income $276,723, State $255,195, Locally Generated Income $21,528. Mats Exp $9,819, Books $900, Per/Ser (Incl. Access Fees) $900, Other Print Mats $8,019. Sal $160,243 (Prof $98,000)
Library Holdings: Bk Titles 300; Per Subs 12
Publications: Regional Rag
Member Libraries: Abbott Memorial Library; Bennington Free Library; Bettendorf Public Library Information Center; Birmingham Public Library; Bloomfield Public Library; Bonaparte Public Library; Burlington Public Library; Cantril Public Library; Cavendish-Fletcher Community Library; Columbus Junction Public Library; Davenport Public Library; Drake Public Library; Eddyville Public Library; Fairfield Public Library; Farmington Public Library; Fletcher Memorial Library; Fort Madison Public Libraries; Fort Madison Public Libraries; Garrett Memorial Library; H J Nugen Public Library; Hedrick Public Library; Hillsboro Public Library; Jamaica Memorial Library; John G McCullough Free Library Inc; Kalona Public Library; Keck Memorial Library; Keokuk Public Library; Keosauqua Public Library; Landgrove Public Library; Letts Public Library; Lydia Taft Pratt Library; Mediapolis Public Library; Mellinger Memorial Library; Milton Public Library; Moore Free Library; Moravia Public Library; Mount Pleasant Correctional Facility Library; Musser Public Library; New Sharon Public Library; Ottumwa Public Library; Pettee Memorial Library; Proctor Library; Putney Public Library; Reading Public Library; Readsboro

Community Library; Richland Public Library; Rockingham Free Public Library; Scott County Library System; Sigourney Public Library; South English Public Library; Springfield Town Library; Stamford Community Library; Stockport Public Library; Townshend Public Library; Tyson Library; Vernon Free Public Library; Wardsboro Free Public Library; West Liberty Free Public Library; West Point Public Library; What Cheer Public Library; Whitingham Free Public Library; Wilder Memorial Library; Wilson Memorial Library; Wilton Public Library; Windham Town Library; Winfield Public Library; Winhall Memorial Library
Provides contract resource sharing for member libraries, reference back-up, continuing education classes, library development services and other supportive services

DAYTON

P DAYTON PUBLIC LIBRARY,* 36 W Skillet, PO Box 378, 50530-0378. SAN 305-3288. Tel: 515-547-2700, 515-547-2703. Toll Free Tel: 800-392-8804. Interlibrary Loan Service Toll Free Tel: 800-392-8804. FAX: 515-547-2700. E-Mail: dpl@netins.net. *Coll Develop, Librn*, Ruth A Anderson
Pop 818; Circ 26,232
Jul 1998-Jun 1999 Income $31,085, State $324, City $13,458, Federal $607, County $11,901, Other $4,795. Mats Exp $8,856, Books $6,105, Per/Ser (Incl. Access Fees) $1,085, AV Equip $553, Other Print Mats $552, Electronic Ref Mat (Incl. Access Fees) $561. Sal $16,082
Library Holdings: Bk Titles 9,979; Per Subs 59
Special Collections: Audio Books (312); Inspirationals; Large Print Books; Videos (656)
Automation Activity & Vendor Info: (Circulation) Sagebrush Corporation
Mem of N Iowa Libr Extension; North Central Regional Library System
Partic in State Of Iowa Libraries Online Interlibrary Loan
Friends of the Library Group

DE SOTO

P DE SOTO PUBLIC LIBRARY, 405 Walnut St, PO Box 585, 50069. SAN 305-3296. Tel: 515-834-2690. FAX: 515-834-2131. E-Mail: desotopl@earthlink.net. *Dir*, Lori Glanz; *Asst Librn*, Lisa Poffenberger
Pop 1,035
Library Holdings: Bk Vols 9,000; Per Subs 34
Mem of Central Iowa Regional Library
Open Mon-Fri 1-6, Sat 9-1

DE WITT

P THE FRANCES BANTA WAGGONER COMMUNITY LIBRARY, 505 Tenth St, 52742-1335. SAN 305-330X. Tel: 319-659-5523. FAX: 319-659-2901. E-Mail: fbwclib@netins.net. *Dir*, Jane Kedley
Founded 1897. Pop 5,000; Circ 81,489
Jul 1999-Jun 2000 Income $119,028. Mats Exp $29,560, Books $21,234, Per/Ser (Incl. Access Fees) $3,028, Micro $655, AV Equip $3,641, Electronic Ref Mat (Incl. Access Fees) $1,002. Sal $62,755
Library Holdings: Bk Vols 24,265; Per Subs 115
Subject Interests: Audio visual mats, Newsp on microfilm
Partic in Am Libr Asn; Iowa Am Libr Asn
Friends of the Library Group

DECORAH

P DECORAH PUBLIC LIBRARY, 202 Winnebago St, 52101. SAN 305-3318. Tel: 319-382-3717. FAX: 319-382-4524. *Dir*, Wanda Gardner; E-Mail: gardnerdecpublib@hotmail.com; *Asst Dir*, Lorraine Borowski; E-Mail: borowslo@luther.edu. Subject Specialists: *Fundraising*, Wanda Gardner; *Grants*, Wanda Gardner; Staff 6 (MLS 2, Non-MLS 4)
Founded 1893. Pop 8,063; Circ 189,069
Jul 1999-Jun 2000 Income $304,800. Mats Exp $45,966, Books $34,560, Per/Ser (Incl. Access Fees) $6,500, AV Equip $2,906, Electronic Ref Mat (Incl. Access Fees) $2,000. Sal $181,722
Library Holdings: Bk Vols 62,659; Per Subs 207
Special Collections: Vera Harris Large Print Book Coll
Automation Activity & Vendor Info: (Cataloging) Sagebrush Corporation; (Circulation) Sagebrush Corporation
Publications: Annual Report
Mem of Northeastern Iowa Regional Library System
Special Services for the Blind - Audiobooks; Large print bks
Library houses toy lending library & genealogy research library (community non-profit), art gallery, county historical archives; Open Mon-Thurs 10-8, Fri & Sat 10-5, Sun 1-4. Community Technology Center (US Dept of Educ funded)
Friends of the Library Group

C LUTHER COLLEGE LIBRARY, Preus Library, 700 College Dr, 52101. SAN 305-3326. Tel: 319-387-1166. Reference Tel: 319-387-1163. FAX: 319-387-1657. Web Site: www.library.luther.edu. *Ref*, Andrea Beckendorf; Tel: 319-387-1227, E-Mail: beckenan@luther.edu; *Ref*, Duane Fenstermann; Tel: 319-387-1164, E-Mail: fenstedu@luther.edu; *Ref*, Elizabeth Kaschins; Tel: 319-387-1196, E-Mail: kascheli@luther.edu; *Ref*, Moeller Lindy; Tel: 319-387-1498, E-Mail: moellind@luther.edu; *Circ, Spec Coll*, Jane Kemp; Tel: 319-387-1195, E-Mail: kempjane@luther.edu; *Tech Servs*, John Goodin; Tel: 319-387-2124, E-Mail: goodinjo@luther.edu; Staff 6 (MLS 6)
Founded 1861. Enrl 2,550; Fac 285; Highest Degree: Bachelor
Jun 1999-May 2000 Income Parent Institution $1,108,391. Mats Exp $429,520, Books $184,640, Per/Ser (Incl. Access Fees) $231,569, Presv $10,560, Manuscripts & Archives $2,751. Sal $477,929 (Prof $308,177)
Library Holdings: Bk Vols 344,640; Bk Titles 203,866; Per Subs 1,037
Subject Interests: Americana, Children's literature, Fine arts, Norwegian hist, Rare books
Special Collections: American Popular Sheet Music; Luther College Archives; Norwegian-American Newspapers
Automation Activity & Vendor Info: (Acquisitions) Innovative Interfaces Inc.; (Cataloging) Innovative Interfaces Inc.; (Circulation) Innovative Interfaces Inc.; (Course Reserve) Innovative Interfaces Inc.; (ILL) Innovative Interfaces Inc.; (OPAC) Innovative Interfaces Inc.; (Serials) Innovative Interfaces Inc.
Database Vendor: Ebsco - EbscoHost, Innovative Interfaces INN - View, OCLC - First Search
Partic in Bibliographical Center For Research, Rocky Mountain Region, Inc; Iowa Private Academic Library Consortium; OCLC Online Computer Library Center, Inc

S VESTERHEIM NORWEGIAN-AMERICAN MUSEUM, Special Library,* 523 W Water St, PO Box 379, 52101. SAN 325-5727. Tel: 319-382-9681. FAX: 319-382-8828. E-Mail: vesterheim@vesterheim.org. *Librn*, Carol A Hasvold; *Archivist*, Charles Langton
Library Holdings: Bk Vols 11,000; Bk Titles 10,000; Per Subs 25
Special Collections: Norwegian Lang Works Published in America
Publications: The Vesterheim Newsletter

DELHI

P DELHI PUBLIC LIBRARY, 316A Franklin St, PO Box 233, 52223. SAN 305-3342. Tel: 319-922-2037. FAX: 319-922-9063. E-Mail: delhi@mwci.net. Web Site: users.mwci.net/~delhi. *Dir*, Brian James Lenane
Founded 1940. Pop 502; Circ 1,827
Jul 1999-Jun 2000 Income $10,790, State $390, City $6,500, County $3,900. Mats Exp $2,200, Books $1,800, Per/Ser (Incl. Access Fees) $250, Electronic Ref Mat (Incl. Access Fees) $150. (Prof $5,800)
Library Holdings: Bk Titles 7,500; Per Subs 12
Mem of Northeastern Regional Libr Syst
Friends of the Library Group

DENISON

P NORELIUS COMMUNITY LIBRARY,* 1403 First Ave S, 51442-2014. SAN 305-3350. Tel: 712-263-9355. FAX: 712-263-8578. E-Mail: denlib@frontiernet.net. *Dep Dir*, Sandra Hayens; *Dir*, Joyce Amdor; *Ch Servs*, Mary Siegner
Pop 6,604; Circ 149,978
Jul 1998-Jun 1999 Income $196,658. Mats Exp $34,610
Library Holdings: Bk Vols 44,437; Per Subs 176
Mem of Northwest Regional Library System
Open Mon-Thurs 10-9, Fri & Sat 10-5
Friends of the Library Group

DENVER

P DENVER PUBLIC LIBRARY,* 201 E Main St, PO Box 692, 50622-0692. SAN 305-3369. Tel: 319-984-5140. FAX: 319-984-5140. E-Mail: dv10063@cedarnet.org. *Librn*, Mary Mumby; *Asst Librn*, Darlene Mohling; *Asst Librn*, Nancy Stoll; *Asst Librn*, Sue Hotzel
Pop 3,654; Circ 50,187
Library Holdings: Bk Titles 23,578; Per Subs 50
Special Collections: Media: Video (821), Audio (200)
Mem of Northeastern Regional Libr Syst
Open Mon 11-7, Tue 11-6, Wed 10-6, Thur 9-7, Fri 10-5 & Sat 9-12

DES MOINES

J AIB COLLEGE OF BUSINESS LIBRARY, (Formerly American Institute Of Business Library), 2500 Fleur Dr, 50321-1749. SAN 371-0955. Tel: 515-244-4221. Interlibrary Loan Service Tel: 515-246-5331. FAX: 515-244-6773. *Dir*, Kathryn A Griffin; *Asst Librn*, Stacy Kent; Staff 2 (MLS 1, Non-MLS 1)
Circ 30,000; Enrl 900; Fac 40
Library Holdings: Bk Vols 5,400; Bk Titles 5,100; Per Subs 175
Special Collections: Court Reporting (Speedbuilding Tape Library Coll), audio & video tapes
Restriction: Open to student, faculty & staff
Function: ILL limited
Special Services for the Deaf - Books on deafness & sign language

L BRADSHAW, FOWLER, PROCTOR & FAIRGRAVE, Law Library,* 801 Grand Ave, Ste 3700, 50309. SAN 372-123X. Tel: 515-243-4191. FAX: 515-246-5808. *Librn*, Kay Iverson; E-Mail: iverson.kay@bradshawlaw.com
Library Holdings: Bk Vols 10,000; Per Subs 50
Open Mon-Fri 8-5

M BROADLAWNS MEDICAL CENTER, Health Sciences Library, 1801 Hickman Rd, 50314. SAN 305-3385. Tel: 515-282-2394. FAX: 515-282-5634. *Librn*, Phyllis A Anderson; E-Mail: panderson@broadlawns.org
Library Holdings: Bk Vols 1,400; Per Subs 200
Subject Interests: Clinical medicine, Nursing, Psychiatry
Partic in Greater Midwest Regional Medical Libr Network; Polk County Biomedical Consortium

S CHILD CARE RESOURCE & REFERRAL OF CENTRAL IOWA LIBRARY, 1200 University Ave, 50314. SAN 325-5743. Tel: 515-286-3536. FAX: 515-283-9293. *Dir*, Karen King; E-Mail: kking@co.polk.ia.us; *Ch Servs*, Janet George; E-Mail: jgeorge@co.polk.ia.us
Library Holdings: Bk Vols 50

L DAVIS, BROWN, KOEHN, SHORS & ROBERTS PC LIBRARY, 666 Walnut, Ste 2500, 50309. SAN 305-3504. Tel: 515-288-2500. FAX: 515-243-0654. E-Mail: info@lawiowa.com. Web Site: www.lawiowa.com. *Ref*, Sharon Kern
Library Holdings: Bk Vols 11,000
Subject Interests: Law
Restriction: Staff use only
Partic in Dialog Corporation

GM DEPARTMENT OF VETERANS AFFAIRS MEDICAL CENTER, Medical & Patients Library,* 3600 30th St, 50310-2774. SAN 305-3512. Interlibrary Loan Service Tel: 515-699-5824. FAX: 515-699-5877. *Librn*, Judith Gottshall
Founded 1934
1997-1998 Income $52,000
Library Holdings: Bk Vols 3,823; Bk Titles 3,447; Per Subs 250
Subject Interests: Hospital administration, Medicine, Nursing, Psychiatry, Psychology, Surgery
Special Collections: Networked Audiovisuals
Publications: Periodicals Holdings List; Source (newsletter)
Partic in Dialog Corporation; Medline; Polk County Biomedical Consortium; Veterans Affairs Library Network
Open Mon-Fri 8-4:30

S DES MOINES ART CENTER LIBRARY, 4700 Grand Ave, 50312-2099. SAN 305-3415. Tel: 515-277-4405. FAX: 515-271-0357. *Librn*, Mary Morman-Graham; E-Mail: mmg@desmoinesartcenter.org; Staff 1 (MLS 1)
Founded 1950
Library Holdings: Bk Titles 15,700; Per Subs 32
Subject Interests: Art (19th Century), Art (20th Century)
Database Vendor: Wilson - Wilson Web
Restriction: By appointment only
Function: Reference only, Research library

S DES MOINES BOTANICAL CENTER, Berkowitz Memorial Library, 909 E River Dr, 50316. SAN 323-8253. Tel: 515-323-8900. FAX: 515-323-8999. *Curator*, Susan Ferguson; Tel: 515-323-8902, E-Mail: skferguson@ci.des-moines.ia.us
Founded 1979
2000-2001 Income Other $1,500. Mats Exp $1,560, Books $900, Per/Ser (Incl. Access Fees) $400, Electronic Ref Mat (Incl. Access Fees) $300
Library Holdings: Bk Titles 1,250; Per Subs 15
Subject Interests: Botany, Gardening, Horticulture
Special Collections: Des Moines Garden Club Historical Book Coll
Open Mon-Fri 10-4, by appt Sat & Sun

S DES MOINES REGISTER, Newsroom Library,* 715 Locust St, 50304. (Mail add: PO Box 957, 50304), SAN 305-3423. Tel: 515-284-8077. FAX: 515-286-2504. *Librn*, Phyllis Wolfe; E-Mail: pwolfe@dmreg.com; Staff 7 (MLS 1, Non-MLS 6)
Library Holdings: Bk Vols 400
Special Collections: Des Moines Register & Tribune Coll 1920 to present, clippings, photogs

CM DES MOINES UNIVERSITY, Osteopathic Medical Center Library,* 3200 Grand Ave, 50312. SAN 305-3407. Tel: 515-271-1430. FAX: 515-271-1625. Web Site: www.vomhs.edu/departments/library/index.html. *Dir*, Larry Marquardt; E-Mail: larry.marquardt@dsmu.edu; Staff 3 (MLS 2, Non-MLS 1)
Founded 1898. Enrl 1,500; Fac 90; Highest Degree: Doctorate Mats Exp $417,500, Per/Ser (Incl. Access Fees) $227,500, Other Print Mats $115,000, Electronic Ref Mat (Incl. Access Fees) $75,000
Library Holdings: Bk Vols 15,031; Bk Titles 12,564; Per Subs 564
Subject Interests: Health sciences, Medicine, Osteopathic med, Physical therapy, Podiatric med
Special Collections: Historical Early Medical Texts Coll
Automation Activity & Vendor Info: (Cataloging) Innovative Interfaces Inc.; (Circulation) Innovative Interfaces Inc.; (Course Reserve) Innovative Interfaces Inc.; (ILL) Innovative Interfaces Inc.; (Media Booking) Innovative Interfaces Inc.; (OPAC) Innovative Interfaces Inc.; (Serials) Innovative Interfaces Inc.
Database Vendor: Innovative Interfaces INN - View
Partic in Bibliographical Center For Research, Rocky Mountain Region, Inc; Greater Midwest Regional Medical Libr Network; Polk County Biomedical Consortium; Quad City Area Biomedical Consortium
Serves medical students & area health professionals. Open Mon-Fri 7:30am-midnight & Sat-Sun 9am-midnight

C DRAKE UNIVERSITY, Cowles Library, 28th & University, 50311-4505. SAN 341-8111. Tel: 515-271-3993. Interlibrary Loan Service Tel: 515-271-2113. FAX: 515-271-3933. Web Site: www.drake.edu/lib/index.html. *Dean*, Rod Henshaw; *Acq, Electronic Resources, Ser*, Teri Koch; *Ref*, Liga L Briedis; *Syst Coordr, Tech Coordr*, Bruce Gilbert; *Instrul Serv*, Karl Schaefer; *Publ Servs*, Mary Beveridge; *Materials Manager*, Claudia Frazer; Staff 8 (MLS 8)
Founded 1881. Enrl 4,818; Fac 256; Highest Degree: Master
Jun 1999-May 2000 Income (Main Library Only) $1,802,210. Mats Exp $753,702, Books $208,242, Per/Ser (Incl. Access Fees) $384,348, Presv $21,412, Micro $30,268, Electronic Ref Mat (Incl. Access Fees) $109,432. Sal $732,195 (Prof $447,976)
Library Holdings: Bk Vols 472,581; Bk Titles 323,674; Per Subs 1,951
Subject Interests: Music, Religion
Special Collections: Ding Darling Coll; Gardner Cowles Papers
Automation Activity & Vendor Info: (Acquisitions) DRA; (Cataloging) DRA; (Circulation) DRA; (OPAC) DRA; (Serials) DRA
Database Vendor: DRA
Partic in Amigos Library Services, Inc; BCR; OCLC Online Computer Library Center, Inc; Polk County Biomedical Consortium
Friends of the Library Group
Departmental Libraries:

CL DRAKE LAW LIBRARY, Opperman Hall, 27th & Carpenter, 50311-4505. SAN 341-8146. Tel: 515-271-2141. Interlibrary Loan Service Tel: 515-271-3759. Circulation Tel: 515-271-3189. FAX: 515-271-2530. Web Site: www.law.drake.edu. *Dir*, John D Edwards; *Acq, Ref*, Rebecca A Lutkenhaus; Tel: 515-271-3784; *Info Tech*, David B Hanson; Tel: 515-271-2077; *Tech Servs*, Julie A Thomas; Tel: 515-271-2052; *Circ*, Karen Wallace; Tel: 515-271-2989; Staff 11 (MLS 5, Non-MLS 6)
Founded 1865. Enrl 400; Fac 23; Highest Degree: Doctorate
Jun 1999-May 2000 Income $1,122,824, Locally Generated Income $75,421, Parent Institution $846,024, Other $201,379. Mats Exp $654,648, Books $66,869, Per/Ser (Incl. Access Fees) $493,322, Presv $7,546, AV Equip $27,621, Electronic Ref Mat (Incl. Access Fees) $59,290. Sal $410,460 (Prof $231,973)
Library Holdings: Bk Vols 292,126; Bk Titles 36,441; Per Subs 3,159
Special Collections: Iowa legal hist
Automation Activity & Vendor Info: (Acquisitions) DRA; (Cataloging) DRA; (Circulation) DRA; (Serials) DRA
Publications: Acquisitions lists; newsletter
Partic in Bibliographical Center For Research, Rocky Mountain Region, Inc; Law Libr Microfilm Consortium; Mid-Am Law Sch Libr Consortium; OCLC Online Computer Library Center, Inc
Friends of the Library Group

C GRAND VIEW COLLEGE LIBRARY, 1351 Grandview Ave, 50316-1494. SAN 305-3431. Tel: 515-263-2877. Interlibrary Loan Service Tel: 515-263-2879. FAX: 515-263-2998. E-Mail: gvclibr@gvc.edu. Web Site: www.library.gvc.edu. *Dir*, Sandra H Keist; *Asst Librn, Tech Servs*, Pam Rees; *Asst Librn, Publ Servs*, David Marshall; Staff 7 (MLS 3, Non-MLS 4)
Founded 1896. Fac 100; Highest Degree: Bachelor
Jul 1998-Jun 1999 Mats Exp $298,200. Sal $154,000
Library Holdings: Bk Vols 120,000; Per Subs 475
Subject Interests: Business, Communication, Education, Graphic design, Liberal arts, Nursing, Social sciences
Special Collections: Iowa Danish Immigrant Archives
Automation Activity & Vendor Info: (Circulation) Brodart; (OPAC) Brodart
Database Vendor: IAC - Info Trac, Lexis-Nexis, OCLC - First Search
Partic in Bibliographical Center For Research, Rocky Mountain Region, Inc; Docline; Iowa Private Academic Library Consortium; OCLC Online Computer Library Center, Inc; SILO

S IOWA DEPARTMENT OF COMMERCE,* 350 Maple St, 50319. SAN 370-2685. Tel: 515-281-4601. FAX: 515-281-5329. *Dir*, Mandy Kirchner; E-Mail: mkirchn@max.state.ia.us; Staff 2 (MLS 1, Non-MLS 1)
Library Holdings: Bk Vols 3,500; Per Subs 300
Subject Interests: Economics, Engineering, Law, Utility regulation
Special Collections: ValueLine - 1976-present
Open Mon-Fri 8-4:30

G IOWA DEPARTMENT OF HUMAN SERVICES LIBRARY, Hoover Bldg, 1305 E Walnut, 50319-0114. SAN 320-1864. Tel: 515-281-6033. Interlibrary Loan Service Tel: 515-281-6032. Circulation Tel: 515-281-6032. FAX: 515-281-4243. E-Mail: dhslib@dhs.state.ia.us. *Dir*, Kay M Elliott; E-Mail: kelliot@dhs.state.ia.us; *Asst Librn*, Karen Kemnitz; E-Mail: kkemnit@dhs.state.ia.us; Staff 2 (MLS 1, Non-MLS 1)
Founded 1968. Highest Degree: Master
Jul 2000-Jun 2001 Income $123,862, State $83,099, Federal $40,763. Mats

Exp $28,000, Books $8,000, Per/Ser (Incl. Access Fees) $13,000, AV Equip $400, Electronic Ref Mat (Incl. Access Fees) $2,500. Sal $95,873
Library Holdings: Bk Vols 9,250; Bk Titles 9,000; Per Subs 75
Subject Interests: Child welfare, Human services, Mental health, Mentally retarded, Social service (social work)
Database Vendor: OCLC - First Search, Silverplatter Information Inc.
Restriction: In-house use for visitors, Staff use only
Function: Research library
Mem of Central Iowa Regional Library
Partic in BCR

G IOWA DEPARTMENT OF NATURAL RESOURCES, (Formerly Iowa State Department Of Natural Resources), Technical Library, Wallace State Office Bldg, 502 E Ninth St, 50319-0034. SAN 320-6742. Tel: 515-242-5818. FAX: 515-281-8895. *Admin Assoc*, Karen Faust; E-Mail: karen.faust@dnr.state.ia.us
Founded 1974
Library Holdings: Bk Vols 1,500; Per Subs 53
Subject Interests: Energy, Environmental law
Special Collections: EPA Publications
Function: Research library

S IOWA GENEALOGICAL SOCIETY LIBRARY,* 6000 Douglas Ave, Ste 145, PO Box 7735, 50322-7735. SAN 321-5741. Tel: 515-276-0287. E-Mail: igs@digiserve.com. Web Site: www.digiserve.com/igs/igs.htm. *Exec Dir*, Rhonda Riordan; *Librn*, Marilyn Elliott
Founded 1965
Library Holdings: Bk Vols 8,000; Bk Titles 7,500; Per Subs 70
Subject Interests: Genealogy, History
Special Collections: Iowa Cemetery, Census & Court House Records; Iowa Pioneers; US Federal Census Microfilm
Publications: Hawkeye Heritage (quarterly)

S IOWA HOSPITALS & HEALTH SYSTEMS LIBRARY,* 100 E Grand, No 100, 50309. SAN 305-3458. Tel: 515-288-1955. FAX: 515-283-9366.
Founded 1974
Library Holdings: Bk Titles 2,000; Per Subs 150
Subject Interests: Government, Health sciences, Hospital administration, Nursing
Special Collections: Rural Health
Partic in Polk County Biomedical Consortium

G IOWA LEAGUE OF CITIES LIBRARY,* 317 Sixth Ave, Ste 1400, 50309-4122. SAN 320-1872. Tel: 515-244-7282. FAX: 515-244-0740.
Founded 1961
Library Holdings: Bk Vols 900; Per Subs 12
Subject Interests: Law, Local government
Special Collections: Iowa Municipal Codes Coll; League Monthly Magazine-Iowa Coll (1899-present); Local Government Subjects Coll

M IOWA LUTHERAN HOSPITAL, Health Science Library,* 700 E University, 50316. SAN 341-8170. Tel: 515-263-5181. FAX: 515-263-2214. E-Mail: celtic@netins.net. *Dir*, Mary Wegner
Founded 1977
Library Holdings: Bk Vols 2,000; Bk Titles 1,650; Per Subs 135
Subject Interests: Education
Partic in Polk County Biomedical Consortium

IOWA METHODIST MEDICAL CENTER
M HEALTH SCIENCES LIBRARY, 1200 Pleasant St, 50309. SAN 341-8235. Tel: 515-241-6490. FAX: 515-241-3383. *Dir*, Mary Wegner; Staff 5 (MLS 2, Non-MLS 3)
Founded 1940
Library Holdings: Bk Titles 7,000; Per Subs 500
Subject Interests: Allied health, Health sciences, Medicine, Nursing, Nutrition
Partic in Greater Midwest Regional Medical Libr Network; Polk County Biomedical Consortium

P IOWA REGIONAL LIBRARY FOR THE BLIND & PHYSICALLY HANDICAPPED, 524 Fourth St, 50309-2364. SAN 305-344X. Tel: 515-281-1333. Toll Free Tel: 800-362-2587. TDD: 515-281-1355. FAX: 515-281-1378. Web Site: www.blind.ia.us. *Adminr*, Karen Keninger; Staff 22 (MLS 4, Non-MLS 18)
Founded 1960
Library Holdings: Bk Vols 277,925; Bk Titles 83,096
Special Collections: Print Coll of Books about Blindness
Special Services for the Deaf - TDD

G IOWA STATE DEPARTMENT OF EDUCATION, Grimes State Office Building Resource Center,* Capital Complex, 50319. SAN 320-1856. Tel: 515-281-5286. FAX: 515-281-8777.
Founded 1967
Library Holdings: Bk Titles 5,150; Per Subs 471
Subject Interests: Education
Special Collections: Education (ERIC Documents Coll), fiche

S LEGISLATIVE SERVICE BUREAU LIBRARY,* State Capitol Bldg, 50319. SAN 320-6750. Tel: 515-281-3566. FAX: 515-281-8027. Web Site: www.legis.state.ia.us. *Senior Librn*, Jonetta Douglas; Tel: 515-281-3312, E-Mail: jdougla@legis.state.ia.us; *Librn*, Judy Neff
Founded 1960
Library Holdings: Bk Vols 6,413; Per Subs 45
Special Collections: Bill Drafts; Bills introduced in the General Assembly with amendments filed since 1953; Interim Committee Reports & Minutes
Publications: Interim study reports to the General Assembly (yearly)

CM MERCY COLLEGE OF HEALTH SCIENCES LIBRARY,* 928 Sixth Ave, 50309-1239. SAN 377-0990. Tel: 515-643-3180. FAX: 515-643-6695. *Librn*, M J Poehler
Library Holdings: Bk Vols 7,000; Bk Titles 3,000; Per Subs 75
Partic in OCLC Online Computer Library Center, Inc

M MERCY MEDICAL CENTER, Levitt Library, 1111 Sixth Ave, 50314-2611. SAN 305-3482. Tel: 515-247-4189. FAX: 515-643-8809. Web Site: www.mercydesmoines.org. *Librn*, Lenetta Atkins; E-Mail: latkins@mercydesmoines.org; *Asst Librn*, Kathleen Dorf; E-Mail: kdorf@mercydesmoines.org
Founded 1961
Library Holdings: Bk Vols 4,384; Per Subs 151
Automation Activity & Vendor Info: (Cataloging) TLC; (Circulation) TLC
Partic in Polk County Biomedical Consortium

L PRINCIPAL FINANCIAL GROUP, Law Library, 711 High St, 50392. SAN 375-3352. Tel: 515-247-5893. FAX: 515-248-3011. *Librn*, Brent Chesson; E-Mail: chesson.brent@principal.com
Founded 1939
Jan 2000-Dec 2000 Income $178,000. Mats Exp $250,000, Books $30,000, Per/Ser (Incl. Access Fees) $10,000, Electronic Ref Mat (Incl. Access Fees) $210,000. Sal $50,000
Library Holdings: Bk Vols 5,000; Bk Titles 1,200; Per Subs 20
Subject Interests: Ins, Law, Pensions, State law

S PRINCIPLE FINANCIAL GROUP, General Library,* 711 High St, 50392-1210. SAN 305-3377. Tel: 515-247-5308. FAX: 515-362-0154. *Librn*, Linda Senecaut
Founded 1879
Library Holdings: Bk Vols 6,000; Per Subs 75

P PUBLIC LIBRARY OF DES MOINES, Des Moines Public, 100 Locust St, 50309. SAN 341-8294. Tel: 515-283-4152. FAX: 515-237-1654. E-Mail: reference@pldminfo.org. Web Site: www.pldminfo.org. *Dir*, Kay K Runge; *Dep Dir*, Lorna R Truck; Tel: 515-283-4102, E-Mail: lrtruck@pldminfo.org; *Commun Servs*, Jan Kaiser; Staff 40 (MLS 40)
Founded 1866. Pop 193,000; Circ 1,406,623
Jul 1999-Jun 2000 Income (Main Library and Branch Library) $5,218,077, State $112,314, City $4,650,749, Federal $5,046, Locally Generated Income $103,591, Other $346,377. Mats Exp $693,000, Books $458,837, Per/Ser (Incl. Access Fees) $65,220, Micro $7,207, AV Equip $117,435, Electronic Ref Mat (Incl. Access Fees) $52,000. Sal $2,493,490
Library Holdings: Bk Vols 427,283; Per Subs 1,152
Subject Interests: History, Iowa
Special Collections: Foundation Center
Automation Activity & Vendor Info: (Acquisitions) epixtech, inc.; (Cataloging) epixtech, inc.; (Circulation) epixtech, inc.; (OPAC) epixtech, inc.
Database Vendor: epixtech, inc., IAC - Info Trac, OVID Technologies, ProQuest, Wilson - Wilson Web
Publications: Calendar of Events
Partic in BCR
Special Services for the Deaf - High interest/low vocabulary books; Staff with knowledge of sign language
Friends of the Library Group
Branches: 5
EAST SIDE, 2559 Hubbell, 50317. SAN 341-8324. Tel: 515-283-4152. FAX: 515-263-8729. *Librn*, Charles Kolb
Library Holdings: Bk Vols 52,982
Friends of the Library Group
FOREST AVENUE, 1326 Forest Ave, 50314. SAN 341-8383. Tel: 515-283-4152. FAX: 515-242-2853. *Librn*, Carolyn Greufe
Library Holdings: Bk Vols 40,926
Friends of the Library Group
FRANKLIN AVENUE, 5000 Franklin, 50310. SAN 341-8359. Tel: 515-283-4152. FAX: 515-271-8734. *Librn*, Kathleen Bognanni
Library Holdings: Bk Vols 106,585
Friends of the Library Group
NORTH SIDE, 3516 Fifth Ave, 50313. SAN 341-8413. Tel: 515-283-4152. FAX: 515-242-2684. Web Site: www.iren.net/pldm/north.html. *Librn*, Steve Goers
Library Holdings: Bk Vols 46,335
Friends of the Library Group
SOUTH SIDE, 1111 Porter Ave, 50315. SAN 341-8448. Tel: 515-283-4152. FAX: 515-256-2567. *Librn*, Nyla Wobig
Library Holdings: Bk Vols 66,415
Friends of the Library Group

L REVENUE & FINANCE LIBRARY,* Hoover State Off Bldg, 4th flr, 50319. SAN 377-5127. Tel: 515-281-8835. FAX: 515-242-6487. *Dir*, Gerald D Bair
Library Holdings: Bk Vols 2,000; Per Subs 12
Restriction: Not open to public

S STATE HISTORICAL SOCIETY OF IOWA-DES MOINES, Library Archives Bureau, Capitol Complex, 600 E Locust, 50319. SAN 305-3466. Tel: 515-281-5070. FAX: 515-281-5070. *Archivist*, Gordon O Hendrickson; *Archivist*, Sharon Avery; *Archivist*, Becki Plunkett; *Archivist*, Beth Brannen; *Librn*, Rosie Springer; *Librn*, Shari Stelling; Staff 7 (MLS 2, Non-MLS 5)
Founded 1892
Library Holdings: Bk Vols 75,000; Per Subs 200
Subject Interests: Genealogy, Historic preservation, Iowa
Special Collections: Manuscripts; State Archives

P STATE LIBRARY OF IOWA, E 12th & Grand, 50319. SAN 341-8472. Tel: 515-281-4105. FAX: 515-242-6543, 281-6191, 515-281-3384 (Medical), 281-5405 (Law). Web Site: www.silo.lib.ia.us. *State Librn*, Sharman B Smith; *Asst Librn*, Mary Wegner; *AV*, Helen Dagley; Fax: 515-281-4307; Staff 17 (MLS 17)
Founded 1838. Pop 2,776,755 Sal $1,059,040 (Prof $621,554)
Library Holdings: Bk Vols 363,539; Bk Titles 259,449; Per Subs 1,228
Special Collections: Attorney General Opinions; Bar Association Proceedings; Iowa State Publications; Medical Coll, bks & journals; Patent
Automation Activity & Vendor Info: (Cataloging) epixtech, inc.
Publications: AV Film Catalog; CE Calendar; Documents Catalog & Index; Footnotes; Inservice to Iowa (Public Libraries Measures of Quality); Iowa Certification Manual for Public Libraries; Library Directory; Library Laws; Long Range Plan; LSCA Handbooks; Periodical Holdings; Public Library Statistics; Summer Reading Program
Partic in Iowa Resource & Info Sharing; OCLC Online Computer Library Center, Inc

L STATE LIBRARY OF IOWA, Iowa State Law Library, State Capitol Bldg, 1007 E Grand Ave, 50319. SAN 372-1248. Tel: 515-281-5124. FAX: 515-281-5405. E-Mail: law@mail.lib.state.ia.us. Web Site: www.silo.lib.ia.us. *Librn*, Linda Robertson; E-Mail: lrobert@mail.lib.state.ia.us; Staff 4 (MLS 2, Non-MLS 2)
Founded 1835
Jul 1999-Jun 2000 Income $416,935, State $400,216, Locally Generated Income $16,719. Mats Exp $271,064, Books $249,564, Per/Ser (Incl. Access Fees) $17,000, Electronic Ref Mat (Incl. Access Fees) $4,500. Sal $118,882
Library Holdings: Bk Vols 185,000; Per Subs 405
Special Collections: English law; Iowa law
Database Vendor: epixtech, inc.
Restriction: Open to public for reference only

G UNITED STATES COURT OF APPEALS, Branch Library,* 110 E Court Ave, Ste 358, 50309. SAN 325-4305. Tel: 515-284-6228. FAX: 515-284-6451. *Librn*, Cheryl Gritton
Library Holdings: Bk Vols 15,000; Per Subs 50
Partic in Westlaw

DEXTER

P DEXTER PUBLIC LIBRARY,* 724 Marshall St, PO Box 37, 50070-0037. SAN 305-3520. Tel: 515-789-4490. FAX: 515-789-4490. E-Mail: dexterpl@netins.net. *Librn*, Linda Adkins
Founded 1930. Pop 669; Circ 10,065
Library Holdings: Bk Vols 7,939; Per Subs 14
Special Collections: Media: Video (200), Audio (200)
Mem of Central Iowa Regional Library
Open Mon-Wed & Fri 1-5, Thurs 7-9, Sat 9-12
Friends of the Library Group

DICKENS

P DICKENS PUBLIC LIBRARY,* PO Box 38, 51333-0038. SAN 376-530X. Tel: 712-836-2217. *Librn*, Marion Lewis
Jul 1999-Jun 2000 Income $3,165
Library Holdings: Bk Vols 3,000
Mem of Northwest Regional Library System
Open Wed 2:30-4:30, Sat 1-4

DIKE

P DIKE PUBLIC LIBRARY, 133 E Elder, 50624-9612. SAN 305-3547. Tel: 319-989-2608. FAX: 319-989-2984. E-Mail: dk10064@www.cedarnet.org. *Dir*, Pat Boe
Pop 925; Circ 35,000
Jul 2000-Jun 2001 Income $56,000, City $39,000, County $17,000. Mats Exp Books $12,800
Library Holdings: Bk Vols 12,000; Per Subs 72
Automation Activity & Vendor Info: (Cataloging) Sagebrush Corporation; (Circulation) Sagebrush Corporation
Mem of Northeastern Regional Libr Syst
Open Mon & Wed 9-12 & 1-7, Tues & Thurs-Fri 9-12 & 1-5, Sat 9-12
Friends of the Library Group

DONNELLSON

P DONNELLSON PUBLIC LIBRARY, 500 Park St, 52625. (Mail add: PO Box 290, 52625), SAN 305-3555. Tel: 319-835-5545. FAX: 319-835-5545. E-Mail: donpulib@interl.net. *Dir*, Brenda Christine Knox; Staff 3 (Non-MLS 3)
Founded 1937. Pop 940; Circ 25,270
Jan 2000-Dec 2000 Income $48,840, State $2,240, City $15,840, County $3,500, Locally Generated Income $19,000, Other $8,260. Mats Exp $11,055, Books $6,190, Per/Ser (Incl. Access Fees) $1,000, AV Equip $3,140, Other Print Mats $725. Sal $28,785
Library Holdings: Bk Titles 13,893; Per Subs 64
Special Collections: Genealogy; Local History
Database Vendor: OCLC - First Search
Function: ILL available
Open Mon, Tues & Thurs 1:30-8:30; Wed 10-8:30; Fri 10:00-6:00; Sat 10-4

DOON

P DOON PUBLIC LIBRARY,* 202 Barton Ave, 51235. SAN 305-3563. Tel: 712-726-3526. *Librn*, Elaine Siebrands
Pop 537; Circ 6,407
Library Holdings: Bk Titles 6,100
Mem of Northwest Regional Library System
Open Mon & Thurs 3-6 & 7-9, Tues, Wed & Fri 3-6, Sat 11-4

DOW CITY

P DOW CITY PUBLIC LIBRARY,* 104 S Franklin St, PO Box 257, 51528. SAN 305-3571. Tel: 712-674-3453. *Librn*, Judy Gordon
Founded 1916. Pop 616; Circ 2,142
Library Holdings: Bk Vols 3,900; Bk Titles 3,800
Mem of Northwest Regional Library System
Open Wed 2-4, Every 3rd Fri 12:30-2:30, Sat 2-4

DOWS

P DOWS COMMUNITY LIBRARY,* 112 Ellsworth, PO Box 427, 50071-0427. SAN 305-358X. Tel: 515-852-4326. FAX: 515-852-4326. E-Mail: dowslib@trvnet.net. *Dir*, Gloria Stover
Founded 1925. Pop 41,680; Circ 42,000
Library Holdings: Bk Vols 9,400; Bk Titles 8,400; Per Subs 15
Special Collections: Newspapers 1896-present, microfilm
Mem of N Iowa Regional Libr Syst
Partic in OCLC Online Computer Library Center, Inc
Open Mon & Wed 2-5 & 7-9, Tues & Fri 2-5, Thurs 7-9, Sat 9-2

DUBUQUE

P CARNEGIE-STOUT PUBLIC LIBRARY, Dubuque Public Library, 360 W 11th St, 52001-4697. SAN 305-3601. Tel: 319-589-4225. FAX: 319-589-4217. E-Mail: cspl@stout.dubuque.lib.ia.us. Web Site: www.dubuque.lib.ia.us. *Dir*, Thomas J Moran; Tel: 319-589-4225, Ext 240, E-Mail: tmoran@stout.dubuque.lib.ia.us; *Tech Servs*, Deb Fliegel; *Ad Servs*, Ann Straley; *Ch Servs*, Jean Gullikson; *Circ*, Mary Wilson; *ILL*, Sherry Ewert; Staff 24 (MLS 7, Non-MLS 17)
Founded 1902. Pop 59,100
Jul 1999-Jun 2000 Income $1,635,158, State $17,390, City $1,454,342, Federal $1,979, County $51,718, Locally Generated Income $109,729. Mats Exp $252,586, Books $173,645, Per/Ser (Incl. Access Fees) $31,855, AV Equip $28,052, Other Print Mats $6,209, Electronic Ref Mat (Incl. Access Fees) $12,825. Sal $823,129 (Prof $329,161)
Library Holdings: Bk Vols 200,853; Per Subs 472; High Interest/Low Vocabulary Bk Vols 495
Subject Interests: History, Iowa, Local history
Automation Activity & Vendor Info: (Circulation) epixtech, inc.; (OPAC) epixtech, inc.
Database Vendor: Ebsco - EbscoHost, epixtech, inc., OCLC - First Search
Publications: Brochures; FYI (Newsletter); Magazine & Newspaper Holdings (annual)
Mem of Northeastern Iowa Regional Library System
Friends of the Library Group

C CLARKE COLLEGE, Nicholas J Schrup Library, 1550 Clarke Dr, 52001. SAN 305-361X. Tel: 319-588-6320. FAX: 319-588-8160. Web Site: www.clarke.edu/library/. *Head Librn*, Paul R Roberts; Tel: 319-588-6418, E-Mail: proberts@keller.clarke.edu; *Tech Servs*, Helen Shaben; *Acq*, Vicki Larson; *Circ*, Heather Kues; *Asst Dir*, Nancy Carroll; Staff 6 (MLS 4, Non-MLS 2)
Founded 1843. Enrl 1,019; Fac 105; Highest Degree: Master

Jun 2000-May 2001 Income $665,925. Mats Exp $232,495, Books $40,662, Per/Ser (Incl. Access Fees) $144,790, Presv $2,310. Sal $236,453 (Prof $200,641)
Library Holdings: Bk Vols 132,000; Bk Titles 111,750
Special Collections: BVM Heritage Coll
Automation Activity & Vendor Info: (Acquisitions) epixtech, inc.; (Cataloging) epixtech, inc.; (Circulation) epixtech, inc.; (Course Reserve) epixtech, inc.; (OPAC) epixtech, inc.; (Serials) epixtech, inc.
Partic in Bibliographical Center For Research, Rocky Mountain Region, Inc; Tri-College Cooperative Effort

R EMMAUS BIBLE COLLEGE LIBRARY, 2570 Asbury Rd, 52001-3096. SAN 304-4998. Tel: 319-588-8000, Ext 403. FAX: 319-588-1216. *Librn*, John Rush; E-Mail: jrush@emmausl.edu; Staff 2 (MLS 1, Non-MLS 1)
Founded 1941. Enrl 280; Highest Degree: Bachelor
Jul 1998-Jun 1999 Income $140,000, Locally Generated Income $4,000, Parent Institution $136,000. Mats Exp $81,000, Books $66,000, Per/Ser (Incl. Access Fees) $7,000, Presv $7,000, Micro $1,000. Sal $36,000 (Prof $31,000)
Library Holdings: Bk Vols 82,000; Bk Titles 67,000; Per Subs 300
Subject Interests: Biblical studies
Special Collections: Plymouth Brethren Writings, bibliog & flm
Partic in Chicago Area Theological Libr Asn

C LORAS COLLEGE, Wahlert Memorial Library, 1450 Alta Vista St, 52004-0178. SAN 305-3644. Tel: 319-588-7009. Circulation Tel: 319-588-7189. Reference Tel: 319-588-7929. Toll Free Tel: 800-367-5672. FAX: 319-588-7292. Web Site: www.loras.edu/~LIB/. *Librn, Rare Bks, Spec Coll*, Robert F Klein; Tel: 319-588-7164, E-Mail: rklein@loras.edu; *Acq*, Mary Kay Haverland; Tel: 319-588-7125, E-Mail: mhaverla@loras.edu; *Acq*, Diane Schulz; Tel: 319-588-7654, E-Mail: dschulz@loras.edu; *Archivist*, Michael Gibson; Tel: 319-588-7163, E-Mail: mgibson@loras.edu; *Bibliog Instr, Online Servs, Ref*, Kristen Smith; Tel: 319-588-7042, E-Mail: ksmith@loras.edu; *Cat, Tech Servs*, Robert Schoofs; Tel: 319-588-7917, E-Mail: rschoofs@loras.edu; *ILL*, DiAnn Kilburg; Tel: 319-588-7009, E-Mail: dkilburg@loras.edu; *Per*, Diane Neumeister; Tel: 319-588-4969, E-Mail: dneumeis@loras.edu; *Publ Servs*, Doug Gullikson; Tel: 319-588-7873, E-Mail: dgulliks@loras.edu; Staff 8 (MLS 4, Non-MLS 4)
Founded 1839. Enrl 1,683; Fac 139; Highest Degree: Master
Jun 1999-May 2000 Income Parent Institution $996,669. Mats Exp $381,128, Books $227,780, Per/Ser (Incl. Access Fees) $138,115, Presv $10,680, Micro $4,553. Sal $210,141 (Prof $147,745)
Library Holdings: Bk Vols 347,082; Bk Titles 214,590; Per Subs 7,971
Subject Interests: Economics, Education, History
Special Collections: Center for Dubuque History Coll; Dubuque County Document Depository; Horace Coll; Loras College Archives; T S Eliot Coll; Torch Press Imprints Coll; William Boyd Allison Government Document Coll
Automation Activity & Vendor Info: (Acquisitions) epixtech, inc.; (Cataloging) epixtech, inc.; (Circulation) epixtech, inc.; (Course Reserve) epixtech, inc.; (OPAC) epixtech, inc.; (Serials) epixtech, inc.
Partic in Bibliographical Center For Research, Rocky Mountain Region, Inc; OCLC Online Computer Library Center, Inc
Friends of the Library Group

M MERCY MEDICAL CENTER - DUBUQUE, Anthony C Pfohl Health Science Library, 250 Mercy Dr, 52001-7398. SAN 305-3652. Tel: 319-589-9620. FAX: 319-589-8185. Web Site: www.mercydubuque.com/educat/index.htm/library. *In Charge*, James H Lander; E-Mail: landerj@trinity-health.org; Staff 2 (MLS 1, Non-MLS 1)
Founded 1973
Jul 2000-Jun 2001 Income Parent Institution $114,742. Mats Exp $55,442, Books $3,300, Per/Ser (Incl. Access Fees) $37,000, AV Equip $5,800, Electronic Ref Mat (Incl. Access Fees) $4,200. Sal $53,500 (Prof $38,000)
Library Holdings: Bk Vols 9,057; Bk Titles 8,820; Per Subs 300
Subject Interests: Business and management, Education, Health sciences, Psychiatry
Publications: Library Lines (recent acquisitions newsletter)
Partic in Dubuque (Iowa) Area Library Information Consortium; Nat Libr of Med; OCLC Online Computer Library Center, Inc

S TELEGRAPH HERALD LIBRARY,* Eighth Ave & Bluff, PO Box 688, 52001-0688. SAN 305-3695. Tel: 319-588-5770. FAX: 319-588-5745. Web Site: www.thonline.com. *Librn*, Steve McAuliff
Founded 1970
Library Holdings: Bk Vols 1,900
Special Collections: City Directories (from 1856, incomplete); History-Dubuque & area; Necrology Card File (from 1974)

C UNIVERSITY OF DUBUQUE LIBRARY, 2000 University Ave, 52001. SAN 305-3687. Tel: 319-589-3100. FAX: 319-588-3722. *Dir*, Joel L Samuels; *Asst Dir, Reader Servs*, Mary Anne Knefel; *Media Spec*, Richard Smith; *Acq*, Dolores Kitelinger; *Tech Servs*, Anastasia Bissell; *Cat, Circ, ILL*, Sue Reiter; Staff 4 (Non-MLS 4)
Founded 1852. Enrl 900; Fac 46; Highest Degree: Doctorate
Library Holdings: Bk Vols 162,780; Per Subs 550
Partic in OCLC Online Computer Library Center, Inc

SR WARTBURG THEOLOGICAL SEMINARY, Reu Memorial Library, 333 Wartburg Pl, 52003. (Mail add: PO Box 5004, 52004-5004), SAN 325-5808. Tel: 319-589-0267. Interlibrary Loan Service Tel: 319-589-0266. FAX: 319-589-0333. E-Mail: wartburg@wartburgseminary.edu. Web Site: www.wartburgseminary.edu/library.htm. *Dir*, Joel L Samuels; *Asst Dir*, Susan Ebertz; *Acq, ILL*, Charlotte Sell; Staff 2 (MLS 1, Non-MLS 1)
Founded 1853. Enrl 174
Jul 1999-Jun 2000 Mats Exp $217,209, Books $36,984, Per/Ser (Incl. Access Fees) $15,537, Presv $1,131. Sal $84,760 (Prof $39,646)
Library Holdings: Bk Vols 68,551; Per Subs 240
Partic in Bibliographical Center For Research, Rocky Mountain Region, Inc
Open Mon-Thurs 8-10, Fri 8-4:30, Sat 9-4:30, Sun 3-10

DUMONT

P BROWN MEMORIAL LIBRARY,* 602 Second St, 50625. SAN 305-3725. Tel: 515-857-3304. FAX: 515-857-3304. *Librn*, Pam Menken; *Asst Librn*, Betty Nielsen
Pop 789; Circ 14,233
Library Holdings: Bk Titles 11,000; Per Subs 71
Mem of Northeastern Regional Libr Syst

DUNCOMBE

P DUNCOMBE PUBLIC LIBRARY, 621 Prince St, PO Box 178, 50532-0178. SAN 376-5210. Tel: 515-543-4646. FAX: 515-543-8186. E-Mail: duncpl@wccta.net. *Librn*, Mary Jane Kudla
Library Holdings: Bk Vols 6,000; Per Subs 30
Special Collections: Media: Video (600), Audio (100)
Mem of North Central Regional Library System
Open Mon 10-12 & 1-6, Tue-Thur 1-5, Fri 1-6 & Sat 9-12

DUNKERTON

P DUNKERTON PUBLIC LIBRARY,* 209 W Main St, PO Box 249, 50626-0249. SAN 305-3733. Tel: 319-822-4610. FAX: 319-822-4664. *Dir*, Janet Peterson; E-Mail: jp11059@dunkerton.net
Pop 1,100; Circ 16,300
Library Holdings: Bk Titles 7,419
Mem of Northeastern Iowa Regional Library System
Open Mon & Thurs 6-9, Tues 1-7, Wed-Sat 9-12

DUNLAP

P DUNLAP PUBLIC LIBRARY,* 102 S Eighth St, 51529. SAN 305-3741. Tel: 712-643-5311. *Librn*, Paula Hess; E-Mail: pjhess@hotmail.com
Pop 1,217; Circ 16,483
Jul 1998-Jun 1999 Income $28,000. Mats Exp $4,800
Library Holdings: Bk Vols 13,175; Bk Titles 11,000; Per Subs 34
Mem of Southwest Iowa Regional Library System
Open Tues, Thurs & Fr 12:30-5:30, Wed 10-5, Sat 9-12
Friends of the Library Group

DYERSVILLE

P MATTHIAS M HOFFMAN PUBLIC LIBRARY, 340 First Ave E, 52040. SAN 305-375X. Tel: 319-875-8912. FAX: 319-875-8912. E-Mail: hoffman00@mwci.net. Web Site: www.hoffmannlib.mwci.net. *Dir*, Shirley J Vonderhaar; *Ch Servs*, Kimshiro Benton; *Librn*, Joyce Bries; Staff 3 (Non-MLS 3)
Founded 1956. Pop 3,703; Circ 85,000
Jul 1999-Jun 2000 Income $173,747, City $138,747, County $20,000, Other $15,000. Mats Exp Books $61,864. Sal $91,246 (Prof $35,000)
Library Holdings: Bk Titles 39,039; Per Subs 125
Special Collections: Videos (1000)
Database Vendor: OVID Technologies
Mem of Northeastern Iowa Regional Library System
Open Mon-Thurs 9-8, Fri & Sat 9-5 & (Sept-May) Sun 1-4
Friends of the Library Group

DYSART

P DYSART PUBLIC LIBRARY,* 424 Main St, PO Box 519, 52224-0519. SAN 305-3768. Tel: 319-476-5210. FAX: 319-476-2671. E-Mail: dysartpl@netins.net. *Dir*, Deb Reed
Founded 1882. Pop 1,230; Circ 25,039
Library Holdings: Bk Vols 12,000; Per Subs 72
Open Mon & Thurs 1-5:30, Tues, Wed & Fri 2-5:30, Sat 9-12

EAGLE GROVE

P EAGLE GROVE MEMORIAL LIBRARY,* 101 S Cadwell, 50533. SAN 305-3776. Tel: 515-448-4115. FAX: 515-448-5279. E-Mail: eaglelib@netins.net. *Librn*, Jan Grandgeorge; *Circ*, Marilyn Schnell; *Ch Servs*, Renee

Nelson; Staff 1 (MLS 1)
Founded 1903. Pop 6,231; Circ 63,430
Library Holdings: Bk Vols 30,000; Per Subs 107
Special Collections: Media: Video (400), Audio (660)
Mem of North Central Regional Library System
Open Mon-Thurs 10-8, Fri-Sat 10-4:30

EARLHAM

P EARLHAM PUBLIC LIBRARY,* 120 Chestnut St, PO Box 310, 50072. SAN 305-3792. Tel: 515-758-2121. FAX: 515-758-2121. E-Mail: COnrad@dwx.com. *Librn*, Barbara Marquardt
Pop 1,140; Circ 27,212
Library Holdings: Bk Titles 16,000; Per Subs 57
Special Collections: Media: Video (600), Audio (200)
Mem of Central Iowa Regional Library
Open Mon, Wed & Fri 10-5, Tues & Thurs 10-7, Sat 9-12

EARLVILLE

P RUTH SUCKOW MEMORIAL LIBRARY, 138 Northern Ave, PO Box 189, 52041-0189. SAN 305-3806. Tel: 319-923-5235. FAX: 319-923-5235. E-Mail: rslibrary@mwci.net. *Librn*, Joanne Laxson
Founded 1937. Pop 844; Circ 11,293
Jul 1999-Jun 2000 Income $18,222, State $910, City $12,500, County $4,574, Locally Generated Income $238. Mats Exp $5,290, Books $4,593, Per/Ser (Incl. Access Fees) $325, Electronic Ref Mat (Incl. Access Fees) $372. Sal $8,665
Library Holdings: Bk Titles 10,123; Per Subs 31
Special Collections: Ruth Suckow Coll
Mem of Northeastern Regional Libr Syst

EARLY

P EARLY PUBLIC LIBRARY,* 107 Main St, PO Box 399, 50535-0399. SAN 305-3814. Tel: 712-273-5334. FAX: 712-273-5251. E-Mail: earlylib@pionet.net. *Librn*, Christine Drey
Founded 1926. Pop 724; Circ 15,228
Jul 1998-Jun 1999 Income $23,324
Library Holdings: Bk Vols 18,023; Per Subs 62
Mem of Northwest Regional Library System
Open Mon 9-12 & 1-5:30, Tues 2-5, Wed 9-12 & 1-5:30, Sat 9-3
Friends of the Library Group

EDDYVILLE

P EDDYVILLE PUBLIC LIBRARY,* Akers Memorial Bldg, 202 S Second St, 52553. (Mail add: PO Box 399, 52553-0399), SAN 305-3822. Tel: 515-969-4815. FAX: 515-969-4815. E-Mail: elibrary@se-iowa.net. *Librn*, Diane Y Sutton
Founded 1897. Pop 1,116; Circ 5,007
Library Holdings: Bk Vols 7,878; Per Subs 27
Special Collections: Media: Video (200), Audio (180)
Mem of Southeastern Library Services
Open Mon 1-7, Tues 1-6, Wed 10-7, Thurs 1-6, Fri 10-4 & Sat 10-2

EDGEWOOD

P EDGEWOOD PUBLIC LIBRARY,* 203 W Union St, PO Box 339, 52042. SAN 305-3830. Tel: 319-928-6242. FAX: 319-928-6242. *Librn*, Cathy Shaw; *Asst Librn*, Rayma Fisher
Founded 1933. Pop 900; Circ 23,677
Library Holdings: Bk Vols 11,000; Bk Titles 10,500; Per Subs 60
Mem of Northeastern Iowa Regional Library System
Open Mon 2-7, Tues 10-5, Wed 2-8, Thurs 3-7, Fri 12-4, Sat 9-1

ELBERON

P ELBERON PUBLIC LIBRARY, 106 Main St, 52225. SAN 377-581X. Tel: 319-439-5345. E-Mail: elbronpl@netins.net. *Librn*, Pat Daniels
Library Holdings: Bk Vols 8,500; Bk Titles 6,310; Per Subs 15
Special Collections: Media: Video (280), Audio (25)
Open Mon 3:30-6:30, Weds 3:30-5:30 & Sat 9-11:30 (Winter hours)

ELDON

P ELDON PUBLIC LIBRARY,* 608 W Elm St, 52554. SAN 305-389X. Tel: 515-652-7517. FAX: 515-652-7517. E-Mail: eldpulib@netins.net. *Librn*, Gail Potts
Pop 1,070; Circ 7,000
Jul 1998-Jun 1999 Income $24,765. Mats Exp $2,950. Sal $12,000
Library Holdings: Bk Vols 10,142; Per Subs 30
Subject Interests: Genealogy
Special Collections: Media: Video (220), Audio (75)
Mem of Southeastern Regional Libr Syst
Open Mon 1206:30, Tues, Thurs & Fri 2-6:30, Wed 2-6:30, Sat 2-5:30
Friends of the Library Group

ELDORA

P ELDORA PUBLIC LIBRARY, 1202 Tenth St, 50627. SAN 305-3857. Tel: 641-939-2173. E-Mail: luvbooks@adiis.net. *Dir*, Dan Gehring; *Asst Dir*, Joan Mooney; Staff 1 (MLS 1)
Pop 3,063; Circ 39,506
Jul 1999-Jun 2000 Income $115,868. Mats Exp $21,419. Sal $50,000 (Prof $28,000)
Library Holdings: Bk Vols 24,343; Per Subs 75
Mem of North Central Regional Library System
Open Mon & Wed 9-8, Tues & Thurs 9-6, Fri 9-5 & Sat 9-3
Friends of the Library Group

ELDRIDGE

P SCOTT COUNTY LIBRARY SYSTEM,* 215 N Second St, 52748-1284. SAN 341-8561. Tel: 319-285-4794. FAX: 319-285-4743. Web Site: www.gl.rbls.lib.il.us/sel/index.html. *Dir*, Anne Conner; *Tech Servs*, Jalois Crotty; *Ad Servs*, Sue Sissel; *Ch Servs*, Mara Wiggins; *ILL*, Elaine Hein; *AV*, Joan Hennigan; *Bkmobile Coordr*, Debbie Hassi
Founded 1950. Pop 27,514; Circ 302,463
Library Holdings: Bk Vols 114,743; Per Subs 632
Special Collections: Scott County History
Automation Activity & Vendor Info: (Circulation) GEAC
Mem of Southeastern Library Services
Partic in Quad-Link Libr Consortium
Friends of the Library Group
Branches: 9
BLUE GRASS BRANCH, 114 N Mississippi St, Blue Grass, 52726. SAN 341-8596. Tel: 319-381-2868. FAX: 319-381-2868. *Librn*, Lynette Swells
Library Holdings: Bk Vols 5,000
BUFFALO BRANCH, 326 Fourth St, Buffalo, 52728. SAN 341-8626. Tel: 319-381-1797. FAX: 319-381-1797. *Librn*, Cindy Mosier
Library Holdings: Bk Vols 5,000
DURANT BRANCH, 402 Sixth St, Durant, 52747. SAN 341-8650. Tel: 319-785-4725. FAX: 319-785-4725. *Librn*, Betty Farrar
Library Holdings: Bk Vols 10,000
LE CLAIRE BRANCH, 104 Ewing St, Le Claire, 52753. SAN 341-8685. Tel: 319-289-3998. FAX: 319-289-3998. *Librn*, Helen Edwards
Library Holdings: Bk Vols 10,000
LONG GROVE BRANCH, Long Grove, 52756. SAN 341-8715. Tel: 319-285-5730. FAX: 319-285-5730. *Librn*, Lorna Lillis
Library Holdings: Bk Vols 3,000
NEW LIBERTY BRANCH, 501 Liberty St, New Liberty, 52765. SAN 341-874X. Tel: 319-843-2456. FAX: 319-843-2456. *Librn*, Sally Telsrow
Library Holdings: Bk Vols 3,000
PARK VIEW, 5 Lincoln Ave Ste D, 52748-9699. SAN 341-8774. Tel: 319-285-7788. FAX: 319-285-7788. *Librn*, Marjorie K Bender
Library Holdings: Bk Vols 7,000
PRINCETON BRANCH, 328 River Dr, Princeton, 52768. SAN 341-8804. Tel: 319-289-4282. FAX: 319-289-4282. *Librn*, Karen Peterson
Library Holdings: Bk Vols 6,000
Friends of the Library Group
WALCOTT BRANCH, 207 S Main St, Walcott, 52773. SAN 341-8839. Tel: 319-284-6612. FAX: 319-284-6612. *Librn*, Judy Rixe
Library Holdings: Bk Vols 6,000
Friends of the Library Group
Bookmobiles: 1

ELGIN

P ELGIN PUBLIC LIBRARY,* 214 Main St, PO Box 36, 52141-0036. SAN 305-3865. Tel: 319-426-5313. FAX: 319-426-5999. E-Mail: elginlib@netins.net. Web Site: www.elginiowa.com. *Librn*, Beverly Strong; *Asst Librn*, Nicki Naling
Founded 1927. Pop 702; Circ 24,603
Library Holdings: Bk Vols 10,660; Per Subs 45
Special Collections: Media: Video (450), Audio (160), CD (30)
Publications: Annual Report
Mem of Northeastern Regional Libr Syst
Partic in OCLC Online Computer Library Center, Inc
Open Mon & Tues 2-6, Wed 11-6, Thurs 2-8, Fri 2-6 & Sat 9-1
Friends of the Library Group

ELK HORN

P ELK HORN PUBLIC LIBRARY,* 2027 Washington St, PO Box 119, 51531. SAN 305-3873. Tel: 712-764-2013. FAX: 712-764-5515. *Librn*, Jo Christopherson

Pop 875
Library Holdings: Bk Vols 4,000; Bk Titles 3,000; Per Subs 24
Mem of Southwest Regional Library Service System
Open Mon, Tues, Thurs & Fri 12:30-4:30, Wed 12:30-6:30, Sat 9-11

ELKADER

P ELKADER PUBLIC LIBRARY,* 130 N Main St, PO Box 310, 52043. SAN 305-3881. Tel: 319-245-1446. FAX: 319-245-1446. E-Mail: elkdrlib@netins.net. *Librn*, Anita Cox; Staff 3 (Non-MLS 3)
Founded 1927
Library Holdings: Bk Vols 13,836; Per Subs 58
Automation Activity & Vendor Info: (Circulation) Sagebrush Corporation
Mem of Northeastern Regional Libr Syst

ELLIOTT

P ELLIOTT PUBLIC LIBRARY, 401 Main St, PO Box 306, 51532-0306. SAN 376-5156. Tel: 712-767-2355. E-Mail: eliotlib@netins.net. *Dir*, June Anne Rush; *Asst Librn*, Marla Turner; Staff 2 (Non-MLS 2)
Founded 1917. Pop 400
Jul 2000-Jun 2001 Income $12,500, State $550, City $4,500, County $6,600, Other $400. Mats Exp $8,500, Books $4,500, Per/Ser (Incl. Access Fees) $250, Micro $1,250, AV Equip $1,000, Other Print Mats $1,000. Sal $4,000
Library Holdings: Bk Vols 9,000; Bk Titles 10,000; Per Subs 15
Database Vendor: OCLC - First Search
Function: ILL available
Mem of Southwest Iowa Regional Library System
Open Mon, Tues & Fri 1-5, Wed 1-7

ELLSWORTH

P ELLSWORTH PUBLIC LIBRARY,* 1549 Dewitt St, PO Box 338, 50075-0338. SAN 305-3903. Tel: 515-836-4852. FAX: 515-836-2162. E-Mail: ellslib@net.ins.net. *Librn*, Sandra Textor
Pop 480; Circ 6,977
Library Holdings: Bk Vols 6,571; Bk Titles 6,000; Per Subs 76
Mem of North Central Regional Library System
Open Mon 10-5, Wed 2-7, Fri 1-6 & Sat 9-12

ELMA

P ELMA PUBLIC LIBRARY,* 710 Busti Ave, PO Box 287, 50628. SAN 305-3911. Tel: 515-393-8100. FAX: 515-393-8100. *Librn*, Connie Ludwig
Founded 1915
Jul 1998-Jun 1999 Income $32,095, State $5,954, City $15,237, Federal $302, County $6,948, Other $3,654. Mats Exp $6,552, Books $4,771, Per/Ser (Incl. Access Fees) $1,319, AV Equip $342, Electronic Ref Mat (Incl. Access Fees) $120. Sal $16,403
Library Holdings: Bk Titles 11,873; Per Subs 54
Special Collections: Local Newspaper on microflim
Mem of Northeastern Iowa Regional Library System

ELY

P ELY PUBLIC LIBRARY,* 1570 Rowley, PO Box 249, 52227-0249. SAN 305-392X. Tel: 319-848-7616. FAX: 319-848-4103. E-Mail: elylib@soli.inav.net. *Dir*, Janine Norman; *Librn*, Dorothy Moorehead
Founded 1974. Pop 575; Circ 5,450
Library Holdings: Bk Vols 7,080; Per Subs 13
Subject Interests: Czechoslovakia, History, Iowa
Open Mon, Tues & Wed 2-8, Thurs 9-11, Fri 2-5, Sat 9-4
Friends of the Library Group

EMERSON

P EMERSON PUBLIC LIBRARY, 410 Manchester, 51533-0313. SAN 328-0756. Tel: 712-824-7866. FAX: 712-824-7845. *Librn*, Karen Gage; Staff 1 (MLS 1)
Founded 1983. Pop 486; Circ 9,689
Jul 1999-Jun 2000 Income $14,557, State $520, City $2,590, County $7,510, Other $3,937. Mats Exp $6,295, Books $1,000, Per/Ser (Incl. Access Fees) $170. Sal $4,402 (Prof $2,970)
Library Holdings: Bk Titles 10,987; Per Subs 20
Subject Interests: Local history
Open Mon, Tues, Thurs & Fri 8-12, Wed 8-12 & 3:30-7:30 & Sat 9-1, Summer Hours also open Mon 1-4

EMMETSBURG

P EMMETSBURG PUBLIC LIBRARY, 707 N Superior, 50536. SAN 305-3938. Tel: 712-852-4009. FAX: 712-852-3785. *Librn*, Mary Ellen Leners; E-Mail: meleners@ilcc.cc.ia.us; *Ch Servs*, Mary Ann Kroesche; E-Mail: skroesche@ilcc.cc.ia.us
Pop 4,900; Circ 49,757
Jul 1998-Jun 1999 Income $138,880, State $880, City $110,000, County $28,000. Mats Exp $19,519, Books $17,000, Per/Ser (Incl. Access Fees) $2,500, Presv $19. Sal $73,000 (Prof $47,300)
Library Holdings: Bk Titles 35,000; Per Subs 100
Mem of Northwest Regional Library System

EPWORTH

CR DIVINE WORD COLLEGE, Matthew Jacoby Memorial Library, 102 Jacoby Dr SW, 52045-0380. SAN 305-3946. Tel: 319-876-3353, Ext 207. FAX: 319-876-3407. Web Site: www.dwci.edu/pr/librarysw/library.htm. *Librn*, Daniel Boice; E-Mail: dboice@dwci.edu; *Asst Librn*, Bro Anthony Kreinus; Tel: 319-876-3353, Ext 206, E-Mail: akreinus@dwci.edu; Staff 3 (MLS 2, Non-MLS 1)
Founded 1915. Enrl 85; Highest Degree: Bachelor
1999-2000 Income Parent Institution $138,575. Mats Exp $47,187, Books $24,709, Per/Ser (Incl. Access Fees) $16,478, Presv $2,093, Micro $90, AV Equip $3,548, Electronic Ref Mat (Incl. Access Fees) $269. Sal $83,729 (Prof $63,911)
Library Holdings: Bk Vols 93,880; Bk Titles 70,972; Per Subs 355; Bks on Deafness & Sign Lang 11
Subject Interests: Art, Geology, History, Linguistics, Literature, Philosophy, Psychology, Religion, Social sciences and issues
Special Collections: LEP; Vietnamese Literature
Automation Activity & Vendor Info: (Cataloging) Sagebrush Corporation; (Circulation) Sagebrush Corporation
Database Vendor: Lexis-Nexis, OCLC - First Search
Partic in BCR; Dubuque (Iowa) Area Library Information Consortium; OCLC Online Computer Library Center, Inc

ESSEX

P ESSEX PUBLIC LIBRARY,* 501 Iowa St, PO Box 298, 51638. SAN 305-3954. Tel: 712-379-3355. FAX: 712-379-3355. E-Mail: elibrar@sheressex.heartland.net. *Chief Librn*, Lucille Carlson; *Asst Librn*, Rosemary Carlson
Founded 1939. Pop 1,001; Circ 13,259
Library Holdings: Bk Vols 17,000; Bk Titles 9,321; Per Subs 13
Special Collections: Media: Video (40), Audio (50)
Mem of Southwest Iowa Regional Library System
Open Mon & Fri 3-6, Tues & Thurs 9:30-12

ESTHERVILLE

P ESTHERVILLE PUBLIC LIBRARY,* 613 Central, 51334-2294. SAN 305-3962. Tel: 712-362-7731. FAX: 712-362-3509. E-Mail: estpub@ncn.net. Web Site: www.ncn.net. *Dir*, Carolyn L Walz; *Coordr*, Beverly Stump; *Coordr*, Betty Lehman; *Coordr*, Vi Ann Bradley; *Coordr*, Marcia Huntsinger; *Automation Syst Coordr*, Deb Anderson. Subject Specialists: *Psychology*, Marcia Huntsinger
Founded 1903. Pop 7,530
Jul 1998-Jun 1999 Income $229,850, City $219,350, County $10,500. Mats Exp $26,027, Books $23,000, Per/Ser (Incl. Access Fees) $2,875, Micro $152. Sal $108,225
Library Holdings: Bk Titles 53,358; Per Subs 85
Subject Interests: Genealogy, Iowa
Special Collections: Expand Your Horizons, (Books for Literacy groups)
Publications: Friends of Library Newsletter
Mem of Northwest Regional Library System
Special Services for the Deaf - Books on deafness & sign language; High interest/low vocabulary books
Friends of the Library Group

J IOWA LAKES COMMUNITY COLLEGES LIBRARY, 300 S 18th St, 51334. SAN 305-3970. Tel: 712-362-7936. Interlibrary Loan Service Tel: 712-362-7991. FAX: 712-362-5970. Web Site: www.ilcc.cc.ia.us/09-14/library.htm. *Dir*, Brenda Colegrove; E-Mail: bcolegrove@ilcc.cc.ia.us; Staff 2 (MLS 2)
Founded 1924. Enrl 3,100
Jul 2000-Jun 2001 Mats Exp $117,000, Books $40,000, Per/Ser (Incl. Access Fees) $27,800, AV Equip $4,000, Electronic Ref Mat (Incl. Access Fees) $20,000. Sal $161,625 (Prof $70,125)
Library Holdings: Bk Vols 36,881; Per Subs 850
Automation Activity & Vendor Info: (Cataloging) Sagebrush Corporation; (Circulation) Sagebrush Corporation
Database Vendor: Ebsco - EbscoHost, Lexis-Nexis, OCLC - First Search, OVID Technologies
Function: Document delivery services, ILL available, Photocopies available

EVANSDALE

P EVANSDALE PUBLIC LIBRARY,* 123 N Evans Rd, 50707. SAN 305-3989. Tel: 319-232-5367. FAX: 319-232-5367. E-Mail: eplib@forben.com. Web Site: www.cv.commonline.net/evansdalepubliclibrary. *Dir*, Shannon Surly

Founded 1968. Pop 5,003; Circ 9,655
Library Holdings: Bk Vols 12,000; Per Subs 20
Special Collections: Media: videos (280), audios (60)
Mem of Northeastern Regional Libr Syst
Open Mon & Thurs 11-7, Tues, Wed, Fri & Sat 11-5
Friends of the Library Group

EVERLY

P EVERLY PUBLIC LIBRARY,* 308 N Main St, 51338-0265. SAN 305-3997. Tel: 712-834-2390. FAX: 712-834-2390. E-Mail: library1@netins.net. *Dir*, Pat Holst
Founded 1917. Pop 850; Circ 4,387
Library Holdings: Bk Vols 6,121; Bk Titles 4,866; Per Subs 16
Special Collections: Media: videos (110), audios (95)
Mem of Northwest Regional Library System
Open Tues-Fri 10-12 & 1-5, Sat 10-12 (Oct-June), Tues-Fri 9:30-12 & 1-5 (June-Oct)
Friends of the Library Group

EXIRA

P EXIRA PUBLIC LIBRARY,* 114 W Washington St, PO Box 368, 50076-0368. SAN 320-8257. Tel: 712-268-5489. E-Mail: exiralib@netins.net. *Chief Librn*, Sandra Bauer; *Asst Librn*, Julie Johnson; *Ch Servs*, Bev Godwin
Pop 978; Circ 27,981
Library Holdings: Bk Vols 16,000; Per Subs 60
Special Collections: Media: Videos- 475; Audios- 600
Mem of Southwest Regional Library Service System
Open Mon 9-12 & 7-9, Tues-Fri 2-5, Sat 9-12 & 2-5

FAIRBANK

P FAIRBANK PUBLIC LIBRARY,* 212 Main St, PO Box 426, 50629-0426. SAN 305-4004. Tel: 319-635-2487. FAX: 319-635-2487. E-Mail: fairbanklib@fairbank.net. *Librn*, Sharon Maricle; *Asst Librn*, Karen Tiedt
Pop 980; Circ 12,832
Jul 1998-Jun 1999 Income $29,000, County $9,000. Mats Exp $7,000. Sal $14,000
Library Holdings: Bk Titles 12,300; Per Subs 36
Mem of Northeastern Regional Libr Syst
Open Mon 2:30-6:30, Tues, Thurs & Fri 1-5, Wed 9-11 & 2:30-6:30, Sat 10-1

FAIRFAX

P FAIRFAX PUBLIC LIBRARY,* 313 Vanderbilt St, 52228. SAN 305-4012. Tel: 319-846-2994. FAX: 319-846-2889. *Dir*, Carol Niles; *Ch Servs*, Susan Kuecker
Pop 683; Circ 3,552
Library Holdings: Bk Vols 7,893; Per Subs 21
Mem of East Central Regional Library
Open Mon 10-8, Tues & Thurs 4-8, Wed 2-8, Fri 10-6 & Sat 9-12
Friends of the Library Group

FAIRFIELD

P FAIRFIELD PUBLIC LIBRARY, 104 W Adams, 52556. SAN 305-4020. Tel: 641-472-6551. FAX: 641-472-3249. E-Mail: fplib@natel.net. Web Site: www.natel.net/fairfieldpubliclibrary. *Dir*, James Rubis; E-Mail: jrubis@natel.net; Staff 6 (MLS 3, Non-MLS 3)
Founded 1853. Pop 10,000; Circ 217,000
Jul 1999-Jun 2000 Income $380,000, State $12,000, City $265,000, County $60,000, Locally Generated Income $43,000. Mats Exp $73,000. Sal $231,000
Library Holdings: Bk Titles 69,000; Per Subs 233
Automation Activity & Vendor Info: (Acquisitions) epixtech, inc.; (Cataloging) epixtech, inc.; (Circulation) epixtech, inc.; (Course Reserve) epixtech, inc.; (ILL) epixtech, inc.; (Media Booking) epixtech, inc.; (OPAC) epixtech, inc.; (Serials) epixtech, inc.
Database Vendor: Ebsco - EbscoHost
Mem of Southeastern Library Services
Friends of the Library Group

C MAHARISHI UNIVERSITY OF MANAGEMENT LIBRARY, (MUM), 1000 N Fourth St, 52557. SAN 305-4039. Tel: 641-472-1148. Interlibrary Loan Service Tel: 641-472-7000, Ext 3334. Circulation Tel: 641-472-1154. Reference Tel: 641-472-7000, Ext 3733. FAX: 641-472-1173. E-Mail: library@mum.edu. Web Site: www.mum.edu/library/home.html. *Dir*, Craig Shaw; E-Mail: cshaw@mum.edu; *Ref*, James Bates; E-Mail: jbates@mum.edu; Staff 4 (MLS 3, Non-MLS 1)
Founded 1971. Enrl 641; Fac 99; Highest Degree: Doctorate
Jul 1999-Jun 2000 Mats Exp $245,855, Books $62,546, Per/Ser (Incl. Access Fees) $103,011, Presv $1,742. Sal $36,161 (Prof $20,081)
Library Holdings: Bk Vols 148,450; Per Subs 817
Subject Interests: American literature, Art, Computer science, Education, English literature, Management, Medicine, Organic gardening, Physics, Physiology, Psychology
Special Collections: Science of Creative Intelligence Coll (Maharishi Mahesh Yogi & M.U.M. Faculty), bks, A-tapes, V-tapes & flm
Automation Activity & Vendor Info: (Acquisitions) SIRSI; (Cataloging) SIRSI; (Circulation) SIRSI; (Course Reserve) SIRSI; (OPAC) SIRSI
Database Vendor: OCLC - First Search
Publications: bibliography of general reference works; Bibliography on www sites for business management; index to Modern Science & Vedic Science; serials holdings lists
Partic in Bibliographical Center For Research, Rocky Mountain Region, Inc; Iowa Librs Ariel Network; Iowa Private Academic Library Consortium; Iowa Res & Educ Network; Nat Libr of Med; OCLC Online Computer Library Center, Inc

FARLEY

P DUBUQUE COUNTY LIBRARY, 105 First St NE, PO Box 10, 52046-0010. SAN 305-3628. Tel: 319-744-3577. FAX: 319-744-3816. E-Mail: library@dubcolib.lib.ia.us. Web Site: www.dubcolib.lib.ia.us. *Dir*, Rebecca S Heil; Staff 4 (MLS 1, Non-MLS 3)
Founded 1951. Pop 18,000; Circ 120,000
Jul 1999-Jun 2000 Income (Main Library and Branch Library) $339,000, State $7,500, City $30,000, County $300,000, Locally Generated Income $1,500. Mats Exp $39,000, Books $32,000, Per/Ser (Incl. Access Fees) $3,000, AV Equip $4,000. Sal $169,000 (Prof $32,500)
Library Holdings: Bk Vols 40,000; Bk Titles 35,000; Per Subs 130
Subject Interests: Local history
Automation Activity & Vendor Info: (Cataloging) TLC; (Circulation) TLC; (OPAC) TLC
Database Vendor: OCLC - First Search
Mem of Northeastern Iowa Regional Library System
Branches: 1
HOLY CROSS BRANCH, 938 Church St, Holy Cross, 52053. SAN 376-6543. Tel: 319-870-2475. *Librn*, Becky Heil
Library Holdings: Bk Vols 2,500; Per Subs 32
Bookmobiles: 1

FARMERSBURG

P FARMERSBURG PUBLIC LIBRARY,* 106 S Main St, PO Box 167, 52047. SAN 305-4047. Tel: 319-536-2229. *Librn*, Sandra Roeder
Founded 1920. Pop 291; Circ 1,519
Library Holdings: Bk Titles 6,900
Subject Interests: Local history
Mem of Northeastern Iowa Regional Library System
Open Mon & Wed 3-5:30, Sat 9-12

FARMINGTON

P FARMINGTON PUBLIC LIBRARY,* 205 Elm St, 52626-0472. SAN 305-4055. Tel: 319-878-3702. FAX: 319-878-3702. *Librn*, Karen Walton; *Asst Librn*, Betty Rider
Pop 688; Circ 17,469
1999-2000 Income $21,732, State $580, City $18,759, County $2,393. Mats Exp $2,508, Books $2,435, Other Print Mats $73. Sal $16,420
Library Holdings: Bk Vols 26,500; Bk Titles 26,458; High Interest/Low Vocabulary Bk Vols 68
Mem of Southeastern Library Services

FARNHAMVILLE

P FARNHAMVILLE PUBLIC LIBRARY, 240 Hardin, PO Box 216, 50538-0216. SAN 376-5261. Tel: 515-544-3660. FAX: 515-544-3703. E-Mail: farnlib@wceta.net. *Librn*, Sharon Vogel
Library Holdings: Bk Vols 3,500; Per Subs 32
Mem of Northwest Regional Library System
Open Mon & Wed 1-6, Sat 9-12

FAYETTE

P FAYETTE COMMUNITY LIBRARY,* 104 W State St, PO Box 107, 52142-0107. SAN 305-4071. Tel: 319-425-3344. FAX: 319-425-3344. Web Site: www.fayetteia.com/library.htm. *Dir*, Linda K Adams; E-Mail: lkadams@trxinc.com
Founded 1934. Pop 1,515; Circ 10,122
Library Holdings: Bk Vols 12,000; Per Subs 35
Mem of Northeastern Regional Libr Syst
Open Mon & Fri 10-5, Tues & Wed 1-8, Thurs & Sat 1-5

C UPPER IOWA UNIVERSITY, Henderson-Wilder Library, 605 Washington, PO Box 1858, 52142. SAN 305-408X. Tel: 319-425-5270. Interlibrary Loan Service Tel: 319-425-5217. Circulation Tel: 319-425-5261. Reference Tel: 319-425-5261. FAX: 319-425-5271. Web Site: www.uiu.edu/library. *Acq, AV,*

Dir, Becky Wadian; E-Mail: wadianb@uiu.edu; *Govt Doc, Per*, Pamela Humphrey; E-Mail: humphreyp@uiu.edu; *ILL*, Carol Orr; E-Mail: orrc@uiu.edu; *Circ*, Mary White; E-Mail: whitem@uiu.edu; Staff 4 (MLS 1, Non-MLS 3)
Founded 1901. Enrl 3,276; Fac 125; Highest Degree: Master
Jul 1999-Jun 2000 Mats Exp $106,934, Books $24,340, Per/Ser (Incl. Access Fees) $49,450, Presv $2,759, Micro $1,216, AV Equip $6,569, Electronic Ref Mat (Incl. Access Fees) $22,600
Library Holdings: Bk Vols 79,589; Bk Titles 64,047; Per Subs 287
Special Collections: NASA Coll, slides, pictures & clippings
Automation Activity & Vendor Info: (Acquisitions) Endeavor; (Cataloging) Endeavor; (Circulation) Endeavor; (ILL) Endeavor; (OPAC) Endeavor; (Serials) Endeavor
Database Vendor: Dialog, IAC - Info Trac, OCLC - First Search
Publications: Proquest Criminal Justice Periodical Index
Partic in Bibliographical Center For Research, Rocky Mountain Region, Inc; OCLC Online Computer Library Center, Inc
Open Sun 2-11, Mon-Thurs 7:30-11, Fri 7:30-5 & Sat 1-4

FERTILE

P FERTILE PUBLIC LIBRARY, 204 W Main St, 50434-1020. (Mail add: PO Box 198, 50434-0198), SAN 305-4101. Tel: 641-797-2787. FAX: 641-797-2787. E-Mail: ferlib@wctatel.net. *Librn*, Nancy Suby; Staff 2 (Non-MLS 2)
Founded 1968. Pop 382; Circ 12,063
Jul 1998-Jun 1999 Income $28,244, State $568, City $9,300, County $8,800, Locally Generated Income $9,576. Mats Exp $4,863, Books $3,884, Per/Ser (Incl. Access Fees) $679, Electronic Ref Mat (Incl. Access Fees) $300. Sal $9,662
Library Holdings: Bk Vols 9,688; Bk Titles 9,676; Per Subs 42
Mem of North Central Regional Library System
Special Services for the Blind - Bks on cassette; Copier with enlargement capabilities; Large print bks
Open Mon-Wed 1-8, Fri 9-12 & 2-5, Sat 9-12
Friends of the Library Group

FONDA

P FONDA PUBLIC LIBRARY,* 104 W Second & Main, 50540. SAN 305-411X. FAX: 712-288-6633. E-Mail: fondalib@ncn.net. *Librn*, Julie Miller
Founded 1942. Pop 1,500; Circ 7,449
Jul 1998-Jun 1999 Income $25,220. Mats Exp $10,900. Sal $14,820
Library Holdings: Bk Titles 6,970; Per Subs 18
Special Collections: Media (videos 486), audio (100)
Mem of Northwest Regional Library System
Open Mon & Fri 1-5, Wed 9-6, Sat 9-12

FONTANELLE

P FONTANELLE PUBLIC LIBRARY,* 303 Washington St, PO Box 387, 50846. SAN 305-4128. Tel: 515-745-4981. FAX: 515-745-4981. E-Mail: fontanelle-lib@aea14.k12.ia.us. *Librn*, Linda Jensen; *Asst Librn*, Phyllis Jacobson
Pop 805; Circ 2,833
Library Holdings: Bk Titles 10,000; Per Subs 28
Mem of Southwest Iowa Regional Library System
Open Mon, Tues, Thurs & Fri 2-5:30, Sat 9:30-11:30

FOREST CITY

P FOREST CITY PUBLIC LIBRARY, 115 East L St, 50436. SAN 305-4136. Tel: 641-585-4542. FAX: 641-585-2939. E-Mail: fcpublib@wctatel.net. *Dir*, Christa Cosgriff
Founded 1897. Pop 4,500; Circ 33,615
Jul 1999-Jun 2000 Income $106,546. Mats Exp $12,000. Sal $64,341
Library Holdings: Bk Vols 18,547; Per Subs 92
Subject Interests: Audio, Scandinavia, Videos
Publications: Library Notes (monthly)

J WALDORF COLLEGE, Voss Memorial Library, 106 S Sixth, 50436. SAN 305-4144. Tel: 641-585-8110. FAX: 641-585-8111. Web Site: www.waldorf.edu. *Dir*, Mary Ann Bartz; Staff 2 (MLS 2)
Founded 1903. Enrl 497; Fac 45
Library Holdings: Bk Vols 39,643; Bk Titles 38,879; Per Subs 312
Special Collections: Bible Coll
Automation Activity & Vendor Info: (Cataloging) EOS; (Circulation) EOS; (OPAC) EOS
Open Mon-Thurs 7:30-10:45, Fri 7:30-5, Sat 2-5 & Sun 3-10:45

FORT ATKINSON

P FORT ATKINSON PUBLIC LIBRARY,* 302 Third St NW, PO Box 277, 52144-0277. SAN 305-4152. Tel: 319-534-2222. FAX: 319-534-2222. *Librn*, Tina Block
Founded 1964. Pop 410; Circ 4,248
Library Holdings: Bk Titles 6,700; Per Subs 26
Mem of Northeastern Iowa Regional Library System
Open Mon-Wed 3:30-7:30, Thurs 1-7, Fri 9-12 & 2-5

FORT DODGE

S BLANDEN MEMORIAL ART MUSEUM, 920 Third Ave S, 50501. SAN 305-4160. Tel: 515-573-2316. FAX: 515-573-2317. E-Mail: blanden@dodgenet.com. Web Site: www.blanden.org.
Founded 1932
Library Holdings: Bk Titles 3,000; Per Subs 10
Subject Interests: Art and architecture, History

P FORT DODGE PUBLIC LIBRARY,* 605 First Ave N, 50501. SAN 341-8863. Tel: 515-573-8167. Interlibrary Loan Service Tel: 515-573-8168. FAX: 515-573-5422. E-Mail: libstaff@dodgenet.com. *Dir*, Lawanda Roudebush; *Asst Dir*, Rita Schmidt; *Ch Servs*, Laurie Hotz; Staff 14 (MLS 3, Non-MLS 11)
Founded 1890. Pop 25,894; Circ 224,000
Jul 1998-Jun 1999 Income $541,675. Mats Exp $62,000. Sal $383,650
Library Holdings: Bk Vols 72,000; Per Subs 225
Subject Interests: Local history, Travel
Publications: Newsletter (quarterly)
Mem of North Central Regional Library System
Open Mon-Wed 9am-9pm, Thurs-Sat 9-5:30
Friends of the Library Group

J IOWA CENTRAL COMMUNITY COLLEGE, Fort Dodge Center Library, 330 Avenue M, 50501. SAN 370-3177. Tel: 515-576-7201, Ext 2618. FAX: 515-576-0099, Ext 2631. Web Site: www.iccc.cc.ia.us/libraries/. *Dir*, Dan Schiefelbein; E-Mail: schiefelbein@triton.iccc.cc.ia.us; Staff 12 (MLS 2, Non-MLS 10)
Founded 1967. Enrl 2,836
Library Holdings: Bk Vols 49,060; Per Subs 510
Subject Interests: Education, Iowa, Local history
Automation Activity & Vendor Info: (Cataloging) Gaylord; (Circulation) Gaylord; (Serials) Gaylord
Departmental Libraries:
EAGLE GROVE, 316 NW Third Ave, Eagle Grove, 50533. SAN 377-7367. Tel: 515-576-7201, Ext 2801. FAX: 515-448-4724. *Dir*, Sherry Hohensee
WEBSTER CITY CENTER, 1725 Beach St, Webster City, 50595. SAN 305-7747. Tel: 515-832-1632, Ext 2820. FAX: 515-576-0099, Ext 261. Web Site: elvis.iccc.cc.ia.us:8000/. *Librn*, Marilyn Jensen; Staff 3 (MLS 1, Non-MLS 2)
Enrl 200; Fac 20
Library Holdings: Bk Titles 17,520; Per Subs 112

FORT MADISON

P FORT MADISON PUBLIC LIBRARIES,* 614 Seventh St, 52627. SAN 305-4187. Tel: 319-372-5721. FAX: 319-372-5726. E-Mail: sftmadiso@interl.net. *Dir*, Rose Reynolds; *Asst Dir*, JoAnne Reida
Founded 1894. Pop 12,050; Circ 94,200
Library Holdings: Bk Vols 62,000; Per Subs 182
Special Collections: Black History (Dr Harry D Harper Sr Coll); Genealogy & Local History; Railroad (Chester S Gross Memorial Coll)
Mem of Southeastern Library Services
Friends of the Library Group
Branches: 1
IDOL RASHID MEMORIAL LIBRARY, 3421 Ave L, 52627. SAN 376-5547. Tel: 319-372-2071. FAX: 319-372-5726. E-Mail: ftmadis2@inter.net. *Librn*, Rose Reynolds
Library Holdings: Bk Vols 85,000; Per Subs 350
Mem of Southeastern Library Services

S IOWA STATE PENITENTIARY LIBRARY,* 31 Ave G, 52627. SAN 305-4195. Tel: 319-372-5432, Ext 255. FAX: 319-372-6967. *Librn*, Charles Hourihan
Library Holdings: Bk Vols 32,000; Bk Titles 31,056; Per Subs 27
Mem of SE Iowa Regional Libr Syst

FREDERICKSBURG

P UPHAM MEMORIAL LIBRARY,* 138 W Main St, 50630-0213. (Mail add: PO Box 281, 50630), SAN 305-4217. Tel: 319-237-6498. FAX: 319-237-6218. E-Mail: fburglib@sbt.net.; Staff 3 (Non-MLS 3) Income $34,000, State $750, County $11,000
Library Holdings: Bk Titles 8,000; Per Subs 40
Mem of Northeastern Regional Libr Syst

GALVA

P GALVA PUBLIC LIBRARY,* 203 S Main St, 51020. SAN 305-4225. Tel: 712-282-4400. FAX: 712-282-4400. E-Mail: bookwrm@netins.net. *Librn*, Judy Kraser
Pop 420; Circ 6,490

Library Holdings: Bk Vols 5,200; Per Subs 31
Special Collections: Media: Video (150), Audio (40)
Mem of Northwest Regional Library System
Open Mon 2-7, Tues, Thurs & Fri 1-5, Sat 9-12
Friends of the Library Group

GARDEN GROVE

P GARDEN GROVE PUBLIC LIBRARY, 103 Main St, PO Box 29, 50103. SAN 376-6829. E-Mail: gglibry@netins.net. *Librn*, Julie Jones
Library Holdings: Bk Vols 3,500
Mem of Southwest Iowa Regional Library System
Open Mon, Wed & Fri 2-4:30
Friends of the Library Group

GARNAVILLO

P GARNAVILLO PUBLIC LIBRARY,* 122 Main St, 52049. SAN 305-4241. Interlibrary Loan Service Tel: 319-964-2119. FAX: 319-964-2119. E-Mail: garnplib@netins.net. *Librn*, Mary Fran Nikolai
Founded 1939. Pop 735; Circ 36,641
Library Holdings: Bk Vols 21,000; Per Subs 38
Special Collections: Media: videos (360), audios (300)
Mem of Northeastern Iowa Regional Library System
Open Tues & Sat 10-4:30, Wed 10-8, Thurs 3-8

GARNER

P GARNER PUBLIC LIBRARY,* 416 State St, PO Box 406, 50438-0406. SAN 305-425X. Tel: 515-923-2850. FAX: 515-923-2339. E-Mail: garnerpl@ncn.net. *Dir*, Ellen Petty; Staff 1 (MLS 1)
Founded 1870. Pop 2,916; Circ 42,066
Jul 1998-Jun 1999 Income $104,000. Mats Exp $23,000. Sal $48,000 (Prof $26,000)
Library Holdings: Bk Vols 25,951; Per Subs 90
Special Collections: Media: videos (800), audios (100)
Mem of North Central Regional Library System
Open Mon 10-5:30 & 7pm-8pm, Tues & Wed 10-5:30, Thurs 12-8, Fri 12-4, Sat 10-12 & 1-3

GARRISON

P GARRISON PUBLIC LIBRARY,* 100 N Birch Ave, PO Box 26, 52229. SAN 320-8265. Tel: 319-477-5531. FAX: 319-472-5531. E-Mail: garrison@netins.net. *Librn*, Betty Baumgartel
Founded 1975. Pop 300
Jul 1998-Jun 1999 Income $9,415. Mats Exp $2,155, Books $1,982, Per/Ser (Incl. Access Fees) $173. Sal $5,292
Library Holdings: Bk Titles 5,428; Per Subs 20
Special Collections: Media: Video (400), Audio (30)
Open Mon 3-7, Tues-Fri 2:30-5, Sat 9-11

GARWIN

P GARWIN PUBLIC LIBRARY,* 208 Main St, PO Box 216, 50632-0216. SAN 305-4268. Tel: 515-499-2024. *Librn*, Kathy Thurston
Pop 626; Circ 3,844
1997-1998 Income $11,953, City $6,000, County $5,953. Mats Exp $11,816, Books $3,525, Per/Ser (Incl. Access Fees) $556, AV Equip $1,598, Other Print Mats $156. Sal $5,303
Library Holdings: Bk Titles 8,730; Per Subs 12
Open Mon 1-5:30, Tues 8-12, Wed 2-7, Fri 2-5:30, Sat 8-12

GEORGE

P GEORGE PUBLIC LIBRARY, 119 S Main St, PO Box 738, 51237. SAN 305-4276. Tel: 712-475-3897. E-Mail: geolibry@rconnect.com. *Dir*, Nadine Dykstra
Founded 1937. Pop 1,066; Circ 20,174
Jul 1999-Jun 2000 Income $19,012, State $457, City $9,348, County $7,652, Other $1,555. Mats Exp $4,906, Books $3,090, Per/Ser (Incl. Access Fees) $1,006, Other Print Mats $810. Sal $11,821
Library Holdings: Bk Vols 11,614; Per Subs 44
Mem of Northwest Regional Library System
Open Mon & Tues 1-5, Wed 1-6, Thurs 1-8, Fri 10-5 & Sat 9-11

GILMAN

P GILMAN PUBLIC LIBRARY,* 106 N Main St, PO Box 383, 50106-0383. SAN 305-4284. Tel: 515-498-2120. E-Mail: gillib@pcpartner.net. *Librn*, Wilma Smith
Pop 642; Circ 4,706
Library Holdings: Bk Vols 5,000
Mem of Central Regional Libr Syst
Open Mon & Wed 8:30-11, Tues & Thurs 1-6, Sat 8:30-12
Friends of the Library Group

GLADBROOK

P GLADBROOK PUBLIC LIBRARY,* 301 Second St, PO Box 399, 50635. SAN 305-4306. Tel: 515-473-3236. FAX: 515-473-3236. *Librn*, C J Thompson
Pop 970; Circ 10,394
Library Holdings: Bk Vols 13,000; Bk Titles 9,862; Per Subs 16
Open Mon 9-6, Wed 12-7, Fri 12-6, Sat 9-12

GLENWOOD

P GLENWOOD PUBLIC LIBRARY, 109 N Vine, 51534. SAN 305-4314. Tel: 712-527-5252. TDD: 712-527-5252. FAX: 712-527-3619. *Dir*, Denise S Crawford; E-Mail: crawford@server.silo.lib.ia.us; *Ch Servs*, Patricia R Conrad; *ILL*, Betty Jo Budd
Founded 1896. Pop 4,960; Circ 64,612
Jul 1999-Jun 2000 Income $197,646. Mats Exp $30,165, Books $24,958, Per/Ser (Incl. Access Fees) $3,707, AV Equip $1,500. Sal $120,438
Library Holdings: Bk Titles 32,174; Per Subs 148
Subject Interests: Genealogy, Local history
Mem of Southwest Iowa Regional Library System
Friends of the Library Group

M GLENWOOD STATE HOSPITAL-SCHOOL, Staff Library,* 711 S Vine St, 51534. SAN 305-4322. Tel: 712-527-4811. FAX: 712-527-2371. *Dir*, Regina Forney
Founded 1960
Library Holdings: Bk Vols 5,000; Per Subs 20
Open Mon-Fri 8-4:30

GLIDDEN

P GLIDDEN PUBLIC LIBRARY,* 131 Idaho St, 51443. SAN 305-4330. Tel: 712-659-3781. E-Mail: glibrary@netins.net. *Librn*, Erin Wolf
Pop 1,076; Circ 21,572
Library Holdings: Bk Vols 16,000; Bk Titles 11,496; Per Subs 41
Special Collections: Media: videos (200), audios (25)
Mem of Northwest Regional Library System
Open MOn, Tues, Wed & Fri 1-5, Thurs 1-8, Sat 10-4

GOWRIE

P GOWRIE PUBLIC LIBRARY,* 1204 Market, PO Box 137, 50543-5052. SAN 305-4349. Tel: 515-352-3315. FAX: 515-352-3713. *Dir*, Judi Tjepkes
Founded 1930. Pop 1,400; Circ 15,282
Jul 1998-Jun 1999 Income $35,022, State $235, City $11,000, County $11,587, Other $12,200. Mats Exp $6,484, Books $6,051, Other Print Mats $433. Sal $16,099
Library Holdings: Bk Vols 7,900; Per Subs 31
Mem of North Central Regional Library System
Open Mon-Fri 1-5, Sat 9-12 & Wed evenings 7-9

GRAETTINGER

P GRAETTINGER PUBLIC LIBRARY, 115 W Robins Ave, PO Box 368, 51342-0368. SAN 305-4357. Tel: 712-859-3592. FAX: 712-859-3592. E-Mail: library@netins.net. *Librn*, Susie Mahan; *Asst Librn*, Mindy Witt
Founded 1939. Pop 820; Circ 13,136
Library Holdings: Bk Titles 10,000; Per Subs 30
Special Collections: Media: videos (306), audios (112)
Mem of Northwest Regional Library System
Open Mon-Thurs 9-5, Fri 10-5, Sat 9-3
Friends of the Library Group

GRAFTON

P GRAFTON PUBLIC LIBRARY,* 203 Fourth Ave, 50440. SAN 305-4365. Tel: 515-748-2735. FAX: 515-748-2739. E-Mail: cjpahl@netins.net. Web Site: www.netins.net/showcase/GraftonLib. *Librn*, Carol Pahl
Pop 300; Circ 8,425
Library Holdings: Bk Vols 10,283; Per Subs 55
Mem of N Cent Iowa Regional Libr Syst
Open Mon & Fri 1:30-5:30, Wed 1:30-9, Sat 1-5:30

GRAND JUNCTION

P GRAND JUNCTION PUBLIC LIBRARY, 106 Main St, PO Box 79, 50107. SAN 305-4373. Tel: 515-738-2506. E-Mail: gjpl@netins.net. *Librn*, Jenon Cody
Founded 1929. Pop 970; Circ 6,500

Library Holdings: Bk Titles 9,000; Per Subs 30
Special Collections: Media: videos (200), audios (200)
Mem of Central Iowa Regional Library
Open Mon-Fri 2-5, Wed 6:30-8:30, Sat 9-2

GRANGER

P GRANGER PUBLIC LIBRARY, 1906 Main St, PO Box 393, 50109. SAN 305-4381. Tel: 515-999-2088. FAX: 515-999-2988. E-Mail: grangerplib@dux.com. *Librn*, Marcia Henry
Pop 619
Library Holdings: Bk Titles 6,062; Per Subs 40
Mem of Central Iowa Regional Library
Open Mon-Thurs 2-7, Sat 9:30-11:30

GREENE

P GREENE PUBLIC LIBRARY,* 231 W Traer, PO Box 280, 50636-0280. SAN 305-439X. Tel: 515-823-4803. FAX: 515-823-4838. E-Mail: gpl@greene.k12.ia.us, grnpublc@netins.net. *Dir, Online Servs*, Cynthia Siemons; *Ch Servs*, Dorothy Leavens; *Circ, Publ Servs*, Judy Steere
Founded 1872. Pop 2,600; Circ 27,707
Jul 1998-Jun 1999 Income $82,000. Mats Exp $16,500. Sal $33,950
Library Holdings: Bk Titles 17,046; Per Subs 89
Special Collections: Media: Videos- 727; Audios- 500; The Greene Recorder (1876-1996), microfilm
Mem of Northeastern Iowa Regional Library System
Open Mon & Wed 9-9, Tues, Thurs & Fri 12-5 & Sat 9-5

GREENFIELD

P GREENFIELD PUBLIC LIBRARY, 202 S First St, PO Box 328, 50849. SAN 305-4403. Tel: 515-743-6120. E-Mail: greenpl@mddc.com. *Dir*, Lynn Heibuch; *Dir*, Lorraine Schneider
Founded 1916. Pop 2,243; Circ 27,531
Library Holdings: Bk Vols 22,000; Per Subs 100
Subject Interests: Genealogy
Mem of Southwest Iowa Regional Library System
Open Mon, Tues, Wed & Fri 10-5:30, Thurs 10-7, Sat 10-12
Friends of the Library Group

GRIMES

P GRIMES PUBLIC LIBRARY,* 200 N James, PO Box 290, 50111. SAN 305-4411. Tel: 515-986-3551. FAX: 515-986-9553. Web Site: www.grimes.lib.ia.us. *Dir*, Karla D Pfaff; E-Mail: pfaffk@web.grimes.lib.ia.us; Staff 9 (Non-MLS 9)
Founded 1972. Pop 5,000
Jan 1999-Dec 1999 Income $151,163, City $138,163, County $13,000. Sal $83,132
Library Holdings: Bk Vols 26,393; Bk Titles 23,616; Per Subs 45
Database Vendor: OCLC - First Search
Mem of Central Iowa Regional Library
Friends of the Library Group

GRINNELL

C GRINNELL COLLEGE LIBRARIES, Burling Library, 1111 Sixth Ave, 50112-1690. SAN 305-442X. Tel: 641-269-3350. Interlibrary Loan Service Tel: 515-269-3362. Reference Tel: 641-269-3353. FAX: 641-269-4283. Web Site: www.lib.grin.edu/. *Chief Librn*, Christopher McKee; Tel: 641-269-3351, Fax: 641-269-3351, E-Mail: mckee@grinnell.edu; *Assoc Librn*, Gail J Bonath; Tel: 641-269-3358, E-Mail: bonath@grinnell.edu; *Archivist, Assoc Librn*, Catherine M Rod; Tel: 641-269-3364, E-Mail: rod@grinnell.edu; *Science*, Kevin Engel; Tel: 641-269-4234, E-Mail: engelk@grinnell.edu; *Cat*, R Cecilia Knight; Tel: 641-269-3368, E-Mail: knight@grinnell.edu; *Archivist*, Leslie Czechowski; Tel: 515-269-3364, E-Mail: czechowl@grinnell.edu; *Coll Develop*, Rebecca Stuhr; Tel: 641-269-3674, E-Mail: stuhrr@grinnell.edu; *Publ Servs*, Christina Coyle; Tel: 641-269-3354, E-Mail: coylec@grinnell.edu; *Publ Servs*, David Weaver; Tel: 641-269-3355, E-Mail: weaverd@grinnell.edu. Subject Specialists: *Naval hist*, Christopher McKee; Staff 23 (MLS 9, Non-MLS 14)
Founded 1846. Enrl 1,295; Fac 136; Highest Degree: Bachelor
Jul 1999-Jun 2000 Mats Exp $1,097,021, Books $376,780, Per/Ser (Incl. Access Fees) $576,000, Presv $38,290, Micro $238, AV Equip $28,250, Electronic Ref Mat (Incl. Access Fees) $77,463. Sal $806,805 (Prof $435,231)
Library Holdings: Bk Vols 454,734; Bk Titles 411,381; Per Subs 3,400
Special Collections: East Asian Coll; Iowa, Local History & College Archives, bks & mss; James Norman Hall, paper & mss; Pinne Coll, bks & mss
Automation Activity & Vendor Info: (Acquisitions) Innovative Interfaces Inc.; (Circulation) Innovative Interfaces Inc.; (Course Reserve) Innovative Interfaces Inc.; (ILL) Innovative Interfaces Inc.; (OPAC) Innovative Interfaces Inc.; (Serials) Innovative Interfaces Inc.
Database Vendor: Dialog, Innovative Interfaces INN - View, Lexis-Nexis, OCLC - First Search, Silverplatter Information Inc., Wilson - Wilson Web
Function: Reference services available, Research library
Partic in Iowa Private Academic Library Consortium; Iowa Resource & Info Sharing

P STEWART LIBRARY,* 926 Broad St, 50112. SAN 305-4438. Tel: 515-236-2661. FAX: 515-236-2667. E-Mail: stewart@netins.net. Web Site: www.avn.net/library homepage/slhomepage.htm or www.netins.net/showcase/stewartlib/stewartlibrary/index.html. *Dir*, Lorna Caulkins; *Ch Servs*, Virginia Cameron; Staff 10 (MLS 2, Non-MLS 8)
Founded 1901. Pop 8,902
Library Holdings: Bk Vols 49,636; Per Subs 196
Friends of the Library Group

GRISWOLD

P GRISWOLD PUBLIC LIBRARY,* 505 Main, PO Box 190, 51535-0190. SAN 305-4446. Tel: 712-778-4130. FAX: 712-778-2619. E-Mail: grislib@netins.net. *Librn*, Jenelia Copenhaver
Founded 1977. Circ 14,630
1998-1999 Income $23,000
Library Holdings: Bk Vols 13,600; Per Subs 20
Mem of Southwest Iowa Regional Library System
Open Tues 10-6, Wed, Thurs & Fri 10-12 & 2-5, Sat 10-12

GRUNDY CENTER

P KLING MEMORIAL LIBRARY,* 706 Seventh St, 50638-1430. SAN 305-4454. Tel: 319-824-3607. FAX: 319-824-5863. E-Mail: grndylib@sbt.net. *Librn*, Dan Bakke
Pop 2,499; Circ 57,306
1997-1998 Income $79,319. Mats Exp $16,595, Books $10,783, Per/Ser (Incl. Access Fees) $3,005, Micro $392, Other Print Mats $2,415. Sal $37,054
Library Holdings: Bk Vols 22,944; Per Subs 99
Subject Interests: Iowa, Large type print
Mem of Northeastern Iowa Regional Library System
Open Mon-Wed & Fri 10-5, Thurs 10-8, Sat 10-4
Friends of the Library Group

GUTHRIE CENTER

P MARY BARNETT MEMORIAL LIBRARY, 400 Grand St, 50115-1439. SAN 305-4462. Tel: 641-747-8110. FAX: 641-747-8110. E-Mail: gthrieoo@iren.net. Web Site: www.guthriecenter.com/library. *Dir*, Pat Sleister; Staff 1 (MLS 1)
Founded 1902. Pop 2,000; Circ 45,000
Library Holdings: Bk Titles 25,000; Per Subs 85
Special Collections: Large Print Books Coll; Media: Videos- 150; Audios- 400
Mem of Southwest Iowa Regional Library System
Open Tues, Thurs & Fri 1:30-5:30pm, Mon & Wed 1:30-8:30pm & Sat 10am-3pm
Friends of the Library Group

GUTTENBERG

P GUTTENBERG PUBLIC LIBRARY,* 603 S Second St, PO Box 130, 52052-0130. SAN 305-4470. Tel: 319-252-3108. FAX: 319-252-3108. E-Mail: guttlib@netins.net. *Librn*, Mary Ackerman
Pop 2,428; Circ 22,032
Jul 1998-Jun 1999 Income $55,000, City $27,000, County $10,000, Parent Institution $5,000. Mats Exp $14,000, Books $12,500, Per/Ser (Incl. Access Fees) $1,000, Other Print Mats $500. Sal $28,000
Library Holdings: Bk Titles 20,000; Per Subs 45
Special Collections: Media: Video (150), Audio (100)
Mem of Northeastern Regional Libr Syst
Open Mon & Wed 1-8, Tues & Thurs 10-5, Fri 1-5, Sat 9-3

HAMBURG

P HAMBURG PUBLIC LIBRARY,* 1301 Main St, 51640. SAN 305-4489. Tel: 712-382-1395. E-Mail: hamlib@hamburg.heartland.net. *Dir*, Emily Seeger
Founded 1917. Pop 1,597; Circ 49,914
Library Holdings: Bk Vols 28,043; Bk Titles 11,500; Per Subs 23
Subject Interests: History, Iowa
Special Collections: Media: Video (362), Audio (50)
Mem of Southwest Iowa Regional Library System
Open Mon 9:30-11, 1:30-4:30 & 7-8:30, Tues 1:30-4:30, Wed 9:30-11 & 1:30-4:30, Thurs 1:30-4:30 & 7-8:30, Fri 9:30-11 & 1:30-4:30, Sat 10-2
Friends of the Library Group

HAMPTON

P HAMPTON PUBLIC LIBRARY,* 4 Federal St S, 50441-1934. SAN 305-4497. Tel: 515-456-4451. FAX: 515-456-2377. E-Mail: hampublib@hampton-dumont.k12.ia.us. *Dir*, Judy Harper; *Asst Librn*, Suzanne Knipfel; *Ch Servs*, Kim Ball; Staff 2 (MLS 2)
Founded 1889. Pop 4,133
Jul 1997-Jun 1998 Income $135,065, Provincial $65,800, City $42,234. Mats Exp $28,368, Books $20,395, Per/Ser (Incl. Access Fees) $4,909, Micro $1,644. Sal $70,804 (Prof $55,364)
Library Holdings: Bk Titles 37,000; Per Subs 125
Subject Interests: Genealogy, Iowa
Mem of North Central Regional Library System
Open Mon-Thurs 10-8, Fri-Sat 10-5
Friends of the Library Group

HANLONTOWN

P KINNEY MEMORIAL LIBRARY,* 214 Main St, PO Box 58, 50444. SAN 305-4500. Tel: 515-896-2888. FAX: 515-896-2888. E-Mail: redhawks@netins.net. *Librn*, Stacey Lunsford
Pop 193; Circ 2,975
Library Holdings: Bk Titles 5,114; Per Subs 21
Special Collections: Media: videos (145)
Mem of North Central Regional Library System
Open Mon & Wed 6:30-8:30, Tues & Thurs 1-7, Sat 9-1

HARCOURT

P HARCOURT COMMUNITY LIBRARY, 106 W Second St, PO Box 358, 50544. SAN 305-4519. Tel: 515-354-5391. FAX: 515-354-5391. E-Mail: harcourt@netins.net. *Librn*, Twila Widen
Founded 1950. Pop 700; Circ 5,200
Library Holdings: Bk Vols 6,000; Per Subs 45
Mem of North Central Regional Library System
Open Tues 2:30-8, Wed 4-8, Thurs 2:30-8:30, Sat 8:30-1

HARLAN

P HARLAN COMMUNITY LIBRARY,* 718 Court, 51537-1317. SAN 305-4527. Tel: 712-755-5934. FAX: 712-755-3952. E-Mail: harlanpl@harlannet.com. Web Site: www.harlan.lib.ia.us. *Dir*, Jill Pannkuk
Pop 12,168; Circ 105,928
Jul 1998-Jun 1999 Income $200,000. Mats Exp $35,000. Sal $92,000
Library Holdings: Bk Vols 55,000; Per Subs 120
Special Collections: Iowa History; Media: videos (1650), audios (2000)
Automation Activity & Vendor Info: (Circulation) Follett
Mem of Southwest Iowa Regional Library System
Open Mon Tues, Wed, Fri & Sat 9:30-4:30, Thurs 9:30-8:30

HARPERS FERRY

P HARPERS FERRY PUBLIC LIBRARY, 234 Fourth St, PO Box 57, 52146-0057. SAN 376-5040. Tel: 319-586-2524. FAX: 319-586-2524. E-Mail: harplib@means.net. *Librn*, Melissa Patrick
Jul 1999-Jun 2000 Income $11,017. Mats Exp $3,013. Sal $5,868
Library Holdings: Bk Vols 8,391; Per Subs 70
Mem of Northeastern Iowa Regional Library System
Open Tues & Sat 9-12, Wed 4:30-8:30, Fri 2-5

S US NATIONAL PARK SERVICE EFFIGY MOUNDS NATIONAL MONUMENT LIBRARY, 151 Hwy 76, 52146. SAN 370-3185. Tel: 319-873-3491. FAX: 319-873-3743.
Library Holdings: Bk Vols 10,000
Subject Interests: Natural history
Special Collections: Ellison Orr, mss
Restriction: Open to others by appointment, Public reference by request
Federal Government National Monument

HARTLEY

P HARTLEY PUBLIC LIBRARY, 91 First St SE, 51346. SAN 305-4535. Tel: 712-728-2080. FAX: 712-728-2823. E-Mail: hpl51346@rconnect.com. *Coll Develop, Librn*, Nona Hengeveld
Founded 1942. Pop 1,550; Circ 31,082
Jul 2000-Jun 2001 Income $52,913, City $40,480, County $5,500, Other $6,933. Mats Exp $11,532, Books $9,741, Per/Ser (Incl. Access Fees) $1,791. Sal $20,363
Library Holdings: Bk Vols 19,245; Per Subs 92
Automation Activity & Vendor Info: (Cataloging) Sagebrush Corporation; (Circulation) Sagebrush Corporation
Friends of the Library Group

HAWARDEN

P HAWARDEN PUBLIC LIBRARY, 803 Tenth St, 51023. SAN 305-456X. Tel: 712-551-2244. FAX: 712-551-1720. E-Mail: haw_library@acsnet.com. Web Site: www.hawardenlibrary.org. *Librn*, Valerie Haverhals
Founded 1901. Pop 2,600; Circ 49,352
Jul 2000-Jun 2001 Income $148,500, State $2,247, City $113,380, County $21,468, Other $5,000. Mats Exp $28,650, Books $21,000, Per/Ser (Incl. Access Fees) $3,750, Presv $200, AV Equip $2,700, Electronic Ref Mat (Incl. Access Fees) $1,000. Sal $81,904 (Prof $28,500)
Library Holdings: Bk Vols 22,465; Per Subs 112
Special Collections: Map Coll of Northwest Iowa
Database Vendor: OCLC - First Search
Mem of Northwest Regional Library System
Open Mon-Thurs 10-8, Fri & Sat 10-5

HAWKEYE

P HAWKEYE PUBLIC LIBRARY,* 104 S Second St, 52147-0216. SAN 305-4586. Tel: 319-427-5536. FAX: 319-427-5536. E-Mail: hawklib@netins.net. *Librn*, Barbara Langerman
Pop 512; Circ 6,300
1998-1999 Income $22,540. Mats Exp $2,850, Books $2,400, Per/Ser (Incl. Access Fees) $350. Sal $7,219
Library Holdings: Bk Titles 7,829; Per Subs 30
Subject Interests: Civil War
Mem of Northeastern Iowa Regional Library System
Open Mon, Wed & Fri 1-5, Tues & Thurs 3-7, Sat 10-12

HEDRICK

P HEDRICK PUBLIC LIBRARY,* 109 Main St, PO Box 427, 52563-0123. SAN 305-4594. Tel: 515-653-4914. FAX: 515-653-2487. E-Mail: hedricpublib@se-iowa.net. *Librn*, Kathleen Cavin
Pop 847; Circ 4,849
Jul 1998-Jun 1999 Income $8,843. Mats Exp $800, Books $700, Per/Ser (Incl. Access Fees) $100. Sal $5,200
Library Holdings: Bk Titles 7,997; Per Subs 20
Mem of Southeastern Library Services
Open Mon, Tues & Thurs 2-5, Wed & Fri 2-6, Sat 8:30-11:30

HIAWATHA

P HIAWATHA PUBLIC LIBRARY,* 150 W Willman St, 52233. SAN 305-4608. Tel: 319-393-1414. FAX: 319-393-6005. *Dir*, Rosemary Earl; *Asst Dir*, Linda Nash; Staff 7 (Non-MLS 7)
Founded 1960. Pop 5,557; Circ 84,659
Jul 1998-Jun 1999 Income $131,419, State $15,596, City $84,767, Federal $2,686, County $19,074, Locally Generated Income $9,296. Mats Exp $20,380, Books $15,351, Per/Ser (Incl. Access Fees) $1,990, AV Equip $3,039. Sal $86,192
Library Holdings: Bk Titles 26,388; Per Subs 91
Automation Activity & Vendor Info: (Cataloging) DRA; (Circulation) DRA
Database Vendor: DRA
Partic in Linn County Library Consortium
Open Mon-Thurs 10-8, Fri & Sat 10-5, Sun 1-4
Friends of the Library Group

HILLSBORO

P HILLSBORO PUBLIC LIBRARY,* 100 W Commercial St, 52630. SAN 305-4616. Tel: 319-253-4000. E-Mail: hillsborobooks@lisco.net. *Librn*, Dianne Runyan
Founded 1937. Pop 208; Circ 3,120
1998-1999 Income $6,400, City $600, County $5,800
Library Holdings: Bk Titles 5,000
Mem of Southeastern Library Services
Open Mon 4-6, Wed & Fri 2-6:30

HOLSTEIN

P STUBBS MEMORIAL LIBRARY, 207 E Second St, PO Box 290, 51025. SAN 305-4624. Tel: 712-368-4563. FAX: 712-368-4483. E-Mail: stubbs@tionet.net. *Librn*, Bonnie Barkema; *Ch Servs*, Sharon Willson
Pop 1,477; Circ 33,312
Library Holdings: Bk Titles 17,767; Per Subs 80
Mem of Northwest Regional Library System

HOPKINTON

P HOPKINTON PUBLIC LIBRARY,* 110 First St SE, PO Box 220, 52237-0220. SAN 305-4632. Tel: 319-926-2514. E-Mail: hopkintonlib@n-connect.net. Web Site: www.hopkintonlib@n-connect.net. *Librn*, Carolyn Wilson

Pop 800; Circ 12,000
Library Holdings: Bk Titles 13,000; Per Subs 28
Mem of Northeastern Regional Libr Syst
Special Services for the Blind - Audio-cassettes; Large print bks

HUBBARD

P HUBBARD PUBLIC LIBRARY,* 323 E Maple St, PO Box 307, 50122. SAN 305-4640. Tel: 515-864-2771. FAX: 515-864-3379. *Librn*, Nancy Filkins
Founded 1930. Pop 843; Circ 4,484
Library Holdings: Bk Titles 7,080; Per Subs 54
Special Collections: Media: videos (1200), audios (260)
Mem of North Central Regional Library System
Open Mon 9-12 & 1-5, Tues, Thurs & Fri 1-5, Wed 1-8, Sat 8-12

HUDSON

P HUDSON PUBLIC LIBRARY, 401 Fifth St, PO Box 480, 50643. SAN 305-4659. Tel: 319-988-4217. E-Mail: hs10097@cedarnet.org. *Dir*, Mary L Bucy; Staff 5 (Non-MLS 5)
Pop 2,050; Circ 3,300
Jul 1999-Jun 2000 Income $97,862, State $1,316, City $78,954, County $6,972, Locally Generated Income $5,805. Mats Exp $44,255, Books $13,267, Per/Ser (Incl. Access Fees) $2,638, Micro $903. Sal $47,256
Library Holdings: Bk Titles 22,418; Per Subs 94
Automation Activity & Vendor Info: (Circulation) Sagebrush Corporation; (OPAC) Sagebrush Corporation
Database Vendor: OCLC - First Search
Function: Reference services available
Special Services for the Blind - Audiobooks; Large print bks
Friends of the Library Group

HULL

P HULL PUBLIC LIBRARY, 1135 Main St, 51239. (Mail add: PO Box 822, 51239), SAN 305-4667. Tel: 712-439-1321. FAX: 712-439-1534. E-Mail: hulllib@rconnect.com. *Librn*, Jan Van Soelen; *Asst Librn*, Phyllis DeJong
Pop 1,800; Circ 54,538
Jul 1999-Jun 2000 Income $76,835, State $963, City $57,472, County $17,803, Other $597. Mats Exp $15,168, Books $9,915, Per/Ser (Incl. Access Fees) $1,920, Micro $75, AV Equip $1,867, Electronic Ref Mat (Incl. Access Fees) $1,391. Sal $32,515
Library Holdings: Bk Titles 16,860; Per Subs 87
Automation Activity & Vendor Info: (Cataloging) Sagebrush Corporation; (Circulation) Sagebrush Corporation
Mem of Northwest Regional Library System
Open Mon, Tues, Wed & Fri 12:30-5:30, Thurs 12:30-9, Sat 9-1
Friends of the Library Group

HUMBOLDT

P HUMBOLDT PUBLIC LIBRARY, 30 Sixth St N, 50548. SAN 305-4675. Tel: 515-332-1925. FAX: 515-332-1926. E-Mail: hmbldtpl@trvnet.net. *Dir*, Stacey Lunsford; *Ch Servs*, Jean Holste; Staff 2 (MLS 1, Non-MLS 1)
Founded 1908. Pop 4,794; Circ 82,395
Library Holdings: Bk Titles 25,831; Per Subs 85
Special Collections: Media: videos (425), audios (250)
Mem of North Central Regional Library System
Open Mon, Tues & Wed 10-8, Thurs, Fri, Sat 10-5
Friends of the Library Group

HUMESTON

P HUMESTON PUBLIC LIBRARY,* PO Box 97, 50123-0097. SAN 305-4683. Tel: 515-877-4811. E-Mail: humlib@pionet.net. *Librn*, LaVonne Casey
Pop 671; Circ 8,180
Library Holdings: Bk Titles 15,405; Per Subs 12
Mem of Southwest Iowa Regional Library System
Open Mon, Wed & Fri 1-5, Sat 9:30-12

HUXLEY

P HUXLEY PUBLIC LIBRARY,* 602 N Main Ave, 50124. (Mail add: PO Box 5, 50124-0005), SAN 305-4691. Tel: 515-597-2552. FAX: 515-597-2552. E-Mail: huxlib@pcpartner.net. *Librn*, Chris Peterson
Founded 1972. Pop 2,047; Circ 21,856
Jul 1998-Jun 1999 Income $58,770. Mats Exp $9,093. Sal $27,536
Library Holdings: Bk Vols 16,000; Per Subs 55
Special Collections: Iowa History; Norwegian Language Books
Mem of Central Iowa Regional Library
Open Mon & Wed 1-5, 6-9, Tues & Thurs 9-12:30, 6-9, Fri 1-5, Sat 9-12:30
Friends of the Library Group

IDA GROVE

P IDA GROVE PUBLIC LIBRARY,* 100 E Second St, 51445. SAN 305-4705. Tel: 712-364-2306. FAX: 712-364-3228. E-Mail: idagrlib@pionet.net. *Librn*, Sharon Zulauf
Pop 2,268
Library Holdings: Bk Titles 17,786; Per Subs 65
Mem of Northwest Regional Library System
Friends of the Library Group

INDEPENDENCE

S BUCHANAN COUNTY HISTORICAL SOCIETY, Genealogical Society Library, PO Box 4, 50644-0004. SAN 323-7923. Tel: 319-334-9333. *Pres*, Ann Gitsch; *VPres*, Gladys Corkery
Founded 1976
Subject Interests: Family hist, Local history
Publications: Newsletter (bi-annually)
Open Mon 10-2

P INDEPENDENCE PUBLIC LIBRARY, 210 Second St NE, 50644. SAN 305-4713. Tel: 319-334-2470. FAX: 319-334-2470. E-Mail: indeelib@independence.lib.ia.us. Web Site: www.independence.lib.ia.us. *Dir*, Don Hiner; *Actg Dir*, Amy McGraw; E-Mail: amcgraw@independence.lib.ia.us; Staff 7 (MLS 1, Non-MLS 6)
Founded 1857. Pop 6,000; Circ 64,825
Jul 1999-Jun 2000 Income $142,687, State $3,123, City $112,748, County $24,773, Locally Generated Income $2,043. Mats Exp $27,559, Books $24,337, Per/Ser (Incl. Access Fees) $3,222. Sal $81,328 (Prof $31,000)
Library Holdings: Bk Vols 23,839; Per Subs 119
Automation Activity & Vendor Info: (Circulation) Sagebrush Corporation; (OPAC) Sagebrush Corporation
Mem of Northeastern Iowa Regional Library System
Open Mon-Thurs 9:30-8, Fri & Sat 9:30-5, Sun 1-4 (except summers)
Friends of the Library Group

M MENTAL HEALTH INSTITUTE, Medical Library,* 2277 Iowa Ave, PO Box 111, 50644. SAN 305-4721. Tel: 319-334-2583. FAX: 319-334-5252. *Librn*, Bernadette Shannon; Tel: 319-334-2583, Fax: 319-334-5252
Library Holdings: Bk Titles 4,000; Per Subs 35
Subject Interests: Medicine, Nursing, Psychiatry, Psychology, Social sciences and issues

INDIANOLA

P INDIANOLA PUBLIC LIBRARY, 207 North B St, 50125. SAN 305-473X. Tel: 515-961-9418. FAX: 515-961-9419. E-Mail: info@indianola.lib.ia.us, winston@netins.net. Web Site: www.indianola.lib.ia.us. *Dir*, Joyce Godwin; E-Mail: igodwin@indianola.lib.ia.us; *Asst Dir*, Alice Gaumer; E-Mail: agaumer@indianola.lib.ia.us; *Cat*, Jennifer Clark; Staff 6 (MLS 1, Non-MLS 5)
Founded 1884. Pop 12,300; Circ 112,321
Jul 1999-Jun 2000 Income $281,048, State $3,366, City $250,500, County $26,331. Mats Exp $276,737, Per/Ser (Incl. Access Fees) $6,219, Electronic Ref Mat (Incl. Access Fees) $350. Sal $163,138 (Prof $45,000)
Library Holdings: Bk Vols 35,292; Per Subs 146
Subject Interests: Genealogy, Local history
Special Collections: Media: videos (500, audios (500)
Automation Activity & Vendor Info: (Acquisitions) Innovative Interfaces Inc.; (Cataloging) Innovative Interfaces Inc.; (Circulation) Innovative Interfaces Inc.; (Serials) Innovative Interfaces Inc.
Function: Some telephone reference
Mem of Central Iowa Regional Library
Partic in Bibliographical Center For Research, Rocky Mountain Region, Inc; OCLC Online Computer Library Center, Inc
Open Mon-Thurs 10-8:30, Fri 10-6, Sat 10-5, Sun 1-4

CR SIMPSON COLLEGE, Dunn Library, 508 North C St, 50125-1297. SAN 305-4748. Tel: 515-961-1663. Circulation Tel: 515-961-1518. Reference Tel: 515-961-1748. FAX: 515-961-1363. Web Site: www.simpson.edu/dunn/dunn.html. *Dir*, Cynthia M Dyer; Tel: 515-961-1519, E-Mail: dyer@simpson.edu; *Info Res*, Steve Duffy; E-Mail: duffy@simpson.edu; *Syst Coordr*, Jay L Robinson; Tel: 515-961-1520, E-Mail: robinjl@simpson.edu; *Ser*, Liz Grimsbo; Tel: 515-961-1485, E-Mail: grimsbo@simpson.edu; Staff 8 (MLS 4, Non-MLS 4)
Founded 1860. Enrl 1,525; Fac 112; Highest Degree: Bachelor
Jun 1999-May 2000 Income $594,625, State $3,578, Parent Institution $591,147. Mats Exp $233,403, Books $90,532, Per/Ser (Incl. Access Fees) $107,239, Presv $2,551, Micro $7,952, AV Equip $13,675, Electronic Ref Mat (Incl. Access Fees) $6,954. Sal $232,454 (Prof $103,204)
Library Holdings: Bk Vols 119,478; Bk Titles 103,068; Per Subs 607; Spec Interest Per Sub 25; Bks on Deafness & Sign Lang 30; Bks on Deafness & Sign Lang 31
Special Collections: Avery O Craven Coll
Automation Activity & Vendor Info: (Acquisitions) Innovative Interfaces Inc.; (Circulation) Innovative Interfaces Inc.; (Course Reserve) Innovative Interfaces Inc.; (OPAC) Innovative Interfaces Inc.; (Serials) Innovative

Interfaces Inc.
Database Vendor: Lexis-Nexis, OCLC - First Search, ProQuest
Publications: Annual report; brochure; serials list
Partic in OCLC Online Computer Library Center, Inc

INWOOD

P INWOOD PUBLIC LIBRARY, 103 S Main, 51240-0069. SAN 305-4756. Tel: 712-753-4814. E-Mail: impublib@netims.net. *Librn*, Clarene Burgers; *Assoc Librn*, Donna Bos
Pop 850; Circ 12,000
Jul 1999-Jun 2000 Income $30,450, State $438, City $17,785, County $7,198, Locally Generated Income $5,000. Mats Exp $11,190, Books $8,600, Per/Ser (Incl. Access Fees) $750, Other Print Mats $450, Electronic Ref Mat (Incl. Access Fees) $1,500. Sal $8,850
Library Holdings: Bk Titles 13,500; Per Subs 34
Automation Activity & Vendor Info: (Acquisitions) Sagebrush Corporation; (Cataloging) Sagebrush Corporation; (Circulation) Sagebrush Corporation
Mem of Northwest Regional Library System

IONIA

P IONIA COMMUNITY LIBRARY,* 101 W Iowa St, PO Box 130, 50645. SAN 305-4764. Tel: 515-394-4803. FAX: 515-394-4803. *Dir*, Jane McGrane; Staff 1 (MLS 1)
Founded 1974. Pop 350
Jul 1998-Jun 1999 Income $16,036. Mats Exp $3,817, Books $3,617, Per/Ser (Incl. Access Fees) $200. Sal $8,460
Library Holdings: Bk Titles 6,000; Per Subs 24
Mem of Northeastern Iowa Regional Library System
Open Mon 4-8, Tues 9:30-11:30 & 1-5, Wed 4-8:30, Thurs 1-5, Sat 9:30-11:30

IOWA CITY

S ACT LIBRARY, 2201 N Dodge, PO Box 168, 52243-0168. SAN 305-4772. Tel: 319-337-1165. FAX: 319-339-3021. *Librn*, Jacqueline Snider; E-Mail: snider@act.org; *Tech Servs*, Kathleen Lynch; Staff 2 (MLS 1, Non-MLS 1)
Founded 1968
Library Holdings: Bk Titles 30,000; Per Subs 600
Subject Interests: Education
Special Collections: ERIC Coll
Publications: New booklist
Partic in OCLC Online Computer Library Center, Inc

S GUILD OF BOOK WORKERS LIBRARY, University of Iowa, 52242. SAN 327-3393. Tel: 319-335-5908. FAX: 319-335-5900. E-Mail: gbwweb@dartmouth.edu. Web Site: palimpsest.stanford.edu/byorg/gbw/. *Librn*, Anna Embree; E-Mail: anna-embree@uiowa.edu
Library Holdings: Bk Titles 800

P IOWA CITY PUBLIC LIBRARY,* 123 S Linn, 52240. SAN 305-4780. Tel: 319-356-5200. FAX: 319-356-5494. E-Mail: icpl@iowa-city.lib.ia.us. Web Site: www.icpl.org. *Dir*, Susan Craig; E-Mail: scraig@iowa-city.lib.ia.us; *Asst Dir, Automation Syst Coordr*, Elizabeth Nichols; E-Mail: lnichols@iowa-city.lib.ia.us; *Ch Servs*, Debb Green; E-Mail: debgreen@iowa-city.lib.ia.us; *Circ*, Heide Lauritzen; E-Mail: hlauritz@iowa-city.lib.ia.us; *Ref*, Maeve Clark; E-Mail: mavclark@iowa-city.lib.ia.us; *Tech Servs*, Barbara Black; E-Mail: bblack@iowa-city.lib.ia.us; *Commun Servs*, Kara Logsden; E-Mail: klogsden@iowa-city.lib.ia.us
Founded 1896. Pop 77,000; Circ 1,155,116
Jul 1998-Jun 1999 Income $3,326,800, State $56,000, City $2,585,000, County $251,000, Locally Generated Income $434,800
Library Holdings: Bk Vols 232,000; Bk Titles 165,000; Per Subs 610
Automation Activity & Vendor Info: (Acquisitions) Innovative Interfaces Inc.; (Cataloging) Innovative Interfaces Inc.; (Circulation) Innovative Interfaces Inc.; (OPAC) Innovative Interfaces Inc.; (Serials) Innovative Interfaces Inc.
Publications: Children's Calendar (bi-monthly); Window (monthly newsletter)
Special Services - Library cable channel programming; Iowa Communications Network Classroom
Friends of the Library Group

C IOWA INSTITUTE OF HYDRAULIC RESEARCH, Floyd A Nagler Reference Room, 300 S Riverside Dr, 52242-1585. SAN 323-6366. Tel: 319-335-5221. FAX: 319-335-5238. Web Site: www.iihr.uiowa.edu. *Info Specialist*, Daniel Lee Daly; E-Mail: dan-daly@uiowa.edu. Subject Specialists: *Fluid mechanics*, Daniel Lee Daly; *Hydraulics*, Daniel Lee Daly; *Hydrodynamics*, Daniel Lee Daly; Staff 1 (Non-MLS 1)
Founded 1930. Enrl 44; Fac 6; Highest Degree: Doctorate
Library Holdings: Bk Vols 2,500; Bk Titles 1,500; Per Subs 15; Spec Interest Per Sub 15
Subject Interests: Fluid mechanics, Hydraulics, Hydrodynamics, Radar, River mat, Sedimentation
Special Collections: Cold Regions Engineering, bks, papers, rpts; Fluid Mechanics; History of Hydraulics; Hydraulics, bks, papers, rpts; Hydrometeorology; Meteorology; Ship Hydrodynamics; Turbulent Shear Flows
Publications: Bibliographies
Function: Research library

M MERCY HOSPITAL, Medical Library, 500 E Market St, 52245. SAN 305-4799. Tel: 319-339-3660. FAX: 319-358-2619. *Librn*, Ambrosya Amlong; E-Mail: ambrosya.amlong@mercyic.org
Jul 1999-Jun 2000 Income $24,500. Mats Exp $24,500, Books $10,000, Per/Ser (Incl. Access Fees) $10,500, Other Print Mats $2,000, Electronic Ref Mat (Incl. Access Fees) $2,000. Sal $12,000
Library Holdings: Bk Vols 700; Per Subs 150
Subject Interests: Medicine, Nursing
Partic in BRS

S SOJOURNER TRUTH LIBRARY, University of Iowa,* 130 N Madison, 52242. SAN 325-7304. Tel: 319-335-1486. FAX: 319-353-1985. Web Site: www.uiowa.edu/~wrac. *Librn*, Linda Kroon
Library Holdings: Bk Vols 1,100; Per Subs 350
Open Mon-Fri 10-5

S STATE HISTORICAL SOCIETY OF IOWA, 402 Iowa Ave, 52240-1806. SAN 305-4802. Tel: 319-335-3916. FAX: 319-335-3935. Web Site: www.iowahistory.org. *Dir*, Shaner Magalhaes; Tel: 319-335-3927, E-Mail: smagalha@blue.weeg.uiowa.edu; *Spec Coll*, Mary Bennett; *Cat*, Paula Smith; *Cat*, Duncan Stewart; *Acq*, David Hudson; Tel: 319-335-3928; *Ref*, Linda Brown-Link; *Spec Coll*, Matthew Schaefer; *ILL*, Kevin Knoot; *Tech Servs*, Nancy Kraft; *Tech Servs*, Jane Meggers; Staff 13 (MLS 8, Non-MLS 5)
Founded 1857
Jul 1999-Jun 2000 Income State $636,850. Mats Exp $116,050. Sal $520,800
Library Holdings: Bk Vols 148,000; Per Subs 575
Subject Interests: Agriculture, Civil law, Genealogy, History, Iowa, Labor law, Maps, Women's hist
Database Vendor: OCLC - First Search
Restriction: Non-circulating to the public, Not a lending library
Function: Research library
Partic in OCLC Online Computer Library Center, Inc

S UNIVERSITY OF IOWA, Old Capitol Library, 24 Old Capitol Museum, 52242. SAN 305-4810. Tel: 319-335-0548. Web Site: www.uiowa.edu/~oldcap/. *Dir*, Ann Smothers
Founded 1838
Library Holdings: Bk Titles 1,008
Subject Interests: Biology, Education, History
Special Collections: Oral History Coll, tapes; State Publications
The Old Capitol library is a re-creation of the 1840-1850's library in the first state capitol of Iowa

S UNIVERSITY OF IOWA - IOWA TESTING PROGRAMS, Blommers Measurement Resources Lab, 304 Lindquist Ctr, 52242-1587. SAN 322-6840. Tel: 319-335-5416. FAX: 319-335-6038. *Librn*, Martha R Wilding; E-Mail: martha-wilding@uiowa.edu; Staff 2 (MLS 1, Non-MLS 1)
Founded 1973
Oct 1999-Sep 2000 Income $72,000. Mats Exp $18,700, Books $6,000, Per/Ser (Incl. Access Fees) $6,500, Micro $200, Other Print Mats $6,000. Sal $45,000
Library Holdings: Bk Titles 4,000; Per Subs 40
Subject Interests: Educ testing, Measurements, Statistics
Special Collections: Current Tests; Historical Tests
Automation Activity & Vendor Info: (Cataloging) Athena; (Cataloging) Athena; (Cataloging) Sagebrush Corporation; (Circulation) Sagebrush Corporation; (OPAC) Athena; (OPAC) Sagebrush Corporation; (Serials) Sagebrush Corporation

CM UNIVERSITY OF IOWA HOSPITALS & CLINICS, Patients' Library, 8016 JCP, 200 Hawkins Dr, 52242-1046. SAN 305-4829. Tel: 319-356-2468. Web Site: www.uihealthcare.com/patientsvisitors/patientlibrary/patientlibrary.html. *Dir*, Mindwell S Egeland; Tel: 319-384-8908, E-Mail: mindwell-egeland@uiowa.edu; Staff 3 (MLS 1, Non-MLS 2)
Founded 1932
Library Holdings: Bk Titles 11,000
Subject Interests: Consumer health
Special Collections: Consumer Health Information; Popular recreational materials
Automation Activity & Vendor Info: (OPAC) Sagebrush Corporation
Database Vendor: IAC - Info Trac
Function: Some telephone reference

C UNIVERSITY OF IOWA LIBRARIES, 100 Main Library, 52242-1420. SAN 341-8928. Tel: 319-335-5867. Interlibrary Loan Service Tel: 319-335-5917. Reference Tel: 319-335-5299. FAX: 319-335-5900. Interlibrary Loan Service FAX: 319-335-5830. E-Mail: lib-ref@uiowa.edu. Web Site: www.lib.uiowa.edu. *Librn*, Nancy L Baker; *Govt Doc*, Carolyn W Kohler; *Spec Coll*, Sidney Huttner
Founded 1855. Enrl 27,000; Fac 1,800; Highest Degree: Doctorate
Jul 1999-Jun 2000 Mats Exp $852,648. Sal $7,890,653 (Prof $4,567,405)

Library Holdings: Bk Vols 3,384,674; Per Subs 33,638
Publications: Univeristy of Iowa News
Mem of Asn of Research Libraries
Partic in CIC; OCLC Online Computer Library Center, Inc; RLIN
Friends of the Library Group
Departmental Libraries:
ART, W145 Art Bldg, 52242. Tel: 319-335-3089. FAX: 319-335-5900. E-Mail: libart@uiowa.edu. Web Site: www.lib.uiowa.edu. *Head Librn*, Rijn Templeton
Library Holdings: Bk Vols 89,674
Friends of the Library Group
BIOLOGICAL SCIENCES, 100 Main Library, 52242-1420. Tel: 319-335-3083. Web Site: www.lib.uiowa.edu. *Librn*, Jeff Dodd; E-Mail: john-dodd@uiowaedu
Library Holdings: Bk Vols 46,541
Friends of the Library Group
CHEMISTRY, 400 Chemistry Bldg, 52242. Tel: 319-335-3085. Web Site: www.lib.uiowa.edu. *Librn*, Leo Clougherty
Library Holdings: Bk Vols 92,039
Friends of the Library Group
ENGINEERING, 100 Main Library, 52242-1420. Tel: 319-335-6047. *Librn*, John W Forys, Jr
Library Holdings: Bk Vols 109,563
Friends of the Library Group
GEOLOGY, 136 Trowbridge Hall, 52242. Tel: 319-335-3084. *Librn*, Leo Clougherty
Library Holdings: Bk Vols 54,641
Friends of the Library Group

CM HARDIN LIBRARY FOR THE HEALTH SCIENCES, 600 Newton Rd, 52242-1098. Tel: 319-335-9871. Interlibrary Loan Service Tel: 319-335-9874. Reference Tel: 319-335-9151. FAX: 319-335-9897. E-Mail: lib-hardin@uiowa.edu. Web Site: www.lib.uiowa.edu/hardin-www/home.html. *Dir*, Larry Woods; *Tech Servs*, Hope Barton; *Rare Bks*, Richard Eimas
Founded 1882
Library Holdings: Bk Vols 285,241
Subject Interests: History of medicine
Publications: Heirs of Hippocrates
Partic in National Network Of Libraries Of Medicine - South Central Region; OCLC Western Service Center
Friends of the Library Group

CL LAW LIBRARY, 200 Boyd Law Bldg, 52242-1166. Tel: 319-335-9002. Reference Tel: 319-335-9005. FAX: 319-335-9039. Web Site: www.uiowa.edu/~lawlib/. *Acq*, Mary Ertl; *Cat*, Karen Nobbs; *Cat*, Virginia Melroy; *Circ*, John Bergstrom; *Doc*, Sue Emde; *Ref*, Val Russell; *Ref*, Tom Eicher; *Ref*, Ellen Jones; *Tech Servs*, Caitlin Robinson; Staff 14 (MLS 14)
Founded 1868. Enrl 680; Fac 44; Highest Degree: Doctorate
Library Holdings: Bk Vols 642,872; Per Subs 11,138
Subject Interests: Environmental studies, Law
Special Collections: UN Doc (Readex Coll)
Publications: Law Library User's Guide; News Briefs
Partic in OCLC Online Computer Library Center, Inc; RLIN
MARVIN A POMERANTZ BUSINESS LIBRARY, C320 PBB, 52242. (Mail add: 108 Pappajohn Business Administration Bldg, 52242-1000), Tel: 319-335-3077. Web Site: www.lib.uiowa.edu. *Head Librn*, J David Martin
Library Holdings: Bk Vols 32,989
Friends of the Library Group
MATHEMATICAL SCIENCES, 125 Maclean Hall, 52242. Tel: 319-335-3076. *Librn*, Lisa Martincik
Library Holdings: Bk Vols 56,650
Friends of the Library Group
PHYSICS, 350 Van Allen Hall, 52242. Tel: 319-335-3082. *Librn*, Lisa Martincik
Library Holdings: Bk Vols 57,282
Friends of the Library Group
PSYCHOLOGY, W202 Seashore Hall, 52242. Tel: 319-335-3079. *Librn*, Dorothy M Persson
Library Holdings: Bk Vols 65,855
Friends of the Library Group

C RITA BENTON MUSIC LIBRARY, 2000 Voxman Music Bldg, 52242. Tel: 319-335-3086. *Librn*, Ruthann Boles McTyre
Library Holdings: Bk Vols 99,484
Friends of the Library Group

IOWA FALLS

J ELLSWORTH COMMUNITY COLLEGE, Osgood Library,* 1100 College Ave, 50126-1199. SAN 305-4853. Tel: 515-648-4611, Ext 233. FAX: 515-648-3128. E-Mail: ecclib@iavalley.cc.ia.us. *Dir*, Rebecca Spriester
Founded 1890. Enrl 950
Library Holdings: Bk Vols 25,664; Bk Titles 24,689; Per Subs 240
Mem of North Central Regional Library System
Partic in Iowa Higher Educ Instrul Resource Consortia
Open Mon-Thurs 7:30-9:30, Fri 7:30-3:30 & Sun 5-9

P ROBERT W BARLOW MEMORIAL LIBRARY, (Formerly Carnegie-Ellsworth Public Library), 921 Washington Ave, 50126. SAN 305-4845. Tel: 641-648-2872. FAX: 641-648-2872. *Dir*, Deanne Henry; E-Mail: dhenry@iafalls.com; *Asst Dir*, Janice Larson; *Tech Servs*, Nancy Hoffman
Founded 1896. Pop 6,100; Circ 89,000
1999-2000 Income $165,000, State $5,000, City $135,000, County $25,000. Mats Exp $35,000, Books $23,000, Per/Ser (Incl. Access Fees) $3,000, Micro $6,000, AV Equip $3,000. Sal $75,000 (Prof $32,000)
Library Holdings: Bk Titles 48,000; Per Subs 150
Special Collections: Travel Guides
Automation Activity & Vendor Info: (Circulation) TLC; (OPAC) TLC
Mem of Iowa Libr Asn; North Central Regional Library System; Northeastern Iowa Regional Library System
Open Mon-Thurs 9-9, Fri & Sat 9-5
Friends of the Library Group

JAMAICA

P JAMAICA PUBLIC LIBRARY, 316 Main St, PO Box 122, 50128. SAN 305-4861. Tel: 515-429-3362. FAX: 515-429-3362. *Librn*, Dana Lowry
Founded 1948. Pop 275; Circ 3,994
Jul 1998-Jun 1999 Income $8,900, City $1,500, County $7,400. Mats Exp $10,450
Library Holdings: Bk Titles 6,500; Per Subs 12
Subject Interests: Genealogy, Local history
Mem of Southwest Iowa Regional Library System
Friends of the Library Group

JANESVILLE

P JANESVILLE PUBLIC LIBRARY,* 227 Main St, PO Box 328, 50647. SAN 305-487X. Tel: 319-987-2925. FAX: 319-987-2925. E-Mail: jv10100@cedarnet.org. *Dir*, Beth Ann Scott
Pop 870; Circ 17,011
Library Holdings: Bk Vols 14,424; Bk Titles 14,153; Per Subs 35
Mem of Northeastern Regional Libr Syst
Friends of the Library Group

JEFFERSON

P JEFFERSON PUBLIC LIBRARY, 200 W Lincolnway, 50129-2185. SAN 305-4888. Tel: 515-386-2835. FAX: 515-386-8163. E-Mail: jeflib@netins.net. *Dir*, Jane Millard
Founded 1903. Pop 4,200; Circ 85,000
Library Holdings: Bk Titles 41,000; Per Subs 110
Subject Interests: Genealogy
Special Collections: Greene County
Automation Activity & Vendor Info: (Cataloging) Gaylord; (Circulation) Gaylord; (OPAC) Gaylord
Database Vendor: OCLC - First Search
Mem of Central Iowa Regional Library
Friends of the Library Group

JESUP

P JESUP PUBLIC LIBRARY,* 721 Sixth St, PO Box 585, 50648. SAN 305-4896. Tel: 319-827-1533. FAX: 319-827-1580. E-Mail: jesuplibrary@jtt.net. Web Site: www.jesupiowa.com. *Librn*, Cynthia Lellig
Pop 2,299; Circ 29,722
Jul 1998-Jun 1999 Income $80,123. Mats Exp $8,600. Sal $39,431
Library Holdings: Bk Titles 14,299; Per Subs 52
Special Collections: Media: videos (69), audios (277)
Mem of Northeastern Iowa Regional Library System
Open Mon, Wed & Fri 11-6, Tues & Thurs 11-8 & Sat 10-2

JEWELL

P MONTGOMERY MEMORIAL LIBRARY,* 711 Main St, PO Box 207, 50130-0207. SAN 305-490X. Tel: 515-827-5112. FAX: 515-827-5112. E-Mail: jewellib@netins.net. *Librn*, Kris Koehnk; *Asst Librn*, Roseann Amundson
Founded 1947. Pop 1,200
Jul 1998-Jun 1999 Income $37,326. Mats Exp $7,493. Sal $15,048
Library Holdings: Bk Vols 11,256; Per Subs 39
Special Collections: History of Hamilton County, Jewell Township
Mem of North Central Regional Library System
Open Mon, Tues & Thurs 1-5, Wed 1-6, Fri 9:30-5, Sat 9:30-12

JOHNSTON

L IOWA LAW ENFORCEMENT ACADEMY LIBRARY,* Camp Dodge, PO Box 130, 50131. SAN 328-3909. Tel: 515-242-5481. FAX: 515-242-5471. *Librn*, Jo Ellen Warne
Library Holdings: Bk Titles 2,200; Per Subs 10
Open Mon-Thurs 1-11

P JOHNSTON PUBLIC LIBRARY, 6221 Merle Hay Rd, 50131-1226. (Mail add: PO Box 327, 50131-0327), SAN 376-5458. Tel: 515-278-5233. FAX: 515-278-4975. *Dir*, Francine Canfield; Staff 13 (MLS 2, Non-MLS 11)
Founded 1992. Pop 7,000; Circ 114,000
Jul 1999-Jun 2000 Income $321,000, State $14,000, City $256,000, County $39,000, Locally Generated Income $12,000. Mats Exp $38,000. Sal $250,000
Library Holdings: Bk Vols 37,000; Per Subs 100
Automation Activity & Vendor Info: (Cataloging) DRA; (Circulation) DRA
Database Vendor: OCLC - First Search
Mem of Central Iowa Regional Library
Partic in BCR
Friends of the Library Group

S PIONEER HI-BRED INTERNATIONAL, INC LIBRARY, 7300 NW 62nd Ave, PO Box 1004, 50131-1004. SAN 324-7120. Tel: 515-270-4199. FAX: 515-253-2184. Web Site: www.pioneer.com. *Dir*, Dana Smith; E-Mail: smithde@phibred.com; *Asst Librn*, Ken Braun; E-Mail: braunkj@phibred.com; *Cat*, Ann Snyder; Staff 6 (MLS 3, Non-MLS 3)
Founded 1983
Library Holdings: Bk Titles 1,800; Per Subs 340
Subject Interests: Agribus, Agriculture, Biotech, Law, Plant genetics
Automation Activity & Vendor Info: (Cataloging) EOS; (Circulation) EOS; (OPAC) EOS; (Serials) EOS

JOICE

P JOICE PUBLIC LIBRARY,* 201 Main St, PO Box 183, 50446-0183. SAN 305-4918. Tel: 515-588-3330. FAX: 515-588-3330. Web Site: www.netins.net/showcase/joicejhawks. *Librn*, Annette Oswald
Pop 236; Circ 3,419
Library Holdings: Bk Vols 7,000; Bk Titles 5,000; Per Subs 17
Mem of North Central Regional Library System
Open Mon & Wed 2-9, Fri 2-7, Sat 9-12

KALONA

P KALONA PUBLIC LIBRARY,* 511 C Ave, PO Box 1212, 52247-1212. SAN 305-4926. Tel: 319-656-3501. FAX: 319-656-3503. E-Mail: kaloplib@kctc.net. Web Site: www.kctc.net/kaloplib. *Dir*, Anne Skaden
Pop 2,000; Circ 25,659
Jul 1998-Jun 1999 Income $49,228. Mats Exp $10,168. Sal $35,880
Library Holdings: Bk Titles 10,000; Per Subs 50
Subject Interests: Amish
Mem of Southeastern Library Services
Open Mon 10-8, Tues & Wed 10-6, Thurs 1-8, Fri 1-5, Sat 10-3
Friends of the Library Group

KANAWHA

P KANAWHA PUBLIC LIBRARY,* 121 N Main, PO Box 148, 50447. SAN 305-4934. Tel: 515-762-3595. FAX: 515-762-3595. *Librn*, Sharon Grimm
Pop 755; Circ 10,424
Jul 1998-Jun 1999 Income (Main Library Only) $17,900. Mats Exp $8,900. Sal $9,000
Library Holdings: Bk Titles 6,441; Per Subs 45
Mem of North Central Regional Library System
Open Mon 10-5, Wed 12-7, Fri 1-5 & Sat 9-12

KENSETT

P KENSETT PUBLIC LIBRARY, 214 Fifth St, PO Box 55, 50448-0055. SAN 305-4942. Tel: 515-845-2222. FAX: 515-845-2222. E-Mail: kenlib@wtcatel.net. *Librn*, Barbara Luckason
Pop 300; Circ 7,200
Jul 1999-Jun 2000 Income $11,200. Mats Exp $4,693, Books $2,800, Per/Ser (Incl. Access Fees) $638, Micro $255, AV Equip $1,000. Sal $8,000
Library Holdings: Bk Titles 5,930; Per Subs 26
Mem of North Central Regional Library System

KEOKUK

P KEOKUK PUBLIC LIBRARY, 210 N Fifth, 52632. SAN 305-4950. Tel: 319-524-1483. FAX: 319-524-2320. E-Mail: keokuk@keokuk.lib.ia.us. *Dir*, EmmaLee Lahmeyer
Founded 1893. Pop 12,451; Circ 112,000
Library Holdings: Bk Titles 80,000; Per Subs 200
Subject Interests: Local history
Mem of Southeastern Library Services

KEOSAUQUA

P KEOSAUQUA PUBLIC LIBRARY, First & Van Buren, PO Box 158, 52565. SAN 305-4977. Tel: 319-293-3766. FAX: 319-293-3766. E-Mail: keolib@netins.net. *Librn*, Kathy Fisher
Founded 1910. Pop 1,020; Circ 18,450
Jul 1998-Jun 1999 Income $28,153, State $787, City $16,480, County $3,600, Locally Generated Income $7,286. Mats Exp $7,594, Books $5,700, Per/Ser (Incl. Access Fees) $269, AV Equip $425, Electronic Ref Mat (Incl. Access Fees) $1,200. Sal $15,000 (Prof $8,000)
Library Holdings: Bk Titles 18,500
Subject Interests: Genealogy, Iowa, Natural history
Automation Activity & Vendor Info: (Cataloging) Athena
Mem of Southeastern Library Services

KEOTA

P WILSON MEMORIAL LIBRARY,* 109 E Washington St, PO Box 302, 52248-0302. SAN 305-4985. Tel: 515-636-3850. FAX: 515-636-3850. E-Mail: keotalib@lisco.com. *Librn*, Julie Tinnes; *Assoc Librn*, Phyllis Wright
Founded 1877. Pop 1,200; Circ 15,000
Library Holdings: Bk Vols 12,500; Bk Titles 10,000; Per Subs 40
Mem of Southeastern Library Services
Open Mon-Fri 11-6 & Sat 10-5

KEYSTONE

P SCHROEDER PUBLIC LIBRARY,* 93 Main St, 52249-0305. SAN 305-4993. Tel: 319-442-3329. FAX: 319-442-3327. E-Mail: keystnpl@netins.net. *Librn*, Pat Jans
Pop 589; Circ 13,072
Jul 1999-Jun 2000 Income $32,505, City $28,005, County $4,500. Mats Exp $4,550, Books $4,000, Per/Ser (Incl. Access Fees) $300, AV Equip $250. Sal $20,480 (Prof $15,000)
Library Holdings: Bk Titles 7,283; Per Subs 61
Automation Activity & Vendor Info: (Acquisitions) Sagebrush Corporation; (Cataloging) Sagebrush Corporation; (Circulation) Sagebrush Corporation
Mem of East Central Regional Library

KIMBALLTON

P KIMBALLTON PUBLIC LIBRARY,* Main St, PO Box 67, 51543. SAN 305-5000. Tel: 712-773-3002. *Librn*, Rose Anne Poldberg
Pop 1,000
Jul 1998-Jun 1999 Income $7,000
Library Holdings: Bk Vols 6,187; Per Subs 34
Special Collections: Danish Coll
Mem of Southwest Iowa Regional Library System
Open Mon-Fri 1-5

KINGSLEY

P KINGSLEY PUBLIC LIBRARY, 220 Main St, PO Box 400, 51028-0400. SAN 305-5019. Tel: 712-378-2410. E-Mail: library@willinet.com. *Dir*, Marilyn Lindgren; *Asst Librn*, Wilma Hauck
Founded 1966. Pop 1,500; Circ 23,280
Jul 1999-Jun 2000 Income $32,197, City $25,062, County $7,135. Mats Exp $7,094, Books $5,863, Per/Ser (Incl. Access Fees) $1,231. Sal $15,086
Library Holdings: Bk Titles 16,924; Per Subs 50
Mem of Northwest Regional Library System

KLEMME

P KLEMME PUBLIC LIBRARY,* 204 E Main St, 50449. SAN 305-5027. Tel: 515-587-2369. FAX: 515-587-2369. E-Mail: klemlibn@ncr.net. *Librn*, Kathy Olthoff
Founded 1967. Pop 587; Circ 4,865
Jul 1998-Jun 1999 Income $35,000. Mats Exp $7,143. Sal $15,358
Library Holdings: Bk Vols 8,000; Per Subs 60
Mem of North Central Regional Library System
Open Mon, Tues, Wed & Fri 10-12 & 1-5, Thurs 10-12 & 1-7, Sat 10-12

KNOXVILLE

P KNOXVILLE PUBLIC LIBRARY, 213 E Montgomery St, 50138-2296. SAN 305-5035. Tel: 641-828-0585. FAX: 641-828-0585. E-Mail: knoxvillelib@se-iowa.net. *Dir*, Jan Behrens; *Assoc Dir*, Elaine Jordan; *Ch Servs*, Lilliams Gonzalez; *Ch Servs*, Mary Popson-Klein; *Ad Servs*, Mary Lane; Staff 10 (MLS 1, Non-MLS 9)
Founded 1912. Pop 8,241; Circ 114,782
Jul 1999-Jun 2000 Income $234,271, State $7,834, City $165,855, County $41,123, Locally Generated Income $7,085, Other $12,374. Mats Exp $41,800, Books $25,172, Per/Ser (Incl. Access Fees) $5,384, AV Equip $6,109, Electronic Ref Mat (Incl. Access Fees) $5,135. Sal $102,933 (Prof

$32,000)
Library Holdings: Bk Vols 34,998; Per Subs 155
Automation Activity & Vendor Info: (Cataloging) Follett; (Circulation) Follett
Database Vendor: Ebsco - EbscoHost, OCLC - First Search
Function: Internet access, Photocopies available
Mem of Central Iowa Regional Library
Friends of the Library Group

GM VETERANS AFFAIRS CENTRAL IOWA HEALTH CARE SYSTEMS-KNOXVILLE DIVISION, Medical Center Library - 142D,* 1515 W Pleasant St, 50138-3399. SAN 305-5043. Tel: 515-828-5127. FAX: 515-828-5084.; Staff 2 (MLS 1, Non-MLS 1)
Founded 1927
Library Holdings: Bk Titles 7,000
Subject Interests: Allied health, Psychiatry, Psychology
Partic in Vets Admin Libr Network

LA PORTE CITY

P HAWKINS MEMORIAL LIBRARY, 308 Main St, 50651. SAN 305-5051. Tel: 319-342-3025. FAX: 319-342-3025. *Librn*, Elaine Gross; *Asst Librn*, Helen Hoppe
Founded 1945. Pop 2,200; Circ 21,712
Jul 1998-Jun 1999 Income $47,292, City $41,204, County $6,000, Other $88. Mats Exp $11,045, Books $8,525, Per/Ser (Incl. Access Fees) $2,520. Sal $22,400
Library Holdings: Bk Vols 19,280; Per Subs 65
Mem of Northeastern Regional Libr Syst
Open Mon 9-12 & 2-5, Tues, Wed & Fri 2-5 & 7-9, Thurs 2-5, Sat 1-5

LACONA

P LACONA PUBLIC LIBRARY,* 107 E Main, 50139. SAN 376-5466. Tel: 515-534-4400. E-Mail: laconalibrary@crosspaths.net. *Librn*, Mary Mitchell
Library Holdings: Bk Vols 4,500; Per Subs 10
Special Collections: Media: videos (400), audios (25)
Mem of Central Iowa Regional Library
Open Mon 3-6, Tues 11-5, Wed 6-9, Thurs 3:30-6 Fri 3:30-5, Sat 9-12
Friends of the Library Group

LAKE CITY

P LAKE CITY PUBLIC LIBRARY,* 120 N Illinois St, 51449-1707. SAN 305-506X. Tel: 712-464-3413. FAX: 712-464-3413. *Asst Librn*, Faith Blaskovich; *Librn*, Norma DeVries
Founded 1901. Pop 3,200; Circ 21,235
Library Holdings: Bk Vols 19,000; Per Subs 72
Mem of Northwest Regional Library System
Open Tues 12:30-8, Wed & Fri 12:30-5:30, Thurs 9-11:30 & 12:30-8, Sat 9-12
Friends of the Library Group

LAKE MILLS

P LAKE MILLS PUBLIC LIBRARY,* 102 S Lake St, 50450. SAN 305-5078. Tel: 515-592-0092. FAX: 515-592-0093. E-Mail: lmpublib@netins.net. *Librn*, Toni Holstad
Pop 2,281; Circ 24,832
Library Holdings: Bk Titles 23,500; Per Subs 80
Mem of North Central Regional Library System
Open Mon-Thurs 10-12 & 2-8, Fri 10-12 & 2-6, Sat 9-1

LAKE PARK

P LAKE PARK PUBLIC LIBRARY,* 217 Market St, PO Box 344, 51347-0344. SAN 305-5086. Tel: 712-832-9505. FAX: 712-832-3669. E-Mail: lppublic@sconnect.com. *Librn*, Glenda Frank
Founded 1922. Pop 1,123; Circ 6,066
Jul 1998-Jun 1999 Income $17,086
Library Holdings: Bk Titles 8,000; Per Subs 14
Special Collections: Media: Video (100), Audio (30)
Open Tues-Fri 10-6, Sat 10-1

LAKE VIEW

P LAKE VIEW PUBLIC LIBRARY, 202 Main St, PO Box 20, 51450. SAN 305-5094. Tel: 712-657-2310. FAX: 712-657-2310. E-Mail: lvl@netins.net. *Dir*, Joyce Kreitlow; *Asst Librn*, Bonnie Peters
Founded 1920. Pop 1,301; Circ 25,398
Library Holdings: Bk Titles 14,000; Per Subs 103
Special Collections: Civil War (Goffrey C Ward Coll), bk, v-tapes; Des Moines Register; Lake View Resort 1941-to-date (weekly paper); Library of America; Wall Street Journal
Mem of Northwest Regional Library System
Partic in OCLC Online Computer Library Center, Inc
Open Mon 10-12 & 2-8, Tues-Fri 2-8, Sat 10-3
Friends of the Library Group

LAKOTA

P LAKOTA PUBLIC LIBRARY,* 204 Third St, PO Box 178, 50451-0178. SAN 305-5108. Tel: 515-886-2312. FAX: 515-886-2312. E-Mail: lakpubli@heartlandtel.com. *Dir*, Susan Kearney; *Asst Librn*, Debra Steven
Pop 281; Circ 7,179
Library Holdings: Bk Vols 5,100; Per Subs 30
Mem of North Central Regional Library System
Open Tues & Thurs 1-5 & 6-8, Wed 9-2, Sat 9-12

LAMONI

C GRACELAND UNIVERSITY, (Formerly Graceland University), Frederick Madison Smith Library, One University Pl, 50140. SAN 305-5116. Tel: 641-784-5301. Interlibrary Loan Service Tel: 641-784-5306. Circulation Tel: 641-784-5361. FAX: 641-784-5497. E-Mail: library@graceland.edu. Web Site: www2.graceland.edu/library/index.html. *Dir Libr Serv*, Diane Shelton; Tel: 641-784-5302, E-Mail: shelton@graceland.edu; *Assoc Librn*, Francis Oliver Acland; Tel: 641-784-5303, E-Mail: acland@graceland.edu; *Circ*, Marsha Jackel; E-Mail: jackel@graceland.edu; *Per*, Judy Payne; Tel: 641-784-5483, E-Mail: payne@graceland.edu; *ILL*, Victory Smith; E-Mail: vsmith@graceland.edu; Staff 7 (MLS 2, Non-MLS 5)
Founded 1895. Enrl 2,044; Fac 87; Highest Degree: Master
Jun 1999-May 2000 Income $456,555, Locally Generated Income $2,698, Parent Institution $453,857. Mats Exp $148,871, Books $64,631, Per/Ser (Incl. Access Fees) $54,632, Presv $2,064, Micro $26,928, Electronic Ref Mat (Incl. Access Fees) $616. Sal $201,460 (Prof $75,785)
Library Holdings: Bk Vols 93,933; Bk Titles 83,123; Per Subs 577
Special Collections: Mormon History Manuscripts, bks & micro
Automation Activity & Vendor Info: (Acquisitions) VTLS; (Cataloging) VTLS; (Circulation) VTLS; (Course Reserve) VTLS; (OPAC) VTLS; (Serials) VTLS
Database Vendor: Lexis-Nexis, OCLC - First Search
Function: Archival collection, ILL available, Outside services via phone, cable & mail, Photocopies available, Reference services available, Some telephone reference
Partic in OCLC Online Computer Library Center, Inc; State Of Iowa Libraries Online Interlibrary Loan

P LAMONI PUBLIC LIBRARY,* 133 E Main St, 50140. SAN 305-5124. Tel: 515-784-6686. FAX: 515-784-6693. E-Mail: lamonipl@netins.net. *Librn*, Barb Houston
Founded 1922. Pop 2,705; Circ 30,030
Jul 1998-Jun 1999 Income $59,190. Mats Exp $10,356. Sal $36,087
Library Holdings: Bk Vols 26,000; Per Subs 72
Mem of Southwest Iowa Regional Library System
Open Mon, Wed & Fri 15:30, Tues 10:30-9, Thurs 10-5:30, Sat 9-12
Friends of the Library Group

LAMONT

P LAMONT PUBLIC LIBRARY,* 616 Bush St, PO Box 116, 50650. SAN 305-5132. Tel: 319-924-3203. FAX: 319-924-3203. E-Mail: lamontlib@mwci.net. *Librn*, Jane Seedorff
Pop 1,147; Circ 7,927
Library Holdings: Bk Titles 7,200; Per Subs 12
Mem of NE Regional Iowa Libr Syst
Open Mon-Fri 1:30-5:30, Sat 8-12, Wed 1:30-7:30 (winter only)

LANSING

P LANSING PUBLIC LIBRARY,* 515 Main St, PO Box 580, 52151-0580. SAN 305-5140. Tel: 319-538-4693. FAX: 319-538-4693. E-Mail: lanslib@rconnect.com. *Librn*, Mabel Stahl
Pop 1,181; Circ 10,697
Jul 1997-Jun 1998 Income $15,559, City $5,050, County $8,225, Other $2,284. Mats Exp $3,533, Books $2,391, Per/Ser (Incl. Access Fees) $643. Sal $7,232
Library Holdings: Bk Titles 9,758; Per Subs 31
Mem of Northeastern Iowa Regional Library System
Open Tues, Thurs & Fri 1-4:30 & 7-9, Sat 1-4:30

LARCHWOOD

P LARCHWOOD PUBLIC LIBRARY,* 1020 Broadway, PO Box 97, 51241. SAN 305-5159. Tel: 712-477-2583. E-Mail: lpblib@netins.net. *Dir*, Laura Simons
Founded 1927. Pop 800; Circ 13,682
1998-1999 Income $21,530, City $15,300, County $5,948, Locally

Generated Income $282. Mats Exp $19,308, Books $4,151, Per/Ser (Incl. Access Fees) $247. Sal $10,431
Library Holdings: Bk Titles 13,445
Mem of Northwest Regional Library System
Friends of the Library Group

LAUREL

P LAUREL COMMUNITY LIBRARY,* c/o City Hall, 104 Market St, 50141. SAN 375-6432. Tel: 515-476-3275. *Librn*, Dorothy Hill
Library Holdings: Bk Vols 3,000
Mem of Central Iowa Regional Library
Open Wed 4:30-7, Fri 2-4, Sat 9-11

LAURENS

P LAURENS PUBLIC LIBRARY, 273 N Third St, 50554. SAN 305-5167. Tel: 712-841-4612. FAX: 712-841-4612. E-Mail: lrnspl@pionet.net. Web Site: www.siouxland.com/laurenslib. *Librn*, Sandi Neary; *Asst Dir*, Joyce Rigby; Staff 4 (Non-MLS 4)
Founded 1910. Pop 1,500; Circ 30,612
Library Holdings: Bk Vols 18,000; Per Subs 75
Mem of Northwest Regional Library System
Open Mon, Wed & Thurs 1-8, Tues 10-8, Fri 1-5, Sat 10-4
Friends of the Library Group

LAWLER

P LAWLER PUBLIC LIBRARY, 412 E Grove, PO Box 235, 52154. SAN 305-5175. Tel: 319-238-2191. FAX: 319-238-5102. E-Mail: lawlerlib@powerbank.net. *Librn*, Jane Lynch
Founded 1965. Pop 517; Circ 5,925
2000-2001 Income $19,861, State $1,319, City $5,859, County $11,636, Other $1,047. Mats Exp $18,691, Books $4,182, Per/Ser (Incl. Access Fees) $425. Sal $9,302
Library Holdings: Bk Titles 5,907; Per Subs 40
Mem of Northeastern Iowa Regional Library System

LE GRAND

P PIONEER HERITAGE LIBRARY,* 204 N Vine St, PO Box 188, 50142-0188. SAN 373-918X. Tel: 515-479-2122. FAX: 515-479-2122. E-Mail: pioner00@marshallnet.com. *Dir*, Shelley Barron; *Asst Librn*, Linda Thompson
Pop 854; Circ 14,809
Jul 1997-Jun 1998 Income $25,500, City $20,500, County $5,000
Library Holdings: Bk Vols 9,581; Bk Titles 9,516; Per Subs 42
Special Collections: Native American Legends
Mem of Central Iowa Regional Library
Open Tues 10-8, Wed 9-12 & 5-8, Thurs 10-5, Sun 3-6
Friends of the Library Group

LE MARS

P LE MARS PUBLIC LIBRARY,* 46 First St SW, 51031-3696. SAN 305-5183. Tel: 712-546-5004. FAX: 712-546-5797. E-Mail: lemarspl@frontiernet.net. *Actg Dir, Circ*, Beth Hartman; *Asst Dir*, Susan Keller
Founded 1894. Pop 9,435
Jul 1998-Jun 1999 Income $260,000. Mats Exp $48,000. Sal $90,000 (Prof $37,000)
Library Holdings: Bk Vols 34,547; Per Subs 149
Subject Interests: Local history
Publications: Library Movers (quarterly newsletter)
Mem of Northwest Regional Library System
Open Mon-Thurs 10-8, Fri-Sat 10-5, Sun 1-5, closed Sun during summer
Friends of the Library Group

LEDYARD

P LEDYARD PUBLIC LIBRARY, Edmund St, PO Box 8, 50556. SAN 305-5205. Tel: 515-646-3111. FAX: 515-646-3111. E-Mail: llibrary@earthlink.net. *Librn*, Sharon K Ehrich
Founded 1971. Pop 198; Circ 3,951
Library Holdings: Bk Titles 6,796; Per Subs 18
Mem of North Central Regional Library System

LEHIGH

P LEHIGH PUBLIC LIBRARY,* 241 Elm St, PO Box 138, 50557-0138. SAN 305-5213. Tel: 515-359-2967. FAX: 515-359-2967. E-Mail: lehilib@netins.net. *Librn*, Barbara Smith
Pop 536; Circ 17,790
Jul 1998-Jun 1999 Income $27,730. Mats Exp $4,800. Sal $12,665
Library Holdings: Bk Titles 7,743; Per Subs 38
Mem of North Central Regional Library System
Open Mon & Fri 10-12 & 1-5:30, Tues 2:30-5:30, Wed 1-8, Sat 9:30-12

LENOX

P LENOX PUBLIC LIBRARY, 101 N Main St, 50851. SAN 305-5221. Tel: 641-333-4411. FAX: 641-333-2506. E-Mail: lenoxlib@lenox.heartland.net. Web Site: www.swirls.lib.ia.us/libspages/lenox/main.html. *Librn*, Bonnie Tyler; *Asst Librn*, Florence Robinson; Staff 1 (MLS 1)
Pop 1,500; Circ 10,000
Library Holdings: Bk Vols 20,000; Bk Titles 16,000; Per Subs 50
Subject Interests: History
Automation Activity & Vendor Info: (Cataloging) Follett; (Circulation) Follett
Mem of Southwest Iowa Regional Library System
Friends of the Library Group

LEON

P LEON PUBLIC LIBRARY,* 200 W First St, 50144. SAN 305-523X. Tel: 515-446-3746, 515-446-6332. FAX: 515-446-3746. E-Mail: leonpl@netins.net. *Librn*, Rene Fierce; *Ch Servs*, Darlene Richardson; *Asst Librn*, Brenda Griffin
Pop 2,119; Circ 20,655
Jul 1998-Jun 1999 Income $54,365. Mats Exp $8,147. Sal $33,106
Library Holdings: Bk Vols 15,349; Per Subs 46
Mem of Southwest Iowa Regional Library System
Open Mon 12:30-7:30, Tues & Thurs 10:30-5:30, Wed & Fri 12:30-5:30, Sat 10:30-1:30
Friends of the Library Group

LETTS

P LETTS PUBLIC LIBRARY,* 135 S Cherry St, PO Box B, 52754. SAN 305-5248. Tel: 319-726-5121. FAX: 319-726-5121. E-Mail: llibrary@lisco.net. *Librn*, Karen Koppe
Founded 1910. Pop 473; Circ 2,094
Library Holdings: Bk Titles 3,000; Per Subs 25
Publications: Newsletter (quarterly)
Mem of Southeastern Library Services
Open Mon & Fri 1-6, Wed 9-1, Thurs 1-7

LEWIS

P LEWIS PUBLIC LIBRARY,* 506 Main St, 51544. SAN 376-5172. Tel: 712-769-2228. *Librn*, Dorothy M Baxter
Pop 470
Jul 1999- 2000 Income City $2,334
Library Holdings: Bk Vols 8,000; Bk Titles 7,500
Mem of Southwest Iowa Regional Library System
Reading hour for preschoolers (May) (Wed)

LIME SPRINGS

P LIME SPRINGS PUBLIC LIBRARY,* 112 W Main St, PO Box 68, 52155. SAN 305-5264. Tel: 319-566-4405. *Librn*, Fran Bonderman; *Asst Librn*, Mary Jones
Library Holdings: Bk Vols 7,289; Per Subs 26
Mem of Northeastern Iowa Regional Library System

LINDEN

P LINDEN PUBLIC LIBRARY,* 131 S Main, 50146. SAN 305-5272. Tel: 515-744-2408. *Dir*, Marjorie Wassen
Pop 264; Circ 2,334
Library Holdings: Bk Titles 4,696; Per Subs 10
Mem of Central Iowa Regional Library
Open Wed 3-5, Fri 9-12

LINN GROVE

P LINN GROVE PUBLIC LIBRARY,* 122 Weaver St, Box 55, 51033. SAN 305-5280. Tel: 712-296-3919. E-Mail: lglib@pionet.net. *Dir*, Lois Schomaker; *Asst Librn*, Lolita Weier
Founded 1934. Pop 250; Circ 1,500
Jul 1998- Jun 1999 Income $9,685, City $687, County $6,039, Locally Generated Income $20, Other $2,939. Mats Exp $759, Books $759. Sal $4,046
Library Holdings: Bk Titles 7,163
Subject Interests: Iowa, Religion

Mem of Northwest Regional Library System
Open Tues & Thurs 2-5, Wed 2-7, Sat 9-12; Winter Tues & Thurs 2:30-5:30, Wed 2-7, Sat 9-12
Friends of the Library Group

LISBON

P LISBON PUBLIC LIBRARY,* 101 E Main St, 52253-0217. SAN 305-5299. Tel: 319-455-2800. FAX: 319-455-2800. *Dir*, Amy White
Founded 1936. Pop 1,458; Circ 6,000
Library Holdings: Bk Vols 5,800; Per Subs 18
Special Collections: Local History

LITTLE ROCK

P LITTLE ROCK PUBLIC LIBRARY, 402 Main St, PO Box 308, 51243-0308. SAN 376-5288. Tel: 712-479-2298. FAX: 712-479-2298. E-Mail: irbooks@mtcnet.net. *Librn*, Joanne Thiesse
Library Holdings: Bk Vols 6,300; Per Subs 32
Mem of Northwest Regional Library System

LIVERMORE

P LIVERMORE PUBLIC LIBRARY,* 402 Fifth St, PO Box 18, 50558. SAN 305-5329. Tel: 515-379-2078. FAX: 515-379-1002. E-Mail: livplib@trvnet.net. *Dir*, Pansy Streit
Founded 1935. Pop 515; Circ 4,056
Library Holdings: Bk Vols 8,053; Per Subs 34
Special Collections: Media: Video (1400), Audio (185)
Mem of North Central Regional Library System
Open Mon 1-6, Wed 9-12 & 1-5, Thurs & Fri 1-5, Sat 10-12 & 1-5

LOGAN

P LOGAN PUBLIC LIBRARY,* 121 E Sixth St, 51546. SAN 305-5337. Tel: 712-644-2551. FAX: 712-644-2551. E-Mail: loganpl@pionet.net. *Librn*, Delila Rife
Founded 1920. Pop 1,550; Circ 28,000
Jul 1999-Jun 2000 Income $45,950. Mats Exp $10,000. Sal $19,860
Library Holdings: Bk Vols 15,021; Per Subs 51
Mem of Southwest Iowa Regional Library System
Open Mon & Wed 11-8, Tues, Thurs & Fri 11-5, Sat 11-3
Friends of the Library Group

LOHRVILLE

P J J HANDS LIBRARY,* 609 Second St, PO Box 277, 51453. SAN 305-5345. Tel: 712-465-4115. FAX: 712-465-4115. E-Mail: jjhand@cal-net.net. *Librn*, Jane Beschorner
Founded 1935. Pop 535; Circ 5,534
Jul 1997-Jun 1998 Income $25,000, City $5,769, County $7,420, Locally Generated Income $317, Other $162. Mats Exp $5,454, Books $1,607, Per/Ser (Incl. Access Fees) $860. Sal $11,547
Library Holdings: Bk Vols 16,500; Per Subs 48
Special Collections: Media: videos (210), audios (48)
Mem of Northwest Regional Library System
Open Mon & Fri 1-6, Tues 9-12, Wed 9-6, Thurs 5-8, Sat 9-12
Friends of the Library Group

LOST NATION

P LOST NATION PUBLIC LIBRARY,* 301 Pleasant St, 52254-0397. SAN 376-4974. Tel: 319-678-2114. *Librn*, Arlene Paulson
Library Holdings: Bk Titles 9,000
Mem of East Central Regional Library
Open Mon 6-7, Tues 9:30-1130am, Wed 3-6:30, Fri 3-5, Sat 9-11

LOWDEN

P LOWDEN PUBLIC LIBRARY,* 605 Main St, PO Box 307, 52255-0307. SAN 320-8273. Tel: 319-941-7629. E-Mail: lowdenpl@netins.net. *Librn*, Vicki Mohr
Pop 726; Circ 11,621
Jul 1998-Jun 1999 Income $31,849, City $16,777, County $15,072. Mats Exp $3,590, Books $3,000, Per/Ser (Incl. Access Fees) $50. Sal $8,620
Library Holdings: Bk Titles 10,948; Per Subs 10
Open Mon & Wed 1-7, Tues & Fri 9-12 & 1-5, Sat 9-12
Friends of the Library Group

LUVERNE

P LUVERNE PUBLIC LIBRARY,* 113 DeWitt St, PO Box 37, 50560. SAN 305-5361. Tel: 515-882-3436. FAX: 515-882-3436. E-Mail: luvpl@trunet.net. *Dir*, Barbara Holmes
Pop 418; Circ 10,200
Library Holdings: Bk Vols 10,406; Per Subs 52
Mem of North Central Regional Library System
Open Mon & Wed 1:30-8, Fri 1:30-5:30 & Sat 10-4

LYNNVILLE

P LYNNVILLE PUBLIC LIBRARY,* 301 South St, PO Box 96, 50153. SAN 376-4982. Tel: 515-527-2590. FAX: 515-527-2591. E-Mail: lynnlib@netins.net. *Librn*, Linda James
Library Holdings: Bk Vols 11,500; Per Subs 45
Mem of Central Iowa Regional Library
Open Mon 2-5, Wed 10-6, Thurs 1-7, Sat 9-12
Friends of the Library Group

LYTTON

P LYTTON PUBLIC LIBRARY, 118 Main St, 50561. SAN 376-5318. Tel: 712-466-2522. *Librn*, Clark Andrea
Pop 350
Jul 1999-Jun 2000 Income $8,720, State $345, County $8,375. Mats Exp Books $250
Library Holdings: Bk Vols 5,000
Mem of Northwest Regional Library System
Open Mon, Wed & Fri 1-5, Tues 10-7, Thurs 1-7
Friends of the Library Group

MADRID

P MADRID PUBLIC LIBRARY, 100 W Third St, 50156-1339. SAN 305-5388. Tel: 515-795-3846. FAX: 515-795-3697. *Librn*, Rosemarie Bertini
Founded 1934. Pop 2,395; Circ 23,687
Jul 1999-Jun 2000 Income $56,231, State $2,400, City $43,831, County $10,000
Library Holdings: Bk Vols 15,000
Mem of Central Iowa Regional Library
Friends of the Library Group

MALLARD

P MALLARD PUBLIC LIBRARY,* 609 Inman St, PO Box 248, 50562. SAN 320-8281. Tel: 712-425-3330. FAX: 712-425-3330. E-Mail: mallard1@ncn.net. *Librn*, Nancy Kacmarynski
Founded 1943. Pop 420; Circ 8,007
Library Holdings: Bk Vols 8,000; Per Subs 30
Mem of Northwest Regional Library System
Open Mon 1-6, Wed 9-12 & 1-5:30, Fri 1-5:30, Sat 9-12

MALVERN

P MALVERN PUBLIC LIBRARY,* 502 Main St, PO Box 180, 51551-0180. SAN 305-5396. Tel: 712-624-8554. FAX: 712-624-8245. E-Mail: malvernlib@radiks.net. *Librn*, Teresa Gonterman
Founded 1914. Pop 2,500; Circ 16,424
Jul 1998-Jun 1999 Income $40,000. Mats Exp $4,885. Sal $15,292
Library Holdings: Bk Vols 24,849; Per Subs 78
Special Collections: Malvern Leader Coll
Mem of Southwest Iowa Regional Library System
Open Mon, Tues, Thurs & Fri 2-5:30, Wed 2-8, Sat 10-12:30 & 2-4
Friends of the Library Group

MANCHESTER

P MANCHESTER PUBLIC LIBRARY, 304 N Franklin St, 52057. SAN 305-540X. Tel: 319-927-3719. FAX: 319-927-3058. E-Mail: manchlib@mwci.net. Web Site: www.manchester-ia.com/library/htm. *Librn*, Dan Bakke; Staff 3 (MLS 1, Non-MLS 2)
Founded 1903. Pop 5,400; Circ 113,256
Jul 1999-Jun 2000 Income $198,042. Mats Exp $41,000. Sal $39,000
Library Holdings: Bk Vols 31,212; Per Subs 93
Subject Interests: Genealogy, History, Large type print, Local history
Special Collections: Manchester Newspapers, 1871-1999, microfilm
Mem of Northeastern Iowa Regional Library System
Open Mon-Thurs 9:30-8, Fri, 9:30-5, Sat 9-3
Friends of the Library Group

MANILLA

P MANILLA PUBLIC LIBRARY, 447 Main St, PO Box 429, 51454. SAN 305-5418. Tel: 712-654-5192. *Dir*, Ann Macumber
Founded 1932. Pop 1,020; Circ 5,795
Library Holdings: Bk Vols 6,200; Bk Titles 5,241
Mem of Northwest Regional Library System
Open Wed 2-5, Sat 9-11 & 2-5

MANLY

P MANLY PUBLIC LIBRARY, Grant & W Main St, PO Box 720, 50456-0720. SAN 305-5426. Tel: 641-454-2982. FAX: 641-454-2982. E-Mail: stardust@netins.net. *Dir*, Daphne Stromley
Pop 1,349; Circ 25,613
Jul 1999-Jun 2000 Income $36,542, State $1,342, City $22,900, County $9,300, Other $3,000. Mats Exp $6,800, Books $6,000, Per/Ser (Incl. Access Fees) $800. Sal $18,775
Library Holdings: Bk Vols 17,000; Bk Titles 13,230; Per Subs 72
Automation Activity & Vendor Info: (Acquisitions) Sagebrush Corporation; (Cataloging) Sagebrush Corporation; (Circulation) Sagebrush Corporation
Database Vendor: OCLC - First Search
Mem of North Central Regional Library System
Open Mon 2-9, Tues, Wed & Fri 2-5, Thurs 10-12 & 2-9, Sat 10-4

MANNING

P MANNING PUBLIC LIBRARY,* 310 Main St, 51455. SAN 305-5434. Tel: 712-653-2260. *Librn*, Renee Pfannkuch
Pop 1,609; Circ 10,536
Library Holdings: Bk Titles 15,000; Per Subs 20
Special Collections: Media: videos (50), audios (50)
Mem of Northwest Regional Library System
Open Mon, Tues, Thurs & Fri 11-5:30, Wed 11-7, Sat 10-12

MANSON

P MANSON PUBLIC LIBRARY,* Tenth Ave & 13th St, PO Box 309, 50563. SAN 305-5442. Tel: 712-469-3986. FAX: 712-469-3986. *Dir*, Ann Schlapkohl; *Asst Librn*, Pam Baughman
Founded 1922. Pop 1,848
Library Holdings: Bk Vols 17,266; Per Subs 65
Mem of NW Iowa Regional Libr Syst
Open Mon & Fri 1-5, Tues & Wed 10-5, Thurs 1-8, Sat 9-5

MAPLETON

P FISHER WHITING MEMORIAL LIBRARY,* 609 Courtright St, 51034. SAN 305-5450. Tel: 712-882-1312. Interlibrary Loan Service Tel: 800-352-4982. FAX: 712-882-1312. *Librn*, Deborah Stodola; E-Mail: dstodola@mapleton.lib.ia.us; *Asst Librn*, Linda Miller; *Asst Librn*, Jean Wessling
Pop 1,495; Circ 24,617
Library Holdings: Bk Titles 16,852; Per Subs 58
Special Collections: Media: Video (462), Audio (281)
Publications: Library Journal
Mem of Northwest Regional Library System
Open Mon 1-8, Tues 1-5, Wed 10-8, Thurs 1-5, Fri 1-8, Sat 10-4
Friends of the Library Group

MAQUOKETA

P MAQUOKETA FREE PUBLIC LIBRARY,* 126 S Second St, 52060. SAN 305-5469. Tel: 319-652-3874. FAX: 319-652-3874. E-Mail: mlibrary@caves.net. *Dir*, Karen Manning
Founded 1878. Pop 6,313; Circ 72,644
Library Holdings: Bk Vols 34,000; Per Subs 92
Subject Interests: Iowa, Literature, Local history
Special Collections: Media: videos (500, audios (700)
Open Mon, Tues & Thurs 12-8, Wed & Fri 10-5:30, Sa 9-4
Friends of the Library Group

MARATHON

P MARATHON PUBLIC LIBRARY,* 103 W Attica St, PO Box 200, 50565. SAN 305-5477. Tel: 712-289-2200. FAX: 712-289-6118. E-Mail: bookloan@sconnect.com. *Librn*, Cathy Jensen
Pop 442; Circ 5,868
Library Holdings: Bk Titles 8,500; Per Subs 42
Special Collections: Videos (268)
Mem of NW Iowa Regional Libr Syst
Open Mon & Wed 2-5:30, Sat 9-12

MARBLE ROCK

P MARBLE ROCK PUBLIC LIBRARY, 105 S Main St, PO Box 236, 50653. SAN 305-5485. Tel: 515-397-4480. FAX: 515-397-4480. E-Mail: mrlib@netins.net. *Librn*, Elaine Ott
Founded 1946. Pop 361; Circ 6,000
Library Holdings: Bk Vols 4,500; Per Subs 42
Mem of North Central Regional Library System

MARCUS

P MARCUS PUBLIC LIBRARY,* 106 N Locust St, PO Box 528, 51035. SAN 305-5493. Tel: 712-376-2328. FAX: 712-376-4628. E-Mail: marcuspl@nwidt.com. *Dir*, Maxine Shea
Founded 1908. Pop 1,206; Circ 16,727
Jul 1998-Jun 1999 Income $40,238, State $144, City $33,229, County $5,500, Locally Generated Income $1,365. Mats Exp $8,789, Per/Ser (Incl. Access Fees) $2,286, AV Equip $6,468, Electronic Ref Mat (Incl. Access Fees) $35. Sal $17,778
Library Holdings: Bk Titles 14,500; Per Subs 68
Subject Interests: Local history, Science/technology, Technology
Mem of Northwest Regional Library System

MARENGO

P MARENGO PUBLIC LIBRARY,* 1020 Marengo Ave, PO Box 245, 52301-0245. SAN 305-5507. Tel: 319-741-3825. FAX: 319-741-3825. E-Mail: mpl@netins.net. *Librn*, Peggy Walton
Founded 1904. Pop 2,235; Circ 35,648
Library Holdings: Bk Vols 15,367; Per Subs 83
Special Collections: Iowa County History, bd vols, micro; Media: videos (790), audios (515)
Open Mon-Thurs 10-7:30, Fri 10-6, Sat 10-3

MARION

P MARION PUBLIC LIBRARY,* 1095 Sixth Ave, 52302. SAN 305-5515. Tel: 319-377-3412. FAX: 319-377-0113. E-Mail: mpl@crpl.cedar-rapids.lib.ia.us. Web Site: www.community.marion.ia.us/library. *Dir*, Susan S Kling; *Asst Dir*, Cynthia Brown; *Ch Servs*, Jean Hampson; *YA Servs*, Chris Grannis; *Ref*, Judy Winistorfer
Pop 23,500; Circ 365,312
Jul 1998-Jun 1999 Income $736,533, State $36,768, City $632,763, County $29,016, Locally Generated Income $37,986. Mats Exp $135,343. Sal $462,345
Library Holdings: Bk Titles 99,647; Per Subs 272
Mem of East Central Regional Library
Friends of the Library Group

MARSHALLTOWN

S CENTRAL IOWA ART ASSOCIATION, INC LIBRARY,* Fisher Community Ctr, 709 S Center St, 50158. SAN 305-5523. Tel: 515-753-9013. *Dir*, Tim Castle
Library Holdings: Bk Vols 500
Our library is a depository for donated books

S EMERSON ELECTRIC, Fisher Control Information Center,* Tech Ctr, 1700 12th Ave, 50158. SAN 329-0557. Tel: 515-754-2161. FAX: 515-754-3159. *Librn, Online Servs, Ref*, Mark Heindselman; E-Mail: mark.heindselman@frco.com; *Acq, Circ, ILL, Per*, Paula Opperman
Library Holdings: Bk Titles 3,500; Per Subs 300
Subject Interests: Computer science, Software engineering
Special Collections: 2,000 videos
Publications: FRETOCS (electronically disseminated)
Partic in BRS; Dialog Corporation; Vutext
Open Mon-Fri 7:30-4:30, other times available thru appointment

S IOWA VETERAN'S HOME LIBRARY, 1301 Summit, 50158-5485. SAN 305-5531. Tel: 641-753-4412. FAX: 641-753-4373. *Librn*, Jean Wilhelmi
Library Holdings: Bk Vols 5,000; Per Subs 50
Subject Interests: Geriatrics and gerontology
Open Mon-Fri 9-4

J MARSHALLTOWN COMMUNITY COLLEGE, Learning Resource Center,* 3700 S Center St, 50158. SAN 320-6777. Tel: 515-752-7106, Ext 263. FAX: 515-754-1442. E-Mail: mcclib@iavalley.cc.ia.us. *Dir*, Rebecca Spriester
Founded 1927
Library Holdings: Bk Vols 25,000; Per Subs 1,224
Open Mon-Thurs 7:30-9, Fri 7:30-3:30

P MARSHALLTOWN PUBLIC LIBRARY, 36 N Center St, 50158. SAN 341-9347. Tel: 641-754-5738. FAX: 641-754-5708. E-Mail: library@marshallnet.com. Web Site: www.marshallnet.com/library. *Dir*, Carole Booker Winkleblack; *Assoc Dir*, Sandra J Gowdy; *Cat*, LoRae Porter; *Ref Serv*, Mary K Middelkoop; *Ch Servs*, Joa LaVille; Staff 12 (MLS 1, Non-MLS 11)
Founded 1898. Pop 39,000; Circ 176,000
Jul 1998-Jun 1999 Income $568,009, City $493,502, County $16,000, Locally Generated Income $50,796, Other $7,711
Library Holdings: Bk Vols 70,000; Per Subs 232
Subject Interests: Genealogy, Local history
Special Collections: Genealogy (Holdings of the Central Iowa Genealogical Society & Holdings of the Marshalltown DAR); Marshall County Heritage Room

Automation Activity & Vendor Info: (Cataloging) epixtech, inc.; (Circulation) epixtech, inc.; (OPAC) epixtech, inc.
Database Vendor: epixtech, inc., OCLC - First Search
Special Services for the Blind - Bks on cassette
Friends of the Library Group

MARTELLE

P MARTELLE PUBLIC LIBRARY,* 202 South St, 52305. SAN 305-5558. Tel: 319-482-4121. E-Mail: mrtllibr@netins.net. *Librn*, Ellen Platner; *Asst Librn*, Neoma Robertson
Founded 1950. Pop 316; Circ 3,831
Library Holdings: Bk Titles 5,200
Open Tues & Thurs 2-6, Wed 9-5, Sat 9-noon

MASON CITY

S CHARLES H MACNIDER MUSEUM LIBRARY,* 303 Second St SE, 50401-3925. SAN 305-5566. Tel: 515-421-3666. FAX: 515-423-2615. *Dir*, Richard E Leet
Founded 1964
Library Holdings: Bk Vols 1,500
Subject Interests: Art, Art history
Restriction: In-house use for visitors, Not a lending library

C HAMILTON COLLEGE LIBRARY, 100 First St NW, 50401. SAN 375-3255. Tel: 515-423-2530. Toll Free Tel: 800-274-2530. FAX: 515-423-7512. Web Site: www.hamiltonia.edu. *Librn*, Beverly Ann Elder; E-Mail: elderb@hamiltonia.edu; Staff 2 (MLS 1, Non-MLS 1)
Founded 1989
Library Holdings: Bk Titles 4,000; Per Subs 40
Automation Activity & Vendor Info: (Circulation) Athena
Database Vendor: Ebsco - EbscoHost, Lexis-Nexis, OCLC - First Search
Publications: Inside Hamilton (newsletter)
Restriction: Open to students
Function: For research purposes, ILL available, ILL to other special libraries, Literary searches, Mail loans to members, Photocopies available, Reference services available, Some telephone reference
Mem of North Central Regional Library System
Special Services for the Deaf - High interest/low vocabulary books
Friends of the Library Group

P MASON CITY PUBLIC LIBRARY, 225 Second St SE, 50401. SAN 305-5574. Tel: 515-421-3668. Reference Tel: 641-421-3670. FAX: 515-423-2615. E-Mail: admin@mcpl.org, librarian@mcpl.org. Web Site: www.mcpl.org. *Dir*, Andrew G Alexander; Tel: 515-421-3669; *Acq, Asst Dir*, Catherine Durivage; *Circ*, Marie Colby; *Ch Servs*, Barbara Madson; *Ref Servs YA*, Fern Robinson; *Automation Syst Coordr*, Harold Price; E-Mail: webmaster@mcpl.org; *Archivist*, Terrence Harrison; *Admin Assoc*, Penny Moorehead; *Tech Coordr*, Thomas Allen; Staff 17 (MLS 1, Non-MLS 16)
Founded 1876. Pop 29,040; Circ 50,000
Jul 1999-Jun 2000 Income $731,060, State $15,114, City $634,461, County $44,690, Locally Generated Income $55,657. Mats Exp $736,344, Books $72,397, Per/Ser (Incl. Access Fees) $18,482, AV Equip $8,112, Electronic Ref Mat (Incl. Access Fees) $3,060. Sal $393,790
Library Holdings: Bk Titles 106,233; Per Subs 327
Subject Interests: Art and architecture, Civil War, Local history
Special Collections: Lee P Loomis Archive of Mason City History
Publications: Annual Report; Mason City Sketchbooks
Open Winter Hours: Mon-Thurs 9-9, Fri-Sat 9-5 & Sun 1-5; Summer Hours: Mon-Thurs 9-8 & Fri-Sat 9-5
Friends of the Library Group

M MERCY MEDICAL CENTER-NORTH IOWA, Medical Library, 1000 Fourth St SW, 50401. SAN 305-5604. Tel: 641-422-7699. Interlibrary Loan Service Tel: 641-422-7938. FAX: 641-422-7698. *Librn*, Judy Madson; E-Mail: madsonj@trinity-health.org
Library Holdings: Bk Vols 5,300; Per Subs 235
Subject Interests: Administration, Medicine, Nursing
Automation Activity & Vendor Info: (Acquisitions) EOS; (Cataloging) EOS; (OPAC) EOS; (Serials) EOS
Database Vendor: Silverplatter Information Inc.
Partic in Greater Midwest Regional Medical Libr Network; Nat Libr of Med

P NORTH CENTRAL REGIONAL LIBRARY SYSTEM, 22 N Georgia, Ste 208, 50401-3435. SAN 305-5582. Tel: 641-423-6917. Toll Free Tel: 800-392-8804. FAX: 641-423-6261. Web Site: www.ncrls.lib.ia.us. *Dir*, Betty B Landon; E-Mail: blandon@ncrls.lib.ia.us; *Mgr*, Karen M Day; E-Mail: kday@ncrls.lib.ia.us. Subject Specialists: *Consulting*, Thomas A Shepley; Staff 3 (MLS 2, Non-MLS 1)
Founded 1973. Pop 237,957
Jul 1999-Jun 2000 Income State $180,216. Sal $127,836 (Prof $95,000)
Database Vendor: OCLC - First Search
Member Libraries: Ackley Public Library; Alexander Public Library; Algona Public Library; Badger Public Library; Bancroft Public Library; Belmond Public Library; Bode Public Library; Britt Public Library; Buffalo Center Public Library; Burt Public Library; Callender Heritage Library; Charles City Public Library; Clare Public Library; Clarion Public Library; Clear Lake Public Library; Corwith Public Library; Coulter Public Library; Dayton Public Library; Dr Grace O Doane Alden Public Library; Duncombe Public Library; Eagle Grove Memorial Library; Eldora Public Library; Ellsworth Community College; Ellsworth Public Library; Fertile Public Library; Fort Dodge Public Library; Garner Public Library; Gowrie Public Library; Hamilton College Library; Hampton Public Library; Harcourt Community Library; Hubbard Public Library; Humboldt Public Library; Joice Public Library; Juanita Earp Media Center Library; Kanawha Public Library; Kendall Young Library; Kensett Public Library; Kinney Memorial Library; Klemme Public Library; Lake Mills Public Library; Lakota Public Library; Ledyard Public Library; Lehigh Public Library; Livermore Public Library; Luverne Public Library; Manly Public Library; Marble Rock Public Library; Meservey Public Library; Montgomery Memorial Library; Nissen Public Library; Nora Springs Public Library; North Central Regional Library; Northwood Public Library; Onaping Falls Public Library; Osage Public Library; Radcliffe Public Library; Rake Public Library; Renwick Public Library; Riceville Public Library; Robert W Barlow Memorial Library; Rockford Public Library; Rockwell Public Library; Rowan Public Library; Rudd Public Library; Sheffield Public Library; Stacyville Public Library; Stanhope Public Library; Steamboat Rock Public Library; Stratford Public Library; Swaledale Public Library; Swea City Public Library; Thompson Public Library; Thornton Public Library; Titonka Public Library; Union Public Library; Ventura Public Library; Wesley Public Library; West Bend Public Library; Whittemore Public Library; Williams Public Library; Woden Public Library

J NORTH IOWA AREA COMMUNITY COLLEGE LIBRARY, 500 College Dr, 50401. SAN 305-5590. Tel: 641-422-4232. Reference Tel: 641-422-4327. FAX: 641-422-4131. Web Site: www.niacc.cc.ia.us/progserv/library/index.html. *Librn*, Karen F Dole; E-Mail: dolekare@niacc.cc.ia.us; Staff 6 (MLS 3, Non-MLS 3)
Founded 1918. Enrl 2,800; Fac 115
Jul 1999-Jun 2000 Mats Exp $86,104, Books $33,000, Per/Ser (Incl. Access Fees) $25,670, Presv $160, Micro $1,862, Electronic Ref Mat (Incl. Access Fees) $25,412. Sal $161,626 (Prof $97,778)
Library Holdings: Bk Vols 28,711; Per Subs 427
Automation Activity & Vendor Info: (Cataloging) Gaylord; (OPAC) Gaylord; (Serials) Gaylord
Database Vendor: Ebsco - EbscoHost, Lexis-Nexis, OCLC - First Search, OVID Technologies
Publications: NIACC Library Handbook
Partic in BCR; OCLC Online Computer Library Center, Inc

MASSENA

P MASSENA PUBLIC LIBRARY, 100 Main, PO Box 86, 50853. SAN 305-5612. Tel: 712-779-3726. *Librn*, Dolores Curry
Founded 1918. Pop 507; Circ 5,281
1998-1999 Income $5,528, City $2,800, County $2,728. Mats Exp $2,591, Books $2,506, Per/Ser (Incl. Access Fees) $85
Library Holdings: Bk Vols 3,767; Bk Titles 3,502
Mem of Southwest Iowa Regional Library System
Open Tues, Wed & Fri 1-4:30
Friends of the Library Group

MAXWELL

P MAXWELL PUBLIC LIBRARY,* 107 Main St, PO Box 128, 50161. SAN 305-5620. Tel: 515-387-8780. FAX: 515-387-8780. *Librn*, Patricia Ann Taylor
Pop 783; Circ 6,977
Jul 1998-Jun 1999 Income $12,000. Mats Exp $3,000. Sal $6,200
Library Holdings: Bk Vols 5,586
Subject Interests: Iowa
Mem of Central Iowa Regional Library
Open Mon-Thurs 3-7, Sat 9-1

MAYNARD

P MAYNARD COMMUNITY LIBRARY,* 225 Main St W, 50655-0225. SAN 376-5253. Tel: 319-637-2330. FAX: 319-637-2330. E-Mail: maynardlibrary@trxinc.com. *Librn*, Lezlie Barry
Library Holdings: Bk Vols 5,475; Per Subs 43
Mem of Northeastern Iowa Regional Library System
Open Tues & Wed 1-5, Thurs 1-7:30, Fri & Sat 9-12

MC GREGOR

P MC GREGOR PUBLIC LIBRARY,* 334 Main St, PO Box 398, 52157-0398. SAN 305-537X. Tel: 319-873-3318. FAX: 319-873-3318. E-Mail: mplib@mwci.net. *Asst Librn*, Sue Henkes; *Librn*, Pettit Michelle; *Asst Librn*, Jenny Kricke
Pop 797; Circ 23,462
Jul 1999-Jun 2000 Income $65,200. Mats Exp $11,700, Books $11,000, Per/Ser (Incl. Access Fees) $700. Sal $30,500

Library Holdings: Bk Titles 12,607; Per Subs 27
Subject Interests: Local history
Mem of Northeastern Iowa Regional Library System
Open Mon & Wed 2:30-8:30, Tues & Thurs 10:30-5:30, Fri 2:30-5:30, Sat 9:30-3:30

MECHANICSVILLE

P MECHANICSVILLE PUBLIC LIBRARY,* 218 E First St, 52306-0370. SAN 305-5647. Tel: 319-432-7135. FAX: 319-432-7135. E-Mail: mcvillib@netins.net. *Dir*, Judy Hartmen; *Asst Librn*, Kelly Eby
Pop 1,012; Circ 7,497
Library Holdings: Bk Vols 11,000; Per Subs 45
Open Mon & Wed 1-7:30, Tues, Thurs & Fri 1-5, Sat 9-11

MEDIAPOLIS

P MEDIAPOLIS PUBLIC LIBRARY, 128 N Orchard St, 52637. (Mail add: PO Box 39, 52637), SAN 305-5655. Tel: 319-394-3895. FAX: 319-394-9323. E-Mail: medlib@netins.net. *Dir*, Carrie M Haverman; E-Mail: mscarrieh@hotmail.com; *Ch Servs*, Tammy Levins; *Circ*, Nadine Miller; *Circ*, Holly Hay; Staff 4 (Non-MLS 4)
Founded 1915. Pop 1,700; Circ 35,000
Jul 2000-Jun 2001 Income $65,800, State $800, City $40,000, County $15,000, Locally Generated Income $10,000. Mats Exp $16,500, Books $12,000, Per/Ser (Incl. Access Fees) $1,500, Other Print Mats $1,000, Electronic Ref Mat (Incl. Access Fees) $1,000. Sal $40,000 (Prof $22,800)
Library Holdings: Bk Vols 12,000; Bk Titles 11,800; Per Subs 65; High Interest/Low Vocabulary Bk Vols 1,000; Bks on Deafness & Sign Lang 10
Function: ILL available
Mem of Southeastern Library Services

MELBOURNE

P MELBOURNE PUBLIC LIBRARY, 603 Main St, PO Box 128, 50162. SAN 376-5431. Tel: 641-482-3115. *Librn*, Sam Halter; Staff 2 (Non-MLS 2)
Founded 1975
Library Holdings: Bk Vols 18,000; Per Subs 24
Automation Activity & Vendor Info: (Cataloging) Follett; (Circulation) Follett
Mem of Central Iowa Regional Library

MELVIN

P MELVIN PUBLIC LIBRARY,* 232 Main St, 51350. SAN 376-5148. Tel: 712-736-2107. *Librn*, Connie Van Engen
Jul 1997-Jun 1998 Income $8,000
Library Holdings: Bk Vols 5,000; Per Subs 40
Mem of Northwest Regional Library System
Open Mon 3-7, Wed 1-5, Sat 9-2

MENLO

P MENLO PUBLIC LIBRARY,* 417 Sherman St, PO Box 39, 50164-0039. SAN 305-568X. Tel: 515-524-4201. FAX: 515-524-2682. *Dir*, Janet Wright
Founded 1942. Pop 356; Circ 9,996
Library Holdings: Bk Vols 10,311; Bk Titles 10,218; Per Subs 43
Mem of Southwest Iowa Regional Library System
Open Mon 12-4:30, Wed & Fri 11-1:30, Sat 9-11:30

MERRILL

P MERRILL PUBLIC LIBRARY,* 321 Fourth St, PO Box 335, 51038. SAN 305-5698. Tel: 712-938-2503. FAX: 712-938-2503. *Dir*, Julie Schultz; *Asst Librn*, Anna Mae Koerselman; *Asst Librn*, Julie Bergquist
Pop 825; Circ 7,950
Library Holdings: Bk Vols 6,400; Per Subs 71
Mem of Northwest Regional Library System
Open Mon & Wed 6-8, Tues & Thurs 1:30-5, Fri & Sat 9-12

MESERVEY

P MESERVEY PUBLIC LIBRARY, 719 First St, 50457. SAN 305-5701. Tel: 641-358-6274. FAX: 641-358-6274. E-Mail: merlib@kalnet.com. *Dir*, Val Koehler; *Asst Librn*, Evelyn Gaetzke
Founded 1965. Pop 300; Circ 4,500
Library Holdings: Bk Titles 7,588; Per Subs 34
Mem of North Central Regional Library System

MIDDLE AMANA

P AMANA SCHOOL-COMMUNITY LIBRARY,* 3023 220th Trail, 52307. SAN 376-7469. Tel: 319-622-3192. FAX: 319-622-3108. *Librn*, Mary Everhart
Library Holdings: Bk Vols 22,000; Per Subs 60
Mem of East Central Regional Library

MILFORD

P MILFORD MEMORIAL LIBRARY,* 1009 Ninth St Ste 5, 51351. SAN 305-571X. Tel: 712-338-4643. FAX: 712-338-4859. E-Mail: milflib@rconnect.com. *Dir*, Cyndi Naig; E-Mail: cnaig@milford.ia.us
Founded 1912. Pop 2,170; Circ 86,000
Jul 1999-Jun 2000 Income $88,861, City $74,622, County $9,200, Locally Generated Income $2,000. Mats Exp $17,950, Books $9,950, Per/Ser (Incl. Access Fees) $2,000, Micro $1,200, AV Equip $500, Electronic Ref Mat (Incl. Access Fees) $4,300
Library Holdings: Bk Vols 22,300; Bk Titles 18,700; Per Subs 145
Function: Photocopies available
Mem of Northwest Regional Library System
Friends of the Library Group

MILO

P MILO PUBLIC LIBRARY,* 123 Main St, 50166. SAN 305-5728. Tel: 515-942-6557. FAX: 515-942-6557. E-Mail: milopu@crosspatls.net. Web Site: www.cityofmilo.org. *Librn*, Paula J Griggs
Founded 1955. Pop 900; Circ 15,200
Jul 1998-Jun 1999 Income $19,684. Mats Exp $5,418. Sal $9,472
Library Holdings: Bk Titles 14,525; Per Subs 74
Special Collections: Local History Coll, bks, newsp, photogs, obituaries; Media: videos (273), audios (201)
Mem of Central Iowa Regional Library
Open Mon 2-7:30, Tues 6-8, Wed & Thurs 2-5:30, Fri 9-11 & 2-5:30, Sat 9-12

MILTON

P MILTON PUBLIC LIBRARY,* 422 N Main St, 52570. SAN 305-5736. Tel: 515-656-4412, 515-656-4611 (City Hall). *Librn*, Jane Hargrove
Pop 567; Circ 5,132
Library Holdings: Bk Vols 5,312
Mem of Southeastern Library Services
Open Wed-Fri 1:30-4:30

MINBURN

P MINBURN PUBLIC LIBRARY,* 315 Baker St, PO Box 23, 50167-0023. SAN 305-5744. Tel: 515-677-2712. FAX: 515-677-2245. E-Mail: minblib@netins.net. *Librn*, Laura Allen; *Asst Librn*, Evelyn Schwartz
Pop 390; Circ 1,532
Library Holdings: Bk Vols 6,000; Per Subs 15
Mem of Central Iowa Regional Library
Open Tues 9-6, Wed 2-5, Thurs 3-6, Sat 9-12

MINGO

P MINGO PUBLIC LIBRARY, 103 W Main St, PO Box 25, 50168-0024. SAN 376-7612. Tel: 641-363-4631. E-Mail: mingolib123@aol.com. *Librn*, Ellen Timm
Library Holdings: Bk Vols 4,750; Per Subs 15
Mem of Central Iowa Regional Library
Open Tues 9-12, Wed & Fri 3-6, Thurs 3-5

MISSOURI VALLEY

P MISSOURI VALLEY PUBLIC LIBRARY,* 119 N Fifth St, 51555. SAN 305-5752. Tel: 712-642-4111. E-Mail: mupub@neonramp.com. *Dir*, Rhonda J Chambers
Founded 1881. Pop 5,000; Circ 33,000
Library Holdings: Bk Titles 23,730; Per Subs 60
Mem of Southwest Iowa Regional Library System
Open Mon-Wed & Fri 10-5:30, Thurs 1-8 & Sat 10-2
Friends of the Library Group

MITCHELLVILLE

P MITCHELLVILLE PUBLIC LIBRARY, 204 Center Ave N, 50169-0727. SAN 305-5779. Tel: 515-967-3339. FAX: 515-967-1868. E-Mail: mplib@dwx.com. Web Site: www.mitchellvillelibrary.org. *Librn*, Sarah Kennedy
Pop 1,670; Circ 19,764
Jul 1999-Jun 2000 Income $72,426, State $1,808, City $50,391, County $8,504, Other $11,723. Mats Exp $11,802, Books $10,923, Per/Ser (Incl.

Access Fees) $879. Sal $32,567
Library Holdings: Bk Titles 11,855; Per Subs 51
Automation Activity & Vendor Info: (Circulation) Sagebrush Corporation
Mem of Central Iowa Regional Library
Friends of the Library Group

S TOMORROW CENTER LIBRARY, Iowa Correctional Institution for Women,* 300 Elm SW, PO Box 700, 50169. SAN 305-6740. Tel: 515-967-4236, Ext 1221. FAX: 515-967-5347. *Librn*, Gary Krob; Tel: 515-967-4236; Staff 1 (Non-MLS 1)
Library Holdings: Bk Vols 20,000; Per Subs 24
Subject Interests: Ethnic studies, Feminism

MODALE

P MODALE PUBLIC LIBRARY, 208 N Main St, PO Box 28, 51556. SAN 305-5787. Tel: 712-645-2826. E-Mail: modpublib@unitedwestern.net. *Librn*, Margaret Vittitoe
Circ 5,080
Jul 1998-Jun 1999 Income $8,500. Mats Exp $3,937. Sal $3,794
Library Holdings: Bk Vols 8,371; Per Subs 20
Mem of Southwest Iowa Regional Library System
Open Wed 2:30-7:30, Sat 9-2
Friends of the Library Group

MONDAMIN

P MONDAMIN PUBLIC LIBRARY, 201 Maple St, PO Box 190, 51557. SAN 305-5795. Tel: 712-646-2888. E-Mail: mondamin@w-harrison.k12.ia.us. *Librn*, Joyce McClannahan
Founded 1934. Pop 450; Circ 560
Library Holdings: Bk Titles 7,086
Mem of Southwest Iowa Regional Library System
Open Tues & Thurs 1-6, Wed 3-8, Sat 9-2, winter hours Weds 1-6

MONONA

P MURPHY MEMORIAL LIBRARY, 111 N Page, 52159-0430. SAN 305-5809. Tel: 319-539-2356. FAX: 319-539-2306. E-Mail: murphy@netins.net. *Librn*, Chris Bee; *Ch Servs*, Jane Lundquist
Founded 1934. Pop 1,530; Circ 15,572
Jul 1998-Jun 1999 Mats Exp $26,340. Sal $12,513
Library Holdings: Bk Titles 13,500; Per Subs 39
Mem of Northeastern Iowa Regional Library System
Open Mon & Wed 2-7, Tues & Thurs 1-5, Sat 9-12

MONROE

P MONROE PUBLIC LIBRARY, 103 W Washington, PO Box 780, 50170-0796. SAN 376-5474. Tel: 515-259-3065. FAX: 515-259-2311. E-Mail: monpubli@netins.net. *Dir*, Randy Bellinger; Staff 2 (MLS 1, Non-MLS 1)
Pop 1,739
Jul 1999-Jun 2000 Income $29,292. Mats Exp $9,405. Sal $17,779
Library Holdings: Bk Vols 13,667; Per Subs 16
Subject Interests: Local history
Automation Activity & Vendor Info: (Cataloging) Follett; (Circulation) Follett
Function: ILL available, Photocopies available
Mem of Central Iowa Regional Library
Open Mon-Thurs 1-7, Fri 1-5, Sat 9-12
Friends of the Library Group

MONTEZUMA

P MONTEZUMA PUBLIC LIBRARY,* 200 S Third St, PO Box 158, 50171. SAN 305-5817. Tel: 515-623-3417. FAX: 515-623-3339. E-Mail: montepl@netins.net, zumapl@netins.net. *Librn*, Mary Van Baalen; *Asst Librn*, Nancy Dorsheimer
Founded 1916. Circ 15,964
Library Holdings: Bk Vols 12,000; Per Subs 55
Open Mon, Wed & Thurs 9-5, Tues & Fri 2:30-5, Sat 9-12

MONTICELLO

P MONTICELLO PUBLIC LIBRARY,* 116 E Grand St, 52310-1617. SAN 376-7493. Tel: 319-465-3354. FAX: 319-465-3354. E-Mail: library@n-connect.net. *Librn*, Jeanne Knopp
Library Holdings: Bk Vols 15,508; Per Subs 86
Mem of East Central Regional Library
Open Mon & Thurs 12-8, Tues & Wed 10-8, Fri 12-5, Sat 9-1
Friends of the Library Group

MONTROSE

P MONTROSE PUBLIC LIBRARY, 202 Main St, PO Box 100, 52639-0100. SAN 305-5833. Tel: 319-463-5532. FAX: 319-463-5532. E-Mail: montros@ainterl.net, montrose@interl.net. *Dir*, Lana Clark
Founded 1928. Pop 957; Circ 14,334
Jul 1998-Jun 1999 Income $11,999, State $421, City $9,000, County $2,578. Mats Exp $1,050, Books $500, Per/Ser (Incl. Access Fees) $300, AV Equip $250. Sal $9,617
Library Holdings: Bk Vols 9,816; Bk Titles 10,034; Per Subs 28
Subject Interests: Local history
Mem of Southeastern Regional Libr Syst
Open Mon, Wed, Thurs & Fri 3-7, Sat 9-1

MOORHEAD

P MOORHEAD PUBLIC LIBRARY,* 40674 County Hwy E 54, PO Box 33, 51558. SAN 376-6810. Tel: 712-886-5211. *Librn*, Joyce Ballantyne
Library Holdings: Bk Vols 3,500
Mem of Northwest Regional Library System
Open Sat 1-4
Friends of the Library Group

MORAVIA

P MORAVIA PUBLIC LIBRARY,* 114 E Chariton, 52571-9999. SAN 305-5841. Tel: 515-724-3440. Interlibrary Loan Service Tel: 800-397-0029. FAX: 515-724-3440. E-Mail: mlibrary@se-iowa.net. *Dir*, Deena Hoffman
Founded 1941
Library Holdings: Bk Titles 8,206; Per Subs 31
Mem of Southeastern Library Services

MORLEY

P MORLEY PUBLIC LIBRARY,* 203 Main St, PO Box 527, 52312. SAN 305-585X. Tel: 319-489-9271. *Librn*, Sue VonBehren
Pop 95; Circ 1,600
Library Holdings: Bk Titles 14,000
Open Wed 4-6, Sat 9-11

MORNING SUN

P MELLINGER MEMORIAL LIBRARY, Division St, PO Box 8, 52640. SAN 305-5868. Tel: 319-868-7505. FAX: 319-868-7505. E-Mail: mslib@netins.net. *Librn*, Pamela Butler
Founded 1915. Pop 956; Circ 14,447
Library Holdings: Bk Vols 11,343; Bk Titles 9,498; Per Subs 50
Mem of Southeastern Library Services

MOULTON

P GARRETT MEMORIAL LIBRARY,* 123 S Main, 52572-1327. SAN 305-5876. Tel: 515-642-3664. FAX: 515-642-3664. E-Mail: gmlib@netins.net. *Librn*, Sandy Gooden
Founded 1968. Pop 762; Circ 6,831
Jul 1998-Jun 1999 Income $14,679. Mats Exp $2,222, Books $1,330, Per/Ser (Incl. Access Fees) $892. Sal $5,364
Library Holdings: Bk Vols 10,000; Per Subs 35
Subject Interests: Genealogy
Mem of Southeastern Library Services
Open Mon 4:30-8, Tues-Thurs 2-5:30, Fri 2-5, Sat 9-12

MOUNT AYR

P MOUNT AYR PUBLIC LIBRARY,* 121 W Monroe St, 50854. SAN 305-5884. Tel: 515-464-2159. FAX: 515-464-2159. E-Mail: mlibrary@mtayr.heartland.net. *Librn*, Nancy Roe; *Asst Librn*, Bobbi Bainum
Founded 1916. Pop 1,938; Circ 33,124
Library Holdings: Bk Vols 14,000; Per Subs 65
Subject Interests: Genealogy, Local history
Mem of Southwest Regional Library Service System
Open Mon-Tues & Wed & Fri 1:30-5, Thurs 9:30-5, Sat 9:30-12

MOUNT PLEASANT

GM IOWA DEPARTMENT OF SOCIAL SERVICES, Mental Health Institute Library,* 1200 E Washington, 52641. SAN 305-5892. Tel: 319-385-9511, Ext 2263. FAX: 319-385-8465. *Librn*, Georgia Houseman McDaniel; E-Mail: ghousem@max.state.ia.us
Founded 1861
Library Holdings: Bk Titles 3,000
Subject Interests: Alcohol and drugs, Drug abuse, Medicine, Nursing, Psychiatry, Self-development, Social sciences and issues
Partic in Regional Med Libr - Region 3; SE Libr Network

C IOWA WESLEYAN COLLEGE, J Raymond Chadwick Library, 107 W Broad St, 52641. (Mail add: 601 N Main St, 52641), SAN 305-5906. Tel: 319-385-6316. Interlibrary Loan Service Tel: 319-385-6318. FAX: 319-385-6324. Web Site: www.iwc.edu/library.htm. *Dir*, Patricia R Newcomer; Tel: 319-385-6315, E-Mail: newcomer@iwc.edu; *Tech Servs*, Nadine Kyle; Tel: 319-385-6319, E-Mail: nkyle@iwc.edu; *Assoc Librn*, Sherril Gibbs; E-Mail: sgibbs@iwc.edu; *Assoc Librn*, Barbara Robb; E-Mail: brobb@iwc.edu; *Media Spec*, Robert Bensmiller; Tel: 319-385-6368; *Circ*, Charis Florendo; Tel: 319-385-6317, E-Mail: florendo@iwc.edu; *Ser*, Lisa Kennedy; Tel: 319-385-6319, E-Mail: lkennedy@iwc.edu; *Acq*, Shirley Farley; E-Mail: sfarley@iwc.edu; *Archivist*, Lynn Ellsworth; Tel: 319-385-6320, E-Mail: iwcarch@iwc.edu. Subject Specialists: *Reference*, Barbara Robb; *Reference*, Sherril Gibbs; *Systs*, Barbara Robb; Staff 7 (MLS 3, Non-MLS 4)
Founded 1857. Enrl 637; Fac 44; Highest Degree: Bachelor
Library Holdings: Bk Vols 107,227; Bk Titles 77,506; Per Subs 431
Special Collections: German-Americanism; Iowa Conference of the United Methodist Church Archives; Iowa History
Automation Activity & Vendor Info: (Circulation) SIRSI; (OPAC) SIRSI
Database Vendor: IAC - Info Trac, Lexis-Nexis, OCLC - First Search
Publications: Library Guides; Off the Shelf (faculty); The Weekly Weeder (student assistants)
Partic in BCR; Iowa Private Academic Library Consortium; OCLC Online Computer Library Center, Inc

S MIDWEST OLD SETTLERS & THRESHERS ASSOCIATION, Old Threshers Office Library,* 405 E Threshers Rd, 52641. SAN 377-5313. Tel: 319-385-8937. FAX: 319-385-0563. E-Mail: info@oldthreshers.org. Web Site: www.oldthreshers.org. *In Charge*, Lennis Moore; *Pub Relations*, Karen Bates Chabal
Library Holdings: Bk Vols 1,500

S MOUNT PLEASANT CORRECTIONAL FACILITY LIBRARY, 1200 E Washington, 52641. SAN 371-5876. Tel: 319-385-9511, Ext 2223. FAX: 319-385-8828. *Librn*, Georgia Houseman McDaniel; Tel: 319-385-9411, Ext 2263, E-Mail: ghousem@max.state.ia.us; Staff 2 (MLS 1, Non-MLS 1)
Founded 1984
Library Holdings: Bk Vols 10,000
Mem of Southeastern Library Services

P MOUNT PLEASANT PUBLIC LIBRARY, 200 N Main St, 52641. SAN 305-5914. Tel: 319-385-1490. TDD: 319-385-1490. FAX: 319-385-1491. E-Mail: mtpplo5@lisco.com. *Dir*, Gayle Trede; Staff 10 (MLS 2, Non-MLS 8)
Founded 1901. Pop 8,027
Jul 1999-Jun 2000 Income $270,509, State $5,000, City $239,995, County $15,844, Locally Generated Income $8,170, Other $1,500. Mats Exp $52,820, Books $43,100, Per/Ser (Incl. Access Fees) $7,300, Micro $120, AV Equip $300, Electronic Ref Mat (Incl. Access Fees) $2,000. Sal $181,149 (Prof $59,363)
Library Holdings: Bk Vols 53,900; Bk Titles 53,000; Per Subs 100
Special Collections: Henry County & Mt Pleasant History
Automation Activity & Vendor Info: (Cataloging) Athena; (Circulation) Athena; (OPAC) Athena
Mem of Southeastern Regional Libr Syst
Special Services for the Deaf - TDD
Friends of the Library Group

MOUNT VERNON

C CORNELL COLLEGE, Russell D Cole Library, 600 First St W, 52314-1098. SAN 305-5922. Tel: 319-895-4260, 895-4271. FAX: 319-895-5936. E-Mail: library@cornell-iowa.edu. Web Site: www.cornell-iowa.edu/library. *Dir*, Jean Donham; *Tech Servs*, Greg Cotton; E-Mail: cotton@cornell-iowa.edu; Staff 5 (MLS 5)
Founded 1853
Library Holdings: Bk Vols 140,463; Bk Titles 122,098; Per Subs 665
Automation Activity & Vendor Info: (Acquisitions) Endeavor; (Cataloging) Endeavor; (Circulation) Endeavor; (Course Reserve) Endeavor; (Serials) Endeavor
Partic in OCLC Online Computer Library Center, Inc

MOVILLE

P WOODBURY COUNTY LIBRARY, 309 Main St, PO Box AL, 51039-0830. SAN 341-9401. Tel: 712-873-3322. FAX: 712-873-3744. *Dir*, Judy A Chesley; E-Mail: judyc@netins.net; *Asst Dir*, Donna Chapman; Staff 1 (MLS 1)
Founded 1949. Pop 12,000
Library Holdings: Bk Titles 53,000; Per Subs 52
Subject Interests: Local history
Mem of Northwest Regional Library System
Friends of the Library Group
Branches: 3
DANBURY BRANCH - CORD MEMORIAL LIBRARY, 215 Main St, Danbury, 51019. SAN 341-9436. Tel: 712-883-2207. *Librn*, Shirley Wright
Library Holdings: Bk Vols 3,500
Friends of the Library Group
HORNICK BRANCH, Main St, Hornick, 51026. SAN 341-9460. *Librn*, Corinne Irvin
Library Holdings: Bk Vols 3,500
Friends of the Library Group
PIERSON BRANCH, Pierson, 51048. SAN 341-9495. *Librn*, Nancy Felts
Library Holdings: Bk Vols 3,500
Bookmobiles: 1

MURRAY

P MURRAY PUBLIC LIBRARY,* 416 Maple St, 50174. (Mail add: PO Box 21, 50174-0021), SAN 305-5930. Tel: 515-447-2711. *Librn*, Joan Callison
Pop 750; Circ 2,400
Library Holdings: Bk Titles 9,000; Per Subs 87
Mem of Southwest Iowa Regional Library System
Open Mon & Wed afternoon, Sat morning

MUSCATINE

S GRAIN PROCESSING CORPORATION, Technical Information Center,* 1600 Oregon St, PO Box 349, 52761. SAN 305-5949. Tel: 319-264-4389. FAX: 319-264-4216. E-Mail: gpcrah@muscanet.com. *Mgr*, Rosemary Hollatz
Founded 1943
Library Holdings: Bk Vols 2,500; Bk Titles 2,000; Per Subs 200
Subject Interests: Analytical chemistry, Biochemistry, Brewing, Chemical engineering, Chemistry, Microbiology, Nutrition, Science/technology, Technology
Open Mon-Fri 8-5

S MUSCATINE ART CENTER, Art Reference Library, 1314 Mulberry Ave, 52761. SAN 373-4544. Tel: 319-263-8282. FAX: 319-263-4702. E-Mail: art@muscanet.com. *Dir*, Barbara Longtin
Library Holdings: Bk Vols 1,000; Per Subs 24
Subject Interests: Decorative arts
Open Tues-Fri 10-5, Thurs 7-9, Sat & Sun 1-5

J MUSCATINE COMMUNITY COLLEGE LIBRARY, 152 Colorado St, 52761. SAN 305-5957. Tel: 319-288-6073. FAX: 319-288-6074. Web Site: www.bridges.eiccd.cc.ia.us/library/mcc.html. *Asst Dean*, Tom Hanifan; E-Mail: thanifan@eiccd.cc.ia.us; Staff 1 (MLS 1)
Founded 1929. Enrl 1,300; Fac 65
Jul 1998-Jun 1999 Income $100,000. Mats Exp $19,000, Books $11,000, Per/Ser (Incl. Access Fees) $8,000. Sal $52,000 (Prof $52,000)
Library Holdings: Bk Vols 20,000; Bk Titles 18,000; Per Subs 50
Automation Activity & Vendor Info: (Cataloging) GEAC; (Circulation) GEAC; (OPAC) GEAC
Mem of Quad-Linc

P MUSSER PUBLIC LIBRARY,* 304 Iowa Ave, 52761-3875. SAN 305-5965. Tel: 319-263-3065, 319-263-3068. FAX: 319-264-1033. E-Mail: mus@libby.rbls.lib.il.us. Web Site: www.rbls.lib.il.us/mus/. *Dir*, Marsha E Tate; *Acq, Asst Dir*, Sheila Chaudoin; *ILL*, Kris Mogle; *Ch Servs*, Jean DeFrance; *Media Spec*, Debbie Grossklaus; *Cat, Tech Servs*, Marianna Haas; *Ref*, Amy Schulte; Staff 4 (MLS 4)
Founded 1901. Pop 40,318; Circ 228,569
Library Holdings: Bk Titles 148,568; Per Subs 242
Special Collections: Area Servicemen; Local History; Media: Videos- 2321; Audios- 3449; CDs- 1394; The Little House Books by Laura Ingalls Wilder; World War II
Publications: MPL Review (newsletter)
Mem of Southeastern Library Services
Partic in Quad-Link Libr Consortium
Open Mon-Thurs 10-9, Fri 10-6 & Sat 10-4
Friends of the Library Group

S STANLEY CONSULTANTS, Technical Library, Stanley Bldg, 225 Iowa Ave, 52761. SAN 325-5840. Tel: 319-264-6234. FAX: 319-264-6658. *Librn*, Marlys A Grete; E-Mail: grete.marlys@stanleygroup.com
Apr 2000-Mar 2001 Income $47,000. Sal $22,500
Subject Interests: Construction

NASHUA

P NASHUA PUBLIC LIBRARY,* 220 Brasher, 50658. SAN 305-5973. Tel: 515-435-4635. FAX: 515-435-4635. *Librn*, Kathryn Pflibsen; *Asst Librn*, Elaine Lantow
Founded 1902. Circ 22,991
Jul 1999-Jun 2000 Income $52,775. Mats Exp $9,900, Books $7,300, Per/Ser (Incl. Access Fees) $2,200, Electronic Ref Mat (Incl. Access Fees) $400. Sal $24,000 (Prof $26,700)
Library Holdings: Bk Vols 18,000; Per Subs 75
Special Collections: Nashua Reporter & Weekly Nashua Post, 1872-present,

micro; Videos (300)
Mem of Northeastern Iowa Regional Library System
Open Mon 9:30-11:30 & 1-8, Tues 1-6, Wed 1-8, Thurs 9:30-11:30 & 1-8, Sat 10-4

NEVADA

SR LUTHERANS FOR LIFE LIBRARY, 1120 S G Ave, 50201-2774. SAN 374-938X. Tel: 515-382-2077. Toll Free Tel: 888-364-5433. FAX: 515-382-3020. E-Mail: info@lutheransforlife.org. Web Site: www.lutheransforlife.org.
Subject Interests: Abortion, Euthanasia

P NEVADA PUBLIC LIBRARY,* 631 K Ave, 50201. SAN 305-5981. Tel: 515-382-2628. FAX: 515-382-3552. *Dir*, Beth Williams
Founded 1896. Pop 7,000; Circ 137,412
Jul 1998-Jun 1999 Income $239,682. Mats Exp $49,270. Sal $114,866 (Prof $34,000)
Library Holdings: Bk Vols 54,000; Per Subs 150
Special Collections: Geneology (Obits)
Mem of Central Iowa Regional Library
Open Mon-Thurs 10-8, Fri 10-6, Sat 10-4
Friends of the Library Group

NEW ALBIN

P NEW ALBIN PUBLIC LIBRARY,* 176 Elm St, PO Box 12, 52160. SAN 305-599X. Tel: 319-544-4747. FAX: 319-544-4747. E-Mail: library@means.net. *Librn*, Patricia Fitzpatrick
Pop 534; Circ 3,821
1998-1999 Income $10,942. Mats Exp $2,357, Books $1,535, Per/Ser (Incl. Access Fees) $822. Sal $4,282
Library Holdings: Bk Titles 4,684; Per Subs 40
Mem of Northeastern Iowa Regional Library System
Open Mon 7:30am-9am & 3-5:30, Wed 9-11, 3-5:30 & 7:30-9, Sat 9-11 & 3-5:30

NEW HAMPTON

P NEW HAMPTON PUBLIC LIBRARY,* 20 W Springs, 50659. SAN 305-6007. Tel: 515-394-2184. FAX: 515-394-5482. E-Mail: nhpl@sbt.net. *Librn*, Patricia Ipsen
Pop 3,660; Circ 57,100
Library Holdings: Bk Vols 23,000; Per Subs 70
Mem of Northeastern Iowa Regional Library System
Friends of the Library Group

NEW HARTFORD

P ELIZABETH RASMUSSEN MARTIN MEMORIAL LIBRARY,* 406 Packwaukee, PO Box 292, 50660-0292. SAN 305-6015. Tel: 319-983-2533. *Librn*, Elizabeth Buss
Pop 764; Circ 5,672
Library Holdings: Bk Titles 10,733; Per Subs 18
Mem of Northeastern Iowa Regional Library System
Open Mon, Tues & Fri 9-12 & 1-4, Wed 9-12 & 1-4, Thurs 9-12 & 4-7, Sat 9-12

NEW LONDON

P H J NUGEN PUBLIC LIBRARY, New London Public Library, 103 E Main St, 52645. SAN 305-6023. Tel: 319-367-7704. FAX: 319-367-7710. E-Mail: hjnugenpl@lisco.net. *Librn*, Rhonda Mixon; *Asst Librn*, Linda Geer
Founded 1937. Pop 1,922
Library Holdings: Bk Titles 21,309; Per Subs 60
Mem of Southeastern Library Services
Open Mon 10-8, Tues, Thurs & Fri 10-6, Wed 1-6, Sat 9-1

NEW MARKET

P NEW MARKET PUBLIC LIBRARY,* 407 Main St, PO Box 116, 51646. SAN 305-6031. Tel: 712-585-3467. *Librn*, Cleva Jobe
Pop 584; Circ 1,841
Library Holdings: Bk Titles 5,677; Per Subs 14
Mem of Southwest Iowa Regional Library System
Open Tues & Thurs 2-4:30

NEW PROVIDENCE

S HONEY CREEK CHURCH PRESERVATION LIBRARY,* c/o Vera Cutler, 30293 O Ave, 50206-8008. SAN 372-638X. *Librn*, Vera Cutler; Tel: 515-497-5458
Founded 1973
Special Collections: Community & School Records, minutes, alumni; Local legal papers, personal memorabilia; Quaker History, bks, flms, tapes, pictures
Publications: Annual newsletter; Diaries; Local Authors
Restriction: By appointment only
Friends of the Library Group

NEW SHARON

P NEW SHARON PUBLIC LIBRARY,* PO Box 92, 50207. SAN 305-604X. Tel: 515-637-4049. *Librn*, Arlene Stilwell
Pop 1,225; Circ 50,013
Library Holdings: Bk Vols 12,000; Bk Titles 10,000
Mem of Southeastern Library Services
Mon-Fri 2-5 & Sat 10-3

NEW VIRGINIA

P NEW VIRGINIA PUBLIC LIBRARY,* 504 Book Alley, PO Box 304, 50210-0304. SAN 305-6058. Tel: 515-449-3614. *Librn*, Gertrude Benedict
Founded 1972. Circ 4,129
1997-1998 Income $11,443, City $5,528, County $3,948, Other $1,863. Mats Exp $2,564, Books $2,322, Per/Ser (Incl. Access Fees) $242. Sal $5,745
Library Holdings: Bk Vols 10,000; Per Subs 20
Mem of Central Iowa Regional Library
Open Tues-Thurs 4-8, Wed 9-11 & 1-8, Sat 9-2

NEWELL

P NEWELL PUBLIC LIBRARY,* 205 E Second, PO Box 667, 50568. SAN 305-6066. Tel: 712-272-4334. *Librn*, Karen Hagen
Founded 1883. Pop 1,200; Circ 6,760
Library Holdings: Bk Titles 12,000; Per Subs 42
Mem of Northwest Regional Library System
Friends of the Library Group

NEWHALL

P NEWHALL PUBLIC LIBRARY,* 14 Main St, 52315-0348. SAN 376-5415. Tel: 319-223-5510. FAX: 319-223-5510. *Librn*, Karen McClain
Jul 1998-Jun 1999 Income $16,000
Library Holdings: Bk Vols 9,000; Per Subs 12
Mem of East Central Regional Library
Friends of the Library Group

NEWTON

P NEWTON PUBLIC LIBRARY,* 100 N Third Ave W, PO Box 746, 50208-0746. SAN 305-6082. Tel: 515-792-4108. FAX: 515-791-0729. E-Mail: newtonpl@server.silo.lib.ia.us. *Dir*, Shirley Houghtaling; *Ch Servs*, Vila Harrison; *Publ Servs*, Randy Landgrebe
Founded 1896. Pop 17,000; Circ 161,468
Jul 1999-Jun 2000 Income $440,349, State $6,266, City $367,219, County $59,595, Other $7,269. Mats Exp $59,383, Books $48,164, Per/Ser (Incl. Access Fees) $12,281. Sal $293,934
Library Holdings: Bk Vols 71,600; Per Subs 198
Automation Activity & Vendor Info: (Acquisitions) SIRSI; (Cataloging) SIRSI; (Circulation) SIRSI; (Course Reserve) SIRSI; (OPAC) SIRSI; (Serials) SIRSI
Mem of Central Regional Libr Syst
Partic in OCLC Online Computer Library Center, Inc
Friends of the Library Group

NORA SPRINGS

P NORA SPRINGS PUBLIC LIBRARY,* 45 N Hawkeye, PO Box 337, 50458. SAN 305-6090. Tel: 515-749-5569. E-Mail: nslib1@netins.net. *Dir*, Marlene Stirling; *Asst Librn*, Vickie Coleman
Pop 1,572; Circ 10,706
Library Holdings: Bk Vols 8,000; Per Subs 46
Mem of North Central Regional Library System
Partic in N Iowa Libr Exten
Open Mon, Tues, Thurs & Fri 1:30-5:30, Wed 1:30-7, Sat 9-12

NORTH ENGLISH

P NORTH ENGLISH PUBLIC LIBRARY,* 123 S Main, PO Box 427, 52316. SAN 305-6104. Tel: 319-664-3725. FAX: 319-664-3725. E-Mail: nepl@netins.net. *Librn*, Jane McCartney
Founded 1934. Pop 990; Circ 16,905
Jul 1998-Jun 1999 Income $45,000
Library Holdings: Bk Vols 9,000; Bk Titles 8,892; Per Subs 35
Special Collections: North English Record (paper) 1902-1998
Partic in Iowa Libr Asn

NORTH LIBERTY

P NORTH LIBERTY COMMUNITY LIBRARY, (NLCL), 520 W Cherry St, 52317-9797. (Mail add: PO Box 320, 52317-0320), SAN 323-5998. Tel: 319-626-5701. FAX: 319-626-5733. E-Mail: nlcl@zeus.ia.net. Web Site: www.zeus.ia.net/~nlcl. *Dir*, Dee Crowner; E-Mail: nlcl@zeus.ia.net; *Asst Dir*, Jennifer Garner; *Ch Servs*, Lois Hatch; Staff 2 (MLS 1, Non-MLS 1)
Founded 1986. Pop 5,000; Circ 93,780
Jul 1999-Jun 2000 Income $246,500, State $18,000, City $187,000, County $24,500, Other $17,000. Mats Exp $28,700, Books $25,000, Per/Ser (Incl. Access Fees) $2,200, Other Print Mats $1,500. Sal $89,000 (Prof $45,000)
Library Holdings: Bk Titles 25,000; Per Subs 118; High Interest/Low Vocabulary Bk Vols 356; Bks on Deafness & Sign Lang 63
Subject Interests: Early childhood
Special Collections: Christian Fiction
Automation Activity & Vendor Info: (Acquisitions) Follett; (Cataloging) Follett; (Circulation) Follett; (OPAC) Follett
Publications: American Libraries; Bookpage; Library Journal
Partic in Am Libr Asn; Iowa Libr Asn
Friends of the Library Group

NORTHWOOD

P NORTHWOOD PUBLIC LIBRARY,* 906 First Ave S, PO Box 137, 50459-0106. SAN 305-6112. Tel: 515-324-1340. E-Mail: nwdpubli@rconnect.com. *Librn*, Connie Kenison
Pop 2,193; Circ 26,149
Library Holdings: Bk Vols 18,542; Bk Titles 18,042; Per Subs 56
Mem of North Central Regional Library System
Open Mon 7-9, Tues & Thurs 1-5:30 & 7-9, Fri 1-5:30 & 10-11, Sat 9-4

NORWALK

P NORWALK EASTER PUBLIC LIBRARY,* 1051 North Ave, 50211-1523. SAN 305-6120. Tel: 515-981-0217. FAX: 515-981-4346. E-Mail: ill@norwalklibrary.org. Web Site: www.ci.norwalk.ia.us/depts/library. *Dir*, Jennifer Nehas; *Asst Dir, Ch Servs*, Carol Albin; Staff 2 (MLS 2)
Founded 1962. Pop 5,725; Circ 26,138
Library Holdings: Bk Vols 29,000; Per Subs 104
Mem of Central Iowa Regional Library
Open Mon-Thurs 11-8, Fri 11-6, Sat 9-4
Friends of the Library Group

NORWAY

P NORWAY PUBLIC LIBRARY,* 107 Railroad St, PO Box 7, 52318-0007. SAN 320-829X. Tel: 319-227-7487. FAX: 319-227-7487. E-Mail: norway@server.silo.lib.ia.us. *Librn*, Diane Riley
Founded 1976. Pop 633; Circ 5,348
Library Holdings: Bk Titles 10,000
Special Collections: Media: videos (150), audios (75)
Open Tues & Thurs 2-8, Wed & Fri 2-5, Sat 10-12
Friends of the Library Group

OAKLAND

P ECKELS MEMORIAL LIBRARY,* 207 S Hwy, 51560. SAN 305-6147. Tel: 712-482-6668. FAX: 712-482-6668. *Librn*, Patrice Vance
Pop 1,700; Circ 13,027
Library Holdings: Bk Titles 27,000; Per Subs 49
Special Collections: Media: videos (806), audios (80)
Mem of Southwest Iowa Regional Library System
Open Tues & Wed 12-5, Thurs 12-7, Fri 1-9, Sat 10-2

OCHEYEDAN

P OCHEYEDAN PUBLIC LIBRARY,* 874 Main St, PO Box 427, 51354. SAN 305-6155. Tel: 712-758-3352. FAX: 712-758-3352. *Librn*, Suzanne Hibma; *Asst Librn*, Susan Jordan
Founded 1969. Pop 530; Circ 16,000
Library Holdings: Bk Vols 15,872; Per Subs 46
Mem of Northwest Regional Library System

ODEBOLT

P FIELD-CARNEGIE LIBRARY,* 200 Maple St, PO Box 426, 51458-0426. SAN 305-6163. Tel: 712-668-2718. FAX: 712-668-4380. E-Mail: fieldcar@netins.net. *Librn*, Donarae Cleveland
Pop 1,256; Circ 17,150
Jul 1998-Jun 1999 Income $33,393. Mats Exp $7,210. Sal $12,895
Library Holdings: Bk Vols 13,922; Per Subs 53
Mem of Northwest Regional Library System
Open Mon, Tues & Fri 2:30-6, Wed 10-12 & 2-7:30, Sat 9-11am
Friends of the Library Group

OELWEIN

P OELWEIN PUBLIC LIBRARY, 22 First Ave NW, 50662-1604. SAN 305-6171. Tel: 319-283-1515. FAX: 319-283-1515. E-Mail: publiclibrary@oelwein.com. *Dir*, Vivian Petrik; *Asst Librn*, Edith Biddinger
Founded 1909. Pop 7,564; Circ 70,842
Jul 1999-Jun 2000 Income $135,952, State $5,424, City $103,992, County $15,328, Locally Generated Income $396, Other $10,812. Mats Exp Books $22,014. Sal $87,489
Library Holdings: Bk Vols 46,466; Per Subs 120
Subject Interests: Audio visual mats, Videos
Mem of Northeastern Iowa Regional Library System
Open Mon-Thurs 10-8:30, Fri 10-5:30 & Sat 12-5:30 (winter hours) Mon, Wed & Fri 10-5:30, Tues & Thurs 10-8 & Sat 12-5:30 (summer hours)

OGDEN

P LEONARD A GOOD COMMUNITY LIBRARY,* 208 W Mulberry St, 50212. SAN 305-618X. Tel: 515-275-4550. *Librn*, Cindy Smith
Founded 1948. Pop 2,000; Circ 38,911
Library Holdings: Bk Titles 12,000; Per Subs 24
Mem of Central Iowa Regional Library
Open Mon 10:30-8, Tues, Wed & Fri 1:30-5, Thurs 9-5, Sat 8:30-12

OLIN

P OLIN PUBLIC LIBRARY,* 303 Jackson St, PO Box 318, 52320. SAN 305-6198. Tel: 319-484-2944. E-Mail: olinlibrary@ins.net. *Librn*, Sheri Ulrich
Pop 735; Circ 3,376
Library Holdings: Bk Titles 7,358
Open Mon-Thurs 1-5, Fri 1-6 & Sat 8-12
Friends of the Library Group

ONAWA

P ONAWA PUBLIC LIBRARY, 707 Iowa Ave, 51040. SAN 305-6201. Tel: 712-423-1733. FAX: 712-423-3828. *Dir*, Virginia Erlandson; Staff 4 (MLS 1, Non-MLS 3)
Founded 1907. Pop 6,401; Circ 53,028
Library Holdings: Bk Vols 26,421; Bk Titles 22,650; Per Subs 109
Subject Interests: Astronomy, Local history
Mem of NW Iowa Regional Libr Syst
Open Mon-Thurs 11-8, Fir & Sat 11-5
Friends of the Library Group

ORANGE CITY

C NORTHWESTERN COLLEGE, Ramaker Library & Learning Resource Center, 101 Seventh St SW, 51041-1996. SAN 305-621X. Tel: 712-737-7234. FAX: 712-737-7247. Web Site: www.nwciowa.edu. *Dir*, Richard Reitsma; E-Mail: richardr@nwciowa.edu; *Ref*, James Lund; *Ref*, Anita Vogel; *Tech Servs*, Anne Mead; *Archivist*, Judy Hilbelink; *Media Spec*, Barry Lawrensen; *Circ*, Denise Sneller; *Per*, Cam Riibe; *ILL*, Judy Hilbelink
Founded 1882. Enrl 1,104; Fac 55; Highest Degree: Bachelor
1998-1999 Income $365,051. Mats Exp $164,233, Books $92,800, Per/Ser (Incl. Access Fees) $49,074, Micro $18,007. Sal $124,256 (Prof $79,000)
Library Holdings: Bk Vols 107,000; Bk Titles 90,500; Per Subs 530
Subject Interests: History, Literature, Religion
Special Collections: Dutch Relatedness-Reformed Church, bks, newsp, micro
Automation Activity & Vendor Info: (Acquisitions) EOS; (Cataloging) EOS; (Circulation) EOS; (OPAC) EOS
Database Vendor: Ebsco - EbscoHost, OCLC - First Search
Partic in Iowa Private Academic Library Consortium; OCLC Online Computer Library Center, Inc

P ORANGE CITY PUBLIC LIBRARY, 112 Albany Ave SE, 51041-1730. (Mail add: PO Box 346, 51041-0346), SAN 305-6228. Tel: 712-737-4302. FAX: 712-737-4431. E-Mail: orange00@iren.net. *Librn*, Karla Chase
Founded 1915. Pop 5,100; Circ 226,472
Jul 1999-Jun 2000 Income $263,465, State $10,244, City $189,400, County $25,134, Locally Generated Income $16,924, Other $21,763. Mats Exp $27,414, Books $23,446, Per/Ser (Incl. Access Fees) $4,242, AV Equip $3,968, Electronic Ref Mat (Incl. Access Fees) $218. Sal $124,942
Library Holdings: Bk Vols 42,553; Per Subs 156
Subject Interests: Iowa, Religion
Special Collections: Books about Iowa by Iowa Authors; Dutch Costume Patterns for Dutch Festival in May
Automation Activity & Vendor Info: (Cataloging) Follett; (Circulation) Follett; (OPAC) Follett
Database Vendor: OCLC - First Search
Mem of Northwest Regional Library System
Open Mon-Thurs 8-9, Fri 8-5, Sat 10-5

OSAGE

S MITCHELL COUNTY HISTORICAL SOCIETY LIBRARY,* Corner of Sixth & Mechanic, PO Box 51, 50461. SAN 375-1562. Tel: 515-732-1269. *In Charge*, Karin Hemrich; Tel: 515-732-5957
Library Holdings: Bk Titles 50

P OSAGE PUBLIC LIBRARY,* 406 Main St, 50461-1449. SAN 305-6236. Tel: 515-732-3323. FAX: 515-732-4419. E-Mail: osagepl@osage.net. *Dir*, Cindi Youngblut
Founded 1876. Circ 76,282
Library Holdings: Bk Vols 38,000
Special Collections: Hamlin Garland Coll
Automation Activity & Vendor Info: (Circulation) Follett
Mem of North Central Regional Library System
Open Mon-Wed 10-9, Thurs 12-9, Fri 10-5:30 & Sat 10-4
Friends of the Library Group

OSCEOLA

P OSCEOLA PUBLIC LIBRARY,* 300 S Fillmore St, 50213-2237. SAN 305-6244. Tel: 515-342-2237. FAX: 515-342-6057. *Librn*, Joyce Turner
Founded 1909. Pop 4,150; Circ 84,880
Library Holdings: Bk Vols 22,000; Per Subs 102
Mem of Southwest Iowa Regional Library System
Open Mon 12-6, Tues, Wed, Thurs & Fri 12-5, Sat 9-1:30

OSKALOOSA

P OSKALOOSA PUBLIC LIBRARY,* 301 S Market St, 52577. SAN 305-6252. Tel: 515-673-0441. FAX: 515-673-6237. E-Mail: opl@wmpenn.edu. Web Site: www.wmpenn.edu/pennweb/opl/opl.html. *Dir*, Nancy L Simpson; *Ch Servs*, Linda Fox; E-Mail: opl-foxl@wmpenn.edu; *Cat*, Claudia Miller; *Automation Syst Coordr*, Paulette Groet; E-Mail: opl-groetp@wmpenn.edu; Staff 9 (MLS 1, Non-MLS 8)
Founded 1903. Pop 22,507; Circ 187,677
Jul 1998-Jun 1999 Income $386,033, State $6,416, City $308,343, County $45,000, Locally Generated Income $12,499, Other $13,775. Mats Exp $52,028, Books $45,437, Per/Ser (Incl. Access Fees) $3,843, Electronic Ref Mat (Incl. Access Fees) $2,748. Sal $206,842 (Prof $40,000)
Library Holdings: Bk Vols 50,859; Bk Titles 48,226; Per Subs 207
Subject Interests: History
Automation Activity & Vendor Info: (Cataloging) DRA; (Circulation) DRA; (OPAC) DRA
Database Vendor: DRA, OCLC - First Search
Function: Some telephone reference
Friends of the Library Group

C WILLIAM PENN UNIVERSITY, Wilcox Library, 201 Trueblood Ave, 52577. SAN 305-6260. Tel: 641-673-1096. FAX: 641-673-1098. Web Site: www.wmpenn.edu/pennweb/library/library.html. *Acq, Dir*, Julie E Hansen; E-Mail: hansenj@wmpenn.edu; *Tech Servs*, Cindy Bracy; *Ref*, Boyd Broughton; Staff 2 (MLS 2)
Founded 1873. Highest Degree: Bachelor
Library Holdings: Bk Vols 68,291; Per Subs 349
Subject Interests: Education, Industrial arts, Social sciences and issues
Special Collections: Quakerism (Quaker Coll)
Automation Activity & Vendor Info: (Cataloging) DRA; (Circulation) DRA; (OPAC) DRA
Partic in OCLC Online Computer Library Center, Inc

OSSIAN

P OSSIAN PUBLIC LIBRARY,* 123 W Main, PO Box 120, 52161-0120. SAN 305-6279. Tel: 319-532-9461. FAX: 319-532-9461. E-Mail: broichlj@means.net. *Librn*, Linda Siver
Founded 1956. Pop 810; Circ 10,841
Jul 1998-Jun 1999 Income $26,400, State $164, City $6,709, County $8,317, Other $2,154. Mats Exp $10,000, Books $2,927, Per/Ser (Incl. Access Fees) $560, AV Equip $486. Sal $10,800
Library Holdings: Bk Vols 8,910; Per Subs 60
Mem of Northeastern Iowa Regional Library System
Member of State Library of Iowa Open Access Program; Participates in Iowa Locator Program; Open Mon, Tues, Thurs 2-5:30, Wed, Fri 2-7, Sat 9-12

OTTUMWA

S AIRPOWER MUSEUM, Library of Flight, Antique Airfield, 22001 Bluegrass Rd, 52501-8569. SAN 326-6419. Tel: 515-938-2773. FAX: 515-438-2773. *In Charge*, Bob Taylor
Founded 1965
Library Holdings: Per Subs 10
Special Collections: Early Airframe Drawings (1920-1965)
Publications: Air Power Museum Bulletin

J INDIAN HILLS COMMUNITY COLLEGE, Special Programs-Learning Resource Center, 525 Grandview Avenue, Bldg 10, 52501-1398. SAN 305-6287. Tel: 641-683-5199. FAX: 641-683-5184. E-Mail: library@ihcc.cc.ia.us. Web Site: www.ihcc.cc.ia.us. *Chairperson*, Mary Stewart; *Publ Servs*, Cheryl Leffler
Founded 1960. Enrl 3,500; Fac 250
Library Holdings: Bk Vols 30,000; Per Subs 270
Publications: Monthly Acquisitions List
Branch campus located in Centerville, Iowa

P OTTUMWA PUBLIC LIBRARY, 102 W Fourth St, 52501. SAN 305-6295. Tel: 641-682-7563. FAX: 641-682-4970. Web Site: www.ci.ottumwa.ia.us/library/. *Dir*, Phyllis Sargent; E-Mail: pmsia@yahoo.com; *Cat*, Julie Wells; *Circ, Spec Coll*, Mary Ann Lemon; *Ch Servs*, Stacy Moran; *Ref*, Richard Ruhnke; *Circ*, Jim Burns; Staff 14 (MLS 4, Non-MLS 10)
Founded 1872. Pop 40,000
Library Holdings: Bk Vols 84,000; Per Subs 200
Special Collections: Media: Videos- 1000; Audios- 400; Ottumwa & Wapello County History (Iowa Coll), bks, clippings, pictures
Automation Activity & Vendor Info: (Cataloging) epixtech, inc.; (Circulation) epixtech, inc.; (OPAC) epixtech, inc.
Database Vendor: epixtech, inc.
Function: ILL available
Mem of Southeastern Library Services
Open Mon-Thurs 9:30-8:30, Fri & Sat 9:30-5:30, Sun 1-5
Friends of the Library Group

M OTTUMWA REGIONAL HEALTH CENTER LIBRARY,* 1001 Pennsylvania Ave, 52501. SAN 377-4856. Tel: 515-682-7511. *Librn*, Elaine Hughs
Library Holdings: Bk Vols 1,300

OXFORD

P OXFORD PUBLIC LIBRARY, 112 Augusta Ave, 52322. SAN 376-6799. Tel: 319-828-4087. *Dir*, Ada Crow
1998-1999 Income $9,000, City $3,000, County $6,000
Library Holdings: Bk Vols 9,000
Mem of East Central Regional Library
Friends of the Library Group

OXFORD JUNCTION

P WREGIE MEMORIAL LIBRARY, 105 W Broadway, 52323. SAN 305-6325. Tel: 319-826-2450. FAX: 319-826-2450. E-Mail: wregieml@netins.net. Web Site: www.netins.net/showcase/wregiememlib. *Dir*, Dawn Kurth
Founded 1940 Sal $5,850
Library Holdings: Bk Titles 5,550; Per Subs 28
Special Collections: Oxford Mirror 1879-1952, micro

PACKWOOD

P PACKWOOD COMMUNITY LIBRARY,* 315 Main St, PO Box 951, 52580. SAN 305-6333. Tel: 319-695-5131. *In Charge*, Jo Chambers
Pop 1,437; Circ 19,161
Library Holdings: Bk Vols 3,000
Mem of Southeastern Regional Libr Syst
Open Mon 9-12

PALMER

P PALMER PUBLIC LIBRARY, 520 Hanson Ave, PO Box 114, 50571-0114. SAN 320-8222. Tel: 712-359-2296. E-Mail: palib@ncn.net. *Librn*, Sally Butcher
Pop 230; Circ 6,457
Jul 1999-Jun 2000 Income $13,633, State $563, City $8,365, County $4,200, Other $505. Mats Exp $3,310, Books $2,649, Per/Ser (Incl. Access Fees) $180, AV Equip $481. Sal $6,858
Library Holdings: Bk Titles 11,187; Per Subs 21
Mem of Northwest Regional Library System
Partic in Iowa Libr Asn
Open Mon 1-5, Wed 1-5:30, Sat 9-12

PANORA

P PANORA PUBLIC LIBRARY,* PO Box 579, 50216. SAN 305-6341. Tel: 515-755-2529. FAX: 515-755-3009. E-Mail: pnrlib@netins.net. *Librn*, Kimberly Finnegan; *Asst Librn*, Lill Kirk
Founded 1902. Pop 1,211; Circ 16,787
Library Holdings: Bk Titles 13,018; Per Subs 78
Special Collections: Audios (125)
Mem of Southwest Iowa Regional Library System
Open Mon 1-7, Tues & Thurs 1-5, Wed 1-8, Fri 9:30-11:30 & 1-5, Sat 9:30-12
Friends of the Library Group

PARKERSBURG

P KOTHE MEMORIAL LIBRARY,* 309 Third St, PO Box 160, 50665. SAN 305-635X. Tel: 319-346-2442. FAX: 319-346-2442. E-Mail: klibrary@forbin.com. *Librn*, Virginia Stukenburg
Pop 1,968; Circ 35,283
Library Holdings: Bk Vols 17,000; Per Subs 51
Special Collections: Media: videos (1000), audios (300)
Mem of Northeastern Iowa Regional Library System
Open Mon & Thurs 1-8:30, Tues Wed & Fri 1-5:30, Sat 10-2
Friends of the Library Group

PATON

P PATON PUBLIC LIBRARY,* 105 Main St, PO Box 70, 50217. SAN 305-6368. Tel: 515-968-4559. E-Mail: patonlib@netins.net. *Librn*, Diana Winger
Pop 255; Circ 7,270
Library Holdings: Bk Titles 13,888; Per Subs 15
Mem of Central Iowa Regional Library
Open Mon 2-7, Wed 9-2, Fri 12:30-5:30, Sat 9-11

PAULLINA

P PAULLINA PUBLIC LIBRARY,* 113 S Mickley St, 51046. (Mail add: PO Box 60, 51046), SAN 305-6376. Tel: 712-448-3941. FAX: 712-448-3866. E-Mail: pplib@pionet.net. *Dir, Librn*, Terri L Tesh; *Asst Librn*, Debra Benner
Founded 1908. Circ 17,436
Jul 1998-Jun 1999 Income $46,685, State $78, City $37,607, County $5,500, Other $3,500. Mats Exp $13,020, Books $10,000, Per/Ser (Incl. Access Fees) $1,600, AV Equip $1,420. Sal $18,337
Library Holdings: Bk Vols 18,367; Per Subs 99
Mem of Northwest Regional Library System
Special Services for the Blind - Bks on cassette

PELLA

C CENTRAL COLLEGE, Geisler Library, Box 6500, 812 University St, 50219-1999. SAN 341-955X. Tel: 641-628-5219. Interlibrary Loan Service Tel: 641-628-5193. FAX: 641-628-5327. Web Site: www.central.edu/library/libhome.htm. *Dir*, Robin Martin; Tel: 641-628-5220, E-Mail: martinr@central.edu; *Bibliog Instr, Online Servs, Ref*, Catherine Cranston; Tel: 641-628-5345, E-Mail: cranstonc@central.edu; *Media Spec*, Tim Hoekstra; Tel: 641-628-5218, E-Mail: hoekstrat@central.edu; *Cat, Syst Coordr*, Lois Smith; Tel: 641-628-5158, E-Mail: smithl@central.edu; *ILL*, Jane Friedman; E-Mail: friedmanj@central.edu; *Circ*, Lana Goodrich; E-Mail: goodrichl@central.edu; *Per*, Sue VanVark; Tel: 641-628-5344, E-Mail: vanvarks@central.edu; *Cat*, Ronda Redman; Tel: 641-628-5158; *Archivist*, Christine Mak; Tel: 641-628-5170, E-Mail: makc@central.edu; *Coll Develop*, Ronald Hardy; Tel: 641-628-5221, E-Mail: hardyr@central.edu; Staff 6 (MLS 4, Non-MLS 2)
Founded 1853. Circ 90,000; Enrl 1,471; Fac 93; Highest Degree: Bachelor
Jul 1999-Jun 2000 Income $880,358. Mats Exp $282,228, Books $103,700, Per/Ser (Incl. Access Fees) $146,600, Presv $8,828, Micro $11,500, AV Equip $11,200, Electronic Ref Mat (Incl. Access Fees) $400. Sal $267,805 (Prof $181,156)
Library Holdings: Bk Vols 212,950; Bk Titles 170,000; Per Subs 850
Special Collections: Dutch in America & Iowa (Scholte Coll), bks & letters; Helen Van Dyke Miniature Book Coll; Pella History, newsp & docs
Automation Activity & Vendor Info: (Acquisitions) Innovative Interfaces Inc.; (Cataloging) Innovative Interfaces Inc.; (Circulation) Innovative Interfaces Inc.; (Course Reserve) Innovative Interfaces Inc.; (OPAC) Innovative Interfaces Inc.; (Serials) Innovative Interfaces Inc.
Database Vendor: Ebsco - EbscoHost, Lexis-Nexis, OCLC - First Search, Silverplatter Information Inc.
Publications: Annual Report; Collection Guides
Partic in Bibliographical Center For Research, Rocky Mountain Region, Inc; Iowa Private Academic Library Consortium; Iowa Res & Educ Network; OCLC Online Computer Library Center, Inc

P PELLA PUBLIC LIBRARY, 603 Main St, 50219. SAN 305-6384. Tel: 515-628-4268. FAX: 515-628-1735. E-Mail: cvpublib@central.edu. *Dir*, Karen L Davidson; *Tech Servs*, Richard Bangma; *Ch Servs*, Suzanne Larson; Staff 3 (MLS 3)
Founded 1903. Pop 11,000; Circ 149,847
Jul 1999-Jun 2000 Income $862,463, State $5,500, City $820,590, County $17,000, Locally Generated Income $11,373, Other $8,000. Mats Exp $66,500, Books $50,500, Per/Ser (Incl. Access Fees) $16,000. Sal $188,015
Library Holdings: Bk Titles 53,174; Per Subs 232
Automation Activity & Vendor Info: (Cataloging) Innovative Interfaces Inc.; (Circulation) Innovative Interfaces Inc.
Mem of Central Iowa Regional Library
Friends of the Library Group

PEOSTA

§R NEW MELLERAY LIBRARY, 6500 Melleray Circle, 52068. SAN 375-4332. Tel: 319-588-2319. FAX: 319-588-4117. E-Mail: melleray@mwci.net. *Librn*, David Bock
Founded 1849
Jan 2000-Dec 2000 Income $7,500. Mats Exp $7,500
Library Holdings: Bk Titles 27,000; Per Subs 40
Subject Interests: Comparative relig, History, Psychology, Scripture, Theology
Restriction: Members only, Residents only, Restricted access

JM NORTHEAST IOWA COMMUNITY COLLEGE, Burton Payne Library,* 10250 Sundown Rd, 52068. SAN 305-3598. Tel: 319-556-5110. FAX: 319-557-0340. Web Site: www.nicc.cc.ia.us.
Founded 1971
Library Holdings: Bk Vols 15,000; Per Subs 250
Subject Interests: Holocaust
Automation Activity & Vendor Info: (Cataloging) epixtech, inc.; (Circulation) epixtech, inc.; (OPAC) epixtech, inc.

PERRY

P PERRY PUBLIC LIBRARY, 1101 Willis Ave, 50220-1649. SAN 305-6392. Tel: 515-465-3569. FAX: 515-465-9881. E-Mail: perrypl@netins.net. Web Site: www.perrypl.org. *Dir*, Donna Emmert; E-Mail: demmert@perrypl.org
Founded 1904. Pop 10,000; Circ 129,325
Library Holdings: Bk Titles 45,000; Per Subs 110
Special Collections: Media: videos (1500), audios (500)
Mem of Central Regional Libr Syst
Open Mon-Thurs 10-8, Fri & Sat 10-5, Sun 1-4
Friends of the Library Group

PETERSON

P KIRCHNER-FRENCH MEMORIAL LIBRARY, 101 Main St, PO Box 203, 51047. SAN 305-6406. Tel: 712-295-6705. FAX: 712-295-6705. *Coll Develop, Dir*, Linda Eaton
Founded 1926. Pop 390; Circ 16,500
1998-1999 Income $26,865, State $56, County $5,510, Locally Generated Income $21,299. Mats Exp $4,295, Books $3,678, Per/Ser (Incl. Access Fees) $575, Other Print Mats $42. Sal $13,931
Library Holdings: Bk Titles 6,967; Per Subs 19
Special Collections: Clay County Historical Material Coll; Iowa Authors Coll; Peterson Patriot (1869-1983)
Mem of Northwest Regional Library System

PLAINFIELD

P PLAINFIELD PUBLIC LIBRARY, 723 Main St, PO Box 327, 50666-0327. SAN 305-6414. Tel: 319-276-4461. FAX: 319-276-4461. E-Mail: bookit@netins.net. *Librn*, Candy Diercks
Circ 9,000
Library Holdings: Bk Vols 6,557; Per Subs 33
Mem of Northeastern Iowa Regional Library System
Open Mon & Fri 1-5, Tues 9-4:30, Wed 12-6

PLEASANT HILL

P PLEASANT HILL PUBLIC LIBRARY,* 5151 Maple Dr, Ste 2, 50317. SAN 376-5032. Tel: 515-266-7815. FAX: 515-266-7793. E-Mail: phlib@netins.net. *Librn*, John Lerdal
Library Holdings: Bk Vols 26,000; Bk Titles 23,000; Per Subs 110
Mem of Central Iowa Regional Library
Open Mon-Thurs 10-8, Fri 10-6, Sat 10-5, Sun 1-4
Friends of the Library Group

PLEASANTVILLE

P WEBB SHADLE MEMORIAL LIBRARY,* 301 W Dallas, PO Box 338, 50225. SAN 305-6422. Tel: 515-848-5617. FAX: 515-848-3272. E-Mail: lconn27769@aol.com. *Dir*, Larry A Conn
Founded 1955. Pop 2,000; Circ 20,000
Library Holdings: Bk Vols 15,000; Per Subs 65
Special Collections: Americana Coll
Mem of Central Iowa Regional Library

PLOVER

P PLOVER PUBLIC LIBRARY,* 301 Main St, 50573. (Mail add: PO Box 112, 50573), SAN 305-6430. Tel: 712-857-3532. *Librn*, Marjorie Spear
Pop 101
Library Holdings: Bk Titles 2,500

Subject Interests: History, Local history
Mem of Northwest Regional Library System
Open Mon & Wed 4-6, Sat 9-11

POCAHONTAS

P POCAHONTAS PUBLIC LIBRARY, 14 Second Ave NW, 50574. SAN 305-6457. Tel: 712-335-4471. FAX: 712-335-4471. E-Mail: pokypl@ncn.net. Web Site: www.ncn.net/~pokypl. *Dir*, Rita Samuelson
Founded 1932. Pop 2,085; Circ 30,000
Jul 1999-Jun 2000 Income $93,723, State $2,110, City $63,218, County $6,000, Other $22,395. Mats Exp $9,381, Books $7,595, Per/Ser (Incl. Access Fees) $1,786. Sal $36,508
Library Holdings: Bk Vols 16,291; Per Subs 77
Subject Interests: Agriculture, Art and architecture, Genealogy, Local history, Railroads
Automation Activity & Vendor Info: (Cataloging) Athena; (Circulation) Athena; (OPAC) Athena
Mem of Northwest Regional Library System
Open Mon, Wed & Fri 11-5, Tues & Thurs 11-8 & Sat 9-3

POLK CITY

P POLK CITY COMMUNITY LIBRARY,* 401 Booth St, PO Box 259, 50226. SAN 305-6465. Tel: 515-984-6119. FAX: 515-984-6119. E-Mail: pcclib@dwx.com. *Dir*, Evelyn Oltmanns
Founded 1974. Pop 1,908; Circ 14,730
Library Holdings: Bk Titles 6,296
Publications: Booklist
Mem of Central Iowa Regional Library
Friends of the Library Group

POMEROY

P POMEROY PUBLIC LIBRARY, Mini Mall, Ontario St, 50575-0369. SAN 305-6473. Tel: 712-468-2311. FAX: 712-468-2311. E-Mail: proylib@ncn.net. *Librn*, Patti Meyer
Pop 895; Circ 10,462
Library Holdings: Bk Vols 8,000; Per Subs 32
Mem of Northwest Regional Library System
Open Mon, Thurs 1-5:30, Fri 1-5, Wed 10-12 & 1-5, Sat 9-12

POSTVILLE

P POSTVILLE PUBLIC LIBRARY,* 235 W Tilden, 52162. SAN 305-6481. Tel: 319-864-7600. FAX: 319-864-7600. E-Mail: postlib@netins.net. *Dir*, Darlene Schutte
Pop 1,475; Circ 19,594
Library Holdings: Bk Vols 9,912; Bk Titles 9,169; Per Subs 45
Mem of Northeastern Iowa Regional Library System
Open Mon 9:30-5:30, Tues, Thurs & Fri 2-5:30, Wed 9:30-9, Sat 8:30-1:30

PRAIRIE CITY

P PRAIRIE CITY PUBLIC LIBRARY,* 203 E Jefferson, 50228. SAN 376-7507. Tel: 515-994-2308. E-Mail: pclibsar@dux.com. *Librn*, Sharon Briles
Library Holdings: Bk Vols 6,000; Per Subs 12
Mem of Central Iowa Regional Library
Open Mon, Wed & Fre 1-5, Tues & Thurs 4-8,, Sat 9-12 & 1-4,

PRESCOTT

P PRESCOTT PUBLIC LIBRARY, 607 Second St, 50859-0177. SAN 376-5199. Tel: 515-335-2238. FAX: 515-335-2238. *Librn*, Veda McCarty
Jul 1999-Jun 2000 Income $12,375, City $8,950, County $2,825. Mats Exp $4,066, Books $3,947, Per/Ser (Incl. Access Fees) $119. Sal $6,427
Library Holdings: Bk Vols 8,000; Per Subs 10
Mem of Southwest Iowa Regional Library System
Open Mon & Thurs 9-5, Wed 2:30-6:30 & Fri 9-1

PRESTON

P PRESTON PUBLIC LIBRARY,* 1 W Gillet, PO Box 605, 52069-0605. SAN 305-649X. Tel: 319-689-3581. FAX: 319-689-3581. E-Mail: plibrary@netins.net. *Librn*, Brenda Mussmann; *Asst Librn*, Mari Snopek
Founded 1974. Circ 14,297
Library Holdings: Bk Vols 13,000; Per Subs 75
Winter hours: Mon, Thurs & Fri 1-5, Tues 9:30-11:30 & 1-5, Wed 1-9, Sat 9:30-4:30; Summer hours: Mon, Thurs & Fri 1-5, Tues 9:30-12, Wed 1-8

PRIMGHAR

P PRIMGHAR PUBLIC LIBRARY,* 320 First St NE, PO Box 9, 51245. SAN 305-6503. Tel: 712-757-8981. FAX: 712-757-8981. E-Mail: primlib@pionet.net. *Librn*, Peggy Watts; *Ch Servs*, Leamn Langfitt
Pop 1,050; Circ 5,760
1997-1998 Income $33,000, City $28,000, County $5,000. Mats Exp $10,000, Books $6,000, Per/Ser (Incl. Access Fees) $750, Other Print Mats $3,000. Sal $16,000
Library Holdings: Bk Titles 12,000; Per Subs 31
Mem of Northwest Regional Library System

QUIMBY

P QUIMBY PUBLIC LIBRARY, 201 N Main, PO Box 186, 51049. SAN 305-6511. Tel: 712-445-2413. FAX: 712-445-2688. E-Mail: qpl@nwidt.com. *Librn*, Dorothy Hanks
Pop 334; Circ 2,736
Library Holdings: Bk Titles 9,862; Per Subs 30
Mem of Northwest Regional Library System
Open Mon-Wed 3-7, Thurs 3-6, Fri 4-6 & Sat 9-Noon

RADCLIFFE

P RADCLIFFE PUBLIC LIBRARY, 210 Isabella, PO Box 348, 50230. SAN 305-652X. Tel: 515-899-7914. FAX: 515-899-7914. E-Mail: rad_lib@netins.net. *Librn*, Kathy Hinderaker
Pop 593; Circ 11,193
Library Holdings: Bk Titles 15,756; Per Subs 50
Mem of North Central Regional Library System
Open (summer) Mon-Sat 9-1, Wed 3-9; (winter) Mon 9:30-11:30 & 1-5, Tues 1-5, Wed 9-12, 1-5 & 7-9, Thurs & Fri 1-5, Sat 9-12

RAKE

P RAKE PUBLIC LIBRARY,* 207 N Second St, 50465. SAN 305-6538. Tel: 515-566-3388. E-Mail: mhoverl@netins.net. *Librn*, Mary Hove
Founded 1962. Pop 400; Circ 5,000
Library Holdings: Bk Titles 7,000
Mem of North Central Regional Library System
Open Tues & Thurs 9-11:30 & 1:30-5, Wed 1:30-5, Fri 9-11 & 1:30-5, Sat 9-10:30

RANDOLPH

P RANDOLPH PUBLIC LIBRARY,* 107 S Main St, PO Box 112, 51649-0112. SAN 305-6546. Tel: 712-625-3561. FAX: 712-625-3561. *Librn*, Kathe Fichter
1999-2000 Income $8,500, City $4,000, County $4,000, Other $500. Mats Exp $2,030, Books $2,000, Per/Ser (Incl. Access Fees) $30. Sal $3,200
Library Holdings: Bk Titles 6,432
Special Collections: Randolph Enterprise Newspapers, 1895-1970
Mem of Southwest Iowa Regional Library System
Open Tues 8-12 & 1-5:30, Thurs 8-12, Sat 8-12

READLYN

P READLYN COMMUNITY LIBRARY,* 309 Main St, PO Box 249, 50668-0249. SAN 305-6554. Tel: 319-279-3432. FAX: 319-279-3432. E-Mail: lbrsj@netins.net. *Librn*, Carol Strottmann; *Asst Librn*, Barb Sowers; *Asst Librn*, Sheri Boehme
Founded 1965. Pop 858; Circ 17,185
Jul 1997-Jun 1998 Income $39,340. Mats Exp $14,018, Books $9,761, Per/Ser (Incl. Access Fees) $1,853, Micro $2,404. Sal $16,919
Library Holdings: Bk Titles 14,000; Per Subs 73
Mem of Northeastern Iowa Regional Library System
Open Mon & Wed 10-8, Tues & Thurs 1-8, Fri 10-5, Sat 9-12

RED OAK

P RED OAK PUBLIC LIBRARY,* 400 N Second St, 51566-2251. SAN 305-6562. Tel: 712-623-6516. FAX: 712-623-6518. E-Mail: ropl@redoak.heartland.net. Web Site: www.redoakiowa.com/ropl/. *Dir*, Joy Tunnell
Founded 1908. Pop 6,264; Circ 63,000
Jul 1996-Jun 1997 Income $123,541, City $103,645, County $18,750. Mats Exp $22,111, Books $17,000, Per/Ser (Incl. Access Fees) $2,800, Presv $1,000, Micro $1,200. Sal $71,088 (Prof $57,425)
Library Holdings: Bk Vols 43,591; Bk Titles 40,571
Special Collections: State & Local History
Publications: Monthly calendar for patron use
Mem of Southwest Iowa Regional Library System
Open Mon-Thurs 10-8, Fri & Sat 10-5

REDFIELD

P REDFIELD PUBLIC LIBRARY,* 1112 Thomas St, PO Box L, 50233. SAN 305-6570. Tel: 515-833-2200. *Librn*, Lori Stonehocker
Pop 959; Circ 11,000
Library Holdings: Bk Titles 10,500; Per Subs 36
Mem of Central Iowa Regional Library

REINBECK

P REINBECK PUBLIC LIBRARY, 501 Clark St, 50669. SAN 305-6589. Tel: 319-345-2652. Interlibrary Loan Service Tel: 800-772-2023. FAX: 319-345-2826. E-Mail: reinlibr@staroute.com. *Librn*, Janet Slessor; *Asst Librn*, Ann Rae Billerbeck; *Asst Librn*, Donna Brandt
Pop 1,605; Circ 34,452
Jul 1999-Jun 2000 Income $84,522, State $871, City $63,096, County $19,048, Locally Generated Income $1,507. Mats Exp $17,085, Books $15,201, Per/Ser (Incl. Access Fees) $1,884. Sal $28,469 (Prof $20,000)
Library Holdings: Bk Vols 18,647; Bk Titles 17,400; Per Subs 85
Mem of Northeastern Iowa Regional Library System

REMBRANDT

P REMBRANDT PUBLIC LIBRARY,* Main St, PO Box 169, 50576. SAN 373-8906. Tel: 712-286-6801. FAX: 712-286-6801. E-Mail: remblib@ncn.net. *Librn*, Joline Anderson; Staff 1 (MLS 1)
Founded 1930. Pop 229; Circ 3,237; Enrl 210
Library Holdings: Bk Titles 6,000; Per Subs 11

REMSEN

P REMSEN PUBLIC LIBRARY,* 211 Fulton, PO Box 440, 51050-0440. SAN 305-6600. Tel: 712-786-2911. FAX: 712-786-3255. E-Mail: rploff@nwidt.com. *Dir*, Mary Riedemann
Founded 1939
Library Holdings: Bk Titles 17,679; Per Subs 90
Mem of Northwest Regional Library System

RENWICK

P RENWICK PUBLIC LIBRARY,* 204 Stoddard St, 50577-0038. SAN 305-6619. Tel: 515-824-3209. FAX: 515-824-3209. E-Mail: renwickl@trvnet.net. *Librn*, Jan Thompson
Pop 410; Circ 6,814
Library Holdings: Bk Vols 4,500; Bk Titles 4,000; Per Subs 15
Mem of North Central Regional Library System
Open Mon & Wed 12-6, Tues & Fri 2-5, Sat 9-12

RICEVILLE

P RICEVILLE PUBLIC LIBRARY,* 307 Woodland Ave, PO Box 269, 50466-0269. SAN 305-6627. Tel: 515-985-2273. FAX: 515-985-4002. E-Mail: ricepubl@netins.net. Web Site: www.netins.net/showcase/ricelib. *Dir*, Randi Krukow; *Asst Librn*, Marian Jensson
Pop 910; Circ 19,358
Library Holdings: Bk Vols 13,050; Bk Titles 12,000; Per Subs 36
Mem of N Iowa Libr Extension; North Central Regional Library System
Open Mon 1-9, Tues 1-6, Wed 9-5 & 7-9, Fri 10-5 & Sat 10-3

RICHLAND

P RICHLAND PUBLIC LIBRARY,* 100 E Main St, 52585. SAN 305-6635. Tel: 319-456-6541. FAX: 319-456-6541. E-Mail: richlib@lisco.com. *Librn*, Joyce Pfeifer
Pop 600; Circ 8,400
Library Holdings: Bk Titles 8,120; Per Subs 11
Mem of Southeastern Library Services

RINGSTED

P RINGSTED PUBLIC LIBRARY,* 8 W Maple St, PO Box 98, 50578-0098. SAN 305-6651. Tel: 712-866-0878. *Librn*, Mrs Orlin Solberg
Pop 557; Circ 3,584
Library Holdings: Bk Titles 9,674; Per Subs 16
Mem of NW Libr Syst

RIPPEY

P RIPPEY PUBLIC LIBRARY, Main St, PO Box 184, 50235. SAN 305-666X. Tel: 515-436-7714. *Librn*, Jean Borgeson
Pop 304; Circ 6,888
Library Holdings: Bk Vols 7,815; Bk Titles 7,349; Per Subs 7
Mem of Central Iowa Regional Library

ROCK RAPIDS

P ROCK RAPIDS PUBLIC LIBRARY, 102 S Greene St, 51246. SAN 305-6678. Tel: 712-472-3541. *Dir*, Linda McCormack
Founded 1893. Pop 2,601; Circ 65,399
Jul 1999-Jun 2000 Income $125,871, State $791, City $86,260, County $13,016, Locally Generated Income $2,048, Other $23,756. Mats Exp $14,034, Books $11,780, Per/Ser (Incl. Access Fees) $2,254. Sal $51,821
Library Holdings: Bk Vols 35,164; Per Subs 69
Mem of Northwest Regional Library System

ROCK VALLEY

P ROCK VALLEY PUBLIC LIBRARY, 1531 Main St, 51247-1127. SAN 305-6686. Tel: 712-476-5651. FAX: 712-476-5261. E-Mail: rvpublib@rconnect.com. *Dir*, Lorna Van Maanen; *Asst Librn*, Linda Deruyter; *Asst Librn*, Beth Vandenberg
Founded 1916. Pop 3,700; Circ 115,980
Library Holdings: Bk Vols 28,000; Per Subs 80
Mem of Northwest Regional Library System

ROCKFORD

P ROCKFORD PUBLIC LIBRARY, 202 W Main Ave, PO Box 496, 50468-0496. SAN 305-6694. Tel: 515-756-3725. FAX: 515-756-3725. E-Mail: rkfdlib@netins.net. *Dir*, Rita Hirv
Founded 1916. Pop 863; Circ 17,403
Jul 1999-Jun 2000 Income $34,828, State $791, City $9,900, County $12,608, Locally Generated Income $11,529. Mats Exp $6,294, Books $5,459, Per/Ser (Incl. Access Fees) $835. Sal $13,576
Library Holdings: Bk Titles 6,524; Per Subs 45
Mem of North Central Regional Library System
Open Mon-Fri 1-5:30, Wed 6-8 & Sat 9-12

ROCKWELL

P ROCKWELL PUBLIC LIBRARY, 307 Main St, PO Box 419, 50469-0419. SAN 305-6708. Tel: 515-822-3268. FAX: 515-822-3168. E-Mail: rkwlpl@netnis.net. *Librn*, Linda Dunning
Pop 1,108; Circ 20,654
2000-2001 Income $39,982, State $1,256, City $27,000, County $11,726. Mats Exp $14,697, Books $13,293, Per/Ser (Incl. Access Fees) $1,404. Sal $17,458
Library Holdings: Bk Vols 11,980; Bk Titles 11,372; Per Subs 72
Automation Activity & Vendor Info: (Cataloging) Sagebrush Corporation; (Circulation) Sagebrush Corporation
Mem of North Central Regional Library System

ROCKWELL CITY

S NORTH CENTRAL CORRECTIONAL FACILITY, Inmate Library,* 313 Lanedale, 50579. SAN 375-3263. Tel: 712-297-7521, Ext 229. FAX: 712-297-9316. *Librn*, Joe Bush; *Librn*, Jon Pagel; Staff 9 (MLS 1, Non-MLS 8)
Library Holdings: Bk Titles 6,000; Per Subs 20
Subject Interests: Law

P ROCKWELL CITY PUBLIC LIBRARY,* 426 Fifth St, 50579-1415. SAN 305-6732. Tel: 712-297-8422. FAX: 712-297-8422. E-Mail: rclib@cal-net.net. Web Site: www.cal-net.net/~rclib. *Dir*, Hilda Hartling; *Ch Servs*, Leslee Mogensen
Founded 1897. Pop 1,919; Circ 21,176
Jul 1998-Jun 1999 Income $46,554, City $28,056, County $15,898, Locally Generated Income $850, Other $1,750. Mats Exp $12,301, Books $9,000, Per/Ser (Incl. Access Fees) $1,551, Micro $1,750. Sal $25,000
Library Holdings: Bk Vols 18,178; Bk Titles 17,762; Per Subs 76; High Interest/Low Vocabulary Bk Vols 80
Special Collections: Calhoun County Genealogical Society Library
Publications: Column Inches (bimonthly newsletter)
Mem of Northwest Regional Library System
Friends of the Library Group

ROLAND

P ROLAND PUBLIC LIBRARY,* 218 Main, PO Box 409, 50236-0409. SAN 376-544X. Tel: 515-388-4086. E-Mail: rolandlib@storycity.net. *Librn*, Todd Reed
Library Holdings: Bk Vols 10,723; Per Subs 40
Mem of Central Iowa Regional Library
Friends of the Library Group

ROLFE

P ROLFE PUBLIC LIBRARY, 401 Garfield St, 50581-1120. SAN 305-6759. Tel: 712-848-3143. FAX: 712-848-3143. E-Mail: spl@ncn.net. *Librn*, Bette Brinkman

Founded 1926. Pop 1,400; Circ 8,930
Library Holdings: Bk Vols 7,291; Per Subs 32
Special Collections: Local Hist Coll, pictures, papers
Mem of Northwest Regional Library System
Open Mon & Wed 2-5, Tues 3-7, Thurs 5-8, Fri 3-5 & Sat 9:30-12:30

ROWAN

P ROWAN PUBLIC LIBRARY,* 103 Main St, PO Box 182, 50470. SAN 305-6767. Tel: 515-853-2327. FAX: 515-853-2390. E-Mail: rowanpl@kalnet.com. *Librn,* Marjorie Osier
Founded 1964. Pop 259; Circ 11,214
Library Holdings: Bk Vols 6,300
Mem of North Central Regional Library System

ROYAL

P ROYAL PUBLIC LIBRARY,* 302 Main St, PO Box 214, 51357. SAN 305-6775. Tel: 712-933-5500. *Librn,* Betty Koster
Pop 522; Circ 4,379
Library Holdings: Bk Vols 5,500; Per Subs 60
Mem of Northwest Regional Library System
Friends of the Library Group

RUDD

P RUDD PUBLIC LIBRARY,* 308 Chickasaw, 50471-0305. SAN 305-6783. Tel: 515-395-2385. FAX: 515-395-2385. *Librn,* Donna Dunbar
Founded 1956. Pop 430; Circ 16,875
Library Holdings: Bk Vols 6,438; Per Subs 48
Mem of North Central Regional Library System

RUTHVEN

P RUTHVEN PUBLIC LIBRARY,* Gowrie & Rolling, 1303 Gowrie St, 51358. SAN 305-6791. Tel: 712-837-4820. FAX: 712-837-4820. E-Mail: rutlib@ncn.net. *Librn,* Erma Johnson
Circ 15,000
1997-1998 Income $15,000, City $5,000, County $10,000
Library Holdings: Bk Vols 6,000; Per Subs 25
Mem of Northwest Regional Library System
Friends of the Library Group

SABULA

P KRABBENHOFT PUBLIC LIBRARY,* 512 Elk St, 52070. SAN 305-6805. Tel: 319-687-2950. FAX: 319-687-2950. E-Mail: krabhoft@gte.net. *Librn,* Ronda Taplin
Founded 1961. Pop 824; Circ 12,724
Library Holdings: Bk Vols 10,907; Per Subs 38
Special Collections: Media: videos (450)
Mem of E Cent Libr Syst
Open Tues, Thurs & Fri 1-5, Wed 7-9, Sat 9-12 & 1-5

SAC CITY

P SAC CITY PUBLIC LIBRARY,* 1001 Main St, 50583. SAN 305-6813. Tel: 712-662-7276. FAX: 712-662-7802. E-Mail: dom123pionet@net. *Librn,* Nancy L Domino; *Asst Librn,* Cathie Hass
Founded 1912. Pop 3,000; Circ 35,000
Library Holdings: Bk Vols 31,000
Special Collections: Local Area History Coll
Mem of Northwest Regional Library System
Open Mon-Thurs 1-8, Fri 10-5 & Sat 10-1
Friends of the Library Group

SAINT ANSGAR

P NISSEN PUBLIC LIBRARY, Saint Ansgar Public Library, 217 W Fifth, PO Box 40, 50472-0040. SAN 305-6821. Tel: 641-736-2218. FAX: 641-736-4716. E-Mail: nissen@smig.net. *Dir,* Marsha Kuntz
Founded 1927. Pop 1,100
Library Holdings: Bk Titles 10,000; Per Subs 40
Automation Activity & Vendor Info: (Cataloging) Sagebrush Corporation; (Circulation) Sagebrush Corporation
Mem of North Central Regional Library System
Open Mon 1-5:30 & 7-9pm, Tues, Wed, Thurs & Sat 1-5:30, Fri 9-12

SALEM

P CREW PUBLIC LIBRARY,* 109 S Main St, PO Box 117, 52649-0117. SAN 305-683X. Tel: 319-258-4691 (Home), 319-258-9007 (Wed & Sat 1-5). *Dir,* Dorothy Mills
Founded 1940. Pop 500; Circ 13,500
Library Holdings: Bk Titles 7,000; Per Subs 15
Mem of SE Iowa Regional Libr Syst

SANBORN

P SANBORN PUBLIC LIBRARY,* 407 Main St, PO Box 430, 51248-0430. SAN 305-6848. Tel: 712-729-3215. FAX: 712-729-3170. E-Mail: spl@mtcnet.net. *Dir, Librn,* Diane Winter
Founded 1901
Library Holdings: Bk Vols 12,000; Per Subs 12
Mem of Northwest Regional Library System

SCHALLER

P SCHALLER PUBLIC LIBRARY,* 103 S Main St, PO Box 427, 51053. SAN 305-6856. Tel: 712-275-4741. E-Mail: splibr@netins.net. *Librn,* Patricia Barlow
Pop 832
Library Holdings: Bk Titles 9,000; Per Subs 20
Mem of Northwest Regional Library System
Open Mon-Fri 2:30-5:30pm & Sat 9am-11pm

SCHLESWIG

P SCHLESWIG PUBLIC LIBRARY,* 202 Cedar St, 51461-0306. SAN 305-6864. Tel: 712-676-3470. *Librn,* Fran Stoneking
Founded 1940. Pop 2,000; Circ 4,810
Library Holdings: Bk Titles 11,017
Special Collections: Schleswig Leader Coll (1909 to 1981), 75th Anniversary, microflim, sound flm
Mem of Northwest Regional Library System

SCRANTON

P SCRANTON PUBLIC LIBRARY,* 1102 Main St, PO Box 68, 51462. SAN 305-6872. Tel: 712-652-3453. E-Mail: scrpblib@netins.net. *Librn,* Sarah Stephens
Pop 583; Circ 15,350
1997-1998 Income $26,785, City $12,000, County $11,365, Other $1,442. Mats Exp $8,635, Books $7,160, Per/Ser (Incl. Access Fees) $570. Sal $11,261
Library Holdings: Bk Vols 13,658; Per Subs 44
Mem of Central Iowa Regional Library
Open Mon, Tues, Thurs & Fri 9-5:30, Sat 9-12, Wed 11:30-5:30
Friends of the Library Group

SEYMOUR

P SEYMOUR COMMUNITY LIBRARY,* 123 N Fifth, 52590. SAN 305-6880. Tel: 515-898-2966. FAX: 515-898-7540. E-Mail: seycomlib@lisco.net. *Librn,* Lisa Perkins
Founded 1940. Pop 1,036; Circ 7,662
Library Holdings: Bk Titles 10,000
Mem of Southwest Iowa Regional Library System

SHEFFIELD

P SHEFFIELD PUBLIC LIBRARY,* 123 S Third St, PO Box 616, 50475-0616. SAN 305-6899. Tel: 515-892-4717. FAX: 515-892-4248. E-Mail: shefflib@frontiernet.net. *Dir,* Vicki Meints
Pop 1,174; Circ 43,288
Library Holdings: Bk Vols 13,028; Per Subs 67
Database Vendor: OCLC - First Search
Mem of North Central Regional Library System

SHELDON

J NORTHWEST IOWA COMMUNITY COLLEGE LIBRARY, 603 W Park St, 51201. SAN 305-6902. Tel: 712-324-5061. FAX: 712-324-4157. Web Site: www.nwicc.com. *Dir,* Molly Galm; E-Mail: mgalm@nwicc.cc.ia.us
Founded 1974. Enrl 850; Fac 50
Library Holdings: Bk Vols 13,000; Bk Titles 11,000; Per Subs 340
Subject Interests: Agriculture, Business and management, Electronics, Mechanical engineering, Science/technology, Technology
Automation Activity & Vendor Info: (Cataloging) Gaylord; (Circulation) Gaylord; (OPAC) Gaylord
Partic in OCLC Online Computer Library Center, Inc; State Of Iowa Libraries Online Interlibrary Loan

P SHELDON PUBLIC LIBRARY,* 925 Fourth Ave, 51201-1517. SAN 305-6910. Tel: 712-324-2442. FAX: 712-324-2442. E-Mail: sheldlib@hch.net. *Librn,* Ruth A Rodvik; *Asst Librn,* Fran Dykstra
Founded 1904. Pop 5,003; Circ 91,231
Jul 1997-Jun 1998 Income $119,650. Mats Exp $34,785, Books $30,000,

Per/Ser (Incl. Access Fees) $3,844. Sal $68,159
Library Holdings: Bk Titles 28,914; Per Subs 107
Special Collections: Local Newspaper 1874-1982, micro
Mem of Northwest Regional Library System
Friends of the Library Group

SHELL ROCK

P BENNY GAMBAIANI PUBLIC LIBRARY,* 104 S Cherry St, PO Box L, 50670-0811. SAN 305-6929. Tel: 319-885-4345. FAX: 319-885-6208. E-Mail: gambaian@netins.net. *Dir*, Diane L Harms; *Librn*, Debra Heidemann
Pop 1,378; Circ 25,000
Jul 1997-Jun 1998 Income $37,424, City $5,607, County $4,393, Locally Generated Income $10,000, Other $17,424. Mats Exp $11,450, Books $8,000, Per/Ser (Incl. Access Fees) $1,350. Sal $20,615
Library Holdings: Bk Titles 12,000; Per Subs 63
Special Collections: Shell Rock Newspapers, microfilm
Mem of Northeastern Iowa Regional Library System
Open Mon & Fri 12-5, Tues & Thurs 12-8, Wed 9-5, Sat 9-3

SHELLSBURG

P SHELLSBURG PUBLIC LIBRARY, 110 Main St, PO Box 248, 52332-0248. SAN 305-6937. Tel: 319-436-2112. FAX: 319-436-2112. E-Mail: spl@netins.net. *Dir*, Ann Marie Kibbie
Founded 1970. Pop 1,200; Circ 10,092
Library Holdings: Bk Titles 7,300
Open Mon 9:30-11:30 & 2-5, Tues 2-7, Wed 9:30-11:30 & 2-7, Thurs & Fri 2-5, Sat 9-11

SHENANDOAH

P SHENANDOAH PUBLIC LIBRARY, 201 S Elm St, 51601. SAN 305-6945. Tel: 712-246-2315. FAX: 712-246-5847. E-Mail: shenlib@heartland.net. *Dir*, Jan Frank-de Ois; *Circ*, Belinda DeBolt; *Tech Coordr*, Carrie Falk; *Ch Servs*, Elizabeth Trippler; Staff 4 (MLS 2, Non-MLS 2)
Founded 1904. Pop 5,610; Circ 65,564
Automation Activity & Vendor Info: (Cataloging) Athena; (Circulation) Athena; (OPAC) Athena
Database Vendor: OCLC - First Search
Mem of Southwest Iowa Regional Library System
Friends of the Library Group

SIBLEY

P SIBLEY PUBLIC LIBRARY, 406 Ninth St, 51249. SAN 305-6953. Tel: 712-754-2888. FAX: 712-754-2590. E-Mail: siblib@rconnect.com. *Librn*, Constance Mataloni; *Ch Servs*, Karen Honken; Staff 5 (Non-MLS 5)
Founded 1917. Pop 2,800; Circ 53,272
2000-2001 Income $103,520, City $95,866, County $7,654. Mats Exp Books $17,381. Sal $57,000
Library Holdings: Bk Titles 20,185; Per Subs 82
Automation Activity & Vendor Info: (Cataloging) Sagebrush Corporation; (Circulation) Sagebrush Corporation
Mem of NW Iowa Regional Libr Syst

SIDNEY

P SIDNEY PUBLIC LIBRARY, (SPL), 604 Clay St, PO Box 479, 51652-0479. SAN 305-6961. Tel: 712-374-2223. FAX: 712-374-2821. *Librn*, Bev Finnigan; E-Mail: bfinnig@sidney.heartland.net
Pop 1,308; Circ 6,418
Library Holdings: Bk Vols 9,611; Bk Titles 8,100; Per Subs 30
Automation Activity & Vendor Info: (Cataloging) Follett
Mem of Southwest Iowa Regional Library System

SIGOURNEY

P SIGOURNEY PUBLIC LIBRARY,* 203 N Jefferson St, 52591. SAN 305-697X. Tel: 515-622-2890. FAX: 515-622-3391. E-Mail: sigopl@se_iowa.net. *Librn*, Roslin Thompson
Pop 2,330; Circ 32,989
Library Holdings: Bk Vols 12,500; Per Subs 40
Mem of Southeastern Library Services
Friends of the Library Group

SIOUX CENTER

C DORDT COLLEGE LIBRARY, 498 Fourth Ave NE, 51250. SAN 305-6996. Tel: 712-722-6040. Interlibrary Loan Service Tel: 712-722-6041. Reference Tel: 712-722-6042. FAX: 712-722-4498. E-Mail: library@dordt.edu. Web Site: www.dordt.edu/services/library. *Dir*, Sheryl Sheeres Taylor; Tel: 712-722-6047, E-Mail: staylor@dordt.edu; *VPres*, David Netz; *Coordr*, Gerlene Meyer; Tel: 712-722-6045; *Tech Servs*, Elaine Wassink; Tel: 712-722-6046; *Publ Servs*, Darlene Reichert; *ILL*, Dawn Van den Hul; Tel: 712-722-6041; *Ref*, Vos Gwen; Tel: 712-722-6042; Staff 4 (MLS 2, Non-MLS 2)
Founded 1955. Enrl 1,400; Fac 84; Highest Degree: Master
Jul 1999-Jun 2000 Mats Exp $160,134, Books $91,430, Per/Ser (Incl. Access Fees) $53,621, Presv $342, Micro $9,988, AV Equip $4,753. Sal $173,764 (Prof $75,670)
Library Holdings: Bk Vols 133,424; Bk Titles 106,497; Per Subs 711
Subject Interests: Education, History, Religion
Special Collections: Dutch History
Automation Activity & Vendor Info: (Acquisitions) SIRSI; (Cataloging) SIRSI; (Circulation) SIRSI; (Course Reserve) SIRSI; (OPAC) SIRSI; (Serials) SIRSI
Database Vendor: Dialog, Ebsco - EbscoHost, Lexis-Nexis, OCLC - First Search, ProQuest
Partic in Amigos Library Services, Inc; BCR; OCLC Online Computer Library Center, Inc

P SIOUX CENTER PUBLIC LIBRARY, 327 First Ave NE, 51250. SAN 305-7003. Tel: 712-722-2138. FAX: 712-722-1235. E-Mail: scplscilo@mtcnet.net. Web Site: siouxcenter.lib.ia.us. *Coll Develop, Dir*, Karen Bjorkman; *Ch Servs*, Dorothy Boeyink; *Cat*, Jean Maatman; *Outreach Serv*, Laurey Zwart; Staff 7 (MLS 1, Non-MLS 6)
Founded 1927. Pop 9,000; Circ 124,000
Jul 2000-Jun 2001 Income $251,297, State $2,754, City $210,000, County $24,000, Locally Generated Income $10,000. Mats Exp $33,900, Books $29,000, Per/Ser (Incl. Access Fees) $4,000, Electronic Ref Mat (Incl. Access Fees) $900. Sal $185,000
Library Holdings: Bk Titles 43,000; Per Subs 141
Subject Interests: Genealogy, History, Iowa
Special Collections: Government Documents
Mem of Northwest Regional Library System
Special Services for the Deaf - Books on deafness & sign language; High interest/low vocabulary books; TDD
Special Services for the Blind - Bks on tape; Homebound services

SIOUX CITY

C BRIAR CLIFF COLLEGE, Mueller Library, 3303 Rebecca St, 51104-2324. SAN 305-7011. Tel: 712-279-5449. FAX: 712-279-1723. E-Mail: library@briarcliff.edu. Web Site: www.briarcliff.edu/library. *Dir*, Kevin R Jones; Tel: 712-279-1771, E-Mail: jonesk@briarcliff.edu; *ILL, Tech Servs*, Sister Mary Jane Koenigs; Tel: 712-279-5535, E-Mail: koenigs@briarcliff.edu; *Instrul Serv*, Patricia Fratangelo; E-Mail: fratangelop@briarcliff.edu; *Electronic Resources*, Gretchen Bogenrief; E-Mail: bogenrief@briarcliff.edu; *Access Serv*, Rosemary Moody; E-Mail: moodyr@briarcliff.edu; Staff 2 (MLS 2)
Founded 1930. Enrl 850; Fac 64; Highest Degree: Master
Jun 2000-May 2001 Income (Main Library Only) $275,000. Mats Exp $97,500, Books $26,000, Per/Ser (Incl. Access Fees) $60,000, Presv $1,500, Micro $7,000, AV Equip $3,000. Sal $125,000 (Prof $90,000)
Library Holdings: Bk Vols 100,000; Per Subs 1,800
Subject Interests: Nursing, Social service (social work), Sociology, Theology
Automation Activity & Vendor Info: (Acquisitions) epixtech, inc.; (Cataloging) epixtech, inc.; (Circulation) epixtech, inc.; (Course Reserve) epixtech, inc.; (ILL) epixtech, inc.; (Media Booking) epixtech, inc.; (OPAC) epixtech, inc.
Partic in Bibliographical Center For Research, Rocky Mountain Region, Inc; Sioux City Library Cooperative
Friends of the Library Group

M MARIAN HEALTH CENTER, Health Science Library,* 801 Fifth St, 51101. SAN 305-7038. Tel: 712-279-2310. FAX: 712-279-5661. *Bibliog Instr, Dir, Online Servs*, Donna Phillips; E-Mail: phillipdm@mercyhealth.com; *Librn*, Barbara Groom
Founded 1976
Jul 1997-Jun 1998 Income $175,000. Mats Exp Books $4,800
Library Holdings: Bk Titles 3,000; Per Subs 500
Subject Interests: Clinical medicine, Hospital administration, Medicine, Nursing, Social sciences and issues
Partic in Greater Midwest Regional Medical Libr Network; Sioux City Library Cooperative

C MORNINGSIDE COLLEGE, Hickman-Johnson-Furrow Library Center, 1501 Morningside Ave, 51106. SAN 305-7046. Tel: 712-274-5195. Reference Tel: 712-274-5193. FAX: 712-274-5224. Web Site: library.morningside.edu. *Dir Libr Serv*, Daria L Bossman; Tel: 712-274-5125, E-Mail: bossman@morningside.edu; *Bibliog Instr, Ref*, Dena Heilik; Tel: 712-274-5246, E-Mail: heilik@morningside.edu; *Electronic Resources*, Rachel Crowley; Tel: 712-274-5247, E-Mail: crowley@morningside.edu; Staff 6 (MLS 3, Non-MLS 3)
Founded 1894. Enrl 979; Fac 75; Highest Degree: Master
Jun 1999-May 2000 Income $420,925. Mats Exp $160,928, Books $53,120, Per/Ser (Incl. Access Fees) $61,589, Presv $363, Micro $12,394, AV Equip $11,578, Electronic Ref Mat (Incl. Access Fees) $21,884. Sal $187,474 (Prof $108,000)

Library Holdings: Bk Vols 114,288; Bk Titles 95,799; Per Subs 607
Subject Interests: Native Am studies
Automation Activity & Vendor Info: (Cataloging) SIRSI; (Circulation) SIRSI; (Course Reserve) SIRSI; (ILL) SIRSI; (Media Booking) SIRSI; (OPAC) SIRSI; (Serials) SIRSI
Publications: Newsletter
Function: Research library
Partic in Bibliographical Center For Research, Rocky Mountain Region, Inc; Iowa Private Academic Library Consortium; Iowa Resource & Info Sharing; OCLC Online Computer Library Center, Inc; Sioux City Library Cooperative; Siouxland Automated Initiative

P NORTHWEST REGIONAL LIBRARY SYSTEM,* 529 Pierce St, PO Box 1319, 51102. SAN 305-7054. Tel: 712-255-2939, Ext 291. FAX: 712-252-3171. E-Mail: nwrldir@server.silo.lib.ia.us. *Dir*, Bonnie McKewon; Staff 2 (MLS 2)
Founded 1973. Pop 364,979
Jul 1997-Jun 1998 Income $222,495. Mats Exp $5,400, Books $2,800, Per/Ser (Incl. Access Fees) $250, AV Equip $1,850. Sal $121,031 (Prof $63,900)
Library Holdings: Bk Titles 500; Per Subs 15
Special Collections: Deaf materials: closed captioned videos & print
Publications: Deaf News; Update
Member Libraries: Akron Public Library; Albert City Public Library; Alton Public Library; Anthon Public Library; Archer Public Library; Arnolds Park Public Library; Arthur Public Library; Ashton Public Library; Battle Creek Public Library; Bay County Public Library Association; Boyden Public Library; Breda Public Library; Carroll Public Library; Charter Oak Public Library; Cherokee Public Library; Coon Rapids Public Library; Correctionville Public Library; Dickens Public Library; Doon Public Library; Dow City Public Library; Early Public Library; Emmetsburg Public Library; Estherville Public Library; Everly Public Library; Farnhamville Public Library; Field-Carnegie Library; Fisher Whiting Memorial Library; Fonda Public Library; Galva Public Library; General N B Baker Public Library; George Public Library; Gilmore City Public Library; Glidden Public Library; Godel Memorial Library; Graettinger Public Library; Hawarden Public Library; Hull Public Library; Ida Grove Public Library; Inwood Public Library; J J Hands Library; King Public Library; Kingsley Public Library; Kirchner-French Memorial Library; Lake City Public Library; Lake View Public Library; Larchwood Public Library; Laurens Public Library; Le Mars Public Library; Linn Grove Public Library; Little Rock Public Library; Lowgap Public Library; Lytton Public Library; Mallard Public Library; Manilla Public Library; Manning Public Library; Marcus Public Library; MC Community Library; Melvin Public Library; Merrill Public Library; Milford Memorial Library; Moorhead Public Library; Mount Airy Public Library; Newell Public Library; Norelius Community Library; Ocheyedan Public Library; Orange City Public Library; Palmer Public Library; Paullina Public Library; Plover Public Library; Pocahontas Public Library; Pomeroy Public Library; Primghar Public Library; Quimby Public Library; Red Lake Falls Public Library; Remsen Public Library; Rock Rapids Public Library; Rock Valley Public Library; Rockwell City Public Library; Rocky Bay First Nation Library; Rolfe Public Library; Roseau Public Library; Royal Public Library; Ruthven Public Library; Sac City Public Library; Sanborn Public Library; Sarah Carpenter Memorial Library; Sargeant Bluff Public-School Library; Schaller Public Library; Schleswig Public Library; Sheldon Public Library; Sioux Center Public Library; Sioux City Public Library; Sioux Narrows Public Library; Sioux Rapids Memorial Library; Sloan Public Library; Soldier Public Library; Somers Public Library; Spencer Public Library; Spirit Lake Public Library; Storm Lake Public Library; Stubbs Memorial Library; Superior Public Library; Terril Community Library; Ute Public Library; Varina Public Library; Wall Lake Public Library; Walnut Cove Public Library; Warroad Public Library; Washta Library; Webb Public Library; Westside Public Library; Whiting Public Library; Wilmington Memorial Library; Woodbury County Library; Yadkin County Public Library

M SAINT LUKE'S REGIONAL MEDICAL CENTER, Media Services, 2720 Stone Park Blvd, 51104. SAN 341-9649. Tel: 712-279-3156. Web Site: www.library.stlukes.org. *Media Spec*, Michelle Tedrow
Library Holdings: Bk Vols 3,800; Bk Titles 3,000; Per Subs 110
Subject Interests: Family practice, Medicine, Nursing
Automation Activity & Vendor Info: (Cataloging) Athena; (Circulation) Athena
Partic in Dialog Corporation; Medline

S SIOUX CITY ART CENTER, Margaret Avery Heffernan Reference Library, 225 Nebraska St, 51101. SAN 305-7062. Tel: 712-279-6272. Reference Tel: 712-279-6272, Ext 208. FAX: 712-255-2921. Web Site: www.sc-artcenter.com. *Dir*, Ronald R Bernier
Jul 1999-Jun 2000 Mats Exp $1,200
Library Holdings: Bk Vols 1,500
Subject Interests: Art (20th Century)
Restriction: Non-circulating to the public
Function: Research library

P SIOUX CITY PUBLIC LIBRARY, 529 Pierce St, 51101-1203. SAN 341-9673. Tel: 712-255-2933. FAX: 712-279-6432. Web Site: www.sc.lib.ia.us. *Dir*, Betsy J Thompson; *Circ*, Marla Kerr; *Ch Servs*, Jeanette E Bobeen; *AV, Branch Mgr*, Joan A Allen; *Ref Serv Ad*, Connie A McKnight; *Coll Develop*, Susan K Hunting; Staff 17 (MLS 8, Non-MLS 9)
Founded 1877. Pop 80,505; Circ 625,000
Jul 1999-Jun 2000 Income (Main Library and Branch Library) $2,140,000. Mats Exp $456,616, Books $329,700, Per/Ser (Incl. Access Fees) $43,800, AV Equip $36,400, Electronic Ref Mat (Incl. Access Fees) $46,716. Sal $1,300,000
Library Holdings: Bk Vols 220,000; Bk Titles 134,000
Automation Activity & Vendor Info: (Acquisitions) epixtech, inc.; (Cataloging) epixtech, inc.; (Circulation) epixtech, inc.; (OPAC) epixtech, inc.
Publications: Book Remarks (newsletter)
Mem of Northwest Regional Library System
Friends of the Library Group
Branches: 2
MARKETPLACE, 2901 Hamilton Blvd, 51104-2405. SAN 341-9797. Tel: 712-255-2926. Web Site: www.sc.lib.ia.us. *Mgr*, Michael V O'Sullivan
Library Holdings: Bk Vols 18,300
Friends of the Library Group
MORNINGSIDE, 4005 Morningside Ave, 51106-2448. SAN 341-9738. Tel: 712-255-2924. Web Site: www.sc.lib.ia.us. *Mgr*, Joan A Allen
Library Holdings: Bk Vols 40,516
Friends of the Library Group

J WESTERN IOWA TECH COMMUNITY COLLEGE, Library Services, 4647 Stone Ave, 51106. SAN 305-7089. Tel: 712-274-8733, Ext 1239. Interlibrary Loan Service Tel: 712-274-8733, Ext 1439. FAX: 712-274-6412. E-Mail: library@witcc.com. Web Site: www.lzone.witcc.com/library. *Mgr*, Sharon Kay Dykshoorn; E-Mail: dykshos@witcc.com; *Publ Servs*, Charles LeMaster; E-Mail: lemastc@witcc.com; *Tech Servs*, Beth Ham; E-Mail: hamb@witcc.com; *Tech Servs*, Rose Peterson; Tel: 712-274-8733, Ext 1304, E-Mail: peterskk@witcc.com; Staff 4 (MLS 2, Non-MLS 2)
Founded 1966. Enrl 2,744; Highest Degree: Associate
Jul 1998-Jun 1999 Income $317,668, State $243,805, Federal $1,237, County $33,649, Other $1,340. Mats Exp $291,724, Books $29,000, Per/Ser (Incl. Access Fees) $50,142, Presv $150, Micro $2,125, AV Equip $10,252. Sal $174,321 (Prof $127,170)
Library Holdings: Bk Vols 26,004; Bk Titles 19,815; Per Subs 315
Automation Activity & Vendor Info: (Circulation) epixtech, inc.; (Course Reserve) epixtech, inc.; (OPAC) epixtech, inc.
Database Vendor: IAC - Info Trac, IAC - SearchBank
Partic in Sioux City Library Cooperative

L WOODBURY COUNTY LAW LIBRARY,* Woodbury County Court House, 6th flr, 51101. SAN 305-7097. Tel: 712-279-6609. FAX: 712-279-6577. *Librn*, Richard P Hustig
Founded 1918
Library Holdings: Bk Titles 300
Special Collections: American Law Coll
Publications: Sioux City Legal Resources

SIOUX RAPIDS

P SIOUX RAPIDS MEMORIAL LIBRARY, 215 Second St, 50585. SAN 305-7100. Tel: 712-283-2064. FAX: 712-283-2064. E-Mail: srlib@nwiowa.com. *Librn*, Martha Landsness
Pop 817; Circ 18,432
Library Holdings: Bk Vols 21,500; Per Subs 35
Special Collections: Sioux Rapids Bulletin Press (1865-1997), micro
Mem of Northwest Regional Library System
Open Mon & Wed 1-7, Tues & Sat 9-3, Thurs 12-6 & Fri 9-12

SLATER

P SLATER PUBLIC LIBRARY,* 105 N Tama St, PO Box 598, 50244. SAN 305-7119. Tel: 515-685-3558. FAX: 515-685-3558. E-Mail: slibrary@pcpartner.net. *Librn*, Paula Armer
Founded 1970. Pop 1,500
Library Holdings: Bk Vols 14,500; Per Subs 40
Special Collections: Palestine Township History
Mem of Central Iowa Regional Library
Friends of the Library Group

SLOAN

P SLOAN PUBLIC LIBRARY,* 311 Fourth St, PO Box 8, 51055. SAN 305-7127. Tel: 712-428-4200. E-Mail: slolib@pinet.net. *Librn*, Marcia Clary
Founded 1935. Pop 978; Circ 2,680
Library Holdings: Bk Vols 6,038; Per Subs 21
Subject Interests: History, Iowa
Mem of Northwest Regional Library System
Special Services for the Deaf - Books on deafness & sign language; Captioned film depository

SOLDIER

P SOLDIER PUBLIC LIBRARY,* 108 Oak St, PO Box 175, 51572-0175. SAN 376-5296. Tel: 712-884-2266. FAX: 712-884-2264. *Librn*, Marceil Frydenlund; Tel: 712-884-2579
Library Holdings: Bk Vols 2,000
Mem of Northwest Regional Library System

SOLON

P SOLON PUBLIC LIBRARY,* 320 W Main St, 52333-9504. SAN 305-7135. Tel: 319-644-2678. FAX: 319-644-2122. E-Mail: solonlib@soli.inav.net. *Librn*, Kris Brown
Founded 1965. Pop 1,000; Circ 6,363
1997-1998 Income $40,200. Mats Exp $18,530. Sal $17,020
Library Holdings: Bk Titles 13,000; Per Subs 15
Friends of the Library Group

SOMERS

P SOMERS PUBLIC LIBRARY,* 502 Sixth St, PO Box 114, 50586-7517. SAN 305-7143. Tel: 515-467-5522. FAX: 515-467-5603. *Librn*, Joyce Erritt
Founded 1973. Pop 167; Circ 3,768
Library Holdings: Bk Titles 5,475
Mem of Northwest Regional Library System
Open Mon & Tues 2-5, Wed 6-9, Sat 8:30-11:30
Friends of the Library Group

SOUTH ENGLISH

P SOUTH ENGLISH PUBLIC LIBRARY, 407 Ives St, PO Box 162, 52335-0162. SAN 305-7151. Tel: 319-667-2715. *Librn*, Elizabeth Seitsinger; Tel: 319-667-5791
Founded 1936. Pop 450
1999-2000 Income $4,919, State $362, City $1,850, County $2,372, Locally Generated Income $335. Mats Exp $1,455, Books $1,213, AV Equip $113, Other Print Mats $129. Sal $2,442
Library Holdings: Bk Titles 6,993; Per Subs 64
Mem of Southeastern Library Services

SPENCER

P SPENCER PUBLIC LIBRARY, 21 E Third St, 51301-4188. SAN 305-716X. Tel: 712-264-7290. FAX: 712-262-7468. E-Mail: spencerpl@surfiowa.com. Web Site: www.surfiowa.com/splibrary. *Dir*, Vicki Myron; E-Mail: vickim@surfiowa.com; *Asst Dir*, Kay Larson; E-Mail: klarson@surfiowa.com; *Ch Servs*, Mary Walk; Staff 11 (MLS 1, Non-MLS 10)
Founded 1906. Pop 11,600
Jul 2000-Jun 2001 Income $366,169, State $4,396, City $348,899, County $12,874. Mats Exp $43,750, Books $28,725, Per/Ser (Incl. Access Fees) $5,825, Micro $225, AV Equip $1,475, Electronic Ref Mat (Incl. Access Fees) $7,500. Sal $237,400
Library Holdings: Bk Vols 45,248; Per Subs 221
Subject Interests: Large type, State hist
Special Collections: Career-Related Materials; Charlotte Brett Genealogy Coll; Kids On The Block Puppets
Automation Activity & Vendor Info: (Cataloging) TLC; (Circulation) TLC; (Course Reserve) TLC; (OPAC) TLC
Database Vendor: OCLC - First Search
Publications: SPLASH (monthly newsletter)
Mem of Northwest Regional Library System
Friends of the Library Group

SPILLVILLE

P SPILLVILLE PUBLIC LIBRARY, 201 Oak St, PO Box 197, 52168. SAN 325-2558. Tel: 319-562-4373. FAX: 319-562-4373. E-Mail: slibrary@rconnect.com. *Dir, Librn*, Joyce Zoulek; *Asst Librn*, Doris Thompson
Founded 1980
Jul 1999-Jun 2000 Income $21,694, State $1,160, City $7,683, County $7,554, Locally Generated Income $641, Other $4,656. Mats Exp $3,627, Books $2,309, Per/Ser (Incl. Access Fees) $518, Electronic Ref Mat (Incl. Access Fees) $800. Sal $10,845
Library Holdings: Bk Vols 6,052; Per Subs 23; Bks on Deafness & Sign Lang 10
Automation Activity & Vendor Info: (Cataloging) Sagebrush Corporation
Mem of Northeastern Iowa Regional Library System

SPIRIT LAKE

P SPIRIT LAKE PUBLIC LIBRARY, 702 16th St, 51360. SAN 305-7178. Tel: 712-336-2667. FAX: 712-336-0511. E-Mail: publib@spirit-lake.ki2.ia.us. *Dir*, Linda Bolluyt
Founded 1912. Pop 3,871; Circ 109,608
Jul 1999-Jun 2000 Income $149,000. Mats Exp $28,210, Books $24,493, Per/Ser (Incl. Access Fees) $3,717. Sal $80,000
Library Holdings: Bk Vols 25,378; Per Subs 117
Special Collections: Northwest Iowa History Coll
Mem of Northwest Regional Library System
Friends of the Library Group

SPRINGVILLE

P SPRINGVILLE MEMORIAL LIBRARY,* 304 Broadway, PO Box 78, 52336-0078. SAN 305-7186. Tel: 319-854-6444. FAX: 319-854-6577. E-Mail: sprlibry@netins.net. *Librn*, Mary LaGrange
Pop 2,610; Circ 13,487
Library Holdings: Bk Vols 14,500; Per Subs 25
Open Mon 3-6, Tues & Fri 3-5, Wed 3-8, Thurs 10-11 & 3-5, Sat 9-12 & 1-3
Friends of the Library Group

STACYVILLE

P STACYVILLE PUBLIC LIBRARY,* 105 W Main St, 50476. SAN 305-7194. Tel: 515-737-2531. FAX: 515-737-2531. E-Mail: stacylib@smig.net. *Librn*, Sydney Heimer
Founded 1967. Pop 481; Circ 19,971
Library Holdings: Bk Titles 10,094
Mem of North Central Regional Library System

STANHOPE

P STANHOPE PUBLIC LIBRARY, 665 Iowa St, PO Box 67, 50246. SAN 305-7208. Tel: 515-826-3211. FAX: 515-826-3211. E-Mail: stanpl@netins.net. *Librn*, Cheryl Haman
Founded 1950. Pop 447; Circ 3,419
Jul 1998-Jun 1999 Income $21,108, State $572, City $10,497, County $10,039
Library Holdings: Bk Vols 7,100; Per Subs 20
Mem of North Central Regional Library System
Open Tues, Wed & Thurs 1-6:30, Fri & Sat 9-12

STANTON

P STANTON COMMUNITY LIBRARY, 310 Broad Ave, PO Box 130, 51573. SAN 305-7216. Tel: 712-829-2290. *Librn*, Jerry S Gilliland; Tel: 712-829-2326, E-Mail: jgilliland@aea14.k12.ia.us; Staff 1 (MLS 1)
Founded 1941. Pop 1,000; Circ 6,000
Jul 1999-Jun 2000 Income $13,688, City $5,610, County $6,000, Locally Generated Income $310. Mats Exp $10,587, Books $3,479, Per/Ser (Incl. Access Fees) $492. Sal $5,500
Library Holdings: Bk Vols 9,446; Per Subs 60
Special Collections: Swedish Coll
Function: ILL available
Mem of Southwest Iowa Regional Library System

STANWOOD

P STANWOOD PUBLIC LIBRARY,* 202 E Broadway, 52337-0234. SAN 305-7224. Tel: 319-942-3531. FAX: 319-942-3531. E-Mail: stwdpl@netins.net. *Dir*, Rita Becker
Founded 1949. Pop 705; Circ 3,366
Library Holdings: Bk Titles 9,000
Friends of the Library Group

STATE CENTER

P GUTEKUNST PUBLIC LIBRARY,* 309 Second St SE, 50247-0550. SAN 305-7232. Tel: 515-483-2741. FAX: 515-483-2131. *Dir*, Rowena Ryan
Circ 55,000
Jul 1997-Jun 1998 Income $60,000, State $500, County $3,500. Mats Exp $10,200. Sal $30,000
Library Holdings: Bk Vols 15,228; Per Subs 90
Automation Activity & Vendor Info: (Cataloging) Follett; (Circulation) Follett
Mem of Central Iowa Regional Library
Friends of the Library Group

STEAMBOAT ROCK

P STEAMBOAT ROCK PUBLIC LIBRARY,* 511 Market St, 50672. SAN 305-7240. Tel: 515-868-2300. FAX: 515-868-2300. E-Mail: srlib@cnsinternet.com. *Librn*, Lois Luiken
Founded 1959. Pop 387; Circ 11,586
Library Holdings: Bk Vols 8,000; Bk Titles 2,390; Per Subs 33
Mem of North Central Regional Library System

STOCKPORT

P STOCKPORT PUBLIC LIBRARY,* Beswick St, PO Box 69, 52651. SAN 305-7259. Tel: 319-796-4681. E-Mail: stocklib@netins.net. *Librn*, Judy Johnson
Pop 250
Jul 1997-Jun 1998 Income $5,524, City $1,300, County $1,943. Mats Exp Books $909. Sal $2,182
Library Holdings: Bk Vols 6,406; Per Subs 12
Mem of Southeastern Library Services
Also serves Van Buren County elementary school

STORM LAKE

C BUENA VISTA UNIVERSITY LIBRARY, 610 W Fourth St, 50588. SAN 305-7267. Tel: 712-749-2127. Interlibrary Loan Service Tel: 712-749-2096. Circulation Tel: 712-749-2096. Reference Tel: 712-749-2203. FAX: 712-749-2059. Web Site: www2.bvu.edu. *Head of Libr*, James R Kennedy; E-Mail: kennedyj@bvu.edu; *Tech Servs*, Margaret Stangohr; Tel: 712-749-2203, E-Mail: stangohrm@bvu.edu; *Ref*, Ann Klavano; E-Mail: klavanoa@bvu.edu; *Ref*, Jodie Morin; E-Mail: morinj@bvu.edu; *Ser*, Jane Fehr; E-Mail: fehrj@bvu.edu; *Acq*, Melissa Richter; *Access Serv*, Florene Cork; E-Mail: corkf@bvu.edu; *Access Serv*, Tom Huntzicker; E-Mail: huntzickert@bvu.edu; Staff 8 (MLS 4, Non-MLS 4)
Founded 1891. Enrl 2,692; Fac 80; Highest Degree: Master
Jul 1999-Jun 2000 Income Parent Institution $777,011. Mats Exp $316,256, Books $111,989, Per/Ser (Incl. Access Fees) $104,150, Presv $6,431, Micro $11,742, AV Equip $4,900, Electronic Ref Mat (Incl. Access Fees) $77,044. Sal $253,913 (Prof $223,207)
Library Holdings: Bk Vols 153,084; Bk Titles 100,384; Per Subs 721
Subject Interests: History, Iowa
Automation Activity & Vendor Info: (Cataloging) epixtech, inc.; (Circulation) epixtech, inc.; (OPAC) epixtech, inc.; (Serials) epixtech, inc.
Database Vendor: Lexis-Nexis, OCLC - First Search, Silverplatter Information Inc.
Function: For research purposes
Partic in BCR; Iowa Private Academic Library Consortium; LVIS

P STORM LAKE PUBLIC LIBRARY, 609 Cayuga St, 50588. SAN 305-7275. Tel: 712-732-8026. FAX: 712-732-7609. E-Mail: slpl@ncn.net. *Dir*, Susan F Stone; *Asst Dir*, Toni Beem-Hayes; *Ch Servs*, Elizabeth Huff; *Circ*, Judy Ferguson; Staff 10 (Non-MLS 10)
Founded 1905. Pop 8,800; Circ 85,000
Jul 1998-Jun 1999 Income City $190,591. Mats Exp $19,700, Books $15,000, Per/Ser (Incl. Access Fees) $3,200, AV Equip $1,500. Sal $95,190
Library Holdings: Bk Vols 43,000; Bk Titles 43,717; Per Subs 99
Special Collections: Spanish-Laotian (Multilingual Coll)
Automation Activity & Vendor Info: (Cataloging) Follett; (Circulation) Follett; (OPAC) Follett
Database Vendor: OCLC - First Search
Publications: Annual Report; Newsletter (monthly)
Mem of Northwest Regional Library System
Friends of the Library Group

STORY CITY

P THE BERTHA BARTLETT PUBLIC LIBRARY, 503 Broad St, 50248-1133. SAN 305-7283. Tel: 515-733-2685. FAX: 515-733-2843. E-Mail: scbbpl@email.roland-story.k12.ia.us. *Librn*, Janice Thompson
Founded 1922. Pop 2,959
Jul 2000-Jun 2001 Income $88,796, State $3,988, City $74,247, County $5,899, Other $4,662. Mats Exp $21,394, Books $17,783, Per/Ser (Incl. Access Fees) $1,631. Sal $40,578
Library Holdings: Bk Vols 34,783; Per Subs 57
Mem of Central Iowa Regional Library
Friends of the Library Group

STRATFORD

P STRATFORD PUBLIC LIBRARY,* 816 Shakesphere, 50249. SAN 305-7291. Tel: 515-838-2131. FAX: 515-838-2131. E-Mail: stratlib@netins.net. *Librn*, Lou Rene Iles; *Asst Librn*, Carolyn Iles
Founded 1926. Pop 715; Circ 9,500
1999-2000 Income $25,238, State $1,501, City $13,500, County $10,237. Mats Exp $7,480, Books $6,814, Per/Ser (Incl. Access Fees) $400, Other Print Mats $266. Sal $12,500
Library Holdings: Bk Vols 5,524; Per Subs 36
Mem of North Central Regional Library System

STRAWBERRY POINT

P STRAWBERRY POINT PUBLIC LIBRARY, 111 Commercial St, 52076. SAN 305-7305. Tel: 319-933-4340. FAX: 319-933-4340. E-Mail: stptlibrary@mwci.net. *Librn*, Lois Cordes; *Asst Librn*, Bonna Fridley; *Asst Librn*, Joan Werner
Pop 1,463; Circ 22,279
Library Holdings: Bk Titles 15,000; Per Subs 60
Mem of Northeastern Iowa Regional Library System

STUART

P STUART PUBLIC LIBRARY,* 1219 Front St, PO Box 220, 50250. SAN 305-7313. Tel: 515-523-2152. E-Mail: stuartpl@netins.net. *Librn*, Nadine Avavey
Founded 1901. Pop 1,650; Circ 28,961
Library Holdings: Bk Vols 18,751; Per Subs 70
Subject Interests: Iowa
Mem of Southwest Iowa Regional Library System
Friends of the Library Group

SULLY

P SULLY COMMUNITY LIBRARY, 318 Sixth Ave, PO Box 226, 50251-0226. SAN 371-5434. Tel: 641-594-4148. FAX: 641-594-2978. E-Mail: sullylib@netins.net. *Librn*, Pam VanDyke
Friends of the Library Group

SUMNER

P SUMNER PUBLIC LIBRARY,* 202 E First St, 50674. SAN 305-7321. Tel: 319-578-3324. FAX: 319-578-3324. E-Mail: sumpublb@sbtek.net. *Librn*, Marcia Sulentic; *Ad Servs*, Bev Thomsen
Pop 2,335; Circ 55,718
Library Holdings: Bk Titles 25,000; Per Subs 75
Mem of Northeastern Iowa Regional Library System

SUPERIOR

P SUPERIOR PUBLIC LIBRARY,* Town Hall, 111 Seventh St, 51363. SAN 376-527X. Tel: 712-858-4528. *Librn*, De Anne Bueltel
Library Holdings: Bk Vols 4,000
Mem of Northwest Regional Library System

SUTHERLAND

P GENERAL N B BAKER PUBLIC LIBRARY, Sutherland Public Library, 315 Ash St, 51058-0280. SAN 305-733X. Tel: 712-446-3839. FAX: 712-446-3839. E-Mail: genbakrlibr@nwidt.com. *Head Librn*, Mary Draper; *Librn*, Rosali Amendt; Staff 2 (Non-MLS 2)
Founded 1875. Pop 714; Circ 9,835
Jul 1999-Jun 2000 Income $18,886, State $1,186, City $12,200, County $5,500. Mats Exp $5,404, Books $3,134, Per/Ser (Incl. Access Fees) $564, AV Equip $1,290, Electronic Ref Mat (Incl. Access Fees) (MEX) $416. Sal $9,068
Library Holdings: Bk Vols 8,088; Per Subs 53
Subject Interests: Gardening, History, Literature, Poetry, Religion
Special Collections: Iowa Coll
Mem of Northwest Regional Library System

SWALEDALE

P SWALEDALE PUBLIC LIBRARY,* 504 Main St, PO Box 114, 50477-0114. SAN 305-7348. Tel: 515-995-2352. FAX: 515-995-2352. *Librn*, Leona Bonner; *Asst Librn*, Lori Reck
Founded 1972. Pop 185; Circ 4,629
Library Holdings: Bk Vols 5,656; Per Subs 25
Special Collections: Large Print
Mem of North Central Regional Library System

SWEA CITY

P SWEA CITY PUBLIC LIBRARY,* 208 Third St N, 50590. SAN 305-7356. Tel: 515-272-4216. FAX: 515-272-4216. E-Mail: swcpl@trvnet.net. *Librn*, Lettie Rowlet; *Asst Librn*, Marilyn Peterson
Founded 1900. Pop 636; Circ 25,000
1999-2000 Income $19,600, State $500, City $7,000, County $7,900, Locally Generated Income $4,200. Mats Exp $9,300, Books $3,500, Per/Ser (Incl. Access Fees) $800. Sal $9,777
Library Holdings: Bk Titles 16,872; Per Subs 32
Mem of North Central Regional Library System
Friends of the Library Group

TABOR

P TABOR PUBLIC LIBRARY,* 805 Main St, PO Box 7, 51653. SAN 305-7364. Tel: 712-629-2735. FAX: 712-629-2735. E-Mail: tlibrar@sidney.heartland.net. *Librn*, Denise Jacobsen

Pop 1,088; Circ 3,954
Library Holdings: Bk Vols 8,286; Per Subs 13
Mem of Southwest Iowa Regional Library System

TAMA

P TAMA PUBLIC LIBRARY,* PO Box 308, 52339-0308. SAN 305-7372. Tel: 515-484-4484. FAX: 515-484-4484. E-Mail: tamalib@pcpartner.net. *Dir*, Julie D Shook; Tel: 515-484-2194, Fax: 515-484-2194, E-Mail: redbeard@pcpartner.net; *Asst Librn*, Francis P Prusha; Tel: 515-484-2892; *Asst Librn*, Anne Rebik; Tel: 515-484-3334
Founded 1906
Jul 1998-Jun 1999 Income $76,320, State $1,860, City $59,554, County $6,625, Other $8,281. Mats Exp $13,375, Books $11,721, Per/Ser (Incl. Access Fees) $1,654. Sal $13,400
Special Collections: Mesquakie Indian; Romance; True Crime
Automation Activity & Vendor Info: (Circulation) Sagebrush Corporation
Database Vendor: OCLC - First Search
Friends of the Library Group

TERRIL

P TERRIL COMMUNITY LIBRARY,* 115 N State St, 51364-0038. SAN 305-7380. Tel: 712-853-6224. FAX: 712-853-6185. E-Mail: terrilib@netins.net. *Dir*, Kathleen Wagner
Founded 1933. Circ 8,001
1998-1999 Income $13,171, City $7,200, County $4,050. Mats Exp $3,676, Books $3,115. Sal $7,929
Library Holdings: Bk Vols 12,000
Special Collections: Terril Record Coll, 1929-52; Terril Tribune Coll, 1900-03
Mem of Northwest Regional Library System

THOMPSON

P THOMPSON PUBLIC LIBRARY,* PO Box 81, 50478-0081. SAN 305-7399. Tel: 515-584-2829. Interlibrary Loan Service Tel: 800-392-8804. *Librn*, Patricia Michaelson
Founded 1937. Pop 668
Library Holdings: Bk Vols 5,300; Bk Titles 4,000; Per Subs 20
Mem of North Central Regional Library System

THORNTON

P THORNTON PUBLIC LIBRARY,* 412 Main, 50479. SAN 305-7402. Tel: 515-998-2416. FAX: 515-998-2470. E-Mail: maplest@frontiernet.net. *Librn*, Deb Tudor
Pop 442; Circ 19,400
Library Holdings: Bk Titles 9,000; Per Subs 20
Mem of North Central Regional Library System
Open Mon 2-6, Tues, Wed & Fri 2-4:30, Thurs 1-4:30, Sat 9-11:30

TIPTON

P TIPTON PUBLIC LIBRARY, 206 Cedar St, 52772-1753. SAN 305-7410. Tel: 319-886-6266. FAX: 319-886-6257. E-Mail: tedybear@netins.net. *Dir*, Ricardo H Sauro; *Asst Librn*, Linda M Dykstra; *Asst Librn*, Louise K Miller; *Ch Servs*, Loretta Martin
Founded 1901. Circ 40,619
Jul 2000-Jun 2001 Income $119,600, City $100,500, County $10,000, Locally Generated Income $4,100. Mats Exp $19,000, Books $17,000, Per/Ser (Incl. Access Fees) $2,000. Sal $69,941 (Prof $31,110)
Library Holdings: Bk Vols 31,539; Bk Titles 31,245; Per Subs 64
Special Collections: Cedar County Genealogical Society; Cedar County History Coll
Automation Activity & Vendor Info: (Cataloging) Sagebrush Corporation; (Circulation) Sagebrush Corporation
Partic in Am Libr Asn; Int Survey Libr Asn
Friends of the Library Group

TITONKA

P TITONKA PUBLIC LIBRARY, 136 Main St, PO Box 323, 50480-0323. SAN 305-7429. Tel: 515-928-2509. FAX: 515-928-2509. E-Mail: tykeplib@netins.net. *Dir*, Dawn M Lloyd
Founded 1913
Jul 1999-Jun 2000 Income $18,207, State $595, City $7,500, Federal $412, County $8,700, Locally Generated Income $1,000. Sal $9,550 (Prof $8,750)
Library Holdings: Bk Vols 7,270; Bk Titles 6,800; Per Subs 50
Special Collections: Wood carving
Automation Activity & Vendor Info: (Cataloging) Follett; (Circulation) Follett; (OPAC) Follett
Database Vendor: IAC - Info Trac, IAC - SearchBank, OCLC - First Search
Function: ILL available
Mem of North Central Regional Library System
Special Services for the Blind - Large print bks
Friends of the Library Group

TOLEDO

S TAMA COUNTY HISTORICAL SOCIETY, Museum Library, 200 N Broadway, 52342. SAN 371-9200. Tel: 515-484-6767. *Pres*, Joyce Wiese; Staff 6 (MLS 6)
Founded 1974
Library Holdings: Bk Titles 5,500; Per Subs 22
Open Tues-Sat 1-4:30

P TOLEDO PUBLIC LIBRARY,* 206 E High St, 52342-1617. SAN 305-7437. Tel: 515-484-3362. FAX: 515-484-3362. E-Mail: tpl@pcpartners.net. *Librn*, Sonia Hayek
Pop 2,450; Circ 23,000
Jul 1997-Jun 1998 Income $58,162, State $834, City $50,974, Federal $365, County $5,989. Mats Exp $22,430, Books $17,000, Per/Ser (Incl. Access Fees) $2,200, Micro $900, Other Print Mats $2,330. Sal $25,500
Library Holdings: Bk Titles 21,000; Per Subs 89
Special Collections: Iowa Coll

TRAER

P TRAER PUBLIC LIBRARY,* 531 Second St, 50675. SAN 305-7445. Tel: 319-478-2180. FAX: 319-478-2180. E-Mail: traerlib@netins.net. *Librn*, Linda McDermott; Staff 1 (MLS 1)
Founded 1916. Pop 1,720; Circ 17,904
Library Holdings: Bk Vols 16,784; Bk Titles 16,500; Per Subs 107
Friends of the Library Group

TRIPOLI

P TRIPOLI PUBLIC LIBRARY,* 101 Fourth Ave SW, 50676. SAN 305-7453. Tel: 319-882-4807. FAX: 319-882-3580. E-Mail: tripplib@netins.net. *Librn*, Sherry Heins
Founded 1951. Pop 1,280; Circ 31,855
Jul 1999-Jun 2000 Income $46,757, State $941, City $23,000, County $14,071, Locally Generated Income $3,027, Other $5,718. Mats Exp $15,023, Books $9,490, Per/Ser (Incl. Access Fees) $1,000, Other Print Mats $2,000. Sal $16,521 (Prof $12,192)
Library Holdings: Bk Titles 13,210; Per Subs 68
Subject Interests: History, Iowa
Mem of Northeastern Iowa Regional Library System

TRURO

P TRURO PUBLIC LIBRARY,* 114 E Center St, 50257. SAN 305-7461. Tel: 515-765-4220. *Librn*, Doris Johnson
Founded 1929. Pop 407; Circ 8,134
Library Holdings: Bk Vols 13,965; Per Subs 83
Mem of Central Iowa Regional Library
Open Mon & Thurs 10-12 & 1-5, Sat 9-12

UNION

P UNION PUBLIC LIBRARY, 406 Commercial St, PO Box 146, 50258-0146. SAN 305-747X. Tel: 641-486-5561. FAX: 641-486-2284. E-Mail: unionlib@netins.net. *Librn*, Nancy Galloway
Founded 1968. Pop 1,500; Circ 50,000
Library Holdings: Bk Vols.19,000; Bk Titles 18,000
Mem of North Central Regional Library System
Open Mon 1-6, Tues 9-6, Wed & Thurs 1-8, Fri & Sat 10-5, Sun 1-5
Friends of the Library Group

UNIVERSITY PARK

CR VENNARD COLLEGE, Jessop-Bruner Library, 2300 Eighth Ave E, PO Box 29, 52595. SAN 305-7488. Tel: 641-673-4345, Ext 240. FAX: 641-673-8365. E-Mail: jessoplb@kdsinet. Web Site: www.vennard.edu/library.html. *Dir*, Rodney Birch; E-Mail: birchr@vennard.edu; Staff 2 (MLS 1, Non-MLS 1)
Founded 1975. Enrl 73; Fac 9; Highest Degree: Bachelor
Jul 2000-Jun 2001 Mats Exp $16,625, Books $12,225, Per/Ser (Incl. Access Fees) $4,000, Electronic Ref Mat (Incl. Access Fees) $400. Sal $38,630 (Prof $24,250)
Library Holdings: Bk Vols 19,720; Bk Titles 15,848; Per Subs 10; High Interest/Low Vocabulary Bk Vols 150
Special Collections: Wesleyan-Holiness Theol Coll
Automation Activity & Vendor Info: (Cataloging) Athena; (Circulation)

Athena
Database Vendor: OCLC - First Search
Partic in Iowa Private Academic Library Consortium; State Of Iowa Libraries Online Interlibrary Loan

URBANDALE

P URBANDALE PUBLIC LIBRARY,* 7305 Aurora Ave, 50322-1799. SAN 305-7496. Tel: 515-278-3945. FAX: 515-278-3918. Web Site: www.urbandale.lib.ia.us. *Dir*, Sara L Pearson; *Asst Dir*, Patricia Dimond; *Ch Servs*, Linda Weiser; *Media Spec*, Susan Clemmensen; *Cat, ILL*, Wendy Street; Staff 17 (MLS 4, Non-MLS 13)
Founded 1961. Pop 28,800; Circ 397,067
Jul 1998-Jun 1999 Income $897,499, State $40,000, City $735,191, County $12,308, Locally Generated Income $30,000. Mats Exp $97,530, Books $82,700, Per/Ser (Incl. Access Fees) $14,830. Sal $599,217
Library Holdings: Bk Vols 86,551; Per Subs 227
Mem of Central Iowa Regional Library
Partic in OCLC Online Computer Library Center, Inc
Friends of the Library Group

VAN HORNE

P VAN HORNE PUBLIC LIBRARY,* 114 Main St, PO Box 280, 52346-0280. SAN 305-750X. Tel: 319-228-8744. FAX: 319-228-8744. *Dir*, Nancy Pickering; *Asst Librn*, Judy Wallace
Pop 1,400; Circ 9,760
Library Holdings: Bk Vols 9,835
Open Mon-Wed & Fri 2-5, Thurs 9-12 & 6-8, Sat 9-12

VAN METER

P VAN METER PUBLIC LIBRARY,* 505 Grant St, PO Box 94, 50261. SAN 305-7518. Tel: 515-996-2435. FAX: 515-996-2207. *Dir*, Shirley L Headlee
Pop 747; Circ 9,743
Library Holdings: Bk Vols 8,000; Per Subs 21
Mem of Central Iowa Regional Library

VARINA

P VARINA PUBLIC LIBRARY,* 107 E Main St, PO Box 207, 50593-0207. SAN 305-7526. Tel: 712-288-6233. *Librn*, Norma Gehrig
Founded 1944. Pop 122; Circ 1,121
Library Holdings: Bk Vols 2,500; Bk Titles 1,285; Per Subs 7
Mem of Northwest Regional Library System
Open Wed 2-4 & Sat 1-4

VENTURA

P VENTURA PUBLIC LIBRARY, 7 W Ventura St, PO Box 200, 50482. SAN 305-7534. Tel: 641-829-4410. FAX: 641-829-4410. E-Mail: ventpl@netins.net. *Librn*, Cheryl Kapka; *Asst Librn*, Carol Clemens
Founded 1968. Pop 614; Circ 9,613
Jul 1998-Jun 1999 Income $42,056, State $3,187, City $22,150, County $10,119, Locally Generated Income $6,600. Mats Exp $22,056, Books $10,000, Per/Ser (Incl. Access Fees) $1,000, AV Equip $2,000, Other Print Mats $9,056. Sal $20,000
Library Holdings: Bk Titles 9,112; Per Subs 50; Bks on Deafness & Sign Lang 20
Publications: Abridged Reader's Guide
Mem of North Central Regional Library System
Home delivery available

VICTOR

P VICTOR PUBLIC LIBRARY,* 710 Second St, PO Box 686, 52347-0686. SAN 305-7542. Tel: 319-647-3646. FAX: 319-647-3646. E-Mail: vpl@netins.net. *Librn*, Elaine Roberts
Library Holdings: Bk Vols 11,480; Bk Titles 6,500; Per Subs 51

VILLISCA

P VILLISCA PUBLIC LIBRARY,* 204 S Third Ave, 50864. SAN 305-7550. Tel: 712-826-2452. E-Mail: villisca-lib@villisca.k12.ia.us. *Bibliog Instr, Librn, Online Servs*, Pat Means
Founded 1903. Pop 1,540; Circ 13,232
Library Holdings: Bk Vols 14,000; Per Subs 55
Special Collections: Chinese Coll, Native American Arrowhead Coll, Pitcher Coll
Mem of Southwest Iowa Regional Library System
Friends of the Library Group

VINTON

P VINTON PUBLIC LIBRARY, 510 Second Ave, 52349. SAN 305-7569. Tel: 319-472-4208. FAX: 319-472-2548. E-Mail: vintonpl@netins.net. *Dir*, Virginia Holsten; *Ch Servs*, Sharon Rhinehart
Founded 1902. Pop 5,103; Circ 103,157
Jul 1999-Jun 2000 Income $141,552, State $4,790, City $89,958, County $12,600, Locally Generated Income $1,204, Other $33,000. Mats Exp $15,240, Books $13,587, Per/Ser (Incl. Access Fees) $1,653. Sal $58,322
Library Holdings: Bk Vols 25,131; Per Subs 110
Automation Activity & Vendor Info: (Circulation) Sagebrush Corporation

VOLGA

P VOLGA PUBLIC LIBRARY, 505 Washington St, PO Box 131, 52077-0131. SAN 305-7577. Tel: 319-767-3511. FAX: 319-767-3511. *Librn*, Lorna Christeleit; Tel: 319-767-4182
Pop 375; Circ 4,537
Library Holdings: Bk Vols 5,500; Bk Titles 5,000; Per Subs 20
Mem of Northeastern Regional Libr Syst

WADENA

P WADENA PUBLIC LIBRARY,* 136 S Mill St, PO Box 19, 52169-0019. SAN 305-7585. Tel: 319-774-2039. FAX: 319-774-2039. E-Mail: wadenalibrar@mwci.net. *Librn*, Viola Lerch
Founded 1950. Pop 237; Circ 5,677
1998-1999 Income $13,950, City $2,850, County $3,119. Mats Exp $1,160, Books $934, Per/Ser (Incl. Access Fees) $226. Sal $600
Library Holdings: Bk Titles 8,164; Per Subs 20
Subject Interests: Education, History, Large type print
Mem of Northeastern Iowa Regional Library System

WALL LAKE

P WALL LAKE PUBLIC LIBRARY, 116 Main St, 51466-0068. SAN 305-7593. Tel: 712-664-2983. FAX: 712-664-2577. E-Mail: wll@netins.net. *Librn*, Jody Fischer
Founded 1909. Pop 950; Circ 7,200
Library Holdings: Bk Vols 10,000; Per Subs 45
Mem of Northwest Regional Library System
Open Mon-Wed 2-5, Thurs 2-6, Fri 11-3 & Sat 10-1

WALNUT

P WALNUT PUBLIC LIBRARY,* 224 Antique City Dr, 51577-0347. SAN 305-7607. Tel: 712-784-3533. E-Mail: wlntlib@netins.net. *Librn*, Kim Knapp
Pop 897; Circ 8,981
Library Holdings: Bk Vols 8,699; Per Subs 46
Mem of Southwest Iowa Regional Library System
Open Mon-Fri 12:30-4:30 & Sat 9-11 (winter hours), Mon-Fri 1-5 & Sat 9-11 (summer hours)

WAPELLO

P KECK MEMORIAL LIBRARY, 119 N Second St, 52653-1501. SAN 305-7615. Tel: 319-523-5261. FAX: 319-523-5261. *Librn*, Llewann Bryant
Pop 2,011; Circ 28,433
Library Holdings: Bk Vols 20,788; Per Subs 55
Mem of Southeastern Library Services
Open Mon & Wed 9-8, Tues, Thurs & Fri 9-5, Sat 9-12
Friends of the Library Group

WASHINGTON

P WASHINGTON PUBLIC LIBRARY,* 120 E Main St, 52353. SAN 305-7623. Tel: 319-653-2726. FAX: 319-653-2097. E-Mail: washlib@lisco.net. Web Site: www.washlib.net. *Dir*, Ellen Hampe
Founded 1878. Pop 13,750
Jul 1997-Jun 1998 Income $191,909. Mats Exp $27,245, Books $15,000, Per/Ser (Incl. Access Fees) $2,500. Sal $99,132
Library Holdings: Bk Titles 49,000; Per Subs 136
Subject Interests: Genealogy
Mem of Southeastern Regional Libr Syst

WASHTA

P WASHTA LIBRARY,* 1005 Fifth St, 51061-0121. SAN 305-7631. Tel: 712-447-6546. *Librn*, Becky Tuttle; *Head of Libr*, Nancy Parrott
Pop 320; Circ 9,605
Library Holdings: Bk Vols 9,327; Per Subs 18
Mem of Northwest Regional Library System
Friends of the Library Group

WATERLOO

M ALLEN MEMORIAL HOSPITAL LIBRARY,* 1825 Logan Ave, 50703. SAN 325-5905. Tel: 319-235-3681. FAX: 319-235-5280. E-Mail: amhlibr@netins.net. *Librn*, Paul Dahl
Library Holdings: Bk Titles 2,100
Subject Interests: Nursing
Special Collections: Radiological Coll
Branches:
BARRETT MEDICAL *Librn*, Paul Dahl
Library Holdings: Bk Titles 250
C W SEIBERT LIBRARY

S JOHN DEERE PRODUCT ENGINEERING CENTER LIBRARY, PO Box 8000, 50704. SAN 305-7658. Tel: 319-292-8020. FAX: 319-292-8028. *Librn*, Shirley Rong; Staff 1 (MLS 1)
Founded 1955
Library Holdings: Bk Vols 3,000; Bk Titles 3,500; Per Subs 45
Subject Interests: Engineering, Science/technology, Technology
Partic in OCLC Online Computer Library Center, Inc

S GROUT MUSEUM OF HISTORY & SCIENCE, Hans J Chryst Archival Library, 503 South St, 50701. SAN 305-7666. Tel: 319-234-6357. FAX: 319-236-0500. *Archivist*, Janice Taylor
Founded 1956
Library Holdings: Bk Titles 1,520
Subject Interests: Genealogy, Local history
Special Collections: Iowa Authors Coll, clippings & memoirs; Photogs; Rare Books Coll (Indian & Iowa History)

J HAWKEYE COMMUNITY COLLEGE LIBRARY,* 1501 E Orange Rd, 50704. SAN 305-7674. Tel: 319-296-4006. FAX: 319-296-9140. *Dir*, Robert Chittenden; *Librn*, Janet Dellinger; Staff 2 (MLS 2)
Founded 1970. Enrl 4,400; Fac 331
Jul 1998-Jun 1999 Income $368,824. Mats Exp $154,080, Books $88,624, Per/Ser (Incl. Access Fees) $40,814, Micro $4,006, Electronic Ref Mat (Incl. Access Fees) $20,636. Sal $162,103 (Prof $108,407)
Library Holdings: Bk Vols 30,193; Bk Titles 23,615; Per Subs 532
Subject Interests: Vocational education
Automation Activity & Vendor Info: (Cataloging) Innovative Interfaces Inc.; (Circulation) Innovative Interfaces Inc.; (OPAC) Innovative Interfaces Inc.; (Serials) Innovative Interfaces Inc.
Partic in BCR; Cedar Valley Libr Consortium

P NORTHEASTERN IOWA REGIONAL LIBRARY SYSTEM, 415 Commercial St, 50701-1317. SAN 305-7682. Tel: 319-233-1200. Toll Free Tel: 800-772-2023. FAX: 319-233-1964. Web Site: www.neirls.org. *Dir*, James E Sixta; E-Mail: sixta@www.neirls.org
Founded 1973
Publications: NE Directions (Newsletter)
Member Libraries: Allison Public Library; Alta Vista Public Library; Arlington Public Library; Aurora Public Library; Beaman Community Memorial Library; Benny Gambaiani Public Library; Carnegie-Stout Public Library; Cascade Public Library; Colesburg Public Library; Conrad Public Library; Decorah Public Library; Dubuque County Library; Dunkerton Public Library; Edgewood Public Library; Elizabeth Rasmussen Martin Memorial Library; Elma Public Library; Farmersburg Public Library; Fort Atkinson Public Library; Garnavillo Public Library; Greene Public Library; Harpers Ferry Public Library; Hawkeye Public Library; Independence Public Library; Ionia Community Library; Jesup Public Library; Kling Memorial Library; Kothe Memorial Library; Lansing Public Library; Lawler Public Library; Lime Springs Public Library; Manchester Public Library; Matthias M Hoffman Public Library; Maynard Community Library; Mc Gregor Public Library; Murphy Memorial Library; Nashua Public Library; New Albin Public Library; New Hampton Public Library; Oelwein Public Library; Ossian Public Library; Plainfield Public Library; Postville Public Library; Readlyn Community Library; Reinbeck Public Library; Robert W Barlow Memorial Library; Robey Memorial Library; Spillville Public Library; Strawberry Point Public Library; Sumner Public Library; Tripoli Public Library; Wadena Public Library; Waterloo Public Library; Waterville Public Library; Waucoma Public Library; Waverly Public Library; Wellsburg Public Library; West Union Community Library; Westgate Public Library; Winthrop Public Library
Partic in Iowa Computer Assisted Network

P WATERLOO PUBLIC LIBRARY, 415 Commercial St, 50701-1385. SAN 341-9851. Tel: 319-291-4521. Interlibrary Loan Service Tel: 319-291-4476. Circulation Tel: 319-291-4480. Reference Tel: 319-291-4476. FAX: 319-291-6736. E-Mail: wl10136@cedarnet.org. Web Site: www.wplwloo.lib.ia.us. *Dir*, Carol French Johnson; Tel: 319-291-4496, Fax: 319-291-9013, E-Mail: johnson@iren.net; *Ch Servs*, Paige Nangle; Tel: 319-287-3976, E-Mail: nangle@iren.net; *Circ*, Gwen Smith; *Tech Servs*, Sheryl Groskurth; Tel: 319-291-4521, E-Mail: sherylgr@wplwloo.lib.ia.us; *Coll Develop, Tech Servs*, Jane Martin; *ILL*, Susan Harnois; *Ref*, Kristi Anhalt; E-Mail: anhaltkr@server.silo.lib.ia.us; *Ref*, Teresa Dahlgren; E-Mail: tdahlgren@aol.com; *Ref*, Cindy Eubank; E-Mail: caeubank@cfu.net; *Ref*, Cathy Meyerhoff; E-Mail: meyerhof@wplwloo.lib.ia.us; *Ref*, Susan Pearson; *Business*, Kim Tovar; Tel: 319-291-4496, Fax: 319-291-9013, E-Mail: kimtovar@wplwloo.lib.ia.us; Staff 12 (MLS 9, Non-MLS 3)
Founded 1896. Pop 66,467; Circ 451,127
Jul 1999-Jun 2000 Income $2,066,231, State $59,155, City $1,768,426, County $54,578, Locally Generated Income $31,263, Other $152,809. Mats Exp $222,251, Books $161,508, Per/Ser (Incl. Access Fees) $7,268, Micro $5,410, Electronic Ref Mat (Incl. Access Fees) $48,065. Sal $1,004,372
Library Holdings: Bk Vols 180,127; Bk Titles 145,986; Per Subs 599
Automation Activity & Vendor Info: (Acquisitions) Innovative Interfaces Inc.; (Cataloging) Innovative Interfaces Inc.; (Circulation) Innovative Interfaces Inc.
Mem of Northeastern Iowa Regional Library System
Partic in Cedar Valley Libr Consortium
Open Mon-Thurs 9-9, Fri & Sat 9-5, Sun 1-5; Closed Sunday of Memorial Day weekend to first Sunday in October
Friends of the Library Group

S WATERLOO-CEDAR FALLS COURIER, Courier Newsroom Library, W Park & Commercial, PO Box 540, 50704-0540. SAN 374-549X. Tel: 319-291-1477. FAX: 319-291-2069. E-Mail: wcfcourier@aol.com. Web Site: www.wcfcourier.com. *Librn*, Teresa Dahlgren; Staff 1 (MLS 1)
Founded 1940
Library Holdings: Bk Vols 100
Special Collections: Waterloo/Cedar Falls Courier from 1859 to present - Local History, clippings, computer, microfilm
Function: Newspaper reference library

WATERVILLE

P WATERVILLE PUBLIC LIBRARY,* 82 Main St, PO Box 68, 52170. SAN 376-5245. Tel: 319-535-7115, 319-535-7295. FAX: 319-535-7295. *Librn*, Michelle Tryggestad
Jul 1997-Jun 1998 Income $6,620. Mats Exp $1,504
Library Holdings: Bk Vols 4,400; Bk Titles 4,200; Per Subs 12
Mem of Northeastern Iowa Regional Library System

WAUCOMA

P WAUCOMA PUBLIC LIBRARY,* 113 First Ave, PO Box 131, 52171. SAN 321-5180. Tel: 319-776-4131. FAX: 319-776-4131. E-Mail: waucomalib@sbtek.net. *Librn*, Susan Zeigler
Founded 1978. Pop 699; Circ 5,963
Jul 1997-Jun 1998 Income $10,000. Mats Exp $3,500, Books $2,422, Per/Ser (Incl. Access Fees) $195. Sal $3,800
Library Holdings: Bk Titles 8,636; Per Subs 40
Mem of Northeastern Iowa Regional Library System
Open Mon, Wed & Thurs 2-5, Tues 9-11 & 2-5, Fri 3:30-7 & Sat 9-12

WAUKEE

P WAUKEE PUBLIC LIBRARY, (WPL), 500 Sixth St, PO Box 68, 50263. SAN 305-7690. Tel: 515-987-1280. FAX: 515-987-5262. E-Mail: wkeelib@netins.net. *Dir*, Linda Mack; Staff 8 (Non-MLS 8)
Pop 5,000; Circ 55,000
Jul 2000-Jun 2001 Income $150,500, State $5,000, City $137,000, County $8,500. Mats Exp $15,400, Books $14,000, Per/Ser (Incl. Access Fees) $1,400. Sal $89,000 (Prof $55,000)
Library Holdings: Bk Vols 18,500; Per Subs 50
Automation Activity & Vendor Info: (Cataloging) Sagebrush Corporation; (Circulation) Sagebrush Corporation
Database Vendor: OCLC - First Search
Publications: City newsletter
Mem of Central Iowa Regional Library
Friends of the Library Group

WAUKON

P ROBEY MEMORIAL LIBRARY, 401 First Ave NW, 52172-1803. SAN 305-7704. Tel: 319-568-4424. FAX: 319-568-5026. E-Mail: robeylib@rconnect.com. Web Site: homepage3.rconnect.com/robeylib. *Dir*, Callie Irons
Founded 1920. Pop 4,863; Circ 50,948
Jul 1998-Jun 1999 Income $94,893, State $478, City $63,734, Federal $515, County $25,994, Locally Generated Income $3,207, Other $965. Mats Exp $20,317, Books $15,867, Per/Ser (Incl. Access Fees) $4,098, Other Print Mats $70, Electronic Ref Mat (Incl. Access Fees) $282. Sal $56,641 (Prof $26,915)
Library Holdings: Bk Vols 32,600; Bk Titles 27,000; Per Subs 139
Subject Interests: Am artists, Iowa
Special Collections: American Artists; Iowa Coll; Large Print Coll
Automation Activity & Vendor Info: (Cataloging) Sagebrush Corporation; (Circulation) Sagebrush Corporation
Mem of Northeastern Iowa Regional Library System
Open Mon-Thurs 10-8, Fri 10-6 & Sat 10-4

WAVERLY

S CUNA MUTUAL LIFE INSURANCE COMPANY LIBRARY,* 2000 Heritage Way, 50677. SAN 325-5034. Tel: 319-352-1000, Ext 2361. FAX: 319-352-5843. *Librn*, Marietta K Sargeant
Jan 1998-Dec 1999 Mats Exp $5,000, Books $3,200, Per/Ser (Incl. Access Fees) $1,800. Sal $40,000 (Prof $31,000)
Library Holdings: Bk Vols 3,000; Per Subs 300
Subject Interests: Bus, Ins, Legal
Restriction: Staff use only
Partic in Dialog Corporation; OCLC Online Computer Library Center, Inc

C WARTBURG COLLEGE LIBRARY,* 222 Ninth St NW, 50677-0903. SAN 305-7712. Tel: 319-352-8500. Interlibrary Loan Service Tel: 319-352-8258. FAX: 319-352-8312. E-Mail: asklibrarian@wartburg.edu. Web Site: www.wartburg.edu/library/. *Dir*, Jill Gremmels; Tel: 319-352-8462, E-Mail: gremmelsg@wartburg.edu; *Bibliog Instr*, Randall Schroeder; Tel: 319-352-8348, E-Mail: schroederr@wartburg.edu; *Cat*, Pam Madden; Tel: 319-352-8461, E-Mail: madden@wartburg.edu; *Publ Servs*, Brian Nevermann; Tel: 319-352-8460, E-Mail: nevermann@wartburg.edu; *Archivist*, Marianne Beck; Tel: 319-352-8457, E-Mail: beck@wartburg.edu; *Acq*, Susan Ohrt; Tel: 319-352-8244, E-Mail: ohrt@wartburg.edu; *Per*, Marnie Hubbard; Tel: 319-352-8426, E-Mail: hubbardm@wartburg.edu; *ILL*, Paula Hemingson; Tel: 319-352-8258, E-Mail: hemingson@wartburg.edu; *Publ Servs*, Eileen Myers; Tel: 319-352-8464, E-Mail: myerse@wartburg.edu; *Circ*, Linda Hennings; Tel: 319-352-8524, E-Mail: hennings@wartburg.edu; Staff 10 (MLS 5, Non-MLS 5)
Founded 1852. Enrl 1,546; Fac 93; Highest Degree: Bachelor
Jun 1998-May 1999 Income Parent Institution $743,442. Mats Exp $243,890, Books $61,674, Per/Ser (Incl. Access Fees) $87,337, Presv $8,203, Micro $5,986, Other Print Mats $37,116, Electronic Ref Mat (Incl. Access Fees) $43,574. Sal $221,275 (Prof $157,804)
Library Holdings: Bk Titles 133,910; Per Subs 760
Special Collections: Archives of Iowa Broadcasting History; College Archives; Koob Coll; Namibia Coll
Automation Activity & Vendor Info: (Cataloging) epixtech, inc.; (Circulation) epixtech, inc.; (Course Reserve) epixtech, inc.; (OPAC) epixtech, inc.; (Serials) epixtech, inc.
Database Vendor: Lexis-Nexis, OCLC - First Search, Silverplatter Information Inc.
Partic in Bibliographical Center For Research, Rocky Mountain Region, Inc; Iowa Private Academic Library Consortium

P WAVERLY PUBLIC LIBRARY, (WAVPL), 1500 W Bremer Ave, 50677-3299. SAN 305-7720. Tel: 319-352-1223. FAX: 319-352-0872. E-Mail: waverly@silo.lib.ia.us. Web Site: www.waverlyia.com. *Dir*, Patricia R Coffie
Founded 1859
Jul 1999-Jun 2000 Income $420,954, State $9,500, City $375,654, Federal $2,000, County $24,000, Locally Generated Income $9,800. Mats Exp $56,900, Books $35,300, Per/Ser (Incl. Access Fees) $7,000, Micro $200, Electronic Ref Mat (Incl. Access Fees) $6,000. Sal $236,057 (Prof $100,000)
Library Holdings: Bk Vols 62,000; Bk Titles 60,000; Per Subs 162; High Interest/Low Vocabulary Bk Vols 100
Automation Activity & Vendor Info: (Cataloging) Gaylord; (Circulation) Gaylord
Mem of Northeastern Iowa Regional Library System
Open Mon-Thurs 10-8, Fri & Sat 10-5, Sun 2-5
Friends of the Library Group

WEBB

P WEBB PUBLIC LIBRARY,* 124 Main St, PO Box 97, 51366-0097. SAN 305-7739. Tel: 712-838-7719. E-Mail: webblibry@netins.net. *Librn*, Linda R Adams
Pop 222; Circ 3,487
Library Holdings: Bk Titles 8,000; Per Subs 35
Mem of Northwest Regional Library System
Open Tues & Thurs 2-5, Wed, Fri & Sat 9-11
Friends of the Library Group

WEBSTER CITY

P KENDALL YOUNG LIBRARY,* 1201 Willson Ave, 50595-2294. SAN 305-7755. Tel: 515-832-9100. FAX: 515-832-9102. E-Mail: info@kendall-young.lib.ia.us. *Dir*, Cynthia A Weiss; *Ad Servs*, Ketta Lubberstedt; *Ch Servs*, Linda Brown; Tel: 515-832-9101; Staff 15 (MLS 3, Non-MLS 12)
Founded 1898. Pop 16,071
Jan 1998-Dec 1998 Income (Main Library Only) $250,854, County $20,060, Locally Generated Income $4,125, Other $224,445. Mats Exp $38,590, Books $25,714, Per/Ser (Incl. Access Fees) $5,223. Sal $151,863 (Prof $65,912)
Library Holdings: Bk Vols 48,091; Per Subs 124
Subject Interests: Genealogy, Local history
Special Collections: Clark R Mollenhoff Coll; MacKinlay Kantor Coll
Automation Activity & Vendor Info: (Cataloging) TLC; (Circulation) Athena
Database Vendor: OCLC - First Search
Mem of North Central Regional Library System
Friends of the Library Group

WELLMAN

P WELLMAN SCOFIELD PUBLIC LIBRARY, 711 Fourth St, PO Box 420, 52356. SAN 305-7763. Tel: 319-646-6858. FAX: 319-646-6561. E-Mail: scofield@netins.net. Web Site: www.netins.net/showcase.wellmanpl/. *Dir*, Sandra L Aggson
Pop 1,085; Circ 26,174
Library Holdings: Bk Titles 15,000; Per Subs 40
Automation Activity & Vendor Info: (Circulation) Sagebrush Corporation
Database Vendor: OCLC - First Search
Function: ILL available
Open Mon & Thurs 10-7, Wed 2-7, Tues & Fri 2-5, Sat 10-4
Friends of the Library Group

WELLSBURG

P WELLSBURG PUBLIC LIBRARY, 515 N Adams, PO Box 489, 50680. SAN 305-7771. Tel: 641-869-5234. FAX: 641-869-5234. E-Mail: wlsbrgpl01@hotmail.com. *Dir*, Laurie Aude; *Asst Librn*, Dee Lindaman; *Circ*, Joyce Meyeraan; Staff 2 (Non-MLS 2)
Pop 660
Jul 2000-Jun 2001 Income $44,184, State $1,300, City $21,000, County $16,769, Locally Generated Income $3,640, Other $1,475. Mats Exp $6,400, Books $5,000, Per/Ser (Incl. Access Fees) $800, AV Equip $600. Sal $24,438
Library Holdings: Bk Titles 11,000; Per Subs 35
Special Collections: Ortssippen books (German genealogy)
Mem of Northeastern Iowa Regional Library System

WESLEY

P WESLEY PUBLIC LIBRARY,* 206 Main, PO Box 37, 50483. SAN 305-778X. Tel: 515-679-4214. FAX: 515-679-4214. E-Mail: wpl@ncn.net. *Dir*, Anne Nygaard; *Librn*, Teresa Lappe
Founded 1950. Pop 444; Circ 9,849
Jul 1997-Jun 1998 Income $16,211, State $367, City $7,500, County $6,854, Locally Generated Income $1,490. Mats Exp $3,956, Books $2,909, Per/Ser (Incl. Access Fees) $1,047. Sal $7,378
Library Holdings: Bk Vols 7,091; Bk Titles 6,877; Per Subs 44
Mem of North Central Regional Library System
Open Mon 1:30-8, Wed 9-11:30 & 1:30-8, Fri 1-5 & Sat 9-11:30

WEST BEND

P WEST BEND PUBLIC LIBRARY,* 316 S Broadway, PO Box 46, 50597-0046. SAN 305-7798. Tel: 515-887-6411. FAX: 515-887-6412. E-Mail: wbpl@ncn.net. *Librn*, Linda Friedow
Founded 1939. Pop 902; Circ 54,000
Jul 1998-Jun 1999 Income $53,386, City $39,045, County $11,641, Locally Generated Income $2,700. Mats Exp $10,500, Books $6,500, Per/Ser (Incl. Access Fees) $1,000, Presv $500, AV Equip $2,500. Sal $29,440
Library Holdings: Bk Vols 10,205; Bk Titles 10,006; Per Subs 75
Automation Activity & Vendor Info: (Cataloging) Follett; (Circulation) Follett; (OPAC) Follett
Mem of North Central Regional Library System

WEST BRANCH

S NATIONAL ARCHIVES & RECORDS ADMINISTRATION, Herbert Hoover Presidential Library, 210 Parkside Dr, PO Box 488, 52358. SAN 305-781X. Tel: 319-643-5301. FAX: 319-643-5825. E-Mail: library@hoover.nara.gov. Web Site: www.hoover.nara.gov. *Dir*, Timothy Walch; E-Mail: timothy.walch@hoover.nara.gov; *Librn*, Patrick Wildenberg
Founded 1962
Library Holdings: Bk Titles 21,141; Per Subs 23
Subject Interests: Economics, History, Political science
Special Collections: Bourke Hickenlooper; Clark R Mollenhoff; Gerald P Nye; Hanford MacNider; Herbert Hoover (1895-1964); Hugh R Wilson; James P Goodrich; James Westbrook Pegler; Laura Ingalls Wilder; Lewis L Strauss; Nathan W MacChesney; Robert E Wood; Rose Wilder Lane; Verne Marshall; Walter Trohan; William C Mullendore; William P MacCracken; William R Castle & others
Publications: Historical Materials in the Herbert Hoover Presidential Library
Partic in RLIN
Friends of the Library Group

P WEST BRANCH PUBLIC LIBRARY,* 300 N Downey, PO Box 460, 52358. SAN 305-7801. Tel: 319-643-2633. FAX: 319-643-2845. E-Mail: wbpl@netins.net. *Librn*, Jon Richardson
Pop 1,897; Circ 25,311
Library Holdings: Bk Titles 28,000; Per Subs 55
Friends of the Library Group

WEST BURLINGTON

M GREAT RIVER MEDICAL CENTER LIBRARY, (Formerly Burlington Medical Center), 1221 S Gear Ave, 52655-1679. SAN 305-2435. Tel: 319-768-4075. FAX: 319-786-4080. *Librn*, Judy Hawk; E-Mail: jhawk@grhs.net; Staff 1 (MLS 1)
Library Holdings: Bk Vols 3,500; Per Subs 283
Partic in Medline

C SOUTHEASTERN COMMUNITY COLLEGE LIBRARY-NORTH CAMPUS, Yohe Memorial Library, 1015 S Gear Ave, 52655-0180. (Mail add: PO Box 180, 52655-0180), SAN 341-9916. Tel: 319-752-2731, Ext 8240. FAX: 319-753-0322. Web Site: www.secc.cc.ia.us. *Dir*, Brian P McAtee; E-Mail: bmcatee@secc.cc.ia.us; *Librn*, Kyle D Winward; E-Mail: kwinward@secc.cc.ia.us; Staff 7 (MLS 3, Non-MLS 4)
Founded 1920. Enrl 2,000; Fac 80
Jul 2000-Jun 2001 Income (Main and Other College/University Libraries) $368,523. Mats Exp $99,030, Books $31,000, Per/Ser (Incl. Access Fees) $27,000, AV Equip $13,200. Sal $269,493
Library Holdings: Bk Vols 30,000; Per Subs 300
Subject Interests: Anthropology, Art and architecture, Environmental studies
Automation Activity & Vendor Info: (Cataloging) Gaylord; (Circulation) Gaylord; (OPAC) Gaylord
Database Vendor: Ebsco - EbscoHost, OCLC - First Search
Mem of Southeastern Regional Libr Syst
Partic in Iowa Computer Assisted Network; Iowa Libr Information Teletype Exchange
Departmental Libraries:
FRED KARRE MEMORIAL LIBRARY-SOUTH CAMPUS, 335 Messenger Rd, PO Box 6007, Keokuk, 52632. SAN 328-9141. Tel: 319-524-3221, Ext 8456. E-Mail: sclib1@secc.cc.ia.us. Web Site: www.secc.cc.ia.us/library/libindex.htm. *Librn*, Elizabeth Gardner; Staff 1 (MLS 1)
Library Holdings: Bk Vols 8,691; Per Subs 75
Subject Interests: Art
Partic in BCS; SE Regional Libr Servs; State Of Iowa Libraries Online Interlibrary Loan

WEST DES MOINES

P WEST DES MOINES PUBLIC LIBRARY,* 4000 George M Mills Civic Pkwy, 50265-2049. SAN 305-7836. Tel: 515-222-3400. FAX: 515-222-3401. *Dir*, Ray Vignovich; E-Mail: rvignovich@city.west-des-moines.ia.us; *Cat*, Leo Kriz; *Circ*, Carol Griffith; *Commun Servs*, Ellen Smith; *Ch Servs*, Judy Proksa
Founded 1940. Pop 41,000; Circ 616,000
Jul 1999-Jun 2000 Income $1,535,400. Mats Exp $266,000, Books $250,000, Per/Ser (Incl. Access Fees) $16,000. Sal $969,900
Library Holdings: Bk Vols 129,788; Bk Titles 104,887; Per Subs 332
Database Vendor: epixtech, inc.
Publications: Cover to Cover (newsletter)
Mem of Central Iowa Regional Library
Friends of the Library Group

WEST LIBERTY

P WEST LIBERTY FREE PUBLIC LIBRARY,* 400 N Spencer, 52776. SAN 305-7844. Tel: 319-627-2084. FAX: 319-627-2135. E-Mail: libwl@netins.net. Web Site: www.netins.net/showcase/wlibolib. *Dir*, Janette McMahon
Pop 2,900; Circ 21,000
1999-2000 Income $78,300, City $71,800, County $6,500. Mats Exp $11,300, Books $10,000, Per/Ser (Incl. Access Fees) $1,300. Sal $38,600 (Prof $12,600)
Library Holdings: Bk Titles 16,000; Per Subs 35
Special Collections: Spanish & Laosian materials
Mem of Southeastern Library Services
Friends of the Library Group

WEST POINT

P WEST POINT PUBLIC LIBRARY,* 311 Ave D, 52656. SAN 305-7852. Tel: 319-837-6315. FAX: 319-837-6315. E-Mail: wppublib@interl.net. *Librn*, Cathy Schwartz
Founded 1946. Pop 1,133; Circ 25,139
Library Holdings: Bk Titles 10,000; Per Subs 60
Mem of Southeastern Library Services

WEST UNION

S FAYETTE COUNTY HISTORICAL SOCIETY LIBRARY, 100 N Walnut, 52175-1347. SAN 371-7763. Tel: 319-422-5797. Web Site: www.rootsweb.com/-infayett/. *Asst Librn*, Ruth Brooks
Founded 1975
Library Holdings: Bk Titles 200
Open Nov-Apr, Mon-Fri 10-3, May-Oct, Mon-Fri 10-4

P WEST UNION COMMUNITY LIBRARY, (Formerly Heiserman Memorial Library), 210 N Vine St, 52175. SAN 305-7860. Tel: 319-422-3103. FAX: 319-422-3103. E-Mail: wulibrary@trxinc.com. *Dir*, Kathryn E Meyer
Pop 2,490; Circ 26,330
Special Collections: Lincoln Coll
Mem of Northeastern Iowa Regional Library System

WESTGATE

P WESTGATE PUBLIC LIBRARY,* PO Box 10, 50681-0010. SAN 305-7887. Tel: 319-578-5151. FAX: 318-578-5151. *Librn*, Mary Belden
Pop 263; Circ 6,510
Library Holdings: Bk Titles 6,110; Per Subs 30
Mem of Northeastern Iowa Regional Library System

WESTSIDE

P WESTSIDE PUBLIC LIBRARY, 150 Main St, 51467-0163. SAN 305-7895. Tel: 712-663-4493. *Librn*, Betty Nobiling
Founded 1927
Jul 2000-Jun 2001 Income $3,500, City $1,000, County $2,500. Mats Exp $2,495, Books $2,000, Per/Ser (Incl. Access Fees) $100, Electronic Ref Mat (Incl. Access Fees) $395
Library Holdings: Bk Vols 7,000
Mem of Northwest Regional Library System

WHAT CHEER

P WHAT CHEER PUBLIC LIBRARY,* 308 S Barnes St, 50268-0008. SAN 321-1770. Tel: 515-634-2859. E-Mail: watchlib@gte. *Librn*, Janis Collins; *Asst Librn*, Ginger Grubb; Staff 1 (Non-MLS 1)
Founded 1897. Pop 803
Library Holdings: Bk Titles 4,600
Mem of Southeastern Library Services
Open Mon ll:30-5:30, Wed 8:30-3:30, Thurs 1:30-5:30, Sat 9-11

WHEATLAND

P CURTIS MEMORIAL LIBRARY,* 205 Jefferson St E, PO Box 429, 52777. SAN 320-8303. Tel: 319-374-1534. *Librn*, Marilynn Hass
Pop 840; Circ 5,665
Library Holdings: Bk Vols 5,800; Bk Titles 5,600
Subject Interests: Local history
Special Collections: Old Local Newspaper Coll (1860-1962)-microfilm
Mem of Southern Maine Library District
Open Mon-Thur 2-6 & Sat 9-12

WHITING

P WHITING PUBLIC LIBRARY, 407 Whittier, PO Box 288, 51063-0288. SAN 305-7917. Tel: 712-458-2612. FAX: 712-458-2612. E-Mail: whting@pionet.net. *Dir*, Margaret A Polly
Founded 1912. Pop 801; Circ 18,578
Jul 1999-Jun 2000 Income $53,101, State $2,730, City $37,113, County $3,587, Locally Generated Income $9,680. Mats Exp $15,456, Books $7,271, Per/Ser (Incl. Access Fees) $960, AV Equip $1,753, Electronic Ref Mat (Incl. Access Fees) $5,472. Sal $26,930
Library Holdings: Bk Vols 13,978; Bk Titles 13,939; Per Subs 73
Mem of Northwest Regional Library System
Friends of the Library Group

WHITTEMORE

P WHITTEMORE PUBLIC LIBRARY, Fourth & Broad, PO Box 356, 50598-0356. SAN 305-7925. Tel: 515-884-2680. FAX: 515-884-2323. E-Mail: whittpl@ncn.net. *Librn*, Sandy Long
Founded 1940. Pop 535; Circ 26,155
Jul 1999-Jun 2000 Income $45,922, State $2,845, City $35,063, County $8,014. Mats Exp $6,415, Books $5,180, Per/Ser (Incl. Access Fees) $1,235. Sal $22,796
Library Holdings: Bk Vols 14,606; Per Subs 61
Automation Activity & Vendor Info: (Circulation) Follett
Mem of North Central Regional Library System
Friends of the Library Group

WILLIAMS

P WILLIAMS PUBLIC LIBRARY,* 216 Main St, PO Box 36, 50271. SAN 305-7933. Tel: 515-854-2643. FAX: 515-854-2643. E-Mail: willpl@ncn.net. *Librn*, Patsy Weldin
Pop 410; Circ 5,907
Library Holdings: Bk Titles 8,727; Per Subs 36
Mem of North Central Regional Library System

WILLIAMSBURG

P WILLIAMSBURG PUBLIC LIBRARY,* 214 W State St, PO Box 48, 52361. SAN 305-7941. Tel: 319-668-1195. FAX: 319-668-9621. E-Mail: lkh@avalon.net, wpl@avalon.net. *Librn*, Loretta Hanson; *Asst Librn*, Carol Uhlman; *Ch Servs*, Erin Gritsch
Founded 1934. Pop 2,033; Circ 37,747
Library Holdings: Bk Titles 19,951; Per Subs 73
Mem of East Central Regional Library
Friends of the Library Group

WILTON

P WILTON PUBLIC LIBRARY,* 106 E Fourth St, 52778. (Mail add: PO Box 447, 52778-0447), SAN 305-795X. Tel: 319-732-2583. FAX: 319-732-2593. E-Mail: wplstaff@netins.net. *Dir*, Ruth Peterson
Founded 1935. Pop 2,822; Circ 30,741
Library Holdings: Bk Vols 16,580; Per Subs 85
Subject Interests: Local history
Special Collections: Wilton Advocate (high school yrbk)
Mem of Southeastern Library Services
Open Mon & Wed 2-8, Tues & Thurs 10-6, Fri 2-6, Sat 10-3
Friends of the Library Group

WINFIELD

P WINFIELD PUBLIC LIBRARY, 112 W Ash, 52659-9511. SAN 305-7968. Tel: 319-257-3247. Interlibrary Loan Service Tel: 800-397-0029. FAX: 319-257-3247. E-Mail: winpubliblm@lisco.net. *Dir*, Mary Wintermeyer; *Asst Dir*, Janet Everett; Staff 2 (MLS 2)
Founded 1916. Pop 2,200; Circ 8,171
Jul 1998-Jun 1999 Income $59,191, State $658, City $23,000, County $7,533, Locally Generated Income $28,000. Mats Exp $3,565, Books $2,418, Per/Ser (Incl. Access Fees) $1,147. Sal $14,022
Library Holdings: Bk Titles 24,344; Per Subs 58
Subject Interests: Agriculture, Education, Religion
Mem of Southeastern Library Services

WINTERSET

P WINTERSET PUBLIC LIBRARY, 124 W Court Ave, 50273-1545. SAN 305-7976. Tel: 515-462-1731. FAX: 515-462-4196. *Librn*, Helen E Sellers; *Ch Servs*, Ann Newbury; Staff 2 (Non-MLS 2)
Founded 1891. Pop 12,483; Circ 100,188
Jul 1999-Jun 2000 Income $175,403, State $4,887, City $137,490, County $27,032, Locally Generated Income $370. Mats Exp Books $18,000. Sal $124,511
Library Holdings: Bk Vols 44,967
Subject Interests: Antiques, Genealogy
Special Collections: John Wayne Videos; Madison County Court Records; Madison County Land Records; Madison County Probate Records; Old Madison County Newspaper Coll, microfilm
Automation Activity & Vendor Info: (Circulation) SIRSI; (OPAC) SIRSI
Database Vendor: OCLC - First Search
Mem of Central Iowa Regional Library
Partic in OCLC Online Computer Library Center, Inc
Friends of the Library Group

WINTHROP

P WINTHROP PUBLIC LIBRARY, (WPL), 354 W Madison, PO Box 159, 50682-0159. SAN 305-7984. Tel: 319-935-3374. FAX: 319-935-3574. E-Mail: winlib@netins.net. *Dir*, Missy Mayfield-Cook; Staff 3 (Non-MLS 3)
Pop 867; Circ 12,399
Library Holdings: Bk Titles 9,250; Per Subs 16
Mem of Northeastern Iowa Regional Library System
Open Mon 1-8, Tues-Fri 1-5 & Sat 9-12

WODEN

P WODEN PUBLIC LIBRARY, 304 Main St, PO Box 156, 50484. SAN 305-7992. Tel: 641-926-5716. FAX: 641-926-5716. *Librn*, Bertha Smidt; *Asst Librn*, Theresa Rudisill
Founded 1960. Pop 250; Circ 6,895
Jul 1998-Jun 1999 Income $14,246, City $5,000, County $8,112, Other $1,134. Mats Exp $14,471, Books $2,478, Per/Ser (Incl. Access Fees) $250. Sal $6,891
Library Holdings: Bk Titles 4,380; Per Subs 43
Mem of North Central Regional Library System

WOODBINE

P WOODBINE PUBLIC LIBRARY,* 58 Fifth St, 51579. SAN 305-800X. Tel: 712-647-2750. FAX: 712-647-2750. E-Mail: carnegie@pionet.net. *Librn*, Connie Ball
Pop 1,463; Circ 21,096
Library Holdings: Bk Titles 24,000; Per Subs 67
Mem of Southwest Iowa Regional Library System
Open Tues, Wed & Fri 10-5, Thurs 10-7, Sat 10-3

WOODWARD

P WOODWARD PUBLIC LIBRARY, 118 S Main St, PO Box 510, 50276-0510. SAN 305-8018. Tel: 515-438-2636. FAX: 515-438-2636. E-Mail: wpublib@netins.net. *Dir*, Judy Grimes; *Librn*, Janice Nelson; *Asst Librn*, Amy Clark
Founded 1946. Pop 1,197; Circ 13,689
Jul 1999-Jun 2000 Income $38,394, State $3,057, City $28,030, County $4,553, Other $2,754. Mats Exp $9,339, Books $8,588, Per/Ser (Incl. Access Fees) $751. Sal $20,806
Library Holdings: Bk Vols 14,910; Per Subs 65
Mem of Central Iowa Regional Library

WOODWARD STATE HOSPITAL-SCHOOL
S CAMPUS LIBRARY, 1251 334th St, 50276. SAN 341-9975. Tel: 515-438-2600, Ext 298. FAX: 515-438-3122. *Librn*, Joanne Anderson; E-Mail: janders3@dhs.state.ia.us
Founded 1969
Library Holdings: Bk Titles 1,600; Per Subs 18
Subject Interests: Special education

WYOMING

P WYOMING PUBLIC LIBRARY, 109 W Main St, PO Box 139, 52362-0139. SAN 305-8026. Tel: 319-488-3975. FAX: 319-488-3975. E-Mail: wlibrary@netins.net.
Founded 1947. Pop 878; Circ 16,135
Jul 1998-Jun 1999 Income $17,046, State $109, City $3,110, County $5,980. Mats Exp $2,506, Books $2,296, Per/Ser (Incl. Access Fees) $210. Sal $6,141
Library Holdings: Bk Titles 15,107; Per Subs 24
Mem of East Central Regional Library
Open Tues 2-5, Thurs 9-11, Fri 2-6, Sat 9-12 (temporary hours)

ZEARING

P ZEARING PUBLIC LIBRARY,* 101 E Main, 50278-0197. SAN 305-8034. Tel: 515-487-7888. FAX: 515-487-7888. *Librn*, Jean Watts; E-Mail: jeanwatt@netins.net
Founded 1975. Pop 630; Circ 7,270
Library Holdings: Bk Vols 7,000; Per Subs 15
Subject Interests: Iowa, World War II
Mem of Central Regional Libr Syst
Open Mon, Tues, Thurs & Fri 3-7, Wed 10-7, Sat 9-12

KANSAS

Date of Statistics: FY 1999
Population, 1999: 2,629,067
Population Served by Public Libraries: 2,628,484
  Unserved: 583
Total Volumes in Public Libraries: 9,836,815
  Volumes Per Capita: 3.7
Total Public Library Circulation: 20,428,087
  Circulation Per Capita: 9.49
Total Public Library Income: $64,590,782
  Expenditures Per Capita: $30.02
  Source of Income: Public funds, donations, federal & state aid
Number of County & Multi-County (Regional) Libraries: 35
Number of Bookmobiles in State: 10
Grants-in-Aid to Public Libraries:
State Aid: $2,320,000 (includes $693,909 in ILDP Resource Grants)

ABILENE

P ABILENE FREE PUBLIC LIBRARY,* 209 NW Fourth, 67410-2690. SAN 305-8042. Tel: 785-263-3082. FAX: 785-263-2274. Web Site: www.abelineks.com. *Dir*, Bruce Chance; *Ch Servs*, Betty Holtzen
Founded 1908. Pop 7,378; Circ 93,420
Library Holdings: Bk Vols 70,250; Per Subs 150
Special Collections: Mamie Eisenhower Doll Coll; WPA Doll Coll
Mem of North Central Kansas Libraries System
Partic in OCLC Online Computer Library Center, Inc
Special Services for the Deaf - TTY machine
Special Services - Job service computer; public access computer center
Friends of the Library Group

S MUSEUM OF INDEPENDENT TELEPHONE LIBRARY, 412 S Campbell, 67410. SAN 326-0984. Tel: 785-263-2681. FAX: 785-263-0380. E-Mail: dchs@ikansas. Web Site: www.geocities.com/museumofindependenttelephony. *Dir*, Robin Sherck
Founded 1973
Library Holdings: Bk Vols 600; Per Subs 10
Restriction: By appointment only, Open to public for reference only

S NATIONAL ARCHIVES & RECORDS ADMINISTRATION, Dwight D Eisenhower Library, 200 SE Fourth St, 67410-2900. SAN 305-8050. Tel: 785-263-4751. Toll Free Tel: 877-746-4453. FAX: 785-263-4218. E-Mail: library@eisenhower.nara.gov. Web Site: www.eisenhower.utexas.edu/. *Dir*, Daniel D Holt; Staff 32 (MLS 20, Non-MLS 12)
Founded 1962
Library Holdings: Bk Vols 25,500; Per Subs 88
Subject Interests: Presidents (US), World War II
Special Collections: World War II & Eisenhower Administration Manuscript Coll
Publications: Overview (newsletter)
Friends of the Library Group

ALLEN

P LYON COUNTY, LIBRARY DISTRICT ONE,* PO Box 447, 66833-0447. SAN 320-4774. Tel: 316-528-3451. E-Mail: library@satelephone.com. *Librn*, Shirley Williams
Founded 1976. Pop 1,104; Circ 5,774
Library Holdings: Bk Titles 8,889
Special Collections: Microfilms of old local newspapers

ALMENA

P ALMENA CITY LIBRARY, 415 Main, PO Box 153, 67622-0153. SAN 320-1880. Tel: 785-669-2336. E-Mail: almenlib@ruraltel.net. *In Charge*, Clara Irene Oman; Staff 1 (Non-MLS 1)
Founded 1903. Pop 373; Circ 4,313
Library Holdings: Bk Vols 4,500; Bk Titles 4,500; Per Subs 10
Subject Interests: General
Function: ILL available
Mem of Northwest Kansas Library System
Open Tues & Thurs 2-5, Sat 9-12

ALTAMONT

P ALTAMONT PUBLIC LIBRARY, PO Box 218, 67330. SAN 305-8077. Tel: 316-784-5530. *Librn*, Freda Edwards; Staff 1 (Non-MLS 1)
Founded 1928. Pop 1,090; Circ 15,366
Library Holdings: Bk Vols 11,366; Per Subs 45
Mem of Southeast Kansas Library System
Open Mon-Fri 1-5pm
Friends of the Library Group

ALTOONA

P ALTOONA PUBLIC LIBRARY,* 714 Main St, PO Box 68, 66710-0068. SAN 305-8085. Tel: 316-568-6645. *Librn*, Veda Roets
Pop 564; Circ 2,970
Library Holdings: Bk Vols 5,000; Per Subs 20
Mem of Southeast Kansas Library System

AMERICUS

P AMERICUS TOWNSHIP LIBRARY,* 710 Main St, PO Box 404, 66835-0404. SAN 305-8093. Tel: 316-443-5503. *Librn*, Sandra Simmons
Pop 1,591; Circ 33,124
Library Holdings: Bk Vols 12,000; Per Subs 28
Mem of North Central Kansas Libraries System
Open Mon-Wed 1-5:30, Thurs & Fri 9-12 & 1:30-5:30

ANDOVER

P ANDOVER PUBLIC LIBRARY,* 937 N Andover Rd, PO Box 550, 67002. SAN 305-8107. Tel: 316-733-4599. E-Mail: andpublib@feist.com. *Dir*, Kate Mutch; Staff 1 (MLS 1)
Pop 5,200
Jan 1998-Dec 1999 Income $114,108, State $8,794, City $105,314. Mats Exp $12,000, Books $9,500, Per/Ser (Incl. Access Fees) $2,500. Sal $49,750 (Prof $25,625)
Library Holdings: Bk Vols 30,000; Per Subs 35
Mem of South Central Kansas Library System

ANTHONY

P ANTHONY PUBLIC LIBRARY, 624 E Main, 67003-2738. SAN 305-8115. Tel: 316-842-5344. FAX: 316-842-5684. E-Mail: library@cyberlodge.com. *Coll Develop, Dir, Head Librn*, Sandy Trotter
Founded 1897. Pop 9,640; Circ 50,477
Library Holdings: Bk Vols 40,000; Bk Titles 39,500; Per Subs 80
Special Collections: County Cemetery Records; County Newspaper Coll,

micro; Dawes Indian Rolls (Enrollment cards for the five civilized tribes 1898-1914)
Automation Activity & Vendor Info: (Cataloging) Follett; (Circulation) Follett
Publications: Weekly Library Newsletter
Mem of South Central Kansas Library System

ARGONIA

P DIXON TOWNSHIP LIBRARY,* 120 W Walnut, PO Box 95, 67004-0095. SAN 305-8123. Tel: 316-435-6979. *Librn*, Anita Busch
Pop 783; Circ 7,366
Library Holdings: Bk Vols 11,000; Per Subs 19
Mem of South Central Kansas Library System

ARKANSAS CITY

P ARKANSAS CITY PUBLIC LIBRARY, 120 E Fifth Ave, 67005-2695. SAN 305-8131. Tel: 316-442-1280. FAX: 316-442-4277. E-Mail: arkcitypl@acpl.org. Web Site: www.acpl.org. *Librn*, Carole Dibben; Staff 6 (MLS 3, Non-MLS 3)
Founded 1907. Pop 12,480; Circ 72,691
Library Holdings: Bk Vols 46,458; Per Subs 119
Special Collections: Kansas Coll
Automation Activity & Vendor Info: (Cataloging) Sagebrush Corporation; (Circulation) Sagebrush Corporation; (OPAC) Sagebrush Corporation
Mem of South Central Kansas Library System
Friends of the Library Group

S CHEROKEE STRIP LAND RUSH MUSEUM, Docking Memorial Reference Library, PO Box 778, 67005. SAN 370-2820. Tel: 316-442-6750. E-Mail: museum@hit.net. Web Site: www.arkcity.org/csm.html. *Dir*, T J Junkins, Jr
Library Holdings: Bk Vols 500
Special Collections: Chilocco Indian School, Cowley County Genealogy
Restriction: Open to public for reference only

J COWLEY COUNTY COMMUNITY COLLEGE, Renn Memorial Library, 125 S Third St, 67005. SAN 305-814X. Tel: 316-442-0430, Ext 5257. FAX: 316-441-5356. Web Site: www.cowley.cc.ks.us. *Dir Libr Serv*, Rhoda M MacLaughlin; Tel: 316-441-5280, E-Mail: maclaughlinr@cowley.cc.ks.us; Staff 3 (MLS 1, Non-MLS 2)
Founded 1922. Enrl 3,758; Fac 47
1999-2000 Income $160,791. Mats Exp $33,665, Books $12,634, Per/Ser (Incl. Access Fees) $5,365, Presv $266, Micro $3,400, Electronic Ref Mat (Incl. Access Fees) $12,000. Sal $70,000 (Prof $34,000)
Library Holdings: Bk Titles 26,000; Per Subs 80
Special Collections: Kansas Room, bks & per
Automation Activity & Vendor Info: (Circulation) Gaylord
Database Vendor: Ebsco - EbscoHost
Mem of South Central Kansas Library System
Open Mon-Thurs 7:45am-9:30pm, Fri 7:45-4, Sat 9-12 & Sun 3-9:30

ARLINGTON

P ARLINGTON CITY LIBRARY,* PO Box 396, 67514-0396. SAN 305-8158. Tel: 316-538-2471. E-Mail: arllib@feist.com. *Librn*, Diana Weaver
Founded 1933. Pop 631; Circ 7,420
Library Holdings: Bk Vols 6,189; Bk Titles 5,500
Mem of South Central Kansas Library System

ARMA

P ARMA CITY LIBRARY, 501 N West St, PO Box 822, 66712. SAN 376-7671. Tel: 316-347-4811. FAX: 316-347-4977. E-Mail: armalibrary@hotmail.com. *Librn*, Christie Wilson
Library Holdings: Bk Vols 7,000; Per Subs 15
Mem of Southeast Kansas Library System
Open Mon-Fri 11-3 (Summer), Mon-Fri 1-5 (Winter)

ASHLAND

P ASHLAND PUBLIC LIBRARY, 604 Main St, PO Box 397, 67831-0397. SAN 305-8166. Tel: 316-635-2589. FAX: 316-635-2931. E-Mail: ashlib@ucom.net. *Librn*, Eldora McMinimy; *Asst Librn*, Pat Graff
Founded 1920. Circ 18,442
Jan 1999-Dec 1999 Income $43,947, State $757, City $8,100, County $7,508, Locally Generated Income $2,058, Other $25,524. Mats Exp $5,119, Books $3,135, Per/Ser (Incl. Access Fees) $1,984. Sal $20,082 (Prof $19,127)
Library Holdings: Bk Vols 19,675; Bk Titles 19,670; Per Subs 41
Mem of Southwest Kansas Library System
Friends of the Library Group

ATCHISON

P ATCHISON LIBRARY, 401 Kansas Ave, 66002-2495. SAN 305-8174. Tel: 913-367-1902. FAX: 913-367-2717.
Pop 11,000; Circ 100,000
Library Holdings: Bk Vols 63,000; Per Subs 80
Subject Interests: History, Music
Special Collections: Local History Coll, microfilm, newsp & prints
Mem of Northeast Kansas Library System
Friends of the Library Group

C BENEDICTINE COLLEGE LIBRARY,* 1020 N Second St, 66002-1499. SAN 342-0000. Tel: 913-367-5340, Ext 2590. FAX: 913-367-6102. Web Site: www.benedictine.edu/bcacadlib1.html. *Dir Libr Serv*, Corinne Cardona; E-Mail: ccardona@raven.benedictine.edu; *Asst Librn, Ref*, Sister Dorothy Heidemann; *ILL*, Florine Muhlenbruck; *Doc, Ser*, Miriam O'Hare; Staff 3 (MLS 3)
Founded 1858. Enrl 802; Fac 58; Highest Degree: Doctorate
Library Holdings: Bk Vols 366,915; Bk Titles 187,020; Per Subs 339
Subject Interests: Agriculture, Education, History, Religion
Special Collections: Belloc; Chesterton; Church Fathers (Abbey Coll); Gerontology (Jay Gatson Coll); Monasticism; Philosophy (Ture Snowden Coll)
Mem of Northeast Kansas Library System
Partic in Bibliographical Center For Research, Rocky Mountain Region, Inc; Health Sciences Library Network of Kansas City, Inc; OCLC Online Computer Library Center, Inc
Open Mon-Thurs 7:45-11, Fri 7:45-5, Sat 10-5, Sun 1-5 & 6:30-11

ATTICA

P ATTICA PUBLIC LIBRARY,* 125 N Main St, PO Box 137, 67009-0137. SAN 305-8190. Tel: 316-254-7767. *Librn*, Lillian Tubb
Pop 730; Circ 4,952
Library Holdings: Bk Vols 11,207; Per Subs 14
Mem of South Central Kansas Library System

ATWOOD

P ATWOOD PUBLIC LIBRARY, 102 S Sixth St, 67730-1998. SAN 305-8204. Tel: 785-626-3805. FAX: 785-626-3670. E-Mail: atwoodli@ruraltel.net. *Librn*, Pamela A Luedke; *Asst Librn*, Denise Maaske
Pop 3,000; Circ 40,211
Jan 1999-Dec 1999 Income $71,000
Library Holdings: Bk Titles 22,372; Per Subs 57
Automation Activity & Vendor Info: (Circulation) Follett; (OPAC) Follett

AUGUSTA

P AUGUSTA PUBLIC LIBRARY, 1609 State St, 67010-2098. SAN 305-8212. Tel: 316-775-2681. FAX: 316-220-1657. E-Mail: augustapl@feist.com. Web Site: www.augusta-ks.org/library/library.html. *Dir*, Teresa Marie Thurman-Zuck; E-Mail: teresa@augusta.lib.ks.us; *Asst Librn*, Sharon Barnes; E-Mail: sbarnes@augusta.lib.ks.us; Staff 4 (MLS 1, Non-MLS 3)
Founded 1919. Pop 8,900; Circ 90,439
Jan 2000-Dec 2000 Income $203,503, State $6,603, City $155,000, Other $41,900. Mats Exp $35,671, Books $24,700, Per/Ser (Incl. Access Fees) $6,993, AV Equip $2,300, Electronic Ref Mat (Incl. Access Fees) $1,678. Sal $114,903 (Prof $30,000)
Library Holdings: Bk Vols 29,517; Per Subs 127
Automation Activity & Vendor Info: (OPAC) Sagebrush Corporation
Database Vendor: Ebsco - EbscoHost, IAC - SearchBank, OCLC - First Search
Mem of South Central Kansas Library System
Open Mon-Thurs 9:30-9, Fri & Sat 9:30-6
Friends of the Library Group

AXTELL

P AXTELL PUBLIC LIBRARY,* 401 Maple, PO Box 241, 66403-0241. SAN 305-8220. Tel: 785-736-2834. *Librn*, Mary H Keegan
Founded 1937. Pop 435; Circ 2,075
Library Holdings: Bk Vols 4,300; Per Subs 12
Mem of North Central Kansas Libraries System
Open Tues, Wed, Fri & Sat 2-5

BALDWIN CITY

C BAKER UNIVERSITY LIBRARY, 518 Eighth St, 66006-0065. (Mail add: PO Box 65, 66006-0065), SAN 305-8239. Tel: 785-594-8414. FAX: 785-594-6721. Web Site: www.bakeru.edu/library. *Dir Libr Serv*, Kay Bradt; E-Mail: bradt@harvey.bakeru.edu; *Govt Doc*, Anne Liebst; Tel: 785-594-8389, E-Mail: liebst@baker.edu; *Archivist*, Brenda Day; Tel: 785-594-8380, E-Mail: day@harvey.bakeru.edu; Staff 7 (MLS 3, Non-MLS 4)
Founded 1858. Enrl 2,366; Fac 165; Highest Degree: Master

Jul 1999-Jun 2000 Income $266,225, Parent Institution $233,887, Other $32,338. Mats Exp $164,544, Books $71,043, Per/Ser (Incl. Access Fees) $87,943, Presv $2,000. Sal $160,217
Library Holdings: Bk Vols 63,670; Per Subs 330
Subject Interests: American history, Biology
Special Collections: Baker University Archives; Quayle Rare Bible Coll; United Methodist Historical Archives (KS East Conf)
Automation Activity & Vendor Info: (Cataloging) DRA; (Circulation) DRA; (Serials) DRA
Database Vendor: Dialog, Ebsco - EbscoHost, GaleNet, IAC - Info Trac, Lexis-Nexis, OCLC - First Search, Silverplatter Information Inc.
Mem of Northeast Kansas Library System
Partic in Kans City Libr Consortium

P BALDWIN CITY LIBRARY,* 800 Seventh St, 66006. SAN 305-8247. Tel: 785-594-3411. FAX: 785-594-3411. *Librn*, Kathy Johnston; *Asst Librn*, Phyllis Braun
Founded 1916. Pop 2,829; Circ 15,366
Library Holdings: Bk Vols 18,000; Per Subs 78
Special Collections: The Kansas Shelf Coll
Mem of Northeast Kansas Library System
Partic in Kansas Info Circuit
Friends of the Library Group

BASEHOR

P BASEHOR COMMUNITY LIBRARY DISTRICT 2, 2812 N 155th St, 66007. (Mail add: PO Box 380, 66007-0380), SAN 326-3967. Tel: 913-724-2828. FAX: 913-724-2898. E-Mail: basehorlib@kcnet.com. Web Site: www.skyways.lib.ks.us/library/basehor. *Dir*, Carla Kaiser; *Asst Dir*, Jenne Laytham; E-Mail: jenne13@juno.com; Staff 4 (Non-MLS 4)
Founded 1985. Pop 6,819; Circ 37,418
Jan 1999-Dec 1999 Income $160,825, State $4,104, Locally Generated Income $138,645, Other $17,611. Mats Exp $21,338, Books $11,210, Per/Ser (Incl. Access Fees) $2,027, AV Equip $7,372, Electronic Ref Mat (Incl. Access Fees) $729. Sal $63,943
Library Holdings: Bk Vols 14,896; Per Subs 58
Automation Activity & Vendor Info: (Cataloging) Follett; (Circulation) Follett
Database Vendor: OCLC - First Search
Mem of Northeast Kansas Library System
Friends of the Library Group

BAXTER SPRINGS

P JOHNSTON PUBLIC LIBRARY, 210 W Tenth St, 66713-1611. SAN 305-8255. Tel: 316-856-5591. FAX: 316-856-4498. *Librn*, Betty Burrows; *Asst Librn*, June Haggard; Staff 1 (MLS 1)
Founded 1905. Pop 5,203; Circ 44,573
Library Holdings: Bk Vols 40,329; Per Subs 77
Subject Interests: American Indians, Civil War, Kansas
Mem of Southeast Kansas Library System

BELLE PLAINE

P BELLE PLAINE CITY LIBRARY,* 222 W Fifth Ave, PO Box 700, 67013-0700. SAN 305-8263. Tel: 316-488-3431. E-Mail: bplib@hit.net. *Librn*, Vicki Bohannon; *Asst Librn*, Sharlene Slaughter
Founded 1915. Pop 1,800; Circ 9,411
Library Holdings: Bk Vols 11,500; Per Subs 25
Mem of South Central Kansas Library System

BELLEVILLE

P BELLEVILLE PUBLIC LIBRARY,* 1327 19th St, 66935-2296. SAN 305-8271. Tel: 785-527-5305. FAX: 785-527-5305. *Dir*, Leah Krotz
Founded 1927. Pop 2,517; Circ 33,841
Library Holdings: Bk Vols 20,242; Per Subs 104
Special Collections: Republic County History Coll; Republic County New papers, 1870-1946, micro; World War II Veterans
Mem of Central Kansas Library System
Open Mon, Wed & Fri 12-5:30, Tues & Thurs 10-8 & Sat 10-4
Friends of the Library Group

BELOIT

P PORT LIBRARY, Beloit City Library, 311 W Main, 67420. SAN 305-828X. Tel: 785-738-3936. E-Mail: portlib@nckcn.com. *Dir*, Patricia A Heidrick; Staff 2 (Non-MLS 2)
Founded 1931. Pop 5,000
Library Holdings: Bk Vols 25,000; Per Subs 93
Special Collections: Quilts & Quilting
Mem of Central Kansas Library System

BELPRE

P HENRY LAIRD LIBRARY,* PO Box 128, 67519-0128. SAN 305-8298. Tel: 316-995-3322. *Librn*, Carlyn Mead
Circ 3,552
Library Holdings: Bk Vols 4,475; Per Subs 21
Special Collections: L Winters Coll, oil painting
Mem of Southwest Kansas Library System
Friends of the Library Group

BERN

P BERN COMMUNITY LIBRARY, 405 Main St, PO Box 1, 66408-0001. SAN 376-5598. Tel: 785-336-3000. FAX: 785-336-3000. E-Mail: bcl@bern.lib.ks.us. Web Site: skyways.lib.ks.us/towns/bern. *Coll Develop, Librn*, Julia Dawdy; Staff 3 (Non-MLS 3)
Founded 1995
1999-2000 Income $16,012. Mats Exp $1,200, Books $800, Per/Ser (Incl. Access Fees) $400. Sal $8,055
Library Holdings: Bk Vols 6,969
Automation Activity & Vendor Info: (Cataloging) Follett; (Circulation) Follett
Mem of Northeast Kansas Library System

BIRD CITY

P MARY L GRITTEN LIBRARY,* 111 E Fourth St, PO Box 175, 67731. SAN 305-8301. Tel: 785-734-2203. FAX: 785-734-2668. E-Mail: bcpl@nwkansas.com. *Librn*, Darla Deeds
Pop 620; Circ 3,491
Library Holdings: Bk Vols 6,743; Per Subs 30
Mem of Northwest Kansas Library System
Open Tues & Sat 2-5:30, Thurs 2-9:30

BISON

P BISON COMMUNITY LIBRARY, 202 Main St, 67520-0406. (Mail add: PO Box 406, 67520-0406), SAN 305-831X. Tel: 785-356-4803. E-Mail: bisonlib@ruraltel.net. *Librn*, Diane Bott
Pop 313; Circ 2,246
Library Holdings: Bk Vols 5,293
Mem of Central Kansas Library System
Open Mon-Fri 2-5 & Thurs 9-12

BLUE MOUND

P LINN COUNTY DISTRICT LIBRARY THREE, 316 Main St, PO Box 13, 66010-0013. SAN 305-8328. Tel: 913-756-2628. *Librn*, Sharon Brahin
Founded 1964. Pop 584; Circ 6,815
Library Holdings: Bk Vols 6,000
Mem of Southeast Kansas Library System
Open Tues & Sat 1-4, Wed-Fri 1-5

BLUE RAPIDS

P BLUE RAPIDS PUBLIC LIBRARY,* PO Box 246, 66411. SAN 305-8336. Tel: 785-363-7709. *Librn*, Lynne Turner
Founded 1874. Pop 1,131; Circ 4,251
Library Holdings: Bk Vols 5,091; Per Subs 19
Mem of North Central Kansas Libraries System
Open Mon, Wed & Fri 1-5, Sat 9-12
Friends of the Library Group

BONNER SPRINGS

P BONNER SPRINGS CITY LIBRARY, 200 E Third St, 66012-1047. SAN 305-8344. Tel: 913-441-2665. FAX: 913-441-2660. E-Mail: bsclib@swbell.net. *Dir*, Kimberly Martin; Staff 4 (MLS 1, Non-MLS 3)
Founded 1946. Pop 6,238; Circ 42,069
Library Holdings: Bk Vols 30,000; Per Subs 50
Automation Activity & Vendor Info: (Cataloging) Sagebrush Corporation; (Circulation) Sagebrush Corporation; (OPAC) Sagebrush Corporation
Database Vendor: IAC - Info Trac, IAC - SearchBank, OCLC - First Search
Mem of Northeast Kansas Library System
Open Mon-Thurs 9-8, Fri & Sat 9-5, Sun 1-5
Friends of the Library Group

S WYANDOTTE COUNTY MUSEUM, Trowbridge Research Library, 631 N 126th St, 66012. (Mail add: U G Clerk - Museum, 701 N Seventh St, 66101), SAN 305-8352. Tel: 913-721-1078. *Curator*, Rebecca Phipps
Founded 1956
Library Holdings: Bk Vols 2,000

Special Collections: 6000 item Photographic file; Census Records; Early Family Records; Genealogical materials (Wyandotte County)
Open Tues-Sat 10-5; ADA accessible

BREWSTER

P NORTHWEST KANSAS HERITAGE CENTER, Library & Museum,* 401 Kansas Ave, PO Box 284, 67732-0284. SAN 376-768X. Tel: 785-694-2891. *Librn*, Betty Wolfe
Library Holdings: Bk Vols 6,000
Mem of Northwest Kansas Library System

BRONSON

P BRONSON PUBLIC LIBRARY,* 411 Clay St, 66716. SAN 305-8360. Tel: 316-939-4910. *Librn*, Karen Wilson
Pop 419; Circ 5,656
Library Holdings: Bk Vols 3,996; Per Subs 28
Mem of Southeast Kansas Library System

BROWNELL

P BROWNELL PUBLIC LIBRARY,* 67521. SAN 305-8379. Tel: 785-481-2300. *Librn*, Ruby Squier
Founded 1941. Pop 85; Circ 3,000
Library Holdings: Bk Vols 4,000
Mem of Southwest Kansas Library System

BUCKLIN

P BUCKLIN PUBLIC LIBRARY, 201 N Main, PO Box 596, 67834-0596. SAN 305-8387. Tel: 316-826-3223. FAX: 316-826-3794. E-Mail: bucklinlibrary@midway.net. *Head Librn*, Edna M Ringwald; *Ch Servs*, Sandra Halling; *Ch Servs*, Kathy Leon; *Cat*, Rebecca Stimpert; Staff 4 (Non-MLS 4)
Founded 1964. Pop 716; Circ 4,500
Jan 2000-Dec 2000 Income $20,286, State $574, City $14,502, Locally Generated Income $515. Mats Exp $2,620, Books $1,500, Per/Ser (Incl. Access Fees) $436, Manuscripts & Archives $684. Sal $8,500
Library Holdings: Bk Vols 14,450; Bk Titles 13,900; Per Subs 33
Special Collections: Kansas History Coll; Large Print Coll
Automation Activity & Vendor Info: (Cataloging) Athena; (Circulation) Athena
Function: Business archives
Mem of Southwest Kansas Library System

BUHLER

P BUHLER PUBLIC LIBRARY,* 121 N Main St, 67522-0118. SAN 305-8395. Tel: 316-543-2241. Web Site: www.skyways.lib.ks.us/kansas/towns/buhler/library.html. *Librn*, Pam Fast
Pop 1,200; Circ 8,398
Library Holdings: Bk Vols 10,000; Per Subs 20
Mem of South Central Kansas Library System

BURDETT

P BURDETT COMMUNITY LIBRARY,* 207 Elm St, 67523. SAN 305-8409. Tel: 316-525-6588. *Librn*, Beverly Steffen
Library Holdings: Bk Vols 2,000
Mem of Central Kansas Library System
Open 2 hrs per week

BURLINGAME

P BURLINGAME COMMUNITY LIBRARY,* 122 W Sante Fe, 66413. SAN 305-8417. Tel: 785-654-3400. FAX: 785-654-3612. E-Mail: burl1lb@kanza.net. *Librn*, Donelda Sage
Founded 1970. Pop 1,293; Circ 10,608
Library Holdings: Bk Vols 8,000
Subject Interests: Large type print
Mem of Northeast Kansas Library System
Friends of the Library Group

BURLINGTON

P COFFEY COUNTY LIBRARY, 410 Juniatta, 66839. SAN 305-8425. Tel: 620-364-2010. FAX: 620-364-2603. Web Site: www.cclibraryks.org. *Adminr*, Jane Hatch; E-Mail: janehatch@yahoo.com; Staff 36 (MLS 2, Non-MLS 34)
Founded 1987. Pop 8,743; Circ 166,264
Jan 1999-Dec 1999 Income (Main Library and Branch Library) $925,708, State $6,688, Federal $6,470, County $888,945, Locally Generated Income $23,605. Mats Exp $45,231, Books $26,876, Per/Ser (Incl. Access Fees) $8,192, Other Print Mats $10,163. Sal $617,911
Library Holdings: Bk Vols 94,954; Per Subs 312
Subject Interests: Genealogy
Automation Activity & Vendor Info: (Cataloging) epixtech, inc.; (Circulation) epixtech, inc.; (OPAC) epixtech, inc.
Database Vendor: epixtech, inc.
Branches: 6
BURLINGTON BRANCH, 410 Juniatta, 66839. Tel: 620-364-5333. FAX: 620-364-2603. Web Site: www.cclibraryks.org. *Dir*, Valerie Williams; E-Mail: valw1@yahoo.com; Staff 6 (MLS 1, Non-MLS 5)
Pop 8,743
GRIDLEY BRANCH, 512 Main, PO Box 251, Gridley, 66852-0251. SAN 305-9316. Tel: 620-836-3905. FAX: 620-836-3401. Web Site: www.cclibraryks.org. *Dir*, Janet Birk; E-Mail: janetbirk23@yahoo.com; Staff 4 (Non-MLS 4)
Pop 8,743
LEBO BRANCH, 327 S Ogden St, Lebo, 66856-9306. SAN 306-0012. Tel: 620-256-6452. FAX: 620-256-6301. Web Site: www.cclibraryks.org. *Dir*, Mary Barker; E-Mail: maryebarker@yahoo.com; Staff 4 (Non-MLS 4)
Pop 8,743
LEROY BRANCH, 725 Main, PO Box 36, LeRoy, 66857-0036. SAN 306-0063. Tel: 620-964-2321. FAX: 620-964-2394. Web Site: www.cclibraryks.org. *Dir*, Cindy Stohs; E-Mail: cjstohs1619@yahoo.com; Staff 3 (Non-MLS 3)
Pop 8,743
Friends of the Library Group
NEW STRAWN BRANCH, 365 N Main St, New Strawn, 66839. SAN 373-5729. Tel: 620-364-8910. FAX: 620-364-8910. Web Site: www.cclibraryks.org. *Dir*, Rhonda Davis; Fax: 620-364-5354, E-Mail: rhondadavis@yahoo.com; Staff 4 (Non-MLS 4)
Pop 8,743
WAVERLY BRANCH, 608 Pearson, Waverly, 66871-9688. SAN 306-1760. Tel: 785-733-2400. FAX: 785-733-2474. Web Site: www.cclibraryks.org. *Dir*, Marcella Chapman; E-Mail: mechapman@yahoo.com; Staff 4 (Non-MLS 4)
Pop 8,743
Publications: Waverly City History Book

BURNS

P BURNS PUBLIC LIBRARY,* 104 Church St, PO Box 233, 66840. SAN 305-8433. Tel: 316-726-5861, 316-728-5272. *Librn*, Albert Gustainis
Pop 363; Circ 1,319
Library Holdings: Bk Vols 4,129
Mem of North Central Kansas Libraries System
Open Tues 7-8 & Fri 3-5

BURR OAK

P BURR OAK CITY LIBRARY,* PO Box 55, 66936-0055. SAN 305-8441. Tel: 785-647-8181. *Librn*, Delores Roesti
Pop 366; Circ 1,696
Library Holdings: Bk Vols 9,350; Per Subs 13
Mem of Central Kansas Library System

BURRTON

P BURRTON PUBLIC LIBRARY, 118 N Burrton Ave, PO Box 400, 67020-0400. SAN 305-845X. Tel: 316-463-7902. *Librn*, Delores Roberts
Pop 1,000; Circ 7,834
Library Holdings: Bk Vols 9,712; Per Subs 44
Mem of South Central Kansas Library System

BUSHTON

P FARMER TOWNSHIP COMMUNITY LIBRARY,* Main St, 460 Ave E, 67427. SAN 305-8468. Tel: 316-562-3352. *Librn*, Barbara Orth
Pop 593; Circ 5,952
Library Holdings: Bk Vols 5,009
Special Collections: Juvenile Book of US Presidents; Kansas Coll
Mem of South Central Kansas Library System

CALDWELL

P CALDWELL CARNEGIE LIBRARY,* 8 N Osage St, 67022. SAN 305-8476. Tel: 316-845-6879. FAX: 316-845-6880. E-Mail: caldw1lb@kan.okla.net. *Librn*, Norma White
Founded 1912. Pop 1,407
Library Holdings: Bk Vols 8,000; Per Subs 35
Mem of South Central Kansas Library System

CANEY

P CANEY CITY LIBRARY,* 100 N Ridgeway, PO Box 38, 67333-2035. SAN 305-8484. Tel: 316-879-5341. *Librn*, Sandra Freidline
Pop 2,284; Circ 13,104
Library Holdings: Bk Vols 10,000; Per Subs 13
Mem of Southeast Kansas Library System

CANTON

P CANTON TOWNSHIP LIBRARY,* 203 N Main St, PO Box 336, 67428-0336. SAN 305-8492. Tel: 316-628-4349. *Librn*, Norma McCary
Founded 1909. Pop 1,187; Circ 6,012
Library Holdings: Bk Vols 4,115; Per Subs 25
Mem of South Central Kansas Library System

CARBONDALE

P CARBONDALE CITY LIBRARY,* 236 Main St, PO Box 330, 66414-0330. SAN 305-8506. Tel: 785-836-7638. *Dir*, Marjean Parker
Library Holdings: Bk Vols 6,500
Mem of Northeast Kansas Library System

CAWKER CITY

P CAWKER CITY PUBLIC LIBRARY, 802 Locust, 67430. SAN 305-8514. Tel: 785-781-4925. *Librn*, Erma Luckey
Founded 1884. Pop 1,000; Circ 6,000
Library Holdings: Bk Titles 9,900; Per Subs 14
Mem of Central Kansas Library System

CEDAR VALE

P CEDAR VALE MEMORIAL LIBRARY,* 608 Cedar St, PO Box 369, 67024-9701. SAN 376-5555. Tel: 316-758-2598. *Dir*, Shirley Myers
Library Holdings: Bk Vols 4,100
Mem of Southeast Kansas Library System

CENTRALIA

P CENTRALIA COMMUNITY LIBRARY,* 608 Fourth St, 66415. SAN 305-8522. Tel: 785-857-3331. *Librn*, Shirley Hiatt
Founded 1880. Pop 521; Circ 4,942
Library Holdings: Bk Vols 4,942; Per Subs 27
Mem of Northeast Kansas Library System
Open Mon 1-5, Wed 1-6, Sat 8-1

CHANUTE

P CHANUTE PUBLIC LIBRARY, 111 N Lincoln, 66720-1819. SAN 305-8530. Tel: 316-431-3820. FAX: 316-431-3848. E-Mail: chanulib@chanute-ks.com. *Dir*, Susan Willis; Staff 5 (MLS 1, Non-MLS 4)
Founded 1905. Pop 17,000; Circ 119,384
Jan 2000-Dec 2000 Income $274,645, State $7,074, City $207,969, Other $25,687. Mats Exp $46,713, Books $35,234, Per/Ser (Incl. Access Fees) $4,899, AV Equip $3,790, Electronic Ref Mat (Incl. Access Fees) $2,790. Sal $113,373 (Prof $30,500)
Library Holdings: Bk Vols 53,558; Per Subs 134
Special Collections: Esther Clark Hill Coll; Local History; Nora B Cunningham Coll, letters
Automation Activity & Vendor Info: (Circulation) Sagebrush Corporation; (OPAC) Sagebrush Corporation
Mem of Southeast Kansas Library System
Friends of the Library Group

J NEOSHO COUNTY COMMUNITY COLLEGE, Chapman Library, 800 W 14th St, 66720-2699. SAN 305-8549. Tel: 316-431-2820, Ext 244. Toll Free Tel: 800-729-6222. Interlibrary Loan Service Toll Free Tel: 800-729-6222, Ext 296. FAX: 316-431-2820, Ext 287. E-Mail: chapmanlibrary@neosho.cc.ks.us. Web Site: www.neosho.cc.ks.us/services/library/library.htm. *Dir*, Susan Weisenberger; Tel: 316-431-2820, Ext 246, E-Mail: sdweisen@neosho.cc.ks.us; Staff 4 (MLS 2, Non-MLS 2)
Founded 1936. Highest Degree: Associate
Jul 1999-Jun 2000 Income $124,000
Library Holdings: Bk Vols 38,000; Per Subs 130
Subject Interests: Nursing
Special Collections: Genealogy
Automation Activity & Vendor Info: (Circulation) Sagebrush Corporation; (OPAC) Sagebrush Corporation
Database Vendor: IAC - Info Trac, OCLC - First Search
Mem of Southeast Kansas Library System
Departmental Libraries:
OTTAWA CAMPUS, 226 Beech St, Ottawa, 66067. SAN 375-4928. Tel: 785-242-2067. FAX: 785-242-0068. *Dir*, Susan Weisenberger; Staff 1 (MLS 1)
Library Holdings: Bk Vols 1,500; Per Subs 40
Automation Activity & Vendor Info: (Circulation) Sagebrush Corporation; (OPAC) Sagebrush Corporation
Database Vendor: IAC - Info Trac, OCLC - First Search
Mem of Southeast Kansas Library System

S THE MARTIN & OSA JOHNSON SAFARI MUSEUM, INC, Stott Explorers Library, 111 N Lincoln Ave, 66720. SAN 325-7320. Tel: 316-431-2730. FAX: 316-431-3848. E-Mail: osajohns@safarimuseum.com. Web Site: www.safarimuseum.com. *Dir*, Conrad G Froehlich; *Curator*, Barbara E Henshall; *Curator*, Jacquelyn Borgeson
Founded 1980
Library Holdings: Bk Vols 10,000
Subject Interests: Africa, Natural history, Pacific
Publications: Wait-A-Bit News
Restriction: Not a lending library
Friends of the Library Group

CHAPMAN

P CHAPMAN PUBLIC LIBRARY,* 402 N Marshall, PO Box F, 67431-2644. SAN 305-8557. Tel: 785-922-6548. E-Mail: chaplib@c.net. *Librn*, Carol Frasure
Pop 1,428; Circ 22,927
1997-1998 Income $19,500. Mats Exp $12,000, Books $3,000, Per/Ser (Incl. Access Fees) $9,000. Sal $7,500
Library Holdings: Bk Vols 14,516; Per Subs 35
Mem of North Central Kansas Libraries System

CHENEY

P CHENEY PUBLIC LIBRARY,* 203 N Main St, PO Box 700, 67025. SAN 305-8565. Tel: 316-542-3331. *Librn*, Susan Sanny
Founded 1940. Pop 1,800; Circ 25,363
Library Holdings: Bk Vols 10,500; Per Subs 17
Mem of South Central Kansas Library System

CHERRYVALE

P CHERRYVALE PUBLIC LIBRARY,* 329 E Main, 67335-1413. SAN 305-8573. Tel: 316-336-3460. *Dir*, Jessie Lickteig
Founded 1913. Pop 2,770; Circ 20,526
Library Holdings: Bk Vols 16,400; Per Subs 26
Mem of Southeast Kansas Library System
Library is a national historic site

CHETOPA

P CHETOPA CITY LIBRARY,* 312 Maple, PO Box 206, 67336-8206. SAN 305-8581. Tel: 316-236-7194. *Librn*, Freda Conard
Founded 1875. Pop 1,650; Circ 16,236
Library Holdings: Bk Vols 25,000; Per Subs 25
Mem of Southeast Kansas Library System
Open Mon-Wed & Fri 1-5, Thurs 4-8

CIMARRON

P CIMARRON CITY LIBRARY, 120 N Main, PO Box 645, 67835-0645. SAN 305-859X. Tel: 316-855-3808. FAX: 316-855-2192. E-Mail: cimarlb@ucom.net. *City Librn*, Sara McFarland; *Asst Librn*, Jeanette Steinkuehler; *Asst Librn*, Sandy Unruh; Staff 3 (Non-MLS 3)
Founded 1934. Pop 1,763; Circ 21,700
2000-2001 Income $87,734, State $2,900, City $68,034, County $13,700, Locally Generated Income $3,100. Mats Exp $11,298, Books $9,198, Per/Ser (Incl. Access Fees) $1,500, Electronic Ref Mat (Incl. Access Fees) $600. Sal $39,240
Library Holdings: Bk Vols 27,870; Per Subs 83
Automation Activity & Vendor Info: (Cataloging) Brodart; (Circulation) Athena; (OPAC) Athena
Database Vendor: OCLC - First Search
Mem of Southwest Kansas Library System
Friends of the Library Group

CLAFLIN

P INDEPENDENT TOWNSHIP LIBRARY,* 108 Main St, PO Box 163, 67525-0163. SAN 305-8603. Tel: 316-587-3488. *Librn*, Judy Wondra; E-Mail: jwondra@ispchannel.com
Pop 914; Circ 8,358
Library Holdings: Bk Vols 8,861; Per Subs 54
Mem of Central Kansas Library System

CLAY CENTER

P CLAY CENTER CARNEGIE LIBRARY,* 706 Sixth St, 67432-2997. SAN 305-8611. Tel: 785-632-3889. E-Mail: ccpublib@kansas.net. Web Site: skyways.lib.ks.us/kansas/norcen/claycenter/claclib.html. *Librn*, Kirsten Young; *Ch Servs*, Kathryn Norton
Founded 1901. Pop 4,640; Circ 44,349
Library Holdings: Bk Titles 40,264; Per Subs 97
Mem of North Central Kansas Libraries System
Friends of the Library Group

CLAYTON

P CLAYTON CITY LIBRARY, HCR 1, Box 76, 67629. SAN 305-862X. Tel: 785-693-4393. *Librn*, Mary Vanover
Pop 117; Circ 600
Library Holdings: Bk Vols 1,877
Mem of Northwest Kansas Library System
Open Sat 9:30-11

CLEARWATER

P CLEARWATER PUBLIC LIBRARY,* 109 E Ross, PO Box 504, 67026-0504. SAN 305-8638. Tel: 316-584-6474. FAX: 316-584-2885. E-Mail: cplstaff@sktc.net. *Dir*, Lee Steen; *Dir*, Sandy Wise
Pop 1,983; Circ 17,791
Library Holdings: Bk Vols 8,000; Per Subs 40
Mem of South Central Kansas Library System
Friends of the Library Group

CLIFTON

P CLIFTON PUBLIC LIBRARY,* 104 E Parallel, PO Box J, 66937-0310. SAN 305-8646. Tel: 785-455-2222. *Librn*, Marilyn Knox
Founded 1954. Pop 738; Circ 5,011
Library Holdings: Bk Vols 4,200
Mem of North Central Kansas Libraries System
Open Mon, Wed & Fri 2-5, Sat 9-11

CLYDE

P CLYDE PUBLIC LIBRARY, Randolph-Decker Library, 101 S Green St, PO Box 85, 66938-0085. SAN 305-8654. Tel: 785-446-3563. E-Mail: rdpl@nckcn.com. Web Site: skyways.lib.ks.us./. *Librn*, Virginia Racette; *Asst Librn*, Pauline Cyr
Founded 1920. Pop 722; Circ 12,305
1998-1999 Income $15,213, State $571, City $8,400, Other $186. Mats Exp $2,900, Books $2,500, Per/Ser (Incl. Access Fees) $400. Sal $7,800
Library Holdings: Bk Vols 14,056
Mem of Central Kansas Library System
Microfiche & Reader for Kansas Union Catalog

COFFEYVILLE

J COFFEYVILLE COMMUNITY COLLEGE, Graham Library, 400 W 11th, 67337-5064. SAN 305-8662. Tel: 316-251-7700, Ext 7220. Circulation Tel: 316-252-7220. FAX: 316-252-7366. Web Site: www.ccc.cc.ks.us/academics/library/library.html. *Dir*, Micaela Ayers; E-Mail: mayers@inetserver.ccc.cc.ks.us; *Mgr*, Janice Lair; E-Mail: janiceL@raven.ccc.cc.ks.us; *Librn*, Roberta Artherton; E-Mail: roberta@raven.ccc.cc.ks.us; *Media Spec*, Garry Foster; E-Mail: garryf@raven.ccc.cc.ks.us; *Tech Servs*, Jean Roberts; E-Mail: jeanr@raven.ccc.cc.ks.us; Staff 1 (MLS 1)
Founded 1923. Enrl 1,170; Fac 45; Highest Degree: Associate
Jul 2000-Jun 2001 Income $107,664. Mats Exp $30,150, Books $10,500, Per/Ser (Incl. Access Fees) $17,650. Sal $63,064 (Prof $29,700)
Library Holdings: Bk Vols 27,626; Bk Titles 25,108; Per Subs 308; Bks on Deafness & Sign Lang 12
Automation Activity & Vendor Info: (Acquisitions) Gaylord; (Cataloging) Gaylord; (Circulation) Gaylord; (OPAC) Gaylord; (Serials) Gaylord
Mem of Southeast Kansas Library System
Partic in BCR
Open Mon-Thurs 8-9, Fri 8-4, Sun 5-9

P COFFEYVILLE PUBLIC LIBRARY, 311 W Tenth, 67337-5816. SAN 305-8670. Tel: 316-251-1370. FAX: 316-251-1512. E-Mail: coffepl@terraworld.net. Web Site: www.skyways.org/library/coffeyville/. *Dir*, Karyl L Buffington; *Circ*, Joy Duvall; *Circ*, Linda McFall; *Ch Servs*, Barbara Powell; *Tech Servs*, Elaine Wylie; *Tech Servs*, Linda Shafer
Founded 1911. Pop 12,100; Circ 88,613
Library Holdings: Bk Titles 69,729; Per Subs 131; Bks on Deafness & Sign Lang 52
Subject Interests: Genealogy
Automation Activity & Vendor Info: (Cataloging) Sagebrush Corporation; (Circulation) Sagebrush Corporation
Mem of Southeast Kansas Library System
Special Services for the Blind - Bks on cassette; Large print bks

COLBY

J COLBY COMMUNITY COLLEGE, H F Davis Memorial Library, 1255 S Range, 67701. SAN 305-8689. Tel: 785-462-4689. FAX: 785-462-4600. Web Site: www.colby.cc.ks.us:8000/www/library. *Dir*, Shelly Huelsman; Tel: 785-462-3984, Ext 266, E-Mail: shelly@colbycc.org; *Acq, Publ Servs*, Rita Wade; Tel: 785-462-3984, Ext 265, E-Mail: rita@colby.cc.ks.us; *Ref*, Jody Engel; E-Mail: jody@colby.cc.ks.us; *Govt Doc, ILL, Publ Servs*, Lana Starkey; Tel: 785-462-3984, Ext 210, E-Mail: lana@colby.cc.ks.us; Staff 4 (MLS 1, Non-MLS 3)
Founded 1964. Enrl 2,402; Fac 75; Highest Degree: Associate
Jul 2000-Jun 2001 Income $158,635. Mats Exp $42,525, Books $22,000, Per/Ser (Incl. Access Fees) $12,000, Presv $850, Micro $2,400, Other Print Mats $275, Electronic Ref Mat (Incl. Access Fees) $5,000. Sal $79,000 (Prof $34,000)
Library Holdings: Bk Titles 26,000; Per Subs 200
Subject Interests: Kansas
Special Collections: Cookbook Coll
Automation Activity & Vendor Info: (Acquisitions) EOS; (Cataloging) EOS; (Circulation) EOS; (OPAC) EOS
Database Vendor: IAC - Info Trac, OCLC - First Search
Publications: Western Plains Heritage Series
Mem of Northwest Kansas Library System
Partic in Kansas Library Network Board

P PIONEER MEMORIAL LIBRARY, 375 W Fourth St, 67701-2197. SAN 305-8697. Tel: 785-462-4470. FAX: 785-462-4472. *Dir*, JoAnne Sunderman; *ILL*, Debbie Tittel; *Ch Servs*, Sheryl Goossen; Staff 3 (Non-MLS 3)
Founded 1926. Pop 5,800; Circ 133,095
Jan 2000-Dec 2000 Income $192,876, State $4,450, City $158,737, Locally Generated Income $26,449, Other $3,240. Mats Exp $23,481, Books $18,781, Per/Ser (Incl. Access Fees) $4,700. Sal $110,306
Library Holdings: Bk Vols 47,000; Per Subs 175
Special Collections: Cake Pans
Automation Activity & Vendor Info: (Circulation) Follett
Mem of Northwest Kansas Library System
Friends of the Library Group

COLDWATER

P COLDWATER-WILMORE REGIONAL LIBRARY, 221 E Main, PO Box 606, 67029. SAN 342-006X. Tel: 316-582-2333. E-Mail: coldlibrary@rh.net. *Librn*, Ellen Seizer; Staff 1 (MLS 1)
Founded 1912. Pop 1,600
Library Holdings: Bk Vols 15,000; Per Subs 27
Mem of Southwest Kansas Library System
Branches: 1
WILMORE BRANCH, PO Box 276, Wilmore, 67155. SAN 342-0094. Tel: 316-738-4464. *Librn*, Margaret Morgan
Library Holdings: Bk Titles 335

COLONY

P COLONY CITY LIBRARY,* 339 Cherry, PO Box 68, 66015-0068. SAN 305-8719. Tel: 316-852-3530. FAX: 316-852-3107. *Librn*, Sharon Wiley
Pop 474; Circ 1,571
1998-1999 Income $4,256, State $303, County $2,072, Parent Institution $1,881. Mats Exp $1,131, Books $1,000, Per/Ser (Incl. Access Fees) $131. Sal $600
Library Holdings: Bk Vols 4,398; Bk Titles 4,368
Mem of Southeast Kansas Library System
Partic in SE Kans Libr Asn

COLUMBUS

P COLUMBUS PUBLIC LIBRARY,* 205 N Kansas, 66725-1221. SAN 305-8727. Tel: 316-429-2086. FAX: 316-429-1950. *Dir*, Katherine VanGilder
Founded 1905. Pop 3,597; Circ 30,418
Library Holdings: Bk Vols 24,500; Per Subs 66
Mem of Southeast Kansas Library System

COLWICH

P COLWICH COMMUNITY LIBRARY, 432 W Colwich, PO Box 8, 67030-0008. SAN 305-8735. Tel: 316-796-1521. *Librn*, Nancy Maus; *Asst Librn*, Karen Jones; Staff 2 (Non-MLS 2)
Founded 1961. Pop 1,750; Circ 16,821
Jan 1999-Dec 1999 Income $58,317, State $3,107, Federal $1,636, Locally Generated Income $36,858, Other $16,716. Mats Exp $5,391, Books $4,022, Per/Ser (Incl. Access Fees) $1,369. Sal $27,161

Library Holdings: Bk Vols 10,500; Per Subs 62
Publications: Newsletter
Mem of South Central Kansas Library System
Friends of the Library Group

CONCORDIA

J CLOUD COUNTY COMMUNITY COLLEGE, Learning Resources Center,* 2221 Campus Dr, PO Box 1002, 66901. SAN 305-8751. Tel: 785-243-1435, Ext 224. FAX: 785-243-1043. Web Site: www.cloudccc.cc.ks.us. *Dir*, Janine Johnson
Founded 1968. Enrl 1,100; Fac 60
Library Holdings: Bk Vols 20,000; Per Subs 135
Open Mon-Thurs 7:45-10, Fri 7:45-5, Sat 8-5 & Sun 6-9

S CLOUD COUNTY HISTORICAL MUSEUM LIBRARY,* 635 Broadway, 66901. SAN 325-7347. Tel: 785-243-2866. *Curator*, Linda J Palmquist
Library Holdings: Bk Vols 550

P FRANK CARLSON LIBRARY,* 702 Broadway, 66901. SAN 305-8743. Tel: 785-243-2250. *Dir*, Denise de Rochefort-Reynolds
Founded 1892. Pop 6,500; Circ 75,000
Library Holdings: Bk Vols 38,000; Per Subs 131
Subject Interests: Travel
Special Collections: Business Resources; Frank Carlson Coll; Kansas Coll; Rural Resources Coll; Travel Video Coll; US Constitution
Mem of Central Kansas Library System

CONWAY SPRINGS

P CONWAY SPRINGS CITY LIBRARY,* 210 W Spring St, PO Box 183, 67031-0183. SAN 376-5563. Tel: 316-456-2859. FAX: 316-456-3294. *Librn*, Danna Fulkerson
Library Holdings: Bk Vols 10,000
Mem of South Central Kansas Library System

COPELAND

P COPELAND PUBLIC LIBRARY,* PO Box 121, 67837. SAN 305-8778. Tel: 316-668-5559. *Librn*, Arline Vann
Pop 310; Circ 1,033
Library Holdings: Bk Vols 7,000
Mem of Southwest Kansas Library System
Open Tues & Thurs 9-12, 1-5

CORNING

P CORNING CITY LIBRARY, Rte 1 Box C-57, 66417-2974. SAN 305-8786. Tel: 785-868-2755. *Librn*, Sharon Steinlage
Founded 1920. Pop 139; Circ 5,129
Library Holdings: Bk Vols 6,000; Per Subs 12
Mem of Northeast Kansas Library System
Open Mon 8-12 & 2-5, Wed 6-9, Sat 8-12

COTTONWOOD FALLS

P BURNLEY MEMORIAL LIBRARY,* 405 N Oak, PO Box 509, 66845. SAN 376-558X. Tel: 316-273-8588. FAX: 316-273-8588. *Librn*, Susan Davis
Library Holdings: Bk Vols 10,000; Per Subs 22
Mem of North Central Kansas Libraries System
Open Mon-Sat 2-5 & Wed 7-9

COUNCIL GROVE

P COUNCIL GROVE PUBLIC LIBRARY, 303 W Main St, 66846. SAN 305-8794. Tel: 316-767-5716. FAX: 316-767-7312. E-Mail: cglib@cgtelco.net. Web Site: www.skyways.lib.ks.us/norcen/cgrove. *Dir*, Anne Teghtmeyer; E-Mail: anneteg@cgtelco.net; *Asst Dir*, Joan Hughes; *Ch Servs*, Linda Shoults-Underwood; Staff 4 (Non-MLS 4)
Founded 1876. Pop 2,500; Circ 18,000
Library Holdings: Bk Vols 19,394; Per Subs 62
Automation Activity & Vendor Info: (Cataloging) Athena; (Circulation) Athena; (OPAC) Athena
Database Vendor: IAC - SearchBank, OCLC - First Search
Function: ILL available
Mem of North Central Kansas Libraries System
Friends of the Library Group

COURTLAND

P COURTLAND COMMUNITY LIBRARY, PO Box 85, 66939-0085. SAN 305-8808. Tel: 785-374-4260. *Dir*, Dolores Erickson
Founded 1922. Pop 377
Library Holdings: Bk Vols 4,976; Per Subs 50
Mem of Central Kansas Library System

CUNNINGHAM

P CUNNINGHAM PUBLIC LIBRARY,* 105 N Main, 67035. SAN 376-7655. Tel: 316-298-3163. *Librn*, Jane Meyers
Library Holdings: Bk Vols 5,000; Per Subs 10
Mem of South Central Kansas Library System

DELPHOS

P DELPHOS PUBLIC LIBRARY,* 114 W Second, PO Box 284, 67436-0284. SAN 376-5679. Tel: 785-523-4668. *Librn*, Sue Elliot
Library Holdings: Bk Vols 8,000; Per Subs 27
Mem of Central Kansas Library System

DERBY

P DERBY PUBLIC LIBRARY, 611 Mulberry, 67037. SAN 305-8816. Tel: 316-788-0760. FAX: 316-788-6067. Web Site: www.derbylibrary.com. *Dir*, Judy K Bennett; E-Mail: judy@derbylibrary.com; *Syst Coordr*, Debbie Thomas; E-Mail: debbie@derbylibrary.com; Staff 16 (MLS 1, Non-MLS 15)
Founded 1957. Pop 19,000; Circ 220,620
Jan 2000-Dec 2000 Income $426,965, State $15,302, City $397,200, Other $14,463. Mats Exp $90,571, Books $76,391, Per/Ser (Incl. Access Fees) $14,180. Sal $237,000 (Prof $42,000)
Library Holdings: Bk Vols 46,840; Bk Titles 57,080; Per Subs 225
Subject Interests: Kansas, Parenting
Automation Activity & Vendor Info: (Cataloging) epixtech, inc.; (Circulation) epixtech, inc.; (OPAC) epixtech, inc.
Database Vendor: Ebsco - EbscoHost, epixtech, inc., OCLC - First Search
Mem of South Central Kansas Library System

DIGHTON

P LANE COUNTY LIBRARY,* 144 South Lane, PO Box 997, 67839-0997. SAN 305-8824. Tel: 316-397-2808, Ext 219. FAX: 316-397-5937. Web Site: www.trails.net/laneco. *Dir*, Ruby Martin; *Asst Librn*, Mona Peck; *Asst Librn*, Maryann McCourt
Founded 1934. Pop 2,790; Circ 15,958
1998-1999 Income $43,000. Mats Exp $6,000. Sal $28,000
Library Holdings: Bk Vols 15,000; Per Subs 55
Subject Interests: Genealogy
Special Collections: Our Kansas Room-Kansas Books
Mem of Southwest Kansas Library System
Open Mon & Wed 9-8, Tues, Thurs & Fri 9-5, Sat 9-12
Friends of the Library Group

DODGE CITY

S BOOT HILL MUSEUM, Special Library & Archives,* Front St, 67801. SAN 373-4552. Tel: 316-227-8188. FAX: 316-227-7673. E-Mail: frontst@pld.com. *Curator*, Susan Dame Sal $17,000
Library Holdings: Bk Vols 1,450; Per Subs 20
Special Collections: Historic Photographs Coll
Partic in Dodge City Library Consortium

J DODGE CITY COMMUNITY COLLEGE, Learning Resources Center-Library Services,* 2501 N 14th, 67801. SAN 305-8840. Tel: 316-225-1321, Ext 287. FAX: 316-225-0918. E-Mail: library@dccc.cc.ks.us. Web Site: www.dccc.cc.ks.us. *Dir*, Cathy L Reeves; Staff 1 (MLS 1)
Founded 1935. Enrl 2,414; Fac 85
Library Holdings: Bk Vols 30,946; Bk Titles 25,620; Per Subs 220
Subject Interests: Agriculture, Nursing
Mem of Southwest Kansas Library System
Partic in Dodge City Library Consortium

P DODGE CITY PUBLIC LIBRARY, 1001 Second Ave, 67801-4484. SAN 305-8859. Tel: 316-225-0248. Toll Free Tel: 800-657-2533. FAX: 316-225-0252. Web Site: trails.net. *Dir*, Rosanne Goble; E-Mail: rgoble@trails.net; *Asst Dir, Coll Develop*, Emily Sitz; *Ref*, Sam Shipley; *Circ*, Esther Cox; Staff 19 (MLS 3, Non-MLS 16)
Founded 1905. Pop 22,033; Circ 239,204
Jan 1999-Dec 1999 Income $636,580, State $17,239, City $574,588, Locally Generated Income $25,653, Other $19,100. Mats Exp $78,998, Books $56,386, Per/Ser (Incl. Access Fees) $8,317, Other Print Mats $7,753, Electronic Ref Mat (Incl. Access Fees) $6,542. Sal $355,823
Library Holdings: Bk Vols 108,150; Per Subs 165
Subject Interests: History, Kansas, Spanish (language)

Special Collections: Cookbook Coll; Large Print Books
Mem of Southwest Kansas Library System
Partic in Bibliographical Center For Research, Rocky Mountain Region, Inc; OCLC Online Computer Library Center, Inc
Friends of the Library Group

S KANSAS HERITAGE CENTER LIBRARY, 1000 N Second Ave, 67801-4415. (Mail add: PO Box 1207, 67801-1207), SAN 305-8832. Tel: 316-227-1616. FAX: 316-227-1695. Web Site: www.ksheritage.org. *Dir*, Jim Sherer; E-Mail: info@ksheritage.com; *Assoc Dir*, Dave Webb; *Mgr*, Barbara Vincent; E-Mail: orders@ksheritage.com; *Res*, Janice Scott; E-Mail: heritage@pld.com; Staff 5 (MLS 1, Non-MLS 4)
Founded 1966
Library Holdings: Bk Vols 9,000; Per Subs 45
Subject Interests: Kansas
Publications: 399 Kansas Characters; Color Kansas Characters Poster/Coloring Book; Color Oklahoma Characters Poster/Coloring Book; Dodge City, Cowboy Capital; Kansas Symbols Coloring Book; Oklahoma Symbols Coloring Book; Santa Fe Trail Adventures; Sentinel to the Cimarron: The Frontier Experience of Fort Dodge, Kansas; West by Southwest
Mem of Kansas State Libr Syst

P SOUTHWEST KANSAS LIBRARY SYSTEM, 1001 Second Ave, 67801-4484. SAN 342-0124. Tel: 316-225-1231. Toll Free Tel: 800-657-2533. FAX: 316-225-0252. Web Site: trails.net. *Dir*, Rosanne Goble; E-Mail: rgoble@trails.net; *Asst Dir*, Carolyn Guernsey; *ILL, Online Servs*, Cindy Shipley; *Ref*, Patti Cummins; Staff 11 (MLS 4, Non-MLS 7)
Founded 1968. Pop 147,330
Jan 1999-Dec 1999 Income $681,046, State $110,009, County $393,289, Other $177,748. Mats Exp Books $45,077. Sal $274,200
Library Holdings: Bk Vols 12,152
Subject Interests: Large type print
Special Collections: Large Print; Spanish (Popular Reading)
Publications: Southwest Kansas Library System Newsletter; System Scene
Member Libraries: Ashland Public Library; Brownell Public Library; Bucklin Public Library; Cimarron City Library; Coldwater-Wilmore Regional Library; Copeland Public Library; Dodge City Community College; Dodge City Public Library; Finney County Public Library; Ford City Library; Fowler Public Library; Grant County Library; Hamilton County Library; Henry Laird Library; Kearny County Library; Kinsley Public Library; Kismet Public Library; Lane County Library; Liberal Memorial Library; Meade Public Library; Meadowlark Public Library; Minneola City Library; Montezuma Township Library; Morton County Library; Ness City Public Library; Plains Community Library; Ransom Public Library; Seward County Community College; Spearville Township Library; Stanton County Library; Stevens County Library; Utica Library Association
Partic in OCLC Online Computer Library Center, Inc; Telecommunications Libr Info Network
Branches: 1
TALKING BOOKS Tel: 316-225-1231. Toll Free Tel: 800-657-2533. FAX: 316-225-0252.
Bookmobiles: 1

DOUGLASS

P DOUGLASS PUBLIC LIBRARY,* 319 S Forest, 67039. SAN 305-8875. Tel: 316-746-2200. FAX: 316-747-2109. *Librn*, Janet Whittington
Pop 1,655
Library Holdings: Bk Vols 15,000; Per Subs 39
Mem of South Central Kansas Library System
Open Mon-Fri 11-6 & Sat 10-3
Friends of the Library Group

DOWNS

P DOWNS CARNEGIE LIBRARY, 504 S Morgan, 67437-2019. SAN 305-8883. Tel: 785-454-3821. FAX: 785-454-6606. E-Mail: dowcarlib@nckcn.com. *Librn*, Helen Seaman
Founded 1905. Pop 1,170; Circ 15,000
Library Holdings: Bk Vols 12,500; Per Subs 40
Subject Interests: History, Kansas
Mem of Central Kansas Library System

DWIGHT

P DWIGHT LIBRARY,* PO Box 278, 66849-0278. SAN 305-8891. Tel: 785-482-3804. *Librn*, Jane Kirkeniude
Pop 392; Circ 2,847
Library Holdings: Bk Vols 3,300; Per Subs 16
Mem of North Central Kansas Libraries System

EDNA

P EDNA PUBLIC LIBRARY, 105 N Delaware, PO Box 218, 67342-0218. SAN 305-8905. Tel: 316-922-3470. *Librn*, Dorothy Ledbetter
Founded 1950. Pop 537
Jan 1999-Dec 1999 Income $4,730, State $330, City $4,400. Sal $4,204
Library Holdings: Bk Vols 6,249
Mem of Southeast Kansas Library System

EFFINGHAM

P EFFINGHAM COMMUNITY LIBRARY,* 414 Main St, PO Box 189, 66023-0189. SAN 305-8913. Tel: 913-833-5881. E-Mail: efflibrary@yahoo.com. *Librn*, Rosie Falk
Pop 540; Circ 9,667
1998-1999 Income $8,235, State $418, City $3,685, Federal $447, Locally Generated Income $3,685. Mats Exp $1,547, Books $1,343, Per/Ser (Incl. Access Fees) $82, Other Print Mats $122. Sal $5,480
Library Holdings: Bk Vols 7,276; Per Subs 18
Mem of Northeast Kansas Library System

EL DORADO

P BRADFORD MEMORIAL LIBRARY,* 611 S Washington St, 67042. SAN 305-8921. Tel: 316-321-3363. FAX: 316-321-5546. E-Mail: brafd1dr@southwind.net. Web Site: www.eldoradokansas.com. *Dir*, Margaret Anderson; *Ch Servs*, Lois Starr; E-Mail: bradf4lb@southwind.net; *ILL*, Patty Jo Grove; E-Mail: bradf4lb@southwind.net; Staff 13 (MLS 1, Non-MLS 12)
Founded 1897. Pop 12,809
Jan 1998-Dec 1998 Income $278,767, Provincial $11,795, City $212,625, Federal $2,275, County $11,386, Locally Generated Income $31,272, Other $9,414. Mats Exp $48,429, Books $41,236, Per/Ser (Incl. Access Fees) $4,153, Other Print Mats $3,040. Sal $142,323 (Prof $26,270)
Library Holdings: Bk Vols 53,458; Per Subs 122
Special Collections: Connell Ornithology Coll; Main Western Americana Coll
Automation Activity & Vendor Info: (Cataloging) epixtech, inc.; (Circulation) epixtech, inc.
Database Vendor: epixtech, inc.
Function: ILL available
Mem of South Central Kansas Library System
Friends of the Library Group

J BUTLER COUNTY COMMUNITY COLLEGE, LW Nixon Library, 901 S Haverhill Rd, 67042-3280. SAN 305-893X. Tel: 316-322-3234. FAX: 316-322-3315. Web Site: www.buccc.cc.ks.us/library/library.htm. *Coll Develop, Dir*, Brian Beattie; E-Mail: bbeattie@butler.buccc.cc.ks.us; *Asst Dir*, Hazel Clothier; E-Mail: hclothie@butler.buccc.cc.ks.us; *Ref*, Martha Gregg; E-Mail: mgregg@butler.buccc.cc.ks.us
Founded 1927
1999-2000 Mats Exp $56,888, Books $36,288, Per/Ser (Incl. Access Fees) $18,600, Micro $2,000. Sal $213,622
Library Holdings: Bk Vols 39,000
Automation Activity & Vendor Info: (Acquisitions) Follett; (Cataloging) Follett; (Circulation) Follett; (OPAC) Follett
Database Vendor: Ebsco - EbscoHost, GaleNet, IAC - SearchBank, OCLC - First Search, ProQuest
Mem of South Central Kansas Library System
Partic in Dialog Corporation

S BUTLER COUNTY HISTORICAL SOCIETY, Olive Clifford Stone Library, 383 E Central, PO Box 696, 67042. SAN 326-4629. Tel: 316-321-9333. FAX: 316-321-3619. *Librn*, Anna Louise Borger; Staff 1 (MLS 1)
Founded 1977
2000-2001 Mats Exp $800, Books $600, Presv $100, Manuscripts & Archives $100. Sal $8,800
Library Holdings: Bk Titles 3,902
Subject Interests: Kansas, Local history
Special Collections: William Allen White Coll
Restriction: Not a lending library
Function: Research library
Open Mon-Sat 9-5, Sun 1-5

ELKHART

P MORTON COUNTY LIBRARY,* 410 Kansas, 67950. (Mail add: PO Box 938, 67950), SAN 305-8948. Tel: 316-697-2025. FAX: 316-697-4205. E-Mail: mortclb@elkhart.com. Web Site: www.elkhart.com/mcch/library/library.htm. *Librn*, Virginia Johnson
Pop 3,408; Circ 139,691
Jan 1997-Dec 1998 Income $207,185, County $203,529, Other $3,656. Mats Exp $13,600, Books $10,000, Per/Ser (Incl. Access Fees) $3,000, Micro $600. Sal $129,540 (Prof $70,084)
Library Holdings: Bk Vols 35,000; Per Subs 110
Special Collections: Doll Coll
Mem of Southwest Kansas Library System

ELLINWOOD

P ELLINWOOD SCHOOL COMMUNITY LIBRARY,* 210 N Schiller, 67526-1651. SAN 305-8956. Tel: 316-564-2306. FAX: 316-564-2848. *Librn*, Sharon Sturgis
Pop 3,240; Circ 39,343
Library Holdings: Bk Vols 34,000; Per Subs 80
Mem of Central Kansas Library System

SR SAINT JOHN'S LUTHERAN CHURCH LIBRARY, Fifth & Wilhelm, 67526. SAN 325-5921. Tel: 316-564-2044. FAX: 316-564-3024. *Librn*, Paula Knop
Library Holdings: Bk Vols 7,000; Per Subs 12
Special Collections: James Dobson Coll, Large Video Coll
Open to home schoolers & the community

ELLIS

P ELLIS PUBLIC LIBRARY, 907 Washington, PO Box 107, 67637-0107. SAN 305-8964. Tel: 785-726-3464. FAX: 785-726-3900. *Librn*, Pamela Newton; *Asst Librn*, Punkie Erbert
Pop 1,740
Library Holdings: Bk Vols 13,036; Per Subs 46
Special Collections: Kansas Coll
Mem of Central Kansas Library System

ELLSWORTH

P J H ROBBINS MEMORIAL LIBRARY, City Library, 219 N Lincoln, 67439-3313. SAN 305-8972. Tel: 785-472-3969. FAX: 785-472-3969. *Dir*, Ruth Vodraska; E-Mail: rvod@idir.net; *Ch Servs*, Linda Homolka
Founded 1913. Pop 3,500; Circ 48,000
Jan 1999-Dec 1999 Income $69,212, State $2,212, City $58,000, Locally Generated Income $6,000, Other $3,000. Mats Exp $10,550, Books $9,000, Per/Ser (Incl. Access Fees) $1,550. Sal $44,000
Library Holdings: Bk Vols 20,100; Per Subs 75
Special Collections: Cemetery Records of Ellsworth County
Automation Activity & Vendor Info: (Cataloging) Athena; (Circulation) Athena
Mem of Central Kansas Library System

EMPORIA

P EMPORIA PUBLIC LIBRARY,* 110 E Sixth, 66801. SAN 305-8980. Tel: 316-342-6524. TDD: 326-342-6524. FAX: 316-342-2633. *Dir*, Sue Blechl; *ILL*, Lynnette Olson; *Ch Servs*, Angela Davis; *Acq, Ad Servs*, Kaite Mediatore; *Ad Servs*, Ron Ratliff; Staff 3 (MLS 3)
Founded 1869. Pop 35,100; Circ 299,450
Library Holdings: Bk Vols 95,724; Per Subs 203
Subject Interests: Art and architecture, Business and management, Genealogy, Local history, Music, Philosophy, Theology
Partic in OCLC Online Computer Library Center, Inc
Special Services for the Deaf - Staff with knowledge of sign language; TDD
Bi-lingual staff member (Spanish/English); Public access internet terminals.
Home Bound Delivery
Friends of the Library Group

C EMPORIA STATE UNIVERSITY, William Allen White Library, 1200 Commercial St, Box 4051, 66801. SAN 342-0183. Tel: 316-341-5207. Interlibrary Loan Service FAX: 316-341-5997. Web Site: www.emporia.edu/s/www/libsu/wawl.htm. *Dir*, Joyce Davis; Tel: 316-341-5043, Fax: 316-341-6208, E-Mail: davisjoy@emporia.edu; *Acq*, Michele Azar; Tel: 316-341-6130, Fax: 316-341-6208, E-Mail: azarmich@emporia.edu; *Online Servs*, Terri Summey; *Media Spec*, Loretta Neufeld; *Spec Coll*, Mary E Bogan; *Circ*, Sally Conard; *ILL*, Steve Hanschu; *Ref*, Lewis Armstrong; Tel: 316-341-5034, Fax: 316-341-6208, E-Mail: armstrol@emporia.edu; *Bibliog Instr*, Sherlene Backhus; Tel: 316-341-5033, Fax: 316-341-6208, E-Mail: backhusz@emporia.edu; *Per*, Patricia Fine; Tel: 316-341-5032, Fax: 316-341-6208, E-Mail: finepatr@emporia.edu; *Archivist*, Barb Robins; Tel: 316-341-5048, Fax: 316-341-5587, E-Mail: robinsba@emporia.edu. Subject Specialists: *Business and management*, Terri Summey; *Technology*, Steve Hanschu; Staff 23 (MLS 9, Non-MLS 14)
Founded 1863. Enrl 6,000; Fac 347
Jul 2000-Jun 2001 Mats Exp $472,890, Books $137,000, Per/Ser (Incl. Access Fees) $184,190, Micro $51,700, Electronic Ref Mat (Incl. Access Fees) $100,000
Library Holdings: Bk Vols 799,200; Bk Titles 481,317; Per Subs 1,357
Special Collections: Children's Books (May Massee Coll), bk, orig illust; Children's Literature (Mary White Coll); Elizabeth Yates Coll; Emporia State University; Lois Lenski Coll, mss, illust; Materials (Normaliana); William Allen White Mss, bk, mss, letter
Automation Activity & Vendor Info: (Acquisitions) Innovative Interfaces Inc.; (Cataloging) Innovative Interfaces Inc.; (Circulation) Innovative Interfaces Inc.; (Course Reserve) Innovative Interfaces Inc.; (ILL) Innovative Interfaces Inc.; (Media Booking) Innovative Interfaces Inc.; (OPAC) Innovative Interfaces Inc.; (Serials) Innovative Interfaces Inc.
Database Vendor: Dialog, OVID Technologies, ProQuest
Departmental Libraries:
TEACHERS COLLEGE RESOURCE CENTER, Visser Hall 224, 66801. SAN 342-0213. Tel: 316-341-5292. FAX: 316-341-5785. *Dir*, Marla Darby
Special Collections: Exceptional Child

P KANSAS STATE LIBRARY, Kansas Talking Books Service, ESU Memorial Union, 1200 Commercial, 66801-5087. SAN 306-1515. Tel: 316-343-7124. Toll Free Tel: 800-362-0699. FAX: 316-343-7124. E-Mail: ksst16Lb@ink.org. *Dir*, Patti Lang; E-Mail: pattilang@ink.org; Staff 1 (MLS 1)
Founded 1970. Circ 368,963
Publications: Newsletter
Special Services for the Blind - Books available with recordings
Friends of the Library Group

ENTERPRISE

P ENTERPRISE PUBLIC LIBRARY,* PO Box 307, 67441-0307. SAN 305-9006. Tel: 785-263-8351. Interlibrary Loan Service Tel: 800-432-2796. *Librn*, Sally S Frank
Pop 995; Circ 12,723
1997-1998 Income $10,509. Mats Exp $1,994, Books $780, Per/Ser (Incl. Access Fees) $1,214. Sal $6,173
Library Holdings: Bk Vols 17,000; Per Subs 48
Publications: Readers Guide
Mem of North Central Kansas Libraries System

ERIE

P ERIE CITY PUBLIC LIBRARY, 204 S Butler, 66733-1349. SAN 305-9014. Tel: 316-244-5119. E-Mail: elibrary@rlrnews.com. *Librn*, Kindra Holland
Pop 1,365; Circ 9,612
Library Holdings: Bk Vols 13,500; Per Subs 25
Special Collections: Kansas Coll
Mem of Southeast Kansas Library System

EUDORA

P EUDORA PUBLIC LIBRARY,* 14 E Ninth St, PO Box 370, 66025-0370. SAN 305-9022. Tel: 785-542-2496. FAX: 785-542-2496. *Librn*, Marlene Evinger
Founded 1967. Pop 4,000; Circ 25,000
Jan 1999-Dec 2000 Income $68,000
Library Holdings: Bk Vols 10,000; Per Subs 35
Mem of Northeast Kansas Library System
Friends of the Library Group

EUREKA

P EUREKA CARNEGIE LIBRARY, 520 N Main St, 67045-1388. SAN 305-9030. Tel: 316-583-6222. FAX: 316-583-6222. E-Mail: carnegie@fox-net.net. *Dir*, Constance Doeden; Staff 3 (Non-MLS 3)
Founded 1892. Pop 2,880; Circ 36,075
Jan 1999-Dec 1999 Income $56,220, State $2,316, City $35,000, Locally Generated Income $5,077, Other $13,827. Mats Exp $7,564, Books $5,351, Per/Ser (Incl. Access Fees) $1,446, AV Equip $767
Library Holdings: Bk Vols 17,711; Bk Titles 16,613; Per Subs 38
Database Vendor: IAC - Info Trac, OCLC - First Search
Mem of Southeast Kansas Library System
Friends of the Library Group

S GREENWOOD COUNTY HISTORICAL SOCIETY LIBRARY, 120 W Fourth, 67045-1445. SAN 371-7941. Tel: 316-583-6682. *Dir*, Alfred Ferguson; *Coll Develop*, Jeff Hokanson
Library Holdings: Bk Titles 500
Subject Interests: Genealogy

EVEREST

P BARNES READING ROOM,* PO Box 204, 66424-0064. SAN 305-9049. Tel: 785-548-7733. *Librn*, Jo Chamberlin
Pop 433; Circ 3,134
Library Holdings: Bk Vols 7,413
Mem of Northeast Kansas Library System
Open Mon 6-8, Tues-Fri 2-4:30

FALL RIVER

P FALL RIVER PUBLIC LIBRARY,* 314 Merchant Ave, 67047. SAN 376-804X. Tel: 316-658-4973. *Librn*, Carol Palsmeier
Library Holdings: Bk Vols 6,000
Mem of Southeast Kansas Library System

FLORENCE

P FLORENCE PUBLIC LIBRARY,* 324 Main St, 66851. SAN 305-9057. Tel: 316-878-4649. *Librn*, Gayle Scriven
Pop 737; Circ 7,460
Library Holdings: Bk Vols 9,680; Per Subs 19
Mem of North Central Kansas Libraries System

FORD

P FORD CITY LIBRARY,* E Eighth St, 67842-0108. SAN 376-7221. Tel: 316-369-2247, 316-369-2820. *Librn*, Marsha Stout
Library Holdings: Bk Vols 5,200
Mem of Southwest Kansas Library System

FORMOSO

P FORMOSO PUBLIC LIBRARY, 204 Main St, PO Box 10, 66942-0010. SAN 305-9065. Tel: 785-794-2424. E-Mail: libfor@nckcn.com. *Librn*, Shelly Haskins
Pop 140; Circ 1,800
Library Holdings: Bk Vols 4,202
Mem of Central Kansas Library System

FORT LEAVENWORTH

UNITED STATES ARMY

A COMBINED ARMS RESEARCH LIBRARY, US Army Command & General Staff College, 250 Gibbon Ave, 66027-2314. SAN 342-0302. Tel: 913-758-3101. FAX: 913-758-3014. E-Mail: carlref@leavenworth.army.mil. Web Site: www.cgsc.army.mil/carl/. *Dir*, Martha Davis; *Ch Servs, Publ Servs*, Edwin Burgess; *Acq*, Stephen Brown; Staff 16 (MLS 16)
Founded 1882
Library Holdings: Bk Vols 253,854; Bk Titles 119,959; Per Subs 604
Subject Interests: Military history, National security
Special Collections: Combined Arms & Fort Leavenworth Archives
Database Vendor: epixtech, inc.
Publications: Guide to Electronic Resources; Guide to Microform & Special Collections; Library Info Brochures; Library Information Guides; Periodical Holdings
Partic in Fedlink; Military Educ Coordination Conf Libr Consortium; Tralinet

A US DISCIPLINARY BARRACKS LIBRARY Tel: 913-684-4313. FAX: 913-651-7108.
Library Holdings: Bk Vols 22,500; Per Subs 84
Partic in Am Correctional Assoc

FORT RILEY

UNITED STATES ARMY

A FORT RILEY POST LIBRARY, Bldg 5306, 66442-6416. SAN 342-0337. Interlibrary Loan Service Tel: 785-239-5305. FAX: 785-239-4971. *Chief Librn*, Arlette Conrad; E-Mail: conrad@ksu.edu; Staff 6 (MLS 2, Non-MLS 4)
Library Holdings: Bk Vols 20,000; Per Subs 50
Subject Interests: Military history
Partic in Fedlink

AM MEDICAL LIBRARY, CDR USAMEDDAC-Med Libr, 600 Caisson Hill Rd, 66442-5037. SAN 320-9288. Tel: 785-239-7874. FAX: 785-239-7626.
Partic in Midcontinental Regional Med Libr Program

S US CAVALRY MUSEUM, Bldg 207, 66442-0160. (Mail add: PO Box 2160, 66442-0160), SAN 329-3025. Tel: 785-239-2737, 785-239-2743. Reference Tel: 785-239-8234. FAX: 785-239-6243. *Dir*, Terry Van Meter; E-Mail: vanmetet@riley.army.mil; *Librn*, Tom Metsala
Library Holdings: Bk Titles 4,800; Per Subs 34
Subject Interests: First infantry div hist, Military history, US cavalry hist
Library is the support library for the museum division at Ft Riley, Kansas

FORT SCOTT

J FORT SCOTT COMMUNITY COLLEGE LIBRARY,* 2108 S Horton, 66701. SAN 305-9073. Tel: 316-223-2700, Ext 82. FAX: 316-223-6530. *Dir*, Connie Park; E-Mail: conniep@fsccax.ftscott.cc.ks.us; Staff 4 (MLS 2, Non-MLS 2)
Founded 1919. Enrl 2,660; Fac 48
1998-1999 Income $115,000. Mats Exp $24,000, Books $8,000, Per/Ser (Incl. Access Fees) $16,000. Sal $86,000 (Prof $67,000)
Library Holdings: Bk Vols 22,000
Subject Interests: Kansas
Mem of Southeast Kansas Library System

P FORT SCOTT PUBLIC LIBRARY,* 201 S National, 66701. SAN 305-9081. Tel: 316-223-2882. *Dir*, Lisa Walter
Pop 8,893
Library Holdings: Bk Vols 38,000; Per Subs 50
Subject Interests: Kansas, Local history
Mem of Southeast Kansas Library System

FOWLER

P FOWLER PUBLIC LIBRARY,* 510 Main St, 67844-0135. SAN 305-909X. Tel: 316-646-5550. *Librn*, Shirley Randall
Founded 1963. Pop 650
Library Holdings: Bk Titles 11,180; Per Subs 30
Mem of Southwest Kansas Library System

FRANKFORT

P FRANKFORT CITY LIBRARY,* 107 N Kansas, 66427-1323. SAN 305-9103. Tel: 785-292-4320. *Librn*, June Warren
Founded 1888
Library Holdings: Bk Vols 8,100; Per Subs 25
Special Collections: Kansas History
Mem of North Central Kansas Libraries System

FREDONIA

P FREDONIA PUBLIC LIBRARY,* 807 Jefferson, 66736. SAN 305-9111. Tel: 316-378-2863. FAX: 316-378-2645. Web Site: www.skyways.lib.ks.us/town/fredonia/index.html.
Founded 1914. Circ 27,865
Jan 1997-Dec 1998 Income $74,173, State $2,019, City $29,075, Locally Generated Income $3,000, Other $21,402. Mats Exp $56,314, Books $6,610, Per/Ser (Incl. Access Fees) $1,383. Sal $34,353
Library Holdings: Bk Vols 35,000; Per Subs 50
Mem of Southeast Kansas Library System
Open Mon-Thurs 10-8, Fri 10-6, Sat 10-12
Friends of the Library Group

S WILSON COUNTY HISTORICAL SOCIETY, Museum Library,* 420 N Seventh, 66736. SAN 325-5948. Tel: 316-378-3965. *Pres*, Richard Wiles
Library Holdings: Bk Vols 100
Subject Interests: Local history
Special Collections: Family Histories; History & Genealogy Coll

GALENA

P GALENA PUBLIC LIBRARY,* 315 W Seventh St, 66739-1293. SAN 305-912X. Tel: 316-783-5132. *Librn*, Nellie Hoskins
Pop 3,731; Circ 22,483
Library Holdings: Bk Vols 35,400; Per Subs 52
Special Collections: Cemetary records for Cherokee County; Genealogy Coll; Local Newspapers, 1877-1930
Mem of Southeast Kansas Library System
Friends of the Library Group

GARDEN CITY

P FINNEY COUNTY PUBLIC LIBRARY, 605 E Walnut, 67846. SAN 305-9146. Tel: 316-272-3680. FAX: 316-272-3682. Web Site: www.fcpl.homestead.com. *Dir*, Todd John Humble; *Head, Cat*, Mary Jo Cousins; E-Mail: fcpl@mail.com; *Dep Dir, ILL*, Earlene Nicholson; *Ch Servs, Dep Dir*, Elaine Scheuerman; Staff 24 (MLS 1, Non-MLS 23)
Founded 1897. Pop 40,000; Circ 240,000
Jan 2001-Dec 2001 Income $183,000, State $38,000, County $105,000, Locally Generated Income $10,000, Other $30,000. Mats Exp $100,000, Books $80,000, Per/Ser (Incl. Access Fees) $12,000. Sal $362,000 (Prof $46,000)
Library Holdings: Bk Vols 126,000; Per Subs 350
Subject Interests: Gardens
Special Collections: Genealogy; Kansas; Spanish & Vietnamese Literature
Automation Activity & Vendor Info: (Cataloging) epixtech, inc.; (Circulation) epixtech, inc.; (OPAC) CARL; (OPAC) epixtech, inc.
Database Vendor: OCLC - First Search
Publications: Newsletter
Mem of Southwest Kansas Library System
Special Services for the Blind - Internet workstation with adaptive software for use by people with visual limitations; Reader services
Involved in outreach programs for the elderly, adult literacy & bilingual children
Friends of the Library Group

J THOMAS F SAFFELL LIBRARY,* Garden City Community College, 801 Campus Dr, 67846. SAN 305-9138. Tel: 316-276-9511. FAX: 316-276-9630. E-Mail: library@gccc.cc.ks.us. *Dir*, William H Utz; Tel: 316-276-9510, E-Mail: wutz@gccc.cc.ks.us; *ILL*, Kathy Winter; Tel: 316-276-9656, E-Mail: kwinter@gccc.cc.ks.us; Staff 4 (MLS 1, Non-MLS 3)
Founded 1919. Enrl 2,320; Fac 110
Library Holdings: Bk Vols 42,000; Bk Titles 33,000; Per Subs 200
Automation Activity & Vendor Info: (Cataloging) epixtech, inc.;

(Circulation) epixtech, inc.; (OPAC) epixtech, inc.
Database Vendor: Ebsco - EbscoHost, epixtech, inc., IAC - SearchBank, OCLC - First Search, OVID Technologies
Publications: Branded Books
Function: ILL available
Partic in Kans Interlibr Syst

GARNETT

P GARNETT PUBLIC LIBRARY,* 125 W Fourth St, PO Box 385, 66032-1398. SAN 305-9154. Tel: 785-448-3388. FAX: 785-448-3936. E-Mail: garlib@kanza.net. *Librn*, Andrea Sobba
Founded 1912. Pop 3,179; Circ 54,000
Library Holdings: Bk Vols 30,000; Per Subs 50
Special Collections: Mary Bridget McAuliffe Walker Art Coll
Mem of Southeast Kansas Library System
Friends of the Library Group

GAYLORD CITY

P GAYLORD CITY LIBRARY,* PO Box 570, 67638-0570. SAN 376-5121. *Librn*, Donna Muck; Tel: 785-697-2650
Library Holdings: Bk Vols 3,000
Mem of Central Kansas Library System

GENESEO

P GENESEO PUBLIC LIBRARY,* 725 Main St, PO Box 166, 67444-0326. SAN 305-9162. Tel: 316-824-6140. *Librn*, Winny Gustus
Pop 521; Circ 5,350
Library Holdings: Bk Vols 5,000; Per Subs 70
Special Collections: Kansas History Coll
Mem of South Central Kansas Library System
Open Mon 9-12, Wed & Fri 1-5

GIRARD

P GIRARD PUBLIC LIBRARY, 128 W Prairie, 66743-1498. SAN 305-9170. Tel: 316-724-4317. FAX: 316-724-8374. E-Mail: girardpl@ckt.net. Web Site: skyways.lib.ks.us/kansas.html. *Librn*, Terri Harley
Founded 1899. Pop 3,000; Circ 22,291
Jan 2000-Dec 2000 Income City $98,116. Mats Exp $8,475, Books $6,000, Per/Ser (Incl. Access Fees) $1,225, AV Equip $1,250. Sal $57,564
Library Holdings: Bk Titles 18,000; Per Subs 65
Special Collections: Crawford County History; Halderman-Julius (Little Blue Books); Kansas Authors; The Girard Press (1869-1999), micro
Mem of Southeast Kansas Library System

GLASCO

P GLASCO CITY LIBRARY,* City Hall, PO Box 595, 67445-0595. SAN 305-9189. Tel: 785-568-2313. *Librn*, Pat Horn
Founded 1916. Pop 600; Circ 5,700
Library Holdings: Bk Vols 6,000; Per Subs 40
Mem of Central Kansas Library System
Open Tues & Fri 2-6, Wed 2-5, Thurs 6-8 & Sat 9-12

GLEN ELDER

P GLEN ELDER LIBRARY, 105 S Mill, PO Box 188, 67446-0188. Tel: 785-545-3632. *Librn*, Robi Clark
Pop 425; Circ 1,716
Library Holdings: Bk Vols 8,025; Per Subs 13
Mem of Central Kansas Library System
Friends of the Library Group

GODDARD

P GODDARD PUBLIC LIBRARY, 315 S Main, PO Box 443, 67052-0443. SAN 305-9200. Tel: 316-794-8771. E-Mail: goddardlib@yahoo.com. *Librn*, Jackilyn A Rundell
Founded 1969. Pop 1,900; Circ 20,120
Jan 1999-Dec 1999 Mats Exp $6,502, Books $4,996, Per/Ser (Incl. Access Fees) $1,425, AV Equip $81. Sal $16,251
Library Holdings: Bk Vols 15,049; Per Subs 50
Mem of South Central Kansas Library System
Open Mon, Wed-Fri 1-5, Tues 10-7, Sat 9-noon

GOESSEL

P GOESSEL CITY LIBRARY,* 214 E Main St, 67053. SAN 305-9219. Tel: 316-367-8440. FAX: 316-367-2774. *Dir*, Kimberly Funk
Founded 1968. Pop 541; Circ 2,500
Library Holdings: Bk Titles 2,914; Per Subs 17
Subject Interests: Aging
Mem of North Central Kansas Libraries System

S MENNONITE HERITAGE MUSEUM,* 200 N Poplar St, 67053. SAN 376-1738. Tel: 316-367-8200.
Library Holdings: Bk Vols 200

GOODLAND

P GOODLAND PUBLIC LIBRARY, 812 Broadway, 67735. SAN 305-9227. Tel: 785-899-5461. FAX: 785-899-5461. E-Mail: glibrary@kansasweb.net. Web Site: www.skyways.lib.ks.us/nwkls/Goodland. *Dir*, Janet Warren; *Ch Servs*, Karen Gillihal; *Ad Servs*, Laura McClung; Staff 6 (MLS 1, Non-MLS 5)
Founded 1912. Pop 8,000; Circ 61,000
Jan 1999-Dec 1999 Income $130,000, State $3,900, City $101,600, County $12,000, Locally Generated Income $3,500, Other $9,000. Mats Exp $26,000, Books $15,000, Per/Ser (Incl. Access Fees) $5,000, Micro $500, AV Equip $4,000, Other Print Mats $1,000, Electronic Ref Mat (Incl. Access Fees) $500. Sal $70,000 (Prof $24,000)
Library Holdings: Bk Vols 41,500; Per Subs 150
Automation Activity & Vendor Info: (Circulation) Sagebrush Corporation; (OPAC) Sagebrush Corporation
Database Vendor: IAC - SearchBank, OCLC - First Search, ProQuest
Mem of Northwest Kansas Library System

GOVE

P GOVE CITY LIBRARY,* K23 Broad St, PO Box 66, 67736. SAN 305-9235. Tel: 785-938-2242. *Librn*, Ethel Beougher
Pop 148; Circ 1,964
Library Holdings: Bk Vols 3,623
Mem of Northwest Kansas Library System
Open Tues & Thurs 2-5

GRAINFIELD

P GRAINFIELD PUBLIC LIBRARY, 242 Main, PO Box 154, 67737. SAN 305-9243. Tel: 785-673-4770. E-Mail: grain1lb@ruraltel.net. *Coll Develop, Librn*, Darlene Shipman
Pop 417; Circ 2,410
Jan 1999-Dec 1999 Income $3,823, State $268, City $2,360, Parent Institution $990. Mats Exp $756, Books $542, Per/Ser (Incl. Access Fees) $66, Other Print Mats $148. Sal $2,160
Library Holdings: Bk Vols 4,086
Mem of Northwest Kansas Library System
OpenTues & Wed 3-6, Thurs 10-12 & Sat 10-11

GREAT BEND

J BARTON COUNTY COMMUNITY COLLEGE LIBRARY,* 245 NE 30 Rd, 67530. SAN 305-9251. Tel: 316-792-9362. FAX: 316-792-3238. Web Site: www.barton.cc.ks.us/library. *Dir*, Carol Barta; *ILL*, Carol Davis
Founded 1969
1998-1999 Mats Exp $27,500. Sal $100,100 (Prof $35,000)
Library Holdings: Bk Vols 33,000
Subject Interests: Nursing
Special Collections: Rural Gerontology Grant Coll
Partic in Cent Kans Libr Syst

P CENTRAL KANSAS LIBRARY SYSTEM,* 1409 Williams St, 67530-4090. SAN 305-926X. Tel: 316-793-4865. Toll Free Tel: 800-362-2642. FAX: 316-792-5495. Web Site: skyways.lib.ks.us/kansas/central/central.html. *Dir*, James Swan; E-Mail: jswan@ckls.org; *Mgr*, Vickie Herl; *Ch Servs*, Marquita Boehnke; *ILL, Ref*, Kathy Mitchum; *AV, Publ Servs*, Chris Rippel; *Automation Syst Coordr*, Steve Thomas; Staff 3 (MLS 3)
Founded 1968. Pop 202,000
1999-2000 Income $900,000
Library Holdings: Bk Vols 25,000
Publications: Post (bi-monthly newsletter); Trustee Handbook
Member Libraries: Barnard Library; Belleville Public Library; Bison Community Library; Burdett Community Library; Burr Oak City Library; Cawker City Public Library; Central Kansas Medical Center Library; Clyde Public Library; Courtland Community Library; Delphos Public Library; Downs Carnegie Library; Ellinwood School Community Library; Ellis Public Library; Formoso Public Library; Frank Carlson Library; Gaylord City Library; Glasco City Library; Glen Elder Library; Great Bend Public Library; Gypsum Community Library; Hays Public Library; Hoisington Public Library; Independent Township Library; J H Robbins Memorial Library; Jamestown City Library; Jewell Public Library; Jordaan Memorial Library; Kanopolis Public Library; Kensington Community Library; Kirwin City Library; Lang Memorial Library; Larned State Hospital; Lebanon-Community Library; Lincoln Carnegie Library; Logan Public Library; Long Island Community Library; Lucas Public Library; Mankato City Library; Mc Cracken Public Library; Minneapolis Public Library; Osborne Public

Library; Otis Community Library; Palco Public Library; Phillipsburg City Library; Plainville Memorial Library; Port Library; Rae Hobson Memorial Library; Randall City Library; Russell Public Library; Salina Public Library; Scandia City Library; Smith Center Public Library; Stockton Public Library; Sunshine City Library; Sylvan Grove Public Library
Partic in BRS; Dialog Corporation; NY Times Info Bank; SDC Info Servs
Branches: 1

P SUBREGIONAL LIBRARY FOR THE BLIND & PHYSICALLY HANDICAPPED, 1409 Williams St, 67530-4090. Tel: 316-793-4865. Toll Free Tel: 800-362-2642. FAX: 316-792-5495. *Librn*, Joanita Masden
Founded 1973. Circ 34,000
1997-1998 Income $80,000
Bookmobiles: 1

M CENTRAL KANSAS MEDICAL CENTER LIBRARY, 3515 Broadway, 67530-3691. SAN 305-9278. Tel: 316-792-2511. Circulation Tel: 316-786-6622. Reference Tel: 316-786-6622. Toll Free Tel: 800-657-5733. FAX: 316-792-1605. E-Mail: library.ckmc@greatbend.com. *Librn*, Romona F Newsome; E-Mail: romona@chi-midwest.org; Staff 1 (Non-MLS 1)
Founded 1988
Jul 1999-Jun 2000 Income $23,435. Mats Exp $11,017, Books $55, Per/Ser (Incl. Access Fees) $10,894, Electronic Ref Mat (Incl. Access Fees) $68. Sal $3,200
Library Holdings: Bk Titles 1,000; Per Subs 40
Subject Interests: Medicine, Nursing
Mem of Central Kansas Library System

P GREAT BEND PUBLIC LIBRARY,* 1409 Williams St, 67530-4090. SAN 305-9286. Tel: 316-792-2409. FAX: 316-792-5495, 793-7270. Web Site: skyways.lib.ks.us/kansas/control/great bend/indexhtml. *Dir*, James A Swan; E-Mail: jswan@ckls.org; *Ch Servs*, Sandy Dayton; *Coll Develop, Ref*, Rose Arnoldy; *Circ*, Marilyn Malbrough; *AV, Publ Servs*, Terri Hurley; Staff 2 (MLS 2)
Pop 15,000; Circ 200,000
1998-1999 Income $488,000. Mats Exp $52,300, Books $37,000, Per/Ser (Incl. Access Fees) $10,000. Sal $260,000
Library Holdings: Bk Vols 98,000; Per Subs 350
Special Collections: Association Law Library Coll); Kansas & Federal Law (Barton County Bar); Petroleum Geology (American Petroleum Institute Coll)
Mem of Central Kansas Library System
Partic in Bibliographical Center For Research, Rocky Mountain Region, Inc; OCLC Online Computer Library Center, Inc
Friends of the Library Group

GREENSBURG

P KIOWA COUNTY LIBRARY, 120 S Main, 67054. SAN 305-9294. Tel: 316-723-2683. *Librn*, Carol Montgomery
Founded 1936. Circ 53,436
Library Holdings: Bk Vols 31,892; Per Subs 85
Open Mon-Fri 9:30-5:30, Sat 9:30-1

GRENOLA

P GRENOLA PUBLIC LIBRARY,* Main St, PO Box 131, 67346-0131. SAN 305-9308. Tel: 316-358-3707. FAX: 316-358-3820. E-Mail: drenlib@sktc.net. *Librn*, Dixie Conklin
Founded 1950. Pop 347; Circ 2,082
Jan 1998-Dec 1998 Income $1,750, State $199, City $1,551. Mats Exp $1,741, Books $1,131, Per/Ser (Incl. Access Fees) $187, Electronic Ref Mat (Incl. Access Fees) $423. Sal $1,808
Library Holdings: Bk Vols 5,000; Bk Titles 5,000; Per Subs 15
Mem of Southeast Kansas Library System
Open Mon 4-7, Thurs & Sat 9-11

GRINNELL

P MOORE FAMILY LIBRARY,* 91 S Adams, PO Box 128, 67738-0128. SAN 376-5512. Tel: 785-824-3885. *Dir*, Pat Baalam
Library Holdings: Bk Vols 5,000
Mem of Northwest Kansas Library System

GYPSUM

P GYPSUM COMMUNITY LIBRARY,* 521 Maple, PO Box 8, 67448-0008. SAN 305-9324. Tel: 785-536-4296. FAX: 785-536-4296. *Librn*, Peggy Woods
Founded 1910. Pop 423; Circ 2,827
Library Holdings: Bk Vols 9,500; Per Subs 20
Mem of Central Kansas Library System

HALSTEAD

P HALSTEAD PUBLIC LIBRARY,* 264 Main St, 67056-0285. SAN 305-9332. Tel: 316-835-2170. FAX: 316-835-2170. E-Mail: hallib@southwind.net. *Dir*, Elizabeth Cain
Founded 1905. Pop 2,000; Circ 14,000
1998-1999 Income $42,000. Mats Exp $5,000
Library Holdings: Bk Vols 17,690; Per Subs 33
Special Collections: Halstead City History; Kansas
Mem of South Central Kansas Library System
Summer Reading Program, Storytime, large & small public reading rooms

HAMILTON

P HAMILTON CITY LIBRARY,* 21st E Main, PO Box 128, 66853-0128. SAN 305-9359. Tel: 316-678-3646. E-Mail: hlibrary@fox-net.net. *Librn*, Leta Harrell
Founded 1970. Pop 380; Circ 2,213
Library Holdings: Bk Vols 7,400; Bk Titles 7,400; Per Subs 14
Mem of Southeast Kansas Library System
Friends of the Library Group

HANOVER

P HANOVER PUBLIC LIBRARY,* 205 Jackson St, PO Box 97, 66945-0097. SAN 305-9367. Tel: 785-337-2424. *Librn*, Judy Springer
Founded 1954. Pop 839
Library Holdings: Bk Vols 14,000; Per Subs 50
Subject Interests: Science/technology, Technology
Mem of North Central Kansas Libraries System

HANSTON

P HANSTON CITY LIBRARY,* 105 N Logan, 67849-9409. SAN 373-8981. Tel: 316-623-2798. FAX: 316-623-2727. *Librn*, Karen S Salmans; E-Mail: salmans@ucom.net; *Asst Librn*, Jamie Casey; Staff 1 (Non-MLS 1)
Founded 1963. Pop 326; Circ 4,639
1998-1999 Income $6,882, State $249, City $2,457, County $528. Mats Exp $2,208, Books $1,376, Per/Ser (Incl. Access Fees) $274, Other Print Mats $558. Sal $3,402
Library Holdings: Bk Vols 5,138; Per Subs 16

HARDTNER

P HARDTNER PUBLIC LIBRARY,* 102 E Central, PO Box 126, 67057. SAN 305-9375. Tel: 316-296-4586. E-Mail: hardt1lb@kanokia.net. *Librn*, Joy Helmer
Pop 336; Circ 1,638
Library Holdings: Bk Vols 10,000; Per Subs 20
Mem of South Central Kansas Library System
Open Tues 7-9, Sat 1-5
Friends of the Library Group

HARPER

P HARPER PUBLIC LIBRARY, 1002 Oak, 67058-1233. SAN 305-9383. Tel: 316-896-2959. FAX: 316-896-7832. E-Mail: harperlib@cyberlodge.com. *Dir*, Cara Lynne Vanderree; *Librn*, Brenda Minnis; *Asst Librn*, Connie Robinson; Staff 2 (Non-MLS 2)
Founded 1876. Pop 1,700; Circ 16,354
Library Holdings: Bk Vols 15,472; Per Subs 86
Mem of South Central Kansas Library System

HARTFORD

P ELMENDARO TOWNSHIP LIBRARY, 229 Commercial St, 66854-0038. (Mail add: PO Box 38, 66854-0038), SAN 305-9391. Tel: 316-392-5518. *Dir*, Catherine Schmidt; *Asst Librn*, Ida Jean Elliott
Founded 1966. Pop 1,650
Library Holdings: Bk Vols 10,000; Per Subs 40
Subject Interests: Children's books, Economics, Health, Social sciences and issues
Mem of North Central Kansas Libraries System
Special Services for the Deaf - Books on deafness & sign language
Special Services for the Blind - Talking Books
Open Mon 1:30-5, Tues 9:30-1:30, Wed 4-7, Thurs 9:30-12 & 2-5, Fri 2-6

HAVANA

P HAVANA LIBRARY,* 205 Mary St, PO Box 296, 67347. SAN 305-9405. Tel: 316-673-5525. *Librn*, Wanda Clark
Pop 121; Circ 1,309
Library Holdings: Bk Vols 4,500
Mem of Southeast Kansas Library System
Open Tues & Fri 12:30-5:30

HAVEN

P HAVEN PUBLIC LIBRARY,* 121 N Kansas, PO Drawer 340, 67543-0340. SAN 373-8973. Tel: 316-465-3524. FAX: 316-465-3524. E-Mail: publib@haven.lib.ks.us. Web Site: skyways.lib.ks.us/kansas/library/haven. *Librn*, Katherine Regier; *Asst Librn*, Mary Jane Biltz; Staff 2 (MLS 1, Non-MLS 1)
Founded 1902
2000-2001 Income $43,989, State $980, City $40,012, Other $2,997. Mats Exp $10,600, Books $8,500, Per/Ser (Incl. Access Fees) $2,100. Sal $20,400
Library Holdings: Bk Vols 11,675; Per Subs 50
Mem of South Central Kansas Library System

HAVILAND

JR BARCLAY COLLEGE, Worden Memorial Library, 100 Cherry St, 67059. SAN 305-9413. Tel: 316-862-5274. FAX: 316-862-5403. E-Mail: library@barclaycollege.edu. Web Site: www.barclaycollege.edu. *Librn*, Heidi Longstroth
Founded 1892. Enrl 102; Fac 18
Library Holdings: Bk Vols 53,000; Per Subs 152
Subject Interests: Religion
Special Collections: Quaker Rare Books
Automation Activity & Vendor Info: (Cataloging) Sagebrush Corporation; (Circulation) Sagebrush Corporation
Partic in S Cent Kans Libr Syst

HAYS

S ELLIS COUNTY HISTORICAL SOCIETY ARCHIVES,* 100 W Seventh St, 67601. SAN 329-7489. Tel: 785-628-2624.; Staff 5 (MLS 2, Non-MLS 3)
Founded 1972
Special Collections: County; Local History, docs, photog; Volga German History, docs, photog
Open Tues-Fri 10-12

C FORT HAYS STATE UNIVERSITY, Forsyth Library, 600 Park St, 67601-4099. SAN 305-9421. Tel: 785-628-4431. Interlibrary Loan Service Tel: 785-628-4351. FAX: 785-628-4096. Web Site: www.fhsu.edu/forsyth_lib/. *Dir*, John Ross; Tel: 785-628-4539, E-Mail: jross@fhsu.edu; *Ref Serv*, Donna Northam; Tel: 785-628-4529; *Circ*, Angela Barger; Tel: 785-628-4434; *ILL*, Carolyn Herrman; *Acq*, Jean Wesselowski; Tel: 785-628-4343; *Cat*, Jerry Wilson; Tel: 785-628-5282; *Archivist*, Judy Salm; Tel: 785-628-5901; *Govt Doc*, Mac Reed; Tel: 785-628-4340; *Electronic Resources*, Lynn Haggard; Tel: 785-628-5566; Staff 18 (MLS 9, Non-MLS 9)
Founded 1902. Circ 175,711; Enrl 5,600; Fac 300
Library Holdings: Bk Vols 350,000; Per Subs 1,800
Special Collections: Children's Literature; History (Ethnic Coll, Volga Germans) bks, tapes; History (Western Coll, Western Kansas)
Automation Activity & Vendor Info: (Cataloging) Endeavor; (Circulation) Endeavor; (OPAC) Endeavor
Partic in Bibliographical Center For Research, Rocky Mountain Region, Inc; OCLC Online Computer Library Center, Inc
Open Mon-Thurs 7:30am-12am, Fri 7:30-7, Sat 9-5, Sun 12-12

P HAYS PUBLIC LIBRARY, 1205 Main, 67601-3693. SAN 305-943X. Tel: 785-625-9014. FAX: 785-625-8683. Web Site: www.hayspublib.org. *Dir*, Melanie Miller; E-Mail: mmiller@fhsu.edu; *Ad Servs*, Anne Millhollen; *Ch Servs*, Norleen Knoll; *Tech Servs*, Geneva Deatrich; Staff 30 (MLS 2, Non-MLS 28)
Founded 1899. Pop 18,866; Circ 512,289
Jan 2000-Dec 2000 Income $898,000, State $24,000, Provincial $25,000, City $816,000, Locally Generated Income $33,000. Mats Exp $196,000, Books $130,000, Per/Ser (Incl. Access Fees) $10,000, Presv $300, Micro $700, AV Equip $15,000, Electronic Ref Mat (Incl. Access Fees) $40,000. Sal $428,000 (Prof $83,000)
Library Holdings: Bk Vols 140,000; Per Subs 205; High Interest/Low Vocabulary Bk Vols 103; Bks on Deafness & Sign Lang 158
Subject Interests: Kansas, Local history
Publications: The Bookmark (Newsletter)
Mem of Central Kansas Library System
Special Services for the Deaf - TTY machine
Friends of the Library Group

HAYSVILLE

P HAYSVILLE COMMUNITY LIBRARY,* 130 W Grand, 67060. SAN 320-4782. Tel: 316-524-5242. FAX: 316-524-0142. E-Mail: haylib@southwind.net. *Librn*, Betty Cattrell; Staff 8 (MLS 5, Non-MLS 3)
Founded 1977. Pop 8,353; Circ 75,970
1998-1999 Income $182,748
Library Holdings: Bk Vols 36,000; Per Subs 132
Special Collections: Genealogy Coll; Kansas (Kansas & Local History), bks, newspapers; Quilting bks; Sports bks
Mem of South Central Kansas Library System
Instituted & supports a community education program which includes an adult literary program teaching English as second language; also offers emergency language banks in Spanish, German, Czech & Vietnamese
Friends of the Library Group

HEPLER

P HEPLER CITY LIBRARY,* PO Box 148, 66746-0148. SAN 305-9448. Tel: 316-368-4379. FAX: 316-368-4779. *Librn*, Penny Smith
Pop 187; Circ 2,155
Library Holdings: Bk Vols 4,126; Per Subs 15
Mem of Southeast Kansas Library System
Open Mon 3-7, Wed 1-5

HERINGTON

P HERINGTON PUBLIC LIBRARY,* 102 S Broadway, 67449-2634. SAN 305-9456. Tel: 785-258-2011. *Librn*, Donna McCullough
Founded 1897. Pop 3,000; Circ 31,250
Library Holdings: Bk Vols 28,700; Per Subs 55
Open Mon-Thurs 12-7, Fri & Sat 10-5

HERNDON

P HERNDON CITY LIBRARY,* PO Box 205, 67739. SAN 305-9464. Tel: 785-322-5298. *Librn*, Ann Martin
Circ 1,920
Library Holdings: Bk Vols 7,500
Open Mon-Thurs 8-12:30 & Fri 8-12:30 & 2:30-4:30

HESSTON

C HESSTON COLLEGE, Mary Miller Library, PO Box 3000, 67062-3000. SAN 342-0361. Tel: 316-327-8245. FAX: 316-327-8300. Web Site: www.hesston.edu/academic/lrc/mml.html. *Bibliog Instr, Librn*, Margaret Wiebe; E-Mail: margaret@hesston.edu; Staff 1 (MLS 1)
Founded 1908. Enrl 400; Fac 35; Highest Degree: Associate
Jul 1999-Jun 2000 Income $88,189, State $3,502. Mats Exp $33,960, Books $18,436, Per/Ser (Incl. Access Fees) $15,000, Presv $524. Sal $56,134 (Prof $35,000)
Library Holdings: Bk Titles 30,000; Per Subs 225
Automation Activity & Vendor Info: (Circulation) Sagebrush Corporation; (OPAC) Sagebrush Corporation
Database Vendor: Ebsco - EbscoHost, GaleNet, IAC - Info Trac, Lexis-Nexis, OCLC - First Search
Mem of South Central Kansas Library System

P HESSTON PUBLIC LIBRARY, 110 E Smith St, PO Box 640, 67062. SAN 305-9472. Tel: 316-327-4666. FAX: 316-327-4459. E-Mail: hesstlib@southwind.net. Web Site: skyways.lib.ks.us/library/hesston/homepage.htm. *Librn*, A Christine Buller; Staff 3 (MLS 1, Non-MLS 2)
Founded 1937. Pop 3,586
Jan 1999-Dec 1999 Income $137,472, State $14,988, City $101,334, County $13,224, Locally Generated Income $6,861, Other $1,065. Mats Exp $32,123, Books $20,890, Per/Ser (Incl. Access Fees) $3,726, Electronic Ref Mat (Incl. Access Fees) $7,507. Sal $72,885 (Prof $29,016)
Library Holdings: Bk Vols 32,196; Per Subs 75
Subject Interests: Amish, Ecology, Landscape architecture, Mennonites, Transportation
Special Collections: Children's videos; educational toys; sewing patterns
Automation Activity & Vendor Info: (Cataloging) Follett; (Circulation) Follett
Function: ILL available, Photocopies available, Some telephone reference
Mem of South Central Kansas Library System

HIAWATHA

P MORRILL PUBLIC LIBRARY,* 431 Oregon, 66434-2290. SAN 305-9480. Tel: 785-742-3831. FAX: 785-742-2054. E-Mail: morril@hiawatha.lib.ks.us.
Founded 1882. Pop 3,702; Circ 83,650
Library Holdings: Bk Vols 36,000; Per Subs 100
Mem of Northeast Kansas Library System
Friends of the Library Group

HIGHLAND

C HIGHLAND COMMUNITY COLLEGE LIBRARY, 606 W Main, 66035. SAN 305-9499. Tel: 785-442-6054. Circulation Tel: 785-442-6053. Reference Tel: 785-442-6053. FAX: 785-442-6101. Web Site: www.highland.cc.ks.us/library/libindex/htm. *Dir Libr Serv*, Mary Ellen Peterson; E-Mail: mpeterso@highland.cc.ks.us; Staff 3 (MLS 1, Non-MLS 2)
Founded 1858. Enrl 3,500; Fac 79; Highest Degree: Associate
Jul 2000-Jun 2001 Income $28,853. Mats Exp $14,165, Books $3,511, Per/Ser (Incl. Access Fees) $8,530, Presv $329, Micro $45, Electronic Ref Mat (Incl. Access Fees) $1,750. Sal $65,000 (Prof $35,000)
Library Holdings: Bk Vols 23,000; Bk Titles 22,000; Per Subs 100
Subject Interests: Social sciences and issues
Special Collections: Local History, videocassettes
Automation Activity & Vendor Info: (Circulation) TLC
Database Vendor: IAC - Info Trac, OCLC - First Search
Mem of Northeast Kansas Library System
Partic in BCR

HILL CITY

P GRAHAM COUNTY PUBLIC LIBRARY, 414 N West St, 67642-1646. SAN 305-9502. Tel: 785-421-2722. FAX: 785-421-5583. E-Mail: gractllb@ruraltel.net. Web Site: www.ghcopublib.excelland.com/. *Librn*, Mary Allen-Balthazor; *Ch Servs*, Frances Belleau; Staff 4 (Non-MLS 4)
Founded 1972. Pop 3,219
Library Holdings: Bk Vols 31,219; Per Subs 60
Special Collections: Graham County Newspapers 1879-present; Wildflowers of Graham County

HILLSBORO

P HILLSBORO PUBLIC LIBRARY, 120 E Grand, 67063-1598. SAN 305-9510. Tel: 316-947-3827. FAX: 316-947-3810. *Dir*, Cathleen J Fish; E-Mail: cfish@teen.k12.ks.us; *Ch Servs*, Delora Kaufman; *Asst Librn*, Rebecca Morris; Staff 3 (Non-MLS 3)
Pop 2,720; Circ 40,272
Library Holdings: Bk Titles 18,000; Per Subs 57
Mem of North Central Kansas Libraries System

C TABOR COLLEGE LIBRARY, 400 S Jefferson St, 67063. SAN 305-9529. Tel: 316-947-3121. FAX: 316-947-2607. Web Site: www.tabor.edu.; Staff 1 (MLS 1)
Founded 1908. Enrl 538; Fac 35
Jul 1999-Jun 2000 Mats Exp $53,264, Books $26,730, Per/Ser (Incl. Access Fees) $16,483, AV Equip $558, Electronic Ref Mat (Incl. Access Fees) $9,493. Sal $44,788
Library Holdings: Bk Vols 80,000; Bk Titles 76,000
Subject Interests: Religion
Special Collections: Mennonite Brethren Historical Library & Archives, bks, mss, per
Partic in S Cent Kans Libr Syst
Open Mon-Thurs 7:30-11pm, Fri 7:30-5:30, Sat 1-5, Sun 1-11, Sept-May

HOISINGTON

P HOISINGTON PUBLIC LIBRARY, 169 S Walnut, 67544. SAN 305-9537. Tel: 316-653-4128. E-Mail: library@carrollsweb.com. *Dir*, Kathy Farrington
Founded 1928. Pop 421,322; Circ 4,144,887
1998-1999 Income $55,557, State $2,200, City $44,897, County $5,960, Other $2,500. Mats Exp $19,304, Books $14,548, Per/Ser (Incl. Access Fees) $2,860, Presv $150, Micro $766, Other Print Mats $980. Sal $32,101
Library Holdings: Bk Vols 28,236; Per Subs 90
Mem of Central Kansas Library System
Friends of the Library Group

HOLTON

P BECK BOOKMAN LIBRARY,* 420 W Fourth St, 66436-1572. SAN 305-9545. Tel: 785-364-3532. FAX: 785-364-5402. *Librn*, Candee Jacobs; *Asst Librn*, Sharon Lane
Founded 1897. Pop 3,207; Circ 37,474
Library Holdings: Bk Vols 31,070; Per Subs 61
Special Collections: Jackson County Coll; Kansas Coll
Mem of Northeast Kansas Library System
Friends of the Library Group

HOPE

P HOPE COMMUNITY LIBRARY, 216 N Main St, PO Box 305, 67451-0336. SAN 376-7663. Tel: 785-366-7218. *Librn*, Betty Penrod
Library Holdings: Bk Vols 3,000
Mem of North Central Kansas Libraries System
Friends of the Library Group

HORTON

P HORTON FREE PUBLIC LIBRARY, 809 First Ave E, 66439-1898. SAN 305-9553. Tel: 785-486-3326. E-Mail: hortonli@nidusa.net. *Dir*, Rita L Higley; E-Mail: rhigley@horton.lib.ks.us; *Librn*, Carolyn Oslen
Founded 1925. Pop 2,000; Circ 18,000
Library Holdings: Bk Vols 15,000; Bk Titles 15,000; Per Subs 41
Special Collections: Kansas Coll
Database Vendor: OCLC - First Search
Mem of Northeast Kansas Library System
Friends of the Library Group

HOWARD

P HOWARD CITY LIBRARY,* 126 S Wabash, PO Box 785, 67349-0785. SAN 305-9561. Tel: 316-374-2890. *Librn*, Judith Harsh
Founded 1921. Pop 976; Circ 6,057
Library Holdings: Bk Vols 17,600; Per Subs 15
Subject Interests: Large type print
Special Collections: Kansas Coll
Mem of Southeast Kansas Library System

HOXIE

P SHERIDAN COUNTY LIBRARY,* 801 Royal Ave, PO Box 607, 67740. SAN 305-957X. Interlibrary Loan Service Tel: 785-675-3102. *Dir*, Cindy Eller; *Asst Librn*, Glenda Farber
Pop 3,500; Circ 34,473
Library Holdings: Bk Vols 14,000; Per Subs 55
Subject Interests: Kansas
Mem of Northwest Kansas Library System
Open Mon 10-8, Tues-Fri 10-4:30 & Sat 10-2
Friends of the Library Group

HUGOTON

P STEVENS COUNTY LIBRARY, 500 Monroe, 67951-2639. SAN 305-9588. Tel: 316-544-2301. FAX: 316-544-2322. E-Mail: steve2lb@pld.com. Web Site: trails.net/hugoton/schr.html. *Dir*, Eunice M Schroeder; Staff 6 (MLS 1, Non-MLS 5)
Founded 1914. Pop 5,347; Circ 82,286
Feb 2001-Jan 2002 Income $402,812, State $4,000, County $398,812. Mats Exp $56,500, Books $40,000, Per/Ser (Incl. Access Fees) $5,000, AV Equip $6,500, Electronic Ref Mat (Incl. Access Fees) $5,000. Sal $107,425 (Prof $35,400)
Library Holdings: Bk Titles 32,812; Per Subs 121
Special Collections: Art Print Coll; Kansas Room Coll; Stevens County Genealogical Society Coll
Automation Activity & Vendor Info: (Cataloging) Nicholas; (Circulation) Nicholas
Database Vendor: OCLC - First Search
Mem of Southwest Kansas Library System
Partic in Tri-State Libr Consortium

HUMBOLDT

P HUMBOLDT PUBLIC LIBRARY,* 916 Bridge St, 66748. SAN 305-9596. Tel: 316-473-2243. *Dir*, Melinda Herder
Founded 1939. Pop 3,500; Circ 19,000
Library Holdings: Bk Vols 18,500; Per Subs 52
Subject Interests: Parenting, Photography, Religion, Science fiction
Special Collections: City History; high school yearbks
Mem of Southeast Kansas Library System
Partic in OCLC Online Computer Library Center, Inc

HUTCHINSON

J HUTCHINSON COMMUNITY COLLEGE, John F Kennedy Library, 1300 N Plum, 67501. SAN 305-9618. Tel: 316-665-3547. FAX: 316-665-3392. Web Site: www.hutchcc.edu/college/library/. *Dir*, Pat Vierthaler; E-Mail: vierthalerp@hutchcc.edu; *Librn*, Cheryl Warkentin; E-Mail: warkentinc@hutchcc.edu; *Librn*, Rebecca Carlson; E-Mail: carlsonr@hutchcc.edu; Staff 5 (MLS 3, Non-MLS 2)
Founded 1928. Enrl 4,330; Fac 99; Highest Degree: Associate
Jul 1999-Jun 2000 Mats Exp $58,947, Books $13,167, Per/Ser (Incl. Access Fees) $12,000, Micro $6,691, AV Equip $5,254, Electronic Ref Mat (Incl. Access Fees) $13,423. Sal $148,038 (Prof $91,331)
Library Holdings: Bk Vols 44,127; Bk Titles 36,742; Per Subs 352
Special Collections: FAA Resource Ctr contains information on flying
Automation Activity & Vendor Info: (Acquisitions) DRA; (Cataloging) DRA; (Circulation) DRA; (OPAC) DRA; (Serials) DRA
Mem of South Central Kansas Library System

P HUTCHINSON PUBLIC LIBRARY, 901 N Main, 67501-4492. SAN 305-9626. Tel: 316-663-5441. Toll Free Tel: 800-234-0529. FAX: 316-663-9506. Web Site: www.hplsck.org. *Dir*, Leroy Gattin; E-Mail: lgatt@hplsck.org; *Asst Dir*, Marcella Kille; E-Mail: mkille@hplsck.org; *ILL*, Ruth Heidebrecht; E-Mail: rheidebr@hplsck.org; *Ad Servs*, Dianna Brown; E-Mail: dbrown@hplsck.org; *Ch Servs*, Terry Christner; E-Mail: tchristn@hplsck.org; *Tech Servs*, Dianne Bogle; E-Mail: dbogle@hplsck.org; *Ref, Spec Coll*, Cheryl Canfield; E-Mail: ccanfiel@hplsck.org; *Coll Develop*, Reta Graber; E-Mail: graber@hplsck.org
Founded 1901. Pop 62,155
Jan 2000-Dec 2000 Income $1,486,926, State $31,250, City $1,297,295, Locally Generated Income $83,000, Other $75,381. Mats Exp $389,800, Books $302,300, Per/Ser (Incl. Access Fees) $72,500, Other Print Mats $15,000. Sal $803,321 (Prof $287,311)
Library Holdings: Bk Vols 583,211; Bk Titles 269,300; Per Subs 425
Automation Activity & Vendor Info: (Acquisitions) epixtech, inc.; (Cataloging) epixtech, inc.; (Circulation) epixtech, inc.; (OPAC) epixtech, inc.
Database Vendor: epixtech, inc.
Mem of South Central Kansas Library System
Partic in BCR; Dialog Corporation
Friends of the Library Group

P SOUTH CENTRAL KANSAS LIBRARY SYSTEM, 901 N Main, 67501. SAN 342-0426. Tel: 316-663-5441, Ext 110. Toll Free Tel: 800-234-0529. FAX: 316-663-9506. Web Site: www.hplsck.org. *Dir*, Leroy Gattin; Tel: 316-663-5441, E-Mail: lgatt@hplsck.org; *Asst Dir*, Paul Hawkins; Tel: 316-663-5441, Fax: 316-663-1215, E-Mail: phawkins@hplsck.org
Founded 1969. Pop 636,159
Jan 2000-Dec 2000 Income $1,775,692, State $210,000, Locally Generated Income $1,449,958, Other $115,734. Mats Exp $158,000, Books $59,000, Per/Ser (Incl. Access Fees) $75,000, AV Equip $24,000. Sal $484,000 (Prof $123,000)
Library Holdings: Bk Vols 121,321
Automation Activity & Vendor Info: (Acquisitions) epixtech, inc.; (Cataloging) epixtech, inc.; (Circulation) epixtech, inc.; (OPAC) epixtech, inc.
Publications: SCKLS (quarterly newsletter)
Member Libraries: Andover Public Library; Anthony Public Library; Arkansas City Public Library; Arlington City Library; Attica Public Library; Augusta Public Library; Belle Plaine City Library; Bethany College; Bradford Memorial Library; Buhler Public Library; Burrton Public Library; Butler County Community College; Caldwell Carnegie Library; Canton Township Library; Central Christian College Of Kansas; Cheney Public Library; Clearwater Public Library; Colwich Community Library; Conway Springs City Library; Cowley County Community College; Cunningham Public Library; Derby Public Library; Dixon Township Library; Douglass Public Library; Edna Bushow Memorial Public Library; Farmer Township Community Library; Friends University; Geneseo Public Library; Goddard Public Library; Halstead Public Library; Hardtner Public Library; Harper Public Library; Haven Public Library; Haysville Community Library; Hesston College; Hesston Public Library; Hutchinson Community College; Hutchinson Public Library; Ida Long Goodman Memorial Library; Inman Public Library; Kansas Wesleyan University; Kingman Carnegie Public Library; Kiowa Public Library; Leon Public Library; Lillian Tear Library; Lincoln Library; Lindsborg Community Library; Little River Community Library; Lyons Public Library; Macksville City Library; Marquette Community Library; Mc Pherson Public Library; McPherson College; Moundridge Public Library; Mount Hope Library; Mulvane Public Library; Newman University; Newton Public Library; Nickerson Public Library; Nora E Larabee Memorial Library; Norwich Public Library; Oxford Public Library; Partridge Public Library; Potwin Public Library; Pratt Community College Library; Pretty Prairie Public Library; Roxbury Library; South Haven Township Library; Southwestern College; Sterling College; Sterling Free Public Library; Sylvia Public Library; Towanda Public Library; Turon Community Library; Udall Public Library; United States Air Force; Viola Township Library; Walton Community Library; Wellington Public Library; Whitewater Memorial Library; Wichita Public Library; Winfield Public Library; Zenda Public Library
Branches: 1
P SUBREGIONAL LIBRARY FOR THE BLIND & PHYSICALLY HANDICAPPED, 67501. SAN 342-0450. Tel: 316-663-5441, Ext 129. Toll Free Tel: 800-234-0529. FAX: 316-663-1215. *Librn*, Karen Socha
Founded 1966
Special Services - Consultant services to individuals, nursing homes & institutions; in-town home bound delivery service; print books available with recordings; magnifying lens available

INDEPENDENCE

C INDEPENDENCE COMMUNITY COLLEGE LIBRARY, PO Box 708, 67301. Tel: 316-331-4100, Ext 4280. FAX: 316-331-8342. Web Site: www.indy.cc.ks.us. *Dir*, Janice C Weir; E-Mail: jweir@indy.cc.ks.us; *Asst Libr Dir*, Melissa Ruberson; E-Mail: mruberson@indy.cc.ks.us; *ILL*, Carol Small; E-Mail: csmall@indy.cc.ks.us; *Media Spec*, Kay Ackerson; E-Mail: kackerson@indy.cc.ks.us; Staff 4 (MLS 2, Non-MLS 2)
Founded 1925
Jul 1999-Jun 2000 Mats Exp $74,517, Books $11,360, Per/Ser (Incl. Access Fees) $5,104, Presv $5,821, AV Equip $23,227, Other Print Mats $17,675, Electronic Ref Mat (Incl. Access Fees) $11,330. Sal $122,286 (Prof $83,910)
Library Holdings: Bk Vols 35,194; Bk Titles 34,000; Per Subs 62
Special Collections: William Inge Coll
Database Vendor: IAC - Info Trac, Lexis-Nexis, OCLC - First Search, ProQuest
Mem of Southeast Kansas Library System

P INDEPENDENCE PUBLIC LIBRARY, 220 E Maple St, 67301-3899. SAN 305-9642. Tel: 316-331-3030. FAX: 316-331-3912. E-Mail: indlib@horizon.hit.net. Web Site: www.terraworld.net/indlib2. *Dir, Librn*, Anne Jaynes; *Asst Dir*, Aprl Nutt; *Ch Servs*, Rebecca Passeaur; *Ad Servs*, Cheryl Greer
Founded 1882. Pop 15,000; Circ 121,613
2000-2001 Income $358,590, State $7,361, City $158,332, Locally Generated Income $34,527, Other $34,565. Mats Exp $200,383, Books $31,896, Per/Ser (Incl. Access Fees) $7,589, Presv $300, AV Equip $10,000, Electronic Ref Mat (Incl. Access Fees) $400. Sal $118,657 (Prof $28,000)
Library Holdings: Bk Titles 5,684; Per Subs 121
Special Collections: Business; Genealogy; local newspapers on micro
Automation Activity & Vendor Info: (Acquisitions) Sagebrush Corporation; (Cataloging) Sagebrush Corporation; (Circulation) Sagebrush Corporation; (Course Reserve) Sagebrush Corporation; (ILL) Sagebrush Corporation; (Media Booking) Sagebrush Corporation; (OPAC) Sagebrush Corporation; (Serials) Sagebrush Corporation
Mem of Southeast Kansas Library System
Open Mon-Thurs 9-8, Fri 12-5 & Sat 9-1
Friends of the Library Group

INMAN

P INMAN PUBLIC LIBRARY,* 100 N Main, PO Box 416, 67546-0416. SAN 305-9650. Tel: 316-585-2474. FAX: 316-585-6418. E-Mail: inmanlib@southwind.net. Web Site: skyways.lib.ks.us/kansas/towns/inman/library.html. *Librn*, Rosetta Bartels
Founded 1943. Pop 1,000; Circ 10,000
Library Holdings: Bk Vols 15,000; Per Subs 24
Mem of South Central Kansas Library System

IOLA

J ALLEN COUNTY COMMUNITY COLLEGE LIBRARY, 1801 N Cottonwood, 66749-1698. SAN 305-9669. Tel: 316-365-5116, Ext 108. FAX: 316-365-3284. E-Mail: accclib@allencc.net. *Dir*, Steven Wells Anderson; Tel: 316-365-5116, Ext 235, E-Mail: anderson@allencc.net; *Asst Librn*, Yvonne Dunlap; Tel: 316-365-5116, Ext 208, E-Mail: ydunlap@allencc.net; *Asst Librn*, Jill Hoffman; Tel: 316-365-5116, Ext 207, E-Mail: hoffman@allencc.net; Staff 3 (MLS 1, Non-MLS 2)
Founded 1970. Enrl 1,066; Fac 45; Highest Degree: Associate
Jul 1999-Jun 2000 Income Other $131,453. Mats Exp $131,453, Books $14,860, Per/Ser (Incl. Access Fees) $16,909, Micro $1,141, Electronic Ref Mat (Incl. Access Fees) $438. Sal $84,495 (Prof $43,571)
Library Holdings: Bk Vols 38,108; Bk Titles 35,229; Per Subs 94
Subject Interests: Local genealogy
Automation Activity & Vendor Info: (Cataloging) Gaylord; (Circulation) Gaylord; (OPAC) Gaylord
Database Vendor: Ebsco - EbscoHost, IAC - SearchBank, OCLC - First Search
Publications: Policies & Procedures Manual
Function: Some telephone reference
Mem of Southeast Kansas Library System
Partic in SE Kans Libr Syst

P IOLA PUBLIC LIBRARY, 218 E Madison, 66749-3384. SAN 305-9677. Tel: 316-365-3262. FAX: 316-365-5137. Web Site: www.iola.lib.ks.us/. *Librn*, Roger Carswell; E-Mail: rogerc@midusa.net; *Ch Servs*, Leah Oswald; *Publ Servs*, Judith Thyer; Staff 4 (MLS 1, Non-MLS 3)
Founded 1884. Pop 6,336; Circ 88,376
Jan 1999-Dec 1999 Income $200,620, State $4,774, City $110,789, Federal $3,000, Locally Generated Income $10,030, Other $82,057. Mats Exp $30,502, Books $18,992, Per/Ser (Incl. Access Fees) $5,861, Electronic Ref Mat (Incl. Access Fees) $2,231. Sal $98,704
Library Holdings: Bk Vols 35,788; Per Subs 126
Special Collections: Genealogy; Kansas History
Automation Activity & Vendor Info: (Cataloging) Sagebrush Corporation; (Circulation) Sagebrush Corporation
Mem of Southeast Kansas Library System
Friends of the Library Group

P SOUTHEAST KANSAS LIBRARY SYSTEM, 218 E Madison, 66749. SAN 305-9685. Tel: 316-365-5136. FAX: 316-365-5137. Web Site: www.sekls.lib.ks.us/. *Dir*, Roger Carswell; E-Mail: rogerc@midusa.net; *Asst Dir*, Harry Willems; *Cat, Tech Servs*, Linda Monninger; *Acq, Coll Develop*, Elaine Brown; *Ref*, Margaret Raines; *ILL*, Brenda Cash; *ILL*, Melissa Sponseller; *Ch Servs*, Betty Burrows; *Automation Syst Coordr*, Nick Fleury; *Librn for Blind*, Liz Nix; Staff 20 (MLS 3, Non-MLS 17)

Pop 221,026
Jan 2000-Dec 2000 Income $959,570, State $119,990, Locally Generated Income $2,414, Other $837,166. Mats Exp $58,327, Books $50,476, Per/Ser (Incl. Access Fees) $750, Micro $36, Electronic Ref Mat (Incl. Access Fees) $2,440. Sal $348,675
Library Holdings: Bk Vols 73,408; Per Subs 16
Special Collections: Art Prints Coll; Genealogy Coll; Kansas Census
Automation Activity & Vendor Info: (Cataloging) Sagebrush Corporation; (Circulation) Sagebrush Corporation
Publications: SEKLS Stacks of News
Member Libraries: Allen County Community College Library; Altamont Public Library; Altoona Public Library; Arma City Library; Bronson Public Library; Caney City Library; Cedar Vale Memorial Library; Chanute Public Library; Cherryvale Public Library; Chetopa City Library; Coffeyville Community College; Coffeyville Public Library; Colony City Library; Columbus Public Library; Edna Public Library; Erie City Public Library; Eureka Carnegie Library; Fall River Public Library; Fort Scott Community College Library; Fort Scott Public Library; Fredonia Public Library; Galena Public Library; Garnett Public Library; Girard Public Library; Graves Memorial Public Library; Grenola Public Library; Hamilton City Library; Havana Library; Hepler City Library; Howard City Library; Humboldt Public Library; Independence Community College Library; Independence Public Library; Iola Public Library; Johnston Public Library; Library District 2 of Linn County; Linn County District Library Three; Linn County Public Library District No 1; Madison Public Library; Mary Sommerville Free Library; McCune City Library; Moline Public Library; Moran Public Library; Mound Valley Public Library; Neosho County Community College; Neosho County Community College; Oswego Public Library; Parsons Public Library; Parsons State Hospital & Training Center; Pittsburg Public Library; Pleasanton-Lincoln Library; Prescott City Public Library; Savonburg Public Library; Sedan Public Library; Thayer Friday Reading Club City Library; Toronto Public Library; W A Rankin Memorial Library; Walnut Public Library; Weir Public Library; Yates Center Public Library

JAMESTOWN

P JAMESTOWN CITY LIBRARY, 415 Walnut, 66948. (Mail add: PO Box 287, 66948-0287), SAN 305-9693. Tel: 785-439-6258. E-Mail: jameslib@nckcn.com. *Librn*, Debbie Kearn; Staff 1 (MLS 1)
Founded 1898. Pop 325; Circ 6,928
Library Holdings: Bk Vols 8,100; Per Subs 22; Spec Interest Per Sub 10
Special Collections: Children Around the World Coll
Mem of Central Kansas Library System
Open Tues 5-7, Wed 1-3, Sat 9-5

JENNINGS

P JENNINGS CITY LIBRARY,* General Delivery, Kansas Ave, 67643. SAN 305-9707. Tel: 785-678-2666. FAX: 785-678-2666. E-Mail: jenlibsg@mail.ruraltel.net. *Librn*, Sonya Gillespie
Pop 194; Circ 3,804
Library Holdings: Bk Vols 4,711; Per Subs 20
Subject Interests: Local history
Mem of Northwest Kansas Library System
Open Mon 2-4:30, Thurs 9-11, Sat 9-11:30

JETMORE

P JETMORE MUNICIPAL LIBRARY,* 308 Main St, PO Box 608, 67854-0608. SAN 305-9715. Tel: 316-357-8336. FAX: 316-357-6398. *Dir*, Jackie Sherrill; Staff 1 (MLS 1)
Library Holdings: Bk Titles 15,386; Per Subs 29
Special Collections: Hodgemon County Census & Newspapers, micro; Hodgemon County Genealogy Coll
Partic in SW Kans Libr Syst
Friends of the Library Group

JEWELL

P JEWELL PUBLIC LIBRARY,* 101 1/2 Washington, PO Box 283, 66949-0283. SAN 305-9723. Tel: 785-428-3630. FAX: 785-428-3600. *Librn*, Eleanor Calahan
Founded 1926. Pop 478; Circ 5,049
Library Holdings: Bk Vols 5,060; Per Subs 15
Mem of Central Kansas Library System

JOHNSON

P STANTON COUNTY LIBRARY,* 103 E Sherman, PO Box 480, 67855. SAN 305-9731. Tel: 316-492-2302. FAX: 316-492-2203. E-Mail: stcpl@pld.com. *Dir*, Denise Smith; *Circ*, Linda Campbell
Pop 2,339; Circ 36,568
1997-1998 Income $144,367. Mats Exp $25,000. Sal $62,000
Library Holdings: Bk Vols 33,000; Per Subs 110
Publications: Library Journal (weekly)
Mem of Southwest Kansas Library System

JUNCTION CITY

P DOROTHY BRAMLAGE PUBLIC LIBRARY,* 230 W Seventh, 66441-3097. SAN 305-974X. Tel: 785-238-4311. FAX: 785-238-7873. E-Mail: jclibrary@jclib.org. *Dir*, Susan Moyer; *Asst Dir*, Carol Franklin
Founded 1907. Pop 31,099; Circ 110,000
Jan 1997-Dec 1998 Income $364,315, State $34,272, City $260,236, County $28,500, Locally Generated Income $41,257. Mats Exp $57,768, Books $49,679, Per/Ser (Incl. Access Fees) $7,089, Presv $1,000. Sal $179,151
Library Holdings: Bk Vols 59,643; Per Subs 168
Subject Interests: Kansas, Local history
Publications: Newsletter
Mem of North Central Kansas Libraries System

KANOPOLIS

P KANOPOLIS PUBLIC LIBRARY,* 221 N Kansas, PO Box 205, 67454-0205. SAN 376-5652. Tel: 785-472-3053. *Librn*, Laura Neuman
1998-1999 Income $7,949
Library Holdings: Bk Vols 8,120; Per Subs 34
Mem of Central Kansas Library System

KANSAS CITY

CENTRAL BAPTIST THEOLOGICAL SEMINARY, Pratt-Journeycake Library, 2915 Minnesota Ave, 66102-3998. (Mail add: 741 N 31st St, 66102-3964), Tel: 913-371-5313. Toll Free Tel: 800-677-2287. FAX: 913-371-8110. Web Site: www.cbts.edu. *Coll Develop, Librn*, Donald Keeney; E-Mail: dkeeney@cbts.edu; *Asst Librn*, Roxanne Grant; E-Mail: astlib@cbts.edu; Staff 2 (MLS 2)
Founded 1901. Enrl 150; Fac 10; Highest Degree: Master
Aug 1998-Jul 1999 Income $274,343. Mats Exp $63,000, Books $45,000, Per/Ser (Incl. Access Fees) $18,000. Sal $135,000
Library Holdings: Bk Vols 105,000; Per Subs 430
Subject Interests: Baptists, Religion
Special Collections: Kansas Qumram Project (Fred E Young Qumran Coll)
Automation Activity & Vendor Info: (Cataloging) DRA; (Circulation) DRA
Database Vendor: DRA
Partic in ECUNET/ABNET

C DONNELLY COLLEGE, Trant Memorial Library, 608 N 18th St, 66102. SAN 305-9774. Tel: 913-621-8735. FAX: 913-621-0354. Web Site: www.donnelly.cc.ks.us. *Dir Libr Serv*, Tom Brown; E-Mail: brown@donnelly.cc.ks.us; *Librn*, Jeanette Gates; *Librn*, Rachel Lee; Staff 6 (MLS 1, Non-MLS 5)
Founded 1949. Enrl 800; Fac 80; Highest Degree: Associate
Jan 1999-Dec 1999 Income Parent Institution $24,000
Library Holdings: Bk Vols 30,000; Bk Titles 27,500; Per Subs 115
Subject Interests: Biblical studies, Women's studies
Special Collections: African-American Heritage (Roe Coll)
Automation Activity & Vendor Info: (OPAC) Inlex
Database Vendor: Dialog, DRA, IAC - SearchBank, OVID Technologies, Wilson - Wilson Web
Function: Reference services available
Partic in Kansas City Metropolitan Library & Information Network

J KANSAS CITY KANSAS COMMUNITY COLLEGE LIBRARY, 7250 State Ave, 66112-3098. SAN 305-9782. Tel: 913-334-1100, Ext 650. FAX: 913-596-9606. Web Site: kckcc.cc.ks.us/lilbrary. *Actg Dir, Tech Servs*, Cheryl Postlewait; E-Mail: cheryl@toto.net; *Publ Servs*, Mary Fenlon; E-Mail: mpfenlon@toto.net; *Media Spec*, Penny Mahon; E-Mail: pennymah@toto.net; *ILL*, Teri Hunter; E-Mail: tjhunter@toto.net; Staff 4 (MLS 4)
Founded 1923. Enrl 7,000
1998-1999 Mats Exp $75,000, Books $47,000, Per/Ser (Incl. Access Fees) $22,000, Micro $6,000
Library Holdings: Bk Vols 60,000; Bk Titles 50,000; Per Subs 400
Subject Interests: Education, Mortuary science, Nursing
Special Collections: Houston Gray film Memorabilia
Partic in Kansas City Libr Consortium; Kansas City Metropolitan Library & Information Network; OCLC Online Computer Library Center, Inc

P KANSAS CITY, KANSAS PUBLIC LIBRARY, 625 Minnesota Ave, 66101. SAN 342-0515. Tel: 913-551-3280. Reference Tel: 913-279-2212. FAX: 913-551-3243. Web Site: www.kckpl.lib.ks.us/. *Dir*, Charles O Perdue; Tel: 913-275-2220; *Asst Dir*, Teresa Garrison; Tel: 913-275-2223, E-Mail: tgarrison@kckpl.lib.ks.us; *Automation Syst Coordr*, Connie Riley; Tel: 913-275-2349, Fax: 913-275-2033, E-Mail: criley@kckpl.lib.ks.us; *Publ Servs*, Jody Becker; Tel: 913-275-2221, E-Mail: jbecker@kckpl.lib.ks.us; *Tech Servs*, Sue Cunningham; Tel: 913-275-2224, Fax: 913-275-2033, E-Mail: scunni@kckpl.lib.ks.us; *ILL*, Jo Gandert; Tel: 913-2792239, E-Mail: jgsnder@kckpl.lib.ks.us. Subject Specialists: *Computer*, Connie Riley; Staff 88 (MLS 25, Non-MLS 63)

Founded 1892. Pop 153,427; Circ 895,691
Jul 1999-Jun 2000 Income (Main Library and Branch Library) $4,962,252, City $3,339,448, County $500,431, Locally Generated Income $906,463, Other $215,910. Mats Exp $610,597, Books $411,531, Per/Ser (Incl. Access Fees) $128,898, Electronic Ref Mat (Incl. Access Fees) $70,168. Sal $2,244,344 (Prof $961,230)
Library Holdings: Bk Vols 401,864; Per Subs 1,165
Subject Interests: Kansas
Special Collections: Fine Arts; Spanish Language; Wyandot Indians (Connelley Coll), bks & mss
Automation Activity & Vendor Info: (OPAC) Inlex
Database Vendor: Ebsco - EbscoHost, GaleNet, ProQuest, Wilson - Wilson Web
Publications: Calendar of Events (Newsletter); Fiction News; Taking Stock
Partic in Kansas City Metropolitan Library & Information Network; NE Kans Libr Syst; OCLC Online Computer Library Center, Inc
Friends of the Library Group
Branches: 2
ARGENTINE BRANCH, 2800 Metropolitan, 66106. SAN 342-054X. Tel: 913-722-7400. FAX: 913-722-7402. *Branch Mgr*, Carol Hanlon; *Coordr*, Sam Bennett
Library Holdings: Bk Vols 102,725
Special Collections: Spanish Language Coll
Friends of the Library Group
WEST WYANDOTTE, 1737 N 82nd St, 66112. SAN 342-0574. Tel: 913-596-5800. FAX: 913-596-5806. *Coordr*, Patricia Gaunce
Library Holdings: Bk Vols 223,609
Special Collections: Fine Arts
Friends of the Library Group
Bookmobiles: 1

§M KANSAS UNIVERSITY MEDICAL CENTER, Clendening History of Medicine Library, 3901 Rainbow Blvd, 66160-7311. SAN 375-4375. Tel: 913-588-7244. FAX: 913-588-7415. E-Mail: clendening@kumc.edu. Web Site: clendening.kumc.edu. *Dir*, Robert Martensen; *Rare Bks*, Kelly Brown; Staff 2 (MLS 1, Non-MLS 1)
Jul 2000-Jun 2001 Income $175,000
Library Holdings: Bk Vols 30,000; Per Subs 50
Subject Interests: Bioethics, History of medicine
Special Collections: Anesthesia, Roentgenology, Hemotology & Microscopy Colls; Florence Nightingale & Joseph Lister Letters; Rudolp Virchow Manuscripts; Samuel Crumbine Papers
Automation Activity & Vendor Info: (Acquisitions) Endeavor; (Cataloging) Endeavor; (Circulation) Endeavor

M PROVIDENCE MEDICAL CENTER LIBRARY,* 8929 Parallel Pkwy, 66112-0430. SAN 342-0604. Tel: 913-596-4795. FAX: 913-596-4906.
Founded 1964
Jun 1997-May 1998 Income $59,285. Mats Exp $19,570, Books $1,500, Per/Ser (Incl. Access Fees) $12,320, Presv $1,000, AV Equip $4,750
Library Holdings: Bk Titles 1,500; Per Subs 69
Subject Interests: Health sciences

S US BUREAU OF THE CENSUS, Information Services Program, 400 State Ave, Ste 600, 66101. SAN 370-2529. Tel: 913-551-6728. FAX: 913-551-6789. Web Site: www.census.gov. *Info Specialist*, Matthew Milbrodt; Tel: 913-551-6711, E-Mail: matthew.s.milbrodt@census.gov
Library Holdings: Bk Vols 100

GL UNITED STATES COURTS, Kansas City Branch Library, 532 US Courthouse, 500 State Ave, 66101-2441. Tel: 913-551-5648. FAX: 913-551-6547. *Librn*, Sharon L Hom; E-Mail: sharon_hom@ksd.uscourts.gov; Staff 1 (MLS 1)
Founded 1994
Library Holdings: Bk Vols 10,000; Per Subs 12

CM UNIVERSITY OF KANSAS MEDICAL CENTER, Dykes Library of the Health Sciences, 2100 W 39th Ave, 66160-7180. SAN 305-9812. Tel: 913-588-7166. Interlibrary Loan Service Tel: 913-588-5073. Reference Tel: 913-588-5070. FAX: 913-588-7304. Web Site: library.kumc.edu. *Dir*, James L Bingham; E-Mail: jbingham@kumc.edu; *Assoc Dir, Coll Develop*, Robert A Pisciotta; *Ref*, Kathy Kosednar; *Ref Serv*, Anne Whitworth; *ILL*, Crystal Vedros; Staff 10 (MLS 8, Non-MLS 2)
Founded 1906. Enrl 2,560; Highest Degree: Doctorate
Library Holdings: Bk Titles 52,000; Per Subs 1,477
Subject Interests: Health sciences
Special Collections: Calkins Educational Resource Ctr
Partic in BRS; Health Sciences Library Network of Kansas City, Inc; Medline; Midcontinental Regional Med Libr Program; OCLC Online Computer Library Center, Inc
Open Mon-Thurs 7:30am-11pm, Fri 7:30am-8pm, Sat 9am-6pm & Sun 1-11pm

G US ENVIRONMENTAL PROTECTION AGENCY, Region VII Information Resource Center, 901 N Fifth St, 66101-2907. SAN 309-0302. Tel: 913-551-7241. Toll Free Tel: 800-223-0425. FAX: 913-551-9241. E-Mail: library-reg7@epa.gov. Web Site: www.epa.gov/region07/newsinfo/irc.; Staff 5 (MLS 3, Non-MLS 2)
Founded 1970. Fac 650
Library Holdings: Bk Vols 7,000; Per Subs 165
Subject Interests: Agriculture, Pesticides

GL WYANDOTTE COUNTY LAW LIBRARY,* Court House, 710 N Seventh St, 66101. SAN 305-9820. Tel: 913-573-2899. FAX: 913-573-2892. *Librn*, Brenda Eaton
Founded 1925
Library Holdings: Bk Vols 20,000
Open Mon-Fri 8:30-5

KENSINGTON

P KENSINGTON COMMUNITY LIBRARY,* 209 E Ash St, 66951. SAN 376-5660. Tel: 785-476-2219. FAX: 785-476-2215. *Librn*, Sheila K Blume
Library Holdings: Bk Vols 7,000; Per Subs 55
Mem of Central Kansas Library System

KINGMAN

P KINGMAN CARNEGIE PUBLIC LIBRARY, 455 N Main St, 67068-1395. SAN 305-9839. Tel: 316-532-3061. FAX: 316-532-2528. E-Mail: kingc1lb@websurf.net. *Librn*, Linda Slack
Founded 1913. Pop 3,200; Circ 56,506
1998-1999 Income $122,133, State $2,500, City $94,600, Other $25,033. Mats Exp $10,565, Books $6,724, Per/Ser (Incl. Access Fees) $2,400, Other Print Mats $667
Library Holdings: Bk Vols 30,969; Per Subs 115
Mem of South Central Kansas Library System
Friends of the Library Group

KINSLEY

P KINSLEY PUBLIC LIBRARY, 208 E Eighth, 67547-1422. SAN 305-9855. Tel: 316-659-3341. FAX: 316-659-3613. E-Mail: kinlib@midway.net. Web Site: trails.net/kinsley/. *Dir*, Joan Weaver; Staff 3 (Non-MLS 3)
Founded 1904. Pop 2,000
Jan 1999-Dec 1999 Income $60,700, State $1,200, City $56,000, Locally Generated Income $3,500. Mats Exp $8,350, Books $5,250, Per/Ser (Incl. Access Fees) $2,500, Micro $600. Sal $45,000 (Prof $20,000)
Library Holdings: Bk Titles 23,000; Per Subs 70
Subject Interests: Carnivals, Genealogy, Local history
Special Collections: DAR Magazines 1914-1963; Kinsley Newspapers 1878-present, micro
Automation Activity & Vendor Info: (Circulation) Sagebrush Corporation
Mem of Southwest Kansas Library System
Open Mon & Wed 9-8, Tues, Thurs & Fri 9:30-11am & 1-5, Sat 1-5

KIOWA

P KIOWA PUBLIC LIBRARY,* 123 N Seventh St, 67070. SAN 305-9863. Tel: 316-825-4630. *Librn*, Sheryl K Farney
Founded 1950. Pop 1,409; Circ 8,629
Library Holdings: Bk Vols 12,000; Per Subs 38
Mem of South Central Kansas Library System
Open Mon 7-9, Tues & Thurs 2-5 & 7-9 & Sat 2-5

KIRWIN

P KIRWIN CITY LIBRARY,* PO Box 445, 67644-0445. SAN 305-9871. Tel: 785-543-6652. *Librn*, Hilda Carol Weems
Pop 267; Circ 5,000
Library Holdings: Bk Vols 7,900; Per Subs 15
Special Collections: Papers Published in Kirwin, 1889-1942
Publications: History of Kirwin, Kansas 1869-1969; The Saga of Fort Kirwin
Mem of Central Kansas Library System

KISMET

P KISMET PUBLIC LIBRARY,* 503 Main St, PO Box 66, 67859-0066. SAN 326-5536. Tel: 316-563-7357. *Librn*, Ina May Davis
Library Holdings: Bk Vols 3,500; Bk Titles 3,500; Per Subs 16
Mem of Southwest Kansas Library System

LA CROSSE

P BARNARD LIBRARY,* PO Box 727, 67548. SAN 305-988X. Tel: 785-222-2826. FAX: 785-222-2826. *Librn*, Ruth Holoperik
Founded 1926. Pop 1,800
Library Holdings: Bk Titles 12,000; Per Subs 50
Special Collections: Gay Nineties (Howard Barnard Coll); Kansas Coll
Mem of Central Kansas Library System

LA CYGNE

P LIBRARY DISTRICT 2 OF LINN COUNTY, 206 N Commercial, 66040-0127. (Mail add: PO Box 127, 66040-0127), Tel: 913-757-2151. FAX: 913-757-2405. E-Mail: lacyg1lb@peoplestelecom.net. *Dir*, Linda Andersen; *Asst Librn*, Janet Reynolds
Founded 1975
Jan 1999-Dec 1999 Income County $85,000. Mats Exp $15,482, Books $13,860, Per/Ser (Incl. Access Fees) $1,622. Sal $42,014
Library Holdings: Bk Titles 20,697; Per Subs 104
Automation Activity & Vendor Info: (Cataloging) Follett; (Circulation) Follett
Database Vendor: OCLC - First Search
Mem of Southeast Kansas Library System

LAKIN

P KEARNY COUNTY LIBRARY,* Main & Prairie, PO Box 773, 67860-0773. SAN 305-9901. Tel: 316-355-6674. FAX: 316-355-6801. E-Mail: kclteach@lgsz.pld.com. *Librn*, Richard Brookman; Staff 4 (MLS 1, Non-MLS 3)
Founded 1956. Pop 3,800; Circ 32,750
1998-1999 Income $251,301, State $3,200, County $245,101, Locally Generated Income $3,000. Mats Exp $56,286, Books $30,000, Per/Ser (Incl. Access Fees) $3,000, AV Equip $1,386. Sal $64,056 (Prof $30,000)
Library Holdings: Bk Titles 20,000; Per Subs 69
Subject Interests: History, Kansas, Large type print
Special Collections: Indian Coll
Publications: Weekly Newspaper
Mem of Southwest Kansas Library System
Open Mon-Fri 8-5, Tues & Thurs 8-9, Sat 10-1

LARNED

S FORT LARNED HISTORICAL SOCIETY, INC, Santa Fe Trail Center Library, Rte 3, 67550. SAN 305-9928. Tel: 316-285-2054. FAX: 316-285-7491. E-Mail: trailctr@larned.net. Web Site: www.larned.net/trailctr/. *Curator*, Betsy Crawford-Gore; Staff 1 (Non-MLS 1)
Founded 1974
1998-1999 Mats Exp $3,900, Books $1,600, Per/Ser (Incl. Access Fees) $300, Presv $500, AV Equip $900, Other Print Mats $100, Manuscripts & Archives $150. Sal $22,500
Library Holdings: Bk Titles 3,400; Per Subs 15
Subject Interests: Kansas
Special Collections: Grand Army of the Republic Records (B F Larned Post); Official Records & Correspondence; R R Smith Glass Magic Lantern Slide Coll; School (Pawnee County, Kansas School Records); War of the Rebellion

P JORDAAN MEMORIAL LIBRARY, 724 Broadway, 67550-3051. SAN 305-991X. Tel: 316-285-2876. FAX: 316-285-7275. E-Mail: jordalib@larned.net. *Dir*, Margaret Larson; Staff 6 (Non-MLS 6)
Founded 1915. Pop 7,000; Circ 61,400
Library Holdings: Bk Vols 36,180; Per Subs 107
Subject Interests: History, Kansas
Mem of Central Kansas Library System
Open Mon-Thurs 12-9, Fri 10-6, Sat 10-4 (winter); Mon 10-8, Tues-Fri 9-6, Sat 10-4 (summer)

LARNED STATE HOSPITAL
M J T NARAMORE MEMORIAL LIBRARY, RR 3 Box 89, 67550. SAN 342-0728. Tel: 316-285-4510. FAX: 316-285-4573. *Librn*, Rita Renfrow
Founded 1953
Jul 1997-Jun 1998 Mats Exp $5,858, Books $833, Per/Ser (Incl. Access Fees) $3,683. Sal $20,304
Special Collections: Dr Homer Davis Coll; J T Naramore Coll
S PATIENTS' LIBRARY, Rte 3 Box 89, 67550. SAN 342-0752. Tel: 316-285-4303. FAX: 316-285-4325. *Librn*, Rita Renfrow; Staff 1 (Non-MLS 1)
Founded 1948
Jul 1997-Jun 1998 Income $36,850, Federal $3,000, Parent Institution $33,850. Mats Exp $2,800, Books $1,200, Per/Ser (Incl. Access Fees) $950, Presv $175, AV Equip $325, Other Print Mats $150. Sal $20,304
Library Holdings: Bk Vols 8,300; Per Subs 30
Subject Interests: Local history
Mem of Central Kansas Library System
Special Services for the Deaf - Videos & decoder
Special Services for the Blind - Braille bks & record players; Large print bks & talking machines
Literacy Volunteers of America Program - 3 participating teachers

S US NATIONAL PARK SERVICE, Fort Larned National Historic Site Library, Rte 3, 67550-9803. SAN 370-3150. Tel: 316-285-6911. FAX: 316-285-3571. Web Site: www.nps.gov/fols. *Librn*, Gia Lane
Library Holdings: Bk Vols 2,000; Per Subs 10
Special Collections: Fort Larned Documents 1859-1878
Open Mon-Sun 8:30-5, closed holidays

LAWRENCE

C HASKELL INDIAN NATIONS UNIVERSITY, Tommaney Library, 155 Indian Ave, PO Box 5016, 66046-4800. SAN 305-9936. Tel: 785-749-8470. FAX: 785-749-8661. E-Mail: khighfill@ross1.cc.haskell.edu. Web Site: www.nass.haskell.edu/asc/asc.html. *Dir*, Pamela Dawes; *Librn*, Karen Highfill
Founded 1884. Enrl 900; Fac 52; Highest Degree: Bachelor
Library Holdings: Bk Vols 43,000; Per Subs 250
Subject Interests: Indians
Special Collections: Indians of North America Coll
Automation Activity & Vendor Info: (Cataloging) DRA; (Circulation) DRA; (ILL) DRA; (OPAC) DRA
Partic in Kans City Pub Libr Consortium
Open Mon-Fri 8am-10pm, Sun 1-10, closed Federal holidays

G KANSAS GEOLOGICAL SURVEY LIBRARY,* University of Kansas, 1930 Constant Ave, 66047-3726. SAN 324-0096. Tel: 785-864-3965. FAX: 785-864-5317. *Librn*, Janice Sorensen; E-Mail: sorensen@kgs.ukans.edu
Founded 1973
Library Holdings: Bk Titles 17,000; Per Subs 55
Subject Interests: Energy, Geology, Kansas, Mineral resources, Natural resources, Water resources
Publications: Bibliography of Kansas Geology; Kansas State Geological Survey Open-file Reports

P LAWRENCE PUBLIC LIBRARY, 707 Vermont St, 66044. SAN 305-9952. Tel: 785-843-3833. Reference Tel: 785-843-1178. FAX: 785-843-3368. Web Site: www.lawrence.lib.ks.us/index.html. *Dir*, Bruce Flanders; Tel: 785-843-3833, Ext 102, E-Mail: flanders@lawrence.lib.ks.us; *Asst Dir*, Sherri Turner; Tel: 785-843-3833, Ext 126, E-Mail: sturner@lawrence.lib.ks.us; *YA Servs*, Joyce Steiner; Tel: 785-843-3833, Ext 116, E-Mail: jsteiner@lawrence.lib.ks.us; *Tech Servs*, Tricia Karlin; Tel: 785-843-3833, Ext 109, E-Mail: tkarlin@lawrence.lib.ks.us; *Ref*, Cecilia Jecha May; Tel: 785-843-3833, Ext 113, E-Mail: cjmay@lawrence.lib.ks.us; *Circ*, Pattie Johnston; Tel: 785-843-3833, Ext 115, E-Mail: johnston@lawrence.lib.ks.us; Staff 26 (Non-MLS 26)
Founded 1904. Pop 80,843; Circ 600,000
Library Holdings: Bk Vols 215,795; Per Subs 447
Automation Activity & Vendor Info: (Circulation) DRA; (OPAC) DRA
Database Vendor: OCLC - First Search
Mem of Northeast Kansas Library System
Partic in BCR
Open Mon-Fri 9-9, Sat 9-6 & Sun 2-6
Friends of the Library Group
Bookmobiles: 1

P NORTHEAST KANSAS LIBRARY SYSTEM, 3300 Clinton Parkway Ct, Ste 100, 66047-2653. SAN 306-1302. Tel: 785-838-4090. Interlibrary Loan Service Tel: 785-843-3654. Toll Free Tel: 888-296-6963 (KS only). FAX: 785-838-3989. Web Site: skyways.lib.ks.us/nekls/noreast.html. *Dir*, Jim Minges; E-Mail: jminges@nekls.lib.ks.us; *Admin Assoc*, Laura DeBaun; E-Mail: ldebaun@nekls.lib.ks.us; *Automation Syst Coordr*, Michelle Rice; E-Mail: mrice@nekls.lib.ks.us; *Ch Servs*, Barbara Stransky; E-Mail: bstransky@nekls.lib.ks.us; *Coordr*, Patti J Butcher; E-Mail: pbutcher@nekls.lib.ks.us; *Tech Servs*, Mark Messenger; E-Mail: messenger@nekls.lib.ks.us; Staff 6 (MLS 4, Non-MLS 2)
Founded 1966. Pop 1,000,000
Automation Activity & Vendor Info: (Circulation) Follett
Publications: Directory; Librarians report; Loose Change (newsletter)
Member Libraries: Atchison Library; Baker University Library; Baldwin City Library; Barnes Reading Room; Basehor Community Library District 2; Beck Bookman Library; Benedictine College Library; Bern Community Library; Bonner Springs City Library; Burlingame Community Library; Carbondale City Library; Centralia Community Library; Corning City Library; Delaware Township Library; Effingham Community Library; Eudora Public Library; Highland Community College Library; Horton Free Public Library; Johnson County Library; Lawrence Public Library; Library District 1 Miami County; Library District Number One, Doniphan County; Lieber Public Library; Linwood Community Library; Lyndon Carnegie Library; Mary Cotton Public Library; Meriden Community Library; Mid-America Nazarene University; Morrill Public Library; Nortonville Public Library; Olathe Public Library; Osawatomie Public Library; Osawatomie State Hospital; Oskaloosa Public Library; Ottawa Library; Ottawa University; Overbrook Public Library; Paola Free Library; Richmond Public Library; Rossville Community Library; Seneca Free Library; Silver Lake Library; Tonganoxie Public Library; Topeka & Shawnee County Public Library; Topeka Technical College Library; Wellsville City Library; Wetmore Public Library; Winchester Public Library
Partic in BCR; Kans City Libr Consortium; Kans City Mo Libr & Info Network

S RESEARCH & TRAINING CENTER ON INDEPENDENT LIVING LIBRARY,* University of Kansas, 4089 Dole Ctr, 66045. SAN 375-1899. Tel: 785-864-4095. FAX: 785-864-5063. E-Mail: rtcil@ukans.edu.
Library Holdings: Bk Vols 300; Per Subs 45

C UNIVERSITY OF KANSAS LIBRARIES, Watson Library, 1425 Jayhawk Blvd, 66045-2800. SAN 342-0787. Tel: 785-864-3956. FAX: 785-864-5311. Web Site: www.lib.ukans.edu. *Actg Dean*, Julia Rholes; *Asst Dean*, George Gibbs; *Asst Dean, Info Tech*, John S Miller; *ILL*, Leon Lars; *Acq, Ser*, Rachel Miller; *Assoc Dean*, Richard Fyffe; Staff 147 (MLS 66, Non-MLS 81)
Founded 1866. Enrl 24,874; Fac 1,577; Highest Degree: Doctorate
Library Holdings: Bk Vols 3,099,335; Per Subs 27,199
Special Collections: 18th Century English History & Literature; 19th Century Spanish Plays; Anglo-Saxon Types; Botany; Children's Books; Chinese Classics; Colombia; Continental Renaissance; Economics; Edmund Curll Coll; English Poetical Miscellanies; French Revolution; Historical Cartography; Irish History & Literature; Joyce Coll; Kansas History; Linnaeus Coll; Modern American Poetry; Modern Extremist Politics; Opera; Ornithology; Rilke Coll; Sir Robert Walpole Coll; Travel; Women; Yeats Coll
Automation Activity & Vendor Info: (Acquisitions) Endeavor; (Cataloging) Endeavor; (Circulation) Endeavor; (OPAC) Endeavor; (Serials) Endeavor
Publications: Bibliographical Contributions, Books & Libraries
Partic in Asn of Research Libraries; Center For Research Libraries; OCLC Online Computer Library Center, Inc
Friends of the Library Group
Departmental Libraries:
ANSCHUTZ SCIENCE LIBRARY, 1301 Hoch Auditoria Dr, 66045-7537. Tel: 785-864-4928. FAX: 785-864-5705. *Librn*, Denise Stephens
DOCUMENTS (REGIONAL DEPOSITORY), 6001 Malott Hall, 66045. SAN 342-0833. Tel: 785-864-4662. FAX: 785-864-5380. *Librn*, Donna Koepp
EAST ASIAN Tel: 785-864-4669. FAX: 785-864-5311. *Librn*, Vickie Doll
KANSAS COLLECTION, Spencer Research Library, 66045. SAN 342-0906. Tel: 785-864-4274. FAX: 785-864-5803. *Librn*, Sheryl Williams
MURPHY ART & ARCHITECTURE LIBRARY, University of Kansas, 1301 Mississippi St, 66045-8500. SAN 342-0817. Tel: 785-864-3020. FAX: 785-864-4608. Web Site: www2.lib.ukans.edu/~artlib. *Librn*, Susan V Craig; E-Mail: scraig@ukans.edu; Staff 4 (MLS 1, Non-MLS 3)
Founded 1980
Library Holdings: Bk Vols 128,000; Per Subs 600
Subject Interests: Architecture, Art, Art history, Design, Photog hist
Database Vendor: IAC - Info Trac, Lexis-Nexis, OCLC - First Search, Silverplatter Information Inc.
Partic in Big Twelve Plus Libr Consortium
MUSIC, Murphy Hall, 66045. SAN 342-1058. Tel: 785-864-3496. FAX: 785-864-5310. Web Site: www2.lib.ukans.edu/~musiclib. *Librn*, Vic Cardell; Tel: 785-864-3282, E-Mail: vcardell@ukans.edu. Subject Specialists: *Dance*, Vic Cardell; *Music*, Vic Cardell; Staff 2 (MLS 1, Non-MLS 1)
Library Holdings: Bk Vols 100,000; Bk Titles 92,000; Per Subs 400
Subject Interests: Applied music, Composition, Music educ, Music theory, Music therapy
REGENTS CENTER LIBRARY, 12600 Quivira Rd, Overland Park, 66213. SAN 342-1074. Tel: 913-864-8570. FAX: 913-864-8573. Web Site: www2.lib.ukans.edu/~rclibrary.
SCHOOL OF LAW LIBRARY, Green Hall, 66045-2384. SAN 342-0930. Tel: 785-864-3025. FAX: 785-864-3680. Web Site: www.law.ukans.edu/library/. *Dir*, Joyce Pearson; *Assoc Dir*, Joseph Custer; *Automation Syst Coordr, Cat, Doc, Tech Servs*, Barbara Ginzburg; Staff 11 (MLS 5, Non-MLS 6)
Founded 1878. Highest Degree: Doctorate
Jul 1997-Jun 1998 Income $1,008,387. Mats Exp $512,458, Books $52,738, Per/Ser (Incl. Access Fees) $459,720. Sal $411,847 (Prof $201,959)
Library Holdings: Bk Vols 252,758; Per Subs 4,473
Friends of the Library Group
SPAHR LIBRARY, Spahr Library-Learned Hall, 66045. SAN 342-099X. Tel: 785-864-3866. FAX: 785-864-5755. Web Site: www2.lib.ukans.edu/~englib/.; Staff 19 (MLS 1, Non-MLS 18)
Library Holdings: Bk Vols 92,000
Automation Activity & Vendor Info: (Circulation) Endeavor; (Course Reserve) Endeavor
Database Vendor: Dialog, IAC - Info Trac, Lexis-Nexis, OCLC - First Search, Silverplatter Information Inc.
Function: Research library
SPECIAL COLLECTIONS, Spencer Research Library, 66045. SAN 342-1112. Tel: 785-864-4334. FAX: 785-864-5803. E-Mail: ksrl-sc@lark.cc.ukans.edu. Web Site: www.ukans.edu/~spencer. *Librn*, Keith Russell
Friends of the Library Group
T R SMITH MAP COLLECTION, Anschutz Science Library, Level 1, 66045. SAN 342-0965. Tel: 785-864-4420. FAX: 785-864-5705. *Librn*, Denise Stephens
UNIVERSITY ARCHIVES, Spencer Research Library, 66045. SAN 342-1147. Tel: 785-864-4188. FAX: 785-864-5803. *Archivist*, Sheryl Williams

R WILLIAM J MOORE READING ROOM,* Smith Hall, Rm 109, 1300 Oread, 66045-2164. SAN 305-9944. Tel: 913-864-4664. E-Mail: wjmoore@kuhub.cc.ukans.edu. *In Charge*, Sally Ahl
Library Holdings: Bk Vols 14,000; Per Subs 45
Restriction: Private library
Library used in connection with Religious Studies Department of the University of Kansas

LEAVENWORTH

GM DEPARTMENT OF VETERANS AFFAIRS, Medical Library, 4101 S Fourth St Trafficway, 66048. SAN 305-9987. Tel: 913-682-2000, Ext 2718. FAX: 913-758-4123. *Librn*, Jan Gosselin
Founded 1900
Library Holdings: Bk Vols 4,000; Per Subs 140
Subject Interests: Medicine, Podiatry, Psychology
Partic in Docline; Vets Admin Libr Network
Open Mon-Fri 8-4:30

P LEAVENWORTH PUBLIC LIBRARY, 417 Spruce, 66048. SAN 305-9960. Tel: 913-682-5666. FAX: 913-682-1248. Web Site: skyways.lib.ks.us/library/leavenworth. *Dir*, Kimberly Baker; *Acq*, Elaine Knapp; *Ch Servs*, Peggy Capps; *Circ*, Gwen Buchanan; *Coll Develop*, Marguerite Spencer; *ILL*, Doris Woodward; *Ref*, Wanda Adams; *Tech Servs*, Stacey Hoeltzel; Staff 6 (MLS 6)
Founded 1895. Pop 41,000
Jan 1999-Dec 2000 Income $649,160, State $30,162, City $534,034, Locally Generated Income $84,964. Mats Exp $109,456, Books $93,538, Per/Ser (Incl. Access Fees) $6,544, Micro $2,000, AV Equip $7,374. Sal $326,231
Library Holdings: Bk Vols 116,867
Subject Interests: Kansas, Local history
Database Vendor: DRA
Publications: Leavenworth Legacy
Friends of the Library Group

C SAINT MARY COLLEGE, De Paul Library, 4100 S Fourth St Trafficway, 66048-5082. SAN 305-9979. Tel: 913-758-6306. Reference Tel: 913-758-6163. FAX: 913-758-6200. Web Site: www.smcks.edu. *Acq, Coll Develop, Dir*, Penelope Lonergan; E-Mail: lonergan@hub.smcks.edu; *Cat*, Barbara Stephens; E-Mail: stephensb@hub.smcks.edu; *Circ, ILL, Spec Coll*, Carol Ayres; E-Mail: ayresc@hub.smcks.edu; *Ref*, Sister Madonna Fink; E-Mail: finksm@hub.smcks.edu; Staff 4 (MLS 4)
Founded 1923. Enrl 600; Fac 52; Highest Degree: Master
Jul 1999-Jun 2000 Income $173,500. Mats Exp $173,000, Books $20,000, Per/Ser (Incl. Access Fees) $24,000, Presv $1,600, Micro $3,100. Sal $119,000
Library Holdings: Bk Vols 116,000; Bk Titles 92,700; Per Subs 302
Special Collections: Abraham Lincoln, bks, pamphlets, music, clippings; Americana (including ethnic minorities), letters, doc, bks, micro; Bible, bks, mss, incunabula; Music, orchestral scores; Shakespeare, bks, microfilm

LEBANON

P LEBANON-COMMUNITY LIBRARY,* 401 N Main, PO Box 67, 66952. SAN 306-0004. Tel: 785-389-5711. E-Mail: leban1lb@ruraltel.net. *Librn*, Esther Delimont
Founded 1901. Pop 440; Circ 575
Jan 1998-Dec 1998 Income $9,590, City $4,094, Other $5,496. Mats Exp $1,716, Books $1,128, Per/Ser (Incl. Access Fees) $331, Other Print Mats $257. Sal $4,124
Library Holdings: Bk Titles 9,000; Per Subs 21
Subject Interests: Environmental studies, History, Medicine, Music, Natural science, Religion
Special Collections: Kansas; Lebanon
Mem of Central Kansas Library System
Open Tues, Wed, Fri & Sat 1:15-5

LENORA

P LENORA PUBLIC LIBRARY,* 1251/2 E Washington St, 67645. SAN 306-0020. Tel: 785-567-4432. *Librn*, Gloria Heikes
Founded 1930. Pop 444; Circ 4,041
Library Holdings: Bk Vols 6,500
Mem of Northwest Kansas Library System
Open Tues-Wed 1-6
Friends of the Library Group

LEON

P LEON PUBLIC LIBRARY,* 111 S Main St, PO Box 57, 67074-0057. SAN 306-0039. Tel: 316-742-3438. *Librn*, Barbara Sears
Pop 667; Circ 5,409
Library Holdings: Bk Vols 4,450
Mem of South Central Kansas Library System
Open Fri 9-12, 1-5

LEONARDVILLE

P LEONARDVILLE CITY LIBRARY,* 103 N Erpelding, 66449. SAN 306-0047. Tel: 785-293-5606. *Librn*, Deanna Tate
Founded 1963. Pop 348; Circ 6,144
Library Holdings: Bk Vols 5,000
Mem of North Central Kansas Libraries System

LEOTI

P WICHITA COUNTY LIBRARY, Fourth & M St, PO Box 490, 67861-0490. SAN 306-0055. Tel: 316-375-4322. E-Mail: wicolib@pld.com. *Dir*, Deandra Gittlein
Founded 1928. Pop 2,900; Circ 18,103
Library Holdings: Bk Titles 19,605; Per Subs 81
Special Collections: Kansas Historical Library; Kansas International Portrait Gallery

LEWIS

P MEADOWLARK PUBLIC LIBRARY,* PO Box 331, 67552. SAN 306-0071. Tel: 316-324-5743. E-Mail: meadowlk@ruraltel.net. *Librn*, Mary Cross
Pop 500; Circ 4,289
Library Holdings: Bk Vols 15,000; Per Subs 23
Mem of Southwest Kansas Library System

LIBERAL

P LIBERAL MEMORIAL LIBRARY,* 519 N Kansas, 67901-3345. SAN 306-008X. Tel: 316-626-0180. FAX: 316-626-0182. E-Mail: libmem7@midus.wet. *Dir*, Brenda Booth; *Ch Servs*, Elizabeth Walker; *ILL*, Lupe Sigala
Founded 1904. Pop 18,100; Circ 150,000
Jan 1997-Dec 1998 Income $309,141. Mats Exp $66,206. Sal $133,547
Library Holdings: Bk Titles 66,000; Per Subs 154
Special Collections: Local Genealogy; Map Coll of Southwest Kansas & Oklahoma Panhandle; Seward County Newspapers, 1886-1995 (microfiche)
Publications: Novel Ideas Newsletter; weekly newspaper articles
Mem of Southwest Kansas Library System
Special Services for the Deaf - Videos & decoder
Special Services for the Blind - Cassette bks; Magna Cam (machine) print enlargers

J SEWARD COUNTY COMMUNITY COLLEGE, Learning Resource Center, 1801 N Kansas, 67901-2054. (Mail add: PO Box 1137, 67905-1137), SAN 306-0098. Tel: 316-629-2656. FAX: 316-629-2725. *Dir*, Denyce G Gammell; E-Mail: dgammell@sccc.net
Founded 1967
Library Holdings: Bk Titles 38,000; Per Subs 300
Automation Activity & Vendor Info: (Cataloging) EOS; (Circulation) EOS; (OPAC) EOS
Mem of Southwest Kansas Library System

LINCOLN

P LINCOLN CARNEGIE LIBRARY,* 203 S Third, 67455. SAN 306-0101. Tel: 785-524-4034. *Librn*, Connie Budreau; *Ch Servs*, Debra Kohrs
Pop 1,400; Circ 27,514
Library Holdings: Bk Vols 19,873; Per Subs 35
Special Collections: Lincoln County Papers from 1873-1999 (Lincoln County Sentinel & Lincoln Republican Coll), micro
Mem of Central Kansas Library System

LINDSBORG

C BETHANY COLLEGE, Wallerstedt Library, 235 E Swensson, 67456-1896. SAN 306-011X. Tel: 785-227-3311, Ext 8342. Web Site: www.bethanylb.edu. *Dir, Librn*, Denise Carson; Staff 2 (MLS 2)
Founded 1907. Enrl 600; Fac 42
Library Holdings: Bk Vols 121,000; Per Subs 598
Automation Activity & Vendor Info: (Cataloging) Innovative Interfaces Inc.; (Circulation) Innovative Interfaces Inc.; (OPAC) Innovative Interfaces Inc.
Mem of South Central Kansas Library System
Partic in Associated Colleges Of Central Kansas

P LINDSBORG COMMUNITY LIBRARY,* 111 S Main St, 67456-2417. SAN 306-0128. Tel: 785-227-2710. E-Mail: biblio@midusa.net. *Dir*, Karen Olson; Staff 3 (MLS 1, Non-MLS 2)
Circ 19,438
Library Holdings: Bk Vols 34,000; Per Subs 50
Subject Interests: Kansas, Scandinavia
Mem of South Central Kansas Library System
Friends of the Library Group

LINWOOD

P LINWOOD COMMUNITY LIBRARY, 302 Main St, PO Box 80, 66052. SAN 320-9997. Tel: 913-723-3686. FAX: 913-723-3686. E-Mail: linwoodlinbrary@sprintmail.com. *Librn*, Hannelore Leach; E-Mail: hleach@linwood.lib.ks.us; Staff 1 (Non-MLS 1)
Founded 1956. Pop 1,817; Circ 4,428
Library Holdings: Bk Titles 12,324; Per Subs 59
Special Collections: Indian 125; Kansas 101; Reference 67
Function: Internet access, Photocopies available
Mem of Northeast Kansas Library System

LITTLE RIVER

P LITTLE RIVER COMMUNITY LIBRARY,* 340 Main St, PO Box 98, 67457. SAN 306-0136. Tel: 316-897-6610. E-Mail: lrcomlib@midusa.net. Web Site: skyways.lib.ks.us/kansas/towns/littleriver/. *Librn*, Dorothy Goodrick
Pop 784; Circ 12,171
Library Holdings: Bk Titles 8,500; Per Subs 30
Subject Interests: Kansas
Mem of South Central Kansas Library System
Friends of the Library Group

LOGAN

P LOGAN PUBLIC LIBRARY,* 109 W Main, 67646. (Mail add: PO Box 356, 67646), Tel: 785-689-4333. *Librn*, Mary Del Gaves
Founded 1900. Pop 770; Circ 3,749
Library Holdings: Bk Vols 5,065; Per Subs 16
Subject Interests: Local history
Mem of Central Kansas Library System

LONG ISLAND

P LONG ISLAND COMMUNITY LIBRARY, Main St, 67647-0195. (Mail add: PO Box 68, 67647-0068), SAN 306-0152. Tel: 785-854-7474. *Librn*, Beth Ponstein
Founded 1921. Pop 187; Circ 2,617
Library Holdings: Bk Titles 2,997
Subject Interests: History, Religion, Social sciences and issues
Mem of Central Kansas Library System

LOUISBURG

P LIBRARY DISTRICT 1 MIAMI COUNTY, Louisburg Public, 206 S Broadway, 66053. (Mail add: PO Box 398, 66053), SAN 306-0179. Tel: 913-837-2217. FAX: 913-837-2218. E-Mail: bookin@micoks.net. *Actg Dir*, Jamie German; Staff 1 (Non-MLS 1)
Founded 1968. Pop 7,359; Circ 52,000
Jan 2000-Dec 2000 Income State $6,000. Sal $90,000 (Prof $26,000)
Library Holdings: Bk Titles 37,000; Per Subs 70
Restriction: Public use on premises
Function: ILL available
Mem of Northeast Kansas Library System
Friends of the Library Group

LUCAS

P LUCAS PUBLIC LIBRARY,* 209 S Main, 67648. (Mail add: PO Box 278, 67648), SAN 306-0187. Tel: 785-525-6305. E-Mail: lucas1lb@midasa.net. *Librn*, Carma Bretz
Founded 1938. Pop 524; Circ 3,196
Library Holdings: Bk Vols 5,329; Per Subs 20
Mem of Central Kansas Library System
Open Mon, Wed, Fri & Sat 1:30-5:30

LYNDON

P LYNDON CARNEGIE LIBRARY,* 127 E Sixth, PO Box 563, 66451-0563. SAN 306-0195. Tel: 785-828-4520. FAX: 785-828-4565. Web Site: www.skyways.lib.ks.us/kansas/towns/lyndon/library.html. *Librn*, Sarah Walker-Hitt
Pop 1,536; Circ 2,968
Library Holdings: Bk Vols 11,000; Per Subs 10
Mem of Northeast Kansas Library System
Friends of the Library Group

LYONS

P LYONS PUBLIC LIBRARY,* 217 East Ave S, 67554-2721. SAN 306-0209. Tel: 316-257-2961. *Dir*, Becky McBeth; Staff 1 (MLS 1)
Founded 1908. Pop 4,395; Circ 47,575
Library Holdings: Bk Vols 28,140; Per Subs 90

Special Collections: Kansas Coll, bks by Kansas authors & bks about Kansas; Local Newspaper; Lyons Daily News on Microfilm; Santa Fe Trail, Coronado & Quivira
Mem of South Central Kansas Library System

MACKSVILLE

P MACKSVILLE CITY LIBRARY,* 333 N Main, PO Box 398, 67557-0398. SAN 306-0241. Tel: 316-348-3555. *Librn*, Rebecca Drake
Founded 1935. Pop 480
Library Holdings: Bk Vols 11,815
Mem of South Central Kansas Library System
Open Mon 2-5, Wed 2-6, Sat 9-12

MADISON

P MADISON PUBLIC LIBRARY,* 112 S First, 66860. SAN 306-0284. Tel: 316-437-2634. E-Mail: madislb@midusa.net. *Librn*, Virginia Pedroja
Pop 1,103; Circ 12,683
Library Holdings: Bk Vols 9,067; Per Subs 47
Subject Interests: Local history
Mem of Southeast Kansas Library System

MANHATTAN

S AMERICAN INSTITUTE OF BAKING, Ruth M Emerson Library, 1213 Bakers Way, 66502. (Mail add: PO Box 3999, 66505-3999), SAN 306-0292. Tel: 785-537-4750, Ext 125. FAX: 785-537-1493. E-Mail: information@aibonline.org. Web Site: www.aibonline.org. *In Charge*, Tammy Popejoy
Founded 1919. Fac 25; Highest Degree: Certificate
Jan 2000-Dec 2000 Income Parent Institution $179,900. Mats Exp $54,050, Books $6,500, Per/Ser (Incl. Access Fees) $35,000, Presv $750, Micro $7,000, Electronic Ref Mat (Incl. Access Fees) $4,800. Sal $78,000
Library Holdings: Bk Vols 6,862; Per Subs 452
Subject Interests: Nutrition
Special Collections: Louis Livingston Baking History & Science Coll
Database Vendor: Ebsco - EbscoHost
Restriction: Not a lending library
Function: Reference services available

C KANSAS STATE UNIVERSITY, Hale Library, Manhattan & Anderson Aves, 66506-1200. SAN 342-1201. Tel: 785-532-3014. Interlibrary Loan Service Tel: 785-532-7441. FAX: 785-532-7415. E-Mail: lib@lib.ksu.edu. Web Site: www.lib.ksu.edu/. *Dean of Libr*, Brice Hobrock; Tel: 785-532-7404, E-Mail: hobrock@ksu.edu; *Assoc Dean*, Karen Cole; E-Mail: kcole@ksu.edu; *Admin Assoc*, Karen McCulloh; *Science*, Daryl Youngman; *Doc*, John Johnson; *ILL*, Cherie Geiser; *Coll Develop*, Nelda Elder; *Humanities and Soc Sci*, Daniel Liestman; Staff 41 (MLS 41)
Founded 1863. Enrl 20,110; Highest Degree: Doctorate
Library Holdings: Bk Vols 1,501,492; Per Subs 16,826
Special Collections: Abraham Lincoln (Rex & Lucille Anderson Coll); Cookery (Clementine Paddleford Coll), bks, papers & recipes; Historical Costume & Textile Coll; History of American Farming Coll; James Joyce Coll; Landon Lecture Coll; Linneana; Local History (Dan Casement Papers Coll); Miniature Book Coll; Political Cartoon Coll; Poultry Coll; Robert Graves Coll; University Archives Coll, mss, newspaper & photog
Automation Activity & Vendor Info: (Acquisitions) Endeavor; (Cataloging) Endeavor; (Circulation) Endeavor; (OPAC) Endeavor; (Serials) Endeavor
Publications: Bibliography Series; Cassette Series on Library Technology
Partic in Bibliographical Center For Research, Rocky Mountain Region, Inc; Center For Research Libraries; OCLC Online Computer Library Center, Inc
Friends of the Library Group
Departmental Libraries:
ARCHITECTURE & DESIGN, Seaton Hall, Rm 323, 66506. SAN 342-1236. Tel: 785-532-5968. *Librn*, Jeff Alger
Library Holdings: Bk Vols 38,806
Subject Interests: Architecture, Construction, Engineering, Historic preservation, Landscape architecture, Planning, Regional studies
MATHEMATICS & PHYSICS LIBRARY, Cardwell Hall, Rm 105, 66506. SAN 342-1295. Tel: 785-532-6827. FAX: 913-532-6806. *Librn*, Barbara Steward
Library Holdings: Bk Vols 27,500
Subject Interests: Mathematics, Physics
CM VETERINARY MEDICAL LIBRARY, Veterinary Medical Complex, Trotter Hall, Rm 408, 66506. SAN 342-1325. Tel: 785-532-6006. FAX: 785-532-2838. *Librn*, Gayle Willard
Library Holdings: Bk Vols 42,216
Subject Interests: Animals, behavior of, Health sciences, Human relations, Nutrition, Veterinary medicine
Special Collections: Animal Nutrition; German Thesis from University of Hanover Veterinary School; Human-Animal Relationships; Veterinary History

C MANHATTAN CHRISTIAN COLLEGE, BD Phillips Memorial Library, 1415 Anderson Ave, 66502-4081. SAN 306-0314. Tel: 785-539-3571. Toll Free Tel: 877-246-4622. FAX: 785-539-0832. Toll Free FAX: 800-563-1859. Web Site: www.mccks.edu. *Dir*, Richard Hathaway; Tel: 785-776-1709, E-Mail: rhathawa@mccks.edu; Staff 2 (MLS 1, Non-MLS 1)
Founded 1927. Enrl 406; Fac 12; Highest Degree: Bachelor
Jul 1999-Jun 2000 Income $73,182, Locally Generated Income $1,772, Parent Institution $71,410. Mats Exp $28,764, Books $10,209, Per/Ser (Incl. Access Fees) $4,954, Presv $857, AV Equip $679, Other Print Mats $5,107, Electronic Ref Mat (Incl. Access Fees) $6,958. Sal $40,836 (Prof $32,500)
Library Holdings: Bk Vols 37,918; Bk Titles 31,400; Per Subs 190; Spec Interest Per Sub 130; Bks on Deafness & Sign Lang 10
Subject Interests: Biblical studies, Counseling, Ministry, Missions and missionaries, Music
Special Collections: Christian Religious Education Center; History of Restoration Movement
Database Vendor: OCLC - First Search
Publications: Student handbook
Partic in Kansas Library Network Board; OCLC Online Computer Library Center, Inc

P MANHATTAN PUBLIC LIBRARY, 629 Poyntz Ave, 66502-6086. SAN 306-0322. Tel: 785-776-4741. Toll Free Tel: 800-432-2796. FAX: 785-776-1545. Web Site: www.manhattan.lib.ks.us. *Dir*, Fred Atchison; *Asst Dir*, Judith Edelstein; E-Mail: fdatch@manhattan.lib.ks.us; *Coll Develop*, Marcia Allen; *Ch Servs*, Jennifer Bergen; *Ref*, Gerry Walton; *Tech Servs*, Sharon Ingrim; *Head, Circ*, Marilyn Fulkerson; Staff 10 (MLS 2, Non-MLS 8)
Founded 1857. Pop 42,000; Circ 535,420
Jan 1999-Dec 1999 Income $1,331,129, State $61,473, City $1,269,656. Mats Exp $184,289, Books $154,985, Per/Ser (Incl. Access Fees) $29,304. Sal $756,934 (Prof $416,314)
Library Holdings: Bk Vols 220,000; Per Subs 296
Automation Activity & Vendor Info: (Circulation) epixtech, inc.
Database Vendor: OCLC - First Search
Publications: Friends newsletter; NCKL newsletter
Mem of North Central Kansas Libraries System
Partic in Bibliographical Center For Research, Rocky Mountain Region, Inc; OCLC Online Computer Library Center, Inc
Friends of the Library Group

P NORTH CENTRAL KANSAS LIBRARIES SYSTEM, 629 Poyntz Ave, 66502-6086. SAN 306-0330. Tel: 785-776-4741. Toll Free Tel: 800-432-2796. FAX: 785-776-1545. Web Site: www.manhattan.lib.ks.us/nckl. *Dir*, Fred Atchison; *Coll Develop*, Marcy Allen; Staff 8 (MLS 4, Non-MLS 4)
Founded 1968. Pop 232,355
Jan 1998-Dec 1999 Income $516,027, State $83,295, Federal $27,500, Locally Generated Income $46,938. Mats Exp $37,000, Books $37,000. Sal $232,343 (Prof $150,013)
Library Holdings: Bk Vols 63,651
Publications: North Central Kansas Libraries Newsletter
Member Libraries: Abilene Free Public Library; Americus Township Library; Axtell Public Library; Blue Rapids Public Library; Burnley Memorial Library; Burns Public Library; Chapman Public Library; Clay Center Carnegie Library; Clifton Public Library; Council Grove Public Library; Dorothy Bramlage Public Library; Dwight Library; Elm Creek Township Library; Elmendaro Township Library; Enterprise Public Library; Florence Public Library; Frankfort City Library; Goessel City Library; Hanover Public Library; Hillsboro Public Library; Hope Community Library; Leonardville City Library; Manhattan Public Library; Marion City Library; Marysville Public Library; Peabody Township Library; Pottawatomie-Wabaunsee Regional Library; Solomon Public Library; Summerfield Public Library; Vermillion Public Library; Wakefield Public Library; Wamego Public Library; Washington Library; Waterville Public Library; White City Public Library
Partic in OCLC Online Computer Library Center, Inc
Branches: 1
P SUBREGIONAL TALKING BOOKS FAX: 913-776-1545. Web Site: www.manhattan.lib.ks.us/bph.html. *Librn*, Marion Rice; Staff 4 (MLS 1, Non-MLS 3)
Oct 1998-Sep 1999 Income $88,538, State $45,822, Federal $15,406
Library Holdings: Bk Vols 3,646
Publications: Newsletter (quarterly)

S RILEY COUNTY HISTORICAL MUSEUM, Seaton Memorial Library, 2309 Claflin Rd, 66502-3421. SAN 306-0349. Tel: 785-565-6490. *Dir*, D Cheryl Collins; *Librn*, Jeanne C Mithen; Staff 1 (MLS 1)
Founded 1916
Library Holdings: Bk Titles 4,500
Subject Interests: Frontier and pioneer lLife, History, Kansas
Special Collections: Local History Coll, photog
Publications: Historic Homes, Manhattan; Indices to Riley County Marriage Records 1887-1918; Land Grant Ladies: KSU Presidential Wives; Memory Lane Map 1976; Parades & Pastimes, Play & Picnics (photographs); Riley County Officials & Their Families 1855-1900 (monograph); The Churches of Manhattan & Vicinity; Tracing Traditions (juvenile coloring book)
Restriction: Non-circulating to the public

S RILEY COUNTY KANSAS GENEALOGICAL SOCIETY LIBRARY, 2005 Claflin, 66502-3415. SAN 326-2421. Tel: 785-565-6495. E-Mail: rcgs@flinthills.com. Web Site: www.flinthills.com/~rcgs. *Cat*, Helen R Long; *Res*, Elizabeth B Love; Staff 35 (MLS 3, Non-MLS 32)

Founded 1962
Library Holdings: Bk Titles 4,100; Per Subs 490
Subject Interests: Genealogy
Special Collections: Genealogy, pedigree charts & surname cards; Local Family History (original material for book Pioneers of the Bluestem Prairie)
Publications: Kansas Kin (Quarterly)

G USDA-AGRICULTURAL RESEARCH SERVICE, Grain Marketing, Production & Research Laboratory Library, 1515 College Ave, 66502-2736. SAN 374-5074. Tel: 785-776-2701. FAX: 785-776-2789. *Head of Libr*, G Glen Dalluge
Library Holdings: Bk Vols 2,000; Per Subs 15
Subject Interests: Agriculture, Biology, Grains

MANKATO

P MANKATO CITY LIBRARY,* 210 N Commercial St, 66956-2006. SAN 306-0357. Tel: 785-378-3885. *Librn*, Sarah Schlotterback
Founded 1902. Pop 1,205; Circ 15,383
Library Holdings: Bk Vols 13,265; Per Subs 44
Mem of Central Kansas Library System
Open Mon & Wed 1-5 & 7-8:30, Tues, Thurs & Fri 1-5 & Sat 10-12

MARION

P MARION CITY LIBRARY,* 208 E Santa Fe, 66861. SAN 306-0365. Tel: 316-382-2442. *Librn*, Janet Marler
Pop 1,951; Circ 19,276
Library Holdings: Bk Vols 17,500; Per Subs 60
Subject Interests: Genealogy
Special Collections: Kansas Coll
Mem of North Central Kansas Libraries System

MARQUETTE

P MARQUETTE COMMUNITY LIBRARY,* 121 N Washington, 67464-0381. SAN 306-0373. Tel: 785-546-2561. E-Mail: marqlib@mfsb.com. *Librn*, Kelly Montgomery
Pop 722; Circ 7,190
Library Holdings: Bk Vols 7,500; Per Subs 31
Mem of South Central Kansas Library System
Open Tues, Wed & Sat 10-12 & 2-5

MARYSVILLE

P MARYSVILLE PUBLIC LIBRARY,* 1009 Broadway, 66508. (Mail add: PO Box 389, 66508-0389), SAN 306-0381. Tel: 785-562-2491. FAX: 785-562-4086. E-Mail: maryslb@bluevalley.net. Web Site: www.skyways.lib.ks.us/library/marysville/. *Dir*, Barbara G Read; E-Mail: bread@bluevalley.net
Founded 1935. Pop 3,359; Circ 26,883
Jan 2000-Dec 2000 Income $130,300, State $85. Mats Exp $130,300, Books $25,000, Per/Ser (Incl. Access Fees) $3,000, AV Equip $2,800. Sal $57,500
Library Holdings: Bk Vols 30,000; Per Subs 80
Subject Interests: Kansas
Special Collections: Marshall County, newsp on microfilm 1898-1981
Database Vendor: Innovative Interfaces INN - View, OVID Technologies
Mem of North Central Kansas Libraries System
Friends of the Library Group

MC CONNELL AFB

UNITED STATES AIR FORCE
A AIR MOBILITY COMMAND, MCCONNELL AIR FORCE BASE LIBRARY, 53476 Wichita St, Bldg 412, 67221. SAN 342-1171. Tel: 316-759-4207. FAX: 316-759-4254. *Dir*, Darla Cooper; Tel: 316-759-4209, E-Mail: darla.cooper@mcconnell.af.mil; Staff 7 (MLS 2, Non-MLS 5)
Founded 1953
Library Holdings: Bk Vols 40,000; Per Subs 60
Special Collections: Air War College Coll; Chief of Staff Reading List; Kansas Coll; Military Aviation History Coll; Project Warrior
Database Vendor: Ebsco - EbscoHost, GaleNet, IAC - Info Trac, OCLC - First Search, ProQuest
Function: ILL available
Mem of South Central Kansas Library System
Partic in Fedlink; OCLC Online Computer Library Center, Inc

MC CRACKEN

P MC CRACKEN PUBLIC LIBRARY,* 303 Main St, 67556-0125. (Mail add: PO Box 125, 67556), SAN 306-0217. Tel: 785-394-2444. *Asst Librn*, Jean Lillie; Tel: 606-781-6166, Ext 11; *Librn*, Marie LePage; Tel: 606-572-5033, E-Mail: mlepage@cc-pl.org
Founded 1936. Pop 292; Circ 1,964
Library Holdings: Bk Vols 8,500
Special Collections: McCracken Newspapers, 1887-1945 & 1951-1953, micro
Mem of Central Kansas Library System

MC CUNE

P MCCUNE CITY LIBRARY, 509 Sixth St, 66753. SAN 306-0225. Tel: 316-632-4112. E-Mail: books@ckt.net. *Librn*, Maxine Allen; E-Mail: books@ckt.net
Pop 419; Circ 2,300
Library Holdings: Bk Vols 3,900; Per Subs 12
Mem of Southeast Kansas Library System

MC DONALD

P MC DONALD PUBLIC LIBRARY,* PO Box 69, 67745. SAN 306-0233. Tel: 785-538-2380. *Librn*, Carleen Atcheson
Pop 238; Circ 3,100
Library Holdings: Bk Vols 3,700; Per Subs 12
Open Tues 2-4 & Sat 10-12

MC PHERSON

J CENTRAL CHRISTIAN COLLEGE OF KANSAS, Briner Library, 1200 S Main, PO Box 1403, 67460. SAN 306-025X. Tel: 316-241-0723. FAX: 316-241-3529. Web Site: www.centralchristianedu/library.html. *Dir*, Nancy Malone; E-Mail: nancy.malone@centralchristian.edu; Staff 2 (MLS 1, Non-MLS 1)
Founded 1894. Enrl 245; Fac 18; Highest Degree: Bachelor
Jul 1999-Jun 2000 Income $64,471, Locally Generated Income $100, Parent Institution $63,871. Mats Exp $18,100, Books $4,600, Per/Ser (Incl. Access Fees) $10,000, AV Equip $1,500, Other Print Mats $2,000. Sal $35,583 (Prof $19,781)
Library Holdings: Bk Vols 30,000; Bk Titles 28,543; Per Subs 212
Subject Interests: Business, Religion
Special Collections: Free Methodist Church Coll, per & bks
Automation Activity & Vendor Info: (Cataloging) Sagebrush Corporation; (Circulation) Sagebrush Corporation; (Course Reserve) Sagebrush Corporation
Mem of South Central Kansas Library System

P MC PHERSON PUBLIC LIBRARY, 214 W Marlin, 67460-4299. SAN 306-0276. Tel: 316-245-2570. FAX: 316-245-2567. Web Site: www.mpks.net/library. *Dir*, Steven D Read; *Ch Servs*, Holly Engle; *Ref*, Elsie Newell; *Circ*, Jennie Hall; Staff 2 (MLS 1, Non-MLS 1)
Founded 1902. Pop 12,800; Circ 167,300
Jan 2000-Dec 2000 Income $434,200. Mats Exp $412,900. Sal $210,700
Library Holdings: Bk Vols 63,000; Per Subs 185
Special Collections: Kansas Coll; Small Business & Entrepreneurship
Automation Activity & Vendor Info: (Cataloging) Gaylord; (Circulation) Gaylord; (OPAC) Gaylord
Mem of South Central Kansas Library System
Special Services for the Blind - CCTV (VisualTex); Kurzweil Reader

MCPHERSON

C MCPHERSON COLLEGE, Miller Library, 1600 E Euclid, PO Box 1402, 67460-1402. SAN 306-0268. Tel: 316-241-0731, Ext 1216. FAX: 316-241-1649. Web Site: www.mcpherson.edu/library/index. html. *Dir Libr Serv*, Rowena Olsen; Tel: 316-241-0731, Ext 1213, E-Mail: olsenr@mcpherson.edu; Staff 3 (MLS 1, Non-MLS 2)
Founded 1906. Enrl 463; Fac 42; Highest Degree: Bachelor
Jul 1999-Jun 2000 Income Parent Institution $220,436. Mats Exp $87,800, Books $23,231, Per/Ser (Incl. Access Fees) $28,378, Presv $2,665, AV Equip $3,203, Electronic Ref Mat (Incl. Access Fees) $24,531. Sal $113,051 (Prof $41,006)
Library Holdings: Bk Vols 90,535; Bk Titles 65,879; Per Subs 308
Special Collections: Church of the Brethren Archives; Kansas & McPherson County Materials Coll; McPherson College Archives
Automation Activity & Vendor Info: (Circulation) Sagebrush Corporation; (OPAC) Sagebrush Corporation; (Serials) Sagebrush Corporation
Database Vendor: Ebsco - EbscoHost, IAC - Info Trac, Lexis-Nexis, OCLC - First Search, Silverplatter Information Inc., Wilson - Wilson Web
Mem of South Central Kansas Library System
Partic in Associated Colleges Of Central Kansas
Open Mon-Thurs 7:30-10, Fri & Sat 8-5, Sun 2-10

MEADE

P MEADE PUBLIC LIBRARY, 104 E West Plains, PO Box 599, 67864-0599. SAN 306-039X. Tel: 316-873-2522. FAX: 316-873-2522. E-Mail: meadelib@midusa.net. *Librn*, Linda Kobs
Founded 1928. Pop 1,600; Circ 30,000

Library Holdings: Bk Vols 22,000; Per Subs 60
Subject Interests: Antiques, Collectibles, Parenting
Mem of Southwest Kansas Library System
Partic in OCLC Online Computer Library Center, Inc
Friends of the Library Group

MEDICINE LODGE

P LINCOLN LIBRARY,* 201 N Main, 67104. SAN 306-0403. Tel: 316-886-5746. E-Mail: lincolnl@cyberlodg.com. Web Site: www.cyberlodg.com/lincoln/index.html. *Librn*, Rosalee Armstrong
Founded 1898. Pop 3,500; Circ 40,804
Library Holdings: Bk Vols 25,360; Per Subs 52
Special Collections: Indians; Kansas History
Mem of South Central Kansas Library System

MERIDEN

P MERIDEN COMMUNITY LIBRARY,* 201 Main St, 66512. SAN 306-0411. Tel: 785-484-3393. *Librn*, Sharon Monhollon
Founded 1968. Circ 15,250
Library Holdings: Bk Vols 12,000
Mem of Northeast Kansas Library System

MINNEAPOLIS

P MINNEAPOLIS PUBLIC LIBRARY,* 519 Delia Ave, 67467. SAN 306-0438. Tel: 785-392-3205. FAX: 785-392-2934. *Librn*, Evelyn Nelson
Founded 1892. Circ 20,382
Library Holdings: Bk Vols 15,715; Per Subs 50
Mem of Central Kansas Library System
Open Mon, Tues & Thurs 12-8, Fri 10-5, Sat 10-3

MINNEOLA

P MINNEOLA CITY LIBRARY,* 112 Main St, PO Box 95, 67865-0095. SAN 306-0446. Tel: 316-885-4749. FAX: 316-885-4278. E-Mail: minlibl@minneola.net. *Librn*, Leta M Locke
Founded 1930. Pop 700; Circ 10,000
Library Holdings: Bk Vols 13,290; Per Subs 15
Mem of Southwest Kansas Library System

MISSION

S NATIONAL SOCIETY OF INSURANCE PREMIUM AUDITORS LIBRARY,* 5800 Foxridge Dr No 115, 66202-2333. SAN 375-0582. Tel: 913-262-0163. FAX: 913-262-0174. E-Mail: nsipa@idir.net. Web Site: www.nsipa.org. *In Charge*, Michelle Reeder-Dauteu

MOLINE

P MOLINE PUBLIC LIBRARY,* 107 N Main, PO Box 96, 67353-0096. SAN 306-0462. Tel: 316-647-3310. *Librn*, Esther Wilson
Pop 553; Circ 8,128
Library Holdings: Bk Vols 5,000; Per Subs 16
Mem of Southeast Kansas Library System
Open Wed 9-5, Sat 9-noon

MONTEZUMA

P MONTEZUMA TOWNSHIP LIBRARY, 309 N Aztec, 67867-0184. (Mail add: PO Box 184, 67867-0184), Tel: 316-846-7032. E-Mail: montelib@ucom.net. *Dir*, Dee Maurer
Founded 1923. Pop 1,287; Circ 5,835
Library Holdings: Bk Vols 12,000
Mem of Southwest Kansas Library System

MORAN

P MORAN PUBLIC LIBRARY, 335 N Cedar, 66755-0186. (Mail add: PO Box 186, 66755-0186), Tel: 316-237-4334. *Librn*, Audrey Maley
Founded 1957. Pop 674; Circ 5,000
Jan 2000-Dec 2000 Income $9,500, State $250, City $2,891, Federal $200, Locally Generated Income $2,500. Mats Exp $3,500, Books $3,000, Per/Ser (Incl. Access Fees) $500. Sal $5,500
Library Holdings: Bk Titles 9,000; Per Subs 15
Mem of Southeast Kansas Library System

MOUND CITY

P MARY SOMMERVILLE FREE LIBRARY, 509 Main St, PO Box 325, 66056-0325. SAN 306-0497. Tel: 913-795-2788. FAX: 913-795-2801. *Librn*, Merleyne New
Pop 874; Circ 10,491
Library Holdings: Bk Vols 9,000; Per Subs 21
Mem of Southeast Kansas Library System

MOUND VALLEY

P MOUND VALLEY PUBLIC LIBRARY,* PO Box 79, 67354-0179. SAN 306-0500. Tel: 316-328-3341. *Librn*, Sharon Billingsly
Founded 1973. Pop 496; Circ 5,293
Library Holdings: Bk Vols 4,679
Mem of Southeast Kansas Library System
Open Mon, Wed & Fri 3-5, Tues & Thurs 9-11

MOUNDRIDGE

P MOUNDRIDGE PUBLIC LIBRARY,* 220 S Christian, PO Box 696, 67107-0696. SAN 306-0519. Tel: 316-345-6355. *Librn*, Helen Bertrand
Pop 1,431; Circ 20,352
Library Holdings: Bk Vols 19,000; Per Subs 63
Mem of South Central Kansas Library System

MOUNT HOPE

P MOUNT HOPE LIBRARY, PO Box 35, 67108. SAN 306-0527. Tel: 316-667-2665. *Librn*, Pauline Moore
Pop 1,096; Circ 12,668
Library Holdings: Bk Vols 8,877; Per Subs 36
Mem of South Central Kansas Library System
Friends of the Library Group

MULVANE

P MULVANE PUBLIC LIBRARY, 101 E Main St, 67110. SAN 306-0535. Tel: 316-777-1211. FAX: 316-777-0307. E-Mail: mulvanelib@feist.com. *Librn*, Marjorie Fox; *Asst Librn*, Pam Thompson; *Asst Librn*, Sue Gerlach
Pop 4,400; Circ 41,463
Jan 1999-Dec 1999 Income $97,239, City $84,676, Federal $3,440, Locally Generated Income $5,208, Other $3,915. Mats Exp $23,421, Books $16,383, Per/Ser (Incl. Access Fees) $3,164, Other Print Mats $1,654, Electronic Ref Mat (Incl. Access Fees) $2,220. Sal $50,946
Library Holdings: Bk Vols 20,000; Per Subs 71
Automation Activity & Vendor Info: (Acquisitions) Follett; (Cataloging) Follett; (Circulation) Follett; (OPAC) Follett
Mem of South Central Kansas Library System

NEODESHA

P W A RANKIN MEMORIAL LIBRARY, 502 Indiana St, 66757-1532. SAN 306-0543. Tel: 316-325-3275. FAX: 316-325-3275. E-Mail: rankin.library@student.neodesha.k12.ks.us. *Librn*, Barbara Shoop; *Asst Librn*, Mary Meckley; *Ch Servs*, Rita Banta
Founded 1912. Pop 2,837; Circ 45,000
Library Holdings: Bk Titles 20,190; Per Subs 43
Special Collections: Neodesha Daily Sun (Mar 1891 - Oct 27, 1983), micro; Neodesha Derrick (Aug 18, 1994 - Apr 27, 1995); Neodesha Register (Nov 1883 - Dec 29, 1983); Neodesha Sun Register (Jan 1990 - Aug 11, 1994)
Mem of Southeast Kansas Library System
Friends of the Library Group

NESS CITY

P NESS CITY PUBLIC LIBRARY, 113 S Iowa, 67560-1992. SAN 306-0551. Tel: 785-798-3415. FAX: 785-798-2313. *Dir, Librn*, Jean Schlegel; E-Mail: jeannepl@ruraltel.net
Founded 1887. Pop 1,540; Circ 14,820
Library Holdings: Bk Vols 12,500; Per Subs 30
Subject Interests: Genealogy
Mem of Southwest Kansas Library System
Partic in OCLC Online Computer Library Center, Inc
Special Services for the Blind - Talking Books

NEWTON

P NEWTON PUBLIC LIBRARY, 720 N Oak, 67114. SAN 306-056X. Tel: 316-283-2890. FAX: 316-283-2916. E-Mail: library@newtonplks.org. Web Site: www.newtonplks.org. *Dir*, Marianne Eichelberger; E-Mail: meichelb@newtonplks.org; *Coll Develop*, Ruth Hartzler; E-Mail: rhartzle@newtonplks.org; *Ad Servs*, Marilyn Schmidt; E-Mail: mschdmit@newtonplks.org; *Ch Servs*, Amy Bayes; E-Mail: abayes@newtonplks.org; Staff 20 (MLS 2, Non-MLS 18)
Founded 1886. Pop 18,116; Circ 189,230
Jan 2000-Dec 2000 Income $551,134, State $23,811, City $478,054, County $13,116, Locally Generated Income $21,200, Other $14,953. Mats Exp $87,450, Books $64,770, Per/Ser (Incl. Access Fees) $11,461, Micro $4,046,

AV Equip $750, Electronic Ref Mat (Incl. Access Fees) $6,423. Sal $294,586
Library Holdings: Bk Titles 87,850; Per Subs 317
Subject Interests: Genealogy
Special Collections: Kansas Coll; Large Print; Spanish Coll
Automation Activity & Vendor Info: (Acquisitions) epixtech, inc.; (Cataloging) epixtech, inc.; (OPAC) epixtech, inc.; (Serials) epixtech, inc.
Database Vendor: Ebsco - EbscoHost, epixtech, inc., IAC - SearchBank, OCLC - First Search
Mem of South Central Kansas Library System
Friends of the Library Group

NICKERSON

P NICKERSON PUBLIC LIBRARY,* 23 N Nickerson, PO Box 368, 67561-0368. SAN 306-0578. Tel: 316-422-3361. Interlibrary Loan Service Toll Free Tel: 800-234-0529. *Librn*, Gay Sykes
Founded 1916
Library Holdings: Bk Vols 10,752; Per Subs 32
Mem of South Central Kansas Library System
Friends of the Library Group

NORCATUR

P NORCATUR PUBLIC LIBRARY, 301 E Ossipee, PO Box 213, 67653-0213. SAN 306-0586. Tel: 785-693-4225. E-Mail: norcaturlib@nwkansas.com. *Librn*, Chris Dempewolf
Founded 1945. Pop 200; Circ 1,365
Library Holdings: Bk Vols 2,875
Mem of Northwest Kansas Library System

NORTH NEWTON

C BETHEL COLLEGE LIBRARY, PO Drawer A, 67117-0531. SAN 342-135X. Tel: 316-283-2500, Ext 361. FAX: 316-284-5286. E-Mail: library@bethelks.edu. Web Site: www.bethelks.edu/services/library/. *Dir, Publ Servs*, Gail Stucky; *Dir, Tech Servs*, Barbara Thiesen; *Acq*, Lori Hein; *ILL*, Greta Hiebert; *Circ*, Rita Kunkel; Staff 3 (MLS 2, Non-MLS 1)
Founded 1891. Enrl 500; Fac 50; Highest Degree: Bachelor
Jul 1998-Jun 1999 Mats Exp $62,279, Books $20,000, Per/Ser (Incl. Access Fees) $34,779, Electronic Ref Mat (Incl. Access Fees) $7,500
Library Holdings: Bk Vols 94,491; Bk Titles 80,620; Per Subs 200
Subject Interests: Environmental studies, Mathematics, Music, Religion
Automation Activity & Vendor Info: (Acquisitions) Endeavor; (Cataloging) Endeavor; (Circulation) Endeavor; (Course Reserve) Endeavor; (ILL) Endeavor; (Media Booking) Endeavor; (OPAC) Endeavor; (Serials) Endeavor
Database Vendor: Ebsco - EbscoHost, IAC - Info Trac, OCLC - First Search, Silverplatter Information Inc.
Partic in Associated Colleges Of Central Kansas; Bibliographical Center For Research, Rocky Mountain Region, Inc; Dialog Corporation; Kansas Info Circuit; OCLC Online Computer Library Center, Inc
Departmental Libraries:
MENNONITE LIBRARY & ARCHIVES, 300 E 27th St, 67117-8061. (Mail add: PO Drawer A, 67117-0531), Tel: 316-284-5304. FAX: 316-284-5286. E-Mail: mla@bethelks.edu. Web Site: www.bethelks.edu/services/mla. *Archivist*, John Thiesen; *Cat*, Barbara Thiesen
Founded 1936
1998-1999 Mats Exp $4,800, Books $2,600, Per/Ser (Incl. Access Fees) $2,200
Library Holdings: Bk Vols 30,788; Per Subs 310
Subject Interests: Baptists, Biblical studies, Dutch (Language), Education, Genealogy, German (Language), History, Mennonites, Reformation
Special Collections: 17th Century Dutch Art; Cheyenne Indian (Rodolphe Petter Coll), mss, photog & bk; Hopi Indian (H R Voth Coll), mss, bk & photog; Peace (H P Krehbiel Coll), mss & bk; Showalter Oral History Coll (numerous topics, especially World War I conscientious objectors & World War II civilian public service)
Publications: Mennonite Life
Partic in Associated Colleges Of Central Kansas; OCLC Online Computer Library Center, Inc

R WESTERN DISTRICT OF THE GENERAL CONFERENCE MENNONITE CHURCH, Resource Library, PO Box 306, 67117. SAN 306-0594. Tel: 316-283-6300. FAX: 316-283-0620. E-Mail: crlib@mennowdc.org. Web Site: www.mennowdc.org. *Librn*, Marlene Bogard
Founded 1936
Library Holdings: Bk Titles 9,000
Subject Interests: Religion
Special Collections: Children's Coll; Sunday School Curriculums; videos
Open Mon-Fri 8-5

NORTON

P NORTHWEST KANSAS LIBRARY SYSTEM, 2 Washington Sq, PO Box 446, 67654-0446. SAN 306-0608. Tel: 785-877-5148. FAX: 785-877-5697. E-Mail: nwkls@ruraltel.net. Web Site: skyways.lib.ks.us/nwkls/norwest.html. *Dir*, Ann C Bailey; E-Mail: abailey@nisc.net; *Asst Dir*, Leslie Bell; E-Mail: leslieb@ruraltel.net; *ILL*, Linda Keith; Staff 9 (MLS 2, Non-MLS 7)
Founded 1966. Pop 42,242
Dec 1999-Jan 2000 Income (Main Library Only) $422,305, State $154,311, Federal $16,197, County $247,778, Locally Generated Income $4,019. Mats Exp $23,604, Books $23,022, Per/Ser (Incl. Access Fees) $582. Sal $203,332 (Prof $91,500)
Library Holdings: Bk Vols 63,966; Per Subs 15
Subject Interests: Genealogy
Special Collections: Kansas Books
Database Vendor: IAC - Info Trac, OCLC - First Search
Publications: NWKLS Exchange
Function: ILL available
Member Libraries: Almena City Library; Clayton City Library; Colby Community College; Goodland Public Library; Gove City Library; Grainfield Public Library; Jay Johnson Public Library; Jennings City Library; Lenora Public Library; Mary L Gritten Library; Moore Family Library; Norcatur Public Library; Northwest Kansas Heritage Center; Norton Public Library; Oakley Public Library; Oberlin City Library; Pioneer Memorial Library; Saint Francis Public Library; Selden Public Library; Sharon Springs Public Library; Sheridan County Library; WaKeeney Public Library
Partic in BCR
Special Services for the Blind - Talking book center
Branches: 1

P WESTERN KANSAS SUBREGIONAL LIBRARY FOR THE BLIND & PHYSICALLY HANDICAPPED Tel: 785-877-5148. FAX: 785-877-5697. E-Mail: tbook@ruraltel.net. Web Site: skyways.lib.ks.us/nwkls/howard/bph.htm. *Librn for Blind*, Clarice Howard; E-Mail: choward@nisc.net; *Dir*, Ann Bailey; E-Mail: nwkls@ruraltel.net; Staff 2 (Non-MLS 2)
Oct 1998-Sep 1999 Income (Main Library Only) $53,817, State $40,317, Federal $13,500. Sal $39,232 (Prof $25,100)

M NORTON CORRECTIONAL FACILITY, Inmate Library,* PO Box 546, 67654. SAN 325-6006. Tel: 785-877-3389. FAX: 785-877-3972. *Librn*, Russell Cart
Library Holdings: Bk Titles 1,500; Per Subs 17
Open 6-9

P NORTON PUBLIC LIBRARY,* One Washington Sq, PO Box 446, 67654. SAN 306-0616. Tel: 785-877-2481. E-Mail: nortonpl@nisc.net. *Dir*, Kay LeBeau; *Librn*, Connie Ward; *Librn*, Helmi Moody; *Asst Dir, Ch Servs*, Mary Luehrs; Staff 1 (MLS 1)
Founded 1909. Pop 7,000; Circ 78,000
1997-1998 Income $69,838. Mats Exp $8,585, Books $6,289, Per/Ser (Incl. Access Fees) $1,255
Library Holdings: Bk Vols 75,000; Bk Titles 33,000; Per Subs 40
Special Collections: Masonic Coll
Mem of Northwest Kansas Library System
Partic in Highlands Regional Library Cooperative
Friends of the Library Group

NORTONVILLE

P NORTONVILLE PUBLIC LIBRARY,* 202 Taggart, PO Box 179, 66060-0179. SAN 306-0624. Tel: 913-886-2060. Interlibrary Loan Service Tel: 913-843-3654. *Dir*, Nancy Banker
Pop 940; Circ 5,275
Library Holdings: Bk Vols 4,050
Mem of Northeast Kansas Library System

NORWICH

P NORWICH PUBLIC LIBRARY,* PO Box 397, 67118. SAN 306-0632. Tel: 316-478-2681. E-Mail: norwi1lb@ink.org. *Librn*, Carol Gray
Founded 1923. Pop 490; Circ 4,674
Library Holdings: Bk Vols 5,422; Per Subs 16
Mem of South Central Kansas Library System
Partic in OCLC Online Computer Library Center, Inc

OAKLEY

P OAKLEY PUBLIC LIBRARY,* 700 W Third St, 67748. SAN 306-0640. Tel: 785-672-4776. FAX: 785-672-3868. E-Mail: oaklellib@ruraltel.net. *Dir*, Joyce Homm
Founded 1923. Pop 2,382; Circ 17,155
Library Holdings: Bk Vols 23,770; Per Subs 36
Mem of Northwest Kansas Library System
Special Services for the Deaf - Captioned film depository
Friends of the Library Group

OBERLIN

P OBERLIN CITY LIBRARY,* 104 E Oak, 67749-1997. SAN 306-0659. Tel: 785-475-2412. FAX: 785-475-2708. *Librn*, Carol Smith
Founded 1903. Pop 2,300; Circ 31,000
Library Holdings: Bk Vols 20,000; Per Subs 56
Mem of Northwest Kansas Library System

OLATHE

GL JOHNSON COUNTY LAW LIBRARY, Courthouse, First Flr, 100 N Kansas Ave, 66061. SAN 306-0667. Tel: 913-715-4154. FAX: 913-715-4152. Web Site: www.jocoks.com/jococourts/law_library.htm. *Dir*, John C Pickett; Tel: 913-715-4150, E-Mail: john.picket@jocoks.com; *Asst Librn*, Bonnie Kanter; Tel: 913-715-4151; *Info Specialist*, Pat Gillgannon; *Info Specialist*, Tami Shay; Staff 1 (MLS 1)
Founded 1954
Jan 2000-Dec 2000 Income $365,000, County $230,000, Locally Generated Income $135,000. Mats Exp $360,000, Books $160,000, Per/Ser (Incl. Access Fees) $9,000. Sal $52,000
Library Holdings: Bk Titles 22,000; Per Subs 80
Restriction: Circulation limited, Non-circulating to the public, Public use on premises
Function: Document delivery services, ILL available, Photocopies available, Reference services available, Some telephone reference

M JOHNSON COUNTY MENTAL HEALTH CENTER LIBRARY,* 1125 W Spruce, 66061. SAN 306-0675. Tel: 913-782-2100. FAX: 913-782-1186.
Founded 1974
Library Holdings: Bk Titles 400; Per Subs 12
Subject Interests: Education, Mental health, Psychiatry, Psychology, Social service (social work)

C MID-AMERICA NAZARENE UNIVERSITY, Mabee Library & Learning Resource Center, 2030 College Way, 66062. SAN 306-0683. Tel: 913-782-3750, Ext 161. FAX: 913-791-3285. Web Site: www.mnu.edu/mabee/. *Dir*, Ray L Morrison; E-Mail: rmorriso@mnu.edu; *Ref*, Bonnie Thornton; E-Mail: bthornto@mnu.edu
Founded 1968. Highest Degree: Master
Jul 1998-Jun 1999 Income $351,005. Mats Exp $118,500, Books $37,000, Per/Ser (Incl. Access Fees) $50,000, Presv $5,000, AV Equip $500. Sal $222,000 (Prof $126,000)
Library Holdings: Bk Titles 115,810; Per Subs 225
Special Collections: Americana; Church of the Nazarene Publications
Mem of Northeast Kansas Library System

P OLATHE PUBLIC LIBRARY,* 201 E Park St, 66061-3499. SAN 306-0691. Tel: 913-764-2259. TDD: 913-393-6855. FAX: 913-764-1009. E-Mail: olref@jcl.lib.ks.us. Web Site: olathe.lib.ks.us. *Dir*, Emily Baker; Tel: 913-393-6880, E-Mail: bakere@jcl.lib.ks.us; *Ch Servs*, Jennifer Adamson; Tel: 913-393-6869, E-Mail: adamson@jcl.lib.ks.us; *Ad Servs*, Kathleen O'Leary; Tel: 913-393-6884, E-Mail: oleary@jcl.lib.ks.us; *Tech Coordr*, Mary Linse; Tel: 913-393-6863, E-Mail: linse@jcl.lib.ks.us; *Circ*, Leslie Ellsworth; Tel: 913-393-6856, E-Mail: ellsworth@jcl.lib.ks.us; Staff 57 (MLS 10, Non-MLS 47)
Founded 1909. Pop 88,081; Circ 618,583
Jan 1998-Dec 1998 Income $1,742,491, State $64,363, City $1,569,198, Locally Generated Income $108,930. Mats Exp $1,416,850. Sal $884,974
Library Holdings: Bk Vols 138,525; Per Subs 319
Special Collections: Grandparents Coll; Kansas Room
Automation Activity & Vendor Info: (Circulation) DRA; (OPAC) DRA
Database Vendor: DRA, IAC - Info Trac, OCLC - First Search
Mem of Northeast Kansas Library System
Special Services for the Deaf - TDD
Special Services for the Blind - Arkenstone, a computer system for the visually handicapped
Friends of the Library Group

OSAGE CITY

P LIEBER PUBLIC LIBRARY,* 515 Main, 66523. SAN 306-0705. Tel: 785-528-3727. FAX: 785-528-4502. *Dir, Librn*, Shirley Earhart; *Asst Librn*, Kristal Annett
Pop 2,667; Circ 26,386
Library Holdings: Bk Vols 16,000; Per Subs 23
Mem of Northeast Kansas Library System
Friends of the Library Group

OSAWATOMIE

P OSAWATOMIE PUBLIC LIBRARY,* 527 Brown St, 66064. SAN 306-0713. Tel: 913-755-2136. FAX: 913-755-2335. E-Mail: osalibr1@micoks.net. *Librn*, Dorothy L Ingram
Pop 4,413; Circ 28,292
Library Holdings: Bk Titles 20,221; Per Subs 60
Special Collections: Kansas Coll
Mem of Northeast Kansas Library System
Friends of the Library Group

M OSAWATOMIE STATE HOSPITAL, Rapaport Professional Library,* 500 State Hospital Dr, PO Box 500, 66064. SAN 306-0721. Tel: 913-755-7212. FAX: 913-755-2637. *Librn*, Rhonda K Ryan; E-Mail: rhondar@srskansas.org; Staff 1 (MLS 1)
Founded 1949
Jul 1999-Jun 2000 Mats Exp $40,000, Books $12,000, Per/Ser (Incl. Access Fees) $17,000, Electronic Ref Mat (Incl. Access Fees) $5,000. Sal $36,500
Library Holdings: Bk Vols 3,000; Per Subs 130
Subject Interests: Medicine, Nursing, Psychiatry, Psychology, Social sciences and issues
Database Vendor: Dialog, Ebsco - EbscoHost, OCLC - First Search
Function: Reference services available
Mem of Northeast Kansas Library System
Partic in Medical Libr Asn; Midcontinental Regional Med Libr Program

OSBORNE

P OSBORNE PUBLIC LIBRARY, 325 W Main St, 67473-2425. SAN 306-073X. Tel: 785-346-5486. FAX: 785-346-2888. E-Mail: osbor1lb@ruraltel.net. *Dir*, Sharon Conway
Founded 1913. Pop 2,120; Circ 24,379
2000-2001 Mats Exp $7,700, Books $7,000, Per/Ser (Incl. Access Fees) $700
Library Holdings: Bk Vols 16,082; Bk Titles 21,000; Per Subs 60
Subject Interests: Genealogy, Local history
Mem of Central Kansas Library System
Partic in Kans Libr Asn
Open Mon & Thurs 1:30-8, Tues, Wed & Sat 1:30-5:30, Fri 10-12 & 1:30-5:30

OSKALOOSA

P OSKALOOSA PUBLIC LIBRARY,* PO Box 347, 66066-0347. SAN 306-0748. Tel: 785-863-2475. FAX: 785-863-2088. E-Mail: opl@ruralnet1.com. Web Site: www.skyways.lib.ks.us/kansas/towns/oskaloosa/library.html. *Librn*, Paula Ware
Pop 2,888; Circ 14,953
1997-1998 Income $22,701, State $1,510, City $8,151, Other $4,755. Mats Exp $3,210, Books $2,400, Per/Ser (Incl. Access Fees) $810. Sal $13,449
Library Holdings: Bk Vols 9,200; Per Subs 31
Subject Interests: Kansas
Mem of Northeast Kansas Library System
Friends of the Library Group

OSWEGO

P OSWEGO PUBLIC LIBRARY,* 704 Fourth St, 67356. SAN 306-0756. Tel: 316-795-4921. *Librn*, Liz Turner
Pop 2,218; Circ 26,500
Library Holdings: Bk Titles 14,000; Per Subs 71
Mem of Southeast Kansas Library System

OTIS

P OTIS COMMUNITY LIBRARY,* 121 S Main, PO Box 7, 67565. SAN 306-0764. Tel: 785-387-2403. FAX: 785-387-2245. E-Mail: otis1lib@ruraltel.net. *Librn*, Lila Baker
Pop 410; Circ 5,181
Library Holdings: Bk Vols 6,000; Per Subs 48
Special Collections: Children's Video Coll; Kansas Shelf
Mem of Central Kansas Library System
Open Mon 7-9pm, Tues 9-12, Thurs 1:30-5, Fri 9-12 & 1:30-5, Sat 9-12:30

OTTAWA

P OTTAWA LIBRARY, 105 S Hickory St, 66067-2306. SAN 306-0772. Tel: 785-242-3080. FAX: 785-242-8789. E-Mail: staff@ottawa.lib.ks.us. Web Site: www.ottawa.lib.ks.us. *Dir*, Barbara Dew; *Circ*, Rosemary Honn; *Tech Servs*, Terry Schaeffer; *ILL*, Kathy Norton; *Ch Servs*, Cheryl Sylvester; Staff 12 (MLS 2, Non-MLS 10)
Founded 1872. Pop 12,000; Circ 110,354
Jan 2000-Dec 2000 Income $486,010, State $9,884, City $428,470, Other $47,656. Mats Exp $48,460, Books $39,797, Per/Ser (Incl. Access Fees) $5,371. Sal $307,344
Library Holdings: Bk Titles 48,062; Per Subs 154
Subject Interests: Genealogy, Local history
Automation Activity & Vendor Info: (Cataloging) SIRSI; (Circulation)

SIRSI; (OPAC) SIRSI
Mem of Northeast Kansas Library System
Partic in Kansas Info Circuit
Friends of the Library Group

CR OTTAWA UNIVERSITY, Myers Library, 1001 S Cedar, 66067-3399. SAN 306-0780. Tel: 785-242-5200, Ext 5444. FAX: 785-229-1017. Web Site: www.ottawa.edu. *Coll Develop, Dir*, Jane Ann Nelson; E-Mail: janelson@ott.edu; *Materials Manager*, Lisa Kai Wellman; Tel: 785-242-5200, Ext 5448, E-Mail: lwellman@ottawa.edu; *Actg Librn*, Janice E Lee; Tel: 785-242-5200, Ext 5445, Fax: 785-229-1017, E-Mail: jlee@ottawa.edu; Staff 2 (MLS 1, Non-MLS 1)
Founded 1865. Enrl 473; Fac 44; Highest Degree: Bachelor
Jul 1999-Jun 2000 Income $90,083. Mats Exp $34,563, Books $5,764, Per/Ser (Incl. Access Fees) $15,451, Presv $466, Micro $46, Electronic Ref Mat (Incl. Access Fees) $4,391. Sal $55,520 (Prof $42,120)
Library Holdings: Bk Vols 78,548; Bk Titles 59,676; Per Subs 166
Special Collections: Chinese Art & Related Asiatic Studies
Database Vendor: Ebsco - EbscoHost, GaleNet, IAC - Info Trac, Lexis-Nexis, OCLC - First Search
Function: ILL available
Mem of Northeast Kansas Library System
Partic in BCR

OVERBROOK

P OVERBROOK PUBLIC LIBRARY, 317 Maple St, 66524. (Mail add: PO Box 389, 66524), SAN 306-0799. Tel: 913-665-7266. FAX: 913-665-7973. *Librn*, Marilyn K Anderson; E-Mail: manderson@overbrook.lib.ks.us
Founded 1928. Pop 930; Circ 13,501
Library Holdings: Bk Vols 11,500; Per Subs 22
Mem of Northeast Kansas Library System
Friends of the Library Group

OVERLAND PARK

S BLACK & VEATCH, Central Library, 11401 Lamar, 66211. SAN 309-023X. Tel: 913-458-7884. FAX: 913-458-2934. *Coll Develop, Dir*, Kevin Nelson; E-Mail: nelsonk@bv.com; *Ref*, Mike Sharpe; Staff 6 (MLS 2, Non-MLS 4)
Library Holdings: Bk Vols 25,000; Bk Titles 20,160; Per Subs 50
Subject Interests: Engineering
Automation Activity & Vendor Info: (Acquisitions) EOS; (Cataloging) EOS; (Circulation) EOS; (Course Reserve) EOS; (ILL) EOS; (Media Booking) EOS; (OPAC) EOS; (Serials) EOS
Partic in Info Mgt & Eng Ltd

S EMPLOYERS REINSURANCE CORP, June Austin Parrish Memorial Library, 5200 Metcalf, PO Box 2991, 66201. SAN 309-0299. Tel: 913-676-5681. FAX: 913-676-6299. *Librn*, Marilyn Downs
Founded 1941
Library Holdings: Bk Vols 1,250; Bk Titles 1,000; Per Subs 50
Subject Interests: Finance, Law
Special Collections: Reinsurance Coll, bks, clippings, pamphlets
Restriction: Staff use only

J JOHNSON COUNTY COMMUNITY COLLEGE, Billington Library, 12345 College Blvd, 66210. SAN 306-0802. Tel: 913-469-3871. FAX: 913-469-4417. Web Site: gold.jccc.net. *Assoc Dean, Dir*, Mel Cunningham; *Coordr, Tech Servs*, Deborah Ludwig; *Ref*, Carol Campbell; *Ref*, Marsha Cousino; *Ref*, Andrea Kempf; *Ref*, John Russell; *Ref*, Judith Vaughn; Staff 11 (MLS 6, Non-MLS 5)
Founded 1969. Enrl 25,000; Fac 800; Highest Degree: Associate
Library Holdings: Bk Vols 100,000; Bk Titles 89,000; Per Subs 600
Special Collections: Education (ERIC Coll), micro
Database Vendor: DRA
Special Services for the Deaf - Books on deafness & sign language; Special interest periodicals; Staff with knowledge of sign language

P JOHNSON COUNTY LIBRARY,* 9875 W 87th St, 66212. (Mail add: PO Box 2933, 66201), SAN 342-1627. Tel: 913-495-2400. TDD: 913-495-2433. FAX: 913-495-2460. E-Mail: jcl@jcl.lib.ks.us. Web Site: www.jcl.lib.ks.us. *Librn*, Mona Carmack; *Tech Servs*, Tim Rogers; *Govt Doc*, Lola Warren; *YA Servs*, Jean Hatfield; *Acq*, Connie Evans; *Tech Coordr*, David Payne; *Ref*, Carolyn Anderson; *Commun Relations*, Marsha Bennett; *Coll Develop*, Mary Anne Hile; Staff 243 (MLS 47, Non-MLS 196)
Founded 1955. Pop 344,600; Circ 4,465,046
Jan 1999-Dec 1999 Income $16,647,270, State $347,808, County $14,044,096, Locally Generated Income $736,589, Other $1,518,777. Mats Exp $2,301,401, Books $1,007,799, Per/Ser (Incl. Access Fees) $742,532, AV Equip $291,000, Other Print Mats $12,850, Electronic Ref Mat (Incl. Access Fees) $247,220. Sal $7,074,349 (Prof $2,516,838)
Library Holdings: Bk Vols 1,070,658; Per Subs 4,119
Subject Interests: Genealogy, Local history
Automation Activity & Vendor Info: (Acquisitions) DRA; (Cataloging) DRA; (Circulation) DRA; (OPAC) DRA; (Serials) DRA
Mem of Northeast Kansas Library System
Partic in Kansas City Metropolitan Library & Information Network; OCLC Online Computer Library Center, Inc
Friends of the Library Group
Branches: 11
ANTIOCH, 8700 Shawnee Mission Pkwy, Merriam, 66202. SAN 376-883X. Tel: 913-261-2300. FAX: 913-261-2320. *Mgr*, Linda Coonley
Library Holdings: Bk Vols 93,697
Database Vendor: DRA
Friends of the Library Group
BLUE VALLEY, 15185 S Lowell, 66223. SAN 342-1678. Tel: 913-897-8200. FAX: 913-897-8204. *Mgr*, Ken Werne
Library Holdings: Bk Vols 31,502
Database Vendor: DRA
Friends of the Library Group
CEDAR ROE, 5120 Cedar, Roeland Park, 66205. SAN 342-1686. Tel: 913-384-8590. FAX: 913-384-8597. *Mgr*, Judy Henry
Library Holdings: Bk Vols 71,886
Database Vendor: DRA
Friends of the Library Group
CORINTH, 8100 Mission Rd, Prairie Village, 66208. SAN 342-1716. Tel: 913-967-8650. FAX: 913-967-8659. *Mgr*, Inge Dugan
Library Holdings: Bk Vols 137,334
Database Vendor: DRA
Friends of the Library Group
DE SOTO BRANCH, 33145 W 83rd St, De Soto, 66018. SAN 342-1740. Tel: 913-583-3106. FAX: 913-583-1702. *Mgr*, Terry Velasquez
Library Holdings: Bk Vols 12,950
Database Vendor: DRA
Friends of the Library Group
GARDNER BRANCH, 116 E Main, Gardner, 66030. SAN 342-1775. Tel: 913-856-7223. FAX: 913-884-5345. *Branch Mgr*, Terry Velasquez
Library Holdings: Bk Vols 18,619
Database Vendor: DRA
Friends of the Library Group
LACKMAN, 15345 W 87th St Pkwy, Lenexa, 66219. SAN 328-6630. Tel: 913-495-7540. FAX: 913-495-7556.
Library Holdings: Bk Vols 71,140
Database Vendor: DRA
Friends of the Library Group
LEAWOOD PIONEER, 4700 Town Center Dr, Leawood, 66211. SAN 375-6300. Tel: 913-344-0250. FAX: 913-344-0253. *Mgr*, Katie Mediatore
Library Holdings: Bk Vols 66,307
Database Vendor: DRA
Friends of the Library Group
OAK PARK, 9500 Bluejacket, 66212. SAN 342-1805. Tel: 913-752-8700. FAX: 913-752-8709. *Mgr*, Andrew Mangels
Library Holdings: Bk Vols 122,642
Database Vendor: DRA
Friends of the Library Group
SHAWNEE BRANCH, 13811 Johnson Dr, Shawnee, 66216. SAN 371-9839. Tel: 913-962-3800. FAX: 913-962-3809. *Mgr*, Kathy Rieger
Library Holdings: Bk Vols 75,000
Database Vendor: DRA
Friends of the Library Group
SPRING HILL BRANCH, 109 S Webster, Spring Hill, 66083. SAN 342-183X. Tel: 913-592-3232. FAX: 913-686-2004. *Mgr*, Terry Velasquez
Library Holdings: Bk Vols 13,176
Database Vendor: DRA
Friends of the Library Group

M MENORAH MEDICAL CENTER, Robert Uhlmann Medical Library, 5721 W 119th St, 66209. SAN 309-0450. Tel: 913-498-6625. FAX: 913-498-6642. Web Site: www.healthmidwest.org.; Staff 3 (MLS 2, Non-MLS 1)
Founded 1931
Library Holdings: Bk Titles 800; Per Subs 225
Subject Interests: Allied health, Medicine, Nursing
Special Collections: Jewish Medical Ethics
Partic in Health Sci Libr Group of Greater Kansas City

OXFORD

P OXFORD PUBLIC LIBRARY, 115 S Sumner St, PO Box 266, 67119-0266. SAN 306-0829. Tel: 316-455-2221. FAX: 316-455-2917. *Librn*, Phyllis Hege
Pop 1,143; Circ 6,490
Library Holdings: Bk Vols 8,000
Subject Interests: History, Kansas
Mem of South Central Kansas Library System

PALCO

P PALCO PUBLIC LIBRARY,* 311 Main St, PO Box 218, 67657. SAN 306-0837. Tel: 785-737-4286. E-Mail: palcolib@ruraltel.net. Web Site: www.skyways.lib.ks.us/kansas/towns/palco.htm. *Librn*, Kim Eichman

Pop 550; Circ 5,637
Library Holdings: Bk Vols 8,900; Per Subs 15
Mem of Central Kansas Library System

PAOLA

P PAOLA FREE LIBRARY,* 101 E Peoria, 66071-1798. SAN 306-0845. Tel: 913-294-3866. FAX: 913-294-4287. *Dir*, Rosemary King; *Asst Librn*, Helen Roberts; Staff 9 (MLS 1, Non-MLS 8)
Founded 1876. Pop 4,850; Circ 50,000
Jan 2000-Dec 2000 Income $186,575, State $3,600, City $103,000, County $10,500, Locally Generated Income $50,000, Other $19,475. Mats Exp $27,650, Books $18,000, Per/Ser (Incl. Access Fees) $3,200, Micro $50, Other Print Mats $1,200, Electronic Ref Mat (Incl. Access Fees) $5,200. Sal $74,135 (Prof $30,135)
Library Holdings: Bk Vols 35,000; Bk Titles 35,000; Per Subs 75
Automation Activity & Vendor Info: (Circulation) Sagebrush Corporation; (OPAC) Sagebrush Corporation
Mem of Northeast Kansas Library System
Open Mon-Thurs 10-8:30, Fri 10-5 & Sat 10-4
Friends of the Library Group

PARKER

P LINN COUNTY PUBLIC LIBRARY DISTRICT NO 1,* 230 Main, 66072-0315. (Mail add: PO Box 315, 66072-0315), Tel: 913-898-4650. *Librn*, Donna Burroughs
Library Holdings: Bk Vols 10,000; Per Subs 40
Mem of Southeast Kansas Library System
Friends of the Library Group

PARSONS

J LABETTE COMMUNITY COLLEGE LIBRARY, 200 S 14th St, 67357. SAN 306-0853. Tel: 316-421-6700, Ext 1168. Interlibrary Loan Service Tel: 316-421-6700, Ext 1154. Circulation Tel: 316-421-6700, Ext 1167. FAX: 316-421-1469. Web Site: www.labette.cc.ks.us. *Dir*, Scotty Zollad; E-Mail: scottz@labette.cc.ks.us; Staff 2 (MLS 1, Non-MLS 1)
Founded 1923. Circ 23,693; Enrl 15,377; Fac 311; Highest Degree: Associate
Jul 1999-Jun 2000 Income Parent Institution $117,650. Mats Exp $58,945, Books $22,298, Per/Ser (Incl. Access Fees) $2,752, Micro $12,000, AV Equip $747, Electronic Ref Mat (Incl. Access Fees) $17,290. Sal $71,181 (Prof $30,883)
Library Holdings: Bk Vols 25,040; Bk Titles 22,844; Per Subs 259
Subject Interests: Academic, Children's literature
Special Collections: Labette County History
Database Vendor: IAC - Info Trac, OCLC - First Search, ProQuest
Function: ILL available, Reference services available, Some telephone reference
Partic in SE Kans Libr Syst
Open Mon-Thurs 8am-8:30pm & Fri 8am-4:30pm; Summer Hours: Mon-Thurs 7am-7pm & Wed-Thurs 7am-4:30pm

P PARSONS PUBLIC LIBRARY, 311 S 17th, 67357. SAN 306-0861. Tel: 316-421-5920. FAX: 316-421-3951. Web Site: skyways.lib.ks.us/kansas/library/parsons/. *Dir*, Dayna Williams-Capone; E-Mail: dwcapone@hit.net; Staff 11 (MLS 1, Non-MLS 10)
Founded 1908. Pop 11,177; Circ 92,696
Jan 1999-Dec 1999 Income $243,552, State $8,656, City $212,600, Other $22,296. Mats Exp $36,614, Books $27,814, Per/Ser (Incl. Access Fees) $3,585, Other Print Mats $4,855, Electronic Ref Mat (Incl. Access Fees) $360. Sal $124,249
Library Holdings: Bk Vols 65,000; Per Subs 100
Subject Interests: Kansas
Automation Activity & Vendor Info: (Cataloging) Follett; (Circulation) Follett; (OPAC) Follett
Mem of Southeast Kansas Library System
Friends of the Library Group

PARSONS STATE HOSPITAL & TRAINING CENTER

M BOOK NOOK, 2601 Gabriel, PO Box 738, 67357. SAN 342-1473. Tel: 316-421-6550, Ext 1796. *Librn*, Deborah Quinzy
Founded 1956
Library Holdings: Bk Vols 6,600; Per Subs 15

S STAFF LIBRARY, 2601 Gabriel, PO Box 738, 67357. SAN 342-1449. Tel: 316-421-6550, Ext 1889. FAX: 316-421-0954. *Librn*, Linda Lee Stahlman; E-Mail: lindalee@falcon.cc.ukans.edu
Founded 1954
Library Holdings: Bk Titles 2,000; Per Subs 178
Subject Interests: Mentally retarded
Mem of Southeast Kansas Library System

PARTRIDGE

P PARTRIDGE PUBLIC LIBRARY,* 23 S Main St, PO Box 96, 67566-0127. SAN 306-087X. Tel: 316-567-2467. E-Mail: partrf1lb@mailink.org. *Librn*, Gladys Miller
Pop 338; Circ 6,496
Library Holdings: Bk Vols 16,798; Per Subs 23
Special Collections: Kansas Author's Coll; Kansas Coll
Mem of South Central Kansas Library System

PEABODY

P PEABODY TOWNSHIP LIBRARY, 214 Walnut, 66866. SAN 306-0896. Tel: 316-983-2502. *Librn*, Mildred Buller; *Asst Librn*, Neva Lou Dyck
Founded 1914. Pop 1,705; Circ 10,909
Library Holdings: Bk Vols 14,500; Per Subs 36
Mem of North Central Kansas Libraries System

PHILLIPSBURG

P PHILLIPSBURG CITY LIBRARY, 888 Fourth St, 67661. SAN 306-090X. Tel: 785-543-5325. FAX: 785-543-5374. E-Mail: pblib1@theclassic.net. Web Site: skyways.lib.ks.us/kansas/towns/phillipsburg/library. *Dir*, Kay Dority
Founded 1926. Pop 2,576; Circ 53,441
Jan 1999-Dec 1999 Mats Exp $13,544, Books $11,226, Per/Ser (Incl. Access Fees) $2,318. Sal $45,994
Library Holdings: Bk Vols 25,818; Per Subs 89
Subject Interests: Genealogy, Kansas
Mem of Central Kansas Library System
Friends of the Library Group

PITTSBURG

P PITTSBURG PUBLIC LIBRARY, 308 N Walnut, 66762-4732. SAN 306-0918. Tel: 316-231-8110. FAX: 316-232-2258. *Dir*, Pat Clement; E-Mail: pclement@pittsburg.lib.ks.us; *Ch Servs*, Gail Sheppard; *Head Ref*, Carol Ann Robb; *Head Tech Servs*, Becky Galindo; *Head, Circ*, Cindy Gier; Staff 29 (MLS 1, Non-MLS 28)
Founded 1902. Pop 18,073; Circ 166,752
Jan 1999-Dec 1999 Income $431,155, State $28,156, City $361,329, Locally Generated Income $41,670. Mats Exp $61,192, Books $49,687, Per/Ser (Incl. Access Fees) $6,346, Electronic Ref Mat (Incl. Access Fees) $2,016. Sal $280,987
Library Holdings: Bk Vols 71,987; Per Subs 202
Subject Interests: Local history, Medicine, Religion
Special Collections: Crawford County Genealogical Society Coll
Automation Activity & Vendor Info: (Cataloging) epixtech, inc.; (Circulation) epixtech, inc.; (OPAC) epixtech, inc.
Database Vendor: IAC - SearchBank, OVID Technologies
Publications: Pittsburg Public Library News (Newsletter)
Mem of Southeast Kansas Library System
Friends of the Library Group

C PITTSBURG STATE UNIVERSITY, Leonard H Axe Library, 1605 S Joplin St, 66762. (Mail add: 1701 S Broadway, 66762-5889), SAN 306-0926. Tel: 316-235-4879. Interlibrary Loan Service Tel: 316-235-4890. FAX: 316-235-4090. Web Site: library.pittstate.edu. *Dean*, Robert Walter; Tel: 316-235-4878, E-Mail: bwalter@pittstate.edu; *ILL*, Richard Samford; E-Mail: samford@pittstate.edu; *Cat*, Barbara Glackin; Tel: 316-235-4895, E-Mail: bglackin@pittstate.edu; *Reader Servs*, Jane Victor; Tel: 316-235-4886, E-Mail: victor@pittstate.edu; *Spec Coll*, Randy Roberts; Tel: 316-235-4883, E-Mail: rerobert@pittstate.edu; *Govt Doc*, JoAnne Beezley; Tel: 316-235-4889, E-Mail: beezley@pittstate.edu; *Automation Syst Coordr*, Susan Johns; Tel: 316-235-4115, E-Mail: suzyq@pittstate.edu; *Online Servs*, Cynthia Pfannenstiel; Tel: 316-235-4888, E-Mail: cynthia@pittstate.edu; *Coll Develop*, Earl W Lee; Tel: 316-235-4885, E-Mail: ewayne@pittstate.edu; *Per*, Leon Divel; Tel: 316-235-4884, E-Mail: divel@pittstate.edu; *Tech Coordr*, Josh Peck; Tel: 316-235-4087, E-Mail: jmpeck@pittstate.edu; Staff 22 (MLS 11, Non-MLS 11)
Founded 1903. Enrl 6,289; Fac 298
Jul 1999-Jun 2000 Income $1,764,939, Locally Generated Income $63,307, Parent Institution $1,701,632. Mats Exp $474,000, Books $149,000, Per/Ser (Incl. Access Fees) $235,000, Presv $10,000, Electronic Ref Mat (Incl. Access Fees) $80,000. Sal $1,140,149 (Prof $685,263)
Library Holdings: Bk Vols 483,150; Bk Titles 317,844; Per Subs 4,119; Bks on Deafness & Sign Lang 142
Special Collections: Southeast Kansas Coll, bks, per, mss, tapes, photogs; University Archives, bks, per, mss, tapes, photogs
Automation Activity & Vendor Info: (Acquisitions) epixtech, inc.; (Cataloging) epixtech, inc.; (Circulation) epixtech, inc.; (OPAC) epixtech, inc.; (Serials) epixtech, inc.
Database Vendor: epixtech, inc., GaleNet, IAC - SearchBank, Innovative Interfaces INN - View, OCLC - First Search, OVID Technologies, Silverplatter Information Inc., Wilson - Wilson Web

Partic in Bibliographical Center For Research, Rocky Mountain Region, Inc; SE Kans Libr Syst
Open Mon-Thurs 7:45am-11pm, Fri 7:45-5, Sat 9-5 & Sun 3-11pm
Friends of the Library Group

PLAINS

P PLAINS COMMUNITY LIBRARY,* 500 Grand Ave, PO Box 7, 67869-0007. SAN 376-5571. Tel: 316-563-7326. FAX: 316-563-6114. E-Mail: plainslibrary@rahab.net. *Librn*, Carolyn Chase
Pop 1,485
Library Holdings: Bk Vols 12,000; Per Subs 35
Mem of Southwest Kansas Library System
Friends of the Library Group

PLAINVILLE

P PLAINVILLE MEMORIAL LIBRARY,* 200 SW First St, 67663. SAN 306-0942. Tel: 785-434-2786. FAX: 785-434-2520. E-Mail: pville2@ruraltel.net. *Librn*, Margaret Wilson; *Asst Librn*, Kathy Rogers
Pop 2,458; Circ 12,000
Library Holdings: Bk Vols 13,000; Per Subs 42
Mem of Central Kansas Library System

PLEASANTON

S LINN COUNTY MUSEUM,* PO Box 137, 66075. SAN 325-6022. Tel: 913-352-8739. FAX: 913-352-8739. *Pres*, Ola May Earnest
Library Holdings: Bk Titles 400; Per Subs 135
Open Sat & Sun 1-5pm (open to public for viewing); Tues & Thurs 9am-4pm (for research)

P PLEASANTON-LINCOLN LIBRARY,* 201 W Ninth, PO Box 101, 66075-0101. SAN 306-0950. Tel: 913-352-8554. *Librn*, Bonnie Ralle
Founded 1905. Pop 1,333; Circ 9,707
Library Holdings: Bk Vols 3,006
Subject Interests: History, Kansas
Mem of Southeast Kansas Library System

POTWIN

P POTWIN PUBLIC LIBRARY,* 126 N Randall, PO Box 189, 67123. SAN 306-0969. Tel: 316-752-3421. FAX: 316-752-3567. E-Mail: whesta@wheatstate.mail.com. *Librn*, Bethany Seal
Founded 1932
Library Holdings: Bk Vols 4,000
Mem of South Central Kansas Library System

PRAIRIE VIEW

P SUNSHINE CITY LIBRARY, Prairie View City Library,* 207 Kansas St, 67664. (Mail add: PO Box 424, 67664), SAN 306-0977. Tel: 785-973-2265. *Librn*, Darline Brown
Founded 1966. Pop 111; Circ 1,773
Jan 1998-Dec 1998 Income $2,153, State $79, City $1,466, Locally Generated Income $608. Mats Exp $947, Books $749, Per/Ser (Incl. Access Fees) $198
Library Holdings: Bk Vols 3,164; Per Subs 12
Mem of Central Kansas Library System

PRAIRIE VILLAGE

R VILLAGE CHURCH LIBRARY,* 6641 Mission Rd, PO Box 8050, 66208-0050. SAN 306-0985. Tel: 913-262-4200. FAX: 913-262-0304. *In Charge*, Nancy Butcher; *Librn*, Karen Lundgrin
Library Holdings: Bk Vols 2,500
Open Mon-Fri 9-5, Sun 9-1

PRATT

J PRATT COMMUNITY COLLEGE LIBRARY,* 348 NE State Rd 61, 67124. SAN 306-0993. Tel: 316-672-5641, Ext 171. FAX: 316-672-2519. Web Site: www.pcc.cc.ks.us. *Dir*, Don Hart; *Asst Librn*, Barbara Allen; Staff 2 (MLS 2)
Founded 1938. Enrl 450; Fac 31
Library Holdings: Bk Titles 26,000; Per Subs 250
Mem of South Central Kansas Library System
Open Mon-Thurs 8am-9pm, Fri 8-5, Sat 9-1, Sun 1-5

P PRATT PUBLIC LIBRARY, Fourth & Jackson St, 67124-1112. SAN 306-1000. Tel: 316-672-3041. E-Mail: library@pratt.net. *Dir*, Janice Hoyt; Staff 5 (MLS 1, Non-MLS 4)
Founded 1910. Pop 9,746; Circ 101,314
Jan 1999-Dec 1999 Income $166,455, State $7,455, City $82,500, County $38,500, Other $38,000. Mats Exp $38,900, Books $27,375, Per/Ser (Incl. Access Fees) $6,469. Sal $90,000 (Prof $30,000)
Library Holdings: Bk Vols 37,560; Per Subs 109
Subject Interests: Genealogy, History, Kansas
Automation Activity & Vendor Info: (Circulation) Sagebrush Corporation
Mon & Thurs story hrs; modern lit discussion group; service to shut-ins

PRESCOTT

P PRESCOTT CITY PUBLIC LIBRARY,* Second & Walnut St, PO Box 112, 66767-0112. SAN 306-1019. Tel: 913-471-4837. *Librn*, Florene Norbury; *Ch Servs*, Patricia Catwell
Founded 1975. Pop 600; Circ 3,915
Library Holdings: Bk Vols 5,000; Per Subs 38
Special Collections: Kansas History
Mem of Southeast Kansas Library System
Open Sat 9-12, Wed 9-2:30 for schoolchildren only. Also open by appointment

PRETTY PRAIRIE

P PRETTY PRAIRIE PUBLIC LIBRARY, 119 W Main St, PO Box 68, 67570-0068. (Mail add: PO Box 68, 67570-0068), SAN 306-1027. Tel: 316-459-6392. FAX: 316-459-7354. E-Mail: prettyp0@southwind.net. Web Site: skyways.lib.ks.us/kansas/towns/PrettyPrairie/index.html. *Coll Develop, Librn*, Patti Brace; *Asst Librn*, Nancy Royer
Founded 1945. Pop 657; Circ 6,537
1998-1999 Income $8,139, State $2,739, City $3,800, Federal $600, County $1,000. Mats Exp $5,300, Books $4,000, Per/Ser (Incl. Access Fees) $900. Sal $2,067
Library Holdings: Bk Vols 14,000; Bk Titles 11,000; Per Subs 35
Mem of South Central Kansas Library System

QUINTER

P JAY JOHNSON PUBLIC LIBRARY,* 411 Main St, PO Box 369, 67752-0369. SAN 306-1035. Tel: 785-754-2171. E-Mail: jjpl@ruraltel.net. *Librn*, Sharon Lee DuBois; *Asst Librn*, Jeanne Mann
Founded 1932. Pop 952; Circ 24,084
Library Holdings: Bk Vols 15,000; Per Subs 27
Special Collections: Religious Coll (Heritage Room)
Mem of Northwest Kansas Library System
Friends of the Library Group

RANDALL

P RANDALL CITY LIBRARY,* PO Box 101, 66963-0101. SAN 306-1043. Tel: 785-739-2380. *Librn*, Lynell Sheahan
Pop 154; Circ 999
Library Holdings: Bk Vols 4,000; Per Subs 12
Mem of Central Kansas Library System
Open Mon-Wed 7:30-9 am, Thurs 3-6, Fri 8-5, Sat 8-12

RANSOM

P RANSOM PUBLIC LIBRARY,* PO Box 263, 67572-0263. SAN 306-1051. Tel: 785-731-2855. *Librn*, Virginia Dietterich
Pop 468; Circ 9,860
Library Holdings: Bk Vols 4,677; Per Subs 15
Mem of Southwest Kansas Library System

REPUBLIC

P RAE HOBSON MEMORIAL LIBRARY,* PO Box 3, 66964-0003. SAN 306-106X. Tel: 785-361-2481. *Librn*, Ruth Holly
Pop 300; Circ 2,301
Library Holdings: Bk Vols 5,000; Per Subs 10
Subject Interests: Fiction
Mem of Central Kansas Library System
Open Sun 1-6 & Tues 3-8
Friends of the Library Group

RICHMOND

P RICHMOND PUBLIC LIBRARY,* 107 E Central, 66080. SAN 306-1078. Tel: 785-835-6163. *Librn*, Nadine Peine
Founded 1938. Pop 410; Circ 7,707
1997-1998 Income $4,186. Mats Exp $1,325, Books $954, Per/Ser (Incl. Access Fees) $94. Sal $1,714
Library Holdings: Bk Vols 3,313; Per Subs 12
Mem of Northeast Kansas Library System

ROSSVILLE

P ROSSVILLE COMMUNITY LIBRARY,* 407 Main St, PO Box 618, 66533. SAN 306-1086. Tel: 785-584-6454. *Librn*, Mary Brennan
Pop 1,635; Circ 19,023
Library Holdings: Bk Vols 10,000; Per Subs 43
Mem of Northeast Kansas Library System

ROXBURY

P ROXBURY LIBRARY, PO Box 46, 67476. SAN 306-1094. Tel: 785-254-7874. *Librn*, Kathy Writer
Founded 1972. Pop 250; Circ 1,250
Library Holdings: Bk Vols 1,900
Mem of South Central Kansas Library System
Open Tues 2-4, Thurs & Sat 9:30-11
Bookmobiles: 1

RUSSELL

P RUSSELL PUBLIC LIBRARY, 126 E Sixth St, 67665. SAN 306-1108. Tel: 785-483-2742. FAX: 785-483-6254. E-Mail: ruspublib@eaglecom.net. *Dir*, Maxine Ganske; Staff 5 (MLS 5)
Founded 1902. Pop 4,597; Circ 36,053
Jan 1999-Dec 1999 Income $103,580, State $5,232, City $83,922, Locally Generated Income $8,526, Other $5,900. Mats Exp $30,116, Books $25,713, Per/Ser (Incl. Access Fees) $3,590, Micro $813. Sal $55,288 (Prof $49,187)
Library Holdings: Bk Vols 31,689; Per Subs 89
Mem of Central Kansas Library System

RUSSELL SPRINGS

S BUTTERFIELD TRAIL ASSOCIATION & LOGAN COUNTY HISTORICAL SOCIETY, INC, Butterfield Trail Museum Library, 515 Hilts Ave, 67764. SAN 306-1116. Tel: 785-751-4242. *Librn*, Dorothy Janke; *Curator*, Joye Rogge
Founded 1965
Library Holdings: Bk Titles 3,850
Subject Interests: Local history
Publications: Butterfield Trail Association Newsletter
Open May-Labor Day: Tues-Sat 9-12 & 1-5, Sun 1-5 (closed Mon)

SABETHA

P MARY COTTON PUBLIC LIBRARY,* 915 Virginia, PO Box 70, 66534-0070. SAN 306-1124. Tel: 785-284-3160. FAX: 785-284-3605. E-Mail: macotton@parod.com. *Librn*, Candee Lehmann
Founded 1912. Pop 2,169; Circ 25,539
Library Holdings: Bk Vols 19,000; Per Subs 83
Mem of Northeast Kansas Library System

SAINT FRANCIS

P SAINT FRANCIS PUBLIC LIBRARY, 121 N Scott St, PO Box 688, 67756. SAN 306-1132. Tel: 913-332-3292. *Librn*, Pat Leibbrandt
Circ 21,202
Library Holdings: Bk Vols 14,000; Per Subs 48
Mem of Northwest Kansas Library System
Open Mon-Fri 10:30-5:30, Sat 10:30-1

SAINT JOHN

P IDA LONG GOODMAN MEMORIAL LIBRARY, 406 N Monroe, 67576-1836. SAN 306-1140. Tel: 316-549-3227. FAX: 316-549-6589. Web Site: skyways.lib.ks.us/library/stjohn. *Dir*, Sue Padilla; E-Mail: spadilla@usd350.k12.ks.us; *Ch Servs*, Christie Snyder; Staff 6 (MLS 1, Non-MLS 5)
Founded 1969. Circ 20,483
Library Holdings: Bk Titles 25,946; Per Subs 110
Subject Interests: Education, Genealogy, History, Kansas, Local history
Special Collections: Sheet Music; St John News (1880-)
Automation Activity & Vendor Info: (Cataloging) Sagebrush Corporation; (Circulation) Sagebrush Corporation
Function: ILL available, Internet access, Photocopies available
Mem of South Central Kansas Library System
Open Winter: Mon-Thurs 8-5 & 7-9, Fri 8-5, Sat 9-12; Summer: Mon 8-8, Tues-Fri 8-12 & 1-4

SAINT MARYS

P POTTAWATOMIE-WABAUNSEE REGIONAL LIBRARY, 306 N Fifth St, 66536-1404. SAN 342-1503. Tel: 785-437-2778. FAX: 785-437-2778. Web Site: www.skyways.lib.ks.us/kansas/library/pottwablib. *Dir*, Freda J Dobbins; E-Mail: dobbinsf@kawvalley.k12.ks.us; Staff 1 (MLS 1)
Founded 1962. Pop 20,961; Circ 80,000
Jan 1999-Dec 1999 Income (Main Library and Branch Library) $262,668, State $15,492, Federal $20,576, County $220,000, Other $6,600. Mats Exp $45,640, Books $40,500, Per/Ser (Incl. Access Fees) $4,420, Electronic Ref Mat (Incl. Access Fees) $720. Sal $132,211
Library Holdings: Bk Vols 118,000; Per Subs 134
Mem of North Central Kansas Libraries System
Branches: 3
ALMA BRANCH, Alma, 66401. SAN 342-1538. Tel: 785-765-3647. FAX: 785-765-3647. E-Mail: powabalm@kansas.net. *Librn*, Joyce Mathies
ESKRIDGE BRANCH, Eskridge, 66423. SAN 342-1562. Tel: 785-449-2296. FAX: 785-449-2296. E-Mail: potwab2lb@ink.org. *Librn*, Sharon Durkes
ONAGA BRANCH, Onaga, 66521. SAN 342-1597. Tel: 785-889-4531. FAX: 785-889-4531. *Librn*, Carla Hibbs

SAINT PAUL

P GRAVES MEMORIAL PUBLIC LIBRARY, PO Box 354, 66771-0354. SAN 306-1159. Tel: 316-449-2001. *Librn*, Angelita Gahman
Pop 965; Circ 5,811
Library Holdings: Bk Vols 5,449; Per Subs 18
Special Collections: W W Graves, writings & bks
Mem of Southeast Kansas Library System

SALINA

J KANSAS STATE UNIVERSITY - SALINA COLLEGE OF TECHNOLOGY & AVIATION LIBRARY,* 2310 Centennial Rd, 67401. SAN 306-1175. Tel: 913-826-2636. FAX: 913-826-2937. *Tech Servs*, Michele Swain; *Librn*, Dr Beverlee Kissick; E-Mail: kissick@sal.ksu.edu; *Asst Librn*, Marilou Wenthe; Staff 4 (MLS 2, Non-MLS 2)
Founded 1966. Enrl 950; Highest Degree: Doctorate
1997-1998 Income $47,500, State $3,750. Mats Exp $51,250, Books $4,000, Per/Ser (Incl. Access Fees) $8,000, Micro $500. Sal $95,500 (Prof $84,500)
Library Holdings: Bk Vols 20,537; Per Subs 163
Subject Interests: Business and management, Engineering, Mathematics
Special Collections: Aeronautics; Civil, Chemical, Computer, Electronic & Mechanical Technology
Open Mon & Wed 8-9, Tues & Thurs 8-12, Fri 8-5, Sat 1-4 & Sun 6-9

C KANSAS WESLEYAN UNIVERSITY, Memorial Library, 100 E Claflin, 67401-6196. SAN 306-1183. Tel: 785-827-5541, Ext 4120. Interlibrary Loan Service Tel: 785-827-5541, Ext 4150. FAX: 785-827-0927. E-Mail: library@kwu.edu. Web Site: www.kwu.edu. *Circ, Dir*, Ruth Cox; E-Mail: rcox@kwu.edu; *ILL*, Lori Berry; E-Mail: lorib@kwu.edu; *Govt Doc*, Donna Werhan; E-Mail: donnaw@kwu.edu; Staff 3 (MLS 1, Non-MLS 2)
Founded 1886. Enrl 600; Fac 47; Highest Degree: Master
Jul 1999-Jun 2000 Mats Exp $68,605, Books $23,720, Per/Ser (Incl. Access Fees) $39,785, Micro $5,100. Sal $57,720 (Prof $28,020)
Library Holdings: Bk Vols 65,534; Bk Titles 57,430; Per Subs 546
Automation Activity & Vendor Info: (Circulation) Sagebrush Corporation; (OPAC) Sagebrush Corporation
Database Vendor: Ebsco - EbscoHost, GaleNet, IAC - SearchBank, Lexis-Nexis, OCLC - First Search
Mem of South Central Kansas Library System
Partic in Associated Colleges Of Central Kansas; BCR; OCLC Online Computer Library Center, Inc

P SALINA PUBLIC LIBRARY, 301 W Elm, 67401. SAN 306-1205. Tel: 785-825-4624. FAX: 785-823-0706. Web Site: www.salpublib.org. *Dir*, Joe McKenzie; E-Mail: joemcken@salpublib.org; *ILL*, Linda Grieve; *Ch Servs*, Kristi Hansen; *Cat*, Nick Berozovsky; *Circ*, Dianna Waite; *Spec Coll*, Judy Lilly; *Ref*, Nancy Jo Leachman; *Coll Develop*, Nancy Reese; Staff 42 (MLS 8, Non-MLS 34)
Founded 1897. Pop 44,600; Circ 493,839
Jan 1999-Dec 1999 Income $1,858,974. Mats Exp $223,703, Books $166,882, Per/Ser (Incl. Access Fees) $18,503, AV Equip $30,756, Electronic Ref Mat (Incl. Access Fees) $7,562. Sal $718,982 (Prof $290,574)
Library Holdings: Bk Vols 226,228; Per Subs 431
Subject Interests: Art, Education, History
Special Collections: Campbell Room of Kansas History
Automation Activity & Vendor Info: (Cataloging) SIRSI; (Circulation) SIRSI; (OPAC) SIRSI
Publications: Cover to Cover Newsletter; Friends Favorites
Mem of Central Kansas Library System
Friends of the Library Group

M SALINA REGIONAL HEALTH CENTER,* 400 S Santa Fe, 67401-5080. SAN 322-7790. Tel: 785-452-7000. FAX: 785-452-7700. *Dir*, Valyne Pochop
Library Holdings: Bk Titles 750; Per Subs 40
Partic in Midcontinental Regional Med Libr Program
Open Mon-Fri 8-5

S WILSON & COMPANY, Engineers & Architects Library,* 1700 E Iron Ave, PO Box 1640, 67401. SAN 306-1213. Tel: 785-827-0433. FAX: 785-827-5949. *Librn*, Linda Newquist
Founded 1956
Library Holdings: Bk Vols 2,000; Per Subs 50

SAVONBURG

P SAVONBURG PUBLIC LIBRARY,* 113 W Main St, 66772. SAN 306-123X. Tel: 316-754-3835. *Librn*, Nancy McMurray
Founded 1961. Pop 113; Circ 3,128
Library Holdings: Bk Vols 2,100; Per Subs 18
Mem of Southeast Kansas Library System

SCANDIA

P SCANDIA CITY LIBRARY,* 409 Fourth St, PO Box 220, 66966-0220. SAN 306-1248. Tel: 785-335-2271. *Librn*, Kathryn Gile
Pop 650
Library Holdings: Bk Vols 8,000; Bk Titles 1,700; Per Subs 69
Subject Interests: Swedish (language)
Mem of Central Kansas Library System

SCOTT CITY

P SCOTT COUNTY LIBRARY,* 110 W Eighth, 67871-1599. SAN 306-1256. Tel: 316-872-5341. FAX: 316-872-0248. E-Mail: sclib@pld.com. *Librn*, Julie O'Brien; *Asst Librn*, Mary Kastleman
Founded 1923. Pop 5,582
1999-2000 Income $135,000. Mats Exp $30,000. Sal $64,000
Library Holdings: Bk Titles 35,000; Per Subs 100

SEDAN

P SEDAN PUBLIC LIBRARY,* 115 N Chautauqua St, 67361-1301. SAN 306-1264. Tel: 316-725-3405. E-Mail: slibrary@hit.net. *Librn*, Kathleen McCorkle; *Asst Librn*, Paula Wolfe; Staff 2 (Non-MLS 2)
Pop 1,450
Library Holdings: Bk Vols 9,000; Per Subs 20
Subject Interests: Audio bks, Large print
Mem of Southeast Kansas Library System

SEDGWICK

P LILLIAN TEAR LIBRARY, 501 N Commercial, PO Box 28, 67135-0028. SAN 306-1272. Tel: 316-772-5727. E-Mail: hearonelb@swbell.net. *Librn*, Karen Barnett
Founded 1929. Pop 1,450; Circ 10,000
Library Holdings: Bk Vols 6,000; Per Subs 20
Special Collections: Sheet Music Coll
Mem of South Central Kansas Library System

SELDEN

P SELDEN PUBLIC LIBRARY,* PO Box 244, 67757-0244. SAN 376-513X. Tel: 785-386-4321. *Librn*, Marsha Rogers
Library Holdings: Bk Vols 8,000
Mem of Northwest Kansas Library System
Open Mon 9-11, Wed 6:30-8:30, Sat 9-11am

SENECA

P SENECA FREE LIBRARY,* 606 Main St, 66538. SAN 306-1280. Tel: 785-336-2377. E-Mail: senec1lb@ink.org. *Librn*, Karen Holthaus
Pop 1,978; Circ 40,000
Library Holdings: Bk Vols 15,000; Per Subs 43
Mem of Northeast Kansas Library System

SHARON SPRINGS

P SHARON SPRINGS PUBLIC LIBRARY,* 113 W Second St, PO Box 640, 67758. SAN 306-1299. Tel: 785-852-4685. *Librn*, Cathy Van Allen
Founded 1930. Pop 1,064; Circ 8,093
Library Holdings: Bk Vols 8,200; Per Subs 17
Subject Interests: Local history
Mem of Northwest Kansas Library System
Open Mon-Thurs 2-6, Fri & Sat 9-12 & 2-6

SHAWNEE MISSION

S BAYER CORP, Animal Health Library,* PO Box 390, 66201. SAN 327-1358. Tel: 913-268-2000. FAX: 913-268-2803. *Librn*, Ruth Lamley; E-Mail: ruth.lamley.b@bayer.com
Library Holdings: Bk Vols 250
Open Mon-Fri 7:30-4

M SHAWNEE MISSION MEDICAL CENTER LIBRARY, 9100 W 74th, PO Box 2923, 66201. SAN 320-1899. Tel: 913-676-2101. Interlibrary Loan Service Tel: 913-676-2103. FAX: 913-676-2106. *Mgr*, Clifford L Nestell
Founded 1963
Library Holdings: Bk Vols 9,282; Per Subs 525
Partic in OCLC Online Computer Library Center, Inc

S WADDELL & REED, INC, Research Library,* 6300 Lamar, PO Box 29217, 66202. SAN 309-0698. Tel: 913-236-2000. FAX: 913-236-1885. *Librn*, Cynthia V Buchanan; Staff 4 (MLS 1, Non-MLS 3)
Founded 1963
Library Holdings: Bk Titles 2,500; Per Subs 300
Subject Interests: Mutual funds, Stock market
Restriction: Private library

SILVER LAKE

P SILVER LAKE LIBRARY, (SLL), 203 Railroad, PO Box 248, 66539. SAN 306-1310. Tel: 785-582-5141. E-Mail: silverlib@cjnetworks.com. Web Site: www.skyways.lib.ks.us/library/silverlake/silver.html. *Dir*, Erica Riley; Staff 2 (Non-MLS 2)
Founded 1975
Library Holdings: Bk Vols 7,100; Bk Titles 7,000; Per Subs 42; Bks on Deafness & Sign Lang 20
Special Collections: Children with Disabilities; Inspirational
Publications: Silver Lake Library Times
Mem of Northeast Kansas Library System
Special Services for the Blind - Audio-cassettes
Friends of the Library Group

SMITH CENTER

P SMITH CENTER PUBLIC LIBRARY,* 117 W Court St, 66967-2601. SAN 306-1329. Tel: 785-282-3361. FAX: 785-282-6740. *Librn*, Joanna Runyon; *Asst Librn*, Diane Depper-Schmidt
Pop 2,100; Circ 30,603
Library Holdings: Bk Vols 16,941; Per Subs 59
Mem of Central Kansas Library System

SOLOMON

P SOLOMON PUBLIC LIBRARY,* 108 N Walnut, PO Box 246, 67480-8245. SAN 306-1337. Tel: 785-655-3521. *Librn*, Connie Avery
Founded 1934. Pop 1,192; Circ 9,492
Library Holdings: Bk Vols 12,500; Per Subs 25
Mem of North Central Kansas Libraries System

SOUTH HAVEN

P SOUTH HAVEN TOWNSHIP LIBRARY, 104 W Baird, PO Box 227, 67140-0027. SAN 306-1345. Tel: 316-892-5268. E-Mail: books@kanokla.com. *Librn*, Bonnie Tompkins
Pop 733; Circ 3,545
Library Holdings: Bk Vols 7,870
Mem of South Central Kansas Library System
Open Thurs, Fri & Sat 1-4:30

SPEARVILLE

P SPEARVILLE TOWNSHIP LIBRARY,* 414 N Main St, PO Box 464, 67876. SAN 306-1353. Tel: 316-385-2501. FAX: 316-385-2508. E-Mail: slibrary@ucom.net. *Librn*, Leesa Shafer
Founded 1929. Pop 1,151; Circ 10,991
Library Holdings: Bk Vols 19,000; Per Subs 50
Mem of Southwest Kansas Library System
Open Mon 1-8, Tues 10-6, Wed-Fri 1-6

STAFFORD

P NORA E LARABEE MEMORIAL LIBRARY,* 108 N Union St, 67578-1339. SAN 306-1361. Tel: 316-234-5762. Web Site: skyways.lib.ks.us/town/stafford/index.html. *Librn*, Dixie A Osborn
Founded 1906. Pop 1,364; Circ 35,000
Library Holdings: Bk Vols 25,000; Per Subs 70
Mem of South Central Kansas Library System
Open Mon & Sat 2-6, Tues-Thurs 7-9pm, Wed 10-12

STERLING

C STERLING COLLEGE, Mabee Library, 125 W Cooper, PO Box 98, 67579-0098. SAN 306-137X. Tel: 316-278-4234. FAX: 316-278-2775. *Dir*, Charles T Kendall; Tel: 316-278-4233, E-Mail: ckendall@sterling.edu; *Tech Servs*, LeAnn Weller; Tel: 316-278-4235, E-Mail: lweller@sterling.edu; Staff 4 (MLS 2, Non-MLS 2)
Founded 1887. Enrl 480; Fac 46; Highest Degree: Bachelor
Function: Reference services available
Mem of South Central Kansas Library System
Partic in Associated Colleges Of Central Kansas; OCLC Online Computer Library Center, Inc

P STERLING FREE PUBLIC LIBRARY, 138 N Broadway, 67579-2131. SAN 306-1388. Tel: 316-278-3191. FAX: 316-278-3891. *Dir*, Sherry Lackey; E-Mail: slackey@sterling.edu; Staff 1 (MLS 1)
Founded 1917. Pop 2,200; Circ 34,100
Library Holdings: Bk Vols 25,000; Per Subs 120
Mem of South Central Kansas Library System

STOCKTON

P STOCKTON PUBLIC LIBRARY,* 124 N Cedar, 67669-1636. SAN 306-1396. Tel: 785-425-6372. Web Site: skyways.lib.ks.us/towns/stockton/library.html/. *Librn*, Neola Breckenridge; *Asst Librn*, Brenda J McClure
Pop 1,825; Circ 14,526
1997-1998 Income $44,331, State $1,173, City $31,204, Locally Generated Income $4,160, Parent Institution $1,000. Mats Exp $4,678, Books $3,526, Per/Ser (Incl. Access Fees) $1,152. Sal $23,434
Library Holdings: Bk Vols 15,000; Per Subs 50
Special Collections: Rooks County Record (1878-1983), Genealogy
Mem of Central Kansas Library System
Partic in OCLC Online Computer Library Center, Inc

SUBLETTE

P HASKELL TOWNSHIP LIBRARY,* 700 Choteau St, PO Box 937, 67877. SAN 306-140X. Tel: 316-675-2771. *Librn*, Jamie Wright
Founded 1922. Pop 1,900; Circ 9,000
Library Holdings: Bk Vols 24,000; Per Subs 50

SUMMERFIELD

P SUMMERFIELD PUBLIC LIBRARY,* PO Box 146, 66541. SAN 306-1418. Tel: 785-244-6531.
Pop 225; Circ 1,542
Library Holdings: Bk Vols 2,122
Mem of North Central Kansas Libraries System

SYLVAN GROVE

P SYLVAN GROVE PUBLIC LIBRARY,* 122 Main St, PO Box 96, 67481-0096. SAN 306-1426. Tel: 785-526-7188. FAX: 785-526-7189. *Librn*, Ramie Schulteis
Founded 1931. Pop 376; Circ 3,245
Library Holdings: Bk Vols 4,236; Per Subs 25
Mem of Central Kansas Library System

SYLVIA

P SYLVIA PUBLIC LIBRARY, 121 S Main St, PO Box 68, 67581. SAN 306-1434. Tel: 316-486-2472. *Librn*, Thelma Ward
Pop 310; Circ 550
Library Holdings: Bk Titles 4,731; Per Subs 13
Mem of South Central Kansas Library System

SYRACUSE

P HAMILTON COUNTY LIBRARY, 102 W Ave C, PO Box 1307, 67878. SAN 306-1442. Tel: 316-384-5622. FAX: 316-384-5623. E-Mail: hamcolib@yahoo.com. Web Site: skyways.lib.ks.us/library/hamilton/. *Librn*, Joyce Armstrong; Staff 2 (Non-MLS 2)
Founded 1932. Pop 2,500; Circ 29,000
Library Holdings: Bk Vols 28,000; Per Subs 70
Subject Interests: Genealogy
Automation Activity & Vendor Info: (Circulation) Athena
Mem of Southwest Kansas Library System
Open Mon-Thurs 9-6 & Fri 9-1

THAYER

P THAYER FRIDAY READING CLUB CITY LIBRARY,* 200 W Neosho Ave, PO Box 36, 66776-0036. SAN 306-1450. Tel: 316-839-5646. FAX: 316-839-5646. *Librn*, Janet Stafford
Pop 330,000
Library Holdings: Bk Vols 8,615; Per Subs 13
Mem of Southeast Kansas Library System
Bookmobiles: 1

TONGANOXIE

P TONGANOXIE PUBLIC LIBRARY, 303 Bury St, 66086-9608. (Mail add: PO Box 890, 66086-0890), SAN 306-1469. Tel: 913-845-3281. FAX: 913-845-3281. Web Site: www.skyways.lib.ks.us/lib/tongie. *Dir*, Beckie Borella; E-Mail: beckie@tongie.lib.ks.us
Pop 3,000; Circ 19,000
Library Holdings: Bk Vols 16,000; Per Subs 40
Special Collections: Kansas
Mem of Northeast Kansas Library System
Special Services for the Blind - Talking Books
Open Mon, Wed & Fri 9-5, Tues & Thurs 12-6 & Sat 9-1
Friends of the Library Group

TOPEKA

M AMERICAN LUNG ASSOCIATION OF KANSAS, Information Center, 4300 SW Drury Lane, 66604-2419. SAN 373-4560. Tel: 785-272-9290. FAX: 785-272-9297. Web Site: www.kslung.org, www.lungusa.org. *In Charge*, Mavis Glenn; E-Mail: mglenn@kslung.org
Subject Interests: Air pollution, Asthma, Research, Smoking
Partic in Am Lung Asn; Am Thoracic Soc
Open Mon-Fri 8-4:30

GM DEPARTMENT OF VETERANS AFFAIRS, Karl A Menninger Medical Library, Colmery O'Neil VA Medical Ctr, 2200 Gage Blvd, 66622. SAN 306-1582. Tel: 785-350-3111, Ext 2779. FAX: 785-350-4421. *ILL*, Donna Seidel; *Tech Servs*, Rosemarie Adkins; E-Mail: adkins.rosemarie@forum.va.gov
Founded 1946
Library Holdings: Bk Vols 28,700; Bk Titles 7,123; Per Subs 297
Subject Interests: Medicine, Psychiatry, Social sciences and issues
Partic in Valnet

G KANSAS DEPARTMENT OF TRANSPORTATION LIBRARY,* 2300 SW Van Buren, 66611. SAN 306-1493. Tel: 785-291-3854. FAX: 785-296-2526. *Librn*, Janice McEvoy
Founded 1962
Library Holdings: Bk Vols 10,200; Per Subs 10
Subject Interests: Engineering
Open Mon-Fri 8-4:30

S KANSAS STATE BOARD OF AGRICULTURE, Division of Water Resources Library,* 901 S Kansas 2nd flr, 66612-1283. (Mail add: 109 SW Ninth St, 66612-1283), SAN 371-408X. Tel: 785-296-3717. FAX: 785-296-1176.
Library Holdings: Bk Vols 250; Per Subs 14
Open Mon-Fri 8-5

G KANSAS STATE DEPARTMENT OF SOCIAL & REHABILITATION SERVICES, Staff Development Library,* 300 SW Oakley St, 66606. SAN 306-1485. Tel: 785-296-4327. FAX: 785-296-3419. *Librn*, Patsy Decker
Founded 1935
Library Holdings: Bk Titles 3,000; Per Subs 128
Subject Interests: Aging, Business and management, Child welfare, Psychology, Social service (social work)
Publications: Acquisitions List (quarterly)

S KANSAS STATE HISTORICAL SOCIETY CENTER FOR HISTORICAL RESEARCH, Library & Archives Div, 6425 SW Sixth Ave, 66615-1099. SAN 306-1507. Tel: 785-272-8681. Reference Tel: 785-272-8681, Ext 117. TDD: 785-272-8683. FAX: 785-272-8682. E-Mail: reference@kshs.org. Web Site: www.kshs.org. *Dir*, Patricia Michaelis; *Ref*, Leslie Cade; *Head Librn*, Margaret Knecht; Staff 18 (MLS 7, Non-MLS 11)
Founded 1875
Jul 2000-Jun 2001 Income $1,725,497, State $1,487,459, Locally Generated Income $238,038. Mats Exp $39,500, Books $17,500, Per/Ser (Incl. Access Fees) $22,000. Sal $1,455,963
Library Holdings: Bk Vols 172,824; Per Subs 475
Subject Interests: American Indians, Civil War, Genealogy, Kansas
Special Collections: Kansas State Archives, AV, maps, ms, newsp & photos
Automation Activity & Vendor Info: (OPAC) Innovative Interfaces Inc.; (Serials) Innovative Interfaces Inc.
Restriction: Non-circulating
Function: ILL limited
Partic in BCR

P KANSAS STATE LIBRARY, State Capitol Bldg, 300 SW Tenth St, Rm 343N, 66612-1593. SAN 342-1864. Tel: 785-296-3296. FAX: 785-296-6650. Web Site: skyways.lib.ks.us/kansas/KSL/. *State Librn*, Duane Johnson; E-Mail: duanej@ink.org; *ILL*, Tom Roth; *Ref*, Cindy Roupe; *Coordr*, Rhonda Moeller; Staff 12 (MLS 11, Non-MLS 1)
Founded 1855. Pop 2,654,052

Jan 1999-Dec 1999 Income $6,979,070
Library Holdings: Bk Vols 150,000; Per Subs 200
Subject Interests: Government, Social sciences and issues
Automation Activity & Vendor Info: (Acquisitions) Innovative Interfaces Inc.; (Cataloging) Innovative Interfaces Inc.; (Circulation) Innovative Interfaces Inc.; (Course Reserve) Innovative Interfaces Inc.; (ILL) Innovative Interfaces Inc.; (Media Booking) Innovative Interfaces Inc.; (OPAC) Innovative Interfaces Inc.; (Serials) Innovative Interfaces Inc.
Database Vendor: Innovative Interfaces INN - View
Publications: Kansas Libraries (newsletter); Kansas Public Library Statistics (annual)
Partic in Dialog Corporation; OCLC Online Computer Library Center, Inc; Westlaw
Open Mon-Fri 8-5
Friends of the Library Group
Branches: 2
KANSAS TALKING BOOKS SERVICE
See Separate Entry in Emporia
LITERACY SERVICE, PO Box 188, Kingman, 67068-0188. SAN 377-6883. Tel: 316-532-1075. FAX: 316-532-1076.

GL KANSAS SUPREME COURT, Law Library, Kansas Judicial Ctr, 301 SW Tenth, 66612-1598. SAN 306-1523. Tel: 785-296-3257. FAX: 785-296-1863. E-Mail: oja06@ink.org. Web Site: www.kscourts.org/ctlib/. *Librn*, Fred W Knecht; *Asst Librn*, Claire King; *Coll Develop*, Jan Cook; Staff 7 (MLS 5, Non-MLS 2)
Founded 1855
Jul 1999-Jun 2000 Income $861,530, State $716,149, Locally Generated Income $145,381. Mats Exp $495,527, Books $149,840, Per/Ser (Incl. Access Fees) $153,156, Presv $11,285, Other Print Mats $181,246. Sal $339,257
Library Holdings: Bk Vols 188,000; Per Subs 500
Special Collections: Judicial Administration
Automation Activity & Vendor Info: (OPAC) Innovative Interfaces Inc.

M MENNINGER CLINIC, Professional Library,* 5800 SW Sixth, PO Box 829, 66601. SAN 306-154X. Tel: 785-350-5975. FAX: 785-273-8625. Web Site: www.menninger.edu. *Librn*, Alice Brand Bartlett; *Coll Develop*, Lois Bogia; E-Mail: bogialv@menninger.edu
Founded 1930
Library Holdings: Bk Vols 30,000
Subject Interests: Psychiatry, Psychoanalysis, Psychotherapy, Social sciences and issues
Partic in Docline; OCLC Online Computer Library Center, Inc
Open Mon-Fri 8:30-5

M SAINT FRANCIS HOSPITAL & MEDICAL CENTER, Library of Health Resources,* 1700 W Seventh St, 66606-1690. SAN 370-5293. Tel: 785-295-8247. FAX: 785-295-8244. *Librn*, Cynthia Perkins; E-Mail: cperkins@stfrancistopekq.org; Staff 1 (MLS 1)
Founded 1984
Library Holdings: Bk Titles 5,000; Per Subs 200

M STORMONT - VAIL HEALTHCARE, Stauffer Health Science Library, 1500 SW Tenth St, 66604-1353. SAN 327-7933. Tel: 785-354-5800. FAX: 785-354-5059. *Dir*, Lenora Kinzie
Library Holdings: Bk Titles 8,000; Per Subs 400
Subject Interests: Medicine, Nursing
Open Mon-Thurs 7-7, Fri 9-5 & Sat 10-2

P TOPEKA & SHAWNEE COUNTY PUBLIC LIBRARY, 1515 SW Tenth Ave, 66604-1374. SAN 342-1929. Tel: 785-233-2040. Interlibrary Loan Service Tel: 785-233-6519. TDD: 785-233-3277. FAX: 785-233-2055. E-Mail: tscpl@tscpl.lib.ks.us. Web Site: www.tscpl.org. *Dir*, David L Leamon; E-Mail: dleamon@tscpl.lib.ks.us; *Dep Dir*, Robert Banks; E-Mail: rbanks@tscpl.lib.ks.us; *Dep Dir*, Nancy Watkins; E-Mail: nwatkins@tscpl.lib.ks.us; *Ch Servs*, Eleanor Strecker; E-Mail: estrecke@tscpl.lib.ks.us; *Pub Relations*, Diana Friend; E-Mail: dfriend@tscpl.lib.ks.us; *Tech Servs*, Dennis Wilson; E-Mail: dwilson@tscpl.lib.ks.us; *Publ Servs*, James McShane; E-Mail: jmcshane@tscpl.lib.ks.us; *Commun Servs*, Barbara Ramirez; E-Mail: bramirez@tscpl.lib.ks.us; *Cat*, Renee Patzer; E-Mail: rpatzer@tscpl.lib.ks.us; *Spec Coll*, Susan Marchant; E-Mail: smarchan@tscpl.lib.ks.us; *ILL*, Sheri Schawo; E-Mail: sschawo@tscpl.lib.ks.us; *Circ*, Paul Brennan; E-Mail: pbrennan@tscpl.lib.ks.us; *Ref*, Donna Gibson; E-Mail: dgibson@tscpl.lib.ks.us; *Bkmobile Coordr*, Ann Newell; E-Mail: anewell@tscpl.lib.ks.us; *Automation Syst Coordr*, John Opgaard; E-Mail: jopgaard@tscpl.lib.ks.us; *Per*, Marta Miles; E-Mail: mmiles@tscpl.lib.ks.us; *Librn for Blind*, Suzanne Bundy; E-Mail: sbundy@tscpl.lib.ks.us; Staff 160 (MLS 40, Non-MLS 120)
Founded 1870. Pop 161,611; Circ 1,623,911; Highest Degree: Doctorate
Jan 1999-Dec 1999 Income (Main Library Only) $8,985,044, State $193,382, Federal $43,200, Locally Generated Income $8,748,462. Mats Exp $1,269,052, Books $1,149,632, Per/Ser (Incl. Access Fees) $119,420. Sal $3,408,161 (Prof $807,015)
Library Holdings: Bk Vols 497,520; Bk Titles 258,023; Per Subs 1,376
Subject Interests: Art and architecture, Music
Special Collections: Fed census; Illustrated Bks; Large Print Books; Miniature Books; Topeka, bks, photos & film
Automation Activity & Vendor Info: (Acquisitions) epixtech, inc.; (Cataloging) epixtech, inc.; (Circulation) epixtech, inc.; (ILL) epixtech, inc.; (OPAC) epixtech, inc.; (Serials) epixtech, inc.
Publications: Library Edition
Mem of Northeast Kansas Library System
Special Services for the Deaf - Books on deafness & sign language; Special interest periodicals; Staff with knowledge of sign language; TDD
Special Services for the Blind - Talking book center
Friends of the Library Group
Branches: 1
P SUBREGIONAL LIBRARY FOR THE BLIND & PHYSICALLY HANDICAPPED Tel: 785-231-0571. Toll Free Tel: 800-432-2925. E-Mail: tscpl@tscpl.lib.ks.us. Web Site: www.tscpl.org. *Librn for Blind*, Suzanne Bundy; E-Mail: sbundy@tscpl.lib.ks.us; Staff 6 (Non-MLS 6)
Founded 1975
Special Services - Red carpet services to Red Cross meal sites, retirement complexes, adult care homes & to individuals who are unable to visit the library (this includes low-vision & large print)
Friends of the Library Group
Bookmobiles: 3

P TOPEKA GENEALOGICAL SOCIETY LIBRARY, 2717 Indiana Ave, 66605-1440. (Mail add: PO Box 4048, 66604-0048), SAN 370-7334. Tel: 785-233-5762. E-Mail: tgs@networksplus.net. Web Site: www.networksplus.net/donno/. *Librn*, Katy Matthews; *Per*, Betty Wood
Founded 1968
Library Holdings: Bk Vols 6,000; Bk Titles 5,800; Per Subs 612
Subject Interests: Genealogy, History
Special Collections: Original Shawnee County Kansas Probate Books 1856-1920; Shawnee County Cemetery Files; Shawnee County Kansas Naturalization Records; Surname Card File
Publications: Topeka Genealogical Society Quarterly; Topeka Society Newsletter
Restriction: Circulation limited, Subscription library
Visitation $1.00 per visit

§C TOPEKA TECHNICAL COLLEGE LIBRARY, 1620 NW Gage Blvd, 66618. SAN 375-4464. Tel: 785-232-5858. Interlibrary Loan Service Tel: 785-232-0006, Ext 221. Circulation Tel: 785-232-0006, Ext 221. Reference Tel: 785-232-0006, Ext 221. Toll Free Tel: 800-808-6735. FAX: 785-235-6745. E-Mail: ttc1libr@idir.net. Web Site: www.educationamerica.com. *Dir*, Judith A Cremer; Tel: 785-232-0006, Ext 221, E-Mail: library_2001@yahoo.com; Staff 2 (MLS 1, Non-MLS 1)
Founded 1968. Enrl 290; Fac 30; Highest Degree: Associate
Jan 2000-Dec 2000 Income $36,000. Mats Exp $23,000, Books $12,000, Per/Ser (Incl. Access Fees) $3,000, AV Equip $2,000, Electronic Ref Mat (Incl. Access Fees) $6,000. Sal $38,750 (Prof $27,000)
Library Holdings: Bk Vols 3,500; Bk Titles 3,000; Per Subs 90
Subject Interests: Bus info, Business tech, Electronics, Legal assts, Medical assistant
Automation Activity & Vendor Info: (Cataloging) ComPanion Corp; (Circulation) ComPanion Corp; (OPAC) ComPanion Corp
Database Vendor: IAC - SearchBank, OCLC - First Search
Restriction: In-house use for visitors, Open to student, faculty & staff
Function: Reference only
Mem of Northeast Kansas Library System
Partic in BCR; OCLC Online Computer Library Center, Inc

S TOPEKA ZOOLOGICAL PARK LIBRARY,* 635 SW Gage Blvd, 66606-2066. SAN 371-540X. Tel: 785-272-5821. FAX: 785-272-2539. E-Mail: zoo@topeka.org.
Founded 1963
Library Holdings: Bk Titles 805; Per Subs 20
Open Mon-Fri 8-5

C WASHBURN UNIVERSITY, Mabee Library, 1700 SW College Ave, 66621. SAN 342-1988. Tel: 785-231-1179. Circulation Tel: 785-231-1485. Reference Tel: 785-231-1483. FAX: 785-357-1240. Web Site: www.washburn.edu/mabee. *Dir*, Wanda Dole; E-Mail: zzwdole@washburn.edu; *Asst Dir*, Michele Reid; E-Mail: zzreid@washburn.edu; *Coll Develop*, David Feinmark; Tel: 785-231-1275, E-Mail: zzfein@washburn.edu; *Access Serv*, Cal Melick; E-Mail: zzmeli@washburn.edu; *Cat*, Dean Corwin; E-Mail: zzcorwin@washburn.edu; *Ser*, David Winchester; E-Mail: zzwinc@washburn.edu; *Instrul Serv*, Patricia Renn-Scanlan; E-Mail: zzrenn@washburn.edu; *Media Spec*, Judy Druse; E-Mail: zzdrus@washburn.edu; *Spec Coll*, Martha Imparato; E-Mail: zzimpa@washburn.edu. Subject Specialists: *Manuscript*, David Feinmark; Staff 19 (MLS 8, Non-MLS 11)
Founded 1865. Enrl 5,000; Fac 250; Highest Degree: Master
Jul 1999-Jun 2000 Income $1,319,645. Mats Exp $525,671, Books $181,440, Per/Ser (Incl. Access Fees) $303,513, Presv $17,272, Micro $12,811, AV Equip $8,037, Other Print Mats $2,598, Electronic Ref Mat (Incl. Access Fees) $60,529. Sal $696,601 (Prof $418,692)
Library Holdings: Bk Vols 324,060; Bk Titles 242,547; Per Subs 1,369
Subject Interests: Education
Special Collections: Bradbury Thompson Materials; College & University History (Washburn Archives); Curriculum Resources Center
Automation Activity & Vendor Info: (Acquisitions) Innovative Interfaces

Inc.; (Cataloging) Innovative Interfaces Inc.; (Circulation) Innovative Interfaces Inc.; (Course Reserve) Innovative Interfaces Inc.; (ILL) Innovative Interfaces Inc.; (OPAC) Innovative Interfaces Inc.; (Serials) Innovative Interfaces Inc.
Publications: Among Friends (Newsletter)
Partic in Dialog Corporation; OCLC Online Computer Library Center, Inc
Friends of the Library Group
Departmental Libraries:
CURRICULUM RESOURCES CENTER, 1700 SW College Ave, 66621. SAN 342-2011. Tel: 785-231-1436. FAX: 785-231-1085. E-Mail: crclbrn@washburn.edu. Web Site: www.washburn.edu/mabee/crc.html. *Librn*, Judy Druse; Tel: 785-231-1277, E-Mail: zzdrus@washburn.edu. Subject Specialists: *Education*, Judy Druse; Staff 2 (MLS 1, Non-MLS 1)
Founded 1984
Jul 1999-Jun 2000 Mats Exp $8,000
SCHOOL OF LAW LIBRARY, 1700 College, 66621-0001. SAN 342-2046. Tel: 785-231-1010, Ext 1088. FAX: 785-232-8087. E-Mail: washburn.lawlib@law.wuacc.edu. Web Site: lib.wuacc.edu. *Dir*, John E Christensen; *Assoc Dir*, Mark Folmsbee; *Doc*, Paul Arrigo; *Tech Servs*, Martin Wisneski; *Circ*, Nancy Gray; *Cat, Ref*, Rebecca Alexander; *Circ*, Marie Mack; *Acq*, John Bostwick
Founded 1903. Enrl 430; Fac 25; Highest Degree: Doctorate
Library Holdings: Bk Vols 289,820; Bk Titles 56,687; Per Subs 3,666
Special Collections: Brow Historic Document Coll; Document Room for Wolf Creek Nuclear Power Project; Kansas Supreme Court Briefs
Partic in Dialog Corporation; OCLC Online Computer Library Center, Inc; Washaw URL; Westlaw

TORONTO

P TORONTO PUBLIC LIBRARY, 107 W Main, PO Box 244, 66777. SAN 376-7213. Tel: 316-637-2661. E-Mail: torlib@fox-net.net. *Dir*, Kristin Ramshaw
Library Holdings: Bk Vols 7,000
Mem of Southeast Kansas Library System
Open Mon-Thurs 2-5

TOWANDA

P TOWANDA PUBLIC LIBRARY, 620 Highland, PO Box 580, 67144-0580. SAN 306-1604. Tel: 316-536-2464. E-Mail: towanilb@powwwer.net. Web Site: skyways.lib.ks.us/towns/towanda/library.html. *Librn*, Janet L VanBuskirk; Staff 1 (Non-MLS 1)
Pop 1,460; Circ 8,080
Jan 1999-Dec 1999 Income $27,152, State $1,200, City $22,000, Locally Generated Income $1,524, Other $2,428. Mats Exp $2,016, Books $2,000, Per/Ser (Incl. Access Fees) $16. Sal $9,000
Library Holdings: Bk Vols 13,013; High Interest/Low Vocabulary Bk Vols 50
Subject Interests: Local history, Reading
Mem of South Central Kansas Library System
Partic in Kansas Library Network Board
Special Services for the Blind - Talking Books
Adult literary program; story hour; summer reading program; home delivery to shut-ins
Friends of the Library Group

TROY

P LIBRARY DISTRICT NUMBER ONE, DONIPHAN COUNTY, 105 N Main, PO Box 220, 66087. SAN 306-1612. Tel: 785-985-2597. FAX: 785-985-2602. *Dir*, Lois E Owens
Founded 1974. Pop 7,766; Circ 38,936
Jan 1999-Dec 1999 Income $155,472, State $5,940, County $139,464, Parent Institution $4,800, Other $5,268. Mats Exp $153,080, Books $16,510, Per/Ser (Incl. Access Fees) $2,632, AV Equip $4,312, Electronic Ref Mat (Incl. Access Fees) $853. Sal $76,125
Library Holdings: Bk Vols 40,911; Per Subs 92; High Interest/Low Vocabulary Bk Vols 80
Subject Interests: Genealogy, Kansas
Special Collections: Doniphan County Hist
Automation Activity & Vendor Info: (Cataloging) Follett; (Circulation) Follett; (OPAC) Follett
Mem of Northeast Kansas Library System
Special Services for the Blind - Bks on cassette
Friends of the Library Group

TURON

P TURON COMMUNITY LIBRARY,* 501 E Price, PO Box 357, 67583-0357. SAN 306-1620. Tel: 316-497-6409. E-Mail: turlib@socencom.net. *Librn*, Sharon Nitzsche
Pop 480
Library Holdings: Bk Vols 5,386; Per Subs 12
Mem of South Central Kansas Library System
Open Tues-Thurs 1-5, Fri 6-9

UDALL

P UDALL PUBLIC LIBRARY, First St, 67146. (Mail add: PO Box 484, 67146-0484), SAN 306-1639. Tel: 316-782-3435. *Librn*, Lorraine Dickerman
Pop 910; Circ 3,000
Jan 1999-Dec 1999 Income City $2,179. Mats Exp $470, Books $445, Electronic Ref Mat (Incl. Access Fees) $25. Sal $8,475
Library Holdings: Bk Vols 3,732
Mem of South Central Kansas Library System
Special Services for the Blind - Bks on cassette
Open Mon-Fri 3-6

ULYSSES

P GRANT COUNTY LIBRARY, 215 E Grant St, 67880-2958. SAN 306-1647. Tel: 316-356-1433. Interlibrary Loan Service Tel: 800-362-9103. FAX: 316-356-1344. E-Mail: frances@pld.com. Web Site: www.trails.net/grant-library, www.userspld.com/frances. *Librn*, Frances Roberts; E-Mail: frances@pld.com; *Asst Librn*, Norma Strickland; *Spec Coll*, Nidia Gallegos; *Ch Servs*, Holly Mathes; *Circ, Tech Servs*, Deanna Hull
Founded 1915. Pop 10,000; Circ 83,111
1999-2000 Income $278,866, State $5,990, County $259,176, Other $7,700. Mats Exp $44,130, Books $26,000, Per/Ser (Incl. Access Fees) $5,400, Micro $7,000, AV Equip $5,000, Other Print Mats $730. Sal $132,045 (Prof $31,500)
Library Holdings: Bk Vols 46,000; Per Subs 140
Subject Interests: Art and architecture, Frontier and pioneer lLife, Genealogy, Kansas, Religion, Social sciences and issues
Special Collections: Large Print Books; Local Newspapers (to 1989), cassettes, micro; Spanish Coll, bks, micro, per & rec
Automation Activity & Vendor Info: (Acquisitions) Sagebrush Corporation; (Cataloging) Sagebrush Corporation; (Circulation) Sagebrush Corporation
Mem of Southwest Kansas Library System
Friends of the Library Group

UTICA

P UTICA LIBRARY ASSOCIATION,* 249 N Ohio, 67584-0146. SAN 306-1655. Tel: 785-391-2419. *Librn*, Marilyn Summey
Pop 288; Circ 3,000
Library Holdings: Bk Vols 2,100
Mem of Southwest Kansas Library System

VALLEY CENTER

P EDNA BUSHOW MEMORIAL PUBLIC LIBRARY,* 321 W First St, 67147. SAN 306-1663. Tel: 316-755-7350. FAX: 316-755-7351. E-Mail: ebml@feist.com. *Librn*, Janice Sharp
Pop 4,008; Circ 37,396
Library Holdings: Bk Vols 42,000; Per Subs 40
Special Collections: Kansas Writers Coll
Mem of South Central Kansas Library System
Friends of the Library Group

VALLEY FALLS

P DELAWARE TOWNSHIP LIBRARY,* 421 Mary St, No A, 66088. SAN 306-1671. Tel: 785-945-3990. FAX: 785-945-3341. *Librn*, Kay Lassiter
Founded 1945. Pop 1,200; Circ 7,024
Library Holdings: Bk Vols 8,000
Mem of Northeast Kansas Library System

VERMILLION

P VERMILLION PUBLIC LIBRARY,* PO Box 139, 66544-0139. SAN 376-5504. Tel: 785-382-6224. *Librn*, Darlene Broxterman
1998-1999 Income $1,280. Mats Exp $1,280
Library Holdings: Bk Vols 4,500
Mem of North Central Kansas Libraries System
Open Sat 9-11:30 & 1st Sat of the month 9-12 & 1-3

VIOLA

P VIOLA TOWNSHIP LIBRARY, 100 N Grice, PO Box 547, 67149-0547. SAN 306-168X. Tel: 316-584-6679. *Dir*, Claire Charlebois
Pop 439; Circ 604
Library Holdings: Bk Vols 5,000; Per Subs 27
Mem of South Central Kansas Library System

WA KEENEY

P WAKEENEY PUBLIC LIBRARY, 610 Russell Ave, 67672-2135. SAN 306-1698. Tel: 785-743-2960. E-Mail: wakeenpl@ruraltel.net. Web Site: skyways.lib.ks.us/kansas/nwkls/trego/wakeeney.htm. *Dir*, Kathryn E Weigel
Founded 1906. Pop 2,016; Circ 29,972
Jan 1999-Dec 1999 Income $50,600, City $46,783, Federal $1,577, Other $2,240. Mats Exp $7,159, Books $6,675, Per/Ser (Incl. Access Fees) $1,250, AV Equip $234. Sal $29,692
Library Holdings: Bk Vols 23,425; Per Subs 68
Subject Interests: Kansas
Function: ILL available, Photocopies available, Reference services available, Some telephone reference
Mem of Northwest Kansas Library System
Open Mon, Wed & Fri 1-5, Tues 9-6, Thurs 1-6, Sat 9:30-1:30

WAKEFIELD

P WAKEFIELD PUBLIC LIBRARY,* 203 Third St, 67487-0348. SAN 306-1701. Tel: 785-461-5510. *Dir*, Shirley Garcia
Founded 1914. Pop 900; Circ 3,800
Library Holdings: Bk Vols 9,500; Per Subs 30
Subject Interests: Large type print, Local history
Mem of North Central Kansas Libraries System
Friends of the Library Group

WALNUT

P WALNUT PUBLIC LIBRARY, 404 S Willow, PO Box 18, 66780-0018. SAN 306-171X. Tel: 316-354-6794. *Librn*, Marie Kearns
Library Holdings: Bk Vols 3,326; Per Subs 16
Mem of Southeast Kansas Library System

WALTON

P WALTON COMMUNITY LIBRARY,* 122 Main St, PO Box 200, 67151. SAN 306-1728. Tel: 316-837-3252. *Librn*, Deborah Herbison
Pop 260; Circ 3,600
Library Holdings: Bk Vols 4,709; Per Subs 18
Mem of South Central Kansas Library System

WAMEGO

P WAMEGO PUBLIC LIBRARY, 408 Elm St, 66547-1620. SAN 306-1736. Tel: 785-456-9181. FAX: 785-456-8986. Web Site: www.skyways.lib.ks.us/library/wamego/wamegopl.html. *Dir*, Claudia Leeds; Staff 5 (Non-MLS 5)
Founded 1937. Pop 5,000; Circ 60,000
Jan 1999-Dec 1999 Income $119,000. Mats Exp $22,000. Sal $73,000
Library Holdings: Bk Titles 19,000; Per Subs 87
Subject Interests: Genealogy, History, Kansas
Automation Activity & Vendor Info: (Cataloging) Athena; (Circulation) Athena
Mem of North Central Kansas Libraries System
Friends of the Library Group

WASHINGTON

P WASHINGTON LIBRARY, 116 E Second St, 66968-1916. SAN 306-1744. Tel: 785-325-2114. E-Mail: wpl@washingtonks.net. *Librn*, Janet Keller
Founded 1909. Pop 6,000
Library Holdings: Bk Titles 34,000
Special Collections: Antique Doll Coll
Mem of North Central Kansas Libraries System
Friends of the Library Group

WATERVILLE

P WATERVILLE PUBLIC LIBRARY,* 129 E Commercial St, 66548. SAN 306-1752. Tel: 785-363-2769. *Librn*, Gladys Lindquist
Founded 1914. Pop 670; Circ 5,490
Library Holdings: Bk Vols 8,000; Per Subs 26
Mem of North Central Kansas Libraries System
Open Mon, Tues, Wed & Fri 2-5, Sat 9-12

WEIR

P WEIR PUBLIC LIBRARY, 612 S Jefferson, PO Box 248, 66781-0248. SAN 306-1779. Tel: 316-396-8899. E-Mail: weirlib@ckt.net. *Dir, Librn*, Susan Adams; Staff 2 (Non-MLS 2)
Pop 800; Circ 5,550
Jan 2000-Dec 2000 Income $16,543, State $676, City $12,000, Other $3,094. Mats Exp $1,704, Books $1,354, Per/Ser (Incl. Access Fees) $350. Sal $9,300
Library Holdings: Bk Titles 6,195; Per Subs 27
Mem of Southeast Kansas Library System
Open Mon, Wed & Fri 1-5, Tues 10-12 & 1-4, Thurs 1-6

WELLINGTON

P WELLINGTON PUBLIC LIBRARY,* 121 W Seventh St, 67152-3898. SAN 306-1787. Tel: 316-326-2011. FAX: 316-326-8193. E-Mail: wlibrary@idir.net. Web Site: www.skyways.lib.ks.us/kansas/kansas.html. *Dir, Librn*, Donna McNeil
Founded 1916. Pop 8,535; Circ 60,081
Jan 1997-Dec 1998 Income $196,800. Mats Exp $25,400. Sal $87,071
Library Holdings: Bk Vols 43,411; Per Subs 105
Mem of South Central Kansas Library System
Friends of the Library Group

WELLSVILLE

P WELLSVILLE CITY LIBRARY,* 115 W Sixth, PO Box 517, 66092-0517. SAN 306-1795. Tel: 785-883-2870. Interlibrary Loan Service Tel: 785-843-3654. FAX: 785-883-2870. E-Mail: citylibrary@wellsville.com. *Librn*, Becky Dodd; *Asst Librn*, Barbara Jones
Pop 1,722; Circ 19,000
Library Holdings: Bk Vols 13,000; Per Subs 35
Special Collections: Wellsville Globes (newsp)
Mem of Northeast Kansas Library System
Partic in Kansas Info Circuit
Friends of the Library Group

WESTWOOD

S SPRINT CORPORATION, Corporate Research Center,* 2330 Shawnee Mission Pkwy, 66205. SAN 323-7826. Tel: 913-624-8500. *Dir*, Kathy Mobley; *Ref*, Denise Marrow; *Ref*, Becky Barger; *Ref*, Dorinda Lanier; *Ref*, Mike Redinger; *Ref*, Deb Robinson; *Ref*, Steve Homan; *Tech Coordr*, Joe Bolduch; *Tech Coordr*, Leslie Wichman; Staff 8 (MLS 6, Non-MLS 2)
Library Holdings: Bk Vols 35,000; Per Subs 500
Subject Interests: Advertising, Engineering, Telecommunications
Publications: Trade Talk (daily news digest)
Partic in OCLC Online Computer Library Center, Inc

WETMORE

P WETMORE PUBLIC LIBRARY, 303 Second St, 66550. (Mail add: PO Box 126, 66550), Tel: 785-866-2250. E-Mail: wetpubli@jbntelco.com. *Dir*, Donna Dorman
Founded 1966. Pop 300; Circ 4,350
Library Holdings: Bk Titles 15,322
Mem of Northeast Kansas Library System

WHITE CITY

P WHITE CITY PUBLIC LIBRARY, 113 N Adolph, PO Box 206, 66872. SAN 306-1817. Tel: 785-349-5551. FAX: 785-349-5551. E-Mail: wclib@tetelco.net. *Librn*, Frank L Nelson
Founded 1933. Pop 900; Circ 7,500
1998-1999 Income $13,700, State $400, City $13,000. Mats Exp $5,000, Books $3,000, Per/Ser (Incl. Access Fees) $300, Micro $200
Library Holdings: Bk Vols 10,000; Per Subs 30
Mem of North Central Kansas Libraries System

WHITEWATER

P WHITEWATER MEMORIAL LIBRARY,* 118 E Topeka, PO Box 9, 67154. SAN 306-1825. Tel: 316-799-2471. FAX: 316-799-1099. E-Mail: whiteilb@swbell.net. *Librn*, Jean Thiessen
Pop 751; Circ 8,711
1997-1998 Income $20,079. Sal $7,269
Library Holdings: Bk Vols 10,792; Per Subs 73
Mem of South Central Kansas Library System
Friends of the Library Group

WICHITA

S THE BOEING COMPANY, WICHITA DIVISION, Technical Library,* 3801 S Oliver, PO Box 7730 Mail Stop K78-38, 67277-7730. SAN 306-1833. Tel: 316-526-3801. FAX: 316-523-1169. *Mgr*, Wade Banks; Tel: 316-526-0051, Fax: 316-526-0051, E-Mail: wade.b.banks@boeing.com
Founded 1941
Library Holdings: Bk Vols 10,000
Subject Interests: Aerospace science, Aviation, Electrical engineering, Electronics, Engineering, Manufacturing, Material culture

CESSNA AIRCRAFT CO

S CESSNA LIBRARY, One Cessna Blvd, 67215. (Mail add: 2617 South Hoover Rd, 67215-1200), SAN 342-2100. Tel: 316-517-6575. FAX: 316-517-7437. Web Site: www.cessna.textron.com. *Head Librn*, Rhonda Inman; E-Mail: rinman@cessna.textron.com; *Asst Librn*, Sarah Sanborn; E-Mail: srsanborn@cessna.textron.com; Staff 2 (MLS 1, Non-MLS 1)
Library Holdings: Bk Titles 10,000; Per Subs 81
Automation Activity & Vendor Info: (Acquisitions) Inmagic, Inc.; (Cataloging) Inmagic, Inc.; (Circulation) Inmagic, Inc.; (Course Reserve) Inmagic, Inc.; (ILL) Inmagic, Inc.; (Media Booking) Inmagic, Inc.; (OPAC) Inmagic, Inc.; (Serials) Inmagic, Inc.

GM DEPARTMENT OF VETERANS AFFAIRS, Medical & Regional Office Center Library,* Library 142D, 5500 E Kellogg, 67218. SAN 306-1922. Tel: 316-651-3612. FAX: 316-651-3669. E-Mail: wivet1lb@ink.org. *Librn, Online Servs*, Alice H Schad
Founded 1946
Library Holdings: Bk Vols 3,250
Subject Interests: Medicine, Nursing
Partic in Vets Admin Libr Network
Open Mon-Fri 8-4:30

CR FRIENDS UNIVERSITY, Edmund Stanley Library, 2100 W University, 67213. SAN 306-1868. Tel: 316-295-5880. FAX: 316-295-5080. E-Mail: askmax@friends.edu. Web Site: www.friends.edu/library/. *Dir*, David L Pappas; E-Mail: pappas@southwind.net; *Asst Dir, Publ Servs*, Max Burson; *Cat*, Anne Crane; *Ser*, Betty Batten; *Circ*, Kathy Edwards; *ILL*, Heather Berkheimer; *Cat, Ref Serv*, Valorie Starr; Staff 8 (MLS 3, Non-MLS 5)
Founded 1898. Pop 3,245; Enrl 3,245; Fac 83; Highest Degree: Master
Jul 1999-Jun 2000 Income $508,066. Mats Exp $190,861, Books $75,138, Per/Ser (Incl. Access Fees) $88,779, Electronic Ref Mat (Incl. Access Fees) $26,944. Sal $260,195 (Prof $111,621)
Library Holdings: Bk Vols 109,500; Bk Titles 81,000; Per Subs 3,350
Special Collections: Quaker Coll
Automation Activity & Vendor Info: (Cataloging) SIRSI; (Circulation) SIRSI; (OPAC) SIRSI
Database Vendor: Ebsco - EbscoHost, IAC - SearchBank, Lexis-Nexis, OCLC - First Search, ProQuest, Wilson - Wilson Web
Mem of South Central Kansas Library System
Partic in Bibliographical Center For Research, Rocky Mountain Region, Inc; OCLC Online Computer Library Center, Inc

G KANSAS GEOLOGICAL SURVEY, Wichita Well Sample Library, 4150 Monroe St, 67209. SAN 374-9576. Tel: 316-943-2343. FAX: 316-943-1261. E-Mail: wwslkgs@swbell.net. Web Site: www.kgs.ukans.edu. *Mgr*, Lawrence H Skelton; E-Mail: lskelton@kgs.ukans.edu; *Librn*, Lois Stewart; E-Mail: lstewart@kgs.ukans.edu; Staff 2 (MLS 1, Non-MLS 1)
Founded 1938
Library Holdings: Bk Vols 2,000
Special Collections: Oil & Gas Well Data; Rock Samples from Gas & Oil Wells

S LEARJET CORP LIBRARY,* One Learjet Way, PO Box 7707, 67277. SAN 306-1876. Tel: 316-946-2000. FAX: 316-946-2809. *Mgr*, Penny Mann; *Librn*, Linda Jesseph
Library Holdings: Bk Vols 1,000; Per Subs 30
Subject Interests: Engineering
Restriction: Staff use only

S MID-AMERICA ALL INDIAN CENTER LIBRARY,* 650 N Seneca, 67203. SAN 376-0766. Tel: 316-262-5221. FAX: 316-262-4216. Web Site: www.southwind.net/~icm/resource.html.
Library Holdings: Bk Vols 1,400

S MIDWEST HISTORICAL & GENEALOGICAL SOCIETY, INC LIBRARY, 1203 N Main, PO Box 1121, 67201-1121. SAN 326-4939. Tel: 316-264-3611. *Librn*, Donna Woods
Founded 1966. Pop 4,110
Library Holdings: Bk Titles 20,000; Per Subs 45
Subject Interests: Genealogy
Publications: MHGS Register
Open Tues & Sat 9-4

CR NEWMAN UNIVERSITY, Ryan Library, 3100 McCormick Ave, 67213-2097. SAN 306-1884. Tel: 316-942-4291. FAX: 316-942-1747. Web Site: www.newmanu.edu. *Dir*, Joseph E Forte; Tel: 316-942-4291, Ext 104, E-Mail: fortej@newmanu.edu; *Cat*, Edwina Pope; Tel: 316-942-4291, Ext 108, E-Mail: popee@newmanu.edu; *Publ Servs*, Rita Sevart; Tel: 316-942-4291, Ext 210, E-Mail: sevartr@newmanu.edu; Staff 4 (MLS 3, Non-MLS 1)
Founded 1933. Enrl 2,100; Highest Degree: Master
Jul 1999-Jun 2000 Income Parent Institution $250,000. Mats Exp $133,000, Books $45,000, Per/Ser (Incl. Access Fees) $65,000, Presv $3,000, Micro $5,000, Electronic Ref Mat (Incl. Access Fees) $15,000. Sal $106,000 (Prof $86,000)
Library Holdings: Bk Vols 110,000; Bk Titles 90,000; Per Subs 550
Subject Interests: Allied health, Catholicism, Nursing, Social work
Special Collections: Cardinal John Henry Newman Coll; Chrysostom Coll; College Archives; College Archives
Database Vendor: Ebsco - EbscoHost, IAC - Info Trac, IAC - SearchBank, OCLC - First Search, Silverplatter Information Inc., Wilson - Wilson Web
Publications: Handbooks for faculty, students, graduate students; Video Catalog
Mem of South Central Kansas Library System
Partic in S Cent Kans Libr Syst

L SEDGWICK COUNTY LAW LIBRARY,* 301 N Main, Ste 700, 67202. SAN 325-6081. Tel: 316-263-2251. *Librn*, Martie Bogle
Library Holdings: Bk Vols 60,000; Bk Titles 2,500
Partic in BRS
Open Mon-Thurs 8-7, Fri 8-5 & Sat 11-3

L UNITED STATES COURTS LIBRARY,* B55 US Courthouse, 401 N Market St, 67202-2011. SAN 372-1256. Tel: 316-269-6162. FAX: 316-269-6168. *Librn*, Sharon L Hom; *Tech Servs*, Lynda R Miller
Library Holdings: Bk Vols 10,000; Per Subs 12

CM UNIVERSITY OF KANSAS SCHOOL OF MEDICINE-WICHITA, George J Farha Medical Library, 1010 N Kansas, 67214-3199. SAN 373-2770. Tel: 316-293-2629. FAX: 316-293-2608. Web Site: www.wichita.kumc.edu/it/library. *Dir*, Teresa Coady; Staff 6 (MLS 3, Non-MLS 3)
Founded 1981. Circ 6,062; Enrl 98; Fac 94; Highest Degree: Master
Library Holdings: Bk Vols 3,800; Per Subs 367
Special Collections: Consumer Health (TLC Coll), bks, videos
Automation Activity & Vendor Info: (Acquisitions) Endeavor; (Cataloging) Endeavor; (Circulation) Endeavor; (OPAC) Endeavor; (Serials) Endeavor

M VIA CHRISTI MEDICAL CENTER, Robert C Tinker Medical Library,* 3600 E Harry St, 67218. SAN 306-1914. Tel: 316-689-5376. FAX: 316-691-6721. *Librn*, Cam Gentry
Founded 1942
Library Holdings: Bk Titles 4,000; Per Subs 400
Subject Interests: Clinical medicine, Education
Open Mon-Fri 8:30-5

M VIA CHRISTI REGIONAL MEDICAL CENTER, Saint Francis Campus Professional Library,* 929 N Saint Francis, 67214-1315. SAN 306-1906. Tel: 316-268-5979. FAX: 316-268-8694. *Librn*, Janet Heidebrecht; E-Mail: janet_heidebrecht@via.christi.org
Founded 1938
Library Holdings: Bk Vols 8,000; Per Subs 540
Subject Interests: Medicine, Nursing
Publications: Wichita Area Health Science Libraries Union List

S VULCAN MATERIALS CO, Chemicals Division Research & Development Library,* 6200 S Ridge, PO Box 12283, 67277. SAN 306-1930. Tel: 316-524-4211, 316-529-7262. FAX: 316-529-7555. *Librn*, Bernie Atherton
Founded 1955
Library Holdings: Per Subs 35
Subject Interests: Chemical engineering, Chemistry
Restriction: Staff use only

S WEATHERDATA INCORPORATED LIBRARY,* 245 N Waco St Ste 310, 67202-1111. SAN 371-4519. Tel: 316-265-9127. FAX: 316-265-1949. Web Site: www.weatherdata.com. *In Charge*, Stephen Pryor
Library Holdings: Per Subs 10
Subject Interests: Climatology, Meteorology

S WICHITA ART MUSEUM LIBRARY, 619 Stackman Dr, 67203-3296. SAN 306-1965. Tel: 316-268-4921. FAX: 316-268-4980. E-Mail: wam@feist.com. Web Site: www.wichitaartmuseum.org. *Librn*, Lois Crane; E-Mail: cranel@wichitaartmuseum.org; Staff 1 (MLS 1)
Founded 1963
Jan 1999-Dec 1999 Income City $4,330. Mats Exp $4,330, Books $3,130, Per/Ser (Incl. Access Fees) $1,200
Library Holdings: Bk Vols 7,886; Per Subs 20
Subject Interests: Art
Special Collections: American Art Coll
Restriction: Open to public for reference only

S WICHITA CENTER FOR THE ARTS, Maude Gowan Schollenberger Memorial Library, 9112 E Central, 67206. SAN 306-1957. Tel: 316-634-2787. FAX: 316-634-0593. Web Site: www.wcfta.com. *Exec Dir*, Howard W Ellington
Founded 1920
Library Holdings: Bk Vols 3,000
Subject Interests: Art
Open Tues-Fri 10-5, Sat & Sun 1-5

S WICHITA EAGLE LIBRARY, 825 E Douglas, PO Box 820, 67201-0820. SAN 306-1973. Tel: 316-455-2221. FAX: 316-268-6646. *Librn*, Deborah Bagby; E-Mail: dbagby@wichitaeagle.com; Staff 2 (Non-MLS 2)
Library Holdings: Bk Vols 2,500; Per Subs 15

P WICHITA PUBLIC LIBRARY, 223 S Main St, 67202. SAN 342-2135. Tel: 316-261-8500. Circulation Tel: 316-261-8508. Reference Tel: 316-261-8510. FAX: 316-262-4540. E-Mail: webmaster@wichita.lib.ks.us. Web Site: www.wichita.lib.ks.us. *Dir*, Cynthia K Berner Harris; Tel: 316-261-8520, E-Mail: cberner@wichita.lib.ks.us; *Ad Servs*, Larry Vos; Tel: 316-261-8540,

E-Mail: lvos@widhita.lib.ks.us; *Exten Serv*, Linda Knupp; Tel: 316-261-8570, E-Mail: lknupp@wichita.lib.ks.us; *Publ Servs*, Virginia Ray; Tel: 316-261-8580, E-Mail: gray@wichita.lib.ks.us; *Publ Servs*, Diana Williams; *Ch Servs*, Jane Dean; *Ch Servs*, Julie Linneman; Tel: 316-261-8590, E-Mail: juliel@wichita.lib.ks.us. Subject Specialists: *Business and management*, Lynn Gunderson; *Technology*, Lynn Gunderson; Staff 30 (MLS 27, Non-MLS 3)
Founded 1876. Pop 320,395; Circ 1,851,637
Jan 1999-Dec 1999 Income $5,986,500, State $281,693, City $4,521,172, Federal $56,368, Locally Generated Income $391,956, Other $635,311. Mats Exp $848,907, Books $658,813, Per/Ser (Incl. Access Fees) $70,202, Micro $391, AV Equip $92,278, Other Print Mats $2,435, Electronic Ref Mat (Incl. Access Fees) $24,788. Sal $3,676,594
Library Holdings: Bk Vols 633,992
Subject Interests: Gen, Kansas, Local history, Music scores, Schematics
Special Collections: American Indian (James H Foulk, Jr Indian Coll); Motor Manuals; Mueller Philatelic Coll
Database Vendor: epixtech, inc., IAC - SearchBank, OCLC - First Search
Publications: Excerpts (Newsletter)
Mem of South Central Kansas Library System
Partic in Bibliographical Center For Research, Rocky Mountain Region, Inc; OCLC Online Computer Library Center, Inc
Special Services for the Deaf - TTY machine
Homebound Deliveries
Friends of the Library Group
Branches: 12
ALEY PARK, 1749 S Martinson, 67218. SAN 342-2143. Tel: 316-337-9066. Web Site: www.wichita.lib.ks.us. *Librn*, Deborah Simpson
Library Holdings: Bk Vols 28,263
Friends of the Library Group
COMOTARA, 2244 N Rock Rd, 67226. SAN 328-7742. Tel: 316-688-9350. Web Site: www.wichita.lib.ks.us. *Librn*, Deborah Simpson
Library Holdings: Bk Vols 12,732
Friends of the Library Group
LINWOOD, 1901 S Kansas Ave, 67211. SAN 342-216X. Tel: 316-337-9125. Web Site: www.wichita.lib.ks.us. *Librn*, Judy Young
Library Holdings: Bk Vols 32,718
Friends of the Library Group
MARINA LAKES, 2021 Amidon, 67204. SAN 342-2372. Tel: 316-838-9647. Web Site: www.wichita.lib.ks.us. *Librn*, Jean Pouncil-Burton
Library Holdings: Bk Vols 30,218
Friends of the Library Group
MAYA ANGELOU NORTHEAST, 3051 E 21st St, 67214. SAN 342-2283. Tel: 316-688-9580. Web Site: www.wichita.lib.ks.us. *Librn*, Ola Sanders
Library Holdings: Bk Vols 28,390
Friends of the Library Group
MINISA, 725 W 13th St, 67203. SAN 342-2259. Tel: 316-337-9154. Web Site: www.wichita.lib.ks.us. *Librn*, Colleen Strouse
Library Holdings: Bk Vols 19,736
Friends of the Library Group
ORCHARD PARK, 4808 W Ninth St, 67212. SAN 342-2291. Tel: 316-941-0634. Web Site: www.wichita.lib.ks.us. *Librn*, Gwen Harris
Library Holdings: Bk Vols 19,120
Friends of the Library Group
PLANEVIEW, 2820 S Roosevelt, 67210. SAN 342-2313. Tel: 316-688-9300. Web Site: www.wichita.lib.ks.us. *Librn*, Zetta Maxwell
Library Holdings: Bk Vols 30,511
Friends of the Library Group
ROCKWELL, 5939 E Ninth, 67208. SAN 342-2194. Tel: 316-688-9361. Web Site: www.wichita.lib.ks.us. *Librn*, Mary Kay Bird-Gillians
Library Holdings: Bk Vols 56,822
Friends of the Library Group
SENECA, 3249 S Seneca, 67217. SAN 342-2348. Tel: 316-529-9950. Web Site: www.wichita.lib.ks.us. *Librn*, Gail Hand
Library Holdings: Bk Vols 35,919
Friends of the Library Group

P SUBREGIONAL LIBRARY FOR THE BLIND & PHYSICALLY HANDICAPPED, 223 S Main St, 67202. SAN 342-2151. Tel: 316-261-3596. Toll Free Tel: 800-362-2869. FAX: 316-262-4540. Web Site: www.wichita.lib.ks.us. *Librn*, Brad Reha
Jan 2000-Dec 2000 Income $104,149, State $75,799, Federal $28,350
Library Holdings: Bk Vols 31,143
Friends of the Library Group
WESTLINK, 8515 Bekemeyer, 67212. SAN 342-2402. Tel: 316-721-7462. Web Site: www.wichita.lib.ks.us. *Dir*, Amy Stahl; *Librn*, Jane Dear
Library Holdings: Bk Vols 74,388
Friends of the Library Group

S WICHITA SEDGEWICK COUNTY HISTORICAL MUSEUM LIBRARY, 204 S Main St, 67202. SAN 325-6103. Tel: 316-265-9314. FAX: 316-265-9319. E-Mail: wschm@feist.com. Web Site: www.wscribe.com/history. *Dir*, Robert A Puckett; *Curator*, Jami Frazier Tracy; E-Mail: jtracy@feist.com; Staff 1 (Non-MLS 1)
Founded 1939
Library Holdings: Bk Vols 330; Per Subs 10
Subject Interests: Local history
Restriction: By appointment only
Function: Archival collection
Open Tues-Fri 11-4, Sat & Sun 1-5

C THE WICHITA STATE UNIVERSITY LIBRARY,* Ablah Library, 67260-0068. SAN 306-1981. Tel: 316-978-3586. Interlibrary Loan Service Tel: 316-978-3167. FAX: 316-978-3048. Web Site: www.twsu.edu/library/. *Asst Dean*, Kathy A Downes; *Curator*, Michael T Kelly; *ILL*, Ted Naylor; *Cat*, Nancy Dayoe; *Cat, Govt Doc*, Nan Myers; *Coll Develop*, Cathy Moore-Jansen. Subject Specialists: *Business and management*, Brian Williams; *Humanities*, Brian Hancock; *Music*, Michelle Wolff; *Science/technology*, Connie Dalrymple; Staff 23 (MLS 23)
Founded 1895. Enrl 9,706; Fac 464; Highest Degree: Doctorate
Jul 1997-Jun 1998 Income $4,540,313, State $4,261,717, County $50,000, Locally Generated Income $228,596. Mats Exp $1,815,281, Books $727,831, Per/Ser (Incl. Access Fees) $1,031,636, Presv $39,420. Sal $1,870,937 (Prof $813,423)
Library Holdings: Per Subs 3,784
Subject Interests: Engineering, History, Manufacturing, Music, Psychology, Urban studies
Special Collections: American Anti-Slavery Movement Coll; American Civil War Sanitary Commission Papers (Kantor Coll); Aviation History of World War I; Congresional Papers of Members of Congress from Kansas & Seven Other States; History of Books & Printing (Aitchison Coll); Hypnotism, Mesmerism & Animal Magnetism (Tinterow Coll); Kansas & the Great Plains (Historical Map Coll); Original Editorial Cartoons of Gene Bassett; Patent & Trademark Dep; W H Auden Coll; Wichita State University Archives; William Lloyd Garrison Papers Coll; World War I & II Pamphlet Coll
Automation Activity & Vendor Info: (Acquisitions) NOTIS; (Cataloging) NOTIS; (Serials) NOTIS
Partic in Amigos Library Services, Inc
Friends of the Library Group
Departmental Libraries:
CHEMISTRY, 118 McKinley Hall, 67260-0051. SAN 324-3311. Tel: 316-978-3764. *Librn*, Connie Dalrymple
MUSIC LIBRARY, C 116 DFAC, 67260-0053. SAN 324-332X. Tel: 316-978-3029. *Librn*, Michele Wolff

WILSEY

P ELM CREEK TOWNSHIP LIBRARY,* 213 Fifth St, 66873. SAN 306-199X. Tel: 785-497-2289. *Librn*, Ann Wittman
Pop 359; Circ 3,500
Library Holdings: Bk Vols 8,000
Mem of North Central Kansas Libraries System
Open Tues 9-12 & 12:30-4:30, Wed 10-1, Sat 9-12

WILSON

P LANG MEMORIAL LIBRARY,* 2405 Ave F, PO Box 310, 67490. SAN 320-4790. Tel: 785-658-3648. E-Mail: langlib@midusa.net. *Librn*, Margaret Stadelman
Founded 1924. Pop 978; Circ 4,266
Library Holdings: Bk Vols 20,100; Per Subs 12
Mem of Central Kansas Library System

WINCHESTER

P WINCHESTER PUBLIC LIBRARY,* 208 Winchester, PO Box 143, 66097-0143. SAN 376-5490. Tel: 913-774-4967. FAX: 913-774-4967. E-Mail: winkslib@hotmail.com. Web Site: www.nekesc.org/~winks/winchester.htm. *Dir*, Raymond Riley
Dec 1998-Dec 1999 Income $21,000, City $4,500, Federal $1,000, County $3,200, Locally Generated Income $11,000. Mats Exp $21,000, Books $2,400, Per/Ser (Incl. Access Fees) $200, Electronic Ref Mat (Incl. Access Fees) $200. Sal $10,000
Library Holdings: Bk Vols 14,799; Per Subs 10
Automation Activity & Vendor Info: (Acquisitions) Follett; (Cataloging) Follett; (Circulation) Follett
Mem of Northeast Kansas Library System
Friends of the Library Group

WINFIELD

S COWLEY COUNTY HISTORICAL SOCIETY MUSEUM LIBRARY, 1011 Mansfield, 67156-3557. SAN 306-2007. Tel: 316-221-4811. *Curator*, Frankie Cullison
Founded 1967
Subject Interests: Family hist, Local history
Special Collections: Military History of the Civil War; Winfield History, photog & newsp
Function: Research library
Open Tues 8:30-11:30, Sat & Sun 2-5

M H L SNYDER MEMORIAL RESEARCH FOUNDATION, Cecil Snyder Laboratory Library, 1407 Wheat Rd, 67156. SAN 306-2023. Tel: 316-221-4080. FAX: 316-221-6825. *Librn*, Toya Smith; Staff 9 (MLS 4, Non-MLS 5)
Founded 1947
Library Holdings: Bk Vols 3,050; Bk Titles 1,500; Per Subs 65
Subject Interests: Biochemistry, Clinical medicine, Surgery
Partic in Midcontinental Regional Med Libr Network

C SOUTHWESTERN COLLEGE, Memorial Library,* 100 College St, 67156-2498. SAN 306-2031. Tel: 316-221-8225. FAX: 316-221-8382. Web Site: www.sckans.edu/library. *Dir*, Gregory Zuck; Tel: 316-221-8310, E-Mail: gzuck1@sckans.edu; *Archivist*, Jerry Wallace; Tel: 316-221-8711, E-Mail: jwallace@sckans.edu; *Coordr*, Terry Quiett; Tel: 316-221-8282, E-Mail: quietly@sckans.edu; *Cat, ILL*, Cheryl Barnett; Tel: 316-221-8312, E-Mail: cheryl@sckans.edu; *Ref*, Mira Greene; Tel: 316-221-8311, E-Mail: mgreene@sckans.edu; *Acq, Ser*, Beth Sheppard; Tel: 316-221-8271, E-Mail: bsheppar@sckans.edu; Staff 6 (MLS 2, Non-MLS 4)
Founded 1885. Enrl 649; Fac 51; Highest Degree: Master
Library Holdings: Bk Vols 75,000; Bk Titles 66,000; Per Subs 360
Subject Interests: Biology, Business and management, Economics, Education, Environmental studies, Feminism, History, Music, Natural science, Nursing, Social sciences and issues, Technology
Special Collections: Arthur Convey Coll; Black History & Literature (Ludgood-Walker Afro-American Studies Coll); Watmull Coll of Indian Studies
Automation Activity & Vendor Info: (OPAC) Innovative Interfaces Inc.; (Serials) Innovative Interfaces Inc.
Mem of South Central Kansas Library System
Partic in Bibliographical Center For Research, Rocky Mountain Region, Inc; Dialog Corporation; OCLC Online Computer Library Center, Inc

P WINFIELD PUBLIC LIBRARY, 605 College, 67156-3199. SAN 306-204X. Tel: 316-221-4470. FAX: 316-221-6135. E-Mail: wpl1@horizon.hit.net. Web Site: www.wpl.org. *Dir*, Tresia Dodson; E-Mail: wpl2@horizon.hit.net; *Ch Servs*, Julia Joy; Staff 11 (MLS 1, Non-MLS 10)
Founded 1912. Pop 12,000; Circ 129,331
Jan 2000-Dec 2000 Income $380,454, State $9,628, City $340,285, Locally Generated Income $16,150, Other $14,391. Mats Exp $58,154, Books $42,918, Per/Ser (Incl. Access Fees) $11,300, Electronic Ref Mat (Incl. Access Fees) $3,936. Sal $166,080 (Prof $127,543)
Library Holdings: Bk Vols 60,381; Per Subs 137
Subject Interests: Art, Genealogy, Kansas
Database Vendor: Innovative Interfaces INN - View
Publications: Newsletter (quarterly)
Mem of South Central Kansas Library System
Partic in Dialog Corporation
Friends of the Library Group

YATES CENTER

P YATES CENTER PUBLIC LIBRARY,* 218 N Main, 66783-1424. SAN 306-2066. Tel: 316-625-3341. FAX: 316-625-3035. E-Mail: yclibrary@yatescenterks.net. *Dir*, Cindy Adams; Staff 4 (Non-MLS 4)
Founded 1908. Pop 1,998; Circ 16,667
Library Holdings: Bk Vols 14,504; Per Subs 41
Mem of Southeast Kansas Library System

ZENDA

P ZENDA PUBLIC LIBRARY,* 306 N Main, PO Box 53, 67159. SAN 306-2074. Tel: 316-243-5791. E-Mail: zenda1lb@ink.org. *Librn*, Kathy Price
Founded 1967. Pop 248; Circ 1,703
Library Holdings: Bk Vols 7,905; Per Subs 11
Mem of South Central Kansas Library System
Open Wed afternoon & Sat morning

KENTUCKY

Date of Statistics: 1999-2000
Population, 1990 Census: 3,685,296
Population Served by Public Libraries & Bookmobiles: 3,651,328
Total Volumes in Public Libraries & Bookmobiles: 7,687,279
Volumes Per Capita (statewide): 2.09
Volumes Per Capita (population served): 2.11
Total Public Library Circulation (including Bookmobiles): 20,092,217
Circulation Per Capita (statewide): 5.45
Circulation Per Capita (population served): 5.50
Total Public Library Income: $71,121,608
Source of Income:
Public Funds: $65,051,549
State & Federal: $5,913,531
Expenditure Per Capita (population served): $18.49
Expenditure Per Capita (statewide): $18.32
Number of (Regional) Libraries: 12
Counties Unserved: 2
Number of Bookmobiles in State: 93
Grants-in-Aid to Public Libraries:
Federal (Library Services & Technology Act): $2,061,219 (No Title II Construction awarded)
Public Library Service Fund: $5,575,500

ALBANY

P CLINTON COUNTY PUBLIC LIBRARY,* 205 Burkesville Rd, 42602. SAN 306-2082. Tel: 606-387-5989. FAX: 606-387-5989. *Librn*, Gayla Duvall; *Bkmobile Coordr*, Deborah Jane Sells
Pop 9,135; Circ 54,076
Library Holdings: Bk Vols 32,981; Per Subs 24
Subject Interests: Kentucky
Mem of Lake Cumberland Regional Libr Syst

APPLIANCE PARK

S GENERAL ELECTRIC CO, Technical Information Center,* AP 35-1217, 40225-0001. SAN 306-3410. Tel: 502-452-5396. FAX: 502-452-3844. *Librn*, Linda Wilson
Founded 1956
Library Holdings: Bk Vols 5,000
Subject Interests: Chemistry, Electrical engineering, Mathematics, Mechanical engineering, Physics
Partic in Dialog Corporation; Dow Jones News Retrieval
Library services contracted through the University of Louisville. Open Mon-Fri 8am-5pm

ASHLAND

J ASHLAND COMMUNITY COLLEGE LIBRARY,* 1400 College Dr, 41101. SAN 306-2090. Tel: 606-326-2169. FAX: 606-326-2186. Web Site: www.ashlandcc.org/library/. *Dir*, Carol M Greene; E-Mail: carol.greene@kctcs.net; *Acq*, Shirley Boyd; *Tech Servs*, Betti George Frye; *Govt Doc*, Matt Onion; Staff 3 (MLS 3)
Founded 1938. Enrl 3,200; Fac 90
Library Holdings: Bk Vols 45,658; Bk Titles 38,132; Per Subs 353
Special Collections: Fed Doc Dep; Jesse Stuart, Kentucky authors
Partic in OCLC Online Computer Library Center, Inc
Ashland Community College is part of the University of Kentucky Community College system

P BOYD COUNTY PUBLIC LIBRARY, 1740 Central Ave, 41101. SAN 306-2112. Tel: 606-329-0090. FAX: 606-329-0578. Web Site: www.thebookplace.org. *Dir*, James C Powers; E-Mail: jcp@wwd.net; *Admin Assoc*, Kitty Tompson; *Ch Servs*, Debra Jonas; *Syst Coordr*, Betty Prince; *Reader Servs*, Martin Hoffman; *Head Ref*, Lois Jackson. Subject Specialists: *Systs*, Betty Prince; Staff 10 (MLS 4, Non-MLS 6)
Founded 1935. Pop 70,000; Circ 294,870
Jul 1999-Jun 2000 Income (Main Library and Branch Library) $1,329,465, State $67,495, County $1,155,846, Locally Generated Income $106,124. Mats Exp $216,579, Books $95,221, Per/Ser (Incl. Access Fees) $20,469, AV Equip $85,889, Electronic Ref Mat (Incl. Access Fees) $15,000. Sal $562,373 (Prof $86,608)
Library Holdings: Bk Vols 113,112; Per Subs 291
Special Collections: Arnold Hanners Photo Coll; Art Gallery; Genealogy & Local History (Minnie C Winder), bks & micro; High Interest/Low Reading; Language Tape Coll; Records from Bellefonte, Buena Vista, Princess & Amanda Furnace Operations
Automation Activity & Vendor Info: (Circulation) epixtech, inc.
Database Vendor: IAC - Info Trac, OCLC - First Search
Publications: Library Times Newsletter
Partic in OCLC Online Computer Library Center, Inc; SE Ind Area Libr Servs Authority
Special Services for the Deaf - Books on deafness & sign language; Captioned film depository
Friends of the Library Group
Branches: 2
CATLETTSBURG BRANCH, 2704 Louisa St, Catlettsburg, 41129. SAN 324-296X. Tel: 606-739-8332. FAX: 606-739-8332. Web Site: www.thebookplace.org.
Library Holdings: Bk Vols 11,288
SUMMIT, 1016 Summit Rd, 41102. SAN 321-8414. Tel: 606-928-3366. FAX: 606-928-3366. Web Site: www.thebookplace.org.
Library Holdings: Bk Vols 18,315
Bookmobiles: 1

R FIRST BAPTIST CHURCH LIBRARY,* 1701 Winchester Ave, PO Box 787, 41105-0787. SAN 306-2120. Tel: 606-324-3109. FAX: 606-324-4344. *Librn*, R L Zimmerman
Library Holdings: Bk Vols 10,000
Open approximately 10 hours each week

AUGUSTA

P KNOEDLER MEMORIAL LIBRARY,* 315 Main St, 41002. SAN 306-2139. Tel: 606-756-3911. *Librn*, Karen Smithers
Founded 1928
Library Holdings: Bk Titles 9,000
Special Collections: Bracken County History; Kentuckiana (Walter Rankins Coll)
Open Mon 1-5, Wed 9-5, Fri 4-8, Sat 10-2

BARBOURVILLE

P KNOX COUNTY PUBLIC LIBRARY,* 206 Knox St, 40906. SAN 306-2147. Tel: 606-546-5339. FAX: 606-546-3602. *Librn*, Lana Hale; E-Mail: lana@barbourville.com; *Bkmobile Coordr*, Pat Mills
Pop 30,239; Circ 74,309
Library Holdings: Bk Titles 43,000; Per Subs 28
Special Collections: Kentucky Coll
Mem of Cumberland Valley Libr Develop District
Partic in Ky Libr Asn

C UNION COLLEGE, Weeks-Townsend Memorial Library, 310 College St, CPO 21, 40906-1499. SAN 306-2155. Tel: 606-546-1240. FAX: 606-546-1239. E-Mail: refdesk@unionky.edu. Web Site: www.unionky.edu. *Dir*, Tara L Cooper; Tel: 606-546-1241; *Publ Servs*, Carrie Stephenson; E-Mail: cstephen@unionky.edu; *Tech Servs*, Kathy Miles; Staff 7 (MLS 3, Non-MLS

4)
Founded 1879. Enrl 597; Fac 56; Highest Degree: Master
Library Holdings: Bk Vols 120,000; Per Subs 469
Subject Interests: Civil War, Education, Genealogy, State hist
Automation Activity & Vendor Info: (Cataloging) SIRSI; (Circulation) SIRSI; (OPAC) SIRSI
Partic in Kentucky Library Network, Inc; OCLC Online Computer Library Center, Inc; SE Libr Network

BARDSTOWN

S OSCAR GETZ MUSEUM OF WHISKEY HISTORY LIBRARY, 114 N Fifth St, 40004. SAN 329-8779. Tel: 502-348-2999. FAX: 502-348-2999. *Curator*, Flaget M Nally; *Curator*, Mary Hite
Library Holdings: Bk Vols 300
Open Mon-Sat 9-5 & Sun 1-5, May 1-Nov 1; Tues-Sat 10-4, Nov 1-May 1

P NELSON COUNTY PUBLIC LIBRARY, 90 Court Sq, 40004-1584. SAN 342-2496. Tel: 502-348-3714. FAX: 502-348-5578. E-Mail: nelsonco.publib@mail.state.ky.us. Web Site: nelsoncopublib.org. *Dir*, Irene Underwood; E-Mail: irene.underwood@mail.state.ky.us; *Assoc Dir*, Vicki Filiatreau; E-Mail: vicki.filiatreau@mail.state.ky.us; *Bkmobile Coordr*, Carol Gritton; E-Mail: carol.gritton@mail.state.ky.us; *Ch Servs*, Betty Cook; E-Mail: betty.cook@mail.state.ky.us; *Web Coordr*, Margaret Scites; E-Mail: margaret.scites@mail.state.ky.us; Staff 14 (MLS 2, Non-MLS 12)
Founded 1967. Pop 29,710; Circ 99,283
Jul 1999-Jun 2000 Income (Main Library and Branch Library) $532,853, State $38,134, City $2,400, Locally Generated Income $454,639, Other $37,680. Mats Exp $74,686, Books $67,645, Per/Ser (Incl. Access Fees) $3,033. Sal $219,350 (Prof $33,170)
Library Holdings: Bk Vols 48,609; Per Subs 61
Special Collections: Genealogy Coll; Kentucky Coll
Automation Activity & Vendor Info: (Cataloging) TLC; (Circulation) TLC; (OPAC) TLC
Database Vendor: Ebsco - EbscoHost, OCLC - First Search
Mem of Lincoln Trail Libraries System
Branches: 3
BLOOMFIELD BRANCH, 141 Depot St, Bloomfield, 40008-0024. (Mail add: PO Box 24, Bloomfield, 40008-0024), SAN 342-2526. Tel: 502-252-9129. Web Site: nelsoncopublib.org. *Branch Mgr*, Jane Cecil; E-Mail: jane.cecil@mail.state.ky.us; Staff 2 (Non-MLS 2)
Pop 1,000; Circ 4,505
Automation Activity & Vendor Info: (Circulation) TLC; (OPAC) TLC
Database Vendor: Ebsco - EbscoHost, OCLC - First Search
BOSTON BRANCH, 61 Lebanon Junction Rd, Boston, 40107. (Mail add: 11406 Boston Rd, Boston, 40107-8602), SAN 342-2550. Tel: 502-833-3381. Web Site: nelsoncopublib.org. *Branch Mgr*, Gladys Greene; E-Mail: gladys.greene@mail.state.ky.us; Staff 2 (Non-MLS 2)
Circ 1,233
Automation Activity & Vendor Info: (Circulation) TLC; (OPAC) TLC
Database Vendor: Ebsco - EbscoHost, OCLC - First Search
NEW HAVEN BRANCH, 240 St Catherine St, New Haven, 40051-6352. SAN 342-2615. Tel: 502-549-6735. E-Mail: nelsonco.publib@mail.state.ky.us. Web Site: www.nelsoncopublib.org. *Dir*, Irene H Underwood; Tel: 502-348-3714, Fax: 502-348-5578, E-Mail: irene.underwood@mail.state.ky.us; *Branch Mgr*, Dolores Head; E-Mail: dolores.head@mail.state.ky.us; Staff 2 (Non-MLS 2)
Pop 900; Circ 3,955
Library Holdings: Bk Vols 2,600
Automation Activity & Vendor Info: (Circulation) TLC; (OPAC) TLC
Database Vendor: Ebsco - EbscoHost, OCLC - First Search
Bookmobiles: 1

BARDWELL

P BALLARD-CARLISLE-LIVINGSTON COUNTY PUBLIC LIBRARY SYSTEM,* PO Box 428, 42023-0428. SAN 320-4804. Tel: 502-335-5059. FAX: 502-335-5059. *Librn*, Sonya Mainord
Founded 1981
Library Holdings: Bk Vols 22,016
Subject Interests: Genealogy
Mem of Purchase Regional Libr Syst
Open Fridays only 9-4
Friends of the Library Group

BEATTYVILLE

P LEE COUNTY PUBLIC LIBRARY,* PO Box V, 41311. SAN 306-2163. Tel: 606-464-8014. FAX: 606-464-2052. *Librn*, Sonya Spencer
Pop 7,754; Circ 74,832
Library Holdings: Bk Vols 30,400; Per Subs 39
Special Collections: Genealogical Coll; Kentucky Coll
Mem of Kentucky Department for Libraries & Archives
Friends of the Library Group

BEDFORD

P TRIMBLE COUNTY PUBLIC LIBRARY, 112 US Hwy 42 E, PO Box 249, 40006. SAN 306-2171. Interlibrary Loan Service Tel: 502-255-7362. FAX: 502-255-7491. E-Mail: tcpl@siglou.com. *Librn*, Libby Powell
Pop 6,090; Circ 41,998
Jul 1998-Jun 1999 Income $157,607, State $21,652, County $135,955. Sal $71,154
Library Holdings: Bk Vols 25,000; Per Subs 50
Subject Interests: Genealogy
Mem of Ky Regional Libr Develop District
Bookmobiles: 1

BENTON

P MARSHALL COUNTY PUBLIC LIBRARY, 1003 Poplar St, 42025. SAN 342-264X. Tel: 270-527-9969. FAX: 270-527-0506. E-Mail: mcpl@marshallcolibrary.org. Web Site: www.marshallcolibrary.org. *Dir*, Kristi Tucker; *Bkmobile Coordr*, Donna Boswell; *Ch Servs*, Kelly Nutt; Staff 1 (MLS 1)
Founded 1968. Pop 27,205
Library Holdings: Bk Vols 55,000; Bk Titles 50,000; Per Subs 110
Special Collections: Local History
Automation Activity & Vendor Info: (Acquisitions) Follett; (Cataloging) Follett; (Circulation) Follett
Partic in Kentucky Library Network, Inc
Branches: 2
CALVERT CITY BRANCH, Calvert City, 42029. SAN 342-2704. Tel: 270-395-5745. FAX: 270-395-8398. E-Mail: ccpl@ldd.net. *Librn*, Nancy Petty
Library Holdings: Bk Titles 35,000; Per Subs 65
Automation Activity & Vendor Info: (Acquisitions) Follett; (Cataloging) Follett; (Circulation) Follett
HARDIN BRANCH, Hardin, 42048. SAN 342-2674. Tel: 270-437-4275. FAX: 270-437-4609. E-Mail: hbpl@ldd.net. *Librn*, Kimberly Darnall
Library Holdings: Bk Titles 29,000; Per Subs 50
Automation Activity & Vendor Info: (Acquisitions) Follett; (Cataloging) Follett; (Circulation) Follett
Bookmobiles: 1

BEREA

C BEREA COLLEGE, Hutchins Library,* 40404. SAN 342-2739. Tel: 606-985-3000. FAX: 606-986-9494. Web Site: www.berea.edu/library/library.html. *Dir*, Anne Chase; E-Mail: anne_chase@berea.edu; *Bibliog Instr, Ref*, Steve Gowler; *Acq*, Marsha Segedy; *Spec Coll*, Gerald Roberts; *ILL*, Patty Tarter; *Coll Develop, Tech Servs*, Catherine Roberts; Staff 9 (MLS 9)
Founded 1870. Enrl 1,500; Fac 133
Jul 1997-Jun 1998 Income $1,183,910. Mats Exp $382,990, Books $173,755, Per/Ser (Incl. Access Fees) $91,343, Presv $14,373, Micro $20,134, Manuscripts & Archives $24,400. Sal $531,847 (Prof $361,073)
Library Holdings: Per Subs 1,530
Special Collections: Berea Archives, mss; Shedd-Lincoln Coll; Weatherford-Hammond Appalachian Coll, bks & mss
Automation Activity & Vendor Info: (Acquisitions) epixtech, inc.; (Circulation) epixtech, inc.; (Serials) epixtech, inc.
Publications: Appalachian Heritage
Mem of Southeastern Regional Libr Syst
Partic in Coun of Independent Ky Cols & Univs; Dialog Corporation; Kentucky Library Network, Inc; OCLC Online Computer Library Center, Inc
Departmental Libraries:
ART Tel: 606-985-3000, Ext 5530. *Librn*, Robert Boyce
Library Holdings: Bk Vols 5,534
MEDIA SERVICES Tel: 606-985-3000. FAX: 606-986-9494. *Coordr*, Duane Semler
SCIENCE RESEARCH Tel: 606-985-3000. FAX: 606-986-9494. *Librn*, Alice Hooker
Library Holdings: Bk Vols 5,569

M SOUTHERN KENTUCKY AHEC LIBRARY, Berea Hospital - SKY AHEC Library, 305 Estill St, 40403. SAN 371-3881. Tel: 859-985-7302. Toll Free Tel: 800-711-0291. FAX: 859-986-0534. Web Site: www.mc.uky.edu/ahec/slib.htm. *Librn*, Mary Congleton; E-Mail: mcongleton@kih.net; Staff 2 (MLS 1, Non-MLS 1)
Founded 1983
Library Holdings: Bk Vols 150; Per Subs 70
Database Vendor: Ebsco - EbscoHost, OCLC - First Search
Partic in Bluegrass Med Librns; Ky AHEC Librns

BOONEVILLE

P OWSLEY COUNTY PUBLIC LIBRARY, 2 Action Pl, 41314. (Mail add: PO Box 280, 41314), Tel: 606-593-5700. FAX: 606-593-5708. E-Mail: marcum1@prtcnet.org. Web Site: www.geocities.com/athens/olympus/2006/. *Dir*, Joyce H Marcum; E-Mail: marcum1@prtcnet.org; Staff 3 (Non-MLS 3)
Founded 1970

Jul 1999-Jun 2000 Income $75,315, State $17,684, County $54,189, Locally Generated Income $3,442. Mats Exp $8,176, Books $5,922, Per/Ser (Incl. Access Fees) $640, Micro $18, AV Equip $1,196, Other Print Mats $500, Electronic Ref Mat (Incl. Access Fees) $400. Sal $46,516 (Prof $21,120)
Library Holdings: Bk Titles 26,698; Per Subs 127
Subject Interests: Genealogy
Special Collections: Kentucky Genealogy Coll
Database Vendor: Ebsco - EbscoHost, OCLC - First Search
Mem of Kentucky Department for Libraries & Archives
Friends of the Library Group

BOWLING GREEN

P BOWLING GREEN PUBLIC LIBRARY,* 1225 State St, 42101. SAN 306-2198. Tel: 502-781-4882. FAX: 502-781-3699. Web Site: www.bgpl.com. *Dir*, Karen T Porter; Tel: 270-781-4884, E-Mail: karenp@bgpl.com; *Assoc Dir*, Alisa R Carmichael; E-Mail: alisac@bgpl.com; *ILL*, Bell Muth; E-Mail: bellm@bgpl.com; *Acq*, Maralyn Williams; E-Mail: marilynw@bgpl.com; *Ch Servs*, Marcia Crabtree; *Bkmobile Coordr*, Tom Durbin; *Coll Develop*, Anita Sanders; E-Mail: anitas@bgpl.com; *Tech Servs*, Stacey Greenwell; *Bkmobile Coordr*, Cindy Gaffney; Tel: 270-781-1441, E-Mail: cindyg@bgpl.com; *Ch Servs, Head of Libr*, Ashley Fowlkes; E-Mail: ashleyf@bgpl.com; Staff 43 (MLS 7, Non-MLS 36)
Founded 1940. Pop 80,000; Circ 530,703
Jul 1998-Jun 1999 Income $1,568,970, State $83,000, City $1,106,000, County $300,000, Locally Generated Income $79,970. Mats Exp $175,000, Books $108,000, Per/Ser (Incl. Access Fees) $15,000, AV Equip $26,000, Electronic Ref Mat (Incl. Access Fees) $26,000. Sal $797,001
Library Holdings: Bk Vols 128,806; Per Subs 220
Subject Interests: Local authors, Rare books
Automation Activity & Vendor Info: (Cataloging) epixtech, inc.; (Circulation) epixtech, inc.; (ILL) epixtech, inc.
Database Vendor: epixtech, inc., OCLC - First Search
Function: ILL available
Mem of Barren River District
Partic in Kentucky Library Network, Inc; Ky Coop Libr Info Project; OCLC Online Computer Library Center, Inc
Friends of the Library Group

C WESTERN KENTUCKY UNIVERSITY LIBRARIES,* 42101-3576. SAN 342-2852. Tel: 270-745-2904. Interlibrary Loan Service Tel: 270-745-6118. Toll Free Tel: 800-922-9585. FAX: 270-745-6422. Interlibrary Loan Service FAX: 270-745-5943. E-Mail: library.web@wku.edu. Web Site: www.wku.edu/library/. *Dean of Libr*, Dr Michael Binder; E-Mail: mike.binder@wku.edu; *Publ Servs*, Dr Brian Coutts; *Tech Servs*, Linda Allan; *Access Serv*, Ruth Kinnersley; *Acq*, Jack Montgomery; Tel: 270-745-6156; *Selection of Elec Mat*, Elaine Moore; *Govt Doc*, Rosemary Meszaros; *Coordr, Ser*, Constance Foster; *Coll Develop*, Dr Marvin Leavy; Staff 79 (MLS 35, Non-MLS 44)
Founded 1907
Jul 1997-Jun 1998 Income $4,620,968. Mats Exp $1,569,679, Books $364,323, Per/Ser (Incl. Access Fees) $965,847. Sal $2,381,173
Library Holdings: Bk Vols 948,927; Per Subs 5,097
Subject Interests: History, Law, Shakers
Automation Activity & Vendor Info: (Cataloging) NOTIS; (Circulation) NOTIS; (Serials) NOTIS
Publications: Collections & Connections (newsletter)
Partic in Center For Research Libraries; OCLC Online Computer Library Center, Inc; SE Libr Network
The library's budget supports a museum with over 60,000 artifacts & an archeological collection of over 150,000 pieces
Friends of the Library Group
Departmental Libraries:
EDUCATIONAL RESOURCES CENTER Tel: 270-745-4552, 270-745-4659. FAX: 270-745-4553. Web Site: www.wku.edu/library/. *In Charge*, Darla Bressler
Subject Interests: Education
Special Collections: Juvenile Literature; Kentucky Education Reform; Thematic Units
GLASGOW, 213 S Liberty St, Glasgow, 42141. SAN 370-5986. Tel: 270-651-7377. FAX: 270-651-7050. Web Site: www.wku.edu/library/. *In Charge*, Adolfina Simpson; E-Mail: fina.simpson@wku.edu
1997-1998 Mats Exp $20,325, Books $793, Per/Ser (Incl. Access Fees) $19,532
Library Holdings: Bk Vols 1,800; Per Subs 128
Friends of the Library Group
KENTUCKY LIBRARY Tel: 270-745-6258. FAX: 270-745-4878, 270-745-6264. Web Site: www.wku.edu/library/. *Spec Coll*, Riley Handy; *Archivist*, Pat Hodges
Library Holdings: Bk Vols 39,615
Special Collections: Literary Coll of Lillie Bland Carter, Anne Pence Davis, Janice Holt Giles, David Morton, Alice Hegan Rice & Cale Young Rice, Robert Penn Warren; Original Cartoons of Whitey Sanders; Papers of Lewis-Starling, Green, Calvert & Underwood Families; Personal & Political papers of Tim Lee Carter & William Natcher, Former Congressmen of Kentucky; Rare Books of Early America, Virginia & Kentucky (McGregor Coll); South Union Shakers
Friends of the Library Group

BRANDENBURG

P MEADE COUNTY PUBLIC LIBRARY, 400 Library Pl, 40108-1045. SAN 306-2201. Tel: 270-422-2094. FAX: 270-422-3133. E-Mail: askus@kvnet.org. Web Site: www.meadereads.org. *Librn*, Laura Thebaud Gibbs; E-Mail: lgibbs@iglou.com; *Asst Librn*, Regan Blanchard; *Bkmobile Coordr*, Deb Huddleston; Staff 2 (MLS 1, Non-MLS 1)
Founded 1967. Pop 24,170; Circ 57,894
Jul 1999-Jun 2000 Income $241,686, State $38,843, County $185,615, Locally Generated Income $17,228. Mats Exp $39,000, Books $31,300, Per/Ser (Incl. Access Fees) $2,185, Other Print Mats $5,515
Library Holdings: Bk Vols 21,790; Per Subs 63
Subject Interests: Genealogy, Local history
Automation Activity & Vendor Info: (Acquisitions) Brodart; (Cataloging) Brodart; (Circulation) Brodart
Database Vendor: Ebsco - EbscoHost, OCLC - First Search
Partic in First Search; Solinet
Bookmobiles: 1

BROOKSVILLE

P BRACKEN COUNTY PUBLIC LIBRARY, 310 W Miami St, 41004-8102. (Mail add: PO Box 305, 41004-0305), Tel: 606-735-3620. E-Mail: brackcpublib@kih.net. *Dir*, Mary Lou Simons
Library Holdings: Bk Vols 18,000; Bk Titles 16,000; Per Subs 28

BROWNSVILLE

P EDMONSON COUNTY PUBLIC LIBRARY, 503 Washington St, PO Box 219, 42210. SAN 306-221X. Tel: 270-597-2146. FAX: 270-597-3282. E-Mail: ecpl@creative-net.net. *Librn*, Jeanie Miller; Staff 5 (Non-MLS 5)
Founded 1956. Pop 10,357; Circ 50,883
Jul 1999-Jun 2000 Income $117,900, State $27,819, County $81,708, Other $8,373. Mats Exp $11,780, Books $9,024, Per/Ser (Incl. Access Fees) $556, Presv $939, Electronic Ref Mat (Incl. Access Fees) $1,509. Sal $57,429 (Prof $30,064)
Library Holdings: Bk Titles 35,460; Per Subs 49
Subject Interests: Genealogy, Local history
Mem of Barren River Regional Libr Syst

BURGIN

G NORTHPOINT TRAINING CENTER, Residents' Library, Shakertown Rd, PO Box 479, 40310. SAN 325-0989. Tel: 606-239-7012, Ext 354. FAX: 606-239-7173. *Librn*, Reda Johnson; E-Mail: rjohnson@mail.state.ky.us; Staff 11 (MLS 1, Non-MLS 10)
Founded 1983. Pop 1,148; Circ 118,400
Oct 1998-Sep 1999 Income $6,719, Federal $3,769, Parent Institution $2,950. Mats Exp $7,500, Books $3,500, Per/Ser (Incl. Access Fees) $4,000. Sal $28,000
Library Holdings: Bk Titles 8,000; Per Subs 115
Database Vendor: OCLC - First Search
Friends of the Library Group

BURKESVILLE

P CUMBERLAND COUNTY PUBLIC LIBRARY,* 114 W Hill St, PO Box 440, 42717-0440. SAN 306-2228. Tel: 270-864-2207. FAX: 270-864-2207. E-Mail: ccplib@hotmail.com. *Dir*, Richard Alexander; *Bkmobile Coordr*, Diana Martin
Pop 6,784; Circ 57,536
Jul 1997-Jun 1998 Income $80,259. Mats Exp $8,637, Books $7,016, Per/Ser (Incl. Access Fees) $1,045. Sal $37,806
Library Holdings: Bk Vols 44,000; Per Subs 60
Mem of Lake Cumberland Regional Libr Syst

CAMPBELLSVILLE

C CAMPBELLSVILLE UNIVERSITY, Montgomery Library, One University Dr, 42718-2799. SAN 306-2252. Tel: 270-789-5272. FAX: 270-789-5363. Web Site: www.campbellsville.edu~library. *Dir*, John R Burch, Jr; Tel: 270-789-5015, E-Mail: jburch@campbellsvil.edu; *Coll Develop*, Karen J Lynema; Tel: 270-789-5390, E-Mail: lynema@campbellsvil.edu
Founded 1906. Enrl 1,365; Fac 92; Highest Degree: Master
Jul 1999-Jun 2000 Mats Exp $114,663, Books $66,853, Per/Ser (Incl. Access Fees) $45,210, Micro $2,600. Sal $150,000
Library Holdings: Bk Vols 120,105; Per Subs 597
Subject Interests: Education, Religion
Special Collections: College Archives

Automation Activity & Vendor Info: (Cataloging) TLC
Publications: Policies & Procedures Handbook
Partic in Association Of Independent Kentucky Colleges & Universities; Kentucky Library Network, Inc
Friends of the Library Group

P TAYLOR COUNTY PUBLIC LIBRARY,* 205 N Columbia, 42718. SAN 306-2260. Tel: 270-465-2562. FAX: 270-465-8026. E-Mail: taybooks@kih.net. *Dir*, Elaine J Munday; *Bkmobile Coordr*, Patricia Jones
Founded 1974. Pop 21,178
Library Holdings: Bk Vols 55,577

CAMPTON

P WOLFE COUNTY LIBRARY, Main St, PO Box 10, 41301. SAN 306-2279. Tel: 606-668-6571. FAX: 606-668-6561. E-Mail: books@mrtc.com. Web Site: www.wolfcopublb.simplenet.com. *Librn*, Billye H Adams; *Asst Librn*, Debra Baker
Pop 6,503; Circ 48,193
Jul 1999-Jun 2000 Income $91,100, State $18,755, County $55,407, Other $16,938. Mats Exp $12,255, Books $10,644, Per/Ser (Incl. Access Fees) $629, Micro $19, Electronic Ref Mat (Incl. Access Fees) $963. Sal $42,175
Library Holdings: Bk Vols 28,255; Per Subs 49
Special Collections: Kentucky Genealogy Coll
Database Vendor: OCLC - First Search
Mem of Kentucky Department for Libraries & Archives
Friends of the Library Group

CARLISLE

P NICHOLAS COUNTY PUBLIC LIBRARY, 223 Broadway, 40311. SAN 306-2287. Tel: 859-289-5595. FAX: 859-289-4340. Web Site: www.users.kih.net/~ncpl/. *Librn*, Becky Reid; Staff 2 (Non-MLS 2)
Founded 1961
Library Holdings: Bk Vols 27,358
Special Collections: Genealogy Reels, Census, Births, Marriages & Deaths, Bonds, Deeds, Wills from 1790
Mem of Bluegrass North Libr District
Bookmobiles: 1

CARROLLTON

P CARROLL COUNTY PUBLIC LIBRARY,* 136 Court St, 41008. SAN 306-2295. Tel: 502-732-7020. FAX: 502-732-7122. E-Mail: carrolllib@kih.net. *Librn*, Mrs Jarrett Boyd; E-Mail: jarrett.boyd@mail.state.ky.us; Staff 5 (Non-MLS 5)
Pop 10,000; Circ 90,000
Jul 1999-Jun 2000 Income $221,220, State $19,220, Locally Generated Income $202,000. Mats Exp $40,150, Books $28,000, Per/Ser (Incl. Access Fees) $4,000, Electronic Ref Mat (Incl. Access Fees) $10,000. Sal $122,900 (Prof $35,666)
Library Holdings: Bk Titles 30,000; Per Subs 55
Special Collections: Kyana
Mem of Northern Ky Regional Libr Develop District
Partic in Kentucky Library Network, Inc; N Ky Video Consortia; Pub Libr Asn of N Ky

CATLETTSBURG

ASHLAND MARATHON PETROLEUM CO
S TECHNICAL INFORMATION CENTER, R & E Bldg, PO Box 911, 41129. SAN 324-7473. Tel: 606-921-6492. FAX: 606-921-2580.
Library Holdings: Bk Vols 5,600; Bk Titles 3,000; Per Subs 100
Subject Interests: Petrochem, Petroleum refining
Special Collections: SRI/PEP (Process Economics Programs Coll)
Publications: Alerted Bulletin (abstracting bulletin)
Restriction: Not open to public
Partic in Dialog Corporation; STN

CENTRAL CITY

S GREEN RIVER CORRECTIONAL COMPLEX LIBRARY, (Formerly Kentucky State Penitentiary), PO Box 9300, 42330. SAN 376-9984. Tel: 270-754-5415. FAX: 270-754-2732. *Librn*, Cher Eaves
Library Holdings: Bk Vols 7,000; Per Subs 40; High Interest/Low Vocabulary Bk Vols 150

COLD SPRING

P CAMPBELL COUNTY PUBLIC LIBRARY DISTRICT, 3920 Alexandria Pike, 41076. SAN 306-3801. Tel: 859-781-6166. FAX: 859-572-5032. Web Site: www.cc-pl.org. *Dir*, Michael Doellman; Tel: 859-781-6166, Ext 21, E-Mail: miked@cc-pl.org; *Assoc Dir*, Jean Lillie; Tel: 859-781-6166, Ext 11, E-Mail: jlillie@cc-pl.org; *Ch Servs, YA Servs*, Marie LePage; Tel: 606-572-5033, E-Mail: mlepage@cc-pl.org; Staff 15 (MLS 10, Non-MLS 5)
Founded 1978. Pop 83,866; Circ 286,146
Jul 2000-Jun 2001 Income $1,463,292, State $82,292, County $1,285,000, Locally Generated Income $96,000. Mats Exp $2,001,000, Books $190,000, Per/Ser (Incl. Access Fees) $11,000, AV Equip $60,000, Electronic Ref Mat (Incl. Access Fees) $6,000. Sal $850,000
Library Holdings: Bk Vols 185,000; Per Subs 275
Automation Activity & Vendor Info: (Acquisitions) Gaylord; (Cataloging) Gaylord; (Circulation) Gaylord; (OPAC) Gaylord
Database Vendor: OCLC - First Search
Publications: Off the Shelf (bi-monthly) (Newsletter)
Mem of Northern Ky Regional Libr Develop District
Partic in Greater Cincinnati Library Consortium
Friends of the Library Group

COLUMBIA

P ADAIR COUNTY PUBLIC LIBRARY,* 307 Greensburg St, 42728-1488. SAN 306-2309. Tel: 270-384-2472. FAX: 270-384-9446. *Librn*, Lee Ann Jessee; *Asst Librn*, Jewel Kimbler; *Bkmobile Coordr*, Bill Bailey; *Ch Servs*, Lisa Burton
Pop 15,233; Circ 49,026
Library Holdings: Bk Vols 39,000
Subject Interests: Kentucky
Special Collections: Janice Holt Giles Coll
Mem of Lake Cumberland Regional Libr Syst
Partic in OCLC Online Computer Library Center, Inc

J LINDSEY WILSON COLLEGE, Katie Murrell Library, 210 Lindsey Wilson St, 42728. SAN 306-2325. Tel: 270-384-8102. FAX: 270-384-4188. Web Site: www.lindsey.edu/library. *Dir*, Philip Hanna; E-Mail: hannap@lindsey.edu; *Tech Servs*, Houston Barnes; E-Mail: barnesh@lindsey.edu; *Publ Servs*, Jason Vance; E-Mail: vancej@lindsey.edu; Staff 7 (MLS 3, Non-MLS 4)
Founded 1903. Enrl 1,440; Fac 64; Highest Degree: Master
Jul 1999-Jun 2000 Income $360,074. Mats Exp $125,750, Books $63,500, Per/Ser (Incl. Access Fees) $50,200, Presv $300, Micro $4,200, AV Equip $3,000, Other Print Mats $2,500, Electronic Ref Mat (Incl. Access Fees) $2,050. Sal $151,350 (Prof $91,800)
Library Holdings: Bk Vols 63,860; Bk Titles 56,523; Per Subs 4,835
Subject Interests: Art, Biology, Children's literature, Counseling, Education, English (language), History, Journalism, Kentucky
Special Collections: Mag Coll
Automation Activity & Vendor Info: (Cataloging) TLC; (Circulation) EOS; (OPAC) EOS
Database Vendor: Ebsco - EbscoHost, IAC - Info Trac, OCLC - First Search
Mem of Southeastern Regional Libr Syst
Partic in Association Of Independent Kentucky Colleges & Universities; Coun of Independent Ky Cols & Univs; Kentucky Library Network, Inc
Special Services for the Blind - Reader services
Support off-campus evening college locations in 1 city

CORBIN

P CORBIN PUBLIC LIBRARY,* 305 E Center St NE, 40701. SAN 306-2333. Tel: 606-528-6366. FAX: 606-523-1895. E-Mail: corbin.publib@mail.state.ky.us. *Dir*, Vicky Jody
Founded 1916. Pop 22,472; Circ 56,233
Library Holdings: Bk Vols 30,000; Per Subs 52
Special Collections: Corbin Time Tribune, 1917-1970, micro
Mem of North Cumberland Valley Libr Develop District
Friends of the Library Group

COVINGTON

S BEHRINGER-CRAWFORD MUSEUM, Lawrence Duba Research Library, PO Box 67, 41012-0067. SAN 373-4579. Tel: 859-491-4003. FAX: 859-491-4006. *Dir*, Laurie Risch
Library Holdings: Bk Vols 1,250

P KENTON COUNTY PUBLIC LIBRARY, 502 Scott Blvd, 41011. SAN 342-300X. Tel: 859-491-7610. FAX: 859-655-7960. E-Mail: admin@kenton.lib.ky.us. Web Site: www.kenton.lib.ky.us. *Dir*, Wayne Onkst; E-Mail: wonkst@kenton.lib.ky.us; *Ad Servs*, Charles King; *Ch Servs*, Patricia Richards; *Commun Servs*, Brenda Clark; *Tech Servs*, Leslie Hoekzema; *Automation Syst Coordr*, Erin Noll; Staff 79 (MLS 17, Non-MLS 62)
Founded 1967. Pop 142,031; Circ 1,290,524
Jul 1998-Jun 1999 Income (Main Library and Branch Library) $4,641,143, State $203,168, Locally Generated Income $4,437,975. Mats Exp $4,128,724, Books $480,614, Per/Ser (Incl. Access Fees) $28,913, AV Equip $67,467, Electronic Ref Mat (Incl. Access Fees) $14,202. Sal $1,847,444
Library Holdings: Bk Vols 351,803; Per Subs 711
Subject Interests: Kentucky, Local history
Special Collections: Northern Kentucky Newspapers Index, 1835-1931, 1984-present
Automation Activity & Vendor Info: (Acquisitions) epixtech, inc.;

(Cataloging) epixtech, inc.; (Circulation) epixtech, inc.; (OPAC) epixtech, inc.
Database Vendor: epixtech, inc., OCLC - First Search
Publications: Bookmark (quarterly)
Partic in Greater Cincinnati Library Consortium
Friends of the Library Group
Branches: 2
ERLANGER BRANCH, 3130 Dixie Hwy, 41018. SAN 342-3034. Tel: 859-341-5115. FAX: 859-344-7242. Web Site: www.kenton.lib.ky.us. *Dir*, Wayne Onkst; Tel: 859-491-7610, Fax: 859-655-7960, E-Mail: wonkst@kenton.lib.ky.us; *Branch Mgr*, Anita Carroll; E-Mail: acarroll@kenton.lib.ky.us; *Ch Servs*, Jill Baurichter
Friends of the Library Group
INDEPENDENCE, 6477 Taylor Mill Rd, 41051. SAN 376-916X. Tel: 859-363-0200. FAX: 859-363-4202. Web Site: www.kenton.lib.ky.us. *Branch Mgr*, J C Morgan; E-Mail: jcmorgan@kenton.lib.ky.us; *Ch Servs*, Mindy Carrico; E-Mail: mcarrico@kenton.lib.ky.us; *Syst Programmer*, Laura Davies. Subject Specialists: *Children's*, Laura Davies
Friends of the Library Group
Bookmobiles: 1

R LATONIA BAPTIST CHURCH LIBRARY,* 38th & Church Sts, PO Box 15103, 41015. SAN 306-2341. Tel: 606-431-8004. FAX: 606-431-1208. *Librn*, Betty McCoy
Library Holdings: Bk Vols 5,000
Subject Interests: Biology, Children's literature

P NORTHERN KENTUCKY TALKING BOOK LIBRARY, 502 Scott Blvd, 41011. SAN 342-3018. Tel: 859-491-7610. Toll Free Tel: 866-491-7610. TDD: 859-491-7610. FAX: 859-655-7956. Web Site: www.kenton.lib.ky.us/talking.html. *Dir*, Julia E Allegrini; E-Mail: jallegri@kenton.lib.ky.us; Staff 3 (MLS 1, Non-MLS 2)
Founded 1980
Oct 1998-Sep 1999 Income $47,900, Provincial $47,200, Other $700. Sal $47,500
Library Holdings: Bk Vols 24,000; Bk Titles 15,000
Publications: Newsletters
Special Services for the Deaf - TDD
Special Services for the Blind - Assistive Technology Center for Persons who are blind or physically handicapped; Perkins Brailers
Special Services - Outreach; referrals

C THOMAS MORE COLLEGE LIBRARY,* 333 Thomas More Pkwy, Crestview Hills, 41017-2599. SAN 306-2597. Tel: 606-344-3300. FAX: 606-344-3342. Web Site: www.thomasmore.edu. *Dir*, James McKellogg; E-Mail: jimmckellogg@thomasmore.edu; *Media Spec*, Ryan Zech; *Cat*, Stuart Pitner; *Acq*, Sr Helen Wilke; *Per*, Sr Juanita Anneken; *Circ*, Patricia Niceley; Staff 3 (MLS 3)
Founded 1921. Enrl 966; Fac 66; Highest Degree: Master
Jun 1997-May 1998 Income $366,533. Mats Exp $112,981, Books $28,920, Per/Ser (Incl. Access Fees) $71,143, Presv $1,850, Micro $9,949. Sal $151,122 (Prof $97,578)
Library Holdings: Bk Vols 131,694; Per Subs 571
Special Collections: Thomas More Coll
Publications: Film & video catalog; Library handbook
Partic in Association Of Independent Kentucky Colleges & Universities; Greater Cincinnati Library Consortium; Kentucky Library Network, Inc; OCLC Online Computer Library Center, Inc; Ohio-Kentucky Coop Libraries; SE Libr Network

CUMBERLAND

J SOUTHEAST COMMUNITY COLLEGE LIBRARY,* 207 Chrisman Hall, 40823. SAN 306-2384. Tel: 606-589-2145, Ext 2046. FAX: 606-589-4941. Web Site: www.uky.edu/communitycolleges/sou/01_library.htm. *Dir Libr Serv*, Warren Grey; *Publ Servs*, Lynn M Cox; *Circ*, Darlene M Coots; *Business*, Willetta Lee; Staff 3 (MLS 3)
Founded 1960. Fac 86
Library Holdings: Bk Vols 35,617; Per Subs 207
Subject Interests: Appalachia, Coal, Engineering, Humanities, Nursing
Special Collections: Kentucky Authors Coll
Partic in OCLC Online Computer Library Center, Inc; SE Libr Network

CYNTHIANA

P CYNTHIANA-HARRISON COUNTY PUBLIC LIBRARY,* 110 N Main St, 41031. SAN 342-3069. Tel: 606-234-4881. FAX: 606-234-0059. *Acq, Dir*, E Susan Ellis; *Bkmobile Coordr*, Senta Stoss; Staff 1 (MLS 1)
Founded 1932. Pop 16,428; Circ 78,000
Library Holdings: Bk Titles 57,000; Per Subs 42
Subject Interests: Economics, Genealogy, Health sciences, History, Home economics
Special Collections: Cissy Gregg Cookbook Coll; Civil War Coll; Kentucky & Local History
Mem of Bluegrass North Libr District
Partic in Kentucky Library Network, Inc
Special Services for the Deaf - Captioned film depository; Special interest periodicals
Headquarters for Adult Literacy Program-Harrison County
Bookmobiles: 1

DANVILLE

P BOYLE COUNTY PUBLIC LIBRARY, Danville Library, Inc, 307 W Broadway, 40422. SAN 306-2406. Tel: 859-236-8466. TDD: 859-236-4921. FAX: 859-236-7692. E-Mail: boylecpl@mis.net. *Asst Dir*, Georgia de Araujo; *Librn*, Karl A Benson; *Bkmobile Coordr*, Sherry Hoskins; *Ch Servs*, Libby McWhorter; Staff 6 (MLS 3, Non-MLS 3)
Founded 1893. Pop 26,000; Circ 218,921
Jul 1999-Jun 2000 Income $674,843, State $37,973, County $491,727, Locally Generated Income $61,163, Other $83,980. Mats Exp $86,841, Books $62,846, Per/Ser (Incl. Access Fees) $3,777, AV Equip $20,218. Sal $303,683
Library Holdings: Bk Vols 87,371; Per Subs 158
Subject Interests: Kentucky, Shakers
Automation Activity & Vendor Info: (Cataloging) Gaylord; (Circulation) Gaylord; (OPAC) Gaylord
Partic in KLN
Special Services for the Deaf - Staff with knowledge of sign language; TTY machine; Videos & decoder
Friends of the Library Group
Bookmobiles: 1

C CENTRE COLLEGE OF KENTUCKY, Grace Doherty Library, 600 W Walnut St, 40422-1394. SAN 306-2392. Tel: 859-238-5372. Circulation Tel: 859-238-5279. Reference Tel: 859-238-5277, 238-5278. FAX: 859-236-7925. Web Site: www.centre.edu/web/library/homepage.html. *Dean of Libr, Dir Libr Serv*, Stanley R Campbell; Tel: 859-238-5271, E-Mail: campbell@centre.edu; *Ref Serv Ad*, Mary Beth Garriott; E-Mail: garriotm@centre.edu; *Ref Serv Ad*, Connie Klimke; E-Mail: klimkec@centre.edu; *Dir, Tech Serv*, Robert Glass; Tel: 859-238-5274, E-Mail: glass@centre.edu; *AV*, Larry Baker; *AV*, Barbara Hanson; *Circ*, Diane Pasick; E-Mail: pasick@centre.edu; *ILL*, Carolyn Frey; Tel: 859-238-5275, E-Mail: carrie@centre.edu; *Acq*, Crystal Wesley; Tel: 859-238-5273, E-Mail: wesley@centre.edu; Staff 9 (MLS 4, Non-MLS 5)
Founded 1819. Enrl 1,050; Highest Degree: Bachelor
Jul 1999-Jun 2000 Income Parent Institution $767,362. Mats Exp $359,096, Books $127,716, Per/Ser (Incl. Access Fees) $174,911, Micro $4,320, Other Print Mats $16,949, Manuscripts & Archives $500, Electronic Ref Mat (Incl. Access Fees) $39,020. Sal $307,258 (Prof $195,144)
Library Holdings: Bk Vols 205,205; Bk Titles 139,561; Per Subs 800
Special Collections: Centre College Archives; LeCompte Davis Coll
Automation Activity & Vendor Info: (Acquisitions) Innovative Interfaces Inc.; (Cataloging) Innovative Interfaces Inc.; (Circulation) Innovative Interfaces Inc.; (Course Reserve) Innovative Interfaces Inc.; (ILL) Innovative Interfaces Inc.; (OPAC) Innovative Interfaces Inc.; (Serials) Innovative Interfaces Inc.
Database Vendor: Dialog, Ebsco - EbscoHost, Lexis-Nexis, OCLC - First Search, Wilson - Wilson Web
Partic in Assoc Cols of the South; Association Of Independent Kentucky Colleges & Universities; Solinet

S KENTUCKY SCHOOL FOR THE DEAF LIBRARY,* S Second St, PO Box 27, 40423-0027. SAN 306-2414. Tel: 606-239-7017. FAX: 606-239-7006. Web Site: www.kfd.k12.ky.us. *Librn*, Gayle Deville; *Librn*, Marybeth Gay
Enrl 340; Fac 75
Library Holdings: Bk Titles 13,654; Per Subs 80
Subject Interests: Deaf
Special Services for the Deaf - Books on deafness & sign language; High interest/low vocabulary books; Special interest periodicals; Videos & decoder

DAWSON SPRINGS

M OUTWOOD ICF-MR LIBRARY, 23524 Dawson Springs Rd, 42408. SAN 306-2422. Tel: 270-797-3771. FAX: 270-797-3592. *Librn*, Fay McCaskill
Library Holdings: Bk Vols 4,000; Per Subs 15

DIXON

P WEBSTER COUNTY PUBLIC LIBRARY,* 101 State Rte 132 E, 42409. SAN 342-3123. Tel: 270-639-9171. FAX: 270-639-6207. E-Mail: web.lib@apex. *Dir*, Peggy Brown; *Br Coordr*, Elaine Price; *Bkmobile Coordr*, LuAnne Riggs
Founded 1954. Pop 13,955; Circ 85,552
1997-1998 Mats Exp $152,000. Sal $72,000
Library Holdings: Bk Titles 48,500; Per Subs 134
Subject Interests: Genealogy, History
Special Collections: Webster County Authors (Rice Coll)
Mem of Green River Libr Develop District
Open Mon-Wed & Fri 9-4, Thurs 9-6 & Sat 9-2

Branches: 1
PROVIDENCE BRANCH, 230 Willow St, Providence, 42450. SAN 342-3158. Tel: 270-667-5658. FAX: 270-667-5658. *Librn*, Elaine Price
Library Holdings: Bk Titles 11,300
Open Mon-Sat 10-4

EDDYVILLE

S KENTUCKY STATE PENITENTIARY, Inmate Library, PO Box 5128, 42038. SAN 306-2430. Tel: 270-388-2211. FAX: 270-388-7753. *Librn*, Graham W Mintz
Founded 1958

P LYON COUNTY PUBLIC LIBRARY,* 261 Commerce St, PO Box 546, 42038-0546. SAN 306-2449. Tel: 270-388-7720. FAX: 270-388-7735. E-Mail: lyonlib@kih.net. *Librn*, Vicki McIntosh; *Asst Librn*, Romona Engler; *Bkmobile Coordr*, Norma P'Pool
Founded 1970. Pop 6,490; Circ 45,556
Library Holdings: Bk Vols 24,992; Per Subs 30
Special Collections: Indian Arrowhead Coll; Lyon County History Coll; Stamp & Foreign Money Coll
Mem of Pennyrile Regional Libr

EDGEWOOD

M SAINT ELIZABETH MEDICAL CENTER, Allnutt Health Sciences Library, 20 Medical Village Dr, Ste 201, 41017. SAN 327-9510. Tel: 859-344-2248. FAX: 859-344-2655. *Librn*, Donald Smith; E-Mail: dsmith@saintelizabeth.com; *Tech Servs*, Mary Ann Hausfeld
Library Holdings: Bk Vols 800; Per Subs 225
Restriction: Staff use only

EDMONTON

P METCALFE COUNTY PUBLIC LIBRARY, Main St, PO Box 626, 42129. SAN 306-2457. Tel: 270-432-4981. FAX: 270-432-4981. E-Mail: metcolib@scrtc.com. *Librn*, Rhonda Glass
Founded 1940
Jul 1999-Jun 2000 Income $107,952. Mats Exp Books $11,211. Sal $54,565
Library Holdings: Bk Titles 37,849; Per Subs 25
Subject Interests: Agriculture, Genealogy
Mem of Barren River District
Bookmobiles: 1

ELIZABETHTOWN

J ELIZABETHTOWN COMMUNITY COLLEGE, Media Center Library, 600 College Street Rd, 42701. SAN 306-2465. Tel: 270-769-2371, Ext 240. FAX: 270-769-1618. Web Site: www.elizabethtowncc.com/Resources/Library. *Dir*, Jimmie Bruce; Tel: 270-769-2371, Ext 424, E-Mail: jimmie.bruce@kctcs.net; *Coordr*, Ann B Thompson; Tel: 270-769-2371, Ext 248, E-Mail: ann.thompson@kctcs.net; *Ref*, Laurie MacKellar; Tel: 270-769-2371, Ext 242, E-Mail: laurie.mackellar@kctcs.net; Staff 9 (MLS 3, Non-MLS 6)
Founded 1964
Library Holdings: Bk Vols 40,000
Subject Interests: Kentucky
Special Collections: Hardin County Genealogical Coll (1793-1900), micro; Local Newspapers, micro
Automation Activity & Vendor Info: (Cataloging) Endeavor; (Circulation) Endeavor; (Course Reserve) Endeavor; (ILL) Endeavor; (OPAC) Endeavor
Database Vendor: Ebsco - EbscoHost, IAC - SearchBank, OCLC - First Search
Function: Research library
Partic in Soline; Solinet; Univ of Ky Commun Col Syst

P HARDIN COUNTY PUBLIC LIBRARY, 201 W Dixie Ave, 42701. SAN 306-2473. Tel: 270-769-6337. FAX: 270-769-0437. *Dir*, Brenda G Macy; *Asst Dir*, Jeffrey B Lanz; *Bkmobile Coordr*, Lisa Waldeck-Huffer; *Ad Servs*, Kim Bland; *Circ*, Tara T Lewis; Staff 11 (MLS 4, Non-MLS 7)
Founded 1958. Pop 88,914; Circ 162,014
Jul 1999-Jun 2000 Income $50,563. Mats Exp $49,120
Library Holdings: Bk Vols 73,025; Per Subs 163
Automation Activity & Vendor Info: (Cataloging) Gaylord; (Circulation) Gaylord; (OPAC) Gaylord
Mem of Lincoln Trail Libraries System
Friends of the Library Group
Branches: 1
RADCLIFF BRANCH, 800 S Logston, Radcliff, 40160. Tel: 270-351-9999. *Librn*, Vi Voge
Library Holdings: Bk Vols 19,000; Per Subs 40
Automation Activity & Vendor Info: (Cataloging) Gaylord; (Circulation) Gaylord; (OPAC) Gaylord

ELKTON

P TODD COUNTY PUBLIC LIBRARY,* 302 E Main St, 42220. SAN 306-2503. Tel: 270-265-9071. FAX: 270-265-2599. E-Mail: toddcopl@kih.net. Web Site: www.anglefire.com/ky/toddcopl. *Dir*, Anise Warden; *Bkmobile Coordr*, Jane Berry
Founded 1977
Library Holdings: Bk Vols 33,638; Per Subs 23
Subject Interests: Genealogy, Kentucky
Special Collections: Robert Penn Warren Coll
Mem of Pennyrile Regional Libr
Friends of the Library Group

EMINENCE

P HENRY COUNTY LIBRARY,* 172 Eminence Terrace, 40019-1146. SAN 306-2511. Tel: 502-845-5682. FAX: 502-845-4807. *Librn*, Tym Ricketts; E-Mail: tymricketts@hotmail.com; *Asst Librn*, Sharon Aynes; *Bkmobile Coordr*, Linda Moore
Pop 12,740; Circ 70,483
1999-1999 Income $254,758. Sal $126,821
Library Holdings: Bk Vols 31,827; Per Subs 64
Automation Activity & Vendor Info: (Cataloging) TLC; (Circulation) TLC
Mem of Ky Libr Network
Friends of the Library Group
Bookmobiles: 1

ERLANGER

§R ARCHS OF THE DIOCESES OF COVINGTON LIBRARY, 947 Donaldson Rd, 41018-0548. (Mail add: PO Box 18548, 41018-0548), Tel: 859-283-6307. FAX: 859-283-6334. *Archivist*, David Schroder; E-Mail: dschroced@dilofcovky.org
Library Holdings: Bk Vols 2,000; Per Subs 30

FALMOUTH

P PENDLETON COUNTY PUBLIC LIBRARY, 228 Main St, 41040-1223. SAN 306-2546. Tel: 606-654-8535. FAX: 606-654-8538. *Dir*, Janie Harter
Founded 1953. Pop 12,036; Circ 99,427
Library Holdings: Bk Vols 28,000; Per Subs 36
Special Collections: E E Barton Genealogy Coll of Northern Kentucky Families; The Falmouth Outlook, microflm
Mem of Northern Ky Regional Libr Develop District
Friends of the Library Group

FANKFORT

§S DEPARTMENT OF MILITARY AFFAIRS, Military Records & Research, Pine Hill Plaza, 1121 Louisville Rd, 40601-6169. Tel: 502-564-4883. FAX: 502-564-4437. *Mgr*, Evan Miller
Library Holdings: Bk Vols 150; Bk Titles 200
Restriction: Not open to public
Function: Research library

FERGUSON

SR FERGUSON BAPTIST CHURCH LIBRARY,* 509 Murphy Ave, PO Box 247, 42533. SAN 373-188X. Tel: 606-679-1690. *Librn*, Kathleen Miller
Library Holdings: Bk Vols 3,400
Subject Interests: History, Religion
Friends of the Library Group

FLEMINGSBURG

P FLEMING COUNTY PUBLIC LIBRARY, 303 S Main Cross, 41041-1298. SAN 306-2570. Tel: 606-845-7851. FAX: 606-845-7045. *Librn*, Beverly Cooper; E-Mail: beverlyc@mail.state.ky.us; *Asst Librn*, Mary Rushing; *Asst Librn*, Connie Saunders; *Bkmobile Coordr*, Barbara Faris; Staff 6 (Non-MLS 6)
Founded 1962. Pop 12,292; Circ 137,929
Jul 1998-Jun 1999 Income $147,600, State $18,000, County $89,000, Locally Generated Income $32,500. Mats Exp $17,600, Books $16,100, Per/Ser (Incl. Access Fees) $1,500. Sal $64,782
Library Holdings: Bk Vols 34,000; Per Subs 70
Subject Interests: Genealogy
Special Collections: Harriet Dudley Grannis Coll
Mem of Buffalo Trace Regional Libr
Friends of the Library Group
Bookmobiles: 1

FORT CAMPBELL

UNITED STATES ARMY

AM MEDICAL LIBRARY, BLANCHFIELD ARMY COMMUNITY HOSPITAL, 650 Joel Dr, 42223-5349. SAN 342-3212. Tel: 502-798-8014. FAX: 502-798-8015, 502-798-8812. *Mgr*, Martha A Short
Founded 1959
Library Holdings: Bk Vols 3,200; Per Subs 169
Partic in Nat Libr of Med

A R F SINK MEMORIAL LIBRARY, Bldg 38, 25th St, 42223-5342. SAN 342-3182. Tel: 270-798-7466. Interlibrary Loan Service Tel: 270-798-4827. FAX: 270-798-0369.; Staff 5 (MLS 5)
Founded 1941
Oct 1997-Sep 1998 Income $500,000. Mats Exp $118,000. Sal $290,000
Library Holdings: Bk Vols 73,900; Bk Titles 65,607; Per Subs 315
Subject Interests: Military history
Special Collections: Local History, microfiche; Official Records of the Civil War; World War II Coll
Publications: In house bibliographies
Partic in Dialog Corporation; Fedlink; OCLC Online Computer Library Center, Inc

FORT KNOX

UNITED STATES ARMY

A ARMOR SCHOOL LIBRARY, 2368 Old Ironsides Ave, Harris Hall, 40121-5200. SAN 342-3395. Tel: 502-624-6231. FAX: 502-624-3365. Web Site: 147.238.100.101/asl. *Dir*, William H Hansen; E-Mail: hansenw@ftknox5-emh3.army.mil; *Res*, Judy C Stephenson; E-Mail: stephensonj@ftknox5-emh3.army.mil; *Ref*, Lorraine A Mitchell; E-Mail: mitchell2@ftknox5-emh3.army.mil; *Circ*, Terri Gates; *Circ*, Janis M Kendall; E-Mail: kendallj@ftknox5-emh3.army.mil. Subject Specialists: *Military history*, Judy C Stephenson; *Military history*, William H Hansen; *Military history*, Lorraine A Mitchell; *Modern*, Judy C Stephenson; Staff 4 (MLS 1, Non-MLS 3)
Founded 1941
Library Holdings: Bk Vols 30,000; Bk Titles 21,000; Per Subs 230
Subject Interests: Military history, US Civil War
Special Collections: Student Papers; WW II Papers & Documents
Automation Activity & Vendor Info: (Cataloging) TLC; (Circulation) TLC
Database Vendor: Ebsco - EbscoHost, OCLC - First Search, OVID Technologies, Silverplatter Information Inc.
Publications: Union List of Periodicals
Restriction: Restricted access
Function: ILL available
Partic in Fedlink; Kentucky Library Network, Inc

A BARR MEMORIAL LIBRARY, 400 Quartermaster St, 40121. Tel: 502-624-5351. Circulation Tel: 502-624-1232. Reference Tel: 502-624-4636. FAX: 502-624-7528. *Tech Servs*, Carmen Curtiss; E-Mail: curtissc@ftknox-emh3.army.mil; *Ref*, Cindy Arnold; E-Mail: arnoldc@ftknox2-emh3.army.mil; *Ref*, Nancy O'Hare; Staff 4 (MLS 4)
Library Holdings: Bk Vols 84,000; Per Subs 315
Subject Interests: Kentucky, Mil sci
Automation Activity & Vendor Info: (Cataloging) TLC; (Circulation) TLC; (OPAC) TLC
Publications: In-house bibliographies
Partic in Kentucky Library Network, Inc; Tralinet

AM IRELAND ARMY HOSPITAL, MEDICAL LIBRARY, Bldg 851, 40121-5520. SAN 324-2358. Tel: 502-624-9550. FAX: 502-624-0280. Web Site: www.iach.knox.amedd.army.mil/iach. *Librn*, Deborah Wallace
Founded 1957
Library Holdings: Bk Vols 2,652; Per Subs 150
Restriction: Staff use only
Partic in Nat Libr of Med

S PATTON MUSEUM OF CAVALRY & ARMOR, Emert L Davis Memorial Library, 4554 Fayette Ave, 40121-0208. SAN 342-3352. Tel: 502-624-3812. FAX: 502-624-2364. E-Mail: museum@ftknox-emh3.army.mil. *Coll Develop*, Candace L Fuller
Founded 1975
Library Holdings: Bk Vols 9,000; Per Subs 20
Special Collections: General George S Patton, Jr Coll, photog; Robert J Icks' Photo & Manuscript Coll on Armored Equipment, bks, maps, photogs
Publications: Selected Bibliographies
Partic in Ky Union List of Serials; Tradoc

FORT MITCHELL

P SOUTHERN OHIO COLLEGE LIBRARY, Fort Mitchell Campus,* 309 Buttermilk Pike, 41017. SAN 376-5776. Tel: 606-341-5627, Ext 48. FAX: 606-341-6483. E-Mail: soc@l.net. Web Site: www.socaec.com. *Librn*, Richard Rosene
Library Holdings: Bk Vols 4,000; Bk Titles 3,500; Per Subs 30
Open Mon-Thurs 9-5

FORT THOMAS

S KENTUCKY COVERED BRIDGE ASSOCIATION LIBRARY, 62 Miami Pkwy, 41075-1137. SAN 325-5379. Tel: 859-441-7000. FAX: 859-441-2112. *Exec Dir*, L K Patton; E-Mail: lkpatton@fuse.net
Founded 1964
Library Holdings: Bk Titles 300
Subject Interests: Covered bridges, Kentucky
Special Collections: Kentucky Bridge Slides (Dr J Winston Coleman, Jr Coll), prints, negatives
Publications: Timbered Tunnel Talk
Restriction: By appointment only

FRAKES

§S HENDERSON SELLEMENT, INC LIBRARY, Hwy 190, PO Box 205, 40940. Tel: 606-337-7729. FAX: 606-337-2225. E-Mail: hendsett@jellico.com. *Outreach Serv*, Blackburn Frankie
Library Holdings: Bk Vols 200; Per Subs 25

FRANKFORT

G GOVERNOR'S OFFICE FOR POLICY & MANAGEMENT LIBRARY, Capitol Annex, Rm 284, 40601. SAN 306-2635. Tel: 502-564-7300. FAX: 502-564-6684. E-Mail: contact@state.ky.us. *In Charge*, Etta Ruth Kepp
Founded 1960
Library Holdings: Bk Vols 2,000; Per Subs 34
Subject Interests: Appalachia, Planning, State budgeting

G KENTUCKY CABINET FOR ECONOMIC DEVELOPMENT, Division of Research Library, Capital Plaza Tower Bldg, 23rd flr, 40601. SAN 306-2619. Tel: 502-564-4886, 502-564-7140. FAX: 502-564-0023. *Librn*, Wanda Sharp; E-Mail: wsharp@mail.state.ky.us
Founded 1966
Library Holdings: Bk Vols 5,000; Per Subs 200
Subject Interests: Economics, Geology, Government, Statistics
Special Collections: Manufacturer's Directories Coll; US Dept of Commerce Coll
Restriction: Open to public for reference only

G KENTUCKY DEPARTMENT FOR ENVIRONMENTAL PROTECTION, EPIC Library, 14 Reilly Rd, 40601. SAN 325-1152. Tel: 502-564-2150, Ext 134. FAX: 502-564-4245. Web Site: www.nr.state.ky.us.
Library Holdings: Per Subs 250
Subject Interests: Environ protection, Legal govt docs
Special Collections: State of Kentucky Environmental Reports, EPA

P KENTUCKY DEPARTMENT FOR LIBRARIES & ARCHIVES, 300 Coffee Tree Rd, 40601. (Mail add: PO Box 537, 40602-0537), SAN 342-3425. Tel: 502-564-8300. FAX: 502-564-5773. Web Site: www.kdla.net. *Dir*, Charlene Davis; *State Librn*, James A Nelson; *Branch Mgr, Publ Servs*, Martha Gregory; *Govt Doc*, Brenda Fuller; *AV*, Ellen Dickerson; *Archivist*, Jim Prichard; Staff 170 (MLS 85, Non-MLS 85)
Founded 1834
Jul 1998-Jun 1999 Income $16,990,600. Mats Exp $233,700, Books $170,600, Per/Ser (Incl. Access Fees) $63,100. Sal $5,882,100 (Prof $4,293,900)
Library Holdings: Bk Vols 115,000; Per Subs 540
Subject Interests: Art, Geology, History, Kentucky, Literature, Social sciences and issues
Special Collections: Civil War Records (Confederate & Union in Kentucky); Confederate Pensions; Kentuckiana Coll; Kentucky Public Records, Maps & Genealogy Coll; Local Government Depository Coll; Louisville Courier-Journal (1868-to-date), micro
Automation Activity & Vendor Info: (Cataloging) Endeavor; (Circulation) Endeavor
Publications: Checklist of Kentucky State Publications; Statistical Report of Kentucky Public Libraries
Partic in Kentucky Library Network, Inc; Ky Coop Libr Info Ctrs; Ky Union List of Serials; OCLC Online Computer Library Center, Inc; RLIN; SE Libr Network
Branches: 1
KENTUCKY REGIONAL LIBRARY FOR THE BLIND & PHYSICALLY HANDICAPPED
See Separate Entry under Kentucky Regional Library for the Blind & Physically Handicapped
Bookmobiles: 110. Cover entire state

L KENTUCKY DEPARTMENT OF PUBLIC ADVOCACY LIBRARY, Leestown Square, Bldg 1, 100 Fair Oaks Lane, 3rd flr, 40601. SAN 325-5638. Tel: 502-564-8006. FAX: 502-564-7890. Web Site: www.dpa.state.ky.us/library.html. *Exec Dir*, David Norat; E-Mail: dnorat@mail.pa.state.ky.us; *Librn*, Will Hilyerd; E-Mail: whilyerd@mail.pa.state.ky.us; Staff 2 (MLS 1, Non-MLS 1)
Founded 1974
Jul 1999-Jun 2000 Income (Main Library and Branch Library) Parent Institution $300,000. Mats Exp $300,000, Books $35,000, Per/Ser (Incl.

Access Fees) $170,000, Electronic Ref Mat (Incl. Access Fees) $95,000
Library Holdings: Bk Vols 30,000; Bk Titles 10,000
Subject Interests: Law
Special Collections: DPA Brief Bank & Motion Files; Kentucky Supreme Court & Court of Appeals Slip Opinions; Training Video Coll
Partic in Kentucky Library Network, Inc

S KENTUCKY HISTORICAL SOCIETY LIBRARY, 100 W Broadway, 40601. SAN 306-2643. Tel: 502-564-1792. FAX: 502-564-4701. Web Site: www.ky.history.org. *Dir*, Anne McDonnell; E-Mail: anne.mcdonnell@mail.state.ky.us; *Mgr*, Mary Ann Conley; *Curator, Rare Bks*, Ron Bryant; *Archivist, Curator*, Mary Winter; *Archivist*, Lynne Hollingsworth; *Tech Servs*, William Shrout
Library Holdings: Bk Titles 85,000
Subject Interests: Genealogy, History, Kentucky, Manuscripts, Maps, Photographs, Rare books
Publications: Bulletin (occasionally); Kentucky Ancestors (quarterly); The Register (quarterly)

P KENTUCKY REGIONAL LIBRARY FOR THE BLIND & PHYSICALLY HANDICAPPED, Kentucky Talking Books Library,* 300 Coffeetree Rd, PO Box 818, 40602. SAN 306-2651. Tel: 502-564-8300. Toll Free Tel: 800-372-2968. FAX: 502-564-5773. *Mgr*, Richard Feindel; E-Mail: rfeindel@ctr.kdla.state.ky.us; Staff 4 (MLS 3, Non-MLS 1)
Founded 1969. Circ 160,000
Jul 1999-Jun 2000 Income $458,500, State $446,000, Federal $12,000, Locally Generated Income $500. Mats Exp $600, Books $500, Per/Ser (Incl. Access Fees) $100. Sal $440,000
Library Holdings: Bk Vols 160,000
Special Collections: Kentucky Coll, bks & tapes
Publications: Newsletter

C KENTUCKY STATE UNIVERSITY, Paul G Blazer Library, 400 E Main St, 40601-2355. SAN 306-2678. Tel: 502-597-6852. Circulation Tel: 502-597-6851. Reference Tel: 502-597-6857. FAX: 502-597-5068. Web Site: www.kysu.edu. *Dir*, Karen C McDaniel; *Asst Dir, Automation Syst Coordr, Tech Servs*, Roberta Kirby; *Asst Dir*, Ann Sullivan; *Coll Develop*, Sheila Stuckey; *Tech Servs*, Margaret Hecker; Staff 12 (MLS 12)
Founded 1886. Enrl 2,100; Fac 120; Highest Degree: Master
Library Holdings: Bk Titles 334,954; Per Subs 1,097
Special Collections: Black Studies, bks, flm & micro
Partic in BRS; Dialog Corporation; OCLC Online Computer Library Center, Inc; SE Libr Network
Friends of the Library Group

S LEGISLATIVE RESEARCH COMMISSION LIBRARY, Capitol Annex, Rm 27, 700 Capitol Ave, 40601. SAN 306-2686. Tel: 502-564-8100, Ext 340. FAX: 502-564-6543. Web Site: www.lrc.state.ky.us. *Head Librn*, Evelyn M Lockwood; *Librn*, Gerard Donovan; *Librn*, John McKee; *Librn, Ref*, Leslie Smith; Staff 4 (MLS 2, Non-MLS 2)
Founded 1948
Library Holdings: Bk Vols 5,500; Bk Titles 3,000; Per Subs 300
Subject Interests: State government
Automation Activity & Vendor Info: (Cataloging) EOS; (OPAC) EOS
Database Vendor: Lexis-Nexis
Publications: Guide to the Legislative Reference Library
Partic in Kentucky Library Network, Inc

S LIBERTY HALL HISTORIC SITE LIBRARY,* 218 Wilkinson St, 40601. SAN 322-8398. Tel: 502-227-2560. FAX: 502-227-3348. E-Mail: libhall@dcr.net. Web Site: www.libertyhall.org. *Dir*, Sara Harder
Library Holdings: Bk Vols 2,000
Subject Interests: Biography, Cooking text bks, Econ, Fict, Gardening, Genealogy, Government, Greek, History, Latin, Law, Medicine, Religion
Special Collections: US Congress (John Brown Coll), bks, documents
Restriction: By appointment only

G OFFICE OF GOVERNMENTAL SERVICES CENTER LIBRARY, Kentucky State University, Academic Services Bldg, 4th Flr, 40601. SAN 325-5611. Tel: 502-564-8170. FAX: 502-564-2732. *Librn*, Mary Jean Reece; E-Mail: maryjean.reece@mail.state.ky.us
Library Holdings: Bk Vols 500; Per Subs 25
Restriction: Staff use only

P PAUL SAWYIER PUBLIC LIBRARY, 305 Wapping St, 40601. SAN 306-2694. Tel: 502-223-1658. FAX: 502-227-2250. Web Site: www.pspl.org. *Dir*, Rita C Douthitt; E-Mail: rita@pspl.org; *Ch Servs*, Mary Greathouse; E-Mail: maryg@pspl.org; Staff 3 (MLS 3)
Founded 1965. Pop 46,000; Circ 370,000
Jul 2000-Jun 2001 Income $1,586,000, State $54,000, County $1,330,000, Locally Generated Income $202,000. Mats Exp $1,118,159, Books $170,000, Per/Ser (Incl. Access Fees) $9,500, AV Equip $47,200, Electronic Ref Mat (Incl. Access Fees) $15,500. Sal $527,900 (Prof $118,961)
Library Holdings: Bk Vols 98,000; Per Subs 233
Automation Activity & Vendor Info: (Acquisitions) Gaylord; (Cataloging) Gaylord; (Circulation) Gaylord; (OPAC) Gaylord; (Serials) Gaylord
Database Vendor: Ebsco - EbscoHost, OCLC - First Search, Wilson - Wilson Web
Bookmobiles: 1

GL STATE LAW LIBRARY,* 700 Capital Ave, Ste 200, 40601-3489. SAN 306-2708. Tel: 502-564-4848. TDD: Voice to TTY 800-648-6057, to voice 800-648-6056. FAX: 502-564-5041. *Librn*, Sallie M Howard; E-Mail: showard@mail.state.ky.us; *Cat, Res*, Linda Sizmore; Staff 8 (MLS 3, Non-MLS 5)
Founded 1954
Library Holdings: Bk Vols 134,000; Bk Titles 10,500; Per Subs 304
Subject Interests: Anglo-American law
Special Collections: Kentucky Law
Publications: Guide to Kentucky Legal Research: A State Bibliography (1985); Index to Kentucky Legal History, 18th & 19th Centuries (1983)
Partic in OCLC Online Computer Library Center, Inc
Special Services for the Deaf - TDD

FRANKLIN

P GOODNIGHT MEMORIAL LIBRARY, 203 S Main St, 42134. SAN 306-2716. Tel: 270-586-8397. FAX: 270-586-8397. E-Mail: goodmeml@apex.net. Web Site: www.goodnightlibrary.org. *Librn*, Audrey Phillips; *Bkmobile Coordr*, Charyl Read; Staff 1 (MLS 1)
Founded 1937. Pop 15,154; Circ 89,136
Library Holdings: Bk Titles 32,000; Per Subs 75
Special Collections: History of Franklin & Simpson County Coll
Mem of Barren River District
Friends of the Library Group

FRENCHBURG

P MENIFEE COUNTY PUBLIC LIBRARY,* PO Box 49, 40322. SAN 306-2724. Tel: 606-768-2212. FAX: 606-768-9676. E-Mail: mlib@mrtc.com. *Librn*, Lillian Ebermann; *Bkmobile Coordr*, Sara Staton
Pop 5,117; Circ 30,789
Library Holdings: Bk Vols 13,000
Subject Interests: Genealogy, Kentucky
Mem of Buffalo Trace Library Develop District
Partic in Regional Libr Syst

FULTON

P FULTON PUBLIC LIBRARY, 312 Main St, 42041. SAN 342-3573. Tel: 270-472-3439. FAX: 270-472-6241. E-Mail: fultonpl@apex.net. *Coll Develop, Dir*, Elaine Allen; *Br Coordr*, Melinda Cagle
Founded 1965. Pop 14,382; Circ 83,680
Library Holdings: Bk Vols 55,587; Per Subs 150
Subject Interests: Antiques, Genealogy, History
Special Collections: Civil War Records
Partic in Kentucky Library Network, Inc
Open Tues 10:30-5 & 6-8, Wed, Fri & Sat 9-12:30 & 1:30-5
Friends of the Library Group
Branches: 1
HICKMAN PUBLIC, 902 Moscow Ave, Hickman, 42050. SAN 342-3603. Tel: 270-236-2464. FAX: 270-236-2464. *Librn*, Melinda Cagle
Friends of the Library Group
Bookmobiles: 1

GEORGETOWN

C GEORGETOWN COLLEGE, Ensor Learning Resource Center, 400 E College St, 40324-1695. SAN 306-2732. Tel: 502-863-8400. Reference Tel: 502-863-8401. FAX: 502-868-7740. Web Site: spider.georgetowncollege.edu/library. *Dir*, Mary Margaret Lowe; Tel: 502-863-8403, E-Mail: mlowe@georgetowncollege.edu; *Head Ref*, JoAnne M Nartowicz; Tel: 502-863-8406; *Coll Develop*, Kenneth Lunceford; Tel: 502-863-8407; *Coll Develop*, Susan H Martin; Tel: 502-863-8407; *Tech Coordr*, Paula McGowan; Tel: 502-863-8405; *Tech Servs*, Victoria Greenwell; *Acq*, Michele D Ruth; Tel: 502-863-8412, Fax: 502-868-8897; *Cat*, Katy Roe; Tel: 502-863-8415. Subject Specialists: *Business*, JoAnne M Nartowicz; *Classics*, Mary Margaret Lowe; *Internet*, JoAnne M Nartowicz; *Japanese*, Mary Margaret Lowe; *Women's studies*, Mary Margaret Lowe; Staff 12 (MLS 4, Non-MLS 8)
Founded 1998. Enrl 1,426; Fac 80; Highest Degree: Master
Jul 2000-Jun 2001 Income Parent Institution $702,000. Mats Exp $266,500, Books $92,000, Per/Ser (Incl. Access Fees) $79,000, Presv $1,000, Micro $25,000, AV Equip $4,500, Electronic Ref Mat (Incl. Access Fees) $65,000. Sal $276,000
Library Holdings: Bk Vols 145,000; Bk Titles 101,000; Per Subs 881
Subject Interests: History, Religion
Special Collections: Christianity (Thompson Coll); Georgetown News & Georgetown Times, newsp; Law (Smith Coll); Pre-1660 English Literature, microbk; Rankin Civil War Coll
Automation Activity & Vendor Info: (Acquisitions) Endeavor; (Cataloging) Endeavor; (OPAC) Endeavor
Database Vendor: Ebsco - EbscoHost, GaleNet, Lexis-Nexis, OCLC - First Search, Wilson - Wilson Web
Partic in AICKU; OCLC Online Computer Library Center, Inc; SE Libr Network

P SCOTT COUNTY PUBLIC LIBRARY, 104 S Bradford Lane, 40324-2335. SAN 306-2740. Tel: 502-863-3566. FAX: 502-863-9621. Web Site: www.scottpublib.org. *Dir*, Earlene Hawkins Arnett; E-Mail: eharnett@mis.net; *Ad Servs*, Patti Burnsides; *Ch Servs*, Shirley Ison; *Ref Serv*, Cathy McGee
Founded 1928. Pop 30,685
Library Holdings: Bk Vols 60,000; Per Subs 120
Partic in Kentucky Library Network, Inc
Friends of the Library Group

GLASGOW

P MARY WOOD WELDON MEMORIAL LIBRARY,* 107 W College St, 42141. SAN 306-2759. Tel: 270-651-2824. FAX: 270-651-2824. E-Mail: publiclibrary@glascow.ky.com. *Librn*, Jim Hyatt; *Asst Librn*, Jane Collins; *Bkmobile Coordr*, Lenora Medcalfe; *Circ*, Deloris Flowers; Staff 1 (MLS 1)
Founded 1925. Pop 34,000; Circ 117,000
Library Holdings: Bk Vols 66,000; Per Subs 115
Special Collections: Genealogy (Kentucky Coll), bks, micro
Mem of Barren River Regional Libr Syst
Friends of the Library Group

GRAYSON

CR KENTUCKY CHRISTIAN COLLEGE, Young Library,* 100 Academic Pkwy, KCC Box 900, 41143-2205. SAN 306-2767. Tel: 606-474-3240. FAX: 606-474-3502. *Dir*, Thomas L Scott; *Librn*, Susan Carpenter
Enrl 430
Library Holdings: Per Subs 350
Subject Interests: Biology, Education, Physical science, Religion
Special Collections: Mission Papers (1969-present); Restoration Church History
Publications: Library News; Search Strategy Handbook; Your Library

GREENSBURG

P GREEN COUNTY PUBLIC LIBRARY,* 116 S Main St, 42743. SAN 306-2775. Tel: 270-932-7081. FAX: 270-932-7081. *Librn*, Evelyn Givens; *Asst Librn*, Ruth Perkins; *Bkmobile Coordr*, Starlot Pierce
Founded 1966. Pop 10,371; Circ 44,181
Library Holdings: Bk Vols 24,205; Per Subs 31
Special Collections: Genealogy & History of Original Green County; National Geographic from 1924 to present
Mem of Lake Cumberland Regional Libr Syst

GREENUP

P GREENUP COUNTY PUBLIC LIBRARIES,* 614 Main St, 41144-1036. SAN 342-3638. Tel: 606-473-6514. FAX: 606-473-6514. *Dir*, Dorothy K Griffith
Founded 1969. Pop 39,132; Circ 237,137
Library Holdings: Bk Vols 95,578; Per Subs 290
Subject Interests: Genealogy, History, Kentucky, Local history
Special Collections: Jesse Stuart Coll, photos
Open Mon, Tues, Thurs & Fri 9-5, Wed 9-8, Sat 9-2
Branches: 2
FLATWOODS PUBLIC, 1705 Argillite Rd, Flatwoods, 41139. SAN 342-3662. Tel: 606-836-3771. FAX: 606-836-8674. *Librn*, Sharon Haines
Founded 1969
Library Holdings: Bk Titles 30,000; Per Subs 40
Subject Interests: Kentucky
Open Mon, Tues & Thurs 10-8, Wed, Fri & Sat 10-5
MCKELL, RR 4, PO Box 330, South Shore, 41175. SAN 342-3697. Tel: 606-932-4478. FAX: 606-932-4478. *Librn*, Sue Evans
Subject Interests: Kentucky
Open Mon, Tues, Thurs & Fri 9-5, Wed 9-8, Sat 9-2
Bookmobiles: 1

GREENVILLE

P MUHLENBERG COUNTY LIBRARIES, 117 S Main, 42345. SAN 342-3727. Tel: 270-338-4760. FAX: 270-338-4000. E-Mail: hmlib@muhlon.com. Web Site: www.mcplib.org. *Dir*, Anniesse Williams; Staff 4 (Non-MLS 4)
Founded 1970. Pop 31,218; Circ 150,476
Jul 1999-Jun 2000 Income (Main Library and Branch Library) $529,093, State $41,451, County $432,897, Locally Generated Income $54,745. Mats Exp $96,750, Books $63,496, Per/Ser (Incl. Access Fees) $10,539, Presv $5,230, Micro $1,000, AV Equip $9,472, Electronic Ref Mat (Incl. Access Fees) $7,013. Sal $279,151 (Prof $96,500)
Library Holdings: Bk Vols 85,454; Per Subs 138
Subject Interests: Genealogy, Local history
Automation Activity & Vendor Info: (Cataloging) Gaylord; (Circulation) Gaylord
Partic in Kentucky Library Network, Inc
Branches: 2
CENTRAL CITY BRANCH, 108 E Broad St, Central City, 42330. SAN 342-3786. Tel: 270-754-4630. FAX: 270-754-2591. E-Mail: cclib@muhlon.com. *Librn*, Ann Page
HARBIN MEMORIAL, 117 S Main, 42345. SAN 342-3751. Tel: 270-338-4760. FAX: 270-338-4000. *In Charge*, Anniesse Williams

HARDINSBURG

P BRECKINRIDGE COUNTY PUBLIC LIBRARY,* 112 S Main St, PO Box 248, 40143. SAN 342-3816. Tel: 502-756-2323, Ext 1. FAX: 502-756-5634. *Dir*, Debra Drane; E-Mail: debbie_drane@hotmail.com
Founded 1953. Pop 16,312; Circ 118,798
Library Holdings: Bk Titles 51,708; Per Subs 86
Subject Interests: Children's, Young adult
Mem of Lincoln Trail Libraries System
Partic in Kentucky Library Network, Inc
Branches: 2
CLOVERPORT BRANCH, 402 Fourth St, Cloverport, 40111. SAN 342-3840. Tel: 270-788-3388, Ext 255. FAX: 270-756-5634. *Librn*, Sandra Carver
IRVINGTON BRANCH, PO Box 391, Irvington, 40146. SAN 342-3875. Tel: 270-547-7404. FAX: 270-756-5634. *Librn*, Mary Rollie-Shilts
Bookmobiles: 1

HARLAN

P HARLAN COUNTY PUBLIC LIBRARY,* 107 N Third St, 40831-2394. SAN 342-3905. Tel: 606-573-5220. FAX: 606-573-5220. *Librn*, Thelma Creech; E-Mail: thelma.creech@mail.state.ky.us; *Bkmobile Coordr*, Rosemary Cantrell
Pop 36,574; Circ 121,020
Jul 1998-Jun 1999 Income (Main Library and Branch Library) $394,996, State $61,809, County $260,252, Locally Generated Income $1,230, Other $71,705. Mats Exp $40,423, Books $29,886, Per/Ser (Incl. Access Fees) $2,623. Sal $161,034 (Prof $95,464)
Library Holdings: Bk Vols 88,768; Per Subs 115
Subject Interests: Coal, Genealogy, Kentucky
Mem of Cumberland Valley Regional Libr Syst
Partic in Kentucky Library Network, Inc
Branches: 1
REBECCA CAUDILL PUBLIC, Cumberland, 40823. SAN 342-393X. Tel: 606-589-2409. FAX: 606-589-2409. *Librn*, Ardelia Evans
Bookmobiles: 1

HARRODSBURG

S HARRODSBURG HISTORICAL SOCIETY, Harrodsburg Mercer County Research Library, 220 S Chiles St, 40330-1631. (Mail add: PO Box 316, 40330-0316), SAN 375-1112. Tel: 859-734-5985. FAX: 859-734-5985. Web Site: www.harrodsburg.org. *Chairperson*, Anne Baker
Library Holdings: Bk Vols 2,000; Per Subs 10
Special Collections: County Historical Archives
Open Tues 10-4 & Wed-Sat 1-4

P MERCER COUNTY PUBLIC LIBRARY,* 109 W Lexington, 40330. SAN 306-2805. Tel: 606-734-3680. FAX: 606-734-7524. E-Mail: mercerpublib.webmaster@mail.state.ky.us. Web Site: www.mercercopublib.state.ky.us/. *Librn*, Robin Ison; *Bkmobile Coordr*, Cathy Worthington; *Coll Develop*, Carolyn W Patterson
Founded 1970. Pop 19,002; Circ 102,733
Library Holdings: Bk Vols 50,000; Per Subs 85
Subject Interests: Genealogy
Special Collections: Kentucky Coll; The Kentucky-Kansas Connection: "Lest We forget"
Mem of Bluegrass South Regional Libr
Open Mon & Thurs 9:30-7:30, Tues, Wed & Fri 9:30-5:30, Sat 9:30-2, Sun 1-5

S SHAKER VILLAGE OF PLEASANT HILL MUSEUM LIBRARY, 3501 Lexington Rd, 40330. SAN 373-4587. Tel: 606-734-5411. FAX: 606-734-5411. Web Site: www.shakervillageky.org. *Curator*, Larrie Spier Curry; E-Mail: lcurry@shakervillageky.org
Founded 1968
Library Holdings: Bk Vols 500; Spec Interest Per Sub 10
Subject Interests: 19th Century, Architecture, Decorative arts, Kentucky, Relig studies, Shakers, Utopianism
Special Collections: Shakers & the village at Pleasant Hill, ephemera, mss, photographs
Restriction: By appointment only
Function: Research library

HARTFORD

P OHIO COUNTY PUBLIC LIBRARY,* 413 Main St, 42347. SAN 306-2813. Tel: 270-298-3790. FAX: 270-298-4214. *Dir*, Melissa Acquaviva
Founded 1967. Pop 21,765; Circ 130,250
Library Holdings: Bk Vols 29,325; Per Subs 85
Special Collections: Charles C Curran Coll, prints, VF; Ohio County History
Mem of Green River Regional Libr
Open Mon & Tues 8:30-7:30, Wed-Fri 8:30-4:30 & Sat 8:30-3

HAWESVILLE

P HANCOCK COUNTY LIBRARY,* 240 Court Sq, PO Box 249, 42348-0249. SAN 342-3964. Tel: 270-927-6760. FAX: 270-927-6847. E-Mail: hancock02@tds.net. *Dir*, Jacquelyn Walton
Founded 1954. Pop 7,864; Circ 54,000
Jul 1999-Jun 2000 Income (Main Library and Branch Library) $197,362, State $19,842, Locally Generated Income $9,020, Other $168,500. Mats Exp $32,100, Books $29,100, Per/Ser (Incl. Access Fees) $3,000. Sal $114,800 (Prof $35,256)
Library Holdings: Bk Vols 34,000; Per Subs 63
Friends of the Library Group
Branches: 1
LEWISPORT BRANCH, 17 Pell St, PO Box 372, Lewisport, 42351. SAN 342-3999. Tel: 502-295-3765. *Librn*, Henry Shillinglow
Library Holdings: Bk Vols 5,000
Friends of the Library Group
Bookmobiles: 1

HAZARD

J HAZARD COMMUNITY COLLEGE LIBRARY, One Community College Dr, 41701. SAN 306-2821. Tel: 606-436-5721, Ext 347. Circulation Tel: 606-436-5721, Ext 349. Reference Tel: 606-436-5721, Ext 349 or 348. FAX: 606-439-1657. Web Site: www.hazcc.kctcs.net/library/library.htm. *Dir*, Eileen C Haddix; E-Mail: eileenhaddix@kctcs.net; Staff 4 (MLS 2, Non-MLS 2)
Founded 1968. Enrl 2,400; Highest Degree: Associate
2000-2001 Mats Exp $63,185
Library Holdings: Bk Vols 40,662; Per Subs 165
Subject Interests: Allied health, Genealogy, Local history
Automation Activity & Vendor Info: (Acquisitions) Endeavor; (Cataloging) Endeavor; (Circulation) Endeavor; (Course Reserve) Endeavor; (ILL) Endeavor; (Media Booking) Endeavor; (OPAC) Endeavor; (Serials) Endeavor

P KENTUCKY DEPARTMENT FOR LIBRARIES & ARCHIVES, Kentucky River Regional Library District, 479 High St, 41701-0928. (Mail add: PO Box 928, 41702), SAN 306-283X. Tel: 606-439-1531. FAX: 606-435-0731. *Dir*, Martha Jane Proctor; Staff 1 (MLS 1)
Pop 134,429
Library Holdings: Bk Titles 50
Subject Interests: Genealogy
Member Libraries: Breathitt County Library; Harry Caudill Memorial Library; Knott County Public Library; Lee County Public Library; Leslie County Library; Owsley County Public Library; Wolfe County Library
Open Mon-Fri 8-4:30

P PERRY COUNTY PUBLIC LIBRARY, 479 High St, PO Box 928, 41702. SAN 306-2848. Tel: 606-436-2475, 606-436-4747. FAX: 606-436-0191. E-Mail: pcpl479@gtemail.net. Web Site: www.geocities.com/pcpl479. *Dir*, Connie Cornett; *Chief Librn*, Elaine Couch
Founded 1970. Pop 33,763; Circ 379,055
2000-2001 Income $572,877. Mats Exp $608,152. Sal $195,138
Library Holdings: Bk Vols 60,000; Per Subs 58
Special Collections: Genealogy Coll; Kentucky, rare bks
Bookmobiles: 1

M SOUTHEAST KENTUCKY AREA HEALTH EDUCATION CENTER, Library Services,* 100 Medical Center Dr, 41701-9429. SAN 370-5277. Tel: 606-439-6792. FAX: 606-439-6798. Web Site: www.mc.uky.edu/ahec/seahec/aheclib.htm. *Dir Libr Serv*, Charlene McGrath; E-Mail: cmcgr1@pop.uky.edu; *Librn*, Laura Davison; Tel: 606-439-6793, E-Mail: ldavison@arh.org; *ILL*, Pansy Adams; Tel: 606-439-6796; Staff 3 (MLS 2, Non-MLS 1)
Founded 1985
Library Holdings: Bk Vols 2,200; Bk Titles 2,000; Per Subs 350
Subject Interests: Medicine, Nursing, Rural health
Database Vendor: IAC - Info Trac, OCLC - First Search, OVID Technologies
Publications: Newsletter
Function: Document delivery services
Partic in Bluegrass Med Librns; Kentucky Health Science Libraries Consortium; Kentucky Library Network, Inc; Nat AHEC Librns; Tennessee Health Science Library Association

HENDERSON

J HENDERSON COMMUNITY COLLEGE, Hartfield Library, 2660 S Green St, 42420-4699. SAN 306-2856. Tel: 270-827-1867, 270-830-5267. FAX: 270-827-8635. Web Site: www.hencc.kctcs.net/library/. *Dir*, Michael Knecht; *Asst Librn*, Kevin Reid; Staff 2 (MLS 2)
Founded 1960. Enrl 1,175; Fac 60
Library Holdings: Bk Vols 30,206; Per Subs 225
Partic in Kentucky Library Network, Inc

P HENDERSON COUNTY PUBLIC LIBRARY,* 101 S Main St, 42420-3599. SAN 306-2864. Tel: 270-826-3712. FAX: 270-827-4226. *Dir*, Donald L Wathen
Founded 1904. Pop 43,044; Circ 223,629
Jul 1997-Jun 1998 Income $696,751, State $41,995, City $7,500, Locally Generated Income $515,405. Mats Exp $73,889, Books $56,483, Per/Ser (Incl. Access Fees) $5,658, Micro $42. Sal $314,941
Library Holdings: Bk Vols 76,833; Per Subs 75
Mem of Green River Regional Libr
Partic in Evansville Area Library Consortium; Kentucky Library Network, Inc; OCLC Online Computer Library Center, Inc; SE Libr Network
Friends of the Library Group

HIGHLAND HEIGHTS

S GENERAL CABLE CO, Research Center Library,* 4 Tesseneer Dr, 41076. SAN 310-5571. Tel: 606-572-8000. FAX: 606-572-8497.
Founded 1943
Library Holdings: Bk Titles 1,400; Per Subs 100
Subject Interests: Electronics, Engineering, Fiber optics, Metallurgy, Patents, Plastics, Polymers, Telecommunication
Restriction: Staff use only
Partic in BRS; Dialog Corporation; Nat Libr of Med; Newsnet

C NORTHERN KENTUCKY UNIVERSITY, W Frank Steely Library, University Dr, 41099. SAN 342-4022. Tel: 859-572-5483. Circulation Tel: 859-572-5457. Reference Tel: 859-572-5456. FAX: 859-572-5390. E-Mail: refdept@nku.edu. Web Site: www.nku.edu/~library. *Dir*, Lois Schultz; E-Mail: schultz@nku.edu; *Head Ref*, Threasa Wesley; Tel: 859-572-5721, E-Mail: wesley@nku.edu; *Bibliog Instr*, Emily Werrell; Tel: 859-572-6523, E-Mail: werrell@nku.edu; *Circ*, Royleen Seibert; Tel: 859-572-5722, E-Mail: seibert@nku.edu; *Govt Doc*, Phil Yannarella; Tel: 859-572-5455, E-Mail: yannarella@nku.edu; *Publ Servs*, Laura Sullivan; Tel: 859-572-5724, E-Mail: sullivanl@nku.edu; *Selection of Elec Mat*, Jack O'Gorman; *Electronic Resources*, Michael Rose; Tel: 859-572-5936, E-Mail: rosemi@nku.edu; *ILL*, Sharon Taylor; Tel: 859-572-6365, E-Mail: taylors@nku.edu; *Automation Syst Coordr*, Perry Bratcher; Tel: 859-572-6309, E-Mail: bratcher@nku.edu; *Coll Develop*, Mary Ellen Elsbernd; *Cat*, Wendy Wood; Tel: 859-572-5480, E-Mail: woodw@nku.edu; *Spec Coll & Archives*, Jason Larson; Tel: 859-572-5863, E-Mail: larsonj@nku.edu; *Tech Servs*, Donna Smith; Tel: 859-572-6140, E-Mail: smithd@nku.edu; Staff 35 (MLS 16, Non-MLS 19)
Founded 1968. Enrl 12,000; Fac 315; Highest Degree: Master
Jul 1999-Jun 2000 Mats Exp $811,469, Books $271,703, Per/Ser (Incl. Access Fees) $532,365, Presv $7,401. Sal $1,180,741 (Prof $704,774)
Library Holdings: Bk Vols 325,731; Bk Titles 251,674; Per Subs 1,488
Special Collections: American Statistics, fiche; Christopher Gist Hist Soc Coll; Confederate Imprints; Kentuckiana Coll; Kentucky One Thousand, ultra fiche; Library of American Civilization; Library of American Literature
Automation Activity & Vendor Info: (Acquisitions) Endeavor; (Cataloging) Endeavor; (Circulation) Endeavor; (OPAC) Endeavor; (Serials) Endeavor
Database Vendor: Dialog, Ebsco - EbscoHost, Lexis-Nexis, OCLC - First Search, Silverplatter Information Inc.
Publications: Annotations (Friends of the Library newsletter)
Mem of SE Libr Network
Partic in Greater Cincinnati Library Consortium; Solinet
Friends of the Library Group

CL NORTHERN KENTUCKY UNIVERSITY, Salmon P Chase College of Law Library, 41099-6110. SAN 306-2368. Tel: 859-572-5340, 859-572-5394. Interlibrary Loan Service Tel: 859-572-5712. FAX: 859-572-6529, 859-572-6664. Web Site: www.nku.edu/~chase/library/lib-home.htm. *Dir*, Carol B Allred; E-Mail: allred@nku.edu; *Assoc Dir, Assoc Prof*, Thomas Heard; *Outreach Serv*, Carol Furnish; *Acq, Ser*, Claudia Zaher; Staff 16 (MLS 6, Non-MLS 10)
Enrl 400; Fac 21
Library Holdings: Bk Vols 242,648
Special Collections: Harold J Siebenthaler Rare Books Coll
Publications: Colloquy; Faculty Services: In a Nutshell; Law Library Handbook; The Liaison; User's Guide
Partic in OCLC Online Computer Library Center, Inc; SE Libr Network

HINDMAN

P KNOTT COUNTY PUBLIC LIBRARY,* 238 S Hwy 160, Box 667, 41822. SAN 306-2880. Tel: 606-785-5412. FAX: 606-785-4299. E-Mail: kclib@tgtel.com. *Dir*, Charlotte Madden; *Asst Librn*, LaDonna Collins; *Bkmobile Coordr*, Audrey Slone

Pop 17,904; Circ 38,856
Library Holdings: Bk Vols 20,925; Per Subs 39
Special Collections: Appalachian: Genealogy
Mem of Kentucky Department for Libraries & Archives
Friends of the Library Group

HODGENVILLE

P LARUE COUNTY PUBLIC LIBRARY,* 201 S Lincoln Blvd, 42748. SAN 306-2899. Tel: 270-358-3851. FAX: 270-358-8647. E-Mail: laruelib@kih.net. *Dir*, Emily Martin; *Ch Servs*, Kathy Crawford
Founded 1917. Pop 11,983; Circ 50,555
Library Holdings: Bk Vols 40,000; Per Subs 65
Special Collections: Lincoln Coll
Mem of Lincoln Trail Libraries System

S ABRAHAM LINCOLN BIRTHPLACE NATIONAL HISTORIC SITE LIBRARY,* 2995 Lincoln Farm Rd, 42748. SAN 370-2790. Tel: 270-358-3137. FAX: 270-358-3874. Web Site: www.nps.gov/abli. *In Charge*, Jennie Jones
Library Holdings: Bk Vols 717
Restriction: Restricted public use
Open 8-6:45 Memorial Day-Labor Day, 8-4:45 balance of year

HOPKINSVILLE

J HOPKINSVILLE COMMUNITY COLLEGE LIBRARY, 720 North Dr, 42240. (Mail add: PO Box 2100, 42241-2100), SAN 306-2910. Tel: 270-886-3921. Interlibrary Loan Service Tel: 270-886-3921, Ext 6123. Circulation Tel: 270-886-3921, Ext 6127. FAX: 270-885-6048. Web Site: www.hopcc.kctcs.net/academics/library/library/main.html. *Librn*, Cynthia Atkins; E-Mail: cynthia.atkins@kctcs.net; *Librn*, Lisa Dick; E-Mail: lisa.dick@kctcs.net; Staff 4 (MLS 2, Non-MLS 2)
Founded 1965. Enrl 2,600; Fac 75; Highest Degree: Associate
Jul 1999-Jun 2000 Mats Exp $70,222, Books $38,222, Per/Ser (Incl. Access Fees) $8,000, Micro $7,000, Other Print Mats $4,000, Electronic Ref Mat (Incl. Access Fees) $13,000
Library Holdings: Bk Vols 44,815; Bk Titles 36,179; Per Subs 126
Subject Interests: Kentucky
Automation Activity & Vendor Info: (Circulation) Endeavor; (Course Reserve) Endeavor; (OPAC) Endeavor

P HOPKINSVILLE-CHRISTIAN COUNTY PUBLIC LIBRARY, 1101 Bethel St, 42240. SAN 306-2902. Tel: 502-887-4263. Interlibrary Loan Service Tel: 502-887-4262. FAX: 502-887-4264. *Dir*, Robert L Satterwhite; *Ad Servs*, Lisa Bond; *Ch Servs*, Joy Windsor; *Coll Develop, Tech Servs*, Julie Antee; Staff 3 (MLS 2, Non-MLS 1)
Founded 1874. Pop 69,502; Circ 179,498
Jul 1999-Jun 2000 Income $434,633, State $71,464, City $167,169, County $40,000, Other $156,000. Mats Exp $73,500, Books $64,600, Per/Ser (Incl. Access Fees) $8,900. Sal $224,167
Library Holdings: Bk Titles 99,743; Per Subs 104
Special Collections: McCarroll Genealogy Coll
Automation Activity & Vendor Info: (Acquisitions) Sagebrush Corporation; (Cataloging) Sagebrush Corporation; (Circulation) Sagebrush Corporation; (OPAC) Sagebrush Corporation
Publications: Newsletter (monthly)
Mem of Green River Regional Libr; Pennyrile Regional Libr
Partic in Ky Coop Libr Info Project
Friends of the Library Group
Bookmobiles: 1

M WESTERN STATE HOSPITAL, Professional Library,* PO Box 2200, 42241. SAN 306-2929. Tel: 502-886-4431, Ext 223. FAX: 502-886-4487. *Dir*, Steve Wiggins
Founded 1940
Library Holdings: Bk Titles 2,600; Per Subs 51
Subject Interests: Business and management, Medicine, Nursing, Psychiatry, Social service (social work)
Publications: Hospital Newsletter
Partic in Ky-Ohio-Mich Regional Med Libr

HORSE CAVE

P HORSE CAVE FREE PUBLIC LIBRARY, 111 Higbee St, 42749-1110. (Mail add: PO Box 127, 42749-0127), SAN 306-2937. Tel: 270-786-1130. FAX: 270-786-1131. E-Mail: hclib@ivprog.com. *Librn*, Denise Ballard; *Asst Librn*, Gloria Laing
Founded 1912. Pop 8,000; Circ 13,200
Library Holdings: Bk Vols 10,500; Per Subs 30
Special Collections: Kentucky Coll
Mem of Barren River District

HYDEN

M FRONTIER NURSING SERVICE LIBRARY,* 130 Kate Ireland Dr, 41749. SAN 375-9121. Tel: 606-672-3162. FAX: 606-672-3626. *Librn*, Juanita Johnson
Library Holdings: Bk Vols 500

P LESLIE COUNTY LIBRARY,* Main St, PO Box 498, 41749. SAN 306-2945. Tel: 606-672-2460. FAX: 606-672-4213. E-Mail: leslib@tds.nat. *Librn*, Mason Collett
Founded 1963. Pop 13,642; Circ 148,880
Library Holdings: Bk Vols 31,726; Per Subs 35
Special Collections: Genealogy (Leslie County Coll); Kentucky
Mem of Kentucky Department for Libraries & Archives
Special Services for the Deaf - Books on deafness & sign language; High interest/low vocabulary books
Open Mon-Fri 8-4

IRVINE

P ESTILL COUNTY PUBLIC LIBRARY,* 246 Main St, 40336-1099. SAN 306-2953. Tel: 606-723-3030. FAX: 606-723-3030. E-Mail: estilcolib@kih.com. *Dir*, Ruth Shaffer; *Bkmobile Coordr*, Sherri Jenkins; *Ch Servs*, Elizabeth Williamson
Founded 1969. Pop 14,500; Circ 81,700
Library Holdings: Bk Vols 30,158; Per Subs 30
Subject Interests: Local history
Special Collections: Kentucky Coll
Publications: Bibliographies; booklists; newsletter
Mem of Bluegrass South Regional Libr

JACKSON

P BREATHITT COUNTY LIBRARY,* 1024 College Ave, 41339. SAN 306-2961. Tel: 606-666-5541. FAX: 606-666-8166. E-Mail: library@tgtel.com. Web Site: www.breathitt.simplenet.com. *Librn*, Jeanette Shouse; *Asst Librn*, Flora Haddix
Founded 1967. Pop 17,000
Library Holdings: Bk Vols 35,000; Per Subs 50
Special Collections: Genealogical Research Library; History & Census Records (Breathitt and surrounding counties); Surname Information Files
Mem of Kentucky Department for Libraries & Archives
Partic in Kentucky Library Network, Inc

J HAZARD COMMUNITY COLLEGE, Lees College Campus Library,* 601 Jefferson Ave, 41339. SAN 306-297X. Tel: 606-666-7521, Ext 653. FAX: 606-666-8910. Web Site: www.leecc.uky.edu/lees-library/index.htm. *Dir*, Robert Hilton; E-Mail: robert.hilton@kcpcs.net; *Acq*, Cathy Branson; *ILL*, Donna Collins; Staff 1 (MLS 1)
Founded 1883. Enrl 300
Library Holdings: Bk Vols 40,000; Per Subs 200
Subject Interests: Local history, Religion
Special Collections: Apalachian Oral Hist; Appalachia & Kentuckiana, bks, flm, cassettes & per
Partic in Coun of Independent Ky Cols & Univs; Kentucky Library Network, Inc
Open Mon-Thurs 8am-11pm; other days irregular

JAMESTOWN

P RUSSELL COUNTY PUBLIC LIBRARY, 94 N Main, PO Box 970, 42629. SAN 306-2988. Tel: 270-343-3545. FAX: 270-343-2019. E-Mail: rcplib@duo-county.com. *Dir*, Irene Black; *Asst Dir*, Christina Johnson; *Ch Servs*, Fillamay Cowell
Founded 1967. Pop 14,716; Circ 72,245
Jul 1999-Jun 2000 Income $185,082, State $28,731, County $20,311, Locally Generated Income $111,534, Other $24,506. Mats Exp $9,461, Books $8,586, Per/Ser (Incl. Access Fees) $875. Sal $90,143 (Prof $24,600)
Library Holdings: Bk Vols 42,418
Subject Interests: Easy bks, Genealogy, Juvenile delinquency, Kentucky, Large type print, Romance languages, Science fiction, Young adult literature
Automation Activity & Vendor Info: (Circulation) Sagebrush Corporation
Database Vendor: OCLC - First Search
Partic in KLN

LA GRANGE

S KENTUCKY STATE REFORMATORY LIBRARY,* 3001 W Hwy 146, 40032. SAN 306-3011. Tel: 502-222-9441. *Librn*, Linda Goble
Founded 1938
Library Holdings: Bk Vols 20,000; Per Subs 220
Subject Interests: Fiction
Friends of the Library Group

P OLDHAM COUNTY PUBLIC LIBRARY, 106 E Jefferson St, 40031. SAN 320-1902. Tel: 502-241-9899 (Admin). FAX: 502-241-6048. Web Site: www.oldhampl.org. *Dir*, Elizabeth Thurman; E-Mail: libby@oldhampl.org; *Asst Dir, Coll Develop*, M Susan Eubank; *Librn*, Sandra Thacker; *Tech Servs*, Jean Small; Staff 24 (MLS 5, Non-MLS 19)
Founded 1968. Pop 33,263; Circ 180,868
Library Holdings: Bk Vols 66,000; Per Subs 166
Special Collections: Census Coll; Genealogy Coll, bks & films; GSA/BSA Coll; Kentucky Coll; Learn Resource; LT Coll; Video Cassette Coll
Automation Activity & Vendor Info: (Cataloging) TLC; (Circulation) TLC; (OPAC) TLC; (Serials) TLC
Mem of Kentuckiana Regional Libr
Partic in Kentucky Library Network, Inc
Branches: 2
MAHAM OLDHAM PUBLIC, PO Box 145, Goshen, 40026. SAN 377-7324. Tel: 502-228-1852. Web Site: oldhampl.org. *Librn*, Janet Calvert; *Librn*, Sue Franklin
SOUTH OLDHAM, PO Box 365, Crestwood, 40014. SAN 377-7340. Tel: 502-241-1108. FAX: 502-241-1108. Web Site: oldhampl.org. *Dir*, Connie Oldham

LANCASTER

P GARRARD COUNTY PUBLIC LIBRARY,* 101 Lexington St, 40444. SAN 306-302X. Tel: 606-792-3424. FAX: 606-792-2366. E-Mail: garlib@hotmail.com. Web Site: www.millennium.fortunecity.com/paddington/739/. *Librn*, Joan Tussey
Pop 10,853; Circ 84,000
Library Holdings: Bk Vols 36,539; Per Subs 45
Mem of Bluegrass South Regional Libr
Partic in Bluegrass Pub Libr Asn

LAWRENCEBURG

P ANDERSON PUBLIC LIBRARY,* 114 N Main, 40342. SAN 306-3038. Tel: 502-839-6420. FAX: 502-839-7243. *Dir*, Jeffrey Sauer; E-Mail: sauer@mis.net; Staff 3 (MLS 1, Non-MLS 2)
Founded 1908. Pop 13,334; Circ 77,857
Jul 1997-Jun 1998 Income $250,709. Mats Exp $46,500. Sal $111,436
Library Holdings: Bk Vols 40,000; Bk Titles 38,000; Per Subs 85
Mem of Bluegrass North Libr District; Ky Libr Network
Open Mon, Wed & Fri 9-6, Tues & Thurs 9-8, Sat 9-4
Friends of the Library Group

LEBANON

P MARION COUNTY PUBLIC LIBRARY,* 201 E Main St, 40033-1133. SAN 306-3046. Tel: 502-692-4698. FAX: 502-692-4698. *Dir*, Kimberly Smith
Pop 16,499; Circ 63,000
Library Holdings: Bk Vols 35,900
Subject Interests: Genealogy, History, Kentucky
Special Collections: Local genealogy
Mem of Lincoln Trail Libraries System
Partic in Kentucky Library Network, Inc
Open Tues & Thurs 10-8, Wed & Fri 10-5:30, Sat 10-3
Friends of the Library Group
Bookmobiles: 1

LEITCHFIELD

P GRAYSON COUNTY PUBLIC LIBRARY, 130 E Market St, 42754. SAN 325-187X. Tel: 502-259-5455. FAX: 502-259-4552. E-Mail: library2@creative-net.net. Web Site: www.graysoncountylibrary.org. *Dir*, Karen Gillespie; *Bkmobile Coordr*, Tracy Wright; E-Mail: tlwright@creative-net.net
Founded 1976. Pop 21,050
Jul 2000-Jun 2001 Mats Exp $32,100, Books $22,000, Per/Ser (Incl. Access Fees) $1,500, Micro $500, AV Equip $3,950, Electronic Ref Mat (Incl. Access Fees) $3,000. Sal $162,200
Library Holdings: Bk Vols 42,000; Bk Titles 35,000; Per Subs 61
Subject Interests: Genealogy, Kentucky, Local history
Automation Activity & Vendor Info: (Cataloging) Brodart; (Circulation) Brodart; (OPAC) Brodart
Database Vendor: Ebsco - EbscoHost, OCLC - First Search
Function: ILL available, Photocopies available, Some telephone reference
Partic in OCLC Online Computer Library Center, Inc
Friends of the Library Group
Bookmobiles: 1

LEXINGTON

S ASHLAND, Henry Clay Memorial Foundation, 120 Sycamore Rd, 40502. SAN 376-0677. Tel: 859-266-8581. FAX: 859-268-7266. Web Site: www.henryclay.org. *Exec Dir*, Kelly Willis; *Curator*, Jeff Meyer
Library Holdings: Bk Titles 18
Restriction: Open to public for reference only
Open Tues-Sat 10-4, Sun 1-4, closed Mon
Friends of the Library Group

S ASHLAND, INC, Technical Learning Center LC-3, 3475 Blazer Pkwy, PO Box 14000, 40512. SAN 325-3023. Tel: 606-357-7176. FAX: 606-357-7265.
Library Holdings: Bk Titles 200; Per Subs 15
Subject Interests: Bus, Computer indust, Computers, Data proc, Mgt
Publications: Articles of Interest; Conference Database; ETC
Restriction: Not open to public
Partic in Dialog Corporation; Dow Jones News Retrieval; OCLC Online Computer Library Center, Inc

S BLOODSTOCK RESEARCH INFORMATION SERVICES, INC LIBRARY, 801 Corporate Dr, 3rd Flr, PO Box 4097, 40544. SAN 375-2356. Tel: 606-223-4444. FAX: 606-223-7024. Web Site: www.brisnet.com. *Pres*, Richard Broadbent III
Library Holdings: Bk Vols 1,000; Per Subs 100

SR CATHOLIC NEWMAN CENTER LIBRARY,* 320 Rose Lane, 40508. SAN 306-3070. Tel: 606-255-8566. FAX: 606-254-7519. *Librn*, Nancy Goodshaw
Founded 1965
Library Holdings: Bk Titles 35,000; Per Subs 12

§M CENTRAL BAPTIST HOSPITAL LIBRARY, 1740 Nicholasville Rd, 40503. Tel: 606-275-6297. FAX: 606-275-6442. *Dir*, Lonnie Wright
Library Holdings: Bk Vols 2,500; Per Subs 300; Bks on Deafness & Sign Lang 10

R CENTRAL CHRISTIAN CHURCH LIBRARY, 205 E Short St, PO Box 1459, 40588. SAN 306-3089. Tel: 606-233-1551. FAX: 606-252-9287. *Librn*, Anne McConnell; Staff 1 (MLS 1)
Library Holdings: Bk Vols 8,500
Subject Interests: Philosophy, Religion

G COUNCIL OF STATE GOVERNMENTS, States Information Center,* 2760 Research Park Dr, PO Box 11910, 40578. SAN 306-3097. Tel: 606-244-8253. FAX: 606-244-8001. Web Site: www.csg.org. *Librn*, Don Hunter; Tel: 606-244-8253, Fax: 606-244-8001
Founded 1947
Library Holdings: Bk Vols 20,000; Bk Titles 20,000; Per Subs 300
Subject Interests: Legislation
Special Collections: State Budgets; State Government, bluebooks and related materials
Publications: State Government Research Checklist

GM DEPARTMENT OF VETERANS AFFAIRS, Medical Center Library,* 141 D-LD VA Med Ctr, 2250 Leestown Rd, 40511. SAN 306-3208. Tel: 606-281-3916. FAX: 606-281-3974. *Mgr*, Robert Bradley; Staff 5 (MLS 3, Non-MLS 2)
Founded 1930
Oct 1996-Sep 1997 Income $99,640
Library Holdings: Bk Vols 11,065; Per Subs 502
Subject Interests: Medicine, Psychiatry, Psychology, Social sciences and issues, Surgery
Publications: Newsletter (monthly)
Partic in Nat Libr of Med; Veterans Affairs Library Network
Statistics include holdings & expenditures for two medical & one patients library. Open Mon-Fri 8-4:30

S DOW AGROSCIENCES, Information Management Center,* 4089 Iron Works Pkwy, 40511. SAN 375-3972. Tel: 317-337-3517. FAX: 317-337-3245. *Mgr*, Margaret B Hentz
Library Holdings: Bk Titles 550
Subject Interests: Agriculture, Organic chemistry
Partic in Indiana Cooperative Library Services Authority

M EASTERN STATE HOSPITAL, Resource Library,* 627 W Fourth, 40508. SAN 306-3100. Tel: 606-246-7538. FAX: 606-246-7677. *Librn*, Shane Shoemaker
Founded 1951
Library Holdings: Bk Vols 5,000
Subject Interests: Medicine, Psychiatry, Psychology, Public health

L GREENEBAUM, DOLL & MCDONALD LIBRARY, 1400 Vine Center Tower, 40507. SAN 323-7222. Tel: 606-288-4717. FAX: 606-255-2742. E-Mail: dlf@gdm.com. *Librn*, Lynn Fogle; *Asst Librn*, Mary Hackworth
Library Holdings: Bk Vols 10,000; Bk Titles 3,000; Per Subs 150

S HEADLEY-WHITNEY MUSEUM LIBRARY,* 4435 Old Frankfort Pike, 40510. SAN 325-545X. Tel: 606-255-6653. FAX: 606-255-8375. E-Mail: hwmusem@mindspring.com. Web Site: www.headley-whitney.org. *Exec Dir*, Diane C Wachs
Library Holdings: Bk Vols 1,500; Per Subs 12
Subject Interests: Art, Art of goldsmiths, Ceramics, Decorative art, French, Furniture, Glassware, Jewels, Silver
Restriction: Non-circulating to the public

S THE JOCKEY CLUB LIBRARY,* 821 Corporate Dr, 40503. SAN 370-1379. Tel: 606-224-2800. FAX: 606-224-2810. Web Site: www.jockeyclub.com. *Cat*, Greg Swinford
Library Holdings: Bk Titles 2,000

S KEENELAND ASSOCIATION, Keeneland Library, Keeneland Race Course, PO Box 1690, 40588. SAN 306-3135. Tel: 606-254-3412, Ext 223. FAX: 606-288-4348. Web Site: www.keeneland.com. *Librn*, Cathy Schenck; E-Mail: cschenck@keeneland.com
Founded 1939
Library Holdings: Bk Vols 5,900; Bk Titles 5,825; Per Subs 45
Subject Interests: Horses
Special Collections: American Racing Coll, photog negative
Restriction: Non-circulating to the public

G KENTUCKY HORSE PARK, International Museum of the Horse,* 4089 Iron Works Pkwy, 40511. Tel: 606-259-4231, Ext 231. Toll Free Tel: 800-678-8813. TDD: 606-233-4303. FAX: 606-225-4613. E-Mail: khp@mis.net. Web Site: www.imh.org/khp. *Curator*, Jenifer Raisor; *Publ Servs*, Pat Woodall
Founded 1977
Library Holdings: Bk Titles 1,600; Per Subs 88
Special Services for the Deaf - TDD

S LEXINGTON COMMUNITY COLLEGE LIBRARY, Learning Resource Center, 220 Oswald Bldg, Cooper Dr, 40506-0235. SAN 306-3151. Tel: 859-257-4872, Ext 4163. FAX: 859-323-1091. Web Site: www.uky.edu/lcc/lib. *Actg Dir*, Charles James; Tel: 859-257-4872, Ext 4162, E-Mail: crjames@pop.uky.edu; *Tech Coordr*, Kathleen Richardson; *Instr, Publ Servs*, Marcia Freyman; *Electronic Resources*, Carol Davis; *AV*, Richard Rydz; Staff 11 (MLS 6, Non-MLS 5)
Founded 1976. Enrl 6,100; Fac 200
Library Holdings: Bk Vols 36,000; Bk Titles 33,000; Per Subs 218
Partic in Kentucky Library Network, Inc; OCLC Online Computer Library Center, Inc; SE Libr Network

S LEXINGTON HERALD-LEADER COMPANY LIBRARY,* 100 Midland Ave, 40508. SAN 306-3143. Tel: 606-231-3335. Web Site: www.kentuckyconnect.com. *Chief Librn*, Lu-Ann Dunn-Farrar; E-Mail: lfarrar@herald-leader.com; Staff 1 (MLS 1)
Founded 1945
Library Holdings: Bk Vols 800
Special Collections: Index to Photograph Coll, 1920-1977; Newspaper Coll 1875-present, micro
Partic in Vutext

P LEXINGTON PUBLIC LIBRARY, 140 E Main St, 40507-1376. SAN 342-4057. Tel: 859-231-5530. Interlibrary Loan Service Tel: 859-231-5520. Reference Tel: 859-231-5520. FAX: 859-231-5598. Web Site: www.lexpublib.org/. *Dir*, Ronald Steensland; Tel: 859-231-5504; *Asst Dir*, Geneva Pullen; Tel: 606-231-5504; *Mgr*, Becky Croft; Tel: 859-231-5510; *Ch Servs*, Toy Lancaster; Tel: 859-231-5534; *ILL, Ser, Spec Coll*, Ida Cornett; *Ad Servs*, Karen Allen; Staff 200 (MLS 30, Non-MLS 170)
Founded 1898. Pop 243,785; Circ 1,846,242
Jul 1999-Jun 2000 Income (Main Library and Branch Library) $8,201,450, State $203,308, City $7,563,150, Locally Generated Income $325,725, Other $109,267. Mats Exp $1,064,804, Books $823,922, Per/Ser (Incl. Access Fees) $52,960, Micro $39,163, Electronic Ref Mat (Incl. Access Fees) $148,755. Sal $3,463,812 (Prof $1,963,478)
Library Holdings: Bk Vols 707,875; Bk Titles 295,118; Per Subs 1,368
Special Collections: African-American Coll; Early Kentucky Books; Early Kentucky Newspapers; Grants Coll; Large Print Coll; Lexington Urban County Doc Coll
Automation Activity & Vendor Info: (Cataloging) DRA; (Circulation) DRA; (OPAC) DRA
Partic in Kentucky Library Network, Inc
Friends of the Library Group
Branches: 4
BEAUMONT, 3080 Fieldstone Way, 40513. SAN 342-4146. Tel: 859-231-5570. FAX: 859-296-4815. Web Site: www.lexpublib.org/. *Librn*, Doris Raney
Library Holdings: Bk Vols 106,711
Friends of the Library Group
EAGLE CREEK, 101 N Eagle Creek Dr, 40509. SAN 342-4081. Tel: 859-231-5560. FAX: 859-231-5561. Web Site: www.lexpublib.org/. *Librn*, John Kalbfleisch
Library Holdings: Bk Vols 94,560
Friends of the Library Group
NORTHSIDE, 1737 Russell Cave Rd, 40505. SAN 322-6352. Tel: 859-231-5590. FAX: 859-294-7796. Web Site: www.lexpublib.org/. *Librn*, William Biles
Library Holdings: Bk Vols 64,671
Friends of the Library Group
TATES CREEK, 3628 Walden Dr, 40517. SAN 342-4111. Tel: 859-231-5580. FAX: 859-231-5581. Web Site: www.lexpublib.org/. *Librn*, Judith Olson
Library Holdings: Bk Vols 84,334
Friends of the Library Group

J LEXINGTON THEOLOGICAL SEMINARY, Bosworth Memorial Library, 631 S Limestone, 40508. SAN 306-316X. Tel: 859-252-0361, Ext 229. FAX: 859-281-6042. Web Site: www.library.lextheo.edu. *Coll Develop, Dir*, Philip Dare; E-Mail: pdare@lextheo.edu; *Asst Librn*, Barbara Pfeifle; *Ser*, Janet Timberlake; *Circ*, Ann Gregory; *Archivist*, J Charles Heaberlin; Staff 5 (MLS 3, Non-MLS 2)
Founded 1865. Enrl 180; Fac 14; Highest Degree: Doctorate
1999-2000 Income $400,000. Mats Exp $151,976, Books $96,021, Per/Ser (Incl. Access Fees) $45,955, Presv $8,000, AV Equip $2,000
Library Holdings: Bk Vols 139,000; Bk Titles 93,000; Per Subs 1,000
Subject Interests: Biblical studies, Religion
Special Collections: John Mason Neale, Disciples of Christ
Database Vendor: Innovative Interfaces INN - View
Publications: Guide to Cane Ridge; Occasional Papers
Partic in SE Libr Network

S LEXINGTON-FAYETTE URBAN-COUNTY PLANNING COMMISSION, Technical Information Library,* 200 E Main St, 40507. SAN 375-0418. Tel: 606-258-3160. FAX: 606-258-3163. *Dir*, Dale B Thoma
Library Holdings: Bk Vols 400; Per Subs 13

S LEXMARK INT, INC, Information Center,* Bldg 005-1, Dept 990L, 40550. SAN 306-3127. Tel: 606-232-6044. FAX: 606-232-5728. E-Mail: techlibl@lexmark.com. *Librn*, Ann Woosley; *Librn*, Debbie Sharp; E-Mail: dsharp@lexmark.com
Founded 1959
Library Holdings: Bk Vols 13,000
Subject Interests: Business and management, Chemistry, Electronic engineering, Mechanical engineering, Metallurgy, Physics
Special Collections: Patents; Products Manuals; Programming Trade Literature
Partic in SE Libr Network

M SAINT JOSEPH HOSPITAL, Medical Library, One Saint Joseph Dr, 40504. SAN 306-3186. Tel: 859-313-1677. FAX: 859-313-3065. Web Site: www.sjhlex.org. *Dir*, Tony Hopkins; E-Mail: tony_hopkins@sjhlex.org
Library Holdings: Bk Vols 935; Per Subs 185
Subject Interests: Medicine, Nursing
Partic in Bluegrass Med Librns; Kentucky Health Science Libraries Consortium; National Library Of Medicine, Medlars; Tri-State Libr Consortium
Open to students & all health related professionals

L STOLL, KEENON & PARK, Law Library,* 201 E Main St, Ste 1000, 40507-1380. SAN 372-1205. Tel: 606-231-3000. FAX: 606-253-1093. *Librn*, Jeffrey L Frey; E-Mail: jlfrey@skp.com
Library Holdings: Bk Vols 10,000; Per Subs 150

C TRANSYLVANIA UNIVERSITY LIBRARY, 300 N Broadway, 40508. SAN 306-3194. Tel: 859-233-8225. FAX: 859-233-8779. Web Site: www.transy.edu/library/library.htm. *Dir*, Kathleen C Bryson; E-Mail: kbryson@mail.transy.edu; *Circ*, Suzie Scott; E-Mail: sescott@mail.transy.edu; *Acq, AV*, Ann Long; E-Mail: along@mail.transy.edu; *Bibliog Instr, ILL, Ref*, Carolyn Tassie; E-Mail: ctassie@mail.transy.edu; *Cat*, Tamara Farnsworth; E-Mail: tfarnsworth@mail.transy.edu; *Rare Bks, Spec Coll*, B J Gooch; E-Mail: bjgooch@mail.transy.edu; *Tech Servs*, Linda Orr; E-Mail: lorr@mail.transy.edu; Staff 8 (MLS 4, Non-MLS 4)
Founded 1780. Enrl 1,080; Fac 80; Highest Degree: Bachelor
Jul 1999-Jun 2000 Income Parent Institution $467,192. Mats Exp $237,291, Books $83,580, Per/Ser (Incl. Access Fees) $78,746, Presv $1,000, Micro $4,800, AV Equip $2,000, Electronic Ref Mat (Incl. Access Fees) $18,872. Sal $229,901 (Prof $151,900)
Library Holdings: Bk Vols 112,114; Bk Titles 92,309; Per Subs 500
Special Collections: Horse, Sporting & Natural History (Clara S Peck Coll); Kentucky History (J Winston Coleman Kentuckiana Coll), bks, photogs; Medicine to 1850 (Transylvania Medical Library); University archives & ms collection
Automation Activity & Vendor Info: (Acquisitions) epixtech, inc.; (Cataloging) epixtech, inc.; (Circulation) epixtech, inc.; (Course Reserve) epixtech, inc.; (OPAC) epixtech, inc.; (Serials) epixtech, inc.
Database Vendor: Ebsco - EbscoHost, OCLC - First Search, ProQuest
Partic in Dialog Corporation; Kentucky Library Network, Inc; OCLC Online Computer Library Center, Inc; SE Libr Network

C UNIVERSITY OF KENTUCKY LIBRARIES, William T Young Library, 40506-0456. SAN 342-4200. Tel: 859-257-0500, Ext 2083. Interlibrary Loan Service Tel: 859-257-0500, Ext 2040. Circulation Tel: 859-257-0500. Ext 2072. Reference Tel: 859-257-0500, Ext 2170. TDD: 859-257-8396. FAX: 859-257-0502. Web Site: www.uky.edu/libraries. *Dir*, Mary Molinaro; Tel: 859-257-0500, Ext 2090, Fax: 859-257-8379, E-Mail: molinaro@email.uky.edu; *Dir*, Paul A Willis; Tel: 859-257-0500, Ext 2087, Fax: 859-257-8379, E-Mail: willis@pop.uky.edu; *Circ*, Judith Brown; Tel: 859-257-0500, Ext 2068, Fax: 859-257-8379, E-Mail: jabrown@pop.uky.edu; *ILL*, Barbara Hale; Tel: 859-257-0500, Ext 2082, E-Mail: bshale@pop.uky.edu; *Ser*, Mary McLaren; Tel: 859-257-0500, Ext 2049, Fax: 859-257-0508, E-Mail: mclaren@pop.uky.edu; *Ref*, Mary Vass; Tel: 859-257-0500, Ext 2114, Fax: 859-257-0505, E-Mail: maryvass@pop.uky.edu; *Business*, Patricia Lloyd; Tel: 859-257-0500, Ext 2085, Fax: 859-257-8379, E-Mail: pat@

email.uky.edu; *Spec Coll*, William Marshall; Tel: 859-257-8371, Fax: 859-257-6311, E-Mail: wjmars01@pop.uky.edu; *Syst Coordr*, Tari Keller; Tel: 859-257-0500, Ext 2116, Fax: 859-257-0505, E-Mail: keller@pop.uky.edu; *Coll Develop*, James Burgett; Tel: 859-257-0500, Ext 2029, Fax: 859-257-0504, E-Mail: jeburg01@pop.uky.edu; Staff 114 (MLS 114)
Founded 1909. Fac 1,348; Highest Degree: Doctorate
Jul 1999-Jun 2000 Mats Exp $7,695,091, Books $1,691,312, Per/Ser (Incl. Access Fees) $5,063,585, Presv $205,289. Sal $8,853,993 (Prof $4,852,504)
Library Holdings: Bk Vols 2,860,457; Per Subs 29,850
Subject Interests: Agriculture, Appalachia, Coal, Education, Engineering, History, Humanities, Law, Medicine, Music
Special Collections: 17th-century English Literature: Milton & Miltoniana; Appalachian Coll, (Appalachian Regional Commission Archives, Frontier Nursing Service, bks, mss, archives); Applied Anthropology Documentation Coll; Broadcast & Audio-Visual Archives; Broadside Ballads & Chapbooks; Dime Novels; Early English Romantics: Wordsworth, Coleridge, Lamb (W Hugh Peal Coll); French English & Spanish Drama, 1600-1930; Graphic Arts; Kentuckiana (Breckinridge Family, Henry Clay, Cassius M Clay, Laura Clay, Zachary Taylor, Wickliffe-Preston Papers); Kentucky Imprints (Samuel M Wilson Coll); Medicine (Daniel Drake Coll); Modern Political Archives (approximately 30 record groups, including Alben Barkley, A B Chandler, Earl Clements, John Sherman Cooper, Thruston & Rogers C B Morton, Stanley Reed, Jouett Shouse, Brent Spence, A O Stanley, Fred Vinson, Wilson Wyatt); Musicology (Alfred Cortot Library); Photographic Archives; Printing & Modern Fine Printing (King Library Press, Victor Hammer, Gravesend & Bur Presses); Spanish Manuscript Coll, 1139-1800; Urban Planning Coll; Western Travel
Publications: Kentucky Review; Occasional Papers
Mem of Asn of Research Libraries
Partic in Center For Research Libraries; Kentucky Library Network, Inc; SE Ind Area Libr Servs Authority; State Assisted Academic Library Council Of Kentucky
Friends of the Library Group
Departmental Libraries:
AGRICULTURAL INFORMATION CENTER, N24 Agr Sci Bldg, 40546-0091. SAN 342-4235. Tel: 859-257-2758. FAX: 859-323-4719. Web Site: webdocs.ca.uky.edu/aic. *Dir*, Antoinette Powell; E-Mail: apowell@ca.uky.edu; *Librn*, Valerie Perry; E-Mail: vperry@pop.uky.edu
Subject Interests: Agriculture, Botany, Entomology, Food industry and trade, Forestry, Horticulture, Landscape architecture, Nutrition, Veterinary medicine
ARCHITECTURE, 200 Pence Hall, 40506-0041. SAN 342-426X. Tel: 859-257-1533. FAX: 859-257-4305. Web Site: www.uky.edu/libraries. *Librn*, Faith Harders; Tel: 859-257-4305, E-Mail: fharders@ukcc.uky.edu
Library Holdings: Bk Vols 34,566; Per Subs 128
Subject Interests: Architecture, Furniture, Interior design, Landscape architecture, Urban planning
Special Collections: Le Corbusier
Publications: Library Guide
CHEMISTRY-PHYSICS, 150 Chemistry/Physics Bldg, 40506-0055. SAN 342-4383. Tel: 859-257-5954. FAX: 859-257-4074. *Dir*, Maggie Johnson; E-Mail: mjohnson@pop.uky.edu
Library Holdings: Bk Vols 69,065; Per Subs 362
Subject Interests: Astronomy, Chemistry, Physics
EDUCATION, 205 Dickey Hall, 40506-0017. SAN 342-4413. Tel: 859-257-7977. FAX: 859-323-1976. Web Site: www.uky.edu/libraries/educ.html. *Librn*, Gillian Buckland; Tel: 859-257-1351, E-Mail: jill@pop.uky.edu
Library Holdings: Bk Vols 90,809; Per Subs 414
Subject Interests: Education, Juvenile delinquency, Young adult literature
Special Collections: ERIC Coll, microfiche
ENGINEERING, 355 Anderson Hall, 40506-0046. SAN 342-4448. Tel: 859-257-2965. FAX: 859-323-1911. Web Site: www.uky.edu/libraries/engin.html. *Librn*, James Manasco; Tel: 859-257-8358, E-Mail: manasco@pop.uky.edu; *Librn*, Reinette Jones; E-Mail: rjones@pop.uky.edu
Library Holdings: Bk Vols 112,891; Per Subs 775
Subject Interests: Coal, Energy, Engineering, Environmental engineering, Transportation
Special Collections: Environmental Reports; Industry Standards; Robotics
GEOLOGICAL SCIENCES, 100 Bowman Hall, 40506-0059. SAN 342-4472. Tel: 859-257-5730. FAX: 859-257-5730. Web Site: www.uky.edu/libraries/geo.htm. *Librn*, Mary Spencer; E-Mail: klimrs@ukcc.uky.edu
Library Holdings: Bk Vols 55,204; Per Subs 388
Subject Interests: Economics, Geochemistry, Geology, Geophysics, Mineralogy, Mining, Paleontology, Petroleum
Special Collections: Kentucky Geology; Map Coll
LAW, 130 College of Law Bldg, 40506-0048. SAN 342-4502. Tel: 859-257-8686. FAX: 859-323-4906. Web Site: www.uky.edu/law. *Dir*, Herbert Cihak; Tel: 859-257-8346, E-Mail: hcihak@pop.uky.edu; *Asst Dir*, Sue Burch; Tel: 859-257-5133, E-Mail: sburch@pop.uky.edu; *Librn*, Nancy Jo Fritz; Tel: 859-257-8122, E-Mail: nfritz@pop.uky.edu; *Librn*, Matt Morrison; Tel: 859-257-6421, E-Mail: mmmorr0@pop.uky.edu; *Librn*, Amy Osborne; Tel: 859-257-8347, E-Mail: amyo@pop.uky.edu; *Librn*, Carol Parris; Tel: 859-257-1081, E-Mail: carol@pop.uky.edu; *Librn*, Dee Wood; Tel: 859-257-2925, E-Mail: owood@pop.uky.edu
Library Holdings: Bk Vols 235,977; Per Subs 3,795
Special Collections: Human Rights; Jurisprudence (Kocourek Coll); US Supreme Court, briefs, records
Publications: Acquisitions List; Bibliographic Guides
LUCILLE LITTLE FINE ARTS LIBRARY & LEARNING CENTER, 40506-0224. SAN 342-4294. Tel: 859-257-2800. FAX: 859-257-4662. Web Site: www.uky.edu/libraries/. *Dir*, Gail Kennedy; Tel: 859-257-4631, E-Mail: gkennedy@pop.uky.edu; *Librn*, Meg Shaw; Tel: 859-257-4908, E-Mail: megshaw@pop.uky.edu; *Librn*, Paula Hickner; Tel: 859-257-4104, E-Mail: plhick00@pop.uky.edu; *Librn*, Kerri Scannell; Tel: 859-257-4630, E-Mail: scannel@pop.uky.edu. Subject Specialists: *Art*, Meg Shaw; *Music*, Paula Hickner
Library Holdings: Bk Vols 104,841; Per Subs 585
Subject Interests: Art, Music, Photography, Theater
Special Collections: Acting Editions of Plays; Early Music Treatises (Alfred Cortot Coll); Wilcox American Music Coll
Publications: Library guide
MATHEMATICAL SCIENCES, OB-9 Patterson Office Tower, 40506-0027. SAN 342-4537. Tel: 859-257-8365. FAX: 859-257-8365. E-Mail: teheck01@pop.uky.edu. *Librn*, Tom Hecker; Tel: 859-257-8343, E-Mail: teheck01@pop.uky.edu
Library Holdings: Bk Vols 40,712; Per Subs 231
Subject Interests: Computer science, Mathematics, Statistics
Special Collections: Programming Languages

CM MEDICAL CENTER LIBRARY, 800 Rose St, 40536-0298. SAN 342-4561. Tel: 859-323-5300. Interlibrary Loan Service Tel: 859-323-6565. FAX: 859-323-1040, 859-323-6805. E-Mail: mclstith@pop.uky.edu. Web Site: www.uky.edu/medicalcenter/medlibrary/info-about/html. *Dir*, Janet Stith; Tel: 859-323-5767, E-Mail: mclstith@pop.uky.edu; *Librn*, Bernadette Baldini; Tel: 859-323-6138, E-Mail: baldini@pop.uky.edu; *Librn*, Jane Bryant; Tel: 859-323-5715, E-Mail: jbryant@pop.uky.edu; *Librn*, Frank Davis; Tel: 859-323-3983, E-Mail: fldavi2@pop.uky.edu; *AV*, Beverly Hilton; Tel: 859-323-8008, E-Mail: bahilt00@pop.uky.edu; *Online Servs*, Stephanie Allen; Tel: 859-323-6567, E-Mail: snalle01@ukcc.uky.edu; *Coll Develop, Ser*, Cindy Cline; Tel: 859-323-6781, E-Mail: mclcindy@pop.uky.edu; *Cat*, Lynne Bowman; Tel: 859-323-8919, E-Mail: lbbowm01@pop.uky.edu; *Ref*, Rick Brewer; Tel: 859-323-5296, E-Mail: rabrew02@pop.uky.edu; *Ref*, Mark Ingram; Tel: 859-323-6568, E-Mail: maingr01@ukcc.uky.edu; *Outreach Serv*, Winn Theirl; Tel: 859-323-8285, E-Mail: mclebt@pop.uky.edu
Founded 1957. Enrl 2,531; Fac 540; Highest Degree: Doctorate
Jul 1999-Jun 2000 Income $2,808,915. Mats Exp $1,429,866. Sal $1,163,140 (Prof $674,272)
Library Holdings: Bk Vols 207,720; Per Subs 1,462
Subject Interests: Allied health, Medicine, Nursing
Mem of University of Ky Libr
Partic in Kentucky Library Network, Inc; National Network Of Libraries Of Medicine - South Central Region; OCLC Online Computer Library Center, Inc; SE Libr Network

LIBERTY

P CASEY COUNTY PUBLIC LIBRARY,* 238 Middleburg St, 42539. SAN 320-8192. Tel: 606-787-9381. FAX: 606-787-7720. E-Mail: ccplstaff@kih.net. *Librn*, Jan J Banks
Pop 14,212; Circ 124,000
Library Holdings: Bk Vols 48,000
Special Collections: Genealogy Coll; Kentucky Coll; Large Print Coll
Mem of Lake Cumberland Regional Libr Syst
Open Mon, Tues, Weds & Fri 2-6, Sat 9-3
Friends of the Library Group

LONDON

P LAUREL COUNTY PUBLIC LIBRARY DISTRICT, 116 E Fourth St, 40741. SAN 306-3224. Tel: 606-864-5759. FAX: 606-864-9061. E-Mail: laurelcolib@sun-spot.com. *Dir*, Lori Acton; *Tech Servs*, Joyce Johnson; *Bkmobile Coordr*, Gina Irvin; *Publ Servs*, Jeanette Smith; Staff 14 (MLS 14)
Founded 1915. Pop 52,790; Circ 150,000
Jul 2000-Jun 2001 Income $950,000, State $53,000, County $819,000, Locally Generated Income $52,869. Mats Exp $185,000, Books $120,000, Per/Ser (Incl. Access Fees) $5,000, AV Equip $5,000. Sal $260,000
Library Holdings: Bk Vols 70,000; Per Subs 214
Partic in Kentucky Library Network, Inc
Open Mon & Tues 9-7, Wed-Fri 9-6 & Sat 9-5
Branches: 1
BENNETT CENTER, 60 Bennett Circle, 40741. Tel: 606-864-5940. *Branch Mgr*, Vickie Nicholson
Open Mon-Fri 8-6 & Sat 9-12

LOUISA

P LAWRENCE COUNTY PUBLIC LIBRARY,* 102 W Main & Jefferson, PO Box 600, 41230. SAN 306-3259. Tel: 606-638-4497. FAX: 606-638-1293. Web Site: ww.kellyswebdesign.com/library. *Dir*, Mary McGuire; E-Mail: mary.mcguire@mail.state.ky.us
Pop 14,121; Circ 99,087
Library Holdings: Bk Vols 25,000; Per Subs 98
Subject Interests: Kentucky

LOUISVILLE

§S AMERICAN AIR FILTER INTERNATIONAL LIBRARY, PO Box 35690, 40232. Tel: 502-637-0451. *Librn*, Cindy Burns
Library Holdings: Bk Vols 275; Per Subs 20

S AMERICAN PRINTING HOUSE FOR THE BLIND, INC, Educational Research Library, 1839 Frankfort Ave, PO Box 6085, 40206-0085. SAN 372-6304. Tel: 502-895-2405, 502-899-2321. FAX: 502-899-2274. Web Site: www.aph.org. *Res*, Andrea Peak; E-Mail: apeak@aph.org
Founded 1968
Library Holdings: Per Subs 80
Special Collections: Blind Education, Development & Research
Restriction: Staff use only

M BAPTIST HOSPITAL EAST, Hagan-Pedigo Library, 4000 Kresge Way, 40207-4676. SAN 324-5977. Tel: 502-897-8183. FAX: 502-897-8020. *Librn*, Dina Burshteyn
Founded 1978
Library Holdings: Bk Titles 1,200; Per Subs 219
Subject Interests: Medicine, Nursing
Restriction: Staff use only
Partic in Kentucky Health Science Libraries Consortium; Kentucky Library Network, Inc; Nat Libr of Med; SE Libr Network

C BELLARMINE UNIVERSITY LIBRARY, (Formerly Bellarmine College Library), 2001 Newburg Rd, 40205-0671. SAN 306-3291. Tel: 502-452-8137. FAX: 502-452-8038. *Dir, Tech Servs*, Marquita Breit; Tel: 502-452-8140, E-Mail: mbreit@bellarmine.edu; *ILL, Ref Serv*, John Boyd; Tel: 502-452-8314, E-Mail: jboyd@bellarmine.edu; *Instrul Serv, Ref Serv*, Martha R Perry; Tel: 502-452-8139, E-Mail: mperry@bellarmine.edu; *Media Spec*, Jeanne Catalano; Tel: 502-452-8142, E-Mail: jcatalano@bellarmine.edu; *Circ*, Kat McMain; Tel: 502-452-8308, E-Mail: kmcmain@bellarmine.edu
Founded 1950. Enrl 2,400; Fac 115; Highest Degree: Master
Jun 1999-May 2000 Income $746,000
Library Holdings: Bk Vols 113,500; Bk Titles 96,000; Per Subs 541
Subject Interests: Health sciences
Special Collections: Louisville Archdiocesan Coll, a-tapes; Louisville Historical League, a-tapes; Miles Coll of US Civil War History; Riebel Literature Coll; Thomas Merton Coll
Database Vendor: Innovative Interfaces INN - View
Publications: Student Library Handbook
Partic in Coun of Independent Ky Cols & Univs; Kentuckiana Metroversity, Inc; OCLC Online Computer Library Center, Inc; SE Libr Network

M CARITAS HEALTH SERVICES, Health Sciences Library,* 1850 Bluegrass Ave, 40215. SAN 324-5403. Tel: 502-361-6428. FAX: 502-361-6799. *Coordr*, Wanda Polley
Library Holdings: Bk Vols 1,720; Per Subs 208
Subject Interests: Medicine, Nursing
Partic in Kentucky Health Science Libraries Consortium

M CARITAS PEACE CENTER, Medical Library,* 2020 Newburg Rd, PO Box 32690, 40232. SAN 306-3534. Tel: 502-451-3330, Ext 594. FAX: 502-459-9075. *Coordr*, Wanda Pauley
Library Holdings: Bk Vols 1,244; Per Subs 50
Subject Interests: Psychiatry

M CENTRAL STATE HOSPITAL LIBRARY,* 10510 LaGrange Rd, 40223. SAN 325-5697. Tel: 502-245-4121, Ext 302. FAX: 502-253-7435. *In Charge*, Rose Sutherland

R CHRIST CHURCH UNITED METHODIST LIBRARY,* 4614 Brownsboro Rd, 40207. SAN 306-333X. Tel: 502-897-6421. FAX: 502-893-2794. *Dir*, Jennie Weeks; E-Mail: jennie@htr.net
Founded 1958
Friends of the Library Group

S COURIER-JOURNAL & LOUISVILLE TIMES CO, INC LIBRARY, 525 W Broadway, PO Box 740031, 40201-7431. SAN 306-3364. Tel: 502-582-4184. FAX: 502-582-4290. *Ref*, Sharon Bidwell; E-Mail: sbidwell@louisv02.gannett.com; Staff 3 (MLS 3)
Founded 1937
Library Holdings: Bk Vols 4,000; Per Subs 50
Subject Interests: Coal, History, Horses, Kentucky, Tobacco
Special Collections: Kentucky History
Partic in Data Time; Dialog Corporation; OCLC Online Computer Library Center, Inc

R CRESCENT HILL BAPTIST CHURCH LIBRARY, 2800 Frankfort Ave, 40206. SAN 306-3372. Tel: 502-896-4425. FAX: 502-896-9855. E-Mail: chbc@aye.net. Web Site: www.chbc-louky.org.
Library Holdings: Bk Vols 3,000; Per Subs 10
Friends of the Library Group

GM DEPARTMENT OF VETERANS AFFAIRS, Hospital Library, 800 Zorn Ave, 40206-1499. SAN 306-3615. Tel: 502-894-6240. FAX: 502-894-6134. *Chief Librn*, Gene Haynes; *Tech Servs*, Cindy Givans; *Tech Servs*, Sue Tomes; Staff 3 (MLS 1, Non-MLS 2)
Founded 1952
Library Holdings: Bk Vols 3,250; Bk Titles 3,200; Per Subs 320
Subject Interests: Allied health, Dentistry, Medicine, Nursing
Automation Activity & Vendor Info: (Circulation) Sagebrush Corporation
Database Vendor: OCLC - First Search, OVID Technologies
Restriction: Not open to public
Function: Literary searches
Partic in Kentucky Health Science Libraries Consortium; Kentucky Library Network, Inc; Veterans Affairs Library Network

R DOUGLASS BOULEVARD CHRISTIAN CHURCH LIBRARY,* 2005 Douglass Blvd, 40205. SAN 306-3380. Tel: 502-452-2629. FAX: 502-452-2225.
Founded 1940
1997-1998 Income $968, Locally Generated Income $225, Parent Institution $600, Other $143. Mats Exp $320, Books $300, Per/Ser (Incl. Access Fees) $20
Library Holdings: Bk Titles 2,500
Subject Interests: Biblical studies, Fiction, Mental health, Missions and missionaries, Religion

S EMBROIDERERS GUILD OF AMERICA INC LIBRARY,* 335 W Broadway, Ste 100, 40202. SAN 325-5735. Tel: 502-589-6956. FAX: 502-584-7900. E-Mail: egahq@aol.com. Web Site: www.egausa.org. *Librn*, Thelma Herweh; *Admin Assoc*, Caroline Deutsch
Library Holdings: Bk Titles 4,500
Subject Interests: History
Special Collections: Clip Art Files; Needleart Videos; Rare Books
Automation Activity & Vendor Info: (Cataloging) Follett
Publications: Needle Arts Magazine & "how to" books

S FILSON CLUB HISTORICAL SOCIETY LIBRARY,* 1310 S Third St, 40208. SAN 306-3402. Tel: 502-635-5083. FAX: 502-635-5086. E-Mail: filson@filsonclub.org. Web Site: www.filsonclub.org. *Dir*, Dr Mark V Wetherington; *Librn*, Judith Partington; *Curator*, James Holmberg; Staff 10 (MLS 7, Non-MLS 3)
Founded 1884
Library Holdings: Bk Vols 55,000; Per Subs 100
Subject Interests: Genealogy, History, Kentucky
Special Collections: Ephemera; historical manuscripts; KY portraits; Maps; newspapers; photographs; Prints; Rare books; Sheet music; Silver (Kentucky Silversmiths Coll)
Publications: Filson Club History Quarterly; Newsletter; Publication Series (history)
Partic in Kentucky Library Network, Inc

L FROST, BROWN & TODD LLC, (Formerly Brown, Todd & Heyburn, PLLC), Law Library, 400 W Market St 32nd flr, 40202. SAN 372-1264. Tel: 502-589-5400. FAX: 502-581-1087. Web Site: www.fbtlaw.com. *Head Librn*, Patsy Bourke; E-Mail: pbourke@fbtlaw.com
Library Holdings: Bk Vols 15,000; Bk Titles 3,000; Per Subs 50
Restriction: Staff use only

L GREENEBAUM, DOLL & MCDONALD, Law Library, 3300 National City Tower, 40202. SAN 372-1272. Tel: 502-589-4200. FAX: 502-587-3695. Web Site: www.gdm.com. *Librn*, Constance Ard; *Asst Librn*, Susan Odewahn; *Ref*, Robert Farmer
Library Holdings: Bk Vols 30,000; Per Subs 172
Automation Activity & Vendor Info: (Cataloging) Inmagic, Inc.
Open Mon-Fri 8am-9pm

J JEFFERSON COMMUNITY COLLEGE, John T Smith Learning Resource Center, 109 E Broadway, 40202. SAN 342-4626. Tel: 502-213-2157. FAX: 502-585-4425. Web Site: www.jctc.kctcs.net/library. *Dir Libr Serv*, Sheree Huber-Williams; Tel: 502-213-2156, E-Mail: sheree.williams@kctcs.net; *ILL*, Nancy Mollette; *Tech Servs*, Nina Deeley; Tel: 502-213-2373, E-Mail: nina.deeley@kctcs.net; *Publ Servs*, Jeffrey Matthias
Founded 1968. Enrl 8,431; Fac 172; Highest Degree: Associate
Jul 1998-Jun 1999 Mats Exp $111,285, Books $58,954, Per/Ser (Incl. Access Fees) $20,828, Micro $8,056, AV Equip $7,619, Electronic Ref Mat (Incl. Access Fees) $15,828. Sal $428,921 (Prof $197,542)
Library Holdings: Bk Vols 53,434; Bk Titles 49,600; Per Subs 300
Automation Activity & Vendor Info: (Acquisitions) Endeavor; (Cataloging) Endeavor; (Circulation) Endeavor; (Course Reserve) Endeavor; (OPAC) Endeavor; (Serials) Endeavor
Database Vendor: Ebsco - EbscoHost, GaleNet
Function: Reference services available
Partic in SE Libr Network
Departmental Libraries:
SOUTHWEST CAMPUS LIBRARY, 1000 Community College Dr, 40272. SAN 342-4650. Tel: 502-935-9840, Ext 3210. FAX: 502-935-8653. Web Site: www.jcc.uky.edu. *Librn*, Larry Rees; *Ref*, Rafe A Johnson; *Tech Servs*, Sarah Cooper; *Circ*, Kelly O'Hara
Founded 1972
Library Holdings: Bk Titles 32,500; Per Subs 190
Partic in SE Libr Network

S JEFFERSON COUNTY HISTORICAL PRESERVATION & ARCHIVES, Urban County Government Center, 810 Barret Ave, 6th flr, 40204. SAN 374-9525. Tel: 502-574-5761. FAX: 502-574-6886. *Archivist*, David Morgan
Library Holdings: Spec Interest Per Sub 2,400
Function: Archival collection

L JEFFERSON COUNTY PUBLIC LAW LIBRARY, Old Jail Bldg, Ste 240, 514 W Liberty St, 40202-2806. SAN 306-3429. Tel: 502-574-5943. FAX: 502-574-3483. E-Mail: jcpll@bluegrass.net. Web Site: www.jcpll.com. *Dir*, Linda Miller Robbins; Staff 1 (MLS 1)
Founded 1839
1998-1999 Income $399,183. Mats Exp $154,616. Sal $132,880
Library Holdings: Bk Vols 90,000
Special Collections: Indiana Coll; Kentucky Coll
Partic in Westlaw
Friends of the Library Group

R JEWISH COMMUNITY CENTER, Israel T Naamani Library, 3600 Dutchman's Lane, 40205. SAN 306-3313. Tel: 502-459-0660, Ext 107. FAX: 502-459-6885. Web Site: www.jccoflouisville.org. *Librn*, Linda Goldberg; E-Mail: lgoldberg@jccoflouisville.org
Founded 1948
Library Holdings: Bk Vols 7,000; Per Subs 20
Special Collections: Jewish Music, Art, Theology, Crafts & Local Jewish History, Holocaust, Genealogy
Publications: Jewish Holiday Bibliographies; Monthly Newsletter

M JEWISH HOSPITAL, Medical Library,* 217 E Chestnut, 40202. SAN 327-6023. Tel: 502-587-4280. FAX: 502-587-4891. *Mgr*, Anne Sabetta; E-Mail: anne.sabetta@jhhs.org; *Tech Servs*, R Michael Steinmacher
Jan 1997-Dec 1998 Income $175,000. Mats Exp $80,000, Books $15,000, Per/Ser (Incl. Access Fees) $55,000, Micro $10,000. Sal $61,100 (Prof $39,600)
Library Holdings: Bk Vols 1,500; Bk Titles 1,200
Partic in Kentucky Health Science Libraries Consortium; Kentucky Library Network, Inc

S KENTUCKY BANKERS ASSOCIATION LIBRARY,* 325 W Main St, Ste 1000, 40202. SAN 306-3437. Tel: 502-582-2453. FAX: 502-584-6390. *Librn*, Debra Stamper; E-Mail: dstamper@kybanks.com

S KENTUCKY SCHOOL FOR THE BLIND LIBRARY, 1867 Frankfort Ave, 40206. SAN 325-1853. Tel: 502-897-1583, Ext 264. FAX: 502-897-2994. *Librn*, Cathy Hicks; E-Mail: chicks@ksb.k12.ky.us
Founded 1842. Enrl 93; Fac 111
Library Holdings: Bk Titles 18,373; Per Subs 25
Subject Interests: Physical handicaps, Recreational reading
Special Collections: Braille, Talking Books
Automation Activity & Vendor Info: (Cataloging) Sagebrush Corporation; (Circulation) Sagebrush Corporation

S LOUISVILLE & JEFFERSON COUNTY PLANNING COMMISSION, Louisville Metropolitan Planning Library,* 531 Court Pl, Ste 900, 40202. SAN 371-1714. Tel: 502-574-6230. FAX: 502-574-8129. *Publ Servs*, Connie Huber
Library Holdings: Bk Vols 400; Per Subs 10

S LOUISVILLE ACADEMY OF MUSIC LIBRARY,* 2740 Frankfort Ave, 40206-2669. SAN 306-3461. Tel: 502-893-7885. *Dir*, Robert B French
Founded 1954
1997-1998 Mats Exp $1,000
Library Holdings: Bk Titles 8,000
Subject Interests: Literature, Local history, Photography
Special Collections: 19th Century First Editions, poster, map & postcards; Antique Piano Rolls; Biographies on Local Musicians; Local History; Music by & about American Composers-Robert Crone, Roy Harris, Roy Nolte & Clifford Shaw, records & written mat; National Geographic Magazine
Open Mon-Fri 2-10

§S LOUISVILLE CHAMBER OF COMMERCE LIBRARY, 600 W Main St, 40202. Tel: 502-625-0000. FAX: 502-625-0010. *Librn*, Curt Martin
Library Holdings: Bk Vols 3,000; Per Subs 75

P LOUISVILLE FREE PUBLIC LIBRARY, 301 York St, 40203-2257. SAN 342-4685. Tel: 502-574-1600. Circulation Tel: 502-574-1781. Reference Tel: 502-574-1616. FAX: 502-574-1657, 574-1666. Web Site: www.lfpl.org. *Dir*, Craig Buthod; Tel: 502-574-1740, E-Mail: buthod@lfpl.org; *Asst Dir*, Jean Varble; Tel: 502-574-1607, Fax: 502-574-1693, E-Mail: jean@lfpl.org; *Asst Dir*, Mary Frances Cooper; Tel: 502-574-1743, E-Mail: cooper@lfpl.org; *Ch Servs*, Susan Moore; *Info Specialist*, Charles Harris; *Coll Develop*, Karen James; Staff 62 (MLS 62)
Founded 1816. Pop 664,937; Circ 3,324,749
Jul 1998-Jun 1999 Income (Main Library and Branch Library) $16,126,457. Mats Exp $3,061,183. Sal $7,816,781
Library Holdings: Bk Vols 1,191,630; Per Subs 776
Special Collections: Foundation Center Regional Coll; Kentucky Author Coll; Kentucky History Coll; US Patent
Publications: Monthly Calendar of Events
Partic in Ky Coop Libr Info Project; SE Libr Network
Special Services for the Deaf - TTY machine
Friends of the Library Group
Branches: 17
BON AIR REGIONAL, 2816 Del Rio Pl, 40220. SAN 342-474X. Tel: 502-574-1795. FAX: 502-454-0169. Web Site: www.flpl.org. *Librn*, Geneva Huttenlocher
Friends of the Library Group
CRESCENT HILL, 2762 Frankfort Ave, 40206. SAN 342-4774. Tel: 502-574-1793. FAX: 502-894-8505. Web Site: www.lfpl.org. *Librn*, Montie Manning
Friends of the Library Group
FAIRDALE BRANCH, 10616 W Manslick Rd, Fairdale, 40118. SAN 378-0260. Tel: 502-375-2051. FAX: 502-375-2016. Web Site: www.lfpl.org. *Mgr*, Polly Price
FERN CREEK, 6768 Bardstown Rd, 40291. SAN 373-8132. Tel: 502-231-4605. FAX: 502-239-3336. Web Site: www.lfpl.org. *Librn*, Laura Kelleher
Friends of the Library Group
HIGHLANDS-SHELBY PARK, Mid-City Mall, 1250 Bardstown Rd, 40204. SAN 342-4987. Tel: 502-574-1672. FAX: 502-451-0548. Web Site: www.lfpl.org. *Librn*, Mona Leitner
Friends of the Library Group
IROQUOIS, 601 W Woodlawn, 40215. SAN 342-5045. Tel: 502-574-1720. FAX: 502-367-1468. Web Site: www.lfpl.org. *Librn*, Stacy DeCoste
Friends of the Library Group
JEFFERSONTOWN BRANCH, 10635 Watterson Trail, Jeffersontown, 40299. SAN 342-507X. Tel: 502-267-5713. FAX: 502-266-6569. Web Site: www.lfpl.org. *Librn*, Nancye Browning
Friends of the Library Group
MIDDLETOWN, 200 N Juneau Dr, 40243. SAN 325-4135. Tel: 502-245-7332. FAX: 502-245-7038. Web Site: www.lfpl.org. *Librn*, Debra Oberhausen
Friends of the Library Group
OKOLONA, 7709 Preston Hwy, 40219. SAN 342-5169. Tel: 502-964-3515. FAX: 502-964-7025. Web Site: www.lfpl.org. *Librn*, Rebecca Miller
Friends of the Library Group
PORTLAND, 3305 Northwestern Pkwy, 40212. SAN 342-5258. Tel: 502-574-1744. FAX: 502-776-9947. Web Site: www.lfpl.org. *Librn*, Beth Pointer
Friends of the Library Group
ST MATTHEWS-ELINE BRANCH, 3940 Grandview Ave, 40207. SAN 342-4804. Tel: 502-574-1771. FAX: 502-894-8709. Web Site: www.lfpl.org. *Librn*, Susan Irving
Friends of the Library Group
SHAWNEE, 3912 W Broadway, 40211. SAN 342-5282. Tel: 502-574-1722. FAX: 502-776-9983. Web Site: www.lfpl.org. *Librn*, Raamesie Umandavi
Friends of the Library Group
SHIVELY-NEWMAN, 3920 Dixie Hwy, 40216. SAN 342-5134. Tel: 502-574-1730. FAX: 502-449-3886. Web Site: www.lfpl.org. *Librn*, Patricia Watson
SOUTHWEST REGIONAL, 10375 Dixie Hwy, 40272. SAN 328-9028. Tel: 502-933-0029. FAX: 502-933-2782. Web Site: www.lfpl.org. *Librn*, Susan Baugh
Friends of the Library Group
P TALKING BOOK LIBRARY, 301 York St, 40203. Tel: 502-574-1625. Web Site: www.lfpl.org. *Librn*, Tom Denning; Staff 8 (MLS 1, Non-MLS 7)
Founded 1976
Special Services - Louisville Courier-Journal, highlights recorded weekly; Louisville, recorded monthly; TV Listings, recorded weekly; volunteer recordings available upon request
Friends of the Library Group
WESTERN, 604 S Tenth St, 40203. SAN 342-5401. Tel: 502-574-1779. FAX: 502-589-9937. Web Site: www.lfpl.org. *Librn*, Carmen Samuels
Special Collections: Black History
Friends of the Library Group
WESTPORT COMMUNITY, 8100 Westport Rd, Ste B, 40222. SAN 376-8848. Tel: 502-394-0379. FAX: 502-394-0377. Web Site: www.lfpl.org. *Librn*, Alison Thielmeier
Bookmobiles: 3

R LOUISVILLE PRESBYTERIAN THEOLOGICAL SEMINARY, Ernest Miller White Library, 1044 Alta Vista Rd, 40205-1798. SAN 306-3488. Tel: 502-895-3411, Ext 265. Reference Tel: 502-895-3411, Ext 214. FAX: 502-895-1096. E-Mail: lptscirc@lpts.edu. Web Site: www.lpts.edu/library/libraryindex.html. *Dir*, Dr Milton J Coalter, Jr; Tel: 502-895-3411, Ext 471, E-Mail: jcoalter@lpts.edu; *Assoc Dir*, Barbara Whittle Terry; Tel: 502-895-3411, Ext 472, E-Mail: bterry@lpts.edu; *Ref*, Angela Morris; Tel: 502-895-3411, Ext 412, E-Mail: amorris@lpts.edu; *Info Tech*, Liz Van Kleeck; Tel: 502-895-3411, Ext 422, E-Mail: lvan_kleeck@lpts.edu; *Circ*, Rick Jones; E-Mail: rjones@lpts.edu; *Acq*, David Scarlott; Tel: 502-895-3411, Ext 421, E-Mail: dscarlott@lpts.edu; Staff 8 (MLS 3, Non-MLS 5)
Founded 1853. Enrl 242; Fac 24; Highest Degree: Doctorate
Jun 1999-May 2000 Income Parent Institution $788,335. Mats Exp $159,278, Books $82,346, Per/Ser (Incl. Access Fees) $46,612, Presv $5,423, Micro $18,543, Manuscripts & Archives $300, Electronic Ref Mat (Incl. Access Fees) $6,054. Sal $362,200 (Prof $225,603)

Library Holdings: Bk Vols 138,329; Bk Titles 92,605; Per Subs 558
Subject Interests: Religion, Social sciences and issues
Special Collections: Presbyterian History
Automation Activity & Vendor Info: (Acquisitions) DRA; (Cataloging) DRA; (Circulation) DRA; (Course Reserve) DRA; (ILL) DRA; (OPAC) DRA; (Serials) DRA
Database Vendor: DRA, Ebsco - EbscoHost, OCLC - First Search
Function: Research library
Partic in Kentuckiana Metroversity, Inc; SE Libr Network; Theological Education Association Of Mid America

S LOUISVILLE SCIENCE CENTER, 727 W Main St, 40202. SAN 373-0557. Tel: 502-561-6100, Ext 6571. FAX: 502-561-6145. *Librn*, Virginia Gregory; *Librn*, Doris Willson; E-Mail: dw40243@aol.com; *Librn*, Mary Wilkerson; Staff 3 (Non-MLS 3)
Founded 1977
Jul 1999-Jun 2000 Income $1,225. Mats Exp $1,224, Books $75, Per/Ser (Incl. Access Fees) $1,149
Library Holdings: Bk Vols 2,287; Per Subs 18
Restriction: Staff use only
Function: Research library

§S NATIONAL SOCIETY OF THE SONS OF THE AMERICAN REVOLUTION, Historical & Genealogical Research Library, 1000 S Fourth St, 40203. Tel: 502-589-1776. FAX: 502-589-1671. E-Mail: library@sar.org. Web Site: www.sar.org/geneal/library.htm. *Librn*, Michael A Christian; E-Mail: mchristi@sar.org
Jan 2000-Dec 2000 Income $70,000
Library Holdings: Bk Vols 50,000; Per Subs 20

S NATIONAL SOCIETY, SONS OF THE AMERICAN REVOLUTION, Genealogy Library, 1000 S Fourth St, 40203. SAN 306-350X. Tel: 502-589-1776. FAX: 502-589-1671. E-Mail: library@sar.org. Web Site: www.sar.org/geneal/library.htm. *Librn*, Michael A Christian
Founded 1889
Jan 2000-Dec 2000 Income $72,000
Library Holdings: Bk Vols 53,000
Subject Interests: American revolution, Census, Genealogy, Local history
Special Collections: Barbour Coll (Conn Colonial period vital records); George Washington Coll; including the Morristown mss coll & the George Washington papers on microfilm); Leach Coll (genealogy of the signers of the Declaration of Independence); revolutionary war pension records; United States Census (1790-1860)
SAR, DAR, SR & Friends of the SAR Library are admitted free of charge, others pay $5.00 per day (9:30-4:30 Eastern Time). Friends of the Library, $25.00/year.
Friends of the Library Group

M NORTON AUDUBON HOSPITAL, R Dietz Wolfe Medical Library, One Audubon Plaza Dr, 40217. SAN 306-3569. Tel: 502-636-7296. FAX: 502-636-7257. *Dir*, Karen C Wright; E-Mail: karen.wright@nortonhealthcare.org; *Librn*, Debra P Fitzpatrick; E-Mail: debra.fitzpatrick@nortonhealthcare.org; Staff 2 (MLS 2)
Founded 1928
Library Holdings: Bk Titles 550; Per Subs 55
Subject Interests: Allied health, Medical
Database Vendor: IAC - Info Trac, OVID Technologies
Function: Reference services available
Partic in Kentucky Health Science Libraries Consortium

M NORTON HEALTHCARE, Medical Library, 200 E Chestnut St, 40202. (Mail add: PO Box 35070, 40232-5070), SAN 306-3526. Tel: 502-629-8125. FAX: 502-629-8138. E-Mail: library@nortonhealthcare.org. *Mgr*, Leslie Pancratz; *Librn*, Ann Schaap. Subject Specialists: *Med info*, Ann Schaap; Staff 4 (MLS 2, Non-MLS 2)
Founded 1959
Library Holdings: Bk Titles 3,200; Per Subs 275
Subject Interests: Aging, Allied health, Consumer health, Medicine, Nursing, Orthopedics, Pediatrics
Special Collections: Hospitals' Archives
Automation Activity & Vendor Info: (Cataloging) Endeavor; (Circulation) Endeavor; (OPAC) Endeavor
Partic in BRS; OCLC Online Computer Library Center, Inc

S OFFICE OF INFORMATION SERVICES, City Archives,* Memorial Auditorium, 970 S Fourth St, 40203. SAN 327-5981. Tel: 502-574-3508. FAX: 502-574-4318.
Special Collections: Archives and Records of the City of Louisville, KY 1778-1986; City Fire Dept Records 1855-current; Small City-Generated Publications Library; Urban Renewal Records 1962-1980
Open Mon-Fri 8-5

CR SIMMONS BIBLE COLLEGE, Parrish Memorial Library,* 1811 Dumesnil St, 40210. SAN 328-1221. Tel: 502-776-1443, 502-776-5549. FAX: 502-776-2227. E-Mail: sbc1811@aol.com. Web Site: www.sbcollege.edu. *Librn*, Ruth Hill Jones; Staff 1 (MLS 1)
Enrl 200; Highest Degree: Master
Library Holdings: Bk Vols 2,800; Per Subs 15
Mem of Ky Libr Asn; SE Libr Asn
Open Mon-Thurs 8-4:30 & 6-9
Friends of the Library Group

R SOUTHERN BAPTIST THEOLOGICAL SEMINARY, James P Boyce Centennial Library, 2825 Lexington Rd, 40280-0294. SAN 342-5436. Tel: 502-897-4807. FAX: 502-897-4600. Web Site: www.sbts.edu. *Dir*, Ronald F Deering; E-Mail: rdeering@lib.sbts.edu; *Assoc Librn*, Bruce L Keisling; Tel: 502-897-4553, E-Mail: bkeisling@lib.sbts.edu; *Syst Coordr*, Martin E Hill; Tel: 502-897-4715, E-Mail: mhill@lib.sbts.edu; *Cat, Online Servs*, Martha C Powell; Tel: 502-897-4096, E-Mail: mpowell@lib.sbts.edu; *Acq*, Timothy M Faile; Tel: 502-897-4598, E-Mail: tfaile@lib.sbts.edu; *Media Spec*, Andrew B Rawls; Tel: 502-897-4508, E-Mail: arawls@lib.sbts.edu; *Archivist*, Sean Lucas; Tel: 502-897-4573, E-Mail: slucas@lib.sbts.edu. Subject Specialists: *Theology*, Ronald F Deering; Staff 27 (MLS 8, Non-MLS 19)
Founded 1859. Enrl 1,493; Fac 95; Highest Degree: Doctorate
Aug 1999-Jul 2000 Income $1,391,296. Mats Exp $250,153, Books $170,518, Per/Ser (Incl. Access Fees) $60,058, Micro $2,764, Other Print Mats $16,813. Sal $801,186 (Prof $407,440)
Library Holdings: Bk Vols 372,261; Bk Titles 307,384; Per Subs 1,503
Subject Interests: Archaeology, Bible, Education, Ethics, History, Music, Psychology, Religion, Theology
Special Collections: (Ingersoll Coll); Archaeology (William F Albright Coll); Evangelism (Billy Graham Coll); Gospel Music; Hymnology (Converse Hymnology Coll); Missions (R Pierce Beaver Coll); Music (Everett Helm Coll)
Automation Activity & Vendor Info: (Acquisitions) DRA; (Cataloging) DRA; (Circulation) DRA; (Course Reserve) DRA; (ILL) DRA; (Media Booking) DRA; (OPAC) DRA; (Serials) DRA
Database Vendor: DRA
Partic in Kentuckiana Metroversity, Inc; SE Libr Network; Team A-Librarians
Branches:
SCHOOL OF CHURCH MUSIC, 2825 Lexington Rd, 40280-0294. Tel: 502-897-4055. Web Site: www.sbts.edu. *Librn*, David A Gregory; Fax: 502-897-4600, E-Mail: dgregory@lib.sbts.edu
Aug 1999-Jul 2000 Income $124,000. Mats Exp $42,045, Books $13,999, Per/Ser (Incl. Access Fees) $6,160, Other Print Mats $16,811, Electronic Ref Mat (Incl. Access Fees) $5,075. Sal $70,301 (Prof $37,070)
Library Holdings: Bk Vols 27,013
Automation Activity & Vendor Info: (Acquisitions) DRA; (Cataloging) DRA; (Circulation) DRA; (Course Reserve) DRA; (ILL) DRA; (Media Booking) DRA; (OPAC) DRA; (Serials) DRA

C SPALDING UNIVERSITY LIBRARY, 853 Library Lane, 40203-9986. SAN 306-3585. Tel: 502-585-7130. FAX: 502-585-7156. *Dir*, Jackie Hinshaw; *Asst Dir*, David Tipton; E-Mail: dtipton@spalding.edu; *Media Spec*, Sister Mary Michelle Naber; *Online Servs*, Janice Poston; *Circ*, Ruth Ann Coomes; *Bibliog Instr, Ref*, Kevin Peers; Staff 5 (MLS 5)
Founded 1920. Enrl 1,200; Fac 128; Highest Degree: Doctorate
Library Holdings: Bk Vols 162,588; Bk Titles 105,249; Per Subs 489
Special Collections: Children's Book Review Coll; Edith Stein Coll; Kentucky Coll; Rare Books Coll
Publications: Library Lane
Partic in Coun of Independent Ky Cols & Univs; Kentuckiana Metroversity, Inc; OCLC Online Computer Library Center, Inc

S SPEED ART MUSEUM LIBRARY,* 2035 S Third St, 40208. SAN 306-3593. Tel: 502-634-2700. FAX: 502-636-2899. *Librn*, Mary Jane Benedict; Tel: 502-634-2710, E-Mail: mbenedict@speedmuseum.org
Founded 1927
Oct 1996-Sep 1997 Income $10,125. Mats Exp $7,200, Books $4,500, Per/Ser (Incl. Access Fees) $1,500, Presv $1,200
Library Holdings: Bk Titles 16,658; Per Subs 50
Subject Interests: Architecture, Art, Decorative arts, Films and filmmaking, Photography
Special Collections: Indian (Weygold Coll); J B Speed's Lincoln Books
Publications: acquisitions list; bibliographies; gallery publications index; Index to the Scrapbooks; Speed Bulletin (in-house periodical index)

L STITES & HARBISON, Law Library,* 400 W Market St Ste 1800, 40202. SAN 372-1280. Tel: 502-587-3400. FAX: 502-587-6391. Web Site: www.stites.com. *Librn*, Lynn H Fritsch; E-Mail: lfritsch@stites.com
Library Holdings: Bk Vols 25,000; Per Subs 114
Special Collections: Historical Kentucky Statutes (back to 1800s)

S SUD-CHEMIE INC, (Formerly United Catalysts, Inc), Technical Library, 1600 W Hill St, 40210. (Mail add: PO Box 32370, 40232), SAN 306-3607. Tel: 502-634-7409. FAX: 502-634-7724. *Librn*, David S Shobe; E-Mail: dshobe@unitedcatalysts.com; Staff 2 (MLS 1, Non-MLS 1)
Founded 1943
Library Holdings: Bk Titles 4,000; Per Subs 50
Subject Interests: Chemistry, Engineering, Physics
Publications: Current Awareness

J SULLIVAN UNIVERSITY LIBRARY, 3101 Bardstown Rd, 40205. (Mail add: PO Box 33-308, 40232), SAN 324-1777. Tel: 502-456-6773. FAX: 502-454-0016. Web Site: at.sullivan.edu/library. *Dir*, Charles Brown; E-Mail: cbrown@sullivan.edu; *Ref*, Linda Taylor; Staff 5 (MLS 3, Non-MLS 2)
Founded 1975. Enrl 2,500; Fac 80; Highest Degree: Master
Library Holdings: Bk Vols 24,000; Bk Titles 18,000; Per Subs 215
Subject Interests: Accounting, Bus mgt, Computer science, Culinary, Paralegal, Travel
Special Collections: Julia Child Cookbook Award Nominees 1991-Present
Restriction: Not open to public
Partic in Kentucky Library Network, Inc

UNITED STATES ARMY
A ENGINEERING DISTRICT, LOUISVILLE TECHNICAL LIBRARY, 600 Dr Martin Luther King Jr Pl, PO Box 59, 40201-0059. SAN 321-8724. Tel: 502-582-6427. FAX: 502-582-6296. *Librn*, Douglas S Blunk; E-Mail: dblunk@smtp.orl.usace.army.mil
Founded 1974
Library Holdings: Bk Titles 15,000; Per Subs 86
Partic in Dialog Corporation; Fedlink; OCLC Online Computer Library Center, Inc

GL UNIVERSITY OF LOUISVILLE, Brandeis School of Law Library, Belknap Campus, 40292. SAN 327-6007. Tel: 502-852-6392. FAX: 502-852-8906. Web Site: www.louisville.edu/library/law.html. *Dir*, David Ensign; E-Mail: david.ensign@louisville.edu; *Circ*, Miriam Schusler Williams; *Assoc Dir*, Michael Whiteman
Library Holdings: Bk Vols 358,620; Bk Titles 40,405; Per Subs 5,300
Automation Activity & Vendor Info: (Acquisitions) Endeavor; (Cataloging) Endeavor; (Circulation) Endeavor; (Course Reserve) Endeavor; (OPAC) Endeavor

C UNIVERSITY OF LOUISVILLE LIBRARIES, 40292. SAN 342-5495. Tel: 502-852-6745. FAX: 502-852-7394. Web Site: www.louisville.edu/library/. *Librn*, Hannelore B Rader; Staff 116 (MLS 41, Non-MLS 75)
Founded 1911. Enrl 20,793; Fac 1,203; Highest Degree: Doctorate
Jul 1999-Jun 2000 Income (Main and Other College/University Libraries) $15,740,987. Mats Exp $6,946,996, Books $1,604,287, Per/Ser (Incl. Access Fees) $3,777,696, Presv $125,218, Micro $481,587, AV Equip $1,187, Other Print Mats $18,159, Manuscripts & Archives $79,074, Electronic Ref Mat (Incl. Access Fees) $818,161. Sal $4,735,297 (Prof $2,305,758)
Library Holdings: Bk Vols 1,700,846; Bk Titles 1,187,802; Per Subs 14,749
Automation Activity & Vendor Info: (Acquisitions) Endeavor; (Cataloging) Endeavor; (Circulation) Endeavor; (Course Reserve) Endeavor; (ILL) Endeavor; (Media Booking) Endeavor; (OPAC) Endeavor; (Serials) Endeavor
Database Vendor: Dialog, Ebsco - EbscoHost, GaleNet, IAC - SearchBank, Lexis-Nexis, OCLC - First Search, ProQuest, Silverplatter Information Inc., Wilson - Wilson Web
Function: Research library
Partic in Kentuckiana Metroversity, Inc; Solinet
Departmental Libraries:
BRANDEIS SCHOOL OF LAW LIBRARY, Belknap Campus, 40292. SAN 342-5584. Tel: 502-852-6392. FAX: 502-852-8906. Web Site: www.louisville.edu/library/la.html. *Dir*, David Ensign; E-Mail: david.ensign@louisville.edu; Staff 12 (MLS 5, Non-MLS 7)
Jul 1999-Jun 2000 Income (Main Library Only) $1,871,090. Mats Exp $1,232,489, Books $708,251, Per/Ser (Incl. Access Fees) $248,616, Presv $8,089, Micro $241,416, Other Print Mats $4,620, Electronic Ref Mat (Incl. Access Fees) $21,497. Sal $472,879 (Prof $238,703)
Library Holdings: Bk Vols 236,843; Per Subs 5,242
Special Collections: Justice (Louis D Brandeis Coll & John M Harlan Sr Coll), mss; US Doc Dep
Automation Activity & Vendor Info: (Acquisitions) Endeavor; (Cataloging) Endeavor; (Circulation) Endeavor; (Course Reserve) Endeavor; (ILL) Endeavor; (Media Booking) Endeavor; (OPAC) Endeavor; (Serials) Endeavor
Database Vendor: Dialog, Ebsco - EbscoHost, GaleNet, Lexis-Nexis, OCLC - First Search, OVID Technologies, ProQuest, Silverplatter Information Inc., Wilson - Wilson Web
Partic in Westlaw
DWIGHT ANDERSON MUSIC LIBRARY, Belknap Campus, 40292. SAN 342-5649. Tel: 502-852-5659. FAX: 502-852-7701. Web Site: www.louisville.edu/library. *Dir*, Karen Little; Staff 6 (MLS 2, Non-MLS 4)
Founded 1947
Jul 1999-Jun 2000 Income (Main Library Only) $425,466. Mats Exp $79,911, Books $28,600, Per/Ser (Incl. Access Fees) $26,031, Presv $17,729. Sal $204,099 (Prof $77,834)
Library Holdings: Bk Vols 85,771; Per Subs 225
Special Collections: Grawemeyer Coll (20th century music); Ricasoli Coll (18th/19th century Plorodine music)
Automation Activity & Vendor Info: (Acquisitions) Endeavor; (Cataloging) Endeavor; (Circulation) Endeavor; (Course Reserve) Endeavor; (ILL) Endeavor; (Media Booking) Endeavor; (OPAC) Endeavor; (Serials) Endeavor
Database Vendor: Dialog, Ebsco - EbscoHost, GaleNet, IAC - Info Trac, Lexis-Nexis, OCLC - First Search, OVID Technologies, ProQuest, Silverplatter Information Inc., Wilson - Wilson Web
Function: For research purposes
EKSTROM LIBRARY, 40292. Tel: 502-852-6745. FAX: 502-852-7394. Web Site: www.louisville.edu/library/. *Dir*, Diane Nichols; Tel: 502-852-8707, E-Mail: dmnich01@gwise.louisville.edu; *Doc*, Mildred Franks; *Media Spec, Per*, David Horvath; *Curator*, James Anderson; *Rare Bks*, Delinda Buie; *Access Serv*, Tyler Goldberg; *Coll Develop*, Judith Niles; Staff 86 (MLS 27, Non-MLS 59)
Founded 1911
Jul 1999-Jun 2000 Income (Main Library Only) $8,564,426. Mats Exp $2,733,309, Books $601,131, Per/Ser (Incl. Access Fees) $1,030,274, Presv $38,651, Micro $218,251, AV Equip $1,187, Other Print Mats $19,113, Manuscripts & Archives $76,420, Electronic Ref Mat (Incl. Access Fees) $720,407. Sal $2,887,704 (Prof $1,337,370)
Library Holdings: Bk Vols 958,188; Per Subs 4,641
Special Collections: Arthur Rackham (Evelyn Parks Rymer Memorial Coll); Astronomy & Mathematics (William Marshall Bullitt Coll); Edgar Rice Burroughs (Neil Dismukes McWhorter Memorial Coll); H L Mencken (Victor Reno Coll); Irish Literature: Joyce & Yeats (Richard M Kain Coll)
Automation Activity & Vendor Info: (Acquisitions) Endeavor; (Cataloging) Endeavor; (Circulation) Endeavor; (Course Reserve) Endeavor; (ILL) Endeavor; (Media Booking) Endeavor; (OPAC) Endeavor; (Serials) Endeavor
Database Vendor: Dialog, Ebsco - EbscoHost, GaleNet, IAC - Info Trac, Lexis-Nexis, OCLC - First Search, OVID Technologies, ProQuest, Silverplatter Information Inc., Wilson - Wilson Web
Function: For research purposes
Partic in Kentuckiana Metroversity, Inc; SE Libr Network
Friends of the Library Group
CM KORNHAUSER HEALTH SCIENCES LIBRARY, Health Sciences Campus, 40292. Tel: 502-852-5775. FAX: 502-852-1631. Web Site: www.louisville.edu/library/kornhauser/. *Dir*, Gary Freiburger; E-Mail: grayf@louisville.edu; *Dep Dir*, Nancy Utterback; *Tech Servs*, Neal Nixon; *Ref*, Michel Atlas; *Cat*, Karen Feder; *Publ Servs*, Felix Garza; *ILL*, Kathy Rodgers; Staff 22 (MLS 8, Non-MLS 14)
Founded 1837. Pop 3,500
Jul 1999-Jun 2000 Income (Main Library Only) $2,632,781. Mats Exp $1,303,837, Books $95,493, Per/Ser (Incl. Access Fees) $1,095,559, Presv $36,551, Electronic Ref Mat (Incl. Access Fees) $59,597. Sal $677,894 (Prof $339,925)
Library Holdings: Bk Vols 213,516; Per Subs 2,984
Subject Interests: Allied health, Dentistry, Medicine, Nursing
Special Collections: Anesthesia; History Coll; Kentucky Medicine; Neurology; Neurosurgery; Pherenology; Psychiatry
Automation Activity & Vendor Info: (Acquisitions) Endeavor; (Cataloging) Endeavor; (Circulation) Endeavor; (Course Reserve) Endeavor; (ILL) Endeavor; (Media Booking) Endeavor; (OPAC) Endeavor; (Serials) Endeavor
Database Vendor: Dialog, Ebsco - EbscoHost, GaleNet, Lexis-Nexis, OCLC - First Search, OVID Technologies, ProQuest, Silverplatter Information Inc., Wilson - Wilson Web
Publications: Synapst (newsletter)
Partic in Greater Midwest Regional Medical Libr Network; OCLC Online Computer Library Center, Inc
Friends of the Library Group
LAURA KERSEY LIBRARY OF ENGINEERING, PHYSICAL SCIENCE & TECHNOLOGY, 40292. SAN 342-5738. Tel: 502-852-6297. FAX: 502-852-0020. Web Site: www.louisville.edu/library. *Dir*, Carol Brinkley; E-Mail: csbrin01@gwise.louisville.edu; Staff 8 (MLS 3, Non-MLS 5)
Founded 1941
Jul 1999-Jun 2000 Income $1,935,118. Mats Exp $1,477,271, Books $89,926, Per/Ser (Incl. Access Fees) $1,329,228, Presv $24,198, Micro $21,870, Electronic Ref Mat (Incl. Access Fees) $12,008. Sal $235,195 (Prof $96,417)
Library Holdings: Bk Vols 130,565; Per Subs 1,317
Subject Interests: Chemistry, Computer science, Engineering, Mathematics, Physics
Database Vendor: Dialog, Ebsco - EbscoHost, Lexis-Nexis, OCLC - First Search, OVID Technologies, ProQuest, Silverplatter Information Inc., Wilson - Wilson Web
MARGARET BRIDWELL ART LIBRARY, Belknap Campus, 40292. SAN 342-5525. Tel: 502-852-6741. FAX: 502-852-6791. Web Site: www.louisville.edu/library. *Librn*, Gail R Gilbert; E-Mail: grgilb01@gwise.louisville.edu; Staff 2 (MLS 1, Non-MLS 1)
Founded 1936
Jul 1999-Jun 2000 Mats Exp $115,476, Books $76,246, Per/Ser (Incl. Access Fees) $31,193, Micro $49
Library Holdings: Bk Vols 71,108; Per Subs 309
Automation Activity & Vendor Info: (Acquisitions) Endeavor; (Cataloging) Endeavor; (Circulation) Endeavor; (Course Reserve) Endeavor; (ILL) Endeavor; (Media Booking) Endeavor; (OPAC) Endeavor; (Serials) Endeavor
Database Vendor: Dialog, Ebsco - EbscoHost, GaleNet, Lexis-Nexis, OCLC - First Search, OVID Technologies, ProQuest, Silverplatter Information Inc.

Budget info included with Ekstrom Library
PHOTOGRAPHIC ARCHIVES, Belknap Campus, 40292. SAN 342-5703. Tel: 502-852-6752. FAX: 502-852-8734. Web Site: www.louisville.edu/library/ekstrom/special/pa-info.html. *Curator*, James C Anderson
Budget info included in total library expenditures
UNIVERSITY ARCHIVES & RECORDS CENTER Tel: 502-852-6674. FAX: 502-852-7394. Web Site: www.louisville.edu/library/uarc/. *Archivist, Dir*, William Morison; E-Mail: bill.morison@louisville.edu; Staff 6 (MLS 5, Non-MLS 1)
Jul 1999- 2000 Income (Main Library Only) $312,106. Mats Exp $54,579. Sal $257,527 (Prof $215,509)
Library Holdings: Bk Vols 4,301; Per Subs 31
Automation Activity & Vendor Info: (Acquisitions) Endeavor; (Cataloging) Endeavor; (Circulation) Endeavor; (Course Reserve) Endeavor; (ILL) Endeavor; (Media Booking) Endeavor; (OPAC) Endeavor; (Serials) Endeavor
Database Vendor: Dialog, Ebsco - EbscoHost, GaleNet, Lexis-Nexis, OCLC - First Search, OVID Technologies, ProQuest, Silverplatter Information Inc., Wilson - Wilson Web

SR URSULINE SISTERS OF THE IMMACULATE CONCEPTION, Archives & Library,* 3115 Lexington Rd, 40206. SAN 375-1678. Tel: 502-897-1811. *Archivist*, Sr Amelia Dues
Library Holdings: Bk Vols 1,000

R WALNUT STREET BAPTIST CHURCH, Media Library,* 1143 S Third St, Ste A, 40203. SAN 306-3623. Tel: 502-589-5290. FAX: 502-589-9323. *Librn*, Alice Arnett
Founded 1943
Library Holdings: Bk Titles 13,000
Friends of the Library Group

S WILLIAM M MERCER INC, Information Center,* 462 S Fourth Ave, Ste 1500, 40202-3431. SAN 327-9383. Tel: 502-561-4500. FAX: 502-561-7841.
Library Holdings: Bk Titles 1,000; Per Subs 50

L WYATT, TARRANT & COMBS LIBRARY,* 2600 Citizens Plaza, 500 W Jefferson St, 40202. SAN 327-6244. Tel: 502-589-5235. FAX: 502-589-0309. E-Mail: wyattlib@iglou.com. *Chief Librn*, Diane Cox
Library Holdings: Bk Vols 5,000; Bk Titles 4,000; Per Subs 40
Subject Interests: Law
Automation Activity & Vendor Info: (Acquisitions) Inmagic, Inc.; (Cataloging) Inmagic, Inc.
Partic in Kentucky Library Network, Inc

LOVELY

P RUFUS M REED PUBLIC LIBRARY, Rt 292, PO Box 359, 41231-0359. Tel: 606-395-5809. *Mgr*, Janet Copley; E-Mail: jcopley@martincolibrary.net
Library Holdings: Bk Vols 19,000; Per Subs 20

MADISONVILLE

P HOPKINS COUNTY-MADISONVILLE PUBLIC LIBRARY, 31 S Main, 42431. SAN 342-5762. Tel: 270-825-2680. FAX: 270-825-2777. E-Mail: library@vci.net. Web Site: www.publiclibrary.org. *Librn*, Lisa Wigley; *Asst Librn*, Lisa Wells; *Bkmobile Coordr*, Theresa Carlisle
Founded 1974. Pop 47,300; Circ 189,714
Jul 1998-Jun 1999 Income $430,000. Mats Exp $60,000, Books $42,000, Per/Ser (Incl. Access Fees) $6,000, Micro $3,500, AV Equip $3,000, Other Print Mats $4,000. Sal $184,000
Library Holdings: Bk Vols 82,000; Per Subs 108
Special Collections: Kentucky Coll; Rare Book Coll
Mem of Green River Regional Libr
Partic in Kentucky Library Network, Inc
Open Mon, Wed & Fri 10-5:30, Tues & Thurs 11-7, Sat 11-3
Friends of the Library Group
Branches: 1
DAWSON SPRINGS BRANCH, 103 Ramsey St, Dawson Springs, 42408. SAN 342-5797. Tel: 502-797-8990. FAX: 502-797-8990. E-Mail: branch@vci.net. Web Site: www.publiclibrary.org. *Librn*, Mary Adams
Library Holdings: Bk Vols 16,000
Friends of the Library Group
Bookmobiles: 1

J MADISONVILLE COMMUNITY COLLEGE, Learning Resource Center,* 2000 College Dr, 42431. SAN 306-364X. Tel: 270-821-2250, Ext 2246. FAX: 270-825-8553. *Dir*, Cherry Berges; *Asst Librn*, Camille Richmond; *Tech Servs*, Tim Stutler
Founded 1968
Library Holdings: Bk Vols 26,284; Bk Titles 21,324; Per Subs 233
Subject Interests: Nursing, Physical therapy
Mem of Univ of Ky
Partic in Kentucky Library Network, Inc

M REGIONAL MEDICAL CENTER, Medical Library,* 900 Hospital Dr, 42431-1694. SAN 323-6331. Tel: 270-825-5252. FAX: 270-825-3411. E-Mail: rmclib@wko.com. *Librn*, Teresa C Ruddell
Library Holdings: Bk Vols 1,500; Per Subs 220
Subject Interests: Consumer health info, Medicine
Partic in Kentucky Library Network, Inc; Ky Area Health Educ Ctr Consortium

MANCHESTER

P CLAY COUNTY PUBLIC LIBRARY, 211 Bridge St, 40962. SAN 306-3658. Tel: 606-598-2617. FAX: 606-598-2617. E-Mail: ccplib@kih.net. *Dir*, Nancy Lee Smith; *Asst Librn*, Donna Gillahan; *Bkmobile Coordr, Commun Servs*, Barbara Macina
Founded 1954. Pop 21,746; Circ 53,470
Jul 1999-Jun 2000 Income $148,515. Mats Exp $14,937, Books $13,596, Per/Ser (Incl. Access Fees) $1,119, Micro $222. Sal $55,426
Library Holdings: Bk Vols 33,000; Per Subs 67
Special Collections: Kentucky Coll; Large Print Books & Magazines; Local History
Partic in Kentucky Library Network, Inc
Participates in Cumberland Valley Audio & Video Consortiums

MARION

P CRITTENDEN COUNTY PUBLIC LIBRARY,* 204 W Carlisle St, 42064. SAN 306-3666. Tel: 270-965-3354. FAX: 270-965-3354. *Librn*, Janice Pritchett
Founded 1953. Pop 9,207; Circ 58,376
Library Holdings: Bk Vols 30,000; Per Subs 92
Subject Interests: Local history

MARTIN

M OUR LADY OF THE WAY HOSPITAL LIBRARY,* PO Box 910, 41649. SAN 328-8323. Tel: 606-285-5181, Ext 2780. FAX: 606-285-6435. *Librn*, Kelly Fraley
Library Holdings: Bk Vols 165; Per Subs 40
Open Mon-Fri 8am-4:30pm

MAYFIELD

P GRAVES COUNTY LIBRARY,* 601 N 17th St, 42066. SAN 306-3674. Tel: 270-247-2911. FAX: 270-247-2990. *Dir*, Diane Bennett
Founded 1940
Library Holdings: Bk Titles 53,934; Per Subs 108
Partic in Kentucky Library Network, Inc

CR MID-CONTINENT COLLEGE, (Formerly Mid-Continent Baptist Bible College), Anne Parrish Markham Library, 99 Powell Rd East, 42066-9007. SAN 325-0709. Tel: 270-247-8521, Ext 275. FAX: 270-247-3115. E-Mail: mcc@midcontinent.edu. Web Site: www.midcontinent.edu.; Staff 2 (MLS 1, Non-MLS 1)
Founded 1968. Fac 12
Library Holdings: Bk Titles 30,500; Per Subs 150
Subject Interests: Computers, Education, English, History, Languages, Literature, Religion, Sci
Automation Activity & Vendor Info: (Cataloging) Sagebrush Corporation; (Circulation) Sagebrush Corporation
Partic in Kentucky Library Network, Inc
Special Services for the Deaf - Books on deafness & sign language

MAYSVILLE

P MASON COUNTY PUBLIC LIBRARY, 218 E Third St, 41056. SAN 306-3690. Tel: 606-564-3286. FAX: 606-564-5408. E-Mail: masonclib@pop.maysvilleky.net. *Dir*, Evelyn Cropper; Staff 5 (MLS 1, Non-MLS 4)
Founded 1876. Pop 17,765; Circ 167,320
1999-2000 Income $402,000. Mats Exp $43,455, Books $37,000, Per/Ser (Incl. Access Fees) $6,455. Sal $139,000
Library Holdings: Bk Vols 34,000; Bk Titles 32,000; Per Subs 70; High Interest/Low Vocabulary Bk Vols 1,700; Bks on Deafness & Sign Lang 14
Subject Interests: Kentucky
Automation Activity & Vendor Info: (Cataloging) Gaylord; (Circulation) Gaylord
Publications: Library Journal; Publisher Weekly
Mem of Buffalo Trace Regional Libr
Partic in Ky Libr Asn
Friends of the Library Group
Bookmobiles: 1

J MAYSVILLE COMMUNITY COLLEGE LIBRARY, 1755 US 68, 41056. SAN 306-3682. Tel: 606-759-7141, Ext 206. FAX: 606-759-7176. Web Site: www.maycc.kctcs.net/library/index.html. *Dir*, Sonja R Eads; E-Mail: sonja.eads@kctcs.net; *Librn*, Margo Hamm; E-Mail: margo.hamm@kctcs.net; *Acq*, Judy Crawford; *Circ*, Dawn Blebins; Staff 2 (MLS 2)
Founded 1968. Enrl 1,300; Fac 39
Library Holdings: Bk Vols 32,458; Bk Titles 27,460; Per Subs 288
Subject Interests: History, Kentucky, Nursing

Special Collections: Buffalo Trace Region Coll; Kentucky History Coll, bks, micro
Automation Activity & Vendor Info: (Cataloging) Endeavor; (Circulation) Endeavor; (Course Reserve) Endeavor; (OPAC) Endeavor
Database Vendor: OCLC - First Search
Publications: Access Point]; Electronic/on-line
Partic in Kentucky Library Network, Inc; OCLC Online Computer Library Center, Inc; SE Libr Network

MC KEE

P JACKSON COUNTY PUBLIC LIBRARY,* David St, PO Box 160, 40447. SAN 306-3631. Tel: 606-287-8113. FAX: 606-287-7774. E-Mail: jcpl@prtcnet.org. *Librn*, Betty L Bingham; *Asst Librn*, Arlie Kay Morgan; *Bkmobile Coordr*, Linda Crocher
Founded 1973. Pop 11,996; Circ 36,438
Library Holdings: Bk Vols 23,432; Per Subs 25
Mem of Cumberland Valley Regional Libr Syst
Partic in Ky Libr Asn

MIDDLESBORO

S CUMBERLAND GAP NATIONAL HISTORICAL PARK LIBRARY,* PO Box 1848, 40965. SAN 370-3088. Tel: 606-248-2817, 606-248-7850. FAX: 606-248-0299, 606-248-7276. Web Site: www.nps.gov/ciga. *In Charge*, Ries Collier; E-Mail: ries_collier@nps.gov
Library Holdings: Bk Vols 1,300
Special Collections: Hensly Settlement Oral History Coll (Appalachian Culture 87 tapes)

P MIDDLESBOROUGH-BELL COUNTY PUBLIC LIBRARY, 126 S 20th St, 40965-1212. (Mail add: PO Box 1677, 40965-1677), SAN 306-3704. Tel: 606-248-4812. FAX: 606-248-8766. E-Mail: mborolib@tcnet.net. Web Site: www.tcnet.net/~pinevillelib. *Dir*, Beverly G Brown; Tel: 606-248-5304, E-Mail: beverly.brown@mail.state.ky.us; *Ch Servs*, Cora King; *Circ*, Lorene Moyers; *Tech Servs*, Michele B Lawson; *Spec Coll*, Kathy Hall; *Bkmobile Coordr*, Patricia Hopkins; Staff 6 (MLS 1, Non-MLS 5)
Founded 1912. Pop 35,000; Circ 81,867
Library Holdings: Bk Vols 46,126; Bk Titles 45,688; Per Subs 124
Subject Interests: Genealogy for local families, Kentucky, Local history
Automation Activity & Vendor Info: (Cataloging) Gaylord; (Circulation) Gaylord; (OPAC) Gaylord
Mem of Cumberland Valley Regional Libr Syst
Partic in Kentucky Library Network, Inc

C SOUTHEAST COMMUNITY COLLEGE & CUMBERLAND VALLEY TECHNICAL COLLEGE, Middlesboro Campus Library, 1300 Chichester Ave, 40965. SAN 371-957X. Tel: 606-242-2145, Ext 2029. FAX: 606-242-2326. Web Site: www.secc.kctcs.net. *Dir*, Kevin Murphy; Tel: 606-242-2145, Ext 2061, E-Mail: kevin.murphy@kctcs.net; *Librn*, Lisa Ahlstedt; *Tech Servs*, Mike Justice
Library Holdings: Bk Vols 10,500; Per Subs 95
Automation Activity & Vendor Info: (Cataloging) Endeavor; (Circulation) Endeavor; (OPAC) Endeavor

MIDWAY

C LITTLE MEMORIAL LIBRARY, 512 E Stephens, 40347-9731. SAN 306-3712. Tel: 859-846-5316. FAX: 859-846-5349. Web Site: www.midway.edu/library. *Dir*, Catherine L Reilender; Tel: 859-846-5315, E-Mail: creilender@midway.edu; *Ref*, Carol Dellapina; Staff 4 (MLS 2, Non-MLS 2)
Founded 1847. Enrl 900; Fac 73; Highest Degree: Bachelor
Jul 1998-Jun 1999 Income $238,000. Mats Exp $113,000, Books $26,000, Per/Ser (Incl. Access Fees) $32,000, Micro $6,000, AV Equip $2,000, Manuscripts & Archives $1,000, Electronic Ref Mat (Incl. Access Fees) $10,000. Sal $125,600
Library Holdings: Bk Vols 54,000; Bk Titles 39,000; Per Subs 450
Special Collections: Horse Industry; Legal Coll for Paralegal Program; Women's Studies
Database Vendor: Ebsco - EbscoHost, OCLC - First Search
Partic in Coun of Independent Ky Cols & Univs; Kentucky Library Network, Inc

MONTICELLO

P WAYNE COUNTY PUBLIC LIBRARY,* 159 S Main St, 42633. SAN 306-3720. Tel: 606-348-8565. FAX: 606-348-3829. *Dir*, Anne Garner; E-Mail: anne.garner@mail.state.ky.us
Founded 1949. Pop 17,468; Circ 139,212
Jul 1997-Jun 1998 Income $176,000, State $26,271, County $133,191, Locally Generated Income $11,745. Mats Exp $18,698, Books $13,813, Per/Ser (Incl. Access Fees) $804, Other Print Mats $84. Sal $78,556
Library Holdings: Bk Vols 35,000; Per Subs 92
Mem of Lake Cumberland Regional Libr Syst

MOREHEAD

M KENTUCKY CANCER PROGRAM LIBRARY,* 120 Normal Ave, Rm 214, 40351. SAN 327-604X. Tel: 606-784-6458. FAX: 606-784-6559.
Library Holdings: Bk Titles 50

C MOREHEAD STATE UNIVERSITY, Camden-Carroll Library, University Blvd, 40351. SAN 306-3739. Tel: 606-783-2200. Interlibrary Loan Service Tel: 606-783-5107. Circulation Tel: 606-783-5490. Reference Tel: 606-783-5491. FAX: 606-783-5037. E-Mail: library@morehead-st.edu. Web Site: www.morehead-st.edu/units/library. *Dir*, Larry X Besant; Tel: 606-783-5100, E-Mail: l.besant@morehead-st.edu; *Publ Servs*, Carol Nutter; Tel: 606-783-5110, Fax: 606-783-2799, E-Mail: c.nutter@morehead-st.edu; *Doc, Per*, Gary Austin; Tel: 606-783-2826, E-Mail: g.austin@morehead-st.edu; *Spec Coll*, Clara Keyes; Tel: 606-783-5122, E-Mail: c.keyes@morehead-st.edu; *Automation Syst Coordr*, Gary Flanagan; Tel: 606-783-5119, E-Mail: g.flanagan@morehead-st.edu; *Online Servs*, Thomas Kmetz; Tel: 606-783-5111, E-Mail: t.kmetz@morehead-st.edu; *Bibliog Instr*, Bill Malone; Tel: 606-783-5114, E-Mail: b.malone@morehead-st.edu; *Tech Servs*, Elsie Pritchard; Tel: 606-783-5120, E-Mail: e.pritch@morehead-st.edu; Staff 13 (MLS 13)
Founded 1922. Enrl 8,344; Fac 400; Highest Degree: Master
Jul 1999-Jun 2000 Income $2,213,586. Mats Exp $796,546, Books $185,614, Per/Ser (Incl. Access Fees) $514,912, Presv $16,777, AV Equip $22,337, Other Print Mats $5,886, Electronic Ref Mat (Incl. Access Fees) $51,020. Sal $1,231,104 (Prof $571,040)
Library Holdings: Bk Vols 479,090; Bk Titles 333,518; Per Subs 2,627
Subject Interests: Appalachia, Education, Mathematics, Music, Nursing, Philosophy, Physical science, Psychology, Social service (social work)
Special Collections: Appalachian Coll; Jesse Stuart Coll; Literature, (James Still Coll), bk & ms; Roger W Barbour Coll
Automation Activity & Vendor Info: (Acquisitions) Endeavor; (Cataloging) Endeavor; (Circulation) Endeavor; (Course Reserve) Endeavor; (OPAC) Endeavor; (Serials) Endeavor
Database Vendor: Ebsco - EbscoHost
Partic in Eastern Kentucky Health Science Information Network; Kentucky Library Network, Inc; Nat Libr of Med; OCLC Online Computer Library Center, Inc; SE Libr Network; State Assisted Academic Library Council Of Kentucky

§S MOREHEAD YOUTH CENTER LIBRARY, 495 Forest Hill Dr, 40351. Tel: 606-784-6421. *Librn*, Betty Pugh
Library Holdings: Bk Vols 5,000

P ROWAN COUNTY PUBLIC LIBRARY,* 185 E First St, 40351. SAN 306-3747. Tel: 606-784-7137. FAX: 606-784-7137. *Dir*, Mrs Frankie Calvert; E-Mail: frankiecalvert@mail.state.ky.us; *Bkmobile Coordr*, Dwayne Fultz
Founded 1952. Pop 20,353; Circ 379,984
1997-1998 Income $215,103, State $27,788, County $171,559, Locally Generated Income $15,755. Mats Exp $14,960, Books $12,155, Per/Ser (Incl. Access Fees) $1,679, Other Print Mats $1,126. Sal $131,790 (Prof $81,261)
Library Holdings: Bk Vols 50,000; Per Subs 34
Mem of Buffalo Trace Regional Libr

M SAINT CLAIRE MEDICAL CENTER LIBRARY,* 222 Medical Circle, 40351. SAN 320-3786. Tel: 606-783-6860. FAX: 606-784-2178. E-Mail: stclaire@mis.net.
Founded 1966
Library Holdings: Bk Titles 1,300; Per Subs 200
Special Collections: Pastoral Care
Partic in Eastern Kentucky Health Science Information Network; Kentucky Library Network, Inc

MORGANFIELD

P UNION COUNTY DISTRICT LIBRARY, 126 South Morgan St, 42437. SAN 342-5827. Tel: 270-389-1696. FAX: 270-389-3925. E-Mail: unionlib@dynasty.net. Web Site: www.uclibrary.8m.com. *Dir*, Laura C Wildey; *Br Coordr*, Betty Lamb; Tel: 270-333-5547, Fax: 270-333-0184; *Br Coordr*, Carol Gough; Tel: 270-822-4244, Fax: 270-822-5075; *Asst Librn*, Shriley Mercer; *Asst Librn*, Gladys F French. Subject Specialists: *Genealogy*, Gladys F French; Staff 6 (Non-MLS 6)
Founded 1964. Pop 16,557; Circ 45,734
Jul 1999-Jun 2000 Income (Main Library and Branch Library) $232,864, State $28,919, County $178,584, Locally Generated Income $25,379. Mats Exp $44,233, Books $40,730, Per/Ser (Incl. Access Fees) $1,499, Electronic Ref Mat (Incl. Access Fees) $2,004. Sal $81,740 (Prof $29,127)
Library Holdings: Bk Vols 39,776; Per Subs 90
Subject Interests: Local history
Database Vendor: Ebsco - EbscoHost, OCLC - First Search
Mem of Green River Regional Libr
Branches: 2
STURGIS BRANCH, 111 W Seventh St, Sturgis, 42459. SAN 342-5851. Tel: 270-333-5547. FAX: 270-333-0184. E-Mail: unionlib@dynasty.net. *Dir*, Laura Wildey; Tel: 270-389-1696; *In Charge*, Betty Lamb; *Asst Librn*, Helen Ayers; Staff 2 (Non-MLS 2)
Founded 1964

Database Vendor: Ebsco - EbscoHost
UNIONTOWN BRANCH, 520 Second St, Uniontown, 42461. (Mail add: PO Box 547, Uniontown, 42461), SAN 342-5886. Tel: 270-822-4244. FAX: 270-822-5075. *In Charge*, Carol Gough; E-Mail: goughcm@hotmail.com; Staff 1 (Non-MLS 1)
Founded 1964
Database Vendor: Ebsco - EbscoHost

MORGANTOWN

P BUTLER COUNTY PUBLIC LIBRARY,* PO Box 247, 42261. SAN 306-3755. Tel: 502-526-4722. FAX: 502-526-4722. E-Mail: bcpl@logantele.com. *Librn*, Sibyl Givens; *Bkmobile Coordr*, Wilma J Howard; *Asst Librn*, Connie Embry
Founded 1954. Pop 11,254; Circ 57,776
Jul 1998-Jun 1999 Income $141,000, State $26,000, County $115,000. Mats Exp $14,000, Books $9,000, Per/Ser (Incl. Access Fees) $862. Sal $80,000
Library Holdings: Bk Vols 35,228; Per Subs 42
Mem of Barren River District
Open Mon, Wed-Fri 8:30-4:30, Tues 8:30-7, Sat 8-4
Bookmobiles: 1

MOUNT OLIVET

P ROBERTSON COUNTY PUBLIC LIBRARY, 407 E Walmut, PO Box 282, 41064. SAN 320-8206. Tel: 606-724-5746. FAX: 606-724-5746. Web Site: www.members.tripod.com/~m22166/index-14.html. *Dir*, Carol Mitchell; E-Mail: cmmitchell7@hotmail.com
Founded 1979. Pop 2,124; Circ 30,737
Library Holdings: Bk Vols 11,503; Per Subs 34
Mem of Buffalo Trace Regional Libr; Ky Libr Info Ctr
Bookmobiles: 1

MOUNT STERLING

P MT STERLING MONTGOMERY LIBRARY,* 241 W Locust St, 40353. SAN 376-5806. Tel: 606-498-2404. FAX: 606-498-7477. E-Mail: mtsterlinglib@kih.net. *Librn*, Karen Kasacavage
Jul 1997-Jun 1998 Income $140,000. Mats Exp $40,000. Sal $60,000
Library Holdings: Bk Vols 36,000; Bk Titles 25,000; Per Subs 75

MOUNT VERNON

P ROCKCASTLE COUNTY LIBRARY,* 60 Ford Dr, 40456. SAN 306-3763. Tel: 606-256-2388. FAX: 606-256-2388. E-Mail: repl@kih.net. *Librn*, Geraldine Robbins
Founded 1954. Pop 13,973; Circ 81,014
Library Holdings: Bk Vols 24,000; Per Subs 65
Subject Interests: Genealogy
Mem of Cumberland Valley Libr Develop District
Open Mon, Tues, Wed & Fri 10am-5pm, Thurs noon-8pm & Sat 10am-4pm

MUNFORDVILLE

P HART COUNTY PUBLIC LIBRARY,* 500 E Union St, PO Box 337, 42765. SAN 306-3771. Tel: 270-524-1953. FAX: 270-524-7323. *Dir*, Vicki Logsdon; *Bkmobile Coordr*, Stacey Bradbury; *Circ*, Christell Bennett
Pop 15,000; Circ 93,652
Library Holdings: Bk Vols 31,000; Per Subs 55
Subject Interests: Genealogy
Mem of Barren River District

MURRAY

P CALLOWAY COUNTY PUBLIC LIBRARY, 710 Main St, 42071. SAN 306-378X. Tel: 270-753-2288. FAX: 270-753-8263. *Dir*, Ben Graves; *Cat, Tech Servs*, Deanna Harmon; *Circ*, Wanda Kimbro; Staff 3 (MLS 3)
Founded 1967. Pop 29,000; Circ 200,000
Library Holdings: Bk Vols 63,000; Per Subs 150
Special Collections: Calloway Company Antique Photographs Coll; Kentucky Authors & Titles (Kentucky Coll)
Publications: Pot Pouri-Calloway County
Friends of the Library Group

C MURRAY STATE UNIVERSITY, Harry Lee Waterfield Library, S 14th St, 42071-3307. SAN 342-5916. Tel: 270-762-2291. Interlibrary Loan Service Tel: 270-762-4298. Circulation Tel: 270-762-4990. Reference Tel: 270-762-2053. FAX: 270-762-3736. Web Site: www.mursuky.edu/msml/library/htm. *Dean of Libr*, Coy L Harmon; E-Mail: coy.harmon@murraystate.edu; *Cat*, Debbra Tate; Tel: 270-762-4818, E-Mail: debbra.tate@murraystate.edu; *Archivist*, Ernie Bailey; Tel: 207-762-6153, E-Mail: ernie.bailey@murray.state.edu; *Publ Servs*, Janet Brewer; Tel: 270-762-3019, E-Mail: janet.brewer@murraystate.edu; Staff 13 (MLS 12, Non-MLS 1)
Founded 1923. Enrl 9,000; Fac 355; Highest Degree: Master
Jul 1999-Jun 2000 Income $2,458,673, State $2,446,102, Locally Generated Income $12,571. Mats Exp $1,155,928, Books $255,388, Per/Ser (Incl. Access Fees) $877,106, Presv $23,434. Sal $1,212,189 (Prof $560,287)
Library Holdings: Bk Vols 380,992; Bk Titles 292,125; Per Subs 2,427
Special Collections: Forrest Pogue Coll; Irvin S Cobb Coll; Jackson Purchase History & Genealogy; Jesse Stuart Coll, bks, mss, memorabilia; National, State & Regional Political Records
Automation Activity & Vendor Info: (Acquisitions) Endeavor; (Cataloging) Endeavor; (Circulation) Endeavor; (Course Reserve) Endeavor; (OPAC) Endeavor; (Serials) Endeavor
Publications: MSU Inform
Partic in OCLC Online Computer Library Center, Inc; SE Libr Network
Special Services for the Blind - Kurzweil Reader
Friends of the Library Group

R UNIVERSITY CHURCH OF CHRIST LIBRARY, 801 N 12th St, 42071-1648. SAN 321-480X. Tel: 502-753-1881. *Librn*, Ernie R Bailey; Staff 1 (MLS 1)
Founded 1953
Library Holdings: Bk Vols 3,500; Bk Titles 3,000
Special Collections: Churches of Christ & Disciples of Christ Coll; Stone/Campbell Movement

NEW HOPE

SR CATHOLICS UNITED FOR LIFE LIBRARY, 3050 Gap Knob Rd, 40052. SAN 373-1898. Tel: 270-325-3061. FAX: 270-325-3091. *Librn, Pres*, Theo Stearns
Library Holdings: Bk Titles 15,000; Per Subs 15
Subject Interests: Law, Literature, Philosophy, Religion, Theology
Publications: Newsletter
Restriction: By appointment only, In-house use for visitors

NICHOLASVILLE

P WITHERS MEMORIAL PUBLIC LIBRARY, 600 S Main, 40356. SAN 306-3828. Tel: 859-885-3523. FAX: 859-885-5164. Web Site: www.withers.org. *Dir*, Susan B Lawrence; Tel: 859-885-3523, Ext 223, E-Mail: lawrence@withers.org; *Tech Servs*, Shirley Mulcahy; Tel: 859-885-5164, Ext 226, E-Mail: shirleym@withers.org; *Ref*, Frederica Smith; Tel: 606-885-3523, Ext 224, E-Mail: fsmith@withers.org; *Ch Servs*, Colleen Hall; Tel: 606-885-3523, Ext 227, E-Mail: chall@withers.org; *Circ*, Kaylene Schember; Tel: 859-885-5164, Ext 229, E-Mail: kschember@withers.org; *Bkmobile Coordr*, Jean Miller; Tel: 859-885-5164, Ext 236, E-Mail: jmiller@withers.org; *Acq*, Sabrina Sawyers; Tel: 885-5164, Ext 225, E-Mail: ssawyers@withers.org; *Ch Servs*, Colleen Hall; Tel: 859-885-5164, Ext 227, E-Mail: chall@withers.org; Staff 23 (MLS 3, Non-MLS 20)
Founded 1968. Pop 30,500; Circ 242,156
Jul 1999-Jul 2000 Income $940,979, State $43,800, County $851,674, Locally Generated Income $45,505. Mats Exp $137,264, Books $133,559, Per/Ser (Incl. Access Fees) $3,705. Sal $327,389 (Prof $91,000)
Library Holdings: Bk Vols 72,998; Per Subs 103
Subject Interests: Kentucky
Special Collections: Jessamine County Genealogy
Automation Activity & Vendor Info: (Cataloging) SIRSI
Database Vendor: Ebsco - EbscoHost, OCLC - First Search
Function: Reference services available
Mem of Bluegrass South Regional Libr
Friends of the Library Group

OWENSBORO

CR BRESCIA UNIVERSITY LIBRARY, 717 Frederica St, 42301. SAN 306-3836. Tel: 270-686-4212. FAX: 502-686-4266. Web Site: library.brescia.edu. *Dir Libr Serv*, Sister Judith N Riney; Tel: 270-686-4213, E-Mail: judithr@brescia.edu; *ILL*, Carol Ranburger; Tel: 270-686-4214, E-Mail: carolr@brescia.edu; *Asst Librn*, Kathy Eby; Tel: 270-686-4288, E-Mail: kathye@brescia.edu; *Ref*, Patty Alvey; E-Mail: pattya@brescia.edu; Staff 5 (MLS 2, Non-MLS 3)
Founded 1950. Enrl 750; Highest Degree: Master
Jun 1999-May 2000 Income Parent Institution $198,100. Mats Exp $57,175, Books $33,912, Per/Ser (Incl. Access Fees) $3,728, Presv $857, Micro $5,796, AV Equip $2,312, Electronic Ref Mat (Incl. Access Fees) $10,570. Sal $75,900
Library Holdings: Bk Vols 84,364; Per Subs 156
Subject Interests: Literature, Music, Religion
Special Collections: Contemporary Woman; Kentuckiana
Database Vendor: Ebsco - EbscoHost, GaleNet, OCLC - First Search, ProQuest, Wilson - Wilson Web
Publications: faculty handbook; List of acquisitions; student handbook
Partic in Association Of Independent Kentucky Colleges & Universities; Kentucky Library Network, Inc; OCLC Online Computer Library Center, Inc; Solinet

P DAVIESS COUNTY PUBLIC LIBRARY,* 450 Griffith Ave, 42301. SAN 306-3860. Tel: 270-684-0211. FAX: 270-684-0218. Web Site: www.dcpl.lib.ky.us. *Dir*, Deborah Mesplay; E-Mail: dmesplay@

dcpl.lib.ky.us; *ILL*, Debbie Hobgood; *Ch Servs*, Cindy Maglinger; *Tech Servs*, Susan McFadden
Founded 1909. Pop 88,813; Circ 400,778
Jul 1997-Jun 1998 Income $1,402,461, State $53,170, Federal $14,430, Locally Generated Income $59,863, Other $1,213,823. Mats Exp $187,832, Books $153,257, Per/Ser (Incl. Access Fees) $19,976, Micro $2,176. Sal $618,025 (Prof $249,156)
Library Holdings: Bk Vols 154,008; Per Subs 236
Subject Interests: Genealogy, History, Kentucky, Local history
Friends of the Library Group

C KENTUCKY WESLEYAN COLLEGE, Library Learning Center, 3000 Frederica St, PO Box 1039, 42302-1039. SAN 306-3852. Tel: 270-926-3111, Ext 5132. FAX: 270-926-3196. Web Site: www.kwc.edu/library/. *Dir*, Pat McFarling; E-Mail: patmc@kwc.edu; *Tech Servs*, Julie Gilmore; E-Mail: juliegi@kwc.edu; *Info Specialist*, April Law; E-Mail: alaw@kwc.edu; Staff 13 (MLS 3, Non-MLS 10)
Founded 1858. Enrl 714; Fac 55; Highest Degree: Bachelor
Jul 1999-Jun 2000 Income $313,192. Mats Exp $95,350, Books $28,250, Per/Ser (Incl. Access Fees) $26,500, Presv $891, Micro $8,947, Electronic Ref Mat (Incl. Access Fees) $12,000. Sal $217,842
Library Holdings: Bk Vols 96,068; Per Subs 352
Special Collections: Dan M King Architecture Coll; First Editions-American & English Literature (Dr & Mrs M David Orrahood Coll); Kentuckiana; Kentucky United Methodist Heritage Center Coll, bks, mss, pamphlets & pictures; KWC Archives; Toraichi Matsumoto Memorial Coll
Publications: Catalog of the Dan M King Architecture Coll; Catalog of the Dr & Mrs M David Orrahood Coll; KWC Non-Graduates 1866-1949, Millersburg-Winchester
Partic in OCLC Online Computer Library Center, Inc; Solinet

S OWENSBORO AREA MUSEUM OF SCIENCE & HISTORY LIBRARY,* 220 Daviess St, 42303. SAN 323-4800. Tel: 270-687-2732. FAX: 270-687-2738. *Exec Dir*, Ed Allen
Library Holdings: Bk Vols 450; Per Subs 12
Subject Interests: Kentucky, Mus studies, Native Am, Natural history

J OWENSBORO COMMUNITY COLLEGE, Learning Resources Center,* 4800 New Hartford Rd, 42303. SAN 323-584X. Tel: 270-686-4448. FAX: 270-686-4594. Web Site: www.owecc.net/library. *Dir Libr Serv*, Fran Davis; E-Mail: fran.davis@kctcs.net; *Librn, Publ Servs*, Shannon Cary; Tel: 570-686-4434, E-Mail: shannon.cary@kctcs.net; Staff 7 (MLS 2, Non-MLS 5)
Founded 1986. Enrl 2,064; Fac 60; Highest Degree: Associate
Jul 1998-Jul 1999 Income $260,116. Mats Exp $52,696, Books $27,755, Per/Ser (Incl. Access Fees) $17,608, AV Equip $4,660, Electronic Ref Mat (Incl. Access Fees) $2,673. Sal $158,863 (Prof $78,973)
Library Holdings: Bk Vols 18,393; Bk Titles 17,053; Per Subs 57
Database Vendor: Ebsco - EbscoHost, OCLC - First Search, Silverplatter Information Inc.
Partic in OCLC Online Computer Library Center, Inc; Solinet

S OWENSBORO MESSENGER-INQUIRER LIBRARY,* 1401 Frederica, 42301. (Mail add: PO Box 1480, 42302), Tel: 270-926-0123. FAX: 270-685-3446. Web Site: www.messenger-inquirer.com. *Librn*, Sherri Heckel; E-Mail: sheckel@messengerinquirer.com
Library Holdings: Bk Titles 1,500; Per Subs 15

S WILLIAMS GAS PIPELINE, Technical & Law Libraries, 3800 Frederica St, 42301. (Mail add: PO Box 20008, 42304-0008), SAN 306-3879. Tel: 270-688-6648. FAX: 270-683-5373. *In Charge*, Joanne Kendall; E-Mail: joanne.t.kendall@williams.com
Founded 1962
Subject Interests: Chemical engineering, Economics, Geology, Kentucky, Law, Natural gas, Petroleum engineering
Open Mon-Fri 8-4:30

OWENTON

P OWEN COUNTY PUBLIC LIBRARY,* 118 N Main St, 40359. SAN 306-3887. Tel: 502-484-3450. FAX: 502-484-3450. *Librn*, Bettina Somerville; *Bkmobile Coordr*, David Washburn
Pop 8,924; Circ 47,431
Library Holdings: Bk Vols 30,000; Per Subs 45
Special Collections: Kentucky Coll; Large Print Coll
Partic in Kentucky Library Network, Inc

OWINGSVILLE

P BATH COUNTY MEMORIAL LIBRARY,* 24 Main St, PO Box 380, 40360. SAN 306-3895. Tel: 606-674-2531. FAX: 606-674-2531. E-Mail: bcml@mail.state.ky.us. *Librn*, Brenda Vance; E-Mail: brenda.vance@mail.state.ky.us; *Bkmobile Coordr*, Sarah Staton
Pop 9,692; Circ 37,078
Library Holdings: Bk Vols 17,000
Special Collections: Kentucky Genealogy
Mem of Buffalo Trace/Gateway Regional Off
Friends of the Library Group

PADUCAH

S LOCKHEED MARTIN UTILITY SERVICES, Paducah Gaseous Diffusion Plant,* PO Box 1410, 42002-1410. SAN 306-3925. Tel: 270-441-6438, Ext 6587. FAX: 270-441-6339. E-Mail: pdgp@usec.com. *Librn*, Ione Romano
Founded 1951
Library Holdings: Bk Vols 10,000
Subject Interests: Aerospace science, Business and management, Chemistry, Computer science, Mathematics, Nuclear energy, Statistics

M LOURDES HOSPITAL, Medical Library,* 1530 Lone Oak Rd, 42001. SAN 327-6392. Tel: 270-444-2138, Ext 2138. FAX: 270-444-2869. *Mgr*, Arlene Dueker; E-Mail: adueker@loudes-pad.org; Staff 1 (MLS 1)
Jan 1998-Dec 1998 Mats Exp $52,000, Books $12,000, Per/Ser (Incl. Access Fees) $40,000
Library Holdings: Bk Vols 600; Per Subs 120
Subject Interests: Consumer health, Quality mgt
Database Vendor: Ebsco - EbscoHost, IAC - Info Trac, OCLC - First Search, Silverplatter Information Inc.
Publications: Library News (Newsletter)
Partic in Bluegrass Med Librns; Kentucky Health Science Libraries Consortium; KLN

P MCCRACKEN COUNTY PUBLIC LIBRARY, (Formerly Paducah Public Library), 555 Washington St, 42003-1735. SAN 306-3917. Tel: 270-442-2510, Ext 13. Circulation Tel: 270-442-2510, Ext 10. Reference Tel: 270-442-2510, Ext 19. FAX: 270-443-9322. Web Site: www.mclib.net. *Dir*, Marie Liang; E-Mail: mliang@ppl.lib.ky.us; *Tech Servs*, Patricia Sallee; *YA Servs*, Iris Garrott; *Ad Servs*, Nancy Reed; Staff 2 (MLS 2)
Founded 1901. Pop 62,880; Circ 292,840
Jul 1999-Jun 2000 Income $877,749, State $66,384, City $619,263, County $71,048, Locally Generated Income $121,054. Mats Exp $191,117, Books $138,747, Per/Ser (Incl. Access Fees) $11,752, AV Equip $17,818, Electronic Ref Mat (Incl. Access Fees) $22,800. Sal $438,333 (Prof $49,458)
Library Holdings: Bk Vols 88,401; Per Subs 262
Special Collections: Genealogy, bks, mss; History (Kentucky Coll), bks, mss; Literature (Irvin S Cobb Coll), bks, mss
Database Vendor: Innovative Interfaces INN - View
Mem of Purchase Regional Libr Syst
Friends of the Library Group

J PADUCAH COMMUNITY COLLEGE LIBRARY, 4810 Alben Barkley Dr, PO Box 7380, 42002-7380. SAN 306-3909. Tel: 270-554-6210. FAX: 270-554-6218. Web Site: www.sats.padcc.kctcs.net/library. *Dir Libr Serv*, Stacey Nickell; Tel: 270-554-9200, Ext 6134, E-Mail: stacey.nickell@kctcs.net; *Tech Servs*, Ken Bradshaw; Tel: 270-554-9200, Ext 6136, E-Mail: ken.bradshaw@kctcs.net; *Publ Servs*, Sandy Farrell; Tel: 270-554-9200, Ext 6132, E-Mail: sandy.farrell@kctcs.net; Staff 9 (MLS 3, Non-MLS 6)
Founded 1932. Enrl 2,759; Fac 75; Highest Degree: Associate
Jul 1999-Jun 2000 Income $363,664. Mats Exp $124,554, Books $73,200, Per/Ser (Incl. Access Fees) $24,800, Micro $3,554, AV Equip $23,000. Sal $262,869
Library Holdings: Bk Vols 39,471; Bk Titles 26,381; Per Subs 148
Automation Activity & Vendor Info: (Cataloging) Endeavor; (Circulation) Endeavor
Database Vendor: GaleNet, IAC - Info Trac, OCLC - First Search, ProQuest
Partic in Kentucky Library Network, Inc; SE Libr Network

PAINTSVILLE

P JOHNSON COUNTY PUBLIC LIBRARY,* 444 Main St, PO Box 788, 41240. SAN 306-3933. Tel: 606-789-4355. FAX: 606-789-6758. E-Mail: jocol@foothills.net. *Librn*, Patricia Patton; *Bkmobile Coordr*, Walta L Pack; *Asst Librn*, Mary Ann Runyon
Pop 24,432; Circ 180,728
Library Holdings: Bk Vols 55,000; Per Subs 55
Mem of FIVCO Libr Develop District

PARIS

P PARIS-BOURBON COUNTY LIBRARY, 701 High St, 40361. SAN 306-395X. Tel: 606-987-4419. FAX: 606-987-2421. Web Site: www.bourbonlibrary.org. *Dir*, Anne M Rogers; E-Mail: arogers@bourbonlibrary.org; *Bkmobile Coordr*, T J Grimes; Staff 2 (MLS 2)
Founded 1905. Pop 19,405; Circ 108,526
Library Holdings: Bk Vols 41,900; Per Subs 75
Special Services for the Deaf - TTY machine
Friends of the Library Group
Bookmobiles: 1

PEWEE VALLEY

S KENTUCKY CORRECTIONAL INSTITUTION FOR WOMEN LIBRARY, 3000 Ash Ave, PO Box 337, 40056-0337. SAN 306-3968. Tel: 502-241-8454, Ext 2224. FAX: 502-241-0372. *Librn*, Lou Sturgill

Library Holdings: Bk Titles 11,000; Per Subs 45
Subject Interests: Ethnic studies, Feminism, Law
Open 7 days a week & 2 evenings

PIKEVILLE

P PIKE COUNTY PUBLIC LIBRARY DISTRICT,* 161 College St Ste 1, 41501-1741. SAN 306-249X. Tel: 606-432-9977. FAX: 606-432-9908. E-Mail: pcpldao@pikelibrary.org. *Dir*, Leean L Allen
Founded 1970
Library Holdings: Bk Vols 140,690; Per Subs 235
Mem of FIVCO Libr Develop District
Branches: 5
BELFRY PUBLIC, PO Box 340, Belfry, 41514. SAN 342-6394. Tel: 606-353-9429. FAX: 606-353-9429. *Librn*, Mary Duncan
ELKHORN CITY PUBLIC, PO Drawer L, Elkhorn City, 41522. SAN 375-541X. Tel: 606-754-5451. FAX: 606-754-5451.
PHELPS PUBLIC, 38575 State Hwy 194E, Phelps, 41553. SAN 328-8773. FAX: 606-456-7860. *Librn*, Mabel M Dotson
PIKEVILLE PUBLIC, 343 Main St, PO Box 415, 41501. SAN 376-9941. Tel: 606-432-1285. *Librn*, Kathy Cantrell
VESTA ROBERTS-JOHNSON MEMORIAL, PO Box 548, Virgie, 41572-0548. SAN 321-3331. FAX: 606-639-9839. *Librn*, Georgia Anderson
Founded 1980
Bookmobiles: 1

C PIKEVILLE COLLEGE, Frank M Allara Library, 147 Sycamore St, 41501-9042. SAN 306-3976. Tel: 606-218-5605, 606-432-9371. FAX: 606-218-5613, 606-432-9372. Web Site: library.pc.edu. *Dir*, Lee Robbins; E-Mail: lrobbins@pc.edu; *Librn*, Cindy Schmidt; Tel: 606-218-5159, Fax: 606-218-5165, E-Mail: cschmidt@pc.edu; *Asst Librn*, Mary Harmon; E-Mail: mharmon@pc.edu; *Per*, Mindy Robertson; E-Mail: mroberts@pc.edu; *Spec Coll & Archives*, Reagan Grimsley; E-Mail: rgrimsle@pc.edu. Subject Specialists: *Med ref*, Cindy Schmidt; Staff 12 (MLS 4, Non-MLS 8)
Founded 1920. Enrl 1,130; Fac 54; Highest Degree: Bachelor
Jul 1999-Jun 2000 Income $400,490, State $4,000, Federal $27,619, Locally Generated Income $5,353, Parent Institution $363,518. Mats Exp $132,345, Books $35,155, Per/Ser (Incl. Access Fees) $73,649, Presv $1,463, AV Equip $3,187, Electronic Ref Mat (Incl. Access Fees) $18,891
Library Holdings: Bk Vols 70,883; Bk Titles 61,071; Per Subs 357
Subject Interests: Appalachia, Genealogy, Kentucky
Special Collections: Pike County Historical Society Coll
Database Vendor: Ebsco - EbscoHost, OCLC - First Search, ProQuest
Partic in Appalachian Col Asn; Coun of Independent Ky Cols & Univs; Kentucky Library Network, Inc; OCLC Online Computer Library Center, Inc; SE Libr Network; Solinet

P PIKEVILLE PUBLIC LIBRARY,* 343 Main St, PO Box 471, 41502. SAN 306-3984. Tel: 606-432-1285. FAX: 606-432-1285. *Librn*, Delania Adkins; Staff 3 (MLS 1, Non-MLS 2)
Founded 1920. Pop 5,000; Circ 35,803
Library Holdings: Bk Vols 37,000; Per Subs 55
Special Collections: Kentucky Authors Coll
Mem of Big Sandy Libr District

PINEVILLE

§S BELL COUNTY FORESTRY CAMP LIBRARY, Rte 2, Box 75, 40977. Tel: 606-337-7065. FAX: 606-337-1312. *In Charge*, Charles Bowling; E-Mail: charles.bowling@mail.state.ky.us
Library Holdings: Bk Vols 3,000; Per Subs 20

§R CLEAR CREEK BAPTIST BIBLE COLLEGE, Brooks Memorial Library, 300 Clear Creek Rd, 40977-9754. Tel: 606-337-3196. FAX: 606-337-2372. E-Mail: ccbbc@tenet.net. *Dir Libr Serv*, Marge Cummings
Library Holdings: Bk Vols 36,000; Bk Titles 29,000; Per Subs 331
Automation Activity & Vendor Info: (Cataloging) TLC; (Circulation) TLC

P PINEVILLE-BELL COUNTY PUBLIC LIBRARY, Tennessee & Walnut, PO Box 1490, 40977-1490. SAN 306-3992. Tel: 606-337-3422. FAX: 606-337-9862. E-Mail: pinevillelib@tcnet.net. Web Site: www.tcnet.net/~pinevillelib/. *Librn*, Beverly Brown; *Asst Librn*, Ron Day; *Bkmobile Coordr*, Patricia Hopkins; *Circ*, Elizabeth Napier; Staff 5 (Non-MLS 5)
Founded 1933. Pop 20,300
Jul 1999-Jun 2000 Income $397,467, State $41,565, County $307,699, Locally Generated Income $48,203. Mats Exp $34,229, Books $26,567, Per/Ser (Incl. Access Fees) $3,861, Other Print Mats $3,201, Electronic Ref Mat (Incl. Access Fees) $600. Sal $171,146
Library Holdings: Bk Vols 80,830; Per Subs 164
Subject Interests: Genealogy, History, Local history
Automation Activity & Vendor Info: (Cataloging) Gaylord; (Circulation) Gaylord; (OPAC) Gaylord
Mem of Cumberland Valley Regional Libr Syst
Partic in Kentucky Library Network, Inc
Bookmobiles: 1

PIPPA PASSES

J ALICE LLOYD COLLEGE, McGaw Library & Learning Center,* 41844. SAN 306-400X. Tel: 606-368-2101, Ext 6112. FAX: 606-368-2125. E-Mail: mcgaw_library@hotmail.edu. *Dir*, Andy Busroe; *Publ Servs*, Jeannie G Galloway; Staff 3 (MLS 3)
Founded 1923
Aug 1997-Jul 1998 Income $90,850. Mats Exp $60,850, Books $33,000, Per/Ser (Incl. Access Fees) $18,000, Presv $850, Micro $5,000, Other Print Mats $4,000. Sal $92,000
Library Holdings: Bk Vols 8
Special Collections: Appalachian Oral History; Appalachian Photographic Coll; Children's Literature Coll
Partic in Kentucky Library Network, Inc; Solinet
Friends of the Library Group

PRESTONSBURG

P FLOYD COUNTY PUBLIC LIBRARY,* 161 N Arnold Ave, 41653. SAN 306-4026. Tel: 606-886-2981. FAX: 606-886-2284. Web Site: www.fclib.org. *Librn*, Homer L Hall; *Bkmobile Coordr*, Buddy W LeMaster
Founded 1957. Pop 48,764; Circ 74,114
Library Holdings: Bk Vols 65,309; Per Subs 50
Special Collections: Kentucky Coll
Mem of Big Sandy Libr District

J PRESTONSBURG COMMUNITY COLLEGE LIBRARY, One Bert T Combs Dr, 41653. SAN 306-4034. Tel: 606-886-3863, Ext 221. FAX: 606-886-8683. Web Site: www.prestonsburgcc.com. *Librn*, Sandra D Robertson; Tel: 606-886-3863, Ext 295, E-Mail: sandra.robertson@kctcs.net; *Asst Librn*, Melissa Forsyth; Tel: 606-886-3864, Ext 240, E-Mail: melissa.forsyth@kctcs.net; *Ref*, Judy Bowen; Tel: 606-886-3863, Ext 216, E-Mail: judy.bowen@kctcs.net; Staff 7 (MLS 3, Non-MLS 4)
Founded 1964. Enrl 2,887; Fac 92; Highest Degree: Associate
Jul 1999-Jun 2000 Mats Exp $83,302, Books $56,789, Per/Ser (Incl. Access Fees) $13,060, Micro $5,952, AV Equip $7,501. Sal $248,658
Library Holdings: Bk Vols 36,838; Bk Titles 36,500; Per Subs 250
Special Collections: Eastern Kentucky History Coll
Automation Activity & Vendor Info: (Cataloging) Endeavor; (Circulation) Endeavor; (Course Reserve) Endeavor; (ILL) Endeavor; (OPAC) Endeavor
Database Vendor: GaleNet, IAC - SearchBank, ProQuest
Publications: User's Guide
Partic in SE Libr Network

PRINCETON

P GEORGE COON PUBLIC LIBRARY, 114 S Harrison St, PO Box 230, 42445. SAN 306-4042. Tel: 270-365-2884. FAX: 270-365-2892. E-Mail: gcl@31994com.net. *Librn*, Judy Boaz; *Bkmobile Coordr*, Margaret Newby; *Ch Servs*, Becky Gray
Founded 1913. Pop 13,232; Circ 106,909
Library Holdings: Bk Vols 43,733; Per Subs 70
Special Collections: Genealogy (Ira Fears Coll), microfilm, bks; Rare Book Coll
Open Mon-Thurs 9-6, Fri & Sat 9-5
Friends of the Library Group
Bookmobiles: 1

RICHMOND

C EASTERN KENTUCKY UNIVERSITY LIBRARIES, 521 Lancaster Ave, 40475-3102. SAN 342-6068. Tel: 859-622-1778. Interlibrary Loan Service Tel: 859-622-1415. FAX: 859-622-1174. Web Site: www.library.eku.edu. *Dean*, Lee VanOrsdel; *Tech Coordr*, Greg Mitchell; *Acq*, Genevieve Clay; *Spec Coll*, Charles Hay III; *Cat*, Carol Thomas; *Coll Develop*, Ken Barksdale; *ILL*, Pat New; *Instrul Serv, Res*, Mary Anne Dewey; Staff 27 (MLS 24, Non-MLS 3)
Founded 1907. Enrl 14,950; Fac 644; Highest Degree: Master
Jul 2000-Jun 2001 Income $3,927,536. Mats Exp $1,361,728, Books $310,168, Per/Ser (Incl. Access Fees) $982,197, Presv $37,895, Electronic Ref Mat (Incl. Access Fees) $31,468. Sal $1,875,288 (Prof $937,661)
Library Holdings: Bk Vols 832,663; Per Subs 3,564
Subject Interests: Education, Humanities, Justice, Music, Nursing, Occupational therapy, Safety
Special Collections: Kentuckiana, bks, microfiche, mss; Learning Resources Center; Madison County-Eastern Kentucky University Law Library Coll, bks, microfiche
Automation Activity & Vendor Info: (Acquisitions) Endeavor; (Cataloging) Endeavor; (Circulation) Endeavor; (Course Reserve) Endeavor; (ILL) Endeavor; (Media Booking) Endeavor; (OPAC) Endeavor; (Serials) Endeavor
Publications: bibliographies; Books & More, (semi-annually) (Newsletter); brochures

Partic in Kentucky Library Network, Inc; OCLC Online Computer Library Center, Inc; SE Libr Network; Westlaw
Special Services for the Deaf - TDD
Friends of the Library Group
Departmental Libraries:
JUSTICE & SAFETY, Stratton Bldg, 40475. SAN 342-6092. Tel: 859-622-1798. FAX: 859-622-8028. E-Mail: libcasey@acs.edu.edu. *Librn*, Verna Casey
Founded 1975. Highest Degree: Master
Library Holdings: Bk Vols 28,921; Per Subs 150
Subject Interests: Corrections, Criminal justice, Criminal law and justice, Fire science, Law enforcement, Loss prevention, Safety
Partic in Kentucky Library Network, Inc; OCLC Online Computer Library Center, Inc; SE Libr Network
Friends of the Library Group
MUSIC, Foster Bldg, 40475. SAN 342-6122. Tel: 859-622-1795. FAX: 859-622-1174. *Actg Librn*, Elizabeth Baker
Library Holdings: Bk Vols 24,388
Subject Interests: Music
Partic in Kentucky Library Network, Inc; OCLC Online Computer Library Center, Inc; SE Libr Network

P MADISON COUNTY PUBLIC LIBRARY, 507 W Main St, 40475. SAN 375-3093. Tel: 859-623-6704. FAX: 859-623-2023. E-Mail: madison.publib@mail.state.ky.us. *Dir*, Sue Hays; Fax: 859-623-2032; *Librn*, Kathy Crouch; *Tech Servs*, Jody Baumgardner; *Bkmobile Coordr*, Beth Madden; *Ch Servs*, Kim Grampp; *Circ*, Bob Eager; Staff 17 (MLS 3, Non-MLS 14)
Founded 1988. Pop 57,508; Circ 330,000
Jul 1999-Jun 2000 Income $895,332, State $62,312, County $743,494, Locally Generated Income $89,526. Mats Exp $140,429, Books $103,330, Per/Ser (Incl. Access Fees) $6,936. Sal $372,532
Library Holdings: Bk Vols 81,177; Per Subs 215
Subject Interests: Genealogy, Kentucky
Automation Activity & Vendor Info: (Cataloging) TLC; (Circulation) epixtech, inc.; (OPAC) epixtech, inc.
Mem of Bluegrass South Regional Libr
Friends of the Library Group
Branches: 1
BEREA BRANCH, 319 Chestnut St, Berea, 40403. SAN 375-3107. Tel: 606-986-7112. FAX: 606-986-7208. *Librn*, Abbie Harris; *Ch Servs*, Michelle Sheyock; *Circ*, Kathy Hamblin
Friends of the Library Group
Bookmobiles: 1

RUSSELLVILLE

P LOGAN COUNTY PUBLIC LIBRARY, 201 W Sixth St, 42276. SAN 306-4093. Tel: 270-726-6129. FAX: 270-726-6127. E-Mail: loganlib@loganlibrary.org. Web Site: loganlibrary.org. *Dir*, Linda Kompanik; E-Mail: lindak@loganlibrary.org; *Dep Dir*, Sherryl Appling; *Bkmobile Coordr*, Beverly Terry; *Cat*, Mila Sledge; *Br Coordr*, Carol McKinney; *YA Servs*, Monica Edwards; *Br Coordr*, Geraldine Hodges; *Tech Servs*, Wanda Gower; Staff 4 (MLS 2, Non-MLS 2)
Founded 1966. Pop 24,416; Circ 238,016
Jul 1999-Jun 2000 Income $368,195, State $34,022, County $277,794, Locally Generated Income $56,379. Mats Exp $84,527, Books $63,437, Per/Ser (Incl. Access Fees) $3,108, Presv $2,786, Electronic Ref Mat (Incl. Access Fees) $600. Sal $188,077 (Prof $31,766)
Library Holdings: Bk Vols 45,000; Per Subs 100
Subject Interests: Genealogy, Photog hist
Automation Activity & Vendor Info: (Acquisitions) Brodart; (Cataloging) Brodart; (Circulation) Brodart; (Course Reserve) Brodart
Friends of the Library Group
Branches: 2
ADAIRVILLE BRANCH, 401 Church St, Adairville, 42202. SAN 320-8141. Tel: 270-539-4601. *Librn*, Carol McKinney
AUBURN BRANCH, 344 W Main St, Auburn, 42206. SAN 320-8168. Tel: 270-542-8180. *Librn*, Geraldine Hodges
Bookmobiles: 1

SAINT CATHARINE

§S DOMINICAN SISTERS ARCHIVES, Congregation of St Catharine of Siena, 2645 Bardstown Rd, 40061. Tel: 606-336-9303. FAX: 859-336-9306. *Dir*, Ilona Burdette; *Archivist*, Sister Louise Quinlan
Library Holdings: Bk Vols 2,000

J SAINT CATHARINE COLLEGE LIBRARY,* 2735 Bardstown Rd, 40061-9988. SAN 306-4107. Tel: 606-336-5082. FAX: 606-336-5031. *Dir*, Ilona Burdette
Founded 1930
Library Holdings: Bk Titles 20,000; Per Subs 100
Special Collections: Elizabeth Madox Roberts Coll

SALYERSVILLE

P MAGOFFIN COUNTY LIBRARY,* 141 Church St, PO Box 435, 41465. SAN 306-4115. Tel: 606-349-2411. FAX: 606-349-1120. E-Mail: mcpls@foothills.net. *Librn*, Carol Jean Howard; *Bkmobile Coordr*, Gency Bailey
Pop 13,515; Circ 29,747
Library Holdings: Bk Vols 22,000; Per Subs 15
Mem of Big Sandy Libr District

SANDY HOOK

§P RHETT BROWN MEMORIAL LIBRARY, Main St, 41171. (Mail add: PO Box 750, 41171-0750), Tel: 606-738-5796. FAX: 606-738-4980. E-Mail: ellcolib@harold.eastky.com. *Librn*, Victoria Hargraves
Library Holdings: Bk Vols 1,500; Per Subs 200

SCOTTSVILLE

P ALLEN COUNTY PUBLIC LIBRARY,* 106 W Main St, 42164. SAN 306-4123. Tel: 502-237-3861. FAX: 502-237-4095. *Dir*, Elaine Reece; E-Mail: ereece@nctc.com; *Bkmobile Coordr*, Ruby Gosser; *Ch Servs*, Susan Stewart
Founded 1953. Pop 14,628; Circ 70,786
Library Holdings: Bk Vols 29,040; Per Subs 70
Subject Interests: Genealogy
Special Collections: Kentucky Coll; Large type bks
Mem of Barren River Regional Libr Syst
Bookmobiles: 1

SHELBYVILLE

P SHELBY COUNTY LIBRARY DISTRICT,* 309 Eighth St, 40065. SAN 306-4131. Tel: 502-633-3803. FAX: 502-633-4025. *Dir*, Pamela W Federspiel; *Circ, Ref*, Deborah Magan; *Tech Servs*, Joyce Lancaster; *Publ Servs*, Jane Walls; *Ch Servs*, Elaine Johnson; Staff 7 (MLS 2, Non-MLS 5)
Founded 1899. Pop 24,824; Circ 155,000
Library Holdings: Bk Vols 50,000
Special Collections: Shelby County Historical Records, micro
Mem of Kentuckiana Libr Develop District
Partic in Kentucky Library Network, Inc
Friends of the Library Group
Bookmobiles: 1

SHEPHERDSVILLE

P BULLITT COUNTY PUBLIC LIBRARY, Ridgway Memorial Library, 127 N Walnut St, PO Box 146, 40165. SAN 342-6157. Tel: 502-543-7675. FAX: 502-543-5487. E-Mail: bcpl@iglou.com. Web Site: www.bcplib.org. *Dir*, Randy Matlow; Staff 19 (MLS 1, Non-MLS 18)
Founded 1954. Pop 60,955; Circ 166,923
Jul 1999-Jun 2000 Income $777,645. Mats Exp $163,519, Books $100,000, Per/Ser (Incl. Access Fees) $4,800. Sal $441,991
Library Holdings: Bk Vols 114,916; Per Subs 121
Mem of Kentuckiana Regional Libr
Partic in Kentucky Library Network, Inc
Branches: 3
DOROTHEA STOTTMAN BRANCH, 1251 Hillview Dr, Louisville, 40229. SAN 342-6246. Tel: 502-957-5759. FAX: 502-957-5759. Web Site: www.bcplib.org. *Librn*, Barbara Cross; E-Mail: dsl@bcplib.org
LEBANON JUNCTION BRANCH, 276 E Main St, Lebanon Junction, 40150. SAN 342-6181. Tel: 502-833-4648. FAX: 502-833-4648. Web Site: www.bcplib.org. *Librn*, Mary Yocum; E-Mail: ljl@bcplib.org
MOUNT WASHINGTON BRANCH, 113 Snapp St, Mount Washington, 40047. SAN 342-6211. Tel: 502-538-7560. FAX: 502-538-7560. Web Site: www.bcplib.org. *Librn*, Beverly Reeks; E-Mail: mwl@bcplib.org

SOMERSET

P PULASKI COUNTY PUBLIC LIBRARY, 107 N Main St, 42501. (Mail add: PO Box 36, 42502), SAN 342-6270. Tel: 606-679-8401. FAX: 606-679-1779. Web Site: www.pcpl.lib.ky.us. *Librn*, Judy Burdine; E-Mail: jburdine@hyperaction.net; *Asst Librn*, Charlotte Keeney; *Bkmobile Coordr*, Wilma Hughes; *Ch Servs*, Carol Sexton; E-Mail: csexton@hyperaction.net
Founded 1905. Pop 49,489; Circ 208,941
Jul 1998-Jun 1999 Income (Main Library and Branch Library) $637,529, State $54,365, County $494,562, Locally Generated Income $88,602. Mats Exp $75,000, Books $64,500, Per/Ser (Incl. Access Fees) $6,500, Electronic Ref Mat (Incl. Access Fees) $3,000. Sal $268,054 (Prof $70,000)
Library Holdings: Bk Vols 80,000; Per Subs 203
Subject Interests: Genealogy
Automation Activity & Vendor Info: (Cataloging) Gaylord; (Circulation) Gaylord; (OPAC) Gaylord
Mem of Lake Cumberland Regional Libr Syst
Partic in Kentucky Library Network, Inc
Friends of the Library Group

Branches: 4
BURNSIDE BRANCH, French Ave, PO Box 7, Burnside, 42519. SAN 342-6300. Tel: 606-561-5287. *Librn*, Joy Halcomb
NANCY BRANCH, Mill Springs Plaza, PO Box 88, Nancy, 42544. SAN 342-6335. Tel: 606-636-4241. FAX: 606-636-4241. *Librn*, Mary Stevenson
SCIENCE HILL BRANCH, PO Box 448, Science Hill, 42553. SAN 342-636X. Tel: 606-423-4221. *Librn*, Donna Pfeiffer
SHOPVILLE STAB, Shopville/Stab Fire Dept, 42501. SAN 377-6727. *Librn*, Wanda Bullock
Bookmobiles: 1

J SOMERSET COMMUNITY COLLEGE LIBRARY, Harold B Strunk Learning Resource Ctr, 808 Monticello St, 42501. SAN 306-414X. Tel: 606-679-8501, Ext 3410. FAX: 606-679-5139. Web Site: www.somcc.uky.edu/library. *Dir Libr Serv*, Shelley Wood Burgett; Tel: 606-679-8501, Ext 3412, E-Mail: shelly.burgett@kctcs.net; *Publ Servs*, Pamela K Rush; E-Mail: pam.rush@kctcs.net; *Distance Educ, Ref Serv*, Mary Taylor Huntsman; Tel: 606-679-8501, Ext 3415, E-Mail: mary.huntsman@kctcs.net; Staff 5 (MLS 3, Non-MLS 2)
Founded 1965. Enrl 1,601; Fac 50; Highest Degree: Associate
Jul 1999-Jun 2000 Mats Exp $85,773, Books $57,984, Per/Ser (Incl. Access Fees) $12,869, Micro $3,000, Electronic Ref Mat (Incl. Access Fees) $11,920
Library Holdings: Bk Vols 52,000; Bk Titles 41,143; Per Subs 190
Subject Interests: Japan, Local history
Database Vendor: Ebsco - EbscoHost, GaleNet, OCLC - First Search
Partic in Kentucky Library Network, Inc
Special Services for the Deaf - Staff with knowledge of sign language

SOUTH UNION

S SOUTH UNION SHAKER VILLAGE, Julia Neal Museum Library, 850 Shaker Museum Rd, PO Box 30, 42283. SAN 375-0736. Tel: 270-542-4167. Toll Free Tel: 800-811-8379. FAX: 270-542-7558. E-Mail: shakmus@logantele.com. *Exec Dir*, Saddler Jones Taylor; *Curator*, Tommy Collier Hines. Subject Specialists: *Architecture*, Saddler Jones Taylor; *Exhibition catalogs*, Tommy Collier Hines
Founded 1986
Library Holdings: Bk Titles 1,000
Subject Interests: Kentucky
Special Collections: Historic photograph; Manuscript; Primary material
Restriction: Non-circulating
Function: Archival collection
Friends of the Library Group

SOUTH WILLIAMSON

M WILLIAMSON APPALACHIAN REGIONAL HOSPITALS, Lake Swigart Memorial Library, 260 Hospital Dr, 41503. SAN 317-8404. Tel: 606-237-1700, Ext 4287. FAX: 606-237-1745. *Librn*, Amy Harris; E-Mail: aharris@arh.org
Founded 1956
Library Holdings: Bk Titles 650; Per Subs 20
Restriction: Employees & their associates, Staff use only
Partic in Medline
Open Mon-Fri 8am-4:30pm

SPRINGFIELD

P WASHINGTON COUNTY PUBLIC LIBRARY,* 210 E Main St, 40069. SAN 306-4158. Tel: 606-336-7655. FAX: 606-336-0256. E-Mail: washclib@kih.net. *Librn*, Lisa Jones; *Ch Servs*, Ione Pinkston
Founded 1964. Pop 10,441; Circ 41,352
Jul 1996-Jun 1997 Income $128,583, State $19,630, County $102,655, Locally Generated Income $1,625, Other $4,673. Mats Exp $19,737, Books $15,927, Per/Ser (Incl. Access Fees) $1,366, Micro $38. Sal $50,528 (Prof $38,108)
Library Holdings: Bk Vols 25,000; Per Subs 47
Special Collections: Elizabeth Madox Roberts
Mem of Lincoln Trail Libraries System
Partic in Kentucky Library Network, Inc
Friends of the Library Group

STANFORD

P HARVEY HELM MEMORIAL LIBRARY, Lincoln County Public Library, 301 Third St, 40484. SAN 306-4174. Tel: 606-365-7513. FAX: 606-365-7513. *Librn*, Kay Peppard; *Asst Librn*, Angela Hensley
Pop 19,000; Circ 136,000
Library Holdings: Bk Vols 33,400; Per Subs 66
Branches: 1
HARVEY HELM HISTORICAL LIBRARY & MUSEUM, 315 W Main St, 40484. SAN 320-0914. FAX: 606-365-7513. *In Charge*, Kay Peppard
Bookmobiles: 1

STANTON

P POWELL COUNTY PUBLIC LIBRARY,* 725 Breckenridge St, 40380. SAN 306-4182. Tel: 606-663-4511. FAX: 606-663-4346. E-Mail: powellpublib@mailcity.com. *Librn*, Linda Rogers; *Asst Librn*, Janice Sipple; *Ch Servs*, Mary Farmer; *Bkmobile Coordr*, Patsy Roe
Founded 1964. Pop 11,886; Circ 92,402
Library Holdings: Bk Vols 19,986; Per Subs 64
Special Collections: New Readers, large print

TAYLORSVILLE

P SPENCER COUNTY PUBLIC LIBRARY, 168 Taylorsville Rd, 40071. SAN 320-8214. Tel: 502-477-8137. FAX: 502-477-5033. E-Mail: scpl@iglou.com. *Librn*, Sue D Snider; *Asst Librn*, Lisa Lewis-Brown
Pop 6,801; Circ 22,449
Library Holdings: Bk Vols 25,000
Mem of Kentuckiana Regional Libr
Partic in ALA; Ky Libr Asn

TOMPKINSVILLE

P MONROE COUNTY PUBLIC LIBRARY, William B Harlan Memorial Library, 500 W Fourth St, 42167-1497. SAN 306-4190. Tel: 270-487-5301. FAX: 270-487-5309. E-Mail: wbhmlib@scrtc.com. *Dir*, Stephanie Penick; *Ch Servs, Publ Servs*, Dawn Shaw; *Bkmobile Coordr*, William D Davis, Jr
Founded 1966. Pop 12,353; Circ 62,000
Library Holdings: Bk Vols 33,000; Per Subs 114
Mem of Barren River District
Open Mon 8:30-8, Tues-Fri 8:30-5, Sat 8:30-2

TRAPPIST

SR GETHSEMANI, Abbey Library, 3642 Monks Rd, 40051. SAN 306-4204. Tel: 502-549-3117. FAX: 502-549-4124. Web Site: www.monks.org.
Founded 1848
Library Holdings: Bk Vols 30,200
Subject Interests: Philosophy, Religion, Theology
Special Collections: Cistercian Monastic History & Liturgy, rare bks; Saint Bernard & DeRance, rare bks; Thomas Merton Coll

UNION

P BOONE COUNTY PUBLIC LIBRARY, 8899 US 42, 41091. SAN 306-2589. Tel: 859-384-5550. FAX: 859-384-5557. E-Mail: info@bcpl.org. Web Site: www.bcpl.org. *Mgr*, Jasbir Chahal; *Mgr*, Tillie Tanfani; *Ad Servs*, Patricia Yannarella; *Dir*, Lucinda A Brown; Tel: 504-286-4785, E-Mail: labrown@bcpl.org; *YA Servs*, Betsy Glick; Staff 41 (MLS 10, Non-MLS 31)
Founded 1973. Pop 57,589; Circ 573,784
Jul 1999-Jun 2000 Income $3,889,236, State $63,000, Federal $14,000, County $3,443,785, Locally Generated Income $370,000. Mats Exp $371,084. Sal $970,475
Library Holdings: Bk Vols 226,000; Bk Titles 215,000; Per Subs 317
Automation Activity & Vendor Info: (Cataloging) Gaylord; (Circulation) Gaylord; (OPAC) Gaylord
Database Vendor: Ebsco - EbscoHost
Mem of Northern Ky Regional Libr Develop District
Partic in Greater Cincinnati Library Consortium

VANCEBURG

P LEWIS COUNTY PUBLIC LIBRARY,* 422 Second St, 41179. SAN 306-4220. Tel: 606-796-2532. FAX: 606-796-2532. *Librn*, Marilyn Conway; *Asst Librn*, Helen Rayburn
Founded 1954. Pop 14,545; Circ 82,402
Library Holdings: Bk Vols 31,000; Per Subs 35
Partic in OCLC Online Computer Library Center, Inc
Friends of the Library Group

VANCLEVE

R KENTUCKY MOUNTAIN BIBLE COLLEGE, Gibson Library, PO Box 10, 41385. SAN 306-4239. Tel: 606-666-5000. FAX: 606-666-7744. Web Site: www.kmbc.edu. *Librn*, Patricia Bowen; E-Mail: pbowen@kmbc.edu
Founded 1931. Enrl 69; Fac 13
Library Holdings: Bk Vols 25,000; Per Subs 191
Special Collections: Holiness, Missionary, Religious Biography
Automation Activity & Vendor Info: (Cataloging) Sagebrush Corporation; (Circulation) Sagebrush Corporation
Open Mon-Fri 8am-5pm & 6:30-9pm

VERSAILLES

P LOGAN-HELM WOODFORD COUNTY PUBLIC LIBRARY,* 115 N Main St, 40383-1289. SAN 306-4247. Tel: 606-873-5191, 606-873-9703. FAX: 606-873-1542. *Dir*, Kelle Hoskins; *Ch Servs, YA Servs*, Rebecca Watson; *Cat*, Carla Tomlin; *Bkmobile Coordr*, Thelma Grimes; *Tech Servs*, Lynchie Duggan; Staff 3 (MLS 3)
Founded 1967. Pop 19,655; Circ 144,542
Jul 1997-Jun 1998 Income $384,194, State $31,888. Mats Exp $62,752, Books $52,679, Per/Ser (Incl. Access Fees) $4,355. Sal $205,521
Library Holdings: Bk Titles 32,117; Per Subs 108
Subject Interests: Local history
Friends of the Library Group

§S WOODFORD COUNTY HISTORICAL SOCIETY LIBRARY, 121 Rose Hill, 40383-1221. Tel: 859-873-6786. E-Mail: woodford@qx.net. Web Site: www.rootsweb.com/kywchs/woodfordpage.htm. *Curator*, Danna Estridge
Library Holdings: Bk Titles 1,000

VILLA HILLS

SR ST WALBURG MONASTERY ARCHIVES,* 2500 Amsterdam Rd, 41017-5316. SAN 375-6521. Tel: 606-331-6324. FAX: 606-331-2136. E-Mail: walburg@iglou.com. *Archivist*, Sr Teresa Wolking
Library Holdings: Bk Titles 200
Special Collections: St Walburg Monastery of Benedictine Sisters

WARSAW

P GALLATIN COUNTY PUBLIC LIBRARY, 209 W Market St, PO Box 848, 41095-0848. SAN 321-0510. Tel: 859-567-2786. FAX: 859-567-4750. E-Mail: gallatinlib@yahoo.com. *Dir*, Brenda Hawkins; *Asst Librn*, Alice Johnson; Staff 3 (MLS 1, Non-MLS 2)
Founded 1978. Pop 5,376; Circ 51,300
Library Holdings: Bk Vols 24,500; Bk Titles 22,000; Per Subs 24
Mem of Northern Ky Regional Libr Develop District

WEST LIBERTY

P JOHN F KENNEDY MEMORIAL LIBRARY, Morgan County Library, 408 Prestonburg St, 41472. SAN 306-4255. Tel: 606-743-4151. FAX: 606-743-2170. E-Mail: kenidlib@mrtc.com. *Librn*, Michael Griffitts; *Bkmobile Coordr*, Jackie Griffitts
Founded 1965. Pop 11,406; Circ 76,576
Library Holdings: Bk Vols 30,000; Per Subs 29
Subject Interests: Genealogy
Mem of Buffalo Trace Library Develop District

WHITESBURG

P HARRY CAUDILL MEMORIAL LIBRARY, 121 E Main St, 41858. SAN 342-6459. Tel: 606-633-7547. FAX: 606-633-3407. E-Mail: hmclib@kih.net. Web Site: www.users.kih.net/~hmclib/. *Dir*, Lina Tidal; *Bkmobile Coordr*, Anna Caudill
Founded 1952. Pop 27,000; Circ 116,932
Jul 1999-Jun 2000 Income (Main Library and Branch Library) $480,266. Mats Exp Books $64,967. Sal $186,619 (Prof $33,000)
Library Holdings: Bk Titles 111,631; Per Subs 188
Subject Interests: Genealogy, Local history
Mem of Kentucky Department for Libraries & Archives
Branches: 3
BLACKEY BRANCH, Blackey, 41804. SAN 374-4566. Tel: 606-633-4013. FAX: 606-633-9808. *Librn*, Mary Grace Raglin
LILLIAN WEBB MEMORIAL, Neon, 41840. SAN 342-6513. Tel: 606-855-7913. FAX: 606-855-4565. *Librn*, Joyce Amburgey
Pop 1,600
MARY JO WOLFE BRANCH, PO Box 687, Jenkins, 41537. SAN 342-6483. Tel: 606-832-4101. FAX: 606-832-0040. *Librn*, Peggy Bentley
Bookmobiles: 1

C SOUTHEAST COMMUNITY COLLEGE, Whitesburg Campus Library,* 201 Long Ave, 41858. SAN 372-6959. Tel: 606-633-0279. FAX: 606-633-7225. Web Site: www.uky.edu/communitycolleges/sou/01_libra.htm.
Special Collections: Terry Cornett Appalachian Coll
Publications: The Gateway (newsletter)

WHITLEY CITY

P MCCREARY COUNTY PUBLIC LIBRARY DISTRICT, 6 N Main St, 42653-4116. (Mail add: PO Box 8, 42653-0008), SAN 320-4812. Tel: 606-376-8738. FAX: 606-376-3631. E-Mail: mcpl@highland.net. *Dir*, Kay Morrow; *Circ*, Debbie Lyons; *Bkmobile Coordr*, Peggy Rector; Staff 1 (Non-MLS 1)
Founded 1975. Pop 15,603; Circ 80,715
Jul 2000-Jun 2001 Income $189,260, Federal $25,400, County $146,000, Locally Generated Income $17,860. Mats Exp $4,300, Per/Ser (Incl. Access Fees) $2,000, Micro $200, Electronic Ref Mat (Incl. Access Fees) $2,100
Library Holdings: Bk Vols 41,000; Bk Titles 39,500; Per Subs 40; Bks on Deafness & Sign Lang 10
Special Collections: Pictorial History of McCreary County
Automation Activity & Vendor Info: (Circulation) Follett
Database Vendor: OCLC - First Search
Mem of Lake Cumberland Regional Libr Syst
Partic in Kentucky Library Network, Inc
Friends of the Library Group
Bookmobiles: 1

WILLIAMSBURG

C CUMBERLAND COLLEGE, Norma Perkins Hagan Memorial Library, 821 Walnut St, 40769. SAN 306-4263. Tel: 606-539-4329. Interlibrary Loan Service Tel: 606-539-4134. Reference Tel: 606-539-4526. FAX: 606-539-4317. Web Site: hagan.cumber.edu. *Dir*, Jan Wren; E-Mail: jwren@cc.cumber.edu; *Publ Servs*, Ru Story-Huffman; *Tech Servs*, Ron Bunger; Staff 8 (MLS 3, Non-MLS 5)
Founded 1889. Enrl 1,505; Fac 105; Highest Degree: Master
Library Holdings: Bk Vols 148,000; Per Subs 653
Subject Interests: Appalachia, Education, Religion
Special Collections: Children's Literature; Kentucky; US Govt
Automation Activity & Vendor Info: (Cataloging) SIRSI
Partic in Appalachian Col Asn; Coun of Independent Ky Cols & Univs; Dialog Corporation; Kentucky Library Network, Inc

P WHITLEY COUNTY LIBRARY, 285 S Third St, 40769. SAN 306-4271. Tel: 606-549-0818. FAX: 606-549-0818. E-Mail: wcpublib@tcnet.net. *Dir*, Tammy Thompson; E-Mail: thompsotam@hotmail.com
Founded 1960. Pop 33,396; Circ 124,937
Library Holdings: Bk Vols 48,663; Per Subs 35
Mem of Cumberland Valley Libr Develop District
Bookmobiles: 1

WILLIAMSTOWN

P GRANT COUNTY PUBLIC LIBRARY DISTRICT, (GCPL), 107 N Main St, 41097-1187. SAN 306-428X. Tel: 859-824-4723, 859-824-7059. FAX: 859-824-4769. E-Mail: elms_grant@yahoo.com. *Dir*, Elizabeth Schneider
Founded 1976. Pop 19,828; Circ 257,125
Jul 1998-Jun 1999 Income $255,330, State $25,496, County $208,941, Locally Generated Income $20,892. Mats Exp $27,683, Books $24,000, Per/Ser (Incl. Access Fees) $1,983, Micro $50, Other Print Mats $1,650. Sal $98,101
Library Holdings: Bk Vols 41,021; Per Subs 101; High Interest/Low Vocabulary Bk Vols 47; Bks on Deafness & Sign Lang 86
Special Collections: Genealogy Coll; Kentuckiana Coll
Automation Activity & Vendor Info: (Cataloging) TLC; (Circulation) TLC; (Serials) TLC
Mem of Northern Ky Regional Libr Develop District
Partic in Ky Coop Libr Info Project
Friends of the Library Group

WILMORE

C ASBURY COLLEGE, Morrison-Kenyon Library, One Macklem Dr, 40390-1198. SAN 306-4298. Tel: 859-858-3511. FAX: 859-858-3921. Web Site: www.asbury.edu. *Dir*, Larry Reining; Tel: 859-858-3511, Ext 2126, E-Mail: larry.reining@asbury.edu; *Bibliog Instr, Online Servs, Publ Servs*, Jennifer Walz; Tel: 859-858-3511, Ext 2269, E-Mail: jlwalz@asbury.edu; *Cat*, Douglas Butler; Tel: 859-858-3511, Ext 2266, E-Mail: doug.butler@asbury.edu; *ILL*, Bonnie Temple; Tel: 859-858-3511, Ext 2143, E-Mail: bonnie.temple@asbury.edu; *Archivist, Ref*, Morgan Tracy; Tel: 859-858-3511, Ext 2292, E-Mail: matracy@asbury.edu; Staff 4 (MLS 4)
Founded 1890. Enrl 1,337; Fac 109; Highest Degree: Bachelor
Jul 1998-Jun 1999 Income Parent Institution $499,640. Mats Exp $217,000, Books $142,000, Per/Ser (Incl. Access Fees) $50,000, Presv $3,000, Micro $15,000, Manuscripts & Archives $1,000, Electronic Ref Mat (Incl. Access Fees) $6,000. Sal $288,000 (Prof $178,323)
Library Holdings: Bk Vols 175,597; Bk Titles 133,741; Per Subs 620
Special Collections: Asbury College faculty & alumni publications; College Archives; Missionary Coll
Automation Activity & Vendor Info: (Acquisitions) epixtech, inc.; (Cataloging) epixtech, inc.; (Circulation) epixtech, inc.; (Course Reserve) epixtech, inc.; (OPAC) epixtech, inc.; (Serials) epixtech, inc.
Database Vendor: Dialog, Ebsco - EbscoHost, OCLC - First Search, Wilson - Wilson Web
Publications: Annual Report; Campus Newsletter; Collegii Asburiensis Bibliotheca
Partic in Association Of Independent Kentucky Colleges & Universities; BRS; Christian Libr Network; Dialog Corporation; Kentucky Library Network, Inc; OCLC Online Computer Library Center, Inc; Southeast Library System; Wilsonline

R ASBURY THEOLOGICAL SEMINARY, B L Fisher Library, 204 N Lexington Ave, 40390-1199. SAN 306-4301. Tel: 859-859-2229. FAX: 859-858-2350. Web Site: www.asburyseminary.edu. *Dir*, David William Faupel; *Dir Libr Serv*, Donald Butterworth; *Spec Coll*, William Kostlevy; *ILL*, John Seery; Staff 16 (MLS 6, Non-MLS 10)
Founded 1939. Enrl 1,300; Fac 67; Highest Degree: Doctorate
Library Holdings: Bk Vols 197,000; Per Subs 1,000
Subject Interests: Biblical studies, Missions and missionaries, Theology
Special Collections: bks & microfilm; Healing (Alfred E Price Coll); Wesleyan/Holiness Evangelicalism; World Council of Churches (Faith & Order Papers Coll)
Publications: Occasional Bibliographic Papers of the B L Fisher Library
Partic in SE Libr Network; Theological Education Association Of Mid America

WINCHESTER

P CLARK COUNTY PUBLIC LIBRARY,* 370 S Burns Ave, 40391. SAN 306-431X. Tel: 606-744-5661. FAX: 606-744-5993. *Ad Servs*, Julie Narvell; *Bkmobile Coordr*, Carol Spicer; *Ch Servs*, Anne Hall
Founded 1950. Pop 29,500; Circ 172,000
Library Holdings: Bk Vols 50,000; Per Subs 140; Per Subs 118
Special Collections: Kentucky History (Doyle Coll & Kentucky Coll); Local Genealogy (Doyle Coll, Family File), bks, micro
Partic in Kentucky Library Network, Inc
Friends of the Library Group

LOUISIANA

Date of Statistics: 1999
Population, 1990 Census: 4,219,973
Population Served by Public Libraries: 4,325,773 (1999 est.)
Total Volumes in Public Libraries: 11,356,307
Volumes Per Capita: 2.63
Total Public Library Circulation: 17,851,898
Circulation Per Capita: 4.13
Total Public Library Income: $103,218,674
Median or Average Income: $1,587,980
Source of Income: Public Funds (Primarily Property Tax)
Expenditures Per Capita: $20.35
Number of County or Multi-county (Regional) Libraries: 65
Counties Served: 64
Grants-in-Aid to Public Libraries:
State Aid: $1,500,000

ABBEVILLE

P VERMILION PARISH LIBRARY, 200 N Magdalen Sq, 70510-4645. (Mail add: PO Drawer 640, 70511-0640), SAN 342-6548. Tel: 337-893-2655. Circulation Tel: 337-893-2674. FAX: 337-898-0526. Web Site: www.vermilion.lib.la.us. *Dir*, Jackie Choate; *Ch Servs*, Tiffany Abshire; *ILL, Ref*, Sharon Herbert; *Ad Servs*, Sally Braud; Staff 3 (MLS 3)
Founded 1941. Pop 53,044; Circ 299,077
Jan 2000-Dec 2000 Income (Main Library and Branch Library) $922,065, State $135,913, County $726,068, Other $60,084. Mats Exp $215,385, Books $199,044, Per/Ser (Incl. Access Fees) $16,341. Sal $383,855 (Prof $97,297)
Library Holdings: Bk Vols 150,674; Bk Titles 110,660; Per Subs 97
Special Collections: Louisiana Coll
Mem of Bayouland Library System
Friends of the Library Group
Branches: 8
ABBEVILLE BRANCH, 200 N Magdalen Square, 70510. (Mail add: PO Drawer 640, 70511-0640), Tel: 337-893-2674. FAX: 337-898-0526. E-Mail: abbeville.b1vm@pelican.state.lib.la.us. *Branch Mgr*, Shelley Choate
Founded 1941
Library Holdings: Bk Vols 61,966; Per Subs 109
Special Collections: Louisiana Coll
Open Mon & Thurs 9:8, Tues, Weds & Fri 9-5:30 & Sat 9-1
Friends of the Library Group
COW ISLAND, 19635 Columbus, 70510. (Mail add: PO Drawer 640, 70511-0640), Tel: 337-642-5474. FAX: 337-898-0526. E-Mail: cowisland.b1vm@pelican.state.lib.la.us. *Branch Mgr*, Susan Stelly; Staff 1 (Non-MLS 1)
Library Holdings: Bk Vols 7,033; Per Subs 12
Special Collections: Louisiana Coll
Open Mon only 9-4:30
DELCAMBRE BRANCH, 206 W Main St, Delcambre, 70528-2918. SAN 342-6602. Tel: 337-685-2388. FAX: 337-685-2388. *Branch Mgr*, Jean Segura
Library Holdings: Per Subs 22
Special Collections: Louisiana Coll
Library shared with Iberia Parish Public Library. Vermilion Parish Library provides personnel & ILL while Iberia supplies the books
ERATH BRANCH, 210 S Broadway, Erath, 70533-4004. SAN 342-6637. Tel: 337-937-5628. FAX: 337-937-5628. E-Mail: erath.blvm@pelican.state.lib.la.us. *Branch Mgr*, Peggy B LeBlanc
Library Holdings: Bk Vols 15,694; Per Subs 19
Special Collections: Louisiana Coll
Open Mon-Thur 12-5:30, Fri 12-5, Sat 9-12
GUEYDAN BRANCH, 605 McMurtry, Gueydan, 70542-4140. SAN 342-6661. Tel: 337-536-6781. FAX: 337-536-6781. E-Mail: gueydan.blvm@pelican.state.lib.la.us. *Branch Mgr*, Angela Touchet
Library Holdings: Bk Vols 16,879; Per Subs 23
Special Collections: Louisiana Coll
Open Mon-Fri 10-5, Sat 9-12
KAPLAN BRANCH, 513 N Cushing, Kaplan, 70548-3315. SAN 342-6696. Tel: 337-643-7209. FAX: 337-643-7209. E-Mail: kaplan.blvm@pelican.state.lib.la.us. *Branch Mgr*, Linda Leonard
Library Holdings: Bk Vols 27,475; Per Subs 33
Special Collections: Louisiana Coll
Open Mon, Wed, Thur & Fri 9-5, Tues 9-8, Sat 9-12
MAURICE BRANCH, 100 E Joseph, Maurice, 70555. (Mail add: PO Box 127, Maurice, 70555-0127), SAN 342-6726. Tel: 337-893-5583. FAX: 337-893-5583. E-Mail: maurice.blvm@pelican.state.lib.la.us. *Branch Mgr*, Cheryl Bergeron
Library Holdings: Bk Vols 12,365; Per Subs 20
Special Collections: Louisiana Coll
Open Mon-Thur 12-5:30, Fri 12-5, Sat 9-12
PECAN ISLAND, 28736 W LA Hwy 82, Kaplan, 70548-9403. SAN 342-6750. Tel: 337-737-2510. FAX: 337-737-2510. E-Mail: pecanisland.b1vm@pellican.state.lib.la.us. *Branch Mgr*, Florine Hardin; Staff 1 (Non-MLS 1)
Library Holdings: Bk Vols 9,262; Per Subs 15
Special Collections: Louisiana Coll
Open Tues-Thurs 10-3

ALEXANDRIA

M CHRISTUS SAINT FRANCES CABRINI HOSPITAL, Medical Library, 3330 Masonic Dr, 71301. SAN 327-6031. Tel: 318-487-1122, Ext 1540. FAX: 318-448-6754. Web Site: www.cabrini.org/main.htm. *Librn*, Mary Zischke; E-Mail: mary.zischke@sfc.christushealth.org
Library Holdings: Bk Vols 100; Per Subs 70
Subject Interests: Medical
Restriction: By appointment only
Partic in Cent La Libr Consortium

G DEPARTMENT OF VETERANS AFFAIRS, Medical & Patient's Library,* VA Medical Center, PO Box 69004, 71306-9004. SAN 342-7056. Tel: 318-473-0010, 318-473-2548. FAX: 318-473-9491. *Chief Librn*, Charles Coker
Circ 15,988
Library Holdings: Bk Vols 5,741; Per Subs 270
Partic in BRS; S Cent Regional Med Libr Program; Vets Admin Libr Network

L GOLD, WEEMS, BRUSER, SUES & RUNDELL, Law Library,* 2001 MacArthur Dr, 71307. SAN 372-1299. Tel: 318-445-6471. FAX: 318-445-6476. *Librn*, Dorothy Shepard; E-Mail: dshepard@goldlawfirm.com
Library Holdings: Bk Titles 1,287; Per Subs 77

C LOUISIANA STATE UNIVERSITY AT ALEXANDRIA, James C Bolton Library, 8100 Hwy 71 S, 71302. SAN 306-4344. Tel: 318-473-6438. Circulation Tel: 318-473-6441. Reference Tel: 318-473-6442. FAX: 318-473-6556. E-Mail: yvonnev@pc01.lsua.edu. Web Site: www.lsua.edu/library/bolton.htm. *Dir*, Dr Anna C Burns; Tel: 318-473-6437, E-Mail: aburns@pobox.lsua.edu; *Head Tech Servs*, Floyd B Bennett; Tel: 318-473-6509,

E-Mail: fbennett@pobox.lsua.edu; *Tech Servs*, Pamela Deloach; Tel: 318-473-6440, E-Mail: pdeloach@pobox.lsua.edu; *Publ Servs*, Mary E Connell; Tel: 318-473-6442, E-Mail: mconnell@pobox.lsua.edu; *Circ*, Callie B Harvey; Tel: 318-473-6441, E-Mail: charvey@pobox.lsua.edu; Staff 6 (MLS 3, Non-MLS 3)
Founded 1960. Enrl 2,386; Highest Degree: Associate
Jul 1999-Jun 2000 Income State $298,024. Mats Exp $56,262, Books $25,002, Per/Ser (Incl. Access Fees) $30,355, Electronic Ref Mat (Incl. Access Fees) $905. Sal $201,796 (Prof $163,903)
Library Holdings: Bk Vols 154,935; Bk Titles 102,850; Per Subs 354
Subject Interests: Nursing
Special Collections: Local History; Louisiana Newspapers; US Census Records; Louisiana Newspapers & United States Census Records, micro
Automation Activity & Vendor Info: (Cataloging) NOTIS
Database Vendor: GaleNet, IAC - Info Trac, IAC - SearchBank, Lexis-Nexis, OCLC - First Search, ProQuest, Silverplatter Information Inc.
Friends of the Library Group

P RAPIDES PARISH LIBRARY, 411 Washington St, 71301-8338. SAN 342-6785. Tel: 318-445-2411, 318-445-6436. Interlibrary Loan Service Tel: 318-448-8125. Circulation Tel: 318-445-2411, Ext 201. Reference Tel: 318-445-2411, Ext 202. E-Mail: info@rpl.org. Web Site: www.rpl.org. *Dir*, Stephen L Rogge; Tel: 318-445-6436, Ext 238, E-Mail: steverogge@hotmail.com; *Asst Dir*, Beth Vandersteen; Tel: 318-445-6436, Ext 225, E-Mail: bethvandersteen@hotmail.com; Staff 86 (MLS 4, Non-MLS 82)
Founded 1942. Pop 131,556; Circ 586,628
Jan 1999-Dec 1999 Income (Main Library and Branch Library) $2,693,325, State $249,340, County $2,068,980, Locally Generated Income $99,941. Mats Exp $311,705, Books $281,068, Per/Ser (Incl. Access Fees) $23,192, Micro $4,600, Electronic Ref Mat (Incl. Access Fees) $2,845. Sal $1,282,545
Library Holdings: Bk Vols 391,924; Bk Titles 139,137; Per Subs 233; Spec Interest Per Sub 12; Bks on Deafness & Sign Lang 65
Subject Interests: Local history
Special Collections: Map coll
Automation Activity & Vendor Info: (Acquisitions) Innovative Interfaces Inc.; (Cataloging) Innovative Interfaces Inc.; (Circulation) Innovative Interfaces Inc.; (ILL) Innovative Interfaces Inc.; (OPAC) Innovative Interfaces Inc.; (Serials) Innovative Interfaces Inc.
Database Vendor: Ebsco - EbscoHost, OCLC - First Search
Publications: Friends Newsletter (adult); Friends of the Rapides Library (Newsletter); Ripple (Newsletter)
Friends of the Library Group
Branches: 9
BOYCE BRANCH, 500A Ulster St, PO Box 792, Boyce, 71409. SAN 342-6815. Tel: 318-793-2182. FAX: 318-793-2182. E-Mail: boycelibrary@hotmail.com. *Librn*, Deborah Boerboorn
Library Holdings: Bk Vols 12,648
FUHRER, 1264 Canterbury Dr, 71303. SAN 342-6939. Tel: 318-442-2483. FAX: 318-442-7256. E-Mail: fuhrerlibrary@hotmail.com. *Librn*, Blanche Williams
Library Holdings: Bk Vols 38,851
GLENMORA BRANCH, 1120 Seventh Ave, PO Box 1206, Glenmora, 71433. SAN 342-6874. Tel: 318-748-4848. FAX: 318-748-4848. E-Mail: glenmoralibrary@hotmail.com. *Librn*, Gail Goldberg
Library Holdings: Bk Vols 17,802
Friends of the Library Group
GUNTER, 5630 Holloway Rd, Pineville, 71360. SAN 342-684X. Tel: 318-443-7259. FAX: 318-443-1293. E-Mail: gunterlibrary@hotmail.com. *Librn*, Karen Gipson
Library Holdings: Bk Vols 45,579
HINESTON BRANCH, 1839 Hwy 121, Hineston, 71438. (Mail add: PO Box 63, Hineston, 71438), Tel: 318-793-8461. FAX: 318-793-8461. E-Mail: hinestonlibrary@hotmail.com. *Mgr*, Judy N Brown; *Circ*, Mrs Donna Crawford; *Circ*, Sally I Wilson; Staff 3 (Non-MLS 3)
Founded 1984
Library Holdings: Bk Vols 14,236
Automation Activity & Vendor Info: (Circulation) Gateway
JOHNSON, 1610 Veterans, PO Box 1207, Lecompte, 71346. SAN 342-6904. Tel: 318-776-5153. FAX: 318-776-5153. E-Mail: johnsonbranch@hotmail.com. *Librn*, Mary Rabalais
Library Holdings: Bk Vols 17,755
Friends of the Library Group
MARTIN, 801 W Shamrock, Pineville, 71360. SAN 342-6963. Tel: 318-442-7575. FAX: 318-442-6604. E-Mail: martinbranch@hotmail.com. *Librn*, Donna LeBlanc; Staff 1 (Non-MLS 1)
Founded 1950
Library Holdings: Bk Vols 43,947
MARTIN LUTHER KING MEMORIAL, 3311 Third St, 71302. SAN 342-6890. Tel: 318-445-3912. FAX: 318-445-3912. *Librn*, Sharon Williams; E-Mail: sawilliams90@hotmail.com
Library Holdings: Bk Vols 12,007
ROBERTSON, 809 Tioga High School Rd, Pineville, 71360. SAN 342-7021. Tel: 318-640-3098. FAX: 318-640-8713. E-Mail: robertsonbranch@hotmail.com. *Librn*, Bobbie Thompson
Library Holdings: Bk Vols 45,114
Bookmobiles: 3. Bookmobile, Preschool Outreach Project & Red Carpet Van Service - Tel: 318-445-2411, Ext 222, 445-6436, Ext 225.

M RAPIDES REGIONAL MEDICAL CENTER, Medical Library,* 211 Fourth St, PO Box 30101, 71301. SAN 306-4352. Tel: 318-473-3563. FAX: 318-473-3489. *Librn*, Lola Purvis; E-Mail: lpurvis@rapides.com
Founded 1963
Library Holdings: Bk Vols 1,800; Per Subs 141
Subject Interests: Allied health, Health sciences, Medicine, Nursing

AMITE

P TANGIPAHOA PARISH LIBRARY,* Admin Office, 200 E Mulberry St, 70422. SAN 342-7110. Tel: 504-748-7559. FAX: 504-748-2812. E-Mail: sledge@i-55.com, slou3010@selu.edu. Web Site: www.tangiphoa.lib.li.us. *Dir*, Pat Sledge; Staff 45 (MLS 1, Non-MLS 44)
Founded 1944. Pop 94,364; Circ 308,740
Jan 1998-Dec 1998 Income $1,498,986, State $165,000, County $860,200, Locally Generated Income $20,000, Other $162,425. Mats Exp $168,664, Books $130,000, Per/Ser (Incl. Access Fees) $26,364, Presv $1,000, Micro $300, AV Equip $1,000. Sal $485,800 (Prof $40,000)
Library Holdings: Bk Vols 152,755
Subject Interests: Genealogy, Local history
Friends of the Library Group
Branches: 6
AMITE BRANCH, 739 W Oak St, 70422. Tel: 504-748-7151. FAX: 504-748-5476. Web Site: www.tangipahoa.lib.la.us. *Librn*, Sherri Alford
Library Holdings: Bk Vols 46,212
HAMMOND BRANCH, 314 E Thomas, Hammond, 70403. SAN 342-7234. Tel: 504-345-0937, 504-345-3909. FAX: 504-345-2188. Web Site: www.tangipahoa.lib.la.us. *Librn*, Bill Dorman
Library Holdings: Bk Vols 42,868
INDEPENDENCE BRANCH, 300 W Fourth St, PO Box 439, Independence, 70443. SAN 342-7269. Tel: 504-878-2970. FAX: 504-878-1996. Web Site: www.tangipahoa.lib.la.us. *Librn*, Kathy Smith
Library Holdings: Bk Vols 13,177
KENTWOOD BRANCH, 101 Avenue F, Kentwood, 70444. SAN 342-7293. Tel: 504-229-3596. FAX: 504-229-4566. Web Site: www.tangipahoa.lib.la.us. *Librn*, Anne Frey
Library Holdings: Bk Vols 15,969
Friends of the Library Group
LORANGER BRANCH, PO Box 515, Loranger, 70446. SAN 342-7315. Tel: 504-878-6224. FAX: 504-878-3571. Web Site: www.tangipahoa.lib.la.us. *Librn*, Joanne Lagatuta
Library Holdings: Bk Vols 6,723
PONCHATOULA BRANCH, 380 N Fifth St, Ponchatoula, 70454. SAN 342-7358. Tel: 504-386-6554. FAX: 504-370-5019. Web Site: www.tangipahoa.lib.la.us. *Librn*, Brenda Neidhamer
Library Holdings: Bk Vols 32,191
Friends of the Library Group
Bookmobiles: 1. Librn, Sandy Cox & Denise Johnson. Bk vols 5731. Tel: 504-747-7060

ANGIE

S WASHINGTON CORRECTIONAL INSTITUTE,* 27268 Hwy 21, 70426. SAN 373-8574. Tel: 504-986-3182, Ext 301. FAX: 504-986-1207. *Librn*, J S Young
Library Holdings: Per Subs 37

ANGOLA

S LOUISIANA STATE PENITENTIARY LIBRARY,* Main Prison Library, A Bldg, 70712. SAN 306-4379. Tel: 225-655-4411, Ext 2028. FAX: 225-655-2790.
Founded 1968
Library Holdings: Bk Vols 17,000
Special Collections: Criminal Justice; Science Fiction

ARCADIA

P BIENVILLE PARISH LIBRARY,* 2678 Maple St, 71001-3699. SAN 306-4387. Tel: 318-263-7410. FAX: 318-263-7428. E-Mail: bvlibl@bienville.lib.la.us. *Dir*, Joyce Lilly; *Asst Dir*, Wanda Bell; Staff 9 (MLS 1, Non-MLS 8)
Founded 1964. Pop 15,979; Circ 150,945
Jan 1999-Dec 1999 Income (Main Library and Branch Library) $473,080, State $35,000, County $414,080, Locally Generated Income $24,000. Mats Exp $50,800, Books $37,000, Per/Ser (Incl. Access Fees) $7,000, AV Equip $5,000, Other Print Mats $500, Manuscripts & Archives $1,300. Sal $188,250 (Prof $35,000)
Library Holdings: Bk Titles 65,497; Per Subs 226
Subject Interests: Genealogy, Louisiana
Special Collections: Large print books, Louisiana material

Branches: 1
RINGGOLD BRANCH, PO Box 792, Ringgold, 71068. SAN 324-3001. Tel: 318-894-9770. *Asst Librn*, Annette McLemore
Bookmobiles: 1

BARKSDALE AFB

UNITED STATES AIR FORCE
A BARKSDALE AIR FORCE BASE LIBRARY, 744 Douhet Dr, Bldg 4244, 71110. SAN 342-7447. Tel: 318-456-4101. Circulation Tel: 318-456-4101. Reference Tel: 318-456-5993. FAX: 318-456-1323. *Dir*, Kelly Bunt Desmond; Tel: 318-456-4182, E-Mail: kelly.desmond@barksdale.af.mil; *Ref*, Carla Jean Clark; Tel: 318-456-5982, E-Mail: carla.clark@barksdale.af.mil; *Acq*, Anthony Joseph Bellucci; Tel: 318-456-2093, E-Mail: anthony.bellucci@barksdale.af.mil; *Circ*, Catherine Lanham; Tel: 318-456-4101, E-Mail: catherine.lanham@barksdale.af.mil; *Tech Servs*, Hsin Yi Lee; Tel: 318-456-5982, E-Mail: hsin.lee@barksdale.af.mil; *Ch Servs*, Linda Romano. Subject Specialists: *Computer*, Hsin Yi Lee; *Economics*, Kelly Bunt Desmond; *Law*, Kelly Bunt Desmond; *Reference*, Carla Jean Clark; Staff 5 (MLS 2, Non-MLS 3)
Founded 1933
Library Holdings: Bk Vols 35,000; Per Subs 109
Subject Interests: Mil hist (US)
Special Collections: Chief of Staff Reading Lists; Louisiana History & Culture; Project Warrior Coll
Automation Activity & Vendor Info: (Acquisitions) EOS; (Cataloging) EOS; (Circulation) EOS; (Course Reserve) EOS; (OPAC) EOS; (Serials) EOS
Database Vendor: Dialog, Ebsco - EbscoHost, GaleNet, Lexis-Nexis, OCLC - First Search, ProQuest
Restriction: Open to government employees only
Function: ILL available
Partic in Amigos Library Services, Inc; Fedlink
Special Services for the Blind - Large print bks

BASTROP

P MOREHOUSE PARISH LIBRARY,* 524 E Madison, 71221-0232. (Mail add: PO Box 232, 71221-0232), Tel: 318-281-3683. *Dir*, Mary Hodgkins; Staff 1 (MLS 1)
Founded 1940. Pop 34,000; Circ 129,402
Jan 1997-Dec 1998 Income $315,000
Library Holdings: Bk Vols 60,000; Per Subs 101
Subject Interests: Genealogy, Local history
Mem of Trail Blazer Libr Syst
Branches: 6
BONITA BRANCH, 15004 Henry St, PO Box 8, Bonita, 71223. SAN 342-7536. Tel: 318-823-2154. *Asst Librn*, Gloria Travis
Library Holdings: Bk Titles 4,000
COLLINSTON BRANCH, 4620 Main St, Collinston, 71229. SAN 342-7560. Tel: 318-874-3531. *Asst Librn*, Martha Crymes
Library Holdings: Bk Titles 2,300
DUNBAR, 1102 Martin Luther King S, 71220. SAN 342-7595. Tel: 318-281-1137. *Asst Librn*, Hattie Mae Nicks
Library Holdings: Bk Titles 4,500
MER ROUGE BRANCH, 107 S 16th, PO Box 70, Mer Rouge, 71261. SAN 342-7625. Tel: 318-647-5639. *Asst Librn*, Gloria Travis
Library Holdings: Bk Titles 4,150
OAK RIDGE BRANCH, Oak St, Oak Ridge, 71264. (Mail add: PO Drawer B, Oak Ridge, 71264), Tel: 318-244-5329. *Asst Librn*, June Fitch
Library Holdings: Bk Titles 5,000

BATON ROUGE

S ALBEMARLE CORPORATION, Information Services, PO Box 14799, 70898-4799. SAN 323-4827. Tel: 504-768-5779. FAX: 504-768-5970.
Library Holdings: Bk Vols 18,000; Per Subs 420
Subject Interests: Chemical engineering, Chemistry

§J BATON ROUGE COMMUNITY COLLEGE, Main Campus Library, 5310 Florida Blvd, 70806. Tel: 225-216-8303. FAX: 225-216-8712. E-Mail: brcclibrary@mail.brcc.cc.la.us. Web Site: www.brcc.cc.la.us. *Dir Libr Serv*, Joanie D Chavis
Library Holdings: Bk Vols 12,000; Per Subs 250; Bks on Deafness & Sign Lang 20
Automation Activity & Vendor Info: (Cataloging) epixtech, inc.; (Circulation) epixtech, inc.; (OPAC) epixtech, inc.
Departmental Libraries:
BUSINESS & TECHNOLOGY ANNEX LIBRARY, 555 Julia St, 70821. Tel: 225-219-0440. FAX: 225-219-0441. E-Mail: brcclibrary@mail.brcc.cc.la.us. Web Site: www.brcc.cc.la.us. *Dir Libr Serv*, Joanie D Chavis
Library Holdings: Bk Vols 5,000; Per Subs 50
Automation Activity & Vendor Info: (Cataloging) epixtech, inc.; (Circulation) epixtech, inc.; (OPAC) epixtech, inc.

S CAPITAL CITY PRESS, The Advocate Library, PO Box 588, 70821-0588. SAN 306-4395. Tel: 225-383-1111, Ext 327. FAX: 225-388-0329. Web Site: www.theadvocate.com. *Dir*, Jill Arnold; E-Mail: jarnold@theadvocate.com; *Asst Dir*, Laurie Christensen
Founded 1922
Library Holdings: Bk Vols 1,500; Per Subs 120
Special Collections: Newspaper Clipping Files (1922-1982)
Open Mon-Sun 9-10

M EARL K LONG MEDICAL CENTER LIBRARY,* 5825 Airline Hwy, 70805-2498. SAN 306-4433. Tel: 504-358-1089. FAX: 504-358-1240. E-Mail: med_libr@mail.ekl.lsumc.edu. *Librn*, Mary DeFoe; Staff 2 (MLS 2)
Founded 1968
Jul 1996-Jun 1997 Mats Exp $55,500, Books $7,000, Per/Ser (Incl. Access Fees) $45,000. Sal $48,000
Library Holdings: Bk Titles 2,200; Per Subs 300
Subject Interests: Medicine

P EAST BATON ROUGE PARISH LIBRARY,* 7711 Goodwood Blvd, 70806-7625. SAN 342-7684. Tel: 225-231-3700. Interlibrary Loan Service Tel: 225-231-3755. FAX: 225-231-3759. Web Site: www.ebr.lib.la.us. *Dir*, John B Richard; Tel: 225-231-3700, Fax: 225-231-3700, E-Mail: jrichard@ebr.lib.la.us; *Asst Dir*, Trudy Jaques; Fax: 225-231-3788, E-Mail: tjaques@ebr.lib.la.us; *ILL*, Dan Forrest; Fax: 225-231-3736, E-Mail: ill@ebr.lib.la.us; *Ad Servs*, Beth Bingham; Tel: 225-231-3745, Fax: 225-231-3734, E-Mail: bbingham@ebr.lib.la.us; *Ch Servs*, Patricia Arnold; Tel: 225-231-3760, Fax: 225-231-3736, E-Mail: parnold@ebr.lib.la.us; *YA Servs*, Mary Stein; Tel: 225-231-3770, Fax: 225-231-3736, E-Mail: mstein@ebr.lib.la.us; *Acq*, Denise Freyou; Tel: 225-231-3717, Fax: 225-231-3788, E-Mail: dfreyou@ebr.lib.la.us; *Cat*, Bobby Ferguson; Tel: 225-231-3717, Fax: 225-231-3788, E-Mail: bferguson@ebr.lib.la.us; *Ref*, Carolyn Flint; Tel: 225-231-3750, Fax: 225-231-3736, E-Mail: cflint@ebr.lib.la.us; *Br Coordr*, Joe Baker; Tel: 225-231-3780, Fax: 225-231-3788, E-Mail: jbaker@ebr.lib.la.us; *Coll Develop*, Tam McConnell; Fax: 225-231-3788, E-Mail: tam@ebr.lib.la.us; Staff 64 (MLS 64)
Founded 1939. Pop 400,000; Circ 2,407,161
Jan 1998-Dec 1998 Income (Main Library and Branch Library) $18,882,597, State $154,415, County $17,330,351, Locally Generated Income $376,944, Other $759,365. Mats Exp $1,468,565, Books $1,116,271, Per/Ser (Incl. Access Fees) $159,418, Presv $16,701, Micro $37,554. Sal $5,827,174
Library Holdings: Bk Vols 1,231,576; Per Subs 2,592
Subject Interests: Genealogy, Louisiana
Publications: Community Information Directory; Staff Information Sheet; The Calendar
Friends of the Library Group
Branches: 12
BAKER BRANCH, 4761 Groom Rd, Baker, 70714. SAN 342-7714. Tel: 504-775-3125. FAX: 225-775-0926. *Librn*, Diane Lewis
Library Holdings: Bk Vols 52,344
BLUEBONNET REGIONAL, 9200 Bluebonnet Blvd, 70810. SAN 373-1243. Tel: 225-763-2240. FAX: 225-763-2254. *Librn*, Sylvia Melancon
Library Holdings: Bk Vols 158,572
CARVER, 1509 Highland Rd, 70802. SAN 342-7749. Tel: 504-389-4978. FAX: 225-389-8750. *Librn*, Geralyn Davis
Library Holdings: Bk Vols 27,284
CENTRAL, 13505 Hooper Rd, 70811. SAN 342-7773. Tel: 225-261-3787. FAX: 225-261-6569. *Librn*, Brenda Eames
Library Holdings: Bk Vols 55,263
CENTROPLEX, 120 St Louis, PO Box 1471, 70821. SAN 342-7803. Tel: 225-389-4967. *Librn*, Anita York
Library Holdings: Bk Vols 89,128
Special Collections: Baton Rouge History; Foundation Center Cooperating Coll
DELMONT GARDENS, 3351 Lorraine St, 70805. SAN 342-7838. Tel: 225-389-5280. FAX: 225-389-5282. *Librn*, E J Carter; Staff 9 (MLS 2, Non-MLS 7)
Pop 500,000
Library Holdings: Bk Vols 93,000; Bk Titles 100,000; Per Subs 100
Subject Interests: Black lit, Romances
Friends of the Library Group
EDEN PARK, 4142 Gus Young Ave, 70802. SAN 342-7811. Tel: 225-389-3829. FAX: 225-389-8751. *Librn*, Barbara Martin
Library Holdings: Bk Vols 20,544
GREENWELL SPRINGS ROAD REGIONAL, 11300 Greenwell Springs Rd, 70815. SAN 376-964X. Tel: 225-274-4440. FAX: 225-274-4454. *Librn*, Sandra Abraham
Library Holdings: Bk Vols 86,159
JONES CREEK REGIONAL, 6222 Jones Creek Rd, 70817. SAN 370-1301. Tel: 225-756-1140. FAX: 225-756-1153. *Librn*, Marjorie Kemp
Library Holdings: Bk Vols 160,009
PRIDE BRANCH, PO Box B, Pride, 70770. SAN 342-7862. Tel: 225-654-8811. FAX: 225-658-8562. *Librn*, Bernice Whitley
Library Holdings: Bk Vols 21,636
SCOTLANDVILLE, 1492 Harding Blvd, 70807. SAN 342-7897. Tel: 225-778-0618. FAX: 225-774-3103. *Librn*, Joanne Looney

Library Holdings: Bk Vols 37,729
ZACHARY BRANCH, 5055 E Mae, Zachary, 70791. SAN 342-7927. Tel: 225-654-5086. *Librn*, Louise Johnson
Library Holdings: Bk Vols 53,690

S EXXON MOBIL PROCESS RESEARCH LABORATORIES LIBRARY, 4045 Scenic Hwy, 70805. (Mail add: PO Box 2226, 70821), SAN 342-801X. Tel: 225-977-7681. FAX: 225-977-7145. E-Mail: emprlib@exxon.sprint.com. *Librn*, Nancy Cash; E-Mail: ncash1@erenj.com
Library Holdings: Bk Vols 6,000; Per Subs 150

EXXONMOBIL CHEMICAL
S BATON ROUGE CHEMICAL PLANT INFORMATION CENTER, 4999 Scenic Hwy, CPWO 2546, 70805. SAN 342-7986. Tel: 225-977-7256. FAX: 225-359-4249. *Head Librn*, Sally D'Aquin; Tel: 225-977-8614; *Asst Librn*, Keith M Sagona; Tel: 225-977-7256, E-Mail: keith.m.sagona@exxon.com; *Asst Librn*, Sue Toney; Tel: 225-977-8620; *Ref*, Brigette Ory; Tel: 225-977-8084; *Ref*, Derek Wells; Tel: 225-977-8260; *Archivist*, Bonnie Blalock; Tel: 225-977-8260
Founded 1990
Library Holdings: Bk Vols 700; Per Subs 45

§S JETSON CORRECTIONAL CENTER FOR YOUTH LIBRARY, 15200 Scenic Hwy, 70874-7527. (Mail add: PO Box 97527, 70874-7527), Tel: 225-778-9171. *Librn*, Miriam Barton
Library Holdings: Bk Vols 5,000; Per Subs 15
Automation Activity & Vendor Info: (Cataloging) Follett; (Circulation) Follett

S LA ROCHE INDUSTRIES INC, R & D Library,* 1200 Airline Hwy at Old MS River Bridge, PO Box 1031, 70805. SAN 373-7993. Tel: 225-356-8566. FAX: 225-356-8444. *Librn*, Marilyn Moore; E-Mail: mmoore@larocheind.com
Founded 1987
Library Holdings: Bk Titles 400; Per Subs 60
Restriction: Staff use only
Partic in Dialog Corporation

L LANE & FERTITTA, Law Library,* 435 Louisiana Ave, 70822. (Mail add: PO Box 3335, 70821), SAN 372-0829. Tel: 225-387-0241. FAX: 225-387-1238. *Librn*, William Janney
Library Holdings: Bk Titles 30
Restriction: Private library

S LOUISIANA ASSOCIATION OF BUSINESS & INDUSTRY LIBRARY, 3113 Valley Creek Dr, 70808. (Mail add: PO Box 80258, 70898-0258), SAN 306-4441. Tel: 225-928-5388. FAX: 225-929-6054. Web Site: www.labi.org. *In Charge*, Frances M Fontenot; E-Mail: francesf@labi.org
Founded 1976
Library Holdings: Bk Vols 5,000; Per Subs 120
Subject Interests: Education, Tourism, Trade
Restriction: Staff use only

S LOUISIANA DEPARTMENT OF ECONOMIC DEVELOPMENT, Research Library, 101 France St, 70802. (Mail add: PO Box 94185, 70804-9185), Tel: 225-342-3071. FAX: 225-342-5389. Web Site: www.lded.state.la.us. *Librn*, Paula Bryars; E-Mail: bryars@mail.lded.state.la.us; Staff 1 (MLS 1)
1999-2000 Mats Exp $13,000. Sal $41,800 (Prof $36,000)
Library Holdings: Bk Titles 5,000; Per Subs 350
Subject Interests: Economics, Louisiana
Special Collections: Business reference; Current Economic Development Material; DED publications, Economic Development Research Studies, Parish & Port Profiles, Louisiana International Trade; Manufacturing Directories from most states

G LOUISIANA DEPARTMENT OF ENVIRONMENTAL QUALITY, Air Quality Information Center,* 7290 Bluebonnet Blvd, 2nd flr, 70810. SAN 371-8387. Tel: 504-765-0169. FAX: 504-765-0222. Web Site: www.deq.state.la.us. *Librn*, Elizabeth Santa; E-Mail: lizs@deq.state.la.us; Staff 1 (MLS 1)
Founded 1990
Library Holdings: Bk Vols 5,500
Subject Interests: Air pollution
Special Collections: Chemical Risk/Hazard Data; United States Air Quality
Automation Activity & Vendor Info: (Cataloging) Inmagic, Inc.

GL LOUISIANA HOUSE OF REPRESENTATIVES, David R Poynter Legislative Research Library, PO Box 94012, 70804-9012. SAN 306-4468. Tel: 225-342-2434, 225-342-6945. FAX: 225-342-2431. *Dir*, Suzanne Hughes
Founded 1952
Library Holdings: Bk Vols 10,000; Per Subs 250
Special Collections: Legislative Archival Coll, staff memoranda, committee rpts; Legislative Documents & Research Publications, per, clippings
Publications: Resume (annual summary of enactments)

A LOUISIANA NAVAL WAR MEMORIAL LIBRARY,* 305 S River Rd, 70802. SAN 374-9401. Tel: 225-342-1942. FAX: 225-342-2039. *Dir*, Maury Drummond
Library Holdings: Bk Vols 350; Per Subs 50

G LOUISIANA OFFICE OF THE SECRETARY OF STATE, Division of Archives, Records Management & History Library,* 3851 Essen Lane, PO Box 94125, 70804. SAN 326-5463. Tel: 225-922-1207. FAX: 225-922-0002. E-Mail: library@sec.state.la.us. Web Site: www.sec.state.la.us. *Archivist, Dir*, Donald Lemieux; *Librn*, John Fowler; *Archivist*, Louis Morris; Staff 1 (MLS 1)
Founded 1956
Library Holdings: Bk Vols 3,500; Bk Titles 3,000; Per Subs 50
Subject Interests: Genealogy, Military history
Special Collections: Birth Certificates (Orleans Parish)-over 100 years beginning with 1790-1898; Death Certificates (Orleans Parish) 1804-1947, (Statewide) 1912-1948; Louisiana Confederate Government (Rebel Archives Coll), docs; Lumber Industry (Louisiana Longleaf Lumber Co Coll); Marriage Certificates (Orleans Parish) 1831-1948
Publications: Legacy (quarterly newsletter)
Friends of the Library Group

GL LOUISIANA STATE DEPARTMENT OF JUSTICE, Attorney General's Law Library,* 301 Main, 7th flr, PO Box 94005, 70801. SAN 327-4829. Tel: 504-342-1361. FAX: 504-342-5991.
Library Holdings: Bk Vols 5,000; Per Subs 10

L LOUISIANA STATE SENATE, Law Library,* PO Box 94183, 70804. SAN 372-0810. Tel: 225-342-2414. FAX: 225-342-2725. Web Site: www.senate.state.la.us. *Librn*, Arthur E McEnany; E-Mail: mcenanya@legis.state.la.us; *Res*, Kim Manning
Library Holdings: Bk Vols 4,500; Per Subs 42

C LOUISIANA STATE UNIVERSITY LIBRARIES, 70803-3300. SAN 342-8133. Tel: 225-388-2217, 225-388-5652, 225-388-8560 (Lending). Interlibrary Loan Service Tel: 225-388-2138. FAX: 225-388-6825 (Admin), 225-388-6992 (ILB). Interlibrary Loan Service FAX: 225-388-5723. Web Site: www.lib.lsu.edu. *Dean of Libr*, Jennifer Cargill; Tel: 225-388-2217, Fax: 225-388-6825, E-Mail: cargill@lsu.edu; *Assoc Dean*, Jane Kleiner; Tel: 225-388-2217, E-Mail: jkleiner@lsu.edu; *ILL*, Robbie Ruiz; Tel: 225-388-2138, E-Mail: rruiz@lsu.edu; *Head, Circ*, Floris St Amant; Tel: 225-388-3216, E-Mail: fstaman@lsu.edu; *Head Ref*, Tom Diamond; Tel: 225-388-6572, E-Mail: notted@lsu.edu; *Bibliog Instr*, Bill Thompson; Tel: 225-388-6823, E-Mail: wthomp2@lsu.edu. Subject Specialists: *English literature*, Bill Thompson; Staff 131 (MLS 41, Non-MLS 90)
Founded 1860. Enrl 30,996; Highest Degree: Doctorate
Jul 1999-Jun 2000 Income (Main Library and Branch Library) $8,817,947. Mats Exp $3,185,612, Books $729,721, Per/Ser (Incl. Access Fees) $2,455,891. Sal $4,076,214 (Prof $1,910,135)
Library Holdings: Bk Vols 3,054,740; Per Subs 18,309
Special Collections: Louisiana & Lower Mississippi Coll; McIlhenny Natural History Coll; Rare Book Coll; US Patent
Automation Activity & Vendor Info: (Acquisitions) NOTIS; (Circulation) NOTIS; (Serials) NOTIS
Database Vendor: Dialog, epixtech, inc., IAC - Info Trac, Lexis-Nexis, Silverplatter Information Inc.
Publications: Guide to Oral History Collections in Louisiana; Guide to the Russell B Long Collection; Historical Collections of Louisiana (CD-ROM edition); Schwing Library Lectures
Partic in Association Of Southeastern Research Libraries (ASERL); La Acad Libr Info Network Consortium; La Online Univ Info Systs; OCLC Online Computer Library Center, Inc; SE Libr Network; USDA SW Regional Doc Delivery Syst
Friends of the Library Group
Departmental Libraries:
CHEMISTRY, 301 Williams Hall, 70803. SAN 342-8168. Tel: 225-388-2530. Interlibrary Loan Service Tel: 225-388-2138. FAX: 225-388-2760. E-Mail: notwwa@lsu.edu. Web Site: www.lib.lsu.edu/sci/chem/intro.html. *Dean of Libr*, Jennifer Cargill; Tel: 225-388-2217, Fax: 225-388-6825, E-Mail: cargill@lsu.edu; *Branch Mgr*, Bill Armstrong; Tel: 225-388-2738; Staff 2 (MLS 1, Non-MLS 1)
Library Holdings: Bk Vols 59,163; Per Subs 700
Subject Interests: Biochemistry, Chemical engineering, Chemistry
Special Collections: Beilstein Coll; Gleian Coll; Sadler Spectra Coll
Automation Activity & Vendor Info: (Acquisitions) NOTIS
Partic in BRS; Dialog Corporation; Medline; STM Chemical Abstracts
Friends of the Library Group
DESIGN RESOURCE CENTER, 104 Design Bldg, 70803. SAN 373-5818. Tel: 225-388-2665. Interlibrary Loan Service Tel: 225-388-2138. Web Site: www.lib.lsu.edu. *Dean of Libr*, Jennifer Cargill; Tel: 225-388-2217, Fax: 225-388-6825, E-Mail: cargill@lsu.edu; *Branch Mgr*, Sandy T Mooney; E-Mail: smooney@lsu.edu; Staff 2 (MLS 1, Non-MLS 1)
Library Holdings: Bk Vols 13,853; Per Subs 59
Subject Interests: Architecture, Art, Landscape architecture
Friends of the Library Group
EDUCATION RESOURCES, 227 Middleton, 70803. SAN 376-852X. Tel: 225-388-2349. Interlibrary Loan Service Tel: 225-388-2138. Web Site:

www.lib.edu/edu/er/index.html. *Dean of Libr*, Jennifer Cargill; Tel: 225-338-2217, Fax: 225-388-6825, E-Mail: cargill@lsu.edu; *Branch Mgr*, Peggy Chalaron; E-Mail: pchalar@lsu.edu; Staff 2 (MLS 1, Non-MLS 1)
Library Holdings: Bk Vols 32,896
Subject Interests: Education
Automation Activity & Vendor Info: (Acquisitions) NOTIS
Friends of the Library Group

CL LAW CENTER, E Campus Dr, 70803-1010. Tel: 225-388-8802. TDD: 225-388-4706. FAX: 225-388-5773. E-Mail: lawrefl@lsu.edu. Web Site: www.law.lsu.edu/library. *Dir*, Christine Corcos; *Media Spec*, Rita Parham; *Online Servs, Ref*, Scott Childs; *Tech Servs*, Rita Millican; *Publ Servs*, Charlotte Melius; *Coll Develop*, Madeline Herbert; Staff 21 (MLS 9, Non-MLS 12)
Founded 1906. Enrl 650; Fac 36; Highest Degree: Doctorate
Library Holdings: Bk Vols 402,195; Bk Titles 128,499
Special Collections: Foreign, Comparative & International Law
Automation Activity & Vendor Info: (Acquisitions) NOTIS; (Cataloging) NOTIS; (Circulation) NOTIS; (Course Reserve) NOTIS; (ILL) NOTIS; (OPAC) NOTIS; (Serials) NOTIS
Mem of Asn Res Librs
Partic in Consortium Of South Eastern Law Libraries

LOUISIANA ENERGY & ENVIRONMENTAL RESOURCE & INFORMATION CENTER (LEERIC), One E Fraternity Circle, 70803-0301. SAN 375-3018. Tel: 504-388-4600. Web Site: www.leeric.lsu.edu. *Dir*, Robert Bradley; *Cat, Librn*, Versa Stickle; *Acq, Cat*, Patty Birkett; *Ref*, Rita Jackson; *Online Servs*, Ric Pincomb; Staff 4 (MLS 4)
Founded 1982. Pop 207,053; Circ 3,523,279
Library Holdings: Bk Titles 15,000; Per Subs 40
Subject Interests: Education, Energy
Publications: The Egret's Watch
Friends of the Library Group

MUSIC RESOURCES, 202 Middleton, 70803. SAN 376-8538. Tel: 225-388-4674. Interlibrary Loan Service Tel: 225-388-2138. E-Mail: notlkre@lsuvm.sncc.lsu.edu. Web Site: www.lib.lsu.edu. *Dean of Libr*, Jennifer Cargill; Tel: 225-388-2217, Fax: 225-388-6825, E-Mail: cargill@lsu.edu; *Branch Mgr*, Lois Kuyper-Rushing; E-Mail: lkuyper@lsu.edu; Staff 3 (MLS 1, Non-MLS 2)
Library Holdings: Bk Vols 57,440; Per Subs 80
Subject Interests: History, Music
Automation Activity & Vendor Info: (Acquisitions) NOTIS
Friends of the Library Group

CM SCHOOL OF VETERINARY MEDICINE LIBRARY, S Stadium at River Rd, 70803-8414. SAN 342-8222. Tel: 225-578-9800. FAX: 225-578-9798. *Dir*, Barbara Sue Loubiere; Tel: 225-578-9793, E-Mail: vtllou@lsu.edu; Staff 8 (MLS 1, Non-MLS 7)
Founded 1974. Enrl 350; Highest Degree: Doctorate
Library Holdings: Bk Vols 40,000; Per Subs 670
Subject Interests: Veterinary medicine
Special Collections: Reprint Coll on Parasitology, 1865-1972
Automation Activity & Vendor Info: (Circulation) NOTIS
Database Vendor: Ebsco - EbscoHost, OCLC - First Search
Partic in National Network Of Libraries Of Medicine - South Central Region
Friends of the Library Group

L MCCOLLISTER & MCCLEARY, Law Library, 11542 Lake Sherwood Ave N, 70816. SAN 371-4322. Tel: 225-292-8898. FAX: 225-293-2720. Web Site: www.mccollistermccleary.com. *Librn*, Susie Dore
Library Holdings: Bk Vols 400

GM NATIONAL HANSEN'S DISEASE PROGRAM, (Formerly United States Public Health Service Hospital), Archives Library, 1770 Physician Park Dr, 70816. SAN 306-4557. Tel: 225-642-1927. FAX: 225-642-1926. *Librn*, Anna Belle Steinbach; E-Mail: steinbacha@usa.net
Founded 1921
Library Holdings: Per Subs 75
Special Collections: National Archives of Leprosy Coll
Partic in Docline; Health Sci Asn of LA; Nat Libr of Med; S Cent Regional Med Libr Program

M OUR LADY OF THE LAKE REGIONAL MEDICAL CENTER LIBRARY, 5000 Hennessy Blvd, 70808. SAN 306-4506. Tel: 225-765-8756. FAX: 225-769-8201. *Librn*, John E Tate; Fax: 225-765-3018, E-Mail: jtate@ololcollege.edu; *Coordr*, Carolyn Langlois; E-Mail: clanglois@ololcollege.edu; Staff 3 (MLS 3)
Founded 1923
May 2000-Apr 2001 Income Parent Institution $100,000. Mats Exp Per/Ser (Incl. Access Fees) $30,000
Library Holdings: Bk Titles 500; Per Subs 78
Subject Interests: Medicine
Special Collections: Pediatric Coll
Function: Reference only
Partic in Baton Rouge Hospital Library Consortium

S PUBLIC AFFAIRS RESEARCH COUNCIL OF LOUISIANA, INC LIBRARY,* 4664 Jamestown Ave, No 300, PO Box 14776, 70898-4776. SAN 306-4514. Tel: 225-926-8414. FAX: 225-926-8417. E-Mail: parbrla@aol.com. Web Site: la-par.org.
Founded 1950
Library Holdings: Bk Vols 5,500
Subject Interests: Local government, Louisiana, State government
Restriction: Non-circulating to the public

SR SACRAMENTIST LIBRARIES, St Peter Julian Eymard Library at Our Lady of the Most Blessed Sacrament Priory,* PO Box 706, 70821-0706. SAN 376-0413. Tel: 225-343-7227. E-Mail: Sacramentists@worldnet.att.net. Interlibrary Loan Service E-Mail: ILL_LBrSBS@worldnet.att.net. *Chief Librn*, Br Mary John
Special Collections: Code of Canon Law; Ecclesiastical Heraldry; Sacred Ceremonies, Liturgies & Rites of the Roman Catholic Church
Function: ILL available, Photocopies available

C SOUTHERN UNIVERSITY, John B Cade Library, Roosvelt Steptoe Ave, 70813. SAN 342-8257. Tel: 225-771-4990. Interlibrary Loan Service Tel: 225-771-2860. FAX: 225-771-4113. Web Site: www.lib.subr.edu. *Dean of Libr*, Emma Bradford Perry; Tel: 225-771-4991, E-Mail: eperry@lib.subr.edu; *Reader Servs*, Sana Alawady; Tel: 225-771-2844, E-Mail: sana@lib.subr.edu; *Spec Coll*, Janice Bell; Tel: 225-771-2843, E-Mail: janice@lib.subr.edu; *Tech Servs*, Mildred Brown; Tel: 25-771-2862, E-Mail: mildred@lib.subr.edu; *Head Ref*, Jane Robinson; Tel: 225-771-2875, E-Mail: jane@lib.subr.edu; Staff 40 (MLS 19, Non-MLS 21)
Founded 1928. Enrl 9,512; Highest Degree: Doctorate
2000-2000 Mats Exp $753,450, Books $503,450, Per/Ser (Incl. Access Fees) $250,000. Sal $1,273,442
Library Holdings: Bk Vols 1,396,602; Per Subs 1,967
Subject Interests: Agriculture, Art and architecture, Business and management, Economics, Education
Special Collections: Archives & Shade Coll
Publications: Code Books & Bytes (Newsletter)
Partic in OCLC Online Computer Library Center, Inc; SE Libr Network
Friends of the Library Group
Departmental Libraries:
ARCHITECTURE LIBRARY, Engineering West, 70808. Tel: 225-771-3290. FAX: 225-771-4113. Web Site: www.lib.subr.edu. *In Charge*, Kelley Roberts; E-Mail: kelley@lib.subr.edu; Staff 2 (MLS 1, Non-MLS 1)
LAB SCHOOL LIBRARY, 129 Swan St, 70813. SAN 342-8311. Tel: 504-771-3490. FAX: 504-771-2782. *Librn*, Nettie Robinson
Library Holdings: Bk Vols 8,500; Per Subs 35

CL LAW CENTER LIBRARY, 2 Roosevelt Steptoe, 70813. (Mail add: PO Box 9294, 70813-9294), Tel: 225-771-2139, 225-771-2315. FAX: 225-771-6254. Web Site: www.sucl.edu. *Dir*, Alvin A Roche, Jr; E-Mail: aroche@sus.edu; *Acq*, Dorothy J Allen; *Acq*, Sylvia Moore; *Ref, Res*, Constance Helkme; *Ref, Res*, Harold Isadore; *Ref, Res*, Phebe Poydras; *Cat*, Valanda Ledoux; *Cat*, Marie Louis; *Doc*, Rose Herbert; *Circ*, Brenda Gordon; Staff 17 (MLS 6, Non-MLS 11)
Founded 1947. Enrl 317; Fac 28; Highest Degree: Doctorate
Jul 1999-Jun 2000 Income $1,184,448. Mats Exp $578,276. Sal $606,172 (Prof $254,418)
Library Holdings: Bk Vols 426,386; Bk Titles 62,261; Per Subs 675
Subject Interests: Civil rights
Publications: Newsletter; Reflections; Southern Univ Law Review
Partic in Dialog Corporation; OCLC Online Computer Library Center, Inc; SE Libr Network; Westlaw

P STATE LIBRARY OF LOUISIANA, Section for the Blind & Physically Handicapped, 701 N Fourth St, 70802. (Mail add: PO Box 131, 70821), SAN 306-4492. Tel: 225-342-4944. Toll Free Tel: 800-543-4702. TDD: 225-219-1696. FAX: 225-342-6817. E-Mail: sbph@pelican.state.lib.la.us. Web Site: www.state.lib.la.us. *Coordr*, Sharilynn A Aucoin; Tel: 225-342-4942, E-Mail: saucoin@pelican.state.lib.la.us; *Coordr*, Virginia R Smith; Tel: 225-342-4920, Fax: 225-219-4725, E-Mail: vsmith@pelican.state.lib.la.us; *Librn for Blind*, Elizabeth Hecker Perkins; Tel: 225-342-4942, Fax: 225-219-4804, E-Mail: eperkins@pelican.state.lib.la.us; Staff 13 (MLS 4, Non-MLS 9)
Founded 1933
Special Collections: Large Print Books, Braille, Descriptive Videos; Louisiana Cassettes
Database Vendor: Ebsco - EbscoHost, epixtech, inc., IAC - Info Trac, IAC - SearchBank, OCLC - First Search
Publications: Louisiana Hotlines (Newsletter)
Function: Research library
Friends of the Library Group

P STATE LIBRARY OF LOUISIANA, 701 N Fourth St, 70802-5345. (Mail add: PO Box 131, 70821-0131), SAN 342-8044. Tel: 225-342-4923. Interlibrary Loan Service Tel: 225-342-4919. Circulation Tel: 225-342-4915. Reference Tel: 225-342-4913. TDD: 225-219-1696. FAX: 225-219-4804, 225-342-3547. E-Mail: admin@pelican.state.lib.la.us. Web Site: www.state.lib.la.us. *State Librn*, Thomas F Jaques; E-Mail: tjaques@pelican.state.lib.la.us; *Dep Dir*, Michael R McKann; E-Mail: mmckann@pelican.state.lib.la.us; *Assoc Dir*, Gary O Rolstad; Tel: 225-342-4931, E-Mail: grolstad@pelican.state.lib.la.us; *Coordr, Publ Servs*, Virginia Rogers Smith; Tel: 225-342-4920, Fax: 225-219-4725, E-Mail: vsmith@pelican.state.lib.la.us; *Tech Servs*, Elisabeth Spanhoff; Tel: 225-342-4938, E-Mail: espanhof@pelican.state.lib.la.us; *Librn for Blind*, Elizabeth Hecker Perkins; Tel: 225-342-4942, Fax: 225-342-6817, E-Mail: eperkins@pelican.state.lib.la.us; *Spec Coll*, Judith D Smith; Tel: 225-342-2791, Fax:

225-342-2791, E-Mail: jsmith@pelican.state.lib.la.us; *Ref*, Margaret Schroth; Tel: 225-342-4917, Fax: 225-219-4725, E-Mail: mschroth@pelican.state.lib.la.us; *AV*, Sally Wellman; Tel: 225-342-4940, Fax: 225-342-4941, E-Mail: swellman@pelican.state.lib.la.us; *Tech Coordr*, Sara Taffae; Tel: 225-219-4647, Fax: 225-342-7962, E-Mail: staffae@pelican.state.lib.la.us; *Doc*, Stacey Hathaway-Bell; Tel: 225-342-4929, Fax: 225-219-4725, E-Mail: sbell@pelican.state.lib.la.us; *Business*, Pam Dier; Tel: 225-342-4926, E-Mail: pdier@pelican.state.lib.la.us; *Circ*, Roblyn W Schwehm; Tel: 225-342-5155, Fax: 225-219-4725, E-Mail: rschwehm@pelican.state.lib.la.us; *Commun Relations*, Dedria Givens; Tel: 225-342-9713, E-Mail: dgivens@pelican.state.lib.la.us; *ILL, Ser*, Baksu Basanti; Tel: 225-342-0007, Fax: 225-219-4725, E-Mail: bbaksu@pelican.state.lib.la.us; *Ch Servs*, Gale Criswell; Tel: 225-342-9716, Fax: 225-342-3547, E-Mail: gcriswel@pelican.state.lib.la.us. Subject Specialists: *Louisiana*, Judith D Smith; Staff 79 (MLS 31, Non-MLS 48)
Founded 1925. Pop 4,219,973
Jul 2000-Jun 2001 Income $9,423,403, State $6,567,620, Federal $2,803,678, Locally Generated Income $20,905, Other $31,200. Mats Exp $615,057. Sal $3,145,043
Library Holdings: Bk Vols 523,000; Per Subs 1,025
Subject Interests: Louisiana
Special Collections: Huey Long Photographs; Louisiana History, Politics, Economics, Literature
Automation Activity & Vendor Info: (Cataloging) epixtech, inc.; (Circulation) epixtech, inc.; (OPAC) epixtech, inc.; (Serials) epixtech, inc.
Database Vendor: Dialog, Ebsco - EbscoHost, GaleNet, IAC - SearchBank, ProQuest, Wilson - Wilson Web
Publications: Book Beat: A Young Adult Services Manual for Louisiana's Public Libraries; Communique; Information Resources Exchange; Insights; LaGIN Directory of State Agency Information Resources; Library Laws of Louisiana; Louisiana Summer Reading Program Manual; Official Publications: Lists of the Public Documents of Louisiana; Public Documents; Public Libraries in Louisiana Statistical Report; Searching for Your Louisiana Ancestors and All That Jazz
Partic in Lasernet; SE Libr Network; Solinet
Friends of the Library Group
Branches: 1

L TAYLOR, PORTER, BROOKS & PHILLIPS, Law Library,* 451 Florida St, 8th flr, PO Box 2471, 70801. SAN 372-1302. Tel: 504-387-3221. FAX: 504-346-8049. *Librn*, Carol Bean
Library Holdings: Bk Vols 10,000; Per Subs 15

R UNIVERSITY BAPTIST CHURCH LIBRARY,* 203 Leeward Dr, 70808. SAN 306-4522. Tel: 504-766-9474. FAX: 504-766-9101. *Librn*, Patsy Perritt
Founded 1955
Library Holdings: Bk Vols 6,500; Bk Titles 6,250
Subject Interests: Church history
Special Collections: Children's Literature (Jim Smith Memorial Coll)

BLANCHARD

R FIRST BAPTIST CHURCH OF BLANCHARD, FBC Media Center,* 201 Attaway, PO Box 65, 71009. SAN 374-826X. Tel: 318-929-2346. FAX: 318-929-4680. *Dir*, Kevin Sandifer
Library Holdings: Bk Vols 1,000

BOSSIER CITY

P BOSSIER CENTRAL LIBRARY,* 2206 Becket St, 71111-3701. SAN 342-8400. Tel: 318-746-1693. FAX: 318-746-7768. *Dir*, Louis Covington; *Tech Servs*, Beverly Miles; *ILL*, Beverly Miles; *Librn*, Patti Risinger; *Ref*, Adrian Lee; *Ref*, Ann Parr; Staff 4 (MLS 4)
Founded 1940. Pop 89,000; Circ 510,000
Jan 1998-Dec 1998 Income $2,271,000. Mats Exp $310,000, Books $280,000, Per/Ser (Incl. Access Fees) $30,000. Sal $810,000
Library Holdings: Bk Titles 153,000; Per Subs 900
Special Collections: Bossier Parish Police Jury Minutes, 1881 to present, microfilm; County Newspaper, beginning 1859 to present, bd vol & microflm
Branches: 7
BENTON BRANCH, PO Box 400, Benton, 71006. SAN 342-8435. Tel: 318-965-2751. FAX: 318-965-2751. *Librn*, Marilyn McGowan
EAST 80 BRANCH, 1050 Bellevue Rd, Haughton, 71037. SAN 329-661X. Tel: 318-949-2665. FAX: 318-949-2067. *Librn*, Anita Fletcher
HAUGHTON BRANCH, 116 W McKinley, PO Box 60, Haughton, 71037. SAN 342-8524. Tel: 318-949-0196. FAX: 318-949-1351. *Librn*, Jackie Baker
HENRY L AULDS MEMORIAL, 3950 Wayne Ave, 71112. SAN 342-8494. Tel: 318-742-2337, 318-752-4034. *Librn*, Bonnie Clark; E-Mail: clark939@hotmail.com
KORAN STATION, 5413 Hwy 527, Haughton, 71037. SAN 342-8508. Tel: 318-987-3915. FAX: 318-987-3915. *Librn*, Nita Wilson
PLAIN DEALING BRANCH, 208 E Mary Lee, PO Box 574, Plain Dealing, 71064. SAN 342-8559. Tel: 318-326-4233. *Librn*, Linda Standford
TECHNICAL SERVICES, 2206 Beckett St, 71111. SAN 342-8419. Tel: 318-746-1903. FAX: 318-746-1903. E-Mail: g1bs@pelican.state.lib.la.us. *Tech Servs*, Sandra Johnson

J BOSSIER PARISH COMMUNITY COLLEGE LIBRARY, (BPCC), 2719 Airline Dr, 71111. SAN 306-4530. Tel: 318-746-9851, Ext 357. FAX: 318-741-1498. Web Site: www.bpcc.cc.la.us/boss/. *Dean*, Virgina Bryan; Tel: 318-746-9851, Ext 237, E-Mail: gbryan@bpcc.cc.la.us; *Tech Servs*, Mary Alice Mosley; Tel: 318-746-9851, Ext 238, E-Mail: mamosley@bpcc.cc.la.us; *Publ Servs*, Brenda Brantley; Tel: 318-746-9851, Ext 356, E-Mail: bbrantley@bpcc.cc.la.us
Founded 1968. Enrl 4,900; Fac 100; Highest Degree: Associate
Library Holdings: Bk Vols 30,000; Bk Titles 20,000; Per Subs 350
Mem of Green Gold Library System

BRIDGE CITY

S BRIDGE CITY CORRECTIONS CENTER FOR YOUTH LIBRARY, 3225 River Rd, 70094. SAN 326-4874. Tel: 504-436-4253. FAX: 504-436-0916. *Librn*, Laura Turner
Library Holdings: Bk Titles 2,200

BURAS

P PLAQUEMINES PARISH LIBRARY,* 35572 Hwy 11, 70041-5212. SAN 342-8583. Tel: 504-657-7121. FAX: 504-657-6175. *Librn*, Janet Cantwell; *Acq*, Tammy Di Bartolo; Staff 5 (MLS 5)
Founded 1959. Pop 26,049; Circ 137,078
Library Holdings: Bk Vols 104,516; Per Subs 291
Special Collections: J Ben Meyer Historical Plaquemines Parish Coll; Louisiana Census Coll, microfilm; Video Cassette Coll
Branches: 2
BELLE CHASSE BRANCH, 8442 Hwy 23, Belle Chasse, 70037. SAN 342-8613. Tel: 504-394-3570. FAX: 504-394-6102. *Asst Librn*, Emelie Savoie; *Asst Librn*, Joanne McClellan
Library Holdings: Bk Vols 20,130
PORT SULPHUR BRANCH, 138 Civic Dr, Port Sulphur, 70083. SAN 342-8702. Tel: 504-564-3681. FAX: 504-564-3274. *Asst Librn*, Tammy Dibartlo; *Asst Librn*, Vicky Kramer
Library Holdings: Bk Vols 17,100
Bookmobiles: 1. Bk vols 11,936

CAMERON

P CAMERON PARISH LIBRARY,* 498 Marshal St, PO Box 1130, 70631-2016. SAN 306-4549. Tel: 318-775-5421. FAX: 318-775-5346. *Dir*, Gwendolyn Reasoner
Founded 1958. Pop 9,336; Circ 76,805
Jan 1999-Dec 2000 Income $289,550, State $13,250, County $260,000, Locally Generated Income $16,300. Mats Exp $44,000, Books $38,000, Per/Ser (Incl. Access Fees) $6,000. Sal $111,396 (Prof $36,500)
Library Holdings: Bk Vols 45,000; Per Subs 85
Subject Interests: Louisiana
Special Collections: Cookbooks
Friends of the Library Group

CHALMETTE

S JEAN LAFITTE NATIONAL HISTORICAL PARK & PRESERVE, Chalmette Battlefield Library, 8606 W St Bernard Hwy, 70043. SAN 321-4486. Tel: 504-281-0511. FAX: 504-281-0515. E-Mail: jela_chalmette_interepretation@nps.gov. Web Site: www.nps.gov/jela. *In Charge*, Wanda Lee Dickey
Founded 1939
Library Holdings: Bk Titles 300
Special Collections: Battle of New Orleans, bks, mss; War of 1812 History
Restriction: Open to public for reference only

§J NUNEZ COMMUNITY COLLEGE LIBRARY, 3710 Paris Rd, 70043. Tel: 504-680-2602. FAX: 504-680-2584. E-Mail: library@nunez.cc.la.us. Web Site: www.nunez.ca.la.us/library/ncclib.htm. *Dir*, Albert Tate, III
Jul 2000-Jun 2001 Income $400,000
Library Holdings: Bk Vols 30,000; Per Subs 300; Bks on Deafness & Sign Lang 30
Automation Activity & Vendor Info: (Cataloging) epixtech, inc.; (Circulation) epixtech, inc.; (OPAC) epixtech, inc.

P SAINT BERNARD PARISH LIBRARY,* 1125 E St Bernard Hwy, 70043-5498. SAN 342-8737. Tel: 504-279-0448. FAX: 504-277-3645. E-Mail: s1br@pelican.state.lib.la.us. *Librn*, Ethel B Llamas
Founded 1957. Pop 67,000; Circ 126,000
Jan 1997-Dec 1998 Income $650,000, State $76,000, County $475,000, Locally Generated Income $37,000. Mats Exp $190,000, Books $100,000, Per/Ser (Incl. Access Fees) $70,000, Presv $2,000, Micro $5,000, Other

Print Mats $4,000. Sal $307,150 (Prof $76,000)
Library Holdings: Bk Vols 80,000; Per Subs 290
Subject Interests: Art, Genealogy, Louisiana
Special Collections: Louisiana Coll
Branches: 1
DUCROS MUSEUM, 1345 Bayou Rd, St Bernard, 70085. SAN 342-8761. Tel: 504-682-2713.
Library Holdings: Bk Vols 4,179

CHAUVIN

G LOUISIANA UNIVERSITIES MARINE CONSORTIUM, Lumcon Library,* 8124 Hwy 56, 70344-2124. SAN 326-4815. Tel: 504-851-2800, 504-851-2875. FAX: 504-851-2874. Web Site: www.lumcon.edu/library.htm. *Res*, Donna Rice; E-Mail: drice@lumcon.edu
Founded 1979
Jul 1998-Jun 1999 Income $141,326, State $115,926, Federal $25,400. Mats Exp $79,458, Books $2,000, Per/Ser (Incl. Access Fees) $77,458. Sal $47,660 (Prof $31,000)
Library Holdings: Bk Titles 5,600; Per Subs 165
Subject Interests: Geochemistry, Marine biology, Oceanography
Publications: Effects of Offshore Oil & Gas Development: A Current Awareness Bibliography (annotated, quarterly); US Minerals Management Service
Partic in SE Libr Network

CLINTON

P AUDUBON REGIONAL LIBRARY, 12220 Woodville St, 70722. (Mail add: PO Box 8389, 70722), Tel: 225-683-4290. Interlibrary Loan Service Tel: 225-634-7508. Reference Tel: 225-683-8753. FAX: 225-683-4634. *Dir*, Lula H Pride; E-Mail: lpride@pelican.state.lib.la.us; *Asst Dir*, Rebecca Hamilton; Tel: 225-784-0260, Fax: 225-635-4986, E-Mail: rhamilto@pelican.state.lib.la.us; Staff 22 (MLS 2, Non-MLS 20)
Founded 1963. Pop 43,000; Circ 147,992
Jan 2000-Dec 2000 Income (Main Library and Branch Library) $640,000, State $62,000, Federal $9,000, County $506,000, Locally Generated Income $25,000, Other $38,000. Mats Exp $118,000, Books $53,000, Per/Ser (Incl. Access Fees) $10,000, Micro $100, AV Equip $2,500. Sal $209,000 (Prof $61,600)
Library Holdings: Bk Vols 92,000; Per Subs 212
Subject Interests: Genealogy, History, Louisiana
Automation Activity & Vendor Info: (Cataloging) TLC; (Circulation) TLC; (ILL) TLC; (OPAC) TLC
Open Mon-Fri 9-5 (except Thurs 9-6), Sat 9-1
Friends of the Library Group
Branches: 4
CLINTON (EAST FELICIANA), 12220 Woodville St, PO Box 8389, 70722. SAN 342-8826. Tel: 225-683-8753. FAX: 225-683-4634. *Branch Mgr*, Doris Buerger
Library Holdings: Bk Vols 36,417
Friends of the Library Group
JACKSON BRANCH, 3312 College St, PO Box 1830, Jackson, 70748. SAN 342-8885. Tel: 225-634-7408. Interlibrary Loan Service Tel: 225-634-7508. FAX: 225-634-5896. *Branch Mgr*, Mary Jordan; Staff 1 (Non-MLS 1)
Library Holdings: Bk Vols 13,581
Friends of the Library Group
ST HELENA BRANCH, Oak Plaza Shopping Center, Hwy 10, Greensburg, 70441. (Mail add: PO Box 368, Greensburg, 70441-0368), SAN 342-8850. Tel: 504-222-4328. Interlibrary Loan Service Tel: 225-634-7508. FAX: 504-222-4335. *Branch Mgr*, Leslie Hoffstadt
Library Holdings: Bk Vols 13,055
Friends of the Library Group
WEST FELICIANA BRANCH, 11865 Ferdinand St, Saint Francisville, 70775-4341. (Mail add: PO Box 3120, Saint Francisville, 70775-3120), SAN 342-8915. Tel: 225-635-3364. Interlibrary Loan Service Tel: 225-634-7508. FAX: 225-635-4986. *Branch Mgr*, Penny Reed; Staff 1 (MLS 1)
Library Holdings: Bk Vols 24,314
Friends of the Library Group
Bookmobiles: 34. Bk vols 4000

COLFAX

P GRANT PARISH LIBRARY,* 300 Main St, 71417-1830. SAN 306-4565. Tel: 318-627-9920. FAX: 318-627-9900. *Dir*, Doris Lively; *Bkmobile Coordr*, Billie Oaks
Founded 1959. Pop 17,495; Circ 90,600
Library Holdings: Bk Vols 62,137; Per Subs 131
Subject Interests: Genealogy, History, Louisiana
Branches: 4
DRY PRONG BRANCH, 605 Elm St, Dry Prong, 71423. (Mail add: PO Box 187, Dry Prong, 71423), Tel: 318-899-7588. FAX: 318-899-7588. Web Site: www.grant.lib.la.us. *Branch Mgr*, Jackie Stills
Library Holdings: Bk Vols 4,650
GEORGETOWN BRANCH, 4570 Hwy 500, PO Box 226, Georgetown, 71432. SAN 377-7561. Tel: 318-827-9427. FAX: 318-827-9427. *Librn*, Wanda Shields
Library Holdings: Bk Titles 2,000
MONTGOMERY BRANCH, 940 Caddo St, Montgomery, 71454. (Mail add: PO Box 157, Montgomery, 71454), Tel: 318-646-3660. FAX: 318-646-3660. Web Site: www.grant.lib.la.us. *Branch Mgr*, Marcia Fletcher
Library Holdings: Bk Vols 6,520; Per Subs 11
POLLOCK BRANCH, 1316 Pine St, Pollock, 71467. (Mail add: PO Box 641, Pollock, 71467), Tel: 318-765-9619. FAX: 318-765-9619. Web Site: www.grant.lib.la.us. *Branch Mgr*, Tonya Chelette
Library Holdings: Bk Vols 5,580

COLUMBIA

P CALDWELL PARISH LIBRARY,* 211 Jackson, 71418-1499. (Mail add: PO Box 1499, 71418-1499), Tel: 318-649-2259. FAX: 318-649-7768. *Librn*, Sue M Childers
Founded 1953. Pop 9,810; Circ 53,096
Library Holdings: Bk Vols 40,275; Per Subs 2,020
Mem of Trail Blazer Libr Syst

COTTONPORT

§S AVOYELLES CORRECTIONAL CENTER LIBRARY, 1630 Prison Rd, 71327. Tel: 318-876-2891, Ext 229. FAX: 318-876-4220. *In Charge*, Terry Barbin
Jul 2000-Jun 2001 Income $5,500
Library Holdings: Bk Vols 9,065

COUSHATTA

P RED RIVER PARISH LIBRARY,* 2022 Alonzo, 71019-2008. (Mail add: PO Box 1367, 71019-2008), SAN 306-4581. Tel: 318-932-5614. FAX: 318-932-6747. E-Mail: g1rr@pelican.state.lib.la.us. *Librn*, Marvin Lewis
Founded 1962. Pop 10,500; Circ 44,000
Library Holdings: Bk Vols 23,000

COVINGTON

P SAINT TAMMANY PARISH LIBRARY,* 310 W 21st Ave, 70433. SAN 342-894X. Tel: 504-871-1220. FAX: 504-871-1224, 504-893-6281. Web Site: www.stpl.com. *Dir*, Janice Butler; Staff 84 (MLS 14, Non-MLS 70)
Founded 1950. Pop 180,692; Circ 1,167,914
Jan 1998-Dec 1998 Income (Main Library and Branch Library) $3,337,816. Sal $1,492,502
Library Holdings: Bk Vols 469,553; Bk Titles 157,803; Per Subs 947
Subject Interests: Local history
Automation Activity & Vendor Info: (Cataloging) GEAC; (Circulation) GEAC; (OPAC) GEAC
Database Vendor: GaleNet, IAC - Info Trac, OCLC - First Search, ProQuest
Publications: STPL News (staff newsletter)
Special Services for the Deaf - Books on deafness & sign language; High interest/low vocabulary books
Friends of the Library Group
Branches: 13
ABITA SPRINGS BRANCH, 71683 Leveson St, PO Box 157, Abita Springs, 70420. SAN 342-8974. Tel: 504-893-6285. FAX: 504-893-6285. Web Site: www.stpl.com. *Mgr*, Sue Wolfe
Library Holdings: Bk Vols 22,147
BUSH BRANCH, 81597 Hwy 41, PO Box 385, Bush, 70431. SAN 342-9008. Tel: 504-886-3588. FAX: 504-886-3588. Web Site: www.stpl.com. *Mgr*, Marjorie Morgan
Library Holdings: Bk Vols 16,358
CAUSEWAY, 3457 Hwy 190, Mandeville, 70471. Tel: 504-626-9779. FAX: 504-626-9783. Web Site: www.stpl.com. *Mgr*, Rodney Jackman
Library Holdings: Bk Vols 9,150
COVINGTON BRANCH, 310 W 21st Ave, 70433. Tel: 504-893-6280. FAX: 504-893-6280. Web Site: www.stpl.com. *Mgr*, Alice Rogers; *Tech Coordr*, Donald Westmoreland
Library Holdings: Bk Vols 102,432
Friends of the Library Group
ELECTRONIC RESOURCE CENTER, 21454 Koop Dr, Mandeville, 70448. Tel: 504-809-0989. FAX: 504-809-1278. Web Site: www.stpl.com.
Subject Interests: Computer software
FOLSOM BRANCH, 82393 Railroad Ave, PO Box 37, Folsom, 70437. SAN 342-9091. Tel: 504-796-9728. FAX: 504-796-9728. Web Site: www.stpl.com. *Mgr*, Becky Scroggins
Library Holdings: Bk Vols 22,860
LACOMBE BRANCH, 28027 Hwy 190, PO Box 929, Lacombe, 70445. SAN 342-9121. Tel: 504-882-7858. Web Site: www.stpl.com. *Mgr*, Diane Barringer

Library Holdings: Bk Vols 13,775
LEE ROAD BRANCH, 79213 Hwy 40, 70433. SAN 329-6512. Tel: 504-893-6284. FAX: 504-893-6284. Web Site: www.stpl.com. *Mgr*, Lisa Haley
Library Holdings: Bk Vols 19,195
MADISONVILLE BRANCH, 400 Cedar St, PO Box 69, Madisonville, 70447. SAN 342-9156. Tel: 504-845-4819. FAX: 504-845-4819. Web Site: www.stpl.com. *Mgr*, Lillie Butler
Library Holdings: Bk Vols 22,321
MANDEVILLE BRANCH, 842 Gerard St, Mandeville, 70448. SAN 342-9180. Tel: 504-626-4293. FAX: 504-624-4621. Web Site: www.stpl.com. *Mgr*, Alison Williams
Library Holdings: Bk Vols 77,803
Friends of the Library Group
PEARL RIVER BRANCH, 64580 Hwy 41, PO Box 508, Pearl River, 70452. SAN 342-9210. Tel: 504-863-5518. FAX: 504-863-5518. Web Site: www.stpl.com. *Mgr*, Adele Salzer; *Ref*, Lesley Dolinger; Tel: 504-893-6280, Ext 21, E-Mail: lesley@mail.sttammany.lib.la.us
Library Holdings: Bk Vols 24,129
PONTCHARTRAIN BRANCH, 4002 Pontchartrain Blvd, Ste 2, Slidell, 70458. SAN 373-8523. Tel: 504-646-6469. Web Site: www.stpl.com. *Mgr*, Jeanie Cucinella
Library Holdings: Bk Vols 18,339
SLIDELL BRANCH, 555 Robert Blvd, Slidell, 70458. SAN 342-9245. Tel: 504-646-6470. FAX: 504-645-3553. Web Site: www.stpl.com. *Mgr*, Rebecca A Taylor; Staff 17 (MLS 3, Non-MLS 14)
Library Holdings: Bk Vols 102,429
Friends of the Library Group

CM TULANE UNIVERSITY OF LOUISIANA, Tulane Regional Primate Research Center Library, 18703 Three Rivers Rd, 70433. SAN 306-459X. Tel: 504-892-2040, Ext 6366. FAX: 504-893-1352. Web Site: www2.tulane.edu/resources_libraries.cfm. *Dir Libr Serv*, Sharon Nastasi; E-Mail: sharon@tpc.tulane.edu
Founded 1963
Library Holdings: Bk Titles 9,535; Per Subs 50
Subject Interests: Immunology, Urology
Partic in Medline; Nat Libr of Med; OCLC Online Computer Library Center, Inc

CROWLEY

P ACADIA PARISH LIBRARY,* 1125 N Parkerson, 70527-1509. (Mail add: PO Drawer 1509, 70527-1509), Tel: 337-788-1880. FAX: 337-788-3759. E-Mail: admin.b1ac@pelican.state.lib.la.us. Web Site: www.acadia.lib.la.us. *Librn*, Lyle C Johnson; *Acq*, Ann Mire; Staff 22 (MLS 2, Non-MLS 20)
Founded 1945. Pop 55,882
Library Holdings: Bk Vols 121,000; Per Subs 200
Special Collections: Paul Freeland's Crowley Coll
Mem of Bayouland Library System
Branches: 7
CHURCH POINT BRANCH, 311 N Vista, Church Point, 70525. SAN 342-9334. Tel: 337-684-5774. FAX: 337-684-1593. E-Mail: churchpoint.b1ac@pelican.state.lib.la.us. *Librn*, Mrs Dell Venable
Library Holdings: Bk Vols 5,290
ESTHERWOOD BRANCH, PO Box 230, Estherwood, 70534. SAN 342-9423. Tel: 337-785-1090. *Librn*, Judy Leger
Library Holdings: Bk Vols 1,769
EVANGELINE BRANCH, 123 Willis Lane, PO Box 221, Evangeline, 70537. SAN 342-9458. Tel: 337-824-6443. E-Mail: evangeline.b1ac@pelican.state.lib.la.us. *Librn*, Comau Christine
Library Holdings: Bk Vols 3,378
IOTA BRANCH, PO Box 950, Iota, 70543. SAN 342-9482. Tel: 337-779-2770. E-Mail: iota.b1ac@pelican.state.lib.la.us. *Librn*, Anne Manuel
Library Holdings: Bk Vols 5,340
MERMENTAU BRANCH, PO Box 369, Mermentau, 70556. SAN 342-9512. Tel: 318-824-0690. *Librn*, Betty Broussard
Library Holdings: Bk Vols 2,109
MORSE BRANCH, PO Box 369, Morse, 70559. SAN 342-9520. Tel: 337-783-0784. E-Mail: morse.b1ac@pelican.state.lib.la.us. *Librn*, Sandra Henry
Library Holdings: Bk Vols 2,000
RAYNE BRANCH, 109 W Perrodin, PO Box 3, Rayne, 70578. SAN 342-9547. Tel: 337-334-3188. FAX: 337-334-1181. E-Mail: rayne.b1ac@pelican.state.lib.la.us. *Librn*, Arleen Stutes
Library Holdings: Bk Vols 34,698

DERIDDER

§P BEAUREGARD PARISH LIBRARY, 205 S Washington Ave, 70634. Tel: 337-463-6217. FAX: 337-462-5434. E-Mail: vickir@beau.lib.la.us. Web Site: www.beau.lib.la.us. *Dir*, Lilly F Smith
Library Holdings: Bk Vols 66,100; Per Subs 138
Automation Activity & Vendor Info: (Acquisitions) DRA; (Cataloging) DRA; (Circulation) DRA; (OPAC) DRA
Branches: 6
EAST BEAUREGARD, 7580 Hwy 26, Dry Creek, 70637. Tel: 337-463-6217. FAX: 337-462-5434. Web Site: www.beau.lib.la.us. *Branch Mgr*, Sue Stretton
Library Holdings: Bk Vols 3,700; Per Subs 10
Automation Activity & Vendor Info: (Acquisitions) DRA; (Cataloging) DRA; (Circulation) DRA; (OPAC) DRA
FIELDS BRANCH, C Fields Volunteer Fire Department, 13287 Hwy 389, Fields, 70653. Tel: 337-463-6217. FAX: 337-462-5434. Web Site: www.beau.lib.la.us. *Branch Mgr*, Lenora Pickering
Library Holdings: Bk Vols 3,600; Per Subs 10
Automation Activity & Vendor Info: (Acquisitions) DRA; (Cataloging) DRA; (Circulation) DRA; (OPAC) DRA
LONGVILLE BRANCH, 234 Longville Rd, Longville, 70652. Tel: 337-463-6217. FAX: 337-462-5434. Web Site: www.beau.lib.la.us. *Branch Mgr*, Carolyn Felice
Library Holdings: Bk Vols 6,500
MERRYVILLE BRANCH, 120 Heard St, Merryville, 70653. Tel: 337-463-6217. FAX: 337-462-5434. Web Site: www.beau.lib.la.us.
Library Holdings: Bk Vols 3,800; Per Subs 11
RAGLEY BRANCH, 6715 Hwy 12, Ragley, 70657. Tel: 337-463-6217. FAX: 337-462-5434. Web Site: www.beau.lib.la.us. *Branch Mgr*, Poppy Reeves
Library Holdings: Bk Vols 3,200
SINGER BRANCH, 9130 Hwy 27, Singer, 70660. Tel: 337-463-6217. FAX: 337-462-5434. Web Site: www.beau.lib.la.us. *Branch Mgr*, Mike Tritico
Library Holdings: Bk Vols 3,100; Per Subs 26

EUNICE

C LOUISIANA STATE UNIVERSITY, Eunice LeDoux Library, 2048 Johnson Hwy, PO Box 1129, 70535-1129. SAN 306-4611. Tel: 337-457-7311, Ext 380. FAX: 337-550-1455. Web Site: www.lsue.edu. *Dir*, Dr Sue P Forrest; E-Mail: sforrest@lsue.edu; *Ref*, Hal Mendelson; *Govt Doc*, Cinderella Hayes; Staff 5 (MLS 5)
Founded 1967. Enrl 2,395; Fac 68
Library Holdings: Bk Vols 89,923; Per Subs 218
Subject Interests: Genealogy, Louisiana
Friends of the Library Group

FARMERVILLE

P UNION PARISH LIBRARY,* 202 W Jackson St, 71241-2799. SAN 306-462X. Tel: 318-368-9226. FAX: 318-368-9224. *Librn*, Dorothy H Killen; E-Mail: dkillen@pelican.state.lib.la.us
Founded 1956. Pop 20,690; Circ 62,068
Library Holdings: Bk Vols 53,975; Per Subs 69
Mem of Trail Blazer Libr Syst

FERRIDAY

P CONCORDIA PARISH LIBRARY, 1609 Third St, 71334-2298. SAN 342-975X. Tel: 318-757-3550. FAX: 318-757-8836. E-Mail: con_libl@alpha.nlu.edu. Web Site: cyberserver01.concordia.lib.la.us, www.concordia.lib.la.us. *Dir*, Amanda Taylor; E-Mail: ataylor@pelican.state.lib.la.us
Founded 1928
Library Holdings: Bk Vols 58,689; Per Subs 95
Database Vendor: GaleNet, IAC - Info Trac, IAC - SearchBank, ProQuest
Mem of Trail Blazer Libr Syst
Branches: 2
CLAYTON BRANCH, 8723 Hwy 566, PO Box 100, Clayton, 71326. SAN 342-9784. Tel: 318-757-6460. Web Site: cyberserver01.concordia.lib.la.us. *Librn*, Delilah Leonard
VIDALIA BRANCH, 405 Carter St, Vidalia, 71373. SAN 342-9814. Tel: 318-336-5043. Web Site: cyberserver01.concordia.lib.la.us. *Librn*, Nell Arnold
Bookmobiles: 1

FORT POLK

S FORT POLK MILITARY MUSEUM LIBRARY,* PO Box 3916, 71459-0916. SAN 374-8286. Tel: 318-531-7905. FAX: 318-531-4202. *Curator*, David S Bingham
Library Holdings: Bk Vols 500; Per Subs 100

UNITED STATES ARMY
A ALLEN MEMORIAL LIBRARY, Bldg 400, 6880 Radio Rd, 71459. SAN 342-9849. Tel: 318-531-1987, 337-531-1987, 337-531-2665. *Dir*, Stephanie R Jones; E-Mail: joness@polk-emhs.army.mil; *Librn*, Freeman Shell Jr
Library Holdings: Bk Vols 65,000; Per Subs 165
Subject Interests: Louisiana, Military history
Partic in OCLC Online Computer Library Center, Inc
AM BAYNE-JONES ARMY COMMUNITY HOSPITAL MEDICAL LIBRARY, 1585 Third St, 71459-5110. Tel: 318-531-3726. Toll Free Tel: 800-752-4658. *Adminr, Librn*, Cecelia B Higginbotham; Fax: 337-531-3082, E-Mail: cecelia.higginbotham@amedd.army.mil; Staff 1 (MLS 1)
Founded 1961

Library Holdings: Bk Titles 3,000; Per Subs 153
Automation Activity & Vendor Info: (Acquisitions) Endeavor; (Cataloging) Endeavor; (Circulation) Endeavor; (OPAC) Endeavor; (Serials) Endeavor
Database Vendor: Ebsco - EbscoHost
Partic in Nat Libr of Med; OCLC Online Computer Library Center, Inc; S Cent Regional Med Libr Program

FRANKLIN

P SAINT MARY PARISH LIBRARY,* 206 Iberia St, 70538-4906. SAN 342-9903. Tel: 318-828-1624, 318-828-5364. FAX: 318-828-2329. *Dir*, Cheryl Cooper; *Asst Dir*, Judy Ordoyne; *Ref*, Don Crook; Staff 19 (MLS 2, Non-MLS 17)
Founded 1953. Pop 48,669; Circ 321,828
Library Holdings: Bk Vols 178,155; Per Subs 239
Subject Interests: Genealogy
Publications: Library Lagniappe
Mem of Bayouland Library System
Friends of the Library Group
Branches: 5
AMELIA BRANCH, PO Box 565, Amelia, 70340. SAN 342-9911. Tel: 504-631-2262. FAX: 504-631-2262. *Asst Librn*, Trudy Landry
Library Holdings: Bk Vols 16,138
BAYOU VISTA BRANCH, 1325 Bellview Dr, Bayou Vista, 70380. SAN 377-9998. Tel: 504-399-9866. FAX: 504-399-4232. E-Mail: lamb040@yahoo.com. *Mgr*, Leisha Mitchell
Founded 1998
BERWICK BRANCH, 3527 Fourth St, Berwick, 70342. SAN 342-9938. Tel: 504-385-2943. FAX: 504-385-2943. *Asst Librn*, Diane Matherne
Library Holdings: Bk Vols 31,406
PATTERSON BRANCH, PO Box 57, Patterson, 70392. SAN 342-9997. Tel: 504-395-2777. FAX: 504-395-2777. *Asst Librn*, Lisa Wilson
Library Holdings: Bk Vols 23,415
WEST END, 100 Charenton Rd, Baldwin, 70514. SAN 374-4175. Tel: 318-923-6205. FAX: 318-923-6205. *Mgr*, Doris Thomas
Bookmobiles: 1. Bk vols 18,511

FRANKLINTON

P WASHINGTON PARISH LIBRARY SYSTEM,* 825 Free St, 70438. SAN 343-0022. Tel: 504-839-7805. FAX: 504-839-7808. E-Mail: washlibrary@yahoo.com. *Librn*, Juanita Barker
Founded 1946. Pop 43,185; Circ 153,776
Library Holdings: Bk Vols 104,800
Special Collections: Washington Parish & local history
Branches: 8
ANGIE BRANCH, 30303 Railroad Ave, Angie, 70426. SAN 343-0057. Tel: 504-986-3672. *Mgr*, Marie Stringer
Library Holdings: Bk Vols 6,000
BOGALUSA BRANCH, 304 Ave F, Bogalusa, 70427. SAN 343-0081. Tel: 504-735-1961. *Mgr*, Emmett Guy Jr
Library Holdings: Bk Vols 40,000
ENON, 14073 Hwy 16, 70438. SAN 343-0146. Tel: 504-839-9385. *Mgr*, Helen Buck
Library Holdings: Bk Vols 4,000
FRANKLINTON, 825 Free St, 70438. SAN 343-0170. Tel: 504-839-7808. *Mgr*, Bobbie Jones
Library Holdings: Bk Vols 39,400
MOUNT HERMON BRANCH, 36015 Hwy 38, Mount Hermon, 70450. SAN 343-026X. Tel: 504-877-9937. *Mgr*, Connie Miller
Library Holdings: Bk Vols 4,200
PINE BRANCH, Pine, 70438. SAN 371-9731. Tel: 504-848-9937. *Mgr*, Sylvia Ledet
Library Holdings: Bk Vols 3,000
THOMAS, 30390 Hwy 424, 70438. SAN 343-0235. Tel: 504-848-7061. *Mgr*, Sylvia Ledet
Library Holdings: Bk Vols 3,000
VARNADO BRANCH, 63086 Main St, Varnado, 70467. SAN 343-0294. Tel: 504-735-5597. *Mgr*, Marie Stringer
Library Holdings: Bk Vols 5,200

GONZALES

P ASCENSION PARISH LIBRARY,* 708 S Irma Blvd, 70737. SAN 342-9660. Tel: 225-647-8924. FAX: 225-644-0063. E-Mail: adeshaut@pelican.state.lib.la.us. Web Site: www.ascension.lib.la.us/apl. *Dir*, Angelle Deshautelles; *Asst Dir*, Larie Myers; Staff 36 (MLS 8, Non-MLS 28)
Founded 1960. Pop 58,000; Circ 237,376
Library Holdings: Bk Vols 198,000
Special Collections: US Army Corps of Engineers, Lower Mississippi Valley Flood Control, doc
Personnel counts, fiscal information & holdings for branches are included in the totals for main library
Branches: 3
DONALDSONVILLE BRANCH, 500 Mississippi St, Donaldsonville, 70346-2535. SAN 342-9679. Tel: 225-473-8052. FAX: 225-473-9522. E-Mail: adeshaut@pelican.state.lib.la.us. Web Site: www.ascension.lib.la.us/apl. *Librn*, Miguel Pacheco
GALVEZ, 40300 Hwy 42, Prairieville, 70769. SAN 325-397X. Tel: 225-622-3339. FAX: 225-622-2550. E-Mail: adeshaut@pelican.state.lib.la.us. Web Site: www.ascension.lib.la.us/apl. *Librn*, Jared Millet
GONZALES BRANCH, 708 S Irma Blvd, 70737. SAN 342-9695. Tel: 225-647-3955. FAX: 225-644-0063. E-Mail: adeshaut@pelican.state.lib.la.us. Web Site: www.ascension.lib.la.us/apl. *Librn*, Roberta August

GRAMBLING

C GRAMBLING STATE UNIVERSITY, A C Lewis Memorial Library, PO Box 3, 71245. SAN 306-4638. Tel: 318-274-2220. FAX: 318-274-3268. Web Site: www.gram.edu. *Dean of Libr*, Pauline W Lee; *Ref*, Claudine Ashton; *Circ*, Carolyn J McNeal; *Ser*, Sally Carroll; *Ser*, Charles Hughes, III; *Head, Ser Acq*, Dr Rosemary Mokia; Staff 9 (MLS 9)
Founded 1935. Enrl 7,533; Fac 278; Highest Degree: Doctorate
Library Holdings: Bk Vols 305,288; Per Subs 866
Special Collections: Afro-American Rare Books, fiche; Crime & Juvenile Delinquency, fiche; Education (ERIC 1970-1980), fiche; English Literature, fiche; Facts on Film, micro; Housing & Urban Affairs 1965-1972, fiche; Library of American Civilization, fiche; Mary Watson Hymon Afro-American, bks; National Woman's Party Papers, micro; Newsbank, micro; Schomburg Coll (partial); Sociology (Black Culture), micro; The Adams' Papers, micro; Update, fiche
Publications: Brochures; handbooks; newsletters
Mem of Trail Blazer Libr Syst
Partic in Dialog Corporation; SE Libr Network
Friends of the Library Group

GREENWELL SPRINGS

M GREENWELL SPRINGS HOSPITAL, Medical Library,* 23260 Greenwell Springs Rd, PO Box 549, 70739. SAN 373-9031. Tel: 504-262-3669. FAX: 504-261-9080. *Librn*, Brenda Eames
Library Holdings: Bk Titles 300; Per Subs 23
Subject Interests: Psychiatry
Restriction: Staff use only

HAMMOND

§S HAMMOND DEVELOPMENT CENTER LIBRARY, 45439 Live Oak Dr, 70401-9420. Tel: 504-567-3111, Ext 388. FAX: 225-567-2017. *Librn*, Antoinette Liuzza; E-Mail: tonyz@mail.com
Library Holdings: Bk Vols 1,200; Per Subs 20; Bks on Deafness & Sign Lang 10
Restriction: Staff use only

C SOUTHEASTERN LOUISIANA UNIVERSITY, Linus A Sims Memorial Library, SLU 10896, SGA Dr, 70402. SAN 306-4646. Tel: 504-549-3860. Interlibrary Loan Service Tel: 504-549-5318. FAX: 504-549-3995. Web Site: www.selu.edu/library/. *Dir*, Kay McIntyre; Staff 16 (MLS 16)
Founded 1925. Enrl 14,252; Fac 441; Highest Degree: Master
Library Holdings: Bk Vols 360,000; Per Subs 2,315
Subject Interests: Genealogy
Partic in SE Libr Network
Friends of the Library Group

HARRISONBURG

P CATAHOULA PARISH LIBRARY,* Bushley St, PO Box 218, 71340-0218. SAN 343-0324. Tel: 318-744-5271. FAX: 318-744-5251. *Librn*, Lou Myers; Staff 1 (MLS 1)
Founded 1949. Pop 11,992; Circ 91,688
Library Holdings: Bk Vols 38,792; Bk Titles 39,219; Per Subs 86
Subject Interests: Genealogy
Special Collections: Catahoula Parish History Coll
Branches: 2
JONESVILLE BRANCH, 205 Pond St, Jonesville, 71343. SAN 343-0359. Tel: 318-339-7070. *Librn*, Lou Myers
SICILY ISLAND BRANCH, PO Box 266, Sicily Island, 71368. SAN 343-0383. Tel: 318-389-5804. *Librn*, Lou Myers
Bookmobiles: 1

HOMER

P CLAIBORNE PARISH LIBRARY, 901 Edgewood Dr, 71040. SAN 343-0413. Tel: 318-927-3845. FAX: 318-927-2016. *Dir*, Pamela Suggs; E-Mail: psuggs@pelican.state.la.us; Staff 15 (MLS 1, Non-MLS 14)

Founded 1951. Pop 17,095; Circ 89,809
Library Holdings: Bk Titles 50,000; Per Subs 250
Subject Interests: Louisiana
Friends of the Library Group
Branches: 2
HOMER BRANCH, 901 Edgewood Dr, 71040. SAN 343-0472. Tel: 318-927-2016. *Librn*, Jacqueline Woods
Library Holdings: Bk Vols 30,000
Friends of the Library Group
JOE W WEBB MEMORIAL LIBRARY, 1919 Main St, Haynesville, 71038. SAN 343-0448. Tel: 318-624-0364. *Librn*, Sandra Bower
Library Holdings: Bk Vols 16,883
Friends of the Library Group
Bookmobiles: 1

§S DAVID WADE CORRECTIONAL CENTER, Wade Library, 670 Bell Hill Rd, 71040. Tel: 318-927-0441. FAX: 318-927-0459. *In Charge*, Larry Cunningham
Library Holdings: Bk Vols 9,120; Per Subs 23

HOUMA

P TERREBONNE PARISH LIBRARY,* 424 Roussell St, 70360. SAN 343-0502. Tel: 504-876-5861. FAX: 504-876-5864. *Dir*, Mary Cosper LeBoeuf; E-Mail: mcosperl@pelican.state.lib.la.us; *Dep Dir*, Amy Whipple
Founded 1939. Pop 96,000; Circ 296,197
Jan 2000-Dec 2000 Income $3,685,000, State $30,000, County $3,600,000, Locally Generated Income $55,000. Mats Exp $1,785,000, Books $200,000, Per/Ser (Incl. Access Fees) $25,000, Micro $6,500. Sal $891,942 (Prof $205,491)
Library Holdings: Bk Vols 168,919; Per Subs 351
Subject Interests: Petroleum
Friends of the Library Group
Branches: 7
BOURG BRANCH, 4405 Grace St, Bourg, 70343. SAN 343-0537. Tel: 504-594-4717. *Mgr*, Malane Naquin
Library Holdings: Bk Vols 9,358
Friends of the Library Group
CHAUVIN BRANCH, 5612 LA Hwy 56, Chauvin, 70344. SAN 343-0596. Tel: 504-594-9771. *Mgr*, Kathleen Freeman
Library Holdings: Bk Vols 6,888
Friends of the Library Group
DULARGE, 837 Bayou Dularge Rd, 70363. SAN 375-460X. Tel: 504-851-1752. *Mgr*, Nancy Theriot
Library Holdings: Bk Vols 4,674
Friends of the Library Group
EAST HOUMA, 778 Grand Caillou Rd, 70363. SAN 343-0626. Tel: 504-876-7072. FAX: 504-876-9658. E-Mail: easthouma.b1tb@pelican.state.lib.la.us. *Branch Mgr*, Rhonda Madison Fitch; Staff 7 (MLS 4, Non-MLS 3)
Founded 1968
Library Holdings: Bk Vols 34,279
MONTEGUT BRANCH, 1135 Hwy 55, Montegut, 70377. SAN 343-0650. *Mgr*, Margaret Herbert
Library Holdings: Bk Vols 10,799
Friends of the Library Group
NORTH, 4130 West Park, Gray, 70359. SAN 343-0669. Tel: 504-868-3050. FAX: 504-868-9404. E-Mail: north.bltb@pelicon.state.lib.la.us. *Mgr*, Evelyn Billiot
Library Holdings: Bk Vols 39,857
WEST TERREBONNE, 6363 S Bayou Black Dr, Gibson, 70356. SAN 326-7512.
Library Holdings: Bk Vols 7,550
Friends of the Library Group

JACKSON

§S DIXON CORRECTIONAL INSTITUTE, Law Library, PO Box 788, 70748. Tel: 225-634-6345. *In Charge*, R C Hudnall, Jr
Library Holdings: Bk Vols 3,600; Per Subs 10

§M EASTERN LOUISIANA MENTAL HEALTH SYSTEMS, Patients' Library-Jackson Campus, Hwy 10, 70748. (Mail add: PO Box 498, 70748-0498), Tel: 225-634-0540. FAX: 225-634-0188. *Librn*, Cheryl B Franklin
Library Holdings: Bk Vols 3,000

§M VILLA FELICIANA MEDICAL COMPLEX LIBRARY, 5002 Hwy 10, 70748. (Mail add: PO Box 438, 70748), Tel: 225-634-4120. FAX: 225-634-4191. *In Charge*, Ellen Fudge
Library Holdings: Bk Vols 1,000

JENA

P LASALLE PARISH LIBRARY, 3108 N First St, PO Drawer 3199, 71342-3199. SAN 343-0675. Tel: 318-992-5675. FAX: 318-992-7374. E-Mail: admin.h1ls@pelican.state.lib.la.us. Web Site: www.lasalle.lib.la.us. *Dir*, Cindy Nash; *Tech Servs*, Debra Poole; *Ch Servs*, Donna Estis; *Admin Assoc*, Carol Jackson; E-Mail: cjackson@pelican.state.lib.la.us; *Per*, Barbara Murphy; *Branch Mgr*, Andrea Book; *Circ*, Amber Andrews; *Outreach Serv*, Becky Davidson; Staff 7 (MLS 1, Non-MLS 6)
Founded 1952. Pop 13,700
Jan 1999-Dec 1999 Income (Main Library and Branch Library) $315,344, State $32,580, Locally Generated Income $233,469, Other $49,295. Mats Exp $31,550, Books $23,500, Per/Ser (Incl. Access Fees) $4,000, Micro $50, AV Equip $3,500, Electronic Ref Mat (Incl. Access Fees) $500. Sal $127,000 (Prof $31,000)
Library Holdings: Bk Vols 51,922; Per Subs 150; Bks on Deafness & Sign Lang 51
Subject Interests: Louisiana
Automation Activity & Vendor Info: (Cataloging) Follett; (Circulation) Follett; (OPAC) Follett
Database Vendor: GaleNet, IAC - Info Trac, IAC - SearchBank, ProQuest
Partic in IAC Searchbank; ProQuest
Friends of the Library Group
Branches: 1
OLLA BRANCH, PO Box 807, Olla, 71465. SAN 343-074X. Tel: 318-495-5570. FAX: 318-495-5593. *Asst Librn*, Andrea Book

JENNINGS

P JEFFERSON DAVIS PARISH LIBRARY,* 118 W Plaquemine St, PO Box 356, 70546-0356. SAN 343-0774. Tel: 337-824-1210. FAX: 337-824-5444. *Dir*, Trudy J Patterson; E-Mail: tpatters@pelican.state.lib.la.us; *ILL*, Rhoda Marsh; E-Mail: b1jd@pelican.state.lib.la.us
Founded 1968. Pop 31,464; Circ 101,878
Jan 1998-Dec 1998 Income (Main Library and Branch Library) $645,949, State $53,532, County $516,386, Locally Generated Income $76,031. Mats Exp $73,567, Books $58,634, Micro $9,305, AV Equip $5,628. Sal $273,674 (Prof $64,008)
Library Holdings: Bk Vols 70,187; Per Subs 254
Subject Interests: Indians, Louisiana
Automation Activity & Vendor Info: (Cataloging) epixtech, inc.; (Circulation) epixtech, inc.
Publications: Christmas Cookbook
Mem of Bayouland Library System
Branches: 4
ELTON BRANCH, PO Box 250, Elton, 70532-0250. SAN 343-0804. Tel: 318-584-2640. FAX: 318-584-2640. *Mgr*, Kitty Marsh
Library Holdings: Bk Vols 9,034
Special Collections: Coushatta Indian Coll
JENNINGS HEADQUARTER BRANCH, 118 W Plaquemine, 70546-0356. SAN 322-5755. Tel: 318-824-1210. FAX: 318-824-5444. *Mgr*, Lettie Marcantel
Library Holdings: Bk Vols 23,564
LAKE ARTHUR BRANCH, 411 Lake St, Lake Arthur, 70549. SAN 343-0839. Tel: 318-774-3661. FAX: 318-774-3661. *Mgr*, Emma LeJeune
Library Holdings: Bk Vols 18,841
MCBURNEY MEMORIAL, 301 S Sarah St, Welsh, 70591. SAN 343-0863. Tel: 318-734-3262. FAX: 318-734-3262. *Mgr*, Deanna LeMaire
Library Holdings: Bk Vols 15,577
Bookmobiles: 1

P JENNINGS CARNEGIE PUBLIC LIBRARY,* 303 Cary Ave, 70546-5223. SAN 306-4654. Tel: 318-821-5517.
Founded 1885. Pop 12,500; Circ 39,157
Library Holdings: Bk Vols 50,000; Per Subs 60

JONESBORO

P JACKSON PARISH LIBRARY,* 614 S Polk, 71251-3442. SAN 306-4662. Tel: 318-259-5697. FAX: 318-259-8984. E-Mail: jklibl@engr.latech.edu. Web Site: www.jklibl.jackson.lib.la.us. *Dir*, Robin Toms; Staff 8 (MLS 2, Non-MLS 6)
Founded 1960. Pop 15,400; Circ 141,452
Library Holdings: Bk Vols 62,322; Per Subs 156
Subject Interests: Local history, Louisiana
Special Collections: Jennifer Blake Coll
Mem of Trail Blazer Libr Syst

KENNER

S SOUTHERN FOREST PRODUCTS ASSOCIATION LIBRARY, PO Box 641700, 70064-1700. SAN 306-4670. Tel: 504-443-4464. FAX: 504-443-6612. E-Mail: mail@sfpa.org. Web Site: www.sfpa.org, www.southernpine.com. *Librn*, Linda Patch
Founded 1915
Special Collections: Historical Data, micro

LAFAYETTE

P BAYOULAND LIBRARY SYSTEM, 301 W Congress, 70501. SAN 306-4689. Tel: 318-261-5793. FAX: 318-261-5782. E-Mail: bayouland1@aol.com. *Dir*, Beverly E Laughlin; Staff 1 (MLS 1)

Founded 1974. Pop 714,041; Circ 30,742
Jan 1999-Dec 1999 Income $4,500
Publications: Bayouland 16mm Films; Bayouland Film Catalogue; Bayouland Genealogical Resources; Bayouland Large Print Holdings; Bayouland Union List of Periodicals; Newsletter
Member Libraries: Acadia Parish Library; Allen Parish Libraries; Jefferson Davis Parish Library; Lafayette Public Library; Opelousas-Eunice Public Library; Saint Martin Parish Library; Saint Mary Parish Library; University Of Louisiana at Lafayette; Vermilion Parish Library

S DIOCESE OF LAFAYETTE ARCHIVES, Immaculata Library, 1408 Carmel Ave, 70501-5298. SAN 370-8454. Tel: 337-261-5639, 337-261-5667. FAX: 337-261-5635. Web Site: www.dol.louisiana.org. *Archivist*, Barbara DeJean; E-Mail: barbarac@dol.louisiana.org; *AV*, Lynne Broussard
Founded 1980
Library Holdings: Bk Titles 1,000; Per Subs 40
Subject Interests: Ecumenism, Sexuality
Friends of the Library Group

S LAFAYETTE NATURAL HISTORY MUSEUM, Research Library, 637 Girard Park Dr, 70503. SAN 374-941X. Tel: 318-291-5548. FAX: 318-291-5464. *Librn*, Heather C Kelly
Library Holdings: Bk Vols 2,900; Per Subs 37

P LAFAYETTE PUBLIC LIBRARY,* 301 W Congress, PO Box 3427, 70501. SAN 306-4700. Tel: 337-261-5775. Interlibrary Loan Service Tel: 337-261-5757. FAX: 337-261-5782. *Dir*, Gail Smith; *Asst Dir*, Sona J Dombourian; *Ch Servs*, Katherine Mulloy; *YA Servs*, Suzanne Pomerleau; *ILL*, Janice Cring; *Circ*, Teresa Elberson; *Exten Serv*, Elizabeth Blomquist; *Reader Servs, Ref*, Terry Roy; Staff 11 (MLS 11)
Founded 1946. Pop 172,193; Circ 1,136,371
Library Holdings: Bk Vols 308,595; Per Subs 622
Special Collections: Adult New Readers; Dolls; Genealogy; Jobs; Large Print; Louisiana
Mem of Bayouland Library System
Partic in SE Libr Network
Friends of the Library Group
Branches: 7
BROUSARD BRANCH, 100 W Main St, Brousard, 70518. SAN 377-7235. Tel: 337-837-3936. *Librn*, Cindy Shaw
BUTLER MEMORIAL, 309 Cora St, 70501. SAN 376-981X. Tel: 337-234-0363. *Mgr*, Julie Linton
Library Holdings: Bk Vols 12,000; Per Subs 10
CARENCRO BRANCH, 215 E Peters St, Carencro, 70520. SAN 376-9828. Tel: 337-896-3866. *Mgr*, Cel Boudreaux
Library Holdings: Bk Vols 12,000; Per Subs 10
DUSON BRANCH, 708 First St, Duson, 70529. SAN 376-9836. Tel: 337-873-3521. *Mgr*, Brenda LaVergne
Library Holdings: Bk Vols 12,000; Per Subs 10
MILTON BRANCH, Cedar Village Shopping Ctr, Hwy 92, Milton, 70558. (Mail add: PO Box 3427, Milton, 70502-3427), SAN 376-7353. Tel: 337-856-5261. *Mgr*, Henrietta Schilling
Library Holdings: Bk Vols 12,000; Per Subs 10
SCOTT BRANCH, 5808 W Cameron St Ste B, Scott, 70583. SAN 376-9844. Tel: 318-232-9321. *Mgr*, Rita Prejean
Library Holdings: Bk Vols 12,000; Per Subs 10
YOUNGSVILLE BRANCH, 300 Iberia St, Youngsville, 70592. SAN 376-9852. Tel: 337-856-9385. *Mgr*, Katy Martin
Library Holdings: Bk Vols 12,000; Per Subs 10

L ONEBANE, BERNARD, TORIAN, DIAZ, MCNAMARA & ABELL, Law Library, 102 Versailles Blvd, Ste 600, 70501. SAN 372-0837. Tel: 337-237-2660. FAX: 337-266-1232. Web Site: www.onebane.com. *Librn*, Peggy Drennan; E-Mail: drennanp@onebane.com
Library Holdings: Bk Vols 15,000; Per Subs 71

M OUR LADY OF LOURDES REGIONAL MEDICAL CENTER, Learning Resource Center,* 611 St Landry, PO Box 4027, 70502. SAN 374-8898. Tel: 318-289-2141. FAX: 318-289-2001. *Librn*, Annette Tremie
Library Holdings: Bk Titles 1,000; Per Subs 150

§C REMINGTON COLLEGE LIBRARY, 303 Rue Louis XIV, 70508. Tel: 337-983-7111. FAX: 337-983-7130. Web Site: www.remingtoncollege.com. *Librn*, Arleen Kern-Broderick; E-Mail: akern1234@aol.com
Library Holdings: Bk Vols 8,000; Per Subs 65

G UNITED STATES GEOLOGICAL SURVEY, (NWRC), National Wetlands Research Center, 700 Cajundome Blvd, 70506-3152. SAN 373-6237. Tel: 337-266-8692. Interlibrary Loan Service Tel: 337-266-8533. FAX: 337-266-8513. Web Site: www.nwrc.gov/library.html. *Coll Develop, Librn*, Judy Buys; E-Mail: judy_buys@usgs.gov; *ILL*, Linda Broussard; Tel: 337-266-8533; Staff 3 (MLS 1, Non-MLS 2)
Founded 1978
Oct 2000-Sep 2001 Mats Exp $38,660, Per/Ser (Incl. Access Fees) $23,000, Electronic Ref Mat (Incl. Access Fees) $15,660
Library Holdings: Bk Vols 11,500; Bk Titles 9,424; Per Subs 48
Subject Interests: Forestry, Global climate change, Wetland ecology
Special Collections: Archive of Center Publications; Field Identification Guides; Statistical Support
Publications: Databases at NWRC; Library Services; Publications List
Partic in Fedlink; LVIS; OCLC Online Computer Library Center, Inc
Circulation limited to NWRC staff & ULAL faculty & graduate students

M UNIVERSITY MEDICAL CENTER LIBRARY,* PO Box 69300, 70596-9300. SAN 306-4697. Tel: 318-261-6127. FAX: 318-261-6129. E-Mail: library@umc.lhca.state.la.us. Web Site: swlaheclibrary.com. *Librn*, Cheryl Smith; Staff 5 (MLS 3, Non-MLS 2)
Founded 1973
Library Holdings: Bk Vols 3,500; Bk Titles 2,178; Per Subs 180
Partic in S Cent Regional Med Libr Program

C UNIVERSITY OF LOUISIANA AT LAFAYETTE, (Formerly University Of Southwestern Louisiana), Edith Garland Dupre Library, 302 E St Mary Blvd, 70503. (Mail add: PO Box 40199, 70504-0199), SAN 343-0898. Tel: 318-482-6396. Circulation Tel: 337-482-6025. Reference Tel: 337-482-6030. FAX: 337-482-6399. Web Site: www.louisiana.edu/InfoTech/Library/. *Dir Libr Serv*, Dr Charles W Triche, III; E-Mail: cwt7840@louisana.edu; *Assoc Dir*, Barbara J Flynn; Tel: 337-482-6041, Fax: 337-483-5841, E-Mail: bjf1855@louisiana.edu; *Tech Servs*, Beate N Kukainis; Tel: 337-482-6033, E-Mail: bnk8912@louisiana.edu; *Cat*, Carol Casey; Tel: 337-482-6197, Fax: 337-482-5841; *Archivist*, Dr I Bruce Turner; Tel: 337-482-5702, E-Mail: bturner@louisiana.edu; *ILL*, Deborah Lazare Johnson; Tel: 337-482-6036, Fax: 337-482-1176, E-Mail: djohnson@louisiana.edu; *Head Ref*, Susan M Richard; Tel: 337-482-6030, Fax: 337-482-5841, E-Mail: smr@louisiana.edu; Staff 48 (MLS 17, Non-MLS 31)
Founded 1901. Enrl 16,000; Highest Degree: Doctorate
Jul 1999-Jun 2000 Income State $2,900,000. Mats Exp $1,774,106, Books $60,463, Per/Ser (Incl. Access Fees) $1,131,120, Presv $37,579, Micro $33,304, AV Equip $11,134, Manuscripts & Archives $506, Electronic Ref Mat (Incl. Access Fees) $500,000. Sal $1,669,034
Library Holdings: Bk Vols 873,173; Bk Titles 425,034; Per Subs 4,965
Special Collections: Acadian & Creole Folklore; Louisiana History (Jefferson Caffery Louisiana Room); Regional Photographic Coll
Database Vendor: CARL, Dialog, Ebsco - EbscoHost, GaleNet, IAC - Info Trac, Innovative Interfaces INN - View, Lexis-Nexis, OCLC - First Search, ProQuest, Silverplatter Information Inc., Wilson - Wilson Web
Publications: Bayou State Periodical Index (Index to periodicals)
Function: Research library
Mem of Bayouland Library System
Partic in LALINC; Solinet
Open to public
Friends of the Library Group

LAKE CHARLES

P CALCASIEU PARISH PUBLIC LIBRARY SYSTEM, 301 W Claude St, 70605-3457. SAN 306-4727. Tel: 337-475-8798. FAX: 337-475-8806. Web Site: www.calcasieu.lib.la.us. *Dir*, Paige LeBeau; E-Mail: paige@calcasieu.lib.la.us; *Mgr*, Cheryl Woodmansee; *Publ Servs*, Pam Edwards; E-Mail: pam@calcasieu.lib.la.us; *Info Res*, Ursula Jones; E-Mail: ursula@calcasieu.lib.la.us; *Coll Develop, Computer Services*, Loretta Gharst; Tel: 337-437-3484, Fax: 337-437-3652, E-Mail: lgharst@calcasieu.lib.la.us; Staff 148 (MLS 10, Non-MLS 138)
Founded 1944. Pop 181,799
Jan 1999-Dec 1999 Income (Main Library and Branch Library) $3,816,000, State $170,777, Locally Generated Income $3,380,273, Other $264,950. Mats Exp $510,192, Books $308,954, Per/Ser (Incl. Access Fees) $43,087, Micro $14,976, AV Equip $133,554, Other Print Mats $3,380, Electronic Ref Mat (Incl. Access Fees) $6,241. Sal $2,251,088
Library Holdings: Bk Vols 388,927; Per Subs 950
Subject Interests: Genealogy
Publications: Check Out (Newsletter); Staff Reporter (Newsletter)
Friends of the Library Group
Branches: 14
BELL CITY BRANCH, 7085 Hwy 14, Bell City, 70630. SAN 374-6895. Tel: 337-622-3606. FAX: 337-622-3606. *Branch Mgr*, Angel Trahan
Library Holdings: Bk Vols 3,900
CARNEGIE MEMORIAL, 411 Pujo St, 70601-4254. Tel: 337-437-3480. FAX: 337-437-4198. E-Mail: carn@calcasieu.lib.la.us. Web Site: www.calcasieu.lib.la.us. *Branch Mgr*, Kathleen Dahm
Library Holdings: Bk Vols 15,000; Per Subs 21; Bks on Deafness & Sign Lang 10
Automation Activity & Vendor Info: (Acquisitions) SIRSI; (Cataloging) SIRSI; (Circulation) SIRSI; (OPAC) SIRSI; (Serials) SIRSI
CENTRAL LIBRARY, 301 W Claude St, 70605. Tel: 337-475-8792. FAX: 337-475-8797. *Branch Mgr*, Catherine Earles
Library Holdings: Bk Vols 125,000
Friends of the Library Group
DEQUINCY BRANCH, 102 W Harrison St, DeQuincy, 70633. SAN 374-6925. Tel: 337-786-4213. FAX: 337-786-4213. *Branch Mgr*, Janet Jordy
Library Holdings: Bk Vols 16,236
EPPS MEMORIAL, 1324 N Simmons St, 70601. SAN 374-6933. Tel: 337-433-0033. FAX: 337-433-0033. *Branch Mgr*, Betty Toussand

Library Holdings: Bk Vols 15,000
FONTENOT MEMORIAL, 1402 Center St, Vinton, 70668. SAN 374-6941. Tel: 337-589-3336. FAX: 337-589-3336. *Branch Mgr*, Theresa Watson
Library Holdings: Bk Vols 12,500
Friends of the Library Group
HAYES BRANCH, 7709 Perier St, PO Box 97, Hayes, 70646. SAN 374-695X. Tel: 337-622-3605. FAX: 337-622-3605. *Branch Mgr*, Angel Trahan
Library Holdings: Bk Vols 3,900
IOWA BRANCH, 107 First St, PO Box 1150, Iowa, 70647. SAN 374-6968. Tel: 337-582-3597. FAX: 337-582-3597. *Branch Mgr*, Margaret Schmidt
Library Holdings: Bk Vols 12,786
MAPLEWOOD, 91 Center Circle, Sulphur, 70663. SAN 374-6976. Tel: 337-625-5692. FAX: 337-625-5692. *Branch Mgr*, Kaye Thorne
Library Holdings: Bk Vols 12,500
MOSS BLUFF, 261 Parish Rd, 70611. SAN 374-6909. Tel: 337-855-3055. FAX: 337-855-1827. *Branch Mgr*, Judy Davidson; E-Mail: judy@calcasieu.lib.la.us
Circ 99,583
Library Holdings: Bk Vols 34,535
Friends of the Library Group
SOUTHWEST LOUISIANA GENEALOGICAL & HISTORICAL LIBRARY, 411 Pujo St, 70601-4254. SAN 374-700X. Tel: 337-437-3490. FAX: 337-437-4198. *Branch Mgr*, Shirley Burwell
Library Holdings: Bk Vols 5,000
STARKS BRANCH, 113 S Hwy 109, PO Box 99, Starks, 70661. SAN 374-6992. Tel: 337-743-6560. FAX: 337-743-6560. *Branch Mgr*, Betty West
Library Holdings: Bk Vols 12,500
Friends of the Library Group
SULPHUR REGIONAL, 1160 Cypress St, Sulphur, 70663. SAN 373-7365. Tel: 337-527-7200. FAX: 337-527-8987. *Branch Mgr*, Kelly Kingrey
Library Holdings: Bk Vols 94,500
Friends of the Library Group
WESTLAKE BRANCH, 937 Mulberry St, Westlake, 70669. SAN 374-7018. Tel: 337-437-3571. FAX: 337-437-3571. *Branch Mgr*, Linda Todd
Library Holdings: Bk Vols 15,790

M LAKE CHARLES MEMORIAL HOSPITAL, Walter O Moss Medical Library, 1701 Oak Park Blvd, 70601-3713. SAN 370-5161. Tel: 337-494-3127. FAX: 337-494-3231. *Dir*, Lezlie Fletcher; E-Mail: lfletcher@lcmh.com
Founded 1980
Library Holdings: Bk Vols 780; Per Subs 125
Restriction: Not open to public

C MCNEESE STATE UNIVERSITY, Lether E Frazar Memorial Library, PO Box 91445, 70609. SAN 306-4735. Tel: 337-475-5716. Interlibrary Loan Service Tel: 337-475-5726. Circulation Tel: 337-475-5723. Reference Tel: 337-475-5725. FAX: 337-475-5719; 337-475-5727. Web Site: www.library.mcneese.edu. *Dir*, Nancy L Khoury; E-Mail: nkhoury@mail.mcneese.edu; *Syst Coordr*, Joseph McNeill; *ILL*, Adrienne Detwiler; *Doc*, Brantley Cagle; *Circ*, Jeffrey Coghill; *Bibliog Instr*, Kenneth Awagain; *Spec Coll*, Kathie Bordelon; *Coll Develop*, Alan Harms; Staff 27 (MLS 14, Non-MLS 13)
Founded 1939. Enrl 7,632; Fac 328; Highest Degree: Master
Jul 1999-Jun 2000 Income (Main Library Only) $1,818,941. Sal $1,028,193
Library Holdings: Bk Vols 270,577; Per Subs 1,679
Subject Interests: Education
Special Collections: 20th Century American First Editions; Fore-edge Paintings; Lake Charles, Southwestern Louisiana Archives
Database Vendor: Ebsco - EbscoHost
Publications: Friends of the Library (newsletter)
Mem of La Online Univ Info Syst
Partic in La Libr Network; SE Libr Network
Friends of the Library Group
Departmental Libraries:
CURRICULUM MATERIALS CENTER, PO Box 91380, 70609. SAN 322-6271. Tel: 318-475-5420. Web Site: library.mcneese.edu/materials/index.htm. *Librn*, Dr Linda LeBert; Fax: 337-475-5398, E-Mail: llebert@mail.mcneese.edu
Founded 1970. Enrl 7,632; Fac 310
Jul 2000-Jun 2001 Mats Exp Books $4,089. Sal $56,948
Library Holdings: Bk Vols 8,500; Bk Titles 7,112
Special Collections: Curriculum Materials; Library Science
Automation Activity & Vendor Info: (Acquisitions) NOTIS; (Cataloging) NOTIS; (Circulation) NOTIS; (Course Reserve) NOTIS; (ILL) NOTIS; (Media Booking) NOTIS; (OPAC) NOTIS; (Serials) NOTIS
Restriction: Open to student, faculty & staff
Partic in La Libr Network
Friends of the Library Group
MUSIC LEARNING CENTER, PO Box 92175, 70609. SAN 322-628X. Tel: 318-475-5027. *Librn*, Mary Sherwood; E-Mail: sherwood@mail.mcneese.edu; Staff 1 (MLS 1)
Special Collections: American Women Composers Coll; Frederick Tooley Opera Coll; Norma & Truman Stacy Record Coll

LAKE PROVIDENCE

P EAST CARROLL PARISH LIBRARY, 109 Sparrow St, 71254-2645. SAN 306-4751. Tel: 318-559-2615. FAX: 318-559-4635. E-Mail: t1ec@pelican.state.lib.la.us. *Chief Librn*, Renee Whatley; Staff 4 (MLS 1, Non-MLS 3)
Founded 1954. Pop 9,709; Circ 43,155
Jan 1999-Dec 1999 Income $240,358, State $55,325, County $167,533, Other $17,500. Mats Exp $27,088, Per/Ser (Incl. Access Fees) $3,135, AV Equip $2,183, AV Equip $21,770. Sal $66,958 (Prof $28,000)
Library Holdings: Bk Vols 30,184; Per Subs 105
Subject Interests: Black history, History, Large type print, Louisiana
Special Collections: Caldecott; Coretta S King; Newbery
Mem of Trail Blazer Libr Syst
Friends of the Library Group
Bookmobiles: 1

LAPLACE

P SAINT JOHN THE BAPTIST PARISH LIBRARY, 1334 W Airline Hwy, 70068-3797. SAN 343-0952. Tel: 504-652-6857. FAX: 504-652-2144. *Dir*, Randy A De Soto; E-Mail: rdesoto@stjohn.lib.la.us; *Asst Librn, Ref*, Kay D McKey; E-Mail: kdmckey@yahoo.com; *Circ*, Sharon Manuel; Staff 39 (MLS 5, Non-MLS 34)
Founded 1966. Pop 42,000
Jan 2000-Dec 2000 Income (Main Library and Branch Library) $1,612,791, State $126,411, County $1,420,905, Locally Generated Income $65,475. Mats Exp $152,525, Books $136,389, Per/Ser (Incl. Access Fees) $15,956, Micro $180. Sal $757,799 (Prof $188,957)
Library Holdings: Bk Vols 147,405; Per Subs 174
Subject Interests: Genealogy, Local history, Louisiana
Special Collections: Parish hist, photos
Database Vendor: Innovative Interfaces INN - View
Delivery to homebound
Branches: 3
FRAZEE HARRIS MEMORIAL BRANCH, PO Box 870, Garyville, 70051. SAN 328-8889. Tel: 504-535-6868. *In Charge*, Karen Tassin
Library Holdings: Bk Vols 6,932
RESERVE BRANCH, 170 W Tenth St, Reserve, 70084. SAN 329-6202. Tel: 504-536-4107. *In Charge*, Tammy Houston
Library Holdings: Bk Vols 22,951
ROLAND BORNE SR MEMORIAL LIBRARY, PO Box 166, Edgard, 70049. SAN 343-0987. Tel: 504-497-3453. *In Charge*, Vergie Johnson
Library Holdings: Bk Vols 10,635
Bookmobiles: 1

LEESVILLE

§S LEESVILLE DEVELOPMENTAL CENTER LIBRARY, PO Box 131, 71446. Tel: 337-239-2687, Ext 253. FAX: 337-238-7011. *In Charge*, Glenn Vincent; E-Mail: lgvincent@dhh.state.la.us
Library Holdings: Bk Vols 200; Per Subs 15
Restriction: Staff use only

P VERNON PARISH LIBRARY, 1401 Nolan Trace, 71446. SAN 343-1010. Tel: 337-239-2027. Interlibrary Loan Service Tel: 337-239-2027. Toll Free Tel: 800-737-2231. FAX: 337-238-0666. E-Mail: leesville.wlvr@pelican.state.lib.la.us, vernonpl@alpha.nsula.edu. *Librn*, Howard L Coy, Jr; E-Mail: hcoy@pelican.state.lib.la.us
Founded 1956. Pop 58,000; Circ 240,401
Library Holdings: Bk Titles 105,969
Subject Interests: Civil War, Genealogy, Louisiana, World War II
Automation Activity & Vendor Info: (Cataloging) Gaylord; (Circulation) Gaylord
Database Vendor: Ebsco - EbscoHost
Branches: 2
PAUL LAWRENCE DUNBAR BRANCH, 1401 N 1003 N Gladys, 71446. (Mail add: 1401 Nolan Trace, 71446), SAN 343-1045. Tel: 337-239-7037.
PITKIN BRANCH, PO Box 159, Pitkin, 70656. SAN 370-1190. Tel: 318-358-3294. FAX: 318-358-3294.
Friends of the Library Group
Bookmobiles: 1

LIVINGSTON

P LIVINGSTON PARISH LIBRARY,* 13986 Florida Blvd, PO Drawer 397, 70754-0397. SAN 343-107X. Tel: 225-686-2436. FAX: 225-686-3888. Web Site: www.192.168.2.12. *Dir*, Allen Cunningham; E-Mail: acunning@pelican.state.lib.la.us; *Asst Dir*, Alex Kropog; *Librn*, Wendy Bobo; *Librn*, Wanda Shank; *Librn*, Iris Stilley; *Librn*, Ann Wheat; Staff 6 (MLS 2, Non-MLS 4)
Founded 1946. Pop 87,311; Circ 281,195
Jan 1998-Dec 1998 Income (Main Library and Branch Library) $1,155,700. Mats Exp $689,200, Books $120,000. Sal $266,000 (Prof $60,847)
Library Holdings: Bk Titles 142,767; Per Subs 434

Automation Activity & Vendor Info: (Cataloging) Gaylord; (Circulation) Gaylord; (OPAC) Gaylord
Publications: Free State
Partic in LOIS
Friends of the Library Group
Branches: 7
ALBANY BRANCH, 30051 W School St, PO Box 391, Albany, 70711. SAN 343-110X. Tel: 225-567-1441. FAX: 225-567-1441. Web Site: www.192.168.2.1Z. *Librn*, Helen Holden; *Librn*, Harriet Pope
Circ 12,705
Library Holdings: Bk Vols 17,349
DENHAM SPRINGS-WALKER BRANCH, 8369 Florida Blvd, PO Box 1838, Denham Springs, 70727-1838. SAN 343-1134. Tel: 225-665-8118. FAX: 225-665-8118. E-Mail: denhamsprings.c1lv@pelican.state.lib.la.us. *Librn*, Debbie Stewart; *Librn*, Carlotta Coates; *Librn*, Eunice Allen
Circ 136,261
Library Holdings: Bk Vols 36,893
Friends of the Library Group
FRENCH SETTLEMENT BRANCH, 16015 Hwy 16, French Settlement, 70733. (Mail add: General Delivery, French Settlement, 70733), SAN 343-1169. Tel: 225-698-3015. FAX: 225-698-3015. E-Mail: frenchsettlement.c1lv@pelican.state.lib.la.us. *Librn*, Atrice Gore
Circ 13,982
Library Holdings: Bk Vols 8,001
KILLIAN, 28284 Hwy 22, PO Box 143A, Springfield, 70462. SAN 343-1223. Tel: 225-695-3537. FAX: 225-695-3537. E-Mail: killian.c1lv@pelican.state.lib.la.us. *Librn*, June Owens
Circ 3,671
Library Holdings: Bk Vols 3,513
MAUREPAS BRANCH, 23923 Hwy 22, Maurepas, 70449. (Mail add: 22921 Koto Rd, Maurepas, 70449), SAN 343-1282. Tel: 504-695-3771. *Librn*, Lori Poche
Circ 3,042
Library Holdings: Bk Vols 8,523
SPRINGFIELD BRANCH, 31626 Hwy 22, Springfield, 70462. SAN 343-1312. Tel: 225-294-2006. FAX: 225-294-2006. E-Mail: springfield@c1lv.pelican.state.lib.la.us. *Librn*, Etna Ratcliff
Circ 5,140
Library Holdings: Bk Vols 7,622
WATSON BRANCH, 34917 Hwy 16, PO Box 149, Watson, 70786. SAN 343-1371. Tel: 225-664-3963. FAX: 225-664-3963. E-Mail: watson.c1lv@pelican.state.lib.la.us. *Librn*, Joan Truax; *Librn*, Mary D Sanders Graves; *Librn*, Vicki Brashier
Circ 36,848
Library Holdings: Bk Vols 21,688

LULING

P SAINT CHARLES PARISH LIBRARY,* 105 Lakewood Dr, PO Box 949, 70070. SAN 343-1401. Tel: 504-785-8471. *Dir*, Mary des Bordes; Tel: 594-785-8464, Fax: 505-785-8499, E-Mail: mdesbord@stcharles.lib.la.us; *Assoc Dir*, Margaret Wilhite; *Ad Servs*, Julie Cancienne; *Ch Servs*, Sean George; Staff 5 (MLS 4, Non-MLS 1)
Founded 1955. Pop 48,000; Circ 325,000
Jan 1999-Dec 1999 Income (Main Library and Branch Library) $1,800,000, State $69,000, County $1,731,000. Mats Exp $263,000, Books $243,000, Per/Ser (Incl. Access Fees) $20,000. Sal $846,000 (Prof $146,000)
Library Holdings: Bk Vols 175,000; Per Subs 450
Subject Interests: History, Louisiana
Automation Activity & Vendor Info: (Circulation) epixtech, inc.; (OPAC) epixtech, inc.
Partic in La Libr Network; Lasernet
Friends of the Library Group
Branches: 3
EAST REGIONAL, 100 River Oaks Dr, Destrehan, 70047. SAN 343-1436. Tel: 504-764-2366. *Librn*, Sean George
Library Holdings: Bk Vols 45,000
HAHNVILLE BRANCH, Hahnville, 70057. SAN 343-1460. Tel: 504-783-2341. *Asst Librn*, Laurie Goodell
Library Holdings: Bk Vols 16,000
NORCO BRANCH, Norco, 70079. SAN 343-1495. Tel: 504-764-6581. *Asst Librn*, Phyllis Smith
Library Holdings: Bk Vols 11,958
Bookmobiles: 1

LUTCHER

P ST JAMES PARISH LIBRARY, 1879 W Main St, 70071-9704. SAN 343-1525. Tel: 225-869-3618. FAX: 225-869-8435. *Dir*, Julie W Champagne; Tel: 225-869-9869, E-Mail: sjpl1@pelican.state.lib.la.us; *Ref*, Sarah Byrd; Staff 12 (MLS 2, Non-MLS 10)
Founded 1966. Pop 22,000; Circ 85,000
2000-2000 Mats Exp $71,500, Books $65,000, Per/Ser (Incl. Access Fees) $6,000, Micro $500. Sal $300,000 (Prof $60,000)
Library Holdings: Bk Vols 66,656; Per Subs 155
Special Collections: Louisiana Coll; St James File (parish hist)
Automation Activity & Vendor Info: (Acquisitions) epixtech, inc.; (Cataloging) epixtech, inc.; (Circulation) epixtech, inc.; (Course Reserve) epixtech, inc.; (ILL) epixtech, inc.; (Media Booking) epixtech, inc.; (OPAC) epixtech, inc.; (Serials) epixtech, inc.
Database Vendor: GaleNet, IAC - SearchBank, ProQuest
Branches: 1
WEST, PO Box 190, Vacherie, 70090. SAN 343-155X. Tel: 225-265-6003. *Mgr*, Margaret Simon
Special Collections: Parish History (St James Parish File), bks, newspapers, microflm, clippings
Bookmobiles: 1

MANDEVILLE

M SOUTHEAST LOUISIANA HOSPITAL, Professional Library,* PO Box 3850, 70448. SAN 324-5535. Tel: 504-626-6596. FAX: 504-626-6424. *Librn*, Jan Landrum; Staff 2 (MLS 1, Non-MLS 1)
Library Holdings: Bk Titles 1,000; Per Subs 80
Subject Interests: Mental health
Restriction: Staff use only

MANSFIELD

P DESOTO PARISH LIBRARY, 109 Crosby St, 71052. SAN 321-7485. Tel: 318-872-6100. FAX: 318-872-6120. E-Mail: dpl1@pelican.state.lib.la.us. Web Site: wksta1.desoto.lib.la.us/desoto.htm. *Librn*, Wanda A Berry; E-Mail: wberry@pelican.state.lib.la.us; *Asst Dir*, Fran Morris; E-Mail: fmorris@pelican.state.lib.la.us; *Mgr*, Doris Ross; E-Mail: dross@pelican.state.lib.la.us; *Acq*, Tarsha Christopher; E-Mail: tchristo@pelican.state.lib.la.us; *Ch Servs*, Karla Springer; *Tech Servs*, Linda Foreman; E-Mail: lforeman@pelican.state.lib.la.us; Staff 8 (MLS 2, Non-MLS 6)
Founded 1941. Pop 25,344; Circ 155,168
Jan 1999-Dec 1999 Income (Main Library and Branch Library) $708,529, State $42,180, County $632,806, Locally Generated Income $33,543. Mats Exp $699,215, Books $84,137, Per/Ser (Incl. Access Fees) $7,062. Sal $336,113 (Prof $73,929)
Library Holdings: Bk Vols 89,990; Bk Titles 73,390; Per Subs 116
Subject Interests: Civil War, World War I, World War II
Special Collections: Louisiana History
Automation Activity & Vendor Info: (Acquisitions) epixtech, inc.; (Cataloging) epixtech, inc.; (Circulation) epixtech, inc.; (OPAC) epixtech, inc.
Publications: Informational Brochure
Friends of the Library Group
Branches: 3
LOGANSPORT BRANCH, PO Box 970, Logansport, 71049. SAN 321-7493. Tel: 318-697-2311. FAX: 318-697-4081. *Librn*, Joni Smith; E-Mail: jsmith@pelican.state.lib.la.us; Staff 4 (Non-MLS 4)
Library Holdings: Bk Vols 20,900
Subject Interests: Local history
PELICAN BRANCH, 139 Jackson Ave, Pelican, 71063. SAN 324-2501. Tel: 318-755-2353. FAX: 318-755-2031. *Librn*, Sarah Crump; E-Mail: sabraham@pelican.state.lib.la.us; *Admin Assoc*, Barbara Jones; Staff 3 (Non-MLS 3)
Library Holdings: Bk Vols 10,550
Friends of the Library Group
STONEWALL BRANCH, 1460 Hwy 171, Stonewall, 71078. SAN 321-7507. Tel: 318-925-9191. FAX: 318-925-3392. *Librn*, Mildred Osborne; E-Mail: mosborne@pelican.state.lib.la.us; Staff 3 (Non-MLS 3)
Library Holdings: Bk Vols 11,900
Friends of the Library Group

MANY

P SABINE PARISH LIBRARY,* 705 Main, 71449-3199. SAN 343-1649. Tel: 318-256-4150. FAX: 318-256-4154. E-Mail: g1sb@pelican.state.lib.la.us. *Librn*, Rebecca Morris
Founded 1933. Pop 22,646; Circ 124,419
Library Holdings: Bk Vols 79,378; Per Subs 249
Special Collections: Sabine Parish History Coll
Mem of Green Gold Library System
Partic in SOQUIJ
Branches: 7
CONVERSE BRANCH, PO Box 69, Converse, 71419. SAN 343-1673. Tel: 318-567-3121. *Asst Librn*, Jerrie Walker
Library Holdings: Bk Vols 4,152
FISHER BRANCH, PO Box 134, Fisher, 71426. SAN 343-1703. Tel: 318-256-4156. *Asst Librn*, Mary Simmons
Library Holdings: Bk Vols 2,934
FLORIEN BRANCH, PO Box 249, Florien, 71429. SAN 328-7351. Tel: 318-586-4553. *Asst Librn*, Joni McNeely
Library Holdings: Bk Vols 2,422
OAK GROVE, 1274 Boliver Rd, Converse, 71419. SAN 343-1827. *Asst Librn*, Pauline Strickland

Library Holdings: Bk Vols 2,730
PLEASANT HILL BRANCH, PO Box 277, Pleasant Hill, 71065. SAN 343-1851. Tel: 318-796-2595. E-Mail: pleasanthill.glsb@pelican.state.lib.la.us. *Asst Librn*, Lena Craig
Library Holdings: Bk Vols 2,979
TOLEDO BRANCH, 12224 Texas Hwy, Mang, 71449. SAN 328-7378. Tel: 318-256-4152. *Asst Librn*, Betty Fields
Library Holdings: Bk Vols 2,550
ZWOLLE BRANCH, PO Box 536, Zwolle, 71486. SAN 343-1886. Tel: 318-645-6955. *Asst Librn*, Erma Jean Martinez
Library Holdings: Bk Vols 6,180

MARKSVILLE

P AVOYELLES PARISH LIBRARY,* 104 N Washington St, 71351-2496. SAN 343-1916. Tel: 318-253-7559. Web Site: www.avoyelles.lib.la.us. *Dir*, Theresa Thevenote; E-Mail: ttheveno@pelican.state.lib.la.us; *Assoc Librn*, Susan Guidry; E-Mail: h1av@pelican.state.lib.la.us
Founded 1949. Pop 40,801; Circ 95,608
Jan 1999-Dec 1999 Income (Main Library and Branch Library) $514,630, State $17,642, Federal $1,415, County $474,508, Locally Generated Income $21,065. Mats Exp $52,008, Books $39,767, Per/Ser (Incl. Access Fees) $6,426, AV Equip $5,815. Sal $185,291 (Prof $32,600)
Library Holdings: Bk Vols 78,200; Per Subs 100
Special Collections: Louisiana Room
Automation Activity & Vendor Info: (Cataloging) Gaylord
Database Vendor: GaleNet, IAC - Info Trac, ProQuest
Partic in La Libr Network
Friends of the Library Group
Branches: 7
BUNKIE BRANCH, 107 W Oak St, PO Box 630, Bunkie, 71322. SAN 343-1940. Tel: 318-346-6122.
Library Holdings: Bk Vols 7,334
COTTONPORT BRANCH, 229 Cottonport Ave, Cottonport, 71327. SAN 343-1975. Tel: 318-876-3411.
Library Holdings: Bk Vols 7,008
MARKSVILLE - HEADQUARTERS, 104 N Washington St, 71351. SAN 343-2068. Tel: 318-253-7559. *Dir*, Theresa Thevenote
Library Holdings: Bk Vols 46,518
MOREAUVILLE BRANCH, Community Ctr, Tassin St, PO Box 130, Moreauville, 71355. SAN 343-2092. Tel: 318-985-2767.
Library Holdings: Bk Vols 4,441
OUTREACH, 2111 Cleco Rd, Mansura, 71350. (Mail add: PO Box 448, Mansura, 71350), Tel: 318-964-2118. FAX: 318-964-2118, 318-964-5701. Web Site: www.avoyelles.lib.la.us. *Branch Mgr*, Karen Jisclair
Library Holdings: Bk Vols 1,000; Per Subs 20
Traveling Branch, open Fri only
PLAUCHEVILLE BRANCH, Town Hall, Gin St, PO Box 27, Plaucheville, 71362. SAN 343-2122.
Library Holdings: Bk Vols 4,033
SIMMESPORT BRANCH, Main St, PO Box 155, Simmesport, 71369. SAN 343-2157. Tel: 318-941-2822.
Library Holdings: Bk Vols 5,840
Friends of the Library Group

METAIRIE

P JEFFERSON PARISH LIBRARY DEPARTMENT, (EBR), East Bank Regional, 4747 W Napoleon Ave, 70001-2310. SAN 343-2181. Tel: 504-838-1100. FAX: 504-849-8834. *Dir*, Joan S Adams; *Asst Dir*, Anne O'Steen; *Br Coordr*, Verdie Richburg; *Ad Servs, YA Servs*, Jamie Elston; *AV*, Chris Stuckwish; *Cat*, Jeanne Gillmore; *Ch Servs*, Marci Saucier; *Circ*, Marylyn Haddican; *Coll Develop*, Thomas Huston
Founded 1949. Pop 477,213
1998-1999 Income (Main Library and Branch Library) $10,224,477. Mats Exp $720,500, Books $540,000, Per/Ser (Incl. Access Fees) $140,000, Micro $40,500. Sal $7,082,730
Library Holdings: Bk Titles 327,621; Per Subs 3,340
Subject Interests: Louisiana
Special Collections: Foreign Languages
Publications: List of government officials; Newsletter (quarterly)
Special Services for the Deaf - Books on deafness & sign language; Captioned film depository
Friends of the Library Group
Branches: 15
BELLE TERRE, 5550 Belle Terre Rd, Marrero, 70072. SAN 343-219X. Tel: 504-349-5910. FAX: 504-349-5913.
Subject Interests: Genealogy
EAST BANK REGIONAL, 4747 W Napoleon Ave, 70010-7490. (Mail add: PO Box 7490, 70010-7490), Tel: 504-838-1190. *Librn*, Mario Dipietrantonio
Subject Interests: Genealogy
Friends of the Library Group
GRAND ISLE BRANCH, PO Box 827, Grand Isle, 70358. SAN 343-2211. Tel: 504-787-3450. FAX: 504-787-2715.
GRETNA BRANCH, 102 Willow Dr, Gretna, 70053. SAN 343-2246. Tel: 504-364-2716. FAX: 504-364-2710. *Librn*, Lisa Ciravolo
HARAHAN BRANCH, 219 Soniat Ave, Harahan, 70123. SAN 343-2270. Tel: 504-736-8745. FAX: 504-736-8746. *Librn*, Suzanne Upshaw
LAFITTE BRANCH, Rte 1, Box 2, Lafitte, 70067. SAN 343-236X. Tel: 504-689-3354. FAX: 504-689-5097. *Librn*, Janice Favaloro
LAKESHORE, 1000 W Esplanade, 70005. SAN 376-9429. Tel: 504-838-4375. FAX: 504-838-4379. *Librn*, Janet Perry
LIVE OAK, 125 Acadia Dr, Waggaman, 70094. SAN 329-6644. Tel: 504-736-8475. FAX: 504-736-8476. *Librn*, Jovana Susic
NORTH KENNER, 630 W Esplanade Ave, Kenner, 70065. SAN 343-2335. Tel: 504-736-8730. FAX: 504-736-8737. *Branch Mgr*, Alice L Hubbard; *Librn*, Alice Luvvorn
Special Collections: Foreign Language Coll; New Readers Coll
Friends of the Library Group
OLD METAIRIE, 2350 Metairie Rd, 70001. SAN 343-2424. Tel: 504-838-4353. FAX: 504-838-1014. *Librn*, Mae Giaimo
ROSEDALE, 4036 Jefferson Hwy, Jefferson, 70121. SAN 329-3173. Tel: 504-838-4350. FAX: 504-838-1829. *Librn*, Claudia Smith
TERRYTOWN BRANCH, 680 Heritage Ave, Terrytown, 70056. SAN 343-2459. Tel: 504-364-2717. FAX: 504-364-2718.
WAGNER BRANCH, 6612 Kawanee Ave, 70003. SAN 343-2483. Tel: 504-838-1193. Web Site: www.jefferson.lib.la.us. *Librn*, Debra Laine; Staff 5 (MLS 1, Non-MLS 4)
Founded 1963
Friends of the Library Group
WEST BANK REGIONAL, 2751 Manhattan Blvd, Harvey, 70058. SAN 370-9493. Tel: 504-364-2660, 504-364-3726. FAX: 540-364-3723. *Librn*, Evalyn Cole
Subject Interests: Genealogy
Friends of the Library Group
WESTWEGO BRANCH, 635 Fourth St, Westwego, 70094. SAN 343-2513. Tel: 504-349-5912. FAX: 504-349-5921. *Librn*, Rania Melhem
Bookmobiles: 2. Vans - Outreach programs to nurseries, senior homes

MINDEN

P WEBSTER PARISH LIBRARY, 521 East & West St, 71055. SAN 343-2548. Tel: 318-371-3080. FAX: 318-371-3081. E-Mail: ehammont@pelican.state.lib.la.us. Web Site: www.webster.lib.la.us. *Coll Develop, Dir*, Eddie Hammontree; E-Mail: ehammont@pelican.state.lib.la.us; *Asst Dir*, Beverly Hammett; Staff 3 (MLS 3)
Founded 1929. Pop 41,989; Circ 103,895
Library Holdings: Bk Vols 67,756; Per Subs 258
Subject Interests: Art and architecture, Business and management, Religion, Technology
Special Collections: Louisiana Coll
Branches: 6
DOYLINE BRANCH, PO Box 8, Doyline, 71023. SAN 343-2637. Tel: 318-745-3800. FAX: 318-745-2170. *Branch Mgr*, Joyce Cook
Library Holdings: Bk Vols 6,578
DR JOHN PUGH MEMORIAL, PO Box 727, Cotton Valley, 71018. SAN 343-2572. Tel: 318-832-4290. FAX: 318-832-5335. *Branch Mgr*, Nancy Windham
Library Holdings: Bk Vols 7,252
HEFLIN BRANCH, PO Box 177, Heflin, 71039. SAN 343-2661. Tel: 318-371-1027. FAX: 318-382-9613. *Branch Mgr*, Ella Rodriguez
Library Holdings: Bk Vols 2,366
MACK MEMORIAL, 217 N Main, Springhill, 71075. SAN 343-2815. Tel: 318-539-4117. FAX: 318-539-3718. *Branch Mgr*, Evelyn Simmons
Library Holdings: Bk Vols 15,396
MINDEN MAIN, 521 East & West St, 71055. SAN 343-2726. Tel: 318-371-3080. FAX: 318-371-3081. *Branch Mgr*, Shelia Phenix
Library Holdings: Bk Vols 27,377
SAREPTA BRANCH, PO Box 127, Sarepta, 71071. SAN 343-2750. Tel: 318-847-4992. FAX: 318-847-4826. *Branch Mgr*, Renee Andrews
Library Holdings: Bk Vols 3,057

MONROE

M LSU HEALTH SCIENCES CENTER-MONROE, EA Conway Medical Center, 4864 Jackson St, 71201-7410. (Mail add: PO Box 1881, 71210-8005), SAN 306-4778. Tel: 318-330-7644. FAX: 318-330-7649. E-Mail: eac-library@lsuhsc.edu. Web Site: www.conway.lsuhsc.edu/library/libraryhome.htm. *Dir Libr Serv*, Lesley Arnott; Staff 2 (MLS 1, Non-MLS 1)
Library Holdings: Bk Vols 612; Per Subs 150
Subject Interests: Clinical medicine

P OUACHITA PARISH PUBLIC LIBRARY, 1800 Stubbs Ave, 71201. SAN 343-284X. Tel: 318-327-1490. FAX: 318-327-1373. E-Mail: help@ouaschita.lib.la.us. Web Site: www.ouachita.lib.la.us. *Dir*, Ben Brady; E-Mail: bbrady@ouachita.lib.la.us; *Asst Dir*, Shirley Montfort
Founded 1916. Pop 142,191; Circ 671,693
Jan 2000-Dec 2000 Income (Main Library and Branch Library) $4,232,602, State $323,229, Federal $50, County $3,528,000, Locally Generated Income $381,323. Mats Exp $1,240,330, Books $281,000, Per/Ser (Incl. Access Fees) $88,800, AV Equip $800,000, Other Print Mats $70,530. Sal

$1,671,000 (Prof $61,215)
Library Holdings: Bk Vols 261,631; Per Subs 584
Subject Interests: Louisiana
Special Collections: Genealogy, bks, microflm, microfiche, clippings, photog, original source mat
Automation Activity & Vendor Info: (Acquisitions) epixtech, inc.; (Cataloging) epixtech, inc.; (Circulation) epixtech, inc.; (Serials) epixtech, inc.
Mem of Trail Blazer Libr Syst
Open Mon-Thurs 9-9, Fri 9-6, Sat 9-5, Sun 2-5
Friends of the Library Group
Branches: 4
ANNA MEYER BRANCH, 1808 Hwy 165 S, 71202. SAN 343-2904. Tel: 318-327-1351. FAX: 318-329-4059. *Librn*, Terrie Wright
Library Holdings: Bk Vols 30,256
Friends of the Library Group
CARVER, 2941 Renwick, 71201. SAN 343-2874. Tel: 318-327-1477. FAX: 318-329-4061. *Librn*, Robert Tanzy
Library Holdings: Bk Vols 23,159
Friends of the Library Group
OUACHITA VALLEY, 601 McMillian Rd, West Monroe, 71291. SAN 343-2939. Tel: 318-327-1470. FAX: 318-327-1473. *Librn*, Dorothy Barker
Library Holdings: Bk Vols 58,781
Friends of the Library Group
WEST MONROE BRANCH, 315 Cypress, West Monroe, 71291. SAN 343-2963. Tel: 318-327-1365. FAX: 318-329-4062. *Librn*, Glynn Arant
Library Holdings: Bk Vols 40,292
Friends of the Library Group
Bookmobiles: 1

C UNIVERSITY OF LOUISIANA AT MONROE LIBRARY, 4100 Northeast Dr, 71209-0720. SAN 306-4794. Tel: 318-342-1071. Interlibrary Loan Service Tel: 318-342-1067. FAX: 318-342-1075. Web Site: www.ulm.edu/~dosmith/SANDELIN.HTM. *Dean*, Donald Smith; Tel: 318-342-1050, E-Mail: libdsmith@ulm.edu; *Assoc Dir*, Rebecca DiCarlo; Tel: 318-342-1076, E-Mail: libdicarlo@ulm.edu; *Syst Coordr*, Lynda Huggins; Tel: 318-342-1059, E-Mail: libhuggins@ulm.edu; *Govt Doc*, Martha Wooden; Tel: 318-342-1065, E-Mail: libwooden@ulm.edu; *Acq*, Emily Higdon; Tel: 318-342-1053, E-Mail: libhigdon@ulm.edu; *Cat*, Barbara Moore; Tel: 318-342-3051, E-Mail: libmoore@ulm.edu; *Ser*, Kathy Gallent; Tel: 318-342-1074, E-Mail: libgallent@ulm.edu; *Spec Coll*, Dr H Glenn Jordan; Tel: 318-342-1054, E-Mail: libjordan@ulm.edu; *Ref*, Dinah Williams; Tel: 318-342-1069, E-Mail: libwilliams@ulm.edu; *ILL*, Melinda Matthews; Tel: 318-342-1067, E-Mail: libmatthews@ulm.edu; Staff 11 (MLS 11)
Founded 1931. Highest Degree: Doctorate
Jul 1999-Jun 2000 Income Parent Institution $2,129,326. Mats Exp $871,400, Books $19,635, Per/Ser (Incl. Access Fees) $762,012, Presv $3,804, Micro $85,949. Sal $929,528
Library Holdings: Bk Vols 619,202; Per Subs 2,931
Subject Interests: Education, Family counseling, Gerontology, Health sciences, Marriage counseling, Pharmacy
Special Collections: Civil War (Gilhula Coll); Governor James Noe Papers; Griffin Photograph Coll; Regional History (Otto E Passman Papers)
Automation Activity & Vendor Info: (Acquisitions) NOTIS; (Cataloging) NOTIS; (Circulation) NOTIS; (Course Reserve) NOTIS; (OPAC) NOTIS; (Serials) NOTIS
Database Vendor: Dialog, epixtech, inc., GaleNet, IAC - Info Trac, IAC - SearchBank, Lexis-Nexis, OCLC - First Search, ProQuest, Silverplatter Information Inc., Wilson - Wilson Web
Partic in Amigos Library Services, Inc; BRS; Dialog Corporation; La Libr Network; LALINC; OCLC Online Computer Library Center, Inc
Friends of the Library Group
Departmental Libraries:
CENTER FOR BUSINESS & ECONOMIC RESEARCH LIBRARY, Admin Bldg 2-104, 700 University Ave, 71209-0101. SAN 327-4845. Tel: 318-342-1215. FAX: 318-342-1209. Web Site: cber.ulm.edu, leap.ulm.edu. *Dir*, Dr Jerry L Wall
Library Holdings: Bk Titles 1,000; Per Subs 100
Special Collections: Partial Federal Repository Census

MORGAN CITY

P MORGAN CITY PUBLIC LIBRARY,* 220 Everett St, PO Box 988, 70380-0988. SAN 306-4816. Tel: 504-380-4646. E-Mail: b1mc@pelican.state.lib.la.us. *Librn*, Malisa Mayon
Founded 1934. Pop 16,114; Circ 44,616
Library Holdings: Bk Vols 65,167; Per Subs 128

NAPOLEONVILLE

P ASSUMPTION PARISH LIBRARY,* 293 Napoleon Ave, 70390. SAN 306-4824. Tel: 504-369-7070. *Librn*, Mary Judice; Staff 16 (MLS 4, Non-MLS 12)
Founded 1968. Pop 24,328; Circ 68,845
Library Holdings: Bk Vols 58,000; Per Subs 400
Special Collections: Assumption Pioneer (1850-), micro; French Language Materials Coll (childrens & adult); Southern Louisiana Genealogy
Friends of the Library Group
Branches: 2
LABADIEVILLE BRANCH, 105 Cherry St, Labadieville, 70372. (Mail add: 293 Napoleon Ave, 70390), Tel: 504-526-7055. *Mgr*, Roslyn Rhodes
PIERRE PART BRANCH, 3103 Lee Dr, Pierre Part, 70339. (Mail add: PO Box 369, Pierre Part, 70339), Tel: 504-252-4220. *Mgr*, Roslyn Rhodes

NATCHITOCHES

P NATCHITOCHES PARISH LIBRARY, 431 Jefferson St, 71457-4699. SAN 343-2998. Tel: 318-357-3280. FAX: 318-357-7073. *Dir*, Bob Black; E-Mail: rblack@pelican.state.lib.la.us; *Asst Dir*, Ann Landon; Staff 9 (MLS 2, Non-MLS 7)
Founded 1939. Pop 38,000; Circ 150,890
1999-2000 Income $804,574, State $58,530, County $746,044. Mats Exp $84,000, Books $60,000, Per/Ser (Incl. Access Fees) $18,000, Micro $6,000. Sal $252,894 (Prof $70,000)
Library Holdings: Bk Vols 68,000; Per Subs 120
Subject Interests: Local history
Special Collections: Natchitoches Authors
Automation Activity & Vendor Info: (Cataloging) Gaylord; (Circulation) Gaylord; (OPAC) Gaylord
Friends of the Library Group

C NORTHWESTERN STATE UNIVERSITY OF LOUISIANA, Eugene P Watson Memorial Library, College Ave, 71497. SAN 343-3234. Tel: 318-357-4477. Interlibrary Loan Service Tel: 318-357-4409. Reference Tel: 318-357-4574. Toll Free Tel: 888-540-9657. FAX: 318-357-4470. Interlibrary Loan Service FAX: 318-357-3201. Web Site: www.nsula.edu/watson_library/index.html. *Dir*, Ada D Jarred; E-Mail: jarred@alpha.nsala.edu; *Head Ref*, Abbie V Landry; E-Mail: laudry@alpha.nsula.edu; *Tech Servs*, Martha V Henderson; Tel: 318-357-4463, E-Mail: henderson@alpha.nsula.edu; *ILL*, Fleming A Thomas; E-Mail: thomas@alpha.nsula.edu; *Govt Doc*, Gail S Kwak; E-Mail: kwak@alpha.nsala.edu; *Ser*, Charles Gaudin; Tel: 318-357-4406, E-Mail: charlesg@alpha.nsula.edu; *Archivist*, Mary Linn Wernet; Tel: 318-357-4585, E-Mail: wernet@alpha.nsula.edu. Subject Specialists: *Education*, Martha V Henderson; Staff 22 (MLS 10, Non-MLS 12)
Founded 1884. Enrl 8,572; Fac 317; Highest Degree: Master
Jul 1999-Jun 2000 Income $1,370,638, State $1,334,071, Locally Generated Income $36,567. Mats Exp $609,733, Books $242,600, Per/Ser (Incl. Access Fees) $253,244, Presv $17,000, Micro $31,889, AV Equip $10,000, Other Print Mats $28,784, Electronic Ref Mat (Incl. Access Fees) $25,000. Sal $779,479 (Prof $522,329)
Library Holdings: Bk Vols 330,145; Per Subs 1,749
Subject Interests: Business, Education, Nursing
Special Collections: Carl F Gauss (Dunnington Coll); Isthmian Canal, United States & Louisiana History (Owen Coll); Literature (Aswell Coll); Louisiana Folklore (Saucier Coll); Louisiana History & Folklore (Melrose Coll); Louisiana History (Egan, Safford, Harris & Cloutier Coll); Louisiana History, Indians & Botany (Dormon Coll); Mexican Revolution (Grass Coll); Poetry (Bancroft Coll)
Automation Activity & Vendor Info: (Acquisitions) NOTIS; (Cataloging) NOTIS; (Circulation) NOTIS; (ILL) NOTIS; (OPAC) NOTIS; (Serials) NOTIS
Database Vendor: GaleNet, IAC - Info Trac, Lexis-Nexis, ProQuest, Silverplatter Information Inc.
Publications: ExLibris (Newsletter); Index & Abstracts of Colonial Documents in the Eugene P Watson Memorial Library; Library handbook; User Guides
Partic in Amigos Library Services, Inc; Dialog Corporation
Friends of the Library Group

NEW IBERIA

P IBERIA PARISH PUBLIC LIBRARY, 445 E Main St, 70560-3710. SAN 343-3269. Tel: 337-373-0075, 337-373-0077. Interlibrary Loan Service Tel: 337-373-0079. FAX: 337-373-0086. E-Mail: b1ib@pelican.state.lib.la.us. Web Site: www.iberia.lib.la.us. *Dir*, Carla S Hostetter; *Asst Librn*, Kathleen Crook; *Circ*, Lauren Salkowitz; *Ref*, Claire Woosley; *Ch Servs*, Cheryl Braud; Staff 6 (MLS 4, Non-MLS 2)
Founded 1947. Pop 72,000; Circ 349,944
Jan 2001-Dec 2001 Income $1,461,500, State $194,000, County $1,269,000, Locally Generated Income $174,500. Mats Exp $180,900, Books $140,000, Per/Ser (Incl. Access Fees) $21,000, Presv $300, AV Equip $1,000. Sal $585,118 (Prof $146,313)
Library Holdings: Bk Vols 209,800; Per Subs 214
Special Collections: Harold Drob-Bunk Johnson Jazz Coll; I A & Carroll Martin Photo Coll
Automation Activity & Vendor Info: (Cataloging) epixtech, inc.; (Circulation) epixtech, inc.; (ILL) TLC; (OPAC) epixtech, inc.
Friends of the Library Group

Branches: 7
CITY PARK, 300 Parkview St, 70563. SAN 343-3293. Tel: 337-373-0081. FAX: 337-373-0081. *In Charge*, Debra Landry
Library Holdings: Bk Vols 8,670
Friends of the Library Group
COTEAU, 6308 Coteau Park Dr, 70560. SAN 375-5746. Tel: 337-373-0120. FAX: 337-373-0120. *In Charge*, Nancy Guidry
Library Holdings: Bk Vols 11,959
Friends of the Library Group
DELCAMBRE BRANCH, 206 W Main, Delcambre, 70528-2918. Tel: 337-685-2388. *In Charge*, Jean Segura
Friends of the Library Group
JEANERETTE BRANCH, 411 Kentucky St, Jeanerette, 70544. SAN 343-3358. Tel: 337-276-4014. FAX: 337-276-4014. *In Charge*, Rita Gouner
Library Holdings: Bk Titles 30,621
Friends of the Library Group
LOREAUVILLE BRANCH, 510 Main St, Loreauville, 70552. SAN 343-3382. Tel: 337-229-6348. FAX: 337-229-6348. *In Charge*, Elizabeth Price
Library Holdings: Bk Titles 11,782
Friends of the Library Group
MORTON, 7205 Weeks Island Rd, 70560. SAN 343-3412. Tel: 337-373-0083. FAX: 337-373-0083. *In Charge*, JoAnn Clay
Library Holdings: Bk Titles 17,038
Friends of the Library Group
WEST END PARK, Martin Luther King Park, 1200 Field St, 70560. SAN 322-6026. Tel: 337-373-0087. FAX: 337-373-0087. *In Charge*, Leona Guillory
Library Holdings: Bk Vols 7,719
Friends of the Library Group

NEW ORLEANS

L ADAMS & REESE LAW LIBRARY, 4500 One Shell Sq, 70139. SAN 372-0888. Tel: 504-581-3234. FAX: 504-566-0210. Web Site: www.arlaw.com. *Librn*, Ronald G Aucoin; E-Mail: aucoinrg@arlaw.com; *Asst Librn*, Barbara Rome
Library Holdings: Bk Vols 15,500; Per Subs 200

S AMISTAD RESEARCH CENTER,* Tulane University, Tilton Hall, 70118. SAN 306-4840. Tel: 504-865-5535. FAX: 504-865-5580. E-Mail: arc@mailhost.tcs.tulane.edu. Web Site: www.tulane.edu/~amistad. *Dir*, Donald E DeVore; *Dir*, Brenda Square; *Archivist*, Rebecca Hankins; *Archivist*, Beatrice Owsley
Founded 1966
Library Holdings: Bk Titles 20,000; Per Subs 200
Subject Interests: Afro-American, Chicano studies, Ethnic studies, Puerto Rican studies
Special Collections: African-American Art
Publications: Amistad Chronicles; Amistad Reports
Partic in OCLC Online Computer Library Center, Inc
Friends of the Library Group

S BUREAU OF GOVERNMENTAL RESEARCH LIBRARY,* 225 Baronne St, Ste 610, 70112. SAN 306-4891. Tel: 504-525-4152. FAX: 504-525-4153. Web Site: www.bgr.org. *Pres*, James C Brandt; E-Mail: jimbrandt@bgr.org
Founded 1932
Library Holdings: Bk Vols 900
Publications: Research Reports

L CHAFFE, MCCALL, PHILLIPS, TOLER & SARPY, Law Library, 2300 Energy Centre, 1100 Poydras St, 70163. SAN 372-0896. Tel: 504-585-7211. FAX: 504-585-7075. Web Site: www.chaffe.com. *Librn*, Virginia L Smith; E-Mail: vsmith@chaffe.com; *Asst Librn*, Karen Christie
Library Holdings: Bk Vols 20,000; Per Subs 10

M CHILDREN'S HOSPITAL, Medical Library, 200 Henry Clay Ave, 70118. SAN 322-8533. Tel: 504-896-9264. FAX: 504-896-3932.
Library Holdings: Bk Vols 3,000; Bk Titles 700; Per Subs 92
Subject Interests: Abused children, Congenital, Developmental anatomy, Malformations, Pediatric emergency, Pediatric intensive care, Pediatric neonatal intensive care, Pediatric neurology, Pediatric neurosurgery, Pediatric oncology, Pediatric surgery, Pediatrics orthopedics
Partic in Health Sciences Library Association Of Louisiana; Medline; Nat Libr of Med

J DELGADO COMMUNITY COLLEGE, Moss Memorial Library, 615 City Park Ave, 70119. SAN 306-493X. Tel: 504-483-4119. FAX: 504-483-1939. Web Site: www.dcc.edu/libr/libi.web.htm. *Dir*, Lenora C Lockett; E-Mail: llocke@dcc.edu; *Cat*, Denise Repman; *Acq, Coll Develop*, Harolyn Cumlet; *Ref*, Constance Varnado; Staff 6 (MLS 6)
Founded 1921. Enrl 15,000
Library Holdings: Bk Vols 120,000; Per Subs 900
Subject Interests: Louisiana
Departmental Libraries:
CITY PARK CAMPUS, 615 City Park Ave, 70119. SAN 321-8562. Tel: 504-483-4119. FAX: 504-483-1939. *Ser*, Carol Craft; *Ref*, Constance Varnado
WESTBANK CAMPUS, 2600 General Mayer, 70114. SAN 321-8732. Tel: 504-361-6435. FAX: 504-361-6411. *Librn*, Robin Leckbee

M DELGADO COMMUNITY COLLEGE, Charity School of Nursing Library, 450 S Claiborne Ave, 70112. SAN 306-4913. Tel: 504-568-6430. FAX: 504-568-5494. *Coordr*, Melanie Tennyson; E-Mail: mtenny@pop3.dcc.edu; Staff 2 (MLS 2)
Founded 1895. Enrl 600
Library Holdings: Bk Vols 7,000; Bk Titles 4,550; Per Subs 110
Subject Interests: Medicine, Nursing

GM DEPARTMENT OF VETERANS AFFAIRS, Medical Center Library,* 1601 Perdido St, 70146. SAN 306-5219. Tel: 504-589-5272. FAX: 504-589-5916. *Chief Librn, Online Servs*, Mark Petersen
Founded 1946
Library Holdings: Bk Vols 2,500; Per Subs 200
Subject Interests: Allied health, Nursing
Partic in Nat Libr of Med; Vets Admin Libr Network

L DEUTSCH, KERRIGAN & STILES, Law Library, 755 Magazine St, 70130-3672. SAN 306-4948. Tel: 504-581-5141, Ext 465. FAX: 504-566-1201. Web Site: www.dkslaw.com. *Librn*, Ransey McDonald; Tel: 504-593-0779, E-Mail: rmcdonald@dkslaw.com
Founded 1926
Library Holdings: Bk Titles 30,000; Per Subs 25
Subject Interests: Great Britain

C DILLARD UNIVERSITY, Will W Alexander Library, 2601 Gentilly Blvd, 70122-3097. SAN 306-4956. Tel: 504-816-4784. Circulation Tel: 504-816-4786. Reference Tel: 504-816-7486. FAX: 504-816-4787. Web Site: www.dillard.edu. *Dean of Libr*, Tommy S Holton; E-Mail: tholton@dillard.edu; *Asst Dean*, Annie Malessia Payton; E-Mail: apayton@dillard.edu; *Cat*, Venola Jones; E-Mail: vjones@dillard.edu; *Librn*, Dr Theodosia T Shields; E-Mail: tshields@dillard.edu; *Acq, Ser*, Beverly Harris; E-Mail: bharris@dillard.edu; *Tech Servs*, Mary Beauchamp; E-Mail: mbeauchamp@dillard.edu; *Circ, Reader Servs*, Shannon Neal; *Circ*, Gayle Wright; *Selection of Gen Ref Mat*, Charles Porter Dunn; Tel: 504-286-4786, E-Mail: cdunn@dillard.edu; *Selection of Gen Ref Mat*, Mrs Assunta Fleming; *Spec Coll & Archives*, Dr Dorothy Smith; E-Mail: dsmith@dillard.edu. Subject Specialists: *Biology*, Mrs Assunta Fleming; *Chemistry*, Mrs Assunta Fleming; *History*, Dr Dorothy Smith; *History*, Charles Porter Dunn; *Psychology*, Mrs Assunta Fleming; *Social sciences*, Charles Porter Dunn; Staff 15 (MLS 6, Non-MLS 9)
Founded 1961. Enrl 1,902; Fac 123; Highest Degree: Bachelor
Jul 2000-Jun 2001 Income $921,490. Mats Exp $173,000, Books $55,000, Per/Ser (Incl. Access Fees) $65,000, Micro $18,000, AV Equip $35,000. Sal $574,346 (Prof $344,607)
Library Holdings: Bk Vols 103,702; Per Subs 495
Subject Interests: Afro-Am studies, Humanities, Nursing, Social sciences and issues
Special Collections: Literature & Architecture (McPherson Memorial Freedom Coll); Spitz (David), Beale (Howard Kennedy), Goldstein (Moise), and Richards (E V) Coll
Automation Activity & Vendor Info: (Acquisitions) Endeavor; (Cataloging) Endeavor; (Circulation) Endeavor; (Media Booking) Endeavor; (OPAC) Endeavor; (Serials) Endeavor
Database Vendor: IAC - Info Trac, Lexis-Nexis, ProQuest, Silverplatter Information Inc.
Publications: Acquisitions list (quarterly); Bibliographies; Gifts & exchange list
Partic in Call; Coop Col Libr Ctr, Inc; La Libr Network; LALINK; OCLC Online Computer Library Center, Inc; Solinet

S ENTERGY SERVICES, Information Resource Center,* 639 Loyola Ave, 70113. SAN 325-5328. Tel: 504-576-6479. FAX: 504-576-4001. *Librn*, Debbie DeSeamus; E-Mail: ddeseam@entergy.com
Founded 1976
Library Holdings: Bk Vols 10,000; Per Subs 40
Partic in Dialog Corporation

L GORDON, ARATA, MCCOLLAM & DUPLANTIS LAW LIBRARY,* 201 Saint Charles Ave, Ste 4000, 70170. SAN 326-2596. Tel: 504-582-1111, Ext 4039. FAX: 504-582-1121. *Librn*, Edward Benefiel; E-Mail: benefiel@acadiacom.net; Staff 1 (MLS 1)
Library Holdings: Bk Vols 10,000; Per Subs 50

S HERMANN-GRIMA HOUSE LIBRARY, 820 Saint Louis St, 70112. SAN 374-8324. Tel: 504-525-5661. FAX: 504-568-9735. E-Mail: hggh@gnofn.org. Web Site: www.gnofn.org/~hggh. *Dir*, Stephen Moses
Library Holdings: Bk Vols 700; Per Subs 10
Special Collections: New Orleans Coll 1830-1860

S HISTORIC NEW ORLEANS COLLECTION, (Formerly Williams Research Center of the Historic New Orleans Collection), William Research Center, 410 Chartres St, 70130-2102. SAN 306-4980. Tel: 504-598-7171. FAX: 504-598-7168. E-Mail: hnocinfo@hnoc.org, wrc@hnoc.org. Web Site: www.hnoc.org. *Head Librn*, Gerald F Patout Jr; Tel: 504-598-7125, E-Mail: geraldp@hnoc.org; *Cat*, Amy Baptist; Tel: 504-588-7157; *Coll Develop*,

Viola Berman; Tel: 504-598-7119, E-Mail: vberman@hnoc.org; *Ref*, Pamela D Arceneaux; Tel: 504-598-7118, E-Mail: pamela@hnoc.org; Staff 9 (MLS 4, Non-MLS 5)
Founded 1966
Library Holdings: Bk Vols 16,000; Per Subs 30
Subject Interests: Louisiana
Special Collections: New Orleans broadsides, directories, imprints, sheet music, selected ephemera; Vieux Carre Survey (information on property in the French Quarter of New Orleans)
Publications: Bibliography of New Orleans Imprints, 1764-1864; Bound to Please (catalog of exhibition of rare bks); Guide to Research at the Historic New Orleans Coll; Guide to the Vieux Carre Survey; This Country of Louisiana
Partic in OCLC Online Computer Library Center, Inc; SE Libr Network

L JONES, WALKER, WAECHTER, POITEVENT, CARRERE & DENEGRE, Law Library,* 201 Saint Charles Ave, 70170-5100. SAN 372-0918. Tel: 504-582-8589. FAX: 504-582-8567. E-Mail: tgambrell@joneswalker.com. *Librn*, Tina Gambrell
Library Holdings: Bk Vols 30,000; Per Subs 100

GL LAW LIBRARY OF LOUISIANA,* Supreme Court Bldg, Rm 100, 301 Loyola Ave, 70112. SAN 306-5014. Tel: 504-568-5705. FAX: 504-568-5069. *Dir*, Carol Billings; *Cat*, Janice Shull; *Publ Servs*, Marie Erickson; *Acq, Ser*, Cathleen Richards; *Ref*, Catherine Lemann; *Acq, Govt Doc*, Georgia Chadwick
Founded 1855
Library Holdings: Bk Vols 190,000; Per Subs 3,500
Special Collections: 19th Century American, British & French Law, Louisiana Law
Publications: Newsletter of the Friends of the Law Library of Louisiana
Partic in SE Libr Network; Westlaw
Friends of the Library Group

L LEMLE & KELLEHER, Law Library, Pan Am Life Ctr, 21st Flr, 601 Poydras St, 70130. SAN 372-0853. Tel: 504-586-1241. FAX: 504-584-9142. *Librn*, Elizabeth Cortez; E-Mail: ecortez@lemle.com; *Asst Librn*, Melinda Dupuy
Library Holdings: Bk Vols 20,000; Per Subs 190

S LOUISIANA INTERNATIONAL TRADE CENTER - SBDC, 2 Canal St, Ste 2926, 70130. SAN 329-7047. Tel: 504-568-8222. FAX: 504-568-8228. E-Mail: litc@uno.edu. Web Site: www.uno.edu/~litc. *Dir*, Ruperto Chavarri; *Asst Dir*, Jennifer Klein
Library Holdings: Bk Vols 4,000; Per Subs 63
Subject Interests: International trade
Publications: Export & Import Guide & Directory/Country Guide Report; Research Report
Restriction: Not a lending library
Function: Research library
Open 9-4:30

S LOUISIANA STATE MUSEUM, Louisiana Historical Center, 400 Esplanade Ave, 751 Chartres, 70176-2448. (Mail add: PO Box 2448, 70176), SAN 306-5022. Tel: 504-568-8214. Toll Free Tel: 800-568-6968. FAX: 504-568-2678. *Curator*, Kathryn Page; E-Mail: kpage@crt.state.la.us; Staff 1 (Non-MLS 1)
Founded 1930
Library Holdings: Bk Titles 30,000
Subject Interests: Local history, Louisiana
Special Collections: Colonial Judicial Documents, mss, maps, sheet music
Restriction: Non-circulating to the public

CM LOUISIANA STATE UNIVERSITY MEDICAL CENTER, John P Ische Library, 433 Bolivar St, 70112-2223. SAN 343-3471. Circulation Tel: 504-568-6100. Reference Tel: 504-568-6102, 504-568-8339. FAX: 504-568-7720. Interlibrary Loan Service FAX: 504-568-7718. Web Site: www.lsuhsc.edu/library/NO/. *Dir Libr Serv*, Wilba Swearingen; E-Mail: wswear@lsuhsc.edu; *Assoc Dir*, Pauline Fulda; Tel: 504-568-7698, E-Mail: pfulda@lsuhsc.edu; *Automation Syst Coordr*, Bruce Abbott; E-Mail: babbot@lsuhsc.edu; *Br Coordr*, Elizabeth A Strother; E-Mail: estrot@lsuhsc.edu; *Ref*, Carolyn Bridgewater; E-Mail: cbridg@lsuhsc.edu; *Ref*, Jennifer Kelly; E-Mail: jkelly1@lsuhsc.edu; *Ref*, Kathryn Kerdolff; E-Mail: kkerdo@lsuhsc.edu; *Ref*, Mary Marix; E-Mail: mmarix@lsuhsc.edu; *Ref*, Julie Schiavo; Tel: 504-619-8550, Fax: 504-619-8723, E-Mail: jschia@lsuhsc.edu; *Cat*, Margaret Jean Rouse; E-Mail: mrouse@lsuhsc.edu; *Ser*, Hanna Kwasik; E-Mail: hkwasi@lsuhsc.edu; *Publ Servs*, Jennifer Lloyd; E-Mail: jlloyd@lsuhsc.edu; *Coll Develop*, Marlene Bishop; Tel: 504-568-6109, E-Mail: mbisho@lsuhsc.edu; Staff 29 (MLS 13, Non-MLS 16)
Founded 1931. Circ 211,500
Jul 1999-Jun 2000 Mats Exp $972,884, Books $80,633, Per/Ser (Incl. Access Fees) $791,700, AV Equip $4,334, Electronic Ref Mat (Incl. Access Fees) $92,770. Sal $876,573
Library Holdings: Bk Vols 214,151; Bk Titles 75,435; Per Subs 1,311
Subject Interests: Allied health, Dentistry, Medicine, Nursing, Nutrition
Automation Activity & Vendor Info: (Acquisitions) Innovative Interfaces Inc.; (Cataloging) Innovative Interfaces Inc.; (Circulation) Innovative Interfaces Inc.; (OPAC) Innovative Interfaces Inc.; (Serials) Innovative Interfaces Inc.
Database Vendor: Dialog, GaleNet, IAC - Info Trac, IAC - SearchBank, Lexis-Nexis, OVID Technologies, ProQuest, Silverplatter Information Inc., Wilson - Wilson Web
Publications: Library Bulletin (Newsletter)
Restriction: Open to faculty, students & qualified researchers
Partic in Amigos Library Services, Inc; La Libr Network; SCAMeL
Departmental Libraries:
PENNINGTON BIOMEDICAL RESEARCH CENTER, 6400 Perkins Rd, Baton Rouge, 70808-4124. SAN 372-7831. Tel: 504-763-2556. FAX: 504-763-2558. *Asst Dir*, Lori Steib; E-Mail: steibll@mhs.pbrc.edu
SCHOOL OF DENTISTRY LIBRARY, 1100 Florida Ave, 70119-2799. SAN 343-3501. Tel: 504-619-8550. FAX: 504-619-8783. *Librn*, Elizabeth Strother; *Ref*, Julie Schiavo; E-Mail: jschia@lsuhsc.edu

C LOYOLA UNIVERSITY NEW ORLEANS, J Edgar & Louise S Monroe Library, 6363 Saint Charles Ave, PO Box 198, 70118. SAN 343-3536. Tel: 504-864-7111. Interlibrary Loan Service Tel: 504-864-7144. FAX: 504-864-7247. Web Site: www.lib.loyno.edu. *Dean of Libr*, Mary Lee Sweat; *Archivist*, Art Carpenter; *Bibliogr*, Laurie Gibson; *Coll Develop*, Richard Snow; *Govt Doc, Publ Servs*, Deborah Poole; *Instrul Serv*, Doreen Simonsen; *ILL*, Pat Doran; *Online Servs*, Jim Hobbs; *Spec Coll*, Rosalee McReynolds; *Syst Coordr*, Robert Cameron; *Tech Servs*, Darla Rushing; Staff 31 (MLS 13, Non-MLS 18)
Founded 1912. Enrl 5,600; Fac 300; Highest Degree: Master
Library Holdings: Bk Vols 329,414; Per Subs 1,696
Subject Interests: Am hist, Am lit, English literature, Philosophy, Religious studies
Special Collections: History (Spanish Documents & French Documents), micro; Louisiana Coll; New Orleans Province of Society of Jesus, archives; University Archives
Automation Activity & Vendor Info: (Acquisitions) SIRSI; (Cataloging) SIRSI; (Circulation) SIRSI; (Course Reserve) SIRSI; (ILL) SIRSI; (Media Booking) SIRSI; (OPAC) SIRSI; (Serials) SIRSI
Partic in LALINC; SE Libr Network
Departmental Libraries:
CL LOYOLA LAW LIBRARY, School of Law, 7214 St Charles Ave, 70118. SAN 343-3625. Tel: 504-861-5539. Interlibrary Loan Service Tel: 504-861-5692. FAX: 504-861-5895. *Dir*, Ed Edmonds; E-Mail: edmonds@loyno.edu; *Acq*, Trina Robinson; *Cat*, Marguerite Florent; *Doc, Ref*, Carla Pritchett; *Publ Servs*, Nancy L Strohmeyer; *Ref*, Nona Beisenherz; *Ref*, Tim Hunt; *Tech Servs*, Elizabeth L Moore; Staff 7 (MLS 7)
Founded 1914. Enrl 745; Fac 59
Library Holdings: Bk Vols 173,000; Per Subs 2,780
Special Collections: GATT; US Supreme Court Records & Briefs
Partic in OCLC Online Computer Library Center, Inc; SE Libr Network; Westlaw
MUSIC LIBRARY Tel: 504-865-2774.

L MCCALLA, THOMPSON, PYBURN, HYMOWITZ & SHAPIRO, Law Library, 650 Poydras St Ste 2800, 70130. SAN 372-0861. Tel: 504-524-2499. FAX: 504-528-3141. Web Site: www.mtphs.com. *Librn*, Melinda St Germain; E-Mail: melinda@mtphs.com
Library Holdings: Bk Vols 6,000; Per Subs 20
Publications: Labor Law Letter

L MCGLINCHEY, STAFFORD, Law Library, 643 Magazine St, PO Box 60643, 70160. SAN 326-2529. Tel: 504-586-1200, Ext 697. FAX: 504-596-2800.; Staff 4 (MLS 2, Non-MLS 2)

MEMORIAL MEDICAL CENTER
M MEDICAL LIBRARY-MID-CITY CAMPUS, 301 N Jefferson Davis Pkwy, 70119. SAN 329-8981. Tel: 504-483-5627. FAX: 504-483-5284. *Coordr*, Sondra L White; Tel: 504-897-5911
Library Holdings: Bk Vols 1,000; Per Subs 54
M MEDICAL LIBRARY-UPTOWN CAMPUS, 2700 Napoleon Ave, 70115-9989. SAN 327-6171. Tel: 504-897-5911. FAX: 504-897-4231.
Library Holdings: Bk Vols 9,945
Subject Interests: Clinical medicine, Nursing
Partic in S Cent Regional Med Libr Program
Open Mon-Thurs 9-5 & Fri 9-3

L MILLING, BENSON, WOODWARD LIBRARY, 909 Poydras St, Ste 2300, 70112-1017. SAN 326-100X. Tel: 504-569-7308. FAX: 504-569-7001. *Mgr Libr*, Vanessa Odems; E-Mail: vodems@millinglaw.com
Library Holdings: Bk Titles 105; Per Subs 25

S WALDEMAR S NELSON & COMPANY INC LIBRARY,* 1200 Saint Charles Ave, 70130. SAN 371-1307. Tel: 504-523-5281, Ext 728. FAX: 504-523-4587. *Librn*, Malcolm Ross
Library Holdings: Bk Vols 10,100; Per Subs 115

R NEW ORLEANS BAPTIST THEOLOGICAL SEMINARY, John T Christian Library, 4110 Seminary Pl, 70126. SAN 343-365X. Tel: 504-282-4455, Ext 3288. FAX: 504-816-8429. Web Site: www.nobts.edu. *Dir*, Michael Garrett; *Cat*, Patty Furr; *ILL*, Eric Benoy; *Coll Develop*, Michael Garrett; *Music*, Dr Harry Eskew; Staff 4 (MLS 4)
Founded 1918. Enrl 1,049; Fac 93; Highest Degree: Doctorate

Library Holdings: Bk Titles 240,000; Per Subs 1,020
Special Collections: Baptists; Music (Keith Coll); Preaching-Pastoral (Lee Coll)
Partic in Dialog Corporation; SE Libr Network
Branches:
MARTIN MUSIC Tel: 504-282-4455, Ext 3289. *Dir*, Harry Eskew

S NEW ORLEANS BOTANICAL GARDEN LIBRARY,* City Park, Victory Ave, 70124. (Mail add: City Park, One Palm Dr, 70124), SAN 377-0699. Tel: 504-483-9386. FAX: 504-483-9485. Web Site: www.neworleanscitypark.com/botanical.html. *Dir*, Paul Soniat
Library Holdings: Bk Vols 2,000; Bk Titles 2,000; Per Subs 20
Subject Interests: Horticulture
Open Tues-Sun 10-4:30

S NEW ORLEANS MUSEUM OF ART, Felix J Dreyfous Library, One Collins Diboll Circle City Park, PO Box 19123, 70179-0123. SAN 306-5057. Tel: 504-488-2631. FAX: 504-484-6662. *Librn*, Norbert E Raacke, Jr; Staff 1 (MLS 1)
Founded 1972
Library Holdings: Bk Vols 20,000; Per Subs 112
Subject Interests: Art (19th Century), Art (20th Century), Glass technology, Louisiana, Oriental art, Paintings, Photography, Pottery, Pre-Columbian art, Prints
Special Collections: WPA Index to New Orleans Artists, 1805-1940
Publications: Arts Quarterly; Handbook of the Collection
Partic in OCLC Online Computer Library Center, Inc

S NEW ORLEANS PSYCHOANALYTIC INSTITUTE INCORPORATED LIBRARY,* 3624 Coliseum St, 70115. SAN 371-2680. Tel: 504-899-5815. FAX: 504-899-5886. *Chairperson*, Denise Dorsey MD; *Librn*, Kelly Barnes
1998-1999 Mats Exp $1,600
Library Holdings: Bk Vols 6,500; Per Subs 10

P NEW ORLEANS PUBLIC LIBRARY, 219 Loyola Ave, 70112-2044. SAN 343-3714. Tel: 504-596-2602. Interlibrary Loan Service Tel: 504-596-2622. FAX: 504-596-2609. E-Mail: nopl@gnofn.org. Web Site: www.nutrias.org. *Librn*, Gertiana C Williams; *ILL*, Penny Atkinson; *Tech Servs*, Elisabeth Konrad; *Cat*, Cathy Wagar; *Rare Bks, Spec Coll*, Collin B Hamer, Jr; *Publ Servs*, Elizabeth Bedikian; *Online Servs*, Penny Lytle; *Head Ref*, Katye Rubin
Founded 1896. Pop 496,938; Circ 954,363
Jan 2000-Dec 2000 Income (Main Library and Branch Library) $8,474,541, State $107,040, City $6,857,916, County $510,040, Locally Generated Income $187,092, Other $812,451. Mats Exp $7,733,456, Books $1,090,493, Per/Ser (Incl. Access Fees) $200,000, Presv $20,000. Sal $5,159,471
Library Holdings: Bk Vols 794,830; Per Subs 999
Special Collections: City Archives, microflm & mss; Foundation Center Coop Coll; Louisiana Division, bks, micro, audio & video tapes, news reels, slides, maps, pictures
Automation Activity & Vendor Info: (Acquisitions) epixtech, inc.; (Circulation) epixtech, inc.
Partic in OCLC Online Computer Library Center, Inc
Friends of the Library Group
Branches: 14
ACQUISITIONS Tel: 504-596-2576. *Librn*, Walter Mascari
ALGIERS POINT, 725 Pelican Ave, 70114-1141. SAN 343-3749. Tel: 504-596-2640. FAX: 504-596-2666. *Librn*, Jane Palmer
Library Holdings: Bk Vols 23,468
ALGIERS REGIONAL, 3014 Holiday Dr, 70131. SAN 343-3773. Tel: 504-596-2642. FAX: 504-596-2661. *Librn*, Joe Clark
Library Holdings: Bk Vols 55,958
ALVAR, 913 Alvar St, 70117-5409. SAN 343-3803. Tel: 504-596-2624. FAX: 504-596-2667. *Librn*, Gauthier Ronald
Library Holdings: Bk Vols 17,957
CHILDREN'S RESOURCE CENTER, 913 Napoleon Ave, 70115-2862. SAN 343-3951. Tel: 504-596-2628. FAX: 504-596-2669. *Librn*, Sonia Castro-Zaimis
Library Holdings: Bk Vols 19,443
EAST NEW ORLEANS REGIONAL, 5641 Read Blvd, 70127-3105. SAN 343-3862. Tel: 504-596-2646. FAX: 504-596-2662. *Librn*, Sung Ja Han
Library Holdings: Bk Vols 57,057
GENTILLY, 2098 Foy St, 70122-3158. SAN 343-3897. Tel: 504-596-2644. FAX: 504-596-2664. *Librn*, Damian lambert
Library Holdings: Bk Vols 34,653
LATTER, 5120 St Charles Ave, 70115-4941. SAN 343-3927. Tel: 504-596-2625. FAX: 504-596-2665. *Librn*, Missy Abbott; Tel: 504-596-2626; Staff 12 (MLS 2, Non-MLS 10)
Founded 1948
Library Holdings: Bk Vols 60,000; Per Subs 20
Friends of the Library Group
MARTIN LUTHER KING JR BRANCH, 1611 Caffin Ave, 70117. SAN 376-9410. Tel: 504-596-2695. FAX: 504-596-2699. *Librn*, Henrietta Kinney
Library Holdings: Bk Vols 31,328
NORA NAVRA BRANCH, 1902 St Bernard Ave, 70116-1317. SAN 343-3986. Tel: 504-596-2623. FAX: 504-596-2670. *Librn*, Lydia Bigard
Library Holdings: Bk Vols 16,842
NIX, 1401 S Carrollton Ave, 70118-2809. SAN 343-401X. Tel: 504-596-2630. FAX: 504-596-2672. *Librn*, Erskine Barbarin
Library Holdings: Bk Vols 22,978
ROBERT E SMITH BRANCH, 6301 Canal Blvd, 70124-3117. SAN 343-4044. Tel: 504-596-2638. FAX: 504-596-2663. *Librn*, Ed Real
Library Holdings: Bk Vols 51,951
ROSA KELLER BRANCH, 4300 S Broad St, 70125. SAN 374-6836. Tel: 504-596-2675. FAX: 504-596-2678. *Librn*, Virginia Williams
Library Holdings: Bk Vols 37,200
SERIALS Tel: 504-596-2578. *Ser*, Maria Forti

R NOTRE DAME SEMINARY LIBRARY,* 2901 S Carrollton Ave, 70118-4391. SAN 306-5065. Tel: 504-866-7426, Ext 3700. FAX: 504-866-3119. E-Mail: ndame@iamerica.net. *Dir*, Sister Barbara Dupuis
Founded 1923
Library Holdings: Bk Vols 92,652
Subject Interests: Philosophy, Theology

M ALTON OCHSNER MEDICAL FOUNDATION, Medical Library, 1516 Jefferson Hwy, 70121-1516. SAN 306-5073. Tel: 504-842-3760. Interlibrary Loan Service Tel: 504-842-3763. FAX: 504-842-5339. E-Mail: infodesk@ochsner.org. Web Site: www.ochsner.org/library. *Dir, Librn*, Ethel U Madden; E-Mail: emadden@ochsner.org; *Outreach Serv*, Leann C Benedict; E-Mail: lbenedict@ochsner.org; *Syst Coordr*, Greg Bodin; E-Mail: gbodin@ochsner.org; *Tech Servs*, Barbara J Attebery; E-Mail: battebery@ochsner.org; Staff 6 (MLS 4, Non-MLS 2)
Founded 1944
Library Holdings: Per Subs 554
Automation Activity & Vendor Info: (Cataloging) EOS; (Circulation) EOS; (OPAC) EOS; (Serials) EOS
Partic in Dialog Corporation; Docline; Nat Libr of Med; OCLC Online Computer Library Center, Inc

C OUR LADY OF HOLY CROSS COLLEGE LIBRARY, Blaine S Kern Library, 4123 Woodland Dr, 70131. SAN 306-5081. Tel: 504-394-7744. Toll Free Tel: 800-259-7744. FAX: 504-391-2421. Web Site: www.olhcc.edu. *Dir*, Sister Helen Fontenot; E-Mail: hfontenot@olhcc.edu; *Acq, Cat, Coll Develop*, Kathleen Devitt; E-Mail: kdevitt@olhcc.edu; *Doc, Ref*, Ramesh Parikh; E-Mail: rparikh@olhcc.edu; *Coll Develop, ILL, Ser*, Diana Schaubhut; E-Mail: dschaubhut@olhcc.edu; Staff 5 (MLS 3, Non-MLS 2)
Founded 1916. Enrl 1,260; Fac 82; Highest Degree: Master
Jul 1999-Jun 2000 Income $289,901. Mats Exp $93,856, Books $29,645, Per/Ser (Incl. Access Fees) $41,782, Presv $1,000, Micro $20,354, AV Equip $1,075. Sal $150,397 (Prof $137,514)
Library Holdings: Bk Vols 49,542; Bk Titles 45,500; Per Subs 998
Subject Interests: Children's literature, Education, Genealogy, Humanities, Louisiana, Natural science, Nursing, Social sciences and issues
Special Collections: Govt Doc Dep
Automation Activity & Vendor Info: (Cataloging) Gaylord; (Circulation) Sagebrush Corporation; (OPAC) Sagebrush Corporation
Partic in Call; La Libr Network; LALINC; OCLC Online Computer Library Center, Inc
Friends of the Library Group

L PHELPS DUNBAR LLP, Law Library, 365 Canal St, Ste 2000, 70130-6534. SAN 372-087X. Tel: 504-566-1311, Ext 287. FAX: 504-568-9130. *Info Res, Mgr*, Cynthia Jones; E-Mail: jonesc@phelps.com
Library Holdings: Bk Vols 50,000; Per Subs 75

L SESSIONS, FISHMAN & NATHAN, LLP LIBRARY, 201 St Charles Ave, Ste 3500, 70170. SAN 326-0127. Tel: 504-582-1500. FAX: 504-582-1555. *Librn*, Jeanne Claudel-Simoneaux; E-Mail: jclaudel@sessions-law.com
Founded 1958
Library Holdings: Bk Vols 15,000; Bk Titles 5,000; Per Subs 75
Publications: Now Hear This (internal newsletter)

L SIMON, PERAGINE, SMITH & REDFEARN LLP, Law Library, Energy Ctr, 1100 Poydras St, 30th Flr, 70163. SAN 372-090X. Tel: 504-569-2961. FAX: 504-569-2999. *Librn*, Frank Schiavo; E-Mail: fschiavo@spsr-law.com; Staff 1 (MLS 1)
Library Holdings: Bk Vols 9,100; Per Subs 23

C SOUTHERN UNIVERSITY IN NEW ORLEANS, Leonard S Washington Memorial Library, 6400 Press Dr, 70126. SAN 306-5111. Tel: 504-286-5224. FAX: 504-284-5490. Web Site: www.suno.edu. *Dir*, E W Young
Founded 1959. Enrl 3,146; Fac 102; Highest Degree: Master
Library Holdings: Bk Vols 218,043; Per Subs 526
Subject Interests: Education, Ethnic studies, Social sciences and issues
Special Collections: Afro-French
Mem of SE La Libr Network Coop

M TOURO INFIRMARY, Hospital Library,* 1401 Foucher St, 70115. SAN 343-4079. Tel: 504-897-8102. FAX: 504-897-8322. *Librn*, Patricia J Greenfield
Founded 1947
Library Holdings: Bk Vols 5,000; Bk Titles 5,000; Per Subs 150
Subject Interests: Clinical medicine, Nursing
Partic in BRS; Medline; S Cent Regional Med Libr Program

C TULANE UNIVERSITY, Howard-Tilton Memorial Library, 7001 Freret St, 70118-5682. SAN 343-4133. Tel: 504-865-5131. Interlibrary Loan Service Tel: 504-865-5610. FAX: 504-865-6773. Web Site: www.tulane.edu/~html. *Asst Librn*, Cecilia Stafford; E-Mail: stafford@mailhost.tcs.tulane.edu; *Govt Doc*, Eric Wedig; E-Mail: wedig@mailhost.tcs.tulane.edu; *Asst Librn*, Wilbur E Meneray; E-Mail: meneray@mailhost.tcs.tulane.edu; *ILL*, Jennifer Cella; E-Mail: jcella@mailhost.tcs.tulane.edu; *Circ*, Felice Maciejewski; E-Mail: felicem@mailhost.tcs.tulane.edu; *Ref*, Andy Corrigan; Tel: 504-865-5679, E-Mail: andyc@mailhost.tcs.tulane.edu. Subject Specialists: *Latin America*, Bill Nanez; Staff 33 (MLS 33)
Founded 1834. Enrl 11,487; Fac 927; Highest Degree: Doctorate
Jul 1998-Jun 1999 Income (Main Library Only) $7,473,000. Mats Exp $2,783,000. Sal $3,035,000 (Prof $1,213,228)
Library Holdings: Bk Vols 1,801,740; Per Subs 9,131
Subject Interests: Latin America
Special Collections: Architecture (Southeastern Architectural Archive); Jazz Music (Hogan Jazz Archive), rec; Louisiana History
Publications: The Jazz Archivist, Annual Report
Partic in Asn of Research Libraries; Dialog Corporation; SE Libr Network
Friends of the Library Group
Departmental Libraries:
A H CLIFFORD MATHEMATICS RESEARCH LIBRARY, Gibson Hall, 70118. SAN 343-4257. Tel: 504-862-3455. FAX: 504-865-5063.
Library Holdings: Bk Vols 26,000; Per Subs 28,053
Subject Interests: Mathematics
Special Collections: Edward D Conway Coll; Frank D Quigley Coll
ARCHITECTURE, Richardson Memorial Bldg, Rm 202, 70118. SAN 343-4168. Tel: 504-865-5391. *In Charge*, Frances Hecker
Library Holdings: Bk Vols 14,817; Per Subs 304
CM MATAS MEDICAL LIBRARY, 1430 Tulane Ave, PO Box SL86, 70112. SAN 343-4281. Tel: 504-588-5155. FAX: 504-587-7417. E-Mail: medlib@mailhost.tcs.tulane.edu. Web Site: www.tulane.edu/~matas. *Dir*, W D Postell, Jr; *Asst Dir*, Cynthia Goldstein; *Per*, Millie Moore; *Cat*, Mary Holt; *ILL*, Ann Elliot; *Online Servs, Ref*, Patricia Copeland; *Circ*, Susan Dorsey; Staff 8 (MLS 8)
Founded 1844
Library Holdings: Bk Vols 164,526; Per Subs 1,000
Subject Interests: Medicine, Public health
Special Collections: Louisiana medicine & medical biography
Publications: Newsletter
Partic in Amigos Library Services, Inc; Coop Libr Agency for Syst & Servs; Ontyme; S Cent Regional Med Libr Program
MEADE NATURAL HISTORY LIBRARY, Howard-Tilton Memorial Libr, 70118. SAN 343-4346. Tel: 504-394-9937, 504-865-5609. FAX: 504-865-6773. *Librn*, Eleanor Elder
Library Holdings: Bk Vols 15,500; Per Subs 500
Subject Interests: Biology, Natural history
Publications: Tulane Studies in Zoology & Botany
CL MONTE M LEMANN MEMORIAL LAW LIBRARY, 6329 Freret St, 70118-5600. SAN 343-4222. Tel: 504-865-5952. FAX: 504-865-5917. Web Site: www.law.tulane.edu/library/lib.htm. *Librn*, David Combe; E-Mail: dcombe@law.tulane.edu; *Publ Servs*, Ray A Lytle; *Cat*, Mary McCorkle; *Circ*, Christine Todd; *Doc*, Katherine Nachod; *Coll Develop*, Margareta Horiba; Staff 10 (MLS 10)
Founded 1847. Enrl 1,000; Fac 48; Highest Degree: Doctorate
Library Holdings: Bk Vols 206,158
Special Collections: French Civil Law Coll; Maritime Law Coll; Roman Law Coll
Partic in Dialog Corporation; OCLC Online Computer Library Center, Inc; SE Libr Network; Westlaw
TURCHIN LIBRARY, 7 McAlister Dr, 70118-5669. SAN 343-4370. Tel: 504-865-5376. FAX: 504-862-8953. Web Site: www.freeman.tulane.edu/turchin. *Dir*, William Strickland; *Per*, Gerald Kelly; E-Mail: gkelly@mailhost.tcs.tulane.edu
1998-1999 Income $446,000. Mats Exp $224,000, Books $15,000, Per/Ser (Incl. Access Fees) $60,000. Sal $156,000 (Prof $37,500)
Library Holdings: Bk Vols 30,000; Per Subs 500
Subject Interests: Accounting, Finance, Organizational behavior
Database Vendor: ProQuest, Silverplatter Information Inc., Wilson - Wilson Web

UNITED STATES ARMY
A CORPS OF ENGINEERS, TECHNICAL LIBRARY, Rm 389, PO Box 60267, 70160-0267. SAN 343-4400. Tel: 504-862-2558. Interlibrary Loan Service Tel: 504-862-2559. FAX: 504-862-1721. *Librn*, Daniel Bates; *Cat*, Marsh Sullivan; Staff 4 (MLS 2, Non-MLS 2)
Founded 1974
1998-1999 Mats Exp $120,000, Books $25,000, Per/Ser (Incl. Access Fees) $80,000, Other Print Mats $15,000. Sal $112,663 (Prof $80,508)
Library Holdings: Bk Titles 12,500; Per Subs 439
Subject Interests: Archaeology, Biology, Engineering, Environmental studies
Special Collections: Environmental Impact Statements; Government Reports; Standards & Specifications
Partic in Dialog Corporation; OCLC Online Computer Library Center, Inc

GL UNITED STATES COURT OF APPEALS, Fifth Circuit Library,* 600 Camp St, Rm 106, 70130. SAN 306-5154. Tel: 504-589-6510. FAX: 504-589-6517. Web Site: www.ca5.uscourts.gov. *Librn*, Kay Guillot; *Librn*, Michael Smith; *Asst Librn*, Cassandra Hyer; *Asst Librn*, Lisa Vinson; *Asst Librn*, Peggy Mitts; *Tech Servs*, Anne Middleton; *Tech Servs*, Cheryl Duthu; *Tech Servs*, Joann Eiserloh; *Coll Develop*, Todd St Pe
Founded 1920
1997-1998 Income $4,074,000. Mats Exp $2,952,000. Sal $1,200,000
Special Collections: Government Documents Coll

G UNITED STATES DEPARTMENT OF AGRICULTURE, Southern Regional Research Center,* 1100 Robert E Lee Blvd, PO Box 19687, 70179. SAN 306-5162. Tel: 504-286-4288. FAX: 504-286-4396. *Librn*, Suhad Wojkowski; E-Mail: suhad@nola.srrc.usda.gov
Founded 1941
Library Holdings: Bk Vols 25,000; Per Subs 500
Subject Interests: Bacteriology, Chemistry, Entomology, Food sci, Microbiology, Textiles
Database Vendor: epixtech, inc.
Publications: Post Harvest News from the Library
Partic in Fedlink; OCLC Online Computer Library Center, Inc

G US DEPARTMENT OF THE INTERIOR, Minerals Management Service - Regional Technical Library, 1201 Elmwood Park Blvd, MS-5031, 70123-2394. SAN 306-4905. Tel: 504-736-2521. FAX: 504-736-2525. *Dir*, Stephen Vincent Pomes; E-Mail: stephen.pomes@mms.gov; Staff 1 (MLS 1)
Oct 1999-Sep 2000 Income $100,000. Mats Exp $42,000, Books $10,000, Per/Ser (Incl. Access Fees) $20,000, Electronic Ref Mat (Incl. Access Fees) $12,000. Sal $60,000 (Prof $40,000)
Library Holdings: Bk Vols 8,500; Per Subs 85
Subject Interests: Environmental law, Geology, Geophysics, Marine biology, Oceanography, Paleontology, Petroleum engineering
Special Collections: Environmental Impact Statements that relate to the offshore oil & gas industries, especially in the Gulf of Mexico & Atlantic Coast of the US
Automation Activity & Vendor Info: (Cataloging) Follett; (Circulation) Follett
Publications: Weekly Report
Restriction: Staff use only
Partic in Fedlink; OCLC Online Computer Library Center, Inc

UNITED STATES NAVY
G NAVAL SUPPORT ACTIVITY LIBRARY, 2300 General Meyer Ave, Bldg 24, 70142-5007. SAN 343-4435. Tel: 504-678-2210. FAX: 504-678-2727. *Librn*, Martha G Cantrell; E-Mail: m.g.cantrell@hotmail.com; Staff 1 (MLS 1)
Oct 2000-Sep 2001 Mats Exp $6,315, Books $3,673, Per/Ser (Incl. Access Fees) $2,642
Library Holdings: Bk Vols 9,085; Per Subs 56
Special Collections: Louisiana, Naval History; McPon Reading List, Master Chief Petty Officer Navy

C UNIVERSITY OF NEW ORLEANS, Earl K Long Library, Lake Front, 70148. SAN 306-5200. Tel: 504-280-6556. Interlibrary Loan Service Tel: 504-280-6548. FAX: 504-280-7277. Web Site: www.uno.edu/liad/. *Dean of Libr*, Dr Sharon Mader; *Ref*, Lea Wade; *Coordr, Res*, Phoebe Timberlake; *Cat*, Marie Morgan; *Archivist*, F Jumonville; *Coll Develop*, Stephen Alleman; Staff 55 (MLS 25, Non-MLS 30)
Founded 1958. Enrl 15,665; Fac 727; Highest Degree: Doctorate
Library Holdings: Bk Vols 845,767; Per Subs 2,845
Subject Interests: Economics, Education, Law, Natural science, Social sciences and issues, Technology
Special Collections: Egyptology (Judge Pierre Crabites Coll); European Community; Louisiana History; Nuclear Regulatory Commission; Orleans Parish School Board; Supreme Court of Louisiana Archives; William Faulkner (Frank A Von der Haar Coll)
Publications: Guide to Photographic Collections in New Orleans; Long View (intramural newsletter)
Mem of La Online Univ Info Syst
Partic in OCLC Online Computer Library Center, Inc; SE Libr Network
Friends of the Library Group

C XAVIER UNIVERSITY OF LOUISIANA LIBRARY, One Drexel Dr, 70125-1098. SAN 343-446X. Tel: 504-483-7304. Circulation Tel: 504-483-7311. Reference Tel: 504-483-7305. FAX: 504-485-7917. Web Site: www.172.16.101.33/. *Dir*, Robert E Skinner; Tel: 504-483-7303, E-Mail: rskinner@xula.edu; *Archivist*, Lester Sullivan; Tel: 504-483-7655, E-Mail: lester.sullivan@xula.edu; *Govt Doc*, Paula Singleton; Tel: 504-483-7309, E-Mail: paula.singleton@xula.edu; *ILL*, Patricia Coston; Tel: 504-485-5056, E-Mail: patricia.coston@xula.edu; *Publ Servs*, Gennice King; Tel: 504-485-7606, E-Mail: gennice.king@xula.edu; *Ser*, Carl Penny; Tel: 504-485-5291, E-Mail: carl.penny@xula.edu; *Syst Coordr*, Jason Calbaugh; Tel: 504-485-5290, E-Mail: jclabaug@xula.edu; *Tech Servs*, Lynn Gaines; Tel: 504-485-5294, E-Mail: lrgaines@xula.edu; Staff 13 (MLS 10, Non-MLS 3)
Founded 1925. Enrl 3,797; Fac 211; Highest Degree: Doctorate
Jul 1999-Jun 2000 Income Parent Institution $1,264,078. Mats Exp $375,817, Books $141,055, Per/Ser (Incl. Access Fees) $214,655, Presv $2,000, Manuscripts & Archives $3,000, Electronic Ref Mat (Incl. Access

Fees) $15,107. Sal $923,958 (Prof $498,500)
Library Holdings: Bk Vols 139,334; Bk Titles 108,597; Per Subs 1,868
Subject Interests: Afro-American, Southern states
Special Collections: Black Studies (Negro History & Culture Coll); Southern & Black Catholica; Southern Writers
Automation Activity & Vendor Info: (Acquisitions) VTLS; (Cataloging) VTLS; (Circulation) VTLS; (OPAC) VTLS; (Serials) VTLS
Publications: Information Literacy: Survival Skills for the Information Age; Xavier Library News; Xavier Review (with Department of English); Xavier Review Occassional Publications Series (with Department of English); Xavier University Annual Report; Xavier University Library Annual Report; Xavier University Library Periodicals List
Partic in Amigos Library Services, Inc; Dialog Corporation; New Orleans Consortium

NEW ROADS

P POINTE COUPEE PARISH LIBRARY, New Roads (Main Branch), 201 Claiborne St, 70760-3403. SAN 343-4524. Tel: 225-638-7593. FAX: 225-638-9847. E-Mail: c1pc@pelican.state.lib.la.us. *Librn*, Melissa Hymel
Pop 22,002; Circ 83,560
Library Holdings: Bk Vols 80,000; Per Subs 200
Subject Interests: Art and architecture, Geology, Humanities
Special Collections: Louisiana Studies
Friends of the Library Group
Branches: 4
INNIS BRANCH, 4306 Nichols Ave, Innis, 70747. (Mail add: PO Box 978, Innis, 70747), SAN 343-4559. Tel: 225-492-2632. *Librn*, Bennie Rice
Library Holdings: Bk Vols 4,623
Friends of the Library Group
LIVONIA BRANCH, 3100 Hwy 78, Livonia, 70755. (Mail add: PO Box 510, Livonia, 70755), SAN 343-4583. Tel: 225-637-2987. *Librn*, Sandra Bailey
Library Holdings: Bk Vols 4,486
Friends of the Library Group
MORGANZA BRANCH, 221 S Louisiana, Hwy 1, Morganza, 70759. (Mail add: PO Box 309, Morganza, 70759), SAN 343-4613. Tel: 225-694-2428. *Actg Dir*, Miriam Hodge
Library Holdings: Bk Vols 4,739
Friends of the Library Group
JULIAN POYDRAS BRANCH, 4985 Julian Poydras Lane, PO Box 587, Rougon, 70773. SAN 343-4648. Tel: 225-627-5846. *Librn*, Debra Soileau
Library Holdings: Bk Vols 4,546
Friends of the Library Group
Bookmobiles: 1

OAK GROVE

P WEST CARROLL PARISH LIBRARY, 101 Marietta St, PO Box 703, 71263-0703. SAN 306-5235. Tel: 318-428-4100. FAX: 318-428-9887. E-Mail: admin.t1wc@pelican.state.lib.la.us. *Dir*, Clay Robertson; Staff 6 (Non-MLS 6)
Founded 1967. Pop 12,100; Circ 112,000
Jan 2000-Dec 2000 Income $184,719, State $27,750, County $130,000, Locally Generated Income $21,400, Other $5,569. Mats Exp $21,000, Books $22,500, Per/Ser (Incl. Access Fees) $3,500, Electronic Ref Mat (Incl. Access Fees) $1,000. Sal $75,936 (Prof $22,000)
Library Holdings: Bk Vols 25,000; Per Subs 110
Special Collections: Louisiana Coll
Automation Activity & Vendor Info: (Cataloging) TLC
Mem of Trail Blazer Libr Syst
Bookmobiles: 1

OBERLIN

P ALLEN PARISH LIBRARIES,* 320 S Sixth St, 70655-0400. (Mail add: PO Box 400, 70655), SAN 343-4702. Tel: 337-639-4315. Toll Free Tel: 800-960-3015. FAX: 337-639-2654. *Dir*, Karen Teigen; E-Mail: kteigen@pelican.state.lib.la.us; Staff 11 (MLS 2, Non-MLS 9)
Founded 1957. Pop 24,242; Circ 137,936
Jan 1999-Dec 1999 Income (Main Library and Branch Library) $520,194, State $66,839, County $442,000, Locally Generated Income $11,355. Mats Exp $76,418, Books $43,117, Per/Ser (Incl. Access Fees) $4,544, AV Equip $18,000, Electronic Ref Mat (Incl. Access Fees) $10,757
Library Holdings: Bk Vols 84,253; Per Subs 181
Automation Activity & Vendor Info: (Circulation) Gaylord; (OPAC) Gaylord
Database Vendor: Ebsco - EbscoHost, IAC - Info Trac
Mem of Bayouland Library System
Friends of the Library Group
Branches: 2
KINDER BRANCH, 832 Fourth St, PO Box 637, Kinder, 70648. SAN 343-4761. Tel: 318-738-2126. FAX: 318-738-2126. *Actg Dir*, Kenneth Parton
Library Holdings: Bk Vols 16,750
Friends of the Library Group
OAKDALE BRANCH, 405 E Sixth Ave, Oakdale, 71463. SAN 343-4737. Tel: 318-335-2690. FAX: 318-335-2690. *Actg Dir*, Dorothy Fournerat
Library Holdings: Bk Vols 28,275
Friends of the Library Group
Bookmobiles: 1

OPELOUSAS

P OPELOUSAS-EUNICE PUBLIC LIBRARY,* 212 E Grolee St, 70570. (Mail add: PO Box 249, 70571), SAN 343-4796. Tel: 337-948-3693. FAX: 337-948-5200. *Dir*, Walter O Stubbs; Staff 12 (MLS 1, Non-MLS 11)
Founded 1967. Pop 88,716
Library Holdings: Bk Vols 91,927; Per Subs 150
Subject Interests: Genealogy, History, Louisiana
Special Collections: Large print bks
Mem of Bayouland Library System
Branches: 1
EUNICE PUBLIC, 222 S Second St, Eunice, 70535. SAN 343-4826. Tel: 337-457-7120. FAX: 337-457-7114. *Librn*, Walter O Stubbs
Library Holdings: Bk Vols 39,896

PINEVILLE

CENTRAL LOUISIANA STATE HOSPITAL
M DISTEFANO MEMORIAL LIBRARY, Shamrock St, PO Box 5031, 71360-5031. SAN 343-4850. Tel: 318-484-6363. FAX: 318-484-6284. *Librn*, Carol McGee; Staff 3 (MLS 1, Non-MLS 2)
Founded 1958
Library Holdings: Bk Vols 5,000; Bk Titles 4,000; Per Subs 180
Subject Interests: Mental health, Neurology, Psychiatry, Psychology, Psychotherapy, Social service (social work)
Partic in S Cent Regional Med Libr Program

S FOREST GLEN PATIENT'S LIBRARY, Shamrock St, PO Box 5031, 71360-5031. SAN 343-4885. Tel: 318-484-6364. FAX: 318-484-6284. *Librn*, Carol McGee
Library Holdings: Bk Vols 12,000; Per Subs 40

C LOUISIANA COLLEGE, Richard W Norton Memorial Library, 1140 College Blvd, 71359. SAN 306-5243. Tel: 318-487-7201. FAX: 318-487-7571. Web Site: norton.lacollege.edu/lacollege/default.asp. *Dir*, W T Martin; E-Mail: martin@lacollege.edu; *Ref*, Bonnie Hines; *Cat*, Margaret Davis; *Circ, Doc*, Lillian Purdy; Staff 7 (MLS 4, Non-MLS 3)
Founded 1906. Enrl 1,084; Fac 59; Highest Degree: Bachelor
Aug 1999-Jul 2000 Income $426,700. Mats Exp $90,560, Books $34,720, Per/Ser (Incl. Access Fees) $54,840, Presv $1,000. Sal $227,401 (Prof $150,830)
Library Holdings: Bk Vols 133,241; Per Subs 442
Special Collections: Baptist History Coll
Automation Activity & Vendor Info: (Cataloging) TLC; (Circulation) TLC; (OPAC) TLC
Publications: LIBlines (newsletter)
Partic in La Online Univ Info Systs; SE Libr Network

§S PINECREST DEVELOPMENT CENTER, Professional Library, PO Box 5191, 71361-5191. Tel: 318-641-2142. FAX: 318-641-2383. *Librn*, Peggy Berlin; E-Mail: pberlin@dhh.state.la.us
Library Holdings: Bk Titles 800; Per Subs 80

§S WORK TRAINING FACILITY-NORTH, 1453 15th St, 71360. Tel: 318-640-0351. FAX: 318-487-5955. *In Charge*, Karen Cummings
Library Holdings: Bk Vols 5,000; Per Subs 39

PLAQUEMINE

S DOW CHEMICAL USA, Technical, 21255 La Hwy 1, Bldg 2507, 70764. (Mail add: PO Box 400, Bldg 2507, 70764), SAN 306-5251. Tel: 225-353-6848. FAX: 225-353-1666.
Founded 1956
Library Holdings: Bk Titles 5,271; Per Subs 147
Subject Interests: Chemistry, Engineering, Safety
Automation Activity & Vendor Info: (Cataloging) SIRSI
Database Vendor: Dialog, OCLC - First Search, Silverplatter Information Inc.
Partic in Dialog Corporation; SDC Info Servs

P IBERVILLE PARISH LIBRARY,* 24605 J Gerald Berret Blvd, 70764. (Mail add: PO Box 736, 70765-0736), SAN 343-4915. Tel: 225-687-2520. FAX: 225-687-9719. E-Mail: admin.c1il@pelican.state.lib.la.us. Web Site: www.iberville.lib.la.us. *Dir*, Dannie Ball; *Asst Dir*, Ted Landry; *Tech Servs*, Caroline LeBlanc; *Circ*, Marion Martin; *Ch Servs*, Anne Reeves; *ILL*, Audrey DeVillier; *Ser*, Betsy Bensen; Staff 10 (MLS 2, Non-MLS 8)
Founded 1951. Pop 32,159; Circ 242,536
Jan 1997-Dec 1998 Income $1,015,355, State $75,135, Federal $11,640, County $885,080, Locally Generated Income $43,500. Mats Exp $152,150, Books $124,500, Per/Ser (Incl. Access Fees) $17,150, Micro $2,000, AV

Equip $500
Library Holdings: Bk Vols 141,200; Per Subs 626
Subject Interests: Local authors, Local history, Louisiana
Friends of the Library Group
Branches: 7
BAYOU PIGEON, 36625 Hwy 75, 70764. SAN 343-4974. Tel: 225-545-8567. E-Mail: bayoupigeon.c1il@pelican.state.lib.la.us. *Librn*, Geraldine Settoon
Library Holdings: Bk Vols 4,615
Friends of the Library Group
BAYOU SORREL, 65755 Tot Carline Dr, 70764. SAN 343-494X. Tel: 225-659-7055. *Librn*, Judy Young
Library Holdings: Bk Vols 4,475
EAST IBERVILLE, 5715 Monticello St, Saint Gabriel, 70776. SAN 343-5008. Tel: 225-642-8380. FAX: 225-642-9888. E-Mail: eastiberville.c1il@pelican.state.lib.la.us. *Librn*, Frances Peltier
Library Holdings: Bk Vols 21,781
Friends of the Library Group
GROSSE TETE BRANCH, 18135 Willow St, PO Box 218, Grosse Tete, 70740. SAN 343-5016. Tel: 225-648-2667. *Librn*, Nelda Brumfield
Library Holdings: Bk Vols 6,486
Friends of the Library Group
MARINGOUIN BRANCH, 77175 Ridgewood Dr, PO Box 37, Maringouin, 70757. SAN 343-5032. Tel: 225-625-2743. FAX: 225-625-2743. *Librn*, Debra Lewis
Library Holdings: Bk Vols 9,146
ROSEDALE BRANCH, 15695 Rosedale Rd, PO Box 410, Rosedale, 70772. SAN 343-5067. Tel: 225-648-2213. E-Mail: rosedale.c1il@pelican.state.lib.la.us. *Librn*, Brenda Coles
Library Holdings: Bk Vols 5,690
Friends of the Library Group
WHITE CASTLE BRANCH, 32835 Bowie St, White Castle, 70788. SAN 343-5121. Tel: 225-545-8424. FAX: 225-545-4536. E-Mail: whitecastle.c1il@pelican.state.lib.la.us. *Librn*, Kitty Wood
Library Holdings: Bk Vols 15,853
Friends of the Library Group

PORT ALLEN

P WEST BATON ROUGE PARISH LIBRARY,* 830 N Alexander, 70767-2327. SAN 306-526X. Tel: 225-342-7920. FAX: 225-342-7918. E-Mail: pawbr1@unix1.sncc.lsu.edu. Web Site: www.wbr.lib.la.us. *Dir*, Anna Marchiafava; E-Mail: pawbr2@unix1.sncc.lsu.edu; *Asst Dir*, Fannie Easterly; Staff 4 (MLS 4)
Founded 1965. Pop 20,412; Circ 97,513
Library Holdings: Bk Vols 67,898; Per Subs 204
Special Collections: Louisiana Material
Automation Activity & Vendor Info: (Cataloging) Gaylord; (Circulation) Gaylord; (OPAC) Gaylord

RAYVILLE

P RICHLAND PARISH LIBRARY,* 1410 Louisa St, 71269-3299. SAN 343-5156. Tel: 318-728-4806. FAX: 318-728-6108. *Dir*, Brenda Doran
Founded 1926. Pop 21,774; Circ 110,051
Library Holdings: Bk Vols 65,000; Per Subs 118
Special Collections: 1927 Flood Coll; Literature (Ruth Hatch Coll); Reference (Innis Morris Ellis Coll)
Mem of Trail Blazer Libr Syst
Partic in Lasernet; SE Libr Network
Branches: 2
DELHI BRANCH, 520 N Main St, Delhi, 71232. SAN 343-5180. Tel: 318-878-5121. FAX: 318-878-0674.
Library Holdings: Bk Vols 18,000
MANGHAM BRANCH, 302 Hixon, Mangham, 71259. SAN 343-5210. Tel: 318-248-2493. FAX: 318-248-3912.
Library Holdings: Bk Vols 7,900

RUSTON

P LINCOLN PARISH LIBRARY, 509 W Alabama, 71270-4231. SAN 306-5286. Tel: 318-251-5030. FAX: 318-251-5045. Web Site: www.lincoln.state.lib.la.us. *Dir*, Katherine Brown; E-Mail: kbrown@pelican.state.lib.la.us; *Head Tech Servs*, Donna Vavrek; *Tech Coordr*, Mary Miller; *Circ*, Amy Hill; *Ch Servs*, Barbara Moore; *Ref*, Ann Roberts; Staff 14 (MLS 3, Non-MLS 11)
Founded 1962. Pop 42,935; Circ 273,703
Jan 1999-Dec 1999 Income $611,187, State $75,041, Federal $10,000, County $457,000, Locally Generated Income $56,146, Other $13,000. Mats Exp $83,029, Books $57,573, Per/Ser (Incl. Access Fees) $17,616, Presv $1,000, Micro $840, AV Equip $6,000. Sal $394,352 (Prof $97,000)
Library Holdings: Bk Vols 91,283; Per Subs 220
Subject Interests: Genealogy, Local history
Publications: Library Pages (newsletter)
Mem of Trail Blazer Libr Syst
Friends of the Library Group

C LOUISIANA TECH UNIVERSITY, Prescott Memorial Library, PO Box 10408, 71272-0046. SAN 306-5294. Tel: 318-257-3555. Interlibrary Loan Service Tel: 318-257-2926. FAX: 318-257-2579. Web Site: www.latech.edu/tech/library. *Dir*, Rebecca Stenzel; E-Mail: stenzel@latech.edu; *Assoc Dir*, Michael DiCarlo; *Ser*, Judy Irvin; *Bibliogr*, Fred Hamilton; *Doc*, Stephen Henson; *Ref*, Lynell Buckley; *ILL*, Laura Ogden; *Coll Develop*, John Calhoun; Staff 31 (MLS 14, Non-MLS 17)
Founded 1895. Enrl 9,500; Fac 398; Highest Degree: Doctorate
Jul 1998-Jun 1999 Income $2,328,037. Mats Exp $955,000, Books $195,000, Per/Ser (Incl. Access Fees) $760,000. Sal $1,040,727 (Prof $533,394)
Library Holdings: Bk Vols 396,405; Per Subs 2,621
Mem of Trail Blazer Libr Syst
Partic in La Acad Libr Info Network Consortium; SE Libr Network

SAINT BENEDICT

CR SAINT JOSEPH SEMINARY COLLEGE, Pere Rouquette Library, 75376 River Rd, 70457. SAN 306-5308. Tel: 504-867-2237. FAX: 504-867-2270. Web Site: www.stjosephabbey.org. *Dir*, George Dansker; E-Mail: gdansker@hotmail.com
Founded 1891. Highest Degree: Bachelor
1998-1999 Mats Exp $23,320, Books $9,000, Per/Ser (Incl. Access Fees) $13,000. Sal $55,076
Library Holdings: Bk Vols 40,000; Per Subs 155
Subject Interests: Education, History, Literature, Philosophy, Religion, Social sciences and issues
Special Collections: Diocesan Coll; Historical Natchez

SAINT GABRIEL

§S HUNT CORRECTIONAL CENTER LIBRARY, 6925 Hwy 74, 70776. (Mail add: PO Box 174, 70776-0174), Tel: 225-319-4346. FAX: 225-319-4596. *Mgr*, Steven Ratcliff
Library Holdings: Bk Vols 7,000; Per Subs 40

S LOUISIANA CORRECTIONAL INSTITUTE FOR WOMEN LIBRARY,* Hwy 74, PO Box 26, 70776. SAN 306-5316. Tel: 225-642-5529. FAX: 225-319-2757. *Librn*, Elmelda Thoman
Founded 1969
Library Holdings: Bk Vols 6,900; Per Subs 14
Friends of the Library Group

SAINT JOSEPH

P TENSAS PARISH LIBRARY,* 135 Plank Rd, PO Box 228, 71366-0228. SAN 306-5324. Tel: 318-766-3781. FAX: 318-766-0098. E-Mail: t1tn@pelican.state.lib.la.us. *Librn*, Byron Temple
Founded 1952. Pop 7,200; Circ 37,453
Library Holdings: Bk Vols 25,600; Per Subs 29
Special Collections: Louisiana Section
Mem of Trail Blazer Libr Syst

SAINT MARTINVILLE

P SAINT MARTIN PARISH LIBRARY, 201 Porter St, PO Box 79, 70582-0079. SAN 306-5332. Tel: 337-394-2207. FAX: 337-394-2248. Web Site: www.beau.lib.la.us/~smpl. *Dir*, Jeanne A Essmeier; *ILL*, Serhania Mitchell; *Coll Develop*, Erica Poirier; Staff 17 (Non-MLS 17)
Founded 1955. Pop 46,262; Circ 199,003
Jan 1998-Dec 1999 Income $758,137. Mats Exp $162,216, Books $125,932, Per/Ser (Incl. Access Fees) $12,150, Presv $800, AV Equip $1,000. Sal $344,060 (Prof $49,400)
Library Holdings: Bk Vols 112,092; Per Subs 457
Subject Interests: Genealogy, History, Louisiana
Publications: Genealogy catalog, microfilm catalog
Mem of Bayouland Library System
Friends of the Library Group
Branches: 6
ARNAUDVILLE BRANCH, 1021 Overton St, PO Box 768, Arnaudville, 70512. SAN 377-6107. Tel: 337-754-5037. FAX: 337-754-5037. Web Site: www.beau.lib.la.us/~smpl.
Friends of the Library Group
BREAUX BRIDGE BRANCH, 102 Courthouse St, Breaux Bridge, 70517. SAN 329-6962. Tel: 337-332-2733. FAX: 337-332-2733. Web Site: www.beau.lib.la.us/~smpl.
Friends of the Library Group
CATAHOULA, 1016-A Catahoula School Hwy, 70582. SAN 377-6123. Tel: 337-394-1900. FAX: 337-394-1900. Web Site: www.beau.lib.la.us/~smpl.
Friends of the Library Group
CECILIA BRANCH, 2040 Cecilia St, High School Hwy, PO Box 247, Cecilia, 70521. SAN 329-6989. Tel: 337-667-7411. FAX: 337-667-7411. Web Site: www.beau.lib.la.us/~smpl.
Friends of the Library Group
PARKS, 1012 Martin St, PO Box 2542, 70582. SAN 377-614X. Tel: 337-845-4693. FAX: 337-845-4693. E-Mail: parks.b1mt@pelican.state.lib.la.us.

Web Site: www.beau.lib.la.us/~smpl.
Friends of the Library Group
STEPHENSVILLE, 3243 Hwy 70, Morgan City, 70380. SAN 377-6166. Tel: 504-385-4687. FAX: 504-385-4687. E-Mail: stephensville.b1mt@pelican.state.lib.la.us. Web Site: www.beau.lib.la.us/~smpl.
Friends of the Library Group
Bookmobiles: 1

SHREVEPORT

M AMERICAN RHINOLOGIC SOCIETY LIBRARY,* LSU Medical Ctr/Dept of OTO, 1501 Kings Hwy, Office No 9-203, 71130. SAN 376-1835. Tel: 318-675-6262. Toll Free Tel: 888-520-9585. FAX: 318-675-6260. Web Site: www.american-rhinologic.org..
Library Holdings: Bk Vols 500

S AMERICAN ROSE SOCIETY LIBRARY, 8877 Jefferson Paige Rd, 71119-8817. (Mail add: PO Box 30000, 71130-0030), SAN 327-4616. Tel: 318-938-5402. FAX: 318-938-5405. E-Mail: ars@ars-hq.org. Web Site: www.ars.org. *Librn*, Darlene Kamperman
Library Holdings: Bk Titles 1,000
Subject Interests: Gardening

R B'NAI ZION CONGREGATION, B'Nai Zion Memorial Library, 245 Southfield Rd, 71105. SAN 306-5359. Tel: 318-861-2122. FAX: 318-861-7961. E-Mail: bzt@microgear.net. *Librn*, Judy Grunes
Founded 1952
Library Holdings: Bk Titles 5,045; Per Subs 12
Subject Interests: Art, History, Judaica (lit or hist of Jews), Literature, Philosophy

C CENTENARY COLLEGE OF LOUISIANA, John F Magale Memorial Library, 2911 Centenary Blvd, 71134-1188. (Mail add: PO Box 41188, 71134-1188), SAN 306-5367. Tel: 318-869-5047. Interlibrary Loan Service Tel: 318-869-5202. Reference Tel: 318-869-5058. FAX: 318-869-5004. Web Site: www.centenary.edu/magale/index2.html. *Dean of Libr*, Roger Becker; Tel: 318-869-5059, E-Mail: rbecker@centenary.edu; *Cat*, Judith K Grunes; E-Mail: jgrunes@centenary.edu; *Dir*, Dr Ronald N Bukoff; Tel: 318-869-5247, E-Mail: rbukoff@centenary.edu; *Acq of Monographs*, Nancy E Middleton; Tel: 318-869-5173, E-Mail: nmiddlet@centenary.edu; *Coordr*, Christy J Wrenn; Tel: 318-869-5057, E-Mail: cwrenn@centenary.edu; *Archivist*, Margery Wright; Tel: 318-869-5172, E-Mail: mwright@centenary.edu; *Circ*, Sharon K Chevalier; E-Mail: schevali@centenary.edu; *Doc Delivery, ILL*, Marcia M Alexander; Tel: 318-869-5220; *Tech Coordr, Web Coordr*, Eric Grunes; Tel: 318-869-5171, E-Mail: egrunes@centenary.edu; *Access Serv, Archivist, Instrul Serv, Res*, Kyle Labor; Tel: 318-869-5123, E-Mail: klabor@centenary.edu; *Ser*, Beth Ackerman; Tel: 318-869-5499, E-Mail: backerman@centenary.edu; *Circ*, Sofia Bennett; Tel: 318-869-5699, E-Mail: sbennett@centenary.edu. Subject Specialists: *Archives*, Margery Wright; *Bibliog instruction*, Judith K Grunes; *Methodist hist*, Beth Ackerman; *Mus studies*, Dr Ronald N Bukoff; Staff 11 (MLS 3, Non-MLS 8)
Founded 1825. Enrl 1,033; Fac 75; Highest Degree: Master
Jun 1999-May 2000 Income $305,000. Mats Exp $344,059, Books $53,872, Per/Ser (Incl. Access Fees) $139,110, Micro $10,000, Manuscripts & Archives $1,070, Electronic Ref Mat (Incl. Access Fees) $19,400. Sal $288,818
Library Holdings: Bk Vols 178,557; Per Subs 928; Spec Interest Per Sub 329; Bks on Deafness & Sign Lang 3
Subject Interests: American literature, Geology, Music educ, Religion
Special Collections: Bill Corrington Papers; Centenary College Archives; Centenary College Archives; Jack London Papers; Jack London Papers; North Louisiana Historical Association Archicves; North Louisiana Historical Association Archives; Rare Books & Cline Room Archives; Sam Peters Research Center; United Methodist Church Archives; United Methodist Church Archives
Automation Activity & Vendor Info: (Acquisitions) Innovative Interfaces Inc.; (Cataloging) Innovative Interfaces Inc.; (Circulation) Innovative Interfaces Inc.; (ILL) Innovative Interfaces Inc.; (OPAC) Innovative Interfaces Inc.; (Serials) Innovative Interfaces Inc.
Database Vendor: CARL, GaleNet, IAC - Info Trac, IAC - SearchBank, Innovative Interfaces INN - View, Lexis-Nexis, OCLC - First Search, Wilson - Wilson Web
Publications: Keys To Magale Library (Library handbook)
Restriction: Private library
Function: For research purposes
Partic in Amigos Library Services, Inc; Assoc Cols of the South; La Libr Network; OCLC Online Computer Library Center, Inc; Phoenix Group
Friends of the Library Group

GM DEPARTMENT OF VETERANS AFFAIRS, Overton Brooks Medical Center Library, 510 E Stoner Ave, 71101-4295. SAN 306-5502. Tel: 318-424-6036. FAX: 318-424-6170. *Chief Librn*, Mary C Hill
Founded 1950
Library Holdings: Bk Vols 20,173; Bk Titles 20,000; Per Subs 310
Subject Interests: Clinical medicine
Partic in Veterans Affairs Library Network

R FIRST PRESBYTERIAN CHURCH LIBRARY,* 900 Jordan St, 71101. SAN 306-5383. Tel: 318-222-0604. FAX: 318-221-8589. *Librn*, Betty Shires
Founded 1952
Library Holdings: Bk Titles 7,500
Special Collections: A-Tapes, Sermons & Lectures

R FIRST UNITED METHODIST CHURCH, Bliss Memorial Library, 500 Common St, 71101. (Mail add: PO Box 1567, 71165-1567), SAN 306-5375. Tel: 318-424-7771. FAX: 318-429-6888. Web Site: www.fumschv.org. *Librn*, Bennette Daniel; *Librn*, Anne King; Tel: 318-798-0307, E-Mail: AWKING@aol.com; *Asst Librn*, Dorothy Moss Hanks; Staff 20 (MLS 3, Non-MLS 17)
Founded 1946
Library Holdings: Bk Vols 12,500
Subject Interests: Children's, Fiction, Religion
Special Services for the Blind - Large print bks

P GREEN GOLD LIBRARY SYSTEM, 424 Texas, PO Box 21523, 71120. SAN 306-5391. Tel: 318-226-5871. FAX: 318-226-4780. *Dir*, James Pelton; Staff 1 (MLS 1)
Founded 1971. Pop 418,000
Subject Interests: Genealogy
Special Collections: Government Documents; Larkin Edwards Coll
Member Libraries: Bossier Parish Community College Library; Sabine Parish Library

S GRINDSTONE BLUFF MUSEUM LIBRARY,* 875 Cotton St, 71101. SAN 326-1026. Tel: 318-222-3325, 318-861-4363.
Founded 1958
Library Holdings: Bk Vols 5,500; Bk Titles 5,500; Per Subs 25
Subject Interests: Archaeology, Folklore, Geography
Special Collections: Archaeology & Social Anthropology; Geology & Physical Geography, bks, journals, slides, tapes; Regional American Indians, Caddo & others
Partic in Am Asn of Museums; Local & State Mus of La; Soc of Am Archaeology

C LOUISIANA STATE UNIVERSITY IN SHREVEPORT, Noel Memorial Library, One University Pl, 71115-2399. SAN 306-5405. Tel: 318-798-5069. Circulation Tel: 318-797-5225. Reference Tel: 318-798-5068. FAX: 318-798-4138. Web Site: www.lsus.edu/library. *Dean*, Dr Alan D Gabehart; Tel: 318-798-4131; *Head, Circ*, Rich Collins; *Head Tech Servs*, James Evans; *Head Ref*, Julienne Wood; *Archivist*, Laura Street; *Res*, Tami Echavarria; *Curator*, Dr Robert Leitz; *Online Servs*, William Peters; *Tech Servs*, Laura Coleman; Staff 22 (MLS 7, Non-MLS 15)
Founded 1966. Enrl 4,500; Fac 175; Highest Degree: Master
Jul 2000-Jun 2001 Income $1,137,633. Sal $670,557
Library Holdings: Bk Vols 241,334; Bk Titles 250,000; Per Subs 1,200
Special Collections: James Smith Noel Coll
Automation Activity & Vendor Info: (Cataloging) NOTIS; (OPAC) NOTIS
Database Vendor: epixtech, inc., GaleNet, IAC - Info Trac, ProQuest, Wilson - Wilson Web
Publications: Shreveport TIMES Index (1871-1890)
Partic in Amigos Library Services, Inc; La Libr Network; OCLC Online Computer Library Center, Inc

CM LOUISIANA STATE UNIVERSITY SCHOOL OF MEDICINE IN SHREVEPORT, Medical Library,* 1501 Kings Hwy, PO Box 33932, 71130-3932. SAN 306-5413. Tel: 318-675-5445. FAX: 318-675-5442. Web Site: lib-sh.lsumc.edu. *Dir*, James Pat Craig; E-Mail: jcraig@lsumc.edu; *Assoc Dir*, Marianne Puckett; *Asst Dir*, Billy Triplett; *Bibliog Instr, Ref*, Dixie Jones; *Cat*, Alice Burnett; *Circ, ILL*, Shirley Dickerson; *Coll Develop*, Betty Tucker; Staff 22 (MLS 16, Non-MLS 6)
Founded 1968. Enrl 400
Library Holdings: Bk Vols 198,083; Per Subs 907
Subject Interests: Allied health, Medicine, Nursing
Special Collections: Archives; History of Medicine; Medical Fiction
Publications: Library Bulletin (bi-monthly); LSUMC Faculty Publications (ann)
Partic in Amigos Library Services, Inc; OCLC Online Computer Library Center, Inc; South Central Academic Medical Libraries Consortium

CM NORTHWESTERN STATE UNIVERSITY OF LOUISIANA, E P Watson Library - Shreveport Division - Nursing Education Center, 1800 Line Ave, 71101. SAN 306-5421. Tel: 318-677-3007. Interlibrary Loan Service Tel: 318-677-3008. Circulation Tel: 318-677-3007. FAX: 318-676-7087. Web Site: www.nsula.edu/department/watson_library/index.html. *Librn*, Barbara D Reilly; Tel: 318-677-3013; *Assoc Librn*, Dorthy Fernandez; Tel: 318-677-3008; *Assoc Librn*, Sandra Rufty; Tel: 318-677-3009; Staff 3 (MLS 1, Non-MLS 2)
Founded 1949. Enrl 1,100; Fac 52; Highest Degree: Master
Jul 2000-Jun 2001 Mats Exp $55,760, Books $37,480, Per/Ser (Incl. Access Fees) $18,280. Sal $80,993 (Prof $34,839)
Library Holdings: Bk Vols 9,979; Bk Titles 6,700; Per Subs 151
Subject Interests: Nursing, Radiologic tech
Special Collections: Historical Nursing Texts, microfilm
Automation Activity & Vendor Info: (Acquisitions) NOTIS; (Cataloging) NOTIS; (Circulation) NOTIS; (OPAC) NOTIS; (Serials) NOTIS

Database Vendor: Silverplatter Information Inc.
Partic in Docline; La Online Univ Info Systs; NLM
Branch of Eugene P Watson, NSU, Natchitoches, LA 71497

S R W NORTON ART GALLERY, Reference & Research Library, 4747 Creswell Ave, 71106-1899. SAN 306-543X. Tel: 318-865-4201. FAX: 318-869-0435. E-Mail: norton@softdisk.com. *Librn*, Ginger Specian; Staff 1 (MLS 1)
Founded 1946
Subject Interests: Fine arts, Genealogy, Ornithology
Special Collections: Early US, State & Local History, especially Virginia (James M Owens Memorial)
Restriction: Non-circulating to the public

M SCHUMPERT MEDICAL CENTER LIBRARY, One Saint Mary Pl, PO Box 21976, 71120-1976. SAN 324-5683. Tel: 318-681-4500. FAX: 318-681-4550.
Library Holdings: Bk Vols 2,200; Per Subs 120

P SHREVE MEMORIAL LIBRARY, (SML), 424 Texas St, 71101. (Mail add: PO Box 21523, 71120-1523), SAN 343-5245. Tel: 318-226-5897. Interlibrary Loan Service Tel: 318-226-5887. Circulation Tel: 318-226-5898. Reference Tel: 318-226-5894. FAX: 318-226-4780. Web Site: www.shreve-lib.org. *Dir*, James R Pelton; Tel: 318-226-5870, E-Mail: jpelton@smlnet.sml.lib.la.us; *Asst Dir*, Jeffrey L Salter; Tel: 318-226-5872, E-Mail: jlsalter@smlnet.sml.lib.la.us; *Automation Syst Coordr*, Grace Simmons; Tel: 318-226-4975, E-Mail: gsimmons@smlnet.sml.lib.la.us; *Head Ref*, Carlos Colon; Tel: 318-226-5886, E-Mail: ccolon@smlnet.sml.lib.la.us; *ILL*, Melba Evans; Tel: 318-226-5887, E-Mail: mevans@smlnet.sml.lib.la.us; *Ch Servs*, Mary Ann Skarda; Tel: 318-226-5880, E-Mail: maskarda@smlnet.sml.lib.la.us; *Cat*, Dana Smith; Tel: 318-226-5874; *Head, Acq*, Julia Gahagan; Tel: 318-226-5876, E-Mail: jgahagan@smlnet.sml.lib.la.us; *Acq*, Susan Wise; Tel: 318-226-4980, E-Mail: swise@smlnet.sml.lib.la.us; *Br Coordr*, Cindy Ortego; Tel: 318-226-5881, E-Mail: cortego@smlnet.sml.lib.la.us; *Spec Coll*, Pat Ferguson; Tel: 318-226-5888, E-Mail: patf@smlnet.sml.lib.la.us; *Head, Circ*, Brenda Jackson; Tel: 318-226-5896; *Admin Assoc*, Kathy Tuminello; Tel: 318-226-4977, E-Mail: kathyt@smlnet.sml.lib.la.us; *Commun Relations*, Ivy Woodard-Latin; Tel: 318-226-4976, E-Mail: ilatin@smlnet.sml.lib.la.us; Staff 25 (MLS 14, Non-MLS 11)
Founded 1923. Pop 260,000
Jan 1999-Dec 1999 Income (Main Library and Branch Library) $18,635,864, State $487,096, County $7,933,580, Locally Generated Income $675,785, Other $9,539,403. Mats Exp $634,176, Books $513,121, Per/Ser (Incl. Access Fees) $67,728, AV Equip $53,327. Sal $2,455,779
Library Holdings: Bk Vols 719,572; Per Subs 4,600
Subject Interests: Genealogy, Geology, Petroleum
Special Collections: Louisiana Coll
Database Vendor: epixtech, inc.
Function: Archival collection, Business archives, Document delivery services, ILL available, Newspaper reference library, Outside services via phone, cable & mail, Photocopies available, Research library, Some telephone reference
Partic in Green Gold Libr Syst
Friends of the Library Group
Branches: 19
ATKINS, 2709 Hassett, 71109. SAN 343-527X. Tel: 318-635-6222. *Branch Mgr*, Dora Rogers; E-Mail: drogers@smlnet.sml.lib.la.us; Staff 1 (Non-MLS 1)
Library Holdings: Bk Vols 33,975
Friends of the Library Group
BELCHER-WYCHE BRANCH, 409 Charles St, PO Box 121, Belcher, 71004. SAN 343-530X. Tel: 318-378-4567. *Branch Mgr*, Lesa Miller; Staff 1 (Non-MLS 1)
Library Holdings: Bk Vols 7,583
Friends of the Library Group
BLANCHARD BRANCH, 344 Alexander St, PO Box 779, Blanchard, 71009. SAN 343-5334. Tel: 318-929-3163. *Branch Mgr*, Frances Andrews; Staff 1 (Non-MLS 1)
Library Holdings: Bk Vols 8,239
Friends of the Library Group
BROADMOOR, 1212 Captain Shreve Dr, 71105. SAN 343-5369. Tel: 318-219-1782, 318-869-0120. FAX: 318-868-9464. *Branch Mgr*, Betty Cannon; E-Mail: bcannon@smlnet.sml.lib.la.us; *Head Ref*, Jeremy Bolom; Staff 6 (MLS 3, Non-MLS 3)
Library Holdings: Bk Vols 60,288
Subject Interests: Genealogy
Friends of the Library Group
CEDAR GROVE-LINE AVENUE, 8303 Line Ave, 71106. SAN 343-5393. Tel: 318-868-3890. FAX: 318-868-2071. *Branch Mgr*, Nancy Solomon; E-Mail: nsolomon@smlnet.sml.lib.la.us; Staff 1 (Non-MLS 1)
Library Holdings: Bk Vols 32,312
Friends of the Library Group
DAVID RAINES BRANCH, 1625 David Raines Rd, 71107. SAN 343-5660. Tel: 318-222-0824. *Branch Mgr*, Yvette Black-Counts; E-Mail: ladycounts@yahoo.com; Staff 1 (Non-MLS 1)
Library Holdings: Bk Vols 20,869
Friends of the Library Group
EXTENSION CENTER, 5802 Union Ave, 71108. SAN 328-8986. Tel: 318-636-5520.; Staff 1 (Non-MLS 1)
Library Holdings: Bk Vols 59,199
Friends of the Library Group
GILLIAM BRANCH, 12797 Main, PO Box 217, Gilliam, 71029. SAN 343-5407. Tel: 318-296-4227. *Branch Mgr*, Betty Hall; Staff 1 (Non-MLS 1)
Library Holdings: Bk Vols 7,609
Friends of the Library Group
HAMILTON, 2604 Hillcrest Ave, 71108. SAN 343-5423. Tel: 318-631-3675. FAX: 318-631-4743. *Branch Mgr*, Bob Gullion; E-Mail: bgullion@smlnet.sml.lib.la.us; Staff 1 (Non-MLS 1)
Library Holdings: Bk Vols 53,769
Friends of the Library Group
HIGGINBOTHAM-BRYSON, 9381 Greenwood Rd, PO Box 48, Greenwood, 71033. SAN 343-5458. Tel: 318-938-1451. *Branch Mgr*, Claire Loveridge; Staff 1 (Non-MLS 1)
Library Holdings: Bk Vols 6,747
Friends of the Library Group
HOSSTON BRANCH, 15487 US Hwy 71, PO Box 355, Hosston, 71043. SAN 343-5482. Tel: 318-287-3265. *Branch Mgr*, Mable Kirby; Staff 1 (Non-MLS 1)
Library Holdings: Bk Vols 6,420
Friends of the Library Group
MEANS, 7016 E Magnolia Lane, PO Box 295, Ida, 71044. SAN 343-5547. Tel: 318-284-3416. *Librn*, Wanda Dial; Staff 1 (Non-MLS 1)
Library Holdings: Bk Vols 7,213
Friends of the Library Group
MOORINGSPORT BRANCH, 603 Latimer St, PO Box 356, Mooringsport, 71060. SAN 343-5571. Tel: 318-996-6720. *Branch Mgr*, Diane Maxwell; Staff 1 (Non-MLS 1)
Library Holdings: Bk Vols 9,291
Friends of the Library Group
NORTH CADDO, 615 N Pine St, Vivian, 71082. SAN 343-5601. Tel: 318-375-3975. FAX: 318-375-4597. *Branch Mgr*, Lynette Parker; Staff 1 (Non-MLS 1)
Library Holdings: Bk Vols 33,239
Friends of the Library Group
OIL CITY BRANCH, 102 Allen St, PO Box 930, Oil City, 71061. SAN 343-5636. Tel: 318-995-7975. *Branch Mgr*, Rose Marie Hopkins; Staff 1 (Non-MLS 1)
Library Holdings: Bk Vols 15,533
RODESSA BRANCH, 10093 Main St, PO Box 176, Rodessa, 71069. SAN 343-5695. Tel: 318-223-4211. *Branch Mgr*, Katheryn Flores; Staff 1 (Non-MLS 1)
Library Holdings: Bk Vols 8,024
Friends of the Library Group
SOUTH CADDO, 9701 Baird Rd, 71118. SAN 343-5725. Tel: 318-687-6824. *Branch Mgr*, Babs Skains; Staff 1 (Non-MLS 1)
Library Holdings: Bk Vols 60,473
Friends of the Library Group
WALLETTE, 363 Hearne Ave, 71103. SAN 343-5512. Tel: 318-425-3630. FAX: 318-226-8311. *Branch Mgr*, Ruth Ann Jackson; Staff 1 (Non-MLS 1)
Library Holdings: Bk Vols 23,141
Friends of the Library Group
WEST SHREVEPORT, 6723 Pines Rd, No 110, 71129. SAN 370-4491. Tel: 318-686-0729. *Branch Mgr*, Charla Streetman; E-Mail: cstreet@smlnet.sml.lib.la.us; Staff 1 (Non-MLS 1)
Library Holdings: Bk Vols 39,630
Friends of the Library Group
Bookmobiles: 1

J SOUTHERN UNIVERSITY, Shreveport-Bossier City Campus Library,* 3050 Martin Luther King Dr, 71107. SAN 306-5480. Tel: 318-674-3400. Interlibrary Loan Service Tel: 318-674-3396. FAX: 318-674-3403. *Librn*, Orella Brazile; *Circ*, Nora Ware; *Ref*, Camille Redden; *Media Spec*, Fred Moss; Staff 4 (MLS 4)
Founded 1967. Enrl 1,483; Fac 56
Library Holdings: Bk Vols 48,143; Bk Titles 32,692; Per Subs 379
Subject Interests: Ethnic studies, Natural science
Special Collections: Black Studies, bks, pictures; Louisiana Coll
Open Mon-Thurs 8-9, Fri 8-5 & Sat 9-1

S TIMES LIBRARY,* 222 Lake St, 71130. SAN 306-5472. Tel: 318-459-3389. FAX: 318-459-3301. *Librn*, Martha Matlock; *Asst Librn*, Dorothy Landry
Founded 1950
Library Holdings: Bk Titles 2,275; Per Subs 13

L UNITED STATES COURTS LIBRARY,* 300 Fannin St Rm 5012, 71101. SAN 372-0934. Tel: 318-676-3230. FAX: 318-676-3231. E-Mail: 5sattib-shreveport@ca5.uscourts.gov. *Librn*, Marian Drey
Library Holdings: Bk Vols 10,000; Per Subs 40

SUNSET

P SOUTH ST LANDRY COMMUNITY LIBRARY,* 235 Marie St, 70584. SAN 373-7659. Tel: 337-662-3442. FAX: 337-662-3475. *Dir*, Golda B Jordan; E-Mail: gjordan@pelican.state.lib.la.us
Founded 1993. Pop 8,500
Jan 1997-Dec 1998 Income $115,917, State $3,500, Provincial $33,227, County $59,000, Locally Generated Income $1,840, Other $1,050. Mats Exp Books $13,000. Sal $26,101
Library Holdings: Bk Vols 18,206
Publications: Library Log (quarterly)
Friends of the Library Group

TALLULAH

P MADISON PARISH LIBRARY, 403 N Mulberry St, 71282. SAN 343-575X. Tel: 318-574-4308. FAX: 318-574-4312. *Dir*, Gary Phillips; E-Mail: gphillip@pelican.state.lib.la.us; *Tech Servs*, Olivia Virgil; Staff 4 (MLS 1, Non-MLS 3)
Founded 1945. Pop 12,930; Circ 19,625
Jan 2000-Dec 2000 Income (Main Library Only) County $166,639. Mats Exp $21,080, Books $18,580, Per/Ser (Incl. Access Fees) $2,500. Sal $75,934
Library Holdings: Bk Vols 30,000; Bk Titles 39,000; Per Subs 80
Subject Interests: Art and architecture, Economics, Horticulture, Music, Religion, World War II
Mem of Trail Blazer Libr Syst

THIBODAUX

P LAFOURCHE PARISH PUBLIC LIBRARY, 303 W Fifth St, 70301-3123. SAN 343-5814. Tel: 504-446-1163. FAX: 504-446-3848. E-Mail: kilgen@pelican.state.lib.la.us. Web Site: www.lafourche.lib.la.us. *Dir*, Kathleen Kilgen; Staff 53 (MLS 4, Non-MLS 49)
Founded 1947. Pop 88,127; Circ 234,623
Library Holdings: Bk Vols 158,244; Bk Titles 89,375; Per Subs 390
Subject Interests: Genealogy, Louisiana
Automation Activity & Vendor Info: (Acquisitions) TLC; (Cataloging) TLC; (Circulation) TLC; (ILL) TLC; (OPAC) TLC; (Serials) TLC
Friends of the Library Group
Branches: 6
CUT OFF GALLIANO BRANCH, Hwy 1 at W 154th St, PO Box 488, Galliano, 70354. SAN 343-5873. Tel: 504-632-7140. FAX: 504-632-4963. E-Mail: galliano.b1la@pelican.state.lib.la.us. *In Charge*, Paul Chiquet
Library Holdings: Bk Vols 27,045; Bk Titles 22,330; Per Subs 50
Subject Interests: Genealogy, Louisiana
Automation Activity & Vendor Info: (Acquisitions) TLC; (Cataloging) TLC; (Circulation) TLC; (ILL) TLC; (OPAC) TLC; (Serials) TLC
Friends of the Library Group
GOLDEN MEADOW BRANCH, 1501 N Bayou Dr, Golden Meadow, 70357. SAN 343-5903. Tel: 504-475-5660. FAX: 504-475-7141. E-Mail: goldenmeadow.b1La@pelican.state.lib.la. *In Charge*, Tammy Robertson
Library Holdings: Bk Vols 17,806; Bk Titles 15,567; Per Subs 43
Automation Activity & Vendor Info: (Acquisitions) TLC; (Cataloging) TLC; (Circulation) TLC; (ILL) TLC; (OPAC) TLC; (Serials) TLC
Friends of the Library Group
LAROSE BRANCH, Bayou Civic Ctr, E Fifth St, PO Box 1430, Larose, 70373. SAN 343-5938. Tel: 504-693-3336. FAX: 504-693-6131. E-Mail: larosecutoff.b1la@pelican.state.lib.la.us. *In Charge*, Diana Uzee
Library Holdings: Bk Vols 20,566; Bk Titles 15,800; Per Subs 50
Automation Activity & Vendor Info: (Acquisitions) TLC; (Cataloging) TLC; (Circulation) TLC; (ILL) TLC; (OPAC) TLC; (Serials) TLC
Friends of the Library Group
LOCKPORT BRANCH, 710 Church, Lockport, 70374. SAN 343-5997. Tel: 504-532-3158. FAX: 504-532-0270. E-Mail: lockport.b1la@pelican.state.lib.la.us. *In Charge*, Brenda Bascle
Library Holdings: Bk Vols 20,958; Bk Titles 17,537; Per Subs 49
Automation Activity & Vendor Info: (Acquisitions) TLC; (Cataloging) TLC; (Circulation) TLC; (ILL) TLC; (OPAC) TLC; (Serials) TLC
Friends of the Library Group
MARTHA SOWELL UTLEY MEMORIAL, 314 St Mary St, 70301. SAN 343-6055. Tel: 504-447-4119. FAX: 504-449-4128. E-Mail: thibodeaux.b1la@pelican.state.lib.la.us. *Librn*, Sherill Faucheux
Library Holdings: Bk Vols 41,784; Bk Titles 34,379; Per Subs 145
Subject Interests: Genealogy, Louisiana
Automation Activity & Vendor Info: (Acquisitions) TLC; (Cataloging) TLC; (Circulation) TLC; (ILL) TLC; (OPAC) TLC; (Serials) TLC
Friends of the Library Group
RACELAND BRANCH, 104 Mississippi St, PO Box 189, Raceland, 70394-0189. SAN 343-6020. Tel: 504-537-6875. FAX: 504-537-9181. E-Mail: raceland.b1la@pelican.state.lib.la.us. *In Charge*, Regina Lauland
Library Holdings: Bk Vols 19,912; Bk Titles 16,976; Per Subs 53
Automation Activity & Vendor Info: (Acquisitions) TLC; (Cataloging) TLC; (Circulation) TLC; (ILL) TLC; (OPAC) TLC; (Serials) TLC
Friends of the Library Group
Bookmobiles: 1

C NICHOLLS STATE UNIVERSITY, Allen J Ellender Memorial Library, Leighton Dr, 70301. (Mail add: PO Box 2028, 70310), SAN 306-5529. Tel: 504-448-4646. Interlibrary Loan Service Tel: 504-448-4633. Circulation Tel: 504-448-4654. Reference Tel: 504-448-4625. FAX: 504-448-4925. Web Site: www.nich.edu/acad/ellender/ellender/html. *Dir*, Mark L Daganaar; E-Mail: el-mld@mail.nich.edu; *Acq, Asst Dir*, Stephen Banister; Tel: 504-448-4653, E-Mail: el-stb@mail.nich.edu; *Archivist, Spec Coll*, Carol Mathias; Tel: 504-448-4621, E-Mail: el-cam@mail.nich.edu; *Cat*, Alice Saltzman; Tel: 504-448-4635, E-Mail: el-abs@mail.nich.edu; *Publ Servs*, Joseph T Butler; Tel: 504-448-4626, E-Mail: el-jtb@mail.nich.edu; Staff 29 (MLS 10, Non-MLS 19)
Founded 1948. Enrl 7,345; Fac 301; Highest Degree: Master
Jul 1999-Jun 2000 Mats Exp $416,440, Books $36,500, Per/Ser (Incl. Access Fees) $291,000, Micro $14,500, AV Equip $13,240, Other Print Mats $61,200. Sal $1,044,273 (Prof $665,631)
Library Holdings: Bk Vols 532,948; Bk Titles 301,477; Per Subs 1,341
Subject Interests: Agriculture, Business and management, Culinary arts, Economics, Education, Marine biology, Nursing
Special Collections: Cajun & Zydeco Music Heritage; Center for Traditional Louisiana Boat Building; Local History (Historic Thibodaux & Historic Lafourche Parish); Sugar Cane Plantations (J Wilson Lepine Coll & Laurel Valley Coll), diaries, mss; United States Senators' Papers (Allen J Ellender Archives)
Automation Activity & Vendor Info: (Acquisitions) NOTIS; (Cataloging) NOTIS; (Circulation) NOTIS; (OPAC) NOTIS; (Serials) NOTIS
Database Vendor: GaleNet, IAC - Info Trac, Lexis-Nexis, OCLC - First Search, Silverplatter Information Inc.
Partic in La Acad Libr Info Network Consortium; La Online Univ Info Systs

VILLE PLATTE

P EVANGELINE PARISH LIBRARY,* 242 W Main St, PO Box 40, 70586-0040. SAN 306-5537. Tel: 318-363-1369. FAX: 318-363-2353. E-Mail: b1ev@pelican.state.lib.la.us. Web Site: www.eplibrary.org. *Dir*, Ramona A Pellerin; E-Mail: rniffene@pelican.state.lib.la.us; *Mgr*, Hope Demouruelle; Staff 12 (MLS 2, Non-MLS 10)
Founded 1948. Pop 33,274; Circ 131,715
Jan 1999-Dec 1999 Income (Main Library and Branch Library) $371,677, State $16,199, County $355,478. Mats Exp $41,423, Books $30,800, Per/Ser (Incl. Access Fees) $4,273, AV Equip $5,350, Electronic Ref Mat (Incl. Access Fees) $1,000. Sal $207,459 (Prof $30,000)
Library Holdings: Bk Vols 65,181; Per Subs 121
Subject Interests: Genealogy
Special Collections: Louisiana, Cajuns and Cajun Music
Automation Activity & Vendor Info: (Circulation) Gaylord; (OPAC) Gaylord
Database Vendor: GaleNet, IAC - Info Trac, ProQuest
Friends of the Library Group
Branches: 1
CHATAIGNIER BRANCH, PO Box 94, Chataignier, 70524. Tel: 318-885-2028. *Librn*, Hope Demouruelle
Library Holdings: Bk Vols 2,949; Bk Titles 2,936; Per Subs 44
Friends of the Library Group

WINNFIELD

P WINN PARISH LIBRARY, 205 W Main St, 71483-2718. SAN 343-608X. Tel: 318-628-4478. FAX: 318-628-9820. Web Site: www.winn.lib.la.us. *Dir*, Mary Doherty; E-Mail: mdoherty@pelican.state.lib.la.us; Staff 10 (MLS 1, Non-MLS 9)
Founded 1937. Pop 16,269; Circ 177,610
Jan 1997-Dec 1998 Income $246,313. Mats Exp $40,200, Books $30,000, Per/Ser (Incl. Access Fees) $7,200. Sal $157,288
Library Holdings: Bk Vols 86,000; Per Subs 120
Special Collections: Genealogy Coll, bks; Louisiana Coll, bks
Branches: 4
ATLANTA BRANCH, 110 School Rd, Atlanta, 71404. SAN 343-611X. Tel: 318-628-7657. *In Charge*, Amy Deen
Library Holdings: Bk Vols 3,200
CALVIN BRANCH, 255 Second St, Calvin, 71410. SAN 343-6144. Tel: 318-727-9644. *In Charge*, Robin Hailey
Library Holdings: Bk Vols 3,200
DODSON BRANCH, 206 E Gresham, Dodson, 71422. SAN 343-6179. Tel: 318-628-2821. *In Charge*, Gaila Cockerham
Library Holdings: Bk Vols 3,200
SIKES BRANCH, 125 Fifth St, Sikes, 71473. SAN 343-6209. Tel: 318-628-2824. *In Charge*, Lizzie Newsom
Library Holdings: Bk Vols 3,200

WINNSBORO

P FRANKLIN PARISH LIBRARY, 705 Prairie St, 71295-2795. SAN 343-6233. Tel: 318-435-4336. FAX: 318-435-1990. E-Mail: t1fr@pelican.state.lib.la.us. Web Site: www.franklin.lib.la.us. *Librn*, Carolyn Flint
Founded 1950. Pop 22,387; Circ 74,046

Library Holdings: Bk Vols 64,000
Special Collections: Louisiana Coll
Mem of Trail Blazer Libr Syst
Friends of the Library Group

Branches: 1
WISNER BRANCH, 129 Fort Scott St, PO Box 246, Wisner, 71378. SAN 343-6268. Tel: 318-724-7399. Web Site: www.franklin.lib.la.us. *In Charge*, Dale Barry
Library Holdings: Bk Vols 10,010

MAINE

Date of Statistics: 1998
Population, 1990 Census: 1,227,928
Population Served by Public Libraries Reporting: 1,032,224
Total Volumes in Public Libraries Reporting: 5,362,750
Volumes Per Capita: 5.19
Total Public Library Circulation: 7,755,850
Circulation Per Capita: 7.51
Total Public Library Expenditures: $21,635,466
Expenditures Per Capita: $20.96
Grants-in-Aid to Public Libraries:
State Aid: $43,000
Number of Regional Districts: 3

ACTON

P ACTON PUBLIC LIBRARY,* PO Box 539, 04001. SAN 306-5545. Tel: 207-636-2781. *Librn*, Doreen Henderson
Founded 1920. Pop 1,050; Circ 1,200
Library Holdings: Bk Vols 5,600
Mem of Southern Conn Libr Coun

ALBION

P ALBION PUBLIC LIBRARY,* CMP Dr, Box 1398, 04910. SAN 376-3803. Tel: 207-437-2616. FAX: 207-437-2001. *Librn*, Flora Wing Champlin
Library Holdings: Bk Vols 12,690; Bk Titles 10,000
Mem of Central Maine Library District

ALFRED

P PARSONS MEMORIAL LIBRARY,* Kennebunk Rd, PO Box 167, 04002. SAN 306-5561. Tel: 207-324-2001. *Librn*, Jean Collins
Pop 1,850; Circ 5,417
Library Holdings: Bk Vols 24,000; Bk Titles 20,000; Per Subs 25
Mem of Southern Conn Libr Coun; Southern Maine Library District
Open Mon & Wed 3-8, Tues & Sat 10-3
Friends of the Library Group

ANDOVER

P ANDOVER PUBLIC LIBRARY,* PO Box 393, 04216-0393. SAN 306-557X. Tel: 207-392-4841. *Librn*, Christie Mulvaney
Pop 850; Circ 4,112
Library Holdings: Bk Vols 7,400; Per Subs 16
Open Tues, Wed & Sat 1-4:30, Thurs 6-8

APPLETON

P MILDRED STEVENS WILLIAMS MEMORIAL LIBRARY, Appleton Public Library, 2957 Sennebec Rd, 04862. (Mail add: 260 Union Rd, 04862), SAN 306-5588. Tel: 207-785-4293. *Librn*, Nancy W Brown; Tel: 707-785-4293
Founded 1946. Pop 850; Circ 1,000
Jun 1998-Jun 1999 Income $1,326, City $500, Locally Generated Income $826. Mats Exp $1,361, Books $129
Library Holdings: Bk Vols 4,000
Special Collections: Maine Coll
Mem of Northeastern Maine Library District

ASHLAND

P ASHLAND COMMUNITY LIBRARY, 57 Exchange St, PO Box 639, 04732. SAN 306-5596. Tel: 207-435-6532. *Librn*, Gladys Craig
Founded 1960. Pop 1,888; Circ 8,863
Jan 1999-Dec 1999 Income $28,576, State $315, City $28,563. Mats Exp Books $5,800. Sal $17,700
Library Holdings: Bk Vols 12,500
Special Collections: Aroostook
Mem of Northeastern Maine Library District

AUBURN

S ANDROSCOGGIN HISTORICAL SOCIETY, Clarence E March Library, County Bldg, 2 Turner St, 04210-5978. SAN 306-5618. Tel: 207-784-0586. E-Mail: itigapa@aol.com. Web Site: www.rootsweb.com/~meandrhs. *In Charge*, Michael C Lord
Founded 1923
Jun 1999-May 2000 Income $5,986, State $1,500, Locally Generated Income $3,986, Other $500. Mats Exp $481, Books $397, Per/Ser (Incl. Access Fees) $84. Sal $13,992
Library Holdings: Bk Vols 3,900; Per Subs 13; Spec Interest Per Sub 12
Subject Interests: Genealogy, Local history
Special Collections: Historical Diaries & Photographs (Local Coll), local maps
Publications: Androscoggin History (3 times a year) (Newsletter)
Restriction: Not a lending library, Open to public for reference only, Open to public with supervision only, Public use on premises
Function: Archival collection, For research purposes, Newspaper reference library, Photocopies available, Reference only, Reference services available, Referrals accepted, Research fees apply, Research library, Some telephone reference

P AUBURN PUBLIC LIBRARY, 49 Spring St, 04210. SAN 306-5626. Tel: 207-782-3191. FAX: 207-782-1859. Web Site: www.auburn.lib.me.us. *Dir*, Steve Norman; E-Mail: snorman@auburn.lib.me.us; *Ch Servs*, Pamela Riley Osborn; *Circ*, John Kelley; *Tech Servs*, Linda Henault; *Ad Servs*, Steve Bouchard; Staff 18 (MLS 4, Non-MLS 14)
Founded 1890. Pop 24,000; Circ 157,500
Jul 1999-Jun 2000 Income $791,800, State $200, City $722,200, Locally Generated Income $69,400. Mats Exp $102,700, Books $72,300, Per/Ser (Incl. Access Fees) $16,000, Presv $1,700, Micro $1,000, Electronic Ref Mat (Incl. Access Fees) $11,700. Sal $452,600 (Prof $167,200)
Library Holdings: Bk Vols 82,765; Per Subs 260
Subject Interests: Genealogy, Local history
Automation Activity & Vendor Info: (Cataloging) epixtech, inc.; (Circulation) epixtech, inc.; (OPAC) epixtech, inc.
Database Vendor: Ebsco - EbscoHost
Publications: APL Quarterly (Newsletter)
Mem of Central Maine Library District
Friends of the Library Group

CM CENTRAL MAINE TECHNICAL COLLEGE LIBRARY, 1250 Turner St, 04210-6498. SAN 377-9785. Tel: 207-755-5265. FAX: 207-755-5494. Web Site: www.cmtc.net/library/. *Dir Libr Serv*, Judith G Frost; E-Mail: jfrost@cmtc.net; jfrost@mtcs.net; Staff 2 (MLS 2)

Library Holdings: Bk Vols 11,000; Per Subs 235
Mem of Central Maine Library District
Partic in Maine Health Sci Librs & Info Consortium

J MID-STATE COLLEGE LIBRARY, Auburn Campus, 88 E Hardscrabble Rd, 04210. SAN 306-5634. Tel: 207-783-1478. FAX: 207-783-1477. Web Site: www.midstatecollege.com. *Librn*, Barbara MacIntosh
Founded 1968
Library Holdings: Bk Titles 3,965; Per Subs 62
Subject Interests: Accounting, Law, Medicine, Tourism, Travel
Partic in Central Maine Libr District
Information also includes library at Mid-State College in Augusta, Maine

L SKELTON, TAINTOR & ABBOTT, Law Library,* 95 Main St, PO Box 3200, 04212-3200. SAN 372-0950. Tel: 207-784-3200. FAX: 207-784-3345. *Librn*, Sue Turgeon
Library Holdings: Bk Vols 5,500; Per Subs 47

AUGUSTA

S AUGUSTA MENTAL HEALTH INSTITUTE, Colonel Black Library, Arsenal St, PO Box 724, 04330. SAN 343-6292. Tel: 207-287-7200, 207-287-7266. FAX: 207-287-7127. Web Site: www.state.me.us/dmhmrsa/amhi/library/index.htm. *AV*, Dennis Dunn
Library Holdings: Bk Vols 16,750; Per Subs 57
Subject Interests: Authors, Maine, Mental health, Native Am lit
Partic in BHSL; Health Science Library Information Consortium; North Atlantic Health Sciences Libraries, Inc

P CENTRAL MAINE LIBRARY DISTRICT,* Maine State Library, State House Sta 64, 04333. SAN 306-5642. Tel: 207-287-5600. FAX: 207-287-5615. Web Site: www.state.me.us/msl/mslhome.htm.
Member Libraries: Albert Church Brown Memorial Library; Albion Public Library; Alvan Bolster Ricker Memorial Library; Auburn Public Library; Bethel Library Association; Boothbay Harbor Memorial Library; Bowdoinham Public Library; Bremen Public Library; Bristol Area Library; Brown Memorial Library; Brownfield Public Library; Cary Memorial Library; Central Maine Power Company; Central Maine Technical College Library; Coolidge Library; Denmark Public Library; Department of Mental Health, Mental Retardation & Substance Abuse Services; Farmington Public Library; Freeland Holmes Library; Gardiner Public Library; Hartland Public Library; Isaac F Umberhine Library; Lawrence Public Library; Lewis Dana Hill Memorial Library; Lewiston Public Library; Lisbon Falls Community Library; Ludden Memorial Library; Madison Public Library; Mechanic Falls Public Library; Mexico Free Public Library; New Sharon Town Library; New Vineyard Public Library; Norridgewock Free Public Library; Norway Memorial Library; Patten Free Library; Phillips Public Library; Pittsfield Public Library; Rangeley Public Library; Rumford Public Library; Skidompha Public Library; Skowhegan Public Library; South China Library; Southport Memorial Library; Stratton Public Library; Strong Public Library; Topsham Public Library; Treat Memorial Library; Underwood Memorial Library; Waldoboro Public Library; Waterville Public Library; Weld Free Library; Wilton Free Public Library
Friends of the Library Group

S CENTRAL MAINE POWER COMPANY, Library Services, 83 Edison Dr, 04336. SAN 321-0367. Tel: 207-623-3521, Ext 2177. Interlibrary Loan Service Tel: 207-621-4761. Reference Tel: 207-621-4761. FAX: 207-623-9384. Web Site: www.cmpco.com. *Res*, Merica Tripp; E-Mail: merica.tripp@cmpco.com; Staff 2 (MLS 1, Non-MLS 1)
Founded 1978
Library Holdings: Bk Titles 7,000; Per Subs 150
Subject Interests: Energy, Environment, Law
Special Collections: Utility Annual Reports
Automation Activity & Vendor Info: (Acquisitions) CASPR; (Cataloging) CASPR; (Circulation) CASPR; (OPAC) CASPR; (Serials) CASPR
Database Vendor: Lexis-Nexis, OCLC - First Search
Restriction: Open to public upon request
Function: ILL available
Mem of Central Maine Library District
Partic in Nelinet, Inc

S DEPARTMENT OF MENTAL HEALTH, MENTAL RETARDATION & SUBSTANCE ABUSE SERVICES, (OSA IRC), (Formerly Office Of Substance Abuse), Information Resource Center, AMHI Complex Marquardt Bldg, 159 State House Sta, 04333-0159. SAN 370-1522. Tel: 207-287-8900. TDD: 800-215-7604. FAX: 207-287-8910. E-Mail: osa.ircosa@state.me.us. Web Site: www.state.me.us/dmhmrsa/osa, www.state.me.us/suicide. *Mgr*, Jo McCaslin; E-Mail: jo.mccaslin@state.me.us; *Librn*, Leanne Morin-Plourde; E-Mail: leanne.morin-plourde@state.me.us; Staff 2 (MLS 2)
Library Holdings: Bk Vols 8,234; Bk Titles 5,426; Spec Interest Per Sub 25
Subject Interests: Substance abuse, Suicide
Automation Activity & Vendor Info: (Cataloging) TLC; (Circulation) TLC; (Media Booking) TLC; (OPAC) TLC
Database Vendor: Ebsco - EbscoHost
Publications: 97 Prevention Data Report; Audiovisual Catalog; Teen Yellow Pages; Web Guide for Substance Abuse Prevention
Mem of Central Maine Library District; Maine State Library
Partic in Regional Alcohol And Drug Abuse Resource Network; Substance Abuse Librarians & Information Specialists

S DEPARTMENT OF THE SECRETARY OF STATE, Maine State Archives, 84 State House Sta, 04333-0084. SAN 373-0565. Tel: 207-287-5790. FAX: 207-287-5739. Web Site: www.state.me/sos/arc/. *Archivist*, James S Henderson; E-Mail: james.henderson@state.me.us; Staff 9 (Non-MLS 9)
Founded 1965
Library Holdings: Bk Titles 400
Subject Interests: Civil War, State government

P LITHGOW PUBLIC LIBRARY, Winthrop St, 04330-5599. SAN 306-5669. Tel: 207-626-2415. FAX: 207-626-2419. *Dir*, Elizabeth L Pohl; E-Mail: betsy@lithgow.lib.me.us; *Publ Servs*, Jodi L Crawford; E-Mail: jodi@lithgow.lib.me.us; *YA Servs*, David H Schumacher; E-Mail: daves@lithgow.lib.me.us; *Cat*, Ann Russell; E-Mail: annr@lithgow.lib.me.us; Staff 3 (MLS 3)
Founded 1896. Pop 21,325; Circ 136,000
Jul 2000-Jun 2001 Income $518,750, City $488,750, Other $30,000. Mats Exp $51,000, Books $44,000, Per/Ser (Incl. Access Fees) $3,000, Electronic Ref Mat (Incl. Access Fees) $4,000. Sal $390,932 (Prof $114,441)
Library Holdings: Bk Vols 54,000; Per Subs 105
Automation Activity & Vendor Info: (Cataloging) DRA; (Circulation) DRA; (OPAC) DRA
Friends of the Library Group

M MAINE GENERAL MEDICAL CENTER LIBRARY, 6 E Chestnut St, 04330. SAN 343-6322. Tel: 207-626-1325. FAX: 207-626-1537. *Librn*, Barbara Harness; E-Mail: bharness@mainegeneral.org; Staff 1 (MLS 1)
Library Holdings: Bk Vols 3,000; Per Subs 100
Subject Interests: History of medicine
Publications: LRC bulletin
Partic in BHSL; HSLC; Nat Libr of Med

P MAINE REGIONAL LIBRARY FOR THE BLIND & PHYSICALLY IMPAIRED, c/o Maine State Library, 64 State House Sta, 04333-0064. SAN 306-5685. Tel: 207-287-5650. Toll Free Tel: 800-762-7106. FAX: 207-287-5654. *Coordr, Librn*, Benita Davis; E-Mail: benitad@ursus1.ursus.maine.edu; Staff 3 (MLS 3)
Founded 1972
Library Holdings: Bk Vols 131,268
Special Collections: French Language, cassette
Publications: Talking Books (newsletter); Talking Books Borrower's Handbook

P MAINE STATE LIBRARY, State House Sta 64, 04333-0064. SAN 343-6357. Tel: 207-287-5600. Toll Free Tel: 800-452-8784. FAX: 207-287-5615. Web Site: www.state.me.us/msl/. *State Librn*, J Gary Nichols; E-Mail: gary.nichols@state.me.us; Staff 25 (MLS 25)
Founded 1839. Circ 160,000
Library Holdings: Bk Vols 300,000; Per Subs 170
Subject Interests: Genealogy, History
Special Collections: History Genealogy, Indians, letters, official rec, Maine Counties, Towns, Boundaries & Rivers, maps; Maine Authors; Maine Government, Baxter State Park, Conservation (Baxter Coll), letters, scrapbooks, personal rec; Mt Katahdin, Lumbering in Northern Maine 1876-1936, & the Appalachian Trail (Avery Coll)
Publications: Maine Entry; Maine Memo
Member Libraries: Berry Memorial Library; Bingham Union Library; Cumston Public Library; Department of Mental Health, Mental Retardation & Substance Abuse Services; Dr Shaw Memorial Library; Eastern Maine Technical College Library; Edythe L Dyer Community Library; Hope Library; Kennebec Valley Technical College; Old York Historical Society Library; Spaulding Memorial Library; West Paris Public Library
Partic in Nelinet, Inc; OCLC Online Computer Library Center, Inc
Branches: 1
MAINE REGIONAL LIBRARY FOR THE BLIND & PHYSICALLY IMPAIRED
See Separate Entry

M MEDICAL CARE DEVELOPMENT, INC LIBRARY,* 11 Parkwood Dr, 04330. SAN 321-5318. Tel: 207-622-7566. FAX: 207-622-3616. *Librn*, Mary Anne Libby; Staff 1 (MLS 1)
Founded 1968
Library Holdings: Bk Titles 200; Per Subs 20

J MID-STATE COLLEGE, Augusta Campus Library,* 218 Water St, 04330. SAN 306-5723. Tel: 207-623-3962. FAX: 207-623-3844. *Dir*, Sue Gammon; *Librn*, Barbara MacIntosh
Founded 1977
Library Holdings: Bk Vols 1,500
Subject Interests: Accounting, Data processing, Secretarial sciences
Special Collections: Maine Coll
Partic in Central Maine Libr District

GL STATE OF MAINE LAW & LEGISLATIVE REFERENCE LIBRARY, 43 State House Sta, 04333-0043. SAN 306-5731. Tel: 207-287-1600. TDD: 207-287-6431. FAX: 207-287-6467. Web Site: www.state.me.us/legis/lawlib. *Librn*, Lynn E Randall; *Tech Servs*, Sheila M Bearor; *Cat, Ser*, Mark R Knierim; *Publ Servs*, Stephanie P Ralph; *Ref*, Robert H Michaud; *Ref*, Sue Wright; Staff 15 (MLS 6, Non-MLS 9)
Founded 1971
Jul 1999-Jun 2000 Income $1,199,713. Mats Exp $250,892. Sal $858,984
Library Holdings: Bk Vols 106,703
Special Collections: Legislative Committee master files (111th Legislative to present)
Publications: Legislative Reference Bibliographies; New Items on our Shelves
Partic in Nelinet, Inc; Westlaw

C UNIVERSITY OF MAINE AT AUGUSTA LIBRARIES, Bennett D Katz Library, 46 University Dr, 04330-9410. SAN 306-574X. Tel: 207-621-3349. Circulation Tel: 207-621-3356. Reference Tel: 207-621-3348. Toll Free Tel: 877-862-1234, Ext 3349. FAX: 207-621-3354. Web Site: www.uma.maine.edu/libraries/. *Dean of Libr*, Thomas E Abbott; E-Mail: tabbott@maine.edu; *Asst Dean*, Jean Thomas; E-Mail: jean.thomas@maine.edu; *Circ, Tech Servs*, Judith Clarke; E-Mail: judithc@maine.edu; *Librn*, Judith Nottage; Fax: 207-262-7901, E-Mail: judyn@ursus3.ursus.maine.edu; *Coll Develop, Ref*, Jay Hoffman; E-Mail: jhoffman@maine.edu; *ILL, Ref*, Gabriella Howard; E-Mail: ghoward@maine.edu; Staff 6 (MLS 5, Non-MLS 1)
Founded 1965. Enrl 6,000; Fac 140; Highest Degree: Bachelor
Jun 1999-Jul 2000 Income Parent Institution $558,820. Mats Exp $179,473, Books $103,292, Per/Ser (Incl. Access Fees) $60,331, Micro $11,500, AV Equip $4,350. Sal $289,859 (Prof $212,208)
Library Holdings: Bk Titles 66,000; Per Subs 520
Subject Interests: Business, Liberal arts, Libr sci, Maine, Music, Nursing, Research
Special Collections: Maine Related Materials; Research Materials
Partic in Health Sci Libr Info Consortium; LVIS; Nelinet, Inc; OCLC Online Computer Library Center, Inc
Financial figures reported include the Bangor campus, Univ of Maine at Augusta

BAILEYVILLE

P WOODLAND PUBLIC LIBRARY,* PO Box 549, 04694-0549. SAN 306-7912. Tel: 207-427-3235. FAX: 207-427-3673. E-Mail: townsendg@woodland.lib.me.us. *Dir*, Gladys Townsend
Founded 1912. Pop 2,200; Circ 10,220
Jul 1998-Jun 1999 Income $26,998, State $200, City $26,798. Mats Exp $4,679, Books $4,000, Per/Ser (Incl. Access Fees) $679. Sal $14,232
Library Holdings: Bk Vols 16,500; Bk Titles 15,000; Per Subs 26
Special Collections: Maine Authors Coll
Mem of Northeastern Maine Library District

BANGOR

S BANGOR DAILY NEWS LIBRARY,* 491 Main St, PO Box 1329, 04402-1329. SAN 370-3886. Tel: 207-990-8000. FAX: 207-990-8081. E-Mail: bdnlib@bangornews.infi.net. Web Site: www.bangornews.com. *Chief Librn*, Charles A Campo; Staff 1 (MLS 1)
Special Collections: 1976-1990 Newspaper clippings on micro; Newspapers 1900-present (available electronically)
Mem of Northeastern Maine Library District
Partic in Dow Jones News Retrieval

S BANGOR HISTORICAL SOCIETY LIBRARY, 159 Union St, PO Box 773, 04402-0773. SAN 371-6651. Tel: 207-942-5766. FAX: 207-941-0266. E-Mail: bangorhistorical@hotmail.com. *Dir*, Christopher Olsen
Founded 1864
Library Holdings: Bk Titles 1,000
Subject Interests: Local history

M BANGOR MENTAL HEALTH INSTITUTE, Health Science Library,* PO Box 926, 04402-0926. SAN 343-6411. Tel: 207-941-4226. FAX: 207-941-4062. *Librn*, Jackie Dodge
Founded 1972
Library Holdings: Bk Vols 2,500; Per Subs 150
Subject Interests: Consumer health, Geriatrics and gerontology, Psychiatry, Psychology
Publications: The right to Refuse Treatment & the Obligation to Treat: A Selected Bibliography (1986)
Mem of Northeastern Maine Library District
Partic in Dialog Corporation
Branches:
PATIENT LIBRARY *Librn*, Jessica Powers

P BANGOR PUBLIC LIBRARY, 145 Harlow St, 04401-1802. SAN 343-6470. Tel: 207-947-8336. Toll Free Tel: 800-427-8336. FAX: 207-945-6694. E-Mail: bplill@ursus3.ursus.maine.edu. Web Site: www.bpl.lib.me.us. *Dir*, Barbara Rice McDade; *Ch Servs*, Anne Mundy; *Tech Servs*, Judith Leighton; *Ref*, Susan Wennrich; Staff 29 (MLS 8, Non-MLS 21)
Founded 1883. Pop 31,431; Circ 420,370
Jul 1999-Jun 2000 Income $1,900,564, State $121,200, City $961,920, Locally Generated Income $687,505, Other $129,939. Mats Exp $1,845,267, Books $174,595, Per/Ser (Incl. Access Fees) $85,685. Sal $876,914
Library Holdings: Bk Vols 442,487; Per Subs 599
Subject Interests: History
Special Collections: Aroostook War of 1839; Genealogy & Town History; Mountaineering; Ornithology; Penobscot Expedition of 1779; World War II Unit History
Automation Activity & Vendor Info: (Acquisitions) Innovative Interfaces Inc.; (Cataloging) Innovative Interfaces Inc.; (Circulation) Innovative Interfaces Inc.; (ILL) Innovative Interfaces Inc.; (OPAC) Innovative Interfaces Inc.; (Serials) Innovative Interfaces Inc.
Database Vendor: Ebsco - EbscoHost, GaleNet, OCLC - First Search, Silverplatter Information Inc.
Mem of Northeastern Maine Library District
Partic in Maine State Libr Network; Nelinet, Inc
Friends of the Library Group

R BANGOR THEOLOGICAL SEMINARY, Moulton Library, 300 Union St, 04401. SAN 306-5766. Tel: 207-942-6781, Ext 123. Toll Free Tel: 800-287-6871. FAX: 207-990-1267. E-Mail: library@bts.edu. Web Site: www.bts.edu. *Dir*, Beth Bidlack; Tel: 207-942-6781, Ext 122; Staff 2 (MLS 2)
Founded 1814. Enrl 115; Fac 11; Highest Degree: Master
Library Holdings: Bk Vols 136,603; Per Subs 431
Automation Activity & Vendor Info: (Cataloging) TLC
Database Vendor: OCLC - First Search
Publications: General Theological Library Bulletin (College journal)
Partic in OCLC Online Computer Library Center, Inc

J BEAL COLLEGE LIBRARY, 629 Main St, 04401. (Mail add: PO Box 450, 04402-0450), SAN 306-5774. Tel: 207-947-4591. FAX: 207-947-0208. E-Mail: beal-college-library@msln.net. Web Site: www.beal-college.lib.me.us. *Librn*, Ann Rea; E-Mail: annrea@saturn.caps.maine.edu; Staff 1 (MLS 1)
Enrl 500; Highest Degree: Associate
Library Holdings: Bk Vols 7,000; Per Subs 125
Subject Interests: Business and management, Law enforcement, Medical assistant, Tourism, Travel
Partic in Maine School & Libr Network

M EASTERN MAINE MEDICAL CENTER, Hadley Parrot Health Sciences Library, 489 State St, PO Box 404, 04402-0404. SAN 320-4502. Tel: 207-973-8228. Interlibrary Loan Service Tel: 207-973-8236. FAX: 207-973-8233. E-Mail: library@emmc.emh.org. Web Site: www.emh.org/hll/hpl. *Dir*, Suellen Jagels; Tel: 207-973-8227, E-Mail: sjagels@emh.org; *Tech Servs*, Pat Bishop; Tel: 207-973-8232, E-Mail: pbishop@emh.org; *Ref*, Wendy Troiano; Tel: 207-973-8235, E-Mail: wtroiano@emmc.lib.me.us; *ILL*, Cindy White; E-Mail: lwhite@emh.org; Staff 6 (MLS 4, Non-MLS 2)
Founded 1892
Library Holdings: Bk Titles 7,541; Per Subs 475
Subject Interests: Consumer health, Medical, Nursing
Special Collections: Hospital Annual Reports & Archives
Automation Activity & Vendor Info: (Acquisitions) Innovative Interfaces Inc.; (Cataloging) Innovative Interfaces Inc.; (Circulation) Innovative Interfaces Inc.; (Course Reserve) Innovative Interfaces Inc.; (Media Booking) Innovative Interfaces Inc.; (OPAC) Innovative Interfaces Inc.; (Serials) Innovative Interfaces Inc.
Database Vendor: Ebsco - EbscoHost, IAC - Info Trac
Partic in Basic Health Sciences Library Network; Health Sci Libr & Info Coop; Maine School & Libr Network

J EASTERN MAINE TECHNICAL COLLEGE LIBRARY,* 354 Hogan Rd, 04401-4280. SAN 306-5782. Tel: 207-941-4600, 207-941-4640. FAX: 207-941-4641. *Librn*, Karen R Reilly; Staff 1 (MLS 1)
Founded 1968. Enrl 892
Library Holdings: Bk Vols 10,148; Bk Titles 9,150; Per Subs 210
Subject Interests: Automotive engineering, Construction, Electronics, Nursing, Radiology
Special Collections: American Welding Society - Reference Coll
Mem of Maine State Library; Northeastern Maine Library District
Friends of the Library Group

C HUSSON COLLEGE LIBRARY, One College Circle, 04401-2999. SAN 306-5790. Tel: 207-941-7188. FAX: 207-941-7989. *Dir*, Amy Averre; E-Mail: averrea@husson.edu; *Cat*, Diane Hanscom
Founded 1947. Highest Degree: Master
Library Holdings: Bk Vols 35,000; Per Subs 500
Database Vendor: Innovative Interfaces INN - View, OCLC - First Search
Mem of Northeastern Maine Library District
Partic in Health Science Library Information Consortium; Nat Libr of Med; Nelinet, Inc

P NORTHEASTERN MAINE LIBRARY DISTRICT, 145 Harlow St, 04401. SAN 320-7501. Tel: 207-947-8336. FAX: 207-945-6694. *In Charge*, Benita Davis; E-Mail: benitad@ursus1.ursus.maine.edu; Staff 1 (MLS 1)
Founded 1973

Publications: Districtly Speaking (biannually); flyers (irregular)
Member Libraries: Abbe Museum Library; Abbott Memorial Library; Abel J Morneault Memorial Library; Alice L Pendleton Library; Aroostook Medical Center; Ashland Community Library; Bagaduce Music Lending Library; Bangor Daily News Library; Bangor Mental Health Institute; Bangor Public Library; Bangor Theological Seminary; Bass Harbor Memorial Library; Belfast Free Library; Blue Hill Memorial Hospital; Blue Hill Public Library; Brewer Public Library; Brooksville Free Public Library, Inc; Buck Memorial Library; Calais Free Library & Reading Room; Camden Public Library; Caribou Public Library; Carver Memorial Library; Cary Library; Case Memorial Library; Charleston Public Library; Chase Emerson Memorial Library; Cherryfield Free Public Library; College Of The Atlantic; Cushing Public Library; Danforth Public Library; Department of Corrections; Dorcas Library; East Millinocket Public Library; Eastern Maine Technical College Library; Ellsworth Public Library; Fort Fairfield Public Library; Fort Kent Public Library; Friend Memorial Public Library; Gallison Memorial Library; Gibbs Library; Glenburn Library; Guilford Memorial Library; Henry D Moore Public Library; Husson College Library; Islesford Library; Jackson Laboratory; Jackson Memorial Library; Jesup Memorial Library; John B Curtis Free Public Library; Katahdin Public Library; Lincoln Memorial Library; Lubec Memorial Library; Madawaska Public Library; Maine Coast Memorial Hospital Library; Maine Maritime Museum; Maine State Prison Library; Mattawamkeag Public Library; Mayhew Library Association; Milbridge Public Library; Mildred Stevens Williams Memorial Library; Millinocket Memorial Library; Milo Free Public Library; Monson Free Public Library; Newport Public Library; North Haven Library; Northeast Harbor Library; Northern Maine Technical College Library; Old Town Public Library; Orono Public Library; Orrington Public Library; Peabody Memorial Library; Peavey Memorial Library; Pen Bay Medical Center; Porter Memorial Library; Quoddy Tides Foundation Marine Library; Robert A Frost Memorial Library; Rockland Public Library; Rockport Public Library; Sangerville Public Library; Searsmont Town Library; Shaw Public Library; Sherman Public Library; Simpson Memorial Library; Southwest Harbor Public Library; Stetson Library; Stewart Free Library; Thomaston Public Library; Thompson Free Library; University of Maine at Machias; University of Maine at Presque Isle Library; Veterans Memorial Library; Vinalhaven Public Library; Vose Library; Walter T A Hansen Memorial Library; Washburn Memorial Library; Washington County Technical College Library; Whitneyville Library Association, Inc; Winter Harbor Public Library; Winterport Memorial Library; Witherle Memorial Library; Woodland Public Library

L PENOBSCOT COUNTY LAW LIBRARY,* 97 Hammond St, 04401. SAN 306-5804. Tel: 207-947-6124. *Librn*, Judith Bennett
Library Holdings: Bk Titles 15,000

J UNIVERSITY OF MAINE AT AUGUSTA, (Formerly University Of Maine), University College Library, Bangor Campus, 124 Eastport Hall, 128 Texas Ave, 04401. SAN 306-5812. Tel: 207-262-7902. FAX: 207-262-7901. *Librn*, Judith Nottage; Staff 3 (MLS 1, Non-MLS 2)
Founded 1968. Enrl 1,000; Fac 55
Library Holdings: Bk Vols 20,000; Per Subs 230
Subject Interests: Allied health

BAR HARBOR

S ABBE MUSEUM LIBRARY, Museum of Stone Age Antiquities Library, PO Box 286, 04609. SAN 371-7615. Tel: 207-288-2179, 207-288-3519. FAX: 207-288-8979. E-Mail: abbe@midmaine.com. *Dir*, Diane Kopec; *Curator*, Rebecca Cole-Will
Founded 1928
Library Holdings: Bk Titles 1,500; Per Subs 10
Special Collections: History of the Northeast (The Jesuit Relations Coll)
Mem of Northeastern Maine Library District

C COLLEGE OF THE ATLANTIC, Thorndike Library, 109 Eden St, 04609. SAN 306-5820. Tel: 207-288-5015. Circulation Tel: 207-288-5015, Ext 275. Web Site: www.coa.edu. *Assoc Dir*, Patricia Cantwell-Keene; Tel: 207-288-5015, Ext 211, E-Mail: tcantwell@ecology.coa.edu; *Asst Dir*, Marcia L Dworak; Tel: 207-288-5015, Ext 210, E-Mail: dwork@ecology.coa.edu; *Asst Librn*, Ingrid Hill; Tel: 207-288-5015, Ext 212, E-Mail: ihill@ecology.coa.edu; *Media Spec Ad*, Anne Swann; Tel: 207-288-5015, Ext 213, E-Mail: swann@ecology.coa.edu; Staff 3 (MLS 3)
Founded 1972. Enrl 277; Fac 23; Highest Degree: Master
Jul 1999-Jun 2000 Income $236,000. Mats Exp $72,330, Books $31,188, Per/Ser (Incl. Access Fees) $39,145, AV Equip $1,997. Sal $151,610 (Prof $100,000)
Library Holdings: Bk Vols 34,947; Per Subs 475
Subject Interests: Botany, Environmental studies, Evolution, Horticulture, Philosophy, Pub policy
Special Collections: Evolution (Philip Darlington Coll); Humanities (R Amory Thorndike Coll); Science & History of Science (Thomas S & Mary T Hall Coll)
Automation Activity & Vendor Info: (Cataloging) Athena; (Circulation) Athena; (Course Reserve) Athena; (ILL) Athena; (OPAC) Athena
Database Vendor: OCLC - First Search
Publications: Thorndike Library News
Mem of Northeastern Maine Library District
Partic in Nelinet, Inc

M JACKSON LABORATORY, Joan Staats Library, 600 Main St, 04609-1500. SAN 306-5839. Tel: 207-288-6146. FAX: 207-288-6079. E-Mail: library@.jax.org. Web Site: www.aretha.jax.org/library. *Dir*, Douglas Macbeth; Staff 4 (MLS 2, Non-MLS 2)
Founded 1929
Library Holdings: Bk Titles 3,500; Per Subs 310
Subject Interests: Biology, Cancer
Special Collections: Historical archives of the Jackson Laboratory
Mem of Northeastern Maine Library District
Partic in BRS; Dialog Corporation; Health Science Library Information Consortium; NRML; OCLC Online Computer Library Center, Inc
Library sponsors seminars on information science

P JESUP MEMORIAL LIBRARY,* 34 Mount Desert St, 04609. SAN 306-5847. Tel: 207-288-4245. FAX: 207-288-9067. E-Mail: jesup@acadia.net. *Librn*, Nancy Howland
Founded 1875. Pop 4,124; Circ 37,009
Library Holdings: Bk Vols 24,000; Per Subs 65
Subject Interests: Genealogy
Special Collections: Local Newspapers from 1881-1968, microfilm
Mem of Northeastern Maine Library District
Partic in Maine Libr Asn; Maine Small Pub Libr Asn

BAR MILLS

P BERRY MEMORIAL LIBRARY,* PO Box 25, 04004. SAN 306-5855. Tel: 207-929-5484. *Librn*, Alice Pease
Founded 1925. Pop 2,500; Circ 6,775
Library Holdings: Bk Titles 7,000
Subject Interests: History
Special Collections: Genealogy (Downeast Ancestry), per; Histories of Several Maine Towns; Maine Authors (Kate D Wiggin Coll); Narragansett & Buxton Town Histories; Saco Valley Settlements & Families
Mem of Maine State Library; Southern Maine Library District
Open Tues 1-5 & 6-8, Fri 1-5

BATH

S MAINE MARITIME MUSEUM, Library Archives, 243 Washington St, 04530. SAN 306-5863. Tel: 207-443-1316, Ext 328. FAX: 207-443-1665. E-Mail: lipfert@bathmaine.com. Web Site: www.bathmaine.com. *Dir*, Nathan Lipfert; E-Mail: lipfert@bathmaine.com; Staff 1 (Non-MLS 1)
Founded 1964
Library Holdings: Bk Titles 8,000; Per Subs 20
Special Collections: Bath, Maine Built Vessels (Photograph Coll); Ship Logs Coll, original doc in bk form; Ship Papers (Sewall Coll), original doc
Mem of Northeastern Maine Library District

P PATTEN FREE LIBRARY, 33 Summer St, 04530. SAN 306-5871. Tel: 207-443-5141. FAX: 207-443-3514. E-Mail: pfl@patten.lib.me.us. Web Site: www.patten.lib.me.us. *Dir*, Elizabeth S Hughes; *Asst Dir*, Anne Phillips; *Ch Servs*, Nyree Thomas; *Ref*, Dean Corner
Founded 1847. Pop 20,000; Circ 141,950
Jul 1999-Jun 2000 Income $464,155. Mats Exp $70,385. Sal $238,600 (Prof $150,000)
Library Holdings: Bk Titles 48,000; Per Subs 243
Subject Interests: Genealogy, Local history, Maritime history
Special Collections: Historic Preservation (Sagadahoc Preservation Inc); Maine History & Genealogy; Maritime (Whitmore) (Stevens) (Bath Iron Works); Native American (Staton)
Database Vendor: Innovative Interfaces INN - View
Publications: Good Times & Hard Times in Bath, 1936-1986; I Am Now a Soldier: The Civil War Diaries of Lorenzo Vanderhoeff; Maine Odyssey; Pattens of Bath, a Seagoing Dynasty
Mem of Central Maine Library District
Serves Bath, Georgetown, Phippsburg, West Bath, Woolwich & Arrowsic

L SAGADAHOC COUNTY LAW LIBRARY,* 752 High St, PO Box 246, 04530-0246. SAN 371-1145. Tel: 207-443-8200, 207-729-0856. FAX: 207-729-7790. E-Mail: email@mb-law.com. *Dir*, Nancy Morin
Library Holdings: Bk Vols 5,000

BELFAST

P BELFAST FREE LIBRARY,* 106 High St, 04915. SAN 306-588X. Tel: 207-338-3884. FAX: 207-338-3895. *Dir*, Jacque Schultze; E-Mail: jschultze@belfast.lib.me.us; *Archivist*, Lawrence T Cole; E-Mail: tcole@belfast.lib.me.us; *Ch Servs*, Jane Thompson; E-Mail: jthompson@belfast.lib.me.us; Staff 7 (MLS 2, Non-MLS 5)
Founded 1887. Pop 12,000; Circ 68,000
Jul 1997-Jun 1998 Income (Main Library Only) $245,191, City $180,179, Locally Generated Income $65,012. Mats Exp $28,985, Books $24,485, Per/

Ser (Incl. Access Fees) $4,000, Manuscripts & Archives $500. Sal $128,617 (Prof $55,000)
Library Holdings: Bk Titles 30,000; Per Subs 20; Spec Interest Per Sub 10
Subject Interests: Genealogy, Local history
Special Collections: Genealogy & Local History
Automation Activity & Vendor Info: (Cataloging) Follett; (Circulation) Follett
Publications: History of Belfast
Function: ILL available
Mem of Northeastern Maine Library District
Special Services for the Blind - Large print bks; Talking Books
Friends of the Library Group

M WALDO COUNTY GENERAL HOSPITAL, Health Sciences Library, 118 Northport Ave, 04915. SAN 377-9246. Tel: 207-338-2500, Ext 4154. FAX: 207-338-6029. Web Site: www.wchi.com. *Librn*, Lois Dutch
Library Holdings: Bk Titles 250; Per Subs 25
Partic in Health Science Library Information Consortium

GL WALDO COUNTY LAW LIBRARY,* Waldo County Courthouse, 137 Church St, PO Box 188, 04915. SAN 327-5949. Tel: 207-338-1940. FAX: 207-338-1086.
Library Holdings: Bk Titles 1,000

BERNARD

P BASS HARBOR MEMORIAL LIBRARY,* Main St, PO Box 99, 04612. SAN 376-351X. Tel: 207-244-3798. *Librn*, Ann Crisafulli
Library Holdings: Bk Vols 8,600; Bk Titles 8,700; Per Subs 30
Mem of Northeastern Maine Library District

BERWICK

P BERWICK PUBLIC LIBRARY,* 43 Rte 236, 03901. SAN 376-3889. Tel: 207-698-5737. *Librn*, Cynthia Hunt
Jul 1996-Jun 1997 Income $20,000
Library Holdings: Bk Vols 18,000; Bk Titles 9,000; Per Subs 18
Mem of Southern Conn Libr Coun
Friends of the Library Group

BETHEL

P BETHEL LIBRARY ASSOCIATION,* Broad St, 04217. SAN 306-5898. Tel: 207-824-2520. *Librn*, Michelle Conroy
Pop 5,000; Circ 20,000
Library Holdings: Bk Vols 19,000; Bk Titles 17,600
Special Collections: Maine History Coll
Mem of Central Maine Library District

BIDDEFORD

S FIBER MATERIALS INC LIBRARY,* 5 Morin St, 04005-4497. SAN 306-5901. Tel: 207-282-5911, Ext 372. FAX: 207-282-7529. E-Mail: fmi@gwi.net. *In Charge*, Sharon Forcier
Founded 1974
Library Holdings: Bk Vols 4,500; Per Subs 63
Subject Interests: Ceramics

P MCARTHUR PUBLIC LIBRARY, 270 Main St, PO Box 346, 04005. SAN 306-591X. Interlibrary Loan Service Tel: 207-284-4181. FAX: 207-284-6761. E-Mail: reference@mcarthur.lib.me.us. Web Site: www.mcarthur.lib.me.us. *Dir*, Robert M Filgate; *Ch Servs*, Vicky J Smith
Founded 1863. Pop 20,710; Circ 161,692
1998-1999 Income $634,000, City $191,000, Locally Generated Income $2,000, Other $441,000. Mats Exp $75,071, Books $52,600, Per/Ser (Incl. Access Fees) $7,700, Presv $541, Micro $4,059, Manuscripts & Archives $171, Electronic Ref Mat (Incl. Access Fees) $10,000. Sal $300,000
Library Holdings: Bk Vols 68,000; Per Subs 188
Subject Interests: History
Automation Activity & Vendor Info: (Cataloging) Sagebrush Corporation; (Circulation) Sagebrush Corporation
Publications: Newsletter
Mem of Southern Conn Libr Coun; Southern Maine Library District

M SOUTHERN MAINE MEDICAL CENTER, Health Sciences Library, One Medical Center Dr, PO Box 626, 04005. SAN 328-4476. Tel: 207-283-7289. FAX: 207-283-7063. E-Mail: mad.djm@smmc.org. *Librn*, Dina McKelvy; Staff 1 (MLS 1)
Library Holdings: Bk Titles 600; Per Subs 85

C UNIVERSITY OF NEW ENGLAND LIBRARIES, Jack S Ketchum Library, 11 Hills Beach Rd, 04005. SAN 322-8142. Tel: 207-283-0171, Ext 2361. Reference Tel: 207-283-0171, Ext 2363. FAX: 207-294-5922. E-Mail: agolub@mailbox.une.edu, library@mailbox.une.edu. Web Site: www.une.edu. *VPres*, Andrew J Golub; Tel: 207-283-0171, Ext 2319, E-Mail: agolub@mailbox.une.edu; *Admin Assoc*, Cindy Vakas; Tel: 207-283-0170, Ext 2811, E-Mail: cvakas@mailbox.une.edu; *Publ Servs*, Barbara Swartzlander; Tel: 207-283-0171, Ext 2315, E-Mail: bswartzlander@mailbox.une.edu; *Ref*, Janice Beal; Tel: 207-283-0170, Ext 2497, E-Mail: jbeal@mailbox.une.edu; *Syst Coordr*, Stew MacLehose; Tel: 207-283-0171, Ext 2830, E-Mail: smaclehose@mailbox.une.edu; *Tech Servs*, Sharon Eckert; Tel: 207-283-0171, Ext 2364, E-Mail: seckert@mailbox.une.edu; Staff 14 (MLS 9, Non-MLS 5)
Founded 1831. Enrl 1,794; Fac 277; Highest Degree: Doctorate
Jul 1998-Jun 1999 Income $1,000,000. Mats Exp $424,257, Books $64,151, Per/Ser (Incl. Access Fees) $276,771, Presv $3,226. Sal $407,159 (Prof $303,938)
Library Holdings: Bk Vols 94,841; Bk Titles 39,457; Per Subs 843
Subject Interests: Allied health, Life sci, Marine biology, Medicine, Social work
Automation Activity & Vendor Info: (Acquisitions) Innovative Interfaces Inc.; (Cataloging) Innovative Interfaces Inc.; (Circulation) Innovative Interfaces Inc.; (ILL) Innovative Interfaces Inc.
Database Vendor: Dialog, Ebsco - EbscoHost, Lexis-Nexis, OCLC - First Search, OVID Technologies, ProQuest, Silverplatter Information Inc.
Partic in Health Sci Libr & Info Consortium; National Network Of Libraries Of Medicine New England Region; New England Libr Info Network; OCLC Online Computer Library Center, Inc
Departmental Libraries:

BLUE HILL

S BAGADUCE MUSIC LENDING LIBRARY,* Greene's Hill, PO Box 829, 04614. SAN 373-0573. Tel: 207-374-5454. FAX: 207-374-2733. E-Mail: musiclib@hypernet.com. Web Site: www.hypernet.com/musiclib.html. *Exec Dir*, Kurt Stoll; *Music*, Mary Cheyney Gould
Library Holdings: Bk Titles 100,000
Special Collections: State of Maine Music Coll
Publications: Collection catalogs
Mem of Northeastern Maine Library District

P BLUE HILL MEMORIAL HOSPITAL, Health Education Center, Water St, PO Box 823, 04614. Tel: 207-374-2836, Ext 1001. E-Mail: bhmhhec@media2.hypernet.com. *Mgr*, Kim Horton
Library Holdings: Bk Vols 200
Mem of Northeastern Maine Library District

P BLUE HILL PUBLIC LIBRARY, Parker Point Rd, PO Box 824, 04614-0821. SAN 306-5944. Tel: 207-374-5515. FAX: 207-374-5254. Web Site: www.bluehill.lib.me.us. *Dir*, Marcia Schatz; Tel: 207-374-5424, Fax: 207-374-5424, E-Mail: marcias@bluehill.lib.me.us; *Asst Dir, Librn*, Holly Williams; E-Mail: hollyw@bluehill.lib.me.us
Founded 1796. Pop 1,644; Circ 74,505
Library Holdings: Bk Vols 32,000; Bk Titles 26,000; Per Subs 93
Special Collections: Large Print Books; Maine Local History
Database Vendor: Ebsco - EbscoHost
Publications: Booklist; Horn Book; Library Journal
Mem of Northeastern Maine Library District
Friends of the Library Group

BOOTHBAY HARBOR

P BOOTHBAY HARBOR MEMORIAL LIBRARY,* 4 Oak St, 04538. SAN 306-5952. Tel: 207-633-3112. Web Site: www.bmpl.lib.me.us. *Dir*, John Clark; *Ref*, Linda Barter; *Ch Servs*, Mary Pinkham
Founded 1924. Pop 4,950; Circ 39,574
Nov 1998-Oct 1999 Income $110,000. Mats Exp $19,000. Sal $63,000
Library Holdings: Bk Vols 24,500
Special Collections: Maine (Osgood Coll); Maritime Coll; Military History (Farmer Coll)
Publications: Summer Events Schedule
Mem of Central Maine Library District
Friends of the Library Group

M SAINT ANDREW'S HOSPITAL, Medical Library, 3 Saint Andrews Lane, PO Box 417, 04538-0417. SAN 329-935X. Tel: 207-633-2121. FAX: 207-633-7414. *Librn*, Brenda LaBreck
Library Holdings: Bk Vols 125

BOWDOINHAM

P BOWDOINHAM PUBLIC LIBRARY,* 13A School St, 04008. SAN 306-5960. Tel: 207-666-8405. Web Site: www.bowdoinham.lib.me.us. *Librn*, Pamela Hanson; *Librn*, Beth French
Pop 2,192; Circ 12,808
Jul 1998-Jun 1999 Income $18,000, State $192, City $6,000, Other $10,015. Mats Exp $6,140, Books $5,545, Per/Ser (Incl. Access Fees) $595. Sal $10,000
Library Holdings: Bk Titles 11,260; Per Subs 30
Special Collections: Maine Coll
Mem of Central Maine Library District
Friends of the Library Group

BRADFORD

P JOHN B CURTIS FREE PUBLIC LIBRARY, Main Rd, RR 2 Box 362, 04410-9700. SAN 378-1283. Tel: 207-327-2923. E-Mail: curtis.free.public.library@msln.net. *Dir, Librn*, Muriel S Parker
Founded 1913. Pop 1,103; Circ 3,300
Jan 1999-Dec 1999 Income $5,360, State $180, City $4,500, Other $680. Mats Exp Books $800. Sal $152,000
Library Holdings: Bk Vols 8,200; Per Subs 14
Subject Interests: Genealogy, Local history
Mem of Northeastern Maine Library District

BREMEN

P BREMEN PUBLIC LIBRARY,* Rte 32, Box 163, 04551. SAN 376-379X. Tel: 207-529-5572. *Librn*, Sue Trouwhorst
Library Holdings: Bk Vols 10,000; Bk Titles 5,000; Per Subs 11
Mem of Central Maine Library District
Open Mon 10-12, Wed & Fri 10-3

BREWER

P BREWER PUBLIC LIBRARY,* 24 Union St, 04412. SAN 306-5979. Tel: 207-989-7943. FAX: 207-989-5262. Web Site: www.geocities.com/athens/parthenon/8485. *Dir*, Elise Adams; E-Mail: eladams@brewer.lib.me.us; *Asst Dir, Cat, Ref*, Frances Payson; E-Mail: fpayson@brewer.lib.me.us
Founded 1908. Pop 9,010; Circ 61,000
Jul 1999-Jun 2000 Mats Exp $115,941, Books $14,000, Per/Ser (Incl. Access Fees) $1,500, AV Equip $600, Electronic Ref Mat (Incl. Access Fees) $500. (Prof $32,000)
Library Holdings: Bk Vols 40,000; Per Subs 83
Special Collections: Fannie Hardy Eckstorm Coll, 1865-1946
Automation Activity & Vendor Info: (Circulation) Sagebrush Corporation
Mem of Northeastern Maine Library District
Friends of the Library Group

BRIDGTON

P BRIDGTON PUBLIC LIBRARY, Dalton Holmes Davis Memorial Library, 65 Main St, 04009. SAN 306-5987. Tel: 207-647-2472. FAX: 207-647-2472. Web Site: www.bridgton.lib.me.us. *Dir, Librn*, Ann Carabia
Founded 1895. Pop 5,400; Circ 28,000
1998-1999 Income $150,000, State $171, City $45,000, Locally Generated Income $25,000, Other $79,829. Mats Exp Per/Ser (Incl. Access Fees) $1,100. Sal $64,925
Library Holdings: Bk Vols 22,000; Per Subs 65
Subject Interests: Local history
Publications: Friends of Library (newsletter)
Mem of Southern Conn Libr Coun; Southern Maine Library District
Friends of the Library Group

M CENTRAL MAINE HEALTHCARE, (BH), (Formerly Northern Cumberland Memorial Hospital), Bridgton Hospital Health Sciences Library, S High St, PO Box 230, 04009-0230. SAN 329-0336. Tel: 207-647-8841, Ext 6084. FAX: 207-647-6009. *Librn*, Sally M MacAuslan; E-Mail: sallymm@bh.cmhc.org; Staff 1 (Non-MLS 1)
Founded 1972
Jul 2000-Jun 2001 Mats Exp $9,000, Books $1,500, Per/Ser (Incl. Access Fees) $5,400, Other Print Mats $100, Electronic Ref Mat (Incl. Access Fees) $2,000. Sal $8,000
Library Holdings: Bk Vols 208; Bk Titles 187; Per Subs 70
Subject Interests: Allied health, Consumer health, Medicine, Nursing
Mem of Southern Conn Libr Coun
Partic in Docline; Medline

BROOKLIN

P FRIEND MEMORIAL PUBLIC LIBRARY,* PO Box 57, 04616. SAN 306-6010. Tel: 207-359-2276. *Librn*, Gretchen Volenik; Staff 2 (MLS 1, Non-MLS 1)
Founded 1900
Library Holdings: Bk Vols 14,000; Per Subs 50
Mem of Northeastern Maine Library District

BROOKSVILLE

P BROOKSVILLE FREE PUBLIC LIBRARY, INC,* Townhouse Bldg, 1 Townhouse Rd, PO Box 38, 04617. SAN 306-6029. Tel: 207-326-4560. FAX: 207-326-4560. E-Mail: bfpl-df@bfpl.lib.me.us. Web Site: www.bfpl.lib.me.us. *Librn*, Leona Gray; Staff 2 (Non-MLS 2)
Founded 1953. Pop 753; Circ 3,960
Library Holdings: Bk Vols 11,960
Subject Interests: Genealogy, Local history
Publications: Newsletter
Mem of Northeastern Maine Library District
Partic in Scoop Purchasing Coop
Friends of the Library Group

BROWNFIELD

P BROWNFIELD PUBLIC LIBRARY,* Main St, Rte 113, PO Box 215, 04010. SAN 374-5473. Tel: 207-935-3003. *Librn*, Frances Jones; Staff 7 (Non-MLS 7)
Founded 1908. Pop 1,010
Library Holdings: Bk Vols 4,030
Mem of Central Maine Library District
Open Wefd & Sat only
Friends of the Library Group

BROWNVILLE

P BROWNVILLE PUBLIC LIBRARY, PO Box 687, 04414-0687. SAN 321-513X. *Librn*, Pauline Thomas
Pop 1,540
Library Holdings: Bk Titles 7,500; Per Subs 16

BRUNSWICK

C BOWDOIN COLLEGE LIBRARY,* 3000 College Sta, 04011. SAN 306-6037. Tel: 207-725-3749. FAX: 207-725-3083. Web Site: www.bowdoin.edu/dept/library. *Dir*, Sherrie Bergman; *Assoc Librn, Publ Servs*, Judith Montgomery; *ILL*, Guy Saldanha; *Acq, Coll Develop*, Penny Schroeder; *Ref*, Katie Sasser; *Ref*, Leanne Pander; *Govt Doc*, Ginny Hopcroft; *Instrul Serv*, Carmen Greenlee; *Cat*, Karl Fattig; Staff 15 (MLS 15)
Founded 1794. Enrl 1,524; Fac 131; Highest Degree: Bachelor
Jul 1998-Jun 1999 Mats Exp $3,420,696, Books $515,777, Per/Ser (Incl. Access Fees) $748,134, Presv $45,200, Micro $26,634. Sal $1,204,811 (Prof $683,435)
Library Holdings: Bk Vols 901,589; Per Subs 2,137
Special Collections: Abbot Coll; Arctic Coll; Carlyle Coll; Hawthorne Coll; Huguenot Coll; Longfellow Coll; Maine; Senator George J Mitchell Papers
Publications: From the Library (faculty & staff newsletter)
Partic in New England Libr Info Network; OCLC Online Computer Library Center, Inc
Open Mon-Sat 8:30am-12am, Sun 10am-12am
Friends of the Library Group
Departmental Libraries:
ART Tel: 207-725-3690. *Librn*, Anne Shankland
LANGUAGE MEDIA CENTER Tel: 207-725-3702. FAX: 207-725-3348. *Librn*, Carmen Greenlee
MUSIC Tel: 207-725-3570. *Librn*, Sydnae Steinhart
SCIENCE Tel: 207-725-3004. FAX: 207-725-3095. *Librn*, Kathleen Kenny

P BRUNSWICK PUBLIC LIBRARY ASSOCIATION, Captain John Curtis Memorial Library, 23 Pleasant St, 04011-2295. SAN 306-6045. Tel: 207-725-5242. FAX: 207-725-6313. Web Site: www.curtislibrary.com. *Dir*, Stephen J Podgajny; E-Mail: spodgajn@curtislibrary.com; *Asst Dir*, Brian Damien; *Ch Servs*, Pam Jenkins; *YA Servs*, Melissa Orth; Staff 5 (MLS 5)
Founded 1883. Pop 26,000; Circ 179,993
Jul 1998-Jun 1999 Income $686,902. Mats Exp $91,717. Sal $482,147
Library Holdings: Bk Vols 110,000; Bk Titles 105,402; Per Subs 398
Publications: Newsletter
Partic in Nelinet, Inc; OCLC Online Computer Library Center, Inc
Friends of the Library Group

M MID-COAST HOSPITAL, Health Sciences Library, 58 Baribeau Dr, 04011. SAN 306-6061. Tel: 207-721-1365, 207-729-0181, Ext 365. FAX: 207-725-6899. E-Mail: library@midcoasthealth.com. *Librn*, Clara M Ackroyd; E-Mail: cmack@gwi.net; Staff 1 (MLS 1)
Founded 1973
Library Holdings: Bk Vols 2,500; Bk Titles 700; Per Subs 130
Partic in Basic Health Sciences Library Network; Health Sci Libr & Info Consortium

S PEJEPSCOT HISTORICAL SOCIETY, 159 Park Row, 04011. SAN 306-6053. Tel: 207-729-6606. FAX: 207-729-6012. E-Mail: pejepscot@curtislibrary.com. Web Site: www.curtislibrary.com/pejepscot.htm. *Dir*, Deborah Smith; *Curator*, Jarrod Diels-Roll
Founded 1888
Library Holdings: Bk Vols 700; Bk Titles 500
Subject Interests: Local history
Special Collections: History of Brunswick, 1803-59 (Lincoln, Isaac, LC MS 65-20001), papers; Joshua Lawrence Chamberlain Coll; Local Franco-American History, Local Industrial History

BRYANT POND

P WHITMAN MEMORIAL LIBRARY,* Main St, PO Box 307, 04219. SAN 306-7920. Tel: 207-665-2505. *Librn*, Rebecca Laipres
Founded 1908. Pop 1,194; Circ 2,456
Library Holdings: Bk Vols 11,219; Per Subs 28
Friends of the Library Group

BUCKSPORT

P BUCK MEMORIAL LIBRARY,* Main St, PO Box DD, 04416. SAN 306-607X. Tel: 207-469-2650. *Librn*, Emeric Spooner; *Librn*, Gerry Spooner
Founded 1806. Pop 4,345; Circ 10,233
Library Holdings: Bk Vols 24,000; Per Subs 35
Mem of Northeastern Maine Library District

CALAIS

P CALAIS FREE LIBRARY & READING ROOM,* Union St, 04619. SAN 306-6096. Tel: 207-454-2758. FAX: 207-454-2765. *Librn*, E Marilyn Sotirelis; *Asst Librn*, Karen Herrick; *Ch Servs*, Kelley Wade; Staff 2 (MLS 2)
Founded 1892. Pop 3,963; Circ 49,420
Jul 1998-Jun 1999 Income $119,700, State $200, City $119,500. Mats Exp $15,128, Books $13,838, Per/Ser (Incl. Access Fees) $1,290. Sal $59,904
Library Holdings: Bk Vols 33,925; Per Subs 42
Special Collections: Champlain Coll; James S Pike Coll; Maine & Genealogy Coll, microfiche; State of Maine Coll
Mem of Northeastern Maine Library District

M CALAIS REGIONAL HOSPITAL, Health Science Library,* 50 Franklin St, 04619-1398. SAN 329-8485. Tel: 207-454-7521, Ext 122. FAX: 207-454-3616. E-Mail: crhlibrary@nemaine.com. *Librn*, Cheryl Mahar
Library Holdings: Bk Vols 1,500; Per Subs 25
Subject Interests: Medicine, Nursing, Orthopedics, Pediatrics, Surgery

C WASHINGTON COUNTY TECHNICAL COLLEGE LIBRARY,* RR 1, Box 22C, 04619. SAN 322-8452. Tel: 207-454-2144, Ext 1050. FAX: 207-454-1026. *Librn*, Barbara Maenhout; *Asst Librn*, Nan Gallant
Library Holdings: Bk Vols 11,000; Per Subs 225
Mem of Northeastern Maine Library District

CAMDEN

P CAMDEN PUBLIC LIBRARY, 55 Main St, 04843-1703. SAN 306-610X. Tel: 207-236-3440. FAX: 207-236-6673. Web Site: www.camden.lib.me.us. *Dir*, Elizabeth Moran; E-Mail: emoran@camden.lib.me.us; *Asst Dir*, Dottie Morales; Staff 12 (MLS 4, Non-MLS 8)
Founded 1896. Pop 5,050; Circ 215,450
Jan 2000-Dec 2000 Income $504,200, State $200, City $174,000, Locally Generated Income $160,000, Other $170,000. Mats Exp $28,400, Books $23,200, Per/Ser (Incl. Access Fees) $2,400, Presv $500, Micro $100, AV Equip $1,700, Electronic Ref Mat (Incl. Access Fees) $500. Sal $244,000
Library Holdings: Bk Vols 42,281; Per Subs 66
Special Collections: Edna St Vincent Millay Coll
Publications: From Harbor Hill (newsletter)
Mem of Northeastern Maine Library District
Friends of the Library Group

CAPE ELIZABETH

P THOMAS MEMORIAL LIBRARY, 6 Scott Dyer Rd, 04107. SAN 322-6786. Tel: 207-799-1720. *Dir*, Jay Scherma; E-Mail: jscherma@thomas.lib.me.us; *Ch Servs*, Rachel A Quenk; E-Mail: rquenk@thomas.lib.me.us; *YA Servs*, Kevin Goody; E-Mail: kgoody@thomas.lib.me.us; *Ref*, Joyce Lourie; E-Mail: jlourie@thomas.lib.me.us; Staff 11 (MLS 4, Non-MLS 7)
Founded 1919. Pop 8,854; Circ 107,669
Jul 1999-Jun 2000 Income $340,950. Mats Exp $39,168, Books $28,324, Per/Ser (Incl. Access Fees) $4,138, AV Equip $2,640, Electronic Ref Mat (Incl. Access Fees) $4,066. Sal $217,088
Library Holdings: Bk Vols 53,283; Per Subs 96
Subject Interests: Contemporary lit, Contemporary poetry, Experimental lit, Experimental poetry
Special Collections: Gabriel A Zimpritch Coll; Maine Coll
Automation Activity & Vendor Info: (Cataloging) Sagebrush Corporation; (Circulation) Sagebrush Corporation
Mem of Southern Maine Library District
Open Mon, Wed, Fri & Sat 9-5, Tues & Thurs 9-8:30
Friends of the Library Group

CARIBOU

P CARIBOU PUBLIC LIBRARY,* 30 High St, 04736. SAN 306-6126. Tel: 207-493-4214. Interlibrary Loan Service Tel: 800-427-8336. FAX: 207-493-4654. Web Site: www.caribou-public.lib.me.us/index.htm. *Dir, Librn*, Diane C Dubois; E-Mail: ddubois@caribou-public.lib.me.us
Founded 1911. Pop 9,920; Circ 65,700
Jan 1998-Dec 1998 Income $162,991. Mats Exp $23,390. Sal $109,000
Library Holdings: Bk Vols 42,000; Per Subs 105
Subject Interests: Local history
Special Collections: Local newspaper 1887-1976, microfilm
Mem of Northeastern Maine Library District
Friends of the Library Group

M CARY MEDICAL CENTER, Health Science Library,* 163 Van Buren Rd, Ste 1, 04736-2599. SAN 306-6134. Tel: 207-498-3111, Ext 380. FAX: 207-496-6761. *Librn*, Betty Walker
Library Holdings: Bk Vols 600; Per Subs 100
Subject Interests: Health sciences

CARMEL

P SIMPSON MEMORIAL LIBRARY,* PO Box 186, 04419. SAN 376-3544. Tel: 207-848-7145. *Librn*, Dixie Carr
Library Holdings: Bk Vols 4,000; Bk Titles 3,500; Per Subs 12
Mem of Northeastern Maine Library District
Open Tues 11-7, Thurs 11-5 & Sat 9-1

CASCO

P CASCO PUBLIC LIBRARY,* 7 Leach Hill Rd, Box 420, 04015. SAN 306-6142. Tel: 207-627-4541. E-Mail: cascolib@casco.lib.me.us. Web Site: www.casco.lib.me.us. *Librn*, Holly Hancock; Staff 2 (MLS 1, Non-MLS 1)
Founded 1946. Pop 3,018; Circ 23,096
Jan 1998-Dec 1998 Income $53,778, City $24,000. Mats Exp $14,000, Books $12,936, Per/Ser (Incl. Access Fees) $626, Micro $300. Sal $15,300
Library Holdings: Bk Vols 15,096; Per Subs 15
Mem of Southern Conn Libr Coun
Partic in Maine School & Libr Network

CASTINE

C NUTTING MEMORIAL LIBRARY, (Formerly Maine Maritime Academy), Maine Maritime Academy, Pleasant St, 04420. (Mail add: PO Box C-1, 04420), Tel: 207-326-2263. FAX: 207-326-2261. Web Site: bell.mma.edu/~wknicker/library2.html. *Dir*, Wendy Knickerbocker; Tel: 207-326-2260, E-Mail: wknicker@bell.mma.edu; *Tech Servs*, Willard H Gilmore; Tel: 207-326-2262, E-Mail: wgilmore@bell.mma.edu; *Publ Servs*, H Brent Hall; E-Mail: bhall@bell.mma.edu; *Acq*, Leone Howard; Tel: 207-326-2264, E-Mail: lhoward@bell.mma.edu; *Doc*, Dale Motycka; Tel: 207-326-2265; *Govt Doc*, Melissa Ferguson; Tel: 207-326-2265, E-Mail: mfaust@bell.mma.edu; Staff 5 (MLS 3, Non-MLS 2)
Founded 1941. Enrl 710; Fac 65; Highest Degree: Master
Jul 1999-Jun 2000 Income Parent Institution $371,431. Mats Exp $143,268, Books $67,803, Per/Ser (Incl. Access Fees) $65,129, Electronic Ref Mat (Incl. Access Fees) $10,336. Sal $198,858 (Prof $134,114)
Library Holdings: Bk Vols 82,115; Per Subs 468
Subject Interests: Marine tech, Maritime history, Military history
Special Collections: Gilmartin Coll (oceanography); Leslie Kanuk Coll of Federal Maritime Commission papers; Schieffelin Coll (military history)
Automation Activity & Vendor Info: (Acquisitions) Innovative Interfaces Inc.; (Cataloging) Innovative Interfaces Inc.; (Circulation) Innovative Interfaces Inc.; (OPAC) Innovative Interfaces Inc.; (Serials) Innovative Interfaces Inc.
Database Vendor: Dialog, Ebsco - EbscoHost, Innovative Interfaces INN - View, OCLC - First Search, Silverplatter Information Inc.
Function: ILL available
Partic in Nelinet, Inc; OCLC Online Computer Library Center, Inc

P WITHERLE MEMORIAL LIBRARY,* One School St, PO Box 202, 04421. SAN 306-6169. Tel: 207-326-4375. E-Mail: refdesk@witherle.lib.me.us. *Dir*, Anne Francis Romans; *Librn*, Patricia M Fowler; Staff 5 (MLS 2, Non-MLS 3)
Founded 1801. Pop 1,191; Circ 18,000
Feb 1998-Jan 1999 Income $88,679, City $53,337, Locally Generated Income $11,342, Other $24,000. Mats Exp $14,498, Books $11,059, Per/Ser (Incl. Access Fees) $1,373, Presv $750, AV Equip $1,316. Sal $53,337 (Prof $18,743)
Library Holdings: Bk Vols 13,161; Per Subs 84
Special Collections: Castine newspapers - 1800s & 1900s
Mem of Northeastern Maine Library District
Special Services for the Deaf - Books on deafness & sign language
Special Services for the Blind - Large print bks; Talking Books
Friends of the Library Group

CHARLESTON

P CHARLESTON PUBLIC LIBRARY, 13 Aitkinson Rd, 04422. (Mail add: PO Box 119, 04422), SAN 372-6800. Tel: 207-285-3637. *Librn*, Joanne Gray
Founded 1900. Pop 1,037; Circ 2,409

Jan 1999-Dec 1999 Income $1,300. Mats Exp $1,200
Library Holdings: Bk Titles 7,000
Mem of Northeastern Maine Library District
Friends of the Library Group

CHEBEAGUE

P CHEBEAGUE ISLAND LIBRARY,* South Rd, Box 511, 04017. SAN 306-6207. Tel: 207-846-4351. FAX: 207-846-4358. *Librn*, Martha O Hamilton
Founded 1965. Pop 2,000; Circ 13,450
Jan 1999-Dec 1999 Income City $30,000. Mats Exp Books $5,000. Sal $30,000
Library Holdings: Bk Vols 11,810; Per Subs 32
Subject Interests: Genealogy, Local history
Mem of Southern Conn Libr Coun
Friends of the Library Group

CHERRYFIELD

P CHERRYFIELD FREE PUBLIC LIBRARY, Main, 04622. (Mail add: RR 1 Box 3, 04622-9702), SAN 321-5989. Tel: 207-546-4228. *Librn*, Esther Goulart; Staff 1 (MLS 1)
Founded 1837. Pop 1,320; Circ 2,106
Oct 2000-Sep 2001 Income $7,391, State $105, City $1,000, Other $6,286. Mats Exp Books $1,895. Sal $3,500
Library Holdings: Bk Titles 9,125
Mem of Northeastern Maine Library District

CHINA

P ALBERT CHURCH BROWN MEMORIAL LIBRARY, Main St, PO Box 146, 04926-0146. SAN 376-687X. Tel: 207-968-2926. *Librn*, Mary Grow
Library Holdings: Bk Vols 16,000; Per Subs 15
Mem of Central Maine Library District

CLINTON

P BROWN MEMORIAL LIBRARY,* 14 Railroad St, PO Box 370, 04927. SAN 376-7434. Tel: 207-426-8686. *Librn*, Louella Bickford
Library Holdings: Bk Vols 8,000; Per Subs 40
Mem of Central Maine Library District; Southern Maine Library District
Open Mon & Wed 2-6, Tues & Thurs 2-8, Sat 10-1

CORINNA

P STEWART FREE LIBRARY,* One Stewart Lane, 04928. SAN 306-6185. Tel: 207-278-2454. FAX: 207-278-5200. *Librn*, June Jaworski; E-Mail: jjaworski@stewart.lib.me.ue
Pop 2,196; Circ 10,290
Jan 1999-Dec 1999 Income City $1,500. Mats Exp $2,320, Books $2,000, Per/Ser (Incl. Access Fees) $320
Library Holdings: Bk Titles 15,580; Per Subs 22
Special Collections: Abraham Lincoln; Civil War Napoleon & (Levi Stewart Private Library Room)
Mem of Northeastern Maine Library District

CORNISH

P BONNEY MEMORIAL LIBRARY, Main St, PO Box 357, 04020-0357. SAN 306-6193. Tel: 207-625-8083. Web Site: www.bonney.lib.me.us. *Librn*, Cheryl Beth Hevey; E-Mail: chevey@bonney.lib.me.us; Staff 1 (MLS 1)
Founded 1928. Pop 1,658
Nov 1999-Oct 2000 Income $38,000, City $2,500, Locally Generated Income $1,700, Other $33,800. Mats Exp $6,132, Books $4,854, Per/Ser (Incl. Access Fees) $713, AV Equip $300, Other Print Mats $265. Sal $21,470 (Prof $21,000)
Library Holdings: Bk Titles 13,675; Per Subs 24
Mem of Southern Maine Library District
Open Mon & Wed 10-1 & 3-8, Tues & Thurs 11-6, Sat 10-1 (except July & August)

CUMBERLAND

P PRINCE MEMORIAL LIBRARY, 266 Main St, 04021-9754. SAN 306-6215. Tel: 207-829-2215. FAX: 207-829-2221. E-Mail: inquiry@princememorial.lib.me.us. Web Site: www.princememorial.lib.me.us. *Dir*, Thomas Bennet; Tel: 207-829-2216, E-Mail: direktor@princememorial.lib.me.us; Staff 10 (MLS 1, Non-MLS 9)
Founded 1923. Pop 8,975; Circ 84,000
Jul 2000-Jun 2001 Income City $277,638. Mats Exp $30,800, Books $26,000, Per/Ser (Incl. Access Fees) $3,000. Sal $150,217 (Prof $115,742)
Library Holdings: Bk Vols 39,947; Bk Titles 35,834; Per Subs 100
Special Collections: Maine Coll
Automation Activity & Vendor Info: (Cataloging) Sagebrush Corporation; (Circulation) Sagebrush Corporation
Mem of Southern Conn Libr Coun; Southern Maine Library District
Friends of the Library Group

DAMARISCOTTA

M MILES MEMORIAL HOSPITAL, Health Science Library,* RR 2 Box 4500, 04543-9767. SAN 377-9807. Tel: 207-563-4367. FAX: 207-563-4380. E-Mail: library@mileshealthcare.org.
Library Holdings: Bk Titles 300
Partic in Maine Health Network; Maine Health Sci Librs & Info Consortium

P SKIDOMPHA PUBLIC LIBRARY, Main St, PO Box 70, 04543. SAN 306-6223. Tel: 207-563-5513. E-Mail: skid@skidompha.lib.me.us. Web Site: www.skidompha.org. *Librn*, Ellen Welsh; *Asst Librn*, Brenda Madore; *Asst Librn*, Ellen Dickens; Staff 3 (MLS 1, Non-MLS 2)
Founded 1905. Pop 4,855; Circ 39,721
1998-1999 Income (Main Library Only) $96,384, City $21,769. Mats Exp $98,405, Books $19,000, Per/Ser (Incl. Access Fees) $1,000. Sal $52,595
Library Holdings: Bk Vols 27,000
Subject Interests: Genealogy, Local history
Mem of Central Maine Library District
Friends of the Library Group

DEER ISLE

P CHASE EMERSON MEMORIAL LIBRARY,* PO Box 9, 04627. SAN 306-6231. Tel: 207-348-2899. *Librn*, Aimee H Eaton
Founded 1922. Pop 1,427; Circ 9,731
Library Holdings: Bk Titles 24,000
Special Collections: Merchant Sail (William A Fairburn Coll)
Mem of Northeastern Maine Library District; Southern Maine Library District

S HAYSTACK MOUNTAIN SCHOOL OF CRAFTS LIBRARY, 89 Haystack School Dr, 04627. SAN 306-624X. Tel: 207-348-2306. FAX: 207-348-2307. E-Mail: haystack@haystack-mtn.org. Web Site: www.haystack-mtn.org. *Dir*, Stuart Kestenbaum
Founded 1950
Library Holdings: Bk Vols 1,000
Subject Interests: Crafts
Restriction: Not a lending library

DENMARK

P DENMARK PUBLIC LIBRARY,* Rte 117, PO Box 50, 04022. SAN 376-3811. Tel: 207-452-2200. E-Mail: denmarklib@denmarklib.me.us. *Librn*, DeDe Rowe
Jul 1998-Jun 1999 Income $15,000. Mats Exp $1,200. Sal $5,800
Library Holdings: Bk Vols 6,800; Bk Titles 6,100; Per Subs 18
Mem of Central Maine Library District
Friends of the Library Group

DEXTER

P ABBOTT MEMORIAL LIBRARY,* One Church St, 04930. SAN 306-6258. Tel: 207-924-7292. E-Mail: aml-lb@abott-memorial.lib.me.us. *Dir*, Liz Breault; Staff 1 (MLS 1)
Founded 1896. Pop 3,580; Circ 24,764
Library Holdings: Bk Titles 19,225; Per Subs 72
Special Collections: Maine History, bks, cht, maps
Mem of Northeastern Maine Library District

DIXFIELD

P LUDDEN MEMORIAL LIBRARY, 40 Main St, PO Box 805, 04224-0805. SAN 306-6266. Tel: 207-562-8838. FAX: 207-562-4311. E-Mail: lml-jn@ludden.lib.me.us. *Librn*, Justina Nazar
Founded 1939. Circ 23,307
Jul 1999-Jun 2000 Income $54,749, State $345, City $52,504, Locally Generated Income $1,900. Mats Exp $12,857, Books $12,166, Per/Ser (Incl. Access Fees) $691. Sal $21,688 (Prof $9,798)
Library Holdings: Bk Vols 12,836; Per Subs 33
Special Collections: Maine Town Histories & Geneologies
Mem of Central Maine Library District

DOVER-FOXCROFT

S MID-MAINE MEDIA (WDME), Library Information Center,* 118 Union Square, 04426. Tel: 207-564-2642. FAX: 207-564-8905. E-Mail: wdme@kynd.com. Web Site: www.wdmefm.com. *Mgr*, Richard Thau; *Coordr*, Joyce Wemer; Staff 2 (MLS 2)
Library Holdings: Bk Vols 750; Bk Titles 500; Per Subs 15

Subject Interests: Broadcasting, Bus, Government, Local history, Music, News
Database Vendor: Lexis-Nexis
Function: Reference services available
For in-person visits, telephone prior to visiting

P THOMPSON FREE LIBRARY, 76 E Main St, 04426. SAN 306-6274. Tel: 207-564-3350. FAX: 207-564-3531. E-Mail: df@thompson.lib.me.us. Web Site: www.dover-foxcroft.org/lib.htm. *Librn*, Helen Austin; *Asst Librn*, Patricia Juska; Staff 3 (MLS 1, Non-MLS 2)
Founded 1898. Pop 4,600; Circ 68,000
Jul 1999-Jun 2000 Income $73,500, State $200, City $73,300. Mats Exp $20,000
Library Holdings: Bk Vols 25,000; Per Subs 30
Subject Interests: Gardening, Genealogy, History
Special Collections: Maine Town Histories
Automation Activity & Vendor Info: (Cataloging) Sagebrush Corporation; (Circulation) Sagebrush Corporation
Mem of Northeastern Maine Library District
Friends of the Library Group

EAST BALDWIN

P BROWN MEMORIAL LIBRARY,* School St, PO Box 24, 04024. SAN 372-7548. Tel: 207-787-3155. *Librn*, Winnie Slocum; Staff 2 (MLS 1, Non-MLS 1)
Founded 1906. Pop 1,100; Circ 2,003
Library Holdings: Bk Vols 8,878
Special Collections: Baldwin History, bks, photogs; Baldwin Town Records
Mem of Southern Conn Libr Coun
Special Services for the Deaf - Books on deafness & sign language
Open Mon 6pm-8pm, Wed 2:30-4:30 & 6-8, Sat 1-5
Friends of the Library Group

EAST LEBANON

P LEBANON AREA LIBRARY,* New Rd, PO Box 339, 04027. SAN 306-669X. Tel: 207-457-1171. *Librn*, Barbara Bridge
Pop 3,237
Library Holdings: Bk Vols 7,500; Bk Titles 7,406
Subject Interests: Art, Genealogy
Special Collections: Genealogy; Lebanon History; Lebanon Town Reports; Maine Coll; Valuation of Real Estate
Mem of Southern Conn Libr Coun; Southern Maine Library District
Open Mon 7am-8pm & Sat 2-4pm
Friends of the Library Group

EAST MACHIAS

P FLORENCE STURDIVANT PUBLIC LIBRARY,* 04630. SAN 306-6290. FAX: 207-255-8480. *Librn*, Holly Costley
Pop 1,200; Circ 2,628
Library Holdings: Bk Vols 6,780; Per Subs 12

EAST MILLINOCKET

P EAST MILLINOCKET PUBLIC LIBRARY,* 53 Main St, 04430. SAN 306-6304. Tel: 207-746-3554. FAX: 207-746-3550. *Librn*, Dorothy Chasse; E-Mail: dchasse@east.millinocket.lib.me.us
Library Holdings: Bk Titles 20,844; Per Subs 15
Mem of Northeastern Maine Library District

EAST SEBAGO

P SPAULDING MEMORIAL LIBRARY, PO Box 300, 04029. SAN 306-7467. Tel: 207-787-2321. E-Mail: directors@spaulding.lib.me.us. *Librn*, Barbara L Thorne; Staff 2 (Non-MLS 2)
Pop 1,300; Circ 5,863
Jan 2000-Dec 2000 Income $26,950, Provincial $14,000, Other $12,950. Mats Exp $5,500, Books $4,500, Per/Ser (Incl. Access Fees) $400, AV Equip $600. Sal $9,672 (Prof $2,707)
Library Holdings: Bk Titles 8,000; Per Subs 14; High Interest/Low Vocabulary Bk Vols 53
Subject Interests: Maine
Mem of Maine State Library; Southern Maine Library District
Open Wed 1-8:30, Sat 10-12:30, Sun 2-4
Friends of the Library Group

EAST VASSALBORO

P VASSALBORO PUBLIC LIBRARY,* PO Box 62, 04935-0062. SAN 306-6312. Tel: 207-923-3233. *Librn*, Julie Rowe; E-Mail: nrowe@vassalboro.lib.me.us
Founded 1910. Pop 3,679; Circ 23,031
Jul 1998-Jun 1999 Income $28,915, City $19,425, Parent Institution $9,490. Mats Exp $7,850, Books $6,750, Per/Ser (Incl. Access Fees) $300, Presv $500. Sal $14,900
Library Holdings: Bk Vols 25,000
Subject Interests: Local history

EAST WATERBORO

P WATERBORO PUBLIC LIBRARY,* HCR 72, Rte 5, Box 1775, 04030. SAN 376-3854. Tel: 207-247-3363. E-Mail: wl_rb@waterboro.lib.me.us. *Librn*, Ruth Blake
1996-1997 Income $34,120. Mats Exp $33,317. Sal $21,114
Library Holdings: Bk Vols 14,255; Bk Titles 13,597; Per Subs 16
Mem of Southern Conn Libr Coun
Open Tues & Thurs 3-8, Sat 9-2
Friends of the Library Group

EASTPORT

P PEAVEY MEMORIAL LIBRARY,* 26 Water St, 04631. SAN 306-6320. Tel: 207-853-4021. FAX: 207-853-4021. E-Mail: eastport@peavey.lib.me.us. *Librn*, Christina Sbaiby
Founded 1893. Pop 1,982; Circ 7,384
Library Holdings: Bk Vols 25,959
Subject Interests: Economics, Environmental studies, History
Special Collections: Civil War Coll; Local Artists Coll; Maine Coll
Mem of Northeastern Maine Library District
Special Services for the Blind - Braille
Friends of the Library Group

S QUODDY TIDES FOUNDATION MARINE LIBRARY, 123 Water St, PO Box 213, 04631. SAN 372-7270. Tel: 207-853-2366, 207-853-4806. FAX: 207-853-4095. E-Mail: qtides@nemaine.com. *Librn*, Serena A Wilson
Founded 1968
Library Holdings: Bk Titles 1,000; Per Subs 10
Mem of NE Libr District; Northeastern Maine Library District

ELIOT

P WILLIAM FOGG LIBRARY, PO Box 359, Old Road, 03903. SAN 306-6339. Tel: 207-439-9437. FAX: 207-439-9437. Web Site: www.william-fogg.lib.me.us. *Ad Servs, Dir*, Mary Jasper Cate; E-Mail: maryjcate@william-fogg.lib.me.us; *Asst Dir, Ch Servs, YA Servs*, Mary P Class; E-Mail: classm@william-fogg.lib.me.us; *Circ*, Laura A Hyson; *Circ Ch*, Nicole LaBranche; *Librn*, Sharon Kibat. Subject Specialists: *Children's*, Nicole LaBranche; Staff 5 (MLS 2, Non-MLS 3)
Founded 1907. Pop 6,000; Circ 20,000
Library Holdings: Bk Vols 18,658; Per Subs 26
Subject Interests: Genealogy, Local history
Mem of Southern Maine Library District
Special Services for the Blind - Large print & cassettes
Friends of the Library Group

ELLSWORTH

P ELLSWORTH PUBLIC LIBRARY, 20 State St, 04605. SAN 306-6347. Tel: 207-667-6363. FAX: 207-667-4901. Web Site: www.ellsworth.lib.me.us. *Dir*, Patricia Foster; E-Mail: pat@seth.ellsworth.lib.me.us; *Assoc Dir*, Charlene Clemons; *Ch Servs*, Lisa Crosby; Staff 9 (Non-MLS 9)
Founded 1897. Pop 13,000; Circ 125,864
Jul 1999-Jun 2000 Income $420,426, State $1,200, City $375,026, Locally Generated Income $14,200, Other $30,000. Mats Exp $33,500, Books $26,000, Per/Ser (Incl. Access Fees) $7,500
Library Holdings: Bk Vols 35,034; Bk Titles 32,996; Per Subs 134
Subject Interests: Local history
Special Collections: Whitmore Genealogy Coll
Mem of Northeastern Maine Library District
Friends of the Library Group

L HANCOCK COUNTY LAW LIBRARY, 50 State St, 04605. SAN 327-330X. Tel: 207-667-7176. *Librn*, Rosemary Merchant
Library Holdings: Bk Vols 10,000

M MAINE COAST MEMORIAL HOSPITAL LIBRARY,* 50 Union St, 04605. SAN 377-9262. Tel: 207-667-5311, Ext 298. *Librn*, Jane Harris; E-Mail: jharris@acadia.net
Library Holdings: Bk Vols 50; Bk Titles 50; Per Subs 30
Mem of Northeastern Maine Library District
Partic in Health Science Library Information Consortium

ENFIELD

P COLE MEMORIAL LIBRARY,* Hammett Rd, PO Box 429, 04493-0429. SAN 325-2698. Tel: 207-732-4270. FAX: 207-732-5335. *Librn*, Donne P Chubbuck

Founded 1974
Jul 1998-Jun 1999 Income $500, City $500. Mats Exp Books $500
Library Holdings: Bk Vols 2,986

FAIRFIELD

J KENNEBEC VALLEY TECHNICAL COLLEGE, Media Center,* 92 Western Ave, 04937-1367. SAN 321-5636. Tel: 207-453-5162. FAX: 207-453-5194. Web Site: www.kvtc.net/library.html. *Librn*, Janet Sibley; E-Mail: jsibley@kvtc.net; Staff 2 (MLS 1, Non-MLS 1)
Founded 1979. Enrl 1,894; Fac 43; Highest Degree: Associate
Jul 1998-Jun 1999 Income $135,840. Mats Exp $25,554, Books $11,778, Per/Ser (Incl. Access Fees) $11,926, Presv $250, AV Equip $1,600. Sal $98,902 (Prof $81,810)
Library Holdings: Bk Vols 19,700; Bk Titles 18,700; Per Subs 150
Subject Interests: Electronics, Nursing
Automation Activity & Vendor Info: (Cataloging) Follett
Database Vendor: Ebsco - EbscoHost
Mem of Maine State Library
Partic in Health Science Library Information Consortium
Special Services for the Deaf - TDD
Special Services for the Blind - Kurzweil Personal Reader

P LAWRENCE PUBLIC LIBRARY,* 33 Lawrence Ave, 04937. SAN 306-6355. Tel: 207-453-6867. FAX: 207-453-9345. Web Site: www.lawrence.lib.me.us. *Ch Servs, Dir*, Edna Hale
Founded 1901. Pop 6,113; Circ 15,597
Library Holdings: Bk Titles 23,400; Per Subs 65
Special Collections: Fairfield Historical Society Coll
Mem of Central Maine Library District

FALMOUTH

P FALMOUTH MEMORIAL LIBRARY, 5 Lunt Rd, 04105-1292. SAN 306-6363. Tel: 207-781-2351. FAX: 207-781-4094. E-Mail: falmouth.memorial.library@msln.net. Web Site: www.falmouth.lib.me.us. *Dir*, Lynda Sudlow; Staff 5 (MLS 5)
Founded 1944. Pop 10,000; Circ 120,000
Jul 1999-Jun 2000 Income $276,301, State $200, City $211,000, Locally Generated Income $24,000, Other $41,101. Mats Exp $28,800, Books $20,000, Per/Ser (Incl. Access Fees) $2,800. Sal $197,948
Library Holdings: Bk Titles 40,000; Per Subs 74
Subject Interests: History
Special Collections: Crafts & Needlepoint Coll; Gardening Coll; Maine Coll
Automation Activity & Vendor Info: (Cataloging) Sagebrush Corporation; (OPAC) Sagebrush Corporation
Database Vendor: Ebsco - EbscoHost
Mem of Southern Maine Library District
Friends of the Library Group

S GOVERNOR BAXTER SCHOOL FOR THE DEAF LIBRARY, (GBSD), One Mackworth Island, 04105-1951. (Mail add: PO Box 799, 04104-0799), SAN 328-1973. Tel: 207-781-6237. TDD: 207-781-6237. FAX: 207-781-6240. E-Mail: librariansb@fc.baxter.pvt.k12.me.us. *Librn for Deaf*, Leona Anderson; Staff 1 (Non-MLS 1)
Library Holdings: Bk Titles 7,000; Per Subs 40
Subject Interests: Am sign lang, Deaf culture, Deaf educ, Deafness
Automation Activity & Vendor Info: (Cataloging) Athena; (Circulation) Athena
Restriction: Circulation limited
Function: ILL limited, Outside services via phone, cable & mail, Photocopies available, Professional lending library, Some telephone reference
Special Services for the Deaf - Collection on deaf education; TTY machine

S MAINE AUDUBON SOCIETY LIBRARY,* PO Box 6009, 04105-6009. SAN 327-3326. Tel: 207-781-2330. FAX: 207-781-0974.
Library Holdings: Bk Vols 3,000; Bk Titles 2,300; Per Subs 40
Restriction: Non-circulating to the public

FARMINGTON

P FARMINGTON PUBLIC LIBRARY,* 2 Academy St, 04938. SAN 306-6371. Tel: 207-778-4312. Web Site: www.farmington.lib.me.us. *Dir*, Jean Oplinger; Staff 4 (MLS 1, Non-MLS 3)
Founded 1890. Pop 7,430; Circ 75,000
Jan 1999-Dec 1999 Income $110,000. Mats Exp $25,000. Sal $65,000
Library Holdings: Bk Vols 31,000; Per Subs 86
Subject Interests: Genealogy, History
Mem of Central Maine Library District

C UNIVERSITY OF MAINE AT FARMINGTON, Mantor Library, 116 South St, 04938-1990. SAN 306-638X. Tel: 207-778-7210. FAX: 207-778-7223. Web Site: www.umf.maine.edu/~library/. *Dir*, Franklin D Roberts; Tel: 207-778-7215, E-Mail: froberts@maine.maine.edu; *Access Serv*, Janet Brackett; *Ref*, Terence Edwards; *Tech Servs*, Judy Steere; *ILL*, Moira Wolohan; *Info Tech*, Shelly Davis; Staff 4 (MLS 4)
Founded 1933. Enrl 2,000; Fac 125; Highest Degree: Bachelor
Jul 1999-Jun 2000 Income $535,368. Mats Exp $143,795, Books $45,261, Per/Ser (Incl. Access Fees) $61,190, Micro $18,713, AV Equip $784, Manuscripts & Archives $10,247, Electronic Ref Mat (Incl. Access Fees) $7,600. Sal $459,678 (Prof $189,661)
Library Holdings: Bk Vols 104,313; Bk Titles 91,048; Per Subs 1,800
Special Collections: University of Maine at Farmington Archives
Publications: Library: The Academic Edge (video)
Partic in Central Maine Libr District; Nelinet, Inc; OCLC Online Computer Library Center, Inc

FAYETTE

P UNDERWOOD MEMORIAL LIBRARY, Main St, RR 2, Box 1305, 04349. SAN 306-6398. Tel: 207-685-3778. E-Mail: faylib@fayette.lib.me.us. *Librn*, Suzanne Rich
Founded 1958. Pop 1,000; Circ 14,500
Jul 1999-Jun 2000 Income City $7,850
Library Holdings: Bk Titles 16,564; Per Subs 12
Subject Interests: Children's books, Cookbooks, Maine
Mem of Central Maine Library District
Partic in Nelinet, Inc
Open Winter: Wed 9-8; Summer: Mon 6-9pm, Tues & Thurs 9-12 & Wed 2-4 & 6-9
Friends of the Library Group

FORT FAIRFIELD

P FORT FAIRFIELD PUBLIC LIBRARY,* 275 Main St, 04742-1199. SAN 306-6401. Tel: 207-472-3880. *Librn*, Janice Fletcher; *Asst Librn*, Inez Lynch
Founded 1895. Pop 3,880; Circ 20,869
Library Holdings: Bk Titles 24,000; Per Subs 50
Special Collections: Civil War (Drew Coll)
Mem of Northeastern Maine Library District
Friends of the Library Group

FORT KENT

P FORT KENT PUBLIC LIBRARY, One Pleasant St, 04743. SAN 306-641X. Tel: 207-834-3048. FAX: 207-834-2630. *Librn*, Marlene Pooler
Founded 1936. Pop 4,268; Circ 22,596
1999-2000 Income City $21,000
Library Holdings: Bk Vols 22,000
Mem of Northeastern Maine Library District

C UNIVERSITY OF MAINE AT FORT KENT, Blake Library, 25 Pleasant St, 04743-1292. SAN 306-6428. Tel: 207-834-7525. FAX: 207-834-7518. Web Site: www.umfk.maine.edu/infoserv/library. *Dean*, Sharon M Johnson; E-Mail: sharonj@maine.edu; *Asst Dir*, Leslie Kelly; Tel: 207-834-7528, E-Mail: lesliek@main.edu; *Cat*, Patricia Whitworth; Staff 6 (MLS 3, Non-MLS 3)
Founded 1878. Enrl 827; Fac 32; Highest Degree: Bachelor
Jan 1999-Dec 1999 Income $223,251. Mats Exp $54,277, Books $7,680, Per/Ser (Incl. Access Fees) $33,160, Micro $10,065, AV Equip $1,272, Electronic Ref Mat (Incl. Access Fees) $2,100. Sal $146,647 (Prof $108,271)
Library Holdings: Bk Vols 64,898; Per Subs 382
Special Collections: Saint John Valley History
Database Vendor: CARL, Ebsco - EbscoHost, OCLC - First Search, Silverplatter Information Inc.

FREEPORT

P FREEPORT COMMUNITY LIBRARY, 10 Library Dr, 04032. SAN 306-6436. Tel: 207-865-3307. FAX: 207-865-1395. *Dir*, Kathryn Haines; E-Mail: khaines@baetol.lib.me.us; *Asst Librn*, Vicki Lowe; Staff 10 (MLS 2, Non-MLS 8)
Pop 6,905; Circ 193,631
Jul 1999-Jun 2000 Income $311,917. Mats Exp $50,017, Books $35,000, AV Equip $8,762, Electronic Ref Mat (Incl. Access Fees) $6,255. Sal $224,700
Library Holdings: Bk Titles 45,008; Per Subs 124
Automation Activity & Vendor Info: (Acquisitions) Sagebrush Corporation
Mem of Southern Maine Library District
Open Mon & Wed 11:30-8, Tues & Thurs 9:30-5, Fri 11:30-5 & Sat 9-3

FRYEBURG

P FRYEBURG PUBLIC LIBRARY, 98 Main St, 04037-1126. SAN 306-6452. Tel: 207-935-2731. *Librn*, Emily D Fletcher; E-Mail: efletcher@fryeburg.lib.me.us
Founded 1890. Pop 3,124; Circ 16,251
Jan 1999-Dec 1999 Income $55,850. Mats Exp $6,500
Library Holdings: Bk Vols 15,581
Special Collections: Clarence E Mulford Coll
Mem of Southern Conn Libr Coun

GARDINER

P GARDINER PUBLIC LIBRARY,* 152 Water St, 04345. SAN 306-6460. Tel: 207-582-3312. FAX: 207-582-6104. E-Mail: staff@gpl.lib.me.us. Web Site: www.gpl.lib.me.us. *Dir*, Anne Davis; *Asst Dir*, Scott Handville; *Ch Servs*, Charlene M Wagner
Founded 1881. Pop 16,588; Circ 141,882
Jul 1998-Jun 1999 Income $200,531, State $1,000, City $112,680, Locally Generated Income $86,851. Mats Exp Books $28,000. Sal $71,186 (Prof $48,476)
Library Holdings: Bk Vols 42,364; Per Subs 89
Special Collections: E A Robinson Coll; Laura E Richards Coll; The Yellow House Papers
Publications: Who Reads What List (annual)
Mem of Central Maine Library District
Friends of the Library Group

GEORGETOWN

P LAURA E RICHARDS LIBRARY,* 5 Island Rd, PO Box 436, 04548. SAN 372-6339. Tel: 207-371-2820. *Librn*, Lois K Klein
Founded 1937. Pop 914; Circ 2,905
Library Holdings: Bk Vols 4,902

GLENBURN

P GLENBURN LIBRARY,* 991 Hudson Rd, 04401. SAN 328-0306. Tel: 207-942-9897. FAX: 207-947-3867. *Librn*, Valerie Rich; E-Mail: vrich@glenburn.k12.me.ur; Staff 1 (MLS 1)
Founded 1978. Pop 3,200; Circ 17,300
Library Holdings: Bk Vols 15,500
Mem of Northeastern Maine Library District
Open School Year: Mon-Fri 9-3, Tues & Thurs 6-8pm; Summers: Tues & Thurs 9-3 & 6pm-8pm
Friends of the Library Group

GORHAM

P BAXTER MEMORIAL LIBRARY, 71 South St, 04038. SAN 306-6479. Tel: 207-839-5031. FAX: 207-839-7749. Web Site: www.baxter-memorial.lib.me.us. *Coll Develop, Dir*, Pamela E Turner; *Asst Dir*, Lorraine Canterbury; *Tech Servs*, Deborah Buker; *Ch Servs*, Elizabeth McDorr
Founded 1908. Pop 11,856; Circ 96,725
Library Holdings: Bk Vols 30,000; Per Subs 92
Special Collections: James Phinney Baxter Coll, papers & mss; Percival Proctor Baxter Coll, papers & mss
Mem of Southern Maine Library District

GRAY

P GRAY PUBLIC LIBRARY, 5 Hancock St, PO Box 1319, 04039-1319. SAN 306-6495. Tel: 207-657-4110. FAX: 207-657-4110. Web Site: www.graylibrary.ourmaine.com. *Dir*, Priscilla Payne; E-Mail: ppayne@maine.rr.com; *Asst Librn*, Kathy George
Pop 7,100; Circ 44,000
Jul 2000-Jun 2001 Income City $70,663. Mats Exp $17,540, Books $13,500, Per/Ser (Incl. Access Fees) $1,400, AV Equip $1,500, Other Print Mats $1,000, Electronic Ref Mat (Incl. Access Fees) $140. Sal $40,492 (Prof $24,720)
Library Holdings: Bk Titles 28,000; Per Subs 37
Subject Interests: Agriculture, Humanities, Medicine, Natural science, Technology
Special Collections: Maine Coll
Automation Activity & Vendor Info: (Cataloging) Sagebrush Corporation; (Circulation) Sagebrush Corporation; (OPAC) Sagebrush Corporation
Mem of Southern Maine Library District
Friends of the Library Group

GREENE

P JULIA ADAMS MORSE MEMORIAL LIBRARY,* Main St, 279 Sprague Mill Rd, 04236. SAN 306-6509. Tel: 207-946-5544. *Librn*, Patricia Rose
Founded 1955. Pop 3,037; Circ 4,620
Library Holdings: Bk Vols 6,227
Open Tues 1-7, Thurs 1-6 & Sat 10-3

GREENVILLE

P SHAW PUBLIC LIBRARY,* Main St, 04441. (Mail add: PO Box 510, 04441), SAN 306-6517. Tel: 207-695-3579. FAX: 207-695-0310. E-Mail: splibrary@shaw-greenville.lib.me.us. *Librn*, Karen Chandler; *Asst Librn*, Etta Hubbard; *Asst Librn*, Deana Ryder; *Asst Librn*, Lauren Muzzy
Pop 1,839; Circ 18,953
Library Holdings: Bk Vols 19,000; Per Subs 60
Mem of Northeastern Maine Library District

GUILFORD

P GUILFORD MEMORIAL LIBRARY,* Library St, PO Box 177, 04443. SAN 306-6525. Tel: 207-876-4547. FAX: 207-876-2569. *Librn*, Linda Packard; Staff 3 (MLS 1, Non-MLS 2)
Founded 1903. Circ 27,500
Library Holdings: Bk Vols 13,500; Per Subs 23
Mem of Northeastern Maine Library District
Friends of the Library Group

HALLOWELL

P HUBBARD FREE LIBRARY,* 115 Second St, 04347. SAN 306-6533. Tel: 207-622-6582. FAX: 207-621-0907. *Librn*, Nancy McGinnis; *AV*, Martha Bourdon; *Asst Librn*, Alfreda Young; *Asst Librn*, Barbara Rohrbaugh
Pop 4,500; Circ 24,380
Library Holdings: Bk Vols 30,000; Bk Titles 19,000; Per Subs 70
Subject Interests: Local history
Partic in Maine Libr Asn; OCLC Online Computer Library Center, Inc
Friends of the Library Group

HAMPDEN

P EDYTHE L DYER COMMUNITY LIBRARY, 269 Main Rd N, 04444. SAN 306-6541. Tel: 207-862-3550. FAX: 207-862-3550. Web Site: www.edl.lib.me.us. *Dir Libr Serv*, Debora Lozito; E-Mail: debbie.lozito@edythedyer.lib.me.us; *Ch Servs*, Donna Beck; Staff 6 (MLS 1, Non-MLS 5)
Founded 1971. Pop 5,974; Circ 107,016
Jul 2000-Jun 2001 Income $143,809, City $132,809, Other $11,000
Library Holdings: Bk Titles 29,236
Subject Interests: Local history
Automation Activity & Vendor Info: (Cataloging) Innovative Interfaces Inc.; (Circulation) Innovative Interfaces Inc.; (OPAC) Innovative Interfaces Inc.
Database Vendor: Ebsco - EbscoHost
Function: ILL available
Mem of Maine State Library
Friends of the Library Group

HARRISON

P CASWELL PUBLIC LIBRARY,* 42 Main St, PO Box 597, 04040-9722. SAN 306-6568. Tel: 207-583-2970. Web Site: www.caswell.lib.me.us. *Librn*, Dianne Jackson; E-Mail: djackson@caswell.lib.me.us
Founded 1908. Pop 1,667; Circ 7,469
Jul 1998-Jun 1999 Income $16,000, State $160, City $10,600, Locally Generated Income $2,561, Other $390. Mats Exp $300, Books $137. Sal $10,400
Library Holdings: Bk Vols 9,500; Per Subs 12
Mem of Southern Conn Libr Coun; Southern Maine Library District
Friends of the Library Group

HARTLAND

P HARTLAND PUBLIC LIBRARY, 8 Mill St, PO Box 620, 04943. SAN 306-6576. Tel: 207-938-4702. *Librn*, Sally P Sargent; E-Mail: s.sargent@hartland.lib.me.us
Founded 1902. Pop 1,860; Circ 13,700
Library Holdings: Bk Vols 27,000; Bk Titles 20,000; Per Subs 22
Subject Interests: Local history
Mem of Central Maine Library District

HIRAM

P SOLDIERS MEMORIAL LIBRARY, 85 Main St, PO Box 281, 04041. SAN 372-7696. Tel: 207-625-4650. *Librn*, Pamela Thomas; E-Mail: slattery-thomas@juno.com
Founded 1915. Pop 1,260; Circ 1,818
Library Holdings: Bk Titles 10,441
Mem of Southern Maine Library District

HOLLIS CENTER

P HOLLIS CENTER PUBLIC LIBRARY, 18 Little Falls Rd, 04042. SAN 343-6594. Tel: 207-929-3911. E-Mail: hclib@hollis.center.lib.me.us. *Dir*, Maureen H Cole; Staff 1 (Non-MLS 1)
Founded 1918. Pop 4,000
1999-2000 Income $19,500, City $18,000, Locally Generated Income $1,500. Mats Exp Books $2,500. Sal $6,000
Library Holdings: Bk Vols 10,500; Bk Titles 10,500
Automation Activity & Vendor Info: (Circulation) Sagebrush Corporation
Database Vendor: Ebsco - EbscoHost
Mem of Southern Conn Libr Coun; Southern Maine Library District
Open Mon 9:30 AM - 12:00, 4 -8 PM; Tues 4 -8 PM, Thurs 4-8 PM & Sat 2-5 PM

P SALMON FALLS VILLAGE LIBRARY,* 27 Salmon Falls Rd, 04042. SAN 376-6489. Tel: 207-929-3990. *Librn*, Zoe Austin
Library Holdings: Bk Vols 8,000
Mem of Southern Maine Library District
Open Mon 3-6, Wed 5-8, Thurs 3-8 & Sat 9-12
Friends of the Library Group

HOULTON

P CARY LIBRARY,* 107 Main St, 04730. SAN 343-6659. Tel: 207-532-1302. FAX: 702-532-4350. Web Site: www.cary.lib.me.us. *Dir*, Betty J Fraser
Founded 1903. Pop 7,000; Circ 83,841
Library Holdings: Bk Vols 40,000; Per Subs 120
Special Collections: Aroostook County Oral History; Aroostook Newspapers (1859-1938), micro
Mem of Northeastern Maine Library District

M HOULTON REGIONAL HOSPITAL LIBRARY,* 20 Hartford St, 04730. SAN 329-3882. Tel: 207-532-9471. FAX: 207-532-7934.
Library Holdings: Bk Vols 200; Per Subs 57

ISLAND FALLS

P KATAHDIN PUBLIC LIBRARY,* Sherman St, PO Box 148, 04747-0148. SAN 306-6592. Tel: 207-463-2091. *Librn*, Trish Prescott
Founded 1939. Pop 1,000; Circ 7,332
Library Holdings: Bk Vols 11,882
Mem of Northeastern Maine Library District

ISLE AU HAUT

P REVERE MEMORIAL LIBRARY,* Revere Memorial Hall, PO Box 8B, 04645-9999. SAN 374-4876. E-Mail: revere.memorial.library@msln.net. *Librn*, Marcia Hart-Quinby
Circ 1,500
Library Holdings: Bk Titles 4,000
Special Collections: Acadia National Park; Isle Au Haut Geological Coll

ISLESBORO

P ALICE L PENDLETON LIBRARY, 309 Main Rd, 04848-4505. (Mail add: PO Box 77, 04848-0077), SAN 306-6606. Tel: 207-734-2218. FAX: 207-734-8394. Web Site: www.alpl.lib.me.us. *Librn*, Linda Graf
Founded 1918. Pop 2,500; Circ 6,668
2000-2001 Mats Exp Books $3,000
Library Holdings: Bk Vols 16,000; Per Subs 48
Subject Interests: Local authors
Special Collections: Maine Genealogy Books; Oil Paintings; Ship Models
Automation Activity & Vendor Info: (Cataloging) Follett; (Circulation) Follett; (OPAC) Follett
Mem of Northeastern Maine Library District
Special Services for the Blind - Bks on tape
Friends of the Library Group

JACKMAN

P JACKMAN PUBLIC LIBRARY,* Main St, PO Box 8, 04945. SAN 321-0383. Tel: 207-668-2110. E-Mail: jackman.public.library@msln.net. *Librn*, Cindy Lacasse; *Coll Develop*, Christine Hughey; Staff 2 (Non-MLS 2)
Founded 1917. Pop 1,500
Jan 1998-Dec 1998 Income $16,100, City $1,600, Locally Generated Income $1,500, Other $13,000. Mats Exp $1,050, Books $800, AV Equip $250
Library Holdings: Bk Vols 6,886; Bk Titles 6,863
Special Collections: Maine Authors Coll

JONESPORT

P PEABODY MEMORIAL LIBRARY,* Main St, Box 210, 04649-0210. SAN 376-3536. Tel: 207-947-8336. *Librn*, Barbara W Hall
Library Holdings: Bk Vols 11,000; Bk Titles 10,000; Per Subs 23
Mem of Northeastern Maine Library District

KENDUSKEAG

P CASE MEMORIAL LIBRARY, PO Box 312, 04450. SAN 306-6622. Tel: 207-884-8598. *Librn*, Diane Smith
Pop 1,210; Circ 1,300
Feb 1998-Jan 1999 Income $3,500. Mats Exp Books $1,500. Sal $2,100
Library Holdings: Bk Vols 6,000
Mem of Northeastern Maine Library District

KENNEBUNK

P KENNEBUNK FREE LIBRARY, 112 Main St, 04043. SAN 306-6649. Tel: 207-985-2173. FAX: 207-985-4730. E-Mail: kflweb@kennebunk.lib.me.us. Web Site: www.kennebunk.lib.me.us. *Dir*, Margaret Mills; *Asst Dir, Ch Servs, Librn*, Janet D Cate; Staff 12 (MLS 1, Non-MLS 11)
Founded 1882. Pop 10,000; Circ 121,436 Income $388,955. Mats Exp Books $55,808
Library Holdings: Bk Vols 33,069; Per Subs 136; Bks on Deafness & Sign Lang 20
Special Collections: Bolton Travel Library; Kenneth Joy Photographic Coll; Walker Diaries
Automation Activity & Vendor Info: (Cataloging) Follett; (Circulation) Follett; (OPAC) Follett
Database Vendor: ProQuest
Publications: History of Kennebunk
Function: ILL available, Reference services available, Some telephone reference
Mem of Southern Maine Library District
Friends of the Library Group

S THE BRICK STORE MUSEUM, Edith Cleaves Barry Library, 117 Main St, 04043. SAN 326-615X. Tel: 207-985-4802. FAX: 207-985-6887. E-Mail: brickstore@cybertours.com. *Dir*, Marcy Molinaro; *Curator*, Catherine Vaillancourt
Library Holdings: Bk Vols 3,000
Subject Interests: Architecture, Decorative arts, Local history
Special Collections: Local
Restriction: Non-circulating to the public

KENNEBUNKPORT

S KENNEBUNKPORT HISTORICAL SOCIETY LIBRARY, 125 North St, 04046-5812. (Mail add: PO Box 1173, 04046-1173), SAN 374-9312. Tel: 207-967-2751. FAX: 207-967-1205. E-Mail: kporthistory@gwi.net. Web Site: www.kporthistory.org. *Exec Dir*, Ellen Driscoll Moy; Staff 1 (Non-MLS 1)
Founded 1952
Library Holdings: Bk Titles 750; Per Subs 40
Subject Interests: Local authors, Local history
Restriction: Not a lending library
Function: Research library

P LOUIS T GRAVES MEMORIAL PUBLIC LIBRARY, 18 Maine St, PO Box 391, 04046. SAN 306-6657. Tel: 207-967-2778. Web Site: www.graves.lib.me.us. *Librn*, Rosalind S Wade; *Ch Servs*, Mary Lou Boucouvalas; Staff 3 (MLS 1, Non-MLS 2)
Founded 1921. Pop 3,356; Circ 49,000
2000-2000 Income $182,000
Library Holdings: Bk Vols 28,000; Per Subs 95
Special Collections: Booth Tarkington Coll; Kenneth Roberts Coll; Margaret Deland Coll
Automation Activity & Vendor Info: (OPAC) Follett
Mem of Southern Maine Library District
Partic in OCLC Online Computer Library Center, Inc
Friends of the Library Group

S SEASHORE TROLLEY MUSEUM LIBRARY,* 195 Log Cabin Rd, 04046. (Mail add: PO Box A, 04046), SAN 377-4503. Tel: 207-967-2712. FAX: 207-967-0867. E-Mail: carshop@gwi.net. Web Site: www.trolleymuseum.org. *Librn*, George Sandborn
Library Holdings: Bk Vols 10,000

KINGFIELD

P WEBSTER LIBRARY CORPORATION,* Depot St, PO Box 518, 04947. SAN 306-6673. Tel: 207-265-2052. *Librn*, Barbara Stewart; *Asst Librn*, Mozelle Tranten
Pop 1,083; Circ 7,610
Library Holdings: Bk Vols 13,000

KITTERY

P RICE PUBLIC LIBRARY, 8 Wentworth St, 03904. SAN 306-6681. Tel: 207-439-1553. FAX: 207-439-1765. E-Mail: arabella@rice.lib.me.us. Web Site: www.rice.lib.me.us/. *Librn*, Hope B Neilson; *Circ*, Margaret Elliott; *Tech Servs*, Joyce Stephens; Staff 2 (MLS 2)
Founded 1875. Pop 9,372; Circ 94,293
Jul 1999-Jun 2000 Income $304,928, City $290,370, Locally Generated Income $14,558. Mats Exp $30,208, Books $25,000, Per/Ser (Incl. Access Fees) $4,908. Sal $170,256
Library Holdings: Bk Vols 53,747; Bk Titles 50,560; Per Subs 190
Special Collections: Kittery History & Genealogy, bks, photog
Automation Activity & Vendor Info: (Cataloging) Follett; (Circulation) Follett

Mem of Southern Maine Library District
Special Services for the Deaf - Books on deafness & sign language; High interest/low vocabulary books
Friends of the Library Group

LEWISTON

C BATES COLLEGE, George & Helen Ladd Library, 48 Campus Ave, 04240. SAN 306-6703. Tel: 207-786-6264. FAX: 207-786-6055. Web Site: www.bates.edu/library. *Dir*, Eugene L Wiemers; E-Mail: ewiemers@bates.edu; *Assoc Dir*, Paul D Matthews; *Tech Servs*, John C Harrison; *Cat*, Sharon K Saunders; *Spec Coll*, Kurt F Kuss; *ILL*, Elaine M Ardia; *Circ*, Julie A Retelle; *Ref*, Laura Juraska; *Doc*, Sandra Groleau; *Bibliog Instr*, Maryann Hight; *Archivist*, Christopher Beam; *Syst Coordr*, Andrew White
Founded 1855. Enrl 1,713; Fac 163; Highest Degree: Bachelor
Jul 1998-Jun 1999 Income $2,650,800. Mats Exp $1,074,042, Books $388,826, Per/Ser (Incl. Access Fees) $480,294, Presv $15,054, Micro $34,039, Electronic Ref Mat (Incl. Access Fees) $126,449. Sal $955,808 (Prof $403,922)
Library Holdings: Bk Vols 525,000; Per Subs 1,964
Special Collections: Books from the Library of Marsden Hartley; Dorothy Freeman Coll; Edmund S Muskie Coll; Freewill Baptist Coll; Jonathan Stanton Natural History Coll; Judaica (Berent Coll); Nineteenth Century works in French & German (Rice Coll); Signed First Editions (Phelps Coll)
Automation Activity & Vendor Info: (Acquisitions) Innovative Interfaces Inc.; (Cataloging) Innovative Interfaces Inc.; (Circulation) Innovative Interfaces Inc.; (Serials) Innovative Interfaces Inc.
Partic in CBB Librs

M CENTRAL MAINE MEDICAL CENTER, Gerrish-True Health Sciences Library, 300 Main St, PO Box 4500, 04240. SAN 306-6711. Tel: 207-795-2560. FAX: 207-795-2569. Web Site: www.cmhc.org. *Tech Servs*, Maureen Fournier; *Doc*, Linda Beauliey; *Ref*, Kaltry Brunjes
Library Holdings: Bk Vols 1,700; Per Subs 280
Special Collections: Health Information Coll
Publications: Info to Go (newsletter)
Partic in Nat Libr of Med

P LEWISTON PUBLIC LIBRARY, 200 Lisbon St, 04240. SAN 343-6713. Tel: 207-784-0135. Circulation Tel: 207-784-0135, Ext 500. TDD: 207-784-3123. FAX: 207-784-3011. E-Mail: lpl@lplonline.org. Web Site: www.lplonline.org. *Dir*, Richard A Speer; Tel: 207-784-0135, Ext 208, E-Mail: rspeer@lplonline.org; *Tech Servs*, Karen Jones; Tel: 207-784-0135, Ext 211, E-Mail: kjones@lplonline.org; *ILL, Ref*, Lizette R Leveille; Tel: 207-784-0135, Ext 210, E-Mail: lleveill@lplonline.org; *Circ*, Claire Ward; Tel: 207-784-0135, Ext 206, E-Mail: cward@lplonline.org; *Ch Servs*, David Moorhead; Tel: 207-784-0135, Ext 202, E-Mail: dmoorhead@lplonline.org; Staff 15 (MLS 4, Non-MLS 11)
Founded 1902. Pop 39,757; Circ 207,000
Jul 1998-Jun 1999 Income $731,878, State $5,300, City $722,578, Other $4,000. Mats Exp $114,400, Books $87,900, Per/Ser (Incl. Access Fees) $19,000, Micro $1,500, Electronic Ref Mat (Incl. Access Fees) $6,000. Sal $378,326
Library Holdings: Bk Vols 105,000; Bk Titles 94,000; Per Subs 312; High Interest/Low Vocabulary Bk Vols 747
Special Collections: French Literature (Dr Eustache N Giguere Memorial); Lewiston History Coll; Lewiston Material (David W Farrar Coll)
Mem of Central Maine Library District
Friends of the Library Group

M SAINT MARY'S REGIONAL MEDICAL CENTER, Health Sciences Library, PO Box 291, 04243-0291. SAN 321-5520. Tel: 207-777-8775. FAX: 207-777-8773. *Librn*, Happy Copley; Staff 2 (MLS 1, Non-MLS 1)
Founded 1970
Library Holdings: Bk Vols 1,380; Bk Titles 1,065; Per Subs 129
Subject Interests: Medicine, Nursing, Psychiatry
Partic in Basic Health Sciences Library Network; Health Sci Libr & Info Coop

C UNIVERSITY OF SOUTHERN MAINE, Lewiston-Auburn College Library, 51 Westminster St, PO Box 1937, 04241-1937. SAN 377-9432. Tel: 207-753-6540. Interlibrary Loan Service Tel: 207-753-6542. Reference Tel: 207-753-6546. FAX: 207-753-6543. E-Mail: laclibrary@usm.maine.edu. Web Site: usm.maine.edu/lac/library. *Dir*, Evelyn Greenlaw; Tel: 207-753-6541, E-Mail: evelyng@usm.maine.edu; *Circ*, Suzanne Maheux; E-Mail: smaheux@usm.maine.edu; *ILL*, Daniel Philbrick; E-Mail: philbrick@usm.maine.edu; *Ref Serv*, Maureen Perry; E-Mail: mperry@usm.maine.edu; Staff 2 (MLS 2)
Founded 1988. Enrl 1,600; Fac 20; Highest Degree: Master
Jul 1999-Jun 2000 Income $175,284. Mats Exp $175,284, Books $25,000, Per/Ser (Incl. Access Fees) $39,400, Micro $7,000, AV Equip $1,287, Electronic Ref Mat (Incl. Access Fees) $1,000. Sal $88,584 (Prof $35,793)
Library Holdings: Bk Vols 16,000; Per Subs 266
Subject Interests: Behav sci, Franco-Am hist, Inter-disciplinary, Leadership-mgt, Occupational therapy, Social sciences
Special Collections: Franco-American Heritage Coll
Automation Activity & Vendor Info: (Circulation) Innovative Interfaces Inc.; (Course Reserve) Innovative Interfaces Inc.; (OPAC) Innovative Interfaces Inc.
Database Vendor: Ebsco - EbscoHost, OCLC - First Search, ProQuest, Silverplatter Information Inc.
Partic in Maine Health Sci Librs & Info Consortium; Nelinet, Inc; OCLC Online Computer Library Center, Inc

LIMERICK

P LIMERICK PUBLIC LIBRARY, 55 Washington St, 04048. SAN 376-3870. Tel: 207-793-8975. FAX: 207-793-8443. *Dir, Librn*, Cindy Smith; Staff 2 (Non-MLS 2)
Jan 2000-Dec 2000 Income $30,291, State $200, City $28,991, Locally Generated Income $1,100. Mats Exp Books $5,500. Sal $17,841
Library Holdings: Bk Vols 13,000
Mem of Southern Conn Libr Coun
Friends of the Library Group

LIMESTONE

P ROBERT A FROST MEMORIAL LIBRARY, 42 Main St, 04750-1399. SAN 306-672X. Tel: 207-325-4706. FAX: 207-325-4706. E-Mail: frostml@yahoo.com. *Librn*, Rea M Caldwell; *Asst Librn*, Vicki A Page; Staff 2 (Non-MLS 2)
Founded 1899. Pop 3,000; Circ 20,000
Jul 1999-Jun 2000 Income City $45,000. Mats Exp $9,800, Books $7,200, Per/Ser (Incl. Access Fees) $800, Micro $800, AV Equip $1,000. Sal $25,000
Library Holdings: Bk Titles 24,542; Per Subs 29
Special Collections: Aroostook History, bks, pamphlets; State & Local History, bks, maps, pamphlets, scrapbks
Publications: Booklist
Mem of Northeastern Maine Library District
Friends of the Library Group

LIMINGTON

P DAVIS MEMORIAL LIBRARY, 928 Cape Rd, PO Box 485, 04049. SAN 306-6738. Tel: 207-637-2422. FAX: 207-637-2422. E-Mail: dauislib@altavista.com. *Librn*, Lea Sutton
Founded 1912. Circ 5,438
Library Holdings: Bk Vols 13,050
Special Collections: Town Histories & Genealogy
Mem of Southern Conn Libr Coun; Southern Maine Library District
Friends of the Library Group

LINCOLN

P LINCOLN MEMORIAL LIBRARY, 11 W Broadway, 04457. SAN 306-6746. Tel: 207-794-2765. Web Site: www.lincolnmaine.org/library.html. *Dir*, Lynn Lowell; *Asst Librn*, Carolyn Johnson; *Ch Servs*, Mary Jo Hammond; Staff 3 (MLS 1, Non-MLS 2)
Founded 1879. Pop 5,066
Jul 2000-Jun 2001 Income $104,322. Mats Exp $12,800, Books $11,600, Per/Ser (Incl. Access Fees) $1,200. Sal $81,440 (Prof $63,400)
Library Holdings: Bk Vols 25,000; Per Subs 44; Bks on Deafness & Sign Lang 10
Automation Activity & Vendor Info: (Cataloging) Athena; (Circulation) Athena
Mem of Northeastern Maine Library District
Friends of the Library Group

LISBON FALLS

P LISBON FALLS COMMUNITY LIBRARY,* 28 Main St, 04252-0028. SAN 306-6762. Tel: 207-353-6564. *Dir*, Diane Nadeau; *Asst Librn*, Christine Mitchell; Staff 1 (MLS 1)
Founded 1920. Pop 13,000; Circ 32,621
Library Holdings: Bk Vols 40,000; Per Subs 40
Special Collections: Maine Coll
Publications: Newsletter
Mem of Central Maine Library District
Friends of the Library Group
Branches: 1
LISBON VILLAGE LIBRARY ASSOCIATION, 28 Main St, Lisbon Falls, 04252. (Mail add: 12 Village St, Lisbon, 04250), Tel: 207-353-2262. E-Mail: lhs17@lisbon.lib.me.us. Web Site: www.lisbon.lib.me.us. *Librn*, Diane Nadean; *Asst Librn*, Christine Mitchell; *Ch Servs*, Sherri McKay
Pop 9,500; Circ 30,000
Jul 1998-Jun 1999 Income (Main Library and Branch Library) Locally Generated Income $102,000. Mats Exp $14,400, Books $12,500, Per/Ser (Incl. Access Fees) $1,200, Other Print Mats $700. Sal $80,809
Library Holdings: Bk Vols 11,000; Bk Titles 33,000; Per Subs 40; Bks on Deafness & Sign Lang 37
Special Collections: Large Print Coll; Maine History Coll
Friends of the Library Group

LIVERMORE FALLS

P TREAT MEMORIAL LIBRARY,* 56 Main St, 04254. SAN 306-6770. Tel: 207-897-3631. *Librn*, Sheila Dorey
Pop 3,572; Circ 24,100
Library Holdings: Bk Titles 19,000; Per Subs 35
Mem of Central Maine Library District
Open Mon, Tues & Thurs 1-5 & 6:30-8:30, Fri 1-5, Sat 2-5, closed Wed & Sun

LOVELL

P CHARLOTTE E HOBBS MEMORIAL LIBRARY, Rte 5, PO Box 105, 04051. SAN 306-6789. Tel: 207-925-3177. FAX: 207-925-3177, Ext 51. *Dir*, Barbara Ann Waters; Fax: 207-925-3177, Ext 521, E-Mail: barbaraannwaters@hotmail.com; *Asst Librn*, Marie Barker; *Asst Librn*, Lynne Evans; Staff 3 (Non-MLS 3)
Founded 1900. Pop 1,200; Circ 12,800
Jan 1999-Dec 1999 Income $36,580, State $200, City $11,000, Locally Generated Income $25,380. Mats Exp $4,080. Sal $14,829
Library Holdings: Bk Vols 16,155; Per Subs 20
Special Collections: Children's Room; Maine Books
Function: ILL available
Mem of Southern Maine Library District

P LEWIS DANA HILL MEMORIAL LIBRARY,* Rte 5, RR 2, Box 470, 04051. SAN 376-3757. Tel: 207-928-2301. *Librn*, Phyliss Adams
Library Holdings: Bk Vols 10,000; Bk Titles 5,000
Mem of Central Maine Library District
Open Sat 9-12

LUBEC

P LUBEC MEMORIAL LIBRARY,* 10 School St, 04652-1122. SAN 324-8097. Tel: 207-733-2491. *Librn*, Suzanne Plaut; Staff 3 (MLS 2, Non-MLS 1)
Founded 1946. Pop 2,045; Circ 16,154
Library Holdings: Bk Titles 17,000; Per Subs 20
Subject Interests: Local history
Special Collections: Maine Description & Travel; Maine History
Mem of NE Libr District; Northeastern Maine Library District
Partic in Nelinet, Inc; OCLC Online Computer Library Center, Inc
Friends of the Library Group

LYMAN

§P LYMAN COMMUNITY LIBRARY, 10 John St, 04002-999. Tel: 207-499-7114. *Head Librn*, Kenneth Scott
Library Holdings: Bk Vols 20,000
Mem of Southern Maine Library District

MACHIAS

P PORTER MEMORIAL LIBRARY,* 52 Court St, 04654. SAN 306-6797. Tel: 207-255-3933. *Librn*, Brenda Layman; *Asst Librn*, Gregory Williams; *Ch Servs*, Elizabeth Hanrahan
Founded 1891. Pop 2,458; Circ 17,300
Library Holdings: Bk Titles 20,000; Per Subs 26
Special Collections: Maine Coll
Mem of Northeastern Maine Library District
Friends of the Library Group

C UNIVERSITY OF MAINE AT MACHIAS, Merrill Library, O'Brien Ave, 04654. SAN 306-6800. Tel: 207-255-1234. FAX: 207-255-1356. Web Site: www.umm.maine.edu/library/welcome.html. *Dir*, Bert Phipps; E-Mail: bertp@acad.umm.maine.edu; *Asst Librn*, Susan Elliott; E-Mail: selliott@acad.umm.maine.edu; Staff 4 (MLS 2, Non-MLS 2)
Founded 1909. Enrl 930; Fac 48
Jul 1998-Jun 1999 Income $210,300. Mats Exp $78,145, Books $26,645, Per/Ser (Incl. Access Fees) $46,500, Micro $5,000. Sal $120,598 (Prof $70,865)
Library Holdings: Bk Vols 68,000; Bk Titles 67,763; Per Subs 461
Special Collections: Maine Coll
Automation Activity & Vendor Info: (Acquisitions) Innovative Interfaces Inc.; (Cataloging) Innovative Interfaces Inc.; (Circulation) Innovative Interfaces Inc.; (Course Reserve) Innovative Interfaces Inc.; (ILL) Innovative Interfaces Inc.; (Media Booking) Innovative Interfaces Inc.; (OPAC) Innovative Interfaces Inc.; (Serials) Innovative Interfaces Inc.
Publications: Library Handbook, URSUS Guide
Mem of Northeastern Maine Library District

MACHIASPORT

S DEPARTMENT OF CORRECTIONS, Down East Correctional Facility Library, HCR 70 Box 428, 04655. SAN 371-666X. Tel: 207-255-1100, Ext 50262. FAX: 207-255-1176. *Librn*, James Dumond; E-Mail: jim.dumond@state.me.us; Staff 4 (Non-MLS 4)
Library Holdings: Bk Titles 7,000
Mem of Northeastern Maine Library District
Special Services for the Deaf - Books on deafness & sign language; High interest/low vocabulary books; Special interest periodicals

MADAWASKA

P MADAWASKA PUBLIC LIBRARY,* 411 E Main St, 04756. SAN 306-6819. Tel: 207-728-3606. *Librn*, Patsy Theriault; *Asst Librn*, Delia LaGasse
Founded 1939. Pop 4,800; Circ 22,622
Library Holdings: Bk Vols 28,267; Per Subs 36
Subject Interests: Genealogy
Mem of Northeastern Maine Library District
Open Mon-Fri 10-8, Sat 1-3

MADISON

P MADISON PUBLIC LIBRARY, 12 Old Point Ave, 04950. SAN 306-6827. Tel: 207-696-5626. *Librn*, Irene Wilder Church; *Asst Librn*, Carol Collins; *Ch Servs*, Julie Forbus
Founded 1906. Pop 4,367; Circ 36,000
Library Holdings: Bk Vols 39,000; Bk Titles 21,000; Per Subs 60
Mem of Central Maine Library District

MANSET

S LEARNING INC LIBRARY,* 353 Seawall Rd, 04679. SAN 306-6835. Tel: 207-244-5015. FAX: 207-244-0035. *Curator*, Ann L Welles; Staff 2 (MLS 1, Non-MLS 1)
Founded 1968
Library Holdings: Bk Titles 7,000
Subject Interests: Learning disabilities

MARS HILL

P WALTER T A HANSEN MEMORIAL LIBRARY,* Ten Hansen St, PO Box 1008, 04758. SAN 306-6843. Tel: 207-429-9625. Web Site: www.cahs.sad42k12.me.us/towns/marshill/library. *Librn*, Cheryl Graves; E-Mail: cherylg@hansen.lib.me.us
Pop 1,910; Circ 6,347
Library Holdings: Bk Vols 14,000; Per Subs 15
Subject Interests: Local history
Mem of Northeastern Maine Library District
Open Tues & Thurs 1:30-5:30, Wed & Fri 6:30-8:30, Sat 9-11

MATTAWAMKEAG

P MATTAWAMKEAG PUBLIC LIBRARY,* Main St, PO Box 26, 04459. SAN 306-6851. Tel: 207-736-7013. FAX: 207-736-4801. *Librn*, Denise Day
Pop 1,000; Circ 8,725
Library Holdings: Bk Titles 12,000
Special Collections: Indian Arrowhead Coll
Mem of Northeastern Maine Library District
Open Mon, Wed & Fri 6:30-8:30, Wed 1-4

MECHANIC FALLS

P MECHANIC FALLS PUBLIC LIBRARY,* 15 Elm St, 04256. SAN 306-686X. Tel: 207-345-9450. *Librn*, Sandra Broun-Eustis
Founded 1897. Pop 2,589; Circ 5,000
Library Holdings: Bk Vols 12,000
Mem of Central Maine Library District
Friends of the Library Group

MEXICO

P MEXICO FREE PUBLIC LIBRARY,* 32 Main St, 04257. SAN 306-6886. Tel: 207-364-3281. FAX: 207-364-5685. E-Mail: mexlib@hotmail.com. *Librn*, Michelle Boucher-Ladd
Founded 1926. Pop 3,344; Circ 11,019
Library Holdings: Bk Vols 8,000; Per Subs 12
Mem of Central Maine Library District
Friends of the Library Group

MILBRIDGE

P MILBRIDGE PUBLIC LIBRARY, School St, PO Box 128, 04658. SAN 376-3552. Tel: 207-546-3066. FAX: 207-546-3066. E-Mail: morna@milbridge.lib.me.us. *Librn*, Morna Bell
Founded 1977
Jan 1999-Dec 1999 Income $17,000, State $200, Other $1,500. Mats Exp

Books $2,700. Sal $12,300
Library Holdings: Bk Vols 6,000; Bk Titles 5,000
Mem of Northeastern Maine Library District
Special Services for the Blind - Bks on cassette
Friends of the Library Group

MILLINOCKET

P MILLINOCKET MEMORIAL LIBRARY, 5 Maine Ave, 04462. SAN 306-6894. Tel: 207-723-7020. FAX: 207-723-7020. E-Mail: illoan@millinocket.lib.me.us. *Coll Develop, Dir*, John McManus; E-Mail: jmcman@millinocket.lib.me.us; *Circ, ILL*, Neva Miller; *Ch Servs*, Marietta Cole; *Circ*, Billie Jean Brilliant; Staff 6 (MLS 1, Non-MLS 5)
Founded 1919. Pop 6,980; Circ 70,519
Library Holdings: Bk Vols 42,000; Per Subs 107
Special Collections: Millinocket & Northern Maine History Coll
Mem of Northeastern Maine Library District
Friends of the Library Group

M MILLINOCKET REGIONAL HOSPITAL, Medical Library,* 200 Somerset St, 04462-1298. SAN 374-5457. Tel: 207-723-5161, Ext 265. FAX: 207-723-4913. *Librn*, Barbara Niznik; Staff 2 (Non-MLS 2)
Library Holdings: Bk Titles 536; Per Subs 44

MILO

P MILO FREE PUBLIC LIBRARY,* 4 Pleasant St, 04463. SAN 306-6908. Tel: 207-943-2612. E-Mail: milo1@milo.lib.me.us. Web Site: www.milo.lib.me.us. *Librn*, Catherine K Ellison; *Asst Librn*, Katherine A Osgood
Founded 1921. Pop 2,650; Circ 11,191
Library Holdings: Bk Vols 18,000; Per Subs 25
Subject Interests: Gardening, Genealogy, History
Publications: Library News & Book Reviews Published in a Local Paper
Mem of Northeastern Maine Library District

MONMOUTH

P CUMSTON PUBLIC LIBRARY, 796 Main St, PO Box 239, 04259. SAN 306-6916. Tel: 207-933-4788. E-Mail: allstaff@curston.lib.me.us. Web Site: www.cumston.lib.me.us/index.html. *Librn*, Veronica Clauss; E-Mail: vclauss@cumston.lib.me.us; *Ch Servs*, Marilyn Wilcox-Cowing; Staff 3 (Non-MLS 3)
Founded 1900. Pop 3,304
Jul 1999-Jun 2000 Income $44,329. Mats Exp $8,672, Books $6,500, Per/Ser (Incl. Access Fees) $922, AV Equip $1,250. Sal $31,300
Library Holdings: Bk Vols 15,892; Bk Titles 16,909; Per Subs 66; High Interest/Low Vocabulary Bk Vols 50
Special Collections: Maine (biographies, history, authors)
Mem of Maine State Library
Friends of the Library Group

MONSON

P MONSON FREE PUBLIC LIBRARY, 10 Tenney Hill Rd, PO Box 282, 04464. SAN 321-5040. Tel: 207-997-3641, 207-997-3785. FAX: 207-997-3785. *Librn*, Van Wentworth
Pop 750
Library Holdings: Bk Titles 3,400
Mem of Northeastern Maine Library District
Open Mon-Fri 1-5, Wed 7-8:30pm

MOUNT DESERT

S MOUNT DESERT ISLAND HISTORICAL SOCIETY LIBRARY,* PO Box 653, 04660. SAN 306-6924. Tel: 207-244-5043. FAX: 207-244-3991. *Pres*, Ann Mazlish; Tel: 207-244-7334
Founded 1929
Library Holdings: Bk Vols 800; Bk Titles 350
Publications: Newsletter

MOUNT VERNON

P DR SHAW MEMORIAL LIBRARY,* RR 1, Box 251, 04352. SAN 322-8592. Tel: 207-293-2565. *Librn*, Alice Olson; *Asst Librn*, Anne Brooks
Founded 1943. Circ 7,012
1999-2000 Income $12,500
Library Holdings: Bk Vols 11,824; Per Subs 12
Mem of Maine State Library
Friends of the Library Group

NAPLES

P NAPLES PUBLIC LIBRARY,* Rte 302, Box 1717, 04055. SAN 306-6932. Tel: 207-693-6841. *Librn*, Diane AmRhein; *Ch Servs*, Christine Powers; Staff 3 (Non-MLS 3)
Founded 1906. Pop 3,000; Circ 20,000
Library Holdings: Bk Titles 15,412
Special Collections: Maine Coll
Publications: Book List
Mem of Southern Conn Libr Coun
Open Tues & Thurs 10-6, Sat 10-2

NEW GLOUCESTER

P NEW GLOUCESTER PUBLIC LIBRARY,* 379 Intervale Rd, PO Box 105, 04260-0105. SAN 306-6940. Tel: 207-926-4840. *Librn*, Sue Hawkins
Founded 1897. Pop 3,180; Circ 14,400
Library Holdings: Bk Titles 17,109; Per Subs 34
Mem of Southern Conn Libr Coun; Southern Maine Library District
Friends of the Library Group

R SHAKER LIBRARY,* Sabbathday Lake, 707 Shaker Rd, 04260. SAN 306-7149. Tel: 207-926-4597. E-Mail: brooks1@shaker.lib.me.us. Web Site: www.shaker.lib.me.us. *Dir*, Leonard L Brooks; *Librn*, Gay Marks
Founded 1882
Library Holdings: Bk Vols 16,500; Bk Titles 14,044; Per Subs 60
Subject Interests: Art, Shakers, Technology
Special Collections: The Koreshan Unity; The Religious Society of Friends and Other Radical and Communal Groups; Thomsonian Medicine
Publications: descriptive brochure; Shaker Quarterly
Mem of Southern Maine Library District

NEW HARBOR

P BRISTOL AREA LIBRARY,* PO Box 173, 04554. SAN 376-3773. Tel: 207-677-2115. *Librn*, Phyllis Levine
Library Holdings: Bk Vols 17,000; Bk Titles 10,000
Mem of Central Maine Library District
Friends of the Library Group

NEW SHARON

P NEW SHARON TOWN LIBRARY,* US Rte 2, PO Box 61, 04955. SAN 376-7426. Tel: 207-779-1128. *Librn*, Faith Dyer
Library Holdings: Bk Vols 1,699
Mem of Central Maine Library District

NEW VINEYARD

P NEW VINEYARD PUBLIC LIBRARY, Lake St, PO Box 255, 04956. SAN 306-6959. Tel: 207-652-2250, 207-652-2265. E-Mail: nvpl@hotmail.com. *Dir*, Cindi Ellen O'Connor; *Librn*, June Johnston
Pop 607
Library Holdings: Bk Vols 4,000
Mem of Central Maine Library District
Open Wed 2-7, Sat 10-12
Friends of the Library Group

NEWPORT

P NEWPORT PUBLIC LIBRARY,* 42 Main St, 04953. SAN 306-6967. Tel: 207-368-5074. FAX: 207-368-5074. Web Site: www.msln.maine.edu. *Librn*, Amy Gallagher
Founded 1899. Pop 20,701
Library Holdings: Bk Vols 13,000; Per Subs 25
Mem of Northeastern Maine Library District
Friends of the Library Group

NOBLEBORO

S NOBLEBORO HISTORICAL SOCIETY, Historical Center, PO Box 122, 04555. SAN 373-496X. Tel: 207-563-5874. *Curator*, George F Dow
Apr 1999-May 2000 Income Locally Generated Income $5,305
Library Holdings: Bk Vols 200
Subject Interests: Local history
Special Collections: Town & Church Records 1793-present
Publications: Brochures

NORRIDGEWOCK

P NORRIDGEWOCK FREE PUBLIC LIBRARY,* Sophie May Lane, PO Box 86, 04957. SAN 306-6975. Tel: 207-634-2828. *Librn*, Diana Alsop
Pop 3,105; Circ 4,007

Library Holdings: Bk Vols 15,132
Mem of Central Maine Library District
Small library open 15 hours a week with librarian & voluntary help

NORTH BERWICK

P D A HURD LIBRARY, 41 High St, PO Box 399, 03906. SAN 306-6983. Tel: 207-676-2215. FAX: 207-676-7976. E-Mail: dahurd@hurd.lib.me.us. Web Site: www.hurd.lib.me.us. *Librn*, Betsy Bragdon; *Asst Librn*, Pamela Smart
Pop 8,475
1999-2000 Income $109,681. Mats Exp $18,500, Books $17,000, Per/Ser (Incl. Access Fees) $1,500. Sal $59,400
Library Holdings: Bk Vols 33,000; Per Subs 125
Special Collections: Local Genealogy (Hilton Coll) recs & res mat; Maine (Riviere Coll) bks
Mem of Southern Conn Libr Coun; Southern Maine Library District
Friends of the Library Group

NORTH BRIDGTON

§S BRIDGTON ACADEMY LIBRARY, PO Box 292, 04057-0292. Tel: 207-647-2121. *Librn*, Linda Kautz
Library Holdings: Bk Vols 8,000

P NORTH BRIDGTON PUBLIC LIBRARY,* Rte 37, PO Box 268, 04057. SAN 306-5995. Tel: 207-647-8563. *Librn*, Sue Black
Pop 4,307; Circ 3,000
Library Holdings: Bk Vols 6,780; Per Subs 13
Mem of Southern Conn Libr Coun
Open Mon 10-12, Wed 3-7, Sat 10-3
Friends of the Library Group

NORTH HAVEN

P NORTH HAVEN LIBRARY, Main St, 04853. SAN 306-6991. Tel: 207-867-9797. FAX: 207-867-9797. *Librn*, Kathryn Quinn; E-Mail: katequinn@northhaven.lib.me.us
Pop 373; Circ 4,304
Library Holdings: Bk Vols 14,000; Bk Titles 12,000; Per Subs 20
Mem of Northeastern Maine Library District
Friends of the Library Group

NORTH JAY

P JAY NILES MEMORIAL LIBRARY, PO Box 5008, 04262-5008. SAN 306-6614. Tel: 207-645-4062. *Librn*, Pat McDonald; *Asst Librn*, Bonnie Samson
Founded 1917. Pop 5,086
Library Holdings: Bk Titles 26,000; Per Subs 85
Open Mon-Wed 3-8:30, Thurs & Fri 10-5, Sat 10-2

NORTHEAST HARBOR

P NORTHEAST HARBOR LIBRARY,* Joy Rd Mount Desert, PO Box 288, 04662. SAN 306-7017. Tel: 207-276-3333. FAX: 207-276-3315. Web Site: www.acadia.net/nehlib/. *Librn*, Robert R Pyle; *Ch Servs*, Anna Carr; Staff 1 (MLS 1)
Pop 2,063; Circ 42,000
Library Holdings: Bk Vols 37,000; Per Subs 67
Special Collections: Architectural Drawings of Local Structures (Gerrish Coll); Collected Works of Samuel Eliot Morison; Horticulture (R Gwynne Stout Coll); Local History (I T Moore Coll), photog
Mem of Northeastern Maine Library District

NORWAY

P NORWAY MEMORIAL LIBRARY,* 258 Main St, 04268. SAN 306-7025. Tel: 207-743-5309. FAX: 207-744-0111. *Librn*, Ann Siekman
Founded 1885. Pop 4,042; Circ 37,539
Library Holdings: Bk Vols 30,000; Bk Titles 13,500; Per Subs 80
Subject Interests: Local history
Special Collections: C A Stephens Coll
Mem of Central Maine Library District
Friends of the Library Group

OAKLAND

P OAKLAND PUBLIC LIBRARY,* 18 Church St, 04963. SAN 306-7033. Tel: 207-465-7533. E-Mail: generaldelivery@opl.lib.me.us. *Librn*, Carol A Cooley
Founded 1913. Pop 5,557; Circ 28,323
Library Holdings: Bk Titles 17,126
Subject Interests: History
Special Collections: Maine Coll, bks on tape
Friends of the Library Group

OGUNQUIT

P OGUNQUIT MEMORIAL LIBRARY,* 74 Shore Rd, PO Box 753, 03907. SAN 306-7769. Tel: 207-646-9024. *Librn*, Mary W Littlefield; *Asst Librn*, Frances Clark; *Asst Librn*, Terri Neill
Founded 1897. Circ 15,000
Library Holdings: Bk Vols 10,000
Mem of Southern Conn Libr Coun; Southern Maine Library District

OLD ORCHARD BEACH

P EDITH BELLE LIBBY MEMORIAL LIBRARY, 27 Staples St, 04064. SAN 306-7041. Tel: 207-934-4351. E-Mail: ooblibrary@customnet.com. *Dir*, Eileen McNally; Staff 3 (MLS 1, Non-MLS 2)
Pop 10,071; Circ 26,338
Library Holdings: Bk Titles 23,000; Per Subs 58
Special Collections: Chess Book Coll; Local History
Automation Activity & Vendor Info: (Cataloging) Follett; (OPAC) Follett
Mem of Southern Maine Library District
Special Services for the Blind - Large print bks

OLD TOWN

P OLD TOWN PUBLIC LIBRARY, 65 Middle St, 04468. SAN 306-705X. Tel: 207-827-3972. FAX: 207-827-3978. Web Site: www.old-town.lib.me.us. *Librn*, Valerie A Osborne; E-Mail: vosborne@old-town; *Asst Librn*, Nancy Blanchard
Founded 1904. Pop 8,422; Circ 85,000
Library Holdings: Bk Vols 60,000; Per Subs 100
Special Collections: Local Newspaper, microfilm (100 yrs)
Publications: Booklist; Bulletin (for the Center for children's books); Hornbook; School Library Journal; The Web
Mem of Northeastern Maine Library District
Friends of the Library Group

ORONO

P ORONO PUBLIC LIBRARY,* Goodridge Dr, 04473. SAN 306-7068. Tel: 207-866-5060. Web Site: www.orono.lib.me.us. *Dir*, Katherine Molloy; E-Mail: kmolloy@orono.lib.me.us; *Ch Servs*, Laurie Rose
Pop 10,573; Circ 43,017
Library Holdings: Bk Vols 30,000; Per Subs 100
Mem of Northeastern Maine Library District
Friends of the Library Group

C UNIVERSITY OF MAINE, Raymond H Fogler Library, 5729 Fogler Library, 04469-5729. SAN 306-7076. Tel: 207-581-1661. FAX: 207-581-1653. Web Site: libraries.maine.edu/umaine/. *Dean*, Elaine Albright; *Bibliog Instr, Online Servs, Ref*, Christine Whittington; *Bibliog Instr, Online Servs, Ref*, James Bird; *Govt Doc*, Frank Wihbey; *Spec Coll*, Richard Hollinger; *Coll Develop*, Mary Casserly; Staff 24 (MLS 22, Non-MLS 2)
Founded 1865. Enrl 10,282; Fac 650; Highest Degree: Doctorate
Jul 1998-Jun 1999 Income $5,096,362. Mats Exp $2,829,495, Books $429,036, Per/Ser (Incl. Access Fees) $2,267,788, Presv $67,085, Micro $42,932. Sal $1,832,425 (Prof $792,342)
Library Holdings: Per Subs 5,600
Subject Interests: Can Am studies, Maine studies
Special Collections: Abolition & Antislavery (O'Brien Coll); Cole Maritime Coll; Folklore, Indian Lore & Etymology (Eckstorm Coll); Hannibal Hamlin Family Papers; Senator William S Cohen Coll; State of Maine Coll, University Archives
Publications: Downeast Magazine Index; InfoLine; Maine Times Index; Maine Union List of Serials; SciLites; The Olive Tree
Partic in OCLC Online Computer Library Center, Inc
Friends of the Library Group

ORRINGTON

P ORRINGTON PUBLIC LIBRARY,* 15 School St, 04474. SAN 376-3528. Tel: 207-825-4938. E-Mail: orrington.public.library@msln.net.; Staff 1 (Non-MLS 1)
Pop 3,309
Jul 1998-Jun 1999 Income (Main Library Only) $46,770. Mats Exp $8,011. Sal $25,025
Library Holdings: Bk Titles 13,942; Per Subs 25
Automation Activity & Vendor Info: (Circulation) Sagebrush Corporation
Mem of Northeastern Maine Library District

ORR'S ISLAND

P ORR'S ISLAND LIBRARY, Rte 24, 04066. (Mail add: PO Box 175, 04066-0175), SAN 376-3846. Tel: 207-833-7811. *Librn*, Joanne M Rogers
Library Holdings: Bk Titles 10,000
Mem of Southern Conn Libr Coun; Southern Maine Library District

OXFORD

P FREELAND HOLMES LIBRARY,* 109 Pleasant St, 04270. SAN 376-382X. Tel: 207-539-4016. *Librn*, Glenda Drapeau; E-Mail: gdrapeau@freeland.holmes.lib.me.us
Library Holdings: Bk Vols 30,000; Per Subs 20
Mem of Central Maine Library District

PARIS

P PARIS HILL LIBRARY ASSOCIATION, Hamlin Memorial Library, Paris Hill, 04271. (Mail add: PO Box 43, 04271), SAN 306-7092. Tel: 207-743-2980. *Librn*, Ann McDonald; E-Mail: amcdonald@hamlin.lib.me.us
Founded 1902. Pop 600; Circ 2,298
Library Holdings: Bk Vols 5,610; Bk Titles 5,000
Special Collections: Hamlin Family Records; Town of Paris History

PARSONSFIELD

§P PARSONSFIELD PUBLIC LIBRARY, PO Box 120, 04047-0120. Tel: 207-625-4684. *Librn*, Charlotte Sharp
Library Holdings: Bk Vols 12,000
Mem of Southern Maine Library District
Open Thurs 1-5, Sat 9-11:30

PATTEN

P VETERANS MEMORIAL LIBRARY, Main St, 04765. (Mail add: PO Box 695, 04765), SAN 306-7106. Tel: 207-528-2164. *Librn*, Christine Shorey
Pop 1,368; Circ 14,600
Library Holdings: Bk Vols 17,000; Bk Titles 16,550; Per Subs 30
Mem of Northeastern Maine Library District
Open Mon 10-12, 1-4 & 7-9, Tues 9-12 & 1-4, Thurs 9-12, 1-4 & 7-9

PEMAQUID

S PEMAQUID HISTORICAL ASSOCIATION, Harrington Meeting House,* 239 Old Harrington Rd, 04558. SAN 370-1921. *In Charge*, Margo Hope
Library Holdings: Bk Vols 100; Bk Titles 100
Subject Interests: Local history, Newsp clipping files, Religion
Special Collections: Cemetery Records; Farmers Journals

PHILLIPS

P PHILLIPS PUBLIC LIBRARY, Main St, PO Box O, 04966-1514. SAN 306-7114. Tel: 207-639-2665. *Librn*, Hedy Langdon; E-Mail: hlangdon@phillips.lib.me.us
Founded 1910. Pop 1,885; Circ 2,975
Library Holdings: Bk Titles 9,000
Subject Interests: Local history, Maine
Publications: Newspaper Releases in local press
Mem of Central Maine Library District
Friends of the Library Group

PHIPPSBURG

§P ALBERT F TOTMAN LIBRARY, 28 Parker Head Rd, 04562-9999. Tel: 207-389-2309. FAX: 207-389-2309.
Library Holdings: Bk Vols 10,000

PITTSFIELD

P PITTSFIELD PUBLIC LIBRARY, 89 S Main St, 04967. SAN 306-7122. Tel: 207-487-5880. *Librn*, Ellyn Smith; E-Mail: lsmith@pittsfield.lib.me.us; Staff 4 (MLS 1, Non-MLS 3)
Founded 1904. Pop 4,000; Circ 40,468
Jan 2000-Dec 2000 Income $110,200, State $200, City $110,000. Mats Exp $13,500, Books $11,500, Per/Ser (Incl. Access Fees) $2,000. Sal $52,300 (Prof $25,000)
Library Holdings: Bk Vols 21,000; Per Subs 70
Subject Interests: Local history
Automation Activity & Vendor Info: (Cataloging) Sagebrush Corporation; (Circulation) Sagebrush Corporation
Database Vendor: Ebsco - EbscoHost
Mem of Central Maine Library District
Special Services for the Blind - Brailling & large print projects

POLAND

P ALVAN BOLSTER RICKER MEMORIAL LIBRARY, (RML), Rte 26, Box 98, 04273. SAN 306-7130. Tel: 207-998-4390. FAX: 207-998-2120. Web Site: www.rm.lib.me.us. *Librn*, Linda Hayman; E-Mail: lhayman@rm.lib.me.us; Staff 5 (MLS 1, Non-MLS 4)
Founded 1963. Pop 3,578; Circ 43,359
1998-1999 Income $83,868. Mats Exp $14,618, Books $12,000, Per/Ser (Incl. Access Fees) $2,414, Other Print Mats $204. Sal $52,000 (Prof $22,000)
Library Holdings: Bk Titles 19,000; Per Subs 77
Special Collections: Local History; Maine
Mem of Central Maine Library District
Friends of the Library Group

PORTLAND

J ANDOVER COLLEGE LIBRARY, 901 Washington Ave, 04103. SAN 306-7157. Tel: 207-774-6126. Toll Free Tel: 800-639-3110. FAX: 207-774-1715. *Dir*, Martha T Ott; E-Mail: mott@andovercollege.com; Staff 3 (MLS 3)
Founded 1967. Enrl 600; Fac 33; Highest Degree: Associate
Jul 1999-Jun 2000 Income $35,000. Mats Exp $30,050, Books $15,500, Per/Ser (Incl. Access Fees) $13,300, Other Print Mats $1,250
Library Holdings: Bk Titles 7,000; Per Subs 100
Subject Interests: Accounting, Business, Computer science, Early childhood, Legal, Medical assistant, Travel and tourism
Mem of Southern Maine Library District
Partic in Maine School & Libr Network
Member Southern Maine Library District

SR BANGOR THEOLOGICAL SEMINARY, General Theological Library,* 159 State St, 04101. SAN 307-1731. Tel: 207-874-2214. FAX: 207-874-2214. Web Site: www.bts.edu. *Dir*, Clifton G Davis; *Asst Librn*, Tom O'Donnell; E-Mail: todonnell@bts.edu
Founded 1860
Library Holdings: Bk Titles 35,000
Subject Interests: Art and architecture, Biblical studies, Church history, Drug abuse, Religion, Theology
Publications: Bulletin of General Theological Library (tri-annual)
Mem of Northeastern Maine Library District
Friends of the Library Group

L BERNSTEIN, SHUR, SAWYER & NELSON, Law Library,* 100 Middle St, PO Box 9729, 04104-5029. SAN 329-1251. Tel: 207-774-1200, Ext 281. FAX: 207-774-1127. E-Mail: cbertsch@mainelaw.com. Web Site: www.mainelaw.com. *Librn*, Christine Bertsch; Staff 2 (MLS 1, Non-MLS 1)
Founded 1981
Library Holdings: Bk Vols 5,000; Per Subs 200
Subject Interests: Construction, Real estate
Mem of Southern Conn Libr Coun

S GREATER PORTLAND LANDMARKS, INC, Frances W Peabody Research Library, 165 State St, 04101. SAN 306-7181. Tel: 207-774-5561. FAX: 207-774-2509. E-Mail: landmark@maine.rr.com. Web Site: www.portlandlandmarks.org. *Exec Dir*, Hilary Bassett; Staff 1 (MLS 1)
Founded 1971
Library Holdings: Bk Titles 1,250; Per Subs 10
Subject Interests: Historic preservation, Local history
Special Collections: Biography of Architects in Maine; Buildings & Architectural Detail, microprint; Scientific American Building Monthly, 1885-1905
Publications: Descriptive Library pamphlet
Restriction: Open to public for reference only

S HARDING ESE, (Formerly Harding Lawson Associates Library), 511 Congress St, 04101. (Mail add: PO Box 7050, 04112-7050), SAN 306-719X. Tel: 207-828-3697. FAX: 207-772-4762. *Librn*, James R Lawson; E-Mail: jlawson@harding.com; Staff 1 (MLS 1)
Founded 1969
Library Holdings: Bk Vols 2,000; Per Subs 30
Subject Interests: Engineering, Waste disposal
Database Vendor: Dialog

S MAINE CHARITABLE MECHANIC ASSOCIATION LIBRARY,* 519 Congress St, 04101. SAN 306-7203. Tel: 207-773-8396. *Librn*, Eleanor Reynolds
Founded 1820
Library Holdings: Bk Vols 32,000
Subject Interests: Fiction, History, Travel

S MAINE COLLEGE OF ART LIBRARY,* 619 Congress St, 04101. SAN 321-0391. Tel: 207-775-5153. FAX: 207-772-5069. Web Site: www.library.meca.edu. *Librn*, Laura Graveline; E-Mail: lgraveline@meca.edu; Staff 3 (MLS 1, Non-MLS 2)
Founded 1974. Enrl 315; Fac 43; Highest Degree: Master
1998-1999 Mats Exp $20,574, Books $6,552, Per/Ser (Incl. Access Fees) $5,567, Presv $1,000. Sal $93,397 (Prof $31,860)
Library Holdings: Bk Vols 18,000; Bk Titles 16,000; Per Subs 99

Subject Interests: Art history, Fine arts, Liberal arts
Automation Activity & Vendor Info: (Cataloging) Innovative Interfaces Inc.; (Circulation) Innovative Interfaces Inc.; (Course Reserve) Innovative Interfaces Inc.; (OPAC) Innovative Interfaces Inc.; (Serials) Innovative Interfaces Inc.
Database Vendor: Innovative Interfaces INN - View, OCLC - First Search

S MAINE HISTORICAL SOCIETY RESEARCH LIBRARY, 485 Congress St, 04101. SAN 306-7211. Tel: 207-774-1822. FAX: 207-775-4301. E-Mail: info@mainehistory.org. Web Site: www.mainehistory.org. *Dir*, Richard D'Abate; *Librn*, Nicholas Noyes; E-Mail: nnoyes@mainehistory.org; Staff 8 (MLS 4, Non-MLS 4)
Founded 1822
Library Holdings: Bk Titles 65,000
Subject Interests: Genealogy, New England
Special Collections: Fogg Autograph Coll; Northeast Boundary Coll; Papers of Governor William King; Portland Company Records; Records of Kennebec Proprietors
Publications: Maine Historical Society Newsletter; Maine History
Restriction: Not a lending library
Function: Archival collection, Research library
Mem of Southern Maine Library District
Friends of the Library Group

M MAINE MEDICAL CENTER LIBRARY, 22 Bramhall St, 04102. SAN 306-722X. Tel: 207-871-2202. FAX: 207-871-6398. E-Mail: library@mail.mmc.org. Web Site: www.mmc.org/mmclibrary.html. *Dir*, Janet L Cowen; *Automation Syst Coordr*, Patricia Williams; Staff 10 (MLS 3, Non-MLS 7)
Founded 1874
Oct 1998-Sep 1999 Income $643,935. Mats Exp $249,759, Books $55,919, Per/Ser (Incl. Access Fees) $193,840. Sal $272,459
Library Holdings: Bk Titles 7,780; Per Subs 559
Subject Interests: Hospital administration, Medicine, Nursing
Mem of Southern Maine Library District
Partic in Health Sci Libr & Info Coop; National Network Of Libraries Of Medicine New England Region; North Atlantic Health Sciences Libraries, Inc

M MERCY HOSPITAL, Health Sciences Library,* 144 State St, 04101-3795. SAN 321-4494. Tel: 207-879-3365. FAX: 207-879-3929. *Librn*, Marj Anderson
Founded 1956
Library Holdings: Bk Titles 2,000; Per Subs 225
Special Collections: Medical Illustrations (CIBA Coll), slides
Publications: Newsletter
Partic in Dialog Corporation; Health Sci Libr & Info Coop

L NATHAN & HENRY B CLEAVES LAW LIBRARY, (Formerly Cumberland Bar Association), 142 Federal St, 04101. SAN 306-7165. Tel: 207-773-9712. FAX: 207-773-2155. Web Site: www.cleaves.org. *Librn*, Nancy Rabasca; Staff 2 (MLS 1, Non-MLS 1)
Founded 1811
Library Holdings: Bk Vols 28,297
Special Collections: Records & Briefs of the Supreme Judicial Court of the State of Maine

L PERKINS, THOMPSON, HINCKLEY & KEDDY LIBRARY,* One Canal Plaza, PO Box 426, 04112-0426. SAN 326-1042. Tel: 207-774-2635, Ext 278. FAX: 207-871-8026. *Librn*, Pam Hogan; E-Mail: phogan@pthklaw.com
Founded 1983
Library Holdings: Bk Vols 449; Bk Titles 181; Per Subs 84
Subject Interests: Law
Restriction: Staff use only

L PIERCE ATWOOD LAW LIBRARY, One Monument Sq, 04101. SAN 372-0969. Tel: 207-791-1142. FAX: 207-791-1350. Web Site: www.pierceatwood.com. *Librn*, Kami Bedard; Staff 3 (MLS 2, Non-MLS 1)
Library Holdings: Bk Vols 25,000; Per Subs 250
Subject Interests: Law

S PORTLAND PRESS HERALD-MAINE SUNDAY TELEGRAM LIBRARY, 390 Congress St, PO Box 1460, 04104. SAN 306-7173. Tel: 207-791-6390. FAX: 207-791-6920. E-Mail: library@pressherald.com. Web Site: www.portland.com/archive. *Reader Servs*, Marcia MacVane; Tel: 207-791-6920, E-Mail: mmacvane@pressherald.com; *Asst Librn*, Susan Butler; Tel: 207-791-6391, E-Mail: sbutler@pressherald.com; *Asst Librn*, Linda Madsen; Tel: 207-719-6393, E-Mail: lmadsen@pressherald.com; *Asst Librn*, Julia McCue; Tel: 207-791-6389, E-Mail: jmccue@pressherald.com; *Asst Librn*, Elizabeth Murphy; Tel: 207-791-6394, E-Mail: bmurphy@pressherald.com
Founded 1912
Library Holdings: Bk Titles 2,000
Special Collections: City Directories, 1898-Present; Maine Registers, 1856-Present
Database Vendor: Lexis-Nexis, ProQuest
Function: Newspaper reference library

P PORTLAND PUBLIC LIBRARY, 5 Monument Sq, 04101. SAN 343-6802. Tel: 207-871-1700. Interlibrary Loan Service Tel: 207-871-1735. Circulation Tel: 207-871-1730. Reference Tel: 207-871-1725. Toll Free Tel: 800-649-7696. FAX: 207-871-1703. Web Site: www.portlandlibrary.com. *Dir*, Sheldon Kaye; Tel: 207-871-1755, E-Mail: kaye@portland.lib.me.us; *Ch Servs*, Mary Peverada; Tel: 207-871-1707, E-Mail: peverada@portland.lib.me.us; *Spec Coll*, Thomas Gaffney; Tel: 207-871-1747, E-Mail: gaffney@portland.lib.me.us; *Tech Servs*, Beth Addison; Tel: 207-871-1750, E-Mail: addison@portland.lib.me.us; *Ref*, Suzanne Thompson; Tel: 207-871-1729, Fax: 207-871-1714, E-Mail: thompson@portland.lib.me.us; *Circ*, Daniel Amsberry; Tel: 207-871-1732, E-Mail: amsberry@portland.lib.me.us; *Outreach Serv*, Karen Valley; Tel: 207-871-1719, Fax: 207-871-1721, E-Mail: valley@portland.lib.me.us; Staff 49 (MLS 16, Non-MLS 33)
Founded 1867. Pop 64,000; Circ 629,789
Jul 1999-Jun 2000 Income (Main Library and Branch Library) $2,940,793, State $135,756, City $2,304,543, County $5,305, Locally Generated Income $110,000, Other $385,189. Mats Exp $429,642, Books $234,254, Per/Ser (Incl. Access Fees) $46,026, Presv $2,000, Micro $14,376, AV Equip $60,402, Electronic Ref Mat (Incl. Access Fees) $72,584. Sal $1,697,188 (Prof $686,147)
Library Holdings: Bk Vols 317,259; Bk Titles 223,886; Per Subs 528
Subject Interests: Art, Consumer health, Ireland
Special Collections: Hugh Thomson (Antique Children's Books); Jacob Abbott; Jewish Bi-Centennial Oral History Program; Music by Maine Composers; Newspapers from 1785; Portland; Press Books (Dun Emer, Mosher, Southworth-Anthoensen, Cuala Shagbark); Sarah Orne Jewett; State of Maine (Maine Authors, Maine & Portland Imprints)
Automation Activity & Vendor Info: (Acquisitions) Innovative Interfaces Inc.; (Circulation) Innovative Interfaces Inc.; (OPAC) Innovative Interfaces Inc.; (Serials) Innovative Interfaces Inc.
Database Vendor: OCLC - First Search
Publications: Annual report; seasonal newsletter; services guide
Mem of Southern Maine Library District
Partic in Nelinet, Inc
Special Services for the Deaf - Books on deafness & sign language; High interest/low vocabulary books; TDD
Special Services for the Blind - CCTV for print enlargement
Branches: 5
BURBANK, 377 Stevens Ave, 04103. SAN 376-1096. Tel: 207-774-4229. FAX: 207-871-1721. Web Site: www.portlandlibrary.com. *Mgr*, James Charette; E-Mail: charette@portland.lib.me.us
Circ 165,527
Automation Activity & Vendor Info: (Circulation) Innovative Interfaces Inc.; (OPAC) Innovative Interfaces Inc.
Friends of the Library Group
HOWARD C REICHE BRANCH, 166 Brackett St, 04102-3825. SAN 343-6950. Tel: 207-774-6871. Web Site: www.portlandlibrary.com. *Mgr*, Terry Farish; E-Mail: farish@portland.lib.me.us
Circ 18,314
Library Holdings: Bk Vols 10,998
Automation Activity & Vendor Info: (Circulation) Innovative Interfaces Inc.; (OPAC) Innovative Interfaces Inc.
MUNJOY, 44 Moody St, 04101-4426. SAN 343-6896. Tel: 207-772-4581. Web Site: www.portlandlibrary.com. *Mgr*, Susanne Duncan; E-Mail: duncan@portland.lib.me.us
Circ 23,417
Library Holdings: Bk Vols 12,020
Automation Activity & Vendor Info: (Circulation) Innovative Interfaces Inc.; (OPAC) Innovative Interfaces Inc.
PEAKS ISLAND, 129 Island Ave, 04108-1112. SAN 343-6926. Tel: 207-766-5540. Web Site: www.portlandlibrary.com. *Mgr*, Priscilla Webster; E-Mail: webster@portland.lib.me.us
Circ 28,910
Library Holdings: Bk Vols 6,162
Automation Activity & Vendor Info: (Circulation) Innovative Interfaces Inc.; (OPAC) Innovative Interfaces Inc.
Friends of the Library Group
RIVERTON, 1600 Forest Ave, 04103-1399. SAN 343-6985. Tel: 207-797-2915. Web Site: www.portlandlibrary.com. *Mgr*, Lynn McCarthy; E-Mail: mccarthy@portland.lib.me.us
Circ 44,056
Library Holdings: Bk Vols 13,495
Automation Activity & Vendor Info: (Circulation) Innovative Interfaces Inc.; (OPAC) Innovative Interfaces Inc.

S SOUTHERN MAINE LIBRARY DISTRICT, 5 Monument Sq, 04101-4072. SAN 306-7238. Tel: 207-871-1766. E-Mail: SMLD@portland.lib.me.us. Web Site: www.state.me.us/msl/smld/. *In Charge*, Shirley Helfrich; E-Mail: helfrich@portland.lib.me.us; Staff 2 (MLS 1, Non-MLS 1)
Founded 1974
Jul 1999-Jun 2000 Income $96,671. Mats Exp $10,513, Other Print Mats $1,307. Sal $86,158 (Prof $53,528)
Library Holdings: Bk Vols 500
Subject Interests: Library and information science
Publications: News Notes
Member Libraries: Andover College Library; Baxter Memorial Library; Berry Memorial Library; Bonney Memorial Library; Bridgton Public

Library; Brown Memorial Library; Caswell Public Library; Charlotte E Hobbs Memorial Library; Chase Emerson Memorial Library; Curtis Memorial Library; D A Hurd Library; Davis Memorial Library; Dyer Library; Edith Belle Libby Memorial Library; Falmouth Memorial Library; Foundation For Blood Research Library; Freeport Community Library; Goodall Hospital; Gray Public Library; Hollis Center Public Library; Jones Museum Of Glass & Ceramics; Kennebunk Free Library; Lebanon Area Library; Long Island Community Library; Louis T Graves Memorial Public Library; Lyman Community Library; Maine Correctional Center; Maine Historical Society Research Library; Maine Medical Center Library; McArthur Public Library; Merrill Memorial Library; New Gloucester Public Library; Newfield Reading Room; Ocean Park Memorial Library; Ogunquit Memorial Library; Orr's Island Library; Parsons Memorial Library; Parsonsfield Public Library; Portland Museum of Art Library; Portland Public Library; Prince Memorial Library; Rice Public Library; Salmon Falls Village Library; Scarborough Public Library; Shaker Library; Shapleigh Community Library; Soldiers Memorial Library; South Portland Public Library; Southern Maine Technical College Library; Spaulding Memorial Library; Springvale Public Library; Steep Falls Public Library; Thomas Memorial Library; Walker Memorial Library; Warren Memorial Library; Wells Public Library; William Fogg Library; York Public Library

CL UNIVERSITY OF MAINE SCHOOL OF LAW, Donald L Garbrecht Law Library, 246 Deering Ave, 04102. SAN 306-7254. Tel: 207-780-4829. Circulation Tel: 207-780-4350. Reference Tel: 207-780-4351. FAX: 207-780-4913. Web Site: www.law.usm.maine.edu/library.htm. *Dir*, William Wells; E-Mail: wells@usm.maine.edu; *Asst Librn*, Martin Cerjan; *Asst Librn, Tech Servs*, Lynn Wilcox; *Coll Develop*, Suzanne Parent; Staff 14 (MLS 7, Non-MLS 7)
Founded 1962. Enrl 270; Fac 16; Highest Degree: Doctorate
Library Holdings: Bk Vols 325,000; Per Subs 1,175
Database Vendor: Ebsco - EbscoHost, IAC - SearchBank, OCLC - First Search, OVID Technologies, Silverplatter Information Inc.
Publications: Law Library Guide
Partic in RLIN; Westlaw

C UNIVERSITY OF NEW ENGLAND, WESTBROOK COLLEGE, Josephine S Abplanalp Library, 716 Stevens Ave, 04103. (Mail add: 11 Hills Beach Rd, 04005), SAN 306-7262. Tel: 207-797-7261. Circulation Tel: 207-797-7261, Ext 4330. Reference Tel: 207-797-7261, Ext 4323. FAX: 207-878-4893. E-Mail: library@mailbox.une.edu. Web Site: www.une.edu. *VPres*, Andrew J Golub; Tel: 207-283-0170, Ext 2319, E-Mail: agolub@mailbox.une.edu; *Head of Libr*, Sharon Ecrck; *Curator*, Cally Gurley; Tel: 207-283-0710, Ext 4324, E-Mail: cgurley@mailbox.une.edu; *Acq*, Steve Bouchard; *Cat*, Pat Milligan; Tel: 207-283-0170, Ext 4328, E-Mail: pmilligan@mailbox.une.edu; *Ref*, Roberta Gray; E-Mail: rgray@mailbox.une.edu; *Acq*, Chris McKinnon; Tel: 207-283-0170, Ext 4327, E-Mail: cmckinnon@mailbox.une.edu; Staff 5 (MLS 4, Non-MLS 1)
Founded 1831. Enrl 1,373; Fac 66; Highest Degree: Master
Library Holdings: Bk Vols 52,385; Bk Titles 46,328; Per Subs 365
Subject Interests: Dent hygiene, Education, Nursing, Social work
Special Collections: Maine Women Writers Coll
Automation Activity & Vendor Info: (Acquisitions) Innovative Interfaces Inc.; (Cataloging) Innovative Interfaces Inc.; (Circulation) Innovative Interfaces Inc.; (Course Reserve) Innovative Interfaces Inc.; (OPAC) Innovative Interfaces Inc.; (Serials) Innovative Interfaces Inc.
Database Vendor: IAC - Info Trac, Lexis-Nexis, OCLC - First Search, OVID Technologies, ProQuest, Silverplatter Information Inc.
Mem of Southern Conn Libr Coun
Partic in Health Science Library Information Consortium; National Network of Libraries of Medicine - Southeastern Atlantic Region; New England Libr Info Network; OCLC Online Computer Library Center, Inc

C UNIVERSITY OF SOUTHERN MAINE, Glickman Family Library, 314 Forest Ave, PO Box 9301, 04104-9301. SAN 306-6487. Tel: 207-780-4276. Interlibrary Loan Service Tel: 207-780-4279. FAX: 207-780-4042. Web Site: library.usm.maine.edu. *Dir*, Stephen Bloom; E-Mail: bloom@usm.maine.edu; *Librn*, Barbara D Smith; *Acq, Ser*, Carolyn C Hughes; *Circ*, Lanier Lumbert; *Ref*, Shelia Johnson; *Curator*, Yolanda Theunissen; *Cat*, Peg Schnupt; Staff 19 (MLS 19)
Founded 1878. Enrl 9,966; Fac 345; Highest Degree: Doctorate
Library Holdings: Bk Vols 371,211; Bk Titles 289,651; Per Subs 3,328
Subject Interests: Allied health, Business and management, Education, Technology
Special Collections: Antique Cartographic Materials; Main Nursing Association Archives
Publications: Reference bibliographies
Mem of Southern Conn Libr Coun
Partic in Data Star; Data Time; Dialog Corporation; First Search; Nelinet, Inc; OCLC Online Computer Library Center, Inc; STN
Library facilities on both campuses & at Lewiston Auburn College. Coordinate with University of Maine System Off Campus Library Services Office

S UNUM LIFE INSURANCE CO, Information Center,* 2211 Congress St, 04122. SAN 343-7019. Tel: 207-575-1506, 207-770-2211. FAX: 207-770-3507. Web Site: www.unum.com. *Res*, John Long; Tel: 207-575-3623; Staff 4 (MLS 4)
Founded 1957
Library Holdings: Bk Titles 4,000; Per Subs 300
Subject Interests: Investing, Law, Real estate
Publications: CIC Review
Partic in BRS; Dialog Corporation; Dow Jones News Retrieval; Westlaw

L VERRILL & DANA LIBRARY, One Portland Sq, PO Box 586, 04112-0586. SAN 328-4417. Tel: 207-774-4000, Ext 4856. FAX: 207-774-7499. Web Site: www.verrilldana.com. *Librn*, Anne M Reiman; E-Mail: areiman@verrilldana.com; Staff 1 (Non-MLS 1)
Library Holdings: Bk Titles 13,000
Partic in Dialog Corporation; Westlaw
Friends of the Library Group

S VICTORIA MANSION LIBRARY,* 109 Danforth St, 04101. SAN 320-8605. Tel: 207-772-4841. FAX: 207-772-6290. E-Mail: victoria@maine.rr.com. *Dir*, Robert Wolterstorff
Founded 1943
Library Holdings: Bk Titles 453
Subject Interests: Art (19th Century), Art and architecture, Decorative arts
Restriction: By appointment only

PRESQUE ISLE

M AROOSTOOK MEDICAL CENTER, Health Sciences Library,* PO Box 151, 04769-0151. SAN 320-1910. Tel: 207-768-4173. FAX: 207-768-4046. *Librn*, Candace Johnson; E-Mail: cjohnson@tamc.org
Founded 1968
Library Holdings: Bk Titles 275; Per Subs 70
Mem of Northeastern Maine Library District
Partic in Health Sci Libr & Info Coop

P MARK & EMILY TURNER MEMORIAL LIBRARY, 39 Second St, 04769. SAN 306-7297. Tel: 207-764-2571. FAX: 207-768-5756. Web Site: www.presqueisle.lib.me.us. *Dir*, Donna M Rasche; E-Mail: drasche@presqueisle.lib.me.us; *Librn*, Marilyn G Clark; E-Mail: mgclark@presqueisle.lib.me.us; *Asst Librn*, Susan McPherson. Subject Specialists: *Research*, Donna M Rasche; *Youth programs*, Susan McPherson; Staff 9 (MLS 1, Non-MLS 8)
Founded 1908. Pop 10,000; Circ 97,000
Library Holdings: Bk Vols 66,000; Bk Titles 55,000; Per Subs 98
Subject Interests: Local history
Special Collections: Local Newspapers, microfilm
Automation Activity & Vendor Info: (Circulation) Sagebrush Corporation; (OPAC) Sagebrush Corporation
Database Vendor: Ebsco - EbscoHost
Function: ILL available
Special Services for the Blind - Optelek

J NORTHERN MAINE TECHNICAL COLLEGE LIBRARY, 33 Edgemont Dr, 04769. SAN 306-7289. Tel: 207-768-2734. FAX: 207-768-2823. Web Site: www.nmtc.net/library/library.htm. *Asst Dean*, O'Kane Peggy; Tel: 207-768-2734, E-Mail: pokane@nmtc.net; *Asst Librn*, Kim Ferguson; Tel: 207-768-2735, E-Mail: kferguson@nmtc.net; Staff 3 (MLS 1, Non-MLS 2)
Founded 1968. Fac 60; Highest Degree: Associate
Jul 1999-Jun 2000 Income $151,000. Mats Exp $90,000, Books $30,000, Per/Ser (Incl. Access Fees) $36,000, Electronic Ref Mat (Incl. Access Fees) $2,500. Sal $65,389 (Prof $42,350)
Library Holdings: Bk Titles 13,000; Per Subs 475
Subject Interests: Business, Computer, Medicine
Publications: Acquisition list
Mem of Northeastern Maine Library District
Partic in Docline; Nelinet, Inc; OCLC Online Computer Library Center, Inc

C UNIVERSITY OF MAINE AT PRESQUE ISLE LIBRARY, 181 Main St, 04769-2888. SAN 306-7300. Tel: 207-768-9591. Interlibrary Loan Service Tel: 207-768-9595. Circulation Tel: 207-768-9595. Reference Tel: 207-768-9594. FAX: 207-768-9644. Web Site: www.umpi.maine.edu/info/lib/. *Dir*, Gregory Curtis; *Cat*, Nancy Roe; *Doc, Reader Servs*, Virginia Fischer; *Circ, ILL*, Nancy Fletcher; Staff 4 (MLS 4)
Founded 1903. Enrl 1,344
Jul 1999-Jun 2000 Income $416,915. Mats Exp $118,154, Books $50,034, Per/Ser (Incl. Access Fees) $47,522, Presv $1,248, Micro $3,189. Sal $280,913 (Prof $158,190)
Library Holdings: Bk Vols 162,377; Bk Titles 70,336; Per Subs 450
Subject Interests: Art, Education
Special Collections: Aroostook County History Coll; Maine Coll; Rare bks
Automation Activity & Vendor Info: (Acquisitions) Innovative Interfaces Inc.; (Cataloging) Innovative Interfaces Inc.; (Circulation) Innovative Interfaces Inc.; (Course Reserve) Innovative Interfaces Inc.; (OPAC) Innovative Interfaces Inc.; (Serials) Innovative Interfaces Inc.
Publications: Faculty Staff Guide; Library Resources & Services Guide
Mem of Northeastern Maine Library District
Partic in Nelinet, Inc; OCLC Online Computer Library Center, Inc

PROSPECT HARBOR

P DORCAS LIBRARY,* Rte 186, 04669. (Mail add: PO Box 167, 04669-0167), Tel: 207-963-4027. *Librn*, Sheila Daley
Library Holdings: Bk Vols 15,000; Bk Titles 9,500
Mem of Northeastern Maine Library District
Friends of the Library Group

RANGELEY

P RANGELEY PUBLIC LIBRARY, PO Box 1150, Lake St, 04970. SAN 306-7319. Tel: 207-864-5529. Web Site: www.rangeley.me.com/library. *Librn*, Anne Haynes; E-Mail: ahaynes@rangeley.lib.me.us; *Asst Librn*, Marge Collins; *Tech Servs*, Connie Coleman
Founded 1909. Pop 6,400; Circ 21,407
Jul 1998-Jun 1999 Income $78,237, State $23,746, Locally Generated Income $1,185, Parent Institution $25,570. Mats Exp $8,200, Books $6,700, Per/Ser (Incl. Access Fees) $500. Sal $28,409 (Prof $17,000)
Library Holdings: Bk Vols 21,830; Per Subs 35
Subject Interests: Literature
Special Collections: Wilhelm Reich Coll
Mem of Central Maine Library District
Friends of the Library Group

S TRANET LIBRARY,* 5 Lake St, 04970-0567. (Mail add: PO Box 567, 04970-0567), SAN 321-8082. Tel: 207-864-3784. E-Mail: tranet@rangeley.org. Web Site: www.nonviolence.org/tranet/. *Dir*, Bill Ellis
Founded 1976
Library Holdings: Bk Vols 7,500
Subject Interests: Alternate econ, Alternative concepts, Alternative technologies, Natural resources conservation, Non-military defense, Organic gardening, Premaculture gardening, Renewable energy, Self-help housing, World governance
Publications: TRANET Newsletter - Directory (bi-monthly)
Restriction: Open to public for reference only
Has supplied 100 best books in Appropriate/Alternative Technologies to over 150 (to date) Third World libraries interested in AT worldwide (Third World nations only)
Friends of the Library Group

RAYMOND

P RAYMOND VILLAGE LIBRARY, 3 Meadow Rd, PO Box 297, 04071-0297. SAN 306-7327. Tel: 207-655-4283. E-Mail: rlibrar1@maine.rr.com. *Dir*, Barbara Thorpe
Founded 1914. Pop 3,609; Circ 19,082
Library Holdings: Bk Vols 10,215
Special Collections: Maine Coll
Open Mon & Wed 2-8, Thurs & Sat 9-12, Sun 11-6
Friends of the Library Group

READFIELD

P READFIELD COMMUNITY LIBRARY, 1151 Main St, 04355-3512. (Mail add: PO Box 246, 04355-0246), SAN 374-6267. Tel: 207-685-4089. *Librn*, Jane Davis; Staff 1 (MLS 1)
Pop 2,033; Circ 10,898
Library Holdings: Bk Vols 8,500; Per Subs 10

RICHMOND

P ISAAC F UMBERHINE LIBRARY,* 82 Main St, 04357. SAN 306-7343. Tel: 207-737-2770. *Librn*, Donna McCluskey
Pop 2,168; Circ 6,968
Library Holdings: Bk Vols 23,000
Mem of Central Maine Library District

ROCKLAND

S CAMBREX CORP, (Formerly FMC Corp), Biowhittaker Molecular Applications Library - BMA Library, 191 Thomaston St, 04841. SAN 306-736X. Tel: 207-594-3478. FAX: 207-594-3426. *Librn*, Susanne Carey; Staff 1 (Non-MLS 1)
Library Holdings: Bk Vols 2,280; Per Subs 90
Subject Interests: Biotechnology, Chemistry, Genetics
Publications: Newsletter

S FARNSWORTH ART MUSEUM LIBRARY, 352 Main St, PO Box 466, 04841. SAN 306-7351. Tel: 207-596-6457. FAX: 207-596-0509. E-Mail: farnswth@midcoast.com. *Dir*, Christopher Crosman; *Librn*, Barbara C Watson; Staff 6 (MLS 1, Non-MLS 5)
Founded 1948
Apr 1999-Mar 2000 Income $3,300. Mats Exp $2,500, Books $1,000, Per/Ser (Incl. Access Fees) $1,500
Library Holdings: Bk Vols 4,500; Per Subs 32
Subject Interests: Art history, Decorative arts, Fine arts, Local history, Rare books
Special Collections: Artist File; Jonathan Fisher; Kosti Ruhoma Archives; Louise Nevelson Biographical Material Coll; N C Wyeth Memorabilia
Restriction: Non-circulating to the public
Function: Reference services available

M MID-COAST MENTAL HEALTH CENTER, Lathbury Library, 12 Union St, PO Box 526, 04841. SAN 328-4328. Tel: 207-594-2541. FAX: 207-596-2064. *In Charge*, Kim Parlin

P ROCKLAND PUBLIC LIBRARY, 80 Union St, 04841. SAN 306-7378. Tel: 207-594-0310. FAX: 207-594-0333. Web Site: midcoast.com/rpl. *Dir*, Nikki Maounis; E-Mail: nmaounis@ci.rockland.me.us; *Dep Dir*, Linda Fairfield; E-Mail: lfairfield@ci.rockland.me.us; *Ch Servs*, Jean Young; E-Mail: jyoung@ci.rockland.me.us; *Circ*, Ned Crocketiere; E-Mail: ncrochetiere@ci.rockland.me.us; Staff 3 (MLS 1, Non-MLS 2)
Founded 1892. Pop 7,919; Circ 60,000
Library Holdings: Bk Vols 38,000; Bk Titles 32,000; Per Subs 55
Special Collections: Children's Coll; Literacy Volunteers Coll; Maine Coll
Mem of Northeastern Maine Library District
Open Mon & Tues 9am-8pm, , Wed-Sat 9-5
Friends of the Library Group

S SHORE VILLAGE MUSEUM, Museum Library, 104 Limerock St, 04841. SAN 374-664X. Tel: 207-594-0311. FAX: 207-594-9481. *Dir*, Ken Black; Tel: 207-785-4609, E-Mail: knb@ime.net; *Curator*, Robert N Davis; Staff 3 (Non-MLS 3)
Founded 1977
Special Collections: Complete Official History of Civil War; GAR Records; Lighthouse Library; Local Publications - Other Area Stories; Photographs; Registry of Merchant Vessels (including yachts & government vessels) of the United States; Shore Village Historical Society Coll; Unpublished Manuscripts - Letters & Other Civil War Material
Publications: Newsletter

ROCKPORT

M PENOBSCOT BAY MEDICAL CENTER LIBRARY,* 6 Glen Cove Dr, 04856. SAN 377-9459. Tel: 207-596-8456. FAX: 207-596-5281. *Librn*, Patricia Kahn; E-Mail: pkahn@nehealth.org; Staff 1 (MLS 1)
Apr 1997-Mar 1998 Mats Exp $37,000
Library Holdings: Bk Titles 1,500; Per Subs 120
Partic in Basic Health Sciences Library Network; Maine Health Sci Librs & Info Consortium; North Atlantic Health Sciences Libraries, Inc

P ROCKPORT PUBLIC LIBRARY, One Limerock St, PO Box 8, 04856. SAN 306-7386. Tel: 207-236-3642. FAX: 207-236-3642. E-Mail: rpl@rockport.lib.me.us. Web Site: www.rockport.lib.me.us. *Dir*, Sally Regan; *Asst Librn*, Holly R Torsey; Staff 3 (MLS 1, Non-MLS 2)
Founded 1914. Pop 2,854; Circ 63,000
Library Holdings: Bk Vols 25,000; Per Subs 36
Subject Interests: Maritime history
Function: ILL available, Photocopies available, Reference services available
Mem of Northeastern Maine Library District
Friends of the Library Group

RUMFORD

M RUMFORD COMMUNITY HOSPITAL, Health Science Library,* 420 Franklin St, PO Box 619, 04276. SAN 377-9823. Tel: 207-364-4581, Ext 359. FAX: 207-369-0834. *Dir*, Gus Carlson
Library Holdings: Bk Titles 300; Per Subs 15

P RUMFORD PUBLIC LIBRARY,* 35 Rumford Ave, 04276-1919. SAN 306-7394. Tel: 207-364-3661. FAX: 207-364-7296. Web Site: www.rumford.lib.me.us. *Librn*, Karl Aromaa; E-Mail: karomaa@rumford.lib.me.us; *Circ*, Susan Bowie; *Ch Servs*, Ginny Todd; *Ref*, Joyce Wanger; Staff 8 (MLS 1, Non-MLS 7)
Founded 1903. Pop 9,439; Circ 75,040
Jul 1996-Jun 1997 Income $200,909, State $200, City $181,789, Locally Generated Income $18,920. Mats Exp $35,510, Books $27,660, Per/Ser (Incl. Access Fees) $3,400, Presv $100, Micro $150. Sal $134,002 (Prof $34,000)
Library Holdings: Bk Vols 38,000; Per Subs 166
Special Collections: Maine History & Fiction
Mem of Central Maine Library District

SACO

P DYER LIBRARY,* 371 Main St, 04072. SAN 306-7408. Tel: 207-282-3031, 207-283-3861. *Librn*, Gerard Morin; E-Mail: gmorin@dyer.lib.me.us
Founded 1881. Pop 15,000; Circ 63,547
1998-1999 Income $280,000. Mats Exp $40,000. Sal $160,000 (Prof $53,000)
Library Holdings: Bk Titles 60,000; Per Subs 120
Special Collections: Bureau of the Census; History (Maine Coll), bks, newspapers & photos (18th & 19th centuries), pamphlets, doc, town hist rec

Publications: Dyer Library Association Newsletter
Mem of Southern Conn Libr Coun; Southern Maine Library District
Open Tues & Thurs 10am-8pm, Wed & Fri 10am-5pm & Sat 9am-noon

SWEETSER CHILDREN'S SERVICES
M PROFESSIONAL LIBRARY, 50 Moody St, 04072. SAN 378-0864. Tel: 207-286-0349. FAX: 207-286-0431. *Librn*, Jan Wertheim; E-Mail: jwertheim@sweetser.org
Library Holdings: Bk Titles 2,000; Per Subs 20
Partic in Health Science Library Information Consortium

S SCHOOL LIBRARY, 50 Moody St, 04072. SAN 378-0880. Tel: 207-286-0349. FAX: 207-286-0431. *Librn*, Jan Wertheim
Library Holdings: Bk Titles 6,000; Per Subs 20
Mem of Southern Conn Libr Coun

S YORK INSTITUTE MUSEUM, Dyer Library,* 371 Main St, 04072. SAN 371-4330. Tel: 207-283-0958. *Dir*, Gerard Morin; *Circ*, Francis Nasse
Library Holdings: Bk Vols 60,000; Per Subs 130

SANFORD

M GOODALL HOSPITAL, Bacon Library, 25 June St, 04073. SAN 377-9289. Tel: 207-324-4310. FAX: 207-490-7328. *Actg Librn*, Donna James; E-Mail: djames@goodallhosp.org
Library Holdings: Bk Titles 200; Per Subs 20
Mem of Southern Maine Library District
Partic in Health & Med Info Coop; Health Science Library Information Consortium

P LOUIS B GOODALL MEMORIAL LIBRARY, Sanford Public Library, 952 Main St, 04073. SAN 343-7078. Tel: 207-324-4714. FAX: 207-324-5982. *Dir*, Jeffrey Christiansen; E-Mail: jeffc@goodall.lib.me.us; *Ch Servs*, Rachel Bannister; *Asst Librn*, Wendy Miller; Staff 2 (MLS 2)
Pop 18,040; Circ 125,067
Library Holdings: Bk Vols 74,000; Bk Titles 65,500; Per Subs 120
Mem of Southern Conn Libr Coun

SANGERVILLE

P SANGERVILLE PUBLIC LIBRARY,* Main St, 04479. (Mail add: PO Box 246, 04479), SAN 376-7582. Tel: 207-876-3491. *Librn*, Priscilla F Soule
Library Holdings: Bk Vols 12,513; Per Subs 18
Mem of Northeastern Maine Library District
Partic in Scoop Coop

SCARBOROUGH

M FOUNDATION FOR BLOOD RESEARCH LIBRARY,* Rte 1, Box 190, 04070-0190. SAN 324-5993. Tel: 207-883-4131. FAX: 207-883-1527. *Dir Libr Serv*, L Talamo
Founded 1978
Library Holdings: Bk Vols 1,500; Bk Titles 1,000
Subject Interests: Genetics, Immunology, Prenatal diagnosis
Mem of Southern Maine Library District
Partic in Health Sci Libr & Info Coop

P SCARBOROUGH PUBLIC LIBRARY,* 48 Gorham Rd, 04074. SAN 306-7432. Tel: 207-883-4723. FAX: 207-883-9728. Web Site: www.library.scarborough.me.us. *Librn*, Nancy E Crowell; *Ch Servs*, Susan L Winch; *Circ*, Deirdre Larson; Staff 2 (MLS 2)
Founded 1899. Pop 12,518; Circ 108,773
Library Holdings: Bk Vols 50,000; Per Subs 204
Publications: Footnotes (newsletter, quarterly)
Mem of Southern Conn Libr Coun; Southern Maine Library District
Friends of the Library Group

SEARSMONT

P SEARSMONT TOWN LIBRARY, Rte 131, Box 105, 04973. SAN 374-7069. Tel: 207-342-5549. FAX: 207-342-3495. E-Mail: stl@searsmont.lib.me.us. *Librn*, Kathy Hoey; Staff 6 (MLS 1, Non-MLS 5)
Founded 1990. Pop 1,000; Circ 4,000
Library Holdings: Bk Titles 7,500; Per Subs 20
Mem of Northeastern Maine Library District
Special Services for the Deaf - High interest/low vocabulary books
Friends of the Library Group

SEARSPORT

P CARVER MEMORIAL LIBRARY, 12 Union St, PO Box 439, 04974. SAN 306-7440. Tel: 207-548-2303. E-Mail: staff@carver.lib.me.us. Web Site: www.carver.lib.me.us. *Librn*, Nancy Morley; Staff 2 (Non-MLS 2)
Pop 5,006; Circ 13,386
Library Holdings: Bk Vols 11,383
Special Collections: Maine Material Coll
Mem of Northeastern Maine Library District
Partic in OCLC Online Computer Library Center, Inc
Friends of the Library Group

S PENOBSCOT MARINE MUSEUM, Stephen Phillips Memorial Library, 9 Church St, PO Box 498, 04974-0498. SAN 306-7459. Tel: 207-548-2529. FAX: 207-548-2520. E-Mail: library@penobscotmarinemuseum.org. Web Site: www.penobscotmarinemuseum.org. *Archivist, Head of Libr*, John G Arrison. Subject Specialists: *Maritime history*, John G Arrison
Founded 1936
Jan 2000-Dec 2000 Income $73,600, Locally Generated Income $3,400, Parent Institution $62,000. Mats Exp $1,700, Books $200, Per/Ser (Incl. Access Fees) $200, Presv $300, Manuscripts & Archives $1,000. Sal $50,000
Library Holdings: Bk Titles 12,000; Per Subs 10
Subject Interests: Genealogy, Local history, Maritime history
Special Collections: Maritime (Logbooks, Journals, Maritime Navigation & Law, Ship Registers)
Automation Activity & Vendor Info: (Cataloging) Athena
Database Vendor: Ebsco - EbscoHost
Restriction: Non-circulating to the public
Function: Research library
Partic in Maine Libr Asn

SEBAGO

S JONES MUSEUM OF GLASS & CERAMICS, Edward W Tinney Memorial Library, 35 Douglas Mountain Rd, 04029. SAN 378-1968. Tel: 207-787-3370. FAX: 207-787-2800. *Dir*, John H Holverson; *Curator*, Dorothy-Lee Jones; Staff 2 (Non-MLS 2)
Founded 1978
Library Holdings: Bk Vols 10,000; Bk Titles 6,000; Per Subs 36
Subject Interests: Ceramics, Glass
Restriction: Non-circulating to the public
Mem of Southern Maine Library District

SHAPLEIGH

P SHAPLEIGH COMMUNITY LIBRARY,* Rte 11, Box 97, 04076. SAN 373-0131. Tel: 207-636-3630. *Librn*, Gene Smith
Founded 1980. Pop 2,400; Circ 3,000
Library Holdings: Bk Vols 5,659; Bk Titles 4,000
Subject Interests: Genealogy, Local history
Mem of Southern Maine Library District

SHERMAN

P SHERMAN PUBLIC LIBRARY, Church St, PO Box 276, 04776-0276. SAN 306-7475. Tel: 207-365-4882. Interlibrary Loan Service Tel: 207-947-8336. FAX: 207-365-4143. *Librn*, Eva Perry
Pop 1,021; Circ 2,549
Library Holdings: Bk Vols 1,048
Subject Interests: Local history
Mem of Northeastern Maine Library District
Sherman Public Libr is open ten hours each week serving a town of 1000 people plus a non-resident population of approximately 400

SKOWHEGAN

M REDINGTON-FAIRVIEW HOSPITAL, Health Sciences Library,* Fairview Ave, PO Box 468, 04976. SAN 377-984X. Tel: 207-474-5121, Ext 419. *Librn*, Rebecca Jordan
Library Holdings: Bk Titles 300; Per Subs 175
Partic in Maine Health Sci Librs & Info Consortium

P SKOWHEGAN PUBLIC LIBRARY,* 5 Elm St, 04976. SAN 306-7483. Tel: 207-474-9072. *Chief Librn*, Helen Shaw; *Asst Librn*, Francoise Labonte; *Ch Servs*, Lois Moody
Founded 1889. Pop 8,098; Circ 51,700
Library Holdings: Bk Vols 45,000; Per Subs 52
Mem of Central Maine Library District
Friends of the Library Group

S SKOWHEGAN SCHOOL OF PAINTING & SCULPTURE, Robert Lehman Library, E Madison Rd, PO Box 449, 04976. (Mail add: 200 Park Ave S, Ste 1116, 10003), SAN 312-0635. Tel: 207-474-9345, 212-529-0505. FAX: 212-473-1342. Web Site: www.skowheganart.org. *Exec Dir*, Marella Consolini; *Exec Dir*, Linda Earle
Library Holdings: Bk Vols 16,000
Subject Interests: Art, Gen ref, Maine
Open Mon-Fri 9:30-5:30; June-Aug for students only

SOLON

P COOLIDGE LIBRARY,* S Main St, PO Box 238, 04979. SAN 306-7491. Tel: 207-643-2562. *Librn*, Tricia LeHay
Pop 822; Circ 6,919
Library Holdings: Bk Vols 6,642
Mem of Central Maine Library District
Open Tues 1-8

SOUTH BERWICK

P SOUTH BERWICK PUBLIC LIBRARY,* 37 Portland St, 03908. (Mail add: PO Box 35, 03908), SAN 306-7505. Tel: 207-384-3308. FAX: 207-384-3308. Web Site: www.south-berwick.lib.me.us. *Librn*, Charlene Parsons; E-Mail: cparsons@south-berwick.lib.me.us
Founded 1971. Pop 1,409; Circ 12,697
Library Holdings: Bk Vols 16,000
Mem of Southern Conn Libr Coun
Open Mon & Wed 1-8, Tues & Thurs 10-5, Fri 1-5, Sat 9-1
Friends of the Library Group

SOUTH CHINA

P SOUTH CHINA LIBRARY,* Old Rte 202 Box 417, 04358. SAN 376-3765. Tel: 207-445-3094. Web Site: www.southchina.lib.me.us. *Librn*, Cheryl Bake
Library Holdings: Bk Vols 10,000; Per Subs 20
Special Collections: Quaker (Rufus Jones Coll)
Mem of Central Maine Library District
Open Wed 10-12, 2-5 & 6:30-8 & Sat 10-12 & 1-3
Friends of the Library Group

SOUTH PARIS

P PARIS PUBLIC LIBRARY, 37 Market Sq, 04281. SAN 306-7513. Tel: 207-743-6994. E-Mail: staff@paris.lib.me.us. *Dep Dir*, Avis Green; *Librn*, Michael F Dignan; E-Mail: mdignan@paris.lib.me.us; *Ch Servs*, John Parker; Staff 5 (MLS 1, Non-MLS 4)
Founded 1926. Pop 4,492; Circ 34,126
Jul 1999-Jun 2000 Income $72,928, State $184, City $69,441, Locally Generated Income $3,303. Mats Exp Books $19,679. Sal $32,624 (Prof $18,000)
Library Holdings: Bk Titles 19,500; Per Subs 32
Special Collections: Advertiser-Democrat Newspaper Coll; Town Histories; Youth's Companion Magazine Coll
Automation Activity & Vendor Info: (Cataloging) Sagebrush Corporation; (Circulation) Sagebrush Corporation

SOUTH PORTLAND

P SOUTH PORTLAND PUBLIC LIBRARY, 482 Broadway, 04106. SAN 343-7132. Tel: 207-767-7660. FAX: 207-767-7626. E-Mail: lsouthp1@maine.rr.com. Web Site: home.maine.rr.com/southportlandlib. *Dir*, Marian Agazarian Peterson; *Ad Servs, ILL*, Marie Chenevert; *Ch Servs*, Tom Werley; *Tech Servs*, Charlotte Spear; *YA Servs*, Reta Nappi; Staff 4 (MLS 4)
Founded 1965. Pop 23,163; Circ 142,548
Jul 2000-Jun 2001 Income $505,342. Mats Exp $61,810, Books $54,410, Per/Ser (Incl. Access Fees) $4,900, Electronic Ref Mat (Incl. Access Fees) $2,500. Sal $374,985 (Prof $55,185)
Library Holdings: Bk Vols 93,820; Bk Titles 73,228; Per Subs 127
Special Collections: Cape Elizabeth Historical Records; Early American Children's Books (James Otis Kaler Coll); South Portland
Automation Activity & Vendor Info: (Cataloging) Innovative Interfaces Inc.; (Circulation) Innovative Interfaces Inc.
Database Vendor: Innovative Interfaces INN - View
Mem of Southern Maine Library District
Friends of the Library Group
Branches: 1
MEMORIAL BRANCH, 155 Wescott Rd, 04106. SAN 343-7167. Tel: 207-775-1835. FAX: 207-773-1036. E-Mail: bsouthp1@maine.rr.com. Web Site: www.home.maine.rr.com/southportlandlib/. *Branch Mgr, Librn*, Josephine Adamo; Staff 5 (MLS 1, Non-MLS 4)
Circ 32,000
Jul 1999-Jun 2000 Mats Exp $15,510, Books $14,510, Per/Ser (Incl. Access Fees) $1,000. Sal $71,377 (Prof $40,326)
Library Holdings: Bk Vols 17,000; Per Subs 25
Friends of the Library Group

S SOUTHERN MAINE JUVENILE CORRECTIONAL FACILITY, 675 Westbrook St, 04106. SAN 321-5075. Tel: 207-822-0001. FAX: 207-822-0023. *Librn*, Deborah Wardwell
Library Holdings: Bk Titles 8,000; Per Subs 15
Restriction: Internal circulation only

J SOUTHERN MAINE TECHNICAL COLLEGE LIBRARY, Fort Rd, 04106. SAN 306-7521. Tel: 207-767-9521. FAX: 207-767-9522. Web Site: www.smtc.net. *Librn*, Don Bertsch; *Ref*, Susan Nester; *Tech Servs*, Carin Dunay; Staff 3 (MLS 2, Non-MLS 1)
Founded 1964. Enrl 2,350; Fac 81; Highest Degree: Associate
Jul 2000-Jun 2001 Income $223,000. Mats Exp $74,000, Books $45,000, Per/Ser (Incl. Access Fees) $29,000. Sal $149,000
Library Holdings: Bk Vols 15,000; Bk Titles 14,200; Per Subs 350
Subject Interests: Allied health, Culinary arts, Electronics, Law enforcement, Nursing, Plants, Technology
Publications: Booklists (annual rpt)
Mem of Southern Maine Library District
Partic in Health Sci Libr & Info Consortium

SOUTHPORT

P SOUTHPORT MEMORIAL LIBRARY, 1032 Hendricks Hill Rd, 04576. (Mail add: PO Box 148, 04576), SAN 376-3781. Tel: 207-633-2741. *Librn*, Linda Brewer
Library Holdings: Bk Vols 24,000; Per Subs 20
Special Collections: Butterfly Coll
Mem of Central Maine Library District
Friends of the Library Group

SOUTHWEST HARBOR

P SOUTHWEST HARBOR PUBLIC LIBRARY, 338 Main St, 04679. (Mail add: PO Box 157, 04679-0157), SAN 306-7556. Tel: 207-244-7065. E-Mail: swhlibrary@acadia.net.; Staff 6 (MLS 1, Non-MLS 5)
Founded 1895. Pop 2,000; Circ 55,675
Jul 2000-Jun 2001 Income $170,900, State $200, City $43,000, Locally Generated Income $94,800. Mats Exp $10,700, Books $9,200, Other Print Mats $1,500, Electronic Ref Mat (Incl. Access Fees) $800. Sal $110,000 (Prof $31,000)
Library Holdings: Bk Vols 26,732; Per Subs 100
Special Collections: Maine History
Automation Activity & Vendor Info: (Cataloging) Sagebrush Corporation; (Circulation) Sagebrush Corporation; (Course Reserve) Sagebrush Corporation; (OPAC) Sagebrush Corporation
Mem of Northeastern Maine Library District
Friends of the Library Group

SPRINGVALE

P SPRINGVALE PUBLIC LIBRARY, 443 Main St, 04083. SAN 306-7424. Tel: 207-324-4624. E-Mail: spl@springvale.lib.me.us. Web Site: www.springvale.lib.me.us. *Librn*, Marlene Parent; E-Mail: mmp@springvale.lib.me.us; Staff 8 (MLS 1, Non-MLS 7)
Founded 1906. Pop 20,000; Circ 92,537
Jul 2000-Jun 2001 Income $149,810, State $50, City $111,953, Locally Generated Income $37,807. Mats Exp $16,110, Books $14,260, Per/Ser (Incl. Access Fees) $1,800, Presv $50. Sal $81,075
Library Holdings: Bk Vols 38,861; Per Subs 70
Subject Interests: Genealogy
Automation Activity & Vendor Info: (Cataloging) Follett; (Circulation) Follett
Mem of Southern Maine Library District
Friends of the Library Group

STANDISH

CR SAINT JOSEPH'S COLLEGE, Wellehan Library, 278 Whitesbridge Rd, 04084-5263. SAN 306-7009. Tel: 207-893-7725. FAX: 207-893-7883. E-Mail: library@sjcme.edu. Web Site: www.sjcme.edu/wellehan. *Dir Libr Serv*, Sister Jackie Hittner; E-Mail: jhittner@sjcme.edu; *Cat*, Maryhope Tobin; E-Mail: mtobin@sjcme.edu; *Ref*, Martha Mitchell; Tel: 207-893-7724, E-Mail: mmitchel@sjcme.edu; Staff 6 (MLS 3, Non-MLS 3)
Founded 1915. Enrl 4,800; Fac 47; Highest Degree: Master
Jul 2000-Jun 2001 Income Locally Generated Income $356,700. Mats Exp $129,000, Books $56,000, Per/Ser (Incl. Access Fees) $63,000, Micro $10,000. Sal $178,850
Library Holdings: Bk Vols 75,000; Bk Titles 47,000; Per Subs 420
Special Collections: Ireland; Maine; Thomas Merton Coll
Automation Activity & Vendor Info: (Cataloging) Sagebrush Corporation; (Circulation) TLC; (Circulation) Sagebrush Corporation
Database Vendor: Dialog, Ebsco - EbscoHost
Partic in Health Sci Libr Info Coop

STEEP FALLS

P STEEP FALLS PUBLIC LIBRARY,* Pequawket Trail, 04085-0140. (Mail add: PO Box 140, 04085-0140), SAN 306-7572. Tel: 207-675-3132. FAX: 207-675-3132. E-Mail: fflib@pirot.net. *Librn*, Paula Paul; *Asst Librn, Ch Servs*, Margaret Dutil
Founded 1916. Pop 7,500; Circ 23,208
Library Holdings: Bk Vols 24,000; Per Subs 12
Subject Interests: History

Special Collections: Hobson Coll; Pierce & Maine Colls
Mem of Southern Conn Libr Coun; Southern Maine Library District
Open Tues & Thurs 4-8, Wed 9-4, Sat 10-2

STETSON

P STETSON LIBRARY,* PO Box 154, 04488. SAN 376-3498. Tel: 207-296-2020. *Librn*, Betty-Ann Seelenbandt
Jul 1997-Jun 1998 Income $3,300. Mats Exp $1,200
Library Holdings: Bk Vols 3,950; Bk Titles 1,000; Per Subs 12
Mem of Northeastern Maine Library District
Open Tues 2-5, Wed 3-5, Thurs 9:30-11:30 & 6-7

STEUBEN

P HENRY D MOORE PUBLIC LIBRARY, PO Box 127, 04680. SAN 325-2183. Tel: 207-546-7301. *Librn*, Jeanne Benedict; E-Mail: jbenedict@moore.lib.me.us
Pop 1,084; Circ 5,202
Library Holdings: Bk Vols 11,599; Per Subs 10
Mem of Northeastern Maine Library District
Open Tues & Thurs 1:30-4:30, Wed & Sat 9-12 (summer hours may vary)

STRATTON

P STRATTON PUBLIC LIBRARY, 88 Main St, PO Box 350, 04982. SAN 372-6711. Tel: 207-246-4401. FAX: 207-246-3267. Web Site: www.stratton.lib.me.us/index.htm. *Librn*, Jerome Hopson, Sr; E-Mail: jhopson@stratton.lib.me.us; *Asst Librn*, Wendy Charest
Founded 1921. Pop 600
Library Holdings: Bk Vols 5,000; Bk Titles 5,000
Mem of Central Maine Library District

STRONG

P STRONG PUBLIC LIBRARY, Foster Memorial Library, Main St, 04983. (Mail add: PO Box 629, 04983), SAN 376-7825. Tel: 207-684-4003. FAX: 207-684-4004. *Librn*, Helen M Scamman; E-Mail: hscmman@strong.lib.me.us
Library Holdings: Bk Vols 73,000; Bk Titles 6,000
Mem of Central Maine Library District

SUNSET

S DEER ISLE-STONINGTON HISTORICAL SOCIETY,* Rte 15A, 04627. (Mail add: PO Box 652, 04627), Tel: 207-348-2897. *Pres*, Paul Stubin
Library Holdings: Bk Vols 678
Subject Interests: Early children's bks, Genealogy, Marine hist, Marine vessels, Sch bks, Steamboats, Yachts

TENANTS HARBOR

P JACKSON MEMORIAL LIBRARY,* Main St, PO Box 231, 04860. SAN 306-7416. Tel: 207-372-8961. *Dir, Librn*, Dawn La Brozzi
Founded 1935. Pop 2,200
1998-1999 Income $32,000, State $200, City $6,000, Locally Generated Income $25,800. Mats Exp $5,000, Books $4,800, Per/Ser (Incl. Access Fees) $200. Sal $14,000
Library Holdings: Bk Vols 11,500; Per Subs 44
Mem of Northeastern Maine Library District
Friends of the Library Group

THOMASTON

S MAINE STATE PRISON LIBRARY,* 392 Main St, Box A, 04861-0500. SAN 306-7688. Tel: 207-354-2535. FAX: 207-354-3004.
Library Holdings: Bk Vols 10,312; Per Subs 42
Subject Interests: Art history, Natural history, Vocational info
Special Collections: State & Federal Criminal Law, bks, per
Mem of Northeastern Maine Library District

P THOMASTON PUBLIC LIBRARY,* 60 Main St, 04861. SAN 306-7599. Tel: 207-354-2453. E-Mail: tpl@thomaston.lib.me.us. *Librn*, Kevin Curtin; *Asst Librn*, Kathy Daley; *Ch Servs*, Deanna Riggins
Founded 1898. Pop 3,306; Circ 44,997
Library Holdings: Bk Vols 34,000; Per Subs 50
Special Collections: Audio-Cassettes; Large Print Coll; Maine Coll
Mem of Northeastern Maine Library District
Friends of the Library Group

TOGUS

GM DEPARTMENT OF VETERANS AFFAIRS LEARNING RESOURCES CENTER, Veterans Affairs Medical & Regional Office Center Library, One VA Center, 04330. SAN 306-5758. Tel: 207-623-5773. FAX: 207-623-5766. *Librn*, June Roullard; *Tech Servs*, Gary Pelletier; *Online Servs*, Christopher Bovie; Staff 3 (MLS 2, Non-MLS 1)
Founded 1943
Library Holdings: Bk Vols 4,000; Per Subs 200
Subject Interests: Health sciences
Automation Activity & Vendor Info: (Circulation) EOS; (OPAC) EOS
Partic in Health Sci Libr & Info Coop; NNLM/SCR, OCLC Online Computer Libr Ctr, Inc; Vets Admin Libr Network

TOPSHAM

L MCTEAGUE HIGBEE LAW LIBRARY, 4 Union Park, PO Box 5000, 04086-5000. SAN 372-5804. Tel: 207-725-5581. FAX: 207-725-1090. *Librn*, Dale Dorr; E-Mail: ddorr@me-law.com; Staff 1 (MLS 1)
Jan 2000-Dec 2000 Mats Exp $34,580, Books $5,370, Per/Ser (Incl. Access Fees) $13,700, AV Equip $310, Electronic Ref Mat (Incl. Access Fees) $15,200. Sal $37,400
Library Holdings: Bk Vols 1,341; Bk Titles 516; Per Subs 12
Subject Interests: Discrimination, Labor
Special Collections: Maine Workers Compensation Law
Restriction: Staff use only

P TOPSHAM PUBLIC LIBRARY, (TPL), 35 Republic Ave, 04086-1137. SAN 306-7602. Tel: 207-725-1727. FAX: 207-725-1735. Web Site: www.topsham.lib.me.us. *Dir*, Linda Prybylo; E-Mail: pry@topsham.lib.me.us; Staff 5 (Non-MLS 5)
Founded 1931. Pop 10,000; Circ 48,836
Jul 1999-Jun 2000 Income $124,722, State $200, City $121,522, Other $3,000. Mats Exp $11,000, Books $10,000, Per/Ser (Incl. Access Fees) $1,000. Sal $75,623
Library Holdings: Bk Titles 23,000; Per Subs 55
Automation Activity & Vendor Info: (Circulation) Athena
Database Vendor: Ebsco - EbscoHost
Mem of Central Maine Library District
Friends of the Library Group

TURNER

P TURNER PUBLIC LIBRARY,* PO Box 216, 04282. SAN 306-7610. Tel: 207-225-2030. *Librn*, Vicki Varney
Pop 3,539
Library Holdings: Bk Vols 13,000; Bk Titles 12,000
Open Tues & Thurs 12-8, Sat 9:30-12

UNION

P VOSE LIBRARY, 343 Common Rd, 04862-4252. (Mail add: PO Box 550, 04862-0550), SAN 306-7629. Tel: 207-785-4733. E-Mail: vose-la@vose.lib.me.us. *Librn*, Lynn Allen
Founded 1932. Pop 2,400; Circ 8,891
Jul 1999-Jun 2000 Income $31,121, State $200, City $7,500. Mats Exp $4,083, Books $3,150, Per/Ser (Incl. Access Fees) $375, AV Equip $303, Other Print Mats $165, Electronic Ref Mat (Incl. Access Fees) $90. Sal $8,190
Library Holdings: Bk Vols 10,000; Per Subs 22
Function: ILL available, Internet access, Photocopies available
Mem of Northeastern Maine Library District
Friends of the Library Group

UNITY

C DOROTHY W QUIMBY LIBRARY, Quaker Hill Rd, 04988-9502. SAN 306-7637. Tel: 207-948-3131, Ext 234. FAX: 207-948-2795. E-Mail: dwquimby@unity.unity.edu. Web Site: www.unity.edu/library/. *Chief Librn*, Dorothy W Quimby; *Asst Librn*, Robert J Doan
Founded 1966. Highest Degree: Bachelor
Library Holdings: Bk Titles 45,000; Per Subs 470
Subject Interests: Environ sci, North American Indians in all aspects
Mem of N Maine Libr Dis

VAN BUREN

P ABEL J MORNEAULT MEMORIAL LIBRARY,* 303 Main St, 04785. SAN 306-7645. Tel: 207-868-5076. *Dir*, Cecile Roy; E-Mail: cecileroy@morneault.lib.me.us
Founded 1974. Pop 2,920; Circ 22,607
Jul 1999-Jun 2000 Income $40,605, City $36,605, Other $4,000. Mats Exp $5,650, Books $5,000, Per/Ser (Incl. Access Fees) $650. Sal $26,430
Library Holdings: Bk Vols 23,000; Bk Titles 23,000; Per Subs 58

Subject Interests: Genealogy
Automation Activity & Vendor Info: (Circulation) Sagebrush Corporation
Mem of Northeastern Maine Library District
Friends of the Library Group

VINALHAVEN

P VINALHAVEN PUBLIC LIBRARY, One Carver St, PO Box 384, 04863. SAN 306-7653. Tel: 207-863-4401. FAX: 207-863-4701. E-Mail: vpl@vhaven.lib.me.us. *Librn*, Betsy Bates; Staff 2 (Non-MLS 2)
Founded 1887. Pop 1,225; Circ 19,902
Library Holdings: Bk Titles 21,000; Per Subs 32
Subject Interests: Large print
Special Collections: Audio & Video Tapes
Mem of Northeastern Maine Library District
Special Services for the Blind - Audio-cassettes; Homebound delivery; Large print bks
Friends of the Library Group

WALDOBORO

P WALDOBORO PUBLIC LIBRARY, 908 Main St, 04572-0768. (Mail add: PO Box 768, 04572-6036), SAN 306-7661. Tel: 207-832-4484. FAX: 207-832-4484. E-Mail: wplstaff@waldoboro.lib.me.us. Web Site: www.midcoast.com/~wpl. *Dir*, Delia W Mohlie; *Asst Librn*, Sara Gallant; *Circ*, Jane Lichtman; *Circ*, Cathrina Skov; Staff 4 (Non-MLS 4)
Founded 1916. Pop 5,000; Circ 19,000
Jul 2000-Jun 2001 Income $69,920, City $48,320, Locally Generated Income $21,600. Mats Exp $10,100, Books $6,000, Per/Ser (Incl. Access Fees) $1,200, AV Equip $1,900, Other Print Mats $1,000. Sal $41,350
Library Holdings: Bk Vols 14,000; Per Subs 60
Publications: Newsletter (monthly)
Function: ILL available
Mem of Central Maine Library District

WALPOLE

C UNIVERSITY OF MAINE, (DAR), Darling Marine Center Library, 193 Clarks Cove Rd, 04573. SAN 306-767X. Tel: 207-563-3146, Ext 226. FAX: 207-563-3119. *Librn*, Lisa Auriemma; E-Mail: lisa.auriemma@umit.maine.edu; Staff 1 (MLS 1)
Founded 1966. Fac 10; Highest Degree: Doctorate
Library Holdings: Bk Titles 10,000; Per Subs 190
Subject Interests: Marine biology, Oceanography

WARREN

P WARREN FREE PUBLIC LIBRARY,* PO Box 346, 04864. SAN 306-7696. Tel: 207-273-2900. *Librn*, Carolyn Wiley
Pop 2,550; Circ 10,522
Library Holdings: Bk Vols 16,050
Open Tues 3:30-8, Thurs 3:30-8:30, Sat 9-11:30
Friends of the Library Group

WASHBURN

P WASHBURN MEMORIAL LIBRARY,* 2 Main St, 04786. (Mail add: PO Box 571, 04786-0571), SAN 306-770X. Tel: 207-455-4814. *Librn*, Barbara D Porter; E-Mail: bporter@washburn.lib.me.us
Feb 1998-Jan 1999 Income $32,796, State $270, City $29,258, Other $900. Mats Exp $7,845, Books $6,381, AV Equip $964, Other Print Mats $500. Sal $18,437
Library Holdings: Bk Titles 16,289; Per Subs 20
Special Collections: Aroostook County Coll
Mem of Northeastern Maine Library District

WASHINGTON

P GIBBS LIBRARY,* 40 Old Union Rd, PO Box 348, 04574. SAN 376-348X. Tel: 207-845-2663. *Librn*, Madelon Kelly
1998-1999 Income $9,000. Mats Exp $6,200, Books $3,450, Per/Ser (Incl. Access Fees) $400, Presv $1,000
Library Holdings: Bk Titles 10,000
Mem of Northeastern Maine Library District
Open Tues 9-12 & 6-9, Thurs 3-9, Sat 9-12, Sun 2-5

WATERVILLE

S THE CHINET CO, Research Library,* 242 College Ave, 04901. SAN 329-9392. Tel: 207-873-3351, 207-877-6339. FAX: 207-877-6203. *Librn*, Dr Peter Foster
Library Holdings: Bk Vols 100; Per Subs 15
Partic in Dialog Corporation; OCLC Online Computer Library Center, Inc

C COLBY COLLEGE LIBRARIES, 04901. SAN 343-7191. Tel: 207-872-3444. Interlibrary Loan Service Tel: 207-872-3288. Reference Tel: 207-872-3463. FAX: 207-872-3287. Web Site: www.colby.edu/college/library_etc.html. *Dir*, Suanne W Muehlner; Tel: 207-872-3286, E-Mail: swmuehln@colby.edu; *Publ Servs*, Frances M Parker; Tel: 207-872-3285, E-Mail: fmparker@colby.edu; *Ref*, Toni Katz; Tel: 207-872-3308, E-Mail: tdkatz@colby.edu; *Ref*, Charles Lakin; Tel: 207-872-3901, E-Mail: crlakin@colby.edu; *Ref*, Margaret Menchen; Tel: 207-872-3308, E-Mail: mpmenche@colby.edu; *Ref*, Marilyn R Pukkila; Tel: 207-872-3901, E-Mail: mrpukkil@colby.edu; *Spec Coll*, Nancy Reinhardt; Tel: 207-872-3284, E-Mail: nsreinha@colby.edu. Subject Specialists: *Art*, Margaret Erickson; *Music*, Margaret Erickson; *Science/technology*, Susan Cole; Staff 9 (MLS 9)
Founded 1820. Enrl 1,700; Fac 175; Highest Degree: Bachelor
Jul 1999-Jun 2000 Income (Main and Other College/University Libraries) $2,650,000. Mats Exp $1,190,000, Books $440,000, Per/Ser (Incl. Access Fees) $580,000, Presv $44,000, Electronic Ref Mat (Incl. Access Fees) $125,250. Sal $854,000 (Prof $649,000)
Library Holdings: Bk Vols 507,000; Per Subs 1,800
Special Collections: A E Housman Coll; Colby Archives; Contemporary Letters (Bern Porter Coll); Henry James Coll; Maine Authors (Jacob Abbot, Sarah Orne Jewett, Edna St Vincent Millay, Kenneth Roberts, Ben Ames Williams, Edwin Arlington Robinson); Modern Irish Literature (Lord Dunsany, Lady Gregory, Seamus Heaney, James Joyce, Cuala Press, J M Synge, William Trevor, W B Yeats); Thomas Hardy Coll; Thomas Mann Coll; Violet Paget Coll (Vernon Lee)
Automation Activity & Vendor Info: (Acquisitions) Innovative Interfaces Inc.; (Cataloging) Innovative Interfaces Inc.; (Circulation) Innovative Interfaces Inc.; (Course Reserve) Innovative Interfaces Inc.; (ILL) Innovative Interfaces Inc.; (OPAC) Innovative Interfaces Inc.; (Serials) Innovative Interfaces Inc.
Database Vendor: Innovative Interfaces INN - View, OCLC - First Search
Partic in Nelinet, Inc
Departmental Libraries:
ART & MUSIC Tel: 207-872-3232. FAX: 207-872-3287. *Librn*, Margaret Erickson; E-Mail: m_ericso@colby.edu
SCIENCE Tel: 207-872-3313. FAX: 207-872-3287. *Librn*, Suzi Cole; Tel: 207-872-3722, E-Mail: swcole@colby.edu

M INLAND HOSPITAL, Medical Library, 200 Kennedy Memorial Dr, 04901. SAN 378-0619. Tel: 207-861-3018. FAX: 207-861-3025. E-Mail: inldlbry@mint.net. Web Site: www.inlandhospital.org/library.html. *Librn*, Janet Bolduc; Staff 1 (MLS 1)
Sep 2000-Aug 2001 Income Parent Institution $23,641. Mats Exp $15,550, Books $7,692, Per/Ser (Incl. Access Fees) $7,858. (Prof $6,959)
Library Holdings: Bk Vols 298; Bk Titles 241; Per Subs 39
Partic in Health Science Library Information Consortium

G MAINE DEPARTMENT OF PUBLIC SAFETY, Maine Criminal Justice Academy-Media Resources Library, 93 Silver St, 04901. SAN 326-338X. Tel: 207-877-8003. FAX: 207-877-8027. *Librn*, Linda J Dwelley; E-Mail: linda.j.dwelley@state.me.us; Staff 1 (MLS 1)
Founded 1976
Library Holdings: Bk Titles 3,721; Per Subs 63
Subject Interests: Corrections, Highways, Law enforcement, Safety
Database Vendor: ProQuest
Publications: Media Catalogue
Partic in Nelinet, Inc

M MAINE GENERAL MEDICAL CENTER, Health Sciences Library,* North St, 04901-1000. SAN 320-1929. Tel: 207-872-1224. FAX: 207-872-1460. E-Mail: mmmclib@mint.net. *Librn*, Cora M Damon
Library Holdings: Bk Vols 4,000; Bk Titles 1,000; Per Subs 175
Subject Interests: Allied health, Literature, Medicine
Partic in BRS; Docline; Health Science Library Information Consortium; Nat Libr of Med

C THOMAS COLLEGE, Marriner Library, 180 W River Rd, 04901. SAN 306-7718. Tel: 207-859-1234. Web Site: www.thomas.edu/library. *Dir*, Stephen LaRochelle; E-Mail: larochelle@thomas.edu; Staff 1 (MLS 1)
Founded 1894. Enrl 800; Fac 30; Highest Degree: Master
Library Holdings: Bk Vols 20,000; Bk Titles 18,000; Per Subs 500
Subject Interests: Business and management, Education

S WATERVILLE HISTORICAL SOCIETY LIBRARY, 64 Silver St, 04901. SAN 306-7726. Tel: 207-872-9439. Web Site: www.redingtonmuseum.org. *Pres*, Willard B Arnold, III; Tel: 207-465-2403, Fax: 207-465-9623, E-Mail: arnold@ctel.net; *Librn*, Diane Johnson
Founded 1903
Library Holdings: Bk Titles 2,500
Subject Interests: Civil War, Local history
Special Collections: Coll of Waterville Mail, A Newspaper Printed From 1846 to 1906, microfilm

P WATERVILLE PUBLIC LIBRARY, 73 Elm St, 04901-6078. SAN 306-7734. Tel: 207-872-5433. Interlibrary Loan Service Tel: 207-873-4779. FAX: 207-873-4779. Web Site: www.wtvl.net/library/. *Dir*, Richard P Sibley, Jr; E-Mail: rsibley@waterville.lib.me.us; *ILL*, Meta Vigue; *Ch Servs*, Marie Benner; *Cat, Tech Servs*, Cathy Perkins; E-Mail: stf-catper@

waterville.lib.me.us; *Circ*, Madeline Boudreau
Founded 1896. Pop 17,173; Circ 126,220
Jul 1998-Jun 1999 Income $397,000, State $200, City $321,000, Locally Generated Income $75,800. Mats Exp $52,871, Books $42,119, Per/Ser (Incl. Access Fees) $6,252, Electronic Ref Mat (Incl. Access Fees) $4,500. Sal $228,674 (Prof $102,814)
Library Holdings: Bk Vols 92,481; Per Subs 109; High Interest/Low Vocabulary Bk Vols 135
Special Collections: Franco-Americans & Lebanese-Americans in Waterville; Waterville-Area Genealogy & Local History
Automation Activity & Vendor Info: (Cataloging) Sagebrush Corporation; (Circulation) Sagebrush Corporation; (OPAC) Sagebrush Corporation
Mem of Central Maine Library District
Friends of the Library Group

WAYNE

P CARY MEMORIAL LIBRARY, Old Winthrop Rd, PO Box 127, 04284. SAN 306-7742. Tel: 207-685-3612. *Librn*, Janet H Adelberg
Pop 1,100; Circ 14,500
1999-2000 Income $26,000
Library Holdings: Bk Vols 12,129; Per Subs 40
Special Collections: Annie Louise Cary Memorabilia (Opera Star 1841-1921); Bookplates (7 vols)
Mem of Central Maine Library District
Friends of the Library Group

P NORTH WAYNE VILLAGE LIBRARY, RR 1, Box 4710, 04284. SAN 321-5725. Tel: 207-685-3689. *Librn*, M Tripp
Founded 1967. Circ 1,391
Library Holdings: Bk Titles 5,000

WELD

P WELD FREE LIBRARY,* Church St, 04285. SAN 306-7750. Tel: 207-585-2439. *Librn*, Diana Demers
Founded 1905. Pop 321; Circ 4,848
Library Holdings: Per Subs 15
Mem of Central Maine Library District
Open Tues 3-8, Fri 1-6

WELLS

P WELLS PUBLIC LIBRARY,* 1434 Post Rd Rte 1, 04090-4508. (Mail add: PO Box 699, 04090-0699), SAN 372-6320. Tel: 207-646-8181. FAX: 207-646-5636. E-Mail: libstaff@wells.lib.me.us. Web Site: www.wells.lib.me.us. *Dir*, Sandra J Broomfield; Tel: 207-646-8181, Ext 206, E-Mail: sbroomfield@wells.lib.me.us; Staff 8 (MLS 2, Non-MLS 6)
Founded 1979. Pop 10,000; Circ 90,000
Jul 1999-Jun 2000 Income $208,000, State $204,000, Other $4,000. Mats Exp $25,800, Books $20,000, Per/Ser (Incl. Access Fees) $4,500, Electronic Ref Mat (Incl. Access Fees) $1,300. Sal $148,600 (Prof $58,000)
Library Holdings: Bk Vols 38,200; Bk Titles 36,700; Per Subs 100
Automation Activity & Vendor Info: (Cataloging) Follett; (Circulation) Follett; (OPAC) Follett
Mem of Southern Maine Library District
Friends of the Library Group

§J YORK COUNTY TECHNICAL COLLEGE LIBRARY, 112 College Dr, 04090-9999. Tel: 207-646-9282. Web Site: www.yctc.net. *Dir*, Sarah Campbell
Library Holdings: Bk Vols 5,000

WEST BOOTHBAY HARBOR

G MAINE DEPARTMENT OF MARINE RESOURCES, Bigelow Laboratory for Ocean Sciences Library, McKown Point Rd, 04575. SAN 306-7777. Tel: 207-633-9500, 207-633-9600. FAX: 207-633-9641. E-Mail: library@bigelow.org. Web Site: www.bigelow.org/. *Librn*, Pamela Shephard-Lupo
Founded 1957
1999-2000 Income $75,000, State $30,000, Parent Institution $45,000. Mats Exp $58,000, Books $4,000, Per/Ser (Incl. Access Fees) $50,000, Electronic Ref Mat (Incl. Access Fees) $4,000. Sal $26,000
Library Holdings: Bk Titles 3,500; Per Subs 252
Subject Interests: Biochemistry, Botany, Environmental studies, Marine biology, Oceanography, Zoology
Special Collections: fishing gear; Foreign Countries Documents; State & Federal Government Publications
Publications: Dept of Marine Resources, Scientific & Technical Publications Index 1946-1983
Partic in Dialog Corporation; OCLC Online Computer Library Center, Inc
Exchange of staff publications with other oceanographic libraries & institutions

WEST BUXTON

P WEST BUXTON PUBLIC LIBRARY, Rte 112, River Rd, PO Box 348, 04093. SAN 306-6088. Tel: 207-727-5898. *Librn*, Kathy Miles
Founded 1926. Pop 4,000; Circ 4,642
Library Holdings: Bk Vols 7,800; Bk Titles 5,800
Open Tues 6-8, Wed 9-11, Thurs 4-7, Sat 9-12

WEST NEWFIELD

P NEWFIELD READING ROOM,* 637 Water St, 04095. (Mail add: PO Box 55, 04056-0055), SAN 376-3862. Tel: 207-793-4348. *Librn*, Doreen Lofgren
Library Holdings: Bk Vols 3,500; Bk Titles 3,000
Mem of Southern Conn Libr Coun; Southern Maine Library District
Open Tues 6-8, Sat 10-12

WEST PARIS

P WEST PARIS PUBLIC LIBRARY,* 226 Main St, PO Box 307, 04289. SAN 321-0529. Tel: 207-674-2004. Web Site: www.bstevwpl.westparis.lib.me.us. *Librn*, Beverly Stevens
Founded 1889. Pop 1,390; Circ 3,963
Library Holdings: Bk Vols 8,000; Per Subs 17
Mem of Maine State Library
Open Mon & Fri 1:30-5 & Wed 1:30-7
Friends of the Library Group

WESTBROOK

S SAPPI FINE PAPER NORTH AMERICA, Technology Center Library, 89 Cumberland St, 04092. (Mail add: PO Box 5000, 04098-1597), SAN 306-7785. Tel: 207-856-3538. FAX: 207-856-3770. *Mgr*, Deborah G Chandler; E-Mail: deborah.chandler@sappi-na.com; Staff 1 (MLS 1)
Library Holdings: Bk Titles 3,500; Per Subs 80
Subject Interests: Chemistry, Engineering, Papermaking, Physics, Printing

P WALKER MEMORIAL LIBRARY, 800 Maine St, 04092. SAN 306-7793. Tel: 207-854-0630. FAX: 207-854-0629. E-Mail: wmlx800@gwi.net. Web Site: www.westbrookmaine.com/library. *Dir*, Carolyn K Watkins; E-Mail: cwatki@westbrook.me.us; *Asst Librn*, Dianne LeConte; E-Mail: dlecon@westbrook.me.us; *AV, Ch Servs*, Patricia Larrabee; E-Mail: plarra@westbrook.me.us; *Curator*, Julie Peterson; E-Mail: jpeter@westbrook.me.us; Staff 6 (MLS 2, Non-MLS 4)
Founded 1894. Pop 16,121; Circ 61,118
Jul 2000-Jun 2001 Income $386,027, State $200, City $338,352, Locally Generated Income $7,475, Other $40,000. Mats Exp $40,692, Books $26,872, Per/Ser (Incl. Access Fees) $3,187, Micro $300, Manuscripts & Archives $350, Electronic Ref Mat (Incl. Access Fees) $9,983. Sal $235,711 (Prof $120,000)
Library Holdings: Bk Vols 49,203; Bk Titles 47,832; Per Subs 116
Subject Interests: Large type print, Local history
Automation Activity & Vendor Info: (Cataloging) Follett; (Circulation) Follett; (ILL) Follett; (OPAC) Follett
Publications: Monthly Calendar
Mem of Southern Maine Library District
Friends of the Library Group

P WARREN MEMORIAL LIBRARY,* 479 Main St, 04092-4330. SAN 306-7807. Tel: 207-854-5891. Web Site: www.javanet.com/~warren.html. *Dir*, Anastasia S Weigle; E-Mail: aweigle@warren.lib.me.us; *Ch Servs*, Mary Lee Kimball; *Coll Develop*, Carol Parks
Founded 1894. Pop 16,300; Circ 98,500
Jan 1997-Dec 1998 Income $49,700, Federal $2,000, Locally Generated Income $10,300, Other $37,400. Mats Exp $21,100, Books $17,500, Per/Ser (Incl. Access Fees) $2,600, Micro $1,000. Sal $79,000
Library Holdings: Bk Titles 33,000; Per Subs 103
Subject Interests: History
Special Collections: Maine Coll; Rowe Slides (Westbrook Industry); Susan Warren Memorial Foundation Archives
Mem of Southern Conn Libr Coun; Southern Maine Library District

WHITNEYVILLE

P WHITNEYVILLE LIBRARY ASSOCIATION, INC, 2 School St, 04654. (Mail add: PO Box 478, 04654), SAN 306-7815. Tel: 207-255-8077. E-Mail: whitstaff@whitneyville.lib.me.us. Web Site: www.whitneyville.lib.me.us. *Librn*, John Bodger; Tel: 207-255-3804, E-Mail: jbodger.whitstaff@whitneyville.lib.me.us; *Asst Librn, Cat*, Renee Brightly; *Ch Servs, ILL*, Patricia Brightly; Staff 4 (MLS 1, Non-MLS 3)
Founded 1966. Pop 900; Circ 13,165
Library Holdings: Bk Vols 14,310
Subject Interests: Art and architecture, Biology, Fiction, History, Literature, Music, Nonfiction, Science, Sports, Technology
Special Collections: All Newberry & Caldecott Medal Winners 1928-97; Children's Books (Lucy Stanton Bodger); Memorial Children's Book Coll, (1956-1963)

Publications: New Booklist (biannual)
Mem of Northeastern Maine Library District
Circulation to 20 teachers at 5 schools in Jonesboro, Machias & Wesley; 1 in Jonesboro, 3 in Machias & 1 in Wesley

WILTON

P WILTON FREE PUBLIC LIBRARY, 6 Goodspeed St, PO Box 454, 04294-0454. SAN 306-7823. Tel: 207-645-4831. *Librn*, Vaughan Gagne; E-Mail: vgagne@wilton-free.lib.me.us; *Ch Servs*, Ellen Soucy; *Asst Librn*, Jill Sampson; Staff 3 (MLS 3)
Founded 1901. Pop 4,242; Circ 33,778
Library Holdings: Bk Vols 18,440; Per Subs 53
Subject Interests: Local history
Special Collections: Genealogy, microfilm
Mem of Central Maine Library District

WINDHAM

P WINDHAM PUBLIC LIBRARY, 217 Windham Center Rd, 04062. SAN 306-784X. Tel: 207-892-1908. E-Mail: windham.public.library@msln.net. Web Site: www.windham.lib.me.us. *Coll Develop, Dir*, Inese Gruber; Fax: 207-892-1915, E-Mail: igruber@windham.lib.me.us; *Ch Servs*, Laurel Parker; Fax: 207-892-1915; *YA Servs*, Aggie Kostovick; Fax: 207-892-1915; Staff 3 (MLS 2, Non-MLS 1)
Founded 1971. Pop 15,000; Circ 100,000
Jul 2000-Jun 2001 Income City $222,000. Mats Exp $29,000, Books $23,000, Per/Ser (Incl. Access Fees) $3,000, AV Equip $3,000. Sal $138,000 (Prof $95,000)
Library Holdings: Bk Vols 35,000; Bk Titles 35,000; Per Subs 105; Bks on Deafness & Sign Lang 10
Special Collections: Stephen King Coll, audios, lg prints, videos, music & CD's
Automation Activity & Vendor Info: (Circulation) Sagebrush Corporation
Mem of Southern Conn Libr Coun
Friends of the Library Group

WINSLOW

P WINSLOW PUBLIC LIBRARY,* Halifax St, RR 4 Box 190, 04901. SAN 372-6347. Tel: 207-872-1978. FAX: 207-872-1979. Web Site: www.winslow.lib.me.us. *Dir*, Judy Larson; Staff 5 (MLS 1, Non-MLS 4)
Founded 1905. Pop 8,143; Circ 51,000
Jul 1997-Jun 1998 Income $106,940, State $200, City $102,740, Locally Generated Income $4,000. Mats Exp $18,000, Books $14,000, Per/Ser (Incl. Access Fees) $2,000. Sal $65,000 (Prof $30,000)
Library Holdings: Bk Titles 36,525; Per Subs 40
Automation Activity & Vendor Info: (Circulation) Sagebrush Corporation
Friends of the Library Group

WINTER HARBOR

P WINTER HARBOR PUBLIC LIBRARY,* 18 Chapel Lane, PO Box 310, 04693. SAN 306-7866. Tel: 207-963-7556. *Librn*, Marilyn Coombs
Founded 1918. Pop 1,120; Circ 4,185
Library Holdings: Bk Vols 6,000
Subject Interests: Large type print
Mem of Northeastern Maine Library District

WINTERPORT

P WINTERPORT MEMORIAL LIBRARY,* PO Box 650, 04496. SAN 306-7874. Tel: 207-223-5540. *Librn*, Cora McLeod
Pop 2,675; Circ 8,506
Library Holdings: Bk Vols 12,000; Bk Titles 11,244; Per Subs 40
Mem of Northeastern Maine Library District
Open Tues, Thurs & Sat 12-5

WINTHROP

P CHARLES M BAILEY PUBLIC LIBRARY, Bowdoin St, 04364. SAN 306-7882. Tel: 207-377-8673. FAX: 207-377-4406. *Librn*, Melora Ranney; *Ch Servs*, Cindy Hinkley; Staff 7 (MLS 1, Non-MLS 6)
Pop 5,889; Circ 48,305
Jul 1999-Jun 2000 Income City $116,728. Mats Exp $16,900, Books $13,500, Per/Ser (Incl. Access Fees) $2,200, Electronic Ref Mat (Incl. Access Fees) $1,200. Sal $70,312 (Prof $25,291)
Library Holdings: Bk Vols 27,841; Bk Titles 26,017; Per Subs 76
Automation Activity & Vendor Info: (Circulation) Athena; (Circulation) Nicholas; (OPAC) Athena
Database Vendor: IAC - Info Trac
Partic in Central Maine Libr District
Open Mon & Fri 12-6, Tues 10-8, Wed 10-6, Sat 10-3
Friends of the Library Group

WISCASSET

GL LINCOLN COUNTY LAW LIBRARY,* High St, PO Box 249, 04578. SAN 306-7890. Tel: 207-882-7517.
Library Holdings: Bk Vols 10,000

P WISCASSET PUBLIC LIBRARY, 21 High St, 04578-4119. (Mail add: PO Box 367, 04578-0367), SAN 306-7904. Tel: 207-882-7161. FAX: 207-882-6698. E-Mail: wpl@wiscasset.lib.me.us. Web Site: www.wiscasset.lib.me.us. *Librn*, Janet Morgan; E-Mail: jmorgan@wiscasset.lib.me.us; *Ch Servs*, Joan Spurgat
Founded 1920. Pop 5,559
Jan 1999-Dec 2000 Income $90,000, City $85,000, Other $5,000. Mats Exp $15,785, Books $14,685, Per/Ser (Incl. Access Fees) $1,000, Manuscripts & Archives $100. Sal $83,507
Library Holdings: Bk Vols 31,770
Subject Interests: Art, Local history
Special Collections: Archives; Nuclear Regulatory Comn Coll (Maine Yankee documents only); Orchestral Sheet Music
Friends of the Library Group

YARMOUTH

P MERRILL MEMORIAL LIBRARY,* 215 Main St, 04096. SAN 306-7939. Tel: 207-846-4763. FAX: 207-846-2422. *Dir*, Nancy Kollias
Founded 1904. Pop 7,400; Circ 68,541
Library Holdings: Bk Vols 44,000; Per Subs 96
Subject Interests: Genealogy, History
Publications: Monthly newsletter
Mem of Southern Conn Libr Coun; Southern Maine Library District
Partic in OCLC Online Computer Library Center, Inc
Open Tues, Wed & Thurs 10-8 & Mon, Fri & Sat 10-5
Friends of the Library Group

YORK

S OLD YORK HISTORICAL SOCIETY LIBRARY, 207 York St, PO Box 312, 03909. SAN 306-7947. Tel: 207-363-4974. FAX: 207-363-4021. Web Site: www.oldyork.org. *Librn*, Virginia Spiller
Library Holdings: Bk Titles 6,000
Subject Interests: American folk art, Decorative arts, Genealogy, Local history
Special Collections: 300 Local Geneologies; Local Photographs; Rare Books & Manuscripts gathered from local 18th Century private libraries & the York Social Libr estab 1796
Mem of Maine State Library; Southern Conn Libr Coun

P YORK PUBLIC LIBRARY,* 172 York St, 03909. SAN 306-7955. Tel: 207-363-2818. FAX: 207-363-7250. E-Mail: yl-bl@york.lib.me.us. Web Site: www.york.lib.me.us/. *Dir*, Rebecca Legro; *Ch Servs*, Agnes Moy; *Ch Servs*, Elaine Cannon; *Circ*, Lynn Eaton
Founded 1912. Pop 12,000; Circ 84,500
Special Collections: Genealogy - large print bks, recorded bks, videos
Mem of Southern Maine Library District
Friends of the Library Group

MARYLAND

Date of Statistics: FY 1999
Population, 1990: 5,029,100
Population Served: 5,108,500
Total Volumes in Public Libraries: 15,628,970
  Volumes Per Capita: 3.0
Total Public Library Circulation: 45,501,261
  Circulation Per Capita: 8.91
Total Public Library Income (including Grants-in-Aid): $168,043,082
  Income Per Capita: $32.46
  Source of Income: Public funds
Counties Served: 23 plus Baltimore City (not a county, but receives state aid)
Number of Bookmobiles: 15
Grants-in-Aid to Public Libraries:
  Federal: $2,217,377
  State Aid:
    Library Operations: $24,656,241
    Library Network: $3,783,438

ABERDEEN PROVING GROUND

S BATTELLE, Chemical Warfare, Chemical & Biological Information & Analysis Center,* Gunpowder Branch APG, PO Box 196, 21010-0196. SAN 372-6509. Tel: 410-676-9030. FAX: 410-676-9703. Web Site: www.cbiac.apgea.army.mil. *Res*, Mary Frances Tracy; Staff 10 (MLS 7, Non-MLS 3)
Founded 1986
Special Collections: Chemical & Biological Warfare, bks, rpts, videos & databases; Chemical Weapons Treaty (Treaty Reference Coll), bks, rpts & bibs
Publications: Bibliographies; Handbooks
Partic in Dialog Corporation

UNITED STATES ARMY

A CENTER FOR HEALTH PROMOTION & PREVENTIVE MEDICINE LIBRARY, Bldg E-1570, 21010-5422. SAN 343-7434. Tel: 410-436-4236. *Librn*, Krishan S Goel
Founded 1945
Library Holdings: Bk Vols 15,170; Bk Titles 13,000; Per Subs 270
Subject Interests: Chemistry, Engineering, Medicine, Occupational safety, Physics, Public health, Toxicology
Publications: Journal Holdings List
Partic in Dialog Corporation; Fedlink; National Library Of Medicine, Medlars; OCLC Online Computer Library Center, Inc

AM KIRK HEALTH CLINIC LIBRARY, 2501 Oakington St, 21005-5131. SAN 343-7302. Tel: 410-278-1726. FAX: 410-278-1783.
Founded 1963
Library Holdings: Bk Titles 210; Per Subs 36
Restriction: Open to public for reference only

AM MEDICAL RESEARCH INSTITUTE OF CHEMICAL DEFENSE, WOOD TECHNICAL LIBRARY, 3100 Ricketts Point Rd, 21010-5400. SAN 343-7396. Tel: 410-436-4135. FAX: 410-436-3176. E-Mail: mricd-wood.techlibrary@amedd.army.mil. *Librn*, Barbara Schultz; E-Mail: barbara.schultz@apg.amedd.army.mil; Staff 3 (MLS 1, Non-MLS 2)
Founded 1979
Library Holdings: Bk Vols 7,026; Bk Titles 6,153; Per Subs 152
Subject Interests: Toxicology
Database Vendor: Dialog
Partic in Fedlink; MAHSL; Nat Libr of Med; OCLC Online Computer Library Center, Inc
Restricted Department of the Army Access

A ORDNANCE CENTER & SCHOOL LIBRARY, Bldg 3071, 21005-5201. SAN 343-7310. Tel: 410-278-4991, 410-278-5615. FAX: 410-278-8882. *Chief Librn*, Lenora Haughton
Founded 1940
Library Holdings: Bk Vols 15,000; Per Subs 300
Subject Interests: Art, Business and management, Education, History
Special Collections: Department of the Army Publications
Publications: Acquisition list (monthly); periodical holdings (annual)
Partic in Fedlink

A ORDNANCE CENTER & SCHOOL ORDNANCE MUSEUM LIBRARY, Bldg 2601, USAOC&S, 21005-5201. SAN 343-7345. Tel: 410-278-2396, 410-278-3602. FAX: 410-278-7473. E-Mail: museum@ocs2.ap8.army.mil. *Dir*, William F Atwater
Founded 1973
1997-1998 Mats Exp $150
Library Holdings: Bk Vols 1,460
Subject Interests: Material culture
Special Collections: US Army Technical Manuels Coll

A POST LIBRARY, Bldg 3320, 21005-5001. SAN 370-0992. Tel: 410-278-3417. FAX: 410-278-9537. E-Mail: library-aa@mwr.apg.army.mil. *Librn*, Daniel Norum
Library Holdings: Bk Vols 40,000; Per Subs 300
Subject Interests: Military history, World War II
Partic in Fedlink

ABINGDON

S EAI CORPORATION LIBRARY, 1308 Continental Dr Ste J, 21009. SAN 323-4754. Tel: 410-676-1449. FAX: 410-671-7241. E-Mail: info@eaicorp.com. Web Site: www.eaicorp.com. *In Charge*, Monica Jakubowski
Library Holdings: Bk Vols 5,000; Per Subs 2
Subject Interests: Biological warfare, Chem warfare, Demilitarization, Environmental studies, Security systs
Special Collections: Conference on Disarmament Documents; OPCW Preparatory Committee Documents

ACCOKEEK

S ACCOKEEK FOUNDATION LIBRARY, 3400 Bryan Point Rd, 20607. SAN 371-2826. Tel: 301-283-2113. FAX: 301-283-2049. E-Mail: accofound@aol.com. Web Site: www.acc.keek.org. *Librn*, Clara Moran
Library Holdings: Bk Vols 2,600; Per Subs 20

ADELPHI

S US ARMY RESEARCH LABORATORY, Technical Library, 2800 Powder Mill Rd, 20783-1197. SAN 306-7963. Tel: 301-394-2536. FAX: 301-394-1465. E-Mail: libraryALC@arl.army.mil. *Chief Librn*, Barbara L McLaughlin; *Tech Servs*, Louise McGovern; Staff 8 (MLS 5, Non-MLS 3)
Library Holdings: Bk Vols 36,000; Per Subs 800
Subject Interests: Chemistry, Economics, Electrical engineering, Electronics, Mechanical engineering
Special Collections: DOD Publications
Partic in Dialog Corporation; OCLC Online Computer Library Center, Inc; SDC Info Servs
Special Services for the Deaf - Staff with knowledge of sign language

ANDREWS AFB

AM UNITED STATES AIR FORCE, Malcolm Grow Medical Center Library, 1050 W Perimeter Rd, Bldg 1053, 20762-6600. SAN 337-0860. Tel: 240-857-2354. FAX: 240-857-8608. *Librn*, Dr Imsoon Kim; E-Mail: imsoon.kim@m9mc.af.mil
Founded 1958
Library Holdings: Bk Vols 8,000; Per Subs 285
Partic in Fedlink; OCLC Online Computer Library Center, Inc

ANNAPOLIS

S ARINC, INC LIBRARY,* 2551 Riva Rd, 21401. SAN 306-798X. Tel: 410-266-4622, Ext 4168. FAX: 410-573-3315. E-Mail: cmb@arinc.com. *Librn*, Carol Bowman
Founded 1966
Library Holdings: Bk Vols 2,000; Per Subs 100
Subject Interests: Aviation
Publications: Monthly library bulletin

GL ANNE ARUNDEL COUNTY CIRCUIT COURT, Law Library, Court House, 7 Church Circle, PO Box 2395, 21404-2395. SAN 321-7701. Tel: 410-222-1387. FAX: 410-268-9762. E-Mail: lawlibaa@clark.net. *Librn*, Joan Bellistri; Staff 2 (MLS 1, Non-MLS 1)
Jul 1999-Jun 2000 Income $185,118. Mats Exp $178,445
Library Holdings: Bk Vols 18,077; Bk Titles 1,865; Per Subs 30
Special Collections: Law (Maryland Coll)
Restriction: Open to public for reference only
Partic in Am Asn of Law Librs; Capcon Library Network; Law Libr Asn of Md

M ANNE ARUNDEL MEDICAL CENTER LIBRARY,* 64 Franklin St, 21401. SAN 306-7998. Tel: 410-267-1562. FAX: 410-267-1561. *Librn*, Joyce Cortright Miller
Founded 1970
Library Holdings: Bk Vols 4,000; Per Subs 160
Partic in Dialog Corporation; National Library Of Medicine, Medlars

S THE CAPITAL NEWSPAPER LIBRARY,* PO Box 911, 21404. SAN 373-4595. Tel: 410-268-5000, Ext 3516. FAX: 410-280-5953. *Mgr*, Janice C Wolod
Special Collections: Newspapers 1976-present

S CENTER FOR PUBLIC JUSTICE LIBRARY, 2444 Solomon's Island Rd, Ste 201, 21401. SAN 376-1789. Tel: 410-571-6300. FAX: 410-571-6365. E-Mail: inquiries@cpjustice.org. *Pres*, James W Skillen
Founded 1977
Library Holdings: Bk Vols 3,000; Per Subs 10

S HISTORIC ANNAPOLIS FOUNDATION RESEARCH CENTER, William Paca House, 186 Prince George St, 21401. (Mail add: 18 Pinkney St, 21401), Tel: 410-263-5553, 410-267-7619. FAX: 410-267-6189. Web Site: www.annapolis.org. *In Charge*, Dan Sams; E-Mail: samsd@annapolis.org
1999-2000 Mats Exp Books $400
Library Holdings: Bk Titles 500
Subject Interests: Architecture, Historic preservation, Maryland, Photogs
Special Collections: Annapolis Related Publications, govt & private; Modern & Historic Photographs of Annapolis, 1983 architectural survey of Annapolis Historic District
Restriction: Open to public for reference only
Branches:
WILLIAM PACA-GARDEN CONSERVATION CENTER, One Martin St, 21401. SAN 329-3904. Tel: 410-267-6656. FAX: 410-267-6189. Web Site: www.annapolis.org.
Library Holdings: Bk Titles 500
Subject Interests: Horticulture, Landscape architecture

S IIT RESEARCH INSTITUTE, Technical Information Services, Joint Spectrum Ctr, 185 Admiral Cochrane Dr, 21401-7388. SAN 306-8021. Tel: 410-573-7075. FAX: 410-573-7403. E-Mail: library@jsc.mil. *Mgr*, Mary Fitzpatrick
Founded 1962
Library Holdings: Bk Vols 150,000; Per Subs 200
Subject Interests: Electronics, Software engineering
Special Collections: ADA/Object-Oriented Systems; EMC Coll, bk, fiche, paper, diskette; Military Publications, paper; R&D Reports, paper, fiche; Spectrum Signatures, paper
Publications: Information Center Bulletin
Restriction: Not open to public
Partic in Aerospace Res Info Network; Defense Technical Information Center; Dialog Corporation; Fedlink; Interlibrary Users Association; OCLC Online Computer Library Center, Inc

GL MARYLAND DEPARTMENT OF LEGISLATIVE SERVICES LIBRARY,* 90 State Circle, 21401. SAN 306-8048. Tel: 410-946-5400. FAX: 410-946-5405. E-Mail: libr@mlis.state.md.us. *Coordr*, Lynda C Davis; *Coll Develop, Tech Servs*, Lynda S Cunningham; Staff 11 (MLS 11)
Founded 1966
1997-1998 Mats Exp $248,000, Books $195,000, Per/Ser (Incl. Access Fees) $53,000
Library Holdings: Bk Vols 80,000; Per Subs 300
Subject Interests: State government
Special Collections: Codes of Fifty States; Maryland County & City Codes; Maryland History; State Publications
Automation Activity & Vendor Info: (Acquisitions) EOS; (Cataloging) EOS; (Serials) EOS
Publications: Maryland Documents
Restriction: Open to public for reference only
Partic in OCLC Online Computer Library Center, Inc
Special Services for the Deaf - TTY machine

§G MARYLAND DEPARTMENT OF NATURAL RESOURCES LIBRARY, IRC, B-3, 580 Taylor Ave, 21401. Tel: 410-260-8830. FAX: 410-260-8951. Web Site: www.dnr.state.md.us-irc. *Dir Libr Serv*, Cecelia Petro; E-Mail: cpetro@dnr.state.md.us
Library Holdings: Bk Vols 4,500; Bk Titles 4,000

G MARYLAND STATE ARCHIVES LIBRARY,* 350 Rowe Blvd, 21401. SAN 306-803X. Tel: 410-974-3915. FAX: 410-974-3895. E-Mail: archives@mdarchives.state.md.us. Web Site: www.mdarchives.state.md.us. *Librn*, Christine E Alvey; E-Mail: christia@mdarchives.state.md.us
Founded 1935
Library Holdings: Bk Titles 16,000; Per Subs 125
Subject Interests: Genealogy, History, Maryland, Natural resources
Special Collections: Archives; County & Municipal Reports; Laws of Maryland; Maryland House & Senate Journals; Maryland State Publications & Reports; Public Documents; Work Project Administration Historical Records Survey Publications

GL MARYLAND STATE LAW LIBRARY,* Courts of Appeal Bldg, 361 Rowe Blvd, 21401-1697. SAN 306-8064. Tel: 410-260-1430. FAX: 410-974-2063. E-Mail: mdlaw.library@courts.state.md.us. Web Site: www.lawlib.state.md.us. *Dir*, Michael S Miller; *Cat*, Joanne She; *Doc, ILL*, Shirley Aronson; Staff 10 (MLS 5, Non-MLS 5)
Founded 1826
Jul 1998-Jun 1999 Income $1,200,000. Mats Exp $500,000. Sal $700,000
Library Holdings: Bk Vols 420,000; Bk Titles 75,000; Per Subs 700
Subject Interests: Genealogy, Maryland, State government
Special Collections: Audubon's Birds of America Coll; Early Maryland Newspapers-1745 to date, bk, micro; Maryland Court of Appeals & Maryland Court of Special Appeals Coll, records & briefs
Automation Activity & Vendor Info: (Acquisitions) Innovative Interfaces Inc.; (Cataloging) Innovative Interfaces Inc.; (OPAC) Innovative Interfaces Inc.; (Serials) Innovative Interfaces Inc.
Partic in OCLC Online Computer Library Center, Inc; Westlaw
Special Services for the Deaf - TTY machine

P PUBLIC LIBRARY ASSOCIATION OF ANNAPOLIS & ANNE ARUNDEL COUNTY, INC, 5 Harry S Truman Pkwy, 21401. SAN 343-7469. Tel: 410-222-7371. Interlibrary Loan Service Tel: 410-222-1750. TDD: 410-222-4516, 410-222-4517. FAX: 410-222-7188. Web Site: www.aacpl.net. *Adminr*, Ronald S Kozlowski; Tel: 410-222-7234, E-Mail: rsk@mail.aacpl.net; *Branch Mgr, Publ Servs*, David C Marshall; Tel: 410-222-7235, E-Mail: dmarshal@mail.aacpl.net; *Tech Servs*, John F McGarty; Tel: 410-222-7091, E-Mail: jmcgarty@mail.aacpl.net; *Circ*, Nancy Choice; Tel: 410-222-7287, E-Mail: nchoice@mail.aacpl.net; *Outreach Serv, Ref*, Betty Morganstern; Tel: 410-222-7075, E-Mail: bmorgans@mail.aacpl.net; *Business*, Scott A Sedmak; Tel: 410-222-7236, E-Mail: ssedmak@mail.aacpl.net; *Materials Manager*, Susan Schmidt; Tel: 410-222-7075, E-Mail: sschmidt@mail.aacpl.net; Staff 254 (MLS 52, Non-MLS 202)
Founded 1936. Pop 485,800; Circ 4,959,837
Jul 1999-Jun 2000 Income $14,584,083, State $1,736,214, Federal $48,107, County $11,172,000, Locally Generated Income $615,583, Other $1,012,179. Mats Exp $13,759,111. Sal $10,213,827
Library Holdings: Bk Vols 1,063,760; Bk Titles 194,349
Subject Interests: Maryland
Automation Activity & Vendor Info: (Circulation) DRA
Database Vendor: DRA
Publications: Library Happenings; Seniors Brochure; Small Business Handbook; Staff Newsletter; Story Time; Welcome Flyer
Special Services for the Deaf - TDD
Branches: 15
ANNAPOLIS BRANCH, 1410 West St, 21401. SAN 343-7493. Tel: 410-222-1750. FAX: 410-222-1116. Web Site: www.aacpl.net. *Branch Mgr*, Gloria Davis; E-Mail: gdavis@mail.aacpl.net
Library Holdings: Bk Vols 162,800
BROADNECK, 1275 Green Holly Dr, 21401. SAN 343-7507. Tel: 410-222-1905. FAX: 410-222-1908. Web Site: www.aacpl.net. *Mgr*, Susan Herron
BROOKLYN PARK, One E 11th Ave, Baltimore, 21225. SAN 343-7523. Tel: 410-222-6260. FAX: 410-222-6263. Web Site: web.aacpl.net. *Mgr*, David LaPenotiere; E-Mail: dlapenot@mail.aacpl.net
CROFTON BRANCH, 1657 Crofton Centre, Crofton, 21114. SAN 343-7558. Tel: 410-222-7915. FAX: 410-222-7269. Web Site: www.aacpl.net. *Mgr*, Ruby Jaby; E-Mail: rjaby@mail.aacpl.net
EASTPORT-ANNAPOLIS NECK, 269 Hillsmere Dr, 21403. SAN 343-7582. Tel: 410-222-1770. FAX: 410-222-1973. Web Site: www.aacpl.net.

Mgr, Maryann Wetterau; E-Mail: mwettera@mail.aacpl.net
EDGEWATER BRANCH, 25 Stepney Lane, Edgewater, 21037. SAN 371-9758. Tel: 410-222-1538. FAX: 410-222-1543. Web Site: web.aacpl.net. *Branch Mgr*, Marc Gluck; E-Mail: mgluck@mail.aacpl.net
LINTHICUM BRANCH, 400 Shipley Rd, Linthicum, 21090. SAN 343-7647. Tel: 410-222-6265. FAX: 410-222-6269. Web Site: web.aacpl.lib.md.us. *Branch Mgr*, Adam Mazurek; E-Mail: amazurek@mail.aacpl.net
MARYLAND CITY AT RUSSETT, 3501 Russett Common, Laurel, 20724. SAN 343-7671. Tel: 301-725-2390. FAX: 301-498-5749. Web Site: web.aacpl.net. *Branch Mgr*, Michael Gannon
MOUNTAIN ROAD, 4730 Mountain Rd, Pasadena, 21122. SAN 374-5260. Tel: 410-222-6699. FAX: 410-222-6705. Web Site: web.aacpl.lnet. *Branch Mgr*, Jennifer Adams; E-Mail: jadams@mail.aacpl.net
NORTH COUNTY, 1010 Eastway, Glen Burnie, 21061. SAN 343-7701. Tel: 410-222-6270. FAX: 410-222-6276. Web Site: web.aacpl.net. *Branch Mgr*, Wanda Wagner; E-Mail: wwagner@mail.aacpl.net
ODENTON BRANCH, 1270 Odenton Rd, Odenton, 21113. SAN 343-7736. Tel: 410-222-6277. FAX: 410-222-6279. Web Site: web.aacpl.net. *Branch Mgr*, Karen Mansbridge; E-Mail: kmansbri@mail.aacpl.net
PROVINCES, 2624 Annapolis Rd, Rte 175, Severn, 21144. SAN 328-6673. Tel: 410-222-6280. FAX: 410-222-6283. Web Site: web.aacpl.net. *Branch Mgr*, Patricia Ferguson; E-Mail: pferguso@mail.aacpl.net
RIVIERA BEACH, 1130 Duvall Hwy, Pasadena, 21122. SAN 343-7760. Tel: 410-222-6285. FAX: 410-222-6287. Web Site: web.aacpl.net. *Branch Mgr*, Timothy Burall
SEVERNA PARK BRANCH, 45 McKinsey Rd, Severna Park, 21146. SAN 343-7795. Tel: 410-222-6290. FAX: 410-222-6297. Web Site: web.aacpl.net. *Branch Mgr*, Joanne Trepp
SOUTH COUNTY, 5940 Deale-Churchton Rd, Deale, 20751. SAN 343-7825. Tel: 410-222-1925. FAX: 410-222-1910. Web Site: web.aacpl.net. *Branch Mgr*, Patricia Guyton; E-Mail: pguyton@mail.aacpl.net
Bookmobiles: 1. Care-A-Van (homebound service)

C ST JOHN'S COLLEGE, Greenfield Library, 60 College Ave, 21401. (Mail add: PO Box 2800, 21404), SAN 306-8080. Tel: 410-626-2548. FAX: 410-295-6936. Web Site: www.sjca.edu. *Librn*, Lisa Richmond; *Cat*, Marilyn Clune; *Reader Servs*, Cara Sabolcik; Staff 7 (MLS 3, Non-MLS 4)
Founded 1696. Enrl 531; Highest Degree: Master
Library Holdings: Bk Vols 98,245; Per Subs 114
Subject Interests: Classical studies, History of science, Philosophy
Special Collections: Annapolitan Library (Bray Coll, Rev Thomas)
Database Vendor: epixtech, inc.
Partic in Capcon Library Network; OCLC Online Computer Library Center, Inc

C UNITED STATES NAVAL ACADEMY, Nimitz Library, 589 McNair Rd, 21402-5029. SAN 321-3404. Tel: 410-293-6900. Interlibrary Loan Service Tel: 410-293-6959. FAX: 410-293-3669. E-Mail: perkins@usna.edu. Web Site: www.usna.edu. *Librn*, Richard Hume Werking; *Assoc Librn*, John P Cummings; *Spec Coll & Archives*, Susan T Dean; *Acq*, Margaret J Danchik; *Circ*, Lillian Blake; *Ref*, Patricia Patterson; *Cat*, Laura Nauta; *Bibliog Instr*, Madeline Copp; *Archivist*, Gary LaValley; *Electronic Resources*, Deborah Robinson; Staff 19 (MLS 18, Non-MLS 1)
Founded 1845. Enrl 4,000; Fac 550; Highest Degree: Bachelor
Oct 1999-Sep 2000 Income $2,935,135. Mats Exp $927,500, Books $90,000, Per/Ser (Incl. Access Fees) $816,000, Presv $21,500. Sal $1,702,000
Library Holdings: Per Subs 1,721
Subject Interests: Mil sci, Naval hist, Naval sci, Sci-tech
Special Collections: Electricity & Magnetism (Benjamin Coll); Naval History & Seapower; Paine Submarine Coll; Physics (Albert A Michelson Coll); Somers Submarine Coll; Steichen Photography Coll, bks & photogs; United States Navy Manuscript Colls, Naval Acad archives
Automation Activity & Vendor Info: (Acquisitions) Innovative Interfaces Inc.; (Cataloging) Innovative Interfaces Inc.; (Circulation) Innovative Interfaces Inc.; (Course Reserve) Innovative Interfaces Inc.; (ILL) Innovative Interfaces Inc.; (Media Booking) Innovative Interfaces Inc.; (OPAC) Innovative Interfaces Inc.; (Serials) Innovative Interfaces Inc.
Publications: Annual Report; newsletter
Partic in Fedlink; OCLC Online Computer Library Center, Inc

UNITED STATES NAVY
A NAVAL INSTITUTE HISTORY, REFERENCE & PRESERVATION DEPARTMENT LIBRARY, 291 Wood Rd, 21402-5035. SAN 324-1033. Tel: 410-295-1021. FAX: 410-269-7940. Web Site: www.usni.org. *Dir*, Paul Stillwell; *Mgr*, Dawn Stitzel
Library Holdings: Bk Titles 5,500; Per Subs 25
Subject Interests: Military history
Special Collections: Photograph Archives
Photographs of ships, aircraft, personnel, equipment, weapons of US & foreign military services available to the public for a fee; library research available for a fee

ARNOLD

J ANNE ARUNDEL COMMUNITY COLLEGE, Andrew G Truxal Library, 101 College Pkwy, 21012-1895. SAN 306-8110. Tel: 410-541-2211. Interlibrary Loan Service Tel: 410-541-2536. Circulation Tel: 410-541-2238. Reference Tel: 410-541-2456. FAX: 410-541-2652. Web Site: www.aacc.cc.md.us/library. *Actg Dir, Coll Develop, Syst Coordr*, Cynthia Steinhoff; *Ref*, Louise Greene; *Cat, Distance Educ*, Vicki Cone; *Instr*, Amy Krug; Staff 18 (MLS 6, Non-MLS 12)
Founded 1961. Enrl 48,347; Fac 198; Highest Degree: Associate
Library Holdings: Bk Vols 105,000; Per Subs 400
Automation Activity & Vendor Info: (Cataloging) DRA; (Circulation) DRA; (Course Reserve) DRA; (ILL) DRA; (OPAC) DRA; (Serials) DRA
Database Vendor: OCLC - First Search
Partic in OCLC Online Computer Library Center, Inc
Friends of the Library Group

S CHRIS OLSON & ASSOCIATES, Marketing Consultants Library,* 857 Twin Harbor Dr, 21012-1027. SAN 372-0985. Tel: 410-647-6708. FAX: 410-647-0415. Web Site: www.chrisolson.com. *Librn*, Christine A Olson; E-Mail: chris@chrisolson.com
Library Holdings: Bk Vols 475; Per Subs 10
Subject Interests: Graphic art, Marketing
Restriction: Not open to public

BALTIMORE

S ADAMS EXPRESS COMPANY LIBRARY,* 7 Saint Paul St Ste 1140, 21202. SAN 328-6258. Tel: 410-752-5900, Ext 2198. FAX: 410-659-0080. *Librn*, Shirley Madden
Library Holdings: Bk Vols 500; Per Subs 50
Restriction: Not open to public

S ALTERNATIVE PRESS CENTER LIBRARY,* 1443 Gorsuch Ave, PO Box 33109, 21218-0401. SAN 326-5935. Tel: 410-243-2471. FAX: 410-235-5325. E-Mail: altpress@altpress.org. Web Site: www.altpress.org/. *Librn*, Margaret D'Adamo; *Acq*, Leslie Wade; E-Mail: lwade@altpress.org; *Ref*, Charles D'Adamo; E-Mail: cdadamo@altpress.org; *Coll Develop*, Deborah Bors; E-Mail: dbors@altpress.org
Jan 2000-Dec 2000 Income $148,000. Mats Exp $148,000. Sal $81,000
Library Holdings: Bk Titles 2,500; Per Subs 350
Publications: Alternative Press Index (quarterly); Annotations: A Directory of the Periodicals Listed in the Alternative Press Index (biennial)

GL ATTORNEY GENERAL'S OFFICE, Law Library, 200 Saint Paul Pl, 18th flr, 21202. SAN 306-8641. Tel: 410-576-6400. FAX: 410-576-7002. Web Site: www.oag.state.md.us. *Librn*, Beverly Rubenstein; E-Mail: brubenstein@oag.state.md.us; Staff 2 (MLS 1, Non-MLS 1)
Founded 1917
Library Holdings: Bk Vols 25,000; Per Subs 25
Automation Activity & Vendor Info: (Acquisitions) Inmagic, Inc.; (Cataloging) Inmagic, Inc.; (ILL) Inmagic, Inc.; (Serials) Inmagic, Inc.
Publications: Library Brief (newsletter)

J BALTIMORE CITY COMMUNITY COLLEGE, Bard Library, 2901 Liberty Heights Ave, 21215. SAN 343-7973. Tel: 410-462-8400. FAX: 410-462-8233. Web Site: www.bcc.state.md.us. *Dir Libr Serv*, Stephanie Reidy; Staff 5 (MLS 5)
Enrl 3,664; Fac 120
Library Holdings: Bk Vols 72,000; Per Subs 1,500
Subject Interests: Allied health, Electronics, Ethnic studies, Nursing, Technology, Telecommunications
Special Collections: Baltimore Sun & News American Clippings; Black History, fiche; Maryland & Baltimore
Publications: Baltimore Is Best
Departmental Libraries:
HARBOR CAMPUS, 600 E Lombard St, 21202. SAN 374-4574. Tel: 410-986-5490. FAX: 410-986-5476. *Dir*, Stephanie Reidy

G BALTIMORE CITY DEPARTMENT OF LEGISLATIVE, Reference Library,* 626 City Hall, 21202-3468. SAN 306-8196. Tel: 410-396-4730. FAX: 410-396-8483. *Librn*, Sarah Bass; Staff 8 (MLS 4, Non-MLS 4)
Founded 1874
Special Collections: Baltimore City Directories 1796-1964; Baltimore City Ordinances 1774-current; Court Proceedings (Maryland Reports 1780-current); Laws of Maryland 1692-current; Niles Register 1811-1848
Publications: Baltimore Charter; Baltimore City Building & Fire Codes; Baltimore City Code; Baltimore Municipal Handbook; Newsletter (Book Beat); Public Local Laws
Restriction: Open to public for reference only

S BALTIMORE DEVELOPMENT CORP LIBRARY,* 36 S Charles St, Ste 1600, 21201. SAN 374-9681. Tel: 410-837-9305. FAX: 410-547-7211. *In Charge*, Paul Coleianne
Library Holdings: Bk Vols 200; Per Subs 10

SR BALTIMORE HEBREW CONGREGATION, Julius & Doris Myerberg Library, 7401 Park Heights Ave, 21208. Tel: 410-764-1587. FAX: 410-764-7948. Web Site: bhcong.org. *Dir Libr Serv*, Susan F Berman; E-Mail: sberman@bhcong.org; Staff 5 (MLS 4, Non-MLS 1)
Founded 1994
Jul 1999-Jun 2000 Income $16,000, Locally Generated Income $8,000, Other $8,000. Mats Exp $16,000, Books $10,000, AV Equip $1,000, Other Print Mats $4,000, Electronic Ref Mat (Incl. Access Fees) $1,000
Library Holdings: Bk Vols 12,000; Per Subs 30
Subject Interests: Judaica
Database Vendor: Ebsco - EbscoHost
Restriction: Members only
Special Services for the Blind - Bks on cassette

C BALTIMORE HEBREW UNIVERSITY, Joseph Meyerhoff Library, 5800 Park Heights Ave, 21215. SAN 343-7884. Tel: 410-578-6926. Circulation Tel: 410-578-6936. Reference Tel: 410-578-6994. FAX: 410-454-1109. E-Mail: library@bhu.edu. Web Site: www.bhu.edu. *Dir*, Dr Steven Fine; *Head Tech Servs*, Andrew Johnson; E-Mail: ajohnson@bhu.edu; *Head, Info Serv*, Barbara Salit-Mischel; E-Mail: bmischel@bhu.edu; *Head, Cat*, Elaine Mael; E-Mail: emael@bhu.edu; Staff 7 (MLS 3, Non-MLS 4)
Founded 1919. Enrl 1,000; Fac 7; Highest Degree: Doctorate
Jul 2000-Jun 2001 Mats Exp $54,000, Books $38,000, Per/Ser (Incl. Access Fees) $16,000
Library Holdings: Bk Vols 68,000; Bk Titles 55,000; Per Subs 300
Special Collections: Holocaust Video Testimonies; Jewish Heritage Coll; Judaica 16th Century rare books
Automation Activity & Vendor Info: (Cataloging) TLC; (Circulation) TLC; (Course Reserve) TLC; (OPAC) TLC
Partic in Baltimore Acad Libr Consortium

S BALTIMORE INTERNATIONAL COLLEGE, George A Piendak Library, 17 Commerce St, 21202-3230. SAN 373-658X. Tel: 410-752-4710, Ext 137 or 138. FAX: 410-752-6720. *Actg Dir*, Virginia Rodes; E-Mail: vrodes@bcpl.net; *Tech Servs*, Christine Brown; Staff 3 (MLS 2, Non-MLS 1)
Founded 1987. Circ 35,138; Enrl 583
Library Holdings: Bk Vols 12,800; Bk Titles 10,500; Per Subs 230
Special Collections: Video (900)
Automation Activity & Vendor Info: (Cataloging) TLC; (Circulation) Follett
Partic in Maryland Interlibrary Organization

S BALTIMORE METROPOLITAN COUNCIL, Regional Information Center, 2700 Lighthouse Point E, Ste 310, 21224-4774. SAN 306-8692. Tel: 410-732-9570. FAX: 410-732-9488. Web Site: www.baltometro.org/reginfo.htm. *Librn*, Mary A Logan; E-Mail: mlogan@baltometro.org; Staff 2 (MLS 1, Non-MLS 1)
Founded 1963
Library Holdings: Bk Vols 9,500; Bk Titles 8,000; Per Subs 250
Subject Interests: Economics, Environmental studies, Finance, Government, International relations, Transportation, Urban planning
Publications: Acquisitions List
Restriction: By appointment only
Function: Reference services available
Partic in Maryland Interlibrary Organization

S BALTIMORE MUSEUM OF ART, E Kirkbride Miller Art Library, 10 Art Museum Dr, 21218. SAN 306-8218. Tel: 410-396-6317. FAX: 410-396-6562. E-Mail: ltompkins@artbma.org. Web Site: www.artbma.org. *Asst Librn*, Alene D Oestreicher; *Cat*, Karen Mason
Founded 1929
Library Holdings: Bk Vols 47,500; Per Subs 300
Subject Interests: Africa, Art, Decorative arts, Modern art, Photography, Prints
Special Collections: American Decorative Arts; Artists' Books & Artists' Illustrated Books; Cone Libr; Cone, mss & papers; Dunton Papers; Lucas Libr; Small exhibit
Partic in OCLC Online Computer Library Center, Inc; PALINET & Union Library Catalogue of Pennsylvania

S BALTIMORE MUSEUM OF INDUSTRY, Research Center, 1415 Key Hwy, 21230. SAN 371-8581. Tel: 410-727-4808, Ext 109. Reference Tel: 410-727-4808, Ext 109. FAX: 410-727-4869. E-Mail: bmi@charm.net. Web Site: www.charm.net/~bmi. *Archivist, Dir*, Nancy Perlman; Staff 2 (MLS 1, Non-MLS 1)
Library Holdings: Bk Titles 5,000; Per Subs 15; Spec Interest Per Sub 15
Subject Interests: Bus, Indust hist, Social history, Urban studies
Special Collections: Archival & Manuscript Colls; Business & Industry in Baltimore & Environs, audio & visual, bks, flm, negatives, photogs & tapes, vertical files, per & rarebooks, trade catalogues
Publications: Research Center Brochure
Restriction: By appointment only
Function: Reference services available, Research library

S BALTIMORE POLICE DEPARTMENT, Education & Training Division Library,* 210 Guilford Ave, 21202. SAN 306-8234. Tel: 410-396-2518. FAX: 410-783-0935. *Librn*, Betty Roberts
Founded 1978
Library Holdings: Bk Titles 2,000; Per Subs 15
Subject Interests: Law, Law enforcement, Psychology, Sociology
Special Collections: International Police Coll; Legal Reference Materials
Publications: Developing a Police Library; The Police Chief (1979 magazine)
Partic in Md Ill

S BALTIMORE SUN LIBRARY,* 501 N Calvert St, 21278-0001. (Mail add: PO Box 1377, 21278-0001), SAN 306-8242. Tel: 410-332-6255, 410-783-2500 ((TTY)). Toll Free Tel: 800-829-8000. FAX: 410-332-6918. Web Site: www.sunspot.net.; Staff 12 (MLS 7, Non-MLS 5)
Founded 1906. Pop 300; Circ 450,000
Jan 2000-Dec 2000 Mats Exp $36,600, Books $6,000, Per/Ser (Incl. Access Fees) $18,800, Presv $300, Electronic Ref Mat (Incl. Access Fees) $11,500. Sal $50,000
Library Holdings: Bk Vols 5,000; Per Subs 80
Subject Interests: History, Journalism
Special Collections: A Aubrey Bodine Coll, black & white photogs; H L Mencken Clipping Coll; Index to The Evening Sun, 1910-1951, flm; Index to The Sun & Sunday Sun, 1891-1951, flm; John F Kennedy Memorial Coll, flm; Maryland Laws Coll
Automation Activity & Vendor Info: (Cataloging) Inmagic, Inc.; (Serials) Inmagic, Inc.
Database Vendor: Lexis-Nexis
Publications: Inquiry (newsletter, 6 per yr)

S BALTIMORE ZOO, Arthur R Watson Library, Druid Hill Park, 21217. SAN 324-1785. Tel: 410-396-6013, 410-396-6464. FAX: 410-545-7351. *Librn*, Ethel R Hardee; Staff 1 (MLS 1)
Founded 1979
Library Holdings: Bk Vols 3,800; Bk Titles 3,000; Per Subs 50
Subject Interests: Ecology, Natural history, Veterinary medicine, Zoological gardens, Zoology
Publications: Serials holdings list

M BON SECOURS HOSPITAL, Health Science Library,* 2000 W Baltimore St, 21223. SAN 306-8285. Tel: 410-362-3000, Ext 3581. *Librn*, Janice Mason
Founded 1970
Library Holdings: Bk Vols 2,000

SR CARMELITE MONASTERY, Library & Archives,* 1318 Dulaney Valley Rd, 21286-1399. SAN 327-5922. Tel: 410-823-7415. FAX: 410-823-7418. E-Mail: carmelite@erols.com. *Archivist, Librn*, Constance FitzGerald
Library Holdings: Bk Titles 30,000
Subject Interests: Theology
Special Collections: Archives of Oldest Community of Religious Women in 13 Original Colonies (1649-); Durham Coll - Maryland Law Suit (1820-1830); Rare Books from 1582

M CARNEGIE INSTITUTION OF WASHINGTON, Department of Embryology Library,* 115 W University Pkwy, 21210. SAN 375-2690. Tel: 410-467-1414. FAX: 410-243-6311. *Librn*, John Watt
Library Holdings: Bk Vols 800; Per Subs 10

J COMMUNITY COLLEGE OF BALTIMORE COUNTY-CATONSVILLE, Library Services, 800 S Rolling Rd, 21228. SAN 343-7949. Tel: 410-455-4588. Interlibrary Loan Service Tel: 410-455-4581. Interlibrary Loan Service FAX: 410-455-4386. Web Site: www.ccbc.cc.md.us/campuses/cat/library/c_library.htm. *Dir Libr Serv*, Suzanne Hill; *Ref*, Bonita Preston; *Tech Servs*, Sally Armistead; Tel: 410-455-4201; *ILL*, Cheryl Gordon; *Bibliog Instr*, Bonita Preston; *Coll Develop*, Cynthia Roberts; *AV*, Janice Wilcox; *Circ*, Dena Ritter; *Web Coordr*, Barbara Lipsky
Founded 1957. Enrl 10,500; Fac 200; Highest Degree: Associate
Library Holdings: Bk Vols 110,975; Bk Titles 105,740; Per Subs 702
Subject Interests: Criminal law and justice, Mortuary science, Nursing
Automation Activity & Vendor Info: (Acquisitions) Innovative Interfaces Inc.; (Cataloging) Innovative Interfaces Inc.; (Circulation) Innovative Interfaces Inc.; (Course Reserve) Innovative Interfaces Inc.; (ILL) Innovative Interfaces Inc.; (Media Booking) Innovative Interfaces Inc.; (OPAC) Innovative Interfaces Inc.; (Serials) Innovative Interfaces Inc.
Publications: Look, Listen & Read; Now is the Time to Discover Your Library (handbook)
Partic in Maryland Interlibrary Organization; OCLC Online Computer Library Center, Inc; PALINET & Union Library Catalogue of Pennsylvania
Special Services for the Deaf - Captioned media; Videos & decoder
Special Services for the Blind - Audiotape library; Talking book & recordings for the blind catalogs; Variable speed audiotape players; VisualTek
Friends of the Library Group

C COPPIN STATE COLLEGE, Parlett Moore Library, 2500 W North Ave, 21216-3698. SAN 306-8331. Tel: 410-383-5926. FAX: 410-383-5931. *Dir*, Mary Wanza; Tel: 410-383-5930; *Circ*, Alice Smith; Tel: 410-383-5951; *Ref*, Robernette Smith; Tel: 410-383-5955; Staff 13 (MLS 7, Non-MLS 6)
Founded 1900. Fac 111; Highest Degree: Master
1999-2000 Mats Exp $295,871, Books $67,327, Per/Ser (Incl. Access Fees) $118,227, Presv $3,000, AV Equip $12,715, Electronic Ref Mat (Incl. Access Fees) $94,602. Sal $577,866 (Prof $335,724)

Library Holdings: Bk Vols 80,068; Bk Titles 67,159; Per Subs 694
Subject Interests: Biology, Education, Nursing, Social sciences and issues
Special Collections: Black Studies; Maryland
Automation Activity & Vendor Info: (Cataloging) CARL; (Circulation) CARL; (OPAC) CARL; (Serials) CARL
Database Vendor: OCLC - First Search
Partic in Capcon Library Network; Colorado Alliance Of Research Libraries; Maryland Interlibrary Organization; OCLC Online Computer Library Center, Inc; Univ Syst of Md

S CYLBURN ARBORETUM ASSOCIATION LIBRARY, 4915 Greenspring Ave, 21209. SAN 328-1493. Tel: 410-367-2217. FAX: 410-367-8039. *Librn*, Adelaide C Rackemann
Founded 1955
Library Holdings: Bk Titles 2,000; Per Subs 3
Subject Interests: Horticulture
Special Collections: Rock Gardening Coll; Wildflower Coll
Restriction: Members only
Function: Reference only

GM DEPARTMENT OF VETERANS AFFAIRS, Library Service, 10 N Greene St, 21201. SAN 306-8889. Tel: 410-605-7092. FAX: 410-605-7905.; Staff 2 (MLS 1, Non-MLS 1)
Founded 1952
Library Holdings: Bk Vols 15,950; Per Subs 295
Subject Interests: Education, Hospital administration, Medicine, Nursing, Psychiatry, Psychology, Social service (social work)
Partic in Vets Admin Libr Network

GM DEPARTMENT OF VETERANS AFFAIRS-REHABILITATION RESEARCH & DEVELOPMENT SERVICE, Scientific & Technical Publications Section,* 103 S Gay St, 5th flr, 21202-4051. SAN 353-832X. Tel: 410-962-1800. FAX: 410-962-9670.
Founded 1949
Library Holdings: Bk Titles 4,000; Per Subs 158
Subject Interests: Aging
Partic in SE-Atlantic Regional Med Libr Servs

J DUNDALK COMMUNITY COLLEGE LIBRARY,* 7200 Sollers Point Rd, 21222. SAN 306-834X. Tel: 410-285-9640. FAX: 410-285-9559. *Dir*, Mary Landry; *Tech Servs*, Lon Fen Hou; *Media Spec*, Sharon Casey
Library Holdings: Bk Vols 32,000; Per Subs 140
Subject Interests: Counseling, Forestry, Photography
Partic in Maryland Interlibrary Organization

S EASTERN PUMA RESEARCH NETWORK LIBRARY, PO Box 3562, 21214. SAN 371-9197. Tel: 410-254-2517. E-Mail: epuma@flash.net. Web Site: members.xoom.com/eprnnews/information.htm. *Dir*, Dr John A Lutz; *Tech Servs*, Dr Jon Vinroot. Subject Specialists: *Wildlife*, Dr John A Lutz; *Wildlife*, Dr Jon Vinroot
Founded 1983. Circ 15,000; Fac 9; Highest Degree: Bachelor
2000-2001 Mats Exp $37,250, Per/Ser (Incl. Access Fees) $250, Manuscripts & Archives $7,000, Electronic Ref Mat (Incl. Access Fees) $30,000
Library Holdings: Bk Titles 3,000; Per Subs 1,000
Special Collections: Eastern Puma - Fact or Fantasy Coll (eastern cougar, puma, mountain lion, panther, black panther); Private
Publications: Eastern Puma Network News (quarterly)
Special Services for the Deaf - High interest/low vocabulary books; Special interest periodicals
Lectures/Speakers available

P ENOCH PRATT FREE LIBRARY, 400 Cathedral St, 21201-4484. SAN 343-8570. Tel: 410-396-5395, 410-396-5430. FAX: 410-837-0582. Web Site: epf12.epflbalto.org, www.epfl.net. *Dir*, Dr Carla D Hayden; *Asst Dir*, James Welbourne; *Chief Librn, Publ Servs*, Judy Cooper; *Coll Develop, Mgr*, Lynn Stonesifer; *Ch Servs*, Ellen Riordan; *Acq*, Ryan Wilkerson; *ILL*, Sharon Smith; *AV*, Marc Sober; Staff 323 (MLS 149, Non-MLS 174)
Founded 1886. Pop 717,500; Circ 1,518,524
Jul 1999-Jun 2000 Income (Main Library and Branch Library) $28,662,711, State $11,245,596, City $13,011,524, Federal $1,706,710, Other $98,881. Mats Exp $5,195,736, Books $3,574,097, Electronic Ref Mat (Incl. Access Fees) $1,621,639. Sal $13,979,326
Library Holdings: Bk Vols 2,412,009
Special Collections: (Howard Beck Memorial Philatelic Coll); Afro-American; Baltimore Views (Cator Coll); Bookplates (Bevan Coll); Cookery, Gastronomy & Wines (Stieff Coll); Edgar Allan Poe; Greeting Cards, 1870 to date; H L Mencken; Illustrations to 1900 (Chronological Record of Illustrated Books); Insurance (Baltimore Life Underwriters); Job & Career Information; Printed Book; Richard Malcolm Johnston Coll, mss, letters; Stamps; War Posters
Automation Activity & Vendor Info: (Acquisitions) SIRSI; (Circulation) CLSI LIBS
Publications: A Whole New World Computer Workbook; Cator prints; Literacy Resources bibliography; Mencheniana; reference books; selection policies
Partic in Milnet; OCLC Online Computer Library Center, Inc; PALINET & Union Library Catalogue of Pennsylvania
Special Services for the Deaf - Books on deafness & sign language; Captioned media; Special interest periodicals; Staff with knowledge of sign language; TTY machine
Special Services for the Blind - Kurzweil Reading Machine; VisualTek print magnifying machine
Friends of the Library Group
Branches: 27
BOOKMOBILE HEADQUARTERS, 2001 N Wolfe St, 21213. SAN 343-866X. Tel: 410-396-0995. FAX: 410-396-0985. *Librn*, Ann Smith
BROADWAY, 301 N Broadway, 21231-1101. SAN 343-9208. Tel: 410-396-0970. FAX: 410-396-0979. *Branch Mgr*, Rebecca Wenninger; *Librn*, Marilyn Wilson
BROOKLYN, 300 E Patapsco Ave, 21225-1828. SAN 343-8724. Tel: 410-396-1120. FAX: 410-396-1698. *Librn*, Caroline Bahr
CANTON, 1030 S Ellwood Ave, 21224-4930. SAN 343-902X. Tel: 410-396-8545. FAX: 410-396-7491. *In Charge*, Marian Johnson
Friends of the Library Group
CHERRY HILL, 606 Cherry Hill Rd, Ste 100, 21225-1011. SAN 343-947X. Tel: 410-396-1168. FAX: 410-396-1174. *Branch Mgr*, Romaine Chase-Bobbitt
CLIFTON, 2001 N Wolfe St, 21213-1477. SAN 343-950X. Tel: 410-396-0984. FAX: 410-396-0985. *In Charge*, Juanita Pilgrim
DUNDALK AVENUE, 912 Dundalk Ave, 21224-3015. SAN 343-8759. Tel: 410-396-8547. FAX: 410-396-1176. *Librn*, Shirley Johnson
EDMONDSON AVE, 4330 Edmondson Ave, 21229-1615. SAN 343-9232. Tel: 410-396-0946. FAX: 410-396-0947. *Librn*, Virginia Fore
Friends of the Library Group
FELLS POINT, 606 S Ann St, 21231-2908. SAN 343-9054. Tel: 410-396-0992. *In Charge*, Hedy Drummond
Friends of the Library Group
FOREST PARK, 3023 Garrison Blvd, 21216. SAN 343-9267. Tel: 410-396-0942. FAX: 410-396-0945. *Librn*, Madalyn Parks
Friends of the Library Group
GARDENVILLE, 5427 Belair Rd, 21206-4209. SAN 343-8783. Tel: 410-396-8557. FAX: 410-396-7490. *Librn*, Wendy Dobson
Friends of the Library Group
GOVANS, 5714 Bellona Ave, 21212-3508. SAN 343-8813. Tel: 410-396-6098. FAX: 410-396-6291. *Librn*, Helen Blumberg
Friends of the Library Group
HAMILTON, 5910 Harford Rd, 21214-1845. SAN 343-8848. Tel: 410-396-6088. FAX: 410-396-6097. *Librn*, Ann Smith
HAMPDEN, 3641 Falls Rd, 21211-1815. SAN 343-9119. Tel: 410-396-6043. FAX: 410-396-7152. *In Charge*, Victoria Bringman
HERRING RUN, 3801 Erdman Ave, 21213-2099. SAN 343-8872. Tel: 410-396-0996. FAX: 410-396-0997. *Librn*, Jacquelyn Purnell
Friends of the Library Group
HIGHLANDTOWN, 3323 Eastern Ave, 21224-4109. SAN 343-9143. Tel: 410-396-1580. FAX: 410-396-6075. *In Charge*, Anne Stepney
HOLLINS-PAYSON, 31 S Payson St, 21223. SAN 343-9291. Tel: 410-396-8558. FAX: 410-396-0331. *Librn*, Stanley Butler
LIGHT STREET, 1251 Light St, 21230-4305. SAN 343-8902. Tel: 410-396-1096. FAX: 410-396-1097. *Librn*, Rebecca Berkeley
Friends of the Library Group
NORTHWOOD, 4420 Loch Raven Blvd, 21218-1553. SAN 343-8937. Tel: 410-396-6076. FAX: 410-396-6547. *Librn*, Jan Westervelt
Friends of the Library Group
PATTERSON PARK, 158 N Linwood Ave, 21224-1255. SAN 343-8961. Tel: 410-396-0983. FAX: 410-396-5215. *In Charge*, Pat Costello
Friends of the Library Group
PENNSYLVANIA AVENUE, 1531 W North Ave, 21217-1735. SAN 343-9321. Tel: 410-396-0399. FAX: 410-396-0025. *Librn*, Betty Boulware; *Librn*, Ann Marie Davis
Subject Interests: Statistics
PIMLICO, 5001 Park Heights Ave, 21215-5894. SAN 343-9356. Tel: 410-396-8549. FAX: 410-396-0957. *Librn*, Deborah Peterson
Subject Interests: Reading
REISTERSTOWN ROAD, 6310 Reisterstown Rd, 21215-2301. SAN 343-9380. Tel: 410-396-0948. FAX: 410-396-0952. *Librn*, Vincent Steadman
Friends of the Library Group
ROLAND PARK, 5108 Roland Ave, 21210-2132. SAN 343-8996. Tel: 410-396-6099. FAX: 410-396-6116. Web Site: www.pratt.lib.md.us. *Librn*, Katherine Harig; Staff 5 (MLS 2, Non-MLS 3)
Friends of the Library Group
WALBROOK, 3203 W North Ave, 21216-3015. SAN 343-9410. Tel: 410-396-0935. FAX: 410-396-0332. *Librn*, Sylvia Coker
WASHINGTON VILLAGE, 856 Washington Blvd, 21230. SAN 377-6824. Tel: 410-396-1099. FAX: 410-396-1115. Web Site: www.pratt.lib.md.us/branches/wsh. *Mgr*, Subhanallah Ali
Library Holdings: Bk Vols 15,000; Bk Titles 10,000
WAVERLY, 400 E 33rd St, 21218-3401. SAN 343-9445. Tel: 410-396-6053. FAX: 410-396-6150. *Librn*, Linda Schwartz
Friends of the Library Group

J ESSEX COMMUNITY COLLEGE, James A Newpher Library, 7201 Rossville Blvd, 21237. SAN 306-8358. Tel: 410-780-6426. FAX: 410-391-2642. Web Site: www.ccbc.cc.md.us. *Dir*, Taylor Ruhl; *Automation Syst Coordr, Tech Servs*, Debra Sambuco; *Coordr, Publ Servs*, Michele Meisart
Founded 1957. Enrl 12,670; Fac 525

Library Holdings: Bk Vols 95,528; Per Subs 455
Subject Interests: Allied health
Special Collections: Cultural diversity
Publications: Library Information Series, What's New in Media Services
Partic in Dialog Corporation; Maryland Interlibrary Organization; Mil Network

R FAITH PRESBYTERIAN CHURCH LIBRARY, 5400 Loch Raven Blvd, 21239. SAN 306-8366. Tel: 410-435-4330. FAX: 410-433-2066. *In Charge*, Len Knighton; E-Mail: lknigh1987@aol.com
Founded 1951
Library Holdings: Bk Vols 1,000
Subject Interests: Church history, Theology

S FEDERAL RESERVE BANK OF RICHMOND, Baltimore Branch Library,* 502 S Sharp St, 21201. SAN 306-8374. Tel: 410-576-3383, 410-576-3392. FAX: 410-576-3678. E-Mail: e2dlw@rich.frb.org. *Publ Servs*, Gordon Woelper
Founded 1960
Library Holdings: Bk Vols 1,000; Per Subs 25
Subject Interests: Banks and banking, Economics, Maryland, Monetary policy

L FIDELITY & DEPOSIT COMPANY OF MARYLAND, Law Library,* Fidelity Bldg, Rm 302, 210 N Charles St, 21203. SAN 306-8382. Tel: 410-659-3358. FAX: 410-659-3205. *Librn*, T J Ormseth
Founded 1922
Library Holdings: Bk Vols 42,000
Special Collections: Laws of Maryland dating back to 1800
Partic in Westlaw

M FRANKLIN SQUARE HOSPITAL CENTER, Health Sciences Library,* 9000 Franklin Sq Dr, 21237. SAN 306-8390. Tel: 410-682-7000, Ext 7363. FAX: 410-682-7563. *Librn*, Joan Pochciol; E-Mail: joanp@helix.org
Library Holdings: Bk Vols 4,200; Per Subs 225
Subject Interests: Nursing, Obstetrics and gynecology

S GOLDEN RADIO BUFFS OF MARYLAND, INC, GRB Tape Library, 301 Jeanwood Ct, 21222. SAN 375-3794. Tel: 410-477-3051. *Librn*, Billy Bratton
Founded 1975

M GOOD SAMARITAN HOSPITAL, Health Sciences Library,* 5601 Loch Raven Blvd, 21239-2905. SAN 306-8412. Tel: 410-532-3891. FAX: 410-532-5444. *Librn*, Kathleen Curry; E-Mail: kathyc@helix.org
Founded 1968
Library Holdings: Bk Vols 1,408; Per Subs 105
Special Collections: Stroke Club Libr

L GORDON, FEINBLATT, ROTHMAN, HOFFBERGER & HOLLANDER, Law Library, 233 E Redwood St, 21202. SAN 372-1019. Tel: 410-576-4255. FAX: 410-576-4246. Web Site: www.gfrlaw.com. *Librn*, Steven Paul Anderson; E-Mail: sanderson@gfrlaw.com; *Librn*, Jean Bell Hessenauer. Subject Specialists: *Law*, Steven Paul Anderson; Staff 4 (MLS 1, Non-MLS 3)
Library Holdings: Bk Vols 10,000; Bk Titles 1,600; Per Subs 100
Subject Interests: Law
Database Vendor: Lexis-Nexis
Function: ILL available

C GOUCHER COLLEGE, Julia Rogers Library, 1021 Dulaney Valley Rd, 21204. SAN 307-059X. Tel: 410-337-6361. Interlibrary Loan Service Tel: 410-337-6365. Reference Tel: 410-337-6361. FAX: 410-337-6419. E-Mail: jrogers@goucher.edu. Web Site: www.goucher.edu/library. *Librn*, Nancy Magnuson; Tel: 410-337-6364, E-Mail: nmagnuso@goucher.edu; *ILL, Ref Serv*, Deborah McKinney; *Per*, Thomasin LaMay; *Access Serv, Ref Serv*, Randy Smith; *Cat*, Elizabeth Lang Jedlicka; *Acq*, Sharon Hartmann; *Bibliog Instr*, Marjorie Simon; *AV*, Linda Fowble; *Spec Coll*, Sydney Roby; *Coll Develop*, Barbara A Snead; *Info Tech*, Margaret Guccione; Staff 14 (MLS 7, Non-MLS 7)
Founded 1885. Enrl 1,336; Fac 96; Highest Degree: Master
Jul 1999-Jun 2000 Income Parent Institution $1,102,637. Mats Exp $441,726, Books $155,596, Per/Ser (Incl. Access Fees) $272,901, Presv $13,229. Sal $478,358 (Prof $328,847)
Library Holdings: Bk Vols 299,568; Per Subs 1,313
Special Collections: BS Corrin & CI Winslow Political Memorablia & Political Humor Coll; Goucher College Archives; History of Costume; HL Mencken Coll; Jane Austen (Alberta H Burke Coll); JW Bright Coll; Mark Twain (Eugene Oberdorfer Coll); Sara Haardt Coll; Southern Women During the Civil War (Passano Coll)
Automation Activity & Vendor Info: (Acquisitions) Innovative Interfaces Inc.; (Cataloging) Innovative Interfaces Inc.; (Circulation) Innovative Interfaces Inc.; (OPAC) Innovative Interfaces Inc.
Database Vendor: Ebsco - EbscoHost, IAC - SearchBank, Lexis-Nexis, OCLC - First Search, ProQuest, Wilson - Wilson Web
Publications: Focus (Friends of Library Newsletter) (Newsletter); Goucher Library News; Special Collections Guides
Partic in Baltimore Acad Libr Consortium; OCLC Online Computer Library Center, Inc; PALINET & Union Library Catalogue of Pennsylvania
Friends of the Library Group

S GRAY, KIRK & VANSANT, INC LIBRARY, World Trade Ctr, 401 E Pratt St, 21202. SAN 306-8862. Tel: 410-539-5400. FAX: 410-234-2512. *Dir*, Kelly Ryan
Library Holdings: Bk Titles 100; Per Subs 300
Subject Interests: Advertising, Marketing

M GREATER BALTIMORE MEDICAL CENTER, John E Savage Medical Library,* 6701 N Charles St, 21204. SAN 306-8420. Tel: 410-828-2530. FAX: 410-828-2664. E-Mail: library@gbmc.org. *AV, Mgr*, Deborah Thomas; Staff 1 (MLS 1)
Founded 1965
Jul 1996-Jun 1997 Income $250,000. Mats Exp $106,991, Books $20,000, Per/Ser (Incl. Access Fees) $37,000, Presv $4,300, Micro $44,691, AV Equip $1,000. Sal $87,000 (Prof $51,000)
Library Holdings: Bk Vols 1,500
Subject Interests: Obstetrics and gynecology, Ophthalmology, Otolaryngology
Publications: Acquisitions List

M HARBOR HOSPITAL CENTER, Health Sciences Library, 3001 S Hanover, 21225-1290. SAN 306-8781. Tel: 410-350-3419. FAX: 410-350-2032. *Librn*, Shirley Lay; E-Mail: shirleyslay@medstar.net; Staff 2 (MLS 1, Non-MLS 1)
Founded 1913
Library Holdings: Bk Vols 2,600; Per Subs 160
Subject Interests: Internal medicine, Obstetrics and gynecology, Surgery
Special Collections: Education Media Coll
Publications: Newsletter (quarterly)
Partic in MAHSL; Nat Libr of Med
Friends of the Library Group

S HENRY LEE MOON LIBRARY & CIVIL RIGHTS ARCHIVES, NAACP National Civil Rights Archives,* 4805 Mount Hope Dr, 21215-3297. SAN 374-8669. Tel: 410-358-8900. FAX: 410-358-3818. *Librn*, James Murray
Library Holdings: Bk Vols 1,500; Per Subs 10

S JEWISH MUSEUM OF MARYLAND LIBRARY,* 15 Lloyd St, 21202. SAN 326-6028. Tel: 410-732-6400. FAX: 410-732-6451. Web Site: www.jhsm.org. *Archivist*, Virginia North; Staff 1 (MLS 1)
Founded 1960
Library Holdings: Bk Titles 3,000; Per Subs 20
Special Collections: Dr Louis L Kaplan Papers; Friedenwald Family Papers; Henrietta Szold Coll, journals, speeches & writings; HIAS Records (Holocaust Survivors & Relatives of Holocaust Victims); Maryland Jewry Rare Bk Coll; Robert L Weinberg Family History Center; World War I & II (Jacob Beser & Family Coll); Yiskor (Memorial) Books; Zionism (Dr Herman Seidel Papers)
Restriction: Non-circulating to the public

M JOHNS HOPKINS BAYVIEW MEDICAL CENTER, Harold E Harrison Medical Library, 4940 Eastern Ave, 21224-2780. SAN 306-817X. Tel: 410-550-0678. FAX: 410-550-2465. *Dir Libr Serv*, Linda Gorman; Staff 4 (MLS 1, Non-MLS 3)
Founded 1958
Library Holdings: Bk Vols 2,000; Per Subs 320
Partic in Maryland Interlibrary Organization
Friends of the Library Group

CM JOHNS HOPKINS HOSPITAL, Wilmer Ophthalmological Institute, Jonas S Friedenwald Library,* 600 N Wolfe St, 21287-9105. SAN 343-8309. Tel: 410-955-3127. FAX: 410-955-0046. *Librn*, Michael Piorunski; E-Mail: mpioruns@welchlink.welch.jhu.edu
Founded 1925
Jul 1997-Jun 1998 Income $100,000. Mats Exp $40,000. Sal $50,000
Library Holdings: Bk Titles 10,000; Per Subs 115
Subject Interests: History of medicine, Ophthalmology
Special Collections: History of Medicine (Wilmer Coll), rare bks; Ophthalmological Drawings (Annette Burgess Art Coll), original art

JOHNS HOPKINS UNIVERSITY LIBRARIES

JOHN WORK GARRETT LIBRARY, Evergreen House, 4545 N Charles St, 21210. SAN 343-8066. Tel: 410-516-5571. FAX: 410-516-7202. Web Site: archives.mse.jhu.edu:8000. *Librn*, Bett Miller; E-Mail: bmiller@jhu.edu
Library Holdings: Bk Vols 28,670
Special Collections: 17th Century Maryland (Books Printed Before 1700 Relating to Maryland); Architecture (Laurence H Fowler Coll); Bibles (Hoffmann Coll); Incunabula; Literature, Travel & Exploration, Natural History; Rare Books
Restriction: By appointment only
Mem of Asn of Research Libraries
Administered by Milton S Eisenhower Library, Special Collections

GEORGE PEABODY LIBRARY, 17 E Mount Vernon Pl, 21202. SAN 343-8635. Tel: 410-659-8179. FAX: 410-659-8137. Web Site: archives.mse.jhu.edu:8000. *Librn*, Carolyn Smith; E-Mail: carolyn.smith@jhu.edu

Founded 1857
Library Holdings: Bk Vols 252,277; Per Subs 30; Spec Interest Per Sub 30
Subject Interests: Art and architecture, British hist, Decorative arts, Geography, Maps, Religion, Travel
Special Collections: Cervantes: Editions of Don Quixote
Mem of Asn of Research Libraries
Became part of Milton S Eisenhower Library Special Collections by transfer 1982; Open Mon-Fri 9-3

CM ABRAHAM M LILIENFELD MEMORIAL LIBRARY, School of Hygiene & Public Health, 624 N Broadway, 9th flr, 21205-1901. SAN 343-8090. Tel: 410-955-3028. FAX: 410-955-0200. Web Site: www.welch.jhu.edu. *Mgr*, Donna D Hesson; *Circ*, Lavinia Wiggs; *Circ*, Michelle Moody
Founded 1963
Library Holdings: Bk Vols 32,000; Per Subs 174
Publications: Library Bulletin (quarterly)
Mem of Asn of Research Libraries
Partic in OCLC Online Computer Library Center, Inc; RLIN
Friends of the Library Group

MILTON S EISENHOWER LIBRARY, 3400 N Charles St, 21218. SAN 343-8031. Tel: 410-516-8325. Circulation Tel: 410-516-8370. FAX: 410-516-5080. Web Site: milton.mse.jhu.edu:8001. *Dean*, James G Neal; Tel: 410-516-8328, E-Mail: jneal@jhu.edu; *Curator*, Cynthia Requardt; Tel: 410-516-5493, E-Mail: cynthia.requardt@jhu.edu; *ILL*, Deborah Slingluff; Staff 51 (MLS 39, Non-MLS 12)
Founded 1876. Enrl 13,137; Fac 1,042; Highest Degree: Doctorate
Jul 1999-Jun 2000 Income $14,630,872. Mats Exp $7,470,891. Sal $4,741,121
Library Holdings: Bk Vols 2,560,917; Per Subs 17,209
Special Collections: 17th Century English Literature; 19th & 20th Century American; Economic Classics (Hutzler Coll); Edmund Spenser (Tudor & Stuart Club Coll); French Drama (Couet Coll); German Literature (Kurrelmeyer Coll); Lord Byron; Louis Zukofsky; Manuscripts, including Sidney Lanier, Francis Lieber, D C Gilman, John Banister Tabb, Edward Lucas White, Arthur O Lovejoy Coll; Modern German Drama (Loewenberg Coll); Sheet Music (Levy Coll); Slavery (Birney Coll); Southey (Havens Coll); Trade Unions (Barnett Coll)
Automation Activity & Vendor Info: (Acquisitions) epixtech, inc.; (Cataloging) epixtech, inc.; (Circulation) epixtech, inc.
Publications: Ex Libris
Function: Research library
Partic in Asn of Research Libraries; Baltimore Acad Libr Consortium; Chesapeake Info & Res Libr Alliance; Maryland Interlibrary Organization; Md Independent Cols & Univs Alliance; Md Libr Asn; PALINET & Union Library Catalogue of Pennsylvania
Open Mon-Sat 8-12, Sun 10-12
Friends of the Library Group

CM WILLIAM H WELCH MEDICAL LIBRARY, 1900 E Monument St, 21205-2113. SAN 343-8155. Tel: 410-955-3411. Interlibrary Loan Service Tel: 410-955-3418. FAX: 410-955-0985. E-Mail: csk@welch.jhmi.edu, library@welch.jhu.edu. Web Site: www.welch.jhu.edu. *Actg Dir*, Jayne M Campbell; *Assoc Dir*, Chung Sook Kim; Tel: 410-955-4938, Fax: 410-955-4695; *Assoc Dir*, Barbara M Koehler; Tel: 410-614-2786, Fax: 410-955-4695, E-Mail: bmk@jhmi.edu; *Asst Dir*, Chung Sook Kim; Tel: 410-614-6801, E-Mail: koliver@jhmi.edu
Founded 1929
Jul 1998-Jun 1999 Income $5,026,452. Mats Exp $1,034,614, Books $129,542, Per/Ser (Incl. Access Fees) $875,521, Presv $29,551. Sal $2,329,560 (Prof $1,007,768)
Library Holdings: Bk Vols 387,494; Per Subs 2,451
Subject Interests: Genetics, History of medicine, Medicine
Special Collections: AV Coll; History of Nursing (Florence Nightingale Coll); History of the Diseases of the Chest & Vaccination (Henry Jacobs Coll); Medical Education, software
Mem of Asn of Research Libraries
Partic in BRS; Dialog Corporation; Nat Libr of Med; OCLC Online Computer Library Center, Inc; PALINET & Union Library Catalogue of Pennsylvania
The Welch Medical Library maintains four satellite libraries to provide distributed services throughout the John Hopkins medical institutions; Psychiatry/Neurosciences Library, core collection in psychiatry, neurology & neurosurgery; Williams & Wilkins Information Resources Center, a study & learning center for medical students with course reserve materials, audiovisual equipment, microcomputers & computer-assisted instructional programs; Nursing Information Resource Center, a study & learning center for medical students

S JOHNS HOPKINS UNIVERSITY-PEABODY CONSERVATORY OF MUSIC, Arthur Friedheim Library, One E Mount Vernon Pl, 21202. SAN 343-8511. Tel: 410-659-8255. FAX: 410-685-0657. E-Mail: quist@peabody.jhu.edu, urs@peabody.jhu.edu. Web Site: www.peabody.jhu.edu/lib/. *Librn*, Edwin A Quist; Staff 5 (MLS 3, Non-MLS 2)
Founded 1866. Enrl 580; Fac 70; Highest Degree: Doctorate
Jul 1998-Jun 1999 Income $373,266. Mats Exp $76,206, Books $25,127, Per/Ser (Incl. Access Fees) $37,020, Presv $7,663, AV Equip $6,396. Sal $199,489 (Prof $115,895)
Library Holdings: Bk Vols 101,874; Per Subs 240
Subject Interests: Dance, Music
Special Collections: Asgar Hamerik & Gustav Strube Coll, mss, published works; Barringer Jazz Coll; Brick Fleagle/Luther Henderson Coll of Jazz Recordings; Franz Bornschein, George Boyle, Louis Cheslock, Robert L Paul, Ronald Roxbury, Bernhard Scholz, Howard Thatcher, Timothy Spelman, Vladimir Padwa & W L Hubbard Colls; Friedman Record Coll; John Charles Thomas & Enrico Caruso Coll; Joseph Schillinger Papers
Partic in Maryland Interlibrary Organization
Friends of the Library Group

M THE KENNEDY KRIEGER INSTITUTE, Training Administration & Information Resources,* 707 N Broadway, 21205. SAN 306-8447. Tel: 410-502-9245, 410-502-9447. FAX: 410-502-9084. E-Mail: hoofnagle@kennedykrieger.org. *Dir*, Bettea J Hoofnagle; Staff 5 (MLS 2, Non-MLS 3)
Founded 1968
Library Holdings: Bk Vols 4,500; Per Subs 98
Subject Interests: Cerebral palsy, Learning disabilities, Mentally retarded
Partic in Capcon Library Network; OCLC Western Service Center

L LEGAL AID BUREAU, INC, Central Library,* 500 E Lexington St, 21202. SAN 323-617X. Tel: 410-539-5340, Ext 6300. FAX: 410-539-1710. *Librn*, Frances Moody
Library Holdings: Bk Vols 25,000; Bk Titles 1,375; Per Subs 55
Subject Interests: Administrative law

L LIBRARY COMPANY OF THE BALTIMORE BAR, 100 N Calvert St, Rm 618, 21202-1723. SAN 306-8455. Tel: 410-727-0280. FAX: 410-685-4791. Web Site: www.barlib.org. *Librn*, Kai-Yun Chiu; E-Mail: kychiu@barlib.org; *Asst Librn*, Joseph W Bennett; E-Mail: jwbennett@barlib.org; *Tech Servs*, Barbara E Karpel; E-Mail: bkarpel@barlib.org; Staff 3 (MLS 2, Non-MLS 1)
Founded 1840
Oct 1999-Sep 2000 Income $792,800, City $503,300, Locally Generated Income $289,500. Mats Exp $746,400, Books $343,300, Presv $6,600, Micro $6,000, Electronic Ref Mat (Incl. Access Fees) $50,500. Sal $194,900
Library Holdings: Bk Vols 200,000; Per Subs 314
Subject Interests: Law
Publications: Bar Library Advance Sheet
Restriction: Members only
Partic in Capcon Library Network; PALINET & Union Library Catalogue of Pennsylvania

S LOCKHEED MARTIN NE&SS-MARINE SYSTEMS, Information Center MP44, 2323 Eastern Blvd, 21220-4207. Tel: 410-682-1574. FAX: 410-682-1710. *Librn*, Deborah C Isenhart; E-Mail: deborah.isenhart@lmco.com
Founded 1981
1999-2000 Mats Exp $150,000
Library Holdings: Bk Titles 7,300; Per Subs 65
Subject Interests: Defense, Missiles, Weapons systs
Database Vendor: Dialog, Lexis-Nexis
Restriction: Company staff only
Partic in Capcon Library Network

CR LOYOLA-NOTRE DAME LIBRARY, INC, 200 Winston Ave, 21212. SAN 306-8463. Tel: 410-532-8787. Circulation Tel: 410-532-8787, Ext 101. Reference Tel: 410-532-8787, Ext 117. FAX: 410-532-6130. Web Site: www.loyola.edu/library. *Dir*, John W McGinty; Tel: 410-532-6895, E-Mail: jmcginty@ndm.edu; *Asst Dir*, Jack G Ray; *Media Spec*, Philip Fryer; *Circ*, Gail Breyer; *Cat*, Jim Seamans; *ILL*, Ginnie Smack-Harper; *Ref*, Laurel Yatsko; *Acq*, Joseph Turkos; *ILL*, Virginia Harper; *Bibliog Instr*, Susan Cooperstein; *Web Coordr*, Jane Birch; Staff 29 (MLS 12, Non-MLS 17)
Founded 1973. Enrl 9,250; Highest Degree: Doctorate
Jul 1999-Jun 2000 Income $3,357,112, Locally Generated Income $112,836, Parent Institution $3,244,276. Mats Exp $3,083,202, Books $554,707, Per/Ser (Incl. Access Fees) $505,403, Presv $22,972, AV Equip $102,238, Electronic Ref Mat (Incl. Access Fees) $55,495. Sal $1,017,721 (Prof $561,039)
Library Holdings: Bk Vols 340,200; Bk Titles 291,500; Per Subs 2,126
Special Collections: Book Decoration (Henry A Knott Fore-Edge; English Literature (Gerard Manley Hopkins Coll), bks, per; Painting Coll)
Automation Activity & Vendor Info: (Acquisitions) CARL; (Cataloging) CARL; (Circulation) CARL; (OPAC) CARL; (Serials) CARL
Database Vendor: CARL, Ebsco - EbscoHost, IAC - Info Trac, Lexis-Nexis, OCLC - First Search, Silverplatter Information Inc.
Publications: Loyola-Notre Dame Library News
Partic in Maryland Interlibrary Organization; PALINET & Union Library Catalogue of Pennsylvania

S MARYLAND COMMITTEE FOR CHILDREN, INC, Peggy Moses Hecht Library, 608 Water St, 21202. SAN 327-3407. Tel: 410-752-7588. FAX: 410-752-6286. E-Mail: mcc@mdchildcare.org. Web Site: www.mdchildcare.org. *Librn*, Mary E K Wharton
Library Holdings: Bk Titles 2,600
Restriction: Non-circulating to the public

G MARYLAND DEPARTMENT OF PLANNING LIBRARY, 301 W Preston St, Rm 1101, 21201-2365. SAN 306-8498. Tel: 410-767-4458, 410-767-4500. FAX: 410-767-4480. Web Site: www.op.state.md.us/info/lib/html. *Librn*, Helene W Jeng; E-Mail: helene@mail.op.state.md.us

Founded 1959
Jan 2001-Dec 2001 Mats Exp $13,000, Books $4,000, Per/Ser (Incl. Access Fees) $9,000. Sal $66,000 (Prof $39,000)
Library Holdings: Bk Titles 9,800; Per Subs 160
Subject Interests: Census, Housing, Land use, Planning, Zoning
Special Collections: Maryland Counties & Municipalities Central Depository of Plans
Publications: Acquisitions list (quarterly)

MARYLAND GENERAL HOSPITAL
M MEDICAL STAFF LIBRARY, 827 Linden Ave, 21201. SAN 343-8333. Tel: 410-225-8383. FAX: 410-225-8119. E-Mail: mghlib@earthlink.net. *Librn*, Monica Yang
Library Holdings: Bk Vols 1,500; Per Subs 72

S MARYLAND HISTORICAL SOCIETY LIBRARY, 201 W Monument St, 21201. SAN 321-4508. Tel: 410-685-3750. Reference Tel: 410-685-3750, Ext 359. FAX: 410-962-0487. Web Site: www.library@mdhs.org.
Founded 1844
Library Holdings: Bk Titles 60,000; Per Subs 250
Subject Interests: Maryland
Special Collections: Historic Prints & Photographs, mss, maps, ephemera & broadsides

C MARYLAND INSTITUTE COLLEGE OF ART, Decker Library, 1401 Mount Royal Ave, 21217. SAN 306-851X. Tel: 410-225-2304, 410-225-2311. FAX: 410-225-2316. Web Site: www.mica.edu. *Dir*, Marjorie Chenoweth; *ILL, Ref*, Irma Sangiamo; *Circ*, Mary Anne Rosinsky; *Cat*, Virginia Forni; *Ref*, Jane Spottheim; Staff 7 (MLS 3, Non-MLS 4)
Founded 1826. Enrl 1,012; Highest Degree: Master
Library Holdings: Bk Vols 51,000; Bk Titles 43,000; Per Subs 300
Subject Interests: Art and architecture
Friends of the Library Group

S MARYLAND PHARMACISTS ASSOCIATION LIBRARY,* Kelly Memorial Bldg, 650 W Lombard St, 21201-1572. SAN 327-814X. Tel: 410-727-0746. FAX: 410-727-2253. E-Mail: mpha@esols.com. *Exec Dir*, Howard Schiff
Library Holdings: Bk Titles 1,000; Per Subs 40
Restriction: By appointment only

M MARYLAND REHABILITATION CENTER, R C Thompson Resource Library, 2301 Argonne Dr, 21218. SAN 327-8522. Tel: 410-554-9255. *In Charge*, T Clinton Williams; Staff 1 (Non-MLS 1)
Founded 1973
Jul 1998-Jun 1999 Income (Main Library Only) $5,000
Library Holdings: Bk Titles 5,000; Per Subs 20; Bks on Deafness & Sign Lang 20
Special Collections: Disability Coll, film/v-tapes
Publications: Limited annotated feature film bibliography; limited annotated film/video documentary bibliography; limited film/videography supplements
Special Services for the Blind - Braille; Cassettes; Large print bks; Talking Books
Open Mon-Fri after 2:30 for limited library service

P MARYLAND STATE DEPARTMENT OF EDUCATION, Division of Library Development & Services, 200 W Baltimore St, 21201-2595. SAN 343-8392. Tel: 410-767-0434. FAX: 410-333-2507. Web Site: www.msde.state.md.us/lds. *State Librn*, J Maurice Travillian
1998-1999 Income $1,858,603, State $1,247,272, Federal $611,331. Sal $337,364 (Prof $400,294)
Branches: 1
LIBRARY FOR THE BLIND & PHYSICALLY HANDICAPPED
See Separate Entry

G MARYLAND STATE HIGHWAY ADMINISTRATION LIBRARY,* 707 N Calvert St, Rm 603C, 21202. SAN 306-8536. Tel: 410-545-5553. FAX: 410-209-5019. *Dir*, William Barnard; Staff 2 (MLS 1, Non-MLS 1)
Founded 1965
Library Holdings: Bk Vols 10,000; Per Subs 175
Subject Interests: Electrical engineering
Publications: Newsletter
Open Mon-Fri 8-4:30

P MARYLAND STATE LIBRARY FOR THE BLIND & PHYSICALLY HANDICAPPED, 415 Park Ave, 21201-3603. SAN 306-8544. Tel: 410-230-2424. Toll Free Tel: 800-964-9209. TDD: 800-934-2541, 410-333-8679. FAX: 410-333-2095. E-Mail: recept@lbph.lib.md.us. Web Site: www.lbph.lib.md.us. *Dir*, Sharron McFarland; E-Mail: smcfar@lbph.lib.md.us; Staff 18 (MLS 4, Non-MLS 14)
Jul 1999-Jun 2000 Mats Exp Other Print Mats $14,000
Library Holdings: Bk Vols 230,000; Bk Titles 38,000
Special Collections: Marylandia, in-house produced a-tapes
Database Vendor: DRA
Publications: Adult newsletter (quarterly), annual report, bibliographies, children's newsletter (semi-annual)
Special Services for the Deaf - TDD; Videos & decoder
Subregional library: Special Needs Library, Bethesda, Md; Other Special Services - After hours telephone ordering; in-house assistive aids; information referral; special programs with Friends group
Friends of the Library Group

MERCY MEDICAL CENTER, INC
M MCGLANNAN HEALTH SCIENCES LIBRARY, 301 St Paul Pl, 21202. SAN 343-8457. Tel: 410-332-9189. FAX: 410-332-0324. *Dir Libr Serv*, Ellen Lindenbaum; E-Mail: elindenbaum@mail.mercymed.org; Staff 2 (MLS 1, Non-MLS 1)
Founded 1874
Library Holdings: Bk Titles 7,000; Per Subs 185
Special Collections: Medical & Nursing, rare bks
Database Vendor: OVID Technologies
Restriction: Access at librarian's discretion, In-house use for visitors, Lending to staff only, Non-circulating to the public, Open to public with supervision only
Function: Archival collection, Document delivery services, ILL available, Literary searches, Mail loans to members, Reference services available, Some telephone reference
Partic in MAHSL; NLM

L MILES & STOCKBRIDGE PC LIBRARY, 10 Light St, 21202. SAN 325-4887. Tel: 410-385-3671. FAX: 410-385-3700. *Librn*, Anna B Cole; E-Mail: acole@milesstockbridge.com; Staff 8 (MLS 2, Non-MLS 6)
Jan 1999-Dec 1999 Income (Main Library and Branch Library) $580,000. Mats Exp $556,000, Books $23,000, Per/Ser (Incl. Access Fees) $530,000, Presv $3,000
Library Holdings: Bk Vols 20,000; Bk Titles 15,000; Per Subs 100
Subject Interests: Law
Automation Activity & Vendor Info: (Acquisitions) Inmagic, Inc.; (Cataloging) Inmagic, Inc.; (Circulation) Inmagic, Inc.; (ILL) Inmagic, Inc.; (Serials) Inmagic, Inc.
Publications: A Guide to the Miles & Stockbridge Library

C MORGAN STATE UNIVERSITY, Morris A Soper Library & Information Technology Center, 1700 E Cold Spring Lane, 21251. SAN 306-8579. Tel: 443-885-3477. Reference Tel: 443-885-3450. FAX: 410-319-3336. Web Site: www.library.morgan.edu. *Dir*, Karen A Robertson; *Tech Servs*, Maggie P Wanza; Tel: 443-885-3469, E-Mail: mwanza@moac.morgan.edu; *Info Tech*, Mei-yiao Lo; Tel: 443-885-3930, E-Mail: mlo@moac.morgan.edu; *ILL*, Donald A Matthews; Tel: 443-885-1711, E-Mail: dmatthews@moac.morgan.edu; *Acq*, James C Yuan; Tel: 443-885-1712, E-Mail: jyuan@moac.morgan.edu; *Media Spec*, Steven A Kinsey; Tel: 443-885-3834, E-Mail: skinsey@moac.morgan.edu; *Ref*, Elaine S Tsubota; Tel: 443-885-1719, E-Mail: etsubota@moac.morgan.edu; *Spec Coll*, Vivian L Fisher; *Circ*, Alan V Poulson; Tel: 443-885-1703, E-Mail: apoulson@moac.morgan.edu; *Cat*, David A Kuan; *Publ Servs*, Strephon H Johnson; Tel: 443-885-3478, E-Mail: johnson@moac.morgan.edu; Staff 29 (MLS 14, Non-MLS 15)
Founded 1867. Enrl 6,179; Fac 293; Highest Degree: Doctorate
Jun 1999-Jun 2000 Income $2,622,836. Mats Exp $803,378. Sal $1,017,397
Library Holdings: Bk Vols 251,500; Per Subs 3,000
Subject Interests: Economics, Education, Ethnic studies
Special Collections: Afro-American History & Life (Beulah M Davis Special Colls Rm); Correspondence of Late Poet & Editor (W S Braithwaite Coll), letters; Negro Employment in WWII (Emmett J Scott Coll), letters; Papers of Emeritus President (D O W Holmes Papers, Martin D Jenkins Papers), letters; Quaker & Slavery (Forbush Coll), bk, mss
Automation Activity & Vendor Info: (Acquisitions) CARL; (Cataloging) CARL; (Circulation) CARL; (Course Reserve) CARL; (ILL) CARL; (OPAC) CARL; (Serials) CARL
Database Vendor: Ebsco - EbscoHost, GaleNet, Lexis-Nexis, OCLC - First Search, ProQuest, Silverplatter Information Inc.
Partic in Capcon Library Network; OCLC Online Computer Library Center, Inc

S NATIONAL AQUARIUM IN BALTIMORE, A Carter Middendorf Library, 501 E Pratt St, Pier 3, 21202-3194. SAN 370-6397. Tel: 410-659-4257. FAX: 410-659-0116. Web Site: www.aqua.org. *Dir*, Susanne Ridenour; Staff 1 (MLS 1)
Founded 1980
Library Holdings: Bk Titles 2,500; Per Subs 75
Subject Interests: Conservation, Ecology, Horticulture
Special Collections: Archival Coll, clippings, reprint files
Publications: Journal Holdings
Partic in American Zoo & Aquarium Association (AZA-LSIG); Capcon Library Network; IAMSLIC; Medical Libr Asn; Sch Libr Asn

G NATIONAL INSTITUTE ON AGING, Gerontology Research Center Library - Library & Information Services Section, 5600 Nathan Shock Dr, 21224-6825. Tel: 410-558-8125. FAX: 410-558-8224. E-Mail: rrb-liss@grc.nia.nih.gov. *Librn*, Joanna C Lin; Staff 4 (MLS 1, Non-MLS 3)
Founded 1977
Library Holdings: Bk Vols 25,000; Bk Titles 10,000; Per Subs 400
Subject Interests: Biological sci, Biomedical res, Cardiovascular med, Cognitive sci, Genetics, Immunology, Neuropsychology, Neuroscience, Personalities
Database Vendor: Dialog, OVID Technologies
Partic in BRS; Dialog Corporation; National Library Of Medicine, Medlars; OCLC Online Computer Library Center, Inc

G NATIONAL INSTITUTE ON DRUG ABUSE, Addiction Research Center Library,* PO Box 5180, 21224. SAN 306-3178. Tel: 410-550-1488. FAX: 410-550-1438. *Librn*, Mary Pfeiffer; E-Mail: mpfeiffe@irp.nida.nih.gov; Staff 2 (MLS 1, Non-MLS 1)
Founded 1935
Library Holdings: Bk Titles 8,700; Per Subs 250
Subject Interests: Biochemistry, Drug (chemistry), Neurology, Pharmacology, Physiology, Psychiatry, Psychology
Partic in Dialog Corporation; Nat Libr of Med; OCLC Online Computer Library Center, Inc

S NATIONAL PARK SERVICE, Fort McHenry National Monument & Historic Shrine Library, End of E Fort Ave, 21230-5393. SAN 306-8595. Tel: 410-962-4290, Ext 244. FAX: 410-962-2500. E-Mail: fomc_superintendent@nps.gov. Web Site: www.nps.gov/fomc.
Founded 1933
Library Holdings: Bk Titles 400
Special Collections: Fort McHenry history; Star Spangled Banner; War of 1812
Restriction: Employees & their associates, Open to others by appointment
Function: Research library

S NATURAL HISTORY SOCIETY OF MARYLAND, INC LIBRARY,* 2643 N Charles St, 21218. SAN 326-0194. Tel: 410-235-6116. *Librn*, Haven Kolb; Staff 1 (MLS 1)
Founded 1929
Library Holdings: Bk Titles 20,200
Subject Interests: Natural history

R NER ISRAEL RABBINICAL COLLEGE LIBRARY, 400 Mount Wilson Lane, 21208. SAN 306-8609. Tel: 410-484-7200. FAX: 410-484-3060. *Librn*, Avvohom S Shnidman
Founded 1933
Library Holdings: Bk Vols 17,372; Per Subs 18
Special Collections: Biblical Commentaries; Hebrew Newspapers of European Communities 1820-1937; Responsa; Talmudic Laws

S NILES, BARTON & WILMER LAW LIBRARY, 111 S Calvert St, Ste 1400, 21202. SAN 327-8182. Tel: 410-783-6300. FAX: 410-783-6363. *Librn*, Stacey Ray; Tel: 410-783-6386, E-Mail: saray@niles-law.com; Staff 1 (Non-MLS 1)
Library Holdings: Bk Vols 10,000

S NORTHROP GRUMMAN CORP, Electronic Sensors & Systems Division, PO Box 746 MS 1138, 21203. SAN 322-4961. Tel: 410-993-7752. FAX: 410-993-7675, 993-1484. *Mgr*, Susan Baker; E-Mail: baker.s@postal.essd.northgrum.com
Library Holdings: Bk Vols 34,000; Bk Titles 32,000; Per Subs 400
Subject Interests: Electronics, Marketing

S OBER, KALER, GRIMES & SHRIVER LAW LIBRARY, 120 E Baltimore St, Ste 1000, 21202-1643. SAN 327-8204. Tel: 410-230-7181. FAX: 410-547-0699. *Librn*, Ginger Gerton; E-Mail: gjgerton@ober.com
Library Holdings: Bk Vols 8,000; Per Subs 300
Partic in Dialog Corporation; Dow Jones News Retrieval; Westlaw

S PENNIMAN & BROWNE, INC LIBRARY,* 6252 Falls Rd, PO Box 65309, 21209. SAN 306-865X. Tel: 410-825-4131. FAX: 410-321-7384. *Pres*, Herbert Wilgis
Library Holdings: Bk Vols 1,000; Per Subs 20
Subject Interests: Analytical chemistry

L PIPER, MARBURY, RUDNICK & WOLFE LLP, Law Library, 6225 Smith Ave, 21209-3600. SAN 306-8668. Tel: 410-580-3010. FAX: 410-580-3261. Web Site: www.piperrudnick.com. *Librn*, Ronelle Manger; Tel: 410-580-4655, Fax: 410-580-3655, E-Mail: ronelle.manger@piperrudnick.com; Staff 5 (MLS 2, Non-MLS 3)
Library Holdings: Bk Vols 27,800; Per Subs 70
Subject Interests: Administrative law, Banks and banking, Labor, Securities
Partic in Westlaw
Branches:
WASHINGTON BRANCH
See separate entry in Washington, DC
NEW YORK BRANCH
See separate entry in New York, NY
PHILADELPHIA BRANCH
See separate entry in Philadelphia, PA

S RAYTHEON, Indentification Systems, Engineering Library,* 1300 E Joppa Rd, 21286-5999. SAN 307-0573. Tel: 410-583-4382. FAX: 410-337-7485. *Librn*, Donna Lepore
Founded 1950
Library Holdings: Bk Vols 4,050; Per Subs 142
Subject Interests: Electronics, Mathematics, Physics, Technology
Partic in Dialog Corporation; OCLC Online Computer Library Center, Inc

M SAINT AGNES HEALTHCARE, Lewis P Gundry Health Sciences Library, 900 Caton Ave, 21229. SAN 306-8714. Tel: 410-368-3123, 410-368-3124. FAX: 410-368-3298. Web Site: www.stagnas.org. *Dir*, Joanne Sullivan; E-Mail: jsulliva@stagnas.org; Staff 3 (MLS 1, Non-MLS 2)
Library Holdings: Bk Vols 4,000; Per Subs 328
Subject Interests: Administrative law, Allied health, Medicine, Nursing
Special Collections: Medicine - Historical (Cohn-Bloodgood Coll)
Publications: Newsletter (quarterly)

SAINT JOSEPH MEDICAL CENTER
M OTTO C BRANTIGAN MEDICAL LIBRARY, 7620 York Rd, Towson, 21204. SAN 343-9747. Tel: 410-337-1210. FAX: 410-337-1116. *Librn*, Marianne Prenger
Founded 1940
Jul 1998-Jun 1999 Mats Exp $68,500, Books $22,500, Per/Ser (Incl. Access Fees) $41,000, Micro $5,000. Sal $30,000
Library Holdings: Bk Vols 1,150; Per Subs 250
Partic in Maryland Association Of Health Science Librarians

R SAINT MARY'S SEMINARY & UNIVERSITY, The Knott Library, 5400 Roland Ave, 21210-1994. SAN 306-8722. Tel: 410-864-3623. FAX: 410-435-8571. *Actg Dir*, Sister Ian Stewart; Staff 3 (MLS 3)
Founded 1791. Enrl 157; Fac 25; Highest Degree: Master
Library Holdings: Bk Vols 101,801; Per Subs 320
Subject Interests: Religion, Theology
Special Collections: Early Catholic Americana; Scripture/Orientalia (Arbez Coll); Semitics
Partic in OCLC Online Computer Library Center, Inc

L SAINT PAUL FIRE & MARINE, Law Library, 5801 Smith Ave, MC 32, 21209. SAN 372-1027. Tel: 410-205-5990. FAX: 410-205-6390.
Library Holdings: Bk Vols 46,000; Per Subs 114

L SAUL, EWING, WEINBERG & GREEN ATTORNEYS-AT-LAW LIBRARY, 100 S Charles St, 21201. SAN 306-8900. Tel: 410-332-8600. FAX: 410-332-8862. Web Site: www.saul.com. *Librn*, Fay Sauchelli; E-Mail: fsauchelli@saul.com
Library Holdings: Bk Vols 15,000; Per Subs 20
Subject Interests: Banks and banking, Commercial law, Corporate law, Real estate, Securities
Restriction: Staff use only

L SEMMES, BOWEN & SEMMES LIBRARY, 250 W Pratt St, 16th flr, 21201. SAN 306-8757. Tel: 410-385-3936. FAX: 410-539-5223. *Dir*, Kathleen Sweeney; E-Mail: ksweeney@mail.semmes.com
Subject Interests: Gen law
Automation Activity & Vendor Info: (Acquisitions) Inmagic, Inc.; (Cataloging) Inmagic, Inc.; (Serials) Inmagic, Inc.

M SINAI HOSPITAL OF BALTIMORE, Eisenberg Medical Staff Library, Belvedere & Greenspring, 21215-5271. SAN 306-8765. Tel: 410-601-5015. FAX: 410-664-7432. *Dir*, Lee Cook; E-Mail: lcook@sinai-balt.com; Staff 4 (MLS 2, Non-MLS 2)
Library Holdings: Bk Vols 4,100; Per Subs 325
Subject Interests: Medicine, Nursing
Special Collections: Jewish Medicine & Health
Restriction: Staff use only
Partic in BRS; Dialog Corporation; National Library Of Medicine, Medlars

G SOCIAL SECURITY ADMINISTRATION LIBRARY, Altmeyer Bldg, Rm 571, 6401 Security Blvd, 21235-6401. (Mail add: PO Box 17728, 21235-7728), SAN 306-8773. Tel: 410-965-6114. Interlibrary Loan Service Tel: 410-965-6113. Circulation Tel: 410-965-6115. Reference Tel: 410-965-6113. FAX: 410-966-2027. *Chief Librn*, Bill Vitek; *Librn*, Keith Searls; *ILL, Ref*, Leo Hollenbeck; *Automation Syst Coordr*, Rick McCarthy; *Acq*, Norma Nunnally; *Circ*, Sandy Kuperberg; *Ref*, Eugene Malkowski; Staff 10 (MLS 6, Non-MLS 4)
Founded 1942
Library Holdings: Bk Titles 80,000; Per Subs 210
Subject Interests: Business and management, Electronic engineering, History, Law, Medicine, Personnel management, Public health, Social sciences and issues
Partic in BRS; Dialog Corporation; Fedlink; OCLC Online Computer Library Center, Inc

C SOJOURNER-DOUGLASS COLLEGE, Walter P Carter Library, 500 N Caroline St, 21205. SAN 325-0660. Tel: 410-276-0306, Ext 269. FAX: 410-675-1810. E-Mail: oali@host.sdc.edu. *Acq, Librn, Per*, Sadiq Omowali Ali; Staff 1 (MLS 1)
Founded 1976
Library Holdings: Bk Vols 22,500; Bk Titles 22,000; Per Subs 50
Subject Interests: African hist, African-Am hist
Special Collections: Africa & African American History (Old Rare Books Coll)

S SPACE TELESCOPE SCIENCE INSTITUTE LIBRARY,* 3700 San Martin Dr, 21218. SAN 323-7729. Tel: 410-338-4961. FAX: 410-338-4949. E-Mail: library@stsci.edu. Web Site: www.sesame.stsci.edu/library.html. *Librn*, Sarah Stevens-Rayburn; Staff 2 (MLS 2)
Founded 1983
Oct 1998-Sep 1999 Mats Exp $108,000, Books $20,000, Per/Ser (Incl. Access Fees) $88,000

Library Holdings: Bk Vols 8,000; Bk Titles 6,000; Per Subs 515
Subject Interests: Astrophysics
Special Collections: Sky Survey Photographs
Automation Activity & Vendor Info: (Acquisitions) SIRSI; (Cataloging) SIRSI; (Circulation) SIRSI; (OPAC) SIRSI; (Serials) SIRSI
Publications: Acquisitions List; STEPsheet (preprint listing)
Partic in Fedlink

S STAR-SPANGLED BANNER FLAG HOUSE ASSOCIATION LIBRARY, 844 E Pratt St, 21202. SAN 373-4609. Tel: 410-837-1793. FAX: 410-837-1812. *In Charge*, Sally Johnston; *Curator*, Kathleen Browning
Library Holdings: Bk Vols 200

S STEAMSHIP HISTORICAL SOCIETY OF AMERICA COLLECTION AT THE UNIVERSITY OF BALTIMORE, University of Baltimore Library, 1420 Maryland Ave, 21201. SAN 306-879X. Tel: 410-837-4334. Web Site: www.ubalt.edu/archives/ship/ship.htm. *Librn*, Ann House; E-Mail: ahouse@ubmail.ubalt.edu
Founded 1946
Library Holdings: Bk Titles 5,500; Per Subs 77
Subject Interests: Transportation
Special Collections: Coll), photog; Corporate Records (Hudson River Day Line Coll), corresp, files, etc; E E Viez Coll, photog, Maryland Shipbuilding & Drydock Co, Shipplans & Photographs; US Coastal Vessels (R L Graham
Publications: Occasional monographs
Partic in OCLC Online Computer Library Center, Inc

SR TALMUDICAL ACADEMY OF BALTIMORE LIBRARY,* 4445 Old Court Rd, 21208. SAN 306-8803. Tel: 410-484-6600, Ext 133. FAX: 410-484-5717. *Librn*, Chaya Statman
Founded 1947
Library Holdings: Bk Vols 11,500

M THE JOHNS HOPKINS UNIVERSITY, Population Information Program, 111 Market Pl, 21202. SAN 306-8676. Tel: 410-659-6300. FAX: 410-659-6266. E-Mail: pip@jhuccp.org. Web Site: www.jhuccp.org. *Dep Dir*, Anne Compton; Staff 14 (MLS 6, Non-MLS 8)
Founded 1972
Library Holdings: Per Subs 450
Subject Interests: Population studies, Statistics
Special Collections: Reproductive health in developing countries
Produces POPLINE, an on-line bibliographic retrieval system, available online through the National Library of Medicine. CD-ROM version produced by and available from National Information Services Corporation

R TRINITARIAN LIBRARY,* Park Heights Ave, PO Box 5719, 21282. SAN 306-8811. Tel: 410-486-5171. FAX: 410-486-0614. *Librn*, Bro Eric Beardsley
Founded 1963
Library Holdings: Bk Vols 20,000; Per Subs 25
Special Collections: Trinitariana

L TYDINGS & ROSENBERG LLP, Law Library, 100 E Pratt St, 26th flr, 21202. SAN 372-0993. Tel: 410-752-9700, 410-752-9804. FAX: 410-539-7475. *Dir*, Jean Hessenauer; E-Mail: jhessenauer@tydingslaw.com; Staff 1 (MLS 1)
Jan 1998-Dec 1999 Mats Exp $120,000
Library Holdings: Bk Vols 10,000; Per Subs 137

UNION MEMORIAL HOSPITAL
M LIBRARY & INFORMATION RESOURCES, 201 E University Pkwy, 21218. SAN 343-9801. Tel: 410-554-2294. FAX: 410-554-2166. *Mgr*, Linda Gorman; E-Mail: lindag@helix.org; Staff 4 (MLS 2, Non-MLS 2)
Founded 1935
Jul 1998-Jun 1999 Income $218,172
Library Holdings: Bk Vols 3,000; Per Subs 300
Subject Interests: Clinical medicine, Medicine, Orthopedics, Sports, Surgery
Special Collections: Administration; History of Nursing
Partic in Docline; Nat Libr of Med

UNITED METHODIST HISTORICAL SOCIETY, Lovely Lane Museum Library, 2200 St Paul St, 21218-5897. SAN 306-8838. Tel: 410-889-4458. FAX: 410-889-1501. E-Mail: lovLnMus@BCPL.net. Web Site: www.bwconf.org/archivehistory/. *Librn*, Edwin Schell; Staff 2 (Non-MLS 2)
Founded 1855
Jan 1999-Dec 1999 Income $60,397, Locally Generated Income $22,770, Parent Institution $37,627. Mats Exp $695, Books $270, Per/Ser (Incl. Access Fees) $175, Presv $200, Micro $50. Sal $22,004 (Prof $6,092)
Library Holdings: Bk Vols 4,857; Per Subs 23
Subject Interests: History
Special Collections: Archives of Baltimore-Washington Conference; Journals of Preachers
Publications: Methodist Union Catalog; Union List of Methodist Serials
Restriction: Open to public for reference only
Non-circulating (except interlibrary loans)
Friends of the Library Group

UNITED STATES ARMY
A CORPS OF ENGINEERS, BALTIMORE DISTRICT LIBRARY, PO Box 1715, 21203-1715. SAN 343-9860. Tel: 410-962-3423. FAX: 410-962-1889.
Founded 1974
Library Holdings: Bk Vols 15,100; Per Subs 361
Subject Interests: Civil engineering, Environmental studies, Law, Soil mechanics, Water resources
Special Collections: American Society of Civil Engineers Proceedings (1803-), micro; Annotated Codes; Corps of Army Engineers (Annual Reports 1800-); Federal Government Regulations; Industrial Standards; Military Specifications; Waterway Legislation (Rivers & Harbors 1800-)
Publications: Library Bulletin
Partic in Dialog Corporation; Fedlink; OCLC Online Computer Library Center, Inc

L UNITED STATES COURTS LIBRARY,* US Courthouse Rm 3625, 101 W Lombard St, 21201. SAN 372-1000. Tel: 410-962-0997. FAX: 410-962-9313. *Librn*, Charmaine Metallo
Library Holdings: Bk Vols 38,000; Per Subs 125

C UNIVERSITY OF BALTIMORE, Langsdale Library, 1420 Maryland Ave, 21201. SAN 343-9925. Tel: 410-837-4319. Circulation Tel: 410-837-4260. Reference Tel: 410-837-4274. TDD: 410-837-4297. FAX: 410-837-4330. Web Site: www.ubalt.edu/www/langlib/index.html. *Dir*, Myrna McCallister; Tel: 410-837-4333, E-Mail: mmccallister@ubmail.ubalt.edu; *Archivist*, Thomas Hollowak; *Circ*, James J Foster; *Info Tech*, Daniel Albert; *ILL*, Carol Vaeth; *Online Servs*, Susan Wheeler; *Ref*, Stephen LaBash; *Tech Servs*, Ted Kruse; Staff 33 (MLS 13, Non-MLS 20)
Founded 1926. Enrl 4,641; Fac 156; Highest Degree: Doctorate
Jul 2000-Jun 2001 Income $1,400,000. Mats Exp $481,600, Books $60,000, Per/Ser (Incl. Access Fees) $259,000, Presv $7,100, Micro $7,500, AV Equip $60,000, Manuscripts & Archives $30,000, Electronic Ref Mat (Incl. Access Fees) $58,000. Sal $1,071,878 (Prof $509,000)
Library Holdings: Bk Vols 436,000; Per Subs 900
Special Collections: Archives of Society of Colonial Wars, correspondence of many local civic orgn, govt agencies & companies, papers, rpt; Corporate Reports; Steamship Historical Society of American Coll; WMAR-TV Film Archives
Automation Activity & Vendor Info: (Acquisitions) EX Libris; (Cataloging) EX Libris; (Circulation) EX Libris; (ILL) EX Libris; (Media Booking) EX Libris; (OPAC) EX Libris; (Serials) EX Libris
Database Vendor: CARL, Ebsco - EbscoHost, OCLC - First Search
Publications: Langsdale Library Link
Partic in Baltimore Acad Libr Consortium; Colorado Alliance Of Research Libraries; Maryland Interlibrary Organization; OCLC Online Computer Library Center, Inc
Special Services for the Deaf - TTY machine
Departmental Libraries:
CL LAW LIBRARY, 1415 Maryland Ave, 21201. SAN 343-995X. Tel: 410-837-4584. Circulation Tel: 410-837-4554. Reference Tel: 410-837-4559. FAX: 410-837-4570. Web Site: www.ubalt.edu/law/lawlib/index.html. *Dir*, Emily Greenberg; *Info Tech*, Will Tress; *Publ Servs*, Harvey Morrell; *Govt Doc*, Pat Behles; *Circ, ILL*, Shah Bijal; *Tech Servs*, Clement Chu-Sing Lau; Staff 20 (MLS 9, Non-MLS 11)
Founded 1925. Pop 1,100; Enrl 1,000; Fac 45; Highest Degree: Master
Jul 2000-Jun 2001 Income State $1,766,500. Mats Exp $847,000, Books $153,000, Per/Ser (Incl. Access Fees) $594,500, Presv $12,500, Electronic Ref Mat (Incl. Access Fees) $87,000. Sal $776,000 (Prof $486,200)
Library Holdings: Bk Vols 312,600; Bk Titles 27,130; Per Subs 3,500
Database Vendor: Ebsco - EbscoHost, IAC - Info Trac, Lexis-Nexis, OCLC - First Search, ProQuest
Publications: Anglo-American law (Research guide)
Partic in Cap Area Libr Consortium; OCLC Online Computer Library Center, Inc

UNIVERSITY OF MARYLAND, BALTIMORE
CM HEALTH SCIENCES & HUMAN SERVICES LIBRARY, 601 W Lombard St, 21201. SAN 344-001X. Tel: 410-706-7545. FAX: 410-706-3101. E-Mail: hslmgr@umaryland.edu. Web Site: www.umaryland.edu/hshsl. *Exec Dir*, Frieda O Weise; E-Mail: fweise@umaryland.edu; *Dep Dir*, M J Tooey; Tel: 410-706-2693, E-Mail: mjtooey@umaryland.edu; *Publ Servs*, Beverly Gresehover; Tel: 410-706-1784, Fax: 410-706-0067; *Acq, Ser*, Beth Jacoby; Tel: 410-706-8856, Fax: 410-706-8860, E-Mail: bjacoby@hshsl.umaryland.edu; *Tech Servs*, Jane Murray; Tel: 410-706-7378, E-Mail: jmurray@hshsl.umaryland.edu; *Publ Servs*, Alexa Mayo; Tel: 410-706-8863, Fax: 410-706-2379, E-Mail: alexa@umaryland.edu. Subject Specialists: *Consulting*, Alexa Mayo; *Education*, Alexa Mayo; *Reference*, Alexa Mayo; Staff 66 (MLS 29, Non-MLS 37)
Founded 1813. Enrl 5,875; Fac 1,600; Highest Degree: Doctorate
Library Holdings: Bk Vols 365,000; Per Subs 2,400
Subject Interests: Dentistry, Medicine, Nursing, Pharm, Social service (social work)
Special Collections: History of Dentistry (Grieves Coll), bks, pictures; History of Medicine (Crawford, Cordell Coll); History of Nursing; History of Pharmacy
Automation Activity & Vendor Info: (Acquisitions) DRA; (Cataloging) DRA; (Circulation) DRA; (Course Reserve) DRA; (OPAC) DRA; (Serials)

DRA
Database Vendor: DRA
Partic in OCLC Online Computer Library Center, Inc; PALINET & Union Library Catalogue of Pennsylvania; Univ Syst of Md
Headquarters for National Network of Libraries of Medicine - Region 2
Friends of the Library Group

CL THURGOOD MARSHALL LAW LIBRARY, 111 S Greene St, 21201-1583. SAN 344-0044. Tel: 410-706-2720. Circulation Tel: 410-706-6502. FAX: 410-706-8354. Web Site: www.law.umaryland.edu/marshall. *Dir*, Barbara Gontrum; *Res*, Maxine Grosshans; *Res*, Susan Herrick; *Ref*, Sara Kelley; *Selection of Elec Mat*, Kimberli Morris; *Circ*, Kinda France; Tel: 410-706-7031, E-Mail: kfrance@law.umaryland.edu; *Assoc Dir, Tech Servs*, Pamela Bluh; Tel: 410-706-2736, E-Mail: pbluh@umaryland.edu; Staff 22 (MLS 9, Non-MLS 13)
Founded 1843
Jul 1999-Jun 2000 Income $1,868,518. Mats Exp $886,083, Books $91,323, Per/Ser (Incl. Access Fees) $706,297, Micro $6,073, Electronic Ref Mat (Incl. Access Fees) $83,456. Sal $844,395 (Prof $424,047)
Library Holdings: Bk Vols 278,400; Bk Titles 73,176; Per Subs 4,052
Special Collections: German & French Civil Law
Automation Activity & Vendor Info: (Cataloging) CARL; (Circulation) CARL
Database Vendor: CARL, Dialog, Ebsco - EbscoHost, GaleNet, IAC - Info Trac, IAC - SearchBank, Lexis-Nexis, OCLC - First Search
Partic in Dialog Corporation; OCLC Online Computer Library Center, Inc; PALINET & Union Library Catalogue of Pennsylvania; Westlaw

C UNIVERSITY OF MARYLAND, BALTIMORE COUNTY, Albin O Kuhn Library & Gallery, 1000 Hilltop Circle, 21250. SAN 306-8854. Tel: 410-455-2356. Interlibrary Loan Service Tel: 410-455-2234. Circulation Tel: 410-455-2354. Reference Tel: 410-455-2346. Interlibrary Loan Service FAX: 410-455-1061. E-Mail: libadmin@umbc.edu. Web Site: www.umbc.edu/library. *Dir*, Dr Larry Wilt; Fax: 410-455-1078, E-Mail: wilt@umbc.edu; *Assoc Dir*, Jonathan LeBreton; E-Mail: lebreton@umbc.edu; *Coll Develop, ILL*, Robin Moskal; Tel: 410-455-2341; *Assoc Dir, Tech Servs*, Judith K Sterling; *Spec Coll*, Tom Beck; Tel: 410-455-2353, Fax: 410-455-1567; *Ser*, Joyce Tenney; *Bibliog Instr*, Michael Romary; *Acq*, Michelle Flinchbaugh; Fax: 410-455-1598; *Archivist*, Marcia Peri; Tel: 410-455-2353, Fax: 410-455-1567. Subject Specialists: *Photography*, Tom Beck; Staff 19 (MLS 18, Non-MLS 1)
Founded 1966. Enrl 7,800; Fac 580; Highest Degree: Doctorate
Jul 1999-Jun 2000 Income $5,125,199, Locally Generated Income $99,723, Parent Institution $5,025,476. Mats Exp $2,437,128, Books $452,816, Per/Ser (Incl. Access Fees) $1,936,814, Presv $41,590, Micro $5,908. Sal $1,976,638 (Prof $772,927)
Library Holdings: Bk Vols 800,000; Bk Titles 600,000; Per Subs 4,200
Special Collections: 19th Century English Graphic Satire (Merkle Coll); American Society for Microbiology Archives, bks, pers, mss; Baltimore Sun Photo Archives; Children's Science Bks; Marylandia (Howard Coll); Photography, bks, pers, photo apparatus; Popular Culture; Tissue Culture Association Archives
Automation Activity & Vendor Info: (Acquisitions) CARL; (Acquisitions) EX Libris; (Cataloging) CARL; (Cataloging) EX Libris; (Circulation) CARL; (Circulation) EX Libris; (OPAC) CARL; (OPAC) EX Libris; (Serials) CARL; (Serials) EX Libris
Database Vendor: OCLC - First Search
Publications: From the Stacks (newsletter); Numerous exhibition cat
Partic in OCLC Online Computer Library Center, Inc; Univ of Md Libr Info Mgt Syst
Friends of the Library Group

L VENABLE, BAETJER & HOWARD, LLP LIBRARY, 1800 Mercantile Bank & Trust Bldg, 2 Hopkins Plaza, 17th flr, 21201-2978. SAN 306-8870. Tel: 410-244-7502. FAX: 410-244-7742. E-Mail: lib01@venable.com. Web Site: www.venable.com. *Dir*, John S Nixdorff; E-Mail: jsnixdorff@venable.com; *Admin Assoc*, Rose Alston; *Ref Serv*, Greg Creamean; *Ref*, Anne Morrison-Low; E-Mail: damorrison-low@venable.com; *Acq*, Vivian V Shern; E-Mail: vvshern@venable.com; Staff 5 (MLS 2, Non-MLS 3)
Founded 1900
Library Holdings: Bk Vols 40,000; Per Subs 50
Subject Interests: Bankruptcy, Banks and banking, Corporate law, Employee benefits, Environmental law, Estates, Finance, Government, Labor, Law, Litigation, Real estate, Securities, Taxation, Transportation, Trusts
Partic in Dialog Corporation; Dun & Bradstreet Info Servs; Westlaw
Branches:
VENABLE, BAETJER & HOWARD, 2010 Corporate Ridge, Ste 400, McLean, 22102. SAN 325-3899. Tel: 703-760-1600, 703-760-1621. FAX: 703-821-8949. Web Site: www.venable.com. *Librn*, Kathleen G Lolich; E-Mail: kglolich@venable.com
Founded 1977
Library Holdings: Bk Vols 7,000; Per Subs 15
Subject Interests: Bankruptcy, Corporate law, Government, Litigation, Real estate, Securities, Taxation, Transportation
Partic in Westlaw
VENABLE, BAETJER & HOWARD, 210 Allegheny Ave, PO Box 5517, Towson, 21204. SAN 370-9388. Tel: 410-494-6200. FAX: 410-821-0147. Web Site: www.venable.com.
Founded 1962
Library Holdings: Bk Vols 1,500
Subject Interests: Ins law, Law, Litigation, Real estate law
Partic in Westlaw
VENABLE, BAETJER & HOWARD LIBRARY, One Church St, Ste 500, Rockville, 20850. SAN 370-937X. Tel: 301-217-5600. FAX: 301-217-5617. Web Site: www.venable.com. *Librn*, John S Nixdorff; E-Mail: jsnixdorff@venable.com; *Librn*, Kathleen Lolich; E-Mail: kglolich@venable.com
Founded 1967
Library Holdings: Bk Vols 1,800
Subject Interests: Labor law, Litigation, Municipal law, Real estate law
Partic in Westlaw
VENABLE, BAETJER, HOWARD & CIVILETTI, 1201 New York Ave NW, Ste 1000, Washington, 20005. SAN 325-3902. Tel: 202-962-4950. Interlibrary Loan Service Tel: 202-962-8325. Reference Tel: 202-962-8325. FAX: 202-962-8300. E-Mail: lib02@venable.com. Web Site: www.venable.com. *Librn*, Elaine Clark; E-Mail: emclark@venable.com; *Librn*, Victoria Kahn; *Ref Serv, Tech Servs*, David Konieczko; *Ref Serv*, Mohammad Nassim; *Computer Services*, Ronny Fritz; Staff 6 (MLS 5, Non-MLS 1)
Founded 1981
Library Holdings: Bk Vols 30,000; Per Subs 50
Subject Interests: Banks and banking, Corporate law, Drug laws, Energy, Environmental law, Estates, Government, Immigration, International trade, Labor, Litigation, Patents, Real estate law, Securities, Taxation, Trademarks, Trusts

S WALTERS ART MUSEUM LIBRARY, 600 N Charles St, 21201-5185. SAN 306-8897. Tel: 410-547-9000, Ext 274. FAX: 410-752-4797. Web Site: www.thewalters.org. *Head Librn*, Kathleen Stacey; E-Mail: kstacey@thewalters.org; Staff 3 (MLS 1, Non-MLS 2)
Founded 1934
Library Holdings: Bk Vols 75,000; Bk Titles 49,000; Per Subs 500
Subject Interests: History
Special Collections: Art Auction Catalogs Coll
Database Vendor: OCLC - First Search
Partic in OCLC Online Computer Library Center, Inc

L WHITEFORD, TAYLOR & PRESTON, Law Library, 7 St Paul St, Ste 1400, 21202. SAN 372-0616. Tel: 410-347-8700. FAX: 443-263-8253. Web Site: www.wtplaw.com. *Librn*, Anne B Garrett; Staff 4 (MLS 1, Non-MLS 3)
Library Holdings: Bk Vols 5,000; Per Subs 50

BEL AIR

J HARFORD COMMUNITY COLLEGE LIBRARY,* 401 Thomas Run Rd, 21015-1698. SAN 306-8935. Tel: 410-836-4316. FAX: 410-836-4198. Web Site: harford.cc.md.us/library/library.htm. *Dir, Librn*, Geraldine Yeager; Tel: 410-836-4144; *Assoc Dir*, Christel Vonderscheer; Tel: 410-836-4145; *Ref*, Mary Somers; Tel: 410-836-4232
Founded 1957. Enrl 5,500; Fac 85
Jul 1999-Jun 2000 Income $1,300,000. Mats Exp $253,000, Books $75,000, Per/Ser (Incl. Access Fees) $52,000, Presv $3,000, AV Equip $60,000, Other Print Mats $23,000, Electronic Ref Mat (Incl. Access Fees) $40,000
Library Holdings: Bk Vols 63,000; Bk Titles 60,000; Per Subs 428
Subject Interests: Art
Special Collections: Maryland Constitutional Convention File; Maryland History; Rosenburg Report
Automation Activity & Vendor Info: (Acquisitions) DRA; (Circulation) DRA; (Course Reserve) DRA; (OPAC) DRA
Database Vendor: OCLC - First Search
Partic in PALINET & Union Library Catalogue of Pennsylvania

R LINCOLN CHRISTIAN COLLEGE-EAST COAST LIBRARY, 2408 Creswell Rd, 21015. SAN 321-5512. Tel: 410-836-2092. FAX: 410-734-4271. *Asst Dir*, Kevin W Larsen; *Cat*, Pam Sarno
Founded 1961
Library Holdings: Bk Vols 16,000; Per Subs 100
Subject Interests: Theology

BELCAMP

P HARFORD COUNTY PUBLIC LIBRARY, (HCPL), 1221-A Brass Mill Rd, 21017-1209. SAN 344-0079. Tel: 410-273-5600, 410-575-6761. FAX: 410-273-5606. Web Site: www.harf.lib.md.us. *Dir*, Irene M Padilla; Tel: 410-273-5600, Ext 225, E-Mail: padilla@harf.lib.md.us; *Assoc Dir*, Audra Caplan; Tel: 410-273-5600, Ext 246, E-Mail: caplan@harf.lib.md.us; *Adminr*, Kenneth D Boyle; Tel: 410-273-5600, Ext 260, E-Mail: boyle@harf.lib.md.us; *Publ Servs*, Sandra Owen; Tel: 410-273-5600, Ext 249, E-Mail: owen@harf.lib.md.us; *Tech Servs*, Irmgarde Brown; Tel: 410-273-5600, Ext 274; *Tech Coordr*, Gia Wilhelm; Tel: 410-273-5600, Ext 248, E-Mail: wilhelm@harf.lib.md.us; *Materials Manager*, Jennifer Ralston; Tel: 410-273-5600, Ext 273, E-Mail: ralston@harf.lib.md.us; Staff 9 (MLS 5, Non-MLS 4)
Founded 1946. Pop 219,586; Circ 2,334,217
Jul 1999-Jun 2000 Income (Main Library and Branch Library) $8,693,182,

State $1,054,803, Federal $14,014, County $7,062,804, Locally Generated Income $542,676, Other $18,885. Mats Exp $1,690,180, Books $1,317,947, Per/Ser (Incl. Access Fees) $58,544, AV Equip $70,274, Electronic Ref Mat (Incl. Access Fees) $243,415. Sal $4,918,123 (Prof $1,277,861)
Library Holdings: Bk Vols 676,596; Bk Titles 170,992; Per Subs 1,415; Bks on Deafness & Sign Lang 165
Subject Interests: Maryland
Special Collections: Juvenile Historical Coll; Learning, Sharing & Caring; PTC Coll
Automation Activity & Vendor Info: (Acquisitions) DRA; (Cataloging) DRA; (Circulation) DRA; (OPAC) DRA; (Serials) DRA
Database Vendor: DRA
Publications: Headlines & Happenings
Partic in Marynet; Sailor
Special Services for the Deaf - TDD
Friends of the Library Group
Branches: 9
ABERDEEN BRANCH, 21 Franklin St, Aberdeen, 21001-2495. SAN 344-0109. Tel: 410-273-5608. FAX: 410-273-5610. Web Site: www.harf.lib.md.us. *Mgr*, Gregory Wollon; E-Mail: wollon@harf.lib.md.us; Staff 5 (MLS 2, Non-MLS 3)
Library Holdings: Bk Vols 87,965
Subject Interests: Maryland
Special Collections: African-American Coll; Parent-Teacher Coll
Database Vendor: DRA
Friends of the Library Group
BEL AIR BRANCH, 100 Pennsylvania Ave, Bel Air, 21014-3799. SAN 344-0133. Tel: 410-638-3151. FAX: 410-638-3155. Web Site: www.harf.lib.md.us. *Mgr*, Joan Stiffler; E-Mail: stiffler@harf.lib.md.us; Staff 15 (MLS 9, Non-MLS 6)
Library Holdings: Bk Vols 234,930
Subject Interests: Maryland
Special Collections: Juvenile Historical Coll; LSC Coll; Parent-Teacher Coll
Database Vendor: DRA
Friends of the Library Group
DARLINGTON BRANCH, 1134 Main St, Darlington, 21034-1418. SAN 344-0168. Tel: 410-638-3750. FAX: 410-638-3752. Web Site: www.harf.lib.md.us. *Branch Mgr*, Cathleen Johnson; E-Mail: johnsonc@harf.lib.md.us; Staff 1 (Non-MLS 1)
Library Holdings: Bk Vols 8,374
Subject Interests: Maryland
Special Collections: Parent-Teacher Coll
Database Vendor: DRA
EDGEWOOD BRANCH, 2205 Hanson Rd, Edgewood, 21040-2607. SAN 344-0192. Tel: 410-612-1600. FAX: 410-612-1602. Web Site: www.harf.lib.md.us. *Mgr*, Nancy McClary; Tel: 410-612-1601, E-Mail: mcclary@harf.lib.md.us; Staff 4 (MLS 3, Non-MLS 1)
Library Holdings: Bk Vols 57,618
Subject Interests: Maryland
Special Collections: AF-AM; Parent-Teacher Coll
Database Vendor: DRA
Friends of the Library Group
FALLSTON-JARRETTSVILLE, 1461 Fallson Rd, Fallston, 21047-1699. SAN 326-7059. Tel: 410-638-3003. FAX: 410-638-3005. Web Site: www.harf.lib.md.us.; Staff 6 (MLS 2, Non-MLS 4)
Library Holdings: Bk Vols 87,912
Subject Interests: Maryland
Special Collections: Parent-Teacher Coll
Database Vendor: DRA
Friends of the Library Group
HAVRE DE GRACE BRANCH, 120 N Union Ave, Havre de Grace, 21078-3000. SAN 344-0222. Tel: 410-939-6700. FAX: 410-939-6702. Web Site: www.harf.lib.md.us. *Mgr*, Susan M Deeney; E-Mail: deeney@harf.lib.md.us; Staff 4 (MLS 3, Non-MLS 1)
Library Holdings: Bk Vols 58,847
Subject Interests: Maryland
Special Collections: African-American Coll; Learn to Earn; Parent-Teacher Coll
Database Vendor: DRA
Friends of the Library Group
JOPPA BRANCH, 655 Towne Center Dr, Joppa, 21085-4497. SAN 344-0214. Tel: 410-612-1660. FAX: 410-612-1662. Web Site: www.harf.lib.md.us. *Mgr*, Elizabeth Ward; E-Mail: ward@harf.lib.md.us; Staff 4 (MLS 3, Non-MLS 1)
Library Holdings: Bk Vols 57,042
Subject Interests: Maryland
Special Collections: Parent-Teacher Coll
Database Vendor: DRA
Friends of the Library Group
NORRISVILLE BRANCH, 5310 Norrisville Rd, White Hall, 21161-8923. SAN 328-7661. Tel: 410-692-7850. FAX: 410-692-7851. Web Site: www.harf.lib.md.us. *Branch Mgr*, Deidrah Reeves; E-Mail: reeves@harf.lib.md.us; Staff 1 (MLS 1)
Library Holdings: Bk Vols 8,981
Database Vendor: DRA
Friends of the Library Group
WHITEFORD BRANCH, 2407 Whiteford Rd, Whiteford, 21160-1218. SAN 344-0249. Tel: 410-638-3608. FAX: 410-638-3610. Web Site: www.harf.lib.md.us. *Mgr*, George W Meyn; E-Mail: meyn@harf.lib.md.us; Staff 3 (MLS 2, Non-MLS 1)
Library Holdings: Bk Vols 41,718
Subject Interests: Maryland
Special Collections: Parent-Teacher Coll
Database Vendor: DRA
Friends of the Library Group

BELTSVILLE

UNITED STATES DEPARTMENT OF AGRICULTURE
S NATIONAL AGRICULTURAL LIBRARY, 10301 Baltimore Ave, 20705-2351. SAN 344-0257. Tel: 301-504-5755. FAX: 301-504-5472. E-Mail: info@nalusda.gov. Web Site: url:www.nal.usda.gov/. *Dir*, Pamela Andre; *Assoc Dir, Tech Servs*, Sally Sinn; *Assoc Dir, Automation Syst Coordr*, Gary McCone; *Assoc Dir, Publ Servs*, Maria Pisa; Staff 187 (MLS 118, Non-MLS 69)
Founded 1862
OctSep
Library Holdings: Bk Vols 2,292,524; Per Subs 16,724
Subject Interests: Agriculture, Aquaculture, Biotechnol, Botany, Chemistry, Econ pertaining to agr, Entomology, Farming, Food, Forestry, Nutrition, Rural society, Soil sci, Tech agr, Water resources
Special Collections: Flock, Herd & Stud; Food & Nutrition, av; Foreign & Domestic Nursery & Seed Trade, catalogs; Forest Service Photo Coll; Milk Sanitation (Charles E North Coll), mss; Poster Coll; Poultry (James M Gwin Coll); Rare Book Coll
Publications: Agricultural Library Information Notes (newsletter); list of journals indexed in AGRICOLA
Mem of Asn of Research Libraries
Partic in BRS; Dun & Bradstreet Info Servs; Fedlink; Nat Libr of Med; OCLC Online Computer Library Center, Inc; Wilsonline
Producer of AGRICOLA Data Base; producer of US input for Agris Database
PUBLIC SERVICES DIVISION - DC REFERENCE CENTER, Rm 1052, South Bldg, US Dept of Agr, 14th & Independence Ave, SW, Washington, 20250. SAN 344-0281. Tel: 202-720-3434. FAX: 202-720-0342. *Librn*, Janet Wright
Subject Interests: Core agri mat, Global change
Partic in BRS; Dialog Corporation; OCLC Online Computer Library Center, Inc

BERLIN

G NATIONAL PARK SERVICE, Assateague Island National Seashore Library, 7206 National Seashore Lane, 21811. SAN 306-8943. Tel: 410-641-1443. FAX: 410-641-1099. *Librn*, Christopher Seymour
Library Holdings: Bk Vols 500; Per Subs 10
Subject Interests: Natural history
Special Collections: Assateague Island Seashore, slides

BETHESDA

M AMERICAN COLLEGE OF CARDIOLOGY, Griffith Resource Library, 9111 Old Georgetown Rd, 20814. SAN 328-0187. Tel: 301-897-2683. FAX: 301-897-9745. *Librn*, Gwen Pigman; E-Mail: gpigman@acc.org; Staff 3 (MLS 2, Non-MLS 1)
Library Holdings: Bk Titles 2,400; Per Subs 130
Subject Interests: Cardiology

M AMERICAN OCCUPATIONAL THERAPY FOUNDATION & ASSOCIATION, Wilma L West Library of Occupational Therapy, 4720 Montgomery Lane, PO Box 31220, 20824-1220. SAN 324-6795. Tel: 301-652-2682, Ext 2557. FAX: 301-656-3620. E-Mail: wlwlib@aota.org. *Dir*, Mary Binderman; Staff 3 (MLS 3)
Founded 1980
Library Holdings: Bk Vols 4,700; Per Subs 50
Subject Interests: Education, Human occupation, Occupational therapy, Practice, Profession, Rehabilitation
Special Collections: A Jean Ayres Coll; AOTA Archives Coll; Mary Reilly Coll
Publications: Occupational Therapy Library Brochure
Partic in Maryland Interlibrary Organization

M AMERICAN SOCIETY OF HEALTH-SYSTEM PHARMACISTS LIBRARY, 7272 Wisconsin Ave, 20814. SAN 377-1636. Tel: 301-657-3000. Interlibrary Loan Service Tel: 301-657-3000, Ext 1255. FAX: 301-664-8857. Web Site: www.ashp.org. *Librn*, Louise Dambrauskas; E-Mail: ldambrauskas@ashp.org; Staff 2 (MLS 1, Non-MLS 1)
Library Holdings: Bk Vols 1,300; Per Subs 550

G ARMED FORCES RADIOBIOLOGY RESEARCH INSTITUTE, William H Chapman Library, 8901 Wisconsin Ave, 20889-5603. SAN 306-8951. Tel: 301-295-0443.
Founded 1962
Library Holdings: Bk Vols 10,000; Per Subs 120

G ASSOCIATION FOR FINANCIAL PROFESSIONAL INFORMATION SERVICES, 7315 Wisconsin Ave, Ste 600W, 20814-3211. SAN 377-385X. Tel: 301-907-2862. FAX: 301-907-2864. E-Mail: info@AFPonline.org, tma@tma-net.org. Web Site: www.AFPonline.org, www.tma-net.org/library/. *Mgr*, Larry Foxman. Subject Specialists: *Finance*, Larry Foxman; Staff 2 (MLS 2)
Library Holdings: Bk Vols 500; Per Subs 100
Subject Interests: Finance

S AUTISM SOCIETY OF AMERICA, Information & Referral Service, 7910 Woodmont Ave, Ste 300, 20814-3015. SAN 370-8365. Tel: 301-657-0881. FAX: 301-657-0869. Web Site: www.autism-society.org/. *Dir*, Rob Beck
Library Holdings: Bk Vols 275; Per Subs 30

R BETHESDA PRESBYTERIAN CHURCH LIBRARY,* 7611 Clarendon Rd, 20814. SAN 306-896X. Tel: 301-986-1137. FAX: 301-986-1230. *Librn*, Marion Kirby
Library Holdings: Bk Vols 1,650

R BETHESDA UNITED METHODIST CHURCH LIBRARY, 8300 Old Georgetown Rd, 20814. SAN 306-8978. Tel: 301-652-2990. FAX: 301-652-1965. *Librn*, Rene McDonald
Founded 1956
Library Holdings: Bk Vols 4,000
Subject Interests: Biblical studies, Biology, Child welfare, Church history, Religion
Publications: Library News (newsletter)
Friends of the Library Group

S CAMBRIDGE SCIENTIFIC ABSTRACTS LIBRARY,* 7200 Wisconsin Ave, 20814. SAN 307-0026. Tel: 301-961-6744. FAX: 301-961-6740. E-Mail: market@csa.com. Web Site: www.csa.com. *Electronic Resources*, Anthea Gotto
Founded 1952
Library Holdings: Bk Vols 14,000
Subject Interests: Aquatic sci, Biological sci, Engineering, Environ scis, Linguistics, Mat sci, Sociology
Publications: ASFA Thesaurus; Life Sciences Thesaurus; Thesaurus of Linguistics Indexing Terms; Thesaurus of Metallurgical Terms; Thesaurus of Sociological Indexing Terms

R CHRIST LUTHERAN CHURCH LIBRARY,* 8011 Old Georgetown Rd, 20814. SAN 306-8994. Tel: 301-652-5160. FAX: 301-652-2301.
Founded 1961. Pop 400
Library Holdings: Bk Vols 2,100; Bk Titles 2,001
Subject Interests: Religion
Special Collections: Archives of the Church; Old Testament, A-tapes
Publications: American Book Publishing Record

S COMSAT CORPORATION LIBRARY,* 6560 Rock Spring Dr, 20817. SAN 377-5402. Tel: 301-214-3682. FAX: 301-214-7100. *Librn*, Mary Clague
Library Holdings: Bk Vols 800; Per Subs 100
Partic in Interlibrary Users Association

S DAMES & MOORE LIBRARY,* 7101 Wisconsin Ave, Ste 700, 20814-4870. SAN 306-9028. Tel: 301-652-2215. FAX: 301-656-8059. *Librn*, Sharon Noyce; Staff 1 (MLS 1)
Founded 1975
1998-1999 Income $60,000. Mats Exp $19,099, Books $4,507, Per/Ser (Incl. Access Fees) $11,242, Other Print Mats $3,350. Sal $39,500
Library Holdings: Bk Titles 6,000; Per Subs 75
Subject Interests: Engineering, Geology, Ground water quality, Water resources, Water treatment
Restriction: Staff use only

S DITTBERNER ASSOCIATES INC, LIBRARY, 4641 Montgomery, 20814-3488. SAN 327-8263. Tel: 301-652-8350. FAX: 301-657-8084. Web Site: www.dittberner.com. *Librn*, Ingrid Mayr; E-Mail: mayr@dittberner.com
Founded 1966
Library Holdings: Bk Vols 1,200; Bk Titles 800; Per Subs 75; Spec Interest Per Sub 50
Subject Interests: Telecommunications
Restriction: Not open to public
Function: Research library
Partic in US Telecommunication Asn

S EDITORIAL PROJECTS IN EDUCATION, 6935 Arlington Rd, 20814. SAN 377-1237. Tel: 301-280-3100. FAX: 301-280-3200. E-Mail: ew@epe.org. Web Site: www.edweek.org, www.teachermagazine.org. *Librn*, Kathryn Dorko; E-Mail: kdorko@epe.org; *Head of Libr*, Kay Dorko; E-Mail: kdorko@epe.edu; *Asst Librn*, Barbara Hiron; E-Mail: bhiron@epe.edu; Staff 2 (MLS 2)
Founded 1995
Library Holdings: Bk Vols 3,156; Bk Titles 3,000; Per Subs 150
Function: Newspaper reference library
Partic in Am Libr Asn; DC Libr Asn; Spec Libr Asn

S JACK FAUCETT ASSOCIATES LIBRARY,* 4550 Montgomery Ave, Ste 300N, 20814. SAN 306-9214. Tel: 301-961-8800. FAX: 301-469-3001. *Librn*, Donald Hutson; Staff 2 (MLS 1, Non-MLS 1)
Founded 1963
Library Holdings: Bk Titles 18,000; Per Subs 20
Subject Interests: Benefits (Labor), Economics, Energy, Environmental studies, Investing, Transportation
Partic in Dialog Corporation; Metrop Wash Libr Coun

S FEDERATION OF AMERICAN SOCIETIES FOR EXPERIMENTAL BIOLOGY, (BIRC), Beaumont Information Resources Center, 9650 Rockville Pike, 20814-3998. SAN 306-9044. Tel: 301-530-7146. FAX: 301-571-1876. *Librn*, Dr Donald G Smith
Library Holdings: Bk Vols 1,000; Per Subs 80
Restriction: Lending to staff only

S FISH & WILDLIFE REFERENCE SERVICE, 5430 Grosvenor Lane, Ste 110, 20814. SAN 329-7942. Tel: 301-492-6403. Toll Free Tel: 800-582-3421. FAX: 301-564-4059. E-Mail: fw9_fa_reference-service@fws.gov. Web Site: fa.r9.fws.gov/r9fwrs/. *Br Coordr*, Geoffrey Yeadon; Staff 6 (MLS 3, Non-MLS 3)
Founded 1967
Subject Interests: Fisheries mgt, Wildlife management
Special Collections: Fish & Wildlife Coll
Publications: Fish & Wildlife Reference Service Newsletter
No inter-library loans. Distribution of photocopies & microfiche copies, indexing & storage of government reports.

S FOSTER ASSOCIATES, INC LIBRARY, 4550 Montgomery Ave, Ste 350N, 20814. SAN 302-6574. Tel: 301-664-7800. FAX: 301-664-7810. E-Mail: lsilkey@foster-fa.com. *Librn*, Le Silkey
Founded 1956
Library Holdings: Bk Vols 18,000; Per Subs 150
Subject Interests: Energy, Telecommunications

SR FOURTH PRESBYTERIAN CHURCH, Media Center, 5500 River Rd, 20816-3399. SAN 371-7321. Tel: 301-320-3434. FAX: 301-320-6315. *Librn*, Ruth Williams; *Asst Librn*, Judy Batten; *Ch Servs*, Vicky Hess; Staff 5 (Non-MLS 5)
Library Holdings: Bk Titles 7,500; Per Subs 50

L LERCH, EARLY & BREWER, Law Library,* 3 Bethesda Metro Ctr Ste 380, 20814. SAN 372-1035. Tel: 301-986-1300. FAX: 301-986-0332. *Librn*, Belinda Cain
Library Holdings: Bk Vols 5,000; Per Subs 50

S MARRIOTT INTERNATIONAL LIBRARY,* 10400 Fernwood Rd, 20817. SAN 377-4341. Tel: 301-380-6799. FAX: 301-380-0030. *Librn*, Cindy Monroe
Library Holdings: Bk Vols 10,000; Per Subs 200
Partic in Am Asn of Law Librs; Law Libr Soc of DC; Spec Libr Asn

GM NATIONAL CANCER INSTITUTE, Library & Information Center,* Bldg 31, Rm 10A34, 9000 Rockville Pike, 20892. SAN 377-4805. Tel: 301-496-6756. FAX: 301-435-2931. *Librn*, Judy Grosberg; E-Mail: grosberj@occ.nci.nih.gov
Library Holdings: Bk Vols 600; Per Subs 230
Partic in Spec Libr Asn

S NATIONAL CLEARINGHOUSE FOR WORKER HEALTH & SAFETY TRAINING, Hazardous Materials, Waste Operations & Emergency Response Library,* 5107 Benton Ave, 20814. SAN 323-5343. Tel: 301-571-4226. FAX: 301-897-5848. Web Site: www.niehs.nih.gov/wetp/clear.htm. *Dir*, Ruth Ruttenberg
Library Holdings: Bk Titles 4,195; Per Subs 10
Partic in Dialog Corporation; Nat Libr of Med

M NATIONAL HEART, LUNG & BLOOD INSTITUTE, Information Center Library, PO Box 30105, 20824-0105. SAN 326-5420. Tel: 301-592-8573. FAX: 301-592-8563. E-Mail: nhlbinfo@rover.nhlbi.nih.gov. Web Site: www.nhlbi.nih.gov. *Librn*, Carol Creech; Staff 3 (MLS 2, Non-MLS 1)
Library Holdings: Bk Titles 500; Per Subs 80
Function: Reference only

S NATIONAL INJURY INFORMATION CLEARINGHOUSE, US Consumer Product Safety Commission, East West Tower, 4330 East West Hwy, Rm 504, 20814. SAN 371-2583. Tel: 301-504-0424. Toll Free Tel: 800-638-2772. FAX: 301-504-0025. E-Mail: clearinghouse@cpsc.gov, info@cpsc.gov. Web Site: www.cpsc.gov. *Dir*, Ann Detemple
Library Holdings: Bk Vols 380
Special Collections: Agency Records; US CPSC Documents
Special Services for the Deaf - TTY machine

G NATIONAL INSTITUTE OF ARTHRITIS & MUSCULOSKELETAL & SKIN DISEASES, (Formerly National Arthritis & Musculoskeletal & Skin Diseases), Information Clearinghouse, One AMS Circle, 20892-3675. SAN 326-3312. Tel: 301-495-4484, 301-565-2966 (TTY). FAX: 301-718-6366 (Faxback service-24 hr/day), 301-718-6366. Web Site: www.nih.gov/niams/. *Librn*, Sardar Zuberi; *Info Specialist*, Anita Scamack; Staff 1 (Non-MLS 1)
Library Holdings: Per Subs 27
Subject Interests: Arthritis, Related musculoskeletal, Skin diseases, Sports injuries
Publications: Bibliographies; Biblio-profiles; Brochures & Info Packages; Catalogs; Directories
Special Services for the Deaf - TTY machine
Open Mon-Fri 8:30-5

S NATIONAL INSTITUTE OF DENTAL & CRANIOFACIAL RESEARCH, Information Technology System & Analysis Branch, Bldg 31, Rm 2C35, 31 Center Dr, MSC 2290, 20892-2290. SAN 371-2923. Tel: 301-496-4261. FAX: 301-496-9988. E-Mail: nidrinfo@od31.nidr.nih.gov. Web Site: www.nidcr.nih.gov/. *Dir*, Dr Harold Slavkin
Library Holdings: Bk Vols 300

G NATIONAL INSTITUTE OF DIABETES, DIGESTIVE & KIDNEY DISEASES, Information Clearinghouse Library,* 2 Information Way, 20892-3570. SAN 370-7741. Tel: 301-654-3810. FAX: 301-907-8906. E-Mail: nddic@info.niddk.nih.gov. Web Site: www.niddk.nih.gov/.
Founded 1980
Branches:
NATIONAL DIABETES INFORMATION CLEARINGHOUSE, One Information Way, 20892-3560. SAN 372-8374. Tel: 301-654-3327. FAX: 301-907-8906. E-Mail: ndic@aerie.com. Web Site: www.niddk.nih.gov/.
Founded 1978
Library Holdings: Bk Titles 8,745
NATIONAL KIDNEY & UROLOGIC INFORMATION CLEARINGHOUSE, 3 Information Way, 20892-3580. SAN 372-8390. Tel: 301-654-4415. FAX: 301-907-8906. E-Mail: nkvdic@aerie.com. Web Site: www.niddk.nih.gov.
Founded 1987
Library Holdings: Bk Titles 3,665

NATIONAL INSTITUTES OF HEALTH
GM NIH LIBRARY, Bldg 10, Rm 1L25G, 10 Center Dr, MSC 1150, 20892-1150. SAN 344-0400. Tel: 301-496-2447. FAX: 301-402-0254. Web Site: www.nihlibrary.nih.gov. *Chief Librn*, Suzanne F Grefsheim; *Coll Develop*, Lisa Wu; *Doc Delivery*, Rosalie Stroman; *Info Specialist, Instrul Serv*, Susan Whitmore; Staff 54 (MLS 24, Non-MLS 30)
Founded 1903
Oct 1999-Sep 2000 Income $8,100,000. Mats Exp $2,678,697, Books $197,000, Per/Ser (Incl. Access Fees) $1,610,000, Presv $55,000, AV Equip $295,697, Electronic Ref Mat (Incl. Access Fees) $521,000. Sal $2,931,523
Library Holdings: Bk Vols 65,000; Per Subs 2,400
Subject Interests: Biology, Chemistry, Health sciences, Medicine, Physiology
Automation Activity & Vendor Info: (Acquisitions) Innovative Interfaces Inc.; (Cataloging) Innovative Interfaces Inc.; (Circulation) Innovative Interfaces Inc.; (ILL) Innovative Interfaces Inc.; (OPAC) Innovative Interfaces Inc.; (Serials) Innovative Interfaces Inc.
Database Vendor: OCLC - First Search
Partic in Fedlink; OCLC Online Computer Library Center, Inc; Ser Holdings Network

GM NATIONAL LIBRARY OF MEDICINE, 8600 Rockville Pike, 20894. SAN 306-9079. Tel: 301-496-6308. Interlibrary Loan Service Tel: 301-496-5511. Toll Free Tel: 888-346-3656. FAX: 301-496-4450. E-Mail: publicinfo@nlm.nih.gov. Web Site: www.nlm.nih.gov. *Dir*, Dr Donald A B Lindberg; *Coll Develop*, Duane Arenales; *Publ Servs*, Robert Mehnert; E-Mail: mehnert@nlm.nih.gov; *Publ Servs*, Eve-Marie Lacroix; E-Mail: eve-marie_lacroix@nlm.nih.gov
Founded 1836
Library Holdings: Bk Vols 2,200,000; Per Subs 22,500
Subject Interests: Health sciences, Medicine
Special Collections: Manuscripts
Publications: Index Medicus; National Library of Medicine
Mem of Asn of Research Libraries
Partic in National Library Of Medicine, Medlars; National Network Of Libraries Of Medicine
Friends of the Library Group

M THE NATIONAL NAVAL MEDICAL CENTER, E R Stitt Library, 8901 Wisconsin Ave, 20889-5600. SAN 344-046X. Tel: 301-295-1184. Toll Free Tel: 800-526-7101. FAX: 301-295-6001. *Librn*, Jerry Meyer; *Ref*, Cathryn Jordan
Founded 1902
Library Holdings: Bk Vols 70,000; Bk Titles 19,000; Per Subs 800
Subject Interests: Allied health, Dentistry, Medicine, Nursing, Surgery
Special Collections: History of Medicine; Hospital Management; Pastoral Care
Publications: Stitt Notes
Restriction: Staff use only
Partic in National Library Of Medicine, Medlars

M NAVAL DENTAL SCHOOL, William L Darnall Library,* Naval Dental School, National Naval Dental Ctr, 20889-5602. SAN 306-9087. Tel: 301-295-0080. E-Mail: evanspa@nnd1o.med.navy.mil. *In Charge*, Patricia Evans
Founded 1947
Library Holdings: Bk Vols 7,000; Per Subs 100
Subject Interests: Dentistry

M NAVAL MEDICAL RESEARCH INSTITUTE, (NMRC), Medical Research Library, 8901 Wisconsin Ave, 20889-5607. SAN 306-9095. Tel: 301-295-0283. FAX: 301-295-2720. *Librn*, Charles Bradsher; Tel: 301-295-2186, E-Mail: bradsherc@nmripo.nmri.nnmc.navy.mil; *Ref*, Paula Clark; *Tech Servs*, Aletha Holser
Founded 1942
Library Holdings: Bk Vols 8,000; Per Subs 330
Subject Interests: Biochemistry, Immunology, Medicine, Physiology, Transportation
Special Collections: Naval Medical Research Institute Reports, 1943 to present
Publications: Summaries of Research; Union List of Serials
Restriction: Open to public for reference only
Partic in Dialog Corporation; National Library Of Medicine, Medlars; OCLC Online Computer Library Center, Inc

S THE REFRIGERATION RESEARCH & EDUCATION FOUNDATION LIBRARY,* 7315 Wisconsin Ave, Ste 1200 N, 20814. SAN 325-9080. Tel: 301-652-5674. FAX: 301-652-7269. E-Mail: email@iarw.org. *Librn*, Angela Steves
Library Holdings: Bk Vols 1,000; Per Subs 50

G SOCIETY OF AMERICAN FORESTERS, Information Center,* 5400 Grosvenor Lane, 20814. SAN 373-1596. Tel: 301-897-8720. FAX: 301-897-3690.
Library Holdings: Bk Vols 2,000
Subject Interests: Forestry

M SUBURBAN HOSPITAL, Medical Library,* 8600 Old Georgetown Rd, 20814-1497. SAN 306-9125. Tel: 301-896-3100. FAX: 301-896-7310. *Dir Libr Serv*, Debbie Skolnik
Founded 1955
Library Holdings: Bk Titles 1,000; Per Subs 100
Subject Interests: Administrative law, Allied health, Geriatrics and gerontology, Nursing, Plastic surgery, Surgery, Urology
Publications: Library Lines (quarterly newsletter)
Partic in SE-Atlantic Regional Med Libr Servs

CM UNIFORMED SERVICES UNIVERSITY OF THE HEALTH SCIENCES, Learning Resource Center, 4301 Jones Bridge Rd, 20814-4799. SAN 324-2226. Tel: 301-295-3350. FAX: 301-295-3795. E-Mail: teleinfo@lrcm.usuhs.mil. Web Site: www.lrc.usuhs.mil. *Dir*, Chester J Pletzke; *Ref*, Judith K Torrence; *Tech Servs*, Janice J Powell Muller; Staff 29 (MLS 8, Non-MLS 21)
Founded 1976. Highest Degree: Doctorate
Library Holdings: Bk Titles 95,533; Per Subs 2,800
Subject Interests: Mil med
Automation Activity & Vendor Info: (Acquisitions) Innovative Interfaces Inc.; (Circulation) Innovative Interfaces Inc.; (Course Reserve) Innovative Interfaces Inc.; (OPAC) Innovative Interfaces Inc.; (Serials) Innovative Interfaces Inc.
Publications: Learning Resource Center Guides; Learning Resource Center Multimedia WEB Tour (computer based); Research Guide Series
Partic in Fedlink; Nat Libr of Med; PALINET & Union Library Catalogue of Pennsylvania
Special Services for the Deaf - Staff with knowledge of sign language
Friends of the Library Group

UNITED STATES ARMY
A CENTER FOR ARMY ANALYSIS, Bldg 1839, Ste 102, 6110 Goethals Rd, Fort Belvoir, 22060-5230. SAN 328-8668. Tel: 703-806-5192. FAX: 703-806-5724. *Chief Librn*, Dale Eliasson; *Tech Servs*, Veronica Brown; E-Mail: brownv@caa.army.mil; Staff 2 (MLS 1, Non-MLS 1)
Library Holdings: Bk Titles 4,550; Per Subs 130
Subject Interests: Computer science, Military history
Automation Activity & Vendor Info: (Cataloging) SIRSI; (Circulation) SIRSI
Database Vendor: Ebsco - EbscoHost, OCLC - First Search
Partic in Defense Technical Information Center; Dialog Corporation; OCLC Online Computer Library Center, Inc

G UNITED STATES CONSUMER PRODUCT SAFETY COMMISSION LIBRARY,* 4330 East West Hwy, Rm 701, 20814. SAN 306-9001. Tel: 301-504-0044. FAX: 301-504-0124. *Chief Librn*, Elizabeth Kythail
Founded 1973
Library Holdings: Bk Titles 10,000; Per Subs 65
Subject Interests: Administrative law, Business and management, Economics, Engineering, Health sciences, Medicine, Safety, Standards

(government), Technology, Toxicology
Special Collections: Indexed Documents Coll; Technical Standards (Standards Coll), doc, bk & micro
Publications: Information Update (monthly newsletter & new accessions list); User's Guide to Library & Information Services
Partic in Dialog Corporation; Fedlink; Westlaw

S UNIVERSITY PUBLICATIONS OF AMERICA LIBRARY, 4520 East-West Hwy, 20814. SAN 323-8873. Tel: 301-654-1550, 301-657-3200. FAX: 301-657-3203. Web Site: www.upa.pubs.com. *Media Spec*, Robert E Lester; E-Mail: robert.lester@lexis-nexis.com
Founded 1985
Library Holdings: Bk Vols 700; Bk Titles 450
Special Collections: Antebellum South; microfilm & fiche; NAACP records; US Diplomatic, Domestic & Military
Restriction: Staff use only

BOWIE

C BOWIE STATE UNIVERSITY, Thurgood Marshall Library, 14000 Jericho Park Rd, 20715. SAN 306-9141. Tel: 301-860-3850. FAX: 301-860-3848. Web Site: www.bowiestate.edu. *Dir*, Dr Richard Bradberry; *Spec Coll*, Cynthia Coleman
Founded 1937
Library Holdings: Bk Vols 290,000; Per Subs 860
Subject Interests: Art
Special Collections: Afro-American Experience, Slave Doc; Maryland subject; Rare books; University history
Automation Activity & Vendor Info: (Circulation) CARL
Partic in Can Asn of Res Librs; Dialog Corporation; OCLC Online Computer Library Center, Inc

CALVERTON

S MACRO INTERNATIONAL, INC LIBRARY,* 11785 Beltsville Dr, Library, 20705-3119. SAN 307-0352. Tel: 301-572-0294, Ext 0351. FAX: 301-572-0999. *Librn*, James Matheny; E-Mail: jmatheny@macroint.com; *Librn*, Jessica Fomalont; Tel: 301-572-0853, E-Mail: jfomalon@macroint.com; *Asst Librn*, Jeffrey Mewbourn
Library Holdings: Bk Titles 1,500
Subject Interests: Criminal law and justice, Education, Employment, Health sciences, Planning

CAMBRIDGE

§GL DORCHESTER COUNTY CIRCUIT COURT, Law Library, 206 High St, 21613. Tel: 410-228-9840. FAX: 410-228-1860. *In Charge*, Pat Tolley
Library Holdings: Bk Vols 3,000; Bk Titles 40

P DORCHESTER COUNTY PUBLIC LIBRARY,* 303 Gay St, 21613. SAN 344-0524. Tel: 410-228-7331. TDD: 410-228-0454. FAX: 410-228-6313. Web Site: www.dorchesterlibrary.org. *Dir*, Jean S Del Sordo; E-Mail: jdelsordo@dorchesterlibrary.org; *Asst Dir, Circ*, Susan Steele; *Ad Servs*, Cheryl Michael; *Bkmobile Coordr, Br Coordr*, Toby Gearhart; Staff 4 (MLS 4)
Founded 1922. Pop 30,400; Circ 164,627
Jul 1997-Jun 1998 Income $631,888. Mats Exp $70,550, Books $61,704, Per/Ser (Incl. Access Fees) $8,846. Sal $337,670
Library Holdings: Bk Vols 85,067
Special Collections: Dorchester County History & Genealogy; Drama Coll; Education Coll; Maryland Coll
Mem of Eastern Shore Regional Library, Inc
Special Services for the Deaf - TDD
Friends of the Library Group
Branches: 1
HURLOCK BRANCH, 220 S Main St, Hurlock, 21643. SAN 344-0559. Tel: 410-943-4331. FAX: 410-943-4331. Web Site: www.dorchesterlibrary.org.
Friends of the Library Group
Bookmobiles: 1

M EASTERN SHORE HOSPITAL CENTER, Professional Library, PO Box 800, 21613. SAN 306-915X. Tel: 410-221-2485. FAX: 410-221-2475. E-Mail: eshclib@shorenet.net.
Founded 1953
Library Holdings: Bk Vols 2,669; Bk Titles 1,820; Per Subs 39
Subject Interests: Medicine, Nursing, Psychiatry
Partic in National Library Of Medicine, Medlars; SE-Atlantic Regional Med Libr Servs

C UNIVERSITY OF MARYLAND, (UMHP), Center for Environmental & Estuarine Studies Horn Point Library, Horn Point Environmental Laboratories, PO Box 775, 21613. SAN 328-8439. Tel: 410-221-8450. FAX: 410-221-8490. Web Site: www.hpl.umces.edu. *Librn*, Darlene Windsor; E-Mail: windsor@hpl.umces.edu; Staff 1 (MLS 1)
Founded 1972. Fac 20; Highest Degree: Doctorate
Jul 1999-Jun 2000 Mats Exp $95,199, Books $2,000, Per/Ser (Incl. Access Fees) $77,399, Other Print Mats $1,400, Electronic Ref Mat (Incl. Access Fees) $14,400
Library Holdings: Bk Vols 2,900; Per Subs 97
Subject Interests: Marine biology, Oceanography
Database Vendor: CARL, Ebsco - EbscoHost
Function: ILL available
Partic in Maryland Interlibrary Organization; Univ Syst of Md

CAMP SPRINGS

S TRANSPORTATION INSTITUTE, Information Resources Center, 5201 Auth Way, 5th Flr, 20746. SAN 302-7902. Tel: 301-423-3335, Ext 11. FAX: 301-423-0634. E-Mail: info@trans-inst.org. Web Site: www.trans-inst.org. *Librn*, Tina Hammonds
Founded 1968
Library Holdings: Bk Titles 1,500; Per Subs 64
Subject Interests: Water transportation
Publications: Monthly new acquisitions

CATONSVILLE

M SPRING GROVE HOSPITAL CENTER, Sulzbacher Memorial Staff Library, Isidore Tuerk Bldg, 60 Wade Ave, 21228. SAN 306-9168. Tel: 410-402-7824. FAX: 410-402-7732. Web Site: www.springgrove.com. *Librn*, Hannah Johnston
Founded 1938
Library Holdings: Bk Titles 2,100; Per Subs 26
Special Collections: American Journal of Insanity, 1846-1921; Hospital Reports from 1897

CENTREVILLE

P QUEEN ANNE'S COUNTY FREE LIBRARY, 121 S Commerce St, 21617. SAN 306-9176. Tel: 410-758-0980. FAX: 410-758-0614. Web Site: www.quan.lib.md.us. *Dir*, Charles V Powers
Founded 1909. Pop 40,000; Circ 350,000
Library Holdings: Bk Vols 90,000; Per Subs 100
Special Collections: Local History; Waterfowl, Decoy Carving & Boat Building Coll
Mem of Eastern Shore Regional Library, Inc
Partic in Maryland Interlibrary Organization
Open Mon-Thurs 10-8, Fri & Sat 9-5
Branches: 1
KENT ISLAND, 200 Library Circle, Stevensville, 21666-4026. SAN 376-9860. Tel: 410-643-8161. FAX: 410-643-7098. *Mgr*, Margaret Ranson

CHARLOTTE HALL

P SOUTHERN MARYLAND REGIONAL LIBRARY ASSOCIATION, INC., PO Box 459, 37600 New Market Rd, 20622. SAN 306-9826. Tel: 301-843-3634, 301-884-0436, 301-934-9442. FAX: 301-884-0438. E-Mail: smrla@lib.md.us. Web Site: www.somd.lib.md.us/. *Dir*, Sharan D Marshall; E-Mail: smarshall@somd.lib.md.us; *Librn*, David J Paul; Staff 10 (MLS 2, Non-MLS 8)
Founded 1959. Pop 299,700
Jul 2000-Jun 2001 Income $658,120, State $482,120, Federal $5,000, Locally Generated Income $84,700, Other $86,300. Mats Exp $78,300, Books $3,200, Per/Ser (Incl. Access Fees) $15,000, Electronic Ref Mat (Incl. Access Fees) $60,100. Sal $383,690 (Prof $116,400)
Library Holdings: Bk Vols 7,200; Per Subs 500
Automation Activity & Vendor Info: (Cataloging) DRA; (Circulation) DRA; (OPAC) DRA
Database Vendor: Ebsco - EbscoHost, epixtech, inc.
Publications: Community Info Directory; Small Business Resource Guide
Partic in Md State Libr Network

CHESTERTOWN

P KENT COUNTY PUBLIC LIBRARY,* 408 High St, 21620-1312. SAN 306-9184. Tel: 410-778-3636. FAX: 410-778-6756. Web Site: www.kent.lib.md.us. *Dir*, Anne Briggs; E-Mail: abriggs@kent.lib.md.us; Staff 5 (MLS 2, Non-MLS 3)
Founded 1961. Pop 18,000; Circ 120,000
Jul 1997-Jun 1998 Income $373,088, State $65,329, Federal $2,150, County $290,463, Locally Generated Income $15,146. Mats Exp $46,322, Books $38,296, Per/Ser (Incl. Access Fees) $4,232, Presv $196. Sal $246,621
Library Holdings: Bk Titles 60,708; Per Subs 110
Mem of Eastern Shore Regional Library, Inc
Partic in Maryland Interlibrary Organization
Friends of the Library Group
Branches: 2
JAIL TWIG, 200 Pangborn Hall, Washington, 20064. *Mgr*, Anne Briggs
Library Holdings: Bk Vols 1,000; Bk Titles 850
ROCK HALL BRANCH, 5585 Main St Municipal Bldg, 21661. SAN 376-8090. Tel: 410-639-7162. Web Site: www.kent.lib.md.us. *Mgr*, Jeanne

Geibel
Library Holdings: Bk Vols 4,000
Mem of Eastern Shore Regional Library, Inc

C WASHINGTON COLLEGE, Clifton M Miller Library, 300 Washington Ave, 21620-1197. SAN 306-9192. Tel: 410-778-7292. FAX: 410-778-7288. E-Mail: the-library@washcoll.edu. Web Site: www.librarywashcoll.edu. *Librn*, William J Tubbs; E-Mail: william.tubbs@washcoll.edu; *Reader Servs*, William J Chaffin; Tel: 410-778-7293, E-Mail: jeff.chaffin@washcoll.edu; *Reader Servs*, Ruth C Shoge; Tel: 410-778-7704, E-Mail: ruth.shoge@washcoll.edu; *Tech Servs*, Judith I Hymes; Tel: 410-778-7278, E-Mail: judith.hymes@washcoll.edu; Staff 10 (MLS 4, Non-MLS 6)
Founded 1782. Enrl 1,175; Fac 85; Highest Degree: Master
Jul 1999-Jun 2000 Income Parent Institution $805,838. Mats Exp $287,330, Books $59,597, Per/Ser (Incl. Access Fees) $112,995, Micro $22,626, Other Print Mats $47,242, Electronic Ref Mat (Incl. Access Fees) $44,870. Sal $361,047
Library Holdings: Bk Vols 158,147; Bk Titles 144,985; Per Subs 860
Special Collections: Maryland Coll
Automation Activity & Vendor Info: (Acquisitions) Innovative Interfaces Inc.; (Cataloging) Innovative Interfaces Inc.; (Circulation) Innovative Interfaces Inc.; (OPAC) Innovative Interfaces Inc.; (Serials) Innovative Interfaces Inc.
Database Vendor: Dialog, Ebsco - EbscoHost, GaleNet, Lexis-Nexis, OCLC - First Search, ProQuest
Publications: Reference guide brochures
Partic in OCLC Online Computer Library Center, Inc; PALINET & Union Library Catalogue of Pennsylvania
Special Services for the Blind - Access to internet through assistive technology is offered
Friends of the Library Group

CHEVERLY

M PRINCE GEORGE'S HOSPITAL CENTER, Saul Schwartzbach Memorial Library, 3001 Hospital Dr, 20785-1193. SAN 306-9206. Tel: 301-618-2490. FAX: 301-618-2983. *Librn, Online Servs*, Penny Martin; E-Mail: penny11bsense@netscape.com
Founded 1944
Library Holdings: Bk Vols 5,500; Bk Titles 1,500; Per Subs 160
Partic in Nat Libr of Med

CHEVY CHASE

S AUDUBON NATURALIST SOCIETY LIBRARY,* 8940 Jones Mill Rd, 20815. SAN 372-6258. Tel: 301-652-9188, Ext 3028. FAX: 301-951-7179.
Library Holdings: Bk Titles 1,000; Per Subs 115

M HOWARD HUGHES MEDICAL INSTITUTE, Purnell W Choppin Library, 4000 Jones Bridge Rd, 20815-6789. SAN 323-7087. Tel: 301-215-8661. FAX: 301-215-8663. *Mgr Libr Serv*, Cathy Harbert; E-Mail: harbertc@hhmi.org; *Asst Librn*, Jenifer Kirin; Staff 3 (MLS 2, Non-MLS 1)
Library Holdings: Bk Titles 5,000; Per Subs 100
Subject Interests: Cell biology, Genetics, Immunology, Law, Neurosciences
Automation Activity & Vendor Info: (Acquisitions) Endeavor; (Cataloging) Endeavor; (Circulation) Endeavor; (OPAC) Endeavor; (Serials) Endeavor
Database Vendor: Dialog, Lexis-Nexis, Silverplatter Information Inc.
Restriction: Not open to public
Function: ILL limited, Research library

R OHR KODESH CONGREGATION, Sisterhood Library, 8402 Freyman Dr, 20815-3897. SAN 373-059X. Tel: 301-589-3880. FAX: 301-495-4801. E-Mail: okcjmm@erols.com. *Coll Develop, Librn*, Leonard Rosenberg
Library Holdings: Bk Vols 2,000
Subject Interests: Holocaust, Judaica

S RACHEL CARSON COUNCIL, INC LIBRARY, 8940 Jones Mill Rd, 20815. SAN 327-0467. Tel: 301-652-1877. E-Mail: rccouncil@aol.com. Web Site: members.aol.com/rccouncil/ourpage/rcc_page.htm. *Exec Dir*, Diana Post
Founded 1965
Library Holdings: Bk Vols 1,500; Per Subs 12
Subject Interests: Pesticides
Special Collections: Rachel Carson's personal library, photographs, materials on her life
Restriction: By appointment only

R SAINT JOHN'S EPISCOPAL CHURCH LIBRARY, 6701 Wisconsin Ave, 20815. SAN 306-9230. Tel: 301-654-7767. *Librn*, Susan Bradley
Library Holdings: Bk Vols 2,000
Subject Interests: Architecture, Church history, Education, Fiction, Music, Poetry, Theology

CLARKSBURG

S LOCKHEED MARTIN GLOBAL, (Formerly Comsat Corp Library), Telecommunications Library, 22300 Comsat Dr, 20871. SAN 306-9257. Tel: 301-428-4512. FAX: 301-428-7747. *Librn*, Merilee J Worsey
2000-2001 Mats Exp $103,000, Per/Ser (Incl. Access Fees) $55,000, Other Print Mats $48,000
Library Holdings: Bk Vols 12,500; Per Subs 295
Subject Interests: Electronic engineering, Marketing, Technology, Telecommunications
Publications: Bulletins; New Book; Serial Holdings
Restriction: By appointment only
Partic in Dialog Corporation; Interlibrary Users Association

CLINTON

S DIVERSE TECHNOLOGIES CORP, Library & Information Services,* 7905 Malcolm Rd, Ste 200, 20735. SAN 377-094X. Tel: 301-868-6300. FAX: 301-868-8690. *Dir*, Ann Cleland
Library Holdings: Bk Vols 200; Per Subs 12

S MARYLAND NATIONAL CAPITAL PARK & PLANNING COMMISSION, Surratt Museum Research Library, 9118 Brandywine Rd, PO Box 427, 20735. SAN 371-8697. Tel: 301-868-1121. TDD: 301-868-1121. FAX: 301-868-8177. Web Site: www.surratt.org. *Dir*, Laurie Verge; Staff 2 (Non-MLS 2)
Founded 1975
Library Holdings: Bk Vols 1,200
Subject Interests: Civil War, Local history
Special Services for the Deaf - TDD
Specialized material on Lincoln assassination studies

M SOUTHERN MARYLAND HOSPITAL CENTER LIBRARY,* 7503 Surratts Rd, 20735. SAN 377-4236. Tel: 301-899-4163. FAX: 301-856-0911. *Librn*, Joyce Strong
Library Holdings: Bk Vols 500; Per Subs 85
Partic in Maryland Association Of Health Science Librarians

COCKEYSVILLE

S BALTIMORE COUNTY HISTORICAL SOCIETY LIBRARY, 9811 Van Buren Lane, 21030. SAN 371-9979. Tel: 410-666-1876. Web Site: www.baltimorecohistsoc.org. *Librn*, Elmer Haile
Founded 1960
Jan 1999-Dec 1999 Income $2,500. Mats Exp Other Print Mats $400
Library Holdings: Bk Titles 1,300
Subject Interests: Genealogy, Local history
Special Collections: Tombstone Inscriptions, bks & mss
Publications: History Trails (quarterly)
Restriction: Not a lending library

COLLEGE PARK

C ACADEMIC INFORMATION TECHNOLOGY SERVICES LIBRARY,* Acad Info Tech Servs, Univ Md, 20742. SAN 324-1793. Tel: 301-405-4261. FAX: 301-405-0726. E-Mail: infotech-library@umail.umd.edu. Web Site: www.oit.umd.edu/library. *Mgr*, Kathy Campoli; Staff 1 (MLS 1)
Founded 1965. Enrl 32,000
Library Holdings: Bk Titles 2,200; Per Subs 89
Subject Interests: Computer science
Special Collections: Software Coll for IBM PC & MacIntosh
Restriction: Circulation limited

S AMERICAN INSTITUTE OF PHYSICS, Niels Bohr Library, One Physics Ellipse, 20740-3843. SAN 311-5844. Tel: 301-209-3177. FAX: 301-209-3144. E-Mail: nbl@aip.org. Web Site: www.aip.org/history. *Head of Libr*, Joseph Anderson; *Librn*, Michele Blakeslee; *Asst Librn*, Heather Lindsay; Staff 8 (MLS 6, Non-MLS 2)
Founded 1962
Library Holdings: Bk Titles 16,400; Per Subs 75
Subject Interests: Astronomy, Hist of physics, Physics
Special Collections: archives, autobiog, bks, dissertations, mss, notebooks, oral hist mat, per, photog; Hist of Astronomy, 1850-1960, misc; History of Physics, 1850-1950
Automation Activity & Vendor Info: (Acquisitions) epixtech, inc.; (Cataloging) epixtech, inc.; (OPAC) epixtech, inc.; (Serials) epixtech, inc.
Publications: Guide to the Archival Collection of the AIP Niels Bohr Library; National Catalog of Sources for History of Physics; Newsletter
Friends of the Library Group

S ASIAN STUDIES NEWSLETTER ARCHIVES, (ASNA), 9225 Limestone Pl, 20740-3943. SAN 371-6929. Tel: 301-935-5614. *Curator*, Frank Joseph Shulman; Staff 1 (MLS 1)
Founded 1970
1999-2000 Mats Exp $5,000, Books $3,000, Per/Ser (Incl. Access Fees) $2,000

Library Holdings: Bk Vols 10,000
Subject Interests: Asia, China, India, Japan, Korea, Southeast Asia
Publications: Bibliographies
Restriction: By appointment only

S NATIONAL ARCHIVES & RECORDS ADMINISTRATION, National Archives Library,* 8601 Adelphi Rd, 20740-6001. SAN 375-3042. Tel: 301-713-6800. FAX: 301-713-6740. *Dir*, Lida Holland Churchville
Library Holdings: Bk Vols 22,500; Per Subs 505
Partic in Fedlink; OCLC Online Computer Library Center, Inc

NATIONAL ARCHIVES & RECORDS ADMINISTRATION
G NATIONAL ARCHIVES LIBRARY, 8601 Adelphi Rd, Rm 2380, 20740. SAN 336-9064. Tel: 301-713-6778. FAX: 301-713-6740. E-Mail: alic@arch2.nara.gov. *Chief Librn, Dir*, Lida Holland Churchville; Staff 10 (MLS 6, Non-MLS 4)
Founded 1934
Oct 1997-Sep 1998 Income $662,000. Mats Exp $57,500, Books $30,000, Per/Ser (Incl. Access Fees) $22,500, AV Equip $5,000. Sal $498,000
Library Holdings: Bk Vols 78,000; Bk Titles 70,000; Per Subs 480
Special Collections: Archival Record Set of Publications of the United States Government; Archives & Records Management Literature; Federal Government Publications Issued by the Government Printing Office; United States History, bks, per
Publications: Library newsletter
Partic in Fedlink; OCLC Online Computer Library Center, Inc; RLIN
ALIC - Archive Library Information Center: Information & research service for archival & records management information (10,000 docs)

C UNIVERSITY OF MARYLAND LIBRARIES, 20742. SAN 344-0583. Tel: 301-405-9128. FAX: 301-314-9408. Web Site: www.lib.umd.edu/umcp/. *Dean of Libr*, Dr Charles B Lowry; E-Mail: clowry@deans.umd.edu; *Dir Info Resources & Res*, Carlen Ruschoff; Tel: 301-405-9299, E-Mail: ruschoff@deans.umd.ude; *Mgr*, Irma F Dillon; Tel: 301-405-9113, E-Mail: id8@umail.umd.edu; *Coll Develop*, Dr Desider Vikor; Tel: 301-405-9112, E-Mail: dvikor@deans.umd.edu; *Info Tech*, Howard Harris; Tel: 301-405-9194, E-Mail: hharris@deans.umd.edu; *Planning Services*, Mildred Jane Williams; Tel: 301-405-9124, E-Mail: mjwillia@deans.umd.edu; *Publ Servs*, Lori Goetsch; Tel: 301-405-0251, E-Mail: lgoetsch@deans.umd.edu; Staff 300 (MLS 115, Non-MLS 185)
Founded 1813. Enrl 33,006; Fac 1,496; Highest Degree: Doctorate
Jul 1999-Jun 2000 Mats Exp $6,994,191, Books $2,271,339, Per/Ser (Incl. Access Fees) $4,361,207, Presv $207,276, Micro $154,369. Sal $5,458,477 (Prof $4,869,246)
Library Holdings: Bk Vols 2,850,285; Per Subs 13,712
Special Collections: Archives & Manuscripts; Books in Many Scholarly Fields; Broadcast Pioneers Library; East Asia Coll, misc; Gordon W Prange Coll; International Piano Archives at Maryland; Katherine Anne Porter Coll, bks, mss, memorabilia; Maryland State Documents; Marylandia, bks, mss; Music Educators' National Conference Historical Center Coll, misc; National & International Music Organizations Coll; National Public Broadcasting Archives; National Trust for Historic Preservation Library Coll; Official Records & Publications of the University of Maryland at College Park; Oral History Records, memorabilia; Personal Papers & Textual Manuscripts of American & English Authors of the Modern Period; Personal/Family Papers; Rare Books; Records of Organizations, photogs; Special Coll of Papers of Maryland Political Figures; US Patents Dep
Automation Activity & Vendor Info: (Acquisitions) CARL; (Cataloging) CARL; (Circulation) CARL; (OPAC) CARL; (Serials) CARL
Database Vendor: CARL
Publications: Library Bulletin; Library Issues
Partic in Asn of Research Libraries; Center For Research Libraries; Chesapeake Info & Res Libr Alliance; PALINET & Union Library Catalogue of Pennsylvania
Friends of the Library Group
Departmental Libraries:
ARCHITECTURE LIBRARY Tel: 301-405-6317. Interlibrary Loan Service Tel: 301-405-9178. FAX: 301-314-9583. Interlibrary Loan Service FAX: 301-314-9416. E-Mail: ac110@umail.umd.edu. Web Site: www.lib.umd.edu/umcp/arch/architecture.html.
Founded 1967
Library Holdings: Bk Vols 40,143; Per Subs 158
Subject Interests: Architecture, Landscape architecture
Special Collections: World Expositions from 1851-1937
ART LIBRARY Tel: 301-405-9061. Interlibrary Loan Service Tel: 301-405-9178. FAX: 301-314-9725. Interlibrary Loan Service FAX: 301-314-9416. E-Mail: cs20@umail.umd.edu, lw64@umail.umd.edu. Web Site: www.lib.umd.edu/umcp/art/art.html. *Head of Libr*, Lynne Woodruff; Tel: 301-405-9065; *Ref*, Louise Green
Founded 1979
Library Holdings: Bk Vols 99,392; Per Subs 394
Subject Interests: African Language, Pre-Columbian art
Special Collections: Art Exhibition Catalog Coll; Art Reproductions Coll; Decimal Index Art of Low Countries; Emblem Books; Index Photographique de l'art de France; Marburg Index
BROADCAST PIONEERS LIBRARY OF AMERICAN BROADCASTING, Hornbake Library, 20742. SAN 302-6000. Tel: 301-405-9160. FAX: 301-314-2634. E-Mail: bp50@umail.umd.edu. Web Site: www.lib.umd.edu/umcp/lab. *Curator*, Charles Howell; *Archivist, Asst Curator*, Karen Fishman; *Archivist, AV*, Suzanne Adamko; Staff 4 (MLS 3, Non-MLS 1)
Founded 1971
Library Holdings: Bk Vols 9,550; Bk Titles 5,768; Per Subs 382
Subject Interests: Radio, Television
Special Collections: "Wisdom" Coll; Alois Havrilla Coll, photog; Arthur Godfrey Coll; BMI Coll, a-tapes; Edythe J Meserand Coll; Elmo Neale Pickerill Coll; Jane Barton Coll, photog; Joseph E Baudino Coll; National Association of Broadcasters Coll; Peter H Bontsema Coll; Radio Advertising Bureau Coll, recording; Ray Stanich Coll; Robert E Lee Coll; Rod E Phillips Coll; St Louis Post-Dispatch Coll, photog; Westinghouse Broadcasting News Coll, a-tapes; William S Hedges Coll
ENGINEERING & PHYSICAL SCIENCES LIBRARY Tel: 301-405-9157. Interlibrary Loan Service Tel: 301-405-9178. FAX: 301-405-9164. Interlibrary Loan Service FAX: 301-314-9416. Web Site: www.lib.umd.edu/umcp/engin/engin.html. *Head of Libr*, Neal Kaske; Tel: 301-405-9144; *Circ*, Dave Wilt; *Ref*, Julie Harding; *Ref*, Jim Miller
Founded 1953
Library Holdings: Bk Vols 349,369; Per Subs 2,546
Subject Interests: Engineering, Physical science
Special Collections: Rand Corp; Technical Reports (NASA & NACA, its predecessor); US Patent & Trademark
R LEE HORNBAKE UNDERGRADUATE LIBRARY Tel: 301-405-9257. FAX: 301-314-9419. Interlibrary Loan Service FAX: 301-314-9416. *Circ*, Glenn Moreton
Founded 1972
Library Holdings: Bk Vols 205,018; Per Subs 34
The Hornbake Undergraduate Collection has been merged with McKeldin Library. The totals reported here are in storage
THEODORE R MCKELDIN LIBRARY Tel: 301-405-9075. Interlibrary Loan Service Tel: 301-405-9178. FAX: 301-314-9408. Interlibrary Loan Service FAX: 301-314-9416. Web Site: www.lib.umd.edu/umcp/. *Acq*, Carole Bell; Tel: 301-405-9307, E-Mail: cb216@umail.umd.edu; *Cat*, John Schalow; Tel: 301-405-9320, E-Mail: js368@umail.umd.edu; *Circ*, Rebecca Nwude; Tel: 301-405-9095, E-Mail: rn15@umail.umd.edu; *Govt Doc*, Marianne Ryan; Tel: 301-405-9169, E-Mail: mr190@umail.umd.edu; *Access Serv*, Terry Sayler; Tel: 301-405-9177, E-Mail: ts6@umail.umd.edu
Library Holdings: Bk Vols 1,975,107; Per Subs 9,711
Subject Interests: Rare books
Special Collections: East Asia Coll (Chinese, Japanese & Korean Language Publications); Gordon W Prange Coll; Katherine Ann Porter Room, bks, photogs, memorabilia; Marylandia; Md, Del & DC Regional; National Trust for Historic Preservation
The figures provided for the number of book volumes & periodical subscriptions include the College of Information Science Library collection
NONPRINT MEDIA SERVICES, 4210 Hornbake Library Bldg, 20742. SAN 344-0788. Tel: 301-405-9236. FAX: 301-314-9419. Interlibrary Loan Service FAX: 301-314-9416. *Head of Libr*, Allan Rough; *Circ, Ref*, Carleton Jackson
Founded 1971
Special Collections: Public Television Archives Collections include: Maryland Public Television, Corporation for Public Broadcasting and NAEB Radio Programs
Supports all programs offered at College Park Campus
PERFORMING ARTS LIBRARY Tel: 301-405-9217. Interlibrary Loan Service Tel: 301-405-9178. FAX: 301-314-7170. Interlibrary Loan Service FAX: 301-314-9416. Web Site: www.lib.umd.edu/umcp/music/music.html. *Head of Libr*, Bruce Wilson; *Circ*, Philip Vandermeer; *Curator*, Donald E Manildi; *Curator, Spec Coll*, Bonnie Jo Dopp
Founded 1982
Library Holdings: Bk Vols 98,548; Per Subs 345
Special Collections: Arts Education (Charles Fowler Papers); Handeliana (Jacob Coppersmith Coll); International Piano Archives at Maryland; Musical Americana (Irving & Magery Lowens Coll); National & International Music Organization Coll; Radio Station WOR/Alfred Wallenstein Score Coll
WHITE MEMORIAL CHEMISTRY LIBRARY Tel: 301-405-9078. Interlibrary Loan Service Tel: 301-405-9176. Interlibrary Loan Service FAX: 301-314-9416. E-Mail: se13@umail.umd.edu. Web Site: www.lib.umd.edu/umcp/chem/chemistry.html. *Actg Librn*, Sylvia O'Brien; Tel: 301-401-9080; *Circ*, Alla Ballanik
Founded 1953
Library Holdings: Bk Vols 82,571; Per Subs 658
Subject Interests: Chemistry, Microbiology

COLUMBIA

S ALLIED-SIGNAL AEROSPACE, Microelectronics & Technology Center,* 9140 Old Annapolis Rd, 21045-1998. SAN 321-3978. Tel: 410-964-4046. FAX: 410-992-5813. *Dir Libr Serv*, Mary Baker
Founded 1981
Library Holdings: Bk Titles 5,640; Per Subs 125
Partic in Dialog Corporation; Maryland Interlibrary Organization; Metrop Wash Libr Coun; OCLC Online Computer Library Center, Inc; PALINET & Union Library Catalogue of Pennsylvania

S HENRY GEORGE FOUNDATION OF AMERICA LIBRARY,* 8775 Cloudleap Court, Ste 212, 21045. SAN 325-464X. Tel: 410-740-1177. FAX: 410-740-3279. E-Mail: hgeorge@smart.net. Web Site: www.smart.net/~hgeorge. *Dir*, Josh Vincent; *Librn*, Sharon Feinman; Staff 2 (MLS 2)
Founded 1926
Library Holdings: Bk Titles 300
Special Collections: Land value & taxation (Henry George Coll), bks, per
Publications: Equal Rights; Incentive Taxation

J HOWARD COMMUNITY COLLEGE LIBRARY, 10901 Little Patuxent Pkwy, 21044. SAN 306-9338. Tel: 410-772-4812. Circulation Tel: 410-772-4922. Reference Tel: 410-772-4921. FAX: 410-772-4993. Web Site: www.howardcc.edu. *Dir*, Lucy K Gardner; E-Mail: lgardner@howardcc.edu; *Asst Dir*, Elzbieta Ciborowski; Tel: 410-772-4788; *Cat*, Yvonda Johnson; Staff 8 (MLS 4, Non-MLS 4)
Founded 1970. Enrl 5,252
Jul 1999-Jun 2000 Income $655,574. Mats Exp $155,090. Sal $348,675 (Prof $156,487)
Library Holdings: Bk Vols 46,633; Bk Titles 43,032; Per Subs 1,201
Subject Interests: Art, Nursing
Automation Activity & Vendor Info: (Acquisitions) SIRSI; (Cataloging) SIRSI; (Circulation) SIRSI; (Course Reserve) SIRSI; (OPAC) SIRSI; (Serials) SIRSI
Database Vendor: GaleNet, IAC - Info Trac, Lexis-Nexis, OCLC - First Search, Silverplatter Information Inc.

P HOWARD COUNTY LIBRARY, 6600 Cradlerock Way, 21045-4912. SAN 344-0850. Tel: 410-313-7750. TDD: 410-313-7883. FAX: 410-313-7742. Web Site: www.howa.lib.md.us. *Dir*, Norma Hill; E-Mail: hilln@howa.lib.md.us; *Assoc Dir*, Joyce Demmitt; E-Mail: demmittj@howa.lib.md.us; *Asst Dir*, Brian K Auger; E-Mail: auger@howa.lib.md.us; *Head Tech Servs*, Holly Johnson; Tel: 410-313-7922, E-Mail: johnsonh@howa.lib.md.us; *Head, Circ*, Lewis Belfont; E-Mail: belfontl@howa.lib.md.us; *Ch Servs*, Hope Chase; E-Mail: chaseh@howa.lib.md.us; *Materials Manager*, Cynthia Jones; E-Mail: jonesc@howa.lib.md.us; *Coordr*, Patricia Bates; E-Mail: batesp@howa.lib.md.us; *Coordr*, Madeline Terrell; E-Mail: terrelm@howa.lib.md.us; *Outreach Serv*, Natalie Weikart; E-Mail: weikartn@howa.lib.md.us; *Branch Mgr*, Ann Gilligan; Tel: 410-313-5580, Fax: 410-313-5575, E-Mail: gilligaa@howa.lib.md.us; *Branch Mgr*, Liz Lancaster; E-Mail: lancastl@howa.lib.md.us; *Branch Mgr*, Phil Lord; Tel: 410-313-5581, Fax: 410-313-5095, E-Mail: lordp@howa.lib.md.us; *Branch Mgr*, Ruth Newton; Tel: 410-313-1978, Fax: 410-313-1999, E-Mail: newtonr@howa.lib.md.us; *Branch Mgr*, Angelo Sanders; Tel: 410-313-7770, Fax: 410-313-7741, E-Mail: sandersa@howa.lib.md.us; *Branch Mgr*, Karen Trennepohl; Tel: 410-880-5990, Fax: 410-880-5999, E-Mail: trennepk@howa.lib.md.us. Subject Specialists: *Adult*, Patricia Bates; *Human resources*, Madeline Terrell; Staff 206 (MLS 47, Non-MLS 159)
Founded 1940. Pop 234,500; Circ 3,142,328
Jul 1999-Jul 2000 Income (Main Library and Branch Library) $10,054,653, State $524,980, Federal $112,682, County $8,397,677, Locally Generated Income $385,048. Mats Exp $1,719,122. Sal $5,518,101
Library Holdings: Bk Vols 953,108; Bk Titles 802,394; Per Subs 1,324
Subject Interests: Health sciences
Special Collections: County Detention (JAIL) Library; Literacy Materials; Materials for the Disabled; Toys
Automation Activity & Vendor Info: (Acquisitions) epixtech, inc.; (Cataloging) epixtech, inc.; (Circulation) epixtech, inc.; (OPAC) epixtech, inc.; (Serials) epixtech, inc.
Database Vendor: epixtech, inc., GaleNet, IAC - Info Trac, IAC - SearchBank, Innovative Interfaces INN - View, ProQuest
Publications: Great Expectations (Newsletter)
Special Services for the Deaf - High interest/low vocabulary books; Staff with knowledge of sign language; TDD; TTY machine
Special Services for the Blind - Screen enlargement software for people with visual disabilities
Literacy Tutor Programs
Friends of the Library Group
Branches: 6
CENTRAL, 10375 Little Patuxent Pkwy, 21044-3499. SAN 344-0915. Tel: 410-313-7800. TDD: 410-313-7883. FAX: 410-313-7864. *Mgr*, Liz Lancaster
Library Holdings: Bk Vols 301,336
Special Services for the Deaf - TDD
EAST COLUMBIA, 6600 Cradlerock Way, 21045-4912. SAN 374-647X. Tel: 410-313-7700. TDD: 410-313-7740. FAX: 410-313-7741. *Mgr*, Glennor Shirley
Library Holdings: Bk Vols 166,664
Special Services for the Deaf - TDD
ELKRIDGE BRANCH, 6540 Washington Blvd, Elkridge, 21227-5532. SAN 328-5049. Tel: 410-313-5077. TDD: 410-313-5090. FAX: 410-313-5095. *Mgr*, Phil Lord
Library Holdings: Bk Vols 78,417
Special Services for the Deaf - TDD
LISBON COMMUNITY, 710 Lisbon Center Dr, Woodbine, 21797-8600. SAN 328-5006. Tel: 410-489-4290.
Library Holdings: Bk Vols 18,000
MILLER BRANCH, 9421 Frederick Rd, Ellicott City, 21042-2119. SAN 344-0885. Tel: 410-313-1950. TDD: 410-313-1957. FAX: 410-313-1999. *Librn*, Ruth Newton
Library Holdings: Bk Vols 196,000
Special Services for the Deaf - TDD
SAVAGE, 9125 Durness Lane, 20723-5991. SAN 328-5022. Tel: 410-880-5980. TDD: 410-880-5979. FAX: 410-880-5999. *Librn*, Karen Trennepohl
Library Holdings: Bk Vols 80,101
Special Services for the Deaf - TDD
Bookmobiles: 1

L MILES & STOCKBRIDGE, Law Library,* 9881 Broken Land Pkwy Ste 400, 21046. SAN 372-056X. Tel: 410-381-6000. FAX: 410-381-6430. Web Site: www.milesstockbridge.com. *Librn*, Mary Ann Redman; E-Mail: mredman@milesstockbridge.com
Library Holdings: Bk Vols 4,500; Per Subs 30

L ROUSE CO, Law Library,* 10275 Little Patuxent Pkwy, 21044. SAN 372-1051. Tel: 410-992-6000. FAX: 410-992-6363. *In Charge*, Dodie Gaudry
Library Holdings: Bk Titles 533; Per Subs 47

S W R GRACE & CO, Information Center, 7500 Grace Dr, 21044. SAN 306-9311. Tel: 410-531-4080. FAX: 410-531-4757. E-Mail: co.jones-quartey@grace.com. *Mgr*, Theo S Jones-Quartey; Staff 3 (MLS 1, Non-MLS 2)
Founded 1953
Library Holdings: Bk Titles 18,000; Per Subs 100
Subject Interests: Chemical engineering, Inorganic chemistry, Organic chemistry, Polymer chemistry
Special Collections: Annual Reports
Automation Activity & Vendor Info: (Acquisitions) epixtech, inc.; (Cataloging) epixtech, inc.; (Circulation) epixtech, inc.; (Serials) epixtech, inc.
Database Vendor: Dialog, Ebsco - EbscoHost, epixtech, inc., Lexis-Nexis
Publications: InfoSource (newsletter)
Function: Research library
Partic in Capcon Library Network

CROWNSVILLE

M CROWNSVILLE HOSPITAL CENTER, Staff Library,* 1520 Crownsville Rd, 21032-2002. SAN 306-9346. Tel: 410-729-6000, Ext 6585. FAX: 410-987-0446. *Dir*, Susan S Merrill; E-Mail: smerrill@mail.bcpl.lib.md.us
Founded 1954
Library Holdings: Bk Vols 1,125; Per Subs 22
Subject Interests: Nursing, Psychiatry, Psychoanalysis, Psychology
Special Collections: Psychiatry (Collected Papers of Adolf Myer); Psychoanalysis (Life & Work of Sigmund Freud)
Partic in Maryland Interlibrary Organization; Md Health Science Libraries' Union List of Biomedical Serials

CUMBERLAND

J ALLEGANY COLLEGE OF MARYLAND LIBRARY, 12401 Willowbrook Rd SE, 21502-2596. SAN 306-9354. Tel: 301-784-5268. Interlibrary Loan Service Tel: 301-784-5241. Circulation Tel: 301-784-5269. Reference Tel: 301-784-5138. FAX: 301-784-5017. Web Site: www.ac.cc.md.us/Library. *Dir Libr Serv*, Robert D Baldwin; *Coordr*, Mona Clites; *Ref, Tech Servs*, Virginia Rasbold; *Ref*, Barbara Browning; Staff 10 (MLS 4, Non-MLS 6)
Founded 1961. Enrl 2,591; Fac 195; Highest Degree: Associate
Jul 1999-Jun 2000 Income (Main and Other College/University Libraries) Parent Institution $506,276. Mats Exp $101,232, Books $33,752, Per/Ser (Incl. Access Fees) $24,130, Presv $470, Micro $12,518, AV Equip $12,332, Electronic Ref Mat (Incl. Access Fees) $16,753. Sal $262,447 (Prof $127,067)
Library Holdings: Bk Vols 56,729; Bk Titles 49,027; Per Subs 440
Subject Interests: Allied health, Criminal law and justice, Social sciences and issues
Special Collections: Local Hist (Appalachian Coll)
Automation Activity & Vendor Info: (Acquisitions) GEAC; (Cataloging) GEAC; (Circulation) GEAC; (Course Reserve) GEAC; (OPAC) GEAC; (Serials) GEAC
Publications: bibliographies & user guides; Western Maryland Materials union list
Function: ILL available, Photocopies available, Reference services available, Some telephone reference
Partic in Maryland Interlibrary Organization; Md Commun Col Libr Consortium
Departmental Libraries:
BEDFORD COUNTY CAMPUS
See Separate Entry in Everett, PA

L ALLEGANY COUNTY CIRCUIT COURT LIBRARY,* Court House, 30 Washington St, 21502. SAN 306-9362. Tel: 301-777-5921. FAX: 301-777-2055. *Librn*, James T Speis Jr
Library Holdings: Bk Vols 15,500

Subject Interests: Law
Special Collections: Maryland County Charters; Maryland Court of Appeals Records and Briefs, 1893-1931

P ALLEGANY COUNTY LIBRARY, 31 Washington St, 21502. SAN 344-0974. Tel: 301-777-1200. FAX: 301-777-7299. E-Mail: lib@allconet.org. Web Site: www.lib.allconet.org. *Dir*, John Taub; *Tech Servs*, Carol A Waugerman; *Bkmobile Coordr*, Judy C Castleman; Staff 4 (MLS 4)
Founded 1924. Pop 72,700; Circ 330,624
1999-2000 Income $1,424,078, State $535,136, Federal $6,686, County $620,000, Locally Generated Income $63,900. Mats Exp $1,300,633, Books $143,602. Sal $651,724
Library Holdings: Bk Vols 162,768; Per Subs 317
Special Collections: Western Maryland (Maryland History & Genealogy)
Mem of Western Maryland Public Libraries
Partic in Maryland Interlibrary Organization
Branches: 4
FROSTBURG PUBLIC, 65 E Main St, Frostburg, 21532. SAN 344-1008. Tel: 301-687-0790. FAX: 301-689-6401. *Branch Mgr*, Patricia Merrbach; *Ch Servs*, Constance Wilson
Library Holdings: Bk Vols 25,965
LAVALE BRANCH, 815 National Hwy, LaVale, 21502. SAN 344-1032. Tel: 301-729-0855. FAX: 301-729-3490. *Branch Mgr*, Sondra A Ritchie
Library Holdings: Bk Vols 24,741
SOUTH CUMBERLAND, 100 Seymour St, 21502. SAN 344-1067. Tel: 301-724-1607. FAX: 301-724-1504. *Branch Mgr*, Lisa Broll; *Branch Mgr*, Linda Burkey
Library Holdings: Bk Vols 20,795
Friends of the Library Group
WESTERNPORT BRANCH, 66 Main St, Westernport, 21562. SAN 344-1091. Tel: 301-359-0455. FAX: 301-359-0046. *Branch Mgr*, Pamela K Neder
Library Holdings: Bk Vols 20,195
Bookmobiles: 1

M WESTERN MARYLAND HEALTH SYSTEM - SACRED HEART CAMPUS, Sr Martha Malloy Medical Library, 900 Seton Dr, 21502. SAN 306-9389. Tel: 301-723-5229. FAX: 301-723-5526. *Librn*, Margie Gacki; E-Mail: mgacki@wmhs.com
Founded 1967
Library Holdings: Bk Vols 500; Per Subs 40

M WESTERN MARYLAND HEALTH SYSTEM MEMORIAL CAMPUS, Library Media Center,* 600 Memorial Ave, 21502. SAN 306-9370. Tel: 301-723-4027. FAX: 301-723-4549. E-Mail: mhmc@mindspring.com. *Librn*, Margie Gacki
Founded 1929
Library Holdings: Bk Vols 1,300; Per Subs 60
Subject Interests: Medicine, Nursing, Surgery
Consumer health information section

DENTON

P CAROLINE COUNTY PUBLIC LIBRARY, 100 Market St, 21629. SAN 344-1121. Tel: 410-479-1343. FAX: 410-479-1443. Web Site: www.caro.lib.md.us/library. *Dir*, George A Sands, Jr; E-Mail: gsands@mail.caro.lib.md.us; *Asst Dir*, Deborah A Bennett; Staff 19 (MLS 4, Non-MLS 15)
Founded 1961. Pop 30,000; Circ 202,186
Jul 1999-Jun 2000 Income (Main Library and Branch Library) $1,046,681, State $201,547, County $845,134. Mats Exp $130,000. Sal $622,953
Library Holdings: Bk Vols 85,023; Bk Titles 76,289; Per Subs 284
Partic in Maryland Interlibrary Organization
Friends of the Library Group
Branches: 2
FEDERALSBURG BRANCH, 123 Morris St, Federalsburg, 21632. SAN 344-1156. Tel: 410-754-8397. FAX: 410-754-3058. *Librn*, Samuel A Smith
Library Holdings: Bk Vols 6,000; Bk Titles 5,000
NORTH COUNTY BRANCH, Cedar Lane, PO Box 336, Greensboro, 21639. SAN 377-7421. Tel: 410-482-2173. FAX: 410-482-2634. *Librn*, Richard O Smith
Bookmobiles: 1

EASTON

S ACADEMY ART MUSEUM, Arts Resource Center & Library, 106 South St, 21601. SAN 306-9397. Tel: 410-822-0455. FAX: 410-822-5997. *Dir*, Christopher Brownawell
Founded 1958
Library Holdings: Bk Vols 2,000; Per Subs 10
Subject Interests: Art and architecture, Arts and crafts, Music, Photography
Special Collections: Fine Art Books
Restriction: Members only

J CALHOON MEBA ENGINEERING SCHOOL LIBRARY, 27050 Saint Michaels Rd, 21601. SAN 306-8293. Tel: 410-822-9600, Ext 322. FAX: 410-822-7220. Web Site: www.mebaschool.com. *Dir*, Henry Phillips; *Librn*, Lisa McNeal; E-Mail: lmcneal@mebaschool.org; Staff 1 (Non-MLS 1)
Founded 1966
Library Holdings: Bk Vols 8,000; Per Subs 125
Subject Interests: Marine eng

M MEMORIAL HOSPITAL, Health Sciences Library,* 219 S Washington St, 21601. SAN 306-9400. Tel: 410-822-1000, Ext 5776. FAX: 410-820-4020. *Librn*, Lois Sanger; Staff 3 (MLS 1, Non-MLS 2)
Founded 1929
Library Holdings: Bk Titles 5,000; Per Subs 250
Subject Interests: Medicine, Nursing, Obstetrics and gynecology, Orthopedics, Pediatrics, Surgery
Partic in Nat Libr of Med Region 2

P TALBOT COUNTY FREE LIBRARY, (TCFL), 100 W Dover St, 21601-2620. SAN 306-9419. Tel: 410-822-1626. TDD: 410-822-8735. FAX: 410-820-8217. Web Site: www.talb.lib.md.us. *Dir*, Robert T Horvath; E-Mail: rhorvath@talb.lib.md.us; *Asst Dir*, Jane E McFarlane; E-Mail: jmac@talb.lib.md.us; *Branch Mgr*, Shauna Beulah; *Ch Servs*, Rosemary Morris; E-Mail: rm0013@mail.pratt.lib.md.us; *ILL*, Mia Y Clark; E-Mail: mia@talb.lib.md.us; *Spec Coll*, Ronald J Keiser; E-Mail: jerry@talb.lib.md.us; *Syst Coordr*, Scott Oliver; E-Mail: soliver@talb.lib.md.us; *Cat*, Jane Steele; *ILL*, Christine Eareckson; *Librn, Ref Serv*, Susan Horvath; Staff 12 (MLS 7, Non-MLS 5)
Founded 1925. Pop 32,400; Circ 179,206
Jul 1999-Jun 2000 Income (Main Library and Branch Library) $752,820, State $76,590, City $4,500, County $511,400, Locally Generated Income $129,000, Other $31,330. Mats Exp $72,775, Books $59,000, Per/Ser (Incl. Access Fees) $7,575, Presv $500, AV Equip $1,500, Manuscripts & Archives $1,200, Electronic Ref Mat (Incl. Access Fees) $3,000. Sal $415,284
Library Holdings: Bk Vols 96,500; Bk Titles 78,517; Per Subs 150
Subject Interests: Maryland
Publications: Talbot County Free Library's Weathervane
Mem of Eastern Shore Regional Library, Inc
Special Services for the Deaf - TTY machine
Friends of the Library Group
Branches: 1
SAINT MICHAELS BRANCH, 106 N Fremont St, PO Box 917, Saint Michaels, 21663-0917. SAN 376-8198. Tel: 410-745-5877. FAX: 410-754-5877. Web Site: www.talb.lib.md.us. *Head of Libr*, Shauna Beulah
Jun 1998-Jul 1999 Income $18,492. Mats Exp $14,593
Library Holdings: Bk Vols 10,000; Bk Titles 5,000; Per Subs 105
Bookmobiles: 1

EDGEWATER

G SMITHSONIAN INSTITUTION LIBRARIES, Smithsonian Environmental Research Center Library, 647 Contees Wharf Rd, 21037. SAN 307-0174. Tel: 301-261-4190. FAX: 301-261-4174. E-Mail: libmail@sil.si.edu. Web Site: www.sil.si.edu. *Librn*, Angela Haggins; Staff 1 (Non-MLS 1)
Library Holdings: Bk Vols 9,000; Per Subs 101
Subject Interests: Ecology, Environ mgt, Land use
Open Mon-Fri 8-4:30

ELK RIDGE

M MHA LIBRARY, 6820 Deerpath Rd, 21075. SAN 306-9915. Tel: 410-379-6200. FAX: 410-379-8239. E-Mail: communicate@mhaonline.org. *In Charge*, Elizabeth B Smith; E-Mail: esmith@mhaonline.org
Library Holdings: Bk Vols 700; Per Subs 25
Partic in Nat Libr of Med

ELKTON

S BASELL USA, (Formerly Montell Usa, Inc), 912 Appleton Rd, 21921. SAN 374-7735. Tel: 410-996-1787. FAX: 410-996-1777. *Tech Servs*, Marlene A Rossing; E-Mail: marlene_rossing@montellna.com; Staff 1 (MLS 1)
Founded 1989
Library Holdings: Bk Vols 3,800; Per Subs 160
Database Vendor: Dialog

§GL CECIL COUNTY CIRCUIT COURT LIBRARY, Courthouse, 2nd flr, 129 E Main St, 21921. Tel: 410-996-5325. FAX: 410-996-5120. E-Mail: cecillaw@iximd.com. *Librn*, Hallie Wolfe
Library Holdings: Bk Vols 5,000; Bk Titles 150

P CECIL COUNTY PUBLIC LIBRARY, 301 Newark Ave, 21921-5441. SAN 344-1180. Tel: 410-996-5600. TDD: 410-996-5609. FAX: 410-996-5604. Web Site: www.ebranch.cecil.lib.md.us. *Dir*, Linda Brammer; *Asst Dir*, Lee O'Brien; *Br Coordr*, Carol Starzmann; *Ref*, Barbara Ramsaur; *Ad Servs*, Nikki Bigley; *YA Servs*, Ruth Ann Johnson; *Ch Servs*, Nancy Heinold; Staff 30 (MLS 6, Non-MLS 24)
Founded 1947. Pop 80,600; Circ 544,699
Jul 1999-Jun 2000 Income (Main Library and Branch Library) $1,685,134, State $404,510, City $5,000, Federal $97,057, County $1,078,091, Locally Generated Income $105,476. Mats Exp $240,984. Sal $1,005,315
Library Holdings: Bk Vols 212,718; Bk Titles 101,273; Per Subs 201

Automation Activity & Vendor Info: (Cataloging) SIRSI; (Circulation) SIRSI
Publications: Cecil County Organizations; Library Link
Partic in Maryland Interlibrary Organization
Friends of the Library Group
Branches: 6
CECILTON BRANCH, PO Box 550, Cecilton, 21913-0550. SAN 344-1210. Tel: 410-275-1091. FAX: 410-275-1092.
CHESAPEAKE CITY BRANCH, PO Box 256, Chesapeake City, 21915. SAN 344-1229. Tel: 410-885-2552.
NORTH EAST BRANCH, 106 W Cecil Ave, North East, 21901. SAN 344-1245. Tel: 410-996-6269. FAX: 410-996-6268.
PERRYVILLE BRANCH, 515 Broad St, Perryville, 21903. SAN 344-1253. Tel: 410-996-6050. FAX: 410-996-6051.
PORT DEPOSIT BRANCH, 64 S Main St, Port Deposit, 21904. SAN 328-7963. Tel: 410-996-6055.
RISING SUN BRANCH, 111 Colonial Way, Rising Sun, 21911. SAN 344-127X. Tel: 410-658-4025. FAX: 410-658-4024.
Friends of the Library Group
Bookmobiles: 1

S THIOKOL CORP, Elkton DLV Operations Library,* 55 Thiokol Rd, 21921. SAN 329-0328. Tel: 410-392-1348. FAX: 410-392-1650. *Actg Librn*, Anthony LoRusso
Founded 1985. Pop 350
Library Holdings: Bk Titles 2,000; Per Subs 100
Subject Interests: Engineering
Special Collections: CPIA Publications
Restriction: Restricted access

EMMITSBURG

C MOUNT SAINT MARY'S COLLEGE & SEMINARY, Hugh J Phillips Library, 16300 Old Emmitsburg Rd, 21727-7799. SAN 306-9435. Tel: 301-447-5244. FAX: 301-447-5099. Web Site: www.msmary.edu/library. *Dir*, D Stephen Rockwood; E-Mail: rockwood@msmary.edu; *Online Servs, Publ Servs*, Joy Allison; *Tech Servs*, Kathleen Sterner; *Bibliog Instr, Ref*, Laurel Thrasher; *Syst Coordr*, Bruce Yelovich; E-Mail: yelovich@msmary.edu
Highest Degree: Master
Jul 1998-Jun 1999 Income $722,197. Mats Exp $309,641, Books $160,000, Per/Ser (Incl. Access Fees) $105,886, Micro $18,155, Electronic Ref Mat (Incl. Access Fees) $25,600. Sal $290,842 (Prof $176,529)
Library Holdings: Bk Vols 202,000; Per Subs 825
Special Collections: 16th & 17th Century Religions; Early Catholic Americana
Automation Activity & Vendor Info: (Acquisitions) CARL; (Cataloging) CARL; (Circulation) CARL; (Course Reserve) CARL; (ILL) CARL; (Media Booking) CARL; (OPAC) CARL; (Serials) CARL
Partic in Maryland Interlibrary Organization; OCLC Online Computer Library Center, Inc; PALINET & Union Library Catalogue of Pennsylvania
Friends of the Library Group

G NATIONAL EMERGENCY TRAINING CENTER, Learning Resource Center, 16825 S Seton Ave, 21727. SAN 325-8939. Tel: 301-447-1030. Toll Free Tel: 800-638-1821. FAX: 301-447-3217. E-Mail: netclrc@fema.gov. Web Site: www.lrc.fema.gov. *In Charge*, Adele Chiesa; Staff 12 (MLS 5, Non-MLS 7)
Oct 2000-Sep 2001 Income (Main Library Only) $742,700. Mats Exp $122,500, Books $77,000, Per/Ser (Incl. Access Fees) $39,000, Presv $5,000, AV Equip $1,500. Sal $540,000 (Prof $210,000)
Library Holdings: Bk Vols 80,000; Per Subs 300
Subject Interests: Emergency care
Database Vendor: OCLC - First Search
Partic in Fed Libr & Info Network

FORT DETRICK

S NATIONAL CANCER INSTITUTE AT FREDRICK SCIENTIFIC LIBRARY, (Formerly Nci-Frederick Cancer Research & Development Center), Bldg 549, Sultan St, 21702-8255. (Mail add: PO Box B, 21702-1201), Tel: 301-846-1093. Interlibrary Loan Service Tel: 301-846-1572. FAX: 301-846-6332. Web Site: www-library.ncifcrf.gov. *Mgr*, Susan W Wilson; E-Mail: wilsonu@mail.ncifcrf.gov
Founded 1972
Library Holdings: Bk Vols 15,500; Per Subs 700
Subject Interests: Biological physics, Biology, Cancer, Chemistry
Database Vendor: Dialog, IAC - Info Trac, Innovative Interfaces INN - View, Silverplatter Information Inc.
Publications: Accessions list; Serial holdings list
Partic in Fedlink

FORT GEORGE G MEADE

UNITED STATES ARMY

AM KIMBROUGH AMBULATORY CARE CENTER, MEDICAL LIBRARY, 2480 Llewellyn Ave, 20755-5800. SAN 344-1326. Tel: 301-677-8228. FAX: 301-677-8108. *In Charge*, Patricia L Passaro; E-Mail: pat_passaro@smtplink.meade.amedd.army.mil
Oct 1999-Sep 2000 Income $60,000. Mats Exp $60,000, Books $36,000, Per/Ser (Incl. Access Fees) $24,000. Sal $38,000
Library Holdings: Bk Titles 2,459; Per Subs 120
Subject Interests: Medical care, Medicine, Nursing
Partic in SE-Atlantic Regional Med Libr Servs

A POST LIBRARY, 4418 Llewellyn Ave, 20755-5068. SAN 344-130X. Tel: 301-677-4509. FAX: 301-677-3590. *Librn*, Ron Argentati; Tel: 301-677-3594, E-Mail: argentar@meade-emh2.army.mil
Oct 1997-Sep 1998 Income $210,000. Mats Exp $60,000, Books $10,000, Per/Ser (Incl. Access Fees) $7,500, Micro $5,000. Sal $130,000
Library Holdings: Bk Vols 30,000; Per Subs 118
Subject Interests: Foreign Language
Partic in Dialog Corporation; Fedlink; OCLC Online Computer Library Center, Inc

FORT HOWARD

GM DEPARTMENT OF VETERANS AFFAIRS, Medical Library, 9600 N Point Rd, 21052-3035. SAN 344-1369. Tel: 410-477-1800, Ext 2729. FAX: 410-477-7207. *In Charge*, Corrine Tippit
Founded 1941
Library Holdings: Bk Vols 2,000; Per Subs 200
Subject Interests: Rehabilitation, physical
Restriction: Members only

FORT MEAD

G US ENVIRONMENTAL PROTECTION AGENCY, (ESCL), (Formerly Environmental Science Center Library), Environmental Science Center Library, 701 Mapes Rd, 20755. SAN 306-8005. Tel: 410-305-2603. Interlibrary Loan Service Tel: 410-305-2695. FAX: 410-305-3092. Web Site: www.epa.gov/reg3esd1/oasqlib. *Librn*, Matthew Moran; E-Mail: moran.matthew@epamail.epa.gov
Founded 1964
Oct 1999-Sep 2000 Income $12,000. Mats Exp $15,400, Books $5,000, Per/Ser (Incl. Access Fees) $6,400, AV Equip $4,000
Library Holdings: Bk Titles 6,000; Per Subs 40
Subject Interests: Analytical chemistry, Chesapeake Bay, Maryland, Virginia
Publications: Federal Register Summary (Newsletter); Infostructure (Newsletter)
Partic in EPA
Special Services for the Deaf - TTY machine

FREDERICK

S BECHTEL CORP, Technical Library, 5275 Westview Dr, 21703-8306. SAN 306-9540. Tel: 301-228-7521. FAX: 301-668-1643. *Librn*, Diane Kavanagh; E-Mail: dkavanag@bechtel.com
Founded 1962
Library Holdings: Bk Vols 3,500; Per Subs 50
Subject Interests: Construction, Electrical engineering, Mechanical engineering, Nuclear energy, Nuclear power, U.S. Government

J FREDERICK COMMUNITY COLLEGE LIBRARY, 7932 Opossumtown Pike, 21702. SAN 306-946X. Tel: 301-846-2444. FAX: 301-846-2498. Web Site: www.fcc.cc.md.us/library. *Dir*, Mick O'Leary; E-Mail: moleary@fcc.cc.md.us; Staff 6 (MLS 4, Non-MLS 2)
Founded 1957. Enrl 5,000; Fac 75; Highest Degree: Associate
Jul 2000-Jun 2001 Income $394,027. Mats Exp $104,000, Books $68,000, Per/Ser (Incl. Access Fees) $9,000, Electronic Ref Mat (Incl. Access Fees) $27,000. Sal $266,884 (Prof $198,611)
Library Holdings: Bk Vols 37,000; Bk Titles 36,000; Per Subs 100; Bks on Deafness & Sign Lang 20
Subject Interests: Nursing
Automation Activity & Vendor Info: (Acquisitions) VTLS; (Cataloging) VTLS; (Circulation) VTLS; (Course Reserve) VTLS; (OPAC) VTLS
Database Vendor: Ebsco - EbscoHost, OCLC - First Search, ProQuest, Silverplatter Information Inc.
Partic in OCLC Online Computer Library Center, Inc
Open Mon-Thurs 8-10, Fri 8-4, Sat 10-4

GL FREDERICK COUNTY CIRCUIT COURT LIBRARY, Courthouse, 100 W Patrick St, 21701. SAN 306-9478. Tel: 301-694-2563. *Librn*, Betty Tucker
Library Holdings: Bk Vols 27,000

P FREDERICK COUNTY PUBLIC LIBRARIES, (FCPL), 110 E Patrick St, 21701. SAN 306-9494. Tel: 301-694-1613. TDD: 301-631-3787. FAX: 301-631-3789. Web Site: www.fcpl.org. *Dir*, Darrell Batson; *Assoc Dir*, Dolores Maminski; *Assoc Dir*, Elizabeth Pelle; E-Mail: bp0012@mail.pratt.lib.ms.us; *Tech Servs*, Pat Short; Tel: 301-631-3762; *Ch Servs*, Barbara White; Tel: 301-631-3775; *Coll Develop*, Mary Hauer; Tel: 301-631-3779; Staff 64 (MLS 17, Non-MLS 47)

Founded 1937. Pop 192,000; Circ 1,183,631; Enrl 81,144
Jul 1999-Jun 2000 Income (Main Library and Branch Library) $3,640,556, State $747,461, Federal $25,700, County $2,717,058, Locally Generated Income $150,337. Mats Exp $776,870, Books $558,281, Per/Ser (Incl. Access Fees) $34,803, Micro $8,632, AV Equip $104,416, Electronic Ref Mat (Incl. Access Fees) $70,738. Sal $2,810,276
Library Holdings: Bk Vols 350,765; Per Subs 717
Special Collections: Maryland Hist (Maryland Coll), bk, micro
Automation Activity & Vendor Info: (Acquisitions) Brodart; (Cataloging) VTLS; (Circulation) VTLS; (OPAC) VTLS
Special Services for the Deaf - Staff with knowledge of sign language; TDD; TTY machine
Friends of the Library Group
Branches: 7
AUDIO-VISUAL SERVICE, 7630A Hayward Rd, 21702. SAN 321-5008. Tel: 301-694-8166. *Librn*, Gail Lowery
BRUNSWICK BRANCH, 915 N Maple, Brunswick, 21716. SAN 320-2844. Tel: 301-834-9065. TDD: 301-843-9065. *Librn*, Maria Yost
C BURR ARTZ CENTRAL, 110 E Patrick St, 21701. SAN 374-7506. Tel: 301-694-1630. TDD: 301-631-3787. FAX: 301-696-2905. Web Site: www.fcpl.org. *Mgr*, Mary Cramer
EMMITSBURG BRANCH, Community Ctr, Emmitsburg, 21727. SAN 320-2852. Tel: 301-447-2682. TDD: 301-447-2682. *Librn*, Joan Fisher
Friends of the Library Group
MIDDLETOWN BRANCH, 101 Prospect, Middletown, 21769. SAN 320-2860. Tel: 301-371-7560. TDD: 301-371-7560. *Librn*, Rick Muthig
Friends of the Library Group
THURMONT BRANCH, 11 Water St, Thurmont, 21788. SAN 320-2879. Tel: 301-271-7721. TDD: 301-271-7721. *Librn*, Erin Dingle
Friends of the Library Group
WALKERSVILLE BRANCH, 57 W Frederick St, Walkersville, 21793. SAN 329-6024. Tel: 301-845-8880. TDD: 301-845-8880. *Librn*, Doris Cooper
Friends of the Library Group
Bookmobiles: 2

M FREDERICK MEMORIAL HOSPITAL, Walter F Prior Medical Library, 400 W Seventh St, 21701-4593. SAN 306-9508. Tel: 301-698-3300, Ext 3459. *Librn*, Dorothy Kinna
Founded 1962
Library Holdings: Bk Vols 1,000; Per Subs 92
Subject Interests: Medicine, Nursing, Obstetrics and gynecology, Ophthalmology, Orthopedics, Pediatrics, Psychiatry, Radiology, Surgery
Restriction: Staff use only
Partic in Johns Hopkins Hosp Continuing Educ Syst

S HISTORICAL SOCIETY OF FREDERICK COUNTY, INC LIBRARY, 24 E Church St, 21701. SAN 371-778X. Tel: 301-663-1188. FAX: 301-663-0526. E-Mail: library@fwp.net. Web Site: www.fwp.net/hsfc. *Head of Libr*, Marie H Washburn; *Archivist*, Rebecca Fitzgerald; *Asst Librn*, C Larry Bishop; Staff 2 (Non-MLS 2)
Founded 1984
Library Holdings: Bk Vols 5,500; Bk Titles 4,000
Subject Interests: Genealogy, Local history
Special Collections: History of Frederick County, diaries, mss, scrapbooks
Automation Activity & Vendor Info: (Cataloging) Inmagic, Inc.
Publications: Historical Society of Frederick County (Newsletter)
Restriction: Non-circulating
Function: Research fees apply
Open Tues-Sat 10-4

C HOOD COLLEGE, Beneficial-Hodson Library, 401 Rosemont Ave, 21701. SAN 306-9524. Tel: 301-696-3909. Circulation Tel: 301-696-3709. Reference Tel: 301-696-3915. FAX: 301-696-3796. Web Site: www.hood.edu/library. *Dir*, Jan Samet; Tel: 301-696-3934, E-Mail: jsamet@hood.edu; *Dir, Tech Serv*, Arthur Martin; Tel: 301-696-3874, E-Mail: amartin@hood.edu; *Tech Servs*, Phyllis Townsend; Tel: 301-696-3933, E-Mail: townsend@hood.edu; *Head, Circ*, Lisa Mitchell; Tel: 301-696-3924, E-Mail: mitchell@hood.edu; *Circ*, Bridget Frey; Tel: 301-696-3902, E-Mail: frey@hood.edu; *Circ*, Anne Thayer; Tel: 301-696-3902, E-Mail: thayer@hood.edu; *ILL*, Cynthia Feher; Tel: 301-696-3921, E-Mail: cfeher@hood.edu; *Head Ref*, Ann Maginnis; Tel: 301-696-3975, E-Mail: maginnis@hood.edu; *Ref*, Darylyne Provost; Tel: 301-696-3917, E-Mail: provost@hood.edu; *Info Tech*, John Urian; Tel: 301-696-3858, E-Mail: urian@hood.edu; Staff 10 (MLS 6, Non-MLS 4)
Founded 1893. Enrl 1,776; Fac 102; Highest Degree: Master
Jul 1999-Jun 2000 Mats Exp $265,413, Books $113,239, Per/Ser (Incl. Access Fees) $152,174. (Prof $152,958)
Library Holdings: Bk Vols 180,000; Per Subs 1,057
Subject Interests: Biology, Civil War
Special Collections: Landauer Civil War Coll; Sylvia Meagher (Kennedy Assassination Archives)
Automation Activity & Vendor Info: (Acquisitions) CARL; (Cataloging) CARL; (Circulation) CARL; (Serials) CARL
Database Vendor: CARL, Ebsco - EbscoHost, GaleNet, IAC - Info Trac, Lexis-Nexis, OCLC - First Search
Function: Research library
Partic in Maryland Interlibrary Organization; PALINET & Union Library Catalogue of Pennsylvania

UNITED STATES ARMY
A FORT DETRICK POST LIBRARY, Fort Detrick, 501 Scott St, 21702-5000. SAN 324-2331. Tel: 301-619-7510. FAX: 301-619-3362. *Librn*, Angelia Reynolds
Library Holdings: Bk Vols 32,857; Per Subs 90
Partic in OCLC Online Computer Library Center, Inc
AM MEDICAL RESEARCH INSTITUTE OF INFECTIOUS DISEASES LIBRARY Tel: 301-619-2717. FAX: 301-663-8936.; Staff 2 (MLS 2)
Library Holdings: Bk Vols 10,000; Bk Titles 4,000; Per Subs 220
Subject Interests: Communicable diseases
Partic in Dialog Corporation; Fedlink; National Library Of Medicine, Medlars; OCLC Online Computer Library Center, Inc

FROSTBURG

C FROSTBURG STATE UNIVERSITY, (Formerly Lewis J Ort Library), Lewis J Ort Library, One Stadium Dr, 21532. SAN 306-9532. Tel: 301-687-4396. Circulation Tel: 301-687-4395. Reference Tel: 301-687-4424. FAX: 301-687-7069. Web Site: www.frostburg.edu/dept/library/library.htm. *Dir*, Dr David M Gillespie; E-Mail: dgillespie@frostubrg.edu; *Assoc Dir*, Lea Messman-Mandicott; Tel: 301-687-4890, E-Mail: lmessman@frostburg.edu; *Assoc Dir*, Pamela S Williams; Tel: 301-687-4887, E-Mail: pwilliams@frostburg.edu; *Coll Develop*, Nathanial M DeBruin; Tel: 301-687-3114, E-Mail: ndebruin@frostburg.edu; *Info Tech*, Randall A Lowe; Tel: 301-687-4313, E-Mail: elowe@frostburg.edu; *Archivist, Spec Coll*, MaryJo Price; Tel: 301-687-4889, E-Mail: mprice@frostburg.edu; *Web Coordr*, Mark de Jong; Tel: 301-687-4425, E-Mail: mdejong@frostburg.edu; *Cat*, Charlie S Lackey; Tel: 301-687-4884, E-Mail: clackey@frostburg.edu; Staff 25 (MLS 8, Non-MLS 17)
Founded 1902. Enrl 5,240; Fac 238; Highest Degree: Master
Jul 1999-Jun 2000 Income $1,304,427, State $1,299,713, Federal $4,714. Mats Exp $247,720, Books $79,348, Per/Ser (Incl. Access Fees) $128,153, Presv $8,225, Micro $35,494, Other Print Mats $7,346, Electronic Ref Mat (Incl. Access Fees) $70,322. Sal $589,519 (Prof $351,400)
Library Holdings: Bk Vols 248,738; Bk Titles 171,122; Per Subs 1,025
Special Collections: Can; George Meyers American Communist Party & Labor Materials Coll; Selected United States Geological Survey Maps
Automation Activity & Vendor Info: (Acquisitions) CARL; (Circulation) CARL; (OPAC) CARL; (Serials) CARL
Database Vendor: CARL, Dialog, Ebsco - EbscoHost, GaleNet, Lexis-Nexis, OCLC - First Search, Wilson - Wilson Web
Publications: Library Handouts; Library Newsletter, Periodical Subscriptions List
Partic in Colorado Alliance Of Research Libraries; OCLC Online Computer Library Center, Inc

GAITHERSBURG

S FOI SERVICES INC LIBRARY, 11 Firstfield Rd, 20878-1703. SAN 329-8744. Tel: 301-975-9400. FAX: 301-975-0702. E-Mail: infofoi@foiservices.com. Web Site: www.foiservices.com. *Pres*, John E Carey; E-Mail: jcarey@foiservices.com; *VPres*, Marlene S Bobka; E-Mail: mbobka@foiservices.com
Founded 1975
Subject Interests: Approval of pharmaceuticals, Med devices, Regulation of pharmaceuticals

S GILLETTE MEDICAL EVALUATION LABORATORIES, Information Center,* 401 Professional Dr, 20879. SAN 307-0077. Tel: 301-590-1551. FAX: 301-590-1588.
Founded 1962
Library Holdings: Bk Vols 9,300; Bk Titles 7,600; Per Subs 300
Subject Interests: Biology, Chemistry, Cosmetics industry, Dermatology, Medicine, Microscopy, Toxicology
Automation Activity & Vendor Info: (Cataloging) Sydney
Publications: Scientific Regulatory Newsletter
Partic in Interlibrary Users Association; Nat Libr of Med

S LOCKHEED MARTIN CORP, Information Resource Center,* 700 N Frederick Ave, 20879. SAN 306-9559. Tel: 301-240-5500. FAX: 301-240-6855. *Librn*, Henry Courtney; *Mgr*, Cheryl Diallo
Founded 1960
Library Holdings: Bk Vols 5,500; Per Subs 250
Subject Interests: Mathematics
Publications: On-Line Bulletin (monthly)

NATIONAL INSTITUTE OF STANDARDS & TECHNOLOGY
G NATIONAL CENTER FOR STANDARDS & CERTIFICATION INFORMATION (NCSCI), 100 Bureau Dr, Stop 2150, 20899. SAN 320-9237. Tel: 301-975-4040. FAX: 301-926-1559. E-Mail: ncsci@nist.gov. Web Site: ts.nist.gov/ncsci. *Chief Librn*, Joanne Overman
Founded 1965
Library Holdings: Per Subs 100
Subject Interests: Analytical chemistry, Engineering, Standards (government)

Publications: Indexes & Directories
Partic in INFO
Primarily a standards information center; inquiry point for Isonet, NAFTA & WTO Agreements

G OFFICE OF INFORMATION SERVICES, NIST RESEARCH LIBRARY, Rte 270 & Quince Orchard Rd. (Mail add: Admin Bldg E106, 20899), SAN 306-9567. Tel: 301-975-2784, 301-975-3052. Interlibrary Loan Service FAX: 301-869-6787. E-Mail: reflib@enh.nist.gov. Web Site: www.nvl.nist.gov. *Res*, Sami W Klein; *Archivist, Curator*, Karma A Beal
Founded 1901
Library Holdings: Per Subs 1,500
Subject Interests: Chemistry, Computer science, Engineering, Library and information science, Mathematics, Physics, Statistics
Special Collections: Artifacts of the National Bureau of Standards (Historical Museum Coll), legal refs, congressional mats; biographical files on NBS and NIST scientists and managers; National Bureau of Standards Personalities; Old & Rare 17th & 18th Century Scientific Meterology Treaties (Historical Coll), bks, tech rpts, mss; Significant Compilations of Atomic & Molecular Properties, Chemical Kinetics (Colloid & Surface), Fundamental Particles, Mechanical, Nuclear, Solid State, Thermodynamic & Transport Properties (National Standard Reference Data Coll); Weights & Measures Historical Coll
Automation Activity & Vendor Info: (Acquisitions) SIRSI; (Circulation) SIRSI; (Serials) SIRSI
Publications: Abstract & Index Collection in the NIST Research Library of the National Institute of Standards & Technology (biennial); An Annotated List of Historically & Scientifically Important Works Published Before 1900 in the Library of the National Bureau of Standards (1977); Data Bases Available at the National Institute of Standards & Technology Research Library (annual); Foundations of Metrology: Important Early Works on Weights & Measures in the Library of the National Bureau of Standards (1980); National Institute of Standards & Technology Research Library Handbook (irregular); National Institute of Standards & Technology, Research Library Serial Holdings (annual); Science-Technology Information, OIS (monthly information bulletin)
Partic in Dialog Corporation; Fedlink; Interlibrary Users Association; Nasa Libraries Information System - Nasa Galaxie; OCLC Online Computer Library Center, Inc

S WATKINS-JOHNSON CO, Engineering Library,* 700 Quince Orchard Rd, 20878. SAN 306-9591. Tel: 301-948-7550. FAX: 301-948-7576. *Coordr*, Shelley Hilgenberg
Library Holdings: Bk Vols 500; Per Subs 100
Subject Interests: Manufacturers' catalogs
Publications: Newsletter

GAMBRILLS

S ECOSYSTEMS INTERNATIONAL INC LIBRARY,* PO Box 225, 21054. SAN 373-1588. Tel: 410-987-4976. FAX: 410-729-1960. E-Mail: ecosystems@erols.com.
1998-1999 Mats Exp $1,500, Books $500, Per/Ser (Incl. Access Fees) $1,000
Library Holdings: Bk Vols 380; Per Subs 88

GERMANTOWN

S MALCOLM PIRNIE INC, Virtual Library, 20250 Century Blvd, 20874. Toll Free Tel: 888-909-1020. FAX: 301-540-0903. *Librn*, Lenore Grossinger; E-Mail: lgrossinger@pirnie.com; Staff 3 (MLS 2, Non-MLS 1)
Library Holdings: Bk Titles 10,000; Per Subs 150
Subject Interests: Engineering
Special Collections: Environmental Protection Agency

GLEN BURNIE

S MILLENNIUM INORGANIC CHEMICALS LIBRARY, 6752 Baymeadow Dr, 21060. Tel: 410-762-1116. FAX: 410-762-1030. E-Mail: librarian@mic-usa.com. *Adminr*, Ellen Hack; *Mgr*, Nancy J Freeman; *Info Specialist*, Dawn S French; Staff 3 (MLS 2, Non-MLS 1)
Founded 1944
Library Holdings: Bk Vols 3,250; Bk Titles 3,000; Per Subs 180
Subject Interests: Analytical chemistry, Ceramics, Chemical engineering, Inorganic chemistry, Polymer chemistry, Technology
Database Vendor: Dialog, Wilson - Wilson Web
Publications: Resource Update (Acquisition list)
Restriction: Open to researchers by request
Function: Research library

GLEN ECHO

S UNITED STATES NATIONAL PARK SERVICE, Clara Barton National Historic Site Library, 5801 Oxford Rd, 20812. SAN 373-1561. Tel: 301-492-6245. FAX: 301-492-5384. Web Site: www.nps.gov/clba.
Library Holdings: Bk Vols 500
Open for tours daily on the hour 10-4

GREENBELT

G NASA, Goddard Space Flight Center Library, Library, Code 292, 20771. SAN 306-9648. Tel: 301-286-7218. TDD: 301-286-7218. FAX: 301-286-1755. E-Mail: library@library.gsfc.nasa.gov. Web Site: library.gsfc.nasa.gov. *Dir*, Janet D Ormes; Tel: 301-286-3217, E-Mail: janet.ormes@gsfc.nasa.gov; *Info Tech*, Robin Miller Dixon; Tel: 301-286-9230, E-Mail: robin.m.dixon@gsfc.nasa.gov; *Online Servs*, Jane Riddle; E-Mail: jane.riddle@gsfc.nasa.gov; *Coll Develop*, Pete Bonholzer; E-Mail: pete.banholzer@gsfc.nasa.gov; Staff 7 (MLS 4, Non-MLS 3)
Founded 1959
Library Holdings: Bk Titles 110,000; Per Subs 1,100
Subject Interests: Astronomy, Computer science, Earth science, Electronics, Mathematics, Physics, Space science
Database Vendor: Dialog, OCLC - First Search
Restriction: By appointment only
Partic in Fedlink; Nat Res Libr Alliance

S SCIENTISTS CENTER FOR ANIMAL WELFARE LIBRARY, 7833 Walker Dr, Ste 410, 20770-3211. SAN 372-7262. Tel: 301-345-3500. FAX: 301-345-3503. E-Mail: info@scaw.com. Web Site: www.scaw.com. *Exec Dir*, Lee Krulisch
Founded 1978
Library Holdings: Bk Vols 1,000
Publications: SCAW Newsletter

HAGERSTOWN

J HAGERSTOWN BUSINESS COLLEGE LIBRARY,* 18618 Crestwood Dr, 21742. SAN 326-9329. Tel: 301-739-2670. FAX: 301-791-7661. *Librn*, Carol Bailey; Staff 1 (MLS 1)
Enrl 600; Fac 32
Library Holdings: Per Subs 79

J HAGERSTOWN COMMUNITY COLLEGE LIBRARY,* 11400 Robinwood Dr, 21742-6590. SAN 306-9664. Tel: 301-790-2800, Ext 237. FAX: 301-393-3681. *Bibliog Instr, Ref*, LuAnn Fisher
Founded 1946. Enrl 1,200
Jul 1997-Jun 1998 Income $474,558. Mats Exp $49,000, Books $29,000, AV Equip $20,000. Sal $300,918 (Prof $198,185)
Library Holdings: Bk Titles 48,294

S REVIEW & HERALD, Editorial Library, 55 W Oak Ridge Dr, 21740. SAN 302-7619. Tel: 301-393-4141. FAX: 301-393-4055. E-Mail: library@rhpa.org. *Dir Libr Serv*, Richard Coffen
Founded 1903
Library Holdings: Bk Titles 40,000; Per Subs 115
Subject Interests: Church history, Theology
Special Collections: Early Seventh-day Adventist Publications; Millerite Coll; Rare Book Collection

G WASHINGTON COUNTY BOARD OF EDUCATION, Instructional Resource Library,* 820 Commonwealth Ave, 21740. SAN 306-9680. Tel: 301-766-2941. FAX: 301-766-2942.; Staff 4 (MLS 1, Non-MLS 3)
Founded 1967
Library Holdings: Bk Titles 20,000; Per Subs 120
Subject Interests: Art, Education, Photography, Television
Special Collections: India, artifacts, slides, flm
Publications: Current Index to Journals in Education; Education Index; Eric Index
Partic in Maryland Interlibrary Organization; Washington County Cooperative Library Services

P WASHINGTON COUNTY FREE LIBRARY,* 100 S Potomac St, 21740. SAN 344-1458. Tel: 301-739-3250. FAX: 301-739-7603. E-Mail: webmaster@pilot.wash.lib.md.us. Web Site: www.wc-link.org/wcfl. *Dir*, Mary C Baykan; *Asst Dir*, Kathleen O'Connell; Tel: 301-739-3250, Ext 166, E-Mail: ko01@pilot.wash.lib.md.us; *Ad Servs*, Barbara Gibney; Tel: 301-739-3250, Ext 124; *Ch Servs*, Donna Parks; *Coll Develop*, Margaret Fraver; *ILL*, Chris Henry; *Spec Coll*, Gloria Urban; *Spec Coll*, John Frye; *Tech Servs*, David Wolf; Staff 84 (MLS 11, Non-MLS 73)
Founded 1898. Pop 128,500; Circ 926,602
Jul 1998-Jun 1999 Income (Main Library and Branch Library) $2,143,382, State $737,499, City $16,000, Federal $17,515, County $1,113,000, Locally Generated Income $129,684, Other $129,684. Mats Exp $325,603. Sal $1,454,436
Library Holdings: Bk Vols 314,873; Per Subs 587
Subject Interests: Business, Genealogy, Government, Local history
Special Collections: video tapes of historical lectures; Western Maryland (Western Maryland Rm), bks, AV
Database Vendor: DRA, Ebsco - EbscoHost, IAC - SearchBank
Publications: A Newspaper History of Washington County; Index to Hagerstown Newspapers
Mem of Western Maryland Public Libraries
Special Services for the Deaf - TTY machine
Friends of the Library Group

Branches: 6
BOONSBORO FREE, 19 N Main St, Boonsboro, 21713. SAN 344-1482. Tel: 301-432-5723. Web Site: www.wash.lib.md.us/wcfl. *Librn*, O Christine Hawkins
Library Holdings: Bk Vols 12,350
HANCOCK WAR MEMORIAL, Park Rd, Hancock, 21750. SAN 344-1512. Tel: 301-678-5300. Web Site: www.wash.lib.md.us/wcfl. *Librn*, Marcella Whitmore
Library Holdings: Bk Vols 16,197
Friends of the Library Group
KEEDYSVILLE LIBRARY, Taylor Park, Keedysville, 21756. SAN 373-8094. Tel: 301-432-5795. Web Site: www.wash.lib.md.us/wcfl. *Librn*, Sarah Hull
SHARPSBURG PUBLIC, 106 E Main St, Sharpsburg, 21782. SAN 344-1547. Tel: 301-432-8825. Web Site: www.wash.lib.md.us/wcfl. *Librn*, Sara Jane Baker
Library Holdings: Bk Vols 10,790
SMITHSBURG BRANCH, PO Box 648, Smithsburg, 21783. SAN 344-1571. Tel: 301-824-7722. Web Site: www.wash.lib.md.us/wcfl. *Librn*, Patricia A Monahan
Library Holdings: Bk Vols 11,497
WILLIAMSPORT MEMORIAL, 104 E Potomac St, Williamsport, 21795. SAN 344-1601. Tel: 301-223-7027. Web Site: www.wash.lib.md.us/wcfl. *Librn*, Kathleen Knode
Library Holdings: Bk Vols 17,512
Bookmobiles: 2

S WASHINGTON COUNTY HISTORICAL SOCIETY, Jamieson Memorial Library, 135 W Washington St, 21740. SAN 371-5183. Tel: 301-797-8782. *Curator*, Elizabeth Graff
Founded 1962
Library Holdings: Bk Vols 1,200
Restriction: Non-circulating to the public
Open Tues-Sat 9-4; please call first

M WASHINGTON COUNTY HOSPITAL, Wroth Memorial Library, 251 E Antietam St, 21740-5771. SAN 306-9699. Tel: 301-790-8801. FAX: 301-790-9026. *Librn*, Myra Binau
Founded 1953
Library Holdings: Bk Titles 5,000; Per Subs 195
Subject Interests: Biochemistry, Health sciences, Medicine, Nursing
Partic in BRS; Dialog Corporation

GL WASHINGTON COUNTY LAW LIBRARY,* Circuit Court House, 95 W Washington St, 21740. SAN 306-9702. Tel: 301-791-3115. FAX: 301-791-2048. *Librn*, Ben Horton
Library Holdings: Bk Vols 20,000; Per Subs 10

S WASHINGTON COUNTY MUSEUM OF FINE ARTS LIBRARY, City Park, PO Box 423, 21741. SAN 325-8858. Tel: 301-739-5727. FAX: 301-745-3741. E-Mail: wcmfa@aol.com. Web Site: www.washcomuseum.org. *Dir*, Jean Woods
1999-2000 Mats Exp $400
Library Holdings: Bk Vols 4,100
Subject Interests: Art

P WESTERN MARYLAND PUBLIC LIBRARIES, 100 S Potomac St, 21740. SAN 306-9729. Tel: 301-739-3250, Ext 135. FAX: 301-739-5839. E-Mail: mmo1@pilot.wash.lib.md.us. Web Site: www.pilot.wash.lib.md.us. *Dir*, John C Venditta; E-Mail: johnv@wc-link.org; *Dir*, Mary S Mallery; *Acq, Coll Develop*, Darlene C Reimond; Staff 4 (MLS 4)
Founded 1968. Pop 229,900
Jul 1998-Jun 1999 Income $450,007, State $345,491, Federal $96,171, Other $8,345. Mats Exp $65,638, Books $25,000. Sal $213,205 (Prof $160,000)
Library Holdings: Bk Vols 51,504; Bk Titles 40,290
Automation Activity & Vendor Info: (Cataloging) DRA; (Circulation) DRA
Publications: Western Maryland Public Libraries Sign System Manual
Member Libraries: Allegany County Library; Ruth Enlow Library Of Garrett County; Washington County Free Library

HUNT VALLEY

S MCCORMICK & CO, INC, Information Resource Center, 204 Wight Ave, 21031. SAN 306-9737. Tel: 410-771-7707. FAX: 410-785-7439. E-Mail: IRC_Requests@mccormick.com. Web Site: www.mccormick.com. *Mgr*, Alice F Tramontana; Tel: 410-771-7983, E-Mail: Alice_Tramontana@mccormick.com; *Ref*, Sarah A Riley; Tel: 410-771-7252, Fax: 410-785-7439, E-Mail: Sally_Riley@mccormick.com; *Senior Info Specialist*, Ellen T Madden; Tel: 410-771-7735, E-Mail: Ellen_Madden@mccormick.com; *Info Specialist*, Jennifer L Heinlein; Tel: 410-771-7086, E-Mail: Jennifer_Heinlein@mccormick.com. Subject Specialists: *Business*, Ellen T Madden; *Chemistry*, Alice F Tramontana; *Flavor*, Alice F Tramontana; *Food indust*, Alice F Tramontana; *Herbs*, Alice F Tramontana; *Marketing*, Ellen T Madden; *Patents*, Alice F Tramontana; Staff 3 (Non-MLS 3)
Founded 1970
Dec 1997-Nov 1998 Mats Exp $43,200, Books $9,000, Per/Ser (Incl. Access Fees) $32,000, Presv $700, Micro $1,000, Manuscripts & Archives $500. Sal $185,000
Library Holdings: Bk Vols 4,000; Bk Titles 2,500; Per Subs 300
Subject Interests: Chemistry, Technology
Special Collections: Flavor Chemistry; Spices & Herbs
Database Vendor: Dialog, Ebsco - EbscoHost
Restriction: Staff use only
Function: For research purposes

S TELEDYNE BROWN ENGINEERING-ENERGY SYSTEMS LIBRARY,* 10707 Gilroy Rd, 21031. SAN 307-0557. Tel: 410-771-8600. FAX: 410-771-8618. *Librn*, Cathy Layne
Founded 1968
Library Holdings: Bk Titles 1,600
Subject Interests: Aerospace science, Electronics, Energy, Mathematics, Metallurgy

HYATTSVILLE

SR FIRST UNITED METHODIST CHURCH LIBRARY,* 6201 Belcrest Rd, 20782. SAN 306-9753. Tel: 301-927-6133. FAX: 301-927-7368.
Founded 1949
Library Holdings: Bk Vols 2,500

GM NATIONAL CENTER FOR HEALTH STATISTICS, Staff Research Library, 6525 Belcrest Rd, Rm 1169, 20782. SAN 306-9788. Tel: 301-458-4775. FAX: 301-458-4019. Web Site: www.library.psc.gov. *Dir*, Kathy Slack; *ILL*, Charlene Brock; *Ref*, Harnethia Cousar; Staff 3 (MLS 1, Non-MLS 2)
Founded 1977
Library Holdings: Bk Vols 1,500; Per Subs 332
Subject Interests: Epidemiology, Health statistics, Public health
Automation Activity & Vendor Info: (Acquisitions) Innovative Interfaces Inc.; (Circulation) Innovative Interfaces Inc.; (OPAC) Innovative Interfaces Inc.; (Serials) Innovative Interfaces Inc.
Database Vendor: Silverplatter Information Inc.
Publications: Guide to Library Resources; Recent Acquisitions List
Restriction: Public use on premises
Function: Research library
Partic in Dialog Corporation; OCLC Online Computer Library Center, Inc

P PRINCE GEORGE'S COUNTY MEMORIAL LIBRARY SYSTEM, 6532 Adelphi Rd, 20782-2098. SAN 344-1636. Tel: 301-699-3500. FAX: 301-699-0122. E-Mail: am@info.prge.lib.md.us. Web Site: www.prge.lib.md.us. *Actg Dir*, Maralita Freeny; E-Mail: mf0004@mail.pratt.lib.md.us; *Assoc Dir*, Doris Goodlett; *Assoc Dir*, Kathryn K Marathon; E-Mail: kathie@info.prge.lib.md.us; *Assoc Dir*, Jo A Schultz
Founded 1946. Pop 764,053; Circ 4,400,000
Jul 1999-Jun 2000 Income (Main Library and Branch Library) $17,302,820, State $4,234,520, Federal $11,000, County $11,834,800, Locally Generated Income $1,222,500. Mats Exp $3,480,000, Books $3,250,000, Electronic Ref Mat (Incl. Access Fees) $230,000. Sal $10,457,500
Library Holdings: Bk Vols 2,234,881; Bk Titles 199,498; Per Subs 549
Special Collections: American Blacks (Sojourner Truth Room); Horses & Horse Racing (Selima Room); Maryland Room; Planned Communities & Consumers' Cooperatives (Rexford G Tugwell Room)
Automation Activity & Vendor Info: (Acquisitions) GEAC; (Circulation) GEAC; (OPAC) GEAC
Database Vendor: IAC - SearchBank, ProQuest
Publications: Directory of Organizations in Prince George's County; Friends Handbook; Selection Policy for Library Materials; Service Code for Information Services; Volunteer's Handbook
Special Services for the Deaf - Captioned media; High interest/low vocabulary books; TDD
Friends of the Library Group
Branches: 22
ACCOKEEK BRANCH, 16200 Livingston Rd, Accokeek, 20607. SAN 344-1660. Tel: 301-283-2521. Web Site: www.prge.lib.md.us/.. *Librn*, Evelyn Tchiyuka
Friends of the Library Group
ADMINISTRATIVE OFFICES, 6532 Adelphi Rd, 20782. SAN 371-4969. FAX: 301-699-0122. Web Site: www.prge.lib.md.us/..
Friends of the Library Group
BADEN BRANCH, 13603 Baden-Westwood Rd, Brandywine, 20613. SAN 344-1695. Tel: 301-888-1152. Web Site: www.prge.lib.md.us/.. *Librn*, Evelyn Tchiyuka
BELTSVILLE BRANCH, 4319 Sellman Rd, Beltsville, 20705. SAN 344-1725. Tel: 301-937-0294. FAX: 301-595-3455. Web Site: www.prge.lib.md.us/.. *Librn*, Kenneth Lewis
Special Services for the Deaf - TTY machine
Friends of the Library Group
BLADENSBURG BRANCH, 4820 Annapolis Rd, Bladensburg, 20710. SAN 344-175X. Tel: 301-927-4916. FAX: 301-454-0324. Web Site: www.prge.lib.md.us/.. *Librn*, Susan Miller
Friends of the Library Group
BOWIE BRANCH, 15210 Annapolis Rd, Bowie, 20715. SAN 344-1784. Tel: 301-262-7000. FAX: 301-809-2792. Web Site: www.prge.lib.md.us/.. *Librn*, Norman P Jacob
Special Collections: Selima Room (horses & horse racing)

Special Services for the Deaf - TTY machine
Friends of the Library Group
CENTRAL SERVICE FACILITY, 9601 Capital Lane, Largo, 20774. SAN 374-7360. Tel: 301-336-4144. FAX: 301-808-6867. Web Site: www.prge.lib.md.us/..
COUNTY CORRECTIONAL CENTER LAW LIBRARY, 13400 Dille Rd, Upper Marlboro, 20772. SAN 371-4977. Tel: 301-952-7089. FAX: 301-952-7285. Web Site: www.prge.lib.md.us./.. *Librn*, Ronald J Kaye, III
Library Holdings: Bk Vols 2,385; Bk Titles 1,415
FAIRMOUNT HEIGHTS BRANCH, 5904 Kolb St, Fairmount Heights, 20743. SAN 344-1873. Tel: 301-883-2650. FAX: 301-925-7936. Web Site: www.prge.lib.md.us/.. *Librn*, Yvonne Harris
Special Services for the Deaf - TTY machine
Friends of the Library Group
GLENARDEN BRANCH, 8724 Glenarden Pkwy, Glenarden, 20706. SAN 344-1903. Tel: 301-772-5477. FAX: 301-322-3410. Web Site: www.prge.lib.md.us/.. *Librn*, Audrey Norman
Friends of the Library Group
GREENBELT BRANCH, 11 Crescent Rd, Greenbelt, 20770. SAN 344-1938. Tel: 301-345-5800. FAX: 301-982-5018. Web Site: www.prge.lib.md.us/.. *Librn*, Ellen Utley
Special Collections: Tugwell Room (Planned Communities & Consumers Cooperatives)
Special Services for the Deaf - TTY machine
Friends of the Library Group
HILLCREST HEIGHTS BRANCH, 2398 Iverson St, Temple Hills, 20748. SAN 344-1962. Tel: 301-630-4900. FAX: 301-316-0825. Web Site: www.prge.lib.md.us/.. *Librn*, Marian Figlio
HYATTSVILLE BRANCH, 6530 Adelphi, 20782. SAN 344-1997. Tel: 301-985-4690. FAX: 301-927-6781. Web Site: www.prge.lib.md.us/.. *Librn*, Cynthia Prine
Library Holdings: Bk Vols 211,996; Bk Titles 84,508
Special Collections: Maryland Room (Maryland & Prince George's County History)
Special Services for the Deaf - TTY machine
Friends of the Library Group
LARGO-KETTERING, 9601 Capital Lane, Largo, 20774. SAN 329-6431. Tel: 301-336-4044. FAX: 301-333-8857. Web Site: www.prge.lib.md.us/.. *Librn*, Roy Joynes
Friends of the Library Group
LAUREL BRANCH, 507 Seventh St, Laurel, 20707. SAN 344-2020. Tel: 301-776-6790. FAX: 301-497-4223. Web Site: www.prge.lib.md.us/.. *Librn*, Dianne Ashworth
Special Services for the Deaf - TTY machine
Friends of the Library Group
MOUNT RAINIER BRANCH, 3409 Rhode Island Ave, Mount Rainier, 20712. SAN 344-211X. Tel: 301-864-8937. Web Site: www.prge.lib.md.us/.. *Librn*, Cynthia Prine
Friends of the Library Group
NEW CARROLLTON BRANCH, 7414 Riverdale Rd, New Carrollton, 20784. SAN 344-2144. Tel: 301-459-6900. FAX: 301-577-5085. Web Site: www.prge.lib.md.us/.. *Librn*, Doris Kirschbaum
Special Services for the Deaf - TTY machine
Friends of the Library Group
OXON HILL BRANCH, 6200 Oxon Hill Rd, Oxon Hill, 20745. SAN 344-2179. Tel: 301-839-2400. FAX: 301-749-1784. Web Site: www.prge.lib.md.us/.. *Librn*, Evelyn Tchiyuka
Special Collections: Sojourner Truth Room (African American Hist)
Special Services for the Deaf - TTY machine
Friends of the Library Group
PUBLIC DOCUMENTS REFERENCE, County Administration Bldg, Rm 2198, Upper Malboro, 20772. SAN 344-2209. Tel: 301-952-3904. FAX: 301-952-4862. Web Site: www.prge.lib.md.us/.. *Librn*, Sandra Emme
SPAULDINGS BRANCH, 5811 Old Silver Hill Rd, District Heights, 20747. SAN 328-7513. Tel: 301-817-3750. FAX: 301-967-7087. Web Site: www.prge.lib.md.us/.. *Librn*, Barbara Spears
Friends of the Library Group
SURRATTS-CLINTON BRANCH, 9400 Piscataway Rd, Clinton, 20735. SAN 344-2268. Tel: 301-868-9200. FAX: 301-856-9369. Web Site: www.prge.lib.md.us/. *Librn*, Harriet Ying
Special Services for the Deaf - TTY machine
Friends of the Library Group
UPPER MARLBORO, 14730 Main St, Upper Marlboro, 20772. SAN 344-208X. Tel: 301-627-9330. FAX: 301-627-8405. Web Site: www.prge.lib.md.us/.. *Librn*, Anne Marie Ramsey
Friends of the Library Group
Bookmobiles: 4

SR RIVERDALE PRESBYTERIAN CHURCH LIBRARY, 6513 Queens Chapel Rd, 20782-2197. SAN 306-9761. Tel: 301-927-0477. TDD: 301-699-2156. FAX: 301-699-2156. *Librn*, Marjorie Crammer; *Librn*, Marna Cary; *AV*, Joan Borchers
Founded 1952
Library Holdings: Bk Vols 2,200

INDIAN HEAD

UNITED STATES NAVY
A GENERAL LIBRARY, Naval Surface Warfare Ctr, Strauss Ave, Bldg 620, 20640. SAN 344-2322. Tel: 301-744-4747. FAX: 301-744-4386. *In Charge*, Vickie C LaFleur; E-Mail: vickielafleur@hotmail; Staff 1 (Non-MLS 1)
1998-1999 Mats Exp $15,000, Books $9,000, Per/Ser (Incl. Access Fees) $5,000. Sal $30,000
Library Holdings: Bk Titles 8,000; Per Subs 135
Special Collections: Maryland & Charles County History Books; Navy Biographical & Historical Books
A LIBRARY 840L Tel: 301-744-4742. FAX: 301-744-4192. *Librn*, Mike Sikora; E-Mail: mikesikora@infotech.ihnavy.mil; Staff 4 (MLS 1, Non-MLS 3)
Library Holdings: Bk Vols 12,150; Per Subs 417
Subject Interests: Chemistry, Engineering
Special Collections: Ordnance; Research; Rocketry; Test & Evaluation Reports
Publications: Accessions Bulletin
Partic in Defense Technical Information Center; Dialog Corporation; OCLC Online Computer Library Center, Inc
A NAVAL EXPLOSIVE ORDINANCE DISPOSAL TECHNOLOGY DIVISION TECHNICAL LIBRARY, Bldg 2172, 20640-5070. SAN 344-2381. Tel: 301-744-6817. *Librn*, Ann Cashin; E-Mail: cashin@eodpoe2.navsea.navy.mil; Staff 3 (MLS 1, Non-MLS 2)
Founded 1954
Library Holdings: Per Subs 100
Special Collections: Ordnance, engineering drawings
Publications: Accession List
Partic in Fedlink; OCLC Online Computer Library Center, Inc

KENSINGTON

S INFORMATION SYSTEMS CONSULTANTS INC LIBRARY, 9707 Elrod Rd, 20895. SAN 307-1847. Tel: 301-946-2240. FAX: 301-946-6505. E-Mail: dickboss@erols.com.
Founded 1978
Jan 1999-Dec 1999 Income $20,500. Mats Exp $8,000, Books $1,000, Per/Ser (Incl. Access Fees) $3,000, Other Print Mats $1,000, Electronic Ref Mat (Incl. Access Fees) $3,000. Sal $12,500
Library Holdings: Bk Vols 2,500; Bk Titles 1,500; Per Subs 70
Subject Interests: Architecture, Info tech
Publications: Library Systems Newsletter
Restriction: Staff use only

S LIBRARY STORE LTD LIBRARY, 10528 Saint Paul St, 20895. SAN 377-4139. Tel: 301-652-8811. Toll Free Tel: 800-858-8117. FAX: 301-654-4960. Web Site: www.librarystoreltd.com. *VPres*, Bill Doudnikoff; E-Mail: bill@librarystoreltd.com; Staff 19 (MLS 3, Non-MLS 16)
Library Holdings: Bk Titles 13,000

S UNDERSEA & HYPERBARIC MEDICAL SOCIETY, Charles W Shilling Library, 10531 Metropolitan Ave, 20895. SAN 377-449X. Tel: 301-942-2980, Ext 105. FAX: 301-942-7804. Web Site: www.uhms.org. *Librn*, Kathy Davidson; E-Mail: kathy@uhms.org
Library Holdings: Bk Vols 800; Per Subs 20
Subject Interests: Hyperbaric med
Function: Research library

LA PLATA

L CHARLES COUNTY CIRCUIT COURT, Law Library,* PO Box 3060, 20646. SAN 329-8574. Tel: 301-932-3322. FAX: 301-932-3324. *Librn*, Mary Rice; E-Mail: ricemary@looksmart.com
Library Holdings: Bk Vols 20,000; Per Subs 10

J CHARLES COUNTY COMMUNITY COLLEGE LIBRARY,* 8730 Mitchell Rd, PO Box 910, 20646-0910. SAN 306-9818. Tel: 301-934-2251, Ext 7626. FAX: 301-934-7699. E-Mail: library@charles.cc.md.us. *Dir*, Thomas Repenning; Tel: 301-934-7630, E-Mail: tomr@charlescc.md.us; *Tech Servs*, Shirley Gross; *Ref*, Erica Roth; Tel: 301-934-7626; *Ref*, Vince Doblos; Tel: 301-934-7626; Staff 4 (MLS 3, Non-MLS 1)
Founded 1958. Enrl 5,897; Fac 86
Jul 1999-Jun 2000 Mats Exp $230,920, Books $35,600, Per/Ser (Incl. Access Fees) $76,070, Micro $3,500, AV Equip $22,670, Electronic Ref Mat (Incl. Access Fees) $93,080. Sal $258,263 (Prof $97,075)
Library Holdings: Bk Vols 40,789; Bk Titles 33,414; Per Subs 1,112
Subject Interests: Local history
Special Collections: Southern Maryland Manuscripts & Genealogy
Automation Activity & Vendor Info: (Circulation) Follett; (Course Reserve) Follett; (OPAC) Follett
Partic in Md Commun Col Libr Consortium; Southern Md Regional Libr Asn

P CHARLES COUNTY PUBLIC LIBRARY, LaPlata Branch, 2 Garrett Ave, 20646-5959. SAN 344-2411. Tel: 301-934-9001. TDD: 301-934-9090. FAX: 301-934-2297. Web Site: www.somd.lib.md.us/chas/libraries. *Dir*, Emily Ferren; E-Mail: eferren@somd.lib.md.us; *Branch Mgr*, Diane Johnson; Staff 72 (MLS 2, Non-MLS 70)
Founded 1923. Pop 122,000; Circ 729,286
Jul 1999-Jun 2000 Income (Main Library and Branch Library) $2,157,147, State $536,029, Federal $27,500, County $1,445,567, Other $148,051. Mats Exp $386,153, Books $260,000. Sal $1,413,560 (Prof $1,161,038)
Library Holdings: Bk Vols 203,114; Bk Titles 178,114; Per Subs 278; High Interest/Low Vocabulary Bk Vols 300; Bks on Deafness & Sign Lang 100
Subject Interests: Local genealogy, Spanish
Special Collections: Spanish
Automation Activity & Vendor Info: (Circulation) DRA; (ILL) DRA
Database Vendor: Dialog, DRA, IAC - SearchBank
Function: Internet access, Reference services available
Partic in Southern Md Regional Libr Asn
Special Services for the Deaf - TDD
Special Services for the Blind - Audio-cassettes
Friends of the Library Group
Branches: 2
P D BROWN MEMORIAL, 50 Village St, Waldorf, 20602-1837. SAN 344-2500. Tel: 301-645-2864. FAX: 301-843-4869. Web Site: www.somd.lib.md.us/chas/libraries/. *Branch Mgr*, Barbara W Smith
Friends of the Library Group
POTOMAC, 3225 Ruth B Swann Dr, Indian head, 20640-3038. Tel: 301-375-7375. FAX: 301-283-0621. Web Site: www.somd.lib.md.us/chas/libraries/. *Branch Mgr*, Janet L Garvey
Friends of the Library Group . 1 outreach van

LANDOVER

M EPILEPSY FOUNDATION, (NEL), National Epilepsy Library, 4351 Garden City Dr, 20785-2223. SAN 302-6469. Tel: 301-459-3700, Ext 684. Toll Free Tel: 800-332-4050. FAX: 301-459-3700. E-Mail: nel@efa.org. Web Site: www.efa.org. *Mgr*, Cecille Jach; E-Mail: cjach@efa.org; *Coll Develop*, Stephanie Eberley; E-Mail: seberley@efa.org
Founded 1982
Library Holdings: Bk Vols 2,000; Per Subs 65
Special Collections: Albert & Ellen Grass Archives
Partic in Dialog Corporation
Open Mon-Fri 9-5

§R FIRST BAPTIST CHURCH OF HIGHLAND PARK LIBRARY, 6801 Sheriff Rd, 20785. Tel: 301-773-6655, Ext 236. FAX: 301-773-1347. E-Mail: library@capu.net. *Head Librn*, Linda C Redmond; *Asst Librn*, Ruby Alexander; Staff 22 (MLS 2, Non-MLS 20)
Founded 1998
Jan 2000-Dec 2000 Income $6,000
Library Holdings: Bk Titles 1,700; Per Subs 25
Restriction: Members only
Function: Reference services available

S PRINCE GEORGE'S COUNTY PUBLIC SCHOOLS, Professional Library, 8437 Landover Rd, 20785-3599. SAN 325-9005. Tel: 301-386-1595. FAX: 301-386-1601. *Librn*, Diane Brady; E-Mail: dbrady1@pgcps.pg.k12.md.us
Library Holdings: Bk Vols 10,000; Per Subs 242
Special Collections: Multicultural Education Coll
Partic in Maryland Interlibrary Organization

LANHAM

S AMERICAN CORRECTIONAL ASSOCIATION LIBRARY,* 4380 Forbes Blvd, 20706-4322. SAN 321-8309. Tel: 301-918-1800. Toll Free Tel: 800-222-5646. FAX: 301-918-1886. *In Charge*, Gabriele Daley
Founded 1975
Library Holdings: Bk Titles 5,000
Subject Interests: Archives, Corrections
Special Collections: Photograph Coll
Restriction: Open to public for reference only

M DOCTORS COMMUNITY HOSPITAL, Medical Library,* 8118 Good Luck Rd, 20706. SAN 377-3841. Tel: 301-552-8072. FAX: 301-552-8052.
Library Holdings: Bk Vols 200; Per Subs 80
Partic in Maryland Association Of Health Science Librarians; Medical Libr Asn; Mid-Atlantic Med Librs

S NATIONAL ASPHALT PAVEMENT ASSOCIATION, Charles R Foster Technical Library, 5100 Forbes Blvd, 20706. SAN 328-0098. Tel: 301-731-4748. FAX: 301-731-4621. Web Site: www.hotmix.com. *In Charge*, Judy Hornung
Library Holdings: Bk Titles 1,000; Per Subs 75

CR WASHINGTON BIBLE COLLEGE-CAPITAL BIBLE SEMINARY, Oyer Memorial Library, 6511 Princess Garden Pkwy, 20706. SAN 306-9834. Tel: 301-552-1400, Ext 231. *Actg Dir*, William Banks; *Tech Servs*, Barbara Sherry; Staff 2 (MLS 2)
Jul 1998-Jun 1999 Income $130,577, Locally Generated Income $15,775, Parent Institution $114,802. Mats Exp $12,192, Books $3,066, Per/Ser (Incl. Access Fees) $8,317, Presv $535. Sal $105,738 (Prof $60,017)
Library Holdings: Bk Titles 68,570; Per Subs 258
Subject Interests: Theology
Special Collections: Rare Books
Partic in Capcon Library Network; OCLC Online Computer Library Center, Inc

LARGO

C PRINCE GEORGE'S COMMUNITY COLLEGE LIBRARY, Media Center, 301 Largo Rd, 20774-2199. SAN 306-9842. Tel: 301-322-0462. Interlibrary Loan Service Tel: 301-322-0021. Circulation Tel: 301-322-0475. Reference Tel: 301-322-0476. FAX: 301-808-8847. E-Mail: loganlb@pg.cc.md.us. Web Site: www.pgcollege.org/library/online.htm. *Dean*, Dr Lynda Byrd Logan; Tel: 301-322-0466; *Tech Servs*, Margaret C Warner; Tel: 310-322-0467, E-Mail: warnermc@pg.cc.md.us; *Publ Servs*, Priscilla C Thompson; Tel: 301-322-0468, E-Mail: thompspc@pg.cc.md.us; *Bibliog Instr*, Norma A Schmidt; Tel: 301-322-0471, E-Mail: schmidna@pg.cc.md.us; *Electronic Resources*, Imogene Zachery; Tel: 301-322-0138, E-Mail: zacherix@pg.cc.md.us; *Coll Develop*, Marianne Rough; Tel: 301-322-0465, E-Mail: MCR@email.pg.cc.md.us; *Syst Coordr*, John D Bartles; Tel: 301-322-0469, E-Mail: bartlejd@pg.cc.md.us; Staff 48 (MLS 12, Non-MLS 36)
Founded 1958. Enrl 6,451; Fac 369
Jul 2000-Jun 2001 Mats Exp $216,456, Books $64,964, Per/Ser (Incl. Access Fees) $29,000, Presv $1,200, Micro $7,292, AV Equip $25,000, Electronic Ref Mat (Incl. Access Fees) $89,635. Sal $1,127,922 (Prof $406,310)
Library Holdings: Bk Titles 93,500; Per Subs 450
Special Collections: Municipal
Automation Activity & Vendor Info: (Cataloging) Endeavor
Database Vendor: GaleNet, IAC - Info Trac, IAC - SearchBank, OCLC - First Search, ProQuest, Wilson - Wilson Web
Partic in Md Commun Col Libr Consortium
Friends of the Library Group

LAUREL

C CAPITOL COLLEGE, John G & Beverly A Puente Library, 11301 Springfield Rd, 20708. SAN 306-9796. Tel: 301-369-2800. FAX: 301-369-2552. E-Mail: rsample@capitol-college.edu. Web Site: www.capitol-college.edu. *Dir Libr Serv*, Rick A Sample; E-Mail: rsample@capitol.college.edu; *Mgr*, Lorraine Trapp; E-Mail: ltrapp@capitol-college.edu; *Librn*, Sandy Pisano; E-Mail: spisano@capitol.college.edu; Staff 3 (MLS 2, Non-MLS 1)
Founded 1966. Enrl 675; Fac 18
Jul 1999-Jun 2000 Income $200,000. Mats Exp $27,000, Books $10,000, Per/Ser (Incl. Access Fees) $7,000, AV Equip $2,000, Electronic Ref Mat (Incl. Access Fees) $8,000. Sal $120,000 (Prof $75,000)
Library Holdings: Bk Vols 8,563; Bk Titles 8,400; Per Subs 98
Subject Interests: Computer science, Electronics, Engineering, Technology, Telecommunications
Automation Activity & Vendor Info: (Acquisitions) EOS; (Cataloging) EOS; (Circulation) EOS; (OPAC) EOS; (Serials) EOS
Publications: Road Map to Borrowing
Partic in Maryland Interlibrary Organization; Md Independent Col & Univ Asn

S JOHNS HOPKINS UNIVERSITY, APPLIED PHYSICS LABORATORY, R E Gibson Library & Information Center,* 11100 Johns Hopkins Rd, 20723-6099. SAN 306-9850. Tel: 443-778-5151. Interlibrary Loan Service Tel: 443-778-5152. FAX: 443-778-5353. Web Site: lib2.jhuapl.edu. *Librn*, Robert S Gresehover; Staff 25 (MLS 13, Non-MLS 12)
Founded 1945
Library Holdings: Bk Titles 30,000; Per Subs 300
Subject Interests: Aerospace science, Biomedical engineering, Electronics, Mathematics, Physics
Automation Activity & Vendor Info: (Cataloging) SIRSI; (Circulation) SIRSI
Publications: Information Exchange

GL MARYLAND STATE DIVISION OF LABOR & INDUSTRY, Occupational Safety & Health Library, 312 Marshall Ave Ste 600, 20707. SAN 370-1565. Tel: 410-880-4970. FAX: 301-483-8332. Web Site: www.dllr.state.md.us.
Library Holdings: Bk Titles 750; Per Subs 15
Subject Interests: Accident prevention, Hazard occupations, Indust hygiene, Occupational med

G UNITED STATES GEOLOGICAL SURVEY BIOLOGICAL RESOURCES DIVISION, Patuxent Wildlife Research Center, 12100 Beech Forest Rd, 20708-4030. SAN 306-9869. Tel: 301-497-5550. Circulation Tel: 301-497-5551. FAX: 301-497-5545. Web Site: www.pwrc.usgs.gov. *Librn*, Lynda Garrett; E-Mail: lynda_garrett@usgs.gov
Founded 1942
Library Holdings: Bk Titles 9,000; Per Subs 350

Subject Interests: Literature
Special Collections: Pesticides & Pollution, reprints
Publications: Journal & serial holdings list
Restriction: Staff use only
Function: ILL available
Partic in Maryland Interlibrary Organization; OCLC Online Computer Library Center, Inc

S WESTVACO CORP, Research Library,* 11101 Johns Hopkins Rd, 20723. SAN 306-9877. Tel: 301-497-1307. FAX: 301-497-1309. *Res*, Jeanne D Lloyd; E-Mail: jdlloyd@westvaco.com
Founded 1967
Library Holdings: Bk Vols 5,100; Per Subs 150
Subject Interests: Chemical engineering, Chemistry, Microbiology, Polymer chemistry, Technology
Special Collections: Institute of Paper Science & Technology Bibliography, senes, technical papers, progress rpts & thesis; NCASI Technology Bulletins & Special Reports
Publications: Acquisitions list; Company Reports Compilation
Partic in Dialog Corporation; Sailor; STN

LEONARDTOWN

S SAINT MARY'S COUNTY HISTORICAL SOCIETY RESEARCH CENTER, PO Box 212, 20650. SAN 306-9885. Tel: 301-475-2467. Web Site: www.somd.lib.md.us/smchs. *Pres*, Richard Gass
Founded 1951
Library Holdings: Bk Titles 2,000; Per Subs 35
Subject Interests: Genealogy, Local history, Religion
Special Collections: Chronicles of St Mary's; Early Maryland & English History; Local Authors
Restriction: Non-circulating to the public

P SAINT MARY'S COUNTY MEMORIAL LIBRARY, 23250 Hollywood Rd, 20650. SAN 344-2535. Tel: 301-475-2846. FAX: 301-884-4415. Web Site: www.somd.lib.md.us/STMA/Libraries/. *Dir*, Mary R Wood; E-Mail: mwood@somd.lib.md.us
Founded 1950. Pop 89,000
Jul 1999-Jun 2000 Income (Main Library and Branch Library) $1,894,682, State $457,930, Federal $15,000, County $1,276,616, Locally Generated Income $145,136. Mats Exp $337,280, Books $254,080, Per/Ser (Incl. Access Fees) $25,216, AV Equip $44,003, Electronic Ref Mat (Incl. Access Fees) $13,981. Sal $1,091,010 (Prof $67,000)
Library Holdings: Bk Vols 163,299; Per Subs 443
Special Collections: Genealogy Society Coll
Automation Activity & Vendor Info: (Cataloging) DRA; (Circulation) DRA; (OPAC) DRA
Database Vendor: DRA
Partic in Maryland Interlibrary Organization; Southern Md Regional Libr Asn
Friends of the Library Group
Branches: 2
CHARLOTTE HALL BRANCH, 37600 New Market Rd, Charlotte Hall, 20622. SAN 344-2543. Tel: 301-884-2211. FAX: 301-884-2113. Web Site: www.somd.lib.md.us/stma/libraries/.
LEXINGTON PARK BRANCH, 21744 S Coral Dr, Lexington Park, 20653. SAN 344-256X. Tel: 301-863-8188. FAX: 301-863-2550. Web Site: www.somd.lib.md.us/stma/libraries/. *Head of Libr*, Janice Hummel
Bookmobiles: 1. Van

LINTHICUM

S CENTER FOR INDOOR AIR RESEARCH LIBRARY,* 1099 Winterson Rd, 21090. SAN 375-7110. Tel: 410-684-3777. FAX: 410-684-3729. *Dir Libr Serv*, Paula Raimondo
Library Holdings: Bk Titles 400; Per Subs 45

MC HENRY

J GARRETT COMMUNITY COLLEGE, Library Resource Center, 687 Mosser Rd, 21541. SAN 306-9923. Tel: 301-387-3009. FAX: 301-387-3055. *Coll Develop, Dir*, Dana Shimrock; Tel: 301-387-3003, E-Mail: dana@gcc.cc.md.us; *AV*, James Matthews; Tel: 301-387-3104; *Acq*, Judy Sconyers; Tel: 301-387-3022, E-Mail: judy@gcc.cc.md.us; *Cat*, Ellen Sheaffer; Tel: 301-387-3002, E-Mail: esheaffer@gcc.cc.md.us; *Circ, ILL*, Linda Tomblin; E-Mail: ltomblin@gcc.cc.md.us; Staff 2 (Non-MLS 2)
Founded 1971. Enrl 620; Fac 18
Jul 1999-Jun 2000 Income $238,034. Mats Exp $38,655, Books $25,000, Micro $2,500, Other Print Mats $2,155, Electronic Ref Mat (Incl. Access Fees) $9,000. Sal $164,364 (Prof $104,243)
Library Holdings: Bk Titles 27,000; Per Subs 210
Subject Interests: Natural resources, Sports, Wildlife
Special Collections: Western Maryland
Automation Activity & Vendor Info: (Cataloging) Follett; (Circulation) Follett; (OPAC) Follett

NORTH EAST

J CECIL COMMUNITY COLLEGE, Veterans Memorial Library, One Seahawk Dr, 21901-1904. SAN 306-9931. Tel: 410-287-6060, Ext 562. FAX: 410-287-1026. Web Site: www.cecil.cc.md.us/lrc/. *Dir*, Shelley Gardner; E-Mail: fgardner@ed.cecil.cc.md.us; *Asst Librn*, Gayle Stauffer
Founded 1968. Enrl 1,400; Fac 40
Library Holdings: Bk Vols 28,530; Bk Titles 27,386; Per Subs 142
Subject Interests: Genealogy, Maryland

OAKLAND

§GL GARRETT COUNTY CIRCUIT COURT LIBRARY, 203 S Fourth St, 21550. Tel: 301-334-1934. FAX: 301-334-5042. *In Charge*, John R Toston
Library Holdings: Bk Vols 500; Bk Titles 10

P RUTH ENLOW LIBRARY OF GARRETT COUNTY,* 6 N Second St, 21550-1393. SAN 344-2659. Tel: 301-334-3996. TDD: 301-334-3997. FAX: 301-334-4152. E-Mail: info@relib.net. Web Site: www.relib.net. *Dir*, Cathy A Ashby; E-Mail: cashby@relib.net; *Publ Servs*, Ann Leighton; *Tech Servs*, Sheila Hughes; E-Mail: sheila@mail.garr.lib.md.us; Staff 3 (MLS 3)
Founded 1946. Pop 28,500; Circ 213,805
Jul 1999-Jun 2000 Income (Main Library and Branch Library) $612,570, State $149,518, County $375,000, Locally Generated Income $30,000. Mats Exp $612,570, Books $30,000, Per/Ser (Incl. Access Fees) $6,800, AV Equip $5,000. Sal $487,230 (Prof $107,504)
Library Holdings: Bk Vols 60,271; Bk Titles 71,427; Per Subs 225
Subject Interests: Local history
Special Collections: Garrett County; Garrett County Families; Western Maryland
Database Vendor: Ebsco - EbscoHost, GaleNet, IAC - Info Trac, IAC - SearchBank
Mem of Western Maryland Public Libraries
Partic in Maryland Interlibrary Organization
Special Services for the Deaf - TDD
Friends of the Library Group
Branches: 4
ACCIDENT BRANCH, PO Box 154, Accident, 21520-0154. SAN 344-2683. Tel: 301-746-8792. FAX: 301-746-8399. *Librn*, Janet Otto
Friends of the Library Group
FRIENDSVILLE BRANCH, PO Box 57, Friendsville, 21531-0057. SAN 344-2748. Tel: 301-746-5663. FAX: 301-746-5663. *Librn*, Susan C Dresley; Tel: 617-494-2117
Friends of the Library Group
GRANTSVILLE BRANCH, PO Box 237, Grantsville, 21536-0237. SAN 344-2772. Tel: 301-895-5298. FAX: 301-245-4411. *Librn*, Kimberly Lishia
Friends of the Library Group
KITZMILLER BRANCH, PO Box 100, Kitzmiller, 21538-0100. SAN 344-2802. Tel: 301-453-3368. FAX: 301-453-3368. *Librn*, Diane Kisner
Friends of the Library Group
Bookmobiles: 1

OWINGS MILLS

M ROSEWOOD CENTER, Miriam Lodge Professional Library,* Rosewood Lane, 21117-2999. SAN 306-9958. Tel: 410-363-2817. FAX: 410-581-4962. E-Mail: racstaffdevelopment@erols.com. *Dir*, Mary Harrell
1997-1998 Mats Exp $5,000
Library Holdings: Bk Vols 2,000; Per Subs 20

OXFORD

G NATIONAL MARINE FISHERIES SERVICE, Southeast Fisheries Science Center, Oxford Cooperative Laboratory Library,* 904 S Morris St, 21654-9724. SAN 306-9966. Tel: 410-226-5193. FAX: 410-226-5925. *Librn*, Susie K Hines; E-Mail: shines@hatteras.bea.nmfs.gov
Founded 1961
Library Holdings: Bk Vols 11,158; Per Subs 75
Subject Interests: Marine biology
Publications: Annual Publications List; Dissertations; Serial & Journal Holdings; Theses List
Partic in Dialog Corporation; OCLC Online Computer Library Center, Inc

PATUXENT RIVER

G NAVAL AIR WARFARE CENTER, MSA Library,* 22347 Cedar Point Rd, Bldg 2185, Ste 1250, Unit 6, 20670-1161. SAN 326-176X. Tel: 301-342-2469. FAX: 301-342-2468. *Librn*, Charlotte London; E-Mail: londoncm@navier.navy.mil; Staff 2 (MLS 1, Non-MLS 1)
Founded 1977
Library Holdings: Bk Vols 7,500; Bk Titles 4,500
Special Collections: S-3 Airplane Info (VS Program Library)
Publications: Lists of holdings

UNITED STATES NAVY

A PATUXENT RIVER CENTRAL LIBRARY, Bldg 407, 22269 Cedar Point Rd, 20670-1120. SAN 344-2837. Tel: 301-342-9785. Interlibrary Loan Service Tel: 301-342-1925. Reference Tel: 301-342-1930. FAX: 301-342-1933. Web Site: navair.navy.mil. *In Charge*, Carolyn K Eaton; E-Mail: eatonck@navair.navy.mil; Staff 6 (MLS 2, Non-MLS 4)
Library Holdings: Bk Vols 55,000; Per Subs 420
Subject Interests: Aeronautics, Computer science, Engineering, Physical science, U.S. Government
Publications: Technical Information Bulletin
Partic in Consortium of Navy Librs; Fedlink

PERRY POINT

GM DEPARTMENT OF VETERANS AFFAIRS, Medical Center Library,* 21902. SAN 306-9974. Tel: 410-642-2411, Ext 5716. FAX: 410-642-1103.; Staff 3 (MLS 2, Non-MLS 1)
Founded 1924
Library Holdings: Bk Vols 12,700; Per Subs 310
Subject Interests: Geriatrics and gerontology, Nursing, Psychiatry, Psychology
Partic in Nat Libr of Med; Veterans Affairs Library Network

PIKESVILLE

S MARYLAND STATE POLICE ACADEMY LIBRARY,* 1201 Reisterstown Rd, 21208-3899. SAN 327-8166. Tel: 410-653-4357. FAX: 410-653-4380. *In Charge*, Patty Garrish
Library Holdings: Bk Titles 4,500; Per Subs 48

PINEY POINT

S SEAFARER'S HARRY LUNDEBERG SCHOOL OF SEAMANSHIP, Paul Hall Library & Maritime Museum, PO Box 75, 20674. SAN 306-9982. Tel: 301-994-0010, Ext 5353. *Dir*, Janice M Smolek; Staff 3 (MLS 2, Non-MLS 1)
Founded 1970. Enrl 437
Library Holdings: Bk Vols 19,000; Per Subs 120
Subject Interests: History, Maritime history

PRINCE FREDERICK

S CALVERT COUNTY HISTORICAL SOCIETY LIBRARY,* Prince Frederick Library Bldg 30 Duke St, PO Box 358, 20678. SAN 373-160X. Tel: 410-535-2452. Web Site: www.somd.lib.us/calv/cchs.
Library Holdings: Bk Vols 1,000
Subject Interests: Genealogy, Local history
Special Collections: Wilfong Collection, photos & clippings

P CALVERT COUNTY PUBLIC LIBRARY, 30 Duke St, PO Box 405, 20678. SAN 307-000X. Tel: 410-535-0291. FAX: 410-535-3022. E-Mail: calvert.director@somd.lib.md.us. Web Site: www.calvert.lib.md.us. *Dir*, Patricia Hofmann; E-Mail: calv.director@somd.lib.md.us; *Librn*, Carolyn Graessle; E-Mail: calv.manager@somd.lib.md.us; *Coll Develop*, Kathleen Eichfeld; E-Mail: calv.ref@somd.lib.md.us
Founded 1959. Pop 67,000; Circ 544,807
Jul 1999-Jun 2000 Income (Main Library and Branch Library) $1,793,511, State $247,399, Federal $15,000, County $1,363,610, Locally Generated Income $72,688, Other $94,814. Mats Exp $254,100. Sal $1,224,855
Library Holdings: Bk Vols 142,166; Per Subs 264
Subject Interests: Maryland
Automation Activity & Vendor Info: (Circulation) DRA; (OPAC) DRA
Partic in Southern Md Regional Libr Asn
Friends of the Library Group
Branches: 3
FAIRVIEW, 8120 Southern Maryland Blvd, Owings, 20736. SAN 321-9585. Tel: 410-257-2101. FAX: 410-257-0662. Web Site: www.somd.lib.md.us/calv/libraries/. *Librn*, Sheila Hejl
SOUTHERN, 20 Appeal Lane, PO Box 599, Lusby, 20657. SAN 329-5516. Tel: 410-326-5289. FAX: 410-326-8370. Web Site: www.somd.lib.md.us/calv/libraries/. *Librn*, Carol Bays
TWIN BEACHES, Captains Quarters, PO Box 910, Chesapeake Beach, 20732. SAN 321-9593. Tel: 410-257-2411. FAX: 410-257-0663. Web Site: www.somd.lib.md.us/calv/libraries/. *Librn*, Joan Roach
Bookmobiles: 1

PRINCESS ANNE

§GL SOMERSET COUNTY CIRCUIT COURT LIBRARY, Courthouse, PO Box 279, 21853. Tel: 410-651-1630. FAX: 410-651-1878. *Librn*, Lynn Cain
Library Holdings: Bk Vols 1,500; Bk Titles 40

P SOMERSET COUNTY LIBRARY SYSTEM, 11767 Beechwood St, 21853. SAN 344-2861. Tel: 410-651-0852, Ext 11. FAX: 410-651-1388. *Dir*, Jean Johnson
Founded 1967. Pop 19,300; Circ 84,382
Library Holdings: Bk Vols 104,672; Per Subs 67
Subject Interests: History, Maryland
Mem of Eastern Shore Regional Library, Inc
Branches: 3
CORBIN MEMORIAL, 4 E Main St, Crisfield, 21817. SAN 344-2896. Tel: 410-968-0955. FAX: 410-968-2363. *Librn*, Yvonne Long
DEAL ISLAND BRANCH, c/o Deal Island School, Deal Island, 21821. SAN 320-5290. Tel: 410-784-2449. *Asst Librn*, Jan Thompson
EWELL BRANCH, Ewell School, Ewell, 21824. SAN 320-5282. Tel: 410-425-5141. *Librn*, Christine Marshall; *Librn*, Janice Kitching

C UNIVERSITY OF MARYLAND-EASTERN SHORE, Frederick Douglass Library, College Bochbone Rd, 21853. SAN 344-2926. Tel: 410-651-2200, Ext 6622. FAX: 410-651-6269. Web Site: www.fdl.umes.edu. *Dean of Libr*, Dr Theodosia Shields; *Tech Servs*, Gwen Scott; *Acq, Coll Develop*, Theresa Dadson; *Media Spec*, Sharon Brooks; *Doc, Ser*, Martha Zimmerman; *Cat*, Marvella Rounds; *Spec Coll*, Lois Peterson; *Ref*, Adbul Aden; Staff 11 (MLS 11)
Founded 1968. Fac 136; Highest Degree: Doctorate
Jun 1998-May 1999 Income $1,264,871. Mats Exp $360,488. Sal $863,497 (Prof $475,669)
Library Holdings: Bk Titles 172,719; Per Subs 937
Subject Interests: Physical therapy
Special Collections: Juvenile Coll; Maryland Coll, bks, micro
Automation Activity & Vendor Info: (Acquisitions) CARL; (Cataloging) CARL; (Circulation) CARL
Publications: A Mini Guide; Departmental Brochures; Library Aides; New Acquisitions List; Periodical Holdings
Partic in Colorado Alliance Of Research Libraries; OCLC Online Computer Library Center, Inc
Departmental Libraries:
MUSIC LEARNING RESOURCES, PAC Bldg, 21853. SAN 344-2950. Tel: 410-651-2200, Ext 6570. FAX: 410-651-7688. Web Site: www.fdl.umes.umd.edu. *Dir*, John R Lamkin, II; E-Mail: jrlamkin@mail.umes.edu
Automation Activity & Vendor Info: (Circulation) CARL
Publications: Annual Report; Douglass Notes; DOUGNET; Mini Library Guide; New Acquisitions; Serials-Documents; State Publications
Partic in Colorado Alliance Of Research Libraries; OCLC Online Computer Library Center, Inc

RANDALLSTOWN

S NORTHWEST HOSPITAL CENTER, Health Sciences Library, 5401 Old Court Rd, 21133. SAN 325-8815. Tel: 410-521-2200, Ext 5682. FAX: 410-922-7549. *Librn*, Janice Mason; Staff 1 (MLS 1)
Library Holdings: Bk Vols 1,500; Per Subs 72

RISING SUN

SR PRISON MINISTRY OF YOKEFELLOW'S INTERNATIONAL LIBRARY, 36 N Queens St, PO Box 482, 21911. SAN 375-6505. Tel: 410-658-2661. Web Site: www.mywebhome.com/yokefellow. *Dir*, Hal E Owens
Library Holdings: Bk Titles 500
Subject Interests: Religion, Theology

ROCKVILLE

S AMERICAN RED CROSS HOLLAND LAB, (AMR), Biomedical Sciences Library, 15601 Crabbs Branch Way, 20855-2743. SAN 377-1725. Tel: 301-738-0640. FAX: 301-738-0660. *In Charge*, Ann Harnsberger; E-Mail: harnsberger@usa.redcross.org; Staff 1 (Non-MLS 1)
Founded 1987
Jul 1998-Jun 1999 Mats Exp $98,000
Library Holdings: Bk Vols 7,000; Per Subs 100
Partic in MAHSL; Medical Libr Asn; National Network of Libraries of Medicine - Greater Midwest Region; Spec Libr Asn
Photocopy only, $.05/page

S AMERICAN SPEECH LANGUAGE HEARING ASSOCIATION LIBRARY,* 10801 Rockville Pike, 20852. SAN 371-2893. Tel: 301-897-5700. FAX: 301-571-0457. *In Charge*, Kathleen Moorehead
Library Holdings: Bk Vols 550
Restriction: Not open to public

M INTRACEL CORPORATION,* 1330 Picard Dr, 20850. SAN 306-980X. Tel: 301-258-5200, Ext 1186. FAX: 301-840-2161. *Librn*, Michele Mickens
Library Holdings: Bk Vols 3,000; Bk Titles 1,000; Per Subs 100
Subject Interests: Cancer, Immunology

JEWISH COMMUNITY CENTER OF GREATER WASHINGTON, Kass Judaic Library, 6125 Montrose Rd, 20852. SAN 307-0085. Tel: 301-881-0100. FAX: 301-881-5512. Web Site: www.jccgw.org. *Dir*, Barbara Winnik; Staff 21 (MLS 1, Non-MLS 20)
Founded 1970
Library Holdings: Bk Titles 6,000; Per Subs 15

S MAMIGONIAN FOUNDATION, Reference Collection,* 14513 Woodcrest Dr, 20853. SAN 373-0611. Tel: 301-460-0353. FAX: 301-460-0353. *Mgr*, John L Gueriguian
Library Holdings: Bk Vols 5,000; Per Subs 12

MONTGOMERY COLLEGE
J GERMANTOWN CAMPUS LIBRARY, 20200 Observation Dr, Germantown, 20876. SAN 321-0804. Tel: 301-353-7850. Interlibrary Loan Service Tel: 301-353-7858. Circulation Tel: 301-353-7858. Reference Tel: 301-353-7853. TDD: 301-353-1971. FAX: 301-353-7859. Web Site: www.mc.cc.md.us. *Head Librn*, Robert Bryce; Tel: 301-353-7855, E-Mail: rbryce@mc.cc.md.us; *Coll Develop, Ref*, Abi Sogunro; *Electronic Resources, Ref*, Brenda Braham; *Per, Ref*, Diane Cockrell; Staff 4 (MLS 4)
Founded 1978. Enrl 4,279; Fac 73; Highest Degree: Associate
Jul 2000-Jun 2001 Mats Exp $242,500, Books $105,000, Per/Ser (Incl. Access Fees) $48,000, Micro $15,000
Library Holdings: Per Subs 477
Automation Activity & Vendor Info: (Acquisitions) Endeavor; (Cataloging) Endeavor; (Circulation) Endeavor; (Course Reserve) Endeavor; (ILL) Endeavor; (Media Booking) Endeavor; (OPAC) Endeavor; (Serials) Endeavor
Publications: Guides & brochures for internal use
Function: ILL available, Reference services available
Partic in Capcon Library Network; Maryland Interlibrary Organization; OCLC Online Computer Library Center, Inc
No community ILL
Friends of the Library Group
J ROCKVILLE CAMPUS LIBRARY, 51 Mannakee St, 20850. SAN 307-0093. Tel: 301-251-7117, 301-279-5067 (recorded message). Interlibrary Loan Service Tel: 301-251-7118. Reference Tel: 301-251-7130. FAX: 301-251-7134. Web Site: montgomerycollege.org.library/, www.montgomerycollege.com. *Head Librn*, Patricia Mehok; Tel: 301-251-7101; *Librn*, Linda Fortney; Tel: 301-251-7127; *Librn*, Vani Murthy; Tel: 301-251-7128; *Librn*, Nancy Nyland; Tel: 301-251-7252; *Librn*, Harriet Reiter; Tel: 301-251-7126; *Librn*, Silvia Santiago; Tel: 301-251-7104; *Librn*, Shelly Summers; Tel: 301-251-7174; *Librn*, Beth Thoms; Tel: 301-251-7128; *Librn*, Douglas Williams; Tel: 301-251-7129; Staff 22 (MLS 7, Non-MLS 15)
Founded 1965. Enrl 14,011; Fac 299; Highest Degree: Associate
2000-2001 Mats Exp $294,500, Books $166,500, Per/Ser (Incl. Access Fees) $80,000, Micro $36,000, Electronic Ref Mat (Incl. Access Fees) $27,000
Library Holdings: Bk Vols 141,573; Bk Titles 119,644; Per Subs 729
Automation Activity & Vendor Info: (Acquisitions) Endeavor; (Cataloging) Endeavor; (Circulation) Endeavor; (Course Reserve) Endeavor; (OPAC) Endeavor; (Serials) Endeavor
Database Vendor: GaleNet, IAC - Info Trac, OVID Technologies, ProQuest
Publications: Guides & brochures for internal use.
Partic in Capcon Library Network; Maryland Interlibrary Organization; OCLC Online Computer Library Center, Inc
Special Services for the Deaf - TDD; Videos & decoder
J TAKOMA PARK CAMPUS LIBRARY, 7600 Takoma Ave, Takoma Park, 20912. SAN 307-0506. Tel: 301-650-1540. Interlibrary Loan Service Tel: 301-251-7118. Reference Tel: 301-650-1536. TDD: 301-650-1546. FAX: 301-650-1550. Web Site: www.montgomerycollege.org/library. *Dir Libr Serv*, Sarah Fisher; Tel: 301-650-1544, E-Mail: sfisher@mc.cc.md.us; Staff 4 (MLS 4)
Founded 1946. Fac 96
Jul 2000-Jun 2001 Mats Exp $286,060, Books $103,000, Per/Ser (Incl. Access Fees) $44,300, Micro $14,000, Electronic Ref Mat (Incl. Access Fees) $124,760
Library Holdings: Per Subs 388
Automation Activity & Vendor Info: (Acquisitions) Endeavor; (Cataloging) Endeavor; (Circulation) Endeavor; (Course Reserve) Endeavor; (OPAC) Endeavor
Database Vendor: IAC - Info Trac, OCLC - First Search, OVID Technologies
Publications: Guides & brochures for internal use
Function: Reference services available
Partic in Capcon Library Network; Maryland Interlibrary Organization; OCLC Online Computer Library Center, Inc
Special Services for the Deaf - TTY machine
Public service & user instruction to students of community
J TECHNICAL SERVICES, 20200 Observation Dr, 20876. Tel: 301-251-7136. FAX: 301-251-7134. Web Site: www.mc.cc.md.us.
Library Holdings: Per Subs 150

GL MONTGOMERY COUNTY CIRCUIT COURT, Law Library, Judicial Ctr, 50 Maryland Ave, Ste 326, 20850. SAN 307-0107. Tel: 240-777-9120. FAX: 240-777-9126. *Dir*, Karen D M Smith; E-Mail: ksmith@mccourt.com; *Librn*, Janet Camillo; E-Mail: jcamillo@mccourt.com; Staff 2 (MLS 1, Non-MLS 1)
Library Holdings: Bk Vols 80,000; Per Subs 110
Subject Interests: Continuing educ, Legal
Special Collections: How To Books for Pro Se Patrons; Maryland, DC & Virginia Legal & Federal Materials
Automation Activity & Vendor Info: (Cataloging) TLC; (OPAC) TLC
Friends of the Library Group

S MONTGOMERY COUNTY HISTORICAL SOCIETY LIBRARY, 111 W Montgomery Ave, 20850. SAN 326-0402. Tel: 301-340-2974. FAX: 301-340-2871. E-Mail: info@montgomeryhistory.org. Web Site: www.montgomeryhistory.org. *Librn*, Patricia A Andersen; E-Mail: pandersen@montgomeryhistory.org; Staff 9 (MLS 1, Non-MLS 8)
Founded 1965
Library Holdings: Bk Titles 35,000
Subject Interests: Genealogy, Local history, Local newsp, Manuscripts
Special Collections: Montgomery Mutual Insurance Papers
Publications: Montgomery County Story (quarterly)
Restriction: Open to public for reference only

P MONTGOMERY COUNTY PUBLIC LIBRARIES, 99 Maryland Ave, 20850-2372. SAN 344-2985. Tel: 240-777-0032. Interlibrary Loan Service Tel: 240-777-0063. TDD: TTY 240-777-0900. FAX: 240-777-0014, 240-777-0064. E-Mail: comments@mont.lib.md.us. Web Site: www.mont.lib.md.us. *Dir*, Harriet Henderson; *Tech Servs*, Alan Bobowski; *Mgr*, Bill Clarke; *Coll Develop*, Kay Ecelbarger; *Publ Servs*, Que Bronson; Staff 184 (MLS 151, Non-MLS 33)
Founded 1951. Circ 10,087,585
Jul 1999-Jun 2000 Income $32,614,546, State $1,642,862, Federal $120,841, County $29,685,161, Locally Generated Income $6,750, Other $1,158,932. Mats Exp $6,170,510, Books $3,580,070, Per/Ser (Incl. Access Fees) $507,000, Micro $37,000, Electronic Ref Mat (Incl. Access Fees) $493,194. Sal $19,776,791
Library Holdings: Bk Vols 2,505,244; Per Subs 4,539
Subject Interests: Government
Special Collections: Business Resource Center; Health Information Center (Wheaton Coll); Library Science (Professional Coll), bks, per; Local History (Rockville Coll), bks, maps, microfilm, oral hist, papers, per; Recent Political & Social History of Montgomery County (Marie Bennett Coll), bks & papers; Urban & Land Use Planning Reference (Vinton Coll), papers
Automation Activity & Vendor Info: (Acquisitions) SIRSI; (Circulation) SIRSI
Database Vendor: Ebsco - EbscoHost
Partic in Capcon Library Network; Md State Libr Network; OCLC Online Computer Library Center, Inc
Special Services for the Deaf - TTY machine
Special Services for the Blind - Newsline for the Blind; SNL for registered users
Friends of the Library Group
Branches: 23
ASPEN HILL LIBRARY, 4407 Aspen Hill Rd, 20853-2899. SAN 344-3019. Tel: 301-871-2094. TDD: 301-871-2097. FAX: 301-871-0443. *Mgr*, Paulette Burt
Special Collections: Foreign Language (Spanish) Coll; Literacy Coll
Special Services for the Deaf - TTY machine
Special Services for the Blind - ADA PC (OPAC) with JAWS & Zoom Text; CCTV for print enlargement; Copier with enlargement capabilities; Large print bks; Magnifiers; Screen enlargement software for people with visual disabilities
Special Services - Wheelchair accessible; chair lift between floors
Friends of the Library Group
BETHESDA LIBRARY, 7400 Arlington Rd, Bethesda, 20814-5399. SAN 344-3043. Tel: 301-986-4300. TDD: 301-986-4304. FAX: 301-986-4309. *Mgr*, Irene Briggs
Special Collections: Business Coll; Foreign Language Colls (Chinese, French, German, Korean, Spanish, Vietnamese); Job Information Coll; Literacy Coll
Special Services for the Deaf - Captioned media; TTY machine
Special Services for the Blind - ADA PC (OPAC) with JAWS & Zoom Text; Audio loop in meeting room; Copier with enlargement capabilities; Large print bks; Magnifiers; Screen enlargement software for people with visual disabilities
Special Services - Wheelchair accessible; study carrel at wheelchair height
Friends of the Library Group
CHEVY CHASE LIBRARY, 8005 Connecticut Ave, Chevy Chase, 20815-5997. SAN 344-3078. Tel: 301-986-4313. TDD: 301-657-0830. FAX: 301-657-0606. E-Mail: chinfo@mont.lib.md.us. *Mgr*, Kathie Meizner; Tel: 301-986-4313, E-Mail: meiznk@mont.lib.md.us; Staff 16 (MLS 7, Non-MLS 9)
Special Collections: Glass Coll
Special Services for the Deaf - TTY machine
Special Services for the Blind - ADA PC (OPAC) with JAWS & Zoom Text; Copier with enlargement capabilities; Large print bks; Screen enlargement software for people with visual disabilities
Special Services - Wheelchair accessible
Friends of the Library Group
DAMASCUS LIBRARY, 9701 Main St, Damascus, 20872-2007. SAN 344-3108. Tel: 301-253-5100. TDD: 301-253-0148. FAX: 301-253-1002. *Mgr*, John Baker
Special Services for the Deaf - Captioned media; TTY machine

Special Services for the Blind - ADA PC (OPAC) with JAWS & Zoom Text; Audio loop in meeting room; Copier with enlargement capabilities; Large print bks; Magnifiers; Screen enlargement software for people with visual disabilities
Special Services - Wheelchair accessible; study carrel at wheelchair height
Friends of the Library Group

DAVIS LIBRARY, 6400 Democracy Blvd, Bethesda, 20817-1638. SAN 344-3132. Tel: 301-897-2200. TDD: 301-897-2203. FAX: 301-564-5055. *Mgr*, Kay Bowman
Special Services for the Deaf - Captioned media; TTY machine
Special Services for the Blind - ADA PC (OPAC) with JAWS & Zoom Text; Audio loop in meeting room; Copier with enlargement capabilities; Large print bks; Screen enlargement software for people with visual disabilities
Special Services - Wheelchair accessible
Friends of the Library Group

DETENTION CENTER LIBRARY, 1307 Seven Locks Rd, 20854. SAN 344-3000. Tel: 240-777-9780. FAX: 240-777-9782. *Librn*, Joan Deacon

FAIRLAND LIBRARY, 14910 Old Columbia Pike, Burtonsville, 20866. SAN 374-7964. Tel: 301-421-5400. TDD: 301-421-5460. FAX: 301-421-5407. *Mgr*, Mildred Nance; E-Mail: nancep@mont.lib.md.us
Special Collections: Foreign Language (Chinese & Korean Coll)
Special Services for the Deaf - Captioned media; TTY machine
Special Services for the Blind - ADA PC (OPAC) with JAWS & Zoom Text; Audio loop in meeting room; Copier with enlargement capabilities; Large print bks; Screen enlargement software for people with visual disabilities
Special Services - Wheelchair accessible; study carrel at wheelchair height
Friends of the Library Group

GAITHERSBURG LIBRARY, 18330 Montgomery Village Ave, Gaithersburg, 20879-3599. SAN 344-3191. Tel: 301-840-2515. TDD: 301-840-2641. FAX: 301-840-2459. *Mgr*, Lillian Snyder
Special Collections: Foreign Language Coll (Chinese, French, German, Korean, Spanish, Vietnamese); Literacy Coll
Special Services for the Deaf - Captioned media; TTY machine
Special Services for the Blind - ADA PC (OPAC) with JAWS & Zoom Text; Copier with enlargement capabilities; Large print bks; Magnifiers; Screen enlargement software for people with visual disabilities
Special Services - Wheelchair accessible; study carrel at wheelchair height
Friends of the Library Group

GERMANTOWN LIBRARY, 12900 Middlebrook Rd, Germantown, 20874. SAN 328-9966. Tel: 240-777-0110. TDD: 240-777-0901. FAX: 240-777-0129. *Mgr*, Maria Pedak-Kari
Special Collections: Foreign Language (Spanish) Coll
Special Services for the Deaf - TTY machine
Special Services for the Blind - ADA PC (OPAC) with JAWS & Zoom Text; Audio loop in meeting room; Copier with enlargement capabilities; Large print bks; Magnifiers; Screen enlargement software for people with visual disabilities
Special Services - Wheelchair accessible; study carrel at wheelchair height
Friends of the Library Group

KENSINGTON PARK LIBRARY, 4201 Knowles Ave, Kensington, 20895-2408. SAN 344-3221. Tel: 301-897-2211. TDD: 301-897-2250. FAX: 301-897-2238. *Mgr*, Keith Fleeman; E-Mail: fleemk@mont.lib.md.us; Staff 7 (MLS 4, Non-MLS 3)
Special Services for the Deaf - TTY machine
Special Services for the Blind - ADA PC (OPAC) with JAWS & Zoom Text; Audio loop in meeting room; Copier with enlargement capabilities; Large print bks; Screen enlargement software for people with visual disabilities
Special Services - Wheelchair accessible; study carrel at wheelchair height

LITTLE FALLS LIBRARY, 5501 Massachusetts Ave, Bethesda, 20816-1932. SAN 344-3256. Tel: 301-320-4880. TDD: 301-320-8813. FAX: 301-320-0164. *Mgr*, Nancy Shaver; E-Mail: nancys@mont.lib.md.us
Special Services for the Deaf - TTY machine
Special Services for the Blind - ADA PC (OPAC) with JAWS & Zoom Text; Copier with enlargement capabilities; Large print bks; Magnifiers; Screen enlargement software for people with visual disabilities
Special Services - Wheelchair accessible
Friends of the Library Group

NOYES CHILDREN'S LIBRARY, 10237 Carroll Pl, Kensington, 20895-3361. SAN 344-3310. Tel: 301-929-5533. FAX: 301-929-5470.
Special Services for the Blind - ADA PC (OPAC) with JAWS & Zoom Text; Screen enlargement software for people with visual disabilities

OLNEY LIBRARY, 3500 Olney-Laytonsville Rd, Olney, 20832-1798. SAN 344-340X. Tel: 301-570-1232. TDD: 301-570-1221. FAX: 301-570-1239. *Mgr*, Elaine Barkley; E-Mail: barkle@mont.lib.md.us
Special Services for the Deaf - TTY machine
Special Services for the Blind - ADA PC (OPAC) with JAWS & Zoom Text; Copier with enlargement capabilities; Large print bks; Screen enlargement software for people with visual disabilities
Special Services - Wheelchair accessible

POOLESVILLE LIBRARY, 19633 Fisher Ave, Poolesville, 20837-2071. SAN 344-3493. Tel: 301-972-7800. TDD: 301-972-7825. FAX: 301-972-7810. *Mgr*, Mark Gochnour
Special Services for the Deaf - TTY machine
Special Services for the Blind - ADA PC (OPAC) with JAWS & Zoom Text; Copier with enlargement capabilities; Large print bks; Screen enlargement software for people with visual disabilities
Special Services - Wheelchair accessible; study carrel at wheelchair height

POTOMAC LIBRARY, 10101 Glenolden Dr, Potomac, 20854-5052. SAN 344-3345. Tel: 301-983-4475. TDD: 301-765-4083. FAX: 301-983-4479. *Mgr*, Rita Isenberg
Special Collections: Chinese Language Coll
Special Services for the Deaf - TTY machine
Special Services for the Blind - ADA PC (OPAC) with JAWS & Zoom Text; Audio loop in meeting room; Copier with enlargement capabilities; Large print bks; Screen enlargement software for people with visual disabilities
Special Services - Wheelchair accessible
Friends of the Library Group

QUINCE ORCHARD LIBRARY, 15831 Quince Orchard Rd, Gaithersburg, 20878. Tel: 240-777-0200. TDD: 240-777-0903. FAX: 240-777-0202. *Mgr*, Cindy Counihan
Special Collections: Foreign Language (Chinese) Coll
Special Services for the Deaf - Captioned media; TTY machine
Special Services for the Blind - ADA PC (OPAC) with JAWS & Zoom Text; Audio loop in meeting room; Copier with enlargement capabilities; Large print bks; Screen enlargement software for people with visual disabilities
Special Services - Wheelchair accessible; study carrel at wheelchair height

ROCKVILLE LIBRARY, 99 Maryland Ave, 20850-2371. SAN 344-337X. Tel: 240-777-0140. Reference Tel: 240-777-0001. TDD: 240-777-0902. FAX: 240-777-0157. *Mgr*, Dan Beavin
Special Collections: Business Resource Center (Business Counselling); Children's Resource Center; County Government Archives; Foreign Language Coll (Chinese, Korean & Vietnamese); Local
Special Services for the Deaf - TTY machine
Special Services for the Blind - ADA PC (OPAC) with JAWS & Zoom Text; Copier with enlargement capabilities; Large print bks; Screen enlargement software for people with visual disabilities
Special Services - Wheelchair accessible; Public Access Catalog (PAC) & tables at wheelchair height
Friends of the Library Group

SILVER SPRING LIBRARY, 8901 Colesville Rd, Silver Spring, 20910-4339. SAN 344-3434. Tel: 301-565-7689. TDD: 301-565-7505. FAX: 301-565-7301. *Mgr*, Ann Irvine
Special Collections: Chinese Language Coll; Literacy Coll; Spanish Language Coll
Special Services for the Deaf - Captioned media; TTY machine
Special Services for the Blind - ADA PC (OPAC) with JAWS & Zoom Text; Copier with enlargement capabilities; Large print bks; Screen enlargement software for people with visual disabilities
Special Services - Wheelchair accessible
Friends of the Library Group

SPECIAL NEEDS LIBRARY, 6400 Democracy Blvd, Lower Level, Bethesda, 20817-1699. SAN 344-2993. Tel: 301-897-2212. FAX: 301-897-2217. *Mgr*, Charlette Stinnett
Special Collections: Disability-related materials incl videos; Large Print & Talking Books
Special Services for the Deaf - Staff with knowledge of sign language; TTY machine
Special Services for the Blind - ADA PC (OPAC) with JAWS & Zoom Text; Audio loop in meeting room; Braille printer (Romeo), Braille translator (MEGA DOTS); Braille translation & printing software & equipment; CCTV (VisualTex); Copier with enlargement capabilities; Kurzweil Reading Machine; Large print bks; Magnifiers; Newsline for the Blind; Reading edge system; Talking book & recordings for the blind catalogs
Other Special Services - Wheelchair accessible; Homebound service; Computer services with adaptive software & hardware; Sub-regional library of the Maryland State Library for the Blind & Physically Handicapped

TWINBROOK LIBRARY, 202 Meadow Hall Dr, 20851-1551. SAN 344-3469. Tel: 240-777-0240. TDD: 240-777-0904. FAX: 240-777-0258. *Mgr*, Jan Baird-Adams
Special Collections: Foreign Language (Chinese, Korean, Spanish, Vietnamese) Coll
Special Services for the Deaf - TTY machine
Special Services for the Blind - ADA PC (OPAC) with JAWS & Zoom Text; Copier with enlargement capabilities; Large print bks; Screen enlargement software for people with visual disabilities
Special Services - Wheelchair accessible; study carrel at wheelchair height

WHEATON LIBRARY, 11701 Georgia Ave, Wheaton, 20902-1997. SAN 344-3523. Tel: 301-929-5520. TDD: 301-929-5524. FAX: 301-929-5525. *Mgr*, Cynthia Hicks
Special Collections: Foreign Language (Chinese, French, German, Korean, Spanish & Vietnamese) Coll; Health Information Center; Literacy Coll; Science & Technology
Special Services for the Deaf - Captioned media; TTY machine
Special Services for the Blind - ADA PC (OPAC) with JAWS & Zoom Text; Audio loop in meeting room; CCTV for print enlargement; Copier with enlargement capabilities; Large print bks; Magnifiers; Screen enlargement software for people with visual disabilities

Special Services - Wheelchair accessible; study carrels at wheelchair height
WHITE OAK LIBRARY, 11701 New Hampshire Ave, Silver Spring, 20904-2898. SAN 344-3558. Tel: 301-622-2492. TDD: 301-622-6596. FAX: 301-989-1921. *Mgr*, David Muse
Special Collections: Foreign Language (Spanish) Coll; Literacy Coll
Special Services for the Deaf - TTY machine
Special Services for the Blind - ADA PC (OPAC) with JAWS & Zoom Text; Copier with enlargement capabilities; Large print bks; Magnifiers; Screen enlargement software for people with visual disabilities
Special Services - Wheelchair accessible; study carrel at wheelchair height
Bookmobiles: 3. Bk vols 34,850

S MONTGOMERY COUNTY PUBLIC SCHOOLS, Professional Library,* 850 Hungerford Dr Rm 50, 20850-1747. SAN 324-5233. Tel: 301-279-3227. FAX: 301-279-3072. Web Site: www.mcps.k12.md.us/departments/media/prof.html. *Librn*, Janet Biggs; E-Mail: janet_biggs@fc.mcps.k12.md.us; Staff 1 (MLS 1)
Enrl 115,000; Fac 8,000
Library Holdings: Bk Vols 13,000; Per Subs 400
Subject Interests: Education
Special Collections: Montgomery County Public Schools Instructional Guides, ERIC
Automation Activity & Vendor Info: (Circulation) Sagebrush Corporation
Publications: Bibliography Series
Partic in Maryland Interlibrary Organization

GL NATIONAL CRIMINAL JUSTICE REFERENCE SERVICE,* 2277 Research Blvd. (Mail add: PO Box 6000, 20849-6000), SAN 322-1717. Tel: 301-519-5500. Toll Free Tel: 800-851-3420. FAX: 301-519-5212. E-Mail: askncjrs@ncjrs.org. Web Site: www.ncjrs.org. *Librn*, Anne Bolin
Founded 1972
Library Holdings: Bk Vols 150,000; Bk Titles 130,000; Per Subs 200
Subject Interests: Criminal law and justice, Drug abuse
Partic in Dialog Corporation

G NUCLEAR REGULATORY COMMISSION, Law-Legislative Information Service, 11555 Rockville Pike, 20852. SAN 377-4260. Tel: 301-415-1526. FAX: 301-415-3725. Web Site: www.nrc.gov. *Librn*, Charlotte Carnahan
1998-1999 Mats Exp Books $80,000
Library Holdings: Bk Vols 5,000; Per Subs 300
Partic in Law Libr Soc of DC; Spec Libr Asn

GM SHADY GROVE ADVENTIST HOSPITAL LIBRARY,* 9901 Medical Center Dr, 20850. SAN 377-4589. Tel: 301-279-6101. FAX: 301-279-6500.
Library Holdings: Bk Vols 400; Per Subs 100

G UNITED STATES BUREAU OF ALCOHOL, TOBACCO & FIREARMS, National Laboratory Library, 1401 Research Blvd, 20850. SAN 371-1315. Tel: 301-217-5756. FAX: 301-315-0519. *Librn*, Adiva R Sotzsky; E-Mail: asotzsky@atfhq.atf.treas.gov; Staff 1 (MLS 1)
Library Holdings: Bk Titles 3,000; Per Subs 100
Subject Interests: Analytical chemistry, Forensic sci
Automation Activity & Vendor Info: (Cataloging) TLC; (Circulation) TLC; (OPAC) TLC

UNITED STATES DEPARTMENT OF HEALTH & HUMAN SERVICES
GM FDA CENTER FOR DEVICES & RADIOLOGICAL HEALTH LIBRARY, 9200 Corporate Blvd, Rm 030, 20850. SAN 344-3736. Tel: 301-827-6901. FAX: 301-594-2352. *Librn*, Harriet Albersheim; Staff 7 (MLS 5, Non-MLS 2)
Founded 1976
Library Holdings: Bk Titles 10,000; Per Subs 600
Subject Interests: Biomedical engineering, Health sciences, Nuclear medicine, Radiation, Radiology
Publications: Library newsletter (irregular)
Partic in Fedlink
GM FOOD & DRUG ADMINISTRATION, MEDICAL LIBRARY, 5600 Fishers Lane, Rm 11B-40/HFD-230, 20857. SAN 344-3760. Tel: 301-827-5701. FAX: 301-443-6385. *Dir*, Carol S Assouad; *Dep Dir*, Kathy Kruse; Staff 21 (MLS 10, Non-MLS 11)
Founded 1948
1996-1997 Mats Exp $750,000. Sal $1,000,000
Library Holdings: Bk Vols 30,000; Per Subs 1,500
Subject Interests: Pharmaceutics (careers), Pharmacology, Toxicology
Special Collections: Adverse Drug Effects; FDA Publications
Publications: Information Update (newsletter)
Partic in Fedlink
GM PARKLAWN HEALTH LIBRARY, 5600 Fishers Lane, Rm 13-12, 20857. SAN 344-3795. Tel: 301-443-2673. FAX: 301-443-2269. E-Mail: refdesk@psc.gov. Web Site: library.psc.gov. *Dir*, Karen M Stakes; Staff 12 (MLS 4, Non-MLS 8)
Founded 1970
Library Holdings: Bk Titles 25,000; Per Subs 1,250
Subject Interests: Health care administration, Health care delivery, Health res, Health servs, Mental health, Public health
Special Collections: Public Health (Public Health Service Publications, Public Health Bulletins), doc
Automation Activity & Vendor Info: (Acquisitions) Innovative Interfaces Inc.; (Circulation) Innovative Interfaces Inc.; (OPAC) Innovative Interfaces Inc.; (Serials) Innovative Interfaces Inc.
Publications: Parklawn Health Library Bulletin (monthly); Periodical Holdings List
Partic in Dialog Corporation; OCLC Online Computer Library Center, Inc
See also National Center for Health Statistics, Hyattsville, MD

G UNITED STATES NUCLEAR REGULATORY COMMISSION LIBRARY, 11545 Rockville Pike, 20852-2738. (Mail add: T2C8, 20555), SAN 320-6300. Tel: 301-415-7204. Reference Tel: 301-415-5610. FAX: 301-415-5365. E-Mail: library@nrc.gov. *In Charge*, Thomas E Smith; E-Mail: tes@nrc.gov
Library Holdings: Bk Titles 20,000; Per Subs 400
Subject Interests: Energy, Nuclear science, Radiation
Special Collections: International Atomic Energy Agency Publications
Restriction: By appointment only
Partic in Dialog Corporation; Fedlink; OCLC Online Computer Library Center, Inc
Branches:
GL LAW LIBRARY, 11555 Rockville Pike, 20852-2738. (Mail add: 0-15 B18, Washington, 20555), SAN 373-1979. Tel: 301-415-1526. FAX: 301-415-3725.
Library Holdings: Bk Vols 7,000; Per Subs 12
Subject Interests: Administrative law, Environmental law, Nuclear energy

M US SUBSTANCE ABUSE & MENTAL HEALTH SERVICES ADMINISTRATION, (NCADI), National Clearinghouse for Alcohol & Drug Information Library, 11426-28 Rockville Pike, Ste 200, 20852-3007. (Mail add: PO Box 2345, 20847-2345), SAN 307-0131. Tel: 301-468-2600. Toll Free Tel: 800-729-6686. TDD: 800-487-4889. FAX: 301-468-6433. E-Mail: info@health.org. Web Site: www.health.org. *Coll Develop, Librn*, John Fay; E-Mail: jfay@health.org; *Ref*, Diane Johnston; E-Mail: djohnston@health.org
Founded 1987
Oct 1998-Sep 1999 Mats Exp $44,800, Books $6,000, Per/Ser (Incl. Access Fees) $38,800
Library Holdings: Bk Vols 3,300; Per Subs 200
Subject Interests: Alcohol and drugs, Drug abuse
Special Collections: Quarterly Journal of Studies on Alcohol, 1940-71
Publications: Clearinghouse publications: Prevention Pipeline (bimonthly); NCADI Publications Catalog (quarterly); Resource Guides
Restriction: Lending to staff only
Partic in District Of Columbia Health Sciences Information Network; National Network of Libraries of Medicine - Greater Midwest Region
Special Services for the Deaf - TDD
The Clearinghouse is an Information Service of the Substance Abuse & Mental Health Services Administration (US Public Health Service) & is operated under contract by Social & Health Services, Ltd

S WESTAT, INC LIBRARY,* 1650 Research Blvd, 20850. SAN 307-0190. Tel: 301-251-1500, Ext 4290. FAX: 301-294-2034. *Librn*, Ken Vaughan; *Librn*, Rebekah Zanditon
Subject Interests: Economics, Education, Health sciences, Labor, Marketing, Psychology, Social sciences and issues, Statistics

SAINT LEONARD

S ESTUARINE RESEARCH CENTER, Academy of Natural Sciences Library, 10545 Mackall Rd, 20685. SAN 374-9738. Tel: 410-586-9700. FAX: 410-586-9705. Web Site: www.anserc.org. *Librn*, Jean Beard; E-Mail: beard@acnatsci.org
Library Holdings: Bk Titles 200

SAINT MARY'S CITY

S HISTORIC SAINT MARY'S CITY, Research Library, PO Box 39, 20686. SAN 329-3920. Tel: 301-862-0974. FAX: 301-862-0968. E-Mail: pndance@osprey.smcm.edu. *Dir*, Henry Miller; *Res*, Patricia Dance
Library Holdings: Bk Vols 375

C SAINT MARY'S COLLEGE OF MARYLAND LIBRARY, 18952 E Fisher Rd, 20686-3001. SAN 307-0204. Tel: 301-862-0264. FAX: 301-862-0400, 301-862-0492. E-Mail: refdesk@osprey.smcm.edu. Web Site: www.smcm.edu/library. *Dir*, Todd Kelley; E-Mail: tdkelley@osprey.smcm.edu; *Librn*, Celia E Rabinowitz; Tel: 301-862-0267, E-Mail: cerabinowitz@smcm.edu; *Librn*, Theresa A Leonard; Tel: 301-862-0265, E-Mail: taleonard@smcm.edu; *Librn*, Kerie L Nickel; Tel: 301-862-0285, E-Mail: klnickel@smcm.edu; *ILL*, Brenda Rogers; *Cat*, Joe L Storey; Tel: 301-862-0260, E-Mail: jlstorey@smcm.edu; *Circ*, Brian Hawk; *Ref*, Joanne Juhnke; *Cat*, Winnie W Fun; Tel: 301-862-0259, E-Mail: wwfun@smcm.edu. Subject Specialists: *Education*, Celia E Rabinowitz; *History*, Theresa A Leonard; *Psychology*, Celia E Rabinowitz; *Religious studies*, Celia E Rabinowitz; *Social sci*, Theresa A Leonard; Staff 18 (MLS 7, Non-MLS 11)
Founded 1840. Enrl 1,650; Fac 112; Highest Degree: Bachelor
Library Holdings: Bk Vols 180,000; Per Subs 1,601
Subject Interests: Art and architecture, History, Literature, Music, Natural science, Social sciences and issues
Special Collections: Marylandiana, St Mary's County History

Automation Activity & Vendor Info: (Acquisitions) epixtech, inc.; (Cataloging) epixtech, inc.; (Circulation) epixtech, inc.; (OPAC) epixtech, inc.; (Serials) epixtech, inc.
Database Vendor: Dialog, DRA, Ebsco - EbscoHost, epixtech, inc., GaleNet, IAC - Info Trac, Lexis-Nexis, OCLC - First Search, ProQuest
Function: ILL available
Partic in Dialog Corporation; PALINET & Union Library Catalogue of Pennsylvania

SAINT MICHAELS

S CHESAPEAKE BAY MARITIME MUSEUM LIBRARY, PO Box 636, 21663. SAN 307-0212. Tel: 410-745-2916. FAX: 410-745-6088. E-Mail: library@cbmm.org. Web Site: www.cbmm.org. *Curator*, Pete Lesher; E-Mail: plesher@cbmm.org; *Coll Develop*, Lindsley Hand; E-Mail: lhand@cbmm.org; Staff 2 (Non-MLS 2)
Founded 1967
May 2000-Apr 2001 Income $3,000. Mats Exp $3,000, Books $2,500, Per/Ser (Incl. Access Fees) $500
Library Holdings: Bk Vols 9,800; Per Subs 17
Subject Interests: History, Maritime history, Maryland, Virginia
Special Collections: Constance Stuart Larrabee Chesapeake Bay Photographs; Downes Curtis Sailmaking Papers; Herman Hollerith Photographs; Howard I Chapelle Papers; John G Earle Ships Plans; Louis Feuchter Notes & Sketches; Ralph Wiley Yacht Designs; Robert G Henry Yacht Designs
Restriction: By appointment only

SALISBURY

P EASTERN SHORE REGIONAL LIBRARY, INC, 122-126 S Division St, PO Box 4148, 21801. SAN 307-0220. Tel: 410-742-1537. FAX: 410-548-5807. Web Site: www.esrl.lib.md.us. *Adminr*, Raineyl Coiro; E-Mail: raineyl@esrl.lib.md.us; *Syst Coordr*, Craig Abresch; E-Mail: craig@esrl.lib.md.us; *Coll Develop*, Rosemary Truitt; *Info Specialist*, Susan Pedersen Upole; E-Mail: susan@esrl.lib.md.us; Staff 10 (MLS 2, Non-MLS 8)
Founded 1965. Pop 299,900
2000-2001 Income $687,948, State $45,000, Locally Generated Income $10,101. Mats Exp $83,239, Books $31,774, Electronic Ref Mat (Incl. Access Fees) $51,465. Sal $305,632 (Prof $141,291)
Automation Activity & Vendor Info: (Circulation) Innovative Interfaces Inc.
Database Vendor: Ebsco - EbscoHost, GaleNet, Innovative Interfaces INN - View, ProQuest
Publications: Annual Plan; Annual Report; AV Catalog; Directory of Libraries; Union List of Periodicals
Member Libraries: Dorchester County Public Library; Kent County Public Library; Kent County Public Library; Queen Anne's County Free Library; Somerset County Library System; Talbot County Free Library; Wicomico County Free Library, Inc; Worcester County Library
Special Services for the Blind - Newsline for the Blind
Special Services - Provides ILL, inservice training, AV coll & referral, technology consulting, consortium purchasing, computer training center for the region

M PENINSULA REGIONAL MEDICAL CENTER, Charles Long-Ulman Health Sciences Library, 100 E Carroll St, 21801. SAN 329-2177. Tel: 410-543-7094. FAX: 410-543-7096. *Librn*, Cathy Moore; E-Mail: cathy.moore@peninsula.org; Staff 1 (MLS 1)
Library Holdings: Bk Vols 1,750; Per Subs 100
Subject Interests: Medicine, Nursing

C SALISBURY STATE UNIVERSITY, Blackwell Library, 1101 Camden Ave, 21801-6863. SAN 307-0239. Tel: 410-543-6130. FAX: 410-543-6203. Web Site: www.ssu.umd.edu/univoffices/blackwell.html. *Assoc Dir*, Judith K Fischer; *Coll Develop*, D Andrews Reese; *Cat*, Neil Jen; *Cat*, Audrey Schadt; *Spec Coll*, Charletta House; *Ref*, Susan Brazer; *Ref*, Kristin Carlson; *Ref*, Terry Daenzer; *Ref*, Stephanie Fridie; *Ref*, Kathryn Kalmanson; *Ref*, Gaylord Robb; Staff 22 (MLS 12, Non-MLS 10)
Founded 1925. Enrl 5,049; Fac 317; Highest Degree: Master
Jul 1998-Jun 1999 Income $1,672,303. Mats Exp $356,458, Books $65,223, Per/Ser (Incl. Access Fees) $248,578, Presv $10,026, Micro $32,631. Sal $990,122 (Prof $508,905)
Library Holdings: Bk Vols 246,294; Per Subs 1,662
Special Collections: Civil War (Les Callette Memorial Coll); Leisure Studies Coll, bks, VF; Maryland Room, bks, micro; Teacher Education (Educational Resources Coll), bks, AV, micro
Automation Activity & Vendor Info: (Circulation) CARL
Partic in Colorado Alliance Of Research Libraries; Dialog Corporation; Maryland Interlibrary Organization; OCLC Online Computer Library Center, Inc; PALINET & Union Library Catalogue of Pennsylvania

P WICOMICO COUNTY FREE LIBRARY, INC,* 122-126 S Division St, PO Box 4148, 21801-4148. SAN 307-0247. Tel: 410-749-3612. FAX: 410-548-2968. E-Mail: askus@wicomico.org. Web Site: www.wicomicolibrary.org. *Dir*, Kathleen S Reif; *Asst Dir*, Judy Quillin; *Ref*, Rosemary Truitt; *Cat*, Kip Martin; *Automation Syst Coordr*, Victoria Greene; *Bkmobile Coordr*, Barbara Prevento; *Ch Servs*, Janice Murphy; *Circ*, Bernadette Canaday; *Coll Develop*, Rosemary Truitt; Staff 8 (MLS 8)
Founded 1927. Pop 76,800
Library Holdings: Bk Vols 190,360; Per Subs 252
Subject Interests: Art, Carving, Genealogy, Maryland
Special Collections: Maryland & Delmarva Peninsula, bks, micro
Publications: Crisis of Opportunities, Wicomico County Free Library Long Range Plan III, 1991-96; Self-Study of the Wicomico County Free Library & Its Service Area
Mem of Eastern Shore Regional Library, Inc
Friends of the Library Group

SANDY SPRING

S SANDY SPRING MUSEUM LIBRARY, (SSM), 17901 Bentley Rd, 20860. SAN 375-6807. Tel: 301-774-0022. FAX: 301-774-8149. Web Site: www.sandyspringmuseum.org. *Dir*, Debbie Heibein; E-Mail: dheibein@sandyspringmuseum.org; *Librn*, Jean M Snyder; *Archivist*, Miriam Sherwin; *Archivist*, Betsy Shimkus. Subject Specialists: *Hist info*, Jean M Snyder; *Music*, Miriam Sherwin; *Photos*, Betsy Shimkus
Library Holdings: Bk Vols 350; Bk Titles 150
Subject Interests: Genealogy, Quakers
Special Collections: Local African American History; Underground Railroad
Publications: Sandy Spring Legacy, 1999
Open Mon, Wed & Thurs 11-4, Sat & Sun 12-4

SEVERNA PARK

S BAND, LAVIS & ASSOCIATES, INC, Technical Library,* 900 Ritchie Hwy, 21146. SAN 370-3924. Tel: 410-544-2800. FAX: 410-647-3411. E-Mail: bla@access.digex.net. Web Site: www.access.digex.net~bla. *Dir*, Shirley Wilson
Library Holdings: Bk Titles 15,500; Per Subs 25
Restriction: Not open to public

R WOODS MEMORIAL PRESBYTERIAN CHURCH LIBRARY,* 611 Baltimore-Annapolis Blvd, 21146. SAN 307-0255. Tel: 410-647-2550. FAX: 410-647-2781.
Library Holdings: Bk Vols 2,400
Subject Interests: Children's literature, Marriage, Religion, Women's studies

SHARPSBURG

S NATIONAL PARK SERVICE, Chesapeake & Ohio Canal National Historical Park Library, 16500 Shepherdstown Pike, PO Box 4, 21782. SAN 371-6228. Tel: 301-739-4200. FAX: 301-739-5275. Web Site: www.nps.gov/choh.
Library Holdings: Bk Titles 500
Restriction: By appointment only

S NATIONAL PARK SERVICE, Antietam National Battlefield Library, PO Box 158, 21782. SAN 307-0263. Tel: 301-432-5124. FAX: 301-432-4590. Web Site: www.antietam.gov. *Librn*, Ted Alexander
Founded 1940
Library Holdings: Bk Titles 2,000
Subject Interests: Civil War, Local history
Special Collections: Battle of Antietam Coll; Civil War Regimental Histories; Civil War Soldiers' Letters & Diaries; Info on Civil War Artillary; National Tribune on microfilm; Park History; Research Reports; War of the Rebellion, Official Records of the Union & Confederate Armies

SILVER SPRING

S ASSOCIATION FOR INFORMATION & IMAGE MANAGEMENT INTERNATIONAL, Resource Center, 1100 Wayne Ave, Ste 1100, 20910. SAN 307-0387. Tel: 301-587-8202. FAX: 301-587-2711. Web Site: www.aiim.org/ebusiness. *Mgr*, Jaqueline Virando; E-Mail: jvirando@aiim.org; *VPres*, Gary Robinson; Tel: 301-755-2622
Founded 1974
1999-2000 Mats Exp $40,000
Subject Interests: Automation, Electronic engineering, Technology
Publications: 1st Resource & Infobits (on-line info products); Publications Catalog; Resource Reports

GENERAL CONFERENCE OF SEVENTH-DAY ADVENTISTS
SR ARCHIVES, 12501 Old Columbia Pike, 20904. SAN 375-2844. Tel: 301-680-5021. FAX: 301-680-6090. E-Mail: 74617.1400@compuserv.com. *Dir*, Bert Haloviak
Subject Interests: Seventh-Day Adventist hist
Special Collections: Administrative Records of the World Headquarters of the Seventh-Day Adventist Church

SR REBOK MEMORIAL LIBRARY, 12501 Old Columbia Pike, PO Box 4999, 20914. SAN 325-5115. Tel: 301-680-6495. FAX: 301-680-6090. E-Mail: 74617.3550@compuserv.com. *Dir*, Alan S Hecht

Founded 1983
Library Holdings: Bk Vols 26,000; Bk Titles 25,200; Per Subs 430
Special Collections: Religion (Seventh-Day Adventists) & Other Religions
Publications: Check It Out (newsletter)
Partic in Capcon Library Network

S GEORGE MEANY MEMORIAL ARCHIVES LIBRARY,* 10000 New Hampshire Ave, 20903. SAN 302-5616. Tel: 301-431-5445. FAX: 301-431-0385. *Librn*, Jannie Cobb; E-Mail: jcobb@clark.net; *Librn*, Ruby U Tyson; Staff 3 (MLS 2, Non-MLS 1)
Founded 1916
Library Holdings: Bk Titles 13,000; Per Subs 4,000
Special Collections: American Federation of Labor Proceedings Coll (1881-1955), per, microfilm; American Federationist Coll (1894-1982), microfilm; CIO News (1937-1955), micro; CIO Proceedings (1938-1955), micro; National & International Trade-Union Proceedings Coll, constitutions & journals; State Labor Proceedings Coll (1884-1974), microfiche
Publications: Acquisitions List
Partic in Capcon Library Network

S HAMMER, SILER & GEORGE ASSOCIATES LIBRARY,* 8601 Georgia Ave, Ste 1010, 20910. SAN 302-6663. Tel: 301-565-5200. FAX: 301-565-4184. *Librn*, Martha Nichols
Library Holdings: Bk Vols 8,000; Bk Titles 6,000; Per Subs 45
Subject Interests: Real estate
Special Collections: Census Materials
Restriction: Staff use only

M HOLY CROSS HOSPITAL OF SILVER SPRING, Medical Library,* 1500 Forest Glen Rd, 20910. SAN 325-8734. Tel: 301-754-7245. FAX: 301-754-7247. *Librn*, Bernetta Payne
Library Holdings: Bk Vols 2,000; Per Subs 185

R HOLY NAME COLLEGE LIBRARY,* 1650 St Camillus Dr, 20903-2559. SAN 302-671X. Tel: 301-434-3400. FAX: 301-434-4624.
Subject Interests: Theology
Special Collections: Franciscan Coll
Partic in Wash Theol Union

S INTERNATIONAL FABRICARE INSTITUTE, Research Center Library,* 12251 Tech Rd, 20904. SAN 307-0336. Tel: 301-622-1900. FAX: 301-236-9320. *Librn*, Elenor Brooks
Founded 1930
Library Holdings: Bk Vols 500
Subject Interests: Chemistry, Textiles

L LINOWES & BLOCHER LLP, Law Library, 1010 Wayne Ave, 20910. SAN 372-0608. Tel: 301-650-7063. FAX: 301-495-9044. E-Mail: inbox@linowes-law.com. Web Site: www.linowes-law.com. *Librn*, Deborah Cannon
Library Holdings: Bk Vols 3,000; Per Subs 35
Subject Interests: Real estate

S MARYLAND COLLEGE OF ART & DESIGN LIBRARY,* 10500 Georgia Ave, 20902. SAN 307-0379. Tel: 301-649-4454. FAX: 301-649-2940. *Librn*, Shelly Summers; E-Mail: shelly.summers@mailcity.com
Founded 1977
Library Holdings: Bk Vols 11,000; Per Subs 28
Subject Interests: Fine arts, Graphic arts

S NATIONAL CAPITAL TROLLEY MUSEUM LIBRARY, 1313 Bonifant Rd, 20905. SAN 326-2782. Tel: 301-384-6088, 301-384-6352. FAX: 301-384-6352. Web Site: www.dctrolley.org. *Librn*, Eric Madison; Staff 2 (Non-MLS 2)
Library Holdings: Bk Titles 600
Subject Interests: Railroads
Open Sat & Sun 12-5

S NATIONAL COUNCIL OF SENIOR CITIZENS LIBRARY, (NSCERC), 8403 Colesville Rd, Ste 1200, 20910-1260. SAN 325-8238. Tel: 301-578-8422. FAX: 301-578-8999.
Library Holdings: Bk Titles 1,000; Per Subs 200
Subject Interests: Legislation
Publications: Acquisitions List (quarterly)
Senior citizens issues

G NATIONAL GEODETIC SURVEY LIBRARY,* 1315 East-West Hwy, 20910. SAN 328-1876. Tel: 301-713-3249. FAX: 301-713-4327. *Chief Librn*, Sharon Faber
Founded 1970
Library Holdings: Bk Vols 5,000; Per Subs 1,200
Subject Interests: Geodesy
Special Collections: 3500 Technical Papers
Publications: C & GS Special Publication; FGCC Publication; NOAA Manual; NOAA Professional Paper; NOAA Technical Memorandum; NOAA Technical Report

G NATIONAL OCEANIC & ATMOSPHERIC ADMINISTRATION, Library & Information Services Division, 1315 East West Hwy, 2nd flr, 20910. SAN 344-3582. Tel: 301-713-2600. FAX: 301-713-4599. E-Mail: reference@nodc.ndaa.gov. Web Site: www.lib.noaa.gov. *In Charge*, Doria Grimes; *Coll Develop*, Steven Quillen
Founded 1809
Library Holdings: Bk Vols 800,000; Bk Titles 600,000; Per Subs 1,000
Subject Interests: Climatology, Marine biology, Ocean engineering, Oceanography, Rare books
Special Collections: Climatology Coll (Daily Weather Maps), bk, flm; Marine Fisheries Data (Technical Reports), micro; Meteorology Coll (Data Publications), bk, flm, micro
Automation Activity & Vendor Info: (OPAC) SIRSI
Partic in Dialog Corporation; Fedlink; OCLC Online Computer Library Center, Inc
Branches:
ATLANTIC OCEANOGRAPHIC & METEOROLOGICAL LAB, 4301 Rickenbacker Causway, Miami, 33149. SAN 377-7405. Web Site: www.aoml.noaa.gov/general/lib. *Librn*, Linda Pikula
SEATTLE REGIONAL, BINC-15700, Bldg 3, 7600 Sand Point Way NE, Seattle, 98115. SAN 344-368X. Tel: 206-526-6241. FAX: 206-526-4535. Web Site: www.wrclib.noaa.gov/lib. *Librn*, Maureen Woods
Library Holdings: Bk Titles 10,000
Subject Interests: Chemistry, Climatology, Mathematics, Meteorology, Oceanography, Physics, Waste disposal
Special Collections: Puget Sound

S NATIONAL REHABILITATION INFORMATION CENTER (NARIC), 1010 Wayne Ave Ste 800, 20910-5633. SAN 371-263X. Tel: 301-562-2400. Toll Free Tel: 800-346-2742. FAX: 301-562-2401. Web Site: www.naric.com/. *Dir*, Mark X Odum; Staff 9 (Non-MLS 9)
Founded 1977
Library Holdings: Bk Vols 59,600; Per Subs 140; Bks on Deafness & Sign Lang 5,600
Subject Interests: Disability, Rehabilitation, Special education
Restriction: Non-circulating to the public
Function: Document delivery services, Referrals accepted
Special Services for the Deaf - TTY machine
Special Services for the Blind - Brailling & large print projects

SR PRESBYTERIAN CHURCH OF THE ATONEMENT LIBRARY, 10613 Georgia Ave, 20902. SAN 327-0505. Tel: 301-649-4131. FAX: 301-649-9633. *Librn*, Angela Riker
Founded 1953
Library Holdings: Bk Vols 4,800; Bk Titles 4,500; Per Subs 11
Special Collections: religious bks
Partic in Churchline Coun; Prof Libr Asn

SR SEVENTH DAY ADVENTISTS GENERAL CONFERENCE, Office of Archives & Statistics,* 12501 Old Columbia Pike, 20904. SAN 377-4481. Tel: 301-680-6000, Ext 6495. FAX: 301-680-6090. E-Mail: 74617.3550@compuserve.com. *Dir*, William Cash; *Librn*, Alan Hecht; *Archivist*, Bert Haloviak
Library Holdings: Bk Vols 27,000; Per Subs 500
Partic in Asn of Seventh Day Adventists Librns; Spec Libr Asn

S SOLID WASTE INFORMATION CLEARINGHOUSE LIBRARY,* 1100 Wayne Ave, Ste 700, PO Box 7219, 20910. SAN 372-6592. Tel: 301-585-2898. FAX: 301-589-7068. E-Mail: technical_services@swana.org. Web Site: www.swana.org.
Founded 1989
Library Holdings: Bk Titles 7,000; Per Subs 15
Publications: List of literature
SWICH is the Solid Waste Association of North America's (SWANA) library information clearinghouse

R WOODSIDE UNITED METHODIST CHURCH LIBRARY,* 8900 Georgia Ave, 20910-2739. SAN 307-0441. Tel: 301-587-1215. *Actg Librn*, Felicia Stokely
Founded 1962
Library Holdings: Bk Vols 1,200

SNOW HILL

P WORCESTER COUNTY LIBRARY,* 307 N Washington St, 21863. SAN 344-3884. Tel: 410-632-2600. FAX: 410-632-1159. E-Mail: worc@dmv.com. *Dir*, Stewart L Wells; *ILL*, Liz Brown; *Ch Servs*, Rose Donoway; *Acq*, Carol Howe; Staff 22 (MLS 1, Non-MLS 21)
Founded 1959. Pop 33,300
1998-1999 Income (Main Library and Branch Library) $939,888, State $90,000, County $814,888, Other $35,000. Mats Exp $185,000, Books $150,000, Per/Ser (Incl. Access Fees) $20,000, AV Equip $15,000. Sal $574,004
Library Holdings: Bk Vols 148,662; Bk Titles 90,773; Per Subs 365
Subject Interests: Real estate
Publications: Agriculture Directory Program Resources Handbook; quarterly program schedules
Mem of Eastern Shore Regional Library, Inc
Partic in Maryland Interlibrary Organization
Friends of the Library Group

Branches: 4
BERLIN BRANCH, 220 N Main St, Berlin, 21811. SAN 344-3914. Tel: 410-641-0650. FAX: 410-641-9566. *Librn*, Janet Bucciere
Friends of the Library Group
OCEAN CITY BRANCH, 200 14th St, Ocean City, 21842. SAN 344-3949. Tel: 410-289-7297. FAX: 410-289-5577. *Librn*, Andrea Schlottman
Friends of the Library Group
POCOMOKE CITY BRANCH, 301 Market St, Pocomoke City, 21851. SAN 344-3973. Tel: 410-957-0878. FAX: 410-957-4773. *Librn*, Elizabeth Barnes
SNOW HILL BRANCH, 307 N Washington St, 21863. SAN 344-4007. Tel: 410-632-2600. FAX: 410-632-1159. *Librn*, Karen Neville
Friends of the Library Group

SOLOMONS

S CALVERT MARINE MUSEUM LIBRARY, 14150 Solomons Island Rd, PO Box 97, 20688-0097. SAN 324-1122. Tel: 410-326-2042, Ext 14. FAX: 410-326-6691. E-Mail: library@calvertmarinemuseum.com. Web Site: www.calvertmarinemuseum.com. *Librn*, Paul L Berry; E-Mail: berrypl@co.cal.md.us
Founded 1970. Pop 250,000
Jul 1999-Jun 2000 Mats Exp $1,700, Books $1,000, Per/Ser (Incl. Access Fees) $300, Presv $350, Manuscripts & Archives $50
Library Holdings: Bk Vols 7,100; Bk Titles 6,800; Per Subs 75
Subject Interests: Ecology, Maritime history, Paleontology
Special Collections: B B Wills steamboat research files; Boat Building (M M Davis & Sons Coll), blueprints, correspondence, clippings; Chesapeake Bay History (M V Brewington Research Coll); History of Solomons Island (Patuxent River Seafood Industries); Seafood Processing (J C Lore & Sons Coll & Warren Denton Oysterhouse Coll); Tobacco Culture in Calvert County
Publications: Publications Catalogue
Restriction: Not a lending library
Function: Research library

C UNIVERSITY OF MARYLAND, Chesapeake Biological Laboratory,* PO Box 38, 20688-0038. SAN 328-8625. Tel: 410-326-7287. FAX: 410-326-7430. *Librn*, Kathy Heil; E-Mail: heil@cbl.umces.edu
Jul 1998-Jun 1999 Income $157,020. Mats Exp $74,000. (Prof $41,000)
Special Collections: Chesapeake Bay; shellfish, early reprints
Partic in Maryland Interlibrary Organization

SPARKS

S EA ENGINEERING SCIENCE & TECHNOLOGY, Resource Center, 15 Loveton Circle, 21152. SAN 329-8973. Tel: 410-771-4950, Ext 5177. Toll Free Tel: 800-876-4950. FAX: 410-771-4204. E-Mail: lbw@eaest.com. *Mgr*, Leslye Wakefield
Library Holdings: Bk Vols 10,000; Per Subs 55
Subject Interests: Engineering

STEVENSON

C VILLA JULIE COLLEGE LIBRARY, 1525 Greenspring Valley Rd, 21153. SAN 307-0468. Tel: 410-602-7233. FAX: 410-486-7329. Web Site: www.vjc.edu/library/. *Dir Libr Serv*, Maureen Anne Beck; Tel: 410-602-7231, E-Mail: mbeck@mail.vjc.edu; *Publ Servs*, Mary Patricia Rickert-Wilbur; *Ref*, Sue Bonsteel; *Cat*, Janet Foote; *Syst Coordr*, Robin Findeisen; *Tech Servs*, Steve Rouzer; *Circ*, Adam Mecinski. Subject Specialists: *Business*, Maureen Anne Beck; Staff 10 (MLS 6, Non-MLS 4)
Founded 1953. Enrl 1,820; Fac 120; Highest Degree: Master
Jul 2000-Jun 2001 Income Parent Institution $590,000. Mats Exp $321,360, Books $75,000, Per/Ser (Incl. Access Fees) $40,000, Presv $2,000, Micro $36,000, AV Equip $12,000, Other Print Mats $75,000, Electronic Ref Mat (Incl. Access Fees) $53,500. Sal $267,900
Library Holdings: Bk Vols 100,000; Bk Titles 67,841; Per Subs 720
Subject Interests: Education, Nursing, Paralegal
Automation Activity & Vendor Info: (Acquisitions) epixtech, inc.; (Cataloging) epixtech, inc.; (Circulation) epixtech, inc.; (Serials) epixtech, inc.
Database Vendor: Dialog, Ebsco - EbscoHost, epixtech, inc., IAC - Info Trac, Silverplatter Information Inc.
Partic in Baltimore Acad Libr Consortium; Capcon Library Network; Dialog Corporation; Dow Jones News Retrieval; OCLC Online Computer Library Center, Inc

STEVENSVILLE

S HISTORICAL EVALUATION & RESEARCH ORGANIZATION, Hero Library, 1407 Love Point Rd, 21666. SAN 324-1297. Tel: 410-643-8807. FAX: 410-643-8807. E-Mail: hero_library@msn.com. Web Site: www.herolibrary.org. *Librn*, Charles Hawkins
Founded 1962
Library Holdings: Bk Titles 4,000
Subject Interests: Military history
Special Collections: Military Law (Wiener Coll)

SUITLAND

S SMITHSONIAN INSTITUTION LIBRARIES, Museum Support Center Library, 4210 Silver Hill Rd, 20746-0534. SAN 376-9348. Tel: 301-238-3666. FAX: 301-238-3667. E-Mail: libmail@sil.si.edu. Web Site: www.sil.si.edu. *Librn*, Gil Taylor
Library Holdings: Bk Vols 25,000; Per Subs 125
Subject Interests: Conservation, Med entomology, Presv

SMITHSONIAN INSTITUTION LIBRARIES, National Museum of the American Indian Library, NMAI Cultural Resources Ctr 2000, MRC 537, 4220 Silver Hill Rd, 20746-0537. Tel: 301-238-6624, Ext 6329.
Library Holdings: Bk Vols 1,971

SYKESVILLE

M THE LIBRARY AT SPRINGFIELD HOSPITAL CENTER, 6655 Sykesville Rd, 21784. SAN 307-0484. Tel: 410-795-2100, Ext 3481. FAX: 410-795-6048. E-Mail: shcpl@ccpl.carr.org. *In Charge*, Bonnie Murray
Founded 1953
Jul 1999-Jun 2000 Mats Exp $21,832, Books $9,832, Per/Ser (Incl. Access Fees) $11,000, AV Equip $500
Library Holdings: Bk Titles 6,000; Per Subs 34; High Interest/Low Vocabulary Bk Vols 57; Bks on Deafness & Sign Lang 60
Subject Interests: Addictions, Art therapy, Dance movement therapy, Deafness, Forensic sci, Gerontology, Music therapy, Neurology, Nursing, Occupational therapies, Physical therapy, Psychiatry, Psychology, Recreational therapy, Rehabilitation, Social service (social work), Social work, Speech therapy
Function: ILL available, Literary searches, Photocopies available .
Bookmobile is from the Carroll County Public Library System in Maryland & comes twice a month during school year & once a month during the summer.

TAKOMA PARK

C COLUMBIA UNION COLLEGE, Weis Library,* 7600 Flower Ave, 20912-7796. SAN 307-0492. Tel: 301-891-4217, 301-891-4218, 301-891-4223. Interlibrary Loan Service Tel: 301-891-4217. FAX: 301-891-4204. E-Mail: library@cuc.edu. Web Site: www.cuc.edu/library/. *Dir*, Margaret J Von Hake; *Bibliog Instr, Ref*, Lee Marie Wisel; *Circ, ILL*, Donald Essex; *Acq*, Debby Szasz; *Ser*, Kathy Hecht; *Cat*, Stanley Cottrell II; Staff 6 (MLS 3, Non-MLS 3)
Founded 1904. Enrl 845; Highest Degree: Bachelor
Library Holdings: Bk Vols 130,000; Per Subs 369
Special Collections: Seventh-day Adventists History & Publications, bks, per
Publications: booklists (quarterly); Newsletter (irregular pub schedule): A Word From The Weis

S LTG ASSOCIATES LIBRARY, 6930 Carrol Ave, Ste 410, 20912. SAN 377-1466. Tel: 301-270-0882. FAX: 301-270-1966. Web Site: www.ltgassociates.com.
Library Holdings: Bk Vols 200

P TAKOMA PARK MARYLAND LIBRARY,* 101 Philadelphia Ave, 20912. SAN 307-0514. Tel: 301-270-1717. FAX: 301-270-8794. E-Mail: takoma@cais.com. Web Site: www.cityoftakomapark.org/library/. *Dir*, Ellen Arnold-Robbins; *Ch Servs*, Jillian Herschberger; *Ref*, Rebecca Brown; *Coordr, Tech Servs*, Nic Fontem
Founded 1935. Pop 16,231; Circ 110,332
Library Holdings: Bk Vols 52,480; Bk Titles 60,000; Per Subs 210
Subject Interests: Children's literature, English (language), Horticulture, Local history, Parenting, Restoration
Special Collections: Takoma Park History (Takoma Journal 1923-1955), unbd issues, microflm
Mem of Polaroid Camera Program
Partic in Maryland Interlibrary Organization; Metropolitan Area ILL Serv; State Libr Network
Open Mon & Wed 1-9, Tues & Thurs 10-9, Fri 12-6 & Sat 10-5
Friends of the Library Group

R TAKOMA PARK PRESBYTERIAN CHURCH LIBRARY, 310 Tulip Ave, 20912. SAN 307-0522. Tel: 301-270-5550, 301-270-5860. FAX: 301-270-8405. *Librn*, Carolyn Tilley; Staff 2 (MLS 1, Non-MLS 1)
Founded 1954
2000-2001 Mats Exp Books $250
Library Holdings: Bk Titles 2,500
Subject Interests: Philosophy, Religion, Social sciences and issues

M WASHINGTON ADVENTIST HOSPITAL, Health Sciences Library, 7600 Carroll Ave, 20912. SAN 307-0530. Tel: 301-891-5260. FAX: 301-891-6087. *Librn*, Cathy Cumbo; E-Mail: ccumbo@juno.com; Staff 2 (Non-MLS 2)

Founded 1956
Jan 1999-Dec 1999 Mats Exp $43,000, Books $10,000, Per/Ser (Incl. Access Fees) $31,500, Electronic Ref Mat (Incl. Access Fees) $1,500. Sal $34,851
Library Holdings: Bk Vols 1,200; Per Subs 162
Subject Interests: Clinical medicine, Hospital administration, Nursing
Restriction: Circulation limited
Partic in Docline; Hospital Coun of Nat Capital Area; MAHSL

TOWSON

GL BALTIMORE COUNTY CIRCUIT COURT LIBRARY, County Courts Bldg, 401 Bosley Ave, 21204. SAN 307-0565. Tel: 410-887-3086. FAX: 410-887-4807. Web Site: www.co.ba.md.us. *Dir Libr Serv*, Betsy Sandison; E-Mail: bsandison@co.ba.md.us; *Asst Librn*, James Gernert; *Asst Librn*, Stephanie Papa
Library Holdings: Bk Vols 100,000; Per Subs 70
Subject Interests: Law
Special Collections: CA & CSA Briefs, microfiche; Micpels

P BALTIMORE COUNTY PUBLIC LIBRARY, 320 York Rd, 21204-5179. SAN 344-4031. Tel: 410-887-6100. FAX: 410-887-6103. E-Mail: bcpl@bcplonline.org. Web Site: www.bcplonline.org. *Dir*, James H Fish; *Asst Dir*, Lynn Lockwood; *Asst Dir*, Deborah Wheeler; *Automation Syst Coordr*, Michael Stevens; *Tech Servs*, Jane Eickhoff; *ILL*, Karen Quinn-Wisniewski; Staff 56 (MLS 56)
Founded 1948. Pop 730,969; Circ 9,543,864
Jul 1999-Jun 2000 Income $28,869,890. Mats Exp $4,914,162. (Prof $13,108,657)
Library Holdings: Bk Vols 1,598,360; Bk Titles 158,811; Per Subs 4,347
Special Collections: Children's Picture Book Spanish Language Coll; Historical Coll; Historical Photograph Coll; Russian Coll
Automation Activity & Vendor Info: (Circulation) CARL
Publications: Baltimore County Directory of Organizations; Branching Out; Day By Day; Your Library Programs & News
Friends of the Library Group
Branches: 16
ARBUTUS, 1581 Sulphur Spring Rd, Ste 105, Baltimore, 21227-2598. SAN 344-4066. Tel: 410-887-1451. FAX: 410-536-0328. Web Site: www.bcplonline.org. *Mgr*, Gail Ross
Library Holdings: Bk Vols 86,807
CATONSVILLE, 1100 Frederick Rd, Baltimore, 21228-5092. SAN 344-4090. Tel: 410-887-0951. FAX: 410-788-8166. Web Site: www.bcplonline.org. *Mgr*, Marlene Kuhl
Library Holdings: Bk Vols 185,918
Friends of the Library Group
COCKEYSVILLE AREA BRANCH, 9833 Greenside Dr, Cockeysville, 21030-2188. SAN 344-4120. Tel: 410-887-7750. FAX: 410-666-0325. Web Site: www.bcplonline.org. *Mgr*, Mary Kay LePage
Library Holdings: Bk Vols 189,841
ESSEX, 1110 Eastern Blvd, Baltimore, 21221-3497. SAN 344-421X. Tel: 410-887-0295. FAX: 410-687-0075. Web Site: www.bcplonline.org. *Mgr*, Carol Dausch
Library Holdings: Bk Vols 102,387
HEREFORD, 16940 York Rd, Monkton, 21111. SAN 378-0473. Tel: 410-887-1919. FAX: 410-329-8203. Web Site: www.bcplonline.org. *Mgr*, Mary Kay LePage
Library Holdings: Bk Vols 45,400
Friends of the Library Group
LOCH RAVEN MINI, 1046 Taylor Ave, 21286. SAN 378-049X. Tel: 410-887-4444. FAX: 410-296-4339. Web Site: www.bcplonline.org. *Mgr*, Jennifer Haire
Library Holdings: Bk Vols 21,231
NORTH POINT, 1716 Merritt Blvd, Baltimore, 21222-3295. SAN 344-4368. Tel: 410-887-7255. FAX: 410-282-3272. Web Site: www.bcplonline.org. *Mgr*, Pamela Brown
Library Holdings: Bk Vols 109,842
PARKVILLE-CARNEY, 9509 Harford Rd, Baltimore, 21234-3192. SAN 344-4392. Tel: 410-887-5353. FAX: 410-668-3678. Web Site: www.bcplonline.org. *Mgr*, Beth McGraw-Wagner
Library Holdings: Bk Vols 109,518
PERRY HALL, 9440 Belair Rd, Baltimore, 21236-1504. SAN 344-4422. Tel: 410-887-5195. FAX: 410-529-9430. Web Site: www.bcplonline.org. *Mgr*, Sarah Stanhope
Library Holdings: Bk Vols 63,428
PIKESVILLE, 1301 Reisterstown Rd, Baltimore, 21208-4195. SAN 344-4457. Tel: 410-887-1234. FAX: 410-486-2782. Web Site: www.bcplonline.org. *Mgr*, Deborah Wheeler
Library Holdings: Bk Vols 124,278
RANDALLSTOWN AREA BRANCH, 8604 Liberty Rd, Randallstown, 21133-4797. SAN 344-4481. Tel: 410-887-0770. FAX: 410-521-3614. Web Site: www.bcplonline.org. *Mgr*, Glennor Shirley; E-Mail: gshirley@bcpl.net; Staff 9 (MLS 4, Non-MLS 5)
Founded 1967
Library Holdings: Bk Vols 159,363
REISTERSTOWN BRANCH, 21 Cockeys Mill Rd, Reisterstown, 21136-1285. SAN 344-4511. Tel: 410-887-1165. FAX: 410-833-8756. Web Site: www.bcplonline.net. *Mgr*, Margaret Prescott; E-Mail: mprescot@bcpl.net
Library Holdings: Bk Vols 102,414
Friends of the Library Group
ROSEDALE, 6105 Kenwood Ave, Baltimore, 21237-2097. SAN 344-4546. Tel: 410-887-0512. FAX: 410-866-4299. Web Site: www.bcplonline.org. *Mgr*, Alene Crenson
Library Holdings: Bk Vols 115,816
TOWSON AREA BRANCH, 320 York Rd, 21204-5179. SAN 344-4570. Tel: 410-887-6166. FAX: 410-887-3170. Web Site: www.bcplonline.org. *Mgr*, Jennifer Haire
Library Holdings: Bk Vols 225,923
Friends of the Library Group
WHITE MARSH, 8133 Sandpiper Circle, Baltimore, 21236-4973. SAN 329-6725. Tel: 410-887-5097. FAX: 410-931-9229. Web Site: www.bcplonline.org. *Mgr*, E J Woznicki
Library Holdings: Bk Vols 103,184
WOODLAWN, 1811 Woodlawn Dr, Baltimore, 21207-4074. SAN 344-466X. Tel: 410-887-1336. FAX: 410-281-9584. Web Site: www.bcplonline.org. *Mgr*, Mary Louise Daneri
Library Holdings: Bk Vols 99,675
Bookmobiles: 2

M SHEPPARD PRATT HEALTH SYSTEMS, Lawrence S Kubie Medical Library,* 6501 N Charles St, 21285. (Mail add: PO Box 6815, 21285-6815), SAN 344-4694. Tel: 410-938-4594. FAX: 410-938-4596. E-Mail: kubie@sheppardpratt.org. *Dir*, Andrea Smith
Founded 1891
Library Holdings: Bk Vols 12,000; Per Subs 90
Subject Interests: Psychiatry, Psychotherapy, Social service (social work)
Restriction: Staff use only
Partic in Dialog Corporation; National Library Of Medicine, Medlars

C TOWSON UNIVERSITY, Albert S Cook Library, 8000 York Rd, 21252-0001. SAN 307-0611. Tel: 410-830-2450. Interlibrary Loan Service Tel: 410-830-3292. Circulation Tel: 410-830-2456. Reference Tel: 410-830-2462. Interlibrary Loan Service FAX: 410-830-3829. Web Site: cooklibrary.towson.edu. *Dean*, Deborah Leather; E-Mail: dleather@towson.edu; *Dir*, Eleanore O Hofstetter; E-Mail: ehofstetter@towson.edu; *Assoc Dir*, Yvonne T Lev; Tel: 410-830-2445, E-Mail: ylev@towson.edu; *Head Tech Servs*, Mary Gilbert; Tel: 410-830-4926, E-Mail: mgilbert@towson.edu; *Govt Doc*, Nancy Gonce; *ILL*, Sharon Mollock; Tel: 410-830-3292, E-Mail: smollock@towson.edu; *Media Spec*, Polley Adams; Tel: 410-830-3182, E-Mail: padams@towson.edu; *Head Ref*, Mary Volland; Tel: 410-830-2618, E-Mail: mvolland@towson.edu; *Tech Coordr*, Paul Peeling; Tel: 410-830-4895, E-Mail: ppeeling@towson.edu; Staff 57 (MLS 21, Non-MLS 36)
Founded 1866. Enrl 12,826; Fac 757; Highest Degree: Master
Jul 1999-Jun 2000 Income $3,907,630. Mats Exp $1,189,436. Sal $2,289,621 (Prof $933,925)
Library Holdings: Bk Vols 579,058; Bk Titles 364,468; Per Subs 2,164
Subject Interests: Art, Education, Ethnic studies, Fine arts, Music, Theater, Women's studies
Special Collections: Educational Resources Information Center, fiche; Library of American Civilization, fiche; Library of English Literature, fiche
Automation Activity & Vendor Info: (Acquisitions) CARL; (Cataloging) CARL; (Circulation) CARL; (OPAC) CARL; (Serials) CARL
Database Vendor: Dialog, Ebsco - EbscoHost, Lexis-Nexis, OCLC - First Search, ProQuest, Silverplatter Information Inc.
Publications: Cook News (Newsletter)
Partic in OCLC Online Computer Library Center, Inc; PALINET & Union Library Catalogue of Pennsylvania; Univ Syst of Md

UPPER MARLBORO

GL PRINCE GEORGE'S COUNTY CIRCUIT COURT, Law Library, 14735 Main St, PO Box 1696, 20773-1696. SAN 307-062X. Tel: 301-952-3438. FAX: 301-952-2770. *Librn*, Pamela J Gregory
Founded 1900
Library Holdings: Bk Titles 37,000; Per Subs 67
Subject Interests: Criminal law and justice, Law, Maryland
Publications: Acquisitions list
Partic in Dialog Corporation; Westlaw
Fee-based searching on Westlaw, Lexis-Nexis & Dialog
Friends of the Library Group

WEST BETHESDA

G NAVAL SURFACE WARFARE CENTER, Carderock Division Technical Information Center,* 9500 MacArthur Blvd, 20817-5700. SAN 337-2065. Tel: 301-227-1433. FAX: 301-227-5307. *In Charge, Online Servs*, David Glenn; E-Mail: glenndc@nswccd.navy.mil
Library Holdings: Bk Vols 38,500
Partic in Defense Technical Information Center; Dialog Corporation

WESTMINSTER

J CARROLL COMMUNITY COLLEGE, Random House Learning Resources Center, 1601 Washington Rd, 21157-6944. SAN 373-2827. Tel: 410-386-8090. Circulation Tel: 410-386-8330. Reference Tel: 410-386-8340. Toll Free Tel: 888-221-9748. FAX: 410-840-0398. Web Site: www.carroll.cc.md.us/lrc. *Dir Libr Serv*, Alan Bogage; Tel: 410-386-8339, E-Mail: abogage@carroll.cc.md.us; *Publ Servs*, Judith Goodyear; Tel: 410-386-8342, E-Mail: jgoodyear@carroll.cc.md.us; *Head Tech Servs*, Christi Karman; Tel: 410-386-8337, E-Mail: ckarman@carroll.cc.md.us; *Media Spec*, Beverly Woerner; Tel: 410-386-8346, Fax: 410-386-8357, E-Mail: bwoerner@carroll.cc.md.us; *Ser*, Barbara Scherrer; Tel: 410-386-8338, E-Mail: bscherrer@carroll.cc.md.us; *Coordr*, Mike Armacost; Tel: 410-386-8345, E-Mail: marmacost@carroll.cc.md.us; *Circ*, Irma Hernandez; Tel: 410-386-8330, E-Mail: ihernandez@carroll.cc.md.us; *Circ*, Marie Wheeler; Tel: 410-386-8330, E-Mail: mwheeler@carroll.cc.md.us; *Circ*, Tracey Lewis; Tel: 410-386-8334, E-Mail: tlewis@carroll.cc.md.us; *Electronic Resources*, Elizabeth Beere; Tel: 410-386-8333, E-Mail: ebeere@carroll.cc.md.us. Subject Specialists: *Administration*, Christi Karman; Staff 12 (MLS 5, Non-MLS 7)
Founded 1976. Enrl 1,300; Fac 140; Highest Degree: Associate
Jun 1999-May 2000 Income Parent Institution $600,000. Mats Exp $131,000, Books $60,000, Per/Ser (Incl. Access Fees) $17,000, Micro $6,000, AV Equip $3,000, Electronic Ref Mat (Incl. Access Fees) $45,000
Library Holdings: Bk Vols 36,518; Bk Titles 32,411; Per Subs 305
Automation Activity & Vendor Info: (Acquisitions) epixtech, inc.; (Cataloging) epixtech, inc.; (Circulation) epixtech, inc.; (Course Reserve) epixtech, inc.; (Media Booking) epixtech, inc.; (OPAC) epixtech, inc.; (Serials) epixtech, inc.
Database Vendor: GaleNet
Function: ILL available
Partic in Carroll Librs in Partnership; Md Commun Col Libr Consortium
Special Services for the Deaf - Books on deafness & sign language
Special Services for the Blind - Magnifiers

GL CARROLL COUNTY COURT LIBRARY,* Court & Willis Sts, 21157. SAN 307-0638. Tel: 410-386-2672. *In Charge*, Florence Green
Library Holdings: Bk Vols 8,000; Per Subs 10
Friends of the Library Group

S CARROLL COUNTY FARM MUSEUM, Landon Burns Memorial Library, 500 S Center St, 21157. SAN 371-201X. Tel: 410-848-7775. FAX: 410-876-8544. *Mgr*, Dottie Freeman; *Curator*, Victoria Fowler
Library Holdings: Bk Vols 650; Per Subs 11

P CARROLL COUNTY PUBLIC LIBRARY, 115 Airport Dr, 21157. SAN 344-4759. Tel: 410-386-4500. Reference Tel: 410-386-4488. FAX: 410-386-4509, 410-386-4509. Web Site: www.carr.org/library. *Dir*, Linda Mielke; Tel: 410-386-4500, Ext 136, E-Mail: lmielke@carr.org; *Dep Dir*, Gail L Griffith; Tel: 410-386-4500, Ext 131, E-Mail: gailg@carr.org; *Asst Dir*, Scott Reinhart; Tel: 410-386-4500, Ext 137, E-Mail: scottr@carr.org; *Outreach Serv*, Dorothy Stoltz; Tel: 410-386-4450, Ext 733, Fax: 410-386-4497, E-Mail: dstoltz@carr.org; *Coll Develop*, Jacqueline Adams; *Coll Develop*, Concetta Pisano; Tel: 410-386-4500, Ext 142, E-Mail: cpisano@carr.org; Staff 138 (MLS 22, Non-MLS 116)
Founded 1958. Pop 150,300; Circ 2,958,738
Jul 1999-Jun 2000 Income (Main Library and Branch Library) $5,988,371, State $725,104, Federal $106,631, County $4,680,658, Locally Generated Income $475,978, Other $900. Mats Exp $878,152, Books $746,152, Per/Ser (Incl. Access Fees) $62,000, Electronic Ref Mat (Incl. Access Fees) $70,000. Sal $3,708,717
Library Holdings: Bk Vols 419,095; Per Subs 1,751
Subject Interests: Local history
Automation Activity & Vendor Info: (Acquisitions) epixtech, inc.; (Cataloging) epixtech, inc.; (Circulation) epixtech, inc.; (OPAC) epixtech, inc.
Database Vendor: Ebsco - EbscoHost, epixtech, inc.
Publications: Directory of Community Services for Carroll County, MD (Annually); Ghosts & Legends of Carroll County, Md
Partic in Carroll Librs in Partnership
Special Services for the Deaf - TTY machine
Branches: 5
ELDERSBURG BRANCH, 6400 W Hemlock Dr, Eldersburg, 21784-6538. SAN 344-4872. Tel: 410-795-3520. FAX: 410-795-7006. Web Site: www.carr.lib.md.us. *Librn*, Jacqueline Sollers; *Ad Servs*, Susan Lohr; *Ch Servs*, Kathleen Kelly
MOUNT AIRY BRANCH, 705 Ridge Ave, Mount Airy, 21771-5221. SAN 344-4813. Tel: 410-386-4470. FAX: 410-386-4477. Web Site: www.carr.lib.md.us. *Librn*, Cynthia Ahmann; *Ch Servs*, Stacey Freedman
Friends of the Library Group
NORTH CARROLL, 2255 Hanover Pike, Greenmount, 21074-1317. SAN 344-4783. Tel: 410-386-4480. FAX: 410-386-4486. Web Site: www.carr.lib.md.us. *Librn*, Lisa Hughes; *Ad Servs*, Kristina Peters; *Ch Servs*, Claudine Hanner
TANEYTOWN BRANCH, 10 Grand Dr, Taneytown, 21787-2421. SAN 344-4848. Tel: 410-751-1980. FAX: 410-751-1984. Web Site: www.carr.lib.md.us. *Librn*, Dorothy Wolf; *Ch Servs*, Helen Sparks
WESTMINSTER BRANCH, 50 E Main St, 21157-5097. SAN 375-6297. Tel: 410-386-4490. FAX: 410-386-4497. Web Site: www.carr.org. *Mgr*, Lois Leasure; *Ad Servs*, Christina Kuntz; *Ch Servs*, Brenda Conaway; *Ad Servs*, Janet Colburn
Special Services for the Deaf - TTY machine
Bookmobiles: 2

S HISTORICAL SOCIETY OF CARROLL COUNTY LIBRARY,* 210 E Main St, 21157. SAN 371-6694. Tel: 410-848-6494. E-Mail: hscc@carr.org. Web Site: www.carr.org/hscc. *Librn*, Jay A Graybeal; Staff 2 (Non-MLS 2)
Founded 1939
Library Holdings: Bk Vols 600; Bk Titles 500; Per Subs 10

C WESTERN MARYLAND COLLEGE, Hoover Library, Two College Hill, 21157-4390. SAN 307-0646. Tel: 410-857-2281. FAX: 410-857-2748. Web Site: www.hoover.wmdc.edu. *Dir*, Harold D Neikirk; *Syst Coordr, Tech Servs*, Robert E Withers; *Ref*, James Feagin; Staff 12 (MLS 5, Non-MLS 7)
Founded 1867. Circ 1,450; Enrl 2,200; Fac 90; Highest Degree: Master
Jul 1999-Jun 2000 Income $950,000. Mats Exp Books $450,000
Library Holdings: Bk Vols 200,000; Bk Titles 150,000; Per Subs 825
Special Collections: ERIC Coll, microfiche
Automation Activity & Vendor Info: (Cataloging) epixtech, inc.; (Circulation) epixtech, inc.; (Course Reserve) epixtech, inc.; (OPAC) epixtech, inc.; (Serials) epixtech, inc.
Database Vendor: Dialog, Ebsco - EbscoHost, epixtech, inc., GaleNet, IAC - Info Trac, Lexis-Nexis, Silverplatter Information Inc.
Partic in Carroll Librs in Partnership; Dialog Corporation; OCLC Online Computer Library Center, Inc; PALINET & Union Library Catalogue of Pennsylvania; SDC Search Serv
Special Services for the Deaf - Books on deafness & sign language; Special interest periodicals

WYE MILLS

C CHESAPEAKE COLLEGE, Learning Resource Center, PO Box 23, 21679. SAN 307-0654. Tel: 410-827-5860. FAX: 410-827-7057. *Assoc Dean*, Pat Cheek; *Ref*, Amy Schisler; *Tech Servs*, Douglass P Gray; E-Mail: doug-gray@crabpot.chesapeake.edu
Founded 1967
Library Holdings: Bk Vols 45,000; Bk Titles 40,000; Per Subs 232
Special Collections: Eastern Shore Literature (Chesapeake Room)
Publications: Directory of Community Services

MASSACHUSETTS

Date of Statistics: Fiscal Year 2000
Population, 1999 (est): 6,175,169
Population Served by Public Libraries: 6,174,032
Unserved: 1137
Number of Cities & Towns: 351
Total Public Library Holdings (Print & Nonprint): 39,361,858
Holdings (Print & Nonprint) Per Capita: 6.37
Total Public Library Operating Income: $193,139,066
Source of Income: Municipal appropriation: $167,933,497
Expenditures Per Capita (excluding Fed. Grants): $29.80
Number of Regional Library Systems: 6
Counties Served: All 351 cities & towns (systems not developed on county basis)
Grants-in-Aid to Public Libraries:
State Aid: $10,889,804
State Funding for 3 Regional Library Systems & Library of Last Recourse: $16,845,377
State Expenditures for Public Library Construction: $24,381,157

ABINGTON

P ABINGTON PUBLIC LIBRARY,* 600 Gliniewicz Way, 02351. SAN 307-5737. Tel: 781-982-2139. FAX: 617-878-7361. *Dir*, Jean K Lothrop; *Ch Servs*, Deborah Grimmett
Founded 1878
Library Holdings: Bk Vols 52,000
Special Collections: Civil War (Arnold Coll); Large Print Coll
Mem of SE Mass Regional Libr Syst
Partic in Old Colony Libr Network
Friends of the Library Group

ACTON

P ACTON MEMORIAL LIBRARY,* 486 Main St, 01720. SAN 307-0670. Tel: 978-264-9641. TDD: 978-635-0072. FAX: 978-635-0073. *YA Servs*, Pamela Parenti; *Dir*, Wanda S Null; *Asst Dir, Coll Develop*, Ellen Clark; *Ref*, Susan Paju; *Ch Servs*, Kristine Adolph; *Ch Servs*, Lee Donohue; *Cat*, Stephanie Knowland; *Circ*, Gloria Reid; *ILL*, Julia Glendon; Staff 5 (MLS 5)
Founded 1890. Pop 18,500; Circ 313,917
Jul 1998-Jun 1999 Income $594,846, State $22,213, Locally Generated Income $549,633, Other $23,000. Mats Exp $92,449, Books $72,929, Per/Ser (Incl. Access Fees) $10,661, Micro $2,985, AV Equip $3,576, Electronic Ref Mat (Incl. Access Fees) $2,298. Sal $453,080 (Prof $84,098)
Library Holdings: Bk Vols 89,655; Per Subs 300
Subject Interests: Local history
Special Collections: Arthur Davis Paintings
Automation Activity & Vendor Info: (Cataloging) DRA; (Circulation) DRA; (OPAC) DRA
Publications: Good Word
Partic in Metrowest Massachusetts Regional Library System; Minuteman Library Network
Special Services for the Deaf - TDD
Friends of the Library Group

P WEST ACTON CITIZEN'S LIBRARY,* 21 Windsor Ave, 01720-2809. SAN 307-0697. Tel: 978-264-9652. *Dir*, Regenia Tischler
Library Holdings: Bk Vols 11,700; Per Subs 25
Mem of Eastern Mass Regional Libr Syst
Friends of the Library Group

ACUSHNET

P RUSSELL MEMORIAL LIBRARY, Acushnet Public Library, 88 Main St, 02743. SAN 307-0700. Tel: 508-998-0270. FAX: 508-998-0271. *Dir, Librn*, Tonya Revell; *Asst Librn*, Claudette J Olivier; Staff 1 (MLS 1)
Founded 1930. Pop 10,111; Circ 21,000
Library Holdings: Bk Titles 16,000; Per Subs 108
Subject Interests: History
Special Collections: Joseph Lincoln Books
Mem of SE Mass Regional Libr Syst
Partic in Sails, Inc
Open Mon & Wed 10-8, Tues & Thurs 1-8, Sat 9-3
Friends of the Library Group

ADAMS

P ADAMS FREE LIBRARY, 92 Park St, 01220-2096. SAN 307-0719. Tel: 413-743-8345. TDD: 413-743-8345. *Dir*, Deborah G Bruneau; *Ch Servs*, Betty Lou Zajac; *Cat*, Beatrice Boisvert; *ILL*, Lorraine M Kalisz; Staff 5 (MLS 1, Non-MLS 4)
Founded 1883. Pop 9,274; Circ 64,740
Jul 1998-Jun 1999 Income $206,245, City $197,059, Other $9,186. Mats Exp $34,989, Books $29,402, Per/Ser (Incl. Access Fees) $3,819, Micro $200, AV Equip $413, Electronic Ref Mat (Incl. Access Fees) $1,155. Sal $148,008 (Prof $75,405)
Library Holdings: Bk Vols 43,047; Bk Titles 39,526; Per Subs 83; Bks on Deafness & Sign Lang 47
Subject Interests: Genealogy, Local history
Automation Activity & Vendor Info: (Cataloging) Follett; (Circulation) Follett; (OPAC) Follett
Mem of Western Massachusetts Regional Library System
Partic in CW Mars
Special Services for the Deaf - TTY machine
Special Services for the Blind - Descriptive videos
Open Mon, Tues & Thurs 9-8, Wed 12-6, Fri 9-6 & Sat 9-12; Access Center Library

AGAWAM

P AGAWAM PUBLIC LIBRARY,* 750 Cooper St, 01001. SAN 307-0727. Tel: 413-789-1550. FAX: 413-789-1552. *Dir*, Donna M Campbell; *Cat*, Jolene Mercadante; *Ref*, Joanne Gentry; *Ch Servs*, Jeanne Hofmann
Founded 1979. Pop 29,000; Circ 219,277
Library Holdings: Bk Vols 86,114; Per Subs 200
Mem of Western Regional Libr Syst
Partic in CW Mars
Open Mon-Thurs 9-9, Fri 10-6, Sat 10-5
Friends of the Library Group

AIR STATION CAPE COD

A US COAST GUARD BASE LIBRARY - OTIS, Bldg 5205, 02542-5017. SAN 326-5471. Tel: 508-968-6456. FAX: 508-968-6686. *Librn*, Candice Wolcott; Staff 2 (MLS 2)
Circ 8,000
Library Holdings: Bk Titles 40,000; Per Subs 55
Subject Interests: World War II

ALFORD

P ALFORD TOWN LIBRARY,* 5 Alford Center Rd, 01230-8920. SAN 307-0735. Tel: 413-528-2190. *Librn*, Edith Byington
Pop 400
Mem of Western Regional Libr Syst
Open Sat 10-12

AMESBURY

P AMESBURY PUBLIC LIBRARY,* 149 Main St, 01913. SAN 307-0743. Tel: 978-388-8148. FAX: 978-388-2662. *Dir*, Marc Lankin; *Ch Servs*, Lori Beth Spector; *Cat*, Suzanne Cote; *Circ, ILL*, Michaela Pelletier; *Ref*, Jennifer Haren
Founded 1856. Pop 15,908
Jul 1997-Jun 1998 Income $325,536, State $16,509, City $281,218, Locally Generated Income $27,809. Mats Exp $47,242, Books $37,651, Per/Ser (Incl. Access Fees) $5,325. Sal $214,395
Library Holdings: Bk Titles 70,000; Per Subs 120
Special Collections: Amesbury Carriage History Material; Charles H Davis Painting Coll; John Greenleaf Whittier Material
Mem of Eastern Mass Regional Libr Syst
Partic in Merrimack Valley Library Consortium
Friends of the Library Group

S WHITTIER HOME ASSOCIATION LIBRARY,* 86 Friend St, 01913. SAN 370-5587. Tel: 978-388-1337. *Pres*, Lavery Sally
Founded 1918
Library Holdings: Bk Titles 300
Subject Interests: Poetry
Special Collections: John Greenleaf Whittier Coll, bks, doc
Publications: Whittier Newsletter (quarterly)

AMHERST

C AMHERST COLLEGE, Robert Frost Library, 01002. SAN 344-4902. Tel: 413-542-2212. Interlibrary Loan Service Tel: 413-542-2666. FAX: 413-542-2662. E-Mail: webridegam@amherst.edu. Web Site: www.amherst.edu/~library. *Librn*, Willis Bridegam; *Ser*, Paul Trumble; *Archivist, Spec Coll*, Daria D'Arienzo; *Circ, ILL*, Alexa Jaffurs; *Ref*, Margaret Groesbeck; *Govt Doc*, Susan Edelberg; *Spec Coll*, John Lancaster; *Ref*, Mary Jane Sobinski-Smith; *Ref*, Michael Kasper; *Tech Servs*, Susan Sheridan; *Cat*, Marjorie Hess; *Librn*, Jan Jourdain; *Librn*, Jane Beebe
Founded 1821. Highest Degree: Bachelor Sal $1,522,542 (Prof $778,178)
Library Holdings: Bk Vols 866,452; Per Subs 2,750
Subject Interests: Theater
Special Collections: Augustine Daly, Emily Dickinson, Clyde Fitch, Robert Frost, Rolfe Humphreys, Richard Mann, John J McCloy, Thomas, Walt Whitman, Dylan Thomas, Richard Wilbur, William Wordsworth
Publications: Newsletter of the Friends of the Amherst College Library
Partic in State University Of New York-NYLINK
Friends of the Library Group
Departmental Libraries:
KEEFE SCIENCE LIBRARY, 01002. Tel: 413-542-8112. Web Site: www.amherst.edu/~library. *Librn*, Susan Kimball
Library Holdings: Bk Vols 44,000
Friends of the Library Group
MUSIC, 01002. Tel: 413-542-2387. Web Site: www.amherst.edu/~library. *Librn*, Jane Beebe
Friends of the Library Group

C HAMPSHIRE COLLEGE, Harold F Johnson Library Center,* 893 West St, 01002-5001. SAN 307-0751. Tel: 413-559-5440. FAX: 413-559-5419. Web Site: www.hampshire.edu. *Dir*, Gai Carpenter; *Tech Servs*, Anita Weigel; *Publ Servs*, Susan Dayall; *Bibliog Instr, Online Servs*, Helaine Selin; *Acq, Ref*, Dan Schnurr; *Bibliog Instr, Online Servs, Tech Servs*, Bonnie Vigeland; *Bibliog Instr, Online Servs, Tech Servs*, Serena Smith; Staff 9 (MLS 9)
Founded 1970. Enrl 1,275; Fac 90; Highest Degree: Bachelor
Jul 1997-Jun 1998 Income Parent Institution $1,062,635. Mats Exp $147,141, Books $59,382, Per/Ser (Incl. Access Fees) $82,658, Micro $5,101. Sal $665,895
Library Holdings: Bk Vols 105,000; Bk Titles 104,000; Per Subs 600
Subject Interests: Environmental studies, Films and filmmaking, Mass communications
Automation Activity & Vendor Info: (Circulation) Innovative Interfaces Inc.
Partic in Nelinet, Inc; OCLC Online Computer Library Center, Inc

P JONES LIBRARY, INC,* 43 Amity St, 01002-2285. SAN 344-502X. Tel: 413-256-4090. FAX: 413-256-4096. *Dir*, Bonnie J Isman; E-Mail: bisman@cwmars.org; *Asst Dir, Ch Servs*, Sondra M Radosh; E-Mail: sradosh@cwmars.org; *Tech Servs*, Carolyn Platt; E-Mail: cplatt@cwmars.org; *Ad Servs*, Beth Girshman; *Ref*, Polly Peterson; *Rare Bks, Spec Coll*, Dan Lombardo; *Circ*, Amy Anaya; E-Mail: aanaya@cwmars.org; *Archivist*, Peter Nelson; E-Mail: pnelson@cwmars.org; Staff 30 (MLS 10, Non-MLS 20)
Founded 1919. Pop 35,827; Circ 510,000
Jul 1998-Jun 1999 Income (Main Library and Branch Library) $1,427,000, State $73,600, City $989,400, Parent Institution $364,000. Mats Exp $186,000, Books $135,700, Per/Ser (Incl. Access Fees) $15,500, Presv $1,000, Micro $5,500. Sal $932,600
Library Holdings: Bk Vols 177,775; Per Subs 386
Subject Interests: English (language)
Special Collections: Early Textbooks & Children's Books (Clifton Johnson Coll); Emily Dickinson Coll; Genealogy (Boltwood); Harlan Fiske Stone Coll; Julius Lester Coll; Local History &; Ray Stannard Baker Coll; Robert Frost Coll; Sidney Waugh Coll
Automation Activity & Vendor Info: (Circulation) CARL
Database Vendor: Innovative Interfaces INN - View
Publications: Annual Report; Tales of Amherst; The Library in North Amherst
Mem of Western Massachusetts Regional Library System
Partic in CW Mars
Special Services for the Deaf - TTY machine
Special Services for the Blind - Descriptive videos; Optelek 20/20 video magnification system
Friends of the Library Group
Branches: 2
MUNSON MEMORIAL, S East St, South Amherst, 01002. SAN 344-5089. Tel: 413-256-4095. FAX: 413-256-4095. *Librn*, Susan Hugus
Library Holdings: Bk Titles 10,000
NORTH AMHERST, 8 Montague Rd, 01002. SAN 344-5054. Tel: 413-256-4099. *Librn*, Cynthia Asebrook
Library Holdings: Bk Titles 9,000

S NATIONAL YIDDISH BOOK CENTER LIBRARY,* Harry & Jeanette Weinberg Bldg, 1021 W St, 01002-3375. SAN 370-5056. Tel: 413-256-4900. Toll Free Tel: 800-535-3595. FAX: 413-256-4700. Web Site: www.yiddishbookcenter.org. *Librn*, Neil Zagorin; E-Mail: nzagorin@bikher.org
Library Holdings: Bk Vols 1,300,000; Bk Titles 20,000

C UNIVERSITY OF MASSACHUSETTS AT AMHERST, W E B Du Bois Library, 154 Hicks Way, 01003-9275. SAN 344-5119. Tel: 413-545-0284. Circulation Tel: 413-545-2622. Reference Tel: 413-545-0150. FAX: 413-545-6873. Web Site: www.library.umass.edu. *Dir*, Margo Crist; E-Mail: mlcrist@library.umass.edu; *Assoc Dir*, Patricia Banach; Tel: 413-545-0241, E-Mail: banach@library.umass.edu; *Assoc Dir*, Gordon Fretwell; Tel: 413-545-0284, E-Mail: gordon.fretwell@library.umass.edu; *Assoc Dir*, Phelix Hanible; Tel: 413-577-0600, E-Mail: hanible@library.umass.edu; *Acq*, Leslie Horner Button; Tel: 413-545-0738, E-Mail: button@library.umass.edu; *Coll Develop*, Jay Schafer; Tel: 413-545-0058, E-Mail: jschafer@library.umass.edu; *Coll Develop*, Peter Stern; Tel: 413-545-0058, E-Mail: pstern@library.umass.edu; *Cat*, Melvin Carlson; Tel: 413-545-2728, E-Mail: melvinc@library.umass.edu; *Govt Doc*, William Thompson; Tel: 413-545-2765, E-Mail: william.thompson@library.umass.edu; *Ref*, J Michael Davis; Tel: 413-545-6822, E-Mail: jmdavis@library.umass.edu; *Info Tech*, Marilyn Hanley; Tel: 413-545-6891, E-Mail: mhanley@library.umass.edu; *Coll Develop*, Ann Wood; Tel: 413-545-0058, E-Mail: awood@library.umass.edu; *Outreach Serv, Ref*, Isabel Espinal; Tel: 413-545-6817, E-Mail: iespinal@library.umass.edu; *Ref*, Emily Silverman; Tel: 413-545-0995, E-Mail: essilverman@library.umass.edu; *Admin Assoc*, Barbara Jones; Tel: 413-545-6872, E-Mail: bjones@library.umass.e; *Doc*, Leonard Adams; Tel: 413-545-2767, E-Mail: len.adams@library.umass.edu; *Ref*, Lori Mestre; Tel: 413-545-6851, E-Mail: lori.mestre@library.umass.edu; *Ref*, Barbara Morgan; Tel: 413-545-6850, E-Mail: bmorgan@library.umass.edu; *Ref*, Elizabeth Fitzpatrick; Tel: 413-545-5963, E-Mail: ebf@library.umass.edu; *Ref*, Beth Lang; Tel: 413-545-0150, E-Mail: bwlang@library.umass.edu; *Ref*, Jeffrey Tenenbaum; Tel: 413-545-6853, E-Mail: jmt@library.umass.edu; *Ref*, Melilnda McIntosh; Tel: 413-545-6802, E-Mail: mmcintosh@library.umass.edu; *Archivist, Ref*, Melissa Watterworth; Tel: 413-545-2780, E-Mail: watterworth@library.umass.edu; *Archivist, Spec Coll*, Linda Seidman; Tel: 413-545-2780, E-Mail: linda.seidman@lilbrary.umass.edu; *Adminr*, Laurence Feldman; Tel: 413-545-2674, E-Mail: larry.feldman@library.umass.edu; *Circ*, Betty Brace; Tel: 413-545-2622, E-Mail: betty.brace@library.umass.edu; *Web Coordr*, MJ Canavan; Tel: 413-545-6824, E-Mail: mjcanavan@library.umass.edu; *ILL*, Anne Moore; Tel: 413-545-0553, E-Mail: amoore@library.umass.edu. Subject Specialists: *Biological sci*, James Craig; *Latin America*, Peter Stern; *Music*, Pamela Juengling; *Physical science*, Eric Esau; Staff 140 (MLS 53, Non-MLS 87)
Founded 1865. Enrl 24,000; Fac 1,182; Highest Degree: Doctorate
Jul 1998-Jun 1999 Mats Exp $4,541,345, Books $1,011,836, Per/Ser (Incl. Access Fees) $2,976,589, Other Print Mats $144,148, Electronic Ref Mat (Incl. Access Fees) $408,772. Sal $6,025,923
Library Holdings: Bk Vols 5,435,411; Per Subs 15,510
Subject Interests: Afro-American, Agriculture, Ethnic studies, Geography, Latin America, Massachusetts, Natural history, New England
Special Collections: Benjamin Smith Lyman Papers & Japanese Coll; Broadside Press; Can; County Atlases of New England, New York & New Jersey (Farm Credit Bank's Coll); French Revolution Coll (Binet Coll); Harvey Swados Papers; Horace Mann Bond Papers; Massachusetts Government Publications; Massachusetts Labor & Business Records; Massachusetts Social Action & Peace Organizations; Massachusetts Social Service Agencies records; Robert Francis Coll; Silvio O Conte Congressional Papers; Slavery & Anti-Slavery Pamphlets 1725-1911; Travel

& Tourism in the Northeast; W B Yeats (R K Alspach Coll); W E B Du Bois Papers; Wallace Stevens
Automation Activity & Vendor Info: (Acquisitions) Innovative Interfaces Inc.; (Cataloging) Innovative Interfaces Inc.; (Circulation) Innovative Interfaces Inc.
Friends of the Library Group
Departmental Libraries:
BIOLOGICAL SCIENCES, Morrill Science Ctr, 01003. SAN 344-5143. Tel: 413-545-2674. FAX: 413-577-1531. Web Site: www.library.umass.edu. *Librn*, Laurence Feldman; Staff 9 (MLS 3, Non-MLS 6)
Friends of the Library Group
MUSIC, W E B Du Bois Libr 19th flr, 01003. SAN 344-5151. Tel: 413-545-2870. Web Site: www.library.umass.edu. *Librn*, Pamela Juengling; Staff 2 (MLS 1, Non-MLS 1)
Friends of the Library Group
PHYSICAL SCIENCES & ENGINEERING, Lederle Graduate Research Ctr, 01003. SAN 344-5178. Tel: 413-545-1370. FAX: 413-577-1534. Web Site: www.library.umass.edu. *Librn*, Eric Esau; Staff 9 (MLS 3, Non-MLS 6)
Friends of the Library Group

ANDOVER

S AGILENT TECHNOLOGIES, INC, Healthcare Soultions Group, 3000 Minuteman Rd, 01810-1099. SAN 322-8274. Tel: 978-659-2228. FAX: 978-687-7941. *Mgr*, Susan Saraidaridis
Library Holdings: Bk Titles 10,000; Per Subs 250
Subject Interests: Bus, Cardiology, Computer science, Intensive care, Ultrasound
Automation Activity & Vendor Info: (Circulation) SIRSI
Partic in Hewlett-Packard Library Information Network

S ANDOVER HISTORICAL SOCIETY, Caroline M Underhill Research Library, 97 Main St, 01810. SAN 325-8696. Tel: 978-475-2236. FAX: 978-470-2741. E-Mail: andhists@ma.ultranet.com. Web Site: www.ultranet.com/~andhists. *Exec Dir*, Barbara Thibault; *Asst Dir*, Margaret Matulsky; *Curator*, Christine P Stelzer
Library Holdings: Bk Vols 3,240
Subject Interests: Decorative arts
Special Collections: 19th & 20th Century Photographs of Andover People, Events, Buildings & Sites; Andover Imprints
Publications: Andover Century of Change 1896-1996; Andover Townswomen by Bessie Goldsmith; Historical Sketches of Andover

S DYNAMICS RESEARCH CORP LIBRARY, (DRC), 60 Frontage Rd, 01810. SAN 307-8078. Tel: 978-475-9090, Ext 2619. FAX: 978-474-8948. Web Site: www.drc.com. *Librn*, Sheila Elfman; E-Mail: selfman@drc.com.
Subject Specialists: *Corporate*, Sheila Elfman
Founded 1962
Library Holdings: Bk Titles 5,600; Per Subs 125
Subject Interests: Computers, Defense
Database Vendor: OCLC - First Search

S OLIVER WENDELL HOLMES LIBRARY,* Phillips Academy, Main St, 01810. SAN 322-7227. Tel: 978-749-4230. FAX: 978-749-4233. Web Site: www.andover.edu/library/ndex.htm. *Dir*, Susan Ezell Noble; *Asst Dir, Ref, Spec Coll*, Tim Sprattler; *Circ*, Muriel Casper; *Tech Servs*, Jo Wang; *Ref*, Roberta McDonald; Staff 5 (MLS 5)
Enrl 1,190; Fac 250
Library Holdings: Bk Vols 101,000; Per Subs 278
Special Collections: Cooper Coll of American Humor; Kelly Wise Photobook Archives; Oliver Wendell Holmes Coll; Vergiliana Coll
Partic in OCLC Online Computer Library Center, Inc
Branches:
ROBERT S PEABODY MUSEUM OF ARCHAEOLOGY, c/o Phillips Acad, Main St, 01810. Tel: 978-749-4490. FAX: 978-749-4495. Web Site: www.andover.edu/rspeabody. *Dir*, Dr James W Bradley; *Mgr*, Dawn Meldrum
Founded 1901
Library Holdings: Bk Vols 5,000; Per Subs 15
Restriction: By appointment only, Non-circulating to the public

L MASSACHUSETTS SCHOOL OF LAW LIBRARY,* 500 Federal St, 01810. SAN 371-5892. Tel: 978-681-0800. FAX: 978-681-6330. Web Site: www.mslaw.edu. *Librn*, Judith A Wolfe; E-Mail: wolfe@mslaw.edu; *Online Servs*, Edward Becker; *Online Servs*, Linda Sheff; *Tech Servs*, Shukla Biswas; *Dir, Tech Servs*, Alan Shutt; Staff 6 (MLS 5, Non-MLS 1)
Enrl 450; Fac 13; Highest Degree: Doctorate
Library Holdings: Bk Vols 70,000
Partic in Nelinet, Inc; NMRLS

P MEMORIAL HALL LIBRARY, Elm Sq, 01810. SAN 344-5208. Tel: 978-623-8401. FAX: 978-623-8406. Web Site: www.mhl.org. *Dir*, James E Sutton; *Asst Dir*, Beth Mazin; *Ch Servs*, Katherine Belczyk; *Ch Servs*, Bridget Bennett; *Circ, Tech Servs*, Nancy Richards; *Circ*, Grace Bouvier; *Per*, Nancy Bartlett; *YA Servs*, Beth Kerrigan; *YA Servs*, Barbara Mortenson; *Ref*, Glenda Schaake; *ILL*, Anna Kjoss; Staff 15 (MLS 15)
Founded 1873. Pop 31,000; Circ 531,419
Jul 1999-Jun 2000 Income $1,990,845, State $464,818, City $1,505,299. Mats Exp $357,869, Books $326,296, Per/Ser (Incl. Access Fees) $21,655, Micro $9,918. Sal $1,381,950
Library Holdings: Bk Vols 192,307; Per Subs 496
Subject Interests: Art, Business and management, Domestic law, Foreign law, Local history, Maps, Travel
Special Collections: Civil War Coll
Automation Activity & Vendor Info: (Cataloging) GEAC; (Circulation) GEAC; (OPAC) GEAC
Publications: Andover in Print
Mem of Northeast Mass Regional Libr Syst
Reference & Interlibrary Loan Center for Northwest Massachusetts Regional Library System
Friends of the Library Group

AQUINNAH

§P AQUINNAH PUBLIC LIBRARY, One Church St, 02535. SAN 375-4367. Tel: 508-645-2314. FAX: 508-645-2188. E-Mail: aquilib@vineyard.net. *Dir*, Agnieszka Meyro; Staff 2 (MLS 1, Non-MLS 1)
Jul 1999-Jun 2000 Income $44,000. Mats Exp $22,000. Sal $22,000
Library Holdings: Bk Vols 8,000; Per Subs 25
Special Collections: Native American Coll
Automation Activity & Vendor Info: (Cataloging) Athena; (Circulation) Athena
Friends of the Library Group

ARLINGTON

S ARLINGTON HISTORICAL SOCIETY, Smith Museum Archives,* 7 Jason St, 02476-6410. SAN 373-1723. Tel: 781-648-4300. Web Site: www.arlhs.org.
Library Holdings: Bk Vols 5,500
Subject Interests: Genealogy

S ARMENIAN CULTURAL FOUNDATION LIBRARY,* 441 Mystic St, 02474. SAN 373-0654. Tel: 781-646-3090. FAX: 781-646-3090. *Curator*, Ara Ghazarian
Library Holdings: Bk Vols 15,000; Per Subs 10
Open TAues, Thurs & Sat 9-12, Fri 1-4
Friends of the Library Group

P ROBBINS LIBRARY,* 700 Massachusetts Ave, 02476. SAN 344-5267. Tel: 781-316-3200. FAX: 781-316-3209. *Asst Dir*, Cindy Diminture; *Dir*, Maryellen Remmert-Loud; *Ad Servs*, Nancy Gentile; *Ch Servs*, Marianne Uttam; *Br Coordr*, Page Lindsay; *Tech Servs*, Susan Neubauer; Staff 13 (MLS 13)
Founded 1835. Pop 44,630; Circ 459,763
Jul 1996-Jun 1997 Income $1,330,918, State $49,195, City $1,207,199, Other $74,524. Mats Exp $181,603, Books $136,521, Per/Ser (Incl. Access Fees) $18,473, Micro $7,140. Sal $852,786
Library Holdings: Bk Vols 180,372; Per Subs 329
Subject Interests: Business and management, Music
Special Collections: Robbins Print Coll, etchings, lithographs, prints
Automation Activity & Vendor Info: (Circulation) DRA
Partic in Minuteman Library Network
Friends of the Library Group
Branches: 1
EDITH M FOX BRANCH, 175 Massachusetts Ave, 02174. SAN 344-5321. Tel: 617-316-3198. *Librn*, Page Lindsay
Library Holdings: Bk Vols 25,391
Friends of the Library Group

S SIMPSON, GUMPERTZ & HEGER, INC LIBRARY,* 297 Broadway, 02474. SAN 373-0662. Tel: 781-643-2000. FAX: 781-643-2009. Web Site: www.sgh.com. *Mgr*, Evelyn Neuburger
Library Holdings: Bk Titles 11,000; Per Subs 45
Subject Interests: Structural engineering

ASHBURNHAM

P STEVENS MEMORIAL LIBRARY,* 20 Memorial Dr, 01430. SAN 307-0808. Tel: 978-827-4115. FAX: 978-827-4116. *Librn*, Cheryl Paul Bradley; *Asst Librn*, Melissa Walker
Pop 5,433; Circ 27,000
Library Holdings: Bk Vols 27,000; Per Subs 28
Mem of Central Massachusetts Regional Library System
Open Mon & Wed 9-7, Tues, Thurs & Fri 2-7
Friends of the Library Group

ASHBY

P ASHBY FREE PUBLIC LIBRARY,* 812 Main St, PO Box 279, 01431-0279. SAN 307-0816. Tel: 978-386-5377. FAX: 978-386-5377. *Librn*, Marja-Leena LePoer
Pop 2,740; Circ 18,500

Library Holdings: Bk Vols 31,000
Mem of Central Massachusetts Regional Library System
Open Tues & Fri 1:30-9, Sat 9-12
Friends of the Library Group

ASHFIELD

P BELDING MEMORIAL LIBRARY,* 344 Main St, PO Box 407, 01330-0407. SAN 307-0824. Tel: 413-628-4414. *Librn*, Anne C Judson; Staff 1 (MLS 1)
Founded 1914. Pop 1,689; Circ 23,795
Jul 1997-Jun 1998 Income $24,000. Mats Exp $6,000
Library Holdings: Bk Titles 17,000; Per Subs 23
Mem of Western Regional Libr Syst
Open Mon, Wed & Sat
Friends of the Library Group

ASHLAND

S ASHLAND HISTORICAL SOCIETY LIBRARY,* 2 Mrytle St, PO Box 145, 01721. SAN 329-8698. Tel: 508-881-8183. *Curator*, Catherine Powers
Library Holdings: Bk Vols 100
Subject Interests: Genealogy, History
Open Wed 7-9pm & Sat 10-12 & by appointment

P ASHLAND PUBLIC LIBRARY,* 66 Front St, 01721-1606. SAN 307-0832. Tel: 508-881-0134. FAX: 508-881-0135. *Dir*, Beth Hoffer; *Ch Servs*, Sandra Leifeld; *ILL*, J Dee Clark
Pop 11,604; Circ 48,500
Library Holdings: Bk Vols 30,000; Per Subs 75
Mem of Eastern Mass Regional Libr Syst
Open Mon 1-8, Tues & Thurs 10-8, Wed & Fri 10-5, Sat 10-3
Friends of the Library Group

ATHOL

P ATHOL PUBLIC LIBRARY,* 568 Main St, 01331. SAN 307-0840. Tel: 508-249-9515. FAX: 508-249-7636. *Dir*, Debra Blanchard; E-Mail: dblancha@cwmarsmail.cwmars.org; *Asst Dir*, Dorothy Hayden; *Archivist, Ch Servs*, Jean Shaughnessy; *ILL*, Marie Lehmann; *Circ, Per*, Ruth Gagliardi; Staff 8 (MLS 3, Non-MLS 5)
Founded 1882. Pop 11,451; Circ 133,032
Jul 1998-Jun 1999 Income City $277,319. Mats Exp $51,723, Books $47,200, Per/Ser (Incl. Access Fees) $4,523. Sal $196,106 (Prof $107,743)
Library Holdings: Bk Vols 52,471; Per Subs 96
Special Collections: Local Art Originals; Local History Archives
Automation Activity & Vendor Info: (Cataloging) Follett; (Circulation) Follett; (OPAC) Follett
Publications: Athol Community Information Directory (biennial)
Mem of Central Massachusetts Regional Library System
Friends of the Library Group

ATTLEBORO

P ATTLEBORO PUBLIC LIBRARY, Joseph L Sweet Memorial,* 74 N Main St, 02703-2280. SAN 344-5356. Tel: 508-222-0157. FAX: 508-226-3326. Web Site: www.attleboro.com/library/apl.htm. *Dir*, Walter Stitt; *Asst Dir*, Joan Pilkington-Smyth; *Librn*, Christine Lefort; *Ref*, Kathlen Hibbert; *Ch Servs*, Christina Renaud; *Tech Servs*, Gayle Gilbert; *Circ*, Patricia Kenaley
Founded 1885. Pop 42,185
Jul 1998-Jun 1999 Income $751,299, State $44,718, City $706,581. Mats Exp $225,000, Books $84,979, Per/Ser (Incl. Access Fees) $15,279, Micro $5,022. Sal $535,000
Subject Interests: Genealogy, Local history
Special Collections: Attleboro History, bks, mss & papers
Publications: Annual Report
Partic in Automated Bristol Library Exchange
Friends of the Library Group
Branches: 1
SOUTH ATTLEBORO BRANCH, 609 Newport Ave, South Attleboro, 02703. SAN 344-5380. Tel: 508-761-6232. *Librn*, Christine Lefort; *Tech Servs*, Heidi Cauley
Library Holdings: Bk Vols 9,500
Open Tues & Thurs
Friends of the Library Group

M STURDY MEMORIAL HOSPITAL, Health Sciences Library,* 211 Park St, 02703. SAN 307-0859. Tel: 508-236-7920. FAX: 508-236-7909. *Librn*, Joseph Holland
Founded 1960
Library Holdings: Bk Vols 1,950; Bk Titles 500; Per Subs 35
Subject Interests: Cardiology, Obstetrics and gynecology, Pediatrics, Surgery, Urology
Partic in North Atlantic Health Sciences Libraries, Inc; Southeastern Massachusetts Consortium Of Health Science Libraries

AUBURN

P AUBURN PUBLIC LIBRARY,* 369 Southbridge St, 01501. SAN 307-0867. Tel: 508-832-7790. FAX: 508-832-7792. *Dir*, Joan Noonan; *Asst Dir*, Donna Galonek; *Ch Servs*, Katherine Mongeon; *ILL*, Marie Carbone; Staff 8 (MLS 3, Non-MLS 5)
Founded 1872. Pop 14,719; Circ 150,997
Jul 1996-Jun 1997 Income $262,356. Mats Exp $59,424. Sal $280,784
Library Holdings: Bk Vols 70,000; Per Subs 129
Special Collections: Local History
Mem of Central Massachusetts Regional Library System
Partic in CW Mars

R FIRST CONGREGATIONAL CHURCH LIBRARY, 128 Central St, 01501. SAN 307-0875. Tel: 508-832-2845. FAX: 508-721-2539. *In Charge*, Florence La Plante
Founded 1959
Library Holdings: Bk Titles 4,000
Subject Interests: Biology, Current events

AVON

P AVON PUBLIC LIBRARY,* 280 W Main St, 02322. SAN 307-0905. Tel: 508-583-0378. FAX: 508-580-2757. Web Site: ocln.org. *Dir*, Marilyn Greeley
Founded 1948
Library Holdings: Bk Titles 40,000; Per Subs 105
Subject Interests: Antiques, Restoration
Special Collections: China, Porcelain, Silver (Barker Coll)
Mem of Eastern Mass Regional Libr Syst
Friends of the Library Group

S KROHN-HITE CORP LIBRARY,* Avon Industrial Park, 255 Bodwell St, 02322. SAN 328-2880. Tel: 508-580-1660. FAX: 508-583-8989. E-Mail: krohnhite@aol.com. Web Site: www.krohn-hite.com. *In Charge*, Joe Inglis
Library Holdings: Bk Vols 200
Subject Interests: Engineering
Publications: Catalog

AYER

P AYER LIBRARY,* 26 E Main St, 01432. SAN 307-0913. Tel: 978-772-8250. FAX: 978-772-8251. *Dir*, Mary Anne Lucht; *Ch Servs*, Mona Blanchette; *ILL, Ref*, Jean Henry
Pop 7,000; Circ 24,000
Library Holdings: Bk Vols 30,000; Per Subs 60
Mem of Central Massachusetts Regional Library System
Open Mon 10-8, Tues & Thurs 12-8, Wed & Fri 10-6, Sat 10-1
Friends of the Library Group

M CARE GROUP - DEACONESS-NASHOBA HOSPITAL, Medical Library, 200 Groton Rd, 01432. SAN 325-8831. Tel: 978-784-9000. Reference Tel: 978-784-9241. FAX: 978-784-9601. Web Site: caregroup.harvard.com. *Coordr*, Thomas A Gentilella; Tel: 978-784-9215, E-Mail: tgentile@caregroup.harvard.edu
Library Holdings: Bk Vols 600; Per Subs 70

BABSON PARK

C BABSON COLLEGE, Horn Library,* 02457. SAN 307-0921. Tel: 781-239-4596. FAX: 781-239-5226. Web Site: www.babson.edu/library/. *Dir*, Hope N Tillman; Tel: 781-239-4259, E-Mail: tillman@babson.edu; *Coll Develop, Instrul Serv, Mgr*, Frances Nilsson; Tel: 781-239-5486, E-Mail: nilsson@babson.edu; *Mgr, Ref*, Ellen Royalty; Tel: 781-239-5024, E-Mail: royalty@babson.edu; *Coll Develop, Mgr, Tech Servs*, Barbara Taub; Tel: 781-239-4568, E-Mail: taub@babson.edu; *Mgr*, Hilary Walsh; Tel: 781-239-5257, E-Mail: hwalsh@babson.edu; *Mgr*, Charles Childress; Tel: 781-239-6428, E-Mail: cchildress@babson.edu; *Ref*, Jane Cloran; Tel: 781-239-4471, E-Mail: cloran@babson.edu; *Ref*, S Kate Buckley; Tel: 781-239-4985, E-Mail: buckley@babson.edu; *Ref*, Mary Gavett-Orsi; Tel: 781-239-5605, E-Mail: gavettorsi@babson.edu; *Ref*, Nancy Dlott; Tel: 781-239-4987, E-Mail: dlott@babson.edu; *Ref*, Christine Drew; Tel: 781-239-5604, E-Mail: drewch@babson.edu; *Ser*, Martha Burk; Tel: 781-239-4988, E-Mail: burk@babson.edu; *Acq*, Jerilyn Cavanagh; Tel: 781-239-5025, E-Mail: cavanagh@babson.edu; *ILL*, P Brendan Harney; Tel: 781-239-4574, E-Mail: harney@babson.edu. Subject Specialists: *Accounting*, Mary Gavett-Orsi; *Arts*, Martha Burk; *Economics*, Jane Cloran; *History*, S Kate Buckley; *Humanities*, Martha Burk; *Law*, Mary Gavett-Orsi; *Marketing*, Nancy Dlott; *Math sci*, Christine Drew; *Society*, S Kate Buckley; Staff 26 (MLS 18, Non-MLS 8)
Founded 1919
Library Holdings: Bk Vols 131,330; Bk Titles 92,721; Per Subs 1,545
Subject Interests: Business and management, Economics
Special Collections: Hinckley Coll (sailing & transportation); Sir Isaac Newton Coll
Automation Activity & Vendor Info: (Acquisitions) SIRSI; (Cataloging) SIRSI; (Circulation) SIRSI; (Course Reserve) SIRSI; (ILL) SIRSI; (OPAC) SIRSI; (Serials) SIRSI

Database Vendor: GaleNet, IAC - Info Trac, IAC - SearchBank, Lexis-Nexis, OCLC - First Search, ProQuest
Publications: Computer & Library Survival Guide; ITSD Update
Partic in Nelinet, Inc; OCLC Online Computer Library Center, Inc; WEBnet Libr Consortium

BARNSTABLE

L BARNSTABLE LAW LIBRARY,* First District Court House, PO Box 427, 02630-0427. SAN 325-8653. Tel: 508-362-2511, Ext 415. FAX: 508-362-1374. *Librn*, Martha W Elkins
Library Holdings: Bk Vols 16,000; Per Subs 22

P STURGIS LIBRARY, 3090 Main St, 02630. (Mail add: PO Box 606, 02630), SAN 307-093X. Tel: 508-362-6636. FAX: 508-362-5467. E-Mail: sturgis@capecod.net. Web Site: www.capecod.net/sturgis. *Coll Develop, Dir*, Christopher J Lindquist; *Ad Servs*, Diane Nielsen; *Ref, Selection of Gen Ref Mat*, Janet Lexow; E-Mail: jlexow@mediaone.net; *Ch Servs*, Nancy Coriaty; E-Mail: stl_nc@clams.lib.ma.us; *Tech Servs*, Rachel J Anderson; Staff 9 (MLS 3, Non-MLS 6)
Founded 1863. Pop 43,000; Circ 65,000
Jul 1999-Jun 2000 Income $320,000. Mats Exp $38,400, Books $27,000, Per/Ser (Incl. Access Fees) $2,900, Presv $765, Micro $1,000, Manuscripts & Archives $1,000. Sal $190,000 (Prof $152,000)
Library Holdings: Bk Titles 65,000; Per Subs 99
Subject Interests: Geography, History
Special Collections: Early Cape Cod Land Deeds, Some Indian (Stanley W Smith Coll); Genealogy & Local History (Hooper Room); Local Authors (Cape Cod Collection); Maritime History (Kittredge Room), bks, micro; Nineteenth Century Literature
Publications: Cape Cod Mariner (quarterly); History of Sturgis Library; Journal of William Sturgis; Literary Gentlemen of 19th Century; Vital Records Newsletter (quarterly)
Mem of SE Mass Regional Libr Syst
Partic in Cape Libraries Automated Materials Sharing
Special Services - To the institutionalized of Barnstable County House of Corrections. Open Mon, Wed & Fri 10-5, Tues & Thurs 1-8, Sat 10-4, Sun 1-5, closed Sun in July & Aug; handicapped accessible
Friends of the Library Group

BARRE

P WOODS MEMORIAL LIBRARY,* 19 Pleasant St, PO Box 489, 01005-0489. SAN 307-0948. Tel: 978-355-2533. FAX: 978-355-2533. *Dir*, Jennifer Jourdain; E-Mail: jjourdai@cwmars.org; Staff 5 (MLS 1, Non-MLS 4)
Founded 1857. Pop 4,900; Circ 35,967
Jul 1999-Jun 2000 Income (Main Library Only) $77,098, State $5,331, Locally Generated Income $71,767. Mats Exp $17,304, Books $15,117, Per/Ser (Incl. Access Fees) $2,187
Library Holdings: Bk Titles 20,825; Per Subs 63; Bks on Deafness & Sign Lang 19
Subject Interests: Local history
Automation Activity & Vendor Info: (Cataloging) Sagebrush Corporation; (Circulation) Sagebrush Corporation
Mem of Central Massachusetts Regional Library System

BECKET

P BECKET ATHENAEUM, INC LIBRARY,* 3367 Main St, PO Box 346, 01223. SAN 307-0956. Tel: 413-623-5483. *Librn*, Margaret Goss
Founded 1889. Pop 1,610
Library Holdings: Bk Titles 18,000; Per Subs 47
Mem of Western Regional Libr Syst

BEDFORD

P BEDFORD FREE PUBLIC LIBRARY,* 7 Mudge Way, 01730-2168. SAN 307-0980. Tel: 781-275-9440. FAX: 781-275-3590. *Dir*, Meredith McCulloch; E-Mail: mmcculloch@mln.lib.ma.us; *Asst Dir*, Christine Friese; *ILL, Ref*, Joanne Poage; *Ch Servs*, Sharon McDonald; *Tech Servs*, Kathleen Ruggeri; *Circ*, Jennifer Dalrymple; *Circ*, Katherine Townsend; Staff 11 (MLS 5, Non-MLS 6)
Founded 1876. Pop 13,066; Circ 206,718
Jul 1998-Jun 1999 Income $747,391. Mats Exp $131,000. Sal $524,916
Library Holdings: Bk Titles 98,000; Per Subs 285
Special Collections: Local History (Bedford Coll), multi-media; Parent's Coll, multi media
Publications: Bedford Sampler; History of the Town of Bedford
Mem of Eastern Mass Regional Libr Syst
Partic in Minuteman Library Network
Friends of the Library Group

DEPARTMENT OF VETERANS AFFAIRS

GM MEDICAL LIBRARY SERVICE, 200 Springs Rd, 01730. SAN 344-5410. Tel: 781-687-2504. FAX: 781-687-2507.
Founded 1928
Library Holdings: Bk Vols 8,700; Per Subs 302
Subject Interests: Medicine, Nursing, Psychology, Social service (social work)

J MIDDLESEX COMMUNITY COLLEGE, Academic Resources Division, 591 Springs Rd, 01730. SAN 307-1014. Tel: 781-280-3708. Reference Tel: 781-280-3706. FAX: 781-280-3771. E-Mail: mcc@noblenet.org. Web Site: www.middlesex.cc.ma.us. *Dir*, Mary Ann Niles; Tel: 781-280-3703; *Syst Coordr, Tech Servs*, Laura Horgan; Tel: 781-280-3702; *Publ Servs*, David Pietrantoni
Founded 1970. Enrl 3,810; Fac 181; Highest Degree: Associate
Library Holdings: Bk Vols 52,960; Per Subs 538
Database Vendor: OCLC - First Search
Publications: Annual Reports; Film & Video List (ann); MCC Libraries Newsletter (occasional); Middlesex Community College Library Periodicals
Partic in Nelinet, Inc; North of Boston Library Exchange, Inc

S MITRE CORP BEDFORD LIBRARY,* 202 Burlington Rd, 01730. SAN 307-1030. Tel: 781-271-7834, 781-271-7838. FAX: 781-271-3593. *Mgr*, Betsy F Cogliano; Staff 18 (MLS 6, Non-MLS 12)
Founded 1959
Library Holdings: Bk Vols 58,000; Bk Titles 30,000; Per Subs 605
Subject Interests: Computer science, Electronics, Engineering, Mathematics
Restriction: Restricted access
Partic in Nelinet, Inc; OCLC Online Computer Library Center, Inc

S NAMETRE COMPANY LIBRARY,* 25 Wiggins Ave, 01730. SAN 328-5669. Tel: 781-275-9660. FAX: 781-275-9665.
Library Holdings: Per Subs 10
Subject Interests: Physics

BELCHERTOWN

P CLAPP MEMORIAL LIBRARY,* 19 S Main St, PO Box 627, 01007. SAN 307-1057. Tel: 413-323-0417. FAX: 413-323-0453. *Dir*, Owen Maloney; Staff 5 (MLS 2, Non-MLS 3)
Founded 1887. Pop 13,500; Circ 107,000
Jul 1997-Jun 1998 Income $173,667. Mats Exp $31,000
Library Holdings: Bk Vols 24,000; Per Subs 100
Mem of Western Massachusetts Regional Library System
Friends of the Library Group

BELLINGHAM

P BELLINGHAM PUBLIC LIBRARY,* 100 Blackstone St, 02019. SAN 307-1065. Tel: 508-966-1660. FAX: 508-966-3189. E-Mail: bell@ma.ultranet.com. Web Site: www.ultranet.com/~bell. *Dir*, Laura Einstadter; Staff 7 (MLS 3, Non-MLS 4)
Founded 1894. Pop 15,000; Circ 90,000
Jul 1999-Jun 2000 Income $342,463. Mats Exp $61,250, Books $55,000, Per/Ser (Incl. Access Fees) $2,300, AV Equip $3,000, Electronic Ref Mat (Incl. Access Fees) $950. Sal $212,289 (Prof $106,512)
Library Holdings: Bk Titles 42,000; Per Subs 70
Automation Activity & Vendor Info: (Cataloging) Innovative Interfaces Inc.; (Circulation) Innovative Interfaces Inc.; (OPAC) Innovative Interfaces Inc.
Database Vendor: IAC - Info Trac
Mem of Central Massachusetts Regional Library System; Central Regional Libr Syst
Friends of the Library Group

BELMONT

P BELMONT PUBLIC LIBRARY,* 336 Concord Ave, PO Box 125, 02478. SAN 344-547X. Tel: 617-489-2000. FAX: 617-489-5725. *Dir*, Maureen Conners; *ILL*, Carol Baer; *Coordr, Tech Servs*, Frederick C Dooe; *Ch Servs*, Joyce D Higgins; *Coordr, Publ Servs, Ref*, Duane E Crabtree; *Circ*, Mary G Hall; Staff 11 (MLS 9, Non-MLS 2)
Founded 1868. Pop 24,762; Circ 397,192
Library Holdings: Bk Vols 151,396; Per Subs 331
Partic in Minuteman Library Network
Friends of the Library Group
Branches: 2
BENTON, Old Middlesex Rd, 02178-0125. SAN 344-550X. *Librn*, Elisabeth Strachen
Library Holdings: Bk Vols 15,035
WAVERLEY READING ROOM, 445 Trapelo Rd, 02178-0125. SAN 344-5534. *Librn*, Elisabeth Strachen
Library Holdings: Bk Vols 15,946

R BETH-EL TEMPLE CENTER, Carl Kales Memorial Library, 2 Concord Ave, 02478-4075. SAN 307-1073. Tel: 617-484-6668. FAX: 617-484-6020. *Librn*, Barbara Lichtman
Library Holdings: Bk Vols 2,400
Open Mon-Thurs 9-5

S MASSACHUSETTS AUDUBON SOCIETY, Habitat Education Center & Wildlife Sanctuary, 10 Juniper Rd, 02478. SAN 307-1081. Tel: 617-489-5050. FAX: 617-484-8664. *Dir*, Roger Wrubel; *Librn*, Barbara Herzstein
Founded 1970
Library Holdings: Bk Titles 1,200
Subject Interests: Ecology, Horticulture, Natural history, Ornithology
Restriction: Staff & members only
Open Mon-Fri 9am-5pm

M MCLEAN HOSPITAL, Mental Health Sciences Library, 115 Mill, 02478. SAN 307-109X. Tel: 617-855-2460. FAX: 617-855-2414. E-Mail: library@mclean.harvard.edu. *Librn*, Marilyn Dietrich; Staff 3 (MLS 1, Non-MLS 2)
Founded 1836
Library Holdings: Bk Titles 10,000; Per Subs 180
Subject Interests: Alcohol and drugs, Drug abuse, Mental health, Psychiatry, Psychoanalysis, Psychology, Psychopharmacology, Psychotherapy, Social sciences and issues
Database Vendor: OCLC - First Search
Partic in BRS; Dialog Corporation; OCLC Online Computer Library Center, Inc

S WORLD PHENOMENOLOGY INSTITUTE,* 348 Payson Rd, 02478. SAN 325-8637. Tel: 617-489-3696. FAX: 802-295-5963. E-Mail: info@phenomenology.org. Web Site: www.phenomenology.org. *In Charge*, Dr Anna-Teresa Tymieniecka
Library Holdings: Bk Vols 500; Per Subs 10

BERKLEY

P BERKLEY PUBLIC LIBRARY,* One N Main St, 02779. SAN 307-1103. Tel: 508-822-3329. FAX: 508-824-2471. *Dir*, Susan Richardson; *Librn*, Kelly Cutner; *Asst Librn*, Doris Caron
Pop 2,400; Circ 10,500
Library Holdings: Bk Vols 13,000; Per Subs 30
Mem of Eastern Mass Regional Libr Syst
Open Mon-Thurs 3-8, Fri & Sat 9-1

BERLIN

P BERLIN PUBLIC LIBRARY,* Carter St, 01503-0115. SAN 307-1111. Tel: 978-838-2812. FAX: 978-838-2812. *Dir*, Randy Kafka; *Ch Servs*, Valeda Dent; Tel: 734-647-3785, Fax: 734-764-1153, E-Mail: ballet@umich.edu; *Asst Librn*, Judy Bridge
Pop 2,280; Circ 18,000
Library Holdings: Bk Vols 14,000
Mem of Central Massachusetts Regional Library System
Friends of the Library Group

BERNARDSTON

P CUSHMAN LIBRARY,* 28 Church St, PO Box 248, 01337. SAN 307-112X. Tel: 413-648-5402. *Librn*, Gloria Freyenhagen
Founded 1863. Pop 1,800; Circ 8,698
Library Holdings: Bk Vols 18,000; Per Subs 26
Mem of Western Massachusetts Regional Library System
Open Wed 10-12 & 1-7:30, Sat 10-4:30
Friends of the Library Group

BEVERLY

S BEVERLY HISTORICAL SOCIETY, Charles W Galloupe Memorial Library, 117 Cabot St, 01915-5107. SAN 307-1138. Tel: 978-922-1186. FAX: 978-922-7387. E-Mail: beverlyhistoricalsociety@nii.net. Web Site: www.beverlyhistory.org. *Dir*, Paige Roberts
Founded 1891
Library Holdings: Bk Vols 2,000
Subject Interests: Genealogy, Historic preservation, Maritime law, New England, Transportation
Special Collections: New England History (Charles W Galloupe Memorial Library); Settlement hist of Essex County, 17th Century; Ship log of vessells from Salem & Beverly, from 1750's to late early 20th century, Walker Transportation Coll, photog
Publications: Beverly Cook Book; Beverly Men in the War of Independence; History of Beverly; North Beverly Remembered; Royal Side From Early Days of Salem Colony
Restriction: Non-circulating to the public

M BEVERLY HOSPITAL LIBRARY,* 85 Herrick St, 01915-1777. SAN 344-5569. Tel: 978-922-3000, Ext 2920. *Librn*, Ann M Tomes; E-Mail: atomes@nhs-healthlink.org
Founded 1900
Library Holdings: Bk Vols 3,000; Per Subs 150
Special Collections: Medical Incunabula (Beverly Hospital Historical Library)
Partic in Essex County Coop Librs; Northeastern Consortium For Health Information

P BEVERLY PUBLIC LIBRARY,* 32 Essex St, 01915-4561. SAN 344-5593. Tel: 978-921-6062. FAX: 978-922-8329. E-Mail: beverely_library@noblenet.org. Web Site: ci.beverly.ma.us/library. *Dir*, Thomas F Scully; *Asst Dir*, Anna Langstaff; *Ch Servs*, Nancy Bonne; *Tech Servs*, Laurie Formichella; *Ref*, Suzanne Nichelson; *Bkmobile Coordr*, Linda Caravaggio; Staff 20 (MLS 14, Non-MLS 6)
Founded 1855. Pop 38,755; Circ 266,634
Jul 1997-Jun 1998 Income $1,142,513, State $37,862, City $1,071,733, Other $32,918. Mats Exp $142,503, Books $98,503, Per/Ser (Incl. Access Fees) $12,000, Micro $25,000. Sal $693,784 (Prof $422,656)
Library Holdings: Bk Vols 137,130; Per Subs 287
Special Collections: Will Barnet Coll of Original Lithographs
Publications: Monthly newsletter
Special Services for the Deaf - Books on deafness & sign language; High interest/low vocabulary books; Special interest periodicals
Friends of the Library Group
Branches: 1
BEVERLY FARMS, 24 Vine St, 01915-2208. SAN 344-5623. Tel: 978-921-6066. FAX: 978-922-0819. Web Site: ci.beverly.ma.us/library. *Librn*, Brenda Wettergreen; *Librn*, Kate Ingalls
Library Holdings: Bk Vols 14,326
Friends of the Library Group
Bookmobiles: 1

S COMMUNICATION & POWER INDUSTRIES (CPI), Technical Library, 150 Sohier Rd, 01915-5595. SAN 307-1170. Tel: 978-922-6000. FAX: 978-922-8914. *Dir*, Sam Cooper
Founded 1963
Library Holdings: Bk Titles 1,400; Per Subs 60
Subject Interests: Electronics, Engineering

J ENDICOTT COLLEGE LIBRARY, 376 Hale St, 01915. SAN 307-1146. Tel: 978-232-2279. FAX: 978-232-2700. E-Mail: end@noblenet.org. Web Site: www.endicott.edu/production. *Dir*, Thomas Cesarz; *Ref*, Michael Moore; *Ref*, Elizabeth Roland; *Circ*, Carol Douglas; Staff 4 (MLS 4)
Founded 1939. Enrl 950
Library Holdings: Bk Vols 115,000; Per Subs 1,890
Publications: New Acquisition List
Partic in North of Boston Library Exchange, Inc; Northeast Consortium Of Colleges & Universities In Massachusetts

C MONTSERRAT COLLEGE OF ART, Paul M Scott Library, 23 Essex St, PO Box 26, 01915. SAN 328-6231. Tel: 978-921-4242, Ext 1208. FAX: 978-922-4268. E-Mail: mon@noblenet.org. Web Site: www.montserrat.edu. *Dir*, Cheri Coe
Library Holdings: Bk Vols 12,000; Bk Titles 11,000; Per Subs 104
Special Collections: Paul M Scott Archives
Automation Activity & Vendor Info: (Circulation) Innovative Interfaces Inc.
Database Vendor: CARL, Dialog, Ebsco - EbscoHost, IAC - Info Trac, Wilson - Wilson Web
Partic in NE Mass Regional Libr Syst; North of Boston Library Exchange, Inc; Northeast Consortium Of Colleges & Universities In Massachusetts

NORTH SHORE COMMUNITY COLLEGE
J LEARNING RESOURCE CENTER, 112 Sohier Rd. (Mail add: PO Box 3340, Danvers, 01923), SAN 321-1363. Tel: 978-762-4000, Ext 5526. FAX: 978-922-5165. E-Mail: nsb@clsn1231.noble.mass.edu. *Dir*, Anne Tullson-Johnsen; *Coordr, Tech Servs*, John Koza; *Coordr, Publ Servs*, William Meunier; Staff 22 (MLS 9, Non-MLS 13)
Founded 1965. Enrl 3,200; Fac 160
Jul 1996-Jun 1997 Mats Exp $157,403. Sal $660,111 (Prof $324,101)
Library Holdings: Bk Titles 65,171; Per Subs 423
Publications: Newsletter
Partic in Nelinet, Inc; North of Boston Library Exchange, Inc; Northeast Consortium Of Colleges & Universities In Massachusetts; OCLC Online Computer Library Center, Inc

S OSRAM SYLVANIA,* 71 Cherry Hill Dr, 01915. SAN 307-3432. Tel: 978-750-1725. FAX: 978-750-1797. *Librn*, David Jelley; E-Mail: david.jelly@sylvania.com
Library Holdings: Bk Titles 9,000; Per Subs 150
Subject Interests: Engineering, Optics, Physical chemistry

BILLERICA

S AERODYNE RESEARCH INC, Technical Information Center,* 45 Manning Rd, 01821-3976. SAN 307-0964. Tel: 978-663-9500, Ext 257. FAX: 978-663-4918. E-Mail: mast@aerodyne.com.
Founded 1975

Library Holdings: Bk Vols 2,000; Bk Titles 200; Per Subs 210
Subject Interests: Chemistry, Optics
Publications: Journal List; Technical Information Center Bytes
Partic in Dialog Corporation

P BILLERICA PUBLIC LIBRARY,* 25 Concord Rd, 01821. SAN 307-1189. Tel: 508-671-0948. FAX: 508-667-4242. Web Site: www.tiac.net/users/ bilerica/depart.htm#librar. *Dir*, Barbara A Flaherty; E-Mail: flaherty@ mvlc.lib.ma.us; *Asst Dir*, Priscilla Vaughn
Pop 38,000; Circ 232,000
Jul 1999-Jun 2000 Income $847,001, State $36,000, City $811,001. Mats Exp $120,200, Books $110,000, Per/Ser (Incl. Access Fees) $3,000, Electronic Ref Mat (Incl. Access Fees) $7,200. Sal $591,481
Library Holdings: Bk Vols 83,445; Per Subs 200
Mem of Eastern Mass Regional Libr Syst
Partic in Merrimack Valley Library Consortium
Open Mon-Thurs 9am-9pm & Fri-Sat 9am-5pm
Friends of the Library Group

S WELCHS, Science & Technology Library,* 749 Middlesex Tpk, 01821. SAN 312-6765. Tel: 978-670-8506. FAX: 978-670-8539. *In Charge*, Lew Benedict
Founded 1950
Library Holdings: Bk Titles 500; Per Subs 15
Subject Interests: Agriculture, Enology, Food chem, Food eng, Food tech, Horticulture, Microbiology
Restriction: Staff use only

BLACKSTONE

P BLACKSTONE PUBLIC LIBRARY, 15 Saint Paul St, 01504-2295. SAN 307-1200. Tel: 508-883-1931. FAX: 508-883-1531. *Dir*, Suzanne Wargo; E-Mail: suewargo@aol.com; Staff 4 (Non-MLS 4)
Founded 1889. Pop 8,729
Jul 1998-Jun 1999 Income (Main Library Only) $104,658, State $8,477, City $93,184, Other $2,997. Mats Exp $16,508, Books $13,280, Per/Ser (Incl. Access Fees) $1,416, Electronic Ref Mat (Incl. Access Fees) $1,812. Sal $66,980 (Prof $32,500)
Library Holdings: Bk Vols 17,042; Per Subs 62
Mem of Central Massachusetts Regional Library System
Open Mon 10-6, Tues & Thurs 12-8, Wed, Fri & Sat 10-2
Friends of the Library Group

BLANDFORD

P PORTER MEMORIAL LIBRARY,* Main St, PO Box 797, 01008. SAN 307-1219. Tel: 413-848-2853. FAX: 413-848-2853. *Librn*, Gale LaScala; Staff 3 (Non-MLS 3)
Founded 1892. Pop 1,016; Circ 15,648
Library Holdings: Bk Vols 9,000; Per Subs 20
Subject Interests: Genealogy
Mem of Western Regional Libr Syst
Open Mon 5-9, Tues 1-5, Thurs 1-5 & 7-9, Sat 10-4

BOLTON

P BOLTON PUBLIC LIBRARY, 738 Main St, 01740-1202. (Mail add: PO Box 188, 01740-0188), SAN 307-1227. Tel: 978-779-2839. FAX: 978-779-2839. Web Site: www.bolton.ma.us/Library/library.html. *Dir*, Kelly Collins; Staff 7 (MLS 1, Non-MLS 6)
Founded 1856. Pop 4,005; Circ 24,996
2000-2001 Income $101,000. Mats Exp $21,500, Books $20,000, Per/Ser (Incl. Access Fees) $1,500. Sal $56,963
Library Holdings: Bk Vols 15,000; Per Subs 60
Subject Interests: Local history
Mem of Central Massachusetts Regional Library System
Open Tues-Thurs 10-8, Fri 10-5, Sat 10-3
Friends of the Library Group

BOSTON

S AEW CAPITOL MANAGEMENT LP, Information Resource Center, World Trade Ctr E, 2 Seaport Lane, 02210-2021. SAN 375-7544. Tel: 617-261-9000. FAX: 617-261-9555. *VPres*, Chai Young; Tel: 617-261-9245; *Asst Dir*, Margarta Solis; Tel: 617-261-9530
Library Holdings: Bk Titles 200; Per Subs 140
Subject Interests: Real estate

R AMERICAN CONGREGATIONAL ASSOCIATION, Congregational Library, 14 Beacon St, 02108-9999. SAN 307-1235. Tel: 617-523-0470. FAX: 617-523-0491. Web Site: www.14beacon.org. *Librn*, Dr Harold F Worthley; E-Mail: hworthley@14beacon.org; Staff 5 (MLS 2, Non-MLS 3)
Founded 1853
Apr 1998-Mar 1999 Income $135,800, Locally Generated Income $16,200, Parent Institution $119,600. Mats Exp $39,150, Books $6,900, Per/Ser (Incl. Access Fees) $2,500, Presv $6,600. Sal $148,000 (Prof $83,450)
Library Holdings: Bk Titles 232,500; Per Subs 105
Subject Interests: Literature, Local history, Missions and missionaries, Natural science, Philosophy, Psychology, Religion, Theology
Special Collections: Church Records, ms, micro, rec; Congregationalism (National & General Council Congregational Christian Churches), rec; Educational & Missionary Societies, ms, rec, printed ann rpt; local church histories, worship & membership data, printed & ms, pamphlets & monographs; Mather Family Coll, ms, printed; modern theology coll, printed; newspapers & periodicals, printed originals & micro; Pratt Bible Coll, printed; State & Intrastate Clerical Organizations, ms rec; theology & sermons, 17th-19th centuries, ms & printed monographs; town histories, printed monographs
Publications: Bulletin

S ARTHUR ANDERSEN & CO LIBRARY,* 225 Franklin, Ste 1500, 02110. SAN 327-3350. Tel: 617-330-4596. FAX: 617-439-9731. *Librn*, Jeannette Silic; *Assoc Librn*, Stacey Potito
Library Holdings: Bk Titles 3,000; Per Subs 100

S APPALACHIAN MOUNTAIN CLUB LIBRARY,* 5 Joy St, 02108-1490. SAN 307-1243. Tel: 617-523-0636, Ext 329. FAX: 617-523-0722. *Librn*, John Gerber
Founded 1876
Library Holdings: Bk Titles 8,000
Subject Interests: Conservation, Mountaineering, Outdoor recreation
Special Collections: Sella Coll; White Mountains (Kilbourne Coll)
Open Mon, Tues & Thurs 8:30-Noon

S ASSOCIATED GRANTMAKERS OF MASSACHUSETTS, INC, Resource Center for Philanthropy,* 294 Washington St, Ste 840, 02108. SAN 327-3377. Tel: 617-426-2606. FAX: 617-426-2849. Web Site: www.agmconnect.org. *Librn*, Philip Conley
Library Holdings: Bk Titles 1,000; Per Subs 20
Special Collections: Massachusetts Foundations 990-PF forms
Open Mon-Fri 10-4:30 & Tues 10-8

J BAY STATE COLLEGE LIBRARY,* 122 Commonwealth Ave, 02116. SAN 307-1278. Tel: 617-236-8004. FAX: 617-236-8023. *Dir*, Virginia K Johnson; E-Mail: vjohnson@baystate.edu; Staff 1 (MLS 1)
Founded 1946
Jul 1998-Jun 1999 Income $37,000. Mats Exp $35,294, Books $6,120, Per/Ser (Incl. Access Fees) $22,400, AV Equip $2,123, Electronic Ref Mat (Incl. Access Fees) $4,651. Sal $31,560 (Prof $31,560)
Library Holdings: Bk Vols 4,022; Bk Titles 3,612
Subject Interests: Accounting, Allied health, Business, Early childhood, Education, Fashion, Hotel administration, Legal, Occupational therapy, Physical therapy, Tourism, Travel
Automation Activity & Vendor Info: (Circulation) Sagebrush Corporation
Database Vendor: OCLC - First Search, Silverplatter Information Inc.
Publications: Bay State College Library Book Bag; Bay State College Library Lingo
Mem of Boston Regional Libr Syst
Open Mon-Thurs 8-8, Fri 8-4

C BERKLEE COLLEGE OF MUSIC LIBRARY, 150 Massachusetts Ave, 02115. SAN 307-1286. Tel: 617-266-1400, Ext 2258, 617-747-2258. FAX: 617-747-2050. Web Site: www.library.berklee.edu. *Dir*, Gary Haggerty; E-Mail: ghaggerty@berklee.edu; *Asst Dir*, Paul Engle; *Circ*, Matt Mitchel; *AV*, Ralph Rosen; Staff 10 (MLS 3, Non-MLS 7)
Founded 1964. Enrl 2,900; Highest Degree: Bachelor
Library Holdings: Bk Vols 35,624; Per Subs 120
Subject Interests: Humanities, Music, Technology
Special Collections: Jazz & Rock Music Coll, scores with matching recordings

BETH ISRAEL DEACONESS MEDICAL CENTER WEST CAMPUS
M WEST CAMPUS LIBRARY, One Deaconess Rd, 02215. SAN 344-7189. Tel: 617-632-8311. FAX: 617-632-8316.
Founded 1926
Library Holdings: Bk Titles 1,000; Per Subs 114
Subject Interests: Medicine, Nursing, Surgery
Special Collections: Neurology & Neurosurgery (Horrax Coll)
Partic in Boston Biomedical Library Consortium

L BINGHAM DANA LLP, Law Library, 150 Federal St, 02110. SAN 307-1308. Tel: 617-951-8313. FAX: 617-951-8736. *Dir*, Amy Lannon; *Ref*, Heather Blagdon
Library Holdings: Bk Vols 30,000

S BOSTON ARCHITECTURAL CENTER, Shaw & Stone Library, 320 Newbury St, 02115. SAN 307-1324. Tel: 617-585-0155. Reference Tel: 617-585-0155. FAX: 617-585-0151. E-Mail: library@the-bac.edu. Web Site: www.the-bac.edu/library. *Coll Develop, Dir*, Susan Lewis; Tel: 617-585-0234, E-Mail: lewis@the-bac.edu; *Assoc Librn*, Lucy Maziar; E-Mail: maziar@the-bc-edu; *Syst Coordr*, Matthew Burfeind; Staff 3 (MLS 3)
Founded 1966. Enrl 650; Fac 150; Highest Degree: Master
Jul 2000-Jun 2001 Income $126,350. Mats Exp $63,900, Books $45,000, Per/Ser (Incl. Access Fees) $9,000, Presv $2,000, Manuscripts & Archives $2,500, Electronic Ref Mat (Incl. Access Fees) $5,400. Sal $193,175 (Prof

$125,400)
Library Holdings: Bk Titles 26,000; Per Subs 140
Subject Interests: Architecture, Conservation, Interior design, Landscape architecture, Photography, Solar energy, Urban planning
Special Collections: Architectural History (Memorial Library Coll)
Automation Activity & Vendor Info: (Acquisitions) Endeavor; (Cataloging) Endeavor; (Circulation) Endeavor; (Course Reserve) Endeavor; (OPAC) Endeavor; (Serials) Endeavor
Restriction: Open to public for reference only
Friends of the Library Group

S BOSTON ATHENAEUM, 10 1/2 Beacon St, 02108-3777. SAN 307-1332. Tel: 617-227-0270. FAX: 617-227-5266. Web Site: www.bostonathenaeum.org. *Dir*, Richard Wendorf; *Acq, Assoc Dir*, John Lannon; *Assoc Dir*, Ruth Morley; *Pres*, John G L Cabot; *Cat*, Robert Kruse; *Ref*, Stephen Z Nonack; *ILL*, Lisa Starzyk-Weldon; Staff 46 (MLS 34, Non-MLS 12)
Founded 1807
Library Holdings: Bk Vols 650,000; Per Subs 475
Subject Interests: Archives, Fine arts, History, Manuscripts
Special Collections: 18th & 19th Century Tracts; American 19th Century Photographs; American Prints & Drawings; Books from the Library of George Washington; Byroniana; Confederate Imprints, bk, micro; European & American 19th Century paintings & sculpture; General Henry Knox Library; Gypsy Literature; Henry Rowe Schoolcraft Coll; John Fowles; John Masefield; Merrymount Press Coll; TS Eliot
Automation Activity & Vendor Info: (OPAC) Athena
Publications: Athenaeum Items (quarterly) (Newsletter)
Function: For research purposes, ILL available, Mail loans to members, Reference services available, Research library, Some telephone reference
Mem of Boston Regional Libr Syst
Partic in OCLC Online Computer Library Center, Inc; RLIN

S BOSTON COMPANY, INC, Research Library,* One Boston Pl, 02108. SAN 307-1340. Tel: 617-722-7954. *Librn*, Lisa McDonough; Staff 2 (MLS 1, Non-MLS 1)
Library Holdings: Bk Titles 200; Per Subs 65
Publications: Publications List
Partic in Dialog Corporation

S BOSTON HERALD, Newspaper Library,* One Herald Sq, PO Box 2096, 02106-2096. SAN 307-1383. Tel: 617-426-3000, Ext 680. FAX: 617-542-1314. E-Mail: library@bostonherald.com. Web Site: www.bostonherald.com. *Librn*, John Cronin
Founded 1972
Library Holdings: Bk Vols 800; Bk Titles 500; Per Subs 70
Subject Interests: Photography, Statistics

S BOSTON MAGAZINE, Research Department Library,* 300 Massachusetts Ave, 02115. SAN 375-7935. Tel: 617-262-9700. FAX: 617-262-4925. *Dir, Res*, Tina Tyler
1997-1998 Income $50,000
Library Holdings: Bk Titles 500

S BOSTON MUNICIPAL RESEARCH BUREAU LIBRARY,* 333 Washington St, Ste 854, 02108. SAN 327-7259. Tel: 617-227-1900. FAX: 617-227-2815. *Pres*, Samuel R Tyler
Library Holdings: Bk Vols 6,000; Per Subs 30
Restriction: Private library

S BOSTON PSYCHOANALYTIC SOCIETY & INSTITUTE, INC, The Hanns Sachs Medical Library, 15 Commonwealth Ave, 02116. SAN 307-1391. Tel: 617-266-0953. FAX: 617-266-3466. E-Mail: bpsilibrary@aol.com. *Librn*, Ann Menashi
Founded 1933
Library Holdings: Bk Titles 5,400; Per Subs 95
Subject Interests: Psychoanalysis
Special Collections: Archives (History of Psychoanalysis)
Partic in Boston Regional Libr Syst

P BOSTON PUBLIC LIBRARY, 700 Boylston St, 02117-0286. SAN 344-5712. Tel: 617-536-5400. FAX: 617-236-4306. Web Site: www.bpl.org. *Pres*, Bernard A Margolis; *Publ Servs*, Katherine Dibble; *Dir*, Ruth Kowal; *Res*, Gunars Rutkovskis; *AV*, Steve Olsen; *Curator*, Janice Chadbourne; *Curator*, William Grealish; *Curator*, Marilyn McLean; *Curator*, Mary Frances O'Brien; *Curator*, Diane Ota; *Govt Doc*, Gail Fithian; *Librn*, Dolores Schueler; *Reader Servs*, Fran Majusky; *ILL*, Dorothy M Keller; *Ch Servs*, Paula Hayes; *Cat*, Nancy Browne. Subject Specialists: *Operations*, Ruth Kowal; Staff 540 (MLS 207, Non-MLS 333)
Founded 1852. Circ 2,258,524
1999-2000 Income City $22,223,961. Mats Exp $5,607,597. Sal $21,534,339
Library Holdings: Bk Vols 6,838,214; Per Subs 29,217
Special Collections: American & English History & Biography incl Fine Editions (Thayer), Spanish & Portuguese (Ticknor); American & English History & Literature, Jurists, Artists, Men of Letters, Anti-slavery; American & Foreign Authors & Rare Editions incl Longfellow Memorial known as Artz Coll; American Accounting to 1900 (Bentley); Astronomy, Mathematics & Navigation (Bowditch); Books By & About Women (Galatea); Christian Science (Works of Mary Baker Eddy); Dance (Lilla Viles Wyman); Defoe & Defoeana (Trent); Drama (Barton, Gilbert & Ticknor); Early & Important Children's Books; Early Boston Imprints (John A Lewis); English & American Literature; Engravings & Early Rare Impressions (Tosti); Frankliniana (works, books printed by him & books from his library); Fred Allen Papers; Genealogy (New England families, English Parish Records); German 18th & 19th Centuries Poetry (Sears-Freiligrath); Government Documents; Great Britain, Ireland, Scotland & United States; Heraldry; Imprints before 1850 (Charlotte Harris); James Brendan Connolly (First Editions); Joan of Arc Coll; Landscape Architecture (Codman); Library of President John Adams deposited by city of Quincy, Americana; Literature; Manuscript Coll; Maps & Atlases; Medieval Manuscripts; Microfilms (Books Printed in England before 1640, Newspapers, City of Boston Records, Government Documents); Military Science & History & Civil War (20th Regiment); Music (Brown); Newspapers (Early American & Current from all over the World); Patents (Early American to present, British, German); Periodicals & Serials (Boston Imprints, Learned Societies, Literary, Foreign Language); Photographs, Early & Civil War, Baseball Players (Michael T McGreevy); Picture Coll; Prince Coll-deposited by Old South Church of Boston, St Francis of Assisi & the Franciscan Order (Sabetier); Printing (Incunabula & Fine Printing & Binding from 16th Century to present); Prints (Albert H Wiggin); Religion & Theology; Robert & Elizabeth Browning-gift of Boston Browning Society; Sacco-Vanzetti Papers; Statistics; The Book of Common Prayer (Benton); Theatre (Brown); Theodore Parker Library; Walt Whitman; Washingtoniana (Lewisson); West Indies (Benjamin P Hunt); Wilfred Beaulieu Papers; William Peterson Trent; Works printed by John Baskerville (Benton); World War I (Mary Boyle O'Reilly)
Publications: Armstrong & Co Artistic Lithographers; BPL Press/Catalogue of Publications; Catalog of the Large Print Collection; Childs Gallery, Boston, 1937-1980; Evolution of a Catalogue: From Folio to Fiche; Irwin D Hoffman, an Artist's Life; Small Talk About Great Books (Bromsen lecture VII); The Sacco-Vanzetti Case: Developments & Reconsiderations, 1979; The Society of Arts & Crafts: Boston Exhibition Record, 1897-1928
Partic in Greater Boston Libr Consortium of Acad & Res Libr
Friends of the Library Group
Branches: 26

ADAMS STREET, 690 Adams St, Dorchester, 02122-1907. SAN 344-5836. Tel: 617-436-6900. FAX: 617-288-7703. Web Site: www.bpl.org. *Librn*, James McConnell
Library Holdings: Bk Vols 28,815
Friends of the Library Group

BRIGHTON BRANCH, 40 Academy Hill Rd, Brighton, 02135-3316. SAN 344-5895. Tel: 617-782-6032. FAX: 617-782-9883. Web Site: www.bpl.org. *Librn*, Mary Jo Campbell
Library Holdings: Bk Vols 79,233
Friends of the Library Group

CHARLESTOWN BRANCH, 179 Main St, Charlestown, 02129-3299. SAN 344-5925. Tel: 617-242-1248. FAX: 617-242-2019. Web Site: www.bpl.org. *Librn*, Maureen Marx
Library Holdings: Bk Vols 38,959
Friends of the Library Group

CODMAN SQUARE, 690 Washington St, Dorchester, 02124-3598. SAN 344-595X. Tel: 617-436-8214. FAX: 617-436-0941. Web Site: www.bpl.org. *Librn*, Deborah Wall
Library Holdings: Bk Vols 84,390
Friends of the Library Group

CONNOLLY, 433 Centre St, Jamaica Plain, 02130-1895. SAN 344-5984. Tel: 617-522-1960. FAX: 617-971-0695. Web Site: www.bpl.org. *Librn*, Olive Knight
Library Holdings: Bk Vols 29,019
Friends of the Library Group

DUDLEY, 65 Warren St, Roxbury, 02119-3206. SAN 344-6018. Tel: 617-442-6186. FAX: 617-427-9752. Web Site: www.bpl.org. *Librn*, Elaine McLean James
Library Holdings: Bk Vols 77,642
Friends of the Library Group

EAST BOSTON, 276 Meridian St, 02128-1654. SAN 344-6042. Tel: 617-569-0271. FAX: 617-569-6665. Web Site: www.bpl.org. *Librn*, Timothea McDonald
Library Holdings: Bk Vols 38,691
Friends of the Library Group

EGLESTON SQUARE, 2044 Columbus Ave, Roxbury, 02119-1123. SAN 344-6077. Tel: 617-445-4340. FAX: 617445-3978. Web Site: www.bpl.org. *Librn*, Joanne Goodman
Library Holdings: Bk Vols 24,426
Friends of the Library Group

FANEUIL, 419 Faneuil St, Brighton, 02135-1699. SAN 344-6107. Tel: 617-782-6705. FAX: 617-787-3654. Web Site: www.bpl.org. *Librn*, Paula Posnick
Library Holdings: Bk Vols 22,416
Friends of the Library Group

FIELDS CORNER, 1520 Dorchester Ave, Dorchester, 02122-1319. SAN 344-6131. Tel: 617-436-2155. FAX: 617-282-2738. Web Site: www.bpl.org. *Librn*, Paul McCallion
Library Holdings: Bk Vols 39,365

GROVE HALL, 5 Crawford St, Roxbury, 02121-2495. SAN 344-6166. Tel: 617-427-3337. FAX: 617-427-3619. Web Site: www.bpl.org. *Librn*,

Jacquelyn Hogan
Library Holdings: Bk Vols 32,167
Friends of the Library Group
HYDE PARK BRANCH, 35 Harvard Ave, Hyde Park, 02136-2862. SAN 344-6190. Tel: 617-361-2524. FAX: 617-361-6791. Web Site: www.bpl.org. *Librn*, Barbara S Wicker
Library Holdings: Bk Vols 50,000
Friends of the Library Group
JAMAICA PLAIN BRANCH, 12 Sedgwick St, Jamaica Plain, 02130-2897. SAN 344-6220. Tel: 617-524-2053. FAX: 617-983-0661. Web Site: www.bpl.org. *Librn*, Alice Roberts
Library Holdings: Bk Vols 37,213
Friends of the Library Group
KIRSTEIN BUSINESS, 20 City Hall Ave, 02108. SAN 344-5771. Tel: 617-523-0860. FAX: 617-523-3153. Web Site: www.bpl.org. *Librn*, Dolores Schueler
Library Holdings: Bk Vols 48,570
LOWER MILLS, 27 Richmond St, Dorchester, 02124-5610. SAN 344-6255. Tel: 617-298-7841. FAX: 617-296-2086. Web Site: www.bpl.org.
Library Holdings: Bk Vols 40,795
Friends of the Library Group
MATTAPAN BRANCH, 10 Hazelton St, Dorchester, 02126-3198. SAN 344-628X. Tel: 617-298-7590. FAX: 617-298-5970. Web Site: www.bpl.org. *Librn*, Cynthia Dromgoole
Library Holdings: Bk Vols 21,995
Friends of the Library Group
NORTH END, 25 Parmenter St, 02113-2306. SAN 344-631X. Tel: 617-227-8135. FAX: 617-723-1617. Web Site: www.bpl.org. *Librn*, Janet Buda
Library Holdings: Bk Vols 28,186
Friends of the Library Group
ORIENT HEIGHTS, 18 Barnes Ave, East Boston, 02128-1234. SAN 344-6328. Tel: 617-567-2516. FAX: 617-561-0288. Web Site: www.bpl.org. *Librn*, Margaret Kelly
Library Holdings: Bk Vols 38,000
PARKER HILL, 1497 Tremont St, Roxbury, 02120-2995. SAN 344-6379. Tel: 617-427-3820. FAX: 617-445-4321. Web Site: www.bpl.org. *Librn*, Janice Knight
Library Holdings: Bk Vols 29,000
Friends of the Library Group
ROSLINDALE BRANCH, 4238 Washington St, Roslindale, 02131-2517. SAN 344-6409. Tel: 617-323-2343. FAX: 617-325-1664. Web Site: www.bpl.org. *Librn*, Dorothy Martin
Library Holdings: Bk Vols 39,977
Friends of the Library Group
SOUTH BOSTON, 646 E Broadway, 02127-1589. SAN 344-6433. Tel: 617-268-0180. FAX: 617-464-2568. Web Site: www.bpl.org. *Librn*, Mary Linn
Library Holdings: Bk Vols 39,664
Friends of the Library Group
SOUTH END, 685 Tremont St, 02118-3198. SAN 344-6468. Tel: 617-536-8241. FAX: 617-266-8993. Web Site: www.bpl.org. *Librn*, Anne Smart
Library Holdings: Bk Vols 33,493
Friends of the Library Group
UPHAMS CORNER, 500 Columbia Rd, Dorchester, 02125-2389. SAN 344-6492. Tel: 617-265-0139. FAX: 617-282-2623. Web Site: www.bpl.org. *Librn*, Kate Brown
Library Holdings: Bk Vols 32,000
Friends of the Library Group
WASHINGTON VILLAGE, 1226 Columbia Rd, South Boston, 02127-3920. SAN 344-6514. Tel: 617-269-7239. FAX: 617-268-7884. Web Site: www.bpl.org. *Librn*, Mary Linn
Library Holdings: Bk Vols 17,463
WEST END, 151 Cambridge St, 02114-2704. SAN 344-6522. Tel: 617-523-3957. FAX: 617-723-1621. Web Site: www.bpl.org. *Librn*, Rhoda Blacker
Library Holdings: Bk Vols 25,873
Friends of the Library Group
WEST ROXBURY, 1961 Centre St, West Roxbury, 02132-2595. SAN 344-6557. Tel: 617-325-3147. FAX: 617-325-1972. Web Site: www.bpl.org. *Librn*, Sheila Scott
Library Holdings: Bk Vols 68,089
Friends of the Library Group . Homemobiles: 2

C BOSTON UNIVERSITY, Stone Science Library,* 675 Commonwealth Ave, Rm 440, 02215. SAN 370-6451. Tel: 617-353-5679. FAX: 617-353-5358. E-Mail: stonelib@bu.edu. *Dir*, Nasim Momen; Staff 2 (MLS 2)
Founded 1988. Enrl 25,000; Fac 2,400
1997-1998 Mats Exp $3,547,912. Sal $5,253,180
Library Holdings: Bk Titles 10,000; Per Subs 200
Subject Interests: Archaeology, Geography, Geology
Special Collections: Balloon Aerial photogs; Geography (George K Lewis Coll), bks; Space Science-Apollo Missions (NASA Photo Archives) photogs
Publications: Newsletter
Partic in BRS

BOSTON UNIVERSITY LIBRARIES
C AFRICAN STUDIES LIBRARY, 771 Commonwealth Ave, 02215. SAN 344-6611. Tel: 617-353-3726. FAX: 617-358-1729. Web Site: www.bu.edu/library/asl/home.html. *Librn*, Gretchen Walsh; E-Mail: gwalsh@bu.edu; Staff 3 (MLS 3)
Library Holdings: Bk Titles 125,000; Per Subs 425
Special Collections: African Government Documents; African Studies
Mem of Asn of Research Libraries
CM ALUMNI MEDICAL LIBRARY, 715 Albany St L-12, 02118-2394. SAN 344-6670. Tel: 617-638-4230. Interlibrary Loan Service Tel: 617-638-4270. Circulation Tel: 617-638-4244. Reference Tel: 617-638-4228. FAX: 617-638-4233. Web Site: med-libwww.bu.edu. *Dir*, David S Ginn; Fax: 617-638-4478, E-Mail: dginn@bu.edu; Staff 8 (MLS 5, Non-MLS 3)
Founded 1848
Jul 1999-Jun 2000 Income $1,838,338. Mats Exp $697,753, Books $35,929, Other Print Mats $661,824. Sal $757,596 (Prof $431,583)
Library Holdings: Bk Vols 128,173; Per Subs 1,884
Subject Interests: Dentistry, Medicine, Public health
Partic in Boston Library Consortium; National Network Of Libraries Of Medicine New England Region
S GEORGE H BEEBE COMMUNICATION REFERENCE LIBRARY, College of Communication, 640 Commonwealth Ave, 02215-9991. SAN 325-8025. Tel: 617-353-7649. *Coordr*, James H Gallagher; Staff 1 (Non-MLS 1)
Library Holdings: Bk Titles 45
Subject Interests: Advertising, Films and filmmaking, Journalism, Mass communications
Special Collections: Boston Herald Newspaper (clippings from late 19th Century - mid 1970's)
Mem of Asn of Research Libraries
C EDUCATIONAL RESOURCES LIBRARY, 605 Commonwealth Ave, 02215-1605. SAN 344-6646. Tel: 617-353-3734. FAX: 617-353-6105.; Staff 1 (MLS 1)
Library Holdings: Bk Vols 60,100; Per Subs 53
Subject Interests: Education
Special Collections: Curriculum Guides; Standardized Psychological and Educational Tests
Mem of Asn of Research Libraries
Partic in OCLC Online Computer Library Center, Inc
Holdings in K-12 textbooks, curriculum guides & children's literature; instructional aids, vertical file
C MUGAR MEMORIAL LIBRARY, 771 Commonwealth Ave, 02215. SAN 344-6581. Tel: 617-353-3710. Interlibrary Loan Service Tel: 617-353-3706. FAX: 617-353-2084. Web Site: web.bu.edu/library/. *Dir*, Robert Hudson; *Ref*, Doris Ann Sweet; *Cat*, Catherine Moulton; *Circ*, Helen Jacoby; *Spec Coll*, Howard B Gotlieb; *Ser*, Craig Brown; *Coll Develop*, Linda Carr; Staff 63 (MLS 63)
Founded 1839. Enrl 29,000
Jul 1997-Jun 1998 Income $13,573,000. Mats Exp $4,930,000, Books $735,000, Per/Ser (Incl. Access Fees) $3,708,000. Sal $6,596,533 (Prof $3,577,933)
Library Holdings: Bk Vols 2,056,350; Per Subs 29,162
Subject Interests: Art and architecture, Business and management, Law, Medicine, Music, Religion, Social sciences and issues
Special Collections: African Studies; Americana to 1920 (Mark & Llora Bortman Coll); Art of the Printed Book; Browning Coll; Endowment for Biblical Research; G B Shaw Coll; H G Wells Coll; History of Nursing; Lincolniana (Edward C Stone & F Lauriston Bullard Colls); Liszt Coll; Military History; Mystery & Suspense Novel Coll; Nineteenth Century English Literature; Pascal Coll; Paul C Richards Literary & Hi Manuscript Holdings in Contemporary Literature; Private Press Books; Public Affairs, Theater, Film, Music, Journalism; Robert Frost Coll; Theodore Roosevelt Coll; Whitman Coll
Partic in Boston Library Consortium; New England Libr Info Network
Friends of the Library Group
S MUSIC LIBRARY, 771 Commonwealth Ave, 02215. SAN 325-3279. Tel: 617-353-3705. FAX: 617-353-2084. E-Mail: musiclib@bu.edu. Web Site: web.bu.edu/library/music/home.htm. *Librn*, Holly E Mockovak; *Publ Servs*, Donald Denniston; *Cat*, Lillian Murray; *Cat*, Archie Elliott; *Cat*, Daryll Yoder; Staff 7 (MLS 4, Non-MLS 3)
Friends of the Library Group
CL PAPPAS LAW LIBRARY, 765 Commonwealth Ave, 02215. Tel: 617-353-3151. FAX: 617-353-5995. Web Site: www.bu.edu/lawlibrary/. *Dir*, Dan Freehling; *Assoc Dir*, Marlene Alderman; Tel: 617-353-8870, E-Mail: alderman@bu.edu; *Tech Servs*, Anne Myers; *Ref*, Russell Sweet
Founded 1872
Library Holdings: Bk Vols 550,000
Special Collections: Anglo-American Law Coll; Banking & Financial Law; Health Law; Intellectual Property; International Law; Taxation
Database Vendor: Innovative Interfaces INN - View
Publications: Law Review Table of Contents; Recent Acquisitions
Partic in Nellco; RLG
S FREDERICK S PARDEE MANAGEMENT LIBRARY, 595 Commonwealth Ave, 02215. SAN 377-8126. Tel: 617-353-4301. Reference Tel: 617-353-4303. FAX: 617-353-4307. Web Site: www.bu.edu/library/management. *Head of Libr*, Arlyne Ann Jackson; Tel: 617-353-4310, E-Mail: ajac@bu.edu; *Access Serv*, Margaret Howe-Soper; Tel: 617-353-4311, E-Mail: msoper@bu.edu; *Bibliog Instr, Ref*, Thomas J Casserly; Tel: 617-353-4312, E-Mail: casserly@bu.edu; Staff 15 (MLS 4, Non-MLS 11)
Founded 1997
Jul 1999-Jun 2000 Mats Exp $363,486, Books $26,575, Per/Ser (Incl.

Access Fees) $152,333, Presv $5,550, Micro $7,642, Electronic Ref Mat (Incl. Access Fees) $171,386
Library Holdings: Bk Vols 92,000; Per Subs 350
Subject Interests: Accounting, Advertising, Business, Economics, Human resources, Management, Marketing
Automation Activity & Vendor Info: (Acquisitions) Innovative Interfaces Inc.; (Cataloging) Innovative Interfaces Inc.; (Circulation) Innovative Interfaces Inc.; (Course Reserve) Innovative Interfaces Inc.; (ILL) Innovative Interfaces Inc.; (Media Booking) Innovative Interfaces Inc.; (OPAC) Innovative Interfaces Inc.; (Serials) Innovative Interfaces Inc.
Database Vendor: GaleNet, Innovative Interfaces INN - View, Lexis-Nexis, OCLC - First Search, ProQuest, Silverplatter Information Inc., Wilson - Wilson Web
Function: Document delivery services, ILL available, Reference services available
Partic in Boston Library Consortium

CR SCHOOL OF THEOLOGY LIBRARY, 745 Commonwealth Ave, 02215. SAN 344-676X. Tel: 617-353-3034. Reference Tel: 617-353-5357. FAX: 617-358-0699. E-Mail: sthlib@bu.edu. Web Site: www.bu.edu/sthlib/library.htm. *Head Librn*, Dr Raymond Van de Moortell; Tel: 617-353-1321, E-Mail: rvdm@bu.edu; *Head Ref*, Dr William Bergmann; E-Mail: bergmann@bu.edu; *Head Tech Servs*, Dr Brian Frykenberg; Tel: 617-353-1310, E-Mail: fryken@bu.edu; *Head, Circ*, Scott Roberts; Tel: 617-353-1317, E-Mail: kenobi@bu.edu; *Archivist*, Stephen Pentek; Tel: 617-353-1323, E-Mail: spentek@bu.edu; *Head, Acq*, Olga Potap; Tel: 617-358-3070, E-Mail: opotap@bu.edu; *Spec Coll*, Dawn Piscitello; Tel: 617-358-0698, E-Mail: dawnp@bu.edu; *Cat*, Caroline Christian; Tel: 617-353-1353, E-Mail: cchristi@bu.edu. Subject Specialists: *Art*, Dawn Piscitello; *Business*, Olga Potap; *History*, Dawn Piscitello; *Medieval studies*, Dr Brian Frykenberg; *Methodist hist*, Stephen Pentek; *Theology*, Dr William Bergmann; *Theology*, Dr Raymond Van de Moortell; Staff 8 (MLS 3, Non-MLS 5)
Founded 1839. Enrl 450; Fac 24; Highest Degree: Doctorate
Jul 1999-Jun 2000 Income $438,845, Locally Generated Income $75,351, Parent Institution $228,106, Other $17,825. Mats Exp $123,163, Books $30,871, Per/Ser (Incl. Access Fees) $30,416, Presv $9,959, Micro $35,029. Sal $302,324 (Prof $191,700)
Library Holdings: Bk Vols 140,049; Per Subs 536
Subject Interests: Biblical studies, Music, Philosophy, Relig hist, Theology
Special Collections: American Guild of Organists Library; History of Christian Missions Coll; Hymnals (Metcalf-Nutter Coll); Kimball Bible Coll; Liturgy and Worship Coll; Massachusetts Bible Society Coll; New England Methodist Hist Soc Coll; Nutter-Metcalf Hymnal Coll; Oriental Art Objects (Woodward Coll)
Database Vendor: Innovative Interfaces INN - View
Mem of Asn of Research Libraries; Nelinet; OCLC ILL Subsystem
Partic in American Theological Library Association; Boston Library Consortium; Boston Theological Institute Library Program; Nelinet, Inc

S SCIENCE & ENGINEERING LIBRARY, 38 Cummington St, 02215. SAN 325-3716. Circulation Tel: 617-353-3733. Reference Tel: 617-353-9474. FAX: 617-353-3470. E-Mail: selill@bu.edu. Web Site: www.bu.edu/library/sel/home.htm. *Head Librn*, Ardelle Legg; Tel: 617-353-7332, E-Mail: alegg@bu.edu; Staff 4 (MLS 3, Non-MLS 1)
Founded 1983. Enrl 1,080; Highest Degree: Doctorate
2000-2000 Mats Exp $1,400,000
Library Holdings: Bk Vols 70,000; Per Subs 1,200
Subject Interests: Aerospace science, Biology, Biomedical engineering, Chemistry, Computer science, Earth science, Electrical engineering, Engineering, Manufacturing, Mathematics, Mechanical engineering, Physics
Automation Activity & Vendor Info: (Circulation) Innovative Interfaces Inc.; (Course Reserve) Innovative Interfaces Inc.; (OPAC) Innovative Interfaces Inc.; (Serials) Innovative Interfaces Inc.
Database Vendor: Silverplatter Information Inc., Wilson - Wilson Web
Restriction: Open to public for reference only
Function: Research library
Partic in Boston Library Consortium

S BOSTONIAN SOCIETY LIBRARY, 15 State St, 3rd Fl. (Mail add: Old State House, 206 Washington St, 02109), SAN 307-143X. Tel: 617-720-1713, Ext 12. FAX: 617-720-3289. E-Mail: library@bostonhistory.org. Web Site: www.bostonhistory.org. *Dir, Spec Coll*, Nancy Richard; Staff 2 (MLS 1, Non-MLS 1)
Founded 1881
Library Holdings: Bk Titles 7,500; Per Subs 13
Subject Interests: History
Special Collections: Boston Architecture (Severy Coll), photog; Boston Charities (Wrenn Coll), pamphlets; Boston Theatre History; Bostoniana, bks; John L Sullivan scrapbook items; mss;; Photographs of 19th-20th Century Boston
Automation Activity & Vendor Info: (Cataloging) Sagebrush Corporation; (OPAC) Sagebrush Corporation
Publications: Bostonian Society Newsletter; Old Boston in Early Photographs; The Last Tenement: Confronting Community & Urban Renewal in Boston's West End (1992)

M BRIGHAM & WOMEN'S HOSPITAL, Medical Library, Tower Bldg, 4th Flr, Rm TR4-91, 75 Francis St, 02115. SAN 377-9157. Tel: 617-732-5684. FAX: 617-975-0890. Web Site: www.bwh.partners.org/medlib. *Librn*, Judith Sacknoff; E-Mail: jsacknoff@partners.org
Library Holdings: Bk Titles 325; Per Subs 101
Partic in Massachusetts Health Sciences Libraries Network; North Atlantic Health Sciences Libraries, Inc

M BRIGHAM & WOMENS-FAULKNER HOSPITAL, (Formerly Faulkner Hospital), Ingersoll Bowditch Library, 1153 Centre St, 02130. SAN 307-4595. Tel: 617-983-7443. Interlibrary Loan Service Tel: 617-983-1747. FAX: 617-983-7555. E-Mail: bpp@world.std.com. *Dir*, Barbara P Pastan; E-Mail: bpastan@faulknerhospital.org; *Asst Librn*, Bruce Glazer; E-Mail: bglazer@faulknerhospital.org
Founded 1940
Oct 1999-Sep 2000 Mats Exp $59,500, Books $5,000, Per/Ser (Incl. Access Fees) $4,500, Presv $10,000, Electronic Ref Mat (Incl. Access Fees) $40,000
Library Holdings: Bk Vols 750; Per Subs 202
Subject Interests: Consumer health, Hospital administration, Medicine, Nursing, Orthopedics, Pathology, Psychiatry, Radiology, Surgery
Database Vendor: OVID Technologies
Partic in Boston Biomedical Library Consortium; Regional Med Libr - Region 1

L BROWN, RUDNICK, FREED & GESMER, Law Library,* One Financial Ctr, 02111. SAN 372-0748. Tel: 617-856-8200, Ext 8213. FAX: 617-856-8201. Web Site: www.brownrudnick.com. *Librn*, Diana Pierce; *Librn*, Kathleen Gerwatowski
Library Holdings: Bk Vols 10,000; Per Subs 400
Partic in Am Asn of Law Librs; Asn of Boston Law Librns; Law Librs New England; Spec Libr Asn

J BUNKER HILL COMMUNITY COLLEGE LIBRARY,* 250 New Rutherford Ave, 02129-2991. SAN 307-1456. Tel: 617-228-2211. FAX: 617-228-3288. E-Mail: bhc@noblenet.org. Web Site: www.mail.noblenet.org. *Dir*, Linda K Weinstein; *Cat*, Svetlana Ordian; *Publ Servs*, Diane Smith; *Tech Servs*, Robert Cabral; *Librn*, Robert Kintz
Library Holdings: Bk Vols 53,000; Per Subs 335
Subject Interests: Europe, Latin America, Nursing
Partic in OCLC Online Computer Library Center, Inc

L BURNS & LEVINSON, Law Library,* 125 Summer St, 02110-1624. SAN 372-073X. Tel: 617-345-3000. FAX: 617-345-3299. E-Mail: amaher@b-l.com. Web Site: www.burnslevinson.com. *Librn*, Abbi Maher
Library Holdings: Bk Vols 500; Per Subs 50

S CHARLES RIVER ASSOCIATES LIBRARY,* 200 Clarendon St T-33, 02116. SAN 307-1499. Tel: 617-425-3000, 617-425-3519. FAX: 617-425-3132. *Bibliog Instr, Head Librn, Online Servs*, Chris Stueart
Founded 1975
Library Holdings: Bk Vols 20,000; Per Subs 300
Subject Interests: Economics, Energy, Environmental studies, Metal working, Transportation
Partic in Nelinet, Inc

M CHILDREN'S HOSPITAL LIBRARY, Fegan Plaza, 300 Longwood Ave, 02115. SAN 377-9173. Tel: 617-355-7232. FAX: 617-734-7763. *Librn*, Alison Clapp; E-Mail: alison.clapp@tch.harvard.edu; *Archivist*, Rebecca Altermatt; Staff 3 (MLS 2, Non-MLS 1)
Founded 1994
Library Holdings: Bk Titles 3,000; Per Subs 285
Automation Activity & Vendor Info: (OPAC) EOS
Database Vendor: OVID Technologies
Partic in Boston Biomedical Library Consortium; National Network Of Libraries Of Medicine - South Central Region
Branches:
WILLIAM STEM LIBRARY, Dept Radiology, Main 2, 02115. SAN 378-0171. Tel: 617-355-6301. *Librn*, Miriam Geller
Library Holdings: Per Subs 34

S CHILDREN'S MUSEUM RESOURCE CENTER, Museum Wharf, 300 Congress St, 02210. SAN 307-1502. Tel: 617-426-6500, Ext 284. FAX: 617-426-1944. Web Site: www.bostonkids.org. *Dir*, Jenny Zanger; *Librn*, Dr Virginia Vogelzanger; Staff 3 (MLS 1, Non-MLS 2)
Founded 1914
Library Holdings: Bk Vols 15,000; Per Subs 69
Subject Interests: Americana, Children's literature, Education, Ethnic studies, Natural science, Physical science
Publications: Activity sheets; Bibliographies; Multicultural Celebrations (children's lit series); Teachers' Guides
Partic in OCLC Online Computer Library Center, Inc
Special Services for the Deaf - Books on deafness & sign language; TTY machine
Open Tues-Sat 10am-5pm

L CHOATE, HALL & STEWART LIBRARY,* Exchange Pl, 53 State St, 02109. SAN 307-1510. Tel: 617-248-5000, Ext 3381. FAX: 617-248-4000. *Dir Libr Serv*, Mary E Rogalski; *Asst Librn*, Thea Frost; Staff 5 (MLS 2, Non-MLS 3)

Library Holdings: Bk Vols 15,000
Subject Interests: Law
Restriction: Private library
Partic in Asn of Boston Law Librns

S CHRISTIAN SCIENCE MONITOR LIBRARY,* One Norway St, 02115. SAN 307-1529. Tel: 617-450-2688. FAX: 617-450-2689. E-Mail: csmlibrary@csps.com. Web Site: www.csmonitor.com. *Librn*, Leigh Montgomery; E-Mail: montgomeryl@csps.com; Staff 1 (MLS 1)
Founded 1909
Library Holdings: Bk Titles 10,000; Per Subs 20
Subject Interests: Current events
Restriction: Not open to public
Partic in Data Time; Dialog Corporation; Dow Jones News Retrieval
Open Mon-Sun 7:30am-5pm

GL COMMONWEALTH OF MASSACHUSETTS, Office of the Attorney General Library, One Ashburton Pl, 02108-1698. SAN 307-1537. Tel: 617-727-2200, Ext 2098. FAX: 617-727-5768. *Chief Librn*, Karin Thurman; Staff 2 (MLS 1, Non-MLS 1)
Founded 1975
Library Holdings: Bk Vols 23,500; Bk Titles 2,000; Per Subs 200
Publications: Index to Opinions of Attorney General; Library Bulletin
Partic in Dialog Corporation; Westlaw

M DANA-FARBER CANCER INSTITUTE, Baruj Benacerraf Library, 44 Binney St, 02115-6084. SAN 325-2787. Tel: 617-632-3508. FAX: 617-632-2488. *Librn*, Christine W Fleuriel; Staff 2 (MLS 1, Non-MLS 1)
Founded 1981
Library Holdings: Bk Titles 1,300; Per Subs 265
Subject Interests: AIDS, Cancer res, Clinical oncology, Nursing, Pharmacology
Restriction: Staff use only
Partic in Boston Biomedical Library Consortium; Massachusetts Health Sciences Libraries Network

L DECHERT, PRICE & RHOADS, Law Library,* 10 Post Off Sq 12th flr, 02109. SAN 372-0659. Tel: 617-728-7100. FAX: 617-426-6567. Web Site: www.dechert.com. *Librn*, Elizabeth D Kenney; E-Mail: ekenney@dechert.com
Library Holdings: Bk Vols 6,000; Per Subs 68

GM DEPARTMENT OF VETERANS AFFAIRS, Medical Library,* 150 S Huntington Ave, 02130. SAN 307-2452. Tel: 617-232-9500, Ext 5077. FAX: 617-278-4531. *Dir*, Irmeli Kilburn
Founded 1952
Oct 1997-Sep 1998 Income $110,000. Mats Exp $131,000, Books $20,000, Per/Ser (Incl. Access Fees) $100,000, Presv $500, Micro $8,000, AV Equip $500
Library Holdings: Bk Vols 6,119; Bk Titles 2,800; Per Subs 380
Publications: Newsletter
Partic in Boston Biomedical Library Consortium; Veterans Affairs Library Network

C EMERSON COLLEGE LIBRARY,* 120 Boylston St, 02116. SAN 307-1588. Tel: 617-824-8668. Interlibrary Loan Service Tel: 617-824-8335. FAX: 617-824-7817. Web Site: www.emerson.edu/library/. *Dir*, Mickey Zemon; E-Mail: mickey_zemon@emerson.edu; *Media Spec*, David Murphy; *Ref*, Ken Rodriguez; *Online Servs, Ref*, Beth Joress; *Ref*, Anna Litten; *Archivist*, Robert Fleming; Staff 10 (MLS 10)
Founded 1880. Enrl 2,912; Fac 199; Highest Degree: Doctorate
Jul 1997-Jun 1998 Income $1,377,887. Mats Exp $397,924, Books $219,651, Per/Ser (Incl. Access Fees) $146,443, Presv $6,086, Micro $11,246, AV Equip $7,015. Sal $731,077 (Prof $431,755)
Library Holdings: Bk Vols 142,661; Bk Titles 127,460; Per Subs 1,015
Subject Interests: Mass communications, Theater
Special Collections: Boston Herald Theatre Clipping Coll
Publications: Film & Video Guide; Library Newsletter; Resources for Advertising; Resources for Communication Policy; Resources for Communication study; Student Library Guide
Partic in Fenway Libraries Online; Nelinet, Inc

C EMMANUEL COLLEGE, Cardinal Cushing Library, 400 The Fenway, 02115. SAN 307-1596. Tel: 617-735-9927. FAX: 617-735-9763. Web Site: www.emmanuel.edu. *Dir*, Dr Mary Ann Tricarico; Tel: 617-264-7656, E-Mail: tricaric@emmanuel.edu; *Assoc Dir*, Dr Susan Von Daum Tholl; Tel: 617-264-7659, E-Mail: tholl@emmanuel.edu; *ILL*, Joleen Westerdale-Robertson; *Media Spec Ad*, Christine Barnhart; *Res*, Irene Ke; *Tech Coordr*, Elena O'Malley; Staff 6 (MLS 4, Non-MLS 2)
Founded 1919. Enrl 1,350; Fac 88; Highest Degree: Master
Jul 1999-Jun 2000 Income Parent Institution $442,609. Mats Exp $179,267, Books $32,034, Per/Ser (Incl. Access Fees) $71,199, Presv $4,439, Micro $6,869, AV Equip $2,870, Electronic Ref Mat (Incl. Access Fees) $16,290. Sal $263,342 (Prof $160,000)
Library Holdings: Bk Vols 98,513; Bk Titles 87,614; Per Subs 876
Subject Interests: Art, Art therapy, Literature, Theology, Women's studies
Automation Activity & Vendor Info: (Acquisitions) DRA; (Cataloging) DRA; (Circulation) DRA; (Course Reserve) DRA; (ILL) DRA; (OPAC) DRA; (Serials) DRA
Database Vendor: Dialog, Ebsco - EbscoHost, IAC - SearchBank, Innovative Interfaces INN - View, OCLC - First Search, OVID Technologies
Partic in Boston Regional Libr Syst; Fenway Libraries Online; Fenway Library Consortium; Nelinet, Inc

R EPISCOPAL DIOCESE OF MASSACHUSETTS, Diocesan Library & Archives, 138 Tremont St, 02111. SAN 307-1618. Tel: 617-482-4826, Ext 504. FAX: 617-482-8431. E-Mail: mem@diomass.org. Web Site: www.diomass.org. *Archivist*, Sandra Sudak
Founded 1884
Library Holdings: Bk Vols 2,800
Subject Interests: Church history
Special Collections: 18th &19th Century Americana, pamphlets & SPG publications; Common Prayer
Publications: Guide to the Parochial Archives of the Episcopal Church in Boston, 1981; Littera Scripta Manet (newsletter)

S ERNST & YOUNG, Center For Business Knowledge, 200 Clarendon St, 02116. SAN 329-0425. Tel: 617-859-6307. FAX: 617-859-6205. *Business*, Ann M Kenny; E-Mail: ann.kenny@ey.com; Staff 4 (MLS 3, Non-MLS 1)
Founded 1970
Library Holdings: Bk Vols 1,600; Bk Titles 1,400; Per Subs 100
Subject Interests: Accounting, Auditing, Taxation
Database Vendor: Dialog, Lexis-Nexis
Function: Research library

S EVERGREEN INVESTMENT MANAGEMENT CO LIBRARY,* 200 Berkeley St, 02116. SAN 307-1901. Tel: 617-338-3435. FAX: 617-210-2786. *Librn*, Kathy Young
Library Holdings: Bk Titles 200; Per Subs 200
Restriction: Private library

S FEDERAL RESERVE BANK OF BOSTON, Research Library, 600 Atlantic Ave, PO Box 2076, 02106-2076. SAN 307-1634. Tel: 617-973-3397. Interlibrary Loan Service Tel: 617-973-3668. FAX: 617-973-4221. E-Mail: boston.library@bos.frb.org. Web Site: www.bos.frb.org. *Dir*, Joyce Hannan; *Librn*, Sandra Cram; *ILL, Ref*, Maki Nakane; *Tech Servs*, Jennifer Caccamo; Staff 10 (MLS 3, Non-MLS 7)
Founded 1921
Library Holdings: Bk Vols 65,000
Subject Interests: Economics, Finance
Special Collections: Federal Reserve System Materials
Publications: Booknews
Partic in Boston Regional Libr Syst; Nelinet, Inc; OCLC Online Computer Library Center, Inc
Open Mon-Fri 9-4:30

S FIDELITY MANAGEMENT & RESEARCH CO, Equity Research Information Center,* 82 Devonshire St, E33B, 02109. SAN 307-1650. Tel: 617-563-7631. FAX: 617-476-9914. *Dir*, Leslie Jacobs; Staff 44 (MLS 21, Non-MLS 23)
Founded 1973
Library Holdings: Bk Titles 1,000
Subject Interests: Finance, Investing
Special Collections: Foreign Corporations; Municipal Coll; US Corporations
Restriction: Not open to public
Partic in Dialog Corporation; Dow Jones News Retrieval; Nelinet, Inc

J FISHER COLLEGE LIBRARY, 118 Beacon St, 02116. SAN 307-1677. Tel: 617-236-8875. Reference Tel: 617-236-4504. Toll Free Tel: 800-446-1226. FAX: 617-262-4946. Web Site: www.fisher.edu/library. *Dir Libr Serv*, Joshua Van Kirk McKain; E-Mail: jmckain@fisher.edu; *Asst Librn*, Kenneth Peterson; *Bibliog Instr*, Tamara Che Spates; E-Mail: tspates@fisher.edu; *Reader Servs*, Carolyn Brownhill; E-Mail: cbrownhill@fisher.edu; *Tech Servs*, Hillary J Corbett; E-Mail: hcorbett@fisher.edu; Staff 8 (MLS 5, Non-MLS 3)
Founded 1903. Enrl 1,239; Fac 138; Highest Degree: Bachelor
Jul 1999-Jun 2000 Mats Exp $301,000, Books $110,000, Per/Ser (Incl. Access Fees) $68,000, AV Equip $27,200, Electronic Ref Mat (Incl. Access Fees) $40,000. Sal $196,000 (Prof $191,000)
Library Holdings: Bk Vols 33,000; Per Subs 210
Subject Interests: Fashion, Hospitality, Physical therapy, Travel
Automation Activity & Vendor Info: (Acquisitions) Gaylord; (Cataloging) Gaylord; (Circulation) Gaylord; (OPAC) Gaylord
Database Vendor: IAC - Info Trac, Wilson - Wilson Web
Publications: Library Handbook
Mem of Boston Regional Libr Syst

S FLEET BOSTON, Research & Information Services, 100 Federal St, PO Box 1896, 02105. SAN 307-1669. Tel: 617-434-8440. FAX: 617-434-7208. *Mgr*, Jane E Gutowski-Connell
Founded 1929
Library Holdings: Bk Titles 8,000
Subject Interests: Business and management, Finance
Partic in Dialog Corporation; Dow Jones News Retrieval

L FOLEY, HOAG & ELIOT LIBRARY, One Post Office Sq, 18th Flr, 02109. SAN 307-1685. Tel: 617-832-7071. FAX: 617-832-7000. *Librn*, Ruth Armstrong; E-Mail: rarmstro@fhe.com; *Ref*, Allen Rines; E-Mail: arines@

fhe.com; *Tech Servs*, Lucinda Valeru
Library Holdings: Bk Vols 25,000
Subject Interests: Corporate law, Environmental law, Labor
Partic in Dialog Corporation; Westlaw

M FORSYTH DENTAL CENTER, Percy R Howe Memorial Library, 140 The Fenway, 02115. SAN 307-1693. Tel: 617-262-5200, Ext 244. FAX: 617-262-4021. Web Site: www.forsyth.org. *Dir*, Susan Orlando; E-Mail: sorlando@forsyth.org; Staff 2 (MLS 2)
Founded 1913
Library Holdings: Bk Vols 6,815; Per Subs 240
Subject Interests: Bacteriology, Biochemistry, Immunology, Microbiology, Microscopy, Molecular biology, Pharmacology
Special Collections: Forsyth Dental Center Archives, photogs, bks, memorabilia
Publications: Collected Reprints of Forsyth Dental Center (newsletter)

S FRANKLIN INSTITUTE OF BOSTON, Lufkin Memorial Library, 41 Berkeley St, 02116. SAN 307-1707. Tel: 617-423-4630, Ext 123. FAX: 617-482-3706. Web Site: www.fib.edu. *Dir*, Sharon B Bonk; Fax: 617-482-8740, E-Mail: sbonk@fib.edu; *Cat*, Julie Hankinson; E-Mail: jhankinson@fib.edu; Staff 4 (MLS 2, Non-MLS 2)
Founded 1908. Enrl 400
Jan 2000-Dec 2000 Mats Exp $16,000, Per/Ser (Incl. Access Fees) $3,000, Electronic Ref Mat (Incl. Access Fees) $13,000
Library Holdings: Bk Titles 13,000; Per Subs 60
Subject Interests: Architecture, Civil engineering, Computer science, Electronic engineering, Mechanical engineering, Technology
Special Collections: Benjamin Franklin Coll; Photographic Science (Dr Leonard E Ravich Coll)
Automation Activity & Vendor Info: (OPAC) CASPR
Database Vendor: Ebsco - EbscoHost, IAC - SearchBank, ProQuest, Wilson - Wilson Web
Publications: Guide to the Library
Partic in Boston Library Consortium; Nelinet, Inc
Open Mon-Thurs 8-8, Fri 8-4

S THE FRENCH LIBRARY & CULTURAL CENTER, 53 Marlborough St, 02116-2099. SAN 307-1715. Tel: 617-912-0400. FAX: 617-912-0450. Web Site: www.frenchlib.org. *Librn*, Jane M Stahl; E-Mail: jstahl@frenchlib.org; Staff 3 (MLS 2, Non-MLS 1)
Founded 1945
Library Holdings: Bk Vols 23,000; Per Subs 65
Subject Interests: Humanities
Special Collections: films; French; French Culture; History & literature of France & French-speaking countries; Marcel Carne Coll, papers, memorabilia
Publications: AdLib (Bimonthly)

L GALLAGHER & GALLAGHER, Law Library,* 120 Second Ave, 02129-4533. SAN 372-0764. Tel: 617-598-3800. FAX: 617-241-7692. *Librn*, Dorothy Miller
Library Holdings: Bk Vols 1,000

J KATHARINE GIBBS SCHOOL LIBRARY,* 126 Newbury St, 02116. SAN 326-1123. Tel: 617-578-7149. FAX: 617-262-6210. Web Site: www.katharinegibbs.com. *Librn*, Heather McCabe; Staff 1 (MLS 1)
Founded 1982
Library Holdings: Bk Vols 3,300; Per Subs 81
Special Collections: Women in Business

S GILLETTE CO, Corporate Research & Development Library,* Gillette Park-5GA4, 02127-1028. SAN 307-174X. Tel: 617-463-3178. FAX: 617-463-2815. Web Site: www.gillette.com.
Library Holdings: Bk Vols 7,000
Subject Interests: Chemistry, Cosmetics industry, Material culture
Publications: Newsletter

L GOLDSTEIN & MANELLO, Law Library,* 265 Franklin St, 02110. SAN 372-0705. Tel: 617-946-8000. FAX: 617-946-8100. *Librn*, Pamela Ross; E-Mail: pross@gmlaw.com; Staff 2 (MLS 1, Non-MLS 1)
Library Holdings: Bk Vols 6,000; Per Subs 24
Subject Interests: Corporate law
Database Vendor: Lexis-Nexis
Partic in Asn of Boston Law Librns

L GOODWIN, PROCTER & HOAR, Law Library,* Exchange Pl, 02109. SAN 328-4654. Tel: 617-570-1333. FAX: 617-523-1231. *Librn*, Mary Jo Poburko; E-Mail: mpoburko@gph.com
Library Holdings: Bk Vols 25,000; Per Subs 2,500
Partic in Dialog Corporation; Westlaw

L GOULSTON & STORRS, Law Library,* 400 Atlantic Ave, 02110. SAN 372-0772. Tel: 617-574-4054. FAX: 617-574-4112. Web Site: www.goulstonstorrs.com. *Librn*, Robert DeFabrizio; *Asst Librn*, Stephanie Tatah
Library Holdings: Bk Vols 10,000; Per Subs 90
Subject Interests: Health, Law, Real estate, Securities
Partic in ABA/NET; ALA; Am Soc Law Libr; Asn of Boston Law Librns; SLA

S GRAND LODGE OF MASONS IN MASSACHUSETTS, (SCLL), Samuel Crocker Lawrence Library, 186 Tremont St, 02111. SAN 307-1774. Tel: 617-426-6040, Ext 221. FAX: 617-426-6115. E-Mail: glamasonsma@aol.com. Web Site: www.masonsmass. *Librn*, Cynthia Alcorn; Staff 3 (MLS 1, Non-MLS 2)
Founded 1814
Library Holdings: Bk Vols 120,000
Special Collections: Freemassonry John Paul Jones Coll, relic & mss; Histories; Medals, Crystal & China of Masonic Interest; New England Town & City; Paul Revere, relics, engravings & mss
Function: Research library

L HALE & DORR LIBRARY,* 60 State St, 02109. SAN 307-1782. Tel: 617-526-5900. FAX: 617-526-5000. *Mgr*, Lynn K Oser; *Ref*, Anne Stemlar; *Ref*, Sara Scott
Library Holdings: Bk Vols 21,000
Subject Interests: Government, Law

S HALEY & ALDRICH INC LIBRARY,* 465 Medford St, 02129. SAN 373-0670. Tel: 617-886-7300, Ext 7426. FAX: 617-886-7600. E-Mail: ejd@haleyaldrich.com. Web Site: www.haleyaldrich.com. *Librn*, Edward Dickie
Library Holdings: Bk Vols 5,500; Bk Titles 6,000; Per Subs 35
Subject Interests: Environmental engineering, Geotechnical
Restriction: Clients only, Staff use only

L JOHN HANCOCK MUTUAL LIFE INSURANCE, Law Library,* PO Box 111, 02117. SAN 372-0756. Tel: 617-572-9191. FAX: 617-572-1565. *Librn*, Nancy McHugh
Library Holdings: Bk Vols 35,400; Per Subs 125

S HARVARD MUSICAL ASSOCIATION LIBRARY, 57A Chestnut St, 02108. SAN 307-1812. Tel: 617-523-2897. FAX: 617-523-2897. *Librn*, Natalie Palme
Founded 1837
Library Holdings: Bk Titles 12,000
Special Collections: Chamber music parts; Two-piano music

L HEMENWAY & BARNES, Law Library, 60 State St, 02109. SAN 372-0667. Tel: 617-227-7940. FAX: 617-227-0781. *Librn*, Chris Laut; E-Mail: claut@hembar.com; Staff 1 (Non-MLS 1)
Founded 1863
Jan 2000-Dec 2000 Income $160,000. Sal $80,000 (Prof $50,000)
Library Holdings: Bk Vols 10,000; Per Subs 100
Special Collections: Massachusetts Statutes Back to 1694

L HILL & BARLOW LIBRARY,* One International Pl, 02110. SAN 327-3431. Tel: 617-428-3000. FAX: 617-428-3500. *Librn*, Julie Snyder
Library Holdings: Bk Titles 13,000; Per Subs 25
Subject Interests: Real estate
Restriction: Not open to public
Partic in Asn of Boston Law Librns; Soc Law Librs

L HOLLAND & KNIGHT LLP, Law Library, 10 Saint James Ave, 02116-3803. SAN 372-0640. Tel: 617-523-2700, Ext 863. FAX: 617-523-6850. *Librn*, Maureen C Kearney; E-Mail: m.kearney@hklaw.com
Library Holdings: Per Subs 55

S INSTITUTE OF CONTEMPORARY ART LIBRARY,* 955 Boylston St, 02115. SAN 374-9533. Tel: 617-266-5152. FAX: 617-266-4021. *Dir*, Jill Medvedow
Library Holdings: Bk Vols 500
Subject Interests: Architecture, Theater
Restriction: Open to public for reference only
Library exchange program

S INSURANCE LIBRARY ASSOCIATION OF BOSTON, 156 State St, 02109. SAN 307-1855. Tel: 617-227-2087. FAX: 617-723-8524. Web Site: www.insurancelibrary.org. *Dir*, Jean Lucey; E-Mail: jlucey@insurancelibrary.org; *Asst Dir*, Phyllis Smithers; E-Mail: psmithers@insurancelibrary.org; *Librn*, Jennifer Doyle; E-Mail: jdoyle@insurancelibrary.org
Founded 1887
Jul 1998-Jun 1999 Income $635,644. Mats Exp $82,770, Presv $2,500. Sal $193,000
Library Holdings: Bk Vols 28,000; Bk Titles 12,000; Per Subs 350
Special Collections: Sanborn Fire Maps
Publications: Monthly trustee newsletter; quarterly membership newsletter
Partic in Asn of Boston Law Librns

S ISABELLA STEWART GARDNER MUSEUM LIBRARY, 2 Palace Rd, 02115-5897. SAN 328-6134. Tel: 617-278-5121. FAX: 617-278-5177. Web Site: www.boston.com/gardner. *Actg Librn*, Richard E Lingner; E-Mail: rlingner@isgm.org; Staff 1 (Non-MLS 1)
Founded 1903
Library Holdings: Bk Vols 2,300; Bk Titles 2,300; Per Subs 10

Subject Interests: Art history, Conservation
Special Collections: Isabella Stewart Gardner Coll, bks, binding, mss, letters, autographs, music scores, archives
Database Vendor: OCLC - First Search
Restriction: Non-circulating
Function: Archival collection

M JOHN SNOW INC, JSI Research & Training Institute Library, 44 Farnsworth St, 02210-1211. SAN 377-9130. Tel: 617-482-9485. FAX: 617-482-0617. Web Site: www.jsi.com.; Staff 2 (MLS 2)
Library Holdings: Bk Titles 10,000; Per Subs 125
Subject Interests: Public health
Partic in Asn of Pop-Family Planning Librs & Info Ctr; Boston Regional Libr Syst; Spec Health Librs Coalition

M JOSLIN DIABETES CENTER, INC, Alexander Marble Library, One Joslin Pl, 02215. SAN 324-6639. Tel: 617-732-2400, 617-732-2641. FAX: 617-732-2542. *Librn*, Saundra Ketner; E-Mail: sketner@joslin.harvard.edu
Library Holdings: Bk Vols 5,000; Per Subs 110
Subject Interests: Biochemistry, Diabetes, Endocrinology, Metabolism
Special Collections: Historical Material on Diabetes Archives, bks, newsp clippings, correspondence; Reprint Coll, staff journal articles
Publications: Joslin Diabetes Center 1898-1988: A History of the First 90 Years Through Its Publications
Restriction: By appointment only
Partic in Boston Biomedical Library Consortium

GL JUDGES' LIBRARY CORP, Thorndike Library, 1300 New Court House, 02108. SAN 307-1898. Tel: 617-557-1000, 617-557-1151. FAX: 617-557-1091. *Librn*, Sally Locke
Founded 1921
Library Holdings: Bk Vols 25,000

L KIRKPATRICK & LOCKHART LLP, Law Library, 75 State St, 02109-1808. SAN 327-6082. Tel: 617-951-9000. FAX: 617-951-9151. Web Site: www.kl.com. *Librn*, Elizabeth Labedz; E-Mail: elizabeth@kl.com; *Librn*, Jeannette Tracy; E-Mail: jtracy@warstack.com
Library Holdings: Bk Vols 6,000; Per Subs 40
Restriction: Not open to public

J LABOURE COLLEGE, Helen Stubblefield Law Library, 2120 Dorchester Ave, 02124. SAN 307-191X. Tel: 617-296-8300, Ext 4012. FAX: 617-296-7947. Web Site: www.librarycollege.org. *Dir*, Andrew M Calo; Staff 1 (MLS 1)
Founded 1971. Enrl 600
Library Holdings: Bk Vols 11,000; Per Subs 155
Subject Interests: Nursing, Technology
Partic in Massachusetts Health Sciences Libraries Network
Friends of the Library Group

S LESLEY COLLEGE, (AIB), Art Institute of Boston Library, 700 Beacon St, 02215-2598. SAN 307-1251. Tel: 617-262-1223, Ext 6670. FAX: 617-437-1226. Web Site: www.aiboston.edu. *Librn*, Valda Bolis; Tel: 617-585-6671; Staff 3 (MLS 1, Non-MLS 2)
Enrl 500; Fac 100; Highest Degree: Bachelor
1998-1999 Income $25,000. Mats Exp $29,000, Books $12,000, Per/Ser (Incl. Access Fees) $7,000, Electronic Ref Mat (Incl. Access Fees) $10,000
Library Holdings: Bk Vols 9,200; Bk Titles 9,000; Per Subs 70
Subject Interests: Art history, Humanities, Photography
Partic in Fenway Libraries Online

LIBERTY MUTUAL GROUP
S EDUCATION INFORMATION RESOURCES, One PPG Pl, Ste 1650, Pittsburgh, 15222-5409. SAN 329-6717. Tel: 412-231-1331.
L LAW LIBRARY, 175 Berkeley St, 02117. SAN 344-6883. Tel: 617-357-9500, Ext 45826. FAX: 617-426-7125. *VPres*, Helen Gilcrist; *Dir*, Rodney Koliha; E-Mail: rodney.koliha@libertymutual.com; Staff 3 (MLS 1, Non-MLS 2)
Founded 1918
Library Holdings: Bk Vols 130,000; Per Subs 120
Subject Interests: Environmental law
Partic in Dialog Corporation; Westlaw

M ERICH LINDEMANN MENTAL HEALTH CENTER LIBRARY,* 25 Staniford St, 02114. SAN 371-4098. Tel: 617-626-8500, Ext 68618. FAX: 617-367-4260. *Librn*, Vishakha Mehta; E-Mail: vmehta@state.ma.us
Library Holdings: Bk Vols 7,000; Per Subs 35

P MASS TRIAL COURT LAW LIBRARIES SYSTEM, (Formerly Trial Court Law Libraries), 2 Center Plaza, 9th flr, 02108. SAN 325-3481. Tel: 617-878-0338. TDD: 800-281-3683 (in-state). FAX: 617-723-8821. Web Site: www.lawlib.state.ma.us.; Staff 57 (MLS 23, Non-MLS 34)
Founded 1978
Jul 2000-Jun 2001 Income State $5,191,211. Mats Exp $2,915,118. Sal $2,144,093 (Prof $1,201,063)
Subject Interests: Law
Database Vendor: IAC - SearchBank, Lexis-Nexis, OCLC - First Search
Partic in Nelinet, Inc; New England Law Library Consortium, Inc; OCLC Online Computer Library Center, Inc
There are 17 public law libraries in the system located in Barnstable, Brockton, Cambridge, Fall River, Fitchburg, Greenfield, Lawrence, Lowell, New Bedford, Northampton, Norwood, Pittsfield, Plymouth, Salem, Springfield, Taunton & Worcester.

P MASSACHUSETTS BOARD OF LIBRARY COMMISSIONERS, 648 Beacon St, 02215. SAN 307-1952. Tel: 617-267-9400. FAX: 617-421-9833. E-Mail: blc@noblenet.org. Web Site: www.mlin.lib.ma.us. *Dir*, Keith Michael Fiels; *Res*, Mary A Litterst; *Ref, Res*, Brian R Donoghue; Staff 18 (MLS 18)
Founded 1890
Jul 1998-Jun 1999 Income $54,196,933, State $50,819,490, Federal $3,377,443. Mats Exp $17,065, Books $4,000, Per/Ser (Incl. Access Fees) $11,065, Other Print Mats $2,000. Sal $1,015,920
Library Holdings: Bk Vols 3,000
Special Collections: Agency Archival Coll
Publications: 1991-1996; Annual Report of Board of Library Commissioners; Data for Massachusetts Series (Public Library Statistics & Personnel Data); Directory of Free Public Libraries in Massachusetts; Massachusetts Long Range Program; MBLC Notes (monthly); Strategic Plan for the Future of Library Services in Massachusetts
Partic in Nelinet, Inc; North of Boston Library Exchange, Inc
The Massachusetts Board of Library Commissioners is the state agency responsible for public library development

C MASSACHUSETTS COLLEGE OF ART, Morton R Godine Library,* 621 Huntington Ave, 02115-5882. SAN 307-1960. Tel: 617-232-1555, Ext 392. FAX: 617-264-7473. Web Site: www.massart.edu/library/library.html. *Dir*, Deborah Johnson; *Cat*, Oscar Palacio; *Curator*, Staci Stull; *Ser*, Gail Lancaster; *Tech Servs*, Anita Bolden; *Archivist*, Paul Dobbs; *AV*, Robert Hilpert; *Publ Servs*, Jonathan Rand; *Publ Servs*, Julia Blake; *Publ Servs*, Leslie Everett; *Publ Servs*, Deborah Johnson; *Publ Servs*, John Keating; *Tech Servs*, Raye Yankauskas; Staff 13 (MLS 5, Non-MLS 8)
Founded 1873. Enrl 1,470; Highest Degree: Master
Jul 1997-Jun 1998 Income $703,206, State $615,356, Parent Institution $87,850. Mats Exp $184,708. Sal $482,783 (Prof $281,015)
Library Holdings: Bk Vols 96,519; Bk Titles 86,880; Per Subs 442
Subject Interests: Art, Art history, Films and filmmaking
Special Collections: Art Educ; College Archives; Design
Automation Activity & Vendor Info: (Circulation) DRA
Publications: New Books
Partic in Fenway Libraries Online; Nelinet, Inc; OCLC Online Computer Library Center, Inc

CM MASSACHUSETTS COLLEGE OF PHARMACY & HEALTH SCIENCES, Sheppard Library, 179 Longwood Ave, 02115. SAN 307-1979. Tel: 617-732-2810. Reference Tel: 617-732-2813. FAX: 617-278-1566. Web Site: www.mcp.edu. *Dir*, Richard Kaplan; *Access Serv*, Joanne Doucette; *Head Ref, Ref*, Julie S Whelan; *Science*, Marilyn Steinberg; Staff 13 (MLS 5, Non-MLS 8)
Founded 1823. Highest Degree: Doctorate
Library Holdings: Bk Vols 71,500; Bk Titles 30,000; Per Subs 750
Subject Interests: Medicine, Nursing, Pharmacology
Database Vendor: DRA
Publications: Acquisitions List (quarterly); Annual Report; Current Serials; Library Guide
Partic in Fenway Library Consortium; OCLC Online Computer Library Center, Inc

G MASSACHUSETTS DEPARTMENT OF EMPLOYMENT & TRAINING, Research Library,* 19 Staniford St, 2nd flr, 02114. SAN 307-2010. Tel: 617-626-5744. FAX: 617-727-0335. Web Site: www.detma.org. *Mgr*, Elliot Winer
Subject Interests: Economics, Employment, Massachusetts

§S MASSACHUSETTS DEPARTMENT OF ENVIRONMENTAL PROTECTION, Massachusetts Environmental Library, One Winter St, 2nd flr, 02108. SAN 378-3804. Tel: 617-292-5802. FAX: 617-348-4007. E-Mail: library.maindeslh@state.ma.us. Web Site: www.state.ma.us/dep/. *Dir*, Thomas G Hughes; *Cat*, Kathy Higgins; *ILL*, Bridget McCormick; *Outreach Serv, Res*, Rich Johnson; *Res*, Aroon Shah
Library Holdings: Bk Vols 8,000; Per Subs 80; Spec Interest Per Sub 1,000
Restriction: By appointment only

G MASSACHUSETTS DEPARTMENT OF PUBLIC HEALTH, Central Library, Central Library Bldg, 3rd Flr, 250 Washington St, 02108-4619. SAN 307-2002. Tel: 617-624-5190. FAX: 617-624-5185. Web Site: www.magnet.state.ma.us/dph/library.htm. *Dir Libr Serv*, Alice M Welch; E-Mail: alice.welch@state.mass.us; Staff 1 (MLS 1)
Library Holdings: Bk Vols 1,200; Per Subs 150
Subject Interests: Public health
Partic in Docline; OCLC Online Computer Library Center, Inc
Open Mon-Fri 8:30-5

M MASSACHUSETTS EYE & EAR INFIRMARY LIBRARIES,* 243 Charles St, 02114. SAN 328-400X. Tel: 617-573-3196. FAX: 617-573-3370. Web Site: www.mgh.harvard.edu (look for libraries magic). *Dir*, Chris Nims; *Librn*, Kathleen Kennedy
Library Holdings: Bk Vols 5,400; Per Subs 203

Partic in Asn for Vision Sci Librns; Massachusetts Health Sciences Libraries Network; Medical Libr Asn
Friends of the Library Group

MASSACHUSETTS GENERAL HOSPITAL
M TRACY BURR MALLORY MEMORIAL LIBRARY, Dept of Pathology, 02114. SAN 344-6948. Tel: 617-726-8892. FAX: 617-726-7474. *Dir*, Dr Robert H Young; Staff 2 (MLS 1, Non-MLS 1)
Founded 1952
Library Holdings: Bk Titles 400; Per Subs 15
Subject Interests: Pathology

M TREADWELL LIBRARY, Bartlett Hall Ext, 55 Fruit St, 02114-2696. SAN 344-6972. Tel: 617-726-8600. FAX: 617-726-6784. E-Mail: treadwellq&a@mgh.harvard.edu. Web Site: www.mgh.harvard.edu/library/library.htm. *Dir*, Elizabeth Schneider; *Res*, Carole Mankin; *Ref*, Martha Stone; *Ser*, Sheila Moran; *Access Serv*, Carolyn Paul; Staff 20 (MLS 9, Non-MLS 11)
Founded 1858
Oct 1998-Sep 1999 Mats Exp $454,255, Books $68,502, Per/Ser (Incl. Access Fees) $372,183, Presv $13,570
Library Holdings: Bk Vols 58,000; Bk Titles 11,956; Per Subs 660
Subject Interests: Biochemistry, Biology, Medicine, Nursing
Restriction: Staff use only
Partic in Dialog Corporation; Docline; OCLC Online Computer Library Center, Inc

S WARREN LIBRARY, Fruit St, 02114. SAN 344-7006. Tel: 617-726-2253. FAX: 617-726-3852. *Librn*, Nancy Marshall
Founded 1841
Oct 1996-Sep 1997 Income $35,000. Mats Exp $5,000. Sal $32,000
Library Holdings: Bk Vols 10,000; Per Subs 60

S MASSACHUSETTS HISTORICAL SOCIETY LIBRARY,* 1154 Boylston St, 02215-3695. SAN 307-2037. Tel: 617-536-1608. FAX: 617-859-0074. E-Mail: library@masshist.org. Web Site: www.masshist.org. *Librn*, Peter Drummey; Tel: 617-646-0501, E-Mail: pdrummey@masshist.org; *Assoc Librn, Curator*, Brenda Lawson; Tel: 617-646-0502, E-Mail: blawson@masshist.org; *Res*, Jennifer Tolpa; Tel: 617-646-0527, E-Mail: jtolpa@masshist.org; *Cat*, Mary Fabiszewski; Tel: 617-646-0504, E-Mail: mfab@masshist.org; *Reader Servs*, Nicholas Graham; Tel: 617-646-0509, E-Mail: ngraham@masshist.org. Subject Specialists: *Manuscripts*, Brenda Lawson; *Rare books*, Mary Fabiszewski; *Reproductive rights*, Jennifer Tolpa; Staff 12 (MLS 7, Non-MLS 5)
Founded 1791
Library Holdings: Bk Vols 200,000; Per Subs 160
Subject Interests: New England
Special Collections: Historical Manuscripts, maps, photographs, prints & broadsides, rare bks
Database Vendor: OCLC - First Search
Restriction: Non-circulating to the public
Partic in Nelinet, Inc; OCLC Online Computer Library Center, Inc

S MASSACHUSETTS HORTICULTURAL SOCIETY LIBRARY,* Horticultural Hall, 300 Massachusetts Ave, 02115. SAN 307-2045. Tel: 617-536-9280, Ext 225. FAX: 617-262-8780. E-Mail: library@masshort.org. Web Site: www.masshort.org. *Librn*, Eric Frazier
Founded 1829
Library Holdings: Bk Titles 40,000; Per Subs 250
Subject Interests: Art, History
Special Collections: Print Coll; Rare Book Coll; Seed & Nursery Catalogs
Partic in Council On Botanical Horticultural Libraries; Nelinet, Inc; OCLC Online Computer Library Center, Inc
Periodicals & catalogs date to the 18th century; 50,000 books-collection dates from the 15th century

M MASSACHUSETTS MENTAL HEALTH CENTER, Charles MacFie Campbell Memorial Library, 74 Fenwood Rd, 02115. SAN 307-2061. Tel: 617-626-9300. FAX: 617-731-9514. *Librn*, Judy Blood; Tel: 617-626-9329
Founded 1921
Library Holdings: Bk Vols 5,000; Per Subs 100
Subject Interests: Geriatrics and gerontology, Neurology, Nursing, Pharmacology, Psychiatry, Psychology, Social service (social work)
Restriction: Staff use only, Use of others with permission of librarian
Partic in BRS; Dialog Corporation

S MASSACHUSETTS SOCIETY FOR THE PREVENTION OF CRUELTY TO ANIMALS LIBRARY (MSPCA), 350 S Huntington Ave, 02130. SAN 327-3253. Tel: 617-522-7400, Ext 5322. FAX: 617-522-4885. Web Site: www.mspca.org. *Librn*, John Julian; E-Mail: jjulian@mspca.org
Library Holdings: Bk Vols 1,500; Bk Titles 1,000; Per Subs 65
Special Collections: Archives of George Angel I

GM MASSACHUSETTS STATE LAB INSTITUTE LIBRARY, Dept of Public Health, 305 South St, 02130. SAN 377-922X. Tel: 617-983-6290. FAX: 617-983-6292. *Librn*, Kathy Noonan; E-Mail: kathryn.noonan@state.ma.us; Staff 1 (MLS 1)
Library Holdings: Per Subs 105
Subject Interests: Laboratory med, Medicine, Pub health med
Function: ILL available
Partic in Boston Regional Libr Syst; National Network Of Libraries Of Medicine - South Central Region; OCLC Online Computer Library Center, Inc

S MASSACHUSETTS TAXPAYERS FOUNDATION LIBRARY,* 333 Washington St Ste 853, 02108. SAN 307-2088. Tel: 617-720-1000. FAX: 617-720-0799. *Librn*, Courtney Cady
Founded 1948
Library Holdings: Bk Vols 6,800; Per Subs 98
Special Collections: Massachusetts Taxpayers Foundation Archives
Publications: Annual report; Ballot Questions (annual); Budget Analysis (annual); Library List (quarterly); Massachusetts Legislative Directory (biennial); Municipal Financial Data (annual); Operating Program (annual-to 1987)
Open Mon-Fri 8:45-4:45

G MASSACHUSETTS WATER RESOURCES AUTHORITY LIBRARY, (MWRA), 100 First Ave, 02129. SAN 371-7682. Tel: 617-242-6000, Ext 4175, 617-788-4175. Interlibrary Loan Service Tel: 617-788-4176. FAX: 617-788-4899. E-Mail: mwralib@mwra.state.ma.us.; Staff 3 (MLS 1, Non-MLS 2)
Founded 1986
1998-1999 Mats Exp $93,000, Books $18,000, Per/Ser (Incl. Access Fees) $65,000, Electronic Ref Mat (Incl. Access Fees) $10,000. Sal $110,000
Library Holdings: Bk Titles 2,010; Per Subs 141
Special Collections: Massachusetts Water Resources Authority Publications
Publications: Information Services (quarterly)

G MENTAL HEALTH LEGAL ADVISORS COMMITTEE, Flaschner Disabilities Library, 294 Washington St, Ste 320, 02108. SAN 373-1634. Tel: 617-338-2345. FAX: 617-338-2347. *Librn*, Eleanor Sarcia
Library Holdings: Bk Vols 500; Per Subs 12
Publications: The Advisor (legal newsletter)

L MINTZ, LEVIN, COHN, FERRIS, GLOVSKY, & POPEO, Law Library,* One Financial Ctr, 02111. SAN 307-2118. Tel: 617-542-6000, Ext 4852. FAX: 617-542-2241. Web Site: www.mintz.com. *Librn*, Lori Tarpinian
Library Holdings: Bk Vols 5,000; Per Subs 600
Partic in Dialog Corporation

L MORRISON, MAHONEY & MILLER, Law Library,* 250 Summer St, 02210. SAN 372-0780. Tel: 617-439-7500, Ext 7014. FAX: 617-439-7590. *Librn*, Julie Piantedosi
Library Holdings: Bk Titles 1,000; Per Subs 25

S MUSEUM OF FINE ARTS, BOSTON, William Morris Hunt Memorial Library, 465 Huntington Ave, 02115-5519. SAN 307-2126. Tel: 617-369-3385. FAX: 617-247-9063. Web Site: www.mfa.org. *Dir*, Kathleen Meszaros; *Cat*, Laila Abdel-Malek; Staff 11 (MLS 4, Non-MLS 7)
Founded 1879
Library Holdings: Bk Titles 250,000; Per Subs 1,000
Subject Interests: Egypt, Fine arts, Museology
Partic in Fenway Libraries Online; Fenway Library Consortium; RLG; RLIN
Branches:
W VAN ALAN CLARK JR LIBRARY, 230 The Fenway, 02115. SAN 307-2134. Tel: 617-369-3650. FAX: 617-424-6271. E-Mail: library@smfa.edu. Web Site: www.smfa.edu. *Dir*, Kathleen Meszaros
Founded 1928
Subject Interests: 20th Century art, Contemporary art
Restriction: Open to student, faculty & staff
Function: AV services, ILL available, Internet access
Partic in Fenway Library Consortium
Open Mon-Thurs 8:45am-9pm, Fri 8:45-5, Sat 10-5 & Sun 1-5

S MUSEUM OF NATIONAL CENTER OF AFRO-AMERICAN ARTISTS, Slide Library,* 300 Walnut Ave, 02119. SAN 307-2142. Tel: 617-442-8614. FAX: 617-445-5525. *Curator, Dir*, Edmund B Gaither
Founded 1969

S MUSEUM OF SCIENCE LIBRARY, Science Park, 02114-1099. SAN 307-2150. Tel: 617-589-0170. FAX: 617-589-0187. E-Mail: library@mos.org. Web Site: www.mos.org. *Archivist*, Carolyn Kirdahy; Staff 2 (MLS 2)
Founded 1831
Library Holdings: Bk Vols 17,000; Per Subs 200
Subject Interests: Education
Special Collections: 19th Century Natural History, bk, journal & mss; Archives of the Boston Society of Natural History (founded 1830, the predecessor of the Museum of Science)

S NATIONAL ARCHIVES & RECORDS ADMINISTRATION, John F Kennedy Library & Museum, Columbia Point, 02125. SAN 307-7438. Tel: 617-929-4500. Interlibrary Loan Service Tel: 617-929-4534. Toll Free Tel: 877-616-4599. FAX: 617-929-4538. Web Site: www.cs.umb.edu/jfklibrary/museum.htm. *Dir*, Brad Gerratt; *AV*, Allan Goodrich; *Librn*, Ronald E Whealan; *Archivist*, Megan Desnoyers; *Curator*, Frank Rigg; Staff 45 (MLS 18, Non-MLS 27)
Founded 1963
1999-1999 Mats Exp Books $6,750

Library Holdings: Bk Vols 35,000; Bk Titles 32,000; Per Subs 10
Special Collections: Ernest Hemingway Coll, film, mss, photog, printed mat; Mid-Twentieth Century American Politics & Government,; The Life & Times of John F Kennedy
Publications: Historical Materials in the John F Kennedy Library
Open Mon-Fri 8:30-4:30, by special request on Sat
Friends of the Library Group

S NEN-LIFE SCIENCE PRODUCTS INC,* 549 Albany St, 02118. SAN 307-2223. Tel: 617-482-9595, Ext 9605. FAX: 617-350-9658.; Staff 3 (Non-MLS 3)
Founded 1963
Library Holdings: Bk Titles 15,500; Per Subs 350
Subject Interests: Cancer, Chemistry, Nuclear medicine
Partic in BRS; Dialog Corporation; Pergamon; STN

S NEW ENGLAND AQUARIUM LIBRARY, Central Wharf, 02110. SAN 328-1922. Tel: 617-973-5237. FAX: 617-973-0251. Web Site: www.neaq.org. *Head of Libr*, Dot Wensink; E-Mail: dwensink@neaq.org; Staff 2 (MLS 1, Non-MLS 1)
Founded 1982
Library Holdings: Bk Titles 5,500; Per Subs 102; Spec Interest Per Sub 75
Subject Interests: Biology, Conservation, Ecology, Ichthyology, Marine biology, Oceanography
Automation Activity & Vendor Info: (Acquisitions) Sagebrush Corporation; (Cataloging) Sagebrush Corporation; (Circulation) Sagebrush Corporation; (Course Reserve) Sagebrush Corporation; (ILL) Sagebrush Corporation; (Media Booking) Sagebrush Corporation; (OPAC) Sagebrush Corporation; (Serials) Sagebrush Corporation
Partic in Boston Regional Libr Syst; Environ Sci Libr
Open Mon-Fri 8:30-3:30, Sat 10-3

NEW ENGLAND BAPTIST HOSPITAL
M PAUL E WOODARD HEALTH SCIENCES LIBRARY, 125 Parker Hill Ave, 02120-2847. SAN 344-7030. Tel: 617-754-5155. FAX: 617-754-6414. Web Site: www.nebh.org/health_library.asp.; Staff 1 (MLS 1)
Founded 1963
1998-1999 Income $83,325. Mats Exp $45,100
Library Holdings: Bk Titles 2,000; Per Subs 121
Subject Interests: Medicine, Nursing, Orthopedics
Special Collections: Orthopaedics & History of Medicine (Morton Smith-Petersen Coll); Otto Aufranc Coll
Partic in Boston Biomedical Library Consortium

S NEW ENGLAND BOARD OF HIGHER EDUCATION LIBRARY,* 45 Temple Pl, 02111. SAN 307-7624. Tel: 617-357-9620. FAX: 617-338-1577. Web Site: www.nebhe.org. *Librn*, Sue Klemer; E-Mail: sklemer@nebhe.org
Founded 1955
Library Holdings: Bk Titles 2,200; Per Subs 80
Subject Interests: Education
Publications: Connection; Facts: The Directory of New England Colleges & Universities; New England's Journal of Higher Education & Economic Development
Partic in Dialog Corporation

CM NEW ENGLAND COLLEGE OF OPTOMETRY LIBRARY, 424 Beacon St, 02115. SAN 307-2185. Tel: 617-236-6263. FAX: 617-236-6293. E-Mail: library@ne-optometry.edu. Web Site: www.ne-optometry.edu/library. *Dir Libr Serv*, Lucinda Hutchison; Tel: 617-369-0187, E-Mail: hutchisonc@ne-optometry.edu; *Syst Coordr*, Gregory Sakal; Tel: 617-236-6265, E-Mail: sakalg@ne-optometry.edu; Staff 6 (MLS 2, Non-MLS 4)
Founded 1894. Enrl 500; Fac 120; Highest Degree: Doctorate
Jul 2000-Jun 2001 Income (Main Library Only) $210,749. Mats Exp $115,000, Books $45,000, Per/Ser (Incl. Access Fees) $50,000, Electronic Ref Mat (Incl. Access Fees) $20,000
Library Holdings: Bk Vols 12,553; Bk Titles 4,936; Per Subs 233
Subject Interests: Ophthalmology, Optometry
Special Collections: History of Optometry
Automation Activity & Vendor Info: (Acquisitions) SIRSI; (Cataloging) SIRSI; (Circulation) SIRSI; (Course Reserve) SIRSI; (OPAC) SIRSI; (Serials) SIRSI
Database Vendor: OCLC - First Search, OVID Technologies
Partic in Asn Vision Sci Librns; BHSL; Boston Biomedical Library Consortium; Boston Regional Libr Syst; LVIS; Nelinet, Inc

S NEW ENGLAND CONSERVATORY OF MUSIC, Harriet M Spaulding Library, 33 Gainsborough St, 02115. SAN 344-712X. Tel: 617-585-1250. FAX: 617-585-1245. Web Site: www.newenglandconservatory.edu. *Head of Libr*, Jean Morrow; Tel: 617-585-1247, E-Mail: jmorrow@newenglandconservatory.edu; *Publ Servs*, Richard Vallone; Tel: 617-585-1251, E-Mail: rvallone@newenglandconservatory.edu; *Tech Servs*, Patrick Maxfield; Tel: 617-585-1256, E-Mail: pmaxfield@newenglandconservatory.edu; *Cat*, Craig Thomas; Tel: 617-585-1253, E-Mail: cthomas@newenglandconservatory.edu; *ILL*, Mary Jane Loizou; Tel: 617-585-1248, E-Mail: mjloizou@newenglandconservatory.edu; Staff 9 (MLS 5, Non-MLS 4)
Founded 1867. Enrl 750; Fac 162; Highest Degree: Doctorate
Jul 1999-Jun 2000 Income (Main Library Only) $536,219. Mats Exp $76,884, Books $49,562, Per/Ser (Incl. Access Fees) $10,622, Presv $12,400, Micro $300, Electronic Ref Mat (Incl. Access Fees) $4,000. Sal $348,598 (Prof $157,000)
Library Holdings: Bk Vols 116,912; Per Subs 255
Special Collections: Firestone Hour Coll Music, rec, v-tapes; New England Composers, mss; Preston Coll of Musicians' Letters; Vaughn Monroe Coll of Camel Caravan, scores
Database Vendor: DRA
Publications: Acquisitions
Partic in Boston Area Music Libraries; Fenway Libraries Online; Fenway Library Consortium; Metro Boston Libr Network; Nelinet, Inc; OCLC Online Computer Library Center, Inc
Branches:
IDABELLE FIRESTONE AUDIO LIBRARY, 290 Huntington Ave, 02115. SAN 344-7154. Tel: 617-585-1255. FAX: 617-585-1245.
Special Collections: Early Jazz Recordings; New England Conservatory Concerts
Partic in Fenway Libraries Online

S NEW ENGLAND FINANCIAL, Corporate Library,* Information Research Ctr, 501 Boylston St, 02116. SAN 307-2215. Tel: 617-578-3836. Interlibrary Loan Service Tel: 617-578-3836. FAX: 617-578-5523. *Mgr*, Pamela Gollis; *Archivist*, Phyllis Steele; Staff 5 (MLS 3, Non-MLS 2)
Founded 1955
Library Holdings: Bk Vols 2,000; Per Subs 200
Subject Interests: Finance
Special Collections: Archives
Database Vendor: OCLC - First Search
Publications: Abstracts from Selected Readings; Selected Readings; The Monitor (newsletter of competitive info)

S NEW ENGLAND HISTORIC GENEALOGICAL SOCIETY LIBRARY, 101 Newbury St, 02116. SAN 307-2193. Tel: 617-536-5740. Circulation Tel: 888-906-3447. FAX: 617-536-7307. E-Mail: nehgs@nehgs.org. Web Site: www.newenglandancestors.org. *Dir Libr Serv*, Chad Leinaweaver; Tel: 617-536-5740, Ext 231, E-Mail: cleinaweaver@nehgs.org; *Dir, Tech Serv*, Lynne Burke; Tel: 617-536-5740, Ext 225, E-Mail: lburke@nehgs.org; *Ref*, Jerome E Anderson; Tel: 617-536-5740, Ext 235, E-Mail: jeanderson@nehgs.org; *Ref*, David Curtis Dearborn; Tel: 617-536-5740, Ext 234, E-Mail: dcdearborn@nehgs.org; *Ref*, Marshall Kirk; E-Mail: marshallk@nehgs.org; *Ref*, David Allen Lambert; Tel: 617-536-5740, Ext 239, E-Mail: dalambert@nehgs.org; *Ref*, Michael J Leclerc; Tel: 617-536-5740, Ext 223, E-Mail: mleclerc@nehgs.org; *Ref*, George Sanborn; Tel: 617-536-5740, Ext 273, E-Mail: gsanborn@nehgs.org; *Ref*, Ruth Wellner; Tel: 617-536-5740, Ext 233, E-Mail: rwellner@nehgs.org; *Ser*, Jean Maguire; Tel: 617-536-5740, Ext 229, E-Mail: jmaguire@nehgs.com; *Acq*, Debra MacEachern; Tel: 617-536-5740, Ext 224, E-Mail: debram@nehgs.org; *Spec Coll & Archives*, Timothy Salls; Tel: 617-536-5740, Ext 232, E-Mail: tsalls@nehgs.org; *Circ*, Alex Woodle; Tel: 888-906-3447, Fax: 617-624-0325, E-Mail: awoodle@nehgs.org; *Acq*, Virginia Yowell; Tel: 617-536-5740, Ext 224; Staff 25 (MLS 5, Non-MLS 20)
Founded 1845
Library Holdings: Bk Titles 175,000; Per Subs 550
Subject Interests: Genealogy
Special Collections: Manuscripts of family histories, town & church records, diaries, heraldry, census records, probate records & deeds of New England states; Microtext Coll, Census Records, Probate Records & Deeds of New England States
Automation Activity & Vendor Info: (Acquisitions) Sydney; (Cataloging) Sydney; (Circulation) Sydney; (OPAC) Sydney; (Serials) Sydney
Database Vendor: OCLC - First Search
Publications: Monographs in Genealogy & Local History; New England Historical & Genealogical Register; NEXUS (5 times yr newsletter)
Partic in Boston Regional Libr Syst; Nelinet, Inc
Seminars, conferences, tours & course instruction in various aspects of genealogy
Friends of the Library Group

CL NEW ENGLAND SCHOOL OF LAW LIBRARY, 154 Stuart St, 02116-5687. SAN 307-2231. Tel: 617-422-7282. Interlibrary Loan Service Tel: 617-422-7418. Circulation Tel: 617-422-7288. Reference Tel: 617-422-7299. FAX: 617-422-7303. Web Site: www.nesl.edu. *Dir*, Frank S Bae; *Assoc Librn*, Anne M Acton; *Reader Servs*, Susan Tatelman; *Tech Servs*, Kyle Kelly; *Govt Doc*, Edward Hart; *Cat*, Sarah Boling; *Access Serv, Ref Serv*, Kristin McCarthy; *Coll Develop*, Helen Litwack; *Ref Serv*, Barry Stearns; *Computer Services*, Sandra Lamar; Staff 11 (MLS 9, Non-MLS 2)
Founded 1917. Enrl 1,100; Fac 76; Highest Degree: Doctorate
Jul 1999-Jun 2000 Income $2,009,287. Mats Exp $965,000, Books $130,000, Per/Ser (Incl. Access Fees) $751,000, Presv $15,000, Micro $62,000, Other Print Mats $7,000. Sal $802,657 (Prof $507,987)
Library Holdings: Bk Vols 300,000; Bk Titles 45,000; Per Subs 3,100
Special Collections: Standard American Law Library Coll, bks, micro, AV & on line resources
Automation Activity & Vendor Info: (Acquisitions) Innovative Interfaces Inc.; (Cataloging) Innovative Interfaces Inc.; (Circulation) Innovative Interfaces Inc.; (Serials) Innovative Interfaces Inc.
Publications: Library guide; Library newsletter; selected list of recent

acquisitions
Partic in Nelinet, Inc; Nellco; Westlaw
Special Services for the Deaf - TTY machine

S NICHOLS HOUSE MUSEUM INC LIBRARY,* 55 Mount Vernon, 02108. SAN 377-516X. Tel: 617-227-6993. *Curator*, William Pear; *Dir*, Flavia Cigliano
Library Holdings: Bk Vols 1,000
Restriction: By appointment only
Open Feb-Apr & Nov-Dec Thurs-Sat 12-4:15, May-Oct Tues-Sat 12-4:15

L NIXON PEABODY LLP, Law Library, 101 Federal St, 02110-1832. SAN 372-0721. Tel: 617-345-1000. FAX: 617-345-1300. *Ref*, Amy Bruce
Library Holdings: Bk Vols 8,500; Per Subs 150
Partic in Asn of Boston Law Librns

NORTHEASTERN UNIVERSITY LIBRARIES

C BURLINGTON CAMPUS LIBRARY, 145 S Bedford St, Burlington, 01803. Tel: 781-238-8410. Interlibrary Loan Service Tel: 781-238-8406. FAX: 781-238-8408. Web Site: www.lib.neu.edu. *Head Librn*, Donna Kennedy; Tel: 781-238-8409, E-Mail: d.kennedy@nunet.neu.edu; *Coll Develop*, Kristin Abbott; Tel: 781-238-8407, E-Mail: k.abbott@nunet.neu.edu; Staff 3 (MLS 3)
Founded 1964
Library Holdings: Bk Vols 70,000; Per Subs 95
Subject Interests: Business, Computer eng, Electrical engineering
Automation Activity & Vendor Info: (Cataloging) CARL; (Circulation) CARL; (Course Reserve) CARL; (OPAC) CARL
Database Vendor: CARL, IAC - SearchBank, OCLC - First Search, OVID Technologies, Silverplatter Information Inc.
Function: ILL available
Partic in Boston Library Consortium; OCLC Online Computer Library Center, Inc

S MARINE SCIENCE, East Point, Nahant, 01908. SAN 344-7383. Tel: 781-581-7370. FAX: 781-581-6076.

CL SCHOOL OF LAW LIBRARY, 400 Huntington Ave, 02115. SAN 344-7367. Tel: 617-373-3222, 617-373-3552. Circulation Tel: 617-373-3332. Reference Tel: 617-373-3594. FAX: 617-373-8705. Web Site: www.slaw.neu.edu/library. *Dir*, Filippa Marullo Anzalone; Tel: 617-373-3994, E-Mail: f.anzalone@nunet.neu.edu; *Assoc Dir*, Kim Dulin; Tel: 617-373-3480, E-Mail: k.dulin@nunet.neu.edu; *Head Tech Servs*, Susan More; Tel: 617-373-3691, E-Mail: s.more@nunet.neu.edu; *Tech Servs*, Rachel Bates; Tel: 617-373-3553; *Tech Servs*, Matthew Kennedy; Tel: 617-373-3622; *ILL*, Stephanie Hudner; Tel: 617-373-3350; *Ref*, Joy Plunket; *Reader Servs*, John Fernald; *Cat*, Damaris Chapin; Tel: 617-373-3716, E-Mail: d.chapin@nunet.neu.edu; *Head, Info Serv*, Diane Murley; Tel: 617-373-3589, E-Mail: d.murley@nunet.neu.edu; *Ref*, Michelle Pearse; Tel: 617-373-3883, E-Mail: m.pearse@nunet.neu.edu; *Circ*, Dennis Turner; Tel: 617-373-3332; *Admin Assoc*, Janice Giordano; Tel: 617-373-3552; Staff 14 (MLS 7, Non-MLS 7)
Founded 1898. Enrl 600; Fac 30; Highest Degree: Doctorate
Library Holdings: Bk Vols 397,000
Special Collections: Abolition of Death & Capital Punishment (Sara R Ehrmann Coll); Pappas Public Interest Law Coll
Database Vendor: CARL, IAC - Info Trac, Lexis-Nexis, OCLC - First Search
Function: Research library
Partic in Boston Library Consortium; New England Law Library Consortium, Inc

C SNELL LIBRARY, 360 Huntington Ave, 02115. SAN 344-7243. Tel: 617-373-2350. Interlibrary Loan Service Tel: 617-373-3198. Circulation Tel: 617-373-8778. Reference Tel: 617-373-2356. TDD: 617-373-3995. Interlibrary Loan Service FAX: 617-373-8681. Web Site: www.library.neu.edu. *Actg Dean*, Filippa M Anzalone; *Assoc Dean, Tech Servs*, Carol E Chamberlain; *Assoc Dean, Head, Circ*, Lesley Milner; *Adminr*, Elizabeth C Habich; Tel: 617-373-4924, E-Mail: e.habich@neu.edu; *Branch Mgr*, Donna Kennedy; *Head, Cat*, Mary Menke; *Head, Acq*, Janet B Belanger; *Media Spec*, Debra Mandel; *Head, Info Serv*, James Dendy; *Doc*, Roxanne B Palmatier; *Syst Coordr*, Rosemary Krol; *Archivist*, Joan Krizack; *Bibliog Instr*, Christine K Oka; *Coll Develop*, Willilam M Wakeling; *AV*, Nancy Frank; Staff 90 (MLS 42, Non-MLS 48)
Founded 1898. Pop 30,079; Enrl 25,940; Fac 743; Highest Degree: Doctorate
Jul 1999-Jun 2000 Income Parent Institution $8,300,000. Mats Exp $3,715,024, Books $728,439, Per/Ser (Incl. Access Fees) $2,480,655, Micro $135,434, Electronic Ref Mat (Incl. Access Fees) $333,571. Sal $3,590,000 (Prof $2,100,000)
Library Holdings: Bk Vols 915,342; Per Subs 8,010
Subject Interests: Allied health, Computer science, Criminal law and justice, Economics, Education, Engineering, Humanities, Technology
Special Collections: Freedom House, Inc Records; Glenn Gray Casa Loma Orchestra Swing Era, original scores & rec; Irish History, 1845-48 Famine, bks & doc; Julius Schweinfurth Papers; Michael S Dukakis US Presidential Campaign Media Coll; Muriel & Otto Snowden Papers; Sara Ehrmann Coll on Capital Punishment; Thomas Hardy Insurance Industry Coll; University Archives, fac papers & publications; YMCA of Greater Boston Records
Automation Activity & Vendor Info: (Acquisitions) CARL; (Cataloging) CARL; (Circulation) CARL; (Course Reserve) CARL; (OPAC) CARL; (Serials) CARL
Restriction: Public use on premises
Partic in Boston Library Consortium; Boston Regional Libr Syst; Nelinet, Inc; OCLC Online Computer Library Center, Inc
Special Services for the Deaf - TTY machine; Videos & decoder
Special Services for the Blind - Talking book center
Special Services for Users with Disabilities - Height adjustable carrels, staff assistance

L NUTTER, MCCLENNEN & FISH, Law Library,* One International Pl, 02110-2699. SAN 307-2266. Tel: 617-439-2483, 617-439-2492. FAX: 617-973-9748. *Librn*, Gina Lynch; *Ref*, Joanne Blinn
Library Holdings: Per Subs 200
Subject Interests: Corporate law, Labor, Planning
Partic in Am Asn New England; Asn of Boston Law Librns; Law Librs New England; Soc Law Librs

L PALMER & DODGE, Law Library, One Beacon St, 02108. SAN 372-0632. Tel: 617-573-0254. FAX: 617-227-4420. *Dir Libr Serv*, Sharen C Leonard; E-Mail: sleonard@palmerdodge.com; *Asst Libr Dir*, Andrea Rasmussen; *Ref*, Wilfred Lawrence Pollender; Staff 6 (MLS 3, Non-MLS 3)
Library Holdings: Bk Vols 30,000; Per Subs 425
Partic in Mass Libr & Info Network

S PAYETTE ASSOCIATES, David J Rowan Library, 285 Summer St, 02210. SAN 327-3458. Tel: 617-895-1000. FAX: 617-895-1002. Web Site: www.payette.com. *Dir*, Nora B Zaldivar; E-Mail: nzaldivar@payette.com; *Ref*, Eric Crockwell
Founded 1979
Library Holdings: Bk Titles 4,000; Per Subs 75
Subject Interests: Architecture
Special Collections: Healthcare
Restriction: Not open to public
Partic in Dialog Corporation

L PEABODY & ARNOLD LLP, Law Library, 50 Rowes Wharf, 02110-3342. SAN 372-0713. Tel: 617-261-5051. FAX: 617-951-2125. *Mgr Libr Serv*, Carol S Wellington; Staff 1 (Non-MLS 1)
Library Holdings: Bk Vols 12,000

S PRICEWATERHOUSECOOPERS LIBRARY, 160 Federal St, 02110. SAN 307-2282. Tel: 617-439-7412. FAX: 617-748-0158. *Dir*, Jean M Scanlan; E-Mail: scanlan@us.pwcglobal.com; Staff 2 (MLS 1, Non-MLS 1)
Founded 1976
Library Holdings: Bk Titles 300; Per Subs 40

S PUTNAM INVESTMENTS LIBRARY,* One Post Office Sq, MS 11, 02109. SAN 307-1944. Tel: 617-292-1335. FAX: 617-292-8545. *Dir*, Ellen Callahan; Staff 7 (MLS 3, Non-MLS 4)
Founded 1970
Library Holdings: Per Subs 300
Subject Interests: Business and management, Economics, Finance
Publications: Putnam's Periodicals (annual)
Restriction: Staff use only

L RACKEMANN, SAWYER & BREWSTER LIBRARY,* One Financial Ctr, 02111-2659. SAN 323-7478. Tel: 617-542-2300. FAX: 617-542-7437. *Librn*, Lynne Serio; Staff 3 (MLS 2, Non-MLS 1)
Library Holdings: Bk Vols 12,000; Per Subs 400
Subject Interests: Real estate
Special Collections: Zoning

S RITTNERS SCHOOL OF FLORAL DESIGN LIBRARY, 345 Marlborough St, 02115. SAN 328-2198. Tel: 617-267-3824. FAX: 617-267-3824. Web Site: www.floralschool.com. *Librn*, Stephen Rittner; E-Mail: stevrt@tiac.net
Library Holdings: Bk Vols 3,000; Per Subs 350

S ROPES & GRAY LIBRARY, One International Pl, 02110-2624. SAN 329-0468. Tel: 617-951-7855. FAX: 617-951-7050. *Librn*, Cornelia Trubey; *Publ Servs*, Kimberly Sweet; Staff 8 (MLS 3, Non-MLS 5)
Library Holdings: Bk Vols 40,000; Bk Titles 10,000; Per Subs 300
Subject Interests: Law
Automation Activity & Vendor Info: (Acquisitions) Innovative Interfaces Inc.; (OPAC) Innovative Interfaces Inc.; (Serials) Innovative Interfaces Inc.
Restriction: Staff use only

J ROXBURY COMMUNITY COLLEGE LIBRARY,* 1234 Columbus Ave, 02120-3400. SAN 307-6466. Tel: 617-541-5323. FAX: 617-541-0339. Web Site: www.rcc.mass.edu/. *Dir*, Timothy DiPace; Staff 10 (MLS 5, Non-MLS 5)
Founded 1973. Enrl 1,000
Library Holdings: Bk Vols 26,264; Bk Titles 23,827; Per Subs 135
Partic in Dialog Corporation; Mass Libr Asn; Nelinet, Inc; New England Libr Info Network; OCLC Online Computer Library Center, Inc

M ST ELIZABETH'S MEDICAL CENTER, Stahlman Library, 736 Cambridge St, 02135. Tel: 617-789-2177. FAX: 617-789-5081. *Librn*, Catherine Guarcello; E-Mail: cguarcel@semc.org; *ILL*, Marybeth Edwards
Library Holdings: Bk Titles 1,800; Per Subs 220

Partic in Boston Biomedical Library Consortium; Boston Regional Network; Massachusetts Health Sciences Libraries Network; National Network Of Libraries Of Medicine New England Region; North Atlantic Health Sciences Libraries, Inc

S SCUDDER KEMPER INVESTMENTS LIBRARY,* 2 International Pl, 02110. SAN 307-2290. Tel: 617-295-2282. FAX: 617-443-7063.; Staff 1 (MLS 1)
Founded 1927
Library Holdings: Per Subs 400
Subject Interests: Investing
Restriction: Staff use only
Partic in Spec Libr Asn
Open Mon-Fri 8:30-5:15

C SIMMONS COLLEGE, Beatley Library, 300 The Fenway, 02115. SAN 307-2312. Tel: 617-521-2741. Circulation Tel: 617-521-2786. Reference Tel: 617-521-2784. Web Site: www.simmons.edu/resources/libraries/. *Actg Dir*, Daphne Harrington; E-Mail: daphne.harrington@simmons.edu; *Acq*, Terri-Leigh Hinkle; E-Mail: hinkle@simmons.edu; *Archivist*, Claire Goodwin; E-Mail: claire.goodwin@simmons.edu; *Coll Develop*, Ilze Olmsted; E-Mail: olmsted@simmons.edu; *Tech Servs*, Judy Narosny; E-Mail: narosny@simmons.edu; *Online Servs, Reader Servs*, Daphne Harrington; E-Mail: harrington@simmons.edu; *Electronic Resources*, Megan Fox; E-Mail: fox@simmons.edu; *Publ Servs*, Patty Durisin; E-Mail: durisin@simmons.edu; Staff 25 (MLS 13, Non-MLS 12)
Founded 1899. Enrl 2,659; Fac 199; Highest Degree: Doctorate
Jul 2000-Jun 2001 Income (Main and Other College/University Libraries) $2,378,554. Mats Exp $897,115, Books $242,140, Per/Ser (Incl. Access Fees) $449,774, Presv $17,000, Micro $38,500, Electronic Ref Mat (Incl. Access Fees) $149,701. Sal $923,594
Library Holdings: Bk Vols 285,698; Bk Titles 188,752; Per Subs 1,861
Subject Interests: Library and information science, Social service (social work), Women's studies
Special Collections: Career Resource Materials; Children's Literature (Knapp Coll); Simmons College Archives
Automation Activity & Vendor Info: (Acquisitions) Innovative Interfaces Inc.; (Cataloging) Innovative Interfaces Inc.; (Circulation) Innovative Interfaces Inc.; (Course Reserve) Innovative Interfaces Inc.; (ILL) Innovative Interfaces Inc.; (OPAC) Innovative Interfaces Inc.; (Serials) Innovative Interfaces Inc.
Database Vendor: Ebsco - EbscoHost, IAC - Info Trac, Innovative Interfaces INN - View, Lexis-Nexis, OCLC - First Search, ProQuest, Silverplatter Information Inc., Wilson - Wilson Web
Partic in Dialog Corporation; Fenway Library Consortium; Nelinet, Inc; OCLC Online Computer Library Center, Inc
Departmental Libraries:
CAREER RESOURCE LIBRARY, 300 The Fenway W-110, 02115. Tel: 617-521-2510. *Librn*, Laura Lidano; Fax: 617-521-3093, E-Mail: lidano@simmons.edu; Staff 2 (MLS 1, Non-MLS 1)
GRADUATE SCHOOL OF MANAGEMENT LIBRARY, 409 Commonwealth Ave, 02115. SAN 326-7784. Tel: 617-521-3851. FAX: 617-521-3885. *Librn*, Denise Davis; E-Mail: denise.davis@simmons.edu; Staff 2 (MLS 2)
LIBRARY & INFORMATION SCIENCE, 300 The Fenway, 02115. Tel: 617-521-2824. *Librn*, Linda Watkins; E-Mail: watkins@simmons.edu; Staff 2 (MLS 1, Non-MLS 1)
SCHOOL OF SOCIAL WORK LIBRARY, 51 Commonwealth Ave, 02116. SAN 326-7822. Tel: 617-521-3905. FAX: 617-521-3981. *Librn*, Gianna Gifford; E-Mail: gifford@simmons.edu; Staff 3 (MLS 1, Non-MLS 2)

L SOCIAL LAW LIBRARY,* 1200 Court House, 02108. SAN 307-2320. Tel: 617-523-0018. FAX: 617-523-2458. *Exec Dir*, Robert J Brink; *Asst Librn*, Brian J Harkins; *Coll Develop*, Elaine Roselli
Founded 1803
Library Holdings: Bk Vols 305,000; Bk Titles 60,000; Per Subs 967
Special Collections: Anglo-American Law
Publications: Legal Video Review; New Acquisitions; Proprietor's Reporter
Partic in New England Law Library Consortium, Inc

S SOCIETY FOR THE PRESERVATION OF NEW ENGLAND ANTIQUITIES LIBRARY & ARCHIVES, 141 Cambridge St, 02114. SAN 307-1928. Tel: 617-227-3956. FAX: 617-973-9050. *Dir*, Lorna Condon; Tel: 617-227-3957, Ext 225, E-Mail: lcondon@spnea.org; *Archivist*, Rebecca Aaronson; Tel: 617-227-3957, Ext 226, E-Mail: raaronson@spnea.org. Subject Specialists: *Archives*, Rebecca Aaronson; *Ref*, Rebecca Aaronson; Staff 5 (MLS 2, Non-MLS 3)
Founded 1910
Library Holdings: Bk Titles 10,000
Subject Interests: Architecture, Decorative arts, History, Photography
Special Collections: 19th & 20th Centuries Collection including Asher Benjamin,Luther Briggs, Frank Chouteau Brown, Hernert Browne, George Clough, Ogden Codman Jr., Robert AllenCook, Arland Dirlam, Halfdan Hanson, Arthur Little, J Luippold & Richard Upjohn; Architectural Drawings, 19th & 20th centuries including Asher Benjamin, Luther Briggs, Frank Chouteau Brown, Herbert Browne, George Clough, Ogden Codman Jr, Robert Allen Cook, Arland Dirlam, Halfdan Hanson, Arthur Little, J Luippold & Richard Upjohn; Builders Guides & Account Books, 19th & 20th Centuries; Edwin Whitefield Coll, sketch bks; Family Papers (Casey Family, Codman Family, Jewett Family, Harrison Gray Otis Business); Historic American Buildings Survey, Mass; Manuscript Coll, Casey Family Papers, Codman Family Papers, Jewett Family Papers, Harrison Gray Otis Business Papers; Photographic Coll including Emma Coleman, Baldwin Coolidge, Alfred Cutting, Boston & Albany Railroad Coll, Boston Elevated Railroad Co & Boston Transit Commission Coll, Halliday Historic Photograph Coll, Wallace Nutting, Henry Peabody, Fred Quimby, N L Stebbins, Yankee Magazine
Publications: indices & inventories of holdings (Archives guide); indices & inventories of holdings
Restriction: By appointment only
Function: Archival collection
Partic in Nelinet, Inc
Friends of the Library Group

M SPAULDING REHABILITATION HOSPITAL, Medical Library, 125 Nashua St, 02114. Tel: 617-573-2415. FAX: 617-573-2419. Web Site: www.spaulding rehabilita.org/home/splash. *Asst Librn*, Terry O'Brien; Tel: 617-573-2415, Fax: 617-573-2419, E-Mail: tmobrien@partners.org
Library Holdings: Bk Vols 1,300; Bk Titles 1,700; Per Subs 105

S STATE LIBRARY OF MASSACHUSETTS, 341 State House, 02133-1099. SAN 307-2339. Tel: 617-727-2590. FAX: 617-727-5819. Web Site: www.state.ma.us/lib. *State Librn*, Stephen A Fulchino; Tel: 617-727-2592, E-Mail: stephen.fulchino@state.ma.us; *Assoc Dir*, Spencer Clough; Tel: 617-727-2403, E-Mail: spencer.clough@state.ma.us; *Ser*, Anne Meringolo; Tel: 617-727-6279, E-Mail: anne.meringolo@state.ma.us; *ILL*, Tina Vegelante; E-Mail: tina.vegelante@state.ma.us; *Cat*, Judith Carlstrom; Tel: 617-727-7456, E-Mail: judith.carlstrom@state.ma.us; *Govt Doc*, Bette Siegel; Tel: 617-727-6279, E-Mail: bette.siegel@state.ma.us; *Tech Servs*, Susan Edmonds; Tel: 617-727-7456, E-Mail: susan.edmonds@state.ma.us; *Tech Servs*, Kathleen McNamara; Tel: 617-727-7456, E-Mail: kathaleen.mcnamara@state.ma.us; *Spec Coll*, Mary Bicknell; Tel: 617-727-2595, E-Mail: mary.bicknell@state.ma.us; *Res*, Eva Murphy; Tel: 617-727-2403, E-Mail: eva.murphy@state.ma.us; *Res*, Pamela Schofield; Tel: 617-727-2403, E-Mail: pamela.schofield@state.ma.us; Staff 21 (MLS 15, Non-MLS 6)
Founded 1826
Jul 1999-Jun 2000 Income State $1,328,976. Mats Exp $317,566. Sal $775,462
Library Holdings: Bk Vols 825,000; Per Subs 1,845
Subject Interests: Law, Legis hist, Political science, Public admin
Special Collections: Americana, early Massachusetts imprints; Massachusetts History & Biography, atlases, city directories, mss, maps; Massachusetts Legislators' Private Papers; Massachusetts State House Coll, docs, photogs & prints; New England History; Revolutionary War Broadsides
Automation Activity & Vendor Info: (Cataloging) Innovative Interfaces Inc.; (Circulation) Innovative Interfaces Inc.; (OPAC) Innovative Interfaces Inc.; (Serials) Innovative Interfaces Inc.
Database Vendor: Innovative Interfaces INN - View
Publications: Annual Checklist of State Publications; Quarterly Checklist of State Publications
Restriction: Lending to staff only
Function: Research library
Mem of Boston Regional Libr Syst
Partic in Boston Library Consortium; CW Mars; Nelinet, Inc
Special Services for the Deaf - TTY machine

S STATE STREET CONSULTANTS, INC, Information Center Library, 31 Milk St, 02109. SAN 326-2197. Tel: 617-482-1234, Ext 240. FAX: 617-482-2060. *Librn*, Maria Moyer
Founded 1970
Library Holdings: Bk Titles 600; Per Subs 80
Restriction: Staff use only

S STATE TRANSPORTATION LIBRARY,* 10 Park Plaza, 02116. SAN 321-9720. Tel: 617-973-8000. FAX: 617-973-7153. Web Site: www.stlibrary.org. *Dir*, Lynn Matis; *Ref*, George Sanborn; *Tech Servs*, Sandra Wong. Subject Specialists: *Law*, Lynn Matis; Staff 4 (MLS 3, Non-MLS 1)
Founded 1983
Library Holdings: Bk Vols 20,000; Per Subs 200
Subject Interests: Transportation, Urban planning
Special Collections: Boston Transportation Planning Review Archives, files, publications, MBTA History; Massachusetts Highway History
Publications: Computer-Assisted Research Services, brochure; List of selected Acquisitions; Transportation Library, brochure
Restriction: Non-circulating to the public
Partic in Dialog Corporation; OCLC Online Computer Library Center, Inc

S STONE & WEBSTER ENGINEERING CORPORATION, Technical Information Center,* 245 Summer St, 02210. SAN 307-2355. Tel: 617-589-6994. FAX: 617-589-2223. E-Mail: library@stoneweb.com. *Acq*, M O'Hara
Founded 1900
Library Holdings: Bk Vols 20,000; Per Subs 100
Subject Interests: Chemistry, Civil engineering, Computer science, Construction, Electrical engineering, Marketing, Mechanical engineering,

Nuclear engineering, Technology
Publications: Guide to the Technical Information Center; List of Stone & Webster Serial & Journal Holdings

C SUFFOLK UNIVERSITY, Mildred F Sawyer Library, 8 Ashburton Pl, 02108-2770. SAN 344-7391. Tel: 617-573-8535. Interlibrary Loan Service Tel: 617-573-8427. Reference Tel: 617-573-8532. FAX: 617-573-8756. E-Mail: sawlib@acad.suffolk.edu. Web Site: www.suffolk.edu/admin/sawlib/sawyer.htm. *Dir*, Robert E Dugan; E-Mail: rdugan@acad.suffolk.edu; *Asst Dir*, Becky Fulweiler; *Asst Dir*, Kathleen Maio; *Ref*, Sonia Didriksson; *Ref*, Kristin Djorup; *Ref*, Connie Sellers; *Archivist*, Robert Allison; *Circ*, Catherine Boyle; Staff 6 (MLS 6)
Founded 1937. Enrl 3,750; Highest Degree: Doctorate
Jul 2000-Jun 2001 Income $1,107,000, Locally Generated Income $7,000, Parent Institution $1,100,000. Mats Exp $428,000, Books $58,000, Per/Ser (Incl. Access Fees) $227,000, Electronic Ref Mat (Incl. Access Fees) $143,000. Sal $600,000 (Prof $350,000)
Library Holdings: Bk Vols 112,000; Per Subs 990
Special Collections: Afro-American Literature Coll
Database Vendor: Innovative Interfaces INN - View
Publications: Help & Research Guide
Partic in Fenway Library Consortium; Nelinet, Inc; PALINET & Union Library Catalogue of Pennsylvania
Departmental Libraries:

CL LAW LIBRARY, 120 Tremont St, 02108-4977. SAN 344-7421. Tel: 617-573-8177. Interlibrary Loan Service Tel: 617-305-1615. FAX: 617-723-3164. Web Site: www.law.suffolk.edu/library. *Dir*, Elizabeth McKenzie; *Tech Servs*, David M Turkalo; *Publ Servs*, Susan Sweetgall; Staff 25 (MLS 11, Non-MLS 14)
Enrl 1,760; Fac 60; Highest Degree: Doctorate
1999-2000 Income $1,407,650. Mats Exp $927,000
Library Holdings: Bk Vols 319,239; Bk Titles 69,221; Per Subs 5,931
Database Vendor: Innovative Interfaces INN - View
Publications: Browsing The Library; Faculty Research Materials; Law Library Research Series
Partic in Dialog Corporation; Nelinet, Inc; New England Law Library Consortium, Inc; OCLC Online Computer Library Center, Inc; Westlaw

L SULLIVAN & WORCESTER, Law Library, One Post Office Sq, 02109. SAN 372-0675. Tel: 617-338-2888. FAX: 617-338-2880. *Dir Libr Serv*, W Leslie Peat; E-Mail: peat@sandw.com; *Ref*, Sarah J Slater; *Tech Servs*, Lucinda Valero; Staff 3 (MLS 2, Non-MLS 1)
Library Holdings: Bk Vols 25,000; Per Subs 100
Subject Interests: Corp law
Automation Activity & Vendor Info: (Cataloging) Inmagic, Inc.; (Circulation) Inmagic, Inc.; (OPAC) Inmagic, Inc.; (Serials) Inmagic, Inc.
Publications: Brochures; newsletter

R TEMPLE ISRAEL LIBRARY,* Longwood Ave & Plymouth St, 02215. SAN 307-2371. Tel: 617-566-3960, 617-566-4202. FAX: 617-731-3711. *Librn*, Ann Abrams
Library Holdings: Bk Titles 10,000; Per Subs 12
Subject Interests: Judaica (lit or hist of Jews)
Friends of the Library Group

L TESTA, HURWITZ & THIBEAULT, Law Library,* High Street Tower, 125 High St, 02110. SAN 372-0683. Tel: 617-248-7000. FAX: 617-248-7100. E-Mail: bitman@tht.com. Web Site: www.tht.com. *Dir Libr Serv*, Leslie Bitman; *Ref*, Lucy Richards; Tel: 617-248-7472; *Asst Librn*, Lorraine Jewkes; Tel: 617-248-7537
Library Holdings: Bk Vols 10,000; Per Subs 425

C THE BOSTON CONSERVATORY, Albert Alphin Music Library, 8 The Fenway, 02215-4099. SAN 307-1359. Tel: 617-536-6340. FAX: 617-536-3176. Web Site: www.bostonconservatory.edu. *Dir*, Reginald A Didham; E-Mail: rdidham@bostonconservatory.edu; *Asst Librn*, Anne Diament; Tel: 617-912-9131
Founded 1867. Highest Degree: Master
Library Holdings: Bk Vols 35,000; Per Subs 85
Subject Interests: Dance, Drama, Music, Opera, Theater
Special Collections: Coll; James Pappoutsakis Memorial Coll; Jan Veen - Katrine Amory Hooper Memorial Art; Jan Veen - Katrine Amory Hooper Memorial Dance Coll; Katherine Rossi Memorial Coll
Partic in OCLC Online Computer Library Center, Inc

SR THE FIRST CHURCH OF CHRIST, SCIENTIST, Mary Baker Eddy Library- Church Records Department, 8221 Huntington Ave, 02115-3187. SAN 326-3525. Tel: 617-450-3501. FAX: 617-450-3415. *Librn*, Shirley Whittle; Tel: 617-450-7116
Founded 1932
1998-1999 Mats Exp $700
Library Holdings: Bk Vols 6,000; Bk Titles 3,000
Special Collections: Church; Historical Bible Coll

CM TUFTS UNIVERSITY, Health Sciences Library,* 145 Harrison Ave, 02111-1843. SAN 307-238X. Tel: 617-636-2458 (Info Servs), 617-636-6705. FAX: 617-636-4039. E-Mail: hsl@tufts.edu. Web Site: lwww.library.tufts.edu/. *Dir*, Dr Elizabeth K Eaton; Tel: 617-636-2481, E-Mail: eeaton@opal.tufts.edu; *Dep Dir*, Cora C Ho; Tel: 617-636-2481, E-Mail: cho-@opal.tufts.edu; *Mgr*, James Verrill; Tel: 617-636-2961, E-Mail: jverri01@emerald.tufts.edu; *Assoc Librn*, Elizabeth J Richardson; E-Mail: erichard@opal.tufts.edu; *Assoc Librn*, Howard Silver; E-Mail: hsilver@opal.tufts.edu; *Assoc Librn*, Amy Lapidow; E-Mail: alapidow@opal.tufts.edu; *Assoc Librn*, Eileen Moyer; Tel: 617-636-2466, E-Mail: emoyer01@emerald.tufts.edu; *Asst Librn*, Frances Burke-Foret; Tel: 617-636-0319, E-Mail: frances.foret@tufts.edu; *Asst Librn*, JoAnne Griffin; Tel: 617-636-2452, E-Mail: jgriffin@emerald.tufts.edu; *Assoc Librn*, Carolyn Waite; Tel: 617-636-2448, E-Mail: cwaite@emerald.tufts.edu; *Publ Servs*, Barbara Hefler; Tel: 617-636-2956, E-Mail: bhefler@opal.tufts.edu; *Mgr*, Susan R Albright; Tel: 617-636-6708, E-Mail: salbrigh@opal.tufts.edu; *Mgr*, Jan Mathews; *Coordr*, John Hanlin; Tel: 617-636-6706, E-Mail: jhanli01@emerald.tufts.edu; *Asst Librn*, Brynn Mays; E-Mail: bmays01@emerald.tufts.edu; *Asst Librn*, Anne Nou; E-Mail: anou@opal.tufts.edu; *Coordr*, Connie Wong; Tel: 617-636-3787, E-Mail: wwong01@emerald.tufts.edu; *Coordr*, Annie Yeung; Tel: 617-636-2424, E-Mail: ayeung@emerald.tufts.edu. Subject Specialists: *Health science*, Dr Elizabeth K Eaton; Staff 31 (MLS 18, Non-MLS 13)
Founded 1906. Pop 2,500; Enrl 1,500; Highest Degree: Doctorate
Jul 1998-Jun 1999 Income (Main Library Only) $2,348,380, Federal $94,224, Locally Generated Income $201,536, Parent Institution $2,052,620. Mats Exp $2,348,380, Books $68,716, Per/Ser (Incl. Access Fees) $588,508, Presv $17,027, Electronic Ref Mat (Incl. Access Fees) $78,372. Sal $1,051,138 (Prof $675,562)
Library Holdings: Bk Vols 154,288; Bk Titles 52,128; Per Subs 1,131
Subject Interests: Basic sciences, Dentistry, History of medicine, Medicine, Nutrition, Veterinary medicine
Automation Activity & Vendor Info: (Circulation) DRA; (OPAC) ComPanion Corp; (Serials) DRA
Database Vendor: CARL, DRA, IAC - Info Trac, OVID Technologies
Publications: Bibliographies; Brochures; Health Science Link (newsletter); Online Library Guide
Function: Document delivery services
Partic in Boston Library Consortium; Nelinet, Inc; OCLC Online Computer Library Center, Inc; UCMP
Friends of the Library Group

SR UNITARIAN UNIVERSALIST ASSOCIATION ARCHIVES, 25 Beacon St, 02108. SAN 326-1107. Tel: 617-742-2100, Ext 652. FAX: 617-367-3237. E-Mail: info@uua.org. Web Site: www.uua.org.
Founded 1832
Library Holdings: Bk Titles 150
Special Collections: Congregational file Historical & Current

R UNITED METHODIST CHURCH - NEW ENGLAND CONFERENCE, Commission on Archives & History, 745 Commonwealth Ave, 2nd flr, 02215. SAN 328-4921. Tel: 617-353-1323. FAX: 617-358-0699. E-Mail: nvdm@bu.edu. Web Site: www.bu.edu/sth/archives/cahhome.htm. *Dir Libr Serv*, Raymond Van de Moortell; Tel: 617-353-1321; *Archivist*, Stephen Pentek; E-Mail: spentek@bu.edu; *Spec Coll*, Emily Oswalt; E-Mail: eoswalt@bu.edu; *Tech Servs*, Brian Frykenburg; Tel: 617-353-1310, E-Mail: fryken@bu.edu; *Publ Servs*, William Carl Bergmann; Tel: 617-353-5357, E-Mail: bergmann@bu.edu. Subject Specialists: *Medieval studies*, Brian Frykenburg; *Methodism*, Stephen Pentek; *Preservation*, Emily Oswalt; *Theology*, Raymond Van de Moortell; *Theology*, William Carl Bergmann
Jan 1998-Dec 1999 Income $8,500. Mats Exp $5,200. Sal $4,000
Subject Interests: Methodism (religion), New England
Special Collections: Archival Records of the New England Conference
Restriction: Non-circulating to the public
Function: Research library
Partic in Boston Library Consortium; Boston Theological Institute Library Program

GL UNITED STATES COURT OF APPEALS, First Circuit Library,* US Courthouse, Ste 9400, One Courthouse Way, 02210. SAN 307-2401. Tel: 617-748-9044. FAX: 617-748-9358. *Librn*, Karen M Moss; E-Mail: karen_moss@ca1.us.courts.gov; Staff 7 (MLS 3, Non-MLS 4)
Library Holdings: Bk Titles 40,000; Per Subs 170
Subject Interests: Law
Special Collections: Government Documents Selective Depository
Publications: Library Handbook; Newsletter (bi-monthly)
Partic in Dialog Corporation; OCLC Online Computer Library Center, Inc; Westlaw

G US DEPARTMENT OF COMMERCE BUREAU OF THE CENSUS, Information Service Program-Boston Regional Office, 2 Copley Pl, Ste 301, PO Box 9108, 02117-9108. SAN 327-3490. Tel: 617-424-0510. FAX: 617-424-0547.
Library Holdings: Bk Vols 5,000; Per Subs 10

G UNITED STATES ENVIRONMENTAL PROTECTION AGENCY, Research Library for RCRA, One Congress St, EPA Region 1, SPP, 02114. SAN 372-6185. Tel: 617-918-1807. FAX: 617-918-1010. Web Site: www.epa.gov/region1/. *Head of Libr*, Fred Friedman; E-Mail: friedman.fred@epa.gov; Staff 2 (MLS 2)
Founded 1989
1998-1999 Income $120,000. Mats Exp $22,700, Books $2,000, Per/Ser (Incl. Access Fees) $600, Other Print Mats $100, Electronic Ref Mat (Incl. Access Fees) $20,000. Sal $120,000 (Prof $79,000)

Library Holdings: Bk Titles 400; Per Subs 100
Subject Interests: Ecology, Toxicology
Publications: Compendia of MSW Series; New Arrivals; Recycling on the Internet; Subject Headings
Restriction: By appointment only
Function: Reference only, Research library

G UNITED STATES INTERNAL REVENUE SERVICE, District Library, JFK Fed Bldg, 02203. (Mail add: PO Box 9112, 02203), SAN 371-8700. Tel: 617-316-2410. FAX: 617-316-2370. *Librn*, Patricia Hopkins Shoyinka; E-Mail: patricia.shoyinka@irs.gov; Staff 1 (MLS 1)
Founded 1987
Oct 1999-Sep 2000 Mats Exp $100,000
Library Holdings: Bk Vols 2,000; Per Subs 60
Special Collections: United States Tax Law, bks, docs, pers, vf
Database Vendor: Lexis-Nexis

C UNIVERSITY OF MASSACHUSETTS AT BOSTON, Joseph P Healey Library, 100 Morrissey Blvd, 02125-3393. SAN 344-7456. Tel: 617-287-5910. Interlibrary Loan Service Tel: 617-287-5929. Reference Tel: 617-287-5940. FAX: 617-287-5950. Web Site: www.lib.umb.edu. *Dir*, Sharon L Bostick; E-Mail: sharon@delphinus.lib.umb.edu; *Assoc Dir*, Daniel Ortiz; E-Mail: daniel.ortiz@umb.edu; *Head Ref*, Janet Stewart; E-Mail: janet@delphinus.lib.umb.edu; *Acq*, Rebecca Breedlove; E-Mail: rebecca@delphinus.lib.umb.edu; *Coll Develop*, Charles A Schwartz; E-Mail: charles.schwartz@umb.edu; *Instrul Serv*, Sara Baron; E-Mail: sara.baron@umb.edu; *Syst Coordr*, Apurva Mehta; E-Mail: apurva.mahta@umb.edu; *ILL*, Sylvana Clarke; Fax: 617-287-5955, E-Mail: sylvana@delphinus..ib.umb.edu; Staff 19 (MLS 17, Non-MLS 2)
Founded 1965. Enrl 12,923; Fac 456; Highest Degree: Doctorate
Jul 1999-Jun 2000 Income $3,613,386, State $3,263,925, Parent Institution $349,461. Mats Exp $1,330,701, Books $160,220, Per/Ser (Incl. Access Fees) $917,169, Presv $8,431, Micro $54,129, AV Equip $34,190, Other Print Mats $63,466, Electronic Ref Mat (Incl. Access Fees) $101,665. Sal $1,858,789 (Prof $1,126,287)
Library Holdings: Bk Vols 583,114; Per Subs 2,772
Database Vendor: Dialog, epixtech, inc., GaleNet, Lexis-Nexis, OCLC - First Search, Silverplatter Information Inc.
Publications: Healey News (Newsletter)
Function: Archival collection, Document delivery services, ILL available
Partic in Boston Library Consortium; Fenway Library Consortium

C WENTWORTH INSTITUTE OF TECHNOLOGY, Alumni Library, 550 Huntington Ave, 02115-5902. SAN 307-2460. Tel: 617-989-4040. FAX: 617-989-4091. Web Site: www.wit.edu/Library/index.html. *Dir*, Rosemary Walker; E-Mail: walkerr@wit.edu; *Asst Dir*, Walter Punch; Tel: 908-989-4092; *Circ*, Kurt Oliver; *ILL*, Don Loughman; *Archivist*, Mary Ellen Flaherty; *Publ Servs*, Holly Nagib; Staff 12 (MLS 6, Non-MLS 6)
Founded 1904. Enrl 3,000; Highest Degree: Bachelor
Library Holdings: Bk Vols 75,000; Per Subs 500
Subject Interests: Architecture, Electrical engineering, Electronics, Manufacturing, Mechanical engineering, Technology
Special Collections: Archives Coll; ASEE/ET Archives; Edward Kingman Coll; Mechanical Engineering (Richard H Lufkin), bks & per
Publications: Accessions list; Library Handbooks (student, staff & faculty); Research Guide
Partic in Dialog Corporation; Fenway Library Consortium; Nelinet, Inc

C WHEELOCK COLLEGE LIBRARY, 132 Riverway, 02215-4815. SAN 307-2479. Tel: 617-879-2220. FAX: 617-232-5165. Web Site: www.wheelock.edu/library/lilibinf.html. *Dir*, Elvernoy Johnson; Tel: 617-879-2225, E-Mail: ejohnson@wheelock.edu; *Tech Servs*, Liping Song; Tel: 617-879-2221, E-Mail: lsong@wheelock.edu; *Ref*, Esme Devault; Tel: 617-879-2222, E-Mail: edevault@wheelock.edu; *Access Serv, Electronic Resources*, Kari Parker; E-Mail: kparker@wheelock.edu; *Acq*, Judith Ceven; Tel: 617-879-2245, E-Mail: jceven@wheelock.edu; *ILL, Ser*, Susan Stella; Tel: 617-879-2223, E-Mail: sstella@wheelock.edu; *Circ, Computer Services*, Theressa Davis; E-Mail: tdavis@wheelock.edu; Staff 8 (MLS 6, Non-MLS 2)
Founded 1889. Enrl 1,052
2000-2001 Income $603,374. Mats Exp $152,000, Books $36,000, Per/Ser (Incl. Access Fees) $83,000, Micro $5,000, Manuscripts & Archives $1,000, Electronic Ref Mat (Incl. Access Fees) $27,000. Sal $394,000
Library Holdings: Bk Vols 96,000; Per Subs 550
Subject Interests: Education, Social service (social work), Special education
Special Collections: Early Childhood Curriculum Resource Coll; History of Kindergarten in the United States; Rare & historical children's literature (US & Great Britian)
Automation Activity & Vendor Info: (Acquisitions) DRA; (Cataloging) DRA; (Circulation) DRA; (Course Reserve) DRA; (ILL) DRA; (OPAC) DRA
Database Vendor: Dialog, IAC - SearchBank, ProQuest, Silverplatter Information Inc., Wilson - Wilson Web
Publications: Bibliographies; Information Handbook
Partic in Boston Regional Libr Syst; Fenway Libraries Online; Fenway Library Consortium; OCLC Online Computer Library Center, Inc

BOURNE

P JONATHAN BOURNE PUBLIC LIBRARY, 19 Sandwich Rd, 02532-3699. SAN 344-7545. Tel: 508-759-0644. Reference Tel: 508-759-0644, Ext 109. FAX: 508-759-0647. *Dir*, Richard W Fitzgerald; Tel: 508-759-0644, Ext 107, E-Mail: rfitzgerald@clams.lib.ma.us; *Asst Dir, Coll Develop*, Diane M Ranney; Tel: 508-759-0644, Ext 103, E-Mail: dranney@clams.lib.ma.us; *Cat*, Randall Mason; Tel: 508-759-0644, Ext 104; *Ch Servs*, Judith Blaisdell; Tel: 508-759-0644, Ext 106; Staff 9 (MLS 3, Non-MLS 6)
Founded 1896. Pop 16,000; Circ 83,763
Jul 1999-Jun 2000 Income $424,609, State $22,306, City $379,632, Locally Generated Income $2,500, Other $20,171. Mats Exp $96,090, Books $57,090, Per/Ser (Incl. Access Fees) $6,400, Micro $100, Electronic Ref Mat (Incl. Access Fees) $32,500. Sal $246,244 (Prof $174,816)
Library Holdings: Bk Vols 51,000; Bk Titles 43,000
Special Collections: Army National Guard Base (Otis) Hazardous Waste Cleanup; Cape Cod Coll; EPA Materials Re: Massachusetts; Genealogy Coll; Large Print Book Coll; Young Adult Coll
Automation Activity & Vendor Info: (Acquisitions) DRA; (Cataloging) DRA; (Circulation) DRA; (ILL) DRA; (OPAC) DRA
Mem of SE Mass Regional Libr Syst
Partic in Cape Libraries Automated Materials Sharing
Special Services for the Deaf - Books on deafness & sign language; High interest/low vocabulary books; TTY machine
Special Services for the Blind - Bks on tape
Open Tues-Thurs 9-8 & Fri-Sat 9-5:30
Friends of the Library Group

BOXBOROUGH

P ALBERT J SARGENT MEMORIAL LIBRARY, 575 Middle Rd, 01719-1408. SAN 307-2487. Tel: 978-263-4680. FAX: 978-263-1275. Web Site: www.ultranet.com/~boxbl/. *Actg Dir*, Judy Reiter; E-Mail: jreiter@cwmarsmail.cwmars.org; *Actg Dir*, Maureen Strapko; E-Mail: mstrapko@cwmarsmail.cwmars.org; Staff 2 (MLS 1, Non-MLS 1)
Library Holdings: Bk Vols 20,000; Per Subs 50
Mem of Central Massachusetts Regional Library System
Friends of the Library Group

BOXFORD

P BOXFORD TOWN LIBRARIES, 10 Elm St, 01921. SAN 344-7669. Tel: 978-887-7323. FAX: 978-887-6352. E-Mail: mbo@mvlc.lib.ma.us. *Coll Develop, Dir*, Adele McConaghy; *Asst Dir*, Jan Dempsey; *Ch Servs*, Joshua Kennedy
Founded 1966. Pop 8,550; Circ 74,943
Jul 1999-Jun 2000 Income (Main Library and Branch Library) $269,588, State $5,986, Locally Generated Income $3,324, Other $15,291. Mats Exp $64,530, Books $58,530, Per/Ser (Incl. Access Fees) $6,000. Sal $168,254 (Prof $49,994)
Library Holdings: Bk Vols 50,618; Per Subs 256
Publications: Library Bulletin (newsletter)
Mem of Northeast Mass Regional Libr Syst
Open Mon-Thurs 10-8, Fri 10-6, Sat 10-3
Friends of the Library Group
Branches: 1
WEST BOXFORD BRANCH, 188 Washington St, West Boxford, 01921. SAN 344-7693. Tel: 978-352-7323. *Coll Develop, Dir*, Adele McConaghy; *Asst Dir*, Jan Dempsey; *Ch Servs*, Joseph Kennedy
Open Mon-Fri 12-6, Sat 10-2
Friends of the Library Group

BOYLSTON

P BOYLSTON PUBLIC LIBRARY, 695 Main, 01505. SAN 307-2495. Tel: 508-869-2371. FAX: 508-869-6195. *Dir*, Nick Langhart; Staff 5 (Non-MLS 5)
Founded 1880. Pop 3,700; Circ 33,776
Jul 1998-Jun 1999 Income $104,448. Mats Exp $35,666, Books $17,172, Per/Ser (Incl. Access Fees) $1,751. Sal $65,724
Library Holdings: Bk Vols 28,000
Publications: Newsletter (semi-annual)
Mem of Central Massachusetts Regional Library System
Partic in CW Mars
Friends of the Library Group

S WORCESTER COUNTY HORTICULTURAL SOCIETY LIBRARY, Tower Hill Botanic Garden, PO Box 598, 01505-0598. SAN 307-8337. Tel: 508-869-6111, Ext 16. FAX: 508-869-0314. E-Mail: thbg@towerhillbg.org. Web Site: www.towerhillbg.org. *Librn*, Jane Milligan; Staff 1 (MLS 1)
Founded 1842
Library Holdings: Bk Vols 8,500; Per Subs 44
Subject Interests: Fruit, Garden hist, Horticulture, Landscape design
Function: Archival collection, Professional lending library
Partic in WACL

BRAINTREE

S BRAINTREE HISTORICAL SOCIETY, INC LIBRARY, 31 Tenney Rd, 02184-6512. SAN 327-5523. Tel: 781-848-1640. FAX: 781-380-0731. *Librn*, Marjorie P Maxham
Library Holdings: Bk Vols 1,500
Subject Interests: Genealogy, Local history
Open Sat-Wed

M HEALTH SOUTH-BRAINTREE REHABILITATION HOSPITAL-PROFESSIONAL LIBRARY,* 250 Pond St, PO Box 859020, 02185. SAN 377-9211. Tel: 781-848-5353, Ext 2113. FAX: 781-849-8171. *Coordr*, Donna Cass
Library Holdings: Bk Titles 150; Per Subs 50
Partic in Massachusetts Health Sciences Libraries Network; National Network Of Libraries Of Medicine - South Central Region

M OLYMPUS SPECIALTY HOSPITAL, Center for Occupational & Environmental Medicine, 2001 Washington St, 02184. SAN 377-919X. Tel: 781-848-2600. FAX: 781-849-3290. *Coordr*, Karen Cassidy; E-Mail: karencassidy@olympushealth.com; *Coordr*, Susan Rosen-Wasser
Library Holdings: Bk Titles 100
Partic in Am Asn of Occupational & Environ Health Claims; Am Pub Health Orgn; Mass Pub Health Orgn; National Network Of Libraries Of Medicine - South Central Region

P THAYER PUBLIC LIBRARY,* 798 Washington St, 02184. SAN 344-7723. Tel: 781-848-0405. FAX: 781-356-0672. E-Mail: brlib@ocln.org. Web Site: www.key-biz.com/ssn/Braintree/newlib.html. *Circ*, Sean Harrington; *Tech Servs*, Thomas Kosman
Pop 34,000; Circ 300,137
Library Holdings: Bk Vols 105,051
Special Collections: Audio Cassettes; Braintree Historical Coll; Cookery Coll, cassettes; Large Type Books & Newspapers; Music; Spoken Art
Mem of Eastern Mass Regional Libr Syst
Friends of the Library Group
Branches: 2
HIGHLANDS, 250 Peach St, 02184. SAN 344-7758. Tel: 781-843-1892. FAX: 781-356-0672. Web Site: www.key-biz.com/ssn/Braintree/library.html. *Librn*, Lois Wasserman
WATSON PARK, 85 Quincy Ave, East Braintree, 02184. SAN 344-7782. Tel: 781-848-0405. *Librn*, Lois Wasserman
Friends of the Library Group
Bookmobiles: 1

BREWSTER

P BREWSTER LADIES' LIBRARY, 1822 Main St, 02631. SAN 307-2509. Tel: 508-896-3913. FAX: 508-896-9372. E-Mail: brewllib@gis.net. Web Site: www.gis.net/~brewllib. *Dir*, Susan Carr; *Ch Servs*, Claire Gradone; Staff 4 (MLS 2, Non-MLS 2)
Founded 1852. Pop 10,043; Circ 122,000
Library Holdings: Bk Titles 48,917; Per Subs 123
Special Collections: Brewster History Coll; Cape Cod Coll; Joseph Lincoln Novels; Plays
Database Vendor: DRA
Partic in Cape Libraries Automated Materials Sharing; SE Mass Regional Libr Syst
Open Tues & Wed 10-8, Thurs & Fri 10-6, Sat 10-4

S CAPE COD MUSEUM OF NATURAL HISTORY, Clarence L Hay Library, Rte 6A, Box 1710, 02631. SAN 307-2517. Tel: 508-896-3867. FAX: 508-896-8844. Web Site: www.ccmnh.org. *Librn*, Deborah Diamond; E-Mail: ddiamond@ccmnh.org; Staff 1 (Non-MLS 1)
Founded 1958
Library Holdings: Bk Vols 10,000; Per Subs 54
Subject Interests: Archaeology, Botany, Conservation, Ecology, Entomology, Geology, Marine biology, Ornithology, Zoology
Special Collections: Scientific Specimens
Publications: Cape Naturalist; Conservation Leaflets; High Tidings; Svenson: The Flora on Cape Cod
Partic in SE Mass Regional Libr Syst
Friends of the Library Group

S NEW ENGLAND FIRE & HISTORY MUSEUM, Library & Archives, 1439 Main St, Rte 6A, 02631. SAN 326-6486. Tel: 508-896-5711. *Librn*, Robert Burger; Staff 1 (MLS 1)
Founded 1960
Library Holdings: Bk Titles 715; Per Subs 2
Special Collections: Antique & Old Fireman's Gazettes; Blacksmithing History; Fire Rating Principles & Risks (Charles Dominge Coll); NFPA Fire Codes; Pharmacy History

BRIDGEWATER

P BRIDGEWATER PUBLIC LIBRARY, 15 South St, 02324-2593. SAN 307-2525. Tel: 508-697-3331. Interlibrary Loan Service Tel: 508-697-9317. TDD: 508-697-3331. FAX: 508-697-9123. Web Site: www.ultranet.com/~bwpl/. *Dir*, Elizabeth L Gregg; *Ch Servs*, Joanne Doherty; *Assoc Dir, Tech Servs*, Diane L Dugal; *Circ*, Ann Gerald; *Assoc Dir, Publ Servs*, Mary O'Connell; Staff 27 (MLS 10, Non-MLS 17)
Founded 1881. Pop 23,240; Circ 176,528
Jul 1999-Jun 2000 Income $930,886. Mats Exp $167,878. Sal $661,357
Library Holdings: Bk Vols 113,255; Per Subs 154
Special Collections: Adaptive equipment & materials for disabled
Automation Activity & Vendor Info: (Acquisitions) SIRSI; (Cataloging) SIRSI; (Circulation) SIRSI; (Media Booking) SIRSI; (OPAC) SIRSI; (Serials) SIRSI
Partic in Sails, Inc
Special Services for the Deaf - TDD
Regional Reference Center for Southeastern Massachusetts Library System
Friends of the Library Group

C BRIDGEWATER STATE COLLEGE, Clement C Maxwell Library, Shaw Rd, 02325. SAN 307-2533. Tel: 508-531-1392. Interlibrary Loan Service Tel: 508-697-1706. FAX: 508-531-1349, 508-531-6103. E-Mail: libraryweb@bridgew.edu. Web Site: www.bridgew.edu/library. *Dir*, David H Carlson; Tel: 508-531-1256, E-Mail: dcarlson@bridgew.edu; *Selection of Gen Ref Mat*, Ratna Chandrasekhar; Tel: 508-531-1742, E-Mail: rchandra@bridgew.edu; *Automation Syst Coordr*, Mark F Johnson; *Coll Develop*, Kendra St Aubin; Tel: 508-531-2035, E-Mail: kstaubin@bridgew.edu; *Cat*, Shu-Chen Tu; Tel: 508-531-1757, E-Mail: stu@bridgew.edu; *Circ*, Kevin Manning; Tel: 508-531-2005, E-Mail: kmanning@bridgew.edu; *Spec Coll*, Mabell Bates; Tel: 508-531-1756, E-Mail: mbates@bridgew.edu; *Coll Develop*, Deborah Sanford; Tel: 508-531-6159, E-Mail: dsanford@bridgew.edu; *Per*, Christine Brown; *Automation Syst Coordr*, Sarah Nesbeitt; Tel: 508-531-6153, E-Mail: snesbeitt@bridgew.edu; *Doc*, Cynthia Svoboda; Tel: 508-531-1740, E-Mail: csvoboda@bridgew.edu; Staff 24 (MLS 11, Non-MLS 13)
Founded 1840. Enrl 8,243
Library Holdings: Bk Vols 337,723; Bk Titles 209,293; Per Subs 2,519
Subject Interests: Art, Education
Special Collections: Abraham Lincoln Coll; Albert G Boyden Coll of Early American Textbooks; Bridgewaterana; Can; Children's Coll; Dicken's Coll; Educational Resources Information Center, micro; Library of American Civilization, micro; Library of English Literature, micro; Standardized Tests; Tests in Microfiche; Theodore Roosevelt Coll
Automation Activity & Vendor Info: (Circulation) Endeavor; (Course Reserve) Endeavor; (OPAC) Endeavor; (Serials) Endeavor
Database Vendor: CARL, Ebsco - EbscoHost, GaleNet, IAC - Info Trac, Lexis-Nexis, OCLC - First Search, Silverplatter Information Inc.
Publications: SE Mass Cooperating Libraries Union List of Serials
Partic in Nelinet, Inc; Southeastern Massachusetts Cooperating Libraries

S MASSACHUSETTS DEPARTMENT OF CORRECTION, State Hospital Library, 20 Administration Rd, 02324. SAN 307-2541. Tel: 508-279-4500, Ext 4600. FAX: 508-279-4502. *Librn*, Dorothy Stanley-Ballard; Staff 1 (MLS 1)
Founded 1975
Library Holdings: Bk Titles 6,850; Per Subs 52
Subject Interests: Law
Partic in SE Mass Health Sci Librs Consortium

BRIGHTON

SR ARCHDIOCESE OF BOSTON ARCHIVES,* 2121 Commonwealth Ave, 02135-3192. SAN 326-0070. Tel: 617-254-0100, Ext 108. FAX: 617-783-5642. *Archivist*, Robert Johnson-Lally; E-Mail: robert_johnson_lally@chancery.rcab.org; Staff 4 (MLS 2, Non-MLS 2)
Founded 1978
Subject Interests: Social history

S NATIONAL TAY-SACHS & ALLIED DISEASES ASSOCIATION LIBRARY,* 2001 Beacon St, 02135. SAN 372-6312. Tel: 617-277-4463. FAX: 617-277-0134. E-Mail: ntsadboston@worldnet.att.net. Web Site: www.ntsad.org. *Dir*, Diana Pangonis
Library Holdings: Bk Vols 3,000

R SAINT JOHN'S SEMINARY LIBRARY, 99 Lake St, 02135-3846. SAN 307-2576. Tel: 617-254-2610, 617-746-5426. FAX: 617-746-5495. *Dir*, Lawrence McGrath
Founded 1884
Library Holdings: Bk Vols 150,000; Per Subs 400
Partic in Boston Theological Institute Library Program; New England Libr Info Network

BRIMFIELD

P BRIMFIELD PUBLIC LIBRARY,* Main St, 01010-9701. SAN 307-2584. Tel: 413-245-3518. Interlibrary Loan Service Tel: 800-922-8326. FAX: 413-245-3518. E-Mail: brimfield@cwmars.org. *Librn*, Claire Milette; *Asst Librn*, Rachel DuBois
Founded 1877. Pop 3,136; Circ 20,179
Jul 1998-Jun 1999 Income $34,697. Mats Exp $6,700, Books $6,200, Per/Ser (Incl. Access Fees) $500. Sal $21,262 (Prof $11,487)

Library Holdings: Bk Vols 13,743
Subject Interests: Genealogy, Local history
Mem of Central Massachusetts Regional Library System
Open Mon 10-1 & 6-9, Tues & Thurs 3-8, Wed 2-6, Sat 9-1

BROCKTON

M BROCKTON HOSPITAL LIBRARY, 680 Centre St, 02302. SAN 371-2028. Tel: 508-941-7207. FAX: 508-941-6412. E-Mail: brocktonhosplibrary@erols.com. Web Site: www.brocktonhospital.com. *Mgr*, Denise Corless; Staff 4 (MLS 1, Non-MLS 3)
2000-2000 Mats Exp $53,000, Books $4,000, Per/Ser (Incl. Access Fees) $42,000, Electronic Ref Mat (Incl. Access Fees) $7,000
Library Holdings: Bk Vols 9,000; Bk Titles 2,500; Per Subs 268
Subject Interests: Medicine, Nursing
Publications: Brochures
Partic in BHSL; Southeastern Massachusetts Consortium Of Health Science Libraries

GL BROCKTON LAW LIBRARY, 72 Belmont St, 02301. SAN 307-2630. Tel: 508-586-7110. FAX: 508-588-8483. Web Site: www.lawlib.state.ma.us.; Staff 2 (MLS 1, Non-MLS 1)
Jul 2000-Jun 2001 Mats Exp $111,512. Sal $102,058
Library Holdings: Bk Vols 14,124
Database Vendor: OCLC - First Search

P BROCKTON PUBLIC LIBRARY SYSTEM, 304 Main St, 02301-5390. SAN 344-7812. Tel: 508-580-7890. FAX: 508-580-7898. E-Mail: brockton@ocin.org. Web Site: www.brocktonpubliclibrary.org. *Dir*, E Diane Pacheco; E-Mail: dpacheco@ocin.org; *Asst Dir*, Katherine Lussier; E-Mail: klussier@ocin.org; *ILL*, Esther Cohen; *Ref*, Lucia Shannon; E-Mail: lshannon@ocin.org; *Ch Servs*, Sharon Quint; E-Mail: squint@ocin.org; *Head Tech Servs*, Keith Choquette; E-Mail: keithc@ocin.org; Staff 47 (MLS 7, Non-MLS 40)
Founded 1867. Pop 95,688; Circ 237,590
Jul 1999-Jun 2000 Income $1,458,526, State $174,747, City $1,251,097, Locally Generated Income $32,682. Mats Exp $169,555, Books $139,261, Per/Ser (Incl. Access Fees) $5,817, AV Equip $17,817, Other Print Mats $3,215, Electronic Ref Mat (Incl. Access Fees) $3,445. Sal $988,648 (Prof $341,837)
Library Holdings: Bk Vols 90,900; Per Subs 122
Automation Activity & Vendor Info: (Cataloging) epixtech, inc.; (Circulation) epixtech, inc.; (OPAC) epixtech, inc.
Database Vendor: epixtech, inc.
Partic in Old Colony Libr Network
Friends of the Library Group
Branches: 2
EAST, 54 Kingman St, 02302. SAN 344-7871. Tel: 508-580-7892. FAX: 508-580-7861. E-Mail: bteast@ocin.org. Web Site: www.brocktonpubliclibrary.org. *Branch Mgr*, Karen King; E-Mail: kking@ocin.org; *Dir*, E Diane Pacheco; Tel: 508-580-7890, Fax: 508-580-7898, E-Mail: dpacheco@ocin.org
Founded 1969
Library Holdings: Bk Vols 22,618
Partic in Old Colony Libr Network
Friends of the Library Group
WEST, 540 Forest Ave, 02301. SAN 344-7936. Tel: 508-580-7894. FAX: 508-580-7863. E-Mail: btwest@ocin.org. Web Site: www.brocktonpubliclibrary.org. *Branch Mgr*, Ann Riccardi; E-Mail: annr@ocin.org; *Dir*, E Diane Pacheco; Tel: 508-580-7890, Fax: 508-580-7898, E-Mail: dpacheco@ocin.org
Founded 1969
Library Holdings: Bk Vols 25,841
Partic in Old Colony Libr Network
Friends of the Library Group
Bookmobiles: 1. Bk vols 6317

S THE ENTERPRISE LIBRARY,* 60 Main St, PO Box 1450, 02303. SAN 307-2606. Tel: 508-586-6200. FAX: 508-586-6506. E-Mail: newsroom@enterprisenews.com. *Librn*, Beth Rose
Founded 1880
Subject Interests: History
Special Collections: News clippings
Restriction: Staff use only

M GOOD SAMARITAN MEDICAL CENTER, Peirce Leavitt Library, 235 N Pearl St, 02301. SAN 377-905X. Tel: 508-427-2676. FAX: 508-427-3475. E-Mail: library1@tiac.net. *Dir*, Nancy Sezak; E-Mail: nsezak@caritas-gsmc.org; Staff 1 (MLS 1)
Founded 1968
Library Holdings: Bk Titles 1,000; Per Subs 120
Database Vendor: IAC - Info Trac
Partic in Basic Health Sciences Library Network; Massachusetts Health Sciences Libraries Network; North Atlantic Health Sciences Libraries, Inc; Southeastern Massachusetts Consortium Of Health Science Libraries

J MASSASOIT COMMUNITY COLLEGE LIBRARY,* One Massasoit Blvd, 02302. SAN 307-2622. Tel: 508-588-9100, Ext 1940. FAX: 508-427-1255. Web Site: www.massasoit.mass.edu. *Ref*, Joanne Jones; *Circ, Ref*, Jennifer Rudolf
Founded 1966
Library Holdings: Bk Vols 74,098; Per Subs 339
Special Collections: Allied Health Resources; New York Times, 1851-date

GM VA MEDICAL CENTER, Medical Library 142D, 940 Belmont St, 02301. SAN 307-2649. Tel: 508-583-4500, Ext 1142. FAX: 508-895-0074. *Librn*, Lynn Lloyd
Founded 1953
Library Holdings: Bk Vols 4,000; Bk Titles 4,000; Per Subs 475
Subject Interests: Alcohol and drugs, Drug abuse, Medicine, Nursing, Psychiatry, Psychology, Social sciences and issues
Partic in Boston Biomedical Library Consortium; Southeastern Massachusetts Consortium Of Health Science Libraries

BROOKFIELD

P MERRICK PUBLIC LIBRARY, Two Lincoln St, PO Box 528, 01506. SAN 307-2657. Tel: 508-867-6339. FAX: 508-867-6339. *Dir*, Brenda Metterville; E-Mail: bmetterv@cwmars.org
Pop 3,100; Circ 13,355
Library Holdings: Bk Vols 14,059
Subject Interests: Local history
Mem of Central Massachusetts Regional Library System
Friends of the Library Group

BROOKLINE

L BRUMBERG PUBLICATIONS, INC, Law Library,* 124 Harvard St, 02146. SAN 372-0799. Tel: 617-734-1979. FAX: 617-734-1989. E-Mail: brumberg@compuserve.com. *Librn*, Bruce Brumberg
Library Holdings: Bk Vols 200; Per Subs 100

C HEBREW COLLEGE, Jacob & Rose Grossman Library, 43 Hawes St, 02146. SAN 307-2665. Tel: 617-278-4927. FAX: 617-264-9264. E-Mail: heblib@gis.net. *Dir*, Maurice Tuchman; *Ref*, Mimi Mazor; *Spec Coll*, Shalva Siegel; *Syst Coordr*, Harvey Sukenic; Staff 5 (MLS 5)
Founded 1918. Enrl 2,000; Fac 90; Highest Degree: Master
2000-2001 Income $405,873, Locally Generated Income $132,000, Parent Institution $273,873. Mats Exp $62,450, Books $25,000, Per/Ser (Incl. Access Fees) $10,000, Presv $3,500, Micro $1,250, AV Equip $3,500, Other Print Mats $7,600, Manuscripts & Archives $2,000, Electronic Ref Mat (Incl. Access Fees) $9,600. Sal $212,423 (Prof $185,000)
Library Holdings: Bk Vols 112,000; Bk Titles 100,000; Per Subs 281; Bks on Deafness & Sign Lang 40
Special Collections: Canadian Jewry; Hassidic & Kabbalistic Literature; Holocaust; Japanese-Judaica; Jewish Education (Herman & Peggy Vershbow Pedagogic Center); Jewish Genealogy; Jewish Medical Ethics (Harry A & Beatrice Savitz Coll); Jewish Women's Studies; John S & Florence G Lawrence Coll, microform; Large Print Books of Jewish Interest; Middle East & Israeli Affairs (Dr Gerald Wohlberg Coll); Modern Hebrew Literature Responsa; Simon & Sylvia Krakon Fund in Jewish Communal Service; Video Coll
Automation Activity & Vendor Info: (Cataloging) EX Libris; (Circulation) EX Libris; (OPAC) EX Libris
Publications: Bibliography of Japanese-Judaica; Bibliography of Russian - Judaica in the Hebrew College Library 2nd Ed; Jewish Genealogical Resources in the Hebrew College Library; Jewish Reference Books 1980-1990; Manuscripts in the Hebrew College Library
Partic in Council Of Archives & Research Libraries In Jewish Studies; Fenway Library Consortium
Consortial type relationship with Boston Univ, Northeastern Univ & Andover-Newton Theological Seminary
Friends of the Library Group

CR HELLENIC COLLEGE-HOLY CROSS GREEK ORTHODOX SCHOOL OF THEOLOGY, Archibishop Iakovos Library, 50 Goddard Ave, 02445-7496. SAN 307-2673. Tel: 617-850-1223. FAX: 617-850-1470. Web Site: www.hchc.edu. *Coll Develop, Dir*, Joachim Cotsonis; Tel: 617-850-1243, E-Mail: jcotsonis@hchc.edu; *Cat*, Athanasia Papademetriou; Tel: 617-850-1246, E-Mail: apapademetriou@hchc.edu; *Acq, Syst Coordr*, Nancy Hughes; Tel: 617-850-1367, E-Mail: nhughes@hchc.edu; *Circ, Per*, Hilary Rogler; Tel: 617-850-1244, E-Mail: hrogler@hchc.edu; Staff 4 (MLS 3, Non-MLS 1)
Founded 1937. Enrl 170; Fac 23; Highest Degree: Master
Jul 1999-Jun 2000 Income $539,900. Mats Exp $59,729, Books $18,137, Per/Ser (Incl. Access Fees) $21,888, Micro $551, AV Equip $87, Electronic Ref Mat (Incl. Access Fees) $19,066. Sal $264,154 (Prof $207,090)
Library Holdings: Bk Vols 110,000; Per Subs 747
Subject Interests: Archival, Greek, History, Orthodox theol
Special Collections: Archbishop Iakovos Coll, rare bks
Automation Activity & Vendor Info: (Acquisitions) SIRSI; (Cataloging) SIRSI; (Circulation) SIRSI; (ILL) SIRSI

Database Vendor: Ebsco - EbscoHost
Partic in Boston Theological Institute Library Program; Nelinet, Inc; OCLC Online Computer Library Center, Inc; OCLC Online Computer Library Center, Inc

S MUSEUM OF TRANSPORTATION LIBRARY & ARCHIVES, 15 Newton St, Larz Anderson Park, 02445. SAN 375-1538. Tel: 617-522-6547, Ext 23. FAX: 617-524-0170. E-Mail: mot@shore.net. Web Site: www.mot.org. *Dir*, Glen Pare'; *Curator*, Amy Beth Friend; E-Mail: friend@mot.org. Subject Specialists: *Automobiles*, Amy Beth Friend; Staff 1 (Non-MLS 1)
Founded 1948
Library Holdings: Bk Vols 1,500; Bk Titles 1,300
Subject Interests: Automobiles
Special Collections: Anderson Isabel and Larson Writing Collection; Anderson Photograph Collection (Weid Estate, Brookline, MA); Roderick Blood Collection, Packard Automobile Mat
Publications: Carriage House Notes (Newsletter)
Restriction: By appointment only, Non-circulating to the public
Function: Research library

J NEWBURY COLLEGE LIBRARY, 129 Fisher Ave, 02445-5796. SAN 307-2258. Tel: 617-730-7070. FAX: 617-730-7239. Web Site: www.newbury.edu/library. *Dir*, Marie A Kascus; Tel: 617-730-7255, E-Mail: m.kascus@newbury.edu; *Coll Develop*, Janet Hayashi; Tel: 617-730-7254, E-Mail: j.hayashi@newbury.edu; *Circ*, Nelie Lyubomirsky; Tel: 617-738-2425, E-Mail: n.lyubomirski@newbury.edu; *Cat*, Panit Satayasai-Crimnin; Tel: 617-738-2428; *Ref*, Kate Silfen; Tel: 617-730-7008, E-Mail: k.silfen@newbury.edu; Staff 9 (MLS 6, Non-MLS 3)
Founded 1961. Enrl 700; Fac 35; Highest Degree: Bachelor
Jul 1999-Jun 2000 Income $447,544. Mats Exp $194,468, Books $77,631, Per/Ser (Incl. Access Fees) $38,336, AV Equip $1,960, Other Print Mats $15,458, Electronic Ref Mat (Incl. Access Fees) $61,083. Sal $253,076
Library Holdings: Bk Titles 25,280; Per Subs 1,010
Subject Interests: Art, Business, Communications, Computer science, Culinary, Hospitality indust, Interior design, Legal
Automation Activity & Vendor Info: (Acquisitions) DRA; (Cataloging) DRA; (Circulation) DRA; (Course Reserve) DRA; (OPAC) DRA
Database Vendor: OCLC - First Search
Partic in Minuteman Library Network; Nelinet, Inc; OCLC Online Computer Library Center, Inc

P PUBLIC LIBRARY OF BROOKLINE, Brookline Public,* 361 Washington St, 02445. SAN 344-7960. Tel: 617-730-2360. FAX: 617-232-7146. *Dir*, Jamec C Flaherty; *Asst Dir*, Dalija P Karoblis; *Circ*, Mary Egan-James; *ILL*, Ben Steinberg; *Tech Servs*, Michael Wofsey; *Coll Develop*, Cynthia J Battis; Staff 22 (MLS 22)
Founded 1857. Pop 54,700; Circ 729,718
1997-1998 Income $2,474,296. Mats Exp $420,342. Sal $1,741,316
Automation Activity & Vendor Info: (Circulation) DRA
Mem of Eastern Mass Regional Libr Syst
Friends of the Library Group
Branches: 2
COOLIDGE CORNER, 31 Pleasant St, 02446. SAN 344-7995. Tel: 617-730-2380. FAX: 617-734-4565. *Librn*, Catherine Dooley
Library Holdings: Bk Vols 100,849
PUTTERHAM, 959 W Roxbury Pkwy, 02467. SAN 344-8029. Tel: 617-730-2385. FAX: 617-469-3947. *Librn*, Karen O'Donnell-Leach
Library Holdings: Bk Vols 40,997

R TEMPLE SINAI LIBRARY, 50 Sewall Ave, 02446. SAN 307-2703. Tel: 617-277-5888. FAX: 617-277-5842. E-Mail: sinaibrook@aol.com. Web Site: uahcweb.org/ma/sinai-brookline. *Librn*, Leann Shamash
Founded 1960
Library Holdings: Bk Vols 1,000
Subject Interests: Israel, Judaica (lit or hist of Jews), Middle East

S US NATIONAL PARK SERVICE FREDERICK LAW OLMSTED NATIONAL HISTORIC SITE, Olmsted Archives, 99 Warren St, 02445. SAN 370-2936. Tel: 617-566-1689. FAX: 617-232-3964. E-Mail: olmsted_archives@nps.gov. Web Site: www.nps.gov/frla/home/htm. *Archivist*, Jill Trebbe; *Archivist*, T Michele Clark; *Archivist, Ref Serv*, Mike Sosch
Library Holdings: Bk Vols 400
Special Collections: Frederick Law Olmsted Plans & Drawings Coll
Restriction: By appointment only

BUCKLAND

P BUCKLAND PUBLIC LIBRARY,* PO Box 149, 01338. SAN 307-2711. Tel: 413-625-9412. FAX: 413-625-9412. *Dir*, Pat Leuchtman; E-Mail: pleucht@cwmarsmail.cwmars.org
Pop 2,165; Circ 13,820
Library Holdings: Bk Vols 11,609; Per Subs 28
Mem of Western Regional Libr Syst

BURLINGTON

S ALPHATECH INCORPORATED LIBRARY,* 50 Mall Rd, 01803. SAN 370-9825. Tel: 781-273-3388, Ext 263. FAX: 781-273-9345. *Librn*, Julie Cohen
Library Holdings: Bk Vols 5,000; Per Subs 70
Open Mon-Fri 8:15-4:45

P BURLINGTON PUBLIC LIBRARY, 22 Sears St, 01803. SAN 307-2738. Tel: 781-270-1690. FAX: 781-270-1693. E-Mail: mbu@mvlc.lib.ma.us. *Dir*, Hilding Hedberg; E-Mail: hhedberg@burlmass.org; *Asst Dir*, Elizabeth Owens; *Cat*, Lucile Liu; *Ref*, Ann Cameron; *Ch Servs*, Charl Magnard; Staff 10 (MLS 7, Non-MLS 3)
Founded 1857. Pop 23,694; Circ 240,515
2000-2000 Income City $798,322. Sal $547,531 (Prof $259,350)
Library Holdings: Per Subs 190
Subject Interests: Business and management, Law
Function: ILL available, Photocopies available
Mem of Eastern Mass Regional Libr Syst
Partic in Merrimack Valley Library Consortium
Friends of the Library Group

M LAHEY CLINIC, Cattell Memorial Library, 41 Mall Rd, 01805. SAN 320-5827. Tel: 781-744-8253. FAX: 781-744-3615. *Dir*, Carol Spencer; E-Mail: carol.spencer@lahey.org; Staff 1 (MLS 1)
Founded 1965
Library Holdings: Bk Titles 10,000; Per Subs 200
Subject Interests: Medicine
Restriction: Staff use only
Partic in Boston Biomedical Library Consortium; National Network Of Libraries Of Medicine New England Region

G VISIDYNE, INC LIBRARY,* 10 Corporate Pl, S Bedford St, 01803. SAN 329-9961. Tel: 781-273-2820.
Library Holdings: Bk Vols 200; Per Subs 12
Subject Interests: Atmospheric optics, Government, Naval, Rpts, Surface analysis

BUZZARDS BAY

S MASSACHUSETTS MARITIME ACADEMY, Captain Charles H Hurley Library, 101 Academy Dr, 02532. SAN 307-2878. Tel: 508-759-5761, 508-830-5034. FAX: 508-830-5074. Web Site: www.sailsinc.com. *Dir*, Maurice H Bosse
Founded 1970. Enrl 950
Library Holdings: Bk Vols 50,000
Subject Interests: Law, Nautical history, Ocean engineering, Oceanography
Publications: Acquisitions list
Partic in Nelinet, Inc

CAMBRIDGE

S ABT ASSOCIATES INC, Corporate Library, 55 Wheeler St, 02138. SAN 307-2886. Tel: 617-492-7100, Ext 2857. FAX: 617-520-2967. *Dir*, Sharon Christenson; E-Mail: sharon_christenson@abtassoc.com; Staff 2 (MLS 1, Non-MLS 1)
Founded 1965
Library Holdings: Per Subs 125
Special Collections: 6000 ABT Associates Reports
Open Mon-Fri 8:30-6

S AMERICAN ASSOCIATION OF VARIABLE STAR OBSERVERS, Charles Y McAteer Library, 25 Birch St, 02138. SAN 323-4894. Tel: 617-354-0484. FAX: 617-354-0665. E-Mail: aavso@aavso.org. Web Site: www.aavso.org. *Dir*, Dr Janet A Mattei
Library Holdings: Bk Vols 2,500; Per Subs 200
Subject Interests: Astronomy
Open Mon-Fri 9-5

M ARIAD PHARMACEUTICALS, Library & Information Services,* 26 Landsdowne St, 02139. SAN 377-9238. Tel: 617-494-0400, Ext 229. FAX: 617-494-8144. *Librn*, Yoland Bator
Library Holdings: Per Subs 40
Partic in National Network Of Libraries Of Medicine - South Central Region

S BBN TECHNOLOGIES LIBRARY, (Formerly GTE Internetworking Library), 10 Moulton St, 02138. SAN 307-2916. Tel: 617-873-3279. FAX: 617-873-2956. E-Mail: library@bbn.com. *Librn*, Jennie Connolly; *Librn*, Andrew Jones; *Librn*, Terry Ladner
Founded 1960
Subject Interests: Architecture, Data processing, Physical science, Technology
Special Collections: BBN Reports 1947-present
Restriction: Staff use only
Open Mon-Fri 8-5

S BIOGEN, INC LIBRARY,* 14 Cambridge Ctr, 02142. SAN 375-8370. Tel: 617-679-3385. FAX: 617-679-2306.
Library Holdings: Bk Titles 2,500; Per Subs 140

S CAMBRIDGE ACOUSTICAL ASSOCIATES, INC LIBRARY,* 84 Sherman St, 02140. SAN 375-7862. Tel: 617-864-1944. FAX: 781-396-1953.
Library Holdings: Bk Titles 1,000; Per Subs 15

S CAMBRIDGE ENERGY RESEARCH ASSOCIATES LIBRARY,* Charles Sq, 20 University Rd, 02138. SAN 328-607X. Tel: 617-497-6446. FAX: 617-497-0423. Web Site: www.cera.com. *Librn*, Barbara J Blodgett
Library Holdings: Bk Vols 700; Per Subs 120
Subject Interests: Political science
Open Mon-Fri 10-5

S CAMBRIDGE HISTORICAL COMMISSION ARCHIVE, 831 Massachusetts Ave, 2nd flr, 02139. SAN 329-0905. Tel: 617-349-4683. FAX: 617-349-3116. E-Mail: histcomm@ci.cambridge.ma.us. Web Site: www.ci.cambridge.ma.us/~historic/. *Asst Dir*, Kathleen L Rawlins; *Exec Dir*, Charles M Sullivan
Library Holdings: Bk Titles 500
Subject Interests: Architecture, Local history, Photog
Publications: Cambridge African American Heritage Trail Guide; Cambridge City Hall, 1890-1990; Maintaining Your Old House in Cambridge; Map: Washington Takes Command: Cambridge During the American Revolution; Survey of Architectural History in Cambridge: Cambridge Port; Survey of Architectural History in Cambridge: Cambridgeport; East Cambridge; Mid Cambridge; Northwest Cambridge; Old Cambridge
Restriction: Non-circulating to the public

M CAMBRIDGE HOSPITAL, Medical Library, 1493 Cambridge St, 02139. SAN 372-6274. Tel: 617-665-1439. FAX: 617-665-1424. *Dir*, Jenny C Lee; E-Mail: jlee@challiance.org; Staff 2 (MLS 1, Non-MLS 1)
Library Holdings: Bk Vols 1,200; Bk Titles 1,000; Per Subs 82
Subject Interests: Medicine, Podiatry, Psychiatry
Database Vendor: OVID Technologies
Publications: Newsletter (bi-monthly)
Mem of Northeastern Consortium for Health Information
Partic in Maryland Association Of Health Science Librarians; Metrowest Massachusetts Regional Library System; MLA

P CAMBRIDGE PUBLIC LIBRARY,* 449 Broadway, 02138. SAN 344-8053. Tel: 617-349-4040. FAX: 617-349-4028. E-Mail: camdir@mln.lib.ma.us. Web Site: www.ci.cambridge.ma/~cpl. *Dir*, Susan Flannery; *Ch Servs*, Daryl Mark; *Acq, Tech Servs*, Frank Gages; *Ref*, Elizabeth Dickinson; *Rare Bks*, Donald York; E-Mail: dyork@ci.cambridge.ma.us; *Circ*, Dave Shaw; *Coll Develop*, Bliss Matteson; Staff 45 (MLS 45)
Jul 1997-Jun 1998 Income $3,372,190, State $120,976, City $3,251,214. Mats Exp $414,940, Books $314,296, Per/Ser (Incl. Access Fees) $43,476. Sal $2,271,668
Library Holdings: Per Subs 890
Partic in Metrowest Regional Libr Syst; Minuteman Library Network
Friends of the Library Group
Branches: 6
BOUDREAU (OBSERVATORY HILL) BRANCH, 245 Concord Ave, 02138. SAN 344-8231. Tel: 617-349-4017. Web Site: www.ci.cambridge.ma/~cpl. *Librn*, Linda Haines
Library Holdings: Bk Vols 17,856
Friends of the Library Group
CENTRAL SQUARE, 45 Pearl St, 02139. SAN 344-8118. Tel: 617-349-4010. Web Site: www.ci.cambridge.ma/~cpl. *Librn*, Jean Williams
Library Holdings: Bk Vols 46,028
COLLINS (MOUNT AUBURN) BRANCH, 64 Aberdeen Ave, 02138. SAN 344-8177. Tel: 617-349-4021. Web Site: www.ci.cambridge.ma/~cpl. *Librn*, Kathy Fitzgerald
Library Holdings: Bk Vols 14,000
O'CONNELL (EAST CAMBRIDGE) BRANCH, 48 Sixth St, 02141. SAN 344-8142. Tel: 617-349-4019. Web Site: www.ci.cambridge.ma/~cpl. *Librn*, Judy Swarden
Library Holdings: Bk Vols 11,351
O'NEILL (NORTH CAMBRIDGE) BRANCH, 70 Rindge Ave, 02140. SAN 344-8207. Tel: 617-349-4023. FAX: 617-349-4422. Web Site: www.ci.cambridge.ma/~cpl. *Librn*, Jessica Rabban
Library Holdings: Bk Vols 27,929
VALENTE (CAMBRIDGE FIELD) BRANCH, 826 Cambridge St, 02141. SAN 344-8088. Tel: 617-349-4015. FAX: 617-349-4416. Web Site: www.ci.cambridge.ma/~cpl. *Librn*, Carole Feeney
Library Holdings: Bk Vols 35,060
Bookmobiles: 1

S CAMBRIDGE SCHOOL DEPARTMENT, Teachers Resource Center Library, 459 Broadway, 02138. SAN 327-5485. Tel: 617-349-6778. FAX: 617-349-6897. Web Site: www.cps.ci.cambridge.ma.us/crls/trc/index.htm. *Librn*, Sheila Morshead; Tel: 617-349-6779, E-Mail: sheila-morshead@cps.ci.cambridgema.us; *Asst Librn*, Joanne Connolly; Staff 3 (MLS 1, Non-MLS 2)
Library Holdings: Bk Titles 3,000; Per Subs 110
Subject Interests: Education
Special Collections: K-12 curriculum videotapes
Automation Activity & Vendor Info: (Cataloging) TLC; (Circulation) TLC
Publications: Cable Connections; TRC Newlsetter (Newsletter)
Partic in Edco
Open Mon-Fri 7:30-4

S CAMP, DRESSER & MCKEE, Herman G Dresser Information Center, 50 Hampshire St, 02139. SAN 307-1472. Tel: 617-452-6778. FAX: 617-452-8000. E-Mail: infocenter@cdm.com. *Dir*, Nancy Moorhouse; *Mgr*, Patricia Anne Lambert; Tel: 617-452-6683, Fax: 617-452-8683, E-Mail: lambertpa@cdm.com; *Senior Librn*, Virginia L Carroll; Tel: 617-452-6781, Fax: 617-452-8781, E-Mail: carrollvl@cdm.com. Subject Specialists: *Engineering*, Virginia L Carroll; Staff 4 (MLS 3, Non-MLS 1)
Founded 1963
Library Holdings: Bk Vols 20,000; Bk Titles 13,000; Per Subs 190; Spec Interest Per Sub 190
Subject Interests: Civil engineering, Environmental engineering, Wastewater
Database Vendor: Dialog, Ebsco - EbscoHost, epixtech, inc., OCLC - First Search
Function: Research library
Partic in Nelinet, Inc

S CHARLES STARK DRAPER LABORATORY INC, Technical Information Center, 555 Technology Sq, Mail Sta 74, 02139. SAN 307-2959. Tel: 617-258-3555. FAX: 617-258-1919. E-Mail: library@draper.com. Web Site: www.draper.com. *In Charge*, Laurie Rotman; *Cat*, Heather Russell; *Acq*, Amy Chapman; *Web Coordr*, Ellen Avery; *Ref Serv*, Linda Petkunas; Staff 6 (MLS 5, Non-MLS 1)
Founded 1973
Library Holdings: Bk Vols 16,000; Bk Titles 10,000; Per Subs 350
Subject Interests: Electronics, Engineering, Mathematics, Physics
Special Collections: C S Draper Laboratory Archives
Restriction: Staff use only
Partic in Nelinet, Inc

S COOPER INFORMATION, Architecture, Engineering & Environmental Consulting Library,* 5 Ellery Pl, 02138. SAN 375-4669. Tel: 617-354-3274. E-Mail: cooperinfo@aol.com. *Pres*, Mary Cooper
Library Holdings: Bk Titles 250
Subject Interests: Architecture, Engineering
Partic in Dialog Corporation; Dowline

S CULTURAL SURVIVAL INC LIBRARY, 215 Prospect St, 02139. SAN 326-8977. Tel: 617-441-5400. FAX: 617-441-5417. E-Mail: csinc@cs.org. *Dir*, Ian McIntosh
Library Holdings: Bk Vols 700; Per Subs 300
Subject Interests: Education, Forestry, Human rights
Publications: CS Occasional Papers; Cultural Survival (quarterly)
Restriction: By appointment only

S DIBNER INSTITUTE FOR THE HISTORY OF SCIENCE & TECHNOLOGY, Burndy Library, MIT E56-100, 38 Memorial Dr, 02139. SAN 302-2889. Tel: 617-258-5240. FAX: 617-253-9858. Web Site: burndydibner.mit.edu. *Librn*, Clark A Elliott; E-Mail: elliottc@mit.edu
Founded 1937
Library Holdings: Bk Vols 40,000
Special Collections: Edison; Leonardo da Vinci & Pasteur; Volta
Publications: Burndy Library Publication Series
Friends of the Library Group

R EPISCOPAL DIVINITY SCHOOL & WESTON JESUIT SCHOOL OF THEOLOGY LIBRARY, 99 Brattle St, 02138. SAN 307-3165. Tel: 617-349-3602. FAX: 617-349-3603. Web Site: www.edswjst.org. *Coll Develop, Dir*, Paul A L LaCharite; *Publ Servs*, Gene Fox; *Cat*, Anne Reece; *Acq*, Sarah F Spencer; *Ref*, Steve Kuehler; *Ser*, Sherrie Tuck; Staff 5 (MLS 5)
Founded 1867. Enrl 250; Fac 35; Highest Degree: Doctorate
Jul 2000-Jun 2001 Mats Exp $194,950. Sal $548,410 (Prof $271,738)
Library Holdings: Bk Vols 228,000; Per Subs 1,174
Subject Interests: Theology
Partic in Boston Theological Institute Library Program; Nelinet, Inc; OCLC Online Computer Library Center, Inc
A joint library of Episcopal Divinity School & Weston Jesuit School of Theology

S GENETICS INSTITUTE, Information Center,* 87 Cambridge Park Dr, 02140. SAN 327-6279. Tel: 617-665-8129. FAX: 617-665-8033. E-Mail: infocenter@genetics.com. Web Site: www.ahp.com.
Library Holdings: Bk Titles 8,500; Per Subs 550
Subject Interests: Genetics
Restriction: Staff use only
Partic in Nelinet, Inc
Open Mon-Fri 8:30-5
Branches:

S ANDOVER BRANCH, 1 Burtt Rd, Andover, 01810. SAN 377-9203. Tel: 978-247-1077. FAX: 978-247-2608. Web Site: www.ahp.com.
Library Holdings: Bk Vols 5,000; Per Subs 500
Partic in National Network Of Libraries Of Medicine - South Central Region; Spec Libr Asn

S GRADIENT CORP, Information Resource Center, 238 Main St, 02142-1016. SAN 370-8764. Tel: 617-395-5000. FAX: 617-395-5001. Web Site: www.gradientcorp.com. *Mgr*, Marcia Olson; Tel: 617-395-5562, E-Mail: molson@gradientcorp.com; Staff 3 (MLS 2, Non-MLS 1)
Founded 1986
Oct 1999-Sep 2000 Income $170,000. Mats Exp $50,000, Books $10,000, Per/Ser (Incl. Access Fees) $25,000
Library Holdings: Bk Titles 7,000; Per Subs 60
Subject Interests: Environ sci, Risk assessment, Toxicology

C HARVARD UNIVERSITY LIBRARY, Wadsworth House, 02138. SAN 344-8266. Tel: 617-495-3650. Interlibrary Loan Service Tel: 617-495-2972. FAX: 617-495-0370. Interlibrary Loan Service FAX: 617-495-2129. Web Site: www.hcl.harvard.edu/. *Dir*, Sidney Verba; *Asst Dir*, Stacy T Kowalczyk; *Assoc Dir*, Dale P Flecker; *Assoc Dir*, Barbara S Graham; *Adminr*, Mathilda Van Es; *Librn*, Jan Merrill-Oldham; *Head, Info Serv*, Tracey Robinson; *Archivist*, Harley P Holden
Founded 1638. Enrl 18,541
Jul 1999-Jun 2000 Mats Exp $21,255,367. Sal $39,955,576
Automation Activity & Vendor Info: (Acquisitions) NOTIS; (Cataloging) NOTIS; (Circulation) NOTIS; (Serials) NOTIS
Publications: Harvard Librarian; Harvard Library Bulletin; HUL Notes; Library Resource Forum
Mem of Asn of Research Libraries
Partic in Nelinet, Inc; OCLC Online Computer Library Center, Inc; RLIN
Special Services for the Deaf - Books on deafness & sign language; Special interest periodicals
Departmental Libraries:

CR ANDOVER-HARVARD THEOLOGICAL LIBRARY, Divinity School, 45 Francis Ave, 02138. SAN 344-8622. Tel: 617-495-5770. FAX: 617-496-4111. *Librn*, Louis Charles Willard; *Tech Servs*, Russell O Pollard; *Archivist, Curator*, Timothy Driscoll; Staff 7 (MLS 7)
Founded 1816. Enrl 550; Fac 36; Highest Degree: Doctorate
1997-1998 Mats Exp $370,827, Books $226,963, Per/Ser (Incl. Access Fees) $64,342, Micro $79,522. Sal $865,490 (Prof $378,348)
Library Holdings: Bk Vols 443,039; Per Subs 2,310
Special Collections: Religion of Liberal Churches
Publications: Collection Development Statement; Guide
Partic in OCLC Online Computer Library Center, Inc

ARNOLD ARBORETUM HORTICULTURE LIBRARY, 125 Arborway, Jamaica Plain, 02130. SAN 344-8657. Tel: 617-524-1718. FAX: 617-524-1418. *Librn*, Sheila Connor
Library Holdings: Bk Vols 35,000
Subject Interests: Horticulture

ARTHUR & ELIZABETH SCHLESINGER LIBRARY ON THE HISTORY OF WOMEN IN AMERICA, 3 James St, 02138-3766. (Mail add: 10 Garden St, 02138), SAN 307-3106. Tel: 617-495-8647. FAX: 617-496-8340. E-Mail: slref@radcliffe.edu. Web Site: www.radcliffe.edu.schles. *Actg Dir*, Jane S Knowles; Tel: 617-495-8263, E-Mail: jane_knowles@radcliffe.edu; *Curator*, Anne Engelhart; *Curator*, Barbara Haber; *Curator*, Mary Harrington; *Curator*, Kathryn Jacob; *AV*, Ruth Hill; *Publ Servs*, Ellen Shea; *Archivist*, Kathy Kraft; Staff 22 (MLS 13, Non-MLS 9)
Founded 1943
Jul 1999-Jun 2000 Income $1,365,982. Mats Exp $84,240, Books $45,848, Per/Ser (Incl. Access Fees) $19,675, Presv $1,800, Manuscripts & Archives $16,917
Library Holdings: Bk Vols 60,556; Per Subs 411
Subject Interests: Women's hist, Women's studies
Special Collections: Culinary History; Social Reform; Women's Rights
Publications: 40th Anniversary Report; A Bibliography for Culinary Historians; Annual & Biennial Reports (1960-1981); annual newsletters; Innocent Documents; New Viewpoints in Women's History: Working Papers from the Schlesinger Library 50th Anniversary Conference; The Black Women Oral History Project, A Guide to the Transcripts; Women of Courage Exhibition Catalogue
Restriction: Non-circulating to the public
Partic in OCLC Online Computer Library Center, Inc; RLIN
Friends of the Library Group

BAKER LIBRARY, Harvard Business School, Soldiers Field, Boston, 02163. SAN 344-8681. Tel: 617-495-6040, 617-495-6395. FAX: 617-496-3811. Web Site: www.library.hbs.edu. *Exec Dir*, Thomas J Michalak; *Coll Develop*, Laura Linard; *Dir*, Melissa Shaffer; *Dir, Tech Serv*, Pat Johnson; *Dir Info Resources & Res*, Elizabeth Bibby; *Coll Develop*, Judith Brink; Staff 38 (MLS 28, Non-MLS 10)
Founded 1908. Enrl 1,475; Fac 220; Highest Degree: Doctorate
Jul 1999-Jun 2000 Income $458,198. Mats Exp $5,247,836, Books $270,554, Per/Ser (Incl. Access Fees) $542,783, Micro $146,424, Electronic Ref Mat (Incl. Access Fees) $601,270. Sal $2,771,009
Library Holdings: Bk Vols 605,960; Per Subs 6,561
Special Collections: Adam Smith (Vanderblue Coll); Business & Economics From 1484 to 1850 (Kress Coll); Credit Reports from 1840's to 1880's (R G Dun & Co Coll); Harvard Business School Archives; Historical Corporate Reports; Pinne Coll, bks & mss; South Sea Bubble
Publications: Baker Books (online only at www.library.hbs.edu/bakerbooks); HBS Working Knowledge (online only at www.hbsworkingknowledge.hbs.edu)
Partic in Nelinet, Inc; OCLC Online Computer Library Center, Inc; RLIN

BELFER CENTER FOR SCIENCE & INTERNATIONAL AFFAIRS LIBRARY, 79 John F Kennedy St, 02138. SAN 345-0600. Tel: 617-495-1408. FAX: 617-495-8963. *Librn*, Anne M Cushing
Founded 1973
Library Holdings: Bk Vols 5,000
Subject Interests: Technology
Publications: Aquisitions List

BIOCHEMICAL SCIENCES TUTORIAL LIBRARY, 7 Divinity Ave, 02138-2092. SAN 344-9947. Tel: 617-495-4106. FAX: 617-496-6148. E-Mail: biochsci@biohp.harvard.edu. *In Charge*, Barbara J Lewis
1999-2000 Mats Exp $18,567, Per/Ser (Incl. Access Fees) $17,274, Other Print Mats $1,293
Library Holdings: Bk Vols 946

BIOLOGICAL LABORATORIES LIBRARY, 16 Divinity Ave, 02138. SAN 344-8746. Tel: 617-495-2332. FAX: 617-495-9300. Web Site: mcb.harvard.edu/admin_res/library. *Librn*, David L Osterbur; E-Mail: dosterbur@mcb.harvard.edu; Staff 2 (MLS 1, Non-MLS 1)
Jul 1999-Jun 2000 Income $297,000. Mats Exp $215,200, Books $6,200, Per/Ser (Incl. Access Fees) $203,000, Presv $6,000. Sal $118,000
Library Holdings: Bk Vols 30,500; Bk Titles 10,000; Per Subs 190
Subject Interests: Biology

BLUE HILL METEOROLOGICAL OBSERVATORY LIBRARY, Pierce Hall, 29 Oxford St, 02138. SAN 344-9289. Tel: 617-495-2836. FAX: 617-495-9837. E-Mail: lib@deas.harvard.edu. Web Site: www.deas.harvard.edu/~library/bluehill.htm. *Librn*, Martha F Wooster; *Publ Servs*, Jack Maniscalco; *Publ Servs*, Diane Pochini; *Ser*, Heidi Simon; *Tech Servs*, Christy Kissileff; *ILL*, Benson Smith
Subject Interests: Atmospheric sci, Climatology, Earth science, Geophysics, Meteorology, Oceanography
Publications: New Acquisitions (monthly)
Expenses included in Gordon McKay Library

CENTER FOR EUROPEAN STUDIES LIBRARY, 27 Kirkland St, 02138. SAN 345-018X. Tel: 617-495-4303. FAX: 617-495-8509. *Librn*, George Cumming; Staff 1 (MLS 1)

CENTER FOR HELLENIC STUDIES LIBRARY, 3100 Whitehaven St NW, Washington, 20008. SAN 344-9106. Tel: 202-745-4415. Reference Tel: 202-745-4414. FAX: 202-797-3745. Web Site: www.chs.wrlc.org. *Librn*, Dr Ellen C Roth; E-Mail: ellen-roth@umail.umd.edu; Staff 4 (MLS 3, Non-MLS 1)
Founded 1961
Jul 1999-Jun 2000 Mats Exp Books $40,000
Library Holdings: Bk Vols 50,000; Per Subs 250
Subject Interests: Art, Civilization, Greek, History, Literature, Philosophy, Roman
Special Collections: Greek & Latin Authors in Original Languages
Automation Activity & Vendor Info: (Acquisitions) Endeavor; (Cataloging) Endeavor; (ILL) Endeavor; (OPAC) Endeavor; (Serials) Endeavor
Database Vendor: OCLC - First Search
Restriction: By permission only, Not open to public
Partic in Capcon Library Network; OCLC Online Computer Library Center, Inc; Washington Research Library Consortium

CENTER FOR MIDDLE EASTERN STUDIES LIBRARY, 1737 Cambridge St, 02138. SAN 345-0422. Tel: 617-495-2173. FAX: 617-495-8292. *Librn*, Malcolm D White
Library Holdings: Bk Vols 5,114
Subject Interest: Middle East

CENTER FOR POPULATION STUDIES LIBRARY, 665 Huntington Ave, Rm 1-1111, Boston, 02115. SAN 345-0546. Tel: 617-432-1234. FAX: 617-566-0365. Web Site: www.hsph.harvard.edu/academics/pih/poplibrary/lib1.html. *Coordr*, Sarah Coit
Library Holdings: Bk Vols 12,000; Per Subs 90
Subject Interests: Demography, Develop, Population, Reproductive health

CHEMISTRY LIBRARY, Converse Memorial Lab, 12 Oxford St, 02138. SAN 344-8770. Tel: 617-495-4079. FAX: 617-495-0788. Web Site: www-chem.harvard.edu/chemlib2.html. *Librn*, Theresa Kavanaugh
Library Holdings: Bk Vols 57,000

CHILD MEMORIAL & ENGLISH TUTORIAL LIBRARY, Widener, Rm Z, 02138. SAN 344-9556. Tel: 617-495-4681. *In Charge*, Larry D Benson
Library Holdings: Bk Vols 17,319

CM FRANCIS A COUNTWAY LIBRARY OF MEDICINE, Boston Med Libr-Harvard Med Libr, 10 Shattuck St, Boston, 02115. SAN 344-8835. Tel: 617-432-2142. Circulation Tel: 617-432-2136. Reference Tel: 617-432-2147. FAX: 617-432-4738. Web Site: www.countway.harvard.edu. *Ref Serv*, Suzy Conway; *Access Serv*, Doris Ann Sweet; *Librn*, Judith Messerle; Fax: 617-432-0693; *Curator, Rare Bks, Spec Coll*, Tom Horrocks. Subject Specialists: *Education*, Suzy Conway; *Reference*, Suzy Conway; Staff 34 (MLS 24, Non-MLS 10)
Founded 1964
Jul 1999-Jun 2000 Income $726,856. Mats Exp $1,462,514, Per/Ser (Incl. Access Fees) $1,209,621, Electronic Ref Mat (Incl. Access Fees)

$252,893. Sal $2,696,168 (Prof $1,673,890)
Library Holdings: Bk Vols 672,195; Per Subs 3,146
Subject Interests: Anatomy, Biochemistry, Biology, Cytology (study Of cells), Dermatology, Genetics, Geriatrics and gerontology, Immunology, Microscopy, Molecular biology, Obstetrics and gynecology, Oncology, Pediatrics, Pharmacology, Physiology, Psychiatry, Public health, Radiology, Statistics
Special Collections: Americana printed before 1821, particularly items bearing New England imprints; Chinese & Japanese med (1650-1850); dissertations, 1498 to date; English imprints before 1701; Incunabula of Medical Interest (William Norton Bullard Coll); Jewish Medicine (Solomon M Hymans Coll); Legal Medicine; Medical Medals (Horatio Robinson Storer Coll); Medieval & Renaissance Manuscripts of Medical Interest; Oliver Wendell Holmes Coll; other foreign imprints before 1701; paintings of Boston physicians; physicians' account bks & case bks, 1729-1850; Spanish imprints, incl Mexico & S Am, before 1826
Serves Harvard University Schools of Medicine, Public Health & Dentistry & membership of Boston Medical Library
Friends of the Library Group

DAVIS CENTER FOR RUSSIAN STUDIES LIBRARY, 1737 Cambridge St, 02138. SAN 344-9408. Tel: 617-495-4030. FAX: 617-495-8319. *Librn*, Susan Jo Gardos; E-Mail: gardos@fas.harvard.edu
Jul 1999-Jun 2000 Mats Exp $23,562. Sal $71,021
Library Holdings: Bk Vols 19,099; Per Subs 130

DEVELOPMENT OFFICE LIBRARY, University Pl, 124 Mount Auburn St, 02138-5762. SAN 345-0058. Tel: 617-495-9750. FAX: 617-496-9140.
Founded 1964
Library Holdings: Bk Vols 6,000
Collection circulates within Development office only

DUMBARTON OAKS RESEARCH LIBRARY & COLLECTION, 1703 32nd St NW, Washington, 20007. SAN 344-886X. Tel: 202-339-6400. FAX: 202-339-6419. Web Site: www.doaks.org. *Head Librn*, Sheila Klos; *Librn*, Bridget Gazzo; *Librn*, Ingrid Gibson; *Librn*, Linda Lott; *Librn*, Irene Vaslef; *Cat*, Clark Kimball. Subject Specialists: *Byzantine studies*, Irene Vaslef; *Rare books*, Linda Lott; Staff 13 (MLS 7, Non-MLS 6)
Founded 1936
Jul 1999-Jun 2000 Mats Exp $359,468, Books $177,641, Per/Ser (Incl. Access Fees) $105,152, Presv $56,675, Other Print Mats $20,000. Sal $459,636 (Prof $328,206)
Library Holdings: Bk Vols 176,550; Per Subs 1,119
Subject Interests: Byzantine studies, Garden design, Landscape architecture, Medieval studies
Automation Activity & Vendor Info: (Acquisitions) SIRSI; (Cataloging) SIRSI; (OPAC) SIRSI; (Serials) SIRSI
Database Vendor: OCLC - First Search
Partic in OCLC Online Computer Library Center, Inc

EDA KUHN LOEB MUSIC LIBRARY - HARVARD COLLEGE LIBRARY, Music Bldg, Harvard University, 02138. Tel: 617-495-2794. FAX: 617-496-4636. Web Site: hcl.harvard.edu/loebmusic. *Actg Mgr*, Sarah Adams; *Librn*, Virginia Danielson; *Librn*, Robert Dennis; *Cat*, Florence Lynch; *Publ Servs*, Constance Mayer
Library Holdings: Bk Vols 145,357
Subject Interests: Music
Special Collections: Archive of World Music, Sound Rec; Isham Memorial Library

FACULTY OF ARTS & SCIENCES OFFICE OF CAREER SERVICES LIBRARY, 54 Dunster St, 02138. SAN 345-0007. Tel: 617-495-2595. FAX: 617-495-3584. *Librn*, Susan M Vacca
Jul 1999-Jun 2000 Income Parent Institution $71,981. Mats Exp $23,118, Books $17,096, Per/Ser (Incl. Access Fees) $5,259, Micro $763. Sal $51,284 (Prof $24,660)
Library Holdings: Bk Vols 5,930; Per Subs 63
Subject Interests: Career develop

FINE ARTS LIBRARY - HARVARD COLLEGE LIBRARY, Fogg Art Museum, 32 Quincy St, 02138. SAN 344-838X. Tel: 617-496-1504. FAX: 617-496-4889. Web Site: hcl.harvard.edu/finearts/. *Librn*, Amanda Bowen; *Librn*, Yenshew Lynn Chao; *Librn*, Katharine Martinez; *Head Ref, Publ Servs*, Mary Clare Altenhofen; *Cat*, Susan Myerson; *Curator*, Martha Mahard; *Bibliogr*, Andreas Riedlmayer
Library Holdings: Bk Vols 295,140
Friends of the Library Group

FRANCES LOEB LIBRARY, Harvard Graduate School of Design, 48 Quincy St, Gund Hall, 02138. SAN 344-922X. Tel: 617-496-0904. Circulation Tel: 617-495-9163. Reference Tel: 617-496-1304. FAX: 617-496-5929. Web Site: www.gsd.harvard.edu/library/. *Librn*, Ann Whiteside; *Librn*, Hugh Wilburn; *Tech Servs*, Janet Rutan; *Spec Coll*, Mary Daniels; *Publ Servs*, Barbara Mitchell; *Coll Develop*, Sarah Dickinson; *Cat*, Page Nelson; Staff 10 (MLS 6, Non-MLS 4)
Founded 1900. Enrl 550; Fac 100; Highest Degree: Doctorate
Library Holdings: Bk Vols 282,000; Per Subs 1,650
Subject Interests: Architecture, Landscape architecture, Urban planning
Special Collections: Le Corbusier Coll; Papers of Charles Eliot II, Daniel Kiley, J C Olmsted, Josep L Luis Sert, Arthur Shurcliff, Hugh Stubbins
Publications: Special Collections in the Frances Loeb Library (an inventory)
Partic in OCLC Online Computer Library Center, Inc
Friends of the Library Group

GEORGE DAVID BIRKHOFF MATHEMATICAL LIBRARY, Science Ctr, One Oxford St, 02138. SAN 344-9971. Tel: 617-495-2147. *In Charge*, Nancy Milller; E-Mail: nancy@math.harvard.edu; Staff 1 (Non-MLS 1)
Library Holdings: Bk Vols 12,385

GODFREY LOWELL CABOT SCIENCE LIBRARY - HARVARD COLLEGE LIBRARY, Science Center, One Oxford St, 02138. SAN 344-8355. Tel: 617-495-5351. FAX: 617-495-5324. Web Site: hcl.harvard.edu/cabot. *Librn*, Thomas Parris; *Librn*, Lynne M Schmelz; *Head Ref*, John Carper; *Circ, Head Tech Servs*, Allen Bourque
Library Holdings: Bk Vols 212,612

GORDON MCKAY LIBRARY, Division of Engineering & Applied Sciences, Pierce Hall, 29 Oxford St, 02138. SAN 344-9254. Tel: 617-495-2836. FAX: 617-495-9837. *Librn*, Martha F Wooster; *Ser*, Heidi Simon; *Tech Servs*, Suzanne Meunier
1997-1998 Income $908,000. Mats Exp $624,365, Books $52,865, Per/Ser (Incl. Access Fees) $559,900, Presv $11,600. Sal $255,055
Library Holdings: Bk Vols 106,241
Subject Interests: Computer science, Electrical engineering, Mechanical engineering, Microbiology, Optics, Water resources
Special Collections: Division Publications
Publications: New Acquisitions (monthly)
Partic in Nelinet, Inc; OCLC Online Computer Library Center, Inc

GROSSMAN LIBRARY FOR UNIVERSITY EXTENSION, Sever Hall, Harvard Yard, 02138. SAN 345-0244. Tel: 617-495-4163. FAX: 617-495-9438. *Mgr*, James Gilligan; E-Mail: gilligan@hudce.harvard.edu; Staff 3 (Non-MLS 3)
Founded 1967. Enrl 14,000; Fac 600; Highest Degree: Master
Jul 1999-Jun 2000 Income (Main Library Only) $18,259. Mats Exp $3,869. Sal $143,081 (Prof $52,908)
Library Holdings: Bk Vols 7,634

GUTMAN LIBRARY-RESEARCH CENTER, Graduate School of Educ, 6 Appian Way, 02138. SAN 344-9041. Tel: 617-495-4225. Circulation Tel: 617-495-3423. Reference Tel: 617-495-3421. FAX: 617-495-0540. Web Site: gseweb.harvard.edu. *Librn*, John W Collins, III; *Ref*, Deborah Garson; *Tech Servs*, Joseph Gabriel; *Circ*, Marcella Flaherty; *Coll Develop*, Gladys Dratch
Library Holdings: Bk Vols 181,895
Subject Interests: Education
Special Collections: Action for Children's Television Coll; Curriculum Materials; Early American Textbooks; Educational Software; Jeanne Chall Coll; Private School Catalogs; Public School Reports
Publications: Current Issues in Education: A Bibliographic Series
Partic in BRS; Dialog Corporation; Nelinet, Inc; OCLC Online Computer Library Center, Inc

HAMILTON A R GIBB ISLAMIC SEMINAR LIBRARY, Widener, Rm Q, 02138. SAN 344-9580. Tel: 617-495-5701. *In Charge*, Muhsin S Mahdi
Library Holdings: Bk Vols 7,478

HARVARD COLLEGE LIBRARY (HEADQUARTERS IN HARRY ELKINS WIDENER MEMORIAL LIBRARY), Harvard University, 02138. Tel: 617-495-2401. FAX: 617-496-4750. Web Site: www.hcl.harvard.edu, www.hcl.harvard.edu/widener. *Librn*, Nancy M Cline; *Assoc Librn*, Jeffrey Horrell; *Assoc Librn*, Lynda Leahy; *Assoc Librn*, Susan Lee; *Res*, Carrie Kent; *Circ*, Elizabeth McKeigue; *Access Serv*, Marilyn Wood; *Curator*, David Cobb; *Ref*, Joe Bourneuf; *Head Tech Servs*, Jane Ouderkirk; *Tech Servs*, Daryl Boone; *Tech Servs*, Elizabeth Eggleston; *Tech Servs*, Ruth Haas; *Tech Servs*, Nancy Hallock; *Tech Servs*, Lynda Kresge; *Tech Servs*, Kathleen Rutter; *Tech Servs*, Bruce Trumble; *Coll Develop*, Jill Coelho; *Coll Develop*, Charles Fineman; *Coll Develop*, Evangelie Flessas; *Coll Develop*, Barbara Halporn; *Coll Develop*, Dan Hazen; *Coll Develop*, Ray Lum; *Coll Develop*, Michael Olson; *Coll Develop*, Allison Scott; *Coll Develop*, Lynn Shirey. Subject Specialists: *American history*, Lynn Shirey; *Greek*, Evangelie Flessas; *Maps*, David Cobb
Jul 1999-Jun 2000 Income $52,669,626. Mats Exp $11,462,857, Books $5,884,787, Per/Ser (Incl. Access Fees) $2,411,626, Presv $879,863, Micro $1,360,290. Sal $22,273,874 (Prof $11,831,820)
Library Holdings: Bk Vols 8,706,475
Subject Interests: American history, Arabic language, Art, Canadiana, Cartography, Church history, Dutch (Language), Education, European history, Folklore, German (Language), History, History of science, Italian (language), Judaica (lit or hist of Jews), Latin (language), Literature, Local history, Maps, Mormons, Music, New England, Numismatics, Persian (language), Photography, Portuguese (language), Quakers, Siam, Slavic history and literature, Spanish (language), Theater, Typography, Yiddish (Language)
Special Collections: Author Collections: Achebe, Alcott Family, Ariosto, Aristophanes, Bacon, Beerbohm, Blake, Bossuet, Byron, Caldecott, Camoes, Carlyle, Carman, Carroll, Cervantes, Chaucer, Coleridge, Walter Crane, Cruikshank, E E Cummings, Dante, Dickens, Emily Dickinson, Donne, Dryden, T S Eliot, Emerson, Erasmus, Faulkner, Fielding, Galsworthy, John Gay, Goethe, Hearn, Heine, Herbert, Hofmannsthal, Horace, Henry James, William James, Johnson, Kipling, T E Lawrence, Lear, Levi, Longfellow, Amy Lowell, Masefield, Melville, Milton, Moliere, Montaigne, Nabokov, Persius, Petrach, Alexander Pope, Rilke, Rousseau, Schiller, Shakespeare, Shelley, Robert E Sherwood, Soyinka, Steinbeck, Stevenson, Strindberg, Tasso, Thackeray, Trotsky, Updike, Villard Family, Gilbert White, Thomas Wolfe; Farnsworth Recreational

Reading Room; Harry Elkins Widener Memorial Coll; John Keats & His Circle; Printing & Graphic Arts; Theatre Coll; Theodore Roosevelt Coll; Winsor Memorial Map Room; Woodberry Poetry Room
Partic in Nelinet, Inc; OCLC Online Computer Library Center, Inc; RLIN
Friends of the Library Group

HARVARD DATA CENTER, Littauer Ctr, Rm M32, North Yard, Harvard University, 02138. SAN 345-0279. Tel: 617-495-4734. FAX: 617-496-5149. Web Site: www.data.fas.harvard.edu. *Exec Dir*, William Wei

HARVARD FOREST LIBRARY, 324 N Main St, Petersham, 01366. (Mail add: PO Box 68, Petersham, 01366), Tel: 978-724-3302. FAX: 978-724-3595. Web Site: www.lternet.edu/hfr/. *Librn*, Barbara Flye
Founded 1907
Library Holdings: Bk Vols 29,326
Subject Interests: Forestry

HARVARD-YENCHING LIBRARY - HARVARD COLLEGE LIBRARY, 2 Divinity Ave, 02138. SAN 344-8444. Tel: 617-495-2756. FAX: 617-496-6008. Web Site: hcl.harvard.edu/harvard-yenching/. *Librn*, James Cheng; *Librn, Publ Servs, Ref*, Hilde DeWeerdt; *Assoc Librn*, James K Lin; *Rare Bks*, Chun Shum
Library Holdings: Bk Vols 951,960
Subject Interests: Japanese (Language), Tibetan (language), Vietnam
Publications: Harvard-Yenching Library Bibliographical Services; Harvard-Yenching Library Occasional Reference Notes
Friends of the Library Group

HILLES LIBRARY-UNDERGRADUATE - HARVARD COLLEGE LIBRARY, 59 Shepard St, 02138. SAN 344-8533. Tel: 617-495-8720. FAX: 617-496-8760. Web Site: hcl.harvard.edu/hilles. *Librn*, Heather E Cole; *Assoc Librn*, Suzanne Kemple
Library Holdings: Bk Vols 207,324

HISTORY DEPARTMENT LIBRARY, Robinson Hall, 02138. SAN 345-0368. Tel: 617-495-2545. FAX: 617-496-3425. *In Charge*, Michael McCormick
Library Holdings: Bk Vols 9,301

HISTORY OF SCIENCE LIBRARY
Library Holdings: Bk Vols 24,312

HOUGHTON LIBRARY-RARE BOOKS & MANUSCRIPTS - HARVARD COLLEGE LIBRARY Tel: 617-495-2441. FAX: 617-495-1376. Web Site: www.hcl.harvard.edu/houghton. *Librn*, William P Stoneman; *Curator*, Leslie Morris; *Curator*, Roger E Stoddard; *Curator*, Fredric W Wilson; *Tech Servs*, Mollie Della-Terza; *Publ Servs*, Rachel Howarth; *Cat*, Karen Nipps. Subject Specialists: *Rare books*, Roger E Stoddard; *Theatre*, Fredric W Wilson
Library Holdings: Bk Vols 453,070

JOHN F KENNEDY SCHOOL OF GOVERNMENT LIBRARY, 79 John F Kennedy St, 02138. SAN 344-8924. Tel: 617-495-1300. Reference Tel: 617-495-1302. FAX: 617-495-1972. Web Site: www.ksg.harvard.edu/library. *Coll Develop, Dir*, Ellen Isenstein; *Circ*, Paula Ebbitt; *Tech Servs*, Beata Panagopoulos; Staff 13 (MLS 6, Non-MLS 7)
Library Holdings: Bk Vols 54,250; Per Subs 1,771
Subject Interests: Government, Nonprofit mgt, Pub administration, Pub policy
Partic in OCLC Online Computer Library Center, Inc

JOHN K FAIRBANK CENTER FOR EAST ASIAN RESEARCH LIBRARY, Coolidge Hall, 1737 Cambridge St, 02138. SAN 345-0120. Tel: 617-495-5753. FAX: 617-495-9976. *Librn*, Nancy Hearst
Library Holdings: Bk Vols 20,000
Subject Interests: Chinese Language, English (language)

JOHN PEABODY MONKS UNIVERSITY HEALTH SERVICES LIBRARY, 75 Mount Auburn St, 02138. SAN 345-0457. Tel: 617-495-9629. *Librn*, Sylvia Gerhard
Library Holdings: Bk Vols 500

KUMMEL LIBRARY OF GEOLOGICAL SCIENCES - HARVARD COLLEGE LIBRARY, Geological Museum, 24 Oxford St, 02138. SAN 344-8983. Tel: 617-495-2029. FAX: 617-495-4711. Web Site: hcl.harvard.edu/kummel. *Librn*, Michael R Leach
Library Holdings: Bk Vols 65,652

LAMONT LIBRARY-UNDERGRADUATE - HARVARD COLLEGE LIBRARY Tel: 617-495-2450. FAX: 617-496-3692. Web Site: hcl.harvard.edu/lamont. *Librn*, Heather E Cole; *Assoc Librn*, Jon Lanham; *Head Ref*, Jeff Kosokoff; *Access Serv*, Linda Collins
Library Holdings: Bk Vols 188,048

CL LAW SCHOOL LIBRARY, Langdell Hall, 1545 Massachusetts Ave, 02138. SAN 344-919X. Tel: 617-495-3174. FAX: 617-495-4449. Web Site: www.law.harvard.edu/library. *Librn*, Harry S Martin, III; *Assoc Librn*, Robert L Buckwalter; *Assoc Librn*, Paul George; *Cat*, Ann G Sitkin; *Ser*, Margaret Cianfarini; *Acq*, Harold Moren; *Spec Coll*, David Warrington; *Ref*, Joan Duckett; *Circ*, Phyllis Askey; *ILL*, Aparna Sen; Staff 43 (MLS 34, Non-MLS 9)
Founded 1817. Enrl 2,000; Fac 150; Highest Degree: Doctorate
2000-2000 Mats Exp $2,877,747, Books $695,974, Per/Ser (Incl. Access Fees) $1,881,707, Micro $146,370, Other Print Mats $1,156, Electronic Ref Mat (Incl. Access Fees) $152,540. Sal $5,133,092 (Prof $2,567,177)
Library Holdings: Bk Vols 1,623,910; Bk Titles 777,414; Per Subs 15,336
Special Collections: English Common Law (Dunn Coll); French Legal History (Violett Coll); International Law (Olivart Coll); Japanese Law (de Becker Coll)
Partic in Nellco; RLIN

LITTAUER LIBRARY - HARVARD COLLEGE LIBRARY, Littauer Center, North Yard, 02138. SAN 344-8479. Tel: 617-495-2106. FAX: 617-496-5770. Web Site: hcl.harvard.edu/littauer. *Librn*, Diane Garner; *Librn*, Heather McMullen; *Coll Develop*, Jan Voogd; *Cat, Tech Servs*, Danila Terpanjian
Library Holdings: Bk Vols 458,834
Special Collections: Manpower & Industrial Relations

NEAR EASTERN LANGUAGES & LITERATURES LIBRARY, Widener, Rm G, 02138. SAN 344-970X. Tel: 617-495-0553.
Library Holdings: Bk Vols 1,986

NIEMAN COLLECTION OF CONTEMPORARY JOURNALISM LIBRARY, One Francis Ave, 02138. SAN 345-0481. Tel: 617-495-2237.
Library Holdings: Bk Titles 1,995; Per Subs 21
Subject Interests: Journalism
Special Collections: Financial Files of PM; Herman Obermeyer American Nazi Party Coll; Herman Obermeyer Rape and Sexual Assault Coll; Nieman Alumni Coll; Roland Steel Walter Lippmann Coll

MILMAN PARRY COLLECTION OF ORAL LITERATURE Tel: 617-496-2499. *In Charge*, Stephen Mitchell
Library Holdings: Bk Vols 583

PHYSICS RESEARCH LIBRARY, 450 Jefferson Laboratory, 17 Oxford St, 02138. SAN 344-9343. Tel: 617-495-2878. FAX: 617-495-0416. E-Mail: Bitnet: library@huhepl. Web Site: www.physics.harvard.edu/. *Librn*, Michael R Leach; Staff 2 (MLS 1, Non-MLS 1)
Library Holdings: Bk Vols 20,968

PSYCHOLOGY RESEARCH LIBRARY, William James Hall, 33 Kirkland St, 02138. SAN 344-9378. Tel: 617-495-3858. *Librn*, Richard E Kaufman; E-Mail: kaufman@wjh.harvard.edu
Library Holdings: Bk Vols 17,088; Per Subs 124

ROBBINS LIBRARY OF PHILOSOPHY, Emerson Hall, 02138. SAN 345-0570. Tel: 617-495-2193. *Librn*, David Macarthur
Library Holdings: Bk Vols 10,038

ROBINSON CELTIC SEMINAR LIBRARY Tel: 617-495-8771. *Curator*, Pamela Hopkins
Library Holdings: Bk Vols 1,396

SANSKRIT LIBRARY, Widener, Rm A, 02138. SAN 344-9793. Tel: 617-495-3295. *In Charge*, James W Benson
Library Holdings: Bk Vols 2,625

HERBERT WEIR SMYTH CLASSICAL LIBRARY Tel: 617-495-4027.
Library Holdings: Bk Vols 9,363

SOCIAL RELATIONS/SOCIOLOGY LIBRARY, William James Hall, 33 Kirkland St, 02138. SAN 344-9467. Tel: 617-495-3838. *Librn*, Richard E Kaufman; E-Mail: kaufman@wjh.harvard.edu
Library Holdings: Bk Vols 24,973; Per Subs 161

STATISTICS LIBRARY, Science Ctr, Rm 607, One Oxford St, 02138. SAN 345-066X. Tel: 617-495-5496. *Librn*, Michelle Dussault
Library Holdings: Bk Vols 2,401

TOZZER LIBRARY - HARVARD COLLEGE LIBRARY, 21 Divinity Ave, 02138. SAN 344-8568. Tel: 617-495-2253. FAX: 617-496-2741. Web Site: hcl.harvard.edu/tozzer. *Librn*, Maija Lutz; *Assoc Librn, Publ Servs, Reader Servs*, Gregory A Finnegan; *Assoc Librn, Coll Develop, Tech Servs*, Janet Steins; *Cat*, Isabel Quintana; *Circ*, Gene DeVita; Staff 16 (MLS 6, Non-MLS 10)
Library Holdings: Bk Vols 225,260
Subject Interests: Anthropology, Archaeology
Publications: Anthropological Literature; Bibliographic Guide to Anthropology & Archaeology

UKRAINIAN RESEARCH INSTITUTE REFERENCE LIBRARY, 1583 Massachusetts Ave, 02138. SAN 345-0724. Tel: 617-496-5891. FAX: 617-495-8097. Web Site: www.huri.harvard.edu/. *Librn*, Ksenya Kiebuzinski; E-Mail: kiebuzin@fas.harvard.edu
Founded 1973
Library Holdings: Bk Vols 2,500; Per Subs 140
Special Collections: Archives of Ukrainian Cultural Institutions & of Ukrainian Civic, Cultural & Political Figures

WEATHERHEAD CENTER FOR INTERNATIONAL AFFAIRS LIBRARY, 1737 Cambridge St, 02138. SAN 344-9165. Tel: 617-495-2173. FAX: 617-495-8292. Web Site: hdc-www.harvard.edu/cfia/library/index.htm. *Librn*, Malcolm White; E-Mail: mwhite@cfia.harvard.edu
Library Holdings: Bk Vols 10,000; Per Subs 80
Subject Interests: Foreign policy, International relations

S HARVARD-SMITHSONIAN CENTER FOR ASTROPHYSICS LIBRARY, John G Wolbach Library, 60 Garden St, MS-56, 02138. SAN 307-3122. Tel: 617-496-5769. FAX: 617-495-7199. E-Mail: library@cfa.harvard.edu. Web Site: cfa-www.harvard.edu/library. *Head Librn*, Donna J Coletti; Tel: 617-495-7289, E-Mail: dcoletti@cfa.harvard.edu; *Asst Librn*, Ewa Basinska; *Acq of New Ser*, Barbara Palmer; Tel: 617-495-5488, E-Mail: bpalmer@cfa.harvard.edu; *Electronic Resources*, Melissa A Hilbert; Tel: 617-496-7601, E-Mail: mhilbert@cfa.harvard.edu; *ILL*, Maria McEachern; Tel: 617-495-7266, E-Mail: mmceachern@cfa.harvard.edu; *Purchasing*, Donna M Thompson; Tel: 617-496-7808, E-Mail: dthompson@cfa.harvard.edu; *Tech Servs*, William Graves; Tel: 617-496-7550, E-Mail: wgraves@cfa.harvard.edu; Staff 6 (MLS 3, Non-MLS 3)
Founded 1959. Enrl 35; Highest Degree: Doctorate
Library Holdings: Per Subs 850

Subject Interests: Astronomy, Astrophysics, Space science
Special Collections: Astronomical Institutes Coll: early observatory publications from around the world; Early Observatory Publications (Al Coll)
Publications: Quarterly acquisition list (Acquisition list)
Combines the library collections of the Harvard College Observatory & the Smithsonian Astrophysical Observatory

S INSTITUTE FOR DEFENSE & DISARMAMENT STUDIES LIBRARY, 675 Massachuetts Ave 8th flr, 02139. SAN 327-5507. Tel: 617-354-4337. FAX: 617-354-1450. Web Site: www.idds.org. *Exec Dir*, Dr Randall Caroline Forsberg; E-Mail: forsberg@idds.org
Founded 1979
Library Holdings: Bk Titles 3,500; Per Subs 200
Special Collections: Analysis of US Army RDT&E Funding (FY 1980-1997); Arms Control Reporter 2000; Arms Control Reporter on CD - 1990-1999; IDDF Almanac Database 2000 Production & Trade; World Compact Aircraft, Ships & Tanks 2000

S INSTITUTE FOR FOREIGN POLICY ANALYSIS, INC, International Relations Library, 675 Massachusetts Ave 10th flr, 02139-3396. SAN 325-0067. Tel: 617-492-2116. FAX: 617-492-8242. E-Mail: mail@ifpa.org, Web Site: www.ifpa.org. *Pres*, Dr Robert L Paltzgraff
Library Holdings: Bk Titles 1,000; Per Subs 50
Subject Interests: Arms control, Int security studies, International relations, NATO, US foreign policy
Publications: Foreign Policy Reports, National Security Papers & Conference Reports; Special Reports

S CAROL R JOHNSON & ASSOCIATES, INC LIBRARY,* 1100 Massachusetts Ave, 02138. SAN 327-7216. Tel: 617-868-6115. FAX: 617-864-7890. *Librn*, Chris Burns
Library Holdings: Bk Vols 1,500; Per Subs 50

C LESLEY UNIVERSITY, Eleanor DeWolfe Ludcke Library, 30 Mellen St, 02138-2790. SAN 307-3025. Tel: 617-349-8840. Interlibrary Loan Service Tel: 617-349-8838. Circulation Tel: 617-349-8850. Reference Tel: 617-349-8872. FAX: 617-349-8849. Web Site: www.lesley.edu/library. *Dir*, Patricia Payne; E-Mail: ppayne@mail.lesley.edu; *Asst Dir*, Katherine Holmes; *Assoc Dir*, Constance Vrattos; *Media Spec*, Marie Gannon; *Tech Servs*, Mary McClure; *Ref*, Jessica Bell; *Cat*, Wen-chieh Kung; *Ref*, Mary Forkin; Staff 18 (MLS 11, Non-MLS 7)
Founded 1909. Enrl 3,580; Fac 81; Highest Degree: Doctorate
Jul 2000-Jun 2001 Income Parent Institution $1,475,936. Mats Exp $309,717, Books $91,000, Per/Ser (Incl. Access Fees) $81,500, Micro $16,800, AV Equip $15,000, Electronic Ref Mat (Incl. Access Fees) $105,417. Sal $929,621 (Prof $619,504)
Library Holdings: Bk Vols 100,000; Per Subs 650
Subject Interests: Art, Education, Feminism, Psychology, Special education, Therapy
Special Collections: Curriculum Materials; Educational Test
Automation Activity & Vendor Info: (Circulation) DRA; (OPAC) DRA
Partic in Fenway Libraries Online; Fenway Library Consortium; Nelinet, Inc; OCLC Online Computer Library Center, Inc

ARTHUR D LITTLE INC
S GLOBAL INFORMATION & RESEARCH SERVICES, 15 Acorn Park, 02140-2390. SAN 307-3033. Tel: 617-498-6012, 617-498-6371, 617-498-6372. FAX: 617-498-7241. E-Mail: ctr.globalresearch@adlittle.com. *Dir*, Beth Jacaruso
Founded 1886
Library Holdings: Per Subs 500
Subject Interests: Bus, Chemistry, Energy, Engineering, Environ, Food indust, Info sci, Mgt safety
Special Collections: Arthur D Little Coll
Publications: Acquisitions List; Union List of Serials
Partic in Nelinet, Inc; OCLC Online Computer Library Center, Inc

C LONGY SCHOOL OF MUSIC, Bakalar Library, One Follen St, 02138. SAN 324-2846. Tel: 617-876-0956, Ext 540. FAX: 617-354-8841. *Librn*, Roy Rudolph; E-Mail: rrudolph@longy.edu. Subject Specialists: *Music*, Roy Rudolph; Staff 1 (MLS 1)
Founded 1915. Enrl 1,350; Fac 148
Library Holdings: Bk Vols 20,500; Per Subs 25
Special Collections: Baroque Dance (Margaret Daniels-Girard Coll); Nadia Baulanger, E Power Biggs & other 20th Century Longy Faculty (Longy Archives Coll), correspondence, photogs
Database Vendor: OCLC - First Search

S LOTUS DEVELOPMENT CORPORATION, Information Resources Group,* 55 Cambridge Pkwy, 02142. SAN 326-0372. Tel: 617-693-5300. FAX: 617-693-1099.; Staff 4 (MLS 3, Non-MLS 1)
Founded 1983
Library Holdings: Bk Vols 300; Bk Titles 300; Per Subs 200
Publications: IRG Industry Newswire; IRG Micro Notes
Restriction: Company library

C MASSACHUSETTS INSTITUTE OF TECHNOLOGY LIBRARIES, Rm 14S-216, 02139-4307. SAN 345-0783. Tel: 617-253-5651. Interlibrary Loan Service Tel: 617-253-5668. Interlibrary Loan Service FAX: 617-253-1690. Web Site: libraries.mit.edu. *Dir*, Ann Wolpert; Fax: 617-253-8894; *Acq*, Marilyn G McSweeney; *Publ Servs*, Virginia Steel; *ILL*, Keith Glitvash; *Coll Develop*, Carol Fleishauer; *Cat*, Sarah G Mitchell; *Doc*, Keith Glavash; *Coll Develop*, Jennifer Banks; Staff 86 (MLS 86)
Founded 1862. Enrl 9,521; Fac 792; Highest Degree: Doctorate
Library Holdings: Per Subs 18,359
Special Collections: 19th Century Glass Manufacture in US (Gaffield Coll); Architecture & Planning, photostats, slides, pamphlets; Civil Engineering (Baldwin Coll); Drawings by Charles Bulfinch & Benjamin Latrobe; Early History of Aeronautics (Vail Coll); Early Works in Mathematics & Physics (Louis Derr Coll); Linguistics (Roman Jakobson Coll); Maps; Microscopy, 17th-19th Century (Melville Eastham Coll); Rand Corp; Spectroscopy (Kayser Coll)
Automation Activity & Vendor Info: (Circulation) GEAC
Publications: MIT Libraries' News
Mem of Asn of Research Libraries
Partic in Boston Library Consortium; BRS; Dialog Corporation; Nelinet, Inc; RLIN; SDC Search Serv
Departmental Libraries:
AERONAUTICS & ASTRONAUTICS, Rm 33-316, 02139. SAN 345-0813. Tel: 617-253-5665. FAX: 617-253-3256. Web Site: libraries.mit.edu/aero/. *Librn*, Eileen Dorschner
Library Holdings: Bk Vols 98,500
BARKER-ENGINEERING, Rm 10-500, 02139. SAN 345-0937. Tel: 617-253-5663. FAX: 617-258-5623. Web Site: libraries.mit.edu/barker/. *Librn*, Steven Gass
Library Holdings: Bk Vols 268,786
Subject Interests: Computer science, Engineering, Manufacturing
DEWEY-SOCIAL SCIENCES & MANAGEMENT, Rm E53-100, 02139. SAN 345-0872. Tel: 617-253-5676. FAX: 617-253-0642. Web Site: libraries.mit.edu/dewey/. *Librn*, Catherine Friedman
Library Holdings: Bk Vols 560,376
HUMANITIES, Rm 14S-200, 02139. SAN 345-0996. Tel: 617-253-5683. FAX: 617-253-3109. Web Site: libraries.mit.edu/humanities/. *Librn*, Theresa A Tobin
Library Holdings: Bk Vols 255,864
INSTITUTE OF ARCHIVES & SPECIAL COLLECTIONS, Rm 14N-118, 02139. SAN 345-102X. Tel: 617-253-5690. FAX: 617-258-7305. Web Site: libraries.mit.edu/archives/. *In Charge*, Megan Sniffin-Marinoff
Library Holdings: Bk Vols 159,568
LEWIS MUSIC LIBRARY, Rm 14E-109, 02139. SAN 345-1054. Tel: 617-253-5636. FAX: 617-253-3109. Web Site: libraries.mit.edu/music/. *Librn*, Peter Munstedt
Library Holdings: Bk Vols 42,154
Publications: Whats the Score? (newsletter)
LINDGREN-EARTH SCIENCES, Rm 54-200, 02139. SAN 345-0902. Tel: 617-253-5679. FAX: 617-252-1621. Web Site: libraries.mit.edu/lindgren. *Librn*, Katherine Keefe
Library Holdings: Bk Vols 45,905
ROTCH LIBRARY-ARCHITECTURE & PLANNING, Rm 7-238, 02139. SAN 345-0848. Tel: 617-258-5594. FAX: 617-253-9331. Web Site: libraries.mit.edu/rotch/. *Librn*, Margaret dePopolo
Library Holdings: Bk Vols 202,692
ROTCH VISUAL COLLECTIONS, Rm 7-304, 02139. SAN 345-1143. Tel: 617-253-7098. FAX: 617-253-9331. Web Site: libraries.mit.edu/rvc/. *Librn*, Katherine Poole
SCHERING-PLOUGH LIBRARY, Rm E25-131, 02139. SAN 345-1070. Tel: 617-253-6366. FAX: 617-252-1657. Web Site: libraries.mit.edu/sp/. *Librn*, Louisa Worthington
Library Holdings: Bk Vols 8,767
SCIENCE, Rm 14S-134, 02139. SAN 345-1089. Tel: 617-253-5685. FAX: 617-253-6365. Web Site: libraries.mit.edu/science/. *Librn*, Virginia Steel
Library Holdings: Bk Vols 300,533
Subject Interests: Chemical engineering, Mathematics, Nuclear engineering, Physics

GL MIDDLESEX LAW LIBRARY AT CAMBRIDGE, Superior Courthouse, 40 Thorndike St, 02141. SAN 307-3068. Tel: 617-494-4148. FAX: 617-225-0026. *Dir*, Sandra K Lindheimer; E-Mail: sandyl@ultranet.com; Staff 5 (MLS 2, Non-MLS 3)
Founded 1815
Library Holdings: Bk Vols 90,000; Bk Titles 4,250; Per Subs 500
Special Collections: Massachusetts, United States & Federal Law
Partic in OCLC Online Computer Library Center, Inc; Westlaw
Friends of the Library Group

S MIT RESEARCH LABORATORY OF ELECTRONICS, Document Room, 77 Massachusetts Ave, 02139. SAN 329-0220. Tel: 617-253-2566. FAX: 617-258-7864. Web Site: www.rleweb.mit.edu.; Staff 2 (MLS 1, Non-MLS 1)
Enrl 7,000; Highest Degree: Doctorate

Library Holdings: Bk Titles 2,000; Per Subs 110
Subject Interests: Electronics, Optics, Physics
Publications: RLE Currents (newsletter biannually); RLE Progress Report (annually); RLE Undercurrents

C MIT SCIENCE FICTION SOCIETY LIBRARY, (MITSFS), W20-473, 84 Massachusetts Ave, 02139-0901. SAN 324-1149. Tel: 617-258-5126. E-Mail: mitsfs@mit.edu. Web Site: www.mit.edu/~mitsfs/. *Pres*, T C Skinner
Founded 1949
Library Holdings: Bk Vols 60,000; Bk Titles 22,533; Per Subs 10
Subject Interests: Fantasy bks, Fantasy mags, Science fiction
Special Collections: Foreign Language materials; Science Fiction Writers of America depository
Publications: Twilight Zine (irregularly published fanzine)

G MIT SEA GRANT COLLEGE PROGRAM, Information Center, MIT Bldg E38-300, 292 Main St, 02139. SAN 329-9090. Tel: 617-253-7041. FAX: 617-258-5730.
Founded 1970
Library Holdings: Bk Titles 4,000; Per Subs 100
Subject Interests: Aquaculture, Chitin, Fisheries, Offshore structures
Restriction: Open to public for reference only
Partic in Dialog Corporation

M MOUNT AUBURN HOSPITAL, Health Sciences Library, 330 Mount Auburn St, 02238. SAN 307-3076. Tel: 617-499-5109. *Dir, Librn*, M Cherie Haitz
Library Holdings: Bk Vols 1,800; Per Subs 130
Subject Interests: Health sciences
Special Collections: Classics in Medicine
Database Vendor: OVID Technologies
Restriction: Non-circulating to the public, Open to public for reference only
Function: Document delivery services, ILL available, Photocopies available, Reference services available
Partic in Boston Biomedical Library Consortium; National Network Of Libraries Of Medicine
Open Mon-Fri 9-5

S POLAROID CORPORATION, Research Library,* 730 Main St, 02139. SAN 307-3092. Tel: 781-386-2000. FAX: 781-386-8241. *Librn*, Micheal Fournier
Founded 1942
Library Holdings: Bk Vols 32,000; Bk Titles 31,000; Per Subs 1,000
Subject Interests: Chemistry, Engineering, Photography, Physics
Publications: Library Bulletin
Partic in Dialog Corporation; SDC Info Servs

S RAYTHEON ENGINEERS & CONSTRUCTORS, INC LIBRARY,* One Broadway, 02142. SAN 307-2398. Tel: 617-494-7000. FAX: 617-494-7277. *Librn*, Jacqueline Bassett
Founded 1908
Library Holdings: Bk Titles 12,000; Per Subs 300
Subject Interests: Civil engineering, Electrical engineering, Energy, Engineering, Industrial engineering
Special Collections: Jackson & Morgland
Publications: Library Bulletin (6 times per yr)
Partic in Dialog Corporation

S US NATIONAL PARK SERVICE LONGFELLOW NATIONAL HISTORIC SITE LIBRARY, 105 Brattle St, 02138. SAN 370-2979. Tel: 617-876-4491. FAX: 617-497-8718. E-Mail: frla_longfellow@nps.gov. Web Site: www.nts.gov/long. *Curator*, Janice Hodson
Library Holdings: Bk Vols 10,000
Publications: Charles Appleton Longfellow: Twenty Months in Japan 1871-1873
Friends of the Library Group

G JOHN A VOLPE NATIONAL TRANSPORTATION SYSTEMS CENTER, Technical Reference Center, Kendall Square, 55 Broadway, 02142. SAN 307-3149. Tel: 617-494-2306. FAX: 617-494-3125. Web Site: www.volpe.dot.gov/library/index.html. *Dir*, Susan C Dresley; Tel: 617-494-2117, Fax: 617-494-3125, E-Mail: dresley@volpe.dot.gov; *ILL, Ref*, Althea Phillips; Tel: 617-494-2117, E-Mail: phillipsa@volpe.dot.gov; *Acq*, Suzanne Ryan; Tel: 617-494-2637, E-Mail: ryans@volpe.dot.gov; *Cat*, Marilyn Gross; Tel: 617-494-2088, E-Mail: gross@volpe.dot.gov; Staff 6 (MLS 5, Non-MLS 1)
Founded 1970
Library Holdings: Bk Vols 32,000; Bk Titles 25,000; Per Subs 300
Subject Interests: Aviation, Engineering, Transportation
Special Collections: Fed Aviation Administration Documents; Motor Vehicle Specifications; Transportation Statistics Documents
Automation Activity & Vendor Info: (Circulation) Sydney; (OPAC) Sydney; (Serials) Sydney
Database Vendor: OCLC - First Search
Publications: Transportation Systems Center Bibliography of Technical Reports; TRC Bulletin (monthly acquisitions)
Restriction: Circulates for staff only, Public use on premises
Partic in Dialog Corporation; Fedlink; OCLC Online Computer Library Center, Inc

S W R GRACE & CO LIBRARY, 62 Whittemore Ave, 02140. SAN 307-2991. Tel: 617-498-4595. FAX: 617-864-7198. *Librn*, Jennifer L Umali; E-Mail: jennifer.l.umali@grace.com; *Asst Librn*, Pauline Chan; Tel: 617-498-4802, E-Mail: pauline.chan@grace.com; Staff 2 (MLS 1, Non-MLS 1)
Founded 1955
1998-1999 Mats Exp $117,000, Per/Ser (Incl. Access Fees) $30,000
Library Holdings: Bk Titles 3,000; Per Subs 125
Subject Interests: Chemistry, Polymer chemistry, Rubber chemistry, Technology
Automation Activity & Vendor Info: (Acquisitions) epixtech, inc.; (Cataloging) epixtech, inc.; (Circulation) epixtech, inc.; (OPAC) epixtech, inc.; (Serials) epixtech, inc.
Database Vendor: Dialog, epixtech, inc., OCLC - First Search
Restriction: By appointment only
Partic in Nelinet, Inc

M WHITEHEAD INSTITUTE FOR BIOMEDICAL RESEARCH, Elizabeth Augustus Whitehead Library, 9 Cambridge Ctr, 02142. SAN 377-9076. Tel: 617-258-5132. FAX: 617-258-6294. *Librn*, David Richardson; E-Mail: richardson@wi.mit.edu
Library Holdings: Bk Titles 300; Per Subs 100
Partic in National Network Of Libraries Of Medicine New England Region

CANTON

S CANTON HISTORICAL SOCIETY LIBRARY, 1400 Washington St, 02021. SAN 375-2615. Tel: 781-828-8537. FAX: 781-821-5780. *Pres*, James Roache
Founded 1893
Library Holdings: Bk Vols 500

P CANTON PUBLIC LIBRARY,* 786 Washington St, 02021-3029. SAN 307-3173. Tel: 781-821-5027. FAX: 781-821-5029. E-Mail: caill@ocln.org. Web Site: canton.mec.edu/library. *Dir*, Mark Lague; *Asst Librn, Tech Servs*, Lisa Barbieri; *ILL*, Sandy Greenfield; *Circ*, Ilene Kramer; *Ch Servs*, Ann Woodman; *Ref*, Patty Ryburn; Staff 6 (MLS 6)
Founded 1902. Pop 20,037; Circ 230,136
Jul 1996-Jun 1997 Income $603,978. Mats Exp $89,438, Books $50,417, Per/Ser (Incl. Access Fees) $35,521, Presv $500, Micro $3,000. Sal $457,316 (Prof $207,299)
Library Holdings: Bk Titles 85,440; Per Subs 190
Subject Interests: Art and architecture, Business and management, Law
Mem of Old Colony Libr Network
Partic in OCLN
Friends of the Library Group

M MASSACHUSETTS HOSPITAL SCHOOL, Medical Library,* 3 Randolph St, 02021. SAN 326-1085. Tel: 781-828-2440, Ext 270. FAX: 781-821-4086. *Dir*, Aruna Sachbev
Library Holdings: Bk Vols 500; Bk Titles 500; Per Subs 75
Restriction: Non-circulating to the public
Partic in Dept of Pub Health; MAHSL; Semco

CARLISLE

P GLEASON PUBLIC LIBRARY,* 22 Bedford Rd, 01741-0905. (Mail add: PO Box 813, 01741-0905), SAN 307-3181. Tel: 978-369-4898. FAX: 978-371-1268. E-Mail: mca@mvlc.lib.ma.us. *Dir*, Ellen Christinw Rauch; E-Mail: rauch@mvlc.lib.ma.us; Staff 9 (MLS 3, Non-MLS 6)
Founded 1872. Pop 4,615; Circ 77,514
Jul 1998-Jun 1999 Income $246,263, State $3,922, City $229,521, Locally Generated Income $1,169, Other $11,651. Mats Exp $53,194, Books $37,881, Per/Ser (Incl. Access Fees) $8,927, AV Equip $4,886, Electronic Ref Mat (Incl. Access Fees) $1,500. Sal $137,998
Library Holdings: Bk Vols 40,313; Per Subs 105
Special Collections: Local History (Wilkins Coll)
Function: ILL available
Mem of Eastern Mass Regional Libr Syst; Northeast Mass Regional Libr Syst
Partic in Merrimack Valley Library Consortium
Open Mon, Tues & Thurs 10-5 & 6:30-9, Wed 1-5 & 6:30-9, Fri 10-5, Sat 9-5
Friends of the Library Group

CARVER

P CARVER PUBLIC LIBRARY,* 2 Meadowbrook Way, PO Box 328, 02330-0328. SAN 307-319X. Tel: 508-866-3415. FAX: 508-866-3416. E-Mail: carref@sailsinc.org. Web Site: www.sailsinc.org/carver/index.html. *Librn*, Joyce H Upham; *Dir*, Carole A Julius; E-Mail: cjulius@sailsinc.org; *Res*, Amy Sheperdson; *Circ*, Patricia Martin; Staff 9 (MLS 1, Non-MLS 8)
Founded 1895. Pop 11,500; Circ 80,000
Jul 1999-Jun 2000 Income City $218,653. Mats Exp $37,000, Books $31,500, Per/Ser (Incl. Access Fees) $5,500. Sal $161,443 (Prof $42,000)
Library Holdings: Bk Vols 51,000; Per Subs 75
Special Collections: Local Genealogy

Automation Activity & Vendor Info: (Cataloging) epixtech, inc.
Database Vendor: epixtech, inc.
Mem of SE Automated Libr
Partic in Sails, Inc
Friends of the Library Group

CENTERVILLE

P CENTERVILLE PUBLIC LIBRARY ASSOCIATION,* 585 Main St, 02632. SAN 307-3203. Tel: 508-790-6220. FAX: 508-790-6218. *Librn*, Janice M LaPorte
Circ 49,937
Library Holdings: Per Subs 103
Special Collections: Private Coll of the Books of Walter Lippmann, non-fiction
Mem of Eastern Mass Regional Libr Syst
Friends of the Library Group

CHARLEMONT

P TYLER MEMORIAL LIBRARY, 153 Main St, PO Box 618, 01339-0618. SAN 307-3211. Tel: 413-339-4335. FAX: 413-339-0320. *Dir*, Bambi Miller
Pop 1,250; Circ 12,274
Library Holdings: Bk Vols 9,200; Per Subs 12
Subject Interests: Local history
Mem of Western Regional Libr Syst
Open Thurs 1-5, Tues 6:30-8:30 & Sat 9-12:30

CHARLESTOWN

S CHARLESTOWN BOYS' & GIRLS' CLUB, Charles Hayden Memorial Library, 15 Green St, 02129. SAN 307-1448. Tel: 617-242-1775. FAX: 617-241-3847. *Dir*, Kenneth Sazama
Founded 1893
Library Holdings: Bk Vols 8,000; Per Subs 15
Restriction: Members only
Open Tues-Fri 2:30-6, 6-12 yrs olds, Sat 10-5, 6-8 yrs old, Tues-Fri 2:30-8 & Sat 10-5, 9-12 yrs old

CHARLTON

P CHARLTON PUBLIC LIBRARY,* 40 Main St, 01507. SAN 307-322X. Tel: 508-248-2052. FAX: 508-248-2052. *Dir*, Anne Hackett; E-Mail: ahackett@cwmarsmail.cwmars.org
Pop 11,400; Circ 70,000
1997-1998 Income $78,000, State $12,000. Mats Exp $18,000, Books $16,500, Per/Ser (Incl. Access Fees) $1,500. Sal $66,000
Library Holdings: Bk Vols 26,000
Mem of Central Massachusetts Regional Library System
Open Mon & Wed 9:30-5, Tues & Thurs 9:30-8, Sat 9:30-3
Friends of the Library Group

CHATHAM

P ELDREDGE PUBLIC LIBRARY,* 564 Main St, 02633-2296. SAN 307-3238. Tel: 508-945-5170. FAX: 508-945-5173. Web Site: www.capecod.net/epl. *Librn*, Irene B Gillies; E-Mail: igillies@clams.lib.ma.us; Staff 7 (MLS 3, Non-MLS 4)
Founded 1895. Pop 6,500; Circ 98,000
Jul 1998-Jun 1999 Income $322,007, State $6,199, City $213,116, Locally Generated Income $102,692. Mats Exp $73,170, Books $42,374, Per/Ser (Incl. Access Fees) $15,617, AV Equip $12,675, Electronic Ref Mat (Incl. Access Fees) $2,504. Sal $248,114
Library Holdings: Bk Vols 45,000; Bk Titles 52,829; Per Subs 78; Bks on Deafness & Sign Lang 18
Subject Interests: Genealogy
Special Collections: Genealogy (Edgar Francis Waterman Coll); Life Saving Service Reports
Automation Activity & Vendor Info: (Circulation) DRA; (ILL) DRA; (Serials) DRA
Database Vendor: DRA
Mem of SE Mass Regional Libr Syst
Partic in Cape Libraries Automated Materials Sharing
Friends of the Library Group

CHELMSFORD

P CHELMSFORD PUBLIC LIBRARY,* 25 Boston Rd, 01824-3088. SAN 345-1208. Tel: 978-256-5521. FAX: 978256-8511. E-Mail: mcd@mvlc.lib.ma.us. Web Site: www.mdc.net/~chelmlib. *Dir*, Mary Mahoney; *Asst Dir*, Nanette Eichell; *Ch Servs*, Cheryl Zani; *Tech Servs*, Christopher Kupec; *Ref*, Debra Perlow; *Acq*, Celeste Crowley; *Librn*, Maureen Foley; *ILL*, Linda Webb; Staff 23 (MLS 6, Non-MLS 17)
Founded 1894. Pop 32,383; Circ 380,313
Jul 1996-Jun 1997 Income $951,847, State $41,045, City $910,802. Mats Exp $135,516, Books $109,816, Per/Ser (Incl. Access Fees) $16,714. Sal $690,733 (Prof $202,301)
Library Holdings: Bk Vols 117,885; Bk Titles 110,595; Per Subs 238
Subject Interests: Local history
Publications: Handbook of Chelmsford Organizations; Library Lines (newsletter); Poetry: Community Connections
Partic in Merrimack Valley Library Consortium
Friends of the Library Group
Branches: 1
MACKAY, 43 Newfield St, North Chelmsford, 01863-1799. SAN 345-1232. Tel: 978-251-3212. *Librn*, Maureen Foley
Library Holdings: Bk Vols 32,000
Friends of the Library Group

CHELSEA

P CHELSEA PUBLIC LIBRARY,* 569 Broadway, 02150-2991. SAN 307-3254. Tel: 617-889-8399. FAX: 617-889-8364. *Dir*, Robert E Collins; *ILL, Ref*, Adelaide Sexton; *Tech Servs*, Dan LeBlanc; *Ch Servs*, Dennis Cooper; *Cat*, George Athas; *Asst Librn*, Bill Martin; Staff 4 (MLS 4)
Founded 1870. Pop 28,222; Circ 75,000
Library Holdings: Bk Titles 80,000; Per Subs 196
Special Collections: Large Print; Local History Archives; Massachusetts Annotated Laws; Massachusetts Law; Spanish
Friends of the Library Group

CHESHIRE

P CHESHIRE PUBLIC LIBRARY,* 80 Church St, PO Box Y, 01225-0015. SAN 307-3262. Tel: 413-743-4746. *Librn*, Judy Bender
Pop 3,357; Circ 15,000
Library Holdings: Bk Vols 6,700; Bk Titles 6,000; Per Subs 15
Mem of Western Regional Libr Syst

CHESTER

P HAMILTON MEMORIAL LIBRARY,* 195 Rte 20, 01011-9648. SAN 307-3270. Tel: 413-354-7808. *Librn*, Gale Andrade
Pop 1,114; Circ 5,269
Library Holdings: Bk Vols 7,000; Per Subs 15
Mem of Western Massachusetts Regional Library System
Summer programs available for children. Open Mon 12-4 & 6-8, Wed 6-8, Fri 10-3 & 6-8

CHESTERFIELD

P CHESTERFIELD PUBLIC LIBRARY,* 408 Main Rd, 01012. SAN 307-3289. Tel: 413-296-4735. *Dir*, Cindy Klein
Pop 1,012; Circ 6,921
Library Holdings: Bk Vols 8,300; Per Subs 22
Special Collections: Hampshire County & Chesterfield
Mem of Western Regional Libr Syst
Open Mon 2-7, Wed 10-4 & Sat 9-1
Friends of the Library Group

CHESTNUT HILL

CR BOSTON COLLEGE LIBRARIES, 140 Commonwealth Ave, 02467. SAN 345-1267. Tel: 617-552-3195. Circulation Tel: 627-552-8038. Reference Tel: 617-552-4472. FAX: 617-552-8828. Web Site: www.bc.edu/libraries.html. *Dir*, Jerome Yavarkovsky; *Assoc Dir*, Kathleen Carney; Tel: 617-552-4470; *Assoc Dir*, Jan Cellucci; Tel: 617-552-4470; *Assoc Dir*, Monique Lowd; Tel: 617-552-4470, Fax: 617-552-0599, E-Mail: lowd@bc.edu. Subject Specialists: *Administration*, Monique Lowd; *Research*, Kathleen Carney; *Systs*, Monique Lowd; Staff 155 (MLS 54, Non-MLS 101)
Founded 1863. Enrl 14,696; Fac 619; Highest Degree: Doctorate
Jun 1999-May 2000 Income (Main Library and Branch Library) $15,040,192. Mats Exp $6,586,998, Books $1,425,260, Per/Ser (Incl. Access Fees) $3,265,824, Presv $186,582, AV Equip $37,565, Other Print Mats $788,257, Electronic Ref Mat (Incl. Access Fees) $883,510. Sal $6,768,713 (Prof $3,634,835)
Library Holdings: Bk Vols 1,858,113; Per Subs 21,296
Special Collections: Balkan Studies; Bookbuilders of Boston Archives, 1938-; Boston History; British Catholic Authors; Caribbeana; Catholic Liturgy & Life in America 1925-1975; Eire Society of Boston Archives; Flann O'Brien Papers; Francis Thomson Coll, 1859-1907; Gilbert Keith Chesterton Coll, 1874-1936; Graham Greene Library & Archive; Hillaire Belloc Collection & Archives; Irish Coll; Irish Music Center; Jane Jacobs Coll; Jesuitana Coll, 1540-1773; Rex Stout Collection & Archives; S J Papers; Samuel Beckett Coll; Seamus Heaney Coll; The Honorable Margaret Heckler Papers; The Reverend Robert F Drinan; Theodore Dreiser Coll; Thomas Merton Coll; William Butler Yeats Coll
Automation Activity & Vendor Info: (Acquisitions) EX Libris; (Cataloging) EX Libris; (Circulation) EX Libris; (Course Reserve) EX Libris; (OPAC) EX Libris; (Serials) EX Libris

Database Vendor: CARL, Dialog, GaleNet, IAC - Info Trac, Lexis-Nexis, OCLC - First Search, OVID Technologies, ProQuest, Silverplatter Information Inc.
Publications: Faculty Newsletter; Guide to the Boston College Libraries
Partic in Boston Library Consortium; Boston Theological Institute Library Program; Greater NE Regional Med Libr Program
Departmental Libraries:
ACADEMIC DEVELOPMENT CENTER Tel: 617-552-8055. Web Site: www.bc.edu/bc_org/avp/ulib/bclib.html. *Dir*, Suzanne Barrett; *Coordr*, Kathleen Duggan; *Coordr*, Bryan Marinelli; *Assoc Librn*, Monique Lowd; Tel: 617-552-2918, Fax: 617-552-0599, E-Mail: lowd@bc.edu
Open Mon-Fri 9-5
BAPST ART LIBRARY, 140 Commonwealth Ave, 02467. SAN 323-5297. Tel: 617-552-3200. FAX: 617-552-0510. Web Site: www.bc.edu/libraries.html. *Librn*, Adeane Bregman
Library Holdings: Bk Vols 41,991; Per Subs 220
Publications: Guide to Bapst Library
Collection of library resources in art & art history
EDUCATIONAL RESOURCE CENTER, 140 Commonwealth Ave, 02467. SAN 323-5319. Tel: 617-552-4920. FAX: 617-552-0812. Web Site: www.bc.edu/libraries.html. *Head Librn*, Stephanie Neely; Tel: 617-552-4919, Fax: 617-552-1769, E-Mail: neelys@bc.edu; *Cat*, Cindy Jones; Tel: 617-552-4619, E-Mail: jonescn@bc.edu. Subject Specialists: *Educ K-12*, Stephanie Neely
Library Holdings: Bk Vols 27,357; Per Subs 102
Subject Interests: Audio, Children's books, Edu, Educ K-12, Psychology, Videos
GRADUATE SCHOOL OF SOCIAL WORK LIBRARY, 140 Commonwealth Ave, 02467. SAN 345-147X. Tel: 617-552-3233. FAX: 617-552-3199. Web Site: www.bc.edu/libraries.html. *Head Librn*, Betty Cohen; Tel: 617-552-3234; *Assoc Librn*, Monique Lowd; Tel: 617-552-2918, Fax: 617-552-0599, E-Mail: lowd@bc.edu
Library Holdings: Bk Vols 40,765; Per Subs 362
Subject Interests: Child welfare, Geriatrics and gerontology
JOHN J BURNS LIBRARY OF RARE BOOKS & SPECIAL COLLECTIONS, 140 Commonwealth Ave, 02467. Tel: 617-552-3282. FAX: 617-552-2465. Web Site: www.bc.edu/libraries.html. *Head Librn*, Robert K O'Neill; E-Mail: oneillro@bc.edu; *Archivist*, Edward Copenhagen; Tel: 617-552-3249, E-Mail: copenhag@bc.edu; *Ref*, John Atteberry; *Music*, Beth Sweeney
Library Holdings: Bk Vols 103,315; Per Subs 32
Subject Interests: Catholic Church, Jesuit, Manuscripts, Medieval mss, Nursing
Special Collections: Balkan Coll; British Catholic Authors Coll; Burns & Oates Coll; Congregationalism (1629-1829); Congressional Archives (Edward P Boland, Robert F Drinan, Margaret Heckler, Thomas P O'Neill Jr); Coventry Kersy Dighton Patmore (1823-1896); David Jones (1895-1973); DeFacto School Segregation; Detective Fiction Coll; Eire Society of Boston; Ethnology; Evelyn Waugh (1903-1966); Fallon Funeral Home; Fatherless Children of France (WW I); Fine Print Coll; Flann O'Brien Papers; Folklore, Jamaica & West Africa; Foulis Press; Freemasons; Golden Cockerel Press; Graham Greene (1904); Graham Greene Coll; Hibernia Bank; Hilaire Belloc Coll; Irish Authors; Irish Coll (Samuel Becket, William Butler Yeats, Seamus Heaney); Irish Land League; Irish Literature; Irish Music Center; Jamaica; Japanese Prints; Jesuitana Coll; John Henry Newman (1801-1890); Judaica; Liturgy & Life Coll; Nativism; Nero Wolfe Attractions; New England Theology; Nicholas M Williams Ethnological Coll; Nicholas M Williams Ethnological Coll; Nonesuch Press (London); Nursing; Oriole Press; Peppercannister Press; Playbills; Publishers & Publishing; Rare Books; Rita P Kelleher Nursing Coll; Salem Divines Coll; Samuel Beckett; St Dominic's Press; St Vincent DePaul Society; Stanbrook Abbey Press; Theater Programs; Thomas P O'Neill Jr Papers; Type Designers; Union Warren Savings Bank Archives; US Congressional Archives; Viola (Dallyn) Meynell (1886-1956); West Indies; William Butler Yeats (1865-1939); Women's History (Janet Wilson James Coll); World War I & II
Publications: Art of the Book (Collection catalog); Catalogue of Books, Manuscripts, etc in the Caribbeana Section of the Nicholas M Williams Memorial Ethnological Collection; Jesuitana at Boston College

CL LAW LIBRARY, Kenny-Cottle Library, 885 Centre St, Newton Centre, 02459. SAN 345-1321. Tel: 617-552-4405. Circulation Tel: 617-552-4434. Reference Tel: 617-552-4434. FAX: 617-552-2889. Web Site: www.bc.edu/lawlibrary. *Librn*, Sharon H O'Connor; *Business, Tech Coordr*, Michael Mitsukawa; Tel: 617-552-2355, E-Mail: michael.mitsukawa@bc.edu; *Ref*, Karen Beck; *Ref*, Irene Good; *Ref*, John Nann; *Ref*, Connie Sellers; *Ref*, J Shear; *Ref*, Mark Sullivan; *Publ Servs*, Susan Sullivan; *Coll Develop*, Jonathan Thomas; *Bibliogr*, Deena Frazier; Staff 23 (MLS 12, Non-MLS 11)
Library Holdings: Bk Vols 217,725; Per Subs 6,510
NEWTON CAMPUS RESOURCE CENTER, Trinity Chapel Lower Level, Newton Ctr, 02459. SAN 345-1356. Tel: 617-552-4412. FAX: 617-552-4839. Web Site: www.bc.edu/libraries.html. *In Charge*, Tim Lynch
CATHERINE B O'CONNOR LIBRARY, Weston Observatory, 381 Concord Rd, Weston, 02467. SAN 307-7934. Tel: 617-552-8321. FAX: 617-552-8388. Web Site: www.bc.edu/bc_org/avp/ulib/bclib.html. *Assoc Librn*, Monique Lowd; Tel: 617-552-2918, Fax: 617-552-0599, E-Mail: lowd@bc.edu; *Coordr*, Patricia Donovan; E-Mail: donovapa@bcvms.bc.edu; Staff 1 (Non-MLS 1)
Founded 1946
Library Holdings: Bk Vols 8,409; Bk Titles 2,777; Per Subs 39
Subject Interests: Geology, Geophysics
Database Vendor: Silverplatter Information Inc.
Restriction: Open to faculty, students & qualified researchers
Function: Research library

CR THOMAS P O'NEILL JR LIBRARY (CENTRAL LIBRARY), 140 Commonwealth Ave, 02467. Tel: 617-552-4470. FAX: 617-552-0599. Web Site: www.bc.edu/libraries.html. *Head, Circ*, Margie Fiels; Tel: 617-552-4834, E-Mail: fiels@bc.edu; *Head, Cat*, Christine Conroy; Tel: 617-552-3210, E-Mail: conroyc@bc.edu; *Head, Ser Acq*, Scott Stangroom; Tel: 617-552-1907, E-Mail: stangroo@bc.edu; *Head, Acq*, Elvira Reynolds; Tel: 617-552-3207, E-Mail: reynolds@bc.edu; *Coll Develop*, Jonas Barciauskas; Tel: 617-552-4447, E-Mail: barciaus@bc.edu; *Media Spec*, Claudia Semper; Tel: 617-552-2183, E-Mail: semper@bc.edu; *Assoc Librn*, Monique Lowd; Tel: 617-552-2918, E-Mail: lowd@bc.edu; *Head Ref*, Edward Tallent; Tel: 617-552-2854, E-Mail: tallent@bc.edu; *Automation Syst Coordr*, Malcolm Norton; Tel: 617-552-4132, E-Mail: mac@bc.edu; *Instrul Serv*, Kwasi Sarkodie-Mensah; Tel: 617-552-4465, E-Mail: sarkodik@bc.edu; *Web Coordr*, Sheila Fehlman; Tel: 617-552-3211, E-Mail: fehlman@bc.edu; *Govt Doc*, Barbara Mento; Tel: 617-552-3354, E-Mail: mento@bc.edu. Subject Specialists: *Bibliographies*, Barbara Mento
Library Holdings: Bk Vols 1,318,387; Per Subs 13,833
Automation Activity & Vendor Info: (Cataloging) NOTIS
Publications: Faculty Newletter, Guide to the Boston College Libraries, Insert to the Student Newspaper
Partic in Boston Library Consortium; Boston Theological Institute Library Program; Greater NE Regional Med Libr Program
Special Services for the Deaf - TDD

SR CONGREGATION MISHKAN TEFILA, Harry & Anna Feinberg Library, 300 Hammond Pond Pkwy, 02167. SAN 326-033X. Tel: 617-332-7770. FAX: 617-332-2871. E-Mail: librarian@m.shkantefila.org. *Librn*, Judith Shapiro Greenblatt; Staff 1 (MLS 1)
Partic in Metrowest Massachusetts Regional Library System
Open Tues-Thurs 3-6

S LONGYEAR MUSEUM LIBRARY, 1125 Boylston St, 02467. SAN 370-1506. Tel: 617-278-9000. Toll Free Tel: 800-277-8943. FAX: 617-278-9003. Web Site: www.longyear.org. *Dir*, John Baehrend; *Curator*, Stephen Howard; *Librn*, Barbara Boenke
Library Holdings: Bk Vols 6,000
Subject Interests: Christian Sci
Special Collections: History of Christian Science 1821-1910; Life of Mary Baker Eddy & her early followers, photogs, diaries, letters, journals & logbks
Restriction: Non-circulating

C PINE MANOR COLLEGE, Annenberg Library & Communications Center,* 310 Heath St, 02467. SAN 307-3297. Tel: 617-731-7081. FAX: 617-731-7045. Web Site: www.pmc.edu/library/library.html. *Dir*, Esther Griswold; *Cat*, Claire Gosselin; *Circ*, Ellen Langer; *ILL*, Sarah Woolf; *Ref*, Vicki Litzinger; *Acq*, Sandra LaFleur; Staff 8 (MLS 5, Non-MLS 3)
Founded 1911. Enrl 350; Fac 59; Highest Degree: Bachelor
Library Holdings: Bk Vols 77,000; Bk Titles 64,000; Per Subs 346
Subject Interests: Education, Psychology
Special Collections: First Editions of Noted American Women Authors
Automation Activity & Vendor Info: (Acquisitions) SIRSI; (Cataloging) SIRSI; (Circulation) SIRSI; (Course Reserve) SIRSI; (OPAC) SIRSI; (Serials) SIRSI
Partic in Metrowest Massachusetts Regional Library System; Nelinet, Inc; OCLC Online Computer Library Center, Inc; Webnet

CHICOPEE

P CHICOPEE PUBLIC LIBRARY,* Main Library Market Sq, 31 Springfield St, 01013. SAN 345-150X. Tel: 413-594-1800. FAX: 413-594-1819. *Dir*, Cheryl Blieler; *Asst Dir*, Dorothy Beam; *Media Spec*, Diane Robillard; *Cat*, Eileen Cullinan; *Ref*, George Swistac; *Ch Servs*, Mary Jane Trybulski
Founded 1853. Pop 55,000; Circ 190,000
Library Holdings: Bk Titles 97,961; Per Subs 903
Subject Interests: Local history, Polish (language)
Mem of Western Regional Libr Syst
Friends of the Library Group
Branches: 3
ALDENVILLE, 527 Grattan St, 01020. SAN 345-1534. Tel: 413-532-4248. *Librn*, Ron Sullivan
Library Holdings: Bk Vols 10,500; Per Subs 30
Friends of the Library Group
CHICOPEE FALLS, 216 Broadway, 01020. SAN 345-1569. Tel: 413-594-1820. *Librn*, Patricia Kusiak
Library Holdings: Bk Vols 18,000; Per Subs 35

Friends of the Library Group
FAIRVIEW, 373 Britton St, 01020. SAN 345-1593. Tel: 413-533-8218. *Librn*, Linda Koske
Library Holdings: Bk Vols 11,516; Per Subs 40
Friends of the Library Group

C COLLEGE OF OUR LADY OF THE ELMS, Alumnae Library, 291 Springfield St, 01013-2839. SAN 307-3300. Tel: 413-594-2761, Ext 280. Interlibrary Loan Service Tel: 413-594-2761, Ext 286. Reference Tel: 413-594-2761, Ext 297. FAX: 413-594-7418. Web Site: www.elms.edu. *Coll Develop, Dir*, Patricia Bombardier; Tel: 413-594-2761, Ext 281, E-Mail: bombardierp@elms.edu; *ILL, Ref*, Elizabeth Sullivan; E-Mail: sullivanel@elms.edu; *Ref*, Mary E Courtney; E-Mail: courtneym@elms.edu; *Ser*, Debra Gomes; Tel: 413-594-2761, Ext 287; *Circ*, Joyce Boucher; E-Mail: boucherj@elms.edu; *Archivist, Spec Coll*, Mary E Gallagher; Tel: 413-594-2761, Ext 354, E-Mail: gallagherm@elms.edu; *Tech Servs*, Elaine Pinkos; Tel: 413-594-2761, Ext 286, E-Mail: pinkose@elms.edu; Staff 11 (MLS 5, Non-MLS 6)
Founded 1928. Enrl 750; Highest Degree: Master
Library Holdings: Bk Vols 109,100; Per Subs 652
Subject Interests: Natural science, Nursing, Religion
Special Collections: 18th Century Editions of English Authors; Ecclesiology, 16th & 17th Century Editions; Sir Walter Scott Coll, First Editions
Automation Activity & Vendor Info: (Cataloging) Innovative Interfaces Inc.; (Circulation) Innovative Interfaces Inc.; (ILL) Innovative Interfaces Inc.; (OPAC) Innovative Interfaces Inc.; (Serials) Innovative Interfaces Inc.
Publications: Barry Collection Catalog; Serials Catalog
Mem of Western Massachusetts Regional Library System
Partic in Cooperating Libraries Of Greater Springfield

CHILMARK

P CHILMARK PUBLIC LIBRARY, 552 South Rd, PO Box 180, 02535-1757. (Mail add: PO Box 180, 02535-0180), SAN 307-3319. Tel: 508-645-3360. FAX: 508-645-3737. E-Mail: chillib@vineyard.net. Web Site: www.ci.chilmark.ma.us/library. *Dir*, Catherine A Thompson; Staff 2 (Non-MLS 2)
Founded 1882. Pop 948
Jul 1999-Jun 2000 Income $135,822, State $3,595, City $120,416, Other $11,811. Mats Exp $26,290, Books $18,444, Per/Ser (Incl. Access Fees) $2,146, AV Equip $4,712, Other Print Mats $2,146. Sal $84,916
Library Holdings: Bk Vols 30,508; Per Subs 75
Special Collections: Brickner Corner; Martha's Vineyard Room, poetry, videos
Automation Activity & Vendor Info: (Acquisitions) Athena; (Acquisitions) Sagebrush Corporation; (Cataloging) Athena; (Cataloging) Sagebrush Corporation; (Circulation) Athena; (Circulation) Sagebrush Corporation; (Course Reserve) Athena; (Course Reserve) Sagebrush Corporation; (ILL) Athena; (ILL) Sagebrush Corporation
Database Vendor: Ebsco - EbscoHost
Mem of SE Mass Regional Libr Syst
Open Mon & Sat 10:30-5:30, Tues 8:30-12:30, Wed 10:30-7:30
Friends of the Library Group

CLARKSBURG

P CLARKSBURG TOWN LIBRARY, 711 W Cross Rd, 01247. SAN 376-7124. Tel: 413-664-6050. FAX: 413-664-6384. E-Mail: clarksburg@cwmars.org. *Dir*, Barbara DiLorenzo
Founded 1898. Pop 1,650; Circ 17,000
Jul 1998-Jun 1999 Income (Main Library Only) $39,035, State $2,573, City $29,232, Locally Generated Income $7,122, Other $108. Mats Exp $7,314, Books $4,500, Per/Ser (Incl. Access Fees) $1,250, AV Equip $1,500, Electronic Ref Mat (Incl. Access Fees) $64. Sal $21,240
Library Holdings: Bk Titles 10,000; Per Subs 53
Mem of Western Massachusetts Regional Library System
Friends of the Library Group

CLINTON

P BIGELOW FREE PUBLIC LIBRARY,* 54 Walnut St, 01510. SAN 307-3335. Tel: 978-365-4160. Interlibrary Loan Service Tel: 978-799-1683. FAX: 978-365-4161. *Librn*, Christine Flaherty
Pop 12,978; Circ 72,455
Library Holdings: Bk Vols 136,384; Per Subs 54
Mem of Central Massachusetts Regional Library System

COHASSET

S COHASSET HISTORICAL SOCIETY, Burtram J Pratt Memorial Library & Archives, 14 Summer St, 02025. SAN 372-6428. Tel: 781-383-1434. *Curator*, David H Wadsworth; *Librn*, Eleanor Smith; Staff 1 (MLS 1)
Founded 1928
Library Holdings: Bk Titles 1,000
Special Collections: Local & Area History (includes Henry F Howe Coll); Local & Area Theater (Arthur Mahoney Coll); Maritime History
Publications: Historical Highlights (newsletter 4 times a year) (Newsletter)
Restriction: By appointment only

P PAUL PRATT MEMORIAL LIBRARY, 106 S Main St, 02025-2097. SAN 307-3343. Tel: 781-383-1348. FAX: 781-383-1698. Web Site: www.cohassetlibrary.org. *Dir*, Janet G Husband; Staff 9 (MLS 3, Non-MLS 6)
Founded 1879. Pop 7,823; Circ 85,500
Jul 1999-Jun 2000 Income $324,136. Mats Exp $65,255. Sal $230,227
Library Holdings: Bk Vols 54,428; Per Subs 164
Partic in Old Colony Libr Network
Friends of the Library Group

COLRAIN

P GRISWOLD MEMORIAL LIBRARY,* PO Box 33, Main St, 01340-0033. SAN 307-3351. Tel: 413-624-3619. FAX: 413-624-3619. *Librn*, Betty Johnson; E-Mail: bjohnson@cwmars.org
Founded 1908. Pop 1,757
Library Holdings: Bk Vols 10,000; Per Subs 16
Friends of the Library Group

CONCORD

P CONCORD FREE PUBLIC LIBRARY,* 129 Main St, 01742-0129. SAN 345-1658. Tel: 978-318-3300. FAX: 978-318-3344. E-Mail: conmail1@mln.lib.ma.us. *Dir*, Barbara Powell; *ILL, Ref*, Ray Gerke; *Ch Servs*, Karen Ahearn; *Acq, Cat, Tech Servs*, Carol Taylor; *Rare Bks, Spec Coll*, Leslie Wilson; *Circ*, Robin McGrath
Founded 1873. Pop 17,071; Circ 328,267
Jul 1997-Jun 1998 Income $1,132,475, State $19,806, City $1,016,595, Locally Generated Income $8,830, Parent Institution $87,244. Mats Exp $166,163, Books $121,265, Per/Ser (Incl. Access Fees) $20,521, Micro $22,661, AV Equip $1,716. Sal $815,218
Library Holdings: Bk Vols 230,856; Per Subs 570
Subject Interests: American literature, History
Special Collections: Alcott Family; Concord History; Henry David Thoreau Coll; Nathaniel Hawthorne Coll; Ralph Waldo Emerson Coll
Publications: Corporation Newsletter; Friends Newsletter
Mem of Eastern Mass Regional Libr Syst
Partic in Minuteman Library Network
Special Services for the Deaf - TTY machine
Friends of the Library Group
Branches: 1
FOWLER MEMORIAL, 1322 Main St, 01742. SAN 345-1682. Tel: 978-318-3350. FAX: 978-371-6252. *Librn*, Pat Pluskal; *Librn*, Sharon McCarrell
Library Holdings: Bk Titles 30,000

S CONCORD MUSEUM LIBRARY, 200 Lexington Rd, PO Box 146, 01742. SAN 373-1677. Tel: 978-369-9763. FAX: 978-369-9660. E-Mail: cm1@concordmuseum.org. Web Site: www.concordmuseum.org. *Pub Relations*, Carol Haines; *Curator*, David Wood
Library Holdings: Bk Vols 950; Per Subs 12
Subject Interests: Decorative arts
Special Collections: Concord history
Restriction: By appointment only
Function: Research library

M EMERSON HOSPITAL LIBRARY,* 133 Old Rd to Nine Acre Corner, 01742. SAN 307-3378. Tel: 978-287-3090. FAX: 978-287-3651. *Librn*, Nancy Callander
Library Holdings: Bk Vols 700; Per Subs 150

S LOUISA MAY ALCOTT MEMORIAL ASSOCIATION LIBRARY,* PO Box 343, 01742. SAN 371-1552. Tel: 978-369-4118. FAX: 978-369-1367. *Dir*, Jan Turnquist
Library Holdings: Bk Vols 550

S MASSACHUSETTS CORRECTIONAL INSTITUTION-CONCORD LIBRARY,* 965 Elm St, PO Box 9106, 01742. SAN 307-3386. Tel: 978-369-3220, Ext 292. FAX: 978-727-7322. *Librn*, Margaret Mubiru-Musoke
Library Holdings: Bk Titles 9,000; Per Subs 51
Subject Interests: Law
Special Collections: Spanish Coll

S SIGNATRON LIBRARY,* 29 Domino Dr, 01742-2845. SAN 307-4854. Tel: 978-371-0550. FAX: 978-371-7414. E-Mail: signatron@signatron.com. Web Site: www.signatron.com. *Librn*, Paul Lane
Library Holdings: Bk Vols 1,000
Subject Interests: Technology
Partic in Dialog Corporation

UNITED STATES ARMY

A CORPS OF ENGINEERS, NEW ENGLAND DISTRICT LIBRARY, 696 Virginia Rd, 01742-2751. SAN 345-7206. Tel: 978-318-8349. FAX: 978-318-8693. *Bibliog Instr, Chief Librn, Online Servs*, Timothy Hays; E-Mail: timothy.p.hays@usace.army.mil
Founded 1947
Oct 1998-Sep 1999 Income $200,000. Mats Exp $60,000, Books $10,000, Per/Ser (Incl. Access Fees) $50,000. Sal $98,000 (Prof $55,000)
Library Holdings: Bk Titles 21,000; Per Subs 375
Subject Interests: Civil engineering, Ecology, Natural science, Real estate, Soil mechanics, Structural engineering, Water resources
Special Collections: New England River Basin Boring Data
Partic in Dialog Corporation; Fedlink; OCLC Online Computer Library Center, Inc

CONWAY

P FIELD MEMORIAL LIBRARY,* One Elm St, 01341. SAN 307-3394. Tel: 413-369-4646. *Librn*, Mildred Willenbrock
Pop 1,152; Circ 12,050
Library Holdings: Bk Vols 15,500; Per Subs 38
Mem of Western Regional Libr Syst

COTUIT

S CAHOON MUSEUM OF AMERICAN ART, American Painting Research Library, 4676 Falmouth Rd, PO Box 1853, 02635. SAN 375-8338. Tel: 508-428-7581. FAX: 508-420-3709. Web Site: www.cahoonmuseum.org. *Dir*, Cindy Nickerson
Founded 1984
Library Holdings: Bk Titles 2,000

P COTUIT LIBRARY, 871 Main St, PO Box 648, 02635. SAN 307-3408. Tel: 508-428-8141. FAX: 508-428-4636. E-Mail: cotuit@cape.com. *Dir*, Barbara A Burrow; *Asst Librn*, Joan Aselton; *Asst Librn*, Susan Boynton; *Asst Librn*, Patricia Hall; *Ref*, Kathleen Pratt; *Ch Servs*, Valerie Morgan
Founded 1874. Circ 56,365
Jul 1999-Jun 2000 Income $216,245, State $3,800, City $125,645, Locally Generated Income $48,200, Parent Institution $29,000, Other $9,600. Mats Exp $27,725, Books $27,525, Electronic Ref Mat (Incl. Access Fees) $200. Sal $145,803
Library Holdings: Bk Titles 48,849; Per Subs 100
Special Collections: Art Books; Old Children's Books
Automation Activity & Vendor Info: (Acquisitions) DRA; (Cataloging) DRA; (Circulation) DRA; (Course Reserve) DRA; (ILL) DRA; (Media Booking) DRA; (OPAC) DRA; (Serials) DRA
Mem of SE Mass Regional Libr Syst
Partic in Cape Libraries Automated Materials Sharing
Friends of the Library Group

CUMMINGTON

P BRYANT FREE LIBRARY,* 455 Berkshire Trail, 01026-9803. SAN 307-3416. Tel: 413-634-0109. *Chief Librn*, Mark DeMaranville
Founded 1872. Pop 800; Circ 10,117
1997-1998 Income $6,200
Library Holdings: Bk Titles 11,462; Per Subs 8
Mem of Western Regional Libr Syst
Friends of the Library Group

G CUMMINGTON HISTORICAL COMMISSION, Kingman Tavern Historical Museum Lyman Library, 41 Main St, 01026. SAN 373-1693. Tel: 413-634-5527. *Chair*, Merrie Bergmann
Library Holdings: Bk Vols 500
Open Sat 2-5, July & Aug

DALTON

P DALTON FREE PUBLIC LIBRARY, 462 Main St, 01226. SAN 307-3424. Tel: 413-684-6112. E-Mail: dalton@cwmars.org. Web Site: www.vgernet.net/dfplib/index.html. *Librn*, Doris J Lamica; *Asst Librn*, Katherine Hoag; Staff 1 (MLS 1)
Founded 1798. Pop 7,177
Jul 2000-Jun 2001 Income $139,112, State $11,509, City $116,603, Other $11,000. Mats Exp $26,200, Books $25,000, Per/Ser (Incl. Access Fees) $1,200. Sal $82,983 (Prof $36,500)
Library Holdings: Bk Titles 38,860; Per Subs 81
Subject Interests: Local history
Special Collections: Dalton Education Plan
Automation Activity & Vendor Info: (Circulation) Follett
Mem of Western Regional Libr Syst
Special Services for the Blind - Descriptive videos; Radio reading receivers
Friends of the Library Group

DANVERS

C NORTH SHORE COMMUNITY COLLEGE, Learning Resource Center, One Ferncroft Rd, 01923. (Mail add: PO Box 3340, 01923-0840), Tel: 978-762-4000, Ext 5524. FAX: 978-922-5165. Web Site: www.nscc.edu. *Dir*, Anne Tullson-Johnsen; E-Mail: atullson@noblenet.org; *Coordr*, David Houle; *Coordr*, Rosemarie Levesque; *Coordr*, William J Meunier; *Ref*, Cynthia Entwistle; *Ref*, Karen Pangallo; *Tech Servs*, John Koza; *Media Spec*, Darren Thompson
Library Holdings: Bk Vols 75,959; Bk Titles 66,763; Per Subs 592
Publications: Re:SEARCH
Partic in Dialog Corporation; Northeast Consortium Of Colleges & Universities In Massachusetts; OCLC Online Computer Library Center, Inc; Westlaw
Open Mon-Thurs 8-9, Fri 8-4, Sat 8:30-12:30 (academic year)

P PEABODY INSTITUTE LIBRARY,* 15 Sylvan St, 01923-2735. SAN 345-1712. Tel: 978-774-0554. FAX: 978-762-0251. Web Site: www.noblenet.org/danvers. *Dir*, Douglas W Rendell; *Asst Dir, Coll Develop*, Nicholas E McAuliffe; *Ch Servs*, JoAnne Dearin; *Tech Servs*, Mary Saratora; *Ref*, Suzanne MacLeod; *Archivist, Rare Bks, Spec Coll*, Richard Trask; *Circ*, Lynn Arnold
Founded 1866. Pop 24,000; Circ 206
Jul 1998-Jun 1999 Income $821,832. Mats Exp $130,634, Books $114,817, Per/Ser (Incl. Access Fees) $15,817. Sal $625,563
Library Holdings: Bk Vols 115,188; Per Subs 300
Special Collections: Anti Slavery (Parker Pillsbury Coll), bks, pamphlets; Danvers (Town Records Coll), mss; Witchcraft (Ellerton J Brehart Coll), bks, pamphlets, photog, mss
Automation Activity & Vendor Info: (Circulation) GEAC
Partic in North of Boston Library Exchange, Inc
Friends of the Library Group

DARTMOUTH

P DARTMOUTH PUBLIC LIBRARIES, Southworth Library, 732 Dartmouth St, 02748. SAN 345-5971. Tel: 508-999-0726. FAX: 508-992-9914. E-Mail: southwth@ultranet.com. Web Site: www.ultranet.com/~southwth. *Dir*, Andrew Katzen; *Asst Dir*, Dolores Tansey; *ILL, Ref*, Brian Walsh; *Ch Servs*, Joanne Sousa; *Tech Servs*, Rebecca Robins
Pop 28,017; Circ 238,418
Library Holdings: Bk Vols 104,564; Per Subs 165
Partic in Sails, Inc
Friends of the Library Group
Branches: 2
NORTH DARTMOUTH BRANCH, 1383 Tucker Rd, 02747. SAN 345-6005. Tel: 508-999-0728. FAX: 508-999-0795. *Librn*, Lynne Antunes
Library Holdings: Bk Vols 24,000
RUSSELL MILLS, 1205 Russell Mills Rd, 02714. SAN 345-603X. Tel: 508-999-0729. *Librn*, Kathleen Whittaker
Library Holdings: Bk Vols 10,000

DEDHAM

S DEDHAM HISTORICAL SOCIETY LIBRARY, 612 High St, 02027. (Mail add: PO Box 215, 02027-0215), Tel: 781-326-1385. FAX: 781-326-5762. E-Mail: library@dedhamhistorical.org. Web Site: www.dedhamhistorical.org. *Dir*, Ronald F Frazier; E-Mail: frazier@dedhamhistorical.org
Founded 1859
Jan 1999-Dec 1999 Income $100,000. Mats Exp $8,000, Books $2,000, Presv $2,000
Library Holdings: Bk Vols 10,000; Bk Titles 20,000; Per Subs 14
Subject Interests: Genealogy
Special Collections: Ames Family Coll; Church Records 1638-1890; Mann Family Coll; Original Dedham Grant Area Residents & Artifacts (including Nathaniel Ames-father & son); Records of Firms & Associations
Partic in Am Asn of State & Local Hist; Nat Trust for Hist Preservation
Open Tues-Fri 9-4, even dated Sat (call as times may change)

P DEDHAM PUBLIC LIBRARY, 43 Church St, 02026. SAN 345-1771. Tel: 781-326-0583. FAX: 781-326-1257. E-Mail: dedham@mln.lib.ma.us. *Dir*, Thomas G Brennan; *Asst Dir*, Maureen Horn; *Ad Servs, ILL*, Paul W Harvey; *Ch Servs*, Pat Riley; *Ref*, Dora Federico; *Circ*, Gretchan Reardan; *Tech Servs*, Isabella Suciu; Staff 19 (MLS 6, Non-MLS 13)
Founded 1872. Pop 21,892; Circ 135,250
Library Holdings: Bk Vols 100,000; Per Subs 242
Subject Interests: Art and architecture, Business and management, History, Social sciences and issues
Special Collections: Dedham Historical Coll
Mem of Eastern Mass Regional Libr Syst
Friends of the Library Group
Branches: 1
ENDICOTT, 257 Mount Vernon St, 02026. SAN 345-1801. Tel: 781-326-5339. *Dir*, Thomas G Brennan
Library Holdings: Bk Vols 25,000

DEERFIELD

S HISTORIC DEERFIELD INC & POCUMTUCK VALLEY MEMORIAL ASSOCIATION LIBRARIES, 6 Memorial St, PO Box 53, 01342-0053. SAN 371-6058. Tel: 413-774-5581, Ext 125. FAX: 413-775-7223. E-Mail: library@historic-deerfield.org. Web Site: www.historic-deerfield.org/libraries.html. *Librn*, David C Bosse; *Assoc Librn*, Sharman E Prouty; Staff 3 (MLS 2, Non-MLS 1)
Founded 1970
Jan 1999-Dec 1999 Income $225,000. Mats Exp $23,000, Books $15,000, Per/Ser (Incl. Access Fees) $3,000, Presv $1,000, Micro $500, Other Print Mats $3,500. Sal $86,000 (Prof $67,200)
Library Holdings: Bk Titles 50,000; Per Subs 50
Subject Interests: Decorative arts, Genealogy, Local history
Automation Activity & Vendor Info: (Cataloging) Endeavor; (Circulation) Endeavor; (OPAC) Endeavor
Publications: Brochure; Research at Deerfield
Partic in Nelinet, Inc; OCLC Online Computer Library Center, Inc

DENNIS

P DENNIS MEMORIAL LIBRARY ASSOCIATION, Old Bass River Rd, 02638-2523. SAN 307-3475. Tel: 508-385-2255. FAX: 508-385-2255. *Librn*, Nancy Symington
Pop 12,805; Circ 25,000
Library Holdings: Bk Vols 15,000; Per Subs 23
Mem of Eastern Mass Regional Libr Syst
Open Mon-Sat 1-5, Mon-Thurs 7pm-8:30pm

DIGHTON

S DIGHTON HISTORICAL SOCIETY MUSEUM LIBRARY, 1217 Williams St, 02715-1013. (Mail add: 1247 Somerset Ave, 02715-1224), SAN 372-6738. Tel: 508-669-5514. *Curator*, Elaine Varley
Founded 1962
Library Holdings: Bk Titles 100
Special Collections: Dightin Area Pictures & Scrapbooks; Indian Artifacts; Military & Children's Clothing; Old School Books

P DIGHTON PUBLIC LIBRARY, 395 Main St, 02715. SAN 307-3483. Tel: 508-669-6421. FAX: 508-669-6963. E-Mail: dpublib@netscape.net. Web Site: www.dighton.com. *Dir*, Ann Rust; E-Mail: arust@sailsinc.org; *Ch Servs*, Margaret St Ours; E-Mail: mstours@sailsinc.org; *Circ*, Phyllis Haskell; E-Mail: phaskell@sailsinc.org; *Cat*, Brenda Carr; E-Mail: bcarr@sailsinc.org; Staff 4 (Non-MLS 4)
Founded 1894. Pop 6,018; Circ 21,913
Jul 1999-Jun 2000 Income $92,829, State $8,219, City $82,300, Locally Generated Income $2,310. Mats Exp $16,745. Sal $57,208
Library Holdings: Bk Vols 17,000; Per Subs 80
Special Collections: Births & Deaths; Town Documents
Database Vendor: CARL, Dialog, Ebsco - EbscoHost, IAC - Info Trac, IAC - SearchBank, OCLC - First Search
Publications: Friend's Newsletter
Mem of SE Mass Regional Libr Syst
Partic in Sails, Inc
Friends of the Library Group

DORCHESTER

S BOSTON GLOBE, Newspaper Library,* 135 Morrissey Blvd, PO Box 2378, 02107. SAN 307-3491. Tel: 617-929-2540. FAX: 617-929-3314. *Librn*, Lisa Tuite
Founded 1887
Library Holdings: Bk Vols 6,500; Per Subs 120
Special Collections: Boston History
Publications: Boston Globe Library (handbook); Library News (recent acquisitions)
Partic in Dialog Corporation; Dow Jones News Retrieval

M CARNEY HOSPITAL, Colpoys Library,* 2100 Dorchester Ave, 02124-5666. SAN 307-3513. Tel: 617-296-4000, Ext 2050. FAX: 617-296-7659. *Librn*, Catherine Moore
Founded 1953
Library Holdings: Bk Titles 2,000; Per Subs 122
Subject Interests: Medicine
Partic in Boston Biomedical Library Consortium; Massachusetts Health Sciences Libraries Network

DOVER

P DOVER TOWN LIBRARY, 56 Dedham St, PO Box 669, 02030-0669. SAN 307-3521. Tel: 508-785-8113. FAX: 508-785-0138. Web Site: www.ultranet.com/~dovlib/. *Dir*, Kathy Killeen; E-Mail: dovmail1@mln.lib.ma.us; *Asst Dir*, Michelle Sampson; *Tech Servs*, Ellie Greim; *Ch Servs*, Lois McAuliffe; *Ch Servs*, Joan Panek; Staff 4 (MLS 4)
Founded 1894. Pop 5,751; Circ 76,926
Jul 2000-Jun 2001 Income $293,790, State $6,800, City $242,990, Other $44,000. Mats Exp $50,860, Books $35,000, Per/Ser (Incl. Access Fees) $6,500, AV Equip $6,500, Electronic Ref Mat (Incl. Access Fees) $2,860. Sal $175,262
Library Holdings: Bk Vols 45,875; Per Subs 110
Special Collections: McGrath Coll; Military & Aviation Coll
Partic in Metrowest Regional Libr Syst; Minuteman Library Network
Friends of the Library Group

DRACUT

P MOSES GREELEY PARKER MEMORIAL LIBRARY, 28 Arlington St, 01826-3997. SAN 307-3548. Tel: 978-454-5474. FAX: 978-454-9120. E-Mail: mdr@mvlc.lib.ma.us. *Dir*, Susan Schwarz; *Ad Servs*, Jeanne Roy; *Ch Servs*, Penny Berube; *Circ*, Julie Sheehan; *Circ*, Eleanor Szafran; *Ref Servs YA*, Gordon Noble
Founded 1922. Pop 28,000; Circ 155,000
Jul 2000-Jun 2001 Income $441,600
Library Holdings: Bk Vols 74,000; Per Subs 97
Subject Interests: Local history
Partic in Merrimack Valley Library Consortium
Friends of the Library Group

DUDLEY

P PEARLE L CRAWFORD MEMORIAL LIBRARY,* One Village St, 01571-3812. SAN 307-3556. Tel: 508-949-8021. FAX: 508-949-8026. *Dir*, Charles Moore; E-Mail: cmoore@cwmars.org; *Ch Servs*, Norma Waterhouse; Staff 4 (MLS 1, Non-MLS 3)
Founded 1897. Pop 9,900; Circ 50,875
Jul 1998-Jun 1999 Income $122,543, State $10,739, City $111,806. Mats Exp $69,774, Books $22,839, Per/Ser (Incl. Access Fees) $1,747
Library Holdings: Bk Vols 29,000; Per Subs 16
Mem of Central Massachusetts Regional Library System
Partic in CW Mars
Open Mon 1-7, Tues, Wed & Fri 10-5, Thurs 10-7
Friends of the Library Group

C NICHOLS COLLEGE, Conant Library, Center Rd, 01571. SAN 307-3564. Tel: 508-213-2334. Interlibrary Loan Service Tel: 508-213-2333. Circulation Tel: 508-213-2334. Reference Tel: 508-213-2333. FAX: 508-213-2323. Web Site: www.nichols.edu/library/homepage.htm. *Coll Develop, Dir*, Kay Lee; Tel: 508-213-2222, E-Mail: kay.lee@nichols.edu; *Asst Dir, Ref*, Jim Douglas; Tel: 508-213-2333, E-Mail: douglajs@nichols.edu; *Acq*, Evelyn Nieszczezewski; Tel: 508-213-2220, E-Mail: evelyn.nieszczezewski@nichols.edu; *Per*, Donna DeNardis; Tel: 508-213-2209, E-Mail: donna.denardis@nichols.edu; *Circ*, Sandra Lobo; Tel: 508-213-2234, E-Mail: sandra.lobo@nichols.edu; *Circ*, Pauline Sroczynski; E-Mail: pauline.sroczynski@nichols.edu; Staff 6 (MLS 2, Non-MLS 4)
Founded 1815. Enrl 877; Fac 53; Highest Degree: Master
Jul 1999-Jun 2000 Income Parent Institution $181,718. Mats Exp $45,822, Books $20,108, Per/Ser (Incl. Access Fees) $18,969, Presv $500, Micro $314, AV Equip $1,015, Electronic Ref Mat (Incl. Access Fees) $4,916. Sal $115,139 (Prof $64,000)
Library Holdings: Bk Vols 43,495; Per Subs 251
Subject Interests: Economics, Finance
Special Collections: History of Dudley, Webster & Nichols Academy
Automation Activity & Vendor Info: (Cataloging) Sagebrush Corporation; (Circulation) Sagebrush Corporation; (OPAC) Sagebrush Corporation
Database Vendor: Ebsco - EbscoHost, GaleNet, OCLC - First Search
Publications: Newsletter, twice per year
Partic in CMRLS; Nelinet, Inc; OCLC Online Computer Library Center, Inc; WACL

DUNSTABLE

P DUNSTABLE FREE PUBLIC LIBRARY,* 588 Main St, PO Box 219, 01827. SAN 307-3572. Tel: 978-649-7830. FAX: 978-649-4215. E-Mail: mdu@mvlc.lib.ma.us. *Dir*, Mary Beth Pallis
Pop 2,500; Circ 25,965
Jul 1996-Jun 1997 Income $55,779. Mats Exp $13,631, Books $12,151, Per/Ser (Incl. Access Fees) $780, Presv $200. Sal $34,278
Library Holdings: Bk Vols 23,500; Per Subs 56
Publications: Dunstable Village; Nason's History of Dunstable, Massachusetts
Mem of Eastern Mass Regional Libr Syst
Partic in Merrimack Valley Library Consortium
Friends of the Library Group

DUXBURY

S ART COMPLEX MUSEUM, Carl A Weyerhaeuser Library, 189 Alden St, PO Box 2814, 02331. SAN 325-318X. Tel: 781-934-6634, Ext 35. FAX: 781-934-5117. *Librn*, Cheryl O'Neill
Library Holdings: Bk Vols 6,000; Bk Titles 5,000; Per Subs 15
Subject Interests: Art history

Special Collections: Asian Art Coll, bks, prints; Shakers Coll
Publications: Acquisition List; Museum Catalogues
Restriction: Open to public for reference only
Open Wed-Sun 1-4
Friends of the Library Group

S BATTELLE OCEAN SCIENCES LIBRARY,* 397 Washington St, 02332. SAN 307-3580. Tel: 781-934-0571. FAX: 781-934-2124. *Librn*, Ellen Rosen; E-Mail: rosene@battele.org
Founded 1934
Library Holdings: Bk Vols 2,508; Bk Titles 1,280
Subject Interests: Chemistry, Marine biology, Oceanography, Toxicology, Water pollution
Restriction: By appointment only

P DUXBURY FREE LIBRARY, 77 Alden St, 02332. SAN 307-3599. Tel: 781-934-2721. FAX: 781-934-0663. Web Site: www.duxburyfreelibrary.org. *Dir*, Elaine Winquist; E-Mail: ewinquis@ocln.org; *Asst Dir*, David Murphy; *Circ*, Carol Jankowski; *Ch Servs*, Nancy Denman; Staff 22 (MLS 9, Non-MLS 13)
Founded 1889. Pop 14,205; Circ 119,600
Jul 2000-Jun 2001 Income $902,977, State $20,000, City $855,477, Other $27,500. Mats Exp $855,477, Books $86,741, Per/Ser (Incl. Access Fees) $3,000. Sal $633,063 (Prof $333,753)
Library Holdings: Bk Vols 100,000; Per Subs 200
Special Collections: Graton Coll on Book Collecting
Automation Activity & Vendor Info: (Cataloging) epixtech, inc.; (Circulation) epixtech, inc.
Mem of Eastern Mass Regional Libr Syst
Partic in Old Colony Libr Network
Open Mon & Thurs 10-9, Tues-Wed, Fri & Sat 10-5, Sun 1-5 (closed Sun in summer)
Friends of the Library Group

EAST BRIDGEWATER

P EAST BRIDGEWATER PUBLIC LIBRARY, 32 Union St, 02333-1598. SAN 307-3602. Tel: 508-378-1616. FAX: 508-378-1617. E-Mail: ebpl@tiac.net. *Dir Libr Serv*, Susan M Peterson; *Asst Libr Dir*, Jane A Finlay; *Ch Servs*, Lorraine M Boyd; *Tech Servs*, Ellen Crete; Staff 15 (MLS 5, Non-MLS 10)
Pop 12,779; Circ 125,242
Jul 2000-Jun 2001 Income $269,334, State $12,942, City $247,392, Other $9,000. Mats Exp $51,500, Books $36,800, Per/Ser (Incl. Access Fees) $3,700, Electronic Ref Mat (Incl. Access Fees) $11,000. Sal $215,876 (Prof $140,546)
Library Holdings: Bk Vols 45,017; Per Subs 123
Database Vendor: IAC - Info Trac
Mem of SE Mass Regional Libr Syst
Partic in Able Network
Special Services for the Blind - OCR scanner to read & translate printed materials not available on special media & translate them to special media (braille, large print, voice)
Has branches in three local schools
Friends of the Library Group

EAST BROOKFIELD

P EAST BROOKFIELD PUBLIC LIBRARY,* Depot Square, PO Box 90, 01515. SAN 307-3610. Tel: 508-867-7928. FAX: 508-867-4181. *Librn*, Cheryl Labonte; E-Mail: clabonte@cwmars
Pop 2,000; Circ 15,992
Library Holdings: Bk Titles 14,000; Per Subs 30
Mem of Central Massachusetts Regional Library System
Friends of the Library Group

EAST DENNIS

P JACOB SEARS MEMORIAL LIBRARY, East Dennis Library,* 23 Center St, PO Box 782, 02641. SAN 307-3629. Tel: 508-385-8151. *Dir*, Nancy Symington
Founded 1898. Pop 4,000; Circ 15,000
Library Holdings: Bk Vols 14,500
Subject Interests: History, Natural science
Mem of Eastern Mass Regional Libr Syst
Friends of the Library Group

EAST DOUGLAS

P SIMON FAIRFIELD PUBLIC LIBRARY,* Main St, PO Box 607, 01516. SAN 307-3637. Tel: 508-476-2695. FAX: 508-476-2695. *Dir*, Ann D Carlsson; Staff 1 (Non-MLS 1)
Founded 1903. Pop 5,021; Circ 20,315
Library Holdings: Bk Titles 20,000; Per Subs 50
Special Collections: Douglas History, bks & realia
Mem of Central Massachusetts Regional Library System
Open Mon & Thurs 12-5, Tues 12-8, Wed 10-5 & Sat 10-1

EAST FREETOWN

P JAMES WHITE MEMORIAL LIBRARY,* Five Washburn Rd, 02717-1220. SAN 307-3645. Tel: 508-763-5344. FAX: 508-763-4876. E-Mail: jwhiteli@ultranet.com. *Chief Librn*, Althea H Brady; *Dir*, Vicki Dawson
Circ 18,003
Jul 1996-Jun 1997 Income $21,834, State $3,882, Locally Generated Income $1,000. Mats Exp $6,000, Books $5,000, Per/Ser (Incl. Access Fees) $600, Other Print Mats $400. Sal $14,386
Library Holdings: Bk Vols 10,000
Subject Interests: Local history
Mem of Eastern Mass Regional Libr Syst
Partic in SE Automated Librs, Inc
Friends of the Library Group
Branches: 1
G H HATHAWAY LIBRARY, N Main St, No 6, Assonet, 02702. SAN 307-4013. Tel: 508-644-2385. FAX: 508-644-3193. E-Mail: ghlibra@ultranet.com. *Dir*, Vicki Dawson; *Librn*, Althea H Brady
Pop 8,600
Library Holdings: Bk Vols 10,000; Per Subs 30
Subject Interests: Large type print, Local history
Open Mon & Wed 3-5 & 7-9, Fri 1-5, Sat 10-12
Friends of the Library Group

EAST LONGMEADOW

P EAST LONGMEADOW PUBLIC LIBRARY, 60 Center Sq, Ste 2, 01028-2459. SAN 307-3653. Tel: 413-525-5432. FAX: 413-525-0344. Web Site: www.eastlongmeadow.org. *Dir*, Gloria Carver; E-Mail: gcarver@eastlongmeadow.org; *Asst Dir*, Susan Teale; E-Mail: steale@cwmars.org
Founded 1896. Pop 14,146
Jul 1999-Jun 2000 Income $533,535, State $20,501, Federal $7,155, Other $13,806. Mats Exp $78,742, Books $62,530, Per/Ser (Incl. Access Fees) $5,124. Sal $325,841
Library Holdings: Bk Vols 66,674; Per Subs 210
Database Vendor: Innovative Interfaces INN - View
Mem of C/W Mars; Western Massachusetts Regional Library System
Friends of the Library Group

EAST SANDWICH

S THE ROBERT S SWAIN LIBRARY, Green Briar Nature Center,* 6 Discovery Hill Rd, 02537. SAN 329-7845. Tel: 508-888-6870. FAX: 508-888-1919. *Librn*, Kathleen Fulton; *Curator*, Bethany Rutlidge
Subject Interests: Natural hist of NE US
Special Services for the Deaf - Special interest periodicals
Friends of the Library Group

EASTHAM

P EASTHAM PUBLIC LIBRARY, 190 Samoset Rd, 02642. SAN 307-3661. Tel: 508-240-5950. FAX: 508-240-0786. E-Mail: slederhouse@clams.lib.ma.us. Web Site: www.capecod.net/~elibrary/. *Dir*, Sue Lederhouse; *Ad Servs*, Martha Magane; *Tech Servs*, Connie Terhune; *Ch Servs*, Curry Hoskey; *Circ*, Linda Gloo; Staff 5 (MLS 3, Non-MLS 2)
Founded 1878. Pop 5,033; Circ 96,186
Jul 1999-Jun 2000 Income $174,165, State $6,233, City $149,585, County $2,029, Other $16,318. Mats Exp $48,749, Books $32,299, Per/Ser (Incl. Access Fees) $4,179, AV Equip $8,191, Electronic Ref Mat (Incl. Access Fees) $4,080. Sal $109,025
Library Holdings: Bk Vols 36,286; Per Subs 90
Subject Interests: Genealogy, Local history
Automation Activity & Vendor Info: (Cataloging) DRA; (Circulation) DRA; (ILL) DRA; (OPAC) DRA; (Serials) DRA
Database Vendor: DRA
Publications: History of the Eastham Library
Mem of SE Mass Regional Libr Syst
Partic in Cape Libraries Automated Materials Sharing
Friends of the Library Group

EASTHAMPTON

P EMILY WILLISTON MEMORIAL LIBRARY,* Nine Park St, 01027. SAN 307-367X. Tel: 413-527-1031. FAX: 413-527-3765. E-Mail: emily@crocker.com. Web Site: www.crocker.com/~emily. *Dir*, Rebecca Plimpton
Pop 16,000; Circ 90,000
1997-1998 Income $192,933. Mats Exp $29,000. Sal $129,634
Library Holdings: Bk Vols 42,000
Automation Activity & Vendor Info: (Circulation) Follett
Mem of Western Massachusetts Regional Library System
Friends of the Library Group

EASTON

CR STONEHILL COLLEGE, MacPhaidin Library, 320 Washington St, 02357-4015. SAN 307-5958. Tel: 508-565-1313. Interlibrary Loan Service Tel: 508-565-1310. Reference Tel: 508-565-1203. FAX: 508-565-1424. Web Site: www.stonehill.edu/library/. *Dir*, Edward Hynes; Tel: 508-565-1223, E-Mail: ehynes@stonehill.edu; *Cat*, Cheryl Brigante; Tel: 505-565-1151, E-Mail: cbrigante@stonehill.edu; *Circ*, Susan Conant; Tel: 508-565-1289, E-Mail: sconant@stonehill.edu; *Coll Develop*, Steve McGinty; Tel: 508-565-1329, E-Mail: smcginty@stonehill.edu; *Per*, Geri Sheehan; Tel: 508-565-1293, E-Mail: gsheehan@stonehill.edu; *Res*, Joe Middleton; Tel: 508-565-1433, E-Mail: jmiddleton@stonehill.edu; *Syst Coordr*, Jennifer Macaulay; Tel: 508-565-1238, E-Mail: jmacaulay@stonehill.edu; Staff 21 (MLS 8, Non-MLS 13)
Founded 1948. Enrl 2,100; Fac 117; Highest Degree: Bachelor
Jul 1998-Jun 1999 Income Parent Institution $1,311,000. Mats Exp $383,060, Books $84,237, Per/Ser (Incl. Access Fees) $215,165, Presv $5,776, Micro $24,207, AV Equip $6,058, Electronic Ref Mat (Incl. Access Fees) $45,189. Sal $560,072 (Prof $343,075)
Library Holdings: Bk Vols 176,408; Per Subs 1,445
Subject Interests: Business and management, Religion
Special Collections: Michael Novak Papers; Rep Joseph W Martin Jr, Papers & Memorabilia; Tofias Business Archives
Automation Activity & Vendor Info: (Acquisitions) Innovative Interfaces Inc.; (Cataloging) Innovative Interfaces Inc.; (Circulation) Innovative Interfaces Inc.; (Course Reserve) Innovative Interfaces Inc.; (OPAC) Innovative Interfaces Inc.; (Serials) Innovative Interfaces Inc.
Database Vendor: CARL, Dialog, IAC - SearchBank, Lexis-Nexis, OCLC - First Search
Partic in Nelinet, Inc; OCLC Online Computer Library Center, Inc; SE Mass Regional Libr Syst; Southeastern Massachusetts Cooperating Libraries

EDGARTOWN

L DUKES LAW LIBRARY,* PO Box 1267, 02539. SAN 373-1650. Tel: 508-627-4668. *Coordr*, Joseph E Sollito Jr
Library Holdings: Bk Vols 1,800; Per Subs 10

P EDGARTOWN FREE PUBLIC LIBRARY,* 58 N Water St, PO Box 5249, 02539. SAN 307-3688. Tel: 508-627-1373. FAX: 508-627-9534. *Dir*, Ann M Tyra; E-Mail: atyra@clams.lib.ma.us; *Asst Dir, Ch Servs*, Deborah A MacInnis
Founded 1892. Pop 2,900; Circ 47,117
Jul 1997-Jun 1998 Income $233,500. Mats Exp $50,000, AV Equip $5,868. Sal $165,180
Library Holdings: Bk Vols 40,000; Per Subs 100
Mem of Eastern Mass Regional Libr Syst
Partic in Cape & Islands Interlibrary Asn; Cape Libraries Automated Materials Sharing
Open Mon 10-2, Tues & Thurs 2-8, Wed 10-6, Fri & Sat 2-6
Friends of the Library Group

S MARTHA'S VINEYARD HISTORICAL SOCIETY, PO Box 1310, 02539-1310. SAN 321-0731. Tel: 508-627-4441. FAX: 508-627-4436. E-Mail: mvhistory@vineyard.net. Web Site: www.vineyard.net/org/mvhs. *Dir*, Matthew Stackpole; *Curator*, Jill Bouck; *Librn*, Peter Van Tassel
Founded 1922
Library Holdings: Bk Titles 3,000; Per Subs 50
Subject Interests: Hist of Martha's Vineyard, Seafaring, Whaling
Special Collections: 19th Century Photography; Genealogy; Logbooks; Wampahoag Indians
Publications: The Dukes County Intelligencer
Restriction: Open to public for reference only

ERVING

P ERVING PUBLIC LIBRARY,* 12 E Main St, PO Box 128, 01344. SAN 307-3696. Tel: 978-544-2765. FAX: 978-544-5436. *Librn*, Kathleen Hammock
Pop 1,308; Circ 9,280
Library Holdings: Bk Vols 11,627
Mem of Western Regional Libr Syst

ESSEX

P T O H P BURNHAM PUBLIC LIBRARY, Martin St, 01929. SAN 307-370X. Tel: 508-768-7410. FAX: 508-768-3370. E-Mail: mes@mvlc.lib.ma.us. *Librn*, Beth Cairns
Founded 1894. Pop 3,400; Circ 26,500
Library Holdings: Bk Vols 15,813; Per Subs 24
Mem of Eastern Mass Regional Libr Syst
Friends of the Library Group

S ESSEX HISTORICAL SOCIETY & SHIPBUILDING MUSEUM, INC, Archives & Library,* 28 Main St, PO Box 277, 01929. SAN 371-6902. Tel: 978-768-7541. FAX: 978-768-2541. *Curator*, Jim Witham; *Coll Develop*, Courtney Ellis Peckham
Founded 1976
Library Holdings: Bk Titles 523; Per Subs 40
Subject Interests: Maritime history
Special Collections: Choate Papers; Essex History, bks, doc & photos; Maritime History, bks, doc & photos; Shipbuilding, bks, doc, drawings & photos
Publications: List of Watercraft Built in Essex 1860-1980

EVERETT

P FREDERICK E PARLIN MEMORIAL LIBRARY, 410 Broadway, 02149. SAN 345-1895. Tel: 617-394-2300. Circulation Tel: 617-394-2300. Reference Tel: 617-394-2302. TDD: 617-389-0784. FAX: 617-389-1230. E-Mail: eve@noblenet.org. Web Site: www.noblenet.org/everett. *Dir*, Deborah Abraham; Tel: 617-394-2303, E-Mail: abraham@noblenet.org; *Acq, Asst Dir*, Anne Marie Letourneau; Tel: 617-394-2304, E-Mail: letourn@noblenet.org; *ILL, Ref*, Susanna Austin; E-Mail: austin@noblenet.org; *Circ*, Julie Matson; E-Mail: matson@noblenet.org; *Cat*, Sharon Morita; Tel: 617-394-2307, E-Mail: morita@noblenet.org; *Ch Servs*, Michael Sullivan; Tel: 617-394-2305, E-Mail: msullivan@noblenet.org; *YA Servs*, Teresa Kerrigan; E-Mail: kerriga@noblenet.org; Staff 10 (MLS 9, Non-MLS 1)
Founded 1879. Pop 35,701; Circ 131,152
Jul 1999-Jun 2000 Income (Main Library and Branch Library) $807,065, State $47,253, City $756,493, Federal $2,393, Other $926. Mats Exp $109,738, Books $79,015, Per/Ser (Incl. Access Fees) $13,831, Micro $100, AV Equip $12,913, Electronic Ref Mat (Incl. Access Fees) $3,879. Sal $561,673 (Prof $322,023)
Library Holdings: Bk Vols 135,799; Per Subs 215; High Interest/Low Vocabulary Bk Vols 25; Bks on Deafness & Sign Lang 115
Subject Interests: City hist
Automation Activity & Vendor Info: (Cataloging) Innovative Interfaces Inc.; (Circulation) Innovative Interfaces Inc.; (ILL) Innovative Interfaces Inc.; (Media Booking) Innovative Interfaces Inc.; (OPAC) Innovative Interfaces Inc.
Database Vendor: CARL, Dialog, Ebsco - EbscoHost, IAC - SearchBank
Publications: Children's Brochure; General Brochure; Internet Services Brochure; Young Adult Brochure
Partic in Noble
Special Services for the Deaf - TDD
Friends of the Library Group
Branches: 1
SHUTE MEMORIAL, 781 Broadway, 02149. SAN 307-3742. Tel: 617-394-2308. FAX: 617-394-2354. E-Mail: evs@noblenet.org. Web Site: www.noblenet.org/everett. *Ad Servs*, Mark Parisi; *Ch Servs*, Ellen Baird; Staff 6 (MLS 2, Non-MLS 4)
Library Holdings: Bk Titles 52,849; Per Subs 60
Automation Activity & Vendor Info: (Cataloging) Innovative Interfaces Inc.; (Circulation) Innovative Interfaces Inc.; (ILL) Innovative Interfaces Inc.; (OPAC) Innovative Interfaces Inc.
Publications: Shute Memorial Library: A Short History
Partic in North of Boston Library Exchange, Inc
Open Mon & Wed 10-8, Tues & Thurs-Sat 10-6
Friends of the Library Group

M WHIDDEN MEMORIAL HOSPITAL, Medical Library,* 103 Garland St, 02149. SAN 307-3750. Tel: 617-389-6270.
Library Holdings: Bk Vols 2,614; Per Subs 70

FAIRHAVEN

P MILLICENT LIBRARY,* 45 Centre St, PO Box 30, 02719-0030. SAN 307-3769. Tel: 508-992-5342. FAX: 508-993-7288. E-Mail: millie@maultranet.com. Web Site: www.tiac.net/users/millie. *Dir*, Carolyn Longworth; *Asst Dir*, Juanita Goulart; *Ch Servs*, Lisa Howard; *Archivist*, Debbie Charpentier; Staff 3 (MLS 3)
Founded 1893. Pop 16,279; Circ 130,259
Library Holdings: Bk Titles 61,189; Per Subs 150
Subject Interests: Art and architecture
Special Collections: Manjiro Nakahama (Journal of His Voyages 1840); Mark Twain (Letters to the Rogers Family)
Publications: Booklets on Fairhaven's history; Henry Huttleson Rogers; Mark Twain and Henry Huttleson Rogers, An Odd Couple; Mark Twain Letter to the Rogers Family
Mem of Eastern Mass Regional Libr Syst
Partic in SE Automated Librs, Inc
Friends of the Library Group

FALL RIVER

JR BRISTOL COMMUNITY COLLEGE, Eileen T Farley Learning Resources Center, 777 Elsbree St, 02720. SAN 307-3777. Tel: 508-678-2811, Ext 2500. Circulation Tel: 508-678-2811, Ext 2105. Reference Tel: 508-678-2811, Ext 2108. FAX: 508-676-7146. Web Site: www.bristol.mass.edu/department_pages/lrc/. *Asst Dean*, James H Ingles; *Assoc Dir, Coll Develop*, Ruth A Sullivan; Tel: 508-678-2811, Ext 2103, E-Mail: rasulliv@bristol.mass.edu; Staff 23 (MLS 4, Non-MLS 19)

Founded 1968. Enrl 2,625; Highest Degree: Associate
Jul 1999-Jun 2000 Income $601,123. Mats Exp $202,902, Books $92,872, Per/Ser (Incl. Access Fees) $69,903, Presv $2,018, Micro $21,500, AV Equip $7,329, Other Print Mats $5,000, Electronic Ref Mat (Incl. Access Fees) $4,280. Sal $328,480
Library Holdings: Bk Vols 63,278; Bk Titles 61,820; Per Subs 357
Subject Interests: Allied health
Automation Activity & Vendor Info: (Cataloging) SIRSI
Database Vendor: CARL, Ebsco - EbscoHost, GaleNet, IAC - Info Trac, IAC - SearchBank, Lexis-Nexis, OCLC - First Search
Function: ILL available
Partic in Nelinet, Inc; SE Automated Librs, Inc

M CHARLTON MEMORIAL HOSPITAL, Ida S Charlton Medical Library, 363 Highland Ave, 02720. SAN 307-3831. Tel: 508-679-3131. FAX: 508-679-7669. *Librn*, Carla Schneider; Tel: 508-679-2385
Founded 1949
Library Holdings: Bk Vols 2,000; Per Subs 75
Special Collections: Rare Books

S FALL RIVER HISTORICAL SOCIETY MUSEUM-LIBRARY,* 451 Rock St, 02720. SAN 370-8500. Tel: 508-679-1071. FAX: 508-675-5754. *Curator*, Michael Martins; *Archivist*, Marie-Claire Lajoie
Library Holdings: Bk Vols 1,500
Open Tues-Fri 9-4:30, closed holidays & weekends

P FALL RIVER PUBLIC LIBRARY, 104 N Main St, 02720. SAN 345-2018. Tel: 508-324-2700. TDD: 508-324-2700. FAX: 508-324-2707. E-Mail: frbooks@ma.ultranet.com. Web Site: www.sailsing.org/fallriver/main.htm. *Adminr*, Keith Stavely; *Publ Servs*, Paula Costa Cullen; *Tech Coordr*, Richard Sterling; *Acq*, Elizabeth Driscoll; *Circ*, Laurel DeStefano; *Ref*, Patricia Redfearn; *Ch Servs*, David Mello; *Tech Servs*, Mary Anne Walsh; Staff 27 (MLS 5, Non-MLS 22)
Founded 1860. Pop 91,066; Circ 225,318
Jul 2000-Jun 2001 Income $1,462,944, State $168,552, City $1,216,916, Federal $65,000, Other $12,476. Mats Exp $174,568, Books $136,898, Per/Ser (Incl. Access Fees) $24,478, Micro $5,613, Electronic Ref Mat (Incl. Access Fees) $7,579. Sal $780,531 (Prof $221,714)
Library Holdings: Bk Vols 350,000; Per Subs 296
Special Collections: Dr David S Greer Coll for Peace, Science & Education; Estes Coll of Books by Individuals Born & Who Have Lived in Fall River; Lizzie Borden Coll; Local History Coll; Portuguese Language Materials Coll
Automation Activity & Vendor Info: (Acquisitions) epixtech, inc.; (Cataloging) epixtech, inc.; (Circulation) epixtech, inc.; (OPAC) epixtech, inc.
Partic in Sails, Inc
Special Services for the Deaf - TDD; TTY machine
Friends of the Library Group
Branches: 2
EAST END, 1386 Pleasant St, 02723. SAN 345-2042. Tel: 508-324-2709. FAX: 508-324-2709. Web Site: www.sailsinc.org/fallriver/main.htm. *Branch Mgr*, Rita Menard; Staff 3 (Non-MLS 3)
SOUTH, 1310 S Main St, 02724. SAN 345-2077. Tel: 508-324-2708. FAX: 508-324-2708. Web Site: www.fallriver.mec.edu/frlibrary/main.htm. *Branch Mgr*, Elizabeth Washburn; Staff 3 (Non-MLS 3)

S MARINE MUSEUM AT FALL RIVER, INC LIBRARY, 70 Water St, 02721. SAN 307-3807. Tel: 508-674-3533. FAX: 508-674-3534. E-Mail: staff@marinmuseum.org. *Dir*, Dr Edwin L Dunbaugh
Founded 1968
Library Holdings: Bk Vols 2,000

M SAINT ANNE'S HOSPITAL, Sullivan Medical Library, 795 Middle St, 02721. SAN 307-3815. Tel: 508-674-5741, Ext 2231. FAX: 508-675-5606. *Librn*, Elaine M Crites
Founded 1955
Library Holdings: Bk Vols 4,044; Per Subs 84
Subject Interests: Geriatrics and gerontology, Medicine, Neurology, Obstetrics and gynecology, Oncology, Orthopedics, Pediatrics, Radiology, Surgery
Partic in SE Mass Health Sci Librs Consortium

R TEMPLE BETH EL, Ziskind Memorial Library, 385 High St, 02720. SAN 307-3823. Tel: 508-674-3529. FAX: 508-674-3058. *Librn*, Ruth Chebot
Founded 1955
Library Holdings: Bk Vols 6,500; Per Subs 35

GL TRIAL COURT OF MASSACHUSETTS, Fall River Law Library, Superior Court House, 441 N Main St, 02720. SAN 307-3793. Tel: 508-676-8971. FAX: 508-677-2966. Web Site: www.lawlib.state.ma.us. *Librn*, Lois Kane; E-Mail: lkane@lawlib.state.ma.us
Library Holdings: Bk Vols 31,000; Per Subs 37
Subject Interests: Law
Database Vendor: OCLC - First Search
Partic in Nellco; OCLC Online Computer Library Center, Inc; SE Mass Regional Libr Syst
Friends of the Library Group

S USS MASSACHUSETTS MEMORIAL COMMITTEE, INC, Archives & Technical Library, Battleship Cove, 02721. SAN 370-3258. Tel: 508-678-1100. FAX: 508-674-5597. E-Mail: battleship@battleshipcove.com. Web Site: www.battleshipcove.com. *Coordr*, Don Shannon; *Coll Develop*, Chris Nardi
Library Holdings: Bk Vols 2,000
Subject Interests: World War II
Special Collections: Blue Prints of Ships & Equipment, Machinery of US Navy

FALMOUTH

S FALMOUTH HISTORICAL SOCIETY, Resources Center History & Genealogy Archives Library, Palmer Ave at the Village Green, PO Box 174, 02541. SAN 326-5080. Tel: 508-548-4857. FAX: 508-540-0968. E-Mail: fhsoc@juno.com. *Archivist, Doc*, Dorothy Svenning
Library Holdings: Bk Vols 1,020
Subject Interests: Genealogy, Local history
Special Collections: Katharine Lee Bates Coll
Publications: Charlotte S Price Compilation (guide to manuscripts & special coll in the archives of Falmouth Historial Society); Dyer Arnold W Hotels & Inns of Falmouth (1993); Dyer Arnold W Residential Falmouth: an 1897 Souvenir brought up-to-date (c1897, 1992); Geoffregy Theodate Suckanesset: Reprint with index (c1928, 1992)

M FALMOUTH HOSPITAL, Medical Library,* 100 Ter Heun Dr, 02540. SAN 377-9092. Tel: 508-548-5300, Ext 3521. FAX: 508-457-3675. E-Mail: falmedli@capecod.net. *Librn*, Patricia Davis
Library Holdings: Bk Vols 800; Per Subs 150
Partic in Massachusetts Health Sciences Libraries Network; National Network Of Libraries Of Medicine New England Region; Southeastern Massachusetts Consortium Of Health Science Libraries

P FALMOUTH PUBLIC LIBRARY, 123 K L Bates Rd, 02540-2895. SAN 345-2107. Tel: 508-457-2555. FAX: 508-457-2559. Web Site: www.falmouthpubliclibrary.org. *Dir*, Nancy Serotkin; E-Mail: nserotkin@clams.lib.ma.us; *Asst Dir*, Lynne Lindley; *Circ*, Tammy Amon; *Tech Servs*, Frances Bordonaro; *Ch Servs*, Phyllis Eastwood; *Ref Serv Ad*, Jill Erickson; *ILL*, Toni Robertson; Staff 10 (MLS 8, Non-MLS 2)
Founded 1902. Pop 31,431; Circ 435,342
Jul 1999-Jun 2000 Income (Main Library and Branch Library) $1,205,314, State $42,098, City $1,163,216. Mats Exp $178,338, Books $118,708, Per/Ser (Incl. Access Fees) $21,972, Micro $3,944, AV Equip $14,734, Electronic Ref Mat (Incl. Access Fees) $18,980. Sal $875,527
Library Holdings: Bk Vols 142,729; Bk Titles 137,804; Per Subs 978
Subject Interests: Local history
Special Collections: Local Author (Katharine Lee Bates Coll); Local History
Automation Activity & Vendor Info: (Acquisitions) DRA; (Cataloging) DRA; (Circulation) DRA; (Course Reserve) DRA; (ILL) DRA; (Media Booking) DRA; (OPAC) DRA; (Serials) DRA
Database Vendor: DRA, OCLC - First Search
Mem of SE Mass Regional Libr Syst
Partic in Cape Libraries Automated Materials Sharing
Special Services for the Deaf - Captioned film depository; TTY machine
Special Services for the Blind - Descriptive videos
Friends of the Library Group
Branches: 2
EAST FALMOUTH BRANCH, 310 E Falmouth Hwy, East Falmouth, 02536. SAN 345-2131. Tel: 508-548-6340. *Librn*, Barbara Gibson
NORTH FALMOUTH BRANCH, 6 Chester St, North Falmouth, 02556. SAN 345-2166. Tel: 508-563-2922. *Librn*, Laurie McNee

FITCHBURG

P FITCHBURG PUBLIC LIBRARY,* 610 Main St, 01420-3146. SAN 307-3866. Tel: 978-345-9635. FAX: 978-345-9689. Web Site: www.net1plus.com/users/fpl. *Dir*, Elizabeth S Watson; *Ch Servs*, Jerry Johnson; *Cat*, Elizabeth L Berry; *Ref*, Kathleen French
Founded 1859. Pop 220,000
Library Holdings: Bk Vols 191,915; Per Subs 317
Automation Activity & Vendor Info: (Acquisitions) Brodart
Mem of Central Massachusetts Regional Library System
Special Services for the Deaf - Videos & decoder
Special Services for the Blind - VisualTek closed circuit TV reading aid
Friends of the Library Group

C FITCHBURG STATE COLLEGE LIBRARY, 160 Pearl St, 01420. SAN 307-3874. Tel: 978-665-3196. Circulation Tel: 978-665-3063. FAX: 978-665-3069. Web Site: www.fsc.edu/library. *Dir*, Robert Foley; E-Mail: rfoley@fsc.edu; *Per*, Janice Ouellette; *Res*, Bruce McSheehy; *Tech Servs*, Simone Blake; *Res*, Jean Missud; *Tech Coordr*, Ron McGuire; E-Mail: romcguire@fsc.edu; *Distance Educ*, Linda LeBlanc; Tel: 978-665-3063, E-Mail: lileblanc@fsc.edu; Staff 15 (MLS 8, Non-MLS 7)
Founded 1894. Enrl 3,603; Fac 225; Highest Degree: Master
Jul 1999-Jun 2000 Income $747,689, State $382,776, Federal $13,400, Parent Institution $351,513. Mats Exp $565,734, Books $221,280, Per/Ser

(Incl. Access Fees) $211,034, Presv $13,096, Micro $23,304, Other Print Mats $811, Electronic Ref Mat (Incl. Access Fees) $96,209. Sal $583,338 (Prof $293,655)
Library Holdings: Bk Vols 245,931; Per Subs 1,363
Subject Interests: Clinical labs, Local history, Nursing, Scis
Special Collections: College Archives; John van cortland Moon Coll; Rice Art Coll; Robert Cormier Coll; Robert Salvatore Coll
Automation Activity & Vendor Info: (Cataloging) Innovative Interfaces Inc.; (Circulation) Innovative Interfaces Inc.; (ILL) Innovative Interfaces Inc.; (OPAC) Innovative Interfaces Inc.; (Serials) Innovative Interfaces Inc.
Database Vendor: Ebsco - EbscoHost, GaleNet, IAC - Info Trac, Lexis-Nexis, OCLC - First Search, OVID Technologies, Silverplatter Information Inc., Wilson - Wilson Web
Publications: directories; Pathfinders (library instruction)
Partic in CW Mars; Dialog Corporation; Nelinet, Inc; OCLC Online Computer Library Center, Inc

L MASSACHUSETTS TRIAL COURT, Fitchburg Law Library, Superior Court House, 84 Elm St, 01420-3296. SAN 307-3858. Tel: 978-345-6726. FAX: 978-345-7334. E-Mail: fll@ma.ultranet.com. Web Site: www.lawlib.state.ma.us. *Librn*, Peter Anderegg; *Asst Librn*, Donna Wilkin
Founded 1871
Subject Interests: Law
Mem of Central Massachusetts Regional Library System
Partic in Nellco; OCLC Online Computer Library Center, Inc

FLORENCE

P LILLY LIBRARY, 19 Meadow St, 01062. SAN 322-7626. Tel: 413-587-1500. FAX: 413-587-1503. E-Mail: lilly@javanet.com. Web Site: www.lillylibrary.org. *Dir*, Mark Kille; *Asst Dir*, Charlotte Carver; *Ch Servs*, Kathryn Marciano; *ILL*, Dylan Gaffney; Staff 11 (MLS 1, Non-MLS 10)
Founded 1888. Pop 12,500; Circ 80,000
Library Holdings: Bk Vols 19,000; Per Subs 130
Mem of Western Massachusetts Regional Library System
Friends of the Library Group

FLORIDA

P FLORIDA FREE LIBRARY,* 56 N County Rd, 01247-9407. SAN 307-3890. Tel: 413-664-6023. FAX: 413-663-3593. *Dir*, Gail A La Gess
Library Holdings: Bk Titles 7,159; Per Subs 36
Mem of Western Massachusetts Regional Library System

FOXBORO

P BOYDEN LIBRARY,* 10 Bird St, 02035. SAN 307-3904. Tel: 508-543-1245. FAX: 508-543-1193. *Dir*, Bertha Chandler; *Ref*, Kathy Bell-Horney; *Ch Servs*, Margaret Rossetti; *Cat*, Diane Monahan; *Ad Servs*, Patrick Marshall; Staff 4 (MLS 4)
Founded 1870. Pop 17,000; Circ 146,125
Library Holdings: Bk Titles 72,420; Per Subs 96
Special Collections: Pace Genealogy Coll
Mem of Eastern Mass Regional Libr Syst
Open Mon-Thurs 10-8, Fri 10-6 & Sat 10-5
Friends of the Library Group

FRAMINGHAM

S DANFORTH MUSEUM OF ART, Marks Fine Arts Library, 123 Union Ave, 01702. SAN 373-1618. Tel: 508-620-0050. FAX: 508-872-5542. *Dir*, Ronald L Crusan
Library Holdings: Bk Vols 3,500
Subject Interests: Dance

P FRAMINGHAM PUBLIC LIBRARY,* 49 Lexington St, 01702-8278. SAN 345-2344. Tel: 508-879-3570. FAX: 508-820-7210. Web Site: www.mln.lib.ma.us. *Dir*, Thomas Gilchrist; *Asst Dir*, Mary Wasmuth; *Ch Servs*, Lucy Loveridge; *Tech Servs*, Linda Benjaminsen; *YA Servs*, Deborah Kelsey; *ILL*, Heather Pisani-Kristl; *Circ*, Judy Noonan; *Ref*, Deborah Ervin; *Coll Develop*, Juliana Melly; Staff 14 (MLS 14)
Founded 1855. Pop 64,536; Circ 769,877
Jul 1997-Jun 1998 Income $1,847,175. Mats Exp $295,878. Sal $1,383,969
Library Holdings: Bk Vols 222,764; Per Subs 466
Special Collections: Basic Education Coll; Local History Coll; Portuguese Language Coll; Spanish Language Coll
Mem of Eastern Mass Regional Libr Syst
Partic in Minuteman Library Network
Special Services for the Deaf - TTY 508-872-2775
Friends of the Library Group
Branches: 1
CHRISTA CORRIGAN MCAULIFFE BRANCH, 10 Nicholas Rd, 01701-3469. SAN 345-2409. Tel: 508-877-3636. FAX: 508-788-1930. *Librn*, Jeanne Kelley

C FRAMINGHAM STATE COLLEGE, Henry Whittemore Library, 100 State St, 01701. SAN 307-3955. Tel: 508-626-4651. Circulation Tel: 508-626-4650. Reference Tel: 508-626-4654. FAX: 508-626-4649. Web Site: www.frc.mass.edu. *Dir*, Bonnie Mitchell; *Ref Serv*, Jonathan Husband; *Ref Serv*, Sandra Rothenberg; *Ref Serv*, Marion Slack; *Cat, Tech Servs*, Richard Boehme; *Acq, Ser*, Maureen Krier; *Circ, ILL*, Allen Keane; *Bibliog Instr*, Irena Bond. Subject Specialists: *Curric*, Mary Pat Craig; Staff 11 (MLS 10, Non-MLS 1)
Founded 1969. Enrl 3,445; Fac 221; Highest Degree: Master
Library Holdings: Bk Vols 180,000; Bk Titles 168,000; Per Subs 1,317
Subject Interests: Biology, Chemistry, Computer science, Education, Natural science, Nursing, Physical science, Psychology, Social sciences and issues
Special Collections: College & Local History Coll; Curriculum Materials; Eric Documents Coll; Faculty Publications; Modern American Poetry
Publications: Staff newsletter; student & faculty handbooks; student employee manual
Partic in Minuteman Library Network; Nelinet, Inc; OCLC Online Computer Library Center, Inc

S GENZYME CORP, Information Services,* One Mountain Rd, PO Box 9322, 01701-9322. SAN 374-8596. Tel: 508-872-8400. FAX: 508-872-9080. *Dir*, Dawn Renear
Library Holdings: Bk Vols 50; Per Subs 3

S INTERNATIONAL DATA CORP LIBRARY, 5 Speen St, 01701-9015. SAN 329-0581. Tel: 508-935-4253. FAX: 508-935-4057. *Dir Libr Serv*, Merrill Walsh; E-Mail: mwalsh@idc.com; Staff 2 (MLS 1, Non-MLS 1)
Library Holdings: Bk Vols 2,400; Per Subs 250
Subject Interests: Bus, Computer science, Finance
Publications: Happenings; Industry News; Library News; Quote Alert; Reference Highlights
Restriction: Staff use only
Partic in Dialog Corporation; Dow Jones News Retrieval; OCLC Online Computer Library Center, Inc

S MASSACHUSETTS CORRECTIONAL INSTITUTION-FRAMINGHAM LIBRARY,* PO Box 9007, 01701-9007. SAN 307-3971. Tel: 508-875-5258, Ext 142. *In Charge*, Nilima Jamsandekar
Founded 1921
Library Holdings: Bk Titles 9,600; Per Subs 28
Subject Interests: Ethnic studies, Fiction, Psychology, Social sciences and issues
Special Collections: Law (West & Lawyers Coop)

M METROWEST MEDICAL CENTER, Tedeschi Library & Information Center,* 115 Lincoln St, 01702. SAN 307-3963. Tel: 508-383-1591. FAX: 508-879-0471. *Dir*, Sandra R Clevesy; Staff 3 (MLS 1, Non-MLS 2)
Founded 1960
Library Holdings: Bk Vols 11,249; Per Subs 228
Subject Interests: Hospital administration, Nursing
Partic in Dialog Corporation; Nat Libr of Med; OCLC Online Computer Library Center, Inc

S NANMAC CORPORATION LIBRARY,* 9-11 Mayhew St, 01702. SAN 328-6193. Tel: 508-872-4811. FAX: 508-879-5450. *Mgr*, Jake Nanigian
Library Holdings: Bk Vols 200

S NEW ENGLAND WILD FLOWER SOCIETY, INC, Lawrence Newcomb Library, 180 Hemenway Rd, 01701-2699. SAN 324-6892. Tel: 508-877-7630. FAX: 508-877-3658. E-Mail: newfs@newfs.org. Web Site: www.newfs.org. *Librn*, John Benson; Staff 6 (MLS 2, Non-MLS 4)
Founded 1969
1998-1999 Income $1,500. Mats Exp $1,500
Library Holdings: Bk Titles 4,000
Subject Interests: Botany, Conservation of native plants, Ecology, Horticulture, Native plants, Natural history, New England
Special Collections: Comprehensive Coll of books on Wildflowers; Native Plant Slides; Newsletters of US Native Plant Societies
Publications: Bibliography of Publications About Gardening with Native Plants; List of Botanical Clubs & Native Plants Societies in the US; Readsources: Book Review Section of Wild Flower Society Magazine

FRANKLIN

J DEAN COLLEGE, E Ross Anderson Library, 99 Main St, 02038-1994. SAN 307-3998. Tel: 508-528-9100, Ext 1771. FAX: 508-541-1918. Web Site: www.dean.edu. *Librn*, Norma Gahl; *ILL*, Karline Wild; *Media Spec*, James Abrams; Staff 3 (MLS 3)
Founded 1865. Enrl 1,400
Library Holdings: Bk Vols 53,000; Bk Titles 42,000; Per Subs 300
Special Collections: Encyclopedia Britannica Library of American Civilization & Basic Library of English Literature, ultra-fiche; New York Times (1851 to date), microfilm
Publications: Student library handbook, style handbook
Partic in Metrowest Regional Libr Syst; SE Asn of Coop Higher Educ Mass Consortium

P FRANKLIN PUBLIC LIBRARY, 118 Main St, 02038. SAN 307-4005. Tel: 508-520-4940. Web Site: www.franklin.ma.us/town/library/index.htm. *Dir*, Mary E Ferris; *Asst Dir*, Felicia Oti; *Ref*, Vicki Buchanio; Staff 17 (MLS 5, Non-MLS 12)
Founded 1790
Jul 1999-Jun 2000 Income $846,493. Mats Exp $138,051. Sal $564,077
Library Holdings: Bk Vols 71,591; Per Subs 242
Subject Interests: Local history
Special Collections: Benjamin Franklin Special Coll; First Books of the Franklin Library
Publications: History of the Franklin Library
Partic in Minuteman Library Network
Open Mon-Thurs 9-9, Fri & Sat 9-5 & Sun 2-5 (closed Sun May-Sept)
Friends of the Library Group

GARDNER

S DEPARTMENT OF CORRECTION, North Central Correctional Institute Library, 500 Colony Rd, 01440. SAN 372-4913. Tel: 978-632-2000, Ext 325. FAX: 978-632-2802. *Librn*, Peggy McCarthy
Library Holdings: Bk Vols 6,350; Bk Titles 4,750; Per Subs 65
Partic in Cent Mass Regional Libr Syst
Open Mon-Fri 8:30-11, 1-3 & 6-7:45 & Sat 7-3

P LEVI HEYWOOD MEMORIAL LIBRARY,* 57 City Hall Ave, 01440-2672. SAN 307-4021. Tel: 978-632-5298. *Dir*, Gail P Landy; Staff 9 (MLS 2, Non-MLS 7)
Founded 1886. Pop 19,000
1997-1998 Income $351,427, State $24,100, City $290,600, Parent Institution $36,700. Mats Exp $49,900, Books $43,100, Per/Ser (Incl. Access Fees) $3,800. Sal $216,400 (Prof $60,000)
Library Holdings: Bk Vols 100,000; Per Subs 155
Subject Interests: Furniture
Mem of Central Massachusetts Regional Library System
Open Children's dept: Mon 9-8, Tues, Thurs & Fri 9-5, Wed 10-5, Sat 9-1, Adult dept: Mon & Tues 9-8, Wed & Thurs 10-8, Fri 9-5, Sat 9-1 (closed Sat, July & Aug)
Friends of the Library Group

J MOUNT WACHUSETT COMMUNITY COLLEGE LIBRARY, 444 Green St, 01440. SAN 307-403X. Tel: 978-632-6600, Ext 126. Interlibrary Loan Service Tel: 978-632-6600, Ext 125. Circulation Tel: 978-632-6600, Ext 125. Reference Tel: 978-632-6600, Ext 338. FAX: 978-632-1210. E-Mail: library@mwcc.mass.edu. Web Site: www.mwcc.mass.edu/library. *Dir*, Linda R Oldach; E-Mail: l_oldach@mwcc.mass.edu; *Asst Librn*, Chris Coolidge; *Cat*, Susan Budd; *Ref*, Heidi McCann; Staff 7 (MLS 5, Non-MLS 2)
Founded 1964. Enrl 3,140; Fac 72
Jul 1999-Jun 2000 Income $421,658, State $107,764, Parent Institution $313,894. Mats Exp $100,644, Books $25,900, Per/Ser (Incl. Access Fees) $74,744. Sal $257,069 (Prof $209,027)
Library Holdings: Bk Vols 56,334; Per Subs 290
Automation Activity & Vendor Info: (Cataloging) Innovative Interfaces Inc.; (Circulation) Innovative Interfaces Inc.; (Course Reserve) Innovative Interfaces Inc.; (OPAC) Innovative Interfaces Inc.; (Serials) Innovative Interfaces Inc.
Database Vendor: Ebsco - EbscoHost, IAC - Info Trac
Partic in CW Mars; Nelinet, Inc; OCLC Online Computer Library Center, Inc
Open Mon-Thurs 7:30-8:30, Fri 7:30-4, Sat 12-4 (academic year), Mon-Thurs 8-5, Fri 8-4, Sat 12-4 (summer hours)

GEORGETOWN

P GEORGETOWN PEABODY LIBRARY,* Lincoln Park, 01833. SAN 307-4056. Tel: 978-352-5728. FAX: 978-352-7415. E-Mail: mge@mvlc.lib.ma.us. *Dir*, Diane Giarrusso; *Ch Servs*, Michelle Patton; Staff 1 (MLS 1)
Founded 1904. Pop 7,100; Circ 59,300
Jul 1998-Jun 1999 Income $142,510, State $6,470, City $135,540, Other $500. Mats Exp $29,500, Books $26,600, Per/Ser (Incl. Access Fees) $2,900. Sal $90,192 (Prof $26,522)
Library Holdings: Bk Titles 45,000; Per Subs 96
Special Collections: historical newspapers.; Local town reports
Mem of Eastern Regional Libr Syst
Friends of the Library Group

GILL

P SLATE MEMORIAL LIBRARY,* 332 Main Rd, 01376. SAN 376-7515. Tel: 413-863-2591. FAX: 413-863-9347. *Dir*, Lissa Greenough
Library Holdings: Bk Vols 3,000; Bk Titles 2,500; Per Subs 10
Mem of Western Massachusetts Regional Library System

GLOUCESTER

M ADDISON GILBERT HOSPITAL, Medical Library,* 298 Washington St, 01930. SAN 377-9114. Tel: 978-283-4001, Ext 608. FAX: 978-281-1129. E-Mail: aghlibr@nhs-healthlink.org. *Librn*, Charlotte Minasian
Library Holdings: Bk Titles 800; Per Subs 54
Partic in Massachusetts Health Sciences Libraries Network; Medical Libr Asn; Northeastern Consortium For Health Information; Spec Libr Asn

S CAPE ANN HISTORICAL ASSOCIATION LIBRARY, 27 Pleasant St, 01930. SAN 307-4080. Tel: 978-283-0455. FAX: 978-283-4141. *Dir*, Judith McCulloch; *Archivist, Librn*, Barbara Lambert; *Archivist, Librn*, Ellen R Nelson
Library Holdings: Bk Vols 2,225
Subject Interests: Genealogy, Local history, Maritime history
Special Collections: City; Manuscript Coll; Rare Book Coll; Turn of the Century Documentary Photography
Restriction: Open to public for reference only

P GLOUCESTER, LYCEUM & SAWYER FREE LIBRARY,* 2 Dale Ave, 01930-5906. SAN 345-2468. Tel: 978-281-9763. FAX: 978-281-9770. *Acq, Dir*, David McArdle; *Asst Dir*, Carol Gray; E-Mail: gray@noblenet.org; *ILL, Ref*, Judith Oski; *Ch Servs*, Catherine Talty; *Cat*, Helen Freeman; *Circ*, Gail Mondello; *Per*, Derek Ketcahopulos; *YA Servs*, Donna Willwerth; Staff 17 (MLS 5, Non-MLS 12)
Founded 1830. Pop 30,000; Circ 202,100
Library Holdings: Bk Vols 112,476; Per Subs 120
Subject Interests: Art and architecture
Special Collections: Charles Olson Coll; T S Eliot Coll; US Census
Publications: Annual report; monthly newsletter
Mem of Noble; Northeast Mass Regional Libr Syst
Special Services for the Deaf - TTY machine
Friends of the Library Group
Bookmobiles: 1

P MAGNOLIA LIBRARY CENTER,* One Lexington Ave, PO Box 5552, 01930. SAN 307-4099. Tel: 978-525-3343. *Librn*, Ellen Fiahlo
Pop 27,209
Library Holdings: Bk Vols 700
Mem of Eastern Mass Regional Libr Syst
Open Mon & Wed 2-4, Thurs 3-5, Sat 10-12

GOSHEN

P GOSHEN FREE PUBLIC LIBRARY,* 42 Main St, PO Box 320, 01032. SAN 307-4110. Tel: 413-268-7856. *Dir*, Virginia Berry
Library Holdings: Bk Vols 8,000; Bk Titles 7,500; Per Subs 24
Mem of Western Massachusetts Regional Library System

GRAFTON

P GRAFTON PUBLIC LIBRARY, 33 Grafton Common, PO Box 387, 01519. SAN 345-2557. Tel: 508-839-4649. FAX: 508-839-7726. Web Site: www.ultranet.com/~graflib. *Librn*, Barbara Braley; E-Mail: bbraley@cwmars.org; *Ch Servs, YA Servs*, Denise Wilson; Staff 6 (MLS 2, Non-MLS 4)
Founded 1858. Pop 13,035; Circ 85,200
Library Holdings: Bk Vols 40,400; Per Subs 60
Mem of Central Massachusetts Regional Library System
Friends of the Library Group
Branches: 2
NELSON MEMORIAL, 2 Prentice St, North Grafton, 01536. SAN 345-2581. Tel: 508-839-4454. FAX: 508-839-4454. *In Charge*, Amanda Diurba
Library Holdings: Bk Vols 14,978; Per Subs 20
Friends of the Library Group
SOUTH GRAFTON BRANCH, Main St, South Grafton, 01560. SAN 345-2611. Tel: 508-839-3850. FAX: 508-839-3850. *In Charge*, Patricia English
Library Holdings: Bk Vols 14,181; Per Subs 20
Friends of the Library Group

GRANBY

P GRANBY FREE PUBLIC LIBRARY,* Library Lane, 01033-9711. SAN 307-4137. Tel: 413-467-3320. FAX: 413-467-3320. Web Site: www.community.masslive.com/cc/granbylibrary. *Librn*, Patricia Kislo; E-Mail: pkislo@cwmars.org; Staff 3 (MLS 1, Non-MLS 2)
Founded 1891. Pop 5,500; Circ 25,500
Library Holdings: Bk Titles 20,000; Per Subs 75
Subject Interests: Genealogy, Local history, Mathematics
Special Collections: Church Records (microfiche); Town Records
Mem of Western Massachusetts Regional Library System
Friends of the Library Group

R SAINT HYACINTH COLLEGE & SEMINARY, Kolbe Memorial Library, 66 School St, 01033. SAN 307-4145. Tel: 413-467-7191, Ext 521. FAX: 413-467-9609. *Coll Develop*, Beverly Wilson
Library Holdings: Bk Vols 69,284; Per Subs 105

Subject Interests: Philosophy, Theology
Special Collections: Fransicana; Incunabula & Rare Books; Materials in the Polish Language; Maximillian Kolbe Coll
Publications: Library Handbook

GRANVILLE

P GRANVILLE PUBLIC LIBRARY,* 2 Granby Rd, 01034-9539. SAN 307-4153. Tel: 413-357-8531. FAX: 413-357-8531. *Librn*, Mary Short
Founded 1900. Pop 1,183; Circ 11,707
Library Holdings: Bk Vols 8,900
Mem of Western Regional Libr Syst
Friends of the Library Group

GREAT BARRINGTON

S AMERICAN INSTITUTE FOR ECONOMIC RESEARCH, EC Harwood Library, AIER Division St, PO Box 1000, 01230-1000. SAN 322-7928. Tel: 413-528-1216. FAX: 413-528-0103. E-Mail: info@aier.org. *Head Librn*, Eric Andelson; Tel: 413-528-1216, Fax: 413-528-0103; Staff 1 (MLS 1)
Founded 1975
Library Holdings: Bk Titles 13,000; Per Subs 300
Subject Interests: Business, Economics, Finance
Special Collections: AIER's Economic Education Bulletins 1961-present; AIER'S Research Reports 1934-present; Commercial & Financial Chronicle, 1923-1974; File of E. C. Harwood's Papers; The Annalist, 1923-1940
Database Vendor: Innovative Interfaces INN - View
Publications: Economic Education Bulletins (monthly); Research Reports (semi-monthly)

P MASON LIBRARY, 231 Main St, 01230. SAN 307-4161. Tel: 413-528-2403. FAX: 413-528-2403 (Call first). *Librn*, Marlene L Drew; *Ch Servs*, Karen Ball
Founded 1861
Library Holdings: Bk Vols 33,500; Per Subs 75
Subject Interests: Genealogy
Automation Activity & Vendor Info: (Cataloging) Follett; (Circulation) Follett
Mem of Western Massachusetts Regional Library System
Open Mon-Thurs 10-6, Fri 10-8, Sat 10-5; Children's: Mon-Wed 1-5, Thurs 10-12 & 1-5, Fri 1-5, Sat 10-12 & 1-5
Friends of the Library Group

C SIMON'S ROCK COLLEGE OF BARD, Alumni Library, 84 Alford Rd, 01230. SAN 307-417X. Tel: 413-528-7370. FAX: 413-528-7380. E-Mail: library@simons-rock.edu, library@simons-rock.edu. Web Site: www.minerva.simons-rock.edu/~library/library.html. *Dir*, Joan Goodkind; Tel: 413-528-7274, E-Mail: goodkind@simons-rock.edu; *Online Servs*, Dana Cummings; Tel: 413-528-7284, E-Mail: cummings@simons-rock.edu; *Reader Servs*, Katie Archey; Tel: 413-528-7273, E-Mail: karchey@simons-rock.edu; *Circ*, Beth Sack; Tel: 413-528-7361, E-Mail: bsack@simons-rock.edu; *Acq*, Beth Moser; Tel: 413-528-7356, E-Mail: bbmoser@simons-rock.edu; Staff 5 (MLS 3, Non-MLS 2)
Founded 1966. Enrl 350; Fac 36; Highest Degree: Bachelor
2000-2001 Mats Exp $124,000, Books $53,000, Per/Ser (Incl. Access Fees) $52,000, Micro $9,000, Electronic Ref Mat (Incl. Access Fees) $10,000
Library Holdings: Bk Vols 65,000; Bk Titles 63,000; Per Subs 350
Subject Interests: American literature, Art, Environmental studies, Liberal arts, Music, Theater
Special Collections: Bernard Krainus Coll of early music scores; W E B DuBois Coll on the Black Experience
Automation Activity & Vendor Info: (Circulation) epixtech, inc.; (Course Reserve) epixtech, inc.; (OPAC) epixtech, inc.
Database Vendor: Dialog, epixtech, inc., GaleNet, IAC - SearchBank, Lexis-Nexis, OCLC - First Search, Silverplatter Information Inc., Wilson - Wilson Web
Publications: Hours & Service Brochure; Library Newsletter (monthly during academic year)
Mem of Western Massachusetts Regional Library System
Partic in Nelinet, Inc; Southeastern New York Library Resources Council; State University Of New York-NYLINK; Western Mass Regional Libr Syst
Since 1979 Simon's Rock has been a part of Bard College, Annandale-on-Hudson, New York

GREENFIELD

M FRANKLIN MEDICAL CENTER, Health Sciences Library,* 164 High St, 01301. SAN 377-9270. Tel: 413-773-2211, Ext 2398. FAX: 413-773-2094. *Librn*, Liz Zemelka
Library Holdings: Bk Titles 800; Per Subs 144
Partic in Basic Health Sciences Library Network; Massachusetts Health Sciences Libraries Network; Western Mass Health Info Consortium

J GREENFIELD COMMUNITY COLLEGE LIBRARY, One College Dr, 01301-9739. SAN 307-4196. Tel: 413-775-1830. TDD: 413-774-2462. Web Site: www.gcc.mass.edu. *Dir*, Carol G Letson; Tel: 413-775-1831, Fax: 413-775-1838, E-Mail: cletson@gcc.mass.edu; *Librn*, Janet Ryan; *Librn*, Jeanne Walsh; *Circ*, Carolyn Bellany; *Acq*, Deborah Chown; *Tech Servs*, Hope Schneider; Staff 6 (MLS 3, Non-MLS 3)
Founded 1962. Enrl 2,274; Highest Degree: Associate
Jul 1998-Jun 1999 Income $121,442, State $81,266, Federal $1,151, Parent Institution $39,025. Mats Exp $84,635, Books $33,414, Per/Ser (Incl. Access Fees) $40,040, Presv $3,825, Electronic Ref Mat (Incl. Access Fees) $7,356. Sal $288,000 (Prof $108,393)
Library Holdings: Bk Vols 50,309; Bk Titles 44,775; Per Subs 351
Special Collections: Archibald MacLeish Coll; Massachusetts Census Data Center; Pioneer Valley Resource Center; Yankee-Rowe Local Public Document Coll
Automation Activity & Vendor Info: (Cataloging) Innovative Interfaces Inc.; (Circulation) Innovative Interfaces Inc.; (OPAC) Innovative Interfaces Inc.; (Serials) Innovative Interfaces Inc.
Database Vendor: Dialog, Ebsco - EbscoHost, IAC - Info Trac
Publications: Annual report; newsletter (semi-annual)
Mem of Western Massachusetts Regional Library System
Partic in Central-Western Mass Automated Resource Sharing; Nelinet, Inc; OCLC Online Computer Library Center, Inc
Special Services for the Deaf - TTY machine

P GREENFIELD PUBLIC LIBRARY,* 402 Main St, 01301. SAN 307-420X. Tel: 413-772-1544. FAX: 413-772-1589. *Dir*, Daniel Brassell; *Asst Dir*, Mary Holmes; *ILL*, Debbi Kern; *Ad Servs*, Susan P Gleason; *Cat*, Pamela J Murphy
Founded 1881. Pop 18,400; Circ 118,145
Library Holdings: Bk Vols 51,000; Per Subs 110
Subject Interests: Local history
Special Collections: Genealogy; Town Histories-Franklin County
Automation Activity & Vendor Info: (Cataloging) Sagebrush Corporation; (Circulation) Sagebrush Corporation
Publications: Newsletter
Mem of Western Massachusetts Regional Library System
Friends of the Library Group

S HANDWRITING ANALYSIS RESEARCH LIBRARY, 91 Washington St, 01301-3411. SAN 326-1271. Tel: 413-774-4667. *Curator*, Robert E Backman
Founded 1964
Library Holdings: Bk Titles 5,616
Special Collections: Ephemera (Anna C Backman Memorial Coll), printed & non-printed items; Graphology (K S Dunn Memorial Coll), print & non-print items; History of Writing (Anna Aab Memorial Coll)
Publications: Autography Revisited; Carmillo Baldi: His Life & Works; Graphological Abstracts; Graphomancy Revisited; Needles in Haystacks
Restriction: Non-circulating to the public

GL MASSACHUSETTS TRIAL COURT, Franklin Law Library, Court House, 425 Main St, 01301. SAN 307-4188. Tel: 413-772-6580. FAX: 413-772-0743. Web Site: www.lawlib.state.ma.us/. *Head of Libr*, Marilyn Lee; E-Mail: marilynl@oit.umass.edu; Staff 2 (MLS 1, Non-MLS 1)
Founded 1812
Jul 1999-Jun 2000 Income $183,617. Mats Exp $100,000, Books $97,764, Per/Ser (Incl. Access Fees) $1,000, Micro $1,236, AV Equip $3,000. Sal $100,981 (Prof $64,997)
Library Holdings: Bk Vols 30,000; Bk Titles 425; Per Subs 334
Automation Activity & Vendor Info: (Cataloging) TLC
Function: Archival collection, ILL available, Photocopies available, Reference services available, Some telephone reference
Partic in Lexus; LOIS; New England Law Library Consortium, Inc; OCLC Online Computer Library Center, Inc; Westlaw

S NORTH EAST SUSTAINABLE ENERGY ASSOCIATION, Resource Center,* 50 Miles St, 01301. SAN 321-7590. Tel: 413-774-6051. FAX: 413-774-6053. *Exec Dir*, Thomas Thompson
Founded 1974
Library Holdings: Bk Vols 2,000; Bk Titles 2,000; Per Subs 50
Restriction: Open to public for reference only

GROTON

P GROTON PUBLIC LIBRARY, 99 Main St, 01450. SAN 307-4218. Tel: 978-448-1167. Reference Tel: 978-448-8000. FAX: 978-448-1169. E-Mail: info@gp1.org. Web Site: www.gpl.org. *Dir*, Owen Shuman; Tel: 978-448-1167, Ext 11; *Ch Servs*, Geraldine Perry; Tel: 978-448-1168; *Ref Serv*, Tina McEvoy; *ILL*, Karen L Bolduc; Tel: 978-448-1167, Ext 13; *YA Servs*, Gaye Kulvete; *Tech Servs*, Jeffrey Pike; Staff 16 (MLS 3, Non-MLS 13)
Founded 1854. Pop 9,500; Circ 135,000
Jul 2000-Jun 2001 Income (Main Library Only) $527,000, State $12,000, City $515,000. Mats Exp $87,373. Sal $296,747 (Prof $140,152)
Library Holdings: Bk Vols 52,000; Bk Titles 43,000; Per Subs 120
Automation Activity & Vendor Info: (Cataloging) TLC; (Circulation) TLC; (OPAC) TLC
Database Vendor: IAC - SearchBank
Mem of Central Massachusetts Regional Library System
Friends of the Library Group

GROVELAND

P LANGLEY-ADAMS LIBRARY,* 185 Main St, 01834-1314. SAN 307-4226. Tel: 978-372-1732. FAX: 978-374-6590. E-Mail: mgr@mvlc.lib.ma.us. *Librn*, Marianne C Burbridge; *Asst Dir*, Lynne Stanton
Pop 5,323; Circ 35,000
Library Holdings: Bk Vols 27,237; Per Subs 59
Partic in Merrimack Valley Library Consortium
Open Mon & Wed 12-5 & 6:30-8:30, Tues & Thurs 10-5:30, Fri 12-5, closed Sat & Sun
Friends of the Library Group

HADLEY

P GOODWIN MEMORIAL LIBRARY,* 50 Middle St, PO Box 55, 01035-9544. SAN 307-4234. Tel: 413-584-7451. FAX: 413-584-7451. E-Mail: library@hadleyma.org. *Librn*, Marylin Mish
Pop 4,125; Circ 14,410
Library Holdings: Bk Vols 14,600; Per Subs 27
Mem of Western Massachusetts Regional Library System
Friends of the Library Group

HALIFAX

P HOLMES PUBLIC LIBRARY,* 470 Plymouth St, 02338. SAN 307-4242. Tel: 781-293-2271, 781-293-4553. FAX: 781-294-8518. E-Mail: hfxpl@tiac.net. Web Site: www.tiac.net/users/hfxpl. *Dir Libr Serv*, Leslie A Morrissey; Fax: 781-294-8515, E-Mail: hallib@tiac.net; *Ch Servs*, Maria MacDonald; *Ch Servs*, Jean Gallant; *Ad Servs*, Catherine Kirby; *Ad Servs*, Larissa Curley; *Tech Servs*, Margaret Benoit; *Tech Coordr*, Elizabeth Randall; Staff 7 (MLS 1, Non-MLS 6)
Founded 1876. Pop 7,031; Circ 53,917
Jul 1998-Jun 1999 Income $205,934, State $7,807, City $196,042, Locally Generated Income $2,085. Mats Exp $64,851, Books $31,780, Per/Ser (Incl. Access Fees) $4,575, Electronic Ref Mat (Incl. Access Fees) $1,600. Sal $121,458 (Prof $39,596)
Library Holdings: Bk Titles 29,198; Per Subs 95
Automation Activity & Vendor Info: (Cataloging) epixtech, inc.; (Circulation) epixtech, inc.; (OPAC) epixtech, inc.
Database Vendor: Ebsco - EbscoHost, epixtech, inc., GaleNet, IAC - Info Trac, OCLC - First Search
Mem of Eastern Mass Regional Libr Syst
Partic in Able Network
Special Services for the Blind - Large print bks; Talking bks & player equipment
Friends of the Library Group

HAMPDEN

P HAMPDEN FREE PUBLIC LIBRARY, 625 Main St, 01036. (Mail add: PO Box 129, 01036), SAN 307-4250. Tel: 413-566-3047. FAX: 413-566-5862. E-Mail: library@hampden.org. Web Site: www.hampdenlibrary.org. *Dir*, Ellen Bump; *Ch Servs*, Monica Tronsky
Founded 1891. Pop 4,572; Circ 36,191
Library Holdings: Bk Vols 24,000
Mem of Western Massachusetts Regional Library System
Open Mon & Wed 11-8, Tues & Thurs 11-5, Sat 10-3
Friends of the Library Group

HANCOCK

P TAYLOR MEMORIAL LIBRARY,* Main St, 01237-1124. SAN 307-4269. Tel: 413-738-5419 (Librn). *Librn*, Joan M Burdick
Pop 697; Circ 7,750
Library Holdings: Bk Vols 7,525
Mem of Western Regional Libr Syst; Winding Rivers Library System

HANOVER

P JOHN CURTIS FREE LIBRARY, 534 Hanover St, 02339. SAN 307-4277. Tel: 617-826-2972. FAX: 617-826-3130. Web Site: www.hanovermass.com. *Dir*, Lorraine Welsh; E-Mail: lwelsh@ocln.org; *Ch Servs*, Tara Grosso; E-Mail: tgrosso@ocln.org
Founded 1907. Pop 12,800; Circ 153,510
Jul 1998-Jun 1999 Income $310,336, State $13,000, City $297,336. Mats Exp $43,571, Books $31,371, Per/Ser (Incl. Access Fees) $7,500, Micro $4,700. Sal $201,134 (Prof $79,878)
Library Holdings: Bk Vols 52,000; Per Subs 72
Special Collections: Historical Coll
Publications: New Books at JCFL
Mem of Eastern Mass Regional Libr Syst
Partic in Old Colony Libr Network
Friends of the Library Group

HANSCOM AFB

UNITED STATES AIR FORCE
A AIR FORCE RESEARCH LABORATORY LIBRARY, AFRL/VSOSA, 5 Wright St Bldg 1103, 01731-3004. SAN 345-2646. Tel: 781-377-4895. Interlibrary Loan Service Tel: 781-377-4619. FAX: 781-377-5627. E-Mail: plses@plh.af.mil. *Dir*, Eleanor Gildersleeve; *Circ*, Bill Reid; *Cat*, Elaine Poirier; *Acq*, Hazel Hanson; *Online Servs*, John Griffin; *Ref*, Mary Latham; Staff 9 (MLS 3, Non-MLS 6)
Founded 1945
Oct 1998-Sep 1999 Income $999,779. Mats Exp $476,425. Sal $431,402
Library Holdings: Bk Vols 252,663; Per Subs 777
Subject Interests: Astronomy, Chemistry, Electronics, Engineering, Geology, Geophysics, Mathematics, Meteorology, Physical science, Physics
Special Collections: Early Ballooning & Aeronautics, 200 vols; Oriental Science Library, 35,000 vols; Rare Books, 2500 vols; Science Manuscripts of Lords Rayleigh III & IV
Publications: Accessions List (weekly); Recurrent Bibliographies
Partic in BRS; Defense Technical Information Center; Dialog Corporation; Fedlink; Nasa Libraries Information System - Nasa Galaxie; OCLC Online Computer Library Center, Inc

A HANSCOM AIR FORCE BASE LIBRARY FL2835, 66 SVS/SVMG, 98 Barksdale St Bldg 1530, 01731-1807. SAN 345-2670. Tel: 781-377-2177. FAX: 781-377-4482. *Dir*, Tae Minn; Staff 5 (MLS 1, Non-MLS 4)
Founded 1952
Library Holdings: Bk Vols 27,800; Bk Titles 23,600; Per Subs 110
Subject Interests: Military history
Special Collections: Air War Coll; Project Warrior
Partic in Fedlink; OCLC Online Computer Library Center, Inc

HANSON

P HANSON PUBLIC LIBRARY,* 132 Maquan St, 02341. SAN 307-4285. Tel: 781-293-2151. FAX: 781-293-6801. E-Mail: hnstaff@ma.ultranet.com. Web Site: www.ma.ultranet.com/~nhstaff. *Dir*, Jacqueline Rafferty; *Acq*, Suzanne Olson; *Ch Servs, YA Servs*, Nancy Cappellini; *Tech Servs*, Antonia Leverone; *Circ*, Donald Colon; *Circ*, Sue Olsen
Pop 8,331; Circ 33,086
Library Holdings: Bk Vols 38,251; Per Subs 45
Subject Interests: Local history
Mem of Eastern Mass Regional Libr Syst
Open Mon & Wed 12-5, Tues & Thurs 12-8 & Fri-Sat 10-3
Friends of the Library Group

HARDWICK

P PAIGE MEMORIAL LIBRARY,* 87 Main St, PO Box 128, 01037. SAN 307-4293. Tel: 413-477-6704. FAX: 413-477-6704. *Librn*, Regina Coffey Nykyel
Pop 2,379; Circ 3,592
Library Holdings: Bk Vols 10,091; Per Subs 27
Mem of Western Regional Libr Syst
Friends of the Library Group

HARVARD

S FRUITLANDS MUSEUMS LIBRARY, 102 Prospect Hill Rd, 01451. SAN 307-4307. Tel: 978-456-3924. FAX: 978-456-8910.
Founded 1914
Library Holdings: Bk Vols 11,200; Per Subs 15
Special Collections: American Indians Coll; American Literature & History Coll; American Paintings Coll; Shaker History Coll
Restriction: By appointment only

P HARVARD PUBLIC LIBRARY,* Harvard Common, PO Box 666, 01451. SAN 307-4315. Tel: 978-456-4114. FAX: 978-456-4115. Web Site: www.ultranet.com~harvardlib. *Librn*, Lisa Dagdigian
Jul 1997-Jun 1998 Income $243,068, State $12,400, Parent Institution $11,438. Mats Exp $43,325, Books $34,556, Per/Ser (Incl. Access Fees) $7,675, Micro $1,094. Sal $179,301 (Prof $120,383)
Library Holdings: Bk Vols 49,747
Subject Interests: Local history, Shakers
Mem of Central Massachusetts Regional Library System
Partic in CW Mars
Friends of the Library Group

HARWICH

P BROOKS FREE LIBRARY, 739 Main St, 02645. SAN 307-4323. Tel: 508-430-7562. FAX: 508-430-7564. Web Site: www.vsg.cape.com/~brooks. *Dir*, Virginia Hewitt; *Librn*, Jo Ann Latimer; *Ref*, Myrna Crowley; *Ch Servs*, Susanne Martell; Staff 7 (MLS 5, Non-MLS 2)
Founded 1855. Pop 12,590; Circ 111,872
Library Holdings: Bk Titles 62,492; Per Subs 205
Special Collections: Local History Rm

Function: ILL available, Reference services available
Mem of SE Mass Regional Libr Syst
Partic in Cape Libraries Automated Materials Sharing
Special Services for the Blind - Reader services
Friends of the Library Group

HARWICH PORT

P HARWICH PORT LIBRARY ASSOCIATION,* 49 Lower Bank St, PO Box 175, 02646-1170. SAN 307-4331. Tel: 508-432-3320. FAX: 508-432-3320. *Librn*, Leslie Brown
Founded 1923. Pop 10,000; Circ 31,632
Library Holdings: Bk Titles 14,000
Special Collections: Mystery Coll
Mem of Eastern Mass Regional Libr Syst

HATFIELD

P HATFIELD PUBLIC LIBRARY, 39 Main St, 01038. SAN 307-434X. Tel: 413-247-9097. FAX: 413-247-9237. *Dir*, Pamela Jacobson; Staff 1 (MLS 1)
Founded 1873. Pop 3,600; Circ 20,000
Jul 1999-Jun 2000 Income $72,763, State $3,687, Provincial $68,632, Other $444. Mats Exp $15,660, Books $13,121, Per/Ser (Incl. Access Fees) $1,501. Sal $38,692
Library Holdings: Bk Titles 23,992; Per Subs 56
Subject Interests: Local history, Poland
Automation Activity & Vendor Info: (Cataloging) Innovative Interfaces Inc.; (ILL) Innovative Interfaces Inc.
Mem of Western Massachusetts Regional Library System
Open Tues & Thurs 10-3, Wed & Fri 6-9 & Sat 9-1
Friends of the Library Group

P WESTERN MASSACHUSETTS REGIONAL LIBRARY SYSTEM,* 58 Main St, PO Box 9, 01038. SAN 307-7020. Tel: 413-247-9306. FAX: 413-247-9740. Web Site: www.wmrls.org. *Dir*, John E Ramsay; *Tech Servs*, Tina Herman; *Librn*, Mary King; *Librn*, Karen Klopfer; *Ch Servs*, Janet Eckert; *Asst Dir, ILL*, N Janeen Resnick; Staff 25 (MLS 7, Non-MLS 18)
Founded 1961. Pop 797,267; Circ 215,220
Jul 1999-Jun 2000 Income $1,812,817. Mats Exp $341,000, Books $142,700, Per/Ser (Incl. Access Fees) $6,300, AV Equip $144,000, Electronic Ref Mat (Incl. Access Fees) $75,000. Sal $826,113
Library Holdings: Bk Vols 143,372
Automation Activity & Vendor Info: (Acquisitions) Innovative Interfaces Inc.; (Cataloging) Innovative Interfaces Inc.; (Circulation) Innovative Interfaces Inc.; (ILL) Innovative Interfaces Inc.; (OPAC) Innovative Interfaces Inc.
Publications: Children's Service News; Wrapper
Member Libraries: Adams Free Library; Berkshire Athenaeum; Clapp Memorial Library; Clarksburg Town Library; College of Our Lady of the Elms; Cushman Library; David & Joyce Milne Public Library; Dickinson Memorial Library; East Longmeadow Public Library; Edwards Public Library; Egremont Free Library; Emily Williston Memorial Library; Florida Free Library; Frederick Sargent Huntington Memorial Library; Goodwin Memorial Library; Goshen Free Public Library; Grace Hall Memorial Library; Granby Free Public Library; Graves Memorial Library; Greenfield Community College Library; Greenfield Public Library; Hamilton Memorial Library; Hampden Free Public Library; Hancock Shaker Village Library; Hatfield Public Library; Haydenville Public Library; Hubbard Memorial Library; Jones Library, Inc; Lanesborough Public Library; Lee Library Association; Lilly Library; Mason Library; Middlefield Public Library; Monson Free Library & Reading Room Association; Monterey Library; North Adams Public Library; Otis Public Library; Palmer Public Library; Peru Library; Ramsdell Public Library; Robertson Memorial Library; S White Dickinson Memorial Library; Sandisfield Free Public Library; Shaw Memorial Library; Simon's Rock College Of Bard; Slate Memorial Library; South Hadley Public Library; Springfield Library; Stockbridge Library Association; Tilton Library; Tolland Public Library; Wales Public Library; Warwick Free Public Library; West Springfield Public Library; West Stockbridge Public Library; Westfield Athenaeum; Wheeler Memorial Library; Wilbraham Public Library; Windsor Free Public Library; Young Men's Library Association
Partic in CW Mars; Nelinet, Inc
Special Services for the Deaf - TDD
Open Mon-Fri 8:30-4:30
Bookmobiles: 2

HATHORNE

S CHARLES V HOGAN REGIONAL CENTER, Staff Library,* PO Box A, 01937. SAN 320-3875. Tel: 978-774-5000, Ext 263. FAX: 978-774-5000. *Librn*, Catherine Riley
Founded 1973
Library Holdings: Bk Titles 3,000; Per Subs 84
Subject Interests: Mental health, Mentally retarded, Psychiatry, Psychology, Special education
Partic in Essex County Coop Librs; Northeastern Consortium For Health Information

HAVERHILL

M HAVERHILL MUNICIPAL (HALE) HOSPITAL, Medical Library, 140 Lincoln Ave, 01830. SAN 307-4382. Tel: 978-521-8542. *Librn*, Eleanor Howard
Library Holdings: Bk Titles 1,680; Per Subs 95
Subject Interests: Allied health, Medicine, Nursing
Partic in Haverhill Libr Res Consortium; Northeastern Consortium For Health Information

P HAVERHILL PUBLIC LIBRARY, 99 Main St, 01830-5092. SAN 345-2700. Tel: 978-373-1586. Circulation Tel: 978-373-1586, Ext 603. Reference Tel: 978-373-1586, Ext 607. FAX: 978-372-8508. Reference FAX: 978-373-8466. E-Mail: library@haverhill.com. Web Site: www.haverhillpl.org. *Librn*, Joseph Dionne; *Spec Coll*, Gregory H Laing; *Tech Servs*, Maureen Johnson; *Circ*, Catherine Page; *Ref*, Susan Katzenstein; *Ch Servs*, Leslie Todd; *Web Coordr*, James Hayes. Subject Specialists: *Literacy*, Virginia Behan; Staff 34 (MLS 9, Non-MLS 25)
Founded 1874. Pop 52,000; Circ 377,612
Jul 1999-Jun 2000 Income $1,521,164, State $71,880, City $1,183,000, Locally Generated Income $167,000, Other $99,284. Mats Exp $458,243, Books $171,327, Per/Ser (Incl. Access Fees) $9,152, Micro $10,906. Sal $1,062,921
Library Holdings: Bk Titles 216,353; Per Subs 333
Special Collections: Fine Arts Coll; Genealogy Coll; Haverhill & New England Towns History; John Greenleaf Whittier Coll; Rare Children's Bks Coll; US Topo Maps, New England States
Automation Activity & Vendor Info: (Cataloging) epixtech, inc.; (Circulation) epixtech, inc.; (Course Reserve) epixtech, inc.; (OPAC) epixtech, inc.
Publications: Architectural Heritage of Haverhill; Holdings of the HPL-J G Whittier Collection; HPL Technical Services Division-Procedures Manual; Library News & Notes (HPL); Merrimack Interlibrary Cooperative (MILC)
Mem of Northeast Mass Regional Libr Syst
Partic in Merimack Valley Libr Consortium
Friends of the Library Group
Bookmobiles: 1. Van

J NORTHERN ESSEX COMMUNITY COLLEGE, Bentley Library, 100 Elliott St, 01830. SAN 307-4390. Tel: 978-556-3400. FAX: 978-556-3738. Web Site: www.necc.mass.edu/library. *Dir*, Linda Hummel-Shea; Tel: 978-556-3423, E-Mail: lshea@necc.mass.edu; *Ref*, Gail Stuart; Tel: 978-556-3421, E-Mail: gstuart@necc.mass.edu; *Cat*, Helen Mansur; Tel: 978-556-3425, E-Mail: hmansur@necc.mass.edu; *Circ*, Louise Bevilacqua; Tel: 978-556-3422; *Electronic Resources*, Ann Grandmaison; E-Mail: agrandmaison@necc.mass.edu; Staff 7 (MLS 5, Non-MLS 2)
Founded 1961. Enrl 3,200; Highest Degree: Associate
Library Holdings: Bk Vols 62,618; Per Subs 302
Automation Activity & Vendor Info: (Cataloging) Innovative Interfaces Inc.; (Circulation) Innovative Interfaces Inc.; (Course Reserve) Innovative Interfaces Inc.; (ILL) Innovative Interfaces Inc.; (OPAC) Innovative Interfaces Inc.
Database Vendor: Innovative Interfaces INN - View
Publications: NECC Periodicals Holdings List
Partic in Nelinet, Inc; Noble
Special Services for the Deaf - Books on deafness & sign language; Special interest periodicals
Departmental Libraries:
LAWRENCE CAMPUS LIBRARY, 45 Franklin St, Lawrence, 01841. SAN 376-0308. Tel: 978-738-7400. FAX: 978-682-4235. Web Site: www.necc.mass.edu/library. *In Charge*, Ellen Madigan Pratt; E-Mail: emadigan@necc.mass.edu; Staff 2 (MLS 2)
Library Holdings: Bk Vols 6,736; Per Subs 87
Subject Interests: Law, Nursing
Automation Activity & Vendor Info: (Acquisitions) Innovative Interfaces Inc.; (Cataloging) Innovative Interfaces Inc.; (Circulation) Innovative Interfaces Inc.; (Course Reserve) Innovative Interfaces Inc.; (ILL) Innovative Interfaces Inc.; (OPAC) Innovative Interfaces Inc.
Partic in Nelinet, Inc; Noble

HAYDENVILLE

P HAYDENVILLE PUBLIC LIBRARY, S Main St, 01039-0516. (Mail add: PO Box 772, 01096-0772), SAN 376-7116. Tel: 413-268-8406. FAX: 413-268-8406. E-Mail: haydenville@cwmars.org. *Dir*, Lisa Wenner
Library Holdings: Bk Titles 6,000
Mem of Western Massachusetts Regional Library System
Open Mon 2-5, Tues 6-8 & Fri 1-6
Friends of the Library Group

HEATH

P HEATH PUBLIC LIBRARY,* One E Main St, 01346. SAN 307-4404. Tel: 413-337-4934. FAX: 413-337-8542. E-Mail: heath@cwmars.org. *Librn*, Laurie Wheeler Burrington; *Asst Librn*, Paul Wood
Founded 1894. Pop 760; Circ 16,525
Library Holdings: Bk Titles 14,000; Per Subs 30
Mem of Western Regional Libr Syst
Friends of the Library Group

HINGHAM

P HINGHAM PUBLIC LIBRARY,* 66 Leavitt St, 02043. SAN 307-4412. Tel: 781-741-1406. FAX: 781-749-0956. Web Site: www.hingham-ma.com/library. *Dir*, Dennis Corcoran; E-Mail: dennisc@ocln.org; *ILL*, Jean Beatty; *Cat*, Jaye Jones; *Ref*, Kathleen Leahy; E-Mail: kleahy@ocln.org; *Ref*, Winifred Grotevant; Staff 29 (MLS 6, Non-MLS 23)
Founded 1869. Pop 19,500; Circ 402,062
Jul 1998-Jun 1999 Income $949,231, State $23,000, City $756,649, Parent Institution $192,582. Mats Exp $158,247, Books $82,188, Per/Ser (Incl. Access Fees) $12,656, Presv $2,000, Micro $300, AV Equip $21,258. Sal $678,970
Library Holdings: Bk Vols 174,519; Per Subs 348
Subject Interests: Local history
Special Collections: Typography (W A Dwiggins Coll)
Database Vendor: epixtech, inc.
Partic in Old Colony Libr Network; SE Mass Regional Libr Syst
Open Mon-Thurs 10-9, Sat 9-5 & Sun 1-5 (fall hours), Mon-Thurs 10-9, Sat 9-1 (summer hours)

HINSDALE

P HINSDALE PUBLIC LIBRARY,* 58 Maple St, PO Box 397, 01235-0397. SAN 307-4420. Tel: 413-655-2303. *Dir*, Laurie Vilord
Founded 1866. Pop 1,780; Circ 29,745
Library Holdings: Bk Vols 8,000; Per Subs 20
Special Collections: First Congregational Church Records (1790-1980); Handwritten records of Burials of Maple Street Cemetary (1790-1912); Israel Bissell Coll; Local Newspaper Clippings (1890-to date)
Mem of Western Regional Libr Syst

HOLBROOK

P HOLBROOK PUBLIC LIBRARY, 2 Plymouth St, 02343. SAN 307-4439. Tel: 781-767-3644. FAX: 781-767-5721. E-Mail: holib@ocln.org. *Dir*, Janet H Meagher; E-Mail: jmeagher@ocln.org; *Asst Librn*, Ruth Hathaway; E-Mail: rhathaway@ocln.org; *Ch Servs*, Carolyn Elkort; E-Mail: celkort@ocln.org; Staff 11 (MLS 3, Non-MLS 8)
Founded 1872. Pop 11,125; Circ 116,677
Jul 2000-Jun 2001 Income $314,190, City $297,190, Federal $17,000. Mats Exp $66,376, Books $60,483, Per/Ser (Incl. Access Fees) $5,001, Micro $892. Sal $201,157 (Prof $112,322)
Library Holdings: Bk Vols 83,518; Per Subs 130
Automation Activity & Vendor Info: (Cataloging) epixtech, inc.; (Circulation) epixtech, inc.; (OPAC) epixtech, inc.
Database Vendor: epixtech, inc., GaleNet, IAC - Info Trac, IAC - SearchBank
Mem of SE Mass Regional Libr Syst
Partic in Old Colony Libr Network
Friends of the Library Group

HOLDEN

S ALDEN RESEARCH LABORATORY INC LIBRARY,* 30 Shrewsbury St, 01520. SAN 370-9841. Tel: 508-829-6000. FAX: 508-829-5939. E-Mail: arlmail@aldenlab.com. *Pres*, George E Hecker
Library Holdings: Bk Vols 8,500; Per Subs 90
Restriction: Staff use only
Open Mon-Fri 8-4:30

P GALE FREE LIBRARY, 23 Highland St, 01520-2599. SAN 307-4447. Tel: 508-829-0228. FAX: 508-829-0232. *Dir*, Jane Dutton; Tel: 508-829-0231, E-Mail: jdutton@cwmars.org; *Ch Servs*, Joan Platt; Tel: 508-829-0230, E-Mail: jplatt@cwmars.org; *Ref Serv*, Stan Haney; Tel: 508-829-0229, E-Mail: shaney@cwmars.org; Staff 15 (MLS 4, Non-MLS 11)
Founded 1888. Pop 15,730; Circ 240,006
Jul 1998-Jun 1999 Income $444,577, State $27,769, City $400,299, Other $16,509. Mats Exp $75,170, Books $62,223, Per/Ser (Incl. Access Fees) $4,765. Sal $330,178
Library Holdings: Bk Titles 59,694; Per Subs 142
Special Collections: Local newspapers, micro
Mem of Central Massachusetts Regional Library System
Partic in CW Mars
Friends of the Library Group

HOLLAND

P HOLLAND PUBLIC LIBRARY,* 23 Sturbridge Rd, 01521-3000. (Mail add: PO Box 9, 01521-0009), SAN 307-6873. Tel: 413-245-3607. E-Mail: hpl@cwmars.org. *Dir*, Joan W Markert
Founded 1912. Pop 2,185; Circ 8,384
Library Holdings: Bk Vols 8,000
Mem of Western Regional Libr Syst
Open Mon 3-8, Wed 12-6, Sat 10-2

HOLLISTON

P HOLLISTON PUBLIC LIBRARY, 752 Washington St, 01746. SAN 307-4455. Tel: 508-429-0617. FAX: 508-429-0625. E-Mail: holdir@mln.lib.ma.us. Web Site: www.ultranet.com/~holpub. *Dir*, Leslie Pasch; *Circ*, Jane Early; *Ch Servs*, Paula Sharaga; *Cat*, Caroline Nie
Founded 1879. Pop 14,000; Circ 91,104
Library Holdings: Bk Titles 55,000; Per Subs 110
Mem of Eastern Mass Regional Libr Syst
Friends of the Library Group

HOLYOKE

J HOLYOKE COMMUNITY COLLEGE LIBRARY,* 303 Homestead Ave, 01040-1099. SAN 307-4463. Tel: 413-538-7000, Ext 261. FAX: 413-552-2729. Web Site: www.hcc.mass.edu. *Dir*, Judith Campbell; *Acq*, Robert Stoddard; *Cat, ILL, Tech Servs*, Theresa Labato; *Ref*, Madeleine Charney; *Coll Develop*, Kathleen McDonough; Staff 3 (MLS 3)
Founded 1946. Enrl 2,980; Fac 140
Library Holdings: Bk Vols 70,635; Per Subs 650
Special Collections: Library of English Literature, ultrafiche
Partic in CW Mars; Nelinet, Inc; OCLC Online Computer Library Center, Inc
Open Mon-Thurs 8am-9pm, Fri 8am-5pm & Sun 1-5pm

P HOLYOKE PUBLIC LIBRARY,* 335 Maple St, 01040-4999. SAN 345-276X. Tel: 413-534-2211. FAX: 413-532-4230. E-Mail: library@ci.holyoke.ma.us. Web Site: www.holyokelibrary.org. *Dir*, Maria G Pagan; *Ch Servs*, Janet Falvey
Founded 1870. Pop 44,678; Circ 72,026
Jul 1997-Jun 1998 Income $380,463, State $53,096, City $167,322, Locally Generated Income $8,680, Other $151,365. Mats Exp $68,519, Books $51,451, Per/Ser (Incl. Access Fees) $6,007, Micro $6,143. Sal $187,928 (Prof $30,996)
Library Holdings: Bk Vols 64,181; Per Subs 110
Special Collections: US Volleyball Association
Publications: Quarterly newsletter
Special Services for the Deaf - TDD
Friends of the Library Group

HOPEDALE

P BANCROFT MEMORIAL LIBRARY,* 50 Hopedale St, 01747-1799. SAN 307-4471. Tel: 508-634-2209. FAX: 508-634-8095. *Dir*, Elaine Malloy; *Ch Servs*, Elaine Kraimer; *Tech Servs*, Anne Mattie
Founded 1898. Pop 4,750; Circ 42,293
1997-1998 Income $118,629. Mats Exp $37,152. Sal $75,000
Library Holdings: Bk Vols 29,861
Special Collections: Adin Ballou Coll; Draper Corporation Coll
Mem of Central Massachusetts Regional Library System
Open Mon 2-8, Tues 10-6, Wed 1-8, Thurs 2-6 & Fri 2-5
Friends of the Library Group

HOPKINTON

P HOPKINTON PUBLIC LIBRARY, 13 Main St, 01748. SAN 307-448X. Tel: 508-497-9777. FAX: 508-497-9778. Web Site: www.hopkintonma.org. *Dir*, Carol Walsh; *Asst Librn*, Frances Sheehey
Founded 1890. Pop 10,534
Jul 1999-Jun 2000 Income $196,162. Mats Exp $52,361, Books $32,471, Per/Ser (Incl. Access Fees) $3,149. Sal $143,800
Library Holdings: Bk Titles 38,074; Per Subs 99
Special Collections: Local History Vital Records Coll
Mem of Central Massachusetts Regional Library System; Central Regional Libr Syst
Friends of the Library Group

HOUSATONIC

P RAMSDELL PUBLIC LIBRARY,* 1087 Main St, PO Box 568, 01236. SAN 307-4498. Tel: 413-274-3738. E-Mail: ramsol@vgernet.net. *Dir*, Marlene Drew; *Tech Servs*, Dawn Barbieri; *Tech Servs*, Marion Forfa; *Tech Servs*, Selma Hawkins
Circ 15,000

Library Holdings: Bk Vols 24,000; Per Subs 34
Mem of Western Massachusetts Regional Library System
Branch of Mason Public Library
Friends of the Library Group

HUBBARDSTON

P HUBBARDSTON PUBLIC LIBRARY,* 7 Main St, PO Box D, 01452-0225. SAN 307-4501. Tel: 978-928-4775. FAX: 978-928-4775. *Librn*, Geraldine Page; E-Mail: gpage@cwmars.org; *Asst Librn*, Anne Long
Founded 1825. Pop 2,400; Circ 11,612
Library Holdings: Bk Vols 10,000; Per Subs 45
Mem of Central Massachusetts Regional Library System
Friends of the Library Group

HUDSON

P HUDSON PUBLIC LIBRARY,* Wood Sq, 01749-2499. SAN 307-451X. Tel: 978-568-9644. FAX: 978-568-9646. Web Site: www.ultranet.com/~hudslib. *Coll Develop, Dir*, Patricia Desmond; E-Mail: tdesmond@cwmarsmail.cwmars.org; *ILL*, Barbara Stout; *Cat*, Deborah Kane; *Ref*, Phyllis Brooks; *Ch Servs, YA Servs*, Rhoda Augarten; Staff 7 (MLS 3, Non-MLS 4)
Founded 1868. Pop 17,614; Circ 130,864
Jul 1996-Jun 1997 Income $344,814, State $19,772, Other $19,000. Mats Exp $54,199, Books $44,304, Per/Ser (Incl. Access Fees) $4,770, Presv $250, Micro $550. Sal $248,567 (Prof $97,544)
Library Holdings: Bk Titles 51,000; Per Subs 199
Publications: The Book Mark
Mem of Central Massachusetts Regional Library System
Partic in CW Mars
Friends of the Library Group

HULL

P HULL PUBLIC LIBRARY,* 9 Main St, 02045-1199. SAN 307-4528. Tel: 781-925-2295. FAX: 781-925-0867. *Dir*, Daniel J Johnson; *Asst Dir, Ref*, Ann Bradford; *Ch Servs*, Josephine Nielsen
Pop 9,600; Circ 32,000
Library Holdings: Bk Vols 30,000; Per Subs 100
Special Collections: Local History Hull & Boston Harbor Islands
Partic in SE Mass Regional Libr Syst
Friends of the Library Group

HUNTINGTON

P HUNTINGTON PUBLIC LIBRARY, 7 E Main St, PO Box 597, 01050-0597. SAN 307-4536. Tel: 413-667-3506. E-Mail: huntington@cwmars.org. *Librn*, Margaret Nareau
Pop 2,095; Circ 10,295
Library Holdings: Bk Vols 7,894; Per Subs 90
Mem of Western Regional Libr Syst
Open Mon & Thurs 1-4 & 5-8, Tues 1-4, Wed 1-6 & Sat 10-3
Friends of the Library Group

HYANNIS

M CAPE COD HOSPITAL, Medical Library, 27 Park St, 02601-5203. (Mail add: PO Box 640, 02601-0640), SAN 377-9122. Tel: 508-862-5443. FAX: 508-775-5688. E-Mail: medlib@capecodhealth.com. *Dir*, Jeanie Vander Pyl; E-Mail: jvanderpyl@capecodhealth.org; *ILL*, Sally Schumann; Staff 5 (MLS 1, Non-MLS 4)
2000-2000 Mats Exp $45,521
Library Holdings: Bk Vols 6,276; Bk Titles 1,808; Per Subs 120
Database Vendor: OVID Technologies
Partic in Basic Health Sciences Library Network; Massachusetts Health Sciences Libraries Network; North Atlantic Health Sciences Libraries, Inc; SE Mass Regional Libr Syst; Southeastern Massachusetts Consortium Of Health Science Libraries
Special Services for the Blind - Talking book center

P HYANNIS PUBLIC LIBRARY ASSOCIATION,* 401 Main St, 02601-3019. SAN 307-4544. Tel: 508-775-2280. FAX: 508-790-0087. Web Site: www.hyannislibrary.org. *Dir*, Ann-Louise Harries; *Asst Dir*, Carol J Saunders
Founded 1865. Pop 12,000; Circ 150,000
Library Holdings: Bk Vols 62,000; Bk Titles 57,500; Per Subs 125
Partic in SE Mass Regional Libr Syst
Open Tues & Wed 11-8, Thur-Sat 11-5 - Summer, Open Mon 11-5, closed Sat
Friends of the Library Group

HYDE PARK

S HYDE PARK HISTORICAL SOCIETY ARCHIVES, 35 Harvard Ave. (Mail add: 30 Ayles Rd, 02136), SAN 371-8298. Tel: 617-361-4398. FAX: 617-361-4398. E-Mail: nhhlaw@aol.com. Web Site: www.bostonhistory.org/hphshome.html. *Pres*, Nancy H Hannan
Founded 1887
2000-2001 Income Locally Generated Income $1,000. Mats Exp AV Equip $480
Library Holdings: Bk Titles 5,000
Subject Interests: Local history
Special Collections: John Antoniazci Coll, videos
Restriction: By appointment only
Function: Archival collection, Some telephone reference

IPSWICH

P IPSWICH PUBLIC LIBRARY, 25 N Main St, 01938-2287. SAN 307-4560. Tel: 978-356-6648. FAX: 978-356-6647. E-Mail: mip@mvlc.lib.ma.us. Web Site: www.town.ipswich.ma.us/library.html. *Dir*, Victor Dyer; Tel: 978-356-6649, E-Mail: vdyer@mailserv.mvlc.lib.ma.us; *ILL, Ref*, Genevieve Picard; *Ch Servs*, Marilyn Pauley; Staff 18 (MLS 3, Non-MLS 15)
Founded 1868. Pop 13,751
Jul 1999-Jun 2000 Income $448,323. Mats Exp $76,734, Books $51,656, Per/Ser (Incl. Access Fees) $12,652. Sal $286,825
Library Holdings: Bk Vols 78,323; Per Subs 147
Subject Interests: Genealogy, Local history
Automation Activity & Vendor Info: (Acquisitions) epixtech, inc.; (Cataloging) epixtech, inc.; (Circulation) epixtech, inc.; (ILL) epixtech, inc.; (OPAC) epixtech, inc.
Partic in Merrimack Valley Library Consortium
Friends of the Library Group

JAMAICA PLAIN

LEMUEL SHATTUCK HOSPITAL

M MEDICAL LIBRARY, 170 Morton St, 02130. SAN 345-2859. Tel: 617-971-3225. FAX: 617-971-3850. *Dir Libr Serv*, Kathryn Noonan; E-Mail: kathryn.noonan@state.ma.us; Staff 2 (MLS 1, Non-MLS 1)
Founded 1954
Library Holdings: Bk Titles 500; Per Subs 110
Function: ILL to other special libraries
Partic in Boston Regional Libr Syst; NNLM/SCR, OCLC Online Computer Libr Ctr, Inc; Southeastern Massachusetts Consortium Of Health Science Libraries

KINGSTON

P KINGSTON PUBLIC LIBRARY,* 6 Green St, 02364. SAN 307-4617. Tel: 781-585-0517. FAX: 781-585-0521. *Dir*, Sia Stewart; E-Mail: sstewart@ocln.org; Staff 9 (MLS 3, Non-MLS 6)
Pop 10,447; Circ 99,179
1997-1998 Income $345,928, State $10,890, City $320,209, Federal $900, Locally Generated Income $13,929. Mats Exp $68,361, Books $49,586, Per/Ser (Incl. Access Fees) $3,962, Micro $2,677. Sal $203,058
Library Holdings: Bk Vols 42,300
Subject Interests: Parenting, Travel
Special Collections: History of Kingston; History of Plymouth County
Friends of the Library Group

S R S MEANS COMPANY, INC,* Construction Plaza, 63 Smiths Lane, 02364. SAN 325-8610. Tel: 781-585-7880, Ext 724. FAX: 781-585-8868. Web Site: www.rsmeans.com. *Librn*, Jennifer Curin; E-Mail: jcurin@rsmeans.com
Founded 1945
Library Holdings: Bk Titles 500; Per Subs 40
Subject Interests: Civil engineering, Construction
Open Mon-Fri 8-5

LAKEVILLE

P LAKEVILLE PUBLIC LIBRARY,* 241 Main St, 02347. SAN 307-4625. Tel: 508-947-9028. FAX: 508-923-9934. *Dir*, Donna Tibbetts; *Ch Servs*, Cathleen Goodfellow
Founded 1914. Pop 7,800; Circ 19,183
Library Holdings: Bk Titles 18,700; Per Subs 49
Mem of Eastern Mass Regional Libr Syst
Open Tues & Thurs 1-8, Wed 10-6, Winter Sat 9-2, Summer Fri 9-2
Friends of the Library Group

LANCASTER

S LANCASTER HISTORICAL COMMISSION, Document Collection,* Town Hall, Thayer Dr, PO Box 351, 01523-0351. SAN 374-5686. Tel: 978-368-1162.

Library Holdings: Bk Titles 150
Special Collections: Alice Greene Chandler Photographic Coll (1860-1900); James Macdonald Photographic Coll; Lancaster Iconographic Coll
Open Tues 10-2

P THAYER MEMORIAL LIBRARY, 717 Main St, PO Box 5, 01523-0005. SAN 307-4633. Tel: 978-368-8928. FAX: 978-368-8929. *Dir*, Joseph Mule; *Ch Servs, Librn*, Betty Ogborn
Founded 1862. Pop 6,661; Circ 48,342
Library Holdings: Bk Vols 50,000; Per Subs 43
Subject Interests: American Indians, Botany, Civil War, Rare books
Special Collections: Botany; Historical Reference Coll
Mem of Central Massachusetts Regional Library System
Partic in CW Mars
Identified by the Massachusetts Board of Library Commissioners as a historical library & dates back to October 4, 1790 when founded as a social library
Friends of the Library Group

LANESBOROUGH

P LANESBOROUGH PUBLIC LIBRARY,* 83 N Main St, PO Box 352, 01237-0352. SAN 307-4641. Tel: 413-442-0222. FAX: 413-443-5811. E-Mail: lanesborough@cwmars.org. *Dir*, Kathy Adams; *Asst Librn*, Christa Sidway
Founded 1871. Pop 3,170
Library Holdings: Bk Titles 15,000
Mem of Western Massachusetts Regional Library System
Open Mon, Wed & Thurs 2-7, Tues 10-7, Sat 10-1
Friends of the Library Group

LAWRENCE

M LAWRENCE GENERAL HOSPITAL, Medical Library,* One General St, PO Box 189, 01842-0389. SAN 307-465X. Tel: 978-683-4000, Ext 2221. *Dir*, Carmel Gram
Library Holdings: Bk Titles 1,800; Per Subs 100
Partic in Northeastern Consortium For Health Information

L LAWRENCE LAW LIBRARY,* 2 Appleton St, 01840-1525. SAN 307-4668. Tel: 978-687-7608. FAX: 978-688-2346. E-Mail: lawlib@ma.ultranet.com. *Librn*, Brian J Archambault
Founded 1905
Open Mon-Fri 8:30-4:30, extended hrs Tues & Thurs til 9:30, Sat 9-1
Friends of the Library Group

P LAWRENCE PUBLIC LIBRARY, 51 Lawrence St, 01841. SAN 345-2913. Tel: 978-682-1727. FAX: 978-688-3142. E-Mail: mla@mvlc.lib.ma.us. Web Site: www.lawrencepl.org. *Actg Dir*, David Thomas Hildt; Tel: 978-794-5786, E-Mail: dhildt@mailserv.mvic.lib.ma.us; *Ad Servs*, Sharon Doyle; *Ad Servs*, Maureen Nimmo; *Circ*, Yvette Iglesia; *AV*, Damaris Lamontagne; *Spec Coll*, Louise Sandberg; *Ch Servs*, Anne Vantran. Subject Specialists: *Technology*, Sharon Doyle
Founded 1872. Pop 70,000; Circ 150,000
Jul 1999-Jun 2000 Income $1,222,004, State $194,574, City $979,630, Locally Generated Income $47,800. Mats Exp $169,538, Books $95,335, Per/Ser (Incl. Access Fees) $13,743, Presv $2,000, AV Equip $13,143, Electronic Ref Mat (Incl. Access Fees) $9,236. Sal $667,330 (Prof $167,330)
Library Holdings: Bk Vols 200,000; Per Subs 350
Special Collections: Adult Basic Education; Career Opportunity Center Computerized Info & Referral; Funding Resources Center; Literacy; Local Historical Archives (1912 Labor Strike - Lawrence Historical Materials); Old Radio Shows (Kelly Tape Coll); Spanish Language Materials
Automation Activity & Vendor Info: (Cataloging) epixtech, inc.; (Circulation) GEAC; (ILL) epixtech, inc.; (OPAC) epixtech, inc.
Database Vendor: Ebsco - EbscoHost, epixtech, inc.
Publications: English & Spanish; ESL Writing Curriculum Guide; Friends Brochure; General Info Brochure
Mem of Northeast Mass Regional Libr Syst
Friends of the Library Group
Branches: 1
SOUTH LAWRENCE BRANCH, 135 Parker St, South Lawrence, 01843. SAN 345-2948. Tel: 978-794-5789. FAX: 978-688-3142. E-Mail: mla@mvlc.lib.ma.us. Web Site: www.lawrence.org. *Librn*, Irene Wolfendon
Friends of the Library Group

LEE

P LEE LIBRARY ASSOCIATION, 100 Main St, 01238-1688. SAN 307-4676. Tel: 413-243-0385. FAX: 413-243-0385. *Dir Libr Serv*, Georgia A Massucco; E-Mail: gmassucc@cwmarsmail.cwmars.org; Staff 10 (MLS 1, Non-MLS 9)
Founded 1874. Pop 6,426; Circ 47,000
Jul 1999-Jun 2000 Income $178,993, State $9,545, City $159,818, Locally Generated Income $9,630. Mats Exp $31,556, Books $28,856, Per/Ser (Incl. Access Fees) $2,700. Sal $103,690 (Prof $40,212)
Library Holdings: Bk Titles 60,978; Per Subs 108
Subject Interests: Local history
Mem of Western Massachusetts Regional Library System; Western Regional Libr Syst
Partic in CW Mars
Open Mon, Tues & Thurs 10-8, Wed & Fri 10-5, Sat 10-2

LEEDS

GM DEPARTMENT OF VETERANS AFFAIRS, Medical Center Library,* 421 N Main St, 01053-9714. SAN 307-5923. Tel: 413-584-4040, Ext 2432. FAX: 413-582-3039. *Chief Librn*, Dorothy Young; Staff 4 (MLS 2, Non-MLS 2)
Library Holdings: Bk Vols 10,258; Per Subs 255
Subject Interests: Psychiatry, Psychology
Special Collections: Patient Health Coll
Restriction: Open to public for reference only
Partic in Medical Libr Asn; Vets Admin Libr Network

LEICESTER

J BECKER COLLEGE, Paul Swan Library, 3 Paxton St, 01524. SAN 307-4684. Tel: 508-791-9241, Ext 411. FAX: 508-892-7422. E-Mail: plummer@go.becker.edu. Web Site: www.beckercollege.edu. *Coll Develop, Dean of Libr*, Bruce Plummer; Tel: 508-791-9241, Ext 212
Founded 1741. Enrl 1,000
Library Holdings: Bk Vols 30,450; Per Subs 478
Subject Interests: Philosophy, Psychology, Veterinary sci, Veterinary tech
Special Collections: Samuel May, 19th Century Religion & Philosophy
Automation Activity & Vendor Info: (Circulation) MultiLIS; (Circulation) DRA; (Course Reserve) MultiLIS; (Media Booking) MultiLIS; (Media Booking) DRA; (OPAC) MultiLIS; (OPAC) DRA; (Serials) MultiLIS; (Serials) DRA
Publications: Acquisitions list; faculty handbook
Partic in OCLC Online Computer Library Center, Inc; Worcester Area Cooperating Libraries

P LEICESTER PUBLIC LIBRARY,* 1136 Main St, 01524-0389. SAN 345-2972. Tel: 508-892-7020. FAX: 508-892-7045. *Dir*, Patricia Faron; *Asst Librn*, Patricia Grady; *Cat*, Donna Johnson
Pop 10,000; Circ 27,261
Library Holdings: Bk Titles 28,000; Per Subs 52
Mem of Central Massachusetts Regional Library System
Open Tues-Thurs 10-8, Fri 10-5, Sat 10-2
Friends of the Library Group

LENOX

P LENOX LIBRARY ASSOCIATION,* 18 Main St, 01240. SAN 307-4706. Tel: 413-637-0197. FAX: 413-637-2115. E-Mail: lenox@cwmars.org. *Dir*, Denis J Lesieur; *Assoc Dir*, Sherry Gaherty; Staff 4 (MLS 4)
Founded 1856. Pop 5,568; Circ 91,177
Jul 1997-Jun 1998 Income $400,437, State $11,288, City $113,500, Locally Generated Income $275,649. Mats Exp $67,574, Books $37,582, Per/Ser (Incl. Access Fees) $5,501, Micro $7,652. Sal $196,585 (Prof $111,111)
Library Holdings: Bk Titles 67,167; Per Subs 110
Subject Interests: Local history, Music
Special Collections: A Pride of Palaces, Photographs by Edwin Hale Lincoln; Art Exhibits; Music Study Scores, Records
Partic in Western Mass Regional Libr Syst

LEOMINSTER

M HEALTH ALLIANCE-BURBANK HOSPITAL, Health Sciences Library, 60 Hospital Rd, 01453. SAN 377-9254. Tel: 978-466-4035. FAX: 978-466-4038. E-Mail: library@healthalliance.com. *Mgr Libr Serv*, Francis R Landry; E-Mail: flandryo@aol.com; Staff 1 (MLS 1)
Founded 1950
Library Holdings: Bk Titles 250; Per Subs 100
Subject Interests: Allied health, Medicine, Nursing
Restriction: Not a lending library
Partic in Cent Mass Regional Libr Syst; Central Massachusetts Consortium Of Health Related Libraries (CMCHRL); Massachusetts Health Sciences Libraries Network; N Cent Mass Librns Alliance; National Network Of Libraries Of Medicine - South Central Region

P LEOMINSTER PUBLIC LIBRARY,* 30 West St, 01453. SAN 307-4730. Tel: 978-534-7522. FAX: 978-840-3357. *Dir*, Susan Theriault Shelton; *Asst Dir*, Meredith Foley; *ILL, Media Spec*, Amy Ricciuti; *Tech Servs*, Linda Newman; *YA Servs*, Diane Sanabria; *Acq*, Marion Saucier; *Circ*, Nancy Tourigny; *Ad Servs*, Edward Bergman
Founded 1856. Pop 38,258; Circ 234,965
Library Holdings: Bk Vols 113,427; Per Subs 182
Special Collections: Career Information Center; Local Historical & Genealogical Coll; Parent Resource Center
Publications: Friend's Newsletter

Mem of Central Massachusetts Regional Library System
Partic in CW Mars
Open Mon-Thurs 9-9, Fri & Sat 9-5
Friends of the Library Group

M UNIVERSITY OF MASSACHUSETTS MEMORIAL HEALTHALLIANCE LIBRARY, (Formerly Health Alliance Hospital Library), 60 Hospital Rd, 01453-8004. SAN 307-4722. Tel: 978-466-4035. FAX: 978-466-4038. E-Mail: library@healthalliance.com. *Mgr Libr Serv*, Francis R Landry. Subject Specialists: *Allied health*, Francis R Landry; *Consumer health*, Francis R Landry; *General med*, Francis R Landry; Staff 1 (MLS 1)
Founded 1950
Library Holdings: Bk Titles 350; Per Subs 150
Subject Interests: Allied health, Medicine, Nursing
Automation Activity & Vendor Info: (OPAC) Endeavor
Database Vendor: IAC - Info Trac, OVID Technologies, Silverplatter Information Inc.
Publications: User Guide
Restriction: By appointment only
Function: Research library
Mem of Central Massachusetts Regional Library System
Partic in Massachusetts Health Sciences Libraries Network
Open Mon-Thurs 7:30-3. Librarian is licensed Notary Public
Branches:
FITCHBURG BRANCH, Burbank Hosp, Nichols Rd, Fitchburg, 01420. SAN 377-6069. Tel: 978-343-5057. FAX: 978-466-4039.
Subject Interests: Allied health, Medicine, Nursing, Psychiatry
Publications: User Guide
Partic in Basic Health Sciences Library Network; Central Massachusetts Consortium Of Health Related Libraries (CMCHRL); Medical Libr Asn; N Cent Mass Librns Alliance; North Atlantic Health Sciences Libraries, Inc
Open Fri 10-3

LEVERETT

P BRADFORD M FIELD MEMORIAL LIBRARY,* One Shutesbury Rd, PO Box 250, 01054. SAN 307-4749. Tel: 413-548-9220. FAX: 413-548-9220. Web Site: www.community/masslive.com/cc/leverettlibrary. *Librn*, Lorna E Rivers
Pop 1,471; Circ 4,253
Library Holdings: Bk Vols 7,000
Mem of Western Regional Libr Syst
Open Winter hours: Tues & Thurs 3-8, Sat 10-3, Summer hours: Tues & Thurs 3-8
Friends of the Library Group

LEXINGTON

P CARY MEMORIAL LIBRARY, 1874 Massachusetts Ave, 02420. SAN 345-3030. Tel: 781-862-6288. FAX: 781-862-7355. Web Site: www.carylibrary.org. *Dir*, Carol A Mahoney; Tel: 781-862-1685, Ext 129; *Asst Dir*, Cynthia Johnson; Tel: 781-862-1685, Ext 132; *Head Ref*, Jane Eastman; *Ch Servs*, Ruth Lynn; *Tech Servs*, Sarah A Nisenson; *Acq*, Janice Franca; *Circ*, Peggy Bateson; Staff 60 (MLS 18, Non-MLS 42)
Founded 1868. Pop 31,984; Circ 698,117
Jul 1999-Jun 2000 Income (Main Library and Branch Library) Locally Generated Income $1,677,988. Mats Exp $245,915. Sal $1,192,657
Library Holdings: Bk Vols 225,013; Per Subs 322
Subject Interests: Architecture, Art
Special Collections: American Revolutionary War Coll; Lexington History (Worthen Coll); Original Prints Coll
Automation Activity & Vendor Info: (Acquisitions) DRA; (Cataloging) DRA; (Circulation) DRA; (Course Reserve) DRA; (ILL) DRA; (Media Booking) DRA; (OPAC) DRA; (Serials) DRA
Database Vendor: DRA
Partic in Minuteman Library Network
Friends of the Library Group
Branches: 1
EAST LEXINGTON, 735 Massachusetts Ave, 02420. SAN 345-3065. Tel: 781-862-2773. FAX: 781-674-0178. Web Site: www.carylibrary.org. *Librn*, Laura Kulin; Staff 3 (Non-MLS 3)
Library Holdings: Bk Vols 10,000
Friends of the Library Group

S INSTRUMENTATION LABORATORY LIBRARY,* 101 Hartwell Ave, 02421-3125. SAN 328-0470. Tel: 781-861-4079. FAX: 781-862-5830. *Mgr*, Kay Dolezal
Founded 1965
Library Holdings: Bk Titles 6,800; Per Subs 100
Subject Interests: Hematology, Medicine
Publications: New Books List
Restriction: Staff use only
Partic in Northeastern Consortium For Health Information; OCLC Online Computer Library Center, Inc

S LEXINGTON HISTORICAL SOCIETY INC, Library Archives,* 1332 Mass Ave, PO Box 514, 02173. SAN 375-1015. Tel: 781-862-1703. FAX: 781-862-4920. E-Mail: lexhiss@tiac.net. Web Site: www.lhs.org. *Dir*, George Comtois
Library Holdings: Bk Titles 200

S LOCKHEED MARTIN IR IMAGING SYSTEMS, INC, Technical Library,* 2 Forbes Rd, 02173. SAN 307-4781. Tel: 781-863-3756. FAX: 781-863-4809. *Librn*, Mary Willis
Founded 1958
Library Holdings: Bk Vols 3,000; Per Subs 100
Subject Interests: Optics
Publications: List of serials

S MASSACHUSETTS CENTER FOR CAREER & TECHNICAL EDUCATION LIBRARY, 758 Marrett Rd, 02421-7313. SAN 324-685X. Tel: 781-863-1863. FAX: 781-863-9965. E-Mail: mccte@tiac.net. Web Site: www.mccte.org. *Librn*, Kathy Dubrovsky; *Asst Librn*, Susan Tinker; Staff 5 (MLS 4, Non-MLS 1)
Founded 1980
Library Holdings: Bk Titles 6,000; Per Subs 10
Subject Interests: Occupational career educ, Tech educ
Publications: Book Catalog (annual); Curriculum Currents (quarterly newsletter); New Acquisitions List (monthly)

S MASSACHUSETTS INSTITUTE OF TECHNOLOGY, Lincoln Laboratory Library & Information Services,* 244 Wood St, 02173-0073. SAN 307-482X. Tel: 781-861-0150. FAX: 781-981-2305. *Tech Servs*, Richard P Burnes; Staff 45 (MLS 11, Non-MLS 34)
Founded 1952
Library Holdings: Bk Vols 160,000; Bk Titles 68,000; Per Subs 3,700
Subject Interests: Aerospace science, Electronics, Engineering, Optics, Solid state physics
Automation Activity & Vendor Info: (Acquisitions) CLSI LIBS
Publications: Classified Reports Announcement; Defense Update; Management Focus; Scanner; Technical Reports Announcement
Partic in Defense Technical Information Center; Dialog Corporation; Nasa Libraries Information System - Nasa Galaxie; OCLC Online Computer Library Center, Inc

S MUSEUM OF OUR NATIONAL HERITAGE, Van Gorden-Williams Library, 33 Marrett Rd, 02421. (Mail add: PO Box 519, 02420), Tel: 781-861-6559, Ext 109. FAX: 781-861-9846 (call first). E-Mail: library@monh.org. *Head Librn*, Nancy Wilson; Tel: 781-861-6559, Ext 127, E-Mail: nwilson@monh.org; *Archivist*, Catherine Compton Swanson; Tel: 781-861-6559, Ext 116, E-Mail: cswanson@monh.org; *Publ Servs*, Helaine Davis; Tel: 781-861-6559, Ext 125, E-Mail: hdavis@monh.org; *Ser*, Julie Triessl; Tel: 781-861-6559, Ext 155, E-Mail: jtriessl@monh.org; Staff 4 (MLS 4)
Founded 1974
Library Holdings: Bk Titles 60,000; Per Subs 150
Subject Interests: American revolution, Americana, Fraternal benefit societies
Special Collections: Archives of Scottish Rite Northern Masonic Supreme Council
Restriction: Non-circulating
Function: Research library
Partic in Metrowest Massachusetts Regional Library System

RAYTHEON CO
S BUSINESS INFORMATION CENTER, Exec Headquarters, 141 Spring St, 02421. SAN 307-4846. Tel: 781-862-6600, Ext 2579. FAX: 781-860-2663. *Mgr*, Roberta Preve
Founded 1961
Library Holdings: Bk Vols 1,240; Bk Titles 1,000; Per Subs 200
Subject Interests: Bus, Finance, Mgt
Restriction: Staff use only
L LAW LIBRARY, 141 Spring St, 02421. SAN 327-2990. Tel: 781-860-3828. FAX: 781-860-3899.
Library Holdings: Bk Vols 5,000
Restriction: Not open to public

LEYDEN

P ROBERTSON MEMORIAL LIBRARY,* 849 Greenfield Rd, 01301-9419. SAN 307-4862. Tel: 413-773-9334. FAX: 413-774-4111. *Dir*, Laura Timmerman
Founded 1913. Pop 702; Circ 8,511
1998-1999 Income $9,991, State $1,576, City $8,415. Mats Exp $2,370. Sal $5,655
Library Holdings: Bk Titles 3,204
Mem of Western Massachusetts Regional Library System
Friends of the Library Group

LINCOLN

S DECORDOVA MUSEUM & SCULPTURE PARK, Dr Robert L & Alice W DeNormandie Library, 51 Sandy Pond Rd, 01773-2600. SAN 307-4870. Tel: 781-259-3612, 781-259-8355. FAX: 781-259-3650.
Founded 1950
1998-1999 Mats Exp $50
Library Holdings: Bk Titles 4,000; Per Subs 20
Restriction: Circulates for staff only, In-house use for visitors, Non-circulating to the public, Not a lending library, Open to public for reference only
Function: For research purposes, Reference only
Open Tues-Sun 11-5

S KALBA INTERNATIONAL, INC LIBRARY, 23 Sandy Pond Rd, 01773. SAN 327-2958. Tel: 781-259-9589. FAX: 781-259-1460. E-Mail: info@kalbainternational.com. Web Site: www.kalbainternational.com. *Dir*, Beverly Spencer
Library Holdings: Bk Vols 1,500; Bk Titles 400; Per Subs 50
Restriction: Staff use only
Open Mon-Fri 9-5

P LINCOLN PUBLIC LIBRARY, Bedford Rd, 01773. SAN 307-4889. Tel: 781-259-8465. FAX: 781-259-1056. *Dir*, Jerry Cirillo; E-Mail: jcirillo@mln.lib.ma.us; *Asst Dir*, Ellen Sisco; *Tech Servs*, Lisa Rothenberg; *Ref*, Jeanne Bracken; *Ch Servs*, Amy Gavalis; *Ch Servs*, Jane Flanders; *ILL*, Nadine Rebovich
Founded 1883. Pop 5,500; Circ 140,237
Jul 1999-Jun 2000 Income $577,480. Mats Exp $97,896, Books $68,039, Per/Ser (Incl. Access Fees) $7,095. Sal $404,723
Library Holdings: Bk Vols 76,225; Per Subs 190
Subject Interests: Local history
Automation Activity & Vendor Info: (Acquisitions) DRA; (Cataloging) DRA; (Circulation) DRA; (ILL) DRA; (OPAC) DRA
Partic in Minuteman Library Network
Friends of the Library Group

S MASSACHUSETTS AUDUBON SOCIETY, Hatheway Environmental Resource Library, 208 S Great Rd, 01773. SAN 307-4897. Tel: 781-259-9506, Ext 7255. Toll Free Tel: 800-283-8266, Ext 7255. FAX: 781-259-8899. E-Mail: edresources@massaudubon.org. Web Site: www.massaudubon.org. *Coordr*, Kristin Eldridge
Founded 1967
Library Holdings: Bk Titles 9,000; Per Subs 40
Subject Interests: Ecology, Massachusetts, Natural science
Special Collections: Environmental Science; Natural History

LITTLETON

P REUBEN HOAR LIBRARY, 41 Shattuck St, 01460-4506. SAN 307-4900. Tel: 978-486-4046. FAX: 978-952-2323. E-Mail: mli@mvlc.lib.ma.us. *Librn*, Marnie Oakes; Staff 16 (MLS 2, Non-MLS 14)
Pop 8,000; Circ 110,000
Jul 1999-Jun 2000 Income $338,860. Mats Exp $65,000, Books $39,691, Per/Ser (Incl. Access Fees) $6,696, Electronic Ref Mat (Incl. Access Fees) $132. Sal $265,903
Library Holdings: Bk Vols 65,000; Per Subs 200
Subject Interests: Local history, Science fiction
Publications: Reuben's Notes (electronic newsletter)
Mem of Northeast Mass Regional Libr Syst
Partic in MVLC
Friends of the Library Group

S INFORONICS, INC LIBRARY,* 25 Porter Rd, 01460. SAN 307-4919. Tel: 978-698-7307. FAX: 978-698-7500. E-Mail: lfb@inforonics.com. Web Site: www.inforonics.com. *Chair*, Lawrence F Buckland; *Librn*, Michael Vandermillen
Founded 1962

S LITTLETON RESEARCH & ENGINEERING CORP LIBRARY,* 95 Russell St, PO Box 128, 01460. SAN 373-1731. Tel: 978-486-3526. *Mgr*, Everit Reid
Library Holdings: Bk Vols 2,400; Per Subs 14

S METEOROLOGICAL & GEOASTROPHYSICAL ABSTRACTS, LIBRARY SERVICES,* 25 Porter Rd, 01460. SAN 377-6301. Tel: 978-698-7358. FAX: 978-698-7500. E-Mail: mga@inforonics.com. Web Site: www.mganet.org. *Coll Develop*, Lawrence F Buckland
Founded 1997
1997-1998 Mats Exp $25,000
Library Holdings: Bk Vols 1,000; Per Subs 400
Subject Interests: Climatology, Geophysics, Meteorology, Oceanography

LONGMEADOW

J BAY PATH COLLEGE, Frank & Marian Hatch Library, 539 Longmeadow St, 01106. (Mail add: 588 Longmeadow St, 01106), SAN 307-4927. Tel: 413-565-1376. FAX: 413-567-8345. E-Mail: library@bapath.edu. Web Site: www.library.baypath.edu. *Dir*, Maureen Horak; *Assoc Librn*, Sharon Bellenoit; Staff 4 (MLS 4)
Founded 1897. Enrl 621; Fac 55
1998-1999 Mats Exp $217,413, Books $109,100, Per/Ser (Incl. Access Fees) $53,021, AV Equip $40,669, Electronic Ref Mat (Incl. Access Fees) $14,623. Sal $156,473
Library Holdings: Bk Vols 45,179; Bk Titles 34,955; Per Subs 315
Automation Activity & Vendor Info: (OPAC) SIRSI
Partic in Cooperating Libraries Of Greater Springfield; Nelinet, Inc

P RICHARD SALTER STORRS LIBRARY,* 693 Longmeadow St, 01106. SAN 307-4935. Tel: 413-565-4181. FAX: 413-565-4183. Web Site: www.longmeadow.org. *Dir*, Carl L Sturgis; *Ref*, Farida Pomerantz; *Ad Servs*, Sue Bosman; *Ch Servs*, Martha Richard; *Circ*, Anne Nicholson
Founded 1908. Pop 17,000; Circ 213,216
Library Holdings: Bk Vols 69,000; Per Subs 149
Subject Interests: Genealogy, Local history
Mem of Western Regional Libr Syst
Friends of the Library Group

LOWELL

M LOWELL GENERAL HOSPITAL, Health Sciences Library,* 295 Varnum Ave, 01854. SAN 307-4951. Tel: 978-937-6247. FAX: 978-937-6855. *Dir*, Donna Beales
Library Holdings: Bk Vols 3,000; Bk Titles 2,500; Per Subs 145
Special Collections: Obstetrics Coll
Partic in Massachusetts Health Sciences Libraries Network; Medical Libr Asn; Northeastern Consortium For Health Information

L MASSACHUSETTS TRIAL COURT, (Formerly Lowell Law Library), Lowell Law Library, Superior Court House, 360 Gorham St, 01852. SAN 307-496X. Tel: 978-452-9301. FAX: 978-970-2000. E-Mail: lowlaw@lawlib.state.ma.us. Web Site: www.lawlib.state.ma.us. *Librn*, Catherine Mello Alves; Staff 2 (MLS 1, Non-MLS 1)
Founded 1815
Library Holdings: Bk Vols 35,000; Per Subs 53
Special Collections: Law books - Legal Periodicals statutes, case reporters, Digests, Legal treatises
Friends of the Library Group

J MIDDLESEX COMMUNITY COLLEGE, City Campus Library,* Derby Bldg, 88 Middle St, 01852. SAN 372-4093. Tel: 978-937-5454. Circulation Tel: 978-656-3004. Reference Tel: 978-656-3005. FAX: 978-656-3031. E-Mail: mcl@clsn1231.noble.mass.edu. Web Site: www.college.noblenet.org. *Librn*, Allyson O'Brien
Library Holdings: Bk Vols 9,000
Open Mon-Thurs 8:30-8, Fri 8:30-4:30 & Sat 9-1

P POLLARD MEMORIAL LIBRARY,* 33 Middle St, 01852-5999. SAN 307-4943. Tel: 978-970-4120. FAX: 978-970-4117. E-Mail: mlo@mvlc.lib.ma.us. Web Site: www.uml.edu/. *Dir*, Mary Johnson-Lally; *Asst Dir*, Silvia Tontar; *Tech Servs*, Emily Classon
Founded 1844. Pop 103,000; Circ 272,000
Jul 1997-Jun 1998 Income $937,699, State $130,351, City $803,603, Other $3,745. Mats Exp $165,931, Books $123,976, Per/Ser (Incl. Access Fees) $22,717, Micro $7,773. Sal $595,400
Library Holdings: Bk Titles 176,750; Per Subs 265
Special Collections: History of Lowell
Automation Activity & Vendor Info: (Circulation) GEAC
Mem of Eastern Mass Regional Libr Syst
Partic in Merrimack Valley Library Consortium
Special Services for the Deaf - TTY machine
Friends of the Library Group

M SAINTS MEMORIAL MEDICAL CENTER, Health Sciences Library,* Hospital Dr, PO Box 30, 01853-0030. SAN 327-3016. Tel: 978-934-8308. FAX: 978-934-8241.
Library Holdings: Bk Vols 2,000; Per Subs 400
Partic in Boston Biomedical Library Consortium; Mashlin; Nat Libr of Med; Northeastern Consortium For Health Information

S TYCO INT'L, M A-COM Technology Information Center, 100 Chelmsford St, Mail Stop L3, 01851-3294. SAN 377-6735. Tel: 978-442-5000. FAX: 978-656-2590. Web Site: infolink.macom.com/Techinfoctr/Default.htm. *Info Specialist*, Sharon Pei; Tel: 978-656-2816, E-Mail: peis@tyelectronics.com; Staff 2 (MLS 1, Non-MLS 1)
Founded 1960
Jan 2000-Dec 2000 Mats Exp $12,197, Books $6,500, Per/Ser (Incl. Access Fees) $3,420, Presv $2,277
Library Holdings: Bk Vols 2,500; Bk Titles 2,200; Per Subs 75
Subject Interests: Bus mgt, Electronic engineering, Manufacturing, Microwave, Quality control
Automation Activity & Vendor Info: (Acquisitions) EOS; (Cataloging) EOS; (Circulation) EOS; (Course Reserve) EOS; (OPAC) EOS; (Serials) EOS
Database Vendor: Dialog, OCLC - First Search

Publications: New Acquisition List
Restriction: Not open to public
Partic in Nelinet, Inc; OCLC Online Computer Library Center, Inc

LUDLOW

P HUBBARD MEMORIAL LIBRARY, 24 Center St, 01056-2795. SAN 307-4986. Tel: 413-583-3408. FAX: 413-583-5646. *Dir*, Judy Kelly; E-Mail: jkelly@cwmarsmail.cwmars.org; Staff 8 (MLS 2, Non-MLS 6)
Founded 1891. Pop 19,000; Circ 122,000
Jul 1999-Jun 2000 Income $287,135, State $30,336, City $256,799. Mats Exp $39,056, Books $30,182, Per/Ser (Incl. Access Fees) $5,500, Micro $948, AV Equip $2,226, Other Print Mats $200. Sal $169,972 (Prof $79,663)
Library Holdings: Bk Titles 49,000; Per Subs 112
Subject Interests: Fiction, Nonfiction, World War II
Automation Activity & Vendor Info: (Cataloging) Follett; (Circulation) Follett; (OPAC) Follett
Mem of Western Massachusetts Regional Library System
Partic in CW Mars
Friends of the Library Group

LUNENBURG

P RITTER MEMORIAL LIBRARY,* 960 Massachusetts Ave, 01462. SAN 307-4994. Tel: 978-582-4140. FAX: 978-582-4141. Web Site: www.net1plus/users/ritter/. *Dir*, Susan Tallman; E-Mail: stallman@cwmars.org; *Asst Dir, Cat*, Patricia Dupont; *Ch Servs*, Karen Kemp
Founded 1909. Pop 9,400
Jul 1998-Jun 1999 Income $180,000, State $10,000, City $165,000, Locally Generated Income $5,000. Mats Exp $36,000. Sal $121,000
Library Holdings: Bk Titles 29,643; Per Subs 80
Automation Activity & Vendor Info: (Circulation) Sagebrush Corporation
Mem of Central Massachusetts Regional Library System
Friends of the Library Group

LYNN

M ATLANTICARE MEDICAL CENTER, Union Hospital Health Sciences Library, 500 Lynnfield St, 01904. SAN 320-3816. Tel: 781-581-9200, Ext 4123. FAX: 781-581-0720. *Dir*, Deborah Almquist; E-Mail: deboraha@nsme.partners.org; Staff 3 (MLS 1, Non-MLS 2)
Library Holdings: Bk Titles 1,272; Per Subs 100
Subject Interests: Medicine, Nursing, Surgery
Special Collections: Consumer Health Coll
Partic in Docline; Essex County Libr Consortium; Northeastern Consortium For Health Information; Regional Med Libr Network
Open Mon-Fri 7:30-4

S DAILY EVENING ITEM LIBRARY,* 38 Exchange St, 01901. SAN 325-5484. Tel: 781-593-7700, Ext 223. FAX: 781-598-2891. E-Mail: lynnitem@shore.net. *Librn*, Judy Johnson
Founded 1933

S GENERAL ELECTRIC CO, Aircraft Engines Library, Technical Info Ctr, 24001, 1000 Western Ave, 01910. SAN 307-5001. Tel: 781-594-5363. FAX: 781-594-1689. E-Mail: ssm@pdd8.ae.ge.com. *In Charge*, Sandra S Moltz; E-Mail: sandra.moltz@ae.ge.com; Staff 1 (MLS 1)
Founded 1954
Jan 1999-Dec 1999 Income $66,000. Mats Exp $66,000, Books $5,000, Per/Ser (Incl. Access Fees) $45,000, Other Print Mats $10,000, Electronic Ref Mat (Incl. Access Fees) $6,000
Library Holdings: Bk Vols 12,000; Per Subs 300
Subject Interests: Mathematics, Mechanical engineering, Metallurgy
Special Collections: Gas-turbine Literature (C W Smith Coll)
Automation Activity & Vendor Info: (Cataloging) TechLIB; (Circulation) TechLIB; (OPAC) TechLIB
Publications: Acquisitions list (bi-weekly); Brochure of Services; Journals Holdings (annual)
Restriction: Not open to public

S LYNN MUSEUM, 125 Green St, 01902. SAN 307-5028. Tel: 781-592-2465. FAX: 781-592-0012. E-Mail: lynnmuse@shore.net. Web Site: www.lynnmuseum.org. *Dir*, Sandra Krein; *Librn*, Diane Shephard
Founded 1897
Library Holdings: Bk Titles 1,000
Subject Interests: Genealogy
Special Collections: Lynn Family papers; organizational records, church records, business records, Government records, Lynn Scrapbooks, maps, architectural drawings, 18th, 19th & 20th century ephemera
Publications: Guide to Manuscripts & Special Collections, 1988
Open Mon-Fri 9-4 for research

P LYNN PUBLIC LIBRARY,* 5 N Common St, 01902. SAN 345-3154. Tel: 781-595-0567. FAX: 781-592-5050. E-Mail: lyn@noblenet.org. Web Site: www.shore.net/~lynnlib. *Acq, Dir*, Joan Reynolds; *Asst Dir*, Kathy Dennis-Prestia; *Mgr*, Lisa Bourque; *ILL*, Linda Hedetniemi; *Ref*, Nadine Mitchell; *Ch Servs*, Diane Kulyk; Staff 8 (MLS 8)
Founded 1815. Pop 78,458
Library Holdings: Bk Titles 253,267; Per Subs 400
Subject Interests: Civil War, Genealogy, History, Law
Special Collections: Shoe Industry
Mem of Eastern Mass Regional Libr Syst
Partic in Noble
Special Services for the Deaf - TTY machine
Friends of the Library Group
Branches: 3
HAYWOOD, 270 Broadway, 01904. SAN 375-5975. Tel: 781-595-3735. FAX: 781-595-3735. *Librn*, Joseph Coffil
Friends of the Library Group
HOUGHTON, 833 Western Ave, 01905. SAN 345-3189. Tel: 781-477-7054. FAX: 781-477-7054. *Librn*, Theresa Hurley
Friends of the Library Group
SHUTE, 15 Parrott St, 01902. SAN 345-3219. Tel: 781-477-7053. FAX: 781-477-7053. *Librn*, Lisa Bourque
Friends of the Library Group

LYNNFIELD

P LYNNFIELD PUBLIC LIBRARY,* 18 Summer St, 01940-1837. SAN 345-3278. Tel: 781-334-5411. FAX: 781-334-2164. *Dir*, Sue Koronowski; E-Mail: koron@noblenet.org; *Asst Dir, Ref*, Nancy Ryan; *Ch Servs*, Mary Puleo; *Tech Servs*, June Hutchinson; *Circ*, Beverly Levy
Founded 1892. Pop 11,903; Circ 144,000
1998-1999 Income $395,000. Mats Exp $75,000, Books $55,000, Per/Ser (Incl. Access Fees) $12,000. Sal $300,000 (Prof $180,000)
Library Holdings: Bk Vols 67,201; Per Subs 174
Subject Interests: Local history
Special Collections: Learning Resources Coll
Database Vendor: Innovative Interfaces INN - View
Publications: Library Link
Mem of Northeast Mass Regional Libr Syst
Partic in North of Boston Library Exchange, Inc
Friends of the Library Group

MALDEN

S MALDEN HISTORICAL SOCIETY, c/o Malden Public Library, 36 Salem St, 02148-5291. SAN 327-3032. Tel: 781-324-0218. FAX: 781-324-4467. E-Mail: maldensup@mbln.lib.ma.us. *Curator*, John E Tramondozzi; *Dir*, Dina Malgeri
Subject Interests: Local history
Restriction: By appointment only

P MALDEN PUBLIC LIBRARY, (MPL), 36 Salem St, 02148-5291. SAN 345-3332. Tel: 781-324-0218. Interlibrary Loan Service Tel: 781-324-0220. FAX: 781-324-4467. E-Mail: maldensup@mbln.lib.ma.us. Web Site: mbln.lib.ma.us/malden/index.htm. *Dir*, Dina G Malgeri; Tel: 781-338-0800; *Asst Dir, Online Servs*, Anthony F Tieuli; E-Mail: ttieuli@mbln.lib.ma.us; *Ad Servs, ILL*, Donna Alger; E-Mail: dalger@mbln.lib.ma.us; *Ad Servs, ILL*, Stacey Holder; E-Mail: sholder@mbln.lib.ma.us; *Cat, Tech Servs*, Ziping Wu; E-Mail: zwu@mbln.lib.ma.us; *Ch Servs*, Ardis Francoeur; Tel: 781-388-0803, E-Mail: afrancoeur@mbln.lib.ma.us; *Coll Develop*, Dina Malgeri; *Media Spec, YA Servs*, Elizabeth Sarkodie-Mensah; *Ref*, Julia Keventzidis; *Ref*, Joel Thiele; *YA Servs*, Kenneth Pease; Staff 22 (MLS 10, Non-MLS 12)
Founded 1879. Pop 53,313; Circ 168,328
Jul 1998-Jun 1999 Income $1,013,520. Mats Exp $106,838, Books $82,826, Per/Ser (Incl. Access Fees) $13,366, Micro $909, Other Print Mats $5,494. Sal $714,173 (Prof $365,862)
Library Holdings: Bk Titles 232,463; Per Subs 308
Subject Interests: Art and architecture, History, Local history, Religion
Special Collections: Abraham Lincoln (Pierce Coll)
Automation Activity & Vendor Info: (Acquisitions) Brodart; (Cataloging) DRA; (Circulation) DRA; (ILL) DRA; (OPAC) DRA
Database Vendor: DRA
Publications: Annual Report; Booklet
Partic in Boston Regional Libr Syst
Friends of the Library Group
Branches: 1
LINDEN BRANCH, Oliver & Clapp Sts, 02148. SAN 329-3157. Tel: 781-397-7067. FAX: 781-397-7067. Web Site: mbln.lib.ma.us/malden/index.htm.. *Librn*, Martha Van Riddle; Staff 1 (MLS 1)
Library Holdings: Bk Vols 11,000

MANCHESTER-BY-THE-SEA

S MANCHESTER HISTORICAL SOCIETY LIBRARY,* 10 Union St, 01944. SAN 329-7403. Tel: 978-526-7230. *Librn*, Esther Proctor
Library Holdings: Bk Titles 700; Per Subs 6
Special Collections: Local Deeds
Open Mon-Fri 10-12, call for appointment

P MANCHESTER-BY-THE-SEA PUBLIC LIBRARY, 15 Union St, 01944. SAN 307-5036. Tel: 978-526-7711. FAX: 978-526-7711. E-Mail: mtl@mvlc.lib.ma.us. Web Site: www.mvlc.org. *Dir*, Jolene Larsen; *Asst Dir*, Dorothy Sieradzki; *Ch Servs, Librn*, Sara Collins; *Ad Servs*, Jo-Ann Roy; Staff 4 (MLS 4)
Founded 1886. Pop 5,512; Circ 41,940
Jul 2000-Jun 2001 Income City $266,900. Mats Exp $44,477. Sal $183,806
Library Holdings: Bk Vols 40,961; Per Subs 101
Mem of Northeast Mass Regional Libr Syst
Partic in Merrimack Valley Library Consortium
Open Mon 10-8, Tues-Thurs 1-8, Fri 10-6, Sat 10-1 (closed Sat July & thru Labor Day)
Friends of the Library Group

MANOMET

S MANOMET CENTER FOR CONSERVATION SCIENCES LIBRARY, (MCCS), (Formerly Manomet Bird Observatory Library), PO Box 1770, 02345. SAN 371-2281. Tel: 508-224-6521. FAX: 508-224-9220. Web Site: www.manomet.org.
Library Holdings: Bk Vols 12,000
Open Mon-Fri 9-5

MANSFIELD

S ALBANY INTERNATIONAL RESEARCH CO LIBRARY,* 777 West St, PO Box 9114, 02048-9114. SAN 371-0386. Tel: 508-339-7300. FAX: 508-339-4996.; Staff 1 (MLS 1)
Library Holdings: Bk Vols 3,000; Per Subs 100
Special Collections: Dye Catalogs Coll
Restriction: Staff use only
Mem of SE Mass Regional Libr Syst
Partic in Nelinet, Inc
Open Mon-Fri 8am-4:30pm

P MANSFIELD PUBLIC LIBRARY,* 255 Hope St, 02048-2353. SAN 307-5044. Tel: 508-261-7380. FAX: 508-339-7327. E-Mail: manlib@ici.net. *Dir*, Leslie Pasch; *Ch Servs*, Janet Campbell; *Circ*, Barbara Sheffield; *Ref*, Mary Tynan
Founded 1884. Pop 20,000; Circ 204,600
Jul 1998-Jun 1999 Income $399,680, State $20,000. Mats Exp Books $92,955. Sal $246,960 (Prof $107,631)
Library Holdings: Bk Titles 72,009; Per Subs 184
Subject Interests: Local history
Mem of SE Mass Regional Libr Syst
Partic in Automated Bristol Library Exchange
Friends of the Library Group

MARBLEHEAD

P ABBOT PUBLIC LIBRARY, 235 Pleasant St, 01945. SAN 307-5052. Tel: 781-631-1481. Reference Tel: 781-631-2554. FAX: 781-639-0558. *Dir*, Bonnie J Strong; E-Mail: bjstrong@noblenet.org; *Asst Dir, Head Ref*, Ann E Connolly; E-Mail: aconnoll@noblenet.org; *Tech Servs*, Christine Evans; E-Mail: evans@noblenet.org; *Ref Servs YA*, Mary Farrell; E-Mail: farrell@noblenet.org; *ILL*, Jonathan Randolph; E-Mail: randolph@noblenet.org; Staff 24 (MLS 6, Non-MLS 18)
Founded 1878. Pop 19,971
Jul 1999-Jun 2000 Income $814,395, State $27,076, City $756,447, Locally Generated Income $30,872
Library Holdings: Bk Vols 115,895; Per Subs 258
Subject Interests: Government
Special Collections: Yachts & Yachting
Automation Activity & Vendor Info: (Cataloging) Innovative Interfaces Inc.; (Circulation) Innovative Interfaces Inc.; (OPAC) Innovative Interfaces Inc.; (Serials) Innovative Interfaces Inc.
Database Vendor: Dialog, Ebsco - EbscoHost
Mem of Northeast Mass Regional Libr Syst
Partic in North of Boston Library Exchange, Inc
Friends of the Library Group

S MARBLEHEAD HISTORICAL SOCIETY LIBRARY,* 170 Washington St, PO Box 1048, 01945. SAN 320-8613. Tel: 781-631-1069. FAX: 781-631-0917. *Res*, Karen MacInnis; E-Mail: macin@greennet.net
Founded 1898
Special Collections: Diary & Genealogy Coll; Ledger & Log Book Coll; Unbound Document Coll

MARION

P ELIZABETH TABER LIBRARY,* 8 Spring St, 02738-0116. (Mail add: PO Box 116, 02738-0116), SAN 307-5060. Tel: 508-748-1252. FAX: 508-748-0939. *Dir*, Judith Kleven; *Ch Servs*, Marsha Rehkamp; Staff 2 (MLS 2)
Founded 1852. Pop 8,000
Library Holdings: Bk Titles 37,000; Per Subs 50
Special Collections: Maritime History Coll, Marion History Coll
Publications: Newsletter
Mem of SE Automated Libr
Story hours & craft activities for children weekly
Friends of the Library Group

S TELEDYNE BROWN ENGINEERING, Information Center,* 513 Mill St, 02738. SAN 307-7500. Tel: 508-748-0103, Ext 122. FAX: 508-748-2029.
Founded 1950
Library Holdings: Bk Vols 1,200; Per Subs 100
Subject Interests: Civil engineering, Mathematics, Mechanical engineering
Publications: Acquisition Bulletins
Partic in Dialog Corporation; Nelinet, Inc; OCLC Online Computer Library Center, Inc
Open 7:30-4:30

MARLBOROUGH

P MARLBOROUGH PUBLIC LIBRARY, 35 W Main St, 01752-5510. SAN 307-5095. Tel: 508-624-6900. FAX: 508-485-1494. Web Site: www.marlborough.com/mpl.html. *Dir*, Ann A Robinson; E-Mail: arobinso@cwmars.org; *Asst Dir, Head, Circ*, Karen M Tobin; Tel: 508-624-6993, E-Mail: ktobin@cwmars.org; *YA Servs*, Susan Alatalo; *Ch Servs*, Mary Lou Audette; *Cat*, Joanne Whittemore; *Ref*, Wayne Noah; Tel: 508-624-6992, E-Mail: wnoah@cwmars.org; *Ref*, Barbara Oberlin; Staff 28 (MLS 3, Non-MLS 25)
Founded 1871. Pop 33,278
Jul 1999-Jun 2000 Income $721,474, State $44,633, City $676,841. Mats Exp $115,804, Books $89,322, Per/Ser (Incl. Access Fees) $10,744, Electronic Ref Mat (Incl. Access Fees) $15,738. Sal $468,255
Library Holdings: Bk Vols 106,099; Per Subs 259
Special Collections: Horatio Alger Coll
Automation Activity & Vendor Info: (Acquisitions) Innovative Interfaces Inc.; (Circulation) Innovative Interfaces Inc.; (OPAC) Innovative Interfaces Inc.
Database Vendor: IAC - Info Trac
Mem of Central Massachusetts Regional Library System
Partic in CW Mars
Friends of the Library Group

S RAYTHEON CO, Research Library, 1001 Boston Post Rd, 01752. SAN 329-112X. Tel: 508-490-2288. FAX: 508-490-2017. *Mgr*, Mark Baldwin; *Senior Librn*, James Cornacchia; *Ser*, Maureen Steudel; Staff 3 (MLS 1, Non-MLS 2)
Founded 1986
Library Holdings: Bk Vols 12,000; Per Subs 250
Subject Interests: Computer science, Electronics, Mathematics, Transportation
Special Collections: ICAO Documents; IEEE Conference Proceedings
Publications: Bulletin
Partic in Dialog Corporation; Nelinet, Inc; OCLC Online Computer Library Center, Inc

MARSHFIELD

P VENTRESS MEMORIAL LIBRARY,* Library Plaza, 02050. SAN 307-5117. Tel: 781-834-5535. FAX: 781-837-8362. *Dir*, Ellen Riboldi; *Ref*, Christine Woods; *Ch Servs*, Stefanie Finnegan; *Cat*, Nancy Kelly; *Circ*, Dorothy Youmans; Staff 7 (MLS 5, Non-MLS 2)
Founded 1895. Pop 21,531; Circ 240,000
Library Holdings: Bk Titles 81,539; Per Subs 200
Subject Interests: New England
Special Collections: Local History, prints, photogs
Mem of Eastern Mass Regional Libr Syst
Partic in Old Colony Libr Network
Friends of the Library Group

MARSTONS MILLS

P MARSTONS MILLS PUBLIC LIBRARY, (MMPL), 2160 Main St, 02648. (Mail add: PO Box 9, 02648), SAN 307-5125. Tel: 508-428-5175. FAX: 508-420-5194. E-Mail: mml@cape.com. Web Site: www.mmpl.org. *Dir*, Koren Stembridge; E-Mail: kstembridge@mmpl.org
Founded 1891. Pop 9,500; Circ 65,000
Jul 1999-Jun 2000 Income $157,000, City $107,000, Locally Generated Income $50,000. Mats Exp $22,000, Books $16,000, Per/Ser (Incl. Access Fees) $1,000, AV Equip $5,000. Sal $85,000 (Prof $40,000)
Library Holdings: Bk Vols 23,642; Per Subs 42
Subject Interests: Cookbooks, Mysteries
Special Collections: Cape Cod Coll; Contemporary American Women Poets
Database Vendor: DRA
Publications: Library Lore (quarterly newsletter)
Mem of SE Mass Regional Libr Syst
Partic in Cape Libraries Automated Materials Sharing
Not handicap accessible
Friends of the Library Group

MASHPEE

P MASHPEE PUBLIC LIBRARY,* 100 Nathan Ellis Hwy, PO Box 657, 02649-0657. SAN 376-7868. Tel: 508-539-1435. FAX: 508-539-1437. *Dir*, Helene DeFoe
Library Holdings: Bk Vols 25,000; Bk Titles 23,000; Per Subs 60
Mem of Eastern Mass Regional Libr Syst
Partic in Cape Libraries Automated Materials Sharing
Friends of the Library Group

MATTAPOISETT

P MATTAPOISETT FREE PUBLIC LIBRARY,* 7 Barstow St, PO Box 475, 02739-0475. SAN 307-5133. Tel: 508-758-4171. FAX: 508-758-4783. *Dir*, Sue Tweedy
Founded 1882. Pop 5,500; Circ 30,000
Library Holdings: Bk Vols 26,354; Bk Titles 25,602; Per Subs 64
Mem of SE Mass Regional Libr Syst
Friends of the Library Group

MAYNARD

S EARTHWATCH INSTITUTE LIBRARY, 3 Clock Tower Place Ste 100, PO Box 75, 01754. SAN 329-9465. Tel: 978-461-0081, Ext 331. Toll Free Tel: 800-776-0188. FAX: 978-461-2332. Web Site: www.earthwatch.org. *Pres*, Roger Bergen; *Librn*, Ann Austin
Library Holdings: Per Subs 45
Subject Interests: Anthropology, Archaeology, Ecology, Humanities, Soc sci
Special Collections: Earthwatch Archive
Publications: Earthwatch Magazine (bi-monthly)
Partic in Dialog Corporation

P MAYNARD PUBLIC LIBRARY, 197 Main St, 01754. SAN 307-515X. Tel: 978-897-1010. FAX: 978-897-9884. E-Mail: maydir@mln.lib.ma.us. *Dir*, Stephen Weiner; E-Mail: maydir@mln.lib.ma.us; *Asst Dir*, Cynthia C Howe; Staff 3 (MLS 3)
Founded 1881. Pop 10,035; Circ 40,000
Library Holdings: Bk Vols 50,000; Per Subs 126
Special Collections: Maynard History
Mem of Eastern Mass Regional Libr Syst
Partic in Minuteman Library Network
Open Mon, Wed & Fri 10-5, Tues & Thurs 2-9, Sat 10-5
Friends of the Library Group

MEDFIELD

S BAYER DIAGNOSTICS, Steinberg Information Center, 63 North St, 02052-0000. SAN 322-7901. Tel: 508-359-7711, Ext 3606. FAX: 508-359-3442. *Mgr*, Kathleen McCabe; Staff 3 (MLS 1, Non-MLS 2)
Founded 1978
Library Holdings: Bk Vols 2,000; Bk Titles 1,800; Per Subs 400
Subject Interests: Biochemistry, Chemistry, Marketing, Medicine
Special Collections: Bio-Medical Patents Coll; Competitive Information Coll; Lab Notebooks
Publications: Competitive Information Newsletter; Competitor Profiles; Meetings Update; New & Interesting; New Books; Reports on Research
Restriction: Staff use only
Partic in BRS; Nelinet, Inc; SDC Info Servs
Open Mon-Fri 8-5
Branches:
WALPOLE INFORMATION CENTER, 333 Coney St, East Walpole, 02032. SAN 371-3474. Tel: 508-660-4476. FAX: 508-668-4575. *Dir*, Kathleen McCabe; Staff 3 (MLS 1, Non-MLS 2)
Library Holdings: Per Subs 63
Restriction: Staff use only
Open Mon-Fri 8-5

S MEDFIELD HISTORICAL SOCIETY LIBRARY,* 6 Pleasant St, PO Box 233, 02052. SAN 375-152X. Tel: 508-359-4773. *Pres*, Albert Clark
Library Holdings: Bk Titles 200
Open Sat 10-1 & by appt

M MEDFIELD STATE HOSPITAL, Medical Library, 45 Hospital Rd, 02052. SAN 345-3480. Tel: 508-242-8260. FAX: 727-983-2462. *Librn*, Jeanne Migliacci; E-Mail: jeanne.migliacci@dmh.state.ma.us
Founded 1950
Library Holdings: Bk Vols 4,100; Per Subs 42
Subject Interests: Nursing, Psychiatry, Psychology
Special Collections: Journal Coll Indices
Partic in Massachusetts Health Sciences Libraries Network
Branches:
GENERAL Tel: 617-359-7312, Ext 221. FAX: 727-983-2462. *Librn*, Jeanne M Migliacci
Library Holdings: Bk Titles 2,135; Per Subs 25

P MEMORIAL PUBLIC LIBRARY, 468 Main St, 02052-2008. SAN 307-5168. Tel: 508-359-4544. FAX: 508-359-8124. *Librn*, Dan Brassell; Staff 13 (MLS 5, Non-MLS 8)
Founded 1872. Pop 11,500; Circ 172,353
2000-2001 Mats Exp $324,571, Books $58,142. Sal $192,782
Library Holdings: Bk Vols 56,000; Per Subs 105
Automation Activity & Vendor Info: (Acquisitions) DRA; (Cataloging) DRA; (Circulation) DRA; (Course Reserve) DRA; (ILL) DRA; (Media Booking) DRA; (OPAC) DRA; (Serials) DRA
Mem of Eastern Mass Regional Libr Syst
Partic in Minuteman Library Network
Friends of the Library Group

MEDFORD

M LAWRENCE MEMORIAL HOSPITAL OF MEDFORD, Robert J Fahey Health Sciences Library, 170 Governors Ave, 02155-1698. SAN 307-5176. Tel: 781-306-6606. FAX: 781-306-6655. *Dir*, Terri Niland; E-Mail: tniland@lmh.edu; Staff 1 (MLS 1)
Founded 1977. Enrl 100; Fac 22
Library Holdings: Bk Vols 4,000; Bk Titles 3,000; Per Subs 125
Subject Interests: Nursing
Special Collections: Helene Fuld Media Network Coll
Mem of Northeastern Consortium for Health Information
Open Mon-Fri 8-4

P MEDFORD PUBLIC LIBRARY,* 111 High St, 02155. SAN 307-5184. Tel: 781-395-7950. FAX: 781-391-2261. *Dir*, Brian G Boutilier; E-Mail: bboutilier@mln.lib.us; *Assoc Dir, Coll Develop*, Barbara E Kerr; *Acq, ILL*, Barbara DelDuca; *Ch Servs*, Phyllis Breslow; *YA Servs*, Gay Hyson; *Media Spec*, Millie Selvitella; *Ref*, Victoria Duly; *Commun Servs*, Mary Gallant; *Cat*, Barbara Kerr; Staff 8 (MLS 8)
Founded 1825. Pop 58,076; Circ 283,115
Library Holdings: Bk Vols 150,000; Per Subs 250
Special Collections: Medford History
Publications: This Month at Medford Public Library
Mem of Eastern Mass Regional Libr Syst
Partic in Minuteman Library Network
Special Services for the Deaf - High interest/low vocabulary books; TTY machine
Friends of the Library Group

C TUFTS UNIVERSITY, Tisch Library, Professors Row, 02155-5816. SAN 345-3545. Tel: 617-627-3345. Interlibrary Loan Service Tel: 617-627-3206. Circulation Tel: 617-627-3347. Reference Tel: 617-627-3460. FAX: 617-627-3002. E-Mail: tischref@tufts.edu. Web Site: www.library.tufts.edu/tisch/. *Dir*, Jo Ann Michalak; E-Mail: jo-ann.michalak@tufts.edu; *Head, Cat, Web Coordr*, Lyn Condron; Tel: 617-627-2399, E-Mail: lyn.condron@tufts.edu; *Admin Dir, Info Tech*, Paul Stanton; E-Mail: paul.stanton@tufts.edu; *Access Serv, Mgr*, Kathleen DiPerna; Tel: 617-627-3346, E-Mail: kathleen.diperma@tufts.edu; *Head Ref*, Laura Walters; Tel: 617-627-2098, E-Mail: laura.walters@tufts.edu; *Music*, Michael Rogan; Tel: 617-627-2846, Fax: 617-627-3967, E-Mail: michael.rogan@tufts.edu; *Archivist*, Greg Colati; Tel: 617-627-3631, E-Mail: gregory.colati@tufts.edu; *Head, Acq*, Tony Kodzis; Tel: 617-627-3595, Fax: 617-627-3204, E-Mail: anthony.kodzis@tufts.edu; Staff 25 (MLS 25)
Founded 1852. Enrl 4,962; Highest Degree: Doctorate
Jul 1999-Jun 2000 Mats Exp $3,444,274, Books $734,336, Per/Ser (Incl. Access Fees) $1,786,713, Presv $82,491, AV Equip $51,111, Other Print Mats $13,935, Electronic Ref Mat (Incl. Access Fees) $775,688. Sal $2,271,462 (Prof $1,171,945)
Library Holdings: Bk Vols 735,050; Per Subs 2,982
Special Collections: Asa Alfred Tufts Coll; Citizens Clearinghouse of Hazardous Waste (Love Canal); Confederate Archives; Edwin Bolles Coll; Henri Gioiran Coll; Hosea Ballou Coll; John Holmes Coll; musicology; P T Barnum Coll; Ritter Coll; Ryder Coll; Stearus Coll; University Archives; William Bentley Sermon Coll
Automation Activity & Vendor Info: (Acquisitions) DRA; (Cataloging) DRA; (Circulation) DRA; (Course Reserve) DRA; (ILL) DRA; (OPAC) DRA; (Serials) DRA
Publications: Bibliotech Connections
Partic in Boston Library Consortium; Metrowest Massachusetts Regional Library System; Nelinet, Inc; New Eng Res Librs; OCLC Online Computer Library Center, Inc
Friends of the Library Group
Departmental Libraries:
EDWIN GINN LIBRARY, Fletcher Sch Law & Diplomacy, 02155-7082. SAN 345-3669. Tel: 617-627-3273. FAX: 617-627-3736. Web Site: www.library.tufts.edu/ginn/ginn.html. *Librn*, Natalie Schatz; *Assoc Librn*, Barbara Boyce; *Ref*, Miriam Seltzer
Founded 1933. Enrl 320
Jul 1997-Jun 1998 Income $745,289. Mats Exp $200,157, Books $33,813, Per/Ser (Incl. Access Fees) $145,980, Presv $7,427, Micro $12,937. Sal $503,510 (Prof $243,853)
Library Holdings: Bk Vols 109,435; Per Subs 513
Subject Interests: International law
Special Collections: Ambassador John Moors Cabot Papers; Ambassador

Phillip K Crowe Papers; Edward R Murrow Papers; International Labor Office; League of Nations; Permanent Court of International Justice; United Nations Coll
Partic in Boston Library Consortium; Nelinet, Inc
MUSIC, Leir Hall, Aidekman Arts Ctr, 02155. SAN 328-7726. Tel: 617-627-3594. FAX: 617-627-3684. Web Site: www.library.tufts.edu/tisch/music_library.htm.

MEDWAY

P MEDWAY PUBLIC LIBRARY,* 26 High St, 02053. SAN 345-3693. Tel: 508-533-3217. FAX: 508-533-3219. E-Mail: mwydir@mln.lib.ma.us. Web Site: www.medway.lib.ma.us. *Ad Servs, Dir*, Philip E McNulty
Founded 1860. Pop 11,391; Circ 150,949
Jul 1998-Jun 1999 Income $303,713, State $13,275, Locally Generated Income $12,500, Other $640. Mats Exp $52,123, Books $34,045, Per/Ser (Incl. Access Fees) $7,810. Sal $194,890
Library Holdings: Bk Vols 50,043; Bk Titles 43,394; Per Subs 131
Special Collections: Medway Coll
Automation Activity & Vendor Info: (Acquisitions) DRA; (Cataloging) DRA; (Circulation) DRA; (OPAC) DRA
Partic in Metrowest Massachusetts Regional Library System
Friends of the Library Group

S NEW ENGLAND WHOLESALERS ASSOCIATION LIBRARY, 116 Main St, 02053-1800. (Mail add: PO Box 738, 02053-0738), SAN 370-1948. Tel: 508-533-3335. FAX: 508-533-3337. E-Mail: newa@newa.org. Web Site: www.newa.org. *VPres*, Brad Sell
Founded 1932

MELROSE

M AMERICAN SOCIETY OF ABDOMINAL SURGEONS, Donald Collins Memorial Library, 675 Main St, 02176. SAN 328-6215. Tel: 781-665-6102. FAX: 781-665-4127. E-Mail: office@abdominalsurg.org. Web Site: www.abdominalsurg.org. *Chief Librn, Pres*, Dr Louis F Alfano, Sr
Library Holdings: Bk Vols 1,000; Per Subs 62

R FIRST BAPTIST CHURCH LIBRARY, 561 Main St, 02176. SAN 307-5192. Tel: 781-665-4470. *Librn*, Christine Swartwout; Tel: 781-665-2147
Library Holdings: Bk Titles 1,025
Subject Interests: Art, Education, Religion

P MELROSE PUBLIC LIBRARY,* 69 W Emerson St, 02176. SAN 345-3758. Tel: 781-665-2313. Interlibrary Loan Service Tel: 781-665-2640. FAX: 781-662-4229. Web Site: www.noblenet.org/melrose. *Dir*, Dennis J Kelley; E-Mail: kelley@noblenet.org; *Asst Dir*, Lois McMullin; *ILL, Ref*, Diane McLaughlin; *ILL, Ref*, Jane D'Alessandro; *Circ*, Diane Wall; *Ch Servs*, Marianne Stanton; Staff 6 (MLS 6)
Founded 1871. Pop 29,994; Circ 205,328
Library Holdings: Bk Titles 109,853; Per Subs 180
Subject Interests: Art, Genealogy, Local history
Special Collections: Fine Arts (Felix A Gendrot Coll); Sadie & Alex Levine Coll
Publications: Friends of Library Newsletter
Mem of Eastern Mass Regional Libr Syst; North of Boston Library Exchange
Partic in Noble
Open Mon-Thurs 9-9, Fri & Sat 9-5, Sun 1-5
Friends of the Library Group

MENDON

P TAFT PUBLIC LIBRARY,* 18 Main St, PO Box 35, 01756. SAN 307-5214. Tel: 508-473-3259. FAX: 508-473-7049. *Librn*, Lorna F Rhodes
Founded 1881. Pop 3,236; Circ 6,079
Library Holdings: Bk Titles 26,000
Subject Interests: History
Mem of Central Massachusetts Regional Library System
Open Mon-Thurs 9-8, Fri 9-5, Sat 9-2

MERRIMAC

P MERRIMAC PUBLIC LIBRARY, Thomas H Hoyt Memorial,* 34 W Main St, 01860. SAN 307-5222. Tel: 978-346-9441. FAX: 978-346-8272. E-Mail: mer@mvlc.lib.ma.us. Web Site: www.library.merrimac.ma.us. *Dir*, Carole McCarthy; *Ch Servs*, Cathy Fowler
Founded 1930. Pop 5,400; Circ 36,008
Library Holdings: Bk Vols 28,000; Per Subs 76
Special Collections: Local History (Thomas H Hoyt Family Coll), bks & papers
Mem of Eastern Mass Regional Libr Syst
Open Mon 12-6, Tues & Thurs 10-8, Wed 12-8, Fri 12-5, Sat 9-2
Friends of the Library Group

METHUEN

M HOLY FAMILY HOSPITAL & MEDICAL CENTER, (BSM), Health Sciences Library, 70 East St, 01844-4597. SAN 307-5230. Tel: 978-687-0151, Ext 2392. FAX: 978-688-7689. *Librn*, Chin-Soon Han; E-Mail: cshan@cchcs.org
Founded 1950. Pop 18,000
Library Holdings: Bk Titles 1,000; Per Subs 116
Subject Interests: Medicine, Nursing
Restriction: Staff use only
Partic in Massachusetts Health Sciences Libraries Network; Medical Libr Asn; North Atlantic Health Sciences Libraries, Inc
Friends of the Library Group

P NEVINS MEMORIAL LIBRARY,* 305 Broadway, 01844-6898. SAN 307-5249. Tel: 978-686-4080, 978-794-3292. FAX: 978-686-8669. E-Mail: mme@mvlc.lib.ma.us. *Dir*, Krista I McLeod; *Tech Servs*, Beverly Winn; *Ad Servs*, Sharon Morley; *Ref*, Janis Tunstall; *Ch Servs*, Kathleen Moran-Wallace; Staff 25 (MLS 5, Non-MLS 20)
Founded 1883. Pop 41,000; Circ 142,981
Jul 1998-Jun 1999 Income $589,389, State $40,700, City $380,000, Locally Generated Income $168,689. Mats Exp $113,988, Books $69,074, Per/Ser (Incl. Access Fees) $10,128, Micro $2,241, AV Equip $4,856, Electronic Ref Mat (Incl. Access Fees) $27,689. Sal $378,047
Library Holdings: Bk Titles 61,831; Per Subs 128
Special Collections: Elise Nevins Morgan Meditation Series, mss & bks
Automation Activity & Vendor Info: (Cataloging) GEAC; (Circulation) GEAC
Mem of Northeast Mass Regional Libr Syst
Partic in Merrimack Valley Library Consortium
Friends of the Library Group

MIDDLEBOROUGH

S MASSACHUSETTS ARCHAEOLOGICAL SOCIETY RESEARCH LIBRARY, 17 Jackson St, PO Box 700, 02346. SAN 370-1573. Tel: 508-947-9005. FAX: 508-947-9005. E-Mail: robbins-museum@angelfire.com. Web Site: bridgew.edu/mas. *Librn*, Mabell Bates; *Asst Librn*, Kathryn Fairbanks; Staff 2 (Non-MLS 2)
1998-1999 Income $200. Mats Exp Books $200
Library Holdings: Bk Titles 1,500; Per Subs 21; Spec Interest Per Sub 21
Subject Interests: Archaeology, Local history
Publications: Bulletin of the Massachusetts Archaelogical Society (society journal); Newsletter; Round Robbins
Restriction: Not a lending library
Open Wed 10-3, Thurs 1:30-4:30

P MIDDLEBOROUGH PUBLIC LIBRARY,* 102 N Main St, PO Box 391, 02346-0391. SAN 307-5257. Tel: 508-946-2470. FAX: 508-946-2473. E-Mail: midlib@sailsinc.org. Web Site: www.salesinc.org/middleboro/midlib.htm. *Dir*, Marjorie L Judd
Founded 1875
Library Holdings: Bk Titles 68,317; Per Subs 120
Special Collections: Cranberry Culture Coll
Mem of Eastern Mass Regional Libr Syst
Open Mon 1-8, Tues-Thurs 10-8, Fri 10-5, Sat 9-3
Friends of the Library Group

MIDDLEFIELD

P MIDDLEFIELD PUBLIC LIBRARY,* 188 Skyline Trail, PO Box 128, 01243-1028. SAN 307-5265. Tel: 413-623-6421. *Dir*, Cynthia Oligny
Library Holdings: Bk Vols 12,000; Bk Titles 11,000
Mem of Western Massachusetts Regional Library System

MIDDLETON

P FLINT PUBLIC LIBRARY, 2 N Main St, PO Box 98, 01949. SAN 307-5273. Tel: 978-774-8132. FAX: 978-777-3270. E-Mail: mmi@mvlc.lib.ma.us. Web Site: www.flintlibrary.org. *Dir*, Adela Carter; E-Mail: flint3@mediaone.com; Staff 6 (MLS 1, Non-MLS 5)
Founded 1891. Pop 6,700; Circ 55,000
Jul 1999-Jun 2000 Income $247,347, State $6,992, City $240,355. Mats Exp $47,440, Books $40,940, Per/Ser (Incl. Access Fees) $5,850, AV Equip $650, Electronic Ref Mat (Incl. Access Fees) $500. Sal $151,635 (Prof $109,049)
Library Holdings: Bk Vols 32,000; Per Subs 130
Database Vendor: CARL, Ebsco - EbscoHost, IAC - Info Trac, IAC - SearchBank
Mem of Eastern Mass Regional Libr Syst
Partic in Merimack Valley Libr Consortium
One person delivers to home-bound
Friends of the Library Group

MILFORD

M BIOMEASURE, INC LIBRARY,* 27 Maple St, 01757. SAN 377-9149. Tel: 508-478-0144. FAX: 508-473-3531. *Librn*, Barbara Catone; E-Mail: barbara.catone@biomeasure.com
Library Holdings: Per Subs 15
Partic in Nat Libr of Med; OCLC Online Computer Library Center, Inc

P MILFORD TOWN LIBRARY, 80 Spruce St, 01757. SAN 307-5281. Tel: 508-473-2145. FAX: 508-473-8651. Web Site: www.infofind.com/library/. *Dir*, Linda Wright; E-Mail: lwright@cwmars.org; *Asst Dir, Tech Servs*, Jennifer Perry; E-Mail: jperry@cwmars.org; *YA Servs*, Sue-Ellen Deianna; *ILL*, Mary Frances Best; E-Mail: mfbest@cwmars.org; *Circ*, Paula Bonetti; E-Mail: pbonetti@cwmars.org; Staff 34 (MLS 5, Non-MLS 29)
Founded 1986. Pop 26,000; Circ 191,000
Jul 1999-Jun 2000 Income $921,238, State $44,092, City $872,093, Locally Generated Income $2,481, Other $2,572. Mats Exp $917,920, Books $93,515, Per/Ser (Incl. Access Fees) $7,875, Micro $10,082, Electronic Ref Mat (Incl. Access Fees) $31,000. Sal $634,372
Library Holdings: Bk Vols 2,399; Bk Titles 86,595; Per Subs 222
Special Collections: Local History (Milford Room)
Automation Activity & Vendor Info: (Cataloging) Innovative Interfaces Inc.; (Circulation) Innovative Interfaces Inc.; (OPAC) Innovative Interfaces Inc.; (Serials) Innovative Interfaces Inc.
Database Vendor: IAC - SearchBank
Mem of Central Massachusetts Regional Library System
Partic in CW Mars
Friends of the Library Group

M MILFORD-WHITINSVILLE REGIONAL HOSPITAL, Medical Library, 14 Prospect St, 01757. SAN 307-529X. Tel: 508-473-1190, Ext 2385. FAX: 508-473-2744. Web Site: www.mwrh.com. *Coll Develop*, Elizabeth Killoran; E-Mail: ekillora@ma.ultranet.com; Staff 1 (MLS 1)
Founded 1974
Oct 2000-Sep 2001 Income $77,742. Mats Exp $32,742, Books $3,000, Per/Ser (Incl. Access Fees) $24,000, AV Equip $2,000
Library Holdings: Bk Vols 8,500; Bk Titles 650; Per Subs 100
Subject Interests: Allied health, Consumer health, Medicine, Nursing
Special Collections: Consumer Health; Hospital Archives Coll; Management Coll; Thurber Medical Association Archives
Database Vendor: CARL, IAC - Info Trac, IAC - SearchBank, OVID Technologies
Publications: Medical library brochure
Restriction: Circulates for staff only, In-house use for visitors, Lending to staff only, Non-circulating to the public, Open to employees & special libraries, Open to others by appointment, Open to public for reference & circulation; with some limitations, Open to public for reference only, Open to public with supervision only, Open to students, Public use on premises
Function: Archival collection, Document delivery services, For research purposes, ILL available, ILL limited, ILL to other special libraries, Literary searches, Mail loans to members, Newspaper reference library, Outside services via phone, cable & mail, Photocopies available, Professional lending library, Reference services available, Referrals accepted, Research fees apply, Research library, Some telephone reference
Mem of Central Massachusetts Regional Library System
Partic in Central Massachusetts Consortium Of Health Related Libraries (CMCHRL); Docline; Friends of the Nat Libr of Med; Massachusetts Health Sciences Libraries Network; Medical Libr Asn; National Network Of Libraries Of Medicine; North Atlantic Health Sciences Libraries, Inc; Worcester Area Cooperating Libraries
New multi-type Central Mass Regional Library System, Pre-Planning Committee, Interim Planning Committee, Planning & Budget Committee, Education Committee Co-Chair, MLA's Academy of Health Information Professionals, & Founding Member, Friends of the National Library of Medicine

S WATERS CORP, Information Center,* 34 Maple St, 01757. SAN 325-2981. Tel: 508-482-3087. FAX: 508-482-2417. *Librn*, Carla Clayton; E-Mail: clara_clayton@waters.com; *Asst Librn*, Grace Lavallee; Staff 3 (MLS 1, Non-MLS 2)
Library Holdings: Bk Titles 2,000; Per Subs 150
Subject Interests: Liquid chromatography
Restriction: Restricted public use
Partic in Dialog Corporation; OCLC Online Computer Library Center, Inc

MILL RIVER

P NEW MARLBOROUGH TOWN LIBRARY,* One Mill River Great Barrington, 01244-0239. SAN 318-1375. Tel: 413-229-6668. FAX: 413-229-6668. E-Mail: n_marlborough@cwmars.org. *Librn*, Debora O'Brien
Pop 1,078; Circ 8,456
Library Holdings: Bk Vols 6,000; Bk Titles 5,000
Mem of Western Regional Libr Syst
Friends of the Library Group

MILLBURY

P MILLBURY PUBLIC LIBRARY, 128 Elm St, 01527. SAN 307-5311. Tel: 508-865-1944. Interlibrary Loan Service Tel: 508-865-1181. FAX: 508-865-0795. *Dir*, Rosemary Waltos
Founded 1869. Pop 12,121; Circ 70,000
Library Holdings: Bk Vols 30,000; Per Subs 46
Mem of Central Massachusetts Regional Library System
Friends of the Library Group

MILLIS

P MILLIS PUBLIC LIBRARY,* 25 Auburn Rd, 02054-1203. SAN 307-5338. Tel: 508-376-8282. FAX: 508-376-1278. E-Mail: millis@mln.lib.ma.us. *Dir*, Merrily C Sparling; *Ch Servs*, Shirley DiCenzo; *ILL*, Patricia Olstead
Founded 1887. Pop 7,900; Circ 45,509
Jul 1998-Jun 1999 Income $191,367, State $7,865, City $179,934, Other $3,568. Mats Exp $32,271, Books $26,653, Per/Ser (Incl. Access Fees) $5,618. Sal $121,870 (Prof $41,663)
Library Holdings: Bk Titles 40,376; Per Subs 169
Subject Interests: Local history
Database Vendor: DRA
Publications: Friends Newsletter
Partic in Metrowest Massachusetts Regional Library System; Minuteman Library Network
Open Mon-Wed 10-8, Thurs & Fri 10-4, Sat 10-1
Friends of the Library Group

MILLVILLE

P MILLVILLE FREE PUBLIC LIBRARY,* 169 Main St, PO Box 726, 01529-0726. SAN 376-7736. Tel: 508-883-1887. FAX: 508-883-1887. *Dir*, Kristin Carlson Wood; E-Mail: kwood@cwmars.org
1998-1999 Income $8,000. Mats Exp $4,200. Sal $1,015
Library Holdings: Bk Titles 10,000; Per Subs 15
Mem of Central Massachusetts Regional Library System

MILTON

C CURRY COLLEGE, Louis R Levin Memorial Library, 1071 Blue Hill Ave, 02186-9984. SAN 307-5346. Tel: 617-333-2177. FAX: 617-333-2164. Web Site: www.curry.edu:8080/academic/library/library.html. *Dir*, Jane Lawless; *Circ*, Leslie Becker; *ILL*, Kathy Russell; *Reader Servs*, Gail Shank; *Tech Servs*, David Miller; Staff 8 (MLS 8)
Founded 1952. Enrl 1,010; Fac 100; Highest Degree: Master
Library Holdings: Bk Vols 90,000; Per Subs 662
Partic in Nelinet, Inc

P MILTON PUBLIC LIBRARY,* 476 Canton Ave, 02186-3299. SAN 345-3847. Tel: 617-698-5757. FAX: 617-698-0441. E-Mail: miref@ocln.org. Web Site: www.miltonlibrary.org. *Dir*, Glenn R Coffman; *Assoc Dir, Ref*, Dan Haacker; *YA Servs*, Pat Bergin; *Tech Servs*, Shirley Pyne; *Ch Servs*, Anne Parker
Founded 1871. Pop 25,600; Circ 221,000
Jul 1999-Jun 2000 Income (Main Library and Branch Library) $837,056, State $34,543, City $706,013, Locally Generated Income $706,013, Parent Institution $30,000, Other $66,500. Mats Exp $140,433, Books $127,540, Per/Ser (Incl. Access Fees) $7,543, Electronic Ref Mat (Incl. Access Fees) $5,350. Sal $561,055 (Prof $211,542)
Library Holdings: Bk Vols 111,457; Per Subs 165
Subject Interests: Art, Local history
Mem of SE Mass Regional Libr Syst
Partic in Old Colony Libr Network
Open Mon-Thurs 9-9, Fri 1-5:30, Sat 9-5, Sun 1-5
Friends of the Library Group
Branches: 1
EAST MILTON, 334 Edge Hill Rd, 02186-5435. SAN 345-3871. Tel: 617-698-1733. *Librn*, Mary Owens
Open Mon 1-6 & 7-9, Tues & Thurs 1-5:30, Fri 9-noon & 1-5:30
Friends of the Library Group

MONROE BRIDGE

P MONROE PUBLIC LIBRARY,* PO Box 35, 01350-0035. SAN 307-5362. Tel: 413-424-7776. *Actg Librn*, Eleanor Willey
Circ 1,581
Library Holdings: Bk Vols 3,000
Mem of Western Regional Libr Syst

MONSON

P MONSON FREE LIBRARY & READING ROOM ASSOCIATION,* 2 High St, 01057-1095. SAN 307-5370. Tel: 413-267-3866. FAX: 413-267-5496. *Dir*, Theresa Rini Percy; Tel: 413-267-9035, E-Mail: tpercy@cwmars.org

Founded 1878. Pop 8,300; Circ 38,000
Library Holdings: Bk Vols 30,500; Per Subs 144
Subject Interests: Arts and crafts, Automotive engineering, Genealogy, Local history
Mem of Western Massachusetts Regional Library System
Open Mon-Thurs 10-8, Fri 10-5 & Sat 9-2
Friends of the Library Group

MONTEREY

P MONTEREY LIBRARY,* Main Rd, PO Box 172, 01245. SAN 307-5397. Tel: 413-528-3795. *Dir*, Anne Marie Makuc; *Asst Dir*, Mark Makuc
Founded 1890. Pop 970; Circ 10,058
Library Holdings: Bk Titles 7,528; Per Subs 14
Subject Interests: Local history
Mem of Western Massachusetts Regional Library System
Open Mon 7-9, Tues 9:30-12, Wed 3-5, Sat 9:30-12 & 7-9

MONTGOMERY

P GRACE HALL MEMORIAL LIBRARY, 48 Birch Bluff Rd, 01085-9619. SAN 307-5400. Tel: 413-862-3894. E-Mail: montgomery@cwmars.org. Web Site: www.community.masslive.com/cc/gracehall. *Librn*, Denise King
Pop 780
Library Holdings: Bk Vols 5,000; Per Subs 13
Mem of Western Massachusetts Regional Library System
Open Tues 1-9, Thurs 3-8, Sat 10-12
Friends of the Library Group

MOUNT WASHINGTON

P MOUNT WASHINGTON PUBLIC LIBRARY, Town Hall 118 East St, 01258. SAN 307-5419. Tel: 413-528-1798. FAX: 413-528-0265. *Librn*, Ellie Lovejoy
Pop 78; Circ 250
Library Holdings: Bk Titles 2,500
Mem of Western Regional Libr Syst

NAHANT

P NAHANT PUBLIC LIBRARY, 15 Pleasant St, 01908-0076. SAN 307-5427. Tel: 781-581-0306. Web Site: www.nahant.com. *Librn*, Daniel A deStefano; *Ch Servs*, Barbara Deines
Founded 1819. Pop 3,900; Circ 30,000
Jul 2000-Jun 2001 Income $122,959. Mats Exp $27,321, Books $26,987, Per/Ser (Incl. Access Fees) $2,400, Presv $1,000. Sal $84,999 (Prof $49,729)
Library Holdings: Bk Titles 73,000; Per Subs 124
Special Collections: Nahant Historical
Publications: Newsletter (occasionally)
Mem of Eastern Mass Regional Libr Syst
Friends of the Library Group

NANTUCKET

P NANTUCKET ATHENEUM, One India St, 02554-3519. (Mail add: PO Box 808, 02554-0808), SAN 307-5435. Tel: 508-228-1110. FAX: 508-228-1973. E-Mail: atheneum@nantucket.net. *Dir*, Charlotte Louisa Maison; Tel: 508-228-1974, Fax: 508-228-1974; Staff 7 (MLS 6, Non-MLS 1)
Founded 1834. Circ 94,228
Jul 1999-Jun 2000 Mats Exp $831,666. Sal $413,447
Library Holdings: Bk Vols 33,276; Per Subs 174
Subject Interests: Travel
Special Collections: 19th Century American Coll; Nantucket Coll
Database Vendor: DRA
Mem of Eastern Mass Regional Libr Syst
Partic in Cape Libraries Automated Materials Sharing
Friends of the Library Group

S NANTUCKET HISTORICAL ASSOCIATION, Fair Street Research Center, 7 Fair St, 02554-3737. (Mail add: PO Box 1016, 02554-1016), SAN 327-3091. Tel: 508-228-1655. FAX: 508-228-5618. E-Mail: library@nha.org. Web Site: www.nha.org. *Dir*, Betsy Lowenstein; *Archivist*, Peter Schmid; *Res*, Elizabeth Oldham; Staff 4 (MLS 2, Non-MLS 2)
1999-2000 Mats Exp $9,400, Books $2,000, Per/Ser (Incl. Access Fees) $200, Presv $2,000, Micro $200, Other Print Mats $2,000, Manuscripts & Archives $3,000. Sal $138,000 (Prof $82,000)
Library Holdings: Bk Titles 5,000
Special Collections: Architectural Drawings; Log Books & Account Books; Manuscript & Audio-Visual Colls; Maps
Publications: Guide to Historical Records & Genealogical Resources of Nantucket, MA; Guide to the Manuscript Coll of the Nantucket Historical Association, 2nd ed, 1991

S NANTUCKET MARIA MITCHELL ASSOCIATION, Maria Mitchell Science Library, 2 Vestal St, 02554-2699. SAN 307-5443. Tel: 508-228-9219. FAX: 508-228-1031. *Librn*, Patricia Hanley
Founded 1902
Library Holdings: Bk Titles 9,000; Per Subs 42
Subject Interests: Astronomy, Biology, Botany, Chemistry, Geology, Oceanography, Physics, Zoology
Special Collections: Maria Mitchell Memorabilia (Original Notebooks & Papers), micro
Publications: Nantucket Maria Mitchell Association Annual Report

NATICK

M METRO WEST MEDICAL CENTER, Leonard Morse Campus Medical Library, 67 Union St, 01760. SAN 307-546X. Tel: 508-650-7000, Ext 7255. FAX: 508-650-7669. *Librn*, Rhoda Moskowitz
Founded 1970
Library Holdings: Bk Titles 800; Per Subs 90
Subject Interests: Allied health, Clinical medicine, Hospital administration, Nursing
Partic in Medline; OCLC Online Computer Library Center, Inc

P MORSE INSTITUTE LIBRARY, 14 E Central St, 01760. SAN 307-5451. Tel: 508-647-6520. Reference Tel: 508-647-6521. FAX: 508-647-6527. E-Mail: natick@mln.lib.ma.us. Web Site: morseinstitute.org. *Dir*, Paula M Polk; Tel: 508-647-6523, E-Mail: ppolk@mln.lib.ma.us; *Asst Dir*, Brenda M Castino; Tel: 508-647-6526, E-Mail: bcastino@mln.lib.ma.us; *Head Ref*, Anna Koch; Tel: 508-647-6521, E-Mail: akoch@mln.lib.ma.us; *Head Tech Servs*, Martha Jones; E-Mail: mjones@mln.lib.ma.us; *Head, Circ*, Paula P Welch; E-Mail: pwelch@mln.lib.ma.us; *Commun Relations*, Joan Craig; Tel: 508-647-6524, E-Mail: jcraig@mln.lib.ma.us; *YA Servs*, Mary Ann Hague; *Ch Servs*, Dale Smith; Tel: 508-647-6522, E-Mail: dsmith@mln.lib.ma.us; *Bkmobile Coordr*, Mary Ellen Womboldt; *AV*, Susan Barnicle; Staff 53 (MLS 13, Non-MLS 40)
Founded 1873. Pop 30,150; Circ 269,471
Jun 1999-May 2000 Income $1,232,629, State $27,000, City $1,113,580, Locally Generated Income $92,049. Mats Exp $569,327, Books $99,253, Per/Ser (Incl. Access Fees) $31,665, Micro $2,800, AV Equip $390,809, Other Print Mats $390,809, Electronic Ref Mat (Incl. Access Fees) $44,800. Sal $868,577
Library Holdings: Bk Vols 112,698; Per Subs 297
Special Collections: Natick Historical Coll
Automation Activity & Vendor Info: (Cataloging) DRA; (Circulation) DRA; (OPAC) DRA
Database Vendor: DRA, GaleNet, IAC - Info Trac, OCLC - First Search
Publications: Off the Shelf (quarterly newsletter)
Mem of Eastern Mass Regional Libr Syst
Partic in Metrowest Massachusetts Regional Library System; Minuteman Library Network; Nelinet, Inc
Friends of the Library Group

UNITED STATES ARMY

A TECHNICAL LIBRARY, AMSSB-REO-L(N), Kansas St, 01760-5056. SAN 345-3936. Tel: 508-233-4249. Interlibrary Loan Service Tel: 508-233-4542. FAX: 508-233-4248. *Cat, Doc*, Patricia E Bremner; E-Mail: pbremner@natick-emh2.army.mil; *ILL*, Denice C Czedik; E-Mail: dczedik@natick-emh2.army.mil; Staff 2 (MLS 1, Non-MLS 1)
Founded 1946
Library Holdings: Bk Vols 47,890; Bk Titles 42,490; Per Subs 115
Subject Interests: Biochemistry, Biology, Chemistry, Engineering, Mathematics, Medicine, Physical science, Psychology, Social sciences and issues, Textiles
Database Vendor: OCLC - First Search
Publications: Annual Bibliography of Technical Publications; Papers & List of Patents
Partic in Defense Technical Information Center; Dialog Corporation; Fedlink; Nelinet, Inc; OCLC Online Computer Library Center, Inc

NEEDHAM

M DEACONESS GLOVER HOSPITAL, Medical Library, 148 Chestnut St, 02492. SAN 307-5508. Tel: 781-453-5419. FAX: 781-453-5786.
Founded 1955
Library Holdings: Bk Titles 200; Per Subs 32
Subject Interests: Allied health, Medicine, Nursing
Partic in OCLC Online Computer Library Center, Inc

S DURACELL, INC, Technical Information Center,* 37 A St, 02494. SAN 307-2789. Tel: 781-449-7600, Ext 234. FAX: 781-449-4825. *Dir*, Marian Farley; Staff 4 (MLS 2, Non-MLS 2)
Founded 1969
Library Holdings: Bk Vols 7,000; Per Subs 220
Subject Interests: Chemistry, Environmental studies, Marketing, Physical chemistry
Publications: IS&S Newsletter
Partic in OCLC Online Computer Library Center, Inc

P NEEDHAM FREE PUBLIC LIBRARY, (NFPL), 1139 Highland Ave, 02494-1109. SAN 345-3960. Tel: 781-455-7559. FAX: 781-455-7591. E-Mail: needham@mln.lib.ma.us. Web Site: www.needhamonline.com/library/home.html. *Dir*, Ann MacFate; *Asst Dir*, Elise MacLennan; *AV*, Catherine Stetson; *Cat*, Susan Park; *Ch Servs*, Janet Prague; *ILL*, Cheryl Steeves; *Ref*, April Asquith
Founded 1888. Pop 29,925; Circ 388,211
Jul 1999-Jun 2000 Income $853,213. Mats Exp $112,618, Books $92,000, Per/Ser (Incl. Access Fees) $11,000, Micro $6,700, Electronic Ref Mat (Incl. Access Fees) $2,918. Sal $675,346
Library Holdings: Bk Titles 141,711; Per Subs 368
Subject Interests: Business and management
Special Collections: Benjamin Franklin; N C Wyeth Art Coll; Needham Archives; Needham History
Automation Activity & Vendor Info: (Cataloging) DRA; (Circulation) DRA; (ILL) DRA; (OPAC) DRA
Database Vendor: DRA
Partic in Metrowest Regional Libr Syst; Minuteman Library Network
Friends of the Library Group

NEEDHAM HEIGHTS

S GENERAL DYNAMICS COMMUNICATIONS SYSTEM LIBRARY, (Formerly GTE Government Systems), 77 A St, 02494. SAN 307-5516. Tel: 781-455-4461. FAX: 781-455-4460. *Dir*, Harriet Randall; E-Mail: harriet.randall@gd-cs.com; Staff 4 (MLS 2, Non-MLS 2)
Library Holdings: Bk Vols 15,000; Per Subs 200
Subject Interests: Computer science, Data processing, Electronics, Telecommunications
Partic in Dialog Corporation; Okla Telecommunications Interlibr Syst

S OMNISYS CORPORATION, Library Services Div,* 32 Wexford St, 02494. SAN 307-2983. Tel: 781-444-4123. Toll Free Tel: 888-884-4124. FAX: 781-444-5590. E-Mail: omnisys@gis.net. Web Site: www.gis.net/~omnisys.
Special Collections: 18th Century French, Hispanic, Italian, Russian & Scandinavian bks; English & American, French, German & Spanish Drama; French Revolutionary Pamphlets; French, German, Hispanic, Italian & Low Countries bks before 1601; Revistas Hispano-Americana; Victorian Fiction

NEW BEDFORD

P NEW BEDFORD FREE PUBLIC LIBRARY, Subregional Headquarters for Eastern Massachusetts Regional Library System,* 613 Pleasant St, 02740-6203. SAN 345-4029. Tel: 508-991-6275, 508-991-6279. FAX: 508-979-1481. E-Mail: nbmref@sailsinc.org. Web Site: www.ci.new-bedford.ma.us/nbfpl.htm. *Dir*, Theresa Coish; E-Mail: tcoish@sailsinc.org; *Circ, Commun Servs*, Carol Bellefeuille; *Ref*, Martine Hargreaves; *Automation Syst Coordr, Tech Servs*, Vicki Lukas; Staff 15 (MLS 15)
Founded 1852. Pop 99,922; Circ 331,240
Jul 1997-Jun 1998 Income $1,633,046. Mats Exp $174,405, Books $131,148, Per/Ser (Incl. Access Fees) $33,183, Micro $3,728. Sal $1,332,625
Library Holdings: Bk Vols 359,011; Bk Titles 320,956; Per Subs 1,063
Subject Interests: Genealogy
Special Collections: Melville Whaling Room, mss, microfilm; Portuguese Coll
Automation Activity & Vendor Info: (Circulation) epixtech, inc.
Mem of Eastern Mass Regional Libr Syst
Friends of the Library Group
Branches: 4
CASA DA SAUDADE, 58 Crapo, 02740. SAN 345-4088. Tel: 508-991-6218. FAX: 508-984-0784. *Librn*, Maria Jose Carvalho; E-Mail: zcarvalh@sailsinc.org; Staff 4 (MLS 1, Non-MLS 3)
Library Holdings: Bk Vols 16,036
Bilingual Branch, Portuguese & English language material
Friends of the Library Group
FRANCIS J LAWLER BRANCH, 745 Rockdale Ave, 02740. SAN 345-4053. Tel: 508-991-6216. FAX: 508-961-3077. *Librn*, Sharon Pinho
Library Holdings: Bk Vols 25,052
Friends of the Library Group
HOWLAND-GREEN, 3 Rodney French Blvd, 02744. SAN 345-4118. Tel: 508-991-6212. FAX: 508-984-0783. *Mgr*, Dale Easton
Library Holdings: Bk Vols 25,511
Special Collections: Spanish Language Coll
Friends of the Library Group
WILKS, 1911 Acushnet Ave, 02745. SAN 345-4142. Tel: 508-991-6214. FAX: 508-998-6039. E-Mail: wilkslib@ma.ultranet.com. *Mgr*, Olivia Melo
Library Holdings: Bk Vols 24,953
Friends of the Library Group

GL NEW BEDFORD LAW LIBRARY, 441 County St, 02740. SAN 307-5532. Tel: 508-992-8077. FAX: 508-991-7411. *Librn*, Margaretha E H Birknes; E-Mail: mbirknes@ultranet.com
Founded 1894
Library Holdings: Bk Vols 25,000; Per Subs 15
Friends of the Library Group

S NEW BEDFORD STANDARD-TIMES LIBRARY, 25 Elm St, 02740. SAN 371-2605. Tel: 508-997-7411. FAX: 508-997-7491. Web Site: www.paho.org. *Librn*, Gail Couture; Tel: 508-979-4436, E-Mail: gcouture@s-t.com
Special Collections: New Bedford Standard Times Coll (1880-present)

S OLD DARTMOUTH HISTORICAL SOCIETY, New Bedford Whaling Museum Library,* 18 Johnny Cake Hill, 02740-6398. SAN 307-5540. Tel: 508-997-0046. FAX: 508-994-4350. E-Mail: whalinglibrary@aol.com. Web Site: www.whalingmuseum.org. *Dir*, Ann Brengle; *Librn*, Judith Downey; Staff 3 (MLS 3)
Founded 1903
Library Holdings: Bk Vols 15,000; Per Subs 25
Subject Interests: History
Special Collections: International Marine Archives, micro; Maritime History (Charles A Goodwin Coll); Whaling (Charles F Batchelder Coll); Whaling Museum Logbook Coll

M SAINT LUKE'S HOSPITAL, Health Sciences Library, 101 Page St, 02741-3400. (Mail add: PO Box 3000, 02741-3000), SAN 307-5559. Tel: 508-961-5267. FAX: 508-999-0219. Web Site: www.southcoast.org/library. *Dir Libr Serv*, Bonnie C Hsu; E-Mail: hsub@southcoast.org
Founded 1954
Oct 1998-Sep 1999 Mats Exp $43,000, Books $8,000, Per/Ser (Incl. Access Fees) $30,000, Electronic Ref Mat (Incl. Access Fees) $5,000
Library Holdings: Bk Vols 1,500; Per Subs 200
Subject Interests: Allied health, Medicine, Nursing
Special Collections: Hospital Archives
Database Vendor: OVID Technologies
Publications: Journal Holdings List; newsletter
Partic in MLA; North Atlantic Health Sciences Libraries, Inc

NEW BRAINTREE

P NEW BRAINTREE PUBLIC LIBRARY,* 45 Memorial Dr, 01531. SAN 307-5583. Tel: 508-867-7650. FAX: 508-867-7650. *Librn*, Alice Webb
Pop 834; Circ 5,814
Library Holdings: Bk Vols 7,000
Mem of Central Massachusetts Regional Library System
Open Mon 1-8:30, Thurs 12:30-3

NEW SALEM

P NEW SALEM PUBLIC LIBRARY,* 24 S Main St, 01355. SAN 307-5591. Tel: 978-544-6334. E-Mail: n_salem@cwmars.org. *Dir*, Diana Smith
Founded 1890. Pop 802; Circ 14,820
Library Holdings: Bk Vols 8,550; Per Subs 24
Mem of Western Regional Libr Syst
Open Tues 12-7, Thurs 9-3, Sat 9-1

NEWBURY

P NEWBURY TOWN LIBRARY,* 50A Main St, 01922. SAN 307-5605. Tel: 978-465-0539. FAX: 978-465-1071. *Dir*, Sandra Small; *Ad Servs*, Suzanne Hussey; *Ch Servs*, Elaine Blackburn
Founded 1926. Pop 6,700; Circ 38,792
Library Holdings: Bk Titles 21,508; Per Subs 71
Partic in Merrimack Valley Library Consortium
Open Mon & Wed noon-8pm, Tues & Thurs 10am-5pm & Sat 10am-3pm
Friends of the Library Group

NEWBURYPORT

S AON CONSULTING, RTS Library, 222 Merrimac St, PO Box 926, 01950. SAN 370-1239. Tel: 978-465-5374. FAX: 978-463-3450. Web Site: www.aon.com. *In Charge*, Qiutong Li; E-Mail: qli@aoncons.com; Staff 3 (MLS 2, Non-MLS 1)
Library Holdings: Per Subs 150
Restriction: Staff use only

S HISTORICAL SOCIETY OF OLD NEWBURY LIBRARY, Cushing House Museum, 98 High St, 01950. SAN 328-2813. Tel: 978-462-2681. FAX: 978-462-0134. E-Mail: hson@greennet.net. *Curator*, Jay Williamson
Library Holdings: Bk Vols 2,500
Special Collections: Local History; Newbury, Newburyport & West Newbury
Open Tues-Fri 9-4 & Sat 11-2 (May-Oct); Open Oct-May for research by appt only

M ANNA JAQUES HOSPITAL, Rogers Medical Library, 25 Highland Ave, 01950. SAN 371-943X. Tel: 978-463-1000, Ext 2480. FAX: 978-463-1286. E-Mail: fmercer@ajh.org. *Dir*, Florence S Mercer; E-Mail: fmercer@ajh.org; *Asst Librn*, Carol Feingold; Staff 2 (MLS 1, Non-MLS 1)
Founded 1970
Oct 1999-Sep 2000 Mats Exp $26,407, Books $5,235, Per/Ser (Incl. Access Fees) $17,400, Electronic Ref Mat (Incl. Access Fees) $3,772. Sal $40,954 (Prof $28,676)

Library Holdings: Bk Vols 800; Per Subs 349
Subject Interests: Clinical medicine
Database Vendor: Ebsco - EbscoHost
Publications: Newsletter (occasional)
Partic in Massachusetts Health Sciences Libraries Network; North Atlantic Health Sciences Libraries, Inc; Northeastern Consortium For Health Information

P NEWBURYPORT PUBLIC LIBRARY,* 112 Parker St, 01950-6619. SAN 307-5621. Tel: 978-465-4428. FAX: 978-463-0394. E-Mail: mne@mvlc.lib.ma.us. Web Site: www.greenet/client/nbptlib. *Librn*, Dorothy R LaFrance; *Ch Servs*, Eloise Schoeppner; *ILL*, Maryanne Delsavio; *Cat*, Ellen Kaminski; *Ad Servs*, Janet Loske
Founded 1854. Pop 16,317; Circ 148,694
Library Holdings: Bk Vols 80,828
Special Collections: Genealogy Coll; Newburyport History, bks, docs, maps, photogs
Partic in Merrimack Valley Library Consortium
Friends of the Library Group

NEWTON

S GEO-CENTERS, INC LIBRARY,* 7 Wells Ave, 02459. SAN 375-7668. Tel: 617-964-7070. FAX: 617-527-7592. *Librn*, Susan Korte Lundgren; E-Mail: slund@corp.geo-centers.com
Library Holdings: Bk Titles 200; Per Subs 75

S H C STARCK LIBRARY,* 45 Industrial Pl, 02461. SAN 307-5664. Tel: 617-969-7690, Ext 4865. FAX: 617-630-5948. *Librn*, Kathy Doyle
Library Holdings: Bk Vols 1,500; Per Subs 175
Subject Interests: Chemistry, Physical chemistry, Physics, Technology
Restriction: Not open to public

S JACKSON HOMESTEAD, Manuscript & Photograph Collection Library, 527 Washington St, 02158. SAN 307-5656. Tel: 617-552-7238. FAX: 617-552-7228. Web Site: www.ci.newton.ma.us/jackson/. *Dir*, Margaret Latimer; *Archivist*, Susan D Abele; E-Mail: sabele@mis12.ci.newton.ma.us. Subject Specialists: *Local history*, Susan D Abele; Staff 1 (MLS 1)
Founded 1950
Library Holdings: Bk Vols 1,000
Subject Interests: Abolitionism, Architectural hist, Black people (ethnic), Decorative arts, Genealogy, Local history, Slavery, State hist for genealogy
Special Collections: Manuscript & Photograph Coll
Function: Reference only
Open Mon-Thurs 8:30-5, most Sun 2-5 (Sept-May)

C LASELL COLLEGE, Brennan Library, 1844 Commonwealth Ave, 02466. SAN 307-0891. Tel: 617-243-2244. FAX: 617-796-4099. E-Mail: lasdir@mln.lib.ma.us. Web Site: www.lasell.edu. *Dir*, Allyson Gray; Tel: 617-243-2243, E-Mail: agray@lasell.edu; *Tech Servs*, Judith Koncz; Tel: 617-243-2207, E-Mail: jkoncz@lasell.edu; *Ref*, June Coughlan; Staff 7 (MLS 4, Non-MLS 3)
Founded 1851. Enrl 800; Fac 90; Highest Degree: Bachelor
Jul 2000-Jun 2001 Income $146,800, Parent Institution $121,800, Other $25,000. Mats Exp $99,000, Books $24,000, Per/Ser (Incl. Access Fees) $31,000, Micro $13,500, AV Equip $500, Electronic Ref Mat (Incl. Access Fees) $30,000. Sal $145,500 (Prof $101,000)
Library Holdings: Bk Vols 55,302; Bk Titles 54,491; Per Subs 478
Subject Interests: Business, Child studies, Education, Fashion, Hotel administration, Physical therapy, Physiology, Retailing, Travel
Special Collections: Lasell Historical Coll
Automation Activity & Vendor Info: (Cataloging) DRA; (Circulation) DRA
Database Vendor: Dialog, IAC - Info Trac, IAC - SearchBank, Lexis-Nexis, OCLC - First Search, Silverplatter Information Inc.
Function: ILL available, Photocopies available
Partic in Minuteman Library Network

S NELINET LIBRARY, 2 Newton Exec Park, 02462. SAN 372-0322. Tel: 617-969-0400. FAX: 617-332-9634. Web Site: www.nelinet.net. *Exec Dir*, Arnold Hirshon; E-Mail: ahirshon@nelinet.net; *Assoc Dir*, Diane G Baden; E-Mail: dbaden@nelinet.net
Library Holdings: Bk Vols 1,500; Per Subs 44
Open Mon-Fri 8:30-5

P NEWTON FREE LIBRARY,* 330 Homer St, 02459-1429. SAN 345-4231. Tel: 617-552-7145. Interlibrary Loan Service Tel: 617-552-7152. FAX: 617-965-8457. Web Site: www.ci.newton.ma.us. *Dir*, Kathy Glick-Weil; E-Mail: kglick_weil@mln.lib.ma.us; *Asst Dir*, Nancy Perlow; *Ad Servs*, Nancy Johnson; *Ch Servs*, Susan Raskin; *ILL*, Elinor Hernon; *Cat*, Andrea Shirley; *Circ*, Gila Vesset
Founded 1870. Pop 81,968; Circ 1,384,656
Jul 1998-Jun 1999 Income (Main Library and Branch Library) $3,574,898, State $115,989, City $3,219,921, Federal $15,000, Locally Generated Income $14,779, Parent Institution $209,209. Mats Exp $737,204, Books $495,848, Per/Ser (Incl. Access Fees) $32,200, Micro $28,858, AV Equip $159,000, Electronic Ref Mat (Incl. Access Fees) $21,298. Sal $2,366,952
Library Holdings: Bk Vols 432,257; Per Subs 787
Special Collections: Newton Historical; Visually & Hearing Handicapped Materials
Automation Activity & Vendor Info: (Acquisitions) DRA; (Cataloging) DRA; (Circulation) DRA; (ILL) DRA; (OPAC) DRA; (Serials) DRA
Publications: bibliography of Newton materials; booklists in subject fields; history of Newton Free Library; monthly newsletter; Newtoniana; People in the Arts
Partic in Metrowest Regional Libr Syst; Minuteman Library Network
Special Services for the Deaf - Books on deafness & sign language; Captioned film depository; Special interest periodicals; TTY machine
Special Services for the Blind - Kurzweil Reading Machine; Optelek
Friends of the Library Group
Branches: 4
AUBURNDALE BRANCH, 375 Auburn St, Auburndale, 02166. SAN 345-4266. Tel: 617-552-7158. Web Site: www.ci.newton.ma.us. *Librn*, Margaret Ellis
NEWTON CORNER, 126 Vernon St, 02158. SAN 345-4290. Tel: 617-552-7157. Web Site: www.ci.newton.ma.us. *Librn*, Nien Lun Tai
NONANTUM, 144 Bridge St, 02158. SAN 345-4479. Tel: 617-552-7163. Web Site: www.ci.newton.ma.us. *Librn*, Marischka Dopp
WABAN BRANCH, 1608 Beacon St, Waban, 02168. SAN 345-4533. Tel: 617-552-7166. Web Site: www.ci.newton.ma.us. *Librn*, Susan Goldberg

NEWTON CENTER

R ANDOVER NEWTON THEOLOGICAL SCHOOL, Franklin Trask Library, 169 Herrick Rd, 02459. SAN 307-5680. Tel: 617-964-1100, Ext 251. FAX: 617-965-9756. Web Site: library.ants.edu. *Dir*, Sharon Taylor; E-Mail: staylor@ants.edu; *Asst Dir, Spec Coll*, Diana Yount; *Online Servs, Tech Servs*, Jeffrey Brigham; *Acq*, James Jaquette; *Tech Servs*, Greg Murphy; *Circ*, Cynthia Bolshaw; Staff 3 (MLS 3)
Founded 1807. Enrl 280; Fac 33
Library Holdings: Bk Vols 230,190; Per Subs 556
Special Collections: Baptist & Congregational Church Records Coll, mss; Isaac Backus Coll, mss; Jonathan Edwards Coll. mss; New England Baptist History Coll
Partic in Boston Theological Institute Library Program; Nelinet, Inc; OCLC Online Computer Library Center, Inc

MOUNT IDA COLLEGE
J LEARNING RESOURCE CENTER, 777 Dedham St, 02159. SAN 307-5699. Tel: 617-928-4552. FAX: 617-928-4038. *Publ Servs*, Bart Hollingsworth; Staff 11 (MLS 11)
Founded 1939. Enrl 18; Fac 47
1996-1997 Income $765,416, Parent Institution $735,412, Other $30,000. Mats Exp $229,027, Books $72,836, Per/Ser (Incl. Access Fees) $64,404, Presv $16,000, Micro $17,787, AV Equip $21,000, Manuscripts & Archives $7,000. Sal $264,389 (Prof $178,637)
Library Holdings: Bk Titles 46,000; Per Subs 530
Subject Interests: Art, Fashion, Literary criticism, Medicine, Veterinary medicine
Special Collections: History of Mount Ida College Archives; National Center for Death Education Library
Partic in Minuteman Library Network; New England Libr Info Network

S NATIONAL CENTER FOR DEATH EDUCATION LIBRARY, 777 Dedham St, 02159. SAN 325-4836. Tel: 617-969-7000, Ext 4649. FAX: 617-928-4713. E-Mail: ncde@mountida.edu.; Staff 1 (MLS 1)
Founded 1984
Library Holdings: Bk Titles 3,000; Per Subs 47
Partic in Minuteman Library Network

SR SWEDENBORG SCHOOL OF RELIGION LIBRARY,* 1320 Center St, Ste 403, 02459-2497. SAN 307-5672. Tel: 617-244-0504. FAX: 617-558-0357. Web Site: www.ssr.com. *Dir*, Johanna Hedbor
Founded 1866
Library Holdings: Bk Titles 33,000; Per Subs 20
Subject Interests: Church history, Counseling, Theology
Special Collections: Church of the New Jerusalem; Emanuel Swedenborg, archives, letters; New Church; Swedenborgian Church
Publications: Studia Swedenborgiana

NEWTON LOWER FALLS

M NEWTON-WELLESLEY HOSPITAL, Paul Talbot Babson Memorial Library,* 2014 Washington St, 02462. SAN 307-5702. Tel: 617-243-6279. FAX: 617-243-6595. E-Mail: new.libr.belc@nwh.org. *Dir Libr Serv*, Christine L Bell
Founded 1945
Library Holdings: Bk Vols 11,000; Per Subs 315
Subject Interests: Health sciences, Hospital administration, Medicine, Nursing, Psychiatry
Special Collections: Newton-Wellesley Hospital Archives
Partic in Boston Biomedical Library Consortium; Massachusetts Health Sciences Libraries Network; OCLC Online Computer Library Center, Inc

NEWTONVILLE

S NEWTON PUBLIC SCHOOLS, Teachers' Professional Library,* 100 Walnut St, 02460. Tel: 617-552-7630. FAX: 617-558-6087. Web Site: www.newton.mec.edu. *Coordr*, Barbara Selvitella
Library Holdings: Bk Titles 2,000
Restriction: By appointment only

NORFOLK

L MCI NORFOLK LAW LIBRARY, 2 Clark St, PO Box 43, 02056. SAN 327-313X. Tel: 508-668-0800, Ext 390. FAX: 617-727-7168. *Head Librn*, William Mongelli
Library Holdings: Bk Vols 8,840; Per Subs 14
Restriction: Not open to public
Branches:
MCI GENERAL LIBRARY *Librn*, William Mongelli
Library Holdings: Bk Vols 6,400; Per Subs 14
RB SEGREGATION UNIT LAW LIBRARY Tel: 508-668-0800. *Librn*, William Mongelli
Library Holdings: Bk Vols 4,000

P NORFOLK PUBLIC LIBRARY, 139 Main St, 02056. SAN 307-5729. Tel: 508-528-3380. FAX: 508-528-6417. Web Site: www.ultranet.com/~npl. *Dir*, Robin Glasser; E-Mail: glasser@ultranet.com; *Assoc Dir*, Francena Johnson; E-Mail: fjohnson@virtualnorfolk.org; *Ch Servs*, Sarina Bluhm; E-Mail: sbluhm@virtualnorfolk.org; *Electronic Resources*, John Spinney; E-Mail: jspinney@virtualnorfolk.org; *Cat*, Marion Graham; E-Mail: mgraham@virtualnorfolk.org. Subject Specialists: *Acquisitions*, Francena Johnson; *Children's*, Sarina Bluhm; *Reference*, Sarina Bluhm; *Reference*, John Spinney; Staff 7 (MLS 2, Non-MLS 5)
Founded 1880. Pop 10,000
Jul 2000-Jun 2001 Income $350,000, State $15,000, City $335,000. Mats Exp $53,000, Books $45,000, Per/Ser (Incl. Access Fees) $3,000, Electronic Ref Mat (Incl. Access Fees) $5,000. Sal $235,000 (Prof $76,000)
Library Holdings: Bk Titles 49,000; Per Subs 150
Automation Activity & Vendor Info: (Acquisitions) SIRSI; (Cataloging) SIRSI; (Circulation) Sydney
Database Vendor: GaleNet, IAC - Info Trac, IAC - SearchBank, OCLC - First Search
Partic in Sails, Inc
Open Mon 2-8:30, Tues-Thurs 10-9-8:30 & Sat 10-4
Friends of the Library Group

NORTH ADAMS

C MASSACHUSETTS COLLEGE OF LIBERAL ARTS, Eugene L Freel Library, 375 Church St Ste 9250, 01247. SAN 307-5753. Tel: 413-662-5321. FAX: 413-662-5286. E-Mail: library@mcla.mass.edu. Web Site: www.mcla.mass.edu. *Asst Dean*, Allen S Morrill; Tel: 413-662-5322, E-Mail: amorrill@mcla.mass.edu; *Publ Servs*, Linda Kaufmann; Tel: 413-662-5325, E-Mail: lkaufman@mcla.mass.edu; *Circ*, Glenn Lawson; Tel: 413-662-5326, E-Mail: glawson@mcla.mass.edu; Staff 14 (MLS 3, Non-MLS 11)
Founded 1894. Enrl 1,400; Fac 92; Highest Degree: Master
Jul 1999-Jun 2000 Income $680,960, State $232,990, Parent Institution $447,970. Mats Exp $217,997, Books $128,726, Per/Ser (Incl. Access Fees) $41,637, Presv $1,388, Micro $16,313, AV Equip $3,300, Electronic Ref Mat (Incl. Access Fees) $26,633. Sal $419,125 (Prof $175,138)
Library Holdings: Bk Vols 170,000; Per Subs 518
Subject Interests: Education, Liberal arts
Special Collections: Hoosac Valley Coll for Local History; Teacher Resources Coll
Automation Activity & Vendor Info: (Cataloging) Innovative Interfaces Inc.; (Circulation) Innovative Interfaces Inc.
Database Vendor: Ebsco - EbscoHost, IAC - Info Trac
Mem of C/W Mars
Partic in Dialog Corporation; Nelinet, Inc

S MRA LABORATORIES LIBRARY, Information Services, 96 Marshall St, 01247-2411. SAN 307-5761. Tel: 413-664-4524, Ext 14. FAX: 413-663-5535. E-Mail: mralib@berkshire.net. Web Site: www.ceramics.com/mra. *Mgr Libr Serv*, Richard Shotwell; E-Mail: shotwell70@hotmail.com
Founded 1951
Library Holdings: Bk Vols 6,800; Per Subs 110
Subject Interests: Ceramics, Chemistry, Electronics, Engineering, Metallurgy, Physics
Partic in Dialog Corporation

P NORTH ADAMS PUBLIC LIBRARY, 74 Church St, 01247. SAN 307-3327. Tel: 413-662-3133. FAX: 413-662-3039. Web Site: www.naplibrary.com. *Dir*, Marcia Gross; E-Mail: lgross@bcn.net; *Ad Servs*, Robin Martin; *Ch Servs*, Marion Grillon; Staff 3 (MLS 2, Non-MLS 1)
Founded 1884. Pop 15,000; Circ 60,662
Jul 1999-Jun 2000 Income $247,406, State $21,263, City $226,143. Mats Exp $42,360, Books $32,500, Per/Ser (Incl. Access Fees) $4,600, Presv $500, Micro $400, AV Equip $2,000, Electronic Ref Mat (Incl. Access Fees) $2,360. Sal $189,158
Library Holdings: Bk Vols 38,160; Per Subs 78
Mem of Western Massachusetts Regional Library System
Friends of the Library Group

M NORTH ADAMS REGIONAL HOSPITAL, Dr Robert Carpenter Memorial Library, 71 Hospital Ave, 01247. SAN 377-9025. Tel: 413-663-3701. FAX: 413-664-5016. E-Mail: library@nbhealth.org. *Librn*, Deborah Lipa
Library Holdings: Bk Titles 300; Per Subs 100
Partic in Basic Health Sciences Library Network; National Network Of Libraries Of Medicine - South Central Region; Western Mass Health Info Consortium

NORTH ANDOVER

S EAGLE TRIBUNE, Editorial Library,* 100 Turnpike St. (Mail add: PO Box 100, 01842), SAN 307-5796. Tel: 978-685-1000, Ext 219. FAX: 978-687-6045. E-Mail: news@eagletribune.com. *Librn*, Tara Mazarella
Library Holdings: Bk Vols 250

C MERRIMACK COLLEGE, McQuade Library, 315 Turnpike Rd, 01845. SAN 307-580X. Tel: 978-837-5215. FAX: 978-837-5434. Web Site: www.web.merrimack.edu/library/mcquade.htm. *Dir*, Barbara Lachance; *Media Spec*, Kevin Salemme; *Coll Develop*, Brian Courtemanche; Tel: 978-837-5000, Ext 4207, E-Mail: bcourtemanche@merrimack-edu; *Cat*, Kathryn Geoffrion; *Publ Servs*, Lori Stalteri; *Electronic Resources, Ser*, Bridget Rawding; Staff 13 (MLS 7, Non-MLS 6)
Founded 1947. Enrl 2,343; Fac 140; Highest Degree: Bachelor
Jul 2000-Jun 2001 Mats Exp $321,040, Books $117,340, Per/Ser (Incl. Access Fees) $132,000, Micro $37,500, AV Equip $6,000, Other Print Mats $1,200, Electronic Ref Mat (Incl. Access Fees) $27,000
Library Holdings: Bk Titles 101,700; Per Subs 1,080
Subject Interests: American history, Literature, Natural history, Philosophy
Special Collections: Augustinian Studies
Database Vendor: Innovative Interfaces INN - View
Publications: A Guide to the Library; Annotated Bibliographies; McQuade Library Skills Handbook
Mem of Northeast Mass Regional Libr Syst
Partic in Nelinet, Inc; Noble; OCLC Online Computer Library Center, Inc

S NORTH ANDOVER HISTORICAL SOCIETY LIBRARY, 153 Academy Rd, 01845. SAN 373-1626. Tel: 978-686-4035. FAX: 978-676-6616. E-Mail: nahistory@juno.com. *Dir*, Carol Majahad
Founded 1913
1997-1998 Mats Exp Presv $700
Library Holdings: Bk Vols 1,500
Subject Interests: Genealogy
Special Collections: Local Architectural History Coll, documents, maps & photos
Restriction: Non-circulating

P STEVENS MEMORIAL LIBRARY, 345 Main St, PO Box 8, 01845. SAN 307-5826. Tel: 978-688-9505. FAX: 978-688-9507. E-Mail: msm@mvlc.lib.ma.us. *Dir*, Sue Ellen Holmes; *Asst Dir*, Barbara Philbrick; *Circ, ILL*, Carol Obert; *Ch Servs*, S Marina Salenikas; *ILL, Ref*, Adelaide Pearson; Staff 10 (MLS 4, Non-MLS 6)
Founded 1907. Pop 25,000; Circ 179,451
1999-2000 Income $644,031, State $21,601, City $601,730, Parent Institution $20,700. Mats Exp $83,145, Books $81,254, Per/Ser (Incl. Access Fees) $7,793, Micro $3,624. Sal $426,833
Library Holdings: Bk Vols 85,715; Per Subs 217
Special Collections: Essex County Ma; Poetry (Anne Bradstreet Coll)
Partic in NE Mass Regional Libr Syst
Friends of the Library Group

NORTH ATTLEBORO

P RICHARDS MEMORIAL LIBRARY, North Attleboro Public Library, 118 N Washington St, 02760. SAN 307-5834. Tel: 508-699-0122. FAX: 508-699-8075. *Ad Servs, Dir*, Francis Ward; *Tech Servs*, David Lockhart
Founded 1878. Pop 24,000; Circ 100,000
Library Holdings: Bk Vols 50,000; Per Subs 120
Mem of Eastern Mass Regional Libr Syst
Friends of the Library Group

NORTH BILLERICA

§M DUPONT PHARMACEUTICALS LIBRARY, 331 Treble Cove Rd, 01862. SAN 375-4499. Tel: 978-671-8972. FAX: 978-671-8080. E-Mail: marilyn.cocorochio@dupontpharma.com. *Info Specialist*, Marilyn Cocorochio
Library Holdings: Bk Vols 1,200; Per Subs 120
Subject Interests: Nuclear medicine
Automation Activity & Vendor Info: (Acquisitions) SIRSI; (Cataloging) SIRSI; (Circulation) SIRSI
Restriction: Employees & their associates

NORTH BROOKFIELD

P HASTON FREE PUBLIC LIBRARY,* 161 Main St, 01535. SAN 307-5842. Tel: 508-867-0208. FAX: 508-867-0216. *Librn*, Ann L Kidd; E-Mail: akidd@cwmarsmail.cwmars.org; *Asst Librn*, Rosemary MacKenzie
Founded 1879. Pop 4,817; Circ 32,829
Jul 1997-Jun 1998 Income $61,511, State $5,365, City $54,157, Locally Generated Income $1,116, Other $873. Mats Exp $10,256, Books $9,115, Per/Ser (Incl. Access Fees) $1,141. Sal $35,242
Library Holdings: Bk Vols 19,100; Bk Titles 20,062; Per Subs 44
Mem of Central Massachusetts Regional Library System
Partic in CW Mars
Friends of the Library Group

NORTH DARTMOUTH

L SOUTHERN NEW ENGLAND SCHOOL OF LAW LIBRARY, 333 Faunce Corner Rd, 02747. SAN 372-0314. Tel: 508-998-9888. FAX: 508-998-2018. *Dir*, Marguerite Most; *Bibliogr*, Kendra Saint Aubin; *Publ Servs*, Howard Senzel
Partic in OCLC Online Computer Library Center, Inc; SE Mass Regional Libr Syst
Friends of the Library Group

C UNIVERSITY OF MASSACHUSETTS DARTMOUTH, Library Communications Center, 285 Old Westport Rd, 02747-2300. SAN 307-5850. Tel: 508-999-8675. Circulation Tel: 508-999-8750. Reference Tel: 508-999-8678. FAX: 508-999-8987. E-Mail: libweb@umassd.edu. Web Site: www.lib.umassd.edu. *Dean of Libr*, Donald G Sweet; Tel: 508-999-8663, E-Mail: dsweet@umassd.edu; *Asst Dean*, Ann Montgomery Smith; Tel: 508-999-8664, E-Mail: asmith@umassd.edu; *Ref*, Jane Booth; *Ref*, Elizabeth Lindsay; *Circ*, Catherine Fortier-Barnes; Tel: 508-999-8665, E-Mail: cfortier@umassd.edu; *Cat*, Pearl Szatek; *ILL, Ser*, Susanne Andrews; Tel: 508-999-8676, E-Mail: sandrews@umassd.edu; *Archivist, Spec Coll*, Judith Farrar; Tel: 508-999-8686, Fax: 508-999-8424, E-Mail: jfarrar@umassd.edu; *Coll Develop*, Bruce Barnes; Tel: 508-999-8666, E-Mail: bbarnes@umassd.edu; *Ref*, Linda Zieper; Tel: 508-999-8526, Fax: 508-999-9240, E-Mail: lzieper@umassd.edu; *Automation Syst Coordr*, Charles McNeil; Tel: 508-999-8680, E-Mail: cmcneil@umassd.edu. Subject Specialists: *Art*, Linda Zieper; Staff 43 (MLS 16, Non-MLS 27)
Founded 1960. Pop 5,966; Enrl 5,966; Fac 372; Highest Degree: Doctorate
Jul 1999-Jun 2000 Income $2,580,536, State $1,744,396, Locally Generated Income $12,000, Parent Institution $824,140. Mats Exp $1,246,560, Books $253,840, Per/Ser (Incl. Access Fees) $656,440, Presv $29,260, Micro $81,600, Electronic Ref Mat (Incl. Access Fees) $208,900. Sal $1,795,779 (Prof $997,808)
Library Holdings: Bk Vols 455,323; Bk Titles 258,189; Per Subs 2,850
Subject Interests: Literature, Portuguese (language), Technology
Special Collections: American Imprints Coll; Archives of the Center for Jewish Culture; Archives of the Franco American League of Fall River; Can; Franco-American Coll; Hansard Parliamentary Debates; Portuguese-American Historical Coll; Robert Kennedy Assassination Archives
Automation Activity & Vendor Info: (Cataloging) MultiLIS; (Circulation) MultiLIS
Database Vendor: CARL, Dialog, Ebsco - EbscoHost, IAC - SearchBank, OCLC - First Search, OVID Technologies, ProQuest, Silverplatter Information Inc., Wilson - Wilson Web
Publications: Library News (Newsletter)
Partic in Boston Library Consortium; Nelinet, Inc; Southeastern Massachusetts Consortium Of Health Science Libraries; Southeastern Massachusetts Cooperating Libraries
Friends of the Library Group

NORTH EASTON

P AMES FREE LIBRARY, Easton's Public Library, 53 Main St, 02356. SAN 307-594X. Tel: 508-238-2000. FAX: 508-238-2980. E-Mail: library@easton.ma.org. Web Site: www.people.ne.mediaone.net/amesfreelibrary. *Exec Dir*, Annalee Bundy; *Assoc Dir*, Madeline Miele; *Ref Servs YA*, Karen Gabbert; *Ref*, Elizabeth Keenan; *ILL*, Willa Richards-Grant; *Circ*, Michael Briody; *Ad Servs*, Kathleen Eastwood; Staff 34 (MLS 20, Non-MLS 14)
Founded 1879. Pop 22,659; Circ 73,512
Jul 1999-Jun 2000 Income (Main Library and Branch Library) $902,022, State $18,522, City $360,000, Locally Generated Income $6,000, Other $517,500. Mats Exp $95,202, Books $87,000, Per/Ser (Incl. Access Fees) $8,202. Sal $353,500 (Prof $232,200)
Library Holdings: Bk Vols 55,300; Per Subs 160
Subject Interests: Decorative arts
Special Collections: 19th Century Periodicals; H H Richardson Materials; Massachusetts Town Reports
Automation Activity & Vendor Info: (Cataloging) SIRSI; (Circulation) epixtech, inc.
Database Vendor: Dialog, epixtech, inc., GaleNet, IAC - Info Trac, OCLC - First Search
Publications: The First Century (a centennial history of Ames Free Library of Easton, Inc)
Friends of the Library Group
Branches: 1
FIVE CORNERS, 670 Depot St, Easton, 02375. SAN 374-6410. Tel: 508-230-8595.

NORTH READING

P FLINT MEMORIAL LIBRARY, 147 Park St, 01864. SAN 307-5869. Tel: 978-664-4942. FAX: 978-664-0812. E-Mail: mnr@mvlc.lib.ma.us. *Dir*, Nancy Sheehan; *Ref*, Debra Hindes; Staff 3 (MLS 3)
Founded 1872. Pop 13,800; Highest Degree: Master
Library Holdings: Bk Vols 56,013; Per Subs 176
Subject Interests: Local history
Special Collections: Genealogy & History (Clara Burnham, North Reading & George Root Colls) bks, mss, maps
Automation Activity & Vendor Info: (Circulation) GEAC
Mem of Northeast Mass Regional Libr Syst
Partic in Merrimack Valley Library Consortium
Friends of the Library Group

NORTH TRURO

P TRURO PUBLIC LIBRARY, 5 Library Lane, 02652-0357. (Mail add: PO Box 357, 02652), SAN 307-5877. Tel: 508-487-1125. FAX: 508-487-3571. Web Site: www.capecod.net/~tlibrary. *Dir*, Elsie K Brainard; E-Mail: ebrainard@clams.lib.ma.us; Staff 1 (MLS 1)
Founded 1999. Pop 1,450; Circ 12,000
Jul 2000-Jun 2001 Income City $97,455. Mats Exp Books $9,500. Sal $56,498
Library Holdings: Bk Titles 17,600; Per Subs 29
Automation Activity & Vendor Info: (Acquisitions) DRA; (Circulation) DRA; (ILL) DRA
Mem of SE Mass Regional Libr Syst
Partic in Cape Libraries Automated Materials Sharing; SE Mass Regional Libr Syst
Special Services for the Blind - Low vision aids & talking readers
Friends of the Library Group

NORTHAMPTON

GL COMMONWEALTH OF MASSACHUSETTS TRIAL COURT, Hampshire Law Library, Courthouse, 99 Main St, 01060. SAN 307-5893. Tel: 413-586-2297. FAX: 413-584-0870. Web Site: www.lawlib.state.ma.us.; Staff 1 (MLS 1)
Founded 1894
Jul 1999-Jun 2000 Mats Exp Books $114,135. Sal $111,000 (Prof $57,000)
Library Holdings: Bk Vols 27,388; Bk Titles 3,865; Per Subs 70
Special Collections: Statutes of New England States & New York
Partic in Nelinet, Inc; OCLC Online Computer Library Center, Inc
Friends of the Library Group

COOLEY DICKINSON HOSPITAL
M RICHARD H DOLLOFF MEDICAL LIBRARY, 30 Locust St, 01060. SAN 345-4592. Tel: 413-582-2291. FAX: 413-582-2985. Web Site: www.pages.map.com/dkurkul.; Staff 2 (MLS 1, Non-MLS 1)
Founded 1969
Oct 1996-Sep 1997 Mats Exp $30,348
Library Holdings: Bk Titles 800; Per Subs 185
Subject Interests: Clinical medicine
Database Vendor: OVID Technologies
Function: Professional lending library
Partic in Basic Health Sciences Library Network; Docline; Massachusetts Health Sciences Libraries Network; Western Mass Health Info Consortium

P FORBES LIBRARY, 20 West St, 01060-3798. SAN 307-5885. Tel: 413-587-1011. Reference Tel: 413-587-1012. FAX: 413-587-1015. Web Site: www.gazettenet.com/forbeslibrary. *Dir*, Blaise Bisaillon; *Ch Servs*, Judith McGowan; *Ref*, Elise Feeley; *Cat*, Paula Elliot; Staff 9 (MLS 9)
Founded 1894. Pop 30,058; Circ 272,000
Jul 1999-Jun 2000 Income $1,038,076, State $40,700, City $824,586, Other $171,000. Mats Exp $165,000, Books $98,000, Per/Ser (Incl. Access Fees) $26,000, Presv $4,900, Electronic Ref Mat (Incl. Access Fees) $7,500. Sal $734,072 (Prof $282,000)
Library Holdings: Bk Vols 225,000; Per Subs 300
Subject Interests: Art and architecture, Music
Special Collections: Calvin Coolidge; Connecticut Valley History; Genealogy Coll; Photography (Walter E Corbin), photog, prints, slides; World War I & World War II Posters
Automation Activity & Vendor Info: (Circulation) Innovative Interfaces Inc.
Mem of Western Regional Libr Syst
Partic in CW Mars
Friends of the Library Group

S HISTORIC NORTHAMPTON, Archives & Library,* 46 Bridge St, 01060. SAN 329-9112. Tel: 413-584-6011. FAX: 413-584-7956. E-Mail: hstnhamp@javanet.com. Web Site: www.historic-northampton.org. *Exec Dir*, Kerry W Buckley

Founded 1905
Library Holdings: Bk Titles 2,500
Subject Interests: Local history
Special Collections: Houses & People (Howes Brothers Coll), docs, ephemera, maps, mss & photog from 19th-20th centuries, archives from 17th-20th centuries
Publications: History of Northampton; Newsletters; Weathervane Series (booklets on local subjects)
Open Tues-Fri 10-4, Sat & Sun 12-4; Researchers by appt
Friends of the Library Group

S NEW SONG LIBRARY, PO Box 295, 01061. SAN 323-7141. Tel: 413-586-9485. Web Site: users.massed.net/~johanna/. *Librn*, Johanna Halbeisen; E-Mail: johanna@massed.net
Library Holdings: Bk Titles 4,000
Special Collections: Civil Rights songs & songs of other freedom movement around the world; Collections of songs about parenting, growing older, family violence, addictions & spiritual growth; labor songs (contemporary & historical); Recordings by gay & lesbian artists; tapes of workshops & songsharings from People's Music Network (1977-1989); Weavers, Malvina Reynolds, Phil Ochs, Pete Seeger, Joan Baez & 60's era recordings

C SMITH COLLEGE LIBRARIES, William Allan Neilson Library, 01063. SAN 345-4657. Tel: 413-585-2910. Interlibrary Loan Service Tel: 413-585-2962. Reference Tel: 413-585-2966. FAX: 413-585-2904. Web Site: www.smith.edu/libraries. *Dir*, Christopher B Loring; Tel: 413-585-2902, E-Mail: cloring@smith.com; *ILL*, Naomi Sturtevant; *Tech Servs*, James Montgomery; *Syst Coordr*, Eric Loehr; *Bibliog Instr, Online Servs, Ref*, Christine Hannon; *Coll Develop*, Maria Brazill; Staff 22 (MLS 22)
Founded 1875. Enrl 3,464; Fac 264; Highest Degree: Doctorate
Jul 1999-Jun 2000 Income (Main and Other College/University Libraries) $5,168,473. Mats Exp $2,002,406, Books $986,462, Per/Ser (Incl. Access Fees) $867,994, Presv $82,579, Micro $65,371. Sal $2,031,667 (Prof $949,222)
Library Holdings: Bk Vols 1,246,348; Per Subs 3,204
Subject Interests: Art and architecture, Feminism, French Canadians, History, Printing
Special Collections: Sylvia Plath, Virginia Woolf & Bloomsbury Colls
Database Vendor: Innovative Interfaces INN - View
Publications: News From the Libraries
Partic in Nelinet, Inc; OCLC Online Computer Library Center, Inc; RLIN
Friends of the Library Group
Departmental Libraries:
COLLEGE ARCHIVES Tel: 413-585-2970. FAX: 413-585-2886. Web Site: www.smith.edu/libraries/ca/home.htm. *Archivist*, Nanci Young; Staff 2 (MLS 2)
Founded 1921
Library Holdings: Per Subs 30
Subject Interests: Education, History, Landscape architecture, Social service (social work)
Special Collections: College Records (Cambridge School of Landscape Architecture; Faculty Papers (Mary Ellen Chase, John Duke, William Allan Neilson & Harris Hawthorne Wilder Colls); Institute for the Coordination of Women's Interests; other college offices & departments); Photographs; School for Social Work; Smith College Relief Unit; Student Diaries & Letters
Restriction: Non-circulating to the public
HILLYER ART LIBRARY, Fine Arts Ctr, 01063. SAN 345-4681. Tel: 413-585-2940. FAX: 413-585-2904. Web Site: www.smith.edu/libraries/hillyer/bpindex.htm. *Librn*, Barbara Polowy; Staff 1 (MLS 1)
Subject Interests: Architecture, Art, Art history
WERNER JOSTEN LIBRARY, Mendenhall Ctr for the Performing Arts, 01063. SAN 345-4711. Tel: 413-585-2930. Web Site: www.smith.edu/libraries/josten.htm. *Librn*, Marlene M Wong; *Assoc Librn*, Kathryn E Burnett; Staff 2 (MLS 2)
Subject Interests: Dance, Music, Theater
Special Collections: Einstein Coll (music of the 16th & 17th Centuries copied in score by Alfred Einstein); Music & correspondence of Werner Josten
Partic in Nelinet, Inc
MORTIMER RARE BOOK ROOM Tel: 413-585-2906. Web Site: www.smith.edu/libraries/mrbr/rare.htm. *Curator*, Martin Antonetti; Staff 2 (MLS 2)
Founded 1942
Library Holdings: Bk Vols 27,723
Subject Interests: American literature, English literature, Printing
Special Collections: Botany (George Salter & E Thornton Colls); English & American Children's Books, 17th-20th Centuries (Ernest Hemingway, Rudyard Kipling & George Bernard Shaw Colls); Iconography (Bloomsbury, Sylvia Plath & Virginia Woolf Colls)
Restriction: Non-circulating to the public
SOPHIA SMITH COLLECTION Tel: 413-585-2970. Web Site: www.smith.edu/libraries/ssc/. *Head of Libr*, Sherrill Redmon; Staff 2 (MLS 2)
Founded 1942
Subject Interests: Art, Birth control, Education, Feminism, Humanities, Journalism, Women's hist
Special Collections: Birth Control (Margaret Sanger Coll), mss; Suffrage & Peace, mss; United States 19th Century Social, Economic & Political Reforms (Garrison & Ames Family Papers), mss; Women in Industry (Mary van Kleeck Papers), mss
Publications: Imposing Evidence (newsletter)
Restriction: Non-circulating to the public
ANITA O'K & ROBERT R YOUNG SCIENCE LIBRARY, Bass Hall, 01063. SAN 345-4746. Tel: 413-585-2950. FAX: 413-585-3786. Web Site: www.smith.edu/libraries/young/scimain.htm. *Librn*, Rocco Piccinino; Staff 1 (MLS 1)
Subject Interests: Astronomy, Chemistry, Computer science, Geology, History of science, Mathematics, Physics
Special Collections: Maps, printed, mss, wall, raised relief & gazetteers
Partic in Nelinet, Inc

NORTHBOROUGH

P NORTHBOROUGH FREE LIBRARY, 34 Main St, 01532-1942. SAN 307-5931. Tel: 508-393-5025. FAX: 508-393-5027. *Dir*, Jean M Langley; E-Mail: jlangley@cwmarsmail.cwmars.org; *Asst Librn*, Daniel Finneran; E-Mail: dfinnera@cwmarsmail.cwmars.org; *Ch Servs*, Doreen Metcalfe; *YA Servs*, Sandra Stafford; Staff 11 (MLS 4, Non-MLS 7)
Founded 1868. Pop 13,300; Circ 175,686
1998-1999 Income $487,573, State $13,000, City $474,573. Mats Exp $77,830, Books $67,920, Per/Ser (Incl. Access Fees) $5,466. Sal $329,691 (Prof $157,545)
Library Holdings: Bk Titles 77,775; Per Subs 170
Publications: Gale Forecast, monthly newsletter
Mem of Central Massachusetts Regional Library System
Partic in CW Mars
Friends of the Library Group

S SAINT GOBAIN INDUSTRIAL CERAMICS, Technology Information Services - (NRDC) Northborough Research & Development Center Library,* Goddard Rd, 01532. SAN 375-6513. Tel: 508-351-7810. FAX: 508-351-7700. *Mgr, Tech Servs*, Brendan Wyly; *Cat*, Dianne Rugh
Library Holdings: Bk Vols 1,000; Bk Titles 800; Per Subs 60
Partic in Nelinet, Inc; OCLC Online Computer Library Center, Inc; Worcester Area Cooperating Libraries

NORTHFIELD

P DICKINSON MEMORIAL LIBRARY, 115 Main St, 01360. SAN 307-5966. Tel: 413-498-2455. FAX: 413-498-5111. E-Mail: dmemlib@shaysnet.com. *Asst Dir*, Sharon Miller
Founded 1878. Pop 3,000; Circ 33,000
Library Holdings: Bk Vols 19,000; Per Subs 40
Mem of Western Massachusetts Regional Library System
Friends of the Library Group

P FIELD LIBRARY,* 39 Four Mile Brook Rd, 01360-9542. SAN 307-5974. Tel: 413-498-0220. *Librn*, Ann Nadolski
Pop 2,470
Library Holdings: Bk Vols 4,000
Mem of Western Regional Libr Syst

NORTON

C MADELEINE CLARK WALLACE LIBRARY, Wheaton College, 26 E Main St, 02766-2322. SAN 345-4770. Tel: 508-285-8200, Ext 8224. FAX: 508-285-8275. *Assoc Librn, Instrul Serv, Ref*, Margaret F Gardner; Tel: 508-285-8200, Ext 3705; *ILL, Ref*, Marcia E Grimes; Tel: 508-285-8200, Ext 3702; *ILL*, Martha J Mitchell; *Acq*, Hilary Murray; *Cat*, Betty L Brown; *Archivist, Spec Coll & Archives*, Zephorene Stickney; *Ser, Syst Coordr*, Jean Callaghan; *Media Spec*, Robert Muttart; *Tech Coordr*, Susan Quagliorol; *Ref*, Judith Aaron; *Acq*, Gloria Barker; *Admin Assoc*, Judy Arsenault; *Tech Servs*, Jennifer Horton; *Circ*, Mary Savolainen; Tel: 508-285-8200, Ext 3708; *Media Spec*, Jeanne Farrell; *Ref*, Kathleen Sheehan
Founded 1840
Library Holdings: Bk Vols 362,933; Per Subs 2,252
Subject Interests: Art and architecture, History, Religion, Women's studies
Special Collections: Children's Coll; Lucy Larcom Coll; Private Press Books; Wheaton Coll & Archives, bks, photog, clippings, rec, cat & misc
Automation Activity & Vendor Info: (Acquisitions) Innovative Interfaces Inc.; (Cataloging) Innovative Interfaces Inc.
Publications: Newsletter (3 issues per year)
Restriction: Open to faculty, students & qualified researchers, Public use on premises
Function: Photocopies available
Partic in Nelinet, Inc; SE Mass Regional Libr Syst; Southeastern Massachusetts Consortium Of Health Science Libraries
Library card available, residents $20.00 annual fee, non-residents $40.00

P NORTON PUBLIC LIBRARY, 68 E Main St, 02766. SAN 307-5982. Tel: 508-285-0265. FAX: 508-285-0266. *Librn*, Elaine Jackson; E-Mail: ejackson@sailsinc.org; Staff 14 (MLS 3, Non-MLS 11)

Pop 15,072; Circ 128,000
1999-2000 Income $304,144
Library Holdings: Bk Titles 34,686; Per Subs 89
Subject Interests: Local history
Partic in Sails, Inc
Friends of the Library Group

NORWELL

S GIGA INFORMATION GROUP, Information Center Library,* One Longwater Circle, 02061. SAN 375-8389. Tel: 781-982-9500. FAX: 781-878-6650. *Dir*, Daniel Bednarek; Tel: 617-577-9595
Library Holdings: Per Subs 60

P NORWELL PUBLIC LIBRARY, 64 South St, 02061-2433. SAN 321-0812. Tel: 781-659-2015. FAX: 781-659-6755. Web Site: www.ssec.org/idis/norwell/nplnew/joanne/npl.htm. *Dir*, Diane Gordon Kadanoff; E-Mail: dianek@ocln.org; *Syst Coordr*, JoAnne Dirk; *Ad Servs*, Jeanne Ryer; *Ch Servs*, Jane Acheson; Staff 4 (MLS 4)
Pop 9,200; Circ 93,827
Library Holdings: Bk Vols 42,099; Per Subs 108
Open Mon-Wed 10-8, Thurs-Sat 10-5
Friends of the Library Group

S SOUTH SHORE NATURAL SCIENCE CENTER, Vinal Library, Jacob's Lane, PO Box 429, 02061. SAN 371-7259. Tel: 781-659-2559, Ext 208. FAX: 781-659-5924. Web Site: www.ssnsc.org. *Exec Dir*, Martha Twigg; *Librn*, Doris Holmes
Founded 1976
Library Holdings: Bk Titles 1,200
Subject Interests: Natural science
Special Collections: William Gould Vinal Coll

§S THE JAMES LIBRARY, 24 West St., 02061. (Mail add: PO Box 164, 02061), Tel: 781-659-7100. *Librn*, Caroline D Chapin; Staff 1 (MLS 1)
Founded 1874
Library Holdings: Bk Titles 20,000
Special Collections: First Parish Church, Norwell; Local History; North River Ship Building
Friends of the Library Group

NORWOOD

M CARITAS NORWOOD HOSPITAL, Library Services, 800 Washington St, 02062. SAN 307-6016. Tel: 781-278-6243. FAX: 781-769-9622. *Dir Libr Serv*, Denise Corless; Staff 1 (MLS 1)
Founded 1965
Oct 1999-Sep 2000 Income $57,200. Mats Exp $52,650, Books $8,000, Per/Ser (Incl. Access Fees) $30,000, Presv $3,000, Micro $220, Electronic Ref Mat (Incl. Access Fees) $4,000. Sal $36,500
Library Holdings: Bk Vols 5,500; Bk Titles 2,000; Per Subs 200
Subject Interests: Medical
Partic in Basic Health Sciences Library Network; Consortium For Information Resources; National Network Of Libraries Of Medicine - South Central Region; Southeastern Massachusetts Consortium Of Health Science Libraries

S FACTORY MUTUAL RESEARCH CORP, Technical Information Center, 1151 Boston-Providence-Tpk, 02062. SAN 307-6008. Tel: 781-255-4764. FAX: 781-762-9375. E-Mail: fmrctic@usal.com. *Bibliog Instr, Librn, Mgr*, Janet B Green; E-Mail: janet.green@fmglobal.com; Staff 6 (MLS 1, Non-MLS 5)
Founded 1968
Library Holdings: Bk Vols 7,500; Per Subs 150
Subject Interests: Technology
Special Collections: Company History
Automation Activity & Vendor Info: (Cataloging) Inmagic, Inc.; (OPAC) Inmagic, Inc.; (Serials) Inmagic, Inc.

GL MASSACHUSETTS TRIAL COURT, (Formerly Norfolk Law Library), Norfolk Law Library, 57 Providence Hwy, 02062. SAN 307-3459. Tel: 781-769-7483. FAX: 781-769-7836. *Librn*, Carol Ewing; *Librn*, Agnes Leathe; E-Mail: agnesml@juno.com; Staff 3 (MLS 1, Non-MLS 2)
Founded 1898
Jul 2000-Jun 2001 Mats Exp $139,000. Sal $117,962
Library Holdings: Bk Titles 15,000; Per Subs 24
Subject Interests: State law
Special Collections: Legal videos for laypeople
Database Vendor: OCLC - First Search
Partic in Metrowest Regional Libr Syst; New England Law Library Consortium, Inc
Friends of the Library Group

P MORRILL MEMORIAL LIBRARY, 14 Peabody Rd, 02062-1206. (Mail add: PO Box 220, 02062-0220), SAN 345-486X. Tel: 781-769-0200. FAX: 781-769-6083. Web Site: www.ci.norwood.ma.us/lib/index.html. *Dir*, Mary R Phinney; E-Mail: mphinney@mln.lib.ma.us; *Ad Servs*, Bettina Blood; E-Mail: bblood@mln.lib.ma.us; *Ad Servs*, Margot Sullivan; E-Mail: msullivan@mln.lib.ma.us; *Ref*, Marie Lydon; E-Mail: mlydon@mln.lib.ma.us; *Tech Servs*, Shelby P Warner; E-Mail: swarner@mln.lib.ma.us; *Ch Servs*, Hope Anderson; E-Mail: handerson@mln.lib.ma.us; *Ad Servs*, Beth Goldman; E-Mail: bgoldman@mln.lib.ma.us. Subject Specialists: *Large print*, Beth Goldman; *Literacy*, Bettina Blood; Staff 15 (MLS 7, Non-MLS 8)
Founded 1873. Pop 28,000; Circ 162,447
Jul 1999-Jun 2000 Income $939,146, State $41,098, City $871,348, Other $26,700. Mats Exp $136,753, Books $103,439, Per/Ser (Incl. Access Fees) $10,431, Presv $2,000, Micro $2,000, Electronic Ref Mat (Incl. Access Fees) $5,762. Sal $701,333
Library Holdings: Bk Titles 74,221; Per Subs 236
Special Collections: Norwood Coll
Automation Activity & Vendor Info: (Acquisitions) DRA; (Cataloging) DRA; (Circulation) DRA; (ILL) DRA; (OPAC) DRA
Publications: Monthly Calendar; New At Your Library
Partic in Minuteman Library Network
Friends of the Library Group

OAK BLUFFS

P OAK BLUFFS PUBLIC LIBRARY, PO Box 2039, 02557. SAN 307-6032. Tel: 508-693-9433. FAX: 508-693-5377. Web Site: www.vineyard.net/org/obpl. *Dir*, Linda N Norton; E-Mail: lnorton@clams.lib.ma.us
Pop 3,306; Circ 33,634
Library Holdings: Bk Vols 13,959; Per Subs 56
Partic in Cape Libraries Automated Materials Sharing; SE Mass Regional Libr Syst
Friends of the Library Group

OAKHAM

P FOBES MEMORIAL LIBRARY,* 4 Maple St, 01068-9790. SAN 307-6040. Tel: 508-882-3372. FAX: 508-882-3372. *Librn*, Maude M Stone; *Asst Librn*, Stella Anderson
Pop 1,079; Circ 14,000
Library Holdings: Bk Vols 15,885; Per Subs 22
Mem of Central Massachusetts Regional Library System
Friends of the Library Group

ORANGE

P WHEELER MEMORIAL LIBRARY,* 49 E Main St, 01364-1267. SAN 307-6067. Tel: 978-544-2495. FAX: 978-544-1116. *Dir*, Janice Lanou; E-Mail: jlanou@cwmars.org; Staff 6 (MLS 1, Non-MLS 5)
Founded 1847. Pop 7,312; Circ 59,669
Jul 1998-Jun 1999 Income $232,422, State $9,213, City $186,305, Locally Generated Income $36,904. Mats Exp $39,219, Books $29,133, Per/Ser (Incl. Access Fees) $3,296, Micro $958, AV Equip $5,472, Electronic Ref Mat (Incl. Access Fees) $360. Sal $118,494 (Prof $36,450)
Library Holdings: Bk Vols 46,843; Per Subs 138
Mem of Western Massachusetts Regional Library System
Friends of the Library Group

ORLEANS

P SNOW LIBRARY, 67 Main St, PO Box 246, 02653. SAN 307-6075. Tel: 508-240-3760. FAX: 508-255-5701. *Dir*, Mary Reuland; E-Mail: orl-mr@clams.lib.ma.us; *Asst Dir*, Tavi Prugno; Staff 2 (MLS 2)
Founded 1877. Pop 6,911; Circ 134,996
Jul 1999-Jun 2000 Income $366,310, State $13,941, City $314,843, Other $37,526. Mats Exp $72,331, Books $52,647, Per/Ser (Incl. Access Fees) $10,093. Sal $225,749 (Prof $75,413)
Library Holdings: Bk Titles 50,564; Per Subs 85
Special Collections: H K Cummings Coll of Historical Photographs (1870-1890)
Automation Activity & Vendor Info: (Acquisitions) DRA; (Cataloging) DRA; (Circulation) DRA; (Course Reserve) DRA; (ILL) DRA; (Media Booking) DRA; (OPAC) DRA; (Serials) DRA
Partic in Cape Libraries Automated Materials Sharing
Friends of the Library Group

OSTERVILLE

P OSTERVILLE FREE LIBRARY,* 43 Wianno Ave, 02655-2088. SAN 307-6083. Tel: 508-428-5757. FAX: 508-428-5557. *Dir*, Barbara Conathan; *Asst Dir*, Lorraine Felt; *Ch Servs*, Linda Dalrymple; Staff 8 (MLS 2, Non-MLS 6)
Founded 1882. Pop 10,500
Library Holdings: Bk Vols 37,500
Subject Interests: Art, History
Mem of Cape Librs Automated Mat Sharing; Eastern Mass Regional Libr Syst
Friends of the Library Group

OXFORD

P OXFORD FREE LIBRARY, Main St, 01540. SAN 345-4924. Tel: 508-987-6003. FAX: 508-987-3896. *Dir*, Timothy A Kelley; E-Mail: tkelley@cwmarsmail.cwmars.org
Founded 1903. Pop 13,100; Circ 72,100
Jul 2000-Jun 2001 Income $337,531, City $263,022. Mats Exp $48,100, Books $45,000, Per/Ser (Incl. Access Fees) $2,600, Presv $500. Sal $249,951 (Prof $50,700)
Library Holdings: Bk Vols 29,000; Per Subs 71
Special Collections: Local History (Records to 1850)
Automation Activity & Vendor Info: (Circulation) Innovative Interfaces Inc.
Mem of Central Massachusetts Regional Library System
Partic in CW Mars
Friends of the Library Group

PALMER

P PALMER PUBLIC LIBRARY,* 1455 N Main St, 01069. SAN 307-6091. Tel: 413-283-3330. FAX: 413-283-9970. Web Site: www.palmer.lib.ma.us. *Dir*, Mark J Contois; E-Mail: mcontois@palmer.lib.ma.us; *Asst Dir*, Nancy E Bauer; *Ch Servs, YA Servs*, Christine F Reim; *Ref*, Mary Bernat; *Coll Develop*, Geraldine B Molleur; Staff 2 (MLS 2)
Founded 1878. Pop 12,112; Circ 201,398
Jul 1998-Jun 1999 Mats Exp $551,254, Books $86,157. Sal $340,749 (Prof $85,984)
Library Holdings: Bk Vols 59,623; Per Subs 147
Subject Interests: Genealogy, Local history
Special Collections: Palmer Coll; Palmer Journal-Register
Mem of Western Massachusetts Regional Library System
Partic in Central-Western Mass Automated Resource Sharing
Special Services for the Deaf - TTY machine
Open Mon-Thurs 10-8, Fri & Sat 10-5
Friends of the Library Group

M WING MEMORIAL HOSPITAL, Medical Library, 40 Wright St, 01069-1187. Tel: 413-283-7651, 413-284-5314. FAX: 413-284-5117. *Librn*, Karen Dorval; E-Mail: karen.dorval@winghealth.org
Library Holdings: Bk Vols 2,500; Bk Titles 2,000; Per Subs 40

PAXTON

CR ANNA MARIA COLLEGE, Mondor-Eagen Library, 50 Sunset Lane, 01612-1198. SAN 307-6105. Tel: 508-849-3405. FAX: 508-849-3408. Web Site: www.annamarie.edu. *Dir Libr Serv*, Ruth Pyne; Tel: 508-849-3406, E-Mail: rpyne@annamaria.edu; *Cat*, Sr Lorraine Bilodeau; Tel: 508-849-3407; *ILL*, Sr Dolores Lavoie; Tel: 508-849-3405; *Acq*, Leona McDonald; Tel: 508-849-3407, E-Mail: lmcdonald@annamaria.edu; Staff 11 (MLS 5, Non-MLS 6)
Founded 1946. Enrl 978; Fac 165; Highest Degree: Master
Jul 1998-Jun 1999 Income Parent Institution $164,297. Mats Exp $83,847, Books $22,300, Per/Ser (Incl. Access Fees) $24,750, Presv $5,297, Other Print Mats $31,500. Sal $106,951 (Prof $74,940)
Library Holdings: Bk Vols 64,442; Bk Titles 48,829; Per Subs 288
Subject Interests: Business, Criminal justice, Education, Religion, Sociology
Automation Activity & Vendor Info: (Cataloging) Innovative Interfaces Inc.; (Circulation) Innovative Interfaces Inc.
Database Vendor: IAC - SearchBank, Innovative Interfaces INN - View, OCLC - First Search
Publications: Introduction to the Library; Library guides
Function: Reference services available
Partic in CMRLS; Nelinet, Inc; Worcester Area Cooperating Libraries

P RICHARDS MEMORIAL LIBRARY,* 44 Richards Ave, 01612. SAN 307-6113. Tel: 508-754-0793. FAX: 508-754-0793. *Librn*, Janet D Porter
Founded 1877. Pop 4,000; Circ 65,134
Library Holdings: Bk Vols 25,795
Mem of Central Massachusetts Regional Library System
Friends of the Library Group

PEABODY

S PEABODY HISTORICAL SOCIETY, Library & Archives,* 35 Washington St, 01960-5520. SAN 329-8892. Tel: 978-531-0805. *Pres*, Rosa Drysdale; *Librn*, Daniel Douchette
Library Holdings: Bk Vols 400
Special Collections: Genealogy; Historical Documents

P PEABODY INSTITUTE LIBRARY,* 82 Main St, 01960-5592. SAN 345-4983. Tel: 978-531-0100. FAX: 978-532-1797. Web Site: www.peabodylibrary.org. *Dir*, J Michael Franceschi; *Asst Dir*, Helena Minton; *Ch Servs*, Mary Puleo; *Tech Servs*, Maria Vagianos; *Ref*, Gwendolyn Charter; *Ad Servs, Coll Develop*, Joanne O'Keefe; *YA Servs*, Nanci Milone; *Ch Servs*, Julianne Driscoll; Staff 21 (MLS 9, Non-MLS 12)
Founded 1852. Pop 48,000; Circ 243,884
Jul 1998-Jun 1999 Income $1,189,657, State $47,000, City $1,067,657, Other $75,000. Mats Exp $164,000, Books $159,000, Micro $5,000. Sal $750,000 (Prof $380,000)
Library Holdings: Bk Vols 137,720; Per Subs 318
Publications: Annual Report; Library News (monthly); Special Pamphlets
Partic in Noble
Special Services for the Blind - Kurzweil Reading Machine
Friends of the Library Group
Branches: 2
SOUTH, 78 Lynn St, 01960. SAN 345-5017. Tel: 508-531-3380. FAX: 508-531-9113. *Librn*, Kathy Walsh
Library Holdings: Bk Vols 22,277
Friends of the Library Group
WEST, 603 Lowell St, 01960. SAN 345-5041. Tel: 508-535-3354. FAX: 508-535-0147. *Librn*, Marcia Cohen
Library Holdings: Bk Vols 24,143
Friends of the Library Group

PELHAM

P PELHAM LIBRARY, 2 S Valley Rd, 01002. SAN 307-6121. Tel: 413-253-0657. FAX: 413-253-0594. E-Mail: pelhamlibrary@hotmail.com. *Dir*, Rebecca Frank; *Asst Librn*, Hope Wright; Staff 3 (MLS 3)
Founded 1893. Pop 1,433; Circ 4,876
Jul 2000-Jun 2001 Income $24,225. Mats Exp $7,676, Books $6,176, Per/Ser (Incl. Access Fees) $100, AV Equip $1,000, Manuscripts & Archives $400
Library Holdings: Bk Vols 9,500; Per Subs 11
Special Collections: Local historical books & pamphlets
Automation Activity & Vendor Info: (Acquisitions) Sagebrush Corporation; (Cataloging) Sagebrush Corporation; (Circulation) Sagebrush Corporation; (Course Reserve) Sagebrush Corporation; (ILL) Sagebrush Corporation
Database Vendor: CARL, IAC - Info Trac
Mem of Western Regional Libr Syst
Friends of the Library Group

PEMBROKE

P PEMBROKE PUBLIC LIBRARY, 140 Center St, PO Box 517, 02359. SAN 307-613X. Tel: 781-293-6771. FAX: 781-294-0742. *Chief Librn*, Margaret Polly Bentley; *Ch Servs*, Rebecca Freer; Staff 6 (MLS 1, Non-MLS 5)
Founded 1878. Pop 16,621; Circ 145,445
Jul 1999-Jun 2000 Income $403,380. Mats Exp $69,268. Sal $264,809 (Prof $46,890)
Library Holdings: Bk Vols 60,571; Per Subs 117
Mem of Eastern Mass Regional Libr Syst
Partic in Sails, Inc
Friends of the Library Group

PEPPERELL

P LAWRENCE LIBRARY,* 15 Main St, 01463. (Mail add: PO Box 1440, 01463), SAN 307-6148. Tel: 978-433-0330. FAX: 978-433-0317. *Dir*, Ann Parsons; E-Mail: aparsons@cwmars.org; *Asst Dir*, Nancy Clune; *Ch Servs*, Cheryl Murray; *Circ*, Jeanne Palmer; Staff 11 (MLS 2, Non-MLS 9)
Founded 1900. Pop 11,145; Circ 91,109
Jul 1998-Jun 1999 Income $296,204, State $11,034, City $257,900, Locally Generated Income $11,467, Other $15,803. Mats Exp $52,283, Books $40,326, Per/Ser (Incl. Access Fees) $4,346, Electronic Ref Mat (Incl. Access Fees) $7,611. Sal $169,582 (Prof $107,013)
Library Holdings: Bk Vols 54,938; Per Subs 130
Subject Interests: Genealogy, History, Local history
Database Vendor: IAC - SearchBank
Publications: Clipboard - Friend of the Library
Mem of Central Massachusetts Regional Library System
Partic in North Cent Libr Coop
Friends of the Library Group

PERU

P PERU LIBRARY,* Main Rd, 01235-9279. SAN 376-7531. Tel: 413-655-8650. E-Mail: perulib@berkshire.net. *Dir*, Alice Halvorsen
Library Holdings: Bk Vols 2,500; Bk Titles 2,000
Mem of Western Massachusetts Regional Library System

PETERSHAM

S PETERSHAM HISTORICAL SOCIETY LIBRARY, Ten N Main St, 01366-0302. SAN 307-6164. Tel: 508-724-3380. *Librn*, Delight G Haines
Founded 1923
Library Holdings: Bk Titles 850
Subject Interests: Local history
Special Collections: Local Houses; Shay's Rebellion
Restriction: By appointment only

P PETERSHAM MEMORIAL LIBRARY,* 23 Common St, 01366-0056. (Mail add: PO Box 56, 01366-9756), SAN 307-6172. Tel: 978-724-3405. FAX: 978-724-0089. *Dir*, Sandra Y Gross
Founded 1890. Pop 1,000; Circ 8,500
Library Holdings: Bk Titles 18,856; Per Subs 30
Subject Interests: Local history
Mem of Central Massachusetts Regional Library System

PHILLIPSTON

P PHILLIPS FREE PUBLIC LIBRARY,* 25 Templeton Rd, 01331-9704. SAN 307-6180. Tel: 978-249-1734. FAX: 978-249-3356. E-Mail: phillipston@cwmars.org. *Librn*, Edna Haley
Pop 962; Circ 6,325
Library Holdings: Bk Vols 9,000
Friends of the Library Group

PITTSFIELD

P BERKSHIRE ATHENAEUM, Pittsfield Public Library, One Wendell Ave, 01201-6385. SAN 345-5076. Tel: 413-499-9480, 413-499-9484. TDD: 413-499-9488. FAX: 413-499-9489. Web Site: www.berkshire.net/pittsfield/library, www.site.cwmars.mass.edu. *Dir*, Ronald B Latham; E-Mail: rlatham@cwmars.org; *ILL, Ref*, Madeline Kelly; Tel: 413-499-9488, E-Mail: mkelly@cwmars.org; *Circ, Coll Develop*, Catherine Congelosi; *Acq, Cat*, Sara Hutchings; E-Mail: shutchin@cwmars.org; Staff 9 (MLS 9)
Founded 1871. Pop 46,437; Circ 275,000
Jul 1998-Jun 1999 Income $779,043, State $55,497, City $700,223, Parent Institution $23,323. Mats Exp $157,692, Books $131,845, Per/Ser (Incl. Access Fees) $11,940, Micro $3,800, AV Equip $5,645, Electronic Ref Mat (Incl. Access Fees) $4,462. Sal $582,471
Library Holdings: Bk Vols 160,000; Per Subs 225
Subject Interests: Genealogy
Special Collections: Berkshire Authors Room; Herman Melville Memorial Room; Morgan Ballet coll
Automation Activity & Vendor Info: (Cataloging) Innovative Interfaces Inc.; (Circulation) Innovative Interfaces Inc.; (OPAC) Innovative Interfaces Inc.
Mem of Western Massachusetts Regional Library System
Partic in CW Mars
Friends of the Library Group

J BERKSHIRE COMMUNITY COLLEGE, Jonathan Edwards Library, 1350 West St, 01201. SAN 307-6199. Tel: 413-499-4660, Ext 201. FAX: 413-448-2700. Web Site: www.cc.berkshire.org. *Dir*, Nancy A Walker; *Asst Librn*, Mary Jo Daly; Staff 1 (MLS 1)
Founded 1960. Enrl 1,551; Fac 100
Library Holdings: Bk Vols 55,000; Per Subs 351
Subject Interests: Art, Environmental studies, Social sciences and issues, Technology
Mem of Nelinet

M BERKSHIRE MEDICAL CENTER, Health Science Library,* 725 North St, 01201. SAN 307-6202. Tel: 413-447-2734. *Dir*, Eleanor M McNutt; Staff 2 (MLS 1, Non-MLS 1)
Founded 1968
Library Holdings: Bk Titles 1,500; Per Subs 160
Subject Interests: Medicine
Partic in Basic Health Sciences Library Network; Cooperating Libraries Of Greater Springfield; Western Mass Health Info Consortium
Library combines resources of the Pittsfield General Hospital Library & Saint-Luke's Medical Science Library

GENERAL ELECTRIC CO
S PLASTICS INFORMATION RESOURCE CENTER, One Plastics Ave, 01201. SAN 345-5203. Tel: 413-448-7345. FAX: 413-448-7601. *Mgr*, Nancy J Kane; E-Mail: nancy.kane@gepex.ge.com; Staff 3 (MLS 2, Non-MLS 1)
Founded 1978
Library Holdings: Bk Vols 5,000; Per Subs 200
Subject Interests: Chemistry, Marketing, Planning, Technology
Publications: Resource Update; Users Guide
Partic in Nelinet, Inc

L MASSACHUSETTS TRIAL COURT, Berkshire Law Library, Court House, 76 East St, 01201. SAN 324-346X. Tel: 413-442-5059. FAX: 413-448-2474. *Head Librn*, Janice B Shotwell; E-Mail: shotwell@external.umass.edu; Staff 1 (MLS 1)
Founded 1842
Library Holdings: Bk Titles 10,000; Per Subs 40
Subject Interests: Law for layman, Mass legal mat
Partic in Nelinet, Inc

PLAINFIELD

P SHAW MEMORIAL LIBRARY,* 312 Main St, 01070-9709. SAN 307-6245. Tel: 413-634-5406. FAX: 413-634-5683. E-Mail: plainfield@cwmars.org. *Librn*, Denise Sessions
Founded 1926. Pop 609; Circ 9,000
Library Holdings: Bk Titles 9,000; Per Subs 18
Mem of Western Massachusetts Regional Library System
Open Tues 1-4 & 6-8, Thurs 6-8, Sat 9-1

PLAINVILLE

P PLAINVILLE PUBLIC LIBRARY,* 198 South St, 02762-1512. SAN 307-6253. Tel: 508-695-1784. FAX: 508-695-6359. *Dir*, Melissa M Campbell; *Assoc Librn*, Stanley Kozcera
Pop 7,465
Jul 1998-Jun 1999 Income $151,882, State $8,569, City $141,863, Other $1,450. Mats Exp $33,565, Books $25,800, Per/Ser (Incl. Access Fees) $3,000. Sal $92,000
Library Holdings: Bk Vols 28,087; Per Subs 72
Friends of the Library Group

PLYMOUTH

S GENERAL SOCIETY OF MAYFLOWER DESCENDANTS, (GSMD), Mayflower Descendant Library, 4 Winslow St, PO Box 3297, 02361. SAN 373-1669. Tel: 508-746-3188. FAX: 508-746-2488. E-Mail: gsmd@tiac.net. Web Site: www.mayflower.org. *Librn*, Linda Ashley; *Asst Librn*, Louise Egowin. Subject Specialists: *Genealogy*, Linda Ashley; *History*, Linda Ashley; Staff 5 (MLS 1, Non-MLS 4)
Founded 1897
Library Holdings: Bk Vols 3,400; Bk Titles 25,000; Per Subs 70
Subject Interests: Genealogy, History, Massachusetts
Special Collections: Pilgrims Coll
Restriction: Non-circulating to the public

M JORDAN HOSPITAL, Daryl A Lima Memorial Library, 275 Sandwich St, 02360. SAN 377-9319. Tel: 508-746-2000. FAX: 508-830-2887. E-Mail: jhosp11@capecod.net. *Librn*, Marian de la Cowr; E-Mail: mdelacowr@jordanhospital.org
Library Holdings: Bk Titles 100; Per Subs 84
Partic in Massachusetts Health Sciences Libraries Network; National Network Of Libraries Of Medicine - South Central Region; North Atlantic Health Sciences Libraries, Inc; SE Mass Regional Libr Syst; Southeastern Massachusetts Consortium Of Health Science Libraries

S PILGRIM SOCIETY, Pilgrim Hall Museum,* 75 Court St, 02360-3891. SAN 307-6261. Tel: 508-746-1620. FAX: 508-747-4228. *Dir, Librn*, Peggy Baker
Founded 1820
Library Holdings: Bk Titles 6,000
Subject Interests: Decorative arts, History
Special Collections: Manuscript Coll; Plymouth, Massachusetts & Pilgrim History Coll
Publications: Pilgrim Society News; Pilgrim Society Notes; The Pilgrim Journal

S PLIMOTH PLANTATION, Research Library,* 137 Warren Ave, PO Box 1620, 02362. SAN 327-3199. Tel: 508-746-1622, Ext 384. FAX: 508-746-4978.
Library Holdings: Bk Titles 4,500; Per Subs 55
Restriction: By appointment only

P PLYMOUTH PUBLIC LIBRARY, 132 South St, 02360-3309. SAN 345-522X. Tel: 508-830-4250. TDD: 508-747-5882. FAX: 508-830-4258. Web Site: www2.pcix.com/users/ppl/public-html/. *Dir*, Dinah O'Brien; *Asst Dir*, Jennifer Conragen; *Ch Servs, YA Servs*, Evelyn Moschella; *Outreach Serv*, Sharon LaRosa; *Tech Servs*, Terry Stano; Staff 31 (MLS 9, Non-MLS 22)
Founded 1811. Pop 49,000; Circ 476,780
Jul 1999-Jun 2000 Income (Main Library and Branch Library) $1,287,625, State $48,519, City $1,190,160, Other $48,946. Mats Exp $191,510, Books $174,500, Per/Ser (Incl. Access Fees) $17,010. Sal $834,986
Library Holdings: Bk Vols 180,000; Per Subs 324
Subject Interests: Genealogy
Special Collections: Plymouth Coll
Publications: Footnotes
Mem of Old Colony Libr Network
Open Mon-Wed 10-9, Thurs 10-6, Fri & Sat 10-5:30, Sun 12:30-5
Friends of the Library Group
Branches: 1
MANOMET BRANCH, 24 Point Rd, Manomet, 02345. SAN 345-5254. Tel: 508-830-4185. *Librn*, Linda Fitzgerald
Friends of the Library Group

PLYMPTON

P PLYMPTON PUBLIC LIBRARY, 248 Main St, 02367-1114. SAN 307-627X. Tel: 781-585-4551. FAX: 781-585-7660. *Actg Dir*, Debra L Batson; E-Mail: plpdebbie@hotmail.com; Staff 3 (MLS 1, Non-MLS 2)
Founded 1894. Pop 2,700; Circ 14,970
Jul 1998-Jun 1999 Income $34,347, State $2,358, City $31,989. Mats Exp $12,135, Books $9,084, Per/Ser (Incl. Access Fees) $1,496, Micro $1,282, AV Equip $273. Sal $32,047 (Prof $19,501)
Library Holdings: Bk Titles 22,308; Per Subs 45
Mem of SE Mass Regional Libr Syst
Partic in Sails, Inc
Friends of the Library Group

PRINCETON

P PRINCETON PUBLIC LIBRARY, 2 Town Hall Dr, 01541. SAN 307-6288. Tel: 978-464-2115. FAX: 978-464-2116. Web Site: www.ultranet.com/~prince. *Dir*, Wendy Pape; E-Mail: wpape@cwmars.org; Staff 1 (MLS 1)
Founded 1884. Pop 3,300; Circ 35,000
Jul 1999-Jun 2000 Income $83,641, State $2,774, City $80,867. Mats Exp $77,699, Books $11,555, Per/Ser (Incl. Access Fees) $2,051. Sal $52,115
Library Holdings: Bk Titles 25,000; Per Subs 78
Subject Interests: Arts, Cookery, Gardening, History
Automation Activity & Vendor Info: (Acquisitions) Brodart; (Cataloging) Sagebrush Corporation; (Circulation) Sagebrush Corporation
Mem of Central Massachusetts Regional Library System
Friends of the Library Group

PROVINCETOWN

P PROVINCETOWN PUBLIC LIBRARY, 330 Commercial St, 02657-2209. SAN 307-6296. Tel: 508-487-7094. Web Site: www.ptownlib.com. *Dir*, Debra DeJonker-Berry; *Asst Dir*, Lu Hetlyn; *Ch Servs*, Irene Gibbs-Brady; Staff 4 (MLS 1, Non-MLS 3)
Founded 1873. Pop 3,947; Circ 48,000
Jul 1999-Jun 2000 Income $185,000. Mats Exp $43,000, Books $28,000, Per/Ser (Incl. Access Fees) $7,000, AV Equip $8,000. Sal $125,000 (Prof $72,000)
Library Holdings: Bk Vols 29,000; Bk Titles 15,000; Per Subs 110
Subject Interests: Am art, Local history, Modern art, Paintings, Theater
Automation Activity & Vendor Info: (Course Reserve) DRA
Mem of SE Mass Regional Libr Syst
Partic in Cape Libraries Automated Materials Sharing
Friends of the Library Group

QUINCY

C EASTERN NAZARENE COLLEGE, Nease Library,* 23 E Elm Ave, 02170. SAN 307-8159. Tel: 617-773-6350, Ext 3455. FAX: 617-745-3913. Web Site: www.library.enc.edu. *Dir*, Susan J Watkins; *Acq*, Laura Constantine; *Tech Servs*, Terttu Savoie; *Circ*, Renee Polerville; *Syst Coordr*, Amy Travaline; Staff 5 (MLS 3, Non-MLS 2)
Enrl 862; Fac 57; Highest Degree: Master
Library Holdings: Bk Vols 122,604; Per Subs 1,078
Special Collections: Theology Coll
Partic in Nelinet, Inc

S MARINE PRODUCTS LIBRARY,* 10 Furnace Brook Pkwy, 02169. SAN 307-1936. Tel: 617-268-0758. FAX: 617-472-9359. *Dir*, Edward J Iorio
Founded 1929
Library Holdings: Bk Titles 5,000
Restriction: Staff use only

S NATIONAL FIRE PROTECTION ASSOCIATION, Charles S Morgan Technical Library, One Batterymarch Park, 02269-9101. SAN 307-2169. Tel: 617-984-7445. FAX: 617-984-7060. E-Mail: library@nfpa.org. Web Site: www.nfpa.org. *Librn*, Teresa Frydryk; *Asst Librn*, Lee Cram; Staff 2 (MLS 1, Non-MLS 1)
Founded 1945
Library Holdings: Bk Titles 18,000; Per Subs 230
Subject Interests: Safety
Special Collections: National Fire Codes; National Fire Protection Association Published Archives Coll
Automation Activity & Vendor Info: (Cataloging) CASPR; (OPAC) CASPR
Publications: Acquisitions Update
Restriction: Not a lending library
Function: Research library

J QUINCY COLLEGE, Anselmo Library, 24 Saville Ave, 02169-5309. SAN 307-6326. Tel: 617-984-1680. FAX: 617-984-1782. Web Site: www.quincycollege.com. *Dir*, Susan Bossa; *Ref, Tech Servs*, Galina Lemdersky
Founded 1958. Enrl 2,800; Fac 44
1998-1999 Mats Exp $103,000. Sal $213,104 (Prof $189,038)
Library Holdings: Bk Vols 50,000; Per Subs 500
Subject Interests: Allied health, Computer science, Criminal law and justice, Environmental studies, Nursing, Psychology, Tourism, Travel

S QUINCY HISTORICAL SOCIETY LIBRARY,* Adams Academy Bldg, 8 Adams St, 02169. SAN 328-1256. Tel: 617-773-1144. FAX: 617-472-4990. *Curator, Dir*, Dr Edward Fitzgerald
Founded 1893
Library Holdings: Bk Titles 5,000; Per Subs 14
Special Collections: Adams Family Coll, bks; Local; Shipbuilding Coll, bks, mss & photogs

M QUINCY HOSPITAL MEDICAL LIBRARY,* 114 Whitwell St, 02169. SAN 307-6318. Tel: 617-773-6100, Ext 4094. FAX: 617-376-1650. *Librn*, JoAnn Donovan
Library Holdings: Bk Vols 600; Per Subs 130
Partic in SE Mass Health Sci Librs Consortium

S STATE STREET BANK & TRUST CO LIBRARY,* 1776 Heritage Dr, 02171. SAN 307-2347. Tel: 617-985-8421. FAX: 617-985-1002.
Founded 1969
Library Holdings: Per Subs 125
Subject Interests: Finance

P THOMAS CRANE PUBLIC LIBRARY, 40 Washington St, 02269-9164. SAN 345-5289. Tel: 617-376-1300. Circulation Tel: 617-376-1301. Reference Tel: 617-376-1316. TDD: 617-376-1314. FAX: 617-376-1313. E-Mail: quref@ci.quincy.ma.us. Web Site: ci/quincy.ma.us/tcpl. *Dir*, Ann E McLaughlin; Tel: 617-376-1312, E-Mail: amclaughlin@ci.quincy.ma.us; *Asst Dir*, Jane E Granstrom; Tel: 617-376-1331, E-Mail: jgranstrom@ci.quincy.ma.us; *ILL*, Megan Allen; Tel: 617-376-1319, Fax: 617-376-1311, E-Mail: mallen@ci.quincy.ma.us; *Ch Servs*, Julie M Rines; Tel: 617-376-1332, Fax: 617-376-1438, E-Mail: jrines@ocln.org; *Circ*, Betty Hillcoat; Tel: 617-689-8321, E-Mail: bettyh@ocln.org; *Acq*, Rita Seegraber; Tel: 617-376-1306, Fax: 617-376-1438, E-Mail: ritas@ocln.org; *Tech Servs*, Josephine Parsley; Tel: 617-376-1318, Fax: 617-376-1438, E-Mail: jparsley@ci.quincy.ma.us
Founded 1871. Pop 88,781; Circ 466,211
Library Holdings: Bk Vols 210,082; Per Subs 970
Subject Interests: Art, Local history, Music
Automation Activity & Vendor Info: (Cataloging) epixtech, inc.; (Circulation) epixtech, inc.; (ILL) epixtech, inc.; (OPAC) epixtech, inc.
Database Vendor: epixtech, inc.
Publications: Quarterly Newsletter
Mem of SE Mass Regional Libr Syst
Partic in OCLC Online Computer Library Center, Inc; Old Colony Libr Network
Special Services for the Deaf - TDD
Open Mon-Thurs 9-9, Fri & Sat 9-5:30
Friends of the Library Group
Branches: 3
ADAMS SHORE, 519 Sea St, 02169. SAN 345-5319. Tel: 617-376-1325, 617-376-1326. FAX: 617-376-1437. Web Site: ci.quincy.ma.us/tcpl. *Librn*, Linda Cohen; *Librn*, Blanche Eckert; *Librn*, Betty Santangelo; Staff 2 (MLS 1, Non-MLS 1)
Founded 1970
NORTH QUINCY, 381 Hancock St, 02171. SAN 345-5408. Tel: 617-376-1320, 617-376-1321. FAX: 617-376-1432. Web Site: ci.quincy.ma.us/tcpl. *Librn*, Louise Dinegan
Founded 1963
WOLLASTON BRANCH, 41 Beale St, Wollaston, 02170. SAN 345-5491. Tel: 617-376-1330. FAX: 617-376-1430. Web Site: ci.quincy.ma.us/tcpl. *Librn*, Marian Ciccariella; *Librn*, Catherine Saville; Staff 2 (Non-MLS 2)
Founded 1923
Bookmobiles: 1

S UNITED STATES DEPARTMENT OF THE INTERIOR, Adams National Historical Park, Stone Library, 135 Adams St, 02169. SAN 307-6334. Tel: 617-773-1177. FAX: 617-471-9683. Web Site: www.nts.gov/adam. *In Charge*, Kelly Cobble
Library Holdings: Bk Vols 14,000
Restriction: Not a lending library
The Library is a historic structure containing the original books owned & used by 2nd President John Adams, 6th President John Quincy Adams, Civil War Minister to England, Charles Frances Adams & his two literary sons Henry & Brooks Adams

RANDOLPH

P TURNER FREE LIBRARY, 2 N Main St, 02368. SAN 307-6342. Tel: 781-961-0932. FAX: 781-961-0933. *Dir*, Charles Michaud; *Asst Dir*, Ann Marie Pokaski
Founded 1874. Pop 30,600; Circ 264,129
Jul 1999-Jun 2000 Income $544,850, State $51,850, City $493,000. Mats Exp $78,200, Books $75,000, Per/Ser (Incl. Access Fees) $3,200. Sal $353,904 (Prof $131,882)
Library Holdings: Bk Titles 60,946; Per Subs 126

Automation Activity & Vendor Info: (Cataloging) epixtech, inc.; (Circulation) epixtech, inc.
Partic in Southeastern Massachusetts Consortium Of Health Science Libraries
Friends of the Library Group

RAYNHAM

P RAYNHAM PUBLIC LIBRARY, 760 S Main St, 02767. SAN 307-6350. Tel: 508-823-1344. FAX: 508-824-0494. E-Mail: lambip@capecod.net. *Dir*, Pat Lambirth; *Ref*, Lorna Sylvia; Staff 3 (MLS 1, Non-MLS 2)
Founded 1888. Pop 10,340; Circ 36,788
Library Holdings: Bk Vols 29,000; Bk Titles 28,535; Per Subs 39
Mem of Eastern Mass Regional Libr Syst
Friends of the Library Group

READING

P READING PUBLIC LIBRARY, 64 Middlesex Ave, 01867. SAN 307-6377. Tel: 781-944-0840. FAX: 781-942-9106. E-Mail: readingpl@noblenet.org. Web Site: www.readingpl.org. *Dir*, Kimberly S Lynn; Tel: 781-942-9110, E-Mail: lynn@noblenet.org; *Asst Dir*, Diane Young; Tel: 781-942-9111, E-Mail: young@noblenet.org; *Ch Servs*, Corinne Fisher; E-Mail: fisher@noblenet.org; *Ad Servs*, Nancy Aberman; E-Mail: aberman@noblenet.orgt; *Circ*, Jamie Penney; E-Mail: jamie@noblenet.org; *Head Tech Servs*, Michael Colford; E-Mail: colford@noblenet.org; *Head, Info Serv*, Esme Green; E-Mail: green@noblenet.org; *ILL*, Allison DaSilva; E-Mail: dasilva@noblenet.org; *YA Servs*, Lorraine Barry; E-Mail: barry@noblenet.org; *YA Servs*, Susan Beauregard; E-Mail: susanb@noblenet.org; Staff 42 (MLS 17, Non-MLS 25)
Founded 1867. Pop 22,000; Circ 305,983
Jul 1999-Jun 2000 Income $926,620, State $35,618, City $865,745, Locally Generated Income $24,757, Other $500. Mats Exp $139,564, Books $106,277, Per/Ser (Incl. Access Fees) $9,103, AV Equip $19,301, Electronic Ref Mat (Incl. Access Fees) $4,883. Sal $616,386 (Prof $451,858)
Library Holdings: Bk Vols 105,619; Per Subs 253
Subject Interests: Local history
Automation Activity & Vendor Info: (OPAC) Innovative Interfaces Inc.
Database Vendor: Dialog, Ebsco - EbscoHost, IAC - Info Trac, OCLC - First Search
Publications: Bibliobits-Off the Shelf
Partic in NMRLS; North of Boston Library Exchange, Inc
Friends of the Library Group

S TASC, INC, Analytic Sciences Corporation Library, 55 Walkers Brook Dr, 01867. SAN 320-1945. Tel: 781-942-2000, Ext 7106. FAX: 781-942-7100. *Dir, Online Servs*, Martha Dionne; E-Mail: medionne@tasc.com; Staff 4 (MLS 1, Non-MLS 3)
Library Holdings: Bk Vols 30,000; Per Subs 450
Subject Interests: Economics, Engineering, Finance, Mathematics, Meteorology, Software engineering
Publications: Library Bulletin
Restriction: Staff use only
Partic in Data Time; Dialog Corporation; Dow Jones News Retrieval; OCLC Online Computer Library Center, Inc

REHOBOTH

P BLANDING PUBLIC LIBRARY,* 124 Bay State Rd, PO Box 377, 02769. SAN 307-6385. Tel: 508-252-4236. FAX: 508-252-5834. *Dir*, Laura Bennett
Founded 1915. Pop 9,000
Library Holdings: Bk Titles 12,000; Per Subs 21
Subject Interests: Art and architecture, Genealogy, Music
Mem of Eastern Mass Regional Libr Syst
Open Mon-Thurs 11:30-8, Sat 11-4
Friends of the Library Group

REVERE

P REVERE PUBLIC LIBRARY, 179 Beach St, 02151. SAN 307-6393. Tel: 781-286-8380. FAX: 781-286-8382. E-Mail: revere@noblenet.org. Web Site: www.noblenet.org/revere. *Dir*, Robert Rice; E-Mail: rice@noblenet.org; *Ch Servs*, Diane S Pitts; Staff 12 (MLS 3, Non-MLS 9)
Founded 1880. Pop 42,786; Circ 48,635
Library Holdings: Bk Vols 48,265; Per Subs 140
Subject Interests: Local history
Special Collections: Horatio Alger Coll
Mem of Eastern Mass Regional Libr Syst
Partic in North of Boston Library Exchange, Inc
Friends of the Library Group

RICHMOND

P RICHMOND FREE PUBLIC LIBRARY, State Rd, 01254-0472. SAN 307-6407. Tel: 413-698-3834. FAX: 413-698-3834. *Dir*, Lauren Losaw; E-Mail: llosaw@cwmarsmail.cwmars.org
Pop 1,689; Circ 10,000
Jul 1999-Jun 2000 Income $41,978, State $2,873, City $39,105. Mats Exp $10,294, Books $8,414, Per/Ser (Incl. Access Fees) $1,002, AV Equip $478, Other Print Mats $870. Sal $23,993 (Prof $11,000)
Library Holdings: Bk Vols 11,000; Bk Titles 10,500; Per Subs 24
Automation Activity & Vendor Info: (Cataloging) Innovative Interfaces Inc.
Mem of Western Regional Libr Syst
Open Tues-Thurs 10-8 & Sat 10-2
Friends of the Library Group

ROCHESTER

P JOSEPH H PLUMB MEMORIAL LIBRARY,* 17 Constitution Way, 02770-0069. (Mail add: PO Box 69, 02770-0069), SAN 307-6415. Tel: 508-763-8600. Interlibrary Loan Service Tel: 508-991-6275. FAX: 508-763-9593. E-Mail: jhplumb@ultranet.com. Web Site: www.geocities.com/~plumblibrary. *Librn*, Lucy Loomis; *Ch Servs*, Kristine Hastreiter
Pop 4,000
Library Holdings: Bk Vols 12,000
Mem of Eastern Mass Regional Libr Syst
Friends of the Library Group

ROCKLAND

P ROCKLAND MEMORIAL LIBRARY, 20 Belmont St, 02370-2232. SAN 307-6423. Tel: 781-878-1236. FAX: 781-878-4013. *Dir Libr Serv*, Denise Medeiros; *Ch Servs*, Jane Gilbert; *Circ*, Lorraine Dixon; *Ref Serv*, Beverly Brown; Staff 4 (MLS 3, Non-MLS 1)
Founded 1878
Jul 2000-Jun 2001 Income $366,985. Mats Exp $57,971. Sal $277,237
Library Holdings: Bk Vols 46,578; Per Subs 98
Subject Interests: Genealogy, Local history
Partic in Old Colony Libr Network
Friends of the Library Group

ROCKPORT

L EDWIN T HOLMES LAW OFFICES LIBRARY,* 146 South St, 01966. SAN 372-0330. Tel: 978-546-3478. FAX: 978-546-6785. *Librn*, Edwin Holmes
Library Holdings: Bk Vols 2,200

P ROCKPORT PUBLIC LIBRARY,* 17 School St, 01966. SAN 307-6431. Tel: 978-546-6934. FAX: 978-546-1011. Web Site: www.mvlc.org. *Dir*, M Hope Coffman; *Tech Servs*, Boyd Coons; *Ch Servs*, Jane Knight
Founded 1874. Pop 7,000; Circ 81,000
Library Holdings: Bk Vols 36,000; Per Subs 130
Subject Interests: Art
Special Collections: Local History
Mem of Eastern Regional Libr Syst
Partic in Essex County Coop Librs; Merimack Valley Libr Consortium
Friends of the Library Group

S SANDY BAY HISTORICAL SOCIETY & MUSEUMS LIBRARY,* 40 King St, PO Box 63, 01966. SAN 329-0913. Tel: 978-546-9533. *Curator*, Cynthia Peckham
Founded 1926
Library Holdings: Bk Vols 1,000
Subject Interests: Massachusetts
Special Collections: Cape Ann Hist
Publications: Quarterly Bulletin, Ad Hoc Brochures, Pamphlets
Library is one room in one of two historic houses (1715 & 1832) which serve as museums for the town's historical society; Open Mon 9-1 (winter) & Mon-Sat 2-5 (summer)

ROWE

P ROWE TOWN LIBRARY,* Zoar Rd, 01367-9998. SAN 307-644X. Tel: 413-339-4761. E-Mail: rowe@cwmars.org. *Librn*, Martha Rice; Staff 1 (MLS 1)
Founded 1787. Pop 380; Circ 12,000
Library Holdings: Bk Vols 12,069; Per Subs 51
Subject Interests: Local history
Mem of Western Regional Libr Syst
Open Tues, Wed & Sat 9-5

ROWLEY

S EARLY SITES RESEARCH SOCIETY LIBRARY,* Long Hill, 01969. SAN 370-8691. Tel: 978-948-8170. FAX: 978-948-8171.
Library Holdings: Bk Vols 5,000; Per Subs 2,000
Special Collections: Epigraphy (Ogam Script Coll)
Publications: Early Sites Bulletin

P ROWLEY PUBLIC LIBRARY, 17 Wethersfield St, 01969. (Mail add: PO Box 276, 01969), SAN 307-6458. Tel: 978-948-2850. FAX: 978-948-2266. E-Mail: mro@mvlc.lib.ma.us. Web Site: www.rowley-ma.com/library/index.htm. *Dir*, Julie Bernier; E-Mail: jbernier@mailserv.mvlc.lib.ma.us; *Ad Servs*, Rebecca Shea; *Ch Servs*, Eilene Chadbourne; Staff 11 (MLS 1, Non-MLS 10)
Founded 1894. Pop 5,194
Library Holdings: Bk Vols 26,000; Per Subs 60
Subject Interests: Genealogy
Automation Activity & Vendor Info: (Circulation) Sagebrush Corporation
Mem of Northeast Mass Regional Libr Syst
Partic in Merimack Valley Libr Consortium
Friends of the Library Group

ROXBURY

S METROPOLITAN COUNCIL FOR EDUCATION OPPORTUNITY LIBRARY,* 40 Dimock St, 02119. SAN 328-4077. Tel: 617-427-1545. FAX: 617-541-0550. *Dir*, Jean McGuire
Library Holdings: Bk Vols 15,000; Per Subs 12

ROYALSTON

P PHINEHAS S NEWTON LIBRARY,* Main St, 01368. SAN 307-6474. Tel: 978-249-3572. FAX: 978-249-3572. *Librn*, Kathy Morris
Pop 1,012; Circ 2,326
Library Holdings: Bk Vols 6,926
Mem of Central Massachusetts Regional Library System
Open Mon 1-5, Thurs 1-5 & Sat 9-12

RUSSELL

P RUSSELL PUBLIC LIBRARY,* 162 Main St, 01071. (Mail add: PO Box 438, 01071-0438), SAN 307-6482. Tel: 413-862-3102. E-Mail: russell@cwmars.org. *Librn*, Gail Duso
Pop 1,580; Circ 4,650
Library Holdings: Bk Vols 6,255
Mem of Western Regional Libr Syst
Open Mon, Wed, Fri 3-8, Tues & Thurs 3-5
Friends of the Library Group

RUTLAND

P RUTLAND FREE PUBLIC LIBRARY,* 246 Main St, 01543. SAN 307-6490. Tel: 508-886-4108. FAX: 508-886-4141. *Dir*, May Lee Tom; E-Mail: mltom@cwmarsmail.cwmars.org; *Asst Librn*, Kerry Remington; *ILL*, Nancy Borglund; *Ch Servs*, Maureen Lynch
Founded 1865. Pop 5,179; Circ 50,959
Jul 1999-Jun 2000 Income $105,477, State $7,821, City $97,656. Mats Exp $18,555. Sal $68,286 (Prof $52,340)
Library Holdings: Bk Vols 20,450; Per Subs 76
Mem of Central Massachusetts Regional Library System
Friends of the Library Group

SALEM

GL ESSEX LAW LIBRARY,* Superior Court House, 34 Federal St, 01970. SAN 307-6512. Tel: 978-744-5500, Ext 372. FAX: 978-745-7224. *Librn*, Richard Adamo
Library Holdings: Bk Vols 35,000; Per Subs 200
Friends of the Library Group

S PEABODY ESSEX MUSEUM, Phillips Library, East India Sq, 01970-3773. SAN 323-8520. Tel: 978-745-9500. FAX: 978-741-9012. Web Site: www.pem.org. *Coll Develop, Librn*, William T La Moy; *Archivist*, MaryAnn Campbell; *Head Ref, Publ Servs*, Kathy Flynn; Staff 8 (MLS 4, Non-MLS 4)
Founded 1799
Library Holdings: Bk Vols 400,000; Per Subs 200
Subject Interests: American folk art, Archaeology, Architecture, Art, Decorative arts, Ethnology, Fine arts, Maritime history, Massachusetts, Natural history, New England
Special Collections: Chinese History (Frederick T Ward Coll), bks, mss, broadsides, photogs
Database Vendor: Ebsco - EbscoHost
Publications: Peabody Essex Museum Collections (annual monographic series); The American Neptune (quarterly journal of maritime art & history)
Restriction: Non-circulating to the public
Partic in Nelinet, Inc; NMRLS
Friends of the Library Group

S SALEM ATHENAEUM,* 337 Essex St, 01970. SAN 371-8344. Tel: 978-744-2540. E-Mail: sal-athm@star.net. *Librn*, John P Adams
Library Holdings: Bk Titles 54,202; Per Subs 31
Special Collections: Personal Library of Dr Edward Holyoke, 18th to early 19th century; Philosophical Library 1781; Social Library of 1760

G SALEM MARITIME NATIONAL HISTORIC SITE LIBRARY, 174 Derby St, 01970. SAN 323-7451. Tel: 978-740-1680. FAX: 978-740-1685. *Curator*, David Kayser
Founded 1937
1999-2000 Mats Exp $400
Library Holdings: Bk Vols 1,100; Bk Titles 925
Subject Interests: Maritime history
Special Collections: New England Maritime History Coll

P SALEM PUBLIC LIBRARY,* 370 Essex St, 01970-3298. SAN 345-5521. Tel: 978-744-0860. FAX: 978-745-8616. E-Mail: sal@noblenet.org. *Dir*, Patrick J Cloherty, Jr; *Ch Servs*, Cheryl Opolski; *Asst Dir*, Lorraine E Jackson; *ILL, Ref*, Jane Walsh; *Circ*, Carol Larrabee; *Tech Servs*, Nancy D'Amico
Founded 1888. Pop 38,545; Circ 379,511
Jul 1998-Jun 1999 Income (Main Library Only) $1,066,980, State $48,246, City $908,478, Locally Generated Income $74,248, Other $36,008. Mats Exp $215,142, Books $146,505, Per/Ser (Incl. Access Fees) $17,259, Micro $8,949, AV Equip $30,035, Electronic Ref Mat (Incl. Access Fees) $12,394. Sal $646,476
Library Holdings: Bk Vols 127,688; Per Subs 241
Partic in Essex County Coop Librs; N of Boston Children's Libr Servs Asn; North of Boston Library Exchange, Inc

C SALEM STATE COLLEGE LIBRARY, 352 Lafayette St, 01970-4589. SAN 307-6547. Tel: 978-542-6230. FAX: 978-542-6596. Web Site: www.salem.mass.edu/library. *Dean of Libr*, Dr Laverna Saunders; Tel: 978-542-6231, E-Mail: saunders@noblenet.org; *Publ Servs*, Camilla Glynn; E-Mail: glynn@noblenet.org; *Circ*, Jill Hennessey; E-Mail: henness@noblenet.org; *Ser*, Susan Sturgeon; E-Mail: susan.sturgeon@salem.mass.edu; *Syst Coordr*, Glenn Macnutt; E-Mail: gmacnutt@salem.mass.edu; *Acq, Coll Develop*, Elizabeth Dole; E-Mail: elizabeth.dole@salem.mass.edu; *Ref*, Eleanor Reynolds; E-Mail: eleanor.reynolds@salem.mass.edu; *Cat*, Stephen Pew; E-Mail: pew@noblenet.org; *ILL*, Martha-Jane Moreland; E-Mail: moreland@noblenet.org; *Archivist*, Susan Edwards; E-Mail: susan.edwards@salem.mass.edu; *Res*, Margaret Andrews; E-Mail: margaret.andrews@salem.mass.edu; *Outreach Serv*, Nancy Dennis; E-Mail: nancy.dennis@salem.mass.edu; *Electronic Resources*, Nancy George; E-Mail: nancy.george@salem.mass.edu; *Instrul Serv*, Barbara Husbands; E-Mail: barbara.husbands@salem.mass.edu; *Info Res*, Mia Morgan; E-Mail: mimorgan@noblenet.org. Subject Specialists: *Education*, Barbara Husbands; Staff 35 (MLS 15, Non-MLS 20)
Founded 1854. Enrl 5,716; Fac 317; Highest Degree: Master
Jul 1998-Jun 1999 Income $1,845,795, State $1,321,814, Locally Generated Income $10,000, Parent Institution $513,981. Mats Exp $634,172, Books $190,051, Per/Ser (Incl. Access Fees) $222,169, Presv $16,543, Micro $32,144, AV Equip $42,404, Electronic Ref Mat (Incl. Access Fees) $130,861. Sal $1,093,665 (Prof $675,086)
Library Holdings: Bk Vols 303,812; Bk Titles 211,946; Per Subs 1,741
Subject Interests: Cartography, Education, Nursing
Special Collections: Annual Reports & 10 K's; Education (19th Century Normal School Texts Coll of the College); Eric 1968 to date; Federal Government (Representative William H Bates Memorial Archives & Representative Michael Harrington Papers); United States Geological Survey Topographical Map Coll
Automation Activity & Vendor Info: (OPAC) GEAC
Database Vendor: Ebsco - EbscoHost
Publications: Library Handbook; Online Brochure; Periodical List; Various Research Guides
Partic in Eccl; Neccum; Nelinet, Inc; Noble; Northeastern Consortium For Health Information; OCLC Online Computer Library Center, Inc
Friends of the Library Group

M THE NORTH SHORE MEDICAL CENTER, Health Sciences Library, 81 Highland Ave, 01970. SAN 324-6647. Tel: 978-354-4950. FAX: 978-744-9110. *Dir Libr Serv*, Anne Fladger; E-Mail: annef@nsmc.partners.org; *Librn*, Nancy Fazzone; E-Mail: nancyf@nsmc.partners.org; *Assoc Librn*, Sue Dhanjal; E-Mail: sue@nsmc.partnrs.org. Subject Specialists: *Consumer health*, Anne Fladger; Staff 3 (MLS 2, Non-MLS 1)
Founded 1928
Library Holdings: Bk Vols 4,110; Bk Titles 3,700; Per Subs 250
Subject Interests: Medicine
Database Vendor: IAC - Info Trac, OCLC - First Search, OVID Technologies
Publications: Newsletter

Restriction: Employees & their associates, Medical staff only
Mem of Northeastern Regional Libr Syst
Partic in Dialog Corporation; Nat Libr of Med

SALISBURY

P SALISBURY PUBLIC LIBRARY, 17 Elm St, 01952. SAN 307-6555. Tel: 978-465-5071. *Dir*, Gail C Lyon
Founded 1895. Pop 7,170; Circ 27,284
Jul 1999-Jun 2000 Income $124,803. Mats Exp $23,700. Sal $81,200
Library Holdings: Bk Titles 23,839; Per Subs 51
Subject Interests: Genealogy, Local history
Mem of Eastern Mass Regional Libr Syst
Friends of the Library Group

SANDISFIELD

P SANDISFIELD FREE PUBLIC LIBRARY,* Rte 57, 01255. SAN 307-6563. Tel: 413-258-4966. *Librn*, Ruth Dwyer
Pop 660
Library Holdings: Bk Titles 3,500
Publications: Fact sheet for town
Mem of Western Massachusetts Regional Library System
Friends of the Library Group

SANDWICH

S THE SANDWICH GLASS MUSEUM LIBRARY, 129 Main St, PO Box 103, 02563-0103. SAN 323-8679. Tel: 508-888-0251, Ext 15. FAX: 508-888-4941. E-Mail: sgm@capecod.net. Web Site: www.sandwichglassmuseum.org. *Dir*, Bruce Courson; *Curator*, Lynne Horton
Founded 1907
Library Holdings: Bk Titles 1,650
Subject Interests: Antiques
Special Collections: B & S Correspondence, Demming Jarves Letters, archival doc; Town of Sandwich Families, archival doc, letters
Restriction: Non-circulating to the public

P SANDWICH PUBLIC LIBRARY,* 142 Main St, 02563. SAN 307-658X. Tel: 508-888-0625. FAX: 508-833-1076. *Dir*, Richard J Connor; *Ref*, M Elizabeth Ellis; *Ch Servs*, Lauren Robinson; *Acq, Media Spec*, Pat Vineis; *Cat, Tech Servs*, Barbara O'Neil; Staff 5 (MLS 5)
Founded 1891. Pop 16,483; Circ 196,063
Jul 1997-Jun 1998 Income $500,000. Mats Exp $75,000. Sal $320,000
Library Holdings: Bk Titles 47,000; Per Subs 247
Subject Interests: Glass technology
Special Collections: Glass Books
Mem of Eastern Mass Regional Libr Syst
Friends of the Library Group

SAUGUS

G NATIONAL PARK SERVICE DEPARTMENT OF INTERIOR, Saugus Iron Works National Historic Site Library, 244 Central St, 01906. SAN 323-7613. Tel: 781-233-0050. FAX: 781-231-7345. Web Site: www.nps.gov/sair. *Dir*, Victoria Earll
Library Holdings: Bk Titles 1,000

P SAUGUS PUBLIC LIBRARY, 295 Central St, 01906-2191. SAN 345-5610. Tel: 781-231-4168. Reference Tel: 781-231-4056. TDD: 781-231-4191. FAX: 781-231-4169. E-Mail: sau@noblenet.org. Web Site: www.saugus.ma.us/Library. *Dir*, Mary Rose Quinn; E-Mail: quinn@noblenet.org; *Asst Libr Dir*, Carolyn Wakefield; E-Mail: wakefiel@noblenet.org; *Head Tech Servs*, Ewa Jankowska; E-Mail: jankowsk@noblenet.org; *Ch Servs*, Charlene Baxendale; E-Mail: baxendal@noblenet.org; *Head, Info Serv*, Dolores O'Hara; E-Mail: ohara@noblenet.org; *Ref Serv Ad*, Judith Floyd; E-Mail: floyd@noblenet.org; *Ref Servs YA*, Tatjana Saccio; E-Mail: saccio@noblenet.org; Staff 25 (MLS 10, Non-MLS 15)
Founded 1888. Pop 26,223; Circ 95,720
Jul 1999-Jun 2000 Income $634,632, State $32,939, City $560,963, Locally Generated Income $39,000. Mats Exp $111,117. Sal $430,642
Library Holdings: Bk Titles 58,117; Per Subs 150
Special Collections: Ceramics & Glass (Dorothy E Lunt Coll); Civil War (Franklin P Bennett Jr Coll); Sheet Music (Lt Col Harry J Jenkins, ret, Coll)
Automation Activity & Vendor Info: (Acquisitions) Innovative Interfaces Inc.; (Cataloging) Innovative Interfaces Inc.; (Circulation) Innovative Interfaces Inc.; (Course Reserve) Innovative Interfaces Inc.; (ILL) Innovative Interfaces Inc.; (OPAC) Innovative Interfaces Inc.; (Serials) Innovative Interfaces Inc.
Database Vendor: CARL, Dialog, Ebsco - EbscoHost, epixtech, inc., GaleNet, IAC - Info Trac
Mem of Noble
Partic in North of Boston Library Exchange, Inc
Friends of the Library Group

SAVOY

P SAVOY HOLLOW LIBRARY, Town Off Bldg, 720 Main Rd, 01256. SAN 307-6598. Tel: 413-743-4290. Reference Tel: 413-743-3759. FAX: 413-743-4292. E-Mail: savoy@cwmars.org. *Librn*, Jane Phinney
Founded 1890. Pop 701; Enrl 52 Sal $200
Library Holdings: Bk Vols 520
Mem of Western Regional Libr Syst
Friends of the Library Group
Bookmobiles: 1

SCITUATE

S SCITUATE HISTORICAL SOCIETY LIBRARY, 43 Cudworth Rd, PO Box 276, 02066. SAN 326-7814. Tel: 781-545-1083. FAX: 781-545-8287. E-Mail: history@ziplink.net. Web Site: www.ziplink.net/~history. *Librn*, Gray Curtis; Staff 1 (MLS 1)
Library Holdings: Bk Titles 675
Subject Interests: Genealogy, History

P SCITUATE TOWN LIBRARY,* 85 Branch St, 02066. SAN 307-6601. Tel: 781-545-8727. FAX: 781-545-8728. *Dir*, Kathleen Meeker
Founded 1893. Pop 17,829; Circ 137,466
Library Holdings: Bk Vols 74,948; Per Subs 121
Mem of Eastern Mass Regional Libr Syst
Friends of the Library Group

SEEKONK

P SEEKONK PUBLIC LIBRARY, 410 Newman Ave, 02771. SAN 345-570X. Tel: 508-336-8230. FAX: 508-336-7062. Web Site: www.seekonkpl.org. *Dir*, Sharon E Saint-Hilaire; *Asst Dir*, Peter Fuller; *Ch Servs*, Mary Ellen Siniak; *Ref*, Anne Klegraefe; Staff 22 (MLS 17, Non-MLS 5)
Founded 1899. Pop 13,000; Circ 254,227
Jul 2000-Jun 2001 Income $572,654. Mats Exp $95,287, Books $61,034, Per/Ser (Incl. Access Fees) $7,664, AV Equip $14,204, Electronic Ref Mat (Incl. Access Fees) $12,385. Sal $412,293
Library Holdings: Bk Titles 66,576; Per Subs 245
Partic in Sails, Inc
Friends of the Library Group

SHARON

S KENDALL WHALING MUSEUM LIBRARY, 27 Everett St, 02067-0297. (Mail add: PO Box 297, 02067-0297), SAN 307-661X. Tel: 781-784-5642. FAX: 781-784-0451. Web Site: www.kwm.org. *Dir*, Stuart M Frank; *Librn*, Michael Dyer
Founded 1956
Library Holdings: Bk Vols 15,000; Bk Titles 12,000; Spec Interest Per Sub 10
Subject Interests: Fine arts, Manuscripts, Navigation, Technology, Voyages, Whaling
Special Collections: Paintings & Drawings, Photogs, Prints, Mss
Publications: 100 Highlights (Gallery Guide); 100 Years, 100 Curiosities (Gallery Guide); Donald E Ridley et al., Frederick Myrick: Scrimshaw Catalogue Raisonne; Donald E Ridley, Janet West, et al., Frederick Myrick: Physical Characteristics of the Scrimshaw; Fifty States: America's Whaling Heritage (Gallery Guide); Honore Forster, The South Sea Whaler: An Annotated Bibliography; Joshua Basseches & Stuart M Frank, Edward Burdett (1805-1833): America's First Master Scrimshaw Artist; Joshua Basseches, The Scrimshaw of Manuel Cunha; Kendall Whaling Museum Monograph Series; Kenneth R Martin, "Naked & a Prisoner": Captain Edward C Barnard's Narrative of Shipwreck in Palau; Whalemen's Paintings & Drawings; Kenneth R Martin, Whalermen's Paintings & Drawings: Selections from the Kendall Whaling Museum; Mary Malloy, "From Boston Harbor We Set Sail!" A Curriculum Unit on African-American Mariners; Mary Malloy, African Americans in the Maritime Trades: A Guide to Resources in New England; "From Boston Harbor We Set Sail!": A Curriculum Unit on African-American Mariners; Pamela A Miller, And the Whale Is Ours! Creative Writing of American Walemen; Sir Gerald Elliot, Whaling 1937-1967: The International Control of Whale Stocks; Stuart M Frank & Robert L Webb, M V Brewington: A Bibliography & Catalogue of the Brewington Press, KWM Newsletter (quarterly); Stuart M Frank, "Musick on the Brain": Frederick Howland Smith's Shipboard Tunes; Stuart M Frank, Biographical Dictionary of Scrimshaw Artists; Stuart M Frank, Corrections to "Brewington": Notes & Revisions; Stuart M Frank, Meditations from Steerage: Two Whaling Journal Fragments; Stuart M Frank, Oooh, You New York Girls!The Urban Pastorale in Ballads & Songs about Sailors Ashore in the Big City; Stuart M Frank, Sea Chanteys & Sailors' Songs: An Introduction...& a Guide for Teachers & Group Leaders; Stuart M Frank, The Book of Pirate Songs; The Africa Connection (Gallery Guide); The Kendall Whaling Museum Newsletter
Restriction: By appointment only
Usage fee or institutional affiliation
Friends of the Library Group

P SHARON PUBLIC LIBRARY, (SPL), 11 N Main St, 02067-1299. SAN 307-6628. Tel: 781-784-1578. FAX: 781-784-4728. Web Site: www.sharonpubliclibrary.org. *Dir*, Kip M Roberson; Tel: 781-784-1524, E-Mail: kipr@ocln.org; *Asst Dir*, Barbra Katz; Tel: 781-784-1578, Ext 54, E-Mail: bkatz@ocln.org; *Ch Servs*, Cheryl McClain; Tel: 781-784-1578, Ext 56, E-Mail: cmclain@ocln.org; *Tech Servs*, Dick Radtke; Tel: 781-784-1578, Ext 26, E-Mail: dradtke@ocln.org; Staff 22 (MLS 5, Non-MLS 17)
Pop 17,000; Circ 198,000
Jul 2000-Jun 2001 Income City $615,157. Mats Exp $130,075, Books $96,408, Per/Ser (Incl. Access Fees) $11,000, Micro $3,700, Electronic Ref Mat (Incl. Access Fees) $18,967. Sal $423,376
Library Holdings: Bk Vols 78,000; Per Subs 125
Special Collections: Deborah Sampson Coll
Publications: Between the Lines (Newsletter)
Mem of SE Mass Regional Libr Syst
Partic in Old Colony Libr Network
Friends of the Library Group

SR TEMPLE ISRAEL, Neipris Library, 125 Pond St, PO Box 377, 02067. SAN 307-6636. Tel: 781-784-3986. FAX: 781-784-0719. *Librn*, Florette Molot Brill
Founded 1953
Library Holdings: Bk Vols 6,350
Subject Interests: Judaica (lit or hist of Jews)
Friends of the Library Group

SHEFFIELD

P BUSHNELL-SAGE LIBRARY,* 48 Main St, 01257. (Mail add: PO Box 487, 01257), SAN 307-6644. Tel: 413-229-7004. FAX: 413-229-7003. Web Site: www.cwmorris.org. *Dir*, John K Campbell
Founded 1892. Pop 2,743; Circ 33,000
Library Holdings: Bk Vols 35,000; Bk Titles 29,000; Per Subs 50
Mem of Western Regional Libr Syst
Friends of the Library Group

SHELBURNE FALLS

P ARMS LIBRARY ASSOCIATION,* Bridge & Main St, 01370. SAN 307-6652. Tel: 413-625-0306. *Librn*, Louis H Battalen
Founded 1854. Pop 2,200; Circ 25,283
Library Holdings: Bk Vols 22,840; Per Subs 48
Mem of Western Regional Libr Syst
Open Mon & Thurs 1-5:30 & 6:30-8:30, Sat 11-3
Friends of the Library Group

P SHELBURNE FREE PUBLIC LIBRARY,* 233 Shelburne Center Rd, 01370. SAN 307-6660. Tel: 413-625-0307. FAX: 413-625-0307. E-Mail: s_falls@cwmars.org. *Librn*, Elizabeth Burnham
Pop 8,000; Circ 8,648
Library Holdings: Bk Vols 9,000; Per Subs 33
Mem of Western Regional Libr Syst

SHERBORN

P SHERBORN LIBRARY, 4 Sanger St, 01770-1499. SAN 307-6679. Tel: 508-653-0770. FAX: 508-650-9243. E-Mail: sherborn@ixl.net. Web Site: people.ne.mediaone.net/sherbornlibrary. *Dir*, M Elizabeth Johnston; *Ch Servs*, Cheryl Stern Ouellette; *Publ Servs*, Donna Bryant; *Tech Servs*, Kathleen Rao; Staff 9 (MLS 5, Non-MLS 4)
Founded 1860. Pop 4,442; Circ 54,000
Jul 1999-Jun 2000 Income $231,707, State $4,601, City $212,966, Other $14,140. Mats Exp $51,469, Books $39,644, Per/Ser (Incl. Access Fees) $5,625, Electronic Ref Mat (Incl. Access Fees) $6,200. Sal $169,863 (Prof $135,495)
Library Holdings: Bk Titles 52,374; Per Subs 163
Automation Activity & Vendor Info: (Cataloging) EOS; (Circulation) EOS; (OPAC) EOS
Publications: First Search
Partic in Metrowest Massachusetts Regional Library System; OCLC Online Computer Library Center, Inc
Friends of the Library Group

SHIRLEY

P HAZEN MEMORIAL LIBRARY,* 3 Keady Way, 01464. (Mail add: PO Box 1129, 01464), SAN 307-6687. Tel: 978-425-2620. FAX: 978-425-2621. Web Site: radio.bienet/~hazenlib/. *Librn*, Elizabeth Wade; E-Mail: bwade@cwmarsmail.cwmars.org
Founded 1893. Circ 19,000
Jul 1997-Jun 1998 Income $97,538, State $8,240, City $74,298, Federal $6,000, Locally Generated Income $9,000. Mats Exp $21,550, Books $19,000, Per/Ser (Incl. Access Fees) $2,000. Sal $40,362
Library Holdings: Bk Vols 29,000; Per Subs 94
Subject Interests: Local history
Mem of Central Massachusetts Regional Library System
Partic in CW Mars
Friends of the Library Group

SHREWSBURY

P CENTRAL MASSACHUSETTS REGIONAL LIBRARY SYSTEM, 8 Flagg Rd, 01545-4665. SAN 307-8221. Tel: 508-757-4110. FAX: 508-757-4370. E-Mail: cmrls@cmrls.org. Web Site: www.cmrls.org. *Dir*, Anne T Parent; Tel: 508-757-4110, Ext 304, Fax: 508-757-4390, E-Mail: aparent@cwmars.org; *Librn*, Paul Ericsson; Tel: 508-757-4110, Ext 307, E-Mail: pericsso@cwmars.org; *Librn*, Margaret Cardello; Tel: 508-757-4110, Ext 306, E-Mail: mcardell@cwmars.org; *Assoc Dir*, Carolyn B Noah; Tel: 508-757-4110, Ext 305, E-Mail: cnoah@cwmars.org; *Tech Coordr*, Richard Levine; Tel: 508-757-4110, Ext 308, E-Mail: rlevine@cwmars.org; Staff 10 (MLS 4, Non-MLS 6)
Founded 1962. Pop 852,104
Jul 2000-Jun 2001 Income $1,862,393, State $1,764,493. Mats Exp $211,261, Books $73,590, Per/Ser (Incl. Access Fees) $3,000, Electronic Ref Mat (Incl. Access Fees) $134,671. Sal $479,484 (Prof $308,677)
Library Holdings: Bk Vols 60,000
Automation Activity & Vendor Info: (Cataloging) Innovative Interfaces Inc.; (Circulation) Innovative Interfaces Inc.; (ILL) Innovative Interfaces Inc.; (Media Booking) Innovative Interfaces Inc.
Database Vendor: CARL, IAC - SearchBank, OCLC - First Search
Publications: Centralities (monthly news brief)
Member Libraries: Albert J Sargent Memorial Library; Ashby Free Public Library; Athol Public Library; Atlantic Union College; Auburn Public Library; Ayer Library; Bancroft Memorial Library; Beals Memorial Library; Beaman Memorial Public Library; Bellingham Public Library; Berlin Public Library; Bigelow Free Public Library; Blackstone Public Library; Bolton Public Library; Boylston Public Library; Boynton Public Library; Brimfield Public Library; Charlton Public Library; Chester C Corbin Public Library; Conant Public Library; East Brookfield Public Library; First Allmerica Financial Life Insurance Company; Fitchburg Public Library; Fobes Memorial Library; Forbush Memorial Library; Gale Free Library; Grafton Public Library; Groton Public Library; Harvard Public Library; Haston Free Public Library; Hazen Memorial Library; Hopkinton Public Library; Hubbardston Public Library; Hudson Public Library; Jacob Edwards Library; Joshua Hyde Public Library; Lawrence Library; Leicester Public Library; Leominster Public Library; Levi Heywood Memorial Library; Marlborough Public Library; Massachusetts Trial Court; Merriam-Gilbert Public Library; Merrick Public Library; Milford Town Library; Milford-Whitinsville Regional Hospital; Millbury Public Library; Millville Free Public Library; New Braintree Public Library; Northborough Free Library; Norton Co Library; Oxford Free Library; Pearle L Crawford Memorial Library; Petersham Memorial Library; Phinehas S Newton Library; Princeton Public Library; Richard Sugden Library; Richards Memorial Library; Ritter Memorial Library; Rutland Free Public Library; Shrewsbury Public Library; Simon Fairfield Public Library; Southborough Public Library; Stevens Memorial Library; Sutton Free Public Library; Taft Public Library; Thayer Memorial Library; Townsend Public Library; University of Massachusetts Memorial HealthAlliance Library; Upton Town Library; Uxbridge Free Public Library; Warren Public Library; Westborough Public Library; Whitinsville Social Library, Inc; Woods Memorial Library; Worcester Public Library
Partic in CW Mars; OCLC Online Computer Library Center, Inc

S QUANTUM CORP, Shrewsbury Library, 333 South St, SHRI-3/G18, 01545-4171. SAN 377-4198. Tel: 508-770-3271. FAX: 508-770-3400. *Librn*, Steven McCulloch; E-Mail: steve.mcculloch@quantum.com
Founded 1984
Library Holdings: Bk Vols 4,000; Per Subs 350
Partic in Cent Mass Regional Libr Syst; Spec Libr Asn

P SHREWSBURY PUBLIC LIBRARY,* 609 Main St, 01545. SAN 307-6695. Tel: 508-842-0081. FAX: 508-841-8540. *Dir*, Bonnie L O'Brien; *Asst Dir, Tech Servs*, Margaret Lesinski; *Ch Servs*, Jacqueline Shartin; *Ad Servs*, George Brown; Staff 17 (MLS 4, Non-MLS 13)
Founded 1872. Pop 22,674; Circ 207,280
Library Holdings: Bk Titles 125,000; Per Subs 200
Special Collections: Early New England History & Biography (Artemas Ward Coll)
Publications: Newsletter (quarterly)
Mem of Central Massachusetts Regional Library System
Partic in CW Mars
Friends of the Library Group

SHUTESBURY

P MN SPEAR MEMORIAL LIBRARY, 10 Cooleyville Rd, 01072-0256. (Mail add: PO Box 256, 01072-0256), SAN 307-6717. Tel: 413-259-1213. FAX: 413-259-1213. E-Mail: shutesbury@cwmars.org. *Librn*, Judith Seelig
Pop 1,600; Circ 3,700

Library Holdings: Bk Vols 10,000; Per Subs 28
Mem of Western Regional Libr Syst
Open Tues & Thurs 3:30-7:30
Friends of the Library Group

SOMERSET

P SOMERSET PUBLIC LIBRARY,* 1464 County St, 02726. SAN 345-5769. Tel: 508-646-2829. FAX: 508-646-2831. *Dir*, Sally Evans; *Ref*, Bonnie Mendes; *Ch Servs*, Mary Lou Martel
Founded 1897. Pop 18,860; Circ 151,394
Jul 1997-Jun 1998 Income $422,115
Library Holdings: Bk Vols 74,000; Per Subs 210
Subject Interests: Local history
Friends of the Library Group

SOMERVILLE

S EARTHWORM, INC, Recycling Information Center,* 35 Medford St, 02143-4211. SAN 370-2308. Tel: 617-628-1844. FAX: 617-628-2773. E-Mail: earthwrm@aol.com. *Exec Dir*, Jeff Coyne
1999-2000 Mats Exp $300, Per/Ser (Incl. Access Fees) $225, Other Print Mats $50. Sal $1,000
Library Holdings: Bk Vols 110; Per Subs 15
Subject Interests: Environ educ, Environ qual, Hazardous waste, Pollution, Recycling, Res recovery, Solid waste mgt
Restriction: By appointment only
Open Mon-Fri 9-5; Special Services - Slide shows

P PUBLIC LIBRARY OF THE CITY OF SOMERVILLE, Somerville Public, 79 Highland Ave, 02143. SAN 345-5882. Tel: 617-623-5000. Circulation Tel: 617-623-5000, Ext 2900. Reference Tel: 617-623-5000, Ext 2955. FAX: 617-628-4052. E-Mail: somdir@mln.lib.ma.us. Web Site: www.ultranet.com/somlib. *Dir*, Paul A DeAngelis; *Asst Dir*, Thelma G Donovan; *Per*, Ron Castile; *Ch Servs*, Ann Dausch; *YA Servs*, Catherine Piantigini; *Cat, Tech Servs*, Shwuing H Wu; *Ref*, Dora St Martin; *AV*, Wendy Wood; *Bkmobile Coordr*, Mary Faith Baker; *Ad Servs*, Josefa M Wrangham; *Circ*, James A Ventura; *Syst Coordr*, Alix Quan; *Coll Develop*, Barbara Nowak; Staff 37 (MLS 21, Non-MLS 16)
Founded 1873. Pop 78,385; Circ 337,330
Jul 1999-Jun 2000 Income (Main Library and Branch Library) $1,888,882, State $125,470, City $1,745,992, Other $17,420. Mats Exp $244,145, Books $178,573, Per/Ser (Incl. Access Fees) $24,198, Micro $10,463, AV Equip $30,911. Sal $1,386,426
Library Holdings: Bk Vols 189,633; Per Subs 431
Subject Interests: Art, Genealogy, Travel, Women's studies
Special Collections: New England & Somerville History Coll
Automation Activity & Vendor Info: (Acquisitions) Brodart; (Circulation) DRA; (OPAC) DRA
Database Vendor: DRA, Ebsco - EbscoHost
Mem of Eastern Mass Regional Libr Syst
Partic in Minuteman Library Network
Friends of the Library Group
Branches: 2
EAST, 115 Broadway, 02145. SAN 345-5912. Tel: 617-623-5000. FAX: 617-623-9403. *Librn*, Susan Lamphier; Staff 3 (MLS 2, Non-MLS 1)
Founded 1918
Library Holdings: Bk Vols 17,560
Partic in Minuteman Library Network
WEST, 40 College Ave, 02144. SAN 345-5947. Tel: 617-623-5000. Web Site: www.ultranet.com/~somlib. *Librn*, Karen Kramer; Staff 4 (MLS 1, Non-MLS 3)
Founded 1909
Library Holdings: Bk Vols 29,449
Database Vendor: Dialog, IAC - Info Trac, OCLC - First Search
Function: ILL available, Reference services available
Friends of the Library Group
Bookmobiles: 1

M SOMERVILLE HOSPITAL, Carr Health Sciences Library, 230 Highland Ave, 02143. SAN 320-3824. Tel: 617-591-4288. FAX: 617-591-4286. *Librn*, Michelle Giberti; E-Mail: mgilberti@challiance.org; Staff 2 (MLS 1, Non-MLS 1)
Library Holdings: Bk Vols 3,000; Bk Titles 2,100; Per Subs 144
Subject Interests: Medicine, Nursing
Special Collections: National League for Nursing Publications
Publications: Acquisitions List; Library Brochure
Partic in Cambridge Health Alliance; Northeastern Consortium For Health Information

SOUTH CHATHAM

P SOUTH CHATHAM PUBLIC LIBRARY,* Rte 28 & Bayview Rd, PO Box 218, 02659. SAN 307-6725. Tel: 508-430-7989. *Librn*, Helen S Warren
Pop 5,000
Library Holdings: Bk Vols 4,300
Mem of Eastern Mass Regional Libr Syst
Friends of the Library Group

SOUTH DARTMOUTH

S LLOYD CENTER FOR ENVIRONMENTAL STUDIES, INC, Katharine Nordell Resource Center, 430 Potomska Rd, 02748-1326. SAN 329-2223. Tel: 508-990-0505. FAX: 508-993-7868. E-Mail: lloydctr@lloydctr.ma.ultranet.com. Web Site: www.thelloydcenter.org. *Exec Dir*, Donald M Tucker
Founded 1981
Library Holdings: Bk Vols 2,031; Bk Titles 2,019
Subject Interests: Natural history

SOUTH DEERFIELD

P TILTON LIBRARY,* 75 N Main St, 01373. SAN 345-1860. Tel: 413-665-4683. FAX: 413-665-9118. *Dir*, Barbara Schuman; E-Mail: tilton@cwmars.org; Staff 1 (MLS 1)
Founded 1871. Circ 30,000
Library Holdings: Bk Titles 18,000; Per Subs 87
Special Collections: Local Histories of Western Massachusetts
Mem of Western Massachusetts Regional Library System
Friends of the Library Group

SOUTH DENNIS

P SOUTH DENNIS FREE PUBLIC LIBRARY,* 389 Main St, PO Box 304, 02660. SAN 307-6733. Tel: 508-394-8954. FAX: 508-394-4392. *Librn*, Pauline Marr
Circ 13,796
Library Holdings: Bk Vols 12,050
Mem of Eastern Mass Regional Libr Syst
Open Mon 6:30-8:30, Wed 3-5, Fri 10-12 & 3-5:30, Sat 10-12

SOUTH EGREMONT

P EGREMONT FREE LIBRARY, One Buttonball Lane, PO Box 246, 01258. SAN 307-6741. Tel: 413-528-1474. FAX: 413-528-6416. E-Mail: s_egremont@cwmars.org. *Dir*, Sally Henderer Caldwell
Founded 1882. Pop 1,070; Circ 5,483
Jul 1998-Jun 1999 Income $17,126. Mats Exp $4,484, Books $3,755, Per/Ser (Incl. Access Fees) $729. Sal $11,880 (Prof $11,580)
Library Holdings: Bk Titles 9,069; Per Subs 20
Database Vendor: Innovative Interfaces INN - View
Mem of Western Massachusetts Regional Library System

SOUTH HADLEY

C MOUNT HOLYOKE COLLEGE LIBRARY, Information & Technology Services, 50 College St, 01075-6404. SAN 307-675X. Tel: 413-538-2225. Interlibrary Loan Service Tel: 413-538-2423. FAX: 413-538-2370. Web Site: www.mtholyoke.edu/lits. *Dir*, Susan L Perry; E-Mail: sperry@mhc.mtholyoke.edu; *Access Serv*, Gail Scanlon; Tel: 413-538-2434, E-Mail: gscanlon@mtholyoke.edu; *Tech Servs*, Sandra Berestka; *Coll Develop*, Kathleen Norton; Staff 16 (MLS 16)
Founded 1837. Enrl 1,945; Fac 192; Highest Degree: Master
Library Holdings: Bk Vols 695,096; Per Subs 2,954
Subject Interests: Economics, Feminism, History, Natural science
Special Collections: Alumnae Letters & Diaries; Faculty Papers; Illustrated Editions of Dante's Divine Comedy (Giamatti Dante Coll); Women's Education 1920-
Automation Activity & Vendor Info: (Acquisitions) Innovative Interfaces Inc.; (Cataloging) Innovative Interfaces Inc.; (Circulation) Innovative Interfaces Inc.; (Media Booking) Innovative Interfaces Inc.
Database Vendor: Lexis-Nexis, OCLC - First Search, OVID Technologies
Partic in New England Libr Info Network

S REXAM IMAGE PRODUCTS, Research Library, 15 Mulligan Dr, 01075. SAN 320-6807. Tel: 413-536-7800. FAX: 413-532-6630. Web Site: www.rexam.com. *VPres*, Wanda Zabawa; Tel: 413-539-5657
Founded 1963
Library Holdings: Bk Vols 2,900; Per Subs 83
Subject Interests: Chemistry, Films and filmmaking, Patents, Polymer chemistry, Printing

P SOUTH HADLEY PUBLIC LIBRARY, Bardwell St, 01075. SAN 345-6064. Tel: 413-538-5045. FAX: 413-539-9250. Web Site: www.shadleylib.org. *Dir*, Richard Callaghan; E-Mail: rcallagh@cwmars.org; *Tech Servs*, Lorraine Ensor; E-Mail: lensor@cwmars.org; *Librn*, Meg

Clancy; E-Mail: mclancy@cwmars.org; *Librn*, Lisa Downing; E-Mail: ldowning@cwmars.org; *Circ*, Sheila Martinelli; E-Mail: smartine@cwmars.org. Subject Specialists: *Reference*, Lisa Downing; Staff 11 (MLS 4, Non-MLS 7)
Founded 1906. Pop 17,000; Circ 205,000
Jul 2000-Jun 2001 Income $477,000. Mats Exp $101,000, Books $86,000, Per/Ser (Incl. Access Fees) $7,750. Sal $320,109
Library Holdings: Bk Vols 45,000; Bk Titles 45,910; Per Subs 130
Subject Interests: Local history
Automation Activity & Vendor Info: (Circulation) Innovative Interfaces Inc.; (OPAC) Innovative Interfaces Inc.
Database Vendor: IAC - Info Trac, Innovative Interfaces INN - View
Publications: South Hadley Library News (Newsletter)
Mem of Western Massachusetts Regional Library System
Partic in CW Mars
Operate public access studio & channel for cable television
Friends of the Library Group

SOUTH HAMILTON

R GORDON-CONWELL THEOLOGICAL SEMINARY, Burton L Goddard Library, 130 Essex St, 01982-2361. SAN 307-6776. Tel: 978-646-4074. FAX: 978-468-4567. E-Mail: glibrary@gcts.edu. Web Site: www.gcts.edu/library. *Dir*, Freeman Barton; Tel: 978-646-4076, E-Mail: febarton@gcts.edu; *Circ*, Brian Jones; Staff 5 (MLS 1, Non-MLS 4)
Founded 1970. Highest Degree: Doctorate
Jul 1998-Jun 1999 Income $315,596. Mats Exp $102,266, Books $57,209, Per/Ser (Incl. Access Fees) $43,283, Micro $1,774. Sal $154,196 (Prof $39,500)
Library Holdings: Bk Vols 250,000; Bk Titles 134,637; Per Subs 990
Special Collections: Assyro-Babylonian (Mercer Coll); Aston Coll-Judism, Christianity 1615-1691 (Richard Babson Coll); John Bunyan Coll; Millerite-Adventual Coll; Rare Bibles (Babson Coll); Washburn Baptist Coll
Database Vendor: CARL, IAC - SearchBank
Partic in Boston Theological Institute Library Program

P HAMILTON PUBLIC LIBRARY,* 299 Bay Rd, 01982-2288. SAN 307-6784. Tel: 978-468-5577. FAX: 978-468-5578. Web Site: www.hamiltonpubliclibrary.org. *Librn*, Annette V Janes; *Asst Dir*, Nancy Day
Founded 1891. Pop 7,020; Circ 99,899 Income $255,292, State $8,970. Mats Exp $58,080, Books $47,000, Per/Ser (Incl. Access Fees) $4,000, Micro $3,000, Other Print Mats $4,000. Sal $160,835
Library Holdings: Bk Titles 56,000; Per Subs 93
Mem of Eastern Mass Regional Libr Syst
Friends of the Library Group

SOUTH LANCASTER

C ATLANTIC UNION COLLEGE, G Eric Jones Library, 338 Main St, PO Box 1209, 01561. SAN 307-6792. Tel: 978-368-2450. FAX: 978-368-2456. E-Mail: library@atlanticuc.edu. Web Site: library.atlanticuc.edu. *Dir*, Margareta Sbacchi; Tel: 978-368-2453; *Per*, Karen Silverthorn; *Circ*, Marjorie Whidbee; Staff 5 (MLS 2, Non-MLS 3)
Founded 1882. Enrl 603
Library Holdings: Bk Vols 150,000; Per Subs 533
Subject Interests: Literary criticism, Religion, Seventh-Day Adventists, Theology
Special Collections: 20th Cent British & American Poets (Stafford Poetry Coll); Career Reference Center; George H Reavis Education material; Seventh-Day Adventist Coll
Publications: Library Handbook; New Titles; Recent Accessions
Mem of Central Massachusetts Regional Library System
Partic in Nelinet, Inc; Worcester Area Cooperating Libraries

SOUTH NATICK

P BACON FREE LIBRARY,* 58 Eliot St, 01760-5596. SAN 372-7602. Tel: 508-653-6730. *Dir*, Anne B Feen
Founded 1870. Circ 16,700
Library Holdings: Bk Vols 13,850; Per Subs 43
Special Collections: Early Christian Native Americans of South Natick; Natick Historical Coll
Mem of Eastern Mass Regional Libr Syst
Friends of the Library Group

S NATICK HISTORICAL SOCIETY LIBRARY, 58 Eliot St, 01760. SAN 371-2567. Tel: 508-647-4841. FAX: 508-651-7013. Web Site: www.ultnanet.com/~elliot/. *Dir*, Anne Schaller
Founded 1870
May 1999-Apr 2000 Income $12,500. Mats Exp $9,000
Library Holdings: Bk Vols 1,800; Per Subs 34
Subject Interests: Local history
Special Collections: Indian Artifacts; Vice-President Henry Wilson
Publications: Images of America-Natick-Arcadia Pub Co
Restriction: Reference only to non-staff
Open Tues 6-8:30, Wed 2-4:30, Sat 10-12:30

SOUTH WALPOLE

S MASSACHUSETTS DEPARTMENT OF CORRECTION, Institution Library at MCI Cedar Junction, PO Box 100, 02071. SAN 307-7330. Tel: 508-668-2100. *Librn*, Beverly Veglas; Staff 10 (MLS 2, Non-MLS 8)
Founded 1956. Pop 700
Library Holdings: Bk Vols 9,800; Bk Titles 3,000
Special Collections: Law Library Coll

SOUTH WEYMOUTH

M SOUTH SHORE HOSPITAL, Medical Library, 55 Fogg Rd, 02190. Tel: 781-340-8528. FAX: 781-331-0834. Web Site: www.southshorehospital.org. *Librn*, Kathy Mc Carthy; E-Mail: kathy-mccarthy@sshop.org
Library Holdings: Bk Titles 1,000; Per Subs 135

SOUTH YARMOUTH

P YARMOUTH TOWN LIBRARIES,* 312 Old Main St, 02664. SAN 307-8450. Tel: 508-760-4820. FAX: 508-760-2699. E-Mail: syar_ms@clams.lib.ma.us. Web Site: www.capecod.net/yarmouthlibraries. *Asst Dir*, Carol Devir; *Librn*, Virginia Gifford
Founded 1866. Pop 21,727; Circ 203,839
1998-1999 Income $624,750, State $18,494. Mats Exp $114,000, Books $88,931, Per/Ser (Incl. Access Fees) $11,014. Sal $320,818
Library Holdings: Bk Titles 34,535; Per Subs 119
Special Collections: Genealogy (New England Historic General Register & Amos Otis Papers); Histories of Cape
Friends of the Library Group
Branches: 2
SOUTH YARMOUTH BRANCH, 312 Main St, 02664. SAN 307-6822. Tel: 508-760-4820. FAX: 508-760-2699. *Dir*, Marcia Shannon
Circ 72,884
Library Holdings: Bk Vols 27,950; Per Subs 46
Subject Interests: History
Special Collections: Joseph C Lincoln Coll, novels
Mem of Eastern Mass Regional Libr Syst
WEST YARMOUTH BRANCH, Rt 28, West Yarmouth, 02673-4797. SAN 307-7853. Tel: 508-775-5206. FAX: 508-778-4812. *Dir*, Marcia Shannon
Founded 1891. Pop 21,000; Circ 65,000
Jul 1996-Jun 1997 Mats Exp $18,532
Library Holdings: Bk Titles 28,000; Per Subs 60
Mem of Eastern Mass Regional Libr Syst
Open Mon, Wed & Fri 10-12 & 1-4:30, Tues & Thurs 2:30-5:30 & 6:30-9
Friends of the Library Group

SOUTHAMPTON

P EDWARDS PUBLIC LIBRARY, 30 East St, 01073-9324. SAN 307-6830. Tel: 413-527-9480. FAX: 413-527-9480. *Ad Servs, Dir*, Dorothy B Frary; E-Mail: dfrary@cwmarsmail.cwmars.org; *Ch Servs*, Sandra Enders-Holmes; E-Mail: senders@ncats.net
Founded 1904. Pop 4,900
Jun 1999-Jun 2000 Income $85,992, State $6,787, City $79,205. Mats Exp $18,140, Books $15,300, Per/Ser (Incl. Access Fees) $1,028, Electronic Ref Mat (Incl. Access Fees) $1,812. Sal $54,724
Library Holdings: Bk Titles 24,900; Per Subs 47
Special Collections: Local History Coll; Vocal Music Coll
Automation Activity & Vendor Info: (Circulation) Follett
Mem of Western Massachusetts Regional Library System
Partic in CW Mars

SOUTHBOROUGH

P SOUTHBOROUGH PUBLIC LIBRARY,* 25 Main St, 01772. SAN 307-6849. Tel: 508-485-5031. FAX: 508-229-4451. *Dir*, Judith Williams; *Asst Librn*, Elizabeth Meyer; *Asst Librn*, Margaret Tuttle; *Asst Librn*, Claire Curran Ball; *Ch Servs*, Kim Keith
Founded 1852. Pop 6,326; Circ 76,156
Library Holdings: Bk Vols 60,000; Per Subs 100
Mem of Central Massachusetts Regional Library System
Friends of the Library Group

SOUTHBRIDGE

P JACOB EDWARDS LIBRARY, 236 Main St, 01550-2598. SAN 307-6865. Tel: 508-764-5426. FAX: 508-764-5428. *Ch Servs*, Mary White; *Tech Servs*, Susan Chaplin; *Circ*, Corinna Pena; *Ref*, Margaret Morrissey; Staff 3 (MLS 1, Non-MLS 2)
Founded 1914. Pop 17,460; Circ 61,619
Jul 1999-Jun 2000 Income $336,887, State $23,732, City $285,081, Other

$28,074. Mats Exp $274,548, Books $38,380, Per/Ser (Incl. Access Fees) $4,204, AV Equip $2,114, Other Print Mats $45,955, Electronic Ref Mat (Incl. Access Fees) $14,987. Sal $202,280
Library Holdings: Bk Vols 54,964; Per Subs 150
Special Collections: Local History (Ammidown & Tucci Colls)
Automation Activity & Vendor Info: (Cataloging) Innovative Interfaces Inc.; (Circulation) Innovative Interfaces Inc.; (ILL) Innovative Interfaces Inc.
Mem of Central Massachusetts Regional Library System
Partic in CW Mars
Friends of the Library Group

S LYCOTT ENVIRONMENTAL INC LIBRARY,* 600 Charlton St, 01550. SAN 328-2511. Tel: 508-765-0101. FAX: 508-765-1352. *In Charge*, Kim Prescott
Library Holdings: Bk Titles 5,000

SOUTHWICK

P SOUTHWICK PUBLIC LIBRARY, 95 Feeding Hills Rd, 01077-9683. SAN 307-6881. Tel: 413-569-1221. FAX: 413-569-0440. E-Mail: swck@concentric.net. *Dir*, Anne Murray; Staff 5 (Non-MLS 5)
Founded 1892. Pop 8,300
Jul 1999-Jun 2000 Income $239,931, State $13,700, City $226,231. Mats Exp $54,000, Books $50,000, Per/Ser (Incl. Access Fees) $4,000. Sal $142,555
Library Holdings: Bk Titles 24,068
Publications: Links Newsletter
Mem of Western Regional Libr Syst
Special Services for the Blind - Talking Books
Friends of the Library Group

SPENCER

SR SAINT JOSEPH'S ABBEY, Monastic Library, 167 N Spencer Rd, 01562. SAN 328-1302. Tel: 508-885-8700, Ext 524. FAX: 508-885-8701. E-Mail: sjalibrary@aol.com. *Cat, Librn*, Basil Byrne
Circ 80
Library Holdings: Bk Titles 35,000; Per Subs 25

P RICHARD SUGDEN LIBRARY,* 8 Pleasant St, 01562. SAN 307-689X. Tel: 508-885-7513. FAX: 508-885-7523. *Dir*, Mary Baker-Wood; E-Mail: mbwood@cwmars.org
Pop 11,500; Circ 77,430
Library Holdings: Bk Vols 46,000; Per Subs 100
Special Collections: Historical Materials of Spencer & Massachusetts
Mem of Central Massachusetts Regional Library System
Houses Spencer Historical Museum
Friends of the Library Group

SPRINGFIELD

C AMERICAN INTERNATIONAL COLLEGE, James J Shea Sr Memorial Library, 1000 State St, 01109. SAN 307-6903. Tel: 413-205-3225. FAX: 413-205-3904. Web Site: aic.map.com. *Dir*, F Knowlton Utley; E-Mail: kutley@cwmars.org; *Tech Servs*, Kerry Adams; *Ref*, Dale LaBonte; Staff 4 (MLS 4)
Founded 1885. Enrl 1,800; Fac 94; Highest Degree: Doctorate
1998-1999 Mats Exp $207,167, Books $65,000, Per/Ser (Incl. Access Fees) $72,000, Presv $160, Micro $33,000, AV Equip $7,000, Other Print Mats $5,000, Electronic Ref Mat (Incl. Access Fees) $32,000
Library Holdings: Bk Vols 75,436; Bk Titles 70,100; Per Subs 525
Subject Interests: Education, Health science, Psychology
Special Collections: Curriculum Libr, rare bks
Automation Activity & Vendor Info: (Acquisitions) Innovative Interfaces Inc.; (Cataloging) Innovative Interfaces Inc.; (Circulation) Innovative Interfaces Inc.; (Course Reserve) Innovative Interfaces Inc.; (ILL) Innovative Interfaces Inc.; (Media Booking) Innovative Interfaces Inc.; (OPAC) Innovative Interfaces Inc.; (Serials) Innovative Interfaces Inc.
Database Vendor: Innovative Interfaces INN - View
Partic in Cooperating Libraries Of Greater Springfield; CW Mars; Western Mass Regional Libr Servs

M BAYSTATE MEDICAL CENTER, Health Sciences Library,* 759 Chestnut St, 01199. SAN 345-6153. Tel: 413-794-1865. FAX: 413-794-1978. *Ser*, Micheline Gaudette; *ILL*, Margaret Whitlock; *Cat*, Diane Mazur; Staff 16 (MLS 5, Non-MLS 11)
Library Holdings: Bk Titles 10,700; Per Subs 500
Subject Interests: Anesthesiology, Cardiology, History of medicine, Literature, Medicine, Nursing, Obstetrics and gynecology, Oncology, Orthopedics, Pediatrics, Surgery
Publications: What's New (quarterly)

S MASSACHUSETTS MUTUAL LIFE INSURANCE CO LIBRARY,* 1295 State St F017, 01111. SAN 307-6938. Tel: 413-744-3361. FAX: 413-744-8440. *Librn*, Suzanne O'Donnell; E-Mail: sodonnell@massmutual.com; Staff 1 (MLS 1)
Founded 1929
Library Holdings: Bk Vols 14,000; Bk Titles 12,000; Per Subs 100
Subject Interests: Business and management, Investing
Branches:
LAW LIBRARY, 1295 State St, 01111. SAN 325-2965. Tel: 413-744-2188, 413-744-5439. FAX: 413-744-6279. *Librn*, Elenor Owczarski; Staff 1 (MLS 1)
Library Holdings: Bk Vols 23,000
Restriction: Company staff only
Partic in Nelinet, Inc

GL MASSACHUSETTS TRIAL COURT, Hampden Law Library, 50 State St, PO Box 559, 01102-0559. SAN 307-692X. Tel: 413-748-7923. FAX: 413-734-2973. Web Site: masslaw.library.net. *Librn*, Kathleen M Flynn; Staff 4 (MLS 1, Non-MLS 3)
Founded 1890
Library Holdings: Bk Vols 52,015; Per Subs 425
Special Collections: Massachusetts Law
Partic in Cooperating Libraries Of Greater Springfield; New England Law Library Consortium, Inc; OCLC Online Computer Library Center, Inc
Friends of the Library Group

M MERCY HOSPITAL, Gilman Health Sciences Library, 271 Carew St, 01102-9012. (Mail add: PO Box 9012, 01102-9012), SAN 328-5588. Tel: 413-748-9050. FAX: 413-748-9059. *Dir*, Roger S Manahan; E-Mail: roger.manahan@sphs.com
Jan 1999-Dec 1999 Mats Exp $32,000, Books $9,000, Per/Ser (Incl. Access Fees) $14,000, Electronic Ref Mat (Incl. Access Fees) $9,000. Sal $40,000
Library Holdings: Bk Titles 750; Per Subs 64
Subject Interests: Allied health, Hospital administration, Medicine, Nursing
Database Vendor: Silverplatter Information Inc.
Partic in Massachusetts Health Sciences Libraries Network; WMHIC

S NAISMITH MEMORIAL BASKETBALL HALL OF FAME, Edward J & Gena G Hickox Library, 1150 W Columbus Ave, 01105. SAN 307-6954. Tel: 413-781-6500, Ext 112. FAX: 413-781-1939. Web Site: www.hoophall.com. *Archivist, Librn*, Doug Stark
Founded 1968
Library Holdings: Bk Titles 2,300; Per Subs 23
Special Collections: Basketball (William G Mokray Coll); Complete set of Basketball rule books (Spalding Coll)
Restriction: By appointment only

M SHRINERS' HOSPITAL FOR CHILDREN, Medical Library, 516 Carew St, 01104. SAN 377-9335. Tel: 413-787-2053. FAX: 413-735-1222. *Librn*, Susan La Forte; *ILL*, Joy Wright; Tel: 413-735-1289
Library Holdings: Bk Titles 1,000; Per Subs 110
Subject Interests: Pediatrics orthopedics
Partic in Basic Health Sciences Library Network; Massachusetts Health Sciences Libraries Network; National Network Of Libraries Of Medicine - South Central Region; Western Mass Health Info Consortium

C SPRINGFIELD COLLEGE, Babson Library, 263 Alden St, 01109-3797. SAN 307-6997. Tel: 413-748-3502. Interlibrary Loan Service Tel: 413-748-3315. FAX: 413-748-3631. Web Site: www.spfldcol.edu/library. *Dir*, Gerald F Davis; Tel: 413-748-3309; *Assoc Dir*, Andrea Taupier; E-Mail: andrea_taupier@spfldcol.edu; *Tech Servs*, Tatyana Eckstrand; *ILL*, Cynthia Kowalczyk; Staff 8 (MLS 8)
Founded 1877. Enrl 3,300; Fac 250; Highest Degree: Doctorate
Library Holdings: Bk Vols 168,797; Bk Titles 142,000; Per Subs 733
Subject Interests: Allied health, Education, History, Humanities, Natural science, Social sciences and issues
Special Collections: Sports rules; US Volleyball Association Materials
Automation Activity & Vendor Info: (Acquisitions) Endeavor; (Cataloging) Endeavor; (Circulation) Endeavor
Partic in CCGS; Cooperating Libraries Of Greater Springfield; WMRLS

P SPRINGFIELD LIBRARY, 220 State St, 01103. SAN 345-6218. Tel: 413-263-6800. Circulation Tel: 413-263-6800, Ext 218. Reference Tel: 413-263-6800, Ext 213. TDD: 413-263-6835. FAX: 413-263-6817. Web Site: www.springfieldlibrary.org. *Dir*, Emily B Bader; Fax: 413-263-6825, E-Mail: ebader@spfldlibmus.org; *Asst Dir*, Molly Fogarty; Tel: 413-263-6800, Ext 293, Fax: 413-263-6825, E-Mail: lfogarty@spfldlibmus.org; *Cat, Tech Servs*, Sandra Birkner; *Ref*, John Clark; *Coll Develop*, Janet Fullerton; *Admin Assoc*, Carol Ann Leaders; Tel: 413-263-6800, Ext 290, Fax: 413-263-6825, E-Mail: cleaders@spfldlibmus.org; Staff 137 (MLS 37, Non-MLS 100)
Founded 1857. Pop 150,000; Circ 755,385
Jul 1999-Jun 2000 Income (Main Library and Branch Library) $6,659,201, State $466,571, City $5,175,520, Federal $332,837, Parent Institution $422,770, Other $261,503. Mats Exp $631,651, Books $449,016, Per/Ser (Incl. Access Fees) $150,048, Electronic Ref Mat (Incl. Access Fees) $32,587. Sal $3,572,887 (Prof $1,569,710)
Library Holdings: Bk Vols 627,930; Per Subs 1,558
Special Collections: American Wood Engravings (Aston Coll); Economics (David A Wells Coll); New England & French Canadian Genealogy Coll; Springfield History Coll; World War I & World War II Propaganda Coll
Automation Activity & Vendor Info: (Cataloging) CARL; (Circulation) CARL

Database Vendor: IAC - Info Trac, IAC - SearchBank, Innovative Interfaces INN - View, OCLC - First Search
Mem of Western Massachusetts Regional Library System
Partic in CW Mars
Special Services for the Deaf - Books on deafness & sign language; Captioned film depository; High interest/low vocabulary books; Special interest periodicals; TDD
Friends of the Library Group
Branches: 9
BRIGHTWOOD BRANCH, 359 Plainfield St, 01107. SAN 345-6242. Tel: 413-263-6805. FAX: 413-263-6810. Web Site: springfieldlibrary.org/scl/home.html. *Librn*, Haydee Hodis; E-Mail: hhodis@spfldlibmus.org; *Admin Assoc*, Carol Ann Leaders; Tel: 413-263-6800, Ext 290, Fax: 413-263-6825, E-Mail: cleaders@spfldlibmus.org
Library Holdings: Bk Vols 36,088
Database Vendor: IAC - Info Trac, IAC - SearchBank, Innovative Interfaces INN - View, OCLC - First Search
Partic in CW Mars
Friends of the Library Group
EAST FOREST PARK BRANCH, 122-124 Island Park Rd, 01108. Tel: 413-263-6836. FAX: 413-263-6838. *Librn*, Ann Keefe; E-Mail: akeefe@spfldlibmus.org
Library Holdings: Bk Vols 19,380
Database Vendor: IAC - Info Trac, IAC - SearchBank, Innovative Interfaces INN - View, OCLC - First Search
Partic in CW Mars
Friends of the Library Group
EAST SPRINGFIELD BRANCH, 21 Osborne Terrace, 01104. SAN 345-6277. Tel: 413-263-6840. FAX: 413-263-6838, 413-263-6842. Web Site: www.springfieldlibrary.org/scl/home.html. *Librn*, Ann Keefe; E-Mail: akeefe@spfldlibmus.org; *Admin Assoc*, Carol Ann Leaders; Tel: 413-263-6800, Ext 290, Fax: 413-263-6825, E-Mail: cleaders@spfldlibmus.org
Library Holdings: Bk Vols 26,338
Database Vendor: IAC - Info Trac, IAC - SearchBank, Innovative Interfaces INN - View, OCLC - First Search
Partic in CW Mars
Friends of the Library Group
FOREST PARK BRANCH, 2380 Belmont Ave, 01108. SAN 345-6307. Tel: 413-263-6843. FAX: 413-263-6845. Web Site: www.springfieldlibrary.org/scl/home.html. *Librn*, Norma Couture; E-Mail: ncouture@spfldlibmus.org; *Admin Assoc*, Carol Ann Leaders; Tel: 413-263-6800, Ext 290, Fax: 413-263-6825, E-Mail: cleaders@spfldlibmus.org
Library Holdings: Bk Vols 63,407
Database Vendor: IAC - Info Trac, IAC - SearchBank, Innovative Interfaces INN - View, OCLC - First Search
Partic in CW Mars
Friends of the Library Group
INDIAN ORCHARD BRANCH, 44 Oak St, Indian Orchard, 01151. SAN 345-6331. Tel: 413-263-6846. FAX: 413-263-6848. Web Site: www.springfieldlibrary.org/scl/home.html. *Librn*, Marianne Pedulla; E-Mail: mpedulla@spfldlibmus.org; *Admin Assoc*, Carol Ann Leaders; Tel: 413-263-6800, Ext 290, Fax: 413-263-6825, E-Mail: cleaders@spfldlibmus.org
Library Holdings: Bk Vols 28,983
Database Vendor: IAC - Info Trac, IAC - SearchBank, Innovative Interfaces INN - View, OCLC - First Search
Partic in CW Mars
Friends of the Library Group
LIBERTY BRANCH, 773 Liberty St, 01104. SAN 345-6366. Tel: 413-263-6849. FAX: 413-263-6851. Web Site: www.springfieldlibrary.org/scl/home.html. *Librn*, Anne Keefe; E-Mail: akeefe@spfldlibmus.org; *Admin Assoc*, Carol Ann Leaders; Tel: 413-263-6800, Ext 290, Fax: 413-263-6825, E-Mail: cleaders@spfldlibmus.org
Library Holdings: Bk Vols 27,344
Database Vendor: IAC - Info Trac, IAC - SearchBank, Innovative Interfaces INN - View, OCLC - First Search
Partic in CW Mars
Friends of the Library Group
MASON SQUARE BRANCH, 765 State St, 01109. SAN 345-6455. Tel: 413-263-6852. FAX: 413-263-6854. Web Site: www.springfieldlibrary.org/scl/home.html. *Librn*, Reggie Wilson; E-Mail: rwilson@spfldlibmus.org; *Admin Assoc*, Carol Ann Leaders; Tel: 413-263-6800, Ext 290, Fax: 413-263-6825, E-Mail: cleaders@spfldlibmus.org
Library Holdings: Bk Vols 33,906
Database Vendor: IAC - Info Trac, IAC - SearchBank, Innovative Interfaces INN - View, OCLC - First Search
Partic in CW Mars
Friends of the Library Group
PINE POINT BRANCH, 204 Boston Rd, 01109. SAN 345-6390. Tel: 413-263-6855. FAX: 413-263-6857. Web Site: www.springfieldlibrary.org/scl/home.html. *Librn*, Marianne Pedulla; E-Mail: mpedulla@spfldlibmus.org; *Admin Assoc*, Carol Ann Leaders; Tel: 413-263-6800, Ext 290, Fax: 413-263-6825, E-Mail: cleaders@spfldlibmus.org
Library Holdings: Bk Vols 52,746
Database Vendor: IAC - Info Trac, IAC - SearchBank, Innovative Interfaces INN - View, OCLC - First Search
Partic in CW Mars
Friends of the Library Group
SIXTEEN ACRES BRANCH, 1187 Parker St, 01129. SAN 345-6420. Tel: 413-263-6858. FAX: 413-263-6860. Web Site: www.springfieldlibrary.org/scl/home.html. *Librn*, Norma Couture; E-Mail: ncouture@spfldlibmus.org; *Admin Assoc*, Carol Ann Leaders; Tel: 413-263-6800, Ext 290, Fax: 413-263-6825, E-Mail: cleaders@spfldlibmus.org
Library Holdings: Bk Vols 44,045
Database Vendor: IAC - Info Trac, IAC - SearchBank, Innovative Interfaces INN - View, OCLC - First Search
Partic in CW Mars
Friends of the Library Group

S SPRINGFIELD LIBRARY & MUSEUMS ASSOCIATION, Connecticut Valley Historical Museum-Genealogy & Local History Library, The Quadrangle, 220 State St, 01103. SAN 307-6911. Tel: 413-263-6800, Ext 230. FAX: 413-263-6898. E-Mail: info@spfldlibmus.org. Web Site: www.quadrangle.org. *Exec Dir, Pres*, Joseph Carvalho; Fax: 413-263-6875, E-Mail: president@spfldlibmus.org; *Dir*, John Hamilton; E-Mail: jhamilton@spfldlibmus.org; *Head Librn*, Margaret Humberston; Tel: 413-263-6800, Ext 311, E-Mail: mhumberston@spfldlibmus.org; *Pub Relations*, Marianne Gambaro; Tel: 413-263-6800, Ext 314, E-Mail: mgambaro@spfldlibmus.org; Staff 4 (MLS 1, Non-MLS 3)
Founded 1876
Jul 1999-Jun 2000 Income $128,145, Locally Generated Income $6,970, Other $121,175. Mats Exp $19,210, Books $3,495, Per/Ser (Incl. Access Fees) $375, Presv $3,060, Other Print Mats $635. Sal $108,935 (Prof $98,965)
Library Holdings: Bk Vols 30,000; Bk Titles 24,000; Per Subs 50
Subject Interests: French Canadian studies, Genealogy, New Eng genealogy
Special Collections: Business & Personal Records of Connecticut Valley (1650-present)
Restriction: Not a lending library
Partic in Western Mass Regional Libr Servs
Friends of the Library Group

S SPRINGFIELD NEWSPAPERS LIBRARY, 1860 Main St, 01103. SAN 371-4357. Tel: 413-788-1018. FAX: 413-788-1301. *Dir*, James S Gleason; Tel: 413-788-1151, E-Mail: jgleason@union-news.com; *Librn*, Stephanie Willen Brown; Staff 5 (MLS 1, Non-MLS 4)
Library Holdings: Bk Titles 500; Per Subs 20
Special Collections: Merlin database of articles from 1988; Microfilm of paperbacks to 1824-no index; Springfield newspapers-1824 to present, database, microfilm
Database Vendor: Lexis-Nexis
Restriction: Company staff only, Not open to public
Function: Business archives

J SPRINGFIELD TECHNICAL COMMUNITY COLLEGE LIBRARY, One Armory Sq, 01101-9000. SAN 307-7012. Tel: 413-755-4845. Reference Tel: 413-755-4549. FAX: 413-733-8403. Web Site: library.stcc.mass.edu. *Dean of Libr*, Tamson M Ely; Tel: 413-755-4531, E-Mail: tely@mail.stcc.mass.edu; *Syst Coordr*, Eric Warren; Tel: 413-755-4555, E-Mail: ewarren@stcc.mass.edu; *Tech Servs*, Lynn Eaton; Tel: 413-755-4565, E-Mail: leaton@stcc.mass.edu; *Ref*, Barbara S Wurtzel; Tel: 413-755-4816, E-Mail: bwurtzel@stcc.mass.edu; *AV*, Lynn Kleindienst; Tel: 413-755-4541, E-Mail: lkliendienst@stcc.mass.edu; Staff 13 (MLS 5, Non-MLS 8)
Founded 1969. Enrl 3,924; Fac 358; Highest Degree: Associate
Jul 1999-Jun 2000 Income $889,177. Mats Exp $177,785, Books $64,257, Per/Ser (Incl. Access Fees) $74,039, Presv $438, Micro $10,101, AV Equip $11,916, Other Print Mats $260, Electronic Ref Mat (Incl. Access Fees) $16,774. Sal $484,397 (Prof $316,479)
Library Holdings: Bk Vols 67,989; Bk Titles 50,991; Per Subs 494
Subject Interests: Allied health, Dental hygiene, Medicine, Nursing, Technology
Automation Activity & Vendor Info: (OPAC) Innovative Interfaces Inc.
Database Vendor: Ebsco - EbscoHost, IAC - Info Trac, IAC - SearchBank, Lexis-Nexis, OCLC - First Search, Wilson - Wilson Web
Publications: Audio-visual Catalog; STCC Library Guide
Partic in CW Mars; Nelinet, Inc; OCLC Online Computer Library Center, Inc; Western Mass Regional Libr Servs; Western Massachusetts Health Information Consortium

G US NATIONAL PARK SERVICE SPRINGFIELD ARMORY SITE, Springfield Armory Site Library & Archives, One Armory Sq, 01105-1299. SAN 323-5955. Tel: 413-734-8551. FAX: 413-747-8062. E-Mail: sparinterpretation@nps.gov. Web Site: www.nps.gov/spar. *Archivist, Coll Develop*, Dru Bronson-Geoffroy Sal $30,805
Special Collections: Former Springfield Armory Workers Oral History Project (SA Historic Library Coll); Springfield Armory Archives
Special library containing Springfield Armory, SA historic library collection, archival material & related publications

WESTERN NEW ENGLAND COLLEGE
C D'AMOUR LIBRARY, 1215 Wilbraham Rd, 01119. SAN 345-648X. Tel: 413-782-1535. FAX: 413-796-2011. Web Site: www.libraries.wnec.edu. *Dir*, May E Stack; Tel: 413-782-1531, E-Mail: mstack@wnec.edu; *Acq*, Stephen Bobowicz; Tel: 413-782-1635, E-Mail: sbobowic@wnec.edu; *Circ*, Valerie Bolden-Marshall; Tel: 413-782-1510, E-Mail: vbolden@

wnec.edu; *Ser*, Daniel Eckert; Tel: 413-782-1654, E-Mail: deckert@wnec.edu; *Coll Develop*, Nancy Contois; Tel: 413-782-1514, E-Mail: ncontois@wnec.edu. Subject Specialists: *American history*, Daniel Eckert; *Business*, May E Stack; *Criminal justice*, Nancy Contois; *Education*, Nancy Contois; *English*, Stephen Bobowicz; *History*, May E Stack; *Physical science*, May E Stack; *Psychology*, Nancy Contois; *Sociology*, Stephen Bobowicz; *World history*, Daniel Eckert; Staff 11 (MLS 5, Non-MLS 6)
Founded 1983. Highest Degree: Master
Jul 1998-Jun 1999 Income Parent Institution $924,136. Mats Exp $783,675, Books $146,800, Per/Ser (Incl. Access Fees) $50,428, Micro $29,734, AV Equip $10,740, Electronic Ref Mat (Incl. Access Fees) $36,875. Sal $415,585 (Prof $263,713)
Library Holdings: Bk Vols 111,659; Bk Titles 93,570; Per Subs 183
Subject Interests: Arts, Business, Criminal justice, Education, Engineering, Sciences
Special Collections: SAEX Judaica Resource Center
Automation Activity & Vendor Info: (Cataloging) Innovative Interfaces Inc.
Database Vendor: Ebsco - EbscoHost, IAC - SearchBank, OCLC - First Search, ProQuest
Publications: Acquisitions Lists (monthly); AV List; BI Syllabus; Self-Help Guide; Subject Guide to Serials
Partic in Cooperating Libraries Of Greater Springfield

CL LAW LIBRARY, 1215 Wilbraham Rd, 01119-2693. SAN 345-651X. Tel: 413-782-1457. Reference Tel: 413-782-1458. FAX: 413-782-1745. Web Site: www.law.wnec.edu/library. *Dir*, Bonnie Koneski-White; Tel: 413-782-1456; *Coll Develop*, Katherine Lamothe; Tel: 413-782-1460; *Tech Servs*, Christine Archambault; Tel: 413-782-1474; *Ref*, Pat Newcombe; Tel: 413-782-1616; *Cat*, Nancy Johnson; Tel: 413-782-1309; *Reader Servs*, Michele Dill LaRose; Tel: 413-782-1484; *Electronic Resources*, Susan Drisko; Tel: 413-782-1459; Staff 7 (MLS 7)
Founded 1973. Enrl 517; Fac 27; Highest Degree: Doctorate
Jul 1999-Jun 2000 Income $1,556,097. Mats Exp $788,107, Books $72,285, Per/Ser (Incl. Access Fees) $649,195, Presv $7,159, Micro $51,683, Electronic Ref Mat (Incl. Access Fees) $7,785. Sal $631,543 (Prof $293,957)
Library Holdings: Bk Vols 366,378; Bk Titles 44,353; Per Subs 4,984
Subject Interests: Labor, Tax
Special Collections: Government Documents; Massachusetts Continuing Legal Education Material
Automation Activity & Vendor Info: (Acquisitions) Innovative Interfaces Inc.; (Cataloging) Innovative Interfaces Inc.; (Circulation) Innovative Interfaces Inc.; (Course Reserve) Innovative Interfaces Inc.; (OPAC) Innovative Interfaces Inc.; (Serials) Innovative Interfaces Inc.
Database Vendor: Innovative Interfaces INN - View
Publications: Cybercites; Readers Guide; Self Guided Tour; Slipped Opinions
Partic in Cooperating Libraries Of Greater Springfield; Nelinet, Inc; New England Law Library Consortium, Inc

STERLING

P CONANT PUBLIC LIBRARY,* 4 Meetinghouse Hill Rd, PO Box 428, 01564-0428. SAN 307-7039. Tel: 978-422-6409. FAX: 978-422-6643. E-Mail: contantpl@ultranet.com. *Dir*, Patrica Campbell; Staff 6 (MLS 3, Non-MLS 3)
Founded 1871. Pop 6,659
Library Holdings: Bk Titles 33,000; Per Subs 80
Publications: Sterling Business Directory (biennial); Sterling Factsheet: A Guide To Community Resources & Services (irregular)
Mem of Central Massachusetts Regional Library System
Friends of the Library Group

STOCKBRIDGE

G BERKSHIRE BOTANICAL GARDEN LIBRARY,* PO Box 826, 01262. SAN 373-174X. Tel: 413-298-3926. FAX: 413-298-4897. *Exec Dir*, John J Parker
Library Holdings: Bk Vols 125; Per Subs 12

S CHESTERWOOD MUSEUM LIBRARY,* 4 Williamsville Rd, Glendale Section, PO Box 827, 01262-0827. SAN 322-6603. Tel: 413-298-3579. TDD: 413-298-3579. FAX: 413-298-3973. *Archivist*, Wanda Magdeleine Styka
Founded 1973
Library Holdings: Bk Titles 6,000
Subject Interests: Am Renaissance, Am sculpture, Architecture, Conservation, Decorative arts, European sculpture, Hist of art, Historic preserv, Landscape architecture, Mus methodology, Sculpture of Daniel Chester French
Special Collections: Daniel Chester French Coll, bks, blueprints, correspondence, mss, memorabilia, papers, photogs; Henry Flagg French Coll, letters; Henry French Hollis (US Senator) Coll, diary "Europe in 1918"; Margaret French Cresson Coll, bks, correspondence, mss, papers, photogs; Mrs Daniel Chester French Coll, literary mss; William Penn Cresson Coll, bks, mss, photogs
Publications: Annual Exhibit Catalogs; Chesterwood: A Guidebook for Students (pamphlets); Chesterwood: A Guidebook for Teachers; The Chesterwood Pedestal (quarterly newsletter)
Special Services for the Deaf - TDD

S NORMAN ROCKWELL MUSEUM AT STOCKBRIDGE, Reference Department, PO Box 308, 01262. SAN 328-6177. Tel: 413-298-4100. FAX: 413-298-4145. Web Site: nrm.org. *Curator*, Pamela A Mendelsohn

M AUSTEN RIGGS CENTER, INC, Austen Fox Riggs Library,* 25 Main St, 01262. SAN 307-7047. Tel: 413-298-5511, Ext 259. FAX: 413-298-4020. E-Mail: arclib@bcn.net. *Librn*, Helen Linton
Founded 1935
Jan 1997-Dec 1998 Income $65,378. Mats Exp $31,905, Books $7,300, Per/Ser (Incl. Access Fees) $15,855. Sal $33,473 (Prof $33,473)
Library Holdings: Bk Vols 12,777; Bk Titles 10,463; Per Subs 85
Special Collections: general literature (David Rapaport Memorial Library); Psychology, psychoanalysis & related subjects
Restriction: Staff use only
Partic in BHSL; MAHSL; NEHSL; WMHIC; WMRLS

P STOCKBRIDGE LIBRARY ASSOCIATION, 46 Main St, PO Box 119, 01262. SAN 307-7055. Tel: 413-298-5501. FAX: 413-298-5501. *Librn*, Rosemary Schneyer; *Asst Librn*, Cheryl Tracy
Founded 1868. Pop 2,312; Circ 59,441
Library Holdings: Bk Titles 27,000; Per Subs 70
Special Collections: Historical Coll
Mem of Western Massachusetts Regional Library System

STONEHAM

P STONEHAM PUBLIC LIBRARY,* 431 Main St, 02180. SAN 307-7063. Tel: 781-438-1324. FAX: 781-279-3836. E-Mail: sto@noblenet.org. Web Site: www.noblenet.org/stoneham. *Dir*, Hugh E Williams Jr; *Asst Dir*, Mary P Todd; *Circ*, Deborah Cunningham; *Ch Servs*, Jennifer P Brown; *Cat*, Janice L Chase; *Ref*, Laurie Lucey; Staff 6 (MLS 6)
Founded 1859. Pop 22,203; Circ 115,000
Jul 1998-Jun 1999 Income $614,182, City $608,882, Other $5,300. Mats Exp $60,885, Books $53,140, Per/Ser (Incl. Access Fees) $6,252, Micro $1,493. Sal $416,992 (Prof $184,000)
Library Holdings: Bk Titles 80,592; Per Subs 226
Special Collections: 18th-20th century (Stoneham Coll), docs on micro
Automation Activity & Vendor Info: (Circulation) GEAC
Publications: Stoneham Public Library Film Catalog; Stoneham Public Library Serial Holdings (annually)
Partic in NE Mass Regional Libr Syst; North of Boston Library Exchange, Inc
Friends of the Library Group

STOUGHTON

M NEW ENGLAND SINAI HOSPITAL, Medical Library,* 150 York St, 02072. SAN 377-9181. Tel: 781-344-0600, Ext 172. FAX: 781-344-0128. *Librn*, Nancy Ling; E-Mail: nling@nesinai.org
Library Holdings: Bk Vols 600; Per Subs 100
Partic in Basic Health Sciences Library Network; Massachusetts Health Sciences Libraries Network; North Atlantic Health Sciences Libraries, Inc; Southeastern Massachusetts Consortium Of Health Science Libraries

P STOUGHTON PUBLIC LIBRARY, 84 Park St, PO Box 209, 02072-0209. SAN 345-6544. Tel: 781-344-2711. FAX: 781-344-7340. E-Mail: stlib@ocln.org. Web Site: www.stoughton.org/library/spl.html. *Dir*, Patricia Basler; *Asst Dir*, Diane Browne; *Ad Servs*, Anita Lehto; *Ch Servs*, Barbara Pally; *YA Servs*, Jacqueline Weber; Staff 5 (MLS 4, Non-MLS 1)
Founded 1874. Pop 26,777; Circ 188,723
Library Holdings: Bk Vols 98,100; Per Subs 207
Special Collections: Stoughton Coll
Publications: Stoughton Houses: 100 Years; Stoughton Public Library: 100 Years
Partic in Old Colony Libr Network

STOW

P RANDALL LIBRARY,* 19 Crescent St, 01775. SAN 307-7071. Tel: 978-897-8572. FAX: 978-897-7379. E-Mail: stow@mln.lib.ma.us. *Dir*, Susan C Wysk; *Asst Librn*, Claire Tozeski
Founded 1892. Pop 5,500; Circ 90,479 Sal $74,029 (Prof $39,947)
Library Holdings: Bk Vols 41,527
Subject Interests: Local history
Mem of Eastern Mass Regional Libr Syst
Partic in Minuteman Library Network
Friends of the Library Group

STURBRIDGE

P JOSHUA HYDE PUBLIC LIBRARY,* 306 Main St, 01566-1242. SAN 307-708X. Tel: 508-347-2512. FAX: 508-347-2872. Web Site: www.ultranet.com/~sturlib. *Librn*, Ellie Chesebrough; E-Mail: echesebr@cwmarsmail.cwmars.org; *Ch Servs*, Dawn Clarke
Founded 1896. Pop 8,000; Circ 99,000
Jul 1997-Jun 1998 Income $210,478. Mats Exp $49,079. Sal $137,936
Library Holdings: Bk Titles 32,647; Per Subs 108
Subject Interests: Local history
Automation Activity & Vendor Info: (Cataloging) Sagebrush Corporation; (Circulation) Sagebrush Corporation
Mem of Central Massachusetts Regional Library System
Friends of the Library Group

S OLD STURBRIDGE VILLAGE, Research Library,* One Old Sturbridge Village Rd, 01566. SAN 307-7098. Tel: 508-347-3362, Ext 232. FAX: 508-347-0295. Web Site: www.osv.org. *Dir*, Jack Larkin; E-Mail: jlarkin@osv.org; *Librn*, Colleen Couture; E-Mail: ccourture@osv.org; *Coll Develop*, Meg Haley; E-Mail: mhaley@osv.org; Staff 4 (MLS 3, Non-MLS 1)
Founded 1946
Library Holdings: Bk Vols 34,784; Per Subs 110
Subject Interests: Agriculture, Architecture, Arts and crafts, Education, Health, History, Law, Medicine, Music, New England
Special Collections: 19th & Early 20th Century Massachusetts Townscapes (Charles W Eddy Coll), glass plate negatives; Fine & Decorative Arts, Crafts &Textiles of Rural New England 1790-1840; Gravestone Rubbings; Historical Agriculture (Powell), bks, mss; Water Power Technology (Kinne Coll), trade cat; Wool Manufacture 1811-1845 (Merino-Dudley Wool Company Coll), mss
Restriction: Lending to staff only
Partic in RLIN
Friends of the Library Group

SUDBURY

P GOODNOW LIBRARY, 21 Concord Rd, 01776-2383. SAN 307-7101. Tel: 978-443-1035. FAX: 978-443-1047. E-Mail: goodnow@mln.lib.ma.us. Web Site: www.mml.lib.ma.us. *Dir*, William Talentino; *Ch Servs*, Betsy Mosher; Tel: 978-443-1037; *Cat*, Sheila Noah; *Circ*, Carolyn Anderson; *Ad Servs, Ref*, Anne Shirley; Staff 8 (MLS 6, Non-MLS 2)
Founded 1862. Pop 16,000; Circ 260,000
Jul 2000-Jun 2001 Income $758,000, State $18,000. Mats Exp $87,600, Books $72,000, Per/Ser (Incl. Access Fees) $7,800, AV Equip $4,800, Electronic Ref Mat (Incl. Access Fees) $3,000. Sal $420,000
Library Holdings: Bk Vols 80,000; Per Subs 130
Subject Interests: Genealogy, Local history
Automation Activity & Vendor Info: (Circulation) DRA
Partic in Minuteman Library Network
Special Services for the Deaf - Staff with knowledge of sign language
Friends of the Library Group

S RAYTHEON CO, Equipment Division Technical Information Center,* 528 Boston Post Rd, 01776-3375. SAN 307-711X. Tel: 978-440-2282. FAX: 978-440-4412. *Librn*, Robert Moore; Staff 1 (MLS 1)
Founded 1962
Library Holdings: Bk Titles 7,000; Per Subs 100
Subject Interests: Electronics
Publications: Union List of Book; Union List of Serials
Restriction: Staff use only
Partic in Bibliotech; Nasa Libraries Information System - Nasa Galaxie; Nelinet, Inc

SUNDERLAND

P GRAVES MEMORIAL LIBRARY, 111 N Main St, 01375. SAN 307-7136. Tel: 413-665-2642. FAX: 413-665-1435. *Dir*, Sharon A Bailey; E-Mail: bailey_sharon@hotmail.com; *Asst Librn*, Laura Williams; *Ch Servs*, Kelly Daniels; Staff 3 (MLS 1, Non-MLS 2)
Founded 1869. Pop 3,519; Circ 41,529
Jul 1999-Jun 2000 Income $96,957, State $6,699, City $77,166, Locally Generated Income $6,651, Other $6,441. Mats Exp $21,958, Books $15,362, Per/Ser (Incl. Access Fees) $1,801, AV Equip $4,722, Electronic Ref Mat (Incl. Access Fees) $73. Sal $48,167 (Prof $30,900)
Library Holdings: Bk Titles 15,879; Per Subs 68
Automation Activity & Vendor Info: (Cataloging) Innovative Interfaces Inc.; (Circulation) Innovative Interfaces Inc.; (OPAC) Innovative Interfaces Inc.
Database Vendor: IAC - SearchBank
Mem of Western Massachusetts Regional Library System
Friends of the Library Group

SUTTON

P SUTTON FREE PUBLIC LIBRARY,* 4 Uxbridge Rd, 01590. SAN 345-6609. Tel: 508-865-8752. FAX: 508-865-8752. E-Mail: suttonlib@ultranet.com. *Librn*, Joanne N Donnelly
Pop 6,790; Circ 35,111
Library Holdings: Bk Vols 25,000; Per Subs 37
Mem of Central Massachusetts Regional Library System
Friends of the Library Group
Branches: 1
MANCHAUG BRANCH, Main St, Manchaug, 01526. SAN 345-6633. Tel: 508-476-7036. *Librn*, Margaret Alger
Library Holdings: Bk Vols 14,500; Per Subs 12
Friends of the Library Group

SWAMPSCOTT

J MARIAN COURT COLLEGE, Lindsay Library, 35 Little's Point Rd, 01907-2896. SAN 370-5404. Tel: 781-595-6768. FAX: 781-595-3560.
Founded 1964. Enrl 185; Fac 20
Jul 1998-Jun 1999 Income $23,000. Mats Exp $14,385, Books $5,045, Per/Ser (Incl. Access Fees) $5,996, Micro $1,964. Sal $5,000
Library Holdings: Bk Vols 5,000; Bk Titles 4,396; Per Subs 121
Subject Interests: Archives
Automation Activity & Vendor Info: (Cataloging) Athena
Partic in Neccum; NMRLS

P SWAMPSCOTT PUBLIC LIBRARY, 61 Burrill St, 01907. SAN 307-7144. Tel: 781-596-8867. FAX: 781-596-8826. E-Mail: swa@noblenet.org. Web Site: www.nolenet.org/swampscott. *Dir*, Alyce Deveau; E-Mail: deveau@noblenet.org; *AV*, Barbara Wermuth; *Cat*, Marcia Harrison; *Ch Servs*, Beth Coughlin; *Ch Servs*, Israela Abrahams; *Ref*, Susan Zbinden Connor; *Ref*, Vicky Pratt; Staff 19 (MLS 5, Non-MLS 14)
Founded 1853. Pop 13,650; Circ 135,265
2000-2001 Mats Exp $99,300. Sal $318,701
Library Holdings: Bk Vols 81,254; Per Subs 100
Special Collections: Railroads & Model Railroads (Albert W Lalime Coll); Town History (Henry Sill Baldwin Coll)
Mem of Eastern Mass Regional Libr Syst
Partic in North of Boston Library Exchange, Inc
Friends of the Library Group

SWANSEA

P SWANSEA FREE PUBLIC LIBRARY,* 69 Main St, 02777. SAN 345-6668. Tel: 508-674-9609. FAX: 508-675-5444. *Dir*, J Kevin Lawton; *Ch Servs*, Frances Mazurak
Founded 1896. Pop 16,000; Circ 82,226
Library Holdings: Bk Titles 52,000; Per Subs 117
Subject Interests: Genealogy, History
Mem of Eastern Mass Regional Libr Syst
Friends of the Library Group
Branches: 1
SOUTH SWANSEA, 34 Maplewood Ave, 02777. SAN 345-6692. Tel: 508-679-8006. FAX: 508-675-9127. *In Charge*, Presephonie Bates
Library Holdings: Bk Vols 16,913
Friends of the Library Group

TAUNTON

GL BRISTOL LAW LIBRARY,* Superior Court House, 9 Court St, 02780. SAN 307-7152. Tel: 508-824-7632. FAX: 508-824-4723. E-Mail: brilaw@ma.ultranet.com. *Librn*, Meg Hayden
Founded 1858
Library Holdings: Bk Vols 28,000; Per Subs 24
Special Collections: Complete Massachusetts Laws, cases, regulations
Friends of the Library Group

M MORTON HOSPITAL & MEDICAL CENTER, INC, Medical Library, 88 Washington St, 02780-2499. SAN 377-9475. Tel: 508-828-7407. FAX: 508-824-6941. *Librn*, Patricia M Vigorito; E-Mail: pvigorito@mortonhospital.org; Staff 1 (MLS 1)
Library Holdings: Bk Vols 500; Per Subs 60
Special Collections: Clinical Medicine Coll
Database Vendor: IAC - Info Trac, OVID Technologies
Function: Research library
Partic in Massachusetts Health Sciences Libraries Network; SE Mass Health Sci Librs Consortium; SE Mass Regional Libr Syst

S OLD COLONY HISTORICAL SOCIETY, 66 Church Green, 02780. SAN 307-7160. Tel: 508-822-1622. *Dir*, Katheryn P Viens
Founded 1853
Library Holdings: Bk Titles 8,000
Subject Interests: Civil War, Genealogy, Local history
Special Collections: Original Manuscripts, Letters & Records
Publications: Library books & pamphlets

P TAUNTON PUBLIC LIBRARY, 12 Pleasant St, 02780. SAN 345-6722. Tel: 508-821-1410, 508-821-1412 (Children's Room). Reference Tel: 508-821-1413. TDD: 508-821-1418. FAX: 508-821-1414. E-Mail: cotlib01@tmlp.com. Web Site: www.tauntonlibrary.org. *Dir*, Susanne Costa Duquette; E-Mail: sduquett@sailsinc.org; *ILL*, Robyn Bryant; *Ad Servs, Ref*, Virginia Johnson; *Ref*, Darrel Ashcraft; *Ch Servs*, Daisy Delano; *Acq*, Carolyn Silva; *Acq*, Marguerite Jacinto; *Asst Librn, Cat*, Judith Sanderson; *Cat*, Joan Ross; *Ser*, Mary Moitoso; *Circ*, Helen Medeiros; *Circ*, Gail Coelho; Staff 19 (MLS 6, Non-MLS 13)
Founded 1866. Pop 50,962; Circ 180,511
Jul 1999-Jun 2000 Income $956,134, State $82,121, City $798,682, Parent Institution $53,000, Other $22,331. Mats Exp $152,615, Books $108,845, Per/Ser (Incl. Access Fees) $5,377, Presv $2,045, Micro $8,125, Electronic Ref Mat (Incl. Access Fees) $28,223. Sal $554,050
Library Holdings: Bk Vols 173,394; Per Subs 150
Subject Interests: American literature, Art and architecture, Genealogy, History, Local history, World War II
Special Collections: American-Portuguese Genealogical Coll; History of Taunton File Reference Coll; Literacy Center; Portuguese Coll; Young Adult Coll
Automation Activity & Vendor Info: (Acquisitions) SIRSI; (Cataloging) SIRSI; (Circulation) SIRSI; (Course Reserve) SIRSI; (ILL) SIRSI; (Media Booking) SIRSI; (OPAC) SIRSI
Publications: Monthly newsletter
Mem of SE Mass Regional Libr Syst
Partic in Sails, Inc; SE Mass Regional Libr Syst
Special Services for the Deaf - TDD
Location for city-wide literacy support as provided by Commonwealth Literacy Campaign; Location for American-Portuguese Genealogical & Historical Library
Friends of the Library Group

M TAUNTON STATE HOSPITAL, Medical Library,* 60 Hodges Ave, PO Box 4007, 02780. SAN 307-7179. Tel: 508-824-7551, Ext 300. FAX: 508-824-1050, Ext 221. *Librn*, Irene Fernandes
Founded 1948
Library Holdings: Bk Vols 909; Per Subs 78
Partic in SE Mass Health Sci Libs Consortium

TEMPLETON

P BOYNTON PUBLIC LIBRARY,* 27 Boynton Rd, PO Box 296, 01468-0296. SAN 345-6846. Tel: 978-939-5582. FAX: 978-939-8755. *Dir*, Jacqueline Prime
Pop 6,079
Library Holdings: Bk Vols 12,500; Per Subs 20
Mem of Central Massachusetts Regional Library System
Friends of the Library Group

TEWKSBURY

S RAYTHEON COMPANY, Raytheon Electronic Systems, Technical Information Center Library - T3MA13,* 50 Apple Hill Dr, 01876. SAN 307-1049. Tel: 978-858-4700. FAX: 978-858-4516.; Staff 3 (MLS 1, Non-MLS 2)
Founded 1952
Subject Interests: Electronics, Physics, Radar
Publications: Accessions list
Partic in Defense Technical Information Center; Dialog Corporation; OCLC Online Computer Library Center, Inc

P TEWKSBURY PUBLIC LIBRARY, 300 Chandler St, 01876. SAN 307-7195. Tel: 978-640-4490. FAX: 978-851-8609. *Dir, Librn*, Elisabeth Desmarais
Founded 1877. Pop 29,500; Circ 125,000
Jul 1999-Jun 2000 Income $824,830. Mats Exp $60,275, Micro $1,000. Sal $324,700
Library Holdings: Bk Vols 63,000; Per Subs 175
Mem of Northeast Mass Regional Libr Syst
Partic in Merrimack Valley Library Consortium
Friends of the Library Group

TOLLAND

P TOLLAND PUBLIC LIBRARY,* 22 Clubhouse Rd, 01034-9551. SAN 376-7108. Tel: 413-258-4201. E-Mail: tolland@cwmars.org. *Dir*, Jo-Ann Carl
Library Holdings: Bk Vols 7,000; Bk Titles 6,500
Mem of Western Massachusetts Regional Library System

TOPSFIELD

P TOPSFIELD TOWN LIBRARY, One S Common St, 01983-1496. SAN 307-7217. Tel: 978-887-1528. FAX: 978-887-0185. Web Site: www.topsfieldtownlibrary.org. *Dir*, Jaclyn Finocchio; E-Mail: jfinocchio@mrlc.lib.ma.us; *Ch Servs*, Jane Johnson; *Tech Servs*, Sibyl Hezlett; *Ad Servs*, Annette Stathopoulos; *Ref*, Wendy Thatcher; Staff 12 (MLS 2, Non-MLS 10)
Founded 1794. Pop 5,709; Circ 83,431
Jul 1999-Jun 2000 Income $415,402, State $10,833, Locally Generated Income $314,759, Other $89,810. Mats Exp $181,325, Books $73,015, Per/Ser (Incl. Access Fees) $54,673, Other Print Mats $49,137, Electronic Ref Mat (Incl. Access Fees) $4,500. Sal $220,015
Library Holdings: Bk Vols 53,000; Per Subs 134
Database Vendor: epixtech, inc.
Mem of Northeast Mass Regional Libr Syst
Partic in Merrimack Valley Library Consortium
Friends of the Library Group

TOWNSEND

P TOWNSEND PUBLIC LIBRARY, 276 Main St, PO Box 526, 01469. SAN 307-7225. Tel: 978-597-1714. FAX: 978-597-2779. E-Mail: tplhart@bicnet.net. Web Site: www.radio.bicnet.net/~tplhart. *Dir*, Heidi E Fowler; *Librn*, Catherine Hill; *Asst Librn*, Joanne Conlon; *Asst Librn*, Sky Randall; *Asst Librn*, Theresa Sawyer; *Ch Servs*, Sheila Brown; *Ch Servs*, Diane Eaton; Staff 6 (MLS 1, Non-MLS 5)
Founded 1929. Pop 9,041
Jul 1999-Jun 2000 Income (Main Library Only) $146,471. Sal $96,891
Library Holdings: Bk Vols 26,852; Per Subs 55
Subject Interests: Genealogy, Local history
Database Vendor: Innovative Interfaces INN - View
Mem of Central Massachusetts Regional Library System
Partic in Central-Western Mass Automated Resource Sharing
Friends of the Library Group

TURNERS FALLS

P MONTAGUE PUBLIC LIBRARIES, Carnegie Library-Main Branch,* 201 Avenue A, 01376-1989. SAN 307-7233. Tel: 413-863-3214. FAX: 413-863-3227. *Dir*, Susan A SanSoucie; E-Mail: ssansouc@cwmarsmail.cwmars.org; *Ch Servs*, Linda Hickman; Staff 7 (MLS 2, Non-MLS 5)
Jul 1997-Jun 1998 Income $179,648, City $179,648. Mats Exp $34,000, Books $29,900, Per/Ser (Incl. Access Fees) $2,100, Micro $2,000. Sal $117,945 (Prof $60,695)
Library Holdings: Bk Vols 16,000; Per Subs 100
Special Collections: Local History Materials
Mem of Western Regional Libr Syst
Branches: 2
MILLERS FALLS BRANCH, 11 Bridge St, Millers Falls, 01349. SAN 307-532X. Tel: 413-659-3801. *Librn*, Nancy Lapean
Pop 1,000; Circ 11,753
Library Holdings: Bk Titles 15,718
Special Collections: Early Town Histories, photogs
Friends of the Library Group
MONTAGUE CENTER BRANCH, 17 Center St, PO Box 157, Montague, 01351. SAN 307-5389. Tel: 413-367-2852. *Asst Librn*, Anna F Greene
Circ 9,870
Library Holdings: Bk Vols 16,412
Special Collections: Early Massachusetts Historical Information
Friends of the Library Group

TYNGSBORO

C BOSTON UNIVERSITY CORPORATE EDUCATION CENTER LIBRARY,* 72 Tyng Rd, 01879-2099. SAN 321-4516. Tel: 978-649-9731, Ext 277. FAX: 978-649-6926. *Librn*, Sherry Bailey; *Coordr*, Donna Gouldson; Staff 1 (MLS 1)
Founded 1979. Enrl 1,800; Fac 50; Highest Degree: Master
Library Holdings: Bk Vols 5,500; Bk Titles 4,300; Per Subs 150
Subject Interests: Computer science, Software engineering
Special Collections: Software Standards; Technical Reports
Partic in Nelinet, Inc; OCLC Online Computer Library Center, Inc

P TYNGSBOROUGH PUBLIC LIBRARY, 25 Bryant Lane, 01879-1003. SAN 307-7241. Tel: 978-649-7361. FAX: 978-649-2578. E-Mail: mty@mvlc.lib.ma.us. *Dir*, Carol Bacon; *Asst Dir*, Terri Ducharme
Founded 1878. Pop 10,300; Circ 76,000
Jul 1999-Jun 2000 Income $234,600, State $13,500, City $212,000, Locally Generated Income $3,100, Other $6,000. Mats Exp $57,000, Books $49,900, Per/Ser (Incl. Access Fees) $5,900, Electronic Ref Mat (Incl. Access Fees) $1,200. Sal $153,600 (Prof $70,500)
Library Holdings: Bk Vols 28,000; Bk Titles 27,500; Per Subs 200
Special Collections: Puppets
Automation Activity & Vendor Info: (Circulation) Sagebrush Corporation; (OPAC) Sagebrush Corporation
Partic in Merrimack Valley Library Consortium; NE Regional Libr Syst
Friends of the Library Group

TYRINGHAM

P TYRINGHAM FREE PUBLIC LIBRARY,* Main Rd, PO Box 440, 01264. SAN 307-725X. Tel: 413-243-1373. *Librn*, Amy Fennelly
Founded 1891. Circ 328
Library Holdings: Bk Vols 8,300
Mem of Western Regional Libr Syst

UPTON

P UPTON TOWN LIBRARY,* Main St, PO Box 1196, 01568. SAN 307-7276. Tel: 508-529-6272. FAX: 508-529-2453. Web Site: www.ultranet.com/~uptonlib. *Dir*, Deborah Hersh
Pop 3,884; Circ 24,000
Jul 1998-Jun 1999 Income $87,034, State $4,255, City $74,918, Locally Generated Income $7,861. Mats Exp $16,506, Books $13,820, Per/Ser (Incl. Access Fees) $2,650. Sal $56,918
Library Holdings: Bk Vols 18,800; Per Subs 101
Mem of Central Massachusetts Regional Library System
Friends of the Library Group

UXBRIDGE

P UXBRIDGE FREE PUBLIC LIBRARY, 15 N Main St, 01569-1822. SAN 307-7284. Tel: 508-278-8624. FAX: 508-278-8618. *Dir, Head Librn*, Susan J Stanovich; E-Mail: sstanovi@cwmarsmai/.cwmars.org; *Asst Librn, Ch Servs*, Debra J Young
Pop 10,804; Circ 77,173
Jul 1999-Jun 2000 Income $268,157. Mats Exp $47,377, Books $31,677, Per/Ser (Incl. Access Fees) $4,427, AV Equip $4,338, Electronic Ref Mat (Incl. Access Fees) $6,935. Sal $187,058
Library Holdings: Bk Vols 42,129; Bk Titles 40,023; Per Subs 76
Mem of Central Massachusetts Regional Library System
Friends of the Library Group

VINEYARD HAVEN

P VINEYARD HAVEN PUBLIC LIBRARY, 200 Main St, RFD 139 A, 02568-9710. SAN 375-3719. Tel: 508-696-4211. FAX: 508-696-7495. Web Site: www.vhlibrary.org. *Dir*, Marjorie P Convery; *Ch Servs*, Barbara Fehl; *Publ Servs*, Nina Mentzel; *Circ*, Wendy Andrews; Staff 7 (MLS 3, Non-MLS 4)
Founded 1878. Pop 10,000; Circ 127,000
1999-2000 Income $323,833, City $289,426, Other $34,407. Mats Exp $68,945, Books $46,432, Per/Ser (Incl. Access Fees) $10,563, AV Equip $10,900, Electronic Ref Mat (Incl. Access Fees) $1,050. Sal $185,973 (Prof $106,218)
Library Holdings: Bk Vols 31,554; Per Subs 150
Automation Activity & Vendor Info: (Acquisitions) DRA; (Cataloging) DRA; (Circulation) DRA; (Course Reserve) DRA; (ILL) DRA; (Media Booking) DRA; (OPAC) DRA; (Serials) DRA
Partic in Cape Libraries Automated Materials Sharing
Friends of the Library Group

WAKEFIELD

P LUCIUS BEEBE MEMORIAL LIBRARY,* 345 Main St, 01880-5093. SAN 345-6900. Tel: 781-246-6334. FAX: 781-246-6385. E-Mail: wakefieldlibrary@noblenet.org. Web Site: www.noblenet.org/wakefield. *Dir*, Sharon Gilley; E-Mail: gilley@noblenet.org; *Assoc Dir*, Charlotte Thompson; Tel: 781-246-6335, E-Mail: thompson@noblenet.org; *Circ*, Marie Field; E-Mail: field@noblenet.org; *Ch Servs*, Kimberlie Monteforte; E-Mail: montefor@noblenet.org; *Selection of Gen Ref Mat*, Jeffrey Klapes; E-Mail: klapes@nonblenet.org; *Tech Servs*, Rebecca Rohr; E-Mail: rohr@noblenet.org; *Ref Servs YA*, Tiffany Grossman; E-Mail: grossman@nonblenet.or; *Reader Servs*, Leane Ellis; E-Mail: ellis@noblenet.org; Staff 31 (MLS 14, Non-MLS 17)
Founded 1856. Pop 25,000; Circ 227,356
Jul 1998-Jun 1999 Income $919,235, State $24,973, City $848,286, Other $45,974. Mats Exp $120,000, Per/Ser (Incl. Access Fees) $10,000. Sal $626,293
Library Holdings: Bk Vols 103,362; Per Subs 231
Special Collections: Rifles, Riflery & Target Shooting (Keough Coll); Wakefield Authors
Automation Activity & Vendor Info: (Circulation) GEAC
Database Vendor: Ebsco - EbscoHost, IAC - SearchBank
Mem of Northeast Mass Regional Libr Syst
Partic in North of Boston Library Exchange, Inc
Open Mon-Thurs 9-9, Fri 9-6 & Sat 9-5 (during school year)
Friends of the Library Group

S METCALF & EDDY INC, Harry L Kinsel Library, PO Box 4071, 01880-5371. SAN 307-210X. Tel: 781-246-5200. FAX: 781-245-6293. *Librn*, Richard Mansfield; E-Mail: richard_mansfield@metcalfeddy.com
Founded 1908
Library Holdings: Bk Titles 8,000; Per Subs 60
Subject Interests: Environmental engineering
Publications: Library service brochure
Restriction: By appointment only

WALES

P WALES PUBLIC LIBRARY,* 77 Main St, 01081-0243. (Mail add: PO Box 243, 01081-0243), SAN 307-7322. Tel: 413-245-9072. E-Mail: wales@cwmars.org. *Dir*, Nancy Baer; *Librn*, Shelby Perry
Pop 1,700; Circ 6,805
Library Holdings: Bk Vols 9,000
Mem of Western Massachusetts Regional Library System
Open Mon & Wed 2-7, Sat 10-1
Friends of the Library Group

WALPOLE

P WALPOLE PUBLIC LIBRARY, Common St, 02081. SAN 345-6994. Tel: 508-660-7340. FAX: 508-660-2714. Web Site: www.walpole.ma.us. *Dir*, Jerry Romelczyk; E-Mail: jerryyr@walpole.ma.us; *Ad Servs, Tech Servs*, Norma Jean Cauldwell; *Ch Servs*, Carol Fitzpatrick; *Ch Servs*, Leslie Loomis; *Ref*, Warren Smith
Founded 1876. Pop 21,151; Circ 235,000
Library Holdings: Bk Vols 92,536; Per Subs 200
Mem of Eastern Mass Regional Libr Syst
Partic in Old Colony Libr Network
Friends of the Library Group

WALTHAM

R AMERICAN JEWISH HISTORICAL SOCIETY, Lee M Friedman Memorial Library, 2 Thornton Rd, 02453. SAN 307-7365. Tel: 781-891-8110. FAX: 781-899-9208. E-Mail: ajhs@ajhs.org. Web Site: www.ajhs.org. *Exec Dir*, Michael Feldberg; E-Mail: feldberg@ajhs.org; Staff 13 (MLS 7, Non-MLS 6)
Founded 1892
1999-1999 Income $1,500,000. Mats Exp $1,400,000
Library Holdings: Bk Vols 60,000; Per Subs 750
Subject Interests: Jewish history and literature
Special Collections: Eleanor & Morris Soble Coll of American Judaica; Rutenberg & Everett Yiddish Film Collection; The Sang Coll of American Judaica; Yiddish Sheet Music; Yiddish Theatre (Kanof-Pascher), posters
Publications: Artifacts & Daguerreotypes; Catalog of Collections of American Judaica; Catalog of Portraits; Newsletter; Quarterly Journal
Open 8:30-5

C BENTLEY COLLEGE, Solomon R Baker Library, 175 Forest St, 02452-4705. SAN 307-7381. Tel: 781-891-2231. FAX: 781-891-2830. Web Site: bnet.bentley.edu/dept/l:. *Dir*, Tjalda Nauta; *ILL*, Dylan Klempner; *Acq, Ser*, Enza Rapatano; *Cat*, Denise Cross; *Circ*, Catherine C Cronin; *Ref*, Sheila Ekman; *Bibliog Instr*, Lisa Scott; *Electronic Resources*, Stephen Tracey; Staff 16 (MLS 10, Non-MLS 6)
Founded 1917. Enrl 5,500; Fac 215; Highest Degree: Master
Jul 1998-Jun 1999 Mats Exp $326,660, Books $70,660, Per/Ser (Incl. Access Fees) $119,000, Electronic Ref Mat (Incl. Access Fees) $137,000. Sal $641,823
Library Holdings: Bk Vols 214,000; Bk Titles 197,000; Per Subs 917
Subject Interests: Accounting, Business and management, Economics, Finance
Special Collections: Accounting, 17th-19th Century (Rare Book); Business Histories
Automation Activity & Vendor Info: (Acquisitions) SIRSI; (Cataloging) SIRSI; (Circulation) SIRSI; (Course Reserve) SIRSI; (ILL) SIRSI; (Media Booking) SIRSI; (OPAC) SIRSI; (Serials) SIRSI
Partic in Dialog Corporation; Dow Jones News Retrieval; Nelinet, Inc; OCLC Online Computer Library Center, Inc
Special Services for the Deaf - Staff with knowledge of sign language

C BRANDEIS UNIVERSITY LIBRARIES, 415 South St, 02454-9110. (Mail add: PO Box 549110, Mailstop 045, 02454-9110), Tel: 781-736-4621. Interlibrary Loan Service Tel: 781-736-4676. Circulation Tel: 781-736-4624. Reference Tel: 781-736-4670. FAX: 781-736-4719. Web Site: www.library.brandeis.edu. *Dir*, Bessie King Hahn; Tel: 781-736-4700, E-Mail: bhahn@brandeis.edu; *Assoc Dir*, Robert Evensen; Tel: 781-736-4647, E-Mail: evensen@brandeis.edu; *Assoc Dir*, Ann Schaffner; Tel: 781-736-4720, E-Mail: schaffner@brandeis.edu; *Head Ref*, Ann Frenkel; Tel: 781-736-4679, E-Mail: frenkel@brandeis.edu; *Head, Circ*, Susan E Swanson; Tel: 781-736-4620, E-Mail: swanson@brandeis.edu; *Spec Coll & Archives*, Dr Charles Cutter; Tel: 781-736-4685, E-Mail: cutter@brandeis.edu; *Archivist*, Lisa C Long; Tel: 781-736-4701, E-Mail: lclong@brandeis.edu; *Info Tech*, Susan V Wawrzaszek; Tel: 781-736-4700, E-Mail: wawrzaszek@brandeis.edu; *Branch Mgr*, Jonathan Nabe; Tel: 781-736-4720, E-Mail: nabe@brandeis.edu; Staff 65 (MLS 26, Non-MLS 39)
Founded 1948. Fac 360; Highest Degree: Doctorate
Jul 1999-Jun 2000 Income (Main Library and Branch Library) $5,840,000.

Mats Exp $3,148,633, Books $1,120,201, Per/Ser (Incl. Access Fees) $1,393,703, Micro $86,347, Other Print Mats $2,253, Electronic Ref Mat (Incl. Access Fees) $546,129. Sal $2,096,263 (Prof $1,361,839)
Library Holdings: Bk Vols 1,100,000; Per Subs 16,119
Subject Interests: Judaica
Special Collections: Da Vinci; Hebraica & American Judaica; Shakespeare (Louis D Brandeis Coll)
Automation Activity & Vendor Info: (Acquisitions) EX Libris; (Cataloging) EX Libris; (Circulation) EX Libris; (OPAC) EX Libris; (Serials) EX Libris
Database Vendor: Dialog, Ebsco - EbscoHost, IAC - Info Trac, IAC - SearchBank, Lexis-Nexis, OCLC - First Search, OVID Technologies, ProQuest, Silverplatter Information Inc., Wilson - Wilson Web
Publications: Library Liaison (Newsletter)
Function: Research library
Partic in ARL; Boston Library Consortium; Center For Research Libraries; Metrowest Regional Libr Syst; Nelinet, Inc; OCLC Online Computer Library Center, Inc; Research Libraries Group, Inc; Scholarly Publ & Acad Resources Coalition
Friends of the Library Group
Departmental Libraries:
GERSTENZANG SCIENCE LIBRARY Tel: 781-736-4728. Interlibrary Loan Service Tel: 781-736-4676. FAX: 781-736-4723.

S CHARLES RIVER MUSEUM OF INDUSTRY LIBRARY, 154 Moody St, 02453. SAN 375-7102. Tel: 781-893-5410. FAX: 781-891-4536. E-Mail: charles_river@msn.com. Web Site: www.crmi.org. *Dir*, Karen M LeBlanc
Founded 1980
Library Holdings: Bk Titles 3,000

M DEACONESS WALTHAM HOSPITAL, Medical Library, Hope Ave, 02254. SAN 307-7519. Tel: 781-647-6261. FAX: 781-647-6018. *Librn*, Ellen Fulton
Library Holdings: Bk Titles 700; Per Subs 62
Subject Interests: Allied health, Clinical medicine, Nursing
Partic in Consortium For Information Resources
Open Mon-Fri 8-10, Wed Closed

S GENOME THERAPEUTICS CORP, Science Library,* 100 Beaver St, 02453. SAN 307-742X. Tel: 781-398-2366, www2.mid-pen.lib.mi.us/midpen/library/ontonagon/home.htm. FAX: 781-893-9535. E-Mail: monti@genomecorp.com. Web Site: www.gonome.com. *Librn*, Karen Monti
Founded 1964
Library Holdings: Bk Vols 40; Per Subs 100
Subject Interests: Biochemistry, Chemistry, Medicine

S GINER, INC LIBRARY,* 14 Spring St, 02451. SAN 323-407X. Tel: 781-899-7270. FAX: 781-894-2762. Web Site: www.ginerinc.com. *Librn*, Anne Bowman
Library Holdings: Bk Vols 1,300; Per Subs 12
Restriction: Not open to public

S GORE PLACE SOCIETY, INC LIBRARY,* 52 Gore St, 02154. SAN 327-3210. Tel: 781-894-2798. FAX: 781-894-5745. E-Mail: gpsinc@erols.com. Web Site: www.goreplace.org. *Dir*, Susan Robertson
Library Holdings: Bk Vols 2,000
Open Tues-Sat 11-5, Sun 1-5 (Apr 15-Nov 15), Nov 15-Apr 15 by appointment

G NATIONAL ARCHIVES & RECORDS ADMINISTRATION, Northeast Region (Boston), 380 Trapelo Rd, 02452-6399. SAN 329-188X. Tel: 781-647-8100. FAX: 781-647-8460. E-Mail: archives@waltham.nara.gov. Web Site: www.nar.gov/regional/boston.html. *Archivist*, Walter Hickey; *Archivist*, James K Owens; Tel: 781-647-1800; *Archivist*, William Read; *Archivist*, Erika Reece; *Archivist*, George Sermuksnis; *Archivist*, Cynthia Winterhalter; Staff 7 (MLS 3, Non-MLS 4)
Founded 1969
Subject Interests: Genealogy
Special Collections: Archival records of Federal agencies & courts in Connecticut, Maine, Massachusetts, New Hampshire, Rhode Island & Vermont
Publications: Guide to Records in the National Archives - New England Region (Washington, DC: National Archives & Records Administration, 1989); Microfilm Publications in the National Archives - New England Region (Washington, DC: National Archives & Records Administration, 1990); National Archives - New England Region (National Archives General Information Leaflet No 46, 1993); National Archives - New England Region, "Sources for Family History" (leaflet) 1993
Restriction: Non-circulating to the public, Reference only to non-staff

S CHARLES RIVER BROADCASTING CO, INC, WCRB Library,* 750 South St, PO Box 9173, 02453. SAN 326-2111. Tel: 781-893-7080, Ext 542. FAX: 781-893-0038.; Staff 4 (MLS 1, Non-MLS 3)
Special Collections: Boston Symphony/Boston Pops: Archival & Broadcast Tapes of Live Concerts (Symphony Hall, Boston & Tanglewood)
Restriction: Non-circulating to the public
Open Mon-Fri 10:30-4

S VERIZON INFORMATION RESEARCH NETWORK, (Formerly GTE Laboratories, Inc Library), 40 Sylvan Rd, 02254. SAN 307-7446. Tel: 781-466-2952, 781-466-2986. FAX: 781-890-5790. *Mgr*, Marcia Schemper-Carlock
Founded 1961
Library Holdings: Bk Vols 20,000; Per Subs 250
Subject Interests: Computer science, Optics, Telecommunications
Special Collections: Bellcore Docs; videotapes
Publications: GTE Union List of Serials
Partic in OCLC Online Computer Library Center, Inc
Open Mon-Fri 7:30-7

S WALTHAM MUSEUM INC LIBRARY,* 17 Noonan St, 02154. SAN 373-0689. Tel: 781-893-8017. *Dir*, Albert Arena
Library Holdings: Bk Vols 5,000
Open Sun 1-4:30

P WALTHAM PUBLIC LIBRARY,* 735 Main St, 02451. SAN 345-7230. Tel: 781-893-1750. FAX: 781-647-5873. E-Mail: walmail1@mln.lib.ma.us. Web Site: www.tiac.com/users/walthampl. *Dir*, Thomas N Jewell; *Asst Dir*, Tamara Chernow; *Circ*, Joyce E Israel; *Tech Servs*, Marcia M Luce; *Ch Servs*, Nancy Rea; *Ref*, Katherine A Tranquada
Founded 1865. Pop 57,090; Circ 530,065
Jul 1997-Jun 1998 Income $1,447,764, State $67,380, City $1,380,384. Mats Exp $201,040, Books $151,349, Per/Ser (Incl. Access Fees) $12,944. Sal $1,015,127 (Prof $457,295)
Library Holdings: Bk Vols 137,404; Per Subs 375
Mem of Eastern Mass Regional Libr Syst
Friends of the Library Group
Bookmobiles: 1

WARE

M MARY LANE HOSPITAL, The Community Health Information Center, 85 South St, 01082. SAN 377-9351. Tel: 413-967-2226. FAX: 413-967-2115. *Librn*, Janet Lussier; E-Mail: jlussier@library.bhs.org
Library Holdings: Bk Vols 400; Per Subs 85
Partic in Massachusetts Health Sciences Libraries Network; National Network Of Libraries Of Medicine - South Central Region; North Atlantic Health Sciences Libraries, Inc; Western Mass Health Info Consortium

P YOUNG MEN'S LIBRARY ASSOCIATION, 37 Main St, 01082-1317. SAN 307-7535. Tel: 413-967-5491. FAX: 413-967-5491. *Librn*, Mary Ann DeSantis; E-Mail: madesant@cwmars.org; *Ch Servs*, Laurel Sullivan; Staff 4 (Non-MLS 4)
Founded 1872. Pop 9,817; Circ 46,188
Jul 1999-Jun 2000 Income $185,168, State $10,833, City $128,521, Locally Generated Income $1,913. Mats Exp $34,687. Sal $90,435
Subject Interests: Local history
Automation Activity & Vendor Info: (Cataloging) Innovative Interfaces Inc.; (Circulation) Innovative Interfaces Inc.
Database Vendor: IAC - SearchBank
Mem of C/W Mars; Western Massachusetts Regional Library System

WAREHAM

S TOBEY HOSPITAL, Stillman Library, 43 High St, 02571. SAN 328-6150. Tel: 508-273-4037. FAX: 508-295-0910. *Librn*, Joan Boyer; E-Mail: boyerj@southcoast.org
Library Holdings: Bk Titles 300; Per Subs 40
Subject Interests: Health, Medical

P WAREHAM FREE LIBRARY,* 59 Marion Rd, 02571. SAN 307-7543. Tel: 508-295-2343. FAX: 508-295-2678. *Dir*, Mary Jane Pillsbury; *Ref*, Susan Pizzolato; *Ch Servs*, Adelaide Gardner; *Ad Servs*, Virginia Murphy; Staff 7 (MLS 5, Non-MLS 2)
Founded 1891. Pop 20,340; Circ 175,000
Jul 1999-Jun 2000 Income $626,189, State $20,556, City $560,633, Locally Generated Income $40,000, Other $5,000. Mats Exp $173,379, Books $97,351, Per/Ser (Incl. Access Fees) $3,400, Micro $500, Electronic Ref Mat (Incl. Access Fees) $3,338. Sal $342,508
Library Holdings: Bk Titles 75,000; Per Subs 108
Special Collections: Wareham Coll
Automation Activity & Vendor Info: (Acquisitions) epixtech, inc.; (Cataloging) epixtech, inc.; (Circulation) epixtech, inc.; (ILL) epixtech, inc.; (OPAC) epixtech, inc.; (Serials) epixtech, inc.
Database Vendor: epixtech, inc.
Mem of Eastern Mass Regional Libr Syst
Partic in SE Automated Librs, Inc
Friends of the Library Group

WARREN

P WARREN PUBLIC LIBRARY,* 934 Main St, 01083-0937. SAN 307-7551. Tel: 413-436-7690. FAX: 413-436-7690. *Librn*, Sylvia G Buck; E-Mail: sbuck@cwmarsmail.cwmars.org; *Asst Librn*, Joanne R Wilson
Founded 1879. Pop 4,500; Circ 24,159

Jul 1998-Jun 1999 Income $84,420, State $3,448, City $73,600, Locally Generated Income $2,755, Other $4,617. Mats Exp $19,247, Books $13,896, Per/Ser (Incl. Access Fees) $1,010, Electronic Ref Mat (Incl. Access Fees) $2,125. Sal $48,796
Library Holdings: Bk Vols 18,318; Per Subs 25; Bks on Deafness & Sign Lang 19
Subject Interests: Genealogy, Local history
Mem of Central Massachusetts Regional Library System
Friends of the Library Group

WARWICK

P WARWICK FREE PUBLIC LIBRARY,* 4 Hotel Rd, 01378-9311. SAN 307-6059. Tel: 978-544-7866. E-Mail: warwick@cwmars.org. *Dir*, Nancy Hickler
Founded 1870. Pop 680
Library Holdings: Bk Titles 8,000; Per Subs 10
Mem of Western Massachusetts Regional Library System
Open Tues 1-8, Thurs 5-8

WATERTOWN

S ARMENIAN LIBRARY & MUSEUM OF AMERICA,* 65 Main St, 02172. SAN 325-8963. Tel: 617-926-2562. FAX: 617-926-0175. *Curator*, Gary Lind-Sinanian; *Exec Dir*, Mary Ellen Margosian
Library Holdings: Bk Vols 12,000
Special Collections: Early Armenian Printings (1514-1700 AD)
Friends of the Library Group

S BACON INDUSTRIES, INC LIBRARY,* 192 Pleasant St, 02472. SAN 370-3894. Tel: 617-926-2550. FAX: 617-926-2022. *In Charge*, Margaret Keating
Library Holdings: Bk Titles 250; Per Subs 20
Restriction: Not open to public

S IONICS, INC, Research Department Library,* 65 Grove St, 02472. SAN 307-756X. Tel: 617-926-2500. FAX: 617-926-9277. *Librn*, Cathy Zarenba
Library Holdings: Bk Vols 1,000; Per Subs 50
Subject Interests: Chemistry, Water treatment
Partic in Dialog Corporation

P PERKINS SCHOOL FOR THE BLIND, (BTBL), Braille & Talking Book Library, 175 N Beacon St, 02472. SAN 345-732X. Tel: 617-972-7240. Reference Tel: 617-972-7245. Toll Free Tel: 800-852-3133. FAX: 617-972-7363. Web Site: www.perkins.pvt.k12.ma.us/btbl.htm. *Dir*, Patricia A Kirk; *Asst Dir*, Kim L Charlson; Staff 28 (MLS 8, Non-MLS 20)
Founded 1829. Pop 16,179; Circ 459,276
Special Collections: Foreign Language, cassettes; French, German, Italian, Polish, Portuguese & Massachusetts, cassettes; Reference material on blindness & other physical handicaps
Publications: Dots & Decibels (newsletter)
Partic in National Library Service For The Blind & Physically Handicapped, Library Of Congress
Open Mon-Fri 8:30-5
Friends of the Library Group
Branches: 3
INSTRUCTIONAL MATERIALS CENTER, 175 N Beacon St, 02472. Tel: 617-972-7291. FAX: 617-926-2027. *Librn*, Shelley Patterson
SAMUEL P HAYES RESEARCH LIBRARY, 175 N Beacon St, 02472. Tel: 617-972-7250. FAX: 617-923-8076. Web Site: www.perkins.pvt.k12.ma.us/research.htm.
Library Holdings: Bk Titles 20,000
Subject Interests: Blindness, Deaf
Special Collections: Historic Coll of Material on Hellen Keller & Anne Sullivan; Postage Stamps Relating to Blindness
SCHOOL LIBRARY, 175 N Beacon St, 02472. Tel: 617-972-7236. FAX: 617-926-2027. Web Site: www.perkins.pvt.k12.ma.us/seconder.htm.
Subject Interests: Children's literature
Special Collections: Audio Cassettes, Large Print, Talking Books

S PROJECT SAVE ARMENIAN PHOTOGRAPH ARCHIVES, 65 Main St, 02472-4400. (Mail add: PO Box 236, 02471-0236), Tel: 617-923-4542, 617-923-4563. FAX: 617-924-0434. E-Mail: archives@projectsave.org. *Exec Dir*, Ruth Thomasian; *Archivist*, Elizabeth Lee Balcom; Staff 4 (MLS 1, Non-MLS 3)
Founded 1975
Library Holdings: Bk Titles 1,000
Subject Interests: Armenian
Restriction: Non-circulating to the public
Function: Archival collection
Project SAVE is an Armenian ethnic photograph archives

S SASAKI ASSOCIATES, INC LIBRARY, 64 Pleasant St, 02172. SAN 307-7578. Tel: 617-926-3300. FAX: 617-924-2748. *Librn*, Heather Magner; E-Mail: h.magner@sasaki.com
Library Holdings: Bk Vols 5,000; Per Subs 150
Subject Interests: Architecture, Landscape architecture, Planning
Special Collections: Company archives
Publications: Newsletter (bi-monthly)

P WATERTOWN FREE PUBLIC LIBRARY,* 123 Main St, 02472. SAN 345-7508. Tel: 617-972-6431. FAX: 617-924-5471. E-Mail: watmail1@mln.lib.ma.us. Web Site: www.watertownlib.org. *Dir*, Leone Cole; *Asst Dir*, Lois Neve; *Ad Servs*, Beverly Shank; *Ch Servs*, Elaine Granche; *YA Servs*, Carey Conkey; *Tech Servs*, Forrest Mack; Staff 17 (MLS 17)
Founded 1868. Pop 33,284; Circ 220,606
Library Holdings: Bk Vols 146,423; Per Subs 346
Subject Interests: Art and architecture, Genealogy, Local history
Special Collections: Armenian Materials (in English & Armenian); Art of 19th Century Watertown women artists
Automation Activity & Vendor Info: (Circulation) CLSI LIBS
Publications: Childcare: A Resource Handbook; Crossroads on the Charles; Get Set, Get Ready, Go Metric; Talking for Keeps (oral history handbook).; To Your Health; Walking Tour of Historic Watertown; Watertown's Victorian Legacy; Where the Action Is
Mem of Eastern Mass Regional Libr Syst
Special Services for the Deaf - Special interest periodicals; Staff with knowledge of sign language
Open Mon-Wed 9-9, Thurs 1-9, Fri & Sat 9-5
Friends of the Library Group
Branches: 2
EAST, 481 Mount Auburn St, 02472. SAN 345-7532. Tel: 617-972-6441. E-Mail: wt1circ@mln.lib.ma.us. *Librn*, Eloise M Lyman; *Ch Servs*, Kathy Caple
Library Holdings: Bk Vols 19,500
Special Collections: Armenian books & phonorecords
NORTH BRANCH, 265 Orchard St, 02472. SAN 345-7567. Tel: 617-972-6442. E-Mail: wt2circ@mln.lib.ma.us. Web Site: www.watertownlib.org. *Asst Dir*, Lois C Neve; Tel: 617-972-6438, Fax: 617-926-4375, E-Mail: watmgr@min.lib.ma.us; *Branch Mgr*, Eloise M Lyman; *Librn*, Maureen Hartman; Staff 2 (MLS 2)
Founded 1921. Circ 16,534
Library Holdings: Bk Vols 14,580; Per Subs 31
Special Collections: Children's CD ROMS
Database Vendor: DRA, GaleNet, IAC - Info Trac, OCLC - First Search
Partic in Minuteman Library Network
Special Services for the Blind - Bks on tape; Large print bks

WAYLAND

P WAYLAND FREE PUBLIC LIBRARY, 5 Concord Rd, 01778. SAN 345-7621. Tel: 508-358-2311. FAX: 508-358-5249. *Dir*, Louise R Brown; E-Mail: lbrown@mln.lib.ma.us; *Asst Dir*, Ann Knight; E-Mail: aknight@mln.lib.ma.us; *Ch Servs*, Deborah Kelsey; Tel: 508-358-2308, E-Mail: dkelsey@mln.lib.ma.us; *Ch Servs*, Pamela Sway; E-Mail: psway@mln.lib.ma.us; *Circ*, Margaret Harper; Tel: 508-358-2311, E-Mail: mharper@mln.lib.ma.us; *Per*, Marian Amare; Staff 12 (MLS 4, Non-MLS 8)
Founded 1848. Pop 13,400; Circ 220,488
Jul 1999-Jun 2000 Income $670,452, State $19,883, Locally Generated Income $623,054, Other $27,515. Mats Exp $128,769, Books $83,287, Per/Ser (Incl. Access Fees) $12,512, Micro $4,389, AV Equip $21,758, Electronic Ref Mat (Incl. Access Fees) $2,765. Sal $459,387 (Prof $170,000)
Library Holdings: Bk Vols 853; Bk Titles 78,771; Per Subs 237
Subject Interests: Gardening
Special Collections: Wayland Local History
Database Vendor: CARL, DRA, GaleNet, IAC - Info Trac, IAC - SearchBank, OCLC - First Search
Publications: Wayland Public Library Update (monthly newsletter)
Partic in Minuteman Library Network
Friends of the Library Group

WEBSTER

P CHESTER C CORBIN PUBLIC LIBRARY, Webster Public Library, 2 Lake St, 01570-2699. SAN 307-7594. Tel: 508-949-3880. FAX: 508-949-0537. *Dir*, Daniel Lekas; *Asst Librn*, Rose Foley; *Ch Servs*, Dorothy Morse
Founded 1889. Pop 15,090; Circ 72,852
Library Holdings: Bk Vols 45,482; Per Subs 69
Subject Interests: Genealogy
Mem of Central Massachusetts Regional Library System
Partic in CW Mars
Open Mon, Tues & Thurs 9-8, Wed 9-1, Fri 9-5, Sat 9-2
Friends of the Library Group

WELLESLEY

S CARR RESEARCH LABORATORY, INC LIBRARY, 17 Waban St, 02482. SAN 371-5248. Tel: 508-651-7027. FAX: 508-647-4737. E-Mail: carr@carr-research-lab.com. *Pres*, Jerome B Carr
Jan 1999-Dec 1999 Mats Exp $13,000, Books $10,000, Per/Ser (Incl. Access

Fees) $3,000
Library Holdings: Bk Titles 4,000; Per Subs 35
Subject Interests: Ecology, Geology, Geophysics, Hydrology, Oceanography, Wetlands
Restriction: Company library

J MASSACHUSETTS BAY COMMUNITY COLLEGE, Perkins Library, 50 Oakland St, 02481. SAN 307-7616. Tel: 617-239-2610. FAX: 617-239-3621. Web Site: www.mbcc.mass.edu/mbcc/lib/lib.html. *Dir*, Catherine Lee; *Bibliog Instr*, Linda Ann Stern; Tel: 781-239-2617, E-Mail: sternlin@mbcc.mass.edu; *Per, Ref*, Kathleen Duggan; Staff 6 (MLS 3, Non-MLS 3)
Founded 1961. Enrl 3,909; Fac 130
Library Holdings: Bk Vols 47,000; Bk Titles 39,700; Per Subs 400
Subject Interests: Allied health
Partic in Nelinet, Inc
Departmental Libraries:
FRAMINGHAM CAMPUS - MBCC, 19 Flagg Dr, Framingham, 01701. SAN 373-2916. Tel: 508-270-4212. Web Site: www.mbcc.mass.edu/mbcc/lib/lib.html. *Asst Dir*, Rene Mandel; Tel: 508-270-4215; Staff 3 (MLS 1, Non-MLS 2)

C WELLESLEY COLLEGE, Margaret Clapp Library, 106 Central St, 02481-8275. SAN 345-7680. Tel: 781-283-2096. Circulation Tel: 781-283-3753. Reference Tel: 781-283-2097. FAX: 781-283-3690. Web Site: www.luna.wellesley.edu, www.wellesley.edu. *Info Res, Librn*, Micheline Jedrey; Tel: 781-283-2095, Fax: 781-283-3640, E-Mail: mjedrey@wellesley.edu; *Bibliog Instr, ILL, Ref*, Joan Campbell; *Bibliog Instr, ILL, Ref*, Sally Linden; *Coll Develop*, Eileen Hardy; *Spec Coll*, Ruth Rogers; *Archivist*, Wilma Slaight; *Doc*, Claire Loranz; *Acq*, Ross Wood; Staff 38 (MLS 14, Non-MLS 24)
Founded 1875. Enrl 2,271; Fac 226; Highest Degree: Bachelor
Jul 1999-Jun 2000 Income (Main Library and Branch Library) $4,848,560. Mats Exp $1,655,533, Books $569,632, Per/Ser (Incl. Access Fees) $955,630, Presv $86,406, Micro $43,865. Sal $1,597,139 (Prof $970,110)
Library Holdings: Bk Vols 765,530; Per Subs 2,577
Special Collections: Book Arts; First & Rare Editions of English & American Poetry; Italian Renaissance (Plimpton Coll), bks & mss; Ruskin; Slavery (Elbert Coll)
Automation Activity & Vendor Info: (Acquisitions) Innovative Interfaces Inc.; (Circulation) Innovative Interfaces Inc.; (Serials) Innovative Interfaces Inc.
Database Vendor: Dialog, epixtech, inc., Lexis-Nexis, OCLC - First Search
Partic in Boston Library Consortium; New England Libr Info Network; OCLC Online Computer Library Center, Inc
Friends of the Library Group
Departmental Libraries:
ART LIBRARY, Jewett Arts Ctr, 02481. SAN 345-7699. Tel: 781-283-2049. Web Site: www.luna.wellesley.edu.
Friends of the Library Group
MUSIC LIBRARY, 106 Central St, 02481-8203. SAN 345-7702. Tel: 781-283-2075. FAX: 781-283-3687. Web Site: www.luna.wellesley.edu.
Friends of the Library Group
SCIENCE LIBRARY, Science Ctr, 106 Central St, 02481. SAN 345-7710. Tel: 781-283-3084. FAX: 781-283-3642. Web Site: www.luna.wellesley.edu. *Librn*, Irene Laursen
Library Holdings: Bk Vols 105,000; Per Subs 625
Friends of the Library Group

C WELLESLEY COLLEGE, Center for Research on Women, Cheever House, 106 Central St, 02481. SAN 374-9886. Tel: 781-283-2500. FAX: 781-283-2504. Web Site: www.wellesley.edu/WCW. *Exec Dir*, Susan McGee Bailey
Library Holdings: Bk Vols 1,000
Restriction: Open to public for reference only

P WELLESLEY FREE LIBRARY, 530 Washington St, 02482. SAN 345-7745. Tel: 781-235-1610. Reference Tel: 781-235-1610, Ext 116. TDD: 781-239-1464. E-Mail: wellesley@min.lib.ma.us. Web Site: www.ci.wellesley.ma.us/library. *Dir*, Janice G Bures; Tel: 781-235-1610, Ext 129, E-Mail: jbures@ci.wellesley.ma.us; *Assoc Dir*, David M Hinkley; Tel: 781-235-1610, Ext 107; *Asst Dir*, Helen Macarof; Tel: 781-235-1610, Ext 130; *Asst Dir*, Merrily Sparling; Tel: 781-235-1610, Ext 107; *Br Coordr*, Josh Olshin; *Automation Syst Coordr*, Mary Rose Quinn; *Ch Servs*, Mary Dalton; Tel: 781-235-1610, Ext 109; *Head Tech Servs*, Mary Stevens; Tel: 781-235-1610, Ext 124; *Acq*, Elaine Schicitano; *ILL*, Sue Kaler; Tel: 781-235-1610, Ext 112; *Per*, Tyson Bolles; Tel: 781-235-1610, Ext 214; *Head, Circ*, Lawrence Maguire; Tel: 781-235-1610, Ext 105; *AV*, Debra Berenbaum; Tel: 781-235-1610, Ext 214; *YA Servs*, Phyllis Wiggin; *Head Ref*, Mary Durda; Tel: 781-235-1610, Ext 110; Staff 66 (MLS 16, Non-MLS 50)
Founded 1881. Pop 26,615; Circ 435,284
Jul 1999-Jun 2000 Income (Main Library and Branch Library) $2,103,976, State $480,749, City $1,623,227. Mats Exp $199,157, Books $168,334, Per/Ser (Incl. Access Fees) $18,028, Micro $11,140. Sal $1,257,467
Library Holdings: Bk Titles 322,692; Per Subs 450
Special Collections: Business
Automation Activity & Vendor Info: (Acquisitions) DRA; (Cataloging) DRA; (Circulation) DRA
Database Vendor: DRA, IAC - Info Trac, OCLC - First Search, ProQuest
Function: Reference services available
Partic in Minuteman Library Network
Special Services for the Deaf - TTY machine
Friends of the Library Group
Branches: 2
FELLS, 308 Weston Rd, 02482. SAN 345-777X. Tel: 781-237-0485. *Dir*, Janice G Bures; Tel: 781-235-1610, Ext 129, Fax: 781-235-0495, E-Mail: jbures@ci.wellesley.ma.us; *Librn*, Janet Drake; *Branch Mgr*, Josh Olshin; Staff 5 (MLS 1, Non-MLS 4)
Founded 1923
Library Holdings: Bk Vols 8,537
Database Vendor: Ebsco - EbscoHost
Partic in Minuteman Library Network
WELLESLEY HILLS BRANCH, 210 Washington St, Wellesley Hills, 02481. SAN 345-780X. Tel: 781-237-0381. *Dir*, Janice G Bures; Tel: 781-235-1610, Ext 129, Fax: 781-235-0495, E-Mail: jbures@ci.wellesley.ma.us; *Branch Mgr*, Josh Olshin; Staff 5 (MLS 1, Non-MLS 4)
Founded 1923
Library Holdings: Bk Vols 15,388
Database Vendor: Ebsco - EbscoHost
Partic in Minuteman Library Network

WELLESLEY HILLS

R FIRST CONGREGATIONAL CHURCH IN WELLESLEY HILLS LIBRARY, 207 Washington St, 02481-3105. SAN 307-7632. Tel: 781-235-4424. FAX: 781-235-9838. *Librn*, Dr Lorraine E Tolman
Founded 1956
Library Holdings: Bk Vols 4,135
Subject Interests: Religion
Special Collections: Children Coll

S SUN LIFE ASSURANCE COMPANY OF CANADA, Reference Library, One Sun Life Executive Park, 02481. SAN 307-7640. Tel: 781-431-4926. Interlibrary Loan Service Tel: 781-431-4927. Toll Free Tel: 800-786-5433. FAX: 781-237-1398. *Librn*, Pamela Ann Mahaney; *Asst Librn*, Angela McKay; Staff 3 (MLS 1, Non-MLS 2)
Founded 1973
1998-1999 Mats Exp $96,500, Books $15,000, Per/Ser (Incl. Access Fees) $18,500. Sal $120,912 (Prof $92,000)
Library Holdings: Bk Vols 15,000; Per Subs 850
Subject Interests: Accounting, Economics, Law, Real estate
Special Collections: Insurance Codes for all States; Life Insurance Marketing & Research Association Coll
Publications: Book News; Library News Service (daily); Limra Accessions List; selected articles of interest; Subject Alert
Partic in Nelinet, Inc

WELLFLEET

S US NATIONAL PARK SERVICE CAPE COD NATIONAL SEASHORE LIBRARY, 99 Marconi Site Rd, 02667. SAN 370-3061. Tel: 508-349-3785. FAX: 508-349-9052.
Library Holdings: Bk Titles 2,225; Per Subs 35

P WELLFLEET PUBLIC LIBRARY, 55 W Main St, 02667. SAN 307-7659. Tel: 508-349-0310, 508-349-0311. FAX: 508-349-0312. Web Site: www.capecod.net/~wlibrary3. *Librn*, Elaine R McIlroy; E-Mail: emcilroy@clams.lib.ma.us; Staff 6 (MLS 1, Non-MLS 5)
Founded 1893. Pop 2,500; Circ 89,000
Jul 1999-Jun 2000 Income $215,404, State $5,822, City $196,098, Other $13,484. Mats Exp $70,119, Books $38,902, Per/Ser (Incl. Access Fees) $5,378, AV Equip $6,664, Electronic Ref Mat (Incl. Access Fees) $19,175. Sal $135,398 (Prof $43,000)
Library Holdings: Bk Vols 40,000; Per Subs 100
Subject Interests: Art
Special Collections: Cape Cod Coll, Local Hist Coll, videos
Mem of SE Mass Regional Libr Syst
Friends of the Library Group

WENDELL

P WENDELL FREE LIBRARY,* 2 Lockesvillage Rd, PO Box 236, 01379-9701. SAN 307-7667. Tel: 978-544-3559. FAX: 978-544-7467. E-Mail: wendell@cumars.org. *Dir*, Rosemary Heidkamp
Jul 1998-Jun 1999 Income $15,000, State $1,700, City $13,300. Mats Exp $3,000. Sal $8,000
Library Holdings: Bk Vols 10,000; Bk Titles 8,000; Per Subs 40
Mem of Western Regional Libr Syst

WENHAM

C GORDON COLLEGE, Jenks Learning Resource Center, 255 Grapevine Rd, 01984-1899. SAN 307-7675. Tel: 978-927-2306, Ext 4339. Interlibrary Loan Service Tel: 978-927-2306, Ext 4416. Circulation Tel: 978-927-2306, Ext

4342. Reference Tel: 978-927-2306, Ext 4342. FAX: 978-524-3725. E-Mail: hope@gordon.edu. Web Site: www.noblenet.org. *Coll Develop, Dir*, John Beauregard; Tel: 978-927-2306, Ext 4140, E-Mail: beauregard@hope.gordon.edu; *Circ, Ref*, Randall Gowman; E-Mail: gowman@hope.gordon.edu; *ILL*, Martha Crain; E-Mail: crain@hope.gordon.edu; *Per*, Janet Bjork; Tel: 978-927-2306, Ext 4345, E-Mail: jbjork@hope.gordon.edu; *Tech Servs*, Shui-Keung Alec Li; Staff 4 (MLS 4)
Founded 1889. Enrl 1,500; Fac 86; Highest Degree: Master
Jul 1999-Jun 2000 Income Parent Institution $641,866. Mats Exp $175,337, Books $78,837, Per/Ser (Incl. Access Fees) $62,300, Presv $6,600, Electronic Ref Mat (Incl. Access Fees) $27,600. Sal $413,466
Library Holdings: Bk Vols 177,067; Per Subs 563
Subject Interests: Education, Fine arts, Humanities, Natural science, Social sciences and issues
Special Collections: American Linguistics; Bibles; Global Circumnavigation; Northwest Exploration; Shakespeare (Vining Coll)
Automation Activity & Vendor Info: (Acquisitions) Innovative Interfaces Inc.; (Cataloging) Innovative Interfaces Inc.; (Circulation) Innovative Interfaces Inc.; (Course Reserve) Innovative Interfaces Inc.; (ILL) Innovative Interfaces Inc.; (Media Booking) Innovative Interfaces Inc.; (OPAC) Innovative Interfaces Inc.; (Serials) Innovative Interfaces Inc.
Database Vendor: CARL, Dialog, Ebsco - EbscoHost, IAC - Info Trac, IAC - SearchBank, Lexis-Nexis
Function: ILL available, Reference services available
Partic in Dialog Corporation; Nelinet, Inc; North of Boston Library Exchange, Inc; OCLC Online Computer Library Center, Inc

S WENHAM MUSEUM, Col Timothy Pickering Library, 132 Main St, 01984. SAN 307-7683. Tel: 978-468-2377. FAX: 978-468-1763. E-Mail: wenham@museum.com. Web Site: www.wenhammuseum.org. *Dir*, Emily Stearns
Founded 1953
Library Holdings: Bk Titles 1,100
Subject Interests: Agriculture, Costume design, Genealogy, History
Special Collections: Historical Association, papers, account bks, diaries, deeds; Massachusetts Society for Promoting Agriculture, publications, medals, paintings, mementoes
Publications: Annual Report of Museum; History of Claflin-Richards House, Allens History of Wenham

P WENHAM PUBLIC LIBRARY,* 138 Main St, 01984-1598. SAN 307-7691. Tel: 978-468-5527. FAX: 978-468-5535. *Dir*, Doris Gallant; E-Mail: gallant@mvlc.lib.ma.us; *Ch Servs*, Karen Conway; Staff 7 (MLS 2, Non-MLS 5)
Founded 1857. Pop 4,423; Circ 63,290
Jul 1999-Jun 2000 Income $231,840. Mats Exp $45,898, Books $40,948, Per/Ser (Incl. Access Fees) $4,950. Sal $132,000 (Prof $66,390)
Library Holdings: Bk Vols 49,150
Subject Interests: Genealogy, Local history
Automation Activity & Vendor Info: (Circulation) GEAC
Mem of Northeast Mass Regional Libr Syst
Partic in Merrimack Valley Library Consortium
Friends of the Library Group

WEST BARNSTABLE

J CAPE COD COMMUNITY COLLEGE, Library-Learning Resource Center, 2240 Iyanough Rd, 02668-1599. SAN 307-7705. Tel: 508-362-2131. Circulation Tel: 508-362-2131, Ext 4342. Reference Tel: 508-362-2131, Ext 4343. FAX: 508-375-4020. E-Mail: refdesk@capecod.mass.edu. Web Site: www.capecod.mass.edu/library. *Dir*, Greg Masterson; Tel: 508-362-2131, Ext 4345, E-Mail: gmasters@capecod.mass.edu; *Bibliog Instr, Chief Librn*, Jeanmarie Fraser; Tel: 508-362-2131, Ext 4618, E-Mail: jfraser@capecod.mass.edu; *Tech Servs*, Brenda Collins; Tel: 508-362-2131, Ext 4617, E-Mail: bcollins@capecod.mass.edu; *Ref*, Patricia Fisher; Tel: 508-362-2131, Ext 4636, E-Mail: pfisher@capecod.mass.edu; *Spec Coll & Archives*, Mary Sicchio; Tel: 508-362-2131, Ext 4445, E-Mail: msicchio@capecod.mass.edu; Staff 4 (MLS 4)
Founded 1961. Enrl 5,000; Fac 93; Highest Degree: Associate
Jul 2000-Jun 2001 Income $591,412, State $556,212, Locally Generated Income $11,000, Other $24,200. Mats Exp $121,350, Books $65,385, Per/Ser (Incl. Access Fees) $31,300, Micro $23,665, AV Equip $1,000, Manuscripts & Archives $2,000. Sal $407,538 (Prof $214,708)
Library Holdings: Bk Vols 54,000; Bk Titles 51,400; Per Subs 483
Special Collections: Cape Cod History Coll; Health Resources Coll; State Census Data
Automation Activity & Vendor Info: (Circulation) DRA; (OPAC) DRA; (Serials) DRA
Database Vendor: CARL, Dialog, Ebsco - EbscoHost, IAC - Info Trac, OCLC - First Search
Function: ILL available, Reference services available
Partic in Cape & Islands Interlibrary Asn; Cape Libraries Automated Materials Sharing; Nelinet, Inc; SE Mass Health Sci Librs Consortium; Southeastern Massachusetts Consortium Of Health Science Libraries
Friends of the Library Group

P WHELDEN MEMORIAL LIBRARY, 2401 Meetinghouse Way, 02668. (Mail add: PO Box 147, 02668), SAN 307-7713. Tel: 508-362-2262. FAX: 508-362-1344. Web Site: people/ne.mediaone.net/whelden/. *Dir*, Lexa Crane; E-Mail: lcrane@clams.lib.ma.us; *Asst Dir*, Carol Silverman; Staff 5 (MLS 1, Non-MLS 4)
Founded 1899. Pop 2,311; Circ 25,779
Jul 1998-Jun 1999 Income $105,569, State $1,771, City $58,823, Locally Generated Income $12,634, Other $32,341. Mats Exp $11,916, Books $11,369, Per/Ser (Incl. Access Fees) $547. Sal $52,413
Library Holdings: Bk Vols 20,473; Per Subs 22
Subject Interests: Local history
Special Collections: Beginning Finnish History Coll
Database Vendor: DRA
Partic in Cape Libraries Automated Materials Sharing
Friends of the Library Group

WEST BOYLSTON

P BEAMAN MEMORIAL PUBLIC LIBRARY,* 8 Newton St, 01583. SAN 307-7721. Tel: 508-835-3711. FAX: 508-835-4770. Web Site: www.ultranet.com/~beaman. *Acq, Commun Servs, Dir*, Ellen M Dolan; E-Mail: edolan@cwmarsmail.cwmars.org; *Asst Dir, Tech Servs*, Louise Howland; *Ad Servs, ILL*, Connie Kalloch; *Ch Servs*, Cecile Lindberg; Staff 10 (MLS 1, Non-MLS 9)
Founded 1912. Pop 6,610; Circ 56,032
Jul 1997-Jun 1998 Income $225,402. Mats Exp $48,155, Books $36,383, Per/Ser (Incl. Access Fees) $6,680. Sal $158,204
Library Holdings: Bk Titles 35,976; Per Subs 115
Publications: Beaman Browser (newsletter, quarterly)
Mem of Central Massachusetts Regional Library System
Partic in CW Mars
Friends of the Library Group

S WORCESTER COUNTY JAIL & HOUSE OF CORRECTION LIBRARY,* 5 Paul X Tivnan Dr, 01583. SAN 372-7254. Tel: 508-854-1800. FAX: 508-852-8754.; Staff 2 (MLS 1, Non-MLS 1)
Library Holdings: Bk Vols 7,050; Per Subs 17
Special Collections: Black History, bks, videotapes
Open Mon-Fri 9-11 & 1-3

WEST BRIDGEWATER

P WEST BRIDGEWATER PUBLIC LIBRARY, (WBPL), 80 Howard St, 02379-1710. SAN 307-773X. Tel: 508-894-1255. FAX: 508-894-1258. *Coll Develop, Dir*, Beth Roll Smith; E-Mail: bsmith@sailsinc.org; *Asst Dir*, April McDermott; *Ch Servs*, Caroline Hammonds; *Tech Servs*, Kathleen Baer; Staff 4 (MLS 1, Non-MLS 3)
Founded 1879. Pop 6,389; Circ 43,000
Jul 2000-Jun 2001 Income $263,056, State $9,000, City $251,056, Locally Generated Income $3,000. Mats Exp $51,706, Books $45,706, Per/Ser (Incl. Access Fees) $3,000, AV Equip $1,000, Other Print Mats $1,000. Sal $155,450 (Prof $49,000)
Library Holdings: Bk Vols 53,000; Bk Titles 50,000; Per Subs 150
Subject Interests: Genealogy, History
Special Collections: W Bridgewater History Coll; World War II Autobiographies
Automation Activity & Vendor Info: (Acquisitions) SIRSI; (Cataloging) SIRSI; (Circulation) SIRSI; (Course Reserve) SIRSI; (Media Booking) SIRSI; (OPAC) SIRSI; (Serials) SIRSI
Publications: Heddalines (quarterly) (Newsletter)
Mem of SE Mass Regional Libr Syst
Partic in Sails, Inc
Open Mon, Thurs & Fri 10-5, Tues & Wed 10-7, Sat 10-2
Friends of the Library Group

WEST BROOKFIELD

P MERRIAM-GILBERT PUBLIC LIBRARY,* 3 Main St, PO Box 364, 01585. SAN 307-7748. Tel: 508-867-1410. FAX: 508-867-1409. *Actg Dir*, Louise Garwood; *Ch Servs*, Lisa Careau
Founded 1880. Pop 3,026; Circ 35,928
Library Holdings: Bk Vols 19,000; Per Subs 40
Mem of Central Massachusetts Regional Library System
Friends of the Library Group

WEST DENNIS

P WEST DENNIS FREE PUBLIC LIBRARY,* 272 Main St, PO Box 158, 02670-0158. SAN 307-7764. Tel: 508-398-2050. FAX: 508-394-6279. E-Mail: westdennis@bpl.org. *Librn*, Jacquelyn Lewis
Pop 5,000; Circ 15,183
Library Holdings: Bk Vols 14,000; Per Subs 42
Mem of Eastern Mass Regional Libr Syst
Open Winter hours: Mon 1:30-6, Wed 10-12 & 2-6, Fri 2-6 & 7-9; Summer hours: Mon 2-5 & 7-9, Wed 10-12, 2-5 & 7-9, Fri 2-5 & 7-9

WEST FALMOUTH

P WEST FALMOUTH LIBRARY,* 575 W Falmouth Hwy, 02574. (Mail add: PO Box 1209, 02574), Tel: 508-548-4709. FAX: 508-457-9534. *Librn*, Ann L Ellis; *Asst Librn*, Rosaleen Egan
Pop 2,500; Circ 12,827
Library Holdings: Bk Vols 10,500; Per Subs 28
Mem of Eastern Mass Regional Libr Syst

WEST HARWICH

P CHASE LIBRARY, 5 Main St, PO Box 457, 02671-0457. SAN 307-7780. Tel: 508-432-2610. Interlibrary Loan Service Tel: 508-548-7455. *Dir*, Mae I Schellhorn; E-Mail: cschell@capecod.net; *Ch Servs*, Ruth Hudson
Founded 1907. Circ 10,000
Library Holdings: Bk Vols 14,850
Mem of Eastern Mass Regional Libr Syst
Open Tues & Sat 1-5

WEST NEWBURY

P G A R MEMORIAL LIBRARY, 490 Main St, 01985-1115. SAN 307-7799. Tel: 978-363-1105. FAX: 978-363-1116. E-Mail: mwy@mvlc.lib.ma.us. *Ch Servs, Dir, Tech Servs*, Katharine M Gove; Staff 1 (Non-MLS 1)
Founded 1819. Pop 4,036
Jul 1999-Jun 2000 Income $186,972, State $7,452, City $172,820, Other $6,700. Mats Exp $57,208, Books $33,037, Per/Ser (Incl. Access Fees) $10,895, Electronic Ref Mat (Incl. Access Fees) $13,276. Sal $106,629 (Prof $45,267)
Library Holdings: Bk Titles 43,423; Per Subs 175
Mem of Northeast Mass Regional Libr Syst
Partic in Merrimack Valley Library Consortium
Friends of the Library Group

WEST ROXBURY

GM MEDICAL LIBRARY VA MEDICAL CENTER, 1400 Veterans of Foreign Wars Pkwy, 02132. SAN 307-7802. Tel: 617-323-7700, Ext 5142. FAX: 617-363-5532. *Librn*, Mary S Abram
Library Holdings: Bk Vols 3,850; Per Subs 300
Subject Interests: Allied health, Cardiology, Medicine, Surgery
Open Mon-Fri 8:30-5

WEST SPRINGFIELD

S STORROWTON VILLAGE MUSEUM LIBRARY, 1305 Memorial Ave, 01089. SAN 373-1758. Tel: 413-787-0136. FAX: 413-787-0166. *In Charge*, Dennis Picard
Library Holdings: Bk Vols 750
Subject Interests: Local history
Open Mon-Fri 8:30-5

P WEST SPRINGFIELD PUBLIC LIBRARY,* 200 Park St, 01089-3398. SAN 307-7810. Tel: 413-736-4561. TDD: 413-732-2599. FAX: 413-736-6469. Web Site: www.wspl.org. *Dir*, Barbara Morse; *Asst Dir*, Nancy Dellapenna; *ILL, Ref*, David Morrell; *Ch Servs*, Antonia Golinski-Folsy; *Cat*, Carol St Amand; Staff 19 (MLS 8, Non-MLS 11)
Founded 1916. Pop 26,192; Circ 209,289
Jul 1998-Jun 1999 Income $714,915, State $28,969, City $604,555, Other $81,391. Mats Exp $94,486, Books $84,062, Per/Ser (Incl. Access Fees) $4,895, Electronic Ref Mat (Incl. Access Fees) $5,529. Sal $406,883
Library Holdings: Bk Vols 105,938; Per Subs 376
Automation Activity & Vendor Info: (Circulation) CARL; (OPAC) CARL
Mem of Western Massachusetts Regional Library System
Special Services for the Deaf - Captioned media; TDD; TTY machine
Special Services for the Blind - Descriptive videos
Friends of the Library Group

WEST STOCKBRIDGE

P WEST STOCKBRIDGE PUBLIC LIBRARY, 9 Main St, PO Box 60, 01266. SAN 307-7829. Tel: 413-232-0308. E-Mail: w_stockbridge@cwmars.org. *Librn*, Leslie Meltzer
Founded 1890. Pop 1,400
Library Holdings: Bk Titles 6,000; Per Subs 15
Mem of Western Massachusetts Regional Library System
Friends of the Library Group

WEST TISBURY

P WEST TISBURY FREE PUBLIC LIBRARY, 1042A State Rd, PO Box 190, 02575. SAN 307-7837. Tel: 508-693-3366. FAX: 508-696-0130. E-Mail: wtlib@gis.net. *Dir*, Mary Jo Joiner; *Asst Librn*, Gay Nelson; *Asst Librn*, Martha Hubbell
Founded 1893. Pop 2,310; Circ 96,465
Jul 1999-Jun 2000 Income $200,988. Mats Exp $34,594, Books $37,731, Per/Ser (Incl. Access Fees) $4,268. Sal $126,967 (Prof $48,462)
Library Holdings: Bk Titles 33,178; Per Subs 147
Special Collections: Nantucket & Vineyard Authors
Friends of the Library Group

WEST WARREN

P WEST WARREN LIBRARY ASSOCIATION,* 2148 Main St, PO Box 143, 01092. SAN 307-7845. Tel: 413-436-9892. *Librn*, Rita Culliton
Circ 5,390
Library Holdings: Bk Titles 9,000; Per Subs 18
Open Mon & Fri 12:30-5, Wed 12:30-7
Friends of the Library Group

WESTBOROUGH

S DATA GENERAL CORPORATION, EMC Corporate Library, 4400 Computer Dr, 01580. SAN 327-344X. Tel: 508-898-7110. FAX: 508-898-4676. *Res, Senior Librn*, Cheryl Cove; E-Mail: cheryl_cove@emc.com; Staff 1 (MLS 1)
Library Holdings: Bk Titles 3,000; Per Subs 250
Subject Interests: Marketing
Database Vendor: CARL, Dialog, IAC - Info Trac
Restriction: Not open to public
Mem of Nelinet
Partic in Nenon Asn

P WESTBOROUGH PUBLIC LIBRARY,* 55 W Main St, 01581. SAN 307-787X. Tel: 508-366-3050. FAX: 508-366-3049. Web Site: www.cwmars.org. *Librn*, Carolyn Delude; *Ad Servs*, Donna Martel; *Ch Servs*, Dorothy Hurley; *Circ*, Lucy Whitin; Staff 15 (MLS 3, Non-MLS 12)
Founded 1859. Pop 13,954; Circ 125,000
Library Holdings: Bk Vols 81,000; Per Subs 223
Subject Interests: Art, Genealogy
Special Collections: Local History (Reed Coll)
Mem of Central Massachusetts Regional Library System
Friends of the Library Group

WESTFIELD

P WESTFIELD ATHENAEUM,* 6 Elm St, 01085. SAN 345-7834. Tel: 413-568-7833. FAX: 568-0988. *Dir*, Patricia Thompson Cramer; E-Mail: pcramer@exit3.com; *Ch Servs*, Jo Ann Bourquard; *Circ*, Donald G Buckley; *Cat*, Jeanne T Peer; *Ref*, Joan Ackerman; *ILL*, Janice Gryszkiewicz; Staff 29 (MLS 1, Non-MLS 28)
Founded 1864. Pop 38,000; Circ 327,211
Library Holdings: Bk Vols 119,311; Per Subs 132
Special Collections: Edward Taylor Colonial Poetry Coll, mss
Mem of Western Massachusetts Regional Library System
Partic in Central-Western Mass Automated Resource Sharing
Friends of the Library Group

C WESTFIELD STATE COLLEGE, Ely Library, 01086. SAN 307-7896. Tel: 413-572-5231. FAX: 413-572-5520. Web Site: www.bondo.wsc.mass.edu/dept/library/library.htm. *Coll Develop, Dir*, Hal Gibson; Tel: 413-572-5233; *Tech Servs*, Judy Carlson; *Ref*, Brian Hubbard; *Circ, Ser*, Mary Ann Nesto; *Bibliog Instr*, Corinne Ebbs; *ILL*, Mary Ann Nest; Staff 7 (MLS 7)
Founded 1839. Enrl 3,801; Fac 219; Highest Degree: Master
Library Holdings: Bk Vols 168,828; Bk Titles 122,807; Per Subs 927
Subject Interests: Criminal law and justice, Education
Automation Activity & Vendor Info: (Acquisitions) Endeavor; (Cataloging) Endeavor; (Circulation) Endeavor; (Course Reserve) Endeavor; (ILL) Endeavor; (Media Booking) Endeavor; (OPAC) Endeavor; (Serials) Endeavor
Publications: Student Guide
Partic in Nelinet, Inc; OCLC Online Computer Library Center, Inc

WESTFORD

P J V FLETCHER LIBRARY,* 50 Main St, 01886-2599. SAN 307-790X. Tel: 978-692-5555. FAX: 978-692-0287. E-Mail: mwf@mvlc.lib.ma.us. Web Site: www.westfordlibrary.org. *Dir*, Ellen Downey Rainville; *Asst Dir*, Linda Schreiber; *Tech Servs*, Catherine Carroll; *Ref*, T G Brennan
Founded 1797. Pop 16,879; Circ 190,911
Library Holdings: Bk Vols 96,707; Per Subs 337
Special Collections: Genealogical Data Coll; Historic Document Coll (pertaining to hist of Merrimack Valley); Textile Mill Histories Coll
Publications: Focus on Friends Newsletter; Library Latest Newsletter
Mem of Mass Regional Libr Syst
Open Mon 1-9, Tues-Thurs 10-9, Fri 1-5 & Sat 10-3
Friends of the Library Group

WESTHAMPTON

P WESTHAMPTON MEMORIAL LIBRARY,* 3 South Rd, 01027. SAN 307-7918. Tel: 413-527-5386. E-Mail: westhampton@cwmars.org. *Dir*, Carolyn A Keating
Founded 1866. Pop 1,403; Circ 17,650
Library Holdings: Bk Vols 8,000
Mem of Western Regional Libr Syst
Friends of the Library Group

WESTMINSTER

P FORBUSH MEMORIAL LIBRARY, 118 Main St, 01473-1444. (Mail add: PO Box 468, 01473-0468), SAN 307-7926. Tel: 978-874-7416. FAX: 978-874-7424. *Dir*, Barbara Friedman; Staff 10 (Non-MLS 10)
Founded 1901. Pop 6,400; Circ 53,258
Jul 1998-Jun 1999 Income $178,073, State $6,612, City $171,461. Mats Exp $32,000, Books $24,000, Per/Ser (Incl. Access Fees) $3,000, Other Print Mats $5,000. Sal $103,317 (Prof $33,889)
Library Holdings: Bk Vols 40,753
Mem of Central Massachusetts Regional Library System
Open Mon, Tues & Thurs 1-8, Wed & Fri 10-6 & Sat 10-2
Friends of the Library Group

S WESTMINSTER HISTORICAL SOCIETY LIBRARY, 110 Main St, PO Box 177, 01473. SAN 375-1872. Tel: 508-874-5569. FAX: 978-874-5569. E-Mail: westminsterhissoc@aol.com. *Coll Develop, Curator*, Betsy Hannula
Founded 1921
Jul 1999-Jun 2000 Income $4,000. Mats Exp $4,000, Presv $1,500. Sal $1,200
Library Holdings: Bk Titles 200
Special Collections: General Nelson A Miles Coll

WESTON

S CARDINAL SPELLMAN PHILATELIC MUSEUM LIBRARY,* 235 Wellesley St, 02493. SAN 307-7942. Tel: 781-768-8367. E-Mail: cspm01@interserv.com. Web Site: www.cspm.com. *Curator*, Kerry Salamone
Founded 1960
Library Holdings: Bk Titles 24,000; Per Subs 105
Subject Interests: Philately
Open Tue & Thur 9-4, Wed 9-4

S GOLDEN BALL TAVERN TRUST, Museum - Library, 662 Boston Post Rd, PO Box 223, 02493. SAN 374-4949. Tel: 781-894-1751. *Librn*, Dorothea Waterbury
Library Holdings: Bk Vols 625
Subject Interests: Local history
Special Collections: Jones History, Six Generations

R POPE JOHN XXIII NATIONAL SEMINARY LIBRARY, 558 South Ave, 02493. SAN 307-7950. Tel: 781-899-5500, Ext 20. FAX: 781-899-9057. E-Mail: pjohn1@shore.net. Web Site: www.ziplink.net~popejohn/index.html. *Asst Librn*, Sr Jacqueline Miller; *Librn*, Timothy J McFadden
Founded 1963. Enrl 78
Jul 1999-Jun 2000 Income $66,065. Mats Exp $30,007, Books $14,502, Per/Ser (Incl. Access Fees) $13,956, AV Equip $497, Electronic Ref Mat (Incl. Access Fees) $1,052. Sal $86,257
Library Holdings: Bk Vols 61,317
Special Collections: Comprehensive English Language Theology, 1958 to date
Database Vendor: OCLC - First Search
Partic in Metrowest Massachusetts Regional Library System

C REGIS COLLEGE LIBRARY,* 235 Wellesley St, 02493. SAN 307-7969. Tel: 781-768-7301. FAX: 781-768-7323. *Dir*, Mary Behrle; *Tech Servs*, Lynn Triplett; *Info Res*, Kristina Worcester; *Ref*, S Eleanor Deady; *ILL*, Armine Bagdasarian; *Circ*, Abby Reidy; *Archivist*, S Jeanne d'Arc O'Hare; *Ser*, Renate Olsen; *Coll Develop*, Susan Harris; Staff 16 (MLS 6, Non-MLS 10)
Founded 1927. Enrl 1,131; Highest Degree: Master
Library Holdings: Bk Vols 131,749; Bk Titles 109,976; Per Subs 890
Subject Interests: Art, Economics, History, Literature, Music, Natural science, Nursing, Women's studies
Special Collections: Cardinal Newman Coll; Madeleine Doran Coll
Automation Activity & Vendor Info: (Acquisitions) SIRSI; (Cataloging) SIRSI; (Circulation) SIRSI; (Course Reserve) SIRSI; (OPAC) SIRSI; (Serials) SIRSI
Database Vendor: OCLC - First Search, Silverplatter Information Inc.
Partic in Metrowest Massachusetts Regional Library System; Nelinet, Inc; OCLC Online Computer Library Center, Inc; West of Boston Network

P WESTON PUBLIC LIBRARY,* 87 School St, 02493. SAN 307-7977. Tel: 781-893-3312 (Adult Serv), 781-893-4089 (Youth Serv), 781-893-4090 (Admin & Tech Servs). FAX: 781-529-0174. Web Site: www.weston.org/library. *Dir*, Elizabeth Drake; E-Mail: drake@mln.lib.ma.us; *Ad Servs, Coll Develop*, Donna Davies; *Ch Servs*, Kelly Wood; *YA Servs*, Tatanya Flannery; *Ref*, Karen Stevens; *Ref*, Madeleine Mullin; *Tech Servs*, Roberta Rothwell; Staff 8 (MLS 8)
Founded 1857. Pop 10,411; Circ 222,463
Jul 1996-Jun 1997 Income $777,525, State $11,793, City $714,050, Other $5,200. Mats Exp $126,774, Books $84,913, Per/Ser (Incl. Access Fees) $16,026, Micro $6,200, AV Equip $3,500. Sal $506,586 (Prof $282,133)
Library Holdings: Bk Vols 91,500; Per Subs 221
Special Collections: Weston
Mem of Eastern Mass Regional Libr Syst
Open Mon-Thurs 10-9, Fri 10-6, Sat 10-5, Sun 2-5
Friends of the Library Group

WESTPORT

P WESTPORT FREE PUBLIC LIBRARY, 408 Old County Rd, PO Box N-157, 02790-0630. SAN 307-7985. Tel: 508-636-1100. FAX: 508-636-1102. *Dir*, Anita E Baron; *Asst Dir*, Susan Branco
Founded 1891. Pop 14,206; Circ 70,186
Jul 1999-Jun 2000 Income $202,955, State $16,309, City $163,126, Other $23,520. Mats Exp $24,568, Books $21,166, Per/Ser (Incl. Access Fees) $3,402. Sal $128,650
Library Holdings: Bk Titles 34,332; Per Subs 77
Mem of Eastern Mass Regional Libr Syst; SE Mass Regional Libr Syst
Partic in Sails, Inc
Friends of the Library Group

S WESTPORT HISTORICAL SOCIETY LIBRARY, 25 Drift Rd, PO Box 3031, 02790-0700. SAN 373-1707. Tel: 508-636-6011. *Dir*, Lincoln S Tripp
Library Holdings: Bk Vols 300
Subject Interests: Local history
Open Tues-Wed 9-12, 1-4

WESTWOOD

P WESTWOOD PUBLIC LIBRARY, 668 High St, 02090. SAN 345-7893. Tel: 781-326-7562. FAX: 781-326-5383. Web Site: www.townhall.westwood.ma.us/library/. *Dir*, Thomas P Viti; Tel: 781-320-1041, E-Mail: tviti@mln.lib.ma.us; *ILL*, Nancy Hogan; *Ad Servs*, Margaret Reucroft; *Ch Servs*, Loretta Eysie; *Tech Servs*, Caroline Nie; Staff 28 (MLS 8, Non-MLS 20)
Founded 1898. Pop 13,500; Circ 216,664
Jul 2000-Jun 2001 Income (Main Library and Branch Library) $756,146, City $745,025, Other $11,121. Mats Exp $124,022, Books $93,000, Per/Ser (Incl. Access Fees) $8,000, Presv $700, Micro $4,000, AV Equip $14,641, Electronic Ref Mat (Incl. Access Fees) $3,681. Sal $574,060
Library Holdings: Bk Vols 94,640; Per Subs 216
Special Collections: Sauter Art Coll
Database Vendor: DRA
Partic in Minuteman Library Network
Friends of the Library Group
Branches: 1
ISLINGTON, 280 Washington St, 02090. SAN 345-7923. Tel: 617-326-5914. *Librn*, Nancy Sullivan
Library Holdings: Bk Vols 16,000
Database Vendor: DRA
Friends of the Library Group

WEYMOUTH

P TUFTS LIBRARY, Public Libraries of Weymouth, 46 Broad St, 02188. SAN 345-7958. Tel: 781-337-1402. FAX: 781-682-6123. *Dir*, Judith A Patt; *Asst Dir*, Robert Roehr; *Dir Libr Serv*, Joanne L Lamothe; E-Mail: jlamothe@ocln.org; *Ad Servs*, Jacqueline Seuss; *YA Servs*, Elizabeth Murphy; *Ch Servs*, Suzanne Mundy; Staff 11 (MLS 11)
Founded 1879. Pop 55,137; Circ 215,006
Jul 1998-Jun 1999 Income $974,158. Mats Exp $158,033, Books $99,325, Per/Ser (Incl. Access Fees) $46,143. Sal $707,605
Library Holdings: Bk Vols 155,151; Per Subs 400
Special Collections: Local History Coll; Teachers' Professional Library
Mem of Eastern Mass Regional Libr Syst
Friends of the Library Group
Branches: 3
FOGG LIBRARY, One Columbian Sq, South Weymouth, 02190. SAN 345-7982. Tel: 617-337-0410. *Dir*, Judith Patt
Library Holdings: Bk Vols 25,000
NORTH BRANCH, 220 North St, 02191. SAN 375-2968. Tel: 718-340-5036. *Dir*, Judith A Patt
Friends of the Library Group
FRANKLIN N PRATT LIBRARY, 1400 Pleasant St, East Weymouth, 02189. SAN 345-8016. Tel: 617-337-1677. *Dir*, Judith Patt
Library Holdings: Bk Vols 14,000

WHATELY

P S WHITE DICKINSON MEMORIAL LIBRARY,* 202 Chestnut Plain Rd, 01093. SAN 307-8000. Tel: 413-665-2170. *Librn*, Nancy Marcheska
Founded 1951. Pop 1,400; Circ 9,380
Library Holdings: Bk Vols 15,200; Per Subs 20

Subject Interests: Local history
Special Collections: New England History of towns, Genealogy books - gift of Stuart Waite
Mem of Western Massachusetts Regional Library System
Open Mon & Wed 10-5, Sat 9-1

WHITINSVILLE

P WHITINSVILLE SOCIAL LIBRARY, INC,* 17 Church St, 01588. SAN 345-8075. Tel: 508-234-2151. FAX: 508-234-0927. *Librn*, Christine McLaughlin
Founded 1844. Pop 12,652; Circ 62,031
Library Holdings: Bk Vols 32,000; Per Subs 60
Special Collections: Northbridge Historical Coll
Mem of Central Massachusetts Regional Library System
Friends of the Library Group

WHITMAN

P WHITMAN PUBLIC LIBRARY, 100 Webster St, 02382. SAN 307-8019. Tel: 781-447-7613. FAX: 781-447-7678. *Librn*, Bat-Ami Sofer; E-Mail: bsofer@ocln.org; *Asst Librn*, Francis Zeoli; *Circ*, Barbara Bryant; *YA Servs*, Cheryl Dunford; Staff 2 (Non-MLS 2)
Founded 1896. Pop 13,743; Circ 57,949
Jul 1999-Jun 2000 Income $235,681, State $22,698, City $207,750, Other $5,233. Mats Exp $44,764, Books $29,979, Per/Ser (Incl. Access Fees) $3,590, AV Equip $9,153, Other Print Mats $680, Electronic Ref Mat (Incl. Access Fees) $1,362. Sal $148,754 (Prof $70,690)
Library Holdings: Bk Vols 40,358; Bk Titles 38,295; Per Subs 109
Subject Interests: Local history
Automation Activity & Vendor Info: (Cataloging) epixtech, inc.; (Circulation) epixtech, inc.; (OPAC) epixtech, inc.
Partic in Old Colony Libr Network
Friends of the Library Group

WILBRAHAM

P WILBRAHAM PUBLIC LIBRARY, 25 Crane Park Dr, 01095-1740. SAN 307-8027. Tel: 413-596-6141. FAX: 413-596-5090. E-Mail: wpl1@javanet.com. Web Site: www.wilbrahamlibrary.org. *Dir*, Christine Bergquist; E-Mail: cbergqui@cwmars.org; *Asst Dir*, Joseph Rodio; E-Mail: jrodio@cwmars.org; *Ad Servs*, Karen Demers; E-Mail: kdemers@cwmars.org; *Ch Servs*, Elaine Crane; E-Mail: ecrane@cwmars.org; Staff 18 (MLS 5, Non-MLS 13)
Founded 1892. Pop 13,900; Circ 197,000
Jul 2000-Jun 2001 Income $483,241. Mats Exp $77,297. Sal $331,394
Library Holdings: Bk Vols 60,193; Per Subs 133
Special Collections: Local History (Wilbraham Coll)
Automation Activity & Vendor Info: (Circulation) Innovative Interfaces Inc.; (OPAC) Innovative Interfaces Inc.
Database Vendor: IAC - Info Trac
Publications: Library News (quarterly) (Newsletter)
Function: ILL available, Outside services via phone, cable & mail, Photocopies available, Some telephone reference
Mem of Western Massachusetts Regional Library System
Partic in Central-Western Mass Automated Resource Sharing
Open Mon, Tues & Thurs 9-8, Wed 12-8, Fri 9-5 & Sat 9-4
Friends of the Library Group

WILLIAMSBURG

SR EARTH SPIRIT COMMUNITY LIBRARY,* PO Box 723, 01096. SAN 370-2294. Tel: 413-238-4240. FAX: 413-238-7785. E-Mail: earthspirit@earthspirit.com. Web Site: www.earthspirit.com. *Dir*, Andras Corban Arthen
Library Holdings: Bk Vols 5,000

P MEEKINS LIBRARY,* 2 Main St, Box 772, 01096-0772. SAN 307-8035. Tel: 413-268-7472. FAX: 413-268-7472. *Librn*, Lisa Wenner; E-Mail: lwenner@cwmars.org
Pop 2,515; Circ 45,000
1997-1998 Income $50,300. Mats Exp $16,500, Books $12,500, Per/Ser (Incl. Access Fees) $1,000, Micro $1,000, Other Print Mats $500
Library Holdings: Bk Titles 25,000; Per Subs 32
Publications: Abridged Readers Guide to Periodical Literature
Mem of Western Regional Libr Syst
Open Tue 10-5, Wed 8-10, Thur 3-8 & Sat 10-3
Friends of the Library Group

WILLIAMSTOWN

S STERLING & FRANCINE CLARK ART INSTITUTE LIBRARY,* 225 South St, 01267. (Mail add: PO Box 8, 01267), SAN 307-8043. Tel: 413-458-9545. FAX: 413-458-9542. E-Mail: library@clark.williams.edu. Web Site: francine.clark.williams.edu. *Librn*, Susan Roeper; Tel: 413-458-9545, Ext 350, E-Mail: susan.roeper@clark.williams.edu; *Cat*, Elizabeth Kieffer; *Reader Servs*, Nancy Spiegel; Tel: 413-458-9545, Ext 261, E-Mail: nancy.spiegel@clark.williams.edu; *Ser*, Peter Erickson; Tel: 413-458-9545, Ext 332, E-Mail: peter.erickson@clark.williams.edu; *Tech Servs*, Penny Baker; Tel: 413-458-9545, Ext 331, E-Mail: penny.baker@clark.williams.edu; Staff 9 (MLS 4, Non-MLS 5)
Founded 1962
Jul 1999-Jun 2000 Income (Main Library Only) $742,405, Locally Generated Income $30,000, Parent Institution $712,405. Mats Exp $398,445. Sal $373,960 (Prof $257,380)
Library Holdings: Bk Vols 175,000; Per Subs 700
Subject Interests: American art, Contemporary art, European art, Medieval art
Special Collections: Auction Catalogues; Mary Ann Beinecke Decorative Arts Coll; Robert Sterling Clark Coll of Rare & Illustrated Books
Automation Activity & Vendor Info: (Cataloging) Innovative Interfaces Inc.; (OPAC) Innovative Interfaces Inc.; (Serials) Innovative Interfaces Inc.
Database Vendor: IAC - SearchBank, Innovative Interfaces INN - View, OCLC - First Search, Silverplatter Information Inc., Wilson - Wilson Web
Restriction: Non-circulating to the public
Function: Research library
Partic in Research Libraries Group, Inc

P DAVID & JOYCE MILNE PUBLIC LIBRARY, 1095 Main St, 01267-2627. SAN 345-813X. Tel: 413-458-5369. FAX: 413-458-3085. Web Site: www.milnelibrary.org. *Dir*, Patricia McLeod; E-Mail: pmcleod@williamstown.net; *Ch Servs*, Mindy Hackner; E-Mail: mhackner@cwmars.org; *Ref*, Fern Sann
Founded 1876. Pop 8,056
Jul 2000-Jun 2001 Income $312,201, State $11,500, City $209,750, Locally Generated Income $85,951, Other $5,000. Mats Exp $60,500, Books $39,500, Per/Ser (Incl. Access Fees) $5,000, AV Equip $14,000, Electronic Ref Mat (Incl. Access Fees) $2,000. Sal $176,000
Library Holdings: Bk Titles 45,000; Per Subs 120
Subject Interests: Local history
Automation Activity & Vendor Info: (Cataloging) Innovative Interfaces Inc.; (Circulation) Innovative Interfaces Inc.
Publications: Biblio-File (quarterly newsletter)
Mem of Western Massachusetts Regional Library System
Open Mon, Tues, Thurs & Fri 10-5:30, Wed 10-8, Sat 10-4
Friends of the Library Group

C WILLIAMS COLLEGE, Sawyer Library, 55 Sawyer Library Dr, 01267. SAN 345-8199. Tel: 413-597-2501. FAX: 413-597-4106. Web Site: www.williams.edu/library/. *Head of Libr*, David M Pilachowski; Tel: 413-597-2502, E-Mail: david.pilachowski@williams.edu; *Acq*, Sandra Ludwig Brooke; Tel: 413-597-2172, E-Mail: sandra.brooke@williams.edu; *Archivist*, Sylvia Kennick-Brown; Tel: 413-597-2596, E-Mail: sylvia.k.brown@williams.edu; *Automation Syst Coordr*, Walter Komorowski; Tel: 413-597-2084, E-Mail: walter.komorowski@williams.edu; *Cat*, M Robin Kibler; Tel: 413-597-3047, E-Mail: m.robin.kibler@williams.edu; *Doc*, Peter Giordano; Tel: 413-597-2514, E-Mail: peter.giordano@williams.edu; *Reader Servs*, Lee B Dalzell; Tel: 413-597-2021, E-Mail: lee.b.dalzell@williams.edu; *Govt Doc*, Rebecca Spencer; Tel: 413-597-4321; Staff 16 (MLS 12, Non-MLS 4)
Founded 1793. Enrl 2,024; Fac 206; Highest Degree: Master
Jul 1999-Jun 2000 Income Parent Institution $3,792,720. Mats Exp $1,826,394, Books $787,009, Per/Ser (Incl. Access Fees) $700,035, Presv $40,995, Micro $37,258, Electronic Ref Mat (Incl. Access Fees) $1,598
Library Holdings: Bk Vols 853,635; Bk Titles 447,773; Per Subs 2,402
Subject Interests: Humanities, Natural science
Special Collections: Paul Whiteman Coll, scores, rec & mss; Shaker, bks, mss & pamphlets; William Cullen Bryant Coll, bks & mss
Database Vendor: Innovative Interfaces INN - View
Partic in Nelinet, Inc; OCLC Online Computer Library Center, Inc
Departmental Libraries:
CHAPIN LIBRARY, 26 Hopkins Hall Dr, 01267-2560. (Mail add: PO Box 426, 01267-0426), SAN 345-8253. Tel: 413-597-2462. FAX: 413-597-2929. Web Site: www.williams.edu/resources/chapin. *Asst Librn*, Wayne G Hammond; E-Mail: wayne.g.hammond@williams.edu; *Head Librn*, Robert L Volz; Tel: 413-597-2930, E-Mail: robert.l.volz@williams.edu; Staff 2 (MLS 2)
Founded 1923
Jul 1999-Jun 2000 Income $121,726, Locally Generated Income $500, Parent Institution $121,226. Mats Exp $123,699, Books $110,579, Per/Ser (Incl. Access Fees) $2,429, Presv $10,691
Library Holdings: Bk Vols 52,000
Subject Interests: Am lit, Americana, English lit (20th century), French (Language), German (Language), Graphic arts, History of science, Italian (language), Latin (language), Manuscripts, Performing arts, Printing, Spanish language
Special Collections: Aldine Press; Bibles & Liturgical Books; C B Falls Coll; Daniel Press; Daniel Webster Coll; Edwin Arlington Robinson (John T Snyder Coll); Field Family Coll; Gelett Burgess Coll; Herman Rosse Coll; James Elroy Flecker (Hugh M MacMullan Coll); Joseph Conrad (Donald S Klopfer Coll); Leo Wyatt Coll; Oliver Herford Coll; Overbrook Press; Rudyard Kipling Coll; Rupert Brooke (Hugh M MacMullan Coll); Samuel Butler (Carroll Atwood Wilson Coll), correspondence, first ed, music & memorabilia, notebks, photogs; Sporting Books; Stereos, photogs;

T S Eliot (Hugh M MacMullan Coll); Theodore Roosevelt Coll; Walt Whitman (Julian K Sprague Coll); William Faulkner Coll; William Saroyan Coll; Winston S Churchill Coll
Automation Activity & Vendor Info: (OPAC) Innovative Interfaces Inc.
Database Vendor: OCLC - First Search
Publications: British Book Illustration 1924-36; British Ecclesiastical Architecture; Catalogue of the Collection of Samuel Butler; Finished by Hand; Graphic Art of C B Falls; London: High Life & Low Life; Short-Title List
Restriction: Not a lending library
Function: Research library
Partic in OCLC Online Computer Library Center, Inc

S WILLIAMSTOWN HOUSE OF LOCAL HISTORY, 1095 Main St, 01267. SAN 373-1995. Tel: 413-458-2160. Web Site: www.williamstown.net/hlh.htm. *Curator*, Nancy Burstein; E-Mail: nancywb947@aol.com
Library Holdings: Bk Vols 1,805
Subject Interests: Local hist of town

WILMINGTON

S TEXTRON DEFENSE SYSTEMS, Research Library,* 201 Lowell St, 01887. SAN 307-806X. Tel: 978-657-2868. FAX: 978-657-4975. *Librn*, Joanne M Campbell
Founded 1956
Library Holdings: Bk Vols 18,000; Per Subs 87
Subject Interests: Electronics

P WILMINGTON MEMORIAL LIBRARY, 175 Middlesex Ave, 01887-2779. SAN 307-8086. Tel: 978-658-2967. TDD: 978-6657-4625. FAX: 978-658-9699. E-Mail: mwl@mvlc.lib.ma.us. Web Site: www.wilmlibrary.org. *Dir*, Christine A Stewart; E-Mail: cstewart@mailserv.mvlc.lib.ma.us; *Head Tech Servs*, Laurel Toole; E-Mail: ltoole@mailserv.mvlc.lib.ma.us; *Admin Assoc*, Gloria Corcoran; E-Mail: gcorcoran@mailserv.mvlc.ma.us; *Ad Servs, Head Ref*, Laura Hodgson; E-Mail: lhodgson@mailserv.mvcl.lib.ma.us; *Circ*, Linda Callahan; *Ch Servs*, Susan MacDonald; E-Mail: smacdonald@mailserv.mvlc.lib.ma.us; Staff 10 (MLS 4, Non-MLS 6)
Founded 1871. Pop 21,672; Circ 157,502
Jul 1999-Jun 2000 Income $563,146. Mats Exp $126,283, Books $69,466, Per/Ser (Incl. Access Fees) $15,619. Sal $420,410 (Prof $211,479)
Library Holdings: Bk Vols 95,831; Per Subs 181
Database Vendor: Dialog, Ebsco - EbscoHost, IAC - SearchBank
Mem of Northwest Regional Library System
Partic in Merrimack Valley Library Consortium
Special Services for the Blind - Kurzweil Reading Machine
Friends of the Library Group

WINCHENDON

P BEALS MEMORIAL LIBRARY,* 50 Pleasant St, 01475. SAN 307-8094. Tel: 978-297-0300. FAX: 978-297-2018. *Dir*, Julia F White
Founded 1867. Pop 8,400; Circ 43,000
Library Holdings: Bk Vols 34,000; Per Subs 87
Subject Interests: Local history
Mem of Central Massachusetts Regional Library System
Friends of the Library Group

WINCHESTER

S FLAG RESEARCH CENTER LIBRARY, 3 Edgehill Rd, PO Box 580, 01890-0880. SAN 327-7232. Tel: 781-729-9410. FAX: 781-721-4817. *Exec Dir*, Whitney Smith
Library Holdings: Bk Vols 13,000; Per Subs 60
Subject Interests: Heraldry
Friends of the Library Group

G UNITED STATES FOOD & DRUG ADMINISTRATION DEPARTMENT OF HEALTH & HUMAN SERVICES, Winchester Engineering & Analytical Center Library,* 109 Holton St, 01890. SAN 307-8108. Tel: 781-729-5700. FAX: 781-729-3593. *In Charge*, Josephine Clancy
Founded 1961
Library Holdings: Bk Titles 1,500; Per Subs 100
Subject Interests: Electronics, Engineering, Medicine, Physics

M WINCHESTER HOSPITAL, Health Sciences Library,* 41 Highland Ave, 01890. SAN 377-9378. Tel: 781-756-2165. FAX: 781-756-2059. *Librn*, Mary Miller; E-Mail: mmiller@winhosp.org
Library Holdings: Bk Vols 400; Per Subs 135
Partic in Massachusetts Health Sciences Libraries Network; North Atlantic Health Sciences Libraries, Inc; Northeastern Consortium For Health Information

P WINCHESTER PUBLIC LIBRARY, 80 Washington St, 01890. SAN 307-8116. Tel: 781-721-7171. FAX: 781-721-7170. E-Mail: windir@mln.lib.ma.us. Web Site: mln.lib.ma.us. *Dir*, Lynda J Wills; *Asst Dir*, Barbara Yuan; *Circ*, Karen Brown; *Ch Servs*, Yvonne K Coleman; *Commun Relations*, Richard Welton; *Ref*, Julie A Kinchla; *Tech Servs*, Nancy Goodwin; Staff 20 (MLS 10, Non-MLS 10)
Founded 1859. Pop 20,652; Circ 336,000
Jul 1999-Jun 2000 Income $1,181,400, State $30,200, City $1,137,000, Other $14,200. Mats Exp $181,000, Books $145,000, Per/Ser (Incl. Access Fees) $12,000, AV Equip $13,700. Sal $903,800
Library Holdings: Bk Vols 109,100; Per Subs 212
Special Collections: Civil War History (Lincoln & Lee Coll)
Automation Activity & Vendor Info: (Circulation) DRA
Publications: A Plan for the Future: FY2000 - FY2005; Art in the Library; Guide to Winchester Public Library
Partic in Minuteman Library Network
Special Services for the Deaf - TTY machine
Special Services for the Blind - Optelek
Friends of the Library Group

WINDSOR

P WINDSOR FREE PUBLIC LIBRARY,* Rte 9, PO Box 118, 01270-0118. SAN 376-7094. Tel: 413-684-3811. *Dir*, Nicole R Pierce
Library Holdings: Bk Vols 3,500; Bk Titles 3,000
Mem of Western Massachusetts Regional Library System

WINTHROP

P WINTHROP PUBLIC LIBRARY & MUSEUM,* 2 Metcalf Sq, 02152-3157. SAN 307-8124. Tel: 617-846-1703. FAX: 617-846-7083. *Dir*, Marjorie Hill-Devine; *Ch Servs*, Ellen J Nickerson; *Circ*, Mary Ann Blair; *Tech Servs*, Richard Allen; Staff 3 (MLS 3)
Founded 1885. Pop 18,263
Library Holdings: Bk Vols 84,000; Bk Titles 78,000; Per Subs 35
Special Collections: Lincoln Memorabilia; Local History (Museum Coll), bks, postcards, artifacts, pamphlets
Mem of Eastern Mass Regional Libr Syst; N of Boston Libr Exchange, Inc
Friends of the Library Group

WOBURN

L COMMONWEALTH OF MASSACHUSETTS TRIAL COURT, Middlesex Law Library, 30 Pleasant St, 01801. SAN 327-635X. Tel: 781-935-4000, Ext 229. FAX: 781-935-4122. *In Charge*, Francine Boykin
Library Holdings: Bk Vols 5,000; Per Subs 19
Special Collections: Massachusetts Legal Materials

S NORTHERN RESEARCH & ENGINEERING CORP LIBRARY,* 39 Olympia Ave, 01801-2073. SAN 307-3084. Tel: 781-935-9050. FAX: 781-935-9052. E-Mail: jbw@nrec.com. *Info Specialist*, Jane B Waks; Staff 1 (MLS 1)
Founded 1965
Library Holdings: Bk Vols 800; Per Subs 125
Subject Interests: Aeronautics, Energy
Special Collections: NACA/NASA publications
Publications: Quarterly updates for serials & book holdings
Partic in Dialog Corporation
Open Mon-Fri 9-5:30

S PORTUGUESE CONTINENTAL UNION OF THE USA LIBRARY,* 30 Cummings Park, 01801. SAN 327-3474. Tel: 781-376-0271. FAX: 781-376-2033. E-Mail: upceua@aol.com. Web Site: members.aol.com/upceua.
Library Holdings: Bk Titles 4,000
Publications: Guiomas; The Portiguese Heritage of John Dos Passos; The Portuguese-Americans

P WOBURN PUBLIC LIBRARY,* 45 Pleasant St, PO Box 298, 01801. SAN 307-8140. Tel: 781-933-0148. FAX: 781-938-7860. Web Site: www.mln.lib.ma.us. *Dir*, Kathleen O'Doherty; *Asst Dir*, Rebecca Deaver; *Acq*, Jeanne Yachkouri; *Ref*, Paul Uek; *Cat*, Beverly Thompson; *Ch Servs*, Anne Nawawi
Founded 1855
Library Holdings: Bk Vols 70,000; Per Subs 152
Subject Interests: Genealogy
Mem of Eastern Mass Regional Libr Syst
Friends of the Library Group

WOODS HOLE

S MARINE BIOLOGICAL LABORATORY, MBL-WHOI Library, 7 MBL St, 02543-1026. SAN 307-8167. Tel: 508-289-7002. FAX: 508-540-6902. E-Mail: Internet: library@mbl.edu. Web Site: mblwhoilibrary.mbl.edu, www.mbl.edu. *Dir*, Cathy Norton; Tel: 508-289-7341, E-Mail: cnorton@mbl.edu; *Asst Dir*, Judy Ashmore; Tel: 508-289-7665, E-Mail: jashmore@mbl.edu; *Asst Dir*, Colleen Hurter; Tel: 508-289-7341, Fax: 508-457-2156, E-Mail: churter@whoi.edu; *Ref*, Amy Stout; E-Mail: astout@mpl.edu; *Syst Coordr*, Maggie Rioux; Tel: 508-289-2538, Fax: 508-457-2156, E-Mail: mrioux@whoi.edu; Staff 22 (MLS 12, Non-MLS 10)
Founded 1888
Library Holdings: Bk Vols 250,000; Per Subs 2,000

Subject Interests: Biology, Biomedical engineering, Chemistry, Geology, Oceanography, Physics
Special Collections: Archives; Data; Rare Books
Automation Activity & Vendor Info: (Acquisitions) Endeavor; (Cataloging) Endeavor; (Circulation) Endeavor; (Course Reserve) Endeavor; (ILL) Endeavor; (Media Booking) Endeavor; (OPAC) Endeavor; (Serials) Endeavor
Partic in Boston Library Consortium; OCLC Online Computer Library Center, Inc; Southeastern Massachusetts Consortium Of Health Science Libraries
Holding library for Woods Hole Oceanographic Institution & National Marine Fisheries Service, NE Center & USGS, Woods Hole Branch

G NATIONAL MARINE FISHERIES SERVICE, Northeast Fisheries Science Center Library,* 166 Water St, 02543-1097. SAN 307-8175. Tel: 508-495-2260. FAX: 508-495-2258. Web Site: www.nefsclibrary.nmfs.gov. *Librn*, J Riley; E-Mail: jriley@whsun1.wh.whoi.edu
Founded 1885
Library Holdings: Per Subs 40
Subject Interests: Biology, Ecology
Special Collections: Laboratory Research (Archives 1871-1979)
Partic in BRS; Dialog Corporation; OCLC Online Computer Library Center, Inc
Field library of National Oceanic & Atmospheric Administration (NOAA) Library System

P WOODS HOLE LIBRARY,* Woods Hole Rd, PO Box 185, 02543. SAN 307-8183. Tel: 508-548-8961. FAX: 508-540-1969. *Librn*, Camilla B Larrey; Staff 2 (MLS 2)
Founded 1910. Pop 5,000; Circ 21,290
1999-1999 Income $89,000
Library Holdings: Bk Vols 25,000; Per Subs 47
Subject Interests: Local history, Theater
Mem of SE Mass Regional Libr Syst

WOODS HOLE OCEANOGRAPHIC INSTITUTION

S DATA LIBRARY & ARCHIVES, McLean MS 8, 360 Woods Hole Rd, 02543-1539. SAN 345-8288. Tel: 508-289-2269, 508-289-3396. FAX: 508-289-2269, 508-289-3396. E-Mail: archivelib@whoi.edu. Web Site: www.mblwhoilibrary.mbl.edu. *Librn*, Melissa Lamont; *Archivist*, Margot Garritt
Founded 1956
Subject Interests: Chemistry, Geology, Geophysics, Meteorology, Ocean engineering, Oceanography
Special Collections: Institution Archives, mss, notebks, instruments
Partic in Boston Library Consortium

C RESEARCH LIBRARY, MS 26, 360 Woods Hole Rd, 02543-1541. SAN 345-8342. Tel: 508-289-2708, 508-289-2865. FAX: 508-457-2156. E-Mail: library@whoi.edu. Web Site: www.mblwhoilibrary.mbl.edu. *Dir*, Catherine Norton; *Librn*, Margaret Rioux; *Asst Librn*, Colleen Hurter; Staff 7 (MLS 4, Non-MLS 3)
Founded 1930. Enrl 138; Fac 100; Highest Degree: Doctorate
Subject Interests: Chemistry, Geophysics, Ocean engineering
Automation Activity & Vendor Info: (Acquisitions) Endeavor; (Cataloging) Endeavor; (Circulation) Endeavor; (Course Reserve) Endeavor; (Media Booking) Endeavor; (OPAC) Endeavor; (Serials) Endeavor
Partic in Boston Library Consortium; Cape Libraries Automated Materials Sharing; Nelinet, Inc

WORCESTER

S AMERICAN ANTIQUARIAN SOCIETY LIBRARY,* 185 Salisbury St, 01609-1634. SAN 307-8191. Tel: 508-755-5221. FAX: 508-753-3311. E-Mail: library@mwa.org. Web Site: americanantiquarian.org. *Pres*, Ellen S Dunlap
Founded 1812
Sep 1998-Aug 1999 Income $3,988,000. Mats Exp $344,700, Books $290,700, Per/Ser (Incl. Access Fees) $20,000, Micro $23,000, Electronic Ref Mat (Incl. Access Fees) $11,000
Library Holdings: Bk Vols 690,000; Per Subs 1,200
Subject Interests: American history, Literature
Special Collections: Manuscripts relating to the history of the American book trades & New England families; Pre-1877 American & Canadian bks, pamphlets, almanacs, directories, children's lit, cook bks, genealogies, broadsides, graphic arts, printed ephemera, local & state histories, songsters, hymnals, sheet music, bibliographies, newspapers & periodicals
Publications: Bibliographies; proceedings; source materials
Partic in Cent Mass Regional Libr Syst; Research Libraries Group, Inc; Worcester Area Cooperating Libraries
Offer visiting fellowships for creative & performing artists, scholars & graduate students
Friends of the Library Group

C ASSUMPTION COLLEGE, Emmanuel d'Alzon Library, 500 Salisbury St, 01615-0005. SAN 307-8205. Tel: 508-767-7135. Interlibrary Loan Service Tel: 508-767-7273. FAX: 508-767-7374. Web Site: www.assumption.edu. *Dir*, Dawn Thistle; *Tech Servs*, Janice Wilbur; *Ref*, Carol Maksian; *Ref*, Larry Spongberg; *Ser*, Julie O'Shea; *Circ*, Nancy Bassett; Staff 13 (MLS 6, Non-MLS 7)
Founded 1904. Fac 110; Highest Degree: Master
Jul 1998-Jun 1999 Income $415,000. Mats Exp $314,700, Books $143,200, Per/Ser (Incl. Access Fees) $155,000, Presv $16,500. Sal $458,000 (Prof $195,000)
Library Holdings: Bk Vols 190,000; Bk Titles 102,000; Per Subs 21,000
Subject Interests: Fr Canadian, Franco-Americans, History, Literature
Automation Activity & Vendor Info: (Acquisitions) epixtech, inc.; (Cataloging) epixtech, inc.; (Circulation) epixtech, inc.; (Course Reserve) epixtech, inc.; (OPAC) epixtech, inc.; (Serials) epixtech, inc.
Database Vendor: OCLC - First Search
Partic in Nelinet, Inc; OCLC Online Computer Library Center, Inc; Worcester Area Cooperating Libraries

J BECKER COLLEGE, William F Ruska Library, 61 Sever St, 01615-0071. SAN 345-8377. Tel: 508-791-9241, Ext 211. FAX: 508-849-5131. E-Mail: plummer@go.becker.edu. *Coll Develop, Dean of Libr*, Bruce Plummer; Tel: 508-791-9241, Ext 212; *Asst Dir*, Sharon Krauss; *Tech Servs*, Alice Baron; Staff 3 (MLS 3)
Founded 1887. Enrl 1,000
Library Holdings: Bk Vols 34,258; Per Subs 241
Subject Interests: Criminal law and justice, Graphic arts, Interior design, Nursing, Physical therapy
Automation Activity & Vendor Info: (Acquisitions) MultiLIS; (Circulation) MultiLIS; (Course Reserve) MultiLIS; (Media Booking) MultiLIS; (OPAC) MultiLIS; (Serials) MultiLIS
Publications: Acquisitions list; faculty handbook
Partic in Worcester Area Cooperating Libraries

L BOWDITCH & DEWEY, Law Library,* 311 Main St, 01608. SAN 372-0349. Tel: 508-791-3511, 508-926-3331. FAX: 508-929-3140. Web Site: www.bowditch.com. *Librn*, Byron C Hill; E-Mail: bhill@bowditch.com
Library Holdings: Bk Vols 14,000; Per Subs 60
Partic in New England Law Library Consortium, Inc

C CLARK UNIVERSITY, Robert Hutchings Goddard Library, 950 Main St, 01610-1477. SAN 345-8407. Tel: 508-793-7573. Interlibrary Loan Service Tel: 508-793-7578. FAX: 508-793-8871. Web Site: www.libref.clarku.edu. *Dir*, Gwen Arthur; Tel: 508-793-7384, E-Mail: garthur@clarku.edu; *Publ Servs*, Mary Hartman; *Online Servs, Ref*, Irene Walch; *Tech Servs*, Page Cotton; *Media Spec*, William Burdette; *Cat*, Cherine Whitney; *ILL*, Cristina Celona; *Coll Develop*, Diane Dolbashian. Subject Specialists: *Science*, Tanya Netch; Staff 30 (MLS 12, Non-MLS 18)
Founded 1889. Enrl 2,700; Fac 163; Highest Degree: Doctorate
Jun 1999-May 2000 Income (Main Library and Branch Library) $2,237,800. Mats Exp $901,143, Books $199,453, Per/Ser (Incl. Access Fees) $565,000, Presv $50,000, Micro $15,000, AV Equip $12,600, Electronic Ref Mat (Incl. Access Fees) $61,798. Sal $862,838 (Prof $439,100)
Library Holdings: Bk Vols 568,879; Bk Titles 281,096; Per Subs 1,310
Special Collections: Census; Rare Books (Robert H Goddard Coll & G Stanley Hall Papers)
Automation Activity & Vendor Info: (Acquisitions) Endeavor; (Cataloging) Endeavor; (Circulation) Endeavor; (Course Reserve) Endeavor; (OPAC) Endeavor; (Serials) Endeavor
Database Vendor: Dialog, GaleNet, IAC - Info Trac, Lexis-Nexis, OCLC - First Search, Silverplatter Information Inc.
Mem of Worcester Area Coop Libr
Partic in Nelinet, Inc; OCLC Online Computer Library Center, Inc
Friends of the Library Group
Departmental Libraries:
MAP Tel: 508-793-7322. FAX: 508-793-8871. *Librn*, Beverly Presley
SCIENCE Tel: 508-793-7712. FAX: 508-793-8871. *Librn*, Eileen M Droscha; E-Mail: droschae@cadl.org
SPECIAL COLLECTIONS-ARCHIVES Tel: 508-793-7572. FAX: 508-793-8871. *Archivist*, Mott Linn
Library Holdings: Bk Vols 10,000

CR COLLEGE OF THE HOLY CROSS, Dinand Library, One College St, 01610. SAN 345-8466. Tel: 508-793-3372. Interlibrary Loan Service Tel: 508-793-2639. Circulation Tel: 508-793-2642. Reference Tel: 508-793-2259. FAX: 508-793-2372. Web Site: campus: www.holycross.edu, library: www.holycross.edu/departments/library/website/. *Dir Libr Serv*, James E Hogan; E-Mail: jhogan@holycross.edu; *Assoc Dir*, Karen J Reilly; Tel: 508-793-2520, E-Mail: kreilly@holycross.edu; *Acq*, Thomas Syseskey; *Archivist*, Mark Savolis; Tel: 508-793-2506, E-Mail: msavolis@holycross.edu; *Cat*, Nancy Singleton; Tel: 508-793-2466, E-Mail: nsinglet@holycross.edu; *Cat*, Mary Moran; *Head, Circ*, Eileen Cravedi; Tel: 508-793-2672, E-Mail: ecravedi@holycross.edu; *Reader Servs*, Patricia Porcaro; Tel: 508-793-2672, E-Mail: pporcaro@holycross.edu; *Ref*, Gudrun Krueger; *Ser*, Diane Gallagher; Tel: 508-793-3543, E-Mail: dgallagh@holycross.edu; Staff 37 (MLS 14, Non-MLS 23)
Founded 1843. Enrl 2,720; Fac 246; Highest Degree: Bachelor
Jul 1999-Jun 2000 Income (Main Library and Branch Library) $2,370,164, Locally Generated Income $33,297, Parent Institution $2,324,555, Other $12,312. Mats Exp $963,268, Books $258,449, Per/Ser (Incl. Access Fees) $601,809, Presv $29,766, Electronic Ref Mat (Incl. Access Fees) $73,244. Sal $1,192,476 (Prof $532,648)

Library Holdings: Bk Vols 566,900; Bk Titles 363,870; Per Subs 1,740
Special Collections: Americana Up to 1840; Early Christian Iberia (Roman-Visigothic-Hispania, 50-711AD), bks & maps; History (David I Walsh, 1872-1947), papers, corresp, scrapbooks; History (James M Curley, 1874-1958), scrapbooks, photog; Holocaust, bks; Literature (Louise I Guiney, 1861-1920), bks, mss, letters; Rare Books 16th-17th Century (Jesuitana Coll); Richard O'Flynn coll, Irish in Worcester, 1880-1890
Automation Activity & Vendor Info: (Acquisitions) DRA; (Cataloging) DRA; (Circulation) DRA; (Course Reserve) DRA; (OPAC) DRA; (Serials) DRA
Database Vendor: DRA, IAC - SearchBank, Lexis-Nexis, OCLC - First Search, Silverplatter Information Inc.
Publications: Handbook; Newsletter; Recent Acquisitions; Subject reference guides
Partic in Nelinet, Inc; Worcester Area Cooperating Libraries
Open Sun-Thurs 8:30am-1am, Fri 8:30am-11pm, Sat 10:30am-11pm
Departmental Libraries:
MUSIC, Fenwick Bldg, 01610-2394. SAN 345-8482. Tel: 508-793-2295. Web Site: campus: www.holycross.edu, library: www.holycross.edu/department/library/website/. *Librn*, Alan Karass; E-Mail: akarass@holycross.edu; Staff 2 (MLS 1, Non-MLS 1)
Library Holdings: Bk Vols 8,002; Per Subs 46
O'CALLAHAN SCIENCE LIBRARY, Swords Bldg, 01610. SAN 345-8490. Tel: 508-793-2643. Circulation Tel: 508-793-2739. FAX: 508-793-3530. Web Site: www.holycross.edu. *Librn*, Anthony V Stankus; E-Mail: tstankus@holycross.edu
Library Holdings: Bk Vols 90,913; Per Subs 304
Subject Interests: Astronomy, Biology, Chemistry, Computer science, History of science, Mathematics, Medicine, Physics

S HIGGINS ARMORY MUSEUM, Olive Higgins Prouty Library & Research Center, 100 Barber Ave, 01606-2444. SAN 307-8248. Tel: 508-853-6015. FAX: 508-852-7697. Web Site: www.higgins.org. *Curator*, Walter J Karcheski, Jr; Tel: 508-853-6015, Ext 23, E-Mail: wkarcheski@higgins.org. Subject Specialists: *Armour*, Walter J Karcheski, Jr; *Arms*, Walter J Karcheski, Jr
Founded 1964
Library Holdings: Bk Vols 3,000
Subject Interests: Armour, Arms, Art, History, Military history
Special Collections: Museum Archives
Publications: John Woodman Higgins Memorial Library Catalogue of Books (circa 1970)
Restriction: Non-circulating
Function: For research purposes
Open Wed 2-4

GL MASSACHUSETTS TRIAL COURT, Worcester Law Library, 2 Main St, 01608. SAN 307-8345. Tel: 508-770-1899, Ext 185. FAX: 508-754-9933. Web Site: www.lawlib.state.ma.us. *Librn*, Suzanne M Hoey; Staff 4 (MLS 1, Non-MLS 3)
Founded 1842
Library Holdings: Bk Vols 103,000; Bk Titles 16,000; Per Subs 110
Special Collections: Early Law Reports (American Coll); History of Worcester County & its Cities & Towns; Legal Textbooks (Major Coll on General Law)

L MIRICK O'CONNELL, Law Library, 100 Front St, 01608-1477. SAN 372-0357. Tel: 508-791-8500. FAX: 508-791-8502. *Librn*, Elaine Apostola; E-Mail: eapostola@modl.com
Library Holdings: Bk Vols 5,000; Per Subs 50

S NORTON CO LIBRARY, One New Bond St, 01606-2698. SAN 307-8264. Tel: 508-795-2278. FAX: 508-795-5755. *Mgr*, Mary Silverberg; E-Mail: mary.e.silverberg@naa.sgna.com; *Librn*, Beth Crenier; *Librn*, Christine Friese; *Ref*, Elaine P Lentini
Founded 1909
Library Holdings: Bk Titles 6,000; Per Subs 75
Subject Interests: Ceramics
Special Collections: Company Newspaper Clippings Coll, micro
Publications: Bi-monthly Acquisitions List; Lit Alerts; User Guide
Mem of Central Massachusetts Regional Library System
Partic in Norton Library Network; OCLC Online Computer Library Center, Inc; Worcester Area Cooperating Libraries

S PRIMEDICA CORP, (Formerly TSI Mason Laboratories), Information Services, 57 Union St, 01608. SAN 374-7654. Tel: 508-890-0100. FAX: 508-753-1834. Web Site: www.primedica.com. *Curator*, Kathy Vanderhoff; E-Mail: kathy.vanderhoff@primedica.com
Library Holdings: Bk Vols 700; Per Subs 50

J QUINSIGAMOND COMMUNITY COLLEGE LIBRARY,* 670 W Boylston St, 01606-2092. SAN 307-8272. Tel: 508-854-4291, 508-854-4366. FAX: 508-852-6943. *Dir*, Loan-Anh Vidmanis; *Coordr, Publ Servs*, Jenny Shih
Founded 1963
Library Holdings: Bk Titles 63,500; Per Subs 320
Partic in Nelinet, Inc; OCLC Online Computer Library Center, Inc; Worcester Area Cooperating Libraries
LRC program includes tutorial services

M SAINT VINCENT HOSPITAL, Dr John J Dumphy Memorial Library, Worcester Medical Center, 20 Worcester Center Blvd, 01608. SAN 307-8280. Tel: 508-363-6117. FAX: 508-798-1118. *Mgr*, Joan Yanicke; E-Mail: joan.yanicke@tenethealth.com; Staff 3 (MLS 2, Non-MLS 1)
Founded 1900
Library Holdings: Bk Vols 1,000; Per Subs 304
Subject Interests: Medicine, Nursing
Special Collections: St Vincent Hospital History
Automation Activity & Vendor Info: (Cataloging) Inmagic, Inc.; (Serials) Inmagic, Inc.
Database Vendor: IAC - SearchBank, OCLC - First Search, OVID Technologies
Partic in BHSL; Central Massachusetts Consortium Of Health Related Libraries (CMCHRL); CMRLS; OCLC-LVIS; WACL

R TEMPLE EMANUEL LIBRARY, 280 May St, 01602. SAN 307-8302. Tel: 508-755-1257. FAX: 508-795-0417. Web Site: www.temple-emanuel.org. *Librn*, Melanie Ullman
Founded 1949
Library Holdings: Bk Vols 6,000; Per Subs 12
Subject Interests: Jewish history and literature, Judaica (lit or hist of Jews), Religion
Open Mon 1-5, Tues 9:30-11:30
Friends of the Library Group

M UMASS MEMORIAL HEALTH CARE, Homer Gage Medical Library, 119 Belmont St, 01605. SAN 307-8256. Tel: 508-334-6421. FAX: 508-334-6527. E-Mail: library@ummhc.org. *Actg Dir*, Andrew Dzaugis; E-Mail: dzaugisa@ummhc.org; Staff 4 (MLS 3, Non-MLS 1)
Founded 1928
Library Holdings: Bk Titles 3,733; Per Subs 265
Open Mon-Fri 8am-5pm
Friends of the Library Group

CM UNIVERSITY OF MASSACHUSETTS MEDICAL SCHOOL, Lamar Soutter Library, 55 Lake Ave N, 01655-2397. SAN 307-8310. Tel: 508-856-2511. Interlibrary Loan Service Tel: 508-856-2029. FAX: 508-856-5899. Web Site: www.library.umassmed.edu. *Dir Libr Serv*, Elaine Martin; *Dep Dir*, Deborah Sibley; E-Mail: deborah.sibley@umassmed.edu; *Coll Develop*, Barbara Ingrassia; *ILL*, Mary Ann Slocomb; *Ref*, James Comes; Staff 35 (MLS 14, Non-MLS 21)
Founded 1966
Library Holdings: Bk Vols 265,000; Per Subs 2,100
Special Collections: Massachusetts Medical History (Worcester Medical Library)
Automation Activity & Vendor Info: (Acquisitions) Endeavor; (Cataloging) Endeavor; (Circulation) Endeavor; (Course Reserve) Endeavor; (OPAC) Endeavor; (Serials) Endeavor
Database Vendor: OVID Technologies
Partic in Boston Library Consortium; OCLC Online Computer Library Center, Inc; Worcester Area Cooperating Libraries

S WORCESTER ART MUSEUM LIBRARY, 55 Salisbury St, 01609-3196. SAN 307-8329. Tel: 508-799-4406, Ext 3070. FAX: 508-798-5646. E-Mail: library@worcesterart.org. Web Site: www.worcesterart.org. *Librn*, Debby Aframe; *Librn*, Jolene deVergess; Staff 3 (MLS 2, Non-MLS 1)
Founded 1909
Library Holdings: Per Subs 200
Subject Interests: European art, Prints
Restriction: Open to public for reference only
Partic in Worcester Area Cooperating Libraries
Open Wed, Thurs & Fri 11-5; Sat 10-5

S WORCESTER HISTORICAL MUSEUM, 30 Elm St, 01609. SAN 307-8361. Tel: 508-753-8278. FAX: 508-753-9070. E-Mail: worchistmu@aol.com. *Exec Dir*, William D Wallace; *Archivist*, William F Carrol; *Librn*, Robyn L Christensen; Staff 6 (MLS 3, Non-MLS 3)
Founded 1875
Library Holdings: Bk Vols 10,000; Bk Titles 6,000; Per Subs 20
Subject Interests: Local history
Special Collections: Anti-Slavery (Kelley-Foster Coll), mss; Architectural Drawings Coll; City of Worcester, mss; Diner Industry; Howland Valentines; Local Information (Worcester pamphlet files); Out-of-Print Worcester Newspaper & Periodicals; Photographic & Graphic Coll

C WORCESTER POLYTECHNIC INSTITUTE, George C Gordon Library, 100 Institute Rd, 01609-2280. SAN 307-8396. Tel: 508-831-5410. Interlibrary Loan Service Tel: 508-831-5414. FAX: 508-831-5829. Web Site: www.library.wpi.edu. *Dir*, Helen Shuster; Tel: 508-831-5058; *ILL*, Diana Johnson; *Publ Servs*, Carmen Brown; *Spec Coll*, Lora Brueck; *Bibliogr, Ref*, Donald Richardson; *Online Servs*, Joanne Williams; *Ser*, Martha Gunnarson; *Circ*, Debra Bockus; Staff 10 (MLS 10)
Founded 1867. Enrl 3,116; Fac 240; Highest Degree: Doctorate
Library Holdings: Bk Vols 339,449; Per Subs 1,036
Subject Interests: Environmental studies, Safety

Special Collections: Charles Dickens (The Robert Fellman Coll); History of Science & Technology; NASA; NASA
Publications: Brochure; Calendar of Library Hours; Handbook; monthly acquisitions; specialized bibliographic instruction material
Partic in Dialog Corporation; Nelinet, Inc; OCLC Online Computer Library Center, Inc; Worcester Area Cooperating Libraries

P WORCESTER PUBLIC LIBRARY,* 160 Fremont St, 01603. SAN 345-8644. Tel: 508-799-1655. Interlibrary Loan Service Tel: 508-799-1697. FAX: 508-799-1652. Web Site: www.worcpublib.org. *Librn*, Penelope B Johnson; E-Mail: pjohnson@cwmars.org; *Reader Servs, Ref*, Christine C Kardokas; *Tech Servs*, E Glenn Musser; *Coll Develop*, Katherine Ogle; Staff 38 (MLS 38)
Founded 1859. Pop 169,759; Circ 583,593
Jul 1997-Jun 1998 Income $3,707,940, City $3,155,783. Mats Exp $412,375. Sal $2,861,944
Library Holdings: Bk Vols 519,407; Per Subs 1,024
Special Collections: US History (Library of American Civilization), micro
Publications: Your Library (quarterly)
Mem of Central Massachusetts Regional Library System
Partic in CW Mars; Nelinet, Inc; Worcester Area Cooperating Libraries
Special Services for the Deaf - TTY machine
Friends of the Library Group
Branches: 3
FRANCES PERKINS BRANCH, 470 W Boylston St, 01606-3226. SAN 345-8733. Tel: 508-799-1687. FAX: 508-799-1693. Web Site: worcpublib.org. *Librn*, Janice Charbonneau
Library Holdings: Bk Vols 48,000
Partic in CW Mars
GREAT BROOK VALLEY, 89 Tacoma St, 01605-3518. SAN 345-8725. Tel: 508-799-1729. Web Site: worcpublib.org. *Librn*, Iris Cotto
Library Holdings: Bk Vols 6,408
Partic in CW Mars

P TALKING BOOK LIBRARY, 160 Fremont St, 01603. SAN 345-8679. Tel: 508-799-1661. FAX: 508-799-1734. E-Mail: talkbook@ultranet.com. Web Site: www.worcpublib.org. *Librn*, James Izatt; Staff 1 (MLS 1)
Founded 1973
Special Services for the Blind - Braille translation & printing software & equipment; Kurzweil Reading Machine; Page magnifiers
Friends of the Library Group

C WORCESTER STATE COLLEGE, Learning Resources Center, 486 Chandler St, 01602-2597. SAN 307-840X. Tel: 508-929-8027. FAX: 508-929-8198. Web Site: www.worc.mass.edu/library. *Dir*, Dr Donald Hochstetler; *Access Serv*, Betsey Brenneman; E-Mail: bbrenneman@worc.mass.edu; *Tech Servs*, Krishna DasGupta; *Cat*, Ruth Webber; *Ref*, Pamela McKay; *Per*, Linda Snodgrass; Staff 5 (MLS 5)
Founded 1874. Enrl 5,300; Fac 245; Highest Degree: Master
Library Holdings: Bk Vols 146,000; Per Subs 974
Subject Interests: Education, Juvenile delinquency, Nursing
Partic in Nelinet, Inc; OCLC Online Computer Library Center, Inc; Worcester Area Cooperating Libraries
Open Mon-Thurs 8-11, Fri 8-5, Sat 9-5, Sun 1-11

S WORCESTER STATE HOSPITAL, Library & Learning Center,* 305 Belmont St, 01604. SAN 345-8881. Tel: 508-368-3300, Ext 89472. E-Mail: wshlib@juno.com. *Librn*, Edward M Hay; Staff 2 (MLS 1, Non-MLS 1)
Founded 1956
Library Holdings: Bk Titles 4,000; Per Subs 75

S WORCESTER TELEGRAM & GAZETTE LIBRARY,* 20 Franklin St, PO Box 15012, 01615-0012. SAN 307-8418. Tel: 508-793-9100. FAX: 508-793-9281. E-Mail: newslibrary@telegram.com. Web Site: www.telegram.com. *Librn*, George Labonte
Library Holdings: Bk Vols 600; Bk Titles 400
Special Collections: Telegram & Gazette, 1989, micro; Worcester Gazette, 1866-1989, micro; Worcester Telegram, 1884-1989, micro

J WORCESTER VOCATIONAL HIGH SCHOOL LIBRARY,* 26 Salisbury St, 01609. SAN 371-7135. Tel: 508-799-1952. E-Mail: vanliew@meol.mass.edu, worctrade@ultranet.com. Web Site: www.ciworcester.ma.us/schools/schools/voke/index.html.
Enrl 1,000; Fac 115
Library Holdings: Bk Titles 15,000; Per Subs 120
Subject Interests: Graphic arts
Special Collections: Integrated Library

WORTHINGTON

P FREDERICK SARGENT HUNTINGTON MEMORIAL LIBRARY,* Huntington Rd, PO Box 598, 01098. SAN 307-8434. Tel: 413-238-5565. *Dir*, Julia J Sharron
Founded 1914. Pop 1,015
Library Holdings: Bk Vols 10,000; Per Subs 48
Special Collections: Russell H Conwell Coll
Mem of Western Massachusetts Regional Library System

WRENTHAM

P FISKE PUBLIC LIBRARY,* 110 Randall Rd, PO Box 340, 02093-0340. SAN 307-8442. Tel: 508-384-5440. FAX: 508-384-5443. E-Mail: fiskepl@ultranet.com. *Dir, Librn*, Mary Tobichuk
Founded 1892. Pop 9,166; Circ 51,500
Library Holdings: Bk Vols 33,000; Per Subs 90
Mem of Eastern Mass Regional Libr Syst
Open Mon, Wed & Thurs 10:30-8, Tues 1-8, Fri 10:30-5, Sat 10-2
Friends of the Library Group

YARMOUTH PORT

S HISTORICAL SOCIETY OF OLD YARMOUTH LIBRARY,* Strawberry Lane, PO Box 11, 02675. SAN 373-2002. Tel: 508-362-3021. *Librn*, Grace T Hudson
Library Holdings: Bk Vols 2,500
Open Mon-Fri 9-5

MICHIGAN

Date of Statistics: 2000
Population, 1990 Census: 9,295,297
STATE LIBRARY ACTIVITIES
Library of Michigan Website: 1,453,336 web pages provided
Michigan Legislature Website: 16,918,517 web pages provided
Reference Requests: 56,345
Circulation/Information Requests:27,251
Total Items Circulated: 24,220
Interlibrary Loan Transactions: 6,515
SBPH Reference/Reader's Advisory Requests:4,392
SBPH Circulation:484,040
Total Number State Aid Grants Awarded: 379
Total LSCA I & III Grants Awarded: 74 LSTA sub-grants awarded
Total Publications Produced: 173
STATE LIBRARY GRANT ACTIVITIES
Total Applications Reviewed: 386
State Aid Grants to Public Libraries: $9,365,875
State Aid Grants to Library Cooperatives: $4,961,579
State Aid to Subregionals (Blind/Handicapped): $554,300
State Aid Grants to Wayne County for Blind/Handicapped: $49,200
Federal Grants Awarded:
Federal Library Services & Technology Act (LSTA): $4,632,550
PUBLIC LIBRARY ACTIVITIES
Total Income Reported by Public Libraries: $281,265,505
Average Income Per Capita: $30.26
Source of Income: Mainly local (approximately 94% local, 6% state & federal)
Expenditures Per Capita: $29.33
Total Number Public Library Employees: 4,439.15 (FTE)
Total Volumes Reported by Public Libraries: 25,959,775
Average Volumes Per Capita: 2.8
Total Items Available: 27,909,315
Total Circulation Reported by Public Libraries: 50,177,814
Average Circulation Per Capita: 5.4
Total Audiovisual Resources Available: 1,837,836

ADA

S AMWAY CORPORATION LIBRARY, Corporate Library 33-2L, 7575 Fulton St E, 49355-0001. SAN 329-871X. Tel: 616-787-7400. FAX: 616-787-7142. E-Mail: corporate_library@amway.com. *In Charge*, Bobbie Minier; Tel: 616-787-5276, E-Mail: bminier@amway.com; Staff 2 (Non-MLS 2)
2000-2001 Mats Exp $370,000, Books $3,000, Per/Ser (Incl. Access Fees) $320,000, Electronic Ref Mat (Incl. Access Fees) $20,000
Library Holdings: Bk Vols 5,000; Per Subs 1,500
Subject Interests: Chemistry, Cosmetics, Direct selling, Food, Multilevel marketing
Automation Activity & Vendor Info: (Acquisitions) EOS; (Cataloging) EOS; (Circulation) EOS; (OPAC) EOS; (Serials) EOS
Restriction: Not open to public, Staff use only
Partic in Michigan Library Consortium

ADRIAN

C ADRIAN COLLEGE, Shipman Library, 110 S Madison St, 49221. SAN 345-8911. Tel: 517-265-5161, Ext 4433. FAX: 517-264-3748. *Head Librn*, Richard Geyer; Tel: 517-265-5161, Ext 4220, E-Mail: rgeyer@adrian.edu; *Electronic Resources*, David Cruse; Tel: 517-265-5161, Ext 4241, E-Mail: dcruse@adrian.edu; *Tech Servs*, Noelle Keller; Tel: 517-265-5161, Ext 4229, E-Mail: nkeller@adrian.edu; *Circ*, Teresa Blomster; E-Mail: tblomster@adrian.edu; *Cat, ILL*, Carol Legenc; Tel: 517-265-5161, Ext 4439, E-Mail: clegenc@adrian.edu; *Acq, Ser*, Elizabeth Maertens; Tel: 517-264-3900, E-Mail: edarnell@adrian.edu; *Archivist*, James Simmons; Tel: 517-265-5161, Ext 4429, E-Mail: jsimmons@adrian.edu; Staff 6 (MLS 3, Non-MLS 3)
Founded 1859. Enrl 1,000; Fac 75; Highest Degree: Bachelor
Jul 2000-Jun 2001 Income Parent Institution $320,400. Mats Exp $252,500, Books $72,000, Per/Ser (Incl. Access Fees) $134,750, Presv $7,000, Micro $12,000, Electronic Ref Mat (Incl. Access Fees) $26,750
Library Holdings: Bk Vols 139,000; Bk Titles 80,000; Per Subs 628
Subject Interests: Liberal arts
Special Collections: Lincolniana (Piotrowski-Lemke); Methodist (Detroit Conference Archives)
Database Vendor: Dialog, DRA, IAC - Info Trac, OCLC - First Search
Partic in Michigan Library Consortium
Departmental Libraries:
EDUCATIONAL CURRICULUM CENTER Tel: 517-265-5161, Ext 4485.
MUSIC Tel: 517-265-5161, Ext 4247.

P ADRIAN PUBLIC LIBRARY,* 143 E Maumee St, 49221-2773. SAN 307-8469. Tel: 517-265-2265. FAX: 517-265-8847. *Dir*, Julie Fosbender; *Asst Dir*, Shirley Ehnis; *Ch Servs*, Kathy Cheser; *Media Spec*, Mary Greenwald; Staff 3 (MLS 3)
Founded 1868. Pop 22,097
Library Holdings: Bk Vols 77,000; Per Subs 161
Subject Interests: Local history
Mem of Woodlands Library Cooperative
Partic in OCLC Online Computer Library Center, Inc

M BIXBY MEDICAL CENTER, Patmos-Jones Memorial Library, 818 Riverside Ave, 49221. SAN 327-6481. Tel: 517-263-0711. FAX: 517-265-0971. *Dir*, Kim Roberts
Library Holdings: Bk Titles 500; Per Subs 11
Mem of Lakeland Library Cooperative

P LENAWEE COUNTY LIBRARY,* 4459 W US 223, 49221-1294. SAN 345-8970. Tel: 517-263-1011. FAX: 517-263-7109. *Dir*, Karen Lindquist; *Asst Dir*, Lee Groeb; *Media Spec*, Phyllis Rickard; *Bkmobile Coordr*, Diane Allen; *Bkmobile Coordr*, Barbara Sell; Staff 3 (MLS 3)
Founded 1935. Pop 43,599; Circ 339,620
Jan 1997-Dec 1998 Income $490,979. Mats Exp $61,610. Sal $321,958
Library Holdings: Bk Vols 130,000; Per Subs 503
Mem of Woodlands Library Cooperative
Branches: 7
ADDISON BRANCH, 102 S Talbot St, PO Box 234, Addison, 49220. SAN 345-9004. Tel: 517-547-3414. FAX: 517-547-3414. *Librn*, Janet Thomas
BRITTON BRANCH, 120 College Ave, PO Box 309, Britton, 49229. SAN 345-9039. Tel: 517-451-2860. FAX: 517-451-2860. *Librn*, Donna Price
CLAYTON BRANCH, 11029 Center St, PO Box 116, Clayton, 49235. SAN 345-9063. Tel: 517-445-2619. FAX: 517-445-2619. *Librn*, Virginia Wentz
ONSTED BRANCH, 261 S Main St, PO Box 248, Onsted, 49265. SAN 345-9098. Tel: 517-467-2623. FAX: 517-467-6298. *Librn*, Barbara Hess
RIDGEWAY BRANCH, Ridge Hwy, PO Box 609, Ridgeway, 49275. SAN 345-9128. *Librn*, Rose DeJonghe
ROBERTS-INGOLD MEMORIAL, 170 Raisin St, PO Box 247, Deerfield, 49238. SAN 345-9152. Tel: 517-447-3400. FAX: 517-447-3400. *Librn*, Regina Holubik
SCHULTZ-HOLMES MEMORIAL, 407 S Lane St, Blissfield, 49228. SAN 345-9187. Tel: 517-486-2858. FAX: 517-486-3565. *Librn*, Barbara Klump
Bookmobiles: 1

C SIENA HEIGHTS COLLEGE LIBRARY,* 1247 E Siena Heights Dr, 49221-1796. SAN 307-8485. Tel: 517-264-7150. FAX: 517-264-7711. Web Site: www.sienahts.edu/~libr/. *Dir*, Susan M Gilbert Black; Tel: 517-264-7152, E-Mail: sbeck@sienahts.edu; *Publ Servs*, Melissa Sissen; Tel: 517-264-7155, E-Mail: msissen@sienahts.edu; *Circ*, Sarah Baker Korth; Tel: 517-264-7150, E-Mail: skorth@sienahts.edu; *Cat*, Mark Dombrowski; Tel: 517-264-7151, E-Mail: mdombrow@sienahts.edu; *Tech Servs*, Lisa Palmer; Tel: 517-264-7153, E-Mail: lpalmer@sienahts.edu; Staff 5 (MLS 3, Non-MLS 2)
Founded 1919. Enrl 1,000; Fac 65; Highest Degree: Master
Jul 1997-Jun 1998 Income $313,233. Mats Exp $75,815, Books $33,370, Per/Ser (Incl. Access Fees) $31,000, Presv $4,000, Micro $5,245. Sal $145,292 (Prof $73,648)
Library Holdings: Bk Vols 107,072; Per Subs 359
Subject Interests: Art and architecture
Database Vendor: Dialog, epixtech, inc., IAC - Info Trac, OCLC - First Search
Partic in Michigan Library Consortium

SR UNITED METHODIST CHURCH, Detroit Conference Archives at Adrian College, c/o Shipman Library, 110 S Madison, 49221. SAN 373-5915. Tel: 517-265-5161, Ext 4429. FAX: 517-264-3748. *Dir*, James G Simmons; E-Mail: jsimmons@adrian.edu; Staff 1 (MLS 1)
Library Holdings: Bk Titles 135,000; Per Subs 800
Publications: Historical Messenger
Friends of the Library Group

S WACKER SILICONES CORP, Technical Library,* 3301 Sutton Rd, 49221. SAN 307-8493. Tel: 517-264-8500. FAX: 517-264-8246. *In Charge*, Kenneth A See Jr
Founded 1964
Library Holdings: Bk Vols 4,000

ALANSON

P ALANSON AREA PUBLIC LIBRARY,* 7631 S US 31 Hwy, PO Box 37, 49706. SAN 376-7744. Tel: 231-548-5465. FAX: 231-548-5465. *Dir*, Mary Ivey
Nov 1997-Oct 1998 Income $42,820. Mats Exp $15,860. Sal $20,920
Library Holdings: Bk Titles 10,000
Mem of Northland Library Cooperative

ALBION

C ALBION COLLEGE, Stockwell - Mudd Libraries, 602 E Cass St, 49224-1879. SAN 307-8507. Tel: 517-629-0285. Interlibrary Loan Service Tel: 517-629-0441. FAX: 517-629-0504. Web Site: www.albion.edu/fac/libr/. *Dir*, John P Kondelik; E-Mail: jkondelik@albion.edu; *Asst Dir*, Michael Van Houten; Tel: 517-629-0382, E-Mail: mvanhouten@albion.edu; *ILL*, Alice Wiley Moore; E-Mail: amoore@albion.edu; *Coll Develop, Tech Servs*, Claudia Diaz; Tel: 517-629-0386, E-Mail: cdiaz@albion.edu; *Doc, Per*, Carolyn Gaswick; Tel: 517-629-0270, E-Mail: cgaswick@albion.edu; *Bibliog Instr*, Cheryl Blackwell; *Circ*, Michelle Gerry; Tel: 517-629-0383, E-Mail: mgerry@albion.edu; Staff 5 (MLS 5)
Founded 1835. Enrl 1,426; Fac 116; Highest Degree: Bachelor
Jul 1999-Jun 2000 Income $1,401,519, Parent Institution $1,380,132, Other $21,387. Mats Exp $540,843, Books $146,922, Per/Ser (Incl. Access Fees) $294,723, Presv $25,863, Micro $14,545, AV Equip $8,750, Electronic Ref Mat (Incl. Access Fees) $50,040. Sal $456,287 (Prof $252,665)
Library Holdings: Bk Vols 346,817; Bk Titles 238,186; Per Subs 1,451; Bks on Deafness & Sign Lang 25
Subject Interests: Liberal arts
Special Collections: Albion Americana; Albion College Archives; Bible Coll; M F K Fisher; Modern Literary First Editions; Western Michigan Conference of United Methodist Church Archives, bks, letters
Automation Activity & Vendor Info: (Acquisitions) Innovative Interfaces Inc.; (Circulation) Innovative Interfaces Inc.; (Course Reserve) Innovative Interfaces Inc.; (ILL) Innovative Interfaces Inc.; (OPAC) Innovative Interfaces Inc.; (Serials) Innovative Interfaces Inc.
Database Vendor: OCLC - First Search
Partic in Dialog Corporation; Michigan Library Consortium; OCLC Online Computer Library Center, Inc; STN; Woodlands Interlibrary Loan
Online Catalog includes Expanded Academic Index
Friends of the Library Group

P ALBION PUBLIC LIBRARY, 501 S Superior St, 49224. SAN 307-8515. Tel: 517-629-3993. Interlibrary Loan Service Tel: 517-629-3993. FAX: 517-629-5354. E-Mail: albion@monroe.lib.mi.us. Web Site: www.forks.org/albionlibrary/. *Dir*, Karen Sherrard; *YA Servs*, Susan Kruger; *ILL*, Kathleen Seidl. Subject Specialists: *History*, Leslie Dick; Staff 4 (MLS 3, Non-MLS 1)
Founded 1919. Circ 66,000
Library Holdings: Bk Vols 44,000; Bk Titles 38,000; Per Subs 149
Subject Interests: Local history
Special Collections: Spanish Coll
Automation Activity & Vendor Info: (Circulation) Follett
Publications: A Michigan Childhood
Mem of Woodlands Library Cooperative
Friends of the Library Group

P WOODLANDS LIBRARY COOPERATIVE, 415 S Superior, Ste A, 49224-2174. SAN 307-8523. Tel: 517-629-9469. Interlibrary Loan Service Tel: 734-241-5277. FAX: 517-629-3812. Web Site: cwic1.jackson.lib.mi.us/woodlands/wlcmain.htm. *Dir*, James C Seidl; E-Mail: jseidl@monroe.lib.mi.us; Staff 1 (MLS 1)
Founded 1978. Pop 499,533
Oct 2000-Sep 2001 Income $539,944, State $495,504, Federal $23,793, Locally Generated Income $20,647. Mats Exp $1,103, Books $915, Per/Ser (Incl. Access Fees) $188. Sal $75,840 (Prof $53,675)
Automation Activity & Vendor Info: (ILL) Brodart
Publications: News Notes (monthly)
Member Libraries: Adrian Public Library; Albion Public Library; Bellevue Township Library; Branch District Library; Burlington Township Library; Burr Oak Township Library; Camden Township Public Library; Colon Township Library; Constantine Township Library; Delton District Library; Homer Public Library; Hudson Public Library; Jonesville District Library; Lenawee County Library; Litchfield District Library; Manchester Township Library; Marshall District Library; Mendon Township Library; Milan Public Library; Mitchell Public Library; Nottawa Township Library; Pittsford Public Library; Putnam District Library; Reading Community Library; Schoolcraft Community Library; Stair Public Library; Sturgis Public Library; Tecumseh Public Library; Tekonsha Public Library; Three Rivers Public Library; Van Buren District Library; Waldron District Library; White Pigeon Township Library
Partic in OCLC Online Computer Library Center, Inc

ALDEN

P HELENA TOWNSHIP PUBLIC LIBRARY,* 8751 Helena Rd, 49612. SAN 307-8531. Tel: 231-331-4318. FAX: 231-331-4245. E-Mail: pbqh@yahoo.com. *Librn*, Gay Anderson
Circ 22,580
Library Holdings: Bk Vols 18,000; Per Subs 25
Mem of Mid-Michigan Library League
Friends of the Library Group

ALLEGAN

P ALLEGAN PUBLIC LIBRARY,* 331 Hubbard St, 49010-1258. SAN 307-854X. Tel: 616-673-4625. FAX: 616-673-8661. E-Mail: apl@triton.net. Web Site: www.web.triton.net/allegan. *Dir*, Ann Perrigo; *Asst Librn*, Linda Lightcap; *Tech Servs*, Joy Masek; *Ch Servs*, Barbara Osborn; Staff 2 (MLS 2)
Founded 1843. Pop 14,821; Circ 78,000
Jul 1998-Jun 1999 Income $310,350. Mats Exp $38,500, Books $31,200, Per/Ser (Incl. Access Fees) $2,800. Sal $136,150 (Prof $49,800)
Library Holdings: Bk Titles 57,106; Per Subs 105
Subject Interests: Civil War, Michigan
Automation Activity & Vendor Info: (Cataloging) Sagebrush Corporation; (Circulation) Sagebrush Corporation; (OPAC) Sagebrush Corporation
Partic in Southwest Michigan Library Cooperative
Friends of the Library Group

ALLEN PARK

P ALLEN PARK PUBLIC LIBRARY,* 8100 Allen Rd, 48101. SAN 307-8558. Tel: 313-381-2425. FAX: 313-381-2124. *Ch Servs*, Sandi Blakney; Staff 5 (MLS 2, Non-MLS 3)
Founded 1927. Pop 34,169; Circ 88,045
Library Holdings: Bk Vols 50,000; Per Subs 157
Mem of The Library Network
Friends of the Library Group

R DETROIT BAPTIST THEOLOGICAL SEMINARY LIBRARY, 4801 Allen Rd, 48101. SAN 373-2010. Tel: 313-381-0111. FAX: 313-381-0798. *Dir Libr Serv*, Mark A Snoeberger; E-Mail: msnoeberger@dbts.edu; Staff 2 (MLS 1, Non-MLS 1)
Founded 1976. Enrl 120; Highest Degree: Master
Library Holdings: Bk Vols 28,000; Bk Titles 24,000; Per Subs 250
Subject Interests: Biblical studies, Theology
Database Vendor: Ebsco - EbscoHost
Partic in Michigan Library Consortium

ALLENDALE

P ALLENDALE TOWNSHIP LIBRARY,* 6175 Library Lane, 49401. SAN 307-8574. Tel: 616-895-4178. FAX: 616-895-5178. *Librn*, Janice Sall; *Ch Servs*, Shirley TenBrink
Founded 1966. Pop 8,022; Circ 63,355
1997-1998 Income $124,648, State $7,352, Other $75,344. Mats Exp Books $19,610. Sal $56,908 (Prof $28,466)
Library Holdings: Bk Vols 20,702; Per Subs 53
Mem of Lakeland Library Cooperative

C GRAND VALLEY STATE UNIVERSITY, Zumberge Library, One Campus Dr, 49401-9403. SAN 307-8582. Tel: 616-895-2619. Circulation Tel: 616-895-3252. Reference Tel: 616-895-3500. FAX: 616-895-2895. Web Site: www.gvsu.edu/library. *Dir*, Lee Lebbin; E-Mail: lebbinl@gvsu.edu; *Archivist*, Robert Beasecker; Tel: 616-895-2635; *Automation Syst Coordr*, Deborah Morrow; *Bibliog Instr*, Kathryn Waggoner; *Cat*, Carole Garey; Tel: 616-895-2623; *ILL*, Laurel Balkema; Tel: 616-895-2630; *Per*, Millie Jackson; Tel: 616-895-2901; Staff 17 (MLS 17)
Founded 1962. Enrl 18,579; Fac 555; Highest Degree: Master
Library Holdings: Bk Vols 497,801; Per Subs 3,207
Special Collections: Limited Edition Series; Lincoln & the Civil War Coll; Michigan; Michigan Novels; US Geological Survey Maps
Automation Activity & Vendor Info: (Acquisitions) Endeavor
Publications: Library newsletter
Partic in Michigan Library Consortium; OCLC Online Computer Library Center, Inc

ALMA

C ALMA COLLEGE LIBRARY, 614 W Superior, 48801. SAN 307-8590. Tel: 517-463-7227. Interlibrary Loan Service Tel: 517-463-7128. Circulation Tel: 517-463-7229. Reference Tel: 517-463-7343. FAX: 517-463-8694. Web Site: www.alma.edu/library. *Dir*, Peter Dollard; E-Mail: dollard@alma.edu; *Tech Servs*, Carol Struble; Tel: 517-463-7343, E-Mail: struble@alma.edu; *Automation Syst Coordr*, Priscilla Perkins; Tel: 517-463-7345, E-Mail: perkinsp@alma.edu; *ILL*, Susan Cross; E-Mail: cross@alma.edu; *Bibliog Instr*, Steven Vest; Tel: 517-463-7344, E-Mail: vest@alma.edu; Staff 4 (MLS 4)
Founded 1889. Enrl 1,350; Fac 98; Highest Degree: Bachelor
Jul 1999-Jun 2000 Income Parent Institution $1,013,863. Mats Exp $516,005, Books $279,218, Per/Ser (Incl. Access Fees) $226,571, Presv $9,845, AV Equip $371. Sal $299,404 (Prof $206,088)
Library Holdings: Bk Vols 238,384; Bk Titles 189,147; Per Subs 1,186
Special Collections: College Archives
Automation Activity & Vendor Info: (Acquisitions) epixtech, inc.; (Cataloging) epixtech, inc.; (Circulation) epixtech, inc.; (OPAC) epixtech, inc.; (Serials) epixtech, inc.
Database Vendor: Dialog, epixtech, inc., IAC - Info Trac, IAC - SearchBank, Lexis-Nexis, OCLC - First Search, Silverplatter Information Inc.
Partic in Michigan Library Consortium

P ALMA PUBLIC LIBRARY,* 351 N Court, 48801-1999. SAN 307-8604. Tel: 517-463-3966. FAX: 517-466-5901. *Librn*, Bryan E Dinwoody; *Asst Librn*, Tina Leonard; Staff 2 (MLS 2)
Founded 1909. Circ 70,226
Library Holdings: Bk Vols 60,000; Per Subs 158
Special Collections: Republic Truck Photography Coll
Publications: Annual Report; Subject Bibliographies
Mem of Capital Library Cooperative

ALMONT

P ALMONT DISTRICT LIBRARY, (ADL), Henry Stephens Memorial Library, 213 W St Clair St, PO Box 517, 48003-0517. SAN 307-8620. Tel: 810-798-3100. FAX: 810-798-2208. E-Mail: adl@expression.org. *Dir*, Judith L Chelekis
Founded 1918. Pop 4,660; Circ 22,950
Library Holdings: Bk Titles 19,600
Function: ILL available, Photocopies available, Some telephone reference
Partic in Mideastern Mich Libr Coop; MLA

ALPENA

J ALPENA COMMUNITY COLLEGE, (ACCLRC), Stephen H Fletcher Library, 666 Johnson St, 49707. SAN 307-8639. Tel: 517-356-9021, Ext 249, 252, 406. FAX: 517-356-6334. E-Mail: acclrc@alpena.cc.mi.us. Web Site: www.alpena.cc.mi.us/library/lrcweb.htm. *Asst Dean*, Charles E Tetzlaff; Tel: 517-356-9021, Ext 249; *Librn*, Kelly Jackson; *AV*, John Parris; Tel: 517-356-9021, Ext 244
Founded 1952. Enrl 1,167; Fac 81; Highest Degree: Associate
Jul 1998-Jun 1999 Income (Main Library Only) Parent Institution $253,872. Mats Exp $58,693, Books $26,950, Per/Ser (Incl. Access Fees) $8,779, Micro $4,571, AV Equip $3,950, Electronic Ref Mat (Incl. Access Fees) $14,443. Sal $128,767
Library Holdings: Bk Vols 34,555; Bk Titles 29,636; Per Subs 185
Publications: Guide to library
Mem of Northern Illinois Library System; Northland Library Cooperative
Partic in Northern Ill Libr Syst

P ALPENA COUNTY LIBRARY, (ACL), George N Fletcher Public Library, 211 N First St, 49707. SAN 307-8647. Tel: 517-356-6188. FAX: 517-356-2765. Web Site: www.nlc.lib.mi.us/members/alpena. *Dir*, Judi Stillion; E-Mail: jsacl@northland.lib.mi.us
Founded 1967. Pop 30,000; Circ 130,000
1998-1999 Income $1,100,000, State $32,450, County $427,320, Locally Generated Income $29,741, Other $228,833. Mats Exp $127,000, Books $110,000, Per/Ser (Incl. Access Fees) $12,000, Electronic Ref Mat (Incl. Access Fees) $5,000. Sal $324,000 (Prof $121,000)
Library Holdings: Bk Titles 77,000; Per Subs 231
Special Collections: Adult Literacy; Cooperating Coll for the Foundation of New York; Education Info Center (Job Launch) Educational Media; Genealogy Center; Michigan Coll
Mem of Northland Library Cooperative
Friends of the Library Group

S JESSE BESSER MUSEUM LIBRARY, Philip M Park Memorial Library, 491 Johnson St, 49707-1496. SAN 320-8621. Tel: 517-356-2202. FAX: 517-356-3133. E-Mail: jbmuseum@northland.lib.mi.us. Web Site: www.oweb.com/upnorth/museum. *Dir*, Dr Janice McLean; *Librn*, Janet Smoak
Founded 1966
Library Holdings: Bk Titles 4,250; Per Subs 20
Subject Interests: Anthropology, Antiques, Archaeology, Art, Astronomy, Decorative arts, Genealogy, Great Lakes, Indians, Michigan
Publications: Pamphlets Concerning Local History
Restriction: Open to public for reference only
Mem of Northland Library Cooperative

P NORTHLAND LIBRARY COOPERATIVE, 316 E Chisholm St, 49707. SAN 307-8655. Tel: 517-356-1622. Toll Free Tel: 800-446-1580. FAX: 517-354-3939. E-Mail: nlcref@northland.lib.mi.us. Web Site: www.nlc.lib.mi.us. *Adminr*, Christine E Johnson; E-Mail: nlcdir@northland.lib.mi.us; Staff 10 (MLS 2, Non-MLS 8)
Founded 1966. Pop 169,915
Special Collections: Audio Books; Book-Cassette Kits; Census
Database Vendor: Dialog, IAC - Info Trac, IAC - SearchBank, OCLC - First Search
Function: ILL available
Member Libraries: Alanson Area Public Library; Alcona County Library System; Alpena Community College; Alpena County Library; Boyne District Library; Charlevoix Public Library; Cheboygan Area Public Library; Crawford County Library; Crooked Tree District Library; Indian River Area Library; Jesse Besser Museum Library; Jordan Valley District Library; Mackinaw Area Public Library; North Central Michigan College Library; Oscoda County Library; Otsego County Library; Petoskey Public Library; Presque Isle District Library; Topinabee Public Library; Wolverine Community Library
Branches: 1

P LIBRARY FOR THE BLIND & PHYSICALLY HANDICAPPED *Librn*, Catherine A Glomski
Founded 1977. Pop 208,704; Circ 25,000
Special Services for the Blind - Brailling & large print projects; Handicapped awareness programs; Reference searches; Student reference materials taped

AMASA

P AMASA COMMUNITY LIBRARY,* 208 Pine St, PO Box 218, 49903-0218. SAN 307-8663. Tel: 906-822-7831.
Pop 404; Circ 1,174
Library Holdings: Bk Vols 2,500
Mem of Mid-Peninsula Library Cooperative

ANN ARBOR

S AMERICAN MATHEMATICAL SOCIETY, Mathematical Reviews Library,* 416 Fourth St, PO Box 8604, 48107. SAN 323-4975. Tel: 734-996-5267. FAX: 734-996-2916. E-Mail: btk@ams.org. *Bibliog Instr*, Bert TePaske-King; *Coll Develop*, Paula Shanks
Library Holdings: Per Subs 2,500

P ANN ARBOR DISTRICT LIBRARY, 343 S Fifth Ave, 48104. SAN 345-9217. Tel: 734-327-4200. Circulation Tel: 734-327-4297. Reference Tel: 734-327-4525. FAX: 734-327-8309. Web Site: www.aadl.org. *Dir*, Mary Anne Hodel; Tel: 734-327-4280, E-Mail: hodelm@aadl.org; *Mgr*, Tim Minick; E-Mail: minickt@aadl.org; *Mgr*, Ginger Sissom; Tel: 734-327-4575, Fax: 734-327-8324, E-Mail: sissomg@aadl.org; *Publ Servs*, Josie Parker; Tel: 734-327-4280, E-Mail: parkerj@aadl.org; *Commun Relations*, Tim Grimes; Tel: 734-327-4265, E-Mail: grimest@aadl.org; *Tech Coordr*, Eli Nieburger; Tel: 734-327-4245, Fax: 734-327-8325, E-Mail: nieburgere@aadl.org; *ILL*, Marcella Zorn; Tel: 734-327-4234, Fax: 734-327-8307, E-Mail: zornm@aadl.org; *Ad Servs*, Jane Conway; Tel: 734-327-4241, Fax: 734-327-8307, E-Mail: conwayj@aadl.org; *Circ*, Janice Savelle; Tel: 734-327-4296, E-Mail: savellej@aadl.org; *Tech Servs*, Janet P Smith; Tel: 734-327-4252, Fax: 734-327-4255, E-Mail: smithj@aadl.org; *Ch Servs*, Rachel Yanikoglu; Tel: 734-327-8319, Fax: 734-327-4283, E-Mail: yanikoglur@aadl.org; *Business*, Ken Nieman; Tel: 734-327-4517, E-Mail: niemank@aadl.org; Staff 196 (MLS 26, Non-MLS 170)
Founded 1856. Pop 136,892; Circ 1,526,184
Jul 1999-Jun 2000 Income (Main Library and Branch Library) $8,807,562, State $345,117, City $7,691,893, Locally Generated Income $648,854, Other $121,698. Mats Exp $661,838, Books $414,415, Per/Ser (Incl. Access Fees) $67,925, Micro $6,236, AV Equip $30,658, Other Print Mats $61,425, Electronic Ref Mat (Incl. Access Fees) $81,179. Sal $4,609,000 (Prof $1,067,279)
Library Holdings: Bk Vols 405,947; Bk Titles 245,193; Per Subs 771
Subject Interests: Art and architecture, Art prints, Basic educ, Bks on cassettes, Black studies, Business and management, Ethnic studies, Large print, Music
Special Collections: Browsing; Small Press
Automation Activity & Vendor Info: (Acquisitions) DRA; (Cataloging) DRA; (Circulation) DRA; (OPAC) DRA; (Serials) DRA
Database Vendor: DRA, Ebsco - EbscoHost, GaleNet, IAC - Info Trac, IAC - SearchBank, OCLC - First Search
Publications: Adult Basic Reading Coll; Ann Arbor Business Guide; Homepage/Hardcopy (newsletter)
Mem of The Library Network

Partic in Michigan Library Consortium; OCLC Online Computer Library Center, Inc
Special Services for the Blind - CCTV (VisualTex)
Friends of the Library Group
Branches: 3
LOVING BRANCH LIBRARY, 3042 Creek Dr, 48108. SAN 345-9241. Tel: 734-994-2353. FAX: 734-971-8637. Web Site: www.aadl.org. *Branch Mgr*, Colleen Verge; E-Mail: vergec@aadl.org; *Commun Relations*, Tim Grimes; Tel: 734-327-4265, Fax: 734-327-8309, E-Mail: grimest@aadl.org
Library Holdings: Bk Vols 37,215; Per Subs 105
Database Vendor: DRA
NORTHEAST BRANCH LIBRARY, 2713 Plymouth Rd, 48105. SAN 345-925X. Tel: 734-996-3180. FAX: 734-996-2012. Web Site: www.aadl.org. *Branch Mgr*, Colleen Verge; E-Mail: vergec@aadl.org; *Commun Relations*, Tim Grimes; Tel: 734-327-4265, Fax: 734-327-8309, E-Mail: grimest@aadl.org
Library Holdings: Bk Vols 31,790; Per Subs 97
WEST BRANCH LIBRARY, 2503 Jackson Rd, 48103. SAN 345-9276. Tel: 734-994-1674. FAX: 734-994-1857. Web Site: www.aadl.org. *Branch Mgr*, Robb Pilkerton; E-Mail: pikertonr@aadl.org; *Commun Relations*, Tim Grimes; Tel: 734-327-4265, Fax: 734-327-8309, E-Mail: grimest@aadl.org
Library Holdings: Bk Vols 40,407; Per Subs 143
Bookmobiles: 1

S ANN ARBOR NEWS LIBRARY,* 340 E Huron St, 48106-1147. SAN 371-280X. Tel: 734-994-6953. FAX: 734-994-6989. *Librn*, Grace Puravs
Library Holdings: Bk Vols 800; Per Subs 10
Special Collections: Newspapers Covering Area since November 1829, microfilm

C CONCORDIA COLLEGE, Zimmerman Library, 4090 Geddes Rd, 48160. SAN 307-8698. Tel: 734-995-7353. FAX: 734-995-7405. Web Site: www.ccaa.edu/ls. *Dir*, Kevin J Brandon; *Acq*, Stephen Parrish; *Doc Delivery*, Jennifer Schumacher; *Publ Servs*, Margaret Goodrich; *Tech Servs*, Richard Buesing
Founded 1963. Enrl 625; Fac 46; Highest Degree: Master
Library Holdings: Bk Vols 110,000; Bk Titles 92,000; Per Subs 1,797
Subject Interests: Education, History, Music, Natural science, Theology
Special Collections: (Partial); ; Classics; ERIC depository; French Language & Literature (Denkinger); History of Science (Annual Volumes & Backfile Bound Periodicals for Creation Research Society Quarterly, vols 1 to date & Journal of Victoria Institute, 1861-1975)
Automation Activity & Vendor Info: (Acquisitions) DRA; (Cataloging) DRA; (Circulation) DRA; (Course Reserve) DRA; (OPAC) DRA
Database Vendor: OCLC - First Search
Mem of Library Network
Partic in Michigan Library Consortium; OCLC Online Computer Library Center, Inc
Friends of the Library Group

GM DEPARTMENT OF VETERANS AFFAIRS, Medical Center Library, 2215 Fuller Rd, 48105. SAN 346-0207. Tel: 734-761-5385. FAX: 734-761-7197. *Librn*, Vickie Smith; E-Mail: smith.vickie@forum.va.gov; *Tech Servs*, Joellen Weller; Staff 2 (MLS 1, Non-MLS 1)
Library Holdings: Bk Vols 5,581; Per Subs 258
Subject Interests: Health sci
Partic in Metrop Detroit Med Libr Group; Michigan Library Consortium; Oakland Washtenaw Wayne Livingston Libr Group; Veterans Affairs Library Network

G ENVIRONMENTAL PROTECTION AGENCY, National Vehicle & Fuel Emission Lab Library,* 2000 Traverwood Dr, 48105. SAN 307-8701. Tel: 734-214-4468. FAX: 734-214-4525. *Librn*, Linda Streeter
Founded 1975
Subject Interests: Air pollution, Automotive engineering, Fuel
Special Collections: Engineering Papers (1962 to present); EPA 460 Report Coll; Legislative Materials, Documents & Reports; Microfiche Federal Register (1977 to present); Soc of Automotive
Publications: EPA MVEL Final Report List; MVEL Technical Report List
Partic in OCLC Online Computer Library Center, Inc

S FEDERAL-MOGUL CORPORATION, Materials Research Library, 3990 Research Park Dr, 48108-0890. SAN 307-871X. Tel: 734-995-8573. FAX: 734-995-3521. *Res*, Margaret Bean; E-Mail: Margaret_Bean@fmo.com. Subject Specialists: *Engineering*, Margaret Bean; Staff 1 (MLS 1)
Founded 1945
Jan 2000-Dec 2000 Mats Exp $16,181, Books $3,636, Per/Ser (Incl. Access Fees) $4,545, Other Print Mats $8,000
Library Holdings: Bk Vols 1,500; Bk Titles 900; Per Subs 65
Subject Interests: Chemical eng, Metallurgy
Database Vendor: Dialog
Publications: Newsletter

S GREAT LAKES COMMISSION LIBRARY,* The Argus II Bldg, 400 Fourth St, 48103-4816. SAN 373-0697. Tel: 734-665-9135. FAX: 734-665-4370. *In Charge*, Julie Wagemakers; E-Mail: juliew@glc.org
Library Holdings: Bk Vols 500; Per Subs 25

S HISTORICAL SOCIETY OF MICHIGAN, Center for the Teaching of Michigan History, 2117 Washtenaw Ave, 48104. SAN 371-8778. Tel: 734-769-1828. FAX: 734-769-4267. E-Mail: hsm@hsofmich.org. *Exec Dir*, Hugh D Gurney
Library Holdings: Bk Titles 1,000; Per Subs 45
Subject Interests: Local history, Mich hist
Special Collections: Michigan History Teaching Resources, bks, pers
Publications: Newsletter
Restriction: Non-circulating to the public

S LIFESPAN RESOURCES, INC LIBRARY, 1212 Roosevelt, 48104. SAN 371-5833. Tel: 734-971-2191. FAX: 734-973-7645. *Pres*, Carol H Tice; Staff 8 (MLS 3, Non-MLS 5)
Founded 1979
1999-2000 Mats Exp $3,000, Books $1,000, Manuscripts & Archives $2,000
Special Collections: Intergenerational Youths at Risk - Their Potential for Schooling & Employment

G MICHIGAN DEPARTMENT OF NATURAL RESOURCES, INSTITUTE FOR FISHERIES RESEARCH, Fisheries Division Library, 212 Museums Annex Bldg, 1109 N University Ave, 48109-1084. SAN 307-8779. Tel: 734-663-3554. FAX: 734-663-9399. Web Site: www.dnr.state.mi.us/www/ifr/ifrlibra/ifrlibra.htm. *Librn*, Tina M Tincher; E-Mail: tinchert@state.mi.us
Founded 1930
Library Holdings: Bk Vols 700; Per Subs 21
Publications: Various research reports & reprints of research findings

S MICHIGAN MUNICIPAL LEAGUE LIBRARY,* 1675 Green Rd, PO Box 1487, 48106-1487. SAN 321-5229. Tel: 734-662-3246. FAX: 313-662-8083. *Librn*, Colleen Layton
Founded 1899
Library Holdings: Bk Titles 3,000
Special Collections: Charters, Codes & Ordinances for Michigan Cities; Michigan Proposed Legislation
Publications: Subject list of MML Publications

G NATIONAL ARCHIVES & RECORDS ADMINISTRATION, Gerald R Ford Library, 1000 Beal Ave, 48109-2114. SAN 321-6497. Tel: 734-741-2218. FAX: 734-741-2341. E-Mail: fordlibrary@nara.gov. Web Site: www.ford.utexas.edu. *Dir*, Dr Dennis Daellenback; *Archivist*, David Horrocks
Founded 1977
Library Holdings: Bk Vols 9,618; Bk Titles 6,550; Per Subs 25
Special Collections: Papers of Gerald Ford & contemporaries
Publications: Gerald Ford Foundation Newsletter; Guide to Historical Materials in the Gerald R Ford Library
Library is part of the system of presidential libraries administered by the National Archives & Records Administration
Friends of the Library Group

S NATIONAL CENTER FOR MANUFACTURING SCIENCES, (MIRC), Manufacturing Information Resource Center, 3025 Boardwalk, 48108. SAN 375-1619. Tel: 734-995-0300. FAX: 734-995-1150. Web Site: www.ncms.org. *Dir*, Cindy Bousley
Founded 1987
Library Holdings: Bk Titles 15,000; Per Subs 500

G NATIONAL OCEANIC & ATMOSPHERIC ADMINISTRATION, Great Lakes Environmental Research Laboratory Library, 2205 Commonwealth Blvd, 48105. SAN 307-8787. Tel: 734-741-2242. FAX: 734-741-2055. E-Mail: ill@lib.glerl.noaa.gov. Web Site: www.lib.glerl.noaa.gov. *Librn*, Barbara J Carrick; E-Mail: carrick@glerl.noaa.gov; Staff 1 (MLS 1)
Founded 1975. Highest Degree: Master
Library Holdings: Bk Vols 8,655; Per Subs 213
Subject Interests: Climatology, Geophysics, Great Lakes, Hydrology, Limnology, Meteorology, Oceanography
Automation Activity & Vendor Info: (Cataloging) SIRSI; (Circulation) SIRSI; (OPAC) SIRSI
Partic in Fed Libr & Info Network; Michigan Library Consortium; OCLC Online Computer Library Center, Inc

S NORTH AMERICAN STUDENTS OF COOPERATION, NASCO Library of Publications on Cooperatives,* PO Box 7715, 48107. SAN 326-3053. Tel: 734-663-0889. FAX: 734-663-5072. *Librn*, Susan Caya; Staff 1 (Non-MLS 1)
Founded 1968
Library Holdings: Bk Titles 750; Per Subs 30

S RIGHT TO LIFE OF MICHIGAN, Resource Center, 24 Frank Lloyd Wright Dr, 48106. (Mail add: PO Box 493, 48106-0493), Tel: 734-930-7474. FAX: 734-930-7479. *Mgr*, Brittany Smith

M ST JOSEPH MERCY HOSPITAL, Riecker Memorial Library, 5301 E Huron River Dr, PO Box 995, 48106. SAN 307-8809. Tel: 734-712-3045. FAX: 734-712-2679. E-Mail: sjmhosp@mlc.lib.mi.us. *Mgr*, Ken Nelson
Library Holdings: Bk Titles 5,000; Per Subs 120
Subject Interests: Clinical medicine, Education, Hospital administration, Surgery
Special Collections: Health Information Library for Patients

Restriction: Private library
Partic in Metrop Detroit Med Libr Group; Michigan Health Sciences Libraries Association; Michigan Library Consortium; National Network of Libraries of Medicine - Greater Midwest Region; OWLSnet

G UNITED STATES GEOLOGICAL SURVEY, John Van Oosten Library, 1451 Green Rd, 48105-2899. SAN 307-8817. Tel: 734-994-3331, Ext 210. FAX: 734-994-8780. E-Mail: gs-glsc-library@usgs.gov. Web Site: www.glsc.usgs.gov/library. *Librn*, Ann Zimmerman; E-Mail: ann_zimmerman@usgs.gov; Staff 2 (MLS 1, Non-MLS 1)
Founded 1965
Oct 1999-Sep 2000 Income $145,000. Mats Exp $40,051, Books $4,450, Per/Ser (Incl. Access Fees) $34,500, Micro $100, Other Print Mats $1,001. Sal $85,000 (Prof $50,000)
Library Holdings: Bk Titles 8,500; Per Subs 90
Subject Interests: Biology, Environmental studies, Great Lakes
Partic in Dialog Corporation; Fedlink; Michigan Library Consortium; OCLC Online Computer Library Center, Inc

UNIVERSITY OF MICHIGAN

C BENTLEY HISTORICAL LIBRARY, 1150 Beal Ave, 48109-2113. SAN 345-9489. Tel: 734-764-3482. FAX: 734-936-1333. E-Mail: bentley.ref@umich.edu. Web Site: www.umich.edu/~bhl/. *Dir*, Francis X Blouin, Jr; *Asst Dir*, William K Wallach; Staff 22 (MLS 12, Non-MLS 10)
Founded 1935
Sep 1998-Aug 1999 Income (Main and Other College/University Libraries) $982,870. Mats Exp $58,000. Sal $919,499
Library Holdings: Bk Vols 60,000; Per Subs 107
Subject Interests: Michigan
Special Collections: Architectural Coll; Papers of Frank Murphy, George Romney, Arthur Vandenburg, G Mennen Williams, Gerald L K Smith, William G Milliken, Detroit Urban League; Records of University of Michigan; Temperance & Prohibition (Women's Christian Temerance Union), micro, printed, mss; US & China; US & Philippines
Publications: Asn of Res Librs
Partic in RLIN
Friends of the Library Group

C ENGLISH LANGUAGE INSTITUTE-LINGUISTICS LIBRARY, 3003 N University Bldg, 48109-1057. SAN 345-9330. Tel: 734-647-0478. FAX: 734-763-0369. *Librn*, Lani Wang; E-Mail: laniwang@umich.edu
Founded 1960
Library Holdings: Bk Titles 4,300; Per Subs 40
Subject Interests: Bilingual Education, Foreign Language, Linguistics
Mem of Asn of Research Libraries

C KRESGE BUSINESS ADMINISTRATION LIBRARY, K3330 Univ of Michigan Business School, 701 Tappan St, 48109-1234. SAN 345-9306. Tel: 734-764-7356. Circulation Tel: 734-764-1375. Reference Tel: 734-764-9464. FAX: 734-764-3839. E-Mail: kresge_library@umich.edu. Web Site: lib.bus.umich.edu. *Actg Dir*, Tomalee Doan; Tel: 734-764-8424, E-Mail: doant@umich.edu; *Ref Serv*, Nancy Karp; Tel: 734-764-4373, E-Mail: nskarp@umich.edu; *Tech Servs*, John Sterbenz; Tel: 734-764-5746, Fax: 734-764-3839, E-Mail: jsterben@umich.edu; *Instrul Serv*, Sally Weston; Tel: 734-764-5532, E-Mail: sweston@umich.edu; *Res*, JoAnn Sokkar; Tel: 734-763-9360, E-Mail: jsokkar@umich.edu; *Coll Develop*, Anne Houston; Staff 17 (MLS 8, Non-MLS 9)
Founded 1925
Jul 1999-Jun 2000 Income $1,900,000. Mats Exp $950,000, Books $58,000, Per/Ser (Incl. Access Fees) $877,000, Presv $15,000. Sal $816,400
Library Holdings: Bk Vols 141,000; Bk Titles 69,000; Per Subs 2,500
Subject Interests: Annual reports, Business, Career info
Automation Activity & Vendor Info: (Acquisitions) Innovative Interfaces Inc.; (Cataloging) Innovative Interfaces Inc.; (Circulation) Innovative Interfaces Inc.; (Course Reserve) Innovative Interfaces Inc.; (ILL) Innovative Interfaces Inc.; (Media Booking) Innovative Interfaces Inc.; (OPAC) Innovative Interfaces Inc.; (Serials) Innovative Interfaces Inc.
Database Vendor: Dialog, GaleNet, IAC - Info Trac, Innovative Interfaces INN - View, Lexis-Nexis, OCLC - First Search, ProQuest
Publications: Bibliographies; newsletters; user guides
Function: Internet access, Research library
Mem of Asn of Research Libraries
Partic in Comt on Institutional Coop; Michigan Library Consortium; OCLC Online Computer Library Center, Inc

CL LAW LIBRARY, 801 Monroe, 48109-1210. SAN 345-942X. Tel: 734-764-9322. FAX: 734-936-3884. *Dir*, Margaret A Leary; *Ref*, Barbara Garavaglia; *ILL*, Barbara Snow; *Tech Servs*, Suzan Burks; Staff 12 (MLS 12)
Founded 1859. Enrl 1,150; Fac 60; Highest Degree: Doctorate
Jul 1997-Jun 1998 Income $3,960,119, State $3,767,747, Locally Generated Income $63,747, Other $128,625. Mats Exp $1,514,946, Books $160,009, Per/Ser (Incl. Access Fees) $1,354,937. Sal $1,732,885 (Prof $574,141)
Library Holdings: Bk Titles 266,423; Per Subs 9,676
Publications: Guide to legal research
Partic in Center For Research Libraries; RLIN; Westlaw

C RESIDENCE HALL LIBRARIES, 1503 Washington Heights, 48109-2015. SAN 345-9543. Tel: 734-647-1152, 734-647-3785. FAX: 734-764-1153. Web Site: www.rhl.housing.umich.edu. *Asst Dir*, Darlene Ray-Johnson; Tel: 734-763-3161; Staff 89 (MLS 1, Non-MLS 88)
Founded 1951. Enrl 10,000; Highest Degree: Master
Jul 1999-Jun 2000 Income $379,140. Mats Exp $32,400, Books $9,600, Per/Ser (Incl. Access Fees) $14,400, Other Print Mats $8,400. Sal $253,651 (Prof $50,000)
Library Holdings: Bk Vols 40,000; Per Subs 730; Spec Interest Per Sub 27; Bks on Deafness & Sign Lang 73
Mem of Asn of Research Libraries
A system of 12 libraries located in University of Michigan residence halls, serving residents with material related to academic programs, cultural development & recreational needs; organized to assist the student within the living-learning enviroment of the residence hall

C SUMNER & LAURA FOSTER LIBRARY, 265 Lorch Hall, 48109-1220. SAN 345-9519. Tel: 734-763-6609. Web Site: www.econ.lsa.umich.edu/library/. *Librn*, Kathleen Folger; Fax: 734-764-2769, E-Mail: kfolger@umich.edu; Staff 1 (MLS 1)
Founded 1986
Jul 2000-Jun 2001 Income Parent Institution $50,000. Mats Exp $13,750, Books $1,000, Per/Ser (Incl. Access Fees) $12,000, Other Print Mats $750. Sal $35,000 (Prof $24,000)
Library Holdings: Bk Vols 2,500; Per Subs 100
Subject Interests: Economics
Special Collections: Working Papers & Research Reports from other Universities & Research Institute
Mem of Asn of Research Libraries

S TRANSPORTATION RESEARCH INSTITUTE LIBRARY, 2901 Baxter Rd, 48109-2150. SAN 345-939X. Tel: 734-764-2171. FAX: 734-936-1081. *Coordr*, Bob Sweet; E-Mail: bsweet@umich.edu; *Asst Dir*, Michelle Wheeler; Staff 5 (MLS 2, Non-MLS 3)
Founded 1966
Library Holdings: Per Subs 300
Subject Interests: Automotive engineering
Publications: UMTRI Bibliography (cumulative); UMTRI Current Acquisitions - A Selected List (weekly - electronic & printed editions)
Partic in Dialog Corporation

C UNIVERSITY OF MICHIGAN, University Library, 818 Hatcher Graduate Library, 48109-1205. SAN 345-9578. Tel: 734-764-9356. Interlibrary Loan Service Tel: 734-764-8584. FAX: 734-763-5080. Web Site: www.lib.umich.edu/. *Dir*, William A Gosling; E-Mail: wgosling@umich.edu; *Publ Servs*, Brenda Johnson; E-Mail: bljohn@umich.edu; *Spec Coll*, Peggy Daub; E-Mail: pdaub@umich.edu; *Ref*, Barbara MacAdam; E-Mail: bmacadam@umich.edu; *Access Serv*, Rebecca Dunkle; E-Mail: rdunkle@umich.edu; *Acq*, *Ser*, Leighann Ayers; E-Mail: layers@umich.edu; *Cat*, Lynn Marko; E-Mail: lfmarko@umich.edu; *Syst Coordr*, Phyllis Valentine; E-Mail: pav@umich.edu; *Access Serv*, Anne Beaubien; E-Mail: beaubien@umich.edu; *Coll Develop*, Mark Sandler; E-Mail: sandler@umich.edu. Subject Specialists: *Syst mgt*, Phyllis Valentine; Staff 370 (MLS 111, Non-MLS 259)
Founded 1817. Enrl 51,199; Fac 3,131; Highest Degree: Doctorate
Jul 1999-Jun 2000 Income (Main Library and Branch Library) $33,324,747. Mats Exp $14,254,482, Books $5,313,093, Per/Ser (Incl. Access Fees) $7,792,408, Presv $567,595, Electronic Ref Mat (Incl. Access Fees) $581,386. Sal $15,150,720
Library Holdings: Bk Vols 6,283,385; Per Subs 56,663
Subject Interests: Astronomy, Bibliographies, Botany, East Asia, English, Geography, Hist of transportation, History, History of science, Mathematics, Near East, Netherlands, Slavic (language), South Asia, Zoology
Special Collections: American Society of Information Sciences, mss; Can; Food & Agriculture Organizations; Human Relations Area Files; Organization of American States; World Health Organizations
Automation Activity & Vendor Info: (Acquisitions) Innovative Interfaces Inc.; (OPAC) NOTIS
Publications: Guides to collections; Newsletters
Partic in CIC; Michigan Library Consortium; OCLC Online Computer Library Center, Inc; Research Libraries Group, Inc
Friends of the Library Group
Departmental Libraries:

CM ALFRED TAUBMAN MEDICAL LIBRARY, 1135 E Catherine 0726, 48109-2038. SAN 345-9721. Tel: 734-764-1210. FAX: 734-763-1473. E-Mail: medical.library@um.cc.umich.edu. Web Site: www.lib.umich.edu/libhome/taubman.lib/. *Dir*, Anthony Aquirre; E-Mail: tonyra@umich.edu; *Info Res*, Theresa Arndt; *Ref*, Patricia M Redman; E-Mail: pmr@umich.edu; *Electronic Resources*, Patricia Martin; E-Mail: pmartin@umich.edu; *Access Serv*, Whitney Field; E-Mail: wfield@umich.edu; *Coll Develop*, Barbara Shipman; E-Mail: bshipman@umich.edu
Founded 1920
Jul 1999-Jun 2000 Mats Exp $1,245,518, Books $36,812, Per/Ser (Incl. Access Fees) $1,208,706
Library Holdings: Bk Vols 362,474
Subject Interests: Medicine, Nursing, Pharmacy
Special Collections: History of Medicine (Crummer, Pilcher & Warthin Colls)
Partic in National Network of Libraries of Medicine - Greater Midwest

Region
Free access to Medline (OVID) for University students, faculty & staff with a minimum appointment of 50%
Friends of the Library Group

ASIA, Hatcher Library, North University, 48109-1205. SAN 345-987X. Tel: 734-764-0406. FAX: 734-747-2885. E-Mail: toasia@umich.edu. Web Site: asia.lib.edu/china/index.htm. *Librn*, Wei-Ying Wan; E-Mail: wywan@umich.edu; Staff 11 (MLS 6, Non-MLS 5)
Founded 1948
1999-2000 Mats Exp $582,481, Books $370,873, Per/Ser (Incl. Access Fees) $211,608
Library Holdings: Bk Vols 665,506; Per Subs 2,271
Subject Interests: China, Far East, Japan, Korea
Special Collections: Ch'ing Archives; Gaimosho Archives; GB PRO Files on China; Hussey Papers; Japanese Diet Proceedings; URI Files
Publications: The Catalogs of the Asia Library, G K Hall, 1979 (25 vols)

CM DENTISTRY LIBRARY, 1100 Dental Bldg, 48109-1078. SAN 345-9632. Tel: 734-764-1526. FAX: 734-764-4477. E-Mail: dentistry.library@umich.edu. Web Site: www.lib.umich.edu/libhome/dentistry.lib/. *Librn*, P F Anderson; E-Mail: pfa@umich.edu
Founded 1875
1998-1999 Mats Exp $106,777, Books $17,880, Per/Ser (Incl. Access Fees) $88,897
Library Holdings: Bk Vols 56,931
Subject Interests: Rare books
Publications: Library Information Guides; Subject Bibliographies
Friends of the Library Group

FILM & VIDEO, 2178 Shapiro Library, 48109-1185. SAN 370-3533. Tel: 734-764-5360. FAX: 734-764-6849. Web Site: www.lib.umich.edu/libhome/fvl.lib/fvl.html.
1999-2000 Mats Exp $76,590, Per/Ser (Incl. Access Fees) $1,867, AV Equip $74,723
Friends of the Library Group

FINE ARTS, 260 Tappan, 48109-1357. SAN 345-9934. Tel: 734-764-5405. FAX: 734-764-5408. E-Mail: finearts@umich.edu. Web Site: www.lib.umich.edu/libhome/finearts.lib/index.html. *Librn*, Deirdre Spencer; E-Mail: deirdres@umich.edu; Staff 4 (MLS 1, Non-MLS 3)
1999-2000 Mats Exp $180,000, Books $136,428, Per/Ser (Incl. Access Fees) $31,275
Library Holdings: Bk Vols 87,427
Subject Interests: Art
Friends of the Library Group

GRADUATE, 209 Hatcher N, 48109-1205. SAN 371-4810. Tel: 734-763-1539. FAX: 734-764-0259. E-Mail: graduate.library.reference@umich.edu. Web Site: www.lib.umich.edu/libhome/grad.lib. *Ref*, Barbara MacAdam; E-Mail: bmacadam@umich.edu; *Access Serv*, Rebecca Dunkle; E-Mail: rdunkle@umich.edu
1999-2000 Mats Exp $3,075,682, Books $1,556,195, Per/Ser (Incl. Access Fees) $1,519,487
Library Holdings: Bk Vols 3,303,858
Subject Interests: English literature, History, Military history
Partic in Michigan Library Consortium; Research Libraries Group, Inc

MEDIA UNION LIBRARY, 2281 Bonnisteel Blvd, 48109-2094. SAN 345-9667. Tel: 734-647-5747. FAX: 734-764-4487. Web Site: www.lib.umich.edu/ummu/. *Librn*, Michael D Miller; E-Mail: xmillerx@umich.edu; *Ref*, James Ottaviani. Subject Specialists: *Architecture*, Rebecca Price-Wilkin; *Art*, Joy Blouin; *Engineering*, Leena Lalwani; Staff 6 (MLS 6)
1999-2000 Mats Exp $1,721,990, Books $388,130, Per/Ser (Incl. Access Fees) $1,333,860
Library Holdings: Bk Vols 625,836
Special Collections: Charles Sawyer Papers; D H Burnham Papers; Geo Bringham Papers; Leonard Eaton Papers; Michigan Reports; Patents; Trademarks; Walter Sanders Papers

MUSEUMS, 2500 Museums Bldg, 48109-1079. SAN 346-0118. Tel: 734-764-0467. FAX: 734-764-3829. Web Site: www.lib.umich.edu/libhome/museums.lib/index.html. *Librn*, Dorothy Riemenschneider; Tel: 734-936-2337, E-Mail: dottie@umich.edu; *Info Res*, Charlene Stachnik
1999-2000 Mats Exp $138,462, Books $40,728, Per/Ser (Incl. Access Fees) $97,734
Library Holdings: Bk Vols 123,423
Subject Interests: Botany, Herpetology, Mammals, Natural history, Paleontology
Friends of the Library Group

MUSIC, School of Music, 3239 Moore Bldg, 48109-2085. SAN 345-9756. Tel: 734-764-2512. E-Mail: music.library@umich.edu. Web Site: www-personal.umich.edu/~celliker.musiclibrary/musiclibrary.html. *Librn*, Calvin Elliker; E-Mail: celliker@umich.edu; *Assoc Librn*, Charles Reynolds
1999-2000 Mats Exp $162,300, Books $58,500, Per/Ser (Incl. Access Fees) $30,800, Other Print Mats $47,000
Library Holdings: Bk Vols 113,876
Subject Interests: Music
Special Collections: American Sheet Music; Music & Musicology Coll (17th-19th Century); Radio Canada Int; Women Composers Coll
Friends of the Library Group

CM PUBLIC HEALTH INFORMATION SERVICES & ACCESS, 109 Observatory, 48109-2029. SAN 345-9810. Tel: 734-936-1391. FAX: 734-763-9851. Web Site: www.sph.umich.edu/phisa/index.html. *Librn*, Nancy Allee; E-Mail: nallee@umich.edu; *Ref*, Helen Look; E-Mail: hlook@umich.edu
1999-2000 Mats Exp $199,018, Books $27,084, Per/Ser (Incl. Access Fees) $171,934
Library Holdings: Bk Vols 81,542
Subject Interests: Education
Publications: PHISA News
Friends of the Library Group

SHAPIRO SCIENCE LIBRARY, 3175 Shapiro Library, 48109-1185. SAN 345-9993. Tel: 734-764-3442. Reference Tel: 734-936-2327. FAX: 734-763-9813. Web Site: www.umich.edu/~scilib/. *Head of Libr*, Kitty Bridges; E-Mail: bridges@umich.edu
1999-2000 Mats Exp $2,531,000, Books $185,000, Per/Ser (Incl. Access Fees) $2,146,000, Electronic Ref Mat (Incl. Access Fees) $12,000
Library Holdings: Bk Vols 446,184
Subject Interests: Astronomy, Biology, Chemistry, Geology, Mathematics, Natural resources, Physics, Statistics
Special Collections: Astronomical Maps; Rare Book Coll
Publications: Newsletter
Friends of the Library Group

SHAPIRO UNDERGRADUATE LIBRARY, 919 S University Ave, 48109-1185. Tel: 734-763-5084. FAX: 734-764-6849. Web Site: www.lib.umich.edu/libhome/ugl/index.html. *In Charge*, Linda TerHaar; E-Mail: terhaar@umich.edu; Staff 20 (MLS 8, Non-MLS 12)
1999-2000 Mats Exp $301,563, Books $197,000, Per/Ser (Incl. Access Fees) $104,563
Library Holdings: Bk Vols 196,912
Friends of the Library Group

SOCIAL WORK LIBRARY, B700 Sch Social Work Bldg, 48109-1106. SAN 345-9845. Tel: 734-764-5169. E-Mail: social.work.library@umich.edu. Web Site: www.lib.umich.edu/libhome/Social.lib/social.html. *Librn*, Karen Reiman-Sendi; E-Mail: karsendi@umich.edu; Staff 3 (MLS 2, Non-MLS 1)
1999-2000 Mats Exp $80,252, Books $38,441, Per/Ser (Incl. Access Fees) $41,811
Library Holdings: Bk Vols 42,155
Subject Interests: Counseling, Gerontology, Social service (social work)
Special Collections: Faculty Authors (SSW)
Friends of the Library Group

SPECIAL COLLECTIONS, Hatcher Graduate Library 7th flr, 48109-1205. SAN 346-0002. Tel: 734-764-9377. FAX: 734-764-9368. E-Mail: special.collections@umich.edu. Web Site: www.lib.umich.edu/libhome/speccoll.lib/spec_coll.html. *Head of Libr*, Peggy Daub; E-Mail: pdaub@umich.edu; *Curator*, Kathryn Beam; *Curator*, Adyebel Evans; *Curator*, Traianos Gagos
1999-2000 Mats Exp $160,000
Library Holdings: Bk Vols 108,262
Special Collections: American Committee for Protection of Foreign-Born, mss; American Drama Coll (19th Century); Anarchism & Radical Social Movements; Anti-Imperialist League, mss; Civil Liberties & Civil Rights Movements; Detroit Artists & Writers of the 1960s; Dutch Historical Pamphlets (17th Century); Early Economics; Early Military Science Coll; Elsevier Imprints Coll; English Drama (17th & 18th Century); English Historical Tracts (1592-1762); Fine Printing Coll; Finerty Irish Papers; French Historical Pamphlets Coll (16th-17th Century); Imaginary Voyages Coll; Incunabula; Medieval, Renaissance & Islamic Colls, mss; Micrographics & Scholarly Communication Coll; National-Sozialististische Deutsch Arbeiter-Partei (1933-45); Papyri Coll; Phillipines (Insurrection & American Occupation Coll); Polar Exploration Coll; Post-Beat Poets Coll; Radical Protest & Reform Literature; Shakespeare, Dryden Swift, Pope, Defoe, Carlyle, Dickens, Swinburne, Trollope, W H Hudson, Whitman, Cabell, Frost & Faulkner Colls; Spanish & Portuguese Poetry & Drama (16th-19th Centuries); Spanish Civil War; Theater Coll; Transportation History
Friends of the Library Group

C UNIVERSITY OF MICHIGAN, William L Clements Library, 909 S University Ave, 48109-1190. SAN 326-4343. Tel: 734-764-2347. FAX: 734-647-0716. E-Mail: clements.library@umich.edu. Web Site: www.clements.umich.edu/. *Dir*, John C Dann; *Curator*, Donald L Wilcox; *Curator, Reader Servs*, Brian Leigh Dunnigan; *Curator*, Barbara DeWolfe; Staff 8 (MLS 7, Non-MLS 1)
Founded 1922
Library Holdings: Bk Vols 77,000; Per Subs 34
Publications: The American Magazine & Historical Chronicle; The Quarto
Partic in RLIN
Friends of the Library Group

M WARNER-LAMBERT PARKE-DAVIS, Knowledge Management Services,* 2800 Plymouth Rd, 48105. SAN 307-8795. Tel: 734-622-4493. FAX: 734-622-7008. E-Mail: libreq@aa.wl.com. *Doc*, Elaine Logan
Founded 1885
Library Holdings: Bk Vols 21,581; Per Subs 780
Subject Interests: Chemistry, Medicine, Microbiology, Pathology,

Toxicology
Partic in Data Star; Dialog Corporation; Michigan Library Consortium; Nat Libr of Med; OCLC Online Computer Library Center, Inc; Questal Orbit; SDC; STN

J WASHTENAW COMMUNITY COLLEGE, Learning Resource Center,* 4800 E Huron River Dr, 48106. (Mail add: PO Box D-1, 48106-1610), SAN 307-8841. Tel: 734-973-3379. FAX: 734-677-2220. Web Site: www.wccnet.org/dept/lrc. *Dean*, Adella Blain; E-Mail: dblain@wccnet.org; *Librn*, Kathleen Scott; Tel: 734-973-3430, E-Mail: kscott@wccnet.org; *Librn*, Sandy McCarthy; Tel: 734-973-5293, E-Mail: mccarthy@wccnet.org; *AV*, Randal Baier; Tel: 734-677-5106, E-Mail: rebaier@wccnet.org; *Online Servs*, Christine Anderson; Tel: 734-973-5179, E-Mail: anderson@wccnet.org; *Publ Servs*, Sheila Rice; Tel: 734-973-3313, E-Mail: sjrice@wccnet.org; *Tech Servs*, Victor Liu; Tel: 734-973-3398, E-Mail: vliu@wccnet.org; Staff 28 (MLS 12, Non-MLS 16)
Founded 1966. Enrl 6,517; Highest Degree: Associate
Jul 1999-Jun 2000 Income (Main Library Only) $2,061,936. Mats Exp $632,333, Books $48,000, Per/Ser (Incl. Access Fees) $90,000, Presv $1,194, Micro $26,055, AV Equip $399,112, Electronic Ref Mat (Incl. Access Fees) $67,972. Sal $1,211,145 (Prof $568,542)
Library Holdings: Bk Vols 73,490; Bk Titles 66,945; Per Subs 553
Special Collections: College Archives; Prof Coll, bks, rpts on higher educ
Database Vendor: epixtech, inc.
Partic in Michigan Library Consortium; Oakland Washtenaw Wayne Livingston Libr Group; OCLC Online Computer Library Center, Inc
LRC facility includes a microcomputer lab for students & staff with 24 computer stations

P WASHTENAW COUNTY LIBRARY,* 4135 Washtenaw Ave, PO Box 8645, 48107-8645. SAN 346-0231. Tel: 734-971-6059. FAX: 734-971-3892. *Dir*, Mary Udoji; Staff 3 (MLS 3)
Founded 1962. Pop 282,939; Circ 76,000
Library Holdings: Bk Titles 5,453
Mem of The Library Network
Partic in Michigan Library Consortium
Houses a network library for the National Library Service for the Blind & Physically Handicapped
Branches: 1

P LIBRARY FOR THE BLIND & PHYSICALLY HANDICAPPED Tel: 734-971-6059. FAX: 734-971-3892. *Librn*, Margaret Wolfe; Staff 1 (MLS 1)
Founded 1972
Library Holdings: Bk Titles 12,000
Special Services for the Blind - Bi-Folkal kits; Kurzweil Personal Reader; Reading edge system; Vantage closed circuit TV magnifier
Special Services - Games & aids for the handicapped; volunteer taping agency/organization presentations

S WASHTENAW COUNTY METROPOLITAN PLANNING COMMISSION LIBRARY,* 110 N Fourth Ave, 48107. SAN 327-5108. Tel: 734-994-2435. FAX: 734-994-8284. *Librn*, Stephanie Gordon
Library Holdings: Bk Titles 2,000

S WILSON ORNITHOLOGICAL SOCIETY, Josselyn Van Tyne Memorial Library, Univ of Michigan Museum of Zoology, 1109 Geddes Ave, 48109-1079. SAN 327-4799. Tel: 734-764-0457. FAX: 734-763-4080. Web Site: www.ummz.lsa.umich.edu/birds/woslibrary.html. *Librn*, Janet Hinshaw; E-Mail: jhinshaw@umich.edu; Staff 1 (Non-MLS 1)
Founded 1930
Library Holdings: Bk Titles 3,000; Spec Interest Per Sub 210
Subject Interests: Ornithology
Function: Mail loans to members
Please see web site for a description of the library, information on holdings & access to on-line catalog.

ARMADA

P ARMADA FREE PUBLIC LIBRARY, 73930 Church St, 48005-3331. SAN 307-885X. Tel: 810-784-5921. FAX: 810-784-8640. Web Site: www.armadalib.org. *Dir*, Diane Burgeson; E-Mail: burgesod@libcoop.net; Staff 4 (MLS 1, Non-MLS 3)
Founded 1901. Pop 5,334; Circ 41,901
Apr 1999-Mar 2000 Income $186,390. Mats Exp $34,000. Sal $81,594
Library Holdings: Bk Titles 27,799; Per Subs 74
Automation Activity & Vendor Info: (Acquisitions) epixtech, inc.; (Cataloging) epixtech, inc.; (Circulation) epixtech, inc.; (ILL) epixtech, inc.; (OPAC) epixtech, inc.; (Serials) epixtech, inc.
Database Vendor: epixtech, inc.
Mem of Libr Coop of Macomb

ATHENS

P ATHENS COMMUNITY LIBRARY,* 106 E Burr Oak St, PO Box 216, 49011-0216. SAN 307-8868. *Chief Librn*, June Eitniear
Circ 1,316
Library Holdings: Bk Vols 4,178
Open Mon-Wed & Fri-Sat 1-5

AUBURN HILLS

P AUBURN HILLS PUBLIC LIBRARY, 3400 E Seyburn Dr, 48326-2759. SAN 329-1332. Tel: 248-370-9466. FAX: 248-370-9364. Web Site: www.auburn-hills.lib.mi.us. *Dir*, Hester Hull; Tel: 248-370-9469, E-Mail: hesthull@tln.lib.mi.us; *Ch Servs*, Linda Coleman; *Ref*, Regina Lawler; *Tech Coordr*, Cheryl DeCovich; Staff 28 (MLS 10, Non-MLS 18)
Founded 1986. Pop 19,310
Jan 2000-Dec 2000 Income $936,285. Sal $390,000
Automation Activity & Vendor Info: (Acquisitions) DRA; (Cataloging) DRA; (Circulation) DRA
Publications: Auburn Hills Highlights (quarterly newsletter)
Mem of The Library Network
Partic in OCLC Online Computer Library Center, Inc

S BUDD CO, Technical Center Library,* 1515 Atlantic Blvd, 48326-1501. SAN 314-5212. Tel: 248-391-9163. FAX: 248-391-0325. *Assoc Librn*, Renee Howes
Founded 1962
Subject Interests: Automotive, Metals, Physics, Plastics, Polymer chemistry, Railroad eng, Welding
Special Collections: Budd Company History & Rail Cars, photog, VF
Partic in Dialog Corporation

S CHRYSLER CORP, Information Resources Center,* 800 Chrysler Dr E, CIMS 483-08-10, 48326. SAN 308-1648. Tel: 248-576-8222, 248-576-8300. FAX: 248-576-2349. *Mgr*, Barbara M Fronczak; *Coll Develop*, Dorothy TeKelly; Staff 6 (MLS 4, Non-MLS 2)
Founded 1933
Library Holdings: Bk Vols 10,000; Per Subs 350
Subject Interests: Automotive engineering

OAKLAND COMMUNITY COLLEGE

J AUBURN HILLS CAMPUS LIBRARY, 2900 Featherstone Rd, 48326. SAN 307-8876. Tel: 248-340-6529. FAX: 248-340-6513. Web Site: www.occ.cc.mi.us/library. *Ref*, James J Weisenborne; E-Mail: jjweisen@vm.occ.cc.mi.us; *Ref*, Calvin Williams; *Ref*, Dennis G Souter; E-Mail: dgsouter@vm.occ.cc.mi.us; *Circ, ILL*, Susanne Taravella; *AV, Media Spec*, John Vavrek; *AV, Media Spec*, Robert Ladd; *Coll Develop*, Dennis Souter; Staff 7 (MLS 3, Non-MLS 4)
Founded 1965. Enrl 8,724; Fac 88
Jul 1997-Jun 1998 Income $781,144. Mats Exp $65,825, Books $29,117, Per/Ser (Incl. Access Fees) $20,027, Micro $13,786, Other Print Mats $600. Sal $354,286 (Prof $210,060)
Library Holdings: Bk Vols 35,000; Bk Titles 32,205; Per Subs 242
Automation Activity & Vendor Info: (Circulation) NOTIS; (Serials) NOTIS
Partic in Detroit Libr Network; Dialog Corporation

J LRC PROCESSING CENTER, 2900 Featherstone Rd, 48326-2817. SAN 320-9121. Tel: 248-340-6506, 248-340-6612. TDD: TTY/ 248-340-6692. FAX: 248-340-6900.; Staff 5 (MLS 1, Non-MLS 4)
Automation Activity & Vendor Info: (Cataloging) NOTIS; (Circulation) NOTIS
Partic in Detroit Libr Network
Special Services for the Deaf - TDD; TTY machine
Central Library Automation & Technical Services for four campus libraries

AUGUSTA

P MCKAY LIBRARY, 105 S Webster St, 49012-9601. SAN 307-8884. Tel: 616-731-4000. Interlibrary Loan Service Tel: 800-451-5021. FAX: 616-731-5323. E-Mail: marlib@tdsnet. *Dir*, Linda Mony; *Librn*, Lee Griffin; *Librn*, Mari Leamy
Circ 23,935
Library Holdings: Bk Vols 24,000; Per Subs 55
Special Collections: Local Newspaper Coll, Augusta Beacon 1902-1964, micro
Automation Activity & Vendor Info: (Cataloging) Follett; (Circulation) Follett
Mem of Southwest Michigan Library Cooperative
Friends of the Library Group

BAD AXE

P BAD AXE PUBLIC LIBRARY,* 200 S Hanselman, 48413. SAN 307-8892. Tel: 517-269-8538. FAX: 517-269-2411. *Dir*, Marilyn Berry
Pop 9,675; Circ 80,345
Library Holdings: Per Subs 110
Mem of White Pine Library Cooperative
Friends of the Library Group

BALDWIN

P PATHFINDER COMMUNITY LIBRARY,* 812 Michigan Ave, PO Box 880, 49304. SAN 307-8906. Tel: 231-745-4010. FAX: 231-745-7681. *Dir*, Bonnie Povilaitis; *Dir*, Millie Pohlman

Founded 1953. Pop 4,200; Circ 14,500
Library Holdings: Bk Vols 26,000; Per Subs 50
Mem of Mid-Michigan Library League

BARRYTON

P BARRYTON PUBLIC LIBRARY, 198 Northern Ave, PO Box 215, 49305-0215. SAN 307-8914. Tel: 517-382-5288. FAX: 517-382-9073. *Dir*, Tammy Knott; Fax: 517-382-9073; *Asst Librn*, Tiffany Smith; Fax: 517-382-9073
Founded 1930. Pop 3,107; Circ 20,000
Jul 1999-Jun 2000 Income $57,909. Mats Exp $15,471. Sal $35,884
Library Holdings: Bk Vols 15,000; Per Subs 35
Mem of Mid-Michigan Library League
Partic in Michigan Library Consortium

BATTLE CREEK

S ART CENTER OF BATTLE CREEK LIBRARY,* 265 E Emmett St, 49017. SAN 307-8922. Tel: 616-962-9511. FAX: 616-969-3838. E-Mail: acbc@net-link.net. *Curator, Spec Coll*, Carol Snapp; *Dir*, Don Desmott; *Librn*, Louise Sweet
Library Holdings: Bk Vols 300
Subject Interests: Art, Art history
Special Collections: Michigan Art Coll & Archival Library

S BATTLE CREEK ENQUIRER, Editorial Department Library,* 155 W Van Buren St, 49017-3093. SAN 307-8949. Tel: 616-964-7161. FAX: 616-964-0299. *Librn*, Shanna Huerta
Founded 1952
Library Holdings: Bk Titles 1,150
Restriction: Staff use only

M BATTLE CREEK HEALTH SYSTEM, Professional Library, 165 N Washington Ave, 49016. SAN 329-9139. Tel: 616-966-8331. FAX: 616-966-8332. *Librn*, Martin Krieger; *Asst Librn*, Bob Clark; Staff 1 (MLS 1)
Founded 1927
Jul 1999-Jun 2000 Income $174,436, Parent Institution $87,218, Other $87,218. Mats Exp $78,186, Books $22,906, Per/Ser (Incl. Access Fees) $46,280, Electronic Ref Mat (Incl. Access Fees) $9,000. (Prof $36,084)
Library Holdings: Bk Vols 2,000; Per Subs 250
Special Collections: Health Sciences
Database Vendor: Silverplatter Information Inc.
Restriction: Circulates for staff only
Partic in Michigan Library Consortium; Nat Network of Libraries of Med - Region 3

GM DEPARTMENT OF VETERANS AFFAIRS, Medical Center Library, 5500 Armstrong Rd, 49016. SAN 307-8981. Tel: 616-660-6093. FAX: 616-660-6031. *Librn*, Linda S Polardino; *Librn*, Brenda Newberry; Tel: 616-966-5600, Ext 6495, E-Mail: Brenda.Newberry@med.va.gov; Staff 4 (MLS 2, Non-MLS 2)
1999-2000 Income $100,000
Library Holdings: Bk Vols 3,000; Per Subs 610
Subject Interests: Psychiatry
Partic in Veterans Affairs Library Network

S KELLOGG CO, Information Center,* One Kellogg Sq, 49016-3232. SAN 307-8957. Tel: 616-961-2000. FAX: 616-961-2871. *Mgr*, Carol A Feltes; E-Mail: carol.feltes@kellogg.com; Staff 4 (MLS 4)
1997-1998 Income $1,400,000
Library Holdings: Per Subs 220
Subject Interests: Nutrition, Technology
Special Collections: Engineering drawings; vendor catalogs
Publications: Dietary Fiber Bibliography
Partic in Dialog Corporation

J KELLOGG COMMUNITY COLLEGE, Emory W Morris Learning Resource Center, 450 North Ave, 49017-3397. SAN 307-8965. Tel: 616-965-4122, Ext 2380. FAX: 616-965-4133. Web Site: www.kellogg.cc.mi.us. *Acq, Dir*, Martha Johnson Stillwell; E-Mail: stillwell.m@kellogg.cc.mi.us; *Coll Develop*, Clara Stewart; *ILL, Ref*, Sally Schuckel; Staff 5 (MLS 5)
Founded 1956
Library Holdings: Bk Vols 51,500; Per Subs 273
Special Collections: Law Reference
Database Vendor: epixtech, inc.
Partic in Michigan Library Consortium; OCLC Online Computer Library Center, Inc

P WILLARD LIBRARY,* 7 W Van Buren, 49017-3009. SAN 307-899X. Tel: 616-968-8166. FAX: 616-968-3284. Web Site: www.willard.lib.mi.us/. *Dir*, Rick Hulsey; *Asst Dir*, Sue Zamzow; *ILL*, Bev Garrett; *Ch Servs*, Sue Steeby; *Media Spec*, Joy Anderton; *Circ*, Sharon Beck; *Coll Develop*, Jean Fleck
Founded 1870. Pop 93,510; Circ 516,409
Jul 1998-Jun 1999 Income $3,815,261, State $168,493, County $341,702. Mats Exp $469,549, Books $387,949, Per/Ser (Incl. Access Fees) $81,600. Sal $2,114,249
Library Holdings: Bk Vols 190,000
Subject Interests: Local history
Mem of Southwest Michigan Library Cooperative
Partic in Michigan Library Consortium; OCLC Online Computer Library Center, Inc
Bookmobiles: 1

BAY CITY

S BAY COUNTY HISTORICAL SOCIETY, Butterfield Memorial Library, 321 Washington Ave, 48708. SAN 327-0246. Tel: 517-893-5733. FAX: 517-893-5741. Web Site: www.bchsmuseum.org. *Dir*, Gay McInerney; *Curator*, Corrine Bloomfield; *Curator*, Ronald Bloomfield; *Admin Assoc*, Claire O'Laughlin
Special Collections: Corporate Archives (Monitor Sugar Co); Patrol Craft Sailors Assoc Archives - military, WWII; Research Materials on Bay County, 1830-present, photos

P BAY COUNTY LIBRARY SYSTEM, 307 Lafayette Ave, 48708-7796. SAN 346-0290. Tel: 517-894-2837. FAX: 517-894-2021. Web Site: www.baycountylibrary.org. *Dir*, Linda Heemstra; *Asst Dir*, K Lynn Derck; *ILL*, Judith Brown; *Ch Servs*, Monica Anderson; *Ref*, Mary McManman; *Bkmobile Coordr*, Marilyn Kaeckmeister; *Tech Servs*, Paulette Fogelsonger; *Coll Develop*, Sheila Pearsons; *Business*, Kevin Ayala; *Tech Coordr*, Beth McQueen; Staff 17 (MLS 14, Non-MLS 3)
Founded 1974. Pop 111,489
Jan 2000-Dec 2000 Income (Main Library and Branch Library) $3,693,132, State $111,397, Federal $13,617, County $2,673,761, Locally Generated Income $823,960, Other $70,397. Mats Exp $470,765, Books $306,940, Per/Ser (Incl. Access Fees) $40,000, Presv $18,000, Micro $12,875, AV Equip $50,600, Electronic Ref Mat (Incl. Access Fees) $42,350. Sal $2,554,291 (Prof $794,225)
Library Holdings: Bk Vols 290,577; Per Subs 781
Subject Interests: Local history
Special Collections: Census Bur; Local History (Michigan Coll)
Automation Activity & Vendor Info: (Acquisitions) epixtech, inc.; (Circulation) epixtech, inc.; (OPAC) epixtech, inc.
Database Vendor: OCLC - First Search
Publications: Branching Out (Newsletter)
Mem of White Pine Library Cooperative
Partic in Michigan Library Consortium; OCLC Online Computer Library Center, Inc; Valley Libr Consortium
Friends of the Library Group
Branches: 5
AUBURN BRANCH, 235 W Midland Rd, Auburn, 48611. SAN 346-0320. Tel: 517-662-2381. FAX: 517-662-2647. *Librn*, Nancy Nicholson
Library Holdings: Bk Vols 36,103
BAY CITY BRANCH, 708 Center Ave, 48708-5989. SAN 346-0355. Tel: 517-893-9566. FAX: 517-893-9799. *Librn*, Barbara Fisher
Library Holdings: Bk Vols 94,471
PINCONNING BRANCH, 204 S Manitou, Pinconning, 48650-0477. SAN 346-041X. Tel: 517-879-3283. FAX: 517-879-5669. *Librn*, Paul Lutenske
Library Holdings: Bk Vols 29,692
SAGE, 100 E Midland St, 48706-4597. SAN 346-0444. Tel: 517-892-8555. FAX: 517-892-2575. *Librn*, Sarah Wohlschlag
Library Holdings: Bk Vols 76,951
SOUTH SIDE, 311 Lafayette Ave, 48708-7796. SAN 346-0479. Tel: 517-893-1287. FAX: 517-894-0505. *Librn*, Sheila Pearsons
Library Holdings: Bk Vols 42,408
Bookmobiles: 1

M BAY MEDICAL CENTER LIBRARY, 1900 Columbus Ave, 48708-6880. SAN 307-9015. Tel: 517-894-3782. FAX: 517-894-4862. *Librn*, Kelly Griffin; *Librn, Online Servs*, Barbara Kormelink; Staff 2 (MLS 1, Non-MLS 1)
Founded 1958
Library Holdings: Bk Titles 2,780; Per Subs 320
Subject Interests: Allied health
Database Vendor: Silverplatter Information Inc.
Publications: Union List of Serials
Restriction: Circulates for staff only, Public use on premises
Function: Document delivery services, ILL available, Literary searches, Photocopies available, Professional lending library, Reference services available, Some telephone reference
Mem of White Pine Library Cooperative
Partic in Greater Midwest Regional Medical Libr Network; Medline; Michigan Health Sciences Libraries Association; Nat Libr of Med; National Network Of Libraries Of Medicine - South Central Region

BELDING

P ALVAH N BELDING LIBRARY,* 302 E Main St, 48809. SAN 307-9031. Interlibrary Loan Service Tel: 616-794-1450. FAX: 616-794-3510. E-Mail: bel@lolas2.lakeland.lib.mi.us. Web Site: www.iserve.net/~wierengt/belding/alvah-library. *Coll Develop, Dir*, Toni Jagger
Founded 1917. Pop 11,068; Circ 55,000
Library Holdings: Bk Titles 43,366; Per Subs 92

Subject Interests: Antiques, Arts and crafts, Genealogy, Local history
Special Collections: Michigan Coll
Automation Activity & Vendor Info: (Circulation) GEAC
Mem of Lakeland Library Cooperative
Friends of the Library Group

BELLAIRE

P BELLAIRE PUBLIC LIBRARY,* 111 S Bridge, PO Box 477, 49615-0477. SAN 307-904X. Tel: 231-533-8814. FAX: 231-533-5064. *Librn*, Linda Offenbecker
Pop 2,697; Circ 23,440
Library Holdings: Bk Vols 19,000; Per Subs 65
Mem of Mid-Michigan Library League
Friends of the Library Group

BELLEVILLE

P FRED C FISCHER LIBRARY,* 167 Fourth St, 48111. SAN 307-9058. Tel: 734-699-3291. FAX: 734-699-6352. *Dir*, Debra L Green; *Asst Librn*, Mary Jo Suchy; Staff 5 (MLS 2, Non-MLS 3)
Founded 1920. Pop 35,500; Circ 134,138
Library Holdings: Bk Vols 45,198; Per Subs 164
Mem of The Library Network
Friends of the Library Group

BELLEVUE

P BELLEVUE TOWNSHIP LIBRARY,* 212 N Main St, 49021. SAN 307-9066. Tel: 616-763-3369. FAX: 616-763-3369. *Librn*, Brenda Harrison
Circ 5,948
Library Holdings: Bk Vols 9,000; Bk Titles 9,000
Publications: Monthly Bulletin on Libr Activities
Mem of Woodlands Library Cooperative
Partic in Woodlands Interlibrary Loan

BENTON HARBOR

P BENTON HARBOR PUBLIC LIBRARY, 213 E Wall St, 49022-4499. SAN 346-0509. Tel: 616-926-6139. FAX: 616-926-1674. E-Mail: bhlibrary@yahoo.com. Web Site: www.grocitier.com/bhlibrary/. *Dir*, Frederick J Kirby; E-Mail: libraryfjk@yahoo.com; *Media Spec*, Jean Lambrecht; *Ch Servs*, Sue Kading; *Doc, Ref*, Jill Rauh; *Cat, Tech Servs*, Sharon Holloway; Staff 20 (MLS 3, Non-MLS 17)
Founded 1899. Pop 30,698; Circ 99,302
Jul 1999-Jun 2000 Income $700,841, State $30,698, City $317,669, County $204,012, Other $148,462. Mats Exp $94,428. Sal $332,390
Library Holdings: Bk Vols 97,833; Per Subs 275
Subject Interests: Ethnic studies
Special Collections: Biological Sciences (Don Farnum Coll); Black Studies (Martin Luther King Jr Coll); Civil War (Randall Perry Coll); Indian Coll; Israelite House of David Coll; Judaica (Lillian Faber Coll); Theater (Helen Polly Klock Coll)
Mem of Southwest Michigan Library Cooperative
Partic in Berrien Library Consortium; Michigan Library Consortium
Bookmobiles: 1

J LAKE MICHIGAN COLLEGE LIBRARY, 2755 E Napier Ave, 49022. SAN 307-9074. Tel: 616-927-8605. FAX: 616-927-6656. Web Site: lmc.cc.mi.us/lib/. *Coll Develop, Dir*, Peter Nachreiner; *ILL, Ref*, Diane Baker; E-Mail: baker@raptor.lmc.cc.mi.us
Founded 1946. Enrl 1,608; Fac 63
Jul 1999-Jun 2000 Income $299,928. Mats Exp $56,536, Books $21,680, Per/Ser (Incl. Access Fees) $27,815, Presv $183, Micro $6,858. Sal $167,485
Library Holdings: Bk Titles 56,000; Per Subs 7,350
Special Collections: Lake Michigan College Archives
Automation Activity & Vendor Info: (Circulation) Follett
Database Vendor: Ebsco - EbscoHost, Lexis-Nexis, OCLC - First Search
Partic in Berrien Library Consortium; Michigan Library Consortium; OCLC Online Computer Library Center, Inc; Southwest Michigan Library Cooperative

S WHIRLPOOL CORPORATION, R&E Technical Information Center,* 750 Monte Rd, 49022. SAN 307-9082. Tel: 616-923-5325. FAX: 616-923-5638.
Founded 1955
Library Holdings: Bk Titles 1,000; Per Subs 100
Subject Interests: Electrical engineering, Mechanical engineering
Publications: WIN Alert (Distributed to Whirlpool personnel only)
Partic in Dialog Corporation; OCLC Online Computer Library Center, Inc; SDC Info Servs

BENZONIA

P BENZONIA PUBLIC LIBRARY, 891 Michigan Ave, 49616-9784. (Mail add: PO Box 445, 49616-0445), SAN 307-9090. Tel: 231-882-4111. E-Mail: benzlib@benzie.com. *Dir*, Roxane Miner
Founded 1925. Pop 2,712; Circ 23,345
Library Holdings: Bk Vols 9,000; Per Subs 32
Subject Interests: Art and architecture, History, Local history, Religion
Publications: Newsletter
Mem of Mid-Michigan Library League
Friends of the Library Group

BERKLEY

P BERKLEY PUBLIC LIBRARY, 3155 Coolidge Hwy, 48072. SAN 307-9104. Tel: 248-546-2440. FAX: 248-546-2447. *Dir*, Celia B Morse; E-Mail: cmorse@tln.lib.mi.us; Staff 20 (MLS 9, Non-MLS 11)
Founded 1927. Pop 16,960; Circ 172,662
Jul 2000-Jun 2001 Income $688,000, State $16,000, City $592,000, County $20,000, Locally Generated Income $60,000. Mats Exp $88,000, Books $70,000. Sal $332,980 (Prof $204,320)
Library Holdings: Bk Vols 60,519; Per Subs 191; High Interest/Low Vocabulary Bk Vols 250
Subject Interests: Art and architecture
Automation Activity & Vendor Info: (Acquisitions) DRA; (Cataloging) DRA; (Circulation) DRA; (OPAC) DRA; (Serials) DRA
Mem of The Library Network
Friends of the Library Group

BERRIEN SPRINGS

C ANDREWS UNIVERSITY, James White Library, 1400 Campus Dr, 49104. SAN 346-0568. Tel: 616-471-3264. Interlibrary Loan Service Tel: 616-471-3506. FAX: 616-471-6166. E-Mail: library@andrews.edu. Web Site: www.andrews.edu/library. *Dir*, Keith Clouten; *ILL*, Sandi White; *Info Res, Online Servs*, Cynthia Helms; *Per*, Marilyn Gane
Founded 1962. Enrl 2,950; Fac 240; Highest Degree: Doctorate
Jul 1998-Jun 1999 Income (Main and Other College/University Libraries) $2,250,000. Mats Exp $792,000, Books $440,000, Per/Ser (Incl. Access Fees) $322,000, Electronic Ref Mat (Incl. Access Fees) $30,000. Sal $1,270,413 (Prof $469,058)
Library Holdings: Bk Vols 550,000; Per Subs 3,033
Subject Interests: Art, Biology, Religion
Special Collections: Environmental Design Research (EDRA); Seventh Day Adventist Church History (Heritage Ctr), bk, mss, personal papers
Database Vendor: Innovative Interfaces INN - View
Partic in Adventist Librs Info Coop; Berrien Library Consortium; Michigan Library Consortium; OCLC Online Computer Library Center, Inc; Southwest Michigan Library Cooperative
Departmental Libraries:
ARCHITECTURAL RESOURCE Tel: 616-471-2418. *Librn*, Kathy Demsky
Library Holdings: Bk Titles 22,000
Subject Interests: Architecture
MUSIC MATERIALS CENTER, Hamel Hall, 49104-0230. Tel: 616-471-3114. Web Site: www2.andrews.edu/~mack. *Librn*, Linda Mack; E-Mail: mack@andrews.edu
Library Holdings: Bk Titles 12,500

S BERRIEN COUNTY HISTORICAL ASSOCIATION LIBRARY, 313 N Cass St, 49103-1038. (Mail add: PO Box 261, 49193-0261), SAN 373-2029. Tel: 616-471-1202. FAX: 616-471-7412. E-Mail: bcha@berrienhistory.org. Web Site: www.berrienhistory.org. *Curator*, Robert Myers
Founded 1967
Library Holdings: Bk Vols 150; Per Subs 4
Subject Interests: Local history
Special Collections: Clark Equipment Archives

P BERRIEN SPRINGS COMMUNITY LIBRARY, 215 W Union St, 49103. SAN 307-9112. Tel: 616-471-7074. FAX: 616-471-4433. *Dir, Librn*, Katherine Smith; E-Mail: kws@qtm.net; Staff 4 (MLS 1, Non-MLS 3)
Founded 1906. Pop 9,823; Circ 90,000
Apr 1999-Mar 2000 Income $233,500, State $9,000, City $143,000, County $62,500, Locally Generated Income $8,500, Other $1,000. Mats Exp Books $35,000. Sal $96,400
Library Holdings: Bk Vols 37,147; Bk Titles 35,453; Per Subs 112; High Interest/Low Vocabulary Bk Vols 80; Bks on Deafness & Sign Lang 32
Subject Interests: Local history
Special Collections: Genealogy Coll of the Berrien County Genealogical Society
Automation Activity & Vendor Info: (Cataloging) Follett; (Circulation) Follett; (OPAC) Follett
Mem of Libr Syst of SW Mich
Partic in Berrien Library Consortium; Southwest Michigan Library Cooperative
Friends of the Library Group

BESSEMER

P BESSEMER PUBLIC LIBRARY,* 411 S Sophie St, 49911. SAN 307-9120. Tel: 906-667-0404. FAX: 906-667-0442. *Librn*, Sharon Baksic
Circ 16,000
Library Holdings: Bk Vols 14,650; Per Subs 53
Mem of Mid-Peninsula Library Cooperative

BEULAH

P BEULAH PUBLIC LIBRARY,* 7228 Commercial St, PO Box 457, 49617-0457. SAN 307-9139. Tel: 231-882-4037. *Librn*, Anne Damm
Circ 5,817
Jul 1996-Jun 1997 Income $30,105. Mats Exp $22,270. Sal $8,176
Library Holdings: Bk Vols 9,300; Per Subs 28
Mem of Mid-Michigan Library League
Friends of the Library Group

BEVERLY HILLS

SR OUR LADY QUEEN OF MARTYRS CHURCH, Saint Lucian Library, 32340 Pierce St, 48025. SAN 307-9171. Tel: 248-644-8620. FAX: 248-644-8623. *Librn*, Eleanor Benkert
Founded 1954
Library Holdings: Bk Vols 3,000

BIG RAPIDS

P BIG RAPIDS COMMUNITY LIBRARY,* 426 S Michigan Ave, 49307. SAN 307-9147. Tel: 231-796-5234. FAX: 231-796-1078. *Librn*, Gaylynn Rorabaugh; Staff 4 (MLS 1, Non-MLS 3)
Founded 1903. Pop 21,000; Circ 122,000
Jul 1996-Jun 1997 Income $259,800, State $18,343, City $74,000, Federal $23,000, County $121,000, Locally Generated Income $10,823. Mats Exp $44,033, Books $38,682, Per/Ser (Incl. Access Fees) $3,189. Sal $98,310 (Prof $33,069)
Library Holdings: Bk Vols 61,000; Per Subs 90
Mem of Mid-Michigan Library League
Partic in Michigan Library Consortium
Friends of the Library Group

C FERRIS STATE UNIVERSITY, (FLITE), Ferris Library for Information, Technology & Education, 1010 Campus Dr, 49307-2747. SAN 307-9155. Tel: 231-591-3727. Interlibrary Loan Service Tel: 231-591-2663. Circulation Tel: 231-591-2669. Reference Tel: 231-591-3602. TDD: 231-591-2669. FAX: 231-591-2662. E-Mail: netref@lib01.ferris.edu. Web Site: www.ferris.edu/library. *Dean of Libr*, Dr Richard Cochran; *Coll Develop*, Joseph Weber; *Govt Doc*, Raymond Dickinson; *Instrul Serv, Ref Serv*, Felix Unaeze; *Automation Syst Coordr*, Richard Bearden; *Tech Servs*, Leah Monger; Staff 35 (MLS 14, Non-MLS 21)
Founded 1884. Enrl 9,847; Fac 450; Highest Degree: Doctorate
Jul 1999-Jun 2000 Income $3,141,137, Locally Generated Income $57,781, Parent Institution $2,958,356, Other $125,000. Mats Exp $891,302, Presv $11,338, Electronic Ref Mat (Incl. Access Fees) $60,677. Sal $1,345,157 (Prof $753,955)
Library Holdings: Bk Vols 312,580; Bk Titles 250,668; Per Subs 2,524
Subject Interests: Health sciences, Law, Optometry, Technology
Special Collections: Northwest Michigan; University Archives; US Bureau of Census; US Patents & Trademarks; Woodbridge N Ferris Papers
Automation Activity & Vendor Info: (Acquisitions) Innovative Interfaces Inc.; (Cataloging) Innovative Interfaces Inc.; (Circulation) Innovative Interfaces Inc.; (Course Reserve) Innovative Interfaces Inc.; (ILL) Innovative Interfaces Inc.; (Media Booking) Innovative Interfaces Inc.; (OPAC) Innovative Interfaces Inc.; (Serials) Innovative Interfaces Inc.
Database Vendor: Lexis-Nexis, OCLC - First Search, Silverplatter Information Inc.
Publications: LIStener (newsletter); Tech Tips
Partic in Michigan Library Consortium; OCLC Online Computer Library Center, Inc

BIRCH RUN

P THOMAS E FLESCHNER MEMORIAL LIBRARY,* 11935 Silver Creek Dr, 48415. (Mail add: PO Box 152, 48415), SAN 325-2655. Tel: 517-624-5171. FAX: 517-624-0120. *Dir*, Audrey J Lewis; Tel: 517-792-4058, E-Mail: lewisa@cris.com; *Asst Librn*, Jeanette Morrish; Staff 2 (MLS 1, Non-MLS 1)
Founded 1979. Pop 5,354; Circ 27,000
Apr 1998-Mar 1999 Income $75,000. Mats Exp $11,400, Books $10,000, Per/Ser (Incl. Access Fees) $1,400. Sal $35,000 (Prof $20,000)
Library Holdings: Bk Titles 16,045; Per Subs 32
Database Vendor: IAC - Info Trac, OCLC - First Search
Mem of White Pine Library Cooperative

BIRMINGHAM

P BALDWIN PUBLIC LIBRARY, 300 W Merrill St, 48009-1483. (Mail add: PO Box 3002, 48012-3002), SAN 307-9163. Tel: 248-647-1700, 248-647-7339. TDD: 248-593-6314. FAX: 248-647-6393. E-Mail: question@baldwinlib.org. Web Site: www.baldwinlib.org. *Dir*, Leslie L Kee; Tel: 248-988-2912, E-Mail: keelesli@baldwinlib.org; *Circ*, Ann Willhite; *Ad Servs*, Sarah Ormond; Tel: 248-647-1700, Ext 641, E-Mail: ormandsa@baldwinlib.org; *YA Servs*, Rita Soltan; Tel: 248-647-1700, Ext 662, E-Mail: soltanri@baldwinlib.org; *Ref Serv*, James Moffet; Tel: 248-647-1700, Ext 629, Fax: 248-644-7297, E-Mail: moffetja@baldwinlib.org; *Tech Servs*, Douglas Koschik; Tel: 248-988-2911, Fax: 248-644-3197, E-Mail: koschikd@baldwinlib.org; Staff 90 (MLS 21, Non-MLS 69)
Founded 1907. Pop 31,608; Circ 300,747
Jul 1999-Jun 2000 Income $2,627,249, State $30,000, City $1,952,360, County $41,000, Locally Generated Income $97,751, Other $506,138. Mats Exp $1,134,199, Books $226,290, Per/Ser (Incl. Access Fees) $18,940, Micro $8,000, AV Equip $80,000, Electronic Ref Mat (Incl. Access Fees) $68,000. Sal $1,493,050 (Prof $789,573)
Library Holdings: Bk Vols 152,524; Bk Titles 131,316; Per Subs 401
Subject Interests: Genealogy, Local history, Mich hist
Automation Activity & Vendor Info: (Cataloging) Endeavor; (Circulation) Endeavor; (OPAC) Endeavor
Database Vendor: IAC - SearchBank, OCLC - First Search, ProQuest
Publications: For Fifty Years, READ community newsletter
Mem of The Library Network
Partic in Metro Net Libr Consortium; Michigan Library Consortium; OCLC Online Computer Library Center, Inc
Special Services for the Deaf - TDD; TTY machine
Special Services for the Blind - Kurzweil Reading Machine
Friends of the Library Group

BLOOMFIELD HILLS

P BLOOMFIELD TOWNSHIP PUBLIC LIBRARY,* 1099 Lone Pine Rd, 48302-2410. SAN 307-9198. Tel: 248-642-5800. FAX: 248-642-4175. Web Site: www.metronet.lib.mi.us/blfd/. *Dir*, Karen Kotulis-Carter; *ILL*, Linda Sessine; *Ad Servs*, Ann M Williams; *Ch Servs*, Marian Rafal; *Circ*, Cathleen Russ; *Automation Syst Coordr*, Douglas Koschik; Staff 23 (MLS 23)
Founded 1964. Pop 46,761; Circ 526,698
Apr 1997-Mar 1998 Income $2,946,484. Mats Exp $533,866. Sal $1,311,054
Library Holdings: Bk Vols 188,222; Per Subs 627
Publications: Answers (three times per year community newsletter)
Mem of The Library Network
Partic in Metro Net Libr Consortium; Michigan Library Consortium; OCLC Online Computer Library Center, Inc
Special Services for the Deaf - TTY machine
Friends of the Library Group

S CRANBROOK ACADEMY OF ART LIBRARY,* 1221 N Woodward Ave, PO Box 801, 48303-0801. SAN 307-9201. Tel: 248-645-3355. FAX: 248-645-3464. Web Site: www.cranbrookart.edu/library/index.cfm. *Dir Libr Serv*, Judy Dyki; E-Mail: jdyki@cranbrook.edu; *Librn*, Mary Beth Kreiner; Staff 3 (MLS 3)
Founded 1928. Enrl 150; Fac 10; Highest Degree: Master
Library Holdings: Bk Titles 25,800; Per Subs 190
Subject Interests: Art and architecture
Special Collections: Artist's Books; Booth Coll of Fine Arts Folios; Cranbrook Press Books; Exhibition Catalogs; Faculty Lectures, tapes; Fine Bindings; Folios; Theses
Automation Activity & Vendor Info: (Cataloging) epixtech, inc.; (Circulation) epixtech, inc.; (OPAC) epixtech, inc.; (Serials) epixtech, inc.
Partic in Dialog Corporation; Michigan Library Consortium; OCLC Online Computer Library Center, Inc; Southeastern Michigan League Of Libraries

S CRANBROOK INSTITUTE OF SCIENCE LIBRARY,* 1221 N Woodward, PO Box 801, 48303-0801. SAN 377-1571. Tel: 248-645-3255. FAX: 248-645-3050. *Librn*, Gretchen Young-Weiner; E-Mail: gretchen_young-weiner@cc.cranbrook.edu
Library Holdings: Bk Vols 18,000; Per Subs 165
Subject Interests: Botany, Geology, Zoology

L DICKINSON WRIGHT PLLC LIBRARY, 38525 Woodward Ave, 48304. SAN 372-0365. Tel: 248-433-7559. FAX: 248-433-7274. Web Site: www.dickinsonwright.com. *Librn*, Jan Bissett; E-Mail: jbissett@dickinson-wright.com; Staff 1 (MLS 1)
Library Holdings: Bk Vols 15,000; Per Subs 600
Subject Interests: Law, US law
Database Vendor: Lexis-Nexis, OCLC - First Search
Function: Research library

L DYKEMA GOSSETT PLLC, Law Library, 1577 N Woodward Ave, Ste 300, 48304-2820. SAN 372-0373. Tel: 248-203-0700. FAX: 248-203-0763. Web Site: www.dykema.com. *Mgr*, Carol Lally
Library Holdings: Bk Vols 6,000; Per Subs 40

R TEMPLE BETH EL, Prentis Memorial Library, 7400 Telegraph Rd, 48301-3876. SAN 307-918X. Tel: 248-851-1100, Ext 3157. FAX: 248-851-1187. Web Site: www.templebethel.org. *Exec Dir*, Tom Jablonski
Founded 1878
Library Holdings: Bk Vols 15,000
Subject Interests: Jewish history and literature, Judaica (lit or hist of Jews)
Special Collections: 16th-19th Century Judaica (Leonard Simons Coll of Rare Judaica); Large Print Books (Goldman Coll); Older American Jewish Periodicals (Irving I Katz Coll of Jewish Americana)

BOYNE CITY

P BOYNE DISTRICT LIBRARY, 201 E Main St, 49712-9331. SAN 307-9236. Tel: 616-582-7861. FAX: 616-582-2998. E-Mail: boynec1@northland.lib.mi.us. *Dir*, Nannette Miller; Staff 5 (Non-MLS 5)
Founded 1918. Pop 6,081; Circ 29,183
May 1998-Apr 1999 Income $248,424. Sal $91,000
Library Holdings: Bk Vols 18,300; Bk Titles 18,000; Per Subs 75
Subject Interests: Local history
Automation Activity & Vendor Info: (Cataloging) Athena; (Circulation) Athena
Mem of Northland Library Cooperative

BRECKENRIDGE

P HOWE MEMORIAL LIBRARY,* 128 E Saginaw St, PO Box 398, 48615. SAN 307-9244. Tel: 517-842-3202. FAX: 517-842-3675. *Librn*, Charlotte Simmons
Founded 1938. Circ 21,310
Library Holdings: Bk Vols 17,000; Per Subs 55
Mem of Capital Library Cooperative

BRIDGEPORT

P BRIDGEPORT PUBLIC LIBRARY,* 3399 Williamson Rd, PO Box 1510, 48722-1510. SAN 376-6144. Tel: 517-777-6030. FAX: 517-777-6880. Web Site: www.vlc.lib.mi.us. *Dir*, Rosemary D Rice; E-Mail: rrice@vlc.lib.mi.us
Library Holdings: Bk Vols 31,500; Bk Titles 28,500; Per Subs 155
Mem of White Pine Library Cooperative

BRIDGMAN

P BRIDGMAN PUBLIC LIBRARY,* 4460 Lake St, 49106-9510. SAN 307-9252. Tel: 616-465-3663. FAX: 616-465-3249. *Dir*, Carol Richardson; E-Mail: richardc@mlc.lib.mi.us
Founded 1966. Pop 4,627; Circ 56,079
1997-1998 Income $172,150, State $35,000, City $54,500, Locally Generated Income $22,650
Library Holdings: Bk Vols 31,623; Per Subs 100
Mem of Southwest Michigan Library Cooperative
Open Mon-Thurs 10-8
Friends of the Library Group

BRIGHTON

P BRIGHTON DISTRICT LIBRARY, 100 Library Dr, 48116. SAN 307-9260. Tel: 810-229-6571. FAX: 810-229-3161. Web Site: www.brighton.lib.mi.us. *Dir*, Charlene Huget; *Ch Servs*, Carla Sharp; *Automation Syst Coordr*, Karen Keller; *Ref*, Ron Loomis; *Tech Servs*, Diana Cunningham. Subject Specialists: *Genealogy*, Gloria Osborne; Staff 16 (MLS 8, Non-MLS 8)
Founded 1992. Pop 35,203; Circ 216,000
Dec 1999-Nov 2000 Income $1,050,213. Mats Exp $120,000, Books $73,500, Per/Ser (Incl. Access Fees) $21,315, Micro $5,000
Library Holdings: Bk Vols 72,000; Per Subs 300
Subject Interests: Genealogy, Local history
Special Collections: Career Coll
Database Vendor: DRA
Publications: Brighton District Library Newsletter
Mem of The Library Network
Friends of the Library Group

BROWN CITY

P BROWN CITY PUBLIC LIBRARY,* 4207 E Main St, 48416-0058. SAN 307-9279. Tel: 810-346-2511. FAX: 810-346-2511. *Librn*, Shirley K Wood
Circ 18,475
Library Holdings: Bk Vols 12,400; Per Subs 62
Mem of White Pine Library Cooperative

BUCHANAN

P BUCHANAN PUBLIC LIBRARY,* 117 W Front St, 49107. SAN 307-9287. Tel: 616-695-3681. FAX: 616-695-0004. *Asst Librn*, Deborah Lynne Berryman; E-Mail: debbieberryman@hotmail.com; Staff 7 (Non-MLS 7)
Pop 9,285; Circ 105,682
Jul 1999-Jun 2000 Income $154,000. Mats Exp $19,000, Books $17,400, Per/Ser (Incl. Access Fees) $1,500, Micro $100. Sal $90,000
Library Holdings: Bk Vols 35,215; Per Subs 105
Subject Interests: Local history
Friends of the Library Group

BURLINGTON

P BURLINGTON TOWNSHIP LIBRARY, 135 Elm St, 49029-0039. (Mail add: PO Box 39, 49029-0039), SAN 307-9309. Tel: 517-765-2702. FAX: 517-765-2702. E-Mail: burlington@cbpu.com. *Dir*, Sheryl Iden
Founded 1935. Pop 1,773; Circ 3,826
Apr 1999-Mar 2000 Income $15,209, State $1,772, County $7,273, Locally Generated Income $4,000, Other $2,164. Mats Exp $2,025, Books $1,356, Per/Ser (Incl. Access Fees) $282, AV Equip $387. Sal $8,686
Library Holdings: Bk Titles 10,082; Per Subs 23
Automation Activity & Vendor Info: (ILL) Brodart
Function: ILL available
Mem of Woodlands Library Cooperative
Open Tues 11-5, Wed 1-5, Thurs 2-7 & Sat 9-12

BURNIPS

P SALEM TOWNSHIP LIBRARY,* PO Box 58, 49314. SAN 346-3532. Tel: 616-896-8170. FAX: 616-896-8035. *Librn*, Sharon Engelsman
Library Holdings: Bk Vols 6,000
Mem of Lakeland Library Cooperative

BURR OAK

P BURR OAK TOWNSHIP LIBRARY,* PO Box 309, 49030-0098. SAN 307-9317. Tel: 616-489-2906. FAX: 616-489-2906. *Dir*, Deanna Stoll
Founded 1905. Pop 2,500; Circ 9,919
Library Holdings: Bk Vols 17,919; Per Subs 29
Mem of Woodlands Library Cooperative
Open Tues 9-5, Thurs 12-5, Fri 12-7 & Sat 9-1
Friends of the Library Group

BURT

P TAYMOUTH TOWNSHIP LIBRARY, 2361 E Burt Rd, PO Box 158, 48417-0158. SAN 376-706X. Tel: 517-770-4651. FAX: 517-770-4651. *Dir*, Diane Snellenberger
Founded 1979. Pop 4,524
Library Holdings: Bk Titles 11,662; Per Subs 32
Subject Interests: Local history

CADILLAC

P CADILLAC-WEXFORD PUBLIC LIBRARY,* 411 S Lake St, 49601-0700. (Mail add: PO Box 700, 49601-0700), SAN 346-0622. Tel: 616-775-6541. FAX: 616-775-1749. *Dir*, Stephen Dix; *Circ, Dep Dir*, Kathleen Kirch; *Ref*, Marlene Ellsworth
Founded 1906. Pop 27,016; Circ 203,540
1998-1999 Income $750,000. Mats Exp $150,000. Sal $275,000
Library Holdings: Bk Vols 147,000; Per Subs 275
Mem of Mid-Michigan Library League
Branches: 3
MANTON BRANCH, 404 W Main, PO Box F, Manton, 49663. SAN 346-0681. Tel: 616-824-3584. *Librn*, Debra Letts
MESICK BRANCH, PO Box 208, Mesick, 49668. SAN 346-0657. Tel: 616-885-1120. *Librn*, Penny Carlsen
TUSTIN BRANCH, 310 S Nielson, Tustin, 49688. SAN 346-0703. Tel: 616-829-3012. *Librn*, Sandra Leach

P MID-MICHIGAN LIBRARY LEAGUE, 411 S Lake St, PO Box 700, 49601-0700. SAN 307-9325. Tel: 616-775-6541. FAX: 616-775-1749. *Dir*, Stephen Dix; E-Mail: dixs@mlc.lib.mi.us; *ILL*, Jack Sheehan; Staff 11 (MLS 3, Non-MLS 8)
Founded 1962. Pop 410,000
Member Libraries: Barryton Public Library; Bellaire Public Library; Benzie Shores District Library; Benzonia Public Library; Beulah Public Library; Big Rapids Community Library; Cadillac-Wexford Public Library; Central Lake District Library; Chase Public Library; Crawford County Library; Elberta Public Library; Elk Rapids District Library; Evart Public Library; Fife Lake Public Library; Gerrish-Higgins School District Public Library; Hart Area Public Library; Helena Township Public Library; Houghton Lake Public Library; Idlewild Public Library; Kalkaska County Library; Leelanau Township Public Library; Leroy Community Library; M Alice Chapin Memorial Library; Mancelona Township Library; Manistee County Library; Mason County District Library; Mason County District Library; Missaukee District Library; Morton Township Public Library; Northwestern Michigan College; Pathfinder Community Library; Peninsula Community Library; Pentwater Township Library; Reed City Public Library;

Richfield Township Public Library; Richland Township Library; Suttons Bay Area Public Library; Traverse Area District Library; Walkerville Public School Library; Walton Erickson Public Library; Wheatland Township Library; White Pine Library
Partic in OCLC Online Computer Library Center, Inc

CALUMET

P CALUMET PUBLIC SCHOOL LIBRARY, 57070 Mine St, 49913-1799. SAN 307-9333. Tel: 906-337-0811, Ext 6. FAX: 906-337-3848. Web Site: www.clk.k12.mi.us/library. *Librn*, Debra Oyler; E-Mail: doyler@clk.k12.mi.us
Pop 9,032; Circ 33,023
2000-2000 Income $153,468, State $9,025, Provincial $126,627, Locally Generated Income $17,816. Mats Exp $35,721, Books $18,143, Per/Ser (Incl. Access Fees) $16,801, AV Equip $777. Sal $105,328
Library Holdings: Bk Vols 25,971; Per Subs 107
Automation Activity & Vendor Info: (Cataloging) epixtech, inc.; (Circulation) epixtech, inc.; (OPAC) epixtech, inc.
Mem of Superiorland Library Cooperative

CAMDEN

P CAMDEN TOWNSHIP PUBLIC LIBRARY,* 119 S Main St, 49232. SAN 307-9341. Tel: 517-368-5554. *Dir*, Barbara Melvin
Circ 13,947
Library Holdings: Bk Vols 8,000; Per Subs 15
Mem of Woodlands Library Cooperative
Friends of the Library Group

CANTON

S ADVANCED INFORMATION CONSULTANTS LIBRARY,* 41575 Joy Rd, 48187. SAN 323-6692. Tel: 734-459-9090. FAX: 734-459-8990. E-Mail: info@advinfoc.com. Web Site: www.advinfoc.com. *In Charge*, Barton B Bryant
Library Holdings: Bk Titles 4,000
Restriction: Staff use only

P CANTON PUBLIC LIBRARY, 1200 S Canton Center Rd, 48188-1600. SAN 321-2645. Tel: 734-397-0999. FAX: 734-397-1130. Web Site: www.cantonpl.org. *Dir*, Jean M Tabor; Tel: 734-397-0999, Ext 111, E-Mail: taborj@metronet.lib.mi.us; *Ch Servs*, Judy Teachworth; E-Mail: teachje@metronet.lib.mi.us; *Ad Servs*, Rebecca Havenstein-Coughlin; E-Mail: havensr@metronet.lib.mi.us; *Tech Servs*, Claire McLaughlin; E-Mail: mclaughc@metronnet.lib.mi.us; Staff 83 (MLS 23, Non-MLS 60)
Founded 1980. Pop 75,000; Circ 733,000
Jan 2000-Dec 2000 Income $3,557,710. Mats Exp $403,408. Sal $1,325,003
Library Holdings: Bk Vols 182,512; Bk Titles 148,370; Per Subs 697
Automation Activity & Vendor Info: (Circulation) Innovative Interfaces Inc.
Database Vendor: GaleNet, OCLC - First Search
Publications: Newsletter (quarterly)
Mem of The Library Network
Partic in Metronet
Friends of the Library Group

CARO

P CARO AREA DISTRICT LIBRARY, 840 W Frank St, 48723. SAN 307-935X. Tel: 517-673-4329. FAX: 517-673-4777. E-Mail: info@mail.carolibrary.org. Web Site: www.carolibrary.org. *Coll Develop, Dir*, Marcia Dievendorf; *Asst Librn*, Betty Gettel; Staff 7 (MLS 1, Non-MLS 6)
Founded 1904. Pop 11,757
Dec 1998-Nov 1999 Income $342,415, State $11,747, Locally Generated Income $286,585, Other $44,083. Mats Exp $57,243, Books $49,141, Per/Ser (Incl. Access Fees) $5,904, Electronic Ref Mat (Incl. Access Fees) $2,198. Sal $179,434 (Prof $33,280)
Library Holdings: Bk Vols 63,181; Per Subs 171; High Interest/Low Vocabulary Bk Vols 122; Bks on Deafness & Sign Lang 22
Subject Interests: Genealogy, Local history
Automation Activity & Vendor Info: (Cataloging) Sagebrush Corporation; (Circulation) Sagebrush Corporation; (OPAC) Sagebrush Corporation
Publications: Indianfields Public Library History 1904-1975
Mem of White Pine Library Cooperative
Open Mon-Fri 9-8, Sat 9-5
Friends of the Library Group

CARSON CITY

M CARSON CITY HOSPITAL, Medical Library,* 406 E Elm, PO Box 879, 48811-0879. SAN 307-9368. Tel: 517-584-3131, Ext 243. FAX: 517-584-3469. *Librn*, Mary Ann Kapustka; Staff 1 (MLS 1)
Founded 1969
Library Holdings: Bk Vols 750; Per Subs 52
Partic in ILL Regional Med Libr, Western Mich Asn of Libr
Open 24 hours daily

P CARSON CITY PUBLIC LIBRARY,* 102 W Main St, 48811-0699. SAN 307-9376. Tel: 517-584-3680. FAX: 517-584-3680. *Coll Develop, Dir*, Beth O'Grady; *Asst Librn*, Brenda Geselman; *Asst Librn*, Janette Kipp
Founded 1900. Pop 9,681; Circ 39,900
Jul 1999-Jun 2000 Income $170,632. Mats Exp $115,576. Sal $55,523 (Prof $25,000)
Library Holdings: Bk Vols 27,313; Per Subs 77
Subject Interests: Genealogy
Mem of Lakeland Library Cooperative
Partic in CLSI Consortium
Branches: 1
CRYSTAL COMMUNITY, 221 W Lake Dr, Crystal, 48818. SAN 376-9232. Tel: 517-235-6111. FAX: 517-235-6111. *Librn*, Brenda Geselman

CASPIAN

S IRON COUNTY MUSEUM, (ICM), Raymond Gustafson Archives Library, Museum Park, PO Box 272, 49915. SAN 326-6281. Tel: 906-265-2617. E-Mail: icmuseum@up.net. Web Site: www.ironcountymuseum.com. *Curator*, Marcia Bernhardt
Founded 1962. Pop 12,000; Highest Degree: Master
Jan 1999-Dec 1999 Income $7,000. Mats Exp Presv $6,000
Library Holdings: Bk Vols 400; Per Subs 3
Subject Interests: Business, Mining, Organization, World War II
Special Collections: Carrie Jacobs-Bond, letters, memorabilia, mining maps; County; Local School Records; Mining & Lumbering Company Records

CASS CITY

C BAKER COLLEGE OF CASS CITY LIBRARY,* 6667 Main St, 48726. SAN 377-1865. Tel: 517-872-1129. FAX: 517-872-1130. Web Site: www.baker.edu. *Actg Librn*, Justine Dregant
Library Holdings: Bk Titles 5,000; Per Subs 25
Partic in Am Libr Asn

P RAWSON MEMORIAL LIBRARY, 6495 Pine, 48726-4073. SAN 307-9384. Tel: 517-872-2856. FAX: 517-872-4073. Web Site: www.rawson.lib.mi.us. *Dir*, Barbara Hutchinson
Circ 70,351
Library Holdings: Bk Vols 20,000; Per Subs 75
Automation Activity & Vendor Info: (Circulation) Sagebrush Corporation; (OPAC) Sagebrush Corporation
Mem of White Pine Library Cooperative
Friends of the Library Group

CASSOPOLIS

P CASS DISTRICT LIBRARY,* 319 Michigan Rd 62 N, 49031-1099. SAN 346-0711. Tel: 616-445-3400. FAX: 616-445-8795. E-Mail: cass@cass.lib.mi.us. Web Site: www.cass.lib.mi.us/. *Dir*, Mary Elizabeth Harper; *Assoc Dir*, Kay McAdam; *Automation Syst Coordr*, Sue Pickar; *Ad Servs*, Lila Toney; *YA Servs*, Kari Black; *Tech Servs*, Georgia Thompson. Subject Specialists: *Local history*, Sue Pickar; Staff 30 (MLS 1, Non-MLS 29)
Founded 1940. Pop 34,616
Subject Interests: Local history
Database Vendor: epixtech, inc.
Friends of the Library Group
Branches: 4
COUNTY HISTORY RESEARCH CENTER, 145 N Broadway St, 49031. SAN 373-7233. Tel: 616-445-3400. *Librn*, Amy Druskovich
EDWARDSBURG BRANCH, Drawer J, Edwardsburg, 49112. SAN 346-0746. Tel: 616-663-5875. FAX: 616-663-5875. *Librn*, Judy Smith
HOWARD COMMUNITY, 1345 Barron Lake Rd, Niles, 49120. SAN 346-0770. Tel: 616-684-1680. FAX: 616-684-1680. *Librn*, Toni Reynolds
MASON-UNION, 17049 US 12 E, Edwardsburg, 49112. SAN 346-0800. Tel: 616-641-7674. FAX: 616-641-7674. *Librn*, Holly Clark

CEDAR SPRINGS

P CEDAR SPRINGS PUBLIC LIBRARY,* 43 W Cherry St, 49319. SAN 307-9406. Tel: 616-696-1910. FAX: 616-696-1910. *Dir*, Eleanor Barber; *Asst Librn*, Phyllis Knoch
Founded 1936
Library Holdings: Bk Vols 22,500; Per Subs 50
Mem of Lakeland Library Cooperative

CENTER LINE

P CENTER LINE PUBLIC LIBRARY, 7345 Weingartz St, 48015-1462. SAN 307-9422. Tel: 810-758-8274. FAX: 810-755-9234.
Founded 1929. Pop 10,379; Circ 43,807
Library Holdings: Bk Vols 33,298; Per Subs 84
Partic in Suburban Library Cooperative
Friends of the Library Group

CENTRAL LAKE

P CENTRAL LAKE DISTRICT LIBRARY, 7900 Maple St, PO Box 397, 49622-0397. SAN 307-9430. Tel: 231-544-2517. FAX: 231-544-5016. E-Mail: cllib@freeway.net. *Dir*, Christine Bachmann; Staff 2 (Non-MLS 2)
Pop 3,309; Circ 19,338
Apr 1999-Mar 2000 Income $306,747, State $2,620, Federal $252,930, Locally Generated Income $51,197. Mats Exp $21,807, Books $14,978, Per/Ser (Incl. Access Fees) $700, AV Equip $309, Other Print Mats $4,507, Electronic Ref Mat (Incl. Access Fees) $1,313. Sal $35,000
Library Holdings: Bk Vols 16,800; Per Subs 67; Bks on Deafness & Sign Lang 12
Special Collections: Michigan Coll
Mem of Mid-Michigan Library League
Friends of the Library Group

CENTREVILLE

J GLEN OAKS COMMUNITY COLLEGE, E J Shaheen Library, 62249 Shimmel Rd, 49032-9719. SAN 307-9449. Tel: 616-467-9945. FAX: 616-467-4114. Web Site: www.glenoaks.cc. *Dir*, Betsy Susan Morgan; Fax: 616-467-8093, E-Mail: bmorgan@glenoaks.cc.mi.us
Founded 1966. Enrl 1,200; Fac 91
Library Holdings: Bk Vols 39,768; Bk Titles 36,066; Per Subs 293
Mem of Southwest Michigan Library Cooperative

P NOTTAWA TOWNSHIP LIBRARY, 112 S Clark St, PO Box 398, 49032. SAN 307-9457. Tel: 616-467-6289. FAX: 616-467-4422. E-Mail: nottawa@monroe.lib.mi.us. *Librn*, Bonnie Heflin
Founded 1871. Pop 6,600; Circ 41,423
Library Holdings: Bk Vols 21,000; Bk Titles 19,500; Per Subs 42
Special Collections: Amish Religion Coll
Automation Activity & Vendor Info: (Cataloging) Follett; (Circulation) Follett; (ILL) Brodart
Mem of Woodlands Library Cooperative
Partic in ALA; Mich Libr Asn

CHARLEVOIX

P CHARLEVOIX PUBLIC LIBRARY, 109 Clinton St, 49720-1399. SAN 307-9465. Tel: 231-547-2651. FAX: 231-547-0678. E-Mail: mwcharle@northland.lib.mi.us. Web Site: 206.153.75.130:4001/htbin/opac/opac_home, www.charlevoix.lib.mi.us/. *Librn*, Mary E Wallick
Pop 7,000; Circ 44,000
Jul 2000-Jun 2001 Income $230,000. Mats Exp $41,100, Books $34,000, Per/Ser (Incl. Access Fees) $6,200, AV Equip $900
Library Holdings: Bk Titles 29,000; Per Subs 90
Special Collections: Michigan History (Babst)
Automation Activity & Vendor Info: (Cataloging) Gaylord; (Circulation) Gaylord; (Course Reserve) Gaylord; (OPAC) Gaylord
Database Vendor: OCLC - First Search
Mem of Northland Library Cooperative
Friends of the Library Group

CHARLOTTE

P CHARLOTTE COMMUNITY LIBRARY, 226 S Bostwick St, 48813. SAN 307-9473. Tel: 517-543-8859. FAX: 517-543-8868. Web Site: www.char.lib.mi.us. *Dir*, William D Siarny, Jr; E-Mail: billsiarny@voyager.net; *Asst Libr Dir*, Amanda Pearsall; *Business*, Marlena Arras; *Per*, Stephany Humenik; *Cat*, Geneva Howe; *YA Servs*, Sally Seifert; *Circ*, Bridget Gregus. Subject Specialists: *Accounting*, Marlena Arras; *Audio visual mats*, Stephany Humenik; *Biology*, Geneva Howe; *Education*, Sally Seifert; *History*, William D Siarny, Jr; *History*, Amanda Pearsall; *Humanities*, Bridget Gregus; Staff 9 (MLS 1, Non-MLS 8)
Founded 1895. Pop 19,608; Circ 96,627
Jul 1999-Jun 2000 Income $382,000. Mats Exp $382,000, Books $38,000, Per/Ser (Incl. Access Fees) $3,000, Electronic Ref Mat (Incl. Access Fees) $3,000. Sal $182,000
Library Holdings: Bk Titles 50,000; Per Subs 112
Subject Interests: Local history
Mem of Capital Library Cooperative
Partic in Capitol Area Library Network; Capitol Area Librs Coop
Friends of the Library Group

CHASE

P CHASE PUBLIC LIBRARY,* 8400 E North St, 49623. SAN 307-9481. Tel: 231-832-9511. *Librn*, Roxanne Ware
Circ 1,906
Library Holdings: Bk Vols 9,289; Per Subs 12
Mem of Mid-Michigan Library League

CHEBOYGAN

P CHEBOYGAN AREA PUBLIC LIBRARY, 107 S Ball St, 49721-1661. SAN 307-949X. Tel: 231-627-2381. FAX: 231-627-2381. E-Mail: cheboy1@northland.lib.mi.us. *Dir*, Susan VerWys
Pop 12,364
Jul 1999-Jun 2000 Income $431,696, State $12,364, Locally Generated Income $419,332. Mats Exp $55,109, Books $38,869, Per/Ser (Incl. Access Fees) $4,971, Micro $435, AV Equip $8,842, Electronic Ref Mat (Incl. Access Fees) $1,992. Sal $143,827 (Prof $45,654)
Library Holdings: Bk Vols 32,959; Per Subs 194
Function: ILL available, Photocopies available, Reference services available
Mem of Northland Library Cooperative
Friends of the Library Group

CHELSEA

M CHELSEA COMMUNITY HOSPITAL, Medical Library, 775 S Main St, 48118. SAN 374-4418. Tel: 734-475-4040, Ext 3309. FAX: 734-475-4025. Web Site: www.cch.org. *Librn*, Kathy Dorsey; Staff 1 (MLS 1)
Jan 1999-Dec 1999 Income $112,555, Parent Institution $82,555, Other $30,000. Mats Exp $29,200, Books $12,000, Per/Ser (Incl. Access Fees) $17,000, Other Print Mats $200
Library Holdings: Bk Titles 1,200; Per Subs 120
Subject Interests: Medicine
Partic in Michigan Library Consortium; Nat Libr of Med

P CHELSEA DISTRICT LIBRARY, 221 S Main St, 48118. SAN 307-9503. Tel: 734-475-8732. FAX: 734-475-6190. Web Site: www.chelsea.lib.mi.us/. *Dir*, Metta T Lansdale, Jr; E-Mail: lansdale@chelsea.lib.mi.us
Founded 1932. Pop 12,164; Circ 78,788
Library Holdings: Bk Titles 30,000; Per Subs 20
Special Collections: Chelsea History, bk, mss, pictures, microfilm; Wastenaw County History Coll, pictures
Mem of The Library Network
Partic in Library Network
Friends of the Library Group

CHESANING

P CHESANING PUBLIC LIBRARY, 227 E Broad St, 48616. SAN 307-9511. Tel: 517-845-3211. FAX: 517-845-2166. Web Site: www.vlc.lib.mi.us/~chelib. *Dir*, Deborah A Schell; E-Mail: schelld@mlc.lib.mi.us; Staff 8 (MLS 1, Non-MLS 7)
Founded 1936. Pop 11,440; Circ 40,219
Apr 1999-Mar 2000 Income $163,800. Mats Exp $22,199, Books $18,505, Per/Ser (Incl. Access Fees) $3,694. Sal $90,312 (Prof $32,000)
Library Holdings: Bk Vols 41,677; Per Subs 70
Subject Interests: Genealogy, Local history
Automation Activity & Vendor Info: (Cataloging) epixtech, inc.; (Circulation) epixtech, inc.; (OPAC) epixtech, inc.; (Serials) epixtech, inc.
Database Vendor: epixtech, inc.
Publications: Monthly newsletter
Mem of White Pine Library Cooperative
Partic in Valley Libr Consortium; White Pine Libr Coop
Friends of the Library Group

CHESTERFIELD

P CHESTERFIELD TOWNSHIP LIBRARY,* 33091 23 Mile Rd, 48047-1927. SAN 377-7537. Tel: 810-725-7732. FAX: 810-725-5422. E-Mail: cheslib@libcoop.net. Web Site: www.libcoop.net/chesterfield. *Dir*, Marion Lusardi; E-Mail: lusardim@libcoop.net; *Mgr*, Sue Archambault; E-Mail: archambs@libcoop.net; *Automation Syst Coordr*, Lynn Marie Minor; E-Mail: minorl@libcoop.net; *Tech Servs*, John Hebert; E-Mail: hebertj@libcoop.net; *Ref*, Lanette Srickland; *Per*, John Stabile; E-Mail: stabilej@libcoop.net; *Circ*, Jean Wilkins; *Ch Servs*, Marta Kwitkowsky; E-Mail: kwitkowm@libcoop.net; Staff 10 (MLS 5, Non-MLS 5)
Founded 1994. Pop 35,000; Enrl 74,614
Jan 1999-Dec 1999 Income $678,400, State $26,000, Locally Generated Income $585,000, Other $67,400. Mats Exp $124,900, Books $100,000, Per/Ser (Incl. Access Fees) $7,500, Electronic Ref Mat (Incl. Access Fees) $6,600. Sal $299,300 (Prof $141,000)
Library Holdings: Bk Titles 38,169; Per Subs 116; Bks on Deafness & Sign Lang 31
Automation Activity & Vendor Info: (Cataloging) epixtech, inc.; (Circulation) epixtech, inc.; (Serials) epixtech, inc.
Partic in Suburban Library Cooperative

CLARE

P GARFIELD MEMORIAL LIBRARY, Clare Public Library, 101 E Fourth St, 48617-1541. SAN 307-952X. Tel: 517-386-7576. FAX: 517-386-3576. E-Mail: garfieldlib@voyager.net. *Dir*, Sheila Bissonnette; Staff 2 (MLS 2)
Founded 1962. Pop 4,875
Library Holdings: Bk Titles 31,121; Per Subs 78
Mem of White Pine Library Cooperative

CLARKSTON

SR COLOMBIERE CENTER, Dinan Library, PO Box 139, 48347. SAN 307-9538. Tel: 248-625-5611. *Librn*, Stephen A Meder
Founded 1959
Library Holdings: Bk Vols 10,000; Bk Titles 9,500; Per Subs 50
Special Collections: Greek & Latin Classics

P INDEPENDENCE TOWNSHIP PUBLIC LIBRARY,* 6495 Clarkston Rd, 48346-1501. SAN 307-9546. Tel: 248-625-2212. FAX: 248-625-8852. *Dir*, Mollie S Lynch; E-Mail: lynchmol@metronet.lib.mi.us; *Ch Servs*, Anne Rose; *Ad Servs*, Patience Beer; *Circ*, Beth Taylor; Staff 3 (MLS 3)
Founded 1955. Pop 24,722; Circ 138,341
1996-1997 Income $509,285, State $16,906, Federal $9,600, County $32,970, Locally Generated Income $17,652, Other $16,853. Mats Exp $42,998, Books $21,348, Per/Ser (Incl. Access Fees) $16,000, Presv $500, Micro $950. Sal $340,000
Library Holdings: Bk Vols 44,000; Per Subs 150
Mem of The Library Network
Partic in Metronet
Open Mon & Tues 1-9, Wed & Thurs 10-6, Fri 1-6, Sat 10-2 & Sun 1-5
Friends of the Library Group

CLAWSON

P BLAIR MEMORIAL LIBRARY, 416 N Main St, 48017-1599. SAN 307-9554. Tel: 248-588-5500. FAX: 248-588-3114. Web Site: www.clawson.lib.mi.us. *Dir*, Elizabeth Levin; *Ch Servs*, Joy Wong
Founded 1929. Pop 13,874; Circ 103,183
Jul 1999-Jun 2000 Income $439,078. Mats Exp $57,000. Sal $270,228
Library Holdings: Bk Vols 58,345; Per Subs 165
Database Vendor: DRA
Mem of The Library Network
Friends of the Library Group

CLIMAX

P LAWRENCE MEMORIAL PUBLIC LIBRARY, 107 N Main St, PO Box 280, 49034. SAN 307-9562. Tel: 616-746-4125. FAX: 616-746-4125. *Dir*, Ralph Weessies
Founded 1882. Pop 2,774; Circ 4,999
Library Holdings: Bk Vols 15,000; Per Subs 4
Special Collections: Historical Society Coll
Partic in Southwest Michigan Library Cooperative

CLINTON

P CLINTON TOWNSHIP PUBLIC LIBRARY,* 100 Brown St, PO Box 530, 49236. SAN 307-9570. Tel: 517-456-4141. FAX: 517-456-4142. *Dir*, Grace Strauss
Founded 1937. Pop 3,557; Circ 33,085
Library Holdings: Bk Vols 25,000; Per Subs 60
Mem of Huron Valley Libr Syst
Friends of the Library Group

CLINTON TOWNSHIP

§P CLINTON-MACOMB PUBLIC LIBRARY, 43245 Garfield Rd, 48038-1115. SAN 375-4251. Tel: 810-226-5000. Circulation Tel: 810-226-5007. Reference Tel: 810-226-5004. FAX: 810-226-5008. Web Site: www.cmpl.org. *Dir*, Christine Lind Hage; Tel: 810-226-5010, E-Mail: christine@cmpl.org; *Asst Dir*, Larry Neal; Tel: 810-226-5011, Fax: 810-226-5078, E-Mail: larry@cmpl.org; Staff 17 (MLS 7, Non-MLS 10)
Founded 1992. Pop 103,048; Circ 200,000
Dec 2000-Nov 2001 Income (Main Library and Branch Library) $3,887,200, State $103,000, City $3,587,400, County $103,300, Locally Generated Income $93,500. Mats Exp $350,000, Books $320,000, Per/Ser (Incl. Access Fees) $12,000, Electronic Ref Mat (Incl. Access Fees) $18,000. Sal $794,600
Library Holdings: Bk Titles 60,000
Subject Interests: Low vision
Automation Activity & Vendor Info: (Acquisitions) epixtech, inc.; (Cataloging) epixtech, inc.; (Circulation) epixtech, inc.; (OPAC) epixtech, inc.; (Serials) epixtech, inc.
Database Vendor: epixtech, inc., IAC - SearchBank, OCLC - First Search
Mem of Suburban Library System
Partic in Michigan Library Consortium
Open Mon-Thurs 9-9, Fri & Sat 9-6
Friends of the Library Group
Branches: 1
SOUTH, 35891 Gratiot, 48035-2859. Tel: 810-226-5072. TDD: 810-226-5009. FAX: 810-226-5078. Web Site: www.cmpl.org. *Branch Mgr*, Larry Neal; Fax: 810-226-5011, E-Mail: larry@cmpl.org
Founded 2001
Library Holdings: Bk Vols 28,000
Automation Activity & Vendor Info: (Acquisitions) epixtech, inc.; (Cataloging) epixtech, inc.; (Circulation) epixtech, inc.; (OPAC) epixtech, inc.; (Serials) epixtech, inc.
Open Mon-Thurs 9-9, Fri & Sat 9-6, Sun 1-6 (during school year)

P MACOMB COUNTY LIBRARY, 16480 Hall Rd, 48038-1132. SAN 308-2857. Tel: 810-286-6660. FAX: 810-412-5958. Web Site: www.libcoop.net/mcl/. *Dir*, Carolyn Deis; *Asst Dir*, Linda S Champion; *Ref*, Sherry Schmidli; *Ch Servs*, Ann Tokarz; *Info Tech*, William Luft; *Acq, Cat*, Sandy Casamer; Staff 16 (MLS 16)
Founded 1946. Pop 717,400
Jan 2000-Dec 2000 Income (Main Library Only) $3,080,915, State $28,020, County $3,052,895. Mats Exp $423,530, Books $220,450, Per/Ser (Incl. Access Fees) $36,000, Micro $24,000, Electronic Ref Mat (Incl. Access Fees) $143,080. Sal $1,717,258
Library Holdings: Bk Vols 140,325; Per Subs 520
Subject Interests: Business, Career info, Consumer health, Foundations, Fund raising, Investment
Automation Activity & Vendor Info: (Cataloging) epixtech, inc.; (Circulation) epixtech, inc.
Database Vendor: OCLC - First Search
Publications: Directory of Government Officials for Macomb; Macomb County Library Newsletter
Partic in Michigan Library Consortium; OCLC Online Computer Library Center, Inc; Suburban Library Cooperative
Friends of the Library Group
Branches: 2
P MACOMB LIBRARY FOR THE BLIND & PHYSICALLY HANDICAPPED, 16480 Hall Rd, 48038-1132. SAN 324-2250. Tel: 810-286-1580. TDD: 810-286-9940. FAX: 810-286-0634. E-Mail: macbld@libcoop.net. Web Site: www.libcoop.net/macspe. *Librn*, Beverlee Babcock; Tel: 810-412-5976, E-Mail: babbev@libcoop.net; Staff 3 (MLS 3)
Founded 1983. Pop 2,600; Circ 38,000
Oct 1999-Sep 2000 Income $246,612, State $46,192, Federal $63,723, County $136,697. Mats Exp Books $12,412. Sal $136,697 (Prof $93,622)
Library Holdings: Bk Vols 30,290; Bks on Deafness & Sign Lang 250
Subject Interests: Handicaps, Large type print, Talking books
Special Collections: Bi-Folkal Kits; Descriptive Videos; Matchingbook & Tape Kits
Publications: LBPH Newsletter
Restriction: Restricted access
Partic in Suburban Library Cooperative
Special Services for the Deaf - TDD
Special Services for the Blind - Braille typewriter
MACOMB LITERACY PARTNERS, 16480 Hall Rd, 48038-1132. SAN 328-9710. Tel: 810-286-2750. FAX: 810-286-4023. *Coordr*, Marsha DeVergilio; Staff 4 (Non-MLS 4)
Founded 1984
Oct 1999-Sep 2000 Income $206,000, Federal $70,000, County $26,000, Other $110,000. Mats Exp Books $10,000. Sal $106,000
Publications: Read On (newsletter); Read to Me Family Literacy Training Manual; Read to Me Parent Manual

CLIO

S AVKO DYSLEXIA RESEARCH FOUNDATION LIBRARY, 3084 W Willard Rd, 48420. SAN 328-5499. Tel: 810-686-9283. FAX: 810-686-1101. E-Mail: donmcabe@aol.com. Web Site: www.avko.org. *Publ Servs*, R J Rayl; Staff 2 (Non-MLS 2)
Founded 1974
Library Holdings: Bk Titles 6,000; Per Subs 20
Subject Interests: Learning disabilities

COLDWATER

P BRANCH DISTRICT LIBRARY,* 10 E Chicago St, 49036. SAN 346-086X. Tel: 517-278-2341. FAX: 517-279-7134. *Dir*, Mary J Hutchins; *Ch Servs*, Christie Kessler; *Automation Syst Coordr*, Bruce E Guy; *Ad Servs*, Linda Grill; Staff 35 (MLS 4, Non-MLS 31)
Founded 1881. Pop 43,000; Circ 134,843
Jan 1998-Dec 1998 Income (Main Library and Branch Library) $664,031, State $53,037, County $554,237, Locally Generated Income $56,754. Mats Exp $55,004, Books $46,901, Per/Ser (Incl. Access Fees) $5,533, AV Equip $2,520, Manuscripts & Archives $50. Sal $331,992 (Prof $132,943)
Library Holdings: Bk Titles 71,464; Per Subs 95
Special Collections: Geneaological Research Materials

Automation Activity & Vendor Info: (Cataloging) Gaylord; (Circulation) Gaylord
Database Vendor: OCLC - First Search
Function: ILL available
Mem of Woodlands Library Cooperative
Partic in Michigan Library Consortium
Friends of the Library Group
Branches: 5
ALGANSEE, 520 S Ray Quincy Rd, Quincy, 49082. SAN 346-0894. Tel: 517-639-4434. *Librn*, Gwen Dove
Library Holdings: Bk Vols 1,148
BRONSON BRANCH, 207 N Matteson Rd, Bronson, 49028. SAN 346-0924. Tel: 517-369-3785. *Librn*, Carole Maddox
Library Holdings: Bk Vols 4,750
QUINCY BRANCH, 11 N Main St, Quincy, 49082. SAN 346-0959. Tel: 517-639-4001.
Library Holdings: Bk Vols 11,772
Friends of the Library Group
SHERWOOD BRANCH, 118 E Sherman St, Sherwood, 49089. SAN 346-0983. Tel: 517-741-7281. *Librn*, Carolyn Robbins
Library Holdings: Bk Vols 1,625
UNION TOWNSHIP BRANCH, 221 N Broadway, Union City, 49094. SAN 346-1017. Tel: 517-741-5091. *Librn*, Linda VanWormer
Library Holdings: Bk Vols 4,727

S FLORENCE CRANE FACILITY LIBRARY, (Formerly Crane Women's Facility Library), Evergreen Program Center, 38 Fourth St, 49036. SAN 377-4872. Tel: 517-279-9165, Ext 1610. FAX: 517-278-8265. *Actg Librn*, Rick Mitchell
Library Holdings: Bk Vols 5,000

S MICHIGAN DEPARTMENT OF CORRECTIONS, Camp Branch Prison Library, 19 Fourth St, 49036. SAN 377-564X. Tel: 517-278-3204, Ext 336. FAX: 517-279-6504. *Librn*, Heidi L Rawson-Ketchum. Subject Specialists: *Law*, Heidi L Rawson-Ketchum; *Recreational reading*, Heidi L Rawson-Ketchum; Staff 1 (Non-MLS 1)
Founded 1994
Library Holdings: Bk Titles 5,000; Per Subs 14
Restriction: Not open to public

COLEMAN

P COLEMAN AREA LIBRARY,* 231 E Railway, PO Box P, 48618. SAN 307-9589. Tel: 517-465-6398. FAX: 517-465-1861. *Dir*, Gail Cook-Nelson
Pop 4,594; Circ 13,340
Library Holdings: Bk Vols 9,000; Per Subs 52

COLOMA

P COLOMA PUBLIC LIBRARY, 262-264 N Paw Paw, PO Box 430, 49038-0430. SAN 307-9597. Tel: 616-468-3431. FAX: 616-468-8077. Web Site: www.ameritech.net/users/cdickinson/index.html. *Dir*, Charles Dickinson; E-Mail: cdickinson@ameritech.net; *Asst Dir*, Viola Viscuso; Staff 3 (MLS 1, Non-MLS 2)
Founded 1963. Pop 11,631; Circ 56,714
Jun 1998-Jul 1999 Income $149,404, State $11,621, Provincial $41,507, Other $96,186. Mats Exp $26,343, Books $22,565, Per/Ser (Incl. Access Fees) $3,778
Library Holdings: Bk Titles 44,000; Per Subs 90
Subject Interests: Michigan
Partic in Southwest Michigan Library Cooperative

COLON

P COLON TOWNSHIP LIBRARY,* 128 S Blackstone Ave, 49040. SAN 307-9600. Tel: 616-432-3958. FAX: 616-432-4554. *Dir*, Patti A Miller; E-Mail: pamiller@monroe.lib.mi.us; Staff 1 (MLS 1)
Founded 1914. Pop 3,685; Circ 12,656
Apr 1998-Mar 1999 Income $44,567. Mats Exp Books $7,300. Sal $18,710
Library Holdings: Bk Vols 12,000; Per Subs 27
Mem of Woodlands Library Cooperative
Friends of the Library Group

COMSTOCK

P COMSTOCK TOWNSHIP LIBRARY, 6130 King Hwy, PO Box 25, 49041. SAN 307-9619. Tel: 616-345-0136. FAX: 616-345-0138. Web Site: www.comstocktownshiplib.org. *Dir*, Margaret King-Sloan; E-Mail: msloan@voyager.net; *Acq, Assoc Librn*, Donna Odar; *Ad Servs, Ref*, Kerry Fitzgerald; Staff 8 (MLS 5, Non-MLS 3)
Founded 1938. Pop 11,825; Circ 128,500
Jan 1999-Dec 1999 Income $591,000, State $30,000, County $22,000, Locally Generated Income $27,000, Parent Institution $512,000. Mats Exp $113,000, Books $75,000, Per/Ser (Incl. Access Fees) $7,500, AV Equip $2,000, Other Print Mats $5,200. Sal $285,000
Library Holdings: Bk Vols 70,600; Bk Titles 61,350; Per Subs 125
Subject Interests: Local history
Special Collections: Comstock History Coll
Automation Activity & Vendor Info: (Cataloging) TLC; (Circulation) TLC; (OPAC) TLC
Mem of Southwest Michigan Library Cooperative

COMSTOCK PARK

P KENT DISTRICT LIBRARY, 814 West River Center, 49321. SAN 346-5489. Tel: 616-336-3250. FAX: 616-336-3201. Web Site: www.kdl.org. *Dir*, Claudya Muller; Tel: 616-336-3261, E-Mail: cmuller@kdl.org; *Dep Dir*, Ruth D McCrank; Tel: 616-336-3260, E-Mail: rmccrank@kdl.org; *Asst Dir*, Sheryl Garrison; Tel: 616-336-2013; *Asst Dir*, Pamela Vander Ploeg; Tel: 616-336-2547; *Assoc Dir*, Jennifer Giltrop; Tel: 616-336-3171, E-Mail: jgiltrop@kdl.org; *Pub Relations*, John Van ValKenburg; Tel: 616-336-2557, E-Mail: jvanvalkenburg@kdl.org; *Computer Services*, Dale Atkins; Tel: 616-336-2558
Founded 1936. Pop 296,810; Circ 2,765,840
Jan 2000-Dec 2000 Mats Exp $1,323,700, Per/Ser (Incl. Access Fees) $99,552, Electronic Ref Mat (Incl. Access Fees) $75,000. Sal $5,440,592
Library Holdings: Bk Vols 797,109; Per Subs 1,650
Automation Activity & Vendor Info: (Acquisitions) epixtech, inc.; (Cataloging) epixtech, inc.; (Circulation) epixtech, inc.; (OPAC) epixtech, inc.
Publications: Index to Grand Rapids Business Journal; What's Next
Mem of Lakeland Library Cooperative
Friends of the Library Group
Branches: 20
ALPINE, 5255 Alpine NW, 49321. SAN 346-5608. Tel: 616-784-0206. FAX: 616-784-0408. *Mgr*, Cathy Neis
Library Holdings: Bk Vols 16,728
ALTO BRANCH, 6071 Linfield, Alto, 49302. SAN 346-5632. Tel: 616-868-6038. FAX: 616-868-7114. *Mgr*, Sandy Graham
Library Holdings: Bk Vols 7,825
BYRON TOWNSHIP, 2456 84th St, Byron Center, 49315. SAN 346-5667. Tel: 616-878-1665. FAX: 616-878-3933. *Mgr*, Marie Van Fleet
Library Holdings: Bk Vols 46,946
Friends of the Library Group
CALEDONIA BRANCH, 240 Emmons, Caledonia, 49316. SAN 346-5691. Tel: 616-891-1502. FAX: 616-891-1550. *Mgr*, Jane Heiss
Library Holdings: Bk Vols 26,470
Subject Interests: Local history
Friends of the Library Group
CASCADE, 2870 Jacksmith SE, Grand Rapids, 49546. SAN 346-5721. Tel: 616-949-3130. FAX: 616-940-3075. *Mgr*, Diane Cutler
Library Holdings: Bk Vols 57,733
Subject Interests: Medicine
Friends of the Library Group
COMSTOCK PARK BRANCH, 3943 W River Dr NE, 49321. SAN 346-5756. Tel: 616-784-5575. FAX: 616-784-8944. *Mgr*, Nancy Mulder
Library Holdings: Bk Vols 22,530
Friends of the Library Group
EAST GRAND RAPIDS BRANCH, 746 Lakeside SE, East Grand Rapids, 49506. SAN 346-5780. Tel: 616-949-1740. FAX: 616-940-3680. *Mgr*, Cathy Clair
Library Holdings: Bk Vols 91,928
Friends of the Library Group
ENGLEHARDT (LOWELL) BRANCH, 200 N Monroe, Lowell, 49331. SAN 346-5969. Tel: 616-897-9596. FAX: 616-897-5890. *Mgr*, Jane Aronson
Library Holdings: Bk Vols 20,303
Friends of the Library Group
GAINES TOWNSHIP, 421 68th St, Grand Rapids, 49548. SAN 346-5810. Tel: 616-455-1430. FAX: 616-455-2097. *Mgr*, Betty Ann Boss
Library Holdings: Bk Vols 42,996
Subject Interests: Local history
GRANDVILLE BRANCH, 4055 Maple, Grandville, 49418. SAN 346-5845. Tel: 616-530-4995. FAX: 616-530-4653. *Mgr*, Martha Smart
Library Holdings: Bk Vols 94,055
Subject Interests: Local history
Friends of the Library Group
KENTWOOD BRANCH, 4700 Kalamazoo Ave SE, Kentwood, 49508. SAN 346-590X. Tel: 616-455-2200. FAX: 616-455-2528. *Mgr*, Cheryl Cammenga
Library Holdings: Bk Vols 95,988

P LIBRARY FOR THE BLIND & PHYSICALLY HANDICAPPED, 4055 Maple, Grand Rapids, 49418. SAN 346-5519. Tel: 616-530-6219. FAX: 616-530-6222.
Special Services - Discussion groups & special programs; homebound services; information & referral; volunteer recordings
Friends of the Library Group
PLAINFIELD, 2650 Five Mile Rd NE, Grand Rapids, 49525. SAN 346-5993. Tel: 616-361-0611. FAX: 616-361-1007. *Mgr*, David Stracke
Library Holdings: Bk Vols 69,605
Subject Interests: Local history

Friends of the Library Group
ROCKFORD BRANCH, 140 E Bridge St, Rockford, 49341. SAN 346-5934. Tel: 616-866-2352. FAX: 616-866-7016. *Mgr*, Jennifer German
Library Holdings: Bk Vols 49,793
Friends of the Library Group
SAND LAKE BRANCH, 2 Maple St, Sand Lake, 49343. SAN 346-6027. Tel: 616-636-8225. FAX: 616-636-8511. *Mgr*, Glenda Middleton
Library Holdings: Bk Vols 25,039
Friends of the Library Group
SERVICE CENTER, 814 West River Center, 49321. SAN 346-5543. Tel: 616-336-3250. FAX: 616-336-3201.
SPENCER TOWNSHIP, 14960 Meddler Ave, Gowen, 49326. SAN 378-1615. Tel: 616-984-2830. FAX: 616-984-2832. *Mgr*, Glenda Middleton
TYRONE TOWNSHIP (KENT CITY), 43 S Main St, PO Box 188, Kent City, 49330. SAN 346-587X. Tel: 616-678-4571. FAX: 616-678-5330. E-Mail: ktcmd@kdl.org. Web Site: www.dl.org. *Branch Mgr*, Marcia DeMeester
Library Holdings: Bk Vols 12,588
Friends of the Library Group
WALKER BRANCH, 4293 Remembrance Rd NW, Walker, 49544. SAN 346-6051. Tel: 616-791-6844. FAX: 616-791-6842. *Mgr*, Jane Seitz
Library Holdings: Bk Vols 39,579
Friends of the Library Group
WYOMING BRANCH, 1575 Gezon Pkwy SW, Wyoming, 49509. SAN 346-6086. Tel: 616-530-3183. FAX: 616-534-4822. *Mgr*, Mary Hollinrake
Library Holdings: Bk Vols 118,687

CONSTANTINE

P CONSTANTINE TOWNSHIP LIBRARY, 165 S Canaris St, 49042-1015. SAN 307-9627. Tel: 616-435-7957. FAX: 616-435-5800. E-Mail: constant@monroe.lib.mi.us. *Librn*, Jane Moe
Founded 1915. Pop 4,907; Circ 34,800
Jan 1999-Dec 1999 Income $118,400. Mats Exp $21,185, Books $14,400, Per/Ser (Incl. Access Fees) $1,800, AV Equip $2,485, Electronic Ref Mat (Incl. Access Fees) $2,500. Sal $46,800
Library Holdings: Bk Vols 17,000; Per Subs 70
Subject Interests: Agriculture, History, Religion
Mem of Woodlands Library Cooperative

COOPERSVILLE

P NORTHEAST OTTAWA DISTRICT LIBRARY,* 333 Ottawa St, 49404-1243. SAN 307-9635. Tel: 616-837-6809. FAX: 616-837-7689. E-Mail: coo@lakeland.lib.mi.us. Web Site: www.lakeland.lib.mi.us/coopersville. *Dir*, Marianne Swanson White
Circ 40,041
Library Holdings: Bk Vols 37,000; Per Subs 72
Special Collections: Coopersville Observers 1880's-1970
Mem of Lakeland Library Cooperative
Friends of the Library Group

CORUNNA

P CORUNNA PUBLIC LIBRARY,* 401 N Shiawassee St, 48817. SAN 307-9643. Tel: 517-743-4800. FAX: 517-743-5502. *Dir*, Sue Huff; *Asst Librn*, Cathy Cramner; Staff 2 (MLS 2)
Founded 1970. Pop 6,928; Circ 33,000
Library Holdings: Bk Vols 16,000; Per Subs 26
Special Collections: Corunna Journal 1887-1913
Mem of Mideastern Michigan Library Cooperative

P SHIAWASSEE COUNTY LIBRARY,* 701 S Norton St, 48817. SAN 346-1041. Tel: 517-743-2278. FAX: 517-743-4891. *Dir*, Judy Berry; E-Mail: jberry@shianet.org; Staff 6 (MLS 1, Non-MLS 5)
Founded 1965. Pop 16,894; Circ 46,839
Jan 1999-Dec 1999 Income (Main Library and Branch Library) $128,254, State $21,756, County $100,498, Locally Generated Income $6,000. Mats Exp Books $11,337. Sal $86,823 (Prof $40,044)
Library Holdings: Bk Vols 37,000
Subject Interests: Large type print
Automation Activity & Vendor Info: (Acquisitions) Sagebrush Corporation; (Cataloging) Sagebrush Corporation; (Circulation) Sagebrush Corporation
Database Vendor: OCLC - First Search
Partic in Mideastern Mich Libr Coop
Branches: 5
BYRON COMMUNITY, 312 W Maple, Byron, 48418. SAN 377-6042. Tel: 810-266-4629. FAX: 810-266-5723. *Librn*, Stephanie Miller; Staff 1 (Non-MLS 1)
Library Holdings: Bk Vols 7,000; Bk Titles 6,100; Per Subs 20
Subject Interests: Audio bks, Large print
MORRICE VILLAGE BRANCH, 300 Main St, Morrice, 48857. SAN 346-1130. Tel: 517-625-7911. FAX: 517-625-7911. *Librn*, LaVerne Wiggins
PERKINS LIBRARY OF LENNON, 11904 Lennon Rd, Lennon, 48449. SAN 346-1106. Tel: 810-621-4285. FAX: 810-621-4896. *Librn*, Lenora Warren
SHIAWASSEE TOWNSHIP BRANCH, 625 Grand River, Bancroft, 48414. SAN 346-1165. Tel: 517-634-5689. FAX: 517-634-5689. *Librn*, LaVerne Wiggins
TWIN TOWNSHIP LIBRARY, 9435 Beech St, PO Box 279, New Lothrop, 48460. SAN 346-1076. Tel: 810-638-7575. FAX: 810-638-7575. *Librn*, Agnes Andres
Bookmobiles: 1

CROSWELL

P WILLIAM H AITKIN MEMORIAL LIBRARY,* 111 N Howard Ave, 48422-1225. SAN 307-9651. Tel: 810-679-3627. FAX: 810-679-3392. E-Mail: wmaitkin@greatlakes.net. *Dir*, Jennifer Jones
Founded 1911. Circ 42,004
Jul 1998-Jun 1999 Income $145,760, State $4,852, City $25,000, County $51,000, Locally Generated Income $5,000, Other $58,000. Mats Exp $32,112, Books $28,000, Per/Ser (Incl. Access Fees) $2,000. Sal $40,252 (Prof $26,000)
Library Holdings: Bk Vols 37,167; Per Subs 102
Partic in Am Libr Asn; White Pine Libr Coop

CRYSTAL FALLS

P CRYSTAL FALLS DISTRICT COMMUNITY LIBRARY, 401 Superior Ave, 49920-1424. SAN 307-966X. Tel: 906-875-3344. FAX: 906-875-3767. *Librn*, Mary J Thoreson
Founded 1955. Circ 29,467
Library Holdings: Bk Vols 16,719; Per Subs 55

DAVISBURG

P SPRINGFIELD TOWNSHIP LIBRARY,* 10900 Andersonville Rd, 48350. SAN 307-9678. Tel: 248-625-0595. FAX: 248-625-0358. *Librn*, Catherine Phillips Forst
Founded 1976. Pop 8,295; Circ 19,100
Jan 1997-Dec 1998 Income $175,000. Mats Exp $20,000. Sal $112,000
Library Holdings: Bk Vols 25,000; Per Subs 95
Mem of The Library Network; Wayne Oakland Libr Federation
Friends of the Library Group

DE TOUR VILLAGE

P DE TOUR AREA SCHOOL & PUBLIC LIBRARY,* 202 S Division St, PO Box 429, 49725-0068. SAN 307-9686. Tel: 906-297-2011. FAX: 906-297-3403. *Librn*, Carole Hiney; E-Mail: chiney@eup.k12.mi.us
Pop 1,829; Circ 11,449
Library Holdings: Bk Vols 12,500; Per Subs 36
Mem of Hiawathaland Library Cooperative
Open Mon-Fri 8-3:30 & 6-8 (winter)

DE WITT

P DE WITT PUBLIC LIBRARY,* 13101 Schavey Rd, 48820. SAN 346-122X. Tel: 517-669-3156. FAX: 517-669-6408. *Dir*, Michael Lamb; *Librn*, Helen Davis
Founded 1934. Pop 26,000
Jul 1997-Jun 1998 Income $180,000. Sal $60,000
Library Holdings: Bk Vols 25,057
Subject Interests: Local history
Mem of Capital Library Cooperative
Friends of the Library Group

DEARBORN

S AUTOMOTIVE HALL OF FAME, INC LIBRARY, 21400 Oakwood Blvd, 48124. SAN 372-6517. Tel: 313-240-4000. FAX: 313-240-8641. Web Site: www.automotivehalloffame.org. *Pub Relations*, Linda Bussei; E-Mail: lbussei@ameritech.net
Founded 1940
Library Holdings: Bk Titles 300
Special Collections: Automotive Biography on Companies & Individuals, bks & per
Open Mon-Fri 10-5. Call first to make arrangements

C DAVENPORT UNIVERSITY, (Formerly Detroit College of Business Library), 4801 Oakman Blvd, 48126. SAN 346-1408. Tel: 313-581-4400, Ext 272. FAX: 313-581-4762. *Actg Dir, Librn*, Marilyn Kwik; *Tech Servs*, Diane Manko-Cliff; *Ser*, Kathleen Maida; Staff 4 (MLS 4)
Founded 1962. Enrl 2,222; Fac 40; Highest Degree: Master
Library Holdings: Bk Vols 32,686; Bk Titles 28,578; Per Subs 257
Automation Activity & Vendor Info: (Acquisitions) epixtech, inc.; (Cataloging) epixtech, inc.; (Circulation) epixtech, inc.; (Course Reserve) epixtech, inc.; (ILL) epixtech, inc.; (Media Booking) epixtech, inc.; (OPAC)

epixtech, inc.; (Serials) epixtech, inc.
Database Vendor: GaleNet, IAC - Info Trac
Mem of Wayne Oakland Libr Federation
Partic in Michigan Library Consortium; Southeastern Michigan League Of Libraries
Departmental Libraries:
WARREN, 27500 Dequindre Rd, Warren, 48092-5279. SAN 378-1402. Tel: 810-558-8700. FAX: 810-558-7868. *Librn*, Carolyn Stingel

S DEARBORN HISTORICAL MUSEUM LIBRARY,* 915 Brady St, 48124. SAN 307-9708. Tel: 313-565-3000. FAX: 313-565-4848. *Curator, Res*, William McElhone; *Curator*, Winfield Arneson; Staff 6 (MLS 2, Non-MLS 4)
Founded 1950
Library Holdings: Bk Vols 2,556; Bk Titles 1,172; Per Subs 18
Special Collections: Local Historical Records & Manuscripts
Publications: Dearborn Historian
Restriction: Open to public for reference only

P DEARBORN PUBLIC LIBRARY, 16301 Michigan Ave, 48126. SAN 346-1289. Tel: 313-943-2037. TDD: 313-943-2193. FAX: 313-943-3063. Web Site: dearborn.lib.mi.us. *Dir*, Reginald P Coady; E-Mail: rcoady@tln.lib.mi.us; *Asst Librn*, Kathy White; Tel: 313-943-2048, E-Mail: klwhite@tln.lib.mi.us; *Ad Servs, ILL, Media Spec*, Jane Fox; *Ch Servs*, Lois Trombley; *Cat, Circ, Tech Servs*, Maryanne Bartles; *Br Coordr*, Carolyn Hook; Staff 70 (MLS 23, Non-MLS 47)
Founded 1919. Pop 89,603; Circ 1,061,983
Jul 1999-Jun 2000 Income (Main Library and Branch Library) $4,365,333, State $89,286, City $4,026,507, Other $249,540. Mats Exp $753,845. Sal $2,895,712
Library Holdings: Bk Vols 299,818; Bk Titles 157,615
Special Collections: City of Dearborn Coll, clippings, pamphlets; Ford Coll
Automation Activity & Vendor Info: (Acquisitions) epixtech, inc.; (Cataloging) epixtech, inc.; (Circulation) epixtech, inc.; (OPAC) epixtech, inc.; (Serials) epixtech, inc.
Database Vendor: epixtech, inc., IAC - Info Trac, OCLC - First Search
Mem of The Library Network
Friends of the Library Group
Branches: 3
BRYANT, 22100 Michigan Ave, 48124. SAN 346-1319. Tel: 313-943-4091. FAX: 313-943-3099. Web Site: dearborn.lib.mi.us. *Librn*, John Oakley
Library Holdings: Bk Vols 42,615
Friends of the Library Group
ESPER, 12929 W Warren, 48126. SAN 346-1343. Tel: 313-943-4096. FAX: 313-943-4097. Web Site: dearborn.lib.mi.us. *Librn*, Peggy Bryan
Library Holdings: Bk Vols 38,611
Friends of the Library Group
SNOW, 23950 Princeton, 48124. SAN 346-1378. Tel: 313-943-4093. FAX: 313-274-1452. Web Site: dearborn.lib.mi.us. *Librn*, Tara Gnau
Library Holdings: Bk Vols 56,869
Friends of the Library Group

J HENRY FORD COMMUNITY COLLEGE, Eshleman Library, 5101 Evergreen Rd, 48128-1495. SAN 307-9724. Tel: 313-845-6379, 313-845-9785. FAX: 313-271-5868. Web Site: www.hfcc.net. *Dir*, Barbara Lukasiewicz; E-Mail: bluka@hfcc.net; *Archivist*, Robert Butler; Tel: 313-845-6521, E-Mail: rbutler@hfcc.net; *Acq, Coll Develop*, Janet Elgas; Tel: 313-845-9764, E-Mail: jelgas@hfcc.net; *Cat, Tech Servs*, Nancy Widman; Tel: 313-845-9786, E-Mail: nwidman@hfcc.net; *Doc*, Vicki Morris; Tel: 313-845-9761, E-Mail: vmorris@hfcc.net; *ILL, Ref*, Terry Potvim; Tel: 313-845-9760; *Media Spec, Ref*, Dan Harrison; Tel: 313-845-6377, E-Mail: dharrisn@hfcc.net; *Ser*, Georgia Lindstrom; Tel: 313-845-6371, E-Mail: glindstm@hfcc.net; Staff 7 (MLS 7)
Founded 1938. Enrl 12,525; Fac 216; Highest Degree: Associate
Jul 2000-Jun 2001 Mats Exp $208,600, Books $67,500, Per/Ser (Incl. Access Fees) $97,500, AV Equip $5,000, Electronic Ref Mat (Incl. Access Fees) $38,600. (Prof $430,960)
Library Holdings: Bk Vols 80,000; Bk Titles 67,000; Per Subs 625
Subject Interests: Law, Nursing, Performing arts
Automation Activity & Vendor Info: (Acquisitions) epixtech, inc.
Database Vendor: epixtech, inc.
Partic in Michigan Library Consortium

S HENRY FORD MUSEUM & GREENFIELD VILLAGE, Research Center Library,* 20900 Oakwood Blvd, PO Box 1970, 48121-1970. SAN 307-9716. Tel: 313-982-6070, Ext 2508. FAX: 313-982-6244. E-Mail: rescntr@hfmgv.org. Web Site: www.hfmgv.org. *Mgr Libr Serv*, Patricia Orr; *Curator*, Judith E Endelman; *Curator*, Cynthia Read-Miller; *Curator*, Robert Casey; *Archivist*, Terry Hoover; Staff 17 (MLS 12, Non-MLS 5)
Founded 1929
1997-1998 Income $220,000. Mats Exp $16,000. Sal $160,000
Library Holdings: Bk Vols 40,000; Per Subs 300
Subject Interests: History, Material culture
Special Collections: Detroit Publishing Company, archives, photogs; Edison Recording Artists; Ephemera Coll, trade lit; Fire Insurance Maps; Ford Motor Company Records; Gebelein Silversmiths; Henry & Clara Ford Papers; Henry Austin Clark Coll; HJ Heinz Co Records; Images Ford Motor Company; Industrial Design Coll; John Burroughs Papers; Stickley Furniture Co Records
Partic in Library Network; Michigan Library Consortium; OCLC Online Computer Library Center, Inc

M OAKWOOD HOSPITAL, Health Science Library, 18101 Oakwood Blvd, 48124-2500. SAN 307-9732. Tel: 313-593-7685. FAX: 313-593-8825. Web Site: www.oakwood.org (hospital homepage), www.ohslibrary.org.; Staff 5 (MLS 2, Non-MLS 3)
Founded 1953
Library Holdings: Bk Vols 12,000; Bk Titles 5,500; Per Subs 400
Subject Interests: Clinical medicine, Health sciences, Hospital administration, Nursing
Automation Activity & Vendor Info: (Cataloging) EOS; (Circulation) EOS; (OPAC) EOS; (Serials) EOS
Database Vendor: OCLC - First Search, OVID Technologies
Partic in Metrop Detroit Med Libr Group; Michigan Health Sciences Libraries Association
Non circulating-periodicals & reference

C UNIVERSITY OF MICHIGAN DEARBORN MARDIGIAN LIBRARY, 4901 Evergreen Rd, 48128-1491. SAN 307-9759. Tel: 313-593-5445. Interlibrary Loan Service Tel: 313-593-3284. Circulation Tel: 313-593-5598. FAX: 313-593-5478. Web Site: www.libraryweb.umd.umich.edu. *Dir*, Timothy F Richards; E-Mail: tim.richards@umich.edu; *Cat*, Mary Nessel; Tel: 313-593-5401, Fax: 313-593-5561, E-Mail: nesselmc@umd.umich.edu; *Cat*, Beth Taylor; Tel: 313-593-5402, Fax: 313-593-5561, E-Mail: bjtaylor@umich.edu; *Syst Coordr*, Erica Fors; Tel: 313-593-5156, Fax: 313-593-5561, E-Mail: efors@umich.edu; *Syst Coordr*, Robert G Kelly; Tel: 313-593-5212, Fax: 313-593-5561, E-Mail: rgk@umd.umich.edu; *Asst Dir, Circ, Tech Servs*, Barbara Kriigel; Tel: 313-593-5614, Fax: 313-593-5561, E-Mail: bkriigel@umich.edu; *Network Services*, Robert M Fraser; Tel: 313-593-3740, E-Mail: rfraser@umd.umich.edu; *Res*, Alicia McCalla; Tel: 313-593-5076, Fax: 313-593-5561, E-Mail: amccalla@umich.edu; *Web Coordr*, Sara Memmott; Tel: 313-593-5617, Fax: 313-593-5561, E-Mail: smemmott@umich.edu; *Media Spec*, Janet Yanosko; Tel: 313-593-5615, Fax: 313-593-5561, E-Mail: jyanosko@umich.edu; *Archivist, Coll Develop*, Karen Morgan; Tel: 313-593-5618, Fax: 313-593-5561, E-Mail: kmissy@umd.umich.edu; *Curator*, Jamie Wraight; Tel: 313-583-6300, Fax: 313-593-5561, E-Mail: jwraight@umd.umich.edu. Subject Specialists: *Holocaust*, Jamie Wraight
Founded 1959
Jul 1999-Jun 2000 Income $1,860,093. Mats Exp $550,767, Books $144,266, Per/Ser (Incl. Access Fees) $281,101, Presv $16,324, AV Equip $7,586, Other Print Mats $8,979, Electronic Ref Mat (Incl. Access Fees) $92,511. Sal $947,437 (Prof $760,586)
Library Holdings: Bk Vols 324,551; Bk Titles 220,192; Per Subs 1,231
Subject Interests: Education, Engineering, Humanities, Management
Automation Activity & Vendor Info: (Acquisitions) Innovative Interfaces Inc.; (Cataloging) Innovative Interfaces Inc.; (Circulation) Innovative Interfaces Inc.; (Course Reserve) Innovative Interfaces Inc.; (ILL) Innovative Interfaces Inc.; (Media Booking) Innovative Interfaces Inc.; (OPAC) Innovative Interfaces Inc.; (Serials) Innovative Interfaces Inc.
Database Vendor: OCLC - First Search
Publications: Occasional Bibliographic Series
Partic in Michigan Library Consortium; OCLC Online Computer Library Center, Inc
Friends of the Library Group

DEARBORN HEIGHTS

P CAROLINE KENNEDY LIBRARY,* 24590 George St, 48127. SAN 307-9767. Tel: 313-277-7762. FAX: 313-277-7005. *Dir*, Mark Andrews
Founded 1961. Pop 67,706; Circ 83,092
Library Holdings: Bk Vols 55,000; Per Subs 120
Mem of The Library Network; Wayne Oakland Libr Federation
Friends of the Library Group

P JOHN F KENNEDY JR LIBRARY,* 24602 Van Born Rd, 48125. SAN 307-9775. Tel: 313-277-7764. FAX: 313-291-7607. *Dir*, Mark Andrews
Pop 67,706
Library Holdings: Bk Titles 55,000; Per Subs 120
Mem of The Library Network; Wayne County Libr Syst
Friends of the Library Group

DECATUR

P VAN BUREN DISTRICT LIBRARY, Webster Memorial Library,* 200 N Phelps St, 49045-1086. SAN 346-1491. Tel: 616-423-4771. FAX: 616-423-8373. E-Mail: decatur@monroe.lib.mi.us. Web Site: cwic1.jackson.lib.mi.us/van/vanburen.htm. *Dir*, David Tate; *ILL*, Susan Marks; *Ch Servs*, Lin Zimmer; *Automation Syst Coordr*, Judith Fasco; *Acq*, Debby Stassek; *Coll Develop*, Debby Stassek; Staff 8 (MLS 8)
Founded 1941. Circ 225,521
Jan 1998-Dec 1999 Income $990,699, State $35,200, County $190,000, Locally Generated Income $55,800, Parent Institution $24,500, Other $5,000. Mats Exp $134,037, Books $105,000, Per/Ser (Incl. Access Fees)

$14,000, Presv $1,595. Sal $470,578
Library Holdings: Bk Vols 130,627; Per Subs 303
Subject Interests: Genealogy, Michigan
Mem of Woodlands Library Cooperative
Friends of the Library Group
Branches: 6
ANTWERP SUNSHINE BRANCH, 24823 Front Ave, Mattawan, 49071. SAN 346-167X. Tel: 616-668-2534. FAX: 616-668-2534. E-Mail: decatur@monroe.lib.mi.us. Web Site: cwic1.jackson.lib.mi.us/van/antwerp.htm. *Librn*, Angela Stair
Friends of the Library Group
BANGOR BRANCH, 420 Division St, Bangor, 49013-1112. SAN 346-1521. Tel: 616-427-8810. FAX: 616-427-8810. E-Mail: decatur@monroe.lib.mi.us. Web Site: cwic1.jackson.lib.mi.us/van/bangor.htm. *Librn*, Bobbi Martindale
Friends of the Library Group
BLOOMINGDALE BRANCH, E Kalamazoo Ave, PO Box 128, Bloomingdale, 49026. SAN 346-1556. Tel: 616-521-7601. FAX: 616-521-7601. E-Mail: decatur@monroe.lib.mi.us. Web Site: cwic1.jackson.lib.mi.us/van/bdale.htm.
COVERT BRANCH, 33805 M-140 Hwy, PO Box 7, Covert, 49043. SAN 346-1580. Tel: 616-764-1298. FAX: 616-764-1298. E-Mail: decatur@monroe.lib.mi.us. Web Site: cwic1.jackson.lib.mi.us/van/covert.htm. *Librn*, Theresa Romano
GOBLES BRANCH, 105 E Main, PO Box 247, Gobles, 49055-0247. SAN 346-1610. Tel: 616-628-4537. FAX: 616-628-4537. E-Mail: decatur@monroe.lib.mi.us. Web Site: cwic1.jackson.lib.mi.us/van/gobles.htm. *Librn*, Shirley Whitt
LAWRENCE BRANCH, 122 W Saint Joseph St, PO Box 186, Lawrence, 49064. SAN 346-1645. Tel: 616-674-3200. FAX: 616-674-3200. E-Mail: decatur@monroe.lib.mi.us. Web Site: cwic1.jackson.lib.mi.us/van/lawrence.htm. *Librn*, Sharon Crotser
Bookmobiles: 1

DECKERVILLE

P DECKERVILLE PUBLIC LIBRARY, 3542 N Main St, 48427-9638. SAN 307-9783. Tel: 810-376-8015. FAX: 810-376-8593. E-Mail: deckpl@thumb.net. Web Site: www.deckervillelibrary.com. *Librn*, Kathy Wedyke; *Asst Librn*, Mayme Decker
Founded 1924. Pop 4,788; Circ 30,976
Library Holdings: Bk Titles 17,932
Special Collections: Census of Sanilac County Cemeteries - Evergreen, Marion Twp, Mt Zion, Rosbury & Tucker; History of Sanilac County 1834-1984; Michigan Census Bk, 1904; Michigan Pioneer & Historical Coll (1881-1912); Sanilac County Atlas, 1906; Sanilac County Portrait & Biographical Album, 1884 & 1984
Automation Activity & Vendor Info: (Cataloging) Sagebrush Corporation
Mem of White Pine Library Cooperative

DELTON

P DELTON DISTRICT LIBRARY, 330 N Grove St, PO Box 155, 49046. SAN 307-9791. Tel: 616-623-8040. FAX: 616-623-6740. E-Mail: ddl@mei.net. Web Site: cwic1.jackson.lib.mi.us/delton/delton.htm. *Dir*, Jane Leavitt; Staff 5 (MLS 1, Non-MLS 4)
Founded 1965. Pop 12,306; Circ 30,000
Apr 2000-Mar 2001 Income $142,700, State $31,000, Other $68,767. Mats Exp $13,000, Books $12,000, Per/Ser (Incl. Access Fees) $1,000. Sal $67,800
Library Holdings: Bk Vols 26,000
Special Collections: Tractor Manuals
Automation Activity & Vendor Info: (Circulation) Brodart; (ILL) Brodart
Mem of Woodlands Library Cooperative
Friends of the Library Group

DETROIT

S ARCHIVES OF AMERICAN ART - SMITHSONIAN INSTITUTION, Midwest Regional Center,* 5200 Woodward Ave, 48202. SAN 320-9156. Tel: 313-226-7544. FAX: 313-226-7620. *Librn*, Cynthia Williams
Special Collections: Archival Material Documenting the History of Visual Arts in the United States, micro
Publications: Update - Midwest Regional Center/Archives of American Art Newsletter (Fall, Winter, Spring)
Friends of the Library Group

S ASH STEVENS, INC LIBRARY,* 5861 John C Lodge Freeway, 48202. SAN 307-9821. Tel: 313-872-6400. FAX: 313-872-6841. *Pres*, Stephen Munk
Founded 1962
Library Holdings: Bk Titles 1,200; Per Subs 10
Subject Interests: Chemistry

AURORA HEALTH CARE

M HEALTH SCIENCE LIBRARY, 3737 Lawton, 48208. SAN 308-0277. Tel: 313-361-7720. *Ref*, Joanne Kowalenok
Founded 1971
Library Holdings: Bk Vols 2,200; Bk Titles 1,850; Per Subs 135
Special Collections: Osteopathy Coll
Partic in Michigan Library Consortium

M BARBARA ANN KARMANOS CANCER INSTITUTE, Leonard N Simons Research Library, 110 E Warren, 48201. SAN 308-0242. Tel: 313-833-0715, Ext 2239. FAX: 313-831-8714. *Dir*, Elliet Mullenmeister; *Librn*, Sandra A Studebaker; E-Mail: studebak@karmanos.org. Subject Specialists: *Cancer*, Sandra A Studebaker
Founded 1948
Library Holdings: Bk Titles 2,500; Per Subs 60
Subject Interests: Cancer
Special Collections: Michigan Cancer Foundation archival files
Publications: CompuScope (newsletter)
Restriction: Not open to public
Function: Research library
Partic in Dialog Corporation; Nat Libr of Med; STN

L BODMAN, LONGLEY & DAHLING, Law Library, 100 Renaissance Ctr 34th flr, 48243. SAN 372-2902. Tel: 313-259-7777. FAX: 313-393-7579. Web Site: www.bodmanlongley.com. *Librn*, Jeanne Stuart; E-Mail: jstuart@bodmanlongley.com; Staff 1 (MLS 1)

SR BUSHNELL CONGREGATIONAL CHURCH LIBRARY,* 15000 Southfield Rd, 48223. SAN 327-2087. Tel: 313-272-3550.

L BUTZEL LONG LIBRARY, 150 W Jefferson, Ste 900, 48226. SAN 307-9856. Tel: 313-225-7000. FAX: 313-225-7080. *Mgr Libr Serv*, A Candace Goss; Tel: 313-983-7442, Fax: 313-225-7080, E-Mail: goss@butzel.com. Subject Specialists: *Legal res*, A Candace Goss; Staff 4 (MLS 1, Non-MLS 3)
Library Holdings: Bk Vols 18,000; Per Subs 10
Subject Interests: Employee benefits, Immigration laws, Labor law
Database Vendor: Lexis-Nexis, OCLC - First Search
Restriction: Staff use only
Function: ILL to other special libraries

C CENTER FOR CREATIVE STUDIES-COLLEGE OF ART & DESIGN LIBRARY,* 201 E Kirby, 48202-4034. SAN 307-9880. Tel: 313-664-7642. FAX: 313-664-7880. *Dir*, Lynell Morr; Tel: 313-664-7641, E-Mail: lmorr@ccscad.edu; *Electronic Resources, Ref*, Beth Walker; Tel: 313-664-7803, E-Mail: bwalker@ccscad.edu
Founded 1966. Highest Degree: Bachelor
Library Holdings: Bk Vols 25,000; Per Subs 183
Subject Interests: Applied arts, Crafts, Fine arts, Graphic design, Industrial design, Photography
Partic in Michigan Library Consortium; OCLC Online Computer Library Center, Inc; Southeastern Michigan League Of Libraries

L CHARFOOS & CHRISTENSEN LAW LIBRARY, 5510 Woodward, 48202. SAN 327-2125. Tel: 313-875-8080. FAX: 313-875-8522, 875-9857. E-Mail: lawyers1@flashnet.com. Web Site: c2law.com. *Dir*, Christine Sikula; E-Mail: clsikula@flash.net; Staff 1 (Non-MLS 1)
Library Holdings: Bk Vols 800; Per Subs 30
Subject Interests: Law, Medicine

M CHILDREN'S HOSPITAL OF MICHIGAN, Medical Library, 3901 Beaubien Blvd, 48201. SAN 307-9899. Tel: 313-745-0252, 313-745-5322. FAX: 313-993-0148. *Librn*, Misa Mi; E-Mail: mmi@dmc.org
Library Holdings: Bk Vols 3,300; Per Subs 270
Subject Interests: Pediatrics

L CITY OF DETROIT, Law Department Library,* First National Bldg, 660 Woodward Ave, Ste 1650, 48226. SAN 307-9902. Tel: 313-224-4550. FAX: 313-224-5505. *Librn*, Thomas R Killian
Founded 1935
Library Holdings: Bk Vols 20,000
Subject Interests: Law, Michigan

L CLARK HILL PLC, Law Library, 500 Woodward Ave, Ste 3500, 48226-3435. SAN 326-3851. Tel: 313-965-8300, Ext 8277. FAX: 965-8252. *In Charge*, Kathleen A Gamache; E-Mail: kgamache@clarkhill.com; Staff 1 (MLS 1)
Library Holdings: Bk Vols 10,000; Per Subs 200

S COMERICA INCORPORATED LIBRARY,* Library 1134, 411 W Lafayette, 48226. (Mail add: Library - 1134, PO Box 75000, 48275-1134), Tel: 313-222-4636. FAX: 313-222-6967. *Senior Librn, VPres*, Beth L Stanton; E-Mail: beth_l_stanton@comerica.com; Staff 3 (MLS 2, Non-MLS 1)
Founded 1974
Jan 1999-Dec 1999 Mats Exp $165,000. (Prof $100,000)
Library Holdings: Bk Vols 7,500; Bk Titles 5,000; Per Subs 250

Subject Interests: Finance
Automation Activity & Vendor Info: (Cataloging) EOS; (Circulation) EOS
Restriction: Company staff only
Function: Research library

GM DEPARTMENT OF VETERANS AFFAIRS MEDICAL CENTER, Library Service, 4646 John R St, 48201. SAN 307-8566. Tel: 313-576-1000, Ext 3380. FAX: 313-576-1048. Web Site: www.webpac.wayne.edu. *Librn*, Karen Tubolino; Tel: 313-576-1085, E-Mail: karen.tubolino@med.va.gov; Staff 2 (MLS 2)
Library Holdings: Bk Vols 5,000; Per Subs 350
Database Vendor: epixtech, inc., OCLC - First Search, OVID Technologies
Partic in Valnet

S DETROIT EDISON CO, Corporate Library,* 2 Service Bldg, 2000 Second Ave, 48226. SAN 307-997X. Tel: 313-235-9216. Interlibrary Loan Service Tel: 313-235-9226. FAX: 313-235-8011. E-Mail: library@detroitedison.com. *Ref*, Dianne White
Founded 1916
Library Holdings: Bk Vols 6,000; Per Subs 50
Subject Interests: Energy, Marketing
Publications: Newsletter
Partic in Michigan Library Consortium

S DETROIT FREE PRESS LIBRARY, 600 W Fort, 48226. SAN 307-9988. Tel: 313-222-6897. Toll Free Tel: 800-678-6400, Ext 6897. FAX: 313-222-8778. E-Mail: library@freepress.com. *Dir, Res*, Shelley Lavey; Staff 7 (MLS 5, Non-MLS 2)
Founded 1925
Special Collections: Detroit Free Press, 1925-Present, clippings, micro & electronic data base
Restriction: Staff use only
Partic in Dialog Corporation

S DETROIT GARDEN CENTER, INC LIBRARY, 1460 E Jefferson Ave, 48207. SAN 324-1017. Tel: 313-259-6363. FAX: 313-259-0107. *Librn*, Beverly Donaldson; Tel: 313-259-6563
Founded 1972
Library Holdings: Bk Titles 6,200
Subject Interests: Horticulture
Publications: Detroit Garden Center Bulletin
Restriction: Non-circulating to the public
Open Tues-Thurs 9:30-3:30

S DETROIT INSTITUTE OF ARTS, Research Library, 5200 Woodward Ave, 48202. SAN 308-0005. Tel: 313-833-3460. Interlibrary Loan Service Tel: 313-833-7926. FAX: 313-833-9169. E-Mail: web@dia.org. Web Site: www.dia.org. *Coll Develop, Head Librn*, Jennifer L S Moldwin; *Ref*, Susan Ballesteros; *Tech Servs*, Mary D Galvin; *Web Coordr*, Ward C Skewes; Staff 4 (MLS 4)
Founded 1905
Library Holdings: Bk Vols 170,000; Per Subs 280
Subject Interests: Art history, Conservation, Decorative arts, Films and filmmaking, Furniture, Paintings, Sculpture
Special Collections: Albert Kahn Architecture Library; Grace Whitney Hoff Coll, fine bindings; Puppetry (Paul McPharlin Coll)
Database Vendor: epixtech, inc.
Publications: Newsletter
Partic in Detroit Associated Libraries Region Of Cooperation; Detroit Libr Network; Horizon Users Group; Michigan Library Consortium; OCLC Online Computer Library Center, Inc

L DETROIT METROPOLITAN BAR ASSOCIATION FOUNDATION LIBRARY,* 645 Griswold St, No 3550, 48226-4220. SAN 307-9945. Tel: 313-961-6120. FAX: 313-965-0842. *Mgr*, Teresa Prince; E-Mail: prince@macomb.cc.mi.us; Staff 1 (MLS 1)
Founded 1836
Library Holdings: Bk Titles 65,000
Partic in Westlaw

P DETROIT PUBLIC LIBRARY, Detroit Associated Libraries, 5201 Woodward Ave, 48202. SAN 346-1769. Tel: 313-833-1000. Interlibrary Loan Service Tel: 313-833-1423. TDD: 313-833-5492. FAX: 313-832-0877. E-Mail: is@detroit.lib.mi.us. Web Site: www.detroit.lib.mi.us. *Dir*, Maurice B Wheeler; *Dep Dir*, Sandra Clemons; *Publ Servs*, Juliet Machie; *Tech Servs*, Nancy Skowronski; *Cat*, J Randolph Call; *Purchasing*, Robert Farms; *ILL*, Andrea Powell; *Res*, James W Lawrence; Tel: 313-833-4835, E-Mail: jlawrenc@detroit.lib.mi.us; Staff 521 (MLS 204, Non-MLS 317)
Founded 1865. Pop 1,027,974
Jul 1999-Jun 2000 Income $29,733,577, State $8,787,404, City $142,697, County $1,126,369, Locally Generated Income $19,677,107. Mats Exp $3,326,000. Sal $20,557,310
Library Holdings: Bk Vols 2,993,000
Subject Interests: Art and architecture, Business and management, Economics, Ethnic studies, History, Maps, Music, Natural science, Social sciences and issues, Technology
Special Collections: Black American in the Performing Arts (E Azalia Hackley Coll), bks, rec, mss; Genealogy, bks, micro; Michigan, Great Lakes, Northwest Territory (Burton Historical Coll), bks, mss; National Automotive History Coll, mfg cat, bks, mss; National Bibliography; Patents, bks, micro; Rare Books, micro, bks
Database Vendor: epixtech, inc., GaleNet, IAC - Info Trac, OCLC - First Search, Wilson - Wilson Web
Member Libraries: McGregor Public Library; The Detroit News, Inc
Partic in Michigan Library Consortium
Special Services for the Deaf - Staff with knowledge of sign language; TTY machine
Friends of the Library Group
Branches: 26

BOWEN, 3648 W Vernor Hwy, 48216-1441. SAN 346-1823. Tel: 313-297-9381. FAX: 313-297-9358. Web Site: www.detroit.lib.mi.us. *Branch Mgr*, Janet Hendrick; *Librn*, Ellen Simmons; E-Mail: esimmon@detroit.lib.mi.us; *Res*, James W Lawrence; Tel: 313-833-4835, Fax: 313-332-0877, E-Mail: jlawrenc@detroit.lib.mi.us; Staff 4 (MLS 4)
Founded 1912
Library Holdings: Bk Vols 26,405
Database Vendor: epixtech, inc., GaleNet, IAC - Info Trac, OCLC - First Search, Wilson - Wilson Web
Friends of the Library Group

CAMPBELL, 5671 W Vernor Hwy, 48209-2977. SAN 346-1882. Tel: 313-297-8442. FAX: 313-297-9359. *Librn*, Edward Solomon; E-Mail: esolomo@detroit.lib.mi.us; *Res*, James W Lawrence; Tel: 313-833-4835, Fax: 313-832-0877, E-Mail: jlawrenc@detroit.lib.mi.us
Library Holdings: Bk Vols 28,061
Database Vendor: epixtech, inc., GaleNet, IAC - Info Trac, OCLC - First Search, Wilson - Wilson Web
Friends of the Library Group

CHANDLER PARK, 12800 Harper, 48213-1898. SAN 346-1912. Tel: 313-852-4346. FAX: 313-852-4347. *Mgr*, Paula M Beaudoin; E-Mail: pbeaudo@detroit.lib.mi.us; *Res*, James W Lawrence; Tel: 313-833-4835, Fax: 313-832-0877, E-Mail: jlawrenc@detroit.lib.mi.us
Library Holdings: Bk Vols 45,516
Database Vendor: epixtech, inc., GaleNet, IAC - Info Trac, OCLC - First Search, Wilson - Wilson Web
Friends of the Library Group

CHANEY, 16101 Grand River, 48227-1898. SAN 346-1947. Tel: 313-852-4545. FAX: 313-852-4545. *Mgr*, Gail Orange; E-Mail: gorange@detroit.lib.mi.us; *Librn*, Darlean Bridges; *Res*, James W Lawrence; Tel: 313-833-4835, Fax: 313-832-0877, E-Mail: jlawrenc@detroit.lib.mi.us
Library Holdings: Bk Vols 35,454
Database Vendor: epixtech, inc., GaleNet, IAC - Info Trac, OCLC - First Search, Wilson - Wilson Web
Friends of the Library Group

CHASE, 17731 W Seven Mile Rd, 48235-3050. SAN 346-1971. Tel: 313-578-8002. FAX: 313-578-8002. *Mgr*, Gail Gilman; E-Mail: ggilman@detroit.lib.mi.us; *Res*, James W Lawrence; Tel: 313-833-4835, Fax: 313-832-0877, E-Mail: jlawrenc@detroit.lib.mi.us
Library Holdings: Bk Vols 25,778
Database Vendor: epixtech, inc., GaleNet, IAC - Info Trac, OCLC - First Search, Wilson - Wilson Web
Friends of the Library Group

CONELY, 4600 Martin, 48210-2343. SAN 346-2005. Tel: 313-224-6461. FAX: 313-224-6461. *Mgr*, Rita Van Brandeghen; E-Mail: rvanbran@detroit.lib.mi.us; *Res*, James W Lawrence; Tel: 313-833-4835, Fax: 313-832-0877, E-Mail: jlawrenc@detroit.lib.mi.us; Staff 7 (MLS 3, Non-MLS 4)
Library Holdings: Bk Vols 32,709
Database Vendor: epixtech, inc., GaleNet, IAC - Info Trac, OCLC - First Search, Wilson - Wilson Web
Friends of the Library Group

P DETROIT SUBREGIONAL LIBRARY FOR THE BLIND & PHYSICALLY HANDICAPPED, 3666 Grand River, 48208-2880. SAN 346-1777. Tel: 313-833-5494. TDD: 313-833-5492. FAX: 313-833-5597. Web Site: www.detroit.lib.mi.us/. *Librn*, Dori V Middleton; Tel: 313-833-5497, E-Mail: dmiddle@detroit.lib.mi.us; *Res*, James W Lawrence; Tel: 313-833-4835, Fax: 313-832-0877, E-Mail: jlawrenc@detroit.lib.mi.us; Staff 5 (MLS 2, Non-MLS 3)
Founded 1980. Circ 7,269
1997-1998 Income $33,101, State $20,983, Federal $12,118
Subject Interests: Braille, Talking books
Database Vendor: epixtech, inc., GaleNet, IAC - Info Trac, OCLC - First Search, Wilson - Wilson Web
Publications: In-Focus (newsletter)
Special Services - Talking Book Encyclopedia; cassettes; discs; mail reading; reference work
Friends of the Library Group

DOUGLASS, 3666 Grand River, 48208-2880. SAN 346-203X. Tel: 313-833-9714. FAX: 313-833-9717. *Coordr*, Michael Wells; E-Mail: mwells@detroit.lib.mi.us; *Res*, James W Lawrence; Tel: 313-833-4835, Fax: 313-832-0877, E-Mail: jlawrenc@detroit.lib.mi.us
Library Holdings: Bk Vols 37,421
Database Vendor: epixtech, inc., GaleNet, IAC - Info Trac, OCLC - First Search, Wilson - Wilson Web
Friends of the Library Group

DOWNTOWN, 121 Gratiot, 48226-2284. SAN 346-2064. Tel: 313-224-0580. FAX: 313-965-1977. *Res*, James W Lawrence; Tel: 313-833-4835,

Fax: 313-832-0877, E-Mail: jlawrenc@detroit.lib.mi.us
Library Holdings: Bk Vols 108,003
Database Vendor: epixtech, inc., GaleNet, IAC - Info Trac, OCLC - First Search, Wilson - Wilson Web
Friends of the Library Group

DUFFIELD, 2507 W Grand Blvd, 48208-1236. SAN 346-2099. Tel: 313-224-6456. FAX: 313-224-6460. *Librn*, Walter Young; E-Mail: wy@detroit.lib.mi.us; *Res*, James W Lawrence; Tel: 313-833-4835, Fax: 313-832-0877, E-Mail: jlawrenc@detroit.lib.mi.us; Staff 9 (MLS 4, Non-MLS 5)
Library Holdings: Bk Vols 44,605
Database Vendor: epixtech, inc., GaleNet, IAC - Info Trac, OCLC - First Search, Wilson - Wilson Web
Friends of the Library Group

EDISON, 18400 Joy Rd, 48228-3189. SAN 346-2129. Tel: 313-852-4515. FAX: 313-852-4581. *Mgr*, Karen Johnson; E-Mail: kjohnson@detroit.lib.mi.us; *Res*, James W Lawrence; Tel: 313-833-4835, Fax: 313-832-0877, E-Mail: jlawrenc@detroit.lib.mi.us
Library Holdings: Bk Vols 37,583
Database Vendor: epixtech, inc., GaleNet, IAC - Info Trac, OCLC - First Search, Wilson - Wilson Web
Friends of the Library Group

ELMWOOD PARK, 550 Chene, 48204-3907. SAN 346-2153. Tel: 313-877-8014. FAX: 313-224-0528. *Mgr*, Cynthia Moreland; E-Mail: cmorla@detroit.lib.mi.us; *Res*, James W Lawrence; Tel: 313-833-4835, Fax: 313-832-0877, E-Mail: jlawrenc@detroit.lib.mi.us
Library Holdings: Bk Vols 28,319
Database Vendor: epixtech, inc., GaleNet, IAC - Info Trac, OCLC - First Search, Wilson - Wilson Web
Friends of the Library Group

FRANKLIN, 13561 E McNichols Rd, 48205-3457. SAN 346-2188. Tel: 313-852-4797. FAX: 313-852-4797. *Mgr*, Constance Jones; E-Mail: cjones@detroit.lib.mi.us; *Res*, James W Lawrence; Tel: 313-833-4835, Fax: 313-832-0877, E-Mail: jlawrenc@detroit.lib.mi.us
Library Holdings: Bk Vols 41,483
Database Vendor: epixtech, inc., GaleNet, IAC - Info Trac, OCLC - First Search, Wilson - Wilson Web
Friends of the Library Group

GRAY, 7737 Kercheval, 48214-2498. SAN 346-2218. Tel: 313-852-4754. FAX: 313-267-6554. *Res*, James W Lawrence; Tel: 313-833-4835, Fax: 313-832-0877, E-Mail: jlawrenc@detroit.lib.mi.us
Library Holdings: Bk Vols 45,248
Database Vendor: epixtech, inc., GaleNet, IAC - Info Trac, OCLC - First Search, Wilson - Wilson Web
Friends of the Library Group

HUBBARD, 12929 W McNichols, 48235-4106. SAN 346-2242. Tel: 313-578-7585. FAX: 313-578-7586. *Res*, James W Lawrence; Tel: 313-833-4835, Fax: 313-832-0877, E-Mail: jlawrenc@detroit.lib.mi.us; *Mgr*, Gerald Fine; E-Mail: gfine@detroit.lib.mi.us
Library Holdings: Bk Vols 24,631
Database Vendor: epixtech, inc., GaleNet, IAC - Info Trac, OCLC - First Search, Wilson - Wilson Web
Friends of the Library Group

JEFFERSON, 12350 E Outer Dr, 48224. SAN 346-2277. Tel: 313-267-6562. FAX: 313-267-6591. *Mgr*, Kenneth Wyatt; E-Mail: kwyatt@detroit.lib.mi.us; *Res*, James W Lawrence; Tel: 313-833-4835, Fax: 313-832-0877, E-Mail: jlawrenc@detroit.lib.mi.us
Library Holdings: Bk Vols 41,291
Database Vendor: epixtech, inc., GaleNet, IAC - Info Trac, OCLC - First Search, Wilson - Wilson Web
Friends of the Library Group

KNAPP, 13330 Conant, 48213-2338. SAN 346-2307. Tel: 313-852-4283. *Mgr*, James Hoogstra; E-Mail: jhoogst@detroit.lib.mi.us; *Res*, James W Lawrence; Tel: 313-833-4835, Fax: 813-832-0877, E-Mail: jlawrenc@detroit.lib.mi.us; Staff 8 (MLS 3, Non-MLS 5)
Library Holdings: Bk Vols 36,517
Database Vendor: epixtech, inc., GaleNet, IAC - Info Trac, OCLC - First Search, Wilson - Wilson Web
Friends of the Library Group

LINCOLN, 1221 E Seven Mile Rd, 48203-2103. SAN 346-2331. Tel: 313-852-4284. *Res*, James W Lawrence; Tel: 313-833-4835, Fax: 313-832-0877, E-Mail: jlawrenc@detroit.lib.mi.us
Library Holdings: Bk Vols 37,206
Database Vendor: epixtech, inc., GaleNet, IAC - Info Trac, OCLC - First Search, Wilson - Wilson Web
Friends of the Library Group

MARK TWAIN ANNEX, 4741 Iroquois, 48213. SAN 346-2390. Tel: 313-924-9272. *Res*, James W Lawrence; Tel: 313-833-4835, Fax: 313-832-0877, E-Mail: jlawrenc@detroit.lib.mi.us
Library Holdings: Bk Vols 37,994
Database Vendor: epixtech, inc., GaleNet, IAC - Info Trac, OCLC - First Search, Wilson - Wilson Web
Friends of the Library Group

MONTEITH, 14100 Kercheval, 48215-2810. SAN 346-2420. Tel: 313-852-5761. FAX: 313-852-5762. *Mgr*, Laurie Townsend; E-Mail: ltownse@detroit.lib.mi.us; *Res*, James W Lawrence; Tel: 313-833-4835, Fax: 313-832-0877, E-Mail: jlawrenc@detroit.lib.mi.us
Library Holdings: Bk Vols 39,850
Database Vendor: epixtech, inc., GaleNet, IAC - Info Trac, OCLC - First Search, Wilson - Wilson Web
Friends of the Library Group

MUNICIPAL REFERENCE, 1004 City County Bldg, 2 Woodward Ave, 48226. SAN 346-1793. Tel: 313-224-3885. FAX: 313-964-6958. *Chief Librn*, Richard Maciejewski; *Res*, James W Lawrence; Tel: 313-833-4835, Fax: 313-832-0877, E-Mail: jlawrenc@detroit.lib.mi.us
Founded 1945
Library Holdings: Bk Vols 4,610; Per Subs 247
Subject Interests: Finance, Government, Housing, Planning, Recreation, Transportation
Special Collections: City of Detroit; Governmental Affairs in Detroit, Wayne County & Michigan (1945-present), newsp clippings; Grantsmanship Center Coll; Municipal Documents Exchange Coll; Wayne County
Database Vendor: epixtech, inc., GaleNet, IAC - Info Trac, OCLC - First Search, Wilson - Wilson Web

PARKMAN, 1766 Oakman Blvd, 48238-2735. SAN 346-2455. Tel: 313-852-4000. FAX: 313-852-4000. *Coordr*, Carolyn Owens; E-Mail: cyowen@detroit.lib.mi.us; *Res*, James W Lawrence; Tel: 313-833-4835, Fax: 313-832-0877, E-Mail: jlawrenc@detroit.lib.mi.us
Library Holdings: Bk Vols 25,499
Database Vendor: epixtech, inc., GaleNet, IAC - Info Trac, OCLC - First Search, Wilson - Wilson Web
Friends of the Library Group

REDFORD, 21200 Grand River, 48219-3896. SAN 346-248X. Tel: 313-578-8000. *Mgr*, Lurine Carter; E-Mail: lcarte@detroit.lib.mi.us; *Res*, James W Lawrence; Tel: 313-833-4835, Fax: 313-832-0877, E-Mail: jlawrenc@detroit.lib.mi.us
Library Holdings: Bk Vols 62,204
Database Vendor: epixtech, inc., GaleNet, IAC - Info Trac, OCLC - First Search, Wilson - Wilson Web
Friends of the Library Group

RICHARD, 9876 Grand River, 48204-2281. SAN 326-8071. Tel: 313-833-1000. FAX: 313-935-4453. *Res*, James W Lawrence; Tel: 313-833-4835, Fax: 313-832-0877, E-Mail: jlawrenc@detroit.lib.mi.us
Library Holdings: Bk Vols 42,169
Database Vendor: epixtech, inc., GaleNet, IAC - Info Trac, OCLC - First Search, Wilson - Wilson Web
Friends of the Library Group

SHERWOOD FOREST, 7117 W Seven Mile Rd, 48221-2240. SAN 346-2544. Tel: 313-578-7593. FAX: 313-935-3506. *Mgr*, Dorothy Williams; E-Mail: dwillia@detroit.lib.mi.us; *Res*, James W Lawrence; Tel: 313-833-4835, Fax: 313-832-0877, E-Mail: jlawrenc@detroit.lib.mi.us
Library Holdings: Bk Vols 47,597
Database Vendor: epixtech, inc., GaleNet, IAC - Info Trac, OCLC - First Search, Wilson - Wilson Web
Friends of the Library Group

WILDER, 7140 E Seven Mile Rd, 48234-3096. SAN 346-2579. Tel: 313-852-4285. FAX: 313-852-4313. *Mgr*, Patricia Petrone; E-Mail: ppetron@detroit.lib.mi.us; *Res*, James W Lawrence; Tel: 313-833-4835, Fax: 313-832-0877, E-Mail: jlawrenc@detroit.lib.mi.us
Library Holdings: Bk Vols 38,482
Database Vendor: epixtech, inc., GaleNet, IAC - Info Trac, OCLC - First Search, Wilson - Wilson Web
Friends of the Library Group

Bookmobiles: 1

M DETROIT RECEIVING HOSPITAL & UNIVERSITY HEALTH CENTER LIBRARY, 4201 Saint Antoine, 48201-2194. SAN 307-9996. Tel: 313-745-4475. FAX: 313-993-0497. *Librn*, Cherrie M Mudloff; E-Mail: cmudloff@dmc.org; Staff 2 (MLS 1, Non-MLS 1)
Founded 1970
Library Holdings: Bk Titles 3,000; Per Subs 296
Subject Interests: Allied health
Partic in Nat Libr of Med

S DETROIT SYMPHONY ORCHESTRA HALL LIBRARY,* 3711 Woodward Ave, 48201. SAN 329-8876. Tel: 313-576-5171. *Librn*, Elkhona Yoffe; *Asst Librn*, Robert Stiles
Library Holdings: Bk Vols 200
Special Collections: Rare Scores

S DETROIT US EXPORT ASSISTANCE CENTER LIBRARY, 211 W Fort St Ste 2220, 48226. SAN 370-2650. Tel: 313-226-3650. FAX: 313-226-3657. E-Mail: odetroit@mail.doc.gov. *Dir*, Neil Hesse
Library Holdings: Bk Vols 25
Restriction: Staff use only

L DICKINSON, WRIGHT, PLLC, Law Library, 500 Woodward, Ste 4000, 48226. SAN 308-0048. Tel: 313-223-3039. FAX: 313-223-3598. Web Site: www.dickinson-wright.com. *Librn*, Mark A Heinrich; *Tech Servs*, Carol M Darga; *Ref*, Jan Bissett; Staff 3 (MLS 3)
Founded 1878
Library Holdings: Bk Vols 25,000; Per Subs 4,000
Subject Interests: Law

Publications: Current awareness bulletin; library guide; research guides
Partic in Dialog Corporation; Dow Jones News Retrieval; Dun & Bradstreet Info Servs; Michigan Library Consortium; OCLC Online Computer Library Center, Inc; Westlaw

S DOSSIN GREAT LAKES MUSEUM,* 100 The Strand-on-Belle Isle, 48207. SAN 327-0289. Tel: 313-852-4051. *Curator*, John Polacsek
Special Collections: Great Lakes Coll
Restriction: Staff use only

L DYKEMA GOSSETT PLLC, Law Library, 400 Renaissance Ctr, 38th Flr, 48243. SAN 308-0056. Tel: 313-568-6715. FAX: 313-568-6735. *Head Librn*, Jennifer Lund; E-Mail: jlund@dykema.com; *Ref*, Baiba Seward; Staff 6 (MLS 3, Non-MLS 3)
Founded 1929
Library Holdings: Bk Vols 55,500; Bk Titles 4,500; Per Subs 500
Subject Interests: Employment, Environmental law, Law, Patents, Securities
Special Collections: Tax Legislative Materials
Automation Activity & Vendor Info: (Acquisitions) EOS; (Cataloging) EOS; (Circulation) EOS; (OPAC) EOS; (Serials) EOS
Database Vendor: Dialog, Lexis-Nexis
Partic in MLC; Westlaw

SR ECUMENICAL THEOLOGICAL SEMINARY, John E Biersdorf Library, 2930 Woodward Ave, 48201. SAN 371-1382. Tel: 313-831-5200, Ext 222. FAX: 313-831-1353. E-Mail: etslibrary@provide.net. *Dir*, Dorothy Huntwork Shields; E-Mail: dhsh@umich.edu; Staff 2 (MLS 1, Non-MLS 1)
Library Holdings: Bk Vols 25,000; Per Subs 100
Automation Activity & Vendor Info: (OPAC) Sagebrush Corporation
Database Vendor: OCLC - First Search
Restriction: In-house use for visitors
Partic in Michigan Library Consortium

S ERNST & YOUNG CENTER FOR BUSINESS KNOWLEDGE, 500 Woodward Ave, Ste 1700, 48226. SAN 308-0064. Tel: 313-596-7100. FAX: 313-596-8840. *Business, Res*, Jennifer Vasquez; E-Mail: jennifer.vasquez@ey.com
Founded 1938
Subject Interests: Accounting, Auditing, Automotive, Law, Manufacturing, Tax
Partic in Spec Libr Asn

M HENRY FORD HOSPITAL, Sladen Library, 2799 W Grand Blvd, 48202. SAN 308-0080. Tel: 313-916-2550. FAX: 313-874-4730. Web Site: www.sladen.hfhs.org. *Dir*, Nardina N Mein; E-Mail: meinn@mlc.lib.mi.us; *Coll Develop*, Audrey Bondar; Staff 22 (MLS 12, Non-MLS 10)
Founded 1915
1997-1998 Income $1,900,000
Library Holdings: Bk Vols 70,000; Per Subs 900
Subject Interests: Hospital administration, Medicine, Nursing
Special Collections: Archives of Henry Ford Health System; Medical History Coll
Partic in National Network Of Libraries Of Medicine - South Central Region; OCLC Online Computer Library Center, Inc

GL RALPH M FREEMAN MEMORIAL LIBRARY FOR THE US COURTS, 436 US Courthouse, 231 W Lafayett, 48226-2719. SAN 308-0420. Tel: 313-234-5255. FAX: 313-234-5383. *Librn*, Linda D Smith; *Asst Librn*, Joan Hollier; Staff 4 (MLS 2, Non-MLS 2)
Founded 1975
Library Holdings: Bk Vols 40,100; Per Subs 35
Subject Interests: Law
Special Collections: Federal Judicial Center Publications
Publications: Acquisitions List; Current Awareness Project; Library Newsletter; Orientation Packet
Restriction: Private library
Partic in OCLC Online Computer Library Center, Inc; Westlaw

GENERAL MOTORS CORP

L LAW LIBRARY, 3031 W Grand Blvd, 48202. SAN 346-2668. Tel: 313-974-1901. FAX: 313-974-0806. *Librn*, Heather Simmons; Staff 1 (MLS 1)
Founded 1941
Library Holdings: Bk Vols 70,000; Per Subs 450
Subject Interests: Anglo-American law, Automotive engineering, Corporate law, Foreign law, History, International law
Partic in Dialog Corporation; Dow Jones News Retrieval; Michigan Library Consortium; OCLC Online Computer Library Center, Inc

L TAX STAFF LIBRARY, 3044 W Grand Blvd, 48202. SAN 346-2692. Tel: 313-556-1567. FAX: 313-556-7616. *Librn*, Sue Connolly
Founded 1965
Library Holdings: Bk Vols 7,000; Bk Titles 5,500; Per Subs 130
Subject Interests: Domestic law

GRACE HOSPITAL

M MEDICAL LIBRARY-AV SERVICES, 6071 W Outer Dr, 48235. SAN 308-0250. Tel: 313-966-3277, 313-966-3300. FAX: 313-966-4089. *Media Spec*, Ronald Garlington
Founded 1939
Library Holdings: Bk Vols 5,000; Per Subs 250
Subject Interests: Allied health, Medicine, Nursing
Partic in Nat Libr of Med; OCLC Online Computer Library Center, Inc
Open Mon-Fri 8am-4:30pm

M OSCAR LE SEURE PROFESSIONAL LIBRARY, 6071 W Outer Dr, 48235. SAN 346-2722. Tel: 313-966-3276. FAX: 313-966-4089. *Librn*, Kathy McPeak; E-Mail: kmcpeak@voyager.net
Founded 1914
Library Holdings: Bk Vols 5,000; Per Subs 250
Subject Interests: Medicine, Nursing, Obstetrics and gynecology, Surgery
Partic in Michigan Library Consortium; Nat Libr of Med; OCLC Online Computer Library Center, Inc
Open Mon-Fri 8am-4:30pm

M GREATER DETROIT HOSPITAL MEDICAL CENTER LIBRARY,* 3105 Carpenter Ave, 48212. SAN 327-0262. Tel: 313-369-3000. FAX: 313-369-3015.

M HARPER HOSPITAL, Department of Libraries, 3990 John R St, 48201-2097. SAN 346-2781. Tel: 313-745-8262. FAX: 313-993-0239. *Coordr*, Jean M Brennan; Tel: 313-745-1444, E-Mail: brennanj@mlc.lib.mi.us; Staff 3 (MLS 1, Non-MLS 2)
Founded 1890
Library Holdings: Bk Vols 9,705; Bk Titles 8,735; Per Subs 302
Special Collections: Archives of Harper-Grace Hospitals
Automation Activity & Vendor Info: (Circulation) epixtech, inc.
Partic in BRS; Dialog Corporation; Nat Libr of Med; OCLC Online Computer Library Center, Inc

L HONIGMAN MILLER SCHWARTZ & COHN, Law Library,* 2290 First National Bldg, 48226. SAN 321-8090. Tel: 313-465-7169. FAX: 313-465-8022. *Mgr*, Patricia A McKanna; *Librn*, Edmund Sonnenberg; *Librn*, Eric Kennedy; *Librn*, Jean Kawata
Library Holdings: Bk Vols 15,000; Bk Titles 8,000; Per Subs 150
Restriction: Staff use only

M HUTZEL HOSPITAL, Medical Library,* 4707 St Antoine St, 48201-1423. SAN 308-0129. Tel: 313-745-7178. FAX: 313-993-0152. *Coordr*, Marilyn Dow; E-Mail: dowm@mlc.lib.mi.us; Staff 2 (MLS 1, Non-MLS 1)
Founded 1936
Library Holdings: Per Subs 200
Subject Interests: Obstetrics and gynecology, Sports
Automation Activity & Vendor Info: (Circulation) epixtech, inc.
Database Vendor: epixtech, inc., GaleNet, OCLC - First Search, OVID Technologies
Function: ILL available

S INTERNATIONAL ASSOCIATION OF CROSS-REFERENCE DIRECTORY PUBLISHERS LIBRARY, c/o Bresser Co, 684 W Baltimore, 48202. SAN 374-7808. Tel: 313-871-1414. FAX: 313-874-3510. *Librn*, Suzanne Kay
Library Holdings: Bk Titles 530
Special Collections: Cross-Index Directories

S INTERNATIONAL UNION OF UNITED AUTOMOBILE, AEROSPACE & AGRICULTURAL IMPLEMENT WORKERS OF AMERICA, Research Library, 8000 E Jefferson Ave, 48214. SAN 308-0412. Tel: 313-926-5386. FAX: 313-331-3640. E-Mail: 71112.243@compuserve.com. *Head Librn*, Jane Catherine Danjin; *Asst Librn*, Maria Catalfio; *Asst Librn*, Helen Levenson; Staff 4 (MLS 3, Non-MLS 1)
Founded 1947
Jan 1998-Dec 1998 Mats Exp $67,351, Books $10,000, Per/Ser (Incl. Access Fees) $43,000, Micro $800, Electronic Ref Mat (Incl. Access Fees) $13,551. Sal $155,896 (Prof $89,804)
Library Holdings: Bk Vols 40,000; Per Subs 362
Subject Interests: Automotive indust
Database Vendor: Dialog, Lexis-Nexis, OCLC - First Search
Publications: New in the Library (monthly acquisition list)
Restriction: Staff use only
Function: Research library

L JAFFE, RAITT, HEUER & WEISS, Law Library,* One Woodward Ave, Ste 2400, 48226. SAN 372-0403. Tel: 313-961-8380. FAX: 313-961-8358. *Librn*, Margi Heinen
Library Holdings: Bk Vols 9,000; Per Subs 25

C MARYGROVE COLLEGE LIBRARY, 8425 W McNichols Rd, 48221-2599. SAN 308-0188. Tel: 313-927-1300. Interlibrary Loan Service Tel: 313-927-1347. Circulation Tel: 313-927-1355. Reference Tel: 313-927-1346. FAX: 313-927-1366. Web Site: www.marygrove.edu. *Dir, Librn*, Frank White; *Access Serv, Ref*, Jeffrey Zachwieja; *Cat*, Zoreh Raein; *Info Tech*, Crystal Agnew; *Head Ref*, Linnea Dudley; *Tech Servs*, Ronald R Stinson; Staff 12 (MLS 7, Non-MLS 5)
Founded 1925. Enrl 4,582; Highest Degree: Master
Library Holdings: Bk Vols 99,000; Bk Titles 82,350; Per Subs 465
Database Vendor: epixtech, inc.
Partic in Michigan Library Consortium; Southeastern Michigan League Of Libraries

S MAURICE C ZEIGER MEMORIAL LIBRARY,* Wayne State University, 667 Grosberg Religious Ctr, 48202. SAN 307-983X. Tel: 313-577-3459. FAX: 313-577-3461. *Exec Dir*, Miriam Starkman
Library Holdings: Bk Vols 2,000; Per Subs 10
Subject Interests: Judaica (lit or hist of Jews)
Special Collections: Periodicals of Jewish Interest
Open Mon-Thurs 9-4:30, Fri 9-2:30

S MICHIGAN CONSOLIDATED GAS COMPANY, Competitive Information Center, 500 Griswold St, 48226. SAN 327-036X. Tel: 313-256-5470. FAX: 313-256-5490. *Librn*, Karen Gulvezan; E-Mail: kareng@michcon.com; *Librn*, Astra Malins; Tel: 313-256-6571, E-Mail: astra_malins@michcon.com; *Librn*, Kirk Nims; Tel: 313-226-9091; Staff 3 (MLS 3)
Library Holdings: Bk Vols 1,200; Per Subs 150
Publications: Corporate Library Update

L MICHIGAN DEPARTMENT OF CIVIL RIGHTS LIBRARY,* 1200 Sixth St, 7th flr, 48226. SAN 327-0440. Tel: 313-256-2622. FAX: 313-256-2678. *Librn*, Ellen McCarthy
Library Holdings: Bk Vols 10,000; Per Subs 200
Special Collections: Civil Rights Law, employment & housing discrimination; Problems of minorities & women
Partic in Detroit Associated Libraries Region Of Cooperation

L MILLER, CANFIELD, PADDOCK & STONE LIBRARY,* 150 W Jefferson, Ste 2500, 48226. SAN 327-0424. Tel: 313-963-6420. FAX: 313-496-8452. *Ref*, Penelope Damore; *Tech Servs*, Nancy Higgerson
Library Holdings: Bk Vols 50,000; Per Subs 500
Subject Interests: Education, Labor, Real estate, Securities

S NBD BANK LIBRARY SERVICES,* 611 Woodward Ave, 48226. SAN 308-0269. Tel: 313-225-2840. *Coll Develop*, Joan Martin; Staff 5 (MLS 3, Non-MLS 2)
Founded 1934
Library Holdings: Bk Titles 3,000; Per Subs 1,000
Subject Interests: Banks and banking, Business and management, Economics, Finance
Special Collections: Conference Board Publications; Federal Reserve Publications

S OMNIGRAPHICS, INC LIBRARY,* 615 Griswold Ste 1400, 48226. SAN 323-5963. Tel: 313-961-1340. Toll Free Tel: 800-234-1340. FAX: 313-961-1383. Toll Free FAX: 800-875-1340. E-Mail: info@omnigraphics.com. Web Site: www.omnigraphics.com. *VPres*, Tom Murphy; Staff 2 (MLS 1, Non-MLS 1)
Founded 1987
Library Holdings: Bk Titles 2,637; Per Subs 213

L PEPPER, HAMILTON LLP, Law Library, 100 Renaissance Ctr, 36th flr, 48243. SAN 372-042X. Tel: 313-259-7110. FAX: 313-259-7926. *Librn*, Elizabeth Stajniak
Library Holdings: Bk Vols 12,000; Per Subs 20

L PHILO, ATKINSON, WHITE, STEPHEN, WRIGHT & WHITAKER, Law Library,* 2920 E Jefferson Ave, 48207. SAN 372-0381. Tel: 313-259-7200. FAX: 313-259-7092. E-Mail: lawyers@philoatconcern.com. *Librn*, Harry Maurice Philo, Jr; *Asst Librn*, Jimmy Durham
Library Holdings: Bk Vols 10,000; Per Subs 70

L PLUNKETT & COONEY, Law Library,* 800 Marquette Bldg, 243 W Congress St, 48226. SAN 371-4101. Tel: 313-983-4877. FAX: 313-983-4350. E-Mail: plunkettinfo@plunkettlaw.com. *Librn*, Bridget Faricy; E-Mail: faricybr@plunkettlaw.com
Library Holdings: Bk Vols 10,000

S PRICE WATERHOUSE COOPERS LLP, Information Center, 400 Renaissance Ctr, Ste 2900, 48243. SAN 308-0293. Tel: 313-394-6331. FAX: 313-394-6010. *Info Specialist*, Jessie Calloway
Founded 1975
Library Holdings: Bk Titles 500; Per Subs 50
Subject Interests: Accounting, Taxes
Publications: Booklets on tax, accounting & auditing
Partic in Dialog Corporation; Westlaw

M REHABILITATION INSTITUTE OF MICHIGAN, Learning Resources Center, 261 Mack Blvd, 48201-2417. SAN 308-0315. Tel: 313-745-9860. FAX: 313-745-9863. *Dir*, Daria Drobny; E-Mail: ddrobnyd@dmc.org
Founded 1958
Library Holdings: Bk Titles 4,100; Per Subs 145
Subject Interests: Education, Medicine, Physical therapy, Vocational education

R SACRED HEART MAJOR SEMINARY, Edmund Cardinal Szoka Library, 2701 Chicago Blvd, 48206. SAN 323-5793. Tel: 313-883-8650. FAX: 313-883-8594. Web Site: www.cardinalszokalibrary.org. *Dir*, Karen Rae Mehaffey; E-Mail: mehaffey.karen@shms.edu; Staff 5 (MLS 1, Non-MLS 4)
Founded 1921. Fac 65; Highest Degree: Master
Jul 2000-Jun 2001 Mats Exp $149,200, Books $69,000, Per/Ser (Incl. Access Fees) $57,000, Manuscripts & Archives $1,200, Electronic Ref Mat (Incl. Access Fees) $22,000
Library Holdings: Bk Vols 113,700; Bk Titles 111,000; Per Subs 500
Subject Interests: Philosophy, Theology
Special Collections: Church History; Early Michigan (Gabriel Richard Coll), bks, mss
Automation Activity & Vendor Info: (Cataloging) epixtech, inc.; (Circulation) epixtech, inc.; (OPAC) epixtech, inc.; (Serials) epixtech, inc.
Database Vendor: epixtech, inc.
Publications: Accessions Lists; Brochure; Straight From the Heart (quarterly newsletter)
Restriction: Restricted borrowing privileges
Partic in Michigan Library Consortium

M ST JOHN DETROIT RIVERVIEW HOSPITAL LIBRARY, 7733 E Jefferson Ave, 48214-2598. SAN 308-0021. Tel: 313-499-4123. FAX: 313-499-4156. *Mgr*, Nora Shumake; Staff 3 (MLS 2, Non-MLS 1)
Library Holdings: Bk Vols 2,300; Per Subs 200
Subject Interests: Allied health, Medicine
Publications: Libraryline (newsletter)
Restriction: Staff use only
Partic in Metrop Detroit Med Libr Group; OCLC Online Computer Library Center, Inc
Open Mon-Fri 8-4:30

M SAINT JOHN HOSPITAL & MEDICAL CENTER LIBRARY, 22101 Moross Rd, 48236. SAN 308-0358. Tel: 313-343-3733. FAX: 313-343-7598. *Dir*, Ellen O'Donnell; *Ref*, Alexia Estabrook; Staff 5 (MLS 2, Non-MLS 3)
Founded 1952
Library Holdings: Bk Titles 3,000; Per Subs 430
Subject Interests: Hospital administration, Medicine, Nursing

M SINAI-GRACE HOSPITAL LIBRARY, 6071 W Outer Dr, 48235. SAN 308-0382. Tel: 313-966-3276. FAX: 313-966-4089. *Librn*, Kathleen E McPeak; E-Mail: kmcpeak@dmc.org; Staff 3 (MLS 1, Non-MLS 2)
Founded 1953
Library Holdings: Bk Vols 35,900; Bk Titles 15,700; Per Subs 255
Subject Interests: Allied health, Medicine, Nursing
Special Collections: History of Medicine (Sydney K Beigler Coll)
Partic in Greater Midwest Regional Medical Libr Network; Nat Libr of Med

S SOUTHEAST MICHIGAN COUNCIL OF GOVERNMENTS LIBRARY,* 660 Plaza Dr, Ste 1900, 48226. SAN 327-0602. Tel: 313-961-4266, Ext 283. FAX: 313-961-4869. Web Site: www.semcog.org. *Librn*, Pamela L Lazar
Library Holdings: Bk Vols 20,000; Per Subs 350
Subject Interests: Environmental studies, Housing, Planning, Transportation
Special Collections: Detroit Metropolitan Area Regional Planning Commission; Detroit Regional Transportation & Land Use Study (TALUS); Master Plans for Southeast Michigan Communities
Publications: SEMOG Library Recent Acquisitions (monthly)
Partic in Detroit Associated Libraries Region Of Cooperation; Michigan Library Consortium

S SPILL CONTROL ASSOCIATION OF AMERICA LIBRARY, Ford Bldg, 7th Flr, 615 Griswold St, 48226. SAN 321-4184. Tel: 313-962-8255. FAX: 313-962-2937. *In Charge*, Marc K Shaye; E-Mail: mshaye@crosswrock.com
Founded 1972
Special Collections: (Coop 1980 proceedings); Hazardous Materials Intelligence Reports; National Oil & Hazardous Materials Conferences Proceedings; Oil Spill Intelligence Reports; Relative to Oil and Hazardous Materials Cleanup; Response Technology; State & National Water Pollution & Hazardous Substances Laws including TSCA, RCRA, CERCLA, SARA; USA, Canadian & World Wide Abstracts on Product Evaluation & Research

S THE DETROIT NEWS, INC, George B Catlin Memorial Library, Detroit News,* 615 W Lafayette Blvd, 48226. SAN 308-0072. Tel: 313-222-2040, 313-222-2090. FAX: 313-222-2059. *Mgr*, Patricia Zacharias; Staff 9 (MLS 7, Non-MLS 2)
Founded 1918
Library Holdings: Bk Vols 10,000; Per Subs 100
Subject Interests: Local history
Special Collections: Detroit News 1873-Present, micro, clips & photos
Restriction: Staff use only
Mem of Detroit Public Library

L THIRD JUDICIAL CIRCUIT COURT, WAYNE COUNTY, Law Library,* 780 City-County Bldg, 48226. SAN 308-0455. Tel: 313-224-5265. FAX: 313-224-6070. *Librn*, Triza Crittle
Library Holdings: Bk Vols 20,000
Partic in Am Asn of Law Librs; Mich Asn of Law Librs; Ohio Regional Asn of Law Librs

L THIRTY SIXTH DISTRICT COURT LIBRARY,* 421 Madison Ave, 48226. SAN 372-0411. Tel: 313-965-2792. FAX: 313-965-4057.
Library Holdings: Bk Vols 30,000; Per Subs 75
Subject Interests: Law

CR UNIVERSITY OF DETROIT MERCY LIBRARY, McNichols Campus, 4001 W McNichols Rd, 48221. (Mail add: PO Box 19900, 48219-0900), SAN 346-3087. Tel: 313-993-1090. Circulation Tel: 313-993-1795. Reference Tel: 313-993-1071. TDD: 313-993-1072. FAX: 313-993-1780.

Web Site: www.ids.udmercy.edu/library/. *Dean of Libr*, Margaret E Auer; E-Mail: auerme@udmercy.edu; *Admin Assoc*, Sally Young; Tel: 313-993-1091, E-Mail: youngsd@udmercy.edu; *Acq*, Linda Hopkins; Tel: 313-993-1073, E-Mail: hopkinl@udmercy.edu; *Cat*, Donna Roe; Tel: 313-993-1075, E-Mail: roedm@udmercy.edu; *Circ*, Betty Nelson; Tel: 313-993-1795, E-Mail: nelsonbj@udmercy.edu; *Materials Manager*, James Rucinski; Tel: 313-993-1073, E-Mail: rucinsje@udmercy.edu; *Govt Doc*, Nancy Piernan; E-Mail: piernank@udmercy.edu; *ILL*, M Teague Orblych; E-Mail: orblycmt@udmercy.edu; *ILL*, Jennifer Stephens; E-Mail: stephejl@udmercy.edu; *Publ Servs*, George H Libbey; Tel: 313-993-1078, E-Mail: libbeygh@udmercy.edu; *Head Ref*, Susan J Homant; Tel: 313-993-1072, E-Mail: homantsj@udmercy.edu; *Tech Servs*, Leo A Papa; Tel: 313-993-1074, E-Mail: papala@udmercy.edu; Staff 24 (MLS 12, Non-MLS 12)
Founded 1877. Enrl 6,212; Fac 582; Highest Degree: Doctorate
Jul 1999-Jun 2000 Income (Main and Other College/University Libraries) $1,704,123. Mats Exp $557,512, Books $154,252, Per/Ser (Incl. Access Fees) $336,617, Presv $10,823, Micro $17,202, AV Equip $22,159, Manuscripts & Archives $11,964, Electronic Ref Mat (Incl. Access Fees) $4,495. Sal $826,558 (Prof $497,229)
Library Holdings: Bk Titles 385,932; Per Subs 660
Subject Interests: Architecture, Education, Philosophy, Theology
Special Collections: Elmore Leonard Coll; Father Edward J Dowling Marine Historical Coll; Great Lakes Shipping; Lawrence DeVine Playbill Coll, manuscripts; Manuscripts; SE Mich Coun on Govt Doc; William Kienzle Manuscript Coll
Automation Activity & Vendor Info: (Acquisitions) epixtech, inc.; (Cataloging) epixtech, inc.; (Circulation) epixtech, inc.; (Course Reserve) epixtech, inc.; (ILL) epixtech, inc.; (OPAC) epixtech, inc.; (Serials) epixtech, inc.
Database Vendor: Dialog, epixtech, inc., GaleNet, IAC - Info Trac, IAC - SearchBank, Lexis-Nexis, OCLC - First Search, OVID Technologies, ProQuest, Wilson - Wilson Web
Publications: Annotated subject bibliographies; Libraries/Media Bibliographic Series; Library Notes; User Guide Sheets
Partic in Asn Jesuit & Univs; Detroit Area Consortium Of Catholic Colleges; Detroit Associated Libraries Region Of Cooperation; Detroit Libr Network; Michigan Library Consortium; OCLC Online Computer Library Center, Inc
Departmental Libraries:
INSTRUCTIONAL DESIGN STUDIO - OUTER DRIVE, 8200 W Outer Dr, PO Box 19900, 48219-0900. SAN 373-5079. Tel: 313-993-6028. FAX: 313-993-6195. Web Site: ids.udmercy.edu/library/. *Dir*, Patrick Misterovich; *Admin Assoc*, Sally Young; Tel: 313-993-1091, Fax: 313-993-1780, E-Mail: youngsd@udmercy.edu; *AV*, Sikawa C Ole; Tel: 313-993-6138, E-Mail: sikawac@udmercy.edu; *Info Tech*, Russell Davidson, III; E-Mail: davidsor@udmercy.edu
Founded 1966. Enrl 6,212; Highest Degree: Doctorate
Jul 1999-Jun 2000 Income $160,290, Locally Generated Income $5,640, Parent Institution $154,650. Mats Exp AV Equip $6,128. Sal $89,880 (Prof $47,000)
Partic in Detroit Libr Network
Special Services - Satellite videoconferencing; instructional design; desktop publishing; graphics hands-on lab; graphic design; television production; photography

CL LAW LIBRARY, 651 E Jefferson, 48226. SAN 346-3206. Tel: 313-596-0239. FAX: 313-596-0245. Web Site: www.law.udmercy.edu. *Assoc Dean, Dir*, Byron D Cooper; E-Mail: cooperbd@udmercy.edu; *Head, Info Serv*, Katherine A Cooper; E-Mail: cooperkt@udmercy.edu; *Assoc Dir*, Colleen Hickey; E-Mail: colleen@udmercy.edu; *Doc*, Gene P Moy; E-Mail: moyg@udmercy.edu; *Syst Coordr*, Sally Moy; E-Mail: sally@udmercy.edu; *Ref*, Mary E Hayes; E-Mail: hayesme@udmercy.edu; *Tech Servs*, Latha Rangarajan; E-Mail: rangari@udmercy.edu; Staff 7 (MLS 5, Non-MLS 2)
Founded 1912. Enrl 375; Fac 20; Highest Degree: Doctorate
Jul 1999-Jun 2000 Income $1,622,592. Mats Exp $1,034,182, Books $23,139, Per/Ser (Incl. Access Fees) $680,127, Electronic Ref Mat (Incl. Access Fees) $47,335. Sal $588,410 (Prof $379,305)
Library Holdings: Bk Vols 136,347; Bk Titles 38,360; Per Subs 604
Subject Interests: Labor, Taxes
Automation Activity & Vendor Info: (Acquisitions) Innovative Interfaces Inc.; (Cataloging) Innovative Interfaces Inc.; (Circulation) Innovative Interfaces Inc.; (Course Reserve) Innovative Interfaces Inc.; (OPAC) Innovative Interfaces Inc.; (Serials) Innovative Interfaces Inc.
Publications: Acquisitions List; Library Handbook
Partic in Dialog Corporation; OCLC Online Computer Library Center, Inc

OUTER DRIVE CAMPUS, 8200 W Outer Dr, PO Box 19900, 48219-0900. SAN 308-0196. Tel: 313-993-6180. Interlibrary Loan Service Tel: 313-993-6241. Reference Tel: 313-993-6181. FAX: 313-993-6329. Web Site: ids.udmercy.edu/library/. *Dir*, Frances O Young; Tel: 313-993-6228, E-Mail: youngfo@udmercy.edu; *Head Ref*, Patricia Setsuko Higo; Tel: 313-993-6149, E-Mail: higopat@udmercy.edu; *Asst Dean*, Sally Young; Tel: 313-993-1091, Fax: 313-993-1780, E-Mail: youngsd@udmercy.edu; *Assoc Librn*, JoAnn Chalmers; Tel: 313-993-6168, E-Mail: chalmejs@udmercy.edu; *Asst Librn*, Beverly Reppert; Tel: 313-993-6248, E-Mail: repperba@udmercy.edu; *Asst Librn*, Marie-Lise Shams; Tel: 313-993-6248, E-Mail: shamsml@udmercy.edu; *Asst Librn*, Jill Spreitzer; Tel: 313-993-6168, E-Mail: werdeljc@udmercy.edu; *Asst Librn*, Kelly Carter; Tel: 313-993-6168, E-Mail: carterkl@udmercy.edu; *ILL*, Sandra Budd; Tel: 313-993-6182, E-Mail: buddsm@udmercy.edu; *Ser*, Loria Walker; Tel: 313-993-6248, E-Mail: walkerlm@udmercy.edu; *Tech Servs*, Darlene Campbell; Tel: 313-993-6248, E-Mail: campbedm@udmercy.edu; *Circ*, Cynthia Mulenga; Staff 12 (MLS 7, Non-MLS 5)
Founded 1877. Enrl 6,212; Highest Degree: Doctorate
Jul 1999-Jun 2000 Income $765,468. Mats Exp $246,151, Books $67,048, Per/Ser (Incl. Access Fees) $163,506, Presv $5,031, Micro $6,072, Electronic Ref Mat (Incl. Access Fees) $4,494. Sal $422,980 (Prof $285,548)
Library Holdings: Bk Titles 156,384; Per Subs 664
Subject Interests: Dentistry, Education, Medicine, Nursing, Psychology, Social service (social work)
Automation Activity & Vendor Info: (Acquisitions) epixtech, inc.; (Cataloging) epixtech, inc.; (Circulation) epixtech, inc.; (Course Reserve) epixtech, inc.; (ILL) epixtech, inc.; (OPAC) epixtech, inc.; (Serials) epixtech, inc.
Database Vendor: Dialog, epixtech, inc., GaleNet, IAC - Info Trac, IAC - SearchBank, Lexis-Nexis, OVID Technologies, ProQuest, Silverplatter Information Inc., Wilson - Wilson Web
Partic in Asn Jesuit & Univs; Detroit Area Consortium Of Catholic Colleges; Detroit Associated Libraries Region Of Cooperation; Detroit Libr Network; Michigan Library Consortium; OCLC Online Computer Library Center, Inc

S US BUREAU OF THE CENSUS, Detroit Regional Census Office Partnership & Data Services, 1395 Brewery Park Blvd, PO Box 33405, 48207. SAN 327-0580. Tel: 313-259-1875. FAX: 313-259-5971. Web Site: www.census.gov/rodet/www. *Info Specialist*, Vincent Kountz
Open Mon-Fri 8:30-4

J WAYNE COUNTY COMMUNITY COLLEGE LIBRARY,* 801 W Fort, 48226. SAN 308-0463. Tel: 313-496-2762. FAX: 313-496-4731. E-Mail: clrcjaf@admin.wccc.edu. *Dean*, Dr Magalene Hester
Founded 1974
Library Holdings: Bk Titles 51,604; Per Subs 559
Subject Interests: Allied health, Ethnic studies, Feminism, Technology
Partic in Educ Resources Info Ctr

C WAYNE STATE UNIVERSITY LIBRARIES, Adamany Undergraduate Library, 3100 Undergraduate Library, 5150 Anthony Wayne Dr, 48202. SAN 346-3230. Tel: 313-577-4012, 313-577-4023. Interlibrary Loan Service Tel: 313-577-4011. FAX: 313-577-5525. E-Mail: aa6499@wayne.edu. Web Site: www.libraries.wayne.edu/. *Assoc Dean*, Lynn Sutton; *Asst Dean*, Robert Harris; *Tech Servs*, Louise Bugg; Staff 292 (MLS 90, Non-MLS 202)
Highest Degree: Doctorate
Oct 1998-Sep 1999 Mats Exp $8,763,860, Books $1,357,302, Per/Ser (Incl. Access Fees) $3,279,638, Presv $87,434, Other Print Mats $2,960,130, Electronic Ref Mat (Incl. Access Fees) $1,079,356. Sal $16,737,261 (Prof $7,973,410)
Library Holdings: Bk Vols 3,081,312; Per Subs 19,960
Automation Activity & Vendor Info: (Acquisitions) epixtech, inc.; (Cataloging) epixtech, inc.; (Circulation) epixtech, inc.; (OPAC) epixtech, inc.; (Serials) epixtech, inc.
Publications: Magazine; Newsletter; papers; reports
Mem of Asn of Research Libraries
Partic in OCLC Online Computer Library Center, Inc
Friends of the Library Group
Departmental Libraries:

CL ARTHUR NEEF LAW LIBRARY, 474 Ferry Mall, 48202. SAN 346-332X. Tel: 313-577-3925. FAX: 313-577-5498. Web Site: www.lib.wayne.edu/lawlibrary/. *Dir*, Georgia A Clark; E-Mail: ad5236@wayne.edu; *Asst Dir*, Janice Selberg; E-Mail: ab1238@wayne.edu; *Asst Dean*, Robert K Harris; Tel: 313-577-4047, Fax: 313-577-5177, E-Mail: aa6499@wayne.edu; *Librn*, Michael Samson; Tel: 313-577-6184, E-Mail: ad4092@wayne.edu; *Ref*, Eric Kennedy; E-Mail: ag3423@wayne.edu; Staff 12 (MLS 4, Non-MLS 8)
Library Holdings: Bk Vols 394,862; Bk Titles 243,745; Per Subs 4,983
Subject Interests: Business and management, Economics, History
Special Collections: fiches; Law Libr Microform Consortium Publications; Social Studies; Women & the Law, flm
Automation Activity & Vendor Info: (Acquisitions) epixtech, inc.; (Cataloging) epixtech, inc.; (Circulation) epixtech, inc.; (OPAC) epixtech, inc.; (Serials) epixtech, inc.
Publications: Recent Acquisitions List; US Documents Information Guide
Partic in OCLC Online Computer Library Center, Inc; Westlaw
Friends of the Library Group

DAVID ADAMANY UNDERGRADUATE LIBRARY, 5155 Gullen Mall, 48202. Tel: 313-577-5121. Interlibrary Loan Service Tel: 313-577-8850. Circulation Tel: 313-577-8854. Reference Tel: 313-577-8852. FAX: 313-577-5265. E-Mail: ac9706@wayne.edu. Web Site: www.ugl.wayne.edu/. *Dir*, Lynn Sutton; Tel: 313-577-6630, E-Mail: ac9706@wayne.edu; *Asst Dir*, Janet Nichols; Tel: 313-577-1706, E-Mail: ab6956@wayne.edu; *Asst Dean*, Robert K Harris; Tel: 313-577-4047, Fax: 313-577-5177, E-Mail: aa6499@wayne.edu; Staff 19 (MLS 7, Non-MLS 12)
Founded 1997
Oct 1999-Sep 2000 Mats Exp $232,309, Books $186,695, Per/Ser (Incl. Access Fees) $45,614
Library Holdings: Bk Vols 35,354; Per Subs 352

Subject Interests: Career planning, Computer educ, Undergrad studies
Automation Activity & Vendor Info: (Acquisitions) epixtech, inc.; (Cataloging) epixtech, inc.; (Circulation) epixtech, inc.; (OPAC) epixtech, inc.; (Serials) epixtech, inc.
Publications: Newsletter
Partic in OCLC Online Computer Library Center, Inc

PURDY-KRESGE LIBRARY, 5265 Cass Ave, 48202. SAN 346-3389. Tel: 313-577-4232. Interlibrary Loan Service Tel: 313-577-4011. FAX: 313-577-3436. *Actg Dir*, Paul Beavers; Tel: 313-577-2360, E-Mail: aa6536@wayne.edu; Staff 17 (MLS 17)
Library Holdings: Bk Vols 1,518,256; Per Subs 5,885
Subject Interests: Business, Education, Humanities, Social sciences and issues
Special Collections: Children & Young People (Eloise Ramsey Coll); Peace & Conflict (Mildred Jeffrey Coll)
Automation Activity & Vendor Info: (Acquisitions) epixtech, inc.; (Cataloging) epixtech, inc.; (Circulation) epixtech, inc.; (Course Reserve) epixtech, inc.; (OPAC) epixtech, inc.; (Serials) epixtech, inc.
Publications: (WSU) Library Leaflets
Partic in OCLC Online Computer Library Center, Inc

SCIENCE & ENGINEERING, 48202. Tel: 313-577-4066. Interlibrary Loan Service Tel: 313-577-4372. FAX: 313-577-3613. Web Site: www.libraries.wayne.edu/sel/. *Dir*, Barton Lessin; *Asst Dir*, H Stephen McMinn; *Coll Develop*, James Ruffner; *Ref*, Kathleen Flemming; *Ref*, Nancy Wilmes; *Tech Servs*, Louise Bugg; Staff 6 (MLS 6)
Founded 1923
Library Holdings: Bk Vols 601,316; Per Subs 3,108
Subject Interests: Natural science, Technology
Special Collections: Chemistry (Hooker Coll), bks, journals; Dubpernell Electro-Chemistry Coll; River Rouge Coll; System on Automotive Safety Information
Automation Activity & Vendor Info: (Cataloging) NOTIS
Publications: SEL Newsletter
Partic in OCLC Online Computer Library Center, Inc

CM VERA P SHIFFMAN MEDICAL LIBRARY, 4325 Brush St, 48201. SAN 346-3354. Tel: 313-577-1088. Interlibrary Loan Service Tel: 313-577-1100. Circulation Tel: 313-577-1089. Reference Tel: 313-577-1094. FAX: 313-577-0706. E-Mail: ask.med@wayne.edu. Web Site: www.libraries.wayne.edu/shiffman. *Dir*, Ellen Marks; Tel: 313-577-1168, Fax: 313-577-6668, E-Mail: emarks@med.wayne.edu; *Asst Dir*, Sandra Martin; Tel: 313-577-6665, E-Mail: smartin@med.wayne.edu; *Librn, Ref*, La Ventra Ellis-Danquah; Tel: 313-577-6666, E-Mail: laventra.ellis-danquah@wayne.edu; *Librn, Ref*, Wendy Gang Wu; Tel: 313-577-0586, E-Mail: wendywu@med.wayne.edu; *Asst Dean*, Robert K Harris; Tel: 313-577-4047, Fax: 313-577-5177, E-Mail: aa6499@wayne.edu; Staff 6 (MLS 6)
Founded 1949
Library Holdings: Bk Vols 300,000; Per Subs 2,821; Bks on Deafness & Sign Lang 13
Subject Interests: Allied health, Basic sciences, Clinical medicine, Consumer health, Health sciences, Medicine, Statistics
Special Collections: Community Health Information Services; Detroit Community AIDS Library; Pharmacy & Allied Health Learning Resources Center Coll
Automation Activity & Vendor Info: (Acquisitions) epixtech, inc.; (Cataloging) epixtech, inc.; (Circulation) epixtech, inc.; (OPAC) epixtech, inc.; (Serials) epixtech, inc.
Database Vendor: GaleNet, IAC - Info Trac, Lexis-Nexis, OCLC - First Search, OVID Technologies, ProQuest, Wilson - Wilson Web
Partic in National Network of Libraries of Medicine - Greater Midwest Region; OCLC Online Computer Library Center, Inc
Friends of the Library Group

WALTER P REUTHER LIBRARY OF LABOR & URBAN AFFAIRS, College of Urban Labor & Metropolitan Affairs, 5401 Cass Ave, 48202. SAN 346-329X. Tel: 313-577-4024. FAX: 313-577-4300. *Assoc Dir*, Patrice R Merritt; E-Mail: p.merritt@wayne.edu; *Librn*, Carrolyn Davis; E-Mail: c.david@wayne.edu; Staff 24 (MLS 14, Non-MLS 10)
Founded 1960
Oct 1998-Sep 1999 Income $66,000, State $49,000, Other $17,000. Sal $596,000 (Prof $545,000)
Library Holdings: Bk Vols 30,000; Per Subs 650
Subject Interests: Archives, Labor
Special Collections: Manuscript Coll; Metropolitan Detroit & University Archives; Photograph Coll
Publications: Reuther Library Newsletter (Newsletter)

R WESTMINSTER CHURCH LIBRARY, 17567 Hubbell Ave, 48235. SAN 308-0471. Tel: 313-341-2697. FAX: 313-341-1514. *Librn*, Lois Brown
Founded 1920
Library Holdings: Bk Titles 2,459; Per Subs 12
Publications: Library Journal

DEXTER

P DEXTER DISTRICT LIBRARY, 8040 Fourth St, 48130. SAN 308-048X. Tel: 734-426-4477, 734-426-7731 (Admin). FAX: 734-426-1217. Web Site: hvcn.org/info/ddl. *Dir*, Paul McCann; E-Mail: pmccann@tln.lib.mi.us
Founded 1964. Pop 10,600; Circ 119,480
Oct 1999-Sep 2000 Income $61,280, State $10,690, County $18,304, Locally Generated Income $19,309, Other $12,977. Mats Exp $56,218, Books $31,500, Per/Ser (Incl. Access Fees) $2,881, Other Print Mats $21,337, Electronic Ref Mat (Incl. Access Fees) $500. Sal $131,093 (Prof $67,000)
Library Holdings: Bk Vols 35,818; Per Subs 60
Special Collections: Bone Science Fiction Coll
Automation Activity & Vendor Info: (Cataloging) DRA; (Circulation) DRA; (OPAC) DRA
Mem of The Library Network
Friends of the Library Group

DIMONDALE

P DOROTHY HULL WINDSOR TOWNSHIP LIBRARY,* 405 W Jefferson, 48821. SAN 308-0498. Tel: 517-646-0633. FAX: 517-646-7061. *Librn*, Joy Slee; *Asst Dir*, Marcie Dailey
Pop 6,000; Circ 31,508
Library Holdings: Bk Vols 18,000; Per Subs 40
Mem of Capital Library Cooperative

DOLLAR BAY

P OSCEOLA TOWNSHIP PUBLIC & SCHOOL LIBRARY,* PO Box 371, 49922-0371. SAN 308-0501. Tel: 906-482-5800. FAX: 906-487-5940. *Librn*, Therese Blissett
Founded 1924. Pop 1,878; Circ 3,000
Library Holdings: Bk Vols 5,500; Per Subs 55

DORR

P DORR TOWNSHIP LIBRARY, 1807 142nd Ave, PO Box 128, 49323. SAN 346-3478. Tel: 616-681-9678. FAX: 616-681-5650. E-Mail: dor@lakeland.lib.mi.us. Web Site: www.dorrlibrary.org. *Dir*, Suanne Wierenga; E-Mail: dorsw@lakeland.lib.mi.us; *Asst Librn*, Kathleen Nyenhuis; *Circ*, Karen Brower; Staff 3 (Non-MLS 3)
Founded 1939. Pop 5,453; Circ 43,558
Apr 1999-Mar 2000 Income $176,111, State $5,449, County $40,776, Locally Generated Income $60,000, Other $60,000, Other $9,886. Mats Exp $14,489, Books $10,722, Per/Ser (Incl. Access Fees) $1,490, AV Equip $2,277. Sal $64,953
Library Holdings: Bk Vols 32,000; Per Subs 84
Database Vendor: epixtech, inc.
Mem of Lakeland Library Cooperative
Open Mon & Thurs 12-8, Wed 10-5, Fri 12-5 & Sat 10-2
Friends of the Library Group

DOUGLAS

P SAUGATUCK-DOUGLAS DISTRICT LIBRARY,* 10 Mixer St, PO Box 789, 49406-0789. SAN 308-4027. Tel: 616-857-8241. FAX: 616-857-3005. Web Site: www.accm.org/~sddl/home.html. *Dir*, Martha M Boetcher
Founded 1965. Pop 7,202; Circ 28,223
Library Holdings: Bk Vols 15,800; Per Subs 62
Mem of Lakeland Library Cooperative
Open Mon, Wed, Thurs & Fri 10-6, Tues 1-8, Sat 10-2
Friends of the Library Group

DOWAGIAC

P DOWAGIAC PUBLIC LIBRARY,* 211 Commercial St, 49047-1728. SAN 346-3567. Tel: 616-782-3826. FAX: 616-782-9798. *Dir, Ref*, John Mohney; *Ch Servs*, Alma Adams; *Circ*, Kay Gray; *Acq*, Kay Hadley; Staff 9 (MLS 2, Non-MLS 7)
Founded 1872. Pop 13,693; Circ 74,625
Oct 1997-Sep 1998 Income $205,000. Mats Exp $40,000. Sal $100,000
Library Holdings: Bk Vols 45,388; Per Subs 123
Subject Interests: Large type print, Local history
Special Collections: Esperanto
Publications: Bibliographies
Mem of Southwest Michigan Library Cooperative
Friends of the Library Group
Branches: 1
CHESTNUT TOWERS, 100 Chestnut St, 49047. SAN 346-3591. *Librn*, Bettie Griffis
Library Holdings: Bk Titles 247; Per Subs 13

J SOUTHWESTERN MICHIGAN COLLEGE, Fred L Mathews Library, 58900 Cherry Grove Rd, 49047. SAN 308-051X. Tel: 616-782-1339. Toll Free Tel: 800-456-8675. FAX: 616-782-9575. Web Site: smc.cc.mi.us/library. *Dir Libr Serv*, Tim Peters; Tel: 616-782-1204, E-Mail: tpeters@smc.cc.mi.us; *Govt Doc*, Sharon Tafunai; Tel: 616 782-1205, E-Mail: sktafu@smc.cc.mi.us; Staff 4 (MLS 1, Non-MLS 3)
Founded 1964. Enrl 3,600; Fac 53; Highest Degree: Bachelor

Jul 2000-Jun 2001 Income $201,500, State $76,973, Federal $3,627, County $43,927, Locally Generated Income $4,634, Parent Institution $58,636, Other $13,703. Mats Exp $53,000, Books $24,000, Per/Ser (Incl. Access Fees) $14,000, Presv $3,000, Micro $10,000, AV Equip $2,000, Electronic Ref Mat (Incl. Access Fees) $10,000. Sal $93,378 (Prof $41,898)
Library Holdings: Bk Vols 38,000; Per Subs 1,200
Special Collections: American Civil War
Automation Activity & Vendor Info: (Cataloging) epixtech, inc.; (Circulation) epixtech, inc.; (OPAC) epixtech, inc.
Database Vendor: epixtech, inc., IAC - SearchBank, OCLC - First Search
Partic in Mich Libr Asn; Michigan Library Consortium; Southwest Michigan Library Cooperative

DRUMMOND ISLAND

S DRUMMOND ISLAND HISTORICAL MUSEUM LIBRARY,* Water St, 49726. SAN 371-7801. Tel: 906-493-5746.
Founded 1962

DRYDEN

P DRYDEN TOWNSHIP LIBRARY,* 5480 Main St, PO Box 280, 48428-9968. SAN 308-0528. Interlibrary Loan Service Tel: 810-796-3586. FAX: 810-796-2634. *Dir*, Desta Ureel; *Asst Librn*, Nancy Wagner
Founded 1975. Pop 3,399
Library Holdings: Bk Vols 11,000; Per Subs 68
Special Collections: Large Print Books (500)
Mem of Blue Water Libr Fedn

EAST GRAND RAPIDS

S ARNOLD'S ARCHIVES LIBRARY, 1106 Eastwood, SE, 49506. SAN 326-3037. Tel: 616-949-1398. *In Charge*, Arnold Jacobsen
Founded 1945
Special Collections: Out-of-Print 78 rpm Records, 1900-1955
Publications: Catalog of holdings

EAST JORDAN

P JORDAN VALLEY DISTRICT LIBRARY, One Library Lane, PO Box 877, 49727. SAN 308-0552. Tel: 231-536-7131. FAX: 231-536-3646. E-Mail: jordan1@northland.lib.mi.us. Web Site: www.nlc.lib.mi.us/members/jvdl/. *Dir*, Dawn Pringle
Pop 6,477; Circ 34,034
Jul 2000-Jun 2001 Income $250,000, State $4,900, City $211,000, County $33,000, Locally Generated Income $1,100. Mats Exp $31,000, Books $25,000, Per/Ser (Incl. Access Fees) $4,000, Other Print Mats $2,000. Sal $87,000
Library Holdings: Bk Vols 34,000
Database Vendor: epixtech, inc.
Publications: Jordan Valley Library News (newsletter-quarterly)
Mem of Northland Library Cooperative

EAST LANSING

CL DETROIT COLLEGE OF LAW LIBRARY, Michigan State University, 115 Law College Bldg, 48824-1300. SAN 307-9953. Tel: 517-432-6860. Circulation Tel: 517-432-6860. FAX: 517-432-6861. E-Mail: declref@msu.edu. Web Site: www.msu-dcl.edu. *Actg Dir*, Hildur Hanna; Tel: 517-432-6863, E-Mail: hannahi@msu.edu; *Tech Coordr*, James La Macchia, Jr; Tel: 517-432-6866, E-Mail: lamacchi@msu.edu; *Head Ref*, Carol Parker; Tel: 517-432-6867, E-Mail: parkerc3@msu.edu; *Ref*, Janet Ann Hedin; Tel: 517-432-6957, E-Mail: hedinj@msu.edu; *Head Tech Servs*, Lynn Sorenson; Tel: 517-432-6864, E-Mail: sorens16@msu.edu; *Web Coordr*, Steven Klukowski; Tel: 517-432-6865, E-Mail: klukows1@msu.edu; Staff 11 (MLS 6, Non-MLS 5)
Founded 1891. Enrl 700; Highest Degree: Doctorate
Jul 2000-Jun 2001 Income $830,000
Library Holdings: Bk Vols 105,262; Bk Titles 25,464; Per Subs 3,460
Subject Interests: Law
Automation Activity & Vendor Info: (Acquisitions) Innovative Interfaces Inc.; (Cataloging) Innovative Interfaces Inc.; (Circulation) Innovative Interfaces Inc.; (OPAC) Innovative Interfaces Inc.; (Serials) Innovative Interfaces Inc.
Database Vendor: Lexis-Nexis
Publications: Acquisitions List
Mem of Mich Libr Consortium
Partic in Lexis, OCLC Online Computer Libr Ctr, Inc; Westlaw

P EAST LANSING PUBLIC LIBRARY,* 950 Abbott Rd, 48823-3105. SAN 308-0560. Tel: 517-351-2420. FAX: 517-351-9536. *Dir*, Sylvia Marabate; *Ad Servs, Ch Servs*, Laurie St Laurent; *Cat*, John Gleason; *Circ*, Hulda Nofzinger
Founded 1923. Pop 50,677; Circ 279,000
Library Holdings: Bk Vols 119,239; Per Subs 392
Mem of Capital Library Cooperative
Open Mon-Thurs 10-9, Fri 10-6, Sat 10-5:30, Sun 1-5 (Sept-June)
Friends of the Library Group

G MICHIGAN DEPARTMENT OF AGRICULTURE LIBRARY,* 1615 S Harrison Rd, 48823. SAN 308-0579. Tel: 517-337-5040. FAX: 517-337-5094.
Founded 1957
Library Holdings: Bk Vols 1,600; Bk Titles 1,400; Per Subs 39
Subject Interests: Animals, behavior of, Bacteriology, Chemistry, Pathology, Pesticides, Toxicology, Veterinary medicine

C MICHIGAN STATE UNIVERSITY LIBRARY, 100 Library, 48824-1048. SAN 346-3621. Tel: 517-353-8700. Interlibrary Loan Service Tel: 517-355-7641. TDD: 517-353-9034. FAX: 517-432-3532. Interlibrary Loan Service FAX: 517-432-1446. Web Site: www.lib.msu.edu. *Dir*, Clifford H Haka; *Coordr*, Colleen F Hyslop; Tel: 517-432-2361, Fax: 517-432-0487, E-Mail: hyslop@pilot.msu.edu; *Assoc Dir, Coll Develop*, Carole S Armstrong; Tel: 517-355-2342, E-Mail: armstr15@mail.lib.msu.edu; *Access Serv*, Jeanne Drewes; Tel: 517-432-7486, E-Mail: drewes@mail.lib.msu.edu; *Publ Servs*, Faye Backie, Tel: 517-355-8465, Fax: 517-432-0487, E-Mail: backie@pilot.msu.edu; *Spec Coll*, Peter I Berg; Tel: 517-355-3770, E-Mail: berg@pilot.msu.edu; Staff 187 (MLS 66, Non-MLS 121)
Founded 1855. Enrl 43,038; Fac 1,993; Highest Degree: Doctorate
Jul 1999-Jun 2000 Mats Exp $8,178,765, Books $2,092,961, Per/Ser (Incl. Access Fees) $4,713,912, Presv $311,525, Other Print Mats $129,157, Electronic Ref Mat (Incl. Access Fees) $931,210. Sal $8,206,493 (Prof $3,060,258)
Library Holdings: Bk Vols 4,359,752; Per Subs 27,324
Special Collections: American Popular Culture; American Radical History; Apiculture Coll; Changing Men Coll; Comic Art; Cookery Coll; Early Works in Criminology; Eighteenth Century English Studies; English & American Authors; Fencing Coll; History of the French Monarchy; Illuminated Manuscripts in Facsimile; Italian Risorgimento History; Natural Science, especially Botany & Entomology; Veterinary History
Automation Activity & Vendor Info: (Acquisitions) Innovative Interfaces Inc.; (Circulation) Innovative Interfaces Inc.; (Serials) Innovative Interfaces Inc.
Mem of Asn of Research Libraries
Partic in Center For Research Libraries; Michigan Library Consortium; Nat Libr of Med; OCLC Online Computer Library Center, Inc
Friends of the Library Group
Departmental Libraries:
AFRICANA LIBRARY, 100 Library, 48824. SAN 346-4075. Tel: 517-355-2366. FAX: 517-432-1446. *Librn*, Joseph Lauer
AGRICULTURAL ECONOMICS REFERENCE ROOM, 219 Agriculture Hall, 488241039. SAN 346-3680. Tel: 517-355-6650. Web Site: www.lib.msu.edu/coll/branches/agecon. *Librn*, Judith Dow; E-Mail: dowj@msu.edu
ANIMAL INDUSTRIES, 3285 Anthony Hall, 48824. SAN 346-3710. Tel: 517-355-8483. FAX: 517-432-7587. *In Charge*, Jane Meyer
AUDIO-VISUAL, W432 Library, 48824. SAN 346-377X. Tel: 517-355-5122. FAX: 517-432-3532. *Librn*, Peter Berg
BUSINESS, 50 DCL Bldg, 48824. SAN 346-380X. Tel: 517-355-3380. FAX: 517-353-6648. *Librn*, Shari Buxbaum
CHEMISTRY, 426 Chemistry, 48824. SAN 346-3834. Tel: 517-355-9715, Ext 363. FAX: 517-432-0439. *Librn*, James W Oliver
CM CLINICAL CENTER, A134-A139 Life Sciences, 48824-1317. SAN 346-3869. Tel: 517-353-3037. FAX: 517-432-1856. *Librn*, John Coffey; E-Mail: coffey@msu.edu; Staff 2 (MLS 1, Non-MLS 1)
CYCLOTRON, 7 Cyclotron, 48824. SAN 346-3958. Tel: 517-353-5959.
ENGINEERING, 1515 Engineering Bldg, 48824. SAN 346-3982. Tel: 517-355-8536. FAX: 517-353-9041. Web Site: www.lib.msu.edu/coll/branches/engin/. *Librn*, Tom Volkening; Staff 3 (MLS 1, Non-MLS 2)
Founded 1963
FINE ARTS-ART, W 403 Library, 48824. SAN 346-3745. Tel: 517-353-4593. FAX: 517-432-3532. *Librn*, Terrie Wilson
FINE ARTS-MUSIC, W 403 Library, 48824. SAN 346-4164. Tel: 517-353-4593. FAX: 517-432-3532. *Librn*, Mary Black
GEOLOGY, 5 Natural Science, 48824. SAN 346-4016. Tel: 517-353-7988. *In Charge*, Diane Baclawski
LABOR & INDUSTRIAL RELATIONS, WG-16 Library, 48824. SAN 346-4105. Tel: 517-355-4647. FAX: 517-432-3532.
MAP LIBRARY, W 308 Library, 48824. SAN 329-6423. Tel: 517-432-6277. FAX: 517-432-3532. *Librn*, Kathleen Weessies
MATHEMATICS, D-101 Wells Hall, 48824. SAN 346-413X. Tel: 517-353-8852. FAX: 517-353-7215. *Librn*, Jan Figa
PHYSICS-ASTRONOMY, 230 Physics-Astronomy, 48824. SAN 346-4199. Tel: 517-353-5244. FAX: 517-353-1357. *Librn*, Judith Matthews
CM VETERINARY MEDICAL LIBRARY, G-201 Veterinary Medical Ctr, 48824. SAN 346-4288. Tel: 517-353-5099. FAX: 517-432-3797. *Librn*, Leslie Behm
VOICE LIBRARY, W 422 Library, 48824. SAN 346-4318. Tel: 517-355-5122. FAX: 517-432-3532. *Librn*, Peter Berg

EASTPOINTE

P EASTPOINTE MEMORIAL LIBRARY, 15875 Oak, 48021-2390. SAN 308-0544. Tel: 810-445-5096. FAX: 810-775-0150. Web Site: www.ci.eastpointe.mi.us/library. *Dir*, Joyce Conte; E-Mail: contej@libcoop.net; *Ad Servs, Asst Dir, ILL*, Carol Sterling; *Ch Servs, YA Servs*, Patricia Price; Staff 7 (MLS 7)
Founded 1939. Pop 35,800; Circ 174,260
Jul 2000-Jun 2001 Income $726,054. Mats Exp $92,000, Books $66,000, Per/Ser (Incl. Access Fees) $15,000, Electronic Ref Mat (Incl. Access Fees) $11,000. Sal $405,716
Library Holdings: Bk Vols 68,400; Per Subs 131
Special Collections: Automobile Manuals Coll
Database Vendor: epixtech, inc.
Partic in Suburban Library Cooperative
Friends of the Library Group

EATON RAPIDS

P EATON RAPIDS PUBLIC LIBRARY,* 220 S Main St, 48827-1256. SAN 308-0595. Tel: 517-663-8744. FAX: 517-663-1940. *Librn*, Nancy Murray
Founded 1876. Pop 10,000; Circ 68,232
1997-1998 Income $126,217. Mats Exp $32,612. Sal $68,416
Library Holdings: Bk Vols 28,000; Per Subs 50
Mem of Capital Library Cooperative

EAU CLAIRE

P EAU CLAIRE DISTRICT LIBRARY,* 6528 E Main St, 49111. SAN 308-0609. Tel: 616-461-6241. FAX: 616-461-3721. *Librn*, Ann Greene; E-Mail: ann.greene@wmich.edu
Founded 1938. Pop 7,716; Circ 34,134
Library Holdings: Bk Vols 29,769; Per Subs 40
Subject Interests: Indians, Local history, Spanish (language)
Mem of Southwest Michigan Library Cooperative
Open Mon & Wed 12-9, Tues, Thurs & Fri 10-6
Friends of the Library Group

ECORSE

P ECORSE PUBLIC LIBRARY,* 4184 W Jefferson Ave, 48229. SAN 308-0617. Tel: 313-389-2030. FAX: 313-389-2032. Web Site: tln.lib.mi.us/~ecor. *Librn*, Reginald Williams; *YA Servs*, Samra Gurpreet
Library Holdings: Bk Vols 28,000; Bk Titles 25,000; Per Subs 110
Mem of The Library Network

EDMORE

P HOME TOWNSHIP LIBRARY,* 329 E Main St, PO Box 589, 48829-0589. SAN 308-0625. Tel: 517-427-5241. FAX: 517-427-3233. *Librn*, Jonelle Ball
Pop 4,208; Circ 19,490
Library Holdings: Bk Vols 17,600; Per Subs 38
Mem of Lakeland Library Cooperative

ELBERTA

P ELBERTA PUBLIC LIBRARY,* 704 Frankfort Ave, 49628-9999. SAN 308-0641. Tel: 231-352-4351. *Librn*, Lois L Holmes
Pop 751; Circ 5,736
Library Holdings: Bk Vols 7,518; Per Subs 20
Mem of Mid-Michigan Library League
Open Mon, Wed & Fri 12-5

ELK RAPIDS

P ELK RAPIDS DISTRICT LIBRARY,* 300 Noble St, PO Box 337, 49629. SAN 308-065X. Tel: 231-264-9979. FAX: 231-264-9975. *Dir*, Debra Ziegler
Founded 1939. Pop 4,223; Circ 25,548
1999-2000 Income $80,500, County $21,500, Locally Generated Income $2,650, Other $4,000. Mats Exp $13,200, Books $12,000, Per/Ser (Incl. Access Fees) $1,200. Sal $33,000 (Prof $19,000)
Library Holdings: Bk Vols 15,500; Per Subs 40
Subject Interests: Local history, Michigan
Mem of Mid-Michigan Library League
Friends of the Library Group

ELSIE

P ELSIE PUBLIC LIBRARY, 145 W Main St, PO Box 545, 48831. SAN 308-0676. Tel: 517-862-4633. FAX: 517-862-4633. *Librn*, Susanne Bensinger; E-Mail: bensinge@edzone.net
Circ 21,953
Jan 2000-Dec 2000 Income $45,000. Mats Exp $20,000. Sal $25,000 (Prof $9,000)
Library Holdings: Bk Vols 23,000; Per Subs 78
Database Vendor: Innovative Interfaces INN - View
Mem of Capital Library Cooperative; Clinton County Libr Syst
Partic in Michigan Library Consortium

ESCANABA

J BAY DE NOC COMMUNITY COLLEGE, Learning Resources Center, 2001 N Lincoln Rd, 49829-2511. SAN 308-0684. Tel: 906-786-5802, Ext 1129. Interlibrary Loan Service Tel: 906-786-5802, Ext 1190. Reference Tel: 906-786-5802, Ext 1128. TDD: 906-786-8320. FAX: 906-789-6912. Web Site: www.lrcweb.baydenoc.cc.mi.us. *Dean of Libr*, Christian Holmes; Tel: 906-786-5802, Ext 1122, E-Mail: holmesc@baydenoc.cc.mi.us; *AV*, Dan Williams; Tel: 906-786-5802, Ext 1192; *Bibliog Instr, Coll Develop, Ref*, Ann Bissell; Tel: 906-786-5802, Ext 1228, E-Mail: bissella@baydenoc.cc.mi.us; *ILL*, C J Havill; E-Mail: havillc@baydenoc.cc.mi.us; Staff 2 (MLS 1, Non-MLS 1)
Founded 1963. Enrl 2,300; Fac 150; Highest Degree: Associate
Jul 2000-Jun 2001 Income $280,000. Mats Exp $44,000, Books $27,000, Per/Ser (Incl. Access Fees) $12,000, Presv $1,000, Micro $1,000, AV Equip $3,000. Sal $136,000
Library Holdings: Bk Vols 45,000; Bk Titles 35,000; Per Subs 230
Special Collections: American Welding Society Coll; Delta County Oral History; Finnish Language Coll; Fire-fighting training videos
Automation Activity & Vendor Info: (Cataloging) DRA; (Circulation) DRA; (Course Reserve) DRA; (OPAC) DRA
Database Vendor: IAC - SearchBank, Lexis-Nexis, OCLC - First Search
Mem of Upper Pennisula Region of Libr Coop
Partic in Michigan Library Consortium; OCLC Online Computer Library Center, Inc
Special Services for the Deaf - TDD

P ESCANABA PUBLIC LIBRARY, 400 Ludington St, 49829. SAN 308-0692. Tel: 906-789-7323. Reference Tel: 906-786-4463. FAX: 906-786-0942. E-Mail: epl@uproc.lib.mi.us. Web Site: www.uproc.lib.mi.us/epl. *Dir*, Mary C Crawford; *Ch Servs*, Patricia J Fittante; *ILL*, Ardith Paarni; *Ref*, Lois Imig; Staff 3 (MLS 2, Non-MLS 1)
Founded 1903. Pop 28,733; Circ 141,036
Jul 1998-Jun 1999 Income $443,422, State $28,709, City $213,825, County $167,953, Locally Generated Income $32,935. Mats Exp $66,664, Books $50,214, Per/Ser (Incl. Access Fees) $10,000, AV Equip $3,000, Electronic Ref Mat (Incl. Access Fees) $3,450. Sal $200,481
Library Holdings: Bk Vols 63,988; Per Subs 153
Subject Interests: Genealogy, Local history
Automation Activity & Vendor Info: (Circulation) epixtech, inc.; (OPAC) epixtech, inc.
Partic in Superiorland Libr Coop
Friends of the Library Group

EVART

P EVART PUBLIC LIBRARY,* 104 N Main St, PO Box 576, 49631. SAN 308-0714. Tel: 616-734-5542. FAX: 616-734-5542. *Librn*, Lilas VanScoyoc; *Asst Librn*, Elsie Connor
Pop 6,000; Circ 34,580
Library Holdings: Bk Titles 24,000
Mem of Mid-Michigan Library League

EWEN

P MCMILLAN TOWNSHIP LIBRARY, 200 Cedar St, PO Box 49, 49925-0049. SAN 376-7078. Tel: 906-988-2515. FAX: 906-988-2255. *Dir*, Lorraine Sain; E-Mail: sainl@midpen.lib.mi.us
Library Holdings: Bk Titles 10,000; Per Subs 28
Mem of Mid-Peninsula Library Cooperative

FAIRGROVE

P FAIRGROVE TOWNSHIP LIBRARY,* 1959 Main St, PO Box 9, 48733. SAN 308-0722. Tel: 517-693-6050. FAX: 517-693-6446. *Dir*, Larry Haubenstricker
Founded 1940. Pop 5,500; Circ 18,000
Library Holdings: Bk Vols 25,000; Per Subs 75
Mem of White Pine Library Cooperative
Partic in OCLC Online Computer Library Center, Inc
Friends of the Library Group

FARMINGTON

M BOTSFORD GENERAL HOSPITAL (OSTEOPATHIC), Hospital Library & Media Center, 28050 Grand River Ave, 48336-5933. SAN 308-0757. Tel: 248-471-8434. FAX: 248-471-8505. Web Site: www.botsfordlibrary.org. *Dir*, Deborah L Adams; E-Mail: dadams@botsford.org; Staff 6 (MLS 3, Non-MLS 3)
Founded 1970. Highest Degree: Master

Jan 1999-Dec 1999 Mats Exp $187,500. Sal $213,600
Library Holdings: Bk Titles 3,500; Per Subs 350
Subject Interests: Medicine, Nursing
Automation Activity & Vendor Info: (Acquisitions) epixtech, inc.
Database Vendor: epixtech, inc.

FARMINGTON HILLS

R ADAT SHALOM SYNAGOGUE, Jacob E Siegel Library, 29901 Middlebelt Rd, 48334. SAN 308-4175. Tel: 248-851-5100. FAX: 248-851-3190. E-Mail: adatshalom@aol.com.
Founded 1960
Library Holdings: Bk Vols 12,000; Per Subs 15
Subject Interests: Archaeology, Israel, Jewish history and literature, Judaica (lit or hist of Jews), Religion
Special Collections: Comparative Religion (I Leeman Memorial Coll); Gendein Yiddish Coll; Jewish Juvenile (B Isaacs Memorial Coll); Katzman Music Coll; Modern Hebrew Literature (I Elpern Coll); William & B Hordes Coll; Zionism
Partic in Jewish Libr Asn; Metrop Detroit Jewish Libr Asn

SR BIRMINGHAM TEMPLE LIBRARY, 28611 W Twelve Mile Rd, 48334. SAN 308-0749. Tel: 248-477-1410. FAX: 248-477-9014. *Librn*, Pera Kane
Founded 1970
Library Holdings: Bk Vols 3,000; Per Subs 20
Subject Interests: Jewish history and literature, Judaism (religion), Philosophy

P FARMINGTON COMMUNITY LIBRARY,* 32737 W 12 Mile Rd, 48334-3302. SAN 346-4342. Tel: 248-553-0300. FAX: 248-553-3228. Web Site: www.farmlib.org/fcl.html. *Dir*, Beverly D Papai; *Asst Dir*, Gerald M Furi; *In Charge*, Tina Theeke; *Coll Develop*, Richard Nagler; Staff 16 (MLS 16)
Founded 1955. Pop 84,784; Circ 714,774
Jul 1997-Jun 1998 Income $3,199,143. Mats Exp $393,199. Sal $1,595,845
Library Holdings: Bk Vols 190,000; Per Subs 557
Special Collections: Business, Law Grantsmanship, parent, teacher, professional; Entrepreneur Coll for Small Business
Automation Activity & Vendor Info: (Circulation) epixtech, inc.
Publications: Info Exchange (Quarterly); Quarterly Program Booklet
Mem of The Library Network; Wayne Oakland Libr Federation
Partic in BRS; Dialog Corporation
Special Services for the Deaf - Books on deafness & sign language; High interest/low vocabulary books; Special interest periodicals; Staff with knowledge of sign language; TTY machine
Friends of the Library Group
Branches: 1
FARMINGTON, 23500 Liberty St, 48335-3570. SAN 346-4407. Tel: 248-474-7770. FAX: 248-474-6915. Web Site: www.farmlib.org/fcl.html. *Librn*, Marilyn Smith
Library Holdings: Bk Vols 68,835; Per Subs 325
Special Collections: Literacy Coll (400 vol); Michigan History Coll (1500 book volumes)

S GALE GROUP, Corporate Research Library, 27500 Drake Rd, 48331-3535. SAN 308-0099. Tel: 248-699-4253, Ext 1223. FAX: 248-699-8074. *Res*, Tory Cariappa; Tel: 248-699-4253, Ext 1546, E-Mail: tory.cariappa@galegroup.com
Founded 1956
Library Holdings: Bk Titles 20,000; Per Subs 1,250
Subject Interests: Biography, Business, Literature
Special Collections: Biographical Dictionaries & Encyclopedias
Restriction: Staff use only

M MERCY HEALTH SERVICES, Resource Center,* 34605 Twelve Mile Rd, 48331. SAN 373-2037. Tel: 248-489-6754. FAX: 248-489-6932. *Librn*, Vicki Hubbard
Library Holdings: Bk Vols 600; Per Subs 82

S MICHIGAN PSYCHOANALYTIC INSTITUTE, Ira Miller Memorial Library, 32841 Middlebelt Rd, Ste 411, 48334. SAN 327-7615. Tel: 248-851-3380. FAX: 248-851-1806. E-Mail: mpi1@ix.netcom.com. Web Site: www.mpi-mps.org. *Librn*, Nancy K Arvai; *Librn*, Johnna Balk; Staff 1 (MLS 1)
Founded 1954
Library Holdings: Bk Titles 2,200; Per Subs 29
Subject Interests: Psychoanalysis
Automation Activity & Vendor Info: (OPAC) Inmagic, Inc.
Database Vendor: OCLC - First Search
Function: For research purposes

S MORPACE INTERNATIONAL, INC, 31700 Middlebelt Rd, Ste 200, 48334. SAN 371-1005. Tel: 248-737-5300. FAX: 248-737-5326. *In Charge*, Patricia A Watkins; E-Mail: pwatkins@morpace.com
1999-2000 Mats Exp $10,000. Sal $60,000
Library Holdings: Bk Vols 1,100; Per Subs 45
Subject Interests: Auto mechanics, Communications, Computer software, Media
Restriction: Company staff only
Function: Research library

J OAKLAND COMMUNITY COLLEGE, King Library, 27055 Orchard Lake Rd, 48334-4579. SAN 346-4431. Tel: 248-522-3525. FAX: 248-522-3530. *Librn*, Thomas Haug; Tel: 248-522-3529, E-Mail: thhaug@occ.cc.mi.us; *Librn*, Ronald Healy; Tel: 248-522-3531; *Librn*, Ann Walaskan; Tel: 248-522-3528; Staff 8 (MLS 3, Non-MLS 5)
Founded 1967. Enrl 7,500; Fac 103
Library Holdings: Bk Titles 105,000; Per Subs 1,100

CR WILLIAM TYNDALE COLLEGE, Boll Mind Lab Library, 35700 W Twelve Mile Rd, 48331. SAN 308-0765. Tel: 248-553-7200. Toll Free Tel: 877-499-6800. FAX: 248-553-5963. Web Site: www.williamtyndale.edu. *Info Specialist*, Gary Oster; E-Mail: goster@williamtyndale.edu; Staff 5 (MLS 3, Non-MLS 2)
Founded 1945. Enrl 700; Fac 24; Highest Degree: Doctorate
Library Holdings: Bk Vols 55,000; Bk Titles 50,000; Per Subs 220
Subject Interests: Theology
Special Collections: Integration of Psychology & Christianity

FARWELL

P SURREY TOWNSHIP PUBLIC LIBRARY,* 105 E Michigan, PO Box 189, 48622-0189. SAN 308-0773. Tel: 517-588-9782. FAX: 517-588-4488. *Librn*, Jane Eisenhauer
Circ 24,227
Library Holdings: Bk Vols 35,000; Per Subs 80
Mem of Chippewa Libr League

FENNVILLE

P FENNVILLE DISTRICT LIBRARY,* 400 W Main St, PO Box 1130, 49408-1130. SAN 308-0781. Tel: 616-561-5050. FAX: 616-561-5251. *Dir*, Kristen Motz
Founded 1924. Pop 11,564; Circ 26,000
Library Holdings: Bk Titles 25,000; Per Subs 90
Subject Interests: Michigan
Mem of Lakeland Library Cooperative
Partic in OCLC Online Computer Library Center, Inc
Special Services for the Deaf - Books on deafness & sign language; High interest/low vocabulary books

FERNDALE

P FERNDALE PUBLIC LIBRARY,* 222 E Nine Mile Rd, 48220. SAN 308-0811. Tel: 248-546-2504. FAX: 248-545-5840. *Librn*, Mary Trenner
Founded 1930. Pop 25,084; Circ 91,575
1998-1999 Income $382,771, State $22,990, City $293,893, County $29,260, Locally Generated Income $36,628. Mats Exp $55,458, Books $29,417, Per/Ser (Incl. Access Fees) $5,119, Micro $20,922. Sal $277,515
Library Holdings: Bk Vols 92,000; Per Subs 133
Publications: Cub Reporter (newsletter for children's programs)
Mem of The Library Network

FIFE LAKE

P FIFE LAKE PUBLIC LIBRARY,* 137 State St, 49633. SAN 308-082X. Tel: 231-879-4101. FAX: 231-879-3360. *Librn*, Julie Gray
Pop 1,000; Circ 2,500
Library Holdings: Bk Vols 11,800; Per Subs 20
Mem of Mid-Michigan Library League

FLAT ROCK

P FLAT ROCK PUBLIC LIBRARY, 25200 Gibraltar Rd, 48134. SAN 308-0838. Tel: 734-782-2430. FAX: 734-789-8265. E-Mail: library@frlib.org. Web Site: www.frlib.org.; Staff 11 (MLS 3, Non-MLS 8)
Founded 1996. Pop 8,900; Circ 77,426
Jul 2000-Jun 2001 Income $489,670, State $15,000, City $90,000, Locally Generated Income $362,670, Other $22,000. Mats Exp $68,000, Books $50,000, Per/Ser (Incl. Access Fees) $2,500, AV Equip $10,000, Electronic Ref Mat (Incl. Access Fees) $5,500. Sal $187,281 (Prof $100,805)
Library Holdings: Bk Vols 32,000; Per Subs 70; Bks on Deafness & Sign Lang 20
Automation Activity & Vendor Info: (Acquisitions) DRA; (Cataloging) DRA; (Circulation) DRA; (ILL) DRA; (OPAC) DRA
Mem of The Library Network
Partic in Michigan Library Consortium; TLN

FLINT

J BAKER COLLEGE SYSTEM LIBRARIES, 1050 W Bristol Rd, 48507-5508. SAN 308-0846. Tel: 810-766-4231. Circulation Tel: 810-766-4237. Reference Tel: 810-766-4236. Toll Free Tel: 888-854-1058. FAX: 810-766-4229. E-Mail: library@baker.edu. Web Site: www.baker.edu. *Dir*, Sandra Hollis; E-Mail: hollis_s@libsl.baker.edu; *ILL*, Alberta Hyvarinen; E-Mail: hyvari_a@libfl.baker.edu; Staff 16 (MLS 7, Non-MLS 9)
Founded 1912. Enrl 17,000
Library Holdings: Bk Vols 182,000; Per Subs 350
Subject Interests: Aviation, Business and management, Computer science, Electronics, Engineering, Fashion, Interior design, Occupational safety, Physical therapy, Technology, Travel
Mem of Falcon; ME Mich Regions of Coop
Partic in Michigan Library Consortium; OCLC Online Computer Library Center, Inc
Baker/Flint Headquarters for 9 campus library systems with libraries at Baker Colleges of Auburn Hills, Cadillac, Cass City, Clinton Township, Jackson, Muskegon, Owosso & Port Huron. Centralized ordering/processing/ILL/Av Booking/Online Reference Services System-wide

S CHARLES STEWART MOTT FOUNDATION LIBRARY,* 1200 Mott Foundation Bldg, 48502. SAN 329-806X. Tel: 810-766-1709. FAX: 810-766-1744. *Librn*, Eve Brown; E-Mail: ebrown@mott.org
Founded 1974
Library Holdings: Bk Vols 2,000; Per Subs 120
Publications: Acquisition list (monthly)
Restriction: Staff use only
Partic in Dialog Corporation

S DELPHI AUTOMOTIVE SYSTEM, (Formerly General Motors Corp), Delphi Engineering Library, 1601 N Averill Ave, 48556. SAN 308-0897. Tel: 810-257-8183. FAX: 810-257-7508. *Librn*, Gloria Browning; Tel: 810-257-7155, E-Mail: gloria.browning@delphiauto.com; *Asst Librn*, Susan C Baroski; E-Mail: susan.baroski@delphiauto.com; Staff 2 (Non-MLS 2)
Founded 1925
Library Holdings: Per Subs 400
Subject Interests: Automotive engineering, Ceramics, Electronic engineering, Material culture
Special Collections: VSMF Documentation Files; VSMF Military Specifications File
Database Vendor: IAC - Info Trac, OCLC - First Search
Partic in Dialog Corporation

C DETROIT COLLEGE OF BUSINESS, Flint Campus Library,* 3488 N Jennings Rd, 48504-1700. SAN 324-4911. Tel: 810-789-2200, Ext 217. FAX: 810-789-2266. E-Mail: flmcgin@dcb.edu. *Librn*, Sheila McGinnis; *Asst Librn*, Elizabeth Roberts; Staff 3 (MLS 3)
Enrl 700; Fac 65; Highest Degree: Bachelor
1998-1999 Income $70,000. Mats Exp $7,300, Books $5,000, Per/Ser (Incl. Access Fees) $2,300
Library Holdings: Bk Vols 9,500; Bk Titles 9,100; Per Subs 130
Subject Interests: Bus, Mgt
Mem of Mideastern Michigan Library Cooperative

SR FIRST PRESBYTERIAN CHURCH OF FLINT, Peirce Memorial Library, 746 S Saginaw St, 48502. SAN 329-8833. Tel: 810-234-8673. FAX: 810-234-1643. *Librn*, Steve Hill
Library Holdings: Bk Vols 4,000

S FLINT JOURNAL, Editorial Library,* 200 E First St, 48502-1925. SAN 308-0862. Tel: 810-766-6192. FAX: 810-767-2278. *Chief Librn*, David W Larzelere; Staff 5 (MLS 1, Non-MLS 4)
Founded 1935
Library Holdings: Bk Titles 3,200; Per Subs 50
Subject Interests: History, Journalism
Restriction: Open to public for reference only

SR FLINT NEWMAN CENTER LIBRARY,* 609 E Fifth Ave, 48502. SAN 308-0870. Tel: 810-239-9391. *Dir*, James B Bettendorf
Founded 1967
Library Holdings: Bk Titles 2,390; Per Subs 45
Subject Interests: Church history, Philosophy, Sociology, Theology
Special Collections: Orestes Brownson's Works
The Flint Newman Center Library is part of the Flint Newman Center, a catholic Campus Ministry, serving the institutions of higher learning in the Flint area

P FLINT PUBLIC LIBRARY,* 1026 E Kearsley St, 48502-1994. SAN 346-4466. Tel: 810-232-7111. FAX: 810-232-8360. *Dir*, Gloria J Coles; E-Mail: gcoles@flint.lib.mi.us; *Asst Dir*, Charles Hansen; *Automation Syst Coordr, Tech Servs*, Patricia Kalstein; *Ad Servs, Coll Develop*, Brent Stokesberry; *Ch Servs, YA Servs*, Cynthia Stilley; Staff 92 (MLS 32, Non-MLS 60)
Founded 1851. Pop 140,761; Circ 875,434
Library Holdings: Bk Vols 638,000; Per Subs 881
Subject Interests: Children's literature, Genealogy, Local history
Publications: Ring A Ring O'Roses
Mem of Mich Libr Consortium; Mideastern Michigan Library Cooperative
Special Services for the Deaf - High interest/low vocabulary books; Staff with knowledge of sign language; TTY machine
Friends of the Library Group
Branches: 3
CODY, 3519 Fenton Rd, 48507. SAN 346-4520. Tel: 810-238-5822. FAX: 810-238-9831. *Librn*, Dennis McMullen
Library Holdings: Bk Vols 16,028
NORTH FLINT, 5005 Clover Lawn Dr, 48504. SAN 346-461X. Tel: 810-785-9879. FAX: 810-785-1151. *Librn*, Brenda Harris
Library Holdings: Bk Vols 11,023
WEST FLINT, 3601 Beecher Rd, 48503. SAN 346-4679. Tel: 810-238-3637. FAX: 810-238-1736. *Librn*, Larry Frounfelter; Staff 3 (MLS 2, Non-MLS 1)
Founded 1971
Library Holdings: Bk Vols 55,837
Bookmobiles: 1

L GENESEE COUNTY CIRCUIT COURT, Law Library,* County Court House Rm 401, 900 S Saginaw St, 48502. SAN 329-7691. Tel: 810-257-3253. FAX: 810-239-9280. *Librn*, Janet Patsy
Library Holdings: Bk Vols 10,000; Per Subs 70

S GENESEE COUNTY METROPOLITAN PLANNING COMMISSION LIBRARY,* 1101 Beach St Rm 223, 48502-1470. SAN 373-0727. Tel: 810-257-3010. FAX: 810-257-3185. E-Mail: gcmpcadmin@attmail.com. *Asst Dir*, Thomas Goergens
Library Holdings: Bk Vols 300
Subject Interests: Housing, Transportation
Open Mon-Fri 8-12 & 1-5

P GENESEE DISTRICT LIBRARY, G-4195 W Pasadena Ave, 48504. SAN 346-4709. Tel: 810-732-5570. Circulation Tel: 810-732-0110. Reference Tel: 810-732-0123. FAX: 810-732-1161. Web Site: gdl.falcon.edu. *Dir, Tech Serv*, Carol Warren; Tel: 810-230-3329, E-Mail: cwarren@gfn.org; Staff 26 (MLS 26)
Founded 1942. Pop 291,000
Library Holdings: Bk Vols 649,100
Subject Interests: Genealogy
Special Collections: American Indians, bks, recs; Civil War (Robert L Calkins Memorial Coll); Genesee County Coll
Partic in Michigan Library Consortium
Special Services for the Deaf - Staff with knowledge of sign language
Branches: 20
BAKER PARK, 3410 S Grand Traverse, Burton, 48529. SAN 346-5128. Tel: 810-742-7860. FAX: 810-742-2927. Web Site: www.gdl.falcon.edu. *Librn*, Karen Upham
Library Holdings: Bk Vols 27,300
BEECHER LIBRARY, 1386 W Coldwater Rd, 48505. SAN 373-8868. Tel: 810-789-2800. FAX: 810-789-2885. Web Site: www.gdl.falcon.edu. *Librn*, Roy Soncrant
Library Holdings: Bk Vols 27,300
BURTON MEMORIAL, G-4012 E Atherton Rd, Burton, 48519. SAN 346-4733. Tel: 810-742-0674. FAX: 810-742-2928. Web Site: www.gdl.falcon.edu. *Librn*, Priscilla Khirfan
Library Holdings: Bk Vols 35,800
CLIO AREA, G-2080 W Vienna Rd, Clio, 48420. SAN 346-4768. Tel: 810-686-7130. FAX: 810-686-0071. Web Site: www.gdl.falcon.edu. *Librn*, Christine Yurgaites
Library Holdings: Bk Vols 44,500
DAVISON AREA, 203 E Fourth St, Davison, 48423. SAN 346-4792. Tel: 810-653-2022. FAX: 810-653-7633. Web Site: www.gdl.falcon.edu. *Librn*, Kirby Thornton
Library Holdings: Bk Vols 70,200
Special Collections: Calkins Civil War Coll
Friends of the Library Group
FENTON AREA (A J PHILLIPS LIBRARY), 200 E Caroline St, Fenton, 48430. SAN 346-4822. Tel: 810-629-7612. FAX: 810-629-0855. Web Site: www.gdl.falcon.edu. *Librn*, Marilyn Brown; *Ch Servs*, Christine Heron; Tel: 810-714-0917, Fax: 810-714-0918
Library Holdings: Bk Vols 42,800
FLUSHING AREA, 120 N Maple, Flushing, 48433. SAN 346-4881. Tel: 810-659-9755. FAX: 810-659-1781. Web Site: www.gdl.falcon.edu. *Librn*, Faye Gulley
Library Holdings: Bk Vols 39,000
FOREST TOWNSHIP, 123 W Main St, Otisville, 48463. SAN 346-5098. Tel: 810-631-6330. FAX: 810-631-6076. Web Site: www.gdl.falcon.edu. *Librn*, Marya Gutek
Library Holdings: Bk Vols 26,300
Friends of the Library Group
GAINES STATION, 103 E Walker, Gaines, 48436. SAN 378-133X. Tel: 517-271-8720. FAX: 517-271-8816. Web Site: www.gdl.falcon.edu. *Librn*, Beverley Wallace
GOODRICH AREA, 10237 Hegel Rd, Goodrich, 48438. SAN 346-4911. Tel: 810-636-2489. FAX: 810-636-3304. Web Site: www.gdl.falcon.edu. *Librn*, Cynthia Fry
Library Holdings: Bk Vols 19,400

Friends of the Library Group
HEADQUARTERS, G-4195 W Pasadena Ave, 48504. SAN 346-4989. Tel: 810-732-0110. Reference Tel: 810-732-0123. FAX: 810-732-3146. Web Site: www.gdl.falcon.edu. *Librn*, Gloria Resteiner; *Cat*, Christine Heron
Library Holdings: Bk Vols 56,000
HEADQUARTERS REFERENCE Tel: 810-732-0123. FAX: 810-732-3146. Web Site: www.gdl.falcon.edu. *Ref*, Tom Rohrer
GENESEE TOWNSHIP (JOHNSON MEMORIAL LIBRARY), 7397 N Genesee Rd, Genesee, 48437. SAN 346-4970. Tel: 810-640-1410. FAX: 810-640-2413. Web Site: gdl.falcon.edu. *Librn*, Cheryl Burtram
Library Holdings: Bk Vols 30,500
Friends of the Library Group
P LIBRARY FOR BLIND & PHYSICALLY HANDICAPPED Tel: 810-732-1120. FAX: 810-732-1715. *Librn*, Deloris King; Tel: 810-230-3325
Mem of Mideastern Michigan Library Cooperative
Special Services for the Blind - Bks on tape; Descriptive videos
LINDEN AREA, Old Mill, Linden, 48451. (Mail add: PO Box 760, Springfield, 65801-0760), SAN 346-5004. Tel: 417-751-2933. FAX: 417-751-2275. Web Site: www.thelibrary.springfield.missouri.org. *Branch Mgr*, Kathy Trompke; E-Mail: kathyt@orion.org; *Librn*, Hans Norbotten; Staff 4 (Non-MLS 4)
Circ 38,032
Library Holdings: Bk Vols 20,000
Database Vendor: Ebsco - EbscoHost, GaleNet, IAC - Info Trac, IAC - SearchBank, Innovative Interfaces INN - View, OCLC - First Search
Friends of the Library Group
FLINT TOWNSHIP (MCCARTY PUBLIC LIBRARY), 2071 S Graham Rd, 48532. SAN 346-4857. Tel: 810-732-9150. FAX: 810-732-0878. Web Site: www.gdl.falcon.edu. *Librn*, Jerri McComb; *Dir, Tech Serv*, Carol Warren; Tel: 810-230-3329, Fax: 810-732-1161, E-Mail: cwarren@gfn.org
Library Holdings: Bk Vols 29,000
Friends of the Library Group
GRAND BLANC AREA (MCFARLEN PUBLIC LIBRARY), 515 Perry Rd, Grand Blanc, 48439. SAN 346-4946. Tel: 810-694-5310. FAX: 810-694-5313. Web Site: www.gdl.falcon.edu. *Librn*, Gail Mock; *Business*, Sharon Van Norwick; Tel: 810-694-5190, Fax: 810-694-5192; *Ch Servs*, Kara Kvasnicka
Library Holdings: Bk Vols 93,400
Friends of the Library Group
MONTROSE-JENNINGS LIBRARY, 241 Feher Dr, Montrose, 48457. SAN 346-5039. Tel: 810-639-6388. FAX: 810-639-3675. Web Site: www.gdl.falcon.edu. *Librn*, Elaine Kinney
Library Holdings: Bk Vols 25,800
Friends of the Library Group
MOUNT MORRIS AREA, 685 Van Buren Ave, Mount Morris, 48458. SAN 346-5063. Tel: 810-686-6120. FAX: 810-686-0661. Web Site: www.gdl.falcon.edu. *Librn*, George Jamison
Library Holdings: Bk Vols 41,200
SWARTZ CREEK AREA (PERKINS LIBRARY), 8095 Civic Dr, Swartz Creek, 48473. SAN 346-5152. Tel: 810-635-3900. FAX: 810-635-4179. Web Site: www.gdl.falcon.edu. *Librn*, Mark Kulig; Staff 1 (Non-MLS 1)
Library Holdings: Bk Vols 40,700

M HURLEY MEDICAL CENTER, Michael H & Robert M Hamady Health Sciences Library, One Hurley Plaza, 48502. SAN 308-0919. Tel: 810-257-9427. FAX: 810-762-7107. E-Mail: circular1@hurleymc.com. *Dir*, Martha Studaker; E-Mail: mstudak1@hurleymc.com; Staff 4 (MLS 4)
Founded 1928
Library Holdings: Bk Titles 450; Per Subs 500
Subject Interests: Health sciences, Hospital administration, Medicine, Nursing
Special Collections: Consumer Health Information
Partic in Flint Area Health Sci Libr Network; Michigan Health Sciences Libraries Association; Nat Libr of Med
Also have Health Information Library for public

S KETTERING UNIVERSITY LIBRARY, 1700 W Third Ave, 48504-4898. SAN 308-0900. Tel: 810-762-7814. FAX: 810-762-9744. Web Site: www.kettering.edu. *Tech Servs*, Dawn Olmsted Swanson; *Publ Servs*, Jim Kangas; *Cat*, Betty Holifield; Staff 13 (MLS 5, Non-MLS 8)
Founded 1928. Enrl 1,330; Fac 154; Highest Degree: Master
Jul 1998-Jun 1999 Income $835,005. Mats Exp $297,568, Books $99,163, Per/Ser (Incl. Access Fees) $171,231, Micro $14,674, Other Print Mats $12,500. Sal $444,947 (Prof $221,036)
Library Holdings: Bk Vols 110,197; Bk Titles 93,876; Per Subs 544
Subject Interests: Business and management, Engineering
Special Collections: ASTM Standards; SAE & SME Technical Coll, papers
Database Vendor: Ebsco - EbscoHost, epixtech, inc., OCLC - First Search
Restriction: Open to faculty, students & qualified researchers
Partic in Michigan Library Consortium

S LIBRARY OF THE FLINT INSTITUTE OF ARTS, 1120 E Kearsley St, 48503. SAN 308-0927. Tel: 810-234-1695. FAX: 810-234-1692.
Founded 1958
Library Holdings: Bk Titles 5,400
Subject Interests: Art and architecture
Publications: Exhibition Catalogues
Restriction: Non-circulating to the public

M MCLAREN REGIONAL MEDICAL CENTER, Medical Library, 401 S Ballenger Hwy, 48532-3685. SAN 324-3907. Tel: 810-342-2141. FAX: 810-342-2269. E-Mail: medlib1@mclaren.org. *Mgr*, D Lea Ann McGaugh; E-Mail: leaannm@mclaren.org; *Asst Librn*, Mary Fitzpatrick; E-Mail: maryk@mclaren.org; *Tech Servs*, Diane Gardner; E-Mail: dianeg@mclaren.org; Staff 3 (MLS 1, Non-MLS 2)
Founded 1951
Library Holdings: Bk Titles 2,065; Per Subs 400
Subject Interests: Clinical medicine, Family practice, Health, Hospital administration, Nursing, Orthopedics, Radiology, Surgery
Automation Activity & Vendor Info: (Cataloging) EOS; (Circulation) EOS; (OPAC) EOS; (Serials) EOS
Partic in Docline; Nat Libr of Med; OCLC Online Computer Library Center, Inc

P MIDEASTERN MICHIGAN LIBRARY COOPERATIVE, 503 S Saginaw St Ste 839, 48502. SAN 346-5187. Tel: 810-232-7119. FAX: 810-232-6639. *Dir*, Roger Mendel; E-Mail: rmendel@gfn.org; Staff 2 (MLS 1, Non-MLS 1)
Founded 1965. Pop 827,000
Oct 1999-Sep 2000 Income $789,000
Publications: The Co-op Connection (monthly newsletter)
Member Libraries: Capital Area District Library; Corunna Public Library; Detroit College Of Business; Edna Bentley Memorial Library; Flint Public Library; Genesee District Library; Lapeer County Library; North Branch Township Library; Ruth Hughes Memorial District Library; Shiawassee District Library
Branches: 1
P LIBRARY FOR THE BLIND & PHYSICALLY HANDICAPPED, G-4195 W Pasadena Ave, 48504. SAN 346-5217. Tel: 810-732-1120. FAX: 810-732-1715. *Dir*, Roger Mendle; Staff 1 (MLS 1)
Founded 1974

J MOTT COMMUNITY COLLEGE, C S Mott Library, 1401 E Court St, 48503. SAN 308-0935. Tel: 810-762-0408. FAX: 810-762-0407. Web Site: www.mcc.edu. *Exec Dir*, Denise Hooks; Tel: 810-762-0415, E-Mail: dhooks@mcc.edu; *Head Tech Servs, ILL*, Martha Lewis; *Publ Servs*, Michael Ugorowski; Staff 9 (MLS 5, Non-MLS 4)
Founded 1960. Fac 152
Jul 1999-Jun 2000 Income $564,708. Mats Exp $82,000, Books $40,000, Per/Ser (Incl. Access Fees) $32,000, Presv $3,000, Electronic Ref Mat (Incl. Access Fees) $7,000. Sal $473,408 (Prof $266,320)
Library Holdings: Bk Vols 101,572; Per Subs 334
Subject Interests: Art, Education, Technology
Special Collections: Children's Literature; Law Reference
Database Vendor: Ebsco - EbscoHost, epixtech, inc., IAC - Info Trac, IAC - SearchBank, OCLC - First Search
Publications: Mott Inklings
Partic in Flint Area Health Sci Libr Network
Friends of the Library Group

S SLOAN MUSEUM, Perry Archives,* 303 Walnut St, 48503. SAN 325-920X. Tel: 810-760-1415. FAX: 810-239-6515. E-Mail: sloan@tir.com. Web Site: www.buickgallery.com. *Curator*, David White
Library Holdings: Bk Vols 4,000
Special Collections: Archives holdings for Flint & Genesee County
Restriction: By appointment only

C UNIVERSITY OF MICHIGAN-FLINT LIBRARY, Frances Willson Thompson Library, 303 E Kearsley, 48502-2186. SAN 308-0951. Tel: 810-762-3400. Interlibrary Loan Service Tel: 810-762-3136. TDD: 810-766-6818. FAX: 810-762-3133. Web Site: www.flint.umich.edu/departments/library/index.html. *Dir*, Robert L Houbeck, Jr; E-Mail: rhoubeck@flint.umich.edu; *Archivist, Rare Bks, Spec Coll*, Paul Gifford; *Doc, Online Servs*, Dorothy Davis; *Publ Servs, Ref*, Grant Burns; *Ref*, Paul Streby; *Ser*, Anh Thach; *Tech Servs*, Dave Hart; Staff 13 (MLS 13)
Founded 1956. Enrl 6,448; Fac 333; Highest Degree: Master
Library Holdings: Bk Vols 215,000; Per Subs 1,143
Special Collections: Foundation Center Regional Coll; Genesee Historical Collection Center
Publications: Library Lexicon
Partic in Dialog Corporation; Michigan Library Consortium; RLIN
Special Services for the Deaf - TDD
Friends of the Library Group

FOSTORIA

P WATERTOWN TOWNSHIP FOSTORIA LIBRARY,* 9405 Foster St, PO Box 39, 48435-0039. SAN 308-096X. Tel: 517-795-2794. FAX: 517-795-2892. *Librn*, Cathy Valentine
Founded 1964. Pop 2,100; Circ 4,800
Library Holdings: Bk Vols 7,000; Per Subs 10
Mem of White Pine Library Cooperative
Open Mon-Thurs 12-5 & Sat 10-12

FOWLERVILLE

P FOWLERVILLE DISTRICT LIBRARY,* 131 Mill St, 48836-0313. SAN 308-0978. Tel: 517-223-9089. FAX: 517-223-0781. E-Mail: library131@yahoo.com. *Librn*, Cheryl Poch
Circ 23,000
Library Holdings: Bk Vols 23,000; Per Subs 50
Mem of Huron Valley Libr Syst; The Library Network
Friends of the Library Group

FRANKENMUTH

S FRANKENMUTH HISTORICAL ASSOCIATION, Frankenmuth Historical Museum Library, 613 S Main St, 48734. SAN 326-0690. Tel: 517-652-9701. FAX: 517-652-9390. E-Mail: frankenmuthmuseum@yahoo.com. Web Site: www.dtimmons.com/frankenmuthmuseum. *In Charge*, Mary Nuechterlein; Staff 1 (MLS 1)
Founded 1972
Library Holdings: Bk Vols 1,500; Bk Titles 1,000
Special Collections: Wilhelm Loehe Memorial Library; Wm Loehe mission activities
Publications: Annual booklet on history of local business or organization
Restriction: Public use on premises

P JAMES E WICKSON MEMORIAL LIBRARY, 359 S Franklin, 48734. SAN 308-0986. Tel: 517-652-8323. TDD: 517-652-8323. FAX: 517-652-3450. E-Mail: wickson@tir.com. Web Site: www.tir.com/~wickson. *Librn*, David Curtis; Staff 11 (MLS 1, Non-MLS 10)
Founded 1974. Pop 6,530; Circ 102,623
Jul 1999-Jun 2000 Income $359,028, State $6,530, City $168,770, County $32,774, Locally Generated Income $150,954. Mats Exp $27,559, Books $23,017, Per/Ser (Incl. Access Fees) $4,542. Sal $107,494 (Prof $39,880)
Library Holdings: Bk Vols 43,159; Per Subs 106
Subject Interests: Genealogy, Local history, Women studies
Automation Activity & Vendor Info: (Cataloging) EOS; (Circulation) EOS; (OPAC) EOS
Database Vendor: IAC - Info Trac, OCLC - First Search
Publications: Newsletter (quarterly)
Mem of White Pine Library Cooperative
Friends of the Library Group

FRANKFORT

P BENZIE SHORES DISTRICT LIBRARY, 630 Main St, PO Box 631, 49635. SAN 308-0994. Tel: 231-352-4671. FAX: 231-352-4671. Web Site: members.ptway.com.faic/library.html. *Librn*, Cathy Carter; E-Mail: bsdl1@benzie.com; Staff 3 (MLS 1, Non-MLS 2)
Pop 2,053; Circ 37,000
Jul 1998-Jun 1999 Income $133,730, State $850, Locally Generated Income $96,270, Other $36,610. Mats Exp $19,300, Books $16,500, Per/Ser (Incl. Access Fees) $2,800. Sal $35,000 (Prof $59,760)
Library Holdings: Bk Vols 20,000; Per Subs 75; High Interest/Low Vocabulary Bk Vols 25
Mem of Mid-Michigan Library League
Fee for out-of-district $200/year
Friends of the Library Group

FRANKLIN

P FRANKLIN PUBLIC LIBRARY,* 32455 Franklin Rd, 48025. SAN 308-1001. Tel: 248-851-2254. FAX: 248-851-5846. *Dir*, Molly Hammerle
Circ 9,144
Library Holdings: Bk Vols 14,500; Per Subs 33
Mem of The Library Network; Wayne Oakland Libr Federation

FRASER

P FRASER PUBLIC LIBRARY,* 16330 Fourteen Mile Rd, 48026-2034. SAN 308-101X. Tel: 810-293-2055. FAX: 810-294-5777. *Dir*, Eric Suess
Oct 1997-Sep 1998 Income $90,000
Library Holdings: Bk Vols 60,000; Bk Titles 55,000; Per Subs 100
Mem of Libr Coop of Macomb
Open 11:00am weekdays, 10:00 am Sat

FREEPORT

P FREEPORT DISTRICT LIBRARY,* 208 S State St, PO Box 5, 49325-0005. SAN 308-1028. Tel: 616-765-5181. FAX: 616-765-5181. Web Site: www.lakeland.lib.mi.us/barry.html. *Librn*, Joanne Hesselink
Founded 1942. Pop 3,589; Circ 5,495
Library Holdings: Bk Titles 10,000
Special Collections: Childrens Cassettes; Jig Saw Puzzles; Large Print Books
Mem of Lakeland Library Cooperative
Open Mon & Fri 1-6, Wed 9-5 & Thurs 6-8

FREMONT

P FREMONT AREA DISTRICT LIBRARY,* 104 E Main, 49412. SAN 308-1036. Tel: 616-924-3480. FAX: 616-924-2355. E-Mail: fmt@lakeland.lib.mi.us. Web Site: www.fadl.ncats.net. *Dir*, Judi McNally; E-Mail: judy@ncats.net; *Ad Servs*, Sandra Enders-Holmes; E-Mail: senders@ncats.net; *Ch Servs, YA Servs*, Darla Lager; E-Mail: dlager@ncats.net; *Spec Coll*, Brenda Wever; E-Mail: brenda@ncats.net. Subject Specialists: *Local history*, Brenda Wever; *Reference*, Sandra Enders-Holmes; Staff 3 (MLS 3)
Founded 1964. Pop 12,600; Circ 147,000
Jul 1998-Jun 1999 Income $513,228, State $12,631, Locally Generated Income $500,597. Mats Exp $63,463, Books $35,267, Per/Ser (Incl. Access Fees) $6,277, Presv $3,293, Micro $500, AV Equip $11,918, Electronic Ref Mat (Incl. Access Fees) $6,208. Sal $238,303 (Prof $102,000)
Library Holdings: Bk Vols 70,334; Per Subs 201
Special Collections: Local History (Harry L Spooner Coll)
Automation Activity & Vendor Info: (Circulation) epixtech, inc.
Publications: Bookworm (quarterly newsletter)
Mem of Lakeland Library Cooperative
Special Services for the Blind - Bks on cassette; Large print bks
Friends of the Library Group

S GERBER PRODUCTS CO, Corporate Library,* 445 State St, 49413-0001. SAN 308-1044. Tel: 616-928-2631. FAX: 616-928-2964. *Librn*, Sherrie Harris
Founded 1946
Library Holdings: Bk Titles 10,000; Per Subs 750
Subject Interests: Agriculture, Annual reports, Biochemistry, Business and management, Microbiology, Nutrition
Publications: Internal Newsletter
Restriction: Staff use only

GALESBURG

P GALESBURG MEMORIAL LIBRARY, 188 E Michigan Ave, 49053. SAN 308-1052. Tel: 616-665-7839. FAX: 616-665-7788. *Dir*, Donna Kowalewski; E-Mail: dnnkwlwsk@hotmail.com
Pop 8,100; Circ 15,327
Jul 1999-Jun 2000 Income $46,835, State $8,173, City $11,309, Locally Generated Income $25,240, Other $2,113. Mats Exp $9,911, Books $7,161, Per/Ser (Incl. Access Fees) $850, AV Equip $1,000, Electronic Ref Mat (Incl. Access Fees) $900. Sal $27,000
Library Holdings: Bk Vols 19,800; Per Subs 34
Subject Interests: Local history
Special Collections: Michigan Collection; Michigan Nut Growers Association; Michigan Pioneer Collection
Automation Activity & Vendor Info: (Circulation) Follett; (OPAC) Follett
Mem of Southwest Michigan Library Cooperative
Special Services for the Deaf - TDD
Friends of the Library Group

GALIEN

P GALIEN TOWNSHIP PUBLIC LIBRARY,* 302 N Main St, PO Box 278, 49113-0278. SAN 308-1060. Tel: 616-545-8281. FAX: 616-545-8281. *Dir*, Caren Woods
1998-1999 Income $32,000. Mats Exp $6,000. Sal $10,000
Library Holdings: Bk Vols 30,000
Mem of Southwest Michigan Library Cooperative

GARDEN CITY

M GARDEN CITY HOSPITAL, Library Services Department,* 6245 Inkster Rd, 48135. SAN 373-2053. Tel: 734-458-4311. *Mgr*, Chris Hunt
Library Holdings: Bk Vols 2,000; Per Subs 155

P GARDEN CITY PUBLIC LIBRARY,* 2012 Middlebelt Rd, 48135-2895. SAN 308-1087. Tel: 734-525-8856. TDD: 734-525-8083. FAX: 734-421-6230. Web Site: garden-city.lib.mi.us. *Dir*, Joan Elmouchi; E-Mail: elmouchi@tln.lib.mi.us
Pop 35,640; Circ 99,000
Jul 1998-Jun 1999 Income $320,250, State $29,042, City $194,000, County $34,000, Locally Generated Income $13,200, Other $5,000. Mats Exp $23,371, Books $16,371, Per/Ser (Incl. Access Fees) $2,000. Sal $165,944 (Prof $116,806)
Library Holdings: Bk Vols 61,153; Per Subs 111
Mem of The Library Network
Special Services for the Deaf - TDD
Friends of the Library Group

GAYLORD

P OTSEGO COUNTY LIBRARY,* 700 S Otsego Ave, 49735. SAN 308-1095. Tel: 517-732-5841. FAX: 517-732-9401. E-Mail: otsego@northland.lib.mi.us. Web Site: www.norhtland.lib.mi.us/member/otsego.htm, www.otsego.lib.mi.us. *Dir*, Maureen Derenzy; E-Mail: mderenzy@

northland.lib.mi.us; *Asst Dir*, Kathleen Olds; *Publ Servs*, Jackie Skinner; E-Mail: jskinner@northland.lib.mi.us; *ILL*, Jean Brown; E-Mail: otsego2@northland.lib.mi.us; *Ch Servs*, Marge Long; Staff 14 (MLS 2, Non-MLS 12)
Pop 17,957; Circ 154,444
Jan 1998-Dec 1998 Income (Main Library and Branch Library) $512,087, State $22,935, Federal $16,839, Locally Generated Income $395,249, Other $77,064. Mats Exp $64,465, Books $45,054, Per/Ser (Incl. Access Fees) $7,264, Micro $200, Electronic Ref Mat (Incl. Access Fees) $11,947. Sal $184,007 (Prof $89,867)
Library Holdings: Bk Vols 57,297; Per Subs 208
Subject Interests: Local history
Automation Activity & Vendor Info: (Cataloging) epixtech, inc.; (Circulation) epixtech, inc.; (OPAC) epixtech, inc.
Mem of Northland Library Cooperative
Partic in Michigan Library Consortium
Special Services for the Blind - Cassette bks; Reading edge system
Friends of the Library Group
Branches: 2
CORWITH TOWNSHIP HALL, 8170 Mill St, Vanderbilt, 49795. SAN 329-3564. Tel: 517-983-3600. FAX: 517-983-3600. *Mgr*, Linda Cole
JOHANNESBURG BRANCH, M-32, Johannesburg, 49751. SAN 329-3548. Tel: 517-732-3928. FAX: 517-732-3928. *Mgr*, Marge Long
Friends of the Library Group

GLADSTONE

P GLADSTONE AREA SCHOOL & PUBLIC LIBRARY,* 300 S Tenth St, 49837-1518. SAN 308-1109. Tel: 906-428-9200, Ext 27. Interlibrary Loan Service Tel: 906-428-4224. FAX: 906-789-8452. *Librn*, Lori Wells; Staff 2 (MLS 2)
Founded 1913. Pop 8,875; Circ 99,884
Library Holdings: Bk Vols 25,000; Per Subs 150
Special Collections: American History (Nebel Memorial Coll), bks, rec
Mem of Mid-Peninsula Library Cooperative; Upper Pennisula Region of Libr Coop
Statistics include central library and four elementary library media centers
Friends of the Library Group

GLADWIN

P GLADWIN COUNTY LIBRARY, 555 W Cedar Ave, 48624-2096. SAN 308-1117. Tel: 517-426-8221. FAX: 517-426-6958. *Dir*, Craig Shuffelt; Staff 14 (MLS 1, Non-MLS 13)
Founded 1934. Pop 21,896; Circ 139,000
Library Holdings: Bk Vols 40,601; Per Subs 126
Special Collections: Local History, local newsp on micro
Automation Activity & Vendor Info: (Circulation) epixtech, inc.
Publications: Annotated Catalog of Large Print Books; Index to Obituaries in the Gladwin County Record; Page 1 (newsletter)
Partic in Valley Libr Consortium

GRAND BLANC

M GENESYS REGIONAL MEDICAL CENTER, Medical Library,* One Genesys Pkwy, 48439-1477. SAN 308-0943. Tel: 810-606-5259. FAX: 810-606-5270. *Librn*, Doris Blauet; *Asst Librn*, Arlene Cousins; *Asst Librn*, Barbara Morey; *Asst Librn*, JoAnn Ellis; Staff 4 (MLS 1, Non-MLS 3)
Founded 1936
Jul 1997-Jun 1998 Income $182,800. Mats Exp $181,000
Library Holdings: Bk Titles 3,000; Per Subs 241
Subject Interests: Cardiology, Geriatrics and gerontology, Obstetrics and gynecology, Oncology
Partic in Flint Area Health Sci Libr Network; Medline

M GENESYS REGIONAL MEDICAL CENTER-FLINT OSTEOPATHIC HOSPITAL, Medical Library,* One Genesys Pkwy, 48439. SAN 308-0889. Tel: 810-606-5260. FAX: 810-606-5270. *Librn*, Doris Blauet; E-Mail: blauet@com.msu.edu
Founded 1960
Subject Interests: Medicine
Partic in Medline; OCLC Online Computer Library Center, Inc

GRAND HAVEN

S COUNCIL OF MICHIGAN FOUNDATIONS, Library & Information Services, One S Harbor Ave, Ste 3, PO Box 599, 49417. SAN 377-1598. Tel: 616-842-7080, Ext 24. FAX: 616-842-1760. E-Mail: cmf@cmif.org. Web Site: www.cmif.org. *Dir*, Gail B Powers-Schaub; E-Mail: gschaub@cmif.org; *Mgr*, Barbara Dryer; Tel: 616-842-7080, Ext 13, E-Mail: bdryer@cmif.org; Staff 2 (MLS 2)
Founded 1972
Library Holdings: Bk Vols 2,500; Bk Titles 2,500; Per Subs 20
Subject Interests: Foundations, Grants, Philanthropy
Automation Activity & Vendor Info: (OPAC) Inmagic, Inc.
Restriction: Circulation limited, Public use on premises
Function: Mail loans to members

P LOUTIT DISTRICT LIBRARY, 407 Columbus St, 49417. SAN 308-1125. Tel: 616-842-5560. Reference Tel: 616-847-2980. FAX: 616-847-0570. E-Mail: gdh@lakeland.lib.mi.us. Web Site: www.loutitlibrary.org. *Dir*, Char Zoet; E-Mail: czoet@lakeland.lib.mi.us; *Ch Servs, YA Servs*, Marilyn Painter; *Ref*, Sharon Piersma; Staff 23 (MLS 4, Non-MLS 19)
Founded 1910. Pop 30,000; Circ 185,000
Jun 1998-May 1999 Income $765,138, State $20,468, City $310,000, Locally Generated Income $23,415, Other $411,255. Mats Exp $87,900, Books $70,000, Per/Ser (Incl. Access Fees) $6,000, Presv $500, Micro $500. Sal $275,035
Library Holdings: Bk Vols 100,000; Per Subs 123
Special Collections: Genealogy & Local History; NOCAA Parent Resource Corner
Automation Activity & Vendor Info: (Circulation) CLSI LIBS
Database Vendor: IAC - Info Trac, OCLC - First Search
Mem of Lakeland Library Cooperative
Partic in Michigan Library Consortium
Computer Users Group; Grand Haven Genealogy Society
Friends of the Library Group

S TRI-CITIES HISTORICAL SOCIETY MUSEUM,* One N Harbor Dr, 49417. SAN 373-2061. Tel: 616-842-0700. FAX: 616-842-3698. E-Mail: tcmuseum@grandhaven.com. Web Site: www.grandhaven.com/museum. *Dir*, Elizabeth Kammeraad
Library Holdings: Bk Vols 500
Subject Interests: Local history
Publications: Riverwinds (bi-monthly newsletter)
Open 10-5, Sat & Sun 12-4 (winter), 10-9:30, Sun 12-9:30 (summer), closed Mon

GRAND LEDGE

P GRAND LEDGE PUBLIC LIBRARY,* 131 E Jefferson St, 48837-1534. SAN 308-1133. Tel: 517-627-7014. FAX: 517-627-6276. *Dir*, Suzanne E Bowles; *Media Spec*, Judy Howard; *Tech Servs*, Suzanne Schramski; Staff 1 (MLS 1)
Founded 1911. Pop 12,358
Library Holdings: Bk Titles 43,000; Per Subs 65
Subject Interests: Local history
Mem of Capital Library Cooperative

GRAND RAPIDS

C AQUINAS COLLEGE, Woodhouse Library, 1607 Robinson Rd SE, 49506-1799. SAN 308-1141. Tel: 616-459-8281, Ext 3704. FAX: 616-732-4534. Web Site: www.aquinas.edu/library. *Dir*, Larry W Zysk; E-Mail: zysk@aquinas.edu; *Media Spec, Ref*, Francine Paolini; *Coll Develop, Tech Servs*, Sister Rose Marie Martin; *Ref, Ser*, Diane Dustin; *Circ*, Pam Luebke; Staff 6 (MLS 6)
Founded 1936. Enrl 2,019; Fac 105; Highest Degree: Master
Jul 1999-Jun 2000 Income $90,783. Mats Exp $325,918, Books $116,545, Per/Ser (Incl. Access Fees) $95,000, Presv $2,130, Micro $26,560, AV Equip $9,000, Electronic Ref Mat (Incl. Access Fees) $10,900. Sal $417,429 (Prof $259,902)
Library Holdings: Bk Vols 119,000; Per Subs 725
Special Collections: Children's Literature Coll (Illustrations & Illustrators of Children's Books, Mother Goose)
Automation Activity & Vendor Info: (Acquisitions) Innovative Interfaces Inc.; (Cataloging) Innovative Interfaces Inc.; (Circulation) Innovative Interfaces Inc.; (Course Reserve) Innovative Interfaces Inc.; (OPAC) Innovative Interfaces Inc.; (Serials) Innovative Interfaces Inc.
Partic in Lakenet, Mich Libr Consortium; OCLC Online Computer Library Center, Inc
Friends of the Library Group

C CALVIN COLLEGE & THEOLOGICAL SEMINARY, Hekman Library, 3207 Burton St SE, 49546-4301. SAN 308-1168. Tel: 616-957-7197. Interlibrary Loan Service Tel: 616-957-8573. Reference Tel: 616-957-6307. FAX: 616-957-6470. Web Site: www.calvin.edu/library/. *Dir*, Glenn A Remelts; Tel: 616-957-6072, E-Mail: remelt@calvin.edu; *Ref*, Kathy DeMey; Tel: 616-957-6310, E-Mail: kdemey@calvin.edu; *Acq, Coll Develop*, Tamara Fetzer; *Cat*, Francene Lewis; *Doc*, Diane Vander Pol; *Archivist*, Richard H Harms; Tel: 616-957-6916, E-Mail: rharms@calvin.edu; *ILL*, Kathy Struck; Staff 17 (MLS 8, Non-MLS 9)
Founded 1892. Enrl 4,200; Fac 280; Highest Degree: Doctorate
Jul 1999-Jun 2000 Income $1,800,000. Mats Exp $915,000, Books $428,000, Per/Ser (Incl. Access Fees) $487,000. Sal $682,000 (Prof $347,000)
Library Holdings: Bk Vols 724,000; Bk Titles 429,000; Per Subs 2,658
Subject Interests: Humanities, Social sciences and issues, Theology
Special Collections: Archives of Christian Reformed Church (Heritage Hall Archives), bk & microfilm; H Henry Meeter Calvinism Research Coll, bk & microfilm
Automation Activity & Vendor Info: (Acquisitions) SIRSI; (Cataloging) SIRSI; (Circulation) SIRSI; (Course Reserve) SIRSI; (OPAC) SIRSI;

(Serials) SIRSI
Publications: Heritage Hall Publications; Origins
Partic in Michigan Library Consortium; OCLC Online Computer Library Center, Inc

CR CORNERSTONE UNIVERSITY, Miller Library, 1001 E Beltline NE, 49525. SAN 308-1265. Tel: 616-949-5300. Circulation Tel: 616-222-1458. FAX: 616-222-1405. Web Site: www.cornerstone.edu/newlib.nsf. *Dir*, Gail Atwood; E-Mail: gatwood@cornerstone.edu; *Publ Servs*, Mary Johnson; E-Mail: mary_johnson@cornerstone.edu; *Ref*, Fred Sweet; E-Mail: fred_sweet@cornerstone.edu. Subject Specialists: *Theology*, Fred Sweet; Staff 8 (MLS 2, Non-MLS 6)
Founded 1941. Enrl 1,573; Fac 63; Highest Degree: Doctorate
Jun 1999-May 2000 Income (Main Library Only) Parent Institution $619,224. Mats Exp $241,560, Books $130,900, Per/Ser (Incl. Access Fees) $110,660. Sal $251,355 (Prof $160,234)
Library Holdings: Bk Vols 111,456; Bk Titles 97,673; Per Subs 1,201
Subject Interests: Religion
Automation Activity & Vendor Info: (Acquisitions) Innovative Interfaces Inc.; (Cataloging) Innovative Interfaces Inc.; (Circulation) Innovative Interfaces Inc.; (Course Reserve) Innovative Interfaces Inc.; (OPAC) Innovative Interfaces Inc.; (Serials) Innovative Interfaces Inc.
Database Vendor: IAC - Info Trac, Lexis-Nexis, OCLC - First Search
Partic in American Theological Library Association; Christian Libr Network; Michiana Acad Libr Consortium; Michigan Library Consortium

C DAVENPORT UNIVERSITY, Margaret Sneden Library, 415 E Fulton St, 49503. SAN 308-1170. Tel: 616-732-1170. FAX: 616-732-1140. Web Site: www.libraries.davenport.edu. *Dir*, Sally A Fagan; Tel: 616-732-1172, Fax: 616-732-1142, E-Mail: sfagan@davenport.edu; *Dir Libr Serv, Tech Servs*, Mark Harris; *Head Ref*, Michael Kruzich; *Ref*, Sally Akehi; *Ref*, JoAnn Marvel; *Ref*, Todd Reed; *Ref*, William Teichert; *Cat*, Julie Gotch; *Circ*, Lori Fischer; *Circ*, Anne Mills; *ILL*, Zofia Dymarksa; *Access Serv*, Kevin Bullerman; *AV*, Robert Slayton; Staff 8 (MLS 5, Non-MLS 3)
Founded 1866. Highest Degree: Master
Jul 1999-Jun 2000 Income $914,586. Mats Exp $240,926, Books $86,880, Per/Ser (Incl. Access Fees) $42,800, Micro $8,370, AV Equip $4,250, Other Print Mats $41,600, Electronic Ref Mat (Incl. Access Fees) $57,026. Sal $331,354
Library Holdings: Bk Vols 35,986; Bk Titles 37,320; Per Subs 996
Subject Interests: Allied health, Business, Computing, Industry, Legal
Automation Activity & Vendor Info: (Cataloging) epixtech, inc.; (Circulation) epixtech, inc.
Database Vendor: GaleNet, IAC - Info Trac, IAC - SearchBank, Lexis-Nexis, OCLC - First Search, ProQuest
Partic in Michigan Library Consortium; MLC; OCLC Online Computer Library Center, Inc

CR GRACE BIBLE COLLEGE, Bultema Memorial Library, 1011 Aldon St SW, PO Box 910, 49509. SAN 308-1249. Tel: 616-261-8575. FAX: 616-538-0599. *Dir*, Kathy Molenkamp; E-Mail: kmolenkamp@gbcol.edu
Founded 1945
Library Holdings: Bk Vols 39,000; Per Subs 174
Subject Interests: Education, Music, Theology
Partic in Lakeland Area Library Network

S GRAND RAPIDS ART MUSEUM, (MRAL GRAM), McBride Art Reference Library, 155 Division North, 49503-3154. SAN 308-1257. Tel: 616-831-1000, 616-831-2901, 616-831-2915 (appt number). FAX: 616-559-0422. E-Mail: collections@gr-artmuseum.org. Web Site: www.gramonline.org. *Librn*, Mary Reusch; Tel: 616-831-2915
Founded 1969
Oct 1998-Sep 1999 Income $1,500. Mats Exp $1,523, Books $1,183, Per/Ser (Incl. Access Fees) $271, Presv $69
Library Holdings: Bk Titles 6,310
Special Collections: Art History; Museum Archival Material

L GRAND RAPIDS BAR ASSOCIATION LIBRARY,* 161 Ottawa Ave NW, No 203-B, 49503-2712. SAN 308-1273. Tel: 616-454-5550. FAX: 616-454-7681. *Librn*, Mary Karpinski
Founded 1887
Library Holdings: Bk Vols 40,000; Per Subs 125
Restriction: Members only
Partic in Westlaw

C GRAND RAPIDS COMMUNITY COLLEGE, Arthur Andrews Memorial Library, 140 Ransom NE, 49503. (Mail add: 143 Bostwick Ave NE, 49503), Tel: 616-234-3867. Interlibrary Loan Service Tel: 616-234-3749. Circulation Tel: 616-234-3871. Reference Tel: 616-234-3868. FAX: 616-771-3878. Web Site: www.grcc.cc.mi.us/library. *Dir Libr Serv*, Susan Bergin; Tel: 616-234-3876, E-Mail: sbergin@grcc.cc.mi.us; *Ref Serv*, Dorothy Terhune; Tel: 616-234-3849, E-Mail: dterhune@grcc.cc.mi.us; *Tech Servs*, Anita Cook; Tel: 616-234-3873, E-Mail: acook@grcc.cc.mi.us; *Ser*, Philip Pikaart; Tel: 616-234-3869, E-Mail: ppikaart@grcc.cc.mi.us; *Bibliog Instr*, Miriam Thompson; Tel: 616-234-3865, E-Mail: mthompso@grcc.cc.mi.us; *Tech Coordr*, Tom Van Dam; Tel: 616-234-3847, E-Mail: tvandam@grcc.cc.mi.us; *Archivist*, Michael Klawitter; Tel: 616-234-3473, E-Mail: mklawitt@grcc.cc.mi.us; Staff 14 (MLS 7, Non-MLS 7)
Founded 1914. Enrl 7,071; Fac 600; Highest Degree: Associate
Jul 2000-Jun 2001 Income $1,264,224, Parent Institution $1,264,224. Mats Exp $245,200, Books $104,600, Per/Ser (Incl. Access Fees) $82,600, Micro $10,000, AV Equip $15,000, Manuscripts & Archives $3,000, Electronic Ref Mat (Incl. Access Fees) $30,000. Sal $742,132 (Prof $450,000)
Library Holdings: Bk Vols 64,559; Bk Titles 60,998; Per Subs 400
Automation Activity & Vendor Info: (Acquisitions) Innovative Interfaces Inc.; (Cataloging) Innovative Interfaces Inc.; (Circulation) Innovative Interfaces Inc.; (Course Reserve) Innovative Interfaces Inc.; (OPAC) Innovative Interfaces Inc.; (Serials) Innovative Interfaces Inc.
Database Vendor: IAC - Info Trac, Innovative Interfaces INN - View, OCLC - First Search, Wilson - Wilson Web
Partic in Michigan Library Consortium

S GRAND RAPIDS PRESS LIBRARY,* 155 Michigan St NW, 49503. SAN 308-129X. Tel: 616-222-5475. FAX: 616-222-5409. *Librn*, Ruth Dryer

P GRAND RAPIDS PUBLIC LIBRARY, 1100 Hynes SW Ste B, 49507. (Mail add: 111 Library St, NE, 49503), SAN 346-5306. Tel: 616-988-5400. Interlibrary Loan Service Tel: 616-456-3626. TDD: 616-456-3614. FAX: 616-988-5419. Web Site: www.grpl.org. *Dir*, Robert E Raz; Tel: 616-988-5402, Ext 5431, E-Mail: rraz@grpl.org; *Mgr*, William Baldridge; Tel: 616-988-5402, Ext 5437, E-Mail: wbaldridge@grpl.org; *ILL*, Richard Vettese; *Asst Dir*, Thomas Genson; *Ch Servs*, Sarah McCarville; *Coll Develop*, Cynthia Gillham; Staff 35 (MLS 35)
Founded 1871. Pop 189,126; Circ 1,196,415
Jul 1999-Jun 2000 Income (Main Library and Branch Library) $10,290,493, State $595,526, City $8,255,845, Federal $23,980, County $633,929. Mats Exp $1,187,830, Books $706,456, Per/Ser (Incl. Access Fees) $173,106, Other Print Mats $248,018, Electronic Ref Mat (Incl. Access Fees) $60,250. Sal $4,682,542 (Prof $2,133,834)
Library Holdings: Bk Vols 670,667; Bk Titles 276,800; Per Subs 1,320
Subject Interests: Art and architecture, Business and management, Education, History, Music, Social sciences and issues
Special Collections: Childrens Literature (May E Quigley); Foundation Center Regional Coll; Fund); Furniture; Gardening (Richmond Fund); Genealogy (Lawrence Fund); History of Old Northwest Territory (Campbell; Landscape Architecture &; Michigan Hist (Stuart Fund); Picture Books (Butler Fund)
Automation Activity & Vendor Info: (Circulation) epixtech, inc.
Publications: Tree That Never Dies
Mem of Lakeland Library Cooperative
Partic in CLSI Consortium; Michigan Library Consortium; OCLC Online Computer Library Center, Inc
Friends of the Library Group
Branches: 6
CRESTON, 1431 Plainfield Ave NE, 49505. SAN 346-5330. Tel: 616-988-5402, Ext 5435. FAX: 616-988-5419. Web Site: www.grapids.lib.mi.us.
MADISON SQUARE, 1167 Madison Ave SE, 49507. SAN 373-5362. Tel: 616-245-4282. FAX: 616-245-2735. Web Site: www.grapids.lib.mi.us. *Librn*, Carmen Vera Rojas
OTTAWA HILLS, 1150 Giddings Ave SE, 49506. SAN 346-5365. Tel: 616-988-5402, Ext 5435. FAX: 616-988-5419. Web Site: www.grapids.lib.mis.us. *Librn*, Kayne Ferrier
Friends of the Library Group
SEYMOUR SQUARE, 2350 Eastern Ave SE, 49507. SAN 346-539X. Tel: 616-241-2316. FAX: 616-241-0461. Web Site: www.grapids.lib.mi.us. *Librn*, Russell Cogar; E-Mail: rcogar@grpl.org
Friends of the Library Group
WEST SIDE, 713 Bridge St NW, 49504. SAN 346-542X. Tel: 616-458-7681. FAX: 616-458-0103. Web Site: www.grapids.lib.mis.us. *Librn*, Deborah Bose
Friends of the Library Group
YANKEE CLIPPER, 2025 Leonard NE, 49505. SAN 346-5454. Tel: 616-235-8316. FAX: 616-235-8349. Web Site: www.grapids.lib.mi.us. *Librn*, Patricia Beechem
Friends of the Library Group

S ITT EDUCATIONAL SERVICES, INC LIBRARY - GRAND RAPIDS, 4020 Sparks Dr SE, 49546-6197. SAN 377-1539. Tel: 616-956-1060. FAX: 616-956-5606. Web Site: vl.ittesi.com/vlib. *Adminr*, John Potter; E-Mail: potter@ittesi.com; Staff 2 (MLS 1, Non-MLS 1)
Founded 1994. Enrl 400; Highest Degree: Associate
Jan 2001-Dec 2001 Income Parent Institution $20,000
Library Holdings: Bk Vols 7,000; Bk Titles 6,000; Per Subs 3,000
Subject Interests: Computers, Design, Electronics, Electronics eng
Automation Activity & Vendor Info: (Acquisitions) Athena; (Cataloging) Athena; (Circulation) Athena
Database Vendor: Ebsco - EbscoHost, IAC - SearchBank, OCLC - First Search, ProQuest
Restriction: Not open to public, Open to students
Partic in Mich Libr Asn; Michigan Library Consortium

S KENDALL COLLEGE OF ART & DESIGN, Van Steenberg Library, 17 Fountain NW, 49503. SAN 308-1311. Tel: 616-451-2787, Ext 121. FAX: 616-451-9867. Web Site: www.kc.ad.edu. *Chief Librn*, Jackie Kenyon; *Assoc Librn*, Dave Shaw; *Curator*, Halina Poplawska; Staff 2 (MLS 2)
Founded 1928. Enrl 600

Library Holdings: Bk Vols 16,633; Bk Titles 14,214; Per Subs 90
Subject Interests: Advertising, Fine arts, Furniture, Illustrators, Interior design
Automation Activity & Vendor Info: (Acquisitions) Innovative Interfaces Inc.

P LAKELAND LIBRARY COOPERATIVE, 4138 Three Mile Rd NW, 49544. SAN 308-132X. Tel: 616-559-5253. FAX: 616-559-4329. Web Site: www.lakeland.lib.mi.us. *Dir*, Dan Siebersma; *Asst Dir*, Martha Pitchford
Founded 1978. Pop 1,058,884
Oct 1999-Sep 2000 Income $1,693,141, State $529,193, Other $1,163,948. Mats Exp $6,000, Books $5,000, Electronic Ref Mat (Incl. Access Fees) $1,000. Sal $417,715
Automation Activity & Vendor Info: (Acquisitions) epixtech, inc.; (Cataloging) epixtech, inc.; (Circulation) epixtech, inc.; (OPAC) epixtech, inc.
Member Libraries: Allendale Township Library; Alvah N Belding Library; Bixby Medical Center; Carson City Public Library; Cedar Springs Public Library; Dorr Township Library; Fennville District Library; Flat River Community Library; Freeport District Library; Fremont Area District Library; Gary Byker Memorial Library of Hudsonville; Georgetown Township Public Library; Grand Rapids Public Library; Grant Public Library; Hackley Public Library; Hall-Fowler Memorial Library; Hastings Public Library; Henika District Library; Herrick District Library; Hesperia Public Library; Home Township Library; Hopkins Public Library; Howard Miller Public Library; J C Wheeler Library; Kent District Library; Lake Odessa Community Library; Leighton Township Public Library; Loutit District Library; Newaygo Carnegie Library; Northeast Ottawa District Library; Reynolds Township Library; Salem Township Library; Saranac Public Library; Saugatuck-Douglas District Library; Sparta Township Library; Tamarack Public Library; Thornapple-Kellogg School & Community Library; Warner Baird District Library; White Cloud Community Library; White Lake Community Library

S MICHIGAN MASONIC LIBRARY & EDUCATIONAL CENTER, 233 E Fulton St, 49503-3270. Tel: 616-459-9336. FAX: 616-459-9436. E-Mail: masonic_heritage@hotmail.com. Web Site: www.angelfire.com/mi/MaHerCenMI. *Dir*, Allison D Bryant; *Archivist*, Cathie M Bryant
Jul 1998-Jun 1999 Income Parent Institution $61,000. Mats Exp $8,500, Books $8,000, Per/Ser (Incl. Access Fees) $250, AV Equip $250. Sal $20,000
Library Holdings: Bk Vols 5,000; Per Subs 15
Subject Interests: Masonic heritage, Philosophy, Symbolism
Publications: Masonic Resources (quarterly)
Friends of the Library Group

L MIKA, MEYERS, BECKETT & JONES, Law Library,* 200 Ottawa Ave NW Ste 700, 49503. SAN 372-0438. Tel: 616-459-3200. FAX: 616-459-8065. *Librn*, Lana Ahumada; E-Mail: lahumada@mmbjlaw.com; Staff 1 (MLS 1)
Library Holdings: Bk Vols 10,000; Per Subs 95
Subject Interests: Law
Special Collections: Energy, Oil & Gas Law
Restriction: Staff use only

L MILLER, JOHNSON, SNELL & CUMMISKEY, Law Library,* 250 Monroe NW, Ste 800, 49503-2250. SAN 372-0446. Tel: 616-831-1875. FAX: 616-831-1701. *Dir Libr Serv*, Kathryn A Vance

S PUBLIC MUSEUM OF GRAND RAPIDS LIBRARY,* 272 Pearl St NW, 49504-5371. SAN 308-1303. Tel: 616-456-3977. FAX: 616-456-3873.
Library Holdings: Bk Vols 6,000
Subject Interests: Furniture

CR REFORMED BIBLE COLLEGE LIBRARY, 3333 E Beltline NE, 49525. SAN 308-1362. Tel: 616-222-3000. FAX: 616-222-3045. E-Mail: library@reformed.edu. Web Site: www.reformed.edu. *Librn*, Dianne Zandbergen; *Librn*, Michelle Norquist; Staff 2 (MLS 2)
Founded 1940. Circ 7,910; Enrl 271; Fac 14; Highest Degree: Bachelor
Jul 1999-Jun 2000 Income $152,603. Mats Exp $40,827, Books $16,989, Per/Ser (Incl. Access Fees) $8,435, Presv $123, Micro $410, AV Equip $10,420, Electronic Ref Mat (Incl. Access Fees) $4,450. Sal $101,631 (Prof $77,007)
Library Holdings: Bk Vols 55,760; Bk Titles 42,854; Per Subs 234
Subject Interests: Biblical studies, Education, History, Religion, Theology
Automation Activity & Vendor Info: (Cataloging) Sagebrush Corporation; (Circulation) Sagebrush Corporation; (OPAC) Sagebrush Corporation
Publications: Library Handbook
Partic in Asn of Christian Librs; Michigan Library Consortium

M RICHARD R SMITH MEDICAL LIBRARY, Spectrum Health Campus,* 1840 Wealthy St SE, 49506. SAN 308-115X. Tel: 616-774-7624. FAX: 616-774-5290. *Librn*, Brian Simmons; E-Mail: brian_simmons@blodgett.com
Founded 1934
Library Holdings: Bk Vols 1,800; Per Subs 350
Subject Interests: Medicine, Surgery
Partic in Dialog Corporation; Medline

S RIGHT TO LIFE OF MICHIGAN, State Central Resource Center, 2340 Porter St SW, 49509. SAN 375-1902. Tel: 616-532-2300. FAX: 616-532-3461. Web Site: www.rtl.org. *Pub Relations*, Pam Sherstad
Library Holdings: Bk Vols 250

M SAINT MARY'S HEALTH SCIENCES LIBRARY, 200 Jefferson SE, 49503. SAN 308-1370. Tel: 616-752-6243. FAX: 616-752-6419. *Librn*, Mary A Hanson; E-Mail: hansonm@mlc.lib.mi.us; Staff 2 (MLS 1, Non-MLS 1)
Library Holdings: Bk Vols 2,500; Bk Titles 2,000; Per Subs 398
Subject Interests: Medicine, Nursing
Publications: Newsletter (quarterly)

R SECOND CONGREGATIONAL CHURCH LIBRARY,* 525 Cheshire Dr NE, 49505. SAN 308-1389. Tel: 616-361-2629. FAX: 616-361-8181. *Librn*, Gerry Klepser
Library Holdings: Bk Vols 2,050

L SMITH, HAUGHEY, RICE & ROEGGE, Law Library,* 250 Monroe Ave NW, 49503. SAN 372-0454. Tel: 616-774-8000. FAX: 616-774-2461. *Librn*, Maria Brummel; E-Mail: mbrummel-schutte@shrr.com
Library Holdings: Bk Vols 6,000; Per Subs 101

S SMITHS INDUSTRIES LIBRARY, 3290 Patterson Ave SE, 49512-1991. SAN 308-1338. Tel: 616-241-7467. FAX: 616-241-7260. E-Mail: library@si.com. *Mgr*, Scott Brackett; E-Mail: brackett_scott@si.com; Staff 3 (MLS 1, Non-MLS 2)
Founded 1954
Library Holdings: Bk Titles 6,500; Per Subs 210
Subject Interests: Aeronautics, Computer science, Electrical engineering, Material culture, Physics
Automation Activity & Vendor Info: (Cataloging) Follett; (Circulation) Follett
Publications: Monthly Acquisitions List
Restriction: By appointment only
Partic in Lakeland Area Library Network

SPECTRUM HEALTH-DOWNTOWN CAMPUS

M JULIUS & DAVID AMBERG HEALTH SCIENCES LIBRARY, 100 Michigan NE, 49503-2560. SAN 346-5276. Tel: 616-391-1655. Interlibrary Loan Service Tel: 616-391-2061. Reference Tel: 616-391-3143. FAX: 616-391-3527. Web Site: www.spectrum-health.org. *Mgr*, Diane Hummel; E-Mail: diane.hummel@spectrum-health.org
Founded 1918
1998-1999 Income $400,000. Mats Exp $190,000, Books $60,000, Per/Ser (Incl. Access Fees) $120,000, AV Equip $10,000
Library Holdings: Bk Vols 2,700; Bk Titles 6,000; Per Subs 475
Subject Interests: Medicine, Nursing
Special Collections: American Nurse's Assoc Publications; National League for Nursing Publications Coll
Automation Activity & Vendor Info: (Acquisitions) EOS; (Cataloging) EOS; (Circulation) EOS; (Course Reserve) EOS; (OPAC) EOS; (Serials) EOS
Database Vendor: OCLC - First Search
Publications: Ex Libris
Friends of the Library Group

L VARNUM, RIDDERING, SCHMIDT & HOWLETT, Law Library,* PO Box 352, 49501-0352. SAN 372-0462. Tel: 616-336-6000. FAX: 616-336-7000. E-Mail: mjmajor@vrsh.com. *Librn*, Marla Major; *Asst Librn*, Bethany Woodard
Library Holdings: Bk Vols 30,000; Per Subs 66

L WARNER, NORCROSS & JUDD LIBRARY,* 111 Lyon St, 49503-2489. SAN 308-1397. Tel: 616-752-2236. FAX: 616-752-2500. *Dir*, Mary Lou Wilker-Calvin; E-Mail: calvinml@wnj.com
Founded 1931
Subject Interests: Law
Partic in Dialog Corporation; Dow Jones News Retrieval; Michigan Library Consortium; Westlaw

R WESTVIEW CHRISTIAN REFORMED CHURCH LIBRARY,* 2929 Leonard St NW, 49504. SAN 308-1400. Tel: 616-453-3105. FAX: 616-453-8891. *Librn*, Beatrice Danke
Library Holdings: Bk Vols 3,283

GRANT

P GRANT PUBLIC LIBRARY,* 51 Front St, PO Box 695, 49327-0695. SAN 308-1419. Tel: 231-834-5713. FAX: 231-834-8466. *Dir*, Jeanette Bazzett; Staff 1 (MLS 1)
Founded 1920. Pop 9,000; Circ 35,814
Library Holdings: Bk Titles 40,000
Subject Interests: Local history
Publications: Grant Area, Yesterday-Today (local history book)
Mem of Lakeland Library Cooperative

GRASS LAKE

S CENTER FOR SCIENTIFIC ANOMALIES RESEARCH LIBRARY, 5010 Willis Rd, 49240. SAN 371-0394. Tel: 517-522-3551. FAX: 517-522-3555. *Dir*, Marcello Truzzi; E-Mail: truzzi@toast.net
Library Holdings: Bk Vols 8,000; Per Subs 50

GRAWN

S ARCHIVE OF THE AMERICAN MUSICAL THEATRE, PO Box 201, 49637-0201. SAN 370-8217. Tel: 616-929-1226. FAX: 616-929-1226 (Call First). *Curator*, David G Hummel; E-Mail: dghummel@core.com
Founded 1970
Subject Interests: Musical comedy, Musical theatre
Publications: The Collector's Guide to the American Musical Theatre
Restriction: Not open to public
Function: Archival collection, Reference services available

GRAYLING

P CRAWFORD COUNTY LIBRARY,* 100 S James St, 49738. SAN 308-1427. Tel: 517-348-9214. FAX: 517-348-9294. Web Site: www.grayling_mi.com/library.htm. *Dir*, Tracie Compton; E-Mail: comptt@k2.kirtland.cc.mi.us; *Asst Dir*, Mary Kay Hinkle
Pop 9,000; Circ 28,000
1997-1998 Income $115,570, State $10,700, County $73,600, Other $31,264. Mats Exp $30,000, Books $22,300, Per/Ser (Incl. Access Fees) $3,600. Sal $75,327
Library Holdings: Bk Vols 27,000; Per Subs 42
Mem of Mid-Michigan Library League; Northland Library Cooperative
Branches: 2
FREDERIC COMMUNITY, 6872 N Old Rte 27, Frederic, 49733. SAN 376-0286. Tel: 517-348-4067.
LOVELLS TOWNSHIP, 8404 Twin Bridge Rd, 49738. SAN 376-0294. Tel: 517-348-9215.

GREENVILLE

P FLAT RIVER COMMUNITY LIBRARY, 200 W Judd St, 48838. (Mail add: PO Box 490, 48838-0490), SAN 308-1435. Tel: 616-754-6359. FAX: 616-754-1398. E-Mail: gre@lakeland.lib.mi.us. Web Site: www.lakeland.lib.mi.us/greenville/homepage.html. *Dir Libr Serv*, Patricia Noordhoorn; Tel: 616-754-6359, Ext 106, E-Mail: grepn@lakeland.lib.mi.us; *Tech Servs*, Timothy J West; E-Mail: gretjw@lakeland.lib.mi.us; *Ch Servs, YA Servs*, Rachel B Potter; E-Mail: grerp@lakeland.lib.mi.us; Staff 9 (MLS 3, Non-MLS 6)
Founded 1868. Pop 15,149; Circ 119,414
Jul 1999-Jun 2000 Income $623,341, State $15,149, County $131,297, Locally Generated Income $322,468, Other $154,427. Mats Exp $84,767, Books $51,904, Per/Ser (Incl. Access Fees) $4,998, AV Equip $3,421, Electronic Ref Mat (Incl. Access Fees) $24,444. Sal $194,108 (Prof $100,330)
Library Holdings: Bk Vols 59,024; Per Subs 165
Subject Interests: Local history
Automation Activity & Vendor Info: (Circulation) epixtech, inc.; (OPAC) epixtech, inc.
Database Vendor: epixtech, inc.
Mem of Lakeland Library Cooperative
Friends of the Library Group

GROSSE ILE

R GROSSE ILE PRESBYTERIAN CHURCH LIBRARY,* 7925 Horse Mill Rd, 48138. SAN 308-1443. Tel: 734-676-8811. FAX: 734-676-2718. *Librn*, Janice Shimmel
Founded 1960
Library Holdings: Bk Vols 850

GROSSE POINTE

M BON SECOURS COTTAGE HEALTH SERVICES, Department of Library Services, 468 Cadieux Rd, 48230. SAN 320-3832. Tel: 313-343-1620. FAX: 313-343-1947. *Dir*, Barbara Platts; Tel: 313-343-1919; Staff 4 (MLS 2, Non-MLS 2)
Founded 1970
Library Holdings: Bk Titles 3,000; Per Subs 250
Subject Interests: Allied health, Consumer health, Medicine, Nursing
Partic in Michigan Library Consortium

GROSSE POINTE FARMS

M BON SECOURS COTTAGE HEALTH SERVICES, Cottage Hospital Library, 159 Kercheval Ave, 48236. SAN 325-9161. Tel: 313-640-2458. FAX: 313-640-2462. *Dir*, Barbara Platts; E-Mail: barbara_platts@bshsi.com; Staff 2 (MLS 1, Non-MLS 1)
Library Holdings: Bk Vols 900; Per Subs 25
Subject Interests: Allied health, Consumer health, Medicine, Nursing
Database Vendor: OVID Technologies
Partic in Michigan Library Consortium; MLC

P GROSSE POINTE PUBLIC LIBRARY, 10 Kercheval, 48236-3693. SAN 346-6116. Tel: 313-343-2074. FAX: 313-343-2437. Web Site: www.gp.lib.mi.us. *Dir*, Vickey Bloom; E-Mail: vbloom@gp.lib.mi.us; *Publ Servs*, Cynthia Zurschmiede; Staff 13 (MLS 13)
Founded 1929. Pop 54,600
Jul 1999-Jun 2000 Income (Main Library and Branch Library) $2,991,577. Mats Exp $387,621, Books $258,913, Per/Ser (Incl. Access Fees) $40,078, AV Equip $63,630, Electronic Ref Mat (Incl. Access Fees) $25,000. Sal $1,097,747 (Prof $744,891)
Library Holdings: Bk Vols 158,618; Per Subs 500
Subject Interests: Business and management, Medicine, Music
Automation Activity & Vendor Info: (Acquisitions) Innovative Interfaces Inc.; (Cataloging) Innovative Interfaces Inc.; (Circulation) Innovative Interfaces Inc.; (OPAC) Innovative Interfaces Inc.
Database Vendor: ProQuest
Publications: Library Pointes
Mem of The Library Network
Friends of the Library Group
Branches: 2
PARK, 15430 Kercheval, Grosse Pointe Park, 48230. SAN 346-6140. Tel: 313-343-2071. FAX: 313-343-2485. Web Site: gp.lib.mi.us. *Librn*, John Clexton; E-Mail: jclexton@gp.lib.mi.us; Staff 2 (MLS 2)
Library Holdings: Bk Vols 36,845; Bk Titles 33,770
Automation Activity & Vendor Info: (Acquisitions) Innovative Interfaces Inc.; (Cataloging) Innovative Interfaces Inc.; (Circulation) Innovative Interfaces Inc.; (OPAC) Innovative Interfaces Inc.
Friends of the Library Group
WOODS, 20600 Mack Ave, Grosse Pointe Woods, 48236. SAN 346-6175. Tel: 313-343-2072. FAX: 313-343-2486. Web Site: gp.lib.mi.us. *Librn*, Leslie Wutzke; Staff 3 (MLS 3)
Library Holdings: Bk Vols 53,831; Bk Titles 46,613
Automation Activity & Vendor Info: (Acquisitions) Innovative Interfaces Inc.; (Cataloging) Innovative Interfaces Inc.; (Circulation) Innovative Interfaces Inc.; (OPAC) Innovative Interfaces Inc.
Friends of the Library Group

GWINN

P FORSYTH TOWNSHIP PUBLIC LIBRARY, 184 W Flint, PO Box 1328, 49841. SAN 308-146X. Tel: 906-346-3433. FAX: 906-346-3433. *Librn*, Kathleen Holman
Pop 8,775; Circ 18,730
Library Holdings: Bk Vols 11,000; Per Subs 52
Partic in Superiorland Libr Coop

HAMBURG

P HAMBURG TOWNSHIP LIBRARY,* 7225 Stone St, PO Box 247, 48139. SAN 308-1478. Tel: 810-231-1771. FAX: 810-231-1520. E-Mail: hamb@tln.lib.mi.us. Web Site: www.hamburg.lib.mi.us. *Coll Develop, Librn*, Holly Hentz
Founded 1966. Pop 18,000; Circ 58,547
Jul 1997-Jun 1998 Income $218,633, State $11,455, County $52,000, Locally Generated Income $17,580, Other $187. Mats Exp $27,700, Books $25,000, Per/Ser (Incl. Access Fees) $1,200, Micro $500, Manuscripts & Archives $1,000. Sal $100,672 (Prof $61,048)
Library Holdings: Bk Vols 35,000
Subject Interests: Arts and crafts, Civil War, Michigan
Special Collections: Depository for Speigleburg Rasmussen Sites; EPA
Mem of The Library Network

HAMTRAMCK

P HAMTRAMCK PUBLIC LIBRARY, Albert J Zak Memorial, 2360 Caniff St, 48212. SAN 308-1486. Tel: 313-365-7050. FAX: 313-365-0160. *Dir*, E Tamara Sochacka; E-Mail: esocha@tlr.lib.mi.us; Staff 3 (MLS 2, Non-MLS 1)
Founded 1924. Pop 18,000; Circ 60,000
1999-1999 Income $150,000, State $25,000, City $125,000. Mats Exp $44,000, Books $34,000, AV Equip $5,000, Electronic Ref Mat (Incl. Access Fees) $5,000. Sal $90,000
Library Holdings: Bk Vols 50,000; Per Subs 122
Special Collections: Polish, Ukrainian, Russian (Foreign Language Coll) & City of Hamtramck Historical File, bks, clippings, microfilm & newspapers
Mem of The Library Network; Wayne Oakland Libr Federation
Friends of the Library Group

HANCOCK

C FINDLANDIA UNIVERSITY, (Formerly Suomi College), Maki Library, 601 Quincy St, 49930-1882. SAN 346-6205. Tel: 906-487-7252. FAX: 906-487-7297. E-Mail: makilib@ccisd.k12.mi.us. Web Site: www.suomi.edu/academic/services/index.html. *Dir*, Marjory Johnston; Tel: 906-487-7253, E-Mail: majohnst@ccisd.k12.mi.us; Staff 3 (MLS 2, Non-MLS 1)
Founded 1896. Enrl 360; Fac 31
Jul 1999-Jun 2000 Income $155,856. Mats Exp $27,923. Sal $99,210
Library Holdings: Bk Vols 37,070; Bk Titles 30,164; Per Subs 392
Subject Interests: Art, Business, Design, Nursing
Special Collections: Finnish-American Life & Culture Coll; Upper Peninsula of Michigan
Mem of Upper Pennisula Region of Libr Coop
Partic in Michigan Library Consortium

S FINNISH-AMERICAN HISTORICAL ARCHIVES HERITAGE CENTER,* Suomi College, 601 Quincy St, 49930. SAN 346-623X. Tel: 906-487-7347. FAX: 906-487-7366. *Archivist, Asst Librn*, Lorraine Richards
Founded 1932
Library Holdings: Bk Vols 6,500
Subject Interests: Church history, Communist movements, Coop movement, Labor, Pioneer libr of rare bks, Socialist movements, Temperance soc
Special Collections: Finnish Language Newspaper, incl 107 titles from 1876-present; Suomi Synod Archives

P HANCOCK SCHOOL PUBLIC LIBRARY,* 501 Campus Dr, 49930-1884. SAN 308-1494. Tel: 906-483-2544. *Librn*, Susan M Zubiena
Founded 1915. Circ 28,000
Library Holdings: Bk Vols 18,000
Subject Interests: History
Mem of Superiorland Library Cooperative; Upper Pennisula Region of Libr Coop

M PORTAGE HEALTH SYSTEM, Health Science Library-Archives,* 200 Michigan Ave, 49930-1495. SAN 308-1508. Tel: 906-487-7846, 906-487-8000. FAX: 906-482-3080. *Librn*, Nancy Manninen
Founded 1976
Library Holdings: Bk Vols 562; Bk Titles 500; Per Subs 45
Special Collections: Photos & material on early physicians, hospitals & diseases
Publications: Serials Holdings List
Partic in Regional Med Libr - Region 3; Upper Peninsula Region Of Library Cooperation, Inc

HARBOR BEACH

P HARBOR BEACH AREA DISTRICT LIBRARY,* 105 N Huron Ave, 48441. SAN 308-1516. Tel: 517-479-3417. FAX: 517-479-6818. *Dir*, Sue Hanson
Founded 1917. Circ 24,262
Library Holdings: Bk Titles 15,000; Per Subs 45
Mem of Blue Water Libr Fedn
Friends of the Library Group

HARPER WOODS

P HARPER WOODS PUBLIC LIBRARY,* 19601 Harper, 48225-2001. SAN 308-1524. Tel: 313-343-2575. FAX: 313-343-2127. *Ad Servs*, Suzanne D Kent; *YA Servs*, Nancy Maxon; *YA Servs*, Cate Fleming
Pop 16,361; Circ 87,048
Library Holdings: Bk Vols 52,000; Per Subs 102
Subject Interests: Large type print
Mem of Wayne Oakland Libr Federation
Friends of the Library Group

HARRISON

P HARRISON COMMUNITY LIBRARY, 105 W Main, PO Box 380, 48625. SAN 308-1532. Tel: 517-539-6711. TDD: 517-539-6711. FAX: 517-539-6301. Web Site: www.glocities.com/athens/ithaca/4577/. *Librn*, Anne Smith; E-Mail: asmith@vlc.lib.mi.us
Founded 1948. Pop 10,325; Circ 45,000
2000-2000 Income $157,992, State $10,316, City $9,900, County $64,791, Locally Generated Income $29,962, Other $43,023. Mats Exp $26,240, Books $18,000, Per/Ser (Incl. Access Fees) $3,345, Presv $300, Micro $160, AV Equip $4,435. Sal $58,018 (Prof $23,712)
Library Holdings: Bk Vols 26,811; Bk Titles 31,256; Per Subs 90
Automation Activity & Vendor Info: (Cataloging) epixtech, inc.; (Circulation) epixtech, inc.; (ILL) epixtech, inc.; (OPAC) epixtech, inc.; (Serials) epixtech, inc.
Database Vendor: epixtech, inc.
Mem of White Pine Library Cooperative
Partic in Valley Libr Consortium
Special Services for the Deaf - TDD
Friends of the Library Group

J MID MICHIGAN COMMUNITY COLLEGE, Charles A Amble Library, 1375 S Clare Ave, 48625. SAN 346-6264. Tel: 517-386-6616. FAX: 517-386-2411. Web Site: www.midmich.cc.mi.us/lib. *Dir*, Linda Ritz; E-Mail: lritz@midmich.cc.mi.us; *Tech Servs*, Rhonica Jankoviak; Staff 1 (MLS 1)
Founded 1969. Enrl 2,200; Fac 59
Library Holdings: Bk Titles 21,000; Per Subs 200
Special Collections: Mid-Michigan History (Meek Coll), still pictures

HARRISON TOWNSHIP

M SAINT JOHN NORTH SHORES HOSPITAL, Medical Library, 26755 Ballard Rd, 48045. SAN 324-5578. Tel: 810-465-5501, Ext 45858. FAX: 810-466-5352. *Librn*, Deborah R Cicchini; Fax: 810-466-5370, E-Mail: cicchd01@stjohn.org; Staff 1 (MLS 1)
Library Holdings: Bk Vols 875; Bk Titles 800; Per Subs 60
Subject Interests: Podiatry
Database Vendor: Ebsco - EbscoHost, OVID Technologies, Silverplatter Information Inc.
Harrison Community Hospital is a 96 bed acute care facility. The Hospital belongs to the St Clair Health Corp of St John's Hospital, Detroit, MI , while maintaining its independence

HARRISVILLE

P ALCONA COUNTY LIBRARY SYSTEM, 312 W Main, 48740. (Mail add: PO Box 348, 48740), SAN 308-1540. Tel: 517-724-6796. FAX: 517-724-6173. E-Mail: alcona1@northland.lib.mi.us. *Dir*, Carol Luck; Staff 3 (MLS 1, Non-MLS 2)
Founded 1940. Pop 10,200; Circ 38,824
Jan 1999-Dec 1999 Income (Main Library and Branch Library) $316,000
Library Holdings: Bk Vols 38,591; Bk Titles 31,000; Per Subs 45
Subject Interests: Local history, Michigan
Automation Activity & Vendor Info: (Acquisitions) Athena; (Cataloging) Athena; (Circulation) Athena
Mem of Northland Library Cooperative
Friends of the Library Group
Branches: 3
CALVIN E WILL CALEDONIA BRANCH, 1499 Hurbert Rd, Hubbard Lake, 49747-9611. (Mail add: PO Box 56, Hubbard Lake, 49747-0056), SAN 376-7949. Tel: 517-727-3105. FAX: 517-727-3105. E-Mail: caledonl@northland.lib.mi.us. *In Charge*, Mary Drooger
Library Holdings: Bk Vols 2,500
LINCOLN BRANCH, 215 S Second, PO Box 115, Lincoln, 48742-0115. SAN 376-8058. Tel: 517-736-3388. FAX: 517-736-3388. E-Mail: lincolnl@northland.lib.mi.us. *In Charge*, Illa Milligan
Library Holdings: Bk Vols 2,500
MIKADO BRANCH, 2291 N F-41, Mikado, 48745. SAN 376-8066. Tel: 517-736-8389. FAX: 517-736-8389. E-Mail: mikadol@northland.lib.mi.us. *In Charge*, Donna Kovacik
Library Holdings: Bk Vols 1,500

HART

P HART AREA PUBLIC LIBRARY,* 407 S State St, 49420-1228. SAN 308-1559. Tel: 231-873-4476. FAX: 231-873-4476. *Dir*, Joan Lundborg
Pop 6,748; Circ 75,000
Library Holdings: Bk Vols 32,000
Subject Interests: History
Mem of Mid-Michigan Library League

HARTFORD

P HARTFORD PUBLIC LIBRARY,* 15 Franklin St, PO Box 8, 49057-0008. SAN 308-1567. Tel: 616-621-3408. FAX: 616-621-3408. *Librn*, Rose A Greter
Pop 6,311; Circ 48,960
Library Holdings: Bk Vols 50,000; Per Subs 60
Special Collections: Hartford Day Spring Newspaper 1881-1973, microflm
Mem of Southwest Michigan Library Cooperative
Partic in OCLC Online Computer Library Center, Inc
Closed Tues & Thurs
Friends of the Library Group

HARTLAND

P CROMAINE DISTRICT LIBRARY, 3688 N Hartland Rd, PO Box 308, 48353-0308. SAN 308-1575. Tel: 810-632-5200. FAX: 810-632-7351. Web Site: www.cromaine.org. *Dir*, Sherry Hupp; E-Mail: shupp@cromaine.org; *YA Servs*, Jeanne Smith; E-Mail: jsmith@cromaine.org; *Ad Servs*, Sallie Brodie; Staff 4 (MLS 4)
Founded 1927. Pop 20,772; Circ 138,145
Jul 1999-Jun 2000 Income $1,131,418, State $20,772, County $102,412, Locally Generated Income $42,868, Other $965,366. Mats Exp $113,591, Books $85,772, Per/Ser (Incl. Access Fees) $10,486, AV Equip $16,333, Electronic Ref Mat (Incl. Access Fees) $1,000. Sal $421,677

Library Holdings: Bk Vols 66,319; Bk Titles 51,372; Per Subs 339
Special Collections: Historical Documents of Hartland & Livingston County (J R Crouse), autographed letters, doc, bks, photog, art works
Automation Activity & Vendor Info: (Acquisitions) epixtech, inc.; (Cataloging) epixtech, inc.; (Circulation) epixtech, inc.; (OPAC) epixtech, inc.
Mem of The Library Network
Partic in Michigan Library Consortium
Friends of the Library Group

HASTINGS

S CHARLTON PARK HISTORIC VILLAGE & MUSEUM LIBRARY, 2545 S Charlton Park Rd, 49058. SAN 323-4169. Tel: 616-945-3775. Web Site: www.charltonpark.org. *Curator*, Joanne Foreman
Founded 1936
Library Holdings: Bk Vols 1,500
Subject Interests: Agriculture, Barry County hist, Gas engines, Steam engines
Special Collections: Museum Books & Journals, Historic Preservation Archival Coll

P HASTINGS PUBLIC LIBRARY, 121 S Church St, 49058-1817. SAN 308-1583. Tel: 616-945-4263. FAX: 616-948-3874. E-Mail: has@lakeland.lib.mi.us. Web Site: www.lakeland.lib.mi.us/hastings.html. *Adminr*, Barbara B Schondelmayer; *Admin Assoc*, Susan Smith; *Circ, Ref*, Darrel Hawbaker; *Tech Servs*, Edward Englerth; Staff 8 (MLS 1, Non-MLS 7)
Founded 1965. Pop 9,075; Circ 71,956
Jul 1999-Jun 2000 Income $335,582, State $9,068, City $215,000, County $20,015, Locally Generated Income $91,501. Mats Exp $28,800, Books $23,000, Per/Ser (Incl. Access Fees) $2,800, AV Equip $3,000. Sal $106,831 (Prof $35,360)
Library Holdings: Bk Vols 37,246; Per Subs 110
Subject Interests: Local history
Automation Activity & Vendor Info: (Circulation) epixtech, inc.; (ILL) epixtech, inc.
Database Vendor: IAC - Info Trac, OCLC - First Search
Mem of Lakeland Library Cooperative
Partic in Michigan Library Consortium
Friends of the Library Group

M PENNOCK HOSPITAL, Health Sciences Library, 1009 W Green St, 49058. SAN 327-0483. Tel: 616-945-3451, Ext 337. FAX: 616-945-3035. E-Mail: penlib@voyager.net. *Librn*, Jacqueline Muma; Staff 1 (MLS 1)
Library Holdings: Bk Vols 300; Per Subs 50
Subject Interests: Medical

HAZEL PARK

P HAZEL PARK MEMORIAL LIBRARY,* 123 E Nine Mile Rd, 48030. SAN 308-1591. Tel: 248-546-4095. FAX: 248-546-4083. Web Site: www.tln.lib.mi.us/~hzpk/. *Dir*, Katherine Rudelich; *Acq, Asst Dir*, Joan E Ludlow; *Ch Servs*, Lisa Saver
Founded 1936. Pop 20,051; Circ 32,000
Jul 1998-Jun 1999 Income $17,000. Mats Exp $45,000. Sal $160,000
Library Holdings: Bk Vols 48,000; Per Subs 100
Special Collections: Large print
Mem of The Library Network
Open Mon-Thurs 12-8, Fri 9-5 & Sat 12-4; Open Sun 12-4 (Sept-May)
Friends of the Library Group

HEMLOCK

P RAUCHHOLZ MEMORIAL LIBRARY, 1140 N Hemlock Rd, 48626. SAN 308-1605. Tel: 517-642-8621. FAX: 517-642-5559. E-Mail: rauchholz@hotmail.com. *Librn*, Christine Ann Haske; *Librn*, Connie Hutfilz; Staff 2 (Non-MLS 2)
Founded 1942. Pop 6,314; Circ 38,029
Apr 1998-Mar 1999 Income $104,614, State $6,283, Locally Generated Income $98,331. Mats Exp $13,000, Books $10,000, Per/Ser (Incl. Access Fees) $1,000, AV Equip $2,000. Sal $56,619 (Prof $31,542)
Library Holdings: Bk Vols 21,560; Per Subs 57
Subject Interests: Amish
Special Collections: Audio History, cassettes; Local History, slides
Mem of White Pine Library Cooperative
Friends of the Library Group

HESPERIA

P HESPERIA PUBLIC LIBRARY,* 80 S Division St, 49421-9004. SAN 308-1613. Tel: 231-854-5125. FAX: 231-854-5125. E-Mail: hesln@lakeland.lib.mi.us. Web Site: www.ncat.net/hesperiapl/. *Librn*, Elizabeth Nordin
Circ 31,942
1997-1998 Income $55,845, State $5,000, Federal $12,845. Mats Exp $5,700. Sal $37,000 (Prof $18,000)
Library Holdings: Bk Vols 19,000; Per Subs 63
Publications: Library Journal
Mem of Lakeland Library Cooperative
Friends of the Library Group

HICKORY CORNERS

C MICHIGAN STATE UNIVERSITY, Walter F Morofsky Memorial Library, 3700 E Gull Lake Dr, 49060-9516. SAN 308-1621. Tel: 616-671-2310. FAX: 616-671-2309. Web Site: www.kbs.msu.edu/library/index.htm. *Librn*, Diane Donham; Tel: 517-432-0808, Fax: 517-432-1191, E-Mail: donham@pilot.msu.edu; Staff 2 (MLS 1, Non-MLS 1)
Founded 1965
Jul 1999-Jun 2000 Income $42,312. Mats Exp $41,912, Books $1,005, Per/Ser (Incl. Access Fees) $40,907
Library Holdings: Bk Vols 6,250; Per Subs 127
Subject Interests: Agriculture, Ecology, Limnology

HIGHLAND

P HIGHLAND TOWNSHIP PUBLIC LIBRARY, 205 W Livingston, PO Box 277, 48357-0277. SAN 308-163X. Tel: 248-887-2218. Web Site: www.milford.lib.mi.us/mcin/groups/highland.htm. *Dir*, Jude Halloran; *Ref Serv Ad*, Kathleen Nash; *Ref Servs Ch*, Kathleen Linn; *Circ*, Marion Reed; Staff 4 (MLS 4)
Founded 1927. Pop 17,941; Circ 108,659
Jan 1999-Dec 1999 Income $824,303. Mats Exp $46,576, Books $43,540. Sal $180,500
Library Holdings: Bk Vols 42,841
Automation Activity & Vendor Info: (Circulation) DRA
Database Vendor: IAC - Info Trac, OCLC - First Search
Mem of The Library Network
Friends of the Library Group

HIGHLAND PARK

P MCGREGOR PUBLIC LIBRARY, Highland Park Library, 12244 Woodward Ave, 48203-3320. SAN 308-1664. Tel: 313-883-4542. FAX: 313-883-0205. Web Site: www.mlc.lib.mi.us/~mcgregor. *Dir*, Laverne Calloway; *Ad Servs*, Robert Wicke; *Ch Servs, Tech Servs*, Cheryl Tatum Scott; Staff 2 (MLS 2)
Founded 1919. Pop 27,909; Circ 57,391
Library Holdings: Bk Vols 78,673; Per Subs 197
Mem of Detroit Public Library
Summer Hrs - Mon, Tues, Thurs 9-5:30, Wed 9-8; Winter Hrs - Tues, Wed 9-9, Thurs, Sat 9-5
Friends of the Library Group

HILLMAN

P HILLMAN-WRIGHT MEMORIAL LIBRARY,* PO Box 247, 49746-0247. SAN 376-5873. Tel: 517-742-4021. FAX: 517-742-4021. *Librn*, Caroline Tracey
Library Holdings: Bk Vols 10,000; Per Subs 24

HILLSDALE

C HILLSDALE COLLEGE, Michael Alex Mossey Library, 33 E College St, 49242. SAN 308-1672. Tel: 517-437-7341. FAX: 517-437-0799. Web Site: www.hillsdale.edu/library. *Head Librn*, Daniel Lee Knoch; E-Mail: dan.knoch@hillsdale.edu; *Ref*, Janet Ryan; *Publ Servs*, Dan Joldersma; E-Mail: dan.joldersma@hillsdale.edu; *Publ Servs*, Linda Anne Moore; Tel: linda.moore@hillsdale.edu; *Coll Develop, Tech Servs*, Daniel Knoch; *Tech Servs*, Maurine Walling McCourry; E-Mail: maurine.mccourry@hillsdale.edu; *Tech Servs*, Martha Jane Spicuzza; E-Mail: martha.spicuzza@hillsdale.edu. Subject Specialists: *Archives*, Linda Anne Moore; *Reference*, Linda Anne Moore; *Reference*, Dan Joldersma; Staff 11 (MLS 5, Non-MLS 6)
Founded 1844. Enrl 1,150; Fac 80; Highest Degree: Bachelor
Jul 2000-Jun 2001 Income Parent Institution $795,000. Mats Exp $450,000, Books $280,000, Per/Ser (Incl. Access Fees) $170,000
Library Holdings: Bk Vols 280,000; Per Subs 1,904
Subject Interests: Economics
Special Collections: Ludwig von Mises Library; Russell Kirk Library
Automation Activity & Vendor Info: (Acquisitions) Innovative Interfaces Inc.; (Cataloging) Innovative Interfaces Inc.; (Circulation) Innovative Interfaces Inc.; (Course Reserve) Innovative Interfaces Inc.; (OPAC) Innovative Interfaces Inc.; (Serials) Innovative Interfaces Inc.
Database Vendor: Dialog, Ebsco - EbscoHost, Lexis-Nexis, OCLC - First Search
Partic in Michigan Library Consortium

P MITCHELL PUBLIC LIBRARY,* 22 N Manning St, 49242. SAN 308-1680. Tel: 517-437-2581. FAX: 517-437-2583. *Dir*, Jacqueline G Morris; Staff 4 (MLS 1, Non-MLS 3)
Founded 1908. Pop 12,500; Circ 65,000
Library Holdings: Bk Vols 30,000; Per Subs 54
Subject Interests: History
Mem of Woodlands Library Cooperative
Friends of the Library Group

HOLLAND

§C DAVENPORT UNIVERSITY LIBRARY, 643 S Waverly Rd, 49423. SAN 378-3839. Tel: 616-395-4670. Toll Free Tel: 616-395-4698. *Dir*, Kimberly Barber; *Librn*, Todd Reed; *Tech Servs*, Diane Rottschaefer; Staff 2 (MLS 1, Non-MLS 1)
Library Holdings: Bk Titles 16,000; Per Subs 250

P HERRICK DISTRICT LIBRARY, 300 S River Ave, 49423-3290. SAN 346-6299. Tel: 616-355-1400. FAX: 616-355-1426 (admin.), 616-355-3083. Web Site: macatawa.org/~herrick/. *Dir*, Robert Sherwood; E-Mail: holrs@lakeland.lib.mi.us; *Automation Syst Coordr, Tech Servs*, Lin Light; *Ad Servs, Circ*, Diane Corradini; *Ch Servs*, Marilyn Brown; *Acq*, Dianna Harrington; *AV*, Bonnie Otis; *Ref*, Kelli Perkins; *Publ Servs*, Gary Pullano; *ILL*, Meredith McCarthy; *Br Coordr*, Ann Prins; Staff 48 (MLS 11, Non-MLS 37)
Founded 1867. Pop 83,888; Circ 597,878
Library Holdings: Bk Vols 143,000
Special Collections: Dutch, Spanish Periodicals; Genealogy (Local & Dutch); Indo-Chinese Language; Spanish Language
Automation Activity & Vendor Info: (Circulation) epixtech, inc.
Mem of Lakeland Library Cooperative
Branches: 2
CROCKERY TOWNSHIP, 17431 12th Ave, Nunica, 49448. SAN 346-6418. Tel: 616-837-6868. FAX: 616-837-7838. *Librn*, Dorothy Way
Library Holdings: Bk Vols 6,637
JAMESTOWN BRANCH, 3246 24th Ave, Jamestown, 49427. SAN 346-6388. Tel: 616-896-9798. FAX: 616-896-9798. *Librn*, Linda Bosma
Library Holdings: Bk Vols 9,872

M HOLLAND COMMUNITY HOSPITAL, Hospital & Medical Staff Library,* 602 Michigan Ave, 49423. SAN 325-9145. Tel: 616-394-3107. FAX: 616-392-8448. *Dir*, Eleanor Lopez; E-Mail: elopez@hoho.org
Library Holdings: Bk Vols 5,000; Per Subs 240
Partic in Am Libr Asn; Michigan Health Sciences Libraries Association; Spec Libr Asn
Branches:
HEALTH INFORMATION LEARNING CENTER, 1061 S Washington St, 49423. SAN 376-9364. Tel: 616-394-3795. Toll Free Tel: 800-304-5182. FAX: 616-394-3794. *Dir*, Eleanor Lopez

SR HOPE CHURCH, Blanche Cathcart Memorial Library, 77 W 11th St, 49423. SAN 325-9129. Tel: 616-392-7947. FAX: 616-392-9037. *Librn*, Jocelynn Yost
Library Holdings: Bk Vols 5,600
Friends of the Library Group

C HOPE COLLEGE, Van Wylen Library, 53 Graves Pl, PO Box 9012, 49422-9012. SAN 308-1710. Tel: 616-395-7790. FAX: 616-395-7965. Web Site: www.hope.edu/lib. *Dir*, David Jensen; E-Mail: jensend@hope.edu; *Publ Servs*, Kelly Jacobsma; *Online Servs*, David O'Brien; *Tech Servs*, Colleen Conway; *Syst Coordr*, Brian Yost; *ILL*, Helen Einberger; *Bibliog Instr*, Priscilla Atkins; *Coll Develop*, Mark Christel; Staff 20 (MLS 9, Non-MLS 11)
Founded 1866. Enrl 2,915; Fac 220; Highest Degree: Bachelor
Jul 1999-Jun 2000 Income $1,917,000. Mats Exp $746,613, Books $243,103, Per/Ser (Incl. Access Fees) $375,925, Presv $18,911, Micro $29,590, Electronic Ref Mat (Incl. Access Fees) $79,084. Sal $676,900
Library Holdings: Bk Vols 330,408; Per Subs 1,548
Special Collections: Church History (Reformed Church in America); Dutch American History; Holland Joint Archives
Automation Activity & Vendor Info: (Acquisitions) DRA; (Cataloging) DRA; (Circulation) DRA; (OPAC) DRA; (Serials) DRA
Publications: Bookbytes
Partic in Michigan Library Consortium; OCLC Online Computer Library Center, Inc

J OTTAWA AREA INTERMEDIATE SCHOOL DISTRICT, Regional Educational Media Center & Professional Library,* 13565 Port Sheldon Rd, 49424. SAN 371-912X. Tel: 616-399-6940, Ext 4075. FAX: 616-399-8263. *Media Spec*, Cynthia Kleinheksel; E-Mail: ckleinhe@remc7.k12.mi.us
Restriction: Not open to public
Partic in Lakeland Area Library Network

S THE JOINT ARCHIVES OF HOLLAND, Hope College Campus, PO Box 9000, 49422. SAN 327-5701. Tel: 616-395-7798. FAX: 616-395-7197. E-Mail: archives@hope.edu. Web Site: www.hope.edu/jointarchives. *Dir*, Larry J Wagenaar; *Admin Assoc*, Lori Tretheway; *Archivist*, Geoffrey D Reynolds; Staff 2 (MLS 1, Non-MLS 1)
Founded 1988
Subject Interests: Immigration, Oral hist, Reform church hist, Regional hist
Special Collections: Archival Coll of the Holland Historical Trust (Holland Museum); Coll of City of Holland, City of Saugatuck & Village of Douglas; Hope College & Western Theological Seminary
Publications: A C Van Raalte: Dutch Leader & American Patriot, 1997; Campus Alive: A Walking Tour of Hope College, 1999; Guide to Collections of The Joint Archives of Holland, 1989; Supplement to The Guide to the Collection, 1991; The Joint Archives Quarterly
Restriction: Non-circulating to the public
Function: Archival collection
Open Mon-Fri 9-5
Friends of the Library Group

R WESTERN THEOLOGICAL SEMINARY, Beardslee Library, 101 E 13th St, 49423. SAN 308-1729. Tel: 616-392-8555. Toll Free Tel: 800-392-8554. FAX: 616-392-8889. Web Site: www.westernsem.org. *Dir*, Paul Smith; Tel: 616-392-8555, Ext 143, E-Mail: pauls@westernsem.org; *Tech Servs*, Ann Nieuwkoop; Tel: 616-392-8555, Ext 141, E-Mail: ann@westernsem.org; *Circ*, Kris Ritton; Tel: 616-392-8555, Ext 140, E-Mail: krisr@westernsem.org; Staff 3 (MLS 2, Non-MLS 1)
Founded 1895. Enrl 166; Fac 17; Highest Degree: Doctorate
Library Holdings: Bk Vols 110,665; Per Subs 442
Subject Interests: Art and architecture, Biblical studies, Church history, Education, Religion, Theology
Special Collections: 15th-18th Century; History of Reformed Church in America (Kolkman Memorial Archives), ms mat; Theology (Rare books), bd vols
Publications: Reformed Review
Partic in American Theological Library Association; Mich Libr Asn; Michigan Library Consortium; OCLC Online Computer Library Center, Inc

HOLLY

P HOLLY TOWNSHIP LIBRARY,* 1116 N Saginaw St, 48442-1395. SAN 308-1737. Tel: 248-634-1754. FAX: 248-634-8088. *Librn*, Shirley Roos; *Ch Servs*, Lucy Summers; *YA Servs*, Evelyn Wheeler
Circ 75,000
Library Holdings: Bk Vols 45,000; Per Subs 101
Special Collections: Large Print Coll
Mem of Mid-Eastern Libr Syst
Special Services for the Deaf - Staff with knowledge of sign language
Friends of the Library Group

HOMER

P HOMER PUBLIC LIBRARY, 104 S Hillsdale St, 49245. SAN 376-7043. Tel: 517-568-3450. FAX: 517-568-4021. E-Mail: hpl@voyager.net. *Dir*, Sandra P VanWert
Library Holdings: Bk Titles 10,000; Per Subs 15
Mem of Woodlands Library Cooperative

HOPKINS

P HOPKINS PUBLIC LIBRARY,* 118 E Main St, 49328-0366. SAN 308-1745. Tel: 616-793-7516. FAX: 616-793-7047. *Librn*, Alice Hazen
Circ 16,186
Library Holdings: Bk Vols 11,500; Per Subs 32
Mem of Lakeland Library Cooperative
Open Fri-Wed

HOUGHTON

C MICHIGAN TECHNOLOGICAL UNIVERSITY, J Robert Van Pelt Library, 49931-1295. SAN 308-1753. Tel: 906-487-2500. Interlibrary Loan Service Tel: 906-487-3207. Circulation Tel: 906-487-2508. Reference Tel: 906-487-2507. FAX: 906-487-2357. Web Site: www.lib.mtu.edu. *Dir*, Phyllis H Johnson; E-Mail: phjohnso@mtu.edu; *Asst Dir, Res*, Theresa Spence; Fax: 906-487-1765, E-Mail: tspence@mtu.edu; *ILL*, Elizabeth Badke; *Instrul Serv, Ref*, Pauline Moore; *Online Servs*, David Lepse; *Syst Coordr*, David Dube; *Archivist*, Erik Nordberg; Staff 16 (MLS 10, Non-MLS 6)
Founded 1887. Enrl 6,321; Fac 399; Highest Degree: Doctorate
Jul 1999-Jun 2000 Income $3,218,600. Mats Exp $1,528,772, Books $121,802, Per/Ser (Incl. Access Fees) $1,145,439, Presv $3,006, Other Print Mats $89,802, Electronic Ref Mat (Incl. Access Fees) $168,723. Sal $1,402,357
Library Holdings: Bk Vols 365,066; Per Subs 2,146
Subject Interests: Engineering, Technology
Special Collections: Copper Country Historical Coll; Copper Mining Company Records; Foundation Center Regional Coll; Isle Royale (Ben Chynoweth Coll), pamphlets, articles, photogs; Spitzbergen (John M Longyear Coll); University Archives; USBM Mine Maps of Michigan
Automation Activity & Vendor Info: (Acquisitions) Endeavor; (Cataloging) Endeavor; (Circulation) Endeavor; (Course Reserve) Endeavor; (OPAC)

Endeavor; (Serials) Endeavor
Partic in Michigan Library Consortium; OCLC Online Computer Library Center, Inc; Upper Peninsula Region Of Library Cooperation, Inc
Friends of the Library Group

P PORTAGE LAKE DISTRICT LIBRARY,* 105 Huron St, 49931-2194. SAN 308-1761. Tel: 906-482-4570. FAX: 906-482-2129. *Dir*, Jim Curtis
Founded 1910. Pop 14,243; Circ 101,200
Library Holdings: Bk Titles 30,000; Per Subs 120
Special Collections: Weaving (Buellwood Weavers Guild), bks bd & per
Mem of Superiorland Library Cooperative
Friends of the Library Group

HOUGHTON LAKE

P HOUGHTON LAKE PUBLIC LIBRARY, 4431 W Houghton Lake Dr, 48629. SAN 308-177X. Tel: 517-366-9230. FAX: 517-366-0063. *Dir*, Donna J Alward; E-Mail: dalward@hlpl.lib.mi.us; Staff 6 (MLS 1, Non-MLS 5)
Founded 1964. Pop 11,918; Circ 50,895
Jul 1999-Jun 2000 Income $520,000, State $12,000, County $438,000, Locally Generated Income $60,000, Other $10,000. Mats Exp $40,000, Books $21,000, Per/Ser (Incl. Access Fees) $5,500, AV Equip $4,000, Electronic Ref Mat (Incl. Access Fees) $9,500. Sal $187,000
Library Holdings: Bk Vols 47,975; Per Subs 114
Automation Activity & Vendor Info: (Cataloging) EOS; (Circulation) EOS; (OPAC) EOS
Mem of Mid-Michigan Library League
Partic in Michigan Library Consortium

HOWARD CITY

P REYNOLDS TOWNSHIP LIBRARY, 215 E Edgerton, PO Box 220, 49329. SAN 308-1788. Tel: 231-937-5575. Reference Tel: 231-937-6175. FAX: 231-937-9240. Web Site: www.lakeland.lib.mi.us. *Librn*, Janice Williams; E-Mail: howjw@lakeland.lib.mi.us
Library Holdings: Bk Titles 17,400; Per Subs 63
Special Collections: Howard City Record, microfilm
Mem of Lakeland Library Cooperative
Partic in Mich Libr Asn

HOWELL

C CLEARY COLLEGE LIBRARY, 3750 Cleary College Rd, 48833. SAN 308-4930. Tel: 517-548-3670. FAX: 517-548-7513. Web Site: www.cleary.edu/library.html. *Librn*, Jane Edwards
Enrl 1,011; Fac 48; Highest Degree: Master
Library Holdings: Bk Titles 7,000; Per Subs 60
Subject Interests: Accounting, Management, Marketing, Quality
Automation Activity & Vendor Info: (Cataloging) SIRSI; (Circulation) SIRSI; (OPAC) SIRSI
Partic in Library Network; Michigan Library Consortium

P HOWELL CARNEGIE DISTRICT LIBRARY, 314 W Grand River Ave, 48843-2146. SAN 308-1796. Tel: 517-546-0720. FAX: 517-546-1494. Web Site: www.howell-carnegie.lib.mi.us. *Librn*, Kathleen Zaenger; *Ad Servs*, Jerri Lee Cook; *Circ*, Suzanne Sherb; *Ch Servs*, Holly Ward-Lamb; Staff 7 (MLS 5, Non-MLS 2)
Founded 1875. Pop 30,271
2000-2001 Income $1,373,661. Mats Exp $1,373,661. Sal $582,052
Library Holdings: Bk Vols 89,244; Per Subs 413
Special Collections: Livingston County Local History, photogs
Automation Activity & Vendor Info: (Acquisitions) epixtech, inc.; (Cataloging) epixtech, inc.; (Circulation) epixtech, inc.; (ILL) epixtech, inc.; (OPAC) epixtech, inc.; (Serials) epixtech, inc.
Partic in Libr Network
Friends of the Library Group

HUDSON

P HUDSON PUBLIC LIBRARY, 205 S Market, 49247. SAN 308-1818. Tel: 517-448-3801. FAX: 517-448-5095. E-Mail: hudson@monroe.lib.mi.us. *Librn*, Kathleen Hepker; *Asst Librn*, JoAnne Crater; Staff 1 (Non-MLS 1)
Founded 1904. Pop 4,604; Circ 69,000
Jul 1999-Jun 2000 Income $128,000, City $90,000. Mats Exp Books $18,000. Sal $75,000
Library Holdings: Bk Vols 49,500; Bk Titles 47,500; Per Subs 91
Special Collections: Carnegie Library; Hudson Historical Coll; Will Carleton Coll
Automation Activity & Vendor Info: (Cataloging) Follett; (Circulation) Follett; (ILL) Brodart
Mem of Woodlands Library Cooperative
Partic in OCLC Online Computer Library Center, Inc

HUDSONVILLE

G GARY BYKER MEMORIAL LIBRARY OF HUDSONVILLE, 3338 Van Buren St, 49426. SAN 308-1826. Tel: 616-669-1255. FAX: 616-669-5150. E-Mail: hudmh@lakeland.lib.mi.us. Web Site: www.hudsonville/library.html. *Dir*, Melissa Ann Huisman; Tel: 616-669-7172, Ext 5, E-Mail: hudmh@lakeland.lib.mi.us; *Ch Servs*, Elizabeth Mazor; Tel: 616-669-7172, Ext 4, E-Mail: hudem@lakeland.lib.mi.us; Staff 14 (MLS 1, Non-MLS 13)
Founded 1967. Pop 7,750; Circ 120,342
Jul 2000-Jun 2001 Income $246,220, State $7,750, City $145,119, County $41,747, Locally Generated Income $18,905, Other $32,699. Mats Exp $29,240, Books $24,955, Per/Ser (Incl. Access Fees) $3,096, AV Equip $739, Electronic Ref Mat (Incl. Access Fees) $450. Sal $137,639 (Prof $41,184)
Library Holdings: Bk Vols 36,972; Per Subs 123
Subject Interests: Local history
Special Collections: Local History Coll
Automation Activity & Vendor Info: (Cataloging) epixtech, inc.; (Circulation) epixtech, inc.; (ILL) epixtech, inc.; (OPAC) epixtech, inc.
Database Vendor: IAC - Info Trac, OCLC - First Search
Function: Photocopies available
Mem of Lakeland Library Cooperative
Partic in Lakeland Libr Coop; Michigan Library Consortium
Friends of the Library Group

HUNTINGTON WOODS

P HUNTINGTON WOODS PUBLIC LIBRARY,* 26415 Scotia, 48070-1198. SAN 308-1834. Tel: 248-543-9720. FAX: 248-543-2559. *Dir*, Shelley Gach; *Ch Servs*, Anne Hage
Founded 1942. Pop 6,514; Circ 55,000
Library Holdings: Bk Vols 45,000; Bk Titles 42,000; Per Subs 120; High Interest/Low Vocabulary Bk Vols 100; Bks on Deafness & Sign Lang 50
Special Collections: Early American Newspapers (Columbian Centinel of Boston 1792-1794)
Mem of The Library Network
Friends of the Library Group

IDLEWILD

P IDLEWILD PUBLIC LIBRARY,* PO Box 148, 49642-0148. SAN 308-1842. Tel: 616-745-7652. FAX: 231-745-7652. *Librn*, Jessie Kinney
Circ 863
Library Holdings: Bk Vols 4,000; Per Subs 20
Special Collections: Black Coll
Mem of Mid-Michigan Library League
Friends of the Library Group

IMLAY CITY

P RUTH HUGHES MEMORIAL DISTRICT LIBRARY, 211 N Almont Ave, 48444-1004. SAN 308-1850. Tel: 810-724-8043. FAX: 810-724-2602. *Dir*, Linda Prendergast; *Adminr*, Julie Toole
Founded 1922. Pop 4,733; Circ 15,000
2000-2000 Income $281,591, County $162,901, Locally Generated Income $51,099, Other $67,591. Mats Exp $35,000, Books $32,000, Per/Ser (Incl. Access Fees) $3,000. Sal $110,000
Library Holdings: Bk Vols 37,000; Per Subs 115
Automation Activity & Vendor Info: (Cataloging) Sagebrush Corporation; (Circulation) Sagebrush Corporation; (OPAC) Sagebrush Corporation
Database Vendor: IAC - Info Trac
Mem of Mideastern Michigan Library Cooperative
Friends of the Library Group

INDIAN RIVER

P INDIAN RIVER AREA LIBRARY, 3546 S Straits Hwy, PO Box 160, 49749. SAN 321-0405. Tel: 231-238-8581. FAX: 231-238-9494. E-Mail: indrivl@northland.lib.mi.us. Web Site: www.libnet.org/iriver/. *Librn*, Cindy Lou Poquette; *Asst Librn*, Janet Doris Koechner; Staff 2 (MLS 1, Non-MLS 1)
Founded 1977. Pop 3,886; Circ 32,972
Jul 1999-Jun 2000 Income $85,398, State $3,886, Provincial $22,702, County $41,902, Locally Generated Income $16,908. Mats Exp $22,010, Books $13,902, Per/Ser (Incl. Access Fees) $1,527, Electronic Ref Mat (Incl. Access Fees) $3,900. Sal $25,232
Library Holdings: Bk Vols 38,000; Per Subs 76; High Interest/Low Vocabulary Bk Vols 200
Subject Interests: Careers, Dance, Law, Music
Publications: Newsletter
Mem of Northland Library Cooperative
Partic in Northland Interlibrary System
Friends of the Library Group

INKSTER

P INKSTER PUBLIC LIBRARY,* 2005 Inkster Rd, 48141. SAN 308-1869. Tel: 313-563-2822. FAX: 313-274-5130. *Dir*, Steven Gulvezan
Pop 35,190
Library Holdings: Bk Vols 38,000; Per Subs 68
Publications: The Roots of Inkster
Mem of The Library Network; Wayne Oakland Libr Federation
Friends of the Library Group

INTERLOCHEN

S INTERLOCHEN CENTER FOR THE ARTS, Academic Library, PO Box 199, 49643. SAN 308-1877. Tel: 231-276-7420. FAX: 231-276-6321. *Head of Libr*, Evelyn R Weliver; Staff 3 (MLS 1, Non-MLS 2)
Founded 1962. Enrl 430
Library Holdings: Bk Titles 22,000
Subject Interests: Art and architecture, Dance, Drama, Music
Special Collections: Music Library Coll
Automation Activity & Vendor Info: (Cataloging) DRA; (Circulation) DRA; (OPAC) DRA
Partic in Michigan Library Consortium

IONIA

P HALL-FOWLER MEMORIAL LIBRARY, 126 E Main St, 48846. SAN 308-1885. Tel: 616-527-3680. FAX: 616-527-6210. E-Mail: ion@lakeland.lib.mi.us. Web Site: www.lakeland.lib.mi.us/ionia/index.html. *Admin Dir*, Heidi Nagel
Founded 1903. Circ 66,676
Jul 1999-Jun 2000 Income $423,699, State $18,805, City $111,156, County $237,140, Locally Generated Income $56,598. Mats Exp $44,658, Books $35,773, Per/Ser (Incl. Access Fees) $3,015, AV Equip $5,870. Sal $148,793
Library Holdings: Bk Vols 36,323; Bk Titles 27,775; Per Subs 100
Special Collections: Civil War Coll; Michigan Historical Coll
Mem of Lakeland Library Cooperative
Friends of the Library Group

M IONIA COUNTY MEMORIAL HOSPITAL, Health Sciences Library,* 479 Lafayette St, PO Box 1001, 48846-1834. SAN 373-9147. Tel: 616-527-4200, Ext 281. FAX: 616-527-5731. *Librn*, Mary Cox
Founded 1980
Library Holdings: Bk Vols 566; Per Subs 36
Restriction: Not open to public
Partic in Michigan Health Sciences Libraries Association; Nat Libr of Med

S IONIA TEMPORARY CORRECTIONAL FACILITY LIBRARY,* 1755 Harwood Rd, 48846. SAN 371-7194. Tel: 616-527-6320, Ext 334. FAX: 616-527-9711. *Asst Librn*, Kathleen E Callahan; *Librn*, Ellen Wood
Founded 1986
Library Holdings: Per Subs 31
Special Services for the Deaf - Books on deafness & sign language

IRON MOUNTAIN

P DICKINSON COUNTY LIBRARY,* 401 Iron Mountain St, 49801-3435. SAN 346-6442. Tel: 906-774-1218. FAX: 906-774-4079. E-Mail: dcl@mid-pen.lib.mi.us. *Actg Dir*, Renee Augustine; E-Mail: augustr@mid-pen.lib.mi.us; *Ch Servs*, Martha Allen; Staff 13 (MLS 1, Non-MLS 12)
Founded 1902. Pop 26,831; Circ 180,446
Jan 1998-Dec 1998 Income (Main Library and Branch Library) $782,984, Provincial $36,874, County $561,818, Other $184,292
Library Holdings: Bk Titles 86,673
Subject Interests: Genealogy, Local history, Michigan
Special Collections: Education & Health (Claire A Lilja Memorial); Wood Industry (Abbott Fox Memorial)
Automation Activity & Vendor Info: (Cataloging) epixtech, inc.; (Circulation) epixtech, inc.; (OPAC) epixtech, inc.
Database Vendor: epixtech, inc.
Publications: Ford Comes to Kingsford; The Evolution of the Public Library in Michigan's Dickinson County
Mem of Mid-Peninsula Library Cooperative
Partic in Michigan Library Consortium
Friends of the Library Group
Branches: 1
NORWAY BRANCH, 620 Section St, Norway, 49870. SAN 346-6477. Tel: 906-563-8617. FAX: 906-563-7224. *Librn*, Cheryl McConnell
Library Holdings: Bk Vols 11,765
Friends of the Library Group
Bookmobiles: 1

GM VETERANS AFFAIRS MEDICAL CENTER LIBRARY,* 325 East H St, 49801. SAN 308-1907. Tel: 906-774-3172. FAX: 906-779-3107. *Librn*, Jeanne Marie Durocher; E-Mail: durocher.jeanne@iron.mtn.va.gov; *ILL*, Sharon Ann Bergstrom; Tel: 906-774-3300, Ext 2440, E-Mail: bergstrom.sharon@iron-mtn.va.gov; Staff 2 (MLS 1, Non-MLS 1)
Founded 1950. Circ 12,493
Oct 1999-Sep 2000 Income (Main Library Only) $42,500, Federal $41,500, Other $1,000. Mats Exp Per/Ser (Incl. Access Fees) $21,700. (Prof $46,000)
Library Holdings: Bk Vols 900; Bk Titles 800; Per Subs 80
Subject Interests: Geriatrics and gerontology
Restriction: Reference only to non-staff
Function: ILL available
Mem of Valnet
Partic in Mid-Peninsula Libr Coop; Veterans Affairs Library Network

IRON RIVER

P WEST IRON DISTRICT LIBRARY,* 116 W Genesee St, PO Box 328, 49935-1437. SAN 308-1915. Tel: 906-265-2831. FAX: 906-265-2062. *Librn*, Barbara Bartel
Founded 1967. Pop 6,964; Circ 27,521
Library Holdings: Bk Titles 15,000; Per Subs 46
Special Collections: Large Print Books
Mem of Mid-Peninsula Library Cooperative

IRONWOOD

J GOGEBIC COMMUNITY COLLEGE, Alex D Chisholm Learning Resources Center,* E4946 Jackson Rd, 49938. SAN 308-1931. Tel: 906-932-4231, Ext 270. FAX: 906-932-0868. Web Site: www2.gogebic.cc.mi.us/library/library.htm. *Tech Servs*, Donna Fowler; E-Mail: donnaf@admin1.gogebic.cc.mi.us; *In Charge*, Sandy Lahtinen; Staff 4 (MLS 2, Non-MLS 2)
Founded 1932
Jul 1999-Jun 2000 Income $196,900. Mats Exp $44,420, Books $25,000, Per/Ser (Incl. Access Fees) $10,500, Presv $520, AV Equip $8,400. Sal $91,420 (Prof $48,100)
Library Holdings: Bk Vols 28,219; Per Subs 204
Subject Interests: Great Lakes, History, Local history
Special Collections: Mining Memorabilia
Partic in Michigan Library Consortium; Upper Peninsula Region Of Library Cooperation, Inc

P IRONWOOD CARNEGIE PUBLIC LIBRARY, 235 E Aurora St, 49938-2178. SAN 308-1923. Tel: 906-932-0203. FAX: 906-932-2447. *Dir*, Sandra E Wulbrecht; E-Mail: sandyw@mid-pen.lib.mi.us; *Asst Librn*, Arla Romo; *Asst Librn*, Mary Pat Baginski; Staff 4 (MLS 1, Non-MLS 3)
Founded 1901. Pop 9,629; Circ 54,607
Library Holdings: Bk Titles 29,152; Per Subs 102
Subject Interests: Arts and crafts, History
Special Collections: Local newspapers on microfilm dating back to 1890; State of Michigan
Automation Activity & Vendor Info: (Cataloging) Brodart; (Circulation) Brodart
Database Vendor: IAC - SearchBank, OCLC - First Search
Mem of Mid-Peninsula Library Cooperative

ISHPEMING

P ISHPEMING CARNEGIE PUBLIC LIBRARY,* 317 N Main St, 49849-1994. SAN 308-194X. Tel: 906-486-4381. TDD: 906-486-4381. FAX: 906-486-6226. *Head Librn*, Linda Peterson; *Asst Librn*, Marsha Gleason; *Ch Servs*, Janet LeFeber; Staff 3 (MLS 2, Non-MLS 1)
Pop 14,344; Circ 60,921
Jan 1998-Jan 1999 Income $131,942. Mats Exp $28,381, Books $16,088, Per/Ser (Incl. Access Fees) $4,638, AV Equip $533, Electronic Ref Mat (Incl. Access Fees) $7,122. Sal $90,722
Library Holdings: Bk Vols 71,616; Per Subs 87
Automation Activity & Vendor Info: (Cataloging) epixtech, inc.; (OPAC) epixtech, inc.
Mem of Superiorland Library Cooperative
Friends of the Library Group

S US NATIONAL SKI HALL OF FAME, Roland Palmedo National Ski Library, 610 Palms Ave, 49849. (Mail add: P O Box 191, 49849), SAN 308-1958. Tel: 906-485-6323. FAX: 906-486-4570. E-Mail: skihall@uplogon.com. Web Site: www.shihall.com. *Curator, Mgr*, Raymond A Leverton; *Archivist*, Burton H Boyum
Founded 1956
Library Holdings: Bk Titles 1,500
Subject Interests: History
Special Collections: Roland Palmedo Coll
Publications: Midwest Skiing-A Glance Back; Nine Thousand Years of Skis: (Norwegian Wood to French Plastic); Seventy-Five Years of Skiing (1904-79); Skiing Then & Now; The Flying Norseman
Friends of the Library Group

ITHACA

P THOMPSON HOME PUBLIC LIBRARY,* 125 W Center St, 48847. SAN 308-1966. Tel: 517-875-4184. FAX: 517-875-3374. *Librn*, Suzanne Bailey
Founded 1926. Pop 10,179

Library Holdings: Bk Vols 24,000; Per Subs 50
Subject Interests: Local history, Michigan
Mem of Capital Library Cooperative

JACKSON

P CAPITAL LIBRARY COOPERATIVE, 4 Universal Way, 49202. SAN 308-2644. Tel: 517-699-1657. FAX: 517-699-4859. Web Site: clc.lib.mi.us/capital. *Dir*, Ann C Holt; E-Mail: aholt@clc.lib.mi.us; Staff 2 (MLS 1, Non-MLS 1)
Founded 1978. Pop 395,313
Oct 2000-Sep 2001 Income $414,908
Member Libraries: Alma Public Library; Benton Township-Potterville District Library; Briggs Public Library; Charlotte Community Library; De Witt Public Library; Dorothy Hull Windsor Township Library; East Lansing Public Library; Eaton Rapids Public Library; Elsie Public Library; Grand Ledge Public Library; Howe Memorial Library; Jackson District Library; Maple Rapids Public Library; Mulliken District Library; Ovid Public Library; Portland District Library; Sunfield District Library; Theodore Austin Cutler Memorial Library; Thompson Home Public Library; Vermontville Public Library
Partic in Michigan Library Consortium; OCLC Online Computer Library Center, Inc

CONSUMERS ENERGY LIBRARY
L LEGAL LIBRARY, 212 W Michigan Ave, 49201. SAN 308-1974. Tel: 517-788-1088. FAX: 517-788-0768. *Librn*, Helen K Sova
Founded 1955
Library Holdings: Bk Vols 32,000; Per Subs 25
Publications: Department letter regarding new material (irregular)
Restriction: Restricted public use
S LIBRARY SERVICES, 1945 Parnall Rd, 49201. SAN 321-8104. Tel: 517-788-0541. FAX: 517-768-3804. *Librn*, Michele Puckett; Staff 2 (MLS 1, Non-MLS 1)
Founded 1977
Library Holdings: Bk Titles 4,200; Per Subs 140
Subject Interests: Energy disciplines, Mgt develop, Mgt training
Special Collections: Industry Standards; NUREG Reports
Database Vendor: Dialog, Lexis-Nexis, OCLC - First Search, ProQuest
Publications: Library Lines
Partic in Capital Area Library Network Inc; OCLC Online Computer Library Center, Inc
American Gas Association Library Services Committee; Edison Electric Institute Library Services Committee; SLA Public Utilities Division; SLA Solo Librarians Division

S ELLA SHARP MUSEUM, Research Library,* 3225 Fourth St, 49203. SAN 327-4039. Tel: 517-787-2320. FAX: 517-787-2933. E-Mail: ellasharp@dmci.net. Web Site: www.ellasharp.org. *Actg Dir*, Lynne Loftis
Library Holdings: Bk Titles 1,500
Friends of the Library Group

S G ROBERT COTTON REGIONAL CORRECTIONAL FACILITY LIBRARY,* 3500 N Elm Rd, 49201. SAN 371-7585. Tel: 517-780-5172. FAX: 517-780-5100. *Librn*, Jonatha Maystead; *Asst Librn*, Jackie Cooke; *Asst Librn*, Kathy Honton; Staff 3 (MLS 1, Non-MLS 2)
Library Holdings: Bk Vols 8,799
Restriction: Not open to public
Special Services for the Deaf - High interest/low vocabulary books; Special interest periodicals

S JACKSON CITIZEN PATRIOT NEWSPAPER LIBRARY, 214 S Jackson St, 49201-2282. SAN 308-2008. Tel: 517-768-4908. Toll Free Tel: 800-878-6397. FAX: 517-787-9711. *Librn*, Susanne M Weible; E-Mail: sweible@citpat.com; Staff 1 (Non-MLS 1)
Library Holdings: Bk Titles 700
Restriction: Access at librarian's discretion, Not open to public
Function: Newspaper reference library

J JACKSON COMMUNITY COLLEGE, Atkinson Learning Resources Center,* 2111 Emmons Rd, 49201. SAN 308-2016. Tel: 517-787-0800, Ext 8622. FAX: 517-796-8623. *Librn*, Cliff Taylor; Staff 2 (MLS 2)
Founded 1928. Enrl 2,749; Fac 115
Library Holdings: Bk Vols 51,940; Bk Titles 46,265; Per Subs 300
Partic in Capitol Area Library Network

P JACKSON DISTRICT LIBRARY, 244 W Michigan Ave, 49201. SAN 346-6507. Tel: 517-788-4087. Reference Tel: 517-788-4087, Ext 234. FAX: 517-782-8635. Web Site: www.jackson.lib.mi.us. *Dir*, Bescye P Burnett; Tel: 517-788-4199, Ext 241, Fax: 517-788-6024, E-Mail: burnettbp@jackson.lib.mi.us; *Publ Servs*, Kenneth Miller; Tel: 517-788-4087, Ext 226; *Tech Servs*, Mike Justian; Tel: 517-788-4087, Ext 257, Fax: 517-788-6024, E-Mail: justianmf@jackson.lib.mi.us; *Ref*, Elaine Piper; Tel: 517-788-4087, Ext 224, E-Mail: piperem@jackson.lib.mi.us; *Adminr, Ch Servs*, Saralinda Tackett; Tel: 517-788-4087, Ext 236, E-Mail: tackettse@jackson.lib.mi.us; *Circ*, Susan McGee; Tel: 517-788-4087, Ext 233, E-Mail: mcgesse@jackson.lib.mi.us; *Purchasing*, George Konopatzki; Tel: 517-788-4087, Ext 239 or 227; *Business*, Vicki Baldwin; Tel: 517-788-4099, Ext 239, E-Mail: baldwinvk@jackson.lib.mi.us. Subject Specialists: *Finance*, George Konopatzki; *Technology*, Mike Justian; Staff 93 (MLS 11, Non-MLS 82)
Founded 1978. Pop 149,756; Circ 659,860
Jan 1999-Dec 1999 Income (Main Library and Branch Library) $3,329,070, State $226,261, County $352,259, Locally Generated Income $2,342,912, Other $407,638. Mats Exp $437,915, Books $250,624, Per/Ser (Incl. Access Fees) $109,893, AV Equip $45,115, Other Print Mats $32,283. Sal $1,471,074
Library Holdings: Bk Vols 397,451; Per Subs 596
Special Collections: Jackson & Michigan History
Automation Activity & Vendor Info: (Cataloging) epixtech, inc.; (Circulation) epixtech, inc.; (OPAC) epixtech, inc.; (Serials) epixtech, inc.
Database Vendor: epixtech, inc., IAC - Info Trac, OCLC - First Search, ProQuest
Mem of Capital Library Cooperative
Friends of the Library Group
Branches: 13
BROOKLYN BRANCH, 207 N Main St, Brooklyn, 49230. SAN 378-1577. Tel: 517-592-3406. FAX: 517-592-3406. Web Site: www.jackson.lib.mi.us. *Branch Mgr*, Judy Barry; E-Mail: barryjh@jackson.lib.mi.us
Pop 6,308; Circ 38,676
Automation Activity & Vendor Info: (Circulation) epixtech, inc.
Friends of the Library Group
CARNEGIE, 244 W Michigan Ave, 49201. SAN 378-1593. Tel: 517-788-4087. FAX: 517-782-8635. Web Site: www.jackson.lib.mi.us. *Dir*, Bescye P Burnett; Tel: 517-788-4199, Ext 241, E-Mail: burnettbp@jackson.lib.mi.us
Pop 37,425; Circ 187,138
CONCORD BRANCH, 110 Hanover St, Concord, 49237. SAN 346-6590. Tel: 517-524-6970. FAX: 517-524-6970. *Branch Mgr*, Karen Veramay; E-Mail: veramayka@jackson.lib.mi.us
Pop 2,408; Circ 28,533
Friends of the Library Group
EASTERN BRANCH, 3125 E Michigan Ave, 49201. SAN 346-6620. Tel: 517-788-4074. FAX: 517-788-4074. Web Site: www.jackson.lib.mi.us. *Branch Mgr*, Elizabeth Spangenberg; E-Mail: spangenbergl@jackson.lib.mi.us
Pop 13,472; Circ 91,652
Friends of the Library Group
GRASS LAKE BRANCH, 130 W Michigan Ave, Grass Lake, 49240. SAN 346-6655. Tel: 517-522-8211. FAX: 517-522-8211. Web Site: www.jackson.lib.mi.us. *Branch Mgr*, Skip Freysinger; E-Mail: freysingerar@jackson.lib.mi.us
Pop 3,774; Circ 25,207
Friends of the Library Group
HANOVER BRANCH, 118 W Main St, Hanover, 49241. SAN 346-668X. Tel: 517-563-8344. FAX: 517-563-8344. Web Site: www.jackson.lib.mi.us. *Branch Mgr*, Valerie Shah; E-Mail: shahva@jackson.lib.mi.us
Pop 3,710; Circ 16,084
Friends of the Library Group
HENRIETTA BRANCH, 11744 Bunkerhill Rd, 49272. SAN 346-6698. Tel: 517-769-6537. FAX: 517-769-6357. Web Site: www.jackson.lib.mi.us. *Branch Mgr*, Becky Turyan; E-Mail: turyanrl@jackson.lib.mi.us
Pop 3,842; Circ 13,044
Friends of the Library Group
MEIJER BRANCH, 2699 Airport Rd, 49202. SAN 346-6736. Tel: 517-788-4480. FAX: 517-788-4480. Web Site: www.jackson.lib.mi.us. *Branch Mgr*, Sonia Sutch; E-Mail: sutchse@jackson.lib.mi.us
Pop 20,492; Circ 127,167
Friends of the Library Group
NAPOLEON BRANCH, 124 S Brooklyn Rd, Napoleon, 49261. SAN 346-6779. Tel: 517-536-4266. FAX: 517-536-4266. Web Site: www.jackson.lib.mi.us. *Branch Mgr*, Karen Heard; E-Mail: heardkp@jackson.lib.mi.us
Pop 6,273; Circ 16,260
Friends of the Library Group
PARMA BRANCH, 102 Church St, Parma, 49269. SAN 346-6809. Tel: 517-531-4908. FAX: 517-531-4908. Web Site: www.jackson.lib.mi.us. *Branch Mgr*, Dot Swanson; E-Mail: swansonde@jackson.lib.mi.us
Pop 2,491; Circ 17,771
Friends of the Library Group
SPRING ARBOR BRANCH, 113 E Main St, Spring Arbor, 49283. SAN 346-6833. Tel: 517-750-2030. FAX: 517-750-2030. Web Site: www.jackson.lib.mi.us. *Branch Mgr*, Mary Frey; E-Mail: freyml@jackson.lib.mi.us
Pop 6,939; Circ 29,312
Friends of the Library Group
SPRINGPORT BRANCH, PO Box 172, Springport, 49284-0172. SAN 346-6868. Tel: 517-857-3833. Web Site: www.jackson.lib.mi.us. *Branch Mgr*, Jackie Merritt; E-Mail: merrittja@jackson.lib.mi.us
Pop 2,090; Circ 11,643
Friends of the Library Group
SUMMIT BRANCH, 104 Bird Ave, 49203. SAN 346-6892. Tel: 517-783-4030. Web Site: www.jackson.lib.mi.us.
Pop 21,130; Circ 57,373
Friends of the Library Group

S MICHIGAN DEPARTMENT OF CORRECTIONS, State Prison of Southern Michigan Central Complex Library,* 4000 Cooper St, 49201. SAN 308-2024. Tel: 517-780-6608, Ext 6671. FAX: 517-780-6021. *Dir*, Washington Daniel
Founded 1936
Subject Interests: Criminal justice, Criminal law

M W A FOOTE HOSPITAL MEDICAL LIBRARY,* 205 N East Ave, 49201. SAN 308-1982. Tel: 517-788-4705. FAX: 517-788-4706. Web Site: www.foote.com. *In Charge*, Janet Zimmerman; E-Mail: janet.zimmerman@wafoote.org; Staff 3 (MLS 1, Non-MLS 2)
Library Holdings: Bk Vols 3,000; Bk Titles 1,900; Per Subs 130
Restriction: Staff use only
Partic in MLC; NLM
Friends of the Library Group

JENISON

P GEORGETOWN TOWNSHIP PUBLIC LIBRARY, 1525 Baldwin St, 49428-8911. SAN 308-2032. Tel: 616-457-9620. FAX: 616-457-3666. E-Mail: jen@lakeland.lib.mi.us. Web Site: www.gtwp.com/library.htm. *Dir*, Sheryl VanderWagen; E-Mail: jensvw@lakeland.lib.mi.us; *Asst Dir, Head Ref*, Pamela Myers; E-Mail: jenpam@lakeland.lib.mi.us; *Ch Servs*, Mary Griffith Reed; E-Mail: jenmr@lakeland.lib.mi.us; *Ref Serv Ad*, Susan Carlson; E-Mail: jensc@lakeland.lib.mi.us; Staff 22 (MLS 4, Non-MLS 18)
Founded 1965. Pop 40,552; Circ 258,736
Jan 2000-Dec 2000 Income $508,952, State $40,522, City $218,500, County $233,500, Locally Generated Income $16,400. Mats Exp $100,500, Books $70,000, Per/Ser (Incl. Access Fees) $14,000, AV Equip $14,000, Electronic Ref Mat (Incl. Access Fees) $2,500. Sal $245,000 (Prof $120,000)
Library Holdings: Bk Vols 111,790; Bk Titles 81,430; Per Subs 140
Automation Activity & Vendor Info: (Cataloging) epixtech, inc.; (Circulation) epixtech, inc.; (OPAC) epixtech, inc.
Database Vendor: GaleNet, IAC - Info Trac, IAC - SearchBank, OCLC - First Search
Function: ILL available
Mem of Lakeland Library Cooperative
Partic in Michigan Library Consortium
Friends of the Library Group

JONESVILLE

P JONESVILLE DISTRICT LIBRARY, 310 Church St, 49250. SAN 308-2040. Tel: 517-849-9701. FAX: 517-849-9701. E-Mail: jonelib@yahoo.com. *Dir*, Mary Miller; *Asst Librn*, Faith Popejoy
Pop 2,500; Circ 28,209
Library Holdings: Bk Vols 22,532; Per Subs 32
Mem of Woodlands Library Cooperative
Friends of the Library Group

KALAMAZOO

M BORGESS MEDICAL CENTER LIBRARY, 1521 Gull Rd, 49048-1666. SAN 314-4658. Tel: 616-226-7360. FAX: 616-226-6881. Web Site: www.borgess.com. *Mgr*, Jennifer Barlow; *Commun Servs*, Carol Aebli; Staff 5 (MLS 2, Non-MLS 3)
Library Holdings: Bk Vols 5,600; Per Subs 400
Subject Interests: Consumer health, Hospital administration, Medicine, Nursing, Patient health info
Partic in National Network of Libraries of Medicine - Greater Midwest Region

M BRONSON METHODIST HOSPITAL, Health Sciences Library,* 252 E Lovell St, 49007. SAN 308-2067. Tel: 616-341-8627. FAX: 616-341-8828. *Dir*, Marge Kars; E-Mail: karsm@bronsonhg.org; *Bibliog Instr, Online Servs*, Jim Sheiley
1997-1998 Mats Exp $60,000, Books $10,000, Per/Ser (Incl. Access Fees) $50,000. Sal $71,000 (Prof $52,000)
Library Holdings: Bk Vols 11,000; Bk Titles 8,000; Per Subs 400
Subject Interests: Allied health, Consumer health, Hospital administration, Medicine, Nursing
Partic in Kalamazoo Consortium For Higher Education; Nat Libr of Med

J DAVENPORT UNIVERSITY, Thomas F Reed Library, 4123 W Main St, 49006. SAN 321-5164. Tel: 616-382-2835, Ext 3373. Toll Free Tel: 800-632-8928. FAX: 616-382-2657. E-Mail: kzlibrary@davenport.edu. Web Site: www.davenport.edu. *Dir*, Judith Bosshart; Tel: 616-562-3373, E-Mail: kzjbosshart@davenport.edu; Staff 4 (MLS 2, Non-MLS 2)
Founded 1982. Enrl 1,200; Fac 125; Highest Degree: Bachelor
Library Holdings: Bk Titles 12,000; Per Subs 1,800
Subject Interests: Accounting, Language arts
Special Collections: Archives
Automation Activity & Vendor Info: (Acquisitions) epixtech, inc.; (Cataloging) epixtech, inc.; (Circulation) epixtech, inc.; (Course Reserve) epixtech, inc.; (OPAC) epixtech, inc.; (Serials) epixtech, inc.
Database Vendor: GaleNet, Lexis-Nexis, OCLC - First Search, ProQuest
Publications: Pathfinders
Restriction: Public use on premises
Function: ILL available, Photocopies available, Professional lending library, Some telephone reference
Mem of Southwest Michigan Library Cooperative
Partic in Kalamazoo Consortium For Higher Education; Michigan Library Consortium

R FIRST PRESBYTERIAN CHURCH LIBRARY,* 321 W South St, 49007. SAN 308-2083. Tel: 616-344-0119. FAX: 616-344-4645. *Librn*, Ginny Kavanaugh; *Librn*, Lillian Anderson; *Cat*, Betty Greene; Staff 8 (MLS 6, Non-MLS 2)
Library Holdings: Bk Titles 3,000
Subject Interests: Adults literature, Children's literature, Religion
Publications: Bulletin (bi-monthly)

R HERITAGE CHRISTIAN REFORMED CHURCH LIBRARY,* 2857 S 11th, 49009. SAN 308-2075. Tel: 616-372-3830. *Librn*, Liz Dow
Founded 1869
Library Holdings: Bk Vols 1,000; Bk Titles 800

C KALAMAZOO COLLEGE, Upjohn Library, 1200 Academy St, 49006-3285. SAN 308-2091. Tel: 616-337-7149. FAX: 616-337-7143. Web Site: kzoo.edu/library/index.html. *Dir*, Lisa L Palchick; *Assoc Dir*, Paul G Smithson; *Acq, Coll Develop*, Ann Haight; *Circ*, Mary Griswold; *ILL*, Carol Smith; *ILL*, Jeanne Taylor; *Ref*, Robin Rank; *Ref Serv*, Stacey Nowicki; Staff 7 (MLS 7)
Founded 1850. Enrl 1,250; Fac 83; Highest Degree: Bachelor
Library Holdings: Bk Vols 350,000; Bk Titles 340,000; Per Subs 911
Subject Interests: Art
Special Collections: Fine Birds Coll; History of Books & Printing; History of Science; Michigan Baptist Coll; Private Presses
Automation Activity & Vendor Info: (Acquisitions) Innovative Interfaces Inc.
Partic in OCLC Online Computer Library Center, Inc

S KALAMAZOO INSTITUTE OF ARTS LIBRARY, 314 S Park St, 49007-5102. SAN 308-2113. Tel: 616-349-7775. FAX: 616-349-9313. Web Site: www.kiarts.org. *Librn*, Rebecca D Steel; E-Mail: rebecca_s@kiarts.org
Founded 1956
Library Holdings: Bk Vols 11,000; Per Subs 65
Subject Interests: Am Art 19th-20th Centuries, Fine arts, Photography
Special Collections: German Expressionist Prints; Weavers Guild of Kalamazoo Coll
Publications: Exhibition Catalogs
Partic in Southwest Michigan Library Cooperative
Collect exhibit catalogs via museum exchanges

P KALAMAZOO PUBLIC LIBRARY, 315 S Rose St, 49007-5264. SAN 346-6981. Tel: 616-342-9837. Interlibrary Loan Service Tel: 616-553-7892. FAX: 616-342-0414. Web Site: www.kpl.gov/index.htl. *Dir*, Saul J Amdursky; E-Mail: saul@kpl.gov; *Asst Dir*, Mary Doud; E-Mail: maryd@kpl.gov; *Asst Dir*, Ann Rohrbaugh; E-Mail: annr@kpl.gov; *Ad Servs*, Jeanne Lawler-Marsac; E-Mail: jeanne@kpl.gov; *Automation Syst Coordr, Tech Servs*, Gary Green; E-Mail: Gary@KPL.gov; *AV, Circ, Outreach Serv*, Terry Lason; E-Mail: terryl@kpl.gov; *Ch Servs*, Mary Rife; E-Mail: maryrife@kpl.gov; *Br Coordr, Ch Servs*, Susan Warner; E-Mail: susan@kpl.gov; Staff 26 (MLS 26)
Founded 1872. Pop 116,925
Jul 1999-Jun 2000 Income (Main Library and Branch Library) $9,475,004, State $427,785, Locally Generated Income $8,270,357, Other $776,862. Mats Exp $878,142, Books $740,782, Per/Ser (Incl. Access Fees) $49,579, Presv $9,650, Electronic Ref Mat (Incl. Access Fees) $78,131. Sal $3,763,542 (Prof $1,609,753)
Special Collections: History, Culture & Contributions of Black People (Martin Luther King Coll); Michigan & Kalamazoo History
Automation Activity & Vendor Info: (Cataloging) Brodart
Publications: Directory of Human Services in Kalamazoo Area; Kalamazoo Gazette Index
Mem of Southwest Michigan Library Cooperative
Partic in Michigan Library Consortium
Friends of the Library Group
Branches: 7
ADULT SERVICES, 315 S Rose St, 49007-5264. Tel: 616-553-7801. FAX: 616-342-0414.
Friends of the Library Group
CHILDREN'S SERVICES, 315 S Rose St, 49007-5264. Tel: 616-553-7804.
EASTWOOD, 1112 Gayle St, 49007. SAN 346-7163. Tel: 616-345-6092. FAX: 616-345-6095. *Librn*, Nancy Stern
OSHTEMO, 7265 W Main St, 49007. SAN 346-7198. Tel: 616-375-5662. FAX: 616-375-6610. *Librn*, Cheryl McKenna
ALMA POWELL BRANCH, 1000 W Paterson St, 49007. SAN 346-7139. Tel: 616-344-0781. FAX: 616-344-0782.
REFERENCE, 315 S Rose St, 49007-5264. Tel: 616-553-7801. FAX: 616-342-0414.
WASHINGTON SQUARE, 1244 Portage Rd, 49001. SAN 346-7228. Tel; 616-345-4279. FAX: 616-342-9261. *Librn*, Nancy Smith
Bookmobiles: 1

J KALAMAZOO VALLEY COMMUNITY COLLEGE LIBRARY, 6767 W O Ave, 49009. (Mail add: PO Box 4070, 49003-4070), Interlibrary Loan Service Tel: 616-372-5380. Circulation Tel: 616-372-5328. Reference Tel: 616-312-5380. FAX: 616-372-5488. Web Site: www.kvcc.edu. *Dir*, Jim Ratliff; E-Mail: jratliff@kvcc.edu; *Coordr*, Pam Fox; Tel: 616-372-5332, E-Mail: pfox@kvcc.edu; *Cat*, Jackie Howlett; *Tech Servs*, Ann Lindsay; Staff 11 (MLS 4, Non-MLS 7)
Founded 1968. Enrl 12,009; Fac 124; Highest Degree: Associate
Jul 1999-Jun 2000 Mats Exp $138,719, Books $49,637, Per/Ser (Incl. Access Fees) $21,403, Presv $4,892, AV Equip $18,787, Electronic Ref Mat (Incl. Access Fees) $44,000. Sal $316,709 (Prof $227,689)
Library Holdings: Bk Vols 92,043; Per Subs 334; Bks on Deafness & Sign Lang 300
Subject Interests: Archives, Career, Sign lang
Special Collections: Alva Dorn Photography Coll; Mary Mace Spradling African American Coll; Michigan History (Ned Rubenstein Memorial Coll)
Database Vendor: Ebsco - EbscoHost, IAC - Info Trac, IAC - SearchBank, OCLC - First Search, ProQuest, Silverplatter Information Inc., Wilson - Wilson Web
Publications: Guides for Effective Use of the Library
Restriction: Restricted loan policy
Partic in Kalamazoo Consortium For Higher Education; Michigan Library Consortium; Southwest Michigan Library Cooperative

S KALSEC INFOCENTER,* 300 Turwill Lane, PO Box 50511, 49006-4232. SAN 327-4012. Tel: 616-349-9711. FAX: 616-349-2062. Web Site: www.kalsec.com. *In Charge*, Linda Bonzo; E-Mail: lbonzo@kalsec.com
Library Holdings: Bk Vols 5,000
Subject Interests: Chemistry

R SAINT LUKE'S EPISCOPAL CHURCH LIBRARY, 247 W Lovell St, 49007. SAN 308-2148. Tel: 616-345-8553. FAX: 616-345-5559. *Librn*, Jean Verseput
Library Holdings: Bk Vols 1,600
Friends of the Library Group

UPJOHN COMPANY

S BUSINESS LIBRARY, 7000 Portage Rd, 49001. SAN 346-7287. Tel: 616-833-4907. FAX: 616-833-6508. *Mgr*, Mark Oudersluys; *ILL, Online Servs*, Tammi S Colvin; Staff 5 (MLS 1, Non-MLS 4)
Founded 1959
Library Holdings: Bk Vols 5,000; Per Subs 100
Subject Interests: Biomedical engineering, Marketing
Publications: Guide to Personal Development; Monthly new materials
Restriction: By appointment only
Partic in Dialog Corporation; Dow Jones News Retrieval; OCLC Online Computer Library Center, Inc

M PHARMACIA AT UPJOHN RESEARCH LIBRARY, 301 Henrietta St, 49001-0199. SAN 346-7252. Tel: 616-833-0914. FAX: 616-833-8603. *Dir*, Fred Einspahr; Staff 31 (MLS 16, Non-MLS 15)
Founded 1941
Library Holdings: Bk Vols 24,000; Per Subs 700
Subject Interests: Biochemistry, Biomedical engineering, Chemistry, Pharmaceutical science, Pharmacology, Statistics
Publications: A Brief Guide to the Corporate Technical Library; Brief Guide to Using LIS; CTL News; Library Additions; Manual for the Preparation of Technical Reports; Preparation of Technical Reports, A Brief Guide

S W E UPJOHN INSTITUTE, Samuel V Bennett Library, 300 S Westnedge Ave, 49007-4868. SAN 371-8174. Tel: 616-343-5541, Ext 418. FAX: 616-343-3308. Web Site: www.upjohninst.org. *Librn*, Linda S Richer; *Asst Librn*, Babette A Schmitt; Staff 2 (MLS 1, Non-MLS 1)
Library Holdings: Bk Vols 8,500; Bk Titles 6,800; Per Subs 300
Subject Interests: Employment, Labour eco, Unemployment
Automation Activity & Vendor Info: (Cataloging) Sydney; (OPAC) Sydney; (Serials) Sydney
Database Vendor: OCLC - First Search
Restriction: Staff use only
Partic in Michigan Library Consortium

C WESTERN MICHIGAN UNIVERSITY, Dwight B Waldo Library, Arcadia at Vande Giessen St, 49008-5080. (Mail add: 1903 W Michigan Ave, 49008-5080), SAN 346-7341. Tel: 616-387-5202. Circulation Tel: 616-387-5156. Reference Tel: 616-387-5178. FAX: 616-387-5077, 616-387-5077. Web Site: www.wmich.edu/library. *Dean*, Dr Lance Query; E-Mail: lance.query@wmich.edu; *Actg Dean*, Joseph Reish; E-Mail: joe.reish@wmich.edu; *Coll Develop*, Bettina Meyer; Tel: 616-387-5143, E-Mail: bettina.meyer@wmich.edu; *Syst Coordr, Tech Coordr*, Dan Marmion; E-Mail: dan.marmion@wmich.edu; *Prof, Ser*, Marcia Kingsley; Tel: 616-387-5147, Fax: 616-387-5193, E-Mail: marcia.kingsley@wmich.edu; *Acq*, Donna Heady; *ILL*, Judy Garrison; Tel: 616-387-5172, Fax: 616-387-5124, E-Mail: judy.garrison@wmich.edu; *Prof, Spec Coll*, Dr Thomas Amos; Tel: 616-387-5221, E-Mail: tom.amos@wmich.edu; *Business*, Regina Buckner; E-Mail: regina.buckner@wmich.edu; *Head Ref*, Marie Perez-Stable; Tel: 616-387-5322, Fax: 616-387-5836, E-Mail: maria.perez-stable@wmich.edu; *Science*, Michael Buckner; Tel: 616-387-5141, Fax: 616-387-5180, E-Mail: michael.buckner@wmich.edu; *Govt Doc*, Michael McDonnell; Tel: 616-387-5187, Fax: 616-387-5012, E-Mail: michael.mcdonnell@wmich.edu; *Head, Cat, Prof*, Ellen Cha; Tel: 616-387-5166, Fax: 616-387-5193, E-Mail: ellen.cha@wmich.edu. Subject Specialists: *Bus*, Regina Buckner; *Children's literature*, Marie Perez-Stable; *Geography*, Michael McDonnell; *German*, Marcia Kingsley; *History*, Marie Perez-Stable; *Medieval studies*, Dr Thomas Amos; *Resource mgt*, Judy Garrison; Staff 96 (MLS 36, Non-MLS 60)
Founded 1903. Enrl 28,500; Fac 817; Highest Degree: Doctorate
Jul 1999-Jun 2000 Income (Main Library and Branch Library) $10,281,674, State $8,526, Federal $19,961, Locally Generated Income $149,360, Parent Institution $9,913,253, Other $190,574. Mats Exp $4,338,749, Books $1,005,469, Per/Ser (Incl. Access Fees) $2,730,667, Presv $67,733, Micro $85,970, Other Print Mats $31,734, Manuscripts & Archives $40,385, Electronic Ref Mat (Incl. Access Fees) $856,973. Sal $4,402,437 (Prof $2,116,582)
Library Holdings: Bk Vols 1,880,453; Bk Titles 937,095; Per Subs 7,262
Special Collections: African Studies (Ann Kercher Memorial); Cistercian Manuscript & Rare Book Coll; D B Waldo Lincoln Coll; Ecology (C C Adams Coll), pamphlets; Haenicke American Women's Poetry Coll; Historical Children's Book Coll; History (Regional History); LeFevre Miniature Book Coll; Medieval Studies (Institute of Cistercian Studies), bks, mss
Automation Activity & Vendor Info: (Acquisitions) Endeavor; (Cataloging) Endeavor; (Circulation) Endeavor; (Course Reserve) Endeavor; (Media Booking) Endeavor; (OPAC) Endeavor; (Serials) Endeavor
Database Vendor: GaleNet, IAC - Info Trac, IAC - SearchBank, Lexis-Nexis, OCLC - First Search, OVID Technologies, ProQuest, Silverplatter Information Inc.
Publications: Gatherings (newsletter)
Function: Reference services available
Partic in Michigan Library Consortium; Southwest Michigan Library Cooperative
Special Services for the Blind - Reading room
Friends of the Library Group
Departmental Libraries:
EDUCATION LIBRARY, 3300 Sangren Hall, 49008. (Mail add: 1093 W Michigan Ave, 49008), SAN 346-7430. Tel: 616-387-5223. FAX: 616-387-5231. Web Site: www.wmich.edu/library/depts/ed-library.html. *Asst Dean*, Bettina Meyer; Tel: 616-387-5143, Fax: 616-387-5077, E-Mail: bettina.meyer@wmich.edu; *Head of Libr*, Dennis Strasser; Tel: 616-387-5230, Fax: 616-387-5231, E-Mail: dennis.strasser@wmich.edu; Staff 5 (MLS 2, Non-MLS 3)
Enrl 28,500; Highest Degree: Doctorate
Library Holdings: Bk Vols 70,003; Bk Titles 56,613; Per Subs 600
Database Vendor: Dialog, GaleNet, IAC - Info Trac, IAC - SearchBank, Lexis-Nexis, OCLC - First Search, OVID Technologies, ProQuest, Silverplatter Information Inc.
Function: Reference services available, Research library
Partic in Michigan Library Consortium
Friends of the Library Group
MUSIC & DANCE, Dalton Ctr, 1903 W Michigan Ave, 49008. SAN 346-7465. Tel: 616-387-5237. FAX: 616-387-5809. Web Site: www.wmich.edu/library/depts/music-dance/. *Asst Dean*, Bettina Meyer; Tel: 616-387-5143, Fax: 616-387-5077, E-Mail: bettina.meyer@wmich.edu; *Head of Libr*, Greg Fitzgerald; Tel: 616-387-5236, E-Mail: gregory.fitzgerald@wmich.edu; Staff 2 (MLS 1, Non-MLS 1)
Enrl 28,500; Highest Degree: Doctorate
Library Holdings: Bk Vols 43,684; Bk Titles 35,656
Subject Interests: Dance, Music
Database Vendor: GaleNet, IAC - Info Trac, IAC - SearchBank, Lexis-Nexis, OCLC - First Search, OVID Technologies, ProQuest, Silverplatter Information Inc.
Function: Reference services available
Partic in Michigan Library Consortium
Friends of the Library Group
REGIONAL HISTORY COLLECTION & ARCHIVES, East Hall, 49008. (Mail add: 1903 W Michigan Ave, 49008), SAN 376-8864. Tel: 616-387-8490. Reference Tel: 616-387-8490. FAX: 616-387-8484. E-Mail: arch_collect@wmich.edu. Web Site: www.wmich.edu/library/depts/archives/. *Dir*, Sharon Carlson; Tel: 616-387-8490, Fax: 616-387-8484, E-Mail: sharon.carlson@wmich.edu; *Assoc Dean*, Bettina Meyer; Tel: 616-387-5143, Fax: 616-387-5077, E-Mail: bettina.meyer@wmich.edu
Founded 1958. Enrl 28,500; Highest Degree: Doctorate
Library Holdings: Bk Vols 17,114
Subject Interests: Census data, County govt rec, Gov doc
Special Collections: Western Michigan University Archives
Database Vendor: GaleNet, IAC - Info Trac, IAC - SearchBank, Lexis-Nexis, OCLC - First Search, OVID Technologies, ProQuest, Silverplatter Information Inc.
Restriction: Non-circulating, Not a lending library
Function: Archival collection
Partic in Michigan Library Consortium
Open Sept 1-June 30 Tues-Fri 8-5, Sat 9-4, July 1-Aug 31 Mon-Fri 10-4
Friends of the Library Group
VISUAL RESOURCES, 2213 Sangren Hall, 49008. (Mail add: 1903 W Michigan Ave, 49008), SAN 377-743X. Tel: 616-387-4111. FAX: 616-387-4114. Web Site: www.wmich.edu/library/vrl/index.html. *Asst Dean*, Bettina Meyer; Tel: 616-387-5143, Fax: 616-387-5077, E-Mail:

bettina.meyer@wmich.edu; *Head of Libr*, Miranda Haddock; Tel: 616-387-4113, Fax: 616-387-414, E-Mail: miranda.haddock@wmich.edu. Subject Specialists: *Art*, Miranda Haddock; *Costumes*, Miranda Haddock; Staff 2 (MLS 1, Non-MLS 1)
Founded 1998. Enrl 28,500; Highest Degree: Doctorate
Database Vendor: GaleNet, IAC - Info Trac, IAC - SearchBank, Lexis-Nexis, OCLC - First Search, OVID Technologies, ProQuest, Silverplatter Information Inc.
Function: Reference services available
Partic in Michigan Library Consortium
Friends of the Library Group

KALKASKA

P KALKASKA COUNTY LIBRARY,* 247 S Cedar St, 49646. (Mail add: PO Box 789, 49646-0789), SAN 308-2164. Tel: 231-258-9411. FAX: 231-258-9412. *Dir*, Kathleen Mosher; Staff 3 (MLS 1, Non-MLS 2)
Pop 11,000; Circ 34,327
Library Holdings: Bk Vols 30,000; Per Subs 45
Special Collections: Northern Michigan History
Mem of Mid-Michigan Library League
Partic in Dialog Corporation; SDC Info Servs
Friends of the Library Group
Bookmobiles: 1

KENTWOOD

R SAINT PAUL'S UNITED METHODIST CHURCH LIBRARY, 3334 Breton Rd SE, 49512. SAN 328-3224. Tel: 616-949-0880. FAX: 616-949-5787. *In Charge*, Marilyn Grimes
Library Holdings: Bk Vols 500

KINGSFORD

P MID-PENINSULA LIBRARY COOPERATIVE, 1525 Pyle Dr, 49802. SAN 308-1893. Tel: 906-774-3005, 906-774-6081. Toll Free Tel: 800-562-9257. FAX: 906-774-3074. Web Site: www.mid-pen.lib.mi.us. *Dir*, Barbara Brewer; E-Mail: brewerb@mid-pen.lib.mi.us; Staff 2 (MLS 2)
Founded 1964
Library Holdings: Bk Vols 5,000
Special Collections: Mail Order Library Coll; Michigan Upper Peninsula History
Publications: Ralph W Secord Press-55 reprint & original titles concerning local history in print
Member Libraries: Amasa Community Library; Bessemer Public Library; Carp Lake Township Library; Dickinson County Library; Gladstone Area School & Public Library; Ironwood Carnegie Public Library; McMillan Township Library; Menominee County Library; Ontonagon Township Library; West Iron District Library
Partic in Comt of Small Mag Ed & Publs; Michigan Library Consortium

KINGSTON

P JACQUELIN E OPPERMAN MEMORIAL LIBRARY, Kingston Community Public Library, 5790 State St, 48741. SAN 308-2180. Tel: 517-683-2500. FAX: 517-683-2081. *Dir*, Mila Brunner; Staff 2 (MLS 1, Non-MLS 1)
Founded 1970. Pop 4,000; Circ 22,000
Jul 1999-Jun 2000 Income Parent Institution $30,000. Mats Exp $8,300, Books $5,500, Per/Ser (Incl. Access Fees) $2,300, AV Equip $250, Electronic Ref Mat (Incl. Access Fees) $250. Sal $46,000
Library Holdings: Bk Vols 30,000; Bk Titles 28,000; Per Subs 85
Automation Activity & Vendor Info: (Acquisitions) Sagebrush Corporation; (Cataloging) Sagebrush Corporation; (Circulation) Sagebrush Corporation; (Course Reserve) Sagebrush Corporation; (ILL) epixtech, inc.; (Media Booking) Sagebrush Corporation; (OPAC) Sagebrush Corporation
Mem of White Pine Library Cooperative
Partic in White Pine Libr Coop

LAINGSBURG

P LAINGSBURG PUBLIC LIBRARY,* 255 E Grand River, PO Box 280, 48848-0254. SAN 308-2210. Tel: 517-651-6282. FAX: 517-651-6371. E-Mail: valleys@mic.lib.mi.us. *Dir*, Susan Pearce; *Asst Librn*, Peggy Hobart
Founded 1905. Pop 3,435; Circ 26,667
Library Holdings: Bk Titles 11,514; Per Subs 29
Subject Interests: Large type print, Local history
Partic in Mideastern Mich Libr Coop
Open Mon & Wed 9-5, Fri 9-7, Sat 9-1
Friends of the Library Group

LAKE CITY

P MISSAUKEE DISTRICT LIBRARY, 210 S Canal St, 49651-0340. (Mail add: PO Box 340, 49651), SAN 308-2229. Tel: 231-839-2166. FAX: 231-839-3865. *Dir*, Kathy J Glass; E-Mail: kate_81@hotmail.com; Staff 8 (MLS 1, Non-MLS 7)
Founded 1907. Pop 14,000; Circ 42,000
Oct 1998-Sep 1999 Income $184,609, State $10,066, City $58,248, County $56,640, Locally Generated Income $24,607, Other $35,048. Mats Exp $32,207, Books $17,574, Per/Ser (Incl. Access Fees) $7,000, AV Equip $2,234, Electronic Ref Mat (Incl. Access Fees) $5,399. Sal $75,000 (Prof $28,500)
Library Holdings: Bk Vols 40,000; Bk Titles 30,721; Per Subs 85
Special Collections: Local History
Function: ILL available
Mem of Mid-Michigan Library League

LAKE LINDEN

P LAKE LINDEN-HUBBELL PUBLIC & SCHOOL LIBRARY, 601 Calumet St, 49945. SAN 308-2237. Tel: 906-296-0698. Reference Tel: 906-296-8020. FAX: 906-296-9332. *Head Librn*, Elizabeth A Martin; E-Mail: martin@lakelinden.k12.mi.us; *Circ*, Julie Audette. Subject Specialists: *Soc studies*, Elizabeth A Martin; Staff 2 (MLS 1, Non-MLS 1)
Founded 1925. Pop 3,372; Circ 25,623
Library Holdings: Bk Titles 14,000; Per Subs 75
Automation Activity & Vendor Info: (Acquisitions) Sagebrush Corporation
Database Vendor: GaleNet, IAC - SearchBank, OCLC - First Search
Function: ILL available
Partic in Superiorland Libr Coop; Upper Peninsula Region Of Library Cooperation, Inc
Friends of the Library Group

LAKE ODESSA

P LAKE ODESSA COMMUNITY LIBRARY, 1007 Fourth Ave, 48849-1023. SAN 376-3714. Tel: 616-374-4591. FAX: 616-374-3054. E-Mail: lko@lakeland.lib.mi.us. Web Site: www.lakeland.lib.mi.us/lakeodessa/index.html. *Dir*, Connie Teachworth
Library Holdings: Bk Vols 18,000; Per Subs 26
Mem of Lakeland Library Cooperative
Friends of the Library Group

LAKE ORION

P ORION TOWNSHIP PUBLIC LIBRARY, 825 Joslyn Rd, 48362. SAN 346-752X. Tel: 248-693-3000. TDD: 248-693-4059. FAX: 248-693-3009. Web Site: www.orion.lib.mi.us. *Dir*, Linda C Sickles; *Ch Servs*, Linda Nixon; *Ad Servs*, Gene Williams; Staff 8 (MLS 7, Non-MLS 1)
Founded 1926. Pop 30,019; Circ 234,640
Jan 2000-Dec 2000 Income $1,888,000, State $58,000, Locally Generated Income $1,830,000. Mats Exp $214,500, Books $136,000, Per/Ser (Incl. Access Fees) $16,000, Other Print Mats $21,000, Electronic Ref Mat (Incl. Access Fees) $30,000. Sal $820,000 (Prof $248,000)
Library Holdings: Bk Vols 104,657; Per Subs 337
Subject Interests: Genealogy, Michigan
Automation Activity & Vendor Info: (Acquisitions) epixtech, inc.; (Cataloging) epixtech, inc.; (Circulation) epixtech, inc.
Publications: Quarterly newsletter
Mem of The Library Network
Special Services for the Deaf - TDD
Friends of the Library Group

LAKEVIEW

P TAMARACK PUBLIC LIBRARY, 407 E Lincoln Ave, PO Box 469, 48850. SAN 308-2245. Tel: 517-352-6274. FAX: 517-352-7713. E-Mail: lvw@lakeland.lib.mi.us. *Librn*, Sherry Mountney; Staff 2 (MLS 1, Non-MLS 1)
Founded 1965. Pop 8,093; Circ 33,620
Jul 1998-Jun 1999 Income $110,000. Mats Exp Books $12,000. Sal $56,000
Library Holdings: Bk Vols 19,000; Per Subs 65
Special Collections: Michigan Coll
Automation Activity & Vendor Info: (Cataloging) epixtech, inc.; (Circulation) epixtech, inc.; (ILL) epixtech, inc.; (OPAC) epixtech, inc.
Mem of Lakeland Library Cooperative
Friends of the Library Group

L'ANSE

P L'ANSE AREA SCHOOL-PUBLIC LIBRARY,* 201 N Fourth St, 49946-1499. SAN 308-2199. Tel: 906-524-6213. FAX: 906-524-5331. *Librn*, Bill A Bennett; *Asst Librn*, Debbie Perrow
Pop 9,140; Circ 7,978

Library Holdings: Bk Vols 16,500; Per Subs 63
Special Collections: Native American Coll
Mem of Superiorland Library Cooperative
Friends of the Library Group

LANSING

S AUTISM SOCIETY OF MICHIGAN LIBRARY, 6035 Executive Dr, Ste 109, 48911. SAN 374-9673. Tel: 517-882-2800. FAX: 517-882-2816. *Librn*, Anne Carpenter
Library Holdings: Bk Vols 700

P CAPITAL AREA DISTRICT LIBRARY, 401 S Capitol Ave, 48933. SAN 346-8453. Tel: 517-367-6300. FAX: 517-374-1068. Web Site: www.cadl.org. *Dir*, Susan J Hill; E-Mail: hills@cadl.org; *Asst Dir*, Nancy Bujold; E-Mail: bujoldn@cadl.org; *Selection of Gen Ref Mat*, Sarah Redman; E-Mail: redmans@cadl.org; *Syst Coordr*, Catherine Welscher; E-Mail: welscherc@cadl.org; Staff 93 (MLS 30, Non-MLS 63)
Pop 235,748; Circ 975,059
Jan 1999-Dec 1999 Income $6,763,600, State $250,000, Federal $127,600, Locally Generated Income $5,400,000, Other $986,000. Mats Exp $725,700, Books $452,000, Per/Ser (Incl. Access Fees) $48,000, Micro $15,000, Other Print Mats $210,700. Sal $2,992,892 (Prof $1,254,000)
Library Holdings: Bk Vols 318,000; Bk Titles 222,600
Automation Activity & Vendor Info: (Acquisitions) Innovative Interfaces Inc.; (Cataloging) Innovative Interfaces Inc.; (Circulation) Innovative Interfaces Inc.; (ILL) Innovative Interfaces Inc.; (OPAC) Innovative Interfaces Inc.
Database Vendor: Innovative Interfaces INN - View
Mem of Mideastern Michigan Library Cooperative
Partic in Michigan Library Consortium
Friends of the Library Group
Branches: 13
AURELIUS, Aurelius Township Hall, 1939 Aurelius Rd, Mason, 48854. SAN 346-8488. Tel: 517-628-3743. FAX: 517-628-2141. E-Mail: aur@cadl.org. *Head of Libr*, Eileen M Droscha; E-Mail: droschae@cadl.org; Staff 3 (Non-MLS 3)
Founded 1936
DANSVILLE BRANCH, 1379 E Mason St, Dansville, 48819. SAN 346-8518. Tel: 517-623-6511. FAX: 517-623-0520. *Librn*, Amy Bolt; E-Mail: bolta@cadl.org; Staff 3 (MLS 1, Non-MLS 2)
FOSTER, 200 N Foster, 48912. SAN 378-2425. Tel: 517-485-5185. FAX: 517-485-5239. E-Mail: fos@cadl.org. *Librn*, Jean S Bolley; E-Mail: bolleyj@cadl.org; Staff 3 (MLS 1, Non-MLS 2)
Friends of the Library Group
HASLETT BRANCH, 5670 School St, Haslett, 48840. SAN 346-8534. Tel: 517-339-2324. FAX: 517-339-0349. *Librn*, Cherry Hamrick; E-Mail: hamrickc@cadl.org; Staff 6 (MLS 1, Non-MLS 5)
Friends of the Library Group
HOLT-DELHI BRANCH, 2078 Aurelius Rd, Holt, 48842. SAN 346-8542. Tel: 517-694-9351. FAX: 517-699-3865. *In Charge*, Nancy Bujold; Staff 4 (Non-MLS 4)
Friends of the Library Group
LANSING LIBRARY & INFORMATION CENTER, 401 S Capitol Ave, 48933. SAN 377-7588. Tel: 517-325-6400. FAX: 517-367-6333. *Librn*, Kathy Johnson; E-Mail: johnsonk@cadl.org; Staff 15 (MLS 10, Non-MLS 5)
Friends of the Library Group
LESLIE BRANCH, 201 Pennsylvania St, Leslie, 49251. SAN 346-8607. Tel: 517-589-9400. FAX: 517-589-0536. *Head Librn*, Pat Worden; E-Mail: wordenp@cadl.org; Staff 3 (Non-MLS 3)
MASON BRANCH, 145 W Ash, Mason, 48854. SAN 346-8631. Tel: 517-676-9088. FAX: 517-676-3780. *Librn*, Sharlene Tietsort; E-Mail: tietsorts@cadl.org; Staff 4 (Non-MLS 4)
Friends of the Library Group
OKEMOS HOPE BORBAS BRANCH, 4660 Ardmore, Okemos, 48864. SAN 346-8666. Tel: 517-349-0250. FAX: 517-381-0396. *Ref Serv*, Joan C Smith; E-Mail: smithj@cadl.org; Staff 7 (MLS 1, Non-MLS 6)
Friends of the Library Group
SOUTH LANSING BRANCH, 3500 S Cedar St, Ste 108, 48910. SAN 378-2441. Tel: 517-272-9840. FAX: 517-272-9901. *Librn*, Virginia McKane; E-Mail: mckanev@cadl.org; Staff 5 (MLS 1, Non-MLS 4)
Friends of the Library Group
STOCKBRIDGE BRANCH, 200 Wood, Stockbridge, 49285. SAN 346-8690. Tel: 517-851-7810. FAX: 517-851-8612. *Librn*, Paul Crandall; E-Mail: crandallp@cadl.org; Staff 5 (MLS 1, Non-MLS 4)
WEBBERVILLE BRANCH, 115 S Main St, Webberville, 48892. SAN 346-8755. Tel: 517-521-3643. FAX: 517-521-1079. *Librn*, Cheryl Miceli; E-Mail: micelic@cadl.org; Staff 3 (Non-MLS 3)
WILLIAMSTON BRANCH, 175 E Grand River, Williamston, 48895. SAN 346-878X. Tel: 517-655-1191. FAX: 517-655-5243. *Librn*, JoAnn Hegedus; E-Mail: hegedusj@cadl.org; Staff 5 (MLS 1, Non-MLS 4)
Friends of the Library Group
Bookmobiles: 1

CR GREAT LAKES CHRISTIAN COLLEGE, Louis M Detro Memorial Library, 6211 W Willow Hwy, 48917. SAN 308-227X. Tel: 517-321-0242, Ext 237. FAX: 517-321-5902. E-Mail: poss@poss.edu. *Librn*, Keith Upton
Founded 1949. Enrl 165; Fac 13; Highest Degree: Bachelor
Library Holdings: Bk Vols 43,000; Per Subs 230
Subject Interests: History, Language arts, Music, Theology
Special Collections: Bibles; C S Lewis
Partic in Cap Area Libr Network Inc; Michigan Library Consortium

M INGHAM REGIONAL MEDICAL CENTER, John W Chi Memorial Medical Library, 401 W Greenlawn Ave, 48910-2819. SAN 320-3840. Tel: 517-334-2270. FAX: 517-334-2939. *Dir, Online Servs*, Judy Barnes; E-Mail: barnesja@irmcmail.irmc.org; *Acq*, Mary Andrick; Staff 5 (MLS 1, Non-MLS 4)
Founded 1960
Oct 1999-Sep 2000 Mats Exp $242,000, Books $90,000, Per/Ser (Incl. Access Fees) $106,000, Presv $27,000, Micro $12,000, Electronic Ref Mat (Incl. Access Fees) $7,000. Sal $153,926
Library Holdings: Bk Titles 9,000; Per Subs 800
Subject Interests: Allied health, Consumer health, Medicine, Nursing, Osteopathy, Pharmacology
Database Vendor: OCLC - First Search
Publications: Acquisition list (monthly)
Partic in Docline; Michigan Health Sciences Libraries Association; MLC; National Network Of Libraries Of Medicine; OCLC Online Computer Library Center, Inc
Branches:

C LANSING COMMUNITY COLLEGE LIBRARY, 419 N Capitol Ave, PO Box 40010, 48901-7210. SAN 346-7589. Tel: 517-483-1657. Circulation Tel: 517-483-1626. Reference Tel: 517-483-1615. TDD: 517-483-1615. FAX: 517-483-5300. E-Mail: er1657@lois.lansing.cc.mi.us. Web Site: www.lansing.cc.mi.us/library/. *Dir Libr Serv*, Elenka Raschkow; Tel: 517-483-1639, E-Mail: raschke@lansing.cc.mi.us; *ILL*, Barbara Shipman; *Distance Educ*, Debby Harris; Tel: 517-483-5241, E-Mail: dharris@lansing.cc.mi.us; *Syst Coordr*, Matt Rademacher; Tel: 517-483-1644, E-Mail: mrademac@lansing.cc.mi.us; *Bibliog Instr*, Kim Farley; Tel: 517-483-1662, E-Mail: kfarley@lansing.cc.mi.us; *Coll Develop*, Bill Kemper; Tel: 517-483-9716, E-Mail: kemper@lansing.cc.mi.us; *Online Servs*, Suzanne Sawyer; Tel: 517-483-9717, E-Mail: sawyers@lansing.cc.mi.us; *Librn, Publ Servs*, Jane Reiter; Tel: 517-483-9656, E-Mail: jreiter@lansing.cc.mi.us; Staff 22 (MLS 8, Non-MLS 14)
Founded 1959. Enrl 16,000
Jul 2000-Jun 2001 Income Parent Institution $1,367,659. Mats Exp $375,181, Books $83,466, Per/Ser (Incl. Access Fees) $81,725, Micro $4,682, AV Equip $4,957, Other Print Mats $25,000, Electronic Ref Mat (Incl. Access Fees) $175,351. Sal $889,601 (Prof $536,188)
Library Holdings: Bk Vols 100,612; Bk Titles 93,512; Per Subs 650
Subject Interests: Computer science, Criminal law and justice, Hotel administration, Law, Medicine, Photography, Travel
Special Collections: Easy Reading Browsing & Career Coll
Automation Activity & Vendor Info: (Acquisitions) Innovative Interfaces Inc.; (Cataloging) Innovative Interfaces Inc.; (Circulation) Innovative Interfaces Inc.; (ILL) Innovative Interfaces Inc.; (Media Booking) Innovative Interfaces Inc.; (OPAC) Innovative Interfaces Inc.; (Serials) Innovative Interfaces Inc.
Database Vendor: Dialog, Ebsco - EbscoHost, GaleNet, IAC - Info Trac, OCLC - First Search, ProQuest, Wilson - Wilson Web
Publications: Focus on (series); Link (library-faculty newsletter)
Function: Reference services available
Partic in Michigan Library Consortium; OCLC Online Computer Library Center, Inc
Special Services for the Deaf - TDD

S LANSING STATE JOURNAL LIBRARY, 120 E Lenawee, 48919. SAN 308-2350. Tel: 517-377-1008. FAX: 517-377-1298. *Chief Librn*, Pam Gawronski
Founded 1950
Library Holdings: Bk Vols 900

P LIBRARY OF MICHIGAN, 717 W Allegan, 48915. (Mail add: PO Box 30007, 48909), SAN 346-7708. Tel: 517-373-1580. TDD: 517-373-8937. FAX: 517-373-5815. Web Site: www.libofmich.lib.mi.us. *State Librn*, Christie Pearson Brandau; *Mgr*, Sue Adamczak; *Info Tech*, Paul Groll; *Business*, Janet Laverty; *Publ Servs*, Susan Nearing; *Rare Bks, Tech Servs*, Nancy Robertson; *Govt Doc*, Ann Sanders; *Coll Develop*, Kirsten Lietz; *Syst Coordr*, Fukang Wang; *Acq, Doc, Ser*, Kim Laird; Tel: 517-373-1574, Fax: 517-373-9438, E-Mail: klaird@libraryofmichigan.org; *Spec Coll*, Randy Riley; Tel: 517-373-5860; *Cat*, Don Todaro. Subject Specialists: *Law*, Ellen Richardson
Founded 1828. Pop 9,295,297
Oct 1998-Sep 1999 Income (Main Library Only) State $7,572,900. Mats Exp $1,047,320, Books $642,071, Per/Ser (Incl. Access Fees) $203,440, Presv $15,865, Micro $91,314, AV Equip $3,405, Manuscripts & Archives $40,896, Electronic Ref Mat (Incl. Access Fees) $50,329. Sal $5,331,376 (Prof $2,917,644)
Library Holdings: Bk Vols 4,639,078; Bk Titles 2,578,680; Per Subs 13,340

Subject Interests: Genealogy, Law, Michigan, Pub policy, Talking books
Special Collections: Federal & Michigan Document Coll; Michigan Resources Coll; Rare Book Room
Automation Activity & Vendor Info: (Acquisitions) Innovative Interfaces Inc.; (Cataloging) Innovative Interfaces Inc.; (Circulation) Innovative Interfaces Inc.; (OPAC) Innovative Interfaces Inc.; (Serials) Innovative Interfaces Inc.
Publications: Abrams Collection Genealogy Highlights; Annual Report of Library of Michigan; Blind & Physically Handicapped Perspective (newsletter); ILL Protocol & Guidelines; Library of Michigan Access Newsletter; Library of Michigan Foundation Focus (newsletter); Library of Michigan Library Laws Handbook; Library of Michigan Long Range Plan; LSCA Long Range Program; LSCA Report; Michigan 1870 Census Index; Michigan Cemetery Atlas; Michigan Documents; Michigan Library Directory; Michigan Library Statistics; Personnel Certification & other brochures; Sourcebook of Michigan Census; State Aid Guidelines
Partic in Michigan Library Consortium
Over 100,000 reference, research questions & title requests are processed for libraries & library users. The Library of Michigan coordinates & administers services & grants to legally established library cooperative & public libraries, multi-type regions & subregional libraries for the blind & physically handicapped. The Library distributes 84,713 Michigan document volumes a year to libraries around the state. There were 314 federal document questions answered from libraries of all types
Branches: 2

L LAW LIBRARY, 525 W Ottawa, PO Box 30007, 48909. SAN 370-9353. Tel: 517-373-0630. FAX: 517-373-3915. *Librn*, Sue Adamczak

P LIBRARY OF MICHIGAN SERVICE FOR THE BLIND & PHYSICALLY HANDICAPPED,* PO Box 30007, 48909. SAN 308-2334. Tel: 517-373-5353. Toll Free Tel: 800-992-9012. FAX: 517-373-5700. *Mgr*, Maggie Bacon; Staff 11 (MLS 3, Non-MLS 8)
Founded 1931
Library Holdings: Bk Vols 275,000
Special Collections: Finnish Language, (cassettes); Michigan History & Authors, cassettes
Publications: LMSBPH Perspective (quarterly, available in large print, braille, cassette)
Special Services - Volunteer taping & brailling services to registered institutions, schools & individuals. Open Mon-Fri 8am-6pm

G MICHIGAN DEPARTMENT OF COMMUNITY HEALTH, Library Resource Center,* 3423 N Martin Luther King Jr Blvd, PO Box 30195, 48909. SAN 308-2350. Tel: 517-335-8394. FAX: 517-335-9397. *Asst Librn*, Ann Mattson; E-Mail: mattsona@state.mi.us
Founded 1873
Library Holdings: Bk Vols 10,000; Per Subs 200
Special Collections: Agent Orange Coll

G MICHIGAN DEPARTMENT OF NATURAL RESOURCES, DNR Fisheries Division Library,* Stevens Mason Bldg, 4th flr, PO Box 30446, 48909. SAN 329-0670. Tel: 517-373-1280. FAX: 517-373-0381. *Asst Librn*, S Jurney; Staff 2 (MLS 1, Non-MLS 1)
Founded 1872
Library Holdings: Bk Titles 1,000; Per Subs 20
Publications: Fisheres Technical Reports; IFR Reports
Restriction: Staff use only
Partic in Dialog Corporation

G MICHIGAN DEPARTMENT OF STATE POLICE, Law Enforcement Resource Center,* 7426 N Canal Rd, 48913. SAN 329-2878. Tel: 517-322-1976. FAX: 517-322-1130. *Librn*, Mary LePiors; E-Mail: lepiorsm@mlc.lib.mi.us; Staff 2 (MLS 2)
Founded 1979
Library Holdings: Bk Vols 4,231; Per Subs 20
Subject Interests: Law enforcement
Partic in Cap Area Libr Network Inc

S MICHIGAN DEPARTMENT OF STATE-HISTORICAL CENTER, State Archives, 717 W Allegan, 48918-1837. SAN 308-2326. Tel: 517-373-1408. Reference Tel: 517-373-1414. FAX: 517-241-1658. E-Mail: archives@state.mi.us. Web Site: www.sos.state.mi.us/history/archive/. *Archivist, Ref Serv*, Mark Harvey; *Archivist*, David J Johnson
Founded 1913
Library Holdings: Bk Vols 500
Special Collections: State & Local Government Records & Personal Papers
Friends of the Library Group

G MICHIGAN DEPARTMENT OF TRANSPORTATION INFORMATION SERVICES,* 425 W Ottawa, PO Box 30050, 48909. SAN 308-2318. Tel: 517-373-1545. FAX: 517-373-0168. *Mgr*, Jeanne F Thomas; E-Mail: thomasj@mdot.state.mi.us
Founded 1964
Library Holdings: Bk Vols 23,000; Bk Titles 9,000; Per Subs 275
Subject Interests: Transportation
Special Collections: Transportation Research Board
Partic in Cap Area Libr Consortium; Michigan Library Consortium; OCLC Online Computer Library Center, Inc

G MICHIGAN FAMILY INDEPENDENCE AGENCY, Grand Tower, 235 Grand Ave, Ste 708, 48919. SAN 373-2118. Tel: 517-373-2390. FAX: 517-335-6221. *Mgr*, Karen Cowles; *Coordr*, Joy Price
Library Holdings: Bk Vols 100

G MICHIGAN PROTECTION & ADVOCACY SERVICE LIBRARY,* 106 W Allegan St, Ste 300, 48933-1706. SAN 373-2126. Tel: 517-487-1755. Toll Free Tel: 800-288-5923. FAX: 517-487-0827. *Exec Dir*, Liz Bauer
Library Holdings: Bk Vols 67; Per Subs 19
Subject Interests: Mental health, Special education

G MICHIGAN STATE DEPARTMENT OF ENVIRONMENTAL QUALITY LIBRARY, 300 S Washington Sq 2nd flr, 48933. SAN 371-733X. Tel: 517-241-9536. FAX: 517-373-9958. *Librn*, Emily Weingartz; E-Mail: weingare@state.mi.us
Founded 1981
Library Holdings: Bk Titles 5,000
Subject Interests: Great Lakes, Pollution, Toxicology
Restriction: Non-circulating to the public
Partic in Sci & Tech Info Network

G MICHIGAN STATE LEGISLATIVE SERVICE BUREAU,* Michigan National Tower, 4th flr, PO Box 30036, 48909-7536. SAN 326-4203. Tel: 517-373-0472. FAX: 517-373-0171. *Dir*, Leo Kennedy; Staff 1 (MLS 1)
Founded 1941
Library Holdings: Bk Vols 17,350; Bk Titles 15,750; Per Subs 115
Subject Interests: Government, Law
Special Collections: Legislative Reports (docs); Michigan Law (bks)
Publications: Guide to Legal Research in the Legislative Service Bureau Library; Legislative Service Bureau Library Periodicals List; Legislative Service Bureau Library Periodicals list by Subject; Recent Acquisitions in the Legislative Service Bureau Library

S RIGHT TO LIFE OF MICHIGAN, Resource Center, 618 Seymour, 48933. SAN 373-210X. Tel: 517-487-3376. FAX: 517-487-6453. Web Site: www.rtl.org. *Coordr*, Laura Hammes
Library Holdings: Bk Vols 200

M SPARROW HOSPITAL, Medical Library, 1215 E Michigan Ave, PO Box 30480, 48909-7980. SAN 308-2342. Tel: 517-483-2274. FAX: 517-483-2273.; Staff 4 (MLS 1, Non-MLS 3)
Library Holdings: Bk Vols 3,780; Bk Titles 2,900; Per Subs 315
Subject Interests: Nursing

L STATE BAR OF MICHIGAN LIBRARY,* 306 Townsend St, 48933. SAN 327-3970. Tel: 517-372-9030, Ext 6379. FAX: 517-482-6248. *Librn*, Evie Breedlove
Library Holdings: Bk Vols 2,500; Per Subs 30

CL THOMAS M COOLEY LAW SCHOOL LIBRARY, 300 S Capitol Ave, 48901. (Mail add: PO Box 13038, 48901-3038), SAN 308-2261. Tel: 517-371-5140. Circulation Tel: 517-371-5140, Ext 3100. Reference Tel: 517-371-5140, Ext 3111. FAX: 517-334-5715. Web Site: www.cooley.edu. *Dir*, Roberta Studwell; *Assoc Dir*, Duane Strojny; *Librn*, Aletha Honsowitz; *Librn*, Sharon Bradley; *Librn*, John Michaud; *Cat*, Pamela Bartlett; *Circ*, Tim Innes; *Publ Servs*, Rita Marsala; *Ser*, Ann Lucas; *ILL*, Ardena Walsh; Staff 10 (MLS 10)
Founded 1972. Enrl 1,600; Fac 60; Highest Degree: Doctorate
Jan 1999-Dec 1999 Income $3,850,000. Mats Exp $1,060,000, Books $85,000, Per/Ser (Incl. Access Fees) $800,000, Presv $20,000, Micro $115,000, Electronic Ref Mat (Incl. Access Fees) $40,000. Sal $2,211,000
Library Holdings: Bk Vols 400,000; Bk Titles 150,000; Per Subs 5,433
Special Collections: Michigan Supreme Court Records & Briefs (1907-present), bound volumes
Automation Activity & Vendor Info: (Acquisitions) Innovative Interfaces Inc.; (Cataloging) Innovative Interfaces Inc.; (Circulation) Innovative Interfaces Inc.; (Course Reserve) Innovative Interfaces Inc.; (OPAC) Innovative Interfaces Inc.; (Serials) Innovative Interfaces Inc.
Publications: Library Research Guides (various subjects); User's Guide to the Thomas M Cooley Law School Library
Partic in First Search; Michigan Library Consortium; OCLC Online Computer Library Center, Inc; Westlaw

LAPEER

P LAPEER COUNTY LIBRARY,* 201 Village West Dr S, 48446-1699. SAN 346-7791. Tel: 810-664-9521. FAX: 810-664-8527. Web Site: www.lapeer.lib.mi.us. *Dir*, Phyllis Clark; E-Mail: pclark@gfn.org; *Asst Dir*, June Mendel; *Ch Servs*, Janet Curtis; Staff 38 (MLS 3, Non-MLS 35)
Founded 1939. Pop 49,237
Library Holdings: Bk Vols 102,236; Per Subs 210
Special Collections: local history, bks, news clippings; Marguerite de Angeli
Mem of Mideastern Michigan Library Cooperative
Partic in Dialog Corporation
Friends of the Library Group
Branches: 8
CLIFFORD, 9530 Main St, PO Box 233, 48727. SAN 346-7821. Tel: 517-761-7393. FAX: 517-761-7541. Web Site: www.lapeer.lib.mi.us. *Librn*,

Linda Long
Library Holdings: Bk Titles 4,240
COLUMBIAVILLE BRANCH, 4718 First St, PO Box 190, Columbiaville, 48421. SAN 346-7856. Tel: 810-793-6100. FAX: 810-793-6243. Web Site: www.lapeer.lib.mi.us. *Librn*, Barbara Harris
Library Holdings: Bk Titles 6,338
Friends of the Library Group
ELBA, 5508 Davison Rd, 48446. SAN 346-7880. Tel: 810-653-7200. FAX: 810-653-4267. Web Site: www.lapeer.lib.mi.us. *Librn*, Nina Flowers
Library Holdings: Bk Titles 2,618
GOODLAND, 2374 N VanDyke Rd, Imlay City, 48444. SAN 346-7910. Tel: 810-724-1970. FAX: 810-724-5612. Web Site: www.lapeer.lib.mi.us. *Librn*, Kathy Arnold
Library Holdings: Bk Titles 2,695
Subject Interests: Genealogy
Friends of the Library Group
HADLEY BRANCH, 3556 Hadley Rd, PO Box 199, Hadley, 48440. SAN 346-7945. Tel: 810-797-4101. FAX: 810-797-2912. Web Site: www.lapeer.lib.mi.us. *Librn*, Debi Rasmussen; *Librn*, Lin Youngblood
Library Holdings: Bk Titles 8,833
Friends of the Library Group
MARGUERITE DE ANGELI BRANCH, 921 W Nepessing St, 48446. SAN 346-797X. Tel: 810-664-6971. FAX: 810-664-5581. Web Site: www.lapeer.lib.mi.us. *Librn*, June Mendel
Library Holdings: Bk Vols 69,078
Special Collections: Career Resource Center; Collection & Exhibit on Marguerite deAngeli; Genealogy
Friends of the Library Group
METAMORA BRANCH, 4018 Oak St, PO Box 77, Metamora, 48455. SAN 346-8003. Tel: 810-678-2991. FAX: 810-678-3253. Web Site: www.lapeer.lib.mi.us. *Librn*, Pam Orr; *Librn*, Carol Kellerman
Library Holdings: Bk Titles 3,884
Special Collections: Michigan Coll
Friends of the Library Group
OTTER LAKE BRANCH, 6361 Detroit St, PO Box 185, Otter Lake, 48464. SAN 346-8038. Tel: 810-793-6300. FAX: 810-793-7040. Web Site: www.lapeer.lib.mi.us. *Librn*, Gena Bunch
Library Holdings: Bk Titles 4,341
Friends of the Library Group

LAWTON

P LAWTON PUBLIC LIBRARY, 125 Main St, PO Drawer 520, 49065-0520. SAN 308-2369. Tel: 616-624-5481. FAX: 616-624-1385. *Asst Librn*, Mary C Roussel
Circ 17,680
Library Holdings: Bk Vols 25,000; Per Subs 56
Automation Activity & Vendor Info: (Cataloging) Follett
Mem of Southwest Michigan Library Cooperative
Closed Thurs & Sun

LE ROY

P LEROY COMMUNITY LIBRARY,* 104 W Gilbert, PO Box 110, 49655-0110. SAN 308-2377. Tel: 231-768-4493. FAX: 231-768-4493. *Librn*, Kim Nelson; *Asst Librn*, Yvonne Peterson
Circ 5,736
Library Holdings: Bk Vols 4,000; Per Subs 40
Subject Interests: Michigan
Mem of Mid-Michigan Library League
Partic in Mich Libr Asn

LELAND

S LEELANAU HISTORICAL SOCIETY, INC, Leelanau Historical Museum,* 203 E Cedar St, PO Box 246, 49654-0246. SAN 371-5698. Tel: 616-256-7475. FAX: 616-256-7650. E-Mail: leemuse@traverse.com. *Curator*, Laura J Quackenbush; *Dir*, R Mark Livengood
1997-1998 Income $116,000, Locally Generated Income $110,000, Other $6,000
Library Holdings: Bk Vols 500

P LELAND TOWNSHIP PUBLIC LIBRARY,* 203 E Cedar, PO Box 736, 49654-0736. SAN 308-2385. Tel: 231-256-9152. FAX: 231-256-8847. *Librn*, Daniel Jamieson
Circ 12,000
Library Holdings: Bk Vols 35,000; Per Subs 50
Special Collections: Michigan History Coll
Friends of the Library Group

LEONARD

P ADDISON TOWNSHIP PUBLIC LIBARY,* 1440 Rochester Rd, 48367-3555. SAN 376-6152. Tel: 248-628-7180. FAX: 248-628-6109. *Dir*, Michele Priesley
Jan 1997-Dec 1998 Income $116,091
Library Holdings: Bk Titles 15,000; Per Subs 54
Mem of The Library Network

LEWISTON

P LEWISTON LIBRARY,* PO Box 148, 49756-0148. SAN 376-5865. Tel: 517-786-2985. FAX: 517-786-2985. *Librn*, Margaret Kujala
Library Holdings: Bk Vols 7,025

LEXINGTON

P MOORE PUBLIC LIBRARY, 7239 Huron Ave, PO Box 189, 48450-0189. (Mail add: PO Box 189, 48450), SAN 308-2393. Interlibrary Loan Service Tel: 810-359-8267. FAX: 810-359-2986. E-Mail: moorepl@greatlakes.net. *Dir*, Marjorie Ann Fruge
Founded 1903. Pop 3,851; Circ 14,787
1998-1999 Income $77,286, State $6,456, City $2,500, Locally Generated Income $2,800, Other $2,631. Mats Exp $13,340, Books $8,256, Per/Ser (Incl. Access Fees) $1,335. Sal $28,073 (Prof $11,896)
Library Holdings: Bk Titles 14,791; Per Subs 43
Automation Activity & Vendor Info: (Circulation) Sagebrush Corporation
Mem of White Pine Library Cooperative
Open Mon 3-8, Wed & Fri 10-5, Sat 10-3

LINCOLN PARK

P LINCOLN PARK PUBLIC LIBRARY,* 1381 Southfield Rd, 48146. SAN 308-2415. Tel: 313-381-0374. FAX: 313-381-2205. Web Site: www.lincoln-park.lib.mi.us. *Dir*, Linda Baum
Founded 1925. Pop 41,832; Circ 65,501
Library Holdings: Bk Vols 48,928; Per Subs 110
Mem of The Library Network
Friends of the Library Group

LITCHFIELD

P LITCHFIELD DISTRICT LIBRARY,* 108 N Chicago St, Box 357, 49252-0357. SAN 308-2423. Tel: 517-542-3887. FAX: 517-542-3207. *Dir*, Paula Wykes
Library Holdings: Bk Vols 11,000; Bk Titles 10,000; Per Subs 12
Mem of Woodlands Library Cooperative

LIVONIA

P LIVONIA PUBLIC LIBRARY,* 32777 Five Mile Rd, 48154-3045. SAN 346-8062. Tel: 734-466-2450. FAX: 734-458-6011. Web Site: livonia.lib.mi.us. *Dir*, A Michael Deller; Staff 90 (MLS 22, Non-MLS 68)
Founded 1958. Pop 100,850; Circ 726,447
Dec 1997-Nov 1998 Income (Main Library and Branch Library) $4,069,458, State $98,247, City $3,650,196, Federal $26,550, County $131,105, Locally Generated Income $163,360. Mats Exp $337,000, Books $307,000, AV Equip $30,000. Sal $2,654,676
Library Holdings: Bk Vols 271,975; Per Subs 654
Automation Activity & Vendor Info: (Cataloging) DRA; (Circulation) DRA; (OPAC) DRA
Mem of The Library Network
Partic in Libr Network
Special Services for the Deaf - TTY machine
Friends of the Library Group
Branches: 4
ALFRED NOBLE BRANCH, 32901 Plymouth Rd, 48150-1793. SAN 346-8097. Tel: 734-421-6600. FAX: 734-421-6606. *Librn*, Carol Harrison; *Ch Servs*, Catherine Huch
Library Holdings: Bk Vols 58,755
Friends of the Library Group
CARL SANDBURG BRANCH, 30100 W Seven Mile Rd, 48152-1918. SAN 346-8127. Tel: 248-476-0700. FAX: 248-476-6230. *Ch Servs*, Dottie Sagoian; *Librn*, Toni Laporte
Library Holdings: Bk Vols 51,052
Friends of the Library Group
CIVIC CENTER LIBRARY, 32777 Five Mile Rd, 48154-3045. SAN 328-9796. Tel: 734-466-2450. FAX: 734-458-6011. *Automation Syst Coordr, Circ*, Delores Hayden; *Ad Servs*, Kathleen Monroe; *Ch Servs*, Trinidad Turse
Founded 1988
Library Holdings: Bk Vols 164,971

Friends of the Library Group
VEST POCKET, 15128 Farmington Rd, 48154-5417. SAN 346-8151. Tel: 734-466-2559. *Librn*, Toni Laporte
Library Holdings: Bk Vols 6,475
Friends of the Library Group

C MADONNA UNIVERSITY LIBRARY, 36600 Schoolcraft Rd, 48150-1173. SAN 346-8186. Tel: 734-432-5703. Interlibrary Loan Service Tel: 734-452-5679. FAX: 734-432-5687. Web Site: ww3.munet.edu/library. *Dir*, Joanne Lumetta; Tel: 734-432-5689, E-Mail: lumetta@smtp.munet.edu; *Coll Develop*, William Alexander Vine; Tel: 734-432-5685, E-Mail: vine@smtp.munet.edu; Staff 18 (MLS 8, Non-MLS 10)
Founded 1947
Library Holdings: Bk Vols 163,678; Bk Titles 81,839; Per Subs 1,106
Subject Interests: Education, Language arts, Literature, Nursing
Special Collections: Artifacts from Diverse Ethnic Cultures; Institutional Archives; Rare Book Collection; Transcultural Nursing Materials (Madeline Leininger Coll)
Automation Activity & Vendor Info: (Acquisitions) epixtech, inc.; (Cataloging) epixtech, inc.; (Circulation) epixtech, inc.; (Course Reserve) epixtech, inc.; (OPAC) epixtech, inc.; (Serials) epixtech, inc.
Database Vendor: epixtech, inc., IAC - Info Trac, Lexis-Nexis, OCLC - First Search, Silverplatter Information Inc., Wilson - Wilson Web
Publications: CD-ROM Guide Series; Information Guide Series; Library Handbook; New Book List; Reference Guide Series; Subject Guide Series
Partic in Dialog Corporation; Michigan Library Consortium; OCLC Online Computer Library Center, Inc; Southeastern Michigan League Of Libraries; Westlaw

M SAINT MARY HOSPITAL, Medical Library,* 36475 Five Mile Rd, 48154. SAN 308-2431. Tel: 734-655-2360, 734-655-2600, Ext 2360. FAX: 734-655-2641. *Mgr*, Christine Miller; Fax: 734-591-2666, E-Mail: christine_miller@stmaryhospital.org; Staff 1 (MLS 1)
Founded 1959
Library Holdings: Bk Titles 1,500; Per Subs 75
Subject Interests: Dermatology, Internal medicine, Nuclear medicine, Nutrition, Obstetrics and gynecology, Orthopedics, Pediatrics, Pharmacology, Surgery
Partic in Metrop Detroit Med Libr Group

J SCHOOLCRAFT COLLEGE, Eric J Bradner Library, 18600 Haggerty Rd, 48152-2696. SAN 308-244X. Tel: 734-462-4400, Ext 5440. FAX: 734-462-4495. E-Mail: library@schoolcraft.cc.mi.us. Web Site: www.schoolcraft.cc.mi.us/library/internet.htm. *Assoc Dean*, Jeanne Bonner; *Ref*, Roy Nuffer; *ILL, Ref*, Wayne Pricer; *Acq*, Gale Buchanan; *Doc, Per*, Janet Schneider; *Tech Servs*, Diane Nesbit
Founded 1964
Library Holdings: Bk Vols 95,000; Per Subs 650
Departmental Libraries:
RADCLIFF CENTER AT GARDEN CITY LIBRARY, 1751 Radcliff, Garden City, 48135. SAN 329-2630. Tel: 734-462-4400, Ext 6019. FAX: 734-462-4743. *Librn*, Graham Burrell
Library Holdings: Bk Vols 13,000; Per Subs 228

S TRW AUTOMOTIVE LIBRARY, 12075 Tech Center Dr, Ste 2, 48150-2172. SAN 326-3142. Tel: 734-266-1478. FAX: 734-266-1671. *Librn*, Steven Johnson; E-Mail: steve.johnson@trw.com
Library Holdings: Bk Titles 300; Per Subs 50

LUDINGTON

P MASON COUNTY DISTRICT LIBRARY, Ludington Branch, 217 E Ludington Ave, PO Box 549, 49431. SAN 308-2458. Tel: 231-843-8465. FAX: 231-843-1491. Web Site: www.masoncounty.lib.mi.us. *Dir*, Robert T Dickson; E-Mail: rdickson@masoncounty.lib.mi.us; *Asst Dir*, Susan Carlson; E-Mail: scarlson@masoncounty.lib.mi.us; Staff 10 (MLS 1, Non-MLS 9)
Founded 1905. Pop 26,000; Circ 150,000
Library Holdings: Bk Vols 140,000; Per Subs 200
Special Collections: Genealogical Coll of Mason County
Publications: Friends of LPL Potpourri (newsletter); Subject bibliographies
Mem of Mid-Michigan Library League
Partic in OCLC Online Computer Library Center, Inc
Outreach to home-bound, hospital, nursing homes; story hours, summer children's reading program; free adult & children's film services; tours & library instruction for elementary, jr high and high schools; custom photocopy service; tax-beneficial memorial & gift donation program
Friends of the Library Group

M MEMORIAL MEDICAL CENTER OF WEST MICHIGAN LIBRARY,* One Atkinson Dr, 49431. SAN 327-3954. Tel: 616-843-2591, 616-845-2362. FAX: 616-845-2292. *Dir*, Dr Marc Keene
Library Holdings: Bk Vols 100

S WHITE PINE VILLAGE, Historical Village Research Library, White Pine Village, 1687 S Lakeshore Dr, 49431. SAN 321-4702. Tel: 231-843-4808. FAX: 231-843-7089. E-Mail: wpv@masoncounty.net. Web Site: www.lumanet.org/whitepine. *Dir*, Ronald M Wood
Founded 1937
Library Holdings: Bk Titles 700; Per Subs 10
Subject Interests: Agriculture, Civil War, Genealogy, Local history, Lumbering, Maritime
Special Collections: Business-Lumbering (Charles Mears Coll), diaries; Civil War (B S Mills Coll); Civil War (Hazel Oldt Coll), letters; Documentary on Wintertime Car Ferry Service across Lake Michigan, video; Lumbering (Jake Lunde Coll), slides, A-tapes, microfilms of Mason County papers; Maritime
Publications: Bones, Dolls & Pomanders; Historic Mason County - 1980; Mason Memories; Nature Power Then & Now; Pictorial History of Mason County - 1987
Part of the Mason County Historical Society
Friends of the Library Group

MACKINAC ISLAND

P MACKINAC ISLAND PUBLIC LIBRARY,* Main St, PO Box 903, 49757-0903. SAN 308-2466. Tel: 906-847-3421. FAX: 906-847-3368. E-Mail: maclibrary@sault.com. *Dir*, Anne L St Onge
Pop 469; Circ 6,500
Library Holdings: Bk Vols 11,000; Per Subs 32
Subject Interests: History
Mem of Hiawathaland Library Cooperative
Partic in OCLC Online Computer Library Center, Inc
Friends of the Library Group

MACKINAW CITY

P MACKINAW AREA PUBLIC LIBRARY,* 528 W Central Ave, PO Box 67, 49701-0067. SAN 346-8240. Tel: 231-436-5451. FAX: 231-436-7344. E-Mail: mackina1@northland.lib.mi.us. Web Site: nlc.lib.mi.us/members/mackinaw.htm. *Dir*, Judy Ranville
Founded 1968. Pop 4,125; Circ 81,937
Jul 1997-Jun 1998 Income $122,003, State $3,781, City $51,304, County $42,715, Locally Generated Income $23,703. Mats Exp $108,187, Books $13,853, Per/Ser (Incl. Access Fees) $2,796. Sal $58,109 (Prof $48,309)
Subject Interests: Michigan
Mem of Northland Library Cooperative
Branches: 3
BLISS, 265 Sturgeon Bay Trail, Levering, 49755. SAN 346-8259. Tel: 231-537-2927. *Librn*, Faith Spierling
LEVERING BRANCH, Lions Club Bldg, 236 Mill St, PO Box 164, Levering, 49755. SAN 346-8267. Tel: 231-537-2150. *Librn*, Debra Lemon
PELLSTON BRANCH, 175 N Milton St, PO Box 456, Pellston, 49769-0456. SAN 346-8275. Tel: 616-539-8858. FAX: 616-539-8858. E-Mail: pellst1@northland.lib.mi.us. Web Site: nlc.lib.mi.us/members/mackinaw.htm. *Librn*, Marcie Shiels
Friends of the Library Group

MADISON HEIGHTS

S HENKEL SURFACE TECHNOLOGIES TECHNICAL LIBRARY, 32100 Stephenson Hwy, 48071. SAN 375-9083. Tel: 248-583-9300. FAX: 248-583-2976. *In Charge*, Kathy Herzek
Library Holdings: Bk Vols 1,500
Restriction: Not open to public

P MADISON HEIGHTS PUBLIC LIBRARY,* 240 W Thirteen Mile Rd, 48071-1894. SAN 308-2474. Tel: 248-588-2029, 248-588-7763. TDD: 248-588-2029. FAX: 248-588-2470. E-Mail: mdht@tln.lib.mi.us. *Dir*, Roslyn Yerman
Founded 1954. Pop 32,196; Circ 173,754
Jul 1996-Jun 1997 Income $464,988. Mats Exp $49,183. Sal $285,041
Library Holdings: Bk Vols 75,000; Per Subs 236
Mem of The Library Network
Partic in Lib Network of Mich
Special Services for the Deaf - TDD
Friends of the Library Group
Branches: 1
MADISON HEIGHTS, 26550 John R Rd, 48071-3612. SAN 377-8363. Tel: 248-541-7880. FAX: 248-541-8955.

M OAKLAND GENERAL HOSPITAL, Medical Library,* 27351 Dequindre, 48071. SAN 373-0735. Tel: 248-967-7575. *Librn*, Jennifer Wang; *Asst Librn*, Jessica Nguyen-Trent
Library Holdings: Bk Vols 7,500; Per Subs 245

MANCELONA

P MANCELONA TOWNSHIP LIBRARY,* 202 W State St, PO Box 499, 49659. SAN 308-2490. Tel: 616-587-9451. FAX: 616-587-0855. *Librn*, Diane Pierce
Circ 16,983
Library Holdings: Bk Vols 11,240; Per Subs 34
Mem of Mid-Michigan Library League

MANCHESTER

P MANCHESTER TOWNSHIP LIBRARY,* 202 W Main St, 48158. SAN 308-2504. Tel: 734-428-8045. FAX: 734-428-1226. *Dir*, Dorothy Davies; *Asst Librn*, Teresa Poland
Founded 1838. Pop 6,547
Jun 1998-Jul 1999 Income (Main Library Only) $78,886, State $6,700, Locally Generated Income $72,186. Mats Exp $5,624, Books $4,044, Per/Ser (Incl. Access Fees) $1,318, AV Equip $262. Sal $51,805 (Prof $34,000)
Library Holdings: Bk Vols 15,963; Bk Titles 15,963; Per Subs 36
Special Collections: Michigan History (Michigan Pioneer Colls)
Mem of Woodlands Library Cooperative

MANISTEE

S MANISTEE COUNTY HISTORICAL MUSEUM, Fortier Memorial Library, 425 River St, 49660. SAN 323-5394. Tel: 231-723-5531. *Dir, Librn*, Steve Harold; Staff 1 (Non-MLS 1)
Library Holdings: Bk Titles 1,000
Subject Interests: Great Lakes maritime hist, Manistee County hist

P MANISTEE COUNTY LIBRARY, 95 Maple St, 49660. SAN 346-8305. Tel: 231-723-2519. FAX: 231-723-8270. *Adminr*, Dawn H Kisley; *YA Servs*, Shirley Trucks; Staff 6 (MLS 1, Non-MLS 5)
Founded 1903. Pop 22,000
1998-1999 Income (Main Library and Branch Library) $681,751, State $23,551, County $389,000, Locally Generated Income $26,700, Other $242,500. Mats Exp $660,391, Books $53,600, Per/Ser (Incl. Access Fees) $9,200. Sal $290,000 (Prof $38,345)
Library Holdings: Bk Vols 97,535; Per Subs 200
Subject Interests: Local history, Victorian literature
Automation Activity & Vendor Info: (Cataloging) epixtech, inc.; (Circulation) epixtech, inc.; (OPAC) epixtech, inc.
Mem of Mid-Michigan Library League
Partic in OCLC Online Computer Library Center, Inc
Friends of the Library Group
Branches: 5
ARCADIA BRANCH, 3422 Lake St, PO Box 109, Arcadia, 49613. SAN 374-4582. Tel: 231-889-4230. *In Charge*, Marcella Guinan
Automation Activity & Vendor Info: (Cataloging) epixtech, inc.; (Circulation) epixtech, inc.; (OPAC) epixtech, inc.
BEAR LAKE-PLEASANTON BRANCH, 7749 Lake St, PO Box 266, Bear Lake, 49614. SAN 346-833X. Tel: 231-864-2700. *In Charge*, Marcella Guinan
Automation Activity & Vendor Info: (Cataloging) epixtech, inc.; (Circulation) epixtech, inc.; (OPAC) epixtech, inc.
KALEVA BRANCH, 9200 Aura St, PO Box 125, Kaleva, 49645. SAN 346-8364. Tel: 231-362-3178. *In Charge*, Judy Czarnecki; Staff 1 (Non-MLS 1)
Automation Activity & Vendor Info: (Cataloging) epixtech, inc.; (Circulation) epixtech, inc.; (OPAC) epixtech, inc.
ONEKAMA BRANCH, 5283 Main St, PO Box 149, Onekama, 49675. SAN 346-8399. Tel: 616-889-4041. *In Charge*, Jane Diesing
Pop 582
Automation Activity & Vendor Info: (Cataloging) epixtech, inc.; (Circulation) epixtech, inc.; (OPAC) epixtech, inc.
WELLSTON BRANCH, 1451 Seaman Rd, PO Box 162, Wellston, 49689. SAN 346-8429. Tel: 231-848-4013. *In Charge*, Joyce Myers
Automation Activity & Vendor Info: (Cataloging) epixtech, inc.; (Circulation) epixtech, inc.; (OPAC) epixtech, inc.

MANISTIQUE

P MANISTIQUE SCHOOL & PUBLIC LIBRARY,* 100 N Cedar, 49854-1293. SAN 308-2512. Tel: 906-341-4316. FAX: 906-341-6751. Web Site: www.uproc.lib.mi.us. *Librn*, Mary Hook; *Asst Librn*, Kay Lawrence
Pop 8,401; Circ 44,459
Library Holdings: Bk Vols 35,000; Per Subs 78
Mem of Hiawathaland Library Cooperative
Friends of the Library Group

MAPLE RAPIDS

P MAPLE RAPIDS PUBLIC LIBRARY, 130 S Maple Ave, PO Box 410, 48853-0410. SAN 321-4672. Tel: 517-682-4464. FAX: 517-682-4149. *Librn*, Marvia Nemetz; E-Mail: mrlibrary@mintcity.com; *Asst Librn*, Kim Salisbury
Founded 1935. Circ 15,009
Library Holdings: Bk Vols 10,158; Bk Titles 9,270; Per Subs 44
Subject Interests: Local history
Mem of Capital Library Cooperative

MARCELLUS

P MARCELLUS TOWNSHIP-WOOD MEMORIAL LIBRARY,* 205 E Main St, PO Box 49, 49067. SAN 308-2520. Tel: 616-646-9654. FAX: 616-646-9603. *Librn*, Christine Nofsinger
Circ 15,860
Jul 1998-Jun 1999 Income $89,925. Mats Exp $12,000, Books $10,000, AV Equip $2,000. Sal $33,000
Library Holdings: Bk Titles 25,000; Per Subs 50
Mem of Southwest Michigan Library Cooperative
Open Mon, Tues & Thurs 12-7, Wed 10-7, Fri 12-5, Sat 10-2
Friends of the Library Group

MARION

P M ALICE CHAPIN MEMORIAL LIBRARY, 120 E Main, 49665. (Mail add: PO Box 549, 49665), SAN 308-2539. Tel: 231-743-2421. FAX: 231-743-2421. E-Mail: machapin@netonecom.net. *Dir*, Shelley Ann Scott; Staff 3 (Non-MLS 3)
Circ 10,432
Library Holdings: Bk Vols 17,000; Per Subs 30
Mem of Mid-Michigan Library League

MARLETTE

P MARLETTE DISTRICT LIBRARY, 3116 Main St, 48453. SAN 308-2547. Tel: 517-635-2838. FAX: 517-635-8005. Web Site: www.vlc.lib.mi.us. *Librn*, Nenette Ricker; Staff 3 (Non-MLS 3)
Founded 1921. Pop 5,396; Circ 34,021
Apr 1998-Mar 1999 Income (Main Library Only) $111,622, State $5,448, County $16,127, Locally Generated Income $32,540, Other $57,507. Mats Exp $52,632, Books $17,122, Per/Ser (Incl. Access Fees) $3,000, AV Equip $7,840, Electronic Ref Mat (Incl. Access Fees) $24,670. Sal $31,609
Library Holdings: Bk Vols 20,500; Per Subs 83
Subject Interests: Bks on tape, Large print, Videos
Special Collections: Michigan Coll; New Reader Coll
Automation Activity & Vendor Info: (Cataloging) epixtech, inc.; (Circulation) epixtech, inc.; (OPAC) epixtech, inc.; (Serials) epixtech, inc.
Mem of White Pine Library Cooperative
Partic in Valley Libr Consortium

MARQUETTE

S BISHOP BARAGA ASSOCIATION ARCHIVES, 347 Rock St, PO Box 550, 49855-0550. SAN 327-5191. Tel: 906-227-9117. FAX: 906-225-0437. *Exec Dir*, Alex Sample; E-Mail: a.sample@dioceseofmarquette.org; *Archivist*, Elizabeth Delene; E-Mail: edelene@dioceseofmarquette.org
Founded 1930
Library Holdings: Bk Vols 1,000
Special Collections: Bishop Frederic Baraga Papers; French Fur Trading Records, microfilm; Monsignor Rezik Coll; Notre Dame Papers; Office of India Affairs Records
Publications: Baraga Bulletin
Restriction: By appointment only

S MARQUETTE COUNTY HISTORICAL SOCIETY, JM Longyear Research Library, 213 N Front St, 49855. SAN 308-2555. Tel: 906-226-3571. E-Mail: mqtcohis@uproc.lib.mi.us. *Librn*, Meg Goodrich; Staff 1 (MLS 1)
Founded 1918
Library Holdings: Bk Vols 15,000; Per Subs 45
Subject Interests: Ethnology, Great Lakes, Mining, Railroads
Special Collections: Breitung-Kaufman Papers; Burt Papers; Business Records; Family Records; J M Longyear Coll; Local Newspapers on microfilm from 1870s; Military (Local Service Men); Municipal Records
Partic in OCLC Online Computer Library Center, Inc

M MARQUETTE GENERAL HOSPITAL, Kevin F O'Brien Health Sciences Library, 580 W College Ave, 49855. SAN 308-2563. Tel: 906-225-3429. FAX: 906-225-3524. E-Mail: library@mgh.org. Web Site: www.mgh.org/library/index.html. *Mgr Libr*, Janis Lubenow
1998-1999 Mats Exp $105,000, Books $22,000, Per/Ser (Incl. Access Fees) $49,000
Library Holdings: Bk Vols 2,348; Per Subs 172
Subject Interests: Administrative law, Allied health, Medicine, Nursing, Planning
Automation Activity & Vendor Info: (Cataloging) epixtech, inc.; (OPAC) epixtech, inc.
Database Vendor: Ebsco - EbscoHost
Partic in Greater Midwest Regional Medical Libr Network; Michigan Health Sciences Libraries Association; Upper Peninsula Health Sci Libr Consort; Upper Peninsula Region Of Library Cooperation, Inc

C NORTHERN MICHIGAN UNIVERSITY, Lydia M Olson Library, 1401 Presque Isle, 49855. SAN 308-258X. Tel: 906-227-2117. Interlibrary Loan Service Tel: 906-227-2065. Circulation Tel: 906-227-2260. Reference Tel: 906-227-2294. TDD: 906-227-1232. FAX: 906-227-1333. Web Site: www.nmu.edu/home.shtml. *Archivist*, Marcus Robyns; Tel: 906-227-1225, E-Mail: mrobyn@nmu.edu; *AV*, Keenen Tunnell; Tel: 906-227-2290, E-Mail: ktunnell@nmu.edu; *Cat*, Stephen Peters; *Circ, ILL*, Kathy Godec; Tel: 906-227-2261, E-Mail: kgodec@nmu.edu; *Coll Develop*, Joanna Mitchell; Tel: 906-227-1208, E-Mail: jmitchel@nmu.edu; *Doc*, Kelly Eastwood; Tel: 906-227-2112, E-Mail: keastwoo@nmu.edu; *Media Spec*, Carolyn Myers; Tel:

906-227-1225, E-Mail: cmyers@nmu.edu; *Ref*, Michael Burgmeier; Tel: 906-227-2187, E-Mail: mburgmei@nmu.edu; *Ref*, Kevin McDonough; Tel: 906-227-2118, E-Mail: kmcdonou@nmu.edu; *Ref*, Michael Strahan; Tel: 906-227-2423, E-Mail: mstrahan@nmu.edu; *Tech Servs*, Krista Clumpner; Tel: 906-227-1205, E-Mail: kclumpne@nmu.edu; Staff 12 (MLS 12)
Founded 1899. Enrl 6,595; Fac 326
Library Holdings: Bk Vols 420,822; Per Subs 1,714
Special Collections: Moses Coit Tyler Coll
Partic in Michigan Library Consortium; OCLC Online Computer Library Center, Inc

P SUPERIORLAND LIBRARY COOPERATIVE,* 1615 Presque Isle Ave, 49855. SAN 308-2598. Tel: 906-228-7697. Toll Free Tel: 800-562-8985. FAX: 906-228-5627. *Dir*, Suzanne Dees; *ILL*, JoAnne Whitley; Staff 1 (MLS 1)
Founded 1974. Pop 131,537
Member Libraries: Calumet Public School Library; Hancock School Public Library; Ishpeming Carnegie Public Library; L'Anse Area School-Public Library; Munising Public Library; Negaunee Public Library; Peter White Public Library; Portage Lake District Library; Republic-Michigamme Public Library; Richmond Township Public Library
Partic in OCLC Online Computer Library Center, Inc
Branches: 1

P UPPER PENINSULA LIBRARY FOR THE BLIND & PHYSICALLY HANDICAPPED,* 1615 Presque Isle Ave, 49855. SAN 308-0706. Tel: 906-228-7697. Toll Free Tel: 800-562-8985. FAX: 906-228-5627. *Librn*, Suzanne Dees; Staff 1 (MLS 1)
Founded 1980. Pop 1,017; Circ 32,000
Special Collections: Coping Skills Information File
Publications: Large Print Books in Upper Peninsula Libraries
Special Services for the Blind - Information on special aids & appliances; Reference services

P PETER WHITE PUBLIC LIBRARY,* 217 N Front St, 49855. SAN 308-2601. Tel: 906-228-9510. FAX: 906-228-7315. Web Site: www.uproc.lib.mi.us/pwpl. *Dir*, Pamela R Christensen; *Ch Servs*, Cathy Sullivan-Seblonka; *Tech Servs*, Ann Ruuska; *Acq, Ref*, Caroline Jordan; *Coll Develop*, Mary Rust; Staff 33 (MLS 6, Non-MLS 27)
Founded 1891. Pop 36,289; Circ 305,223 Sal $452,000
Library Holdings: Bk Vols 152,713; Per Subs 416
Special Collections: Children's Historical Book Coll; Finnish Coll; Guns, Railroads, Ships (Miller Coll); Merrit Coll; Nadeau Coll; Shiras Coll
Automation Activity & Vendor Info: (Circulation) NOTIS
Mem of Superiorland Library Cooperative
Partic in Michigan Library Consortium; Upper Peninsula Region Of Library Cooperation, Inc
Friends of the Library Group

MARSHALL

S AMERICAN MUSEUM OF MAGIC LIBRARY, Lund Memorial Library, 111 Mansion St, PO Box 5, 49068. SAN 325-5042. Tel: 616-781-7666, 616-781-7674. *Librn*, Elaine Lund
Founded 1943
Library Holdings: Bk Vols 12,000; Per Subs 12
Restriction: By appointment only
In addition to books & periodicals, the library includes more than 250,000 photographs, letters, newspaper clippings, scrapbooks, films, video tapes, audio tapes, notebooks, programs, posters, etc all on the subject of magic & magicians. Subject to certain conditions & at our convenience, scholars can obtain access to the library

P MARSHALL DISTRICT LIBRARY, 124 W Green St, 49068. SAN 308-2628. Tel: 616-781-7821. FAX: 616-781-7090. *Dir*, Renwick Garypie; *Coll Develop*, Dawn Hernandez
Founded 1912. Pop 19,154; Circ 164,018
Jul 1999-Jun 2000 Income $502,830, State $19,138, Locally Generated Income $353,462, Other $130,230. Mats Exp $83,200, Books $63,000, Per/Ser (Incl. Access Fees) $5,500, AV Equip $3,500. Sal $266,382
Library Holdings: Bk Vols 55,292; Bk Titles 55,000; Per Subs 120
Mem of Woodlands Library Cooperative
Partic in OCLC Online Computer Library Center, Inc

S MARSHALL HISTORICAL SOCIETY ARCHIVES,* 107 N Kalamazoo Ave, 49068. SAN 308-261X. Tel: 616-781-8544. FAX: 616-789-0371.
Founded 1960
Library Holdings: Bk Vols 300
Special Collections: Genealogies (1830-1925); Marshall History

MARTIN

P J C WHEELER LIBRARY,* 1593 S Main St, PO Box 226, 49070-0226. SAN 308-2636. Tel: 616-672-7875. FAX: 616-672-7875. *Librn*, Shirley A Moore
Founded 1922
Library Holdings: Bk Vols 11,290; Per Subs 23
Mem of Lakeland Library Cooperative
Open Mon, Tues & Fri 12-5, Wed 12-7 & Sat 10-3
Friends of the Library Group

MAYVILLE

S MAYVILLE AREA MUSEUM OF HISTORY & GENEALOGY,* 2124 Ohmer Rd, PO Box 242, 48744. SAN 326-2014. Tel: 517-843-6712. *Pres*, H J Brumley Sr
Founded 1971. Circ 1,930
Friends of the Library Group

P MAYVILLE DISTRICT PUBLIC LIBRARY, 6090 Fulton St, PO Box 440, 48744-0440. SAN 308-2652. Tel: 517-843-6522. FAX: 517-843-0078. E-Mail: maylib@mill.tds.net. *Librn*, Jill Fox; *Asst Librn*, Kathy Jansen
Founded 1946. Pop 5,189; Circ 33,000
Jul 1999-Jun 2000 Income $90,000, State $5,400, City $5,000, County $61,000, Other $18,600. Mats Exp $86,000, Books $13,600, Per/Ser (Incl. Access Fees) $1,900. Sal $17,900
Library Holdings: Bk Titles 12,659; Per Subs 54
Automation Activity & Vendor Info: (Cataloging) Sagebrush Corporation; (Circulation) Sagebrush Corporation
Mem of White Pine Library Cooperative
Partic in Mich Libr Asn

MECOSTA

P MORTON TOWNSHIP PUBLIC LIBRARY, 110 S James, PO Box 246, 49332-0246. SAN 308-2660. Tel: 616-972-8315. FAX: 616-972-4332. E-Mail: mortwplib@centurytel.net. *Dir*, Mary Ann Lenon; *Asst Dir*, Holly Swincicki; Staff 3 (Non-MLS 3)
Founded 1966. Pop 3,702; Circ 29,110
Jul 1998-Jun 1999 Income $147,000, State $3,700, County $25,700, Locally Generated Income $103,500, Other $14,100. Mats Exp $28,020, Books $19,600, Per/Ser (Incl. Access Fees) $2,000, AV Equip $5,700, Electronic Ref Mat (Incl. Access Fees) $720. Sal $56,400
Library Holdings: Bk Vols 15,950; Per Subs 70
Automation Activity & Vendor Info: (Cataloging) EOS; (Circulation) EOS
Mem of Mid-Michigan Library League
Friends of the Library Group

MELVINDALE

P MELVINDALE PUBLIC LIBRARY,* 18650 Allen Rd, 48122. SAN 308-2679. Tel: 313-381-8677. FAX: 313-388-0432. Web Site: www.melvindale.lib.mi.us. *Dir*, Theresa Kieltyka; E-Mail: kieltyka@tln.lib.mi.us
Founded 1928. Pop 11,216; Circ 42,668
1998-1999 Mats Exp $28,000, Books $22,000, Per/Ser (Incl. Access Fees) $6,000
Library Holdings: Bk Vols 50,000; Bk Titles 40,000; Per Subs 100; Bks on Deafness & Sign Lang 12
Subject Interests: Bks on tape, Large print bks
Mem of The Library Network
Special Services for the Deaf - TDD
Special Services for the Blind - Bks on cassette; Large print bks
Friends of the Library Group

MENDON

P MENDON TOWNSHIP LIBRARY,* 314 W Main St, PO Box 38, 49072. SAN 308-2687. Tel: 616-496-4865. FAX: 616-496-4635. E-Mail: mendon@monroe.lib.mi.us. *Dir*, Karrie Waarala
Founded 1882. Pop 4,999; Circ 10,916
Library Holdings: Bk Vols 17,000
Subject Interests: Foreign Language, Genealogy, Local history
Special Collections: Large Print; Local History, scrapbks, bks; Mich & Local History; Mich & Local History, albums; Talking Books
Mem of Woodlands Library Cooperative
Friends of the Library Group

MENOMINEE

P SPIES PUBLIC LIBRARY, 940 First St, 49858-3296. SAN 308-2695. Tel: 906-863-3911. FAX: 906-863-5000. Web Site: www.spiespubliclibrary.org. *Dir*, Cheryl Hoffman; Tel: 906-863-2900, E-Mail: cherylh@uproc.lib.mi.us; Staff 1 (MLS 1)
Founded 1903. Pop 10,585; Circ 126,562
Jun 1999-Jun 2000 Income $336,138, State $10,576, City $63,058, County $7,964, Locally Generated Income $254,540. Mats Exp $49,623, Books $32,682, Per/Ser (Incl. Access Fees) $7,565, AV Equip $1,832, Electronic Ref Mat (Incl. Access Fees) $7,544. Sal $132,837 (Prof $35,000)

Library Holdings: Bk Titles 53,300; Per Subs 139
Automation Activity & Vendor Info: (Cataloging) epixtech, inc.; (Circulation) epixtech, inc.; (OPAC) epixtech, inc.
Friends of the Library Group

MERRILL

P MERRILL DISTRICT LIBRARY,* 136 N Midland St, 48637-0009. SAN 308-2709. Tel: 517-643-7300. FAX: 517-643-7300. *Dir, Librn*, Norma Brown
Circ 24,512
Library Holdings: Bk Vols 23,158; Per Subs 52
Subject Interests: Large type print, Michigan
Mem of White Pine Library Cooperative

MIDDLEVILLE

P THORNAPPLE-KELLOGG SCHOOL & COMMUNITY LIBRARY,* 3885 Bender Rd, 49333-9273. SAN 308-2717. Tel: 616-795-5434. FAX: 616-795-8997. Web Site: www.tk.k12.mi.us. *Librn*, Deb Jones
Circ 45,000
Library Holdings: Bk Vols 37,000; Per Subs 85
Mem of Lakeland Library Cooperative

MIDLAND

THE DOW CHEMICAL CO
S COMMERCIAL & TECHNICAL INFORMATION SERVICES, 566 Bldg, 48667. SAN 346-881X. Tel: 517-636-1098, 517-636-2919. FAX: 517-636-8135.; Staff 70 (MLS 10, Non-MLS 60)
Founded 1920
Library Holdings: Bk Titles 14,000; Per Subs 350
Subject Interests: Chemistry, Engineering, Physics

P GRACE A DOW MEMORIAL LIBRARY, Midland Public Library,* 1710 W St Andrews Ave, 48640-2698. SAN 308-2725. Tel: 517-837-3430. FAX: 517-837-3468. Web Site: www.gracedowlibrary.org. *Dir*, Melissa Barnard; *ILL*, Shirley Schroeder; *Circ*, Joyce Fisher; Staff 14 (MLS 14)
Founded 1895. Pop 69,363
Library Holdings: Bk Vols 223,105; Per Subs 510
Special Collections: Fine Arts (Alden B Dow Coll), bks, rec, art prints; Genealogy
Publications: Readers Review (activities)
Mem of White Pine Library Cooperative
Friends of the Library Group

R MEMORIAL PRESBYTERIAN CHURCH, Greenhoe Library, 1310 Ashman St, 48640. SAN 308-2733. Tel: 517-835-6759. *Librn*, Esther Frost; *Chair*, Esther Arnold; *Ch Servs*, Karen Sheppard; Staff 14 (MLS 3, Non-MLS 11)
Founded 1945
Jan 1998-Dec 1999 Income $2,150, Parent Institution $1,300, Other $850. Mats Exp $2,150, Books $1,345, Per/Ser (Incl. Access Fees) $230
Library Holdings: Bk Titles 5,500; Per Subs 14
Subject Interests: Biblical studies, Church history, Fiction
Special Collections: Children's Library, bks, compact discs, flm & tapes

C MICHIGAN MOLECULAR INSTITUTE, Raymond F Boyer Resource Center,* 1910 W St Andrews Rd, 48640. SAN 324-7139. Tel: 517-832-5555, Ext 552. FAX: 517-832-5560. E-Mail: eastland@mmi.org. Web Site: www.mmi.org/mmi. *Librn*, Judy Eastland; Staff 1 (MLS 1)
Jan 1999-Dec 1999 Mats Exp $70,000, Books $15,000, Per/Ser (Incl. Access Fees) $40,000, Other Print Mats $5,000, Electronic Ref Mat (Incl. Access Fees) $10,000
Library Holdings: Bk Vols 5,000; Bk Titles 4,000; Per Subs 125
Subject Interests: Polymer sci, Polymer tech
Database Vendor: Ebsco - EbscoHost, OCLC - First Search
Restriction: Staff use only
Function: Research library
Partic in LVIS; Michigan Library Consortium

S MIDLAND COUNTY HISTORICAL SOCIETY, Archives Library,* 1801 W Saint Andrews Rd, 48640. SAN 327-4373. Tel: 517-631-5931, Ext 1300. *Dir*, Gary F Skory
Founded 1952
Library Holdings: Per Subs 10
Special Collections: Area Genealogy Coll; Dow Chemical Company Archival Material, photos

S MIDLAND PUBLIC SCHOOLS INSTRUCTIONAL MEDIA CENTER, 600 E Carpenter St, 48640-5499. SAN 326-632X. Tel: 517-923-5001. FAX: 517-923-5004. Web Site: www.mps.k12.mi.us. *Coordr*, Norman Neher; Tel: 517-923-5120, E-Mail: neherna@mps.k12.mi.us; *Cat*, Jennifer Joseph
Enrl 9,800; Fac 1,500
Library Holdings: Bk Vols 4,862; Per Subs 80
Subject Interests: Education
Mem of White Pine Library Cooperative

M MIDMICHIGAN MEDICAL CENTER, Health Sciences Library, 4005 Orchard Dr, 48670. SAN 325-2248. Tel: 517-839-3262. FAX: 517-631-1401. *Mgr*, Patricia Wolfgram
Library Holdings: Bk Vols 3,000; Per Subs 400
Special Collections: Health Sciences Coll
Open weekdays 9-4:30

C NORTHWOOD UNIVERSITY, Strosacker Library, 4000 Whiting, 48640-2398. SAN 346-8933. Tel: 989-837-4333. Toll Free Tel: 800-837-2291. FAX: 989-832-5031. E-Mail: nulib@vlc.lib.mi.us. Web Site: www.northwood.edu/mi/library. *Dir*, Sandra Potts; Tel: 989-837-4339; *Librn*, Judy Gourdji; *Librn*, Rochelle Zimmerman; Staff 9 (MLS 3, Non-MLS 6)
Founded 1969. Enrl 1,700; Fac 38; Highest Degree: Master
Library Holdings: Bk Vols 43,000; Bk Titles 37,000; Per Subs 520
Automation Activity & Vendor Info: (Cataloging) epixtech, inc.; (Circulation) epixtech, inc.; (Course Reserve) epixtech, inc.; (OPAC) epixtech, inc.
Database Vendor: IAC - Info Trac, IAC - SearchBank, Lexis-Nexis, OCLC - First Search, ProQuest
Partic in Michigan Library Consortium; OCLC Online Computer Library Center, Inc; Valley Libr Consortium
Departmental Libraries:
CEDAR HILL CAMPUS
See Separate Entry in Cedar Hill, TX
DR & MRS PETER C COOK LIBRARY
See Separate Entry in West Palm Beach, FL

MILAN

S FEDERAL CORRECTIONAL INSTITUTION LIBRARY,* Arkona Rd, PO Box 9999, 48160-9999. SAN 308-2741. Tel: 734-439-1511, Ext 241. FAX: 734-439-3608. *Librn*, Carol Yoakum
Library Holdings: Bk Vols 20,000; Per Subs 35
Special Collections: Bureau of Prison Program Statements & Institutions Supplements; Federal Law Books & Statutes; Reference Works
Partic in Washtenaw-Livingston Libr Network

G MICHIGAN DEPARTMENT OF MENTAL HEALTH, Center for Forensic Psychiatry-Staff Medical Library, 3501 Willis Rd, 48160. (Mail add: PO Box 2060, 48106-2060), Tel: 313-429-2531, Ext 296. TDD: 313-429-2531. FAX: 313-429-7951. E-Mail: staresinal@state.mi.us. *Dir*, Lois Staresina; Staff 2 (MLS 1, Non-MLS 1)
Founded 1974
Library Holdings: Bk Vols 7,104; Bk Titles 5,724; Per Subs 75
Subject Interests: Forensic psychiat, Forensic psychol
Automation Activity & Vendor Info: (Acquisitions) Inmagic, Inc.; (Cataloging) Inmagic, Inc.; (Circulation) Inmagic, Inc.
Restriction: Not open to public
Partic in MDMLG; Michigan Library Consortium
Special Services for the Deaf - TDD

P MILAN PUBLIC LIBRARY, 151 Wabash St, 48160. SAN 308-275X. Tel: 734-439-1240. FAX: 734-439-5625. E-Mail: milan@monroe.lib.mi.us. Web Site: woodlands.lib.mi.us/milan. *Dir*, Gail Hardenbergh; E-Mail: gailhardenbergh@yahoo.com; Staff 2 (MLS 2)
Founded 1935. Pop 13,681; Circ 62,000
Library Holdings: Bk Vols 31,000; Per Subs 90
Subject Interests: Genealogy, Local history
Publications: Milan Pathfinder
Mem of Woodlands Library Cooperative
Partic in OCLC Online Computer Library Center, Inc
Friends of the Library Group

MILFORD

S MILFORD HISTORICAL SOCIETY, Historical Museum Reference Room, 124 E Commerce St, 48381. SAN 371-6376. Tel: 248-685-7308.

P MILFORD TOWNSHIP LIBRARY,* 1100 Atlantic St, 48381-2000. SAN 308-2768. Tel: 248-684-0845. FAX: 248-684-2923. Web Site: milford.lib.mi.us. *Dir*, Jill Morey
Founded 1929. Pop 15,404; Circ 126,971
Jan 1998-Dec 1999 Income $493,916. Mats Exp $63,000, Books $42,000, Per/Ser (Incl. Access Fees) $4,000, Micro $17,000. Sal $258,200 (Prof $138,000)
Library Holdings: Bk Vols 34,052; Per Subs 159
Subject Interests: Large type print, Local history, Michigan
Special Collections: Art Geyer Civil War Coll
Publications: Library Register (bi-monthly newsletter)
Mem of The Library Network
Friends of the Library Group

MILLINGTON

P MILLINGTON TOWNSHIP LIBRARY,* 8530 Depot St, PO Box 306, 48746-0306. SAN 308-2776. Tel: 517-871-2003. FAX: 517-871-5594. *Dir*, Margaret Olsen; *Dir*, Katherine G Halloran
Founded 1938. Pop 7,381; Circ 40,000
Library Holdings: Bk Vols 24,000; Bk Titles 19,500; Per Subs 65

MIO

P OSCODA COUNTY LIBRARY, 430 W Eighth St, 48647. SAN 308-2784. Tel: 517-826-3613. FAX: 517-826-5461. E-Mail: oscodal@northland.lib.mi.us. *Librn*, Kathleen Flynn; Tel: 651-266-7024, E-Mail: kathleen@stpaul.lib.mn.us; Staff 4 (Non-MLS 4)
Founded 1948. Pop 7,832; Circ 41,249
Jan 1999-Dec 1999 Income $95,573, State $7,835, County $77,947, Locally Generated Income $9,791. Mats Exp $11,700, Books $9,000, Per/Ser (Incl. Access Fees) $2,200, AV Equip $500. Sal $34,399 (Prof $18,425)
Library Holdings: Bk Vols 28,000; Per Subs 90; High Interest/Low Vocabulary Bk Vols 100; Bks on Deafness & Sign Lang 10
Subject Interests: Talking books
Special Collections: County Papers 1932-Present
Automation Activity & Vendor Info: (Cataloging) Athena; (Circulation) Athena; (ILL) Athena
Mem of Northland Library Cooperative
Friends of the Library Group

MOLINE

P LEIGHTON TOWNSHIP PUBLIC LIBRARY,* 4451 12th St, Drawer H, 49335. SAN 346-3508. Tel: 616-877-4143. FAX: 616-877-4484. *Dir*, Martha Jackson
Library Holdings: Bk Vols 20,000
Mem of Lakeland Library Cooperative

MONROE

J MONROE COUNTY COMMUNITY COLLEGE, Learning Resources Center, 1555 S Raisinville Rd, 48161. SAN 308-2792. Tel: 734-384-4204. FAX: 734-384-4160. E-Mail: aksalibrarian@mail.monroe.cc.mi.us. Web Site: www.monroe.cc.mi.us/library. *Dir*, David Reiman; Tel: 734-384-4244, E-Mail: dreiman@mail.monroe.cc.mi.us; *ILL, Per, Ref*, Jennifer Carmody; Tel: 734-384-4162, E-Mail: jcarmody@mail.monroe.cc.mi.us; *Acq, Cat, Coll Develop, Ref*, Terri Kovach; Tel: 734-384-4161, E-Mail: tkovach@mail.monroe.cc.mi.us; Staff 4 (MLS 4)
Founded 1966. Enrl 3,629
Jul 2000-Jun 2001 Income $656,105. Mats Exp $96,770, Books $48,770, Per/Ser (Incl. Access Fees) $33,712, Presv $7,000, Micro $7,288. Sal $334,815 (Prof $193,575)
Library Holdings: Bk Vols 47,692; Bk Titles 44,246; Per Subs 343
Special Collections: Professional Library
Automation Activity & Vendor Info: (Acquisitions) epixtech, inc.; (Cataloging) epixtech, inc.; (Circulation) epixtech, inc.; (OPAC) epixtech, inc.; (Serials) epixtech, inc.
Database Vendor: OCLC - First Search
Mem of Mich Libr Consortium

S MONROE COUNTY HISTORICAL MUSEUM, Archives, 126 S Monroe St, 48161. SAN 327-439X. Tel: 734-240-7787. FAX: 734-240-7788. *Dir*, Matthew Switlik; *Asst Dir*, Ralph Naveaux; *Archivist*, Christine Kull
Library Holdings: Bk Vols 600

GL MONROE COUNTY LAW LIBRARY, Court House, 106 E First St, 48161. SAN 325-8556. Tel: 734-240-7070. FAX: 734-240-7056. *In Charge*, William F LaVoy
Library Holdings: Bk Vols 4,500

P MONROE COUNTY LIBRARY SYSTEM, 3700 S Custer Rd, 48161. SAN 346-8968. Tel: 734-241-5277. Toll Free Tel: 800-462-2050. FAX: 734-241-4722. Web Site: monroe.lib.mi.us. *Dir*, Nancy Colpaert; Tel: 734-241-5277, Ext 203, E-Mail: njc@monroe.lib.mi.us; *Asst Dir, Publ Servs*, Nancy Bellaire; Tel: 734-241-5277, Ext 204; *Tech Coordr*, Rachel Braden; *Cat*, Janice Kirch; *Coll Develop*, Heidi McCraw; *Ref*, Carl Katafiasz; *Circ*, Bill Reiser; Staff 17 (MLS 17)
Founded 1934. Pop 140,488; Circ 821,364
Jan 2000-Dec 2000 Income (Main Library and Branch Library) $3,752,866, State $154,560, Federal $35,089, County $2,185,403, Locally Generated Income $384,955, Other $992,859. Mats Exp $448,277, Books $294,000, Per/Ser (Incl. Access Fees) $42,000, Electronic Ref Mat (Incl. Access Fees) $12,000. Sal $1,883,025
Library Holdings: Bk Vols 457,561; Bk Titles 311,664; Per Subs 2,000
Subject Interests: Genealogy, Local history
Special Collections: Battle of Little Big Horn (General George A Custer Coll); Enrico Fermi Atomic Power Plant & NRC - Pub Doc; Michigan-Monroe Coll
Automation Activity & Vendor Info: (Cataloging) Brodart; (Circulation) Gaylord; (ILL) Brodart; (OPAC) Gaylord
Publications: Custeriana Series; Poetry Anthologies
Partic in Southern Michigan Region Of Cooperation
Special Services for the Deaf - Captioned media; TDD
Friends of the Library Group
Branches: 16
BEDFORD, 8575 Jackman Rd, Temperance, 48182-9493. SAN 346-9387. Tel: 734-847-6747. TDD: 734-847-6747. FAX: 734-847-6591. Web Site: www.monroe.lib.mi.us. *Librn*, Lois White; E-Mail: lwhite@monroe.lib.mi.us
Library Holdings: Bk Vols 84,755
Subject Interests: Genealogy, Local history
Special Services for the Deaf - TDD
Friends of the Library Group
BLUE BUSH, 2210 Blue Bush, 48162-9643. SAN 328-7505. Tel: 734-242-4085. TDD: 734-242-4085. FAX: 734-242-0023. *Librn*, Diane Flor
Library Holdings: Bk Vols 9,158
Special Services for the Deaf - TDD
CARLETON BRANCH, 1444 Kent St, PO Box 267, Carleton, 48117-0267. SAN 346-8992. Tel: 734-654-2180. TDD: 734-654-2180. FAX: 734-654-8767. *Librn*, Marie D Chulski
Library Holdings: Bk Vols 26,415
Special Services for the Deaf - TDD
Friends of the Library Group
DORSCH MEMORIAL, 18 E First St, 48161-2227. SAN 346-9026. Tel: 734-241-7878. TDD: 734-241-7878. FAX: 734-241-7879. Web Site: www.monroe.lib.mi.us. *Librn*, Cindy Green
Library Holdings: Bk Vols 42,601
Special Services for the Deaf - TDD
Friends of the Library Group
DUNDEE BRANCH, 144 E Main St, Dundee, 48131-1202. SAN 346-9050. Tel: 734-529-3310. TDD: 734-529-3310. FAX: 734-529-3310. *Librn*, Allison Enger
Library Holdings: Bk Vols 18,551
Special Services for the Deaf - TDD
Friends of the Library Group
ELLIS REFERENCE & INFORMATION CENTER, 3700 S Custer Rd, 48161-9732. SAN 346-9085. Tel: 734-241-5277. TDD: 734-241-5277. FAX: 734-242-9037. *Ref*, Carl Katafiasz; *Circ*, Bill Reiser
Library Holdings: Bk Vols 148,432
Special Services for the Deaf - TDD
Friends of the Library Group
ERIE BRANCH, 2065 Erie Rd, Erie, 48133. SAN 346-9115. Tel: 734-848-4420. TDD: 734-848-4420. FAX: 734-848-4420. *Librn*, Dawn Shock
Library Holdings: Bk Vols 10,171
Special Services for the Deaf - TDD
Friends of the Library Group
FRENCHTOWN-DIXIE BRANCH, 2881 Nadeau Rd, 48162-9355. SAN 346-914X. Tel: 734-289-1035. TDD: 734-289-1035. FAX: 734-289-3867. *Librn*, Jane Steed
Library Holdings: Bk Vols 17,244
Special Services for the Deaf - TDD
Friends of the Library Group
IDA BRANCH, 3014 Lewis Ave, PO Box 56, Ida, 48140-0056. SAN 346-9174. Tel: 734-269-2191. TDD: 734-269-2191. FAX: 734-269-2191. *Librn*, Barb Drodt
Library Holdings: Bk Vols 8,589
Special Services for the Deaf - TDD
Friends of the Library Group
MAYBEE BRANCH, 9060 Raisin St, PO Box 165, Maybee, 48159-0165. SAN 346-9239. Tel: 734-587-3680. TDD: 734-587-3680. FAX: 734-587-3680. *Librn*, Sue Hartford
Library Holdings: Bk Vols 14,197
Special Services for the Deaf - TDD
Friends of the Library Group
LILLIAN STEWART NAVARRE BRANCH, 1135 E Second St, 48161-1920. SAN 346-9263. Tel: 734-241-5577. TDD: 734-241-5577. FAX: 734-241-5577. *Librn*, Jennifer Hensley
Library Holdings: Bk Vols 18,612
Special Services for the Deaf - TDD
NEWPORT BRANCH, 8120 N Dixie Hwy, Newport, 48166. *Librn*, Judy LaFleur
RASEY MEMORIAL, 4349 Oak St, PO Box 416, Luna Pier, 48157-0416. SAN 346-9204. Tel: 734-848-4572. TDD: 734-848-4572. FAX: 734-848-4572. *Librn*, Dawn Shock
Library Holdings: Bk Vols 9,694
Special Services for the Deaf - TDD
Friends of the Library Group
ROBERT A VIVIAN BRANCH, 2664 Vivian Rd, 48162-9212. SAN 346-9417. Tel: 734-241-1430. TDD: 734-241-1430. FAX: 734-241-1430. *Librn*, Jane Steed
Library Holdings: Bk Vols 11,206
Special Services for the Deaf - TDD
SOUTH ROCKWOOD BRANCH, 12776 Fort St, PO Box 47, South Rockwood, 48179-0047. SAN 346-9352. Tel: 734-379-3333. TDD: 734-379-3333. FAX: 734-379-3333. *Chief Librn*, Judy LaFleur
Library Holdings: Bk Vols 12,653

Special Services for the Deaf - TDD
Friends of the Library Group
SUMMERFIELD - PETERSBURG BRANCH, 60 E Center St, PO Box 567, Petersburg, 49270-0567. SAN 346-9328. Tel: 734-279-1025. TDD: 734-279-1025. FAX: 734-279-2328. *Librn*, Jodi Russ
Library Holdings: Bk Vols 14,460
Special Services for the Deaf - TDD

SR SISTERS, SERVANTS OF THE IMMACULATE HEART OF MARY, Congregational Library,* 610 W Elm Ave, 48162. SAN 308-2806. Tel: 734-241-3660, Ext 233. FAX: 734-242-2947. *Dir*, Sr Marie Gabriel Hungerman; *Acq*, Sr Christine Hattendorf; *AV, Per*, Sr Ruth Glaser
Founded 1927
Jul 1998-Jun 1999 Income $67,500. Mats Exp $17,500
Library Holdings: Bk Vols 54,500; Per Subs 95
Subject Interests: Art, Ecology, Fiction, Large type print, Religion, Theology
Partic in Catholic Libr Conference of Mich; Mich Libr Asn

MORENCI

P STAIR PUBLIC LIBRARY,* 228 W Main St, 49256-1421. SAN 308-2822. Tel: 517-458-6510. FAX: 517-458-3378. *Dir*, Elizabeth Stella; E-Mail: estella@monroe.lib.mi.us
Founded 1930. Pop 2,800; Circ 17,402
Jul 1997-Jun 1998 Income $50,000. Mats Exp $9,000. Sal $30,000
Library Holdings: Bk Vols 17,000; Per Subs 81
Mem of Woodlands Library Cooperative
Friends of the Library Group

MORLEY

P WALTON ERICKSON PUBLIC LIBRARY,* 4808 Northland Dr, Rte 2, 49336-9522. SAN 308-2830. Tel: 231-856-4298. FAX: 231-856-0307. *Librn*, Cory Taylor
Founded 1965. Pop 6,142; Circ 17,986
Library Holdings: Bk Titles 21,000; Per Subs 40
Mem of Mid-Michigan Library League

MOUNT CLEMENS

S MACOMB COUNTY HISTORICAL SOCIETY, Crocker House Library, 15 Union St, 48043. SAN 328-560X. Tel: 810-465-2488. *Librn*, Betty Lou Morris
Library Holdings: Bk Titles 2,500

M MOUNT CLEMENS GENERAL HOSPITAL, Medical Library,* 1000 Harrington Blvd, 48043. SAN 308-2865. Tel: 810-493-8147. FAX: 810-493-8739. *Librn*, Jill VanBuskirk; E-Mail: jvanbusk@mcgh.org; Staff 1 (MLS 1)
Founded 1957
Library Holdings: Bk Titles 3,000; Per Subs 150
Subject Interests: Allied health, Medicine
Restriction: Open to public for reference only
Partic in Michigan Health Sciences Libraries Association

P MOUNT CLEMENS PUBLIC LIBRARY, 150 Cass Ave, 48043. SAN 308-2873. Tel: 810-469-6200. FAX: 810-469-6668. E-Mail: mcpl@libcoop.net. Web Site: www.libcoop.net/mountclemens. *Dir*, Donald E Worrell, Jr; E-Mail: worrelld@libcoop.net; *Asst Dir*, Deborah J Larsen; E-Mail: larsend@libcoop.net; *Coordr, Publ Servs*, Heather McCallister; E-Mail: mccallih@libcoop.net; *Ch Servs*, Lois Sprengnether; E-Mail: sprengnl@libcoop.net; *Circ*, Jayne Kasuba; E-Mail: kasubaj@libcoop.net; Staff 20 (MLS 7, Non-MLS 13)
Founded 1865. Pop 23,937; Circ 154,000
Jul 1999-Jun 2000 Income $1,265,000, State $22,000, Locally Generated Income $1,100,000, Other $143,000. Mats Exp Books $75,000. Sal $64,000
Library Holdings: Bk Vols 124,000; Per Subs 212
Special Collections: Local History & Genealogy (Michigan Coll) bks, per, doc, flm, pamphlets
Automation Activity & Vendor Info: (Cataloging) epixtech, inc.; (Circulation) epixtech, inc.; (OPAC) epixtech, inc.
Database Vendor: IAC - Info Trac, IAC - SearchBank, OCLC - First Search
Publications: Library Online
Mem of Surburban Libr Syst
Friends of the Library Group

M SAINT JOSEPH'S MERCY HOSPITALS & HEALTH SERVICES, Medical Library,* 215 North Ave, 48043-1617. SAN 327-4004. Tel: 810-466-9485. FAX: 810-466-9487. *Asst Librn*, Elaine Wisley
Library Holdings: Bk Titles 3,000; Per Subs 400
Subject Interests: Consumer health, History, Medicine, Nursing
Publications: Acquisitions List
Open Mon-Fri 8-4:30

MOUNT PLEASANT

C CENTRAL MICHIGAN UNIVERSITY, Charles V Park Library, Park 132, 48859. SAN 308-2881. Tel: 517-774-3500. Interlibrary Loan Service Tel: 517-774-3022. Circulation Tel: 517-774-3114. Reference Tel: 517-774-3470. FAX: 517-774-2179. Web Site: www.lib.cmich.edu. *Dean of Libr*, Thomas J Moore; *Assoc Dean*, Stephen Foster; *Head of Libr*, Daniel Ferrer; *Doc*, Pat Barbour; *Tech Servs*, John Riddick; *Govt Doc*, David Shirley; *Ref Serv*, Julie Voelck; *Coll Develop*, Pamela Grudzien; *Circ*, Diane Thomas; Staff 27 (MLS 27)
Founded 1892. Enrl 18,471; Fac 967; Highest Degree: Doctorate
Library Holdings: Bk Vols 935,722; Per Subs 4,358
Publications: The Off-Campus Library Services Conference Proceedings
Partic in Michigan Library Consortium; OCLC Online Computer Library Center, Inc
Departmental Libraries:
CLARKE HISTORICAL LIBRARY, Rose 143, 48859. SAN 323-8741. Tel: 517-774-3352. FAX: 517-774-2160. *Dir*, Frank Boles; *Coordr, Publ Servs*, Evelyn Leasher; *Archivist*, Marian Matyn
Founded 1954
Library Holdings: Bk Vols 88,000; Per Subs 300
Subject Interests: Afro-American, American history, Children's literature, Michigan, Presidents (US)
Special Collections: Africana & Afro-American (Wilbert Wright Coll); Angling (Reed T Draper Coll); Class of 1968 Presidential Campaign Biography Coll; Lucille Clarke Memorial Children's Library; Robert P Griffin, Edford A Cederberg, Russell Kirk, papers
Publications: Michigan Historical Review (annual report)
INSTRUCTIONAL MATERIALS CENTER, Ronan Hall, Rm 109, 48859. SAN 320-0531. Tel: 517-774-3549. *Librn*, Cynthia Whitaker

P CHIPPEWA RIVER DISTRICT LIBRARY, Veterans Memorial Library, 301 S University Ave, 48858-2597. SAN 346-9476. Tel: 517-773-3242. FAX: 517-772-3280. E-Mail: vetsmeml@vml.lib.mi.us. Web Site: www.crdl.lib.mi.us. *Dir*, Lise Mitchell; Tel: 517-772-3488, Ext 12, E-Mail: lhmitch@vml.lib.mi.us; *Cat*, Dianne Holt; Tel: 517-772-3488, Ext 24, E-Mail: dholt@vml.lib.mi.us; *Circ*, Connie Kreiner; Tel: 517-772-3488, Ext 17, E-Mail: ckreiner@vml.lib.mi.us; *Ad Servs*, Alice Jenicke; Tel: 517-772-3488, Ext 20, E-Mail: ajenicke@vml.lib.mi.us; *Ch Servs*, Noah Haiduc-Dale; Tel: 517-772-3488, Ext 15, E-Mail: noahhd@vml.lib.mi.us; *Ch Servs*, Anne Heidemann; Tel: 517-772-3488, Ext 16, E-Mail: aheide@vml.lib.mi.us; *Ch Servs*, Margaret Pavelka; Tel: 517-772-3488, Ext 14, E-Mail: mpavelka@vml.lib.mi.us; *Commun Relations*, Sue Ellen Deni; Tel: 517-772-3488, Ext 27, E-Mail: sdeni@vml.lib.mi.us; Staff 13 (MLS 4, Non-MLS 9)
Founded 1909. Pop 54,616; Circ 190,000
Jan 1999-Dec 1999 Income (Main Library and Branch Library) $1,380,000, State $450,000, County $245,000, Locally Generated Income $500,000, Other $185,000. Mats Exp $1,000,000, Books $140,000, Electronic Ref Mat (Incl. Access Fees) $20,000. Sal $500,000
Library Holdings: Bk Vols 140,000; Bk Titles 90,000; Per Subs 300
Special Collections: Indian Culture & Heritage
Automation Activity & Vendor Info: (Acquisitions) TLC; (Cataloging) TLC; (Circulation) TLC; (OPAC) TLC; (Serials) TLC
Database Vendor: GaleNet, IAC - Info Trac, OCLC - First Search
Function: ILL available
Mem of White Pine Library Cooperative
Partic in MLC; OCLC Online Computer Library Center, Inc
Friends of the Library Group
Branches: 5
COE TOWNSHIP, 308 W Wright St, Shepherd, 48883. SAN 346-9506. Tel: 517-828-6801. FAX: 517-828-6801. *Librn*, Janet Silverthorn; Fax: 517-828-6801, E-Mail: jsilvert@vml.lib.mi.us
Library Holdings: Bk Vols 4,390
FAITH JOHNSTON MEMORIAL, 4026 Michigan St, PO Box 235, Rosebush, 48878. SAN 325-4178. Tel: 517-433-0006. FAX: 517-433-0006. *Librn*, Judy Snook
Library Holdings: Bk Vols 2,750
Friends of the Library Group
FREMONT TOWNSHIP, 2883 W Blanchard Rd, PO Box 368, Winn, 48896. SAN 346-9573. Tel: 517-866-2550. FAX: 517-866-2550. *Librn*, Carole Keene
Library Holdings: Bk Vols 3,325
ROLLAND TOWNSHIP, 430 Harry St, PO Box 39, Blanchard, 49310. SAN 346-9565. Tel: 517-561-2480. FAX: 517-561-2480. *Librn*, Rhonda Clingersmith
Library Holdings: Bk Vols 2,456
WEIDMAN PUBLIC, 3453 N School Rd, PO Box 97, Weidman, 48893. SAN 346-9530. Tel: 517-644-5131. FAX: 517-644-5131. *Librn*, Marsha Huzzey
Library Holdings: Bk Vols 3,230
Friends of the Library Group

R FIRST UNITED METHODIST CHURCH LIBRARY, 400 S Main St, 48858. SAN 308-2911. Tel: 517-773-6934. FAX: 517-773-1855. Web Site: www.mtpfumc.org.
Library Holdings: Bk Vols 2,035

MULLIKEN

P MULLIKEN DISTRICT LIBRARY, 135 Main St, PO Box 246, 48861-0246. SAN 308-292X. Tel: 517-649-8611. FAX: 517-649-2207. *Librn*, Bobbette Walling
Founded 1903. Circ 23,385
Library Holdings: Bk Vols 15,638; Bk Titles 13,668; Per Subs 30
Subject Interests: Local history
Special Collections: Books on Tape; Large Print Books
Mem of Capital Library Cooperative

MUNISING

S ALGER MAXIMUM CORRECTIONAL FACILITY LIBRARY,* Industrial Park Dr, PO Box 600, 49862. SAN 371-6759. Tel: 906-387-5000, Ext 1302. FAX: 906-387-5033. *Librn*, Theresa Larson; Staff 1 (Non-MLS 1)
Founded 1990
Library Holdings: Bk Vols 37,000; Per Subs 38
Subject Interests: Law
Special Collections: ABE, preGED & GED Prepatory Materials; Native American, African-American & Hispanic History
Automation Activity & Vendor Info: (Circulation) Follett
Restriction: Residents only

P MUNISING PUBLIC LIBRARY, 810 State Hwy M28 West, Ste A, 49862. SAN 308-2938. Tel: 906-387-2125. FAX: 906-387-5179. Web Site: www.als.uproc.lib.mi.us/mspl/index.htm. *Dir*, Charlotte Dugas; E-Mail: cdugas@uproc.lib.mi.us; *Librn*, Betty Karbon; E-Mail: bkarbon@uproc.lib.mi.us; Staff 2 (Non-MLS 2)
Founded 1902. Pop 13,219; Circ 66,002
Library Holdings: Bk Vols 16,000; Per Subs 60
Publications: Acquisitions list (newsletter)
Mem of Superiorland Library Cooperative
Open Summer: Mon & Fri 10-4, Tues-Thurs 10-8; Winter: Mon-Thurs 10-8, Fri 10-4, Sun 12-16
Friends of the Library Group

MUSKEGON

J BAKER COLLEGE OF MUSKEGON LIBRARY,* 1903 Marquette Ave, 49442-3404. SAN 308-2970. Tel: 231-777-5330, 231-777-8800. FAX: 231-777-5334. Web Site: www.baker.edu. *Librn*, Margaret Moon; *Circ*, Janis Wayne; *Ref*, Ruth Schnelle
Founded 1885. Enrl 1,600
Library Holdings: Bk Vols 35,000; Per Subs 140
Subject Interests: Accounting, Business and management, Data processing, Law, Secretarial sciences
Open Mon-Thurs 8-8:30, Fri 8-2:30

M HACKLEY HOSPITAL LIBRARY,* 1700 Clinton, PO Box 3302, 49443-3302. SAN 308-2954. Tel: 231-728-4766. FAX: 231-728-0365. *Librn*, Betty Marshall; E-Mail: marshalb@mlc.lib.mi.us
Founded 1957
Library Holdings: Bk Vols 6,000; Per Subs 389
Subject Interests: Allied health, Medicine, Nursing
Partic in Medline

P HACKLEY PUBLIC LIBRARY,* 316 Webster Ave W, 48440. SAN 308-2962. Tel: 231-772-7276. FAX: 231-726-5567. E-Mail: hplref@muskegon.k12.mi.us. Web Site: www.muskegon.k12.mi.us/library/hackley/htm/. *Dir*, Martha Ferriby; E-Mail: mferriby@muskegon.k12.mi.us; *Tech Servs*, Susan Kroes; *Per*, Ann Kelly; *Coll Develop, ILL, Ref*, Marilyn Ryan; *Ch Servs*, James Horan; Staff 29 (MLS 7, Non-MLS 22)
Founded 1888. Pop 39,865
Jul 1999-Jun 2000 Income $1,166,451, State $39,865, Locally Generated Income $449,690, Parent Institution $543,066, Other $133,830. Mats Exp $88,124, Books $74,024, Per/Ser (Incl. Access Fees) $8,500, Presv $200, Micro $5,400. Sal $688,267 (Prof $314,775)
Library Holdings: Bk Vols 190,000; Per Subs 330
Subject Interests: Genealogy
Special Collections: Civil War; Lumbering Era History; Muskegon Regional History
Database Vendor: IAC - SearchBank, OCLC - First Search
Mem of Lakeland Library Cooperative
Partic in Michigan Library Consortium
Friends of the Library Group

M MERCY GENERAL HEALTH PARTNERS, Amos-Crist Health Science Library, PO Box 358, 49443. SAN 329-8949. Tel: 231-739-3972, Ext 8329. FAX: 231-739-3842. *Librn*, Mary Jo Wyels; E-Mail: wyelsm@trinity-health.org
Library Holdings: Bk Titles 1,628; Per Subs 200
Subject Interests: Allied health, Medicine, Nursing
Partic in Medical Libr Asn; Michigan Library Consortium

S MUSKEGON CHRONICLE, Editorial Library,* 981 Third St, 49443. SAN 327-4357. Tel: 231-725-6386. FAX: 231-722-2552. Web Site: www.mlives.com. *Librn*, Linda Thompson
Library Holdings: Bk Titles 350

J MUSKEGON COMMUNITY COLLEGE, Allen G Umbreit Library, 221 S Quarterline Rd, 49442. SAN 308-2989. Tel: 231-777-0269. Interlibrary Loan Service Tel: 231-777-0205. FAX: 231-777-0279. Web Site: library.muskegon.cc.mi.us. *Acq, Coll Develop, Coordr, Ref*, Roger Stoel; *Cat, Ref*, Robert Vanderlaan; *ILL*, Paula McClurg-Ziemelis; *Selection of Elec Mat*, Carol Briggs-Erickson
Founded 1926. Enrl 5,000; Fac 105
Library Holdings: Bk Titles 53,000; Per Subs 230
Subject Interests: Careers, Children's literature
Special Collections: Michigan Authors
Publications: Newsletter
Partic in Dialog Corporation; Michigan Library Consortium; OCLC Online Computer Library Center, Inc

P MUSKEGON COUNTY LIBRARY, 97 E Apple Ave, 49442-3404. SAN 346-959X. Tel: 231-724-6248. TDD: 231-722-4103. FAX: 231-724-6675. E-Mail: mclew@lakeland.lib.mi.us. Web Site: www.lakeland.lib.mi.us/muskegonco/index.html. *Dir*, Elizabeth Winsche; *Cat, Tech Servs*, Sheila Miller; *Online Servs*, Karla Bates; Staff 40 (MLS 7, Non-MLS 33)
Founded 1938. Pop 110,367; Circ 482,018
Oct 1999-Sep 2000 Income (Main Library and Branch Library) $1,512,867, State $156,557, Federal $7,593, County $1,118,931, Locally Generated Income $70,604, Other $169,182. Mats Exp $234,749, Books $191,194, Per/Ser (Incl. Access Fees) $17,160, AV Equip $26,395. Sal $688,298
Library Holdings: Bk Vols 222,330; Bk Titles 104,828; Per Subs 567
Automation Activity & Vendor Info: (Circulation) epixtech, inc.; (ILL) epixtech, inc.; (OPAC) epixtech, inc.
Database Vendor: epixtech, inc., IAC - Info Trac, IAC - SearchBank, OCLC - First Search
Partic in Lakeland Libr Coop
Special Services for the Deaf - TDD
Branches: 10

P BLIND & PHYSICALLY HANDICAPPED LIBRARY, 97 E Apple Ave, 49442. Tel: 231-724-6248. Toll Free Tel: 877-569-4801. TDD: 231-722-4103. FAX: 231-724-6675. E-Mail: mclsm@lakeland.lib.mi.us. Web Site: www.lakeland.lib.mi.us/muskegonco/index.html. *Librn*, Sheila Miller
Founded 1979
Special Services for the Deaf - TDD
Special Services for the Blind - Bks on tape; Descriptive videos

DALTON, 3175 Fifth St, Twin Lake, 49457-9501. SAN 346-9654. Tel: 231-828-4188. E-Mail: dal@lakeland.lib.mi.us. Web Site: www.lakeland.lib.mi.us/muskegonco/dalton.html. *Librn*, Sue Monson
Library Holdings: Bk Vols 9,303
Friends of the Library Group

EGELSTON BRANCH, 5428 E Apple Ave, 49442-3008. SAN 346-9689. Tel: 231-788-6477. TDD: 231-722-4106. FAX: 231-724-6675. E-Mail: ege@lakeland.lib.mi.us. Web Site: www.lakeland.lib.mi.us/muskegonco/egelston.html. *Librn*, Andrew Hammond
Circ 52,379
Library Holdings: Bk Vols 23,437; Per Subs 49
Automation Activity & Vendor Info: (Circulation) epixtech, inc.; (ILL) epixtech, inc.; (OPAC) epixtech, inc.
Friends of the Library Group

FRUITPORT BRANCH, Park & Third Sts, Fruitport, 49415-0911. SAN 346-9719. Tel: 231-865-3461. TDD: 231-722-4103. FAX: 231-724-6675. E-Mail: fru@lakeland.lib.mi.us. Web Site: www.lakeland.lib.mi.us/muskegonco/fruitport.html. *Librn*, Laura Oldt
Library Holdings: Bk Vols 13,258; Per Subs 30
Automation Activity & Vendor Info: (Circulation) epixtech, inc.; (ILL) epixtech, inc.; (OPAC) epixtech, inc.
Partic in Lakeland Libr Coop
Friends of the Library Group

HOLTON BRANCH, 8776 Holton-Duck Lake Rd, PO Box 98, Holton, 49425-9616. SAN 346-9743. Tel: 231-821-0268. TDD: 231-722-4103. FAX: 231-724-6675. E-Mail: hlt@lakeland.lib.mi.us. Web Site: www.lakeland.lib.mi.us/muskegonco/holton.html. *Librn*, Marlene Noble
Circ 14,719
Library Holdings: Bk Vols 11,610; Per Subs 28
Automation Activity & Vendor Info: (Circulation) epixtech, inc.; (ILL) epixtech, inc.; (OPAC) epixtech, inc.
Partic in Lakeland Libr Coop
Friends of the Library Group

MONTAGUE BRANCH, 8778 Ferry St, Montague, 49437-1233. SAN 346-9778. Tel: 231-893-2675. TDD: 231-722-4103. FAX: 231-724-6675. E-Mail: mon@lakeland.lib.mi.us. Web Site: www.lakeland.lib.mi.us/muskegonco/montague.html. *Librn*, Sharon Smith; Staff 2 (Non-MLS 2)
Circ 36,446
Library Holdings: Bk Vols 21,252; Per Subs 59
Automation Activity & Vendor Info: (Circulation) epixtech, inc.; (ILL) epixtech, inc.; (OPAC) epixtech, inc.
Partic in Lakeland Libr Coop

Friends of the Library Group
MUSKEGON HEIGHTS BRANCH, 2808 Sanford St, Muskegon Heights, 49444-2010. SAN 346-9808. Tel: 231-739-6075. TDD: 231-722-4103. FAX: 231-724-6675. E-Mail: muh@lakeland.lib.mi.us. Web Site: www.lakeland.lib.mi.us/muskegonco/heights.html. *Mgr*, Elisia Hardiman
Circ 8,345
Library Holdings: Bk Vols 21,980; Per Subs 35
Automation Activity & Vendor Info: (Circulation) epixtech, inc.; (ILL) epixtech, inc.; (OPAC) epixtech, inc.
Partic in Lakeland Libr Coop
NORTON SHORES BRANCH, 705 Seminole Rd, 49441-4797. SAN 346-9832. Tel: 231-780-8844. TDD: 231-722-4103. FAX: 231-780-5436. E-Mail: nor@lakeland.lib.mi.us. Web Site: www.lakeland.lib.mi.us/muskegonco/norton.html. *Librn*, Carol Knowlton
Founded 1974. Pop 25,000; Circ 136,210
Library Holdings: Bk Vols 53,051; Per Subs 130
Automation Activity & Vendor Info: (Circulation) epixtech, inc.; (ILL) epixtech, inc.; (OPAC) epixtech, inc.
Partic in Lakeland Libr Coop
Friends of the Library Group
RAVENNA BRANCH, 12278 Stafford, Ravenna, 49451-9410. SAN 346-9867. Tel: 231-853-6975. TDD: 231-722-4103. FAX: 231-724-6675. E-Mail: rav@lakeland.lib.mi.us. Web Site: www.lakeland.lib.mi.us/muskegonco/ravenna.html. *Librn*, Diane Landheer
Circ 29,591
Library Holdings: Bk Vols 16,181; Per Subs 30
Automation Activity & Vendor Info: (Circulation) epixtech, inc.; (ILL) epixtech, inc.; (OPAC) epixtech, inc.
Partic in Lakeland Libr Coop
WALKER MEMORIAL BRANCH, 1522 Ruddiman Dr, North Muskegon, 49445-3038. SAN 346-9891. Tel: 616-724-6080. TDD: 231-722-4103. FAX: 231-719-8056. E-Mail: nmu@lakeland.lib.mi.us. Web Site: www.lakeland.lib.mi.us/muskegonco/walker.html. *Librn*, Mark Ames
Circ 65,563
Library Holdings: Bk Vols 22,735; Per Subs 101
Automation Activity & Vendor Info: (Circulation) epixtech, inc.; (ILL) epixtech, inc.; (OPAC) epixtech, inc.
Partic in Lakeland Libr Coop
Friends of the Library Group

S MUSKEGON COUNTY MUSEUM ARCHIVES, Muskegon Mercantile Bldg, 471 W Western Ave, 49440. (Mail add: 430 W Clay Ave, 49440), SAN 372-8013. Tel: 231-722-0278. FAX: 231-728-4119. Web Site: www.muskegonmuseum.org. *Archivist*, Barbara L Martin; E-Mail: barbara@muskegonmuseum.org. Subject Specialists: *Lumbering*, Barbara L Martin; Staff 1 (Non-MLS 1)
Founded 1986. Pop 160,000
Oct 1998-Sep 1999 Income $27,000, County $25,000, Locally Generated Income $1,000, Parent Institution $1,000. Mats Exp $2,600, Per/Ser (Incl. Access Fees) $50, Presv $500, Micro $50, Other Print Mats $500, Manuscripts & Archives $500, Electronic Ref Mat (Incl. Access Fees) $1,000. Sal $20,000
Library Holdings: Bk Vols 2,225; Bk Titles 1,725; Per Subs 12; Spec Interest Per Sub 10
Subject Interests: Local history
Special Collections: Lumbering (Charles Yates Coll), photogs; Muskegon County History, bks, mss, photogs
Restriction: By appointment only
Function: Archival collection

NASHVILLE

P PUTNAM DISTRICT LIBRARY,* 327 N Main St, PO Box C, 49073-9578. SAN 308-2997. Tel: 517-852-9723. FAX: 517-852-0778. *Dir*, Deidre Bryans; Staff 1 (MLS 1)
Founded 1923. Pop 6,362; Circ 25,689
Library Holdings: Bk Vols 14,894; Per Subs 30
Subject Interests: Local history
Publications: F O L Cookbook
Mem of Woodlands Library Cooperative

NEGAUNEE

P NEGAUNEE PUBLIC LIBRARY,* 319 W Case St, PO Box 548, 49866-0548. SAN 308-3012. Tel: 906-475-9400. FAX: 906-475-4880. Web Site: www.uproc.lib.mi.us. *Librn*, Katherine Thurner; *Asst Librn*, Laura Jandron
Founded 1890. Circ 34,723
Library Holdings: Bk Vols 32,707; Per Subs 80
Mem of Superiorland Library Cooperative

NEW BALTIMORE

P MACDONALD PUBLIC LIBRARY, (NBL), 36480 Main St, 48047-2509. SAN 308-3020. Tel: 810-725-0273. FAX: 810-725-8360. Web Site: www.libcoop.net/newbaltimore. *Dir*, Margaret A Thomas
Founded 1941. Pop 7,315
Jul 1998-Jun 1999 Income $321,112. Mats Exp $300,000. Sal $136,191 (Prof $79,976)
Library Holdings: Bk Vols 34,000; Per Subs 81
Automation Activity & Vendor Info: (Acquisitions) SIRSI; (Cataloging) SIRSI; (Circulation) SIRSI; (Course Reserve) SIRSI; (ILL) SIRSI; (Media Booking) SIRSI; (OPAC) SIRSI; (Serials) SIRSI
Friends of the Library Group

NEW BUFFALO

P NEW BUFFALO TOWNSHIP PUBLIC LIBRARY, 33 N Thompson St, 49117. SAN 308-3039. Tel: 616-469-2933. FAX: 616-469-3521. *Dir*, Bonnie Kliss
Library Holdings: Bk Vols 50,000; Per Subs 112
Subject Interests: Local history, Michigan
Automation Activity & Vendor Info: (Cataloging) Sagebrush Corporation; (Circulation) Sagebrush Corporation
Mem of Libr Syst of SW Mich; SW Libr Coop

NEW HAVEN

P LENOX TOWNSHIP LIBRARY,* 58976 Main St, PO Box 0367, 48048-0367. SAN 308-3047. Tel: 810-749-3430. FAX: 810-749-3245. *Dir*, Joanne Johnson
Pop 4,899; Circ 12,191
Library Holdings: Bk Vols 20,000; Per Subs 49
Subject Interests: Black people (ethnic)
Partic in Suburban Library Cooperative

NEW HUDSON

P LYON TOWNSHIP PUBLIC LIBRARY,* 27005 S Milford Rd, PO Box 326, 48165-0326. SAN 308-3055. Tel: 248-437-8800. FAX: 248-437-4621.
Pop 8,828; Circ 38,014
Library Holdings: Bk Vols 28,842; Per Subs 76
Subject Interests: Genealogy
Automation Activity & Vendor Info: (Cataloging) GEAC; (Circulation) GEAC
Mem of The Library Network

NEWAYGO

P NEWAYGO CARNEGIE LIBRARY,* 45 N State Rd, PO Box 427, 49337-0427. SAN 308-3063. Tel: 231-652-6723. FAX: 231-652-6616. E-Mail: new@lakeland.lib.mi.us. Web Site: webpac.lakeland.lib.mi.us/webclientnew.html. *Librn*, Phyllis M Douglas
Pop 7,623
Jul 1997-Jun 1998 Income $106,756. Mats Exp $110,170. Sal $42,806
Library Holdings: Bk Vols 33,697; Per Subs 55
Mem of Lakeland Library Cooperative
Special Services for the Blind - Talking book center

NEWBERRY

S NEWBERRY CORRECTIONAL FACILITY LIBRARY, 3001 Newberry Ave, 49868. SAN 377-161X. Tel: 906-293-6200. FAX: 906-293-6323. *Librn*, Janice Yoak; E-Mail: yoakjl@state.mi.us; Staff 1 (MLS 1)
Founded 1995
Library Holdings: Bk Vols 5,600; Per Subs 31; High Interest/Low Vocabulary Bk Vols 150
Restriction: Residents only
Partic in Am Libr Asn

P TAHQUAMONAN AREA PUBLIC SCHOOL LIBRARY,* 700 Newberry Ave, 49868. SAN 308-3071. Tel: 906-293-5214. FAX: 906-293-3780. Web Site: www.eup.k12.mi.us/tahquamonan/library. *Librn*, Sally Carlson
Pop 7,000; Circ 18,568
Library Holdings: Bk Vols 33,000; Per Subs 145
Mem of Eastern Peninsula Libr Syst
Friends of the Library Group

NILES

P NILES COMMUNITY LIBRARY,* 620 E Main St, 49120. SAN 308-308X. Tel: 616-683-8545. FAX: 616-683-0075. *Dir*, Eileen Doyle; *Tech Servs*, Doris Gill; *Ad Servs, Ref*, Diana J Hiles; *ILL*, Ann Flora; *Ad Servs*, Syd Duncan; *Ad Servs*, Vickie Semeric
Founded 1903. Pop 32,171; Circ 194,678
Library Holdings: Bk Vols 100,000
Special Collections: Niles Newspapers, 1834 to date, microflm; Ring Lardner (Complete Works)
Mem of Southwest Michigan Library Cooperative
Friends of the Library Group

NORTH BRANCH

P NORTH BRANCH TOWNSHIP LIBRARY, 3714 Huron St, PO Box 705, 48461. SAN 308-3101. Tel: 810-688-2282. FAX: 810-688-3165. *Librn*, Karen Lambert; E-Mail: klambert@edcen.ehhs.cmich.edu
Pop 7,705; Circ 38,523
Library Holdings: Bk Titles 27,000; Per Subs 48
Mem of Mideastern Michigan Library Cooperative

NORTHPORT

P LEELANAU TOWNSHIP PUBLIC LIBRARY, 119 E Nagonaba, PO Box 235, 49670-0235. SAN 308-311X. Tel: 616-386-5131. FAX: 616-386-5874. E-Mail: ltlib@traverse.com. *Librn*, Deborah Stannard
Pop 2,500; Circ 16,605
Apr 1998-Mar 1999 Income $85,890. Mats Exp $74,830, Books $10,000, Other Print Mats $5,000. Sal $25,000
Library Holdings: Bk Vols 20,000; Per Subs 46
Subject Interests: Local history
Special Collections: US Constitution Coll, bks
Publications: Library Report (newsletter)
Mem of Mid-Michigan Library League
Open Tues, Thurs, Fri, & Sat 9:30-5, Wed 3-8
Friends of the Library Group

NORTHVILLE

P NORTHVILLE DISTRICT LIBRARY, 212 W Cady St, 48167-1560. SAN 308-3136. Tel: 248-349-3020. FAX: 248-349-8250. E-Mail: nort@tln.lib.mi.us. Web Site: www.northville.lib.mi.us. *Dir*, Julie Herrin; E-Mail: jherrin@tln.lib.mi.us
Pop 23,539
Library Holdings: Bk Vols 65,000; Per Subs 158
Subject Interests: Large type print
Mem of The Library Network
Friends of the Library Group

NOVI

S CLAYTON GROUP SERVICES, INC, Library & Information Center, 22345 Roethel Dr, 48375-4710. SAN 308-4167. Tel: 248-344-1770. FAX: 248-344-2654. *Dir*, Marjorie Corey; E-Mail: mcorey@claytongrp.com; Staff 1 (MLS 1)
Founded 1954
Library Holdings: Bk Vols 10,000; Per Subs 150
Subject Interests: Air pollution, Chemistry, Environmental engineering, Noise pollution, Occupational safety, Pollution, Public health, Toxicology, Waste disposal, Water pollution
Special Collections: OSHA & EPA Govt Doc

P NOVI PUBLIC LIBRARY, (NPL), 45245 W Ten Mile Rd, 48375. SAN 308-3152. Tel: 248-349-0720. FAX: 248-349-6520. Web Site: novi.lib.mi.us. *Dir*, Brenda Evans; Tel: 248-349-0976; *Asst Dir*, Pauline Druschel; Tel: 248-349-0976, E-Mail: druschel@tlm.lib.mi.us; *Ch Servs*, Margi Karp-Opperer; *Circ*, Betty Prost; *Ref*, Donna Hollis; *AV*, Cindy Rooks; *Tech Coordr*, Karen Knox; *Tech Servs*, Mary Ellen Mulcrone; Staff 51 (MLS 18, Non-MLS 33)
Founded 1960. Pop 33,148; Circ 324,767
Jul 2000-Jun 2001 Income $1,679,620. Mats Exp $204,137, Books $154,223, Micro $21,669, AV Equip $28,245. Sal $888,801
Library Holdings: Bk Vols 96,454; Per Subs 269
Subject Interests: Careers, Finance, Law
Special Collections: Adult Basic Readers
Automation Activity & Vendor Info: (Circulation) DRA; (ILL) DRA; (OPAC) DRA
Publications: Annual Report
Mem of Libr Network Coop; The Library Network
Friends of the Library Group
Bookmobiles: 1

OAK PARK

S BUILDING TECHNOLOGY CONSTRUCTION CONSULTANTS, INC LIBRARY,* 21850 Greenfield, 48237. SAN 307-9910. Tel: 248-967-4620. FAX: 248-967-4640. *Librn*, Richard Racusien
Founded 1974
Library Holdings: Bk Titles 500; Per Subs 20

R CONGREGATION BETH SHALOM, Rabbi Mordecai S Halpern Memorial Library, 14601 W Lincoln Blvd, 48237. SAN 308-3160. Tel: 248-547-7970. FAX: 248-547-0421. E-Mail: cbs@congbethshalom.org. *Librn*, Masha Silver
Founded 1965
Library Holdings: Bk Vols 8,000
Subject Interests: Judaica (lit or hist of Jews)

P OAK PARK PUBLIC LIBRARY, 14200 Oak Park Blvd, 48237-2089. SAN 308-3209. Tel: 248-691-7480. TDD: 248-547-8216. FAX: 248-691-7155. Web Site: www.oak-park.lib.mi.us. *Dir*, John Martin; E-Mail: jmartin@oak-park.lib.mi.us; *Ad Servs*, Mary Bernhardt; *Ad Servs*, Richard L Churgay; *Ad Servs*, Marjorie Lusko; *Ch Servs*, Gayle Branzburg; *Ch Servs*, Kimberly Goonis; Staff 32 (MLS 11, Non-MLS 21)
Founded 1957
Jun 1999-Jul 2000 Income $771,760, State $30,468, City $668,848, Federal $11,622, County $38,137, Locally Generated Income $22,685. Mats Exp $102,526, Books $67,924, Per/Ser (Incl. Access Fees) $8,478, AV Equip $26,124. Sal $448,918 (Prof $232,789)
Library Holdings: Bk Vols 85,985; Per Subs 215; High Interest/Low Vocabulary Bk Vols 300; Spec Interest Per Sub 9
Subject Interests: Arabic language, Judaica (lit or hist of Jews), Russian (language)
Automation Activity & Vendor Info: (Acquisitions) DRA; (Cataloging) DRA; (Circulation) DRA; (ILL) DRA; (OPAC) DRA; (Serials) DRA
Database Vendor: DRA
Mem of The Library Network
Special Services for the Deaf - TDD
Friends of the Library Group

OKEMOS

S BLIND CHILDREN'S FUND LIBRARY, 4740 Okemos Rd, 48864. Tel: 517-347-1357. FAX: 517-347-1459. E-Mail: blindchfnd@aol.com. Web Site: www.blindchildrensfund.org. *Pres*, Sherry Raynor
Library Holdings: Bk Titles 1,500; Per Subs 15
Publications: VIP newsletter

OLIVET

C OLIVET COLLEGE, Burrage Library, 333 S Main St, 49076-9730. SAN 346-9921. Tel: 616-749-7608. FAX: 616-749-7121. Web Site: www.olivetcollege.edu. *Dir*, Mary Jo Blackport; E-Mail: mjblackport@olivetcollege.edu; *Tech Servs*, Marja Hendrick; E-Mail: mhendrick@olivetcollege.edu; *Per*, Julie Walker; E-Mail: jwalker@olivetcollege.edu; *Circ*, Elaine Hoeltzel; E-Mail: ehoeltzel@olivetcollege.edu; *ILL*, Robert Barnes; E-Mail: rbarnes@olivetcollege.edu; Staff 5 (MLS 1, Non-MLS 4)
Founded 1844. Enrl 934; Fac 69; Highest Degree: Master
Jul 1999-Jun 2000 Income Parent Institution $218,514. Mats Exp $65,810, Books $30,342, Per/Ser (Incl. Access Fees) $22,680, Micro $4,378, Electronic Ref Mat (Incl. Access Fees) $8,410. Sal $126,328 (Prof $71,669)
Library Holdings: Bk Vols 105,516; Bk Titles 89,238; Per Subs 399
Subject Interests: Arctic, Education
Special Collections: Arctic Coll
Database Vendor: IAC - SearchBank, OCLC - First Search
Partic in Capital Area Library Network Inc; Michigan Library Consortium; OCLC Online Computer Library Center, Inc

ONTONAGON

P ONTONAGON TOWNSHIP LIBRARY, 311 N Steel St, 49953-1398. SAN 308-3233. Tel: 906-884-4411. FAX: 906-884-2829. Web Site: www2.mid-pen.lib.mi.us/midpen/library/ontonagon/home.htm. *Dir Libr Serv*, Barbara Morin
Pop 5,260; Circ 33,636
Library Holdings: Bk Vols 35,700; Per Subs 69
Special Collections: Finnish Books; Michigan Local History
Automation Activity & Vendor Info: (Cataloging) Brodart; (Circulation) Brodart
Database Vendor: OCLC - First Search
Mem of Mid-Peninsula Library Cooperative

ORCHARD LAKE

S GREATER WEST BLOOMFIELD HISTORICAL SOCIETY, Museum Library, 3951 Orchard Lake Rd, PO Box 240514, 48324. SAN 373-2150. Tel: 248-682-2279. *Pres*, Thad Radzilowski
Library Holdings: Bk Vols 120
Subject Interests: Local history

CR SAINT MARY'S COLLEGE, Alumni Memorial Library, 3535 Indian Trail, 48324. SAN 308-3241. Tel: 248-683-0524. Circulation Tel: 248-683-0525. Reference Tel: 248-683-0524. FAX: 248-683-0526. E-Mail: alumnlib@rust.net. Web Site: www.mi.verio.com/~alumnblib. *Dir*, Nancy Ward; E-Mail: nward@mi.verio.com; *Tech Servs*, Judith Edwards; *Ref*, Marie Bookless; Staff 5 (MLS 3, Non-MLS 2)
Founded 1885. Enrl 5,000; Fac 35; Highest Degree: Master
Jul 1999-Jun 2000 Income $219,823. Mats Exp $73,943, Books $45,920, Per/Ser (Incl. Access Fees) $15,574, Presv $408, Micro $1,493, AV Equip $400, Electronic Ref Mat (Incl. Access Fees) $10,148
Library Holdings: Bk Titles 79,103; Per Subs 335; High Interest/Low Vocabulary Bk Vols 50
Subject Interests: Culture, Ethnic studies, Lang, Polish (language), Theology

Special Collections: Polish Language Coll; Polish Language Rare Books
Automation Activity & Vendor Info: (Cataloging) DRA; (Circulation) DRA; (OPAC) DRA
Database Vendor: DRA, IAC - Info Trac, OVID Technologies
Publications: Library Pulse (Acquisition list)
Restriction: Open to student, faculty & staff
Function: ILL limited
Partic in Detroit Area Consortium Of Catholic Colleges; Michigan Library Consortium; OCLC Online Computer Library Center, Inc

ORTONVILLE

P BRANDON TOWNSHIP PUBLIC LIBRARY, 304 South St, PO Box 1008, 48462. SAN 308-325X. Tel: 248-627-1460. E-Mail: brandon@tln.lib.mi.us. Web Site: www.brandonlibrary.org. *Dir*, JoAnn Foster Gavey; E-Mail: jgavey@tln.lib.mi.us; *Ch Servs, YA Servs*, Frances Runnells; *Ref*, Cynthia Ann Neer; *Ad Servs*, Dan T Hutchins; E-Mail: hutch668@flash.net; Staff 21 (MLS 3, Non-MLS 18)
Founded 1924. Pop 14,401
Jan 2000-Dec 2000 Income $709,993, State $14,343, County $18,029, Locally Generated Income $641,121, Other $56,279. Mats Exp $583,053, Books $91,308, Per/Ser (Incl. Access Fees) $5,500, AV Equip $16,154, Electronic Ref Mat (Incl. Access Fees) $10,000. Sal $214,274 (Prof $112,653)
Library Holdings: Bk Titles 44,000; Per Subs 76
Subject Interests: Genealogy
Special Collections: Local History, unabridged audiobooks
Database Vendor: DRA
Publications: Newsletter (bi-annual)
Mem of The Library Network
Friends of the Library Group

OTSEGO

P OTSEGO DISTRICT PUBLIC LIBRARY, 219 S Farmer St, 49078-1313. SAN 308-3268. Tel: 616-694-9690. FAX: 616-694-9129. Web Site: www.otsegolibrary.org. *Dir*, Ryan S Wieber; Tel: 616-694-6455, E-Mail: rwieber@otsegolibrary.org; *Asst Librn*, Brenda Morris; Staff 10 (MLS 1, Non-MLS 9)
Founded 1844. Pop 12,916; Circ 69,304
Jan 1999-Dec 1999 Income $334,653, State $12,336, County $2,892, Locally Generated Income $319,425. Mats Exp $258,013, Books $32,550, Per/Ser (Incl. Access Fees) $3,246. Sal $105,255 (Prof $33,500)
Library Holdings: Bk Vols 40,639; Bk Titles 36,252; Per Subs 109
Special Collections: History of Otsego, 12 volume Coll, bks & micro; Michigan Pioneer Coll
Automation Activity & Vendor Info: (Circulation) Follett
Database Vendor: OCLC - First Search, Wilson - Wilson Web
Function: ILL available
Mem of Southwest Michigan Library Cooperative
Partic in Michigan Library Consortium; Southwest Michigan Library Cooperative
Friends of the Library Group

OVID

P OVID PUBLIC LIBRARY, 206 N Main St, 48866-0048. (Mail add: PO Box 48, 48866-0048), SAN 320-4847. Tel: 517-834-5800. FAX: 517-834-5113. *Librn*, Sharlyn S Huyck; Staff 3 (MLS 1, Non-MLS 2)
Founded 1949. Pop 5,559; Circ 31,100
Library Holdings: Bk Vols 16,000; Per Subs 30
Database Vendor: Innovative Interfaces INN - View
Mem of Capital Library Cooperative

OWOSSO

C BAKER COLLEGE LIBRARY OF OWOSSO,* 1020 S Washington, 48867-4400. SAN 370-0097. Tel: 517-723-5251. FAX: 517-729-3330. Web Site: www.baker.edu. *Librn*, Jessica Janego
Founded 1984. Enrl 900
Library Holdings: Bk Titles 35,000; Per Subs 200
Subject Interests: Electronics, Engineering, Fashion, Interior design, Travel
Open Mon-Thurs 7:45am-9pm, Fri 8am-3pm, Sat 9am-3pm & Sun 1-4pm

P SHIAWASSEE DISTRICT LIBRARY, Owosso, 502 W Main St, 48867-2687. SAN 308-3306. Tel: 517-725-5134. FAX: 517-723-5444. E-Mail: info@sdl.lib.mi.us. Web Site: sdl.lib.mi.us. *Dir*, Kenneth R Uptigrove; *Ad Servs, Asst Dir*, Margaret Ann Bentley; *Ch Servs*, Marjorie Cox; Staff 5 (MLS 2, Non-MLS 3)
Founded 1910. Pop 29,267; Circ 100,791
Dec 2000-Nov 2001 Income (Main Library and Branch Library) $718,300, State $29,250, Locally Generated Income $653,350, Other $35,700. Mats Exp $100,450, Books $71,500, Per/Ser (Incl. Access Fees) $4,100, AV Equip $15,250, Electronic Ref Mat (Incl. Access Fees) $9,600. Sal $409,500
Library Holdings: Bk Vols 90,079; Per Subs 220
Subject Interests: Local history
Special Collections: Genealogy(Includes surname file); ; James Oliver Curwood Coll, bks, mss, pictures
Automation Activity & Vendor Info: (Circulation) Sagebrush Corporation; (OPAC) Sagebrush Corporation
Mem of Mideastern Michigan Library Cooperative
Partic in Michigan Library Consortium
Hours: Open Mon-Thurs 10-9, Fri 1-5, Sat 10-5; (June-Aug) Sat 10-2; (Oct-June) Fri 10-5, Sun 1-5
Friends of the Library Group
Branches: 1
DURAND MEMORIAL BRANCH, 700 N Saginaw St, Durand, 48429-1245. SAN 308-0536. Tel: 517-288-3743. FAX: 517-288-3740. Web Site: www.sdl.lib.mi.us/. *Dir*, Kenneth Uptigrove; *Librn*, Nancy Folaron
Founded 1954. Pop 4,647
Library Holdings: Bk Vols 16,000; Per Subs 52
Subject Interests: Genealogy, Michigan
Special Collections: City of Durand Coll
Hours: Open Mon-Thurs 9:30-8, Fri 9:30-6, Sat 9:30-3
Friends of the Library Group

OXFORD

P OXFORD PUBLIC LIBRARY,* 530 Pontiac Rd, 48371. SAN 308-3314. Tel: 248-628-3034. FAX: 248-628-5008. Web Site: www.oxford.lib.mi.us. *Dir*, Judith Doublestein; Staff 2 (MLS 2)
Founded 1916. Pop 11,933; Circ 62,505
Library Holdings: Bk Vols 47,000; Per Subs 110
Mem of The Library Network
Friends of the Library Group

PALMER

P RICHMOND TOWNSHIP PUBLIC LIBRARY,* Smith St, PO Box 35, 49871-0035. SAN 308-3322. Tel: 906-475-5241. Interlibrary Loan Service Tel: 906-229-7697. FAX: 906-475-7516. *Librn*, Denise Jeske; E-Mail: djeske@bresnenlink.net; Staff 1 (MLS 1)
Founded 1975. Pop 1,095
Library Holdings: Bk Vols 6,475; Bk Titles 5,450; Per Subs 28
Special Collections: Finnish Coll
Mem of Superiorland Library Cooperative

PARADISE

P WHITEFISH TOWNSHIP COMMUNITY LIBRARY, 7247 N Hwy 123, 49768-0197. (Mail add: PO Box 197, 49768-0197), Tel: 906-492-3500. FAX: 906-492-3500. E-Mail: westlund@upk12.mi.us. Web Site: eup.k12.mi.us. *Dir*, Anne Westlund
Circ 1,470
Library Holdings: Bk Vols 10,000; Bk Titles 8,700
Mem of Hiawathaland Library Cooperative

PARCHMENT

P PARCHMENT COMMUNITY LIBRARY,* 401 S Riverview Dr, 49004-1200. SAN 308-3330. Tel: 616-343-7747. FAX: 616-343-7749. E-Mail: parlib@hotmail.com. Web Site: www.mlc.lib.mi.us/~moeningk/index.html. *Dir*, Karen B Moening; *Librn*, Linda Hall; Staff 3 (MLS 3)
Founded 1963. Pop 9,626; Circ 75,273
Library Holdings: Bk Vols 38,500
Special Collections: Parchment History, newspapers, pictures
Mem of Southwest Michigan Library Cooperative
Friends of the Library Group

PAW PAW

P PAW PAW DISTRICT LIBRARY, 609 W Michigan Ave, 49079-1072. SAN 308-3349. Tel: 616-657-3800. FAX: 616-657-2603. Web Site: www.pawpaw.lib.mi.us. *Dir*, John A Mohney; E-Mail: johnamohney@rocketmail.com; Staff 2 (MLS 2)
Pop 11,354; Circ 60,523
Jan 2000-Dec 2000 Income $526,750, State $15,060, County $64,930, Locally Generated Income $419,380, Other $27,380. Mats Exp $93,195, Books $76,780, Per/Ser (Incl. Access Fees) $5,000, AV Equip $7,300, Electronic Ref Mat (Incl. Access Fees) $4,115. Sal $190,777 (Prof $45,650)
Library Holdings: Bk Vols 53,848; Per Subs 137
Special Collections: Michigan Coll
Mem of Southwest Michigan Library Cooperative
Partic in Mich Libr Asn; Southwest Michigan Library Cooperative
Open Mon 9-8, Tues, Wed & Thurs noon-8, Fri & Sat 9-5

P SOUTHWEST MICHIGAN LIBRARY COOPERATIVE,* 305 Oak St, 49079. SAN 308-2156. Tel: 616-657-4698. FAX: 616-657-4494. Web Site: www.smlc.lib.mis.us. *Dir*, Alida Geppert
Founded 1977
Oct 1997-Sep 1998 Income $440,615, State $393,914, Locally Generated

Income $46,701. Mats Exp $142,956. Sal $296,320
Member Libraries: Benton Harbor Public Library; Bridgman Public Library; Comstock Township Library; Davenport University; Dowagiac Public Library; Eau Claire District Library; Galesburg Memorial Library; Galien Township Public Library; Glen Oaks Community College; Hartford Public Library; Kalamazoo Public Library; Lawton Public Library; Lincoln Township Public Library; Marcellus Township-Wood Memorial Library; Maud Preston Palenske Memorial Library; McKay Library; Michigan Career & Technical Institute Library; Niles Community Library; Otsego District Public Library; Parchment Community Library; Paw Paw District Library; Portage District Library; Sodus Township Library; South Haven Memorial Library; Vicksburg District Library; Watervliet District Library; Willard Library

PECK

P ELK TOWNSHIP LIBRARY, 29 E Lapeer St, 48466-0268. SAN 308-3357. Tel: 810-378-5409. FAX: 810-378-5016. *Dir*, Janet Dyki
Founded 1938. Pop 3,494; Circ 11,650
Apr 1999-Mar 2000 Income $53,000. Mats Exp $43,000, Books $7,000, Per/Ser (Incl. Access Fees) $1,600
Library Holdings: Bk Vols 13,000; Per Subs 45
Mem of White Pine Library Cooperative

PENTWATER

P PENTWATER TOWNSHIP LIBRARY,* 402 E Park, PO Box 946, 49449-0946. SAN 308-3365. Tel: 231-869-8581. FAX: 231-869-4000. *Dir*, Marilyn Cluchey; E-Mail: mcluchey.lib@lakeshore.net
Circ 19,000
Apr 1997-Mar 1998 Income $94,000, State $1,600, City $64,000, County $15,000, Locally Generated Income $4,900, Other $8,000. Mats Exp $19,000, Books $14,000, Per/Ser (Incl. Access Fees) $3,300. Sal $57,000
Library Holdings: Bk Vols 17,000; Per Subs 100
Special Collections: Michigan Coll
Mem of Mid-Michigan Library League
Friends of the Library Group

PERRY

P EDNA BENTLEY MEMORIAL LIBRARY,* 135 S Main, PO Box 17, 48872-0017. SAN 308-3373. Tel: 517-625-3166. FAX: 517-625-7214. *Librn*, Sandy MacPherson
Founded 1935. Circ 48,000
Jan 1998-Dec 1999 Income $60,000
Library Holdings: Bk Vols 13,574; Per Subs 40
Mem of Mideastern Michigan Library Cooperative
Branches: 1
DUNHAM LIBRARY, 13021 S Shaftsburg, 48882. SAN 329-3661. Tel: 517-675-5900. FAX: 517-675-5900. *Librn*, Sandy MacPherson
Open Tues 1-7

PETOSKEY

S LITTLE TRAVERSE HISTORICAL SOCIETY, INC LIBRARY,* 100 Depot Ct, PO Box 162, 49770. SAN 321-2335. Tel: 231-347-2620. FAX: 231-347-2875. *Dir*, Mary Candace Eaton; Staff 1 (Non-MLS 1)
Founded 1972
Library Holdings: Bk Titles 5,000; Per Subs 12
Subject Interests: Local history
Special Collections: Little Traverse Bay Area; Petoskey Newspapers 1875-1979

J NORTH CENTRAL MICHIGAN COLLEGE LIBRARY, 1515 Howard St, 49770. SAN 308-3381. Tel: 616-348-6615. FAX: 616-348-6629. Web Site: www.library.nmc.cc.mi.us. *Dir*, Eric Grandstaff; E-Mail: grandste@ncmc.cc.mi.us; *Librn*, Eunice Teel; E-Mail: eteel@ncmc.cc.mi.us; *Asst Librn*, Nancy Henry; Staff 4 (MLS 2, Non-MLS 2)
Founded 1958. Enrl 2,100; Fac 32; Highest Degree: Associate
Jul 1999-Jun 2000 Income $250,685, Locally Generated Income $6,000, Parent Institution $244,685. Mats Exp $125,380, Books $16,800, Presv $3,800, Micro $9,000, AV Equip $75,030, Manuscripts & Archives $3,850, Electronic Ref Mat (Incl. Access Fees) $16,900. Sal $149,799 (Prof $133,335)
Library Holdings: Bk Titles 30,000; Per Subs 240
Subject Interests: History, Science, Social sciences and issues, Technology
Special Collections: Nuclear Documents
Automation Activity & Vendor Info: (Circulation) Athena; (Course Reserve) Athena; (OPAC) Athena
Database Vendor: Dialog, Ebsco - EbscoHost, GaleNet, IAC - Info Trac, Lexis-Nexis, OCLC - First Search
Mem of Northland Library Cooperative
Partic in Dialog Corporation; Northland Interlibrary System

M NORTHERN MICHIGAN HOSPITAL & BURNS CLINIC FOUNDATION, Dean C Burns Health Sciences Library, 416 Connable Ave, 49770. SAN 308-339X. Tel: 231-487-4500. FAX: 231-487-7892. E-Mail: deanbib@northland.lib.mi.us. *Librn*, Anne Foster
Library Holdings: Per Subs 400
Subject Interests: Health sciences
Partic in Medline

P PETOSKEY PUBLIC LIBRARY, 451 E Mitchell St, 49770. SAN 308-3403. Tel: 231-347-4211. FAX: 231-348-8662. E-Mail: ppl1@freeway.net. Web Site: www.nlc.lib.mi.us/members/petoskey.htm. *Dir*, Rex F Miller; E-Mail: petosky1@northland.lib.mis.us; *Ch Servs*, Ronald A Fowler; Staff 10 (MLS 1, Non-MLS 9)
Founded 1908. Pop 17,469; Circ 79,617
Jan 1999-Dec 1999 Income $363,836, State $17,454, City $240,069, County $83,401, Other $22,912. Mats Exp $55,923, Books $45,788, Per/Ser (Incl. Access Fees) $5,763, Micro $560, Other Print Mats $2,702, Electronic Ref Mat (Incl. Access Fees) $1,110. Sal $215,102 (Prof $37,788)
Library Holdings: Bk Vols 37,000; Bk Titles 35,000; Per Subs 198; Per Subs 175
Special Collections: Great Lakes Americana (William H Ohle Coll)
Automation Activity & Vendor Info: (Cataloging) Gaylord; (Circulation) Gaylord; (OPAC) Gaylord
Function: ILL available
Mem of Northland Library Cooperative
Partic in Michigan Library Consortium
Friends of the Library Group

PIGEON

P PIGEON DISTRICT LIBRARY,* 7236 Nitz St, Box 357, 48755. SAN 308-3411. Tel: 517-453-2341. Interlibrary Loan Service Tel: 517-792-0001. FAX: 517-453-2266. E-Mail: pdl@avci.net. Web Site: www.avci.net/~pdl. *Librn*, Naomi R Jantzi; Staff 2 (MLS 2)
Founded 1913. Pop 8,576; Circ 73,422
Jul 1998-Jun 1999 Income (Main Library Only) $129,678. Mats Exp $16,302, Books $15,000, Per/Ser (Incl. Access Fees) $1,302. Sal $68,892
Library Holdings: Bk Titles 30,431; Per Subs 40
Subject Interests: Adult literature, Michigan
Mem of White Pine Library Cooperative

PINCKNEY

P PINCKNEY COMMUNITY PUBLIC LIBRARY,* 350 Mower Rd, PO Box 379, 48169-0379. SAN 308-342X. Tel: 734-878-3888. FAX: 734-878-2907. Web Site: www.pinckney.lib.mi.us. *Librn*, Sara Castle; E-Mail: scastle@tln.lib.mi.us; *Asst Librn*, Judy Aschenbrenner; *Asst Librn*, Beverly Sternbergh
Founded 1952. Pop 9,100; Circ 20,564
Library Holdings: Bk Vols 14,700; Per Subs 28
Subject Interests: Juvenile delinquency
Mem of The Library Network

PITTSFORD

P PITTSFORD PUBLIC LIBRARY, 9268 E Hudson Rd, 49271. SAN 308-3438. Tel: 517-523-2565. FAX: 517-523-2565. E-Mail: pittfor@monroe.lib.mi.us. *Librn*, Susan Ruder
Founded 1962. Pop 4,111; Circ 11,281
Library Holdings: Bk Vols 14,000; Per Subs 40
Automation Activity & Vendor Info: (Cataloging) Follett; (Circulation) Follett; (OPAC) Follett
Mem of Woodlands Library Cooperative

PLAINWELL

P CHARLES A RANSOM DISTRICT LIBRARY, 180 S Sherwood Ave, 49080-1896. SAN 308-3446. Tel: 616-685-8024. FAX: 616-685-2266. *Dir*, Teresa Stannard; E-Mail: teresastannard@hotmail.com; *YA Servs*, Lynne Bridges; *Ch Servs*, Amy Chase; *Ref*, David Michael
Founded 1868. Pop 12,463
Library Holdings: Bk Vols 46,000
Subject Interests: Adult education
Automation Activity & Vendor Info: (Cataloging) Sagebrush Corporation; (Circulation) Sagebrush Corporation
Partic in Southwest Michigan Library Cooperative
Special Services for the Blind - Kurzweil Reader
Friends of the Library Group

J MICHIGAN CAREER & TECHNICAL INSTITUTE LIBRARY,* 11611 W Pine Lake Rd, 49080. SAN 371-9235. Tel: 616-664-4461, 616-664-9252 (library). FAX: 616-664-5850. *In Charge*, Kathy Fretz; *Librn*, Jane Leavitt; Staff 1 (MLS 1)
Library Holdings: Bk Titles 4,000; Per Subs 100
Automation Activity & Vendor Info: (Circulation) Follett

Mem of Southwest Michigan Library Cooperative
Partic in Dialog Corporation
Special Services for the Deaf - Books on deafness & sign language; High interest/low vocabulary books; Special interest periodicals; Staff with knowledge of sign language

PLYMOUTH

SR INDUSTRIAL TECHNOLOGY LIBRARY DBA MMTC, (Formerly Michigan Manufacturing Technology Center Library), 47911 Halyard Dr, PO Box 8064, 48170-8064. SAN 327-523X. Tel: 734-769-4286. FAX: 734-213-3405. E-Mail: kaf@itl.org. *Info Specialist, Web Coordr*, Frost Kendra; E-Mail: kfrost@mmtc.org; Staff 1 (MLS 1)
Library Holdings: Bk Vols 50; Per Subs 50
Subject Interests: Engineering, Manufacturing
Database Vendor: IAC - Info Trac, OCLC - First Search, ProQuest
Publications: ITI Inside Information
Function: For research purposes

P PLYMOUTH DISTRICT LIBRARY, 223 S Main St, 48170-1687. SAN 308-3454. Tel: 734-453-0750. FAX: 734-453-3501. E-Mail: plymouth@plymouth.lib.mi.us. Web Site: www.plymouth.lib.mi.us. *Dir*, Patricia Thomas; E-Mail: thomasp@plymouth.lib.mi.us; *Dep Dir*, Pan Rawlinson; *Ref*, Gerry Barlage; *YA Servs*, Eva Davis; *Business*, Diane Anderson; *YA Servs*, Carol Champagne; Staff 42 (MLS 15, Non-MLS 27)
Founded 1923. Pop 33,208
Jan 2001-Dec 2001 Income $3,118,600, State $144,100, City $2,540,000, Locally Generated Income $437,500. Mats Exp $445,400, Books $260,000, Per/Ser (Incl. Access Fees) $63,800, AV Equip $60,000, Other Print Mats $31,000, Electronic Ref Mat (Incl. Access Fees) $31,000. Sal $1,091,000
Library Holdings: Bk Vols 122,702; Per Subs 403
Automation Activity & Vendor Info: (Acquisitions) epixtech, inc.; (Cataloging) epixtech, inc.; (Circulation) epixtech, inc.; (OPAC) epixtech, inc.; (Serials) epixtech, inc.
Mem of The Library Network
Friends of the Library Group

S PLYMOUTH HISTORICAL MUSEUM ARCHIVES, 155 S Main St, 48170. SAN 371-6546. Tel: 313-455-8940. FAX: 313-455-7797. Web Site: www.plymouth.lib.mi.us/~history. *Dir*, Beth Stewart; E-Mail: bstew03@aol.com; *Tech Servs*, Dalton Quilts; *Archivist*, Elaine Pierce; Staff 1 (MLS 1)
Library Holdings: Bk Titles 5,000; Per Subs 10
Special Collections: Civil War History (War of the Rebellion Coll), bks, rec; Local Newspapers & Census Records, microfilm; Michigan History; Petz Abraham Lincoln Coll, bks, papers, photos

PONTIAC

GL ADAMS-PRATT OAKLAND COUNTY LAW LIBRARY,* 1200 N Telegraph Rd, Dept 450, 48341-0450. SAN 308-3519. Tel: 248-858-0012. FAX: 248-452-9145. Web Site: www.oakland.lib.mi.us/oakllaw.htm. *Librn*, Dianne Zyskowski; Staff 1 (MLS 1)
Founded 1904
Library Holdings: Bk Vols 60,000; Bk Titles 3,560; Per Subs 450
Subject Interests: State law
Special Collections: Michigan Law (Supreme Court Records & Briefs, 1976 to date, House & Senate Bills, 1973 to date, Michigan Statutes, 1838 to date), micro, bk, binders
Automation Activity & Vendor Info: (OPAC) epixtech, inc.
Restriction: Non-circulating to the public
Partic in Detroit Libr Network; Michigan Library Consortium; OCLC Online Computer Library Center, Inc
Open Mon-Thurs 8:30am-8:30pm, Fri 8:30-5 & Sat 9-4
Friends of the Library Group

C MIDWESTERN BAPTIST COLLEGE, B R Lakin Library, 825 Golf Dr, 48341. SAN 308-3500. Tel: 248-334-0961. FAX: 248-334-2185. *Librn*, Myundga Prusky; Staff 1 (MLS 1)
Founded 1975. Enrl 250; Fac 26; Highest Degree: Doctorate
Library Holdings: Bk Titles 25,000
Subject Interests: Education, History, Religion, Shakespearean literature

M NORTH OAKLAND MEDICAL CENTERS LIBRARY, 461 W Huron, 48341. SAN 308-3535. Tel: 248-857-7412. FAX: 248-857-6732.
Founded 1934
Jan 1999-Dec 1999 Mats Exp Books $20,000
Library Holdings: Bk Vols 2,000; Per Subs 280
Subject Interests: Medicine, Nursing
Restriction: Not open to public
Partic in Dialog Corporation; Medline; Michigan Library Consortium
Open Mon-Fri 8-5

S OAKLAND COUNTY LIBRARY FOR THE VISUALLY & PHYSICALLY IMPAIRED, 1200 N Telegraph, 48341-0482. SAN 346-4377. Tel: 248-858-5050. FAX: 248-858-9313. Web Site: oaklandlib.mi.us/oakllbph.htm. *Dir*, Betty Ramey; E-Mail: bramey@tln.lib.mi.us; *Tech Servs*, Stacey Boucher-Tabor; Staff 1 (MLS 1)
Founded 1973. Pop 3,000; Circ 98,430
Library Holdings: Bk Vols 60,000; Spec Interest Per Sub 10
Subject Interests: Braille
Special Services for the Deaf - Books on deafness & sign language; Special interest periodicals; TTY machine
Special Services for the Blind - Demonstration low-vision aids & appliances; Newsletter in large print, braille & cassettes, story hours in American Sign Language, summer reading club

S OAKLAND COUNTY PIONEER & HISTORICAL SOCIETY, Library & Archives, 405 Oakland Ave, 48342. SAN 373-2169. Tel: 248-338-6732. FAX: 248-338-6731. E-Mail: ocphs@wwnet.net. Web Site: wwnet.net/~ocphs/index.html. *Admin Dir*, Leslie S Edwards; *Librn*, Patricia Fisher. Subject Specialists: *Archives admin*, Leslie S Edwards; Staff 1 (MLS 1)
Founded 1874
Library Holdings: Bk Vols 3,500
Subject Interests: Civil War, Local history, Manuscripts, Oral hist, Photographs
Publications: Oakland Gazette (Newsletter)
Restriction: Non-circulating
Function: Research library

S OAKLAND COUNTY RESEARCH LIBRARY,* 1200 N Telegraph Rd, Dept 453, 48341-0453. SAN 308-3527. Tel: 248-858-0738. FAX: 248-452-9145. E-Mail: oaklrsch@tln.lib.mi.us. Web Site: www.oakland.lib.mi.us. *In Charge*, Betty Ramey; Staff 4 (MLS 1, Non-MLS 3)
Founded 1973
Jan 1998-Dec 1999 Income $336,059. Mats Exp $53,975. Sal $140,231 (Prof $53,800)
Library Holdings: Bk Vols 18,000; Per Subs 330
Subject Interests: Business and management, Census, Local government, Personnel management, Planning, Sewage, Sociology, Transportation
Special Collections: Census; Fed; Local Documents
Automation Activity & Vendor Info: (Circulation) DRA
Publications: New Book List (quarterly); Oakland County Union List of Serials
Mem of Coun on Resource Development; The Library Network
Partic in Library Network

M POH MEDICAL CENTER, Medical Library, 50 N Perry St, 48342-2217. SAN 308-3543. Tel: 248-338-5000, Ext 3155. E-Mail: pohlib@mlc.lib.mi.us. *Librn*, Diana Balint; Staff 2 (MLS 1, Non-MLS 1)
Founded 1962
Jul 1999-Jun 2000 Income $98,000. Mats Exp $58,000, Books $22,000, Per/Ser (Incl. Access Fees) $36,000
Library Holdings: Bk Vols 11,500; Per Subs 172
Subject Interests: Orthopedics, Radiology
Publications: MLA bulletin; Special libraries
Partic in Michigan Health Sciences Libraries Association

P PONTIAC PUBLIC LIBRARY,* 60 E Pike St, 48342. SAN 346-9980. Tel: 248-857-7667. FAX: 248-857-9020. E-Mail: pont@tln.lib.mi.us. Web Site: www.pontiac.lib.mius/. *Librn*, David Tacia; *Circ*, Claude Williams
Jul 1998-Jun 1999 Income $474,196. Mats Exp $33,000. Sal $315,000
Library Holdings: Bk Vols 90,000; Bk Titles 80,000; Per Subs 150
Subject Interests: History
Mem of The Library Network
Friends of the Library Group

M SAINT JOSEPH MERCY OAKLAND LIBRARY, (SJMO), 44405 Woodward Ave, 48341-2985. SAN 308-3551. Tel: 248-858-3495. FAX: 248-858-6496. *Librn*, Patty Scholl; E-Mail: schollp@trinity-health.org; Staff 2 (MLS 1, Non-MLS 1)
1999-2000 Income $224,620. Mats Exp $98,938, Books $27,938, Per/Ser (Incl. Access Fees) $71,000. Sal $72,000 (Prof $48,000)
Library Holdings: Bk Titles 4,000; Per Subs 450
Subject Interests: Consumer health, Medicine, Nursing
Automation Activity & Vendor Info: (Acquisitions) EOS; (Cataloging) EOS; (Circulation) EOS
Database Vendor: OVID Technologies
Partic in Nat Libr of Med; OCLC Online Computer Library Center, Inc; Regional Med Libr - Region 3

PORT AUSTIN

S HURON CITY MUSEUM LIBRARY, 7930 Huron City Rd, 48467. SAN 371-8182. Tel: 517-428-4123. FAX: 517-428-4123. *Dir*, Charles A Scheffner
Library Holdings: Bk Titles 10,000

P PORT AUSTIN TOWNSHIP LIBRARY,* 114 Railroad St, 48467-0325. SAN 308-3586. Tel: 517-738-7212. FAX: 517-738-7983. *Librn*, Mary Jaworski
Founded 1947. Pop 4,074; Circ 17,500
Library Holdings: Bk Vols 10,890; Per Subs 46
Subject Interests: Local history
Mem of White Pine Library Cooperative
Friends of the Library Group

PORT HURON

S ACHESON INDUSTRIES, INC, Corporate Information Center,* 511 Fort St, PO Box 610489, 48061-0489. SAN 370-9906. Tel: 810-984-5583. FAX: 810-984-5980.
Library Holdings: Bk Vols 4,500; Per Subs 50

S PORT HURON-TIMES HERALD LIBRARY,* 911 Military St, PO Box 5009, 48061-5009. SAN 370-1972. Tel: 810-985-7171. FAX: 810-989-6294. E-Mail: tmshrld@ic.net. *Librn*, Allison Arnold

J SAINT CLAIR COUNTY COMMUNITY COLLEGE, Learning Resources Center,* 323 Erie St, PO Box 5015, 48061-5015. SAN 308-3608. Tel: 810-989-5640. FAX: 810-984-2852. *Dean*, Cindy Rourke; *Dir*, Kathleen James; *Online Servs, Publ Servs*, Nancy Nyitray; *Publ Servs*, Shelia Paige; *Publ Servs*, Alice Ketchum; *Publ Servs*, Jane Lewandoski; *Coll Develop, Tech Servs*, Judy Wager; Staff 16 (MLS 7, Non-MLS 9)
Founded 1923. Enrl 3,033; Fac 80
1998-1999 Income $834,072. Mats Exp $114,871, Books $77,871, Per/Ser (Incl. Access Fees) $37,000. Sal $476,514 (Prof $284,527)
Library Holdings: Bk Vols 59,077; Per Subs 595
Database Vendor: epixtech, inc.
Partic in Dialog Corporation; Michigan Library Consortium; OCLC Online Computer Library Center, Inc

P SAINT CLAIR COUNTY LIBRARY,* 210 McMorran Blvd, 48060-4098. SAN 347-013X. Tel: 810-987-7323. FAX: 810-987-7327. Web Site: www.sccl.lib.mi.us. *Exec Dir*, James F Warwick; *Ch Servs*, Janet Rose; *Ad Servs, Ref*, Stanley K Arnett II; *Tech Servs*, Lorraine Datres
Founded 1974. Pop 178,893
1997-1998 Income $3,596,077, State $151,000, City $8,000, Federal $11,840, County $998,460, Locally Generated Income $1,760,174. Mats Exp $674,130, Books $491,130, Per/Ser (Incl. Access Fees) $35,000. Sal $1,900,000 (Prof $636,642)
Library Holdings: Bk Vols 285,300
Publications: Library News (bi-monthly newsletter)
Partic in BRS; Dialog Corporation
Friends of the Library Group
Branches: 2
LIBRARY LITERACY PROJECT OF SAINT CLAIR COUNTY, 210 McMorran Blvd, 48060. SAN 371-8808. Tel: 810-987-7323. FAX: 810-987-7327. *In Charge*, Jane Bardon
Library Holdings: Bk Vols 2,000
Publications: Ready to Read
P SAINT CLAIR COUNTY LIBRARY FOR THE BLIND & PHYSICALLY HANDICAPPED, 210 McMorran Blvd, 48060. SAN 347-0164. Tel: 810-982-3600. Toll Free Tel: 800-272-8570. FAX: 810-987-7327. *Librn*, Mary Jo Koch
Publications: Blue Water District Library BPHL Newsletter

P SAINT CLAIR COUNTY LIBRARY SYSTEM,* 210 McMorran Blvd, 48060-4098. SAN 347-0199. Tel: 810-987-7323. FAX: 810-987-7874. *Dir*, Lawrence Frank; *Ad Servs, Ref*, Stanley K Arnett II; *Ch Servs*, Janet Rose; *Tech Servs*, Lorraine Datres; *Commun Relations*, Laura Rittman; *Doc, Per*, Katherine Thomson; *Circ*, Marianne Kemp; *ILL*, Brenda Arnold; Staff 10 (MLS 10)
Founded 1917. Pop 145,607; Circ 554,221
Jan 1998-Dec 1999 Income $3,723,910. Mats Exp $695,025, Books $550,025, Per/Ser (Incl. Access Fees) $34,500. Sal $2,055,890
Library Holdings: Bk Vols 296,000; Per Subs 560
Special Collections: Can & Prov; Michigan & the Great Lakes (W L Jenks Historical Coll), bks, maps, microfilm, mss, per, photog
Mem of The Library Network
Partic in Library Network; Michigan Library Consortium
Friends of the Library Group
Branches: 10
ALGONAC-CLAY BRANCH, 2011 St Clair River Dr, Algonac, 48001. SAN 347-0288. Tel: 810-794-4471. FAX: 810-794-2940. *Librn*, Kathy Lisco
Library Holdings: Bk Vols 16,207
G LYNN CAMPBELL BRANCH, 1955 N Allen Rd, Kimball, 48074. SAN 347-0229. Tel: 810-982-9171. FAX: 810-987-9689. *Librn*, Jane Perukel
Library Holdings: Bk Vols 10,110
Friends of the Library Group
CAPAC PUBLIC, 111 N Main St, Capac, 48014. SAN 347-0253. Tel: 810-395-7000. FAX: 810-395-2863. *Librn*, Patsy Beisher
Library Holdings: Bk Vols 18,837
Friends of the Library Group
IRA TOWNSHIP, 7013 Meldrum Rd, Fair Haven, 48023. SAN 347-0318. Tel: 810-725-9081. FAX: 810-725-1256. *Librn*, Gary Kupper
Library Holdings: Bk Vols 13,030
Friends of the Library Group
MAIN, 210 McMorran Blvd, 48060. SAN 347-0431. Tel: 810-987-7323. FAX: 810-987-7327. *Dir*, Lawrence Frank
Library Holdings: Bk Vols 128,337
Friends of the Library Group
MARINE CITY PUBLIC, 300 S Parker Rd, Marine City, 48039. SAN 347-0342. Tel: 810-765-5233. FAX: 810-765-4376. *Librn*, Lois Kaufman
Library Holdings: Bk Vols 19,375
Friends of the Library Group
MARYSVILLE PUBLIC, 1175 Delaware, Marysville, 48040. SAN 347-0377. Tel: 810-364-9493. FAX: 810-364-7491. *Librn*, Vickie Hurley
Library Holdings: Bk Vols 21,645
Friends of the Library Group
MEMPHIS PUBLIC, 34830 Potter St, Memphis, 48041. SAN 347-0407. Tel: 810-392-2980. FAX: 810-392-3206. *Librn*, Gladys Owen
Library Holdings: Bk Vols 12,814
Friends of the Library Group
SAINT CLAIR PUBLIC, 310 S Second St, Saint Clair, 48079. SAN 347-0466. Tel: 810-329-3951. FAX: 810-329-7142. *Librn*, Leona Moran
Library Holdings: Bk Vols 22,038
Mem of The Library Network
Friends of the Library Group
YALE PUBLIC, 2 Jones St, Yale, 48097. SAN 347-0490. Tel: 810-387-2940. FAX: 810-387-2051. *Librn*, Kaye Ray
Library Holdings: Bk Vols 19,166
Friends of the Library Group
Bookmobiles: 1

M SAINT CLAIR COUNTY MENTAL HEALTH SERVICE LIBRARY,* 1011 Military St, 48060. SAN 373-2177. Tel: 810-985-8900. FAX: 810-985-7620. *Dir*, Peg Lawton
Library Holdings: Bk Vols 600; Per Subs 40

PORT SANILAC

P SANILAC DISTRICT LIBRARY, 7130 Main St, 48469. (Mail add: PO Box 525, 48469), SAN 308-3616. Tel: 810-622-8623. E-Mail: sanilacdistrictlibrary@yahoo.com. Web Site: www.sanilacdistrictlibrary.lib.mi.us. *Coll Develop, Dir*, Beverly Dear; Staff 1 (Non-MLS 1)
Founded 1935. Pop 4,152; Circ 23,261
Jan 2000-Dec 2000 Income $108,952, State $4,152, County $19,800, Locally Generated Income $65,000, Other $20,000. Mats Exp $28,900, Books $25,000, Per/Ser (Incl. Access Fees) $1,400, AV Equip $2,500. Sal $49,740
Library Holdings: Bk Vols 28,726
Subject Interests: Aviation, Local history
Publications: BookTalk (newsletter)
Mem of White Pine Library Cooperative
Friends of the Library Group

PORTAGE

P PORTAGE DISTRICT LIBRARY,* 300 Library Lane, 49002. SAN 308-3624. Tel: 616-329-4544. FAX: 616-324-9222. *Dir*, Christine Berro; *Ad Servs, Ref*, Marsha Meyer; *Ch Servs*, Shirley Newberry; *ILL*, Rosemary Comptom; *Circ*, Johanna Green
Founded 1962. Pop 41,042; Circ 421,700
1996-1997 Income $1,887,000. Mats Exp $302,750, Books $262,750, Per/Ser (Incl. Access Fees) $17,500. Sal $807,000 (Prof $660,000)
Library Holdings: Bk Titles 109,400; Per Subs 237
Special Collections: Local History (Heritage Room Coll), letters, bks, archival mat
Publications: Portage & Its Past; Women in Business & Management - A Bibliography
Mem of Southwest Michigan Library Cooperative
Partic in Kalamazoo Consortium For Higher Education; OCLC Online Computer Library Center, Inc
Special Services for the Deaf - Books on deafness & sign language; Special interest periodicals; Videos & decoder
Friends of the Library Group

PORTLAND

P PORTLAND DISTRICT LIBRARY, 334 Kent St, 48875-1735. SAN 308-3632. Tel: 517-647-6981. FAX: 517-647-2738. *Librn*, Janice Mosser; E-Mail: jmosser@voyageur.net; *Ch Servs*, Erika Avery
Founded 1905. Pop 11,462; Circ 60,780
Jul 1998-Jun 1999 Income $120,000, State $10,600, City $7,500, County $77,153, Locally Generated Income $30,147. Mats Exp $60,190, Books $15,925, Per/Ser (Incl. Access Fees) $1,818, Micro $167, AV Equip $4,408, Electronic Ref Mat (Incl. Access Fees) $4,050. Sal $68,190
Library Holdings: Bk Vols 21,222; Per Subs 100
Subject Interests: Genealogy, Local history
Automation Activity & Vendor Info: (Cataloging) Follett
Mem of Capital Library Cooperative

POTTERVILLE

P BENTON TOWNSHIP-POTTERVILLE DISTRICT LIBRARY,* 150 Library Lane, PO Box 158, 48876. SAN 308-3640. Tel: 517-645-2989. FAX: 517-645-0268. *Librn*, Evelyn VanFossen
Pop 3,500; Circ 19,000

Library Holdings: Bk Vols 16,000; Per Subs 25
Mem of Capital Library Cooperative
Open Mon, Tues, Thurs & Fri 12-5, Wed 12-8, Sat 10-1
Friends of the Library Group

READING

P READING COMMUNITY LIBRARY,* 103 N Main St, 49274-0649. SAN 308-3659. Tel: 517-283-3916. FAX: 517-283-2510. *Librn*, Dorothy Kramer
Pop 4,019; Circ 14,000
Library Holdings: Bk Vols 15,000; Per Subs 40
Mem of Woodlands Library Cooperative
Open Mon 4-8, Tues & Fri 10-5, Wed 10-5:30 & 6:30-8, Sat 9-12

REDFORD

P REDFORD TOWNSHIP DISTRICT LIBRARY, 15150 Norborne, 48239-3223. SAN 308-0307. Tel: 313-538-4257. FAX: 313-531-1721. Web Site: www.redford.lib.mi.us. *Dir*, Fred Paffhausen; Tel: 313-531-6900, E-Mail: macpaff@oeonline.com; *Ad Servs*, Carol Deckert; *Ch Servs*, Pat Slater; *Ref*, Brooke Somerville; E-Mail: brookes@tln.lib.mi.us; Staff 6 (MLS 5, Non-MLS 1)
Founded 1947. Pop 54,387; Circ 185,000
Apr 1999-Mar 2000 Income $1,395,000. Mats Exp $274,000, Books $196,000, Per/Ser (Incl. Access Fees) $8,000, Other Print Mats $15,000, Electronic Ref Mat (Incl. Access Fees) $12,000. Sal $390,000 (Prof $245,000)
Library Holdings: Bk Vols 96,000; Per Subs 176; High Interest/Low Vocabulary Bk Vols 375; Bks on Deafness & Sign Lang 50
Automation Activity & Vendor Info: (Circulation) DRA
Database Vendor: DRA, Ebsco - EbscoHost, OCLC - First Search
Restriction: Restricted access
Mem of The Library Network
Friends of the Library Group

REED CITY

P REED CITY PUBLIC LIBRARY,* 410 W Upton Ave, 49677-1152. SAN 308-3667. Tel: 231-832-2131. FAX: 231-832-2131. E-Mail: rcpl@jackpine.com. *Dir*, Phyllis Obermier; *Librn*, Dolores Bolyard
Circ 24,038
Library Holdings: Bk Vols 20,000; Per Subs 50
Mem of Mid-Michigan Library League

REESE

P UNITY DISTRICT LIBRARY,* 9978 Saginaw, Ste B, 48757-9567. SAN 376-6322. Tel: 517-868-4120. FAX: 517-868-4123. E-Mail: libraryre@hotmail.com. *Dir*, Carole Brown
Library Holdings: Bk Vols 11,000; Bk Titles 10,000; Per Subs 26
Mem of White Pine Library Cooperative
Friends of the Library Group

REMUS

P WHEATLAND TOWNSHIP LIBRARY, 100 W Wheatland, PO Box 217, 49340. SAN 308-3675. Tel: 517-967-8271. FAX: 517-967-8271. *Librn*, Becky Kurtz
Pop 2,377; Circ 8,856
Library Holdings: Bk Vols 8,856
Mem of Mid-Michigan Library League
Friends of the Library Group

REPUBLIC

P REPUBLIC-MICHIGAMME PUBLIC LIBRARY,* Rte 1, Box 201A, 49879-9998. SAN 308-3683. Tel: 906-376-2277. FAX: 906-376-8299. *Librn*, Dee Ann Truscott; *Librn*, Bonnie Mattson
Library Holdings: Bk Vols 9,000; Bk Titles 8,000; Per Subs 9
Mem of Superiorland Library Cooperative

RICHMOND

P LOIS WAGNER MEMORIAL LIBRARY,* 35200 Division, 48062. SAN 308-3691. Tel: 810-727-2665. FAX: 810-727-3774. Web Site: www.libcoop.net/richmond/, www.macomb.lib.mi.us/richmond. *Librn*, Janis M Reghi; E-Mail: reghij@libcoop.us; *Circ*, Colleen Kelley
Founded 1912. Circ 58,076
Jul 1998-Jun 1999 Income $203,997, City $114,570. Mats Exp $20,000. Sal $118,542
Library Holdings: Bk Vols 27,103; Per Subs 33
Special Collections: Pictorial History of Richmond, photos
Publications: Library Information Hand-outs; Newsletter (quarterly)
Mem of Libr Coop of Macomb
Friends of the Library Group

RIVER ROUGE

P WAYNE COUNTY LIBRARY, (Formerly River Rouge Public Library), River Rouge Branch, 221 Burke, 48218. SAN 308-3705. Tel: 313-843-2040. FAX: 313-842-4716. E-Mail: rrou@tln.lib.mi.us. Web Site: www.river-rouge.lib.mi.us/. *Dir*, Maria McCarville-Ogg; E-Mail: mtm@tln.lib.mi.us
Pop 11,314; Circ 24,000
1997-1998 Income $188,494, State $20,950, City $167,544. Mats Exp $23,000, Books $21,000, Per/Ser (Incl. Access Fees) $2,000. Sal $78,700
Library Holdings: Bk Vols 21,000; Per Subs 75
Subject Interests: African Language
Publications: Welcome to River Rouge Public Library
Mem of The Library Network

RIVERDALE

P SEVILLE TOWNSHIP PUBLIC LIBRARY, 6734 N Lumberjack Rd, PO Box 160, 48877-0160. SAN 308-3713. Tel: 517-833-7776. FAX: 517-833-7776. E-Mail: seville@power-net.net. *Dir*, Marlene Fockler
Founded 1941
Library Holdings: Bk Vols 12,200; Bk Titles 11,217
Open Mon, Tues & Fri 10-2, Wed 2-7, Sat 9-12

RIVERVIEW

P RIVERVIEW PUBLIC LIBRARY, 14300 Sibley Rd, 48192. SAN 308-3721. Tel: 734-283-1250. FAX: 734-283-6843. *Dir*, Kirk A Borger; E-Mail: kborger@tln.lib.mi.us; *Ad Servs, Asst Dir*, Alice Gorgas. Subject Specialists: *Youth activities*, Kirk A Borger; Staff 8 (MLS 2, Non-MLS 6)
Founded 1962. Pop 13,894; Circ 65,137
Library Holdings: Bk Vols 34,230; Per Subs 95
Database Vendor: DRA
Mem of The Library Network; Wayne Oakland Libr Federation
Open Mon-Thurs 1-9, Sat 12-5 & Sun 1-5

ROCHESTER

C OAKLAND UNIVERSITY LIBRARY, Kresge Library, 48309-4484. SAN 308-3756. Tel: 248-370-4425. FAX: 248-370-2458. Web Site: www.kl.oakland.edu. *Dean of Libr*, Elaine K Didier; Tel: 248-370-2486, E-Mail: didier@oakland.edu; *Asst Prof, Head Ref*, Linda Hildebrand; Tel: 248-370-2483, E-Mail: hildebra@oakland.edu; *Assoc Dean*, Frank J Lepkowski; Tel: 248-370-2486, E-Mail: lepkowsk@oakland.edu; *Archivist, Spec Coll*, Richard Pettergill; Tel: 248-370-2490, E-Mail: pettergl@oakland.edu; *Automation Syst Coordr*, Kristine Condic; Tel: 248-370-2469, E-Mail: salomen@oakland.edu; *Business*, Brenda Pierce; Tel: 248-370-2488, E-Mail: pierce@oakland.edu; *Syst Coordr*, Eric Condic; Tel: 248-370-2467, E-Mail: condic@oakland.edu; *Doc*, William S Cramer; Tel: 248-370-2480, E-Mail: wcramer@oakland.edu; *Circ*, Louann Stewart; Tel: 248-370-2496, E-Mail: lstewart@oakland.edu; *Coll Develop*, Mildred Merz; Tel: 248-370-2457, E-Mail: merz@oakland.edu; *Tech Servs*, Ann Pogany; Tel: 248-370-2487, E-Mail: pogany@oakland.edu; Staff 38 (MLS 13, Non-MLS 25)
Founded 1959. Enrl 15,000; Fac 442; Highest Degree: Doctorate
Jul 1998-Jun 1999 Income $3,758,942, State $3,371,428, Locally Generated Income $387,514. Mats Exp $1,302,000, Books $579,000, Per/Ser (Incl. Access Fees) $625,000, Electronic Ref Mat (Incl. Access Fees) $98,000. Sal $1,270,143 (Prof $575,623)
Library Holdings: Bk Vols 80,094; Bk Titles 372,312; Per Subs 2,120
Subject Interests: Biology
Special Collections: Book Room Coll; Children's Books (Bingham Coll); Folklore (James Coll); Lincolniana (William Springer Coll); Women in Literature, 17th-19th Centuries (Hicks Coll)
Automation Activity & Vendor Info: (Cataloging) Endeavor; (Circulation) Endeavor; (Course Reserve) Endeavor; (OPAC) Endeavor; (Serials) Endeavor
Database Vendor: CARL, Dialog, Ebsco - EbscoHost, GaleNet, IAC - Info Trac, IAC - SearchBank, Lexis-Nexis, OCLC - First Search, Silverplatter Information Inc.
Partic in Michigan Library Consortium
Friends of the Library Group

P ROCHESTER HILLS PUBLIC LIBRARY, 500 Olde Towne Rd, 48307-2043. SAN 308-373X. Tel: 248-656-2900. Circulation Tel: 248-650-7174. Reference Tel: 248-650-7130. TDD: 248-650-7153. FAX: 248-650-7121. E-Mail: adult-rh@rhpl.org. Web Site: www.rhpl.org. *Dir*, Sandra Matsco; Tel: 248-650-7122, E-Mail: matscosa@rhpl.org; *Ad Servs*, Sharon Campbell; Tel: 248-650-7132, Fax: 248-650-7131, E-Mail: campbels@rhpl.org; *Circ*, Ginger Olson; Tel: 248-650-7162, E-Mail: olsong@rhpl.org; *Outreach Serv*, June Hopaluk; Tel: 248-650-7152, E-Mail: hopalukj@rhpl.org; *Tech Servs*, Marjorie Chu; Tel: 248-650-7172, E-Mail: chumarjo@rhpl.org; Staff 47 (MLS 19, Non-MLS 28)

Founded 1924. Pop 77,000; Circ 1,000,000
Jan 2001-Dec 2001 Income $3,492,000, State $77,000, City $2,958,000, County $80,000, Locally Generated Income $115,000, Other $262,000. Mats Exp $604,000. Sal $1,735,000 (Prof $870,000)
Library Holdings: Bk Vols 202,000; Per Subs 350
Subject Interests: Technology
Special Collections: Photographic Archives
Automation Activity & Vendor Info: (Circulation) epixtech, inc.; (OPAC) epixtech, inc.
Database Vendor: GaleNet, IAC - SearchBank, OCLC - First Search
Publications: The Rhpl Reader (Newsletter)
Function: ILL available
Mem of The Library Network
Partic in Metro Net Libr Consortium; Michigan Library Consortium
Special Services for the Blind - Kurzweil Personal Reader; Magnifiers; Optelek
Public access to the Internet
Friends of the Library Group

ROCHESTER HILLS

J ROCHESTER COLLEGE, Muirhead Library, 800 W Avon Rd, 48307. SAN 308-3748. Tel: 248-218-2106. FAX: 248-218-2005. E-Mail: library@rc.edu. Web Site: www.rc.edu/offices/library. *Mgr*, Steven Bowers; Staff 2 (MLS 1, Non-MLS 1)
Founded 1959. Enrl 600; Highest Degree: Bachelor
Library Holdings: Bk Vols 53,797; Per Subs 285
Subject Interests: Biblical studies, Business, Literature, Psychology, Religion
Friends of the Library Group

ROGERS CITY

P PRESQUE ISLE DISTRICT LIBRARY,* 181 E Erie, 49779-1709. SAN 308-3764. Tel: 517-734-2477. FAX: 517-734-4899. E-Mail: pidl1@freeway.net. *Actg Dir*, Jan Stevenson; Staff 12 (MLS 1, Non-MLS 11)
Founded 1945. Pop 15,020; Circ 69,297
Jan 1997-Dec 1998 Income $321,000. Mats Exp $53,000, Books $40,000, Per/Ser (Incl. Access Fees) $3,000. Sal $142,500
Mem of Northland Library Cooperative
Partic in Michicard Borrowing Serv
Friends of the Library Group
Branches: 3
GRAND LAKE, 8797 E Grand Lake Rd, PO Box 40, Presque Isle, 49777. SAN 321-4087. Tel: 517-595-5051. FAX: 517-595-5051. E-Mail: grandlk1@northland.lib.mi.us. *In Charge*, Wendy Lewis
Friends of the Library Group
ONAWAY BRANCH, State St, PO Box 742, Onaway, 49765. SAN 321-4079. Tel: 517-733-6621. FAX: 517-733-6621. E-Mail: onaway1@northland.lib.mi.us. *Librn*, Anna Mero
Friends of the Library Group
POSEN BRANCH, 6987 Turtle, Posen, 49776. SAN 321-4095. Tel: 517-766-2233. FAX: 517-766-2233. E-Mail: posen1@northland.lib.mi.us.
Friends of the Library Group

ROMULUS

P ROMULUS PUBLIC LIBRARY,* 11121 Wayne Rd, 48174. SAN 308-3780. Tel: 734-942-7589. FAX: 734-941-3575. *Dir*, Diane Hazen; *Ch Servs*, Shelley DeLano
Pop 34,000; Circ 58,344
Library Holdings: Bk Vols 48,000; Per Subs 200
Mem of The Library Network; Wayne Oakland Libr Federation
Friends of the Library Group

ROSCOMMON

P GERRISH-HIGGINS SCHOOL DISTRICT PUBLIC LIBRARY, 10600 Oakwood Rd, 48653-7638. (Mail add: PO Box 825, 48653-0825), SAN 347-0520. Tel: 517-275-6688. FAX: 517-275-6618. *Dir Libr Serv*, Dawn Ann Humphreys; E-Mail: humphd@k2.kirtland.cc.mi.us; *ILL*, Mary Anna Miller; Tel: 517-275-6687, E-Mail: millera@k2.kirtland.cc.mi.us; Staff 4 (MLS 1, Non-MLS 3)
Founded 1961. Pop 10,266; Circ 23,479
Jul 1998-Jun 1999 Income (Main Library Only) $119,000. Mats Exp $16,000, Books $10,000, Per/Ser (Incl. Access Fees) $3,500, AV Equip $2,000, Other Print Mats $4,000. Sal $91,000
Library Holdings: Bk Vols 25,000; Per Subs 98
Mem of Mid-Michigan Library League
Special Services for the Deaf - High interest/low vocabulary books; Staff with knowledge of sign language
Branches: 1
HIGGINS LAKE BRANCH, PO Box 177, Higgins Lake, 48627. SAN 347-0555. Tel; 517-821-9111. FAX: 517-821-9111. *Librn*, Susa McIntosh
Library Holdings: Bk Titles 4,245

J KIRTLAND COMMUNITY COLLEGE LIBRARY, 10775 N St Helen Rd, 48653. SAN 308-3799. Tel: 517-275-5000, Ext 246. FAX: 517-275-8510. E-Mail: library@kirtland.cc.mi.us. Web Site: www.kirtland.cc.mi.us/~library/. *Coll Develop, Dir*, Louise Bucco; *Ref*, Raye Bransdorfer-Polasek; Staff 3 (MLS 2, Non-MLS 1)
Founded 1968. Enrl 1,500; Fac 32; Highest Degree: Associate
Jul 2000-Jun 2001 Income $208,866. Mats Exp $60,200, Books $25,000, Per/Ser (Incl. Access Fees) $20,000, Presv $500, Micro $3,500, Other Print Mats $9,200, Manuscripts & Archives $1,000, Electronic Ref Mat (Incl. Access Fees) $1,000. Sal $96,266 (Prof $58,656)
Library Holdings: Bk Vols 30,000; Bk Titles 29,000; Per Subs 250; Bks on Deafness & Sign Lang 10
Automation Activity & Vendor Info: (Cataloging) SIRSI; (Circulation) SIRSI; (OPAC) SIRSI
Partic in Michigan Library Consortium

ROSE CITY

P OGEMAW DISTRICT LIBRARY,* 107 W Main St, 48654. (Mail add: PO Box 427, 48654-0427), SAN 322-6484. Tel: 517-685-3300. FAX: 517-685-3647. E-Mail: ogemaw@northland.lib.mi.us. *Librn*, Jeanette Nathan; *Asst Librn*, Sandra Bean
Founded 1977. Pop 9,961; Circ 61,728
Library Holdings: Bk Vols 37,817; Bk Titles 24,193
Subject Interests: Genealogy, Local history
Mem of White Pine Library Cooperative
Branches: 2
OGEMAW EAST, 200 Washington, PO Box 111, Prescott, 48756. SAN 325-3406. Tel: 517-873-5807. FAX: 517-873-4591. *Librn*, Sharon Arndt
SKIDWAY LAKE, 2129 Greenwood Rd, Prescott, 48756. Tel: 517-873-5086. FAX: 517-873-4646. *Librn*, Melissa Stachurski

ROSEVILLE

P ROSEVILLE PUBLIC LIBRARY, 29777 Gratiot, 48066. SAN 308-3802. Tel: 810-445-5407. TDD: 810-445-4386. FAX: 810-445-5499. Web Site: www.libcoop.net/roseville. *Dir*, Rose M Kollmorgen; *Asst Dir*, Rita Paniccia; *AV, Ch Servs*, Elizabeth Sulkowski; *Ch Servs*, Ann Busch; *Ref*, Annamarie Lindstrom; *Ref*, Phyllis Jones; *Archivist, Ref*, Jacquelyn Saturley; *Ref*, Mary Szczesiul; Staff 8 (MLS 8)
Founded 1936. Pop 51,412; Circ 257,084
Jul 1998-Jun 1999 Income $881,679, State $51,705, City $829,974. Mats Exp $106,654, Books $75,522, Per/Ser (Incl. Access Fees) $8,293, Micro $9,501, AV Equip $13,338, Other Print Mats $8,293. Sal $686,097
Library Holdings: Bk Vols 128,892; Per Subs 211
Special Collections: Roseville Archives Coll
Automation Activity & Vendor Info: (Acquisitions) epixtech, inc.; (Cataloging) epixtech, inc.; (Circulation) epixtech, inc.; (OPAC) epixtech, inc.; (Serials) epixtech, inc.
Partic in Suburban Library Cooperative
Friends of the Library Group

ROYAL OAK

C OAKLAND COMMUNITY COLLEGE,* 739 S Washington Ave, 48067. Tel: 248-246-2525. FAX: 248-246-2520. Web Site: www.occ.cc.mi.us/library. *Ref*, Tom Lewandowski

J OAKLAND COMMUNITY COLLEGE, Royal Oak Campus Library, 739 S Washington Ave, 48067. SAN 308-3829. Tel: 248-246-2525. Reference Tel: 248-246-2519. FAX: 248-246-2520. Web Site: www.occ.cc.mi.us/library. *Coll Develop, Librn*, Carol Benson; *Librn*, Thomas Lewandowski; Staff 8 (MLS 4, Non-MLS 4)
Founded 1971. Enrl 7,800; Fac 54
Library Holdings: Bk Titles 20,432; Per Subs 218
Subject Interests: Careers
Departmental Libraries:
ELECTRONIC RESOURCE CENTER, 22322 Rutland Dr, Southfield, 48075-4793. SAN 376-9801. Tel: 248-233-2825. Reference Tel: 248-233-2826. FAX: 248-233-2828. Web Site: www.occ.cc.mi.us/library/. *Librn*, Richard B Nagler; E-Mail: ranagler@occ.cc.mi.us
1998-1999 Mats Exp $6,000, Books $4,000, Per/Ser (Incl. Access Fees) $1,000. Sal $113,713 (Prof $76,585)
Library Holdings: Bk Titles 500; Per Subs 15
Subject Interests: Allied health
Database Vendor: GaleNet, IAC - Info Trac, OCLC - First Search
Partic in Detroit Libr Network

P ROYAL OAK PUBLIC LIBRARY, 222 E Eleven Mile Rd, PO Box 494, 48068-0494. SAN 308-3837. Tel: 248-246-3700. Reference Tel: 248-246-3727. FAX: 248-246-3701. Web Site: www.ci.royal-oak.mi.us/library/index.html. *Dir*, Carol Windorf; *Ad Servs, Ref*, Pamela Gosik; *AV*, Anna Vidal; *Ch Servs*, Donna Blotkamp; *Circ*, Diane McGovern; *Doc*, Grace Brainin; *ILL*, Lori Boden; *Per*, Judith Ryan; *Tech Servs*, Matthew Day; Staff 9 (MLS 9)
Founded 1922. Pop 68,185; Circ 210,000

Jul 2000-Jun 2001 Income $1,249,000. Mats Exp $141,000, Books $115,800, Per/Ser (Incl. Access Fees) $20,000, Electronic Ref Mat (Incl. Access Fees) $5,200. Sal $735,742
Library Holdings: Bk Vols 102,310; Per Subs 250
Special Collections: Auto Repair Manuals; Royal Oak History Coll
Automation Activity & Vendor Info: (Circulation) DRA; (OPAC) DRA
Database Vendor: DRA
Publications: Leaflet (Newsletter)
Mem of The Library Network
Friends of the Library Group

M WILLIAM BEAUMONT HOSPITAL, Medical Library, 3601 W 13 Mile Rd, 48073-6769. SAN 308-3810. Tel: 248-551-1750. Interlibrary Loan Service Tel: 248-551-1744. FAX: 248-551-1060. *Dir*, Nancy Bulgarelli; E-Mail: nbulgare@beaumont.edu; *Coll Develop*, Joan E Emahiser
Founded 1956
Library Holdings: Bk Vols 30,000; Bk Titles 10,000; Per Subs 700
Subject Interests: Biomedical engineering
Database Vendor: epixtech, inc.

RUDYARD

P RUDYARD SCHOOL PUBLIC LIBRARY,* 11185 W Second St, 49780-0246. (Mail add: PO Box 246, 49780-0246), SAN 308-3845. Tel: 906-478-4504. FAX: 906-478-3303. *Librn*, Jim McDonald; E-Mail: jimm@eup.k12.mi.us; *Asst Librn*, Donna Porterfield
Circ 28,322
Library Holdings: Bk Vols 15,000; Per Subs 50
Publications: Newsletter
Mem of Hiawathaland Library Cooperative
Open Mon, Wed & Fri 8-5:30, Tues & Thurs 8-8, Sat 9-1
Friends of the Library Group

SAGINAW

GM DEPARTMENT OF VETERANS AFFAIRS, Aleta E Lutz VA Medical Center & Health Science Libary, 1500 Weiss St, 48602. SAN 308-3896. Tel: 517-793-2340, Ext 3302. FAX: 517-791-2224. *Chief Librn*, Debbie Zapolski
Library Holdings: Bk Vols 3,200; Per Subs 200
Special Collections: Health Education, AV
Partic in Dialog Corporation; Medline; Michigan Library Consortium; Vets Admin Libr Network

R MICHIGAN LUTHERAN SEMINARY LIBRARY,* 2777 Hardin St, 48602. SAN 308-3853. Tel: 517-793-1041. FAX: 517-793-4213. *Dir*, Carolyn Zeiger
Founded 1952
Library Holdings: Bk Vols 10,000
Restriction: Not open to public

P PUBLIC LIBRARIES OF SAGINAW, 505 Janes St, 48607. SAN 347-058X. Tel: 517-755-0904. FAX: 517-755-9828. E-Mail: saginaw@vlc.lib.mi.us. Web Site: www.saginawlibrary.org. *Actg Dir*, Sherrill Smith; *Actg Dir*, Marcia Warner; *ILL*, Mike Sullivan; *Media Spec*, Kate Tesdell; *Cat*, Anne Menard; *YA Servs*, Jeanine Collison; *Coll Develop*, Ruth Ann Reinert; *Govt Doc*, Anne Birkam
Founded 1890. Pop 137,920; Circ 679,842
Jul 1998-Jun 1999 Income (Main Library and Branch Library) $5,757,310, State $137,806, City $3,183,983, Federal $38,212, Locally Generated Income $1,439,676, Other $957,633. Mats Exp $374,928, Books $297,946, Per/Ser (Incl. Access Fees) $31,094, Micro $14,537, Other Print Mats $5,735, Electronic Ref Mat (Incl. Access Fees) $25,616. Sal $2,676,956
Library Holdings: Bk Vols 495,056; Per Subs 634
Subject Interests: Art, Genealogy, Local history, Multicultural, Parenting, Science/technology
Special Collections: Genealogy, Saginaw Valley History & Michigan History (Eddy Historical & Genealogy Coll)
Automation Activity & Vendor Info: (Acquisitions) epixtech, inc.; (Circulation) epixtech, inc.
Database Vendor: OCLC - First Search
Mem of White Pine Library Cooperative
Friends of the Library Group
Branches: 5
BUTMAN-FISH, 1716 Hancock, 48602. SAN 347-061X. Tel: 517-799-9160. FAX: 517-799-8149. *Librn*, Elinor Saunders
Library Holdings: Bk Vols 92,754
Special Collections: African Heritage; Hispanic Heritage; Large Print Books
Friends of the Library Group
ARCHER A CLAYTOR LIBRARY, 1410 N 12th St, 48601. SAN 347-0644. Tel: 517-753-5591. FAX: 517-753-6850. *Librn*, Rhonda Farrell-Butler
Library Holdings: Bk Vols 27,799
Special Collections: African Heritage; Hispanic Heritage
Friends of the Library Group
HOYT PUBLIC, 505 Janes St, 48607. SAN 347-0660. Tel: 517-755-0904. FAX: 517-755-9829. Web Site: www.saginaw.lib.mi.us. *Assoc Dir*, Marcia Warner; Tel: 517-755-9823, Fax: 517-755-9828, E-Mail: mwarner@vlc.lib.mi.us
Founded 1890
Library Holdings: Bk Vols 408,825
Special Collections: African Heritage; Genealogy; Hispanic Heritage; Saginaw Valley History & Michigan History (Eddy Historical & Genealogy Coll)
RUTH BRADY WICKES LIBRARY, 1713 Hess, 48601. SAN 347-0679. Tel: 517-752-3821. FAX: 517-752-8685. *Librn*, Deb Trombley
Library Holdings: Bk Vols 42,623
Special Collections: African Heritage; Hispanic Heritage; Spanish Language Materials
Friends of the Library Group
RUDOLPH C ZAUEL LIBRARY, 3100 N Center, 48603. SAN 347-0709. Tel: 517-799-2771. FAX: 517-799-1771. *Head of Libr*, Tricia Anne Deming-Burns; E-Mail: tdem@vlc.lib.mi.us
Library Holdings: Bk Vols 115,788
Special Collections: African Heritage; Greek History Coll; Hispanic Heritage
Friends of the Library Group

S SAGINAW ART MUSEUM LIBRARY,* 1126 N Michigan Ave, 48602. SAN 308-3861. Tel: 517-754-2491. FAX: 517-754-9387. Web Site: www.members.zoom.com/saginawart/. *Dir*, Russell Thayer
Founded 1948
Library Holdings: Bk Titles 800
Subject Interests: Art
Special Collections: E Irving Couse Coll

L SAGINAW COUNTY LAW LIBRARY,* 111 S Michigan Ave, Rm 400, 48602. SAN 329-4218. Tel: 517-790-5470. FAX: 517-793-8180.
Library Holdings: Bk Vols 20,000

M SAGINAW HEALTH SCIENCES LIBRARIES, 1000 Houghton, Ste 2000, 48602-5398. SAN 320-8109. Tel: 517-583-6846. FAX: 517-583-6898. Web Site: www.schi.org. *Dir*, Stephanie John; E-Mail: johnste@msu.ed; *Acq, Cat, Coll Develop*, Janis Van Tiflin; *Assoc Dir*, June Cronenberger; *Doc*, Mary Schmidt; *Publ Servs*, Barbara Wood; *Ser*, Donald Ziehmer; *Ref*, Cheryl Putnam; Staff 11 (MLS 4, Non-MLS 7)
Founded 1978
Library Holdings: Bk Vols 4,500; Bk Titles 3,600; Per Subs 334
Subject Interests: Clinical medicine
Automation Activity & Vendor Info: (Cataloging) EOS; (Circulation) EOS; (OPAC) EOS; (Serials) EOS
Database Vendor: Dialog, OCLC - First Search, OVID Technologies
Partic in Michigan Health Sciences Libraries Association; Michigan Library Consortium
Library founded in 1978 through a merger of the libraries of three independent, competitive Saginaw General Hospital, St Luke's Hospital & St Mary's Hospital; also serves as library for satellite campus of MSU's medical school; provides paid memberships to 26 institutions; has one branch library

S SAGINAW NEWS, Editorial Library,* 203 S Washington Ave, 48607-1283. SAN 324-4180. Tel: 517-776-9672. FAX: 517-752-3115. *Librn*, Lorri D Lea; *Asst Librn*, Suzanne Grant
Founded 1946
Special Collections: Complete Library of Saginaw News, microfilm
Restriction: Not open to public

P THOMAS TOWNSHIP LIBRARY,* 8207 Shields Dr, 48609-4814. SAN 376-7884. Tel: 517-781-3770. FAX: 517-781-3881. *Dir*, Tari L Dusek
Library Holdings: Bk Vols 40,000; Bk Titles 37,000; Per Subs 85
Mem of White Pine Library Cooperative

P WHITE PINE LIBRARY COOPERATIVE, (EZW), 3210 Davenport Ave, 48602. SAN 308-390X. Tel: 517-793-7126. FAX: 517-793-7257. Web Site: www.wplc.org. *Dir*, Dave Simmons; E-Mail: dsimmons@vlc.lib.mi.us; *Adminr*, Karen Puszykowski; E-Mail: kpowski@vlc.lib.mi.us; *ILL*, Pam Kerr; Staff 7 (MLS 1, Non-MLS 6)
Founded 1960
Library Holdings: Bk Titles 478; Per Subs 42
Subject Interests: Library and information science
Publications: Madame Audrey's Book for speedy reference; White Pine Library Cooperative Newsletter
Member Libraries: Bad Axe Public Library; Bay County Library System; Bay Medical Center Library; Bridgeport Public Library; Brown City Public Library; Bullard-Sanford Memorial Library; Caro Area District Library; Chesaning Public Library; Chippewa River District Library; Columbia Township Library; Deckerville Public Library; Dow Corning Corp; Elk Township Library; Fairgrove Township Library; Garfield Memorial Library; Grace A Dow Memorial Library; Harrison Community Library; Iosco-Arenac District Library; Jacquelin E Opperman Memorial Library; James E Wickson Memorial Library; Marlette District Library; Mayville District Public Library; Merrill District Library; Midland Public Schools Instructional Media Center; Moore Public Library; Ogemaw District Library; Pigeon District Library; Port Austin Township Library; Public Libraries Of Saginaw; Rauchholz Memorial Library; Rawson Memorial Library; Saint

Charles District Library; Sandusky District Library; Sanilac District Library; Sebewaing Township Library; Thomas E Fleschner Memorial Library; Thomas Township Library; Unity District Library; Watertown Township Fostoria Library; West Branch Public Library
Partic in Michigan Library Consortium; OCLC Online Computer Library Center, Inc

SAINT CHARLES

P SAINT CHARLES DISTRICT LIBRARY,* 104 W Spruce St, 48655-1238. SAN 308-3918. Tel: 517-865-9451. FAX: 517-865-9451. *Dir*, John Sheridan; *Asst Dir*, Dorothy Bodhaine; Staff 1 (MLS 1)
Founded 1907. Pop 7,796; Circ 30,135
Library Holdings: Bk Vols 25,000; Per Subs 96
Special Collections: Michigan Coll
Mem of White Pine Library Cooperative
Friends of the Library Group

SAINT CLAIR SHORES

P SAINT CLAIR SHORES PUBLIC LIBRARY,* 22500 11 Mile Rd, 48081-1399. SAN 308-3926. Tel: 810-771-9020. FAX: 810-771-8935. Web Site: web.macomb.lib.mi.us/saintclaireshores. *Dir*, Arthur M Woodford; E-Mail: woodfora@lcm.macomb.lib.mi.us; *Asst Dir*, Augusta Eller; *Librn*, Rosemary Orlando; *Librn*, Donna Sakowski; *Ch Servs*, Sue A Mihalik; *Archivist*, Cynthia Bieniek; Staff 10 (MLS 10)
Founded 1935. Pop 68,107; Circ 308,172
Jul 1998-Jun 1999 Income $1,450,337, State $25,750, City $1,293,261, County $56,811, Locally Generated Income $28,266. Mats Exp $115,625, Books $92,625, Per/Ser (Incl. Access Fees) $16,000, Micro $2,000. Sal $743,072
Library Holdings: Bk Vols 121,259; Per Subs 417
Subject Interests: Careers, Great Lakes, Michigan
Special Collections: Great Lakes History; Local History, bks, photogs
Automation Activity & Vendor Info: (Circulation) epixtech, inc.
Publications: Inside the Library (newsletter); Muskrat Tales (local history magazine)
Mem of Libr Coop of Macomb
Open Mon-Thurs 9-9, Fri & Sat 9-5
Friends of the Library Group

SAINT HELEN

P RICHFIELD TOWNSHIP PUBLIC LIBRARY, 1410 N M76, PO Box 402, 48656. SAN 308-3934. Tel: 517-389-7630. FAX: 517-389-7795. E-Mail: rtplib@kirtland.cc.mi.us. *Dir*, Suzanne Zoli; Staff 2 (MLS 1, Non-MLS 1)
Founded 1965. Pop 4,500; Circ 16,000
Library Holdings: Bk Vols 11,000; Per Subs 52
Mem of Mid-Michigan Library League
Open Mon, Wed, Thurs & Fri 9:30-4:30, Tues 9:30-7:30, Sat 10-1
Friends of the Library Group

SAINT IGNACE

P SAINT IGNACE PUBLIC LIBRARY,* 6 Spring St, 49781-1606. SAN 308-3942. Tel: 906-643-8318. FAX: 906-643-9809. Web Site: www.uproc.lib.mi.us. *Librn*, Cindy Patten; E-Mail: cindy@uproc.lib.mi.us
Pop 4,284; Circ 26,000
Jan 1997-Dec 1998 Income $101,000, State $4,100, City $13,000, Other $79,000. Mats Exp $7,900, Books $6,200, Per/Ser (Incl. Access Fees) $700. Sal $20,000 (Prof $16,000)
Library Holdings: Bk Vols 15,000; Per Subs 70
Mem of Hiawathaland Library Cooperative

SAINT JOHNS

P BRIGGS PUBLIC LIBRARY,* 108 E Railroad St, 48879-1533. SAN 308-3950. Tel: 517-224-4702. FAX: 517-224-1205. *Dir*, Christina McKillop; *Asst Dir*, Kathleen Beagle; *Asst Librn*, Marie Geller
Pop 17,875; Circ 71,730
Library Holdings: Bk Vols 25,592; Per Subs 55
Subject Interests: History
Mem of Capital Library Cooperative
Partic in Cap Area Libr Network Inc; OCLC Online Computer Library Center, Inc
Open Mon-Fri 10-8, Sat 10-5
Friends of the Library Group

SAINT JOSEPH

R FIRST CONGREGATIONAL CHURCH OF SAINT JOSEPH LIBRARY,* 2001 Niles Ave, 49085. SAN 308-3969. Tel: 616-983-5519. FAX: 616-983-5988. *Librn*, Carol Geldhof
Founded 1957
Library Holdings: Bk Vols 3,680
Subject Interests: Biblical studies, Education, Psychology
Special Collections: Video Tapes for Children & Adults

P MAUD PRESTON PALENSKE MEMORIAL LIBRARY, Saint Joseph Public Library, 500 Market St, 49085. SAN 308-3977. Tel: 616-983-7167. FAX: 616-983-5804. E-Mail: sjlibrary@qtm.net. *Dir*, Mary Kynast; *Ch Servs*, JoAnn Wurz; *Circ*, Jacquie Schneider; *Ref Serv Ad*, Laura Lyles; *Tech Servs*, Charla Pearson; Staff 7 (MLS 2, Non-MLS 5)
Founded 1903. Pop 18,827; Circ 219,597
Jul 1999-Jun 2000 Income $537,316. Mats Exp $90,000. Sal $277,557
Library Holdings: Bk Vols 90,000; Per Subs 161
Subject Interests: Local history
Special Collections: Cook Nuclear Plant NRC Documents
Automation Activity & Vendor Info: (Cataloging) Gaylord; (Circulation) Gaylord; (OPAC) Gaylord
Function: Document delivery services, ILL available, Photocopies available, Some telephone reference
Mem of Southwest Michigan Library Cooperative
Friends of the Library Group

SAINT LOUIS

P THEODORE AUSTIN CUTLER MEMORIAL LIBRARY, Saint Louis Public Library, 312 Michigan Ave, 48880. SAN 308-3985. Tel: 517-681-5141. FAX: 517-681-2077. *Dir*, Pamela Carberry; E-Mail: t.a.pam@cmsinter.net; Staff 4 (MLS 1, Non-MLS 3)
Founded 1936. Pop 6,946; Circ 37,000
Sep 2000-Jun 2001 Income $134,500, City $17,500, County $107,000, Locally Generated Income $10,000. Mats Exp $21,000, Books $8,000, Per/Ser (Incl. Access Fees) $2,000, Electronic Ref Mat (Incl. Access Fees) $11,000. Sal $65,000 (Prof $36,500)
Library Holdings: Bk Titles 34,000; Per Subs 65
Subject Interests: Local history
Automation Activity & Vendor Info: (Cataloging) Follett; (Circulation) Follett
Mem of Capital Library Cooperative
Open Mon-Thurs 10-8, Fri 10-5:30 & Sat 10-12

S MID-MICHIGAN CORRECTIONAL FACILITY LIBRARY,* 8201 N Croswell Rd, 48880. SAN 373-9139. Tel: 517-681-4361, Ext 2315. FAX: 517-681-4203.; Staff 1 (MLS 1)
Founded 1990
Library Holdings: Bk Vols 30,000; Bk Titles 13,000
Subject Interests: History
Special Collections: Law
Partic in Cap Area Libr Network Inc
Special Services for the Deaf - Books on deafness & sign language; High interest/low vocabulary books

SALINE

P SALINE DISTRICT LIBRARY, 555 N Maple Rd, 48176. SAN 308-3993. Tel: 734-429-5450. FAX: 734-944-0600. Web Site: server.saline.lib.mi.us/. *Dir*, Leslee Niethammer; Tel: 734-429-2313, E-Mail: leslee@saline.lib.mi.us; *Circ*, Karen Gillette; *Coll Develop*, Marlee Horrocks; Staff 30 (MLS 7, Non-MLS 23)
Founded 1900. Pop 15,698
Dec 2000-Nov 2001 Income $937,969, State $19,783, County $20,000, Locally Generated Income $807,186, Other $81,000. Mats Exp $937,969, Books $83,000, Per/Ser (Incl. Access Fees) $6,500, Micro $800, Electronic Ref Mat (Incl. Access Fees) $5,000. Sal $422,163 (Prof $191,788)
Library Holdings: Bk Titles 52,476; Per Subs 120
Subject Interests: Local history
Automation Activity & Vendor Info: (Cataloging) Gaylord; (Circulation) Gaylord; (OPAC) Gaylord
Mem of The Library Network
Friends of the Library Group

SANDUSKY

P SANDUSKY DISTRICT LIBRARY, 55 E Sanilac Rd, 48471. (Mail add: PO Box 271, 48471-0271), SAN 308-4000. Tel: 810-648-2644. FAX: 810-648-1904. E-Mail: sandistlib@hotmail.com. *Dir*, Gail Ann Nartker; *Asst Librn*, Jackie Graves; Staff 5 (Non-MLS 5)
Founded 1937. Pop 6,700; Circ 75,000
Jan 1999-Dec 1999 Income $209,000, State $7,000, County $67,500, Locally Generated Income $123,000, Other $11,500. Mats Exp $122,800, Books $24,000, Other Print Mats $2,200. Sal $59,500 (Prof $25,000)
Library Holdings: Bk Vols 35,000; Per Subs 125
Subject Interests: Genealogy, Local history
Special Collections: Genealogy & local history materials
Database Vendor: IAC - Info Trac, IAC - SearchBank, OCLC - First

Search, Silverplatter Information Inc.
Mem of White Pine Library Cooperative
Partic in White Pine Libr Coop
Friends of the Library Group

SARANAC

P SARANAC PUBLIC LIBRARY,* 61 Bridge St, PO Box 27, 48881-0027. SAN 308-4019. Tel: 616-642-9146. FAX: 616-643-6430. E-Mail: sar@lakeland.lib.mi.us. *Dir*, Patricia Zander; *Asst Dir*, Mike Platte
Circ 18,726
Library Holdings: Bk Vols 35,000; Per Subs 100
Mem of Lakeland Library Cooperative
Partic in Mich Libr Asn
Friends of the Library Group

SAULT SAINTE MARIE

P BAYLISS PUBLIC LIBRARY,* 541 Library Dr, 49783. SAN 308-4035. Tel: 906-632-9331. FAX: 906-635-0210. *Dir*, Janus Storey; *Ch Servs*, Debra Lehman; *Cat*, Mary Frances Morden; *Ref*, Teresa Gray; Staff 2 (MLS 2)
Founded 1903. Pop 29,140; Circ 187,920
Library Holdings: Bk Titles 110,139; Per Subs 279
Special Collections: History (Judge Joseph H Steere Coll), bks, mss
Mem of Hiawathaland Library Cooperative
Friends of the Library Group

P HIAWATHALAND LIBRARY COOPERATIVE,* 541 Library Dr, 49783. SAN 308-4043. Tel: 906-632-4342. FAX: 906-635-0210. E-Mail: janus@uproc.lib.mi.us. *Dir*, Janus Storey; Staff 2 (MLS 2)
Founded 1978
Restriction: Not a lending library
Member Libraries: Bayliss Public Library; De Tour Area School & Public Library; Mackinac Island Public Library; Manistique School & Public Library; Rudyard School Public Library; Saint Ignace Public Library; Whitefish Township Community Library

C LAKE SUPERIOR STATE UNIVERSITY LIBRARY,* 650 Easterday Ave, 49783. SAN 308-4051. Tel: 906-635-2402. FAX: 906-635-2193. Web Site: www.lssu.edu/library/. *Dir*, Fredrick Michels; E-Mail: fmichels@gw.lssu.edu; *AV*, Charles Gustafson; *Cat, Tech Servs*, Maureen DeLaney Lehman; *Coll Develop, Govt Doc, Publ Servs, YA Servs*, Ruth Neveu; *ILL*, Chris Roll; *Publ Servs*, Beth Hronek; Staff 5 (MLS 5)
Founded 1946. Enrl 2,517; Fac 110; Highest Degree: Master
Jul 1997-Jun 1998 Income $754,690. Mats Exp $229,601, Books $80,317, Per/Ser (Incl. Access Fees) $149,284. Sal $454,698
Library Holdings: Bk Vols 131,553; Per Subs 811
Special Collections: Great Lakes (Marine-Laker); Michigan History (Michigan Room)
Publications: Folio (quarterly-internal only)
Partic in Michigan Library Consortium; OCLC Online Computer Library Center, Inc; Sault Area Int Libr Asn; Upper Peninsula Region Of Library Cooperation, Inc

S LE SAULT DE SAINTE MARIE HISTORICAL SITES, Manse Maritime Research Library,* 501 E Water, 49783. SAN 373-2193. Tel: 906-632-3658. FAX: 906-632-9344. *In Charge*, Jimmy Hobaugh; *Librn*, Phyllis Weaver
Library Holdings: Bk Vols 300
Open Tues in winter months

SCHOOLCRAFT

P SCHOOLCRAFT COMMUNITY LIBRARY, 330 N Centre, PO Box 566, 49087-0566. SAN 371-5701. Tel: 616-679-5959. FAX: 616-679-5599. E-Mail: schoolcr@monroe.lib.mi.us. *Dir*, Shirley Cody; E-Mail: scody@monroe.lib.mi.us; *Ch Servs*, Bobbi Truesdell
Founded 1988. Pop 4,730; Circ 23,000
Mar 1998-Feb 1999 Income (Main Library Only) $79,585. Mats Exp $10,996, Books $8,395, Per/Ser (Incl. Access Fees) $250, AV Equip $1,500. Sal $42,240 (Prof $20,000)
Library Holdings: Bk Titles 16,000; Per Subs 20
Mem of Woodlands Library Cooperative
Friends of the Library Group

SCOTTVILLE

P MASON COUNTY DISTRICT LIBRARY, Scottville Branch, 204 E State St, 49454-9506. SAN 308-406X. Tel: 231-757-2588. FAX: 231-757-3401. E-Mail: library@masoncounty.lib.mi.us. Web Site: www.masoncounty.lib.mi.us. *Librn*, Robert T Dickson; Staff 7 (MLS 1, Non-MLS 6)
Founded 1941. Pop 26,000; Circ 75,000
Mem of Mid-Michigan Library League
Friends of the Library Group

J WEST SHORE COMMUNITY COLLEGE, Instructional Media Center,* 3000 N Stiles Rd, 49454. SAN 308-4078. Tel: 231-845-6211, Ext 3305. Toll Free Tel: 800-848-9722. FAX: 231-843-2680. *Librn*, Mike Hypio
Founded 1968. Enrl 1,000
Library Holdings: Bk Vols 21,000; Per Subs 150

SEBEWAING

P SEBEWAING TOWNSHIP LIBRARY,* 41 North Center St, 48759-1406. SAN 308-4086. Tel: 517-883-3520. FAX: 517-883-3902. E-Mail: seb@avci.net. *Librn*, Tammy Haag
Pop 4,509; Circ 31,294
Library Holdings: Bk Vols 23,405; Per Subs 50
Special Collections: Local Newspapers on Microfilm
Mem of White Pine Library Cooperative
Friends of the Library Group

SELFRIDGE AIR NATIONAL GUARD BASE

UNITED STATES ARMY
A GARRISON-SELFRIDGE LIBRARY, Bldg 780 West, 48045-5016. SAN 347-0733. Tel: 810-307-5238. *Librn*, Jo Ann Bonnett; Staff 2 (MLS 2)
Founded 1972
Library Holdings: Bk Vols 26,390; Per Subs 331
Subject Interests: Military history
Partic in Fedlink

SHELBY

P SHELBY AREA DISTRICT LIBRARY, 189 Maple St, 49455-1134. SAN 308-4094. Tel: 231-861-4565. FAX: 231-861-6868. *Dir, Librn*, Sally Diepen; E-Mail: sdiepen@voyager.net
Founded 1907. Pop 9,519
Library Holdings: Bk Vols 34,000; Per Subs 115
Partic in Mich Libr Asn
Open Mon-Wed 9-9, Tues, Thurs & Fri 9-5, Sat 9-4
Friends of the Library Group

SHELBY TOWNSHIP

P SHELBY TOWNSHIP LIBRARY,* 51680 Van Dyke, 48316-4459. SAN 308-4604. Tel: 810-739-7478. FAX: 810-726-0535. *Dir*, Delight Dean; *Ch Servs*, Anne Tobian; *Ad Servs*, Judith Chambers; Staff 3 (MLS 3)
Founded 1972. Pop 40,000; Circ 98,216
Library Holdings: Bk Vols 69,664; Per Subs 210
Subject Interests: Women's studies
Publications: Friends of the Shelby Township Library Newsletter
Mem of Libr Coop of Macomb
Friends of the Library Group

SIDNEY

J MONTCALM COMMUNITY COLLEGE LIBRARY,* 2800 College Dr SW, PO Box 300, 48885-0300. SAN 308-4108. Tel: 517-328-2111, 517-328-2282, Ext 261. FAX: 517-328-2950. Web Site: www.montcalm.cc.mi.us/library. *Dir*, Richard Leigh Parker; E-Mail: rickp@montcalm.cc.mi.us; Staff 3 (MLS 1, Non-MLS 2)
Founded 1966. Enrl 2,000; Fac 24; Highest Degree: Associate
Library Holdings: Bk Titles 28,000; Per Subs 180
Database Vendor: IAC - SearchBank, OCLC - First Search, ProQuest
Function: ILL available
Partic in Michigan Library Consortium

SODUS

P SODUS TOWNSHIP LIBRARY,* 3776 Naomi Rd, 49126-9714. SAN 308-4116. Tel: 616-925-0903. FAX: 616-925-1823. *Librn*, Bea Rodgers
Founded 1939. Pop 2,260; Circ 7,200
Apr 1997-Mar 1998 Income $39,700. Mats Exp $6,300. Sal $9,600
Library Holdings: Bk Titles 15,800; Per Subs 46
Mem of Southwest Michigan Library Cooperative

SOUTH HAVEN

P SOUTH HAVEN MEMORIAL LIBRARY, 314 Broadway, 49090. SAN 308-4124. Tel: 616-637-2403. FAX: 616-639-1685. E-Mail: shlibrary@yahoo.com. *Dir*, Martha Gray; Staff 7 (MLS 1, Non-MLS 6)
Pop 9,748; Circ 141,500
Jul 1999-Jun 2000 Income $236,881, State $9,748, City $136,213, County $53,700, Locally Generated Income $20,871, Other $13,203. Mats Exp $26,895, Books $20,000, Per/Ser (Incl. Access Fees) $5,000, Presv $200, Micro $1,200, Other Print Mats $215. Sal $112,013
Library Holdings: Bk Titles 48,000; Per Subs 105

Subject Interests: Great Lakes, Local history
Automation Activity & Vendor Info: (Cataloging) Follett; (Circulation) Follett
Mem of Southwest Michigan Library Cooperative
Friends of the Library Group

SOUTH LYON

P SALEM-SOUTH LYON DISTRICT LIBRARY, 9800 Pontiac Trail, 48178-1307. SAN 308-4132. Tel: 248-437-6431. FAX: 248-437-6593. Web Site: www.south-lyon.lib.mi.us. *Dir*, Nancy Noble; E-Mail: nnoble@tln.lib.mi.us; Staff 20 (MLS 4, Non-MLS 16)
Founded 1939. Pop 11,500; Circ 186,434
Jul 1999-Jun 2000 Income $596,023. Mats Exp $73,750. Sal $246,000
Library Holdings: Bk Vols 48,827; Per Subs 85
Automation Activity & Vendor Info: (Circulation) DRA; (ILL) DRA; (OPAC) DRA
Database Vendor: DRA
Mem of The Library Network
Friends of the Library Group

SOUTHFIELD

S ARCADIS GIFFELS LIBRARY, 25200 Telegraph Rd, PO Box 5025, 48086-5025. SAN 308-4248. Tel: 248-936-8110, Ext 6151. FAX: 248-936-8387. *Librn*, Richard Sofota
Library Holdings: Bk Vols 1,100; Per Subs 100
Subject Interests: Architecture, Engineering
Mem of Wayne Oakland Libr Federation

R CONGREGATION SHAAREY ZEDEK LIBRARY & AUDIO VISUAL CENTER, 27375 Bell Rd, 48034. SAN 308-4191. Tel: 248-357-5544. FAX: 248-357-0227. *Librn*, Sharon Cohen
Founded 1932
Library Holdings: Bk Vols 40,000; Bk Titles 35,000; Per Subs 20
Subject Interests: Holocaust, Judaica (lit or hist of Jews), Juvenile delinquency, Literature
Special Collections: Modern Hebrew lit, Holtzman Coll
Automation Activity & Vendor Info: (Cataloging) Sagebrush Corporation

S EATON CORP, Innovation Center Research Library,* 26201 Northwestern Hwy, PO Box 766, 48037. SAN 308-4213. Tel: 248-354-6979. FAX: 248-354-2739. *Librn*, Cheryl Pfeifer; E-Mail: cheryl.pfeifer@eaton.com; Staff 2 (MLS 1, Non-MLS 1)
Founded 1963
Library Holdings: Bk Titles 4,000; Per Subs 250
Subject Interests: Automotive engineering, Metallurgy
Publications: 30 Minutes (monthly bulletin of accessions); INFO ALERT (management business info); SAE Handbook, SAE Technical papers 94-96
Restriction: Staff use only
Partic in Data Time; Dialog Corporation; Michigan Library Consortium; OCLC Online Computer Library Center, Inc; Orbit; ProQuest; Questal Orbit

C LAWRENCE TECHNOLOGICAL UNIVERSITY LIBRARY, 21000 W Ten Mile Rd, 48075-1058. SAN 308-4256. Tel: 248-204-3000. FAX: 248-204-3005. E-Mail: ltu_library@ltu.edu. Web Site: www.ltu.edu/library. *Dir*, Gary R Cocozzoli; E-Mail: grc@ltu.edu; *Tech Servs*, Cathy Phillips; E-Mail: phillips@ltu.edu; *Publ Servs*, Gretchen Young Weiner; E-Mail: weiner@ltu.edu; *Publ Servs*, Gerald DiLoreto; E-Mail: diloreto@ltu.edu; *ILL*, Mary Alice Power; E-Mail: power@ltu.edu; *Publ Servs*, Sheila Gaddie; E-Mail: gaddie@ltu.edu; Staff 10 (MLS 6, Non-MLS 4)
Founded 1932. Enrl 4,273; Highest Degree: Master
Jul 2000-Jun 2001 Income $704,139. Mats Exp $253,000, Books $93,000, Per/Ser (Incl. Access Fees) $140,000, Presv $10,000, Micro $10,000. Sal $296,399 (Prof $201,000)
Library Holdings: Bk Vols 108,000; Bk Titles 41,000; Per Subs 1,000
Subject Interests: Architecture, Engineering, Management
Special Collections: Architectural Materials (Albert F Kahn Coll)
Automation Activity & Vendor Info: (Acquisitions) DRA; (Cataloging) DRA; (Circulation) DRA; (OPAC) DRA; (Serials) DRA
Database Vendor: Dialog, DRA, IAC - Info Trac, Lexis-Nexis, OCLC - First Search
Function: ILL available
Partic in Coun on Resources Develop; Michigan Library Consortium; OCLC Online Computer Library Center, Inc; Southeastern Michigan League Of Libraries

M PROVIDENCE HOSPITAL, Helen L DeRoy Medical Library, 16001 W Nine Mile Rd, 48075. SAN 308-4272. Tel: 248-424-3294. FAX: 248-424-3201. Web Site: www.providence-hospital.org/library. *Dir*, Carole M Gilbert; E-Mail: cgilbert@providence-hospital.org; Staff 3 (MLS 2, Non-MLS 1)
Founded 1950
Library Holdings: Bk Vols 4,500; Per Subs 410
Subject Interests: Medicine

S RIGHT TO LIFE OF MICHIGAN, Resource Center, 29610 Southfield Rd Ste 119, 48076. SAN 373-2142. Tel: 248-552-3742. FAX: 248-552-3747. Web Site: www.rtl.org. *Mgr*, Kim Kenson
Library Holdings: Bk Vols 200

L SOMMERS, SCHWARTZ, SILVER & SCHWARTZ, Law Library, 2000 Town Ctr, Ste 900, 48075. SAN 372-0470. Tel: 248-355-0300. FAX: 248-746-4001. *Head Librn*, Angela Booth; E-Mail: abooth@s4online.com
Library Holdings: Bk Vols 14,000; Per Subs 250
Database Vendor: Lexis-Nexis
Restriction: Company library, Not a lending library, Not open to public, Private library
Function: For research purposes, Research library

P SOUTHFIELD PUBLIC LIBRARY, David Stewart Memorial Library, 26000 Evergreen Rd, PO Box 2055, 48037-2055. SAN 308-4299. Tel: 248-948-0460. Reference Tel: 248-948-0480. FAX: 248-354-5319. Web Site: www.metronet.lib.mi.us/SFLD. *City Librn*, Douglas A Zyskowski; Tel: 248-948-0489, Fax: 248-208-8040, E-Mail: daz@metronet.lib.mi.us; *Asst Librn*, Carol Mueller; Tel: 248-948-0488, Fax: 248-208-8040, E-Mail: csm@metronet.lib.mi.us; *Tech Coordr*, Robin Gardella; Tel: 248-948-0477, E-Mail: rg@metronet.lib.mi.us; *Ad Servs*, Ann Abdoo; Tel: 248-948-0455, E-Mail: aa@metronet.lib.mi.us; *Tech Servs*, Catherine Schmidt; Tel: 248-948-0464, E-Mail: schmidt2@metronet.lib.mi.us; Staff 42 (MLS 19, Non-MLS 23)
Founded 1960. Pop 75,728; Circ 390,282
Jul 1999-Jun 2000 Mats Exp $275,473, Books $187,972, Per/Ser (Incl. Access Fees) $36,804, Micro $14,955, AV Equip $32,273, Electronic Ref Mat (Incl. Access Fees) $2,569. Sal $1,754,214
Library Holdings: Bk Vols 184,238; Per Subs 457
Subject Interests: Foreign lang materials
Special Collections: United States Census Affiliate Center
Automation Activity & Vendor Info: (Acquisitions) Innovative Interfaces Inc.; (Cataloging) Innovative Interfaces Inc.; (Circulation) Innovative Interfaces Inc.; (OPAC) Innovative Interfaces Inc.; (Serials) Innovative Interfaces Inc.
Publications: Newsletter (bimonthly)
Mem of The Library Network
Partic in Metronet
Friends of the Library Group
Branches: 1
JOHN GRACE BRANCH, 21030 Indian St, 48034. SAN 373-2924. Tel: 248-948-0409. FAX: 248-948-0409.
Friends of the Library Group

S W B DONER ADVERTISING, (Formerly W B Doner & Company Advertising), Resource Center, 25900 Northwestern Hwy, 48075. SAN 325-5077. Tel: 248-354-9700. FAX: 248-827-0880. *Mgr Libr Serv*, Rita M Simmons; E-Mail: rsimmons@donerus.com; *Librn*, Jennifer Gannod; E-Mail: jgannod@donerus.com; Staff 3 (MLS 3)
Founded 1982
Mar 1999-Feb 2000 Income $150,000. Mats Exp $60,000, Books $15,000, Per/Ser (Incl. Access Fees) $16,000, Electronic Ref Mat (Incl. Access Fees) $20,000. Sal $84,000 (Prof $75,000)
Library Holdings: Bk Vols 350; Bk Titles 300; Per Subs 150
Subject Interests: Marketing and advertising
Database Vendor: Dialog, Ebsco - EbscoHost, Lexis-Nexis, OCLC - First Search, ProQuest
Restriction: Staff use only
Function: Research library
Partic in Michigan Library Consortium

SOUTHGATE

P SOUTHGATE VETERANS MEMORIAL LIBRARY,* 14680 Dix-Toledo Rd, 48195. SAN 308-4310. Tel: 734-284-3268. FAX: 734-284-9477. Web Site: www.tln.lib.mi.us/~sogt/. *Dir*, Joyce Farkas
Pop 30,771; Circ 92,159
Library Holdings: Bk Vols 63,000; Per Subs 134
Mem of The Library Network; Wayne Oakland Libr Federation
Open Mon-Thurs 10-9, Fri-Sat 10-5

P THE LIBRARY NETWORK, (TLN), 13331 Reeck Rd, 48195. SAN 347-1632. Tel: 734-281-3830. FAX: 734-281-1905. E-Mail: mdeller@tln.lib.mi.us. Web Site: tln.lib.mi.us. *Dir*, A Michael Deller; Tel: 734-281-3830, Ext 106, E-Mail: mdeller@tln.lib.mi.us; *Dep Dir*, Eileen Palmer; Tel: 734-281-3830, Ext 107, E-Mail: empalmer@tln.lib.mi.us; *Purchasing*, Lianne Clair; Tel: 734-281-3830, Ext 102, E-Mail: lclair@tln.lib.mi.us; *Cat*, Mary Feltz; *Acq*, Jim Flury; *Automation Syst Coordr*, Anne Neville; Staff 39 (MLS 8, Non-MLS 31)
Founded 1978. Pop 2,564,512; Circ 11,000,000
Oct 1998-Sep 1999 Income $5,638,745, State $1,284,922, Federal $35,563, Locally Generated Income $1,977,953, Other $2,340,307. Mats Exp $2,269,898. Sal $1,161,666
Library Holdings: Bk Vols 4,177,329
Automation Activity & Vendor Info: (Acquisitions) DRA; (Cataloging) DRA; (Circulation) DRA; (OPAC) DRA; (Serials) DRA
Database Vendor: DRA
Publications: Annual Report; Newsletter (weekly)

Member Libraries: Addison Township Public Libary; Allen Park Public Library; Ann Arbor District Library; Auburn Hills Public Library; Bacon Memorial Public Library; Baldwin Public Library; Berkley Public Library; Blair Memorial Library; Bloomfield Township Public Library; Brandon Township Public Library; Brighton District Library; Canton Public Library; Caroline Kennedy Library; Chelsea District Library; Cromaine District Library; Dearborn Public Library; Dexter District Library; Ecorse Public Library; Farmington Community Library; Ferndale Public Library; Flat Rock Public Library; Fowlerville District Library; Franklin Public Library; Fred C Fischer Library; Garden City Public Library; Grosse Pointe Public Library; Hamburg Township Library; Hamtramck Public Library; Hazel Park Memorial Library; Highland Township Public Library; Huntington Woods Public Library; Independence Township Public Library; Inkster Public Library; John F Kennedy Jr Library; Lincoln Park Public Library; Livonia Public Library; Lyon Township Public Library; Madison Heights Public Library; Melvindale Public Library; Milford Township Library; Northfield Township Area Library; Northville District Library; Novi Public Library; Oak Park Public Library; Oakland County Research Library; Orion Township Public Library; Oxford Public Library; Pinckney Community Public Library; Plymouth District Library; Pontiac Public Library; Redford Township District Library; Riverview Public Library; Rochester Hills Public Library; Romulus Public Library; Royal Oak Public Library; Royal Oak Township Library; Saint Clair County; Saint Clair County Library System; Saint Clair County Library System; Salem-South Lyon District Library; Saline District Library; Southfield Public Library; Southgate Veterans Memorial Library; Springfield Township Library; Taylor Community Library; Trenton Veterans Memorial Library; Walled Lake City Library; Washtenaw County Library; Waterford Township Public Library; Wayne County Library; Wayne County Regional Library For The Blind & Physically Handicapped; Wayne Public Library; West Bloomfield Township Public Library; White Lake Township Library; Wixom Public Library; Ypsilanti District Library
Non-public member libraries: Chrysler Information Resource Center, Clarenceville Middle School, Clayton Environmental Consultants Information Center, Cleary College (Bonisteel Library), Concordia College (Zimmerman Library), Eastern Michigan University (Halle Library), Father Gabriel Richara High School, Hamtramck Public School, Henry Ford Academy of Manufacturing Arts & Sciences; Henry Ford Museum & Greenfield Village, John D Dingell Dept VAMG, John Glenn High School, Johnson Controls-Technical Information Center, Oakland Schools Library Services, Our Lady of Mt Carmel High School, Roeper School, Southfield Christian School, Southgate Community Schools, St Clair Community College Library, St Clair County Intermediate School District, University of Michigan (Mardigian Library), Waterford School District, William Tyndale College

SPARTA

P SPARTA TOWNSHIP LIBRARY, 80 N Union St, 49345. SAN 308-4329. Tel: 616-887-9937. FAX: 616-887-0179. Web Site: www.lakeland.lib.mi.us/. *Librn*, Lois Lovell; E-Mail: llovell@lakeland.lib.mi.us
Founded 1917. Pop 8,447; Circ 43,987
Library Holdings: Bk Vols 50,661; Per Subs 131
Subject Interests: Genealogy, Local history
Mem of Lakeland Library Cooperative
Friends of the Library Group

SPRING ARBOR

C SPRING ARBOR COLLEGE, Hugh A White Library, 106 E Main St, 49283. SAN 308-4337. Tel: 517-750-6441. Interlibrary Loan Service Tel: 517-750-6439. Circulation Tel: 517-750-6442. Reference Tel: 517-750-6445. Toll Free Tel: 800-968-9103. FAX: 517-750-2108. Web Site: www.arbor.edu/whitelibrary/. *Dir*, Roy Meador; Tel: 517-750-6444, E-Mail: rmeador@arbor.edu; *Publ Servs, Ref*, Karen Parsons; Tel: 517-750-6436, E-Mail: kparsons@arbor.edu; *ILL*, Angie Hiler; E-Mail: ahiler@arbor.edu; *Tech Servs*, David Burns; Tel: 517-750-1443, E-Mail: dburns@arbor.edu; *Circ*, Lois Hunt; Tel: 517-750-6442, E-Mail: lhunt@arbor.edu. Subject Specialists: *Adult education*, Stephanie Davis; Staff 9 (MLS 4, Non-MLS 5)
Founded 1873. Enrl 2,478; Fac 77; Highest Degree: Master
Nov 1999-Oct 2000 Mats Exp $143,178, Books $76,396, Per/Ser (Incl. Access Fees) $45,380, Micro $1,972, AV Equip $14,222, Other Print Mats $4,550, Manuscripts & Archives $658. Sal $265,410 (Prof $137,752)
Library Holdings: Bk Vols 91,940; Per Subs 566
Partic in Cap Area Libr Network Inc; Michigan Library Consortium; OCLC Online Computer Library Center, Inc

SPRING LAKE

P WARNER BAIRD DISTRICT LIBRARY, 123 E Exchange St, 49456-2018. SAN 308-4353. Tel: 616-846-5770. FAX: 616-844-2129. Web Site: www.warnerbaird.org. *Dir*, Claire Sheridan; *Asst Dir*, Barbara Anderson; Staff 3 (MLS 2, Non-MLS 1)
Pop 10,751
Jan 2000-Dec 2000 Mats Exp $35,000
Library Holdings: Bk Vols 34,825
Mem of Lakeland Library Cooperative
Friends of the Library Group

ST CLAIRE SHORES

S RIGHT TO LIFE OF MICHIGAN, Resource Center, 27417 Harper, 48081. Tel: 810-774-6050. FAX: 810-774-5192. *Mgr*, Andrea Trella

STANTON

P WHITE PINE LIBRARY, 106 E Walnut, 48888-9294. SAN 308-4361. Tel: 517-831-4327. FAX: 517-831-4976. *Dir, Librn*, Katie Arwood; *Asst Librn*, Tammy Bowen
Founded 1935. Pop 9,284; Circ 34,050
Library Holdings: Bk Vols 19,839; Per Subs 50
Subject Interests: Genealogy, Local history
Mem of Mid-Michigan Library League
Open Mon & Fri 9-5:30, Tues 12:30-5:30, Wed 12:30-5:30 & 7-9, Thurs 9-7, Sat 10-12
Friends of the Library Group

STEPHENSON

P MENOMINEE COUNTY LIBRARY,* S319 Railroad St, PO Box 128, 49887-0128. SAN 347-0768. Tel: 906-753-6923. FAX: 906-753-4678. E-Mail: mcl@mid-pen.lib.mi.us. *Dir*, Patricia F Cheski; E-Mail: cheskip@mid-pen.lib.mi.us; Staff 6 (Non-MLS 6)
Founded 1944. Pop 16,342; Circ 127,504
Library Holdings: Bk Vols 56,860; Per Subs 90
Automation Activity & Vendor Info: (Cataloging) Brodart; (Circulation) Brodart; (OPAC) Brodart
Function: ILL available
Mem of Mid-Peninsula Library Cooperative
Friends of the Library Group
Branches: 1
HERMANSVILLE BRANCH, Hermansville, 49847. SAN 347-0792. Tel: 906-498-2253. FAX: 906-498-2253. *In Charge*, Louise Chelmacki
Library Holdings: Bk Vols 6,129; Per Subs 31
Bookmobiles: 1

STERLING HEIGHTS

S GENERAL DYNAMICS LAND SYSTEMS, Technical & Administrative Information Services (TAIS), 38500 Mound Rd, 48310. SAN 329-0956. Tel: 810-825-4402. FAX: 810-825-4013. *Librn*, Michaelene Iwanyckyj; E-Mail: iwanycky@gdls.com; Staff 3 (MLS 1, Non-MLS 2)
Founded 1985
Library Holdings: Bk Vols 24,076; Per Subs 50
Special Collections: Army Technical Manuals & DMWR's
Restriction: Staff use only
Partic in Macomb Region of Coop

P STERLING HEIGHTS PUBLIC LIBRARY, 40255 Dodge Park Rd, 48313-4140. SAN 308-4388. Tel: 810-446-2640. Interlibrary Loan Service Tel: 810-446-2642. Circulation Tel: 810-446-2665. Reference Tel: 810-446-2642. FAX: 810-276-4067. Web Site: www.shpl.net. *Dir*, Carol Lingeman; E-Mail: lingemac@libcoop.net; *Ch Servs*, Judy Kotulis; Tel: 810-446-2644, E-Mail: kotulisj@libcoop.net; *Ad Servs*, Margaret Hanes; Tel: 810-446-2642, E-Mail: hanesm@libcoop.net; *Tech Servs*, Ellen Lasky; Tel: 810-446-2649, E-Mail: laskye@libcoop.net; Staff 16 (MLS 16)
Founded 1971. Pop 117,810; Circ 671,017
Jul 1999-Jun 2000 Income $1,951,970, State $117,713, City $1,759,991, Federal $10,000, County $125,020, Other $64,266. Mats Exp $255,791, Books $199,858, Per/Ser (Incl. Access Fees) $16,912, AV Equip $19,312, Electronic Ref Mat (Incl. Access Fees) $19,709. Sal $1,125,264
Library Holdings: Bk Titles 183,167; Per Subs 343
Subject Interests: Careers, Children's literature, Large print
Special Collections: Polish Lit Coll; Term Paper Topics
Automation Activity & Vendor Info: (Acquisitions) epixtech, inc.; (Cataloging) epixtech, inc.; (Circulation) epixtech, inc.; (ILL) epixtech, inc.; (OPAC) epixtech, inc.; (Serials) epixtech, inc.
Function: Document delivery services, ILL available, Photocopies available, Reference services available
Mem of Suburban Library System
Friends of the Library Group

STEVENSVILLE

P LINCOLN TOWNSHIP PUBLIC LIBRARY, 2099 W John Beers Rd, 49127. SAN 308-4396. Tel: 616-429-9575. TDD: 616-429-9575. FAX: 616-429-3500. Web Site: www.lincolnpublic.lib.mi.us. *Dir*, Virginia Bedunah; E-Mail: vbedunah@remcll.k12.mi.us; *Cat*, Sandra Andert; *ILL*, Ann Wilkinson; *Ref*, Sue Vandermolen; Staff 7 (MLS 3, Non-MLS 4)

Founded 1959. Pop 19,470; Circ 194,000
Apr 1999-Mar 2000 Income $652,682. Mats Exp $474,206. Sal $314,906
Library Holdings: Bk Vols 79,055; Per Subs 142
Automation Activity & Vendor Info: (Cataloging) epixtech, inc.; (Circulation) epixtech, inc.; (OPAC) epixtech, inc.
Database Vendor: epixtech, inc.
Mem of Southwest Michigan Library Cooperative
Partic in Berrien Library Consortium
Friends of the Library Group

STURGIS

P STURGIS PUBLIC LIBRARY, 255 North St, 49091. SAN 308-440X. Tel: 616-659-7224. FAX: 616-651-4534. E-Mail: sturgis@monroe.lib.mi.us. *Dir*, Karrie Waarala; *Asst Dir*, Chandler Jackson; Tel: 406-791-5317; *Head, Circ*, Funches Debora; *Cat*, Jill Peck; *Ad Servs*, Mary Murphy; *Ch Servs*, Barbara Rowe; Staff 11 (MLS 1, Non-MLS 10)
Founded 1846. Pop 16,130; Circ 175,000
Library Holdings: Bk Vols 57,275; Per Subs 156
Subject Interests: Business and management
Special Collections: Genealogy, bks, microfilm; Local History, maps, bks, pictures; Michigan History
Mem of Woodlands Library Cooperative
Friends of the Library Group

SUNFIELD

P SUNFIELD DISTRICT LIBRARY,* 112 Main St, PO Box 97, 48890-0097. SAN 308-4418. Tel: 517-566-8065. FAX: 517-566-8065. E-Mail: sdl@pathfindermail.com. *Librn*, Ward MacCready
Pop 2,086; Circ 23,237
Library Holdings: Bk Vols 12,000; Per Subs 40
Mem of Capital Library Cooperative
Friends of the Library Group

SUTTONS BAY

P SUTTONS BAY AREA PUBLIC LIBRARY, 416 Front St, 49682. (Mail add: PO Box 340, 49682), SAN 308-4426. Tel: 231-271-3512. FAX: 231-271-2914. E-Mail: sbapl@traverse.com. *Librn*, Tina Ulrich; Staff 3 (MLS 1, Non-MLS 2)
Pop 4,200; Circ 30,243
Jul 2000-Jun 2001 Income $85,852, State $4,012, County $72,726, Locally Generated Income $9,114. Mats Exp $22,134, Books $19,109, Per/Ser (Incl. Access Fees) $3,025. Sal $38,928 (Prof $23,296)
Library Holdings: Bk Vols 21,949; Bk Titles 18,670; Per Subs 58
Publications: Newsletter
Mem of Mid-Michigan Library League
Friends of the Library Group

TAWAS CITY

P IOSCO-ARENAC DISTRICT LIBRARY,* 951 Turtle Rd, 48763-9563. SAN 347-0822. Tel: 517-362-2651. FAX: 517-362-6056. *Dir*, Stephanie Olson; E-Mail: solson@voyager.net; *Circ, ILL*, Mark Ewing; *Bkmobile Coordr*, Lynne Bigelow; *Cat*, Gloria Ulman; Staff 8 (MLS 2, Non-MLS 6)
Founded 1935. Pop 45,115; Circ 201,400
Library Holdings: Bk Titles 101,447; Per Subs 251
Subject Interests: Genealogy, Local history, Michigan
Publications: Annual report
Mem of White Pine Library Cooperative
Friends of the Library Group
Branches: 8
AU GRES BRANCH, 110 S Mackinaw, Au Gres, 48703. SAN 347-0857. Tel: 517-876-8818. FAX: 517-876-8818. *Librn*, Linda Kauffman
Library Holdings: Bk Vols 4,600
EAST TAWAS BRANCH, 120 W Westover, East Tawas, 48730. SAN 347-0881. Tel: 517-362-6162. FAX: 517-362-6736. *Librn*, Luann Elvey
Library Holdings: Bk Vols 5,600
OMER BRANCH, 205 E Center St, Omer, 48749. SAN 325-4283. Tel: 517-653-2230. FAX: 517-653-2230. *Librn*, Charmaine Ploof
OSCODA BRANCH, 6010 Skeel St, Oscoda, 48750. SAN 347-0946. Tel: 517-739-9581. FAX: 517-653-2230. *Librn*, Rita Bennett
Library Holdings: Bk Vols 8,400
Friends of the Library Group
PLAINFIELD TOWNSHIP, N Washington, Hale, 48739. SAN 347-0911. Tel: 517-728-2811. FAX: 517-728-4086. *Librn*, Cheryl Tyler
Library Holdings: Bk Vols 4,300
Friends of the Library Group
STANDISH BRANCH, PO Box 698, Standish, 48658-0698. SAN 347-0970. Tel: 517-846-6611. FAX: 517-846-6611. *Librn*, Hildegard Carruthers
Library Holdings: Bk Vols 6,600
Friends of the Library Group
TAWAS CITY BRANCH, 208 North St, PO Box 577, 48763. SAN 347-1004. Tel: 517-362-6557. FAX: 517-362-6557. *Librn*, Shirley Klenow
Library Holdings: Bk Vols 4,700
WHITTEMORE BRANCH, City Hall M-65, Whittemore, 48770. SAN 347-1039. Tel: 517-756-3186. FAX: 517-756-3186. *Librn*, Marie Burkholder
Library Holdings: Bk Vols 5,200
Bookmobiles: 1

TAYLOR

P TAYLOR COMMUNITY LIBRARY,* 12303 Pardee Rd, 48180-4219. SAN 308-4434. Tel: 734-287-4840. FAX: 734-287-4141. Web Site: www.tln.lib.mi.us. *Dir*, Nancy B Pollock; *Asst Dir*, Kirk Borger; *Ch Servs*, Jacqueline Whinihan
Pop 70,800
Library Holdings: Bk Titles 106,498; Per Subs 215
Automation Activity & Vendor Info: (Circulation) GEAC
Mem of The Library Network; Wayne Oakland Libr Federation
Open Mon-Thurs 10-8, Fri & Sat 10-5, Sun 1-5

TECUMSEH

P TECUMSEH PUBLIC LIBRARY, 215 N Ottawa St, 49286. SAN 308-4450. Tel: 517-423-2238. FAX: 517-423-5519. Web Site: www.scnc.tps.k12.mi.us/~tpl. *Dir*, Barbara Smith; E-Mail: bsmith@tps.k12.mi.us; Staff 4 (MLS 1, Non-MLS 3)
Founded 1883. Pop 15,304
1999-2000 Mats Exp $57,446, Books $43,741, Per/Ser (Incl. Access Fees) $13,705, Electronic Ref Mat (Incl. Access Fees) $6,644. Sal $216,431 (Prof $99,563)
Library Holdings: Bk Vols 42,518; Per Subs 133
Subject Interests: Civil War, Indians, Local history
Automation Activity & Vendor Info: (Circulation) Follett; (ILL) Brodart; (OPAC) Follett
Database Vendor: GaleNet, IAC - Info Trac, OCLC - First Search, ProQuest
Mem of Woodlands Library Cooperative

TEKONSHA

P TEKONSHA PUBLIC LIBRARY,* 109 E Canal, 49092-9796. SAN 308-4469. Tel: 517-767-4769. FAX: 517-767-4769. E-Mail: tekonlib@cbpu. *Librn*, Leslie Waltz
Circ 4,800
Library Holdings: Bk Vols 6,466; Per Subs 15
Mem of Woodlands Library Cooperative
Friends of the Library Group

THREE OAKS

P THREE OAKS TOWNSHIP LIBRARY,* 3 N Elm St, 49128-1303. SAN 308-4477. Tel: 616-756-5621. FAX: 616-756-3004. *Librn*, Stephanie Daniels; E-Mail: daniels55@yahoo.com
Founded 1859. Pop 6,278; Circ 22,471
Library Holdings: Bk Vols 27,500; Per Subs 52
Partic in SW Mich Libr Network
Open Mon, Tues, Wed 10-6, Thurs 12-8, Fri 9-5, Sat 10-2
Friends of the Library Group

THREE RIVERS

P THREE RIVERS PUBLIC LIBRARY, 920 W Michigan Ave, 49093-2137. SAN 308-4485. Tel: 616-273-8666. FAX: 616-279-9654. E-Mail: threer@monroe.lib.m.us. *Dir*, Shirley Cody; *Coll Develop*, Linda Hilton
Founded 1889. Pop 13,681; Circ 94,000
Jul 1999-Jun 2000 Income $305,928, State $19,206, City $286,722. Mats Exp $44,308, Books $34,274, Per/Ser (Incl. Access Fees) $4,534, Micro $500, AV Equip $5,000. Sal $190,812 (Prof $32,900)
Library Holdings: Bk Vols 45,863; Per Subs 167
Subject Interests: Local history, Science fiction
Publications: Quarterly newsletter
Mem of Woodlands Library Cooperative

TOPINABEE

P TOPINABEE PUBLIC LIBRARY, 1576 Straits Hwy, 49791-9999. SAN 308-4493. Tel: 616-238-7514. FAX: 616-238-7514. E-Mail: topinabee@northern.lib.mi.us. *Librn*, Elizabeth Benson
Pop 1,197; Circ 13,021
Library Holdings: Bk Vols 7,126; Per Subs 40
Mem of Northland Library Cooperative
Friends of the Library Group

TRAVERSE CITY

J NORTHWESTERN MICHIGAN COLLEGE, Mark & Helen Osterlin Library, 1701 E Front St, 49686-3061. SAN 347-1063. Tel: 231-922-1060. Interlibrary Loan Service Tel: 616-922-1062. Circulation Tel: 31-995-1062. Reference Tel: 231-995-1540. FAX: 231922-1056. E-Mail: library@elmo.nmc.edu. Web Site: www.nmc.edu/library. *Exec Dir*, Craig Mulder; E-Mail: cmulder@nmc.edu; *Tech Servs*, David Dalquist; Tel: 231-922-1056, E-Mail: ddalquist@nmc.edu; *Publ Servs*, Douglas Campbell; Tel: 231-922-1063, E-Mail: dcampbell@nmc.edu; *Ad Servs, Media Spec*, Ronda Edwards; Tel: 231-922-1075, Fax: 231-922-1080, E-Mail: redwards@nmc.edu; *Ser*, Charla Kramer; Tel: 231-995-1973, E-Mail: ckramer@message.nmc.edu; *Govt Doc*, Ann Swaney; Tel: 231-995-1065, E-Mail: aswaney@nmc.edu. Subject Specialists: *Distance learning classroom*, Ronda Edwards; Staff 6 (MLS 4, Non-MLS 2)
Founded 1951. Enrl 4,000; Fac 100; Highest Degree: Associate
Jul 1999-Jun 2000 Income $672,372, Locally Generated Income $33,000, Parent Institution $639,372. Mats Exp $42,700, Presv $1,100, Micro $3,600, AV Equip $38,000. Sal $713,000 (Prof $339,000)
Library Holdings: Bk Vols 110,000; Bk Titles 41,212; Per Subs 630
Special Collections: American Culture Series, microfilm; American Periodicals Series, microfilm
Automation Activity & Vendor Info: (Cataloging) SIRSI; (Circulation) SIRSI; (Course Reserve) SIRSI; (OPAC) SIRSI
Database Vendor: GaleNet, IAC - Info Trac, Lexis-Nexis, OCLC - First Search, ProQuest
Mem of Mid-Michigan Library League

P PENINSULA COMMUNITY LIBRARY,* 2735 Island View Rd, 49686. SAN 308-4515. Tel: 231-223-7700. FAX: 231-223-7708. *Dir*, Julie Maxson
Pop 4,423; Circ 39,107
Jul 1996-Jun 1997 Income $101,200. Mats Exp $20,508, Books $15,158, Per/Ser (Incl. Access Fees) $2,000. Sal $57,130
Library Holdings: Bk Vols 16,400; Per Subs 85
Mem of Mid-Michigan Library League
Friends of the Library Group

P TRAVERSE AREA DISTRICT LIBRARY, (TADL), 610 Woodmere Ave, 49686. SAN 347-1128. Tel: 231-932-8500. FAX: 231-932-8578. E-Mail: tcpublib@tcnet.org. Web Site: tadl.tcnet.org. *Dir*, Michael McGuire; Fax: 231-932-8538; *Asst Dir*, Barbara Nowinski; Staff 53 (MLS 9, Non-MLS 44)
Founded 1897. Pop 70,279; Circ 398,073
Library Holdings: Bk Vols 118,000; Per Subs 340
Subject Interests: Deaf, Genealogy, Hearing impaired, Local history, Sheet music
Publications: TADL-Tales (monthly newsletter)
Mem of Mid-Michigan Library League
Partic in Michigan Library Consortium
Open Mon-Thurs 9-9, Fri & Sat 9-6, Sun 12-5
Friends of the Library Group
Branches: 3
EAST BAY BRANCH, 1989 Three Mile Rd N, 49686. SAN 347-1152. Tel: 231-922-2085. FAX: 231-922-2087.
Founded 1972
Library Holdings: Bk Vols 9,000; Per Subs 70
Special Services for the Blind - Recordings of textbook material

P KINGSLEY BRANCH, 104 S Brownson Ave, PO Box 427, Kingsley, 49649-0427. SAN 308-2172. Tel: 231-263-5484. FAX: 231-263-5526. E-Mail: kt1@tadl.tcnet.org. *In Charge*, Mary Fraquelli
Pop 3,475; Circ 13,423
Library Holdings: Bk Vols 8,400; Per Subs 60
Partic in OCLC Online Computer Library Center, Inc
Open Tues, Wed, Fri 9-5, Thurs 10-6

P SUBREGIONAL LIBRARY FOR THE BLIND & PHYSICALLY HANDICAPPED, 610 Woodmere, Traverse, 49686. SAN 377-7782. Tel: 213-932-8558. FAX: 231-932-8578. E-Mail: lbph@tcnet.org. *Librn*, Kathy Kelto

TRENTON

S NATIONAL STEEL CORP, Technology Information Center, 1745 Fritz Dr, 48183. SAN 317-8536. Interlibrary Loan Service Tel: 734-676-6750. FAX: 734-676-2030. *Coll Develop, Res*, Joyce E Lawson; E-Mail: jlawson@nationalsteel.com; *ILL*, Joan P Wheaton
Founded 1960
Library Holdings: Bk Vols 5,000; Per Subs 505
Subject Interests: Chemistry, Electron microscopy, Engineering, Metallurgy, Steel
Automation Activity & Vendor Info: (Acquisitions) Sydney; (Cataloging) Sydney; (Circulation) Sydney; (ILL) Sydney; (OPAC) Sydney; (Serials) Sydney
Partic in Dialog Corporation; Dow Jones News Retrieval; Michigan Library Consortium

M RIVERSIDE OSTEOPATHIC HOSPITAL, Medical Library,* 150 Truax, 48183. SAN 322-8517. Tel: 734-676-4200, Ext 3237. FAX: 734-676-0419. Web Site: www.sladen.hfhs.org/library/riverside. *Dir*, Susan E Skoglund; E-Mail: skogluns@mlc.lib.mi.us; Staff 1 (MLS 1)
Founded 1966
Jan 1998-Dec 1999 Mats Exp $32,100, Books $13,000, Per/Ser (Incl. Access Fees) $19,100
Library Holdings: Bk Titles 1,300; Per Subs 200
Subject Interests: Medicine, Nursing

P TRENTON VETERANS MEMORIAL LIBRARY, 2790 Westfield, 48183-2482. SAN 308-4523. Tel: 734-676-9777. FAX: 734-676-9895. E-Mail: tren@tln.lib.mi.us. Web Site: www.tln.lib.mi.us. *Ch Servs*, Christine Gogolowski; *Librn*, Francene Sanak
Founded 1928. Pop 54,487; Circ 153,870
Library Holdings: Bk Vols 64,866; Per Subs 204
Automation Activity & Vendor Info: (Cataloging) DRA; (Circulation) DRA
Database Vendor: DRA
Mem of The Library Network
Special Services for the Deaf - TTY machine
Friends of the Library Group

TROY

S ARVIN MERITOR, INC, (Formerly Arvin Meritor Inc), Reference Center, 2135 W Maple Rd, 48084-7186. SAN 308-4531. Tel: 248-435-1668. FAX: 248-435-1670. *Librn*, Cheryl A Barden; E-Mail: bardenca@meritorauto.com
Founded 1960
Library Holdings: Bk Vols 2,600; Per Subs 550
Subject Interests: Advertising, Engineering, Marketing, Metallurgy
Special Collections: Annual Reports 732; ASTM Standards; Focus on the Family; ISO/Din Specs; SAE Paper Coll; Service Manuals-Auto & Truck
Partic in Dialog Corporation; Dow Jones News Retrieval; Profound

S D'ARCY, MASIUS, BENTON & BOWLES, Information Center,* 3310 W Big Beaver, PO Box 5012, 48007-5012. SAN 307-9228. Tel: 248-458-8533. FAX: 248-458-8520. *Dir*, Beth Salzwedel; E-Mail: basalzwe@darcyww.com; Staff 3 (MLS 2, Non-MLS 1)
Library Holdings: Bk Vols 8,000; Per Subs 500
Subject Interests: Advertising, Marketing
Publications: What's New?

L HARNESS, DICKEY & PIERCE, Law Library,* 5445 Corporate Dr, 48098. SAN 372-0489. Tel: 248-641-1600. FAX: 248-641-0270. Web Site: www.hdp.com. *Librn*, Chris Potter
Library Holdings: Bk Vols 10,000; Per Subs 37

P TROY PUBLIC LIBRARY, 510 W Big Beaver, 48084-5289. SAN 347-1187. Tel: 248-524-3538. TDD: 248-740-0253. FAX: 248-524-0112. E-Mail: stoutenb@libcoop.net. Web Site: www.libcoop.net/troy. *Dir*, Brian Stoutenburg; *Asst Dir*, Hedy Brodak; *Asst Dir*, Esther Crum; *Ch Servs, YA Servs*, Bonny Avery; Staff 112 (MLS 24, Non-MLS 88)
Founded 1962. Circ 775,584
Jul 1998-Jun 1999 Income (Main Library and Branch Library) $3,042,818. Mats Exp $557,510. Sal $1,571,890
Library Holdings: Bk Vols 222,927; Per Subs 699
Special Collections: Frances Teasdale (Civil War); Morgan - West White House Memorabilia; Oakland Co Genealogical Society Coll
Automation Activity & Vendor Info: (Circulation) SIRSI
Partic in Suburban Library Cooperative
Special Services for the Deaf - TDD
Friends of the Library Group
Branches: 1
OAKLAND PARK TOWERS READING CENTER, 920 John R, 48084. SAN 347-1276. Tel: 248-588-6727.
Library Holdings: Bk Vols 3,520

C WALSH COLLEGE OF ACCOUNTANCY & BUSINESS ADMINISTRATION LIBRARY,* 3838 Livernois, PO Box 7006, 48007-7006. SAN 308-454X. Tel: 248-689-8282. FAX: 248-689-9066. Web Site: www.walshcol.edu/library/library.html. *Coll Develop, Dir*, Dave Murphy; E-Mail: dmurphy@walshcol.edu
Enrl 3,842; Fac 120; Highest Degree: Master
1998-1999 Income $642,600, Locally Generated Income $2,600, Parent Institution $640,000. Mats Exp $287,460, Books $55,300, Per/Ser (Incl. Access Fees) $84,300, Micro $9,000, Other Print Mats $97,000, Manuscripts & Archives $3,500. Sal $282,000 (Prof $166,400)
Library Holdings: Bk Vols 27,500; Bk Titles 23,000; Per Subs 450
Subject Interests: Business and management, Economics, Taxation (finance)

UBLY

P SLEEPER PUBLIC LIBRARY,* 2236 Main St, 48475-9726. SAN 308-4558. Tel: 517-658-8901. FAX: 517-658-8788. E-Mail: sleeprpl@ubly.k12.mi.us. *Dir*, Geraldine Taylor
Circ 8,117
Library Holdings: Bk Vols 13,635; Per Subs 84
Mem of Blue Water Libr Fedn
Friends of the Library Group

UNIONVILLE

P COLUMBIA TOWNSHIP LIBRARY, 6643 Merry St, 48767. SAN 308-4574. Tel: 517-674-2651. FAX: 517-674-2651. *Librn*, Virginia VanHoost
Founded 1952. Circ 13,780
Library Holdings: Bk Vols 9,000; Per Subs 45
Mem of White Pine Library Cooperative

UNIVERSITY CENTER

J DELTA COLLEGE LIBRARY,* 48710-0001. SAN 308-4582. Tel: 517-686-9822. FAX: 517-686-4131. *Dir*, Gloria Kriewall; E-Mail: gakriewa@alpha.delta.edu; *Librn*, Jennean Kabat-Cyrul; *Librn*, Judith Brow; *Media Spec*, Sandy Watt
Founded 1961
Library Holdings: Bk Titles 92,000
Special Collections: Federal
Automation Activity & Vendor Info: (Circulation) epixtech, inc.

C SAGINAW VALLEY STATE UNIVERSITY, Melvin J Zahnow Library, 7400 Bay Rd, 48710. SAN 308-4590. Tel: 517-790-4240. Interlibrary Loan Service Tel: 517-790-4249. FAX: 517-790-4383. *Dir*, Jean Houghton; *Archivist, Circ*, Jack G Wood; *AV*, Brian Mudd; *Head Ref*, Anita Dey; *Tech Servs*, Laura Kinner; Staff 24 (MLS 10, Non-MLS 14)
Founded 1963. Enrl 8,622; Fac 226; Highest Degree: Master
2000-2001 Mats Exp $534,175
Library Holdings: Bk Vols 205,705; Per Subs 3,240
Special Collections: Cramton Jazz Coll, rec; Local History Coll; University Archives
Automation Activity & Vendor Info: (Acquisitions) Innovative Interfaces Inc.; (Cataloging) Innovative Interfaces Inc.; (Circulation) Innovative Interfaces Inc.; (OPAC) Innovative Interfaces Inc.; (Serials) Innovative Interfaces Inc.
Publications: Annual Reports; Newsletter; Periodicals Holdings List
Partic in Michigan Library Consortium; OCLC Online Computer Library Center, Inc
Host Institution for Valley Library Consortium

UTICA

P UTICA PUBLIC LIBRARY, 7530 Auburn Rd, 48317-5216. SAN 308-4612. Tel: 810-731-4141. FAX: 810-731-0769. Web Site: www.libcoop.net/utica. *Dir*, Mary Kay Eschenburg; Staff 1 (Non-MLS 1)
Founded 1933. Pop 5,081; Circ 31,564
Jul 1999-Jun 2000 Income $141,000, State $5,081, City $120,451, County $5,392, Other $10,076. Mats Exp $62,700, Books $9,811, Per/Ser (Incl. Access Fees) $738, AV Equip $1,420, Electronic Ref Mat (Incl. Access Fees) $850. Sal $84,600 (Prof $35,000)
Library Holdings: Bk Vols 18,500; Per Subs 60
Special Collections: Utica Sentinel Newspaper Coll (1876-1971), micro (1986 to present)
Automation Activity & Vendor Info: (Acquisitions) epixtech, inc.; (Cataloging) epixtech, inc.; (Circulation) epixtech, inc.; (Serials) epixtech, inc.
Mem of Libr Coop of Macomb

VASSAR

P BULLARD-SANFORD MEMORIAL LIBRARY, 520 W Huron St, 48768. SAN 308-4620. Tel: 517-823-2171. FAX: 517-823-8573. Web Site: www.vassarlib.org. *Dir*, James M Rancilio; E-Mail: jrancili@wolv.tds.net; Staff 6 (MLS 1, Non-MLS 5)
Founded 1906. Pop 10,000; Circ 52,000
Jul 1999-Jun 2000 Income $270,000. Mats Exp $50,000. Sal $80,000
Library Holdings: Bk Vols 40,000; Per Subs 100
Subject Interests: Large type print
Automation Activity & Vendor Info: (Acquisitions) Sagebrush Corporation; (Cataloging) Sagebrush Corporation; (Circulation) Sagebrush Corporation
Mem of White Pine Library Cooperative
Partic in White Pine Libr Coop
Special Services for the Blind - Talking Books
Friends of the Library Group
Bookmobiles: 1

VERMONTVILLE

P VERMONTVILLE PUBLIC LIBRARY,* 120 E First St, PO Box G, 49096. SAN 308-4639. Tel: 517-726-1362. FAX: 517-726-1366. E-Mail: thebookbags@mvcc.com. *Dir*, Katherine Sharpe
Founded 1949. Circ 10,309
Library Holdings: Bk Vols 12,479
Mem of Capital Library Cooperative

VERNON

P VERNON DISTRICT PUBLIC LIBRARY,* 316 Main St, PO Box 190, 48476. SAN 308-4647. Tel: 517-288-6486. FAX: 517-288-2422. *Librn*, Louise Goward
Circ 12,044
Library Holdings: Bk Vols 8,000; Per Subs 22

VESTABURG

P RICHLAND TOWNSHIP LIBRARY,* 8821 Third St, PO Box 220, 48891-0220. SAN 308-4655. Tel: 517-268-5044. FAX: 517-268-5044. *Librn*, Pauline Kane
Pop 53,313; Circ 168,328
Apr 1997-Mar 1998 Income $59,000. Mats Exp $31,000. Sal $16,000
Library Holdings: Bk Vols 31,172; Per Subs 59
Mem of Mid-Michigan Library League
Friends of the Library Group

VICKSBURG

P VICKSBURG DISTRICT LIBRARY, 215 S Michigan Ave, 49097. SAN 308-4663. Tel: 616-649-1648. FAX: 616-649-3666. E-Mail: vicksburglibrary@yahoo.com.; Staff 4 (MLS 1, Non-MLS 3)
Founded 1902. Circ 49,100
Library Holdings: Bk Vols 29,677; Per Subs 71
Special Collections: Museum Cases (179)
Mem of Southwest Michigan Library Cooperative

WAKEFIELD

P WAKEFIELD PUBLIC LIBRARY,* 401 Hancock St, 49968. SAN 308-4671. Tel: 906-229-5236. FAX: 906-229-5974. *Librn*, Lois Perona
Founded 1934. Circ 23,584
Library Holdings: Bk Vols 20,000; Per Subs 52
Special Collections: Foreign Language (Italian, Polish & Finnish)

WALDRON

P WALDRON DISTRICT LIBRARY, 107 N Main St, PO Box 136, 49288-0136. SAN 376-7051. Tel: 517-286-6511. FAX: 517-286-6511. E-Mail: waldron@monroe.lib.mi.us. *Dir*, Carol Newcomer
Pop 2,526
Library Holdings: Bk Vols 10,000; Bk Titles 7,500
Mem of Woodlands Library Cooperative
Open Tues 3-8, Weds-Fri 1-4:30 & Sat 9-12
Friends of the Library Group

WALKERVILLE

P WALKERVILLE PUBLIC SCHOOL LIBRARY,* 125 N Franklin St, PO Box 68, 49459-0068. SAN 308-468X. Tel: 231-873-2017. FAX: 231-873-2017. *Dir*, Sharon Burrell; E-Mail: sburrell@edcen.ehhs.cmich.edu
Jul 1998-Jun 1999 Mats Exp $12,000. Sal $23,000
Library Holdings: Bk Vols 12,000; Per Subs 42
Mem of Mid-Michigan Library League

WALLED LAKE

P WALLED LAKE CITY LIBRARY,* 1499 E West Maple Rd, 48390. SAN 308-4698. Tel: 248-624-3772. FAX: 248-624-0041. *Dir*, Donna Rickabaugh; *Asst Librn*, Susan Wess; Staff 5 (MLS 2, Non-MLS 3)
Founded 1963. Pop 15,956; Circ 135,000
Jul 1999-Jun 2000 Income $389,141. Mats Exp $46,000, Books $40,000, Per/Ser (Incl. Access Fees) $3,000, Electronic Ref Mat (Incl. Access Fees) $3,000. Sal $199,800 (Prof $82,000)
Library Holdings: Bk Vols 49,694; Per Subs 70
Mem of The Library Network
Friends of the Library Group

WALLOON LAKE

P CROOKED TREE DISTRICT LIBRARY, 2203 Walloon St, PO Box 518, 49796-0518. SAN 376-6470. Tel: 231-535-2111. FAX: 231-535-2790. *Dir*, Susan Conklin
Jul 1999-Jun 2000 Income (Main Library and Branch Library) $58,000. Mats Exp $6,500. Sal $27,000
Library Holdings: Bk Vols 5,000; Per Subs 29
Mem of Northland Library Cooperative
Friends of the Library Group
Branches: 1
BOYNE FALLS BRANCH, Railroad St, PO Box 17, Boyne Falls, 49713. SAN 376-8201. Tel: 616-549-2277. *Librn*, Judith Planck
Library Holdings: Bk Vols 5,000

WARREN

M BI-COUNTY COMMUNITY HOSPITAL MEDICAL LIBRARY,* 13355 E Ten Mile Rd, 48089. SAN 327-5272. Tel: 810-759-7300. FAX: 810-759-1490. *Dir*, Gayle Williams
Library Holdings: Per Subs 200
Subject Interests: Medicine

S CAMPBELL-EWALD ADVERTISING, Reference Center, 30400 Van Dyke Ave, 48093. SAN 308-4701. Tel: 810-558-6102. E-Mail: refcen@cecom.com. *In Charge*, Susan B Stepek; Staff 9 (MLS 6, Non-MLS 3)
Founded 1925
Library Holdings: Bk Titles 4,000; Per Subs 2,000
Subject Interests: Advertising, Automotive engineering, Business and management, Marketing
Special Collections: Automotive Coll, ad clips; Client History Coll; Company History (Campbell-Ewald Archives); Pictures (Art Library)
Publications: Social Change Briefs

GENERAL MOTORS CORP
S DESIGN CENTER LIBRARY, GM Technical Ctr, 48090-9030. SAN 347-1330. Tel: 810-986-4675. FAX: 810-986-4671.
Founded 1945
Library Holdings: Bk Titles 3,200; Per Subs 151
Subject Interests: Fine arts
Special Collections: Domestic & Foreign Automobile Advertising Brochures
S RESEARCH & DEVELOPMENT LIBRARY, GM Technical Ctr, 30500 Mound Rd, 48090-9059. SAN 347-1365. Tel: 810-986-3314. FAX: 810-986-9378.
Founded 1917
Library Holdings: Bk Titles 51,000; Per Subs 450
Subject Interests: Automotive, Chemistry, Engineering, Physics
Automation Activity & Vendor Info: (Acquisitions) epixtech, inc.; (Cataloging) epixtech, inc.; (Circulation) epixtech, inc.; (Serials) epixtech, inc.
Partic in Michigan Library Consortium; OCLC Online Computer Library Center, Inc

M KERN HOSPITAL, Medical Library,* 21230 Dequindre Rd, 48091. SAN 371-6724. Tel: 810-759-4520, Ext 3405. FAX: 810-757-6467. *Librn*, Mary Kordyban
Founded 1973
Library Holdings: Bk Vols 700; Per Subs 173
Subject Interests: Podiatry

J MACOMB COMMUNITY COLLEGE LIBRARIES, South Campus,* 14500 E 12 Mile Rd, 48093-3896. SAN 308-4728. Tel: 810-445-7401. FAX: 810-445-7157. Web Site: www.macomb.cc.mi.us/. *Publ Servs*, Jerry Bosler; *Publ Servs*, Jim Doyle; *Publ Servs*, Jan Miller; *Electronic Resources*, Teresa Prince; E-Mail: prince@macomb.cc.mi.us; *Publ Servs*, Terence Standifer; *Publ Servs*, Elaine Trice; *Electronic Resources*, Bruce Bett; Tel: 810-445-7880, E-Mail: bett@macomb.cc.mi.us; Staff 26 (MLS 20, Non-MLS 6)
Founded 1954. Enrl 23,236; Fac 300; Highest Degree: Associate
Library Holdings: Bk Vols 134,521; Bk Titles 100,411; Per Subs 852
Subject Interests: Law
Automation Activity & Vendor Info: (Acquisitions) epixtech, inc.; (Cataloging) epixtech, inc.; (Circulation) epixtech, inc.; (Course Reserve) epixtech, inc.; (ILL) epixtech, inc.; (Media Booking) epixtech, inc.; (OPAC) epixtech, inc.; (Serials) epixtech, inc.
Partic in Detroit Libr Network; OCLC Online Computer Library Center, Inc
Departmental Libraries:
CENTER, 44575 Garfield Rd, Clinton Township, 48038-1139. SAN 346-9441. Tel: 810-286-2104. FAX: 810-286-2002. Web Site: www.macomb.cc.mi.us/. *Publ Servs*, Laura Sidlek; *Publ Servs*, Steve Rybicki; *Publ Servs*, Ruth Ewald; *Selection of Elec Mat*, Teresa Prince
Friends of the Library Group

M ST JOHN MACOMB HOSPITAL CENTER LIBRARY, (Formerly Detroit-Macomb Hospital Corporation), 11800 E 12 Mile Rd, 48093. SAN 320-3859. Tel: 810-573-5117. FAX: 810-573-5042. *Asst Librn, Mgr Libr Serv*, Jennifer Randazzo; *Tech Servs*, Lynn Hall; Staff 2 (MLS 1, Non-MLS 1)
Library Holdings: Bk Vols 2,500; Bk Titles 2,200; Per Subs 200
Subject Interests: Allied health, Medicine
Publications: Libraryline

P WARREN PUBLIC LIBRARY,* 5951 Beebe St, 48092-1604. SAN 347-1454. Tel: 810-264-8720. Interlibrary Loan Service Tel: 810-751-5377. FAX: 810-264-2811. Web Site: www.libcoop.net/warren. *Dir*, Wlodek Zaryczny; E-Mail: zarycznw@libcoop.net; *Commun Servs*, Spike Musselman; *Ref*, Oksana Urban
Founded 1958. Pop 144,864; Circ 709,854
Jul 1998-Jun 1999 Income (Main Library and Branch Library) $2,631,959, State $288,864, Federal $25,000, Locally Generated Income $1,791,330. Mats Exp $253,776, Books $121,970, Per/Ser (Incl. Access Fees) $24,000, Micro $3,030, Electronic Ref Mat (Incl. Access Fees) $32,475. Sal $1,243,201 (Prof $990,554)
Library Holdings: Bk Vols 283,094; Per Subs 732
Subject Interests: EPA, Large print
Special Collections: Foreign Language; Warren Historical Coll
Automation Activity & Vendor Info: (Cataloging) epixtech, inc.; (Circulation) epixtech, inc.; (ILL) epixtech, inc.; (OPAC) epixtech, inc.; (Serials) epixtech, inc.
Database Vendor: GaleNet
Publications: Friends Newsletter
Mem of Libr Coop of Macomb
Friends of the Library Group
Branches: 5
ARTHUR J MILLER BRANCH, 4700 E Thirteen Mile Rd, 48092. SAN 347-1578. Tel: 810-751-5377. FAX: 810-751-5902. *Librn*, Amy Henderstein; *Librn*, Oksana Urban
Friends of the Library Group
DOROTHY M BUSCH BRANCH, 23333 Ryan Rd, 48091. SAN 347-1519. Tel: 810-755-5750. FAX: 810-755-5750. *Librn*, Sharon Linsday
EDGAR A GUEST BRANCH, 14060 E Stephens Dr, 48089. SAN 347-1543. Tel: 810-772-0240. FAX: 810-772-9772. *Librn*, Amy Henderstein
MAYBELLE BURNETTE BRANCH, 22005 VanDyke Ave, 48089. SAN 347-1489. Tel: 810-758-2115. FAX: 810-758-1267. Web Site: www.libcoop.net/warren. *Librn*, Kate A Pohjola; E-Mail: pohjolak@libcoop.net; Staff 4 (MLS 2, Non-MLS 2)
Database Vendor: epixtech, inc.
Partic in Suburban Library Cooperative
Friends of the Library Group
WALT WHITMAN BRANCH, 30033 Schoenherr Rd, 48093. SAN 347-1608. Tel: 810-751-0771. FAX: 810-751-0811.

WASHINGTON

P ROMEO DISTRICT LIBRARY, 65821 Van Dyke, 48095. SAN 370-758X. Tel: 810-752-0603. FAX: 810-752-9927. Web Site: www.libcoop.net/romeo. *Dir*, Marina B Kruse; E-Mail: krusem@libcoop.net; *Asst Dir*, Cynthia McIntyre; E-Mail: mcintyrc@libcoop.net; *Head Ref*, Elizabeth Martin; E-Mail: martinb@libcoop.net; *Ch Servs*, Michelle Yochim; E-Mail: yochimm@libcoop.net; Staff 21 (MLS 7, Non-MLS 14)
Founded 1909. Pop 19,099; Circ 291,421
Jul 1999-Jun 2000 Income (Main Library and Branch Library) $1,608,373, State $60,017, Federal $19,099, Locally Generated Income $1,254,632, Other $274,625. Mats Exp $125,000, Books $72,521, Per/Ser (Incl. Access Fees) $11,961, AV Equip $30,233, Electronic Ref Mat (Incl. Access Fees) $10,285. Sal $483,336 (Prof $307,422)
Library Holdings: Bk Vols 74,180; Bk Titles 68,000; Per Subs 360
Automation Activity & Vendor Info: (Acquisitions) epixtech, inc.; (Cataloging) epixtech, inc.; (Circulation) epixtech, inc.; (OPAC) epixtech, inc.; (Serials) epixtech, inc.
Database Vendor: epixtech, inc.
Open Mon-Thurs 10-8, Sat 10-5 (Sept-June); Mon & Tues 10-8, Wed & Thurs 10-6, Fri 10-5 (June-Aug)
Friends of the Library Group
Branches: 1
ROMEO KEZAR BRANCH, 107 Church St, Romeo, 48065. SAN 308-3772. Tel: 810-752-2291. FAX: 810-752-6238. Web Site: www.libcoop.net/romeo. *Br Coordr*, Jacqueline McIntyre; Tel: 810-781-9787, Fax: 810-781-9072, E-Mail: mcintyrj@libcoop.net; *Ch Servs*, Chuck Schacht; E-Mail: cchactc@libcoop.net; Staff 7 (MLS 7)
Founded 1909. Pop 19,099; Circ 270,090
Jul 1998-Jun 1999 Income $1,325,989, State $59,241, Federal $19,083, Locally Generated Income $1,132,201, Other $115,464. Mats Exp $110,518, Books $94,378, Per/Ser (Incl. Access Fees) $12,051, Electronic Ref Mat (Incl. Access Fees) $4,089. Sal $442,366 (Prof $290,000)
Library Holdings: Bk Vols 80,776; Bk Titles 70,000; Per Subs 343
Automation Activity & Vendor Info: (Cataloging) epixtech, inc.; (Circulation) epixtech, inc.; (OPAC) epixtech, inc.; (Serials) epixtech, inc.
Database Vendor: GaleNet
Mem of Libr Coop of Macomb
Open Mon-Thurs 10-8, Fri & Sat 10-5
Friends of the Library Group

WATERFORD

J OAKLAND COMMUNITY COLLEGE, Highland Lakes Campus Library,* 7350 Cooley Lake Rd, 48327-2113. SAN 308-4566. Tel: 248-360-3080, 248-360-3178. FAX: 248-360-3202. Web Site: www.occ.cc.mi.us/library. *Librn*, Laura Kolehmainen; *Media Spec*, Neil Atkins; Tel: 248-360-3101; *Ref*, Jim McMahon; *Cat*, Virginia Wilcox; *AV*, Tim Lepard; Tel: 248-360-3175; Staff 2 (MLS 2)
Founded 1965. Enrl 5,224; Fac 50
Library Holdings: Bk Vols 28,000; Bk Titles 26,000; Per Subs 150
Subject Interests: Allied health
Automation Activity & Vendor Info: (Acquisitions) epixtech, inc.; (Cataloging) epixtech, inc.; (Circulation) epixtech, inc.; (Course Reserve) epixtech, inc.; (ILL) epixtech, inc.; (OPAC) epixtech, inc.; (Serials) epixtech, inc.
Publications: Oakland County Union List of Serials
Mem of Wayne Oakland Libr Federation

P WATERFORD TOWNSHIP PUBLIC LIBRARY,* 5168 Civic Center Dr, 48329. SAN 347-0075. Tel: 248-674-4831. FAX: 248-674-1910. Web Site: www.tln.lib.mi.us/~wate. *Dir*, Nancy Smith; *Asst Dir*, Joan Rogers; *Ref*, Nancy McDonald; *Br Coordr, Commun Servs*, Karen O'Connor; *Ch Servs*, Mary Rice; Staff 12 (MLS 12)
Founded 1964. Pop 67,010; Circ 300,000
Jan 1997-Dec 1998 Income $1,766,347, State $140,000, Locally Generated Income $38,000, Other $72,000. Mats Exp $270,000, Books $192,075, Per/Ser (Incl. Access Fees) $10,025, Presv $100, Micro $13,300, Other Print Mats $600. Sal $796,187 (Prof $488,374)
Library Holdings: Bk Titles 100,000; Per Subs 250
Subject Interests: Careers, Michigan
Mem of The Library Network
Friends of the Library Group
Branches: 1
WATERFORD TOWNSHIP CAI BRANCH, 5640 Williams Lake Rd, 48329. SAN 347-0105. Tel: 248-673-6220. FAX: 248-673-1082. Web Site: www.tln.mi.us/~wate. *Librn*, Karen O'Connor
Library Holdings: Bk Titles 11,000
Friends of the Library Group

WATERVLIET

P WATERVLIET DISTRICT LIBRARY, 333 N Main St, PO Box 217, 49098. SAN 308-4760. Tel: 616-463-6382. FAX: 616-463-3117. Web Site: www.ameritech.net/users/hartmanlr/index.html. *Dir*, Lois R Hartman; E-Mail: lhartman@ameritech.net; Staff 5 (Non-MLS 5)
Founded 1923. Pop 5,509; Circ 34,439
Library Holdings: Bk Vols 29,500; Bk Titles 24,000; Per Subs 40; High Interest/Low Vocabulary Bk Vols 25; Bks on Deafness & Sign Lang 30
Special Collections: Civil War Coll
Automation Activity & Vendor Info: (Cataloging) Follett; (Circulation) Follett
Mem of Southwest Michigan Library Cooperative
Partic in Michigan Library Consortium
Open Mon 1-8, Tues & Fri 1-5, Wed 10-8, Thurs 10-5, Sat 10-2

WAYLAND

P HENIKA DISTRICT LIBRARY, 149 S Main St, 49348-1208. SAN 308-4779. Tel: 616-792-2891. FAX: 616-792-0399. E-Mail: way@lakeland.lib.mi.us. *Dir*, Lynn Mandaville
Pop 6,761; Circ 44,174
Library Holdings: Bk Vols 42,000; Per Subs 56
Mem of Lakeland Library Cooperative

WAYNE

S SENIOR ALLIANCE, Area Agency on Aging Region 1C Library,* 3850 Second St Ste 201, 48184. SAN 375-1708. Tel: 734-722-2830. FAX: 734-722-2836. E-Mail: senior_alliance@state.mi.us. Web Site: www.aaa1c.org. *Dir*, Michael J Simowski
Library Holdings: Bk Vols 300; Per Subs 20

P WAYNE PUBLIC LIBRARY,* 3737 S Wayne Rd, 48184. SAN 308-4809. Tel: 734-721-7832. FAX: 734-721-0341. Web Site: wayne.lib.mi.us. *Librn*, Lois Van Stipdonk; *AV*, John MacDonald
Founded 1927. Pop 19,899; Circ 187,897 Sal $365,445 (Prof $203,234)
Library Holdings: Bk Vols 61,267; Per Subs 131
Publications: Communique
Mem of The Library Network
Friends of the Library Group

WEST BLOOMFIELD

R CONGREGATION BETH AHM, (Formerly Congregation Beth Abraham-Hillel-Moses), Judge Nathan J Kaufman Library, 5075 W Maple Rd, 48322. SAN 308-4817. Tel: 248-851-4170, 248-851-6880. FAX: 248-851-6488. E-Mail: bahm@cbahm.org. Web Site: www.cbahm.org. *Librn*, Mae Weine; Staff 1 (MLS 1)
Founded 1973
Sep 1999-Aug 2000 Mats Exp $3,815, Books $3,171, Per/Ser (Incl. Access Fees) $644. Sal $3,070
Library Holdings: Bk Titles 5,073; Per Subs 13
Subject Interests: Judaica (lit or hist of Jews)
Serves congregation & Hebrew school, also open to the public

R JEWISH COMMUNITY CENTER OF METROPOLITAN DETROIT, Henry & Delia Meyers Memorial Library, 6600 W Maple, 48322. SAN 308-4825. Tel: 248-661-7639. FAX: 248-661-3680. *Librn*, Julie Solomon
Founded 1959
Library Holdings: Bk Titles 11,000; Per Subs 35
Subject Interests: Judaica (lit or hist of Jews)
Special Collections: American-Jewish Coll, per & newsp
Mem of Wayne Oakland Libr Federation

R TEMPLE ISRAEL LIBRARIES & MEDIA CENTER, 5725 Walnut Lake Rd, 48323. SAN 308-0390. Tel: 248-661-5700. FAX: 248-661-1302. E-Mail: TILibrary@aol.com. Web Site: www.temple-israel.org. *Dir*, Rachel Beth Erlich; Staff 1 (MLS 1)
Founded 1961
Library Holdings: Bk Vols 16,000; Per Subs 25
Subject Interests: Holocaust, Jewish hist, Judaism
Automation Activity & Vendor Info: (Cataloging) Athena; (Circulation) Athena

P WEST BLOOMFIELD TOWNSHIP PUBLIC LIBRARY, 4600 Walnut Lake Rd, 48323. SAN 347-1756. Tel: 248-682-2120. Circulation Tel: 248-232-2201. Reference Tel: 248-232-2290. TDD: 248-232-2292. FAX: 248-232-2291. E-Mail: webmaster@wblib.org. Web Site: www.wblib.org. *Dir*, Clara N Bohrer; Fax: 248-232-2333, E-Mail: bohrercn@wblib.org; *Ch Servs*, Wendy Wilcox; Tel: 248-232-2252, E-Mail: wilcoxwe@wblib.org; *Head Tech Servs*, Jackie Licalzi; Tel: 248-232-2221, E-Mail: licalzij@wblib.org; *Circ*, Anna Pacitto; *Automation Syst Coordr*, Katherine Miller; *Ad Servs, Head, Info Serv*, Brenda Plizga; Tel: 248-232-2293, E-Mail: plizgabr@wblib.org; *Tech Coordr*, Jennifer Zimmer; Tel: 248-232-2315, E-Mail: zimmerje@wblib.org; *Branch Mgr*, Elizabeth McKay-Hutchison; Tel: 248-363-4022, E-Mail: hutchis1@wblib.org; Staff 90 (MLS 30, Non-MLS 60)
Founded 1938. Pop 61,648; Circ 717,917
Apr 2000-Mar 2001 Income $5,233,235. Mats Exp $674,506. Sal $1,740,965
Library Holdings: Bk Titles 165,501; Per Subs 468
Database Vendor: Innovative Interfaces INN - View
Mem of The Library Network
Special Services for the Deaf - TDD; TTY machine
Friends of the Library Group
Branches: 1
WESTACRES, 7321 Commerce Rd, 48324. SAN 347-1780. Tel: 248-363-4022. FAX: 248-363-7243. Web Site: metronet.lib.mi.us/west/wbpl.html. *Librn*, Elizabeth Hutchison
Library Holdings: Bk Titles 43,651; Per Subs 150
Friends of the Library Group

WEST BRANCH

P WEST BRANCH PUBLIC LIBRARY,* 119 N Fourth St, 48661. SAN 308-4833. Tel: 517-345-2235. FAX: 517-345-2235. *Librn*, Marsha Boyd; *Asst Librn*, Amy Winter-Nausedas; Staff 6 (MLS 1, Non-MLS 5)
Founded 1905. Pop 8,720; Circ 62,000
Jul 1999-Jun 2000 Income $168,000. Mats Exp $28,000. Sal $65,000 (Prof $31,500)
Library Holdings: Bk Vols 25,000; Per Subs 76
Automation Activity & Vendor Info: (Acquisitions) epixtech, inc.; (Cataloging) epixtech, inc.; (Circulation) epixtech, inc.; (Course Reserve) epixtech, inc.; (ILL) epixtech, inc.; (Media Booking) epixtech, inc.; (OPAC) epixtech, inc.; (Serials) epixtech, inc.
Mem of White Pine Library Cooperative
Friends of the Library Group

WESTLAND

P WAYNE COUNTY REGIONAL LIBRARY FOR THE BLIND & PHYSICALLY HANDICAPPED, 30555 Michigan Ave, 48186-5310. SAN 308-4787. Tel: 734-727-7300. FAX: 734-727-7333. E-Mail: wcrlbph@wayneregional.lib.mi.us. Web Site: www.wayneregional.lib.mi.us. *Dir*, Frederick R Howkins; E-Mail: fhowkins@wayneregional.lib.mi.us
Founded 1931. Pop 25,792; Circ 363,399
Library Holdings: Bk Vols 125,000
Mem of The Library Network
Special Services for the Blind - Large print bks; Talking bks & player equipment
Friends of the Library Group
Bookmobiles: 1

WHITE CLOUD

P WHITE CLOUD COMMUNITY LIBRARY, (WCCL), 1038 E Wilcox Ave, PO Box 995, 49349-0995. SAN 308-485X. Tel: 616-689-6631. FAX: 616-689-6699. E-Mail: wcl@lakeland.lib.mi.us. Web Site: wcpl.ncats.net. *Dir*, Nancy Harper; Fax: 231-689-6631; *Asst Librn*, Linda Foondle; Fax: 231-689-6631; *Cat*, Karen Becker; Fax: 231-689-6631, E-Mail: wcclpro@ncats.net; *Circ*, Jessie Long; Fax: 231-689-6631, E-Mail: wcllibrary@ncats.net
Founded 1956. Pop 6,350; Circ 55,257
Jul 1999-Jun 2000 Income $282,424. Mats Exp $122,700. Sal $138,530
Library Holdings: Bk Vols 36,033; Per Subs 120
Special Collections: Civil War - Lincoln Coll (Louis Fry); Douglass Coll, bks & photos; Martha Evan Memorial Historical Coll; Newaygo County Historical Coll, bks & microfilm
Automation Activity & Vendor Info: (Acquisitions) epixtech, inc.; (Cataloging) epixtech, inc.; (Circulation) epixtech, inc.; (ILL) epixtech, inc.; (OPAC) epixtech, inc.

Database Vendor: epixtech, inc.
Publications: Newsletter (quarterly)
Mem of Lakeland Library Cooperative
Friends of the Library Group

WHITE LAKE

P WHITE LAKE TOWNSHIP LIBRARY, 7527 E Highland Rd, 48383. SAN 375-376X. Tel: 248-698-4942. FAX: 248-698-2550. *Dir*, Silvia Makowski; E-Mail: makowski@tln.lib.mi.us; Staff 9 (MLS 3, Non-MLS 6)
Founded 1980. Pop 28,000; Circ 53,000
1998-1999 Mats Exp $140,500, Books $130,000, Per/Ser (Incl. Access Fees) $3,000, AV Equip $7,500. Sal $188,000
Library Holdings: Bk Titles 30,000; Per Subs 83
Automation Activity & Vendor Info: (Cataloging) DRA; (Circulation) DRA
Mem of The Library Network
Friends of the Library Group

WHITE PIGEON

P WHITE PIGEON TOWNSHIP LIBRARY, 105 N Kalamazoo St, PO Box 399, 49099. SAN 308-4868. Tel: 616-483-7409. FAX: 616-483-9923. E-Mail: pigeon@monroe.lib.mi.us. *Librn*, Mrs David Kistler
Founded 1881. Pop 5,160; Circ 24,249
Jul 1998-Jun 1999 Income $112,200. Mats Exp $21,000, Books $11,000, Per/Ser (Incl. Access Fees) $1,000, AV Equip $4,000, Electronic Ref Mat (Incl. Access Fees) $5,000. Sal $43,000
Library Holdings: Bk Vols 20,443; Per Subs 56
Automation Activity & Vendor Info: (Cataloging) Brodart; (Circulation) Brodart
Mem of Woodlands Library Cooperative
Open Mon, Wed & Fri 9-5, Tues & Thurs 9-7, Sat 9-1
Friends of the Library Group

WHITE PINE

P CARP LAKE TOWNSHIP LIBRARY,* 10 Cedar St, PO Box 307, 49971-0307. SAN 308-4876. Tel: 906-885-5888. FAX: 906-885-5611. *Coll Develop, Librn*, Olivia Sanders; E-Mail: sanderso@mid-pen.lib.mi.us
Founded 1954. Circ 5,702
1997-1998 Income $21,061, State $1,086, City $7,859, County $9,302, Locally Generated Income $373. Mats Exp $7,402, Books $4,615, Per/Ser (Incl. Access Fees) $1,174, Other Print Mats $544. Sal $9,743 (Prof $8,081)
Library Holdings: Bk Vols 12,565; Per Subs 50
Mem of Mid-Peninsula Library Cooperative
Friends of the Library Group

WHITEHALL

P WHITE LAKE COMMUNITY LIBRARY,* 3900 White Lake Dr, 49461. SAN 308-4884. Tel: 231-894-9531. FAX: 231-893-4708. E-Mail: whi@lakeland.lib.mi.us. *Librn*, Bette Carlson; E-Mail: whieac@lakeland.lib.mi.us; Staff 3 (MLS 1, Non-MLS 2)
Founded 1880. Pop 8,751; Circ 40,300
Jul 1997-Jun 1998 Income $79,516, State $5,687, City $47,000, County $16,368, Locally Generated Income $3,251, Other $7,210. Mats Exp Per/Ser (Incl. Access Fees) $2,000. Sal $47,718
Library Holdings: Bk Titles 24,025; Per Subs 96
Subject Interests: Local history, Michigan
Mem of Lakeland Library Cooperative
Friends of the Library Group

WIXOM

P WIXOM PUBLIC LIBRARY, (1973), 49015 Pontiac Trail, 48393-2567. SAN 308-4892. Tel: 248-624-2512. FAX: 248-624-0862. E-Mail: wixom@tln.lib.mi.us. *Dir*, Kimberley A Potter; E-Mail: kpotter@tln.lib.mi.us; *Ch Servs*, Jane Kahan; *Ref*, Sheila Hooker; *Circ*, Laura Kreza; Staff 12 (MLS 5, Non-MLS 7)
Founded 1973
Library Holdings: Bk Titles 33,175; Per Subs 134
Special Collections: Large Print Coll
Database Vendor: DRA
Mem of The Library Network
Partic in TLN
Friends of the Library Group

WOLVERINE

P WOLVERINE COMMUNITY LIBRARY,* 5716 W Main St, PO Box 310, 49799. SAN 308-4906. Tel: 231-525-8800. FAX: 231-525-8713. E-Mail: wolveri@northland.lib.mi.us. *Librn*, Sue Warner
Founded 1950. Circ 6,620
Library Holdings: Bk Vols 12,000; Per Subs 35
Mem of Northland Library Cooperative

WYANDOTTE

P BACON MEMORIAL PUBLIC LIBRARY, 45 Vinewood, 48192-5221. SAN 308-4914. Tel: 734-246-8357. FAX: 734-282-1540. E-Mail: bacon@tln.lib.mi.us. Web Site: www.wyandotte.lib.mi.us. *Dir*, Barbara R Wallace; *Ad Servs*, Beth Kowaleski; *Ch Servs*, Janet Cashin; *Commun Servs*, Wallace Hayden
Founded 1869. Pop 30,938; Circ 125,000
Jul 2000-Jun 2001 Income $700,500, State $62,500, County $38,000, Locally Generated Income $600,000. Mats Exp $86,000, Books $64,700, Per/Ser (Incl. Access Fees) $6,000, Electronic Ref Mat (Incl. Access Fees) $3,300. Sal $354,000 (Prof $254,000)
Library Holdings: Bk Vols 75,000; Per Subs 202
Special Collections: Local History, Military history
Automation Activity & Vendor Info: (Acquisitions) DRA; (Cataloging) DRA; (Circulation) DRA; (ILL) DRA; (OPAC) DRA; (Serials) DRA
Mem of The Library Network
Friends of the Library Group

S FORD-MACNICHOL HOME, WYANDOTTE MUSEUM, ARCHIVES, 2610 Biddle Ave, 48192. SAN 321-0413. Tel: 734-324-7297. FAX: 734-324-7283. E-Mail: wymuseum@ili.net. *Dir*, Marc M Partin
Founded 1958
Library Holdings: Bk Titles 2,000; Per Subs 10
Subject Interests: Detroit hist, Local history, Mich hist, Wayne County hist

S RIGHT TO LIFE OF MICHIGAN, Resource Center, 1638 Eureka Rd, 48192. Tel: 734-282-6100. FAX: 734-282-6218. *Mgr*, Chris MacDonald

YPSILANTI

C BRUCE T HALLE LIBRARY, Eastern Michigan University, 955 W Circle Dr, 48197. SAN 308-4949. Tel: 734-487-0020, Ext 2202. Interlibrary Loan Service Tel: 734-487-0020, Ext 2052. Circulation Tel: 734-487-0020, Ext 2140. Reference Tel: 734-487-0020, Ext 2100. FAX: 734-487-5399. E-Mail: library_ILL@online.emich.edu. Web Site: www.emich.edu/halle/. *Dean of Libr*, Morell B Boone; Tel: 734-487-0020, Ext 2222, Fax: 734-484-1151, E-Mail: morell.boone@emich.edu; *Head of Libr*, Sandra Yee; Fax: 734-484-1151, E-Mail: sandra.yee@emich.edu; *Bibliog Instr*, Linda Shirato; Tel: 734-487-0020, Ext 2130, Fax: 734-487-8861, E-Mail: lib_shirato@online.emich.edu; *Coll Develop*, Twyla Mueller Racz; Tel: 734-487-0020, Ext 2119, Fax: 734-487-8861, E-Mail: lib_racz@online.emich.edu; *Doc*, Barbara Glover; Tel: 734-487-0020, Ext 2233, Fax: 734-487-8861, E-Mail: lib_glover@online.emich.edu; *ILL*, Joe Badics; Tel: 734-487-0020, Ext 2053, E-Mail: lib_badics@online.emich.edu; *Ref*, Rhonda Fowler; Tel: 734-487-0020, Ext 2128, Fax: 734-487-8861, E-Mail: lib_fowler@online.emich.edu; *Tech Servs*, Walter Hogan; Tel: 734-487-0020, Ext 2054, E-Mail: lib_hogan@online.emich.edu. Subject Specialists: *Technologies*, Morell B Boone; *Technologies*, Sandra Yee; Staff 34 (MLS 28, Non-MLS 6)
Founded 1849. Enrl 23,463; Fac 674; Highest Degree: Doctorate
Jul 1999-Jun 2000 Income $6,350,134, Parent Institution $6,262,985, Other $87,149. Mats Exp $2,050,964, Books $772,388, Per/Ser (Incl. Access Fees) $820,780, Presv $11,104, Micro $60,917, AV Equip $5,221, Manuscripts & Archives $1,144, Electronic Ref Mat (Incl. Access Fees) $379,410. Sal $2,745,692 (Prof $1,809,615)
Library Holdings: Bk Vols 699,264; Bk Titles 586,895; Per Subs 4,423
Subject Interests: African-American, Education
Automation Activity & Vendor Info: (Acquisitions) Endeavor; (Cataloging) Endeavor; (Circulation) Endeavor; (OPAC) Endeavor; (Serials) Endeavor
Database Vendor: OCLC - First Search
Publications: Numbered Bibliography Series; Study Guides
Partic in Michigan Library Consortium; OCLC Online Computer Library Center, Inc
Open Mon-Thurs 7:30am-midnight, Fri 7:30am-11pm, Sat 8am-11pm & Sun noon-midnight (fall & winter semesters only)
Friends of the Library Group

P YPSILANTI DISTRICT LIBRARY, 229 W Michigan, 48197-5485. SAN 308-4957. Tel: 734-482-4110. FAX: 734-482-2212. Web Site: www.ypsilibrary.org. *Dir*, Jill Morey; Fax: 734-482-0047, E-Mail: jmorey@tln.lib; *Ad Servs*, Paula Drummond; *Ch Servs, YA Servs*, Lori Coryell; *Tech Servs*, Claire Lathrop; Staff 23 (MLS 11, Non-MLS 12)
Founded 1868. Pop 77,095; Circ 220,000
Library Holdings: Bk Vols 140,000; Bk Titles 110,000; Per Subs 300
Special Collections: Ypsilanti & Michigan History
Automation Activity & Vendor Info: (Acquisitions) epixtech, inc.; (Cataloging) epixtech, inc.; (Circulation) epixtech, inc.; (OPAC) epixtech, inc.
Publications: The Library Connection (semi-annual)
Mem of The Library Network
Partic in Libr Network
Friends of the Library Group

ZEELAND

R FIRST CHRISTIAN REFORMED CHURCH LIBRARY, 15 S Church St, 49464. SAN 308-4965. Tel: 616-772-2866. FAX: 616-772-2620. *Librn*, Betty G Shoemaker
Founded 1930
Jan 1999-Dec 1999 Income $1,500, Parent Institution $1,500. Mats Exp $1,600, Books $1,000, Per/Ser (Incl. Access Fees) $100, AV Equip $500
Library Holdings: Bk Titles 4,500; Per Subs 15
Subject Interests: Biographies, Fiction, Inspirational
Special Collections: Church History (Acts of Synod, 1857-present), bound

P HOWARD MILLER PUBLIC LIBRARY, 14 S Church St, 49464. SAN 308-499X. Tel: 616-772-0874. FAX: 616-772-3253. Web Site: www.ci.zeeland.mi.us/hml/hmpl/htm. *Coll Develop, Dir*, Tara L Conaway; E-Mail: tconaway@lakeland.lib.mi.us; Staff 6 (MLS 2, Non-MLS 4)
Founded 1969. Pop 11,469; Circ 182,316
Jul 2000-Jun 2001 Income $460,422, State $10,954, City $279,468, County $57,000, Locally Generated Income $20,000, Other $93,000. Mats Exp $422,500, Books $30,000, Per/Ser (Incl. Access Fees) $7,000, Presv $400, Micro $200, Electronic Ref Mat (Incl. Access Fees) $2,000. Sal $199,100 (Prof $48,000)
Library Holdings: Bk Vols 56,500; Per Subs 140; High Interest/Low Vocabulary Bk Vols 50
Automation Activity & Vendor Info: (Acquisitions) epixtech, inc.; (Cataloging) epixtech, inc.; (Circulation) epixtech, inc.; (ILL) epixtech, inc.; (ILL) epixtech, inc.; (OPAC) epixtech, inc.; (Serials) epixtech, inc.
Database Vendor: epixtech, inc.
Publications: Children's Services (quarterly newsletter)
Mem of Lakeland Library Cooperative
Partic in Lakeland Libr Coop

R NORTH STREET CHRISTIAN REFORMED CHURCH LIBRARY, 20 E Main Ave, 49464. SAN 308-4981. Tel: 616-772-6971. FAX: 616-772-6928. E-Mail: nscrc@drenthenet.com. *Librn*, Joan Walcott
Library Holdings: Bk Vols 1,800
Subject Interests: Fiction, Juvenile delinquency

MINNESOTA

Date of Statistics: 1999
Population, 1999 (est): 4,836,398
Number of Public Libraries: 130 administrative units; 4 regional public library systems which offer library service through bookmobile service.
Total materials in Public Libraries: 16,952,256
Items Per Capita: 3.5
Total Public Library Circulation: 42,223,587
Circulation Per Capita: 8.73
Total Public Library Operating Expenditures (includes grants): $134,768,684
Operating Expenditures Per Capita: $27.85
Source of Income: Local: 84.7%, State: 8.0%, Federal: 0.8%, Other: 6.5%
Local Tax Support: Minimum 82% of adjusted net tax capacity of taxable property of city or county.
Number of Regional Public Library Systems: 12
Number of Bookmobiles: 18
Number of Multitype Library Systems: 7
State Aid: (FY2000): 12 regional public library systems basic support: $8,570,000;
Regional Library Telecommunication Aid: $1,200,000; 7 multicounty multitype library systems $903,000

ADA

P ADA PUBLIC LIBRARY,* 107 E Fourth Ave, 56510-1223. SAN 347-7126. Tel: 218-784-4480. FAX: 218-784-2594. E-Mail: ada@northernlights.lib.mn.us. *Librn*, Audrey Thomas
Founded 1945. Pop 3,964
Library Holdings: Bk Vols 7,730; Per Subs 52
Mem of Lake Agassiz Regional Library
Partic in Northern Lights Library Network
Friends of the Library Group

AITKIN

P AITKIN PUBLIC LIBRARY,* 110 First Ave NE, 56431-1319. SAN 347-2388. Tel: 218-927-2339. E-Mail: aimail@ecrl.lib.mn.us. *Librn*, Mary Beth Woodrow
Pop 7,450; Circ 58,110
Library Holdings: Bk Vols 5,166; Per Subs 40
Mem of East Central Regional Library
Branch of East Central Regional Library
Friends of the Library Group

ALBANY

P ALBANY PUBLIC LIBRARY,* PO Box 687, 56307-0687. SAN 347-8203. Tel: 320-845-4843. FAX: 320-845-4843. Web Site: www.griver.org. *In Charge*, Helen Manion
Founded 1960. Pop 2,466; Circ 40,393
Library Holdings: Bk Vols 13,422; Per Subs 43
Mem of Great River Regional Library
Open Mon & Thurs 1-6, Wed 10-1 & 2-6, Fri 2-8, Sat 9am-12pm

ALBERT LEA

P ALBERT LEA PUBLIC LIBRARY, 211 E Clark St, 56007. SAN 308-5015. Tel: 507-377-4350. FAX: 507-377-4339. Web Site: www.city.albertlea.org. *Dir*, Lori Barkema; *Ad Servs*, Ben Tri; *Ch Servs*, Theresa Schmidt; *YA Servs*, Staci Waltman; Staff 10 (MLS 4, Non-MLS 6)
Founded 1897. Pop 33,060; Circ 326,000
Jan 1998-Dec 1998 Income $610,928, City $462,928, County $148,000. Mats Exp $82,000, Books $65,000, Per/Ser (Incl. Access Fees) $7,000, AV Equip $10,000. Sal $377,745
Library Holdings: Bk Vols 52,000; Per Subs 226
Special Collections: Obituary Index to Local Newspaper
Database Vendor: DRA
Mem of Selco; Southeastern Libraries Cooperating (SELCO)
Friends of the Library Group

S FREEBORN COUNTY HISTORICAL SOCIETY LIBRARY, 1031 N Bridge Ave, 56007. SAN 308-5023. Tel: 507-373-8003. FAX: 507-373-4172. E-Mail: fchm@smig.net. Web Site: www.smig.net/fchm. *Librn*, L Evenson
Founded 1968
Library Holdings: Bk Titles 400
Subject Interests: Genealogy
Special Collections: Lea College 1966-72; Lt Col Albert Miller Lea Coll; Morin Coll; Obituaries; Photo Coll of County; Sorenson Cartoon Coll; Spicer Coll
Restriction: Not a lending library
Function: For research purposes

ALEXANDRIA

§J ALEXANDRIA TECHNICAL COLLEGE LIBRARY, 1601 Jefferson St, 56308. SAN 378-3863. Tel: 320-762-4695. Toll Free Tel: 888-234-1222. FAX: 320-762-4501. *Dir*, Sheree Cochran; E-Mail: shereec@aln.tec.mn.us
Library Holdings: Bk Titles 7,000; Per Subs 100

P DOUGLAS COUNTY LIBRARY,* 720 Fillmore St, 56308-1790. SAN 308-504X. Tel: 320-762-3014. FAX: 320-762-3036. E-Mail: docolib@means.net. Web Site: douglascountylibrary.org. *Dir*, Patricia Conroy; *Asst Dir, Ch Servs*, Karen Simmons; *ILL*, Betty Ann Hegland; Staff 2 (MLS 2)
Founded 1878. Pop 30,000; Circ 311,000
Jan 1998-Dec 1998 Income $411,000, City $98,790, County $260,744, Locally Generated Income $7,459. Mats Exp $64,700, Books $58,000, Per/Ser (Incl. Access Fees) $6,700. Sal $214,700
Library Holdings: Bk Vols 60,150; Per Subs 176
Special Collections: Kensington Runestone
Mem of Viking Library System
Friends of the Library Group

S INTERNATIONAL REAL ESTATE INSTITUTE LIBRARY, 1224 N Nokomis NE, 56308. SAN 328-3984. Tel: 320-763-4648. FAX: 320-763-9290. E-Mail: irei@iami.org. Web Site: www.iami.org/irei.html. *Exec Dir*, Robert G Johnson
Founded 1965
Library Holdings: Bk Vols 18

ANNANDALE

P ANNANDALE PUBLIC LIBRARY,* 20 Cedar St E, 55302-0207. SAN 347-8238. Tel: 320-274-8448. FAX: 320-274-8448. Web Site: www.griver.org. *In Charge*, Sandra Otto
Pop 5,348; Circ 33,986
Library Holdings: Bk Vols 13,373; Per Subs 30
Mem of Great River Regional Library
Open Mon 2-5, Tues 9-1 & 2-5, Wed 2-8, Fri 9-12 & 2-5, Sat 9am-12pm

ANOKA

S ANOKA COUNTY HISTORICAL-GENEALOGICAL RESOURCE LIBRARY, 1900 Third Ave S, 55303. SAN 308-5066. Tel: 612-421-0600. *Dir*, Jean Smith; *Dir*, Vickie Wendel
Founded 1976

Library Holdings: Bk Titles 420
Special Collections: Anoka County History; Genealogical Books for Research throughout US & Foreign Countries

L ANOKA COUNTY LAW LIBRARY,* 325 E Main St, 55303. SAN 323-8563. Tel: 612-422-7487. FAX: 612-422-7453. Web Site: www.county.anoka.mn.us. *Librn*, Gene Myers; E-Mail: gcmyers@cmonster.county.anoka.mn.us; *Assoc Librn*, Merry Conway
Jan 1998-Dec 1999 Income $253,000. Mats Exp $178,500, Books $130,000, Per/Ser (Incl. Access Fees) $2,000, Presv $1,000, Micro $7,500, AV Equip $8,000, Other Print Mats $500, Manuscripts & Archives $1,000. Sal $81,190 (Prof $50,023)
Library Holdings: Bk Vols 18,000; Bk Titles 1,200
Special Collections: Local Municipal Ordinances

J ANOKA HENNEPIN TECHNICAL COLLEGE, Media Center,* 1355 W Hwy 10, 55303. SAN 308-5058. Tel: 612-576-4820. FAX: 612-576-4821. *Media Spec, Online Servs*, Deborah Brude
Enrl 1,200; Fac 80
Jul 1998-Jun 1999 Mats Exp $27,876, Books $17,164, Per/Ser (Incl. Access Fees) $4,501. Sal $228,674
Library Holdings: Bk Vols 9,031; Per Subs 367
Subject Interests: Allied health, Careers, Nursing, Technology
Publications: New Acquisitions
Partic in Metronet; Minn Interlibr Telecommunication Exchange
Friends of the Library Group
Bookmobiles: 3

M ANOKA METRO REGIONAL TREATMENT CENTER,* 3301 Seventh Ave, 55303-4516. SAN 308-5082. Tel: 612-576-5500. FAX: 612-576-5531. *In Charge*, Betty Palfalvi
Founded 1952
Library Holdings: Bk Vols 1,000; Per Subs 13
Subject Interests: Nursing, Psychiatry, Psychology

APPLE VALLEY

G MINNESOTA ZOOLOGICAL GARDEN LIBRARY, 13000 Zoo Blvd, 55124-8199. SAN 326-016X. Tel: 952-431-9230. FAX: 952-431-9427. *Librn*, Angela Norell; E-Mail: angela.norell@state.mn.us
Founded 1976
Library Holdings: Bk Titles 3,000; Per Subs 70
Subject Interests: Conservation, Horticulture, Natural history, Southeast Asia, Veterinary medicine
Publications: Animal Index 1972-1998; AZA Proceedings
Restriction: Staff use only
Partic in Minn Interlibr Telecommunication Exchange

APPLETON

P APPLETON PUBLIC LIBRARY,* 323 W Schlieman Ave, 56208-1299. SAN 347-6855. Tel: 320-289-1681. FAX: 320-289-1681. *Librn*, Cindy Hendrick
Pop 3,482; Circ 23,801
Library Holdings: Bk Vols 15,400; Per Subs 43
Mem of Pioneerland Library System
Branch of Pioneerland Library System

ARDEN HILLS

R BETHEL THEOLOGICAL SEMINARY LIBRARY, 3949 Bethel Dr, 55112. SAN 308-7530. Tel: 612-638-6184. FAX: 612-638-6006. Web Site: www.bethel.edu/seminary/student/library/library.htm. *Dir*, Sandra Oslund; *Cat, Dir*, Pam Jervis
Founded 1871. Enrl 401; Fac 21; Highest Degree: Doctorate
Library Holdings: Bk Vols 219,000; Per Subs 628
Special Collections: 19th Century Pietism (Skarstedt); Archives (Baptist General Conference); Devotional Literature; Klingberg Puritan Coll; Nelson-Lundquist Coll
Partic in Coop Librs in Consortium; MINITEX Library Information Network; Minnesota Theological Library Association

ARLINGTON

BLUE EARTH COUNTY LIBRARY SERVICES, Arlington Branch, 55307-0391. SAN 347-4216. Tel: 507-964-2490. FAX: 507-964-2378.
Library Holdings: Bk Vols 10,071
Friends of the Library Group

ATWATER

P ATWATER PUBLIC LIBRARY,* 318 Atlantic Ave N, PO Box 465, 56209-0465. SAN 348-0992. Tel: 320-974-3042. FAX: 320-974-8276. *Librn*, Lynda Behm
Pop 2,358; Circ 8,884
Library Holdings: Bk Titles 4,750; Per Subs 18
Subject Interests: Animals, Farming
Mem of Pioneerland Library System
Branch of Pioneerland Library System

AURORA

P AURORA PUBLIC LIBRARY,* 14 W Second Ave N, 55705-2021. SAN 308-5120. Tel: 218-229-2021. FAX: 218-229-3140. *Librn*, Joyce M Banttari
Founded 1914. Pop 1,932; Circ 41,250
Library Holdings: Bk Vols 22,400; Per Subs 90
Subject Interests: Career, College, Handcrafts, How-to
Mem of Arrowhead Library System
Special Services for the Deaf - TTY machine

AUSTIN

P AUSTIN PUBLIC LIBRARY,* 323 Fourth Ave NE, 55912-3370. SAN 347-190X. Tel: 507-433-2391. TDD: 507-433-8665. FAX: 507-433-8787. *Ref*, Linda Anderson; *Ch Servs*, Maureen Steenblock; *Cat*, Gayle Heimer; Staff 4 (MLS 3, Non-MLS 1)
Founded 1904. Pop 38,890; Circ 280,069
Jan 1999-Dec 1999 Income $880,108, City $621,507, County $198,842, Locally Generated Income $59,759. Mats Exp $75,796, Books $58,646, Per/Ser (Incl. Access Fees) $9,000, Micro $150, AV Equip $8,000. Sal $380,267 (Prof $158,204)
Library Holdings: Bk Vols 10,000; Bk Titles 84,928; Per Subs 324
Subject Interests: Local history
Publications: Library Link; Reading Reporter
Mem of Southeastern Libraries Cooperating (SELCO)
Friends of the Library Group
Branches: 3
BROWNSDALE PUBLIC, PO Box 302, Brownsdale, 55918-0302. SAN 347-1934. Tel: 507-567-2177. *Librn*, Shelly Sturdevant
GRAND MEADOW PUBLIC, PO Box 535, Grand Meadow, 55936-0535. SAN 347-1969. Tel: 507-754-5859.
LE ROY PUBLIC, PO Box 357, Le Roy, 55951-0357. SAN 347-1993. Tel: 507-324-5641. *Librn*, Jan Soltau
Bookmobiles: 1

J RIVERLAND COMMUNITY COLLEGE, Austin Campus Library, 1600 Eighth Ave NW, 55912. SAN 308-5139. Tel: 507-433-0533. FAX: 507-433-0515. Web Site: www.riverland.cc.mn.us/Library/index.htm. *Librn*, Kathleen Nelson; Staff 4 (MLS 1, Non-MLS 3)
Founded 1940. Enrl 2,500
Jul 1998-Jun 1999 Income $148,000, State $48,000. Mats Exp $99,400, Books $70,000, Per/Ser (Incl. Access Fees) $26,200, Micro $3,200. Sal $74,383 (Prof $42,062)
Library Holdings: Bk Vols 27,092; Bk Titles 21,790; Per Subs 871
Database Vendor: IAC - Info Trac, OCLC - First Search
Partic in MINITEX Library Information Network; OCLC Online Computer Library Center, Inc
Departmental Libraries:
ALBERT LEA CAMPUS, 2200 Riverland Dr, Albert Lea, 56007. SAN 376-9976. Tel: 507-379-3368. FAX: 507-379-3333. *Dir*, Kathleen Nelson

C UNIVERSITY OF MINNESOTA, Hormel Institute Library, 801 16th Ave NE, 55912. SAN 308-5147. Tel: 507-433-8804. FAX: 507-437-9606. *Librn, Online Servs*, Judith A Mullen
Founded 1942
Library Holdings: Bk Vols 2,000
Subject Interests: Biochemistry, Chemistry, Microbiol of lipids
Partic in Minn Interlibr Loan Network

BABBITT

P BABBITT PUBLIC LIBRARY, 71 South Dr, 55706-1232. SAN 308-5155. Tel: 218-827-3345. FAX: 218-827-3345. E-Mail: als@arrowhead.lib.mn.us. *Librn*, Susan Sowers; E-Mail: ssowers@arrowhead.lib.mn.us; *Asst Librn*, Sandy Gibson
Founded 1959. Pop 1,562; Circ 37,043
Library Holdings: Bk Vols 33,429; Per Subs 43
Special Collections: Babbitt History Coll, bulletins, clippings, pictures; Insect Coll
Mem of Arrowhead Library System
Friends of the Library Group

BAGLEY

P BAGLEY PUBLIC LIBRARY,* PO Box G, 21 Main Ave S, 56621. SAN 328-6975. Tel: 218-694-6201. FAX: 218-694-6201. E-Mail: bagley@northernlights.lib.mn.us. *Librn*, Karen Swanberg
Founded 1910. Pop 9,500; Circ 19,247
Library Holdings: Bk Vols 5,400; Per Subs 30

Mem of Lake Agassiz Regional Library
Partic in Northern Lights Library Network
Branch of Lake Agassiz Regional Library
Friends of the Library Group

BAUDETTE

P BAUDETTE PUBLIC LIBRARY,* 110 First Ave SW, PO Box 739, 56623-0739. SAN 308-5163. Tel: 218-634-2329. *Dir*, Roxanne Larson; *Librn*, Dena Pieper; *Librn*, Lucille Hoscheid
Founded 1912. Pop 1,170; Circ 25,281
Library Holdings: Bk Vols 10,413; Per Subs 38
Mem of Arrowhead Library System
Friends of the Library Group

S LAKE OF THE WOOD COUNTY HISTORICAL SOCIETY LIBRARY, 119 8th Ave SE, 56623. SAN 323-455X. Tel: 218-634-1200. FAX: 218-634-1200. *Curator*, Marlys Hirst
Library Holdings: Bk Titles 485
Subject Interests: Local history

BAYPORT

P BAYPORT PUBLIC LIBRARY, 582 N Fourth St, 55003-1111. SAN 308-5171. Tel: 651-439-7454. FAX: 651-439-0332. Web Site: www.bayportlibrary.org. *Librn*, Kathy L MacDonald
Founded 1960. Pop 3,220; Circ 58,908
Library Holdings: Bk Vols 22,408; Per Subs 110
Subject Interests: Large print, Local history
Publications: Library Log
Mem of Metrop Libr Serv Agency
Friends of the Library Group

S MINNESOTA CORRECTIONAL FACILITY, Education Library, 970 Pickett St N, 55003-1490. SAN 308-8103. Tel: 651-779-2700, Ext 2575. FAX: 651-351-3602. *Librn*, Ron Hauser; E-Mail: rhauser@stw.doc.state.mn.us; Staff 1 (MLS 1)
Founded 1979
Library Holdings: Bk Vols 8,000; Bk Titles 7,500; Per Subs 53; High Interest/Low Vocabulary Bk Vols 100
Subject Interests: Law

BELGRADE

P BELGRADE LIBRARY, 324 Washburn Ave, PO Box 388, 56312-0388. SAN 347-853X. Tel: 320-254-8842. Web Site: www.griver.org. *In Charge*, Kathie Harris
Founded 1477. Circ 19,040
Library Holdings: Bk Vols 8,500; Per Subs 36
Mem of Great River Regional Library
Open Mon & Wed 2-5, Thurs 10-1 & 2-5 Fri 2-5 & 6-8, Sat 9am-12pm

BEMIDJI

S BELTRAMI COUNTY HISTORICAL SOCIETY ARCHIVES, Beltrami County History Center, 130 Minnesota Ave SW, 56601. (Mail add: PO Box 683, 56619), SAN 373-2231. Tel: 218-444-3376. FAX: 218-444-3377. E-Mail: depot@paulbunyan.net. *Dir*, Wanda Hoyum
Library Holdings: Bk Vols 230
Subject Interests: Local history

P BEMIDJI PUBLIC LIBRARY, 509 America Ave NW, 56601. SAN 320-4529. Tel: 218-751-3963. FAX: 218-751-1645. *Librn*, Bona-Carol Enstrom; Staff 6 (MLS 2, Non-MLS 4)
Founded 1907. Pop 30,982; Circ 198,158
Library Holdings: Bk Titles 62,182; Per Subs 150
Subject Interests: Native Am studies
Database Vendor: DRA
Publications: Friends (newsletter)
Mem of Kitchigami Regional Library
Special Services for the Blind - Books available with recordings
Friends of the Library Group

C BEMIDJI STATE UNIVERSITY, A C Clark Library, 1500 Birchmont Dr, 56601-2699. SAN 308-518X. Tel: 218-755-3342. Interlibrary Loan Service Tel: 218-755-2968. Circulation Tel: 218-755-3345. FAX: 218-755-2051. Web Site: cswww.bemidji.msus.edu/~library. *Cat*, Warren Gumeson; *Circ, Govt Doc*, Stuart Rosselet; Tel: 218-755-4233, E-Mail: stuross@cslab.bemidji.msus.edu; *Ref*, Gwen Salner; *ILL, Online Servs*, Pat Conely; *Coll Develop*, Carol Bodien; Staff 13 (MLS 7, Non-MLS 6)
Founded 1919. Enrl 4,441; Fac 253; Highest Degree: Master
Jul 1999-Jun 2000 Income Parent Institution $1,524,809. Mats Exp $405,792, Books $165,782, Per/Ser (Incl. Access Fees) $220,920, Presv $13,795, Other Print Mats $2,066, Electronic Ref Mat (Incl. Access Fees) $3,229. Sal $742,223 (Prof $434,898)
Library Holdings: Bk Vols 334,919; Bk Titles 219,168; Per Subs 979
Subject Interests: Am Indian hist, Northern Minn hist
Special Collections: Holdings; National Indian Education Association Coll
Publications: Newsletter
Partic in Minn Interlibr Telecommunication Exchange; OCLC Online Computer Library Center, Inc

R OAK HILLS CHRISTIAN COLLEGE, Cummings Library, 1600 Oak Hills Rd SW, 56601-8832. SAN 308-5198. Tel: 218-751-8670, Ext 246. FAX: 218-751-8825. Web Site: www.oakhills.edu. *Dir*, Keith Bush; E-Mail: keithjbush@hotmail.com; Staff 2 (Non-MLS 2)
Founded 1946. Enrl 155; Fac 13
Library Holdings: Bk Vols 25,000; Per Subs 160
Subject Interests: Philosophy, Relig studies

BENSON

P BENSON PUBLIC LIBRARY,* 200 13th St N, 56215-1223. SAN 308-5201. Tel: 320-842-7981. FAX: 320-843-4948. *Librn*, Patricia Cina; E-Mail: patc@benson.lib.mn.us; *Asst Librn*, Judy Anderson; *Asst Librn*, Karen Peterson
Founded 1913. Circ 53,129
Jan 2000-Dec 2000 Income $66,521, City $31,309, County $29,052, Other $6,160. Mats Exp $10,057, Books $8,813, Per/Ser (Incl. Access Fees) $1,244. Sal $45,496
Library Holdings: Bk Vols 17,000; Per Subs 77
Mem of Pioneerland Library System
Partic in Southwest Area Multicounty Multitype Interlibrary Exchange

SR OUR REDEEMERS LUTHERAN CHURCH LIBRARY,* Tenth St S & Oakwood Ave, 56215. SAN 308-521X. Tel: 320-843-3151. *Librn*, Marlene Skold; E-Mail: mskold@willmn.com
1997-1998 Income $100
Library Holdings: Bk Vols 1,900

BIG LAKE

P BIG LAKE LIBRARY,* 160 Lake St N, 55309. SAN 322-6336. Tel: 612-263-6445. FAX: 612-263-6445. Web Site: www.griver.org. *In Charge*, Nancy Lee
Founded 1984. Pop 6,813; Circ 34,826
Library Holdings: Bk Vols 12,000; Per Subs 47
Mem of Great River Regional Library
Open Mon 2-8, Wed & Thurs 2-6, Fri 9-1 & 2-5 & Sat 9-1
Friends of the Library Group

BIRD ISLAND

P BIRD ISLAND PUBLIC LIBRARY, 260 S Main, PO Box 217, 55310-0226. SAN 348-1026. Tel: 320-365-4640. FAX: 320-365-4640. E-Mail: birdisland@birdisland.lib.mn.us. *Librn*, Shirley Schulte
Pop 1,320; Circ 16,266
Jan 1999-Dec 1999 Income $40,287, City $15,439, County $13,240, Other $11,608. Mats Exp $28,508, Books $5,200, Per/Ser (Incl. Access Fees) $1,050. Sal $18,000
Library Holdings: Bk Vols 7,667; Per Subs 23
Automation Activity & Vendor Info: (Circulation) PALS; (OPAC) PALS
Mem of Pioneerland Library System
Open Mon 6-8, Tues & Wed 10-5, Thurs 10-4 & 6-8, Fri 10-2 & Sat 10-12

BLACKDUCK

P BLACKDUCK COMMUNITY LIBRARY, 64 First St SE, PO Box 326, 56630-0119. SAN 347-772X. Tel: 218-835-6600. FAX: 218-835-6600. E-Mail: blackduck@northernlights.lib.mn.us. Web Site: www.nlln.org. *In Charge*, Nancy M Kunkel; *Asst Librn*, Michele Krueth; Staff 2 (Non-MLS 2)
Founded 1909. Pop 5,000; Circ 20,000
Library Holdings: Bk Vols 15,000; Per Subs 22
Database Vendor: DRA, GaleNet, IAC - Info Trac, IAC - SearchBank, OCLC - First Search, ProQuest
Function: ILL available
Mem of Kitchigami Regional Library
Partic in Northern Lights Library Network
Branch of Kitchigami Regional Library

BLAINE

P ANOKA COUNTY LIBRARY, 707 Hwy 10 NE, 55434-2398. SAN 347-2027. Tel: 763-785-3695. FAX: 763-717-3262. E-Mail: anoka@anoka.lib.mn.us. Web Site: www.anoka.lib.mn.us. *Dir*, Beverly Flaherty; *Ch Servs*, Kathleen Baxter; Staff 30 (MLS 23, Non-MLS 7)
Founded 1958. Pop 277,010; Circ 2,793,254
Jan 1999-Dec 1999 Income (Main Library and Branch Library) County $5,604,534. Mats Exp $827,100. Sal $3,707,316
Library Holdings: Bk Vols 580,647; Per Subs 1,707

Automation Activity & Vendor Info: (Acquisitions) DRA; (Cataloging) DRA; (Circulation) DRA; (OPAC) DRA; (Serials) DRA
Database Vendor: DRA
Partic in Metropolitan Library Service Agency
Friends of the Library Group
Branches: 9
CENTENNIAL, 100 Civic Heights Circle, Circle Pines, 55014-1786. (Mail add: 707 Hwy 10 NE, 55434-2398), SAN 347-2051. Tel: 763-717-3294. FAX: 763-717-3297. E-Mail: anoka@anoka.lib.mn.us. Web Site: www.anoka.lib.mn.us. *Librn*, Chad Lubbers
Library Holdings: Bk Vols 55,089; Per Subs 128
Database Vendor: DRA
CROOKED LAKE, 11440 Crooked Lake Blvd, Coon Rapids, 55433-3441. (Mail add: 707 Hwy 10 NE, 55434-2398), SAN 347-2116. Tel: 763-576-5972. FAX: 763-576-5973. E-Mail: anoka@anoka.lib.mn.us. Web Site: www.anoka.lib.mn.us. *Librn*, Kathy Petron
Library Holdings: Bk Vols 85,362; Per Subs 195
Database Vendor: DRA
JOHNSVILLE, 12461 Oak Park Blvd, 55434. (Mail add: 707 Hwy 10 NE, 55434-2398), SAN 326-8039. Tel: 763-767-3853. FAX: 763-767-3854. E-Mail: anoka@anoka.lib.mn.us. Web Site: www.anoka.lib.mn.us. *Librn*, Krista Stumo
Library Holdings: Bk Vols 51,217; Per Subs 118
Database Vendor: DRA
MISSISSIPPI, 410 Mississippi St NE, Fridley, 55432-4416. (Mail add: 707 Hwy 10 NE, 55434-2398), SAN 347-2140. Tel: 763-571-1934. FAX: 763-571-1935. E-Mail: anoka@anoka.lib.mn.us. Web Site: www.anoka.lib.mn.us. *Librn*, Peggy Feldick
Library Holdings: Bk Vols 62,396; Per Subs 210
Database Vendor: DRA
NORTH CENTRAL, 17565 Central Ave NE, Ham Lake, 55304-4302. (Mail add: 707 Hwy 10 NE, 55434-2398), SAN 347-2175. Tel: 763-434-6542. FAX: 763-434-6542. E-Mail: anoka@anoka.lib.mn.us. Web Site: www.anoka.lib.mn.us. *Librn*, Susan Webb
Library Holdings: Bk Vols 30,718; Per Subs 67
Database Vendor: DRA
NORTHDALE, 408 Northdale Blvd NW, Coon Rapids, 55448-3364. (Mail add: 707 Hwy 10 NE, 55434-2398), SAN 347-2086. Tel: 763-767-3851. FAX: 763-767-3852. E-Mail: anoka@anoka.lub.mn.us. Web Site: www.anoka.lib.mn.us. *Librn*, Carol Moen
Library Holdings: Bk Vols 42,482; Per Subs 117
Database Vendor: DRA
NORTHTOWN CENTRAL, 711 Hwy 10 NE, 55434-2398. (Mail add: 707 Hwy 10 NE, 55434-2398), SAN 347-2035. Tel: 763-717-3267. FAX: 763-717-3259. E-Mail: anoka@anoka.lib.mn.us. Web Site: www.anoka.lib.mn.us. *Librn*, Louann Smith
Library Holdings: Bk Vols 252,150; Per Subs 467
Database Vendor: DRA
RUM RIVER, 4201 Sixth Ave N, Anoka, 55303. (Mail add: 707 Hwy 10 NE, 55434-2398), SAN 329-5842. Tel: 763-576-4695. FAX: 763-576-4699. E-Mail: anoka@anoka.lib.mn.us. Web Site: www.anoka.lib.mn.us. *Librn*, Karen Hand
Database Vendor: DRA
SAINT FRANCIS BRANCH, 3519 Bridge St NW, Saint Francis, 55070-9754. (Mail add: 707 Hwy 10 NE, 55434-2398), SAN 347-2191. Tel: 763-753-2131. FAX: 763-753-2131. E-Mail: anoka@anoka.lib.mn.us. Web Site: www.anoka.lib.mn.us. *Librn*, Diana Gilbertson
Library Holdings: Bk Vols 17,433; Per Subs 54
Database Vendor: DRA

BLOOMINGTON

L LARKIN, HOFFMAN, DALY & LINDGREN, Law Library,* 7900 Xeres Ave S Ste 1500, 55431. (Mail add: 1500 Norwest Financial Ctr, 55431), SAN 372-283X. Tel: 612-835-3800. FAX: 612-896-3333. *Librn*, Ardis Jacobson
Library Holdings: Bk Vols 15,000; Per Subs 142

J NORMANDALE COMMUNITY COLLEGE LIBRARY,* 9700 France Ave S, 55431. SAN 308-5252. Tel: 612-832-6380. FAX: 612-832-6571. Web Site: www.nr.cc.mn.us/library/default.htm. *Acq, Coordr*, Rosalie Bunge; *Ref*, Susan Mills; *Cat, Tech Servs*, Adam Marsnik; *Bibliog Instr*, Al Mamaril
Founded 1968
1998-1999 Income $615,000. Mats Exp $133,564, Books $48,751, Per/Ser (Incl. Access Fees) $62,793, Presv $621
Library Holdings: Bk Vols 80,771; Per Subs 675
Special Collections: Minnesota Authors Coll
Automation Activity & Vendor Info: (Acquisitions) PALS; (Cataloging) PALS; (Circulation) PALS; (ILL) PALS; (OPAC) PALS; (Serials) PALS
Partic in Minn Interlibr Telecommunication Exchange; OCLC Online Computer Library Center, Inc

C NORTHWESTERN HEALTH SCIENCE UNIVERSITY, Greenawalt Library, 2501 W 84th St, 55431-1599. SAN 308-7816. Tel: 952-885-5419. Interlibrary Loan Service Tel: 952-885-5463. FAX: 952-884-3318. Web Site: www.nwhealth.edu. *Dir*, Della Shupe; E-Mail: dshupe@nwhealth.edu
Founded 1966. Enrl 538; Fac 56; Highest Degree: Doctorate
Library Holdings: Bk Titles 11,500; Per Subs 315
Special Collections: Chiropractic Journals
Publications: New Materials list (monthly)
Partic in Chiropractic Libr Consortium; Health Scis Librs of Minn; Twin Cities Biomedical Consortium

S THERMO KING CORPORATION LIBRARY, 314 W 90th St, 55420-3393. SAN 326-6273. Tel: 952-887-2336. FAX: 952-887-2617. *Librn*, Julie Ann Shea; E-Mail: julie_shea@thermoking.com; Staff 1 (MLS 1)
Founded 1975
Library Holdings: Bk Titles 3,000; Per Subs 100
Automation Activity & Vendor Info: (Circulation) Inmagic, Inc.
Database Vendor: Dialog
Restriction: Staff use only

BLUE EARTH

P BLUE EARTH COMMUNITY LIBRARY, 124 W Seventh St, 56013-1308. SAN 372-5790. Tel: 507-526-5012. TDD: 507-526-5638. FAX: 507-526-4683. E-Mail: libtfb@tds.lib.mn.us, tfblib@tds.lib.mn.us. Web Site: libraries.tds.lib.mn.us/blueearth. *Dir*, Nancy K Steele; E-Mail: nsteele@tds.lib.mn.us; Staff 6 (MLS 1, Non-MLS 5)
Founded 1902
Jan 1999-Dec 1999 Income $128,922, City $57,436, County $38,382, Locally Generated Income $33,104. Mats Exp $128,922, Books $11,000, Per/Ser (Incl. Access Fees) $2,600, Presv $250, Micro $600, AV Equip $1,200. Sal $63,016
Library Holdings: Bk Vols 38,693; Bk Titles 23,029; Per Subs 104
Subject Interests: Local history
Special Collections: DVD videos; Local newspapers from 1861
Automation Activity & Vendor Info: (Cataloging) PALS; (Circulation) PALS; (ILL) PALS; (OPAC) PALS
Database Vendor: IAC - Info Trac, OCLC - First Search, ProQuest
Mem of Traverse Des Sioux Library System
Friends of the Library Group

P FARIBAULT COUNTY LIBRARY SERVICE,* 120 S Main, PO Box 215, 56013-0215. SAN 375-331X. Tel: 507-526-7182. FAX: 507-526-6227. *Dir*, Virgie Ann Murra; Staff 1 (MLS 1)
Circ 19,509
Jan 1998-Dec 1999 Income $160,000. Mats Exp $7,615, Books $7,260, Per/Ser (Incl. Access Fees) $355. Sal $40,000 (Prof $31,600)
Library Holdings: Bk Titles 16,700
Mem of Traverse Des Sioux Library System
Branches: 1
FROST BRANCH, Frost, 56033. SAN 375-3956. Tel: 507-878-3102. *Librn*, Shellie Poetter

BOVEY

P BOVEY PUBLIC LIBRARY,* PO Box 130, 55709. SAN 308-5279. Tel: 218-245-3691. FAX: 218-245-3691. *Dir*, Patrick Perry; E-Mail: pperry@arrowhead.lib.mn.us
Founded 1930. Pop 858; Circ 12,574
Library Holdings: Bk Vols 17,500; Per Subs 50
Subject Interests: Genealogy
Mem of Arrowhead Library System

BRAINERD

S A W RESEARCH LABORATORIES LIBRARY,* 2403 Airport Rd NE, 56401. SAN 374-6720. Tel: 218-829-7974. FAX: 218-829-1316. E-Mail: awrl@mcimail-com. *Pres*, Alan Cibuzar; Staff 10 (MLS 10)
Library Holdings: Bk Titles 175; Per Subs 30
Special Collections: A W Research Laboratories Environmental Coll, computer software & analysis programs
Publications: AWRL Report/Newsletter (seasonally)
Restriction: Company library

P BRAINERD PUBLIC LIBRARY,* 416 S Fifth St, 56401. SAN 320-4537. Tel: 218-829-5574. FAX: 218-829-0055. E-Mail: brainerd@northernlights.lib.mn.us. Web Site: www.brainerd.com/library. *Ad Servs*, Susan Hardy; *AV*, Diane Holz; *Ch Servs*, Jeanne Fields; Staff 5 (MLS 1, Non-MLS 4)
Founded 1882. Pop 40,000; Circ 322,555
Jan 1999-Dec 2000 Mats Exp $51,256, Books $48,956, Per/Ser (Incl. Access Fees) $2,300
Library Holdings: Bk Vols 60,000; Per Subs 138
Mem of Kitchigami Regional Library
Friends of the Library Group

M BRAINERD REGIONAL HUMAN SERVICES CENTER LIBRARY,* 1777 Hwy 18 E, 56401. SAN 327-7828. Tel: 218-828-2420. FAX: 218-828-2207.
Library Holdings: Bk Vols 20,000; Per Subs 30

J CENTRAL LAKES COLLEGE, Learning Resource Center,* 501 W College Dr, 56401. SAN 308-5287. Tel: 218-828-2525. FAX: 218-825-3094. Web Site: www.clc.cc.mn.us/users/lrc/1.htm. *Librn*, Larry M Kellerman
Founded 1938. Enrl 3,600; Fac 180
1998-1999 Income $41,400. Mats Exp $44,600, Books $21,600, Per/Ser (Incl. Access Fees) $15,000, AV Equip $8,000
Library Holdings: Bk Titles 32,000
Subject Interests: Bus, Education, History, Nursing, Sci-tech
Special Collections: American Indian Coll; Local Government; Scandinavian Coll
Publications: Library Handbook
Partic in OCLC Online Computer Library Center, Inc
Special Services for the Blind - Special programs

S CROW WING COUNTY HISTORICAL SOCIETY ARCHIVES LIBRARY, 320 Laurel St, PO Box 722, 56401. SAN 326-0291. Tel: 218-829-3268. FAX: 218-828-4434. E-Mail: history@twwn.com. *Exec Dir*, Mary Lou Moudry
Founded 1983
Library Holdings: Bk Vols 300
Subject Interests: Local history
Special Collections: Brainerd Address Directories 1901-2000; Forsythe-Hoffman Diaries
Restriction: Non-circulating to the public
Mem of Northern Lights Libr Network

BRECKENRIDGE

P BRECKENRIDGE PUBLIC LIBRARY,* 205 N Seventh St, 56520-1519. SAN 347-7185. Tel: 218-643-2113. FAX: 218-643-2113. E-Mail: breckenridge@northernlights.lib.mn.us. *Br Coordr*, Nanci Tobias
Founded 1912. Pop 6,554
Library Holdings: Bk Vols 16,653; Per Subs 61
Mem of Lake Agassiz Regional Library
Partic in Northern Lights Library Network
Friends of the Library Group

M SAINT FRANCIS MEDICAL CENTER, Community Health Science Library,* 415 Oak St, 56520. SAN 327-7844. Tel: 218-643-3000. FAX: 218-643-7487. *Dir*, Karla R Lovaasen; Fax: 218-643-7452, E-Mail: karlalovaasen@chi-midwest.org
Library Holdings: Bk Vols 200
Partic in Minn Asn of Libr; Prairie Libr Network Consortium; Valley Med Ctr Consortium

S WILKIN COUNTY MUSEUM LIBRARY, 704 Nebraska Ave, 56520. SAN 373-224X. Tel: 218-643-1303. *In Charge*, Elaine Andrews
Library Holdings: Bk Vols 1,000
Subject Interests: Genealogy, Local history

BROOKLYN PARK

J NORTH HENNEPIN COMMUNITY COLLEGE LIBRARY, 7411 85th Ave N, 55445-2298. SAN 308-5295. Tel: 763-424-0732, 763-424-0733. Circulation Tel: 763-424-0732. Reference Tel: 763-424-0734. FAX: 763-493-0569. Web Site: www.nh.cc.mm.us/college.services/library/. *Librn*, Theresa Crosby; Tel: 763-424-0738, E-Mail: tcrosby@nh.cc.mn.us; Staff 6 (MLS 2, Non-MLS 4)
Founded 1966. Enrl 5,000; Fac 200; Highest Degree: Associate
Jul 2000-Jun 2001 Mats Exp $92,100, Books $60,000, Per/Ser (Incl. Access Fees) $17,000, Presv $100, Electronic Ref Mat (Incl. Access Fees) $15,000
Library Holdings: Bk Vols 43,000; Bk Titles 42,000
Automation Activity & Vendor Info: (Acquisitions) PALS; (Circulation) PALS; (OPAC) PALS
Database Vendor: IAC - Info Trac, OCLC - First Search
Partic in MINITEX Library Information Network; OCLC Online Computer Library Center, Inc

BROWNS VALLEY

P BROWNS VALLEY PUBLIC LIBRARY,* 15 S Third St, PO Box 307, 56219-0307. SAN 320-894X. Tel: 320-695-2318. FAX: 320-695-2125. E-Mail: vgrimli@brownsvalley.lib.mn.us. *Librn*, Vicki Grimli
Pop 773; Circ 21,311
Jan 1997-Dec 1997 Income $47,798, City $40,726, County $3,403, Locally Generated Income $2,779, Other $890. Mats Exp $9,049, Books $5,846, Per/Ser (Incl. Access Fees) $1,451. Sal $23,956
Library Holdings: Bk Vols 10,188; Per Subs 72
Mem of Viking Library System

BROWNTON

P BROWNTON PUBLIC LIBRARY,* PO Box 97, 55312-0097. SAN 348-1050. Tel: 320-328-5900. FAX: 320-328-5318. *Librn*, Diane Sweely
Pop 801; Circ 10,176
Library Holdings: Bk Vols 6,295; Per Subs 21
Mem of Pioneerland Library System
Open Mon 4:30-8, Tues 1-5, Wed 2:30-5, Thurs 9-12 & 1-5, Sat 9-12, Fri closed

BUFFALO

P BUFFALO LIBRARY,* 18 NW Lake Blvd, 55313. SAN 347-8262. Tel: 612-682-2753. FAX: 612-682-9290. Web Site: www.griver.org. *In Charge*, Amy Wickesberg
Pop 11,194; Circ 166,067
Library Holdings: Bk Vols 32,047; Per Subs 93
Mem of Great River Regional Library
Open Mon, Tues & Wed 10-8, Thurs 12-8, Fri 12-6 & Sat 10-2

BUHL

P BUHL PUBLIC LIBRARY,* 400 Jones Ave, PO Box 664, 55713-0664. SAN 308-5309. Tel: 218-258-3391. FAX: 218-258-3391. Web Site: www.buhl.lib.mn.us. *Librn*, Sara Samuelson; *Asst Librn*, Julie Kaipainen
Founded 1918. Circ 27,000
Library Holdings: Bk Vols 18,087; Bk Titles 18,000; Per Subs 50
Mem of Arrowhead Library System

BURNSVILLE

M FAIRVIEW-RIDGES HOSPITAL, Medical Staff Library,* 201 E Nicollet Blvd, 55337. SAN 370-8519. Tel: 612-925-5005.
Library Holdings: Bk Titles 200; Per Subs 100

CALEDONIA

P CALEDONIA PUBLIC LIBRARY,* 231 E Main St, 55921-1321. SAN 308-5317. Tel: 507-724-2671. FAX: 507-724-5258. *Librn*, Marla Burns; E-Mail: marla@selco.lib.mn.us; *Asst Librn*, Eileen Jacobson; Staff 1 (MLS 1)
Founded 1895. Pop 3,465; Circ 13,670
Library Holdings: Bk Titles 21,752; Per Subs 78
Subject Interests: Architecture, Art, Education, History, Travel
Special Collections: Caledonia Argus (newspaper) 1900 - present; Caledonia Journal, 1868-1956
Partic in SE Libr Coop
Friends of the Library Group

CALUMET

P CALUMET PUBLIC LIBRARY,* PO Box 356, 55716. SAN 308-5325. Tel: 218-247-3108. FAX: 218-247-3108. *Asst Librn*, Helen Serich
Pop 460; Circ 2,446
Library Holdings: Bk Vols 8,000; Per Subs 45
Mem of Arrowhead Library System
Friends of the Library Group

CAMBRIDGE

M CAMBRIDGE REGIONAL HUMAN SERVICES, Resident Library,* 1235 S Hwy 293, 55008. SAN 308-5333. Tel: 612-689-7266. FAX: 612-689-7261. *In Charge*, Richard Colond
Library Holdings: Bk Titles 625
Subject Interests: Mental retardation
Partic in Glen Lake Med Libr Consortium

P EAST CENTRAL REGIONAL LIBRARY, 244 S Birch, 55008-1588. SAN 347-2353. Tel: 763-689-7390. Toll Free Tel: 888-234-1293. FAX: 612-689-7389. E-Mail: ecrl@ecrl.lib.mn.us. Web Site: ecrl.lib.mn.us. *Dir*, Robert Boese; E-Mail: bob@ecrl.lib.mn.us; *Asst Dir*, Bob Gray; *Ch Servs, YA Servs*, Vickie Sorn; Staff 5 (MLS 5)
Founded 1959. Pop 146,555; Circ 717,026
Jan 2001-Dec 2001 Income $1,827,923, State $450,000, Federal $31,000, County $1,075,444, Locally Generated Income $100,000. Mats Exp $320,000, Books $250,000, Per/Ser (Incl. Access Fees) $22,000, Presv $300, Other Print Mats $500. Sal $1,139,523 (Prof $220,000)
Library Holdings: Bk Vols 230,000; Bk Titles 130,000; Per Subs 160
Subject Interests: Minn
Automation Activity & Vendor Info: (Acquisitions) epixtech, inc.; (Cataloging) epixtech, inc.; (Circulation) epixtech, inc.; (ILL) PALS; (OPAC) epixtech, inc.
Member Libraries: Aitkin Public Library; Hinckley Public Library; Lindstrom Public Library; McGregor Public Library; Milaca Community Library; Mille Lacs Community Library; Mora Public Library; North Branch Area Library; Pine City Public Library; Princeton Area Library; Rush City Public Library; Sandstone Public Library

Partic in Central Minnesota Libraries Exchange; MINITEX Library Information Network
Friends of the Library Group
Bookmobiles: 1

S ISANTI COUNTY HISTORICAL SOCIETY, Reference Research Library, 1400 Hwy 293 McBroom NE, PO Box 525, 55008. SAN 323-7257. Tel: 763-689-4229. FAX: 763-689-4229. *Admin Dir, Bibliog Instr, Librn*, Valorie Arrowsmith; E-Mail: varrow2@ecenet.com; Staff 3 (Non-MLS 3)
Founded 1965
Jan 1998-Dec 1999 Income $38,000, City $6,000, County $10,000, Locally Generated Income $22,000. Mats Exp $75, Per/Ser (Incl. Access Fees) $60, AV Equip $15. (Prof $22,000)
Library Holdings: Bk Vols 400
Subject Interests: Swedish immigrants hist
Special Collections: Swedish Immigration from Dalarna Sweden to Isanti County, bks, photogs, tapes
Publications: Art & History Passport; Braham Minnesota, 100 years 1899-1999; Guide to Swedish Sites; Guide to Swedish sites; Isonti, Minnesota Centennial; Local Cemetery Records; Preserving A Sense of Heritage
Restriction: In-house use for visitors, Not a lending library, Open to students, Public use on premises
Function: Archival collection, Business archives, Newspaper reference library, Photocopies available, Reference only, Research fees apply, Research library

CANBY

M CANBY COMMUNITY HEALTH SERVICES, Medical Library,* 112 St Olaf Ave S, 56220. SAN 328-5243. Tel: 507-223-7277, Ext 235. FAX: 507-223-7465. *Dir*, Cheryl Ferguson
Library Holdings: Bk Titles 1,100

P CANBY PUBLIC LIBRARY,* 110 Oscar Ave N, 56220-1332. SAN 308-5341. Tel: 507-223-5738. FAX: 507-223-5170. *Librn*, Lola Reckoff
Pop 2,081; Circ 51,399
Library Holdings: Bk Vols 31,000; Per Subs 81
Friends of the Library Group

CANNON FALLS

P CANNON FALLS LIBRARY,* 306 W Mill St, 55009-2045. SAN 308-535X. Tel: 507-263-2804. FAX: 507-263-5843. *Dir*, Janice Kunkel; E-Mail: janice@selco.lib.mn.us
Founded 1951. Pop 7,715; Circ 91,484
Jan 1997-Dec 1998 Income $158,734, State $1,573, City $82,662, County $55,946, Locally Generated Income $5,777, Other $11,005. Mats Exp $23,447, Books $20,713, Per/Ser (Incl. Access Fees) $2,734. Sal $69,445
Library Holdings: Bk Titles 29,681; Per Subs 101
Subject Interests: Regional hist especially city, Regional hist especially county
Special Collections: Cannon Falls Beacon, microfiche, bd per; Family Search Geneological; Local Cemetery Indexes; Minnesota Census, microfilm (Goodhue County & Dakota County)
Mem of Southeastern Libraries Cooperating (SELCO)
Special Services for the Deaf - TTY machine
Friends of the Library Group

CARLTON

P CARLTON PUBLIC LIBRARY,* 310 Chestnut Ave, PO Box 309, 55718. SAN 308-5368. Tel: 218-384-3726. FAX: 218-384-4229. *Librn*, Kimberly R Goad
Pop 884; Circ 5,661
Library Holdings: Bk Vols 7,500; Per Subs 21
Mem of Arrowhead Library System

CASS LAKE

P CASS LAKE COMMUNITY LIBRARY,* 223 Cedar, PO Box 836, 56633-0836. SAN 347-7789. Tel: 218-335-8865. *Librn*, Evelyn Minzghor
Pop 3,500; Circ 22,091
Library Holdings: Bk Vols 10,420; Per Subs 20
Branch of Kitchigami Regional Library

CENTER CITY

S HAZELDEN LIBRARY & INFORMATION RESOURCES, 15245 Pleasant Valley Rd, PO Box 11, CO-4, 55012. SAN 371-7372. Tel: 651-213-4093. Toll Free Tel: 800-257-7800. FAX: 651-213-4411. Web Site: www.hazelden.org/library. *Info Res*, Barbara Weiner; E-Mail: bweiner@hazelden.org; Staff 1 (MLS 1)
Library Holdings: Bk Titles 10,700; Per Subs 85
Subject Interests: Addictions, Chem dependency, Family, Health, Lifestyle, Recovery, Self help, Spirituality, Substance abuse
Special Collections: History of Alcoholism, Spirituality & Temperance, bks, journals, pamphlets (Pittman Archives at Hazelden)
Restriction: Staff use only
Partic in Central Minnesota Libraries Exchange; Substance Abuse Librarians & Information Specialists; Twin Cities Biomedical Consortium
Federal government RADAR Specialty Site for alcohol & other drug prevention

CHANHASSEN

C UNIVERSITY OF MINNESOTA, Andersen Horticultural Library, Minnesota Landscape Arboretum, 3675 Arboretum Dr, PO Box 39, 55317. SAN 308-5376. Tel: 952-443-1405. FAX: 952-443-2521. Web Site: www.arboretum.umn.edu. *Bibliogr, Head Librn*, Richard T Isaacson; E-Mail: r-isaa@tc.umn.edu
Founded 1970
Library Holdings: Bk Vols 12,000
Subject Interests: Horticulture
Special Collections: Nursery Catalogs; Seed and Nursery; Williams Hosta Coll
Restriction: Non-circulating
Open Mon-Fri 8-4:30, Sat & Sun 11-4:30
Friends of the Library Group

CHASKA

P CARVER COUNTY LIBRARY,* 4 City Hall Plaza, 55318-1963. SAN 347-2655. Tel: 612-448-9395. FAX: 612-448-9392. *Dir*, Melissa Brechon; E-Mail: melissa@carver.lib.mn.us; *Asst Dir*, Janet Karius; Staff 5 (MLS 5)
Founded 1975. Pop 57,010; Circ 320,000
Library Holdings: Bk Vols 125,000; Per Subs 225
Partic in Metropolitan Library Service Agency
Branches: 5
CHANHASSEN BRANCH, 690 Coulter Dr, Chanhassen, 55317-0306. SAN 347-2671. Tel: 612-934-8689. *Librn*, Kathy Perschmann
Friends of the Library Group
CHASKA COMMUNITY LIBRARY, 3 City Hall Plaza, 55318-1963. SAN 347-268X. Tel: 612-448-3886. *Librn*, Sara Nagel
Friends of the Library Group
NORWOOD YOUNG AMERICA BRANCH, 102 Main St E, Young America, 55397-0058. SAN 347-2779. Tel: 612-467-2665. *Librn*, Brenda Youngdahl
WACONIA BRANCH, 101 S Elm St, Waconia, 55387-1414. SAN 347-271X. Tel: 612-442-4714. *Librn*, Susan Loedner
Friends of the Library Group
WATERTOWN BRANCH, 309 Lewis Ave, Watertown, 55388-0277. SAN 347-2744. Tel: 612-955-2939. *Librn*, Brenda Youngdahl
Friends of the Library Group

CHATFIELD

S CHATFIELD BRASS BAND, INC, Music Lending Library,* PO Box 578, 55923-0398. SAN 326-0658. Tel: 507-867-3275. *Asst Librn*, Helen Mercer; *Asst Librn*, Mike Erickson; *Asst Librn*, Wilma Zylstra; Staff 6 (Non-MLS 6)
Founded 1971. Circ 50,000
1998-1999 Income $18,000, Locally Generated Income $17,500, Parent Institution $300. Mats Exp Per/Ser (Incl. Access Fees) $50. Sal $8,500
Library Holdings: Bk Titles 50,000
Special Collections: Jan Bily Small Orchestra Coll
Publications: Newsletter (biennial)

P CHATFIELD PUBLIC LIBRARY,* 314 S Main St, 55923-1284. SAN 308-5384. Tel: 507-867-3480. FAX: 507-867-3480. *Librn*, Monica Erickson; E-Mail: monica@selco.lib.mn.us; *Ch Servs*, Janice Welch; *Asst Librn*, Charlotte Brevig
Founded 1911. Pop 2,226; Circ 14,244
Library Holdings: Bk Vols 14,000; Per Subs 40
Mem of Southeastern Libraries Cooperating (SELCO)
Friends of the Library Group

CHISHOLM

P CHISHOLM PUBLIC LIBRARY,* 300 W Lake, 55719-1718. SAN 308-5392. Tel: 218-254-7913. FAX: 218-254-7952. *Librn*, Elizabeth Kenyon
Pop 5,000; Circ 45,000
Jan 1999-Dec 1999 Income $199,000. Mats Exp $18,000. Sal $120,000
Library Holdings: Bk Vols 32,000; Per Subs 110
Mem of Arrowhead Library System

G IRON RANGE RESEARCH CENTER, Hwy 169 W, PO Box 392, 55719-0392. SAN 324-7716. Tel: 218-254-7959. Toll Free Tel: 800-372-6437. FAX: 218-254-7971. E-Mail: debf@ironworld.com. Web Site: www.ironworld.com/ancestry. *Archivist*, Edward Nelson; *Res*, Debra Fena; Staff 2 (MLS 2)
Founded 1979
Library Holdings: Bk Titles 5,000; Per Subs 100
Subject Interests: Cuyuna iron range, Ethnicity, Genealogy, Labor, Local

history, Mining, Oral hist, Photog hist, Vermilion iron range
Special Collections: Butler Brothers/Hanna Mining Company records; Iron Range City and township government records; Iron Range manuscript records for local organizations; Jones & Laughlin Hill Annex Mining Records; LTV Hist Coll; Oliver Mining Co drawings, survey materials, photographs; US Steel Photo Coll; USDA Superior National Forest Records
Publications: Entrepreneurs & Immigrants: Life on the Industrial Frontier of Northeastern Minnesota
Partic in Arrowhead Libr Systs; Minn Interlibr Telecommunication Exchange; North Country Library Cooperative; OCLC Online Computer Library Center, Inc
Friends of the Library Group

CLARA CITY

P CLARA CITY PUBLIC LIBRARY,* 42 W Center Ave, 56222-0651. SAN 347-688X. Tel: 320-847-3535. FAX: 320-847-3535. *Librn*, Karen Rothers
1997-1998 Income $34,745. Mats Exp $9,660, Books $7,650, Per/Ser (Incl. Access Fees) $1,400. Sal $21,950
Library Holdings: Bk Vols 16,875
Mem of Pioneerland Library System

CLIMAX

P CLIMAX PUBLIC LIBRARY,* 102 Great Northern Ave Box 6, 56523-0006. SAN 347-7215. Tel: 218-857-2455. E-Mail: climax@northernlights.lib.mn.us. *Br Coordr*, Jane Vigness
Founded 1960. Pop 787
Library Holdings: Bk Vols 5,410; Per Subs 18
Mem of Lake Agassiz Regional Library
Partic in Northern Lights Library Network
Friends of the Library Group

CLOQUET

S CARLTON COUNTY HISTORY & HERITAGE CENTER,* 406 Cloquet Ave, 55720. SAN 328-1639. Tel: 218-879-1938. *Dir*, Marlene Wisuri
Library Holdings: Bk Titles 300
Subject Interests: Local history
Special Collections: Carlton County History Coll; The Fires of 1918 Coll, Photog
Publications: Crossroads in Time: History of Carlton County Fury of The Flames; Reflections of our Past, pictorial history of Carlton County
Restriction: Non-circulating to the public

P CLOQUET PUBLIC LIBRARY,* 320 14th St, 55720-2100. SAN 308-5406. Tel: 218-879-1531. FAX: 218-879-6531. Web Site: www.cloquet.lib.mn.us. *Librn*, Mary Lukkarila; E-Mail: mlukkari@arrowhead.lib.mn.us; *Ch Servs*, Judy Nelson; Staff 9 (MLS 2, Non-MLS 7)
Founded 1895. Pop 11,122; Circ 187,113
Jan 1998-Dec 1999 Income $419,183, City $394,077, Locally Generated Income $25,106. Mats Exp $47,135, Books $36,135, Per/Ser (Incl. Access Fees) $6,000. Sal $285,592
Library Holdings: Bk Vols 42,430; Per Subs 177
Automation Activity & Vendor Info: (Cataloging) CARL
Mem of Arrowhead Library System
Partic in North Country Library Cooperative
Friends of the Library Group

COKATO

P COKATO LIBRARY,* 175 Fourth St W, PO Box 686, 55321-0269. SAN 347-8297. Tel: 320-286-5760. FAX: 320-286-5760. Web Site: www.griver.org. *In Charge*, Mary Ackerman
Pop 4,053; Circ 46,467
Library Holdings: Bk Vols 13,771; Per Subs 40
Mem of Great River Regional Library
Open Mon 2-6, Tues & Thurs 2-8, Wed 10-2, Fri 10-12 & 2-6, Sat 10-12

COLD SPRING

P COLD SPRING LIBRARY,* 27 Red River Rd, 56320. SAN 347-8327. Tel: 320-685-8281. FAX: 320-685-8281. Web Site: www.griver.org. *In Charge*, Jan Ross
Pop 5,499; Circ 59,132
Library Holdings: Bk Vols 11,722; Per Subs 38
Mem of Great River Regional Library
Mon 12-6, Tues & Thurs 2-8, Wed 10-1 & 2-6, Fri 10-1 & 2-5, Sat 10-1

COLERAINE

P COLERAINE PUBLIC LIBRARY,* 203 Cole Ave, PO Box 225, 55722-0225. SAN 308-5422. Tel: 218-245-2315. FAX: 218-245-2315. *Librn*, Peggy Karstens
Founded 1911. Pop 2,921; Circ 23,283
Library Holdings: Bk Titles 17,000; Per Subs 40
Special Collections: Historic Photographs of Local Area; Local History Items; Promotional Items of Local Businesses of the Past
Mem of Arrowhead Library System

COLUMBIA HEIGHTS

P COLUMBIA HEIGHTS PUBLIC LIBRARY,* 820 40th Ave NE, 55421. SAN 308-5449. Tel: 612-782-2805. FAX: 612-717-3262. *Dir*, Rebecca Loader; *Ad Servs*, Mary M Kloss; *Ch Servs*, Marsha Tubbs; Staff 3 (MLS 1, Non-MLS 2)
Founded 1928. Pop 23,977; Circ 120,000
Library Holdings: Bk Titles 67,000; Per Subs 120
Mem of Metrop Libr Serv Agency
Special Services for the Deaf - TTY machine
Friends of the Library Group

COMFREY

P COMFREY PUBLIC LIBRARY,* 305 Ochre St W, 56019-1166. SAN 308-5457. Tel: 507-877-6600. *In Charge*, Jane Evers
Library Holdings: Bk Vols 12,000; Bk Titles 11,000; Per Subs 30
Mem of Traverse Des Sioux Library System
Friends of the Library Group

COOK

P COOK PUBLIC LIBRARY,* PO Box 126, 55723-0126. SAN 320-8958. Tel: 218-666-2210. FAX: 218-666-2210. *Librn*, Lois Larson
Pop 800; Circ 4,885
Library Holdings: Bk Vols 5,000
Subject Interests: Fishing, Outdoor hunting
Mem of Arrowhead Library System
Friends of the Library Group

COON RAPIDS

J ANOKA-RAMSEY COMMUNITY COLLEGE LIBRARY, 11200 Mississippi Blvd NW, 55433. SAN 308-5465. Tel: 763-422-3378. Interlibrary Loan Service Tel: 763-422-3370. FAX: 763-422-3341. *Librn*, Gina Pancerella-Willis; Tel: 763-422-3376, E-Mail: panccrgi@an.cc.mn.us; Staff 3 (MLS 2, Non-MLS 1)
Founded 1965
Library Holdings: Bk Vols 40,481; Per Subs 250
Automation Activity & Vendor Info: (Circulation) PALS; (Course Reserve) PALS; (ILL) PALS; (OPAC) PALS
Partic in Mintex Libr Info Network; OCLC Online Computer Library Center, Inc
Departmental Libraries:
CAMBRIDGE CAMPUS, 300 Polk St S, Cambridge, 55008. SAN 377-838X. Tel: 612-689-7011. FAX: 612-689-7050. Web Site: www.cc.cc.mn.us/library/. *Dir*, Bonnie Boese; Tel: 612-689-7012, E-Mail: boesebo@cc.cc.mn.us
Library Holdings: Bk Vols 10,000; Per Subs 125
Automation Activity & Vendor Info: (Cataloging) PALS; (Circulation) PALS; (Course Reserve) PALS; (OPAC) PALS
Database Vendor: IAC - Info Trac, IAC - SearchBank, OCLC - First Search
Partic in MINITEX Library Information Network; MNSCU/PALS

S YAMAHA MOTOR CORPORATION USA, Minnesota Research & Development Library, 1255 Main St, 55448. SAN 324-6906. Tel: 763-755-2743. FAX: 763-754-6939.; Staff 1 (MLS 1)
Founded 1979
Library Holdings: Bk Vols 500; Per Subs 110
Subject Interests: Bus, Engineering, Mgt
Special Collections: Patent Records; Snowmobile Laws & Accident Records; Snowmobile maps; Society of Automotive Engineers, papers
Restriction: Not open to public

COSMOS

P COSMOS PUBLIC LIBRARY, 209 Milky Way St S, PO Box 68, 56228-0068. SAN 348-1085. Tel: 320-877-7757. FAX: 320-877-7757. E-Mail: cosmos@cosmos.lib.mn.us. *Librn*, Brenda Zins; E-Mail: brendaz@cosmos.lib.mn.us; Staff 1 (Non-MLS 1)
Pop 597; Circ 16,722
Jan 2000-Dec 2000 Income $31,241, County $21,067, Locally Generated Income $70, Other $10,104. Mats Exp $2,800, Books $2,300, Per/Ser (Incl. Access Fees) $500. Sal $20,544
Library Holdings: Bk Vols 4,216; Per Subs 65
Mem of Pioneerland Library System

CROOKSTON

P CROOKSTON PUBLIC LIBRARY, 110 N Ash St, 56716-1702. SAN 347-724X. Tel: 218-281-4522. FAX: 218-281-4523. E-Mail: crookston@northernlights.lib.mn.us. *Br Coordr*, Sister Laurian Lasha; Staff 10 (MLS 2, Non-MLS 8)
Founded 1903. Pop 11,000
Library Holdings: Bk Vols 56,590; Per Subs 107
Mem of Lake Agassiz Regional Library
Partic in Northern Lights Library Network
Friends of the Library Group

C UNIVERSITY OF MINNESOTA, CROOKSTON, Media Resources - Kiehle Library, 2900 University Ave, 56716-0801. SAN 308-5481. Tel: 218-281-8399. FAX: 218-281-8080. Web Site: www.zrk.umn.edu. *Dir*, Owen Williams; *Acq, Coll Develop*, Jim Carlson; *ILL*, Krista Proulx
Founded 1966. Enrl 1,500; Fac 75 Sal $111,000
Library Holdings: Bk Titles 31,785; Per Subs 766
Special Collections: Agriculture, Business, Foods, Equine Research Center, Hospitality, Minnesota Census Data, UMC Archives, Vertical Files
Partic in Minn Interlibr Telecommunication Exchange; Northern Lights Library Network; OCLC Online Computer Library Center, Inc

CROSBY

P JESSE F HALLETT MEMORIAL LIBRARY,* 101 First St SE, 56441. SAN 308-549X. Tel: 218-546-8005. FAX: 218-546-7287. *Librn*, Jeanette Smith
Founded 1914. Pop 2,241; Circ 11,869
Library Holdings: Bk Vols 40,000; Per Subs 89
Friends of the Library Group

DASSELL

P DASSEL PUBLIC LIBRARY,* 460 Third St N, PO Box 385, 55325-0385. SAN 348-1115. Tel: 320-275-3756.
Founded 1972
Library Holdings: Bk Titles 7,000; Per Subs 25
Mem of Pioneerland Library System
Branch of Pioneerland Library System

DAWSON

P DAWSON-CARNEGIE LIBRARY, 676 Pine St, 56232-0469. SAN 347-691X. Tel: 320-769-2069. FAX: 320-769-2170. E-Mail: dawson@dawson.lib.mn.us. *Dir*, Pamela Helgeson; E-Mail: pamh@dawson.lib.mn.us
Pop 3,972; Circ 53,511
Library Holdings: Bk Vols 25,000; Per Subs 55
Publications: Article Dawson Sentinel
Mem of Pioneerland Library System
Reading to sight-impaired every Thurs 2-3 pm

DELANO

P DELANO LIBRARY, 140 Bridge Ave E, PO Box 677, 55328-0677. SAN 347-8351. Tel: 612-972-3467. FAX: 612-972-3467. Web Site: www.griver.org. *In Charge*, Carol Plocher
Pop 5,451; Circ 49,958
Library Holdings: Bk Vols 11,804; Per Subs 51
Mem of Great River Regional Library
Open Mon 10-1 & 2-6, Tues 10-1 & 2-8, Wed 2-6, Thurs 2-8, Sat 10-2
Friends of the Library Group

DETROIT LAKES

S BECKER COUNTY HISTORICAL SOCIETY, Walter D Bird Memorial Historical Library, PO Box 622, 56502. SAN 327-831X. Tel: 218-847-2938. FAX: 218-847-5048. *Dir*, Dean Sather
Library Holdings: Bk Vols 4,000
Friends of the Library Group

P DETROIT LAKES PUBLIC LIBRARY, 1000 Washington Ave, 56501-3035. SAN 347-7274. Tel: 218-847-2168. FAX: 218-847-2160. E-Mail: detroit@northernlights.lib.mn.us. Web Site: www.dlpl.org. *Dir*, Ruth Solie; E-Mail: solier@northernlights.lib.mn.us; Staff 2 (MLS 2)
Founded 1908. Pop 21,190
Library Holdings: Bk Vols 32,669; Per Subs 134
Database Vendor: DRA
Mem of Lake Agassiz Regional Library
Partic in Northern Lights Library Network
Friends of the Library Group

DODGE CENTER

P DODGE CENTER PUBLIC LIBRARY, 13 First Ave NW, PO Box 430, 55927-0430. SAN 308-5503. Tel: 507-374-2275. FAX: 507-374-2694. *Librn*, Angela Meyer; *Asst Librn*, Jean Kent
Founded 1909. Pop 4,702; Circ 33,391
Library Holdings: Bk Vols 15,504
Database Vendor: DRA
Mem of Southeastern Libraries Cooperating (SELCO)
Friends of the Library Group

DULUTH

C COLLEGE OF SAINT SCHOLASTICA LIBRARY, 1200 Kenwood Ave, 55811-4199. SAN 347-2809. Tel: 218-723-6140. Interlibrary Loan Service Tel: 218-723-6178. FAX: 218-723-5948. E-Mail: library@.css.edu. Web Site: www.css.edu/depts/library/lib.htm. *Coll Develop, Dir*, Rachel Applegate; *Per*, Kevin McGrew; *Cat*, Laura Hoelter; *Online Servs, Ref*, Todd White; *ILL*, Barbara Werner; *Circ*, Karen Ostovich; *Acq*, Julie Walkowiak; *Tech Servs*, Barbara Werner; Staff 4 (MLS 4)
Enrl 1,850; Fac 110; Highest Degree: Master
Library Holdings: Bk Vols 100,000; Per Subs 759
Subject Interests: Gerontology, Health sci, Indian studies, Nursing, Physical therapy, Relig studies
Special Collections: American Indian Studies Coll; Children's Coll
Publications: Student Handbook for Off-Campus Programs; The Browser
Partic in MINITEX Library Information Network; MNSCU/PALS; North Country Library Cooperative; OCLC Online Computer Library Center, Inc

S DULUTH NEWS-TRIBUNE LIBRARY,* 424 W First St, 55802. SAN 326-3304. Tel: 218-723-5309. FAX: 218-720-4120. Web Site: www.duluthnews.com. *Librn*, June M Rudd
Founded 1975
Restriction: Staff use only

P DULUTH PUBLIC LIBRARY, 520 W Superior St, 55802. SAN 347-2922. Tel: 218-723-3821. Circulation Tel: 218-723-3814. Reference Tel: 218-723-3802. TDD: 218-723-3809. FAX: 218-723-3822. E-Mail: webmail@duluth.lib.mn.us. Web Site: www.duluth.lib.mn.us. *Dir*, Beth Kelly; Tel: 218-723-3825, E-Mail: bkelly@duluth.lib.mn.us; *Ad Servs, Br Coordr*, Mary Caven; *ILL, Ref*, David Ouse; *Ch Servs*, Judy Sheriff; *Acq*, Myra Kenner; *Spec Coll*, Kristine Aho; *Tech Servs*, Jan Simmons; *Commun Servs*, Karen Richgruber; *Doc*, Ann Jenkins; *Online Servs*, Denise Perry; Staff 77 (MLS 22, Non-MLS 55)
Founded 1890. Pop 85,249; Circ 902,640
Jan 1999-Dec 2000 Income (Main Library and Branch Library) $3,714,554, State $76,332, City $3,346,396, Other $291,826. Mats Exp $356,928, Books $301,848, AV Equip $43,359, Electronic Ref Mat (Incl. Access Fees) $11,721. Sal $2,573,698
Library Holdings: Bk Vols 381,687; Per Subs 666
Special Collections: Adaptive Toys; Duluth; Great Lakes Region; Minnesota Coll; Sign Language Video Tapes
Database Vendor: GaleNet, ProQuest
Publications: Index to Duluth Newspapers
Mem of Arrowhead Library System
Partic in Minn Interlibr Telecommunication Exchange; North Country Library Cooperative
Special Services for the Deaf - TTY machine
Special Services for the Blind - Kurzweil Reading Machine
Special services to persons with disabilities - adaptive micros, reading equipment; Special Needs Center - 218-723-3809
Friends of the Library Group
Branches: 3
MOUNT ROYAL, 105 Mount Royal Shopping Circle, 55803. SAN 378-1976. Tel: 218-723-3844. FAX: 218-723-3846. *In Charge*, Patricia Whalen
Friends of the Library Group
SPECIAL NEEDS FOR HANDICAPPED Tel: 218-723-3809. FAX: 218-723-3815. *Librn*, Lucie Holzemer
Special Collections: Adaptive toys; Literacy Coll; Sign Language; video cassettes
Friends of the Library Group
WEST DULUTH, 5830 Grand Ave, 55807. SAN 372-4905. Tel: 218-723-3801. FAX: 218-723-3820. *In Charge*, Clarice Hietala
Library Holdings: Bk Vols 29,000

S LAKE SUPERIOR MUSEUM OF TRANSPORTATION LIBRARY, 506 W Michigan, 55802. SAN 373-0751. Tel: 218-733-7590. FAX: 218-733-7596. E-Mail: lsrm@cpinternet.com. *Curator, Dir*, Tom Gannon
Library Holdings: Bk Vols 550; Per Subs 20
Subject Interests: Railroads

M MILLER-DWAN MEDICAL CENTER, Tilderquist Memorial Library, 502 E Second St, 55805. SAN 308-5570. Tel: 218-720-1362. FAX: 218-733-2322. *Librn, Online Servs*, Annelie Sober; E-Mail: asober@mdmc.sisunet.org; Staff 1 (MLS 1)
Founded 1973
Library Holdings: Bk Titles 600; Per Subs 168

Subject Interests: Allied health, Medicine, Nursing, Supvr mgt
Partic in Arrowhead Health Sciences Library Network; Greater Midwest Regional Medical Libr Network; North Country Library Cooperative

G NATURAL RESOURCES RESEARCH INSTITUTE, Natural Resources Library,* University of Minnesota - Duluth, 5013 Miller Trunk Hwy, 55811. SAN 325-190X. Tel: 218-720-4235. FAX: 218-720-4219. *Librn*, Susan Rhead Hendrickson; E-Mail: shendric@d.umn.edu; Staff 3 (MLS 1, Non-MLS 2)
Library Holdings: Bk Titles 7,000; Per Subs 250
Subject Interests: Ecosystems, Environ sci, Forest products, Minerals, Peat
Special Collections: Peat
Publications: Quarterly Report
Partic in Dialog Corporation; MINITEX Library Information Network; North Country Library Cooperative; OCLC Online Computer Library Center, Inc

S NORTHEAST MINNESOTA HISTORICAL CENTER, University of Minnesota-Duluth Library, Annex 209, 10 University Dr, 55812. SAN 308-5589. Reference Tel: 218-726-8526. FAX: 218-726-6205. Web Site: www.d.umn.edu/lib. *Curator*, Patricia Maus; E-Mail: pmaus@d.umn.edu
Founded 1977
Library Holdings: Bk Titles 2,000
Subject Interests: Commercial fishing on Lake Superior's N shore, Environ, Hist of NE Minn, Lumbering, Mining, Soc welfare, Transportation, Women in bus
Special Collections: Historical Photographs
Publications: Guide to the Collections of the NEMHC (1988)
Partic in North Country Library Cooperative

R PILGRIM CONGREGATIONAL CHURCH LIBRARY, 2310 E Fourth St, 55812. SAN 328-1159. Tel: 218-724-8503.; Staff 2 (MLS 1, Non-MLS 1)
Founded 1918
Library Holdings: Bk Vols 1,900; Bk Titles 1,850; Per Subs 5
Special Collections: Bible (Liberal Theology Coll), bks; UCC & Congregational History Coll

L SAINT LOUIS COUNTY LAW LIBRARY,* 100 N Fifth Ave W, Rm 515, 55802. SAN 308-5538. Tel: 218-726-2611. FAX: 218-726-2612. *Librn*, Michele Des Rosier
Library Holdings: Bk Titles 20,000; Per Subs 15

M ST LUKE'S HOSPITAL, Hilding Medical & Health Sciences Library, 915 E First St, 55805. SAN 308-5627. Tel: 218-726-5320. FAX: 218-726-5181. Web Site: www.slhduluth.com/. *Librn*, Doreen Roberts; E-Mail: droberts@slhduluth.com
Founded 1941
Library Holdings: Per Subs 230
Subject Interests: Clinical medicine, Nursing
Publications: Hilding Library Letter
Partic in Arrowhead Health Sciences Library Network

M SAINT MARY'S MEDICAL CENTER, Health Sciences Library, 407 E Third St, 55805-1984. SAN 308-5635. Tel: 218-786-4396. FAX: 218-786-4249. E-Mail: library@smdc.org. *Librn*, Elizabeth Sobczak
Library Holdings: Bk Titles 1,792; Per Subs 275
Subject Interests: Allied health, Medicine, Nursing
Partic in Arrowhead Health Sciences Library Network

G UNITED STATES ENVIRONMENTAL PROTECTION AGENCY, Mid Continent Ecology Division, 6201 Congdon Blvd, 55804. SAN 308-5554. Tel: 218-529-5000. Interlibrary Loan Service Tel: 218-529-5085. Reference Tel: 218-529-5085. FAX: 218-529-5003. *Librn*, John Bankson; Tel: 218-529-5085, E-Mail: bankson.john@epamail.epa.gov; Staff 2 (MLS 1, Non-MLS 1)
Founded 1967
Oct 2000-Sep 2001 Income $80,000
Library Holdings: Bk Vols 12,000; Bk Titles 5,000; Per Subs 145
Subject Interests: Effluent testing, Freshwater toxicology, Predictive toxicity model
Partic in Arrowhead Health Sciences Library Network; Fedlink; LVIS; MINITEX Library Information Network; North Country Library Cooperative

C UNIVERSITY OF MINNESOTA, DULUTH, 10 University Dr, 55812-2496. SAN 347-3104. Tel: 218-726-8102. Circulation Tel: 218-726-6120. Reference Tel: 218-726-8100. FAX: 218-726-6205. Web Site: www.d.umn.edu/lib. *Dir*, Basil Sozansky; Tel: 218-726-6562, E-Mail: bsozansk@d.umn.edu; *Asst Dir*, Elizabeth Benson Johnson; Tel: 218-726-6561, E-Mail: ejohnso1@d.umn.edu; *ILL*, Adele Krusz; *Acq*, Anne Houde; *Archivist*, Kathryn Fuller; *Syst Coordr*, Darlene Morris; *Tech Servs*, Joe Holtermann; Staff 38 (MLS 16, Non-MLS 22)
Founded 1947. Enrl 7,789; Fac 484; Highest Degree: Master
Jul 1999-Jun 2000 Income (Main Library Only) $2,945,977. Mats Exp $1,232,522, Books $167,327, Per/Ser (Incl. Access Fees) $841,734, Presv $27,462, Electronic Ref Mat (Incl. Access Fees) $195,999. Sal $1,402,052 (Prof $479,239)
Library Holdings: Bk Vols 621,141; Bk Titles 310,385; Per Subs 4,684
Special Collections: Ramseyer Bible; UMD Archives; Voyager
Automation Activity & Vendor Info: (Acquisitions) SIRSI; (Cataloging) SIRSI; (Circulation) SIRSI; (Course Reserve) SIRSI; (Media Booking) SIRSI; (OPAC) SIRSI; (OPAC) SIRSI; (Serials) TLC
Publications: Serials Holding List
Partic in MINITEX Library Information Network; OCLC Online Computer Library Center, Inc
Friends of the Library Group
Departmental Libraries:
CM HEALTH SCIENCE LIBRARY, 10 University Dr, 55812. SAN 347-3139. Tel: 218-726-8733. Interlibrary Loan Service Tel: 218-726-8166. FAX: 218-726-6205. Web Site: www.d.umn.edu/lib. *Bibliog Instr, Dir, Online Servs, Ref*, Martha Eberhart; *ILL*, Heather McLean; *Coll Develop*, Diane Ebro; Staff 4 (MLS 1, Non-MLS 3)
Founded 1971. Enrl 109; Fac 45; Highest Degree: Master
Jul 1997-Jun 1998 Mats Exp $214,483, Books $4,500, Per/Ser (Incl. Access Fees) $200,829, Presv $9,154. Sal $174,931 (Prof $82,143)
Library Holdings: Bk Vols 26,289; Bk Titles 22,093; Per Subs 336
Publications: Serials Holdings List for Health Science Library, University of Minn-Duluth & Arrowhead Professional Library Asn
Partic in Greater Midwest Regional Medical Libr Network; Minn Interlibr Telecommunication Exchange
Friends of the Library Group

EAGAN

P DAKOTA COUNTY LIBRARY, 1340 Wescott Rd, 55123-1099. SAN 347-2205. Tel: 651-688-1500. FAX: 651-688-1530. E-Mail: library@dakota.lib.mn.us. Web Site: www.co.dakota.mn.us/library. *Dir*, William G Asp; *Asst Dir*, Roseanne Byrne; *Ref*, Elizabeth Zdon; *Ch Servs*, Bernadette Couillard; *Tech Servs*, Ardell Bengtson; *Govt Doc*, Pat Odell; *Media Spec*, Paul Deaven; Staff 62 (MLS 51, Non-MLS 11)
Founded 1959. Pop 318,988; Circ 3,346,331
Jan 1999-Dec 1999 Income $7,082,538, County $6,690,009, Locally Generated Income $267,956, Other $124,573. Mats Exp $1,013,780, Books $936,241, Per/Ser (Incl. Access Fees) $58,427, Other Print Mats $19,112. Sal $5,115,005
Library Holdings: Bk Vols 902,640; Per Subs 1,852
Automation Activity & Vendor Info: (Acquisitions) epixtech, inc.; (Cataloging) epixtech, inc.; (Circulation) epixtech, inc.
Partic in Metropolitan Library Service Agency
Friends of the Library Group
Branches: 8
BURNHAVEN COMMUNITY, 1101 W County Rd 42, Burnsville, 55337. SAN 347-223X. Tel: 651-435-7177. FAX: 651-435-3476. Web Site: www.co.dakota.mn.us/library. *Librn*, Nancy Wisser
Circ 630,627
Library Holdings: Bk Vols 188,092; Per Subs 322
FARMINGTON BRANCH, 508 Third St, Farmington, 55024-1394. SAN 347-2264. Tel: 651-463-7990. FAX: 651-463-7979. Web Site: www.co.dakota.mn.us/library. *Librn*, Judy Bonniwell
Circ 139,124
Library Holdings: Bk Vols 62,372; Per Subs 137
Friends of the Library Group
GALAXIE, 14955 Galaxie Ave, Apple Valley, 55124. SAN 370-9272. Tel: 651-891-7045. FAX: 651-891-7048. Web Site: www.co.dakota.mn.us/library. *Librn*, Sandra Moe
Circ 909,286
Library Holdings: Bk Vols 190,173; Per Subs 334
HERITAGE, 20085 Heritage Dr, Lakeville, 55044. *Librn*, Mary Johnson
Library Holdings: Bk Vols 56,000; Per Subs 156
Friends of the Library Group
INVER GLEN, 8098 Blaine Ave, Inver Grove Heights, 55076. Tel: 651-552-7527. FAX: 651-552-7522. *Librn*, Kalla Kalloway
Library Holdings: Bk Vols 27,000; Per Subs 83
Friends of the Library Group
PLEASANT HILL, 1490 S Frontage Rd, Hastings, 55033. SAN 347-2299. Tel: 651-437-5286. FAX: 651-480-4944. Web Site: www.co.dakota.mn.us/library. *Librn*, Murray Wilson
Circ 284,072
Library Holdings: Bk Vols 90,072; Per Subs 186
Friends of the Library Group
WENTWORTH, 199 E Wentworth Ave, West Saint Paul, 55118. SAN 347-2329. Tel: 651-457-8497. FAX: 651-451-1914. Web Site: www.co.dakota.mn.us/library. *Librn*, Kay Brown
Circ 497,024
Library Holdings: Bk Vols 130,326; Per Subs 219
WESCOTT, 1340 Wescott Rd, 55123. SAN 347-2256. Tel: 651-688-1500. FAX: 651-688-1515. Web Site: www.co.dakota.mn.us/library. *Librn*, Eric Austin
Circ 841,589
Library Holdings: Bk Vols 241,585; Per Subs 357
Friends of the Library Group
Bookmobiles: 1

S INTERNATIONAL RESEARCH & EVALUATION, Information & Technology Transfer Resource Center Library, 21098 IRE Control Ctr, 55121-0098. SAN 308-5643. Tel: 952-888-9635. Reference Tel: 952-491-1882. Toll Free Tel: 888-888-9245. FAX: 952-888-9124. E-Mail: ireittn@gte.net. Web Site: ire-ittn.com. *Librn*, Randall L Voight; E-Mail: voight/

ireittn@gte.net; *Online Servs*, George Franklin; *Bibliog Instr*, Sharon King; Staff 88 (MLS 31, Non-MLS 57)
Founded 1972
Jan 1999-Dec 1999 Income $20,410,685, Federal $3,179,635, Parent Institution $17,231,050. Mats Exp $10,696,990, Books $3,769,961, Per/Ser (Incl. Access Fees) $2,136,613, Micro $336,092, AV Equip $479,835, Other Print Mats $875,337, Manuscripts & Archives $537,219, Electronic Ref Mat (Incl. Access Fees) $2,561,933. Sal $3,768,607 (Prof $1,611,005)
Library Holdings: Bk Titles 5,913,654; Per Subs 17,502; Spec Interest Per Sub 1,735
Subject Interests: Acid rain, Alternative fuels, Alternative healing, Artificial intelligence, Biometrics, Derivatives, Disaster planning, Ergonomics, Genetics, Geothermal, GIS, Global warming, Law enforcement, Photovoltaic cells, Resource recovery mgt, Risk mgt, Robotics, Wellness
Special Collections: Health Sciences & Infrastructure
Publications: Airport Guide; Capsule Newsletter; Index to Indexes; Information Age (monthly newsletter); New Business Register; Reference Guide to Surveys; The Source (reference guide)
Restriction: Staff use only
Partic in Dialog Corporation
Parent Company is providing to five Third-World countries a 2 million documents embedded supercomputer
Friends of the Library Group

S LOCKHEED-MARTIN TACTICAL DEFENSE SYSTEMS, Information Resources, 3333 Pilot Knob Rd, 55121. (Mail add: PO Box 64445, 55164-0445), SAN 308-7948. Tel: 651-456-4879. FAX: 651-456-3098. *Librn*, Janep J Perron; E-Mail: jperron@lmco.com. Subject Specialists: *Aerospace eng*, Janep J Perron; *Avionics*, Janep J Perron; *Computer science*, Janep J Perron; Staff 3 (MLS 1, Non-MLS 2)
Library Holdings: Bk Titles 17,000; Per Subs 250
Subject Interests: Computers, Electronics, Mathematics, Mfg, Mgt, Physics
Database Vendor: OCLC - First Search
Restriction: Not open to public
Function: Research library
Partic in Dialog Corporation; OCLC Online Computer Library Center, Inc

L WEST GROUP, Library Services, 610 Opperman Dr, 55123. SAN 371-7143. Tel: 651-687-4173. FAX: 651-687-5440. *Librn*, Aimee Blatz; E-Mail: a.blatz@westgroup.com; Staff 6 (MLS 1, Non-MLS 5)
Library Holdings: Bk Vols 300,000; Bk Titles 6,000; Per Subs 500
Subject Interests: Law

EAGLE BEND

P EAGLE BEND LIBRARY,* 127 E Main, PO Box 238, 56446-0238. SAN 321-9267. Tel: 218-738-4590. FAX: 218-738-4590. *In Charge*, Kay Lundgren
Pop 2,902; Circ 28,265
Library Holdings: Bk Vols 15,000; Per Subs 45
Mem of Great River Regional Library
Open Mon 9-12 & 4-7, Tues & Thurs 9-1 & 2-6, Sat 9am-12pm

EAST GRAND FORKS

P EAST GRAND FORKS PUBLIC LIBRARY,* 915 22nd St NW, PO Box 419, 56721. SAN 308-5651. Tel: 218-773-9121. FAX: 218-773-9121. *Librn*, Charlotte Helgeson
Founded 1963. Pop 8,537; Circ 59,872
Library Holdings: Bk Vols 20,000; Per Subs 59
Friends of the Library Group

EDEN PRAIRIE

G UNITED STATES DEPARTMENT OF ENERGY, Environmental Measurements Lab Library-Technical Library, 376 Hudson St, 55344. SAN 312-1178. Tel: 952-934-4920. FAX: 952-934-3604. Web Site: www.eml.doe.gov. *Tech Servs*, Frances DiPasqua; E-Mail: fdipasq@eml.doe.gov
Founded 1947
Library Holdings: Bk Vols 13,500
Subject Interests: Chemistry, Environmental studies, Physics
Publications: Topical, Quarterly & Internal
Mem of US Govt Libr
Partic in Dialog Corporation

EDGERTON

P RUNALS MEMORIAL LIBRARY,* 750 First Ave W, PO Box 25, 56128-0025. SAN 324-1416. Tel: 507-442-7071. *Librn*, Elberta De Jager; E-Mail: edejager@edgerton.lib.mn.us; *Asst Librn*, Jo Anne Landhuis
Founded 1950. Pop 1,123; Circ 32,480
1998-1999 Income $22,034, City $11,300, County $7,258, Locally Generated Income $1,407, Other $2,069. Mats Exp $5,884, Books $4,607, Per/Ser (Incl. Access Fees) $757. Sal $10,755
Library Holdings: Bk Vols 11,000
Mem of Plum Creek Library System

EDINA

M FAIRVIEW-SOUTHDALE HOSPITAL, Mary Ann King Health Sciences Library, 6401 France Ave S, 55435. SAN 308-5678. Tel: 612-924-5005. FAX: 612-924-5933. E-Mail: mcarlso1@fairview.org. *Librn*, Mary B Carlson; E-Mail: mcarlsol@fairview.org
Founded 1975
Library Holdings: Bk Vols 1,100; Bk Titles 1,000; Per Subs 170
Subject Interests: Business, Cardiology, Nursing, Obstetrics, Orthopedics
Partic in Metronet; Midwest Health Sci Libr Network; Twin Cities Biomedical Consortium

ELBOW LAKE

P ELBOW LAKE PUBLIC LIBRARY, Thorsen Memorial Library, PO Box 1040, 56531-1040. SAN 308-5686. Tel: 218-685-6850. FAX: 218-685-6852. E-Mail: library@runestone.net. Web Site: www.runestone.net/~library/. *Coll Develop, Librn*, Gail Hedstrom; *Asst Librn*, Liza Goergen
Pop 1,484; Circ 5,293
Library Holdings: Bk Vols 13,000; Per Subs 40
Subject Interests: Norwegian lit
Mem of Viking Library System

ELK RIVER

P ELK RIVER LIBRARY, 413 Proctor Ave, 55330. SAN 347-8386. Tel: 612-441-1641. FAX: 612-241-9286. Web Site: www.griver.org. *In Charge*, Margaret Stoffers
Pop 18,267; Circ 163,731
Library Holdings: Bk Vols 31,921; Per Subs 69
Mem of Great River Regional Library
Open Mon & Wed 10-8, Tues & Thurs 12-8, Fri 10-5, Sat 9am-12pm
Friends of the Library Group

ELMORE

P ELMORE PUBLIC LIBRARY,* 302 E Willis St, PO Box 56, 56027-0056. SAN 376-7159. Tel: 507-943-3150. FAX: 507-943-3234. *Librn*, Nancy Ziegler
Library Holdings: Bk Titles 1,000
Mem of Traverse Des Sioux Library System
Open Tues 4-6, Wed 2-8 & Fri 2-5

ELY

J ARROWHEAD COMMUNITY COLLEGE, Vermilion Campus Library,* 1900 E Camp St, 55731. SAN 308-5716. Tel: 218-365-7226. FAX: 218-365-7218.
Founded 1922. Enrl 475
Library Holdings: Bk Vols 20,000; Per Subs 200
Partic in Minn Interlibr Telecommunication Exchange; OCLC Online Computer Library Center, Inc

P ELY PUBLIC LIBRARY, 30 S First Ave E, 55731. SAN 308-5708. Tel: 218-365-5140. FAX: 218-365-6107. Web Site: www.elylibrary.org. *Dir*, Rachel Heinrich; Staff 2 (MLS 1, Non-MLS 1)
Founded 1922. Pop 3,883; Circ 42,529
Jan 1999-Dec 1999 Income $141,920. Mats Exp $22,034
Library Holdings: Bk Vols 30,000; Per Subs 80
Function: Photocopies available
Mem of Arrowhead Library System
Friends of the Library Group

ELYSIAN

S LESUEUR COUNTY HISTORICAL SOCIETY MUSEUM LIBRARY,* 301 NE Second, 56028-0240. (Mail add: PO Box 240, 56028-0240), SAN 326-1336. Tel: 507-267-4620. *Dir*, Nancy Burhop; Staff 4 (MLS 1, Non-MLS 3)
Library Holdings: Bk Vols 2,000
Special Collections: Adolf Dehn (Dehn Art Coll), originals, signed lithos; Albert-Christ-Janner, Artist; David Maass Wildlife Coll; Lloyd Herfindahl (Herfindahl Coll), originals, signed lithos; Roger Puess, Artist Wildlife; signed lithos; Victor Christ-Janer, Architect
Special Services for the Deaf - Staff with knowledge of sign language
Open May weekends, June, July & Aug, Wed-Sun 1:00-5:00, Sept weekends except Labor Day weekend, also by appt, closed winter

EVELETH

P EVELETH PUBLIC LIBRARY, 614 Pierce St, 55734-1697. SAN 308-5724. Tel: 218-744-4913. FAX: 218-744-0743. *Dir*, Mary Beth Kafut; E-Mail: mkafut@arrowhead.lib.mn.us; Staff 1 (MLS 1)
Founded 1914. Pop 7,384; Circ 36,015
Jan 1999-Dec 1999 Income City $130,300. Mats Exp $18,500, Books $15,000, Per/Ser (Incl. Access Fees) $3,500. Sal $56,500 (Prof $37,840)
Library Holdings: Bk Vols 19,503; Per Subs 98
Subject Interests: Architecture, Art
Database Vendor: CARL
Mem of Arrowhead Library System

S UNITED STATES HOCKEY HALL OF FAME LIBRARY,* 801 Hat Trick Ave, PO Box 657, 55734. SAN 326-0569. Tel: 218-744-5167. FAX: 218-744-2590.
Library Holdings: Bk Titles 122

FAIRFAX

P FAIRFAX PUBLIC LIBRARY,* 124 SE First St, PO Box Q, 55332-0108. SAN 376-7728. Tel: 507-426-7269. FAX: 507-426-7256. *Librn*, Carol Thompson
Library Holdings: Bk Vols 4,500; Bk Titles 4,200; Per Subs 18
Mem of Pioneerland Library System

FAIRMONT

S MARTIN COUNTY HISTORICAL SOCIETY, INC, Pioneer Museum Library, 304 E Blue Earth Ave, 56031. SAN 370-1557. Tel: 507-235-5178. E-Mail: mchistry@bevcomm.net. *Curator*, Helen Simon; *Curator*, Muriel Malliat; Staff 4 (Non-MLS 4)
Founded 1929
Library Holdings: Bk Vols 25
Subject Interests: Am Indians, Civil War, Minnesota
Special Collections: Local newspaper file, 1874 to present
Open May-Oct: Mon-Sat 1-4:30

P MARTIN COUNTY LIBRARY,* 110 N Park St, 56031-2893. SAN 308-5767. Tel: 507-238-4207. FAX: 507-238-4208. Web Site: www.tds.lib.mn.us/martinco.htm. *Dir*, Barbara J Shultz; E-Mail: bshult@tds.lib.mn.us; *Ch Servs*, Jennifer Tow; *Tech Servs*, Nancy Warner; *Circ*, Deena Frerichs; *ILL*, Rebecca Perrine; Staff 1 (MLS 1)
Founded 1943. Pop 24,607; Circ 180,605
Library Holdings: Bk Vols 102,798; Bk Titles 79,829
Mem of Traverse Des Sioux Library System
Partic in OCLC Online Computer Library Center, Inc
Friends of the Library Group
Branches: 6
CEYLON BRANCH, 108 W Main, Ceylon, 56122. SAN 378-1992. Tel: 507-632-4496. Web Site: www.tds.lib.mn.us/martinco.htm. *Librn*, Sharon Rosen
DUNNELL BRANCH, PO Box 187, Dunnell, 56127-0187. SAN 376-9909. Tel: 507-695-2942. *Librn*, Pat Shultz
Library Holdings: Bk Vols 1,500; Bk Titles 1,000
Friends of the Library Group
SHERBURN BRANCH, 21 N Main St, Sherburn, 56171-9999. SAN 376-9917. Tel: 507-764-7611. *Librn*, Linda Hanson
Library Holdings: Bk Titles 10,000; Per Subs 16
TRIMONT BRANCH, 190 W Main, Trimont, 56176. SAN 378-2018. Tel: 507-639-2571. *Librn*, Dianne Adamson
Pop 131,556; Circ 586,628
Friends of the Library Group
TRUMAN BRANCH, 101 E Ciro, Box 97, Truman, 56088-0846. SAN 376-9925. Tel: 507-776-2717. *Librn*, Karen Vrieze
Library Holdings: Bk Titles 5,000; Per Subs 12
WELCOME BRANCH, 304 First St, Welcome, 56181. SAN 376-9933. Tel: 507-728-8740. *Librn*, Pat Schultz
Library Holdings: Bk Vols 4,000; Bk Titles 3,500

FALCON HEIGHTS

S MINNESOTA STATE HORTICULTURAL SOCIETY LIBRARY,* 1755 Prior Ave N, 55113-5549. SAN 328-4034. Tel: 651-643-3601. FAX: 651-643-3638. Web Site: www.northerngardener.org. *Dir*, Terri Goodfellow-Heyer; *Coll Develop*, Norman G Wente
Library Holdings: Bk Vols 2,000
Subject Interests: Horticulture
Special Collections: Historical Volumes relating to horticulture; Minnesota Horticulturist bound volumes from 1870s to present; Video tapes-topics relating to Northern horitcultural

FARIBAULT

P BUCKHAM MEMORIAL LIBRARY,* 11 E Division St, 55021-6056. SAN 308-5775. Tel: 507-334-2089. FAX: 507-332-9632. Web Site: www.selco.lib.mm.us/fpl. *Dir*, Peter Press; *Ch Servs*, Kathleen Ahern; *Ad Servs, Ref*, Renee Lowery; *Cat, Tech Servs*, Lisa Boevers
Founded 1897. Pop 46,087; Circ 215,881
1999-2000 Income $616,192
Library Holdings: Bk Vols 63,000; Per Subs 150
Mem of Southeastern Libraries Cooperating (SELCO)
Friends of the Library Group

P MINNESOTA LIBRARY FOR THE BLIND & PHYSICALLY HANDICAPPED, Hwy 298, PO Box 68, 55021. SAN 308-5791. Tel: 507-332-4828. Reference Tel: 507-333-4830. FAX: 507-333-4832. E-Mail: libblnd@state.mn.us. Web Site: cfl.state.mn.us/library/mlbph.html. *Librn for Blind*, Rene Perrance; Tel: 507-333-4830, E-Mail: rene.perrance@state.mn.us; Staff 11 (MLS 2, Non-MLS 9)
Founded 1933
Jul 1999-Jun 2000 Income $498,000. Mats Exp $4,600, Books $2,800, Per/Ser (Incl. Access Fees) $600, Presv $500, AV Equip $700. Sal $415,000
Automation Activity & Vendor Info: (Circulation) DRA; (OPAC) DRA
Database Vendor: DRA
Publications: Patron Newsletter (Newsletter)

S RICE COUNTY MUSEUM OF HISTORY, Archives Library, 1814 Second Ave NW, 55021. SAN 327-8336. Tel: 507-332-2121. *In Charge*, Jon Velishek
Library Holdings: Bk Vols 1,400
Publications: Portraits & Memories of Rice County; Reprinted Rice County 1882; Rice County Families

§C SOUTH CENTRAL TECHNICAL COLLEGE LIBRARY, Faribault Campus, 1225 SW Third St, 55021. SAN 375-4286. Tel: 507-334-3965. FAX: 507-332-5888. Web Site: www.sctc.mnscu.edu. *Librn, Media Spec*, Ala Garlinska; E-Mail: garlinsa@sctc.mnscu.edu
Jul 1999-Jun 2000 Income $72,423
Library Holdings: Bk Vols 3,200; Per Subs 24
Subject Interests: Carpentry
Automation Activity & Vendor Info: (Acquisitions) PALS; (Cataloging) PALS; (Circulation) PALS; (ILL) PALS; (Serials) PALS

FERGUS FALLS

SR CHURCH OF THE LUTHERAN BRETHREN - LUTHERAN BRETHREN SCHOOLS, Christiansen Memorial Library, 815 W Vernon Ave, 56537. SAN 327-7747. Tel: 218-739-3375. FAX: 218-739-3372. Web Site: www.lbs.edu/seminary. *Librn*, Barbara Ellis; E-Mail: bellis@clba.org
May 1999-Apr 2000 Income (Main Library Only) $8,000. Mats Exp $7,600, Books $4,000, Per/Ser (Incl. Access Fees) $2,600, Micro $200, AV Equip $800. Sal $11,100
Library Holdings: Bk Vols 18,000; Per Subs 100
Subject Interests: Church history, Missions, New Testament, Religion, Theology
Mem of Northern Lights Libr Network

J FERGUS FALLS COMMUNITY COLLEGE LIBRARY, 1414 College Way, 56537-1000. SAN 308-5805. Tel: 218-739-7531. FAX: 218-739-7475. Web Site: www.ff.cc.mn.us. *Librn*, Deb Kelman; E-Mail: dkelman@mail.ff.cc.mn.us
Founded 1960. Enrl 1,208; Fac 77
Library Holdings: Bk Titles 31,000; Per Subs 150
Subject Interests: Environment, Minn hist, Womens' studies
Automation Activity & Vendor Info: (Cataloging) PALS; (Circulation) PALS; (Course Reserve) PALS
Partic in Minn Interlibr Telecommunication Exchange; Northern Lights Library Network; OCLC Online Computer Library Center, Inc

P FERGUS FALLS PUBLIC LIBRARY, 205 E Hampden, 56537-2194. SAN 308-5813. Tel: 218-739-9387. FAX: 218-736-5131. E-Mail: library@fergusfalls.lib.mn.us. *Dir*, Walter J Dunlap; *Ref*, Candace Herbert; *Ch Servs*, Betty Johansen; Staff 7 (MLS 4, Non-MLS 3)
Founded 1891. Pop 13,079; Circ 310,983
Library Holdings: Bk Vols 82,100; Per Subs 208
Automation Activity & Vendor Info: (Acquisitions) epixtech, inc.; (Circulation) epixtech, inc.; (OPAC) epixtech, inc.
Database Vendor: epixtech, inc.
Mem of Viking Library System
Friends of the Library Group

M FERGUS FALLS REGIONAL TREATMENT CENTER READING ROOM,* 1400 N Union Ave, 56537-1200. SAN 327-7763. Tel: 218-739-7200. FAX: 218-739-7243.
Library Holdings: Bk Vols 980; Per Subs 20

S OTTER TAIL COUNTY HISTORICAL SOCIETY, E T Barnard Library, 1110 Lincoln Ave W, 56537. SAN 329-2789. Tel: 218-736-6038. FAX: 218-739-3075. E-Mail: otchs@prtel.com. *Librn*, Kathy Evavold; *Asst Librn*, Ann

Jordan
Founded 1927
Library Holdings: Bk Titles 300; Per Subs 25
Subject Interests: Education
Special Collections: Otter Tail County Newspapers (1871-present)
Publications: Otter Tail Record (quarterly)
Restriction: Non-circulating to the public

S OTTER TAIL POWER CO LIBRARY,* 215 S Cascade St, 56537. SAN 377-5194. Tel: 218-739-8594. FAX: 218-739-8952. *Librn*, Jo Ann Thompson; E-Mail: jthompson@otpco.com
Library Holdings: Bk Vols 450; Per Subs 500

P VIKING LIBRARY SYSTEM,* 204 N Cascade, PO Box 717, 56538-0717. SAN 308-583X. Tel: 218-739-5286. FAX: 218-739-5287. *Dir*, Peg Werner; E-Mail: pwerner@viking.lib.mn.us; *Automation Syst Coordr*, Nancy Alsop; Staff 9 (Non-MLS 9)
Founded 1975. Pop 112,970
Jan 1998-Dec 1999 Income $703,758. Mats Exp $47,000. Sal $341,000
Library Holdings: Bk Vols 27,790
Publications: AV Catalog (annual); Newsletter (bimonthly)
Member Libraries: Browns Valley Public Library; Douglas County Library; Elbow Lake Public Library; Fergus Falls Public Library; Glenwood Public Library; Hancock Community Library; New York Mills Public Library; Pelican Rapids Public Library; Perham Area Public Library; Wheaton Community Library
Partic in Minn Interlibr Telecommunication Exchange; Northern Lights Library Network

FERTILE

P FERTILE PUBLIC LIBRARY,* 101 Mill St S, PO Box 418, 56540-0418. SAN 347-7304. Tel: 218-945-6137. E-Mail: fertile@northernlights.lib.mn.us. *Br Coordr*, Linda Black
Founded 1967. Pop 2,050
Library Holdings: Bk Vols 6,700; Per Subs 31
Mem of Lake Agassiz Regional Library
Partic in Northern Lights Library Network

FOLEY

P FOLEY LIBRARY,* 251 N Fourth Ave, PO Box 340, 56329-0340. SAN 347-8416. Tel: 320-968-6612. FAX: 320-968-6612. Web Site: www.griver.org. *In Charge*, Judy Weis
Pop 5,248; Circ 49,049
Library Holdings: Bk Vols 16,263; Per Subs 40
Mem of Great River Regional Library
Open Mon & Wed 2-8, Tues & Fri 9-1 & 2-6, Thurs 2-6, Sat 9am-12pm

FOREST LAKE

P FOREST LAKE PUBLIC LIBRARY,* 220 N Lake St, 55025. SAN 308-5848. Tel: 651-464-4088. FAX: 651-464-4296. Web Site: www.washington.lib.mn.us. *Mgr*, Linda Bergerson; *Publ Servs*, Josephine E Halbach; Tel: 651-731-8487, Fax: 651-731-3758, E-Mail: jhalbach@washco.washington.lib.mn.us
Founded 1941. Circ 229,068
Library Holdings: Bk Vols 59,189; Per Subs 180
Automation Activity & Vendor Info: (OPAC) epixtech, inc.
Mem of Washington County Libr Syst
Open Mon 1-9, Tues-Thurs 10-9, Fri 10-5, Sat 10-3

FOSSTON

P FOSSTON PUBLIC LIBRARY,* 421 Fourth NE, 56542-1449. SAN 347-7339. Tel: 218-435-1320. FAX: 218-435-1320. E-Mail: fosston@northernlights.lib.mn.us. *Br Coordr*, Irene Lindfors
Founded 1918. Pop 4,530
Library Holdings: Bk Vols 13,150; Per Subs 34
Mem of Lake Agassiz Regional Library
Partic in Northern Lights Library Network

FOUNTAIN

S FILLMORE COUNTY HISTORICAL SOCIETY, Historical Center,* 202 County Rd #8, 55935. SAN 373-3696. Tel: 507-268-4449. *Exec Dir*, Jerry Henke
Library Holdings: Bk Vols 2,000
Subject Interests: Local history

FULDA

P FULDA MEMORIAL LIBRARY, 101 Third St NE, 56131-1106. (Mail add: PO Box 346, 56131-0364), Tel: 507-425-3277. *Dir*, Beth Cuperus
Pop 1,330; Circ 19,108
Library Holdings: Bk Vols 14,890; Per Subs 68
Database Vendor: epixtech, inc.
Mem of Plum Creek Library System
Friends of the Library Group

GAYLORD

P GAYLORD PUBLIC LIBRARY, (Formerly Sibley County Library Services), PO Box 77, 55334-0077. SAN 347-4240. Tel: 507-237-2280. FAX: 507-237-5121. *Librn*, Wanda Messner
Library Holdings: Bk Vols 10,300
Friends of the Library Group

GIBBON

P GIBBON PUBLIC LIBRARY, (Formerly Sibley County Library Services), 985 First Ave, 55335-0138. SAN 347-4275. Tel: 507-834-6551. FAX: 507-834-6551. *Librn*, Elaine Kent; *Librn*, Diane Schwecke
Library Holdings: Bk Vols 7,592; Per Subs 30
Friends of the Library Group

GILBERT

P GILBERT PUBLIC LIBRARY,* 17 N Broadway, 55741-0758. SAN 308-5880. Tel: 218-741-6023. FAX: 218-741-1826. Web Site: www.gilbert.lib.mn.us. *Dir*, Marta Edwardson; Staff 4 (MLS 1, Non-MLS 3)
Founded 1934. Pop 1,997; Circ 46,000
Jan 1999-Dec 1999 Income $120,000, City $81,000, Locally Generated Income $1,500, Other $1,200. Mats Exp $20,000. Sal $39,000
Library Holdings: Bk Titles 16,284; Per Subs 50
Mem of Arrowhead Library System; North Country Library System

GLENCOE

P GLENCOE PUBLIC LIBRARY, 719 13th St E, 55336-1597. SAN 348-114X. Tel: 320-864-3919. FAX: 320-864-1919. E-Mail: noritak@glencoe.lib.mn.us. *Librn*, Norita Kath
Pop 5,247; Circ 39,686
Jan 1999-Dec 1999 Income $82,764, City $42,000, County $29,409, Other $11,355. Mats Exp $73,570, Books $10,892, Per/Ser (Incl. Access Fees) $3,000. Sal $50,756
Library Holdings: Bk Vols 21,322; Per Subs 133
Automation Activity & Vendor Info: (Circulation) PALS; (OPAC) PALS
Mem of Pioneerland Library System

GLENWOOD

P GLENWOOD PUBLIC LIBRARY,* 108 SE First Ave, 56334-1622. SAN 308-5899. Tel: 320-634-3375. FAX: 320-634-5099. *Librn*, Leslie Randall
Founded 1907 Sal $53,375 (Prof $902)
Library Holdings: Bk Vols 21,253; Per Subs 70
Mem of Viking Library System

S POPE COUNTY MUSEUM & HISTORY CENTER LIBRARY,* 809 S Lake Shore Dr, 56334. SAN 326-0631. Tel: 320-634-3293. FAX: 320-634-3293. Web Site: pcmuseum@runestone.net.
Founded 1932
Library Holdings: Bk Vols 1,000
Subject Interests: Genealogy
Special Collections: History of Pope County, bks, bibles, ed, fiction; Newspapers (1891-present); Pope County Platt Book (from 1874); Population Census 1880-1920 (not 1890), microfilm
Restriction: Open to public for reference only
Open Tues-Sat 10-5

GOLDEN VALLEY

S NORTHWEST TERRITORY CANADIAN & FRENCH HERITAGE CENTER, Minnesota Genealogical Society Library,* 5768 Olson Memorial Hwy, 55422-5014. SAN 372-7971. Tel: 612-595-9347. *Asst Librn*, Dorthy Chandler
Subject Interests: Genealogy
Special Collections: Canadian Vital Records, bks, per; Loiselle Marriage Index, fiche
Publications: Canadian-American Journal of History & Genealogy for Canadian, French & Metis Study

GRACEVILLE

P GRACEVILLE PUBLIC LIBRARY,* 415 Studdart Ave, PO Box 457, 56240-0457. SAN 347-6944. Tel: 320-748-7332. FAX: 320-748-7338. E-Mail: gracevil@graceville.lib.mn.us. *Librn*, Ann Lauer
Pop 659; Circ 16,794
1998-1999 Income $33,750, City $14,545, County $13,600. Mats Exp

$5,616, Books $4,500, Per/Ser (Incl. Access Fees) $1,116. Sal $17,775
Library Holdings: Bk Vols 14,171; Per Subs 36
Mem of Pioneerland Library System
Branch of Pioneerland Library System

GRAND MARAIS

P GRAND MARAIS PUBLIC LIBRARY, 104 Second Ave W, PO Box 280, 55604-0280. SAN 308-5929. Tel: 218-387-1140. FAX: 218-387-2562. E-Mail: gmlib@arrowhead.lib.mn.us. Web Site: www.grandmaraismn.com. *Librn*, Linda Chappell
Pop 4,300; Circ 65,000
Jan 2000-Dec 2000 Income $173,912. Mats Exp $16,500. Sal $102,312 (Prof $35,859)
Library Holdings: Bk Vols 20,000; Per Subs 104
Subject Interests: Cook County, Local history, North Eastern Minn
Automation Activity & Vendor Info: (Cataloging) CARL; (Circulation) CARL; (ILL) CARL; (OPAC) CARL
Database Vendor: GaleNet
Mem of Arrowhead Library System
Friends of the Library Group

S US NATIONAL PARK SERVICE GRAND PORTAGE MONUMENT LIBRARY, 315 S Broadway, 55604-0668. (Mail add: PO Box 668, 55604), SAN 370-3134. Tel: 218-387-2788. FAX: 218-387-2790. *In Charge*, Timothy Cochrane
Library Holdings: Bk Vols 1,050; Per Subs 50
Restriction: Open to public for reference only

GRAND RAPIDS

P GRAND RAPIDS AREA LIBRARY, 140 NE Second St, 55744-2601. SAN 308-5937. Tel: 218-326-7640. TDD: 218-326-7640. FAX: 218-326-7644. E-Mail: illrap@arrowhead.lib.mn.us. Web Site: www.itascanet.org/library. *Dir*, Janet Crawford; Tel: 218-326-7643, E-Mail: jcrawford@ arrowhead.lib.mo.us; *Ref*, Steve Bean; Tel: 218-326-7641, E-Mail: sbean@ arrowhead.lib.mn.us; *Ch Servs*, Rosalie Mclouden; *Circ*, Faye Chessmen; Tel: 218-326-7641, E-Mail: fchessman@arrowhead.lib.mn.us; *ILL*, Donna Kosola; Tel: 218-326-7641; Staff 11 (MLS 2, Non-MLS 9)
Founded 1900. Pop 19,138; Circ 195,000
Library Holdings: Bk Vols 57,000; Bk Titles 46,127; Per Subs 221; High Interest/Low Vocabulary Bk Vols 180; Bks on Deafness & Sign Lang 120
Subject Interests: Judy Garland, Local authors, Minn, World War I
Automation Activity & Vendor Info: (Acquisitions) CARL; (Circulation) CARL; (Course Reserve) CARL; (OPAC) CARL
Database Vendor: CARL
Mem of Arrowhead Library System
Open Mon-Thurs 9-8, Fri & Sat 10-6
Friends of the Library Group

C ITASCA COMMUNITY COLLEGE LIBRARY, 1851 E Hwy 169, 55744. SAN 308-5945. Tel: 218-327-4472. Web Site: pals.ms.edu. *Librn*, Patricia M Akerman; Fax: 218-327-4753, E-Mail: pakerman@it.cc.mn.us; *Librn*, Michael M McGinnis
Founded 1922. Enrl 750; Fac 40
Library Holdings: Bk Titles 20,363; Per Subs 293
Mem of North Country District
Partic in Minn Interlibr Telecommunication Exchange; OCLC Online Computer Library Center, Inc; Project for Automated Systs
Friends of the Library Group

S ITASCA COUNTY HISTORICAL SOCIETY, Karjala Research Center, Central School Bldg, 10 Fifth St NW, 55744-2660. (Mail add: PO Box 664, 55744-0664), SAN 373-2258. Tel: 218-326-6431. FAX: 218-326-7083. E-Mail: ichs@paulbunyan.net. *Exec Dir*, Lilah Crowe
Library Holdings: Bk Vols 750
Subject Interests: Local history

GRANITE FALLS

P GRANITE FALLS PUBLIC LIBRARY, 155 Seventh Ave, 56241. SAN 308-5953. Tel: 320-564-3738. FAX: 320-564-4666. E-Mail: granite@ granitefalls.lib.mn.us. *Branch Mgr*, Madelyn Bronson; Staff 2 (Non-MLS 2)
Founded 1877. Pop 3,098; Circ 26,421
Jan 2000-Dec 2000 Income $99,648, City $32,717, County $38,077, Other $28,854. Mats Exp $81,220, Books $10,707, Per/Ser (Incl. Access Fees) $2,866. Sal $65,002
Library Holdings: Bk Vols 16,177; Per Subs 87
Subject Interests: Am Indians, Large print, Local history
Special Collections: Sons of Norway (Bks on/of/about Norway)
Mem of Pioneerland Library System

GREENBUSH

P GREENBUSH PUBLIC LIBRARY,* PO Box 9, 56726. SAN 348-0607. Tel: 218-782-2218. *Librn*, Ann Novacek
Founded 1970. Pop 817; Circ 14,082
Library Holdings: Bk Vols 5,500; Per Subs 19
Branch of Northwest Regional Library

GREY EAGLE

P GREY EAGLE LIBRARY, 118 State St E, PO Box 157, 56336. SAN 375-6114. Tel: 320-285-2505. FAX: 320-285-2505. Web Site: www.griver.org. *Librn*, Cindy Bruggenthies
Pop 1,762; Circ 17,645
Library Holdings: Bk Vols 10,114; Per Subs 31
Mem of Great River Regional Library
Open Mon 9-2, Wed & Thurs 2-8, Sat 9am-12pm

GROVE CITY

P GROVE CITY PUBLIC LIBRARY, 210 Atlantic Ave W, PO Box 248, 56243-0248. SAN 348-1174. Tel: 320-857-2550. FAX: 320-857-2322. E-Mail: grovecit@grovecity.lib.mn.us. *Librn*, Loyce Knutson; Staff 1 (Non-MLS 1)
Pop 597; Circ 6,330
Jan 2000-Dec 2000 Income $23,280, County $18,749, Other $4,531. Mats Exp $20,219, Books $2,605, Per/Ser (Incl. Access Fees) $780. Sal $15,860
Library Holdings: Bk Vols 4,693; Per Subs 38
Automation Activity & Vendor Info: (Circulation) PALS; (OPAC) PALS
Mem of Pioneerland Library System

HALLOCK

P HALLOCK PUBLIC LIBRARY,* PO Box 537, 56728. SAN 348-0631. Tel: 218-843-2401. FAX: 218-843-2401. E-Mail: hallock@ northernlights.lib.mn.us. Web Site: www.hallock.northernlights.lib.mn.us. *In Charge*, Jeanette Haubrich
Pop 2,000; Circ 19,895
Library Holdings: Bk Vols 10,000; Per Subs 21
Branch of Northwest Regional Library
Friends of the Library Group

HANCOCK

P HANCOCK COMMUNITY LIBRARY,* 662 Sixth St, PO Box 305, 56244-9998. SAN 308-5961. Tel: 320-392-5666. FAX: 320-392-5285. *Librn*, Roxane Malland
Founded 1920. Pop 750; Circ 10,083
Library Holdings: Bk Titles 7,890; Per Subs 36
Subject Interests: Large print
Special Collections: National Geographics
Mem of Viking Library System
Partic in Northern Lights Library Network
Friends of the Library Group

HANSKA

P HANSKA COMMUNITY LIBRARY, 200 E Second St, PO Box 82, 56041-0082. SAN 376-7167. Tel: 507-439-6294. *Dir*, Kathy Grothem; E-Mail: kgroth@tds.lib.mn.us; *Asst Librn*, Aryn Gustafson; Staff 2 (Non-MLS 2)
Jan 2000-Dec 2000 Income $20,000, City $8,500, County $11,500. Mats Exp Books $2,000. (Prof $10,300)
Library Holdings: Bk Titles 5,000; Per Subs 14
Automation Activity & Vendor Info: (Acquisitions) PALS; (Circulation) PALS; (ILL) PALS
Database Vendor: OCLC - First Search
Mem of Traverse Des Sioux Library System
Open Mon & Thurs 3-7:30, Tues 9-12:30 & 3-7:30, Sat 10-1
Friends of the Library Group

HARMONY

P HARMONY PUBLIC LIBRARY, 225 Third Ave SW, PO Box 426, 55939-0426. SAN 308-597X. Tel: 507-886-8133. FAX: 507-886-8133. *Librn*, Paula S Michel; E-Mail: paulam@selco.lib.mn.us; Staff 3 (MLS 1, Non-MLS 2)
Founded 1916. Pop 2,500; Circ 24,125
Jan 1999-Dec 1999 Income $68,497, City $45,250, County $18,682, Locally Generated Income $4,565. Mats Exp $16,396, Books $8,456, Per/Ser (Incl. Access Fees) $1,488, AV Equip $6,430, Other Print Mats $22. Sal $37,129 (Prof $16,250)
Library Holdings: Bk Vols 14,049; Per Subs 75
Special Collections: Beginning Genealogy; Local Old Photographs & History

Database Vendor: DRA
Function: ILL available
Mem of Southeastern Libraries Cooperating (SELCO)

HASTINGS

P PLEASANT HILL LIBRARY,* 1490 S Frontage Rd, 55033. SAN 376-9356. Tel: 651-437-5286. FAX: 651-480-4944. Web Site: www.co.dakota.mn.us/library/index.html. *Mgr*, Mary Wilson
Jan 1999-Dec 1999 Income $6,700,000
Library Holdings: Bk Titles 80,000; Per Subs 130
Partic in Metropolitan Library Service Agency
Friends of the Library Group

HAWLEY

P HAWLEY PUBLIC LIBRARY,* 421 Hartford St, PO Box 519, 56549-0519. SAN 347-7363. Tel: 218-483-4549. E-Mail: hawley@northernlights.lib.mn.us. *Librn*, Rita Erickson
Founded 1950. Pop 3,580
Library Holdings: Bk Vols 11,508; Per Subs 58
Mem of Lake Agassiz Regional Library

HECTOR

P HECTOR PUBLIC LIBRARY, 126 S Main, PO Box 368, 55342-0368. SAN 376-7191. Tel: 320-848-2841. FAX: 320-848-2841. E-Mail: hector@northernlights.lib.mn.us. *Branch Mgr, Commun Relations*, Jill Sing; Staff 1 (Non-MLS 1)
Pop 1,146; Circ 22,955
Jan 2000-Dec 2000 Income $39,500, City $17,070, County $12,034, Other $9,187. Mats Exp $4,509, Books $3,916, Per/Ser (Incl. Access Fees) $593. Sal $26,436
Library Holdings: Bk Titles 11,000; Per Subs 15
Mem of Pioneerland Library System
Friends of the Library Group

HERON LAKE

P HERON LAKE PUBLIC LIBRARY,* 409 9th St, PO Box 348, 56137. SAN 322-6719. Tel: 507-793-2641. FAX: 507-793-2641. *Commun Relations*, Brenda Martin-Granstra
Pop 1,000; Circ 9,723
Library Holdings: Bk Vols 5,000; Per Subs 45
Mem of Plum Creek Library System

HIBBING

P HIBBING PUBLIC LIBRARY, 2020 E Fifth Ave, 55746-1702. SAN 308-5996. Tel: 218-262-1038. TDD: 218-262-3214. FAX: 218-262-5407. E-Mail: hibbingpl@arrowhead.lib.mn.us. Web Site: www.hibbing.lib.mn.us. *Dir*, J Terry Moore; E-Mail: jmoore@arrowhead.lib.mn.us; *Acq, Cat, Ref*, Nancy Riesgraf; E-Mail: nriesgra@arrowhead.lib.mn.us; *AV*, Bill Trelford; E-Mail: wtrelfor@arrowhead.lib.mn.us; *Ch Servs*, Enid Costley; E-Mail: ecostley@arrowhead.lib.mn.us; *Per*, Chris Magnusson; E-Mail: cmagnuss@arrowhead.lib.mn.us; Staff 10 (MLS 3, Non-MLS 7)
Founded 1908. Pop 17,671; Circ 158,297
Jan 2000-Dec 2000 Income City $681,625. Mats Exp $88,825, Books $66,975, Per/Ser (Incl. Access Fees) $6,750, Micro $100, Electronic Ref Mat (Incl. Access Fees) $15,000. Sal $335,083 (Prof $128,430)
Library Holdings: Bk Vols 80,202; Per Subs 198
Special Collections: Bob Dylan Coll
Automation Activity & Vendor Info: (Circulation) CARL; (OPAC) CARL
Database Vendor: CARL, IAC - SearchBank, ProQuest
Mem of Arrowhead Library System
Partic in MINITEX Library Information Network; North Country Library Cooperative
Special Services for the Deaf - TDD
Toy Library for Day Care Providers; circulating videotapes; Technology Center includes: Arkenstone open book (scanner/reader), computer with screen enhancer, voice synthesizer, braille embosser & closed circuit television
Friends of the Library Group

HINCKLEY

P HINCKLEY PUBLIC LIBRARY, 106 First St SE, PO Box 336, 55037-0366. SAN 347-2418. Tel: 320-384-6351. FAX: 320-384-7492. E-Mail: hinckley@ecrl.lib.mn.us. Web Site: ecrl.lib.mn.us. *Librn*, Cecile M Cross-Maser; Staff 1 (Non-MLS 1)
Pop 2,602; Circ 26,413
Library Holdings: Bk Vols 8,000; Per Subs 60
Automation Activity & Vendor Info: (Cataloging) epixtech, inc.; (Circulation) epixtech, inc.
Database Vendor: epixtech, inc., IAC - Info Trac, IAC - SearchBank, ProQuest
Mem of East Central Regional Library; East Central Regional Library
Branch of East Central Regional Library
Friends of the Library Group

HOKAH

P HOKAH PUBLIC LIBRARY,* 57 Main, PO Box 503, 55941-0503. SAN 376-7833. Tel: 507-894-2665. FAX: 507-894-4190. *Librn*, Barbara Bissen; E-Mail: barbb@selco.lib.mn.us
Library Holdings: Bk Vols 15,000; Bk Titles 13,000; Per Subs 20
Mem of Southeastern Libraries Cooperating (SELCO)
Friends of the Library Group

HOPKINS

S ALLIANT TECHSYSTEMS, INC, Technical Library,* 600 Second St NE, 55343. SAN 308-6003. Tel: 612-931-6851. FAX: 612-931-5152. *Librn*, Terry Bonstrom
Founded 1957
Library Holdings: Bk Titles 4,000; Per Subs 90
Subject Interests: Defense, Electronics
Publications: Infoscan; Library Home Page with links
Restriction: Staff use only
Function: Literary searches
Friends of the Library Group

HOWARD LAKE

P HOWARD LAKE LIBRARY, 617 Sixth Ave, PO Box 207, 55349-0207. SAN 347-8440. Tel: 320-543-2020. FAX: 320-543-2020. Web Site: www.howard-lake.mn.us/library/index.html. *In Charge*, Nancy Harrold
Pop 3,443; Circ 36,105
Library Holdings: Bk Vols 13,332; Per Subs 51
Mem of Great River Regional Library
Open Mon & Wed 2-8, Tues & Thurs 2-6, Fri 10-1 & 2-6, Sat 10-2
Friends of the Library Group

HOYT LAKES

P HOYT LAKES PUBLIC LIBRARY, 206 Kennedy Dr, 55750. SAN 308-6011. Tel: 218-225-2412. FAX: 218-225-2399. *Librn*, Audrey L Evers
Founded 1959. Circ 36,000
Library Holdings: Bk Vols 23,000
Automation Activity & Vendor Info: (Circulation) CARL; (OPAC) CARL; (Serials) CARL
Database Vendor: OCLC - First Search
Mem of Arrowhead Library System
Friends of the Library Group

HUTCHINSON

P HUTCHINSON PUBLIC LIBRARY, 50 Hassan St SE, 55350-1881. SAN 348-1204. Tel: 320-587-2368. FAX: 320-587-4286. E-Mail: hutch@hutchinson.lib.mn.us. *Librn*, Mary Henke; Staff 4 (Non-MLS 4)
Pop 12,989; Circ 83,544
Jan 2000-Dec 2000 Income $227,666, City $86,998, County $47,352, Locally Generated Income $5,510, Other $87,806. Mats Exp $32,017, Books $27,757, Per/Ser (Incl. Access Fees) $4,160, Presv $100. Sal $109,302
Library Holdings: Bk Vols 37,150; Per Subs 112
Automation Activity & Vendor Info: (Circulation) PALS; (OPAC) PALS
Mem of Pioneerland Library System
Friends of the Library Group

§J RIDGEWATER COLLEGE LIBRARY, Hutchinson Campus, 2 Century Ave, 55350. SAN 378-3715. Tel: 320-234-0216. FAX: 320-234-0223. Web Site: www.ridgewater.mnscu.edu. *Librn*, Yvonne Johnson; E-Mail: yjohnson@ridgewater.mnscu.edu

INTERNATIONAL FALLS

P INTERNATIONAL FALLS PUBLIC LIBRARY, 750 Fourth St, 56649. SAN 308-602X. Tel: 218-283-8051. FAX: 218-283-4379. *Dir*, Thomas Shilts; E-Mail: tshilts@arrowhead.lib.mn.us; Staff 8 (MLS 1, Non-MLS 7)
Founded 1912. Pop 7,704; Circ 106,781
Jan 1999-Dec 1999 Income $297,053, State $6,772, City $255,111, County $10,195. Mats Exp $294,846, Books $40,612, AV Equip $5,552, Electronic Ref Mat (Incl. Access Fees) $12,576
Library Holdings: Bk Vols 48,514; Per Subs 130
Subject Interests: Minn hist
Automation Activity & Vendor Info: (Acquisitions) CARL; (Cataloging)

CARL; (Circulation) CARL; (ILL) CARL; (OPAC) CARL
Database Vendor: CARL
Mem of Arrowhead Library System
Friends of the Library Group

S KOOCHICHING COUNTY HISTORICAL MUSEUM LIBRARY,* 214 Sixth Ave, PO Box 1147, 56649. SAN 326-2456. Tel: 218-283-4316, 218-283-9484. *Exec Dir*, Edgar Oerichbauer
Pop 17,500
Library Holdings: Bk Vols 400
Special Collections: industry, logging, papermill; International Lumber Co (photogs & records); Mando/Boise Cascade (photogs & records); sawmill
Restriction: Non-circulating to the public

J RAINY RIVER COMMUNITY COLLEGE LIBRARY,* 1501 Hwy 71, 56649. SAN 308-6038. Tel: 218-285-7722, Ext 220. FAX: 218-285-2239. *Librn*, Scott Crowe; *Tech Servs*, Patricia Dieren; Staff 1 (MLS 1)
Founded 1967. Enrl 475
Library Holdings: Bk Vols 19,000; Bk Titles 17,000; Per Subs 140
Publications: LRC Handbook
Partic in Dialog Corporation

INVER GROVE HEIGHTS

J INVER HILLS COMMUNITY COLLEGE LIBRARY, 2500 80th St E, 55076-3209. SAN 308-6046. Tel: 612-450-8623. Interlibrary Loan Service Tel: 651-450-8624. Circulation Tel: 612-450-8632. FAX: 612-450-8679. *Dir*, Donald Langworthy; Tel: 651-450-8623, E-Mail: dlangwo@ih.cc.mn.us; *Ref*, Julie Benolken; Tel: 651-450-8622, E-Mail: jbenolk@ih.cc.mn.us; *Tech Servs*, Kathy Wille; Tel: 651-450-8624, E-Mail: kwille@ih.cc.mn.us; *Tech Servs*, Kathleen Daniels; Tel: 651-450-8387, E-Mail: kdaniels@ih.cc.mn.us; Staff 4 (MLS 3, Non-MLS 1)
Founded 1970. Enrl 2,475; Fac 140; Highest Degree: Associate
Jul 1999-Jun 2000 Income $123,000. Mats Exp $123,000, Books $90,000, Per/Ser (Incl. Access Fees) $20,000, Presv $300, Micro $5,000, Other Print Mats $750. Sal $190,000 (Prof $125,000)
Library Holdings: Bk Titles 42,000; Per Subs 250
Partic in Minn Interlibr Teletype Exchange; OCLC Online Computer Library Center, Inc

ISLE

P MILLE LACS COMMUNITY LIBRARY,* PO Box 147, 56342-0147. SAN 329-1510. Tel: 320-676-3929. E-Mail: mlmail@ecrl.lib.mn.us. *Librn*, Diane M Skelnik
Pop 3,915; Circ 21,455
Library Holdings: Bk Titles 3,800; Per Subs 50
Mem of East Central Regional Library
Branch of East Central Regional Library
Friends of the Library Group

IVANHOE

P IVANHOE PUBLIC LIBRARY,* 401 N Harold, PO Box 25, 56142-0025. SAN 376-7574. Tel: 507-694-1555. FAX: 507-694-1738. *Librn*, Barbara Herschberger
Library Holdings: Bk Vols 15,000; Bk Titles 10,000
Mem of Plum Creek Library System

JACKSON

P JACKSON COUNTY LIBRARY SYSTEM,* 311 Third St, 56143-1606. SAN 308-6054. Tel: 507-847-4748. FAX: 507-847-5470. *Librn*, Tamera Erickson; Staff 6 (MLS 1, Non-MLS 5)
Pop 11,677; Circ 109,825
Library Holdings: Bk Vols 42,073; Per Subs 226

KASSON

P KASSON PUBLIC LIBRARY, 16 NW First Ave, 55944-1471. SAN 308-6062. Tel: 507-634-7615. *Dir*, Marcia Savela; E-Mail: marcia@selco.lib.mn.us
Founded 1899. Pop 8,576; Circ 70,881
Library Holdings: Bk Vols 17,000; Per Subs 38
Friends of the Library Group

KEEWATIN

P KEEWATIN PUBLIC LIBRARY,* 125 W Third Ave, PO Box 220, 55753-0220. SAN 308-6070. Tel: 218-778-6377. FAX: 218-778-6193. *Librn*, Cathe Bocich; *Librn*, Janet Kunze
Pop 1,300; Circ 11,614
Library Holdings: Bk Vols 7,390
Partic in Arrowhead Health Sciences Library Network

KENYON

P KENYON PUBLIC LIBRARY,* 632 Second St, 55946. SAN 308-6089. Tel: 507-789-6821. *Dir*, Linda Barsness; E-Mail: lbarsness@selco.lib.mn.us
Pop 3,889; Circ 9,414
Library Holdings: Bk Vols 14,500; Per Subs 35
Mem of Southeastern Libraries Cooperating (SELCO)
Closed Mon

KERKHOVEN

P KERKHOVEN PUBLIC LIBRARY, 208 N Tenth, PO Box 508, 56252-0508. SAN 347-6952. Tel: 320-264-2141. FAX: 320-264-2141. E-Mail: kerk@kerkhoven.lib.mn.us. *Branch Mgr*, Faye Helms; Staff 1 (MLS 1)
Pop 740; Circ 7,098
Jan 2000-Dec 2000 Income $28,130, City $9,702, County $12,369, Other $6,059. Mats Exp $5,376, Books $4,813, Per/Ser (Incl. Access Fees) $563. Sal $17,120
Library Holdings: Bk Vols 4,085; Per Subs 16
Automation Activity & Vendor Info: (Circulation) PALS; (OPAC) PALS
Mem of Pioneerland Library System
Branch of Pioneerland Library System

KIMBALL

P KIMBALL LIBRARY,* 5 Main St N, PO Box 540, 55353-0308. SAN 347-8475. Tel: 320-398-3915. FAX: 320-398-3915. Web Site: www.griver.org. *In Charge*, Carla Asfeld
Pop 3,355; Circ 32,144
Library Holdings: Bk Vols 8,237; Per Subs 32
Mem of Great River Regional Library
Open Mon & Fri 2-6, Wed 10-1 & 2-6, Thurs 2-8, Sat 9-1
Friends of the Library Group

KINNEY

P KINNEY PUBLIC LIBRARY,* 400 Main St, PO Box A, 55758. SAN 308-6097. Tel: 218-258-2232. FAX: 218-258-2232. *Librn*, Don Penn
Pop 447; Circ 4,270
Library Holdings: Bk Vols 8,500; Per Subs 30
Mem of Arrowhead Library System
Friends of the Library Group

LA CRESCENT

P LA CRESCENT PUBLIC LIBRARY, 321 Main St, 55947. SAN 375-6157. Tel: 507-895-4047. FAX: 507-895-7153. Web Site: www.selco.lib.mn.us. *Dir*, LaVonne Beach; E-Mail: lbeach@selco.lib.mn.us; *Asst Librn*, Judy Ready; *Cat*, Alice Johnson; Staff 5 (MLS 1, Non-MLS 4)
Founded 1985. Pop 7,000
Jan 2000-Dec 2000 Income $80,729, City $44,036, County $15,073, Locally Generated Income $2,691, Other $18,929. Mats Exp $17,300, Books $15,000, Per/Ser (Incl. Access Fees) $800, Electronic Ref Mat (Incl. Access Fees) $1,500. Sal $29,080
Library Holdings: Bk Vols 20,845; Bk Titles 22,647; Per Subs 40
Mem of Selco
Special Services for the Deaf - Books on deafness & sign language
Special Services for the Blind - Bks on tape
Friends of the Library Group

LAKE BENTON

P LAKE BENTON PUBLIC LIBRARY, 112 W Benton, 56149. SAN 376-690X. Tel: 507-368-4252. *Librn*, Nancy Christensen; E-Mail: nancyc@lakebenton.lib.mn.us
Library Holdings: Bk Titles 9,000
Mem of Plum Creek Library System

LAKE CITY

P LAKE CITY PUBLIC LIBRARY,* 201 S High St, 55041. SAN 308-6100. Tel: 612-345-4013. FAX: 612-345-5923. Web Site: www.selco.lib.mn./us/lcpl. *Librn*, Kathleen A Durand
Founded 1904. Pop 4,505; Circ 40,174
Library Holdings: Bk Vols 33,200; Per Subs 110
Mem of Southeastern Libraries Cooperating (SELCO)

LAKE LILLIAN

P LAKE LILLIAN PUBLIC LIBRARY, 136 Lakeview St, PO Box 38, 56253-0038. SAN 348-1239. Tel: 320-664-4514. FAX: 320-664-4514. E-Mail: lakelil@lakelillian.lib.mn.us. *Branch Mgr*, Villa Lippert; E-Mail: villa1@lakelillian.lib.mn.us; Staff 1 (Non-MLS 1)
Pop 228; Circ 22,282

Jan 2000-Dec 2000 Income $28,479, County $20,800, Locally Generated Income $4,000, Other $50. Mats Exp $4,004, Books $3,364, Per/Ser (Incl. Access Fees) $640. Sal $18,991
Library Holdings: Bk Vols 6,393; Per Subs 43
Mem of Pioneerland Library System
Branch of Pioneerland Library System. Open Tues-Fri 2-5, Sat 9-12
Friends of the Library Group

LAKEFIELD

S JACKSON COUNTY HISTORICAL SOCIETY LIBRARY,* 307 N Hwy 86, 56150. SAN 328-820X. Tel: 507-662-5505. *Mgr*, Judy Nelson
Library Holdings: Bk Titles 200
Special Collections: Genealogical Publications
Publications: History of Jackson County (1910); Jackson County History Volumn II (1978)

P LAKEFIELD PUBLIC LIBRARY,* 219 Third Ave, PO Box 723, 56150-0723. Tel: 507-662-5782. FAX: 507-662-5782. *Commun Relations*, Carol Smith
Library Holdings: Bk Titles 5,000; Per Subs 30
Mem of Plum Creek Library System

LAMBERTON

P LAMBERTON PUBLIC LIBRARY,* 101 E Second Ave, PO Box 505, 56152-0505. SAN 308-6127. Tel: 507-752-7220. *Librn*, Karen Nissel
Founded 1933. Pop 1,010; Circ 8,000
Library Holdings: Bk Vols 6,500
Mem of Plum Creek Library System
Friends of the Library Group

LANESBORO

P LANESBORO PUBLIC LIBRARY,* 202 Parkway S, 55949-0338. (Mail add: PO Box 330, 55949-0330), SAN 376-7892. Tel: 507-467-2649. Web Site: www.lanesboro.cfa.org/~timebomb/homepage.htm. *Librn*, Kathy Buzza; E-Mail: kathyb@selco.lib.mn.us
Library Holdings: Bk Vols 9,000; Bk Titles 8,500; Per Subs 50
Friends of the Library Group

LEWISTON

S EARLY CHILDHOOD FAMILY EDUCATION LIBRARY,* Lewiston Elementary School, PO Box 741, 55952. SAN 327-8824. Tel: 507-523-2194. FAX: 507-523-2609. *In Charge*, Retha Finger; *Ch Servs*, Kathy Patterson
Library Holdings: Bk Vols 200

LINDSTROM

P LINDSTROM PUBLIC LIBRARY,* 30275 Linden St, PO Box 569, 55045-9619. SAN 347-2442. Tel: 651-257-2817. *Librn*, Susan Wilson
Pop 10,500; Circ 27,310
Library Holdings: Bk Vols 10,000; Per Subs 40
Mem of East Central Regional Library
Branch of East Central Regional Library
Friends of the Library Group

LITCHFIELD

P LITCHFIELD PUBLIC LIBRARY, 216 N Marshall Ave, 55355-2111. SAN 320-5274. Tel: 320-693-2483. FAX: 320-693-2483. Web Site: www.litch.com/library. *Head Librn*, Carolyn R Barid; E-Mail: carolb@litchfield.lib.mn.us; Staff 10 (MLS 1, Non-MLS 9)
Founded 1904
Jan 2000-Dec 2000 Income $137,668, City $85,991, County $51,177, Other $500. Mats Exp $27,700, Books $22,000, Per/Ser (Incl. Access Fees) $2,700, Other Print Mats $3,000. Sal $94,612
Library Holdings: Bk Titles 35,000; Per Subs 65
Subject Interests: County hist
Database Vendor: GaleNet, ProQuest
Mem of Pioneerland Library System
Friends of the Library Group

LITTLE FALLS

P CARNEGIE LIBRARY, (Formerly Little Falls Carnegie Library), 108 NE Third St, 56345-2708. SAN 308-6143. Tel: 320-632-9676. FAX: 320-632-1697. Web Site: www.griver.org. *Librn*, Will Hecht
Founded 1904. Pop 11,993; Circ 93,345
Library Holdings: Bk Vols 25,159; Per Subs 106
Mem of Great River Regional Library
Open Mon & Wed 12-8, Tues & Thurs 10-8, Fri 12-6, Sat 12-5
Friends of the Library Group

S CHARLES A WEYERHAEUSER MEMORIAL MUSEUM, R D Musser Library, 2151 Lindbergh Dr S, PO Box 239, 56345-0239. SAN 326-470X. Tel: 320-632-4007. E-Mail: mchs@fallsnet.com. *Exec Dir*, Jan Warner; Staff 2 (Non-MLS 2)
Founded 1975
Library Holdings: Bk Vols 2,000; Per Subs 15
Subject Interests: Genealogy, Local history
Special Collections: Little Falls Transcript 1892-1982, bd vols; Morrison County Record 1969-present
Restriction: Non-circulating to the public
Function: Reference only

M SAINT GABRIEL'S HOSPITAL LIBRARY, 815 SE Second St, 56345. SAN 329-9902. Tel: 320-632-5441. FAX: 320-632-1190. *In Charge*, Peggy Martin
Library Holdings: Bk Vols 300; Bk Titles 20; Per Subs 10

LONG LAKE

S WEST HENNEPIN COUNTY PIONEERS ASSOCIATION LIBRARY,* 1953 W Wayzata Blvd, PO Box 332, 55356. SAN 326-4416. Tel: 612-473-6557. *Librn*, Tom Turnham
Library Holdings: Bk Titles 1,100; Per Subs 25
Subject Interests: Local history
Publications: Newsletter (quarterly)

LONG PRAIRIE

P LONG PRAIRIE LIBRARY, City Hall, 42 Third St N, 56347. SAN 347-8505. Tel: 320-732-2332. FAX: 320-732-2332. Web Site: www.griver.org. *In Charge*, Mary Noble
Pop 6,688; Circ 58,164
Library Holdings: Bk Vols 13,865; Per Subs 49
Mem of Great River Regional Library
Open Mon & Thurs 10-8, Tues, Wed & Fri 1-5, Sat 9am-12pm
Friends of the Library Group

LONGVILLE

P MARGARET WELCH MEMORIAL LIBRARY, 5051 State Hwy 84, PO Box 106, 56655-0106. SAN 347-7878. Tel: 218-363-2710. FAX: 218-363-2710. *Librn*, Nora Shepard
Founded 1954
Library Holdings: Bk Vols 12,000; Per Subs 208
Special Collections: Cookbks Coll; Mystery Bks Coll
Mem of Kitchigami Regional Library
Friends of the Library Group

LUVERNE

P ROCK COUNTY COMMUNITY LIBRARY,* 201 W Main, 56156. SAN 308-6151. Tel: 507-283-5040. FAX: 507-283-5034. *Dir*, Glenda L Bremer; E-Mail: gbremer@luverne.lib.mn.us; *Circ*, Barbara Verhey; *Ch Servs*, April Gangestad; Staff 3 (MLS 3)
Founded 1907. Pop 10,000; Circ 91,401
Jan 2000-Dec 2000 Income $204,000. Mats Exp $29,000. Sal $108,000
Library Holdings: Bk Vols 38,000; Bk Titles 32,000; Per Subs 108
Subject Interests: Linguistics
Mem of Plum Creek Library System
Friends of the Library Group

MABEL

P MABEL PUBLIC LIBRARY, 110 E Newburg, PO Box 118, 55954-0118. SAN 308-616X. Tel: 507-493-5336. FAX: 507-493-3336. *Dir*, Donna Johnson; E-Mail: donnaj@selco.lib.mn.us
Founded 1920. Pop 900; Circ 5,690
Library Holdings: Bk Titles 8,000
Partic in SE Libr Coop
Friends of the Library Group

MADISON

S LAC QUI PARLE COUNTY HISTORICAL SOCIETY, Museum Library, 250 Eighth Ave S, 56256. SAN 328-3771. Tel: 320-598-7678. *Curator, Librn*, Lorraine Connor
Founded 1948
Library Holdings: Bk Vols 1,500; Per Subs 60

P MADISON PUBLIC LIBRARY, 401 Sixth Ave, 56256-1236. SAN 347-6979. Tel: 320-598-7938. FAX: 320-598-7526. E-Mail: madison@madison.lib.mn.us. *Librn*, Kathie Behrens; E-Mail: kathieb@madison.lib.mn.us
Pop 1,930; Circ 37,578
1998-1999 Income $81,993, City $28,453, County $27,293, Locally

Generated Income $1,500, Other $2,500. Mats Exp $8,054, Books $5,301, Per/Ser (Incl. Access Fees) $753. Sal $43,446
Library Holdings: Bk Vols 23,894; Per Subs 35
Mem of Pioneerland Library System

MAHNOMEN

P MAHNOMEN PUBLIC LIBRARY,* 203 S Main St, PO Box 476, 56557. SAN 308-6186. Tel: 218-935-2843. E-Mail: mahnomen@northernlights.lib.mn.us. *Librn*, Jean Luhman; *Coordr*, Marci King
Pop 5,000; Circ 10,000
Library Holdings: Bk Vols 13,000; Per Subs 24
Mem of Lake Agassiz Regional Library
Partic in Northern Lights Library Network
Friends of the Library Group

MANKATO

CR BETHANY LUTHERAN COLLEGE, Memorial Library,* 700 Luther Dr, 56001-4490. SAN 308-6194. Tel: 507-344-7349. FAX: 507-344-7376. Web Site: www.edu/blc/lib/mainframe.html. *Dir*, Norma J Brown; Staff 7 (MLS 2, Non-MLS 5)
Founded 1927. Enrl 400; Fac 40
Jul 1997-Jun 1998 Mats Exp $40,725, Books $23,100, Per/Ser (Incl. Access Fees) $14,425, Presv $1,200, AV Equip $2,000. Sal $162,000 (Prof $64,976)
Library Holdings: Bk Vols 45,000; Per Subs 230
Partic in Minn Interlibr Telecommunication Exchange; OCLC Online Computer Library Center, Inc

S BLUE EARTH COUNTY HISTORICAL SOCIETY, Museum Archives, 415 E Cherry St, 56001. SAN 329-2207. Tel: 507-345-5566. E-Mail: bechs@juno.com. Web Site: www.ic.mankato.mn.us/reg9/bechs/bechs1.html. *Librn*, Carol Oney
Founded 1901
Library Holdings: Bk Titles 1,000; Per Subs 10
Subject Interests: Local history
Publications: Newsletter (monthly)

P BLUE EARTH COUNTY LIBRARY SERVICES, 100 E Main St, 56001-3501. SAN 347-4186. Tel: 507-387-1856. Circulation Tel: 507-387-1856, Ext 285. Reference Tel: 507-387-1856, Ext 248. FAX: 507-387-1060. Web Site: www.beclibrary.org. *Dir*, Tim Hayes; Tel: 507-387-1856, Ext 222, Fax: 507-387-6029, E-Mail: tim.hayes@co.blue-earth.mn.us; *Asst Dir*, Kathie Kading; Tel: 507-387-1856, Ext 238, E-Mail: kathie.kading@co.blue-earth.mn.us; *Asst Dir*, Renee Schneider; Tel: 507-387-1856, Ext 230, E-Mail: renee.schneider@co.blue-earth.mn.us
Founded 1902
Library Holdings: Bk Vols 259,770; Bk Titles 132,239; Per Subs 513
Special Collections: Minnesota print materials
Automation Activity & Vendor Info: (Circulation) PALS
Database Vendor: OCLC - First Search
Mem of Traverse Des Sioux Library System
Special Services for the Deaf - TTY machine; Videos & decoder
Friends of the Library Group
Branches: 3
HENDERSON BRANCH, 110 S Sixth St, Henderson, 56044-7734. (Mail add: PO Box 404, Henderson, 56044-0404), SAN 347-4305. Tel: 507-248-3880. FAX: 507-248-3235. E-Mail: libtvh@tds.lib.mn.us.
Library Holdings: Bk Vols 9,376
LAKE CRYSTAL BRANCH, 100 Robinson St, Lake Crystal, 56055. (Mail add: PO Box 86, Lake Crystal, 56055-0086), Tel: 507-726-2726. FAX: 507-726-2265. Web Site: www.beclibrary.org.
Founded 1919
Friends of the Library Group
MAPLETON BRANCH, 104 First Ave, Mapleton, 56065. (Mail add: PO Box 405, Mapleton, 56065-0405), SAN 347-4364. Tel: 507-524-3513. FAX: 507-524-4536. Web Site: www.beclibrary.org.
Founded 1910
Friends of the Library Group
Bookmobiles: 1

C MINNESOTA STATE UNIVERSITY, MANKATO, Memorial Library, ML3097, 56002-8419. (Mail add: PO Box 8419, 56002-8419), SAN 308-6216. Tel: 507-389-5952. FAX: 507-389-5155. Web Site: www.lib.mankato.mnsu.edu/. *Actg Dir*, Joan Roca; *Acq*, Gary Hudson; *Archivist*, Daardi Sizemore; *Cat*, Yen Yen Chin; *Circ*, Sandy Ready; *Coll Develop*, Diane Richards; *Govt Doc*, Mark McCullough; *ILL*, Polly Frank; *Music*, Lance Leipold; *Ref*, Marilyn Montgomery; *Ser*, Becky Schwartzkopf. Subject Specialists: *Music*, Lance Leipold; Staff 18 (MLS 17, Non-MLS 1)
Founded 1868. Circ 110,104; Enrl 13,000; Fac 650
Jul 1998-Jun 1999 Income Parent Institution $3,200,000. Mats Exp $1,292,275, Books $457,560, Per/Ser (Incl. Access Fees) $682,500, Presv $25,000, Micro $14,000, AV Equip $20,000, Other Print Mats $1,675, Electronic Ref Mat (Incl. Access Fees) $91,540. Sal $1,782,309 (Prof $1,008,607)
Library Holdings: Bk Vols 787,936; Bk Titles 423,817; Per Subs 2,195
Special Collections: Curriculum Materials Coll; Minnesota History (Center for Minnesota Studies Coll); University Archives
Automation Activity & Vendor Info: (Acquisitions) PALS; (Cataloging) PALS; (Circulation) PALS; (Course Reserve) PALS; (ILL) PALS; (Media Booking) PALS; (OPAC) PALS; (Serials) PALS
Publications: Quaterly newsletter
Function: ILL available, Reference services available
Partic in MINITEX Library Information Network; OCLC Online Computer Library Center, Inc; S Cent Minn Interlibr Exchange, Smile
Special Services for the Blind - Kurzweil Reading Machine
Open Mon-Thurs 7:45am-11:45pm, Fri 7:45-6, Sat 10-6 & Sun 1-11:45

P TRAVERSE DES SIOUX LIBRARY SYSTEM,* 110 S Broad St, PO Box 608, 56002-0608. SAN 308-6224. Tel: 507-625-6169. FAX: 507-625-4049. Web Site: www.tds.lib.mn.us. *Dir*, John D Christenson; E-Mail: jchris@tds.lib.mn.us; *ILL, Ref*, Jane Engh; *Asst Dir, Tech Servs*, Patricia Biesterfeld; *Automation Syst Coordr*, John Miller; Staff 7 (MLS 7)
Founded 1975. Pop 220,000
Jan 1999-Dec 2000 Income $974,990, State $375,666, Federal $114,635, Locally Generated Income $354,265. Mats Exp $24,550, Books $500, Per/Ser (Incl. Access Fees) $23,850. Sal $385,501
Library Holdings: Bk Vols 1,690
Subject Interests: Agriculture, Econ develop
Special Collections: Native American Videos
Publications: Siouxline
Member Libraries: Blue Earth Community Library; Blue Earth County Library Services; Comfrey Public Library; Elmore Public Library; Faribault County Library Service; Hanska Community Library; Martin County Library; Muir Library; New Ulm Public Library; Springfield Public Library; Waseca-Le Sueur Regional Library; Watonwan County Library; Wells Public Library
Partic in Minn Interlibr Telecommunication Exchange; OCLC Online Computer Library Center, Inc; S Cent Minn Interlibr Exchange, Smile

MANTORVILLE

S DODGE COUNTY HISTORICAL SOCIETY LIBRARY, 615 N Main, PO Box 433, 55955-0433. SAN 373-370X. Tel: 507-635-5508. *Dir*, Idella Conwell
Library Holdings: Bk Vols 1,000
Subject Interests: Genealogy

MAPLEWOOD

M HEALTHEAST SAINT JOHN'S HOSPITAL, Medical Library, 1575 Beam Ave, 55109. SAN 347-9161. Tel: 651-232-7193. FAX: 651-232-5740. *Librn*, Sherry Oleson; E-Mail: soleson@healtheast.org
Founded 1941
Library Holdings: Bk Titles 1,150; Per Subs 200
Subject Interests: Medicine, Nursing
Restriction: Staff use only
Partic in Metronet; Midwest Health Sci Libr Network; Minn Interlibr Telecommunication Exchange; Twin Cities Biomedical Consortium

MARBLE

P MARBLE PUBLIC LIBRARY,* 302 Alice Ave, PO Box 409, 55764-0409. SAN 308-6232. Tel: 218-247-7676. FAX: 218-247-7133. *Librn*, Linda Veith
Pop 770
1999-2000 Income $25,000
Library Holdings: Bk Vols 17,000; Per Subs 38
Special Collections: Gilbert Morris Series; Stephen King, Dean Koontz & Danielle Steel Colls
Mem of Arrowhead Library System
Open Mon & Fri 9:30-11:30 & 2-4:30, Tues 2-4:30, Wed 2-8, Thurs 2-4:30 & 6:30-8

MARINE ON SAINT CROIX

S CARL L WESCHCKE LIBRARY,* 16363 Norell Ave N, 55047. SAN 327-2060. Tel: 651-433-2321. FAX: 651-433-2322. *Librn*, Carl L Weschcke
Library Holdings: Bk Vols 15,600
Subject Interests: Astrology

MARSHALL

P MARSHALL-LYON COUNTY LIBRARY,* 301 W Lyon St, 56258-1391. SAN 347-4488. Tel: 507-537-7003. FAX: 507-537-6745. Web Site: www.marshall-mn.org/library. *Dir*, Richard MacDonald; *Ch Servs*, Mary Beth Sinclair; *Br Coordr*, Paula Nemes; Staff 10 (MLS 2, Non-MLS 8)
Founded 1886
Jan 1998-Dec 1999 Income $534,285, City $344,723, County $172,362, Locally Generated Income $17,200. Mats Exp $69,750, Books $51,000, Per/Ser (Incl. Access Fees) $6,500, Presv $250, Other Print Mats $2,000. Sal $299,284 (Prof $108,968)
Library Holdings: Bk Vols 92,440; Per Subs 229

Subject Interests: Large print
Special Collections: Cake Pans
Mem of Plum Creek Library System
Partic in Southwest Area Multicounty Multitype Interlibrary Exchange
Friends of the Library Group
Branches: 2
BALATON COMMUNITY, 134 Third St, PO Box 326, Balaton, 56115-0326. SAN 347-4518. Tel: 507-734-2034. FAX: 507-734-2316. *Librn*, Jenny Kirk
Library Holdings: Bk Vols 3,680; Bk Titles 3,665
COTTONWOOD COMMUNITY, 86 W Main St, Cottonwood, 56229-0106. SAN 347-4542. Tel: 507-423-6488. FAX: 507-423-5368. *Librn*, Char Rekedal
Library Holdings: Bk Vols 5,806; Bk Titles 5,400
Bookmobiles: 1

C SOUTHWEST STATE UNIVERSITY LIBRARY, N Highway 23, 56258. SAN 347-4577. Tel: 507-537-7210 (University), 507-537-7278 (Library). Reference Tel: 507-537-6176. FAX: 507-537-6200. Web Site: www2.southwest.msus.edu/. *Dir*, John M Bowden; *Online Servs, Ref*, Mary Jane Striegel; *Media Spec*, Carolyn Bruning; *Acq, Per*, Sandra Hoffbeck; *Acq*, Karen Schmitz; *Cat*, Kristi Akland; *Cat*, Kathleen Ashe; *Bibliog Instr, Ref*, Dicksy Howe; *ILL*, Nancy DeRoode; *Govt Doc*, Connia Stensrud; *Distance Educ*, Pam Sukalski; Staff 5 (MLS 5)
Founded 1967. Enrl 3,000; Fac 126; Highest Degree: Master
Jul 1999-Jun 2000 Income $1,218,000, State $1,200,000, Locally Generated Income $18,000. Mats Exp $259,902, Books $79,244, Per/Ser (Incl. Access Fees) $100,070, Micro $11,697, AV Equip $4,000, Electronic Ref Mat (Incl. Access Fees) $34,878. Sal $325,650 (Prof $235,600)
Library Holdings: Bk Vols 167,111; Bk Titles 145,183; Per Subs 737
Special Collections: Autographs (Z L Begin Coll); Grants-Scholarship Coll; Rare Bks Coll
Publications: Handbook
Partic in Minn Interlibr Telecommunication Exchange; OCLC Online Computer Library Center, Inc; Southwest Area Multicounty Multitype Interlibrary Exchange

MAYNARD

P MAYNARD PUBLIC LIBRARY, 123 Mabel Ave, PO Box 368, 56260-0368. SAN 347-7002. Tel: 320-367-2143. FAX: 320-367-2143. E-Mail: maynard@maynard.lib.mn.us. *Branch Mgr*, Gloria Sims; Staff 1 (Non-MLS 1)
Pop 429; Circ 9,611
Jan 2000-Dec 2000 Income $21,258, County $18,316, Other $2,942. Mats Exp $2,288, Books $1,642, Per/Ser (Incl. Access Fees) $646. Sal $16,223
Library Holdings: Bk Vols 6,258; Per Subs 23
Automation Activity & Vendor Info: (Circulation) PALS; (OPAC) PALS
Mem of Pioneerland Library System
Branch of Pioneerland Library System

MC GREGOR

P MCGREGOR PUBLIC LIBRARY, 55760-0056. SAN 347-2477. Tel: 218-768-3305. FAX: 218-768-3305. E-Mail: mgmail@ecrl.lib.mn.us. *Librn*, Penny R Olson
Pop 3,250; Circ 30,153
Library Holdings: Bk Vols 2,072; Per Subs 15
Mem of East Central Regional Library
Branch of East Central Regional Library
Friends of the Library Group

MCINTOSH

P MCINTOSH PUBLIC LIBRARY, 115 Broadway NW, PO Box 39, 56556-0039. SAN 347-7398. Tel: 218-563-4555. E-Mail: mcintosh@northernlights.lib.mn.us. *Br Coordr*, Connie Bensen
Founded 1941. Pop 977
Library Holdings: Bk Vols 7,000; Per Subs 15
Mem of Lake Agassiz Regional Library
Partic in Northern Lights Library Network

MCKINLEY

P MCKINLEY PUBLIC LIBRARY, 5454 Grand Ave, 55741-9502. (Mail add: PO Box 2085, 55741-2085), SAN 308-6178. Tel: 218-749-5313. FAX: 218-749-5313. *Librn*, Lora Wyrick
Library Holdings: Bk Vols 11,000; Per Subs 20
Mem of Arrowhead Library System
Friends of the Library Group

MELROSE

P MELROSE LIBRARY,* 225 E First St N, PO Box 027, 56352-0027. SAN 347-8564. Tel: 320-256-3885. FAX: 320-256-3885. Web Site: www.griver.org. *In Charge*, Janet Atkinson
Pop 5,397; Circ 29,791
Library Holdings: Bk Vols 13,200; Per Subs 40
Mem of Great River Regional Library
Open Mon & Wed 2-8, Tues & Fri 2-6, thurs 10-12 & 2-6, Sat 10-12
Friends of the Library Group

MILACA

P MILACA COMMUNITY LIBRARY,* 145 S Central, 56353-1122. SAN 347-2507. Tel: 320-983-3677. E-Mail: mimail@ecrl.lib.mn.us. *Librn*, Mary Jane Bridge
Pop 7,587; Circ 30,568
Library Holdings: Bk Vols 3,370; Per Subs 40
Mem of East Central Regional Library
Branch of East Central Regional Library
Friends of the Library Group

MILAN

P MILAN PUBLIC LIBRARY,* 235 N Main St, PO Box 187, 56262-0187. SAN 347-7037. Tel: 320-734-4792. FAX: 320-734-4792. *Librn*, Anita Zelenka
Pop 341; Circ 9,167
Library Holdings: Bk Vols 9,335; Per Subs 12
Mem of Pioneerland Library System

MINNEAPOLIS

P ALLINA HEALTH SYSTEM LIBRARY SERVICES, Nicollet Avenue Center, 1801 Nicollet Ave, 55403. SAN 308-7840. Tel: 612-775-7900. FAX: 612-775-7946. E-Mail: library@allina.com. Web Site: www.allina.com/library. *Coordr*, Betsy Moore; Tel: 612-775-7905, E-Mail: moore@allina.com
Library Holdings: Bk Vols 9,500; Per Subs 630
Open Mon-Fri 8-4:30
Branches: 4
ABBOTT NORTHWESTERN HOSPITAL, 800 E 28th St, 55407. SAN 308-6917. Tel: 612-863-4312. FAX: 612-863-5695. E-Mail: library@allina.com. Web Site: www.allina.com/library. *Dir*, Donna Johnson
Founded 1943
Library Holdings: Bk Vols 7,000; Per Subs 1,300
Subject Interests: Cardiology, Neurology, Nursing, Pediatrics, Perinatology, Rehabilitation med, Spinal cord injury
Restriction: Open to public for reference only
Open Mon-Wed 8-8, Thurs 8-5:30, Fri 8-4:30
MERCY HOSPITAL, 4050 Coon Rapids Blvd, Coon Rapids, 55433. SAN 308-5473. Tel: 763-422-4556. FAX: 763-422-6020.
Library Holdings: Bk Vols 1,000; Per Subs 200
Subject Interests: Cardiology, Emergency med, Neurology, Pediatrics
Special Collections: General Clinical Medicine; Nursing
Open Mon-Fri 7:30-4
UNITED HOSPITAL, 333 N Smith Ave, Saint Paul, 55102. Tel: 651-220-8720. FAX: 651-220-7260.
Open Mon-Fri 8-4:30
UNITY HOSPITAL, 550 Osborne Rd, Fridley, 55432. Tel: 763-780-6774. FAX: 763-780-7873.
Open Mon-Thurs 7:30-4

S AMERICAN EXPRESS FINANCIAL ADVISORS, Investment Resource Center,* IDS Tower No 10, 55402. SAN 308-6569. Tel: 612-671-3131. FAX: 612-671-2262. *Librn*, Ann Becker
Founded 1958
Library Holdings: Bk Vols 800; Per Subs 450
Subject Interests: Investing, Mutual funds
Restriction: Staff use only

S AMERICAN SWEDISH INSTITUTE ARCHIVES & LIBRARY, 2600 Park Ave, 55407. SAN 308-6291. Tel: 612-871-4907. FAX: 612-871-8682. Web Site: www.americanswedishinst.org. *Dir*, Bruce N Karstadt; *Archivist, Librn*, Marita Karlisch; Staff 1 (MLS 1)
Founded 1929
Library Holdings: Bk Vols 14,000; Per Subs 10
Subject Interests: Culture, Swedish life, Swedish-American history
Special Collections: immigrant docs); microfilm church records; Swedish History & Literature (Swan J Turnblad Library); Swedish Immigration History Coll (Victor Lawson Coll); Turnblad Lending Library
Restriction: Non-circulating to the public
Friends of the Library Group

C AUGSBURG COLLEGE, The James G Lindell Family Library, 2211 Riverside Ave, 55454. SAN 308-6305. Tel: 612-330-1604. FAX: 612-330-1436. Web Site: www.augsburg.edu/library. *Dir*, Jane Ann Nelson;

Automation Syst Coordr, Tech Servs, Karen Mateer; *Publ Servs*, William Wittenbreer; *Coll Develop, Ref*, Grace Sulerud; *Ref*, Diane Van Weele; *Ref*, Mary Lee McLaughlin; *Bibliog Instr, Ref*, Boyd Koehler; Staff 7 (MLS 7)
Founded 1869. Enrl 3,086; Fac 292; Highest Degree: Master
Library Holdings: Bk Vols 170,000; Bk Titles 150,000; Per Subs 950
Special Collections: Meridel LeSueur Papers; Modern Scandinavian Music, rec, tapes & scores
Automation Activity & Vendor Info: (Circulation) epixtech, inc.
Partic in Coop Librs in Consortium; Minn Interlibr Telecommunication Exchange; OCLC Online Computer Library Center, Inc

S THE BAKKEN - A LIBRARY & MUSEUM OF ELECTRICITY IN LIFE, 3537 Zenith Ave S, 55416. SAN 326-4459. Tel: 612-927-6508. FAX: 612-927-7265. Web Site: www.thebakken.org. *Dir*, David Rhees; Tel: 612-926-3878, Ext 213, E-Mail: rhees@thebakken.org; *Librn*, Elizabeth Ihrig; Tel: 612-926-3878, Ext 227, E-Mail: ihrig@thebakken.org; *Curator*, Ellen Kuhfeld; Tel: 612-926-3878, Ext 217, E-Mail: kuhfeld@thebakken.org; Staff 1 (MLS 1)
Library Holdings: Bk Titles 11,000; Per Subs 30
Subject Interests: Electricity, Magnetism
Publications: The Bakken Library and Museum (newsletter)
Restriction: Not a lending library
Function: Reference only, Research library
Partic in OCLC Online Computer Library Center, Inc
Friends of the Library Group

S BARR ENGINEERING COMPANY LIBRARY,* 4700 W 77th St, 55435. SAN 327-7739. Tel: 612-832-2863. FAX: 612-832-2601. *Librn*, Kellie Sundheim; *Asst Librn*, Laurie Hare
Library Holdings: Bk Vols 10,000; Per Subs 300

L BOWMAN & BROOKE, Law Library,* 150 S Fifth St, Ste 2600, 55402. SAN 372-0500. Tel: 612-339-8682. FAX: 612-672-3200. *Librn*, Donna Trimble
Library Holdings: Bk Vols 7,000; Per Subs 49

S CAMPBELL-MITHUN-ESTY, Library & Information Services,* 222 S Ninth St, 21st flr, 55402. SAN 308-6313. Tel: 612-347-1509. FAX: 612-347-1041. *Ref*, Peg Sjolander; Staff 2 (MLS 2)
Founded 1953
Library Holdings: Bk Titles 1,300; Per Subs 1,300
Subject Interests: Advertising, Marketing
Special Collections: Scrap Art, picture files
Publications: Information Alert (bimonthly bulletin)
Restriction: Staff use only

S CARGILL, INC, Information Center,* PO Box 5670, 55440. SAN 308-6321. Tel: 612-742-6498. FAX: 612-742-6062. *Dir*, Peter Sidney; E-Mail: peter_sidney@cargill.com; *Ref*, Cindy Acton; *Ref*, Kathrine Hayes; *Ref*, Mary Louise Lose; *Archivist*, Shaleen Culbert-Kivlin; Staff 11 (MLS 8, Non-MLS 3)
Founded 1956
Library Holdings: Bk Vols 30,000; Bk Titles 950; Per Subs 900
Subject Interests: Bus, Commodity trading, Corn wet milling, Feeding, Finance, Grain storage, Hybrid corn, Int trading, Livestock, Mgt, Oilseed proc, Poultry feeds, Products, Raw mat for coatings, Resins, Salt, Sorghum seeds, Transportation
Publications: Cargill Information Center Wiss; Information Center Video, Products & Services Catalog
Partic in Dialog Corporation; Dow Jones Interactive; Medline; MINITEX Library Information Network; OCLC Online Computer Library Center, Inc; Sci & Tech Info Network
Open Mon-Fri 8am-4:30pm

S CARMICHAEL LYNCH ADVERTISING, Information Center,* 800 Hennepin Ave, 55403. SAN 328-509X. Tel: 612-334-6242. FAX: 612-334-6216.
Library Holdings: Per Subs 1,400
Subject Interests: Advertising, Marketing

R CENTRAL LUTHERAN CHURCH LIBRARY, 333 12th St S, 55404. SAN 308-6348. Tel: 612-870-4416. FAX: 612-870-0417. *Librn*, Elizabeth Shelver
Library Holdings: Bk Vols 3,500; Per Subs 12

M A CHANCE TO GROW, Kretsch Brain Resource Library, 1800 Second St NE, 55418. SAN 370-3282. Tel: 612-789-1236. FAX: 612-706-5555. Web Site: actg.org. *Dir*, Bob DeBore; *Coordr, Res*, Kathy DeBore
Library Holdings: Bk Vols 2,000

J COLLEGE OF SAINT CATHERINE, Minneapolis Campus Library & AV Services,* 601 25th Ave S, 55454. SAN 308-6895. Tel: 651-690-7784. FAX: 651-690-7852. Web Site: www.stkate.edu/library. *Librn*, Cynthia Stromgren; E-Mail: ckstromgren@stkate.edu; *Asst Librn, ILL*, Monica Olmschenk; *AV*, Mary Ellen Brown; *Ref*, Jill Lagerstrom
Founded 1964. Enrl 1,200; Fac 200
Jun 1997-May 1998 Income $280,098. Mats Exp $73,109, Books $28,162, Per/Ser (Incl. Access Fees) $28,858, AV Equip $5,879. Sal $157,556 (Prof $75,971)
Library Holdings: Bk Vols 32,000; Per Subs 280
Subject Interests: Allied health, Nursing
Partic in Coop Librs in Consortium; MINITEX Library Information Network; OCLC Online Computer Library Center, Inc
Special Services for the Deaf - Captioned film depository; Special interest periodicals
Special Services for the Blind - Braille bks, CCTV; Voice synthezier, online text enlargement
Friends of the Library Group

S DAIN RAUSHER INC, Research Library MS P16B,* 60 S Sixth St, 55402. SAN 326-5625. Tel: 612-371-2774. FAX: 612-371-7922. *Librn*, Diane M Wiederhoeft; Staff 2 (MLS 1, Non-MLS 1)
Library Holdings: Per Subs 10
Special Collections: Files on Public Company
Restriction: Staff use only

S DELOITTE & TOUCHE LLP LIBRARY, 400 One Financial Plaza, 120 S Sixth St, 55402. SAN 308-6372. Tel: 612-397-4636. FAX: 612-397-4550. Web Site: www.dttus.com. *Librn*, Richard G Reynen; E-Mail: rreynen@dttus.com; *Asst Librn*, Lisa Harrington; *Asst Librn*, Lori Dahl
Library Holdings: Bk Vols 3,500; Per Subs 300
Subject Interests: Accounting, Bus, Mgt, Taxation
Partic in Dialog Corporation; Dow Jones News Retrieval; Westlaw

GM DEPARTMENT OF VETERANS AFFAIRS, Medical Center Library, One Veterans Dr, 55417. SAN 308-6976. Tel: 612-725-2000, Ext 4200. FAX: 612-725-2046. *Mgr*, Dorothy Sinha; E-Mail: sinha.dorothy@forum.va.gov; *Librn*, Clare Lee; E-Mail: lee.clare@forum.va.gov; *Librn*, Barbara Winge; E-Mail: winge.barbara@forum.va.gov; Staff 3 (MLS 3)
Library Holdings: Bk Vols 8,000
Subject Interests: Allied health, Hospital administration, Medicine, Nursing
Special Collections: Medical AV Coll; Patient Education
Automation Activity & Vendor Info: (OPAC) EOS
Branches:
PATIENT EDUCATION CENTER LIBRARY, One Veterans Dr, 55417. Tel: 612-725-2000, Ext 4212. FAX: 612-725-2046. *Librn*, Kathy McKay; E-Mail: mackay.kathleen@forum.va.gov; Staff 1 (MLS 1)
Founded 1978
Library Holdings: Bk Titles 500
Subject Interests: Patient health educ

L DOHERTY, RUMBLE & BUTLER, Law Firm Library,* 100 S Fifth St, Ste 1200, 55402-1216. SAN 308-7611. Tel: 651-265-4000. FAX: 651-265-3900. *Librn*, Ann S Turner; E-Mail: turnea@drblaw.com; *Asst Librn*, Carol Saunders; *Asst Librn*, Nadine Gergen
Library Holdings: Bk Vols 17,000; Per Subs 250
Partic in Dialog Corporation; Westlaw

S DONALDSON CO, INC, Information Center, PO Box 1299, 55440-1299. SAN 308-6399. Tel: 612-887-3019. FAX: 612-887-3155. *Adminr, Info Res*, Julie Eskritt; E-Mail: jeskritt@mail.donaldson.com; *Info Specialist*, Melissa Gray; Staff 2 (MLS 2)
Founded 1969
Library Holdings: Bk Vols 4,000; Per Subs 200
Subject Interests: Bus, Eng with emphasis on filtration, Pollution control
Restriction: Company staff only

L DORSEY & WHITNEY, Law Library,* 220 S Sixth St, 55402. SAN 308-6402. Tel: 612-340-2613. FAX: 612-340-8704. Web Site: library.dorseylaw.com. *Dir*, Ann M Carter
Library Holdings: Bk Vols 60,000; Per Subs 400
Restriction: Not open to public

S DRUG INFORMATION CENTER LIBRARY,* 279 Diehl Hall, 505 Essex St SE, 55455. SAN 375-1252. Tel: 612-624-6492. FAX: 612-626-2454. E-Mail: drugref@tc.umn.edu. Web Site: www.biomed.lib.umn.edu. *Librn*, Gail Weinberg
Library Holdings: Bk Titles 100; Per Subs 62
Subject Interests: Tobacco

J DUNWOODY INSTITUTE LIBRARY, John A Butler Learning Center, 818 Dunwoody Blvd, 55403. SAN 308-6410. Tel: 612-374-5800, Ext 2404. FAX: 612-374-4128. Web Site: www.woody.tec.mn.us. *Librn*, Kristina Oberstar; *Librn*, Ann Wilberton
Library Holdings: Bk Vols 10,000; Per Subs 100

R EDGEWATER BAPTIST CHURCH LIBRARY, 5501 Chicago Ave S, 55417. SAN 308-6429. Tel: 612-827-3803. FAX: 612-824-6154. *Librn*, Gordon Krantz
Subject Interests: Fiction, Missions

L FAEGRE & BENSON, Law Library,* 2200 Norwest Ctr, 90 S Seventh St, 55402. SAN 308-6437. Tel: 612-336-3724. FAX: 612-336-3026. *Dir*, Nina Platt; *Assoc Librn, Ref*, Susan Rafter; Staff 4 (MLS 4)
Library Holdings: Bk Vols 33,000

M FAIRVIEW UNIVERSITY MEDICAL CENTER, Health Science Library,* 2450 Riverside Ave, 55454. SAN 308-6615. Tel: 612-672-6546. FAX: 612-672-2675. *Librn*, Cynthia Robinson; *Mgr*, Michael Scott; Tel: 612-672-6595, E-Mail: mscott2@fairview.org; *ILL*, Andrea Norman; Tel: 612-672-6545,

E-Mail: anorman1@fairview.org; *Per*, Isaura Brandt; E-Mail: ibrandt1@fairview.org; Staff 3 (MLS 1, Non-MLS 2)
Library Holdings: Bk Vols 2,500; Per Subs 350
Subject Interests: Health sci, Nursing
Database Vendor: OVID Technologies
Partic in Medline; Midwest Health Sci Libr Network; Twin Cities Biomedical Consortium

S FEDERAL RESERVE BANK OF MINNEAPOLIS, Research Library,* PO Box 291, 55480-0291. SAN 308-6461. Tel: 612-204-5509. Web Site: research.mpls.frb.fed.us/library/library.html. *Mgr*, Janet Swan; *Librn*, Karen Hovermale
Founded 1940
Library Holdings: Bk Vols 15,000; Per Subs 2,000
Subject Interests: Econ, Finance, Monetary policy
Special Collections: Federal Reserve System Publications Coll
Restriction: Staff use only
Partic in MINITEX Library Information Network

L FELHABER, LARSON, FENLON & VOGT, Law Library,* 601 Second Ave S, Ste 4200, 55402-4302. SAN 372-2864. Tel: 612-339-6321. FAX: 612-338-0535. *Librn*, Mary E Cunningham
Library Holdings: Bk Vols 10,500; Per Subs 107

R FIRST BAPTIST CHURCH LIBRARY, 1021 Hennepin Ave, 55403. SAN 308-647X. Tel: 612-332-3651. FAX: 612-332-3661. E-Mail: firstbaptistofmpls@hotmail.com. *In Charge*, Ruth Dalman
Library Holdings: Bk Vols 4,050
Special Collections: Commentaries & Sermons (Dr W B Riley, founder of Northwestern Bible College)

L FREDRIKSON & BRYON, Law Library,* 1100 International Centre, 55402. (Mail add: 900 Second Ave S, 55402), SAN 372-0519. Tel: 612-347-7086. FAX: 612-347-7077. Web Site: www.fredlaw.com. *Librn*, Marilyn L Hallen; E-Mail: mhallen@fredlaw.com; *Asst Librn*, Krispen Lam
Library Holdings: Bk Vols 20,000; Per Subs 300

GENERAL MILLS, INC

S BUSINESS INFORMATION CENTER, PO Box 1113, 55440-1113. SAN 347-4631. Tel: 612-540-3536. FAX: 612-540-4742. E-Mail: genmills@class.org. *Mgr*, Collen McQuillan; Staff 6 (MLS 4, Non-MLS 2)
Founded 1965
Library Holdings: Bk Vols 700; Per Subs 200
Subject Interests: Bus, Food indust, Marketing, marketing res, Mgt

S JAMES FORD BELL TECHNICAL INFORMATION CENTER, 9000 Plymouth Ave N, 55427. SAN 347-4666. Interlibrary Loan Service Tel: 763-764-2761. FAX: 763-764-3166. *Mgr*, Laura Baird
Founded 1961
Library Holdings: Bk Vols 20,000; Bk Titles 18,000; Per Subs 750
Subject Interests: Food sci
Automation Activity & Vendor Info: (Acquisitions) Sydney; (Cataloging) Sydney; (Circulation) Sydney; (OPAC) Sydney; (Serials) Sydney
Database Vendor: Dialog, OCLC - First Search
Publications: Foods Adlibra; Internal newsletters (Newsletter); Periodical Holdings List (annual)
Restriction: Not open to public
Partic in Dialog Corporation; Dow Jones News Retrieval; OCLC Online Computer Library Center, Inc; STN

L GRAY, PLANT, MOOTY, Law Library,* 3400 City Ctr, 55402. (Mail add: 33 S Sixth St, 55402), SAN 329-9678. Tel: 612-343-2955. FAX: 612-333-0066. *Librn*, Jill T Sonnesyn; E-Mail: jill.sonnesyn@gpmlaw.com; *Asst Librn*, Scott Raver; Staff 3 (MLS 2, Non-MLS 1)
Library Holdings: Bk Titles 2,000; Per Subs 150
Subject Interests: Law
Restriction: Staff use only

S GUTHRIE THEATER FOUNDATION, Staff Reference Library, 725 Vineland Pl, 55403. SAN 327-7909. Tel: 612-347-1185. FAX: 612-347-1188. *Librn*, Mary Jo Beall Holcomb
Library Holdings: Bk Vols 5,500
Subject Interests: Architecture, Decorative arts, Music, Poetry
Special Collections: Guthrie Production Coll, scripts, programs; Ladies Home Companion, The Designer Delineator 1908-1950
Restriction: Not open to public

M HAMILTON HMC LIBRARY,* 120 S Sixth St, Ste 1600, 55402. SAN 375-2054. Tel: 612-378-1700. FAX: 612-339-4477.
Library Holdings: Bk Vols 500; Bk Titles 200; Per Subs 20
Restriction: Not open to public

GL HENNEPIN COUNTY LAW LIBRARY,* C-2451 Government Ctr, 55487. SAN 308-6526. Tel: 612-348-3022. FAX: 612-348-4230. Web Site: www.co.hennepin.mn.us/lawlibrary/lawlib.htm. *Dir*, Anne W Grande; *Tech Servs*, Margaret Hall; *Publ Servs*, Judy Zetterberg; Staff 12 (MLS 6, Non-MLS 6)
Founded 1883
1998-1999 Income $1,500,000, County $350,000, Locally Generated Income $1,150,000. Mats Exp $660,000, Books $20,000, Per/Ser (Incl. Access Fees) $614,000, Micro $25,000. Sal $610,000
Library Holdings: Bk Vols 100,000
Subject Interests: Law
Publications: Library guide; newsletter (irregular)
Open Mon-Fri 8am-6pm & Sat 10am-4pm (Sept-Apr)

M HENNEPIN COUNTY MEDICAL CENTER, Library & Media Services Library,* 701 Park Ave, 55415. SAN 308-6585. Tel: 612-347-2710. FAX: 612-904-4248. *Dir*, Sherry Anderson; E-Mail: sherry.anderson@co.hennepin.mn.us; *Librn*, Anne Dougherty; E-Mail: anne.dougherty@co.hennepin.mn.us; *Librn*, Sarah Lofquist; Staff 12 (MLS 3, Non-MLS 9)
Founded 1901
Library Holdings: Bk Vols 60,000; Per Subs 600
Subject Interests: Clinical medicine
Publications: Information Access (newsletter)
Partic in Midwest Health Sci Libr Network
Open Mon-Fri 7am-9pm, Sat 9-5 & Sun 10-5

S HENNEPIN HISTORY MUSEUM LIBRARY, 2303 Third Ave S, 55404-3599. SAN 326-5773. Tel: 612-870-1329. FAX: 612-870-1320. *Curator*, Jack A Kabrud
Pop 1,500; Fac 4
Special Collections: Historic Photographs; Manuscripts
Publications: Hennepin History Magazine (quarterly periodical)

R HOLY TRINITY LUTHERAN CHURCH LIBRARY, 2730 E 31st St, 55406. SAN 308-6542. Tel: 612-729-8358. FAX: 612-729-6773. *In Charge*, Janice Lehman
Founded 1963
Library Holdings: Bk Vols 4,000; Per Subs 3
Subject Interests: Holocaust

HONEYWELL, INC

S LABORATORIES LIBRARY, 3660 Technology Dr, 55418. (Mail add: Mail Sta MN65-2000, 55418), SAN 347-4720. Tel: 612-951-7400. FAX: 612-951-7402. E-Mail: htc-library-mn65@htc.honeywell.com. Web Site: www.web-library.htc.honewell.com. *Mgr*, Nelson Soken; Staff 8 (MLS 6, Non-MLS 2)
Founded 1951
Library Holdings: Bk Titles 8,000; Per Subs 475
Subject Interests: Aero-space tech, Computer science, Control systs tech, Human factors eng, Info systs, Optical sci
Special Collections: Company Internal Reports; Government Technical Documents, bks, micro
Automation Activity & Vendor Info: (Cataloging) Sydney
Publications: InfoBriefs; Library Bulletin
Restriction: Staff use only
Partic in Dialog Corporation; Dow Jones News Retrieval; MINITEX Library Information Network; OCLC Online Computer Library Center, Inc; STN
This is the major corporate research library at Honeywell serving most of the Minnesota facilities

M INTERNATIONAL DIABETES CENTER LIBRARY,* 3800 Park Nicollet Blvd, 55416. SAN 325-5433. Tel: 612-993-3393. FAX: 612-993-1302. *Librn*, Karen Friederich
Library Holdings: Per Subs 50
Subject Interests: Diabetes mellitus
Publications: Educational materials for Diabetics

S JEWISH COMMUNITY RELATIONS COUNCIL OF MINNESOTA & THE DAKOTAS LIBRARY,* 1201 Marquette Ave S, Ste 110, 55403-2456. SAN 327-8212. Tel: 612-338-7816. FAX: 612-349-6569. *Exec Dir*, Jay Tcath
Library Holdings: Bk Vols 100
Open Mon-Fri 9-5

S KPMG LLP, Publication & Subscription Management Services, 4200 Norwest Ctr, 90 S Seventh St, 55402-3900. SAN 308-6852. Tel: 612-305-5180. FAX: 612-305-5039. *Coordr*, Jeanne Peterson; Tel: 612-305-5512, E-Mail: jepeterson@kpmg.com; Staff 2 (MLS 1, Non-MLS 1)
Founded 1973
Library Holdings: Bk Vols 4,000; Bk Titles 3,000; Per Subs 150
Subject Interests: Accounting, Auditing, Bus, Mgt, Taxation
Automation Activity & Vendor Info: (Cataloging) Sydney; (Serials) Sydney

L LAW LIBRARY CONSULTANTS, INC, 5305 Portland Ave S, 55417. SAN 372-2821. Tel: 612-823-3945. FAX: 612-823-0437. Web Site: www.lawlibraryconsultants.com. *Pres*, Kathleen Bedor; E-Mail: kbedor@lawlibraryconsultants.com
Restriction: Not open to public

L LEONARD, STREET & DEINARD, Law Library, 150 S Fifth St, Ste 2300, 55402. SAN 372-0527. Tel: 612-335-1616. FAX: 612-335-1657. E-Mail: library@leonard.com. *Res*, Susan Catterall; *Res*, Patricia K Cummings; Staff 6 (MLS 3, Non-MLS 3)
Library Holdings: Bk Vols 20,000

L LOCKRIDGE, GRINDAL, NAUEN PLLP, Law Library, 100 Washington Ave S, Ste 2200, 55401. SAN 372-0497. Tel: 612-339-6900. FAX: 612-339-0981. *Librn*, Kathy Kelly; E-Mail: kjkelly@locklaw.com

S LUTHERAN BROTHERHOOD CORPORATE LIBRARY,* 625 Fourth Ave S, 55415. SAN 308-6607. Tel: 612-340-7269. FAX: 612-340-8601. *Librn*, Greta Hanson; *Librn*, Marilyn Thompson
Founded 1956
Library Holdings: Bk Vols 2,000
Subject Interests: Bus, Fraternal benefit societies, Health insurance, Life, Lutherism, Martin Luther biographies, Mgt
Special Collections: Antique Scandinavian Bible Coll; Reformation Research Library, micro of original doc

L MACKALL, CROUNSE & MOORE, Law Library, AT&T Tower, 901 Marquette Ave, No 1400, 55402-2859. SAN 372-0535. Tel: 612-305-1687. FAX: 612-305-1414. E-Mail: llc@mcmlaw.com.
Library Holdings: Bk Vols 11,000; Per Subs 92

S MARTIN-WILLIAMS ADVERTISING INC, Library-Information Center, 60 S Sixth St, Ste 2800, 55402-4444. SAN 371-2710. Tel: 612-342-9739. FAX: 612-342-9700. *Dir*, Julia Hally; *Mgr*, Jennifer Leora Hahs; E-Mail: jhahs@martinwilliams.com. Subject Specialists: *Marketing and advertising*, Jennifer Leora Hahs
Library Holdings: Bk Vols 1,200; Per Subs 14
Restriction: Staff use only

S MEDTRONIC, INC, Information Resource Center,* 7000 Central Ave NE, 55432-9987. SAN 308-6631. Tel: 612-514-3496. FAX: 612-514-5421.
Library Holdings: Bk Vols 5,000; Per Subs 600
Special Collections: Cardiovascular & Neurological Article Coll

C MINNEAPOLIS COLLEGE OF ART & DESIGN LIBRARY,* 2501 Stevens Ave, 55404-3593. SAN 308-6674. Tel: 612-874-3791. FAX: 612-874-3795. E-Mail: library@mn.mcad.edu. Web Site: www.library.mcad.edu. *Dir*, Suzanne Degler; Tel: 612-874-3799, E-Mail: suzanne_degler@mn.mcad.edu; *AV*, Allan Kohl; Tel: 612-874-3781; *Ref*, Kathy Heuer; Tel: 612-874-3752; Staff 9 (MLS 3, Non-MLS 6)
Founded 1886. Enrl 500; Fac 90; Highest Degree: Master
Jun 1998-May 1999 Income $255,300, Parent Institution $255,300. Mats Exp $36,498, Books $17,000, Per/Ser (Incl. Access Fees) $13,248, Presv $2,500, AV Equip $250, Electronic Ref Mat (Incl. Access Fees) $3,500. Sal $199,237
Library Holdings: Bk Vols 58,050; Bk Titles 47,450; Per Subs 196
Subject Interests: Contemporary art, Film, Photog, Visual arts
Special Collections: Artists Books, MSA & MCAD Archives
Publications: Accession List; Bibliographic Guides
Restriction: Circulation limited
Partic in MINITEX Library Information Network; OCLC Online Computer Library Center, Inc

J MINNEAPOLIS COMMUNITY & TECHNICAL COLLEGE LIBRARY,* 1501 Hennepin Ave, 55403. SAN 308-664X. Tel: 612-341-7087. FAX: 612-341-7480. Web Site: www.mctc.tec.mn.us/scu.edu/academicaffair/library/index.html. *Librn*, Julie Setnosky; *Librn*, Anne Ryan; *Librn*, Tom Eland; *Librn*, Jane Jergeus; *Librn*, Kathleen Daniels; *Tech Servs*, Marilee Crowell; Staff 4 (MLS 4)
Founded 1965. Enrl 4,310
Subject Interests: Acad
Partic in MINITEX Library Information Network; Minn Interlibr

S MINNEAPOLIS INSTITUTE OF ARTS, Art Research & Reference Library, 2400 Third Ave S, 55404. SAN 308-6682. Tel: 612-870-3117. FAX: 612-870-3004. Web Site: www.artsconnected.com. *Librn*, Harold Peterson; Staff 4 (MLS 4)
Founded 1915. Highest Degree: Master
Library Holdings: Bk Vols 50,000; Per Subs 120
Subject Interests: American, Art history, Chinese bronzes, Drawing, English silver, Furniture, Jades, Painting, Porcelains, Prints, Sculpture, Textiles
Special Collections: Botany & Fashion (Minnich Coll); Five Hundred Years of Sporting Books (John Daniels Coll), drawings; History of Printing (Lesli Coll)
Database Vendor: OCLC - First Search
Publications: Surrealism: Beyond the Printed Work; The Minneapolis Institute of Arts Research & Reference Library: History & Guide; Villa I Tatti
Restriction: Non-circulating to the public
Friends of the Library Group

P MINNEAPOLIS PUBLIC LIBRARY, 300 Nicollet Mall, 55401-1992. SAN 347-4755. Tel: 612-630-6000, 612-630-6200 (Admin). Interlibrary Loan Service Tel: 612-630-6140. FAX: 612-630-6210. Web Site: www.mpls.lib.mn.us. *Dir*, Mary Lawson; *Assoc Dir*, Janice Feye-Stukas; *Tech Servs*, Marsha Fralick; *Acq*, Louise Merriam; *Cat*, David Klaiber; *Coll Develop*, Carol VanWhy; Staff 77 (MLS 77)
Founded 1885. Pop 360,591; Circ 2,456,727
Jan 1999-Dec 1999 Income (Main Library and Branch Library) $18,582,412, State $6,240,673, City $11,620,829, Federal $21,320, Other $699,590. Mats Exp $2,335,260. Sal $13,859,822
Library Holdings: Bk Vols 2,569,723; Per Subs 4,338
Special Collections: Minneapolis Athenaeum includes Early American Exploration & Travel Coll, Heffelfinger Aesop's & Others' Fables Coll, North American Indians Coll, Spencer Natural History Coll; others include Environmental Conservation Library of Minnesota, Picture Coll; Spec Coll Dept includes History of Books & Printing Coll, Hoag Mark Twain Coll, Huttner Abolition & Anti-Slavery Coll, Kittleson World War II Coll, Louis Dodge Autograph Coll, Minneapolis Coll including Oral History, 19th Century American Studies Coll
Automation Activity & Vendor Info: (Acquisitions) Innovative Interfaces Inc.; (Circulation) Innovative Interfaces Inc.
Publications: booklists & brochures; Currents; Events at Your Minneapolis Public Library; Minneapolis Public Library Periodical List; Rainbow Collection: Multicultural Children's Books; Speaking Volumes, A Newsletter of the Minneapolis Public Library & the Friends of the Minneapolis Public Library; The Book 'Zine...Especially for Teens
Partic in Metronet; Metropolitan Library Service Agency; MINITEX Library Information Network; OCLC Online Computer Library Center, Inc
Special Services for the Deaf - TTY machine
Friends of the Library Group
Branches: 15
PIERRE BOTTINEAU BRANCH, 1224 NE Second St, 55413-1130. SAN 347-4992. Tel: 612-630-6890. Web Site: www.mpls.lib.mn.us. *Librn*, Gloria Busch
Library Holdings: Bk Vols 10,409; Per Subs 50
EAST LAKE, 2727 E Lake St, 55406-1927. SAN 347-481X. Tel: 612-630-6550. *Librn*, Jerry Blue
Library Holdings: Bk Vols 62,287; Per Subs 220
FRANKLIN, 1314 E Franklin Ave, 55404-2924. SAN 347-4844. Tel: 612-630-6800. *Librn*, Sally Munger
Library Holdings: Bk Vols 34,309; Per Subs 89
HOSMER, 347 E 36th St, 55408-4567. SAN 347-4879. Tel: 612-630-6950. *Librn*, Roy Woodstrom
Library Holdings: Bk Vols 47,917; Per Subs 159
LINDEN HILLS, 2900 W 43rd St, 55410-1515. SAN 347-4909. Tel: 612-630-6750. FAX: 612-630-6755. Web Site: www.mpls.lib.mn.us.
Founded 1931
Library Holdings: Bk Vols 31,034; Per Subs 131
MUNICIPAL INFORMATION LIBRARY, City Hall, Rm 300, 350 S Fifth St, 55415. SAN 328-9176. Tel: 612-673-3029.
NOKOMIS, 5100 34th Ave S, 55417-1545. SAN 347-4933. Tel: 612-630-6700. *Librn*, Carol Dosse
Library Holdings: Bk Vols 48,368; Per Subs 151
NORTH REGIONAL, 1315 Lowry Ave N, 55411-1398. SAN 347-478X. Tel: 612-630-6600. *Librn*, Constance Hill
Library Holdings: Bk Vols 94,138; Per Subs 224
NORTHEAST, 2200 Central Ave NE, 55418-3708. SAN 347-4968. Tel: 612-630-6900.
Library Holdings: Bk Vols 51,798; Per Subs 150
ROOSEVELT, 4026 28th Ave S, 55406-3119. SAN 347-5026. Tel: 612-630-6590.
Founded 1927
Library Holdings: Bk Vols 32,123; Per Subs 136
SOUTHEAST, 1222 SE Fourth St, 55414-2027. SAN 347-5050. Tel: 612-630-6850. *Librn*, Jeanette Larsen
Library Holdings: Bk Vols 30,437; Per Subs 128
SUMNER, 611 Emerson Ave N, 55411-4196. SAN 347-5085. Tel: 612-630-6390. *Librn*, Dan Kelty
Library Holdings: Bk Vols 25,679; Per Subs 112
WALKER, 2880 Hennepin Ave, 55408-1957. SAN 347-5115. Tel: 612-630-6650. *Librn*, Susan Brown
Library Holdings: Bk Vols 69,454; Per Subs 204
WASHBURN, 5244 Lyndale Ave S, 55419-1222. SAN 347-514X. Tel: 612-630-6500. FAX: 612-630-6505.
Circ 450,000
Library Holdings: Bk Vols 92,638; Per Subs 215
Automation Activity & Vendor Info: (Acquisitions) Innovative Interfaces Inc.; (Cataloging) Innovative Interfaces Inc.; (Circulation) Innovative Interfaces Inc.; (OPAC) Innovative Interfaces Inc.
WEBBER PARK, 4310 Webber Pkwy, 55412-1340. SAN 347-5174. Tel: 612-630-6640. *Librn*, Joseph Saporito
Library Holdings: Bk Vols 17,231; Per Subs 94
Bookmobiles: 1. Bk vols 13,438

S MINNEGASCO BUSINESS INFORMATION,* 800 LaSalle Ave, 11th flr, PO Box 59038, 55459-0038. SAN 308-6712. Tel: 612-321-5063. FAX: 612-321-4873. *Librn*, Janet Reid; Staff 3 (MLS 2, Non-MLS 1)
Founded 1959
Library Holdings: Bk Titles 3,000; Per Subs 450
Subject Interests: Bus, Energy, Engineering, Gas indust, Mgt
Automation Activity & Vendor Info: (Cataloging) Inmagic, Inc.
Publications: Current Topics Resource Lists; InfoSource
Restriction: Staff use only
Partic in American Gas Association-Library Services; Metronet

GM MINNESOTA DEPARTMENT OF HEALTH, R N Barr Public Health Library, 717 SE Delaware St, PO Box 9441, 55440-9441. SAN 308-6704. Tel: 612-623-5090. FAX: 612-623-5385. E-Mail: library@health.state.mn.us. *Librn*, D Jordan; Staff 6 (MLS 2, Non-MLS 4)
Founded 1872
Library Holdings: Bk Titles 7,000; Per Subs 180
Subject Interests: Environ health, Health planning, Health promotion, Pub, Public health, Socioeconomic aspects of health care
Automation Activity & Vendor Info: (Cataloging) PALS; (Circulation) PALS; (Media Booking) PALS; (Serials) PALS
Publications: CHECK IT OUT (quarterly)
Partic in Capitol Area Library Consortium; Metronet; MINITEX Library Information Network; Twin Cities Biomedical Consortium
Open Mon-Fri 8-4:30

S MINNESOTA ORCHESTRA, Music Library,* 1111 Nicollet Mall, 55403. SAN 329-9155. Tel: 612-371-5622. FAX: 612-371-0838. E-Mail: pbglib@mnorch.org.
Library Holdings: Bk Vols 300; Bk Titles 200; Per Subs 12
Subject Interests: Orchestra performance mat
Special Collections: Minnesota Orchestra Archives

S MISSING CHILDREN MINNESOTA LIBRARY,* 420 N Fifth St, Ste 570, 55401-1318. SAN 372-6266. Tel: 612-521-1188. FAX: 612-521-2204. *Exec Dir*, Carol Watson
Library Holdings: Bk Titles 40
Special Collections: Missing Children, posters

SR MOUNT CARMEL LUTHERAN CHURCH LIBRARY,* 1701 NE Saint Anthony Blvd, 55418. SAN 308-6739. Tel: 612-781-2796. FAX: 612-781-1621. *Librn*, Claudia Kolb
Library Holdings: Bk Vols 2,200

C NORTH CENTRAL UNIVERSITY, T J Jones Information Resource Center, 915 E 14th St, 55404. (Mail add: 910 Elliot Ave, 55404-1391), SAN 308-6798. Tel: 612-343-4490. TDD: 612-343-5012. FAX: 612-343-5012. Web Site: www.northcentral.edu. *Dir*, Dr Don Smeeton; E-Mail: ddsmeeto@northcentral.edu; *Asst Dir*, Joy Jewett; *Tech Servs*, Connie Sylvester; Staff 5 (MLS 2, Non-MLS 3)
Founded 1930. Enrl 1,200; Fac 35; Highest Degree: Bachelor
Jun 1999-May 2000 Income $312,209. Mats Exp $46,350, Books $18,000, Per/Ser (Incl. Access Fees) $20,000, Presv $1,800, Micro $5,200, AV Equip $1,350. Sal $144,500 (Prof $109,000)
Library Holdings: Bk Vols 71,652
Special Collections: Classical Pentecostal Materials
Partic in OCLC Online Computer Library Center, Inc

S NORTHERN STATES POWER COMPANY, Communications Department - Library & Record Center,* 414 Nicollet Mall, 55401. SAN 375-1481. Tel: 612-330-6936. FAX: 612-330-6947.
Library Holdings: Bk Titles 20

PILLSBURY COMPANY
S TECHNOLOGY KNOWLEDGE CENTER, 330 University Ave SE, 55414. SAN 347-5239. Tel: 612-330-8497. FAX: 612-330-8245. *Librn*, Gretchen Haase; Staff 2 (MLS 1, Non-MLS 1)
Founded 1941
Library Holdings: Bk Vols 9,000; Bk Titles 5,000; Per Subs 300
Subject Interests: Analytical chemistry, Cereal chem, Food sci, Microbiology, Plant sci, Technology
Publications: Current Literature (monthly); Food Patient Digest (monthly)
Restriction: Private library

G PLANNED PARENTHOOD OF MINNESOTA & SOUTH DAKOTA, Phyllis Cooksey Resource Center,* 1200 Lagoon Ave S, 55408. SAN 327-2028. Tel: 612-823-6568. FAX: 612-825-3522. Web Site: www.plannedparenthood.org. *Coll Develop, Librn*, Theresa Wolner; E-Mail: twolner@usinternet.com
1998-1999 Mats Exp $5,500
Library Holdings: Bk Vols 2,000; Per Subs 75
Subject Interests: Abortion
Special Collections: Archives Coll, audio-visual
Publications: Various pamphlets, catalogs

S RELIASTAR, Corporate Library,* 20 Washington Ave S, 55401. SAN 377-3612. Tel: 612-372-5432. FAX: 612-342-5339. E-Mail: corporatelibrary@reliastar.com. *Librn*, Laura Allard
Library Holdings: Bk Titles 500; Per Subs 300

S RESOURCE CENTER OF THE AMERICAS, Penny Lernoux Memorial Library on Latin America, 3019 Minnehaha Ave, 55406. SAN 374-4779. Tel: 612-276-0788. FAX: 612-276-0898. E-Mail: info@americas.org. Web Site: www.americas.org. *Librn*, Mary Swenson
Founded 1983
Library Holdings: Bk Titles 10,000; Per Subs 120
Subject Interests: Human rights
Special Collections: Latin America (Penny Lernoux Coll)
Automation Activity & Vendor Info: (Cataloging) Sagebrush Corporation; (Circulation) Sagebrush Corporation

S RIDER, BENNETT, EGAN & ARUNDEL LAW LIBRARY, 333 S 7th St Ste 2000, 55402. SAN 326-0151. Tel: 612-335-3824. FAX: 612-340-7900. *Librn*, Kimberley J Jones; E-Mail: kjjones@riderlaw.com; Staff 2 (Non-MLS 2)
Library Holdings: Bk Vols 5,000; Bk Titles 440; Per Subs 45
Restriction: Not open to public

L ROBINS, KAPLAN, MILLER & CIRESI LLP, Law Library, 2800 LaSalle Plaza, 55402. (Mail add: 800 LaSalle Ave, 55402), SAN 372-0551. Tel: 612-349-8529. Circulation Tel: 612-349-8500. Toll Free Tel: 800-553-9900. FAX: 612-339-4181. Web Site: www.rkmc.com. *Dir*, Carol Crego; Tel: 612-349-0940, E-Mail: cregcj@rkmc.com; *Librn*, Marshall Hambro; E-Mail: mjhamboro@rkmc.com
Library Holdings: Bk Vols 12,000; Per Subs 72

SR SAINT LAWRENCE CATHOLIC CHURCH, Newman Center Library,* 1201 Fifth Sta SE, 55414. SAN 308-6771. Tel: 612-331-3437. FAX: 612-378-1771. *Dir*, Fr John Behmke
Founded 1946
Library Holdings: Bk Titles 11,500; Per Subs 15
Subject Interests: Biblical, Relig studies, Scriptural works, Social justice, Theology

R SAINT OLAF LUTHERAN CHURCH LIBRARY, Carlsen Memorial, 2901 Emerson Ave N, 55411. SAN 308-6909. Tel: 612-529-7726. FAX: 612-529-4385. *Librn*, Eleanor Grant
Founded 1963
Library Holdings: Bk Vols 1,750

S SONS OF NORWAY INTERNATIONAL LIBRARY, 1455 W Lake St, 55408. SAN 308-6925. Tel: 612-827-3611. Toll Free Tel: 800-945-8851. FAX: 612-827-0658. Web Site: www.sofn.com. *Librn*, Liv Dahl
Founded 1962
Library Holdings: Bk Vols 2,500; Bk Titles 1,000; Per Subs 20
Special Collections: Norwegian-American Culture & Immigration (Norwegian-American Studies)
Friends of the Library Group

S STAR TRIBUNE NEWSPAPER OF THE TWIN CITIES LIBRARY, 425 Portland Ave, 55488. SAN 308-6690. Tel: 612-673-7398. FAX: 612-673-4459. *Librn*, Robert H Jansen; E-Mail: bjansen@startribune.com; *Asst Librn*, Sandy Date; *Res*, Roberta Hovde; *Res*, Linda Scheimann
Founded 1946
Library Holdings: Bk Vols 4,000

R TEMPLE ISRAEL LIBRARY, 2324 Emerson Ave S, 55405-2695. SAN 308-6933. Tel: 612-377-8680. FAX: 612-377-6630. *Librn*, Georgia Kalman; Tel: 612-374-0338, E-Mail: gkalman@templeisrael.com
Founded 1929
Library Holdings: Bk Titles 15,000; Per Subs 46
Subject Interests: Art, Biography, History, Holocaust

S UNITED DEFENSE ARMAMENT SYSTEMS DIVISION, Library & Information Center, 4800 E River Rd, 55421-1498. SAN 327-8174. Tel: 612-572-7900. FAX: 612-572-6037.; Staff 2 (MLS 2)
Library Holdings: Bk Vols 8,000; Per Subs 200
Subject Interests: Armament, Ordnance
Database Vendor: Dialog, Lexis-Nexis
Publications: Acquisitions Newsletter (monthly)
Restriction: Company library, Not open to public
Function: Document delivery services, Reference services available, Research library

R UNITED METHODIST CHURCH, Minnesota Annual Conference Archives & Historical Library, 122 W Franklin Ave, Ste 400, 55404. SAN 308-695X. Tel: 612-870-0058, Ext 249. FAX: 612-870-1260. *Archivist*, Thelma B Boeder; E-Mail: thelma.boeder@mnumc.org; Staff 1 (MLS 1)
Library Holdings: Bk Vols 2,500; Bk Titles 2,000
Special Collections: History of the United Methodist Church & Antecedents

G UNITED STATES COURT OF APPEALS, Branch Library, 1102 US Courthouse, 300 Fourth St, 55415. SAN 325-4348. Tel: 612-664-5830. FAX: 612-664-5835. Web Site: www.c28.uscourts.gov/library/library.html. *Librn*, Joyce Larson Schampel; E-Mail: joyce_larson_schampel@mnd.uscourts.gov; Staff 2 (MLS 1, Non-MLS 1)
Library Holdings: Bk Vols 18,000

C UNIVERSITY OF MINNESOTA, Immigration History Research Center, 311 E L Andersen Library, 222 21st Ave S, 55455. SAN 329-7306. Tel: 612-625-4800. FAX: 612-626-0018. E-Mail: ihrc@tc.umn.edu. Web Site: www.umn.edu/ihrc. *Curator*, Joel Wurl; Staff 5 (MLS 2, Non-MLS 3)
Library Holdings: Bk Titles 30,000; Per Subs 150
Publications: Conference Proceedings; IHRC News; Spectrum
Partic in RLIN
Friends of the Library Group

C UNIVERSITY OF MINNESOTA LIBRARIES-TWIN CITIES, (MNU), 499-O Meredith Wilson Libr, 309 19th Ave S, 55455-0414. SAN 347-5298. Tel: 612-624-4520. FAX: 612-626-9353. Web Site: www.lib.umn.edu. *Librn*, Thomas Shaughnessy; *Asst Librn*, Peggy Johnson; *Coll Develop*, Jim

Cogswell; *Tech Servs*, Jon Nichols; Tel: 612-626-0801; *Acq*, Barbara Stelmasik; Tel: 612-625-8074; *Ref*, Kay Kane; Staff 427 (MLS 112, Non-MLS 315)
Founded 1851. Enrl 44,755; Fac 1,446; Highest Degree: Doctorate
Jul 1998-Jun 1999 Income $29,715,493. Mats Exp $9,945,563. Sal $14,268,202
Library Holdings: Bk Vols 5,747,805; Per Subs 45,696
Subject Interests: Philosophy
Special Collections: African-American Literature & Life (Givens Coll); Archives for the History of Quantum Physics; Children's Literature Research Coll; History of European Expansion Prior to 1800 (J F Bell Coll); History of Information Processing (Charles Babbage Institute); John Berryman Coll; Northwest Architectural Archives; Performing Arts Archives (Minnesota Orchestra, Guthrie Theatre); Private Presses Coll; Social Welfare History Archives; Wangensteen Historical Library of Biology & Medicine
Automation Activity & Vendor Info: (Acquisitions) NOTIS; (Cataloging) NOTIS; (OPAC) NOTIS; (Serials) NOTIS
Publications: Friends of the Library (Newsletter); Library Line
Mem of Asn of Research Libraries
Partic in CIC; MINITEX Library Information Network; OCLC Online Computer Library Center, Inc; Research Libraries Group, Inc
Friends of the Library Group
Departmental Libraries:
AMES LIBRARY OF SOUTH ASIA, S-10 Wilson Libr, 309 19th Ave S, 55455. SAN 347-5719. Tel: 612-624-4857. FAX: 612-626-9353. *Librn*, Donald Clay Johnson
ANDERSEN HORTICULTURAL LIBRARY, 3675 Arboretum Dr, PO Box 39, Chanhassen, 55317. SAN 378-0759. Tel: 612-443-2440. FAX: 612-443-2521. *Assoc Librn*, Richard Isaacson
ARCHITECTURE, 1422 University Ave SE, 55455. SAN 329-756X. Tel: 612-624-6383. FAX: 612-625-5597. *Mgr*, Joon Mornes
CM BIO-MEDICAL, Diehl Hall, 505 Essex St SE, 55455. SAN 347-5352. Tel: 612-626-0998. FAX: 612-626-5822. E-Mail: biomcirc@tc.umn.edu. Web Site: www.biomed.lib.umn.edu. *Dir*, Ellen Nagle
CM BIOMEDICAL INFORMATION SERVICES, Diehl Hall, 505 Essex St SE, 55455. Tel: 612-626-3730. FAX: 612-626-3824. *Librn*, Vicki Glasgow
Fee-based services
CHARLES BABBAGE INSTITUTE, Elmer L Andersen Library, 222 21st Ave S, 55455. SAN 371-3083. Tel: 612-624-5050. FAX: 612-625-8054. *Asst Librn*, Elisabeth Kaplan
CHILDREN'S LITERATURE RESEARCH COLLECTIONS, Elmer L Andersen Library, 222 21st Ave S, 55455. SAN 347-6103. Tel: 612-624-4576. FAX: 612-625-5525. *Curator*, Karen Nelson Hoyle
CM CIRCULATION & ILL SERVICES Tel: 612-626-5653. FAX: 612-626-2454. *Mgr*, Maggie Lindorfer
CM CIRCULATION SERVICES (BIO-MEDICAL LIBRARY), Diehl Hall, 505 Essex St SE, 55455. SAN 347-5417. Tel: 612-626-5653. FAX: 612-626-2454. *Mgr*, Maggie Lindorfer
CIRCULATION SERVICES (MAGRATH LIBRARY), 1984 Buford Ave, Saint Paul, 55108. SAN 378-0856. Tel: 612-624-2233. FAX: 612-624-3134. *In Charge*, Nancy Soldatow
CIRCULATION SERVICES (NORRIS HALL), 60 Norris Hall, 172 Pillsbury Dr SE, 55455. SAN 371-3172. Tel: 612-624-3366. FAX: 612-625-5525. *In Charge*, Amy Schaefer
CIRCULATION SERVICES (WILSON LIBRARY), 309 19th Ave S, 55455. SAN 347-6405. Tel: 612-624-3321. FAX: 612-626-8968. *Mgr*, Joan Mouchet
DISTANCE LEARNING INSTRUCTION PROJECT, 499 Wilson Libr, 309 19th Ave S, 55455. SAN 378-0872. Tel: 612-624-4362. FAX: 612-626-9353. *Assoc Librn*, John Butler
DOCUMENTS TO U (ILL LENDING-MINITEX), 15 Andersen Library, 222 21st Ave S, 55455. Tel: 612-624-4388. Web Site: kinglear.lib.umn.edu/dtu/. *In Charge*, Obinnaya Oji
DRUG INFORMATION SERVICE: SUBSTANCE ABUSE COLLECTION, 279 Diehl Hall, 505 Essex St SE, 55455. SAN 378-0899. Tel: 612-624-6492. FAX: 612-626-2454. *Assoc Librn*, Gail Weinberg
EAST ASIAN, S-75 Wilson Libr, 309 19th Ave S, 55455. SAN 347-657X. Tel: 612-624-9833. FAX: 612-626-9353.
ELECTRONIC TEXT RESEARCH CENTER, 179 Wilson Libr, 309 19th Ave S, 55455. SAN 371-3121. Tel: 612-624-6370. FAX: 612-626-9353. *Assoc Prof*, Miranda Remnek
ENTOMOLOGY, FISHERIES & WILDLIFE, 375 Hodson Hall, 1980 Folwell Ave, Saint Paul, 55108. SAN 378-0910. Tel: 612-624-9288. FAX: 612-624-9245. *Asst Prof*, Loralee Kerr
ERIC SEVAREID LIBRARY (JOURNALISM), 20 Murphy Hall, 206 Church St SE, 55455. SAN 378-1208. Tel: 612-625-7892. FAX: 612-626-8251. *Prof*, Kathleen Hansen; *Asst Librn*, Jan Nyberg
ESTIS (FEE BASED SERVICES), Norris Hall, 172 Pillsbury Dr SE, 55455. SAN 378-0937. Tel: 612-624-2356. FAX: 612-624-8518. *Mgr*, Paul McKinney
Fee-based services
FORESTRY, B-50 Natural Resources Admin Bldg, 2003 Upper Buford Circle, Saint Paul, 55108. SAN 378-0953. Tel: 612-624-3222. FAX: 612-624-3733. *Assoc Prof*, Jean Albrecht
GIFTS, 30 Wilson Libr, 309 19th Ave S, 55455. SAN 378-097X. Tel: 612-624-4183. FAX: 612-626-9353.
GOVERNMENT PUBLICATIONS, Wilson Libr, 309 19th Ave S, 55455. SAN 347-6588. Tel: 612-624-5073. FAX: 612-626-9353. *Librn*, Julia Wallace
IMMIGRATION HISTORY RESEARCH CENTER, Elmer L Andersen Library Ste 311, 222 21st Ave S, 55455. SAN 378-0996. Tel: 612-625-4800. *Dir*, Rudolph J Vecoli
Jun 1998-May 1999
INTERLIBRARY LOAN (BIO-MEDICAL LIBRARY), 314 Diehl Hall, 505 Essex St SE, 55455. SAN 378-1003. Tel: 612-626-2969. FAX: 612-626-2454. Web Site: www.biomed.lib.umn.edu/other.html. *Mgr*, Maggie Lindorfer
INTERLIBRARY LOAN (MAGRATH LIBRARY), 1874 Buford Ave, Saint Paul, 55108. SAN 378-102X. Tel: 612-624-3793. FAX: 612-624-9245. *In Charge*, Mary Mortenson
INTERLIBRARY LOAN BORROWING (WILSON LIBRARY), 110 Wilson Libr, 309 19th Ave S, 55455. SAN 347-643X. Tel: 612-624-1806. FAX: 612-626-7585. *Mgr*, Cherie Weston
JAMES FORD BELL LIBRARY, 462 Wilson Libr, 309 19th Ave S, 55455. SAN 347-5328. Tel: 612-624-1528. FAX: 612-626-9353. *Curator, Prof*, Carol Urness
JOHN R BORCHERT MAP LIBRARY, S-76 Wilson Libr, 309 19th Ave S, 55455. SAN 347-6642. Tel: 612-624-4549. FAX: 612-626-9353. *Librn*, Brent Allison
CL LAW, 120 Law Bldg, 229 19th Ave S, 55455. SAN 378-1046. Tel: 612-625-4300. FAX: 612-625-3478. *Dir*, Joan Howland
LEARNING RESOURCES CENTER, 153 Norris Hall, 172 Pillsbury Dr SE, 55455. SAN 347-6197. Tel: 612-624-1584. FAX: 612-625-5525. *Mgr*, Dan Donnelly
MACHINE READABLE DATA CENTER, 170 Wilson Libr, 309 19th Ave S, 55455. SAN 378-1062. Tel: 612-624-4389. FAX: 612-626-9353. *Coordr*, Wendy Treadwell
MANUSCRIPTS DIVISION, Elmer L Andersen Library, 222 21st Ave S, 55455. SAN 347-6227. Tel: 612-627-4199. FAX: 612-627-4110. *Curator, Prof*, Alan Lathrop
MATERIALS ACQUISITIONS & CONTROL (TECHNICAL SERVICES), 160 Wilson Libr, 309 19th Ave S, 55455. SAN 378-1089. Tel: 612-625-4343. FAX: 612-625-3428. *In Charge*, Barbara Stelmasik
MATHEMATICS, 310 Vincent Hall, 206 Church St SE, 55455. SAN 347-5891. Tel: 612-624-6075. FAX: 612-624-4302. *Asst Librn*, Kris Fowler
MUSIC, 70 Ferguson Hall, 2106 Fourth St S, 55455. SAN 347-6251. Tel: 612-624-5890. FAX: 612-626-9353. *Assoc Librn*, Laurel Haycock; *Assoc Librn*, Laura Probst
PLANT PATHOLOGY, 395 Borlaug Hall, 1991 Upper Buford Circle, Saint Paul, 55108. SAN 378-1100. Tel: 612-625-9777. FAX: 612-624-9245.
REFERENCE & INSTRUCTIONAL SERVICES Tel: 612-626-3260.
REFERENCE SERVICES (BIO-MEDICAL LIBRARY), Diehl Hall, 505 Essex St SE, 55455. SAN 347-5387. Tel: 612-626-3260. FAX: 612-626-2454. *Assoc Librn*, Kathy Robbins
REFERENCE SERVICES (BUSINESS), Wilson Libr, 309 19th Ave S, 55455. SAN 347-6553. Tel: 612-624-9066. FAX: 612-626-9353. *Asst Prof*, Judy Wells
REFERENCE SERVICES (MAGRATH LIBRARY), 1984 Buford Ave, Saint Paul, 55108. SAN 378-1127. Tel: 612-624-1212. FAX: 612-624-9245. E-Mail: magrath@tc.umn.edu. *Assoc Librn*, Gregg Richardson
REFERENCE SERVICES (SCIENCES & ENGINEERING), 60 Norris Hall, 172 Pillsbury Dr SE, 55455. SAN 371-3105. Tel: 612-624-0224. FAX: 612-625-5525. *Assoc Librn*, Gary Fouty
REFERENCE SERVICES (WILSON LIBRARY), 309 19th Ave S, 55455. SAN 371-3156. Tel: 612-626-2227. FAX: 612-626-9353. *Librn*, Barbara Kautz; *Assoc Librn*, Charles Spetland
RESERVES (MAGRATH LIBRARY), 60 Magrath Libr, 1874 Buford Ave, Saint Paul, 55108. SAN 378-1143. Tel: 612-624-2233. FAX: 612-625-3134. *In Charge*, Nancy Soldatow
RESERVES (NORRIS HALL), 172 Pillsbury Dr SE, 55455. SAN 378-116X. Tel: 612-624-0283. FAX: 612-625-5525. *In Charge*, Perry Dean
RESERVES (WILSON LIBRARY), 65 Wilson Libr, 309 19th Ave S, 55455. SAN 378-1186. Tel: 612-624-6576. FAX: 612-626-9353. *Mgr*, Jerrie Bayer
SOCIAL WELFARE HISTORY ARCHIVES, Elmer L Andersen Library, 222 21st Ave S, 55455. SAN 347-6286. Tel: 612-624-6394. FAX: 612-625-5525. *Curator, Prof*, David Klaassen
SPECIAL COLLECTIONS & RARE BOOKS, Elmer L Andersen Library, 222 21st Ave S, 55455. SAN 347-6731. Tel: 612-624-3855. FAX: 612-626-9353. *Asst Librn, Curator*, Timothy Johnson
UNIVERSITY ARCHIVES, Elmer L Andersen Library, 222 21st Ave S, 55455. SAN 347-6316. Tel: 612-624-0562. FAX: 612-625-5525. *Assoc Prof, Curator*, Penelope Krosch
CM VETERINARY MEDICAL, 450 Veterinary Science, 1971 Commonwealth Ave, Saint Paul, 55108. SAN 378-1224. Tel: 612-624-4281. FAX: 612-624-9782. *Asst Prof*, Livija Carlson
CM WANGENSTEEN HISTORICAL LIBRARY OF BIOLOGY & MEDICINE, 568 Diehl Hall, 505 Essex St SE, 55455. SAN 347-5506. Tel: 612-626-6881. FAX: 612-626-2454. *Asst Librn*, Elaine Challacombe
YMCA ARCHIVES, Elmer L Anderson Library, 222 21st Ave S, 55455. SAN 370-3207. Tel: 612-625-3445. *Curator, Prof*, Andrea Hinding

S WALKER ART CENTER, Staff Reference Library/Archives, Vineland Pl, 55403. SAN 308-6984. Tel: 612-375-7680. FAX: 612-375-7590. *Librn*, Rosemary Furtak; E-Mail: rosemary.furtak@walkerart.org; *Asst Librn*, Mary Ellyn Johnson; E-Mail: mary.ellyn.johnson@walkerart.org
Founded 1950
Library Holdings: Bk Vols 35,000; Per Subs 110
Subject Interests: Architecture, Art, Art history, Design, Graphics, Painting, Photog, Sculpture
Special Collections: Artists Books, Audio Archive, Artist Catalogues 1940-present; Edmond R Ruben Film Study Coll
Partic in OCLC Online Computer Library Center, Inc

L ZELLE, HOFMANN, VOELBEL & GETTE, Law Library, City Ctr, 33 S Sixth St, Ste 4400, 55402. SAN 372-2813. Tel: 612-336-9129. FAX: 612-336-9100. Web Site: www.zelle.com. *Librn*, Janet L Rongitsch; E-Mail: jrongits@zelle.com
Library Holdings: Bk Vols 10,000; Per Subs 200

MINNEOTA

P MINNEOTA PUBLIC LIBRARY,* 103 N Jefferson St, 56264-0217. SAN 308-6992. Tel: 507-872-5473. FAX: 507-872-6144. *Librn*, Mary Buysse
Pop 1,500; Circ 3,027
Library Holdings: Bk Vols 5,889; Bk Titles 6,369; Per Subs 14

MINNETONKA

S CARLSON COMPANIES, INC, Information Center,* 701 Carlson Pkwy, 55305. SAN 308-633X. Tel: 612-449-2543. FAX: 612-449-2546. *Mgr*, Wendy Stotts
Founded 1962
Library Holdings: Per Subs 300
Subject Interests: Advertising, Bus incentives, Marketing, Real estate, Retail, Trading stamps, Wholesale food marketing
Restriction: Not open to public

P HENNEPIN COUNTY LIBRARY, 12601 Ridgedale Dr, 55305-1909. SAN 347-3163. Tel: 952-847-8500. Interlibrary Loan Service Tel: 952-847-8589. TDD: 952-847-8880. FAX: 952-847-8600. Web Site: www.hennepin.lib.mn.us. *Dir*, Charles M Brown; Tel: 952-847-8580, E-Mail: cbrown@hclib.org; *Tech Coordr*, Sharon Charles; Tel: 952-847-8558, E-Mail: scharles@hclib.org; *Cat*, Bruce Willms; Tel: 952-847-8607, E-Mail: bwillms@hclib.org; *Coll Develop*, Elizabeth Feinberg; Tel: 952-847-8622, E-Mail: efeinberg@hclib.org; *Commun Relations*, Nancy Perron; Tel: 952-847-8516, E-Mail: nperron@hclib.org; Staff 465 (MLS 81, Non-MLS 384)
Founded 1922. Pop 727,973; Circ 10,539,250
Jan 2000-Dec 2000 Income (Main Library and Branch Library) $30,445,270, State $300,000, County $28,445,270, Other $1,700,000. Mats Exp $3,746,362, Books $3,065,043, Per/Ser (Incl. Access Fees) $330,084, Other Print Mats $77,545, Electronic Ref Mat (Incl. Access Fees) $273,690. Sal $15,415,911
Library Holdings: Bk Vols 2,000,000; Bk Titles 400,000; Per Subs 5,864; Bks on Deafness & Sign Lang 605
Subject Interests: World languages
Automation Activity & Vendor Info: (Acquisitions) epixtech, inc.; (Cataloging) epixtech, inc.; (Circulation) epixtech, inc.; (OPAC) epixtech, inc.
Database Vendor: epixtech, inc., OCLC - First Search
Mem of Metropolitan Libr Serv Agency
Friends of the Library Group
Branches: 26
AUGSBURG PARK, 7100 Nicollet Ave S, Richfield, 55423-3117. SAN 347-3198. Tel: 952-847-5300. Interlibrary Loan Service Tel: 952-847-8589. FAX: 952-847-5302. Web Site: www.hennepin.lib.mn.us. *Senior Librn*, Vicki Oeljen; E-Mail: voeljen@hclib.org
Library Holdings: Bk Vols 59,708
Friends of the Library Group
BROOKDALE-HENNEPIN AREA, 6125 Shingle Creek Pkwy, Brooklyn Center, 55430-2110. SAN 347-3228. Tel: 952-847-5600. Interlibrary Loan Service Tel: 952-847-8589. TDD: 952-847-5606. FAX: 612-847-5605. Web Site: www.hennepin.lib.mn.us/pub/. *Actg Librn*, Michael McConnell; E-Mail: mmcconnell@hclib.org
Library Holdings: Bk Vols 137,584
Friends of the Library Group
BROOKLYN PARK BRANCH, 8600 Zane Ave N, Brooklyn Park, 55443-1897. SAN 347-3252. Tel: 763-424-8002. Interlibrary Loan Service Tel: 952-847-8589. FAX: 763-424-8295. Web Site: www.hennepin.lib.mn.us. *Senior Librn*, Joann Frankena; E-Mail: jfrankena@hclib.org
Library Holdings: Bk Vols 58,529
Friends of the Library Group
CHAMPLIN BRANCH, 12154 Ensign Ave N, Champlin, 55316-9998. SAN 347-3287. Tel: 763-427-1010. Interlibrary Loan Service Tel: 952-847-8589. FAX: 763-427-7982. Web Site: www.hennepin.lib.mn.us. *Senior Librn*, Sharyll Smith; E-Mail: ssmith@hclib.org
Library Holdings: Bk Vols 49,492
Friends of the Library Group
EDEN PRAIRIE BRANCH, 479 Prairie Center Dr, Eden Prairie, 55344-5319. SAN 347-3317. Tel: 952-829-5460. Interlibrary Loan Service Tel: 952-847-8589. FAX: 952-941-6035. Web Site: www.hennepin.lib.mn.us. *Actg Librn*, Lois Langer; E-Mail: llanger@hclib.org
Library Holdings: Bk Vols 73,438
Friends of the Library Group
EDINA BRANCH, 4701 W 50th St, Edina, 55424-1397. SAN 347-3341. Tel: 952-922-1611. Interlibrary Loan Service Tel: 952-847-8589. FAX: 952-922-2035. Web Site: www.hennepin.lib.mn.us. *Senior Librn*, Marica Wattson; E-Mail: mwattson@hclib.org
Library Holdings: Bk Vols 74,827
Friends of the Library Group
EXCELSIOR BRANCH, 343 Third St, Excelsior, 55331-1878. SAN 347-3376. Tel: 952-847-5450. Interlibrary Loan Service Tel: 952-847-8589. FAX: 952-474-7913. Web Site: www.hennepin.lib.mn.us. *Librn*, Peggy Bauer; E-Mail: pbauer@hclib.org
Library Holdings: Bk Vols 32,063
Friends of the Library Group
GOLDEN VALLEY BRANCH, 830 Winnetka Ave N, Golden Valley, 55427-4532. SAN 347-3406. Tel: 763-540-8290. Interlibrary Loan Service Tel: 952-847-8589. FAX: 763-540-8292. Web Site: www.hennepin.lib.mn.us. *Actg Librn*, Ardis Wiley; E-Mail: awiley@hclib.org
Library Holdings: Bk Vols 67,188
Friends of the Library Group
HOPKINS BRANCH, 22 11th Ave N, Hopkins, 55343-7575. SAN 347-3430. Tel: 952-930-2740. Interlibrary Loan Service Tel: 952-847-8589. FAX: 952-930-2745. Web Site: www.hennepin.lib.mn.us. *Head Librn*, Carolyn Muchow; E-Mail: cmuchow@hclib.org
Library Holdings: Bk Vols 56,333
Friends of the Library Group
LONG LAKE BRANCH, 1865 Wayzata Blvd W, Long Lake, 55356-9587. SAN 328-7335. Tel: 952-847-5525. Interlibrary Loan Service Tel: 952-847-8589. FAX: 763-475-4697. Web Site: www.hennepin.lib.mn.us. *Assoc Librn*, Nancy Donahue; E-Mail: ndonahue@hclib.org
Library Holdings: Bk Vols 14,917
Friends of the Library Group
MAPLE GROVE BRANCH, 8351 Elm Creek Blvd, Maple Grove, 55369-4617. SAN 328-9184. Tel: 763-420-8377. Interlibrary Loan Service Tel: 952-847-8589. FAX: 763-420-4475. Web Site: www.hennepin.lib.mn.us. *Head Librn*, Margaret Gillespie; E-Mail: mgillespie@hclib.org
Library Holdings: Bk Vols 79,872
Friends of the Library Group
MAPLE PLAIN BRANCH, 5184 Main St E, Maple Plain, 55359-9648. SAN 347-349X. Tel: 952-847-5700. Interlibrary Loan Service Tel: 952-847-8589. FAX: 763-479-3949. Web Site: www.hennepin.lib.mn.us. *Assoc Librn*, Virginia Matanic; E-Mail: vmatanic@hclib.org
Library Holdings: Bk Vols 13,962
Friends of the Library Group
MINNETONKA BRANCH, 17524 Excelsior Blvd, 55345-1099. SAN 347-3554. Tel: 952-847-5725. Interlibrary Loan Service Tel: 952-847-8589. FAX: 952-949-4692. Web Site: www.hennepin.lib.mn.us. *Senior Librn*, Nan Nystrom-Hilk; E-Mail: nnystrom@hclib.org
Library Holdings: Bk Vols 36,265
Friends of the Library Group
OSSEO BRANCH, 415 Central Ave, Osseo, 55369-1194. SAN 347-3589. Tel: 763-425-3837. Interlibrary Loan Service Tel: 952-847-8589. FAX: 763-425-4920. Web Site: www.hennepin.lib.mn.us. *Assoc Librn*, Sandy Fischbach; E-Mail: sfischbach@hclib.org
Library Holdings: Bk Vols 11,207
Friends of the Library Group
OXBORO, 8801 Portland Ave S, Bloomington, 55420-2997. SAN 347-3619. Tel: 952-847-5775. Interlibrary Loan Service Tel: 952-847-8589. FAX: 952-881-2537. Web Site: www.hennepin.lib.mn.us. *Senior Librn*, Marilyn Lustig; Tel: 952-847-5778, E-Mail: mlustig@hclib.org
Library Holdings: Bk Vols 53,512
Friends of the Library Group
PENN LAKE, 8800 Penn Ave S, Bloomington, 55431-2022. SAN 347-3643. Tel: 952-884-3667. Interlibrary Loan Service Tel: 952-847-8589. FAX: 952-881-2623. Web Site: www.hennepin.lib.mn.us. *Head Librn*, Ann Eccles; E-Mail: aeccles@hclib.org
Library Holdings: Bk Vols 72,220
Friends of the Library Group
PLYMOUTH BRANCH, 15700 36th Ave N, Plymouth, 55446. SAN 375-6130. Tel: 952-847-5825. Interlibrary Loan Service Tel: 952-847-8589. FAX: 763-551-6004. Web Site: www.hennepin.lib.mn.us. *Head Librn*, Cathy Fischer; E-Mail: cfischer@hclib.org
Library Holdings: Bk Vols 70,753
Friends of the Library Group
RIDGEDALE-HENNEPIN AREA, 12601 Ridgedale Dr, 55305-1909. Tel: 952-847-8800. Interlibrary Loan Service Tel: 952-847-8589. TDD: 952-847-8880. FAX: 952-847-8839. Web Site: www.hennepin.lib.mn.us. *Head Librn*, Sandy Louis; E-Mail: slouis@hclib.org
Friends of the Library Group
ROCKFORD ROAD, 6401 42nd Ave N, Crystal, 55427-1499. SAN 347-3678. Tel: 612-533-5010. FAX: 612-531-0453. *Librn*, J Michael

McConnell
Library Holdings: Bk Vols 84,569
Friends of the Library Group
ROGERS BRANCH, 21300 John Milless Dr, 55374-9998. SAN 347-3686. Tel: 612-428-4822. FAX: 612-428-4210. *Librn*, Nan Nystrom-Hilk
Library Holdings: Bk Vols 16,930
Friends of the Library Group
SAINT ANTHONY BRANCH, 2900 NE Pentagon Dr, Saint Anthony, 55418-3209. SAN 347-3708. Tel: 612-781-1900. FAX: 612-781-9037. *Librn*, Amy Worwa
Library Holdings: Bk Vols 18,522
Friends of the Library Group
SAINT BONIFACIUS BRANCH, 8264 Kennedy Memorial Dr, Saint Bonifacius, 55375-9998. SAN 347-3732. Tel: 612-446-1418. FAX: 612-446-1418. *Asst Librn*, Patricia Hasse
Library Holdings: Bk Vols 6,790
Friends of the Library Group
SAINT LOUIS PARK BRANCH, 3240 Library Lane, Saint Louis Park, 55426-4101. SAN 347-3767. Tel: 612-929-8108. FAX: 612-920-7735. *Librn*, Eileen Hansen
Library Holdings: Bk Vols 63,605
Friends of the Library Group
SOUTHDALE-HENNEPIN AREA, 7001 York Ave S, Edina, 55435-4287. SAN 347-3791. Tel: 612-830-4900. FAX: 612-830-4976. Web Site: www.hennepin.lib.mn.us. *Dir*, Charles M Brown; *Coordr*, Rosanne Byrne; *Coordr, Librn*, Mark Ranum
Pop 720,895; Circ 10,539,250
1998-1999 Income $28,363,401
Library Holdings: Bk Vols 263,537
Friends of the Library Group
WAYZATA BRANCH, City Hall, 620 Rice St, Wayzata, 55391-1734. SAN 347-3821. Tel: 612-475-4690. FAX: 612-475-4692.
Library Holdings: Bk Vols 38,174
Friends of the Library Group
WESTONKA, 2079 Commerce Blvd, Mound, 55364-1594. SAN 347-3856. Tel: 612-472-4105. FAX: 612-472-3570. *Librn*, Bill Erickson
Library Holdings: Bk Vols 32,659
Friends of the Library Group
Bookmobiles: 1

MONTEVIDEO

P MONTEVIDEO-CHIPPEWA COUNTY PUBLIC LIBRARY, 224 S First St, 56265-1425. SAN 347-6820. Tel: 320-269-6501. FAX: 320-269-8696. Web Site: www.montelibrary.org. *Coll Develop, Librn*, David Lauritsen; E-Mail: davidl@montevideo.lib.mn.us
Founded 1879. Pop 8,000; Circ 85,000
Jan 1999-Dec 1999 Income $162,000, City $85,000, County $82,000. Mats Exp $34,500, Books $30,000, Per/Ser (Incl. Access Fees) $4,500. Sal $87,000 (Prof $37,300)
Library Holdings: Bk Vols 53,000; Per Subs 198; High Interest/Low Vocabulary Bk Vols 400; Bks on Deafness & Sign Lang 10
Subject Interests: 16mm, Film
Special Collections: Spanish Language Uruguayan Materials
Automation Activity & Vendor Info: (Acquisitions) PALS; (Cataloging) PALS; (Circulation) PALS
Mem of Pioneerland Library System

GL C A ROLLOFF LAW LIBRARY, Chippewa County Courthouse, 11th St & Hwy 7, 56265. SAN 321-8317. Tel: 320-269-8550. FAX: 320-269-7733. *Librn*, Nancy Johnson
Founded 1951
Library Holdings: Bk Titles 6,000

MONTICELLO

P MONTICELLO LIBRARY,* 404 Walnut St, 55362-8832. SAN 347-8599. Tel: 612-295-2322. FAX: 612-295-8321. Web Site: www.griver.org. *Librn*, Marge Bauer
Pop 8,922; Circ 102,530
Library Holdings: Bk Vols 25,729; Per Subs 69
Mem of Great River Regional Library
Mon & Thurs 1-8, Tues & Fri 10-6, Wed 1-6, Sat 10-3

MOORHEAD

S CLAY COUNTY HISTORICAL SOCIETY MUSEUM & ARCHIVES,* 202 First Ave N, PO Box 501, 56560. SAN 327-7771. Tel: 218-299-5520. FAX: 218-299-5525. *Archivist*, Mark Peihl
Library Holdings: Bk Vols 250; Per Subs 30

C CONCORDIA COLLEGE, Carl B Ylvisaker Library, 901 S Eighth St, 56562. SAN 308-700X. Tel: 218-299-4640. Interlibrary Loan Service Tel: 218-299-3239. Reference Tel: 218-299-4656. FAX: 218-299-4253. Web Site: cord.edu/dept/library/. *Dir*, Elizabeth Raum; E-Mail: raum@cord.edu; *Head Ref*, Theresa Borchert; *Bibliog Instr*, Molly Pederson; *Ref*, James Hewitt; *Ref*, Connie Jones; *ILL*, Lola Quam; *Circ*, Erika Rux; *Cat*, Linda Swanson; *Archivist*, Sharon Hoverson; *Coll Develop*, Mary Larson; Staff 10 (MLS 9, Non-MLS 1)
Founded 1891. Enrl 2,826; Fac 210; Highest Degree: Bachelor
May 1999-Apr 2000 Income $1,147,517. Mats Exp $511,715, Books $183,935, Per/Ser (Incl. Access Fees) $170,893, Presv $10,287, Manuscripts & Archives $1,600, Electronic Ref Mat (Incl. Access Fees) $145,000. Sal $481,612
Library Holdings: Bk Vols 299,808; Per Subs 1,433
Subject Interests: International studies, Lutheran hist, Philosophy, Relig studies, Scandinavian studies
Partic in MINITEX Library Information Network; Minn Interlibr Telecommunication Exchange; OCLC Online Computer Library Center, Inc; Tri-College University Libraries Consortium

P LAKE AGASSIZ REGIONAL LIBRARY,* 118 S Fifth St, PO Box 900, 56561-0900. SAN 347-7096. Tel: 218-233-3757. FAX: 218-233-7556. E-Mail: lakeagassiz@northernlights.lib.mn.us. *Tech Servs*, Deborah Janzen; Staff 11 (MLS 11)
Founded 1961. Pop 130,981; Circ 815,385
Jan 1997-Dec 1998 Income $2,234,034, State $375,219, City $846,031, Federal $128,658, County $628,096, Locally Generated Income $40,973. Mats Exp $262,942, Books $176,380, Per/Ser (Incl. Access Fees) $35,089. Sal $1,030,014
Library Holdings: Bk Vols 270,404; Bk Titles 229,789; Per Subs 1,071
Member Libraries: Ada Public Library; Bagley Public Library; Breckenridge Public Library; Climax Public Library; Crookston Public Library; Detroit Lakes Public Library; Fertile Public Library; Fosston Public Library; Hawley Public Library; Mahnomen Public Library; McIntosh Public Library; Moorhead Public Library
Partic in Northern Lights Library Network
Friends of the Library Group
Branches: 1
BARNESVILLE BRANCH, PO Box 549, Barnesville, 56514-0549. SAN 347-7150. Tel: 218-354-2301. *Librn*, Kay Martens
Founded 1949. Pop 3,452
Library Holdings: Bk Vols 7,600; Per Subs 35
Friends of the Library Group
Bookmobiles: 3

C MINNESOTA STATE UNIVERSITY MOORHEAD, (Formerly Moorhead State University), Livingston Lord Library, 1104 Seventh Ave S, 56563. SAN 308-7018. Tel: 218-236-2461, 218-236-2924. FAX: 218-299-5924. *Dir*, Patrick Max; *ILL*, Dianne Schmidt; *Tech Servs*, Jean Kramer; *Govt Doc*, William Kenz; *Circ*, Werre Pam; *Archivist*, Terry Shoptaugh; *Coll Develop, Per*, Larry Schwartz; *Electronic Resources*, Stacy Voeller; Staff 19 (MLS 9, Non-MLS 10)
Founded 1887. Enrl 6,665; Fac 313; Highest Degree: Master
Jul 1998-Jun 1999 Income $1,495,551. Mats Exp $507,024, Books $298,468, Per/Ser (Incl. Access Fees) $198,998, Presv $9,558. Sal $859,060 (Prof $469,316)
Library Holdings: Bk Vols 365,000; Per Subs 1,426
Subject Interests: Juv
Automation Activity & Vendor Info: (Acquisitions) PALS; (Cataloging) PALS; (Circulation) PALS; (Course Reserve) PALS; (ILL) PALS; (Media Booking) PALS; (OPAC) PALS; (Serials) PALS
Partic in Minn Interlibr Teletype Exchange; OCLC Online Computer Library Center, Inc; Tri-College University Libraries Consortium

P MOORHEAD PUBLIC LIBRARY, 118 S Fifth St, PO Box 900, 56561-0900. SAN 347-7428. Tel: 218-233-7594. FAX: 218-236-7405. E-Mail: moorhead@northernlights.lib.mn.us. *Dir*, Anne B Fredine; Tel: 218-233-7594, Ext 111, E-Mail: anne@northernlights.lib.mn.us; *Circ*, Helen Goodin; Tel: 218-233-7594, E-Mail: goodinh@northernlights.lib.mn.us; Staff 4 (MLS 4)
Founded 1906. Pop 41,245
Library Holdings: Bk Vols 123,228; Per Subs 299
Database Vendor: DRA
Mem of Lake Agassiz Regional Library
Partic in Northern Lights Library Network
Friends of the Library Group

R TRINITY LUTHERAN CHURCH LIBRARY, 210 S Seventh, 56560-2794. (Mail add: PO Box 188, 56561-0188), SAN 308-7026. Tel: 218-236-1333. FAX: 218-236-8918. *Librn*, Gertrude Knutson; Staff 9 (MLS 5, Non-MLS 4)
Founded 1959
Library Holdings: Bk Titles 4,170
Subject Interests: Bible study resources, Biblical ref, Personal faith

MOOSE LAKE

P MOOSE LAKE PUBLIC LIBRARY,* 205 Elm Ave, PO Box 277, 55767-0277. SAN 308-7034. Tel: 218-485-4424. FAX: 218-485-4424. *Dir*, Deb Shaw; Staff 1 (MLS 1)
Founded 1938. Pop 1,700; Circ 35,508
Library Holdings: Bk Titles 14,800; Per Subs 70
Mem of Arrowhead Library System

GM MOOSE LAKE REGIONAL STATE OPERATED SERVICES,* 1111 Hwy 73, 55767. SAN 308-7042. Tel: 218-485-5300, Ext 5453. FAX: 218-485-5316. *Librn*, Joann Flynn
Founded 1939
Library Holdings: Bk Vols 500; Per Subs 15
Subject Interests: Chem dependency, Geriatrics, Mental retardation, Psychiatry
Partic in Midwest Health Sci Libr Network

MORA

S KANABEC COUNTY HISTORICAL SOCIETY, Kanabec History Center, 805 W Forest Ave, PO Box 113, 55051. SAN 373-2274. Tel: 320-679-1665. FAX: 320-679-1673. E-Mail: kanabechistory@ncis.com. Web Site: www.kanabechistory.com. *Dir*, Janet L Franz; *Dir*, Sharon L Nelson
Founded 1978
Library Holdings: Bk Vols 2,800

P MORA PUBLIC LIBRARY,* 200 W Maple Ave, 55051-1330. SAN 347-2531. Tel: 320-679-2642. E-Mail: momail@ecrl.lib.mn.us. *Librn*, Wendy Prokosch
Pop 11,266; Circ 71,622
Library Holdings: Bk Vols 10,300; Per Subs 40
Mem of East Central Regional Library
Branch of East Central Regional Library
Friends of the Library Group

MORGAN

P MORGAN PUBLIC LIBRARY,* 210 Vernon Ave, PO Box 128, 56266-0128. SAN 308-7050. Tel: 507-249-3153. *Librn*, Jean Brockemeier; E-Mail: jbrockem@morgan.lib.mn.us; Staff 3 (Non-MLS 3)
Pop 1,000; Circ 10,000
Library Holdings: Bk Titles 11,200; Per Subs 25
Automation Activity & Vendor Info: (ILL) epixtech, inc.
Mem of Plum Creek Library System

MORRIS

P MORRIS PUBLIC LIBRARY,* 102 E Sixth St, 56267-1211. SAN 308-7069. Tel: 320-589-1634. FAX: 320-589-1634. *Librn*, Rita Mulcahy; Staff 4 (MLS 1, Non-MLS 3)
Pop 5,366; Circ 128,000
Jan 1999-Dec 1999 Income $195,000. Mats Exp $40,000. Sal $105,000
Library Holdings: Bk Vols 50,000; Per Subs 100
Subject Interests: Local history
Open Mon & Wed 1-9, Tues & Thurs 9-9, Fri & Sat 9-5
Friends of the Library Group

C UNIVERSITY OF MINNESOTA-MORRIS, Rodney A Briggs Library, 600 E Fourth St, 56267-2199. SAN 308-7077. Tel: 320-589-6180. FAX: 320-589-6168. Web Site: www.mrs.umn.edu/library. *Actg Dir, Publ Servs*, LeAnn Dean; Tel: 320-589-6173; *Tech Servs*, Ardath Larson; Staff 9 (MLS 5, Non-MLS 4)
Founded 1960. Enrl 1,990; Fac 121; Highest Degree: Bachelor
Jul 1998-Jun 1999 Income $903,314. Mats Exp $360,584, Books $110,822, Per/Ser (Incl. Access Fees) $194,708, Electronic Ref Mat (Incl. Access Fees) $55,054. Sal $386,538 (Prof $217,258)
Library Holdings: Bk Vols 184,642; Per Subs 927
Automation Activity & Vendor Info: (Cataloging) CLSI LIBS
Database Vendor: IAC - Info Trac, Lexis-Nexis, OCLC - First Search
Publications: Summoner (campus publication)
Partic in Minn Interlibr Teletype Exchange; Mintex Libr Info Network; Northern Lights Library Network; OCLC Online Computer Library Center, Inc; Research Libraries Group, Inc

C WEST CENTRAL MINNESOTA HISTORICAL CENTER,* University of Minnesota, 56267. SAN 371-6236. Tel: 320-589-6172. FAX: 320-589-3811. *Dir*, Stephen Gross
Founded 1960
Library Holdings: Bk Vols 457
Subject Interests: Local history
Special Collections: Campus Archives, Local Records & Manuscripts; Univ

MOUNTAIN IRON

P MOUNTAIN IRON PUBLIC LIBRARY,* 5742 Mountain Ave, PO Box 477, 55768-0477. SAN 308-7085. Tel: 218-735-8625. FAX: 218-735-8252. *Librn*, Karen Luoma; *Asst Librn*, Darlene Anderson
Pop 4,134; Circ 29,300
Library Holdings: Bk Vols 29,500; Per Subs 90
Subject Interests: Local history
Mem of Arrowhead Library System

MOUNTAIN LAKE

P MOUNTAIN LAKE PUBLIC LIBRARY,* 1054 Fourth Ave, PO Box 477, 56159. SAN 308-7093. Tel: 507-427-2506. *Librn*, Carol Lehman
Pop 2,000; Circ 35,408
Library Holdings: Bk Vols 18,500; Per Subs 95
Special Collections: Mennonite Heritage Coll
Mem of Plum Creek Library System
Friends of the Library Group

NEW BRIGHTON

R UNITED THEOLOGICAL SEMINARY OF THE TWIN CITIES, The Spencer Library, 3000 Fifth St NW, 55112-2598. SAN 308-7115. Tel: 651-633-4311. FAX: 651-633-4315. E-Mail: library@unitedseminary-mn.org. Web Site: www.spencerlibrary.org. *Dir*, Susan K Ebbers; *Asst Dir*, Dale Dobias; Staff 2 (MLS 2)
Founded 1962. Enrl 250; Fac 15; Highest Degree: Doctorate
1999-2000 Income Parent Institution $165,948. Mats Exp $41,550, Books $24,500, Per/Ser (Incl. Access Fees) $11,800, Electronic Ref Mat (Incl. Access Fees) $5,250. Sal $120,300 (Prof $98,100)
Library Holdings: Bk Titles 81,200; Per Subs 278
Subject Interests: Bus, Liberation theol, Native Am, Reformed tradition, Women's studies in relig
Automation Activity & Vendor Info: (Acquisitions) Endeavor; (Cataloging) Endeavor; (Circulation) Endeavor; (Course Reserve) Endeavor; (OPAC) Endeavor; (Serials) Endeavor
Partic in MINITEX Library Information Network; Minnesota Theological Library Association

NEW LONDON

P NEW LONDON PUBLIC LIBRARY,* PO Box 156, 56273. SAN 348-1298. Tel: 320-354-2943. *Librn*, Sheila Bosch
Pop 1,000; Circ 12,253
1998-1999 Income $22,062, County $18,563, Other $200. Mats Exp $5,093, Books $4,400, Per/Ser (Incl. Access Fees) $500. Sal $11,375
Library Holdings: Bk Vols 7,500; Per Subs 20
Mem of Pioneerland Library System
Open Mon-Fri 2-5, Sat 9-1

NEW ULM

P BROWN COUNTY HISTORICAL SOCIETY, Research Library,* 2 N Broadway, 56073. SAN 370-5250. Tel: 507-354-2016. FAX: 507-354-1068. E-Mail: bchs@newulm.tel.net. *Librn*, Darla Gebhard
Founded 1930
Library Holdings: Bk Titles 1,000
Publications: News Notes (quarterly)
Restriction: Non-circulating to the public

C MARTIN LUTHER COLLEGE LIBRARY,* 1995 Luther Ct, 56073-3300. SAN 308-7123. Tel: 507-354-8221, Ext 242. FAX: 507-233-9107. *Librn*, David M Gosdeck; E-Mail: gosdecdm@mlc-wels.edu; *Cat*, Connie Cartright
Founded 1995. Enrl 851
1998-1999 Mats Exp $138,651, Books $82,468, Per/Ser (Incl. Access Fees) $31,105, Presv $1,773, Micro $528, AV Equip $10,972. Sal $210,306 (Prof $162,334)
Library Holdings: Bk Titles 160,753; Per Subs 385
Subject Interests: Education, Music, Relig studies
Special Collections: American Civilization Coll, micro, bks
Partic in Minn Interlibr Telecommunication Exchange; OCLC Online Computer Library Center, Inc
Open Mon-Thurs 7:45am-12am, Fri 7:45-5, Sat 11-5, Sun 2pm-12am

P NEW ULM PUBLIC LIBRARY,* 17 N Broadway, 56073-1786. SAN 308-7131. Tel: 507-354-2151. FAX: 507-354-3255. *Dir*, Daniel Reilly; *Asst Dir, Ref*, Marni Blomquist; *Cat*, Betty Roiger; *Ch Servs*, David Coward; *ILL*, Darlis Bode; Staff 12 (MLS 3, Non-MLS 9)
Pop 13,700; Circ 122,900
Library Holdings: Bk Vols 70,000; Per Subs 200
Mem of Traverse Des Sioux Library System

NEW YORK MILLS

P NEW YORK MILLS PUBLIC LIBRARY,* 30 N Main St, PO Box 279, 56567-0176. SAN 376-7175. Tel: 218-385-2436. FAX: 218-385-2508. *Librn*, Julie Adams
Library Holdings: Bk Vols 15,000; Bk Titles 10,000; Per Subs 75
Mem of Viking Library System
Friends of the Library Group

NORTH BRANCH

P NORTH BRANCH AREA LIBRARY, 6381 Main St, PO Box 480, 55056-9479. SAN 321-9240. Tel: 651-674-8443. E-Mail: nbmail@ecrl.lib.mn.us. *Librn*, Susan Monroe; Staff 2 (Non-MLS 2)
Pop 10,427; Circ 48,819
Library Holdings: Bk Vols 8,000; Per Subs 45
Mem of East Central Regional Library; East Central Regional Library
Branch of East Central Regional Library
Friends of the Library Group

NORTH MANKATO

P NORTH MANKATO PUBLIC LIBRARY, 1001 Bell Grade Ave, 56003. SAN 347-4399. Tel: 507-345-5120. FAX: 507-625-4151. E-Mail: libtnm@tds.lib.mn.us. Web Site: www.northmankato.com/library. *In Charge*, Steve Mork
Library Holdings: Bk Vols 7,000

C SOUTH CENTRAL TECHNICAL COLLEGE, North Mankato Campus Library, 1920 Lee Blvd, 560032504. SAN 374-7263. Tel: 507-389-7223, 507-389-7245. FAX: 507-625-7534. Web Site: www.sctc.mnscu.edu. *Librn*, Joan Klanderud; E-Mail: joank@sctc.mnscu.edu; *Tech Servs*, Romelle Quast; *Tech Servs*, Judy Reich; *Tech Servs*, Lee Sutton; Staff 2 (MLS 1, Non-MLS 1)
Library Holdings: Bk Vols 20,000; Per Subs 250
Automation Activity & Vendor Info: (Cataloging) PALS
Partic in Smile

NORTH SAINT PAUL

S NORTH SAINT PAUL HISTORICAL SOCIETY, Museum Library,* 2666 E Seventh Ave, 55109. SAN 373-2282. Tel: 651-779-6402. *Curator*, Betty Lyon
1999-2000 Mats Exp Presv $250
Library Holdings: Bk Vols 3,175
Special Collections: Local Authors, bks, vf
Friends of the Library Group

NORTHFIELD

C CARLETON COLLEGE, Laurence McKinley Gould Library, One N College St, 55057-4097. SAN 347-7452. Tel: 507-646-4260. Interlibrary Loan Service Tel: 507-646-4257. FAX: 507-646-4087. Web Site: www.library.carleton.edu/. *Head of Libr*, Samuel Demas; Tel: 507-646-4267, E-Mail: sdemas@carleton.edu; *Ref*, Karen Fischer; Tel: 507-646-4266, E-Mail: kfischer@carleton.edu; *Head, Info Serv*, Terry Metz; Tel: 507-646-4265, E-Mail: temetz@carleton.edu; *Archivist*, Eric Hillemann; Tel: 507-646-4270, E-Mail: ehillema@carleton.edu; *Science*, Charles Priore; *Tech Servs*, Carol Eyler; Tel: 507-646-4268, E-Mail: ceyler@carelton.edu; *Coll Develop*, Kathy Tezla; Tel: 507-646-5447, E-Mail: ktezla@carleton.edu; Staff 14 (MLS 10, Non-MLS 4)
Founded 1867. Enrl 1,868; Fac 166; Highest Degree: Bachelor
Jul 1998-Jun 1999 Income $2,327,487. Mats Exp $1,273,708, Books $579,184, Per/Ser (Incl. Access Fees) $500,921, Presv $53,455. Sal $708,453 (Prof $465,480)
Library Holdings: Bk Vols 706,950; Per Subs 1,674
Subject Interests: Am studies, Art history, Econ, English, Mathematics
Special Collections: Lucas Jazz Records; Photos of Famous Authors by Famous Photographers; Thorsten Veblen's Library; Warming Orchid Books; Western Americana (Donald Beaty Bloch Coll)
Automation Activity & Vendor Info: (Cataloging) Innovative Interfaces Inc.; (Circulation) Innovative Interfaces Inc.; (Course Reserve) Innovative Interfaces Inc.; (ILL) Innovative Interfaces Inc.; (OPAC) Innovative Interfaces Inc.; (Serials) Innovative Interfaces Inc.
Partic in MINITEX Library Information Network; OCLC Online Computer Library Center, Inc

P NORTHFIELD PUBLIC LIBRARY, 210 Washington St, 55057. SAN 308-7158. Tel: 507-645-6606. TDD: 507-645-1823. FAX: 507-645-1820. Web Site: www.ci.northfield.mn.us/library. *Dir*, Lynne Young; Tel: 507-645-6608, E-Mail: lynney@selco.lib.mn.us; *Tech Servs*, Leota Stewart; E-Mail: leota@selco.lib.mn.us; *Ch Servs*, Leesa Wisdorf; E-Mail: leesa@selco.lib.mn.us; *Circ*, Joanne Kaye; E-Mail: joni@selco.lib.mn.us; *Ad Servs*, Joan Ennis; Tel: 507-645-6608, E-Mail: joane@selco.lib.mn.us; Staff 12 (MLS 4, Non-MLS 8)
Founded 1857. Pop 24,773; Circ 294,998
Jan 1999-Dec 1999 Income $586,621, State $5,372, City $434,958, County $102,433, Locally Generated Income $43,858. Mats Exp $586,621, Books $69,500, Per/Ser (Incl. Access Fees) $7,200, Presv $1,200, Micro $500, AV Equip $4,000, Other Print Mats $500, Electronic Ref Mat (Incl. Access Fees) $2,370. Sal $405,790
Library Holdings: Bk Vols 88,000; Per Subs 297
Subject Interests: Local history
Database Vendor: DRA, IAC - SearchBank, OVID Technologies, ProQuest
Mem of Southeastern Regional Libr Syst
Special Services for the Deaf - TDD
Friends of the Library Group

S NORWEGIAN-AMERICAN HISTORICAL ASSOCIATION ARCHIVES, 1510 St Olaf Ave, 55057. SAN 327-1692. Tel: 507-646-3221. FAX: 507-646-3734. E-Mail: naha@stolaf.edu. Web Site: www.naha.stolaf.edu. *Archivist*, Forrest Brown; *In Charge*, Kim Holland
Founded 1925
Library Holdings: Bk Vols 8,000

SAINT OLAF COLLEGE

S GLASOE SCIENCE LIBRARY, SCIENCE CENTER, 1520 St Olaf Ave, 55057-1098. SAN 347-7541. Tel: 507-646-3099. *Librn*, Charles Priore

S HALVORSON MUSIC LIBRARY, CHRISTIANSEN HALL OF MUSIC, 1520 St Olaf Ave, 55057-1098. SAN 347-7576. Tel: 507-646-3209. *Librn*, Beth Christensen

C HOWARD V & EDNA H HONG KIERKEGAARD LIBRARY, 1510 Saint Olaf Ave, 55057-1097. SAN 374-7077. Tel: 507-646-3846. FAX: 507-646-3858. *Curator*, Gordon Marino; E-Mail: marino@stolaf.edu; *Asst Curator*, Cynthia Wales Lund; E-Mail: lundc@stolaf.edu; Staff 2 (MLS 1, Non-MLS 1)
Founded 1976
Jun 1999-May 2000 Income $81,000. Mats Exp $24,100, Books $22,000, Per/Ser (Incl. Access Fees) $100, Presv $2,000. Sal $47,146 (Prof $42,146)
Library Holdings: Bk Vols 10,000
Automation Activity & Vendor Info: (Cataloging) Innovative Interfaces Inc.; (OPAC) Innovative Interfaces Inc.; (Serials) Innovative Interfaces Inc.
Publications: Soren Kierkegaard Society Newsletter
Restriction: Not a lending library
Partic in MINITEX Library Information Network; OCLC Online Computer Library Center, Inc
Friends of the Library Group

C ROLVAAG MEMORIAL LIBRARY, 1510 St Olaf Ave, 55057-1097. SAN 347-7517. Tel: 507-646-3634. Interlibrary Loan Service Tel: 507-646-3223. Circulation Tel: 507-646-3224. Reference Tel: 507-646-3452. FAX: 507-646-3734. Web Site: www.stolaf.edu/library. *Dir*, Robert Bruce; Tel: 507-646-3771, E-Mail: rkbruce@stolaf.edu; *Dir*, David Lesniaski; Tel: 507-646-3597, E-Mail: lesniask@stolaf.edu; *Br Coordr*, Beth Christensen; Tel: 507-646-3362, E-Mail: christeb@stolaf.edu; *Br Coordr*, Charles Priore; Tel: 507-646-3099, E-Mail: priore@stolaf.edu; *Cat*, Melissa Kalpin; Tel: 507-646-3244, E-Mail: kalpin@stolaf.edu; *Bibliog Instr, Ref*, Bryn Geffert; Tel: 507-646-3226, E-Mail: geffert@stolaf.edu; *Bibliog Instr, Ref*, Elizabeth Hutchins; Tel: 507-646-3793, E-Mail: hutchine@stolaf.edu; *Bibliog Instr, Ref*, Mary Sue Lovett; Tel: 507-646-3598, E-Mail: lovett@stolaf.edu; *Bibliog Instr, Ref*, Kristina MacPherson; Tel: 507-646-6798, E-Mail: macphers@stolaf.edu; *Cat*, Susanne Nevin; Tel: 507-646-3829, E-Mail: nevin@stolaf.edu; *Cat*, Kathy Blough; Tel: 507-646-3794, E-Mail: blough@stolaf.edu. Subject Specialists: *Science*, Charles Priore; Staff 24 (MLS 11, Non-MLS 13)
Founded 1874. Enrl 2,948; Fac 315; Highest Degree: Bachelor
Jun 1999-May 2000 Mats Exp $982,400, Books $391,000, Per/Ser (Incl. Access Fees) $378,500, Presv $31,000, Micro $70,000, AV Equip $15,000, Electronic Ref Mat (Incl. Access Fees) $96,900. Sal $718,725 (Prof $331,485)
Library Holdings: Bk Titles 521,383; Per Subs 1,780
Subject Interests: Relig studies, Scandinavian hist, Scandinavian lit
Special Collections: Norwegian-American Historical Association Coll, bks & per; Pre-1801 Imprints (Vault Coll), bks & per
Database Vendor: IAC - SearchBank, Innovative Interfaces INN - View, Lexis-Nexis, OCLC - First Search
Partic in MINITEX Library Information Network

OLIVIA

P OLIVIA PUBLIC LIBRARY, 405 S Tenth St, 56277-1287. SAN 308-7166. Tel: 320-523-1738. FAX: 320-523-1570. E-Mail: olivia@olivia.lib.mn.us. Web Site: www.olivia.mn.us. *Branch Mgr*, Sue Hilgert; Staff 2 (Non-MLS 2)
Founded 1916. Pop 2,621; Circ 32,398
Jan 2000-Dec 2000 Income $73,779, City $36,120, County $30,996, Locally Generated Income $1,000, Other $5,663. Mats Exp $71,270, Books $9,517, Per/Ser (Incl. Access Fees) $2,000. Sal $57,524
Library Holdings: Bk Vols 20,747; Per Subs 64
Special Collections: Local Newspaper Depository
Automation Activity & Vendor Info: (Circulation) PALS; (OPAC) PALS
Mem of Pioneerland Library System

ORTONVILLE

P ORTONVILLE PUBLIC LIBRARY,* 412 Second St NW, 56278-1415. SAN 308-7182. Tel: 320-839-2494. FAX: 320-839-3784. *Asst Librn*, Laverne Doering
Founded 1903. Circ 28,773
Jan 1998-Dec 1998 Income $67,400, City $40,000, County $27,400. Mats

Exp $7,100, Books $4,700, Per/Ser (Incl. Access Fees) $2,400. Sal $35,000 (Prof $25,000)
Library Holdings: Bk Vols 18,605; Per Subs 40
Mem of Pioneerland Library System
Friends of the Library Group

OWATONNA

P OWATONNA PUBLIC LIBRARY,* 105 N Elm St, PO Box 387, 55060-7488. SAN 347-7606. Tel: 507-444-2460. FAX: 507-444-2465. Web Site: www.owatonna.lib.mn.us. *Dir*, Graham Benoit; *Asst Dir*, Mary Kay Feltes; *AV, Per*, Mary Gontarek; *Ad Servs, Ref*, Bonnie Krueger
Founded 1900. Pop 20,753; Circ 365,164
Jan 1999-Dec 1999 Income $825,235. Sal $570,955
Library Holdings: Bk Vols 122,555; Per Subs 460
Database Vendor: DRA
Mem of Southeastern Libraries Cooperating (SELCO)
Branches: 1
BLOOMING PRAIRIE BRANCH, 138 Highway Ave S, PO Box 187, Blooming Prairie, 55917-0187. SAN 347-7630. Tel: 507-583-7750. FAX: 507-583-4520. *Branch Mgr*, Darlene Grams; E-Mail: dgrams@selco.lib.mn.us; Staff 3 (Non-MLS 3)
Founded 1976. Pop 2,043; Circ 34,238
Jan 1999-Dec 1999 Income City $79,559. Mats Exp $18,950, Books $14,150, Electronic Ref Mat (Incl. Access Fees) $4,800. Sal $36,900 (Prof $20,077)
Library Holdings: Bk Vols 16,770; Per Subs 60
Automation Activity & Vendor Info: (Circulation) DRA
Mem of Southeastern Libraries Cooperating (SELCO)
Friends of the Library Group

PARK RAPIDS

P PARK RAPIDS PUBLIC LIBRARY,* 210 W First St, 56470-8925. SAN 308-7190. Tel: 218-732-4966. FAX: 218-732-4966. E-Mail: parkrapids@northernlights.lib.mn.us. *Librn*, Julianna Stangland; *Asst Librn*, Karen Zwirtz; *Ch Servs*, Julie Volden
Founded 1903. Circ 105,815
Library Holdings: Bk Vols 25,000
Database Vendor: OCLC - First Search
Mem of Kitchigami Regional Library
Friends of the Library Group
Bookmobiles: 1

PAYNESVILLE

P PAYNESVILLE LIBRARY,* 119 Washburne Ave, 56362. SAN 308-7204. Tel: 320-243-7343. FAX: 320-243-7343. Web Site: www.griver.org. *In Charge*, Gretchen Vork
Founded 1908. Pop 4,374; Circ 40,793
Library Holdings: Bk Vols 12,990; Per Subs 32
Mem of Great River Regional Library
Open Mon & Fri 2-8, Tues & Thurs 2-6, Wed 10-1 & 2-6, Sat 10-2
Friends of the Library Group

PELICAN RAPIDS

P PELICAN RAPIDS PUBLIC LIBRARY,* 25 W Mill St, PO Box 371, 56572-0371. SAN 376-7183. Tel: 218-863-7055. FAX: 218-863-7056. E-Mail: library@pelicanrapids.lib.mn.us. Web Site: viking.lib.mn.us. *Librn*, Pamela Westby
Jan 1999-Dec 1999 Income $110,384. Mats Exp $20,605. Sal $55,150
Library Holdings: Bk Titles 18,900; Per Subs 85
Mem of Viking Library System
Friends of the Library Group

PERHAM

P PERHAM AREA PUBLIC LIBRARY, 225 Second Ave NE, 56573-1819. SAN 308-7212. Tel: 218-346-4892. FAX: 218-346-4906. *Librn*, Susan Heusser-Ladwig; E-Mail: sheusser-ladwig@perham.lib.mn.us; Staff 4 (MLS 1, Non-MLS 3)
Founded 1922. Pop 5,912; Circ 68,283
Jan 1999-Dec 1999 Income $99,515, City $66,557, County $18,218, Locally Generated Income $14,740. Mats Exp $19,280, Books $15,136, Per/Ser (Incl. Access Fees) $2,100, AV Equip $1,872, Electronic Ref Mat (Incl. Access Fees) $172. Sal $55,221 (Prof $27,038)
Library Holdings: Bk Vols 21,931; Per Subs 138
Automation Activity & Vendor Info: (Acquisitions) epixtech, inc.; (Cataloging) epixtech, inc.; (Circulation) epixtech, inc.; (OPAC) epixtech, inc.
Mem of Viking Library System

PIERZ

P PIERZ LIBRARY, 220 Main St, 56364. SAN 347-8629. Tel: 320-468-6486. FAX: 320-468-6486. Web Site: www.griver.org. *In Charge*, Beverly Gold
Pop 3,393; Circ 18,782
Library Holdings: Bk Vols 8,808; Per Subs 35
Mem of Great River Regional Library
Mon & Fri 2-6, Wed 2-8, Thurs 10-1 & 2-6, Sat 9-1
Friends of the Library Group

PINE CITY

P PINE CITY PUBLIC LIBRARY,* 300 Fifth St, 55063-1799. SAN 347-2566. Tel: 320-629-6403. FAX: 612-629-6403. E-Mail: pcmail@ecrl.lib.mn.us. *Librn*, Christy Koch
Founded 1921. Pop 8,858; Circ 51,225
Library Holdings: Bk Vols 10,000; Per Subs 40
Mem of East Central Regional Library
Branch of East Central Regional Library
Friends of the Library Group

PINE ISLAND

P VAN HORN PUBLIC LIBRARY, Pine Island Public Library, 115 SE Third St, 55963-6783. (Mail add: PO Box 38, 55963-0038), SAN 308-7239. Tel: 507-356-8558. FAX: 507-356-8230. *Dir*, Jeanne Acker; E-Mail: jeanne_a@selcol.lib.mn.us; Staff 1 (MLS 1)
Pop 2,926; Circ 58,516
1998-1999 Income $94,658. Mats Exp $16,955, Books $11,200, Per/Ser (Incl. Access Fees) $2,428, Presv $62. Sal $55,267
Library Holdings: Bk Vols 20,000; Per Subs 35
Mem of Southeastern Libraries Cooperating (SELCO)

PINE RIVER

P KITCHIGAMI REGIONAL LIBRARY,* 403 Barclay Ave, 56474-0084. (Mail add: PO Box 84, 56474-0084), SAN 347-7665. Tel: 218-587-2171, 218-587-4639. FAX: 218-587-4855. E-Mail: krladm@northernlights.lib.mn.us. *Acq, Dir*, Marian Ridge; E-Mail: ridgem@northernlights.lib.mn.us; *ILL*, Happy Micheau; *Tech Servs*, Alison Edgerton
Founded 1969. Pop 128,784; Circ 407,674
Jan 1997-Dec 1998 Income $1,439,445, Other $17,220. Mats Exp $146,480. Sal $679,492
Library Holdings: Per Subs 525
Subject Interests: Am Indian-Chippewa (Ojibway)
Member Libraries: Bemidji Public Library; Blackduck Community Library; Brainerd Public Library; Margaret Welch Memorial Library; Park Rapids Public Library; Wadena City Library
Partic in Northern Lights Library Network; OCLC Online Computer Library Center, Inc
Special Services for the Deaf - Books on deafness & sign language; High interest/low vocabulary books; Staff with knowledge of sign language
Friends of the Library Group
Branches: 2
PINE RIVER PUBLIC LIBRARY, 409 Barclay Ave, PO Box 14, 56474-0084. SAN 347-7800. Tel: 218-587-4639. FAX: 218-587-4855. E-Mail: pineriver@northernlights.lib.mn.us. Web Site: northernlights.lib.mn.us. *Mgr*, Muriel Erickson; E-Mail: ericksonm@northernlights.lib.mn.us
Founded 1965
Library Holdings: Bk Vols 39,700; Per Subs 35
Special Collections: American Chippewa Indian; Antiques, Collecting & Identifying; Cookbooks
Database Vendor: DRA
Partic in Minn Interlibr Telecommunication Exchange; Northern Lights Library Network; OCLC Online Computer Library Center, Inc
WALKER PUBLIC LIBRARY, 207 Fourth St, PO Box 550, Walker, 56484-0208. SAN 347-7843. Tel: 218-547-1019. FAX: 218-547-1019. *Dir*, Cheryl Stephens; Staff 2 (Non-MLS 2)
Founded 1909. Circ 46,084
Library Holdings: Bk Titles 19,746; Per Subs 33
Database Vendor: DRA

PIPESTONE

P PIPESTONE COMMUNITY LIBRARY,* 400 Second Ave SW, 56164-1569. SAN 376-7132. Tel: 507-825-6714. FAX: 507-825-6729. *Librn*, Rosemarie Loose
Jul 1999-Jun 2000 Income $85,000. Mats Exp $25,000. Sal $62,000
Library Holdings: Bk Titles 26,000; Per Subs 110
Mem of Plum Creek Library System

S PIPESTONE COUNTY HISTORICAL SOCIETY, Pipestone County Museum Research Library, 113 S Hiawatha, 56164. SAN 328-1175. Tel: 507-825-2563. Toll Free Tel: 866-747-3687. FAX: 567-825-2563. Toll Free FAX: 866-747-3687. E-Mail: pipctymu@rconnect.com. Web Site:

www.pipestone.mn.us/museum/homepa~1.htm. *Exec Dir*, Chris Roelfsema-Hummel; *Asst Dir*, Rebecca Ostrom
Library Holdings: Bk Titles 500
Subject Interests: Local history
Special Collections: County Newspapers, 1879-1996 Coll; Doctors' Records Coll; Indian School Coll; Photo Coll

S US DEPARTMENT OF INTERIOR NATIONAL PARK SERVICE, Pipestone National Monument Library & Archives, 36 Reservation Ave, 56164-1269. SAN 370-2847. Tel: 507-825-5464. FAX: 507-825-5466. Web Site: www.nps.gov/pipe. *In Charge*, Jim LaRock
Library Holdings: Bk Vols 2,000
Restriction: Open to public for reference only

PLAINVIEW

P PLAINVIEW PUBLIC LIBRARY, 345 First Ave NW, 55964-1295. SAN 308-7247. Tel: 507-534-3425. *Librn*, Kathie Roussopoulos
Founded 1865. Pop 7,438; Circ 52,800
Library Holdings: Bk Titles 15,000; Per Subs 50
Subject Interests: Old photos
Database Vendor: DRA
Partic in SE Libr Coop

PLATO

S FAR EASTERN RESEARCH LIBRARY, 9 First Ave NE, PO Box 181, 55370-0181. SAN 324-0304. Tel: 320-238-2591. FAX: 320-238-2591. *Librn*, Dr Jerome Cavanaugh; *Acq, Per*, Liao Chia-ch'ing; *Cat*, Lin Ming-chih; Staff 4 (MLS 3, Non-MLS 1)
Founded 1969
Library Holdings: Bk Vols 42,309; Bk Titles 35,120; Per Subs 323
Subject Interests: Chinese hist, Culture, Lang, Literature
Special Collections: Chinese Cultural Revolution Col; Chinese Dialect Materials Coll, bks, mss, journals; Studies on the City of Tianjin
Publications: Far Eastern Research Library Bibliographical Aids Series
Restriction: Open to public for reference only

PLYMOUTH

S HONEYWELL, INC, Solid State Electronics Center Library,* 12001 Hwy 55, 55441. SAN 308-7255. Tel: 612-951-1000. Web Site: www.honeywell.com/buildings.com. *Librn*, Diane Cook
Library Holdings: Bk Titles 800; Per Subs 150
Subject Interests: Electronic engineering, Integrated circuits, Semiconductor devices
Partic in Dialog Corporation

PRESTON

P PRESTON PUBLIC LIBRARY,* PO Box 198, 55965-0198. SAN 308-7271. Tel: 507-765-4511. Web Site: www.selco.lib.mn.us/preston/. *Librn*, Janene Roessler
Founded 1908. Pop 1,478; Circ 17,100
Library Holdings: Bk Vols 19,000; Per Subs 31
Mem of Southeastern Libraries Cooperating (SELCO)
Friends of the Library Group

PRINCETON

P PRINCETON AREA LIBRARY, 100 S Fourth St, 55371. SAN 347-2590. Tel: 612-389-3753. Toll Free Tel: 888-234-1293. FAX: 612-389-3753. E-Mail: princeton@ecrl.lib.mn.us. Web Site: ecrl.lib.mn.us. *Librn*, Robin B Suhsen
Founded 1995. Pop 15,000; Circ 70,000
Library Holdings: Bk Vols 20,000; Per Subs 75
Mem of East Central Regional Library
Branch of East Central Regional Library
Friends of the Library Group

RAYMOND

P RAYMOND PUBLIC LIBRARY,* PO Box 203, 56282-0203. SAN 348-1328. Tel: 320-967-4411. FAX: 320-967-4226. *Librn*, Nancy Rhode
Pop 1,553; Circ 14,732
Library Holdings: Bk Vols 6,200; Per Subs 19
Mem of Pioneerland Library System
Branch of Pioneerland Library System. Open Mon, Tues & Wed 1-4:30, Thurs 1-7:30

RED LAKE FALLS

P RED LAKE FALLS PUBLIC LIBRARY,* 105 Champagne Ave, PO Box 115, 56750. SAN 348-0666. Tel: 218-253-2992. *In Charge*, Lois Steer
Pop 2,100; Circ 20,729
Library Holdings: Bk Vols 8,300; Per Subs 20
Mem of Northwest Regional Library System
Friends of the Library Group

RED WING

R FIRST LUTHERAN CHURCH, Schendel Memorial Library, 615 W Fifth St, 55066. SAN 308-728X. Tel: 651-388-9311. *Librn*, Delma Rigelman
Founded 1951
Library Holdings: Bk Titles 3,750
Subject Interests: Attitudes, Beliefs, Bible study, Children's literature, Christian life, Christianity, Devotional studies, Inspirational reading, Interpersonal relations, Recreational reading

S GOODHUE COUNTY HISTORICAL SOCIETY LIBRARY,* 1166 Oak St, 55066-2447. SAN 327-1714. Tel: 651-388-6024. FAX: 651-388-3577. E-Mail: mail@goodhistory.org. Web Site: www.goodhistory.org. *Archivist, Librn*, Heather Craig; *Curator*, Char Henn
Library Holdings: Bk Vols 2,050
Publications: Goodhue County Historical News

P RED WING PUBLIC LIBRARY, 225 East Ave, 55066-2298. SAN 308-7298. Tel: 651-385-3673. Reference Tel: 651-385-3645. TDD: 651-385-3673. FAX: 651-385-3644. E-Mail: rwpl@selco.lib.mn.us. Web Site: www.selco.lib.mn.us/redwing. *Dir*, Kathryn Rynders; *Circ*, Sally Setzer; *Tech Servs*, Janet Brandt; *Ch Servs*, Pat Martin; Staff 8 (MLS 3, Non-MLS 5)
Founded 1894. Pop 22,200; Circ 197,000
Jan 1999-Dec 1999 Income $799,800, State $2,800, City $688,300, County $61,700, Locally Generated Income $47,000. Mats Exp $174,000, Books $78,200, Per/Ser (Incl. Access Fees) $8,500, Presv $600, Micro $200, Electronic Ref Mat (Incl. Access Fees) $36,500. Sal $399,400 (Prof $229,900)
Library Holdings: Bk Titles 66,100; Per Subs 325; High Interest/Low Vocabulary Bk Vols 40; Bks on Deafness & Sign Lang 40
Special Collections: Red Wing Area Genealogy Index; Red Wing History
Automation Activity & Vendor Info: (Acquisitions) DRA; (Cataloging) DRA; (Circulation) DRA; (ILL) DRA; (Media Booking) DRA; (OPAC) DRA; (Serials) DRA
Database Vendor: GaleNet, IAC - Info Trac, OCLC - First Search, ProQuest
Publications: Contemporary Authors; Junior Reference Collection; Newspaper Indexes; NoveList Biography Resource Center; NovelList Biography Resource Center; Reference USA
Function: ILL available, Photocopies available, Reference services available
Mem of Southeastern Libraries Cooperating (SELCO)
Special Services for the Deaf - TDD
Special Services for the Blind - Kurzweil Reading Machine
Non-resident cards available for a fee
Friends of the Library Group

REDWOOD FALLS

P REDWOOD FALLS PUBLIC LIBRARY, 509 S Lincoln St, 56283. SAN 308-7301. Tel: 507-637-8650. FAX: 507-637-5004. E-Mail: rwf@redwoodfalls.lib.mn.us. Web Site: www.ci.redwood-falls.mn.us. *Acq, Dir, ILL*, Judith Jensen; *Asst Librn, Ch Servs*, Doris Guggisberg; Staff 4 (Non-MLS 4)
Founded 1904. Pop 5,210; Circ 113,323
Library Holdings: Bk Titles 34,000; Per Subs 110
Subject Interests: Native Am
Special Collections: Minnesota Life & History Coll
Publications: American Libraries; Library Journal
Mem of Plum Creek Library System; Southwest Area Multi-county Multi-type Interlibr Exchange
Friends of the Library Group

RENVILLE

P RENVILLE CITY LIBRARY, 221 N Main, PO Box 609, 56284-0609. SAN 348-1336. Tel: 320-329-8193. FAX: 320-329-8367. E-Mail: renville@renville.lib.mn.us. *Branch Mgr*, Esther Fisher
Pop 1,375; Circ 27,584
Jan 2000-Dec 2000 Income $41,418, City $17,937, County $14,902, Other $8,579. Mats Exp $9,590, Books $8,020, Per/Ser (Incl. Access Fees) $1,570. Sal $25,630
Library Holdings: Bk Vols 18,321; Per Subs 63
Automation Activity & Vendor Info: (Circulation) PALS; (OPAC) PALS
Mem of Pioneerland Library System

RICHFIELD

R OAK GROVE LUTHERAN CHURCH, Juanita Carpenter Library, 7045 Lyndale Ave S, 55423-3099. SAN 308-731X. Tel: 952-869-4917. *Coll Develop, Librn*, Juanita Carpenter; Tel: 952-894-3435; Staff 9 (MLS 1, Non-MLS 8)
Founded 1959
Library Holdings: Bk Vols 5,500
Subject Interests: Admin, Aging, Biography, Educ of ch, Ethics, Fiction, Psychology, Religion

RICHMOND

P RICHMOND LIBRARY, 63 Hall Ave SW, PO Box 130, 56368-0130. SAN 347-8653. Tel: 320-597-3739. FAX: 320-597-3739. Web Site: www.griver.org. *In Charge*, Marleen Philabaum
Pop 2,220; Circ 22,225
Library Holdings: Bk Vols 7,143; Per Subs 32
Mem of Great River Regional Library
Open Mon 2-8, Wed 10-1 & 2-6, Fri 2-6 & Sat 9-12

ROBBINSDALE

M NORTH MEMORIAL HEALTH CARE, Medical Library, 3300 Oakdale N, 55422. SAN 308-681X. Tel: 763-520-5673. FAX: 763-520-1453. E-Mail: library@northmemorial.com. Web Site: www.northmemorial.com. *Dir*, Donna Barbour-Talley; E-Mail: donna.barbour-talley@cl.nmmc.com; *Online Servs*, Patrick W Costigan; Staff 5 (MLS 3, Non-MLS 2)
Founded 1968
Library Holdings: Bk Vols 2,900; Per Subs 560
Subject Interests: Hospitals, Medicine, Nursing, Paramed training

ROCHESTER

S IBM CORP, Rochester Information Resource Center Library, Dept 205 005-1, 3605 Highway 52 NW, 55901-7829. SAN 308-7336. Interlibrary Loan Service Tel: 507-253-4512. Reference Tel: 507-253-0557. FAX: 507-253-2593. *Librn*, Melanie Huntington; *Circ*, Marlys Livingood; Staff 3 (MLS 1, Non-MLS 2)
Library Holdings: Bk Vols 20,000; Bk Titles 16,000; Per Subs 525
Subject Interests: Bus, Computer programming, Computers, Engineering, Mgt
Restriction: By appointment only
Partic in OCLC Online Computer Library Center, Inc

MAYO FOUNDATION

M MAYO CLINIC LIBRARY, LEARNING RESOURCE CENTER, 200 First St SW, 55905. SAN 347-7991. Tel: 507-284-3893. FAX: 507-266-4065. *Librn, Online Servs*, Judy Lorrig; *Asst Librn*, Colleen Farley
Founded 1972
Library Holdings: Bk Vols 3,995; Per Subs 42
Subject Interests: Medicine
Special Collections: Perspectives on Women in Medicine & Health

M MAYO MEDICAL CENTER LIBRARIES, 200 First St SW, 55905. SAN 347-7908. Tel: 507-284-2061. Interlibrary Loan Service Tel: 507-284-2042. FAX: 284-1038, 507-284-2215. Web Site: www.mayo.edu. *Dir*, J Michael Homan; Tel: 507-284-9595, E-Mail: homan@mayo.edu; Staff 48 (MLS 20, Non-MLS 28)
Founded 1907. Enrl 1,654; Fac 1,500; Highest Degree: Doctorate
Jan 1999-Dec 1999 Income (Main Library and Branch Library) $5,820,000, Locally Generated Income $720,000, Parent Institution $5,100,000. Mats Exp $2,987,000, Books $285,000, Per/Ser (Incl. Access Fees) $1,755,000, Presv $65,000, Electronic Ref Mat (Incl. Access Fees) $882,000. Sal $1,623,911
Library Holdings: Bk Vols 320,000; Bk Titles 98,765; Per Subs 4,151
Subject Interests: Biomedical res, Clinical medicine
Special Collections: History of Medicine
Automation Activity & Vendor Info: (Acquisitions) Innovative Interfaces Inc.; (Cataloging) Innovative Interfaces Inc.; (Circulation) Innovative Interfaces Inc.; (Course Reserve) Innovative Interfaces Inc.; (Media Booking) Innovative Interfaces Inc.; (OPAC) Innovative Interfaces Inc.; (Serials) Innovative Interfaces Inc.
Database Vendor: OVID Technologies
Publications: Mayo Authors database of Mayo-authored Scientific and Medical Publications
Restriction: By appointment only, Private library
Mem of Minitex Libr Info Network; Nat Network of Librs of Med
Partic in Docline; MINITEX Library Information Network; Nat Libr of Med; OCLC Online Computer Library Center, Inc
Branch libraries include: Learning Resource Center; Venables Health-Related Sciences Library; RMH-Colonial library; Saint Mary's Hospital staff library; Patients' libraries at Rochester Methodist Hospital & Saint Mary's Hospital

M MAYO FOUNDATION, Methodist-Kahler Library, 201 W Center St, 55902. SAN 308-7379. Tel: 507-266-7428. FAX: 507-266-7492. *Chief Librn*, Karen Larsen; *Librn*, Paul Dahl
Founded 1930
Library Holdings: Bk Vols 12,000; Per Subs 700
Subject Interests: Hospital administration, Hospital mgt, Nursing, Nursing educ
Special Collections: History of Nursing
Branches:
HEALTH RELATED SCIENCES, 200 First St SW, 55905. SAN 377-8711. Tel: 507-284-0227. FAX: 507-284-1652. *Librn*, Jill Thompson-Riese
MEDICAL SCHOOL LIBRARY LRC, 200 First St SW, 55905. SAN 377-869X. Tel: 507-284-3420. FAX: 507-266-4065. *Librn*, Judy Lorrig
PATIENT, 201 W Center St, 55902. SAN 377-8673. Tel: 507-266-1006. *In Charge*, Mary Graddy
PLUMMER, 200 First St SW. SAN 378-2034. Tel: 507-284-9595. FAX: 507-284-1038. *Librn*, J Michael Homan
STAFF, 1216 Second St SW, 55902. SAN 377-8533. Tel: 507-266-7425. FAX: 507-255-6536. *Librn*, Mona Stevermer

CR MINNESOTA BIBLE COLLEGE LIBRARY,* 920 Mayowood Rd SW, 55902. SAN 308-7344. Tel: 507-288-4563, Ext 250. FAX: 507-288-9046. E-Mail: mbc@milcom.com. *Librn*, Dr Harold G Mahan
Founded 1924. Highest Degree: Bachelor
Library Holdings: Bk Titles 30,000; Per Subs 120
Special Collections: G H Cachiarias Memorial Library (Disciples of Christ authors)
Publications: Filmstrip list; Library Materials Selection Policy; personnel handbook; student handbook

S OLMSTED COUNTY HISTORICAL SOCIETY ARCHIVES, 1195 W Circle Dr SW, 55902. SAN 326-114X. Tel: 507-282-9447. FAX: 507-289-5481. E-Mail: ochs@olmstedhistory.com. Web Site: www.selco.lib.mn.us/ochs/index.htm. *Archivist*, Sherry Sweetman; *Assoc Librn*, Marilyn Hensley
Founded 1926
1999-2000 Income $10,000. Mats Exp $2,280, Books $80, Presv $2,000, AV Equip $200. Sal $20,000
Special Collections: Olmsted County & Rochester
Restriction: Non-circulating to the public

J ROCHESTER COMMUNITY & TECHNICAL COLLEGE, Goddard Library, 851 30 Ave SE, 55904. SAN 308-7360. Tel: 507-285-7233. FAX: 507-281-7772. E-Mail: goddardlib@roch.edu. Web Site: www.roch.edu/library. *Librn*, Mary Dennison; *Librn*, Cindy Dull; *Librn*, Jeff Taylor; *Librn*, Sharon Wieners; *Coordr*, Dale Pedersen; Staff 8 (MLS 4, Non-MLS 4)
Founded 1915. Enrl 3,073; Fac 175
Library Holdings: Bk Vols 85,000; Per Subs 779
Subject Interests: Commun college educ, Nursing
Partic in Minn Interlibr Telecommunication Exchange; OCLC Online Computer Library Center, Inc; Pals
Provides libr servs for Rochester Centers of Winona State University, University of Minnesota, St Marys University

S ROCHESTER POST-BULLETIN LIBRARY,* 18 First Ave SE, 55904-6118. SAN 322-9084. Tel: 507-285-7737. FAX: 507-285-7772. *In Charge*, Gretchen Meredith; *In Charge*, Jerry Reising; Staff 2 (MLS 1, Non-MLS 1)
Founded 1965
Library Holdings: Bk Titles 150; Per Subs 30
Restriction: Staff use only

P ROCHESTER PUBLIC LIBRARY, 101 Second St SE, 55904-3776. SAN 308-7387. Tel: 507-285-8011. Interlibrary Loan Service Tel: 507-287-2610. Circulation Tel: 507-285-8005. Reference Tel: 507-285-8002. TDD: 507-287-2110. FAX: 507-287-1910. Web Site: www.ci.rochester.mn.us/library/. *Dir*, Audrey Betcher; E-Mail: audrey@rochester.lib.mn.us; *ILL, Online Servs, Ref*, Louise Moe; E-Mail: louise@rochester.lib.mn.us; *Outreach Serv*, Kimberly Edson; Tel: 507-285-8018, E-Mail: kedson@rochester.lib.mn.us; *Cat, Online Servs, Tech Servs*, Rebecca Splitstoesser; Tel: 507-287-2129, E-Mail: rebecca@rochester.lib.mn.us; *Ch Servs*, Beth Warfield; Tel: 507-285-8013, E-Mail: beth@rochester.lib.mn.us; Staff 14 (MLS 14)
Founded 1895. Pop 112,786; Circ 1,060,336
Jan 2000-Dec 2000 Income $3,976,052, State $189,961, City $2,898,915, County $637,373, Locally Generated Income $249,803. Mats Exp $427,715, Books $341,223, AV Equip $67,731, Other Print Mats $954, Electronic Ref Mat (Incl. Access Fees) $17,807. Sal $2,764,848
Library Holdings: Bk Vols 305,183; Per Subs 588
Special Collections: City of Rochester
Mem of Southeastern Libraries Cooperating (SELCO)
Partic in Minn Interlibr Telecommunication Exchange; OCLC Online Computer Library Center, Inc
Friends of the Library Group
Bookmobiles: 1. 1998 Thomas

S SAINT MARY'S HOSPITAL, Sister Joseph Patient & Visitor Library, 1216 Second St SW, 55902. SAN 347-7967. Tel: 507-255-5434. FAX: 507-255-5254. E-Mail: patientlibrary@mayo.edu. *Librn*, Stephanie Wentz; Tel: 507-266-1006
Founded 1921

Library Holdings: Bk Vols 6,500; Per Subs 110
Subject Interests: Consumer health info, Foreign lang materials
Special Services for the Blind - Talking bks & player equipment; Talking bks for the blind & physically handicapped
Branches:
PATIENT LIBRARY, 1216 Second St SW, 55902. SAN 377-8517. Tel: 507-255-5434. FAX: 507-255-5254. *Librn*, Mary Ellen Smith

P SOUTHEASTERN LIBRARIES COOPERATING (SELCO), 2600 19th St NW, 55901-0767. SAN 308-7417. Tel: 507-288-5513. FAX: 507-288-8697. Web Site: www.selco.lib.mn.us. *Dir*, Ann B Huton; *Automation Syst Coordr*, Donovan Lambright; *Cat*, Kirby Johnson; *Publ Servs*, Judith Jordan; Staff 9 (MLS 9)
Founded 1971. Pop 420,094
Jul 1998-Jun 1999 Income $1,900,000, State $857,000, City $550,000, Federal $150,000, County $126,000, Other $217,000. Mats Exp $274,000, Books $106,000, Per/Ser (Incl. Access Fees) $5,000, Micro $5,000. Sal $580,000 (Prof $300,000)
Automation Activity & Vendor Info: (Acquisitions) DRA; (Circulation) DRA
Publications: Update
Member Libraries: Albert Lea Public Library; Austin Public Library; Buckham Memorial Library; Cannon Falls Library; Chatfield Public Library; Dodge Center Public Library; Harmony Public Library; Hokah Public Library; Kenyon Public Library; Lake City Public Library; Owatonna Public Library; Owatonna Public Library; Preston Public Library; Red Wing Public Library; Rochester Public Library; Van Horn Public Library; Wabasha Public Library; Winona Public Library
This a federated system which serves members in the following ways: central acquisitions; staff development; bookmobiles; delivery; consultation on all library matters; interlibrary loan coordination; materials grants; large print, cooperative programming & performing artists; integrated library automation system; public relations; continuing education & training; management of 11- county wide area network; cataloging; regional back-up reference; library space planning assistance grants; scholarships; homepage hosting; dial-in access & web catalog; library advocacy

ROCKFORD

P ROCKFORD PUBLIC LIBRARY,* 8220 Cedar St, 55373. SAN 373-904X. Tel: 612-477-4216. FAX: 612-477-4216. Web Site: www.griver.org. *Librn*, Gale Bacon
Pop 6,045; Circ 42,895
Library Holdings: Bk Vols 11,876; Per Subs 44
Mem of Great River Regional Library
Open Mon & Wed 10-1 & 3-8, Thurs 3-8, Fri 12-6, Sat 10-2
Friends of the Library Group

ROSEAU

P ROSEAU PUBLIC LIBRARY, 110 Second Ave NE, 56751. SAN 348-0690. Tel: 218-463-2825. FAX: 218-463-2825. *Librn*, Charles Erickson
Pop 2,272; Circ 25,258
Library Holdings: Bk Vols 6,000; Per Subs 20
Mem of Northwest Regional Library System
Friends of the Library Group

ROSEMOUNT

J DAKOTA COUNTY TECHNICAL COLLEGE LIBRARY,* 1300 E 145th St, 55068. SAN 320-6831. Tel: 651-423-8345, 651-423-8406. FAX: 651-423-8775. *Librn*, Richard Blasjo
Founded 1973
Library Holdings: Bk Vols 11,000; Per Subs 243
Automation Activity & Vendor Info: (Cataloging) PALS
Partic in Minn Interlibr Telecommunication Exchange

ROSEVILLE

S MINNESOTA DEPARTMENT OF CHILDREN, FAMILIES & LEARNING, Educational Resource Center,* 1500 Hwy 36 W, 55113. SAN 308-7719. Tel: 651-582-8719. FAX: 651-582-8898. *Dir*, Pat Tupper
Founded 1970
Library Holdings: Per Subs 600
Subject Interests: Census, Education, Planning
Special Collections: Census publications (print & microfiche); Minnesota State Documents (microfiche)
Publications: Bibliographies
Partic in Capital Area Consortium; Metronet; Minn Interlibr Telecommunication Exchange; OCLC Online Computer Library Center, Inc
Reports to MN State Libr Agency, Libr Develop & Serv. Open Mon-Fri 8 am-5 pm

P MINNESOTA STATE LIBRARY AGENCY, DEPARTMENT OF CHILDREN, FAMILIES & LEARNING, Library Development & Services, 1500 Hwy 36 W, 55113. SAN 308-7778. Tel: 651-582-8722. Reference Tel: 651-582-8719. FAX: 651-582-8897. Web Site: cfl.state.mn.us/library. *Dir*, Joyce Swonger; *Librn*, Darlene Arnold; Staff 22 (MLS 9, Non-MLS 13)
Founded 1899
Library Holdings: Bk Titles 27,000; Per Subs 975
Subject Interests: Education, Libr sci, Physically handicapped
Automation Activity & Vendor Info: (Serials) Inmagic, Inc.
Publications: Minnesota Libraries Newsletter; Resources in Library & Information Science
Partic in MINITEX Library Information Network
Friends of the Library Group

S ROSEVILLE AREA SCHOOLS ECFE PARENT RESOURCE CENTER, 701 W County Rd B, 55113. SAN 326-4890. Tel: 651-487-4361. *Librn*, Nancy Busse; E-Mail: nancy.busse@pcs.roseville.k12.mn.us
Library Holdings: Bk Titles 2,500
Special Collections: Educational Toys; Parenting Resource Materials

S UNISYS CORPORATION, Roseville Information Center,* 2470 Highcrest Rd, 55113. SAN 329-0298. Tel: 651-635-7211. FAX: 651-635-7523. *Tech Servs*, Marge Johnson; *Tech Servs*, Linda Lockrem; *Tech Servs*, Terri Mercado
Founded 1965
Library Holdings: Bk Titles 15,000; Per Subs 450
Subject Interests: Computer science, Engineering
Automation Activity & Vendor Info: (Acquisitions) SIRSI; (Cataloging) SIRSI; (Circulation) SIRSI

ROYALTON

P ROYALTON LIBRARY,* 13 N Cedar St, PO Box 285, 56373-0285. SAN 347-8688. Tel: 320-584-8151. FAX: 320-584-8151. Web Site: www.griver.org. *In Charge*, Carol Cassman
Pop 2,236; Circ 10,663
Library Holdings: Bk Vols 9,500; Per Subs 26
Mem of Great River Regional Library
Open Mon 2-6, Wed 2-8, Thurs 9-12 & 2-6, Sat 9am-12pm

RUSH CITY

P RUSH CITY PUBLIC LIBRARY,* PO Box 556, 55069-0556. SAN 347-2612. Tel: 320-358-3948. E-Mail: rcmail@ecrl.lib.mn.us. *Librn*, Jeanette Monthye
Pop 4,832; Circ 30,939
Library Holdings: Bk Vols 4,580; Per Subs 45
Mem of East Central Regional Library
Branch of East Central Regional Library
Friends of the Library Group

RUSHFORD

P RUSHFORD PUBLIC LIBRARY, 101 N Mill St, 55971-0250. (Mail add: PO Box 250, 55971-0250), SAN 308-7433. Tel: 507-864-7600. FAX: 507-864-7003. Web Site: www.selco.lib.mn.us/rushpl/default.html. *Dir*, Susan Hart; E-Mail: shart@selco.lib.mn.us
Founded 1856. Pop 2,500
Library Holdings: Bk Vols 11,000; Per Subs 24
Subject Interests: Local history
Database Vendor: DRA, GaleNet, IAC - SearchBank, ProQuest
Partic in SE Libr Coop
Open Tues & Thurs 12-8, Wed & Fri 10-6 & Sat 10-2

SAINT BONIFACIUS

CR CROWN COLLEGE, Peter Watne Memorial Library, 6425 County Rd 30, 55375-9001. SAN 308-5228. Tel: 952-446-4240. Circulation Tel: 952-446-4241. FAX: 952-446-4149. Web Site: www.crown.edu/go/. *Actg Dir*, Pam Pitts; Tel: 952-446-4415, E-Mail: pittsp@crown.edu; *Asst Librn*, Janet Derby; E-Mail: derbyj@crown.edu; *Per*, Elaine Johnson; Tel: 952-446-4242, E-Mail: johnsone@crown.edu; Staff 3 (Non-MLS 3)
Founded 1916. Enrl 897; Fac 42; Highest Degree: Master
Jul 2000-Jun 2001 Mats Exp $46,500, Books $27,000, AV Equip $1,500, Other Print Mats $12,000, Electronic Ref Mat (Incl. Access Fees) $6,000. Sal $83,700
Library Holdings: Bk Vols 100,000; Bk Titles 95,000; Per Subs 450
Subject Interests: Bus, Education, Relig studies
Special Collections: Bible & Theology (Dr Stanton W Richardson Coll); Evangelism (Dr Howard O Jones Coll); Evans Coll, micro print
Automation Activity & Vendor Info: (OPAC) PALS
Database Vendor: Ebsco - EbscoHost, OCLC - First Search
Partic in Metronet; MINITEX Library Information Network; OCLC Online Computer Library Center, Inc

SAINT CHARLES

P SAINT CHARLES PUBLIC LIBRARY,* 125 W 11th St, 55972-1141. SAN 308-7441. Tel: 507-932-3227. FAX: 507-932-3227. *Dir*, Sharon Grossardt
Founded 1913. Pop 5,548; Circ 29,137
Library Holdings: Bk Vols 16,750; Per Subs 70
Special Collections: Photographs of Early St Charles
Partic in SE Libr Coop
Special Services for the Deaf - Staff with knowledge of sign language
Friends of the Library Group

SAINT CLOUD

S CENTRAL MINNESOTA HISTORICAL CENTER LIBRARY,* Saint Cloud State University, 720 Fourth Ave S, 56301. SAN 323-4029. Tel: 320-255-2084 (Learning Resource Ctr), 320-255-3165 (History Dept). FAX: 320-255-4778.
Subject Interests: Church history, Hist of county regions, Polit hist
Special Collections: Cent Minn, letters, papers, ms, photos; World War II Veterans Project
Open Mon-Fri 8am-4pm

GM DEPARTMENT OF VETERANS AFFAIRS MEDICAL CENTER, Medical Library,* 4801 Eighth St N, 56303. SAN 308-745X. Interlibrary Loan Service Tel: 320-255-6342. FAX: 320-255-6493.; Staff 4 (MLS 3, Non-MLS 1)
Founded 1925
Library Holdings: Bk Vols 1,500; Per Subs 205
Subject Interests: Geriatrics, Nursing, Psychiatry, Psychology
Publications: PLEASE
Partic in Central Minnesota Libraries Exchange; Medline; Vets Admin Libr Network

SR DIOCESE OF SAINT CLOUD, Catholic Education Ministries, 305 Seventh Ave N, 56303. SAN 327-1730. Tel: 320-252-1021. FAX: 320-251-0259. E-Mail: cem@gw.stcdio.org.
Library Holdings: Bk Vols 5,200; Per Subs 5

C EVELYN PAYNE HATCHER MUSEUM OF ANTHROPOLOGY LIBRARY,* 262 Stewart Hall, 720 Fourth Ave S, 56301. SAN 327-1757. Tel: 320-255-2294, 320-255-3034. FAX: 320-654-5198. *Dir*, Robert Lavenda; *Curator*, Richard Lane
Library Holdings: Bk Vols 500

S SAINT CLOUD HOSPITAL, Health Sciences Library,* 1406 Sixth Ave N, 56303. SAN 327-8271. Tel: 320-251-2700, Ext 54686. FAX: 320-656-7039. Web Site: www.saintcloudhospital.com. *Librn*, Judith Heeter
Library Holdings: Bk Vols 1,500; Per Subs 200

P SAINT CLOUD LIBRARY, Great River Regional Library,* 405 W Saint Germain, 56301-3697. SAN 347-8718. Tel: 320-251-7282, 320-650-2500. FAX: 320-650-2501. Web Site: www.griver.org. *Dir*, Ken Behringer; *Dep Dir*, Pat Christianson
Circ 723,541
Library Holdings: Bk Vols 305,385; Per Subs 649
Mem of Great River Regional Library
Mon-Thurs 10-9, Fri 10-6, Sat 10-5
Friends of the Library Group
Branches: 1
BECKER LIBRARY, 11500 Sherburne Ave, PO Box 414, Becker, 55308. SAN 322-564X. Tel: 612-261-4454. FAX: 612-261-4454. Web Site: www.griver.org. *Librn*, Gail Wilkinson
Founded 1984. Pop 4,463; Circ 47,071
Library Holdings: Bk Vols 12,937; Per Subs 34
Open Mon & Thurs 2-8, Tues 10-1 & 2-6, Wed & Fri 2-6, Sat 10-1

C SAINT CLOUD STATE UNIVERSITY, James W Miller Learning Resources Center, 112 Miller Ctr, 720 Fourth Ave S, 56301-4498. SAN 347-8807. Tel: 320-255-2022. FAX: 320-255-4778. Web Site: lrs.stcloudstate.edu. *Dean of Libr*, Kristi M Tornquist; *Coll Develop*, Phyllis Lacroix
Founded 1869. Enrl 15,000; Fac 570; Highest Degree: Master
Jul 1999-Jun 2000 Mats Exp $1,221,284, Books $428,784, Per/Ser (Incl. Access Fees) $623,316, AV Equip $15,000, Electronic Ref Mat (Incl. Access Fees) $154,184
Library Holdings: Bk Vols 636,133; Per Subs 1,938
Special Collections: Archives, Government Documents & Maps; ERIC Documents of Education, micro; Library of American Civilization; Minnesota Coll; NASA Coll; Rare Book Coll; State Author Manuscript Coll
Publications: Information Media Newsletter
Partic in MINITEX Library Information Network; OCLC Online Computer Library Center, Inc

J SAINT CLOUD TECHNICAL COLLEGE, Learning Resource Center,* 1540 Northway Dr, 56303-1240. SAN 320-6858. Tel: 320-654-5000, Ext 5966. FAX: 320-654-5981. *In Charge*, Beverly F Wochnick; Staff 4 (MLS 1, Non-MLS 3)
Founded 1975. Enrl 1,600; Fac 100
Library Holdings: Bk Vols 14,000; Bk Titles 12,500; Per Subs 450
Publications: Staff Newsletter
Partic in Central Minnesota Libraries Exchange; Minn Interlibr Telecommunication Exchange

S STEARNS HISTORY MUSEUM, Research Center Archives Library, 235 33rd Ave S, 56301. SAN 325-4712. Tel: 320-253-8424. FAX: 320-253-2172. E-Mail: info@stearns-museum.org. Web Site: www.stearns-museum.org. *Archivist, Ref*, John W Decker; *Ref*, Robert Lommel; Staff 3 (Non-MLS 3)
Founded 1936
Jan 1999-Dec 1999 Income $96,000. Mats Exp $7,200, Books $1,200, Per/Ser (Incl. Access Fees) $500, Presv $100, Micro $1,000, Manuscripts & Archives $2,900. Sal $86,000
Library Holdings: Bk Vols 2,350; Bk Titles 2,000; Per Subs 47
Subject Interests: Dairying, Genealogy, Granite indust, Historic preservation, Immigration, Luxembourg-settlement, Stearns County hist
Special Collections: County
Partic in Central Minnesota Libraries Exchange

SAINT JAMES

P WATONWAN COUNTY LIBRARY,* 511 Second Ave S, 56081-1736. SAN 308-7468. Tel: 507-375-1278. FAX: 507-375-5415. E-Mail: libtwa@tds.lib.mn.us. Web Site: www.tds.lib.mn.us. *Dir*, Cheryl Bjoin; E-Mail: cbjoin@tds.lib.mn.us; *Assoc Dir*, Susan D Kuyper; *Circ*, Cheryl Brown; *Ch Servs, Media Spec*, Pam Dammer; *Acq*, Shirley Coleman; Staff 9 (MLS 1, Non-MLS 8)
Founded 1943. Pop 11,500; Circ 135,991
Jan 1998-Dec 1998 Income (Main Library and Branch Library) $420,054, City $4,310, County $362,793, Locally Generated Income $26,442, Other $26,509. Mats Exp $56,532, Books $48,742, Per/Ser (Incl. Access Fees) $6,641, Presv $504, Electronic Ref Mat (Incl. Access Fees) $645. Sal $234,852 (Prof $48,070)
Library Holdings: Bk Vols 99,862; Per Subs 180
Subject Interests: Agriculture, Antique tractor repair, Tractors
Automation Activity & Vendor Info: (Circulation) PALS; (ILL) PALS
Mem of Traverse Des Sioux Library System
Partic in OCLC Online Computer Library Center, Inc
Friends of the Library Group
Branches: 4
BUTTERFIELD BRANCH, 111 Second St N, PO Box L, Butterfield, 56120-0237. SAN 328-6819. Tel: 507-956-2361. E-Mail: libtwb@tds.lib.mn.us. Web Site: www.tds.lib.mn.us. *Dir*, Cheryl Bjoin; Tel: 507-375-1278, Fax: 507-375-5415, E-Mail: cbjoin@tds.lib/.mn.us; *Br Coordr*, Carol Freitag; Staff 1 (Non-MLS 1)
Founded 1970. Pop 573; Circ 11,291
Library Holdings: Bk Vols 11,383; Per Subs 16
Automation Activity & Vendor Info: (Circulation) PALS; (ILL) PALS
DARFUR BRANCH, PO Box 191, Darfur, 56022-0190. SAN 328-6835. Tel: 507-877-5010. E-Mail: libtwd@tds.lib.mn.us. Web Site: www.tds.lib.mn.us. *Dir*, Cheryl Bjoin; Tel: 507-375-1278, Fax: 507-375-5415, E-Mail: cbjoin@tds.lib.mn.us; *Br Coordr*, Sofianne Evers
Founded 1941. Pop 138; Circ 4,888
Library Holdings: Bk Vols 2,104
Automation Activity & Vendor Info: (Circulation) PALS; (ILL) PALS
LEWISVILLE BRANCH, PO Box 314, Lewisville, 56060-9998. SAN 325-1748. Tel: 507-435-2781. FAX: 507-435-2781. E-Mail: libtwl@tds.lib.mn.us. Web Site: www.tds.lib.mn.us. *Dir*, Cheryl Bjoin; Tel: 507-375-1278, Fax: 507-375-5415, E-Mail: cbjoin@tds.lib.mn.us; *Br Coordr*, Heidi Cooling
Founded 1941. Pop 249; Circ 6,212
Library Holdings: Bk Vols 4,707; Per Subs 20
Automation Activity & Vendor Info: (Circulation) PALS; (ILL) PALS
Friends of the Library Group
MADELIA BRANCH, 23 First St NW, Madelia, 56062. SAN 328-6797. Tel: 507-642-3511. FAX: 507-642-8144. E-Mail: libtwm@tds.lib.mn.us. Web Site: www.tds.lib.mn.us. *Dir*, Cheryl Bjoin; Tel: 507-375-1278, Fax: 507-375-5415, E-Mail: cbjoin@tds.lib.mn.us; *Br Coordr*, Shari Byro; Staff 2 (Non-MLS 2)
Founded 1941. Pop 2,234; Circ 37,136
Library Holdings: Bk Vols 23,107; Per Subs 42
Automation Activity & Vendor Info: (Circulation) PALS; (ILL) PALS
Friends of the Library Group

SAINT JOSEPH

C SAINT JOHN'S UNIVERSITY, Alcuin Library - College of Saint Benedict, Clemens Library, 37 S College Ave, 56374. SAN 308-5430. Tel: 320-363-2119. FAX: 320-363-2126 (St John's), 320-363-5197 (St Benedict). Web Site: www.csbsju.edu/library. *Dir*, Michael D Kathman; Tel: 320-363-2121; *Assoc Dir, Publ Servs*, Jim Parsons; *Tech Servs*, Theresa Kasling; *ILL, Publ Servs*, Molly Ewing; *Publ Servs, Syst Coordr*, W Thomas Nichol; *Publ Servs*, Peggy Roske; *Publ Servs*, David Malone; *Publ Servs*, Norma Dickau; *Govt Doc*, Kirsten Clark; *Cat*, Janice Rod; *Coll Develop*, Sister Stefanie Weisgram; Staff 10 (MLS 10)
Founded 1856. Enrl 1,740; Fac 137; Highest Degree: Master

Library Holdings: Per Subs 2,269
Subject Interests: Benedictina, Liturgy, Nursing, Theology, Women studies
Partic in Central Minnesota Libraries Exchange; MINITEX Library Information Network; Minnesota Theological Library Association; OCLC Online Computer Library Center, Inc
Alcuin Library at St John's University & Clemens Library at the College of St Benedict are a joint library. Figures reported are for both institutions

SAINT LOUIS PARK

R BETH-EL SYNAGOGUE, Max Shapiro Memorial Library, 5224 W 26th St, 55416. SAN 308-7484. Tel: 952-920-3512. FAX: 612-920-8755. *Librn*, Marcia Oleisky
Founded 1929
Library Holdings: Bk Vols 5,000; Per Subs 26
Special Collections: Music Coll

M PARK NICOLLET INSTITUTE, Arneson Methodist Library, 3800 Park Nicollet Blvd, 55416. SAN 308-6879. Tel: 952-993-5451. FAX: 952-993-1322. *Dir*, Penny Marsala; E-Mail: marsap@parknicollet.com; Staff 3 (MLS 3)
Founded 1952
Library Holdings: Bk Vols 6,500; Per Subs 250
Restriction: Staff use only, Use of others with permission of librarian
Partic in Twin Cities Biomedical Consortium

SAINT MICHAEL

P ST MICHAEL (ROY SIMMS) LIBRARY,* 403 Central Ave E, 55376-0309. SAN 373-9058. Tel: 612-497-1998. FAX: 612-497-1998. Web Site: www.griver.org. *In Charge*, Debra Luken
Pop 7,978; Circ 69,667
Library Holdings: Bk Vols 19,000; Per Subs 48
Mem of Great River Regional Library
Open Mon & Wed 10-12 & 2-8, Tues 2-6, Thurs 2-8, Fri 12-6, Sat 10-2
Friends of the Library Group

SAINT PAUL

S AERO SYSTEMS ENGINEERING INC LIBRARY, 358 E Fillmore Ave, 55107. SAN 308-6488. Tel: 612-220-1209. FAX: 612-227-0519. *Librn*, Glenn Payton; Staff 1 (MLS 1)
Founded 1967
Library Holdings: Bk Titles 2,800; Per Subs 150
Subject Interests: Aerospace res, Aircraft engine, Develop, Hush houses, Test cells, Testing, Wind tunnel design
Partic in Dialog Corporation; Metronet; Nasa Libraries Information System - Nasa Galaxie; Nasa Libraries Information System - Nasa Galaxie

SR BAPTIST GENERAL CONFERENCE ARCHIVES & HISTORICAL LIBRARY,* 3949 Bethel Dr, 55112. SAN 327-1862. Tel: 612-638-6282. *Archivist, Librn*, Norris Magnuson
Library Holdings: Bk Vols 1,000
Special Collections: Skarstedt Coll in Pietism
Partic in Minnesota Theological Library Association

CR BETHEL COLLEGE LIBRARY, 3900 Bethel Dr, 55112. SAN 308-7522. Tel: 651-638-6222. FAX: 651-638-6001. Web Site: www.bethel.edu. *Dir*, Robert C Suderman; *Coll Develop, Ref*, Carol Hansen; *Media Spec*, Frank Schiffer; *Cat*, Amy Reinhold; *ILL*, Betty Bond; Staff 7 (MLS 7)
Founded 1871. Enrl 1,845; Fac 112; Highest Degree: Bachelor
Library Holdings: Bk Titles 156,000; Per Subs 642
Subject Interests: Education, History
Partic in Cooperating Libraries in Consortium; Minn Interlibr Telecommunication Exchange

L BRIGGS & MORGAN, Law Library,* 332 Minnesota St W 2200, 55101. SAN 372-2856. Tel: 651-223-6600. FAX: 651-223-6450. E-Mail: morgan@email.briggs.com. *Dir*, Kate McGown; *Librn*, Susan J Redalen
Library Holdings: Bk Vols 53,500; Per Subs 290

M CHILDREN'S HOSPITALS & CLINICS, Medical Library, 345 N Smith Ave, 55102. SAN 308-7573. Tel: 651-220-6145. FAX: 651-220-6408. *Librn*, Nancy W Battaglia
Founded 1927
Library Holdings: Bk Titles 1,000; Per Subs 95
Subject Interests: Pediatrics
Partic in Regional Med Libr - Region 3; Twin Cities Biomedical Consortium

C COLLEGE OF SAINT CATHERINE LIBRARY-SAINT PAUL CAMPUS,* 2004 Randolph Ave, 55105-1794. SAN 347-8866. Tel: 651-690-6650. Interlibrary Loan Service Tel: 651-690-6655. Reference Tel: 651-690-6652. FAX: 651-690-8636. *Dir*, Carol P Johnson; *Media Spec*, John Lange; *Coll Develop, Tech Servs*, Karen Harwood; *Publ Servs*, James Newsome; *Archivist*, Sister Margery Smith; Staff 8 (MLS 8)
Founded 1905. Fac 172; Highest Degree: Master
Jun 1997-May 1998 Income $1,111,893. Mats Exp $219,139, Books $92,925, Per/Ser (Incl. Access Fees) $110,044, Presv $3,760, Micro $8,677, AV Equip $1,217. Sal $631,258 (Prof $349,829)
Library Holdings: Bk Vols 228,726; Per Subs 850
Special Collections: Autographs & Manuscripts (Mother Antonia McHugh Coll), bks, letters; Children's Literature (Ruth Sawyer Coll), multi media; Liturgical Art (Ade Bethune Coll); Muellerleile Coll of Printing; Rare Books (Charlotte Hill Slade Coll & Mitsch Coll), first editions & fine bindings
Partic in Coop Librs in Consortium; Metronet; Mintex Libr Info Network; OCLC Online Computer Library Center, Inc
Friends of the Library Group
Departmental Libraries:
PERFORMING ARTS, 2004 Randolph Ave, St Paul, 55105. Tel: 651-690-6696. *Librn*, Amy Kreitzer
Friends of the Library Group

S COMO ZOO LIBRARY,* 1250 Kaufman Dr, 55103. SAN 371-196X. Tel: 651-487-8201. FAX: 651-487-8203. *Dir*, Victor Camp; *Librn*, Jan Turhajetz
Library Holdings: Bk Vols 1,350
Subject Interests: Conservation, Natural history
Restriction: Staff use only

C CONCORDIA UNIVERSITY, Buenger Memorial Library, 275 N Syndicate St, 55104-5494. SAN 308-759X. Tel: 651-641-8278. FAX: 651-659-0207. Web Site: www.csp.edu. *Cat, Chief Librn*, Charlotte Knoche; *AV*, Jeff Burkart
Founded 1893. Enrl 750; Fac 60; Highest Degree: Bachelor Sal $230,000
Library Holdings: Bk Vols 120,000; Per Subs 900
Subject Interests: Education, History, Music
Special Collections: Curriculum Coll); Education (Children's Coll; Historical Textbooks; Hymnbook Coll; Sixteenth Century Coll
Publications: The Reformation as Media Event: a Bibliography of 16th century Materials
Partic in Coop Librs in Consortium; Minn Interlibr Telecommunication Exchange; OCLC Online Computer Library Center, Inc
Open Mon-Thurs 7:15-11, Fri 9-4:30, Sat 10-5, Sun 2-11

S DAYTONS BLUFF AREA EARLY CHILDHOOD & FAMILY EDUCATION PROGRAM, Adult & Children's Library,* 262 Bates Ave, 55106. SAN 327-1889. Tel: 651-293-5343. FAX: 651-771-3428. *Dir*, Mary Ann Cogelow
Library Holdings: Bk Vols 1,600

G DEPARTMENT OF ECONOMIC SECURITY LIBRARY,* 390 N Robert St, 55101. SAN 320-6866. Tel: 612-297-3419. FAX: 612-297-4501. *Librn*, Linda Woodstrom; E-Mail: linda.woodstrom@state.mn.us
Library Holdings: Bk Vols 4,000; Per Subs 50
Partic in Dialog Corporation; Minn Interlibr Telecommunication Exchange; OCLC Online Computer Library Center, Inc

SR EVANGELICAL LUTHERAN CHURCH IN AMERICA, Region III Archives, 2481 Como Ave, 55108. SAN 373-2290. Tel: 612-641-3205. FAX: 612-641-3354. *Archivist*, Paul Daniels; E-Mail: pdaniels@luthersem.edu
Founded 1960
Library Holdings: Bk Vols 1,500

R FIRST BAPTIST CHURCH LIBRARY, 499 Wacouta St, 55101. SAN 308-7646. Tel: 651-222-0718. FAX: 651-227-7887. *Librn*, Norma Sommerdorf
Library Holdings: Bk Vols 3,000

S DEBRA S FISH EARLY CHILDHOOD RESOURCE LIBRARY, 450 N Syndicate, Ste 5, 55104-4125. SAN 327-2184. Tel: 651-641-3544. TDD: 651-641-0332. FAX: 651-645-0990. *Exec Dir*, Carol Rhode; *Librn*, Patricia J Palahniuk; E-Mail: ppalahniuk@resourcesforchildcare.org; Staff 1 (MLS 1)
Founded 1997
Library Holdings: Bk Titles 2,600; Bks on Deafness & Sign Lang 10
Subject Interests: Cambodia, Spanish, Vietnam

S FORTIS COMPANY LIBRARY,* PO Box 64271, 55164. SAN 323-4614. Tel: 612-738-4589. FAX: 612-738-4680. *Librn*, Sandy Scott
Library Holdings: Bk Titles 1,000; Per Subs 150

HAMLINE UNIVERSITY

C BUSH MEMORIAL LIBRARY, 1536 Hewitt, 55104. SAN 347-8920. Tel: 651-523-2048, 651-523-2375. FAX: 651-641-2199. Web Site: www.hanline.edu/library. *Dir*, Diane Clayton; E-Mail: dclayton@gw.hamline.edu; *Dir*, Julie Rochat; *Ref*, Karen Campbell; *Ref*, Kimberly Feil Meyer; *Ref*, Kate Borowske; *Circ*, Barbara Brokopp; *Ser*, Jon George
Founded 1854. Enrl 2,000
Jul 1998-Jun 1999 Income $803,000. Mats Exp $255,000. Sal $459,000
Library Holdings: Bk Vols 137,244; Per Subs 1,454
Special Collections: Brass Rubbing Coll; Methodism; S Asia Coll
Partic in Coop Librs in Consortium; Dialog Corporation; Minn Interlibr Telecommunication Exchange; OCLC Online Computer Library Center, Inc
Friends of the Library Group

CL SCHOOL OF LAW LIBRARY, 1536 Hewitt Ave, MS-D2010, 55104-1237. SAN 347-8955. Tel: 651-523-2125. FAX: 615-523-2236. Web Site: www.hamline.edu/law/library/index.html. *Dir*, Susan Kiefer; E-Mail: skiefer@gw.hamline.edu; *Cat*, Miki Scholl; E-Mail: mscholl@

gw.hamline.edu; *Acq, Coll Develop, Ser*, Frances Singh; E-Mail: fsingh@gw.hamline.edu; *Publ Servs*, John Tessner; E-Mail: jtessner@gw.hamline.edu; *Online Servs*, Elizabeth Robb; E-Mail: erobb@gw.hamline.edu; Staff 6 (MLS 6)
Founded 1972. Enrl 587; Fac 30
Jul 1998-Jun 1999 Income $566,650. Mats Exp $206,317, Books $69,005, Per/Ser (Incl. Access Fees) $57,378, Micro $79,610
Library Holdings: Bk Vols 254,595; Per Subs 750
Automation Activity & Vendor Info: (Acquisitions) epixtech, inc.
Publications: Library Guide; Pathfinders
Partic in Coop Librs in Consortium; Metronet; MINITEX Library Information Network; OCLC Online Computer Library Center, Inc; Westlaw

M HEALTHEAST - SAINT JOSEPH'S HOSPITAL, Jerome Medical Library, 69 W Exchange St, 55102. SAN 308-7859. Tel: 651-232-3193. FAX: 651-232-3296. E-Mail: kbrudvig@healtheast.org.; Staff 1 (MLS 1)
Founded 1949
Library Holdings: Bk Vols 500; Per Subs 230
Restriction: Open to public for reference only
Partic in Twin Cities Biomedical Consortium

S JAMES J HILL REFERENCE LIBRARY, 80 W Fourth St, 55102-1669. SAN 308-7662. Tel: 651-265-5400, 651-265-5500. Toll Free Tel: 877-700-4455. FAX: 651-265-5544. E-Mail: customer_support@jjhill.org. Web Site: www.jjhill.org. *Pres*, Pam Sveinson; Staff 30 (MLS 15, Non-MLS 15)
Founded 1921
Library Holdings: Bk Vols 240,000; Bk Titles 32,709; Per Subs 989; Spec Interest Per Sub 950
Subject Interests: Business, Economics
Special Collections: James Jerome Hill Papers; Louis Warren Hill Papers
Automation Activity & Vendor Info: (Acquisitions) PALS; (Cataloging) PALS; (ILL) PALS; (OPAC) PALS; (Serials) PALS
Database Vendor: GaleNet, IAC - SearchBank, ProQuest
Publications: Dir of Minnesota Business & Prof Asns; Index to Minnesota Business Periodicals
Restriction: Not a lending library, Open to public for reference only
Function: Archival collection, Document delivery services, ILL limited, Reference only, Reference services available, Some telephone reference
Partic in MINITEX Library Information Network; MNSCU/PALS; OCLC Online Computer Library Center, Inc
Privately-supported business & commerce library. Document Delivery Service provides photocopies of articles available locally & nationally. Custom research service offers fee based research & online searches

S INTERMEDICS, INC LIBRARY,* 4100 Hamline Ave N, 55112-5700. SAN 325-4682. Tel: 409-848-4573. FAX: 409-848-6000, Ext 4573. E-Mail: library@mails.imed.com. *Mgr*, Charlene Kanter; Staff 3 (MLS 1, Non-MLS 2)
Library Holdings: Bk Vols 14,600; Bk Titles 1,500
Subject Interests: Electronics, Engineering
Special Collections: Articles from 1966 to present on pacing; Pacers
Automation Activity & Vendor Info: (Acquisitions) Inmagic, Inc.; (Cataloging) Inmagic, Inc.; (Circulation) Inmagic, Inc.; (Serials) Inmagic, Inc.
Publications: Pacers monthly update, Bookshelf
Restriction: Staff use only
Partic in S Cent Regional Med Libr Program

G INTERTECHNOLOGIES GROUP LIBRARY,* Centennial Office Bldg, 658 Cedar 5th flr, 55155. SAN 370-162X. Tel: 651-296-4621. FAX: 651-296-6362. *Librn*, Pat Loehlein; E-Mail: pat.loehlein@state.mn.us; *Asst Librn*, Robert Livingston; Tel: 651-297-2696, E-Mail: bob.livingston@state.mn.us
Library Holdings: Bk Titles 2,000; Per Subs 60
Subject Interests: Info mgt, Telecommunication tech
Special Collections: Proprietary Vender Manuals
Publications: Newsletter
Partic in MINITEX Library Information Network

S LAND O'LAKES INC LIBRARY,* PO Box 64101, 55164-0101. SAN 327-7941. Tel: 651-481-2691. FAX: 651-766-1346. *Librn*, Donna Koenig
Library Holdings: Bk Vols 4,000; Per Subs 250
Subject Interests: Agriculture

S LEAGUE OF MINNESOTA CITIES LIBRARY, 145 University Ave W, 55103-2044. SAN 327-1943. Tel: 651-281-1200. FAX: 651-281-1299. Web Site: www.lmnc.org. *Librn*, Jeannette Bach
Founded 1913
Library Holdings: Bk Vols 1,000
Subject Interests: City, Government
Special Collections: Minnesota City Charters
Publications: Information memos on municipal topics
Restriction: Staff use only
Friends of the Library Group

R LUTHER SEMINARY LIBRARY, 2481 Como Ave, 55108. SAN 308-7689. Tel: 651-641-3447, 651-641-3456. FAX: 651-641-3280. Web Site: www.luthersem.edu. *Acq*, Reid Westrem; Tel: 651-641-3263, E-Mail: rwestrem@luthersem.edu; *Cat*, Mary Ann Teske; Tel: 651-641-3446, E-Mail: mteske@luthersem.edu; *Ser*, Paula Vestermark; Tel: 651-641-3231, E-Mail: pvesterm@luthersem.edu; *Circ*, Sally Sawyer; Tel: 651-641-3301, E-Mail: ssawyer@luthersem.edu; *Ref*, Bruce E Eldevik; Staff 7 (MLS 2, Non-MLS 5)
Founded 1869. Enrl 770; Fac 50; Highest Degree: Doctorate
Jul 1998-Jun 1999 Mats Exp $199,985, Books $98,202, Per/Ser (Incl. Access Fees) $32,672, Presv $11,500, Micro $50,439, Electronic Ref Mat (Incl. Access Fees) $7,172. Sal $293,748 (Prof $168,449)
Library Holdings: Bk Vols 232,872; Per Subs 765
Subject Interests: Reformation
Special Collections: Doving Hymnal Coll; Lutheran Brotherhood Reformation Research Coll; Tanner Catechism Coll
Automation Activity & Vendor Info: (Cataloging) Endeavor; (Circulation) Endeavor; (Serials) Endeavor
Database Vendor: OCLC - First Search
Partic in Minnesota Theological Library Association
Special Services for the Blind - Adapted computers & special software with speech output to assist learning disabled, mentally retarded & uneducated

C MACALESTER COLLEGE, DeWitt Wallace Library, 1600 Grand Ave, 55105-1899. SAN 347-9013. Tel: 651-696-6346. Interlibrary Loan Service Tel: 651-696-6530. Circulation Tel: 651-696-6610. Reference Tel: 651-696-6618. FAX: 651-696-6617. Web Site: www.macalester.edu/~library. *In Charge*, Joel G Clemmer; *Dir*, Teresa Fishel; Tel: 651-696-6343, E-Mail: fishel@macalester.edu; *Publ Servs*, Ron Joslin; Staff 18 (MLS 9, Non-MLS 9)
Founded 1874. Enrl 1,742; Fac 147; Highest Degree: Bachelor
Library Holdings: Bk Vols 407,321; Bk Titles 251,510; Per Subs 1,869
Special Collections: Early Minnesota; Sinclair Lewis, bks, per, letters & ephemera
Mem of Coop Libr in Consortium; Minitex Libr Info Network
Partic in OCLC Online Computer Library Center, Inc

S METROPOLITAN COUNCIL LIBRARY,* 230 E Fifth St, 55101. SAN 308-7697. Tel: 651-602-1310. FAX: 651-602-1464. *Librn*, Jan Price; E-Mail: jan.price@metc.state.mn.us
Founded 1967
Library Holdings: Bk Titles 8,400; Per Subs 300
Subject Interests: Housing, Transportation
Special Collections: Local Government Comprehensive Plans
Automation Activity & Vendor Info: (Cataloging) Inmagic, Inc.
Publications: Recent Additions to the Library
Restriction: Staff use only
Partic in Dialog Corporation; Dow Jones News Retrieval

P METROPOLITAN LIBRARY SERVICE AGENCY (MELSA),* 1619 Dayton Ave, Rm 314, 55104-6206. SAN 308-7700. Tel: 612-645-5731. FAX: 612-649-3169. E-Mail: melsa@melsa.lib.mn.us. Web Site: www.melsa.mn.us. *Exec Dir*, James V Wroblewski; *Assoc Dir*, Tzvee Morris; Staff 5 (MLS 3, Non-MLS 2)
Founded 1969
Jul 1997-Jun 1998 Income $4,675,580. Sal $225,000
Publications: Subscription microfiche index titled Handicraft/Hobby Index
This is a federated public library system covering seven counties which serves its nine members in the following ways: interlibrary loan; reciprocal borrowing & return; delivery

§C METROPOLITAN STATE UNIVERSITY, Main Campus (Saint Paul Downtown) Library, Library Services, New Main L 105, 700 E Seventh St, 55106. SAN 378-3766. Tel: 651-772-6143, 651-772-7504. FAX: 651-772-3700. E-Mail: sage.holben@metrostate.edu. Web Site: www.metrostate.edu. *Dir*, Jeff Jackson; *Asst Librn*, Adela Peskorz; *Acq*, Sage Holben; Staff 4 (MLS 2, Non-MLS 2)
Library Holdings: Bk Vols 3,579; Per Subs 135
Automation Activity & Vendor Info: (Acquisitions) PALS; (Cataloging) PALS; (Circulation) PALS; (ILL) PALS; (OPAC) PALS

GL MINNESOTA ATTORNEY GENERAL LIBRARY, (MAG), NCL Tower Ste 1050, 445 Minnesota St, 55101-2109. SAN 321-8325. Tel: 651-296-8152. TDD: 651-296-1410. FAX: 651-297-4139. *Dir*, Anita Anderson; E-Mail: anita.anderson@state.mn.us; *Librn*, Karla Gedell; Staff 3 (MLS 2, Non-MLS 1)
Library Holdings: Bk Vols 27,000; Bk Titles 2,873; Per Subs 800
Special Collections: Minnesota Attorney General Opinions Coll, micro, VF
Automation Activity & Vendor Info: (Cataloging) PALS; (ILL) PALS; (OPAC) PALS
Database Vendor: OCLC - First Search
Restriction: Staff use only
Partic in MINITEX Library Information Network; OCLC Online Computer Library Center, Inc

S MINNESOTA DEPARTMENT OF REVENUE LIBRARY, 600 N Robert St, 55101. (Mail add: Mail Sta 2230, 55146), SAN 327-1846. Tel: 651-296-3529. Interlibrary Loan Service Tel: 651-296-5193. Circulation Tel: 651-296-5193. FAX: 612-297-2850. *Dir*, Donna Davis; E-Mail: donna.davis@state.mn.us; Staff 1 (Non-MLS 1)
Founded 1986. Pop 1,200
Jul 1999-Jun 2000 Income State $163,000. Mats Exp $40,000, Books

$12,000, Per/Ser (Incl. Access Fees) $9,300, Electronic Ref Mat (Incl. Access Fees) $16,000. Sal $125,000 (Prof $49,000)
Library Holdings: Bk Vols 10,000; Bk Titles 5,000; Per Subs 100
Subject Interests: Taxation
Special Collections: CCH, RIA Tax Looseleaf Services
Automation Activity & Vendor Info: (Cataloging) PALS; (OPAC) PALS
Database Vendor: OCLC - First Search
Publications: Revenue Library monthly booklist
Restriction: By appointment only
Partic in Capital Area Library Consortium; Metronet; MINITEX Library Information Network; OCLC Online Computer Library Center, Inc

G MINNESOTA DEPARTMENT OF TRANSPORTATION LIBRARY, 395 John Ireland Blvd, MS 155, 55155. SAN 308-7735. Tel: 651-297-4532. Toll Free Tel: 800-657-3774. TDD: 651-296-9930. FAX: 651-297-2354. E-Mail: library@dot.state.mn.us. Web Site: www.dot.state.mn.us/library. *Dir*, Jerome C Baldwin; Tel: 651-297-4532, Fax: 651-297-2354, E-Mail: jerry.baldwin@dot.state.mn.us; *Librn*, Anne Mackereth; Tel: 651-297-4168, E-Mail: anne.mackereth@dot.state.mn.us; *Librn*, Jim Byerly; Tel: 651-296-7702, E-Mail: jim.byerly@dot.state.mn.us; *Librn*, Shirlee Sherkow; Tel: 651-296-5272, E-Mail: shirlee.sherkow@dot.state.mn.us; *Publ Servs*, Pamela Newsome; Tel: 651-296-1494, E-Mail: pam.newsome@dot.state.mn.us; *Tech Servs*, Qin Tang; Tel: 651-215-0447, E-Mail: qin.tang@dot.state.mn.us; Staff 10 (MLS 5, Non-MLS 5)
Founded 1957
Jul 2000-Jun 2001 Income $563,000, Parent Institution $513,000, Other $50,000. Mats Exp $92,000. Sal $471,000
Library Holdings: Bk Vols 25,000; Bk Titles 15,000; Per Subs 400
Subject Interests: Civil engineering, Mgmt, Transportation
Automation Activity & Vendor Info: (Circulation) PALS; (OPAC) PALS
Database Vendor: Dialog, OCLC - First Search, Silverplatter Information Inc.
Publications: Minnesota Transportation Libraries Recent Acquisitions
Partic in Capitol Area Consortium; Metronet; MINITEX Library Information Network; OCLC Online Computer Library Center, Inc

G MINNESOTA GEOLOGICAL SURVEY LIBRARY,* University of Minnesota, 2642 University Ave W, 55114-1057. SAN 324-766X. Tel: 612-627-4780. FAX: 612-627-4778. *Librn*, Lynn Swanson
Founded 1974
Library Holdings: Bk Vols 1,700; Per Subs 130
Subject Interests: Minn geology, Seasonal thermal energy storage, Underground construction, Underground space
Restriction: Non-circulating to the public

MINNESOTA HISTORICAL SOCIETY
S LIBRARY, 345 Kellogg Blvd W, 55102-1906. SAN 347-9137. Tel: 651-296-2143. FAX: 651-297-7436. E-Mail: reference@mnhs.org. Web Site: www.mnhs.org. *Archivist*, Robert Horton; Tel: 651-215-5866, E-Mail: robert.horton@mnhs.org; *Head, Acq*, James E Fogerty; Tel: 651-296-9989, E-Mail: james.fogerty@mnhs.org; *Head Ref*, Denise Carlson; Tel: 651-297-3874, E-Mail: denise.carlson@mnhs.org; *Tech Servs*, Lydia Lucas; Tel: 651-297-5542, E-Mail: lydia.lucas@mnhs.org; *Coll Develop*, Patrick Coleman; Tel: 651-296-9986, E-Mail: patrick.coleman@mnhs.org
Founded 1849
Library Holdings: Bk Vols 500,000; Bk Titles 165,000; Per Subs 1,300
Subject Interests: Minn hist
Special Collections: Great Northern & Northern Pacific Railroad Papers; History of Native Peoples of Minnesota; Hubert H Humphrey Papers; Minnesota Newspapers, 1849-present; Minnesota State Archives, records of agencies of Minnesota state & local government
Automation Activity & Vendor Info: (OPAC) PALS
Publications: Chippewa & Dakota Indians: A Subject Catalog (1969); Genealogical Resources at MHS: A Guide (1993); Guide to Records of Northern Pacific Branch Lines (1977); Guide to the Public Affairs Collection of the Minnesota Historical Society (1968); Manuscripts Collections of the Minnesota Historical Society (1955 & 1977); MHS Oral History Collections (1984); Minnesota State Archives Preliminary Checklist (1979)
Restriction: Open to public for reference only
Partic in Capitol Area Librs Coop; MINITEX Library Information Network; OCLC Online Computer Library Center, Inc; Research Libraries Group, Inc

G MINNESOTA LEGISLATIVE REFERENCE LIBRARY, (LPL), 645 State Off Bldg, 100 Constitution Ave, 55155. SAN 308-7751. Tel: 651-296-3398. Reference Tel: 651-296-8338. FAX: 651-296-9731. E-Mail: refdesk@library.leg.state.mn.us. Web Site: www.library.leg.state.mn.us. *Dir*, Robbie LaFleur; Tel: 651-296-8310, E-Mail: rlafleur@library.leg.state.mn.us; *Dep Dir*, Elizabeth Lincoln; Tel: 651-296-0594, E-Mail: elincoln@library.leg.state.mn.us
Founded 1969
Jul 2000-Jun 2001 Income State $1,247,000. Mats Exp $89,300, Books $22,000, Per/Ser (Incl. Access Fees) $51,600, Electronic Ref Mat (Incl. Access Fees) $15,700. Sal $1,048,000
Library Holdings: Bk Titles 39,000; Per Subs 600
Subject Interests: Government
Special Collections: Bills Introduced for Ten Years; Interim Committee Reports; Minnesota Documents Coll; Minnesota Government Manual, 1887-present; Minnesota Government Publications, on fiche; Senate & House Journals, tapes, committee minutes
Automation Activity & Vendor Info: (OPAC) PALS
Database Vendor: Ebsco - EbscoHost
Publications: Introductions, Minnesota Resources
Partic in Capital Area Library Consortium; MINITEX Library Information Network; OCLC Online Computer Library Center, Inc

L MINNESOTA MINING & MANUFACTURING CO, Law Library, PO Box 33355, 55133-3355. SAN 372-2880. Tel: 651-733-1460. FAX: 651-733-2560. *Librn*, C Jean Johnson; E-Mail: cjjohnson@mmm.com
Library Holdings: Bk Vols 25,000; Per Subs 225

S MINNESOTA MUSEUM OF AMERICAN ART LIBRARY,* 505 Landmark Center, 75 W Fifth St, 55102. SAN 308-776X. Tel: 612-292-4355. FAX: 612-292-4340. E-Mail: library@mtn.org. *Dir*, Bruce A Lilly; *Curator*, Lin Nelson-Mayson
Jul 1998-Jun 1999 Income $3,000
Library Holdings: Bk Vols 2,500; Per Subs 10
Special Collections: Slide Coll Documenting Museum's Coll, Paul Manship Bequest Files
Restriction: Non-circulating to the public
Function: Reference services available

G MINNESOTA POLLUTION CONTROL AGENCY LIBRARY, 520 Lafayette Rd, 55155-4194. SAN 320-684X. Tel: 651-296-6623, 651-296-7719. FAX: 651-215-1537. *Librn*, Helena Peskova; E-Mail: helena.peskova@pca.state.mn.us
Library Holdings: Bk Vols 20,000; Per Subs 300
Subject Interests: Air pollution, Hazardous wastes, Pollution control, Solid wastes, Water pollution
Special Collections: EPA Coll, micro
Partic in OCLC Online Computer Library Center, Inc

GL MINNESOTA STATE LAW LIBRARY, 25 Constitution Ave, Rm G-25, 55155. SAN 308-7794. Tel: 651-296-2775. FAX: 651-296-6740. Web Site: www.courts.state.mn.us/library. *Librn*, Marvin Roger Anderson; *Publ Servs*, R Daniel Lunde; *Tech Servs*, Sara Galligan
Founded 1849
Jul 1998-Jun 1999 Income $1,744,000, County $8,500. Mats Exp $291,500, Books $8,000, Per/Ser (Incl. Access Fees) $36,000, Presv $12,000, Micro $8,500, Other Print Mats $227,000. Sal $551,000
Library Holdings: Bk Vols 215,000
Subject Interests: Am law, Minn law
Special Collections: Minnesota Legal Periodical Index; MN Trial Coll; Program to Collect Prof Papers of Retired Justices of Minnesota Supreme Court
Publications: County Law Library Bulletin; Loquitur (newsletter)
Partic in Metronet; MINITEX Library Information Network; OCLC Online Computer Library Center, Inc

G MINNESOTA TRADE & ECONOMIC DEVELOPMENT LIBRARY, 121 Seventh Pl E, 55101-2146. SAN 308-7743. Tel: 651-296-8902. FAX: 651-215-3841. E-Mail: dted@state.mn.us. Web Site: www.dted.state.mn.us. *Librn*, Kristi Burt; E-Mail: kristi.burt@state.mn.us; *Librn*, Pat Fenton; E-Mail: pat.fenton@state.mn.us; Staff 2 (MLS 1, Non-MLS 1)
Founded 1976
Jul 2000-Jun 2001 Income (Main Library Only) Parent Institution $56,000. Mats Exp $56,000, Books $4,000, Per/Ser (Incl. Access Fees) $32,000, Electronic Ref Mat (Incl. Access Fees) $20,000
Library Holdings: Bk Vols 5,500; Bk Titles 5,000; Per Subs 200
Subject Interests: Commerce, Econ develop, Energy
Automation Activity & Vendor Info: (Cataloging) PALS; (ILL) PALS; (OPAC) PALS
Database Vendor: Dialog, Lexis-Nexis, OCLC - First Search
Restriction: Open to public for reference only
Partic in Capital Area Library Consortium; MINITEX Library Information Network; OCLC Online Computer Library Center, Inc

R MOUNT ZION TEMPLE LIBRARY, 1300 Summit Ave, 55105. SAN 308-7808. Tel: 651-698-3881. FAX: 651-698-1263. *Librn*, Robert A Epstein
Founded 1929
Library Holdings: Bk Titles 9,000; Per Subs 16
Subject Interests: Judaica
Special Collections: Children's Coll; Margolis Coll on Jewish Feminism

C NORTHWESTERN COLLEGE, (BRC), Berntsen Resource Center, 3003 Snelling Ave N, 55113. SAN 320-9326. Tel: 651-631-5241, 651-631-5343. FAX: 651-631-5598. *Dir*, Dale Solberg; *Cat, Ref*, Candy Sherry; *Circ*, Becky Schleicher; *Acq, Tech Servs*, Nathan Farley; *Ref, Ser*, Ruth McGuire; *Doc, Ref*, Mark Hail; *Ref*, Linda Rust; *Archivist*, Mary Lou Houda; Staff 9 (MLS 6, Non-MLS 3)
Founded 1902. Enrl 1,500; Fac 65; Highest Degree: Bachelor
Library Holdings: Bk Vols 90,000; Per Subs 1,800
Special Collections: W B Riley Coll, bks, mss, scrapbooks
Automation Activity & Vendor Info: (Circulation) Innovative Interfaces

Inc.
Partic in CLC; Cooperating Libraries in Consortium; Metronet; Minn Interlibr Telecommunication Exchange; OCLC Online Computer Library Center, Inc

L OPPENHEIMER WOLFF & DONNELLY LIBRARY,* 1700 First Bank Bldg, 332 Minnesota Ave, 55101. SAN 308-7824. Tel: 651-223-2522, 651-605-2527. FAX: 651-605-2100. *Dir*, Trudy Busch; Staff 6 (MLS 3, Non-MLS 3)
Library Holdings: Bk Vols 35,000; Bk Titles 16,000; Per Subs 400
Subject Interests: Antitrust law, Corporate law, Int bus law, Minn law, Taxes
Restriction: Staff use only
Partic in Metronet

S ORPHAN VOYAGE & CONCERNED UNITED BIRTH PARENTS, Kamman Dale Libraries, 57 N Dale St, 55102-2228. SAN 326-1255. Tel: 651-224-5160. *Mgr*, Jeanette G Kamman; *Librn*, Clark B Hansen; Tel: 612-722-3630. Subject Specialists: *Genealogy*, Robert J Olson
Founded 1975
1998-1999 Income $26,347. Mats Exp $600, Books $500, Per/Ser (Incl. Access Fees) $100
Library Holdings: Bk Titles 50,000
Subject Interests: Genealogy, History, Religion
Special Collections: Genealogies, bks, directories, historical mat, references; Minn Genealogical Soc; Minn Historical Society; Ramsey & Dakota Agencies Genealogy & History
Special Services - Local Book Scout services; political & government fact gathering
Friends of the Library Group

S THE QUATREFOIL LIBRARY, 1619 Dayton Ave, 55104-6206. SAN 329-1588. Tel: 651-641-0969. Web Site: www.metronet.lib.mn.us/mnlibs/spec0002.htm. *Coll Develop*, Kathy Robbins
Founded 1983
1998-1999 Income $30,000. Mats Exp $1,100, Books $500, Per/Ser (Incl. Access Fees) $600
Library Holdings: Bk Vols 7,500
Publications: Quatrefolio (quarterly)
Serves the gay/lesbian/bisexual/transgender community

GL RAMSEY COUNTY LAW LIBRARY,* 1815 Court House, 55102. SAN 308-7832. Tel: 651-266-8391. FAX: 651-266-8399. *Librn*, Carol Florin; E-Mail: carol.florin@co.ramsey.mn.us
Founded 1936
Library Holdings: Bk Vols 28,000; Per Subs 30
Subject Interests: Minn law
Automation Activity & Vendor Info: (Serials) Inmagic, Inc.
Partic in Metronet; Westlaw

M REGIONS HOSPITAL, Medical Library,* 640 Jackson St, 55101. SAN 308-7883. Tel: 612-221-3607. FAX: 612-292-4023. *In Charge*, Kris Libro
Founded 1940
Library Holdings: Bk Vols 4,000; Per Subs 390
Partic in Twin Cities Biomedical Consortium

S RESOURCES & COUNSELING FOR THE ARTS LIBRARY, 308 Prince St, Ste 270, 55101-1437. SAN 370-6486. Tel: 612-292-4381. FAX: 612-292-4315. E-Mail: info@rc4arts.org. *Exec Dir*, Joan Wells; Staff 5 (Non-MLS 5)
Founded 1978
Library Holdings: Bk Titles 700; Per Subs 20

S ROCK-TENN CO, Technical Center Library,* 2250 Wabash Ave, 55114. SAN 323-4088. Tel: 651-641-4125, 651-641-4938. FAX: 651-641-4197. Web Site: www.rocktenn.com. *Librn*, Melissa Soukup
Library Holdings: Bk Vols 1,500
Subject Interests: Chemistry, Technology

S SAINT PAUL FIRE & MARINE INSURANCE CO CORPORATE LIBRARY,* 385 Washington St, 55102. SAN 308-7875. Tel: 612-310-8226.
Founded 1954
Subject Interests: Bus, Ins, Mgt
Restriction: Staff use only

S ST PAUL PIONEER PRESS LIBRARY, 345 Cedar St, 55101. SAN 308-7867. Tel: 651-228-5557. FAX: 651-222-5010.
Library Holdings: Bk Vols 6,000
Subject Interests: Local history
Special Collections: Historic Photos from 1900-present; Newspaper Clippings from 1946-present
Restriction: Not open to public

P SAINT PAUL PUBLIC LIBRARY, 90 W Fourth St, 55102-1668. SAN 347-9226. Tel: 651-266-7000. Interlibrary Loan Service Tel: 651-292-7008. TDD: 651-298-4184. FAX: 651-292-6660. Web Site: www.stpaul.lib.mn.us. *Dir*, Carole L Williams; Tel: 651-266-7070, E-Mail: carolew@stpaul.lib.mn.us; *Tech Servs*, Francis Galt; Tel: 651-266-7072, E-Mail: frang@stpaul.lib.mn.us; *Tech Coordr*, Doug Guthrie; Tel: 651-266-7078, E-Mail: dougg@stpaul.lib.mn.us; *Ad Servs*, Kathleen Flynn; Tel: 651-266-7024, E-Mail: kathleef@stpaul.lib.mn.us; *Publ Servs*, Linda Wilcox; Tel: 651-266-7071, E-Mail: lindaw@stpaul.lib.mn.us; *Coll Develop*, Judi Devine; Tel: 651-266-7045, E-Mail: judid@stpaul.lib.mn.us; *ILL*, Laura Johnson; E-Mail: lauraj@stpaul.lib.mn.us; *Govt Doc*, Phyllis Kendig; E-Mail: phyllisk@stpaul.lib.mn.us; *Automation Syst Coordr*, Joan Hoover; Tel: 651-266-7055, E-Mail: joanh@stpaul.lib.mn.us; *Commun Relations*, Steve Nelson; Tel: 651-266-7029, E-Mail: stevenel@stpaul.lib.mn.us; *Bkmobile Coordr*, Jim Vogt; Tel: 651-642-0379, Fax: 651-642-0382, E-Mail: jimv@stpaul.lib.mn.us; Staff 37 (MLS 26, Non-MLS 11)
Founded 1882. Pop 266,927; Circ 1,970,475
Jan 1999-Dec 1999 Income (Main Library and Branch Library) $10,950,565, State $233,791, City $10,112,864, Federal $70,887, County $4,636, Other $528,387. Mats Exp $1,173,015. Sal $8,476,196
Library Holdings: Bk Vols 983,131; Per Subs 1,936
Special Collections: City
Automation Activity & Vendor Info: (Cataloging) Innovative Interfaces Inc.; (Circulation) Innovative Interfaces Inc.; (ILL) Innovative Interfaces Inc.; (OPAC) Innovative Interfaces Inc.; (Serials) Innovative Interfaces Inc.
Database Vendor: Dialog, GaleNet, IAC - Info Trac, IAC - SearchBank, OCLC - First Search, ProQuest
Publications: Communique (Newsletter)
Mem of Metrop Libr Serv Agency
Partic in Metronet; Metropolitan Library Service Agency; Minn Interlibr Telecommunication Exchange; OCLC Online Computer Library Center, Inc
Special Services for the Deaf - TDD
Friends of the Library Group
Branches: 13
ARLINGTON HILLS, 1105 Greenbrier St, 55106-2504. SAN 347-9250. Tel: 651-793-3930. FAX: 651-793-3932. Web Site: www.stpaul.lib.mn.us. *Librn*, Karen Kolb Peterson; Tel: 651-793-3931, E-Mail: karenkp@library.stpaul.lib.mn.us; Staff 1 (MLS 1)
Founded 1917. Pop 26,550; Circ 68,334
Library Holdings: Bk Vols 28,800; Per Subs 50
Automation Activity & Vendor Info: (Acquisitions) Innovative Interfaces Inc.; (Cataloging) Innovative Interfaces Inc.; (Circulation) Innovative Interfaces Inc.; (Course Reserve) Innovative Interfaces Inc.; (ILL) Innovative Interfaces Inc.; (Media Booking) Innovative Interfaces Inc.; (OPAC) Innovative Interfaces Inc.
Friends of the Library Group
BOOKMOBILE, 1080 University Ave, 55104. SAN 347-9544. Tel: 651-642-0379. FAX: 651-642-0382. Web Site: www.stpaul.lib.mn.us. *Bkmobile Coordr*, James Vogt; E-Mail: jimv@library.stpaul.lib.mn.us; Staff 1 (MLS 1)
Circ 46,364
Library Holdings: Bk Vols 21,779; Per Subs 30
Automation Activity & Vendor Info: (Acquisitions) Innovative Interfaces Inc.; (Cataloging) Innovative Interfaces Inc.; (Circulation) Innovative Interfaces Inc.; (ILL) Innovative Interfaces Inc.; (OPAC) Innovative Interfaces Inc.; (Serials) Innovative Interfaces Inc.
Friends of the Library Group
HAMLINE - MIDWAY, 1558 W Minnehaha Ave, 55104-1264. SAN 347-9285. Tel: 651-642-0293. FAX: 651-642-0323. Web Site: www.stpaul.lib.mn.us. *In Charge*, Peg Doheny; E-Mail: pegd@library.stpaul.lib.mn.us; Staff 1 (Non-MLS 1)
Founded 1930. Pop 19,656; Circ 73,018
Library Holdings: Bk Vols 27,750; Per Subs 35
Automation Activity & Vendor Info: (Acquisitions) Innovative Interfaces Inc.; (Cataloging) Innovative Interfaces Inc.; (Circulation) Innovative Interfaces Inc.; (ILL) Innovative Interfaces Inc.; (OPAC) Innovative Interfaces Inc.; (Serials) Innovative Interfaces Inc.
Friends of the Library Group
HAYDEN HEIGHTS, 1456 White Bear Ave, 55106-2405. SAN 347-9315. Tel: 651-793-3934. FAX: 651-793-3936. Web Site: www.stpaul.lib.mn.us. *In Charge*, Karen Smith; E-Mail: karens@library.stpaul.lib.mn.us; Staff 2 (Non-MLS 2)
Founded 1979. Pop 26,919; Circ 166,244
Library Holdings: Bk Vols 65,255; Per Subs 131
Automation Activity & Vendor Info: (Acquisitions) Innovative Interfaces Inc.; (Cataloging) Innovative Interfaces Inc.; (Circulation) Innovative Interfaces Inc.; (ILL) Innovative Interfaces Inc.; (OPAC) Innovative Interfaces Inc.; (Serials) Innovative Interfaces Inc.
Friends of the Library Group
HIGHLAND PARK, 1974 Ford Pkwy, 55116-1922. SAN 347-934X. Tel: 651-695-3700. FAX: 651-695-3701. Web Site: www.stpaul.lib.mn.us. *In Charge*, Virginia Stavn; E-Mail: ginnys@library.stpaul.lib.mn.us; Staff 2 (MLS 2)
Founded 1954. Pop 37,781; Circ 354,145
Library Holdings: Bk Vols 94,439; Per Subs 158
Automation Activity & Vendor Info: (Acquisitions) Innovative Interfaces Inc.; (Cataloging) Innovative Interfaces Inc.; (Circulation) Innovative Interfaces Inc.; (ILL) Innovative Interfaces Inc.; (OPAC) Innovative Interfaces Inc.; (Serials) Innovative Interfaces Inc.
Friends of the Library Group
LEXINGTON, 1080 University Ave, 55104-4704. SAN 347-9374. Tel: 651-642-0359. FAX: 651-642-0381. Web Site: www.stpaul.lib.mn.us. *In Charge*, Alice Neve; E-Mail: alicen@stpaul.lib.mn.us; Staff 3 (MLS 3)
Founded 1967. Pop 28,703; Circ 133,014

Library Holdings: Bk Vols 54,258; Per Subs 158
Automation Activity & Vendor Info: (Acquisitions) Innovative Interfaces Inc.; (Cataloging) Innovative Interfaces Inc.; (Circulation) Innovative Interfaces Inc.; (ILL) Innovative Interfaces Inc.; (OPAC) Innovative Interfaces Inc.; (Serials) Innovative Interfaces Inc.
Friends of the Library Group

MERRIAM PARK, 1831 Marshall Ave, 55104-6010. SAN 347-9404. Tel: 651-642-0385. FAX: 651-642-0391. Web Site: www.stpaul.lib.mn.us. *In Charge*, Cheryl Anderson; E-Mail: cheryla@library.stpaul.lib.mn.us; Staff 2 (MLS 2)
Founded 1993. Pop 29,107; Circ 283,473
Library Holdings: Bk Vols 61,837; Per Subs 131
Automation Activity & Vendor Info: (Acquisitions) Innovative Interfaces Inc.; (Cataloging) Innovative Interfaces Inc.; (Circulation) Innovative Interfaces Inc.; (ILL) Innovative Interfaces Inc.; (OPAC) Innovative Interfaces Inc.; (Serials) Innovative Interfaces Inc.
Friends of the Library Group

RICE STREET, 995 Rice St, 55117-4952. SAN 347-9439. Tel: 651-558-2223. FAX: 651-558-2225. Web Site: www.stpaul.lib.mn.us. *Librn*, Carole Brysky; E-Mail: caroleb@library.stpaul.lib.mn.us; Staff 1 (MLS 1)
Founded 1952. Pop 28,041; Circ 81,579
Library Holdings: Bk Vols 34,951; Per Subs 50
Automation Activity & Vendor Info: (Acquisitions) Innovative Interfaces Inc.; (Cataloging) Innovative Interfaces Inc.; (Circulation) Innovative Interfaces Inc.; (ILL) Innovative Interfaces Inc.; (OPAC) Innovative Interfaces Inc.; (Serials) Innovative Interfaces Inc.
Friends of the Library Group

RIVERVIEW, One E George St, 55107-2906. SAN 347-9463. Tel: 651-292-6626. FAX: 651-292-6575. Web Site: www.stpaul.lib.mn.us. *In Charge*, Mary Margaret Sullivan; E-Mail: marymars@library.stpaul.lib.mn.us; Staff 1 (MLS 1)
Founded 1917. Pop 15,312; Circ 64,737
Library Holdings: Bk Vols 25,738; Per Subs 65
Automation Activity & Vendor Info: (Acquisitions) Innovative Interfaces Inc.; (Cataloging) Innovative Interfaces Inc.; (Circulation) Innovative Interfaces Inc.; (ILL) Innovative Interfaces Inc.; (OPAC) Innovative Interfaces Inc.; (Serials) Innovative Interfaces Inc.
Friends of the Library Group

SAINT ANTHONY PARK, 2245 Como Ave, 55108-1719. SAN 347-9498. Tel: 651-642-0411. FAX: 651-642-0358. Web Site: www.stpaul.lib.mn.us. *In Charge*, Rose Ann Foreman; E-Mail: roseannf@library.stpaul.lib.mn.us; Staff 1 (MLS 1)
Founded 1917. Pop 6,485; Circ 30,154
Library Holdings: Bk Vols 35,482; Per Subs 80
Automation Activity & Vendor Info: (Acquisitions) Innovative Interfaces Inc.; (Cataloging) Innovative Interfaces Inc.; (Circulation) Innovative Interfaces Inc.; (ILL) Innovative Interfaces Inc.; (OPAC) Innovative Interfaces Inc.; (Serials) Innovative Interfaces Inc.
Friends of the Library Group

SKYWAY, 201 Norwest Ctr, 56 E Sixth St, 55101. SAN 328-8005. Tel: 651-292-7141. FAX: 651-292-6688. Web Site: www.stpaul.lib.mn.us. *In Charge*, Janet Van Tassel; E-Mail: janetv@stpaul.lib.mn.us
Founded 1986. Pop 25,308; Circ 41,654
Library Holdings: Bk Vols 8,073
Automation Activity & Vendor Info: (Acquisitions) Innovative Interfaces Inc.; (Cataloging) Innovative Interfaces Inc.; (Circulation) Innovative Interfaces Inc.; (ILL) Innovative Interfaces Inc.; (OPAC) Innovative Interfaces Inc.; (Serials) Innovative Interfaces Inc.
Friends of the Library Group

SUN RAY, 2105 Wilson Ave, 55119-4033. SAN 347-9528. Tel: 651-292-6640. FAX: 651-292-6578. Web Site: www.stpaul.lib.mn.us. *In Charge*, Kathleen Heiderich; E-Mail: kathyh@library.stpaul.lib.mn.us; Staff 2 (MLS 2)
Founded 1970. Pop 23,789; Circ 166,821
Library Holdings: Bk Vols 77,784; Per Subs 155
Automation Activity & Vendor Info: (Acquisitions) Innovative Interfaces Inc.; (Cataloging) Innovative Interfaces Inc.; (Circulation) Innovative Interfaces Inc.; (ILL) Innovative Interfaces Inc.; (OPAC) Innovative Interfaces Inc.; (Serials) Innovative Interfaces Inc.
Friends of the Library Group

WEST 7TH POPULAR, 265 Oneida, 55102-2883. SAN 322-6344. Tel: 651-298-5516. FAX: 651-292-6736. Web Site: www.stpaul.lib.mn.us. *In Charge*, John Ohr; E-Mail: johno@stpaul.mn.us
Founded 1984. Pop 4,584; Circ 39,770
Library Holdings: Bk Vols 14,704; Per Subs 22
Automation Activity & Vendor Info: (Acquisitions) Innovative Interfaces Inc.; (Cataloging) Innovative Interfaces Inc.; (Circulation) Innovative Interfaces Inc.; (ILL) Innovative Interfaces Inc.; (OPAC) Innovative Interfaces Inc.; (Serials) Innovative Interfaces Inc.
Friends of the Library Group

Bookmobiles: 1

J SAINT PAUL TECHNICAL COLLEGE LIBRARY,* 235 Marshall Ave, 55102. SAN 308-7905. Tel: 651-221-1410. FAX: 651-221-1416. *Librn*, Susan Collett; Staff 1 (MLS 1)
Founded 1966. Enrl 3,000; Fac 170
Library Holdings: Bk Vols 12,000; Per Subs 200
Partic in Minn Interlibr Telecommunication Exchange

S SCIENCE MUSEUM OF MINNESOTA, Louis S Headley Memorial Library, 120 W Kellogg Blvd, 55102. SAN 308-793X. Tel: 651-221-9435, 651-221-9488. FAX: 651-221-4777. Web Site: www.smm.org. *In Charge*, Lori Benson; E-Mail: benson@smm.org
Founded 1930
Library Holdings: Bk Vols 25,000; Per Subs 100
Subject Interests: Anthropology, Earth science, Natural history
Special Collections: (Kate Farnham Memorial Coll); Birds; Egypt (Ames Coll); General Science (Museum Publications); Geology (US Geological Survey)
Restriction: Open to public for reference only

S 3M LIBRARY & INFORMATION SERVICES, 3M Center Bldg 201-1S-12a, 55144-1000. SAN 347-9560. Tel: 651-736-1943. FAX: 651-736-0902. *Dir*, Barbara J Peterson; *Coll Develop*, Thea Welsh; Tel: 651-736-0100; Staff 67 (MLS 45, Non-MLS 22)
Library Holdings: Bk Vols 98,000; Bk Titles 67,000; Per Subs 1,600
Automation Activity & Vendor Info: (OPAC) DRA; (Serials) DRA
Publications: 3M Union List of Serials
Partic in Beilstein; Dialog Corporation; OCLC Online Computer Library Center, Inc; Questal Orbit; STN
Information Services is a unified system which includes the seven libraries as well as Systems Services (computer support), a centralized technical service function & Current Awareness Service

UNITED STATES ARMY

A CORPS OF ENGINEERS, SAINT PAUL DISTRICT TECHNICAL LIBRARY, 190 Fifth St E, 55101-1638. SAN 347-9854. Tel: 651-290-5680. FAX: 651-290-5256. *Librn*, Jean M Schmidt; E-Mail: jean.m.schmidt@usace.army.mil
Founded 1972
Library Holdings: Bk Vols 4,884; Per Subs 350
Subject Interests: DM construction, Engineering, Environmental studies, Hydrol, Military hist, Water resources
Special Collections: Annual Reports of the Chief of Engineers, US Army
Partic in Dialog Corporation; Fedlink; OCLC Online Computer Library Center, Inc

GL US COURTS LIBRARY, Eighth Circuit Library, 541 Federal Court Bldg, 316 N Robert St, 55101. SAN 308-7964. Tel: 651-848-1320. FAX: 651-848-1325. Web Site: www.ca8.uscourts.gov. *Librn*, Nancee Halling; Tel: 651-848-1321, E-Mail: nancee_halling@mnd.uscourts.gov; Staff 2 (MLS 1, Non-MLS 1)
Library Holdings: Bk Vols 20,000
Automation Activity & Vendor Info: (Cataloging) SIRSI; (Circulation) SIRSI

C UNIVERSITY OF MINNESOTA, Saint Paul Campus Libraries,* Magrath Library, 1984 Buford Ave, 55108. SAN 347-9889. Tel: 612-624-2233. Interlibrary Loan Service Tel: 612-624-3793. FAX: 612-624-9245. E-Mail: m.mort@tc.umn.edu. Web Site: www.lib.umn.edu. *ILL*, Mary Mortenson
Library Holdings: Bk Vols 398,600; Per Subs 3,307
Automation Activity & Vendor Info: (Acquisitions) NOTIS; (Cataloging) NOTIS; (Serials) NOTIS
Partic in Midwest Region Libr Network; MINITEX Library Information Network; OCLC Online Computer Library Center, Inc; Research Libraries Group, Inc
Friends of the Library Group
Departmental Libraries:

ENTOMOLOGY, FISHERIES & WILDLIFE LIBRARY, 375 Hodson Hall, 55108. SAN 347-9978. Tel: 612-624-9288. *Librn*, Loralee Kerr; Staff 1 (MLS 1)
Library Holdings: Bk Vols 74,998
Friends of the Library Group

FORESTRY LIBRARY, B50 Natural Resources Admin Bldg, 55108. SAN 348-0003. Tel: 612-624-3222. *Librn*, Jean Albrecht; Staff 1 (MLS 1)
Library Holdings: Bk Vols 54,295
Publications: Social Sciences in Forestry; Trails Bibliography; Urban Bibliography
Friends of the Library Group

PLANT PATHOLOGY LIBRARY, 395 Borlaug Hall, 55108. SAN 348-0038. Tel: 612-625-9777. Web Site: plant.lib.umn.edu. *Head of Libr*, Melissa Pauna; E-Mail: pauna001@tc.umn.edu; *Librn*, Katherine Allen; Tel: 612-624-4751, E-Mail: kallen@tc.umn.edu; Staff 1 (Non-MLS 1)
Library Holdings: Bk Vols 11,045; Per Subs 85
Friends of the Library Group

CM VETERINARY MEDICAL LIBRARY, 450 Veterinary Science, 55108. SAN 348-0062. Tel: 612-624-4281. FAX: 612-624-9782. Web Site: www.stp.lib.umn.edu/vetmed. *Librn*, Livija Carlson; Tel: 612-624-3078, E-Mail: l-carl@tc.umn.edu; Staff 3 (MLS 1, Non-MLS 2)
Enrl 372; Fac 87; Highest Degree: Doctorate
Jul 1998-Jun 1999 Mats Exp $272,376, Books $45,615, Per/Ser (Incl.

Access Fees) $226,760. (Prof $57,000)
Library Holdings: Bk Vols 83,775; Per Subs 939
Subject Interests: Animal behavior, Animal welfare
Friends of the Library Group

CR UNIVERSITY OF SAINT THOMAS, O'Shaughnessy-Frey Library Center, 2115 Summit Ave, Mail No 5004, 55105. SAN 308-7581. Tel: 651-962-5014. Circulation Tel: 651-962-5494. Reference Tel: 651-962-5001. FAX: 651-962-5460. Web Site: www.lib.stthomas.edu. *Dir*, Daniel Ross Gjelten; Tel: 651-962-5005, E-Mail: drgjelten@stthomas.edu; *Ref*, Marianne Hageman; *ILL*, Faith E Bonitz; Tel: 651-962-5405, E-Mail: febonitz@stthomas.edu; *Spec Coll*, John B Davenport; *Per*, Greg D Bull; Tel: 651-962-5408, E-Mail: gdbull@stthomas.edu; *Coll Develop*, Bob Pillow; *Archivist*, Ann Kenne; Tel: 651-962-5468, E-Mail: amkenne@stthomas.edu
Founded 1885. Enrl 10,123; Fac 704; Highest Degree: Doctorate
Jul 1999-Jun 2000 Mats Exp $1,012,912, Books $289,780, Per/Ser (Incl. Access Fees) $446,311, Presv $29,120, Micro $33,256, Electronic Ref Mat (Incl. Access Fees) $214,445. (Prof $745,083)
Library Holdings: Bk Vols 329,871; Bk Titles 228,366; Per Subs 1,805
Subject Interests: Business, Education, Literature, Medicine, Psychology
Special Collections: Belloc-Chesterton; Celtic Coll; French Memoir Coll; Luxembourgian Coll; University Archives
Automation Activity & Vendor Info: (Acquisitions) epixtech, inc.; (Cataloging) epixtech, inc.; (Circulation) epixtech, inc.
Database Vendor: CARL, Ebsco - EbscoHost, IAC - Info Trac, Innovative Interfaces INN - View, Lexis-Nexis, OCLC - First Search, ProQuest, Silverplatter Information Inc., Wilson - Wilson Web
Partic in Coop Librs in Consortium; MINITEX Library Information Network; OCLC Online Computer Library Center, Inc
Departmental Libraries:
ARCHBISHOP IRELAND MEMORIAL LIBRARY, 2260 Summit Ave, Mail No IRL, 55105. SAN 377-0214. Tel: 651-962-5450. Reference Tel: 651-962-5453. FAX: 612-962-5460. Web Site: www.lib.stthomas.edu/ireland. *Dir*, Mary E Martin; Tel: 651-962-5451, E-Mail: memartin@stthomas.edu; *Acq*, Judy Quick; *Per*, Betsy J Polakowski; Tel: 651-962-5452, E-Mail: ejpolakowski@stthomas.edu; *Circ*, Judith A Michalski; Tel: 651-962-5456, E-Mail: jamichalski@stthomas.edu; *Ref*, Jan Malcheski; E-Mail: j9malcheski@stthomas.edu; *Coll Develop*, Margaret Mary Bannigan; Staff 5 (MLS 2, Non-MLS 3)
Founded 1894. Enrl 150; Fac 24; Highest Degree: Doctorate
Jul 1999-Jun 2000 Income (Main Library Only) $383,305. Mats Exp $81,110, Books $49,308, Per/Ser (Incl. Access Fees) $22,265, Presv $5,000, Electronic Ref Mat (Incl. Access Fees) $4,537. (Prof $163,453)
Library Holdings: Bk Vols 85,430; Per Subs 426
Subject Interests: Theology
Special Collections: Belloc-Chesterton; Celtic Coll; French Memoir Coll; Luxembourgian Coll; University Archives
Automation Activity & Vendor Info: (Cataloging) epixtech, inc.; (Circulation) epixtech, inc.; (Serials) epixtech, inc.
Partic in Coop Librs in Consortium; Minnesota Theological Library Association; OCLC Online Computer Library Center, Inc
MINNEAPOLIS CAMPUS, MPL-104, 1000 LaSalle Ave, Minneapolis, 55403. SAN 377-0230. Tel: 612-962-4642. FAX: 651-962-4648. Web Site: www.lib.stthomas.edu/mpls.
1997-1998 Mats Exp $52,863, Books $31,692, Per/Ser (Incl. Access Fees) $17,752, Micro $3,419. Sal $133,150 (Prof $92,075)
Library Holdings: Bk Vols 5,529

CL WILLIAM MITCHELL COLLEGE OF LAW, Warren E Burger Library, 871 Summit Ave, 55105. SAN 308-7980. Tel: 651-290-6333. Reference Tel: 651-290-6424. FAX: 651-290-6318. E-Mail: reference@wmitchell.edu. Web Site: www.wmitchell.edu/library/. *Dir*, Ann L Bateson; *Acq*, Ann Poulter; E-Mail: apoulter@wmitchell.edu; Staff 16 (MLS 8, Non-MLS 8)
Founded 1958. Enrl 1,000
1999-2000 Income $1,967,462, Federal $37,447, Parent Institution $1,930,015. Mats Exp $913,490, Books $252,318, Per/Ser (Incl. Access Fees) $87,850, Presv $15,752, Micro $43,701, Other Print Mats $432,557, Electronic Ref Mat (Incl. Access Fees) $81,312. Sal $672,879 (Prof $393,280)
Library Holdings: Bk Vols 305,891; Bk Titles 102,916; Per Subs 1,178
Subject Interests: Law, Taxation
Automation Activity & Vendor Info: (Acquisitions) Innovative Interfaces Inc.; (Cataloging) Innovative Interfaces Inc.; (Circulation) Innovative Interfaces Inc.; (Course Reserve) Innovative Interfaces Inc.; (OPAC) Innovative Interfaces Inc.; (Serials) Innovative Interfaces Inc.
Database Vendor: GaleNet, IAC - Info Trac, IAC - SearchBank, Innovative Interfaces INN - View, OCLC - First Search, OVID Technologies, Wilson - Wilson Web
Partic in MINITEX Library Information Network; OCLC Online Computer Library Center, Inc

L WINTHROP & WEINSTINE, Law Library, 3200 Minnesota World Trade Ctr, 30 E Seventh St, 55101. SAN 372-2872. Tel: 651-290-8450. FAX: 651-292-9347. *Librn*, Nancy Evans; E-Mail: nevans@winthrop.com; *Librn*, Ann Turner; Staff 2 (MLS 1, Non-MLS 1)
Library Holdings: Bk Vols 15,400; Per Subs 217
Restriction: Private library

S WORKING OPPORTUNITIES FOR WOMEN, Resource Center Library,* 1295 Bandana Blvd N, Ste 110, 55108. SAN 327-8239. Tel: 651-647-9961. FAX: 651-647-1424. *Dir*, Yvette Oldendorf
Library Holdings: Bk Vols 500

SAINT PETER

C GUSTAVUS ADOLPHUS COLLEGE, Folke Bernadotte Memorial Library, 800 W College Ave, 56082. SAN 348-0097. Tel: 507-933-7556. Interlibrary Loan Service Tel: 507-933-7564. Circulation Tel: 507-933-7558. Reference Tel: 507-933-7567. FAX: 507-933-6292. E-Mail: folke@gustavus.edu. Web Site: www.gac.edu/oncampus/academics/Resources/Library/index.htm. *Head of Libr*, Barbara Fister; Tel: 507-933-7553, E-Mail: fister@gustvus.edu; *Tech Servs*, Dong-fa Zhou; Tel: 507-933-7554, E-Mail: dzhou@gustavus.edu; *Librn*, Michelle Anderson; Tel: 507-933-7563, E-Mail: manders2@gustavus.edu; *Reader Servs*, Howard Cohrt; Tel: 507-933-7566, E-Mail: hcohrt@gustavus.edu; *Coll Develop, Govt Doc*, Daniel Mollner; Tel: 507-933-7569, E-Mail: dmollner@gustavus.edu; *Archivist*, Michael Haeuser; Tel: 507-933-7572, E-Mail: haeuser@gustavus.edu; *ILL*, Kathleen Martin; Tel: 507-933-7564, E-Mail: kmartin@gustavus.edu. Subject Specialists: *Aviation*, Kathleen Martin; *Electrical*, Kathleen Martin; *Electronic resources*, Michelle Anderson; *Machining*, Kathleen Martin; Staff 16 (MLS 6, Non-MLS 10)
Founded 1862. Enrl 2,516; Fac 193; Highest Degree: Bachelor
Jun 1999-May 2000 Income $1,508,051. Mats Exp $487,433. Sal $704,226 (Prof $328,808)
Library Holdings: Bk Vols 267,677; Bk Titles 228,513; Per Subs 1,061
Special Collections: Gene Basset Political Cartoons; Hasselquist International Studies; Heitzig Coll; Lutheran Church Archives; Mettetal Record Coll; Scandinavian American; Selma Lagerloff (Nils Sahil Coll); Selma Lagerloff (Nils Sahil Coll), bks, pamphlets; Swedish American (Historical Archives Coll)
Automation Activity & Vendor Info: (Circulation) PALS; (Course Reserve) PALS; (ILL) PALS; (OPAC) PALS
Database Vendor: CARL, Dialog, GaleNet, Lexis-Nexis, OCLC - First Search, OVID Technologies, Silverplatter Information Inc.
Partic in MINITEX Library Information Network; OCLC Online Computer Library Center, Inc
Friends of the Library Group

S NICOLLET COUNTY HISTORICAL SOCIETY, Tready Site History Center Museum & Archives Library, 1851 N Minnesota Ave, 56001. SAN 325-500X. Tel: 507-934-2160. FAX: 507-934-0172. E-Mail: weal@mnic.net. Web Site: www.nchs.st-peter.mn.us. *Curator*, Jessica Potter; E-Mail: jessica@mnic.net; *Asst Dir*, Reta M Casper
Library Holdings: Bk Vols 500; Bk Titles 300
Subject Interests: Genealogy, History, Nicholette County, Southern Minn
Special Collections: County & township records
Database Vendor: OCLC - First Search
Partic in Smile

P SAINT PETER PUBLIC LIBRARY, 101 W Nassau St, 56082-2526. SAN 347-4429. Tel: 507-931-1228. FAX: 507-931-4917. *Head Librn*, Doug Wolfe; E-Mail: dwolfe@tds.lib.mn.us; Staff 4 (MLS 1, Non-MLS 3)
Library Holdings: Bk Vols 21,025; Per Subs 127
Friends of the Library Group

M SAINT PETER REGIONAL TREATMENT CENTER LIBRARIES,* 100 Freeman Dr, 56082. SAN 348-0151. Tel: 507-931-7248.; Staff 5 (MLS 1, Non-MLS 4)
Founded 1878
Library Holdings: Bk Vols 12,600; Bk Titles 12,000; Per Subs 25
Subject Interests: Alcoholic dependents, Bks in gen for retarded readers, Drug dependents, Media in gen for retarded readers, Mentally ill patients
Partic in Nat Libr of Med; S Cent Minn Interlibr Exchange, Smile
Branches:
MINNESOTA SECURITY HOSPITAL LIBRARY, 2100 Sheppard Dr, 56082. SAN 348-0178. Tel: 507-931-7137. *Dir*, Robert Idso
ELIZABETH SEAQUIST PATIENTS LIBRARY, Saint Peter Regional Treatment Ctr, 100 Freeman Dr, 56082. SAN 348-0240. Tel: 507-931-7248. *Librn*, Ron Riley

R TRINITY LUTHERAN PARISH LIBRARY, 511 S Fifth St, 56082. SAN 308-7999. Tel: 507-931-4786. FAX: 507-934-4562. *In Charge*, Eric Natwick
Founded 1959
Library Holdings: Bk Vols 2,500; Per Subs 12
Subject Interests: Bible, Christian life, Martin Luther, Psychology, Relig studies
Friends of the Library Group

SANDSTONE

P SANDSTONE PUBLIC LIBRARY,* PO Box 599, 55072-0599. SAN 347-2620. Tel: 320-245-2270. E-Mail: samail@ecrl.lib.mn.us. *Librn*, Susan Thue
Pop 6,582; Circ 45,250

Library Holdings: Bk Vols 7,000; Per Subs 40
Mem of East Central Regional Library
Branch of East Central Regional Library
Friends of the Library Group

SAUK CENTRE

P BRYANT (SAUK CENTRE) PUBLIC LIBRARY,* 430 Main St, 56378. SAN 308-8006. Tel: 320-352-3016. FAX: 320-352-3016. Web Site: www.griver.org. *In Charge*, Karen Pundsack
Founded 1878. Pop 6,367; Circ 46,559
Library Holdings: Bk Vols 22,000; Per Subs 42
Special Collections: James Hendryx; Sinclair Lewis
Mem of Great River Regional Library
Open Mon & Fri 12-5, Tues & Thurs 2-8, Wed 10-1 & 2-5, Fri 12-5, Sat 10-1
Friends of the Library Group

SAVAGE

P SCOTT COUNTY LIBRARY SYSTEM, 13090 Alabama Ave S, 55378-1479. SAN 348-0305. Tel: 612-707-1760. FAX: 612-707-1775. *Dir*, Janet Williams
Founded 1969. Pop 81,990; Circ 618,330
2000-2000 Mats Exp Books $173,212
Library Holdings: Bk Vols 144,386
Automation Activity & Vendor Info: (Circulation) DRA
Mem of Metrop Libr Serv Agency
Friends of the Library Group
Branches: 7
BELLE PLAINE COMMUNITY LIBRARY, 125 W Main St, Belle Plaine, 56011-1245. SAN 348-033X. Tel: 612-873-6767. FAX: 612-873-6767. *Librn*, Georgine Gansen
Library Holdings: Bk Vols 13,409
JORDAN PUBLIC LIBRARY, 230 S Broadway, Jordan, 55352-1508. SAN 348-0364. Tel: 612-492-2500. FAX: 612-492-2500. *Librn*, Pat Mitton
Library Holdings: Bk Vols 15,677
NEW MARKET PUBLIC LIBRARY, 50 Church St, New Market, 55054-9999. SAN 348-0399. Tel: 612-461-3460. FAX: 612-461-3460. *Librn*, Karen Peterson
Library Holdings: Bk Vols 6,156
NEW PRAGUE PUBLIC LIBRARY, 400 E Main St, New Prague, 56071-2429. SAN 348-0429. Tel: 612-758-2391. FAX: 612-758-2391. *Librn*, Lori Weldon
Library Holdings: Bk Vols 21,980
PRIOR LAKE COMMUNITY LIBRARY, 16210 Eagle Creek Ave SE, Prior Lake, 55372-9202. SAN 348-0453. Tel: 612-447-3375. FAX: 612-447-3375. *Librn*, Hilary Toren
Library Holdings: Bk Vols 26,595
SAVAGE PUBLIC LIBRARY, 13090 Alabama Ave S, 55378. SAN 348-0488. Tel: 612-707-1770. FAX: 612-707-1775. *Librn*, Vanessa Birdsey
Library Holdings: Bk Vols 17,964
SHAKOPEE PUBLIC LIBRARY, 235 S Lewis St, Shakopee, 55379. SAN 348-0518. Tel: 612-445-3936. FAX: 612-445-3938. *Librn*, Barbara Hegfors
Library Holdings: Bk Vols 35,925

SHOREVIEW

P RAMSEY COUNTY PUBLIC LIBRARY, 4570 N Victoria St, 55126. SAN 347-8025. Tel: 651-486-2200. FAX: 651-486-2220. *Dir*, Marianne L Roos; *Dir Libr Serv*, Alice-Jo Carlson; Tel: 651-486-2201, E-Mail: acarlson@ramsey.lib.mn.us; *ILL, Tech Servs*, Judy Guidarelli; *Coll Develop*, Faye Herold; Staff 160 (MLS 50, Non-MLS 110)
Founded 1951. Pop 217,566; Circ 2,570,624
Library Holdings: Bk Vols 550,000; Per Subs 2,500
Subject Interests: State geog, State hist
Automation Activity & Vendor Info: (Acquisitions) epixtech, inc.; (Circulation) epixtech, inc.
Partic in Metronet; Metropolitan Library Service Agency; MINITEX Library Information Network
Friends of the Library Group
Branches: 7
ARDEN HILLS BRANCH, 1941 W County Rd E-2, Arden Hills, 55112-2895. SAN 347-805X. Tel: 612-628-6831. FAX: 612-628-6833. Web Site: www.ramsey.lib.mn.us. *Librn*, Faye Herold; Staff 10 (MLS 4, Non-MLS 6)
Library Holdings: Bk Vols 71,240
Friends of the Library Group
HEADQUARTERS LIBRARY (ROSEVILLE), 2180 N Hamline Ave, Roseville, 55113-4241. SAN 347-8122. Tel: 651-628-6803. FAX: 651-628-6818. *Librn*, Lynn Wyman
Library Holdings: Bk Vols 262,638
Friends of the Library Group
MAPLEWOOD BRANCH, 1670 Beam Ave, Maplewood, 55109. SAN 347-8084. Tel: 651-704-2033. FAX: 651-704-2038. *Librn*, Judy Siegle
Library Holdings: Bk Vols 102,638
Friends of the Library Group
MOUNDS VIEW BRANCH, 2576 Hwy 10, Mounds View, 55112-4032. SAN 370-1298. Tel: 612-717-3272. FAX: 612-717-3275. *In Charge*, Therese Sonnek
Library Holdings: Bk Vols 62,261
Friends of the Library Group
NORTH SAINT PAUL BRANCH, 2640 E Seventh Ave, North Saint Paul, 55109-3199. SAN 347-8114. Tel: 651-704-2040. FAX: 651-704-2043. *Mgr Libr*, Karen Byerly; *Librn*, Audrey Lerdahl
Library Holdings: Bk Vols 91,636
Friends of the Library Group
SHOREVIEW BRANCH, 4570 N Victoria St, 55126. SAN 373-5184. Tel: 651-486-2300. FAX: 651-486-2313. Web Site: www.ramsey.lib.mn.us. *Librn*, Sandra Walsh
Library Holdings: Bk Vols 85,022
Friends of the Library Group
WHITE BEAR LAKE BRANCH, 4698 Clark Ave, White Bear Lake, 55110-3415. SAN 347-8149. Tel: 651-407-5302. FAX: 651-407-5305. *Librn*, Eilenne Boder
Library Holdings: Bk Vols 116,089
Friends of the Library Group

SILVER BAY

P SILVER BAY PUBLIC LIBRARY,* 9 Davis Dr, 55614-1318. SAN 308-8014. Tel: 218-226-4331. FAX: 218-226-3140. *Librn*, Julie Billings
Founded 1958. Pop 2,900; Circ 44,184
Library Holdings: Bk Titles 28,000; Per Subs 20
Special Collections: Minnesota History (E W Davis Coll)
Automation Activity & Vendor Info: (Acquisitions) CARL; (Cataloging) CARL; (Serials) CARL
Mem of Arrowhead Library System
Open Mon-Thurs 10-8 & Fri 10-6

SLAYTON

P SLAYTON PUBLIC LIBRARY,* 2451 Broadway Ave, 56172. SAN 308-8022. Tel: 507-836-8778. FAX: 503-836-6301. E-Mail: larson1@slayton.lib.mn.us. *Librn*, Sharyl Larson
Founded 1946. Pop 2,451; Circ 30,573
Library Holdings: Bk Vols 22,000; Per Subs 50
Special Collections: Song Books
Mem of Plum Creek Library System

SLEEPY EYE

P DYCKMAN FREE LIBRARY, 345 W Main, 56085-1331. SAN 308-8030. Tel: 507-794-7655. *Librn*, Gail Christensen; *Asst Librn*, Carole Plahn; Staff 1 (MLS 1)
Founded 1900. Pop 5,000; Circ 34,500
Jan 1999-Dec 1999 Income $94,350, City $80,000, County $12,500, Locally Generated Income $1,850. Mats Exp $9,650, Books $8,000, Per/Ser (Incl. Access Fees) $500, Other Print Mats $1,150. Sal $50,200 (Prof $27,500)
Library Holdings: Bk Vols 23,500; Per Subs 32
Special Collections: Local History Artifacts
Automation Activity & Vendor Info: (Circulation) PALS; (ILL) PALS; (OPAC) PALS
Database Vendor: OCLC - First Search
Partic in Traverse Des Sioux Libr Syst

SOUTH SAINT PAUL

S DAKOTA COUNTY HISTORICAL SOCIETY, Research Center, 130 Third Ave N, 55075. SAN 329-7268. Tel: 651-451-6260. FAX: 651-552-7265. E-Mail: dchs@mtn.org. *Assoc Dir, Res*, Rebecca Snyder; Staff 3 (Non-MLS 3)
Founded 1935
2000-2001 Mats Exp $2,000, Books $500, Per/Ser (Incl. Access Fees) $500, Micro $1,000
Library Holdings: Bk Titles 600; Per Subs 20
Subject Interests: Dakota County, History, Minn
Publications: Census Transcription; Over the Years; Society Happenings (newsletter)

P SOUTH SAINT PAUL PUBLIC LIBRARY, 106 Third Ave N, 55075-2098. SAN 308-8057. Tel: 651-554-3240. TDD: 651-554-3240. FAX: 651-554-3241. Web Site: www.southstpaul.org/library. *Dir*, Jane Kroschel; E-Mail: kroschel@dakota.lib.mn.us; Staff 3 (MLS 3)
Founded 1922. Pop 20,000; Circ 182,000
Jan 2000-Dec 2000 Income $495,406. Mats Exp $56,500, Books $50,000, Per/Ser (Incl. Access Fees) $6,000, Presv $500. Sal $292,000
Library Holdings: Bk Titles 81,000; Per Subs 178
Subject Interests: Original art, State artists
Automation Activity & Vendor Info: (Cataloging) epixtech, inc.; (Circulation) epixtech, inc.
Database Vendor: epixtech, inc., IAC - Info Trac, OCLC - First Search,

ProQuest
Mem of Metrop Libr Serv Agency
Special Services for the Deaf - High interest/low vocabulary books; TDD
Adult Basic Education Coll; Active Adopt-a-Shelf Group

SPICER

P SPICER LIBRARY,* 198 Manitoba, PO Box 160, 56288-0160. SAN 348-1352. Tel: 320-796-5560. FAX: 320-796-3013. E-Mail: sheilab@spicer.lib.mn.us. *Librn*, Sheila Bosch
Pop 1,164; Circ 19,660
Jul 1999-Jun 2000 Income $26,400, County $20,000, Locally Generated Income $200, Other $6,200. Mats Exp $9,390, Books $8,710, Per/Ser (Incl. Access Fees) $650, Presv $30. Sal $11,770
Library Holdings: Bk Vols 9,200; Per Subs 17
Mem of Pioneerland Library System
Open Tues, Thurs & Fri 1-5, Wed 3-7, Sat 9-1
Friends of the Library Group

SPRING VALLEY

P SPRING VALLEY PUBLIC LIBRARY, 201 S Broadway, 55975-1301. SAN 308-8065. Tel: 507-346-2100. FAX: 507-346-1908. *Librn*, Vicki M Tate; E-Mail: vickit@selco.lib.mn.us
Founded 1901. Circ 46,000
Jan 2000-Dec 2000 Income $92,000, City $65,000, County $20,000, Locally Generated Income $7,000. Mats Exp $14,500, Books $12,500, Per/Ser (Incl. Access Fees) $2,000. Sal $39,000
Library Holdings: Bk Vols 19,600; Per Subs 50
Automation Activity & Vendor Info: (Acquisitions) DRA; (Cataloging) DRA; (Circulation) DRA; (Course Reserve) DRA; (ILL) DRA; (Media Booking) DRA; (OPAC) DRA; (Serials) DRA
Mem of Selco
Partic in SE Libr Coop
Friends of the Library Group

SPRINGFIELD

P SPRINGFIELD PUBLIC LIBRARY, 120 N Cass, 56087-1506. SAN 308-8073. Tel: 507-723-3510. FAX: 507-723-6422, 507-723-6780. E-Mail: libtbs@tds.lib.mn.us.
Founded 1932. Pop 2,303; Circ 36,851
1999-2000 Income $146,601, State $10,548, City $75,225, County $12,300, Locally Generated Income $7,528, Other $41,000. Mats Exp $23,675, Books $18,521, AV Equip $1,389, Other Print Mats $3,396, Electronic Ref Mat (Incl. Access Fees) $369. Sal $67,103 (Prof $26,400)
Library Holdings: Bk Vols 30,000; Bk Titles 25,000; Per Subs 100
Subject Interests: Local history
Publications: Booklist; Library Journal
Mem of Traverse Des Sioux Library System
Partic in OCLC Online Computer Library Center, Inc

STAPLES

P STAPLES PUBLIC LIBRARY,* 611 Iowa Ave NE, 56479. SAN 308-8081. Tel: 218-894-1401. FAX: 218-894-1401. Web Site: www.griver.org. *In Charge*, Viretta Neidhardt
Founded 1909. Pop 2,999; Circ 56,816
Library Holdings: Bk Vols 14,730; Per Subs 58
Mem of Great River Regional Library
Open Mon & Thurs 12-5 & 6-8, Tues 12-6, Wed 10-1 & 2-6, Fri 12-5, Sat 10-1

STEWARTVILLE

P STEWARTVILLE PUBLIC LIBRARY,* 110 Second St SE, 55976-1306. SAN 308-809X. Tel: 507-533-4902, 507-533-9557. *Librn*, Glynis Sturm; *Librn*, Patricia A Johnson; *Asst Librn*, Debra Lofgren
Founded 1938. Pop 6,519
Library Holdings: Bk Vols 20,000; Per Subs 72
Mem of Olmstead County Libr Syst
Partic in SE Libr Coop
Open Mon 12-8pm, Tues 10am-6pm, Wed 12-6pm, Thurs 10am-8pm, Fri 12-5pm & Sat 9am-1pm
Friends of the Library Group

STILLWATER

P STILLWATER PUBLIC LIBRARY,* 223 N Fourth St, 55082. SAN 308-8111. Tel: 651-439-1675. FAX: 651-439-0012. *Dir*, Lynne Bertalmio; *Asst Dir*, Carolyn Blocher; *Ref*, Jan Brewer; *Ch Servs*, Gail Nordstrom
Pop 16,000; Circ 245,500
Library Holdings: Bk Vols 65,000; Bk Titles 63,500; Per Subs 280
Subject Interests: Local history
Publications: Shelf Life
Partic in Metropolitan Library Service Agency

SWANVILLE

P SWANVILLE LIBRARY, 213 DeGraff St, PO Box 295, 56382-0295. SAN 347-8742. Tel: 320-547-2346. FAX: 320-547-2346. Web Site: www.griver.org. *In Charge*, Diane Borgert
Pop 2,074; Circ 17,377
Library Holdings: Bk Vols 7,278; Per Subs 26
Mem of Great River Regional Library
Open Mon 9-12 & 2-6, Wed 2-8, Fri 2-6, Sat 9am-12pm

TAYLORS FALLS

P TAYLORS FALLS PUBLIC LIBRARY,* PO Box 195, 55084-9998. SAN 325-1608. Tel: 651-465-6905. *Librn*, Marilyn Rimestad
Founded 1871. Pop 700; Circ 2,499
Library Holdings: Bk Titles 11,680
Special Collections: History of Taylors Falls Colls, bks; The St Croix River Valley Coll, bks

THIEF RIVER FALLS

J NORTHLAND COMMUNITY & TECHNICAL COLLEGE LIBRARY, 1101 Hwy One E, 56701. SAN 308-812X. Tel: 218-681-0756. FAX: 218-681-0724. Web Site: www.northland.cc.mn.us/library. *Librn*, Judith Whaley; E-Mail: jwhaley@nctc.mnscu.edu
Founded 1965. Enrl 1,350
Library Holdings: Bk Vols 23,000; Bk Titles 19,000; Per Subs 175
Mem of Northern Lights Libr Network
Partic in MINITEX Library Information Network; Minn Interlibr Telecommunication Exchange; MPALS; OCLC Online Computer Library Center, Inc

P NORTHWEST REGIONAL LIBRARY, 210 LaBree Ave N, 56701. SAN 348-0542. Tel: 218-681-1066. FAX: 218-681-1095. Web Site: www.nlln.org/aurora/nwrl. *Dir*, Barbara Jauquet Kalinoski; E-Mail: barbara@northernlights-lib.mn.us; *Automation Syst Coordr*, Heidi Hoks; *ILL, Ref Serv*, Barbara Lunsetter; *Tech Servs*, Tammee Bacon; *Bkmobile Coordr*, Margaret Moeglein; Staff 2 (MLS 2)
Pop 49,617; Circ 304,318
Library Holdings: Bk Vols 100,532; Per Subs 411
Subject Interests: High interest-low vocabulary, Large print, Literacy, Toddler's
Member Libraries: Elkin Public Library
Friends of the Library Group

TRACY

P TRACY PUBLIC LIBRARY,* 117 Third St, 56175-1211. SAN 308-8138. Tel: 507-629-5548. *Librn*, Mary Donaldson; *Asst Librn*, Vicky Olsen
Founded 1936. Pop 2,516; Circ 18,000
Library Holdings: Bk Vols 30,000; Per Subs 56
Friends of the Library Group

TWO HARBORS

P TWO HARBORS PUBLIC LIBRARY, 320 Waterfront Dr, 55616-3201. SAN 308-8162. Tel: 218-834-3148. FAX: 208-692-3131. E-Mail: thpl@arrowhead.lib.mn.us. Web Site: www.two-harbors.lib.mn.us. *Dir*, Susan Thompson
Founded 1896. Circ 50,000
Jan 1999-Dec 1999 Income $132,730, City $100,000, County $20,000, Locally Generated Income $7,000, Other $5,730. Mats Exp $18,500, Books $16,000, Per/Ser (Incl. Access Fees) $2,500
Library Holdings: Bk Vols 25,700
Mem of Arrowhead Library System
Friends of the Library Group

TYLER

P TYLER PUBLIC LIBRARY,* 230 N Tyler, PO Box L, 56178-0461. SAN 308-8170. Tel: 507-247-5556. FAX: 507-247-5557. *Librn*, Carla Skjong; E-Mail: cskjong@tylerlib.mn.us
Library Holdings: Bk Vols 6,000; Per Subs 50
Mem of Plum Creek Library System
Friends of the Library Group

UPSALA

P UPSALA LIBRARY,* PO Box 158, 56384. SAN 328-8870. Tel: 320-573-4282. FAX: 320-573-4282. Web Site: www.griver.org. *In Charge*, Wanda Erickson

Pop 1,218; Circ 23,445
Library Holdings: Bk Vols 11,179; Per Subs 37
Mem of Great River Regional Library
Open Mon 10-2, Wed & Fri 2-8, Sat 9-1
Friends of the Library Group

VICTORIA

S LOWRY NATURE CENTER LIBRARY, Carver Park Reserve, Suburban Hennepin,* PO Box 270, 55386. SAN 308-5759. Tel: 612-472-4911. FAX: 612-472-5420. *In Charge*, Mary Vanderforde
Founded 1969
Library Holdings: Bk Vols 1,000; Per Subs 10
Subject Interests: Birding, Conservation, General reading, Incl gardening, Natural history, Outdoor educ, Wildlife mgt
Restriction: Non-circulating to the public

VIRGINIA

P ARROWHEAD LIBRARY SYSTEM, 701 N 11th St, 55792-2298. SAN 308-8189. Tel: 218-741-3840. FAX: 218-741-3519. E-Mail: arrowhead@virginia.k12.mn.us. Web Site: www.arrowhead.lib.mn.us. *Dir*, Jim Weikum; *Admin Assoc*, Ghari Fisher; *Syst Coordr*, Harmon Seaver; *Tech Servs*, Bradley Snelling; Staff 23 (MLS 5, Non-MLS 18)
Founded 1966. Pop 306,743
Jan 1999-Dec 1999 Income $2,167,337, State $965,397, Federal $157,717, County $633,026, Other $411,197. Mats Exp $1,836,705, Books $103,041, Per/Ser (Incl. Access Fees) $3,300, Electronic Ref Mat (Incl. Access Fees) $22,000. Sal $659,113 (Prof $231,178)
Library Holdings: Bk Vols 92,549; Per Subs 33
Special Collections: AIDS; Described Videos; Native Americans
Automation Activity & Vendor Info: (Circulation) CARL; (OPAC) CARL; (Serials) CARL
Database Vendor: CARL, OCLC - First Search
Member Libraries: Aurora Public Library; Babbitt Public Library; Baudette Public Library; Bovey Public Library; Buhl Public Library; Calumet Public Library; Carlton Public Library; Chisholm Public Library; Cloquet Public Library; Coleraine Public Library; Cook Public Library; Duluth Public Library; Ely Public Library; Eveleth Public Library; Gilbert Public Library; Grand Marais Public Library; Grand Rapids Area Library; Hibbing Public Library; Hoyt Lakes Public Library; International Falls Public Library; Kinney Public Library; Marble Public Library; McKinley Public Library; Moose Lake Public Library; Mountain Iron Public Library; Silver Bay Public Library; Two Harbors Public Library; Virginia Public Library
Bookmobiles: 1

J MESABI RANGE COMMUNITY & TECHNICAL COLLEGE LIBRARY,* 1001 Chestnut St W, 55792. SAN 308-8197. Tel: 218-741-3095, Ext 764. Toll Free Tel: 800-657-3860. FAX: 218-749-7782. *Librn*, Laurel Tekautz
Founded 1922. Enrl 700
Library Holdings: Bk Vols 25,000; Per Subs 160

P VIRGINIA PUBLIC LIBRARY, 215 Fifth Ave S, 55792-2642. SAN 308-8200. Tel: 218-748-7525. FAX: 218-748-7526. Web Site: www.virginia.lib.mn.us. *Dir, Ref*, Nancy Maxwell; E-Mail: nancy@arrowhead.lib.mn.us; *Tech Servs*, Susan Krause; *Ch Servs*, Dawn Heisel; Staff 10 (MLS 1, Non-MLS 9)
Founded 1905. Pop 8,740; Circ 243,502
Library Holdings: Bk Vols 85,848; Per Subs 264
Automation Activity & Vendor Info: (Acquisitions) CARL; (Cataloging) CARL; (Circulation) CARL; (Course Reserve) CARL; (ILL) CARL; (Media Booking) CARL; (OPAC) CARL; (Serials) CARL
Mem of Arrowhead Library System
Partic in North Country Library Cooperative
Special Services for the Deaf - TDD
Open Mon-Thurs 9-8, Fri 9-6 & Sat 9-5
Friends of the Library Group

WABASHA

P WABASHA PUBLIC LIBRARY,* 168 Alleghany Ave, 55981-1286. SAN 308-8219. Tel: 651-565-3927. FAX: 651-565-3927. *Librn*, Judith A Schierts
Founded 1868. Pop 2,812; Circ 22,505
Library Holdings: Bk Vols 20,000; Per Subs 70
Special Collections: Local History (Wabasha-A Sense of Place); Local Paper, Wabasha County Herald 1863-1982, micro
Mem of Southeastern Libraries Cooperating (SELCO)
Friends of the Library Group

WABASSO

P WABASSO PUBLIC LIBRARY,* PO Box 190, 56293-0190. SAN 320-8966. Tel: 507-342-5279. FAX: 507-342-2329. *Librn*, Marilyn Daub
Pop 1,090; Circ 15,975
1999-2000 Income $32,861, City $25,861, County $7,000. Mats Exp $5,200, Books $4,000, Per/Ser (Incl. Access Fees) $1,200. Sal $18,039 (Prof $16,019)
Library Holdings: Bk Vols 10,000; Per Subs 42
Mem of Plum Creek Library System
Friends of the Library Group

WACONIA

S CARVER COUNTY HISTORICAL SOCIETY LIBRARY,* 555 W First St, 55387. SAN 325-5182. Tel: 612-442-4234. FAX: 612-442-3025. *Dir*, Leanne Brown; Staff 1 (Non-MLS 1)
Founded 1940
Library Holdings: Bk Titles 1,000
Special Collections: German & Swedish Language Reading Society Coll c.1860, 300 vols each

WADENA

P WADENA CITY LIBRARY,* 304 First St SW, 56482-1460. SAN 347-7819. Tel: 218-631-2476. FAX: 218-631-2476. Web Site: www.catalogue.nlln.org/welcome2.html. *Branch Mgr*, Catherine Edinger
Pop 4,699; Circ 27,238
Library Holdings: Bk Vols 17,000; Per Subs 65
Mem of Kitchigami Regional Library
Friends of the Library Group

WAITE PARK

P WAITE PARK LIBRARY, 253 N Fifth Ave, PO Box 307, 56387-0395. SAN 347-8777. Tel: 320-253-9359. FAX: 320-253-9359. Web Site: www.griver.org. *In Charge*, Julene Mayer
Pop 5,020; Circ 40,861
Library Holdings: Bk Vols 10,527; Per Subs 39
Mem of Great River Regional Library
Mon & Thurs 12-8, Tues 9-12 & 2-6, Wed 2-6 & Sat 9-12

WALNUT GROVE

S LAURA INGALLS WILDER MUSEUM & TOURIST INFORMATION,* 330 Eighth St, 56180. SAN 374-924X. Tel: 507-859-2358. Web Site: www.walnutgrove.org. *In Charge*, Shirley Knakmuhs; Tel: 507-859-2155
Library Holdings: Bk Vols 200

WARREN

P GODEL MEMORIAL LIBRARY, 314 E Johnson Ave, PO Box 115, 56762. SAN 348-0577. Tel: 218-745-5465. FAX: 218-745-8807. *Librn*, JoAnne Ranstrom; E-Mail: jranstrom@northernlights.lib.mn.us
Pop 2,105; Circ 19,561
Library Holdings: Bk Vols 10,000; Per Subs 27
Mem of Northwest Regional Library System
Friends of the Library Group

WARROAD

P WARROAD PUBLIC LIBRARY,* 202 Main Ave NE, 56763. SAN 348-0720. Tel: 218-386-1283. FAX: 218-386-3408. Web Site: www.nlln.org/aurora/nwrl/warroad.htm. *In Charge*, Barbara Larson
Pop 2,187; Circ 9,189
Library Holdings: Bk Vols 12,500; Per Subs 97
Mem of Northwest Regional Library System
Friends of the Library Group

WASECA

G WASECA COUNTY HISTORICAL SOCIETY LIBRARY, 315 Second Ave, NE, PO Box 314, 56093. SAN 326-5102. Tel: 507-835-7700. E-Mail: director@historical.waseca.mn.us. Web Site: www.historical.waseca.mn.us. *Dir*, Margaret Sinn
Founded 1938
Library Holdings: Bk Titles 350; Per Subs 10
Special Collections: Archives; Bus & Organization Rec; Diaries; Family Hist; Manuscripts; Waseca County Genealogy
Partic in S Minnesota Interlibr Res Exchange; Waseca Interlibrary Resource Exchange
Friends of the Library Group

P WASECA-LE SUEUR REGIONAL LIBRARY,* 408 N State St, 56093. SAN 348-0755. Tel: 507-835-2910. FAX: 507-835-3700. *Dir*, Theresa Meadows; *Asst Dir*, Judy Hanks; E-Mail: jhanks@tbs.lib.mn.us; *Acq*, Sue Nelson; Staff 4 (MLS 4)
Founded 1965. Pop 41,882; Circ 241,437

Jan 2000-Dec 2000 Income $627,531
Library Holdings: Bk Vols 125,000; Per Subs 460
Mem of Traverse Des Sioux Library System
Partic in OCLC Online Computer Library Center, Inc; Smile
Branches: 10
CLEVELAND BRANCH, City Hall, Cleveland, 56017. SAN 376-2092. Tel: 507-931-2490. *Librn*, Lauri Jones
Library Holdings: Bk Vols 3,000
ELYSIAN BRANCH, W Main St, Elysian, 56028. SAN 376-2106. Tel: 507-267-4411. *Librn*, Julaine Jacobson
Library Holdings: Bk Vols 3,000
JANESVILLE PUBLIC, 102 W Second, PO Box H, Janesville, 56048. SAN 348-078X. Tel: 507-234-6605. *Librn*, Kathleen Groh
Library Holdings: Bk Vols 10,480
KILKENNY BRANCH, Community Bldg, Kilkenny, 56052. SAN 376-2122. Tel: 507-362-8422. *Librn*, Janet Schmidtke
Library Holdings: Bk Vols 3,000
LE CENTER PUBLIC, 10 W Tyrone St, Le Center, 56057. SAN 348-081X. Tel: 507-357-6792. *Librn*, Dianne Paulsen-Wild
Library Holdings: Bk Vols 10,000
LESUEUR PUBLIC, E 118 Ferry St, LeSueur, 56058. SAN 348-0844. Tel: 507-665-2662. *Librn*, Dianne Pinney
Library Holdings: Bk Vols 13,407
MONTGOMERY PUBLIC, 201 W Ash Ave, Montgomery, 56069. SAN 348-0879. Tel: 507-364-7615. E-Mail: libtlm@tds.lib.ma.us. *In Charge*, Joan Ouradnick
Library Holdings: Bk Vols 11,000
NEW RICHLAND PUBLIC, 129 S Broadway, PO Box 385, New Richland, 56072. SAN 348-0909. Tel: 507-465-3708. *Librn*, Kathy Felsheim
Library Holdings: Bk Vols 10,000
WALDORF BRANCH, City Hall, Waldorf, 56091. SAN 376-2130. Tel: 507-239-2248. *Librn*, N Ruth Anderson
Library Holdings: Bk Vols 3,000
WATERVILLE PUBLIC, 210 E Paquin St, Waterville, 56096. SAN 348-0933. Tel: 507-362-8462. *Librn*, Gayle Appel
Library Holdings: Bk Vols 8,000

WAYZATA

L CARGILL, INC, Law Library,* 15407 McGinty Rd W. (Mail add: PO Box 5624, 55340), SAN 374-7085. Tel: 612-642-7575, 612-742-6235. FAX: 612-742-7503. *Librn*, Richard Wiebelhaus; E-Mail: richard_wiebelhaus@cargill.com; Staff 2 (MLS 1, Non-MLS 1)
Library Holdings: Bk Vols 11,000; Bk Titles 530; Per Subs 120
Automation Activity & Vendor Info: (Acquisitions) Inmagic, Inc.; (Serials) Inmagic, Inc.

R GRACE LUTHERAN CHURCH LIBRARY, 18360 Minnetonka Blvd, 55391-3295. SAN 308-8235. Tel: 612-473-2362. *Librn*, Betty W LeDell
Founded 1958
Jan 1999-Dec 1999 Income $360
Library Holdings: Bk Titles 3,850; Per Subs 10

S PREGNANCY & INFANT LOSS CENTER, Lending Library, 1421 E Wayzata Blvd, No 70, 55391. SAN 373-2304. Tel: 952-473-9372. FAX: 952-473-8978. *In Charge*, Donna Roehl
Library Holdings: Bk Vols 100

R WAYZATA COMMUNITY CHURCH LIBRARY, 125 E Wayzata Blvd, 55391. SAN 308-8243. Tel: 952-473-8876. FAX: 952-473-2695. E-Mail: welcome@wayzatacommunitychurch.org. Web Site: www.wayzatacommunitychurch.org. *In Charge*, Pat Kamrud
Library Holdings: Bk Vols 3,500; Per Subs 12

WELLS

P WELLS PUBLIC LIBRARY,* 54 First St SW, 56097-1913. SAN 308-8251. Tel: 507-553-3702. FAX: 507-553-6141. *Librn*, Barbara Stensrud
Founded 1976. Pop 3,000
1997-1998 Income $56,000, City $33,000, County $23,000. Mats Exp $12,600, Books $8,750, Per/Ser (Incl. Access Fees) $750, Micro $500. Sal $27,000
Library Holdings: Bk Vols 24,000
Mem of Traverse Des Sioux Library System

WEST CONCORD

P WEST CONCORD PUBLIC LIBRARY,* 180 E Main St, PO Box 468, 55985-0468. SAN 376-7140. Tel: 507-527-2031. FAX: 507-527-2031. *Librn*, Rita Lynn Hawes
Library Holdings: Bk Titles 11,980; Per Subs 35
Automation Activity & Vendor Info: (Circulation) DRA
Database Vendor: DRA, GaleNet, IAC - Info Trac, OCLC - First Search
Function: ILL available
Friends of the Library Group

WESTBROOK

P WESTBROOK PUBLIC LIBRARY, 556 First Ave, PO Box 26, 56183-0026. SAN 376-6527. Tel: 507-274-6174. FAX: 507-274-6174. *Librn*, Nancy Boeck
Library Holdings: Bk Vols 9,500; Bk Titles 9,000; Per Subs 20
Mem of Plum Creek Library System

WHEATON

P WHEATON COMMUNITY LIBRARY,* 901 First Ave N, 56296. SAN 320-8974. Tel: 320-563-8487. FAX: 320-563-8815. *Librn*, Marian Nelson
Pop 1,969; Circ 26,000
Jan 1999-Dec 1999 Income $58,000. Mats Exp $10,500. Sal $38,000
Library Holdings: Bk Vols 16,000; Per Subs 50
Mem of Viking Library System

WHITE BEAR LAKE

J CENTURY COMMUNITY COLLEGE LIBRARY, West Campus,* 3300 Century Ave N, 55110-5655. SAN 308-826X. Tel: 651-779-3263. FAX: 651-779-3417. *Acq, Cat, Circ*, Raymond Murray; *Per, Ref*, Bonnie Oldre; Staff 2 (MLS 2)
Founded 1967
Library Holdings: Bk Vols 34,000; Per Subs 220
Partic in MINITEX Library Information Network; OCLC Online Computer Library Center, Inc

WILLMAR

S KANDIYOHI COUNTY HISTORICAL SOCIETY, Lawson Research Library, 610 NE Hwy 71, 56201. SAN 326-3045. Tel: 320-235-1881. E-Mail: kandhist@wecnet.com. Web Site: freepages.genealogy.rootsweb.com/~kchs123/index.html. *Dir*, Mona Nelson-Balcer; Staff 1 (Non-MLS 1)
Founded 1969
Library Holdings: Bk Vols 1,700; Bk Titles 1,500; Per Subs 100
Subject Interests: Archives, Local history, Ref
Special Collections: Local Newspapers Coll, micro-film
Publications: Kandi Express (quarterly)
Restriction: Non-circulating to the public

P PIONEERLAND LIBRARY SYSTEM, 410 Fifth St SW, PO Box 327, 56201. SAN 348-0968. Tel: 320-235-6106. FAX: 320-214-0187. *Dir*, John Houlahan; E-Mail: johnh@pioneerland.lib.mn.us; *Asst Dir*, Katherine A Matson; E-Mail: kathym@pioneerland.lib.mn.us; *Tech Servs*, Jean Clark; E-Mail: jeanc@pioneerland.lib.mn.us; *Tech Coordr*, Beth Lunn; E-Mail: bethl@pioneerland.lib.mn.us; Staff 53 (MLS 7, Non-MLS 46)
Founded 1983. Pop 166,431; Circ 860,555
Jan 2000-Dec 2000 Income $3,097,717, State $409,759, City $801,014, Federal $30,079, County $910,522, Locally Generated Income $116,144, Other $507,325. Mats Exp $331,031, Books $278,876, Per/Ser (Incl. Access Fees) $51,687, Presv $468. Sal $1,801,766
Library Holdings: Bk Vols 464,540; Per Subs 1,905
Automation Activity & Vendor Info: (Cataloging) PALS; (Circulation) PALS; (ILL) PALS; (OPAC) PALS
Database Vendor: GaleNet, ProQuest
Member Libraries: Appleton Public Library; Atwater Public Library; Benson Public Library; Bird Island Public Library; Brownton Public Library; Clara City Public Library; Cosmos Public Library; Dassel Public Library; Dawson-Carnegie Library; Fairfax Public Library; Glencoe Public Library; Graceville Public Library; Granite Falls Public Library; Grove City Public Library; Hector Public Library; Hutchinson Public Library; Kerkhoven Public Library; Lake Lillian Public Library; Litchfield Public Library; Lyons School District Public Library; Madison Public Library; Maynard Public Library; Milan Public Library; Montevideo-Chippewa County Public Library; New London Public Library; Olivia Public Library; Ortonville Public Library; Raymond Public Library; Renville City Library; Spicer Library; Willmar Public Library; Winsted Public Library
Partic in Minn Interlibr Telecommunication Exchange; OCLC Online Computer Library Center, Inc
Bookmobiles: 1

M RICE MEMORIAL HOSPITAL LIBRARY, 301 Becker Ave SW, 56201. SAN 329-0948. Tel: 320-231-4248. FAX: 320-231-4463. *Librn*, Wendy Larson
Library Holdings: Bk Titles 2,000; Per Subs 200
Subject Interests: Hosp admin, Medicine, Nursing

J RIDGEWATER COLLEGE LIBRARY, Willmar Campus, 2101 15th Ave NW, 56201. SAN 308-8278. Tel: 320-231-5135. Toll Free Tel: 800-722-1151. FAX: 320-231-5194. Web Site: www.willmar.ridgewater.mnscu.edu/library. *Coll Develop, Librn*, Carolyn Kelleher; E-Mail: ckelleher@ridgewater.mnscu.edu; Staff 3 (MLS 1, Non-MLS 2)
Founded 1962. Enrl 2,000; Fac 80; Highest Degree: Doctorate
Jul 1999-Jun 2000 Mats Exp $86,000, Books $62,000, Per/Ser (Incl. Access Fees) $21,000, Micro $3,000. Sal $106,144 (Prof $58,738)

Library Holdings: Bk Vols 30,318; Per Subs 299
Special Collections: Private Library of Local Publisher (Lawson Library)
Automation Activity & Vendor Info: (Cataloging) PALS; (Circulation) PALS; (ILL) PALS; (OPAC) PALS
Partic in Minn Interlibr Telecommunication Exchange; Southwest Area Multicounty Multitype Interlibrary Exchange

P WILLMAR PUBLIC LIBRARY, 410 Fifth St SW, 56201-3298. SAN 372-8536. Tel: 320-235-3162. FAX: 320-235-3169. E-Mail: willmar@willmar.lib.mn.us. *Librn*, Earleen Warner; *Ref*, Amanda Raetzman; *Ch Servs*, Carolyn Olson; Staff 8 (MLS 2, Non-MLS 6)
Founded 1904. Pop 18,889; Circ 93,089
Jan 2000-Dec 2000 Income $392,560, City $212,000, County $87,925, Locally Generated Income $6,600, Other $30,998. Mats Exp $356,960, Books $57,404, Per/Ser (Incl. Access Fees) $55,904, Presv $1,500. Sal $272,024
Library Holdings: Bk Vols 55,951; Per Subs 277
Automation Activity & Vendor Info: (Circulation) PALS; (OPAC) PALS
Mem of Pioneerland Library System
Friends of the Library Group

M WILLMAR REGIONAL TREATMENT CENTER, Staff & Patient Library,* PO Box 1128, 56201. SAN 308-8286. Tel: 320-231-5100. FAX: 320-231-5329. *In Charge*, Karen Ochsendorf
Founded 1917
Library Holdings: Bk Vols 2,000; Per Subs 25
Subject Interests: Adolescence, Alcoholism, Chem dependency, Mental illness, Mental retardation, Nursing, Pharm, Psychiatry, Soc work

WINDOM

S COTTONWOOD COUNTY HISTORICAL SOCIETY LIBRARY, 812 Fourth Ave, 56101. SAN 326-3975. Tel: 507-831-1134. FAX: 507-831-2665. Web Site: www.mtn.org/mgs/othersoc/cottonwd.html. *Dir*, Linda Fransen
Oct 2000-Sep 2001 Income $42,000, State $6,000, County $30,000, Locally Generated Income $1,000, Other $5,000. Mats Exp $800, Presv $500, AV Equip $300. Sal $15,000
Library Holdings: Bk Vols 500
Restriction: Public use on premises
Function: Archival collection, Photocopies available, Research fees apply, Research library

P WINDOM PUBLIC LIBRARY,* 904 Fourth Ave, 56101-1639. SAN 308-8294. Tel: 507-831-6131. *Librn*, Joan Hunter
Founded 1883. Pop 4,666; Circ 59,000
Jan 1998-Dec 1998 Income $120,000. Mats Exp $45,000, Books $27,000, Per/Ser (Incl. Access Fees) $8,000. Sal $55,000
Library Holdings: Bk Titles 21,200; Per Subs 85
Subject Interests: Art and architecture, History, Music
Automation Activity & Vendor Info: (Cataloging) epixtech, inc.; (Circulation) epixtech, inc.
Mem of Plum Creek Library System
Friends of the Library Group

WINNEBAGO

P MUIR LIBRARY, 36 Main St N, PO Box 218, 56098. SAN 308-8308. Tel: 507-893-3196. FAX: 507-893-3473. *Librn*, Judy Tupper
Pop 1,562; Circ 29,761
Library Holdings: Bk Titles 19,000; Per Subs 76
Mem of Traverse Des Sioux Library System
Open Mon 9-12, 2-5 & 7-9, Tues, Wed & Thurs 2-5 & 7-9, Fri 10-12 & 2-5, Sat 10-12
Friends of the Library Group

WINONA

C MINNESOTA STATE COLLEGE- SOUTHEAST TECHNICAL LIBRARY, (Formerly Winona Technical College-Red Wing Campus), 1250 Homer Rd, 55987. SAN 320-6823. Tel: 507-453-2406. FAX: 507-453-2715. Web Site: www.southeasttech.mnscu.edu/library/default.htm. *Chief Librn*, Connie L Braun; Tel: 507-453-2410, E-Mail: cbraun@win.tec.mn.us; Staff 2 (MLS 1, Non-MLS 1)
Library Holdings: Bk Vols 2,000; Per Subs 100
Database Vendor: CARL, GaleNet, IAC - Info Trac
Partic in MINITEX Library Information Network

C SAINT MARY'S UNIVERSITY OF MINNESOTA, Bishop Fitzgerald Library, 700 Terrace Heights No 26, 55987-1399. SAN 308-8324. Tel: 507-457-1561. Interlibrary Loan Service Tel: 507-457-1489. Reference Tel: 507-457-1562. FAX: 507-457-1565. Web Site: www.smumn.edu/deptpages/~library. *Dir*, Richard Lemberg; Tel: 507-457-6962, E-Mail: rlemberg@smumn.edu; *Access Serv*, Mariann Alsum; Tel: 507-457-1489, E-Mail: malsum@smumn.edu; *Tech Servs*, Sigrid Docken Mount; Tel: 507-457-6665, E-Mail: smount@smumn.edu; *Ref*, Mary J Moxness; Tel: 507-457-6909, E-Mail: mmoxness@smumn.edu; *Coll Develop*, Cora Mae Berg; Tel: 507-457-1564, E-Mail: cberg@smumn.edu; Staff 5 (MLS 5)
Founded 1925. Enrl 1,364; Fac 104; Highest Degree: Master
Jun 1998-May 1999 Income (Main Library Only) $540,471. Mats Exp $247,870, Books $128,000, Per/Ser (Incl. Access Fees) $75,000, Presv $3,900, Micro $8,970, Electronic Ref Mat (Incl. Access Fees) $32,000. Sal $255,563 (Prof $189,335)
Library Holdings: Bk Vols 169,449; Bk Titles 145,667; Per Subs 711
Partic in MNSCU/PALS; OCLC Online Computer Library Center, Inc
Friends of the Library Group

S WINONA COUNTY HISTORICAL SOCIETY, Laird Lucas Memorial Library, 160 Johnson St, 55987. SAN 308-8332. Tel: 507-454-2723. FAX: 507-454-0006. E-Mail: archives@hbci.com. Web Site: www.winonanet.com/orgs/wchs/archives.htm. *Dir*, Mark Peterson; *Archivist*, Kathy Arnold; *Archivist*, Walter Bennick; *Archivist*, Sigrid Docken Mount; Staff 2 (MLS 1, Non-MLS 1)
Founded 1935. Pop 47,828
Library Holdings: Bk Vols 4,000
Subject Interests: Genealogy, Local history, Lumbering, Railroading, Steamboating
Automation Activity & Vendor Info: (Cataloging) Sagebrush Corporation; (OPAC) Sagebrush Corporation
Publications: Argus: A Winona County Historical Society newsletter (bimonthly)
Restriction: Non-circulating to the public
Function: Archival collection, Research fees apply

P WINONA PUBLIC LIBRARY, 151 W Fifth St, 55987-1247. (Mail add: PO Box 1247, 55987), SAN 308-8340. Tel: 507-452-4582. Reference Tel: 507-452-4860. FAX: 507-452-5842. Reference FAX: 507-452-2162. E-Mail: kc@selco.lib.mn.us. Web Site: www.selco.lib.mn.us/winona/default.htm. *Dir*, Kathleen Davidson-Braun; Tel: 507-457-8204; *Ref Serv Ad*, Sandra Beth; Fax: 507-452-2162, E-Mail: sandra_b@selco.lib.mn.us; *Ref Serv Ad*, Devon Harle; E-Mail: devon@selco.lib.mn.us; *Ch Servs*, Jane Enright; *Ch Servs*, Sally Mogren; Tel: 507-452-4592, E-Mail: smogren@selco.lib.mn.us; *Cat*, Patricia Ann Kollas; E-Mail: patk@selco.lib.mn.us; *ILL*, Carol Borzyskowski; E-Mail: carolb@selco.lib.mn.us; *Circ*, Deborah Lilla; E-Mail: debbiel@selco.lib.mn.us; Staff 7 (MLS 4, Non-MLS 3)
Founded 1899. Pop 45,186; Circ 325,807
Library Holdings: Bk Titles 110,001; Per Subs 347
Subject Interests: Mgt, Minn mat, Winona city, Winona County
Database Vendor: DRA, Ebsco - EbscoHost, IAC - Info Trac, OCLC - First Search, ProQuest
Mem of Southeastern Libraries Cooperating (SELCO)
Partic in Minn Interlibr Teletype Exchange; OCLC Online Computer Library Center, Inc
Open Mon 12-6, Wed & Fri 10-6, Tues & Thurs 10-9, Sat 10-5
Friends of the Library Group

C WINONA STATE UNIVERSITY LIBRARY, 175 W Mark St, PO Box 5838, 55987-5838. Tel: 507-457-5140. Circulation Tel: 507-457-5149. Reference Tel: 507-457-5146. FAX: 507-457-5594. Web Site: www.winona.msus.edu/library/index.html. *Dean of Libr*, Richard J Bazillion; Tel: 507-457-5151, E-Mail: rbazillion@winona.msus.edu; *Mgr*, Russell F Dennison; Tel: 507-457-5143, E-Mail: rdennison@winona.msus.edu; *Access Serv, Coordr*, Mark J Eriksen; Tel: 507-457-5486, Fax: 507-457-2679, E-Mail: meriksen@winona.msus.edu; *Coordr, Govt Doc, Publ Servs*, H Vernon Leighton; Tel: 507-457-5148, E-Mail: vleighton@winona.msus.edu; *Acq, Coll Develop*, Joe Mount; Tel: 507-457-5147, E-Mail: jmount@winona.msus.edu; *Info Tech, Instrul Serv*, Joe Jackson; Tel: 507-457-5152, E-Mail: jjackson@winona.msus.edu; *Ref*, William Palzer; Tel: 507-457-2644, E-Mail: wpalzer@winona.msus.edu; *Tech Servs*, Richard Hastings; Tel: 507-457-5503, E-Mail: rhastings@winona.msus.edu; *Distance Educ*, Kathryn Sullivan; Tel: 507-457-5150, E-Mail: ksullivan@winona.msus.edu; *Admin Assoc*, Nancy Nelton; Tel: 507-457-5151, E-Mail: nnelton@winona.msus.edu. Subject Specialists: *Automation*, Richard Hastings; *Distance learning classroom*, Kathryn Sullivan; *Nonprint mat*, Kathryn Sullivan; Staff 9 (MLS 9)
Founded 1860. Enrl 7,050; Fac 340; Highest Degree: Master
Jul 1999-Jun 2000 Income $380,336, State $217,605, Locally Generated Income $8,170, Parent Institution $154,561. Mats Exp $519,193, Books $246,716, Per/Ser (Incl. Access Fees) $272,477. Sal $813,523 (Prof $534,822)
Library Holdings: Bk Titles 198,994; Per Subs 53,029
Special Collections: Archives (WSU), curriculum, video, Eric, micro
Automation Activity & Vendor Info: (Acquisitions) PALS; (Cataloging) PALS; (Circulation) PALS; (Course Reserve) PALS; (ILL) PALS; (OPAC) PALS; (Serials) PALS
Database Vendor: OCLC - First Search
Partic in Minn Interlibr Telecommunication Exchange; OCLC Online Computer Library Center, Inc

WINSTED

P WINSTED PUBLIC LIBRARY,* PO Box 175, 55395-0175. SAN 348-1387. Tel: 320-485-3909. FAX: 320-485-3909. *Librn*, Sharon Noerenberg
Pop 2,698; Circ 8,049

Library Holdings: Bk Vols 7,000; Per Subs 15
Mem of Pioneerland Library System
Branch of Pioneerland Library System
Friends of the Library Group

WINTHROP

SIBLEY COUNTY LIBRARY SYSTEM, Winthrop Branch, 302 N Main St, 55396-9998. SAN 347-4453. Tel: 507-647-5308. FAX: 507-647-3200. E-Mail: libtsw@tds.lib.mn.us. *In Charge*, Mary Jane Ohland
Library Holdings: Bk Vols 7,869
Friends of the Library Group

WOODBURY

P WASHINGTON COUNTY LIBRARY, 2150 Radio Dr, 55125-9453. SAN 347-3880. Tel: 651-731-8487. FAX: 651-731-3758. Web Site: www.washington.lib.mn.us. *Dir*, James L Wells; *Mgr*, Kathleen Schuller; *Publ Servs*, Josephine E Halbach; E-Mail: jhalbach@washco.washington.lib.mn.us; *Commun Relations*, Erin Stahl; *Automation Syst Coordr, Coll Develop*, Carla Prakash; *Ref*, Linda Rehbein; *Ch Servs*, Vivian Perry
Founded 1967. Pop 179,344; Circ 1,607,040
Jan 1999-Dec 1999 Income (Main Library and Branch Library) $4,098,289, State $38,403, City $158,592, County $3,862,139, Other $39,155. Mats Exp $654,165, Books $509,500, AV Equip $120,246, Electronic Ref Mat (Incl. Access Fees) $24,419. Sal $2,338,412
Library Holdings: Bk Vols 398,469; Per Subs 1,433
Automation Activity & Vendor Info: (OPAC) epixtech, inc.
Partic in Metropolitan Library Service Agency; Mintex Libr Info Network
Branches: 9
FOREST LAKE, 220 N Lake, 55025. SAN 376-2149. Tel: 651-464-4088. FAX: 651-464-4296. Web Site: www.washington.lib.mn.us. *Actg Mgr*, Marlyce Lee; *Publ Servs*, Josephine E Halbach; Tel: 651-731-8487, Fax: 651-731-3758, E-Mail: jhalbach@washington.lib.mn.us
Library Holdings: Bk Vols 56,937
Mem of Washington County Libr Syst
LAKE ELMO BRANCH, 3459 Lake Elmo Ave N, Lake Elmo, 55042-9429. SAN 347-3910. Tel: 651-777-5002. FAX: 651-777-5002. Web Site: www.washington.lib.mn.us. *Mgr*, Carol Warner
Library Holdings: Bk Vols 17,866
Automation Activity & Vendor Info: (OPAC) epixtech, inc.
MARINE BRANCH, 790 Judd St, Marine-on-St Croix, 55047-0042. SAN 347-3945. Tel: 651-433-2820. FAX: 651-433-2820. Web Site: www.washington.lib.mn.us. *Actg Mgr*, Marlyce Lee
Library Holdings: Bk Vols 11,603
Automation Activity & Vendor Info: (OPAC) epixtech, inc.
NEWPORT BRANCH, 405 Seventh Ave, Newport, 55055-1410. SAN 347-3953. Tel: 651-459-9631. Web Site: www.washington.lib.mn.us. *Mgr*, Jim Langmo
Library Holdings: Bk Vols 11,052
Automation Activity & Vendor Info: (OPAC) epixtech, inc.
Mem of Washington County Libr Syst
Friends of the Library Group
OAKDALE BRANCH, 1010 Heron Ave N, Oakdale, 55128. SAN 373-9104. Tel: 651-730-0504. FAX: 651-714-1013. Web Site: www.washington.lib.mn.us. *Mgr*, Carol Warner
Library Holdings: Bk Vols 43,123
Automation Activity & Vendor Info: (OPAC) epixtech, inc.
Mem of Washington County Libr Syst
Friends of the Library Group
PARK-GROVE, 7900 Hemingway Ave S, Cottage Grove, 55016-1833. SAN 347-397X. Tel: 651-459-2040. FAX: 651-459-7051. Web Site: www.washington.lib.mn.us. *Mgr*, Jim Langmo
Library Holdings: Bk Vols 89,579
Automation Activity & Vendor Info: (OPAC) epixtech, inc.
Mem of Washington County Libr Syst
Friends of the Library Group
VALLEY, 380 Saint Croix Trail, PO Box 128, Lakeland, 55043-0128. SAN 347-4003. Tel: 651-436-5882. FAX: 651-436-5882. Web Site: www.washington.lib.mn.us. *Mgr*, Vivian Perry
Library Holdings: Bk Vols 23,978
Automation Activity & Vendor Info: (OPAC) epixtech, inc.
Mem of Washington County Libr Syst
Friends of the Library Group
WILDWOOD, 763 Stillwater Rd, Mahtomedi, 55115-2008. SAN 347-4038. Tel: 651-426-2042. FAX: 651-653-1388. Web Site: www.washington.lib.mn.us. *Mgr*, Marlyce Lee
Library Holdings: Bk Vols 50,403
Automation Activity & Vendor Info: (OPAC) epixtech, inc.
Mem of Washington County Libr Syst
Friends of the Library Group
WOODBURY, 2150 Radio Dr, 55125-9453. SAN 347-4062. Tel: 651-731-1320. FAX: 651-731-4076. Web Site: www.washington.lib.mn.us. *Mgr*, Linda Rehbein
Library Holdings: Bk Vols 93,928
Automation Activity & Vendor Info: (OPAC) epixtech, inc.
Mem of Washington County Libr Syst
Friends of the Library Group

WORTHINGTON

J MINNESOTA WEST COMMUNITY & TECHNICAL COLLEGE LIBRARY, 1450 College Way, 56187-3024. SAN 308-8383. Tel: 507-372-3462. FAX: 507-372-3463. Web Site: www.mnwest.mnscu.edu. *Dir*, JoAnn Amundson; E-Mail: jamundson@wr.mnwest.mnscu.edu; *Bibliog Instr, Coll Develop, Ref Serv*, Marcia G Johnson; E-Mail: mjohnson@wr.mnwest.mnscu.edu; *Bibliog Instr, Cat, Ref*, Sandi Mead; E-Mail: smead@wr.mnwest.mnscu.edu; *Bibliog Instr, Coll Develop, Ref Serv*, Christine Schafer; E-Mail: cschafer@gf.mnwest.mnscu.edu; Staff 4 (MLS 4)
Founded 1936. Enrl 1,885
Library Holdings: Bk Titles 39,000; Per Subs 500
Partic in Minn Interlibr Telecommunication Exchange
Open Mon-Fri 7:45-9
Departmental Libraries:
CANBY CAMPUS, 1011 First St W, Canby, 56220. Tel: 507-223-7252. FAX: 507-223-5291.
Open Mon & Wed 9:30-4, Tues 2-8, Thurs 9:30-6 & Fri 8-12
GRANITE FALLS CAMPUS, 1593 11th Ave, Granite Falls, 56241. Tel: 320-564-4511. FAX: 320-564-2318.
Open Mon & Thurs 8:30-4, Tues & Wed 8:30-8 & Fri 8-12
JACKSON CAMPUS, 401 West St, Jackson, 56143. Tel: 507-847-3320. FAX: 507-847-5389.
Open Mon & Wed 8:30-4, Tues & Thurs 8:30-8 & Fri 8-12
PIPESTONE CAMPUS, 1314 N Hiawatha Ave, PO Box 250, Pipestone, 56164. Tel: 507-825-5471. FAX: 507-825-4656.
Open Mon & Wed 9:30-4, Tues 11:30-8, Thurs 8-2:30 & Fri 8-12
WORTHINGTON CAMPUS, 1450 Collegeway, 56187. Tel: 507-372-3462. FAX: 507-372-3463.
Open Mon-Thurs 8-9 & Fri 8-4

P NOBLES COUNTY LIBRARY & INFORMATION CENTER, 407 12th St, 56187-2411. SAN 308-8367. Tel: 507-372-2981. FAX: 507-372-2982. *Dir*, Roger Spillers; *Ch Servs*, Gail Rahn; *Circ*, Myra Palmer; *Ref*, Laurie Ebbers
Founded 1947. Pop 50,000; Circ 166,524
Jan 2001-Dec 2001 Income $377,153. Mats Exp $36,197, Books $31,526, Per/Ser (Incl. Access Fees) $4,275, Micro $396. Sal $203,797 (Prof $153,695)
Library Holdings: Bk Vols 88,000; Per Subs 110
Mem of Plum Creek Library System
Partic in Minn Interlibr Telecommunication Exchange
Friends of the Library Group
Branches: 1
ADRIAN BRANCH, 214 Maine Ave, Adrian, 56110-0039. SAN 325-1713. Tel: 507-483-2541. E-Mail: adrianlb@adrian.mn.frontiercomm.net. Web Site: www.frontiercomm.net/~adrianlb. *Librn*, Meredith Vaselaar
Pop 1,500; Circ 14,301
Library Holdings: Bk Titles 8,000; Per Subs 16

P PLUM CREEK LIBRARY SYSTEM,* 290 S Lake St, PO Box 697, 56187-0697. SAN 308-8375. Tel: 507-376-5803. FAX: 507-376-9244. *Dir*, Jodi Reng; E-Mail: jreng@plumcreek.lib.mn.us
Founded 1974. Pop 119,523
Jul 1996-Jun 1997 Income $342,727, State $224,284, Federal $40,743, County $77,700. Mats Exp $36,452, Books $33,403, Per/Ser (Incl. Access Fees) $2,049. Sal $206,339 (Prof $75,000)
Subject Interests: Foreign lang materials, Large type publications
Special Collections: framed art prints; Puppet Resources; Song Book Coll; sound film strips
Member Libraries: Fulda Memorial Library; Heron Lake Public Library; Ivanhoe Public Library; Lake Benton Public Library; Lakefield Public Library; Lamberton Public Library; Marshall-Lyon County Library; Morgan Public Library; Mountain Lake Public Library; Nobles County Library & Information Center; Pipestone Community Library; Redwood Falls Public Library; Rock County Community Library; Runals Memorial Library; Slayton Public Library; Tyler Public Library; Wabasso Public Library; Westbrook Public Library; Windom Public Library
Partic in Minn Interlibr Telecommunication Exchange; Southwest Area Multicounty Multitype Interlibrary Exchange
Open Mon-Fri 8am-5pm

ZUMBROTA

P ZUMBROTA PUBLIC LIBRARY, 100 West Ave, 55992. SAN 308-8391. Tel: 507-732-5211. FAX: 507-732-1212. E-Mail: zpl@selco.lib.mn.us. *Dir*, Jeannie Honhart-Johnson
Pop 6,901
Jan 2000-Dec 2000 Income $234,480, City $125,480, County $96,000, Locally Generated Income $13,000. Mats Exp $49,000, Books $30,000, Per/Ser (Incl. Access Fees) $3,000, AV Equip $16,000. Sal $110,000
Library Holdings: Bk Vols 26,000; Per Subs 155

Automation Activity & Vendor Info: (Acquisitions) DRA; (Cataloging) DRA; (Circulation) DRA; (Course Reserve) DRA; (ILL) DRA; (Media Booking) DRA; (OPAC) DRA
Database Vendor: DRA
Partic in SE Libr Coop

Date of Statistics: Fiscal 1998
Population, 1995 Census: 2,697,243
Population Served by Public Libraries: 2,716,115
Total Volumes in Public Libraries: 6,544,729
Volumes Per Capita: 2.41
Total Public Library Circulation: 9,059,775
Total Public Library Income (includes Grants-in-Aid): $31,669,336
Source of Income: Mainly public funds
Expenditures Per Capita: $11.66
Number of County or Multi-County (Regional) Libraries: 47
Counties Served: 82
Number of Bookmobiles in State: 2
Grants-in-Aid to Public Libraries:
Federal & State: $5,856,916

ALCORN STATE

C ALCORN STATE UNIVERSITY, J D Boyd Library, 1000 ASU Dr, No 539, 39096-7500. SAN 308-8901. Tel: 601-877-6350. FAX: 601-877-3885. *Dir*, Jessie B Arnold; E-Mail: jarnold@lorman.alcorn.edu; *Acq*, Bobbie Fells; Tel: 601-877-6354, E-Mail: bpfells@lorman.alcorn.edu; *Ref*, Mary Harris; Tel: 601-877-6357, E-Mail: mharris@lorman.alcorn.edu; *Circ, Ser*, Hazel Bell; Tel: 601-877-6362, E-Mail: hazel@lorman.alcorn.edu; *Automation Syst Coordr*, Eric Speas; Tel: 601-877-6360, E-Mail: espeas@lorman.alcorn.edu; Staff 19 (MLS 7, Non-MLS 12)
Founded 1871. Enrl 2,800; Fac 149
Jul 1998-Jun 1999 Income $1,190,164, State $1,190,164. Mats Exp $264,186, Books $12,645, Per/Ser (Incl. Access Fees) $180,650, Presv $21,318, Micro $5,000, AV Equip $12,645, Electronic Ref Mat (Incl. Access Fees) $31,928. Sal $407,723 (Prof $163,124)
Library Holdings: Bk Vols 189,364; Bk Titles 161,445; Per Subs 1,046
Subject Interests: Agriculture, Education
Special Collections: Alcorn Archives
Automation Activity & Vendor Info: (Acquisitions) Endeavor; (Cataloging) Endeavor; (Circulation) Endeavor; (Course Reserve) Endeavor; (Media Booking) Endeavor; (OPAC) Endeavor; (Serials) Endeavor
Partic in BRS; SE Libr Network

ASHLAND

P ROBERT M BOND MEMORIAL LIBRARY, PO Box 216, 38603-0216. SAN 376-6357. Tel: 662-224-6400. FAX: 662-224-6304. E-Mail: bondmem@benton.lib.ms.us. *Dir*, Sue Poff; E-Mail: suepoff@benton.lib.ms.us
Founded 1959
Library Holdings: Bk Titles 47,000; Per Subs 16
Friends of the Library Group

BAY SAINT LOUIS

P HANCOCK COUNTY LIBRARY SYSTEM, 312 Hwy 90, 39520-3595. SAN 348-1417. Tel: 228-467-5282. FAX: 228-467-5503. E-Mail: hcls@hancock.lib.ms.us. Web Site: www.hancock.lib.ms.us. *Dir*, Prima Plauche; *Asst Dir*, David Woodburn; Tel: 228-467-6836, E-Mail: dwoodburn@hancock.lib.ms.us; *Coordr*, Jeanne Pierce; *Publ Servs*, Mary Perkins; Staff 24 (MLS 3, Non-MLS 21)
Founded 1934. Pop 38,304; Circ 220,000
Oct 1998-Sep 1999 Income (Main Library and Branch Library) $1,088,743, State $70,322, City $218,397, Federal $5,541, County $665,168, Locally Generated Income $100,522. Mats Exp $135,539, Books $125,982, Per/Ser (Incl. Access Fees) $8,194, Presv $590, Micro $590. Sal $521,191 (Prof $183,737)
Library Holdings: Bk Vols 99,188; Bk Titles 61,616; Per Subs 120
Special Collections: Mississippi-Louisianna (Mississippiana Coll)
Database Vendor: Ebsco - EbscoHost, epixtech, inc., OCLC - First Search
The Library Foundation of Hancock County, a non-profit corporation formed for the sole support of the library system
Branches: 3
KILN BRANCH, 16603 Hwy 603, PO Box 628, Kiln, 39556. SAN 348-1433. Tel: 228-255-1724. FAX: 228-255-1724. *Librn*, Sandra Ladner
Library Holdings: Bk Titles 5,199
PEARLINGTON PUBLIC, 6096 First St, Pearlington, 39572. SAN 378-1585. *In Charge*, Caprice Smith
WAVELAND LIBRARY LITERACY CENTER, 333 Coleman Ave, Waveland, 39576-3595. SAN 348-1441. Tel: 601-467-9240. FAX: 601-467-9240. *Librn*, Evelyn Necaise
Library Holdings: Bk Titles 5,689

BELZONI

P HUMPHREYS COUNTY LIBRARY SYSTEM,* 105 S Hayden, 39038. SAN 348-1476. Tel: 662-247-3606. FAX: 662-247-3443. *Dir*, Shirley H Keenum
Founded 1958. Pop 12,134; Circ 26,904
Library Holdings: Bk Vols 40,000; Per Subs 76
Open Mon-Fri 9-12:30 & 1:30-5, Sat 10-4
Branches: 1
ISOLA PUBLIC, Isola, 38754. SAN 348-1530. Tel: 662-962-3606. *Librn*, Kathleen Session

BILOXI

P BILOXI PUBLIC LIBRARY,* 139 Lameuse St, 39530-4298. SAN 348-1565. Tel: 228-374-0330. FAX: 228-374-0375. Web Site: www.harrison.lib.ms.us. *Librn*, Charline J Longino; *Ref*, Stanley Hastings; Staff 3 (MLS 3)
Founded 1924. Pop 49,600; Circ 179,898
Oct 1997-Sep 1998 Income $841,500, City $420,000, County $421,500
Library Holdings: Bk Vols 83,998; Per Subs 220
Special Collections: Genealogy, bk & micro; Local History, bk, photo/image, VF; Mississippiana, bk & micro
Publications: Harrison County Soundings
Friends of the Library Group
Branches: 3
DIVISION STREET, 595 Division St, 39530-2303. SAN 348-159X. Tel: 228-435-2435. Web Site: www.harrison.lib.ms.us/. *Librn*, Janice Spencer
Founded 1955
Library Holdings: Bk Vols 2,770
Subject Interests: Children's literature
Friends of the Library Group
MARGARET S SHERRY MEMORIAL LIBRARY, 2141 Popps Ferry Rd, 39532-4104. SAN 348-1611. Tel: 228-388-1633. FAX: 228-388-1633. Web Site: www.harrison.lib.ms.us. *Librn*, Kathy Sparkman
Founded 1983
Library Holdings: Bk Vols 23,157
Friends of the Library Group
WEST BILOXI, 2047 Pass Rd, 39531-3127. SAN 348-162X. Tel: 228-388-5696. FAX: 228-388-5696. Web Site: www.harrison.lib.ms.us/. *Librn*,

Deborah Lundy
Founded 1968
Library Holdings: Bk Vols 34,367; Per Subs 60
Friends of the Library Group

GM DEPARTMENT OF VETERANS AFFAIRS, Information Management Services,* 400 Veterans Ave, 39531-2410. SAN 308-843X. Tel: 228-385-5751. FAX: 228-385-5718. *Assoc Dir*, Gwen Vanderfin; *Librn*, Marvett Burns; Staff 7 (MLS 3, Non-MLS 4)
Library Holdings: Per Subs 500
Partic in Miss Health Sci Info Network; Mississippi Biomedical Library Consortium; Nat Libr of Med; Vets Admin Libr Network

BLUE MOUNTAIN

C BLUE MOUNTAIN COLLEGE, Guyton Library, PO Box 160, 38610*0160. SAN 308-8448. Tel: 662-685-4771, Ext 147. FAX: 662-685-4776. *Dir*, Carolyn Mounce; *Asst Librn*, Sally Derrick; Staff 2 (MLS 2)
Founded 1875. Enrl 440; Fac 30; Highest Degree: Bachelor
Library Holdings: Bk Vols 60,000; Per Subs 197
Subject Interests: Liberal arts
Open Mon-Fri 7:50-9:45, Sat 9-3

BOONEVILLE

R FIRST BAPTIST CHURCH LIBRARY, 401 W Church St, 38829. SAN 308-8456. Tel: 601-728-6272. FAX: 601-728-6273. *Dir*, Denise Bray
Founded 1945
Library Holdings: Bk Vols 4,000
Subject Interests: 200's relig
Special Collections: Bound Church Bulletins

J NORTHEAST MISSISSIPPI COMMUNITY COLLEGE, Eula Dees Memorial Library, Cunningham Blvd, 38829. SAN 308-8464. Tel: 662-720-7408, 662-728-7751. FAX: 662-728-2428. Web Site: www.necc.cc.ms.us. *Dir*, Carol Killough; E-Mail: ckillou@necc.cc.ms.us; *Librn*, Glenice Stone; *Librn*, Lynn Baragona; Staff 6 (MLS 3, Non-MLS 3)
Founded 1948. Fac 120
Jul 1999-Jun 2000 Income $282,462. Mats Exp $90,000, Books $16,000, Per/Ser (Incl. Access Fees) $20,000, Electronic Ref Mat (Incl. Access Fees) $6,000. Sal $132,000 (Prof $93,000)
Library Holdings: Bk Vols 45,256; Bk Titles 34,572; Per Subs 283
Special Collections: Mississippi
Database Vendor: Ebsco - EbscoHost, GaleNet, IAC - Info Trac, IAC - SearchBank, OCLC - First Search, OVID Technologies, ProQuest, Wilson - Wilson Web
Publications: Tiger Tales (newsletter)

BRANDON

P BRANDON PUBLIC LIBRARY,* PO Box 1537, 39043. SAN 329-2835. Tel: 601-825-2672. FAX: 601-824-7094. E-Mail: brandon@cmrls.lib.ms.us. *Librn*, Ann Graham; Staff 7 (MLS 3, Non-MLS 4)
Founded 1958. Pop 13,200; Circ 64,000
Library Holdings: Bk Vols 27,000; Per Subs 60
Subject Interests: Genealogy
Mem of Central Mississippi Regional Library System
Friends of the Library Group

P CENTRAL MISSISSIPPI REGIONAL LIBRARY SYSTEM,* 104 Office Park Dr, 39042-2404. (Mail add: PO Box 1749, 39043-1749), SAN 329-5109. Tel: 601-825-0100. FAX: 601-825-0199. *Dir*, Rose Johnson; *Asst Dir*, Sandra Sanders; *Tech Servs*, Ray Myers; *Ch Servs, YA Servs*, Mary Thompson
Founded 1986
Library Holdings: Bk Vols 331,000; Bk Titles 250,000; Per Subs 600
Automation Activity & Vendor Info: (Acquisitions) epixtech, inc.; (Cataloging) epixtech, inc.; (Circulation) epixtech, inc.; (OPAC) epixtech, inc.; (Serials) epixtech, inc.
Member Libraries: Brandon Public Library; D'Lo Public Library; Evon A Ford Public Library; Florence Public Library; Forest Public Library; Harrisville Public Library; Lake Public Library; Magee Public Library; Mendenhall Public Library; Mize Public Library; Morton Public Library; Northwest Point Library; Pearl Public Library; Pelahatchie Public Library; Polkville Public Library; Puckett Public Library; Raleigh Public Library; Richland Public Library; Sand Hill Public Library; Sebastopol Public Library
Open Mon-Thurs 9-8, Fri 9-5 & Sat 11-4
Friends of the Library Group

P NORTHWEST POINT LIBRARY, (Reservoir Branch),* 2230 Spillway Rd, 39047. SAN 377-5755. Tel: 601-992-2539. FAX: 601-992-2539. E-Mail: reservoi@carls.lib.ms.us. *Librn*, Ann Marsh
Library Holdings: Bk Vols 15,000; Per Subs 20
Mem of Central Mississippi Regional Library System
Friends of the Library Group

BROOKHAVEN

P LINCOLN-LAWRENCE-FRANKLIN REGIONAL LIBRARY, 100 S Jackson St, PO Box 541, 39602. SAN 348-1654. Tel: 601-833-3369. FAX: 601-833-3381. E-Mail: 6pll@llf.lib.ms.us. Web Site: www.llf.lib.ms.us. *Dir*, Henry J Ledet; E-Mail: hledet@llf.lib.ms.us; *Librn*, Rebecca Nations; E-Mail: rnations@llf.lib.ms.us; *Ch Servs*, Donna Kenney; E-Mail: dkenney@llf.lib.ms.us; Staff 19 (MLS 3, Non-MLS 16)
Founded 1956. Pop 50,861
Oct 1999-Sep 2000 Income (Main Library and Branch Library) $597,856, State $135,019, City $78,031, Federal $37,033, County $267,850, Other $79,923. Mats Exp $72,548, Books $41,145, Per/Ser (Incl. Access Fees) $18,747, Other Print Mats $6,096, Electronic Ref Mat (Incl. Access Fees) $6,560. Sal $341,599
Library Holdings: Bk Titles 99,180; Per Subs 211
Special Collections: Lincoln County History
Automation Activity & Vendor Info: (Circulation) Sagebrush Corporation; (OPAC) Sagebrush Corporation
Open Mon & Wed 9-6, Tues & Thurs 9-8, Fri & Sat 9-5
Branches: 4
BUDE PUBLIC, PO Box 69, Bude, 39630. SAN 348-1689. Tel: 601-384-2348. FAX: 601-384-2348. E-Mail: bude@llf.lib.ms.us. *In Charge*, Kathy Zumbro; Staff 1 (Non-MLS 1)
Library Holdings: Bk Titles 5,223
FRANKLIN COUNTY, PO Box 336, Meadville, 39653. SAN 348-1719. Tel: 601-384-2997. FAX: 601-384-2997. E-Mail: frankcpl@telapex.com. *Librn*, Jo Porter; Staff 2 (MLS 1, Non-MLS 1)
Library Holdings: Bk Titles 10,679
LAWRENCE COUNTY, PO Box 446, Monticello, 39654. SAN 348-1743. Tel: 601-587-2471. FAX: 601-587-2471. *Librn*, Dianne Jones; Staff 3 (MLS 1, Non-MLS 2)
Library Holdings: Bk Titles 15,067
NEW HEBRON PUBLIC, PO Box 202, New Hebron, 39140. SAN 348-176X. Tel: 601-694-2623. FAX: 601-694-2623. *In Charge*, Karen Turnage; Staff 1 (Non-MLS 1)

CANTON

P MADISON COUNTY LIBRARY SYSTEM, Madison County-Canton Public Library, 102 Priestley St, 39046-4599. SAN 348-1808. Tel: 601-859-3202. FAX: 601-859-0014, 601-859-2728. Web Site: www.mad.lib.ms.us. *Dir*, Beverly Herring; *Coll Develop*, Elizabeth Urbanik; *Ch Servs*, Linda Johnson; *Cat*, Marty Warstler; Staff 9 (MLS 7, Non-MLS 2)
Pop 74,000; Circ 268,316
Oct 1999-Sep 2000 Income (Main Library and Branch Library) $1,177,546, State $173,103, City $234,746, County $712,192, Locally Generated Income $39,877, Other $17,628. Mats Exp $215,585, Books $198,385, Per/Ser (Incl. Access Fees) $17,000, Presv $200. Sal $611,126 (Prof $231,617)
Library Holdings: Bk Vols 150,094; Bk Titles 95,812; Per Subs 140
Subject Interests: Black hist, Local history, Miss writers
Special Collections: Local History; Local Picture Coll; Madison County Historical Materials
Automation Activity & Vendor Info: (Acquisitions) SIRSI; (Cataloging) SIRSI; (Circulation) SIRSI
Publications: Newsletter (bimonthly)
Partic in OCLC Online Computer Library Center, Inc
Friends of the Library Group

CARROLLTON

P CARROLLTON-NORTH CARROLLTON PUBLIC LIBRARY,* PO Box 329, 38917-0329. SAN 376-6411. Tel: 662-237-6268. FAX: 662-237-6268. *Dir*, Patricia Ball
Library Holdings: Bk Titles 8,000; Per Subs 20

CHARLESTON

P TALLAHATCHIE COUNTY LIBRARY,* 102 N Walnut, PO Box 219, 38921-0219. SAN 348-1921. Tel: 662-647-2638. FAX: 662-647-2638. *Librn*, Annie V Davis; *Dir*, Angela Etheridge; *Asst Librn*, Shirley Williams
Founded 1939. Pop 16,400; Circ 102,402
Library Holdings: Bk Vols 39,000
Branches: 3
SUMNER BRANCH, PO Box 386, Sumner, 38957. SAN 348-1948. Tel: 662-375-8901. FAX: 662-375-8901. *Librn*, Sarah Jenkins
TUTWILER BRANCH, PO Box 214, Tutwiler, 38963. SAN 348-1956. Tel: 662-345-8475. FAX: 662-345-8475.
WEBB BRANCH, PO Box 618, Webb, 38966. SAN 348-1980. Tel: 662-375-8787. FAX: 662-375-8787. *Librn*, Elsie Hanks

CLARKSDALE

P CARNEGIE PUBLIC LIBRARY OF CLARKSDALE & COAHOMA COUNTY, 114 Delta Ave, 38614-4212. (Mail add: PO Box 280, 38614-0280), SAN 348-2014. Tel: 662-624-4461. FAX: 662-627-4344. *Dir*, Missie Craig; *Circ*, Connee Webster; *ILL, Ref*, Linda White; *Tech Servs*, Charlotte

Huddleston; Staff 3 (MLS 1, Non-MLS 2)
Founded 1914. Pop 31,300
Oct 1998-Sep 1999 Income $476,000, State $51,000, City $202,000, County $165,000, Other $58,000
Library Holdings: Bk Vols 65,000; Per Subs 189
Subject Interests: Archeology, Genealogy
Special Collections: Delta Blues Museum Coll, bks
Automation Activity & Vendor Info: (Cataloging) epixtech, inc.; (Circulation) epixtech, inc.
Partic in Miss Libr Comn Interlibr Loan Network
Open Mon-Thurs 9-5:30, Fri 9-5, Sat 9-1
Friends of the Library Group

J COAHOMA COMMUNITY COLLEGE, Dickerson Johnson Library, 3240 Friars Point Rd, 38614. SAN 308-8480. Tel: 662-627-2571, Ext 461. FAX: 662-627-9530. *Dean of Libr*, Yvonne Stanford; E-Mail: ystanford@ccc.cc.ms.us; *Media Spec*, Mary Caradine
Founded 1949. Enrl 1,362
Library Holdings: Bk Vols 30,000; Per Subs 126
Subject Interests: Bus, Child development, Child growth, Education, Mgt
Special Collections: Special Black Studies Coll

CLEVELAND

P BOLIVAR COUNTY LIBRARY, Robinson-Carpenter Memorial Library, 104 S Leflore Ave, 38732. SAN 348-2073. Tel: 662-843-2774. FAX: 662-843-4701. Web Site: www.bolivar.lib.ms.us. *Dir*, Ronnie W Wise; E-Mail: rwise@tecinfo.com; *Ch Servs*, Cindy Duffee; *ILL*, Emily Bell; *Circ*, Judy Williamson; Staff 3 (MLS 3)
Founded 1958. Pop 41,000; Circ 121,366
Library Holdings: Bk Vols 100,000; Per Subs 275
Subject Interests: Genealogy, Local history
Partic in Westlaw
Friends of the Library Group
Branches: 7
BENOIT PUBLIC, PO Box 307, Benoit, 38725. SAN 372-7912. Tel: 662-742-3402. Web Site: www.bolivar.lib.ms.us. *Librn*, Gloria Twilley
CLEVELAND DEPOT, 101 S Bayou Ave, 38732. SAN 376-0278. Tel: 662-843-7323. FAX: 662-843-7323. Web Site: www.bolivar.lib.ms.us.
FIELD MEMORIAL, Shaw, 38773. SAN 348-2103. Tel: 662-754-6381. FAX: 662-754-6381. Web Site: www.bolivar.lib.ms.us. *Librn*, Beatrice Wadlington
GUNNISON PUBLIC, Gunnison, 38746. SAN 348-2138. Tel: 662-747-2213. Web Site: www.bolivar.lib.ms.us. *Librn*, Mary J Snyder
ROSEDALE PUBLIC, Rosedale, 38769. SAN 348-2162. Tel: 662-759-6332. FAX: 662-759-6332. Web Site: www.bolivar.lib.ms.us. *Librn*, Joyce Applegate
SHELBY PUBLIC, Shelby, 38774. SAN 348-2197. Tel: 662-398-7748. FAX: 662-398-7748. Web Site: www.bolivar.lib.ms.us. *Librn*, Vivian A Malatesta
THELMA RAYNER MEMORIAL, Merigold, 38759. SAN 348-2227. Tel: 662-748-2105. Web Site: www.bolivar.lib.ms.us. *Librn*, Sara Bess Meek

C DELTA STATE UNIVERSITY, W B Roberts Library, 38733. SAN 308-8499. Tel: 662-846-4440. FAX: 662-846-4443. Web Site: www.lib.deltast.edu. *Dir*, Terry S Latour; *Asst Dir*, Margaret Evans; *Instrul Serv, Ref*, Joi Jones; Tel: 662-846-4431; *Ref*, Jean Liddell; Tel: 662-846-4431; *Doc, Ref*, David Salinero; Tel: 662-846-4431; *Media Spec*, Frieda Quon; Tel: 662-846-4345; *Media Spec*, Bill Wilson; *Cat, Tech Servs*, Sheryl Stump; Tel: 662-846-4458; *Tech Servs*, Rick Torgerson; Tel: 662-846-4438; *Circ*, Jane Waldrup; Tel: 662-846-4430; *Automation Syst Coordr*, Meredith Johnston; Tel: 662-846-4432; *Archivist*, Tara Zachary; Tel: 662-846-4780; *Instrul Serv*, Vicki Bond; Tel: 662-846-4341; Staff 30 (MLS 14, Non-MLS 16)
Founded 1925. Enrl 4,082; Fac 250; Highest Degree: Doctorate
Library Holdings: Bk Vols 234,892; Bk Titles 210,309; Per Subs 1,368
Special Collections: Archives (Walter Sillers Coll); Art Coll; Mississippiana, mss
Automation Activity & Vendor Info: (Acquisitions) GEAC; (Circulation) GEAC
Partic in Magnolia; SE Libr Network
Friends of the Library Group

CLINTON

P CLINTON PUBLIC LIBRARY,* 111 Clinton Blvd, 39056. SAN 308-8502. Tel: 601-924-5684. FAX: 601-924-5086. *Mgr*, William M Yount; Staff 5 (MLS 1, Non-MLS 4)
Founded 1971. Pop 24,000
1998-1999 Mats Exp Books $44,000
Library Holdings: Bk Vols 50,000
Mem of Jackson Metro Libr Syst
Friends of the Library Group

SR MISSISSIPPI BAPTIST HISTORICAL COMMISSION LIBRARY, PO Box 4024, 39058. SAN 327-2168. Tel: 601-925-3434. FAX: 601-925-3435. E-Mail: lib@mc.edu. *Librn*, Rachel A Pyron; E-Mail: mbhc@mc.edu; Staff 2 (MLS 1, Non-MLS 1)
Jan 2000-Dec 2000 Income $54,330
Library Holdings: Bk Titles 900
Publications: A History of Mississippi Baptists 1780-1970; Highlights of Mississippi Baptist History (Revised 1990); Mississippi Baptist Convention Ministers: Current Biographies
Selective index to The Baptist Record

C MISSISSIPPI COLLEGE, Leland Speed Library, College & Monroe St, 39058. (Mail add: PO Box 127, 39060), SAN 348-2251. Tel: 601-925-3232. FAX: 601-925-3435. E-Mail: library@mc.edu. Web Site: mc.edu/campus/library/. *Coll Develop, Dir*, David A Wright; Tel: 601-925-3438, E-Mail: wright@mc.edu; *Assoc Dir, Syst Coordr*, Rachel H Smith; Tel: 601-925-3870, E-Mail: smith@mc.edu; *Cat*, Ruth Ann Gibson; Tel: 601-925-3433, E-Mail: gibson@mc.edu; *Spec Coll*, Rachel Pyron; Tel: 601-925-3434, E-Mail: pyron@mc.edu; *Media Spec*, Wanda Mosley; Tel: 601-925-3429, E-Mail: mosley@mc.edu; *Ref*, Ann M Weill; Tel: 601-925-3905, E-Mail: weill@mc.edu; Staff 16 (MLS 9, Non-MLS 7)
Founded 1826. Highest Degree: Doctorate
Jun 2000-May 2001 Income $814,616. Mats Exp $287,182, Books $100,505, Per/Ser (Incl. Access Fees) $111,990, Presv $10,000, Micro $11,687, AV Equip $15,000, Electronic Ref Mat (Incl. Access Fees) $38,000. Sal $459,809 (Prof $334,398)
Library Holdings: Bk Vols 239,531; Per Subs 750
Special Collections: Mississippi Baptist Historical Coll
Automation Activity & Vendor Info: (Acquisitions) Innovative Interfaces Inc.; (Cataloging) Innovative Interfaces Inc.; (Circulation) Innovative Interfaces Inc.; (Course Reserve) Innovative Interfaces Inc.; (ILL) Innovative Interfaces Inc.; (Media Booking) Innovative Interfaces Inc.; (OPAC) Innovative Interfaces Inc.; (Serials) Innovative Interfaces Inc.
Database Vendor: Ebsco - EbscoHost, Lexis-Nexis, OCLC - First Search, Silverplatter Information Inc.
Publications: Library Associates Newsletter (annual)
Restriction: Public use on premises
Function: ILL available
Partic in Central Mississippi Library Council (CMLC); OCLC Online Computer Library Center, Inc; Solinet
Friends of the Library Group
Departmental Libraries:
LAW LIBRARY
See Separate Entry in Jackson

COFFEEVILLE

P COFFEEVILLE PUBLIC LIBRARY,* 14432 Main St, PO Box 359, 38922-0420. SAN 324-3737. Tel: 662-675-8822. FAX: 662-675-2001. *Librn*, Patty M Bailey; *Asst Librn*, Joyce Snider
Founded 1960. Pop 1,100; Circ 1,500
Library Holdings: Bk Vols 9,040; Per Subs 40
Open Mon & Fri 9-12 & 1-5, Tues & Wed 1-5, Thurs 1-8
Friends of the Library Group

COLUMBIA

S MISSISSIPPI DEPARTMENT OF HUMAN SERVICES - YOUTH SERVICES DIVISION, Columbia Training School Library, 1730 Hwy 44, 39429. SAN 371-862X. Tel: 601-736-4592, Ext 128. FAX: 601-736-5667. *Media Spec*, Rosemary Massey Gonzalez; Staff 1 (MLS 1)
Enrl 250; Fac 20
Library Holdings: Bk Titles 6,800; Per Subs 81

P SOUTH MISSISSIPPI REGIONAL LIBRARY, (SMRL), Columbia Marion County Library, 900 Broad St, 39429. SAN 348-2316. Tel: 601-736-5516. FAX: 601-736-1379. *Dir*, Sara Carter Swinney; *Librn*, Faye Speights; *Branch Mgr*, Melinda Hathorn; *Ch Servs*, Ann Fortenberry; Staff 4 (MLS 2, Non-MLS 2)
Founded 1972. Pop 41,508
Oct 1998-Sep 1999 Income (Main Library and Branch Library) $372,412. Mats Exp $43,350. Sal $199,961
Library Holdings: Bk Vols 52,300; Bk Titles 31,602; Per Subs 228
Automation Activity & Vendor Info: (Cataloging) Gaylord; (Circulation) Gaylord; (OPAC) Gaylord
Friends of the Library Group
Branches: 2
BASSFIELD PUBLIC, PO Box 310, Bassfield, 39421. SAN 348-2340. Tel: 601-943-5420. FAX: 601-943-5420. *Mgr*, Melinda Hathorn
Friends of the Library Group
PRENTISS PUBLIC, PO Box 1315, Prentiss, 39474. SAN 348-2375. Tel: 601-792-5845. FAX: 601-792-8159. *Librn*, Faye Speights
Friends of the Library Group

COLUMBUS

P COLUMBUS-LOWNDES PUBLIC LIBRARY, 314 N Seventh St, 39701-4699. SAN 348-2405. Tel: 662-329-5300. FAX: 662-329-5156. E-Mail: pres@lowndes.lib.ms.us. *Dir*, Mrs Douglas Bateman; *Asst Dir*, Charon

Hardy; *Ref*, Susan Nawrocki; *Ch Servs*, Brenda Pritchett; *Ch Servs*, Edwina Williams; *Archivist*, Marty Sparrow; *ILL*, Ann Easley; *Circ*, Brenda Durrett; *Automation Syst Coordr, Cat*, Christy Burks; Staff 26 (MLS 2, Non-MLS 24)
Founded 1940. Pop 58,900; Circ 134,283
Oct 1998-Sep 1999 Income (Main Library and Branch Library) $847,422. Mats Exp $371,614. Sal $385,980
Library Holdings: Bk Titles 98,788; Per Subs 140
Special Collections: Eudora Welty Special Coll; Genealogy & Local History (Margaret Latimer Buckley Room), bks, per & micr; Genealogy (Annie Laurie Leech Coll); Lowndes County Archives & Tennessee Williams Special
Publications: 1870 Federal Census Lowndes Co, Mississippi, Vol I Vol II; Cumulative Index to the Journal of Mississippi History Vol I-XV 1939-1953
Friends of the Library Group
Branches: 3
ARTESIA PUBLIC, Artesia, 39736. SAN 348-243X. Tel: 662-272-5255. FAX: 662-272-5255.
CALEDONIA PUBLIC, Main St, Caledonia, 39740. SAN 348-2464. Tel: 662-356-6384. FAX: 662-356-6384. *Librn*, Mary Betts-Williams
Friends of the Library Group
CRAWFORD PUBLIC, Main St, Crawford, 39743. SAN 348-2472. Tel: 662-272-5144. *Librn*, Mamie Brown

GL LOWNDES COUNTY LAW LIBRARY,* County Courthouse, Rm 210, PO Box 1364, 39703. SAN 327-2087. Tel: 662-329-5889. *Librn*, Lena Mae Duncan; Fax: 662-329-5870
Library Holdings: Bk Vols 12,000; Bk Titles 80
Open Mon-Fri 8-5

C MISSISSIPPI UNIVERSITY FOR WOMEN, John Clayton Fant Memorial Library, PO Box W1625, 39701. SAN 348-2499. Tel: 601-329-7332. Interlibrary Loan Service Tel: 601-329-7338. FAX: 601-329-7348. Web Site: www.muw.edu. *Dir, Ser, Syst Coordr*, Patricia H Matthes; Tel: 662-329-7333, E-Mail: pmatthes@mww.edu; *Circ*, Gail P Gunter; Tel: 662-329-7336, E-Mail: ggunter@mww.edu; *Cat*, Nancy J Wheeley; *Doc*, Laura M Young; Tel: 662-329-7339, E-Mail: lyoung@mww.edu; Staff 14 (MLS 6, Non-MLS 8)
Founded 1884
Library Holdings: Bk Vols 255,487; Per Subs 1,619
Subject Interests: Art and architecture, Behav sci, Education, Feminism, Home econ, Music, Nursing, Soc sci
Special Collections: George Eliot (Blanche Colton Williams' Biography of George Eliot), original mss; George Eliot First Editions & Criticisms; Mississippiana; State & Local Histroy (General E T Sykes Scrapbook Coll), clippings; University history, bks, micro
Database Vendor: DRA
Publications: Library Handbook
Partic in Magnolia; SE Libr Network; Solinet
Friends of the Library Group

COLUMBUS AFB

UNITED STATES AIR FORCE
A COLUMBUS AIR FORCE BASE LIBRARY, FL 3022 (AETC), 39710-5102. SAN 348-2553. Tel: 601-434-2934. FAX: 601-434-6291. *Librn*, Linda Dodson; Staff 6 (MLS 1, Non-MLS 5)
Library Holdings: Bk Vols 16,635; Per Subs 87
Subject Interests: Aviation, Mil strategy

CORINTH

P NORTHEAST REGIONAL LIBRARY,* 1023 Fillmore, 38834-4199. SAN 348-2588. Tel: 601-287-7311. FAX: 601-286-8010. Web Site: www.nereg.lib.ms.us. *Dir*, Elizabeth Cranwell; *Ch Servs*, Ann Coker; *Cat*, Suzanne Horton; *Cat*, Tommie Rafidi; *Coll Develop*, William McMullin; Staff 23 (MLS 5, Non-MLS 18)
Founded 1951. Pop 95,507; Circ 299,719
Oct 1997-Sep 1998 Income $737,604, State $196,369, City $61,500, Federal $8,416, County $360,350, Locally Generated Income $89,098. Mats Exp $77,000, Books $63,390, Per/Ser (Incl. Access Fees) $5,224, Presv $293. Sal $405,408 (Prof $146,142)
Library Holdings: Bk Vols 165,581; Bk Titles 93,334; Per Subs 237
Subject Interests: Genealogy
Friends of the Library Group
Branches: 13
ANNE SPENCER COX LIBRARY, Baldwyn, 38824. SAN 348-2642. Tel: 601-365-3305. FAX: 601-365-3305. *Librn*, Teresa Littlejohn
Library Holdings: Bk Vols 13,219
Friends of the Library Group
BELMONT LIBRARY, Belmont, 38827. SAN 348-2677. Tel: 601-454-7841. FAX: 601-454-7841. *Librn*, Shara Holley
Library Holdings: Bk Vols 10,567
Friends of the Library Group
BLUE MOUNTAIN LIBRARY, Blue Mountain, 38610. SAN 348-2707. Tel: 601-685-4721. *Librn*, Eva Marie Keith
Library Holdings: Bk Vols 4,509
BURNSVILLE LIBRARY, Burnsville, 38833. SAN 348-2731. Tel: 601-427-9258. FAX: 601-427-9258. *Librn*, Donna Burns
Library Holdings: Bk Vols 8,400
Friends of the Library Group
CHALYBEATE, Walnut, 38683. SAN 348-2766. *Librn*, Genette McKinney
Library Holdings: Bk Vols 4,990
CORINTH LIBRARY Tel: 601-287-2441. FAX: 601-286-8010. *Librn*, Ann Coker
Library Holdings: Bk Vols 50,728
Friends of the Library Group
GEORGE E ALLEN LIBRARY, Booneville, 38829. SAN 348-2820. Tel: 601-728-6553. FAX: 601-728-4127. *Librn*, Dana Moffitt
Library Holdings: Bk Vols 22,276
Friends of the Library Group
IUKA LIBRARY, Iuka, 38852. SAN 348-288X. Tel: 601-423-6300. FAX: 601-423-6300. *Librn*, Fredda Sanderson
Library Holdings: Bk Vols 19,285
Friends of the Library Group
MARGARET MCRAE MEMORIAL LIBRARY, Tishomingo, 38873. SAN 348-3002. Tel: 601-438-7640. FAX: 601-438-7640. *Librn*, Kathy Byram
Library Holdings: Bk Vols 5,729
Friends of the Library Group
MARIETTA LIBRARY, Marietta, 38856. SAN 348-291X. Tel: 601-728-9320. *Librn*, Cindy Ramey
Library Holdings: Bk Vols 3,347
RIENZI LIBRARY, Rienzi, 38865. SAN 348-2944. Tel: 601-462-5015. *Librn*, Rita Millsaps
Library Holdings: Bk Vols 5,286
RIPLEY LIBRARY, Ripley, 38663. SAN 348-2979. Tel: 601-837-7773. FAX: 601-837-7773. *Librn*, Tommy Covington
Library Holdings: Bk Vols 17,880
WALNUT LIBRARY, Walnut, 38683. SAN 348-3037. Tel: 601-223-6768. FAX: 601-223-6768. *Librn*, Helen Ray
Library Holdings: Bk Vols 5,882

DECATUR

J EAST CENTRAL COMMUNITY COLLEGE, Burton Library, PO Box 129, 39327. SAN 308-8510. Tel: 601-635-2111, Ext 219. FAX: 601-635-2150. Web Site: ccc.cc.ms.us. *Dir*, Ann Burkes; *Asst Librn*, Gail Wood; *Asst Librn*, Gloria Johnson; *Asst Librn, Tech Servs*, Todd Eldridge
Founded 1977. Enrl 1,200
Library Holdings: Bk Vols 38,000; Per Subs 237

D'IBERVILLE

P D'IBERVILLE LIBRARY,* 10391 Auto Mall Pkwy, 39532. SAN 376-625X. Tel: 228-392-2279. FAX: 228-396-9573. Web Site: www.harrison.ms.us. *Librn*, Nancy Soder; E-Mail: nsoder@harrison.lib.ms.us
Oct 1998-Sep 1999 Income $188,000. Mats Exp $42,650. Sal $100,000
Library Holdings: Bk Vols 14,500; Per Subs 30
Friends of the Library Group

D'LO

P D'LO PUBLIC LIBRARY, PO Box 147, 39062. SAN 376-6292. Tel: 601-847-7474. FAX: 601-847-1721. E-Mail: d'lo@cmrls.lib.ms.us. *Head of Libr*, Dana Phillips
Library Holdings: Bk Vols 1,000; Bk Titles 910
Mem of Central Mississippi Regional Library System
Friends of the Library Group

ELLISVILLE

J JONES COUNTY JUNIOR COLLEGE, T Terrell Tisdale Library, 900 S Court St, 39437. SAN 308-8529. Tel: 601-477-4055. FAX: 601-477-2600. E-Mail: library@jcjc.cc.ms.us. Web Site: www.jcjc.oc.ms.us/depts/lrc/index.html. *Dir*, Sandra Broadhead; *Media Spec*, Charles Cox; *Cat*, Gary Herring; *Publ Servs*, Kathleen Holifield; *Acq*, Barbara Jordan; *Online Servs*, Basil Smith
Founded 1924. Enrl 4,173; Fac 192
Library Holdings: Bk Titles 68,000; Per Subs 500
Special Collections: Genealogy; Literary Criticism on William Faulkner, James Joyce, Katherine Anne Porter & Eudora Welty, bks & flm; Mississippi Coll; Mississippiana flm
Automation Activity & Vendor Info: (Acquisitions) SIRSI; (Circulation) SIRSI
Publications: Library Handbook
Open Mon-Thurs 7:30-9, Fri 7:30-3:30

FLORA

P MADISON COUNTY LIBRARY SYSTEM, Flora Public Library, 168 Carter St, 39071. (Mail add: PO Box 356, 39071), SAN 348-1832. Tel: 601-879-8835. FAX: 601-879-8835. *Librn*, Janis B Watkins; E-Mail: jwatkins@mad.lib.ms.us; *Circ*, Sharon F Ertle; Staff 2 (Non-MLS 2)
Pop 2,000; Circ 11,268
Library Holdings: Bk Vols 15,000; Per Subs 10
Special Collections: Local history coll & old photographs of area
Automation Activity & Vendor Info: (Circulation) SIRSI
Database Vendor: Ebsco - EbscoHost
Partic in Madison County Libr Asn

FLORENCE

P FLORENCE PUBLIC LIBRARY,* PO Box 95, 39073. SAN 376-6276. Tel: 601-845-6032. FAX: 601-845-4625. E-Mail: florence@smrls.lib.ms.us. *Librn*, Jeanette Harper
Library Holdings: Bk Vols 16,000; Bk Titles 15,000; Per Subs 12
Mem of Central Mississippi Regional Library System
Friends of the Library Group

J WESLEY COLLEGE LIBRARY,* 111 Wesley Circle, PO Box 1070, 39073-1070. SAN 308-8537. Tel: 601-845-2265. FAX: 601-845-2266. E-Mail: weslib@netdoor.com. *Librn*, Janice G Parker
Library Holdings: Bk Vols 22,000; Per Subs 103
Subject Interests: English literature, Holiness lit
Partic in Central Mississippi Library Council (CMLC); Miss Libr Asn
Open Mon, Tues & Thurs 8:30-5 & 6-9:30, Wed & Fri 8:30-5

FOREST

P FOREST PUBLIC LIBRARY, 210 S Raleigh St, PO Box 737, 39074. SAN 376-6233. Tel: 601-469-1481. FAX: 601-469-5903. E-Mail: forest@cmrls.lib.ms.us. Web Site: www.cmrls.lib.ms.us. *Branch Mgr*, Tammy Jones
Oct 1997-Sep 1998 Income $48,630
Library Holdings: Bk Titles 10,000; Per Subs 25
Database Vendor: Ebsco - EbscoHost, epixtech, inc., GaleNet, OCLC - First Search, Wilson - Wilson Web
Function: Photocopies available
Mem of Central Mississippi Regional Library System
Friends of the Library Group

FULTON

J ITAWAMBA COMMUNITY COLLEGE, Learning Resource Center,* 602 W Hill, 38843. SAN 348-324X. Tel: 601-862-8000, Ext 237. FAX: 601-862-8410. *Dir*, Dr Glenda Segars; *Media Spec*, Terry Graham; *Ref*, Kelly Ann Griffiths; *Tech Servs*, Jennifer McFerrin; Staff 2 (MLS 2)
Library Holdings: Bk Titles 38,000; Per Subs 254
Special Collections: Mississippi Coll, vf
Partic in Loanet; Miss Interlibr Loan Syst; SE Libr Network

GAUTIER

C MISSISSIPPI GULF COAST COMMUNITY COLLEGE, Jackson County Campus Library, PO Box 100, 39553. SAN 308-8545. Tel: 228-497-7830. FAX: 228-497-7643. Web Site: www.2.mgccc.cc.ms.us/~lrc/jd-lrc-library-index.htm. *Dir*, Adner Pamela; *ILL*, Sandra Briggs; *Circ*, Cheryl Hinton; Staff 3 (MLS 3)
Founded 1965. Enrl 2,941; Fac 185 Sal $223,535 (Prof $169,512)
Library Holdings: Bk Vols 31,770; Per Subs 297
Partic in SE Libr Network

GOODMAN

J HOLMES COMMUNITY COLLEGE, McMorrough Library, PO Box 439, 39079. SAN 308-8553. Tel: 662-472-2312, Ext 1049. FAX: 662-472-2054. *Librn*, Kay Boggan; *Coll Develop*, Janet Halteman
Founded 1928. Enrl 1,136; Fac 75
Library Holdings: Bk Vols 46,000; Per Subs 514
Subject Interests: Juv, Mississippi, Shakespeare

GREENVILLE

P WASHINGTON COUNTY LIBRARY SYSTEM, (WCLS), William Alexander Percy Memorial Library, 341 Main St, 38701-4097. SAN 348-3274. Tel: 601-335-2331. FAX: 601-390-4758. *Dir*, Kay Clanton; E-Mail: kclanton@washington.lib.ms.us; *Ad Servs*, Chris Balducci; *Ch Servs*, Barbara Johnston; *Circ*, Valerie Moore; *ILL*, Ruth Ford; *Tech Servs*, Carolyn Oglesby; Staff 7 (MLS 2, Non-MLS 5)
Founded 1964. Pop 67,935; Circ 114,972
Oct 1999-Sep 2000 Income $802,767, State $139,229, City $264,242, County $399,296. Mats Exp $134,000, Books $110,000, Per/Ser (Incl. Access Fees) $15,000, Presv $1,000, Micro $8,000. Sal $641,639
Library Holdings: Bk Vols 280,188; Per Subs 394
Subject Interests: Genealogy, Local history, Miss hist
Special Collections: Greenville Writers Exhibit
Automation Activity & Vendor Info: (Cataloging) Gaylord
Friends of the Library Group
Branches: 5
ARCOLA LIBRARY, Arcola, 38722. SAN 348-3304. Tel: 601-827-5262. FAX: 601-827-5262. *Librn*, Geneva Hamilton
AVON LIBRARY, Avon, 38723. SAN 348-3339. Tel: 601-332-9346. FAX: 601-332-9346. *Librn*, Doris Jean Wilson
GLEN ALLAN LIBRARY, PO Box 39, Glen Allan, 38744. SAN 348-3428. Tel: 601-839-4066. FAX: 601-839-4066. *Librn*, Winnie Darnell
LELAND LIBRARY, 107 N Broad St, Leland, 38756. SAN 348-3363. Tel: 601-686-7353. FAX: 601-686-7353. *Librn*, Ellen Walker
Friends of the Library Group
TORREY WOOD MEMORIAL, 302 East Ave N, Hollandale, 38748. SAN 348-3398. Tel: 601-827-2335. FAX: 601-827-2335. *Librn*, Andrea Ross
Bookmobiles: 1

GREENWOOD

S COTTONLANDIA EDUCATIONAL & RECREATIONAL FOUNDATION, INC, R A Billups Memorial Library, 1608 Hwy 82 W, 38930. SAN 370-7555. Tel: 662-453-0925. FAX: 662-455-7556. *Exec Dir*, Robin S Person; E-Mail: rsperson@tecinfo.com
Founded 1974
1999-2000 Mats Exp $600, Books $500, Presv $100
Library Holdings: Bk Vols 800; Per Subs 10
Special Collections: Archeology (Mississippi) bks, papers; History (Mississippi) bks

P GREENWOOD-LEFLORE PUBLIC LIBRARY SYSTEM,* 405 W Washington, 38930-4297. SAN 348-3452. Tel: 601-453-3634. *Dir*, Susan Harris; *Ad Servs, Circ*, Diane Mosley; Staff 14 (MLS 4, Non-MLS 10)
Founded 1914. Pop 36,907; Circ 110,670
Oct 1996-Sep 1997 Income $389,924, State $68,511, City $153,527, County $148,750, Locally Generated Income $19,136. Mats Exp $47,233, Books $38,766, Per/Ser (Incl. Access Fees) $6,235, Micro $2,232. Sal $304,230 (Prof $77,361)
Library Holdings: Bk Vols 93,624; Per Subs 209
Subject Interests: Genealogy
Special Collections: Genealogy (Mae Wilson McBee Coll), bk, microfilm
Branches: 2
ITTA BENA BRANCH, 305 Thurman, Itta Bena, 38941. SAN 348-3487. Tel: 601-254-7790. *Librn*, Peggy Muse
Library Holdings: Bk Vols 2,000
JODIE WILSON BRANCH, 209 E Martin Luther King Jr Dr, 38930. SAN 348-3606. Tel: 601-453-1761. *Librn*, Alma Ward
Library Holdings: Bk Vols 925; Per Subs 14

GRENADA

P ELIZABETH JONES LIBRARY, 1050 Fairfield Ave, 38901-3605. (Mail add: PO Box 130, 38902-0130), SAN 308-8561. Tel: 662-226-2072. FAX: 662-226-2072. E-Mail: 2pej@elizabeth.lib.ms.us. Web Site: www.elizabeth.lib.ms.us. *Librn*, Mary Hardy McElwain; *Circ*, Sandra McCaulla; *Circ*, Stella Topps; *Tech Servs*, Pam Davis; Staff 4 (MLS 1, Non-MLS 3)
Founded 1933. Pop 21,043; Circ 87,563
Oct 1999-Sep 2000 Income $232,273. Sal $101,104 (Prof $48,000)
Library Holdings: Bk Vols 46,043; Per Subs 80
Automation Activity & Vendor Info: (Acquisitions) Gaylord
Partic in Miss Libr Asn; Miss Libr Comn Interlibr Loan Network
Open Mon-Sat 10-5:30

GULFPORT

R FIRST UNITED METHODIST CHURCH LIBRARY, 2301 15th St, 39501. SAN 308-857X. Tel: 228-863-0047. FAX: 228-863-7729.
Founded 1965
Library Holdings: Bk Vols 1,400
Special Collections: Christian Literature
Open Mon-Fri 8:30-4

GL HARRISON COUNTY LAW LIBRARY,* 1801 23rd Ave, 39501. SAN 308-8588. Tel: 228-865-4068. FAX: 228-865-4067. *Librn*, Fran J Perry
Founded 1967
Library Holdings: Bk Vols 24,000; Bk Titles 1,500
Subject Interests: Mississippi
Partic in Westlaw

P HARRISON COUNTY LIBRARY SYSTEM, 1300 21st Ave, 39501-2081. SAN 308-8596. Tel: 228-868-1383. FAX: 228-863-7433. Web Site: www.harrison.lib.ms.us. *Dir*, Robert Lipscomb; Tel: 228-868-1383, Ext 22, E-Mail: robertl@harrison.lib.ms.us; *Tech Servs*, Michael Webb; *ILL*, Diane McGee; Staff 74 (MLS 8, Non-MLS 66)
Founded 1916. Pop 190,000; Circ 660,447

Oct 1998-Sep 1999 Income (Main Library and Branch Library) $2,699,575, State $346,742, City $972,000, County $900,941, Locally Generated Income $80,000, Other $523,777. Mats Exp $533,500, Books $385,000, Per/Ser (Incl. Access Fees) $40,000, Electronic Ref Mat (Incl. Access Fees) $108,500. Sal $1,589,300
Library Holdings: Bk Vols 275,560; Per Subs 608
Subject Interests: Art, Careers, Genealogy, Local history, Maps
Automation Activity & Vendor Info: (Cataloging) epixtech, inc.; (Circulation) epixtech, inc.
Database Vendor: epixtech, inc.
Publications: Directory of Academic, High School, Public & Special Libraries in Harrison County
Friends of the Library Group
Branches: 1
ORANGE GROVE, 12031 Mobile Ave, 39503-3175. SAN 377-0001. Tel: 228-832-6924. FAX: 228-832-6926. *Librn*, Gwen Farned
Founded 1975
Library Holdings: Bk Titles 10,000; Per Subs 15
Friends of the Library Group

J MISSISSIPPI GULF COAST COMMUNITY COLLEGE, (MGK), Jefferson Davis Campus Learning Resource Center, 2226 Switzer Rd, 39507. SAN 308-860X. Tel: 228-896-2514. FAX: 228-896-2521. Web Site: www2.mgccc.cc.ms.us/~lrc/jd_lrc_library_index.htm. *Dir*, Foster Flint; *Asst Librn*, Dianne Hurlbert; Tel: 228-897-3880, E-Mail: dianne.hurlbert@mgccc.cc.ms.us; *Asst Librn*, Nancy Wilcox; E-Mail: nancy.wilcox@mgccc.cc.ms.us; *Coll Develop*, Charles M Clark; E-Mail: charles.clark@mgccc.cc.ms.us
Enrl 3,203
Library Holdings: Bk Vols 40,107; Per Subs 280
Special Collections: McNaughton
Automation Activity & Vendor Info: (OPAC) SIRSI
Publications: Acquisitions Bibliographies; Orientation & Reference Guides
Partic in Solinet
Open Mon-Thurs 7:30-8:30, Fri 7:30-4

UNITED STATES NAVY
A NAVAL CONSTRUCTION BATTALION CENTER BASE LIBRARY, MWR CBC Library Code 300, Rm 201, 1800 Dong Xoai Ave, 39501. SAN 348-372X. Tel: 228-871-2409. FAX: 228-871-2539. *Librn*, Marie Ritson; Tel: 228-871-3326. Subject Specialists: *English literature*, Marie Ritson; Staff 2 (Non-MLS 2)
Founded 1966
Library Holdings: Bk Vols 12,600; Per Subs 45
Restriction: Circulation to military employees only

C WILLIAM CAREY COLLEGE ON THE COAST, McMullan Learning Resources Center, 1856 Beach Dr, 39507. SAN 348-3932. Tel: 228-897-7100. FAX: 228-897-7212. E-Mail: wccc@mail.netdoor.com, wccl@netdoor.com. *Librn*, Peggy H Gossage; *Tech Servs*, Theresa Addison; Staff 2 (MLS 1, Non-MLS 1)
Library Holdings: Bk Titles 18,000; Per Subs 100

HARRISVILLE

P HARRISVILLE PUBLIC LIBRARY,* 1767 Simpson Hwy 469, PO Box 307, 39082. SAN 376-6373. Tel: 601-847-1268. *Librn*, Willie Jean Shorter
Library Holdings: Bk Titles 4,000
Mem of Central Mississippi Regional Library System
Friends of the Library Group

HATTIESBURG

R FIRST BAPTIST CHURCH, DH Reed Memorial Library, 510 W Pine St, 39401. SAN 308-8626. Tel: 601-544-0100. FAX: 601-584-8592. *Dir*, Dr Al Foy; Staff 3 (Non-MLS 3)
Founded 1953
Library Holdings: Bk Vols 10,000; Per Subs 20
Special Collections: Bible Study Commentaries
Open Mon-Fri 9-4

M FORREST GENERAL HOSPITAL, Library Services, 6051 Hwy 49 S, 39402. (Mail add: PO Box 16389, 39402), SAN 325-478X. Tel: 601-288-4260. FAX: 601-288-4280. *Librn*, Bettye M Duncan; Tel: 601-288-4261; Staff 1 (MLS 1)
Founded 1973
Library Holdings: Bk Vols 495; Per Subs 42
Subject Interests: Medicine
Partic in Mississippi Biomedical Library Consortium; Nat Libr of Med

S HATTIESBURG AMERICAN LIBRARY,* 825 N Main St. (Mail add: PO Box 1111, 39403-1111), SAN 372-5650. Tel: 601-582-4321. FAX: 601-584-3130. *Librn*, Stephan Payne
Founded 1986
Library Holdings: Bk Titles 200
Special Collections: Newspaper on Microfilm since 1908

P THE LIBRARY OF HATTIESBURG, PETAL, FORREST COUNTY, 329 Hardy St, 39401-3496. SAN 348-3754. Tel: 601-582-4461. Reference Tel: 601-584-3163. FAX: 601-582-5338. E-Mail: staffmail@hpfc.lib.ms.us. Web Site: www.hpfc.lib.ms.us. *Dir*, Pamela J Pridgen; E-Mail: ppridgen@hpte.lib.ms.us; *Ad Servs*, Donna Davis; *Ch Servs*, Philis Bodl; *Ref, Syst Programmer*, Sean Farrell; *Head, Cat, Head Tech Servs*, Alisa St Amant; Tel: 601-584-3164, Fax: 601-584-3168, E-Mail: hpfctraining@yahoo.com; *Head, Circ*, Deborah Herrington; Staff 37 (MLS 5, Non-MLS 32)
Founded 1916. Pop 74,927; Circ 184,569
Oct 1999-Sep 2000 Income (Main Library and Branch Library) $1,172,802. Mats Exp $172,000. Sal $526,000
Library Holdings: Bk Vols 120,000; Per Subs 222
Subject Interests: Genealogy, Mississippi
Special Collections: Adult New Reader's Coll
Automation Activity & Vendor Info: (Cataloging) Gaylord
Database Vendor: DRA, Ebsco - EbscoHost, GaleNet, OCLC - First Search, Wilson - Wilson Web
Publications: The Library Newsletter (Newsletter)
Friends of the Library Group
Branches: 1
PETAL BRANCH, 714 S Main St, Petal, 39465. SAN 348-3789. Tel: 601-584-7610. FAX: 601-582-0176. Web Site: www.hpfc.lib.ms.us. *Mgr*, Pamela S Pridgen
Library Holdings: Bk Vols 12,748
Friends of the Library Group

C UNIVERSITY OF SOUTHERN MISSISSIPPI LIBRARY, Box 5053, 39406. SAN 348-3843. Tel: 601-266-4241. Interlibrary Loan Service Tel: 601-266-4256. Circulation Tel: 601-266-4250. Reference Tel: 601-266-4249. FAX: 601-266-6033. Web Site: www.lib.usm.edu. *Dean of Libr*, James R Martin; E-Mail: jim.martin@usm.edu; *Publ Servs*, Kay Wall; Tel: 601-266-4362, E-Mail: kay.wall@usm.edu; *Cat*, Ann Branton; Tel: 601-266-4350, E-Mail: ann.branton@usm.edu; *Acq*, Nancy Kaul; Tel: 601-266-5078, E-Mail: nancy.kaul@usm.edu; *ILL*, Karolyn Thompson; Tel: 601-266-5111, E-Mail: karolyn.thompson@usm.edu; *Circ*, Kaylene Behm; Tel: 601-266-4251, E-Mail: kaylene.behm@usm.edu; *Ref*, Cheryl Laughlin; Tel: 601-266-4270, E-Mail: sherry.laughlin@usm.edu; *Dir, Tech Serv*, Carol Cubberley; E-Mail: carol.cubberley@usm.edu; *Ser*, Carol Green; Tel: 601-266-4476, E-Mail: carol.green@usm.edu; Staff 65 (MLS 30, Non-MLS 35)
Founded 1910. Enrl 14,500; Fac 618; Highest Degree: Doctorate
Jul 1999-Jun 2000 Income (Main Library Only) $5,562,338, State $5,254,066, Locally Generated Income $142,852, Other $165,420. Mats Exp $2,321,396, Books $272,093, Per/Ser (Incl. Access Fees) $1,821,455, Presv $62,430, Micro $109,969, AV Equip $55,449. (Prof $1,304,448)
Library Holdings: Bk Vols 972,812; Per Subs 21,599
Subject Interests: Biology, Bus, Chemistry, Computers, Criminal justice, Education, Letters, Libr sci, Mgt, Music, Nursing, Polymer sci, Psychology
Automation Activity & Vendor Info: (Acquisitions) SIRSI; (Cataloging) SIRSI; (Circulation) SIRSI; (Course Reserve) SIRSI; (Media Booking) SIRSI; (OPAC) SIRSI; (Serials) SIRSI
Database Vendor: CARL, Ebsco - EbscoHost, IAC - Info Trac, OCLC - First Search, ProQuest, Silverplatter Information Inc., Wilson - Wilson Web
Publications: Juvenile Miscellany; Library Focus Newsletter
Partic in SE Libr Network
Departmental Libraries:
RICHARD G COX LIBRARY
See Separate Entry in Long Beach
MEDIA RESOURCES CENTER, PO Box 5082, 39406-5082. SAN 369-7754. Tel: 601-266-4356. FAX: 601-266-4410. Web Site: www.lib.usm.edu/.
Founded 1976
1996-1997 Income $130,502. Mats Exp $25,624, AV Equip $22,160. Sal $88,368 (Prof $32,880)
WILLIAM DAVID MCCAIN LIBRARY & ARCHIVES, PO Box 5148, 39406-5148. SAN 369-772X. Tel: 601-266-4345. Web Site: www.lib.usm.edu/mccain.htm/. *Cat, Ref*, Antoinette Nelson; *Curator, Spec Coll*, Dolores A Jones; *Archivist*, Bobs Tusa; *Spec Coll*, P Toby Graham; Staff 6 (MLS 4, Non-MLS 2)
Founded 1976
1997-1998 Income $268,539
Library Holdings: Bk Vols 79,379
Subject Interests: 19th-20th Century Am Lit, 19th-20th Century British, Art for children, Civil War, Drawings, Editorial cartoons, Genealogy, Hist of South, Lit for children, Literary criticism, Miss docs, Miss fiction, Miss mss, Miss publications
Special Collections: Association of American Editorial Cartoonists Coll; Association of American Railroads Coll; Children's Literature (Lena Y de Grummond Coll); Cleanth Brooks Literature Coll; Confederate Literature (Ernest A Walen Coll); Genealogy Coll; Gulf, Mobile & Ohio Railroad Records Coll; Mississippiana Coll; Papers of Mississippi Governor & United States Senator Theodore C Bilbo, 1915-1947; Papers of Mississippi Governors Paul Johnson Sr & Paul Johnson Jr, 1917-1970; Papers of United States Representatives William M Colmer, 1933-1973; Paul Yoder Marching Band Music Coll; Rare Book Coll; University Archives
Publications: Juvenile Miscellany (newsletter of the de Grummond Coll)
Partic in OCLC Online Computer Library Center, Inc; SE Libr Network

C WILLIAM CAREY COLLEGE, I E Rouse Library, 498 Tuscan Ave, 39401. SAN 348-3878. Tel: 601-582-6169. FAX: 601-582-6171. Web Site: www.wmcarey.edu. *Dir*, Dr Kyle S Jones; Tel: 601-582-6170, E-Mail: kjones@wmcarey.edu; *Admin Assoc*, Kay Cummins; Tel: 601-582-6782, E-Mail: kcummins@wmcarey.edu; *Publ Servs*, Jim D Myers; E-Mail: jmyers@wmcarey.edu; *Librn*, Peggy Gossage; Tel: 228-897-7212; *Librn*, Julie Schiavo; Tel: 504-286-3291; *Tech Servs*, Patrivan Yuen; Tel: 601-582-6781, E-Mail: pyuen@wmcarey.edu; *Cat*, John Ochola; Tel: 601-582-6783; *Regional Librarian*, Peggy Gossage; Tel: 228-897-7212, Fax: 228-897-7212, E-Mail: wccl@mail.netdoor.com. Subject Specialists: *History*, Jim D Myers; Staff 7 (MLS 4, Non-MLS 3)
Founded 1911. Enrl 2,400; Fac 116; Highest Degree: Master
Jul 2000-Jun 2001 Income (Main Library Only) Parent Institution $445,880. Mats Exp $92,929, Books $46,729, Per/Ser (Incl. Access Fees) $41,291, Micro $4,909. Sal $214,344
Library Holdings: Bk Titles 73,057; Per Subs 371
Subject Interests: Business, Education, Music, Nursing, Relig studies
Special Collections: Church Music (Clarence Dickinson Coll)

HAZLEHURST

P COPIAH-JEFFERSON REGIONAL LIBRARY, George W Covington Memorial Library, 223 S Extension St, 39083-3339. SAN 348-3967. Tel: 601-894-1681. FAX: 601-894-1672. Web Site: www.copjef.lib.ms.us. *Coll Develop, Dir*, Paul C Cartwright; Staff 17 (MLS 1, Non-MLS 16)
Founded 1950. Pop 36,500; Circ 70,760
Oct 1998-Sep 1999 Income (Main Library and Branch Library) $320,000, State $120,000, City $65,000, County $135,000. Mats Exp $37,200, Books $30,000, Per/Ser (Incl. Access Fees) $2,800, Other Print Mats $4,400. Sal $170,000 (Prof $32,000)
Library Holdings: Bk Vols 45,000
Subject Interests: Black hist
Special Collections: Mississippi Coll
Automation Activity & Vendor Info: (Cataloging) Sagebrush Corporation; (Circulation) Sagebrush Corporation
Friends of the Library Group
Branches: 5
GEORGETOWN PUBLIC, PO Box 138, Georgetown, 39078-0138. SAN 377-9955.
HAZELHURST BRANCH (HQ) Tel: 601-894-1681. FAX: 601-844-1672. Web Site: www.copjef.lib.ms.us. *Librn*, Catherine P Young
Friends of the Library Group
J T BIGGS JR MEMORIAL, 200 S Jackson St, Crystal Springs, 39059. SAN 348-4025. Tel: 601-892-3205. *Librn*, Gwen Gallman
Friends of the Library Group
JEFFERSON COUNTY, PO Box 578, Fayette, 39069. SAN 348-405X. Tel: 601-786-3982. FAX: 601-786-9646. *Librn*, Marilyn Felton
LONGIE DALE HAMILTON MEMORIAL, PO Box 299, Wesson, 39191. SAN 348-4084. Tel: 601-643-5725. *Librn*, Elene Hutson
Friends of the Library Group
Bookmobiles: 1

M HARDY WILSON MEMORIAL HOSPITAL LIBRARY,* 233 Magnolia St, PO Box 889, 39083. SAN 308-8642. Tel: 601-894-4541, Ext 338. FAX: 601-894-5800. *Dir*, Rachel McCardle
Library Holdings: Bk Vols 90; Per Subs 4
Open Mon-Fri 7:30-4

HERNANDO

P FIRST REGIONAL LIBRARY, 370 W Commerce St, PO Box 386, 38632. SAN 348-4114. Tel: 662-429-4439. FAX: 662-429-8853. Web Site: www.first.lib.ms.us. *Dir*, James F Anderson; E-Mail: jima@first.lib.ms.us; *Asst Libr Dir, Publ Servs*, Catherine Nathan; E-Mail: cnathan@first.lib.ms.us; *Librn*, Diane Davis; *Ch Servs*, Victoria Penny; E-Mail: vpenny@first.lib.ms.us; *Cat*, Clara Gibson; *Tech Servs*, Kim Polk; E-Mail: kpolk@first.lib.ms.us; *Ref*, Ruth Pierce; E-Mail: rpierce@first.lib.ms.us; Staff 90 (MLS 17, Non-MLS 73)
Founded 1950. Pop 203,610; Circ 1,170,657
Oct 1999-Sep 2000 Income (Main Library and Branch Library) $3,057,913, State $483,018, City $640,587, Federal $125,781, County $1,454,431, Locally Generated Income $193,490, Other $160,606. Mats Exp $475,265, Books $362,177, Per/Ser (Incl. Access Fees) $29,233, AV Equip $80,599. Sal $1,677,872 (Prof $647,586)
Library Holdings: Bk Vols 498,005; Bk Titles 249,002
Special Collections: Mississippi Authors & History
Automation Activity & Vendor Info: (Acquisitions) epixtech, inc.; (Cataloging) epixtech, inc.; (Circulation) epixtech, inc.
Database Vendor: Ebsco - EbscoHost, GaleNet, OCLC - First Search, Wilson - Wilson Web
Publications: What's Happening (quarterly newsletter)
Open Mon-Fri 9:30-7
Branches: 13
BATESVILLE PUBLIC, 206 Hwy 51 N, Batesville, 38606. SAN 348-4149. Tel: 601-563-4447. FAX: 601-563-6640. *Librn*, Mollie Gillespie
Friends of the Library Group
BJ CHAIN LIBRARY, 6619 S Cockrum, Olive Branch, 38654. SAN 348-4173. Tel: 601-895-5900. FAX: 601-895-9171. *Librn*, Mary Agnes Ledbetter
COLDWATER PUBLIC, PO Box 591, Coldwater, 38618. SAN 348-4203. Tel: 662-622-5573. FAX: 662-622-5573. *Librn*, Tenise Faulkner
Friends of the Library Group
EMILY JONES POINTER LIBRARY, PO Box 128, Como, 38619. SAN 348-4262. Tel: 601-526-5283. FAX: 601-526-5283. *Librn*, Maggie Moran
Friends of the Library Group
HERNANDO PUBLIC, 370 W Commerce St, PO Box 386, 38632. Tel: 662-429-4439. FAX: 662-429-8853. *Head Librn*, Diane Davis
Open Mon-Thurs 9:30-7, Fri 9:30-5:30, Sat 9:30-3
LAFAYETTE COUNTY-OXFORD PUBLIC, 401 Bramlett Blvd, Oxford, 38655. SAN 348-4351. Tel: 601-234-5751. FAX: 601-234-3155. *Librn*, Dorothy Fitts
Friends of the Library Group
MR DAVIS LIBRARY, 8889 Northwest Dr, Southaven, 38671. SAN 348-4440. Tel: 601-342-0102. FAX: 601-342-0556. *Librn*, Linda Jowers
Friends of the Library Group
MR DYE PUBLIC, 2885 Goodman Rd, Horn Lake, 38637. SAN 348-4297. Tel: 601-393-5654. FAX: 601-393-5654. *Librn*, Sandy Farrell
Friends of the Library Group
ROBERT C IRWIN LIBRARY, 1285 Kenny Hill Ave, Tunica, 38676. SAN 348-4327. Tel: 601-363-2162. FAX: 601-357-5929. *Librn*, Millee Wrenn
Friends of the Library Group
SAM LAPIDUS MEMORIAL LIBRARY, PO Box 246, Crenshaw, 38621. SAN 348-4238. Tel: 601-382-7479. FAX: 601-382-7479. *Librn*, Cathy Carter
Friends of the Library Group
SARDIS PUBLIC, 101 McLaurin St, Sardis, 38666. SAN 348-4386. Tel: 601-487-2126. FAX: 601-487-2126. *Librn*, Barbara Evans
Friends of the Library Group
SENATOBIA PUBLIC, 222 Ward St, Senatobia, 38668. SAN 348-4416. Tel: 601-562-6791. FAX: 601-562-6791. *Librn*, Laurie Madsen
Friends of the Library Group
WALLS PUBLIC, 7181 Delta Bluff Pkwy, Walls, 38680. Tel: 662-781-3664. FAX: 662-781-3427. *Head Librn*, Mary Jane Starnes
Open Mon-Thurs 10-6, Fri 10-5:30 & Sat 10-2

HICKORY FLAT

P HICKORY FLAT PUBLIC LIBRARY,* PO Box 309, 38633. SAN 376-6268. Tel: 662-333-7663. FAX: 662-333-7663. E-Mail: hflat@benton.lib.ms.us. Web Site: www.hflat.lib.ms.us. *Librn*, Earlene Reed
Library Holdings: Bk Titles 6,000; Per Subs 20

HOLLY SPRINGS

P MARSHALL COUNTY LIBRARY SYSTEM, 109 E Gholson Ave, 38635. SAN 348-4475. Tel: 662-252-3823. FAX: 662-252-3066. *Dir*, Diane Schule; Staff 10 (MLS 1, Non-MLS 9)
Founded 1955. Pop 33,000; Circ 55,000
Library Holdings: Bk Titles 40,000; Per Subs 75
Special Collections: Marshall County Historical & Genealogical Coll
Database Vendor: Dialog, IAC - Info Trac, OVID Technologies, Wilson - Wilson Web
Function: Some telephone reference
Open Mon-Fri 8-6, Sat 9-1
Friends of the Library Group
Branches: 2
POTTS CAMP PUBLIC, PO Box 427, Potts Camp, 38659. SAN 348-4564. Tel: 601-333-7068. *Librn*, Mrs Willie Clayton
RUTH B FRENCH LIBRARY, 213 Church St, PO Box 325, Byhalia, 38611. SAN 348-4505. Tel: 662-838-4024. *Librn*, Esther Jones

C RUST COLLEGE, Leontyne Price Library, 150 E Rust Ave, 38635. SAN 308-8669. Tel: 662-252-4661. FAX: 662-252-6107. *Librn*, Anita W Moore; E-Mail: amoore@rustcollege.edu; Staff 7 (MLS 2, Non-MLS 5)
Founded 1866. Enrl 1,100; Fac 56; Highest Degree: Bachelor
Library Holdings: Bk Titles 115,000; Per Subs 366
Special Collections: International Coll; Roy Wilkins Coll; United Methodist Religious Coll
Publications: acquisition list (quarterly); circulation handbook, collection development handbook; library manual; Roy Wilkins Special Collections Book
Partic in Coop Col Libr Ctr, Inc; Solinet
Library is named for Metropolitan Opera star, Leontyne Price

INDIANOLA

P SUNFLOWER COUNTY LIBRARY SYSTEM,* 201 Cypress Dr, 38751-2499. SAN 348-4599. Tel: 601-887-1672. Interlibrary Loan Service Tel: 601-887-2298. FAX: 601-887-2153. *Dir*, Mike Jones; *Asst Librn*, Joann Ware; *ILL, Tech Servs*, Darlene Bradshaw

Founded 1938. Pop 35,129; Circ 63,129
Library Holdings: Bk Vols 93,788; Bk Titles 58,259; Per Subs 147
Partic in OCLC Online Computer Library Center, Inc
Friends of the Library Group
Branches: 6
DREW PUBLIC, 290 W Park Ave, Drew, 38737-3340. SAN 348-4629. Tel: 601-745-2237. FAX: 601-745-2237. *Librn*, Denise Fountain
Library Holdings: Bk Vols 17,000
HENRY M SEYMOUR LIBRARY, 200 E Percy St, 38751-2499. SAN 348-4718. Tel: 601-887-1672. FAX: 601-887-2641. *Librn*, Geneva Allen
Library Holdings: Bk Vols 45,588
Friends of the Library Group
HORACE STANSEL MEMORIAL, 112 Ruby St, Ruleville, 38771-3939. SAN 348-4653. Tel: 601-756-2226. FAX: 601-756-2226. *Librn*, Maudine Richardson
Library Holdings: Bk Vols 12,200
Friends of the Library Group
INVERNESS PUBLIC, 802 E Grand Ave, PO Box 206, Inverness, 38753-0206. SAN 348-4688. Tel: 601-265-5179. FAX: 601-265-5179. *Librn*, Elloise Sheffield
Library Holdings: Bk Vols 10,000
KATHY JUNE SHERIFF LIBRARY, 1001 Delta Ave, PO Box 178, Moorhead, 38761-0178. SAN 348-4742. Tel: 601-246-8263. FAX: 601-246-8263. *Librn*, Lillian Nash
Library Holdings: Bk Vols 10,000
SUNFLOWER PUBLIC, PO Box 280, Sunflower, 39778-0280. SAN 348-4777. Tel: 601-569-2335. *Librn*, Leslie Downey
Library Holdings: Bk Vols 5,987

ITTA BENA

C MISSISSIPPI VALLEY STATE UNIVERSITY, James Herbert White Library, 14000 Hwy 82 W, 38941. SAN 308-8685. Tel: 662-254-3495. FAX: 662-254-6704. Web Site: www.mvsu.edu/library. *Actg Librn*, Katie Dugan; *Asst Librn, Circ*, Nathan McDonald; Tel: 662-254-3500, E-Mail: bigmac@mvsu.edu; *Media Spec*, Bobbie Wicks; Tel: 662-254-7831, E-Mail: bwicks@mvsu.edu; *Ser*, Ethel B Bowen; Tel: 662-254-3496, E-Mail: ebowen@mvsu.edu; *Cat*, Henry O White; Tel: 662-254-3498, E-Mail: hwhite@mvsu.edu; Staff 14 (MLS 5, Non-MLS 9)
Founded 1952. Enrl 2,509; Highest Degree: Master
Jun 1999-Jul 2000 Income $875,992. Mats Exp $343,410. Sal $532,582
Library Holdings: Bk Vols 130,918; Per Subs 599
Subject Interests: Education, Mississippi, Negroes
Special Collections: Martin Luther King Shelf; Mississippi Coll
Automation Activity & Vendor Info: (Acquisitions) Endeavor; (Cataloging) Endeavor; (Circulation) Endeavor; (Serials) Endeavor
Publications: James Herbert White Library Newsletter
Function: Reference services available
Mem of ALA American Library Association, AMBAC, AMEREI
Partic in Magnolia
Open Mon-Fri 8-10, Sun 2-10

JACKSON

M BAPTIST HEALTH SYSTEMS, J Manning Hudson Health Science Library,* 1225 N State St, 39202-2002. SAN 370-5048. Tel: 601-968-4187. FAX: 601-960-3307. *Librn*, Cecelia Delbridge; E-Mail: cdelbridge@mbmc.org
Sep 1997-Aug 1998 Mats Exp $40,000, Books $8,000, Per/Ser (Incl. Access Fees) $32,000. Sal $35,000
Library Holdings: Per Subs 150
Subject Interests: Medicine, Nursing
Restriction: Medical staff only
Partic in Mississippi Biomedical Library Consortium; Nat Libr of Med

C BELHAVEN COLLEGE, Warren A Hood Library, 1500 Peachtree St, 39202. SAN 308-8693. FAX: 601-968-5968. Web Site: www.belhaven.edu/hood.htm. *Dir*, Gretchen Cook; Tel: 601-968-5948, Ext 5947; *Circ*, Chris Cullnane; *Circ*, Leslie Gentry; *Tech Servs*, Andy Evers; *Cat*, Geraldine Harrison; *Per, Ref*, Margaret Root; *Acq*, Carrie Wallis
Founded 1910. Enrl 1,300
Library Holdings: Bk Vols 107,000; Per Subs 483
Subject Interests: Art, Music, Presbyterian records, Relig studies
Partic in SE Libr Network
Open Mon-Thurs 8-11pm, Fri 8-5, Sat 9-5, hours vary during breaks & summer

SR CATHOLIC DIOCESE OF JACKSON ARCHIVES, 237 E Amite St, PO Box 2248, 39225-2248. SAN 375-040X. Tel: 601-969-1880. FAX: 601-960-8455. *Archivist*, Jo Ann B Haien; Staff 1 (MLS 1)
Special Collections: Papers of the Diocese dating back to 1837
Restriction: By appointment only, Circulates for staff only, Not a lending library, Not open to public, Open to others by appointment, Open to public with supervision only, Open to students, Private library
Function: Archival collection, For research purposes, Photocopies available

GM DEPARTMENT OF VETERANS AFFAIRS, Medical Center Library,* 1500 E Woodrow Wilson Dr, 39216. SAN 308-8855. Tel: 601-364-1273. FAX: 601-364-1316. *Chief Librn*, Carol Sistrunk
Founded 1946
Oct 1997-Sep 1998 Income $104,000. Mats Exp $146,000. Sal $96,000
Library Holdings: Bk Titles 2,120; Per Subs 316
Partic in Central Mississippi Consortium Of Medical Libraries (CMCML); Mississippi Biomedical Library Consortium; Veterans Affairs Library Network
Open Mon-Fri 8-4:30

L HEIDELBERG & WOODLIFF, Law Library,* PO Box 23040, 39225. SAN 372-4352. Tel: 601-948-3800. FAX: 601-353-2961. Web Site: www.hwpa.com. *Librn*, Debbie Hardin
Library Holdings: Bk Vols 7,000; Per Subs 200
Restriction: Private library

C INFORMATION SERVICES LIBRARY, 3825 Ridgewood Rd, 39211. SAN 308-8839. Tel: 601-432-6313. FAX: 601-432-6314. *Dir*, Dr L H Sanders; *Librn*, Alma Blakely; *Librn*, Linda Lewis
Founded 1971
Library Holdings: Bk Vols 30,000; Per Subs 500
Subject Interests: Bus, Census, Demographic, Soc work
Partic in Miss Libr Asn
Affiliated with Jackson State University - H T Sampson Library

C JACKSON STATE UNIVERSITY, Henry Thomas Sampson Library, 1325 J R Lynch St, 39217. SAN 308-8723. Tel: 601-979-2123. FAX: 601-979-2358. *Dir*, Dr Lou Helen Sanders; *Circ*, Melissa Druckery; *Per*, Bernadine Beasley; *Cat, Online Servs*, Linda Lewis; *ILL*, Etherlene Norwood; *Ref*, William Jones
Founded 1877. Enrl 6,700; Fac 330; Highest Degree: Doctorate
Library Holdings: Bk Vols 1,000,000; Bk Titles 600,000; Per Subs 1,589
Subject Interests: Humanities, Soc sci
Special Collections: Black Studies (Afro-American), bks, discs, pamphlets
Automation Activity & Vendor Info: (Circulation) Innovative Interfaces Inc.
Publications: Bibliographies; library handbook; reference guides
Partic in BRS; Dialog Corporation; SE Libr Network

P JACKSON-HINDS LIBRARY SYSTEM, 300 N State St, 39201-1799. SAN 348-4807. Tel: 601-968-5811. Reference Tel: 601-968-5803, 601-968-5809. FAX: 601-968-5817. *Exec Dir*, Marion W Francis; E-Mail: mfrancis@jhls.lib.ms.us; *Dep Dir*, Carolyn McCallum; *Automation Syst Coordr*, Randy Wilson; *Tech Servs*, Loraine Bethany; *Coll Develop*, Marsha Case; Staff 38 (MLS 12, Non-MLS 26)
Founded 1986. Pop 251,031; Circ 634,537
Library Holdings: Bk Vols 506,495; Per Subs 889
Special Collections: Mississippi Writers
Friends of the Library Group
Branches: 15
A E WOOD LIBRARY, 111 Clinton Blvd, Clinton, 39056-5121. SAN 348-498X. Tel: 601-924-5684. FAX: 601-924-5086. *Librn*, William Yount; Staff 5 (MLS 1, Non-MLS 4)
Open: Mon-Thurs 9-9, Fri 9-6, Sat 9-5
Friends of the Library Group
BEVERLY J BROWN LIBRARY, 7395 S Siwell Rd, PO Box 72013, 39272-0013. SAN 374-4159. Tel: 601-372-0954, 601-373-7164. FAX: 601-373-7164. *Librn*, Carolyn Carter; Staff 2 (Non-MLS 2)
Open: Mon-Thurs 10-7, Fri 10-6, Sat 10-2
Friends of the Library Group
COLONIAL MART, 5070 Parkway Dr, 39211-4322. SAN 370-7903. Tel: 601-956-4606. FAX: 601-899-0056. *Actg Librn*, Dorothy Burnes; Staff 1 (Non-MLS 1)
Open: Mon-Thurs 10-7, Fri 10-6, Sat 10-5
Friends of the Library Group
EDWARDS PUBLIC, 101 Front St, PO Box 140, Edwards, 39066-0140. SAN 328-8196. Tel: 601-852-2230. FAX: 601-852-2230. *Librn*, Alfenette Robinson
Library Holdings: Bk Vols 3,500
Open Tues & Thurs 2-6, Wed & Fri 9-1
ELLA BESS AUSTIN LIBRARY, 320 W Cunningham, PO Box 155, Terry, 39170-0155. SAN 348-5765. Tel: 601-878-5336. FAX: 601-878-5336. *Librn*, Merrie Anderson; Staff 1 (Non-MLS 1)
Open Tues, Thurs & Sat 10-2, Wed & Fri 1-5
EUDORA WELTY LIBRARY (HQ), 300 N State St, 39201-1799. SAN 348-517X. Tel: 601-968-5811. Reference Tel: 601-968-5803, 601-968-5809. FAX: 601-968-5806. *AV, Circ*, E Terrell Blackman; *Ref*, Gordon Saucier; Staff 10 (MLS 3, Non-MLS 7)
Open Mon-Thurs 9-9, Fri & Sat 9-6, Sun 1-5
Friends of the Library Group
EVELYN TAYLOR MAJURE LIBRARY, White Oak St, PO Box 340, Utica, 39175-0340. SAN 348-582X. Tel: 601-885-8381. FAX: 601-885-8381. *Librn*, Barbara Barlow
Open Tues, Thurs & Sat 10-2, Wed & Fri 1-5
FANNIE LOU HAMER LIBRARY, 3450 Albermarle Rd, 39213-6513. SAN 348-4831. Tel: 601-362-3012. FAX: 601-362-3012. *Librn*, Vivian Clay; Staff 1 (Non-MLS 1)

Open Mon-Fri 10-5
Friends of the Library Group
ANNIE THOMPSON JEFFERS LIBRARY, 111 Madison St, PO Box 358, Bolton, 39041-0358. SAN 370-7911. Tel: 601-866-4247. FAX: 601-866-4247. *Librn*, Alfenette Robinson
Open Tues & Thurs 9-1, Wed & Fri 2-6 & Sat 10-2
MARGARET WALKER ALEXANDER LIBRARY, 2525 Robinson Rd, 39209. SAN 348-5226. Tel: 601-354-8911. FAX: 601-354-8912. *Librn*, Charlotte Moman; Staff 2 (MLS 1, Non-MLS 1)
Open Mon-Thurs 10-7, Fri & Sat 10-6
Friends of the Library Group
MEDGAR EVERS BOULEVARD, 4215 Medgar Evers Blvd, 39213-5210. SAN 348-5048. Tel: 601-982-2867. FAX: 601-982-2868. *Librn*, Pamela Reed; Staff 1 (MLS 1)
Open Mon-Sat 9-6
Friends of the Library Group
NORTHSIDE, 807 E Northside Dr, 39206-5537. SAN 348-5374. Tel: 601-366-0021, 601-366-9364. FAX: 601-366-9364.; Staff 2 (MLS 1, Non-MLS 1)
Open Mon-Thurs 9-8, Fri & Sat 9-5
Friends of the Library Group
RAYMOND PUBLIC, PO Box 14, Raymond, 39154-0014. SAN 348-5587. Tel: 601-857-8721. FAX: 601-857-8721. *Librn*, Margaret Bell; Staff 1 (Non-MLS 1)
Open Mon-Fri 9-6
Friends of the Library Group
SOUTH HILLS, 515 W McDowell Rd, 39204-5547. SAN 348-5706. Tel: 601-372-1621, 601-372-1676. FAX: 601-372-7038. *Librn*, Fredna Hinkle; Staff 2 (MLS 1, Non-MLS 1)
Open Mon-Thurs 9-9, Fri 9-6, Sat 9-5
Friends of the Library Group
WHITEROCK, 560 Country Club Dr, 39209-2541. SAN 348-5889. Tel: 601-922-6076. FAX: 601-992-6076. *Librn*, Diana Brown; Staff 1 (Non-MLS 1)
Open Mon-Fri 10-5
Friends of the Library Group

M METHODIST HEALTH CARE-JACKSON HOSPITAL, William M Suttle Medical Library, 1850 Chadwick Dr, 39204. SAN 327-1900. Tel: 601-376-1000, 601-376-1085. FAX: 601-376-2761. Web Site: www.methodisthealth.org. *Librn*, Wanda Cane
Library Holdings: Bk Vols 1,200; Bk Titles 500; Per Subs 110

C MILLSAPS COLLEGE, Millsaps-Wilson Library, 1701 N State St, 39210-0001. SAN 308-8731. Tel: 601-974-1070, 601-974-1073. Interlibrary Loan Service Tel: 601-974-1090. FAX: 601-974-1082. Web Site: library.millsaps.edu/library/. *Actg Dir*, Tom Henderson; E-Mail: hendetw@millsaps.edu; *Acq*, Allison Mays; Tel: 601-974-1083, E-Mail: maysap@millsaps.edu; *ILL*, Jan Allison; E-Mail: allisjg@millsaps.edu; *Ref*, Larry Madison; Tel: 601-974-1072, E-Mail: madisle@millsaps.edu; *Tech Servs*, Elizabeth Beck; Tel: 601-974-1076, E-Mail: beckea@millsaps.edu; Staff 6 (MLS 6)
Founded 1890. Enrl 1,257; Fac 90; Highest Degree: Master
Jul 1999-Jun 2000 Income $673,000. Mats Exp $263,500, Books $67,000, Per/Ser (Incl. Access Fees) $118,000, Presv $10,000, AV Equip $500, Electronic Ref Mat (Incl. Access Fees) $68,000. Sal $320,699 (Prof $220,000)
Library Holdings: Bk Vols 205,427; Bk Titles 144,206; Per Subs 3,087
Subject Interests: Applied ethics, Art, Literature, Mgt, Relig studies
Special Collections: Eudora Welty: Rare Books; Military History (Johnson Coll); Mississippi Methodism Archives; Paul Ramsey (Ethics), Theatre (Lehman Engel), bks, rec, mss.
Automation Activity & Vendor Info: (Acquisitions) DRA; (Cataloging) DRA; (Circulation) DRA; (Course Reserve) DRA; (OPAC) DRA; (Serials) DRA
Publications: Annual Report; Library Handbook; Research Guides
Partic in Assoc Cols of the South; Solinet

CL MISSISSIPPI COLLEGE, Law Library, 151 E Griffith St, 39201-1391. SAN 348-2286. Tel: 601-925-7120. FAX: 601-925-7112. *Dir*, Mary Miller; E-Mail: mmiller@mc.edu; *Acq*, Joyce Zeigler; *Cat*, Karin Den Bleyker; *Online Servs*, Thomas Walter; *Ref*, Rebecca Blahut; Staff 5 (MLS 4, Non-MLS 1)
Founded 1975. Enrl 350; Fac 19; Highest Degree: Doctorate
Library Holdings: Bk Vols 300,000; Per Subs 3,500
Automation Activity & Vendor Info: (Acquisitions) Innovative Interfaces Inc.
Partic in OCLC Online Computer Library Center, Inc; SE Libr Network; Westlaw

G MISSISSIPPI DEPARTMENT OF ENVIRONMENTAL QUALITY LIBRARY, Southport Ctr, 2380 Hwy 80 W, 39204. (Mail add: PO Box 20307, 39289), SAN 308-8758. Tel: 601-961-5024. FAX: 601-961-5774. *Librn*, Ronnie Sanders; E-Mail: ronnie_sanders@deq.state.ms.us; Staff 1 (MLS 1)
Founded 1850
Library Holdings: Bk Vols 48,000; Per Subs 126
Subject Interests: Environ geol, Environmental eng, Geohydrology, Geology, Hazardous wastes mgt, Hydrology, Paleontology, Petroleum geol
Special Collections: National, State & International Government Publications; Topographic Maps; United States & State Geological Survey Publications
Database Vendor: Ebsco - EbscoHost, OCLC - First Search, Silverplatter Information Inc., Wilson - Wilson Web
Function: Research library

P MISSISSIPPI LIBRARY COMMISSION, 1221 Ellis Ave, 39209-7328. (Mail add: PO Box 10700, 39289-0700), SAN 348-5919. Tel: 601-961-4111. Reference Tel: 877-594-5733. Toll Free Tel: 800-647-7542. TDD: 601-354-7081. FAX: 354-4181, 601-354-6713. E-Mail: mlcref@mail.mlc.lib.ms.us. Web Site: www.mlc.lib.ms.us. *In Charge*, Emma Ainsworth; Tel: 601-961-4041, E-Mail: emmalou@mlc.lib.ms.us; *Dir Libr Serv*, Keith Coleman; Tel: 601-961-4010, E-Mail: keithc@mlc.lib.ms.us; *Dir*, Rahye Puckett; Tel: 601-713-3233, E-Mail: rahye@mlc.lib.ms.us; *Info Specialist*, Velma Champion; Tel: 601-961-4117, E-Mail: champion@mlc.lib.ms.us; *Dir, Tech Serv*, Glenda Tilson; Tel: 601-961-4124, E-Mail: gtilson@mlc.lib.ms.us; *Coll Develop*, Sara Tubb; Tel: 601-961-4133, E-Mail: stubb@mlc.lib.ms.us; *Govt Doc*, Indira Bhowal; Tel: 601-961-4119, E-Mail: jbhowal@mlc.lib.ms.us; *Head, Cat*, D Bowles; Tel: 601-961-4165, E-Mail: dbowles@mlc.lib.ms.us; *Head Ref*, Sherry Dixon; E-Mail: sdixon@mlc.lib.ms.us; Staff 32 (MLS 20, Non-MLS 12)
Founded 1926. Pop 2,618,700
Jul 1999-Jun 2000 Income $13,333,460, State $11,593,330, Federal $1,740,130. Mats Exp $1,312,044, Books $236,872, Per/Ser (Incl. Access Fees) $57,843, Micro $49,718, Electronic Ref Mat (Incl. Access Fees) $967,612. Sal $2,230,027 (Prof $1,521,364)
Library Holdings: Bk Vols 180,197; Bk Titles 173,743; Per Subs 508; High Interest/Low Vocabulary Bk Vols 12; Spec Interest Per Sub 10; Bks on Deafness & Sign Lang 90
Subject Interests: Large print, Libr sci, Mississippiana
Special Collections: Fed, US Patent & Trademark
Publications: Mississippi State Government Publications: Index; Reading Light
Partic in Soline
Special Services for the Deaf - TDD
Miss Library for the Blind & Physically Handicapped
Friends of the Library Group

P MISSISSIPPI LIBRARY FOR THE BLIND & PHYSICALLY HANDICAPPED, 5455 Executive Pl, 39206-4104. SAN 308-8766. Tel: 601-713-3409. Toll Free Tel: 800-446-0892. TDD: 601-713-3395. FAX: 601-713-3405. E-Mail: lbph@mail.mlc.lib.ms.us, lbph@mlc.lib.ms.us. Web Site: www.mlc.lib.ms.us/lbph.htm. *Dir, Librn*, Rahye Puckett; Tel: 601-713-3233, E-Mail: rahyep@mlc.lib.ms.us; *Librn for Blind*, John L Whitlock; Tel: 601-713-3219, E-Mail: jwhit@mlc.lib.ms.us; Staff 9 (MLS 2, Non-MLS 7)
Founded 1970
Jul 1998-Jun 1999 Income $331,360, State $248,779, Federal $82,581
Library Holdings: Bk Vols 157,231; Bk Titles 42,969
Special Collections: Books & magazines on cassette about Mississippi & by Mississippi Authors; Large print books & descriptive videos; Reference Material on Blindness & Other Disabilities, print
Publications: Bibliography of locally recorded materials; Instruction Manual for Institutions & Libraries; Patron Handbook; Reader Newsletter (braille, large print & cassette); The Reading Light (braille, large print & cassette) (Newsletter); User Manual
Special Services for the Blind - Assistive Technology Center for Persons who are blind or physically handicapped; Large print & cassettes; Reference in braille; Telephone Pioneers equipment repair group; Volunteer recording program
Open Mon-Fri 8-5
Friends of the Library Group

S MISSISSIPPI MUSEUM OF ART, Howorth Library, 201 E Pascagoula, 39201. SAN 327-2141. Tel: 601-960-1515. FAX: 601-960-1505. Web Site: www.msmuseumart.org. *Dir*, Andy Maas
Library Holdings: Bk Vols 3,000
Open Mon-Fri 10-4

S MISSISSIPPI MUSEUM OF NATURAL SCIENCE LIBRARY,* 2148 Riverside Dr, 39202. SAN 308-8774. Tel: 601-354-7303. FAX: 601-354-7227. E-Mail: mmns.library@its.state.ms.us. *Librn*, Mary P Stevens
Founded 1974
Library Holdings: Bk Vols 18,000; Per Subs 104
Subject Interests: Botany, Environmental studies, Herpetology, Ichthyology, Invertebrates, Mammalogy, Ornithology, Paleontology
Partic in Dialog Corporation; OCLC Online Computer Library Center, Inc
Open Mon-Fri 8-5, Sat 9:30-4:30 (first Sat of the month)

G MISSISSIPPI STATE DEPARTMENT OF ARCHIVES & HISTORY, Archives & Library Division,* 100 S State St, 39201. (Mail add: PO Box 571, 39205), Tel: 601-359-6876. FAX: 601-359-6964. E-Mail: refdesk@mdah.state.ms.us. Web Site: www.mdah.state.ms.us. *Dir*, H T Holmes
Founded 1902
Jul 1997-Jun 1998 Income $1,897,848, State $1,744,026, Federal $153,822. Mats Exp $33,000. Sal $1,177,582
Library Holdings: Bk Vols 68,000; Bk Titles 42,000; Per Subs 300

Special Collections: County Records, micro; Federal Government Records Pertaining to Mississippi; Map Coll; Mississippi Businesses & Organizations, private papers, mss; Mississippi Coll, newspapers; Mississippi Confederate Records; newsfilm; Photograph Coll; State, Territorial & Provincial Government, archives
Publications: Guide to Official Records in the Department of Archives & History; Research in the Department of Archives & History
Restriction: Non-circulating to the public
Function: Archival collection
Open Mon-Fri 8-5 & Sat 8-1

MISSISSIPPI STATE DEPARTMENT OF HEALTH
S AUDIO-VISUAL LIBRARY, PO Box 1700, 39215-1700. SAN 348-6001. Tel: 601-576-7675. FAX: 601-576-7517. *Librn*, Peggy Montgomery
Founded 1947

GL MISSISSIPPI SUPREME COURT, State Law Library, Carroll Gartin Justice Bldg, 450 High St, 39201. (Mail add: PO Box 1040, 39215-1040), SAN 308-8804. Tel: 601-359-3672. FAX: 601-359-2912. *State Librn*, Charlie Pearce; E-Mail: cpearce@mssc.state.ms.us; *Head, Info Serv*, Ken Raigins; E-Mail: kraigins@mssc.state.ms.us; *Head Tech Servs*, Liz Thompson; E-Mail: lthompson@mssc.state.ms.us; Staff 4 (MLS 2, Non-MLS 2)
Founded 1838
Library Holdings: Bk Vols 206,000; Per Subs 267
Subject Interests: Fed law, State law
Special Collections: Mississippiana
Database Vendor: Ebsco - EbscoHost, Lexis-Nexis, OCLC - First Search, Wilson - Wilson Web
Restriction: Circulation limited
Function: ILL by photocopy only
Open Mon-Fri 8-5

L PHELPS DUNBAR, Law Library, 200 S Lamar, 39201-3066. (Mail add: PO Box 23066, 39225), SAN 372-4662. Tel: 601-352-2300. FAX: 601-360-9777. *Librn*, Joe Xu; E-Mail: xuj@phelps.com; Staff 2 (MLS 2)
Library Holdings: Bk Vols 10,000; Per Subs 45
Subject Interests: Labor
Database Vendor: Lexis-Nexis

R REFORMED THEOLOGICAL SEMINARY LIBRARY,* 5422 Clinton Blvd, 39209-3099. SAN 308-8812. Tel: 601-923-6204. FAX: 601-923-6203. Web Site: www.rts.edu. *Dir*, Kenneth R Elliott; E-Mail: kelliott@rts.edu; *Tech Servs*, Sara Morrison; *Per*, Stephen Berry; *Publ Servs*, John McCarty; Staff 2 (MLS 2)
Founded 1965. Enrl 285; Fac 18; Highest Degree: Doctorate
Library Holdings: Bk Vols 93,010; Per Subs 640
Special Collections: Southern Presbyterianism (Blackburn Coll)
Partic in SE Libr Network

M SAINT DOMINIC-JACKSON MEMORIAL HOSPITAL, Luther Manship Medical Library, 969 Lakeland Dr, 39216. SAN 308-8820. Tel: 601-364-6445. FAX: 601-713-8075. Web Site: www.stdom.com. *Coordr*, Tammy Beard; E-Mail: tbeard@stdom.com
Founded 1974
Library Holdings: Bk Vols 980; Per Subs 100
Subject Interests: Clinical nursing, Ethics, Total quality mgt

G STATE OF MISSISSIPPI DEPARTMENT OF MENTAL HEALTH LIBRARY, 1101 Robert E Lee Bldg, 39201-1311. SAN 322-7170. Tel: 601-359-1288. FAX: 601-359-6295. *Librn*, Margueritte Ransom
Founded 1975
Jul 1999-Jun 2000 Income $2,500. Mats Exp Books $2,500
Library Holdings: Bk Vols 2,200
Subject Interests: Alcohol abuse, Drug abuse, Mental health, Mental illness, Mental retardation
Publications: Bibliography (yearly); Newsletter (quarterly)

CM UNIVERSITY OF MISSISSIPPI MEDICAL CENTER, Rowland Medical Library, 2500 N State St, 39216-4505. SAN 308-8847. Tel: 601-984-1290. Interlibrary Loan Service Tel: 601-984-1234. Circulation Tel: 601-984-1230. Reference Tel: 601-984-1231. FAX: 601-984-1251. Web Site: www.library.umc.edu. *Dir*, Ada Seltzer; E-Mail: aseltzer@rowland.umsmed.edu; *Assoc Dir, Tech Servs*, Walter Morton; Tel: 601-984-1287, E-Mail: wmorton@rowland.umsmed.edu; *Assoc Dir, Publ Servs*, Virginia Segrest; Tel: 601-984-1288, E-Mail: vsegrest@rowland.umsmed.edu; *Head, Cat*, Connie Machado; Tel: 601-984-1273, E-Mail: cmachado@rowland.umsmed.edu; *Coll Develop*, David Juergens; Tel: 601-984-1270, E-Mail: djuergens@rowland.umsmed.edu; *ILL*, Jennifer Lyle; Fax: 601-984-1262, E-Mail: jlyle@rowland.umsmed.edu; *Head Ref*, Ardis Haaland; Tel: 601-984-1239, Fax: 601-984-1262, E-Mail: ahaaland@rowland.umsmed.edu; *Ser*, John Lucas; Tel: 601-984-1277, E-Mail: jlucas@rowland.umsmed.edu; Staff 30 (MLS 12, Non-MLS 18)
Founded 1955. Enrl 1,700; Fac 708; Highest Degree: Doctorate
Jul 1999-Jun 2000 Income $3,391,557, State $3,342,318, Locally Generated Income $49,239. Mats Exp $1,869,529, Books $176,247, Per/Ser (Incl. Access Fees) $1,582,429, Presv $45,624, Other Print Mats $1,148, Electronic Ref Mat (Incl. Access Fees) $64,081. Sal $1,009,690 (Prof $730,035)
Library Holdings: Bk Vols 222,692; Bk Titles 62,955; Per Subs 2,362
Subject Interests: Allied health, Dentistry, Medicine, Nursing, Prof mat
Special Collections: History of Medicine; UMC Theses & Dissertations
Automation Activity & Vendor Info: (Acquisitions) epixtech, inc.; (Cataloging) epixtech, inc.; (Circulation) epixtech, inc.; (Course Reserve) epixtech, inc.; (OPAC) epixtech, inc.; (Serials) epixtech, inc.
Database Vendor: OCLC - First Search, OVID Technologies
Publications: Dial Access Guide; Handbook; Reference Guide; Romeo Search Guide; Rowland Medical Library Source; Topic Tracks
Partic in Consortium Of Southern Biomedical Libraries (CONBLS); National Network of Libraries of Medicine - Southeastern Atlantic Region Headquarters - Mississippi Health Sciences Information Network
Friends of the Library Group

L WATKINS, LUDLAM, WINTER & STENNIS, Law Library,* 6331 N State St, 39202. (Mail add: PO Box 427, 39205), SAN 372-2899. Tel: 601-949-4792. FAX: 601-949-4804. *Librn*, Maurine B Mattson; E-Mail: mmattson@wlslaw.com
Library Holdings: Bk Vols 14,000; Bk Titles 3,000; Per Subs 52
Partic in Am Asn of Law Librs; Spec Libr Asn

R WESLEY BIBLICAL SEMINARY LIBRARY,* 5980 Floral Dr, 39206-0938. (Mail add: PO Box 9938, 39286), SAN 375-2143. Tel: 601-957-1314. FAX: 601-991-2100. E-Mail: gowesley@aol.com. Web Site: www.gowesley.edu. *Dir Libr Serv*, David L Steveline
Jul 1998-Jun 1999 Income $73,247. Mats Exp $73,247, Books $7,135, Per/Ser (Incl. Access Fees) $8,464. Sal $52,629
Library Holdings: Bk Vols 54,570; Per Subs 270
Subject Interests: Religion

KEESLER AFB

UNITED STATES AIR FORCE
A MCBRIDE LIBRARY FL3010, 81 SPTG/SVMG, 512 Larcher Blvd Bldg 2222, 39534-2345. SAN 348-6036. Tel: 228-377-2181. FAX: 228-435-0203. Web Site: www.keesler.af.mil/. *Dir*, William R Province; Tel: 228-377-2827; *Ref*, Joan Wing; *Cat*, Claudia Garcia; Tel: 228-377-2827; Staff 8 (MLS 2, Non-MLS 6)
Founded 1942. Pop 59,000; Circ 160,000
Library Holdings: Bk Vols 51,100; Per Subs 300
Subject Interests: Bus admin, Computer eng, Computer science, Data communications, Electronics, History, Mathematics, Mil sci, Television, Weather
Special Collections: Air War College; Chief of Staff Professional Reading Test; McNaughton Lease Books; Professional Military Education; Transition Assistance Program; US Air Force periodicals
Publications: A Guide to Resources & Services of the Base Library (monthly newsletter); Bibliographies
Partic in Fedlink; OCLC Online Computer Library Center, Inc

AM MEDICAL CENTER LIBRARY, 81st Medical Group/SGSFL, 301 Fisher St Rm 1A239, 39534-2519. SAN 348-6044. Tel: 228-377-6249. FAX: 228-377-6127. *Librn*, Sherry Nave; E-Mail: sherry.nave@keesler.af.mil; Staff 2 (MLS 1, Non-MLS 1)
Founded 1942
Oct 1999-Sep 2000 Mats Exp $110,000. Sal $85,484 (Prof $52,623)
Library Holdings: Bk Vols 6,000; Per Subs 350
Subject Interests: Allied health, Clinical medicine, Dentistry, Nursing
Automation Activity & Vendor Info: (Cataloging) EOS; (Circulation) EOS; (Serials) EOS
Database Vendor: OVID Technologies
Partic in Gulf Coast Biomedical Libr Consortium; Mississippi Biomedical Library Consortium; SE-Atlantic Regional Med Libr Servs

KOSCIUSKO

P MID-MISSISSIPPI REGIONAL LIBRARY SYSTEM, 201 S Huntington St, 39090-9002. SAN 348-6095. Tel: 662-289-5151. Interlibrary Loan Service Tel: 601-289-5162. FAX: 662-289-5106. *Dir*, Richard O Greene; E-Mail: director@midmissregional.lib.ms.us; *Asst Dir*, Linda Milner; E-Mail: asstdirector@midmissregional.lib.ms.us; *Tech Coordr*, Carolyn B Steen; E-Mail: genadmin@midmissregional.lib.ms.us; *Cat*, Doug Potter; E-Mail: cataloger@midmissregional.lib.ms.us; *Acq*, Pam Chadick; E-Mail: acquisitions@midmissregional.lib.ms.us; *Ch Servs*, Jean Fenwick; E-Mail: youthservices@midmissregional.lib.ms.us; *ILL*, Tim Fancher; E-Mail: refill@midmissregional.lib.ms.us; Staff 7 (MLS 2, Non-MLS 5)
Founded 1957. Pop 90,389; Circ 299,534
Oct 1998-Sep 1999 Income (Main Library and Branch Library) $1,061,063. Mats Exp $142,921. Sal $782,580
Library Holdings: Bk Titles 140,000; Per Subs 447
Subject Interests: Education, Genealogy
Special Collections: Barrett Civil War Coll (Lexington); Hendrix Genealogy Coll (Louisville); Sanders Genealogy Coll (Attala)
Automation Activity & Vendor Info: (Acquisitions) EOS; (Cataloging) EOS; (Circulation) EOS; (OPAC) EOS
Function: ILL available
Friends of the Library Group

Branches: 13

ATTALA COUNTY, 201 S Huntington St, 39090-9002. SAN 348-6125. Tel: 662-289-5141. FAX: 662-289-9983. E-Mail: attala@midmissregional.lib.ms.us. *Librn*, Carolyn Pilgram; Staff 7 (Non-MLS 7)
Special Collections: Blaylock-Sanders Coll; Education (Reavis Coll); Miss History & Geneology
Automation Activity & Vendor Info: (Cataloging) EOS; (Circulation) EOS; (OPAC) EOS
Friends of the Library Group

CARTHAGE-LEAKE COUNTY, 114 E Franklin St, Carthage, 39051-3716. SAN 348-615X. Tel: 601-267-7821. FAX: 601-267-5530. E-Mail: carthage@midmissregional.lib.ms.us. *Librn*, Mary Ellen Ellis; Staff 5 (Non-MLS 5)
Automation Activity & Vendor Info: (OPAC) EOS
Friends of the Library Group

DUCK HILL PUBLIC, PO Box 279, Duck Hill, 38925-0279. SAN 348-6184. Tel: 662-565-2391. FAX: 662-565-2391. E-Mail: duckhill@midmissregional.lib.ms.us. *Librn*, Tiny Mears; Staff 1 (Non-MLS 1)
Automation Activity & Vendor Info: (OPAC) EOS

DURANT PUBLIC, 15338 N Jackson St, Durant, 39063-3708. SAN 348-6214. Tel: 662-653-3451. FAX: 662-653-3108. E-Mail: durant@midmissregional.lib.ms.us. *Librn*, Betty Hatchcock; Staff 2 (Non-MLS 2)
Automation Activity & Vendor Info: (OPAC) EOS

GOODMAN PUBLIC, PO Box 374, Goodman, 39079-0374. SAN 348-6249. Tel: 662-472-2263. FAX: 662-472-2513. E-Mail: goodman@midmissregional.lib.ms.us. *Librn*, Shirley Jobe; Staff 1 (Non-MLS 1)
Automation Activity & Vendor Info: (OPAC) EOS

KILMICHAEL PUBLIC, PO Box 316, Kilmichael, 39747-0316. SAN 348-6273. Tel: 662-262-7615. FAX: 662-262-7615. E-Mail: kilmichael@midmissregional.lib.ms.us. *Librn*, Patricia Rose; Staff 1 (Non-MLS 1)
Automation Activity & Vendor Info: (OPAC) EOS

LEXINGTON PUBLIC, 208 Tchula St, Lexington, 39095-3134. SAN 348-6303. Tel: 662-834-2571. FAX: 662-834-4578. E-Mail: lexington@midmissregional.lib.ms.us. *Librn*, Laura Lawson; Staff 2 (Non-MLS 2)
Automation Activity & Vendor Info: (OPAC) EOS

PICKENS PUBLIC, PO Box 188, Pickens, 39146-0188. SAN 348-6338. Tel: 662-468-2391. FAX: 662-468-2391. E-Mail: pickens@midmissregional.lib.ms.us. *Librn*, Jean McNeese; Staff 1 (Non-MLS 1)
Automation Activity & Vendor Info: (OPAC) EOS

TCHULA PUBLIC, PO Box 248, Tchula, 39169-0248. SAN 348-6362. Tel: 662-235-5235. FAX: 662-235-4925. E-Mail: tchula@midmissregional.lib.ms.us. *Librn*, Yvonne Clark; Staff 1 (Non-MLS 1)
Automation Activity & Vendor Info: (OPAC) EOS

WALNUT GROVE PUBLIC, PO Box 206, Walnut Grove, 39189-0206. SAN 348-6397. Tel: 601-253-2483. FAX: 601-253-9374. E-Mail: walnutgrove@midmissregional.lib.ms.us. *Librn*, Linda Bounds; Staff 1 (Non-MLS 1)
Automation Activity & Vendor Info: (OPAC) EOS

WEST PUBLIC, PO Box 9, West, 39192-0009. SAN 348-6427. Tel: 662-967-2510. FAX: 662-967-2510. E-Mail: west@midmissregional.lib.ms.us. *Librn*, Angie Burrell; Staff 1 (Non-MLS 1)
Automation Activity & Vendor Info: (OPAC) EOS

WINONA-MONTGOMERY COUNTY, 115 N Quitman St, Winona, 38967-2228. SAN 348-6451. Tel: 662-283-3443. FAX: 662-283-2642. E-Mail: winona@midmissregional.lib.ms.us. *Librn*, Virginia Weed; Staff 2 (Non-MLS 2)
Automation Activity & Vendor Info: (OPAC) EOS

WINSTON COUNTY, 301 W Park St, Louisville, 39339-2942. SAN 348-6486. Tel: 662-773-3212. FAX: 662-773-8434. E-Mail: winston@midmissregional.lib.ms.us. *Librn*, Beth Edwards; Staff 4 (Non-MLS 4)
Special Collections: Miss Genealogy Coll
Automation Activity & Vendor Info: (OPAC) EOS

CR PAUL & PHILIP GAUNT LIBRARY, (Formerly Magnolia Bible College), PO Box 1109, 39090. SAN 321-1673. Tel: 662-289-2896, Ext 121. Toll Free Tel: 800-748-8655. FAX: 662-289-2876. E-Mail: pljw@kopower.com. Web Site: www.kopower.com. *Actg Dir*, Lewis Prince; *Asst Librn*, Janie A Wallace; Staff 3 (MLS 2, Non-MLS 1)
Founded 1976. Enrl 26; Fac 10; Highest Degree: Bachelor
Library Holdings: Bk Titles 36,650; Per Subs 278
Special Collections: Churches of Christ - History
Partic in Christian Col Libr; Miss Libr Asn

LAKE

P LAKE PUBLIC LIBRARY,* City Hall, 39092. SAN 376-6179. Tel: 601-775-3552. *Librn*, Selena Swink
Oct 1997-Sep 1998 Mats Exp $2,000
Library Holdings: Bk Titles 2,000
Subject Interests: Genealogy, Local history
Mem of Central Mississippi Regional Library System
Open Tues & Wed 9-12 & 1-4
Friends of the Library Group

LAUREL

P LAUREL-JONES COUNTY LIBRARY, 530 Commerce St, 39440. SAN 348-6516. Tel: 601-428-4313. FAX: 601-428-4314. Web Site: www.laurel.lib.ms.us. *Dir*, Paulette D Entrekin; E-Mail: pentrekin@laurel.lib.ms.us; *Asst Dir, Ch Servs*, Linda Montgomery; *Ref*, James Kennedy; Staff 4 (MLS 2, Non-MLS 2)
Founded 1919. Pop 62,500; Circ 184,393
Oct 1999-Sep 2000 Income (Main Library and Branch Library) $461,397, State $108,700, City $92,300, Federal $2,279, County $190,000, Locally Generated Income $25,150, Other $42,968. Mats Exp $91,197, Books $61,797, Per/Ser (Incl. Access Fees) $4,300, Presv $4,100, AV Equip $21,000. Sal $262,095 (Prof $99,500)
Library Holdings: Bk Vols 103,150
Subject Interests: Genealogy
Automation Activity & Vendor Info: (Cataloging) Gaylord; (Circulation) Gaylord
Open Mon-Fri 8-6, Sat 9:30-3
Friends of the Library Group
Branches: 2

ELLISVILLE PUBLIC, Ellisville, 39437. SAN 348-6540. Tel: 601-477-9271. *Librn*, Dana Bullock
Friends of the Library Group

SANDERSVILLE PUBLIC, Sandersville, 39477. SAN 348-6575. Tel: 601-425-3551. *Librn*, Bernadette Kinney
Friends of the Library Group

S LAUREN ROGERS MUSEUM OF ART LIBRARY, Fifth Ave & Seventh St, 39441-1108. (Mail add: PO Box 1108, 39441-1108), SAN 308-8863. Tel: 601-649-6374, Ext 25. FAX: 601-649-6379. Web Site: www.lrma.org. *Librn*, Donna C Smith; Staff 2 (MLS 1, Non-MLS 1)
Founded 1923
Library Holdings: Bk Vols 10,000; Per Subs 75
Subject Interests: Am art, Georgian silver, Local history, Mississippiana, Native Am basket
Special Collections: Artists' Clipping Files; Bookplates; Local History, photog, mss; Museum Archives; Postcard Coll; Rare Books
Publications: Jean Leon Gerome Ferris (1863-1930), American Painter Historian; Lauren Rogers Museum of Art Handbook of Collections; Lauren Rogers Museum of Art Newsletter (quarterly); Mississippi Art Colony (exhibit catalog); Mississippi Portraiture; Recent Acquisitions, Lauren Rogers Museum of Art; The French Legacy (exhibit catalog); The Gibbons Silver Collection (catalog)
Open Tues-Sat 10-4

CR SOUTHEASTERN BAPTIST COLLEGE, A R Reddin Memorial Library, 4229 Hwy 15 N, 39440. SAN 308-8871. Tel: 601-426-6346. FAX: 601-426-6347.; Staff 1 (MLS 1)
Founded 1955. Enrl 111; Fac 12; Highest Degree: Doctorate
Library Holdings: Bk Titles 25,000; Per Subs 280
Special Collections: Baptist Missionary Association of America Coll, doc

LONG BEACH

P LONG BEACH PUBLIC LIBRARY, 209 Jeff Davis Ave, 39560. SAN 308-8898. Tel: 228-863-0711. FAX: 228-863-8511. E-Mail: dixies@longbeach.lib.ms.us. Web Site: www.longbeach.lib.ms.us. *Dir*, Dixie Stevens; *Asst Dir, Ref*, Jeannie Ripoll; *Librn*, Shannon Wilson; *Circ*, Barbara Brewer; *Ch Servs*, Renee Rayburn
Founded 1895. Pop 16,500; Circ 115,495
Library Holdings: Bk Titles 41,387; Per Subs 95
Special Collections: Cook Books & Craft Coll
Friends of the Library Group

C THE UNIVERSITY OF SOUTHERN MISSISSIPPI, GULF COAST, Richard G Cox Library, 730 E Beach Blvd, 39560-2699. SAN 325-3422. Tel: 228-865-4510. FAX: 228-865-4544. Web Site: www.lib.usm.edu/~coxlib/. *Dir*, Edward McCormack; Tel: 228-865-4541, E-Mail: edward.mccormack@usm.edu; *Publ Servs*, Allisa Beck; Tel: 228-867-2618, E-Mail: allisa.beck@usm.edu; *Electronic Resources, Ser*, Kathy Davis; *Coll Develop*, Faye Brophy; Staff 11 (MLS 4, Non-MLS 7)
Founded 1972. Enrl 1,700; Fac 61
Jul 1999-Jun 2000 Income $474,263. Mats Exp $201,672. Sal $324,416 (Prof $169,764)
Library Holdings: Bk Vols 68,595; Per Subs 321
Subject Interests: Bus admin, Education, Hospitality management, Humanities, Nursing, Psychology
Special Collections: Curriculm Materials Center; Gulf of Mexico Program; PDK Fastbacks
Automation Activity & Vendor Info: (Acquisitions) SIRSI; (Cataloging) SIRSI; (Circulation) SIRSI
Publications: Cox Connection
Partic in Magnolia; SE Libr Network; Solinet

MACON

P NOXUBEE COUNTY LIBRARY SYSTEM, 103 E King St, 39341-2832. SAN 308-891X. Tel: 662-726-5461. FAX: 662-726-4694, 662-726-5461. Web Site: noxubee.lib.ms.us. *Dir*, Beth Freshour; *Librn*, Judy E Proffitt
Founded 1933. Pop 12,604; Circ 21,762
Library Holdings: Bk Vols 26,925
Subject Interests: Mississippiana
Special Collections: Harold G Brown Memorial Library
Friends of the Library Group
Branches: 2
BROOKSVILLE BRANCH, PO Box 325, Brooksville, 39739. SAN 321-9429. Tel: 601-738-4559. *Librn*, Irene Durham
Friends of the Library Group
VISTA J DANIEL MEMORIAL, PO Box 248, Shuqualak, 39361. SAN 321-9437. Tel: 601-793-9576. *Librn*, Polly Bateman
Library Holdings: Bk Vols 18,943
Friends of the Library Group

MADISON

P MADISON COUNTY LIBRARY SYSTEM, Rebecca Baine Rigby Library, 105 Old Canton Rd, 39110. SAN 348-1867. Tel: 601-856-2749. FAX: 601-856-2749. Web Site: www.mad.lib.ms.us. *Librn*, Jane Phillips; *Ch Servs*, Kristie Williamson
Pop 13,000; Circ 114,296
Library Holdings: Bk Vols 32,000
Friends of the Library Group

MAGEE

P MAGEE PUBLIC LIBRARY,* 120 NW First St, 39111. SAN 376-6195. Tel: 601-849-3747. FAX: 601-849-6609. *Librn*, Billie Terrell
Oct 1997-Sep 1998 Income $45,000. Mats Exp $17,000. Sal $20,500
Library Holdings: Bk Titles 31,000; Per Subs 20
Mem of Central Mississippi Regional Library System
Friends of the Library Group

MARKS

P MARKS-QUITMAN COUNTY LIBRARY,* 315 E Main St, 38646. SAN 308-8928. Tel: 662-326-7141. FAX: 662-326-7141. *Librn*, Anne Kerr; E-Mail: akerr@marks.lib.ms.us
Pop 12,636; Circ 23,202
Library Holdings: Bk Titles 30,233; Per Subs 29
Subject Interests: Agriculture, Genealogy, History, Industry, Mississippi
Open Mon-Sat 9-5

MATHISTON

J WOOD COLLEGE, Wood Memorial Library,* PO Box 289, 39752. SAN 308-8936. Tel: 601-263-5352, Ext 78. FAX: 601-263-4964. E-Mail: abs@ra.msstate.edu. *Librn*, Julie Dukes
Founded 1886
Jul 1997-Jun 1998 Income $20,000. Mats Exp $17,749, Books $5,033, Per/Ser (Incl. Access Fees) $8,021, Presv $85, AV Equip $700
Library Holdings: Bk Vols 26,748; Per Subs 147
Subject Interests: Miss writers
Special Collections: Bennett Academy
Publications: Library guide; operations manual; student library handbook; student worker handbook

MC COMB

P PIKE-AMITE-WALTHALL LIBRARY SYSTEM, Mc Comb Public Library (Headquarters), 1022 Virginia Ave, 39648. SAN 348-663X. Tel: 601-684-7034. Interlibrary Loan Service Tel: 601-684-2661. Circulation Tel: 601-684-2661. Reference Tel: 601-684-2661. FAX: 601-250-1213. *Dir*, Toni James; *Asst Dir*, Gail Bracey; *Circ*, Marlene Carruth; *Ch Servs*, Mattie J Rials; *Tech Servs*, Stewart Carpenter; *Ref*, Laura Porta; Staff 14 (MLS 4, Non-MLS 10)
Founded 1964. Pop 66,041; Circ 187,202
Oct 1999-Sep 2000 Income (Main Library and Branch Library) $764,354, State $146,244, City $66,420, Federal $42,187, County $349,865, Locally Generated Income $159,638. Mats Exp $99,016, Books $84,191, Per/Ser (Incl. Access Fees) $13,773, Presv $373, Electronic Ref Mat (Incl. Access Fees) $679. Sal $377,624
Library Holdings: Bk Vols 122,539; Per Subs 258
Subject Interests: Genealogy
Automation Activity & Vendor Info: (Cataloging) Gaylord
Branches: 8
ALPHA CENTER, 414 McComb St, 39648. SAN 348-6664. Tel: 601-684-8312. *Librn*, Linda Brister; Staff 1 (Non-MLS 1)
Library Holdings: Bk Vols 3,311
CROSBY PUBLIC, Crosby, 39633. SAN 348-6699. Tel: 601-639-4633. *Librn*, Yvonne Perry; Staff 1 (Non-MLS 1)
Library Holdings: Bk Vols 3,681
GLOSTER PUBLIC, PO Drawer 460, Gloster, 39638. SAN 348-6729. Tel: 601-225-4341. FAX: 601-225-4341. *Librn*, Joyce Hall; Staff 1 (Non-MLS 1)
Library Holdings: Bk Vols 10,984
LIBERTY PUBLIC, PO Box 187, Liberty, 39645. SAN 348-6753. Tel: 601-657-8781. FAX: 601-657-8781. *Librn*, Cheryl Ott; Staff 1 (Non-MLS 1)
Library Holdings: Bk Vols 12,220
MAGNOLIA PUBLIC, Magnolia, 39652. SAN 348-6788. Tel: 601-783-6565. FAX: 601-783-6565. *Librn*, JoAnn Jones; Staff 1 (Non-MLS 1)
Library Holdings: Bk Vols 12,257
OSYKA PUBLIC, Osyka, 39657. SAN 348-6842. Tel: 601-542-5147. *Mgr*, Anne Johnson; Staff 1 (Non-MLS 1)
Library Holdings: Bk Vols 7,302
PROGRESS PUBLIC Tel: 601-542-5501. *Librn*, Alice Overall; Staff 1 (Non-MLS 1)
Library Holdings: Bk Vols 4,464
Friends of the Library Group
WALTHALL, 707 Union Rd, Tylertown, 39667. SAN 348-6931. Tel: 601-876-4348. FAX: 601-876-4348. *Librn*, Ellis Barthe; Staff 2 (Non-MLS 2)
Library Holdings: Bk Vols 17,958
Friends of the Library Group

MENDENHALL

P MENDENHALL PUBLIC LIBRARY, 1630 Simpson Hwy 149, 39114. SAN 376-6187. Tel: 601-847-2181. FAX: 601-847-2188. E-Mail: mendenha@cmrls.lib.ms.us. *Librn*, Lu Ann Bailey
Library Holdings: Bk Vols 30,000; Bk Titles 25,000; Per Subs 30
Mem of Central Mississippi Regional Library System

MERIDIAN

J MERIDIAN COMMUNITY COLLEGE, L O Todd Library, 910 Hwy 19 N, 39307. SAN 308-8944. Tel: 601-483-8241, 601-484-8760. FAX: 601-482-3936. Web Site: www.mcc.cc.ms.us. *Dean of Libr*, Billy C Beal; *Bibliog Instr*, Douglas Jernigan; Tel: 601-484-8762; *Circ*, Rita McClure; Tel: 601-484-8761; *Tech Servs*, Suzanne Grafton; Tel: 601-484-8766; Staff 14 (MLS 6, Non-MLS 8)
Founded 1937. Enrl 2,900
Jul 1998-Jun 1999 Income $735,414. Mats Exp $78,100, Books $40,000, Per/Ser (Incl. Access Fees) $33,000, Presv $1,500, Micro $3,600. Sal $513,568
Library Holdings: Bk Vols 65,000
Database Vendor: Ebsco - EbscoHost, GaleNet, IAC - Info Trac, OCLC - First Search, Wilson - Wilson Web
Publications: Todd Library Timesavers
Open Mon-Thurs 7:30-9:30, Fri 7:30-3:30, Sat 10-2, Sun 1-5, hours may vary in summer & holidays

P MERIDIAN-LAUDERDALE COUNTY PUBLIC LIBRARY,* 2517 Seventh St, 39301. SAN 308-8952. Tel: 601-693-4913, 601-693-6771. FAX: 601-486-2260. *Dir*, D Steven McCartney; *Librn*, Lois Worrell; *Tech Servs*, Brenda Notgrass; *Circ*, Shirley Koch; *Ch Servs*, Donna McLendon; Staff 2 (MLS 2)
Founded 1913. Pop 76,700; Circ 217,624
Oct 1996-Sep 1997 Income $1,000,988, State $250,000, Federal $20,000, County $634,037, Locally Generated Income $96,951. Mats Exp $100,000, Books $56,200, Per/Ser (Incl. Access Fees) $12,400, Micro $4,000. Sal $468,000 (Prof $86,000)
Library Holdings: Bk Vols 107,511; Per Subs 225
Subject Interests: Genealogy, Local history, Meridian star, Mississippi
Publications: Friends (newsletter monthly); Mailibrary Catalog (monthly supplements)
Partic in Miss Libr Comn Interlibr Loan Network; SE Libr Network
Friends of the Library Group
Branches: 1
MAIL Tel: 601-486-2263.
Friends of the Library Group

UNITED STATES NAVY
A NAVAL AIR STATION LIBRARY, 1155 Rosenbaum Ave, Ste 13, 39309. SAN 348-6966. Tel: 601-679-2623. FAX: 601-679-5106. *In Charge*, Betty Hardy
Founded 1960
Oct 1998-Sep 1999 Income $12,000. Mats Exp $11,483, Books $1,983, Per/Ser (Incl. Access Fees) $4,121, AV Equip $1,396, Other Print Mats $1,547
Library Holdings: Bk Titles 14,990; Per Subs 70
Friends of the Library Group

MISSISSIPPI STATE

S COBB INSTITUTE LIBRARY, Mississippi State University, PO Box AR, 39762. SAN 348-7024. Tel: 662-325-3826. FAX: 662-325-8690. *In Charge*, Kathleen Elliott

Founded 1975
Library Holdings: Bk Vols 1,604
Special Collections: Indians of the Southeastern United States; Middle Eastern & Biblical Archaeology; North American Archaeology; Numismatic literature

S INSTITUTE FOR BOTANICAL EXPLORATION LIBRARY,* PO Box EN, 39762. SAN 374-7816. Tel: 601-325-7570. FAX: 601-325-7939. *Dir*, Sidney McDaniel
Library Holdings: Bk Vols 14,000; Per Subs 12

C MISSISSIPPI STATE UNIVERSITY, Mitchell Memorial Library, Hardy Rd, PO Box 5408, 39762-5408. SAN 348-6990. Tel: 662-325-3061. FAX: 662-325-4263. Web Site: www.msstate.edu/library. *Dean of Libr*, Frances N Coleman; E-Mail: fcoleman@library.msstate.edu; *Tech Servs*, Eula Betts; *Coordr*, June Breland; *Syst Coordr*, Stephen Conetto; *Publ Servs*, Susanna Turner; Staff 26 (MLS 26)
Founded 1881. Highest Degree: Doctorate
Library Holdings: Bk Vols 1,700,000; Per Subs 15,574
Subject Interests: Agriculture, Energy, Engineering, Forestry
Special Collections: David Bowen Coll; Delta & Pineland Company Papers; Eugene Butler; Gil Carmichael; GV (Sonny) Montgomery Coll; Hodding Carter Papers; John C Stennis Coll, notes, photogs, mss, correspondence, papers, genealogy; John Grisham; Mississippi Journalists; Mississippiana, bks, mss, newsp; Republican Party of Mississippi Papers; Sid Salter; Southern History & Politics, micro; State & Local History; Turner Catledge Papers
Automation Activity & Vendor Info: (Circulation) DRA
Publications: Guide to Resources in Mammology; Guide to Resources in Ornithology; Guide to Resources of MSU Library in Education; Library Skills Workbook; Science Resources
Partic in SE Libr Network
Friends of the Library Group
Departmental Libraries:
ARCHITECTURE, PO Box 9633, 39762. SAN 348-7059. Tel: 662-325-2202. FAX: 662-325-8872. *Librn*, Emilie White
Friends of the Library Group
VETERINARY MEDICINE, PO Box 9825, 39759. SAN 348-7083. Tel: 662-325-1240. FAX: 662-325-1141.
Friends of the Library Group

MIZE

P MIZE PUBLIC LIBRARY,* 210 Hwy 28, PO Box 247, 39116. SAN 376-639X. Tel: 601-733-9414. *Librn*, Monica Boykin; E-Mail: monica@cmrls.lib.ms.us
Library Holdings: Bk Vols 1,500; Bk Titles 1,100
Mem of Central Mississippi Regional Library System

MOORHEAD

J MISSISSIPPI DELTA COMMUNITY COLLEGE, Stanny Sanders Library, PO Box 668, 38761. SAN 308-8960. Tel: 662-246-6375. FAX: 662-246-8627. *Dir*, Beverly B Nobile; *Media Spec*, Lawrence Kenneth; *Circ*, Marsha Kenneth; *Ref*, Judy Woodcock; Staff 5 (MLS 4, Non-MLS 1)
Enrl 1,501
Library Holdings: Bk Titles 35,000; Per Subs 249
Publications: Library Handbook; Resume Guide
Accesses information from NASA research files & Federal Laboratory Consortium, as well as other agencies & commerical databases

MORTON

P MORTON PUBLIC LIBRARY,* 16 Fourth Ave, 39117. SAN 376-6160. Tel: 601-732-6288. FAX: 601-732-6288. *Librn*, Dot Purvis
Oct 1997-Sep 1998 Income $51,062. Mats Exp $12,169. Sal $30,000
Library Holdings: Bk Titles 10,000; Per Subs 25
Mem of Central Mississippi Regional Library System
Open Mon-Wed 10-5:30, Thurs 1-8 & Fri 9:30-5:30
Friends of the Library Group

P POLKVILLE PUBLIC LIBRARY,* HCR 66 Box 113, Town Hall Hwy 13, 39117. SAN 376-6012. Tel: 601-537-3115. *Librn*, Pat Wiggins
Library Holdings: Bk Vols 600
Mem of Central Mississippi Regional Library System
Friends of the Library Group

NATCHEZ

J COPIAH-LINCOLN COMMUNITY COLLEGE, Willie Mae Dunn Library, 11 Co-Lin Circle, 39120. SAN 308-8987. Tel: 601-446-1101. FAX: 601-446-1297. *Dir*, Joan M McLemore; E-Mail: joan.mclemore@colin.cc.ms.us; Staff 3 (MLS 2, Non-MLS 1)
Founded 1972. Enrl 748; Fac 20
Jul 1998-Jun 1999 Mats Exp $26,797, Per/Ser (Incl. Access Fees) $16,367, Presv $150, Micro $4,950, AV Equip $5,330
Library Holdings: Bk Vols 21,109; Per Subs 523

P HOMOCHITTO VALLEY LIBRARY SERVICE,* 220 S Commerce St, 39120. SAN 308-8979. Tel: 601-445-8862. FAX: 601-446-7795. *Dir*, Donna Janky; Staff 15 (MLS 1, Non-MLS 14)
Founded 1883. Pop 55,000
Oct 1999-Sep 2000 Income (Main Library and Branch Library) $409,000, City $255,000, Federal $80,000, County $64,000, Locally Generated Income $10,000. Mats Exp $48,300. Sal $195,000
Library Holdings: Bk Vols 90,000; Bk Titles 92,000; Per Subs 230
Subject Interests: Local history
Special Collections: Local History; Natchez Mississippi Coll
Automation Activity & Vendor Info: (Cataloging) epixtech, inc.
Database Vendor: Dialog, epixtech, inc., OVID Technologies
Function: Photocopies available
Open Mon-Thurs 9-6, Fri 9-5 & Sat 9-1
Friends of the Library Group
Branches: 3
JUDGE GEORGE W ARMSTRONG LIBRARY, 220 S Commerce St, 39120. SAN 321-9550. Tel: 601-445-8862. FAX: 601-446-7795. *Dir*, Donna Janky
Friends of the Library Group
KEVIN POOLE VAN CLEAVE MEMORIAL LIBRARY, PO Box 517, Centreville, 39631. SAN 348-9515. Tel: 601-645-5771. *Dir*, Donna Janky
Library Holdings: Bk Vols 6,890
WOODVILLE PUBLIC LIBRARY, PO Box 397, Woodville, 39669. SAN 348-954X. Tel: 601-888-6712. *Dir*, Donna Janky
Library Holdings: Bk Vols 6,805
Bookmobiles: 1. Also have 1 station wagon

NEW ALBANY

P UNION COUNTY LIBRARY, Jennie Stephens Smith Library, 219 King St, 38652. (Mail add: PO Box 846, 38652), SAN 348-7113. Tel: 601-534-1991. FAX: 601-534-1937. E-Mail: tdj@union.lib.ms.us. *Dir*, Tonja Johnson; Staff 9 (MLS 1, Non-MLS 8)
Founded 1933. Pop 22,500; Circ 43,500
Library Holdings: Bk Vols 60,000; Per Subs 75
Subject Interests: Miss hist
Special Collections: Genealogy Coll
Automation Activity & Vendor Info: (Cataloging) Follett; (Circulation) Follett; (ILL) Follett; (OPAC) Follett
Database Vendor: Ebsco - EbscoHost, GaleNet, IAC - Info Trac, OCLC - First Search, Wilson - Wilson Web
Friends of the Library Group
Branches: 2
BLUE SPRINGS PUBLIC, PO Box 11, Blue Springs, 38828. SAN 348-7148. Tel: 601-534-6942. *In Charge*, Ann Sherman
NANCE MCNEELY PUBLIC, PO Box 225, Myrtle, 38650. SAN 374-731X. Tel: 601-988-2895. *In Charge*, Betty McNeely
Friends of the Library Group

OAKLAND

P OAKLAND PUBLIC LIBRARY, PO Box 69, 38948. SAN 308-9029. Tel: 662-623-8651. FAX: 662-623-0089. *Librn*, Walter Moores; E-Mail: wmoores@yalobusha.lib.ms.us
Pop 2,000; Circ 7,262
Library Holdings: Bk Vols 10,000; Per Subs 18
Subject Interests: Local history
Partic in Miss Libr Comn Interlibr Loan Network
Friends of the Library Group

OCEAN SPRINGS

S UNIVERSITY OF SOUTHERN MISSISSIPPI-INSTITUTE OF MARINE SCIENCES, Gulf Coast Research Laboratory-Gunter Library, 703 E Beach Dr, 39564. (Mail add: PO Box 7000, 39566-7000), Tel: 601-872-4213, 601-872-4253. FAX: 601-872-4264. Web Site: www.ims.usm.edu. *Librn*, Joyce M Shaw; E-Mail: joyce.shaw@usm.edu; Staff 4 (MLS 1, Non-MLS 3)
Founded 1956. Fac 25; Highest Degree: Doctorate
Jul 1999-Jun 2000 Mats Exp $97,000, Books $2,000, Per/Ser (Incl. Access Fees) $95,000. Sal $65,000
Library Holdings: Bk Vols 30,000; Per Subs 166
Subject Interests: Botany, Ecology, Ichthyology, Marine biology, Microbiology, Toxicology
Special Collections: GCRL History; GCRL Publications; Marine Biology (Expedition Reports); Marine Invertebrate Zoology Coll
Publications: Gulf Research Reports
Restriction: Open to public for reference only
Partic in Gulf Coast Biomedical Libr Consortium; IAMSLIC; Sails, Inc

Branches:
J L SCOTT MARINE EDUCATION CENTER & AQUARIUM, 115 Beach Blvd, Biloxi, 39530. SAN 321-8597. FAX: 601-374-5550.
Subject Interests: Aquarium mgt, Marine educ
Special Collections: Wildflower, Fish & Reptile Color Slides (35 mm)

OXFORD

J NORTHWEST MISSISSIPPI COMMUNITY COLLEGE, Lafayette-Yalobusha Center Library, 1310 Belk Dr, 38655. SAN 370-4939. Tel: 662-238-7953. FAX: 662-236-4764. *Librn*, Jeanette Stone; E-Mail: jstone@nwcc.cc.ms.us
Library Holdings: Bk Vols 9,000; Per Subs 200

G USDA-ARS, National Sedimentation Laboratory Library, 598 McElroy Dr, 38655-1157. (Mail add: PO Box 1157, 38644), SAN 373-0778. Tel: 662-232-2900. FAX: 662-232-2920. Web Site: www.sedlab.olemiss.edu. *Dir*, Dr Mathias Romkens
Library Holdings: Bk Vols 20,000; Per Subs 34
Open Mon-Fri 8:30-5

PASCAGOULA

P JACKSON-GEORGE REGIONAL LIBRARY SYSTEM, (JGRLS), 3214 Pascagoula St, 39567. SAN 348-7202. Tel: 228-769-3060. Interlibrary Loan Service Tel: 228-769-3223. FAX: 228-769-3146. Web Site: www.jgrl.lib.ms.us. *Dir*, Robert Willits; E-Mail: bwillits@jgrl.lib.ms.us; *Publ Servs*, Rex Bridges; Tel: 228-769-3130, E-Mail: rbridges@jgrl.lib.ms.us; *YA Servs*, Mary Ann Louviere; E-Mail: mlouvier@jgrl.lib.ms.us; *Tech Servs*, William Majure; Tel: 228-769-3078, E-Mail: mjohnson@jgrl.lib.ms.us; *Tech Servs*, Katy Yarber; Staff 20 (MLS 12, Non-MLS 8)
Founded 1940. Pop 155,000; Circ 736,956
Oct 1998-Sep 1999 Income (Main Library and Branch Library) $2,652,137. Mats Exp $300,217, Books $269,405, Per/Ser (Incl. Access Fees) $30,812. Sal $1,281,270 (Prof $560,616)
Library Holdings: Bk Vols 270,499; Per Subs 819
Special Collections: Genealogy Coll, mat
Friends of the Library Group
Branches: 8
EAST CENTRAL, PO Box 999, Hurley, 39555. SAN 348-7237. Tel: 228-588-6263. FAX: 228-588-6268. *Librn*, Jean Goff
Friends of the Library Group
KATHLEEN MCILWAIN-GAUTIER PUBLIC LIBRARY, 2100 Library Lane, Gautier, 39553. SAN 348-7326. Tel: 228-497-4531. FAX: 228-497-4560. *Librn*, Jo Anne West
Friends of the Library Group
LUCEDALE-GEORGE COUNTY, 110 Beaver Dam Rd, Lucedale, 39452. SAN 348-7261. Tel: 601-947-2123. FAX: 601-766-3360. *Librn*, Cindy Williams; Tel: 505-599-0248, E-Mail: williamsc@sjc.cc.nm.us
Friends of the Library Group
MOSS POINT CITY, 4401 McInnis St, Moss Point, 39563. SAN 348-7296. Tel: 228-475-7462. FAX: 228-475-7484. E-Mail: jgrl@lib.ms.us. Web Site: www.jgrl.lib.ms.us. *Librn*, Carol C Hewlett; E-Mail: chewlett@jgrl.lib.ms.us
Founded 1900
Library Holdings: Per Subs 102
OCEAN SPRINGS MUNICIPAL, 525 Dewey Ave, Ocean Springs, 39564. SAN 348-7350. Tel: 228-875-1193. FAX: 228-875-1535. *Librn*, Jill Tempest
Friends of the Library Group
PASCAGOULA PUBLIC, 3214 Pascagoula St, 39567. SAN 348-7385. Tel: 228-769-3060. FAX: 228-769-3113. *Asst Dir*, Max Johnson; *Dir*, Robert Willits
Friends of the Library Group
SAINT MARTIN PUBLIC, 15004 LeMoyne Blvd, Biloxi, 39532-5205. SAN 348-7415. Tel: 228-392-3250. FAX: 228-392-0522. *Librn*, Janice Zuleeg
Friends of the Library Group
VANCLEAVE PUBLIC, 12604 Hwy 57, Vancleave, 39565. SAN 348-744X. Tel: 228-826-5857. FAX: 228-826-5893. *Librn*, Carol Mars
Friends of the Library Group

G NATIONAL MARINE FISHERIES SERVICE, Mississippi Laboratories Library,* 3209 Frederick St, PO Mailing Drawer 1207, 39568-1207. SAN 308-9045. Tel: 228-762-4591. FAX: 228-769-9200. Web Site: www.lib.noaa.gov.
Founded 1950
Library Holdings: Bk Vols 4,000; Per Subs 200
Subject Interests: Marine biology, Oceanography, Seafood analysis, Seafood tech
Partic in Dialog Corporation; Fedlink
Holdings accessible through the Nat Oceanic & Atmospheric Admin Cent Libr, Silver Springs, Md

M SINGING RIVER HOSPITAL SYSTEM, Medical Library,* 2809 Denny Ave, 39581. SAN 325-3163. Tel: 228-938-5040. FAX: 228-809-5439. *Librn*, Janice Debose; Staff 2 (MLS 1, Non-MLS 1)
Founded 1979
Library Holdings: Bk Vols 4,000; Per Subs 275
Subject Interests: Allied health, Clinical medicine, Nursing
Special Collections: Community Health Information
Mem of Gulf Coast Biomed Libr Consortium

PASS CHRISTIAN

P PASS CHRISTIAN PUBLIC LIBRARY, 111 Hiern Ave, 39571. SAN 308-9053. Tel: 228-452-4596. FAX: 228-452-3247. E-Mail: passlib@harrison.lib.ms.us. Web Site: www.harrison.lib.ms.us. *Head Librn*, John Batson; *Head, Circ*, Jerry Sellier; *Circ*, Jan Delaune; *Ch Servs*, Sally James; Staff 2 (MLS 1, Non-MLS 1)
Founded 1970
Library Holdings: Bk Vols 32,000; Bk Titles 30,000; Per Subs 60
Special Collections: Postage Stamps
Open Mon-Thurs 8-6, Fri 8-5, Sat 9-5
Friends of the Library Group

PEARL

P PEARL PUBLIC LIBRARY,* 3470 Hwy 80 E, 39208. SAN 377-5739. Tel: 601-932-3535. *Librn*, Kaileen Thieling
Pop 22,000
Mem of Central Mississippi Regional Library System
Friends of the Library Group

PELAHATCHIE

P PELAHATCHIE PUBLIC LIBRARY,* PO Box 959, 39145. SAN 376-6225. Tel: 601-854-8764. FAX: 601-854-8764. *Librn*, Wilmath McCrary
1997-1998 Income $9,000
Library Holdings: Bk Titles 2,000
Mem of Central Mississippi Regional Library System

PERKINSTON

J MISSISSIPPI GULF COAST COMMUNITY COLLEGE, Perkinston Campus Learning Resource Center,* PO Box 849, 39573-0048. SAN 348-7474. Tel: 601-928-5211, Ext 6286. FAX: 601-928-6359. Web Site: www2.mgccc.cc.ms.us/~lrc/jv-lrc-library-index.htm. *Dir*, Liz Mixon; E-Mail: elizabeth.mixon@mgccc.cc.ms.us; *Asst Librn*, Glenda Redmond; *Media Spec*, Richard Marlowe; *Ref*, Brenda Rivero; *Cat*, Pam Ladner; Staff 4 (MLS 4)
Founded 1925. Enrl 850; Fac 45
Library Holdings: Bk Vols 30,571; Per Subs 212
Subject Interests: Career, Faculty, Young adult

PHILADELPHIA

P NESHOBA COUNTY PUBLIC LIBRARY,* 230 Beacon St, 39350. SAN 308-907X. Tel: 601-656-4911. FAX: 601-656-6894. E-Mail: 4pns@neshoba.lib.ms.us. Web Site: www.neshoba.lib.ms.us. *Ref*, Patsy McWilliams; *Tech Servs*, Brenda Smith; *Ch Servs*, Bobbie Jackson; *Dir*, Bill Majure
Founded 1929. Pop 26,747; Circ 55,307
Oct 1997-Sep 1998 Income $205,151, State $51,187, City $30,680, County $104,886, Locally Generated Income $18,398. Mats Exp $33,613. Sal $93,333 (Prof $26,136)
Library Holdings: Bk Titles 36,500; Per Subs 64
Subject Interests: Choctaw Indians, Genealogy, Local history
Publications: Cemetery Records of Neshoba County; Our Links to the Past; The Red Clay Hills of Neshoba
Open Mon, Wed & Fri 9-5, Tues & Thurs 9-7, Sat 9-12

PICAYUNE

P PEARL RIVER COUNTY LIBRARY SYSTEM, Margaret Reed Crosby Memorial Library, 900 Goodyear Blvd, 39466. SAN 348-7504. Tel: 601-798-5081. FAX: 601-798-5082. *Actg Dir*, Linda Tufaro; *Asst Dir, Tech Coordr*, Susan Cassagne; *Ref*, Janet Teague; *ILL*, Robert Tucker; Staff 2 (MLS 2)
Founded 1926. Pop 39,700; Circ 150,000
Library Holdings: Bk Vols 90,000; Per Subs 70
Subject Interests: Drug abuse, Genealogy, Local history
Special Collections: Genealogy Family Files; Miss Municipal Assn Digitizing Project; W A Zeltner Mississippi Coll
Automation Activity & Vendor Info: (Cataloging) epixtech, inc.; (Circulation) epixtech, inc.
Special Services for the Deaf - High interest/low vocabulary books
Friends of the Library Group

Branches: 1
POPLARVILLE PUBLIC, 202 W Beers St, Poplarville, 39470. SAN 348-7539. Tel: 601-795-8411. FAX: 601-795-8411. *Librn*, Cynthia Hornsby
Library Holdings: Bk Vols 30,000; Per Subs 20
Bookmobiles: 1

PONTOTOC

P DIXIE REGIONAL LIBRARY SYSTEM, (DRLS), 111 N Main St, 38863-2103. SAN 348-7598. Tel: 662-489-3960. FAX: 662-489-7777. Web Site: www.dixie.lib.ms.us. *Dir*, Joe Tynes; *Asst Dir*, Jan Willis; *Tech Servs*, Mary A Hamilton; Staff 3 (MLS 3)
Founded 1961. Pop 58,066; Circ 174,876
Oct 1999-Sep 2000 Income (Main Library and Branch Library) $599,743, State $165,327, City $96,853, Federal $47,381, County $232,000, Locally Generated Income $58,182. Mats Exp $81,176, Books $77,180, Per/Ser (Incl. Access Fees) $1,580, Electronic Ref Mat (Incl. Access Fees) $2,416. Sal $361,652 (Prof $109,367)
Library Holdings: Bk Vols 92,921; Per Subs 188
Subject Interests: Genealogy, Local history
Publications: Dixie News (quarterly newsletter)
Partic in Magnolia
Open Mon-Thurs 9-6, Fri 9-5 & Sat 8-4
Friends of the Library Group
Branches: 8
CALHOUN CITY BRANCH, PO Box 646, Calhoun City, 38916. SAN 348-7652. Tel: 662-628-6331. FAX: 662-628-6331. *Librn*, Charlotte Naomi James
Library Holdings: Bk Vols 7,618
Friends of the Library Group
HOULKA PUBLIC, PO Box 275, Houlka, 38850-0275. SAN 348-7687. Tel: 662-568-2747. FAX: 662-568-2747. *Librn*, Martha Hinton
Library Holdings: Bk Vols 2,717
HOUSTON CARNEGIE BRANCH, PO Box 186, Houston, 38851-0186. SAN 348-7717. Tel: 662-456-3381. FAX: 662-456-3381. *Librn*, Mrs Gene Philpot
Library Holdings: Bk Vols 5,586
Friends of the Library Group
JESSE YANCY MEMORIAL, 314 N Newberger Ave, Bruce, 38915. (Mail add: PO Box 517, Bruce, 38915-0096), Tel: 662-983-2220. FAX: 662-983-2220. E-Mail: brlib@dixie.lib.ms.us. Web Site: www.dixie.lib.ms.us. *Librn*, Ann Ivy King
Founded 1959
Library Holdings: Bk Vols 20,000
Friends of the Library Group
OKOLONA CARNEGIE BRANCH, PO Box 126, Okolona, 38860-0126. SAN 348-7741. Tel: 662-447-2401. FAX: 662-447-2401. *Librn*, Vickie Ross
Library Holdings: Bk Vols 5,131
Friends of the Library Group
PONTOTOC COUNTY LIBRARY, 111 N Main St, 38863-2103. SAN 348-7628. Tel: 662-489-3960. FAX: 662-489-7777. *Librn*, Regina Grahm
Founded 1934. Pop 20,918
Library Holdings: Bk Vols 25,148
Subject Interests: Local history
Friends of the Library Group
SHERMAN PUBLIC, PO Box 81, Sherman, 38869-0181. SAN 373-1766. Tel: 662-840-2513. FAX: 662-840-2513. *Librn*, Grace Caldwell
Library Holdings: Bk Vols 3,265
Friends of the Library Group
EDMONDSON MEMORIAL, PO Box 174, Vardaman, 38878-0174. SAN 348-7776. Tel: 662-682-7333. FAX: 662-682-7333. *Librn*, Jo Anne Blue
Library Holdings: Bk Vols 4,024

POPLARVILLE

J PEARL RIVER COMMUNITY COLLEGE LIBRARY,* 101 Hwy 11 N, PO Box 5660, 39470. SAN 308-9088. Tel: 601-403-6801, Ext 330. FAX: 601-403-1135. Web Site: www.prcc.cc.ms.us. *Librn*, Jeanne Dyar
Founded 1926. Enrl 2,751; Fac 115
Library Holdings: Bk Vols 53,000; Per Subs 326
Subject Interests: Behav sci, History, Literature, Sci-tech, Soc sci
Special Collections: Mississippi Coll
Partic in SE Libr Network
Open Mon-Thurs 7:45 am-9 pm, Fri 7:45-3
Departmental Libraries:
FOREST COUNTY CENTER, 5448 US Hwy 49 S, Hattiesburg, 39401. SAN 377-7758. Tel: 601-554-5522. FAX: 601-554-5470. *Librn*, Mary Wallace
Subject Interests: Allied health

PORT GIBSON

P HARRIETTE PERSON MEMORIAL LIBRARY, 606 Main, 39150-2330. (Mail add: PO Box 1017, 39150-1017), SAN 308-910X. Tel: 601-437-5202. FAX: 601-437-5787. *Coll Develop, Librn*, Nancy S Batton-Butler; E-Mail: nanbutlr@harriette.lib.ms.us
Founded 1818. Pop 11,370
Oct 1999-Sep 2000 Income $137,011, State $30,484, City $27,571, Federal $2,456, County $40,000, Locally Generated Income $21,185, Other $15,315. Mats Exp $27,400, Books $20,815, Per/Ser (Incl. Access Fees) $1,838, Presv $190, Micro $2,172, Electronic Ref Mat (Incl. Access Fees) $2,385. Sal $65,206 (Prof $63,506)
Library Holdings: Bk Titles 31,527; Per Subs 55
Special Collections: Miss Coll
First public library in Mississippi
Friends of the Library Group

PUCKETT

P PUCKETT PUBLIC LIBRARY,* PO Box 550, 39151. SAN 376-6217. Tel: 601-824-0180. E-Mail: puckett@cmrls.lib.ms.us. *Librn*, Regina Hudson
Library Holdings: Bk Titles 6,000; Per Subs 14
Mem of Central Mississippi Regional Library System

PURVIS

P LAMAR COUNTY LIBRARY SYSTEM,* 122 Shelby Speights Dr, 39475. (Mail add: PO Box 289, 39475-0289), Tel: 601-794-8651. *Dir*, Stella Wheat; E-Mail: swheat@lamar.lib.ms.us; *Librn*, Donna Fite; Staff 9 (MLS 2, Non-MLS 7)
Founded 1997. Pop 30,000
Library Holdings: Bk Vols 30,000; Per Subs 80; Bks on Deafness & Sign Lang 10
Subject Interests: Genealogy, Local history
Automation Activity & Vendor Info: (Acquisitions) Brodart; (Cataloging) Brodart; (Circulation) Brodart; (OPAC) Brodart
Database Vendor: Ebsco - EbscoHost, OCLC - First Search
Friends of the Library Group
Branches: 3
LUMBERTON PUBLIC, 106 W Main St, Lumberton, 39455. SAN 348-8284. Tel: 601-796-4227. FAX: 601-796-4227. *Librn*, Patti Beall; E-Mail: pbeall@lamar.lib.ms.us; Staff 2 (Non-MLS 2)
Library Holdings: Bk Titles 8,500; Per Subs 20
Subject Interests: Local history, Photographs
Automation Activity & Vendor Info: (Acquisitions) Brodart; (Cataloging) Brodart; (Circulation) Brodart; (OPAC) Brodart
Database Vendor: OCLC - First Search
Friends of the Library Group
PURVIS PUBLIC, Shelby Speights Dr, PO Box 289, 39475. SAN 348-8438. Tel: 601-794-8768. FAX: 601-794-8768. *Librn*, Donna Fite; Staff 2 (Non-MLS 2)
Library Holdings: Bk Titles 10,500; Per Subs 25
Automation Activity & Vendor Info: (Acquisitions) Brodart; (Cataloging) Brodart; (Circulation) Brodart; (OPAC) Brodart
Database Vendor: OCLC - First Search
SUMRALL PUBLIC - L R BOYER MEMORIAL LIBRARY, 103 Poplar, PO Box 327, Sumrall, 39482. SAN 329-3335. Tel: 601-758-4711. FAX: 601-758-4711. E-Mail: lamar@lamar.lib.ms.us. *Librn*, Billy Landrigan; E-Mail: landrigan@lamar.lib.ms.us
Library Holdings: Bk Titles 8,500; Per Subs 35
Automation Activity & Vendor Info: (Acquisitions) Brodart; (Cataloging) Brodart; (Circulation) Brodart; (Media Booking) Brodart; (OPAC) Brodart
Database Vendor: OCLC - First Search

QUITMAN

P EAST MISSISSIPPI REGIONAL LIBRARY,* 116 Water St, 39355-2336. SAN 348-7830. Tel: 601-776-3881. FAX: 601-776-6559. *Dir*, Susan T Byra; E-Mail: sbyra@emrl.lib.ms.us; *Asst Dir*, Lorraine M Russell; *Librn*, Anissa McCarty; *Asst Librn*, Angie Thornton; Staff 2 (MLS 2)
Founded 1966. Pop 53,944; Circ 127,331
Oct 1997-Sep 1998 Income $314,889, State $126,006, City $35,659, County $131,091, Other $22,133. Mats Exp $55,078, Books $50,350, Per/Ser (Incl. Access Fees) $4,022. Sal $188,083
Library Holdings: Bk Titles 123,652; Per Subs 300
Branches: 8
BAY SPRINGS MUNICIPAL, PO Drawer N, Bay Springs, 39422. SAN 348-7865. Tel: 601-764-2291. *Librn*, Shiloh Walker
Library Holdings: Bk Vols 16,503
ENTERPRISE PUBLIC, Enterprise, 39330. SAN 348-789X. Tel: 601-659-3564. *Librn*, Jane Evans
Library Holdings: Bk Vols 7,470
LOUIN PUBLIC, Hwy 15, Louin, 39338. SAN 348-7903. Tel: 601-739-3630. *Librn*, Carol Byrd-Brown
Library Holdings: Bk Vols 4,081
MARY WEEMS PARKER MEMORIAL, 1016 N Pine Ave, Heidelberg, 39439. SAN 348-792X. Tel: 601-787-3857. *Librn*, Margie McClellan
Library Holdings: Bk Vols 13,276
PACHUTA PUBLIC, PO Box 189, Pachuta, 39347. Tel: 601-776-3131. *Librn*, Sue Sexton

Library Holdings: Bk Vols 7,460
SHUBUTA PUBLIC, PO Box 786, Shubuta, 39360. SAN 348-8012. *Librn*, Monica Hearn
Library Holdings: Bk Vols 4,813
STONEWALL PUBLIC, Stonewall, 39363. SAN 348-8047. Tel: 601-659-7033. *Librn*, Vallie Molony
Library Holdings: Bk Vols 14,897
WAYNESBORO MEMORIAL LIBRARY, 712 Wayne, Waynesboro, 39367. SAN 348-8071. Tel: 601-735-2268. FAX: 601-735-6407. E-Mail: wlib@wwcls.lib.ms.us. Web Site: www.wayneco.com. *Dir*, Patsy Brewer
1999-2000 Income $174,000
Library Holdings: Bk Vols 30,084
Special Collections: Genealogy Coll
Friends of the Library Group

RALEIGH

P RALEIGH PUBLIC LIBRARY, Floyd J Robinson Memorial Library, PO Box 266, 39153. SAN 376-6349. Tel: 601-782-4277. FAX: 601-782-4400. E-Mail: raleigh@cmrls.lib.ms.us. *Librn*, Betty Currie
Library Holdings: Bk Titles 15,000
Mem of Central Mississippi Regional Library System
Friends of the Library Group

RAYMOND

J HINDS COMMUNITY COLLEGE DISTRICT, Learning Resources Center-McLendon Library, Raymond Campus, PMV 11258, 39154-1100. (Mail add: PO Box 1100, 39154-1100), SAN 348-8101. Tel: 601-857-3253. FAX: 601-857-3293. Web Site: www.lrc.hinds.cc.ms.us. *Dir, Tech Servs*, Helen J Flanders; E-Mail: hjflandors@hinds.cc.ms.us; *Acq*, Faye Martin; *Bibliog Instr, Ref*, Nancy Tenhet; *Coll Develop*, Alice Margolis; *ILL*, Peggy Sweeney; Staff 14 (MLS 14)
Founded 1922. Enrl 12,164; Fac 488
Library Holdings: Bk Vols 169,784; Bk Titles 103,793; Per Subs 1,180
Special Collections: Black Heritage Coll; Government (John Bell Williams Coll)
Automation Activity & Vendor Info: (Acquisitions) SIRSI
Publications: HLR Spotlight (monthly newsletter)
Partic in SE Libr Network
Departmental Libraries:
ACADEMIC & TECHNICAL CENTER LIBRARY, 3925 Sunset Dr, Jackson, 39213-5899. SAN 308-8715. Tel: 601-987-8123. FAX: 601-982-5804. *Librn*, Theresa Ellison; Tel: 601-987-8102, E-Mail: jyquinn@hinds.cc.ms.us; *Circ*, Yolonda Cavett; Tel: 601-987-8109, E-Mail: ycavett@netscape.net; Staff 3 (MLS 1, Non-MLS 2)
Automation Activity & Vendor Info: (Circulation) SIRSI
Database Vendor: Ebsco - EbscoHost, GaleNet, IAC - Info Trac, OCLC - First Search, Wilson - Wilson Web
Function: Research library
NURSING ALLIED HEALTH CENTER, 1750 Chadwick Dr, Jackson, 39204-3490. SAN 324-427X. Tel: 601-371-3523. FAX: 601-371-3703. *Tech Servs*, Heloise Bostick; *Tech Servs*, Sandra McNair
RANKIN CAMPUS, 3805 Hwy 80 E, Pearl, 39208-4295. SAN 324-4288. Tel: 601-936-5538. FAX: 601-936-5542. *Librn*, Renita Lane
VICKSBURG-WARREN COUNTY, 755 Hwy 27 S, Vicksburg, 39180-8699. SAN 324-4261. Tel: 601-629-6846. FAX: 601-629-6862. Web Site: www.lrc.hinds.cc.ms.us. *In Charge*, Margaret Jane Stauble; Staff 2 (MLS 1, Non-MLS 1)
Highest Degree: Associate
Automation Activity & Vendor Info: (OPAC) SIRSI
WILLIAM HOLTZCLAW BRANCH, Hwy 18 W, Utica, 39175-9599. SAN 308-9207. Tel: 601-885-6062, Ext 233. FAX: 601-885-8453. *Librn*, Alma M Fisher; *Ref*, Esther Owens; *Media Spec*, Charles R Porter; *Ref*, Theresa Akbar; *Tech Servs*, Amanda Hubbard; Staff 3 (MLS 3)
Founded 1903. Enrl 751
Subject Interests: Behav sci, Education, English literature, Soc sci
Special Collections: Black Heritage Coll
Friends of the Library Group

RICHLAND

P RICHLAND PUBLIC LIBRARY,* PO Box 180098, 39218. SAN 376-6284. Tel: 601-932-1846. FAX: 601-932-1688. *Librn*, Diane Mitchell
Library Holdings: Bk Vols 19,000; Bk Titles 18,000; Per Subs 60
Mem of Central Mississippi Regional Library System
Friends of the Library Group

RICHTON

P PINE FOREST REGIONAL LIBRARY,* 210 Front St, PO Box 1208, 39476-1510. SAN 348-8136. Tel: 601-788-6539. FAX: 601-788-9743. *Dir*, Brenda Knight; Staff 29 (MLS 3, Non-MLS 26)
Founded 1958. Pop 70,638; Circ 184,283
Oct 1997-Sep 1998 Income $374,212. Mats Exp $49,000. Sal $272,473
Library Holdings: Bk Titles 150,000; Per Subs 2,400
Subject Interests: Local history
Branches: 12
BEAUMONT PUBLIC, General Delivery, Beaumont, 39423. SAN 348-8160. *Librn*, Joyce Breland
CONWAY HALL PUBLIC, 9220 Hwy 42, Petal, 39465. SAN 348-8225. *Librn*, Laura Odom
JANE BLAIN BREWER MEMORIAL, PO Box 279, Mount Olive, 39119. SAN 348-8373. Tel: 601-797-4955. FAX: 601-797-4955. E-Mail: mto@pineforest.lib.ms.us. *Librn*, Elaine Lack
LEAKESVILLE PUBLIC, PO Box 1089, Leakesville, 39451. SAN 348-825X. Tel: 601-394-2897. FAX: 601-394-2897. *Librn*, Betty Glass
MCHENRY PUBLIC, PO Box 14, McHenry, 39561. SAN 348-8314. *Librn*, Susan Spiker
MCLAIN PUBLIC, PO Box 65, McLain, 39456. SAN 348-8349. *Librn*, Mable Cochran
NEW AUGUSTA PUBLIC, PO Box 387, New Augusta, 39462. SAN 348-8403. Tel: 601-964-3774. *Librn*, Melissa Dunham
R E BLACKWELL MEMORIAL, PO Box 1539, Collins, 39428. SAN 348-8195. Tel: 601-765-8582. FAX: 601-765-8582. *Librn*, Jaylyn Allen
RICHTON PUBLIC Tel: 601-788-6539. FAX: 601-788-9743. *Librn*, James Freeman
SEMINARY PUBLIC, Seminary, 39479. SAN 348-8497. Tel: 601-722-9041. FAX: 601-722-9041. *Librn*, Shirley Crenshaw
STATE LINE PUBLIC, PO Box 279, State Line, 39362. SAN 348-8527. Tel: 601-848-7011. *Librn*, Eunice Corners
STONE COUNTY PUBLIC, 242 Second St, Wiggins, 39577. SAN 348-8551. Tel: 601-928-4993. FAX: 601-928-4993. *Librn*, Laura Simpson
Friends of the Library Group

RIDGELAND

P MADISON COUNTY LIBRARY SYSTEM, Elsie E Jergens Memorial Library, 397 Hwy 51, 39157. SAN 348-1891. Tel: 601-856-4536. FAX: 601-856-3748. *Librn*, Nan Smith; *Ch Servs*, Pam Reed; *Circ*, Tammie Terry; Staff 2 (MLS 2)
Pop 15,000; Circ 94,422
Library Holdings: Bk Vols 39,911
Friends of the Library Group

ROSEDALE

R FIRST BAPTIST CHURCH, Mattie D Hall Memorial Library, 407 Front St, PO Box 822, 38769. SAN 308-9134. Tel: 662-759-6378.
Founded 1955
Library Holdings: Bk Vols 4,001
Publications: Consumer Reports; Home Missions; Ideals; Media; The Commission

SAND HILL

P SAND HILL PUBLIC LIBRARY,* 698 Pisgah Rd, 39042. SAN 376-6381. Tel: 601-829-1653. FAX: 601-829-1653. *Librn*, Della Fitzhugh
Library Holdings: Bk Vols 6,500; Per Subs 10
Mem of Central Mississippi Regional Library System
Open Mon-Thurs 8-12 & 12:30-3:30

SCOOBA

J EAST MISSISSIPPI COMMUNITY COLLEGE, Tubb-May Memorial Library, 1527 Kemper, 39358. (Mail add: PO Box 158, 39358), SAN 348-8586. Tel: 662-476-5054. FAX: 662-476-5053. Web Site: www.emcc.cc.ms.us. *Dir*, Roger F Smith; E-Mail: rsmith@emcc.cc.ms.us; *Asst Librn*, Janice Irby
Founded 1927. Enrl 1,200
Jul 2000-Jun 2001 Income $150,000. Mats Exp $39,937, Books $23,378, Per/Ser (Incl. Access Fees) $10,359, AV Equip $6,200. Sal $90,000
Library Holdings: Bk Vols 27,500; Per Subs 100
Subject Interests: Miss hist
Special Collections: Mississippi Coll
Departmental Libraries:
INSTRUCTIONAL MATERIALS CENTER

SEBASTOPOL

P SEBASTOPOL PUBLIC LIBRARY,* PO Box 173, 39359. SAN 376-6209. Tel: 601-625-7200. FAX: 601-625-8826. E-Mail: sebastop@cmrls.lib.ms.us. *Librn*, Wanda Bishop
Library Holdings: Bk Vols 8,000; Bk Titles 7,000
Mem of Central Mississippi Regional Library System

SENATOBIA

J NORTHWEST MISSISSIPPI COMMUNITY COLLEGE, R C Pugh Library, 4975 Hwy 51 N, 38668. (Mail add: PO Box L - NWCC, 38668), SAN 348-8640. Tel: 662-562-3278. Reference Tel: 662-562-3268. FAX: 662-562-3280. Web Site: www.nwcc.cc.ms.us. *Dir*, Margaret N Rogers; Tel: 662-562-3277, E-Mail: mrogers@nwcc.cc.ms.us; *Media Spec*, Marvelene McCullar; Tel: 662-562-3279; *Cat*, Betty Sykes Green; Tel: 662-562-3261; *Publ Servs*, Catherine Warren; E-Mail: cawarren@nwcc.cc.ms.us; *Circ*, Wanda Pegues; Staff 11 (MLS 5, Non-MLS 6)
Founded 1926. Enrl 2,191; Fac 122; Highest Degree: Associate
Library Holdings: Bk Vols 70,011; Per Subs 589
Automation Activity & Vendor Info: (Cataloging) SIRSI; (Circulation) SIRSI; (OPAC) SIRSI; (Serials) SIRSI
Database Vendor: Ebsco - EbscoHost, GaleNet, IAC - Info Trac, OCLC - First Search, ProQuest, Wilson - Wilson Web
Partic in SE Libr Network

SOUTHAVEN

J NORTHWEST MISSISSIPPI COMMUNITY COLLEGE, DeSoto Center Library,* 5197 WE Ross Pkwy, 38671. SAN 308-9142. Tel: 662-280-6164. FAX: 662-280-6161. E-Mail: bc_lib1@nwcc.cc.ms.us. *Librn*, Betty L McCollough
Founded 1979. Enrl 600; Fac 41
Library Holdings: Bk Vols 16,000; Per Subs 250
Open Mon-Fri 8 am-9 pm, Sat 8:30-12

STARKVILLE

P STARKVILLE - OKTIBBEHA COUNTY PUBLIC LIBRARY SYSTEM,* 326 University Dr, PO Box 1406, 39760-1406. SAN 348-8675. Tel: 601-323-2766, 601-323-2783. FAX: 601-323-9140. *Dir*, Virginia Holtcamp
Pop 36,600; Circ 113,000
Oct 1996-Sep 1997 Income $417,120. Mats Exp $57,000. Sal $180,600
Library Holdings: Bk Vols 55,000; Per Subs 115
Special Collections: Genealogy (Katie-Prince Eskar Coll)
Friends of the Library Group
Branches: 3
MABEN BRANCH, Maben, 39750. SAN 348-8705. Tel: 601-263-5619. FAX: 601-263-5734. *Circ, Ser*, Katie Brand
Friends of the Library Group
STARKVILLE (HQ) Tel: 601-323-2766, 601-323-2783. FAX: 601-263-5734. *Dir*, Virginia Holtcamp; *Circ, Ser*, Shirley Richter; *Ch Servs*, Carolyn Reed
Friends of the Library Group
STURGIS BRANCH, Sturgis, 39769. SAN 348-8764. Tel: 601-465-7493. FAX: 601-465-7493. *Librn*, Debbie Etheridge

STENNIS SPACE CENTER

UNITED STATES NAVY
A MATTHEW FONTAINE MAURY OCEANOGRAPHIC LIBRARY, 1002 Balch Blvd., Blvd. 1003, 30522-5001. Tel: 228-688-4597. FAX: 228-688-4191. Web Site: 128.160.4.61. *Librn*, Martha Elbers; Staff 6 (MLS 4, Non-MLS 2)
Founded 1871
Library Holdings: Bk Vols 70,000; Per Subs 480
Subject Interests: Biological, Cartography, Chemistry, Engineering, Geol oceanog, Meteorology, Ocean engineering, Photogrammetry, Phys oceanog
Special Collections: Hydrographic Office Publications Coll; Oceanographic Expeditions Coll
Publications: Accessions list
Partic in Defense Technical Information Center; Dialog Corporation; Fedlink; OCLC Online Computer Library Center, Inc

STONEVILLE

C MISSISSIPPI STATE UNIVERSITY AGRICULTURAL & FORESTRY EXPERIMENT STATION, Delta Research & Extension Center Library, DREC Bldg U-101, Rm 216, 82 Stoneville Rd, 38776. (Mail add: PO Box 197, 38776), Tel: 662-686-3261. FAX: 662-686-3342. Web Site: www.msstate.edu/dept/drec/. *Librn*, Rhonda Holman Watson; E-Mail: rhwatson@drec.msstate.edu; Staff 1 (MLS 1,)
Founded 1966
Library Holdings: Bk Vols 25,000; Per Subs 200
Subject Interests: Agriculture, Botany, Chemistry, Economics, Entomology, Mathematics, Mechanical engineering, Meteorology, Publications of all state experiment stations, Zoology
Database Vendor: CARL, Ebsco - EbscoHost, Lexis-Nexis, OCLC - First Search, Silverplatter Information Inc., Wilson - Wilson Web
Publications: (Serials catalog)
Function: Research library

SUMMIT

J SOUTHWEST MISSISSIPPI COMMUNITY COLLEGE, Library-Learning Resources Center,* College Dr, 39666. SAN 308-9169. Tel: 601-276-2004. FAX: 601-276-3748. *Librn*, Jo Ann Young; *Asst Librn*, Maxine Bierbaum; Staff 2 (MLS 2)
Founded 1977. Enrl 1,462
Library Holdings: Bk Vols 32,330; Per Subs 191
Special Collections: Mississippi Coll

TAYLORSVILLE

P EVON A FORD PUBLIC LIBRARY,* PO Box 430, 39168. SAN 376-6241. Tel: 601-785-4361. FAX: 601-785-6611. *Librn*, Frances Gregg
Library Holdings: Bk Vols 16,000; Per Subs 12
Mem of Central Mississippi Regional Library System
Friends of the Library Group

TOUGALOO

C TOUGALOO COLLEGE, L Zenobia Coleman Library, 39174-9989. SAN 308-9177. Tel: 601-977-7705. FAX: 601-977-7714. *Dir*, Charlene J Cole; E-Mail: charlene.cole@tougaloo.edu; *ILL, Ref*, Bernice Smith; Staff 3 (MLS 3)
Founded 1872. Enrl 775; Fac 64; Highest Degree: Bachelor
Library Holdings: Bk Vols 139,000; Bk Titles 125,000; Per Subs 389
Special Collections: African Materials (Ross Coll); Baily-Ward African American Coll (archives); Civil Rights & Liberties (Charles Horowitz Papers); Civil Rights Movement (Tracy Sugarman Print Coll of 1964), prints; Mississippi Civil Rights Lawsuits of the 1960's, bks, papers; Music (B B King Coll), awards, pamphlets, papers, per; Radical Papers (Kudzu File)
Publications: A Classified Bibliography of the Special Collections in the L Zenobia Coleman Library
Partic in Coop Col Libr Ctr, Inc; OCLC Online Computer Library Center, Inc

TUPELO

J ITAWAMBA COMMUNITY COLLEGE, Tupelo Branch, Learning Resource Center,* 2176 S Eason, 38804. SAN 308-9185. Tel: 662-620-5091. FAX: 662-620-5095. Web Site: www.lcc.cc.ms.us. *Dir*, Dr Glenda Segars; E-Mail: grsegars@icc.cc.ms.us; *Librn*, Ruth Ann Free; *AV*, Colby Hannon
Founded 1976. Enrl 1,400; Fac 125
1997-1998 Income $220,000. Mats Exp $50,000, Books $20,000, Per/Ser (Incl. Access Fees) $6,500. Sal $142,000
Library Holdings: Bk Titles 11,000; Per Subs 300
Also houses University of Mississippi, Tupelo Branch library. Open Mon-Thurs 8-8:45, Fri 8-3

P LEE-ITAWAMBA LIBRARY SYSTEM, Lee County Library,* 219 N Madison St, 38801-3807. SAN 348-8799. Tel: 601-841-9027. Interlibrary Loan Service Tel: 601-841-9013. FAX: 601-840-7615. *Dir*, Louann Hurst; *Circ*, Bonnie Gaines; *Tech Servs*, Barbara Anglin; *Ch Servs*, Brian Hargett; Staff 12 (MLS 12)
Founded 1942. Pop 83,808; Circ 272,926
Library Holdings: Bk Vols 209,373; Per Subs 286
Subject Interests: Genealogy
Open Mon-Thurs 9:30-8:30, Fri & Sat 9-5
Branches: 1
ITAWAMBA COUNTY, 210 Cedar St, Fulton, 38843. SAN 348-8829. Tel: 601-862-4926. *Librn*, Cindy Jamason
Library Holdings: Bk Vols 35,566

M NORTH MISSISSIPPI MEDICAL CENTER, Resource Center,* 830 S Gloster St, 38801. SAN 371-0947. Tel: 601-841-4399. FAX: 601-690-7239, 841-3552. *Librn*, Mary Lillian Randle; Staff 2 (MLS 1, Non-MLS 1)
Founded 1975
Library Holdings: Bk Titles 1,151; Per Subs 150
Partic in Mississippi Biomedical Library Consortium

UNION

P KEMPER-NEWTON REGIONAL LIBRARY SYSTEM, 101 Peachtree St, 39365-2617. SAN 348-8888. Tel: 601-774-5096. FAX: 601-774-8735. *Dir*, Barbara Betts Gough; Tel: 601-774-9297, E-Mail: bargo@kemper.lib.ms.us; *Asst Dir*, Jane Wolverton; Tel: 601-774-9297, E-Mail: jawo@kemper.lib.ms.us; *Br Coordr*, Jo Barron; E-Mail: bargo@kemper.lib.ms.us; *Librn*, Rita Dube; Tel: 601-635-2777; *Librn*, Linda Hamm; E-Mail: linha@kemper.lib.ms.us; *Librn*, Ethel Jarvis; Tel: 662-476-8452; *Librn*, Lynette Long; Tel: 601-743-5981, E-Mail: lynlong@kemper.lib.ms.us; *Librn*, Lavanda Yorks; Tel: 601-683-3367, E-Mail: vanyo@kemper.lib.ms.us; *Asst Librn*, Brenda Pierce; E-Mail: brenpie@kemper.lib.ms.us; *Asst Librn*, Eliana Richardson; E-Mail: eliana@kemper.lib.ms.us; *Asst Librn*, Fay Vandevender; Tel: 601-743-5981, E-Mail: fayvan@kemper.lib.ms.us; *Cat*, Brenda Williams; E-Mail: brenwill@kemper.lib.ms.us. Subject Specialists: *Art*,

Eliana Richardson; *Children's literature*, Lynette Long; *Children's literature*, Linda Hamm; *Children's literature*, Ethel Jarvis; *Fiction*, Brenda Pierce; *Fiction*, Lavanda Yorks; *Fiction*, Fay Vandevender; *Fiction*, Rita Dube; Staff 11 (MLS 1, Non-MLS 10)
Founded 1969. Pop 31,685; Circ 50,312
Oct 1999-Sep 2000 Income (Main Library and Branch Library) $243,924, State $11,860, City $31,650, Federal $10,882, County $104,134, Other $8,801. Mats Exp $17,060, Books $14,000, Per/Ser (Incl. Access Fees) $1,860, AV Equip $1,200. Sal $142,943
Library Holdings: Bk Titles 58,830; Per Subs 62
Subject Interests: Genealogy, Miss authors, Miss hist
Function: ILL available
Friends of the Library Group
Branches: 7
CHUNKY BRANCH, Chunky, 39323-0086. SAN 348-8918. *Librn*, Paula Snowden
DECATUR PUBLIC, PO Box 40, Decatur, 39327-0040. SAN 348-8942. Tel: 601-635-2777. *Librn*, Bonnie Russell
DEKALB BRANCH, PO Box 710, DeKalb, 39328-0710. SAN 348-8977. Tel: 601-743-5981. *Librn*, Lynette Long
Special Collections: Kemper County History Coll
Friends of the Library Group
HICKORY BRANCH, Hickory, 39332. SAN 370-8020.
NEWTON PUBLIC, 300 W Church St, Newton, 39345-2208. SAN 348-9000. Tel: 601-683-3367. FAX: 601-683-3367. *Librn*, Vanda Yorks
Special Collections: Mississippi Authors & History Coll
SCOOBA BRANCH, PO Box 217, Scooba, 39358-0217. SAN 348-9035. Tel: 601-476-8452. *Librn*, Janice Irby
Friends of the Library Group
UNION Tel: 601-774-5096. FAX: 601-774-8735. *Librn*, Ella Rathod; E-Mail: er@gi.lib.ne.us
Special Collections: Newton County History Coll

UNIVERSITY

CL UNIVERSITY OF MISSISSIPPI, Law Library, PO Box 1848, 38677-1848. SAN 308-9193. Tel: 662-915-6824. FAX: 662-915-7731. E-Mail: lawlibad@olemiss.edu. Web Site: www.sunset.backbone.olemiss.edu/depts/law_library_school/libndex.html. *Dir*, Kris Gilliland; *Asst Dir*, Christopher Noe; *Tech Servs*, Julianna S Davis; *Cat*, Eugenia Minor; *Publ Servs*, Anne Klinger; *Publ Servs*, Lynn Murray; *ILL, Ref*, Linda Scott; Staff 8 (MLS 8)
Founded 1854. Enrl 540; Fac 26; Highest Degree: Doctorate
Library Holdings: Bk Vols 160,000
Subject Interests: Space law, Tax law
Special Collections: Senator James O Eastland Papers Coll
Publications: Law Library (newsletter)
Partic in SE Libr Network

C UNIVERSITY OF MISSISSIPPI, John Davis Williams Library, PO Box 1848, 38677-1848. SAN 348-906X. Tel: 662-915-7092. TDD: 662-915-7907. FAX: 662-915-5734. Web Site: sunset.backbone.olemiss.edu/depts/general_library. *Dean of Libr*, John M Meador, Jr; E-Mail: jmm@olemiss.edu; *Adminr*, Diane Tillman; Tel: 662-915-7656, E-Mail: dtillman@cypress.mcsr.olemiss.edu; *Tech Servs*, JoAnn Stefani; Tel: 662-915-7013, E-Mail: uljhs@cypress.mcsr.olemiss.edu; *Spec Coll*, Thomas Verich; Tel: 662-915-5933, E-Mail: ulverich@olemiss.edu; *Online Servs*, Gail Herrera; Tel: 662-915-7677; Staff 31 (MLS 28, Non-MLS 3)
Founded 1848. Enrl 11,575; Fac 449; Highest Degree: Doctorate
Jul 1998-Jun 1999 Mats Exp $5,224,244. Sal $1,697,345 (Prof $944,650)
Library Holdings: Bk Vols 1,200,000; Per Subs 7,000
Subject Interests: Blues, Southern culture, Southern hist
Special Collections: Blues Archives; Lumber Archives; Mississippiana; Southern Culture; Space Law; Stark Young Coll; William Faulkner Coll
Automation Activity & Vendor Info: (Acquisitions) Innovative Interfaces Inc.; (Cataloging) Innovative Interfaces Inc.; (Circulation) Innovative Interfaces Inc.; (Circulation) Innovative Interfaces Inc.
Publications: Library Letter
Partic in SE Libr Network
Special Services for the Deaf - Staff with knowledge of sign language
Special Services - ADA room. Home Page address for special collections: http://sunset.backbone.olemiss.edu/depts/general_library/files/archhome.htm. Home page address for government documents: http://sunset.backbone.olemiss.edu/depts/general_library/files/govserv.htm
Friends of the Library Group
Departmental Libraries:
MUSIC-BLUES ARCHIVE, Farley Hall, Rm 340, 38677. SAN 369-7797. Tel: 601-232-7753. FAX: 601-232-5161.
Blues Archives: sunset.backbone.olemiss.edu/depts/general_library/files/bluesarc.htm, Music: sunset.backbone.olemiss.edu/depts/general_library/files/musiclib.htm *Librn*, Edward Komara
Subject Interests: American folk music, Blues music, English folk music
Special Collections: B B King Coll; Kenneth Goldstein Coll
Publications: From the Blues Archives (magazine column)
CM SCIENCE LIBRARY, 1031 Natural Products Ctr, 38677. SAN 369-7800. Tel: 662-915-7381. FAX: 662-915-7549. Web Site: www.olemiss.edu/depts/general_library/files/science/index.html. *Head of Libr*, Nancy F Fuller; Tel: 662-915-5877, E-Mail: ulfuller@olemiss.edu; *Bibliogr*, Elizabeth M Choinski; Tel: 662-915-7910, E-Mail: ulemc@olemiss.edu; *Bibliogr*, Sherie S Rikard; Tel: 662-915-5341, E-Mail: ulsam@olemiss.edu; *ILL*, Deborah V McCain; Tel: 662-915-5668, E-Mail: dmccain@olemiss.edu; Staff 5 (MLS 4, Non-MLS 1)
Founded 1997. Enrl 397; Fac 47; Highest Degree: Doctorate
Library Holdings: Bk Vols 68,000; Per Subs 450
Subject Interests: Clinical pharm, Med (selected areas), Medicinal chem, Organic chemistry, Pharm, Pharm admin, Pharmaceutics, Pharmacognosy-natural products, Pharmacology
Publications: Dispense as Written (irregular newsletter)
Partic in Association Of Memphis Area Health Science Libraries; Mississippi Biomedical Library Consortium

VAIDEN

P VAIDEN PUBLIC LIBRARY,* PO Box 108, 39176. SAN 376-6365. Tel: 601-464-7736. FAX: 601-464-7736. E-Mail: vailiblp@carroll.lib.mu.us. *Librn*, Linda Parks
Library Holdings: Bk Vols 1,500; Bk Titles 1,200; Per Subs 13
Partic in Carroll County Library Cooperative

VICKSBURG

M PARK VIEW REGIONAL MEDICAL CENTER LIBRARY,* 100 McAuley Dr, PO Box 590, 39181-0590. SAN 348-9094. Tel: 601-631-2131. FAX: 601-631-2124. *Librn*, Jeanne Monsour
Founded 1945
Library Holdings: Bk Vols 400; Per Subs 50
Subject Interests: Allied fields, Medicine, Surgery
Partic in Medline

UNITED STATES ARMY
A ENGINEER WATERWAYS EXPERIMENT STATION RESEARCH LIBRARY, 3909 Halls Ferry Rd, 39180-6199. SAN 308-9223. Tel: 601-634-2355. FAX: 601-634-2542. Web Site: libweb.wes.army.mil/index.htm. *Chief Librn*, Debbie Carpenter; Staff 8 (MLS 8)
Founded 1930
Library Holdings: Per Subs 1,500
Subject Interests: Aquatic plant control, Coastal engineering, Concrete, Dredged material research, Environ effects, Explosive excavation, Hydraulics, Pavements, Soil mechanics, Trafficability, Vehicle mobility, Weapons effects
Publications: List of Periodicals; WES List of Publications
Partic in Defense Technical Information Center; Dialog Corporation; OCLC Online Computer Library Center, Inc
A MISSISSIPPI RIVER COMMISSION TECHNICAL LIBRARY, 4155 Clay St, PO Box 60, 39180-0080. SAN 308-924X. Tel: 601-631-7216. Interlibrary Loan Service Tel: 601-631-7218. FAX: 601-631-7217. *Librn*, Sherrie Moran; *Librn*, Bettie Wiley
Founded 1943
Library Holdings: Bk Titles 21,000; Per Subs 530
Subject Interests: Environ issues, Geology, Harbors, Hydraulics, Inland waterways, Law, Rivers, Soils, Wetlands
Special Collections: Archives - Mississippi River Commission
Publications: Acquisitions List (monthly); Database Guide; Library Handbook; Periodical Guide
Partic in Dialog Corporation; Legislate; OCLC Online Computer Library Center, Inc

S VICKSBURG & WARREN COUNTY HISTORICAL SOCIETY, McCardle Library, Old Court House Museum, 1008 Cherry St, 39183. SAN 370-3045. Tel: 601-636-0741. FAX: 601-636-0741. *Curator, Dir*, Gordon Cotton; *Asst Dir*, Blanche Terry
Library Holdings: Bk Vols 2,000
Subject Interests: Genealogy, History
Open Mon-Fri 8:30am-4:30pm

G VICKSBURG NATIONAL MILITARY PARK LIBRARY,* 3201 Clay St, 39183-3495. SAN 308-9231. Tel: 601-636-0583, Ext 8013. FAX: 601-636-9497.
Library Holdings: Bk Vols 1,000
Special Collections: American Civil War Coll

P WARREN COUNTY-VICKSBURG PUBLIC LIBRARY,* 700 Veto St, 39180-3595. SAN 308-9266. Tel: 601-636-6411. FAX: 601-634-4809. Web Site: www.warren.lib.ms.us. *Dir*, Deborah Mitchell; E-Mail: deb@warren.lib.ms.us; *Assoc Dir*, Pamela Gee; *Ch Servs*, Lottie Walker; *Per*, Rosemary Fairchild; *ILL*, Denise Whitten; *AV*, Linda Chandler; *Circ*, Sandra Mayfield; *Cat*, Mary Ann Brennan; *Purchasing*, Paula Benard; Staff 18 (MLS 4, Non-MLS 14)
Founded 1915. Pop 49,800; Circ 212,811
Oct 1997-Sep 1998 Income $632,169, State $88,282, County $499,500, Locally Generated Income $44,387. Mats Exp $102,386, Books $85,266, Per/Ser (Incl. Access Fees) $4,500, Micro $1,000, AV Equip $9,090, Electronic Ref Mat (Incl. Access Fees) $2,530. Sal $355,772
Library Holdings: Bk Vols 108,267; Per Subs 170
Subject Interests: Civil War, Mississippi, Mississippi River, Mystery novels

Automation Activity & Vendor Info: (Cataloging) Gaylord; (Circulation) Gaylord; (OPAC) Gaylord
Database Vendor: Ebsco - EbscoHost, GaleNet, IAC - SearchBank, OCLC - First Search, Wilson - Wilson Web
Publications: Newsletter
Function: ILL available
Story Line 601-636-1300
Friends of the Library Group

WALLS

P FIRST REGIONAL LIBRARY, James D (Jake) Pearson Public,* PO Box 417, 38650. SAN 378-0287. Tel: 601-781-3664. FAX: 601-781-3427. *Librn*, Amy Gharaibeh

WASHINGTON

G HISTORIC JEFFERSON COLLEGE LIBRARY,* PO Box 700, 39190. SAN 321-0421. Tel: 601-442-2901. FAX: 601-442-2902.
Founded 1979. Pop 25,000
Library Holdings: Bk Titles 1,033
Subject Interests: Miss hist
Special Collections: 1840 Library Restoration
Restriction: Open to public for reference only
Open Mon-Fri 8-5

WATER VALLEY

P BLACKMUR MEMORIAL LIBRARY,* 608 Blackmur Dr, 38965. SAN 308-9274. Tel: 662-473-2444. *In Charge*, Alma Goodwin
Founded 1959. Pop 8,000; Circ 16,610
Library Holdings: Bk Vols 16,351; Per Subs 39
Subject Interests: Genealogy, Local history
Special Collections: Mississippi History
Open Mon, Wed & Fri 9-5, Tues 9-9, Thurs 9-7, Sat 9-12

WESSON

J COPIAH-LINCOLN COMMUNITY COLLEGE, Evelyn W Oswalt Library, PO Box 649, 39191. SAN 308-9282. Tel: 601-643-8365, Ext 365. FAX: 601-643-8212. *Dir*, Kendall P Chapman
Founded 1928. Enrl 1,135; Fac 135
Library Holdings: Bk Vols 47,000; Per Subs 194

WEST POINT

J MARY HOLMES COLLEGE, Helen R Walton Learning Resources Center, Hwy 50 W, PO Box 1257, 39773. SAN 308-9290. Tel: 662-494-6820, Ext 3401. Web Site: www.maryholmescollege.com. *Dir*, Dr Evelyn K Bonner; Tel: 662-494-6820, Ext 3431, E-Mail: ekb@maryholmes.edu; *Circ, Ref*, Katie Gaston; *AV*, J'Lyn Moore; *Acq, ILL*, Linda Bankhead
Founded 1892. Fac 21; Highest Degree: Associate
Oct 2000-Sep 2001 Income $290,000. Mats Exp $32,300, Books $10,000, Per/Ser (Incl. Access Fees) $6,500, Presv $500, Micro $5,000, AV Equip $5,000, Manuscripts & Archives $1,600, Electronic Ref Mat (Incl. Access Fees) $3,700. Sal $105,000 (Prof $50,000)
Library Holdings: Bk Vols 30,000; Bk Titles 28,000; Per Subs 121; Spec Interest Per Sub 36
Subject Interests: Languages, Literature
Special Collections: Sharecropper Papers Oral History Project
Automation Activity & Vendor Info: (Circulation) VTLS; (OPAC) VTLS
Database Vendor: OCLC - First Search
Partic in SE Libr Network
Friends of the Library Group

P TOMBIGBEE REGIONAL LIBRARY SYSTEM, Bryan Public Library, Headquarters, 338 Commerce, PO Box 675, 39773-0675. SAN 348-9159. Tel: 662-494-4872. FAX: 662-494-0300. *Dir*, Mary Helen Waggoner; E-Mail: mwag@tombigbee.lib.ms.us; *Asst Dir*, Caroline Dinwiddie; *Ch Servs*, Sandra White; *Res*, Dorothy Calvert; *Tech Servs*, Tina Waits; E-Mail: twaits@tombigbee.lib.ms.us; Staff 28 (MLS 3, Non-MLS 25)
Founded 1916. Pop 79,390; Circ 108,102
Library Holdings: Bk Vols 116,000; Per Subs 193
Subject Interests: Genealogy, Local history
Automation Activity & Vendor Info: (Acquisitions) Gaylord; (Cataloging) Gaylord; (Circulation) Gaylord; (ILL) Gaylord; (OPAC) Gaylord
Database Vendor: Ebsco - EbscoHost, IAC - Info Trac, OCLC - First Search, Wilson - Wilson Web
Publications: BPL-News from Friends
Friends of the Library Group
Branches: 9
AMORY MUNICIPAL, 402 Second Ave N at Fourth St, Amory, 38821. SAN 348-9183. Tel: 601-256-5261. FAX: 601-256-6321. *Librn*, Brenda Wilson; E-Mail: bwilson@tombigbee.lib.ms.us
Circ 87,189
Library Holdings: Bk Vols 18,403
Automation Activity & Vendor Info: (OPAC) Gaylord
Friends of the Library Group
CHOCTAW COUNTY PUBLIC, PO Box 755, Ackerman, 39735. SAN 348-9213. Tel: 601-285-6348. FAX: 601-285-6348. *Librn*, Amy Roberson; Staff 2 (MLS 1, Non-MLS 1)
Circ 6,640
Library Holdings: Bk Vols 6,004
Automation Activity & Vendor Info: (OPAC) Gaylord
Friends of the Library Group
EVANS MEMORIAL, 105 N Long St, Aberdeen, 39730. SAN 348-9248. Tel: 601-369-4601. FAX: 601-369-2971. *Librn*, Kathy Bailey; E-Mail: kab@tombigbee.lib.ms.us; Staff 6 (MLS 1, Non-MLS 5)
Circ 24,494
Library Holdings: Bk Vols 54,384
Subject Interests: Genealogy, Local history
Special Collections: Photographs (McKnight Coll)
Automation Activity & Vendor Info: (OPAC) Gaylord
Friends of the Library Group
HAMILTON PUBLIC, PO Box 96, Hamilton, 39746. SAN 348-9272. Tel: 601-343-8962. *Librn*, Oma Faye Dahlem; E-Mail: odahlem@tombigbee.lib.ms.us
Library Holdings: Bk Vols 3,156
MATHISTON PUBLIC, PO Box 82, Mathiston, 39752. SAN 348-9302. Tel: 601-263-4772. *Librn*, Gail Shurden; E-Mail: gshurden@tombigbee.lib.ms.us
Pop 4,024
Library Holdings: Bk Vols 3,238
Automation Activity & Vendor Info: (OPAC) Gaylord
NETTLETON PUBLIC, PO Box 1310, Nettleton, 38858. SAN 348-9337. Tel: 601-963-2014. *Librn*, Charlotte Ann Thompson
Circ 3,238
Library Holdings: Bk Vols 2,824
Automation Activity & Vendor Info: (OPAC) Gaylord
WEBSTER COUNTY PUBLIC, 202 W Fox Ave, PO Box 205, Eupora, 39744. SAN 348-9396. Tel: 601-258-7515. FAX: 601-258-7515. *Librn*, Glenda Morrow
Circ 8,772
Library Holdings: Bk Vols 5,906
Automation Activity & Vendor Info: (OPAC) Gaylord
Friends of the Library Group
WEIR PUBLIC, PO Box 248, Weir, 39772. SAN 348-9426. Tel: 601-547-6747. *Librn*, Eula Faye Bailey
Circ 4,615
Library Holdings: Bk Vols 3,389
Automation Activity & Vendor Info: (OPAC) Gaylord
WREN PUBLIC, 32655 Hwy 45 N, Aberdeen, 39730. SAN 348-9450. Tel: 601-256-8532. *Librn*, Opal Williams
Circ 4,412
Library Holdings: Bk Vols 3,620
Automation Activity & Vendor Info: (OPAC) Gaylord
Bookmobiles: 1. Mini-van

WHITFIELD

MISSISSIPPI STATE HOSPITAL
M MEDICAL LIBRARY, Whitfield Rd, 39193. SAN 308-9304. Tel: 601-351-8000, Ext 4541. *Dir*, June Lee
Library Holdings: Bk Vols 1,000; Per Subs 25
Subject Interests: Alcoholism, Drug addiction, Psychiatry
M PATIENT LIBRARY, Whitfield Rd, 39193. SAN 376-0324. Tel: 601-351-8000, Ext 4278. *Librn*, Jane Hull
Library Holdings: Bk Vols 12,000

YAZOO CITY

S MISSISSIPPI CHEMICAL CORP, Technical Data Services Library, 4612 Hwy 49 E, PO Box 388, 39194-0388. SAN 308-9312. Tel: 662-751-2539. *Head Tech Servs*, Patricia D Cranston
Founded 1951
Library Holdings: Bk Vols 1,500
Subject Interests: Environmental studies, Equip improvement, Process improvements
Restriction: Lending to staff only

P SOUTH DELTA LIBRARY SERVICES, Ricks Memorial Library,* 310 N Main St, 39194-4253. SAN 348-9574. Tel: 601-746-5557. FAX: 601-746-7309. *Dir*, Kathryn Merkle; *Asst Dir*, Susie Bull; *Ref*, John Ellzey; *Coordr, Publ Servs*, Janet Nail; *Circ*, Miranda Henderson; Staff 4 (MLS 4)
Founded 1838. Pop 34,082; Circ 46,500
Oct 1997-Sep 1998 Income $251,116, State $50,517, City $40,000, County $123,400, Locally Generated Income $8,640, Other $13,174. Mats Exp $21,684, Books $15,134, Per/Ser (Incl. Access Fees) $1,882, Micro $355, Other Print Mats $468. Sal $147,950
Library Holdings: Bk Vols 36,890; Per Subs 110

Special Collections: Local History Coll
Automation Activity & Vendor Info: (Cataloging) Gaylord; (Circulation) epixtech, inc.
Partic in SE Libr Network
Branches: 1
SHARKEY-ISSAQUENA COUNTY LIBRARY, 300 E China St, Rolling Fork, 39159. SAN 323-794X. Tel: 601-873-4076. FAX: 601-873-4076.
Librn, Kathleen Hawkins; *Circ*, Karenthia Jones
Oct 1997-Sep 1998 Income $99,200. Mats Exp $9,585. Sal $44,420
Library Holdings: Bk Vols 19,161; Per Subs 42
Friends of the Library Group
Bookmobiles: 1

MISSOURI

Date of Statistics: 1998-99
Population, 1998 Census: 5,438,559
Population Served by Public Libraries: 4,702,614
  Unserved: 735,945
Total Volumes in Public Libraries: 23,432,461
  Volumes Per Capita: 4.3
Total Public Library Circulation: 40,047,058
  Circulation Per Capita: 7.36
  Total Public Library Income: $130,233,703
  Source of Income: 86% local, 2% state, 12% other
  Expenditure Per Capita: $19.82
Number of County & Multi-county: 43 county, 14 regional serving multicounties
Counties Served:114
Number of Bookmobiles in State: 49
Grants-in-Aid:
  Federal (Library Services & Construction Act): $1,229,552
  State Aid: $2,089,570

ALBANY

P CARNEGIE PUBLIC LIBRARY, 101 W Clay, 64402. SAN 308-9320. Tel: 660-726-5615. FAX: 660-726-4213. E-Mail: librarian@carnegie.lib.mo.us. Web Site: carnegie.lib.mo.us. *Dir*, Cheryl Noble; Staff 1 (MLS 1)
Founded 1906. Pop 1,968; Circ 13,886
Library Holdings: Bk Vols 12,045; Per Subs 25
Partic in Grand Rivers Libr Conference
Friends of the Library Group

ALTON

P OREGON COUNTY LIBRARY DISTRICT, Alton Branch,* PO Box 158, 65606. SAN 377-1016. Tel: 417-778-6414. FAX: 417-778-6414. *Librn*, Janice Richardson
Library Holdings: Bk Vols 12,000; Per Subs 13
Partic in Mo Libr Asn

APPLETON CITY

P APPLETON CITY PUBLIC LIBRARY, (ACL), 105 W Fourth St, 64724-1401. SAN 308-9339. Tel: 660-476-5513. *Dir*, Barbara Franzone; Staff 1 (Non-MLS 1)
Founded 1870
Jul 1999-Jun 2000 Mats Exp $2,450, Books $2,000, Per/Ser (Incl. Access Fees) $200, Electronic Ref Mat (Incl. Access Fees) $250. Sal $10,000
Library Holdings: Bk Vols 24,000; Per Subs 25
Function: Internet access
Special Services for the Blind - Bi-Folkal kits
Open Tues & Thurs 1-7, Sat 8-12

AVA

P DOUGLAS COUNTY PUBLIC LIBRARY, 301 SW Third Ave, 65608. (Mail add: PO Box 277, 65608-0277), SAN 308-9355. Tel: 417-683-5633. FAX: 417-683-5633. *Librn*, Anita Dodd; Staff 2 (Non-MLS 2)
Founded 1977. Pop 11,876; Circ 36,920
Library Holdings: Bk Vols 29,000; Per Subs 34
Automation Activity & Vendor Info: (Cataloging) TLC; (Circulation) TLC; (OPAC) TLC
Partic in Mo State Database
Friends of the Library Group

BLOOMFIELD

P BLOOMFIELD PUBLIC LIBRARY,* 200 Seneca St, PO Box 294, 63825. SAN 308-9363. Tel: 573-568-3626. FAX: 573-568-3626. E-Mail: hix000@mail.connect.more.net. *Librn*, Virginia Hampton
Founded 1967. Pop 1,800; Circ 6,275
Jul 1997-Jun 1998 Income $20,000, State $825, City $15,000, Locally Generated Income $4,175. Mats Exp $1,200, Books $1,150, Per/Ser (Incl. Access Fees) $50. Sal $5,700
Library Holdings: Bk Vols 10,500
Special Collections: 1850 Newspaper Coll, microfilm; Stoddard County Records, bks, microfilm
Open Mon, Wed & Fri noon-5pm & Sat 9am-1pm
Friends of the Library Group

BLUE SPRINGS

S BLUE SPRINGS HISTORICAL SOCIETY, Archives & Research Library,* 101 SW 15th St, 64015. SAN 373-2347. Tel: 816-229-2659. *Archivist*, Karol Witthar
Subject Interests: Local history

S BURROUGHS AUDUBON LIBRARY,* 21509 SW Wood Chapel Rd, 64015. SAN 371-8212. Tel: 816-795-8177. *Mgr*, Anne Duffer
Founded 1971
Library Holdings: Bk Titles 3,000; Per Subs 10
Subject Interests: Natural history, Ornithology
Open Tues, Thurs, Fri & Sat 12:30-4:30 (winter); Open Tues, Thurs & Sat 12:30-4:30 (summer)

J METROPOLITAN COMMUNITY COLLEGES, Blue River Community College Library, 1501 W Jefferson St, 64015. SAN 377-8258. Tel: 816-655-6080. FAX: 816-655-6064. Web Site: www.kcmetro.cc.mo.us/lib/libpage.html. *Dir*, Connie Migliazzo; *ILL, Ref*, Susanne Boatright; *Ref*, Bill Osment; Staff 5 (MLS 4, Non-MLS 1)
Founded 1984. Fac 25; Highest Degree: Associate
Jul 1998-Jun 1999 Income Parent Institution $171,712. Mats Exp $25,030, Books $14,066, Per/Ser (Incl. Access Fees) $9,220, Other Print Mats $1,602, Electronic Ref Mat (Incl. Access Fees) $142. Sal $97,384 (Prof $88,037)
Library Holdings: Bk Vols 8,200; Bk Titles 8,000; Per Subs 95; High Interest/Low Vocabulary Bk Vols 255
Subject Interests: Liberal arts
Automation Activity & Vendor Info: (Circulation) Innovative Interfaces Inc.; (OPAC) Innovative Interfaces Inc.
Function: ILL available, Reference services available
Partic in Kans City Mo Libr & Info Network; Mobius
Special Services for the Blind - Assistive Technology Center for Persons who are blind or physically handicapped

BOLIVAR

P POLK COUNTY LIBRARY,* 1690 W Broadway St, 65613. SAN 348-9639. Tel: 417-326-4531. FAX: 417-326-4366. E-Mail: hwn000@mail.connect.more.net. Web Site: www.mlnc.com/~polk/. *Librn*, Glenda Smithson; Staff 1 (MLS 1)
Founded 1947
Jan 1998-Dec 1998 Income $168,905, State $9,626, Federal $16,855, County $108,375, Locally Generated Income $34,049. Mats Exp $22,217, Books $20,000, Per/Ser (Incl. Access Fees) $2,100, Micro $117. Sal $111,499 (Prof

$26,060)
Library Holdings: Bk Vols 29,010; Per Subs 98
Database Vendor: OCLC - First Search
Friends of the Library Group
Branches: 1
HUMANSVILLE BRANCH, PO Box 191, Humansville, 65674. SAN 348-9752. Tel: 417-754-2455. FAX: 417-754-2455. *Librn*, Sharon Anderson

CR SOUTHWEST BAPTIST UNIVERSITY LIBRARY, 1600 University Ave, 65613. SAN 308-9371. Tel: 417-328-1619. Circulation Tel: 417-328-1613. Reference Tel: 417-328-1604. FAX: 417-328-1652. Web Site: falcon.sbuniv.edu/lib/libhome.htm. *Dean of Libr*, Betty VanBlair; *Actg Dean, Coll Develop*, Eldonna DeWeese; E-Mail: edeweese@sbuniv.edu; *Bibliog Instr, Publ Servs*, Ann Kitchin; Tel: 417-328-1626, E-Mail: akitchin@sbuniv.edu; *Tech Servs*, Coleen Rose; E-Mail: crose@sbuniv.edu; *Media Spec*, Bob McGlasson; *Ref*, Sandra Brown; Tel: 417-328-1561, E-Mail: sbrown@sbuniv.edu; Staff 20 (MLS 4, Non-MLS 16)
Founded 1878. Enrl 3,500; Fac 105; Highest Degree: Master
Jul 1999-Jun 2000 Mats Exp $213,182, Books $70,622, Per/Ser (Incl. Access Fees) $119,986, Presv $6,960, Micro $8,300, AV Equip $6,364, Electronic Ref Mat (Incl. Access Fees) $950
Library Holdings: Bk Vols 590,200; Bk Titles 400,391; Per Subs 632
Special Collections: Butler Baptist Heritage Coll; Christian Education Resource Lab; Library of American Civilization - Microbook Coll; Southern Baptist Convention Resource Lab
Automation Activity & Vendor Info: (Acquisitions) Innovative Interfaces Inc.
Database Vendor: Ebsco - EbscoHost, Lexis-Nexis, OCLC - First Search
Publications: Southern Baptist Periodical Index
Partic in Mobius; OCLC Online Computer Library Center, Inc

BONNE TERRE

P BONNE TERRE MEMORIAL LIBRARY, 5 SW Main St, 63628. SAN 308-938X. Tel: 573-358-2260. FAX: 573-358-5941. E-Mail: xbj000@mail.connect.more.net. *Dir*, McClure Becky; *Circ*, Tina Johnston; E-Mail: xbj002@mail.connect.more.net; *Tech Servs*, Loretta Dodson; *Tech Servs*, Loretta Polette; Staff 1 (Non-MLS 1)
Founded 1867. Circ 18,000
Library Holdings: Bk Vols 18,000; Per Subs 40
Subject Interests: Local history
Automation Activity & Vendor Info: (Cataloging) Sagebrush Corporation; (Circulation) Sagebrush Corporation
Database Vendor: OCLC - First Search
Open Mon, Wed & Fri 10-5, Tues & Thurs 2-8, Sat 10-2
Friends of the Library Group

BOONVILLE

S FRIENDS OF HISTORIC BOONVILLE, Archival Collection, 614 E Morgan, PO Box 1776, 65233. SAN 373-2312. Tel: 660-882-7977. FAX: 660-882-9194. E-Mail: friendsart@mid-mo.net. *In Charge*, Judy Shields
Founded 1971
Library Holdings: Bk Vols 250

J KEMPER MILITARY SCHOOL & COLLEGE LIBRARY,* 701 Third St, 65233. SAN 308-9398. Tel: 660-882-5623. FAX: 660-882-3332. *Chief Librn*, Janis Tate; Staff 1 (MLS 1)
Enrl 296; Fac 30
Library Holdings: Bk Vols 18,000; Bk Titles 29,000; Per Subs 125
Subject Interests: History
Special Collections: Military (McNeeley, Crim & Randolph Colls)

BRANSON

P TANEYHILLS COMMUNITY LIBRARY,* 200 S Fourth St, 65616-2738. SAN 308-9401. Tel: 417-334-1418. FAX: 417-334-1470. *Librn*, Randy Sisco
Founded 1933
Jun 1997-May 1998 Income $75,000, Locally Generated Income $7,000, Other $68,000. Mats Exp $20,000, Books $15,000, Per/Ser (Incl. Access Fees) $2,000, Other Print Mats $3,000. Sal $15,500
Library Holdings: Bk Vols 40,000; Per Subs 50
Special Collections: DAR Genealogy Coll; Missouri Coll; Taney County & Ozark Region Coll
Publications: Newsletter, semi-annual
Special Services - Juvenile programs: Summer Story Hour; Summer Reading Program; word processor for public use; free distribution of Federal & State tax forms
Friends of the Library Group

BRENTWOOD

P BRENTWOOD PUBLIC LIBRARY, 8765 Eulalie Ave, 63144. SAN 308-941X. Tel: 314-963-8630. FAX: 314-962-8675. *Librn*, John Furlong; Staff 2 (MLS 2)
Founded 1939. Pop 8,000; Circ 65,569
Library Holdings: Bk Vols 51,650; Per Subs 98
Partic in Municipal Libr Coop; Saint Louis Regional Library Network

BRIDGETON

M DEPAUL HEALTH CENTER, Medical Library,* 12303 DePaul Dr, 63044. SAN 326-0232. Tel: 314-344-6397. FAX: 314-344-6035. *Dir*, Joan Laneman
Library Holdings: Bk Vols 4,300
Subject Interests: Psychiatry

BROOKFIELD

P BROOKFIELD PUBLIC LIBRARY,* 102 E Boston, 64628. SAN 308-9428. Tel: 660-258-7439. FAX: 660-258-5626. E-Mail: itdoo1@mail.connect.more.net. *Dir*, Gina Phillips
Founded 1918. Pop 4,888; Circ 31,434
Library Holdings: Bk Vols 32,168
Subject Interests: Am states hist, Genealogy, Linn Co hist
Partic in NE Mo Libr Network
Open Mon-Fri 10-6 & Sat 10-4

BRUNSWICK

P BRUNSWICK AREA PUBLIC LIBRARY, 115 W Broadway, 65236. SAN 375-0299. FAX: 660-548-3360. *Librn*, Geraldine Stroemer; Tel: 660-548-3284, E-Mail: dutche@magic.com
Founded 1973. Pop 2,000
Library Holdings: Bk Vols 30,000; Per Subs 22
Open Mon & Fri 10-12 & 2-4, Wed 10-12 & 2-8

BUFFALO

S DALLAS COUNTY HISTORICAL SOCIETY, Historical & Genealogical Library,* HCR 85, Box 291B6, 65622. SAN 373-2320. Tel: 417-345-7297.
Library Holdings: Bk Vols 465

P DALLAS COUNTY LIBRARY, 219 W Main, 65622. (Mail add: PO Box 1008, 65622), SAN 308-9436. Tel: 417-345-2647. FAX: 417-345-2647. E-Mail: sgy000@mail.connect.more.net. *Dir*, Nancy Bradley
Founded 1972. Pop 12,646; Circ 114,782
Library Holdings: Bk Vols 26,000
Friends of the Library Group

BUTLER

P BUTLER PUBLIC LIBRARY, 100 W Atkinson, 64730. SAN 308-9444. Tel: 660-679-4321. FAX: 660-679-4321. *Dir*, Linda Hunter
Founded 1926. Pop 15,000
Library Holdings: Bk Vols 27,000; Per Subs 17
Friends of the Library Group

CALIFORNIA

P WOOD PLACE LIBRARY,* 501 S Oak St, 65018. SAN 308-9452. Tel: 573-796-2642. *Librn*, Cory Mayfield; E-Mail: cmay@socket.net
Founded 1956. Pop 10,472
Library Holdings: Bk Titles 8,000; Per Subs 19
Friends of the Library Group

CAMDENTON

P CAMDEN COUNTY LIBRARY DISTRICT,* 35 Camden Ct, PO Box 1320, 65020-0903. SAN 377-1032. Tel: 573-346-7733. FAX: 573-346-1263. E-Mail: bhv000@mail.connect.more.net, bhv007@mail.connect.more.net. *Dir*, Carrie Ruggles
Library Holdings: Bk Vols 30,000; Bk Titles 29,500; Per Subs 101
Partic in Am Libr Asn; Mo Libr Asn
Branches: 2
CLIMAX SPRINGS BRANCH, PO Box 43, Climax Springs, 65324. SAN 377-4147. Tel: 573-347-2722. FAX: 573-347-2722. E-Mail: bhv000@mail.connect.more.net. *Librn*, Carolee Apperson
Library Holdings: Bk Vols 9,500; Bk Titles 9,000; Per Subs 21
Partic in Am Libr Asn; Mo Libr Asn
SUNRISE BEACH BRANCH, RR 3, Box 1205, Sunrise Beach, 65079. SAN 377-2764. Tel: 573-374-6982. FAX: 573-374-6982. *Librn*, Donna Thompson
Library Holdings: Bk Vols 12,308

CANTON

P CANTON PUBLIC LIBRARY, 409 Lewis St, 63435. SAN 308-9460. Tel: 573-288-5279. FAX: 573-288-5279. *Dir*, Sandra Howe; E-Mail: sjhowe@yahoo.com

Founded 1929. Pop 2,616; Circ 18,618
Jul 1997-Jun 1998 Income $34,407, State $1,212, City $27,771, Locally Generated Income $5,041, Other $383. Mats Exp $3,838, Books $3,638. Sal $12,878
Library Holdings: Bk Vols 33,946
Subject Interests: Adult fiction, Adult non-fiction, Juvenile fiction, Juvenile non-fiction
Special Collections: Meridian Library; War of the Rebellion

CR CULVER-STOCKTON COLLEGE, Carl Johann Memorial Library, 1 College Hill, 63435. SAN 308-9479. Tel: 217-231-6321. FAX: 217-231-6615. Web Site: www.culver.edu. *Dir*, Sharon K Upchurch; Tel: 217-231-6478, E-Mail: supchurch@culver.edu; *Admin Assoc, Ser*, Julie Wright; Tel: 217-231-6640, E-Mail: jwright@culver.edu; *Asst Librn, Ref*, Renee Gorrell; Tel: 217-231-6369, E-Mail: rgorrell@culver.edu; *Acq*, Sandy Monhollen; Tel: 217-231-6641, E-Mail: samonhollen@culver.edu; *Archivist*, Judith William Gaston; Tel: 217-231-6569, E-Mail: jgaston@culver.edu; *Rare Bks*, John Sperry, Jr. Subject Specialists: *Children's literature*, Sharon K Upchurch; Staff 5 (MLS 2, Non-MLS 3)
Founded 1853. Enrl 1,001; Fac 56; Highest Degree: Bachelor
Library Holdings: Bk Vols 151,979; Per Subs 777
Subject Interests: Bus, History, Mgt, Relig studies
Special Collections: American Freedom Studies; History & Literature of Missouri & Midwest (Mark Twain Coll); History of Christian Church (Disciples of Christ Coll); Midwest Americana (Johann Coll)
Database Vendor: Ebsco - EbscoHost, epixtech, inc., Innovative Interfaces INN - View, Lexis-Nexis, OCLC - First Search, ProQuest
Publications: EXLIBRIS (Newsletter)
Partic in Ebsco Masterfile; MLNC; Mobius; Morenet; OCLC Online Computer Library Center, Inc
Friends of the Library Group

CAPE GIRARDEAU

P CAPE GIRARDEAU PUBLIC LIBRARY, 711 N Clark, 63701. SAN 308-9487. Tel: 573-334-5279. FAX: 573-334-8334. E-Mail: sctooo@mail.connect.morenet. Web Site: www.showme.net/cgpl/. *Dir*, Elizabeth Martin; Staff 10 (MLS 2, Non-MLS 8)
Founded 1922. Pop 34,438
Jul 1999-Jun 2000 Income $649,766, State $23,265, City $585,074, Federal $6,112, Locally Generated Income $35,315. Mats Exp $92,409, Books $83,604, Per/Ser (Incl. Access Fees) $5,209, Micro $931, Other Print Mats $819, Electronic Ref Mat (Incl. Access Fees) $27,886. Sal $284,048
Library Holdings: Bk Vols 99,208; Bk Titles 96,808; Per Subs 155
Special Collections: DAC & DAR Coll; Groves Genealogy; Hirsch Foreign Language for Children; Mississippi River Valley
Automation Activity & Vendor Info: (Acquisitions) epixtech, inc.; (Cataloging) epixtech, inc.; (Circulation) epixtech, inc.; (OPAC) epixtech, inc.
Database Vendor: epixtech, inc., OCLC - First Search
Partic in Missouri Library Network Corporation
Friends of the Library Group

S COTTONWOOD RESIDENTIAL TREATMENT CENTER LIBRARY,* 1025 N Sprigg St, 63701. SAN 377-1059. Tel: 573-290-5888. FAX: 573-290-5895. *Adminr*, Martha Cassel; *Librn*, Cindy Snow
Library Holdings: Bk Vols 5,000

C SOUTHEAST MISSOURI STATE UNIVERSITY, Kent Library, One University Plaza, 63701. SAN 308-9495. Tel: 573-651-2235. Interlibrary Loan Service Tel: 573-651-2152. FAX: 573-651-2666. Web Site: www2.semo.edu/library/. *Dir*, Sarah Cron; E-Mail: scron@semovm.semo.edu; *Bibliog Instr*, Catherine Roeder; *Coll Develop*, Ed Buis; Staff 11 (MLS 11)
Founded 1873. Enrl 5,993; Fac 400
Library Holdings: Bk Vols 422,915; Per Subs 2,757
Special Collections: Brodsky Coll of William Faulkner Materials; Charles Harrison Rarebooks Coll; Regional History Coll
Automation Activity & Vendor Info: (Acquisitions) NOTIS; (Circulation) NOTIS
Partic in MLNC; OCLC Online Computer Library Center, Inc

S SOUTHEAST MISSOURIAN NEWSPAPER LIBRARY, 301 Broadway, 63701-7330. (Mail add: PO Box 699, 63702-0699), SAN 329-7128. Tel: 573-335-6611, Ext 136. Toll Free Tel: 800-879-1210. FAX: 573-334-7288. Web Site: www.semissourian.com. *Librn*, Sharon K Sanders; E-Mail: sksanders@semissourian.com
Founded 1965
Library Holdings: Bk Vols 500
Special Collections: Historical Research Notes; Newspaper Clippings (1965-present); Southeast Missourian & Bulletin-Journal Newspapers, microfilm
Research done at librarian's discretion. Charge: $40/hour with 1 hour minimum

CARROLLTON

P CARROLLTON PUBLIC LIBRARY,* 206 W Washington, 64633. SAN 308-9509. Tel: 660-542-0183. FAX: 660-542-0183. E-Mail: hgn000@mail.connect.more.net. Web Site: www.carolnet.com/library.htm. *Librn*, Angee Germann; *Asst Librn*, Charline Spangler
Founded 1943. Pop 4,406; Circ 35,188
Library Holdings: Bk Vols 22,000; Per Subs 50
Partic in Missouri Library Network Corporation

CARTHAGE

P CARTHAGE PUBLIC LIBRARY, 612 S Garrison, 64836. SAN 308-9517. Tel: 417-237-7040. FAX: 417-237-7041. E-Mail: kzh015@mail.connect.more.net. Web Site: carthage.lib.mo.us. *Admin Dir*, Jennifer Richardson; *Ch Servs*, Debra Haynes; *ILL*, Terry John; Staff 11 (Non-MLS 11)
Founded 1902. Pop 10,747; Circ 85,926
Jul 1999-Jun 2000 Income $260,769, State $8,645, City $208,212, Federal $3,029, Locally Generated Income $40,883. Mats Exp $59,715, Books $48,490, Per/Ser (Incl. Access Fees) $6,566, Micro $334, AV Equip $4,325. Sal $137,212 (Prof $29,175)
Library Holdings: Bk Vols 50,489; Bk Titles 46,557; Per Subs 152; Bks on Deafness & Sign Lang 25
Automation Activity & Vendor Info: (Cataloging) Follett; (Circulation) Follett; (OPAC) Follett
Database Vendor: Ebsco - EbscoHost
Publications: Library Notes (monthly)
Partic in Missouri Library Network Corporation
Friends of the Library Group

CARUTHERSVILLE

P CARUTHERSVILLE PUBLIC LIBRARY, 1002 Ward Ave, 63830. SAN 308-9525. Tel: 573-333-2480. FAX: 573-333-0552. E-Mail: dvd000@mail.connect.more.net. Web Site: www.geocities.com/heartland/prairie/6031. *Dir*, Sam Duckworth
Founded 1922. Pop 7,958; Circ 23,874
Library Holdings: Bk Vols 27,636; Per Subs 59
Subject Interests: Behav sci, Education, Genealogy, Law, Relig studies, Soc sci

CENTER

P RALLS COUNTY LIBRARY,* 100 N Public, PO Box 296, 63436. SAN 377-2721. Tel: 573-267-3200. FAX: 573-267-3200. *Librn*, Kay Amos
Library Holdings: Bk Vols 9,000; Per Subs 50

CENTERVILLE

P REYNOLDS COUNTY LIBRARY DISTRICT, Centerville Branch,* PO Box 175, 63633. SAN 349-8727. Tel: 573-648-2471. FAX: 573-648-2471. *Dir*, Joyce Sylcox; *Asst Librn*, Janice Meyers
Jan 1998-Dec 1998 Income $119,625. Mats Exp $21,496. Sal $56,200
Library Holdings: Bk Titles 20,000
Open Mon, Wed & Fri 8-4:30
Branches: 4
BUNKER BRANCH, Main St, Bunker, 63629. SAN 349-8697. Tel: 573-689-2718. *Librn*, Dormalee Schafer
Open Mon-Fri 9:30-4:30
ELLINGTON BRANCH, 110 N Main, Ellington, 63638. (Mail add: PO Box 485, Ellington, 63638), SAN 349-8751. Tel: 573-663-7289. *Librn*, Patricia Walker
Open Mon-Fri 9-5
LESTERVILLE BRANCH, Hwy 21, Lesterville, 63654. SAN 349-8875. Tel: 573-637-2532. *Librn*, Janice Myers
Open Tues & Thurs 8:30-4:30
OATES, PO Box 125, Black, 63625. SAN 349-8964. *Librn*, Phoebe White
Open Mon, Wed & Fri 8:30-11:30am

CENTRALIA

P CENTRALIA PUBLIC LIBRARY,* 210 S Jefferson, 65240. SAN 308-9533. Tel: 573-682-2036. FAX: 573-682-5556. *Dir*, Margaret Doty
Founded 1903. Pop 3,623; Circ 42,942
Library Holdings: Bk Vols 19,500; Per Subs 55
Special Collections: Missouri Bks
Mem of Mid-Missouri Libr Network
Open Mon-Sat (hours vary)
Friends of the Library Group

CHAFFEE

P CHAFFEE PUBLIC LIBRARY,* 202 Wright Ave, 63740. SAN 308-9541. Tel: 573-887-3298. FAX: 573-887-3298. *Librn*, Emily Whitfield
Founded 1929
Library Holdings: Bk Vols 11,877
Partic in OCLC Online Computer Library Center, Inc
Open Mon & Fri 1-5, Tues & Wed 1-6, Sat 9-1

CHARLESTON

P MISSISSIPPI COUNTY LIBRARY,* 105 E Marshall, 63834. (Mail add: PO Box 160, 63834), SAN 348-9817. Tel: 573-683-6748. FAX: 573-683-2761. Web Site: www.207.160.125.241/. *Dir*, Joseph W Dark
Founded 1947. Pop 14,442; Circ 59,579
Library Holdings: Bk Vols 43,150; Per Subs 180
Special Collections: State & Local Hist, print, micro & VF
Partic in Missouri Library Network Corporation
Open Mon, Tues & Thurs 8-5, Wed 8-8, Sat 8-4
Branches: 1
MITCHELL MEMORIAL, 204 E Washington St, East Prairie, 63845. SAN 348-9841. Tel: 573-649-2131. FAX: 573-649-2131. *Librn*, Joseph W Dark
Open Mon 12-8, Tues-Fri 12-5 & Sat 10-2

CHESTERFIELD

CM LOGAN COLLEGE OF CHIROPRACTIC LIBRARY, Learning Resources Center, 1851 Schoettler Rd, PO Box 1065, 63006-1065. SAN 308-955X. Tel: 636-227-2100. Circulation Tel: 636-227-2100, Ext 181. Reference Tel: 636-227-2100, Ext 188. Toll Free Tel: 800-782-3344. FAX: 636-207-2421. E-Mail: library@logan.edu. Web Site: www.logan.edu. *Dir*, Rosemary Elizabeth Buhr; Tel: 636-227-2100, Ext 187, E-Mail: buhrr@logan.edu; *Publ Servs*, Robert E Snyders; E-Mail: bob@logan.edu; *Tech Servs*, Jean Marie Rose; Tel: 636-227-2100, Ext 183. Subject Specialists: *Human relations*, Rosemary Elizabeth Buhr; *Management*, Rosemary Elizabeth Buhr; *Reference*, Robert E Snyders; Staff 7 (MLS 3, Non-MLS 4)
Founded 1960. Highest Degree: Doctorate
Sep 1999-Aug 2000 Income $463,650, Locally Generated Income $29,250, Parent Institution $434,400. Mats Exp $93,400, Books $35,000, Per/Ser (Incl. Access Fees) $50,450, Electronic Ref Mat (Incl. Access Fees) $11,250. Sal $291,000
Library Holdings: Bk Vols 12,500; Bk Titles 11,000; Per Subs 250
Subject Interests: Chiropractic, Neurology, Nutrition, Orthopedics, Radiology, Sports med
Special Collections: Osseous human & synthetic; State Chiropractic Association newsletters; State statutes regarding chiropractic
Automation Activity & Vendor Info: (Acquisitions) epixtech, inc.; (Cataloging) epixtech, inc.; (Circulation) epixtech, inc.; (OPAC) epixtech, inc.; (Serials) epixtech, inc.
Database Vendor: Ebsco - EbscoHost, epixtech, inc., OCLC - First Search
Function: Reference services available
Partic in Chiropractic Libr Consortium; Mobius

CHILLICOTHE

P LIVINGSTON COUNTY LIBRARY, 450 Locust St, 64601-2597. SAN 308-9568. Tel: 660-646-0547. FAX: 660-646-5504. E-Mail: lclibr@greenhills.net. Web Site: www.livcolibrary.org. *Librn*, Karen L Hicklin; Staff 2 (MLS 1, Non-MLS 1)
Founded 1921. Pop 14,592; Circ 166,035
Library Holdings: Bk Vols 52,866; Per Subs 100
Special Collections: Missouri History (George Somerville Coll); Ruddy Smithson Coll
Database Vendor: Ebsco - EbscoHost
Publications: LISTEN
Friends of the Library Group

CLAYTON

GL SAINT LOUIS COUNTY LAW LIBRARY,* Courts Bldg, Ste 536, 7900 Carondelet Ave, 63105. SAN 308-9584. Tel: 314-889-2726. *Librn*, Mary C Dahm
Library Holdings: Bk Vols 27,000; Per Subs 20

CLINTON

P HENRY COUNTY LIBRARY,* 123 E Green St, 64735. SAN 308-9592. Tel: 660-885-2612. FAX: 660-885-8953. E-Mail: ayc0001@mail.connect.more.net. Web Site: www.tacnet.missouri.org/hc. *Dir*, Elizabeth A Cashell
Founded 1946. Pop 16,732; Circ 92,553
Library Holdings: Bk Vols 45,000; Per Subs 97
Subject Interests: Local history
Open Mon-Thurs 8-9, Fri & Sat 8-5
Friends of the Library Group

COLUMBIA

S AMERICAN AUDIO PROSE LIBRARY, 600 Crestland Ave, PO Box 842, 65205-0842. SAN 326-7660. Tel: 573-443-0361. FAX: 573-499-0579. E-Mail: aaplinc@compuserve.com. Web Site: www.americanaudioprose.com. *Dir*, Kay Callison; Staff 2 (MLS 2)
Founded 1980
Special Collections: 280 titles of writers reading their work & talking about their life, work & related matters on audio cassette-all produced by the American Audio Prose Library, Inc
Publications: Annual Catalogue listing tapes for sale
Open Mon-Fri 9-5

P DANIEL BOONE REGIONAL LIBRARY, 101 Park de Ville Dr, PO Box 1267, 65205. SAN 348-9876. Tel: 573-443-3161. FAX: 573-499-0191. Web Site: dbrl.library.missouri.org. *Dir*, Melissa Carr; E-Mail: mcarr1@coin.org; *Head Tech Servs*, Patricia Kopp; *Tech Servs*, Mike Mullett; *Head, Circ*, Connie Bush; *Head Ref*, Marilyn McLeod; *Outreach Serv*, Karen Neely; *Publ Servs*, Elinor Barrett; *Coll Develop*, Doyne McKenzie; Staff 93 (MLS 17, Non-MLS 76)
Founded 1959. Pop 171,896; Circ 1,397,768
Jan 1999-Dec 1999 Income $4,252,909, Locally Generated Income $3,866,323, Other $386,586. Mats Exp $631,059. Sal $2,170,281
Library Holdings: Bk Vols 364,317; Per Subs 1,120
Automation Activity & Vendor Info: (Circulation) Inlex
Friends of the Library Group
Branches: 3
CALLAWAY COUNTY PUBLIC LIBRARY, 710 Court St, Fulton, 65251. SAN 348-9906. Tel: 573-642-7261. TDD: 573-642-0662. FAX: 573-642-4439. *Librn*, Linda Hodgkins; *Ref*, Carolyn Amos
Special Services for the Deaf - TDD
Friends of the Library Group
FAYETTE PUBLIC LIBRARY, 201 S Main St, Fayette, 65248. SAN 308-9789. Tel: 660-248-3348. FAX: 660-248-3348. E-Mail: fayetlib@coin.org. *Branch Mgr*, Cathey Monckton
Founded 1913
Friends of the Library Group
SOUTHERN BOONE COUNTY PUBLIC LIBRARY, 117 E Broadway, Ashland, 65010. Tel: 573-657-7378. FAX: 573-657-0448. *Branch Mgr*, Neely Karen
Founded 1999
Bookmobiles: 1

SR CALVARY EPISCOPAL CHURCH LIBRARY,* 123 S Ninth St, 65201. SAN 326-0771. Tel: 573-449-3194. FAX: 573-442-9392. *Librn*, Donald Foster; *Assoc Librn*, E Clarendon Hyde; *Coordr*, Robert Bussabarger; *Coordr*, Sue Breyfogle
Founded 1975
Library Holdings: Bk Titles 1,250
Subject Interests: Biblical studies, Church history

S COLUMBIA DAILY TRIBUNE LIBRARY, 101 N Fourth St, PO Box 798, 65201. SAN 373-4633. Tel: 573-815-1703. Toll Free Tel: 800-333-6799. FAX: 573-815-1701. Web Site: www.columbiatribune.com. *Librn*, Cassidy Rohrer; E-Mail: crohrer@tribmail.com; Staff 1 (MLS 1)
Founded 1970
2000-2000 Mats Exp $1,445, Books $435, Per/Ser (Incl. Access Fees) $386, Micro $204, Manuscripts & Archives $420. (Prof $24,000)
Library Holdings: Bk Vols 410; Bk Titles 350; Per Subs 10
Restriction: Company library, Not a lending library, Restricted public use

G COLUMBIA ENVIRONMENTAL RESEARCH CENTER LIBRARY,* US Geological Survey, 4200 New Haven Rd, 65201. SAN 308-9657. Tel: 573-876-1853. FAX: 573-876-1896. E-Mail: cerc_library@usgs.gov. *Librn*, Julia Towns
Founded 1970
Library Holdings: Bk Vols 8,500; Bk Titles 7,000; Per Subs 80
Subject Interests: Biol toxicity, Chem pesticides, Environ contaminants, Missouri River, Water quality
Special Collections: Pesticides (Reprint Coll)
Partic in Fedlink; OCLC Online Computer Library Center, Inc

GM DEPARTMENT OF VETERANS AFFAIRS, Harry S Truman Memorial Hospital Library, 800 Hospital Dr, 65201. SAN 308-9673. Tel: 573-814-6515. FAX: 573-814-6516.; Staff 2 (MLS 2)
Founded 1972
Library Holdings: Bk Vols 2,000; Per Subs 100
Subject Interests: Allied health topics, Medicine
Partic in BRS; Coop Libr Agency for Syst & Servs; Dialog Corporation; Medline; Mid-Mo Libr Network; Vets Admin Libr Network
Special Services for the Deaf - High interest/low vocabulary books

R FIRST CHRISTIAN CHURCH LIBRARY, 101 N Tenth St, 65201. SAN 308-9614. Tel: 573-449-7265. FAX: 573-875-8673. *Librn*, Edith Taylor
Library Holdings: Bk Vols 6,125
Subject Interests: Bible, Family life, Inspiration devotions, Missions, Morals, Soc aspects of relig, Travel
Special Collections: Children's Library; Clarence Lemmon Coll; Doris

Bradshaw Coll; Eric Carlson Coll; Large Print Coll; Missionary; Missions (Dr Jennie Fleming Coll); Seth Slaughter Coll
Publications: Annual newsletter

S INVESTIGATIVE REPORTERS & EDITORS, INC LIBRARY, Univ Missouri, Sch Journalism, 138 Neff Annex, 65211. SAN 329-8132. Tel: 573-882-2042. FAX: 573-882-5431. E-Mail: info@ire.org. Web Site: www.ire.org. *Exec Dir*, Brant Houston; *Dep Dir*, Len Bruzzese
Library Holdings: Bk Vols 100
Subject Interests: Investigative reporting
Special Collections: Help/Resource for Journalists & Historians
Publications: IRE Journal (bi-monthly); Uplink (monthly newsletter)

C JW & LOIS STAFFORD LIBRARY, (Formerly Columbia College), 1001 Rogers St, 65216. SAN 308-9606. Tel: 573-875-7381. Circulation Tel: 573-875-7373. Reference Tel: 573-875-7381. FAX: 573-875-7379. E-Mail: reference@email.ccis.edu. Web Site: www.ccis.edu/departments/library. *Dir*, Carolyn M Jones; Tel: 573-875-7372, E-Mail: cmjones@email.ccis.edu; *Head Tech Servs*, Vandy Evermon; Tel: 573-875-7370, E-Mail: vlevermon@email.ccis.edu; *Syst Coordr*, Marcia Stockham; Tel: 573-875-7380, E-Mail: mgstockham@email.ccis.edu; *AV*, Janet Caruthers; Tel: 573-875-7376, E-Mail: jaocaruthers@email.ccis.edu; Staff 7 (MLS 4, Non-MLS 3)
Founded 1851. Enrl 2,600; Fac 72; Highest Degree: Master
Library Holdings: Bk Vols 75,343; Bk Titles 65,169; Per Subs 619
Subject Interests: Biography, History
Special Collections: History of Costumes, slides; Library of American Civilization, microbooks; Quarles Coll, monograph, music; Religion (Lemmon Coll)
Automation Activity & Vendor Info: (Acquisitions) Innovative Interfaces Inc.; (Cataloging) Innovative Interfaces Inc.; (Circulation) Innovative Interfaces Inc.; (Course Reserve) Innovative Interfaces Inc.; (Media Booking) Innovative Interfaces Inc.; (OPAC) Innovative Interfaces Inc.; (Serials) Innovative Interfaces Inc.
Database Vendor: Ebsco - EbscoHost, IAC - Info Trac, Lexis-Nexis, OCLC - First Search
Publications: Newsletter (for reference only, distributed on campus)
Partic in Mobius; Morenet; OCLC Online Computer Library Center, Inc

M MID-MISSOURI MENTAL HEALTH CENTER LIBRARY,* 3 Hospital Dr, 65201. SAN 377-1660. Tel: 573-884-1300. FAX: 573-884-1010. *Dir*, Mark Stansberry
Library Holdings: Bk Vols 50

S NATIONAL ASSOCIATION OF ANIMAL BREEDERS LIBRARY, 401 Bernadette Dr, 65203. (Mail add: PO Box 1033, 65205-1033), SAN 371-2532. Tel: 573-445-4406. FAX: 573-446-2279. E-Mail: naab-css@naab-css.org. Web Site: www.naab-css.org. *Pres*, Gordon A Doak
Founded 1947
Library Holdings: Bk Vols 400

G ORTHOPEDIC FOUNDATION FOR ANIMALS, OFA Hip Dysplasia Registry,* 2300 Nifong Blvd, 65201. SAN 373-1529. Tel: 573-442-0418. FAX: 573-875-5073.
Library Holdings: Bk Vols 100; Per Subs 11

S STATE HISTORICAL SOCIETY OF MISSOURI LIBRARY, 1020 Lowry St, 65201-7298. SAN 308-9649. Tel: 573-882-7083. Toll Free Tel: 800-747-6366. FAX: 573-884-4950. E-Mail: shsofmo@umsystem.edu. Web Site: www.system.missouri.edu/shs. *Exec Dir*, James W Goodrich; E-Mail: goodrichj@umsystem.edu; *Assoc Dir*, Lynn Wolf Gentzler; E-Mail: gentzlerl@umsystem.edu; *Senior Info Specialist*, Laurel Boeckman; E-Mail: boeckmanl@umsystem.edu; *Senior Info Specialist*, Ara Kaye; E-Mail: kayea@umsystem.edu; Staff 23 (MLS 16, Non-MLS 7)
Founded 1898
Jul 1999-Jun 2000 Income $1,117,895, State $974,862, Parent Institution $135,935, Other $7,098. Mats Exp $123,079, Books $14,639, Per/Ser (Incl. Access Fees) $17,792, Presv $85,461, Electronic Ref Mat (Incl. Access Fees) $5,187. Sal $597,162
Library Holdings: Bk Vols 455,000; Per Subs 875
Subject Interests: Genealogy, Missouri hist, Western hist
Special Collections: Church History (Bishop William F McMurry Coll); Joint Manuscript Coll with University of Missouri Western Historical Manuscript Coll; Literature (Mahan Memorial Mark Twain Coll & Eugene Field Coll); Map Coll; Mid-Western History (J Christian Bay Coll); Missouri Newspapers (1808-present); Missouri's Literary Heritage for Children & Youth (Alice Irene Fitzgerald Coll); Photograph Coll; United States Census Coll, micro
Publications: Directory of Local Historical, Museum, & Genealogical Agencies in Missouri, 1998-1999 (1998); Grand Army of the Republic-Missouri Division-Index to Death Rolls, 1882-1940 (1995); Guide to Selected Holdings of Microfilm at the State Historical Society of Missouri (1997); Guide to Selected Holdings of Microfilm at the State Historical Society of Missouri (1998); Historic Preservation Research: A Selective Bibliography of Resources Available at the State Historical Society of Missouri (1999); Index to Missouri Military Pensioners, 1883 (1997); Index to Residents, State Federal Soldiers' Home of Missouri, St James, Missouri, 1899-1946 (1998); Marking Missouri History (1998); Missouri Newspapers on Microfilm at the State Historical Society of Missouri (revised 1996); Missouri Plat Books in the State Historical Society of Missouri, 1987
Restriction: Public use on premises
Function: ILL limited, Photocopies available, Research library
Partic in Missouri Library Network Corporation
Friends of the Library Group

C STEPHENS COLLEGE, Hugh Stephens Library, 1200 E Broadway, 62515. SAN 348-9930. Tel: 573-876-7182. FAX: 573-876-7264. Web Site: www.ac.stephens.edu/library/hsl.htm. *Dir*, Joni Blake; *ILL*, Nina Stawski; *Publ Servs*, Betty Kite; *Tech Servs*, Georgia Baskett; *Tech Servs*, Laura Wells; Staff 7 (MLS 5, Non-MLS 2)
Founded 1833. Enrl 700; Fac 73; Highest Degree: Master
Jun 1999-May 2000 Income $274,000. Mats Exp $119,000, Books $14,000, Per/Ser (Incl. Access Fees) $70,000, Presv $2,200, Micro $14,800, AV Equip $800. Sal $155,000 (Prof $89,000)
Library Holdings: Bk Vols 123,120; Bk Titles 120,000
Subject Interests: Women's studies
Special Collections: Educational Resources & Childrens Literature; Women's Studies Coll (Monographic)
Automation Activity & Vendor Info: (Acquisitions) Innovative Interfaces Inc.; (Cataloging) Innovative Interfaces Inc.; (Circulation) Innovative Interfaces Inc.; (Course Reserve) Innovative Interfaces Inc.; (ILL) Innovative Interfaces Inc.; (Media Booking) Innovative Interfaces Inc.; (OPAC) Innovative Interfaces Inc.; (Serials) Innovative Interfaces Inc.
Publications: Annual report; Bibliographies
Partic in Mobius; OCLC Online Computer Library Center, Inc
Friends of the Library Group

C UNIVERSITY OF MISSOURI, Western Historical Manuscript Collection - Columbia, 23 Ellis Library, 65201-5149. SAN 329-0115. Tel: 573-882-6028. FAX: 573-884-0345. E-Mail: whmc@umsystem.edu. Web Site: www.system.missouri.edu/whmc. *Assoc Dir*, Laura Bullion; *Asst Dir*, David Moore
Founded 1943
Branches of the Western Historical Manuscript Collection exist on all four campuses of the University of Missouri

C UNIVERSITY OF MISSOURI-COLUMBIA, Academic Support Center Film & Video Library, 505 E Stewart Rd, 65211-2040. SAN 308-9665. Tel: 573-882-3601. FAX: 573-882-6110. E-Mail: asc-media-lib@missouri.edu. Web Site: web.missouri.edu/~ascwww/medialib.html. *Assoc Dir*, John S Fick
Publications: Subject area catalogs

UNIVERSITY OF MISSOURI-COLUMBIA

C COLUMBIA MISSOURIAN NEWSPAPER LIBRARY, School of Journalism, 301 S Ninth St, Lee Hills Hall, Rm 315, PO Box 917, 65205. SAN 329-8124. Tel: 573-882-4876. FAX: 573-882-4876. *Librn*, Pat Timberlake; Staff 1 (MLS 1)
Founded 1974
Library Holdings: Bk Vols 110; Bk Titles 80; Per Subs 5

C ELMER ELLIS LIBRARY, Ellis Library Bldg, Rm 104, 65201-5149. Tel: 573-882-4701. Interlibrary Loan Service Tel: 573-882-3224. FAX: 573-882-8044. Interlibrary Loan Service FAX: 573-884-4857. E-Mail: ellisref@showme.missouri.edu. Web Site: www.missouri.edu/~elliswww/. *Dir*, Martha S Alexander; E-Mail: alexanderms@missouri.edu; *Assoc Dir*, Alice Allen; Tel: 573-882-1685, Fax: 573-884-5243, E-Mail: allenaj@missouri.edu; *Asst Dir*, Robert A Almony, Jr; Fax: 573-882-8044, E-Mail: almonyr@missouri.edu; *ILL*, Delores Fisher; Tel: 573-882-3224, Fax: 573-884-4857, E-Mail: fisherd@missouri.edu; *Spec Coll*, Margaret Howell; Tel: 573-882-0076, Fax: 513-884-5004, E-Mail: howellm@missouri.edu; *Head Ref*, Mary Ryan; Tel: 573-882-9165, Fax: 573-882-6034, E-Mail: ryanm@missouri.edu; *Archivist*, Mike Holland; Tel: 573-882-4602, Fax: 572-884-0027, E-Mail: hollandm@missouri.edu; *Archivist*, Rhonda Whithaus; Tel: 573-882-9164, Fax: 573-884-0027, E-Mail: whithausr@missouri.edu; *Govt Doc*, Geoffrey Swindells; Tel: 573-884-8123, E-Mail: swindellsg@missouri.edu. Subject Specialists: *Black studies*, Paula Roper; *Business and management*, Gwen Gray; *Economics*, Gwen Gray; *Education*, Paula Roper; *Education*, Wayne Barnes; *Fine arts*, Michael Muchow; *History*, Rachel Brekhus; *International studies*, Goodie Bhullar; *Language arts*, Anne Barker; *Life sci*, Brenda Graves Blevins; *Literature*, Anne Barker; *Physical science*, Janice Dysart; *Psychology*, Wayne Barnes; *Social sciences and issues*, Nancy Myers; Staff 57 (MLS 57)
Founded 1839. Enrl 23,000; Fac 1,669; Highest Degree: Doctorate
Jul 1999-Jun 2000 Mats Exp $5,829,133, Books $956,385, Per/Ser (Incl. Access Fees) $4,664,959. Sal $5,457,794 (Prof $2,661,601)
Library Holdings: Bk Vols 2,968,062; Per Subs 20,524
Special Collections: American Best Sellers (Frank Luther Mott Coll); Cartoons (John Tinney McCutcheon Coll); Fourth of July Oration Coll; Philosophy (Thomas Moore Johnson Coll); Rare Book Coll; World War I & II Poster Coll
Publications: UMC Libraries (newsletter); University of Missouri Library Series
Partic in Mobius; OCLC Online Computer Library Center, Inc
Friends of the Library Group

C ENGINEERING LIBRARY, W2001 Engineering Bldg E, 65211-5149. SAN 349-0025. Tel: 573-882-2379. FAX: 573-884-4499. Web Site: www.missouri.edu/~engjudy. *Librn*, Judy Siebert Maseles; E-Mail: maselesj@missouri.edu; Staff 1 (MLS 1)

Founded 1906
JulJun
Library Holdings: Bk Vols 93,221; Per Subs 703
Subject Interests: Computing sci, Engr
Database Vendor: Ebsco - EbscoHost, IAC - Info Trac, IAC - SearchBank, Innovative Interfaces INN - View, Lexis-Nexis, OCLC - First Search, OVID Technologies, Silverplatter Information Inc.
Partic in Big Twelve Plus Libr Consortium; Merlin; Missouri Library Network Corporation; Mobius
Friends of the Library Group

C FREEDOM OF INFORMATION CENTER, 127 Neff Annex, 65211. SAN 372-5022. Tel: 573-882-4856. FAX: 573-882-5136. Web Site: www.missouri.edu/~foiwww. *Mgr*, Kathleen Edwards; *Asst Librn*, Robert Anderson
Founded 1958
Library Holdings: Bk Vols 200; Per Subs 140

C GEOLOGY LIBRARY, 201 Geology Bldg, 65211. SAN 349-005X. Tel: 573-882-4860. Interlibrary Loan Service Tel: 573-882-3224. FAX: 573-882-5458. *Librn*, Stephen Stanton
Library Holdings: Bk Vols 68,774; Per Subs 683
Subject Interests: Econ geol, Exploration, Geochemistry, Geophysics, Hydrol, Paleontology, Petrology, Siesmology, Solid-earth geophysics, Statigraphy, Structural geol
Special Collections: 19th Century Federal Survey Publications; 19th Century State Geological Survey Publications
Partic in OCLC Online Computer Library Center, Inc

C INTERLIBRARY LOAN DEPARTMENT Tel: 573-882-0467. *Librn*, Alice Edwards

CM J OTTO LOTTES HEALTH SCIENCES LIBRARY, 1 Hospital Dr, 65211. Tel: 573-882-7033. FAX: 573-882-5574. Interlibrary Loan Service FAX: 573-884-4136. Web Site: hsc.missouri.edu/library/. *Dir*, Deborah Ward; *ILL*, Alice Edwards; *Tech Servs*, Richard Rexroat; Staff 8 (MLS 8)
Library Holdings: Bk Vols 223,367; Per Subs 1,750
Partic in Docline; Library Systems Service; Midcontinental Regional Med Libr Program; Nat Libr of Med; OCLC Online Computer Library Center, Inc

C JOURNALISM LIBRARY, 117 Walter Williams Hall, 65211. SAN 349-0084. Tel: 573-882-7502. Interlibrary Loan Service Tel: 573-882-3224. FAX: 573-884-4963. Web Site: www.missouri.edu/~jourss/. *Chief Librn, Coll Develop*, Pat Timberlake; Tel: 573-882-9156, E-Mail: timberlakep@missouri.edu; Staff 1 (MLS 1)
Founded 1908. Enrl 750; Fac 75; Highest Degree: Doctorate
Library Holdings: Bk Vols 37,500; Per Subs 316
Subject Interests: Advertising, Broadcasting, Journalism, Mass media, Newspapers, Newswriting, Photo journalism, Pub relations
Special Collections: Freedom of Information Center; Newspaper Library
Publications: Journalism Index
Partic in Big Twelve Plus Libr Consortium; Dialog Corporation; Dow Jones News Retrieval; Lexus; Merlin; Mobius; Morenet; PLS

CL LAW LIBRARY, Hulston Hall School of Law, 65211-4190. SAN 349-0114. Tel: 573-882-4597. FAX: 573-882-9676. Web Site: www.law.missouri.edu/library/. *Dir*, Martha J Dragich; Tel: 573-882-2052, E-Mail: dragichm@missouri.edu; *Assoc Dir*, Randy Diamond; Tel: 573-882-2935, E-Mail: diamondr@missouri.edu; *Cat*, Darcy Jones; Tel: 573-882-9680, E-Mail: jonesdl@missouri.edu; *Ref*, Steven Lambson; Tel: 573-882-6464, E-Mail: lambsons@missouri.edu; *Tech Servs*, Needra Jackson; Tel: 573-882-9675, E-Mail: jacksonn@missouri.edu; *Govt Doc*, Cindy Shearrer; Tel: 573-882-1125, E-Mail: shearrerc@missouri.edu; Staff 7 (MLS 7)
Founded 1872. Enrl 500; Fac 40; Highest Degree: Doctorate
Library Holdings: Bk Vols 311,976; Per Subs 4,960
Special Collections: 19th Century Trials (John D Lawson Coll)
Publications: Law Library Guide
Partic in Westlaw

CM LIBRARY FOR FAMILY & COMMUNITY MEDICINE, SOCIAL & BEHAVIORAL SCIENCES, Medical Sciences Bldg, M246, 65212. SAN 349-0130. Tel: 573-882-6183. FAX: 573-882-9096. E-Mail: smeadows@fcm.missouri.edu. *Librn*, Susan Meadows; *Tech Servs*, Susan Elliot; Staff 1 (MLS 1)
Founded 1966. Highest Degree: Master
Library Holdings: Bk Vols 2,000; Per Subs 60
Subject Interests: Gerontology, Healthcare systs, Med ethics, Rural health, Soc aspects of med care

C MATH SCIENCES, 206 Math Sciences Bldg, 65211. SAN 349-0173. Tel: 573-882-7286. Interlibrary Loan Service Tel: 573-882-3224. FAX: 573-884-0058. E-Mail: mthdixie@showme.missouri.edu. *Asst Librn*, Dixie L Fingerson
Founded 1969
Jul 1996-Jun 1997 Mats Exp Per/Ser (Incl. Access Fees) $162,415. Sal $39,011
Library Holdings: Bk Vols 50,919; Per Subs 283
Subject Interests: Mathematics, Statistics
Friends of the Library Group

CM VETERINARY MEDICAL LIBRARY, W-218 Veterinary-Medicine Bldg, 65211. SAN 349-0262. Tel: 573-882-2461. Interlibrary Loan Service Tel: 573-882-2844. FAX: 573-882-2950. E-Mail: vetlib@showme.missouri.edu. *Dir*, Trenton Boyd; Staff 1 (MLS 1)
Founded 1951. Enrl 252; Fac 100; Highest Degree: Doctorate
Jul 1997-Jun 1998 Income $178,630. Mats Exp $84,294, Books $16,159, Per/Ser (Incl. Access Fees) $58,578. Sal $94,346 (Prof $50,345)
Library Holdings: Per Subs 290
Subject Interests: Clydesdales, Mules, Veterinary hist

CONCEPTION

R CONCEPTION ABBEY & SEMINARY LIBRARY,* 64433. SAN 308-9681. Tel: 660-944-2803. FAX: 660-944-2833. E-Mail: abbeylibrary@msc.net. *Librn*, Thomas Sullivan OSB; E-Mail: tsullivan@msc.net; *ILL, Ref*, Carolyn Fisher; *Cat*, Jack Neville; Staff 3 (MLS 3)
Founded 1873. Enrl 93; Fac 15; Highest Degree: Bachelor
Jun 1997-May 1998 Income $199,238. Mats Exp $46,207, Books $34,000, Per/Ser (Incl. Access Fees) $12,207. Sal $114,697 (Prof $74,000)
Library Holdings: Bk Titles 109,912; Per Subs 364
Subject Interests: Art, Medieval European hist, Philosophy, Relig studies, Roman Catholic religion
Special Collections: 17th-19th Century Catholic Theology Coll; American Catholic Church History Coll; Incunabula & Manuscripts
Partic in OCLC Online Computer Library Center, Inc

CRYSTAL CITY

P CRYSTAL CITY PUBLIC LIBRARY, 736 Mississippi Ave, 63019-1646. SAN 308-9711. Tel: 636-937-7166. FAX: 636-937-7166. E-Mail: cme000@mail.connect.more.net. *Dir*, Tania Laughlin; *Asst Librn*, Head Mary; *Asst Librn*, Marilyn Parr
Founded 1916. Pop 3,573; Circ 30,497
Apr 1999-Mar 2000 Income $68,849, State $1,900, City $60,349, Locally Generated Income $6,600. Mats Exp $67,974, Books $15,000, Per/Ser (Incl. Access Fees) $2,100, AV Equip $500. Sal $37,428
Library Holdings: Bk Vols 22,000; Bk Titles 21,100; Per Subs 67
Automation Activity & Vendor Info: (Cataloging) Sagebrush Corporation; (Circulation) Sagebrush Corporation; (OPAC) Sagebrush Corporation
Database Vendor: Ebsco - EbscoHost, GaleNet, OCLC - First Search
Partic in Saint Louis Regional Library Network
Open Mon-Thurs 12-8, Fri 12-5, Sat 10-1
Friends of the Library Group

DE SOTO

P DE SOTO PUBLIC LIBRARY, 712 S Main St, 63020. SAN 308-972X. Tel: 314-586-3858. FAX: 314-586-1707. E-Mail: azz000@mail.connect.more.net. *Librn*, Betty Olson; Staff 1 (MLS 1)
Founded 1935. Pop 10,000; Circ 69,000
Nov 2000-Oct 2001 Income $125,000, State $2,500, City $105,000, Locally Generated Income $17,500. Mats Exp $17,000, Books $15,000, Per/Ser (Incl. Access Fees) $2,000. Sal $60,000 (Prof $25,000)
Library Holdings: Bk Titles 28,000; Per Subs 50
Subject Interests: Jefferson County hist
Special Collections: Local History (Felix Milfeld), negatives, photog
Publications: Quarterly newsletter
Partic in Missouri Library Network Corporation
Friends of the Library Group

DEXTER

P KELLER PUBLIC LIBRARY, (KPL), 402 W Grant, 63841. SAN 308-9738. Tel: 573-624-3764. FAX: 573-624-1501. *Dir*, Loyce L LReed; Staff 4 (Non-MLS 4)
Founded 1934. Pop 7,035
Jul 1999-Jun 2000 Income $193,321, State $4,126, City $90,294, Federal $10,122, Other $28,589. Mats Exp $110,818, Books $28,162, Other Print Mats $37,651, Electronic Ref Mat (Incl. Access Fees) $45,005. Sal $61,269
Library Holdings: Bk Vols 35,595; Per Subs 39
Subject Interests: Genealogy
Automation Activity & Vendor Info: (Acquisitions) SIRSI; (Cataloging) SIRSI; (Circulation) SIRSI
Staff member who is legally blind
Friends of the Library Group

DIAMOND

S US NATIONAL PARK SERVICE, George Washington Carver National Monument Library, 5646 Carver Rd, 64840. SAN 370-3142. Tel: 417-325-4151. FAX: 417-325-4231. E-Mail: gwca_superintendent@nps.gov. Web Site: www.nps.gov. *In Charge*, Lana Henry
Oct 2000-Sep 2001 Mats Exp $2,500
Library Holdings: Bk Vols 550
Special Collections: Carver Coll (3019 archives & artifacts) Original Carver Letters (97 items)

EDINA

S KNOX COUNTY HISTORICAL SOCIETY LIBRARY,* PO Box 75, 63537-0075. SAN 373-3718. Tel: 660-397-2349. FAX: 660-397-3331. *Pres*, Brenton Karhoff
Library Holdings: Bk Vols 2,041
Restriction: By appointment only

ELDON

P ELDON PUBLIC LIBRARY,* 308 E First St, 65026. SAN 377-1075. Tel: 573-392-6657. FAX: 573-392-4071. *Mgr*, Ruby Bunch
Library Holdings: Bk Vols 20,000; Per Subs 30
Mem of Heartland Regional Libr Syst

FARMINGTON

P FARMINGTON PUBLIC LIBRARY,* 108 W Harrison St, 63640. SAN 308-9762. Tel: 573-756-5779. FAX: 573-756-0614. E-Mail: gcw000@mail.connect.more.net. *Librn*, Lynn Crites; Staff 3 (MLS 1, Non-MLS 2)
Founded 1916. Pop 11,589; Circ 103,694
Library Holdings: Bk Vols 35,000; Per Subs 100
Special Collections: Local History & Genealogy Coll
Open Mon & Fri 10-5:30, Tues-Thurs 10-8, Sat 11-3

FAYETTE

CR CENTRAL METHODIST COLLEGE, Smiley Memorial Library, 411 Central Methodist Sq, 65248. SAN 308-9770. Tel: 660-248-6271, 660-298-6292. FAX: 660-248-6392. Web Site: www.cmc.edu. *Librn*, Rita Gulstad; E-Mail: rgulstad@cmc2.cmc.edu; *Tech Servs*, Leasa Strodtman; *Publ Servs*, Joy Dodson; E-Mail: jdodson@cmc.edu; *ILL*, Karen Monnig; E-Mail: kmonnig@cmc.edu; *Per*, Michelle Vale; E-Mail: mvalle@cmc.edu; Staff 2 (MLS 2)
Founded 1857. Enrl 1,200; Highest Degree: Master
1999-2000 Income $261,128. Mats Exp $99,500, Books $22,505, Per/Ser (Incl. Access Fees) $44,847, Presv $428, Electronic Ref Mat (Incl. Access Fees) $5,573. Sal $122,903 (Prof $74,500)
Library Holdings: Bk Vols 94,841; Bk Titles 70,330; Per Subs 354
Subject Interests: Methodism
Special Collections: Religion (Missouri United Methodist Archives)
Automation Activity & Vendor Info: (Cataloging) epixtech, inc.; (Circulation) epixtech, inc.; (OPAC) epixtech, inc.
Partic in Missouri Library Network Corporation

FENTON

S MARITZ INC LIBRARY,* 1400 S Highway Dr, 63099. SAN 308-9797. Tel: 314-827-1501. FAX: 314-827-5505.
Founded 1969
Library Holdings: Bk Vols 10,000; Per Subs 365
Subject Interests: Bus, Graphic art, Incentives, Marketing, Organizational behavior, Quality, Training, Travel
Special Collections: Annual Reports Coll; Archives Coll
Mem of St Louis Regional Libr Network
Partic in Dialog Corporation; OCLC Online Computer Library Center, Inc

FERGUSON

P FERGUSON MUNICIPAL PUBLIC LIBRARY, 35 N Florissant Rd, 63135. SAN 308-9800. Tel: 314-521-4820. TDD: 314-521-4828. FAX: 314-521-1275. E-Mail: fya000@mail.connect.more.net. *Dir*, Sandra Stewart; Tel: 314-521-1275; Staff 10 (MLS 2, Non-MLS 8)
Founded 1933. Pop 22,286; Circ 173,103
Jul 2000-Jun 2001 Mats Exp Books $35,000
Library Holdings: Bk Vols 80,047; Per Subs 115
Subject Interests: City hist
Automation Activity & Vendor Info: (Cataloging) epixtech, inc.; (Circulation) epixtech, inc.; (OPAC) epixtech, inc.
Database Vendor: Ebsco - EbscoHost, epixtech, inc.
Function: ILL available
Partic in Municipal Libr Coop
Special Services for the Deaf - TDD
Friends of the Library Group

FESTUS

P FESTUS PUBLIC LIBRARY,* 222 N Mill St, 63028. SAN 308-9819. Tel: 314-937-2017. FAX: 314-937-3439. *Dir*, Lollie Gray
Founded 1934. Pop 7,574; Circ 91,617
Library Holdings: Bk Vols 31,049; Per Subs 55
Mem of Saint Louis Regional Libr Network
Open Mon-Wed 12-7, Thurs & Fri 12-5, Sat 10-3
Friends of the Library Group

FLORISSANT

CR SAINT LOUIS CHRISTIAN COLLEGE LIBRARY,* 1360 Grandview Dr, 63033. SAN 308-9843. Tel: 314-837-6777, Ext 8512. FAX: 314-837-8291. E-Mail: librarian@slcc4ministry.edu. Web Site: www.slcc4ministry.edu. *Dir*, Philip E Orr; *Tech Servs*, Janis Fordyce; Staff 1 (Non-MLS 1)
Founded 1956
Jul 1997-Jun 1998 Income $65,989. Mats Exp $6,702, Books $1,877, Per/Ser (Incl. Access Fees) $3,377, Presv $390, AV Equip $303. Sal $50,690 (Prof $27,700)
Library Holdings: Bk Vols 39,738; Per Subs 155
Subject Interests: Bible, Biblical theol, Church history, Linguistics, Restoration movement hist (19th century Am relig movement)
Special Collections: Carl Kitcherside Library; Library of American Civilization Coll, micro
Partic in Saint Louis Regional Library Network

FORT LEONARD WOOD

UNITED STATES ARMY

A BRUCE C CLARKE COMMUNITY LIBRARY, 597 Engineer Loop, Ste 100, 65473-8928. SAN 349-0297. Tel: 573-563-4113. FAX: 573-563-4118. Web Site: www.wood.army.mil/isd/comlib.htm.; Staff 1 (MLS 1)
Founded 1941
Library Holdings: Bk Vols 63,000; Per Subs 120
Subject Interests: Bus, Foreign Language, Mil art, Sci
Special Collections: Children's Library
Partic in Fed Libr & Info Network; OCLC Online Computer Library Center, Inc; Tralinet; United States Army Training & Doctrine Command (TRADOC)
Open Tues-Thurs 11-8, Sat & Sun 12-6

AM GEN LEONARD WOOD ARMY COMMUNITY HOSPITAL-MEDICAL LIBRARY, 126 Missouri Ave, 65473-5700. SAN 349-0378. Tel: 573-596-0131, Ext 69110. FAX: 573-596-0072.
Founded 1945
Oct 1998-Sep 1999 Mats Exp $27,500. Sal $40,000
Library Holdings: Bk Titles 2,500; Per Subs 90
Restriction: Staff use only

S MANSCEN ACADEMIC LIBRARY, Bldg 3202, 597 Engineer Loop, Ste 200, 65473-8928. SAN 362-8957. Tel: 573-563-4109. FAX: 573-563-4118. Web Site: www.wood.army.mil. *In Charge*, Ron Novy; E-Mail: novyr@wood.army.mil; Staff 6 (MLS 3, Non-MLS 3)
Founded 1935
Library Holdings: Bk Vols 49,407; Per Subs 90
Subject Interests: Mil eng, Military history
Special Collections: Civil War Era (Rare Book Coll), military publications; Military Engineering
Automation Activity & Vendor Info: (Acquisitions) SIRSI; (Cataloging) SIRSI; (Circulation) SIRSI; (Course Reserve) SIRSI; (ILL) SIRSI; (Media Booking) SIRSI; (OPAC) SIRSI; (Serials) SIRSI
Publications: handbook; New book accessions list; periodical holdings catalogs
Partic in OCLC Online Computer Library Center, Inc

FULTON

FULTON STATE HOSPITAL

S PATIENT'S LIBRARY, 600 E Fifth St, 65251. SAN 349-0440. Tel: 573-592-2261. FAX: 573-592-3011. *Librn*, Tonya Hayes
Founded 1949
Library Holdings: Bk Vols 6,500; Per Subs 100

M PROFESSIONAL LIBRARY, 600 E Fifth St, 65251. SAN 349-0416. Tel: 573-592-2261. FAX: 573-592-3011. *Librn*, Tonya Hayes
Library Holdings: Bk Vols 1,850; Bk Titles 1,400; Per Subs 90
Subject Interests: Medicine, Nursing, Psychiatry, Psychology, Soc work

S MISSOURI SCHOOL FOR THE DEAF, Grover C Farquhar Library, 505 E Fifth St, 65251. SAN 373-0786. Tel: 573-592-2513. FAX: 573-592-2570. Web Site: www.msd.k12.mo.us. *Librn*, Patsy Craghead; E-Mail: pcraghead@msd.k12.mo.us
Library Holdings: Bk Vols 12,000; Per Subs 33

WESTMINSTER COLLEGE

C REEVES MEMORIAL LIBRARY, 501 Westminster, 65251-1299. SAN 308-9886. Tel: 573-642-5246. FAX: 573-642-6356. E-Mail: mitchel@micro.wcmo.edu. Web Site: www.westminster-mo.edu. *Dir*, Lorna Mitchell; *ILL*, Vera Woodworth; *Doc, Tech Servs*, Jim Dutton; *Coll Develop, Ref*, William B Lowe; Staff 9 (MLS 3, Non-MLS 6)
Founded 1905. Highest Degree: Bachelor
Jul 1996-Jun 1997 Income $418,012. Mats Exp $124,810, Books $50,510, Per/Ser (Incl. Access Fees) $35,528, Presv $2,616, Micro $3,955, AV Equip $20,369. Sal $194,561
Library Holdings: Bk Vols 111,079; Per Subs 409
Partic in Missouri Library Network Corporation; OCLC Online Computer Library Center, Inc

S WINSTON CHURCHILL MEMORIAL LIBRARY, Westminister College, 501 Westminster Ave, 65251-1299. SAN 308-9878. Tel: 573-592-5369. FAX: 573-592-5222. *Dir*, Dr Gordon Davis; Staff 4 (MLS 4)
Founded 1962
Library Holdings: Bk Vols 1,300
Special Collections: British-American Relations; Christopher Wren Coll; Sir Winston Churchill Coll
Publications: Churchill Memorial Memory (4 times yearly); Guide for visitors to the Winston Churchill Memorial & Library
Restriction: Non-circulating to the public
Partic in OCLC Online Computer Library Center, Inc

C WILLIAM WOODS UNIVERSITY, Dulany Memorial Library, One University Ave, 65251. SAN 308-9894. Tel: 573-592-1115, 573-592-4289, 573-592-4291. Interlibrary Loan Service Tel: 573-592-4289. Circulation Tel: 573-592-1160. Reference Tel: 573-592-4279. FAX: 573-592-1159. E-Mail: libref@williamwoods.edu. Web Site: www.williamwoods.edu. *Dir*, Erlene A Dudley; *Ref*, Catherine Craven; *ILL*, Helen Renaud; *Tech Servs*, Tom Schultz; Staff 4 (MLS 4)
Founded 1870. Enrl 1,150; Fac 59; Highest Degree: Master
Library Holdings: Bk Vols 120,411; Per Subs 556
Subject Interests: Equestrian studies, Interpreter training
Special Collections: Education Coll; Equestrian Science Coll
Automation Activity & Vendor Info: (Acquisitions) Innovative Interfaces Inc.; (Cataloging) Innovative Interfaces Inc.; (Circulation) Innovative Interfaces Inc.; (Course Reserve) Innovative Interfaces Inc.; (ILL) Innovative Interfaces Inc.; (Media Booking) Innovative Interfaces Inc.; (OPAC) Innovative Interfaces Inc.; (Serials) Innovative Interfaces Inc.
Publications: Dulany Library Handbook
Mem of Mo Libr Network Corp
Partic in Mobius
Special Services for the Deaf - Books on deafness & sign language

GAINESVILLE

P OZARK COUNTY LIBRARY,* 200 Elm St, 65655. (Mail add: PO Box 518, 65655), SAN 377-2233. Tel: 417-679-4442. *Librn*, Donna Mader
Library Holdings: Bk Vols 10,000

GALENA

P STONE COUNTY LIBRARY, 106 E Fifth St, 65656. (Mail add: PO Box 225, 65656-0225), Tel: 417-357-6410. Toll Free Tel: 888-711-3100. FAX: 417-357-6695. E-Mail: cvw000@mail.connect.more.net. *Dir*, David R Doennig; Staff 6 (MLS 1, Non-MLS 5)
Founded 1948. Pop 19,078; Circ 38,175
Jan 1999-Dec 1999 Income $220,882, State $7,177, Federal $7,626, County $187,671, Other $18,408. Mats Exp $35,887, Books $34,340, Per/Ser (Incl. Access Fees) $1,547. Sal $93,251
Library Holdings: Bk Vols 53,000; Bk Titles 44,527; Per Subs 60
Automation Activity & Vendor Info: (Cataloging) Innovative Interfaces Inc.; (Circulation) Innovative Interfaces Inc.; (OPAC) Innovative Interfaces Inc.
Database Vendor: Ebsco - EbscoHost
Function: Some telephone reference
Partic in SW Mo Libr Serv
Branches: 1
CRANE AREA, 111 Main St, PO Box 25, Crane, 65633-0025. SAN 308-9703. Tel: 417-723-8261. FAX: 417-723-8261. *Librn*, Murel Carr
Founded 1938. Pop 2,000; Circ 8,000
Library Holdings: Bk Vols 19,000
Bookmobiles: 1

GALLATIN

P DAVIESS COUNTY LIBRARY, 306 W Grand, 64640. SAN 349-0475. Tel: 660-663-3222. FAX: 660-663-3250. Web Site: www.grm.net/~daviess. *Librn*, Jan Johnson; *Asst Librn*, Jone Perry
Founded 1947. Pop 7,865; Circ 47,335
Jan 1999-Dec 1999 Income (Main Library and Branch Library) $158,555, State $9,640, Federal $7,888, County $128,221, Locally Generated Income $12,806. Mats Exp Books $12,367. Sal $83,388
Library Holdings: Bk Titles 26,972; Per Subs 51
Subject Interests: Amish culture, Genealogy
Automation Activity & Vendor Info: (Acquisitions) SIRSI; (Cataloging) SIRSI; (Circulation) SIRSI; (OPAC) SIRSI
Friends of the Library Group
Branches: 1
JAMESPORT BRANCH, Jamesport, 64648. SAN 349-0505. Tel: 660-684-6120. *Librn*, Martha Moulin
Library Holdings: Bk Vols 4,600

GERALD

P GERALD AREA LIBRARY,* 357 S Main, PO Box 212, 63037. SAN 377-2217. Tel: 573-764-7323. *In Charge*, Edie Heath
Library Holdings: Bk Vols 10,000

GLASGOW

P LEWIS LIBRARY OF GLASGOW, (Formerly Lewis Library), 315 Market St, 65254-1537. SAN 308-9924. Tel: 660-338-2395. FAX: 660-338-2395. *Dir*, Mary Haskamp
Founded 1866. Pop 1,336; Circ 3,745
Library Holdings: Per Subs 20
Special Collections: Local Papers (dated back to 1866)
Database Vendor: OCLC - First Search
Open Mon-Fri 3-7, Sat 1-5
Friends of the Library Group

HAMILTON

P HAMILTON PUBLIC LIBRARY,* 312 N Davis, 64644. SAN 308-9932. Tel: 816-583-4832. *Librn*, Delores Humphrey
Founded 1919. Pop 1,582; Circ 11,441
Jul 1997-Jun 1998 Income $26,900. Mats Exp $4,000. Sal $12,000
Library Holdings: Bk Vols 15,000; Per Subs 42
Open Tues-Sat 1-5

HANNIBAL

P HANNIBAL FREE PUBLIC LIBRARY, 200 S Fifth St, 63401. SAN 308-9940. Tel: 573-221-0222. FAX: 573-221-0369. E-Mail: mdu000@mail.connect.more.net. *Librn*, Ann Sundermeyer
Founded 1845. Pop 18,004; Circ 139,382
Library Holdings: Bk Vols 70,000; Per Subs 200
Subject Interests: Hannibal hist, Mark Twain
Automation Activity & Vendor Info: (Cataloging) SIRSI; (Circulation) SIRSI; (OPAC) SIRSI; (Serials) SIRSI

C HANNIBAL-LAGRANGE COLLEGE, L A Foster Library, 2800 Palmyra Rd, 63401-1999. SAN 308-9959. Tel: 573-221-3675, Ext 219. FAX: 573-248-0294. E-Mail: library@hlg.edu. Web Site: www.hlg.edu. *Dir*, Julie Andresen; *Assoc Dir*, Robert Lindsey; *Per*, Bernice Bueler; Staff 7 (MLS 2, Non-MLS 5)
Founded 1858. Enrl 865; Fac 78; Highest Degree: Bachelor
Aug 2000-Jul 2001 Income (Main Library Only) $331,464. Mats Exp $92,188, Books $40,367, Per/Ser (Incl. Access Fees) $17,649, Presv $513, Micro $8,169, AV Equip $20,911, Electronic Ref Mat (Incl. Access Fees) $4,579. Sal $141,497
Library Holdings: Bk Vols 90,832; Bk Titles 71,680; Per Subs 516
Subject Interests: Archives, Baptist mat, Rare books
Automation Activity & Vendor Info: (Cataloging) TLC; (Circulation) TLC; (OPAC) TLC
Database Vendor: Ebsco - EbscoHost, GaleNet, Lexis-Nexis, OCLC - First Search, Silverplatter Information Inc.
Partic in MLNC; Mobius; Morenet; OCLC Online Computer Library Center, Inc

S MARK TWAIN HOME FOUNDATION, Mark Twain Museum Library, 208 Hill St, 63401-3316. SAN 326-0542. Tel: 573-221-9010. FAX: 573-221-7975. *Dir*, Henry Sweets
Founded 1937
Library Holdings: Bk Titles 1,600; Per Subs 10
Subject Interests: Mark Twain
Special Collections: First Editions of Mark Twain's works
Publications: The Fence Painter (quarterly newsletter)
Restriction: By appointment only
Friends of the Library Group

HARRISONVILLE

P CASS COUNTY PUBLIC LIBRARY, 400 E Mechanic, 64701. SAN 349-0564. Tel: 816-884-3483. TDD: 816-331-8242. FAX: 816-884-2301. *Dir*, Jo Irwin; Tel: 816-380-4600, E-Mail: xrt003@mail.connect.more.net; *Asst Dir*, Whitney Davison-Turley; E-Mail: whitneydt@yahoo.com; Staff 4 (MLS 2, Non-MLS 2)
Founded 1947. Pop 80,000; Circ 354,676
Jan 1999-Dec 1999 Income (Main Library and Branch Library) $1,256,800, State $43,449, County $1,172,492, Other $40,859. Mats Exp $197,108, Books $178,004, Per/Ser (Incl. Access Fees) $13,768, Presv $1,918, Micro $3,418. Sal $616,850 (Prof $33,622)
Library Holdings: Bk Vols 155,000; Per Subs 264; Bks on Deafness & Sign Lang 50
Subject Interests: Genealogy
Special Collections: Cass County & Missouri, hist doc
Automation Activity & Vendor Info: (Acquisitions) DRA; (Cataloging) DRA; (Circulation) DRA; (ILL) DRA; (OPAC) DRA; (Serials) DRA

Database Vendor: DRA, Ebsco - EbscoHost, GaleNet, OCLC - First Search
Publications: Annual Report; Summer Reading Kit
Partic in Kansas City Libr Consortium; Kansas City Metropolitan Library & Information Network; Morenet
Special Services for the Deaf - TDD
Friends of the Library Group
Branches: 9
ARCHIE BRANCH, 315 S Main, PO Box 64, Archie, 64725. SAN 349-0599. Tel: 816-293-5579. *Librn*, Christy Ogle
Friends of the Library Group
BELTON BRANCH, 422 Main St, Belton, 64012. SAN 349-0629. Tel: 816-331-0049. *Librn*, Christina Zibers
Friends of the Library Group
DREXEL BRANCH, 211 E Main St, Drexel, 64742. SAN 349-0688. Tel: 816-657-4740. *Librn*, Kay Edmonds
Friends of the Library Group
GARDEN CITY BRANCH, 207C Date St, PO Box 334, Garden City, 64747. SAN 349-0718. Tel: 816-862-6611. *Librn*, Marilyn Thomas
Friends of the Library Group
GENEALOGY, 400 E Mechanic, 64701. Tel: 816-884-6285. *Librn*, Jacqueline Polsgrove
Friends of the Library Group
HARRISONVILLE BRANCH, 400 E Mechanic, 64701. SAN 349-0742. Tel: 816-884-3483. *Librn*, John Thulin
Friends of the Library Group
PECULIAR BRANCH, 220 N Main St, PO Box 356, Peculiar, 64078-0356. SAN 349-0777. Tel: 816-758-5412. *Librn*, Claudine Mitchell
Friends of the Library Group
PLEASANT HILL BRANCH, 1204B N Hwy 7, Pleasant Hill, 64080. SAN 349-0807. Tel: 816-987-2231. *Librn*, Marianna Decker
Friends of the Library Group
RAYMORE BRANCH, 112 N Madison, Raymore, 64083. SAN 349-0831. Tel: 816-331-8024. *Librn*, Margaret Shaffer
Friends of the Library Group

HARTVILLE

P WRIGHT COUNTY LIBRARY,* 125 Court Square, PO Box 70, 65667. SAN 349-0866. Tel: 417-741-7595. FAX: 417-741-7927. *Dir*, Carrie Cline; *Librn*, Judy Epperly
Founded 1947. Pop 19,241; Circ 186,984
Library Holdings: Bk Vols 152,163; Per Subs 62
Branches: 4
MANSFIELD BRANCH, PO Box 586, Mansfield, 65704-3245. SAN 349-0955. Tel: 417-924-8068. FAX: 417-924-3045. *Librn*, Helen Euler
MOUNTAIN GROVE BRANCH, 219 E Second St, Mountain Grove, 65711. SAN 349-098X. Tel: 417-926-4453. FAX: 417-926-4453. *Librn*, Karen Moore
NORWOOD BRANCH, 248 S Eagle St, Norwood, 65717. SAN 349-1013. Tel: 417-746-1404. FAX: 417-746-1404. *Librn*, Rebecca Sutterwaite; Tel: 402-559-6841, E-Mail: rsattert@unmc.edu
Bookmobiles: 1. Circ 69,524

HAYTI

P CONRAN MEMORIAL LIBRARY, 302 E Main St, 63851. SAN 308-9967. Tel: 573-359-0599. E-Mail: conranlibrary@hotmail. *Librn*, Jeanie Stewart
Founded 1934. Pop 3,841
Library Holdings: Bk Vols 17,500; Per Subs 16
Subject Interests: Town hist
Open Tues-Fri 1:30-5:30

HERMANN

S DEUTSCHHEIM STATE HISTORIC SITE LIBRARY,* 109 W Second St, 65041. SAN 372-7459. Tel: 573-486-2200. FAX: 573-486-2249. *Adminr*, Steve Sitton
Founded 1980
Special Collections: German Immigrants & German Americans in Missouri 1785-1900

HIGGINSVILLE

P ROBERTSON MEMORIAL LIBRARY,* 19 W 20th St, 64037. SAN 308-9975. Tel: 660-584-2880. FAX: 660-584-8181. *Librn*, Mary E Helms; Tel: 402-559-7099, E-Mail: mhelms@unmc.edu
Pop 4,693; Circ 25,587
Library Holdings: Bk Vols 19,831
Open Tues 10-7, Wed-Fri 10-5, Sat 10-2, closed Mon
Friends of the Library Group

HIGH RIDGE

P JEFFERSON COUNTY LIBRARY, 3021 High Ridge Blvd, 63049. SAN 372-7505. Tel: 636-677-8689. FAX: 636-677-1769. E-Mail: wyz006@mail.connect.more.net. *Dir*, Martha Maxwell; *Tech Servs*, Robert Nador; Staff 4 (MLS 2, Non-MLS 2)
Founded 1989. Pop 104,933
Jan 2000-Dec 2000 Income (Main Library and Branch Library) $2,692,709, State $37,484, Federal $11,852, County $2,356,979, Locally Generated Income $65,696, Other $220,698. Mats Exp $278,480, Books $183,262, Per/Ser (Incl. Access Fees) $12,115, Presv $505, Micro $3,311, AV Equip $39,470, Other Print Mats $2,392, Electronic Ref Mat (Incl. Access Fees) $37,580. Sal $924,922 (Prof $178,751)
Library Holdings: Bk Vols 154,233; Bk Titles 86,448; Per Subs 443; High Interest/Low Vocabulary Bk Vols 1,500; Bks on Deafness & Sign Lang 50
Subject Interests: Business, Genealogy, Local history, Parenting
Automation Activity & Vendor Info: (Acquisitions) SIRSI; (Cataloging) SIRSI; (Circulation) SIRSI; (OPAC) SIRSI
Partic in Saint Louis Regional Library Network
Special Services for the Deaf - FullTalk for communication with persons who are deaf
Special Services for the Blind - Low-cost screen magnifier software utilities for PCs
Friends of the Library Group
Branches: 3
FOX, 2103 Jeffco Blvd, Arnold, 63010. SAN 372-7513. Tel: 636-296-2204. FAX: 636-296-5975. E-Mail: wyz001@mail.connect.more.net. *Mgr*, Elizabeth Link; *Ch Servs*, Amy Held; *Ref*, Jeane Tornatore; *Ref*, Meredith McCarthy; Staff 5 (MLS 1, Non-MLS 4)
Partic in Saint Louis Regional Library Network
Friends of the Library Group
NORTHWEST, 3033 High Ridge Blvd, 63049. SAN 372-8064. Tel: 636-677-8186. FAX: 636-677-8243. E-Mail: wyz004@mail.connect.more.net. *Branch Mgr*, Cindy Hayes; *YA Servs*, Georgia Nassar; Staff 5 (Non-MLS 5)
Subject Interests: Genealogy, Local history
Friends of the Library Group
WINDSOR, 7479 Metropolitian Blvd, Barnhart, 63012. SAN 378-2182. Tel: 636-461-1914. FAX: 636-461-1915. *Mgr*, Karen Duree; *Ch Servs*, Christy Kerr; *Ref*, Don Turner; *Ref*, Jay Manning; Staff 8 (MLS 2, Non-MLS 6)
Friends of the Library Group

HILLSBORO

C JEFFERSON COLLEGE LIBRARY,* 1000 Viking Dr, 63050. SAN 308-9983. Tel: 314-166, 314-789-3951, Ext 162. FAX: 314-789-3954. Web Site: www.jeffco.edu. *Dir*, Linda Bigelow; E-Mail: lbigelow@jeffco.edu; *Publ Servs*, Susan Morgan; E-Mail: smorgan@jeffco.edu; *Tech Servs*, Loretta Ponzar; Staff 3 (MLS 3)
Founded 1964. Enrl 2,546; Fac 88
Library Holdings: Bk Vols 63,915; Per Subs 485
Special Collections: County History Center; Fed
Automation Activity & Vendor Info: (Acquisitions) Innovative Interfaces Inc.
Partic in Missouri Library Network Corporation; Mobius; OCLC Online Computer Library Center, Inc; Saint Louis Regional Library Network
Open Mon-Thurs 7:30am-9pm, Fri 7:30-4 & Sat 10-2

HOLDEN

P HOLDEN PUBLIC LIBRARY,* 101 W Third St, 64040. SAN 308-9991. Tel: 816-732-4545. E-Mail: holdlib@iland.net. *Coll Develop, Dir*, Jeannae Dickerson
Founded 1941. Pop 2,389; Circ 10,901
Jul 1997-Jun 1998 Income $21,084, State $1,055, City $19,245, Other $784. Mats Exp $6,249, Books $5,375, Per/Ser (Incl. Access Fees) $629. Sal $7,495 (Prof $6,275)
Library Holdings: Bk Vols 17,681; Per Subs 24
Friends of the Library Group

HOLLISTER

S WORLD ARCHAEOLOGICAL SOCIETY, (WAS), Information Center, 120 Lakewood Dr, 65672-9718. SAN 320-4871. Tel: 417-334-2377. Web Site: www.page1htmlhttphometownaolcommi7.htmindex.html. *Dir*, Ron Miller; E-Mail: mi7689974@aol.com
Founded 1971
Library Holdings: Bk Titles 7,000; Per Subs 30
Subject Interests: Ancient med, Anthropology, Archaeology, Art history, Biblical archaeol, Democracy, Hist of books, Military history, Museology, Writing
Special Collections: Archaeology (Steve Miller Coll)
Publications: Special Publications; WAS Newsletter
Function: Research library
Extensive research and/or consultation by fee (negotiable). Custom illustrations available

HOUSTON

P TEXAS COUNTY LIBRARY, 117 W Walnut, 65483. SAN 349-1048. Tel: 417-967-2258. FAX: 417-967-2262. *Librn*, Blanche McKinney; Staff 7 (MLS 1, Non-MLS 6)
Founded 1946. Pop 22,000; Circ 140,330
1998-1999 Income (Main Library and Branch Library) $124,000. Mats Exp $26,500, Books $25,000, Per/Ser (Incl. Access Fees) $1,500. Sal $103,400 (Prof $30,000)
Library Holdings: Bk Vols 46,000
Database Vendor: Innovative Interfaces INN - View
Partic in SW Mo Libr Network
Friends of the Library Group
Branches: 3
CABOOL BRANCH, PO Box 72, Cabool, 65689. SAN 349-1072. Tel: 417-962-3722. FAX: 417-962-3722.; Staff 2 (Non-MLS 2)
LICKING BRANCH, 121 S Main, Licking, 65542. SAN 349-1102. Tel: 314-674-2038.; Staff 2 (Non-MLS 2)
Friends of the Library Group
SUMMERSVILLE BRANCH, On the Square, Summersville, 65571. SAN 349-1137. Tel: 417-932-5261.; Staff 1 (Non-MLS 1)

IBERIA

P MILLER COUNTY LIBRARY SERVICE CENTER,* 304 N St Louis St, 65486. (Mail add: PO Box 386, 65486), SAN 377-1113. Tel: 573-793-6746. FAX: 573-793-6037. *Mgr*, Catherine Ponder
Library Holdings: Bk Vols 16,000; Per Subs 20
Mem of Heartland Regional Libr Syst

INDEPENDENCE

M CONSUMER HEALTH INFORMATION RESEARCH INSTITUTE (CHIRI), Medical Information Center, 300 Pink Hill Rd, 64057. SAN 324-7910. Tel: 816-228-4595, Ext 109. FAX: 816-228-4995. *Pres*, Dr John H Renner; E-Mail: drrenner@msn.com; Staff 3 (MLS 1, Non-MLS 2)
Founded 1947
Library Holdings: Bk Vols 5,000; Per Subs 75
Subject Interests: Clinical medicine
Special Collections: Eponym Index; Medical Literature Reprints Index
Publications: Periodic Medical Literature Critiques
Functions in conjunction with the information resources of the National Council against Health Fraud

M GRACELAND UNIVERSITY, Dr Charles F Grabske Sr Library, 1401 W Truman Rd, 64050. SAN 309-0000. Tel: 816-833-0524. FAX: 816-833-2990. Web Site: www2.graceland.edu. *Librn*, Katie Voss; E-Mail: kvoss@graceland.edu; Staff 2 (MLS 1, Non-MLS 1)
Founded 1968
Jun 1999-May 2000 Income Parent Institution $74,100. Mats Exp $36,000, Books $11,000, Per/Ser (Incl. Access Fees) $25,000. Sal $55,000 (Prof $36,000)
Library Holdings: Bk Titles 24,000; Per Subs 300
Subject Interests: Medicine, Nursing
Special Collections: Religious Works (Publications of Herald Publishing House)

C INTERNATIONAL UNIVERSITY LIBRARY,* 1301 S Noland Rd, 64055. SAN 309-0361. Tel: 816-461-3633. FAX: 816-461-3634. *Librn*, Frances Shoaf; *Asst Librn*, Israel Abundis; *Media Spec*, Michael McSpadden; *Acq*, John Wayne Johnston; *Cat*, Hazel Robinson; *Ref*, Susan Ellmaker; *Rare Bks*, Cecil Johnston; Staff 1 (MLS 1)
Founded 1973. Enrl 12,500; Fac 975; Highest Degree: Doctorate
Library Holdings: Bk Vols 17,150; Bk Titles 15,850; Per Subs 40
Special Collections: Ireland (Hibernian), bks & pers

S JACKSON COUNTY HISTORICAL SOCIETY, Archives Book Shop & Research Library, Independence Square Courthouse, 112 W Lexington, Rm 103, 64050-3700. SAN 320-197X. Tel: 816-252-7454. FAX: 816-461-1510. Web Site: www.jchs.org. *Dir*, Daivd W Jackson; E-Mail: djackson@jchs.org; *Archivist*, Janet Russell; E-Mail: jrussell@jchs.org. Subject Specialists: *Jackson County, Mo hist*, Janet Russell; *Jackson County, Mo hist*, Daivd W Jackson; Staff 2 (Non-MLS 2)
Founded 1960
Library Holdings: Bk Titles 1,500; Per Subs 10
Subject Interests: Jackson County, Mo hist, Missouri hist
Publications: The Jackson County Historical Society Journal (Newsletter)
Restriction: Not a lending library, Public use on premises
Function: Archival collection

P MID-CONTINENT PUBLIC LIBRARY, 15616 E 24 Hwy, 64050. SAN 349-1161. Tel: 816-836-5200. FAX: 816-521-7253. E-Mail: info@mcpl.lib.mo.us. Web Site: www.mcpl.lib.mo.us. *Dir*, Paul A White; *Asst Dir*, Richard Wilding; *ILL*, Barbara Mull; *Acq, Purchasing*, Cindy Coburn; *Ch Servs*, Anitra Steele; *Media Spec*, Billy Windes; *Tech Servs*, Judith Listrom; *Bibliog Instr, Online Servs, Ref*, Martha Lear; *Commun Servs*, Bill Deacon; *Rare Bks*, Martha Henderson; *Br Coordr*, John Martin; *Br Coordr*, Steve Potter; *Automation Syst Coordr*, Todd Caviness; *Ad Servs*, Marlene Boggs; Staff 27 (MLS 27)
Founded 1965. Pop 582,063; Circ 7,348,198
Jul 2000-Jun 2001 Income (Main Library and Branch Library) $26,223,117, State $396,599, Federal $139,727, County $25,115,958, Locally Generated Income $570,833. Mats Exp $6,443,000, Books $4,400,000, Per/Ser (Incl. Access Fees) $360,000, Presv $60,000, Micro $190,000, AV Equip $800,000, Electronic Ref Mat (Incl. Access Fees) $633,000. Sal $13,937,286
Library Holdings: Bk Vols 2,730,138; Bk Titles 566,431; Per Subs 5,994; High Interest/Low Vocabulary Bk Vols 6,965
Special Collections: Handicapped Coll, bks, AV, toys, puzzles; Missouriana & Genealogy Coll; United States Census Coll, micro
Automation Activity & Vendor Info: (Cataloging) Inlex; (Circulation) Inlex; (ILL) Inlex; (OPAC) Inlex
Partic in Kansas City Metropolitan Library & Information Network; Missouri Library Network Corporation; OCLC Online Computer Library Center, Inc
Special Services for the Deaf - Books on deafness & sign language; High interest/low vocabulary books; Special interest periodicals
Host Newsline for the Blind
Friends of the Library Group
Branches: 29
ANTIOCH BRANCH, 6060 N Chestnut Ave, Gladstone, 64119. SAN 349-1196. Tel: 816-454-1306. FAX: 816-454-7111. Web Site: www.mcpl.lib.mo.us. *Librn*, John Jasumback
BLUE RIDGE BRANCH, 9253 Blue Ridge Blvd, Kansas City, 64138. SAN 349-1765. Tel: 816-761-3382. FAX: 816-761-7074. Web Site: www.mcpl.lib.mo.us. *Librn*, Haile Geraldine; E-Mail: br_librarian@mcpl.lib.mo.us
Founded 1956
BLUE SPRINGS NORTH BRANCH, 850 NW Hunter Dr, Blue Springs, 64015. SAN 373-7195. Tel: 816-224-8772. FAX: 816-224-4723. Web Site: www.mcpl.lib.mo.us. *Librn*, Terri Clark
BLUE SPRINGS SOUTH BRANCH, 2220 South West St, Rte 7, Blue Springs, 64014. SAN 349-1226. Tel: 816-229-3571. FAX: 816-224-2078. Web Site: www.mcpl.lib.mo.us. *Librn*, Amy Davis
BOARDWALK BRANCH, 8600 N Ambassador Dr, Kansas City, 64154. SAN 375-5681. Tel: 816-741-9011. FAX: 816-741-4793. Web Site: www.mcpl.lib.mo.us. *Librn*, Mary Celeste
BUCKNER BRANCH, 19 E Jefferson St, Buckner, 64016. SAN 349-1250. Tel: 816-650-3212. FAX: 816-650-3212. Web Site: www.mcpl.lib.mo.us. *Librn*, Marybeth Hopper
CAMDEN POINT BRANCH, 401 Hardesty St, PO Box 127, Camden Point, 64018. SAN 349-1285. Tel: 816-280-3384. FAX: 816-280-3384. Web Site: www.mcpl.lib.mo.us. *Librn*, Wanda Campbell
CLAYCOMO BRANCH, 309 E US Hwy 69, Claycomo, 64119. SAN 373-7209. Tel: 816-455-5030. FAX: 816-455-5030. Web Site: www.mcpl.lib.mo.us. *Librn*, Pat Bogue
COLBERN ROAD BRANCH, 1000 NE Colbern Rd, Lee's Summit, 64086. SAN 373-7217. Tel: 816-525-9924. FAX: 816-525-3682. Web Site: www.mcpl.lib.mo.us. *Librn*, Gayla Spurlock
DEARBORN BRANCH, 206 Maple Leaf St, Dearborn, 64439. SAN 349-1315. Tel: 816-450-3502. FAX: 816-450-3502. Web Site: www.mcpl.lib.mo.us. *Librn*, Juanita Davidson
EDGERTON BRANCH, 404 Frank St, PO Box 109, Edgerton, 64444. SAN 349-134X. Tel: 816-790-3569. FAX: 816-790-3569. Web Site: www.mcpl.lib.mo.us. *Librn*, Myrna Weese
EXCELSIOR SPRINGS BRANCH, 1460 Kearney Rd, Excelsior Springs, 64024. SAN 349-1374. Tel: 816-630-6721. FAX: 816-630-5021. Web Site: www.mcpl.lib.mo.us. *Librn*, Kirsten Grubbs
GRAIN VALLEY BRANCH, 110 Front St, Grain Valley, 64029. SAN 349-1439. Tel: 816-228-4020. FAX: 816-228-4020. Web Site: www.mcpl.lib.mo.us. *Librn*, Mary Reeder
GRANDVIEW BRANCH, 12930 Booth Lane, Grandview, 64030. SAN 349-1463. Tel: 816-763-0550. FAX: 816-763-3924. Web Site: www.mcpl.lib.mo.us. *Librn*, Linda Tarantino
KEARNEY BRANCH, 100 S Platte-Clay Way, PO Box 1149, Kearney, 64060. SAN 349-1498. Tel: 816-628-5055. FAX: 816-628-5055. Web Site: www.mcpl.lib.mo.us. *Librn*, Marian Hurtubise
LEE'S SUMMIT BRANCH, 150 NW Oldham Pkwy, Lee's Summit, 64081. SAN 349-1528. Tel: 816-524-0567. FAX: 816-246-5342. Web Site: www.mcpl.lib.mo.us. *Librn*, Vicky Baker
LIBERTY BRANCH, 1000 Kent St, Liberty, 64068. SAN 349-1536. Tel: 816-781-9240. FAX: 816-781-5119. Web Site: www.mcpl.lib.mo.us. *Librn*, Janet Heitzman Smith
LONE JACK BRANCH, 211 N Bynum Rd, Lone Jack, 64070. SAN 326-8365. Tel: 816-697-2528. FAX: 816-697-2528. Web Site: www.mcpl.lib.mo.us. *Librn*, Kathy Dunson
NORTH INDEPENDENCE BRANCH, 317 W US Hwy 24, 64050. SAN 349-1552. Tel: 816-252-0950. FAX: 816-252-0950. Web Site: www.mcpl.lib.mo.us. *Librn*, Peggy Henry
NORTH OAK BRANCH, 8700 N Oak Trafficway, Kansas City, 64155. SAN 349-1404. Tel: 816-436-4385. FAX: 816-436-1946. Web Site: www.mcpl.lib.mo.us. *Librn*, Betty Johnson
OAK GROVE BRANCH, 2320 S Broadway, Oak Grove, 64075. SAN 349-1587. Tel: 816-690-3213. FAX: 816-690-3213. Web Site:

www.mcpl.lib.mo.us. *Librn*, Pam Bishop
PARKVILLE BRANCH, 8815 NW 45 Hwy, Parkville, 64152. SAN 373-7225. Tel: 816-741-4721. FAX: 816-741-6215. Web Site: www.mcpl.lib.mo.us. *Librn*, Amy Fisher
PLATTE CITY BRANCH, 412 Main St, Platte City, 64079. SAN 349-1617. Tel: 816-858-2322. FAX: 816-858-2322. Web Site: www.mcpl.lib.mo.us. *Librn*, Karen Dwight
RAYTOWN BRANCH, 6131 Raytown Rd, Raytown, 64133. SAN 349-1676. Tel: 816-353-2052. FAX: 816-353-5518. Web Site: www.mcpl.lib.mo.us. *Librn*, Susan Haley
RED BRIDGE BRANCH, 11140 Locust St, Kansas City, 64131. SAN 349-1706. Tel: 816-942-1780. FAX: 816-942-2657. Web Site: www.mcpl.lib.mo.us. *Librn*, Kevin Zeller
RIVERSIDE BRANCH, 2700 NW Vivion Rd, Riverside, 64150. SAN 349-1730. Tel: 816-741-6288. FAX: 816-741-8596. Web Site: www.mcpl.lib.mo.us. *Librn*, Patrice Nollette
SMITHVILLE BRANCH, 205 Richardson St, PO Box 424, Smithville, 64089. SAN 349-179X. Tel: 816-532-0116. FAX: 816-532-0116. Web Site: www.mcpl.lib.mo.us. *Librn*, Shari Ellison
SOUTH INDEPENDENCE BRANCH, 13700 E 35th St S, 64055. SAN 349-182X. Tel: 816-461-2050. FAX: 816-461-4759. Web Site: www.mcpl.lib.mo.us. *Librn*, Steven Campbell
WESTON BRANCH, 18204 Library Dr, PO Box 517, Weston, 64098. SAN 349-1889. Tel: 816-640-2874. FAX: 816-640-2874. Web Site: www.mcpl.lib.mo.us. *Librn*, Susan Fedrizzi

S NATIONAL ARCHIVES & RECORDS ADMINISTRATION, Harry S Truman Library, US Hwy 24 & Delaware, 64050. SAN 309-0035. Tel: 816-833-1400. Toll Free Tel: 800-833-1225. FAX: 816-833-4368. E-Mail: library@truman.nara.gov. Web Site: www.trumanlibrary.org. *Dep Dir*, Scott Roley; E-Mail: scroley@truman.nara.gov
Founded 1957
Library Holdings: Bk Vols 38,329
Subject Interests: Admin of President Harry S Truman, Career
Special Collections: Papers of Harry S Truman & 400 Other Individuals
Publications: Guide to Historical Materials in the Truman Library (1995)
Friends of the Library Group

S NATIONAL ASSOCIATION OF PARLIAMENTARIANS, 213 S Main St, 64050-3850. SAN 325-5964. Tel: 816-833-3892. Toll Free Tel: 888-NAP-2929. FAX: 816-833-3413, 816-833-3893. E-Mail: nap2@prodigy.net. Web Site: www.parliamentarians.org. *Exec Dir*, Sarah Nieft
Founded 1930
Subject Interests: Parliamentary procedure
Restriction: Members only

SR REORGANIZED CHURCH OF JESUS CHRIST OF LATTER DAY SAINTS LIBRARY, 201 N River, 64051. (Mail add: PO Box 1059, 64051), SAN 349-1919. Tel: 816-833-1000, Ext 2400. Toll Free Tel: 800-825-2806, Ext 2400. FAX: 816-521-3089. E-Mail: rlds_ill@kcpl.lib.mo.us. Web Site: www.rlds.org. *Dir*, Suzanne McDonald; Tel: 816-833-1000, Ext 2399, E-Mail: smcdonald@rlds.org; *Archivist*, Ron Romig; *Asst Librn*, Beverly Ann Spring; Tel: 816-833-1000, Ext 2401, E-Mail: bsprings@rlds.org; Staff 2 (MLS 1, Non-MLS 1)
Founded 1865
Library Holdings: Bk Vols 15,980; Bk Titles 20,000; Per Subs 150
Subject Interests: Christianity, Mormon (Latter Day Saints) hist, Mormon (Latter Day Saints) theol, Peace studies
Special Collections: Book of Mormon, mss; Early Origins of the Mormon Church; Herald Publishing House Publications; Histories of States Related to Latter Day Saints Movement; Inspired Version of the Bible; Latter Day Saints History and Theology, archives, foreign language scriptures, Herald House Preservation, pamphlets,vault, unpublished, audios and videos; Latter Day Saints Pamphlets; Reorganized Church of Jesus Christ of Latter Day Saints, journals, papers, photog & rec
Database Vendor: OCLC - First Search, ProQuest
Partic in Kansas City Metropolitan Library & Information Network
Branches:
AUDIO-VISUAL

IRONTON

P OZARK REGIONAL LIBRARY, 402 N Main St, 63650. SAN 349-1978. Tel: 573-546-2615. FAX: 573-546-7225. *Dir*, John F Mertens; *Ch Servs*, Patricia Cooper; *Ref*, Dan Roberts; Staff 18 (MLS 4, Non-MLS 14)
Founded 1947. Pop 55,987; Circ 182,814
Jan 2000-Dec 2000 Income (Main Library and Branch Library) $709,624, State $36,133, County $592,224, Locally Generated Income $28,928, Other $52,339. Mats Exp $115,207, Books $96,406, Per/Ser (Incl. Access Fees) $6,969, AV Equip $5,080, Electronic Ref Mat (Incl. Access Fees) $6,752. Sal $328,960 (Prof $113,212)
Library Holdings: Bk Vols 128,408; Bk Titles 73,053; Per Subs 303
Special Collections: Eastern US Genealogy (Floyd Coll)
Database Vendor: OCLC - First Search
Branches: 8
ANNAPOLIS BRANCH, School St, Annapolis, 63620. SAN 349-2001. *Librn*, Charlotte Brown
Library Holdings: Bk Vols 3,852
BOURBON BRANCH, 575 Elm, Bourbon, 65441. SAN 349-2036. Tel: 573-732-5313. *Librn*, Elizabeth Miller
Library Holdings: Bk Vols 8,989
FREDERICKTOWN BRANCH, 137 W Main St, Fredericktown, 63645. SAN 349-2060. Tel: 573-783-2120. *Librn*, Deborah Anderson
Library Holdings: Bk Vols 15,409
IRONTON BRANCH, 402 N Main St, 63650. SAN 349-2095. Tel: 573-546-2615. *Librn*, John F Mertens
Library Holdings: Bk Vols 37,238
RECKLEIN MEMORIAL, 305 N Smith St, Cuba, 65453. SAN 349-2125. Tel: 573-885-3431. *Librn*, Imogene Bowers
Library Holdings: Bk Vols 10,273
SAINTE GENEVIEVE BRANCH, 21388 Hwy 32, Sainte Genevieve, 63670. (Mail add: PO Box 386, Sainte Genevieve, 63670-0386), SAN 349-215X. Tel: 573-883-3358. *Librn*, Mae Elder
Library Holdings: Bk Vols 30,818
Friends of the Library Group
STEELVILLE BRANCH, 107 Third St, Steelville, 65565. (Mail add: PO Box 266, Steelville, 65565-0266), SAN 349-2184. Tel: 573-775-2338. *Librn*, Rosemary Kehr
Library Holdings: Bk Vols 17,977
VIBURNUM BRANCH, City Hall Missouri Ave, Viburnum, 65566. (Mail add: PO Box 33, Viburnum, 65566-0033), SAN 349-2214. Tel: 573-244-5986. *Librn*, Kathryn Snyder
Library Holdings: Bk Vols 3,852
Bookmobiles: 1

JACKSON

P JACKSON PUBLIC LIBRARY,* 100 N Missouri St, 63755-2024. SAN 309-0051. Tel: 573-243-5150. FAX: 573-243-8292. E-Mail: jxk000@mail.connect.more.net. *Librn*, Sally K Pierce
Founded 1926. Pop 9,256; Circ 31,531
Library Holdings: Bk Vols 30,000; Per Subs 106
Subject Interests: Genealogy
Special Collections: Missouri Coll

P RIVERSIDE REGIONAL LIBRARY,* 204 S Union Ave, PO Box 389, 63755-0389. SAN 349-2249. Tel: 573-243-8141. FAX: 573-243-8142. Web Site: www.showme.net/rrl. *In Charge*, Paula Gresham-Bequette
Founded 1955. Circ 265,948
Library Holdings: Bk Vols 134,644; Per Subs 135
Subject Interests: Genealogy for local families
Special Collections: Large Print
Friends of the Library Group
Branches: 5
ALTENBURG BRANCH, 66 Poplar St, PO Box 32, Altenburg, 63732. SAN 349-2362. Tel: 573-824-5267. FAX: 573-824-5267. Web Site: www.showme.net/rrl. *Librn*, Kathleen Schlimpert
Library Holdings: Bk Titles 13,214
Friends of the Library Group
BENTON BRANCH, 44 N Winchester, PO Box 108, Benton, 63736. SAN 349-2303. Tel: 573-545-3581. FAX: 573-545-3581. Web Site: www.showme.net/rrl. *Librn*, Bernice Kern
Library Holdings: Bk Titles 11,213
Friends of the Library Group
ORAN BRANCH, 120 Mountain St, PO Box 298, Oran, 63771. SAN 328-8447. Tel: 573-262-3745. FAX: 573-262-3745. Web Site: www.showme.net/rrl. *Librn*, Virginia Robert
Library Holdings: Bk Titles 9,757
Friends of the Library Group
PERRYVILLE BRANCH, 800 City Park Dr. Ste A, Perryville, 63775. SAN 349-2338. Tel: 573-547-6508. FAX: 573-547-3715. Web Site: www.showme.net/rrl. *Librn*, Julie Sauer
Library Holdings: Bk Titles 61,238
Friends of the Library Group
SCOTT CITY BRANCH, 2016 Main St, Scott City, 63780. SAN 349-2273. Tel: 573-264-2413. FAX: 573-264-2413. Web Site: www.showme.net/rrl. *Librn*, Glenda Kenkel
Library Holdings: Bk Titles 22,197
Friends of the Library Group

JEFFERSON CITY

GL COMMITTEE ON LEGISLATIVE RESEARCH, Legislative Library, State Capitol Bldg, 117A, 65101. SAN 309-0086. Tel: 573-751-4633. FAX: 573-751-0130. *Librn*, Anne G Rottmann; Staff 3 (MLS 1, Non-MLS 2)
Founded 1943
Library Holdings: Bk Vols 5,200; Per Subs 125
Special Collections: Missouri Bills, 1909 to date; Missouri House & Senate Journals, 1837 to date; Missouri Laws, Territorial days to date

C LINCOLN UNIVERSITY, Inman E Page Library, 820 Chestnut St, 65102-0029. SAN 309-006X. Tel: 573-681-5000, 573-681-5512. FAX: 573-681-5511. Web Site: www.arthur.missouri.edu. *Librn*, Elizabeth A Wilson; *Cat, Tech Servs*, Inas El-Sayed; *Per*, Connie May; *Media Spec*, Katrina Blau;

Staff 7 (MLS 7)
Founded 1866. Enrl 4,100; Fac 154; Highest Degree: Master
Library Holdings: Bk Vols 175,696; Per Subs 607
Special Collections: Ethnic Studies Center Coll
Publications: Bibliography of Books by and About Blacks
Partic in MLNC; OCLC Online Computer Library Center, Inc
Friends of the Library Group

S MISSOURI DEPARTMENT OF CORRECTIONS OFFENDER LIBRARIES, 2729 Plaza Dr, PO Box 236, 65102-0236. SAN 349-2540. Tel: 573-522-1928. FAX: 573-751-4099. *Coordr*, Margaret Booker; E-Mail: mbooker@mail.doc.state.mo.us; Staff 26 (MLS 5, Non-MLS 21)
Subject Interests: Civil rights, General, Law
Restriction: Internal circulation only
Function: Photocopies available, Reference services available
Branches:
ALGOA CORRECTIONAL CENTER, Fenceline Rd, PO Box 528, 65102-0538. Tel: 573-751-3911, Ext 243. FAX: 573-751-7375.; Staff 1 (Non-MLS 1)
BOONVILLE CORRECTIONAL CENTER, E Morgan St, PO Box 379, Boonville, 65233-0379. SAN 349-2575. Tel: 660-882-6521, Ext 346. FAX: 660-882-7825. *Librn*, Terri Lucas; *Librn*, Connie Bowman; Staff 2 (MLS 1, Non-MLS 1)
CENTRAL MISSOURI CORRECTIONAL CENTER, Rte 1 Hwy 179, PO Box 539, 65102-0539. Tel: 573-751-2053, Ext 254. FAX: 573-751-9037.; Staff 1 (Non-MLS 1)
CHILLICOTHE CORRECTIONAL CENTER-HYDE SCHOOL LIBRARY, 1500 W Third St, Chillicothe, 64601-2079. Tel: 660-646-4032, Ext 275. FAX: 660-646-1217.; Staff 1 (Non-MLS 1)
CROSSROADS CORRECTIONAL CENTER, 1115 E Pence Rd, Cameron, 64429-8804. Tel: 816-632-2727, Ext 285. FAX: 816-632-5249.; Staff 2 (Non-MLS 2)
FARMINGTON CORRECTIONAL CENTER, 1012 W Columbia St, Farmington, 63640-2902. SAN 377-1091. Tel: 573-756-8001, Ext 346. FAX: 573-756-4354. *Librn*, Wanda M Kreitler; Staff 1 (Non-MLS 1)
Library Holdings: Bk Vols 11,914; Per Subs 61
FULTON RECEPTION & DIAGNOSTIC CENTER, PO Box 190, Fulton, 65251-0190. Tel: 573-592-4040. FAX: 573-592-4020.; Staff 1 (Non-MLS 1)
JEFFERSON CITY CORRECTIONAL CENTER, 631 State St, PO Box 597, 65102-0597. SAN 349-263X. Tel: 573-751-3224, Ext 511. FAX: 573-751-0355. *Librn*, Robyn Combs; Staff 1 (Non-MLS 1)
MARYVILLE TREATMENT CENTER, 30227 US Hwy 136, Maryville, 64468. Tel: 660-582-6542. FAX: 660-582-8071.; Staff 2 (MLS 1, Non-MLS 1)
MISSOURI EASTERN CORRECTIONAL CENTER, 18701 US Hwy 66, Pacific, 63069-3525. SAN 329-9171. Tel: 636-257-3322, Ext 219. FAX: 636-257-5296. *Librn*, Mary Merseal; Staff 1 (Non-MLS 1)
Founded 1981. Enrl 11,000; Highest Degree: Bachelor
Library Holdings: Bk Vols 21,000; Bk Titles 17,800; Per Subs 60
Special Collections: Afro-American Coll
Publications: Freedom at last ... (guide for prisoners who are ready for parole); MECC Bookworm (monthly classified list of accessions); The Past Year (annual report); Unto Light ... (guide for users)
Special Services for the Deaf - Books on deafness & sign language; High interest/low vocabulary books
MOBERLY CORRECTIONAL CENTER, PO Box 7, Moberly, 65270-0007. Tel: 660-263-3778, Ext 421. FAX: 660-263-1730.; Staff 2 (Non-MLS 2)
NORTHEAST CORRECTIONAL CENTER, 13698 Pike 46 Airport Rd, Bowling Green, 63334. Tel: 573-324-9975. FAX: 573-324-5028.; Staff 2 (Non-MLS 2)
OZARK CORRECTIONAL CENTER, 929 Honor Camp Lane, Fordland, 65652-9700. Tel: 417-767-4491. FAX: 417-738-2400.; Staff 1 (Non-MLS 1)
POTOSI CORRECTIONAL CENTER, Rte 2, Box 2222, Mineral Point, 63660-9600. Tel: 573-438-6000, Ext 560. FAX: 573-438-6006.; Staff 2 (Non-MLS 2)
SOUTH CENTRAL CORRECTIONAL CENTER, 255 W Hwy 32, Licking, 65542. Tel: 573-674-4470. FAX: 573-674-3899.; Staff 2 (Non-MLS 2)
TIPTON CORRECTIONAL CENTER, 619 N Osage Ave, Tipton, 65081-8038. Tel: 660-433-2031, Ext 2325. FAX: 660-433-2804. *Librn*, Kimberly Bresnahan; Staff 2 (MLS 1, Non-MLS 1)
WESTERN MISSOURI CORRECTIONAL CENTER, 609 E Pence Rd, Cameron, 64429-8823. SAN 372-5758. Tel: 816-632-1390, Ext 421. FAX: 816-632-7882. *Librn*, Norma Beck; Staff 1 (Non-MLS 1)
Library Holdings: Bk Titles 17,000; Per Subs 55
WESTERN RECEPTION & DIAGNOSTIC CORRECTIONAL CENTER, 3502 Frederick, Saint Joseph, 64506. Tel: 816-387-2158. FAX: 816-387-2217.; Staff 1 (Non-MLS 1)
WOMEN'S EASTERN RECEPTION & DIAGNOSTIC CORRECTIONAL CENTER, PO Box 300, Vandalia, 63382-0300. Tel: 573-594-6686. FAX: 573-594-6789.; Staff 2 (MLS 1, Non-MLS 1)

G MISSOURI DEPARTMENT OF ECONOMIC DEVELOPMENT, Research Library,* 301 W High Truman Bldg, PO Box 118, 65102. SAN 327-0106. Tel: 573-751-3674. FAX: 573-751-7385. *Res*, Gary Beahan
Library Holdings: Bk Vols 950
Publications: Economic reports; Newsletter
Restriction: By appointment only

P MISSOURI RIVER REGIONAL, 214 Adams St, 65101. (Mail add: PO Box 89, 65102), SAN 349-2427. Tel: 573-634-2464. Toll Free Tel: 800-949-7323. FAX: 573-634-7028. E-Mail: mrrl@mrrl.org. Web Site: www.mrrl.org. *Dir*, Margaret Conroy; Tel: 573-634-6064, Ext 234, E-Mail: conroym@mrrl.org; *Asst Dir*, Betty Hagenhoff; Tel: 573-634-6064, Ext 249, E-Mail: hagenhoffb@mrrl.org; *Syst Coordr*, Michael Howard; Tel: 573-634-6064, Ext 257, E-Mail: howardm@mrrl.org; *Tech Servs*, Natasha Grando; Tel: 573-634-6064, Ext 232, E-Mail: grandon@mrrl.org; *Ch Servs*, Ruth Ann Stratman; Tel: 573-634-6064, Ext 229, E-Mail: stratmanr@mrrl.org; *Coll Develop*, Claudia Schoonover; Tel: 573-634-6064, Ext 245, E-Mail: schoonoverc@mrrl.org; *Publ Servs*, George Dillard; Tel: 573-634-6064, Ext 250; *Commun Relations*, Mary Schlueter; Tel: 573-634-6064, Ext 261, E-Mail: schlueterm@mrrl.org; *Outreach Serv*, Margaret Snow; Tel: 573-634-6064, Ext 248, E-Mail: snowm@mrrl.org; *Automation Syst Coordr*, Michael Washburn; Tel: 573-634-6064, Ext 241, E-Mail: washburnm@mrrl.org; *Circ*, Jessica Wieberg; Tel: 573-634-6064, Ext 223, E-Mail: wiebergj@mrrl.org; Staff 45 (MLS 8, Non-MLS 37)
Founded 1994. Pop 81,343; Circ 483,876
Jan 1999-Dec 1999 Income (Main Library and Branch Library) $2,070,545, State $35,471, Federal $31,651, County $1,844,268, Locally Generated Income $158,655. Mats Exp $354,680, Books $247,054, Per/Ser (Incl. Access Fees) $24,370, Presv $272, Micro $3,204, AV Equip $54,578, Electronic Ref Mat (Incl. Access Fees) $25,202. Sal $1,081,763
Library Holdings: Bk Vols 192,133; Per Subs 414; High Interest/Low Vocabulary Bk Vols 100; Bks on Deafness & Sign Lang 12
Subject Interests: Local history, Mo hist
Automation Activity & Vendor Info: (Acquisitions) DRA; (Cataloging) DRA; (Circulation) DRA; (ILL) DRA; (OPAC) DRA; (Serials) DRA
Database Vendor: DRA, Ebsco - EbscoHost, GaleNet, IAC - Info Trac, ProQuest
Publications: MRRLIN (bimonthly newsletter)
Open Mon-Thurs 9-9, Fri & Sat 9-5, Sun 1-5
Branches: 1
OSAGE COUNTY, 401 Main St, Linn, 65051. (Mail add: PO Box 349, Linn, 65051), SAN 378-2468. Tel: 573-897-2951. FAX: 573-897-3815. E-Mail: mrrl@mrrl.org. Web Site: www.mrrl.org. *Branch Mgr*, Jan Crow; E-Mail: crowj@mrrl.org; *Asst Dir*, Betty Hagenhoff; Tel: 573-634-6064, Ext 249, Fax: 573-634-7028, E-Mail: hagenhoffb@mrrl.org
Founded 1994
Bookmobiles: 2

P MISSOURI STATE LIBRARY, (MOSL), 600 W Main, PO Box 387, 65102. (Mail add: PO Box 387, 65102), SAN 309-0094. Tel: 573-751-3615. Interlibrary Loan Service Tel: 573-751-2696. Toll Free Tel: 800-325-0131. FAX: 573-751-3612. E-Mail: libref@mail.more.net. Web Site: mosl.sos.state.mo.us/lib-ser/libser.html. *State Librn*, Sara Parker; Tel: 573-751-2751, E-Mail: parkes@sos.mail.state.mo.us; *Govt Doc*, John Finley; Tel: 573-751-3075, E-Mail: finlej@sos.mail.state.mo.us; Staff 55 (MLS 18, Non-MLS 37)
Founded 1907
Jul 1999-Jun 2000 Income $7,995,649, State $5,023,448, Federal $2,972,201. Mats Exp Books $311,213. Sal $1,669,293
Library Holdings: Bk Vols 77,189; Per Subs 486
Subject Interests: State government
Special Collections: Library for the Blind & Physically Handicapped (braille, cassettes & records)
Publications: Directory of Missouri Libraries; Info to Go; Missouri Library World; Missouri State Government Publications; Newsline; Wolfner Library News
Friends of the Library Group

P MISSOURI STATE LIBRARY, Wolfner Library for the Blind & Physically Handicapped, 600 W Main St, PO Box 387, 65102-0387. SAN 309-2216. Tel: 573-751-8720. Toll Free Tel: 800-392-2614. TDD: 800-347-1379. FAX: 573-526-2985. *State Librn*, Sara Parker; E-Mail: parker@sosmail.state.mo.us
Founded 1924. Pop 16,372; Circ 506,100
Jul 1998-Jun 1999 Income $726,644. Mats Exp $211,929. Sal $399,678
Library Holdings: Bk Vols 321,832; Per Subs 70
Database Vendor: DRA
Publications: Newsletter (quarterly)
Special Services for the Deaf - TDD
Friends of the Library Group

GL MISSOURI SUPREME COURT LIBRARY, Supreme Court Bldg, 207 W High St, 65101. SAN 309-0108. Tel: 573-751-2636. FAX: 573-751-2573. *Librn*, Tyronne M Allen; Staff 5 (MLS 2, Non-MLS 3)
Founded 1820
Library Holdings: Bk Vols 110,000; Per Subs 180
Partic in Mead Data Cent

G OFFICE OF SECRETARY OF STATE, Missouri State Archives,* 600 W Main. (Mail add: PO Box 778, 65102), SAN 371-5655. Tel: 573-751-3280, 573-751-4217. FAX: 573-526-7333. E-Mail: archref@mail.sos.state.mo.us. Web Site: mosl.sos.stste.mo.us/rec_man/arch.html. *Archivist*, Kenneth H

Winn; *Archivist*, Shelly J Croteau; *Archivist*, Patricia Luebbert; *Archivist*, Christyn Elley; *Archivist*, Laura Jolley; *Archivist*, Joanna Perkins; Staff 12 (MLS 9, Non-MLS 3)
Founded 1965
Jul 1997-Jun 1998 Income $565,000. Mats Exp $95,000. Sal $435,000
Library Holdings: Bk Vols 6,600; Bk Titles 6,300; Per Subs 6
Special Collections: French & Spanish Land Records; Governor's Papers; Land Records; Local Records; Manuscript Coll; Missouri Military Records; State Documents; State Records
Publications: Annual Report; Guide to County Records on Microfilm; Resources for Family & Community History; The Record; Tracing Your Roots
Open Mon-Wed & Fri 8-5, Thurs 8am-9pm, Sat 8:30-3:30
Friends of the Library Group

JOPLIN

P JOPLIN PUBLIC LIBRARY, 300 S Main, 64801. SAN 309-0116. Tel: 417-623-7953. Reference Tel: 417-624-5465. FAX: 417-624-5217. E-Mail: hzz004@mail.connect.more.net. Web Site: www.mlnc.com/~jpl/. *Dir*, Carolyn Trout; *Ch Servs*, Jennifer McQuilkin; *Ref*, Patty Crane; *Cat, Tech Servs*, Phyllis Seesengood; *Automation Syst Coordr*, Linda Cannon; Staff 34 (MLS 6, Non-MLS 28)
Founded 1902. Pop 43,693; Circ 368,562
Nov 1999-Oct 2000 Income $1,254,683. Mats Exp $160,800. Sal $465,500
Library Holdings: Bk Vols 96,120; Bk Titles 75,221; Per Subs 253
Special Collections: Fine & Decorative Arts (Winfred L & Elizabeth C Post Memorial Art Reference Library); Genealogy Coll
Automation Activity & Vendor Info: (Acquisitions) epixtech, inc.; (Cataloging) epixtech, inc.; (Circulation) epixtech, inc.; (OPAC) epixtech, inc.; (Serials) epixtech, inc.
Database Vendor: Ebsco - EbscoHost, epixtech, inc., OCLC - First Search
Partic in Missouri Library Network Corporation; SW Mo Libr Network

C MISSOURI SOUTHERN STATE COLLEGE, George A Spiva Library, 3950 E Newman Rd, 64801-1595. SAN 309-0132. Tel: 417-625-9362, 417-625-9703. FAX: 417-625-9734. E-Mail: kemp-c@mail.mssc.edu. Web Site: www.mssc.edu. *Dir*, Charles H Kemp; Tel: 417-625-9386; *Circ, ILL*, Gaye Pate; Tel: 417-625-9362; *Online Servs*, Robert Black; *Archivist*, Charles E Nodler; *AV, Govt Doc*, Edward Wuch; *Ref*, Wendy McGrane; Staff 7 (MLS 7)
Founded 1937. Enrl 4,051; Fac 250; Highest Degree: Bachelor
Library Holdings: Bk Vols 264,038; Per Subs 1,234
Subject Interests: Education, Nursing
Special Collections: Arrell Morgan Gibson Coll; Gene Taylor Congressional papers; Tri-State Mining Maps
Automation Activity & Vendor Info: (Acquisitions) NOTIS; (Cataloging) NOTIS; (Circulation) NOTIS; (Serials) NOTIS
Publications: Southern Footnotes (newsletter)
Partic in Missouri Library Network Corporation
Friends of the Library Group

C OZARK CHRISTIAN COLLEGE, Seth Wilson Library, 1111 N Main, 64801-4804. SAN 309-0140. Tel: 417-624-2518, Ext 2708. Interlibrary Loan Service Tel: 417-624-2518-2724. Circulation Tel: 417-624-2518, Ext 2700. Reference Tel: 417-624-2518, Ext 2724. FAX: 417-624-0090. E-Mail: library@occ.edu. Web Site: occ.library.net. *Dir*, Dr William F Abernathy; E-Mail: libman@occ.edu; *Coll Develop*, Mark Sloneker; Tel: 417-624-2518, Ext 2713, E-Mail: msloneker@occ.edu; Staff 2 (MLS 2)
Founded 1942. Enrl 750; Highest Degree: Bachelor
Jul 1999-Jun 2000 Income $19,295. Mats Exp $96,592, Books $65,273, Per/Ser (Incl. Access Fees) $10,214, Presv $5,841, AV Equip $592, Other Print Mats $2,069, Electronic Ref Mat (Incl. Access Fees) $12,603. Sal $173,962
Library Holdings: Bk Vols 54,881; Bk Titles 43,331; Per Subs 366; Bks on Deafness & Sign Lang 50
Subject Interests: Archaeology, Biblical studies
Special Collections: Restoration Movement (Christianity)
Automation Activity & Vendor Info: (Acquisitions) Sagebrush Corporation; (Cataloging) TLC; (Circulation) TLC; (Course Reserve) TLC; (Media Booking) TLC; (OPAC) TLC; (Serials) Inmagic, Inc.
Database Vendor: Ebsco - EbscoHost, OCLC - First Search
Function: ILL available, Photocopies available, Reference services available
Partic in Asn of Christian Librs; MLNC

S WINFRED L & ELIZABETH C POST FOUNDATION, Post Memorial Art Reference Library, 300 Main St, 64801-2384. SAN 325-1756. Tel: 417-782-7678. FAX: 417-782-8802. Web Site: www.clandjop.com/~lsimpson/. *Dir*, Leslie T Simpson; Tel: 417-782-3733, E-Mail: lsimpson@clandjop.com. Subject Specialists: *Historic preservation*, Leslie T Simpson; Staff 2 (MLS 1, Non-MLS 1)
Founded 1981
Library Holdings: Bk Titles 3,800; Per Subs 30
Subject Interests: Antiques, Architecture, Calligraphy, Costumes, Decorative arts, Fine arts, Gardens, Heraldry, Historic preservation, Photog
Special Collections: Antique Furniture & Original Artwork Coll; art objects; Joplin Historic Architecture; Painting Reproductions; Photograph Coll; Yi Dynasty Reproductions
Restriction: Non-circulating
Function: For research purposes

KAHOKA

P NORTHEAST MISSOURI LIBRARY SERVICE,* 207 W Chestnut, 63445. SAN 349-2729. Tel: 660-727-2327. TDD: 660-727-3262. FAX: 660-727-2327. *Actg Dir*, Cathy James; Staff 13 (MLS 1, Non-MLS 12)
Founded 1961. Pop 26,498; Circ 137,000
Jan 1998-Dec 1999 Income $241,768, State $8,454. Mats Exp $44,126, Books $39,626, Per/Ser (Incl. Access Fees) $4,500. Sal $130,167
Library Holdings: Bk Vols 115,592; Bk Titles 105,228; Per Subs 43
Subject Interests: Genealogy
Special Collections: Large Print Material
Special Services for the Deaf - TDD
Friends of the Library Group
Branches: 5
H E SEVER MEMORIAL, 207 W Chestnut, 63445. SAN 349-2877. Tel: 660-727-3262. TDD: 660-727-3262. FAX: 660-727-2327. *Librn*, Peggy Haas
Library Holdings: Bk Vols 58,922; Bk Titles 53,765
Subject Interests: Medicine
Special Collections: Four County (Knox, Lewis, Clark, Schuyler) Histories & Genealogy Coll, micro; Large Print Materials
Special Services for the Deaf - TDD
Friends of the Library Group
KNOX COUNTY PUBLIC, 120 S Main St, Edina, 63537. SAN 349-2753. Tel: 660-397-2460. FAX: 660-397-2460. *Librn*, Marilyn Goodwin; E-Mail: marlawgood@hotmail.com
Pop 5,500
Library Holdings: Bk Titles 20,000
Special Services for the Blind - Large print bks; Talking Books
LEWIS COUNTY BRANCH-LABELLE, 425 State St, LaBelle, 63447. (Mail add: PO Box 34, LaBelle, 63447), SAN 349-2788. Tel: 660-213-3600. FAX: 660-462-3600. *Librn*, Ida Byers
Library Holdings: Bk Vols 10,632; Bk Titles 7,892
LEWIS COUNTY BRANCH-LAGRANGE, 1115 Main, PO Box 8, LaGrange, 63448. SAN 349-2818. Tel: 573-655-2288. FAX: 573-655-2288. *Librn*, Patricia Stambaugh
Library Holdings: Bk Vols 12,199; Bk Titles 10,032
SCHUYLER COUNTY, 1655 Main, PO Box 446, Lancaster, 63548. SAN 349-2842. Tel: 660-457-3731. FAX: 660-457-3731. *Librn*, Dianna Kinney
Library Holdings: Bk Vols 11,541; Bk Titles 9,903
Friends of the Library Group

KANSAS CITY

C AVILA COLLEGE, Hooley-Bundschu Library, 11901 Wornall Rd, 64145. SAN 309-0183. Tel: 816-501-3621. FAX: 816-501-2456. Web Site: www.avila.edu. *Dir*, Kathleen Finnegan; *Asst Librn*, Farrukh Hasan; E-Mail: hasan.fj@mail.avila.edu
Founded 1916. Enrl 1,500
Library Holdings: Bk Vols 70,000; Per Subs 500
Subject Interests: Nursing
Partic in Kansas City Libr Consortium; Kansas City Regional Council for Higher Education

M BAPTIST MEDICAL CENTER LIBRARY, 6601 Rockhill Rd, 64131. SAN 309-0191. Tel: 816-276-7863. FAX: 816-926-2265. E-Mail: penixon@healthmidwest.org. *Dir*, Paul E Nixon; Staff 2 (MLS 1, Non-MLS 1)
Founded 1972
Jan 2000-Dec 2000 Income $125,446, Parent Institution $87,646, Other $37,800. Mats Exp $57,790, Books $6,570, Per/Ser (Incl. Access Fees) $51,220. Sal $42,627
Library Holdings: Bk Vols 5,000; Bk Titles 2,400; Per Subs 224
Subject Interests: Allied health, Hospital administration, Medicine, Nursing
Special Collections: Sherry Morris Memorial Audio Library
Publications: Newsletter (bi-monthly)
Partic in Kansas City Metropolitan Library & Information Network

R BETH SHALOM CONGREGATION, Blanche & Ira Rosenblum Memorial Library, 9400 Wornall, 64114. SAN 309-0221. Tel: 816-361-2990, 816-363-3331. FAX: 816-361-4495. *Librn*, Frances Wolf; E-Mail: franwolf@sky.net
1998-1999 Mats Exp $1,000
Library Holdings: Bk Vols 9,500; Per Subs 20

L BLACKWELL, SANDERS, PEPER & MARTIN, Law Library,* 2300 Main St, Ste 1100, 64108. SAN 372-4719. Tel: 816-983-8791. FAX: 816-983-8080. *Librn*, Paula G Hilkemeyer; E-Mail: philkemeyer@bspmlaw.com
Library Holdings: Bk Vols 10,000; Per Subs 200

S BURNS & MCDONNELL ENGINEERING CO, Central Library,* 9400 Ward Pkwy, 64114. SAN 309-0248. Tel: 816-822-3550. FAX: 816-822-3412. E-Mail: library@burnsmcd.com. *Librn*, Gail Kammer; Staff 3 (MLS 1, Non-MLS 2)
Library Holdings: Bk Vols 40,000; Per Subs 200

Subject Interests: Mechanical engineering
Special Collections: Standards, Manufacturers' catalogs
Publications: Burns & McDonnell Central Library News
Partic in MLNC; OCLC Online Computer Library Center, Inc

CR CALVARY BIBLE COLLEGE THEOLOGICAL SEMINARY, Hilda Kroeker Library, 15800 Calvary Rd, 64147-1341. SAN 309-0264. Tel: 816-322-0110, Ext 1206, 816-322-5152. FAX: 816-331-4474. E-Mail: library@calvary.edu. Web Site: www.calgary.edu. *Assoc Librn*, Jann VanderMey; *Librn*, Lynn Spencer; Staff 1 (Non-MLS 1)
Founded 1932. Highest Degree: Master
Library Holdings: Bk Vols 59,000; Per Subs 100
Subject Interests: Education, History, Music
Publications: Calvary Review
Partic in Kansas City Libr Consortium

R CENTRAL PRESBYTERIAN CHURCH LIBRARY, 3501 Campbell, 64109. SAN 328-0926. Tel: 816-931-2515. FAX: 816-931-0882. *Librn*, Helen Gordon
Library Holdings: Bk Vols 5,500; Per Subs 12
Subject Interests: Presbyterianism, Religion

M CHILDREN'S MERCY HOSPITAL, Health Sciences Library, 2401 Gillham Rd, 64108. SAN 309-0272. Tel: 816-234-3800. FAX: 816-234-3125. *Librn*, Anne Palmer; Staff 3 (MLS 1, Non-MLS 2)
Founded 1914
Library Holdings: Bk Titles 5,000; Per Subs 325
Subject Interests: Pediatrics
Special Collections: Library of History of Pediatrics (William L Bradford, MD)
Partic in Docline; Health Sciences Library Network of Kansas City, Inc; OCLC Online Computer Library Center, Inc

S CHURCH OF THE NAZARENE, International Headquarters Resource Center - Sunday School Ministries Library, 6401 The Paseo, 64131. SAN 327-0122. Tel: 816-333-7000, Ext 2287 or 2497. FAX: 816-333-4439. *In Charge*, Terri Callison
Library Holdings: Bk Vols 6,000; Per Subs 80
Open Mon-Fri 8-4:30

S CITY PLANNING & DEVELOPMENT LIBRARY, City Hall, 414 E 12th St 15th flr, 64106. SAN 327-0181. Tel: 816-513-2818. FAX: 816-513-2808. *Librn*, Alma Lee
Library Holdings: Bk Vols 3,500; Bk Titles 4,000; Per Subs 65
Partic in American Planning Assoc; ICMT; Urban Land Institute

M CLEVELAND CHIROPRACTIC COLLEGE, Ruth R Cleveland Memorial Library, 6401 Rockhill Rd, 64131. SAN 324-7147. Tel: 816-501-0143. FAX: 816-501-0230. *Librn*, Marcia M Thomas; Staff 3 (MLS 1, Non-MLS 2)
Founded 1976. Enrl 400; Fac 45
Library Holdings: Bk Titles 11,600; Per Subs 261
Subject Interests: Acupuncture, Chiropractic, Nutrition, Orthopedics, Radiology
Special Collections: Chiropractic texts, journals
Publications: Library News (monthly); quarterly list of new books; Subject bibliographies
Partic in Health Sciences Library Network of Kansas City, Inc; Ontyme
Open Mon-Fri 7-5, Sat 9-1
Friends of the Library Group

GM DEPARTMENT OF VETERANS AFFAIRS MEDICAL LIBRARY,* 4801 E Linwood Blvd, 64128-2295. SAN 309-068X. Tel: 816-922-2315. FAX: 816-922-3340. *Dir*, Shirley Ting
Founded 1932
Library Holdings: Bk Vols 3,034; Per Subs 198
Subject Interests: Allied health, Medicine
Publications: Current New Acquistion Lists
Restriction: Medical staff only
Partic in Health Sciences Library Network of Kansas City, Inc; Midcontinental Regional Med Libr Program; Veterans Affairs Library Network

J DEVRY INSTITUTE OF TECHNOLOGY LIBRARY, 11224 Holmes Rd, 64131. SAN 309-0493. Tel: 816-941-0430, Ext 5220. Interlibrary Loan Service Tel: 816-941-0430, Ext 5395. Reference Tel: 816-941-0430, Ext 5392. FAX: 816-941-0896. E-Mail: library@kc.devry.edu. Web Site: www.kc.devry.edu. *Dir*, Colleen Kennedy; Tel: 816-941-0430, Ext 5490, E-Mail: ckennedy@kc.devry.edu; *Ref*, Jared Rinck; E-Mail: jrinck@kc.devry.edu; Staff 7 (MLS 2, Non-MLS 5)
Enrl 2,600; Fac 200; Highest Degree: Master
Library Holdings: Bk Vols 14,000; Bk Titles 13,500; Per Subs 40
Subject Interests: Business, Computer science, Electronics, Technology, Telecommunications
Automation Activity & Vendor Info: (Acquisitions) Endeavor; (Cataloging) Endeavor; (Circulation) Endeavor; (OPAC) Endeavor
Database Vendor: IAC - Info Trac, ProQuest
Partic in Kansas City Metropolitan Library & Information Network

S FEDERAL RESERVE BANK OF KANSAS CITY, Research Library, 925 Grand Blvd, 64198. (Mail add: PO Box 419560, 64141-6560), SAN 309-0345. Tel: 816-881-2970. FAX: 816-881-2807. E-Mail: research.library@kc.frb.org. *Librn*, Ellen M Johnson; Staff 5 (MLS 2, Non-MLS 3)
Library Holdings: Bk Vols 15,500
Subject Interests: Agriculture, Economics, Finance, Statistics
Restriction: Open to public for reference only
Partic in OCLC Online Computer Library Center, Inc

SR FIRST CALVARY BAPTIST CHURCH LIBRARY,* 3921 Baltimore, 64111. SAN 373-2355. Tel: 816-531-1208. FAX: 816-753-6307. *Librn*, Lola Tate
Library Holdings: Bk Vols 500; Per Subs 8

S LINDA HALL LIBRARY,* 5109 Cherry St, 64110. SAN 309-0353. Tel: 816-363-5020 (Admin). Reference Tel: 816-363-4600. FAX: 816-926-8785. Web Site: www.lhl.lib.mo.us. *Pres*, C Lee Jones; *Tech Servs*, James Huesmann; *Cat*, Julie Brinkman; *Ser*, Gail Van Auken; *ILL*, Kelly Pangrac; *Coll Develop*, Nancy Day. Subject Specialists: *History of science*, Bruce Bradley; Staff 67 (MLS 19, Non-MLS 48)
Founded 1946
Jan 1997-Dec 1998 Income $6,511,000, Locally Generated Income $900,000, Parent Institution $5,611,000. Mats Exp $2,397,000, Books $252,000, Per/Ser (Incl. Access Fees) $2,145,000. Sal $1,597,000
Library Holdings: Bk Vols 1,050,000; Per Subs 16,000
Subject Interests: Engineering
Special Collections: History of Science; NASA & DOE Tech Reports; Sci-Tech Conference Proceedings; Soviet & European Sci-Tech Publications; Standards & Specifications; US Patent & Trademark Specifications, maps, govt docs
Publications: Arbor Scientiae: A Guide to the Trees & Perennial Beds at Linda Hall Library; Various History of Science Exhibits Catalogs
Partic in Asn of Research Libraries; Big Twelve Plus Libr Consortium; Dialog Corporation; OCLC Online Computer Library Center, Inc; Research Libraries Group, Inc
An independent funded research library of science engineering & technology
Friends of the Library Group

S HALLMARK CARDS, INC, Creative Resource Library,* 2501 McGee No 146, 64108. SAN 349-2907. Tel: 816-274-7470. FAX: 816-274-7245. *In Charge*, Carol A Carr; Staff 4 (MLS 2, Non-MLS 2)
Founded 1930
Library Holdings: Bk Vols 20,000; Per Subs 175
Subject Interests: Fine arts
Special Collections: Andrew Szoeke Design Coll
Publications: Monthly Newsletter (new bks & upcoming events)
Branches:
BUSINESS RESEARCH LIBRARY, 2501 McGee No 203, 64108. SAN 349-2931. Tel: 816-274-4648. FAX: 816-274-7394. Web Site: www.hallmark.com. *Mgr*, Isidro Delaherran
LAW LIBRARY, 2501 McGee, No 339, 64108. SAN 372-4689. Tel: 816-274-5583, 816-274-8583. FAX: 816-274-7171.
Library Holdings: Bk Vols 12,000; Per Subs 20

M HEALTH MIDWEST RESEARCH MEDICAL CENTER, Carl R Ferris Medical Library, 2316 E Meyer Blvd, 64132-1199. SAN 309-0582. Tel: 816-276-4309. FAX: 816-276-3106.; Staff 4 (MLS 1, Non-MLS 3)
Founded 1963
Library Holdings: Bk Titles 4,000; Per Subs 404
Subject Interests: Nursing
Publications: Acquisition List
Partic in Health Sci Libr Group of Greater Kansas City; Kans City Mo Libr & Info Network; National Network Of Libraries Of Medicine - South Central Region

S HEART OF AMERICA GENEALOGICAL SOCIETY & LIBRARY, INC, 311 E 12th St, 64106. SAN 327-7968. Tel: 816-701-3445. FAX: 816-701-3401. *Librn*, Candy Novak
Library Holdings: Bk Vols 13,000; Per Subs 130
Open Sat 10-2 & Sun 1-4:30 & when volunteers are available

M HOECHST, MARION, ROUSSEL LIBRARY,* 10236 Marion Park Dr, 64137. SAN 309-0442. Tel: 816-966-5000. FAX: 816-966-6749. *Librn*, Terry Weaver
Library Holdings: Bk Vols 600; Per Subs 1,200

S IRISH GENEALOGICAL FOUNDATION LIBRARY, PO Box 7575, 64116. SAN 378-0015. Tel: 816-454-2410. FAX: 816-454-2410. Web Site: www.irishroots.com. *In Charge*, Mike O'Laughlin; E-Mail: mike@irishroots.com
Library Holdings: Bk Vols 3,000
Subject Interests: Genealogy, Heraldry, Irish hist
Special Collections: Journal of the American Irish Historical Society 1898-various by county in Ireland
Friends of the Library Group

GL JACKSON COUNTY LAW LIBRARY, INC, (JCLL), 1125 Grand Blvd Ste 1050, 64106. SAN 321-8333. Tel: 816-221-2221. FAX: 816-221-6607. Web Site: www.jcll.org. *Dir*, Jan D Medved; E-Mail: jmedved@jcll.org; *Librn*,

Linda B Roser; E-Mail: lroser@jcll.org; *Asst Librn*, Debbie S Steel; E-Mail: dsteel@jcll.org
Founded 1871
Jan 2000-Dec 2000 Income $512,758, County $419,400, Locally Generated Income $93,358. Mats Exp $220,000, Books $200,000, Electronic Ref Mat (Incl. Access Fees) $20,000. (Prof $111,000)
Library Holdings: Bk Vols 43,500; Bk Titles 2,150
Subject Interests: Fed law, Jury instructions, Legal res, Regulations, State law, Statute law
Automation Activity & Vendor Info: (Acquisitions) CASPR; (Cataloging) CASPR; (OPAC) CASPR; (Serials) CASPR
Publications: Brochure; Pathfinder (newsletter)
Restriction: Not a lending library, Staff & members only, Subscription library
Function: Research library
Open Mon-Fri 8:30-5

S KANSAS CITY ART INSTITUTE LIBRARY,* 4415 Warwick Blvd, 64111. SAN 309-037X. Tel: 816-561-4852, Ext 224. FAX: 816-802-4750. *Dir*, Allen S Morrill
Founded 1885
Jul 1997-Jun 1998 Income $179,987. Mats Exp $19,000, Books $12,500, Per/Ser (Incl. Access Fees) $6,500. Sal $145,267 (Prof $77,721)
Library Holdings: Bk Vols 30,000; Per Subs 110
Subject Interests: Fine arts
Special Collections: Artists books
Open Mon-Thurs 8:30-10, Fri 8:30-5, Sat 12-5, Sun 1:30-10

S KANSAS CITY MUSEUM, Library & Archives, 30 W Pershing Rd, 64108-2422. SAN 309-040X. Tel: 816-460-2052. FAX: 816-460-2260. E-Mail: archive@sciencecity.com. *Archivist*, Denise Morrison
Founded 1939
Special Collections: Aviation (Holland Coll); Local History (Kansas City Archives)
Publications: A guide to the Economic Development of Kansas City Oral History Project (1990); Guide to the Archival Collections (1986)
Restriction: By appointment only

P KANSAS CITY PUBLIC LIBRARY, 311 E 12th St, 64106-2454. SAN 349-2990. Tel: 816-701-3400. Circulation Tel: 816-701-3670. Reference Tel: 816-701-3541. TDD: 816-701-3544. FAX: 816-701-3401. E-Mail: webadmin@kclibrary.org. Web Site: www.kclibrary.org. *Dir*, Daniel J Bradbury; Tel: 816-701-3410, E-Mail: dan@kclibrary.org; *Assoc Dir*, Therese Bigelow; Tel: 816-701-3412, E-Mail: therese@kclibrary.org; *Ch Servs*, Helma Hawkins; Tel: 816-701-3450, E-Mail: helma@kclibrary.org; *Circ*, Pat Mulsoff; Tel: 816-701-3550, E-Mail: ma_pat@kclibrary.org; *Doc Delivery*, Terry Ann Anderson; Tel: 806-701-3551, E-Mail: md_terry@kclibrary.org; *Govt Doc*, Carol Bruegging; Tel: 816-701-3546, E-Mail: mr_carolb@kclibrary.org; *Ref*, Lillie Brack; Tel: 816-701-3530, E-Mail: mr_lillie@kclibrary.org; *YA Servs*, Claudine Jackson; Staff 79 (MLS 79)
Founded 1873. Pop 257,940; Circ 2,337,096
Jul 1999-Jun 2000 Income (Main Library Only) $14,486,843, State $139,161, Federal $360,251. Mats Exp $1,736,526, Books $1,342,044, Per/Ser (Incl. Access Fees) $386,660, Presv $7,822. Sal $6,499,211 (Prof $2,280,741)
Library Holdings: Bk Vols 1,204,992; Per Subs 23,174
Subject Interests: Statistics
Special Collections: Black History (Ramos); Missouri Valley History & Genealogy
Automation Activity & Vendor Info: (Circulation) DRA
Publications: Annual Report; Communique (staff); Comprehensive Annual Financial Report
Partic in Kansas City Metropolitan Library & Information Network; OCLC Online Computer Library Center, Inc
Friends of the Library Group
Branches: 9
LUCILE H BLUFORD BRANCH, 3050 Prospect, 64128. SAN 349-3202. Tel: 816-701-3595. FAX: 816-701-3591. Web Site: www.kclibrary.org. *Librn*, Mary Roberson
Library Holdings: Bk Vols 68,338
NORTH-EAST, 6000 Wilson Rd, 64123. SAN 349-3148. Tel: 816-701-3585. FAX: 816-701-3581. Web Site: www.kclibrary.org. *Librn*, Edward Heeger-Brehm
Library Holdings: Bk Vols 66,428
PLAZA, 4801 Main St, 64112. SAN 349-3172. Tel: 816-701-3575. FAX: 816-701-3576. Web Site: www.kclibrary.org. *Librn*, Diane Swanson
Library Holdings: Bk Vols 118,786
SOUTHEAST, 6242 Swope Pkwy, 64130. SAN 349-3261. Tel: 816-701-3606. FAX: 816-701-3601. Web Site: www.kclibrary.org. *Librn*, Joel Jones
Library Holdings: Bk Vols 46,658
SUGAR CREEK BRANCH, 102 S Sterling, Sugar Creek, 64054. Tel: 816-701-3645. FAX: 816-701-3641. Web Site: www.kclibrary.org. *Librn*, Susan Wray
Library Holdings: Bk Vols 10,234
TRAILS-WEST, 11401 E 23rd St, Independence, 64052. SAN 349-3326. Tel: 816-701-3615. FAX: 816-701-3611. Web Site: www.kclibrary.org. *Librn*, Kathy Simmons
Library Holdings: Bk Vols 77,696
WALDO COMMUNITY, 201 E 75th St, 64114. SAN 349-3296. Tel: 816-701-3625. FAX: 816-701-3621. Web Site: www.kclibrary.org. *Librn*, Dorothy Arneson
Library Holdings: Bk Vols 73,385
WEST, 525 Southwest Blvd, 64108. SAN 349-3350. Tel: 816-701-3655. FAX: 816-701-3657. Web Site: www.kclibrary.org. *Librn*, Aaron Rennick
Library Holdings: Bk Vols 12,843
WESTPORT, 118 Westport Rd, 64111. SAN 349-3385. Tel: 816-701-3635. FAX: 816-701-3631. Web Site: www.kclibrary.org. *Librn*, Magaly Vallazza
Library Holdings: Bk Vols 42,784

P KANSAS CITY REGIONAL CENTER LIBRARY,* 821 E Admiral Blvd, 64141. SAN 377-5356. Tel: 816-889-3400. FAX: 816-889-3325. *Dir*, Gail Claire
Library Holdings: Bk Vols 40

S KANSAS CITY STAR LIBRARY,* 1729 Grand Blvd, 64108. SAN 309-0418. Tel: 816-234-4406. FAX: 816-234-4925. *Dir*, Gayle Hornaday; E-Mail: hornaday@intermind.net
Library Holdings: Bk Titles 5,000; Per Subs 40
Special Collections: Star/Times Newspaper Reference Coll, micro
Publications: Weekly Newsletter
Kansas City Star available online via Datatimes, file name: KCST

L LATHROP & GAGE LC LIBRARY, 2345 Grand Blvd, Ste 2800, 64108. SAN 327-0165. Tel: 816-460-5668. FAX: 816-292-2001. *Chief Librn*, Jamie Frank; *Asst Librn*, Tasha Quick; Tel: 816-460-5669, E-Mail: quicktn@lathropgage.com; *Asst Librn*, Rebecca Regan; Tel: 816-460-5857, E-Mail: reganrg@lathropgage.com
Library Holdings: Bk Vols 30,000; Bk Titles 5,000; Per Subs 150
Database Vendor: Lexis-Nexis

METROPOLITAN COMMUNITY COLLEGES

J LONGVIEW COMMUNITY COLLEGE LIBRARY, 500 SW Longview Rd, Lee's Summit, 64081-2105. SAN 309-0787. Tel: 816-672-2080, 816-672-2266. FAX: 816-672-2087. *Dir*, Scarlett Swall; E-Mail: swalls@longview.cc.mo.us; *Mgr*, Ann Wedaman; Staff 3 (MLS 3)
Founded 1969. Enrl 6,800; Fac 85
1998-1999 Income (Main and Other College/University Libraries) $381,940. Mats Exp $118,793, Books $67,793, Per/Ser (Incl. Access Fees) $25,000, Electronic Ref Mat (Incl. Access Fees) $26,000. Sal $220,549 (Prof $78,478)
Library Holdings: Bk Vols 46,000; Per Subs 260
Partic in Kansas City Metropolitan Library & Information Network; OCLC Online Computer Library Center, Inc

J MAPLE WOODS COMMUNITY COLLEGE LIBRARY, 2601 NE Barry Rd, 64156. SAN 309-0434. Tel: 816-437-3080. FAX: 816-437-3082. *Librn*, Linda Wilson; *Acq*, Darla Luckey; *Ref*, Marieta Knogf; *Ref*, Mary Northrup; Staff 2 (MLS 2)
Founded 1969. Enrl 5,000; Fac 58
Library Holdings: Bk Titles 30,000; Per Subs 273
Special Collections: Veterinary Medicine Coll, bks & per
Mem of Metrop Commun Cols
Partic in Kansas City Metropolitan Library & Information Network; Kansas City Regional Council for Higher Education; Mobius

C PENN VALLEY COMMUNITY COLLEGE LIBRARY, 3200 Pennsylvania Ave, 64111. (Mail add: 3201 SW Trafficway, 64111), SAN 309-0574. Tel: 816-759-4090. FAX: 816-759-4374. E-Mail: refdesk@pennvalley.cc.mo.us. *Dir*, Denise Zortman; *Mgr*, Maureen McGinty; *Head Ref, Librn*, Gloria Maxwell; *Tech Servs*, Ted Ostaszewski; Staff 4 (MLS 4)
Founded 1969. Enrl 4,500; Fac 110
Library Holdings: Bk Vols 83,011; Per Subs 187
Automation Activity & Vendor Info: (Acquisitions) Innovative Interfaces Inc.; (Cataloging) Innovative Interfaces Inc.; (Circulation) Innovative Interfaces Inc.; (Course Reserve) Innovative Interfaces Inc.; (ILL) Innovative Interfaces Inc.; (Media Booking) Innovative Interfaces Inc.; (OPAC) Innovative Interfaces Inc.; (Serials) Innovative Interfaces Inc.
Publications: Bookmarks; New Books List; Student Guides
Partic in Kansas City Metropolitan Library & Information Network; Kansas City Regional Council for Higher Education; Mobius; Morenet

S MIDWEST RESEARCH INSTITUTE, C J Patterson Memorial Library, 425 Volker Blvd, 64110. SAN 349-3504. Tel: 816-753-7600. FAX: 816-753-0209. *Mgr*, Michelle Lahey; E-Mail: mlahey@mriresearch.org; *Librn*, Kimberly Carter; E-Mail: kcarter@mriresearch.org; Staff 2 (MLS 2)
Founded 1945
Library Holdings: Bk Titles 2,000; Per Subs 100
Subject Interests: Biotechnology, Chemistry, Engineering, Environmental studies, Health, Microbiology
Database Vendor: Dialog
Publications: Library Acquisitions List
Restriction: Staff use only
Partic in Health Sci Libr Network; Kans City Mo Libr & Info Network; MLNC; Nat Libr of Med

R MIDWESTERN BAPTIST THEOLOGICAL SEMINARY LIBRARY, 5001 N Oak St, Trafficway, 64118. SAN 309-0477. Tel: 816-414-3729. FAX: 816-414-3790. Web Site: www.mbts.edu. *Librn*, J Craig Kubic; Tel: 816-414-3730, E-Mail: ckubic@mbts.edu; *Tech Servs*, Susan Beyer; Tel: 816-414-3725, E-Mail: sbeyer@mbt.edu; *Res*, Judy Howie; Tel: 816-414-3728, E-Mail: jhowie@mbts.edu; *Acq*, Lynel Willis; Tel: 816-414-3726, E-Mail: lwillis@mbts.edu; *Circ*, Diana Tripp; E-Mail: dtripp@mbts.edu; *AV*, Stacey Jones; *AV*, Jay Sparks. Subject Specialists: *Administration*, J Craig Kubic; *Reference*, Judy Howie; *Research*, Judy Howie; *Research*, J Craig Kubic; Staff 8 (MLS 1, Non-MLS 7)
Founded 1951. Highest Degree: Doctorate
Aug 1999-Jul 2000 Income $275,000. Mats Exp $86,000, Books $38,000, Electronic Ref Mat (Incl. Access Fees) $48,000. Sal $110,000
Library Holdings: Bk Vols 101,000; Bk Titles 89,000; Per Subs 26,000
Subject Interests: Biblical studies
Special Collections: Baptist Denominational Coll
Automation Activity & Vendor Info: (Cataloging) DRA; (Circulation) DRA
Database Vendor: OCLC - First Search, ProQuest
Restriction: Staff use only, Students only
Function: ILL to other special libraries
Mem of OCLC ILL Subsystem
Partic in Kansas City Libr Consortium; Kansas City Metropolitan Library & Information Network

GL MISSOURI COURT OF APPEALS LIBRARY, Western District,* 1300 Oak, 64106. SAN 309-0485. Tel: 816-889-3639. FAX: 816-889-3668. *Librn*, Janine Estrada-Lopez
Founded 1885
Library Holdings: Bk Vols 32,500; Per Subs 150
Partic in Westlaw

L MORRISON & HECKER LIBRARY,* 2600 Grand Ave, 64108. SAN 309-0507. Tel: 816-691-2600. FAX: 816-474-4208. *Librn*, Cindy Crary
Library Holdings: Bk Vols 21,000; Per Subs 50
Subject Interests: Law
Partic in Westlaw

L NAIC RESEARCH LIBRARY, 2301 McGee St, Ste 800, 64108. SAN 329-8345. Tel: 816-783-8252. FAX: 816-889-4446. E-Mail: reslib@naic.org. Web Site: www.naic.org. *Mgr*, Deborah Scott; *Res*, Sharon Sampson; *Res*, Kay J Tyrrell; Staff 4 (MLS 3, Non-MLS 1)
Founded 1871
Library Holdings: Bk Vols 13,000; Bk Titles 10,000; Per Subs 275
Restriction: Open to public upon request
Function: Archival collection, Document delivery services, Reference services available, Research fees apply
Partic in OCLC Online Computer Library Center, Inc

G NATIONAL ARCHIVES & RECORDS ADMINISTRATION, Central Plains Region, 2312 E Bannister Rd, 64131-3011. SAN 309-0515. Tel: 816-926-6272. FAX: 816-926-6235. Web Site: www.nar.gov/regional/kansas.html. *Dir*, R Reed Whitaker; *Archivist*, Diana Duff
Founded 1969
Special Collections: Archival records of Federal agencies & courts in Iowa, Kansas, Missouri & Nebraska; Federal Government Field Office Records of Federal Agencies within the states of Iowa, Kansas, Minnesota, Missouri, Nebraska, North Dakota, & South Dakota, 1850-1950; Records of Indian Territory, Kansas, Nebraska & Dakota Territories, 1854-89
Restriction: Reference only to non-staff

G NATIONAL WEATHER SERVICE, Central Region Hq Library, Federal Bldg, Rm 1836, 601 E 12th St, 64106-2897. SAN 326-0798. Tel: 816-426-5672, Ext 708. FAX: 816-426-3301. *Admin Assoc*, Paula J Guarino; E-Mail: paula.guarino@noaa.gov
Library Holdings: Bk Titles 225; Per Subs 14
Subject Interests: Climatology, Meteorology
Special Collections: National Weather Service Central Region
Publications: Computer Programs; NWS Technical Memorandums; Operational Notes; Scientific Journal Articles; Technical Attachments

R NAZARENE THEOLOGICAL SEMINARY, Broadhurst Library, 1700 E Meyer Blvd, 64131. SAN 309-0531. Tel: 816-333-6254. FAX: 816-822-9025. *Dir*, William C Miller; E-Mail: wcmiller@nts.edu; Staff 2 (MLS 2)
Founded 1945. Enrl 260; Fac 18; Highest Degree: Doctorate
Library Holdings: Bk Vols 98,000; Per Subs 524
Special Collections: History of the Holiness Movement; Methodistica-Wesleyana
Partic in Dialog Corporation; Kansas City Metropolitan Library & Information Network; Missouri Library Network Corporation; OCLC Online Computer Library Center, Inc

S NELSON-ATKINS MUSEUM OF ART, Spencer Art Reference Library, 4525 Oak St, 64111-1873. SAN 309-054X. Tel: 816-751-1216. FAX: 816-561-7154. E-Mail: sarl@nelson-atkins.org. Web Site: www.nelson-atkins.org. *Tech Servs*, Martha Patton Childers; Tel: 816-751-1381, E-Mail: mchilders@nelson-atkins.org; *Coll Develop, Publ Servs*, Jeffrey Weidman; Tel: 816-751-1215, E-Mail: jweidman@nelson-atkins.org; *Acq*, Xiangyuan Zhang; Tel: 816-751-1209, E-Mail: szhang@nelson-atkins.org; *Cat*, Jane Cheng; Tel: 816-751-1231, E-Mail: jcheng@nelson-atkins.org; *Cat*, Jane Zander; Tel: 816-751-1217, E-Mail: jzander@nelson-atkins.org; *Ser*, Karen Harrell; Tel: 816-751-0408, E-Mail: kharrell@nelson-atkins.org; *ILL*, Katharine Reed; Tel: 817-751-1287, E-Mail: kreed@nelson-atkins.org; Staff 13 (MLS 6, Non-MLS 7)
Founded 1933. Circ 19,000
May 2000-Apr 2001 Income $38,000. Mats Exp $104,260, Books $62,000, Per/Ser (Incl. Access Fees) $41,000, Electronic Ref Mat (Incl. Access Fees) $1,260. Sal $291,306 (Prof $223,444)
Library Holdings: Bk Vols 120,000; Bk Titles 60,000; Per Subs 800
Subject Interests: Art history, Asian art, Decorative arts, European art
Special Collections: Auction Catalogs; Decorative Arts, per; Oriental Art; Prints & Drawings (The John H Bender Library)
Automation Activity & Vendor Info: (Cataloging) epixtech, inc.; (Circulation) epixtech, inc.; (Course Reserve) epixtech, inc.; (OPAC) epixtech, inc.; (Serials) epixtech, inc.
Database Vendor: epixtech, inc., OCLC - First Search
Restriction: Non-circulating to the public
Mem of Mo Libr Network Corp
Friends of the Library Group

L POLSINELLI, WHITE, VARDEMAN & SHALTON, Law Library,* 700 W 47th, Ste 1000, 64112. SAN 323-8911. Tel: 816-753-1000. FAX: 816-753-1536. *Librn*, Karin Weaver; Staff 2 (MLS 1, Non-MLS 1)
Library Holdings: Bk Vols 15,000; Bk Titles 2,500
Automation Activity & Vendor Info: (Acquisitions) Inmagic, Inc.; (Cataloging) Inmagic, Inc.; (Serials) Inmagic, Inc.
Restriction: Staff use only

C ROCKHURST UNIVERSITY, Greenlease Library, 1100 Rockhurst Rd, 64110-2561. SAN 309-0590. Tel: 816-501-4144. Interlibrary Loan Service Tel: 816-501-4142. Circulation Tel: 816-501-4142. Reference Tel: 816-501-4188. TDD: 816-501-4833. FAX: 816-501-4666. Web Site: www.rockhurst.edu/3.0/services_and_resources/library/. *Dir*, Jeanne M Langdon; E-Mail: jeanne.langdon@rockhurst.edu; *Cat*, Carolyn Smith; *Publ Servs*, Laurie Hathman; *Acq, Per*, Buddy Pennington; *Head Tech Servs*, Martha Grimes; *Circ, Ref*, Karen Fiegerbaum; *ILL*, Verna Rutz; Staff 11 (MLS 5, Non-MLS 6)
Founded 1917. Enrl 2,922; Fac 212; Highest Degree: Master
2000-2000 Mats Exp $228,735, Books $60,000, Per/Ser (Incl. Access Fees) $70,659, Micro $28,000, Other Print Mats $1,300, Electronic Ref Mat (Incl. Access Fees) $68,776. Sal $266,935 (Prof $169,250)
Library Holdings: Bk Vols 114,200; Bk Titles 97,500; Per Subs 720
Automation Activity & Vendor Info: (Acquisitions) DRA; (Cataloging) DRA; (Circulation) DRA; (Course Reserve) DRA; (ILL) DRA; (OPAC) DRA; (Serials) DRA
Database Vendor: DRA, OCLC - First Search
Publications: Greennotes (Newsletter)
Partic in Kansas City Libr Consortium; Kansas City Metropolitan Library & Information Network
Special Services for the Deaf - TDD
Friends of the Library Group

M SAINT JOSEPH HEALTH CENTER, Health Science Library,* 1000 Carondelet Dr, 64114. SAN 309-0604. Tel: 816-942-4400, Ext 2160. FAX: 816-943-2592. *Librn*, Janice M Foster
Library Holdings: Bk Vols 3,000; Per Subs 155

M SAINT LUKE'S HOSPITAL, Health Sciences Library, 4400 Wornall Rd, 64111. SAN 309-0612. Tel: 816-932-2333. FAX: 816-932-5197. *Dir*, Karen Wiederaenders; E-Mail: kwiederaenders@saint-lukes.org; *Ser*, Mary Webb
Founded 1948
Library Holdings: Bk Vols 5,000; Per Subs 600
Subject Interests: Nursing
Publications: Newsletter
Restriction: Staff use only
Partic in Dialog Corporation; Health Sciences Library Network of Kansas City, Inc; Kansas City Metropolitan Library & Information Network; Libr User Info Syst; Medline

SR SAINT PAUL SCHOOL OF THEOLOGY, Dana Dawson Library, 5123 Truman Rd, 64127. SAN 309-0639. Tel: 816-483-9600. FAX: 816-483-9605. *Dir*, Logan Wright; Staff 1 (MLS 1)
Founded 1958. Highest Degree: Doctorate
Library Holdings: Bk Titles 82,000; Per Subs 550
Special Collections: Methodistica Coll; Wesleyana Coll
Partic in Dialog Corporation; Missouri Library Network Corporation; OCLC Online Computer Library Center, Inc

L SHOOK, HARDY & BACON, Law Library, 1200 Main St, 28th flr, 64105. SAN 309-0647. Tel: 816-474-6550. FAX: 816-421-5547. *Dir*, Lori Weiss; *Cat, Ref*, Mike McReynolds; *Ref*, Marit Bang; *Ref*, Heidi Knight; *Ref*, Julie Parmenter; *Ref*, R Scott Russell; *Ref*, Jeff Sewell; *Ref*, Joyce Sickel; *Ref*, Valerie Vogt; *Ref*, Eddie White; *Tech Servs*, Janet Peters; *Electronic Resources*, Janet McKinney
Library Holdings: Bk Vols 40,000; Per Subs 900
Partic in Health Sciences Library Network of Kansas City, Inc
Maintains 5 branch libraries of 2000 vols each

L SHUGHART, THOMSON & KILROY, Law Library,* 120 W 12th St, Ste 1800, 64105. SAN 372-4670. Tel: 816-421-3355. FAX: 816-374-0509. Web Site: www.kcstklaw.com. *Librn*, Avis C Bates
Library Holdings: Bk Vols 12,000; Per Subs 37

CM THE UNIVERSITY OF HEALTH SCIENCES LIBRARY, 1750 Independence Ave, 64106-1453. SAN 309-0388. Tel: 816-283-2290. Interlibrary Loan Service Tel: 816-283-2292. Reference Tel: 816-283-2294. FAX: 816-283-2237. E-Mail: library@uhs.edu. Web Site: stillpoint.ush.edu. *Acq, Dir*, Marilyn J DeGeus; Tel: 816-283-2295, E-Mail: mdegeus@uhs.edu; *Circ, ILL*, Nancy Stroud; E-Mail: nstroud@uhs.edu; *Circ, Tech Servs*, Robyn Oro; Tel: 816-283-2298, E-Mail: roro@uhs.edu; *Cat*, Lynn Mousseau; Tel: 816-283-2293, E-Mail: lmousseau@uhs.edu; *Circ, Ser*, Connie Brown; E-Mail: cdbrown@uhs.edu; *Ref*, Bonnie Anderson; E-Mail: bjanderson@uhs.edu; *Circ*, Angie Bowen; E-Mail: abowen@uhs.edu; Staff 9 (MLS 3, Non-MLS 6)
Founded 1916. Enrl 960; Fac 154; Highest Degree: Doctorate
Jul 1999-Jun 2000 Mats Exp $231,251, Books $98,692, Per/Ser (Incl. Access Fees) $115,860, Presv $3,026, AV Equip $1,985, Manuscripts & Archives $1,962, Electronic Ref Mat (Incl. Access Fees) $9,726. Sal $269,402 (Prof $126,385)
Library Holdings: Bk Vols 30,789; Bk Titles 58,211; Per Subs 354
Subject Interests: Medicine
Special Collections: Osteopathic History (Osteopathic Coll), bk, flm, slides, tapes
Automation Activity & Vendor Info: (Acquisitions) Endeavor; (Cataloging) Endeavor; (Circulation) Endeavor; (Course Reserve) Endeavor; (ILL) Endeavor; (Media Booking) Endeavor; (OPAC) Endeavor; (Serials) Endeavor
Publications: The Bookbag
Restriction: Circulation limited, Open to student, faculty & staff
Partic in Docline; Health Sci Libr Group of Greater Kansas City; National Network Of Libraries Of Medicine - Midcontinental Region; OCLC Online Computer Library Center, Inc

M TRINITY LUTHERAN HOSPITAL, Florence L Nelson Memorial Library, 3030 Baltimore Ave, 64108. SAN 309-0655. Tel: 816-751-2270. FAX: 816-751-2273. *Dir*, Desi Bravo; E-Mail: debravo@healthmidwest.org; Staff 1 (MLS 1)
Founded 1972
Library Holdings: Bk Vols 6,100; Per Subs 425
Subject Interests: Allied health, Medicine, Nursing
Special Collections: Local History (Oscar D Nelson Coll)
Automation Activity & Vendor Info: (Acquisitions) EOS; (Cataloging) EOS; (Circulation) EOS; (Serials) EOS
Restriction: Medical staff only
Partic in Health Sci Libr Network

UNITED STATES ARMY

A CORPS OF ENGINEERS, DISTRICT LIBRARY, 601 E 12th St, Rm 747, 64106-2896. SAN 349-3652. Tel: 816-983-4321. FAX: 816-426-2730. Web Site: www.nwk.usace.army.mil/library.html.
Library Holdings: Bk Vols 15,000; Per Subs 248
Partic in Dialog Corporation; OCLC Online Computer Library Center, Inc

GL UNITED STATES COURTS, Branch Library,* 9440 US Court House, 400 E Ninth St, 64106. SAN 309-0663. Tel: 816-512-5790. FAX: 816-512-5799. *Librn*, M Tranne Pearce
Library Holdings: Bk Vols 35,000
Partic in Fedlink; Westlaw

C UNIVERSITY OF MISSOURI, (WHMC-KC), Western Historical Manuscript Collection - Kansas City, 302 Newcomb Hall, 5100 Rockhill Rd, 64110-2499. SAN 329-2754. Tel: 816-235-1543. FAX: 816-235-5500. E-Mail: whmckc@umkc.edu. Web Site: www.umkc.edu/whmckc/. *Assoc Dir*, David Boutros; Staff 3 (MLS 2, Non-MLS 1)
Founded 1980
Library Holdings: Bk Titles 1,500
Subject Interests: Kansas City area hist, Missouri hist
Publications: Guide to collections

C UNIVERSITY OF MISSOURI-KANSAS CITY LIBRARIES,* 5100 Rockhill Rd, 64110-2499. SAN 349-3687. Tel: 816-235-1531. Interlibrary Loan Service Tel: 816-235-1586. FAX: 816-333-5584. Interlibrary Loan Service FAX: 816-235-5531. Web Site: www.umkc.edu/lib. *Dir*, Ted P Sheldon; *Asst Dir*, Jennifer Eigsti; *Assoc Dir*, Helen H Spalding; *Tech Servs*, Brenda Dingley; *Access Serv*, Mary Anderson; *Coll Develop*, Marilyn Carbonell; *Ref*, Rebecca Schreiner-Robles; *Publ Servs*, Elizabeth Ader; *Librn*, Michelle Beattie; *Govt Doc*, Christine Angolia; *ILL*, Nancy Radonovich; *Acq, Ser*, Robert Cleary. Subject Specialists: *Music*, Laura Gayle Green; Staff 40 (MLS 40)
Founded 1933. Enrl 10,200; Fac 546; Highest Degree: Doctorate
Jul 1998-Jun 1999 Income $6,112,278. Mats Exp $1,952,381. Sal $3,168,307
Library Holdings: Bk Vols 1,057,609; Per Subs 6,844
Special Collections: (Baker Coll of English & American Literature); American Sheet Music Coll; Americana (Snyder Coll of Americana), bk, mss; English & American; Holocaust Studies; Midwest Center for American Music (Amy Beach & Paul Creston Coll); Sound Archives
Publications: BiblioTech (Newsletter); Bookmark (UMKC Friends of the Library); UMKC Libraries Staff Announcements
Partic in Center For Research Libraries; Kansas City Regional Council for Higher Education; Mo Res Consortium of Librs; OCLC Online Computer Library Center, Inc
Music/Media Library houses collection of sound recordings, non-print materials & AV equipment
Friends of the Library Group
Departmental Libraries:

CM DENTAL LIBRARY, 650 E 25th St, 64108-2784. SAN 349-3806. Tel: 816-235-2030. Web Site: www.umkc.edu/depts/lib. *Librn*, Ann Marie Corry
Jul 1997-Jun 1998 Income $241,495. Mats Exp $41,031. Sal $187,246
Library Holdings: Bk Vols 24,361; Per Subs 424
Special Collections: History of Dentistry Coll
Publications: Library Update
Partic in Health Sciences Library Network of Kansas City, Inc

CM HEALTH SCIENCES LIBRARY, 2411 Holmes St, 64108-2795. SAN 349-3717. Tel: 816-235-1880. Interlibrary Loan Service Tel: 816-235-1878. FAX: 816-235-5194. Web Site: www.umkc.edu/lib/. *Asst Dir*, Margaret Mullaly-Quijas; *ILL*, Janice Rogers; *Media Spec*, Marlene Smith; Staff 4 (MLS 4)
Founded 1965. Highest Degree: Doctorate
Jul 1997-Jun 1998 Income $570,713. Mats Exp $227,958. Sal $246,866
Library Holdings: Bk Vols 79,789
Subject Interests: Clinical medicine, Nursing
Partic in Bibliog Retrieval Servs Inc; Dialog Corporation; Health Sciences Library Network of Kansas City, Inc; Midcontinental Regional Med Libr Program; Nat Libr of Med; SDC Search Serv

CL LEON E BLOCH LAW LIBRARY, 5100 Rockhill Rd, 64110-2499. SAN 349-3741. Tel: 816-235-1650. FAX: 816-235-5274. Web Site: www.law.umkc.edu/library.htm. *Dir*, Patricia O'Connor; *Circ, Ref*, Larry MacLachlan; *Cat*, Nancy Stancel; *Acq, Govt Doc, Ser*, Janet McKinney; Staff 13 (MLS 7, Non-MLS 6)
Founded 1895
Jul 1997-Jun 1998 Income $1,503,887. Mats Exp $360,594, Books $23,666, Per/Ser (Incl. Access Fees) $320,158, Presv $4,948, Micro $11,241. Sal $464,082 (Prof $320,665)
Library Holdings: Bk Vols 193,203; Per Subs 1,754
Subject Interests: Law
Special Collections: Urban Law Coll
Publications: Acquisitions List
Partic in Dialog Corporation; OCLC Online Computer Library Center, Inc; Westlaw

CL SCHOOL OF LAW LIBRARY, 500 E 52nd St, 64110. SAN 377-6905. Tel: 816-235-1650. FAX: 816-235-5274. Web Site: www.law.umkc.edu. *Dir*, Pat Harris-O'Connor; *Asst Librn*, Nancy Morgan
Library Holdings: Bk Vols 185,000

R WESTERN BAPTIST MEMORIAL LIBRARY,* 2119 Tracy, 64108-2997. SAN 309-0701. Tel: 816-842-4195. FAX: 816-842-3050.
Library Holdings: Bk Vols 13,020
Subject Interests: Am hist, Am lit, Archaeology, Bible hist, Black hist, Drama, Eng lit, European history, Music, Philosophy, Psychology, Relig hist educ, Religion, Sociology, Theology, World history

M WESTERN MISSOURI MENTAL HEALTH CENTER, Charles B Wilkinson MD Memorial Library, 600 E 22nd St, 64108. SAN 309-071X. Tel: 816-512-4638. FAX: 816-512-4637. *Librn*, Tyron Emerick; E-Mail: muemert@mail.dmh.state.mo.us; Staff 2 (MLS 1, Non-MLS 1)
Founded 1968
Jul 1998-Jun 1999 Income $45,000. Mats Exp $8,500, Books $1,000, Per/Ser (Incl. Access Fees) $6,000, Micro $300. Sal $40,000 (Prof $32,000)
Library Holdings: Bk Vols 2,780; Bk Titles 2,600; Per Subs 55
Subject Interests: Behav sci, Psychiatry, Psychology, Soc sci
Partic in Health Sciences Library Network of Kansas City, Inc; Kansas City Metropolitan Library & Information Network; OCLC Online Computer Library Center, Inc

KENNETT

P DUNKLIN COUNTY LIBRARY,* 226 N Main, 63857. SAN 349-3865. Tel: 573-888-3561. FAX: 573-888-6393. E-Mail: qjgoo1@mail.connect.more.net. *Dir*, Richard Reynolds; Staff 1 (MLS 1)
Founded 1947. Pop 30,000; Circ 316,825
Library Holdings: Bk Vols 130,000; Per Subs 150
Subject Interests: Genealogy
Partic in SE Libr Network
Branches: 8
ARBYRD BRANCH, Arbyrd, 63821. SAN 349-389X. Tel: 573-654-2385. *Librn*, Teri Long
Library Holdings: Bk Titles 5,607
CAMPBELL BRANCH, Campbell, 63933. SAN 349-392X. Tel: 573-246-2112. *Librn*, Betty Provance
Library Holdings: Bk Titles 15,264
CARDWELL BRANCH, Main St, PO Box 305, Cardwell, 63829. SAN 349-3954. Tel: 573-654-3366. *Librn*, Teri Long

Library Holdings: Bk Titles 5,479
CLARKTON BRANCH, Clarkton, 63837. SAN 349-3989. Tel: 573-448-3803. *Librn*, Peggy Gilkey
Library Holdings: Bk Titles 3,977
HOLCOMB BRANCH, Main St, Holcomb, 63852. SAN 349-4012. Tel: 573-792-3268. *Librn*, Marge Schubert
Library Holdings: Bk Titles 4,615
HORNERSVILLE BRANCH, PO Box 37, Hornersville, 63855-0037. SAN 349-4047. Tel: 573-737-2728. E-Mail: dcls002@dunklin-co.lib.mo.us. *Librn*, Donna Hargraves
Library Holdings: Bk Titles 7,541
MALDEN BRANCH, 113 N Madison, Malden, 63863. SAN 349-4071. Tel: 314-276-3674. *Librn*, Helen Clingingsmith
Library Holdings: Bk Titles 23,517
SENATH BRANCH, 110-112 N Main, Senath, 63876. SAN 349-4101. Tel: 573-738-2363. *Librn*, Jessie Fern Buck
Library Holdings: Bk Titles 16,689

R FIRST BAPTIST CHURCH LIBRARY,* 300 Saint Francis St, 63857. SAN 309-0728. Tel: 573-888-4689. *Librn*, David LaGore; *Librn*, Sara LaGore
Founded 1948
Library Holdings: Bk Vols 3,450; Bk Titles 3,400
Subject Interests: Bible characters, Child missionaries, Devotions, Holidays

KIRKSVILLE

P ADAIR COUNTY PUBLIC LIBRARY, One Library Lane, 63501. SAN 309-0752. Tel: 660-665-6038. FAX: 660-627-0028. Web Site: adair.lib.mo.us/. *Dir*, Glenda Davis
Founded 1986. Pop 24,501; Circ 250,000
Jan 2000-Dec 2000 Income $365,000, State $12,700, Federal $30,000, County $280,000, Locally Generated Income $22,000. Mats Exp $68,000, Books $60,000, Per/Ser (Incl. Access Fees) $8,000. Sal $170,000
Library Holdings: Bk Titles 72,000; Per Subs 180; Bks on Deafness & Sign Lang 50
Subject Interests: Missouri hist
Special Collections: Adair County
Automation Activity & Vendor Info: (Circulation) epixtech, inc.; (OPAC) epixtech, inc.
Database Vendor: OCLC - First Search
Partic in Grand Rivers Libr Conference
Friends of the Library Group

CM KIRKSVILLE COLLEGE OF OSTEOPATHIC MEDICINE, A T Still Memorial Library, 800 W Jefferson, 63501. SAN 309-0736. Tel: 660-626-2345. FAX: 660-626-2031. Web Site: www.kcom.edu. *Dir*, Lawrence W Onsager; E-Mail: lonsager@kcom.edu; *Online Servs, Ref*, Jean Sidwell; *AV*, Leisa Walter; *Tech Servs*, Mary Sims; Staff 3 (MLS 3)
Founded 1897. Enrl 500; Fac 107; Highest Degree: Doctorate
Library Holdings: Bk Vols 90,000; Per Subs 850
Subject Interests: Behav sci, Medicine, Osteopathic med, Para-med, Sci-tech, Soc sci
Special Collections: Ostepathic med
Automation Activity & Vendor Info: (Acquisitions) Innovative Interfaces Inc.
Partic in Docline; Missouri Library Network Corporation; OCLC Online Computer Library Center, Inc
Library also serves Northeast Regional Medical Center

P KIRKSVILLE REGIONAL CENTER LIBRARY,* 1702 E Laharpe St, 63501. SAN 377-1792. Tel: 660-785-2500. FAX: 660-785-2520. Web Site: www.kirksvillergeionalcenter. *Librn*, Kathy Stewart; E-Mail: mlstewk@mail.dmh.state.mo.us
Library Holdings: Bk Vols 200

C TRUMAN STATE UNIVERSITY, Pickler Memorial Library, 100 E Normal, 63501-4211. SAN 309-0744. Tel: 660-785-4038. Interlibrary Loan Service Tel: 660-785-4534. Circulation Tel: 660-785-4533. Reference Tel: 660-785-4051. Interlibrary Loan Service FAX: 660-785-4536. Web Site: www2.truman.edu/pickler/. *Dir*, Richard J Coughlin; E-Mail: coughlin@truman.edu; *Circ*, Gayla McHenry; Tel: 660-785-4037, E-Mail: gmchenry@truman.edu; *Publ Servs*, Karen McClaskey; Tel: 660-785-7416, E-Mail: karenmc@truman.edu; *Bibliogr, Tech Servs*, Patricia Teter; Tel: 660-785-4539, E-Mail: pteter@truman.edu; *Archivist, Spec Coll*, Elaine Doak; Tel: 660-785-7368, E-Mail: emdoak@truman.edu; *Media Spec*, Sharon Hackney; Tel: 660-785-7366, E-Mail: shackney@truman.edu
Founded 1867. Enrl 6,169; Fac 364
Jul 1999-Jun 2000 Income $3,082,130. Mats Exp $1,465,598, Books $488,646, Per/Ser (Incl. Access Fees) $542,297, Micro $164,505, AV Equip $101,188, Manuscripts & Archives $6,075, Electronic Ref Mat (Incl. Access Fees) $119,227. Sal $1,128,904 (Prof $581,442)
Library Holdings: Bk Vols 427,286; Per Subs 2,109
Subject Interests: Business, Health, Liberal arts, Nursing, Sciences
Special Collections: Eugenics Coll (Harry Laughlin), mss; Glenn Frank Coll, mss; Lincoln (Fred & Ethal Schwengel Coll), bks & artifacts; Missouriana (Violette McClure Coll); Rare Books Coll
Automation Activity & Vendor Info: (Course Reserve) Innovative Interfaces Inc.; (OPAC) Innovative Interfaces Inc.; (Serials) Innovative Interfaces Inc.
Database Vendor: OCLC - First Search
Partic in Missouri Library Network Corporation; Mobius
Special Services for the Blind - Print scanner & software for conversion to speech
Open Mon-Thurs 7:30-2am, Fri 7:30-10, Sat 12-10, Sun 12-2am

KIRKWOOD

P KIRKWOOD PUBLIC LIBRARY, 140 E Jefferson Ave, 63122. SAN 309-0760. Tel: 314-821-5770. FAX: 314-822-3755. E-Mail: jtz005@mail.connect.more.net. Web Site: kpl.lib.mo.us. *Dir*, Wicky Sleight; Tel: 314-821-3849, E-Mail: jtz000@mail.connect.more.net; *Asst Dir*, Pamela R Klipsch; Tel: 314-821-5770, Ext 22, E-Mail: prklipsch@netscape.net; *Ad Servs*, Mary Jo Tuchschmidt; Tel: 314-821-5770, Ext 13; *Ch Servs*, Joan Deuschle; Tel: 314-821-5770, Ext 16; *Ref Servs YA*, Carol Boeckmann; Tel: 314-821-5770, Ext 19; *Automation Syst Coordr, Tech Servs*, Joel Shedlofsky; Tel: 314-821-5770, Ext 11; Staff 14 (MLS 9, Non-MLS 5)
Founded 1924. Pop 27,291; Circ 281,048
May 1999-Apr 2000 Income $1,159,130, State $22,224, City $949,790, Federal $55,129, Locally Generated Income $131,987. Mats Exp $157,262, Books $136,074, Per/Ser (Incl. Access Fees) $21,188. Sal $506,132
Library Holdings: Bk Vols 76,576; Per Subs 263
Subject Interests: Storytelling
Special Collections: Early Missouri, St Louis City, County & Kirkwood History; Louisiana Exposition; Nonprofit Resources Special Coll
Automation Activity & Vendor Info: (Cataloging) epixtech, inc.; (Circulation) epixtech, inc.; (OPAC) epixtech, inc.
Database Vendor: Dialog, epixtech, inc., IAC - Info Trac, Wilson - Wilson Web
Publications: Source (bi-monthly) (Newsletter); Sourcery (staff newsletter)
Mem of St Louis Regional Libr Network
Partic in Municipal Libr Coop
Special Services for the Deaf - TDD
Friends of the Library bookstore
Friends of the Library Group

KOSHKONONG

P OREGON COUNTY LIBRARY DISTRICT, Koshkonong Branch,* 302 Luyster, 65692. SAN 377-5542. Tel: 417-867-5472. FAX: 417-867-5472. *Librn*, Paula Miller
Library Holdings: Bk Vols 5,000

LA PLATA

P LA PLATA PUBLIC LIBRARY, 103 E Moore, 63549. (Mail add: 30006 Kodiak Pl, 63549), SAN 309-0779. Tel: 660-332-4945. FAX: 660-332-4945. E-Mail: laplib@istlaplata.net. *Librn*, Cynthia A Moore; E-Mail: mcmoore@istlaplata.net
Founded 1939. Pop 1,401; Circ 11,105
Library Holdings: Bk Vols 15,170; Per Subs 25
Subject Interests: Genealogy, Local history
Special Collections: Doc Savage Coll
Mon, Wed & Fri 1-6, Tues & Thurs 8-1, Sat 10-12

LAWSON

P MISSOURI DEPARTMENT OF NATURAL RESOURCES, Watkins Woolen Mill State Historic Site Research Library, 26600 Park Rd N, 64062. SAN 327-8808. Tel: 816-296-3357, 816-580-3387. FAX: 816-580-3784. E-Mail: nrwatki@mail.dnr.state.mo.us. Web Site: www.mostateparks.com/wwmill/. *Adminr*, Michael Beckett
Founded 1964
Library Holdings: Bk Vols 600; Per Subs 1,000
Special Collections: 19th Century Agriculture, 19th Century Woolen Textile Manufacturing; 19th Century Gristmilling; Watkins Family Letters 1820's-1940's; Watkins Mill Association Records 1959-1990
Restriction: By appointment only
Function: Archival collection
Friends of the Library Group

LEAWOOD

M HERB L HUFFINGTON MEMORIAL LIBRARY SERVICES, (Formerly American Academy Of Family Physicians), 11400 Tomahawk Creek Pkwy, 66211. SAN 329-3424. Tel: 913-906-6000. Reference Tel: 913-906-6000, Ext 4260. Toll Free Tel: 800-274-2237. FAX: 913-906-6077. *Dir, Librn, Res*, David W Wright; E-Mail: dwright@aafp.org; Staff 1 (MLS 1)
Library Holdings: Bk Titles 1,500
Subject Interests: Clinical medicine
Special Collections: Archives for Family Practice

LEBANON

P LEBANON-LACLEDE COUNTY LIBRARY, 135 Harwood Ave, 65536. SAN 349-4136. Tel: 417-532-2148. FAX: 417-532-7424. E-Mail: krlref@llion.org. *Dir*, Patricia Lamb; *Librn*, Renee Hawkins
Pop 89,281; Circ 357,389
Library Holdings: Bk Vols 104,000; Per Subs 140
Subject Interests: Genealogy, Local history
Partic in Mo Libr Film Coop; SW Mo Libr Network
Branches: 1
LEBANON-LACLEDE COUNTY, 135 Harwood Ave, 65536. SAN 349-4160. Tel: 417-532-2148 (Office), 417-532-4212. FAX: 417-532-7424. E-Mail: krlref@llion.org. Web Site: www.lebanon.lacled.library.missouri.org. *Dir*, Patricia Anne Lamb; E-Mail: plamb@llion.org; Staff 13 (MLS 3, Non-MLS 10)
Founded 1938. Pop 32,468; Circ 240,509
Jan 1999-Dec 1999 Income (Main Library Only) $572,866, Federal $42,110, County $366,647, Locally Generated Income $15,028, Other $14,081. Mats Exp $73,870, Books $53,017, Per/Ser (Incl. Access Fees) $4,543, Micro $100, AV Equip $12,015, Electronic Ref Mat (Incl. Access Fees) $4,195. Sal $234,734 (Prof $124,859)
Library Holdings: Bk Vols 56,199; Per Subs 116
Subject Interests: Business, Genealogy, Local history
Automation Activity & Vendor Info: (Cataloging) Innovative Interfaces Inc.; (Circulation) Innovative Interfaces Inc.; (OPAC) Innovative Interfaces Inc.
Database Vendor: Ebsco - EbscoHost, OCLC - First Search
Function: Some telephone reference
Non-resident user fees
Bookmobiles: 2

LEXINGTON

J WENTWORTH MILITARY ACADEMY, Sellers-Coombs Library, 1880 Washington Ave, 64067. SAN 309-0809. Tel: 660-259-2221. FAX: 660-259-2677. Web Site: www.wma1880.org. *Librn*, Linda Tanner
Founded 1884. Enrl 350
Library Holdings: Bk Vols 18,000; Per Subs 35
Subject Interests: Mil sci

LIBERTY

S CLAY COUNTY ARCHIVES & HISTORICAL LIBRARY, 210 E Franklin, PO Box 99, 64069. SAN 323-5238. Tel: 816-781-3611. E-Mail: ccarch@qni.com. Web Site: www.qni.com/~ccarch. *Pres*, Patty King Rendon
Library Holdings: Bk Vols 1,000; Per Subs 15
Subject Interests: Family hist, Genealogy
Open Mon-Wed 10-4, 1st Wed of month 6:30 pm-9 pm

C PARTEE CENTER FOR BAPTIST HISTORICAL STUDIES, Missouri Baptist Archives, William Jewell College, 500 College Hill, 64068. SAN 327-0092. Tel: 816-781-7700, Ext 5490. FAX: 816-415-5027. E-Mail: parteecenter@william.jewell.edu. Web Site: www.jewell.edu/academic/currylibrary/partee/html. *Dir*, Angela N Stiffler; Staff 2 (Non-MLS 2)
Library Holdings: Bk Titles 2,000; Per Subs 300
Restriction: By appointment only
Open Mon-Fri 9-4
Friends of the Library Group

C WILLIAM JEWELL COLLEGE, Charles F Curry Library, 500 College Hill, 64068-1896. SAN 309-0825. Tel: 816-781-7700. FAX: 816-415-5021. Web Site: www.jewell.edu/academia/currylibrary/. *Dir*, John P Young; Tel: 816-781-7700, Ext 5460, E-Mail: youngj@william.jewell.edu; *Media Spec*, Suzanne Barrett; Tel: 816-781-7700, Ext 5189, E-Mail: barretts@william.jewell.edu; *Cat*, Cheryl Couch-Thomas; Tel: 816-781-7700, Ext 5463, E-Mail: couch-thoma@william.jewell.edu; *Coll Develop, Ref*, Bonnie Knauss; Tel: 816-781-7700, Ext 5465, E-Mail: knaussb@william.jewell.edu; *Govt Doc*, Kenette Harder; Tel: 816-781-7700, Ext 5467, E-Mail: harderk@william.jewell.edu; *Circ*, Elise Fisher; Tel: 816-781-7700, Ext 5474, E-Mail: fishere@william.jewell.edu; Staff 6 (MLS 5, Non-MLS 1)
Founded 1849. Enrl 1,150; Fac 105; Highest Degree: Bachelor
Jul 1998-Jun 1999 Income $819,278. Mats Exp $306,929, Books $134,445, Per/Ser (Incl. Access Fees) $78,446, Presv $6,428, Micro $13,765, Electronic Ref Mat (Incl. Access Fees) $73,845. Sal $342,975
Library Holdings: Bk Vols 255,875; Per Subs 865
Special Collections: Baptist History (Partee Center for Baptist Historical Studies); Children's Literature (Lois Lenski Coll), bk, drawing; Missouri History (Missouri Coll); Puritan Literature (Charles Haddon Spurgeon Coll); Western Americana (Settle Coll), bk, photo, slides
Automation Activity & Vendor Info: (Cataloging) DRA; (Circulation) DRA; (Course Reserve) DRA; (OPAC) DRA; (Serials) DRA
Partic in BRS; Dialog Corporation; Kansas City Metropolitan Library & Information Network; Missouri Library Network Corporation; Mobius; OCLC Online Computer Library Center, Inc

LILBOURN

P LILBOURN MEMORIAL LIBRARY,* Lewis Ave, 63862. (Mail add: PO Box 282, 63862), SAN 309-0833. Tel: 573-688-2622. *Librn*, Naomi Peeler
Founded 1936. Pop 1,152; Circ 9,798
Library Holdings: Bk Vols 10,390
Open Tues-Fri 2-5

LOCKWOOD

P LOCKWOOD PUBLIC LIBRARY,* PO Box 286, 65682. SAN 309-0841. Tel: 417-232-4204. E-Mail: locklbr@ipa.net. *Librn*, Leota Queen
Pop 1,050; Circ 14,500
Library Holdings: Bk Vols 17,000
Special Collections: Dade County History; Lockwood Newspapers from 1890-1980
Open Mon, Tues & Thurs 8-5, Sat 8-12

LOUISIANA

P LOUISIANA PUBLIC LIBRARY,* 121 N Third St, 63353. SAN 309-085X. Tel: 573-754-4491. FAX: 573-754-4208. *Librn*, Aimee Preston
Founded 1904. Pop 3,954; Circ 17,323
Library Holdings: Bk Titles 16,000; Per Subs 57

MACKS CREEK

S GREEN GABLES LODGE LIBRARY,* Rte 1, Box 158, 65786. SAN 377-2136. Tel: 573-363-5352. FAX: 573-363-0012. *Librn*, Paul Schaefer
Library Holdings: Bk Vols 2,000; Per Subs 10

MACON

P MACON PUBLIC LIBRARY,* 210 N Rutherford, 63552. SAN 309-0868. Tel: 660-385-3314. FAX: 660-385-6610. *Dir*, Sarah Brown
Founded 1912. Pop 5,680; Circ 34,538
Jan 1997-Dec 1998 Income $92,411. Mats Exp $20,526. Sal $55,038
Library Holdings: Bk Vols 21,600; Per Subs 62
Subject Interests: Genealogy, Macon County, Mo hist
Partic in NE Mo Libr Network
Friends of the Library Group

MAPLEWOOD

P MAPLEWOOD PUBLIC LIBRARY, 7601 Manchester Ave, 63143. SAN 309-0876. Tel: 314-781-2174. FAX: 314-781-2191. Web Site: www.geocities.com/maplewoodpl. *Librn*, Terrence Donnelly; *Ch Servs*, Barbara Patten; Staff 2 (MLS 1, Non-MLS 1)
Founded 1935. Pop 9,009; Circ 65,201
Jul 1999-Jun 2000 Income $264,045, State $8,886, City $240,041, Locally Generated Income $15,118. Mats Exp $47,675, Books $32,424, Per/Ser (Incl. Access Fees) $5,093, Electronic Ref Mat (Incl. Access Fees) $10,158. Sal $138,571
Library Holdings: Bk Titles 42,065; Per Subs 118
Subject Interests: Local history
Automation Activity & Vendor Info: (Cataloging) epixtech, inc.; (Circulation) epixtech, inc.; (ILL) epixtech, inc.; (OPAC) epixtech, inc.; (Serials) epixtech, inc.
Publications: Booked Up (newsletter)
Partic in Municipal Libr Coop; Saint Louis Regional Library Network

MARBLE HILL

P BOLLINGER COUNTY LIBRARY,* 302 Conrad St, 63764. (Mail add: PO Box 919, 63764), SAN 309-0884. Tel: 573-238-2713. FAX: 573-238-2879. E-Mail: emz000@mail.connect.more.net. *Dir*, Eva M Dunn
Founded 1947
Library Holdings: Bk Vols 65,000; Per Subs 50
Subject Interests: Agriculture, Feminism, Handicraft, History, Natural science
Mem of SE Mo Libr Network
Open Tues, Wed & Fri 9-5, Thurs 9-8, Sat 9-1

MARCELINE

P MARCELINE CARNEGIE LIBRARY,* 119 E California, 64658. SAN 309-0892. Tel: 660-376-3223. FAX: 660-376-3577. *Librn*, Joyce Clapp
Founded 1920. Pop 2,622; Circ 7,096
Library Holdings: Bk Titles 14,850; Per Subs 46
Special Collections: Walt Disney Coll
Mem of NE Mo Libr Network
Open Mon-Fri 9-5 & Sat 9-12
Friends of the Library Group

MARSHALL

P MARSHALL PUBLIC LIBRARY, 214 N Lafayette B, 65340. SAN 370-6680. Tel: 660-886-3391. FAX: 660-886-2492. E-Mail: mplibrary@mid-mo.net. Web Site: www.marshallpubliclibrary.com. *Dir*, Karl Brockfeld; E-Mail: kbrockfeld@hotmail.com. Subject Specialists: *History*, Karl Brockfeld; Staff 10 (MLS 1, Non-MLS 9)
Founded 1990. Pop 12,711; Circ 83,941
Oct 1999-Sep 2000 Income (Main Library Only) $158,026, City $148,026, Locally Generated Income $10,000. Mats Exp Electronic Ref Mat (Incl. Access Fees) $3,500. Sal $50,000 (Prof $30,000)
Library Holdings: Bk Titles 37,054; Per Subs 98; Bks on Deafness & Sign Lang 35
Special Collections: Saline County Genealogy & Local History Coll
Automation Activity & Vendor Info: (Cataloging) Sagebrush Corporation; (Circulation) Sagebrush Corporation
Database Vendor: Ebsco - EbscoHost, OCLC - First Search
Open Mon-Thurs 9-9, Fri 9-6, Sat 9-5 & Sun 1-5
Friends of the Library Group

C MISSOURI VALLEY COLLEGE, Murrell Memorial Library, 500 E College, PO Box 1000, 65340. SAN 309-0906. Tel: 660-831-4123, 660-831-4181. FAX: 660-831-4037. Web Site: www.moval.edu. *Dir*, Pamela K Reeder; E-Mail: reederp@moval.edu; Staff 2 (MLS 2)
Founded 1889. Enrl 1,200; Fac 59
Library Holdings: Bk Vols 62,000; Per Subs 870
Subject Interests: Bus, Education
Special Collections: Cumberland Presbyterian Church Archives
Publications: Newsletter
Friends of the Library Group

MARYLAND HEIGHTS

S MARCHEM CORP LIBRARY,* 2500 Adie Rd, 63043. SAN 328-4042. Tel: 314-872-8700. FAX: 314-872-8750. *Librn*, John Lockard
Library Holdings: Bk Vols 100; Per Subs 25
Restriction: Staff use only

MARYVILLE

P MARYVILLE PUBLIC LIBRARY,* 509 N Main, 64468. SAN 309-0914. Tel: 660-582-5281. FAX: 660-582-2411. *Librn*, Diane Houston
Founded 1904. Pop 9,558; Circ 67,613
Library Holdings: Bk Vols 41,500; Per Subs 58
Subject Interests: Cookbooks, Genealogy, Local history
Open Mon, Tues, Wed & Fri 9-6, Thurs 9-7, Sat 9-3
Friends of the Library Group

S NODAWAY COUNTY HISTORICAL SOCIETY, Genealogy Society, 110 N Walnut St, 64468-2251. (Mail add: PO Box 214, 64468-0214), SAN 373-2363. Tel: 660-582-8176. *Curator*, Tom Carneal; *Librn*, Margaret Kelley
Subject Interests: Genealogy

C NORTHWEST MISSOURI STATE UNIVERSITY, B D Owens Library, 800 University Dr, 64468-6001. SAN 349-4284. Tel: 660-562-1192. Interlibrary Loan Service Tel: 660-562-1592. Circulation Tel: 660-562-1193. Reference Tel: 660-562-1591. FAX: 660-562-2153. Web Site: www.nwmissouri.edu/ww-root/northwest/admissions/library/index.html. *Dean of Libr*, Dr Patricia VanDyke; E-Mail: vandyke@mail.nwmissouri.edu; *ILL*, Glenn Morrow; *Tech Servs*, Madonna Kennedy; *Tech Servs*, Jean Osborn; *Ref*, Joyce M Meldrem; *Ref*, Frank Baudino; *Ref*, Vicki Wainscott; *Automation Syst Coordr*, Chuck Vaughn; *Ref*, Carolyn Johnson; *Bibliog Instr*, Connie Ury; *Coll Develop*, Mary Ellen Kimble; Staff 25 (MLS 7, Non-MLS 18)
Founded 1905. Highest Degree: Doctorate
Jul 1999-Jun 2000 Income $1,694,641. Mats Exp $563,387. Sal $684,129
Library Holdings: Bk Vols 227,054; Bk Titles 191,239; Per Subs 1,838
Special Collections: Missouri History & Government (Missouriana), multi-media
Partic in Missouri Library Network Corporation; OCLC Online Computer Library Center, Inc
Departmental Libraries:
HORACE MANN LEARNING CENTER LIBRARY, NWMSU, Brown Hall 121, 64468. SAN 349-4314. Tel: 660-562-1271. FAX: 660-562-1992. Web Site: www.nwmissouri.edu. *Librn*, Mary Jane Stiens; Staff 1 (MLS 1)
Subject Interests: Children lit
Special Collections: Elementary Curriculum; Learning Disabled Materials

MEMPHIS

P SCOTLAND COUNTY MEMORIAL LIBRARY, 306 W Madison, 63555. SAN 309-0922. Tel: 660-465-7042. TDD: 660-465-7192. FAX: 660-465-7334. *Librn*, Melissa Schuster; Staff 4 (Non-MLS 4)
Founded 1958. Pop 4,822; Circ 49,752
Jan 1999-Dec 1999 Income $104,454, State $6,512, County $78,240, Other $19,702. Mats Exp $18,208, Books $15,249, Per/Ser (Incl. Access Fees) $1,164, AV Equip $1,795. Sal $49,485
Library Holdings: Bk Vols 30,379; Per Subs 71; Bks on Deafness & Sign Lang 18
Subject Interests: Consumer health, Genealogy, Local history, Missouriana
Database Vendor: OCLC - First Search
Publications: Ella Ewing, Missouri Giantess
Partic in Missouri Library Network Corporation; OCLC Online Computer Library Center, Inc
Special Services for the Deaf - TDD
Open Mon, Wed & Fri 9-5:30, Tues & Thurs 9-7, Sat 9-1

MEXICO

S AUDRAIN COUNTY HISTORICAL SOCIETY, (Formerly Graceland), Graceland Library-American Saddlebred Museum Library, 501 S Muldrow St, 65265. (Mail add: PO Box 398, 65265), SAN 326-4726. Tel: 573-581-3910. E-Mail: achs@mexicomo.net. *Dir*, Kathryn Adams
Founded 1958
Library Holdings: Bk Vols 1,000
Subject Interests: Genealogy, Local history

P MEXICO-AUDRAIN COUNTY LIBRARY DISTRICT,* 305 W Jackson St, 65265. SAN 349-4349. Tel: 573-581-4939. FAX: 573-581-7510. E-Mail: macld@maain.missouri.org. Web Site: www.maain.missouri.org/library.html. *Librn*, Ray Hall; Staff 21 (MLS 2, Non-MLS 19)
Founded 1912
Library Holdings: Bk Vols 150,000; Bk Titles 86,000; Per Subs 154
Special Collections: Audrain County Genealogy
Partic in Mid-Mo Libr Network
Friends of the Library Group
Branches: 4
ED FRENCH MEMORIAL, 204 Second St, Laddonia, 63352. SAN 349-4403. Tel: 573-373-2393. Web Site: www.maain.missouri.org/library.html. *Librn*, Nancy Ware
Friends of the Library Group
FARBER BRANCH, 113 W Front St, Farber, 63345. SAN 349-4373. Tel: 573-249-2012. Web Site: www.maain.missouri.org/library.html. *Librn*, Vernelle Hull
Friends of the Library Group
MARTINSBURG BRANCH, 201 E Washington, Martinsburg, 65264. (Mail add: PO Box 12, Martinsburg, 65264), SAN 370-002X. Tel: 573-492-6254. Web Site: www.maain.missouri.org/library.html. *Librn*, Jean Aulbur
Friends of the Library Group
VANDALIA BRANCH, 309 S Main, Vandalia, 63382. SAN 349-4438. Tel: 573-594-6600. FAX: 573-594-3590. Web Site: www.maain.missouri.org/library.html. *Librn*, Helen Carter
Friends of the Library Group
Bookmobiles: 1. Librn, Linda Griffin

MILAN

P SULLIVAN COUNTY PUBLIC LIBRARY, 109 E Second St, 63556. SAN 309-0930. Tel: 660-265-3911. FAX: 660-265-3911. E-Mail: dax001@mail.connect.more.net. *Dir*, Susan O'Connor; *Asst Librn*, Evelyn Franklin; *Bkmobile Coordr*, Glenda Clark; Staff 4 (Non-MLS 4)
Founded 1972
Library Holdings: Bk Vols 38,895
Open Tues, Wed & Fri 9-5, Thurs 9-9, Sat 9-3
Bookmobiles: 1

MOBERLY

CR CENTRAL CHRISTIAN COLLEGE LIBRARY,* 911 Urbandale Dr E, 65270. SAN 321-1819. Tel: 660-263-3900. FAX: 660-263-3936. Web Site: cccb.edu. *Librn*, Gareth L Reese; E-Mail: glreese@cccb.edu; Staff 1 (MLS 1)
Founded 1957. Enrl 105; Fac 11; Highest Degree: Bachelor
1998-1999 Income $53,650. Mats Exp $6,525, Books $2,655, Per/Ser (Incl. Access Fees) $3,434, Presv $436. Sal $42,558
Library Holdings: Bk Vols 34,634; Bk Titles 23,515; Per Subs 140
Special Collections: Walter S Coble Mission Files Coll
Partic in Missouri Library Network Corporation

P LITTLE DIXIE REGIONAL LIBRARIES, 111 N Fourth St, 65270-1577. SAN 349-4462. Tel: 660-263-4426. FAX: 660-263-4024. Web Site: www.little-dixie.lib.mo.us. *Coll Develop, Dir*, Karen Hayden; *Ch Servs*, Paula Hayslip; *Ref*, Beverly Holder; Staff 3 (MLS 1, Non-MLS 2)
Founded 1966. Pop 31,198; Circ 172,697
Jan 2000-Dec 2000 Income (Main Library and Branch Library) $601,901, State $8,092, Federal $38,309, County $539,000, Other $16,500. Mats Exp $117,884, Books $87,738, Per/Ser (Incl. Access Fees) $16,732, AV Equip $13,414. Sal $260,481
Library Holdings: Bk Vols 136,000; Per Subs 268
Automation Activity & Vendor Info: (Cataloging) SIRSI; (Circulation) SIRSI; (Media Booking) SIRSI; (OPAC) SIRSI; (Serials) SIRSI
Friends of the Library Group

Branches: 3
DULANY MEMORIAL LIBRARY, 101 N Main, Paris, 65275-1398. SAN 349-4551. Tel: 660-327-4707. FAX: 660-327-4094. Web Site: www.little-dixie.lib.mo.us. *Librn*, Eleanor Roegge
HUNTSVILLE LIBRARY, 102 E Library St, Huntsville, 65259-1125. SAN 349-4497. Tel: 660-277-4518. FAX: 660-277-4518. Web Site: www.little-dixie.lib.mo.us. *Librn*, Lenora McMahan
MADISON BRANCH, PO Box 147, Madison, 65263-0147. SAN 349-4527. Tel: 660-291-3695. FAX: 660-291-8695. Web Site: www.little-dixie.lib.mo.us. *Librn*, Libby Brisendine

J MOBERLY AREA COMMUNITY COLLEGE, Kate Stamper Wilhite Library, 101 College Ave, 65270-1304. SAN 309-0957. Tel: 660-263-4110. FAX: 660-263-6448. Web Site: www.macc.cc.mo.us. *Librn*, Valerie Darst; E-Mail: valeried@macc.cc.mo.us
Founded 1927. Enrl 1,600; Fac 24
Library Holdings: Bk Titles 23,000; Per Subs 100
Subject Interests: Behav sci, Bus, History, Mgt, Natural science, Soc sci
Special Collections: Jack Conroy Memorial Library; Stamper Science & Technology Coll
Partic in Mobius
Open Mon-Thurs 7:30-8:30, Fri 7:30-4

S MOBERLY CORRECTIONAL CENTER LIBRARY, Missouri Department of Corrections, Bus Rte 63 S, 65270. (Mail add: PO Box 7, 65270), SAN 309-0949. Tel: 660-263-3778, Ext 421. FAX: 660-263-1730. *Librn*, Ronald R Hodill; Staff 2 (MLS 1, Non-MLS 1)
Founded 1963
Library Holdings: Bk Vols 6,949; Bk Titles 6,324; Per Subs 64; High Interest/Low Vocabulary Bk Vols 50
Subject Interests: Law
Publications: Chess Club Newsletter; MCC Library Newsletter
Partic in Mid-Mo Libr Network
Recreational reading, Law library

MONETT

P BARRY-LAWRENCE REGIONAL LIBRARY, 213 Sixth St, 65708. SAN 349-4586. Tel: 417-235-6646. FAX: 417-235-6799. E-Mail: exc000@mail.connect.more.net. Web Site: tlc.library.net/bll/. *Dir*, Jean H Berg; *ILL, Ref*, Cindy Frazier; Staff 33 (MLS 1, Non-MLS 32)
Founded 1954. Pop 56,393; Circ 435,668
Jul 1999-Jun 2000 Income (Main Library and Branch Library) $1,123,173, State $75,743, Federal $74,067, County $922,065, Other $51,298. Mats Exp $180,343, Books $164,383, Per/Ser (Incl. Access Fees) $14,532, Other Print Mats $1,428. Sal $455,549
Library Holdings: Bk Vols 143,537; Per Subs 278
Special Collections: Local History (Missouri Coll)
Automation Activity & Vendor Info: (Cataloging) TLC; (Circulation) TLC
Branches: 9
AURORA BRANCH, 202 Jefferson, Aurora, 65605. SAN 349-4594. Tel: 417-678-2036. FAX: 417-678-2041. E-Mail: sgt000@mail.connect.more.net. Web Site: tlc.library.net/bll/. *Br Coordr*, Martha Pettegrew
Library Holdings: Bk Vols 22,009
Open Mon-Thurs 8:30-7, Fri & Sat 8:30-5:30
Friends of the Library Group
CASSVILLE BRANCH, 1007 Main St, Cassville, 65625. SAN 349-4616. Tel: 417-847-2121. FAX: 417-847-4679. E-Mail: wcm000@mail.connect.more.net. Web Site: tlc.library.net/bll/. *Br Coordr*, Marion Stubblefield
Library Holdings: Bk Vols 17,593
Open Mon-Thurs 8:30-7, Fri & Sat 8:30-5:30
Friends of the Library Group
EAGLE ROCK BRANCH, PO Box 147, Eagle Rock, 65641. SAN 375-8745. Tel: 417-271-3186. FAX: 417-271-3186. E-Mail: wcm005@mail.connect.more.net. Web Site: tlc.library.net/bll/. *Br Coordr*, Arlene Burton
Library Holdings: Bk Vols 4,291
Open Tues-Fri 10-6, Sat 9-1
MARIONVILLE BRANCH, 22 E Washington, Marionville, 65705. SAN 349-4640. Tel: 417-463-2675. FAX: 417-463-2675. E-Mail: wcm220@mail.connect.more.net. Web Site: tlc.library.net/bll/. *Br Coordr*, Janea Kay Coker
Library Holdings: Bk Vols 11,348
Open Mon-Fri 9-5, Sat 9-1
MILLER BRANCH, 112 E Main St, PO Box 84, Miller, 65707. SAN 349-4675. Tel: 417-452-3466. FAX: 417-452-3466. E-Mail: wcm003@mail.connect.more.net. Web Site: tlc.library.net/bll/. *Br Coordr*, Frances Gardner
Library Holdings: Bk Vols 10,149
Open Mon-Fri 9-5, Sat 9-1
MONETT BRANCH, 213 Sixth St, 65708. SAN 349-4705. Tel: 417-235-6646, 417-235-7350. FAX: 417-235-6799. E-Mail: exc001@mail.connect.more.net. Web Site: tlc.library.net/bll/. *Br Coordr*, Cindy Frazier
Library Holdings: Bk Vols 33,530
Open Mon-Thurs 8:30-7, Fri & Sat 8:30-5:30
MOUNT VERNON BRANCH, 206 W Water, Mount Vernon, 65712. SAN 349-4764. Tel: 417-466-2921. FAX: 417-466-2936. E-Mail: sgt001@mail.connect.more.net. Web Site: tlc.library.net/bll/. *Br Coordr*, Connie Prater
Library Holdings: Bk Vols 23,769
Open Mon-Thurs 8:30-7, Fri & Sat 8:30-5:30
Friends of the Library Group
PURDY BRANCH, Hwy C at Fourth St, Purdy, 65734. SAN 349-473X. Tel: 417-442-7314. FAX: 417-442-7314. E-Mail: wcm004@mail.connect.more.net. Web Site: tlc.library.net/bll/. *Br Coordr*, Roxanne Wolf
Library Holdings: Bk Vols 8,572
Open Tues-Fri 9-6, Sat 9-1
SHELL KNOB BRANCH, Bridgeway Plaza, PO Box 349, Shell Knob, 65747. SAN 349-4756. Tel: 417-858-3618. FAX: 417-858-3618. E-Mail: wcm001@mail.connect.more.net. Web Site: tlc.library.net/bll. *Br Coordr*, Gina McIlrath
Library Holdings: Bk Vols 12,276
Open Tues-Fri 8:30-5:30, Sat 8:30-12:30

MONROE CITY

P MONROE CITY PUBLIC LIBRARY,* 220 N Main, 63456. SAN 309-0965. Tel: 573-735-2665. FAX: 573-735-2665. *Librn*, Mrs Welton Hood
Founded 1916. Pop 2,457
Library Holdings: Bk Titles 11,050; Per Subs 38
Subject Interests: Recreation
Open Summer: Mon-Fri 10-12 & 1-5 & Sat 10-12; Winter: Mon-Fri 1-5 & Sat 10-12

MONTGOMERY CITY

P MONTGOMERY CITY PUBLIC LIBRARY, 123 E Third St, 63361. SAN 309-0973. Tel: 573-564-8022. FAX: 573-564-6159. E-Mail: rnd000@mail.connect.more.net. Web Site: www.mlnc.org/~montgomery. *Librn*, Linda Eatherton
Founded 1927. Pop 2,281; Circ 30,110
Library Holdings: Bk Vols 14,097; Per Subs 41
Automation Activity & Vendor Info: (Cataloging) SIRSI; (Circulation) SIRSI; (OPAC) SIRSI
Open Mon 8-8, Tues & Thurs 8-6:30, Wed & Fri 8-5, Sat 9-1

MOUND CITY

P MOUND CITY PUBLIC LIBRARY,* 205 E Sixth St, 64470. SAN 309-0981. Tel: 660-442-5700. *Librn*, Melba Tebbe
Founded 1908. Circ 11,000
Library Holdings: Bk Vols 10,000; Per Subs 24
Subject Interests: Ch lit, Fiction
Open Mon-Fri 12-5, Sat 11-3

MOUNT VERNON

S MISSOURI VETERANS' HOME LIBRARY, 600 N Main, 65712. SAN 377-1148. Tel: 417-466-7103. FAX: 417-466-4040. *Librn*, James Dennis
Library Holdings: Bk Vols 300; Per Subs 10

MOUNTAIN VIEW

P MOUNTAIN VIEW PUBLIC LIBRARY,* 105 S Oak St, PO Box 1389, 65548. SAN 309-1007. Tel: 417-934-6154. FAX: 417-934-5100. E-Mail: vhh000@mail.connect.more.net. *Librn*, Lois Bostic; *Asst Librn*, Lois Smith
Founded 1950. Pop 2,036; Circ 26,452
Jul 1997-Jun 1998 Income $43,902, State $941, City $40,856, Locally Generated Income $2,060. Mats Exp $6,227, Books $6,000, Other Print Mats $138. Sal $32,402
Library Holdings: Bk Vols 20,000; Per Subs 50
Subject Interests: Hist of Ozarks scenic river
Publications: Poems for Children; Seasons of the Ozarks
Open Mon & Thurs 9-6, Tues, Wed & Fri 9-5, Sat 9-4
Friends of the Library Group

NEOSHO

J CROWDER COLLEGE, Learning Resources Center,* 601 Laclede Ave, 64850. SAN 309-1015. Tel: 417-451-3223, Ext 239. FAX: 417-451-4280. Web Site: www.crowder.college.net. *Dir*, Barbara Schade; E-Mail: bschade@crowdercollege.net; Staff 1 (MLS 1)
Founded 1964. Enrl 1,024; Fac 75 Sal $81,739 (Prof $36,572)
Library Holdings: Bk Vols 36,495; Bk Titles 34,258; Per Subs 167
Subject Interests: Hazardous mats, Waste water, Water
Automation Activity & Vendor Info: (Cataloging) Innovative Interfaces Inc.; (Circulation) Innovative Interfaces Inc.
Friends of the Library Group

P NEOSHO NEWTON COUNTY LIBRARY,* 201 W Spring, 64850. SAN 349-4799. Tel: 417-451-4231. FAX: 417-451-6438. E-Mail: ymf004@mall.connect.more.vet. *Dir*, Jack Wood
Founded 1956. Pop 42,000; Circ 157,180
Jan 1999-Dec 1999 Income $379,808, State $11,521, County $345,287, Locally Generated Income $23,000. Mats Exp $72,000, Books $69,000, Per/Ser (Incl. Access Fees) $3,000. Sal $166,251 (Prof $28,500)
Library Holdings: Bk Titles 88,222; Per Subs 120
Database Vendor: epixtech, inc.
Partic in OCLC Online Computer Library Center, Inc
Friends of the Library Group

NEVADA

J COTTEY COLLEGE, Blanche Skiff Ross Memorial Library, 225 S College St, 64772. (Mail add: 1000 W Austin, 64772), SAN 309-1023. Tel: 417-667-8181, Ext 2153. FAX: 417-448-1040. Web Site: www.cottey.edu. *Dir*, Nancy A Hill; E-Mail: nhill@cottey.edu; *Ref*, Rebecca Kiel; E-Mail: rkiel@cottey.edu; Staff 5 (MLS 2, Non-MLS 3)
Founded 1884. Enrl 300; Fac 35; Highest Degree: Associate
Library Holdings: Bk Titles 54,525; Per Subs 205
Subject Interests: Gen liberal arts, Women, Women's issues
Special Collections: College Archives
Automation Activity & Vendor Info: (Acquisitions) SIRSI; (Cataloging) SIRSI; (Circulation) SIRSI; (OPAC) SIRSI; (Serials) SIRSI
Database Vendor: Ebsco - EbscoHost, OCLC - First Search, ProQuest
Function: ILL available
Partic in Morenet

M NEVADA HABILITATION CENTER LIBRARY,* 2323 N Ash St, 64772. SAN 309-104X. Tel: 417-667-7833. FAX: 417-448-1138.
Founded 1975
Library Holdings: Bk Vols 500
Subject Interests: Mental retardation

P NEVADA PUBLIC LIBRARY, 218 W Walnut, 64772-0931. (Mail add: PO Box B, 64772-0931), SAN 309-1031. Tel: 417-448-2770. FAX: 417-448-2771. E-Mail: rpr000@mail.connect.more.net. *Coll Develop, Dir*, Marlene Hizer; *Ad Servs*, Kathe Dipman; Staff 3 (Non-MLS 3)
Founded 1898. Pop 8,599; Circ 80,000
Jul 1999-Jun 2000 Income $228,831, State $6,336, City $178,951, Federal $26,282, Other $17,262. Mats Exp $21,315, Books $15,630, Per/Ser (Incl. Access Fees) $3,755, Presv $100, Micro $230, Other Print Mats $1,500, Manuscripts & Archives $100. Sal $84,929 (Prof $27,500)
Library Holdings: Bk Vols 40,710; Bk Titles 40,600; Per Subs 68; High Interest/Low Vocabulary Bk Vols 25; Spec Interest Per Sub 12; Bks on Deafness & Sign Lang 18
Database Vendor: OCLC - First Search
Special Services for the Deaf - TDD
Special Services for the Blind - Computers with Voice Synthesizer
Friends of the Library Group

NORBORNE

P NORBORNE PUBLIC LIBRARY, 109 E Second St, 64668. SAN 309-1066. Tel: 660-593-3514. FAX: 660-593-3514. *Librn*, Doris S Wightman
Founded 1930. Pop 931; Circ 7,844
Apr 1999-Mar 2000 Income $6,514, State $421, City $5,058, Other $1,035. Mats Exp $4,600, Books $4,000, Per/Ser (Incl. Access Fees) $400, AV Equip $200. Sal $1,500 (Prof $2,100)
Library Holdings: Bk Vols 10,000; Per Subs 20; High Interest/Low Vocabulary Bk Vols 10
Subject Interests: Town hist
Open Mon-Fri 8-12 & 1-5, Sat 8-12

NORTH KANSAS CITY

R FIRST BAPTIST CHURCH LIBRARY, 2205 Iron St, 64116. SAN 309-1074. Tel: 816-842-1175. FAX: 816-842-4425. *In Charge*, Craig Kubic
Founded 1958 Income $1,200. Mats Exp $1,200
Library Holdings: Bk Vols 2,500; Per Subs 10
Subject Interests: Biog, Fiction, Religious lit
Friends of the Library Group

M NORTH KANSAS CITY HOSPITAL, Medical Library,* 2800 Clay Edwards Dr, 64116. SAN 373-2371. Tel: 816-691-1692. FAX: 816-346-7192.
1997-1998 Income $159,439. Mats Exp $103,000, Books $25,000, Per/Ser (Incl. Access Fees) $70,000, Micro $8,000. Sal $32,000
Library Holdings: Bk Vols 3,500; Per Subs 22
Subject Interests: Allied health, Nursing
Partic in Health Sciences Library Network of Kansas City, Inc; OCLC Online Computer Library Center, Inc

P NORTH KANSAS CITY PUBLIC LIBRARY,* 715 E 23rd Ave, 64116-3372. SAN 309-1082. Tel: 816-221-3360. FAX: 816-221-8298. E-Mail: nkc_jud@kcpl.lib.mo.us. Web Site: www.nkcpl.lib.mo.us. *Dep Dir*, Jobeth Bradbury; *Librn*, Walter J Hartmetz; *Ch Servs*, Nancy Robinson; *Tech Servs*, Carol Bryant; *Per*, Paula Kemper; *ILL*, Kathy Perry; Staff 7 (MLS 2, Non-MLS 5)
Founded 1939. Pop 4,130; Circ 76,994
Oct 1998-Sep 1999 Income $557,523, State $1,500, City $541,140, Federal $7,217, Other $7,666. Mats Exp $107,505, Books $51,578, Per/Ser (Incl. Access Fees) $22,470, Micro $529, Electronic Ref Mat (Incl. Access Fees) $22,800. Sal $273,998 (Prof $82,000)
Library Holdings: Bk Vols 45,347; Per Subs 180
Automation Activity & Vendor Info: (Acquisitions) DRA; (Cataloging) DRA; (Circulation) DRA; (ILL) DRA; (OPAC) DRA; (Serials) DRA
Database Vendor: DRA
Partic in Kansas City Libr Consortium; Kansas City Metropolitan Library & Information Network
Friends of the Library Group

OREGON

P OREGON PUBLIC LIBRARY,* 103 S Washington St, PO Box 288, 64473. SAN 309-1112. Tel: 660-446-3586. FAX: 660-446-3586. E-Mail: lib1@southholt.net. *Librn*, Allison Russell
Founded 1938. Pop 1,000; Circ 6,741
Library Holdings: Bk Vols 14,000; Per Subs 15
Open Mon-Sat 2-5

OSCEOLA

P SAINT CLAIR COUNTY LIBRARY,* Chestnut & Main, PO Box 575, 64776-0370. SAN 309-1120. Tel: 417-646-2214. FAX: 417-646-8643. E-Mail: jgf000@mail.connect.more.net. *Dir*, Ruth Lewis
Founded 1948. Pop 7,365; Circ 60,885
Library Holdings: Bk Titles 34,697; Per Subs 32
Special Collections: County Historical Society
Bookmobiles: 1

OZARK

P CHRISTIAN COUNTY LIBRARY,* 1005 N Fourth Ave, 65721. SAN 309-1139. Tel: 417-581-2432. FAX: 417-581-8855. E-Mail: ruf000@mail.connect.more.net. Web Site: www.mlnc.com/~ccl/. *Librn*, Mabel Gaye Phillips; *Asst Librn*, Ruth Davis; *Ch Servs, Ref*, Lucinda Dailey; *Tech Servs*, Kenneth Huff; Staff 3 (MLS 3)
Founded 1956. Pop 32,644
Jan 1997-Dec 1998 Income $290,118. Mats Exp $52,833, Books $35,544, Per/Ser (Incl. Access Fees) $7,549, Presv $1,000. Sal $177,060 (Prof $72,000)
Library Holdings: Bk Vols 55,000
Subject Interests: Antiques, Crafts
Special Collections: Southwest Missouri & the Ozarks
Friends of the Library Group

PALMYRA

P PALMYRA BICENTENNIAL PUBLIC LIBRARY,* 212 S Main St, 63461. SAN 309-1147. Tel: 573-769-2830. FAX: 573-769-2830. E-Mail: pbpl@nemonet.com. *Librn*, Carol Brentlinger
Founded 1913. Pop 9,000
Library Holdings: Bk Vols 14,000; Per Subs 24
Subject Interests: Local history
Special Collections: Civil War; History Local Battles; Mary Poppins Coll
Publications: Local paper column (weekly)
Open Mon & Wed-Fri 12:30-5, Tues 10-11:30 & 12:30-7, Sat 10-2:30

PARK HILLS

J MINERAL AREA COLLEGE, Learning Resources Center,* Hwy 67, PO Box 1000, 63601-1000. SAN 308-9835. Tel: 573-518-2177. FAX: 573-518-2162. Web Site: www.mac.cc.mo.us/lrc/. *Dir*, Chris Burns; E-Mail: chris@mail.mac.cc.mo.us; Staff 1 (MLS 1)
Founded 1969. Enrl 3,000; Fac 81
Jul 1998-Jun 1999 Mats Exp $185,854. Sal $117,571
Library Holdings: Bk Vols 52,489; Bk Titles 28,869; Per Subs 203

P PARK HILLS PUBLIC LIBRARY,* 8 Municipal Dr, 63601. SAN 308-9827. Tel: 573-431-4842. FAX: 573-431-2110. E-Mail: jmm002@pop.connect.more.net. *Dir*, Leann Marler; *Asst Dir*, Mary Russell
Founded 1934. Pop 7,866; Circ 34,633
Oct 1999-Sep 2000 Income $84,080. Mats Exp $14,700, Books $13,000, Per/Ser (Incl. Access Fees) $1,700. Sal $53,720
Library Holdings: Bk Vols 32,919; Per Subs 50
Subject Interests: Local history
Automation Activity & Vendor Info: (Cataloging) Follett; (Circulation) Follett
Open Mon & Tues 11-8, Wed-Fri 11-5, Sat 9-12
Friends of the Library Group

PARKVILLE

C PARK UNIVERSITY LIBRARY, 8700 NW River Park Dr, 64152-3795. SAN 309-1155. Tel: 816-741-2000, Ext 6285. FAX: 816-741-4911. Web Site: www.kepl.lib.mo.us. *Dir*, Ann Schultis; E-Mail: aschultis@mail.park.edu; *ILL*, Betty Vestal; *Cat*, Betty Dusing; *Acq*, Louise Bagley; *Circ*, Carolyn Elwess
Founded 1875. Enrl 935; Fac 56; Highest Degree: Master
Library Holdings: Bk Titles 134,750; Per Subs 775
Special Collections: History (Platte County Historical Society Archives); Park College History
Automation Activity & Vendor Info: (Cataloging) DRA; (Circulation) DRA
Publications: Friends of the Library Newsletter; The Dusty Shelf
Partic in Health Sci Libr Group of Greater Kansas City; Kansas City Metropolitan Library & Information Network
Friends of the Library Group

PIERCE CITY

P PIERCE CITY PUBLIC LIBRARY, 100 W Main, 65723. SAN 309-1171. Tel: 417-476-5419. E-Mail: pclibrary@sofnet.com. *Librn*, Carmen Archer
Founded 1933. Pop 1,300; Circ 4,888
Library Holdings: Bk Vols 20,000; Per Subs 12
Open Mon-Sat 2:30-4:30, Tues 7-9, Thurs 12-4
Friends of the Library Group

PINEVILLE

P MCDONALD COUNTY LIBRARY, 1/4 mile N of Square, 808 Bailey Rd, 64856. SAN 309-118X. Tel: 417-223-4489. FAX: 417-223-4011. E-Mail: bwk000@mail.connect.more.net. Web Site: www.mlnc.org/~mcdonald. *Coll Develop, Dir*, Nancy Campbell; *Asst Librn*, Joyce Hollums
Founded 1949. Pop 19,738; Circ 68,539
Jan 1999-Dec 1999 Income $185,558, State $20,900, Federal $22,914, County $129,876, Locally Generated Income $10,759, Other $1,109. Mats Exp $39,858, Books $27,985, Per/Ser (Incl. Access Fees) $2,692, AV Equip $6,735, Electronic Ref Mat (Incl. Access Fees) $2,446. Sal $83,778 (Prof $23,304)
Library Holdings: Bk Vols 33,000; Per Subs 50
Special Collections: Jess James Coll
Database Vendor: Ebsco - EbscoHost, OCLC - First Search
Friends of the Library Group

POINT LOOKOUT

COLLEGE OF THE OZARKS
C LYONS MEMORIAL LIBRARY, 1 Opportunity Ave, 65726. Tel: 417-334-6411, Ext 3411. FAX: 417-334-3085. Web Site: www.cofo.edu. *Dir, Tech Servs*, Nancy S Anderson; E-Mail: n-anders@cofo.edu; *Media Spec*, Gwen Simmons; *Online Servs, Ref*, Ronald D Wyly; *Circ*, Tammy Montavy; Staff 3 (MLS 3)
Founded 1906. Enrl 1,478; Fac 93; Highest Degree: Bachelor
Jun 1997-May 1998 Income $408,206. Mats Exp $146,780, Books $66,232, Per/Ser (Incl. Access Fees) $55,548. Sal $238,117 (Prof $148,035)
Library Holdings: Bk Vols 114,549; Per Subs 644
Special Collections: Ozarks (Ozarkiana Coll), bks, photogs, tapes, mss, letters
Partic in Missouri Library Network Corporation; OCLC Online Computer Library Center, Inc
C RALPH FOSTER MUSEUM - BROWNELL RESEARCH CENTER LIBRARY, One Opportunity Ave, PO Box 17, 65726. Tel: 417-334-6411, Ext 3564. FAX: 417-335-2618. *In Charge*, Annette Sain
Founded 1975
Library Holdings: Bk Titles 3,500; Per Subs 12
Subject Interests: History
Special Collections: Artifacts & Antiques Coll

POPLAR BLUFF

P POPLAR BLUFF PUBLIC LIBRARY,* 318 N Main St, 63901-5199. SAN 349-4918. Tel: 573-686-8639. FAX: 573-785-6876. Web Site: poplarbluff.library.org. *Dir*, Jacqueline Thomas
Founded 1916. Pop 25,000; Circ 100,356
Oct 1999-Sep 2000 Income $345,000. Mats Exp $49,000, Books $30,000, Per/Ser (Incl. Access Fees) $7,000, AV Equip $12,000. Sal $176,000
Library Holdings: Bk Vols 40,000; Per Subs 152
Automation Activity & Vendor Info: (Acquisitions) TLC; (Cataloging) TLC; (Circulation) TLC
Database Vendor: OCLC - First Search
Friends of the Library Group
Branches: 1
TWIN TOWERS, 506 Hazel Eer, 63901. SAN 349-4977. Tel: 573-785-9901. *Librn*, Geneva Winsome
Friends of the Library Group

P POPLAR BLUFF REGIONAL CENTER LIBRARY,* 2351 Kanell Blvd, PO Box 460, 63902. SAN 377-4066. Tel: 573-840-9300. FAX: 573-840-9311. *Librn*, Sharon Wagner
Library Holdings: Bk Vols 30

S W E SEARS YOUTH CENTER LIBRARY,* 9400 Sears Lane, 63901. SAN 309-1198. Tel: 573-840-9280. FAX: 573-686-6904.
Jul 1998-Jun 1999 Income $4,000. Mats Exp $4,000
Library Holdings: Bk Titles 5,000; Per Subs 15
Partic in Mo Statewide ILL Network

J THREE RIVERS COMMUNITY COLLEGE, Rutland Library, 2080 Three Rivers Blvd, 63901. SAN 309-1201. Tel: 573-840-9654. FAX: 573-840-9659. *Dir*, Gordon Johnston; E-Mail: gordonj@trcc.cc.mo.us; Staff 1 (MLS 1)
Founded 1966
Library Holdings: Bk Titles 25,000; Per Subs 250
Special Collections: Civil War; Missouri History; Ozarks History
Automation Activity & Vendor Info: (Acquisitions) Sagebrush Corporation
Publications: Stack Attack
Partic in SE Mo Libr Network

GM VETERANS ADMINISTRATION MEDICAL CENTER, (Formerly Department Of Veterans Affairs), John J Pershing Library, 1500 N Westwood, 63901-3318. SAN 309-121X. Tel: 573-686-4120. FAX: 573-778-4121. *Dir*, Genise Denton
Library Holdings: Bk Vols 2,344; Bk Titles 1,581; Per Subs 83
Partic in Dialog Corporation; Medline; Midcontinental Regional Med Libr Program; Vets Admin Libr Network

PORTAGEVILLE

P NEW MADRID COUNTY LIBRARY, 309 E Maine, 63873. SAN 309-1228. Tel: 573-379-3583. FAX: 573-379-9220. E-Mail: ysm001@mail.connect.more.net. *Dir*, Tom Sadler
Founded 1948. Pop 18,954; Circ 65,721
Jan 1999-Dec 2000 Income $429,430, State $8,360, County $365,371, Locally Generated Income $15,249, Other $40,450. Mats Exp $50,597, Books $42,000, Per/Ser (Incl. Access Fees) $2,397, AV Equip $6,200. Sal $165,195 (Prof $30,000)
Library Holdings: Bk Vols 67,320
Subject Interests: Genealogy, Local history
Branches: 3
MOREHOUSE SERVICE CENTER, 204 Beech St, Morehouse, 63868. SAN 377-3744. Tel: 573-667-5003. *Librn*, Maxine Launius
Library Holdings: Bk Vols 5,000; Bk Titles 20
NEW MADRID MEMORIAL, 431 Mill, New Madrid, 63869. SAN 321-9453. Tel: 573-748-2378. *Librn*, Martha Hunter
RHODES MEMORIAL, Main St, Gideon, 63848. SAN 308-9916. Tel: 573-448-3554. *Librn*, Ida Werner

POTOSI

P WASHINGTON COUNTY LIBRARY, 235 E High, 63664. SAN 309-1236. Tel: 573-438-4691. FAX: 573-438-6423. E-Mail: vrp000@mail.connect.more.net. Web Site: www.rootsweb.com/~mowashin/wclib.html. *Librn*, Dorothy A Lore
Founded 1948. Pop 20,212; Circ 65,197
Jan 1999-Dec 1999 Income $244,346. Mats Exp $65,950. Sal $98,893
Library Holdings: Bk Vols 56,515; Bk Titles 48,472; Per Subs 132
Special Collections: Historical Coll, bks & micro
Mem of Missouri Libr Film Coop
Partic in Missouri Library Network Corporation
Bookmobiles: 1

PRINCETON

P MERCER COUNTY LIBRARY,* 601 Grant, 64673. SAN 309-1244. Tel: 660-748-3725. FAX: 660-748-3723. E-Mail: pii000@mail.connect.more.net. *Librn*, Judy Cox
Founded 1954. Pop 4,610; Circ 35,475
Library Holdings: Bk Vols 20,000
Subject Interests: Genealogy
Partic in OCLC Online Computer Library Center, Inc

REPUBLIC

S NATIONAL PARK SERVICE, Mr & Mrs John K Hulston Civil War Library, Wilson's Creek National Battlefield, 6424 W Farm Rd 182, 65738-9514. SAN 321-0006. Tel: 417-732-2662. FAX: 417-732-1167. E-Mail: wicrnb@hotmail.com. Web Site: www.nps.gov/wicr. *In Charge*, Richard Lusardi; Staff 2 (Non-MLS 2)
Founded 1960

Library Holdings: Bk Titles 4,500
Subject Interests: Civil War, SW MO
Special Services for the Deaf - Staff with knowledge of sign language
Friends of the Library Group

RICHLAND

P PULASKI COUNTY LIBRARY DISTRICT, 111 Camden St, PO Box 340, 65556. SAN 349-4225. Tel: 573-765-3642. FAX: 573-765-5395. E-Mail: okays@llion.org. *Librn*, Osa Kays
Library Holdings: Bk Vols 50,000
Friends of the Library Group
Branches: 2
CROCKER BRANCH, PO Box 854, Crocker, 65452. Tel: 573-736-5592. *Librn*, Sharon McIntosh
WAYNESVILLE BRANCH, 306 Historic Rte 66 W, Waynesville, 65583. SAN 349-425X. Tel: 573-774-2965. FAX: 573-774-3424. *Librn*, Sharon Hanby
Friends of the Library Group

RICHMOND

S RAY COUNTY HISTORICAL SOCIETY & MUSEUM LIBRARY,* 901 W Royle, PO Box 2, 64085-0002. SAN 372-6568. Tel: 816-776-2305. *Librn*, Willie Parker
Founded 1973
Library Holdings: Bk Vols 10,000
Special Collections: Jesse James Coll; Russell Ogg Coll; William Burke Coll
Publications: The Looking Glass (quarterly newsletter)
Open Wed-Sat 12-5

P RAY COUNTY LIBRARY,* 219 S College, 64085. SAN 309-1252. Tel: 816-470-3291. FAX: 816-776-5794. E-Mail: janicecoxproffit@hotmail.com. *Dir*, Janice G Cox Proffitt
Founded 1947. Pop 22,100
Jan 1997-Dec 1997 Income $222,211, State $9,690, Federal $177,239, Locally Generated Income $9,377, Other $25,905. Mats Exp $35,874, Books $33,933, Per/Ser (Incl. Access Fees) $1,941. Sal $87,887 (Prof $22,000)
Library Holdings: Bk Titles 80,000; Per Subs 117
Mem of NW Mo Libr Network
Partic in Missouri Library Network Corporation; NW Missouri Libr Network
Open Mon-Thur 8:30-6, Fri 8:30-5 & Sat 9-12
Friends of the Library Group

RICHMOND HEIGHTS

P RICHMOND HEIGHTS MEMORIAL LIBRARY, 8001 Dale Ave, 63117. SAN 309-1260. Tel: 314-645-6202. FAX: 314-655-3565. E-Mail: phvoo1@mail.connect.more.net. *Dir*, Jeanette Piquet; E-Mail: jpiquet@richmondheights.org; *Ad Servs*, Thomas Cooper; *Ch Servs*, Betsy Simmons; E-Mail: phv002@mail.connect.more.net; Staff 5 (MLS 2, Non-MLS 3)
Founded 1935. Pop 9,463
Jul 2000-Jun 2001 Income $518,800. Mats Exp $122,700, Books $83,000, Per/Ser (Incl. Access Fees) $10,500, AV Equip $9,200, Electronic Ref Mat (Incl. Access Fees) $20,000. Sal $186,900
Library Holdings: Bk Titles 39,804; Per Subs 5,642
Automation Activity & Vendor Info: (Cataloging) epixtech, inc.
Partic in Municipal Libr Coop; Saint Louis Regional Library Network
Open Mon-Thurs 9-9, Fri & Sat 9-5

ROCK HILL

P ROCK HILL PUBLIC LIBRARY,* 9620 Manchester Rd, 63119. SAN 309-1279. Tel: 314-962-4723. FAX: 314-962-3932. E-Mail: cht000@mail.connect.more.net. Web Site: www.vcpl.lib.mo.us.5555. *Dir*, Mrs K Sallade
Founded 1943. Pop 5,217; Circ 29,111
Library Holdings: Bk Vols 28,000; Per Subs 65
Mem of St Louis Regional Libr Network
Partic in Municipal Libr Coop
Open Mon-Fri 12:30-9 & Sat 10-2
Friends of the Library Group

ROCK PORT

P ATCHISON COUNTY LIBRARY,* 200 S Main St, 64482-1532. SAN 349-5000. Tel: 660-744-5404. FAX: 660-744-2861. *Dir*, Janice S Rosenbohm; *Librn*, Darlene Schmidt; *Librn*, Karen Culjat; *Librn*, Rebecca Adams
Founded 1946. Pop 8,605; Circ 46,998
Jan 1998-Dec 1999 Income $220,822. Mats Exp $27,486. Sal $87,873
Library Holdings: Bk Vols 60,000; Per Subs 85
Subject Interests: Genealogy, Local history
Partic in Mo Libr Film Coop; NW Missouri Libr Network
Open Mon-Fri 9-5, Sat 9-12
Branches: 2
FAIRFAX BRANCH, 111 E Main, Fairfax, 64446. SAN 349-5035. Tel: 660-686-2204. *Librn*, Shirley Adams
TARKIO BRANCH, 308 Main, Tarkio, 64491. SAN 349-506X. Tel: 660-736-5832. *Librn*, Cheryl Freeman
Bookmobiles: 1. Circ 11,000

ROLLA

G MISSOURI DEPARTMENT OF NATURAL RESOURCES, Division of Geology & Land Survey Library,* 111 Fairgrounds Rd, PO Box 250, 65401. SAN 309-1287. Tel: 573-368-2100. FAX: 573-368-2111. *In Charge*, Carolyn Ellis
Founded 1853
Library Holdings: Bk Titles 57,400; Per Subs 37
Special Collections: Missouri Geology (Fowler File & Ed Clark Museum), bks, artifacts, maps

P ROLLA FREE PUBLIC LIBRARY, 900 Pine St, 65401. SAN 309-1295. Tel: 573-364-2604. FAX: 573-341-5768. Interlibrary Loan Service E-Mail: illrpl@fidmail.com. *Dir*, Cheryl A Goltz; Staff 1 (MLS 1)
Founded 1938. Pop 14,100; Circ 267,441
Jul 1999-Jun 2000 Income $299,031, State $10,878, City $250,089, Locally Generated Income $19,292, Other $18,772. Mats Exp $296,395, Books $39,154, Per/Ser (Incl. Access Fees) $6,889, Presv $127, Micro $638, AV Equip $6,148, Electronic Ref Mat (Incl. Access Fees) $2,842. Sal $167,654 (Prof $42,360)
Library Holdings: Bk Vols 48,000; Per Subs 121
Subject Interests: Missouriana
Automation Activity & Vendor Info: (Cataloging) TLC; (Circulation) TLC
Special Services for the Deaf - TDD
Special Services for the Blind - Bks on tape; Braille
Open: Mon-Thurs 9-9, Fri & Sat 9-5, Sun 1:30-5
Friends of the Library Group

C UNIVERSITY OF MISSOURI, Western Historical Manuscript Collection - Rolla, G-3 UMR Library, 1870 Miner Circle, 65409-0060. SAN 326-4548. Tel: 573-341-4874. E-Mail: whmcinfo@umr.edu. Web Site: www.umr.edu/~whmcinfo/. *Assoc Dir*, Mark C Stauter; E-Mail: mstauter@umr.edu; Staff 2 (Non-MLS 2)
Subject Interests: History, Minerals, Mining, Missouri hist
Special Collections: State Historical Society of Missouri; Western Historical Manuscript Coll
Function: Archival collection
Partic in Asn of Research Libraries

C UNIVERSITY OF MISSOURI-ROLLA, Curtis Laws Wilson Library, 1870 Miner Circle, 65409-0060. SAN 309-1317. Tel: 573-341-4227. Circulation Tel: 573-341-4008. Reference Tel: 573-341-4007. FAX: 573-341-4233. E-Mail: library@umr.edu. Web Site: www.umr.edu/~library/. *Dir*, Jean S Eisenman; Tel: 573-341-4011, E-Mail: jse@umr.edu; *Acq*, Betty Sanders; *Acq of Monographs*, Minnie Bruer; Tel: 573-341-4009, E-Mail: mbreuer@umr.edu; *Per*, Fay Watkins; *Govt Doc*, Georgia Hall; E-Mail: georgiah@umr.edu; *Head Ref*, J Andrew Stewart; Tel: 573-341-4015, E-Mail: astewart@umr.edu; *Acq of New Ser*, Rebecca Merrell; Tel: 573-341-4013, E-Mail: rmerrell@umr.edu; *Head, Circ*, Mary Jo Barbush-Weiss; Tel: 573-341-4008, E-Mail: mjbw@umr.edu; *ILL*, Annette Howard; Tel: 573-341-4006, E-Mail: ahoward@umr.edu; *Syst Coordr*, Allen Wilkins; Tel: 573-341-4010, E-Mail: awilkins@umr.edu; Staff 26 (MLS 11, Non-MLS 15)
Founded 1871. Enrl 4,715; Fac 400; Highest Degree: Doctorate
Jul 1999-Jun 2000 Income $2,242,402, State $2,183,030, Locally Generated Income $32,519, Other $26,853. Mats Exp $1,219,651, Books $205,331, Per/Ser (Incl. Access Fees) $785,513, Presv $21,974, Micro $10,583, Electronic Ref Mat (Incl. Access Fees) $112,254. Sal $649,202 (Prof $277,845)
Library Holdings: Bk Vols 393,039; Bk Titles 255,768; Per Subs 1,495
Subject Interests: Engineering, Geology, Manufacturing, Mat sci, Metallurgy, Mining
Automation Activity & Vendor Info: (Acquisitions) Innovative Interfaces Inc.; (Cataloging) Innovative Interfaces Inc.; (Circulation) Innovative Interfaces Inc.; (OPAC) Innovative Interfaces Inc.; (Serials) Innovative Interfaces Inc.
Database Vendor: Dialog, Ebsco - EbscoHost, GaleNet, IAC - SearchBank, Lexis-Nexis, OCLC - First Search, OVID Technologies, ProQuest, Silverplatter Information Inc., Wilson - Wilson Web
Partic in Missouri Library Network Corporation; OCLC Online Computer Library Center, Inc

SAINT CHARLES

C LINDENWOOD UNIVERSITY, Margaret L Butler Library, 209 S Kings Hwy, 63301. SAN 309-1333. Tel: 636-949-4820. FAX: 636-949-4822. E-Mail: library@lindenwood.edu. Web Site: www.lindenwood.edu/butlerlibrary. *Info Res*, Shawn Strecker; Tel: 636-949-4818, E-Mail: sstrecker@lindenwood.edu; *Librn*, Anne Booker; Tel: 636-949-4820, E-Mail: abooker@lindenwood.edu; *Ref*, Carl Hubenschmidt; Tel: 636-949-4818, E-Mail: chubenschmidt@lindenwood.edu; *Ref*, Mark McWeeney. Subject

Specialists: *Science*, Carl Hubenschmidt; Staff 6 (MLS 4, Non-MLS 2)
Founded 1827. Pop 10,000; Enrl 3,400; Fac 105; Highest Degree: Master
Library Holdings: Bk Vols 140,167; Per Subs 523
Special Collections: McKissack Center for Black Children's Literature
Database Vendor: Ebsco - EbscoHost, Innovative Interfaces INN - View, OCLC - First Search, Silverplatter Information Inc., Wilson - Wilson Web
Partic in Higher Educ Coun of St Louis; Missouri Library Network Corporation; Mobius; OCLC Online Computer Library Center, Inc; Saint Louis Regional Library Network
Open Mon-Thurs 8-12, Fri 8-5, Sat 8-4:30 & Sun 2-12

S SAINT CHARLES COUNTY HISTORICAL SOCIETY ARCHIVES,* 101 S Main St, 63301-2802. SAN 329-9295. Tel: 636-946-9828. *Archivist*, Carolyn Roth
Library Holdings: Bk Titles 325
Special Collections: Circuit & Probate Court Records- St Charles County; indexes; photographs
Open Mon, Wed & Fri 10-3 & Sat 10-3 (2nd & 4th Sat of each month)

S SAINT JOSEPH HEALTH CENTER, Health Science Library, 300 First Capitol Dr, 63301. SAN 327-1595. Tel: 636-947-5109. FAX: 636-947-5253. *Coordr, Mgr*, Lucille Dykas; E-Mail: ldykas@ssmhcs.com
Library Holdings: Bk Titles 400; Per Subs 80
Subject Interests: Medicine
Partic in Saint Louis Medical Librarians Consortia

SAINT JAMES

P JAMES MEMORIAL LIBRARY, 300 W Scioto St, 65559. SAN 309-135X. Tel: 573-265-7211. FAX: 573-265-8770. E-Mail: tjamesf@stjames.k12.mo.us. *Dir*, Diana Jenkins
Founded 1951. Pop 6,500; Circ 67,366
Library Holdings: Bk Titles 27,000; Per Subs 90
Special Collections: History of Ozarks, photog
Publications: Monthly newsletter
Open Mon 12-8, Tues-Sat 10-5

S MISSOURI VETERANS' HOME LIBRARY, 620 N Jefferson St, 65559. SAN 309-1368. Tel: 573-265-3271. FAX: 573-265-5771. *Librn*, Sandy Pauley; *Librn*, Sharon Tolliver
Library Holdings: Bk Vols 500

SAINT JOSEPH

S BOEHRINGER INGELHEIM ANIMAL HEALTH, INC LIBRARY,* 2621 N Belt Hwy, 64506. SAN 309-1422. Tel: 816-233-2571. FAX: 816-233-0215. *Dir Libr Serv, Librn*, Sharon Clary
Founded 1955
Library Holdings: Bk Vols 1,000
Subject Interests: Bacteriology, Chemotherapy, Immunology, Med res, Parasitology, Pathology, Pharmaceuticals, Veterinary medicine, Virology
Open Mon-Fri 7:30-4

R FIRST CHRISTIAN CHURCH LIBRARY, 927 Faraon St, 64501. SAN 309-1392. Tel: 816-233-2556. *Librn*, Maxine Klikenbeard
Founded 1957
Library Holdings: Bk Vols 3,000
Subject Interests: Biog, Children's bks, Fiction, Religious bks
Restriction: Not open to public

M HEARTLAND REGIONAL MEDICAL CENTER, Library Services, 5325 Faraon St, 64506-3398. SAN 326-4831. Tel: 816-271-6075. FAX: 816-271-6074. *Librn*, Cynthia Nicks; E-Mail: cindi.nicks@mail.heartland-health.com
Library Holdings: Bk Titles 640; Per Subs 387
Subject Interests: Medicine, Nursing
Publications: Newsletter

R HUFFMAN MEMORIAL UNITED METHODIST CHURCH LIBRARY, 2802 Renick, 64507-1897. SAN 309-1406. Tel: 816-233-0239. FAX: 816-233-0683. *Librn*, Dorothy Thomann
Founded 1958
Library Holdings: Bk Vols 4,444

C MISSOURI WESTERN STATE COLLEGE, Hearnes Learning Resources Center, 4525 Downs Dr, 64507-2294. SAN 309-1414. Tel: 816-271-4368. Interlibrary Loan Service Tel: 816-271-4572. Circulation Tel: 816-271-4360. Reference Tel: 816-271-4573. Toll Free Tel: 866-866-6972. TDD: 816-271-5690. FAX: 816-271-4574. E-Mail: refdesk@mwsc.edu. Web Site: www.mwsc.edu/~libwww. *Dir*, Julia Schneider; E-Mail: schneide@mwsc.edu; *ILL*, Rodema Gnuschke; *Media Spec*, Max Schlesinger; E-Mail: schlesin@mwsc.edu; *Tech Servs*, Andrew McGarrell; E-Mail: mcgarrel@mwsc.edu; *Ref*, Darrin Daugherty; E-Mail: daughert@mwsc.edu; *Ref*, Christie Zimmerman; E-Mail: zimmer@mwsc.edu; *Circ*, Sandra Phillips; E-Mail: phillj@mwsc.edu; *Coll Develop, Per*, Audrey Fenner; E-Mail: fenner@mwsc.edu; *Ref*, Jackie Burns; E-Mail: burns@mwsc.edu; *Ref*, James Mulder; E-Mail: mulder@mwsc.edu; Staff 7 (MLS 7)
Founded 1915. Enrl 5,200; Fac 300; Highest Degree: Bachelor
Jul 1999-Jun 2000 Income $1,024,833. Mats Exp $335,780, Books $100,000, Per/Ser (Incl. Access Fees) $180,000, Presv $900, Micro $11,200, Electronic Ref Mat (Incl. Access Fees) $43,680. Sal $604,120 (Prof $354,676)
Library Holdings: Bk Vols 221,500; Bk Titles 161,000; Per Subs 1,481
Special Collections: Women Writers Along the River
Automation Activity & Vendor Info: (Acquisitions) Inlex; (Cataloging) Inlex; (Circulation) Inlex; (OPAC) Inlex
Database Vendor: Dialog, Ebsco - EbscoHost, Lexis-Nexis, OCLC - First Search, Silverplatter Information Inc.
Publications: Library Link
Partic in Missouri Library Network Corporation; Mobius
Special Services for the Deaf - TDD
Special Services for the Blind - Braille printer & software; Reading edge system; ZoomText software to enlarge computer screen

P RIVER BLUFFS REGIONAL LIBRARY, 927 Felix St, 64501-2799. SAN 349-5450. Tel: 816-232-7729. Reference Tel: 816-232-8151. TDD: 816-236-2160. FAX: 816-279-3372. Web Site: www.rbrl.lib.mo.us. *Dir*, Dorothy Sanborn Elliott; *Dep Dir, Publ Servs*, Victoria Swadley; *ILL*, Gena Fisher; *Dep Dir, Publ Servs*, Noel Good; Staff 16 (MLS 10, Non-MLS 6)
Founded 1989. Pop 97,715; Circ 638,938
Jul 1999-Jun 2000 Income (Main Library and Branch Library) $2,531,753. Mats Exp $382,103. Sal $1,214,413
Library Holdings: Bk Vols 405,759; Per Subs 321
Special Collections: Literature (Eugene Field Coll); Medicine (Dr Wayne Toothaker Medical Library)
Database Vendor: DRA
Friends of the Library Group
Branches: 4
CARNEGIE, 316 Massachusetts St, 64504-1449. SAN 349-5485. Tel: 816-238-0526. FAX: 816-238-9438. *Mgr*, Audrey Sheets
Library Holdings: Bk Vols 30,124
EASTSIDE, 1904 N Belt Hwy, 64506-2201. SAN 349-5396. Tel: 816-232-5479. FAX: 816-236-2137. *Mgr*, Mary Beth Crouch
Library Holdings: Bk Vols 90,141
SAVANNAH, 514 W Main St, Savannah, 64485-1670. SAN 349-5426. Tel: 816-324-4569. FAX: 816-324-3562. *Mgr*, Melissa Middleswart
Library Holdings: Bk Vols 34,976
WASHINGTON PARK, 1821 N Third St, 64505-2533. SAN 349-5515. Tel: 816-232-2052. FAX: 816-236-2151. *Mgr*, Steven K Olson
Library Holdings: Bk Vols 34,576

S ST JOSEPH MUSEUM LIBRARY, 1100 Charles, 64501. (Mail add: PO Box 128, 64502-0128), SAN 309-1430. Tel: 816-232-8471. Toll Free Tel: 800-530-8866. FAX: 816-232-8482. E-Mail: sjm@stjosephmuseum.org. Web Site: www.stjosephmuseum.org. *Dir*, Richard A Nolf; *Curator*, Sarah M Elder; Staff 13 (MLS 9, Non-MLS 4)
Founded 1927
Library Holdings: Bk Titles 5,000; Per Subs 15
Subject Interests: California, Civil War, Ethnology, Missouri hist, Native Am, Native Am hist, Natural history, Oregon Trail
Publications: Happenings (Newsletter)
Function: Reference only, Research library

SAINT LOUIS

S ADVANSWERS MEDIA-PROGRAMMING, INC, Information Center,* 10 S Broadway, 63102. SAN 309-166X. Tel: 314-444-2100. FAX: 314-444-2199. E-Mail: mediapro@advanswers.com. *In Charge*, Larry Goldstein
Library Holdings: Bk Vols 2,750; Per Subs 48

M AMERICAN ASSOCIATION OF ORTHODONTISTS, Charles R Baker Reference Library, 401 N Lindbergh Blvd, 63141. SAN 372-6207. Tel: 314-993-1700. FAX: 314-997-1745. Web Site: www.aaortho.org. *Librn*, Celia Giltinan
Library Holdings: Bk Vols 800; Bk Titles 750; Per Subs 80
Restriction: Members only

S AMERICAN AUTOMOBILE ASSOCIATION LIBRARY,* 12901 N Forty Dr, 63141. SAN 377-5607. Tel: 314-523-7350, Ext 6312. FAX: 314-523-6982. *Librn*, Lori Mushkowsky
Library Holdings: Bk Titles 100

S AMERICAN SOYBEAN ASSOCIATION, Technical Information Center,* 12125 Woodcrest Executive Dr, 63141. SAN 321-6195. Tel: 314-576-1770. FAX: 314-576-2786. *Librn*, Roseann Huddleston
Library Holdings: Bk Titles 500; Per Subs 200
Partic in Saint Louis Regional Library Network
Open Mon-Fri 8-4:30

S ANHEUSER-BUSCH CO, INC, Corporate Library, One Busch Pl, Bechtold Sta PO Box 1828, 63118. SAN 309-1457. Tel: 314-577-2669, 314-577-3492. FAX: 314-577-2006. *Librn*, Ann Lauenstein; *Asst Librn*, Mary Butler; Staff 3 (MLS 2, Non-MLS 1)
Founded 1932
Library Holdings: Bk Vols 40,000; Per Subs 1,000
Subject Interests: Beer, Brewing, Corporate hists
Automation Activity & Vendor Info: (Circulation) Sydney; (OPAC)

Sydney; (Serials) EOS
Publications: New Publications (bimonthly); union list of periodicals
Mem of St Louis Regional Libr Network
Partic in Dialog Corporation; Dow Jones News Retrieval; OCLC Online Computer Library Center, Inc

S ARTHUR ANDERSEN LLP LIBRARY, 1010 Market St, 63101. SAN 329-9619. Tel: 314-425-3592. FAX: 314-621-1956. *Info Specialist*, Valerie Rohrbaugh; Staff 2 (MLS 1, Non-MLS 1)
Founded 1982
Library Holdings: Bk Vols 4,000; Per Subs 180
Subject Interests: Accounting
Database Vendor: Lexis-Nexis
Restriction: Not open to public
Function: Research library

BARNES-JEWISH HOSPITAL
M ROTHSCHILD MEDICAL LIBRARY, 216 S Kingshighway Blvd, Mail Stop 90-32-639, 63110. SAN 349-5604. Tel: 314-454-7208. FAX: 314-454-5301. *Librn*, Reka Kozak; E-Mail: kozakr@medicine.wustl.edu, kozakr@msnotes.wustl.edu; Staff 1 (MLS 1)
Library Holdings: Bk Vols 2,262; Per Subs 42
Partic in Library Systems Service

L BLACKWELL, SANDERS, PEPER & MARTIN, Law Library,* 720 Olive St 24th flr, 63101. SAN 372-4700. Tel: 314-345-6871. FAX: 314-345-6060. *Librn*, Lee Ann Genovese; E-Mail: lgenovese@bspmlaw.com
Library Holdings: Bk Vols 20,000; Per Subs 20

BOEING COMPANY
S TECHNICAL LIBRARY, M/C S111-1025, PO Box 516, 63166-0516. SAN 349-5876. Tel: 314-232-6134, 314-232-8516. FAX: 314-232-7528. E-Mail: techlib@boeing.com. *Mgr*, Mercedes Cobb
Founded 1948
Library Holdings: Bk Vols 31,900; Per Subs 500
Subject Interests: Aeronautics, Astronautics, Business, Computer tech, Engineering, Mat, Mgt, Sci, Technology
Publications: Acronyms, Abbreviations & Initialisms dictionary; Weekly Announcement Bulletin
Partic in Defense Technical Information Center

L BRYAN CAVE LLP, Law Library, One Metropolitan Sq, 211 N Broadway Ste 3600, 63102-2750. SAN 328-3054. Tel: 314-259-2298. FAX: 314-259-2020. *Dir Libr Serv*, Judy Harris; E-Mail: jlharris@bryancave.com
Library Holdings: Bk Vols 22,000; Per Subs 100
Special Collections: Annual Reports
Publications: Annual Report; Library Bulletin; Library Guide
Partic in Missouri Library Network Corporation; OCLC Online Computer Library Center, Inc

SR CATHOLIC CENTRAL UNION OF AMERICA, Central Bureau Library, 3835 Westminster Pl, 63108. SAN 328-5618. Tel: 314-371-1653. *Dir*, John Miller; Staff 2 (MLS 1, Non-MLS 1)
Founded 1907
Jul 1998-Jun 1999 Income $80,000. Mats Exp Books $20,000. Sal $60,000
Library Holdings: Bk Vols 250,000; Per Subs 20
Subject Interests: History, Philosophy, Theology
Special Collections: German Americana Coll
Publications: Social Justice Review (bi-monthly)
Restriction: Non-circulating to the public, Open to students

S CENTER FOR REFORMATION RESEARCH LIBRARY,* 6477 San Bonita Ave, 63105-3517. SAN 371-1684. Tel: 314-505-7199. FAX: 314-505-7198. E-Mail: cslcrr@crf.cuis.edu. *Exec Dir*, Dr Robert Rosin
Library Holdings: Bk Vols 15,000
Subject Interests: Theology
Publications: Center for Reformation Research Newsletter
Friends of the Library Group

S CENTRAL INSTITUTE FOR THE DEAF, Speech, Hearing & Education Library, Clinic & Research Bldg, 909 South Taylor, 63110-1511. (Mail add: 4560 Clayton Ave, 63110-1502), SAN 322-7588. Tel: 314-977-0268. TDD: 314-977-0001. FAX: 314-977-0030. Web Site: www.cid.wustl.edu. *Librn*, Cathy Sarli; E-Mail: csarli@cid.wustl.edu
Founded 1931. Enrl 50; Fac 30; Highest Degree: Doctorate
Library Holdings: Bk Titles 3,500; Per Subs 75
Subject Interests: Acoustics, Otolaryngology
Restriction: By appointment only
Partic in Missouri Library Network Corporation; Spec Libr Asn
Member of the Greater Saint Louis Libr Club
Friends of the Library Group

S CHRISTIAN HOSPITAL NORTHEAST LIBRARY,* 11125 Dunn Rd Ste 110, 63136. SAN 377-1164. Tel: 314-355-2300, Ext 5421. FAX: 314-653-4117. E-Mail: rjs@bjcmail.carenet.org. *Librn*, Robbie Jean Shumpert
Library Holdings: Bk Vols 1,800; Per Subs 145
Partic in Spec Libr Asn

R CONCORDIA SEMINARY, Ludwig E Fuerbringer Library, 801 Demun Ave, 63105-3199. SAN 309-1570. Tel: 314-505-7038. Circulation Tel: 314-505-7030. Reference Tel: 314-505-7032. FAX: 314-505-7046. Web Site: www.csl.edu/library. *Coll Develop, Dir*, David O Berger; E-Mail: cslbergerdo@crf.cuis.edu; *Asst Dir*, Joann Mirly; *Tech Servs*, Mark Bliese; Staff 11 (MLS 3, Non-MLS 8)
Founded 1839. Enrl 550; Fac 36; Highest Degree: Doctorate
Jul 1999-Jun 2000 Income $636,985. Mats Exp $216,278, Books $143,269, Per/Ser (Incl. Access Fees) $45,179, Presv $6,427, Micro $10,334, AV Equip $10,233, Electronic Ref Mat (Incl. Access Fees) $7,970. Sal $400,370 (Prof $142,300)
Library Holdings: Bk Vols 143,269; Bk Titles 121,780; Per Subs 1,039; Bks on Deafness & Sign Lang 200
Subject Interests: Biblical studies, Lutheranism, Reformation
Special Collections: Hymnology & Liturgics; Lutherana Coll; Peasant's War
Database Vendor: OCLC - First Search
Restriction: Open to student, faculty & staff, Public use on premises
Function: ILL available, Reference services available, Research library
Partic in Missouri Library Network Corporation; Saint Louis Regional Library Network

R COVENANT THEOLOGICAL SEMINARY, Buswell Library, 12330 Conway Rd, 63141. SAN 309-1589. Tel: 314-434-4044. FAX: 314-434-4819. Web Site: www.covenantseminary.edu. *Dir*, James Cotton Pakala; E-Mail: jpakala@covenantseminary.edu; *Ref*, Christopher Per Almquist; *Tech Servs*, Denise Marchand Pakala; *Circ, Ser*, Heather Dryden; Staff 7 (MLS 2, Non-MLS 5)
Founded 1956
Jul 1999-Jun 2000 Income Parent Institution $294,878. Mats Exp $57,331, Books $35,849, Per/Ser (Incl. Access Fees) $10,679, Presv $3,446, Micro $89, AV Equip $1,799, Electronic Ref Mat (Incl. Access Fees) $5,469. Sal $162,880 (Prof $98,218)
Library Holdings: Bk Vols 55,079; Bk Titles 46,760; Per Subs 362
Subject Interests: Counseling, Religion
Special Collections: Bible & Theology; Church History (post-Reformation); Practical Theology; Presbyterian Church in America Archives
Automation Activity & Vendor Info: (Circulation) Innovative Interfaces Inc.
Database Vendor: Innovative Interfaces INN - View, OCLC - First Search
Partic in MLNC; Mobius; Saint Louis Regional Library Network

S D'ARCY, MASIUS, BENTON & BOWLES,* One Memorial Dr S, 63102. SAN 309-1597. Tel: 314-342-8600. FAX: 314-342-8644. Web Site: www.dmbb.com. *Dir*, Roseanne Hadjri; E-Mail: hadjrir@darcyww.com
Library Holdings: Bk Vols 1,500; Per Subs 75
Partic in Spec Libr Asn

GM DEPARTMENT OF VETERANS AFFAIRS, Medical Library, 142D/JC, 915 N Grand Blvd, 63106. SAN 309-2186. Tel: 314-289-6421. FAX: 314-289-6321. *Librn*, Ann M Repetto; E-Mail: repetto@inlink.com; Staff 2 (MLS 1, Non-MLS 1)
Founded 1954
Library Holdings: Bk Titles 1,700; Per Subs 200
Automation Activity & Vendor Info: (Cataloging) EOS; (Circulation) EOS; (OPAC) EOS
Partic in Library Systems Service; Veterans Affairs Library Network

G EAST WEST GATEWAY COORDINATING COUNCIL LIBRARY, 10 Stadium Plaza, 2nd Flr, 63102-1714. SAN 327-1676. Tel: 314-421-4220. FAX: 314-231-6120. Web Site: www.ewgateway.org, www.postmaster@ewgateway.org. *In Charge*, Toni Phillips; E-Mail: toni.phillips@ewgateway.org
Library Holdings: Bk Titles 5,000

CR EDEN-WEBSTER LIBRARY, 475 E Lockwood, 63119-3192. SAN 309-2208. Tel: 314-968-6950. FAX: 314-968-7113. E-Mail: askref@library2.webster.edu. Web Site: www.library.webster.edu. *Dir*, Laura Rein; Tel: 314-968-7152, E-Mail: lrein@library2.webster.edu; *Acq*, Maya Grach; *Doc Delivery*, Rick Kaeser; *Cat, Tech Servs*, Sue Wartzok; *Circ*, Ellen Eliceiri; *ILL*, Sara Fitzpatrick; *Per*, Mary O'Neal; Staff 29 (MLS 13, Non-MLS 16)
Founded 1969. Enrl 10,500; Highest Degree: Doctorate
Jul 1999-Jun 2000 Income $2,694,341. Mats Exp $965,848, Books $302,500, Per/Ser (Incl. Access Fees) $253,755, Presv $22,550, Electronic Ref Mat (Incl. Access Fees) $387,043. Sal $754,549 (Prof $446,116)
Library Holdings: Bk Vols 250,000; Per Subs 1,400
Subject Interests: Catechism
Special Collections: Children's Literature (Hochschild Coll); Harry James Cargas Coll; Reformed Church History (James I Good Coll)
Automation Activity & Vendor Info: (Acquisitions) epixtech, inc.; (Cataloging) epixtech, inc.; (Circulation) epixtech, inc.; (Serials) epixtech, inc.
Database Vendor: Dialog, GaleNet, IAC - SearchBank, Lexis-Nexis, OCLC - First Search, OVID Technologies, ProQuest, Silverplatter Information Inc., Wilson - Wilson Web
Partic in Higher Educ Coun of St Louis; Missouri Library Network Corporation; OCLC Online Computer Library Center, Inc; Saint Louis Regional Library Network

S EMERSON ELECTRIC LIBRARY,* 8000 W Florissant, 63136. SAN 377-2403. Tel: 314-553-3485. FAX: 314-553-3672. *Mgr*, David Moon
Library Holdings: Bk Vols 20
Partic in Spec Libr Asn

SR THE EPISCOPAL DIOCESE OF MISSOURI ARCHIVES,* 1210 Locust St, 63103-2322. SAN 325-2280. Tel: 314-231-1220. FAX: 314-231-3373. E-Mail: diocese@missouri.anglican.org.; Staff 1 (MLS 1)
Founded 1840
Library Holdings: Bk Titles 700; Per Subs 10
Subject Interests: Anglican Church, Church history, Episcopal church
Special Collections: Diocesan Archives & Historical Coll

S EUGENE FIELD HOUSE & THE SAINT LOUIS TOY MUSEUM,* 634 S Broadway, 63102. SAN 370-8543. Tel: 314-421-4689. *Dir*, Frances Kerber Walrond
Library Holdings: Bk Vols 200

S FEDERAL RESERVE BANK OF SAINT LOUIS, Research Library, 411 Locust St, PO Box 442, 63166. SAN 309-1643. Tel: 314-444-8552. Interlibrary Loan Service Tel: 314-444-4291. FAX: 314-444-8694. E-Mail: reslib@stls.frb.org. *Mgr*, Carol J Thaxton; E-Mail: thaxton@stls.frb.org; Staff 5 (MLS 3, Non-MLS 2)
Founded 1922
Library Holdings: Bk Vols 15,000; Per Subs 800
Subject Interests: Banking, Econ, Money
Automation Activity & Vendor Info: (Acquisitions) EOS; (Cataloging) EOS; (Circulation) EOS; (OPAC) EOS; (Serials) EOS
Database Vendor: Dialog, Ebsco - EbscoHost, Lexis-Nexis
Function: Research library
Partic in OCLC Online Computer Library Center, Inc

CR FONTBONNE COLLEGE LIBRARY, 6800 Wydown Blvd, 63105. SAN 309-1651. Tel: 314-889-1417. FAX: 314-719-8040. Web Site: www.fontbonne.edu/libserv/. *Dir*, John L Gresham; Tel: 314-889-4567, E-Mail: jgresham@fontbonne.edu; *Ref*, Joseph Rogers; Tel: 314-719-8088, E-Mail: jrogers@fontbonne.edu; *Ref*, Ling Thumin; Tel: 314-889-4570, E-Mail: lthumin@fontbonne.edu; *Circ*, Germaine Komor; Tel: 317-719-8026, E-Mail: gkomor@fontbonne.edu; *AV*, Sr Jane Behlmann; Tel: 314-889-4566, E-Mail: jbehlman@fontbonne.edu; *Tech Servs*, June Williams; Tel: 314-889-4569, E-Mail: jwilliam@fontbonne.edu; *Ser*, Jean Ferguson; Tel: 314-889-4568, E-Mail: jferguso@fontbonne.edu; Staff 7 (MLS 5, Non-MLS 2)
Founded 1923. Enrl 2,000; Fac 60; Highest Degree: Master
Jul 2000-Jun 2001 Income $361,000. Mats Exp $116,000, Books $40,000, Per/Ser (Incl. Access Fees) $25,000, Presv $2,000, AV Equip $17,000, Electronic Ref Mat (Incl. Access Fees) $32,000. Sal $216,000
Library Holdings: Bk Titles 100,000; Per Subs 4,000
Subject Interests: Bus, Communications disorders, Education, Home econ
Database Vendor: Ebsco - EbscoHost, GaleNet, Lexis-Nexis, OCLC - First Search
Partic in Missouri Library Network Corporation; Mobius; OCLC Online Computer Library Center, Inc; Saint Louis Regional Library Network

M FOREST PARK HOSPITAL, (Formerly Deaconess Central Hospital), Drusch Professional Library, 6150 Oakland Ave, 63139. SAN 309-1600. Tel: 314-768-3137.; Staff 1 (MLS 1)
Founded 1942
Library Holdings: Bk Vols 4,319; Bk Titles 3,806; Per Subs 222
Subject Interests: Medicine, Nursing
Database Vendor: OCLC - First Search
Partic in Nat Libr of Med; OCLC Online Computer Library Center, Inc; Saint Louis Regional Library Network

J FOUNDATION FOR LATIN AMERICAN ANTHROPOLOGICAL RESEARCH LIBRARY,* 5 Conway Lane, 63124. SAN 323-9071. Tel: 314-997-4540. Web Site: www.maya-art-books.org. *Dir*, Dr Nicholas M Hellmuth; E-Mail: nhellmuth@yahoo.com
Founded 1969
Library Holdings: Bk Titles 3,000
Special Collections: Aztec, Maya art, Olmec, pre-Columbian archit, Teotihuacan & Inca, slides & prints; flora & fauna of Guatemala & Mexico

L GALLOP, JOHNSON & NEUMAN LC, Law Library, 101 S Hanley, Ste 1600, 63105. SAN 374-4809. Tel: 314-862-1200, Ext 458. FAX: 314-862-1219. Web Site: www.gjn.com. *Librn*, Elliott Blevins; E-Mail: ecblevins@gjn.com; *Asst Librn*, Susan Reeves; Staff 2 (MLS 1, Non-MLS 1)
Library Holdings: Bk Vols 9,500
Partic in Westlaw

S GAZETTE INTERNATIONAL NETWORKING INSTITUTE LIBRARY,* 4207 Lindell Blvd, No 110, 63108. SAN 375-2062. Tel: 314-534-0475. FAX: 314-534-5070. E-Mail: gini_intl@msn.com. Web Site: www.post-polio.org. *Librn*, Joan Headley
Library Holdings: Bk Vols 3,500; Per Subs 15

S GREENSFELDER, HEMKER & GALE, PC LIBRARY, 10 S Broadway, Ste 2000, 63102. SAN 329-7713. Tel: 314-241-9090. FAX: 314-241-8624. E-Mail: hsc@greensfelder.com. Web Site: www.greensfelder.com. *Librn*, Sally Crowley
Library Holdings: Bk Vols 10,000; Per Subs 400

C HARRIS-STOWE STATE COLLEGE LIBRARY, Southwestern Bell Library & Technology Center, 3026 Laclede Ave, 63103-2199. SAN 309-1708. Tel: 314-340-3622. FAX: 314-340-3630. Web Site: www.hssc.edu. *Dir*, Martin Knorr; E-Mail: knowwm@hssc.edu; *Librn*, Linda Orzel; *Librn*, Marian Shapiro; *Librn*, Bettye Brown; *Librn*, Shirley McCullough
Founded 1857. Highest Degree: Bachelor
Library Holdings: Bk Vols 91,235; Per Subs 333
Subject Interests: Education, Ethnic studies, Urban studies
Special Collections: St Louis Public School Archives
Partic in Saint Louis Regional Library Network

S HEALTH CAPITAL CONSULTANTS LIBRARY, 10420 Old Olive Street Rd Ste 200, 63141-5938. SAN 377-824X. Toll Free Tel: 800-394-8258. FAX: 314-994-7641. E-Mail: library@healthcapital.com. Web Site: www.healthcapital.com. *Librn*, Tim Alexander; Staff 3 (MLS 1, Non-MLS 2)
Founded 1993
Library Holdings: Bk Vols 1,200; Bk Titles 1,000; Per Subs 110
Automation Activity & Vendor Info: (Cataloging) Inmagic, Inc.; (Circulation) Inmagic, Inc.

S HELLMUTH, OBATA & KASSABAUM, INC LIBRARY,* 211 N Broadway, Ste 600, 63102. SAN 327-0629. Tel: 314-421-2000, Ext 2217. FAX: 314-421-6073. *Librn*, Susan Baerwald; E-Mail: susan.baerwald@hok.com; *Asst Librn*, Rita Kozek
Library Holdings: Bk Vols 7,000; Per Subs 270
Special Collections: Architecture; HOK History
Restriction: By appointment only

L HUSCH & EPPENBERGER, Law Library,* 100 N Broadway Ste 1300, 63102. SAN 372-4751. Tel: 314-421-4800. FAX: 314-421-0239. Web Site: www.husch.com. *Librn*, Karla A Morris-Holmes
Library Holdings: Bk Vols 10,000; Per Subs 95

S INTERNATIONAL BOWLING MUSEUM & HALL OF FAME, 111 Stadium Plaza, 63102. SAN 318-0182. Tel: 314-231-6340. FAX: 314-231-4054. Web Site: www.bowlingmuseum.com. *Exec Dir*, Gerald Baltz; *Curator*, Travis Boley
Founded 1940
Library Holdings: Bk Vols 5,000
Special Collections: Bowling, all published materials

M INTERNATIONAL LIBRARY, ARCHIVES & MUSEUM OF OPTOMETRY,* 243 N Lindbergh Blvd, 63141-7881. SAN 309-1716. Tel: 314-991-0324. FAX: 314-991-4101. *Librn*, Bridget Kowalczyk; *Asst Dir*, Sandra Smith; *Cat*, Linda Draper; *Per*, Aleen Fish; *Circ*, Joan Nohova; *Coll Develop*, Helen Staehle
Founded 1902
Library Holdings: Bk Vols 10,000; Per Subs 450
Subject Interests: Archives, Clinical aspects, ITS hist, Museum of optometry, Ophthalmic sci, Related sci, Socioeconomic aspects, With emphasis on optometry
Special Collections: Rare Books & Periodicals; Topical Research Conducted at Library
Publications: Calendar of Meetings (quarterly); Visionlink (monthly newsletter)
Friends of the Library Group

S JEFFERSON NATIONAL EXPANSION MEMORIAL LIBRARY, 11 N Fourth St, 63102. SAN 309-1724. Tel: 314-655-1600. FAX: 314-655-1652. Web Site: www.nps.gov/jeff. *Librn*, Tom Dewey
Founded 1935
Library Holdings: Bk Vols 6,150; Per Subs 60
Subject Interests: St Louis hist, Westward expansion
Special Collections: Jefferson National Expansion Memorial Association Archives; Lewis & Clark

CM JEWISH HOSPITAL COLLEGE OF NURSING & ALLIED HEALTH LIBRARY, 306 S Kingshighway Blvd, MS 90-30-625, 63110-1091. SAN 349-5639. Tel: 314-454-8474. FAX: 314-454-5303. E-Mail: ecm3213@bjcmail.carenet.org. Web Site: jhconah.org. *Head of Libr*, Dr Mark A Spasser; Tel: 314-454-8171, E-Mail: mas1200@bjc.org; *Asst Librn*, Robert J Addison; E-Mail: rja3089@bjc.org; *Asst Librn*, Anise M Gilliam; E-Mail: amg5270@bjc.org. Subject Specialists: *Biblometrics*, Dr Mark A Spasser; Staff 3 (MLS 1, Non-MLS 2)
Founded 1920. Enrl 600; Fac 30; Highest Degree: Master
Library Holdings: Bk Vols 12,000; Bk Titles 3,000; Per Subs 145
Subject Interests: Clinical labs, Cytology (study Of cells), Dietetics, Nursing, Radiation therapy, Radiologic tech
Special Collections: ALA Publications
Database Vendor: OCLC - First Search
Restriction: In-house use for visitors, Open to student, faculty & staff
Partic in Library Systems Service; MLNC; OCLC Online Computer Library Center, Inc; Saint Louis Regional Library Network

R KENRICK-GLENNON SEMINARY, Charles L Souvay Memorial Library, 5200 Glennon Dr, 63119. SAN 309-1740. Tel: 314-644-0266. FAX: 314-792-6500. *Dir*, Andrew J Sopko; E-Mail: sopko@kenrick.edu; *Acq, ILL*, Terese Wiley; *Tech Servs*, William Toombs; Staff 1 (MLS 1)
Founded 1893. Enrl 65; Fac 15; Highest Degree: Master
Library Holdings: Bk Vols 76,000; Per Subs 300
Subject Interests: Archives, Canon law, Liturgics, Patristics, Roman Catholic theology, Scripture
Special Collections: Cuneiform Tablets; Official Catholic Directory; Pre-Vatican II Catechism Coll; Rare Book Coll; Thomas Merton Coll
Partic in OCLC Online Computer Library Center, Inc

M LAFAYETTE GRAND HOSPITAL LIBRARY,* 3545 Lafayette Ave, 63104. SAN 320-6874. Tel: 314-865-6813. FAX: 314-865-6885. *Librn*, Karen Launsby
Library Holdings: Bk Vols 2,400; Per Subs 60
Partic in Saint Louis Regional Library Network

L LASHLY & BAER PC, Law Library, 714 Locust St, 63101. SAN 375-0523. Tel: 314-621-2939, Ext 1010. FAX: 314-621-6844. Web Site: www.lashlybaer.com. *Librn*, Carol R Teaney; E-Mail: crteaney@lashlybaer.com; Staff 1 (Non-MLS 1)
Library Holdings: Bk Vols 10,000
Restriction: Not open to public

S LAUMEIER SCULPTURE PARK LIBRARY,* 12580 Rott Rd, 63127. SAN 374-5708. Tel: 314-821-6386. FAX: 314-821-1248.; Staff 1 (MLS 1)
Founded 1986
Library Holdings: Bk Titles 3,200; Per Subs 10
Special Collections: Contemporary Sculpture Coll

L LAW LIBRARY ASSOCIATION OF SAINT LOUIS,* 1300 Civil Courts Bldg, 63101-2096. SAN 309-1775. Tel: 314-622-4470. FAX: 314-241-0911. *Librn*, Jean Moorleghen; Staff 7 (MLS 1, Non-MLS 6)
Founded 1838
Library Holdings: Bk Vols 85,000; Per Subs 135
Restriction: Members only
Partic in Dialog Corporation; LOIS; Westlaw

L LEGAL SERVICES OF EASTERN MISSOURI INC LIBRARY,* 4232 Forest Park Ave, 63108. SAN 329-9589. Tel: 314-534-4200, Ext 1308. FAX: 314-534-1028. E-Mail: lsem@lsem.org. Web Site: www.lsem.org. *Librn*, Marcia Griffin
Library Holdings: Bk Vols 7,800; Per Subs 93
Open Mon-Fri 9:30-5

S LEWIS, RICE & FINGERSH LAW LIBRARY,* 500 N Broadway Ste 2000, 63102-2147. SAN 327-7437. Tel: 314-444-7600. FAX: 314-241-6056. Web Site: www.lewisrice.com. *Librn*, Helen Capdevielle; E-Mail: hcapdevielle@lewisrice.com; *Asst Librn*, Teresa Kent
Library Holdings: Bk Vols 20,000
Publications: Monthly accessions list
Restriction: Staff use only
Partic in Westlaw

LUTHERAN CHURCH-MISSOURI SYNOD

R CENTRAL LIBRARY, 1333 S Kirkwood Rd, 63122-7295. SAN 324-7686. Tel: 314-965-9000, Ext 1298. FAX: 314-822-8307. *Librn*, Shari S Stelling; Staff 1 (MLS 1)
Library Holdings: Bk Vols 23,000; Bk Titles 9,000; Per Subs 200
Subject Interests: Evangelism, Lutheranism, Parish educ, Stewardship, Worship
Restriction: By appointment only
Partic in Saint Louis Regional Library Network

R CONCORDIA HISTORICAL INSTITUTE LIBRARY, 801 DeMun Ave, 63105. SAN 309-1783. Tel: 314-505-7900. FAX: 314-505-7901. E-Mail: chi@chi.lcms.org. Web Site: www.chi.lcms.org. *Dir*, Daniel Preus; Tel: 314-505-7911, E-Mail: dpreus@chi.lcms.org; *Assoc Dir*, Marvin A Huggins; Tel: 314-505-7921, E-Mail: mhuggins@chi.lcms.org; *Reader Servs*, Mark Loest; Tel: 314-505-7930, E-Mail: mloest@chi.lcms.org; Staff 10 (Non-MLS 10)
Founded 1927
Jul 1998-Jun 1999 Income (Main Library Only) $510,659, Locally Generated Income $180,659, Parent Institution $330,000. Mats Exp $217,630. Sal $305,768
Library Holdings: Bk Vols 59,000; Per Subs 180
Subject Interests: Lutheran churches, Lutheranism, Lutheranism in America, Lutheranism in history, Lutheranism in theology
Special Collections: Archives of the Lutheran Church-Missouri Synod, 1839-present, mss; History of Lutheranism, bks, mss; Lutheran Foreign Missions (Walter A Maier, Buenger, Graebner, Behnken & Rehwinkel Manuscript Coll); Lutheran Hour, broadcast discs; Lutheranism in America, History & Theology
Publications: Archives & History (biennial); Concordia Historical Institute Quarterly; Historical Footnotes (quarterly); Microfilm Index and bibliography (decennial)
Friends of the Library Group

M LUTHERAN MEDICAL CENTER SCHOOL OF NURSING & MEDICAL STAFF LIBRARY, Louise Kraus-Ament Memorial Library, 3547 S Jefferson, 63118. SAN 309-1791. Tel: 314-577-5864. FAX: 314-268-6160. E-Mail: southpointehosp@hotmail.com.
Library Holdings: Bk Vols 5,000; Per Subs 73
Subject Interests: Nursing educ, Primary educ

S MALLINCKRODT MEDICAL INC, Information Resource Center,* 675 McDonnell Blvd, PO Box 5840, 63134. SAN 372-7297. Tel: 314-654-2000. FAX: 314-658-7385. *Librn*, Grace Brill; *Acq*, Addie Deal; *Ref*, Patrick Hendershot; *Online Servs*, Maribeth Sledbodnik; Staff 5 (MLS 3, Non-MLS 2)
Library Holdings: Bk Vols 4,000

S MALLINCKRODT, INC, Pharmaceutical & Chemical Library,* 3600 N Second St, PO Box 5439, 63147. SAN 309-1813. Tel: 314-539-1515. FAX: 314-539-1513. *Librn*, Phyllis A Fischer; Staff 3 (MLS 2, Non-MLS 1)
Library Holdings: Bk Vols 11,500; Per Subs 460
Subject Interests: Bus, Chemistry, Mgt, Pharmaceutical chem
Partic in OCLC Online Computer Library Center, Inc

C MARYVILLE UNIVERSITY LIBRARY, 13550 Conway Rd, 63141. SAN 309-1821. Tel: 314-529-9595. FAX: 314-529-9941. Web Site: www.library.maryville.edu/librarydir/. *Dir*, Eugenia V McKee; E-Mail: mckee@maryville.edu; *Ref, Syst Coordr*, Melissa Belvadi; *Ref*, Paula Hubbard; *Ref*, Gail Keutzer; *Tech Servs*, Mary Ann Mercante; Staff 13 (MLS 5, Non-MLS 8)
Founded 1872. Enrl 3,764; Fac 321; Highest Degree: Master
Jun 1999-May 2000 Income $761,145. Mats Exp $302,278, Books $78,082, Per/Ser (Incl. Access Fees) $68,700, Presv $907, Micro $28,536, Electronic Ref Mat (Incl. Access Fees) $56,822. Sal $447,337 (Prof $230,690)
Library Holdings: Bk Vols 200,318; Bk Titles 125,742; Per Subs 1,355
Subject Interests: Education, Music therapy
Special Collections: Curriculum materials; Maryville archives; Murphy-Meisgeier Coll; Papers of Edward S Dowling
Database Vendor: Lexis-Nexis, OCLC - First Search, ProQuest
Partic in Missouri Library Network Corporation; Mobius; OCLC Online Computer Library Center, Inc; Saint Louis Regional Library Network
Friends of the Library Group

S MAXIM TECHNOLOGIES INC,* 1908 Innerbelt Business Center Dr, 63114. SAN 309-1635. Tel: 314-426-0880. FAX: 314-426-4212.
Founded 1972
Library Holdings: Bk Vols 3,500; Per Subs 75
Subject Interests: Air pollution, Chem laboratory analysis, Environmental engineering, GC, Hazardous wastes, Indust water supply, Industrial waste treatment, Lab analysis, Municipal waste treatment, Noise abatement, Waste mgt, Water pollution
Restriction: By appointment only

L MAY DEPARTMENT STORES CO, Law Library, 611 Olive St, Ste 1750, 63101. SAN 372-4697. Tel: 314-342-6697. FAX: 314-342-3066. *Mgr Libr Serv*, Diane R Burnett; E-Mail: diane_burnett@may-co.com; *Asst Librn*, Debbie E Clymer; Tel: 314-342-6696, E-Mail: deborah_clymer@may-co.com; Staff 2 (Non-MLS 2)
Library Holdings: Bk Vols 10,000; Per Subs 55
Automation Activity & Vendor Info: (Cataloging) Inmagic, Inc.
Database Vendor: Lexis-Nexis
Restriction: Company staff only

C MISSOURI BAPTIST COLLEGE LIBRARY, One College Park Dr, 63141-8698. SAN 309-1864. Tel: 314-434-1115. Circulation Tel: 314-392-2320. Reference Tel: 314-392-2340. FAX: 314-392-2343. Web Site: www.mobap.edu. *Dir*, Nitsa Hindeleh; Tel: 314-392-2319, E-Mail: hindeleh@mobap.edu; *Tech Servs*, Elaine Trost; Tel: 314-392-2342, E-Mail: trosteh@mobap.edu; *Ref*, Irene Baker; Tel: 314-392-2340, E-Mail: bakerei@mobap.edu; *Circ*, Greg Rhinehart; Tel: 314-392-2320, E-Mail: circdsk@mobap.edu; *Circ*, Jeri Schmidt; Tel: 314-392-2320, E-Mail: circdsk@mobap.edu
Founded 1968. Enrl 2,800; Fac 140; Highest Degree: Master
Jul 1998-Jun 1999 Mats Exp $144,970, Books $87,000, Per/Ser (Incl. Access Fees) $21,000, Micro $7,000, Other Print Mats $5,970, Electronic Ref Mat (Incl. Access Fees) $24,000. Sal $131,299 (Prof $49,949)
Library Holdings: Bk Vols 119,102; Bk Titles 93,940; Per Subs 350
Special Collections: Southern Baptist Convention Curriculum
Automation Activity & Vendor Info: (Circulation) Innovative Interfaces Inc.; (Course Reserve) Innovative Interfaces Inc.; (OPAC) Innovative Interfaces Inc.; (Serials) Innovative Interfaces Inc.
Database Vendor: OCLC - First Search
Partic in MLNC; Mobius; Morenet; Saint Louis Regional Library Network

M MISSOURI BAPTIST MEDICAL CENTER, Medical Library,* 3015 N Ballas Rd, 63131. SAN 321-6209. Tel: 314-996-5000. FAX: 314-996-5031. *Librn*, Sandra Decker; E-Mail: deckers@medicine.wustl.edu
Founded 1965
Library Holdings: Bk Titles 500; Per Subs 100
Restriction: Staff use only

S MISSOURI BOTANICAL GARDEN LIBRARY, 4500 Shaw Blvd, 63110. SAN 309-1872. Tel: 314-577-5155. Reference Tel: 314-577-5159. FAX: 314-577-0840. E-Mail: library@mobot.org. Web Site: www.mobot.org/mobot.molib/. *Dir*, Constance P Wolf; Tel: 314-577-5156, E-Mail: connie.wolf@mobot.org; Staff 9 (MLS 4, Non-MLS 5)
Founded 1859
Jan 2000-Dec 2000 Income $393,051. Mats Exp $397,600, Books $57,500, Per/Ser (Incl. Access Fees) $75,200, Presv $4,000, Other Print Mats $1,139. Sal $221,700
Library Holdings: Bk Vols 126,000; Per Subs 1,800
Subject Interests: Bot exploration, Botanical hist, Botany, Horticulture
Special Collections: Archives; Bryology (Steere Coll); Ewan Coll; Folio Coll; Post-Linnaean Rare Book Coll; Pre-Linnaean Coll; Pre-Linnean Botany (Sturtevant Coll); Rare Book Coll
Database Vendor: epixtech, inc., OVID Technologies
Publications: Accessions List (monthly)
Partic in OCLC Online Computer Library Center, Inc
Open Mon-Fri 8:30-5

L MISSOURI COURT OF APPEALS EASTERN DISTRICT LIBRARY, 111 N Seventh, No 350, 63101. SAN 372-4131. Tel: 314-340-6416, 314-340-6960. FAX: 314-340-6964. Web Site: www.osca.state.mo.us. *Librn*, Laura Roy
Library Holdings: Bk Vols 29,000; Per Subs 12
Special Collections: Regional Reports Appellate; United States Supreme Court Records
Restriction: Staff use only

S MISSOURI HISTORICAL SOCIETY LIBRARY, 225 S Skinker, 63105. (Mail add: PO Box 11940, 63112-0040), SAN 309-1880. Tel: 314-746-4500. FAX: 314-746-4548. E-Mail: library@mohistory.org. Web Site: www.mohistory.org. *Librn*, Emily Jaycox; *Asst Librn*, Randall Blomquist; *Asst Librn*, Carol S Verble; *Tech Servs*, Stephanie A Klein; *Cat*, Debbie Schraut; Staff 9 (MLS 3, Non-MLS 6)
Founded 1866
Library Holdings: Bk Vols 80,000; Per Subs 250
Subject Interests: Am fur trade, Family hist, Genealogy, Hist of Mo, Hist of St Louis, Sheet music, St Louis World's Fair 1904, Trade catalogs, Westward expansion
Special Collections: Charles Lindbergh; Lewis & Clark Expedition; Trade Catalogs
Publications: In Her Own Write
Restriction: Non-circulating
Partic in Saint Louis Regional Library Network
Closed Sun & Mon

C MISSOURI INSTITUTE OF MENTAL HEALTH LIBRARY, University of Missouri, 5400 Arsenal St, 63139-1494. SAN 309-1899. Tel: 314-644-8838. Interlibrary Loan Service Tel: 314-644-8806. FAX: 314-644-8839. Web Site: www.mimh.edu/mimhweb/pie/lib/library.htm. *Bibliog Instr, Coll Develop, Online Servs*, Mary E Johnson; E-Mail: johnsonm@mimh.edu; Staff 8 (MLS 2, Non-MLS 6)
Founded 1962
1998-1999 Income $312,609. Mats Exp $134,740, Books $8,000, Per/Ser (Incl. Access Fees) $68,000. Sal $177,869 (Prof $78,000)
Library Holdings: Bk Titles 11,000; Per Subs 400
Subject Interests: Psychiat nursing, Psychiatry, Psychology, Psychopharmacology
Special Collections: National Association of State Mental Health Program Directory Archive; SLSH Archives
Partic in Dialog Corporation; Library Systems Service; Midcontinental Regional Med Libr Program; OCLC Online Computer Library Center, Inc; Saint Louis Regional Library Network

S MISSOURI SCHOOL FOR THE BLIND LIBRARY, 3815 Magnolia Ave, 63110. SAN 372-6703. Tel: 314-776-4320, Ext 257. FAX: 314-776-1875. Web Site: www.msb.k12.mo.us. *Librn*, Mary Dingus; *Asst Librn*, Chris Davidson; *Asst Librn*, Lisa Sagrati; Staff 3 (MLS 1, Non-MLS 2)
Enrl 116
Library Holdings: Bk Vols 14,256; Bk Titles 8,160; Per Subs 126
Special Collections: Blind Education
Partic in Saint Louis Regional Library Network

S MONSANTO CO, Monsanto Information Organization,* PO Box 7090, 63167-7090. SAN 309-1902. Interlibrary Loan Service Tel: 314-694-4747. FAX: 314-694-8748. E-Mail: lcc@monsanto.com. *In Charge*, Mark H Williams; Staff 25 (MLS 16, Non-MLS 9)
Founded 1961
Library Holdings: Bk Vols 38,000; Bk Titles 26,000; Per Subs 1,100
Subject Interests: Agriculture, Biology, Biotech, Chemistry, Econ, Medicine, Pharmaceuticals
Automation Activity & Vendor Info: (Circulation) epixtech, inc.; (Serials) epixtech, inc.
Publications: Catalogs; Indexes; In-House Alerting Services; Newsletter
Mem of Mo Libr Network Corp; St Louis Regional Libr Network
Partic in OCLC Online Computer Library Center, Inc

S NATIONAL MUSEUM OF TRANSPORTATION, Reference Library, 3015 Barrett Sta Rd, 63122. SAN 309-1910. Tel: 314-965-7998. FAX: 314-965-0242. Web Site: www.museumoftransport.org. *Librn*, Willis Goldschmidt
Founded 1944
Library Holdings: Bk Vols 3,500
Special Collections: Transportation & Communication Coll

S NOOTER CORPORATION, Technical Library,* PO Box 451, 63166. SAN 327-005X. Tel: 314-621-6000. FAX: 314-421-7580. Web Site: www.nooter.com.
Library Holdings: Bk Titles 1,000; Per Subs 15

P PLANNED PARENTHOOD OF SAINT LOUIS, Family Planning Library,* 4251 Forrest Park Ave, 63108. SAN 327-0076. Tel: 314-531-7526. FAX: 314-531-9731. *Librn*, Karen Omvig
Library Holdings: Bk Vols 920; Per Subs 25

S PULITZER, INC, St Louis Post-Dispatch News Research Department, 900 N Tucker Blvd, 63101. SAN 309-1953. Tel: 314-340-8270. Toll Free Tel: 800-365-0820, Ext 8270. FAX: 314-340-3006. Web Site: www.postnet.com. *Dir*, Gerald D Brown; Tel: 314-340-8274, Fax: 314-340-3006, E-Mail: gbrown@postnet.com; *Asst Dir*, Charles Shipman; Tel: 314-340-8275, E-Mail: cshipman@postnet.com. Subject Specialists: *News*, Gerald D Brown; Staff 16 (MLS 3, Non-MLS 13)
Founded 1922
Library Holdings: Bk Titles 3,500
Subject Interests: Int news, Local, Newsp clipping files, Newsp photogs, Newsp subjects related to nat
Special Collections: Housing (Pruitt-Igoe Housing Development Coll), flm; Post-Dispatch Authors Coll; St. Louis Post-Dispatch Archives; Theater (St Louis Municipal Opera Coll), clippings
Database Vendor: Dialog, GaleNet, Lexis-Nexis, ProQuest
Restriction: Not open to public
Function: Archival collection, Research library

S RALSTON PURINA CO, Information Center,* Checkerboard Sq 2S, 63164. SAN 309-1961. Tel: 314-982-2056. FAX: 314-982-3259. *Mgr*, Linda Recklein; E-Mail: lrecklein@ralston.com; *Tech Servs*, Yvonne Ali; *Coordr*, Leah Holler; Staff 3 (MLS 3)
Founded 1929
Library Holdings: Bk Vols 9,000; Per Subs 500
Subject Interests: Animal, Food proc, Human nutrition, Sanitation, Veterinary medicine
Publications: Column in Company Newspaper
Mem of St Louis Regional Libr Network
Partic in Dialog Corporation; Dow Jones News Retrieval; Nat Libr of Med; OCLC Online Computer Library Center, Inc

M SAINT JOHN'S MERCY MEDICAL CENTER, Thomas F Frawley Medical Center Library, 621 S New Ballas Rd, 63141. SAN 309-1988. Tel: 314-569-6340. FAX: 314-995-4299. *Dir*, Saundra H Brenner; E-Mail: brensh@stlo.smhs.com; *Asst Dir*, Jennifer Plaat; *ILL*, Mayris Woods
Library Holdings: Bk Vols 10,000; Per Subs 475
Subject Interests: Clinical medicine, Dentistry, Nursing
Database Vendor: OCLC - First Search, OVID Technologies
Partic in BRS; Dialog Corporation; Docline; Nat Libr of Med; OCLC Online Computer Library Center, Inc; Philnet
Open Mon-Thurs 7-7, Fri 7-6

S SAINT LOUIS ART MUSEUM, Richardson Memorial Library, One Fine Arts Dr, Forest Park, 63110-1380. SAN 309-1996. Tel: 314-655-5252. FAX: 314-721-6172. E-Mail: library@slam.org. Web Site: www.slam.org. *Librn*, Stephanie Sigala; Tel: 314-655-5253, E-Mail: athena@slam.org; *Assoc Librn*, Marianne L Cavanaugh; *Archivist*, Norma Sindelar; Staff 11 (MLS 3, Non-MLS 8)
Founded 1915
1998-1999 Income $362,000
Library Holdings: Bk Titles 70,000; Per Subs 130
Subject Interests: Art history
Special Collections: Contemporary Art Ephemera; Louisiana Purchase Exposition 1904 rec; Museum History Coll; Rare Art Books Coll
Automation Activity & Vendor Info: (OPAC) VTLS
Restriction: Non-circulating to the public
Partic in RLIN

M SAINT LOUIS CHILDREN'S HOSPITAL MEDICAL LIBRARY, (Formerly Saint Louis Children'S Hospital Library), One Children's Pl, 63110. SAN 329-3823. Tel: 314-454-2767, 314-454-2768, 314-454-6000. FAX: 314-454-2340. *Mgr Libr Serv*, Kathryn P Ray; E-Mail: kpr7535@bjc.org; *Librn*, Yvonne Hill; *Librn*, Suzzanne Dunmire. Subject Specialists: *Pediatrics*, Kathryn P Ray; Staff 1 (Non-MLS 1)
Library Holdings: Bk Titles 1,226; Per Subs 32
Subject Interests: Medicine, Nursing, Pediatrics
Database Vendor: OVID Technologies
Partic in Saint Louis Medical Librarians Consortia
Holdings networked through hospital in virtual format

CM SAINT LOUIS COLLEGE OF PHARMACY, O J Cloughly Alumni Library, 4588 Parkview Pl, 63110. SAN 309-2003. Tel: 314-367-8700, Ext 1002. FAX: 314-367-2784. E-Mail: library@eutectic.stlcop.edu. Web Site: www.stlcop.edu/library/. *Dir*, Jill Nissen; Tel: 314-367-8700, Ext 1006, E-Mail: jnissen@stlcop.edu; *Ref*, Barbara Pope; Tel: 314-367-8700, Ext 1001, E-Mail: bpope@stlcop.edu; Staff 7 (MLS 3, Non-MLS 4)
Founded 1948. Enrl 850; Highest Degree: Doctorate
Library Holdings: Bk Vols 54,221; Bk Titles 29,204; Per Subs 400
Subject Interests: Pharmacy
Special Collections: Archives
Partic in Library Systems Service; OCLC Online Computer Library Center, Inc; Saint Louis Regional Library Network

SAINT LOUIS COMMUNITY COLLEGE

J FLORISSANT VALLEY CAMPUS LIBRARY, 3400 Pershall Rd, 63135-1499. SAN 349-5965. Tel: 314-595-4511. Interlibrary Loan Service Tel: 314-644-9556. TDD: 314-595-2295. FAX: 314-595-2053. Web Site: www.stlcc.cc.mo.us. *Dir Libr Serv*, Stephanie Tolson; Tel: 314-595-4529, E-Mail: stolson@stlcc.cc.mo.us; *Ref*, Sharon Fox; Tel: 314-595-4585; *Ref*, Joanne Galanis; Tel: 314-595-4512; *Ref*, Janice Patton; Tel: 314-595-4530; *Ref*, Cathy Reilly; Tel: 314-595-4554; Staff 25 (MLS 8, Non-MLS 17)
Founded 1963. Enrl 3,639; Fac 244; Highest Degree: Associate
Jul 1999-Jun 2000 Income (Main Library Only) $917,788. Mats Exp $215,891, Books $95,786, Per/Ser (Incl. Access Fees) $93,511, Micro $7,409, Electronic Ref Mat (Incl. Access Fees) $15,135. Sal $557,489 (Prof $385,815)
Library Holdings: Bk Vols 99,725; Bk Titles 88,970; Per Subs 491
Automation Activity & Vendor Info: (Circulation) Innovative Interfaces Inc.; (Course Reserve) Innovative Interfaces Inc.; (OPAC) Innovative Interfaces Inc.; (Serials) Innovative Interfaces Inc.
Database Vendor: Dialog, Ebsco - EbscoHost, IAC - Info Trac, Lexis-Nexis, OCLC - First Search
Partic in Missouri Library Network Corporation; Mobius; Morenet; Saint Louis Regional Library Network

INSTRUCTIONAL RESOURCES, 5460 Highland Park, 63110. SAN 349-5930. Tel: 314-644-9555. Interlibrary Loan Service Tel: 314-644-9561. TDD: 314-644-9977. FAX: 314-652-9269. Web Site: www.stlcc.cc.mo.us. *Dir, Instrul Serv*, Cathye Dierberg; Tel: 314-644-9556, E-Mail: cdierberg@stlcc.cc.mo.us; *Head, Acq*, Sheila Ouellette; Tel: 314-644-9557; *Head, Cat*, Carol Bennett; Tel: 314-644-9558; *Syst Coordr*, Bonnie Sanguinet; Tel: 314-644-9562; Staff 22 (MLS 4, Non-MLS 18)
Founded 1962. Highest Degree: Associate
Jul 1998-Jun 1999 Income (Main Library Only) $973,741. Mats Exp $73,084, Books $3,267, Per/Ser (Incl. Access Fees) $7,864, Presv $1,500, Micro $4,062, Electronic Ref Mat (Incl. Access Fees) $45,213. Sal $592,514 (Prof $263,647)
Library Holdings: Bk Vols 876; Bk Titles 469; Per Subs 26
Special Collections: College Archives; Video Library
Automation Activity & Vendor Info: (Acquisitions) Innovative Interfaces Inc.; (Cataloging) Innovative Interfaces Inc.; (Circulation) Innovative Interfaces Inc.; (Serials) Innovative Interfaces Inc.
Database Vendor: Dialog, Ebsco - EbscoHost, IAC - SearchBank, Lexis-Nexis, OCLC - First Search
Partic in Higher Educ Coun of St Louis; Missouri Library Network Corporation; Mobius; Morenet

J MERAMEC CAMPUS LIBRARY, 11333 Big Bend Blvd, 63122. SAN 349-6023. Tel: 314-984-7797. Interlibrary Loan Service Tel: 314-644-9555. TDD: 314-984-7744. FAX: 314-984-7225. Interlibrary Loan Service FAX: 314-652-9555. Web Site: www.stlcc.cc.mo.us. *Dir Libr Serv*, Ann Riley; Tel: 314-984-7624; *Coll Develop*, Donna Saltermann; Tel: 314-984-7486; *Coll Develop*, Damaris Schmitt; Tel: 314-984-7487; Staff 22 (MLS 5, Non-MLS 17)
Founded 1963. Enrl 7,065; Fac 344
Jul 1999-Jun 2000 Income $1,115,602. Mats Exp $394,909, Books $233,470, Per/Ser (Incl. Access Fees) $118,686, Micro $10,497, Electronic Ref Mat (Incl. Access Fees) $32,256. Sal $434,991 (Prof $268,482)
Library Holdings: Bk Vols 84,511; Bk Titles 78,065; Per Subs 538
Automation Activity & Vendor Info: (Circulation) Innovative Interfaces Inc.; (Course Reserve) Innovative Interfaces Inc.; (OPAC) Innovative Interfaces Inc.; (Serials) Innovative Interfaces Inc.
Database Vendor: Dialog, Ebsco - EbscoHost, IAC - Info Trac, OCLC - First Search, Silverplatter Information Inc.
Publications: A Brief Guide to Meramec Instructional Resources, Looseleaf pages explaining Catalog; Other services & products assembled into booklets for classroom instruction
Partic in Higher Educ Coun of Metrop St Louis; MLNC; Mo Res & Educ Network; Mobius; Saint Louis Regional Library Network

J FOREST PARK CAMPUS LIBRARY, 5600 Oakland Ave, 63110-1393. SAN 349-599X. Tel: 314-644-9210. Interlibrary Loan Service Tel: 314-644-9555. TDD: 314-644-9977. FAX: 314-652-9240. Interlibrary Loan Service FAX: 314-652-9269. Web Site: www.stlcc.cc.mo.us. *Dir Libr Serv*, Carol Warrington; Tel: 314-644-9209; *Media Spec*, Randy Malta; Tel: 314-644-9270; *Online Servs*, Carol Shahriary; Staff 11 (MLS 4, Non-MLS 7)
Founded 1965. Enrl 3,491; Fac 128; Highest Degree: Associate
Jul 1999-Jun 2000 Income $674,102. Mats Exp $182,321, Books $68,761, Per/Ser (Incl. Access Fees) $79,158, Micro $14,785, Electronic Ref Mat (Incl. Access Fees) $18,158. Sal $440,611 (Prof $209,100)
Library Holdings: Bk Vols 76,510; Bk Titles 67,226; Per Subs 428
Subject Interests: Allied health, Food indust, Medicine, Nursing, Restaurant mgt, Tourism
Special Collections: Black Studies (Afro-American) bks, per
Automation Activity & Vendor Info: (Circulation) Innovative Interfaces Inc.; (Course Reserve) Innovative Interfaces Inc.; (OPAC) Innovative Interfaces Inc.; (Serials) Innovative Interfaces Inc.
Database Vendor: Dialog, Ebsco - EbscoHost, IAC - Info Trac, Lexis-Nexis, OCLC - First Search
Publications: Collection Development Statement; Library Guide; Library Services for the Faculty
Partic in Missouri Library Network Corporation; Mobius; Morenet; Saint Louis Regional Library Network

G SAINT LOUIS COMPTROLLERS OFFICE, Record Retention, 1200 Market St Rm 1, 63103. SAN 375-2097. Tel: 314-622-4274. *Mgr*, Ruth Brown; Staff 4 (Non-MLS 4)

P SAINT LOUIS COUNTY LIBRARY,* 1640 S Lindbergh Blvd, 63131. SAN 349-6058. Tel: 314-994-3300. TDD: 314-994-9255. FAX: 314-997-7602. Web Site: www.slcl.lib.mo.us. *Dir*, C Daniel Wilson, Jr; *Asst Dir*, George Durnell; Tel: 314-994-3300, Ext 211, E-Mail: gdurnell@slcl.lib.mo.us; *Assoc Dir*, Gary P Holdefer; Tel: 314-994-3300, Ext 212, Fax: 314-997-2896, E-Mail: gholdefer@slcl.lib.mo.us; *Ch Servs*, Natalie Oleshchuk; Staff 491 (MLS 52, Non-MLS 439)
Founded 1946. Pop 860,000; Circ 8,327,623
Jan 1999-Dec 1999 Income (Main Library and Branch Library) $21,363,500, State $470,000, Federal $148,000, County $19,439,000, Locally Generated Income $2,167,500, Other $730,000. Mats Exp $4,200,000, Books $2,325,000, Per/Ser (Incl. Access Fees) $600,000, Micro $100,000. Sal $12,200,000 (Prof $2,075,000)
Library Holdings: Bk Vols 2,777,056; Per Subs 9,258
Subject Interests: Bus, Fiction, Finance, Genealogy, Mgt
Automation Activity & Vendor Info: (Acquisitions) Innovative Interfaces Inc.; (Cataloging) Innovative Interfaces Inc.; (Circulation) Innovative Interfaces Inc.; (ILL) Innovative Interfaces Inc.; (Media Booking) Innovative Interfaces Inc.; (OPAC) Innovative Interfaces Inc.; (Serials) Innovative Interfaces Inc.
Database Vendor: Innovative Interfaces INN - View
Publications: Co-Lib Chronicle (staff newsletter)
Partic in Missouri Library Network Corporation
Special Services for the Deaf - Books on deafness & sign language; High interest/low vocabulary books; Special interest periodicals; TDD
Special Services for the Blind - Arkenstone, a computer system for the visually handicapped; Magnifier lamps & electronic reading machine
Friends of the Library Group
Branches: 19

DANIEL BOONE BRANCH, 300 Clarkson Rd, Ellisville, 63011. SAN 349-6112. Tel: 636-227-9630. Web Site: www.slcl.lib.mo.us. *Branch Mgr*, Marion Sood; *Publ Servs*, George Durnell; Tel: 314-994-3300, Ext 211, Fax: 314-997-7602, E-Mail: gdurnell@slcl.lib.mo.us
Library Holdings: Bk Vols 144,398

BRIDGETON TRAILS BRANCH, 3455 McKelvey Rd, Bridgeton, 63044. SAN 349-6082. Tel: 314-291-7570. Web Site: www.slcl.lib.mo.us. *Branch Mgr*, Juanita Tunnell; E-Mail: jtunnell@slcl.lib.mo.us; *Publ Servs*, George Durnell; Tel: 513-994-3000, Ext 211, Fax: 513-997-7602, E-Mail: gdurnell@slcl.lib.mo.us
Library Holdings: Bk Vols 88,442

P CLIFF CAVE BRANCH, 5430 Telegraph Rd, 63129-3556. SAN 374-4590. Tel: 314-487-6003. Web Site: www.slcl.lib.mo.us. *Branch Mgr*, Marsha Ramey; E-Mail: mramey@slcl.lib.mo.us; *Publ Servs*, George Durnell; Tel: 314-994-3300, Ext 211, Fax: 314-997-7602, E-Mail: gdurnell@slcl.lib.mo.us
Library Holdings: Bk Vols 86,184

P EUREKA HILLS BRANCH, 103 Hilltop Village Ctr, Eureka, 63025-1108. SAN 323-8113. Tel: 636-938-4520. Web Site: www.slcl.lib.mo.us. *Branch Mgr*, Louise Powderly; E-Mail: lpowderly@slcl.lib.mo.us; *Librn*, Joan Stewart; *Publ Servs*, George Durnell; Tel: 314-994-3300, Ext 211, Fax: 314-997-7602, E-Mail: gdurnell@slcl.lib.mo.us
Library Holdings: Bk Vols 17,250

P FLORISSANT VALLEY BRANCH, 195 New Florissant Rd S, Florissant, 63031-6796. SAN 349-6147. Tel: 314-921-7200. Web Site: www.slcl.lib.mo.us. *Branch Mgr*, Diana Fox; E-Mail: dfox@slcl.lib.mo.us; *Publ Servs*, George Durnell; Tel: 314-994-3300, Ext 211, Fax: 314-997-7602, E-Mail: gdurnell@slcl.lib.mo.us
Library Holdings: Bk Vols 105,867

GRAND GLAIZE BRANCH, 1010 Meramec Sta Rd, Manchester, 63021-6943. SAN 349-6171. Tel: 636-225-6454. FAX: 314-225-6072. Web Site: www.slcl.lib.mo.us. *Branch Mgr*, Pat Woodward; E-Mail: pwoodard@slcl.lib.mo.us; *Publ Servs*, George Durnell; Tel: 314-994-3300, Ext 211, Fax: 314-997-7602, E-Mail: gdurnell@slcl.lib.mo.us
Library Holdings: Bk Vols 86,436

INDIAN TRAILS BRANCH, 8400 Delport Dr, 63114-5904. SAN 349-6201. Tel: 314-428-5424. Web Site: www.slcl.lib.mo.us. *Branch Mgr*, Robbin Oehler; E-Mail: roehler@slcl.lib.mo.us; *Publ Servs*, George Durnell; Tel: 314-994-3300, Ext 211, Fax: 314-997-7602, E-Mail: gdurnell@slcl.lib.mo.us

Library Holdings: Bk Vols 78,886
JAMESTOWN BLUFFS BRANCH, 4153 Hwy 67, 63034-2825. SAN 377-6085. Tel: 314-741-6800. Web Site: www.slcl.lib.mo.us. *Branch Mgr*, Kenneth Cieslak; E-Mail: kcieslak@slcl.lib.mo.us
Library Holdings: Bk Vols 77,660
LEWIS & CLARK BRANCH, 9909 Lewis-Clark Blvd, 63136-5322. SAN 349-6260. Tel: 314-868-0331. FAX: 314-868-6891. Web Site: www.slcl.lib.mo.us. *Branch Mgr*, Mildred Rias; E-Mail: mrias@slcl.lib.mo.us; *Publ Servs*, George Durnell; Tel: 314-994-3300, Ext 211, Fax: 314-997-7602, E-Mail: gdurnell@slcl.lib.mo.us
Library Holdings: Bk Vols 89,299
MERAMEC VALLEY, 625 New Smizer Mill Rd, Fenton, 63026-3518. SAN 328-6878. Tel: 636-349-4981. Web Site: www.slcl.lib.mo.us. *Branch Mgr*, Charlene Zinkl; E-Mail: czinkl@slcl.lib.mo.us; *Librn*, Phyllis Dahlem; *Publ Servs*, George Durnell; Tel: 314-994-3300, Ext 211, Fax: 314-997-7602, E-Mail: gdurnell@slcl.lib.mo.us
Library Holdings: Bk Vols 11,522
MID-COUNTY, 7821 Maryland, 63105. SAN 349-6295. Tel: 314-721-3008. Web Site: www.slcl.lib.mo.us. *Branch Mgr*, John Spears; E-Mail: jspears@slcl.lib.mo.us; *Librn*, Suzanne Bromschwig; *Publ Servs*, George Durnell; Tel: 314-994-3300, Ext 211, Fax: 314-997-7602, E-Mail: gdurnell@slcl.lib.mo.us
Library Holdings: Bk Vols 86,511
NATURAL BRIDGE, 7606 Natural Bridge Rd, 63121-4905. SAN 349-6325. Tel: 314-382-3116. Web Site: www.slcl.lib.mo.us. *Branch Mgr*, Vicki Krueger; E-Mail: vkrueger@slcl.lib.mo.us; *Publ Servs*, George Durnell; Tel: 314-994-3300, Ext 211, Fax: 314-997-7602, E-Mail: gdurnell@slcl.lib.mo.us
Library Holdings: Bk Vols 83,925
OAK BEND, 842 S Holmes Ave, 63122-6507. SAN 328-6894. Tel: 314-822-0051. Web Site: www.slcl.lib.mo.us. *Branch Mgr*, Donna Spaulding; E-Mail: dspaulding@slcl.lib.mo.us; *Publ Servs*, George Durnell; Tel: 314-994-3300, Ext 211, Fax: 314-997-7602, E-Mail: gdurnell@slcl.lib.mo.us
Library Holdings: Bk Vols 90,414
PRAIRIE COMMONS, 915 Utz Lane, Hazelwood, 63042-2739. SAN 328-6851. Tel: 314-895-1023. Web Site: www.slcl.lib.mo.us. *Branch Mgr*, Julia Mangner; E-Mail: jmangner@slcl.lib.mo.us; *Librn*, Lee Kiesling; *Publ Servs*, George Durnell; Tel: 314-994-3300, Ext 211, Fax: 314-997-7602, E-Mail: gdurnell@slcl.lib.mo.us
Library Holdings: Bk Vols 88,803
ROCK ROAD, 10267 St Charles Rock Rd, Saint Ann, 63074-1812. SAN 349-635X. Tel: 314-429-5116. Web Site: www.slcl.lib.mo.us. *Branch Mgr*, Eric Button; E-Mail: ebutton@slcl.lib.mo.us; *Librn*, Louise Powderly; *Publ Servs*, George Durnell; Tel: 314-994-3300, Ext 211, Fax: 314-997-7602, E-Mail: gdurnell@slcl.lib.mo.us
Library Holdings: Bk Vols 91,277
SPECIAL COLLECTIONS DEPT, 1640 S Lindbergh Blvd, 63131-3598. SAN 328-476X. Tel: 314-994-3300, Ext 230. FAX: 314-997-7602. Web Site: www.slcl.lib.mo.us. *Spec Coll*, Joyce Loving; E-Mail: jloving@slcl.lib.mo.us; *Publ Servs*, George Durnell; Tel: 314-994-3300, Ext 211, Fax: 314-997-7602, E-Mail: gdurnell@slcl.lib.mo.us
Library Holdings: Bk Vols 25,000
Subject Interests: African Amer, Genealogy, Local history
Publications: Journal (quarterly); Newsletter (monthly)
TESSON FERRY, 9920 Lin-Ferry Dr, 63123-6914. SAN 349-6384. Tel: 314-843-0560. Web Site: www.slcl.lib.mo.us. *Branch Mgr*, June Sommer; E-Mail: jsommer@slcl.lib.mo.us; *Publ Servs*, George Durnell; Tel: 314-994-3300, Ext 211, Fax: 314-997-7602, E-Mail: gdurnell@slcl.lib.mo.us
Library Holdings: Bk Vols 119,416
Subject Interests: African-Am, Genealogy, Local history
THORNHILL, 12863 Willowyck Dr, 63146-3771. SAN 349-6414. Tel: 314-878-7730. Web Site: www.slcl.lib.mo.us. *Branch Mgr*, Dottie Wobbe; E-Mail: dwobbe@slcl.lib.mo.us; *Publ Servs*, George Durnell; Tel: 314-994-3300, Ext 211, Fax: 314-997-7602, E-Mail: gdurnell@slcl.lib.mo.us
Library Holdings: Bk Vols 94,002
Subject Interests: African-Am, Genealogy, Local history
WEBER ROAD, 4444 Weber Rd, 63123-6744. SAN 349-6449. Tel: 314-638-2210. FAX: 314-638-2212. Web Site: www.slcl.lib.mo.us. *Branch Mgr*, Carol Besch; E-Mail: cbesch@slcl.lib.mo.us; *Publ Servs*, George Durnell; Tel: 314-994-3300, Ext 211, Fax: 314-997-7602, E-Mail: dgurnell@slcl.lib.mo.us
Library Holdings: Bk Vols 95,993
Subject Interests: African Amer, Genealogy, Local history
Bookmobiles: 19

S SAINT LOUIS MERCANTILE LIBRARY AT THE UNIVERSITY OF MISSOURI-ST LOUIS, Thomas Jefferson Library Bldg, 8001 Natural Bridge Rd, 63121-4499. SAN 309-2054. Tel: 314-516-7240. FAX: 314-516-7241. *Exec Dir*, John Neal Hoover; E-Mail: jhoover@umsl.edu
Founded 1846
Library Holdings: Bk Vols 250,000
Special Collections: Alchemy Coll; American Railroads 1913-1976 (John W Barriger III Coll), bks, comn rpts, monographs, mss, pamphlets, papers, photogs, speeches; Early Western Americana; National Inland Waterways Coll, bks, mss, maps, photogs, rpts & pamphlets; St Louis History Coll, atlases, maps, newsp, photogs from the early 19th cent
Publications: Annual report; New Books (bulletin); newsletter (quarterly)
Partic in Missouri Library Network Corporation; OCLC Online Computer Library Center, Inc; Saint Louis Regional Library Network
Open Mon-Fri 8:30-4:30
Friends of the Library Group

S SAINT LOUIS METROPOLITAN POLICE DEPARTMENT, Saint Louis Police Library, 315 S Tucker Blvd, 63102. SAN 325-447X. Tel: 314-444-5581. FAX: 314-444-5689. *Librn*, Barbara Miksicek
Founded 1947
Jul 1999-Jun 2000 Income $41,000. Mats Exp $41,000, Books $21,000, Per/Ser (Incl. Access Fees) $20,000
Library Holdings: Bk Vols 30,000; Per Subs 160
Subject Interests: Law enforcement
Special Collections: Annual Reports for Police Department from 1861 to present
Publications: Directory of Law Enforcement Agencies in Metropolitan St Louis; In the Line of Duty
Partic in SLA

S SAINT LOUIS PSYCHIATRIC REHABILITATION CENTER, Clients Library,* 5300 Arsenal St, 63139. SAN 372-6363. Tel: 314-644-8000, 314-644-8136. *Librn*, Jacquelyn Foster
Library Holdings: Bk Titles 6,000; Per Subs 30
Special Services for the Deaf - Books on deafness & sign language; High interest/low vocabulary books
Open Sun-Thurs 8:30-5, Tues & Thurs 6pm-8pm, Fri & Sat 8-4:30

S SAINT LOUIS PSYCHOANALYTIC INSTITUTE, Betty Golde Smith Library,* 4524 Forest Park Blvd, 63108. SAN 309-2062. Tel: 314-361-7075. FAX: 314-361-6269. E-Mail: bgsmlib@stlnet.com. *Librn*, Vera Emmons
Founded 1957
Jul 1999-Jun 2000 Income $35,000. Mats Exp $20,000, Books $3,900, Per/Ser (Incl. Access Fees) $5,300, Manuscripts & Archives $300. (Prof $15,000)
Library Holdings: Bk Vols 6,000; Per Subs 60
Subject Interests: Behav sci, Psychiatry, Psychoanalysis, Psychology, Soc
Partic in Columbus Area Library & Information Council Of Ohio (CALICO)

P SAINT LOUIS PUBLIC LIBRARY, 1301 Olive St, 63103-2389. SAN 349-6597. Tel: 314-241-2288. Interlibrary Loan Service Tel: 314-539-0322. Circulation Tel: 314-539-0342. Reference Tel: 314-539-0353. TDD: 314-539-0364. FAX: 314-241-3840. E-Mail: webmaster@slpl.lib.mo.us. Web Site: www.slpl.lib.mo.us. *Exec Dir*, Glen E Holt; E-Mail: gholt@slpl.lib.mo.us; *Dep Dir*, Waller McGuire; E-Mail: wmcguire@slpl.lib.mo.us; *Dir, Tech Serv*, Kim Peterson; E-Mail: kpeterson@slpl.lib.mo.us; *Commun Relations, YA Servs*, Leslie Edmonds Holt; E-Mail: lholt@slpl.lib.mo.us; *Commun Relations*, Gerald Brooks; E-Mail: gbrooks@slpl.lib.mo.us; *Dir, Tech Serv*, David Smith; E-Mail: dsmith@slpl.lib.mo.us; Staff 121 (MLS 59, Non-MLS 62)
Founded 1865. Pop 361,565; Circ 2,505,182
Oct 1998-Sep 1999 Income (Main Library and Branch Library) $19,145,116, State $243,738, Federal $628,609, Locally Generated Income $16,609,253, Other $1,663,516. Mats Exp $2,707,318, Books $1,456,335, Per/Ser (Incl. Access Fees) $409,706, AV Equip $366,923, Electronic Ref Mat (Incl. Access Fees) $474,354. Sal $7,393,211
Library Holdings: Bk Vols 3,782,690; Per Subs 7,719
Subject Interests: Ch lit, Civil War, Genealogy, Heraldry, Mo hist, St Louis hist
Special Collections: Architecture (Steedman Coll); Black History (Julia Davis Coll); Genealogy Coll; NJ Werner Coll of Typography; St Louis Media Archives
Automation Activity & Vendor Info: (Acquisitions) DRA; (Cataloging) DRA; (Circulation) DRA; (ILL) DRA; (OPAC) DRA; (Serials) DRA
Database Vendor: DRA, OCLC - First Search
Publications: African-American Heritage of St Louis; German-American Heritage of St Louis; St Louis by the Numbers
Partic in OCLC Online Computer Library Center, Inc; Saint Louis Regional Library Network
Special Services for the Deaf - Books on deafness & sign language; Captioned media; Special interest periodicals; TDD
Special Services for the Blind - Assistive Technology Center for Persons who are blind or physically handicapped; Braille translation & printing software & equipment; Magnifier lamps & electronic reading machine; Screen enlargement software for people with visual disabilities
Open Mon 10-9, Tues-Fri 10-6, Sat 9-5, Sun 1-5
Friends of the Library Group
Branches: 15
BADEN, 8448 Church Rd, 63147-1898. SAN 349-6627. Tel: 314-388-2400. FAX: 314-388-0529. *In Charge*, Helen Stephens; Staff 1 (Non-MLS 1)
Library Holdings: Bk Vols 27,270
Open Mon & Sat 9-6, Tues-Thurs 12-7, Fri 11-6
BARR, 1701 S Jefferson Ave, 63104-2699. SAN 349-6651. Tel: 314-771-7040. FAX: 314-771-9054. *Librn*, Adele Heagney; Staff 2 (MLS 2)
Library Holdings: Bk Vols 28,085
Open Mon & Sat 9-6, Tues-Thurs 12-7, Fri 11-6
BUDER, 4401 Hampton Ave, 63109-2237. SAN 349-6716. Tel: 314-352-2900. FAX: 314-352-5387. *Librn*, James Moses; Staff 6 (MLS 5, Non-MLS 1)

Library Holdings: Bk Vols 86,783
Open Mon-Thurs 9-9, Fri & Sat 9-6, Sun 1-5
CABANNE, 1106 N Union Blvd, 63113-1599. SAN 349-6740. Tel: 314-367-0717. FAX: 314-367-7802. *Librn*, Leandrea Lucas; Staff 2 (MLS 1, Non-MLS 1)
Library Holdings: Bk Vols 35,956
Open Mon & Sat 9-6, Tues-Thurs 12-7, Fri 11-6
Friends of the Library Group
CARONDELET, 6800 Michigan Ave, 63111-2896. SAN 349-6775. Tel: 314-752-9224. FAX: 314-752-7794. *Librn*, Fred Fernow; Staff 2 (MLS 1, Non-MLS 1)
Library Holdings: Bk Vols 53,840
Open Mon & Sat 9-6, Tues-Thurs 12-7, Fri 11-6
CARPENTER, 3309 S Grand Ave, 63118-1001. SAN 349-6805. Tel: 314-772-6586. FAX: 314-772-1871. *Librn*, Craig Clark; Staff 4 (MLS 2, Non-MLS 2)
Library Holdings: Bk Vols 65,726
Open Mon-Thurs 9-9, Fri & Sat 9-6, Sun 1-5
CHARING CROSS, 356 N Skinker Blvd, 63130-4808. SAN 322-5917. Tel: 314-726-2653. FAX: 314-726-6541. *In Charge*, Charles Lamkin; Staff 1 (Non-MLS 1)
Library Holdings: Bk Vols 3,863
Open Tues-Fri 1-6, Sat 9-6
COMPTON FILM LIBRARY, 1624 Locust St, 63103-1802. SAN 370-4831. Tel: 314-241-0478. FAX: 314-241-5052. *AV*, Vince Andrzejewski; Staff 1 (Non-MLS 1)
Open Mon-Fri 8:30-6
JULIA DAVIS BRANCH, 4415 Natural Bridge Rd, 63115-5398. SAN 349-6864. Tel: 314-383-3021. FAX: 314-383-0251. *Librn*, Barbara Murphy; Staff 4 (MLS 1, Non-MLS 3)
Library Holdings: Bk Vols 71,850
Open Mon-Thurs 9-9, Fri & Sat 9-6, Sun 1-5
Friends of the Library Group
DIVOLL, 4234 N Grand Blvd, 63107-1898. SAN 349-6929. Tel: 314-534-0313. FAX: 314-534-3353.; Staff 1 (Non-MLS 1)
Library Holdings: Bk Vols 28,051
Open Mon & Sat 9-6, Tues-Thurs 12-7, Fri 11-6
KINGSHIGHWAY, 4641 Shenandoah Ave, 63110-3423. SAN 349-6988. Tel: 314-771-5450. FAX: 314-771-9877. *Librn*, Joe Sedey; Staff 2 (MLS 1, Non-MLS 1)
Library Holdings: Bk Vols 41,578
Open Mon & Sat 9-6, Tues-Thurs 12-7, Fri 11-6
Friends of the Library Group
LASHLY, 4537 W Pine Blvd, 63108-2192. SAN 349-7011. Tel: 314-367-4120. FAX: 314-367-4814. *Librn*, Judith Bruce; Staff 2 (MLS 1, Non-MLS 1)
Library Holdings: Bk Vols 50,160
Open Mon, Wed, Fri & Sat 9-6, Tues & Thurs 12-9
Friends of the Library Group
MACHACEK, 6424 Scanlan Ave, 63139-2498. SAN 349-7046. Tel: 314-781-2948. FAX: 314-781-8441. *Librn*, Trevor Rees; Staff 2 (MLS 1, Non-MLS 1)
Library Holdings: Bk Vols 58,240
Open Mon & Wed 12-9, Tues & Thurs-Sat 9-6
Friends of the Library Group
SAINT LOUIS MARKET PLACE, 6548 Manchester Ave, 63139-3520. SAN 376-9526. Tel: 314-647-0939. FAX: 314-647-1062. *In Charge*, Christie Harkins; Staff 1 (Non-MLS 1)
Open Tues-Fri 11-7, Sat 9-6
WALNUT PARK, 5760 W Florissant Ave, 63120-2444. SAN 349-7135. Tel: 314-383-1210. FAX: 314-383-2079. *Librn*, Barbara Boyd; Staff 2 (MLS 1, Non-MLS 1)
Library Holdings: Bk Vols 36,888
Open Mon & Sat 9-6, Tues-Thurs 12-7, Fri 11-6
Bookmobiles: 3. Vans

S SAINT LOUIS SCIENCE CENTER LIBRARY, 5050 Oakland Ave, 63110. SAN 327-1633. Tel: 314-533-8282. FAX: 314-289-4423.
Library Holdings: Bk Titles 3,500
Partic in Saint Louis Regional Library Network

S SAINT LOUIS SYMPHONY COMMUNITY MUSIC SCHOOL, Mae M Whitaker Library, 560 Trinity Ave, 63130. SAN 309-202X. Tel: 314-286-4425. FAX: 314-286-4421. Web Site: www.symphonymusicschool.org. *Librn*, Tim Gebauer; E-Mail: timg@slso.org
Founded 1974. Enrl 10; Fac 4
Library Holdings: Bk Vols 2,727; Bk Titles 2,487; Per Subs 40
Subject Interests: Music performance
Special Collections: Max Risch Jr Bassoon & Wind Ensemble Music Coll; Robert Orchard Opera Coll, tapes; Thomas B Sherman Coll, recordings, scores & bks

C SAINT LOUIS UNIVERSITY, Pius XII Memorial Library, 3650 Lindell Blvd, 63108-3302. SAN 349-7194. Tel: 314-977-3100. Interlibrary Loan Service Tel: 314-977-3104. FAX: 314-977-3108. Web Site: pius.slu.edu. *Business, Mgr*, Catherine R Riedesel; Tel: 314-977-3101, E-Mail: riedesck@slu.edu; *Librn*, Frances Benham; E-Mail: benham@slu.edu; *ILL*, David Shocklee; Tel: 314-977-3104, E-Mail: shockldg@slu.edu; *Online Servs, Ref*, Patricia Gregory; Tel: 314-977-3107, E-Mail: gregorypl@slu.edu; *Circ*, Doris Beeson; Tel: 314-977-3086, E-Mail: beesondj@slu.edu; *Tech Servs*, Patrick McCarthy; Tel: 314-977-3093, E-Mail: mccartpg@slu.edu; Staff 29 (MLS 21, Non-MLS 8)
Founded 1818. Highest Degree: Doctorate
Jul 1999-Jun 2000 Income (Main Library Only) $5,650,496. Mats Exp $2,612,203, Books $756,267, Per/Ser (Incl. Access Fees) $1,734,956, Presv $99,839. Sal $1,991,968 (Prof $1,192,782)
Library Holdings: Bk Vols 1,277,447; Per Subs 6,673
Subject Interests: Am studies, Catholic Church, Church history, Earth science, Philosophy, Soc sci, Soc work, Urban affairs
Special Collections: Medieval Manuscripts; Western Americana
Publications: Library Guides; Manuscripta; Research Aids; Subject Bibliographies
Partic in Higher Educ Coord Coun of Metrop St Louis; Merlin; Missouri Library Network Corporation; OCLC Online Computer Library Center, Inc; Saint Louis Regional Library Network
Friends of the Library Group
Departmental Libraries:
CM HEALTH SCIENCES CENTER LIBRARY, 1402 S Grand Blvd, 63104. SAN 349-7259. Tel: 314-577-8605. FAX: 314-772-1307. Web Site: www.slu.edu/libraries/hsc. *Dir*, Audrey P Newcomer; Tel: 314-577-8607, E-Mail: newcomer@slu.edu; *Automation Syst Coordr*, Chengren Hu; Tel: 314-577-8604, E-Mail: huc@slu.edu; *Coll Develop*, Kathy Gallagher; E-Mail: gallagherk@slu.edu; Staff 10 (MLS 9, Non-MLS 1)
Founded 1890. Highest Degree: Doctorate
Jul 1999-Jun 2000 Mats Exp $1,023,807, Books $99,512, Per/Ser (Incl. Access Fees) $513,805, Presv $17,135. Sal $959,916 (Prof $447,646)
Library Holdings: Bk Titles 33,551; Per Subs 1,690
Subject Interests: Allied health sci, Health care admin, Medicine, Nursing, Ophthalmology, Public health
Automation Activity & Vendor Info: (Circulation) Innovative Interfaces Inc.
Publications: Infolink Newsletter; Library Fact Sheets; Library Guide; New Books
Partic in Nat Libr of Med; OCLC Online Computer Library Center, Inc; Philnet; Saint Louis Regional Library Network
Friends of the Library Group
CL OMER POOS LAW LIBRARY, Morrissey Hall, 3700 Lindell Blvd, 63108-3478. SAN 349-7283. Tel: 314-977-3947. FAX: 314-977-3966. Web Site: law.slu.edu/library/. *Dir*, Patricia Cervenka; Tel: 314-977-3393, E-Mail: cervenka@slu.edu; *Publ Servs*, Peggy McDermott; Tel: 314-977-2735, E-Mail: mcdermott@slu.edu; *Ref*, Lynn Hartke; Tel: 314-977-2756, E-Mail: hartkelk@slu.edu; *Acq, Web Coordr*, Liz Glankler; Tel: 314-977-2759, E-Mail: glankler@slu.edu; *Tech Servs*, Richard Amelung; *Govt Doc*, Kathleen Casey; Tel: 314-977-2742, E-Mail: caseyke@slu.edu; *Cat*, Ting James; Tel: 314-977-3356, E-Mail: jamests@slu.edu; Staff 9 (MLS 9)
Founded 1842. Highest Degree: Doctorate
Jul 1999-Jun 2000 Income $1,805,079. Mats Exp $908,467, Books $129,832, Per/Ser (Incl. Access Fees) $756,283, Presv $12,965. Sal $700,468 (Prof $389,622)
Library Holdings: Bk Vols 370,746; Per Subs 6,424
Subject Interests: Bus law, Constitutional law, Ill law, Irish law, Labor law, Legal hist, Med-legal, Mo law, Polish law, Urban problems
Special Collections: Early State Records, microfilm; Father Brown Labor Arbitration Coll; Missouri & Illinois Briefs; Smurfit Irish Law Coll; Sullivan Manuscript Coll; US Briefs, microcard & fiche
Partic in Council of Law Librs of AJCU; LVIS; Merlin; Mid-Am Law Sch Libr Consortium; MLNC
Friends of the Library Group

S SAINT LOUIS ZOO LIBRARY, One Government Dr, 63110. SAN 328-4018. Tel: 314-781-0900, Ext 321. FAX: 314-768-5457. *Librn*, Jill Gordon; Tel: 314-781-0900, Ext 319, E-Mail: gordon@stlzoo.org
Library Holdings: Bk Vols 5,000; Per Subs 100
Subject Interests: Conservation, Natural history, Zoology
Special Collections: St Louis Zoo History Coll
Automation Activity & Vendor Info: (Cataloging) EOS; (OPAC) EOS
Database Vendor: Dialog
Partic in Saint Louis Regional Library Network

M SAINT MARY'S HEALTH CENTER, Health Sciences Library, 6420 Clayton Rd, 63117. SAN 349-7348. Tel: 314-768-8112. FAX: 314-768-8974. *Dir*, Sue Schoening; E-Mail: sschoening@ssmhc.com; *Asst Librn*, Ruby Graise
Library Holdings: Bk Vols 16,000; Bk Titles 1,000; Per Subs 305
Subject Interests: Clinical medicine, Consumer health
Partic in Medline; OCLC Online Computer Library Center, Inc
Branches:
NANCY SUE CLAYPOOL HEALTH INFORMATION CENTER, 6420 Clayton Rd, 63117. SAN 376-8600. Tel: 314-768-8636. *Librn*, Sue Schoening
Subject Interests: Consumer health

R SAUL BRODSKY JEWISH COMMUNITY LIBRARY, 12 Millstone Campus Dr, 63146-5776. SAN 309-1732. Tel: 314-432-0020. FAX: 314-432-6150. *Chief Librn*, Barbara Raznick; E-Mail: barbrazn@aol.com
Founded 1983

Library Holdings: Bk Titles 22,000; Per Subs 100
Subject Interests: History, Jewish art, Literature, Philosophy
Special Collections: Hebrew Literature; Holocaust; Israel; Jewish Children's Books; National & International Newspapers in English, Yiddish, Hebrew & Russian; Russian Literature
Publications: Newsletter; Sagarin Review: The St Louis Jewish Literary Journal
Friends of the Library Group

R SHAARE EMETH TEMPLE, Fleischer Library, 11645 Ladue Rd, 63141. SAN 321-5822. Tel: 314-569-0010. FAX: 314-569-0271. *Librn*, Diana J Kline
Founded 1960
Library Holdings: Bk Vols 15,000; Per Subs 11

S SIGMA CHEMICAL CO, Research Library,* 3500 Dekalb St, PO Box 14508, 63118. SAN 377-2748. Tel: 314-771-5765. FAX: 314-772-8826. Web Site: www.sigma-aldrich.com.
Library Holdings: Bk Vols 4,500; Per Subs 100

L SUELTHAUS & WALSH, Law Library,* 7733 Forsyth Blvd Ste 1200, 63105. SAN 372-4727. Tel: 314-727-7676 Ext 7151. FAX: 314-727-7166. E-Mail: swlaw@suelthauswalsh.com. Web Site: www.suelthauswalsh.com. *Librn*, Mary K Macaulay
Library Holdings: Bk Vols 3,000; Per Subs 21

S TEAM FOUR, INC LIBRARY,* 14 N Newstead Ave, 63108. SAN 327-1374. Tel: 314-533-2200. FAX: 314-533-2203.
Library Holdings: Bk Titles 1,000; Per Subs 12
Special Collections: Architecture Catalogs & Books

R THIRD BAPTIST CHURCH LIBRARY, 620 N Grand Blvd, 63103. SAN 309-2097. Tel: 314-533-7340, Ext 21. FAX: 314-533-2926. *AV*, Rea Finn
Founded 1943
Library Holdings: Bk Titles 5,200; Per Subs 12
Restriction: Members only

L THOMPSON COBURN LLP, Law Library, One Firstar Plaza, 63101. SAN 372-4468. Tel: 314-552-6000. FAX: 314-552-7000. Web Site: www.thompsoncoburn.com. *Dir Libr Serv*, Mary Kay Jung; Tel: 314-552-6275, Fax: 314-552-7275, E-Mail: mkjung@thompsoncoburn.com; *Res*, Shirley G Canup; Tel: 314-552-6260, Fax: 314-552-7260, E-Mail: scanup@thompsoncoburn.com; *Tech Servs*, Donna Barratt; Staff 9 (MLS 2, Non-MLS 7)
Library Holdings: Bk Vols 40,000
Database Vendor: Lexis-Nexis

R TRINITY UNITED CHURCH OF CHRIST, Edith L Stock Library, 4700 S Grand Blvd, 63111. SAN 309-2119. Tel: 314-352-6645. *In Charge*, Ruth Cox
Founded 1960
Library Holdings: Bk Titles 2,600
Restriction: Members only

R UNITED HEBREW CONGREGATION LIBRARY, 13788 Conway Rd, 63141. SAN 309-2151. Tel: 314-469-0700. FAX: 314-434-7821. *Librn*, Elaine Amitin
Library Holdings: Bk Vols 3,400
Subject Interests: History, Jewish holidays

UNITED STATES ARMY

A TECHNICAL INFORMATION & LIBRARY SERVICES, 1222 Spruce St, 63103-2833. SAN 349-7437. Tel: 314-331-8883. FAX: 314-331-8873. Web Site: 155.76.89.200/lib/tils_lib.htm. *Coll Develop, Librn, Ref*, Arthur R Taylor; E-Mail: arthur.r.taylor@mvs02.usace.army.mil; Staff 2 (MLS 1, Non-MLS 1)
Founded 1968
Oct 1997-Sep 1998 Mats Exp $63,000. Sal $109,000 (Prof $52,338)
Library Holdings: Bk Vols 8,510; Bk Titles 8,412; Per Subs 688
Subject Interests: Civil engineering, Environ, Outdoor recreation, Water resources, Wildlife mgt
Special Collections: River & Harbor acts, Congressional Documents, 1899-date; River Basin Studies
Publications: Holdings List (biannual); Library Users Guide; New Books List (quarterly)
Partic in Dialog Corporation; Fedlink; OCLC Online Computer Library Center, Inc
Merged USACE Saint Louis & other collections under the Cooperative Administrative Support Unit, 1990, dissolved 1997; Reestablished as Technical Information & Library Services for US Army Corps of Engineers, Saint Louis District, 1997

GL UNITED STATES COURT OF APPEALS, Eighth Circuit Library, Thomas F Eagleton US Courthouse, 111 S Tenth St, Rm 22300, 63102. SAN 309-216X. Tel: 314-244-2665. FAX: 314-244-2675. E-Mail: library8@ca8.uscourts.gov. Web Site: www.ca8.uscourts.gov/library/library.html. *Dir*, Ann T Fessenden; *Dep Dir*, James R Voelker; *Ref*, Kris Albertus; *Cat, Ref*, Joan Stevens; *Tech Servs*, Terry Ellen Ferl; Staff 6 (MLS 5, Non-MLS 1)
Library Holdings: Bk Vols 47,000; Per Subs 200
Subject Interests: Fed law
Automation Activity & Vendor Info: (Acquisitions) SIRSI; (Cataloging) SIRSI; (OPAC) SIRSI; (Serials) SIRSI
Database Vendor: Dialog, Lexis-Nexis, OCLC - First Search
Restriction: Non-circulating to the public
Partic in Fedlink

G UNITED STATES DEPARTMENT OF DEFENSE, National Imagery & Mapping Agency Reference Library,* L-37/ISLSS, 3200 S Second St, 63118-3399. SAN 349-7402. Tel: 314-263-4266. FAX: 314-263-4441. *Chief Librn*, Barbara Bick; E-Mail: bickb@nima.mil; *Ref*, Jennie Paton; Staff 6 (MLS 2, Non-MLS 4)
Founded 1943
Library Holdings: Bk Vols 15,000; Per Subs 450
Subject Interests: Astronautics, Astronomy, Cartography, Computer science, Geodesy, Geophysics, Mgt, Photogrammetry
Partic in Defense Technical Information Center; Dialog Corporation; Fedlink; OCLC Online Computer Library Center, Inc

C UNIVERSITY OF MISSOURI-SAINT LOUIS, Thomas Jefferson Library, 8001 Natural Bridge Rd, 63121-4499. SAN 349-7496. Tel: 314-516-5050. Interlibrary Loan Service Tel: 314-516-5066. FAX: 314-516-5828. Web Site: www.umsl.edu/services/library. *Access Serv, Actg Dir*, Sandy Arnott; *ILL*, Mary Zettwoch; *Cat*, David Owens; Staff 63 (MLS 24, Non-MLS 39)
Founded 1963. Enrl 15,575; Fac 663; Highest Degree: Doctorate
Library Holdings: Bk Vols 967,249; Per Subs 2,828
Special Collections: Colonial Latin American History; Utopian Literature & Science Fiction
Publications: Libraries' Newsletter
Partic in BRS; Dialog Corporation; Midwest Region Libr Network; OCLC Online Computer Library Center, Inc; Saint Louis Regional Library Network
Friends of the Library Group
Departmental Libraries:
WARD E BARNES LIBRARY, 8001 Natural Bridge Rd, 63121. SAN 349-7526. Tel: 314-516-5571. FAX: 314-516-6468. *In Charge*, Cheryl Carr; E-Mail: carr@umsl.edu
Library Holdings: Bk Vols 70,000; Per Subs 400
Subject Interests: Education, Nursing
Special Collections: Autism; Curriculum Guides

S VULCAN VENTURES PRINT MEDIA INC, (Formerly Sporting News Publishing Company Archives), Sporting News Publishing Company Archives, 10176 Corporate Sq Dr Ste 200, 63132. SAN 371-5302. Tel: 314-993-7787. FAX: 314-997-0765. E-Mail: tsnspg@aol.com. Web Site: www.sportingnews.com/archives/. *Librn*, James R Meier; Staff 2 (MLS 2)
Founded 1987
Library Holdings: Bk Vols 10,000
Subject Interests: Sports
Special Collections: Archives of the Sporting News
Automation Activity & Vendor Info: (Cataloging) Athena; (Circulation) Athena
Restriction: By appointment only

C WASHINGTON UNIVERSITY LIBRARIES, One Brookings Dr, Campus Box 1061, 63130-4899. SAN 349-7550. Tel: 314-935-5400. Interlibrary Loan Service Tel: 314-935-5442. Circulation Tel: 314-935-5420. Reference Tel: 314-935-5410. FAX: 314-935-4045. E-Mail: virginia@library.wustl.edu. *Dean of Libr*, Shirley Baker; E-Mail: baker@wustl.edu; *Admin Dir*, Virginia Toliver; *Access Serv, Asst Dean*, Judy Fox; Tel: 314-935-5421, E-Mail: jfox@library.wustl.edu; *Asst Dean, Coll Develop*, B J Johnston; Tel: 314-935-5468, E-Mail: bjj@library.wustl.edu; *Asst Dean, Ref*, Vicky Witte; Tel: 314-935-5466, E-Mail: vwitte@library.wustl.edu; *Acq*, William Wibbing; Tel: 314-935-4551, Fax: 314-935-7273, E-Mail: wibbing@library.wustl.edu; *Spec Coll*, Ann Posega; Tel: 314-935-5413, E-Mail: posega@library.wustl.edu; *ILL*, Nada Vaughn; Tel: 314-935-4087, Fax: 314-935-4719, E-Mail: nvaughn@library.wustl.edu; *Electronic Resources*, Carol Antoniewick; Tel: 314-935-5498, E-Mail: cmanton@wustl.edu; *Ser*, Marianna Mercurio; Staff 102 (MLS 98, Non-MLS 4)
Founded 1853. Enrl 12,088; Fac 669; Highest Degree: Doctorate
Jul 1999-Jun 2000 Income (Main and Other College/University Libraries) $24,142,003. Mats Exp $7,431,430, Books $1,300,710, Per/Ser (Incl. Access Fees) $4,585,642, Presv $138,390, Micro $133,823, Electronic Ref Mat (Incl. Access Fees) $1,272,865. Sal $8,597,954 (Prof $4,481,197)
Library Holdings: Bk Vols 3,422,372; Bk Titles 1,478,760; Per Subs 18,750
Subject Interests: Behav sci, Sci-tech, Soc sci
Special Collections: 19th Century & Modern Literature, mss, bks; American & New; Classical Archaeology & Numismatics (John M Wolfing Coll); Dickey, Robert Creely & Ford Maddox Ford; Early History of Communications-Semantics (Philip M Arnold Coll); Ernst Krohn Musicological Coll; George N Meissner Rare Book Department; German Language & Literature (Praetorius Memorial Coll); History of Architecture (Bruce Coll); History of Printing (Isador Mendle Coll); History of Russian Revolutionary Movement & the Soviet Union (Edna Gellhorn Coll); Literature Coll of Samuel Beckett, Conrad Aiken, James; Romance Languages & Literature (Max W Bryant Coll); York Stock Exchange Reports
Automation Activity & Vendor Info: (Acquisitions) Innovative Interfaces

Inc.; (Cataloging) Innovative Interfaces Inc.; (Circulation) Innovative Interfaces Inc.; (Course Reserve) Innovative Interfaces Inc.; (ILL) Innovative Interfaces Inc.; (OPAC) Innovative Interfaces Inc.; (Serials) Innovative Interfaces Inc.
Publications: FACTS
Partic in Higher Educ Coun of Metrop St Louis; Missouri Library Network Corporation; Mobius; OCLC Online Computer Library Center, Inc; Saint Louis Regional Library Network
Departmental Libraries:
ART & ARCHITECTURE LIBRARY Tel: 314-935-5268. FAX: 314-935-4362. Web Site: library.wustl.edu/~artarch/. *Librn*, Dana Beth; Tel: 314-935-5218, E-Mail: beth@library.wustl.edu; *Librn*, Ellen Petraits; Tel: 314-935-7658; Staff 2 (MLS 2)
Library Holdings: Bk Vols 92,673; Per Subs 372
Subject Interests: Architecture, Art, Art history, Classical archeol, Communication arts, East Asian art, Fashion design, Landscape architecture, Photog, Planning design
Special Collections: Bryce Coll; Eames & Young Coll; East Asian Coll (oriental art); Sorger Coll
Partic in Missouri Library Network Corporation

CM BERNARD BECKER MEDICAL LIBRARY, Campus Box 8132, 660 S Euclid Ave, 63110. SAN 349-7828. Tel: 314-362-7080. FAX: 314-362-0190. Web Site: www.becker.wustl.edu/library/. *Dir*, Paul Schoening; Tel: 314-362-2773, Fax: 314-747-4416, E-Mail: pas@msnotes.wustl.edu; *ILL*, Barbara Halbrook; Tel: 314-362-2786, E-Mail: halbrookb@msnotes.wustl.edu; *Ref*, Carol Murray; Tel: 314-362-4736, E-Mail: murray@msnotes.wustl.edu; *Instrul Serv*, Betsy Kelly; Tel: 314-362-2783, Fax: 314-367-9534, E-Mail: kellyb@msnotes.wustl.edu; *Rare Bks*, Lilla Vekerdy; Tel: 314-362-4235, E-Mail: vekerdyl@msnotes.wustl.edu; *Archivist*, Paul Anderson; Tel: 314-362-4239, E-Mail: andersop@msnotes.wustl.edu; Staff 12 (MLS 12)
Founded 1837. Enrl 1,062; Fac 831
Jul 1998-Jun 1999 Mats Exp $1,685,573, Books $113,644, Per/Ser (Incl. Access Fees) $1,110,635, Presv $58,929, Micro $33,588, Other Print Mats $368,777. Sal $3,327,436 (Prof $2,096,285)
Library Holdings: Bk Vols 280,248; Per Subs 2,099
Subject Interests: Health admin, Medicine, Occupational therapy, Physical therapy
Special Collections: Dental Medicine (Henry J McKellops Coll); Opthalmology (Bernard Becker Coll); Otology & Deaf Education (Max A Goldstein - CID Coll); Robert E Schlueter Paracelsus Coll
Publications: Library Guide; Library Newsletter; Special Collections Guide
Partic in Dialog Corporation; Saint Louis Regional Library Network

BIOLOGY LIBRARY Tel: 314-935-5405. FAX: 314-935-4046. E-Mail: biology@library.wustl.edu. Web Site: library.wustl.edu. *Librn*, Ruth Lewis; Tel: 314-935-4819, E-Mail: ruth@library.wustl.edu; Staff 1 (MLS 1)
Library Holdings: Bk Vols 64,167; Per Subs 562
Subject Interests: Botany, Embryology, Genetics, Molecular biology, Mycology, Neurosci
Partic in CDP; Dialog Corporation

CHEMISTRY Tel: 314-935-6591. FAX: 314-935-4778. *Librn*, Robert McFarland; Tel: 314-935-4814, E-Mail: rtm@library.wustl.edu; Staff 1 (MLS 1)
Library Holdings: Bk Vols 41,510; Per Subs 392
Subject Interests: Biophys, Inorganic, Organic, Physical chemistry, Spectroscopy
Partic in CDP; Dialog Corporation; Medline; STN

EARTH & PLANETARY SCIENCE Tel: 314-935-5406. FAX: 314-935-4800. *Librn*, Clara McLeod; Tel: 314-935-4817, E-Mail: cpmcleod@library.wustl.edu; Staff 1 (MLS 1)
Library Holdings: Bk Vols 36,093; Per Subs 251
Subject Interests: Geochemistry, Geology, Geomorphology, Geophysics, Paleontology, Petrology, Planetary sci, Sedimentation, Structural geol
Special Collections: Missouri State Geological Survey; US Geological Survey & Defense Mapping Agency
Partic in Dialog Corporation

EAST ASIAN LIBRARY Tel: 314-935-5155. FAX: 314-935-7505. Web Site: library.wustl.edu/~ea/. *Librn*, Haruko Nakamuro; E-Mail: hnakamur@library.wustl.edu; *Librn*, Tony Chang; Tel: 314-935-4816, E-Mail: thc@library.wustl.edu; *Librn*, Suad Mohammed-Gamal; E-Mail: suad@library.wustl.edu; Staff 3 (MLS 3)
Library Holdings: Bk Vols 123,537; Per Subs 321
Subject Interests: Art history, History, Lang, Literature, Philosophy, Religion, Soc sci
Special Collections: Cultural Revolution of China, 1966-69 (Robert Elegant Coll)
Publications: A Guide to Library Resources for Japanese Studies (1987)
Partic in OCLC Online Computer Library Center, Inc

GAYLORD MUSIC Tel: 314-935-5563. FAX: 314-935-4263. E-Mail: music@library.wustl.edu, short@library.wustl.edu. Web Site: library.wustl.edu/~music. *Librn*, Bradley Short; Tel: 314-935-5529; *Cat*, Mark Scharff; Tel: 314-935-5560, E-Mail: scharff@library.wustl.edu; Staff 2 (MLS 2)
Jul 1998-Jun 1999 Mats Exp $87,350
Library Holdings: Bk Vols 90,389; Per Subs 542
Special Collections: Early Music Editions; Local Music Manuscripts; Sheet Music

GWB SCHOOL OF SOCIAL WORK, One Brookings Dr, Campus Box 1196, 63130. SAN 349-7917. Tel: 314-935-6633. FAX: 314-935-8511. *Dir*, Michael E Powell; Tel: 314-935-6681, E-Mail: mikep@gwbmail.wustl.edu; *Librn*, Karri Marshall; Tel: 314-935-8644, E-Mail: ksm1@gwbmail.wustl.edu; Staff 3 (MLS 3)
Enrl 400; Fac 28; Highest Degree: Doctorate
Library Holdings: Bk Vols 52,837; Per Subs 542
Subject Interests: Alcoholism, Children, Econ develop, Family therapy, Gerontology, Mental health, Soc develop, Soc work, Women's issues, Youth

KOPOLOW BUSINESS LIBRARY, One Brookings Dr, Campus Box 1133, 63130. SAN 349-764X. Tel: 314-935-6332. FAX: 314-935-4970. Web Site: www.olin.wustl.edu/library/. *Dir*, Ron Allen; Staff 3 (MLS 3)
Highest Degree: Doctorate
Jul 1999-Jun 2000 Income Locally Generated Income $3,032. Mats Exp $626,731, Books $10,656, Per/Ser (Incl. Access Fees) $382,035, Micro $8,828, Electronic Ref Mat (Incl. Access Fees) $225,212. Sal $239,538 (Prof $123,409)
Library Holdings: Bk Vols 29,476; Per Subs 475
Subject Interests: Bus, Mgt
Database Vendor: CARL, Dialog, IAC - Info Trac, Lexis-Nexis, OCLC - First Search, ProQuest
Publications: Recent Acquistions

CL LAW LIBRARY, One Brookings Dr, Campus Box 1171, 63130. SAN 349-7798. Tel: 314-935-6450. FAX: 314-935-7125. Web Site: ls.wustl.edu/Infores/Library. *Info Res*, Phillip Berwick; *Cat*, Rosemary Hahn; *Publ Servs*, Dorie Bertram; Tel: 314-935-6484, E-Mail: bertram@wulaw.wustl.edu; *Publ Servs*, Mark Kloempken; *Tech Servs*, Wei Luo; *Access Serv, Govt Doc*, Katrina Stierholz; *Selection of Elec Mat*, Aris Woodham; *Res*, Hyla Bondareff; Staff 18 (MLS 8, Non-MLS 10)
Founded 1867. Enrl 670; Fac 44; Highest Degree: Doctorate
Library Holdings: Bk Vols 602,918; Bk Titles 122,191; Per Subs 6,367
Subject Interests: Chinese law, Corp law, European Union law, Int trade law, Intellectual property law, Tax law
Special Collections: Ashman British Coll; Matthew Bender Authority on the Web; Neuhoff Rare Book Coll
Automation Activity & Vendor Info: (Cataloging) Innovative Interfaces Inc.; (Circulation) Innovative Interfaces Inc.; (Course Reserve) Innovative Interfaces Inc.; (OPAC) Innovative Interfaces Inc.; (Serials) Innovative Interfaces Inc.
Database Vendor: IAC - Info Trac, Lexis-Nexis, Silverplatter Information Inc., Wilson - Wilson Web
Publications: Faculty Services Guide; Law Library Guide; New Student Orientation Guide; Research Guides; Select Acquisitions List
Partic in Mid-Am Law Sch Libr Consortium; OCLC Online Computer Library Center, Inc; Westlaw

MATHEMATICS Tel: 314-935-5048. FAX: 314-935-4045. Web Site: library.wustl.edu/~math. *Librn*, Barbara Luszczynska; Tel: 314-935-6177, E-Mail: barbaral@library.wustl.edu; Staff 1 (MLS 1)
Library Holdings: Bk Vols 10,389; Per Subs 229
Subject Interests: Advanced math
Partic in BRS

PFEIFFER PHYSICS LIBRARY, One Brookings Dr, Campus Box 1105, 63130. SAN 349-7887. Tel: 314-935-6215. FAX: 314-935-6219. Web Site: library.wustl.edu/units/physics. *Librn*, Alison Verbeck; E-Mail: alisonv@library.wustl.edu; Staff 1 (MLS 1)
Library Holdings: Bk Vols 44,179; Per Subs 281
Subject Interests: Astronomy, Astrophysics, Atomic, High energy particles, Mathematics, Nuclear physics, Physics, Quantum mechanics, Solid state physics
Automation Activity & Vendor Info: (Cataloging) Innovative Interfaces Inc.; (Circulation) Innovative Interfaces Inc.; (Course Reserve) Innovative Interfaces Inc.; (OPAC) Innovative Interfaces Inc.

SAINT PETERS

P SAINT CHARLES CITY COUNTY LIBRARY DISTRICT,* 425 Spencer Rd, 63376-0529. (Mail add: PO Box 529, 63376-0529), SAN 349-5094. Tel: 636-441-2300. FAX: 636-441-3132. E-Mail: library@mail.win.org. Web Site: www.win.org/library/scccld.htm. *Dir*, Carl Sandstedt; *Dep Dir*, Betty Murr; *Br Coordr*, Georgia Gidden; *Ch Servs, Commun Relations*, Margaret Preiss; *Coll Develop*, Dotty Steele. Subject Specialists: *Business and management*, Jim Hicks; *Government*, Jim Hicks; *Local history*, Ann King; Staff 62 (MLS 29, Non-MLS 33)
Founded 1973. Pop 268,000; Circ 3,282,649
Jul 1997-Jun 1998 Income $7,666,701. Mats Exp $1,261,748, Books $1,035,731, Per/Ser (Incl. Access Fees) $78,626. Sal $3,714,351
Library Holdings: Bk Vols 820,000; Bk Titles 234,457; Per Subs 1,130
Subject Interests: Bus, Local history, Mgt
Special Collections: Bizelli-Fleming Local History Coll
Publications: Good Libraries - Good Business; News & Views; Salary Survey of West North Central States
Partic in Missouri Library Network Corporation; Saint Louis Regional

Library Network
Co-sponsors Business Connection - One Stop Micro: - Business Development Program with Service Corps of Retired Executives (SCORE)
Friends of the Library Group
Branches: 10
BOONE'S TRAIL, 4600 Hwy Z, New Melle, 63365. SAN 377-676X. Tel: 636-398-6200. FAX: 636-398-6200. E-Mail: library@mail.win.org. Web Site: www.win.org/library/scccld.htm.
Library Holdings: Bk Vols 6,446
CORPORATE PARKWAY, 1200 Corporate Pkwy, Wentzville, 63385. SAN 349-5302. Tel: 636-332-9966. TDD: 636-327-4010. FAX: 636-327-0548. E-Mail: library@mail.win.org. Web Site: www.win.org/library/scccld.htm. *Mgr*, Chang Liu
Library Holdings: Bk Titles 80,850
Special Services for the Deaf - TDD
DEER RUN, 1300 N Main, O'Fallon, 63366. SAN 375-6270. Tel: 314-980-1332. TDD: 314-978-3261. FAX: 314-978-3209. E-Mail: drrefer@mail.win.org. Web Site: www.win.org/library. *Mgr*, Georgia Glidden; *Ch Servs*, Julie Hafley
Founded 1995
Library Holdings: Bk Vols 68,315
Special Services for the Deaf - TDD
Friends of the Library Group
KISKER ROAD, 1000 Kisker Rd, Saint Charles, 63304. SAN 370-1115. Tel: 636-447-7323, 636-926-7323. TDD: 636-926-7323. FAX: 636-926-0869. E-Mail: library@mail.win.org. Web Site: www.win.org/library/scccld.htm. *Mgr*, Bill Strecker
Library Holdings: Bk Vols 87,000
Special Services for the Deaf - TDD
LINNEMANN, 2323 Elm St, Saint Charles, 63301. SAN 349-5159. Tel: 636-723-0232, 636-946-6294. TDD: 636-946-0789. FAX: 636-947-0692. E-Mail: library@mail.win.org. Web Site: www.win.org/library/scccld.htm. *Mgr*, Mary Heinbokel; *Ch Servs*, Patsy Molina
Library Holdings: Bk Titles 183,253
Special Collections: Local History
Special Services for the Deaf - TDD
MCCLAY, 2760 McClay Rd, Saint Charles, 63303. SAN 377-6786. Tel: 636-441-6454. FAX: 636-441-5898. E-Mail: library@mail.win.org. Web Site: www.win.org/library/scccld.htm. *Mgr*, Martha Radginski
Library Holdings: Bk Vols 70,322
MIDDENDORF-KREDELL, 2750 Hwy K, O'Fallon, 63366. SAN 375-6289. Tel: 636-978-7926. TDD: 636-978-7997. FAX: 636-978-7998. E-Mail: library@mail.win.org. Web Site: www.win.org/library/scccld.htm. *Mgr*, Patricia Kern; *Govt Doc*, Anna Sylvan
Library Holdings: Bk Vols 150,000
Special Services for the Deaf - TDD
NORTH COUNTY, 1825 Commonfield Rd, Portage des Sioux, 63373. SAN 349-5183. Tel: 636-753-3070. FAX: 636-753-3070. E-Mail: library@mail.win.org. Web Site: www.win.org/library/scccld.htm.
Library Holdings: Bk Vols 7,360
SOUTH COUNTY, 5577 Walnut St, Augusta, 63332. SAN 349-5272. Tel: 314-228-4855. FAX: 314-228-4855.
Library Holdings: Bk Vols 8,948
SPENCER ROAD, 427 Spencer Rd, PO Box 529, 63376-0529. SAN 349-5248. Tel: 636-441-0522, 636-447-2320. TDD: 636-441-0794. FAX: 636-926-3948. *Mgr*, Jim Brown; *Business*, Jim Hicks; *Ch Servs*, Cindy Barnard
Library Holdings: Bk Vols 159,569
Special Collections: Business Services
Special Services for the Deaf - TDD
Bookmobiles: 1

J SAINT CHARLES COUNTY COMMUNITY COLLEGE LIBRARY, 4601 Mid Rivers Mall Dr, 63376. SAN 309-1090. Tel: 636-922-8512. FAX: 636-922-8433. Web Site: www.stchas.edu/library. *Dean*, Joan Clarke; E-Mail: jclarke@chuck.stchas.edu; *Publ Servs*, Ying Li; Tel: 636-922-8000, Ext 4438, E-Mail: yli@chuck.stchas.edu; *Tech Servs*, Frances Stumpf; Tel: 636-922-8000, Ext 4439, E-Mail: fstumpf@chuck.stchas.edu; Staff 11 (MLS 5, Non-MLS 6)
Founded 1987. Enrl 3,151; Fac 161
Jul 1998-Jun 1999 Income $578,000. Mats Exp $202,000, Books $70,000, Per/Ser (Incl. Access Fees) $44,000, Electronic Ref Mat (Incl. Access Fees) $9,000. Sal $376,000
Library Holdings: Bk Vols 47,000; Per Subs 485
Automation Activity & Vendor Info: (Acquisitions) Innovative Interfaces Inc.; (Cataloging) Innovative Interfaces Inc.; (Circulation) Innovative Interfaces Inc.; (Course Reserve) Innovative Interfaces Inc.; (ILL) Innovative Interfaces Inc.; (Media Booking) Innovative Interfaces Inc.; (OPAC) Innovative Interfaces Inc.; (Serials) Innovative Interfaces Inc.
Database Vendor: Ebsco - EbscoHost, GaleNet, Lexis-Nexis, OCLC - First Search
Publications: Library editions
Partic in Mobius; Saint Louis Regional Library Network

SALEM

P SALEM PUBLIC LIBRARY, 102 N Jackson, 65560. SAN 309-2224. Tel: 573-729-4331. FAX: 573-729-2123. E-Mail: ixz010@mail.connect.more.net. *Librn*, Glenda Brown
Founded 1930. Pop 4,474; Circ 40,436
Library Holdings: Bk Vols 25,235; Per Subs 44
Subject Interests: Genealogy
Automation Activity & Vendor Info: (Cataloging) TLC; (Circulation) TLC
Database Vendor: OCLC - First Search
Friends of the Library Group

SALISBURY

P DULANY MEMORIAL LIBRARY,* 501 S Broadway, 65281. SAN 309-2232. Tel: 660-388-5712. FAX: 660-388-5712. *Librn*, Cheryl Springer
Founded 1928. Pop 1,960; Circ 19,600
Library Holdings: Bk Titles 16,750; Per Subs 37
Open Mon-Fri 12-5

SARCOXIE

P SARCOXIE PUBLIC LIBRARY, 506 Center St, PO Box 604, 64862-0604. SAN 329-2533. Tel: 417-548-2736. TDD: 417-548-2736. FAX: 417-548-3104. *Dir*, Jeannine Wormington; E-Mail: jwormington@hotmail.com
Founded 1960. Pop 2,000; Circ 13,591
Library Holdings: Bk Titles 14,000
Friends of the Library Group

SEDALIA

P BOONSLICK REGIONAL LIBRARY,* 219 W Third, 65301-4347. SAN 349-7941. Tel: 660-827-7111. TDD: 660-827-4668. FAX: 660-827-4668. Web Site: www.brl.lib.mo.us. *Dir*, Linda Allcorn; *Ref*, Debbie Mueller; Staff 12 (MLS 1, Non-MLS 11)
Founded 1953. Pop 44,706; Circ 299,348
Library Holdings: Bk Vols 131,321; Per Subs 235
Publications: Adult Book List; Annual Report; Bookmobile Schedules; Childrens Newsletter; Informational Brochures; Seasonal Ideas
Partic in Mid-Mo Libr Network; Mo Libr Asn
Special Services for the Deaf - TDD
Open Mon-Fri 8-5
Friends of the Library Group
Branches: 4
BOONVILLE BRANCH, 618 Main St, Boonville, 65233. SAN 349-7976. Tel: 660-882-5864. FAX: 660-882-7953. Web Site: www.brl.lib.mo.us. *In Charge*, Melanie Spencer
COLE CAMP BRANCH, 104 E Main St, Cole Camp, 65325. SAN 349-800X. Tel: 660-668-3887. FAX: 660-668-3852. Web Site: www.brl.lib.mo.us. *In Charge*, Patricia Beckman
Friends of the Library Group
PETTIS COUNTY, 219 W Third, 65301. SAN 329-5834. Tel: 660-827-7323. FAX: 660-827-4668. Web Site: www.brl.lib.mo.us. *In Charge*, Lynn Murray
Friends of the Library Group
WARSAW BRANCH, 950 E Main, Warsaw, 65355. SAN 349-8034. Tel: 660-438-5211. FAX: 660-438-9567. Web Site: www.brl.lib.mo.us. *In Charge*, Judy Gaylord
Bookmobiles: 1

P SEDALIA PUBLIC LIBRARY, (SPL), 311 W Third St, 65301-4399. SAN 309-2240. Tel: 660-826-1314. TDD: 660-826-1314. FAX: 660-826-0396. E-Mail: uzx000@mail.connect.more.net. Web Site: spl.lib.mo.us. *Dir*, Norma R Fowler; *Ch Servs*, Bea Ingersoll; Staff 1 (MLS 1)
Founded 1895. Pop 19,425; Circ 97,276
Apr 1999-Mar 2000 Income $374,301. Mats Exp $64,672, Books $45,565, Per/Ser (Incl. Access Fees) $5,413, AV Equip $3,705, Electronic Ref Mat (Incl. Access Fees) $9,989. Sal $177,132
Library Holdings: Bk Vols 60,242; Per Subs 130
Subject Interests: Local history
Automation Activity & Vendor Info: (Cataloging) Sagebrush Corporation; (Circulation) Sagebrush Corporation; (OPAC) Sagebrush Corporation
Database Vendor: Ebsco - EbscoHost
Special Services for the Deaf - Staff with knowledge of sign language
Outreach Service for physically handicapped; chair lift for handicapped accessibility
Friends of the Library Group

J STATE FAIR COMMUNITY COLLEGE, (SFCC), Learning Resources Center, 3201 W 16th, 65301-2199. SAN 309-2259. Tel: 660-530-5800, Ext 211. FAX: 660-530-5506. Web Site: www.sfcc.cc.mo.us. *Coll Develop, Head Librn*, Arja Crampton; E-Mail: crampton@sfcc.cc.mo.us; Staff 1 (Non-MLS 1)
Founded 1969. Enrl 1,800
Jul 1999-Jun 2000 Mats Exp $41,838, Books $20,685, Per/Ser (Incl. Access Fees) $12,624, Presv $2,040, Micro $526, AV Equip $4,963, Electronic Ref

Mat (Incl. Access Fees) $1,000. Sal $107,991 (Prof $43,307)
Library Holdings: Bk Vols 41,479; Per Subs 273
Subject Interests: Academic, Agriculture, Art, Bus educ, Machinery, Nursing
Special Collections: Audio Visual (videotapes & cassette tape kits); Juvenile Coll; Missouri Coll; Ragtime Coll
Automation Activity & Vendor Info: (Cataloging) epixtech, inc.; (Circulation) epixtech, inc.; (OPAC) epixtech, inc.; (Serials) epixtech, inc.
Database Vendor: Ebsco - EbscoHost
Publications: Library Handbook (Library handbook); Recent Acquisitions Bulletin
Partic in MLNC; Mobius

SHELBINA

P SHELBINA CARNEGIE PUBLIC LIBRARY,* 102 N Center, 63468. SAN 309-2267. Tel: 573-588-2271. FAX: 573-588-2271. E-Mail: fgf001@mail.connect.more.net. *Dir*, Linda K Kropf; *Asst Dir*, Bonnie Wood; *Asst Dir*, Lillian Smith; Staff 1 (MLS 1)
Founded 1917. Pop 2,175; Circ 40,500
Library Holdings: Bk Titles 31,761; Per Subs 73
Special Collections: Centennial Farms Records of Shelby County; Early Census Records of Shelby County; Genealogy (Burial Records of Shelby County, History of Schools, Churches & Families in Area); Shelby County Newspapers

SHELDON

P SHELDON LIBRARY,* PO Box 205, 64784. SAN 377-2179. Tel: 417-884-2909. E-Mail: sheldonlibrary@yahoo.com. *Librn*, Adonna White
Library Holdings: Bk Vols 6,000

SIKESTON

P SIKESTON PUBLIC LIBRARY,* 121 East North St, PO Box 1279, 63801. SAN 309-2275. Tel: 573-471-4140. FAX: 573-471-6048. Web Site: www.sikeston.lib.mo.us. *Dir*, Suzanne Tangeman
Founded 1938. Pop 17,329; Circ 54,758
1998-1999 Income $519,272, State $11,352, City $175,713, Federal $7,380, Other $324,827. Mats Exp $29,568, Books $25,266, Per/Ser (Incl. Access Fees) $4,302. Sal $103,374 (Prof $30,000)
Library Holdings: Bk Vols 32,838; Bk Titles 32,738; Per Subs 110

SLATER

P SLATER PUBLIC LIBRARY,* 311 N Main, 65349. SAN 309-2291. Tel: 660-529-3100. *Librn*, Barbara Usnick
Founded 1927. Pop 2,610; Circ 22,752
Library Holdings: Bk Vols 40,438
Special Collections: Dickens & Mark Twain Coll
Open Mon-Fri 2-5

SPRINGFIELD

CR ASSEMBLIES OF GOD THEOLOGICAL SEMINARY, Cordas C Burnett Library, 1435 N Glenstone Ave, 65802. SAN 309-2305. Tel: 417-268-1000. Toll Free Tel: 800-467-2487. FAX: 417-268-1001. E-Mail: info@agseminary.edu. *Dir Libr Serv*, Joseph F Marics, Jr; *Acq*, Stephanie Thomas; *Publ Servs*, Kevin Folk; *Cat*, Belinda Cruz; Staff 1 (MLS 1)
Founded 1973. Enrl 273; Fac 24; Highest Degree: Doctorate
May 1999-Apr 2000 Mats Exp $76,853, Books $41,655, Per/Ser (Incl. Access Fees) $20,147, Micro $4,926, AV Equip $1,474, Electronic Ref Mat (Incl. Access Fees) $8,651. Sal $121,253
Library Holdings: Bk Vols 82,606; Per Subs 455
Subject Interests: Anthropology, Biblical studies, Communication, Missions, Pastoral counselling, Pentecostalism, Theology
Automation Activity & Vendor Info: (Acquisitions) Endeavor; (Cataloging) Endeavor; (Circulation) Endeavor; (Course Reserve) Endeavor; (OPAC) Endeavor; (Serials) Endeavor
Partic in Missouri Library Network Corporation; OCLC Online Computer Library Center, Inc

CR BAPTIST BIBLE COLLEGE LIBRARY, G B Vick Memorial Library, 628 E Kearney St, 65803. SAN 349-8069. Tel: 417-268-6074. FAX: 417-268-6690. Web Site: www.bbcnet.edu/library, www.seebbc.edu/vick.html. *Dir*, Gregory A Smith; *Circ*, Camille May; *Tech Servs*, Mandie Bruyn
Founded 1956. Enrl 807; Fac 35; Highest Degree: Bachelor
Library Holdings: Bk Vols 66,454; Per Subs 372
Subject Interests: Education, Music, Relig studies
Special Collections: Baptist History
Partic in OCLC Online Computer Library Center, Inc; SW Mo Libr Network
Departmental Libraries:
MUSIC Tel: 417-268-6106. FAX: 417-268-6694. *Dir*, Robin Dowell
Subject Interests: Classical music

CR CENTRAL BIBLE COLLEGE, Pearlman Memorial Library, 3000 N Grant, 65803. SAN 309-2313. Tel: 417-833-2551. FAX: 417-833-5478. Web Site: www.cbcag.edu/library. *Dir*, Lynn Robert Anderson; E-Mail: anderson@cbcag.edu; *Tech Servs*, Alice Murphy; E-Mail: amurphy@cbcag.edu; *Circ*, Neda Reighard; E-Mail: nreighar@cbcab.edu; *Ser*, Sharlotte Campbell; E-Mail: scambel@cbcag.edu; Staff 10 (MLS 2, Non-MLS 8)
Founded 1922. Enrl 950; Fac 42; Highest Degree: Bachelor
May 1998-Apr 1999 Income Parent Institution $186,610. Mats Exp $66,845, Books $34,096, Per/Ser (Incl. Access Fees) $7,473, Presv $1,185, Micro $3,308, Electronic Ref Mat (Incl. Access Fees) $2,435. Sal $119,765
Library Holdings: Bk Vols 112,328; Per Subs 443
Special Collections: Assemblies of God Coll
Automation Activity & Vendor Info: (Cataloging) Innovative Interfaces Inc.; (Circulation) Innovative Interfaces Inc.; (Course Reserve) Innovative Interfaces Inc.; (OPAC) Innovative Interfaces Inc.
Database Vendor: IAC - Info Trac
Function: ILL available

M COX HEALTH SYSTEMS LIBRARIES,* 1423 N Jefferson Ave, 65802. SAN 323-5580. Tel: 417-269-3460. *Dir*, Wilma Bunch; E-Mail: wbunch@coxnet.org
1998-1999 Mats Exp $66,819, Books $19,269, Per/Ser (Incl. Access Fees) $39,705, Presv $4,145. Sal $112,406
Library Holdings: Bk Titles 5,546; Per Subs 514
Subject Interests: Medicine, Nursing
Publications: InforMed (quarterly newsletter)
Partic in MCMLA; Medical Libr Asn; Missouri Library Network Corporation; OCLC Online Computer Library Center, Inc; Philnet
Branches:
DAVID MILLER MEMORIAL, Medical Arts Ctr, 1000 E Primrose, 65807. Tel: 417-269-6192. FAX: 417-269-6140. *Librn*, Pat Leembruggen
Library holdings & expenditures included with Cox Health Systems Libraries

C DRURY COLLEGE, F W Olin Library, 900 N Benton Ave, 65802. SAN 309-2321. Tel: 417-873-7283. Circulation Tel: 417-873-7338. Reference Tel: 417-873-7337. FAX: 417-873-7432. Web Site: www.drury.edu/Olin/library.html. *Dir*, Stephen Stoan; Tel: 417-873-7282, E-Mail: sstoan@drury.edu; *Head, Info Serv*, Craig Smith; Tel: 417-873-7339, E-Mail: csmith@drury.edu; *Govt Doc, Ref, Spec Coll & Archives*, William Garvin; Tel: 417-873-7482, E-Mail: wgarvin@drury.edu; *Outreach Serv, Ref*, Allan Metz; Tel: 417-873-7483, E-Mail: ametz@drury.edu; *ILL, Ref*, Katherine Bohenkamper; Tel: 417-873-7485, E-Mail: kbohnenk@drury.edu; *Cat, Ref*, Phyllis Holzenberg; Tel: 417-873-7487, E-Mail: pholzenb@drury.edu; *Ref*, Jaqueline Tygart; Tel: 417-873-7496, E-Mail: jtygart@drury.edu. Subject Specialists: *Architecture*, Jaqueline Tygart; *Art*, Jaqueline Tygart; *Behavior sci*, Craig Smith; *Biology*, Katherine Bohenkamper; *Business*, Craig Smith; *Edu*, Katherine Bohenkamper; *English (language)*, William Garvin; *Environ sci*, Katherine Bohenkamper; *Exercise*, Craig Smith; *History*, Allan Metz; *Music*, William Garvin; *Philosophy*, Allan Metz; *Political science*, Allan Metz; *Religion*, Allan Metz; *Sports*, Craig Smith; *Theatrical dance*, Phyllis Holzenberg; *Women studies*, Phyllis Holzenberg; Staff 12 (MLS 7, Non-MLS 5)
Founded 1873. Highest Degree: Master
Jun 1999-May 2000 Income Parent Institution $786,980. Mats Exp $217,156, Books $79,282, Per/Ser (Incl. Access Fees) $78,839, Presv $13,130, Micro $12,338, AV Equip $14,091, Electronic Ref Mat (Incl. Access Fees) $19,476. Sal $504,288 (Prof $299,165)
Library Holdings: Bk Vols 244,804; Bk Titles 121,553; Per Subs 717
Subject Interests: Architecture, Womens studies
Special Collections: Claude Thornhill Music Coll; John F Kennedy Memorabilia
Automation Activity & Vendor Info: (Acquisitions) Innovative Interfaces Inc.; (Cataloging) Innovative Interfaces Inc.; (Circulation) Innovative Interfaces Inc.; (Course Reserve) Innovative Interfaces Inc.; (OPAC) Innovative Interfaces Inc.; (Serials) Innovative Interfaces Inc.
Database Vendor: Dialog, Ebsco - EbscoHost, GaleNet, Lexis-Nexis, OCLC - First Search, Silverplatter Information Inc.
Partic in Librunam; Missouri Library Network Corporation; Mobius

C EVANGEL UNIVERSITY, Klaude Kendrick Library, 1111 N Glenstone, 65802. SAN 309-233X. Tel: 417-865-2815, Ext 7268. FAX: 417-865-1574. Web Site: www.evangel.edu. *Acq, Dir*, Woodvall R Moore; E-Mail: woodie@mail.orion.org; *ILL, Tech Servs*, Joyce Moore; *Ref*, Beth Gudmestad; *Per, Ref*, Murl Winters; Staff 4 (MLS 4)
Founded 1955. Enrl 1,500; Fac 88; Highest Degree: Master
May 1999-Apr 2000 Income $527,368. Mats Exp $137,700, Books $40,000, Per/Ser (Incl. Access Fees) $60,000, Presv $2,200, Micro $27,500, AV Equip $8,000. Sal $245,300 (Prof $126,280)
Library Holdings: Bk Vols 123,500; Bk Titles 114,000; Per Subs 685
Subject Interests: Civil War, Indian hist
Special Collections: Library of American Civilization, micro
Automation Activity & Vendor Info: (Acquisitions) Endeavor; (Cataloging) Endeavor; (Circulation) Endeavor; (Course Reserve) Endeavor; (ILL) Endeavor; (Media Booking) Endeavor; (OPAC) Endeavor; (Serials) Endeavor
Partic in BRS; Christian Libr Network; Dialog Corporation; Missouri Library Network Corporation; OCLC Online Computer Library Center, Inc

R GLENSTONE BAPTIST CHURCH, Media Library, 413 S Glenstone, 65802. SAN 309-2348. Tel: 417-869-6361. *Librn*, Becky Ward
1998-1999 Income $350. Mats Exp $150
Library Holdings: Bk Vols 5,700; Per Subs 12

GL MISSOURI STATE COURT OF APPEALS, Southern District Law Library,* University Plaza, 300 Hammons Pkwy, 65806. SAN 309-2364. Tel: 417-895-6813. FAX: 417-895-6817. *Librn*, Beverly Heist
Library Holdings: Bk Vols 16,086; Per Subs 30
Restriction: Not open to public

S NOBLE & ASSOCIATES, Noble Strategic Information Resources, 2155 W Chesterfield Blvd, 65807. SAN 328-185X. Tel: 417-875-5067. FAX: 417-875-5051. *Adminr*, Shelley M Pirnak; E-Mail: shelley.pirnak@noble.net; Staff 3 (MLS 1, Non-MLS 2)
Library Holdings: Bk Vols 1,600; Bk Titles 1,500; Per Subs 750
Subject Interests: Advertising, Architecture, Food, Marketing
Database Vendor: GaleNet, IAC - Info Trac

R SAINT PAUL UNITED METHODIST CHURCH LIBRARY, 413 E Walnut, 65806-2303. SAN 309-2380. Tel: 417-866-4326. FAX: 417-866-6869. *Librn*, Marilyn Moore; *Librn*, Virginia Gleason
Founded 1964
Library Holdings: Bk Titles 5,400
Special Collections: Methodism
Publications: Annual Report

JM SOUTHWEST BAPTIST UNIVERSITY, Springfield Center Library, 4431 S Fremont, 65804. SAN 309-2372. Tel: 417-885-2104. FAX: 417-882-4193. *Branch Mgr*, Kerry Hargrave
Founded 1909
Library Holdings: Bk Vols 4,197; Bk Titles 2,984; Per Subs 88
Subject Interests: Nursing
Special Collections: Archive Coll
Database Vendor: Ebsco - EbscoHost, Lexis-Nexis, OCLC - First Search

C SOUTHWEST MISSOURI STATE UNIVERSITY, Duane G Meyer Library, 901 S National, 65804-0095. SAN 349-8158. Tel: 417-836-4525. Interlibrary Loan Service Tel: 417-836-4540. TDD: 417-836-6794. FAX: 417-836-4764. Interlibrary Loan Service FAX: 417-836-4538. Web Site: library.smsu.edu. *Dean of Libr*, Karen Horny; E-Mail: nam756f@smsu.edu; *Assoc Dean*, Neosha A Mackey; E-Mail: nam756f@mail.smsu.cdu; *Asst Prof, Head Ref*, Douglas Stehle; Tel: 417-836-4537, E-Mail: avl272f@smsu.edu; *Acq*, Lynn S Cline; Tel: 417-836-4658, E-Mail: lsc085f@mail.smsu.edu; *Cat*, Marilyn A McCroskey; Tel: 417-836-4541, E-Mail: mam417f@mail.smsu.edu; *Doc*, Byron Y Stewart; Tel: 417-836-4533, E-Mail: bys274f@mail.smsu.edu; *Spec Coll*, David E Richards; Tel: 417-836-4299, E-Mail: der725f@mail.smsu.edu; *Circ*, Esther I Siler; Tel: 417-836-4700, E-Mail: eis706t@mail.smsu.edu; *Music*, Brian Doherty; Tel: 417-836-5499, E-Mail: bjd895f@mail.smsu.edu; *Science*, Dr J B Petty; Tel: 417-836-4529, E-Mail: jbpetty@mail.smsu.edu; *Automation Syst Coordr*, David L Adams; Tel: 417-836-6211, E-Mail: dla977f@mail.smsu.edu; *Br Coordr*, Suzanne R Teghtmeyer; Tel: 417-926-4105, Fax: 417-926-6646, E-Mail: srt175f@mail.smsu.edu; Staff 63 (MLS 27, Non-MLS 36)
Founded 1907. Enrl 17,300; Fac 673; Highest Degree: Doctorate
Jul 1998-Jun 1999 Income (Main Library and Branch Library) $4,979,397. Mats Exp $1,822,905, Books $425,185, Per/Ser (Incl. Access Fees) $1,253,702, Presv $81,775. Sal $2,500,322 (Prof $1,165,686)
Library Holdings: Bk Vols 1,617,130; Bk Titles 711,122; Per Subs 4,655
Special Collections: African-American History of the Ozarks (Katherine Lederer Coll); Jean Arthur Rimbaud (William Jack Jones Coll); Lena Wills Genealogical Coll; Michel Butor Coll; Ozarks Labor Union Archives
Database Vendor: CARL, Dialog, Ebsco - EbscoHost, GaleNet, IAC - Info Trac, Lexis-Nexis, OCLC - First Search, Silverplatter Information Inc.
Publications: The William J Jones Coll - Rimbaud-Butor at Southwest Missouri State University
Partic in Missouri Library Network Corporation; Mobius; Morenet
Special Services for the Deaf - TDD
Friends of the Library Group
Departmental Libraries:
GREENWOOD LABORATORY SCHOOL, 901 S National, 65804-0095. SAN 349-8182. Tel: 417-836-5958. *Librn*, Dea Borneman
MUSIC, 901 S National, 65804-0095. SAN 328-6916. Tel: 417-836-5434. *Librn*, Brian Doherty
Special Collections: Missouri Music Educators Association Archives
SMSU-WP GARNETT, 304 Cleveland, West Plains, 65775. SAN 376-2300. Tel: 417-256-9865. FAX: 417-256-2303. Web Site: www.wp.smsu.edu/library/. *Librn*, Evelyn Vetter
1996-1997 Income $217,758, State $182,415, Locally Generated Income $5,735, Parent Institution $18,000, Other $11,607. Mats Exp $35,594, Books $15,794, Per/Ser (Incl. Access Fees) $19,028, Micro $472. Sal $86,377 (Prof $67,639)
Library Holdings: Bk Vols 19,570
Subject Interests: Gen, Law, Nursing
Special Collections: Local History Audiocassette Coll
Publications: Footnotes Newsletter
Friends of the Library Group

S SPRINGFIELD ART MUSEUM, Reference Library, 1111 E Brookside Dr, 65807. SAN 309-2399. Tel: 417-837-5700. FAX: 417-837-5704. Web Site: www.springfield.missouri.org/gov/sam/. *Librn*, Gloria Short; E-Mail: gshort@mail.orion.org; Staff 1 (Non-MLS 1)
Founded 1928
Jul 1999-Jun 2000 Income City $39,805. Mats Exp $6,000, Books $1,800, Per/Ser (Incl. Access Fees) $4,000, AV Equip $200. Sal $26,864
Library Holdings: Bk Vols 6,120; Per Subs 53
Subject Interests: Am painting, Decorative arts, European painting, Prints, Sculpture
Restriction: Public use on premises
Partic in SW Mo Libr Network

S SPRINGFIELD NEWS-LEADER LIBRARY,* 651 Boonville, 65806. SAN 373-465X. Tel: 417-836-1215. FAX: 417-837-1381. *Librn*, Maudie Lawson; E-Mail: mlawson@springfi.gannett.com
Restriction: Not open to public
Open Mon-Fri 8-5

P SPRINGFIELD-GREENE COUNTY LIBRARY, 4653 S Campbell, 65810. (Mail add: PO Box 760, 65810-0760), SAN 349-8212. Tel: 417-874-8120. FAX: 417-874-8113. E-Mail: comrel@orion.org. Web Site: thelibrary.springfield.missouri.org. *Exec Dir*, Annie Busch; Tel: 417-874-8120, Fax: 417-874-8121, E-Mail: annieb@orion.org; *Mgr*, Ellen Kerr; Tel: 417-874-8120, Ext 214, Fax: 417-874-8121, E-Mail: ellenk@orion.org; *Business*, Debbie Eckert; Fax: 417-874-8121, E-Mail: debbiee@orion.org; *Coordr*, Carol Grimes; Tel: 417-874-8120, Ext 213, Fax: 417-874-8121, E-Mail: carolg@orion.org; *Selection of Gen Ref Mat*, Dorothy Davidson; Tel: 417-874-8111, Fax: 417-874-8113; *Ch Servs*, Vera Florea; Tel: 417-874-8120, Ext 216, Fax: 417-874-8121, E-Mail: veraf@orion.org; *Tech Servs*, Ann Gilmore; Tel: 417-874-8120, Ext 236, Fax: 417-874-8113, E-Mail: anng@orion.org; *Bkmobile Coordr*, Lisa Sampley; Tel: 417-874-8120, Ext 231, Fax: 417-874-8113, E-Mail: lisas@orion.org; *Commun Relations*, Jeanne Duffey; Tel: 417-874-8120, Ext 217, Fax: 417-874-8121, E-Mail: jeanned@orion.org; *Coll Develop*, Paul Duckworth; Tel: 417-874-8210, Ext 223, Fax: 417-874-8121, E-Mail: pauld@orion.org; *Info Tech*, David Patillo; Fax: 417-874-8121, E-Mail: davidp@orion.org; Staff 175 (MLS 16, Non-MLS 159)
Founded 1903. Pop 226,758; Circ 2,299,498
Jul 1999-Jun 2000 Income (Main Library and Branch Library) $7,542,233, State $157,191, Federal $158,702, Locally Generated Income $7,226,340. Mats Exp $1,132,383, Books $783,782, Per/Ser (Incl. Access Fees) $53,098, AV Equip $114,518, Electronic Ref Mat (Incl. Access Fees) $180,985. Sal $3,036,062 (Prof $576,368)
Library Holdings: Bk Vols 474,368; Per Subs 1,298
Special Collections: Genealogy & Missouri History; Max Hunter Folk Songs Coll; Turnbo Papers
Automation Activity & Vendor Info: (Acquisitions) Innovative Interfaces Inc.; (Cataloging) Innovative Interfaces Inc.; (Circulation) Innovative Interfaces Inc.; (ILL) Innovative Interfaces Inc.; (OPAC) Innovative Interfaces Inc.; (Serials) Innovative Interfaces Inc.
Database Vendor: Dialog, Ebsco - EbscoHost, GaleNet, IAC - Info Trac, IAC - SearchBank, Innovative Interfaces INN - View, OCLC - First Search
Partic in OCLC Online Computer Library Center, Inc; SW Mo Libr Network
Special Services for the Deaf - TDD; Videos & decoder
Special Services for the Blind - Audiobooks; Newsline for the Blind
Friends of the Library Group
Branches: 9
ASH GROVE BRANCH, 101 E Main, Ash Grove, 65604. (Mail add: PO Box 760, 65801-0760), SAN 349-8247. Tel: 417-751-2933. FAX: 417-751-2275. Web Site: www.thelibrary.springfield.missouri.org. *Branch Mgr*, Kathy Trompke; E-Mail: kathyt@orion.org; Staff 4 (Non-MLS 4)
Circ 38,032
Database Vendor: Ebsco - EbscoHost, GaleNet, IAC - Info Trac, IAC - SearchBank, Innovative Interfaces INN - View, OCLC - First Search
Friends of the Library Group
BRENTWOOD, 2214 Brentwood Blvd, 65804. (Mail add: PO Box 760, 65801-0760), SAN 349-8271. Tel: 417-874-8130. FAX: 417-874-8131. Web Site: www.thelibrary.springfield.missouri.org. *Branch Mgr*, Polly C Dross; E-Mail: pollyd@orion.org; Staff 18 (MLS 1, Non-MLS 17)
Founded 1970. Circ 443,524
Database Vendor: Ebsco - EbscoHost, GaleNet, IAC - Info Trac, IAC - SearchBank, Innovative Interfaces INN - View, OCLC - First Search
Friends of the Library Group
KEARNEY, 630 W Kearney, 65803. (Mail add: PO Box 760, 65801-0760), SAN 349-8301. Tel: 417-874-8140. FAX: 417-874-8141. Web Site: www.thelibrary.springfield.missouri.org. *Branch Mgr*, Donna Bacon; E-Mail: donnab@orion.org; *Librn*, Polly Dross; Staff 16 (MLS 1, Non-MLS 15)
Circ 325,282
Database Vendor: Ebsco - EbscoHost, GaleNet, IAC - Info Trac, IAC - SearchBank, Innovative Interfaces INN - View, OCLC - First Search
Friends of the Library Group
MIDTOWN CARNEGIE BRANCH, 397 E Central, 65802. (Mail add: PO Box 760, 65801-0760), Tel: 417-874-8150. FAX: 417-874-8151. Web Site: www.thelibrary.springfield.missouri.org. *Branch Mgr*, Martha Love; E-Mail: marthal@orion.org; Staff 22 (MLS 1, Non-MLS 21)

Circ 296,443
Database Vendor: Ebsco - EbscoHost, GaleNet, IAC - Info Trac, IAC - SearchBank, Innovative Interfaces INN - View, OCLC - First Search
Friends of the Library Group

OUTREACH SERVICES, 4653 S Campbell, 65810. (Mail add: PO Box 760, 65801-0760), SAN 376-2386. Tel: 417-874-8120, Ext 232. FAX: 417-874-8121. Web Site: www.thelibrary.springfield.missouri.org. *Librn*, Dorothy Miller; *Outreach Serv*, Lisa Sampley; Tel: 417-874-8120, Ext 231, E-Mail: lisa1@orion.org; Staff 8 (MLS 1, Non-MLS 7)
Circ 68,258
Database Vendor: Ebsco - EbscoHost, GaleNet, IAC - Info Trac, IAC - SearchBank, Innovative Interfaces INN - View, OCLC - First Search
Friends of the Library Group

REPUBLIC BRANCH, 205 US Hwy 60 W, Republic, 65739. (Mail add: PO Box 760, Republic, 65738), SAN 349-8360. Tel: 417-732-7284. FAX: 417-732-1256. Web Site: www.thelibrary.springfield.missouri.org. *Branch Mgr*, Jim Schmidt; E-Mail: jls@orion.org; *Librn*, Lisa Sampley; E-Mail: lisas1@orion.org; Staff 7 (Non-MLS 7)
Circ 145,136
Database Vendor: Ebsco - EbscoHost, GaleNet, IAC - Info Trac, IAC - SearchBank, Innovative Interfaces INN - View, OCLC - First Search
Friends of the Library Group

THE LIBRARY CENTER, 4653 S Campbell, 65810. (Mail add: PO Box 760, 65801-0760), SAN 349-8328. Tel: 417-874-8110. Reference Tel: 417-874-8111. FAX: 417-874-8113. Web Site: www.thelibrary.springfield.missouri.org. *Branch Mgr*, Lorraine Sandstrom; Tel: 417-874-8110, Ext 116, E-Mail: lorraine@orion.org; Staff 57 (MLS 5, Non-MLS 52)
Circ 908,189
Database Vendor: Ebsco - EbscoHost, GaleNet, IAC - Info Trac, IAC - SearchBank, Innovative Interfaces INN - View, OCLC - First Search
Friends of the Library Group

WILLARD BRANCH, East Shopping Ctr, Willard, 65781. (Mail add: PO Box 760, 65801-0760), SAN 376-2378. Tel: 417-742-4258. FAX: 417-742-4589. Web Site: www.thelibrary.springfield.missouri.org. *Branch Mgr*, Kathy Trompke; E-Mail: kathyt@orion.org; Staff 4 (Non-MLS 4)
Circ 63,852
Database Vendor: Ebsco - EbscoHost, GaleNet, IAC - Info Trac, IAC - SearchBank, Innovative Interfaces INN - View, OCLC - First Search
Friends of the Library Group
Bookmobiles: 1

M ST JOHN'S HEALTH SYSTEMS, INC, Medical Library, 1235 E Cherokee St, 65804-2263. SAN 326-4823. Tel: 417-885-2795. Interlibrary Loan Service Tel: 417-885-2070. Reference Tel: 417-885-5399. FAX: 417-885-5399. E-Mail: libstaff@sprg.smhs.com. *Dir Libr Serv*, Anna Beth Crabtree; Tel: 417-885-3253, E-Mail: acrabtree@sprg.smhs.com; *Librn*, Jean M Lewis; E-Mail: jlewis@sprg.smhs.com; *ILL*, LaRee LaMar; Tel: 417-885-2070, E-Mail: llamar@sprg.smhs.com; *Cat*, Cynthia Avallone; Staff 7 (MLS 3, Non-MLS 4)
Founded 1940
Library Holdings: Bk Vols 14,800; Bk Titles 5,700; Per Subs 410
Subject Interests: Administration, Allied health, Health care mgt, Medicine, Nursing
Database Vendor: OCLC - First Search, OVID Technologies
Restriction: Open to others by appointment
Function: ILL available
Partic in Docline; IVLS; Saint Louis Medical Librarians Consortia
Branches:
VAN K SMITH EDUCATION CENTER, Mid-America Cancer Center at Saint John's, 1235 E Cherokee, 65804-2263. Tel: 417-885-2539. Toll Free Tel: 800-432-2273. FAX: 417-888-8761. *Dir, Tech Serv*, Anna Beth Crabtree; Tel: 417-885-3253, Fax: 417-885-2795, E-Mail: acrabtree@sprg.smhs.com; *Librn*, Sabrina W Miller; E-Mail: swmiller@sprg.smhs.com; Staff 1 (MLS 1)
Founded 1990
Library Holdings: Bk Vols 5,125; Bk Titles 4,000; Per Subs 100
Subject Interests: Health
Database Vendor: OVID Technologies

STANBERRY

P GENTRY COUNTY LIBRARY, Second & Park, 64489. SAN 309-2402. Tel: 660-783-2335. FAX: 660-783-2335. E-Mail: tgn002@mail.connect.more.net. Web Site: www.mlnc.org/~gentry. *Dir*, Judy Beatty; *Asst Dir*, Lana Smith
Founded 1955. Pop 6,256; Circ 70,186
Library Holdings: Bk Titles 52,000; Per Subs 70
Subject Interests: Genealogy, Missouri
Open Tues, Thurs & Fri 8-5, Wed 8-7, Sat 9-12
Friends of the Library Group
Bookmobiles: 1

STEELE

P STEELE PUBLIC LIBRARY,* 117 S Walnut St, 63877-1712. SAN 309-2410. Tel: 573-695-3561. *Dir*, Myrna McKay
Founded 1937. Pop 2,419; Circ 10,426
Library Holdings: Bk Titles 15,000; Per Subs 18
Partic in SE Mo Libr Network
Open Mon-Fri 1-5
Friends of the Library Group

STOUTSVILLE

S MARK TWAIN BIRTHPLACE STATE HISTORIC SITE, Research Library, 37352 Shrine Rd, 65283-9722. SAN 327-8786. Tel: 573-565-3449. FAX: 573-565-3718. *In Charge*, John Huffman
Library Holdings: Bk Titles 500
Subject Interests: Local history
Special Collections: Works by & about Mark Twain including several first editions & a foreign language coll

SULLIVAN

P SULLIVAN PUBLIC LIBRARY, 104 W Vine St, 63080. SAN 329-1057. Tel: 573-468-4372. Web Site: www.ne3.com/library. *Librn*, Betty Brown; *Cat*, Babe Stratman
Founded 1948
Library Holdings: Bk Vols 30,000; Per Subs 50
Friends of the Library Group

SWEET SPRINGS

P SWEET SPRINGS PUBLIC LIBRARY,* 217 Turner St, 65351. SAN 309-2429. Tel: 816-335-4314. *Librn*, Jennie Aiken
Founded 1939
Library Holdings: Bk Vols 11,597; Per Subs 21

THAYER

P THAYER LIBRARY,* 121 N Second St, 65791. SAN 377-2160. Tel: 417-264-3091. FAX: 417-264-3091. E-Mail: sfy000@pop.connect.more.net. *Librn*, Grace Mainprize
Library Holdings: Bk Vols 25,000; Bk Titles 20,000; Per Subs 14
Mem of Oregon County Libr Syst

TIPTON

S PRICE JAMES MEMORIAL LIBRARY,* 104 E Morgan, 65081. (Mail add: PO Box 187, 65081), SAN 309-2445. Tel: 660-433-5622. *Librn*, Linda Schuster
Library Holdings: Bk Vols 30,000
Subject Interests: Classics, Fiction, Humanities, Ref, Relig studies, Sci
Special Collections: Law (Missouri Digest, Southwestern Reporter & Missouri Revised Statutes)
Open Mon, Wed & Fri 10-12 & 2-5, Tues 9-12 & 6-8, Sat 9-12

TRENTON

P GRUNDY COUNTY-JEWETT NORRIS LIBRARY,* 1331 Main St, 64683. SAN 309-2453. Tel: 660-359-3577. FAX: 660-359-6220. E-Mail: dxc000@mail.connect.more.net. Web Site: www.mogrundy/library. *Dir*, Peggy Ausmus; *Ad Servs*, Margaret Wavada
Founded 1890. Pop 11,819; Circ 200,000
Jul 1997-Jun 1998 Income $130,111. Mats Exp $12,685. Sal $84,878
Library Holdings: Bk Titles 31,252; Per Subs 53
Subject Interests: Genealogy
Partic in OCLC Online Computer Library Center, Inc
Open Mon 9-9, Tues-Fri 9-5 & Sat 9-12

J NORTH CENTRAL MISSOURI COLLEGE LIBRARY, 1301 Main St, 64683. SAN 309-2461. Tel: 660-359-3948, Ext 322. FAX: 660-359-3202. *Librn*, Robert M Shields; E-Mail: bshields@mail.ncmc.cc.mo.us
Founded 1967. Enrl 1,321
Jul 2000-Jun 2001 Income $136,287. Mats Exp $21,500, Books $9,500, Per/Ser (Incl. Access Fees) $9,500, AV Equip $2,500. Sal $85,921 (Prof $47,653)
Library Holdings: Bk Vols 23,252; Bk Titles 20,454; Per Subs 131
Automation Activity & Vendor Info: (Circulation) Follett; (OPAC) Follett
Partic in Mobius

TROY

P POWELL MEMORIAL LIBRARY,* 951 W College, 63379. SAN 309-247X. Tel: 314-528-7853. *Librn*, Sharon Hasekamp
Founded 1949. Pop 9,000; Circ 40,000

Library Holdings: Bk Titles 26,450; Per Subs 20
Subject Interests: Local history
Special Collections: Missouri Genealogical Coll
Friends of the Library Group

UNION

J EAST CENTRAL COLLEGE, Library Services, 1964 Prairie Dell Rd, PO Box 529, 63084-0529. SAN 309-2488. Tel: 636-583-5193, Ext 2245. FAX: 636-583-1897. E-Mail: library@ecmail.ecc.cc.mo.us. Web Site: www.ecc.cc.mo.us/ecc/library/web/index.htm. *Librn*, Rebecca Grady; *Asst Librn*, Jennifer Dodillet; *Tech Servs*, Kathleen Schlump; Staff 5 (MLS 3, Non-MLS 2)
Founded 1969. Enrl 3,000; Fac 85
Library Holdings: Bk Vols 35,000; Per Subs 300
Automation Activity & Vendor Info: (Circulation) Innovative Interfaces Inc.; (OPAC) Innovative Interfaces Inc.
Database Vendor: Ebsco - EbscoHost, OCLC - First Search
Partic in Saint Louis Regional Library Network
Friends of the Library Group

R FIRST BAPTIST CHURCH LIBRARY, 801 E Hwy 50, 63084. SAN 309-2496. Tel: 636-583-2386. FAX: 636-583-4281. *Librn*, Rodger Davis
Library Holdings: Bk Vols 3,800

P SCENIC REGIONAL LIBRARY OF FRANKLIN, GASCONADE & WARREN COUNTIES,* 308 Hawthorne Dr, 63084. SAN 349-8395. Tel: 636-583-3224. FAX: 636-583-6519. *Dir*, Sallie Hancox; *Asst Dir*, Kenneth J Rohrbach; *Ref*, Carolyn Scheer; Staff 3 (MLS 3)
Founded 1959. Pop 86,147; Circ 375,216
Library Holdings: Bk Vols 160,000; Bk Titles 85,000; Per Subs 403
Partic in Mo Libr Film Coop; Saint Louis Regional Library Network
Branches: 7
HERMANN SERVICE CENTER, 113 E Fourth St, Hermann, 65041. SAN 349-8425. Tel: 573-486-2024. FAX: 573-486-2024. *Librn*, Sheri Hausman
Library Holdings: Bk Vols 19,206
Special Collections: City Newspapers, micro City Records, micro; County Census Records, micro
NEW HAVEN SERVICE CENTER, 901 Maupin, New Haven, 63068. SAN 349-845X. Tel: 573-237-2189. FAX: 573-237-2189. *Librn*, Judy Brock
Library Holdings: Bk Vols 11,225
OWENSVILLE SERVICE CENTER, 107 N First St, Owensville, 65066. SAN 349-8484. Tel: 573-437-2188. FAX: 573-437-2188. *Librn*, Linda G Little
Library Holdings: Bk Vols 15,265
PACIFIC SERVICE CENTER, 140 W St Louis St, Pacific, 63069. SAN 349-8514. Tel: 636-257-2712. FAX: 636-257-2712. *Librn*, Sue Reed
Library Holdings: Bk Vols 14,238
SAINT CLAIR SERVICE CENTER, 570 S Main St, Saint Clair, 63077. SAN 349-8549. Tel: 636-629-2546. FAX: 636-629-2546. *Librn*, Mary E Davis; *Librn*, Rebecca Cokley
Library Holdings: Bk Vols 17,471
UNION SERVICE CENTER, 308 Hawthorne, 63084. SAN 349-8573. Tel: 636-583-3224. FAX: 636-583-6519. *Librn*, Sallie Hancox
Library Holdings: Bk Vols 43,060
Special Collections: Area Newspapers, micro; County Census records; Selected County records, micro
WARRENTON SERVICE CENTER, 100-2 E Main St, Warrenton, 63383. SAN 349-8603. Tel: 636-456-3321. FAX: 636-456-3321. *Librn*, Marlys Mertens
Library Holdings: Bk Vols 19,266
Special Collections: Census records & area newspapers, micro
Bookmobiles: 1. Bk vols 11,236

UNIONVILLE

P PUTNAM COUNTY PUBLIC LIBRARY,* 115 S 16th St, PO Box 305, 63565. SAN 309-250X. Tel: 660-947-3192. FAX: 660-947-7039. E-Mail: jnr000@mail.connect.more.net. *Librn*, Diane Beatty
Founded 1946. Pop 5,079; Circ 39,207
Library Holdings: Bk Vols 26,994; Per Subs 65
Subject Interests: Genealogy of Putnam County, Local history
Publications: 1877 & 1897 Atlas of Putnam Co
Partic in Mo Res & Educ Network; OCLC Online Computer Library Center, Inc
Friends of the Library Group

UNITY VILLAGE

R UNITY SCHOOL OF CHRISTIANITY LIBRARY, 1901 NW Blue Pkwy, 64065-0001. SAN 309-2518. Tel: 816-524-3550, Ext 2370. FAX: 816-251-3555. E-Mail: library@unityworldhq.org. *Dir*, Priscilla Richards; Tel: 816-524-3550, Ext 2010; *Archivist*, Carolyn Stewart; Tel: 816-524-3550, Ext 2020
Founded 1965. Enrl 80; Fac 13
Library Holdings: Bk Titles 47,785; Per Subs 170
Subject Interests: Relig studies
Special Collections: Unity School of Christianity Archives from 1889, bks, per, AV
Publications: Unity Library & Unity Archives Newsletter

UNIVERSITY CITY

P UNIVERSITY CITY PUBLIC LIBRARY, 6701 Delmar Blvd, 63130. SAN 309-2534. Tel: 314-727-3150. FAX: 314-727-6005. E-Mail: webmaster@ucpl.lib.mo.us. Web Site: ucpl.lib.mo.us. *Dir*, Linda V Ballard; E-Mail: prx002@mail.connect.more.net; *Tech Servs*, Sally Master; *Ref Serv Ad*, Patrick Wall; E-Mail: pjwall@ucpl.lib.mo.us; *Ad Servs*, Elizabeth Farley; E-Mail: farley@ucpl.lib.mo.us; *Ch Servs*, Marilyn Phillips; E-Mail: prx005@mail.connect.more.net; *Ch Servs*, Candace Virgil; E-Mail: cvirgil@ucpl.lib.mo.us; *Ch Servs*, LaRita Wright; E-Mail: lwright@ucpl.lib.mo.us; *Info Tech*, Michael Novak; E-Mail: mjnovak@ucpl.lib.mo.us; *AV*, Michael Ludwig; E-Mail: mludwig@ucpl.lib.mo.us; Staff 35 (MLS 9, Non-MLS 26)
Founded 1939. Pop 40,087; Circ 272,019
Jul 1999-Jun 2000 Income $1,413,568, State $36,734, City $1,179,775, Federal $8,406, Locally Generated Income $188,653. Mats Exp $278,554, Books $190,500, Per/Ser (Incl. Access Fees) $16,649, AV Equip $18,300, Electronic Ref Mat (Incl. Access Fees) $53,105. Sal $564,079
Library Holdings: Bk Vols 156,911; Per Subs 350
Special Collections: Archive of local history, collection of locally produced art pottery and artifacts c. 1910
Automation Activity & Vendor Info: (Cataloging) epixtech, inc.; (Circulation) epixtech, inc.; (OPAC) epixtech, inc.; (Serials) epixtech, inc.
Database Vendor: Ebsco - EbscoHost, epixtech, inc., OVID Technologies
Publications: Checkout (Newsletter)
Partic in Municipal Libr Coop; Saint Louis Regional Library Network
Friends of the Library Group

VALLEY PARK

P VALLEY PARK COMMUNITY LIBRARY,* 320 Benton St, 63088. SAN 309-2542. Tel: 636-225-5608. FAX: 636-825-0079. E-Mail: rjh000@mail.connect.more.net. *Dir*, Bonnie Morris; *Asst Librn*, Judy Piotraschke
Founded 1943. Pop 3,859; Circ 7,900
1997-1998 Income $53,000, State $1,600, City $49,500, Other $550. Mats Exp $13,000, Books $12,000, Per/Ser (Incl. Access Fees) $1,000. Sal $25,000 (Prof $24,000)
Library Holdings: Bk Vols 15,000
Subject Interests: Local history
Partic in Municipal Libr Coop

VAN BUREN

P CARTER COUNTY LIBRARY DISTRICT, Van Buren Library,* PO Box 309, 63965. SAN 349-8638. Tel: 573-323-4315. *Librn*, Shirley Chitwood; Staff 1 (MLS 1)
Founded 1947. Pop 28,967; Circ 325,000
Library Holdings: Bk Vols 245,000
Subject Interests: Children's folklore, Genealogy, Local history
Partic in SE Mo Libr Network
Branches: 2
ELLSINORE BRANCH, Rte 2, Ellsinore, 63937. (Mail add: PO Box 2003, Ellsinore, 63937), SAN 349-8786. *Librn*, Gloria Copeland
GRANDIN BRANCH, PO Box 274, Grandin, 63943. SAN 349-8816. *Librn*, Debbie Norcross
Bookmobiles: 1

S NATIONAL PARK SERVICE, Ozark National Scenic Riverways Reference Library, PO Box 490, 63965-0490. SAN 309-2550. Tel: 573-323-4236. FAX: 573-323-4140. *Dir*, Angela Smith
Founded 1974
Library Holdings: Bk Vols 1,000; Per Subs 5
Subject Interests: Background studies associated with Riverways area, General natural, Hist data relative to Ozark area

VERSAILLES

P MORGAN COUNTY LIBRARY, 102 N Fisher, 65084. SAN 309-2569. Tel: 573-378-5319. *Dir*, Lucy M Middleton; E-Mail: nea001@mail.connect.more.net; *Librn*, Glenn Housworth; Staff 5 (Non-MLS 5)
Founded 1946. Pop 18,908; Circ 97,154
Jan 2000-Dec 2000 Income $192,373, State $4,037, County $173,872, Other $14,464. Mats Exp $29,393, Books $17,009, Per/Ser (Incl. Access Fees) $1,228, AV Equip $11,000, Electronic Ref Mat (Incl. Access Fees) $156. Sal $118,566
Library Holdings: Bk Vols 21,000; Per Subs 55; High Interest/Low Vocabulary Bk Vols 50; Spec Interest Per Sub 20; Bks on Deafness & Sign Lang 10
Subject Interests: Local history
Automation Activity & Vendor Info: (Cataloging) Athena; (Circulation)

Athena
Partic in Morenet
Open Mon-Fri 9-5, Thurs 9-6, Sat 9-12

WARRENSBURG

C CENTRAL MISSOURI STATE UNIVERSITY, James C Kirkpatrick Library, 64093. SAN 349-9111. Tel: 660-543-4140. FAX: 660-543-8001. E-Mail: pal@cmsuvmb.cmsu.edu. Web Site: library.cmsu.edu. *Chair*, Dr Larry D Dorrell; Tel: 660-543-8633, E-Mail: dorrell@libserv.com; *ILL, Publ Servs*, Linda Medaris; *Acq*, George Millen; *Tech Servs*, Mollie Lawson; *Doc*, Pat Antrim; *Cat*, Cheryl Riley; *Cat*, Stephen Walker; *Media Spec*, Mary Griffis; *Coll Develop*, Charles Slattery; Staff 17 (MLS 17)
Founded 1872. Enrl 11,130; Fac 456
Library Holdings: Bk Vols 483,975; Bk Titles 401,678; Per Subs 2,691
Special Collections: Civil War (Personal Narratives & Unit Histories), bks, flm; Geography (Missouri & International Speleology); Literature (Izaac Walton's Compleat Angler); Missouri Coll; Research Coll in Children's Literature
Automation Activity & Vendor Info: (Acquisitions) NOTIS; (Cataloging) NOTIS; (Circulation) NOTIS; (Serials) NOTIS
Publications: Info One (newsletter)
Partic in Kansas City Metropolitan Library & Information Network; MLNC; OCLC Online Computer Library Center, Inc
Includes Ward Edwards Library, University Media Services, & Library Science & Information Services

S JOHNSON COUNTY HISTORICAL SOCIETY, Mary Miller Smiser Heritage Library, 302 N Main St, 64093. SAN 328-0195. Tel: 660-747-6480. *Pres*, Jane Reynolds
Founded 1969
Library Holdings: Bk Titles 1,800
Special Collections: Johnson County; Local History, Newsp

P TRAILS REGIONAL LIBRARY, Consolidated Public Library District (Johnson-Lafayette Counties), 125 N Holden St, PO Box 498, 64093. SAN 349-9170. Tel: 660-747-1699. Reference Tel: 660-747-9177. FAX: 660-747-5774. E-Mail: scg000@mail.connect.more.net. Web Site: www.mlnc.com/~trails. *Dir*, Susan Bonett; *Asst Dir, Br Coordr*, Alicia Morgan; *Ch Servs*, Virginia Brooks; *Ref*, Jean Millen; *Tech Servs*, Anita Ewing; Staff 20 (MLS 5, Non-MLS 15)
Founded 1957. Pop 67,417; Circ 307,213
Jul 1998-Jun 1999 Income $1,259,057, State $33,965, County $1,171,572, Other $53,520. Mats Exp $141,104, Books $123,376, Per/Ser (Incl. Access Fees) $14,285, Presv $3,205, Micro $237. Sal $712,377
Library Holdings: Per Subs 432
Partic in Kansas City Metropolitan Library & Information Network
Friends of the Library Group
Branches: 7
CONCORDIA BRANCH, 709 Main St, Concordia, 64020. SAN 349-9200. Tel: 660-463-2277. FAX: 660-747-5774. E-Mail: scg004@mail.connect.more.net. Web Site: www.mlnc.com/~trails. *Librn*, Kathy Oetting
Library Holdings: Bk Vols 15,608
Friends of the Library Group
CORDER BRANCH, 221 N Lafayette, Corder, 64021. SAN 349-9235. Tel: 660-394-2565. E-Mail: mpr000@mail.connect.more.net. Web Site: www.mlnc.com/~trails. *Librn*, Ann Schumaker; Fax: 660-747-5774
Library Holdings: Bk Vols 6,063
KNOB NOSTER BRANCH, 112 N State, Knob Noster, 65336. SAN 349-926X. Tel: 660-563-2997. Web Site: www.mlnc.com/~trails. *Librn*, Julie Dolph; Fax: 660-747-5774, E-Mail: mpr002@mail.connect.more.net
Library Holdings: Bk Vols 7,432
LEXINGTON BRANCH, 1008 Main St, Lexington, 64067. SAN 349-9294. Tel: 660-259-3071. FAX: 660-259-3071. Web Site: www.mlnc.com/~trails. *Librn*, Fran Rushing; Fax: 660-747-5774, E-Mail: scg005@mail.connect.more.net
Library Holdings: Bk Vols 25,792
Friends of the Library Group
ODESSA BRANCH, 107 W Mason, Odessa, 64076. SAN 349-9324. Tel: 816-633-4089. E-Mail: scg006@mail.connect.more.net. Web Site: www.mlnc.com/~trails. *Librn*, Elaine Miller
Library Holdings: Bk Vols 16,771
Friends of the Library Group
WARRENSBURG BRANCH, 125 N Holden St, 64093. SAN 349-9359. Tel: 660-747-9177. FAX: 660-747-5774. Web Site: www.mlnc.com/~trails. *Librn*, Mary Barnhart
Library Holdings: Bk Vols 86,114
Friends of the Library Group
WAVERLY BRANCH, 203 E Kelling, PO Box 175, Waverly, 64096. SAN 349-9383. Tel: 660-493-2987. E-Mail: mpr001@mail.connect.more.net. Web Site: www.mlnc.com/~trails. *Librn*, Linda Burkhardt
Library Holdings: Bk Vols 5,172
Bookmobiles: 1

WARRENTON

S WARREN COUNTY HISTORICAL SOCIETY, Museum & Historical Library, Market & Walton, PO Box 12, 63383. SAN 373-4668. Tel: 314-456-3820.
Library Holdings: Bk Vols 240
Subject Interests: Local history
Special Collections: Central Wesleyen College

WASHINGTON

P WASHINGTON PUBLIC LIBRARY,* 415 Jefferson, 63090. SAN 309-2577. Tel: 636-390-1070. FAX: 636-390-0171. *Librn*, Carolyn Witt; Staff 1 (Non-MLS 1)
Founded 1924. Pop 9,251; Circ 74,000
Library Holdings: Bk Vols 34,000; Per Subs 110
Mem of Saint Louis Regional Libr Network

WEBB CITY

P WEBB CITY PUBLIC LIBRARY,* 101 S Liberty, 64870. SAN 309-2585. Tel: 417-673-4326. FAX: 417-673-5703. E-Mail: jhh001@mail.connect.more.net. *Librn*, Sue Oliveira
Founded 1913. Pop 7,449; Circ 33,628
Nov 1997-Oct 1998 Income $80,000, State $2,582, City $68,232, Locally Generated Income $5,186, Other $4,000. Mats Exp $19,425, Books $14,000, Per/Ser (Incl. Access Fees) $1,000. Sal $33,992
Library Holdings: Bk Vols 24,000
Subject Interests: Genealogy, Local history
Publications: The Miner (quarterly)
Friends of the Library Group

WEBSTER GROVES

P ARCHIVES OF THE EVANGELICAL SYNOD OF NORTH AMERICA, 475 E Lockwood Ave, 63119-3192. SAN 326-0755. Tel: 314-961-3627, Ext 348. FAX: 314-961-9063. E-Mail: archives@library2.websteruniv.edu. Web Site: library.websteruniv.edu/edemarch.html. *Archivist*, Val Detjen; Tel: 314-918-2515; *Archivist*, Lowell H Zuck; Tel: 314-918-2516
Founded 1925
Library Holdings: Bk Vols 4,400

P WEBSTER GROVES PUBLIC LIBRARY,* 301 E Lockwood Ave, 63119-3195. SAN 309-2593. Tel: 314-961-3784. FAX: 314-961-4233. Web Site: www.wgpl.lib.mo.us. *Dir*, Mary Grashoff; *Ad Servs, Coll Develop*, Pat Linehan; *Ch Servs*, Michelle Haffer; *Ref*, Christopher Johnson
Founded 1928. Pop 22,987; Circ 335,776
Jul 1997-Jun 1998 Income $664,277. Mats Exp $84,300. Sal $364,264
Library Holdings: Bk Vols 69,406; Per Subs 152
Subject Interests: Local history
Automation Activity & Vendor Info: (Cataloging) Inlex; (Circulation) Inlex
Database Vendor: DRA
Partic in Saint Louis Regional Library Network
Friends of the Library Group

WELLSVILLE

P WELLSVILLE PUBLIC LIBRARY,* 108 W Hudson St, 63384. SAN 309-2607. Tel: 573-684-6151. FAX: 573-684-6151. E-Mail: ttd000@mail.connect.more.net. *Librn*, Margaret Harrelson
Pop 1,430; Circ 8,972
Library Holdings: Bk Vols 12,500
Open Mon & Wed 12-5:30, Fri 10-5 & Sat 10-12
Friends of the Library Group

WEST PLAINS

P WEST PLAINS PUBLIC LIBRARY,* 750 W Broadway, 65775. SAN 309-2615. Tel: 417-256-4775. FAX: 417-256-8316. *Chief Librn*, Debra Fite; *Ch Servs*, Kelli Cook
Founded 1948. Pop 10,000; Circ 115,000
Library Holdings: Bk Titles 44,169; Per Subs 97
Partic in SW Mo Libr Network
Friends of the Library Group

WHITEMAN AFB

UNITED STATES AIR FORCE
A WHITEMAN AIR FORCE BASE LIBRARY FL4625, 509 SVS/SVMG, 750 Arnold Ave Bldg 527, 65305-5382. SAN 349-9413. Tel: 660-687-5614. FAX: 660-687-6240. *Ref*, Linda Jacobs
Oct 1998-Sep 1999 Income $241,374. Mats Exp $52,000, Per/Ser (Incl.

Access Fees) $31,000. Sal $164,393
Library Holdings: Bk Vols 23,115; Per Subs 115
Subject Interests: Bus, Mgt, Mil, Political science
Automation Activity & Vendor Info: (Circulation) GEAC
Partic in Fedlink

WILDWOOD

S PSYCHIC SCIENCE INSTITUTE, Haunt Hunters Library, 509 Big Horn Basin Ct, 63011. SAN 375-9067. Tel: 314-831-1379.
Library Holdings: Bk Vols 5,000
Restriction: Not open to public

WINDSOR

P LENORA BLACKMORE PUBLIC LIBRARY,* 115 E Benton, 65360. SAN 309-2623. Tel: 660-647-2298. *Dir*, Phyllis Jones
Founded 1937. Pop 3,053; Circ 19,307
Library Holdings: Bk Vols 18,300; Per Subs 4
Open Mon-Fri 11-5, Sat 12-5

MONTANA

Date of Statistics: 1999-2000
Population, 1998 Census: 880,453
Population Served by Public Libraries:880,453
Counties Served: 56
Number of Public Libraries: 79
Number of Public Library Branches: 28
Number of Academic Libraries: 28
Number of Institutional Libraries: 6
Number of Special Libraries: 52
Number of School Libraries: 573
Total Volumes in Public Libraries: 2,751,550
Volumes Per Capita: 3.13
Total Public Library Circulation: $4,818,643
Circulation per Capita: 5.47

Total Public Library Income: $16,043,377
Income per Capita: 18.22
Source of Income: Mainly public funds
State Tax Rate: 5-Mill county tax (permissive); 7-Mill for cities & towns (permissive)
Total Public Library Expenditures: 14,180,952
Expenditures Per Capita: $16.11
Number of Bookmobiles in State: 3
Federal Grants-in-Aid to Public Libraries-Library Services and Construction Act (includes Title II): 10,000
Federal Grants-in-Aid to Public Libraries-Library Services and Technology Act: $662,302
Grants-in-State Aid to Public Libraries: 595,130

ANACONDA

P HEARST FREE LIBRARY,* 401 Main St, 59711. SAN 309-2631. Tel: 406-563-6932. FAX: 406-563-5393. Web Site: www.hosts2.in-tch.com/. *Cat, Dir*, Honore Bray; E-Mail: hbray@mtlib.org; *Asst Dir, Ref*, Colleen Fergusen
Founded 1895. Pop 10,365; Circ 37,650
1998-1999 Income $154,772, State $2,130, County $146,407, Locally Generated Income $6,235. Mats Exp $18,884, Books $15,137, Per/Ser (Incl. Access Fees) $3,247. Sal $52,065 (Prof $39,488)
Library Holdings: Bk Titles 47,000; Per Subs 83
Publications: Anaconda's Treasure: Hearst Free Library
Mem of Broad Valleys Fedn of Librs

BAKER

P FALLON COUNTY LIBRARY,* 6 W Fallon Ave, PO Box 1037, 59313-1037. SAN 309-2666. Tel: 406-778-7160. FAX: 406-778-3431. *Librn*, Judy Gunderson; E-Mail: jgunder@libmail.mtlib.org
Pop 3,103; Circ 22,024
Library Holdings: Bk Vols 32,000; Per Subs 27
Mem of Sagebrush Fedn of Librs
Open Mon-Thurs 10:30-8, Fri 10:30-5 & Sat 1-5

BELGRADE

P BELGRADE COMMUNITY LIBRARY,* 106 N Broadway, PO Box 929, 59714-0929. SAN 309-2674. Tel: 406-388-4346. FAX: 406-388-6586. Web Site: www.mtbel.mtlib.org. *Librn*, Ilene Casey; E-Mail: icasey@mtlib.org
Pop 8,500; Circ 24,000
Jul 1997-Jun 1998 Income $113,000, City $49,000, County $64,000. Mats Exp $10,000. Sal $43,350
Library Holdings: Bk Titles 12,898; Per Subs 40
Database Vendor: epixtech, inc., OCLC - First Search
Mem of Broad Valleys Fedn of Librs

BELT

P BELT PUBLIC LIBRARY,* 70 Castner St, PO Box 467, 59412. SAN 309-2682. Tel: 406-277-3136. FAX: 406-277-3376. E-Mail: beltlib@3rivers.net. *Librn*, Verna Nicola
Pop 800; Circ 61,524
Library Holdings: Bk Titles 8,000; Per Subs 13
Mem of Pathfinder Regional Library Service System
Open Mon & Wed-Fri 12-4, Tues 2-4 & 7-9

BIG TIMBER

P CARNEGIE PUBLIC LIBRARY,* 314 McLeod St, PO Box 846, 59011-0846. SAN 309-2690. Tel: 406-932-5608. *Librn*, Lauren McMullen
Pop 3,211; Circ 29,953
Library Holdings: Bk Titles 23,800; Per Subs 60
Special Collections: County Newspapers
Partic in S Cent Fedn of Libr

BILLINGS

S BILLINGS GAZETTE LIBRARY,* 401 N Broadway, PO Box 36300, 59107-6300. SAN 309-2704. Tel: 406-657-1200. FAX: 406-657-1208. E-Mail: library@billingsgazette.com. Web Site: www.billingsgazette.com. *Librn*, Sally Rose
Founded 1970
Member Libraries: Anaconda

L CROWLEY, HAUGHEY, HANSON, TOOLE & DIETRICH LIBRARY, 490 N 31st St Ste 500, 59101-1288. (Mail add: PO Box 2529, 59103-2529), Tel: 406-252-3441. FAX: 406-256-0277. Web Site: www.crowleylaw.com. *Librn*, Margaret Webster; Tel: 406-255-7201, E-Mail: mwebster@crowleylaw.com; Staff 1 (MLS 1)
Library Holdings: Bk Vols 32,000
Subject Interests: Law
Database Vendor: Lexis-Nexis, OCLC - First Search
Restriction: Not open to public
Function: ILL by photocopy only
Partic in OCLC Online Computer Library Center, Inc

M DEACONESS BILLINGS CLINIC, Medical Library, 2825 Eighth Ave N. (Mail add: PO Box 35100, 59107-5100), SAN 375-3808. Tel: 406-238-2226. FAX: 406-238-2253. *Librn*, Connie Younkin; E-Mail: cyounkin@billingsclinic.org; *ILL*, Sara Morris; Staff 2 (MLS 1, Non-MLS 1)
Library Holdings: Bk Titles 2,000; Per Subs 500
Partic in Billings Area Health Sciences Information Consortium

S HKM ENGINEERING INC LIBRARY, (Formerly MSE-HKM, Inc Library), 222 N 32nd, Ste 700, 59101. (Mail add: PO Box 31318, 59107-1318), SAN 327-1471. Tel: 406-656-6399. FAX: 406-656-6398. *Librn*, Irene Nelson; E-Mail: inelson@msehkm.com
Library Holdings: Bk Vols 12,500
Subject Interests: Civil engineering

S INTERMOUNTAIN PLANNED PARENTHOOD LIBRARY,* 721 N 29th St, 59101. SAN 375-3425. Tel: 406-248-3636. FAX: 406-245-8182. E-Mail: impp@impp.org. Web Site: www.impp.org. *Librn*, Jackie Lloyd
Library Holdings: Bk Titles 1,000; Per Subs 12
Partic in Billings Area Health Sciences Information Consortium

S MONTANA STATE UNIVERSITY LIBRARIES, Billings College of Technology Library, 3803 Central Ave, 59102. SAN 323-6935. Tel: 406-656-4445. FAX: 406-652-1729. *Librn*, Joan Bares
Enrl 350
Library Holdings: Bk Vols 2,850; Bk Titles 3,500; Per Subs 80

C MONTANA STATE UNVERSITY-BILLINGS LIBRARY,* 1500 N 30th St, 59101-0298. SAN 309-2720. Tel: 406-657-2262. Interlibrary Loan Service Tel: 406-657-1666. Reference Tel: 406-657-1662. FAX: 406-657-2037. E-Mail: Lib_howell@vino.emcmt.edu. Web Site: www.msubillings.edu. *Dir*, Jane L Howell; E-Mail: jlhowell@msubillings.edu; *Acq, Tech Servs*, John Bratton; Tel: 406-657-1659; *AV*, Dennis Schuld; Tel: 406-657-2329; *Doc, Tech Coordr*, Jeff Edgmond; Tel: 106-657-1664; *Doc*, Paula Duffy; *Ref*, Cheryl Hoover; E-Mail: choover@msubillings.edu; Staff 17 (MLS 8, Non-MLS 9)
Founded 1927. Enrl 3,300; Fac 146; Highest Degree: Master
Library Holdings: Bk Vols 302,000; Bk Titles 221,000; Per Subs 870
Subject Interests: Bus, Health, Native Am studies, Special education
Special Collections: Billings, Yellowstone County & Eastern Montana, mss; Montana & Western History (Dora C White Memorial Coll); USGS Montana Maps Coll
Automation Activity & Vendor Info: (Acquisitions) SIRSI; (Cataloging) SIRSI; (Circulation) SIRSI
Publications: Montana Foundations Guide
Partic in BCR; OCLC Online Computer Library Center, Inc
Special Services for the Blind - VisualTek closed circuit TV reading aid
Open Mon-Thurs 7:30 am-10:00 pm, Fri 7:30-4, Sat 9-3, Sun 2-8
Friends of the Library Group

S NORTHERN PLAINS RESOURCE COUNCIL LIBRARY,* 2401 Montana Ave, Ste 200, 59101. SAN 328-3046. Tel: 406-248-1154. FAX: 406-248-2110. E-Mail: info@nprcmt.org. Web Site: www.nprcmt.org.
Library Holdings: Bk Vols 1,500; Per Subs 48

S PARENTS, LET'S UNITE FOR KIDS, (PLUK), Training, Resource & Information Center, 516 N 32nd St, 59101. SAN 377-4422. Tel: 406-255-0540. FAX: 406-255-0523. Web Site: www.pluk.org. *Librn*, Janice Sand; E-Mail: jsand@pluk.org
Library Holdings: Bk Vols 10,000
Partic in BAHSIC Health Scis Libr Network; Billings Area Health Sciences Information Consortium

P PARMLY BILLINGS LIBRARY, 510 N Broadway, 59101-1196. SAN 309-2747. Tel: 406-657-8257. Interlibrary Loan Service Tel: 406-657-8255. Circulation Tel: 406-657-8290. Reference Tel: 406-657-8258. TDD: 406-657-3079. FAX: 406-657-8293. E-Mail: refdesk@billings.lib.mt.us. Web Site: www.billings.lib.mt.us. *Dir*, William M Cochran; Tel: 406-657-8292, E-Mail: cochran@billings.lib.mt.us; *Asst Dir*, Jim Peters; Tel: 406-657-8291, E-Mail: jpeters@billings.lib.mt.us; *Admin Assoc*, Sandra Raymond; Tel: 406-657-8391, E-Mail: sraymond@billings.lib.mt.us; *Tech Coordr*, Thurman Smith; Tel: 406-657-8295, E-Mail: tsmith@billings.lib.mt.us; Staff 30 (MLS 9, Non-MLS 21)
Founded 1901. Pop 120,614; Circ 742,470
Jul 1999-Jun 2000 Income $2,637,384, State $44,969, City $1,690,069, County $335,000, Locally Generated Income $439,167, Other $128,179. Mats Exp $325,005, Books $252,412, Per/Ser (Incl. Access Fees) $51,266, Micro $3,996, Electronic Ref Mat (Incl. Access Fees) $17,331. Sal $1,134,230 (Prof $510,403)
Library Holdings: Bk Vols 278,170; Bk Titles 183,613; Per Subs 260; High Interest/Low Vocabulary Bk Vols 272; Bks on Deafness & Sign Lang 98
Subject Interests: Genealogy, Mont hist
Special Collections: Montana Room
Automation Activity & Vendor Info: (Acquisitions) epixtech, inc.; (Cataloging) epixtech, inc.; (Circulation) epixtech, inc.; (ILL) epixtech, inc.; (OPAC) epixtech, inc.; (Serials) epixtech, inc.
Database Vendor: Dialog, epixtech, inc., IAC - Info Trac
Publications: The Turning Page (monthly public newsletter) (Union list of periodicals); The Turning Page (monthly public newsletter)
Partic in S Cent Fedn of Libr
Special Services for the Deaf - TDD; TTY machine
Special Services for the Blind - Arkenstone, a computer system for the visually handicapped; Bks on cassette
Friends of the Library Group
Bookmobiles: 1

S RIMROCK FOUNDATION LIBRARY,* 1231 N 29th St, 59101-0147. SAN 324-0711. Tel: 406-248-3175. Toll Free Tel: 800-227-3953, Ext 404. FAX: 406-248-3821. E-Mail: comm@rimrock.org. Web Site: www.rimrock.org. *Dir*, Hugh Kilborne
Founded 1975
Library Holdings: Bk Vols 2,000
Subject Interests: Adolescent substance abuse, Adult children of alcoholics, Co-dependency, Compulsive behaviors, Eating disorders
Partic in Billings Area Health Sciences Information Consortium
Chemical dependency resource center & research materials

C ROCKY MOUNTAIN COLLEGE, Paul M Adams Memorial Library, 1511 Poly Dr, 59102-1796. SAN 309-2755. Tel: 406-657-1087. Interlibrary Loan Service Tel: 406-657-1087. FAX: 406-657-1085. Web Site: www.library.rocky.edu. *Dir*, Janet S H Jelinek; *Asst Librn*, Bill Kehler; Staff 3 (MLS 2, Non-MLS 1)
Founded 1878. Enrl 680; Fac 45; Highest Degree: Bachelor
Jul 1999-Jun 2000 Income $150,518. Mats Exp $55,000, Books $32,000, Per/Ser (Incl. Access Fees) $23,000. Sal $99,740
Library Holdings: Bk Vols 87,900; Per Subs 359
Subject Interests: Geology, Liberal arts, Mont hist
Automation Activity & Vendor Info: (Circulation) SIRSI; (Course Reserve) SIRSI; (OPAC) SIRSI; (Serials) SIRSI
Database Vendor: OCLC - First Search
Partic in OCLC Online Computer Library Center, Inc; OMNI
Open Mon-Thurs 7:30am-10pm, Fri 7:30-4:30, Sat 1-5, Sun 1-10

S US DEPARTMENT OF LABOR-OSHA-BILLINGS AREA OFFICE LIBRARY, 2900 Fourth Ave N Ste 303, 59101. SAN 370-2456. Tel: 406-247-7494. FAX: 406-247-7499. Web Site: www.osha.gov. *Librn*, Bonnie Albright
Library Holdings: Bk Vols 550

S WESTERN ORGANIZATION OF RESOURCE COUNCILS LIBRARY,* 2401 Montana Ave, No 301, 59101. SAN 371-4535. Tel: 406-252-9672. FAX: 406-252-1092. Web Site: www.wore.org. *In Charge*, John Smillie
Library Holdings: Bk Titles 200; Per Subs 31

CR YELLOWSTONE BAPTIST COLLEGE, Ida Owen Dockery Library, 1515 Shiloh Rd, 59106. SAN 377-242X. Tel: 406-656-9950. *Librn*, Andrea Todd
Founded 1974. Enrl 51; Fac 15; Highest Degree: Bachelor
1998-1999 Mats Exp Per/Ser (Incl. Access Fees) $1,246
Library Holdings: Bk Vols 19,200; Bk Titles 19,000; Per Subs 57

P YELLOWSTONE BOYS & GIRLS RANCH, Psychiatric Library,* 1732 S 72nd St W, 59106-3599. SAN 370-5749. Tel: 406-655-2100, Ext 2216. FAX: 406-656-8189. *Dir*, Jeanine Holt Seavy
Library Holdings: Bk Titles 750; Per Subs 30

BOULDER

P BOULDER COMMUNITY LIBRARY, 202 S Main St, PO Box 589, 59632-0589. SAN 376-6888. Tel: 406-225-3241. FAX: 406-225-3241. E-Mail: bldrlib@mtlib.org. *Librn*, Cynthia A Kreizwald; Staff 1 (MLS 1)
Founded 1974
Jul 1998-Jun 1999 Income (Main Library and Branch Library) $155,741, State $1,322, City $5,000, County $137,651, Other $11,768. Mats Exp $17,660, Books $14,760, Per/Ser (Incl. Access Fees) $1,400, Electronic Ref Mat (Incl. Access Fees) $1,500. Sal $89,514 (Prof $35,856)
Library Holdings: Bk Vols 13,000; Per Subs 30
Mem of Broad Valleys Fedn of Librs
Open Mon 6:30-8:30, Tues & Thurs 10-2 & 1-5, Wed 10-12, 1-5 & 6:30-8:30, Fri & Sun 1-5
Friends of the Library Group
Branches: 1
JOHN GREGORY (WHITEHALL) BRANCH, 110 First St W, Whitehall, 59759. (Mail add: PO Box 659, Whitehall, 59259), SAN 376-6462. Tel: 406-287-3763. FAX: 406-287-3763. *Librn*, Donna Worth; E-Mail: dworth@mtlib.org; Staff 1 (Non-MLS 1)
Library Holdings: Bk Vols 22,000; Bk Titles 20,000; Per Subs 26; High Interest/Low Vocabulary Bk Vols 200
Automation Activity & Vendor Info: (Cataloging) Sagebrush Corporation; (Circulation) Sagebrush Corporation; (OPAC) Sagebrush Corporation
Database Vendor: GaleNet
Open Mon & Sat 12-5, Tues & Thurs 3-7:30, Wed & Fri 10-12 & 1-5

M THE MONTANA DEVELOPMENTAL CENTER, Client Services,* PO Box 87, 59632-0087. SAN 309-278X. Tel: 406-225-4411. FAX: 406-225-4414.
Founded 1975
Library Holdings: Bk Titles 700; Per Subs 35
Subject Interests: Behav modification, Behav therapy, Child develop, Mental retardation, Psychology
Restriction: Not open to public

BOX ELDER

J STONE CHILD COLLEGE, Rocky Boy Public Library, Rocky Boy Rte 1 Box 1082, 59521-1082. SAN 375-6262. Tel: 406-395-4313, Ext 125. FAX: 406-395-4138. *Librn*, Tracy Jilot; Staff 2 (MLS 1, Non-MLS 1)
Founded 1986. Enrl 200
Library Holdings: Bk Vols 10,800; Bk Titles 10,000; Per Subs 136
Partic in OCLC
Open Mon-Fri 8-4:30

BOZEMAN

P BOZEMAN PUBLIC LIBRARY, 220 E Lamme, 59715. SAN 309-2798. Tel: 406-582-2400. Interlibrary Loan Service Tel: 406-582-5402. Circulation Tel: 406-582-2407, 406-582-2408. Reference Tel: 406-582-2410, 406-582-2411. FAX: 406-582-2424. E-Mail: mtb@mtlib.org. Web Site: www.bozemanlibrary.org. *Dir*, Alice Meister; Tel: 406-582-2401, E-Mail: ameister@mtlib.org; *Automation Syst Coordr, Tech Servs*, Lois Dissly; Tel: 406-582-2403, E-Mail: ldissly@mtlib.org; *Ad Servs, Ref*, Liza McClelland; Tel: 406-582-2406, E-Mail: lizamc@mtlib.org; *Circ*, Mary Jo Stanislao; Tel: 406-582-2409, E-Mail: mstanisl@mtlib.org; Staff 20 (MLS 6, Non-MLS 14)
Founded 1891. Pop 45,631; Circ 437,535
Jul 2000-Jun 2001 Income $984,082, State $14,000, City $643,523, County $326,559. Mats Exp $117,900, Books $95,000, Per/Ser (Incl. Access Fees) $17,900, Electronic Ref Mat (Incl. Access Fees) $5,000. Sal $644,339 (Prof $199,000)
Library Holdings: Bk Vols 85,167; Per Subs 236
Subject Interests: Local, Mont hist
Automation Activity & Vendor Info: (Cataloging) epixtech, inc.; (Circulation) epixtech, inc.; (OPAC) epixtech, inc.
Publications: Check It Out (Newsletter)
Function: ILL available, Photocopies available, Reference services available, Some telephone reference
Mem of Broad Valleys Fedn of Librs
Friends of the Library Group

CR MONTANA BIBLE COLLEGE LIBRARY, 3625 S 19th Ave, 59718. (Mail add: PO Box 6070, 59771), SAN 377-5577. Tel: 406-586-3585. FAX: 406-586-3107. E-Mail: mbc@avicom.net. Web Site: www.link-usa.com/mbc. *Librn*, Sandra Oertli
Founded 1987. Enrl 50; Fac 10; Highest Degree: Bachelor
Library Holdings: Bk Titles 4,000

C MONTANA STATE UNIVERSITY LIBRARIES, Roland R Renne Library, PO Box 173320, 59717-3320. SAN 349-9448. Tel: 406-994-3119. Interlibrary Loan Service Tel: 406-994-3161. FAX: 406-994-2851. Web Site: www.lib.montana.edu. *Dean of Libr*, Bruce Morton; *Spec Coll*, Kim Allen Scott; Staff 20 (MLS 18, Non-MLS 2)
Founded 1893. Enrl 10,798; Fac 564; Highest Degree: Doctorate
Library Holdings: Bk Vols 597,609; Per Subs 3,561
Subject Interests: Agriculture, Health sci, Natural science, Sci-tech
Special Collections: Burton K Wheeler Coll; Canadian; Montana History; Trout; Yellowstone National Park, bks, mss, pictures
Automation Activity & Vendor Info: (Cataloging) SIRSI; (OPAC) SIRSI
Partic in OCLC
Friends of the Library Group
Departmental Libraries:
CREATIVE ARTS LIBRARY, 207 Cheever Hall, 59717. SAN 349-9472. Tel: 406-994-4091. *Librn*, Bruce Morton

BRIDGER

P BRIDGER PUBLIC LIBRARY,* 119 W Broadway Ave, PO Box 428, 59014. SAN 309-281X. Tel: 406-662-3598. FAX: 406-662-3598. *Librn*, Pat Hayden; E-Mail: haydn@wtp.net
Founded 1909. Pop 724; Circ 11,437
Library Holdings: Bk Vols 11,460
Special Collections: Bridger Times, 1909-1958
Mem of S Cent Fedn of Librs
Open Mon & Wed 1-5, Tues 9-12 & 1-5
Friends of the Library Group

BROADUS

P HENRY A MALLEY MEMORIAL LIBRARY,* 101 S Lincoln, PO Box 345, 59317-0345. SAN 309-2828. Tel: 406-436-2812. E-Mail: broaduslibrary@mcn.net. *Librn*, Diane Stuver; *Asst Librn*, June Ray
Pop 2,950; Circ 19,450
Library Holdings: Bk Vols 19,000; Per Subs 35
Mem of Sagebrush Fedn of Librs

BROWNING

J BLACKFEET COMMUNITY COLLEGE LIBRARY,* US Hwy 2 & 89, 59417-0819. (Mail add: PO Box 819, 59417-0819), SAN 321-107X. Tel: 406-338-5411, Ext 223. FAX: 406-338-5454. *Asst Librn*, Leona Skunk-Cap; Staff 2 (MLS 1, Non-MLS 1)
Founded 1981. Enrl 350; Fac 52
1997-1998 Mats Exp $15,000, Books $10,000, Per/Ser (Incl. Access Fees) $5,000. Sal $50,000
Library Holdings: Bk Titles 7,500; Per Subs 80
Subject Interests: Blackfeet hist, Culture, Native Am studies
Special Collections: Blackfoot Community College Archives

BUTTE

P BUTTE-SILVER BOW PUBLIC LIBRARY,* 226 W Broadway St, 59701-9297. SAN 309-2836. Interlibrary Loan Service Tel: 406-723-3361. FAX: 406-782-1825. E-Mail: bplref@mtlib.org. *Dir*, Ann Drew; *Tech Servs*, Sally Carlson
Founded 1890. Pop 34,814; Circ 124,000
Library Holdings: Bk Vols 85,000; Per Subs 190
Subject Interests: Fishing, Mont hist
Special Collections: Fishing Books Coll; Old & Rare Books
Mem of Broad Valleys Fedn of Librs
Hq for Montana Public Library Film Service
Friends of the Library Group

J COLLEGE OF TECHNOLOGY AT UNIVERSITY OF MONTANA,* 25 Basin Creek Rd, 59701. SAN 320-6890. Tel: 406-496-3737. FAX: 406-496-3710. *Librn*, Kathy Reick
Founded 1969
Library Holdings: Bk Vols 700; Per Subs 24
Subject Interests: Auto mechanics, Bus, Civil engineering, Computers, Draft, Electronics, Nursing, Welding

S MONTANA POWER COMPANY, Law Library,* 40 E Broadway, 59701-9989. SAN 327-1498. Tel: 406-497-2111. FAX: 406-497-2451. *Librn*, Maureen Hammer; E-Mail: mhammer@mtpower.com
Library Holdings: Bk Vols 7,000; Bk Titles 1,000

C MONTANA TECH OF THE UNIVERSITY OF MONTANA LIBRARY, 1300 W Park St, 59701-8997. SAN 309-2844. Tel: 406-496-4281. Reference Tel: 406-496-4282. FAX: 406-496-4133. Web Site: www.mtech.edu/library/menu1.htm. *Actg Dir, Ref*, Ann St Clair; Tel: 406-496-4284, E-Mail: astclair@mtech.edu; *Ref*, Jean Bishop; E-Mail: jbishop@mtech.edu; *Tech Servs*, Carol A Rhoads; Tel: 406-496-4285, E-Mail: crhoads@mtech.edu; *Circ, ILL*, Julie Buckley; Tel: 406-496-4222, E-Mail: jbuckley@mtech.edu; *Archivist*, Marcia Lubick; Tel: 406-496-4287, E-Mail: mlubick@mtech.edu; Staff 10 (MLS 2, Non-MLS 8)
Founded 1900. Enrl 2,456; Fac 92; Highest Degree: Master
Jul 1999-Jun 2000 Income $476,814. Mats Exp $159,344, Books $32,844, Per/Ser (Incl. Access Fees) $123,000, Presv $3,500. Sal $273,206 (Prof $120,888)
Library Holdings: Bk Vols 160,086; Bk Titles 57,275; Per Subs 553
Subject Interests: Environmental engineering, Geochemistry, Geology, Geophysics, Metallurgy, Mining, Petroleum engineering
Special Collections: US Patent & Trademark Coll
Automation Activity & Vendor Info: (Cataloging) epixtech, inc.; (Circulation) epixtech, inc.; (Course Reserve) epixtech, inc.; (OPAC) epixtech, inc.
Database Vendor: CARL, Dialog, epixtech, inc., IAC - Info Trac, OCLC - First Search, Silverplatter Information Inc.
Special Services for the Deaf - TDD

MSE, INC
S WETO TECHNICAL LIBRARY, Industrial Park, PO Box 4078, 59702. SAN 327-151X. Tel: 406-494-7417. FAX: 406-494-7230. *Librn*, Tonya Holmes; E-Mail: tholmes@mse-ta.com
Library Holdings: Bk Vols 9,500; Per Subs 90

S NATIONAL CENTER FOR APPROPRIATE TECHNOLOGY, Research Library,* PO Box 3838, 59702-3838. SAN 320-3921. Tel: 406-494-8643. FAX: 406-494-2905. *Dir*, Rose Sullivan; E-Mail: roses@ncat.org
Founded 1978
Library Holdings: Bk Titles 7,000; Per Subs 300
Subject Interests: Alternative energies, Biofuels, Commun develop, Energy conservation, Greenhouses, Internet, Low cost tech, Low income housing, Marketing, Micro-hydro power, Small scale, Solar energy, Superinsulation

M SAINT JAMES COMMUNITY HOSPITAL, Health Sciences Library,* 400 S Clark, 59701. SAN 323-6323. Tel: 406-723-2523. FAX: 406-723-2813. *Librn*, Laurel Egan
Founded 1981
Library Holdings: Bk Titles 750; Per Subs 131
Partic in Medline

CASCADE

P WEDSWORTH MEMORIAL LIBRARY, 9 1/2 Front St N, PO Box 526, 59421-0526. SAN 309-2852. Interlibrary Loan Service Tel: 406-468-2848. FAX: 406-468-2740. E-Mail: wedsworth@mcn.net. Web Site: www.mcn.net/~wedsworth. *Librn*, Jacqueline Strandell
Founded 1936. Pop 900; Circ 15,288
Jul 1998-Jun 1999 Income $7,123, State $1,817, County $2,000, Other $3,306. Mats Exp $3,475, Books $1,927, Electronic Ref Mat (Incl. Access Fees) $1,548. Sal $8,000
Library Holdings: Bk Vols 10,251; Bk Titles 9,170; Per Subs 20
Special Collections: Cascade Historical Coll, photog; Local Newspaper, microflm
Function: ILL available, Photocopies available
Mem of Pathfinder Regional Library Service System

CHESTER

P LIBERTY COUNTY LIBRARY, 100 E First St, PO Box 458, 59522-0458. SAN 309-2860. Tel: 406-759-5445. FAX: 406-759-5445. E-Mail: library@ttc-cmc.net. *Librn*, Cynthia Rooley
Founded 1945. Pop 3,280; Circ 16,000
1998-1999 Income $54,700, County $43,700, Locally Generated Income $21,000. Mats Exp $14,400, Books $12,000, Per/Ser (Incl. Access Fees) $2,400. Sal $31,000 (Prof $17,500)
Library Holdings: Bk Vols 22,300; Per Subs 92
Special Collections: Broken Mountains Genealogical Library Coll
Automation Activity & Vendor Info: (Acquisitions) Sagebrush Corporation; (Cataloging) Sagebrush Corporation; (Circulation) Sagebrush Corporation; (Course Reserve) Sagebrush Corporation; (ILL) Sagebrush Corporation; (Media Booking) Sagebrush Corporation; (OPAC) Sagebrush Corporation
Database Vendor: OCLC - First Search
Mem of Pathfinder Regional Library Service System
Friends of the Library Group

CHINOOK

P BLAINE COUNTY LIBRARY,* 94 Fourth St, PO Box 610, 59523-0610. SAN 349-9502. Tel: 406-357-2932. FAX: 406-357-2552. E-Mail: blcolib@cmc.ttc.net. *Librn*, Diane Doughten
Founded 1920. Pop 6,800; Circ 25,000
Library Holdings: Bk Vols 13,500; Bk Titles 12,187; Per Subs 39
Mem of Pathfinder Regional Library Service System

CHOTEAU

P CHOTEAU PUBLIC LIBRARY,* 17 N Main, PO Box 876, 59422-0876. SAN 309-2879. Tel: 406-466-2052. FAX: 406-466-2052. E-Mail: chotlibr@montanavision.net. *Dir*, Dina Van Setten
Pop 3,200; Circ 17,504
Library Holdings: Bk Titles 16,000; Per Subs 13
Mem of Pathfinder Regional Library Service System
Friends of the Library Group

CIRCLE

P GEORGE MCCONE MEMORIAL COUNTY LIBRARY,* 300 Second St, PO Box C, 59215. SAN 309-2887. Tel: 406-485-2350. *Dir*, Joan Pawlowski
Founded 1930. Pop 2,702
Library Holdings: Bk Vols 19,314; Per Subs 42
Subject Interests: Montana, Western states
Mem of Sagebrush Fedn of Librs; WLN
Friends of the Library Group

COLUMBIA FALLS

S COLUMBIA FALLS ALUMINUM COMPANY LIBRARY,* 2000 Aluminum Dr, PO Box 10, 59912. SAN 309-2895. Tel: 406-892-8215. FAX: 406-892-3273. *Dir*, Ty Wilson
Founded 1955
Library Holdings: Bk Vols 1,000; Per Subs 30
Subject Interests: Aluminum tech, Analytical chemistry, Carbon tech, Environmental control, Industrial hygiene

COLUMBUS

P STILLWATER COUNTY LIBRARY, 27 N Fourth St, PO Box 266, 59019. SAN 349-9561. Tel: 406-322-5009. E-Mail: slibrary@wtp.net. *Librn*, Deanna M King; Staff 2 (Non-MLS 2)
Founded 1928. Pop 7,200
1999-1999 Income $90,918, Federal $2,000, County $88,918. Mats Exp $18,300, Books $16,000, Per/Ser (Incl. Access Fees) $800, Electronic Ref Mat (Incl. Access Fees) $1,500. Sal $39,376 (Prof $21,238)
Library Holdings: Bk Vols 32,000; Per Subs 34
Special Collections: Montana; Stillwater County
Automation Activity & Vendor Info: (Acquisitions) Sagebrush Corporation; (Cataloging) Sagebrush Corporation; (Circulation) Sagebrush Corporation
Database Vendor: Ebsco - EbscoHost, OCLC - First Search
Friends of the Library Group

CONRAD

P CONRAD PUBLIC LIBRARY, 15 Fourth Ave SW, 59425. SAN 309-2909. Tel: 406-278-5751. FAX: 406-278-5751. E-Mail: conradlib@montana.com. *Dir*, Ruth Fladstol; *Asst Librn*, Carolyn Donath; Staff 4 (Non-MLS 4)
Founded 1925. Pop 6,900; Circ 37,163
Jul 1999-Jun 2000 Income $81,950, State $3,884, City $41,456, County $28,080, Locally Generated Income $8,530. Mats Exp $9,829, Books $8,810, Per/Ser (Incl. Access Fees) $760, Electronic Ref Mat (Incl. Access Fees) $259. Sal $45,452
Library Holdings: Bk Titles 22,300; Per Subs 27; Bks on Deafness & Sign Lang 32
Special Collections: Montana Coll
Database Vendor: OCLC - First Search
Mem of Pathfinder Regional Library Service System
Special Services for the Blind - Talking book center
Friends of the Library Group

CUT BANK

P GLACIER COUNTY LIBRARY, 21 First Ave SE, 59427. SAN 349-9715. Tel: 406-873-4572. FAX: 406-873-4845. E-Mail: glibrary@northerntel.net. *Dir*, Sheryl Chapman; Staff 8 (Non-MLS 8)
Founded 1944. Pop 12,540; Circ 39,000
Jul 1999-Jun 2000 Income (Main Library and Branch Library) $236,039, State $3,298, County $151,711, Other $81,030. Mats Exp $36,254, Books $27,019, Per/Ser (Incl. Access Fees) $1,718, Electronic Ref Mat (Incl. Access Fees) $7,517. Sal $92,218
Library Holdings: Bk Vols 33,493; Per Subs 64
Special Collections: Lewis & Clark Coll; Montana Authors & History
Automation Activity & Vendor Info: (Cataloging) Follett; (Circulation) Follett
Database Vendor: Ebsco - EbscoHost, IAC - SearchBank
Open Mon 11-8, Tues-Fri 11-5
Branches: 2
BROWNING BRANCH, PO Box 550, Browning, 59417. SAN 349-974X. Tel: 406-338-7105. FAX: 406-338-7105.
Open Mon 2-8, Tues-Fri 11-5
EAST GLACIER PARK BRANCH, East Glacier Park, 59434. SAN 349-9774.

DARBY

P DARBY PUBLIC LIBRARY,* 102 S Main St, PO Box 37, 59829-0337. SAN 309-2917. Tel: 406-821-4771. FAX: 406-821-4771. E-Mail: library@in-tch.com. *Librn*, Tana Fisher
Founded 1921. Circ 3,500
Library Holdings: Bk Titles 7,500
Mem of Tamarack Fedn of Librs
Open Mon-Fri 1-5

DEER LODGE

S MONTANA STATE PRISON LIBRARY, Conley Lake Rd, 59722. SAN 309-2941. Tel: 406-846-1320, Ext 2410. FAX: 406-846-2951. *Librn*, Dave Beatty
Library Holdings: Bk Vols 8,000; Per Subs 30
Subject Interests: College reference works, Law

S NATIONAL PARK SERVICE, Grant-Kohrs Ranch, National Historic Site Library, 210 Missouri Ave, 59722. (Mail add: PO Box 790, 59722), SAN 323-8504. Tel: 406-846-2070. FAX: 406-846-3962. *In Charge*, Scott Eckberg
Library Holdings: Bk Titles 2,000; Per Subs 20

P WILLIAM K KOHRS MEMORIAL LIBRARY, 501 Missouri Ave, 59722-1152. SAN 309-2933. Tel: 406-846-2622. FAX: 406-846-2622. E-Mail: nsillima@millib.org. *Librn*, Nancy M Silliman; Staff 3 (Non-MLS 3)
Founded 1902. Pop 7,000; Circ 26,360
Library Holdings: Bk Vols 16,000
Special Collections: Newspapers (The New Northwest 1869-1885 & Silver State Post 1893-Present), bd
Automation Activity & Vendor Info: (Cataloging) Sagebrush Corporation; (Circulation) Sagebrush Corporation; (OPAC) Sagebrush Corporation
Mem of Broad Valleys Fedn of Librs
Friends of the Library Group

DENTON

P DENTON PUBLIC LIBRARY, 515 Broadway, PO Box 986, 59430-0986. SAN 376-7841. Tel: 406-567-2571. FAX: 406-567-2571. E-Mail: dentonpl@ttc-cmc.net. *Dir*, Julie Rice
Library Holdings: Bk Titles 5,000
Mem of S Cent Fedn of Librs
Open Mon-Fri 9-5

DILLON

S BEAVERHEAD COUNTY MUSEUM ASSOCIATION LIBRARY,* 15 S Montana St, 59725. SAN 321-8481. Tel: 406-683-5027. E-Mail: bvhdmuseum@bmt.net. *Dir*, Stan Smith
Founded 1947
Library Holdings: Bk Titles 250

Subject Interests: SW Mont
Publications: Newsletter (quarterly)
Restriction: Non-circulating to the public
Mon-Fri 8:30-5

P DILLON CITY LIBRARY, 121 S Idaho, 59725-2500. SAN 309-2976. Tel: 406-683-4544. E-Mail: dillon@mt.lib.org. Web Site: www.mt.di.mt.lib.org. *Dir*, Barbara Fredrickson; Staff 5 (MLS 2, Non-MLS 3)
Founded 1890. Pop 4,889; Circ 26,741
Jul 1999-Jun 2000 Income $53,457, State $2,475, City $44,250, Other $6,732. Mats Exp $10,300, Books $5,800, AV Equip $3,450, Electronic Ref Mat (Incl. Access Fees) $1,050. Sal $24,627
Library Holdings: Bk Titles 16,918; Per Subs 40
Automation Activity & Vendor Info: (Circulation) Follett
Database Vendor: OCLC - First Search
Mem of Broad Valleys Fedn of Librs

C WESTERN MONTANA COLLEGE, Lucy Carson Memorial Library, 710 S Atlantic St, 59725. SAN 309-2984. Tel: 406-683-7541. Interlibrary Loan Service Tel: 406-683-7491. Circulation Tel: 406-683-7542. Reference Tel: 406-683-7492. Toll Free Tel: 800-962-6662. FAX: 406-683-7493. Web Site: www.wmc.edu/academics/library. *Dir*, Mike Schulz; E-Mail: m_schulz@wmc.edu; *Tech Servs*, Jo Thompson; E-Mail: j_thompson@wmc.edu; Staff 2 (MLS 2)
Founded 1897. Enrl 1,100; Fac 55
Jul 2000-Jun 2001 Income $319,519. Mats Exp $104,050, Books $64,150, Per/Ser (Incl. Access Fees) $39,900. Sal $149,164 (Prof $89,119)
Library Holdings: Bk Vols 65,890; Bk Titles 64,176; Per Subs 387
Subject Interests: Education
Special Collections: Emerick Art Coll; EPA Educational Libr; Montana History Coll; NASA Teacher Resource Center; State Educational Media Library
Publications: Unravelling the Patchwork: A Handbook for Rural School Librarians
Partic in OCLC Online Computer Library Center, Inc
Friends of the Library Group

DRUMMOND

P DRUMMOND PUBLIC LIBRARY,* 114 A St, PO Box 378, 59832-0378. SAN 325-2590. Tel: 406-288-3231 (Town Hall). FAX: 406-288-3104. *Dir*, Jeanne Finley
Circ 943
Library Holdings: Bk Titles 4,609
Subject Interests: History, Montana, Mysteries, Romances, Westerns
Special Collections: Montana Coll
Mem of Broad Valleys Fedn of Librs
Friends of the Library Group

DUTTON

P DUTTON PUBLIC LIBRARY,* General Delivery, 59433-9999. SAN 309-295X. Tel: 406-476-3382. E-Mail: dutlibry@mt.net. *Dir*, Phyllis Goodmundson
Library Holdings: Bk Vols 7,000; Bk Titles 5,000
Mem of Pathfinder Regional Library Service System

EKALAKA

S CARTER COUNTY MUSEUM & LIBRARY,* 100 Main St, 59324. SAN 321-8996. Tel: 406-775-6886. *Librn*, Warren White; Staff 1 (MLS 1)
Founded 1936
Library Holdings: Bk Titles 500
Subject Interests: Cretaceous periods, Invertebrate paleontology, Late Cretaceous, Paleocene, Tertiany periods, Vertebrate paleontology
Special Collections: Western Plains Archaeology
Restriction: Staff use only

P EKALAKA PUBLIC LIBRARY,* Main St, PO Box 482, 59324-0482. SAN 325-0199. Tel: 406-775-6336. E-Mail: epl@midrivers.com. *Librn*, Jackie Dalzell
Founded 1976. Pop 1,503; Circ 4,900
Library Holdings: Bk Vols 11,065
Subject Interests: Local history, Local lit
Special Collections: Carter County History Books (series of 3); Montana History; National Geographics 1967-92
Partic in OCLC
Carry-in library to shut-ins & nursing homes; mailing network to Carter County Rural Schools

ENNIS

P MADISON VALLEY PUBLIC LIBRARY,* 210 Main St, PO Box 178, 59729. SAN 309-300X. Tel: 406-682-7244. FAX: 406-682-7669. E-Mail: ennislib@3rivers.net. *Dir*, Kathy Knack; Staff 1 (MLS 1)
Founded 1974. Pop 1,700; Circ 16,407
Library Holdings: Bk Vols 15,500; Per Subs 24
Subject Interests: Large type print
Special Collections: Western Coll
Mem of Broad Valleys Fedn of Librs
Open Mon & Wed-Fri 9-1 & 2-5, Sat 10-2
Friends of the Library Group

FAIRFIELD

P FAIRFIELD PUBLIC LIBRARY,* 14 Fourth St N, PO Box 324, 59436. SAN 309-3018. Tel: 406-467-2477. FAX: 406-467-2477. E-Mail: ftlib@3rivers.net. *Librn*, Blanche Ginther
Pop 638; Circ 14,441
Jul 1997-Jun 1998 Income $15,678. Mats Exp $1,806. Sal $3,780
Library Holdings: Bk Vols 7,000; Per Subs 24
Mem of Pathfinder Regional Library Service System
Open Tues 3:30-8, Wed & Thurs 2-5:30 & Fri 9-1
Friends of the Library Group

FORSYTH

P ROSEBUD COUNTY LIBRARY, 201 N Ninth Ave, PO Box 7, 59327-0007. SAN 309-3026. Tel: 406-356-7561. FAX: 406-356-7685. E-Mail: rbudcountylib@mcn.net. *Librn*, Cheryl J Heser; *Asst Librn*, Susan Martin; *Asst Librn*, Lila Nansel; *Cat*, Catherine Byron; Staff 4 (Non-MLS 4)
Pop 6,092; Circ 21,801
Library Holdings: Bk Vols 26,500; Bk Titles 26,000; Per Subs 50
Subject Interests: Local, Western hist
Special Collections: Local newspapers from 1894-present
Mem of Sagebrush Fedn of Librs
Friends of the Library Group
Branches: 1
COLSTRIP BICENTENNIAL, 415 Willow Ave, PO Box 1947, Colstrip, 59323-1947. SAN 373-9120. Tel: 406-748-3040. *Librn*, Nancy Brennan; *Asst Librn*, Louise Davenport
Founded 1976. Pop 5,689; Circ 30,158
Library Holdings: Bk Titles 14,830; Per Subs 45
Automation Activity & Vendor Info: (Circulation) Follett
Special Services for the Deaf - Books on deafness & sign language
Friends of the Library Group

FORT BENTON

P CHOUTEAU COUNTY LIBRARY,* 1518 Main St, PO Box 639, 59442-0639. SAN 349-9804. Tel: 406-622-5222. FAX: 406-622-5294. E-Mail: choucolib@mcn.net. *Dir*, Mary Meissner; *Asst Librn*, Patti McKenzie
Founded 1915. Pop 5,900; Circ 57,000
Library Holdings: Bk Vols 46,250; Per Subs 100
Subject Interests: Montana
Mem of Pathfinder Regional Library Service System
Friends of the Library Group
Branches: 3
BIG SANDY BRANCH, PO Box 1247, Big Sandy, 59520-0007. SAN 349-9839. Tel: 406-378-2161. *Librn*, Lorna Springer
Friends of the Library Group
GERALDINE BRANCH, PO Box 316, Geraldine, 59446-0326. SAN 349-9863. Tel: 406-737-4331. *Librn*, Bernadine Fairbanks
HIGHWOOD BRANCH, Senior Citizens Ctr, Highwood, 59450. SAN 349-9898. Tel: 406-733-5141. *Librn*, Lucille Davison

FORT HARRISON

GM VETERANS ADMINISTRATION CENTER, Fort Harrison, 59636. SAN 309-3034. Tel: 406-442-6410, Ext 7345. FAX: 406-447-7948. *Chief Librn*, Gail Wilkerson; Tel: 406-232-8328, Fax: 406-232-8297, E-Mail: gail.wilkerson@med.va.gov; Staff 2 (MLS 1, Non-MLS 1)
Founded 1930
Oct 1999-Sep 2000 Mats Exp $45,000
Library Holdings: Bk Titles 2,900; Per Subs 118
Subject Interests: Health, Veterans
Partic in Docline; Medline; Vets Admin Libr Network
Open Mon-Fri 8-4;30

FORT SMITH

S BIGHORN CANYON NATIONAL RECREATION AREA LIBRARY, Hwy 313, PO Box 7458, 59035. SAN 309-3042. Tel: 406-666-2412. FAX: 406-666-2415. Web Site: www.nps.gov. *In Charge*, James Staebler; E-Mail: james_staebler@nps.gov
Founded 1950
Library Holdings: Bk Vols 1,600
Subject Interests: Human hist of the Bighorn Canyon country, National parks, Natural hist of the Bighorn Canyon country
Restriction: Circulation limited

GLASGOW

P GLASGOW CITY-COUNTY LIBRARY, 408 Third Ave S, 59230. SAN 309-3050. Tel: 406-228-2731. FAX: 406-228-8193. *Dir*, Emory Robotham
Founded 1908. Pop 10,500; Circ 62,500
Library Holdings: Bk Titles 33,534; Per Subs 107
Subject Interests: Crafts, Culinary, Mont genealogy
Special Collections: Glasgow Courier 1895-1988
Automation Activity & Vendor Info: (Cataloging) Sagebrush Corporation; (Circulation) Sagebrush Corporation
Mem of Golden Plains Library Federation
Partic in Pacific NW Bibliog Ctr
Open Mon-Thurs 9-8, Fri 9-5, Sat 10-3 & Sun 1-4
Friends of the Library Group

P GOLDEN PLAINS LIBRARY FEDERATION,* 408 Third Ave S, 59230. SAN 309-3069. Tel: 406-228-2731. FAX: 406-228-8193. E-Mail: 2maizey@3rivers.net. *Dir*, Emory Robotham
Founded 1972. Pop 36,000
Jul 1997-Jun 1998 Income $160,536. Mats Exp $35,080, Books $30,500, Per/Ser (Incl. Access Fees) $4,500, Micro $80. Sal $74,160
Library Holdings: Bk Vols 37,574
Automation Activity & Vendor Info: (Cataloging) Sagebrush Corporation; (Circulation) Sagebrush Corporation
Member Libraries: Daniels County Free Library; Fort Peck Community College; Glasgow City-County Library; Opheim Community Library; Phillips County Public Library; Roosevelt County Library; Sheridan County Library
Open Mon-Thurs 9-8, Fri 9-5, Sat 10-3 & Sun 1-4
Friends of the Library Group

GLENDIVE

J DAWSON COMMUNITY COLLEGE, Jane Carey Memorial Library, 300 College Dr, 59330. (Mail add: PO Box 421, 59330), SAN 309-3077. Tel: 406-377-9413. Interlibrary Loan Service Tel: 406-377-9414. Circulation Tel: 406-377-9414. Reference Tel: 406-377-9413. FAX: 406-377-8132. Web Site: www.dawson.cc.mt.us. *Dir*, Andrine J Haas; E-Mail: andrine_h@dawson.cc.mt.us; *Asst Librn*, Mary Ann Clingingsmith; E-Mail: clinger@dawson.cc.mt.us; Staff 2 (MLS 1, Non-MLS 1)
Founded 1940. Enrl 400; Fac 35; Highest Degree: Associate
Library Holdings: Bk Vols 18,901; Per Subs 211
Subject Interests: Art, Law enforcement
Automation Activity & Vendor Info: (Acquisitions) SIRSI; (Cataloging) SIRSI; (Circulation) SIRSI; (Course Reserve) SIRSI; (OPAC) SIRSI; (Serials) SIRSI
Database Vendor: IAC - Info Trac, Lexis-Nexis
Partic in OCLC Online Computer Library Center, Inc

S FRONTIER GATEWAY MUSEUM LIBRARY, E of Glendive, Belle Prairie Frontage Rd, PO Box 1181, 59330. SAN 373-4676. Tel: 406-377-8168. *Curator*, Louise Cross
Library Holdings: Bk Vols 500

P GLENDIVE PUBLIC LIBRARY, 200 S Kendrick, 59330. SAN 349-9928. Tel: 406-377-3633. FAX: 406-377-4568. *Dir*, Gail Nagle; E-Mail: gnagle@midrivers.com; *ILL*, Teresa Skerritt
Founded 1915. Pop 9,000; Circ 45,000
1998-1999 Income $122,000, State $1,340, Federal $1,100. Mats Exp $12,000. Sal $76,000
Library Holdings: Bk Vols 23,000; Bk Titles 20,000; Per Subs 85
Special Collections: German-Russian Immigrations; Montana History
Automation Activity & Vendor Info: (Cataloging) Follett
Database Vendor: GaleNet, IAC - Info Trac
Function: ILL available, Internet access
Mem of Sagebrush Fedn of Librs
Open Mon-Wed 11-7, Thurs & Fri 11-5, Sat 1-5
Friends of the Library Group
Branches: 1
RICHEY PUBLIC LIBRARY, Main & Meadowlark, PO Box 149, Richey, 59259-0149. SAN 349-9952. Tel: 406-773-5585. *Librn*, Betty Keysor
Library Holdings: Bk Titles 4,000
Function: ILL available, Internet access
Open Mon, Wed & Fri 12-4

GREAT FALLS

M BENEFIS, West Library,* 500 15th Ave S, PO Box 5013, 59403-5013. SAN 309-3093. Tel: 406-455-2631. FAX: 406-455-2626.
Founded 1961
1997-1998 Mats Exp $30,000, Books $7,200, Per/Ser (Incl. Access Fees) $531
Library Holdings: Bk Vols 8,600; Bk Titles 7,000; Per Subs 450
Subject Interests: Cancer, Heart surgery, Med educ, Nursing, Obgyn, Orthopedics, Pediatrics, Rehabilitation, Surgery
Special Collections: Nursing Journals, micro
Partic in Dialog Corporation; Medline; Pac NW Regional Med Libr Network
Participates in Class Electronic Mail

S BENEFIS HEALTH SCIENCES LIBRARY, 1101 26th St S, 59405. SAN 371-5787. Tel: 406-455-5594. FAX: 406-455-4112. *Librn*, Patricia J Mueller; E-Mail: muelpatj@benefis.org; Staff 2 (Non-MLS 2)
Founded 1986
Jan 1999-Dec 1999 Mats Exp $45,000, Books $5,000, Per/Ser (Incl. Access Fees) $35,000, Manuscripts & Archives $4,000, Electronic Ref Mat (Incl. Access Fees) $1,000. Sal $60,000 (Prof $40,000)
Library Holdings: Bk Titles 2,500; Per Subs 378
Partic in Nat Libr of Med; RML

S C M RUSSELL MUSEUM LIBRARY, 400 13th St N, 59401. SAN 327-1552. Tel: 406-727-8787. FAX: 406-727-2402. *Curator*, Elizabeth Dear; E-Mail: edear@cmrussell.org
Library Holdings: Bk Titles 2,000; Per Subs 10
Special Collections: Branson Stevenson Archives; Charles M Russell & Joe DeYong, archival mats; Flood Coll of Art; Karl Yost Archives

S CASCADE COUNTY HISTORICAL SOCIETY, Information Center & Archives, High Plains Heritage Ctr, 422 Second St S, 59405. SAN 321-8112. Tel: 406-452-3462. FAX: 406-761-3805. *Dir*, Cindy Kittredge
Founded 1976
Library Holdings: Bk Titles 500
Subject Interests: Hist of Cent Mont area
Special Collections: County Immigration Records; Great Falls Leaders; Great Falls Tribune Coll
Publications: History News

S GREAT FALLS GENEALOGY SOCIETY LIBRARY, 1400 First Ave N, 59401-3299. SAN 326-4025. Tel: 406-727-3922. E-Mail: gfgs@mcn.net.
Founded 1975
Library Holdings: Bk Vols 3,600; Per Subs 104
Subject Interests: Genealogy
Special Collections: Local Cemeteries
Publications: Treasure State Lines (quarterly)

P GREAT FALLS PUBLIC LIBRARY, 301 Second Ave N, 59401-2593. SAN 309-3115. Tel: 406-453-9706. Reference Tel: 406-453-0349. FAX: 406-453-0181. Web Site: www.mtgr.mtlib.org/www/library. *Dir*, Jim Heckel; E-Mail: jheckel@orion.mtgr.mtlib.org; *Adminr*, Kathy Mora; E-Mail: kathy@orion.mtgr.mtlib.org; *Acq*, Marla Wilckens; *Bkmobile Coordr, Circ*, Gwen Carter; Tel: 406-453-0349; *Cat, Tech Servs*, Judith Strong; *Ch Servs*, Heidi Haymaker; *Info Specialist*, Ellen Thompson; *ILL*, Jude Smith; E-Mail: jude@orion.mtgr.mtlib.org; Staff 26 (MLS 21, Non-MLS 5)
Founded 1890. Pop 82,000; Circ 341,000
Jul 1999-Jun 2000 Income $1,139,950, State $19,570, City $590,000, Federal $1,750, County $190,000, Other $338,630. Mats Exp $162,415, Books $142,135, Per/Ser (Incl. Access Fees) $15,650, Micro $200, Electronic Ref Mat (Incl. Access Fees) $4,430. Sal $465,078
Library Holdings: Bk Vols 136,000; Bk Titles 133,232; Per Subs 350
Special Collections: City; Montana History Coll
Automation Activity & Vendor Info: (Acquisitions) Brodart; (Circulation) DRA; (OPAC) DRA
Database Vendor: OCLC - First Search
Partic in OCLC; OCLC Online Computer Library Center, Inc
Bookmobiles: 1

S MONTANA SCHOOL FOR THE DEAF & BLIND LIBRARY, 3911 Central Ave, 59405-1697. SAN 320-6904. Tel: 406-771-6051. TDD: 406-771-6063. FAX: 406-771-6164. *Librn*, Tee Holcomb; E-Mail: tholcomb@sdb.state.mt.us; Staff 1 (Non-MLS 1)
Pop 300; Enrl 80; Fac 30; Highest Degree: Doctorate
Jul 2000-Jun 2001 Mats Exp $2,200, Books $1,000, Per/Ser (Incl. Access Fees) $1,200
Library Holdings: Bk Vols 10,648; Per Subs 43; High Interest/Low Vocabulary Bk Vols 30; Bks on Deafness & Sign Lang 180
Special Services for the Deaf - Captioned film depository
Special Services for the Blind - Braille

C MONTANA STATE UNIVERSITY, Great Falls College of Technology Library, 2100 16th Ave S, PO Box 6010, 59406. SAN 373-6784. Tel: 406-771-4398. FAX: 406-771-4317. Web Site: www.msugf.edu/library/library.html. *Librn*, Sheila Bonnand
Founded 1976. Enrl 660; Fac 40
Library Holdings: Bk Vols 5,688; Bk Titles 4,966; Per Subs 200

CR MOUNTAIN STATES BAPTIST COLLEGE LIBRARY, 824 Third Ave N, 59401. SAN 377-1180. Tel: 406-761-0308. *Librn*, Janet Jonas; E-Mail: msbcjonas@montana.com; *Coll Develop*, Dr Richard Jonas
Founded 1982. Enrl 13; Fac 5; Highest Degree: Doctorate
Jan 1999-Dec 1999 Income $681, Parent Institution $186, Other $495. Mats Exp $681, Books $220, Per/Ser (Incl. Access Fees) $392, Electronic Ref Mat (Incl. Access Fees) $69
Library Holdings: Bk Vols 4,975; Bk Titles 4,375; Per Subs 65
Subject Interests: Religion
Restriction: Private library

CR UNIVERSITY OF GREAT FALLS LIBRARY, 1301 20th St S, 59405-4948. SAN 309-3085. Tel: 406-791-5315. Reference Tel: 406-791-5318. FAX: 406-791-5395. E-Mail: library@ugf.edu. Web Site: 206.127.69.152/slee. *Dir*, Chandler Jackson; Tel: 406-791-5317, E-Mail: cjackson@ugf.edu; *Ref*, Susan M Lee; Tel: 406-791-5318, E-Mail: slee@ugf.edu; Staff 7 (MLS 2, Non-MLS 5)
Founded 1932. Enrl 1,050; Highest Degree: Master
Jul 2000-Jun 2001 Income Parent Institution $513,501. Mats Exp $262,000, Books $120,000, Per/Ser (Incl. Access Fees) $60,500, AV Equip $21,000, Electronic Ref Mat (Incl. Access Fees) $60,500. Sal $200,851 (Prof $73,687)
Library Holdings: Bk Vols 101,109; Bk Titles 68,723; Per Subs 560
Subject Interests: Criminal justice, Education, Sociology
Special Collections: Americana (Microbook Library of American Civilization); Science Education
Automation Activity & Vendor Info: (Cataloging) SIRSI; (Circulation) SIRSI; (Course Reserve) SIRSI; (OPAC) SIRSI
Database Vendor: IAC - Info Trac, OCLC - First Search, ProQuest
Function: ILL available
Partic in OMNI

HAMILTON

P BITTERROOT PUBLIC LIBRARY, 306 State St, 59840-2759. SAN 309-3123. Tel: 406-363-1670. FAX: 406-363-1678. *Coll Develop, Dir*, Gloria Langstaff; E-Mail: glolang@montana.com; *Publ Servs*, Nansu Roddy Haynes; Staff 4 (Non-MLS 4)
Founded 1903. Pop 24,945; Circ 82,675
Jul 1999-Jun 2000 Income $241,314, State $6,675, County $14,000, Locally Generated Income $157,733, Other $62,906. Mats Exp $42,043, Books $31,140, Per/Ser (Incl. Access Fees) $3,230, AV Equip $2,800, Electronic Ref Mat (Incl. Access Fees) $4,873. Sal $83,432 (Prof $50,669)
Library Holdings: Bk Vols 25,822; Bk Titles 24,822; Per Subs 53; High Interest/Low Vocabulary Bk Vols 324; Bks on Deafness & Sign Lang 10
Database Vendor: Dialog, IAC - Info Trac
Mem of Tamarack Fedn of Librs
Friends of the Library Group

G NATIONAL INSTITUTES OF HEALTH, Rocky Mountain Laboratories Library, 903 S Fourth St, 59840-2999. SAN 309-3131. Tel: 406-363-9212. FAX: 406-363-9336. *Librn*, Martha Thayer; Tel: 406-363-9211, E-Mail: mthayer@niaid.nih.gov; Staff 2 (MLS 1, Non-MLS 1)
Founded 1927
2000-2001 Mats Exp $240,000, Books $40,000, Per/Ser (Incl. Access Fees) $200,000. Sal $74,000 (Prof $50,000)
Library Holdings: Bk Vols 3,500; Bk Titles 3,000; Per Subs 300
Subject Interests: Allergy, Bacteriology, Biochemistry, Chemistry, Immunology, Med entomology, Microbiology, Parasitology, Venereal disease, Veterinary sci, Virology, Wildlife, Zoology
Automation Activity & Vendor Info: (Circulation) Innovative Interfaces Inc.; (OPAC) Innovative Interfaces Inc.
Database Vendor: OCLC - First Search
Partic in Medline; Mont Libr Asn

S RAVALLI COUNTY MUSEUM, Miles Rommey Memorial Library, 205 Bedford, 59840. SAN 324-3605. Tel: 406-363-3338. FAX: 406-363-3338. E-Mail: rcmuseum@cybernet1.com. Web Site: www.cybernet1.com/rcmuseum. *Dir*, Helen A Bibler
Founded 1979
Jan 1999-Dec 1999 Income Locally Generated Income $2,216. Mats Exp $2,135, Per/Ser (Incl. Access Fees) $341, AV Equip $561, Other Print Mats $1,233
Library Holdings: Bk Titles 500; Per Subs 15
Special Collections: Bitter Root Valley Historical Society Coll; Bitter Root Valley Newspapers; Museum Collections 35 Display
Restriction: Not a lending library
Function: Research library
Open Mon & Thurs-Sat 10-4 & Sun 1-4

HARDIN

P BIG HORN COUNTY PUBLIC LIBRARY, 419 N Custer Ave, 59034. SAN 309-314X. Tel: 406-665-1808. FAX: 406-665-1888. *Dir*, Eric Halverson; E-Mail: eric@bighorn.lib.mt.us; *Publ Servs*, Helen Turney; E-Mail: helen@bighorn.lib.mt.us; *Ch Servs*, Donnelle Sharpe; E-Mail: donelle@bighorn.lib.mt.us; Staff 7 (MLS 1, Non-MLS 6)
Founded 1910. Pop 11,337; Circ 66,854
Library Holdings: Bk Vols 27,450; Bk Titles 29,500; Per Subs 67
Subject Interests: Mont hist, Montana
Special Collections: Battle of Little Big Horn; Cheyenne Indian Culture and History; Crow Indian Culture and History
Automation Activity & Vendor Info: (Cataloging) epixtech, inc.; (Circulation) epixtech, inc.
Database Vendor: IAC - Info Trac, OCLC - First Search
Mem of S Cent Fedn of Librs
Partic in BCR
Friends of the Library Group
Bookmobiles: 1

HARLEM

J FORT BELKNAP COLLEGE LIBRARY & TRIBAL ARCHIVES,* Hwy 2 & 66 Box 159, 59526-0159. SAN 375-3522. Tel: 406-353-2607, Ext 262. FAX: 406-353-2898. E-Mail: eenglish@fortbelknap.cc.mt.us, evaenglish@yahoo.com. *Dir*, Eva English; Staff 1 (MLS 1)
Founded 1984. Enrl 176; Fac 10
1997-1998 Income $60,000. Mats Exp $27,500, Books $22,500, Per/Ser (Incl. Access Fees) $5,000. Sal $30,500 (Prof $27,000)
Library Holdings: Bk Vols 15,000; Bk Titles 12,000; Per Subs 95
Partic in OCLC
Open Mon-Fri 8-5

P HARLEM PUBLIC LIBRARY,* 37 First Ave S, PO Box 519, 59526. SAN 349-9537. Tel: 406-353-2712. FAX: 406-353-2616. *Dir*, Ethel Siemens
Circ 16,271
Library Holdings: Bk Titles 10,500; Per Subs 45

HARLOWTON

P HARLOWTON PUBLIC LIBRARY,* 17 S Central Ave, PO Box 663, 59036-0663. SAN 309-3158. Tel: 406-632-5584. E-Mail: harlowlibrary@mcn.net. *Librn*, Kathleen Schreiber
Founded 1932. Pop 2,246; Circ 16,902
Library Holdings: Bk Vols 22,954; Bk Titles 21,954; Per Subs 38

HAVRE

P HAVRE HILL COUNTY LIBRARY, 402 Third St, 59501. SAN 309-3174. Tel: 406-265-2123. FAX: 406-262-1091. Web Site: www.mtha.mt.lib.org. *Dir*, Bonnie Williamson; E-Mail: bwilliam@mtlib.org; *Ref*, Francine Brady; *Coll Develop*, Margaret Stallkamp; *Ch Servs*, Carrie Wilson; *Circ*, Shelma Seidel; Staff 5 (MLS 5)
Founded 1983. Pop 17,654; Circ 88,679
Jul 1999-Jun 2000 Income $228,535. Mats Exp $22,800, Books $20,000, Per/Ser (Incl. Access Fees) $2,800. Sal $113,234
Library Holdings: Bk Vols 70,231; Bk Titles 68,926; Per Subs 103; Bks on Deafness & Sign Lang 200
Subject Interests: Montana
Database Vendor: epixtech, inc.
Mem of Pathfinder Regional Library Service System
Friends of the Library Group

C MONTANA STATE UNIVERSITY-NORTHERN, Vande Bogart Library, Box 7751, 59501. SAN 309-3182. Tel: 406-265-3706. FAX: 406-265-3550. Web Site: www.msun.edu/infotech/library. *Actg Librn*, Vicki Gist; E-Mail: gist@msun.edu; *Archivist, Tech Servs*, Valerie Hickman; E-Mail: hickman@msun.edu; *Circ, Doc*, Carol Jestrab; E-Mail: jestrab@msun.edu; *ILL*, Laurie Catt; E-Mail: catt@msun.edu; Staff 5 (MLS 1, Non-MLS 4)
Founded 1929. Enrl 1,525; Fac 121; Highest Degree: Master
Jul 1999-Jun 2000 Mats Exp $106,000. Sal $235,409
Library Holdings: Bk Vols 151,830; Bk Titles 96,100; Per Subs 1,083
Subject Interests: Applied tech, Bus, Education, Nursing, Western hist
Special Collections: Education (Educational Resources Information Center Coll), micro
Automation Activity & Vendor Info: (Cataloging) SIRSI; (Circulation) SIRSI; (Course Reserve) SIRSI; (OPAC) SIRSI; (Serials) SIRSI
Partic in OCLC
Open Mon-Thurs 7:30am-10pm, Fri 7:30-5, Sun 1-10
Friends of the Library Group

HELENA

S ALTERNATIVE ENERGY RESOURCES ORGANIZATION LIBRARY,* 432 N Last Chance Gulch St, 59601-5014. SAN 329-4420. Tel: 406-443-7272. FAX: 406-442-9120. E-Mail: aero@aeromt.org. *Actg Dir*, Marga Lincoln
Library Holdings: Bk Vols 425; Per Subs 50

C CARROLL COLLEGE, Jack & Sallie Corette Library, 1601 N Benton Ave, 59625. SAN 309-3204. Tel: 406-447-4340. Interlibrary Loan Service Tel: 406-447-4343. FAX: 406-447-4525. Web Site: www.carroll.edu. *Dir*, Lois A Fitzpatrick; Tel: 406-447-4341, E-Mail: lfitzpat@carroll.edu; *Circ*, Peggy Kude; Tel: 406-447-4346, E-Mail: pkude@carroll.edu; *Govt Doc, Per, Ref*, Christian Frazza; Tel: 406-447-4344, E-Mail: cfrazza@carroll.edu; *ILL, Ref*, John Thomas; E-Mail: jthomas@carroll.edu; *Tech Servs*, Cathi Burgoyne; Tel: 406-447-4342, E-Mail: cburgoyn@carroll.edu; Staff 6 (MLS 3, Non-MLS 3)
Founded 1928. Enrl 1,300; Fac 85; Highest Degree: Bachelor
Jul 2000-Jun 2001 Income $390,764, Locally Generated Income $2,232, Parent Institution $388,532. Mats Exp $145,888, Books $55,741, Per/Ser

(Incl. Access Fees) $76,687, Micro $5,060, Electronic Ref Mat (Incl. Access Fees) $8,000. Sal $186,333
Library Holdings: Bk Vols 99,386; Bk Titles 83,425; Per Subs 603
Subject Interests: Allied health, Dante, Natural science, State hist, Theology
Automation Activity & Vendor Info: (Acquisitions) Gaylord; (Cataloging) Gaylord; (Circulation) Gaylord; (Course Reserve) Gaylord; (OPAC) Gaylord; (Serials) Gaylord
Database Vendor: GaleNet, Lexis-Nexis, OCLC - First Search
Publications: Library handbook, subject bibliographies
Partic in BCR; Nat Libr of Med; OCLC Online Computer Library Center, Inc

S GRAND LODGE OF MASONS LIBRARY, 425 N Park Ave, PO Box 1158, 59624-1158. SAN 309-3212. Tel: 406-442-7774. FAX: 406-442-1321. E-Mail: mtglsec@ixi.net. Web Site: www.ixi.net/glofmt. *Librn*, Dean M Lindahl
Pop 15,000
Library Holdings: Bk Vols 500
Subject Interests: Masonry

C HELENA COLLEGE OF TECHNOLOGY OF THE UM LIBRARY, 1115 N Robert St, 59601. SAN 373-6865. Tel: 406-444-2743. FAX: 406-444-6892. Web Site: www.hct.umontana.edu. *Librn*, Lois Baker; E-Mail: lbaker@selway.umt.edu; *Librn*, Ginny Richmond Ulberg; E-Mail: ulbergg@hct.umt.edu; *Media Spec*, Debbie Carlson; Staff 3 (MLS 1, Non-MLS 2)
Founded 1992. Enrl 710; Highest Degree: Associate
Jul 1999-Jun 2000 Income State $18,000. Mats Exp $14,800, Books $2,500, Per/Ser (Incl. Access Fees) $4,300, AV Equip $6,000, Electronic Ref Mat (Incl. Access Fees) $2,000. (Prof $30,000)
Library Holdings: Bk Vols 2,800; Bk Titles 2,500; Per Subs 120
Subject Interests: Aviation, Bus, Computer tech, Construction, Diesel, Electronic, Fire protection, Nursing, Teaching, Technologies, Trades
Automation Activity & Vendor Info: (Cataloging) epixtech, inc.; (Circulation) epixtech, inc.
Database Vendor: IAC - Info Trac, OCLC - First Search
Function: ILL available
Partic in BCR; Mont Libr Asn; OCLC Western Service Center

P LEWIS & CLARK LIBRARY, 120 S Last Chance Gulch, 59601. SAN 349-9987. Tel: 406-447-1690. FAX: 406-447-1687. E-Mail: librarians@mth.mtlib.org. Web Site: www.lewisandclarklibrary.org. *Dir*, Deborah L Schlesinger; Tel: 406-447-1690, Ext 17, E-Mail: dschlesi@mtlib.org; *Mgr*, Rebecca W Foster; Tel: 406-447-1690, Ext 12, E-Mail: rwfoster@mtlib.org; *Info Tech*, Matthew A Beckstrom; Tel: 406-447-1690, Ext 11, E-Mail: mbeckstr@mtlib.org; *Cat*, Molly B Herrin; Tel: 406-447-1690, Ext 13, E-Mail: mherrin@mtlib.org; *Circ*, Gail S Wilson; Tel: 406-447-1690, Ext 22, E-Mail: gswilson@mtlib.org; *Publ Servs*, Candice Morris; Tel: 406-447-1690, Ext 15, E-Mail: cmorris@mtlib.org; *Publ Servs*, Bruce Newell; *Coll Develop*, Karla Ritten; Tel: 406-447-1690, Ext 33, E-Mail: kritten@mtlib.org; Staff 26 (MLS 5, Non-MLS 21)
Founded 1886. Pop 52,000; Circ 418,455
Jul 1999-Jun 2000 Income (Main Library and Branch Library) $2,073,940, State $15,212, City $218,805, County $1,256,164, Locally Generated Income $83,759, Other $500,000. Mats Exp $197,226, Books $183,015, Presv $14,211. Sal $614,044
Library Holdings: Bk Vols 118,903; Bk Titles 97,316; Per Subs 198
Subject Interests: Energy resources, Govt info
Special Collections: Local Energy Resource Info Center; Local Government Info Center; Local Montana History
Automation Activity & Vendor Info: (Acquisitions) Brodart; (Cataloging) Brodart; (Circulation) GEAC; (OPAC) GEAC
Database Vendor: Ebsco - EbscoHost, epixtech, inc., IAC - SearchBank, OCLC - First Search
Publications: Annual Report
Mem of Broad Valleys Fedn of Librs
Partic in OCLC Online Computer Library Center, Inc
Friends of the Library Group
Branches: 2
AUGUSTA BRANCH, 205 Main St, PO Box 387, Augusta, 59410. Tel: 406-562-3348. FAX: 406-562-3348. *Branch Mgr*, Janet Varland; Tel: 406-362-4300, E-Mail: jvarland@mtlib.org
LINCOLN COMMUNITY, 102 Ninth Ave S, PO Box 480, Lincoln, 59639. Tel: 406-362-4300. FAX: 406-362-4300. *Branch Mgr*, Sherri Wood; E-Mail: swood@mtlib.org

G MONTANA DEPARTMENT OF COMMERCE, Census & Economic Information Center,* 1424 Ninth Ave, PO Box 200501, 59620-0505. SAN 320-1996. Tel: 406-444-2896. FAX: 406-444-1518. Web Site: www.commerce.state.mt.us/ceic. *Librn*, Pamela Harris; *Res*, David R Martin; Staff 4 (MLS 1, Non-MLS 3)
Founded 1970
1999-2000 Mats Exp $4,100, Per/Ser (Incl. Access Fees) $3,800, Electronic Ref Mat (Incl. Access Fees) $300
Library Holdings: Bk Titles 4,000; Per Subs 125
Subject Interests: Demographic, Econ, Soc data
Publications: Montana County Statistical Reports
Partic in OCLC

S MONTANA HISTORICAL SOCIETY LIBRARY & ARCHIVES PROGRAM, 225 N Roberts St, PO Box 201201, 59620-1201. SAN 309-3220. Tel: 406-444-2681. Interlibrary Loan Service Tel: 406-444-3485. FAX: 406-444-5297. *Cat*, Vivian Hayes; *Ref*, Brian Shovers; E-Mail: bshovers@mcn.net; *Archivist*, Lory Morrow; *Archivist*, Kathyrn Otto; *ILL*, Lea Solberg. Subject Specialists: *Conservation*, Diana Wilkison; *Preservation*, Diana Wilkison; Staff 15 (MLS 8, Non-MLS 7)
Founded 1865
Library Holdings: Bk Vols 115,500; Per Subs 385
Subject Interests: Montana, Western Americana
Special Collections: 20th Century Homesteading Photos (Cameron Coll); Cattle Industry (Huffmann Coll) photogs; Genealogy (Daughters of American Revolution Coll); George Armstrong Custer (Edgar I Stewart Coll); Montana Newspapers; Montana State Archives; Range Cattle Industry 1860-1945 (Teakle Coll); Yellowstone Park, Pacific Northwest & North Plains Photos (Haynes Coll)
Automation Activity & Vendor Info: (Serials) EOS
Database Vendor: OCLC - First Search
Publications: Montana: The Magazine of Western History (Society quarterly); The Montana Post (Society newsletter)
Restriction: Non-circulating to the public
Partic in OCLC Online Computer Library Center, Inc

G MONTANA LEGISLATIVE REFERENCE CENTER, State Capitol, Rm 10, PO Box 201206, 59620-1706. SAN 320-2003. Tel: 406-444-3064. FAX: 406-444-2588. Web Site: www.leg.state.mt.us. *Head Librn*, Beth Furbush; E-Mail: efurbush@state.mt.us; Staff 2 (MLS 1, Non-MLS 1)
Founded 1975
Jul 1999-Jun 2000 Income State $37,211. Mats Exp $38,197, Books $5,210, Per/Ser (Incl. Access Fees) $26,048, Micro $985, Electronic Ref Mat (Incl. Access Fees) $5,954. Sal $62,236 (Prof $44,936)
Library Holdings: Bk Vols 10,456; Bk Titles 7,581; Per Subs 489
Subject Interests: Law, Legis hist, Mont constitutional, Pub admin, Pub affairs
Special Collections: Montana Legislature Interim Study Archives
Automation Activity & Vendor Info: (Acquisitions) Inmagic, Inc.; (Cataloging) Inmagic, Inc.; (Circulation) Inmagic, Inc.; (ILL) Inmagic, Inc.; (OPAC) Inmagic, Inc.; (Serials) Inmagic, Inc.
Database Vendor: Lexis-Nexis, OCLC - First Search
Publications: Catalog of Publications & Interim Study Final Reports (1957-1999); Sources of Information & Publications (8th ed 2000)
Restriction: Non-circulating to the public
Function: ILL limited, Photocopies available, Some telephone reference
Partic in BRS; OCLC Western Service Center

S MONTANA NATURAL HERITAGE PROGRAM LIBRARY,* 1515 E Sixth Ave, 59620-1800. SAN 328-1027. Tel: 406-444-3009. FAX: 406-444-0581. E-Mail: mtnhp@nris.state.mt.us. *Coordr*, Sue Crispen. Subject Specialists: *Botany*, Bonnie Heidel; *Ecology*, Steve Cooper; *Ecology*, Tim McGarvey
Pop 300,000
Library Holdings: Bk Titles 35; Per Subs 12
Special Collections: Animal Species Abstracts (Vertebrate Characterization Abstracts), computer files; Rare & Endangered Species (Element Occurence Records), computer files, maps

G MONTANA OFFICE OF PUBLIC INSTRUCTION, Resource Center, PO Box 202501, 1300 Eleventh Ave, 59620-2501. SAN 309-3239. Tel: 406-444-2082. FAX: 406-444-3924. Web Site: 161.7.114.15/opi/opi.html. *Librn*, Cheri Bergeron; E-Mail: cbergeron@state.mt.us
Subject Interests: Educ policy
Special Collections: Education Resources Information Center Coll, micro; Montana Education Archives
Partic in Mont Info Network & Exchange

G MONTANA STATE DEPARTMENT OF NATURAL RESOURCES & CONSERVATION, Research & Information Center, PO Box 201601, 59620-1601. SAN 320-6912. Tel: 406-444-6603. FAX: 406-444-5918. Web Site: www.dnrc.mt.gov, www.dnrc.state. *Dir*, Arthur Clinch
Library Holdings: Bk Titles 9,000; Per Subs 91
Special Collections: (includes Columbia, Missouri & Yellowstone River basin studies & general natural resource planning); Energy Planning & Development; Environmental Impact Statements; Montana Department of Natural Resources Publications & Water Planning
Publications: DNRC Publications List & Addendum

P MONTANA STATE LIBRARY, 1515 E Sixth Ave, 59620-1800. (Mail add: PO Box 201800, 59620-1800), SAN 350-0136. Tel: 406-444-3115 (Admin). Circulation Tel: 406-444-3016. Reference Tel: 406-444-5351. TDD: 406-444-3005. FAX: 406-444-5612. E-Mail: dmstaff@wln.com. Web Site: www.msl.state.mt.us. *Dir*, Bruce Newell; Tel: 406-444-9816, E-Mail: bnewell@state.mt.us; *Dir Libr Serv*, Darlene M Staffeldt; Tel: 406-444-5381, E-Mail: dstaffeldt@state.mt.us; *State Librn*, Karen Strege; E-Mail: kstrege@state.mt.us; *Librn for Blind*, Christie O Briggs; Tel: 406-444-5399, E-Mail: cbriggs@state.mt.us; *Coll Develop*, Don Cornish; Tel: 406-444-5432, E-Mail: dcornish@state.mt.us; *Info Res*, Jim Hill; Tel: 406-444-5354, E-Mail: jimhill@state.mt.us; Staff 38 (MLS 10, Non-MLS 28)
Founded 1946. Pop 880,453

Jul 1999-Jun 2000 Income $4,228,817, State $3,423,678, Federal $805,139. Mats Exp $118,349. Sal $1,537,280
Library Holdings: Bk Vols 65,122; Bk Titles 60,775; Per Subs 527
Subject Interests: Heritage, Info systs, Natural resources
Special Collections: Geographic Information System; MT Natural Resource Index; Natural Resource Infor System; Water Information System
Automation Activity & Vendor Info: (Cataloging) epixtech, inc.; (Circulation) epixtech, inc.
Database Vendor: epixtech, inc., GaleNet, IAC - Info Trac, IAC - SearchBank, OCLC - First Search, Wilson - Wilson Web
Publications: Annual Montana Library Directory; Big Sky Libraries Newletter (Newsletter); Montana Certification Program Manual; Montana Library Directory; Montana Public Library Annual Statistics; MSL Public Library Statistics
Partic in BCR; Mountain Plains Libr Asn; OCLC; OCLC Online Computer Library Center, Inc; Pac NW Libr Asn
Special Services for the Blind - Talking book center

M SAINT PETER'S HOSPITAL, Medical Library, 2475 Broadway, 59601. SAN 320-8656. Tel: 406-447-2462. FAX: 406-447-2627. Web Site: www.stpetes.org/resource/library.htm. *Librn*, Janice Bacino; E-Mail: jbacino@stpetes.org; Staff 1 (MLS 1)
Founded 1973
Library Holdings: Bk Titles 200; Per Subs 60
Subject Interests: Medicine
Database Vendor: OCLC - First Search
Restriction: Not a lending library
Partic in National Network Of Libraries Of Medicine - Pacific Northwest Region

M SHODAIR HOSPITAL, Medical Library,* 2755 Colonial Dr. (Mail add: PO Box 5539, 59604), SAN 320-6920. Tel: 406-444-7500. FAX: 406-444-7536. *Tech Servs*, Donna Stone; Tel: 406-444-7518, E-Mail: dstone@shodair.org; Staff 1 (Non-MLS 1)
Founded 1979
Library Holdings: Bk Titles 1,800; Per Subs 65
Subject Interests: Birth defects, Child psychology, Clinical genetics, Cytogenetics, Genetic counseling, Genetic disorders, Med genetics, Prenatal diagnosis
Special Collections: lay information on genetic disorders
Database Vendor: Ebsco - EbscoHost, GaleNet, IAC - Info Trac, OCLC - First Search
Partic in Nat Libr of Med; OCLC; OCLC Online Computer Library Center, Inc
Open Mon-Fri 9-2:30

GL STATE LAW LIBRARY OF MONTANA, Justice Bldg, 215 N Sanders, 59620-3004. (Mail add: PO Box 203004, 59620-3004), SAN 309-3263. Tel: 406-444-3660. FAX: 406-444-3603. E-Mail: infodesk@state.mt.us. Web Site: www.lawlibrary.state.mt.us. *Dir*, Judith Meadows; *Coll Develop*, Brenda Grasmick; *Ref Serv*, Meredith Hoffman; *Electronic Resources*, Lisa Jackson; *ILL*, Charlotte LeVasseur; Staff 8 (MLS 4, Non-MLS 4)
Founded 1866
Jul 2000-Jun 2001 Income $646,000. Mats Exp $242,300. Sal $319,000
Library Holdings: Bk Vols 150,000; Bk Titles 19,000; Per Subs 550
Subject Interests: Legal hist, Legislative hist
Special Collections: State Justice Institute Depository
Automation Activity & Vendor Info: (Acquisitions) epixtech, inc.; (Cataloging) epixtech, inc.; (Circulation) epixtech, inc.; (ILL) epixtech, inc.; (OPAC) epixtech, inc.; (Serials) epixtech, inc.
Database Vendor: Lexis-Nexis
Publications: A Guide to Montana Legal Research; Audio/Visual Catalogs; Historic Sketch of the State Law Library of Montana; Legal Materials for Non-lawyers; Periodicals Catalog; State Law Library Users Guide
Partic in OCLC Online Computer Library Center, Inc

G US GEOLOGICAL SURVEY WATER RESOURCES DIVISION LIBRARY, 3162 Bozeman Ave, 59601. SAN 328-0799. Tel: 406-457-5900. FAX: 406-457-5990. *Librn*, Cynthia J Harksen; E-Mail: charksen@usgs.gov; Staff 1 (MLS 1)
Library Holdings: Bk Titles 5,000; Per Subs 10

HERON

P LAURIE HILL LIBRARY, PO Box 128, 59844-9521. SAN 376-7701. Tel: 406-847-2520. *Dir*, Mary Williams; *Coll Develop*, Mary Edith Hoelke
1998-1999 Income Other $2,000. Mats Exp $500
Library Holdings: Bk Vols 9,000; Bk Titles 8,000

HOT SPRINGS

P PRESTON TOWN-COUNTY LIBRARY OF HOT SPRINGS,* 203 E Main St, PO Box 850, 59845-0127. SAN 309-328X. Tel: 406-741-3491. FAX: 406-741-3491. E-Mail: hslibrar@hotsprings.net. *Dir*, Jean Patton
Founded 1963
Library Holdings: Bk Titles 20,000
Subject Interests: Law
Special Collections: Chinese-Herbal Therapy Coll; Montana & Western Coll
Partic in OCLC
Friends of the Library Group
Bookmobiles: 1

JOLIET

P JOLIET COMMUNITY LIBRARY,* PO Box 590, 59041-0168. SAN 376-785X. Tel: 406-962-3541. FAX: 406-962-3958. *Librn*, Paula Samuelson
1998-1999 Income $5,000. Mats Exp $1,500. Sal $2,000
Library Holdings: Bk Vols 1,900; Bk Titles 1,300; Per Subs 30
Mem of S Cent Fedn of Librs
Open Mon & Wed 4-7:30, Tues & Thurs 4-6
Friends of the Library Group

JORDAN

P GARFIELD COUNTY LIBRARY,* E Main St, PO Box 69, 59337-0069. SAN 309-3298. Interlibrary Loan Service Tel: 406-557-2297. E-Mail: garflibr@midrivers.com. *Librn*, Clara Smith
Founded 1948. Pop 1,589; Circ 7,000
Jul 1997-Jun 1998 Income $16,473. Mats Exp $6,550. Sal $8,100
Library Holdings: Bk Titles 10,261
Mem of Sagebrush Fedn of Librs
Open Mon-Thurs 12:30-5:30 & Tues evening 7-9

KALISPELL

P FLATHEAD COUNTY LIBRARY, 247 First Ave E, 59901. SAN 350-0195. Tel: 406-758-5820. Interlibrary Loan Service Tel: 406-758-5823. Circulation Tel: 406-758-5819. Reference Tel: 406-758-5815. FAX: 406-758-5868. Web Site: www.flatheadcountylibrary.org. *Dir*, Dorothy P Laird; E-Mail: dlaird@co.flathead.mt.us; *Tech Coordr*, Rita M Kraus; Tel: 406-758-5817, E-Mail: rkraus@co.flathead.mt.us; Staff 6 (MLS 3, Non-MLS 3)
Founded 1943. Pop 71,707; Circ 582,643
Jul 1999-Jun 2000 Income (Main Library and Branch Library) $900,493, State $23,079, County $789,581, Other $87,833. Mats Exp $110,518, Books $88,400, Per/Ser (Incl. Access Fees) $11,400. Sal $591,434 (Prof $44,500)
Library Holdings: Bk Vols 188,235; Per Subs 231
Special Collections: Montana Author & Subject Coll
Automation Activity & Vendor Info: (Cataloging) epixtech, inc.; (Circulation) epixtech, inc.
Database Vendor: IAC - SearchBank
Mem of Tamarack Fedn of Librs
Partic in OCLC Online Computer Library Center, Inc
Friends of the Library Group
Branches: 4
BIGFORK BRANCH, 525 Electric Ave, PO box 472, Bigfork, 59911. Tel: 406-837-6976. *Branch Mgr*, Rita Shaw
Library Holdings: Bk Vols 9,528
Friends of the Library Group
COLUMBIA FALLS BRANCH, 130 Sixth St W, Columbia Falls, 59912. SAN 350-025X. Tel: 406-892-5919. FAX: 406-892-5919. *Branch Mgr*, Deena Stacy; E-Mail: dstacy@co.flathead.mt.us; Staff 1 (Non-MLS 1)
Library Holdings: Bk Vols 28,734
Friends of the Library Group
MARION BRANCH, PO Box 1048, Marion, 59925. SAN 323-8105. Tel: 406-854-2333. *In Charge*, Kathy Franken
Library Holdings: Bk Vols 1,324
WHITEFISH BRANCH, 9 Spokane Ave, Whitefish, 59937. SAN 350-0373. Tel: 406-862-6657. FAX: 406-862-6657. *Branch Mgr*, Joey Kositzky; E-Mail: jkositzky@co.flathead.mt.us; Staff 1 (Non-MLS 1)
Library Holdings: Bk Vols 26,404
Friends of the Library Group

J FLATHEAD VALLEY COMMUNITY COLLEGE LIBRARY, (MTKF), 777 Grandview Dr, 59901. SAN 309-331X. Tel: 406-756-3856, 756-3853. FAX: 406-756-3854. Web Site: www.fvcc.cc.mt.us/depts/library. *Dir*, Michael J Ober; Tel: 406-756-3863, E-Mail: mober@fvcc.cc.mt.us; *Acq, Tech Servs*, Colleen Wade; Tel: 406-756-3855, E-Mail: cwade@fvcc.cc.mt.us; *Circ, ILL*, Sinda M Puryer; Tel: 406-756-3856, E-Mail: spuryer@fvcc.cc.mt.us; Staff 3 (MLS 1, Non-MLS 2)
Founded 1967. Pop 65,000; Enrl 1,440; Fac 42; Highest Degree: Associate
Jul 2000-Jun 2001 Income $163,000, State $5,000, Locally Generated Income $2,000, Parent Institution $156,000. Mats Exp $63,000, Books $30,000, Per/Ser (Incl. Access Fees) $17,000, Electronic Ref Mat (Incl. Access Fees) $16,000. Sal $84,264 (Prof $44,000)
Library Holdings: Bk Vols 20,952; Bk Titles 18,902; Per Subs 138
Subject Interests: Classical literature, Forestry, Tourism
Automation Activity & Vendor Info: (Cataloging) epixtech, inc.; (Circulation) epixtech, inc.; (OPAC) epixtech, inc.
Database Vendor: OCLC - First Search
Partic in OCLC
Open Mon-Thurs 8-8 & Fri 8-5

M KALISPELL REGIONAL MEDICAL CENTER LIBRARY, 310 Sunnyview Lane, 59901. SAN 309-3328. Tel: 406-752-1739. FAX: 406-752-8771. E-Mail: krh05@digisys.net. Web Site: www.krmc.org. *Librn*, Heidi Sue Adams; E-Mail: hadams@krmc.org; Staff 1 (MLS 1)
Founded 1976
Library Holdings: Bk Vols 480; Bk Titles 450; Per Subs 125
Subject Interests: Allied health, Consumer health, Medicine, Nursing
Database Vendor: Ebsco - EbscoHost, IAC - Info Trac, OCLC - First Search
Partic in Nat Libr of Med; OCLC

LAME DEER

J DULL KNIFE MEMORIAL COLLEGE, Dr John Woodenlegs Memorial Library, One College Dr, 59043. (Mail add: PO Box 98, 59043), SAN 321-8120. Tel: 406-477-8293. FAX: 406-477-6575. Web Site: www.dkmc.cc.mt.us. *Dir*, Sally Schmidt; E-Mail: sschmidt@dkmc.cc.mt.us; *Asst Librn*, Michal Arpan; E-Mail: marpan@dkmc.cc.mt.us; Staff 2 (MLS 1, Non-MLS 1)
Founded 1979. Pop 9,000; Enrl 405; Fac 18
Oct 1999-Sep 2000 Income $74,000. Mats Exp $17,000, Books $6,000, Per/Ser (Incl. Access Fees) $6,000, Electronic Ref Mat (Incl. Access Fees) $5,000. Sal $45,000
Library Holdings: Bk Vols 12,000; Bk Titles 11,000; Per Subs 100; High Interest/Low Vocabulary Bk Vols 500; Spec Interest Per Sub 10; Bks on Deafness & Sign Lang 20
Subject Interests: Local history, Native Am studies
Special Collections: Northern Cheyenne Oral History Coll
Database Vendor: IAC - Info Trac
Partic in OCLC

LAUREL

P LAUREL PUBLIC LIBRARY,* 720 W Third St, PO Box 68, 59044-0068. SAN 309-3336. Tel: 406-628-4961. *Dir*, Peggy A Arnold
Founded 1917. Pop 6,017; Circ 38,000
Jul 1997-Jun 1998 Income $116,206. Mats Exp $12,675. Sal $58,470
Library Holdings: Bk Vols 16,100; Per Subs 22
Mem of S Cent Fedn of Librs
Partic in OCLC
Open Mon-Thurs 10-7:30 & Sat 10-12

LEWISTOWN

P LEWISTOWN PUBLIC LIBRARY, 701 W Main St, 59457. SAN 309-3344. Tel: 406-538-5212. FAX: 406-538-3323. E-Mail: library@lewistown.net. Web Site: lewistownlibrary.org. *Dir Libr Serv*, Bridgett Johnson; *Publ Servs*, Honey Little; E-Mail: hbunhony98@yahoo.com; *Ad Servs*, Nancy Watts; E-Mail: nancyw@lewis-carnegie-library.org; *Tech Servs*, Vickie Dubbs; *Ch Servs*, Nancy Bostrom; Staff 6 (Non-MLS 6)
Founded 1905. Pop 12,000; Circ 81,000
Jul 1999-Jun 2000 Income $214,951, State $4,936, City $161,825, County $16,900, Locally Generated Income $28,878. Mats Exp $42,166, Books $27,166, Electronic Ref Mat (Incl. Access Fees) $15,000. Sal $129,205
Library Holdings: Bk Titles 40,441; Per Subs 54
Subject Interests: Local history, Montana
Automation Activity & Vendor Info: (Cataloging) Follett; (Circulation) Follett; (ILL) Follett; (OPAC) Follett
Database Vendor: Dialog, IAC - Info Trac, IAC - SearchBank
Mem of S Cent Fedn of Librs
Special Services for the Blind - Magnifiers; Talking Books
Friends of the Library Group

LIBBY

P LINCOLN COUNTY PUBLIC LIBRARIES,* 220 W Sixth St, 59923-1898. SAN 350-0403. Tel: 406-293-2778. FAX: 406-293-4235. E-Mail: library@libby.org. Web Site: www.libby.org/library/libhome.html. *Coll Develop*, Jeanne Linn
Founded 1920. Pop 18,000; Circ 79,401
Library Holdings: Bk Titles 30,754; Per Subs 125
Subject Interests: History
Publications: Library Journal
Mem of Tamarack Fedn of Librs
Friends of the Library Group
Branches: 2
EUREKA BRANCH, 318 Dewey Ave, PO Box 401, Eureka, 59917-0401. SAN 350-0438. Tel: 406-296-2613. FAX: 406-296-2613. Web Site: www.libby.org/library/libhome.html. *Librn*, Esther Brandt; E-Mail: ebrandt@libby.org; Staff 2 (Non-MLS 2)
Friends of the Library Group
TROY BRANCH, Third & Kalispell, PO Box 430, Troy, 59935. SAN 350-0462. Tel: 406-295-4040. FAX: 406-295-4040. Web Site: www.libby.org/library/libhome.html. *Librn*, Judith Williams
Friends of the Library Group

LIVINGSTON

S ANTHRO RESEARCH INCORPORATED LIBRARY,* PO Box 1218, 59047. SAN 371-4543. Tel: 406-222-3168. FAX: 406-222-3168. *In Charge*, Larry Larin
Library Holdings: Bk Vols 1,000; Per Subs 26

S FEDERATION OF FLYFISHERS, International Fly Fishing Center, 215 E Lewis, 59047. SAN 374-8227. Tel: 406-222-9369. FAX: 406-222-9369. E-Mail: iffc@wtp.net. Web Site: www.fedflyfishers.org. *Librn*, Bob Wiltshire
Library Holdings: Bk Vols 2,500; Bk Titles 2,300; Per Subs 15; Spec Interest Per Sub 15
Subject Interests: Fly fishing

P LIVINGSTON-PARK COUNTY LIBRARY,* 228 W Callender St, 59047-2618. SAN 309-3379. Tel: 406-222-0862. E-Mail: lpcpublib@ycsi.net. Web Site: www.library.ycsi.net. *Librn*, Milla Cummins
Founded 1901. Circ 91,436
Jul 1997-Jun 1998 Income $183,555. Mats Exp $22,306. Sal $95,546
Library Holdings: Bk Vols 44,000; Bk Titles 42,000; Per Subs 225
Subject Interests: Montana
Publications: Monthly Newsletter
Mem of Broad Valleys Fedn of Librs
Open Mon-Wed 12-8, Thurs 10-8, Fri 10-6 & Sat 10-5
Friends of the Library Group

S PARK COUNTY MUSEUM LIBRARY,* 118 W Chinook, 59047. SAN 329-790X. Tel: 406-222-4184.; Staff 1 (Non-MLS 1)
Founded 1976. Pop 8,000
Special Collections: Park County Newspapers, bks

MALMSTROM AFB

UNITED STATES AIR FORCE
A MALMSTROM AIR FORCE BASE ARDEN G HILL MEMORIAL LIBRARY FL4626, 341 SVS/SVMG, 7356 Fourth Ave N, 59402-7506. SAN 350-0497. Tel: 406-731-2748. Interlibrary Loan Service Tel: 406-731-2301. Circulation Tel: 406-731-4638. FAX: 406-727-6104. *Librn*, Carol Banas; E-Mail: banasc83@hotmail.com; Staff 4 (MLS 1, Non-MLS 3)
Founded 1953
Library Holdings: Bk Vols 56,000; Per Subs 200
Publications: Bulletin (monthly)
Partic in Dialog Corporation; OCLC Online Computer Library Center, Inc

MALTA

P PHILLIPS COUNTY PUBLIC LIBRARY,* 10 S Fourth St E, PO Box 840, 59538. SAN 350-0527. Tel: 406-654-2407. FAX: 406-654-2407. *Dir*, Janeen Brookie; *Asst Librn*, Billie Rae Maxie
Founded 1917. Pop 5,163; Circ 35,346
Library Holdings: Bk Titles 24,431
Mem of Golden Plains Library Federation
Branches: 2
DODSON BRANCH, Dodson, 59524. SAN 350-0551. *Librn*, Bonnie Marney
SACO BRANCH, PO Box 74, Saco, 59261. SAN 350-0586. *Librn*, Esther Brosseau

MANHATTAN

P MANHATTAN COMMUNITY LIBRARY,* 416 N Broadway, PO Box 425, 59741-0008. SAN 309-3395. Tel: 406-284-3341. FAX: 406-284-3104. *Librn*, Julie Herdina
Pop 2,500; Circ 10,400
Library Holdings: Bk Titles 10,800
Mem of Broad Valleys Fedn of Librs

MILES CITY

GM DEPARTMENT OF VETERANS AFFAIRS, Ambulatory Care Clinic Library, 210 S Winchester Ave, 59301. SAN 309-3425. Tel: 406-232-3060, Ext 2280. FAX: 406-232-8297. *Dir Libr Serv*, Gail Shaw Wilkerson; E-Mail: gail.wilkerson@med.va.gov; Staff 2 (MLS 1, Non-MLS 1)
Founded 1951
Library Holdings: Bk Vols 1,100
Database Vendor: IAC - Info Trac, Silverplatter Information Inc.
Partic in Vets Admin Libr Network

P MILES CITY PUBLIC LIBRARY, Sagebrush Federation of Libraries, One S Tenth St, 59301-3398. SAN 309-3409. Tel: 406-232-1496. FAX: 406-232-2095. *Dir*, Mike Hamlett; E-Mail: mhamlett@mt.lib.org; *Archivist*, Esther Kornemann; *Ch Servs*, Stephanie Silvers; *Circ*, Gloria Archdale; *Circ*, Kathy Corbin; *Acq*, Dyan Fidel; Staff 6 (MLS 2, Non-MLS 4)
Founded 1902. Pop 12,000
Library Holdings: Bk Vols 60,000; Bk Titles 43,000; Per Subs 65
Special Collections: Census Materials Center; Montana Hist; Montana

History
Automation Activity & Vendor Info: (Circulation) epixtech, inc.; (OPAC) epixtech, inc.
Database Vendor: IAC - Info Trac, OCLC - First Search
Function: ILL available
Friends of the Library Group

J MILES COMMUNITY COLLEGE LIBRARY,* 2715 Dickinson, 59301. SAN 309-3417. Tel: 406-234-3550. Toll Free Tel: 800-541-9281. FAX: 406-234-3598. *Librn*, Laurence H Torstenbo; E-Mail: torstenbol@mcc.cc.mt.us; *Asst Librn*, Joanna Tsao; Tel: 406-233-3549, E-Mail: jtsao@clark.njpublib.org
Library Holdings: Bk Vols 17,450; Per Subs 275

S MONTANA DEPARTMENT OF CORRECTIONS, Pine Hills Youth Correctional Facility,* N Haynes, PO Box 1058, 59301-1058. SAN 375-314X. Tel: 406-232-1377, Ext 2230. FAX: 406-232-7432. *Dir*, Bill Zook
Library Holdings: Bk Titles 5,000
Special Collections: Native American Coll, bks & videos

G USDA AGRICULTURAL RESEARCH SERVICE, Fort Keogh Livestock & Range Research Laboratory Library, Montana Agricultural Experiment Sta, Rte 1, Box 2021, 59301. SAN 375-183X. Tel: 406-232-4970. FAX: 406-232-8209.
Library Holdings: Bk Titles 800; Per Subs 25

MISSOULA

M CENTER FOR HEALTH INFORMATION, Medical Library, 500 W Broadway, 59802-4587. SAN 309-3441. Tel: 406-329-5710. FAX: 406-329-5688. Web Site: www.saintpatrick.org/chi. *Librn*, Marianne Farr; E-Mail: farr@saintpatrick.org
Founded 1946
Jan 1998-Dec 1999 Income $150,000
Library Holdings: Bk Titles 3,500
Subject Interests: Hospital administration, Nursing
Special Collections: Bioethics; Medical Humanities
Mem of Pac Northwest Regional Health Sci Libr
Partic in Consortium of Acad & Spec Libr in Mont

S DOUGLAS GRIMM LIBRARY, 2524 Sycamore, 59802-3402. SAN 328-0241. Tel: 406-543-7970. *Librn*, Douglas Grimm
Founded 1967
Subject Interests: Ceramics, Furniture, Paintings, Prints, Sculpture
Special Collections: American Contemporary Art Coll, photos
Publications: Catalogs

P MISSOULA PUBLIC LIBRARY, 301 E Main, 59802-4799. SAN 350-0616. Tel: 406-721-2665. FAX: 406-728-5900. E-Mail: mslaplib@missoula.lib.mt.us. Web Site: www.missoula.lib.mt.us. *Dir*, Bette Ammon; *Ref Servs YA*, Suzette Dussault; E-Mail: suzette@missoula.lib.mt.us; *Ch Servs*, Karen Rehard; E-Mail: rose@missoula.lib.mt.us; *Ref*, Vaun Stevens; E-Mail: vstevens@missoula.lib.mt.us; *Cat*, Paulette Parpart; E-Mail: parpart@missoula.lib.mt.us; *Spec Coll*, Donald Spritzer; E-Mail: sprizter@missoula.lib.mt.us; *Head, Circ*, Claire Morton; E-Mail: claire1@missoula.lib.mt.us; *Info Res*, Mitch Waylett; E-Mail: waylett@ronan.net; Staff 21 (MLS 2, Non-MLS 19)
Founded 1894. Pop 89,000; Circ 624,160
Jul 1999-Jun 2000 Income (Main Library and Branch Library) $994,087, State $35,276, County $958,811. Mats Exp Books $110,000. Sal $671,637
Library Holdings: Bk Vols 202,012; Per Subs 312
Special Collections: Montana Hist Coll; Northwest History Coll, bk & doc
Automation Activity & Vendor Info: (Cataloging) epixtech, inc.
Database Vendor: epixtech, inc., IAC - Info Trac, OCLC - First Search
Publications: Friends of the Library (quarterly newsletter)
Partic in OCLC
Friends of the Library Group
Branches: 2
SEELEY LAKE COMMUNITY, Seeley Lake, 59868. SAN 329-5575. Tel: 406-677-2224. FAX: 406-677-2255. *Librn*, Sue Stone
SWAN VALLEY COMMUNITY, Condon, 59847. SAN 350-0691. Tel: 406-754-2521. *Librn*, Fern Kauffman
Friends of the Library Group
Bookmobiles: 1

P MISSOULA PUBLIC LIBRARY,* 301 E Main, 59802-4799. SAN 309-345X. Tel: 406-721-2665. FAX: 406-728-5900. E-Mail: msplib@marsweb.com. Web Site: www.marsweb.com/~mslaplib. *Coordr*, Bette Ammon
Founded 1976. Pop 250,000
Branches: 1
ALBERTON BRANCH, PO Box 87, Alberton, 59820. SAN 377-0346. Tel: 406-722-3372. *Librn*, Eleanor Brovold
Library Holdings: Bk Titles 9,000

S MISSOULIAN NEWSPAPER LIBRARY,* PO Box 8029, 59807. SAN 375-684X. Tel: 406-523-5240. FAX: 406-523-5294. E-Mail: newsdesk@missoulian.com. Web Site: www.missoulian.com.
1997-1998 Mats Exp $3,000, Books $200
Library Holdings: Bk Titles 400

UNIVERSITY OF MONTANA
C MAUREEN & MIKE MANSFIELD LIBRARY, 32 Campus Dr, 59812. Tel: 406-243-6860. Interlibrary Loan Service Tel: 406-243-6736. FAX: 406-243-2060. E-Mail: libadmin@selway.umt.edu. Web Site: www.lib.umt.edu. *Dean of Libr*, Karen A Hatcher; *Bibliog Instr*, Dr Jack Hutslar; Tel: 336-784-4926, Fax: 336-784-5546; *Dir, Publ Servs*, Erling Oelz; *Dir, Tech Servs*, Susan Mueller; *Circ*, Martin Landry; *Doc*, Dennis Richards; *ILL*, Patricia Collins; *Online Servs*, William Elison; *Spec Coll*, Christopher Mullin; *Archivist*, Jodi Allison-Bunnell; *Acq*, Carol Leese; Staff 15 (MLS 15)
Founded 1893. Enrl 10,644; Fac 319; Highest Degree: Doctorate
Jul 1997-Jun 1998 Income $3,694,259, Locally Generated Income $176,294. Mats Exp $1,240,665, Books $304,163, Per/Ser (Incl. Access Fees) $772,644. Sal $1,708,905
Library Holdings: Bk Vols 850,000
Special Collections: (All aspects of the State of Montana & nearby areas - Economics; Lumber Industry & Other Montana Business; Mirsilees Coll (Chaucer & his times); Montana Coll; Montana History) Montana Politicians (Mike Mansfield, James Murray, James Gerard, Joseph Dixon Coll), mss; Natural History; Whicker Coll (English & American literature)
Automation Activity & Vendor Info: (Acquisitions) epixtech, inc.; (Cataloging) epixtech, inc.
Publications: Mansfield Library Notes
Partic in Coop Libr Agency for Syst & Servs; Dialog Corporation; OCLC; OCLC Online Computer Library Center, Inc
Friends of the Library Group
CL SCHOOL OF LAW LIBRARY, Law Library, Law School, 59812. Tel: 406-243-6171. FAX: 406-243-6358. *Librn*, Fritz Snyder; E-Mail: fritz@selway.umt.edu; *Asst Librn*, Carole Ann Granger; Staff 5 (MLS 3, Non-MLS 2)
Founded 1911. Enrl 226; Fac 17; Highest Degree: Doctorate
Jul 1997-Jun 1998 Income $726,085. Mats Exp $309,142. Sal $416,943
Library Holdings: Bk Titles 19,437; Per Subs 1,795
Special Collections: Indian Law, bks & micro
Partic in Westlaw

C THE UNIVERSITY OF MONTANA-MISSOULA, Mansfield Library Instructional Media Services, 132 Campus Dr, 59812-4968. Tel: 406-243-4071. FAX: 406-243-2689. *Dean of Libr*, Frank D'Andraia; *Instrul Serv*, Karen C Driessen; Tel: 406-243-2856, E-Mail: karend@selway.umt.edu
Library Holdings: Bk Vols 1,000,000; Bk Titles 1,000,000
Automation Activity & Vendor Info: (Acquisitions) epixtech, inc.; (Cataloging) epixtech, inc.; (Circulation) epixtech, inc.; (Course Reserve) epixtech, inc.; (ILL) epixtech, inc.; (Media Booking) epixtech, inc.; (OPAC) epixtech, inc.; (Serials) epixtech, inc.
Database Vendor: epixtech, inc.

M WESTERN MONTANA CLINIC LIBRARY, 515 W Front, PO Box 7609, 59807-7609. SAN 309-3468. Tel: 406-721-5600, Ext 7343. FAX: 406-721-3907. *Librn*, Paulette Cote; E-Mail: pcote@wmclinic.com
Founded 1930
Jan 1999-Dec 1999 Mats Exp $10,500, Books $300, Per/Ser (Incl. Access Fees) $7,500, Presv $2,000, Electronic Ref Mat (Incl. Access Fees) $700
Library Holdings: Bk Titles 450; Per Subs 29
Partic in Medline; Pacific NW Regional Health Sci Libr
Serves health care consumers only if referred by physician or staff

MOORE

P MOORE MEMORIAL LIBRARY, 403 Fergus Ave, PO Box 125, 59464-0125. SAN 309-3476. Tel: 406-374-2480 (City Clerk). *In Charge*, Laura Pace
Library Holdings: Bk Vols 200; Bk Titles 150
Mem of S Cent Fedn of Librs
Open Tues & Thurs 12-5

OPHEIM

P OPHEIM COMMUNITY LIBRARY,* 100 Rock St, PO Box 108, 59250-0108. SAN 376-7876. Tel: 406-762-3213. FAX: 406-762-3348. E-Mail: ohs@montanavision.net. *Librn*, Terry Risa
Feb 1997-Jan 1998 Income $59,000. Mats Exp $29,000. Sal $27,000
Library Holdings: Bk Vols 10,000; Bk Titles 9,000; Per Subs 35
Mem of Golden Plains Library Federation
Open Mon-Thurs 8-4 & Fri 8-2:30
Friends of the Library Group

PABLO

C SALISH KOOTENAI COLLEGE, D'arcy McNickle Library, 5200 Hwy 93, 59855. (Mail add: PO Box 117, 59855), SAN 373-6326. Tel: 406-675-4800. Reference Tel: 406-675-4800, Ext 279. FAX: 406-675-4801. Web Site: www.skc.edu. *Dir*, Carlene Barnett; E-Mail: carlene_barnett@skc.edu; *Cat, Tech Servs*, Mary Tevebaugh; E-Mail: mary_l_young@skc.edu; *Ref*, Mary

Lou Mires; *Ser*, Maureen McElderry; Staff 4 (MLS 1, Non-MLS 3)
Founded 1979. Enrl 881; Fac 24; Highest Degree: Bachelor
Library Holdings: Bk Vols 46,000; Per Subs 150
Subject Interests: Environmental studies, Native Am studies, Nursing
Special Collections: Confederated Salish & Kootenai Tribal History
Automation Activity & Vendor Info: (Circulation) CASPR

PHILIPSBURG

P PHILIPSBURG PUBLIC LIBRARY, (MTPH), 102 S Sansome, PO Box 339, 59858-0339. SAN 321-7817. Tel: 406-859-5030. FAX: 406-859-3821. E-Mail: phl5030@montana.com. *Dir*, Susan McCann
Library Holdings: Bk Vols 4,500
Mem of Broad Valleys Fedn of Librs

PLAINS

P PLAINS PUBLIC LIBRARY DISTRICT, 108 W Railroad, PO Box 399, 59859-0339. SAN 309-3484. Tel: 406-826-3101. FAX: 406-826-3101. *Librn*, Carrie M Terrell; E-Mail: cterrell@mtlib.org
Pop 3,678; Circ 15,000
Library Holdings: Bk Vols 13,801; Bk Titles 13,601; Per Subs 25
Special Collections: Montana Coll; Vertebrate Paleontology
Mem of Tamarack Fedn of Librs
Open Mon 11-5, Tues 1-5, Wed 1-7:30, Thurs 3-7 & Sat 10-12
Friends of the Library Group

PLENTYWOOD

P SHERIDAN COUNTY LIBRARY,* 100 W Laurel Ave, 59254. SAN 309-3492. Tel: 406-765-2317. FAX: 406-765-2129. *Librn*, Sheila Lee
Founded 1911. Pop 4,434; Circ 27,076
Jul 1998-Jun 1999 Income $109,719, County $97,486, Other $12,233. Mats Exp $28,506, Books $20,448, Micro $2,283, AV Equip $566, Electronic Ref Mat (Incl. Access Fees) $5,209. Sal $53,067
Library Holdings: Bk Vols 28,000; Bk Titles 25,979; Per Subs 81
Special Collections: Sheet Music Coll
Automation Activity & Vendor Info: (Circulation) Sagebrush Corporation
Database Vendor: Ebsco - EbscoHost, OCLC - First Search
Mem of Golden Plains Library Federation
Open Mon-Wed 10-8 & Thurs-Sat 10-5
Friends of the Library Group

POLSON

P POLSON CITY LIBRARY,* 2 First Ave E, PO Box 820, 59860-0820. SAN 309-3506. Tel: 406-883-8225. FAX: 406-883-8239. E-Mail: polsoncl@mtlib.org. *Dir*, Marilyn M Trosper
Founded 1910. Pop 15,000; Circ 62,619
Jul 1997-Jun 1998 Income $138,798, State $2,871, City $71,228, County $15,315, Other $49,384. Mats Exp Books $8,584. Sal $49,418 (Prof $20,800)
Library Holdings: Bk Vols 45,000; Per Subs 35
Mem of Tamarack Fedn of Librs
Friends of the Library Group

POPLAR

J FORT PECK COMMUNITY COLLEGE, Tribal Library, Highway 2 E, PO Box 398, 59255-0398. SAN 326-7032. Tel: 406-768-5551, Ext 16. FAX: 406-768-5552. *Dir, Librn*, Anita A Scheetz; E-Mail: anitas@fpcc.cc.mt.us; Staff 1 (Non-MLS 1)
Founded 1981. Enrl 285; Highest Degree: Associate
Oct 1998-Sep 1999 Income $14,000, Federal $4,000, Parent Institution $10,000. Mats Exp $13,200, Books $2,000, Per/Ser (Incl. Access Fees) $5,200, Electronic Ref Mat (Incl. Access Fees) $6,000. Sal $31,000
Library Holdings: Bk Titles 10,000; Per Subs 170; Spec Interest Per Sub 25
Subject Interests: Native Am, Western Americana
Special Collections: Fort Peck Assiniboine
Database Vendor: IAC - Info Trac
Function: ILL available
Mem of Golden Plains Library Federation
Partic in OCLC
Special Services - Book Discussion Group meets once a month

RED LODGE

P RED LODGE CARNEGIE LIBRARY,* Eighth St & Broadway, PO Box 1068, 59068-1068. SAN 309-3514. Tel: 406-446-1905. E-Mail: rlibrary@wtp. *Librn*, Robert W Moran
Pop 8,000; Circ 30,000
Library Holdings: Bk Vols 15,000; Bk Titles 10,500; Per Subs 100
Mem of S Cent Fedn of Librs
Friends of the Library Group

RONAN

P RONAN CITY LIBRARY,* 203 Main St SW, 59864-2706. SAN 309-3522. Tel: 406-676-3682. FAX: 406-676-3683. E-Mail: ronanlib@ronan.net. Web Site: www.ronan.net/~ronanlib/.
Founded 1923. Pop 5,813; Circ 21,000
Library Holdings: Bk Titles 19,170; Per Subs 25
Special Collections: Montana Coll
Mem of Tamarack Fedn of Librs
Partic in Mont Libr Asn
Friends of the Library Group

ROUNDUP

P ROUNDUP COMMUNITY LIBRARY,* Sixth St & Sixth Ave W, PO Box 70, 59072-0717. SAN 309-3530. Tel: 406-323-1802. FAX: 406-323-1346. E-Mail: rdpcoml@midrivers.com. *Dir*, Dale R Alger; *Asst Librn*, Vera Stockert; Staff 1 (MLS 1)
Founded 1931. Pop 4,106; Circ 29,482
Jul 1997-Jun 1998 Income $66,968. Mats Exp $13,103, Books $10,371, Per/Ser (Incl. Access Fees) $1,200. Sal $42,916 (Prof $34,716)
Library Holdings: Bk Vols 25,351; Bk Titles 22,852; Per Subs 54
Mem of S Cent Fedn of Librs
Facility is a combined junior-high, high school & public library

SAINT IGNATIUS

P SAINT IGNATIUS PUBLIC LIBRARY,* First Ave, PO Box 309, 59865. SAN 309-3549. Tel: 406-745-2800. *Librn*, Brett Allen
Founded 1948. Pop 3,126; Circ 7,800
Library Holdings: Bk Vols 15,000
Special Collections: National Geographics 1927-present
Mem of Tamarack Fedn of Librs
Friends of the Library Group

SCOBEY

P DANIELS COUNTY FREE LIBRARY,* 203 Timmons St, PO Box 190, 59263-0190. SAN 309-3557. Tel: 406-487-5502. FAX: 406-487-5502. *Librn*, Marlene MacHart
Founded 1946. Pop 1,486; Circ 23,286
Library Holdings: Bk Vols 16,055; Per Subs 45
Mem of Golden Plains Library Federation
Special Services for the Deaf - Captioned film depository
Friends of the Library Group

SHELBY

P TOOLE COUNTY FREE LIBRARY,* 229 Maple Ave, 59474. SAN 350-0764. Tel: 406-434-5411. E-Mail: tocolibshelbymt@mcn.net. *Librn*, Heidi Alford
Founded 1948. Pop 5,046; Circ 19,000
Library Holdings: Bk Titles 19,000; Per Subs 33
Special Collections: Montana Indian Coll
Mem of Pathfinder Regional Library Service System
Open Mon, Wed & Thurs 1-5 & 7-9, Tues 10-5 & 7-9, Fri 10-12 & 1-5, Sat 1-4
Branches: 1
SUNBURST BRANCH, 201 First St N, PO Box 158, Sunburst, 59482. SAN 350-0799. Tel: 406-937-6980. *Librn*, Judith Reighard
Library Holdings: Bk Titles 8,000
Open Mon & Wed 10-12, 1-5 & 7-8:30, Fri 10-2, Sat 10-12

SHERIDAN

P SHERIDAN PUBLIC LIBRARY,* 103 E Hamilton, PO Box 417, 59749-0417. SAN 309-3565. Tel: 406-842-5770.
Founded 1902. Pop 636; Circ 14,000
Library Holdings: Bk Vols 12,300; Per Subs 21
Special Collections: Montana Authors Coll
Mem of Broad Valleys Fedn of Librs
Friends of the Library Group

SIDNEY

S MONDAK HERITAGE CENTER, Lillian Anderson Jensen Library, 120 Third Ave SE, 59270-0050. (Mail add: PO Box 50, 59270-0050), SAN 309-3573. Tel: 406-482-3500. FAX: 406-482-3500. Web Site: mondakheritagecenter@hotmail.com. *Dir*, Judith Deitz; *Admin Assoc*, Melissa Lapham; *Librn*, Gail Staffansen
Founded 1972
Library Holdings: Bk Titles 1,500
Subject Interests: Genealogy, Regional history
Restriction: Non-circulating to the public

P SIDNEY PUBLIC LIBRARY,* 121 Third Ave NW, 59270-4025. SAN 309-3581. Tel: 406-482-1917. FAX: 406-482-4642. Web Site: www.richland.org. *Dir*, Renee Goss; E-Mail: rgoss@mtlib.org; Staff 1 (MLS 1)
Founded 1914. Pop 10,100; Circ 163,604
Library Holdings: Bk Vols 25,718; Bk Titles 25,518; Per Subs 60; Bks on Deafness & Sign Lang 6
Automation Activity & Vendor Info: (Cataloging) Follett; (Circulation) Follett; (OPAC) Follett
Mem of Sagebrush Fedn of Librs
Friends of the Library Group

STANFORD

P JUDITH BASIN COUNTY FREE LIBRARY,* 19 Third N, PO Box 486, 59479. SAN 350-0829. Tel: 406-566-2277. E-Mail: spclk@3rivers.net. *Dir*, Debra Kramer
Founded 1946. Pop 2,282; Circ 15,587
Jul 1997-Jun 1998 Income $46,700. Mats Exp $5,500. Sal $29,200
Library Holdings: Bk Titles 24,125; Per Subs 27
Open Mon-Fri 8-12 & 1-5, Wed 5-7
Branches: 3
GEYSER LIBRARY STATION, PO Box 23, Geyser, 59447. SAN 350-087X. Tel: 406-735-4357. *Librn*, Annie Sherman
Open Mon-Sat 10-6
HOBSON LIBRARY BRANCH, Hobson, 59452. SAN 350-0861. *Librn*, Helen Perrine
MOCCASIN LIBRARY STATION, Moccasin, 59462. SAN 350-0888. Tel: 406-423-5295. *Librn*, Pam Von Bergen
Open Mon-Fri 7:30-3:30, Sat 7:30-12:30

STEVENSVILLE

P NORTH VALLEY PUBLIC LIBRARY, 208 Main St, 59870. SAN 309-359X. Tel: 406-777-5061. *Dir, Librn*, Patti Jo Thomas; *Asst Librn*, Bill Stoudt
Pop 12,000; Circ 48,400
Library Holdings: Bk Vols 58,000; Bk Titles 51,000; Per Subs 16
Mem of Tamarack Fedn of Librs
Friends of the Library Group

SUPERIOR

S MINERAL COUNTY MUSEUM & HISTORICAL SOCIETY LIBRARY, 301 Second Ave E, PO Box 533, 59872-0533. SAN 371-7119. Tel: 406-822-4626. *Librn*, Cathryn Strombo
1998-1999 Income $3,500
Library Holdings: Bk Titles 100; Per Subs 60
Special Collections: John Mullan & Mullan Military Road Coll; Montana Civil War Veterans Coll
Publications: Mullan Chronicles (quarterly)
Friends of the Library Group

P MINERAL COUNTY PUBLIC LIBRARY, 301 Second Ave E, PO Box 430, 59872. SAN 350-0977. Tel: 406-822-3563. FAX: 406-822-3563. E-Mail: mcpl@blackfoot.net. *Dir*, Patsy Foote; Staff 5 (Non-MLS 5)
Founded 1936. Pop 3,633; Circ 21,682
Jul 1998-Jun 1999 Income $50,411, State $3,125, City $350, Federal $4,136, County $42,000, Locally Generated Income $800. Sal $18,307
Library Holdings: Bk Titles 17,564; Per Subs 43; High Interest/Low Vocabulary Bk Vols 150; Bks on Deafness & Sign Lang 20
Subject Interests: Mont hist
Automation Activity & Vendor Info: (Circulation) Sagebrush Corporation
Database Vendor: IAC - SearchBank
Function: ILL available
Mem of Tamarack Fedn of Librs
Special Services for the Blind - Talking Books
Friends of the Library Group

SWAN LAKE

P SWAN LAKE PUBLIC LIBRARY,* PO Box 5115, 59911-5115. SAN 376-5067. Tel: 406-886-2086.
Library Holdings: Bk Vols 10,000; Bk Titles 9,000
Mem of Tamarack Fedn of Librs

TERRY

P PRAIRIE COUNTY LIBRARY,* 309 Garfield Ave, PO Box 275, 59349-0275. SAN 309-3603. Tel: 406-635-5546. FAX: 406-635-5546. *Dir*, Rolane Christofferson
Library Holdings: Bk Vols 12,500; Bk Titles 12,000
Mem of Sagebrush Fedn of Librs

THOMPSON FALLS

P THOMPSON FALLS PUBLIC LIBRARY,* 108 Fulton St, PO Box 337, 59873-0337. SAN 309-3611. Tel: 406-827-3547. FAX: 406-827-4937. E-Mail: tfl4937@montana.com. *Dir*, Catherine Roberts
Pop 1,356; Circ 19,000
Library Holdings: Bk Titles 17,000; Per Subs 28
Mem of Tamarack Fedn of Librs
Friends of the Library Group

THREE FORKS

P THREE FORKS COMMUNITY LIBRARY,* 121 Second Ave E, PO Box 175, 59752-0175. SAN 309-362X. Tel: 406-285-3747. *Librn*, Emma Prokop; Staff 3 (Non-MLS 3)
Founded 1934. Pop 4,500
Jul 1998-Jul 1999 Income $44,905. Mats Exp $4,572. Sal $14,585
Library Holdings: Bk Titles 17,000; Per Subs 25
Mem of Broad Valleys Fedn of Librs
Friends of the Library Group

TOWNSEND

P BROADWATER SCHOOL & COMMUNITY LIBRARY, 201 N Spruce, 59644. SAN 309-3638. Tel: 406-266-5060. FAX: 406-266-4962. *Librn*, Cindy Hangas; E-Mail: changas@townsend.kiz.mt.us; Staff 4 (Non-MLS 4)
Founded 1995. Pop 4,000; Circ 15,949
Library Holdings: Bk Vols 34,000; Per Subs 72; Bks on Deafness & Sign Lang 25
Automation Activity & Vendor Info: (Cataloging) Sagebrush Corporation; (Circulation) Sagebrush Corporation
Database Vendor: IAC - Info Trac
Mem of Broad Valleys Fedn of Librs
Friends of the Library Group

TWIN BRIDGES

P TWIN BRIDGES PUBLIC LIBRARY, 206 S Main St, PO Box 246, 59754-0246. SAN 373-790X. Tel: 406-684-5416. E-Mail: twin@3rivers.net. *Dir*, Sheila Giltrap; Staff 2 (MLS 1, Non-MLS 1)
Founded 1897. Pop 674; Circ 11,680
Jul 1999-Jun 2000 Income $14,311, State $400, City $4,000, County $2,100, Other $7,811. Mats Exp $3,100. Sal $6,200
Library Holdings: Bk Vols 8,079; Bk Titles 8,433
Friends of the Library Group

VALIER

P VALIER PUBLIC LIBRARY,* 400 Teton Ave, PO Box 247, 59486-0247. SAN 309-3646. Tel: 406-279-3366. FAX: 406-279-3366. *Dir*, Duane B Sheble; *Librn*, Raylene Stark
Pop 651; Circ 10,073
Library Holdings: Bk Vols 12,000; Per Subs 10
Mem of Pathfinder Regional Library Service System
Open Mon, Tues & Fri 1-5, Wed 11-2, Thurs 1-6
Friends of the Library Group

VIRGINIA CITY

P THOMPSON-HICKMAN FREE COUNTY LIBRARY, Madison County Library, 217 Idaho St, PO Box 128, 59755-0128. SAN 309-3654. Tel: 406-843-5346. FAX: 406-843-5347. E-Mail: vclibry@3rivers.net. *Dir*, Joanne C Erdall
Founded 1924. Pop 3,647; Circ 3,500
Library Holdings: Bk Titles 6,000; Per Subs 13
Special Collections: Dick Pace Archives
Mem of Broad Valleys Fedn of Librs

WARM SPRINGS

M MONTANA STATE HOSPITAL, Patients Library, 59756. SAN 309-2925. Tel: 406-693-7133. FAX: 406-693-7127. *Librn*, Terry Ferguson; E-Mail: teferguson@state.mt.us; Staff 3 (Non-MLS 3)
Founded 1968. Pop 600
2000-2001 Income $7,500, State $6,000, Parent Institution $1,500. Sal $34,000 (Prof $30,000)
Library Holdings: Bk Vols 5,000; Per Subs 25
Subject Interests: Music, Psychology, Self-help
Partic in OCLC

WEST GLACIER

S NATIONAL PARK SERVICE, Glacier National Park, George C Ruhle Library, PO Box 128, 59936. SAN 309-3670. Tel: 406-888-7800, 406-888-7932. FAX: 406-888-7808. E-Mail: interp@nps.gov/glac. Web Site: www.nps.gov/glac.
Founded 1975
Library Holdings: Bk Titles 13,500
Special Collections: Plains Indians (James Willard Schultz Coll)

WEST YELLOWSTONE

P WEST YELLOWSTONE PUBLIC LIBRARY,* 220 Yellowstone Ave, PO Box 370, 59758-0370. SAN 321-7825. Tel: 406-646-9017. FAX: 406-646-7311. E-Mail: wylibrary@mtlib.org. *Librn*, Elizabeth Kearney; *Asst Librn*, Nancy Bostrom
Founded 1981. Pop 900; Circ 6,000
Library Holdings: Bk Vols 13,500; Bk Titles 12,000; Per Subs 25
Mem of Broad Valleys Fedn of Librs

WHITE SULPHER SPRINGS

P MEAGHER COUNTY CITY LIBRARY,* 15 First Ave SE, PO Box S, 59645. SAN 309-3689. Tel: 406-547-2250. FAX: 406-547-3691. E-Mail: mccl@svn.3rivers.net. Web Site: www.meagherchamber.com. *Librn*, Lisa Bond
Founded 1940. Pop 2,000; Circ 9,730
Library Holdings: Bk Titles 12,000
Special Collections: Montana History (Historical Society); Rare Books
Mem of Broad Valleys Fedn of Librs

WIBAUX

P WIBAUX PUBLIC LIBRARY, 115 S Wibaux, PO Box 332, 59353-0332. SAN 309-3697. Tel: 406-796-2452. FAX: 406-796-2452. *Librn*, Ruby Tennant; E-Mail: rubyt@mtlib.org
Pop 532; Circ 1,191
Library Holdings: Bk Vols 12,157; Per Subs 11
Automation Activity & Vendor Info: (Cataloging) Follett; (Circulation) Follett
Mem of Sagebrush Fedn of Librs
Friends of the Library Group

WINNETT

P PETROLEUM COUNTY COMMUNITY LIBRARY,* 205 S Broadway, PO Box 188, 59087-0188. SAN 309-3700. Tel: 406-429-2451. FAX: 406-429-7631. *Librn*, Dianna Babcock; E-Mail: d.babcock@usa.net; *Librn*, Nancy Freburg
Founded 1957. Pop 600; Circ 10,012
Jul 1997-Jun 1998 Income $34,686. Mats Exp $15,142. Sal $23,161
Library Holdings: Bk Titles 16,000; Per Subs 30
Special Collections: Local History, tape, written mat
Partic in OCLC
Open Mon 8-4, Tues & Thurs 8-5 & 7-9, Wed 8-4 & 7-9, Fri 8-2:40

WOLF POINT

P ROOSEVELT COUNTY LIBRARY, 220 Second Ave S, 59201-1599. SAN 350-106X. Tel: 406-653-2411. FAX: 406-653-1365. E-Mail: read@nemontel.net. *Dir*, Andrea Hayes
Pop 10,999
Jul 1999-Jun 2000 Income (Main Library and Branch Library) $232,446. Mats Exp Books $30,777. (Prof $118,435)
Library Holdings: Bk Titles 58,150; Per Subs 108
Mem of Golden Plains Library Federation
Friends of the Library Group
Branches: 3
CULBERTSON PUBLIC, 202 Broadway Ave, PO Box 415, Culbertson, 59218-0031. SAN 350-1124. Tel: 406-787-5275. FAX: 406-487-5275. E-Mail: culberts@3rivers.net. *Librn*, Karen Baxter
Library Holdings: Bk Titles 6,200
Open Mon 11-5, Tues 1-7, Thurs 11-5
FROID PUBLIC, 110 Main, PO Box 334, Froid, 59226-0334. SAN 350-1159. Tel: 406-766-2492. E-Mail: 4hbranch@nemontel.net. *Librn*, Roma Portra
Library Holdings: Bk Titles 6,500
Open Mon-Thurs 2:30-5
POPLAR CITY PUBLIC, 208 Third Ave W, PO Box 515, Poplar, 59255-0515. SAN 350-1183. Tel: 406-768-3749. E-Mail: poplar@nemontel.net. *Librn*, Jackie Hagadone
Library Holdings: Bk Titles 7,250
Open Tues 9-5, Wed 9-3, Thurs 9-1

NEBRASKA

Date of Statistics: Fiscal 1999
Population, 1998 Census (est): 1,666,028
Population Served by Public Libraries: 1,406,495
Total Book Volumes in Public Libraries: 5,440,669
Total Items in Public Libraries: 6,662,736
Total Public Library Circulation: 10,806,699
Total Public Library Income: $34,343,679
Source of Income: Property Tax 93.05%
Number of County or Multi-County (Regional) Libraries: 12
Number of Bookmobiles in State: 9
Grants-in-Aid to Public Libraries (1999):
Federal: $450,903
State Aid: $416,142
Matching State Funds: $3,069,019

ADAMS

P ADAMS PUBLIC LIBRARY,* 300 Eighth St, PO Box 46, 68301. SAN 309-3719. Tel: 402-988-2565. *Librn*, Elaine Harms
Pop 395; Circ 9,278
1997-1998 Income $1,700. Mats Exp Books $200. Sal $119
Library Holdings: Bk Titles 7,000

AINSWORTH

P AINSWORTH PUBLIC LIBRARY, Fifth & N Main St, PO Box 207, 69210-0207. SAN 309-3727. Tel: 402-387-2032. FAX: 402-387-0209. E-Mail: apl@bloomnet.com. *Librn*, Gail J Irwin
Founded 1911. Pop 4,031; Circ 35,000
Oct 1998-Sep 1999 Income $64,378, State $929, City $49,793, Federal $391, County $9,000, Other $4,264. Mats Exp $16,572, Books $15,572, Per/Ser (Incl. Access Fees) $1,000. Sal $32,000
Library Holdings: Bk Vols 24,260; Per Subs 92
Automation Activity & Vendor Info: (Cataloging) Follett; (Circulation) Follett
Mem of Meridian Libr Syst
Partic in ILL Network - Nebr
Friends of the Library Group

ALBION

P ALBION PUBLIC LIBRARY,* 437 S Third St, 68620. SAN 309-3735. Tel: 402-395-2021. E-Mail: albionpl@albion.net. *Librn*, Mari Hosford
Founded 1900. Pop 2,500; Circ 23,394
Library Holdings: Bk Titles 15,560; Per Subs 37
Mem of Northern Lights Libr Network
Open Mon, Wed & Thurs 2-6 & 7-9, Tues, Fri & Sat 2-6

ALEXANDRIA

P TUCKER MEMORIAL PUBLIC LIBRARY,* 313 Harbine St, PO Box 184, 68303. SAN 309-3743. Tel: 402-749-3550. *Dir*, Maxine Strain
Pop 200; Circ 4,500
Library Holdings: Bk Vols 3,662
Mem of Southeastern Regional Libr Syst
Open Tues 8:30-11:30am, Thurs 9-11:30 & 2-4, Sat 9-11:30 & 1-4

ALLEN

P SPRINGBANK TOWNSHIP LIBRARY, 100 E Second St, PO Box 158, 68710-0158. SAN 309-3751. *Librn*, Bonnie Kellogg
Pop 539; Circ 3,300
Jul 1999-Jun 2000 Income Locally Generated Income $1,200
Library Holdings: Bk Titles 7,627; Per Subs 36
Open Fri 4:30-6:30 & Sat 8-12

ALLIANCE

P ALLIANCE PUBLIC LIBRARY,* 1750 Sweetwater Ave Ste 101, 69301-4438. SAN 309-376X. Tel: 308-762-1387. FAX: 308-762-4148. E-Mail: alibrary@panhandle.net. *Librn*, Mavis McLean
Pop 9,869; Circ 91,000
Library Holdings: Bk Vols 41,000; Per Subs 123
Mem of Panhandle Library System
Friends of the Library Group

GL BOX BUTTE COUNTY LAW LIBRARY,* Courthouse, 515 Box Butte Ave, Ste 302, 69301. SAN 374-9762. Tel: 308-762-5354. FAX: 308-762-7703.
Library Holdings: Bk Titles 10,000

ALMA

P HOESCH MEMORIAL PUBLIC LIBRARY,* City Park W Second, PO Box 438, 68920-0438. SAN 309-3778. Tel: 308-928-2600. FAX: 308-928-2662. E-Mail: libry@megavision.com. *Librn*, LaDonna Schluterbusch
Founded 1910. Pop 1,226; Circ 16,936
Library Holdings: Bk Vols 11,061; Per Subs 36
Subject Interests: History
Friends of the Library Group

ARAPAHOE

P ARAPAHOE PUBLIC LIBRARY,* 302 Nebraska Ave, PO Box 598, 68922-0598. SAN 309-3794. Tel: 308-962-7806. *Librn*, Cheryl Ahrens; *Asst Librn*, Cheryl Koller
Pop 1,050; Circ 5,061
Library Holdings: Bk Titles 17,500; Per Subs 33
Mem of Holdrege Public Library System

ARCADIA

P ARCADIA TOWNSHIP LIBRARY,* 100 S Reynolds, PO Box 355, 68815-0355. SAN 309-3808. Tel: 308-789-6346. *Librn*, Donette Holconb
Circ 6,337
Library Holdings: Bk Vols 6,222; Per Subs 20

ARLINGTON

P ARLINGTON PUBLIC LIBRARY,* PO Box 39, 68002-0039. SAN 309-3816. Tel: 402-478-4545. *Dir*, Kay Stork
Pop 1,117; Circ 6,809
Library Holdings: Bk Titles 7,251
Partic in Bellevue Pub Libr Syst

ARNOLD

P FINCH MEMORIAL PUBLIC LIBRARY,* 205 N Walnut, PO Box 247, 69120-0247. SAN 309-3824. Tel: 308-848-2219. *Librn*, Darlene Rimpley; *Asst Librn*, Marcy Lucas
Pop 1,400; Circ 8,381
Library Holdings: Bk Vols 12,500; Per Subs 28
Mem of Meridian Libr Syst
Friends of the Library Group

ARTHUR

P ARTHUR COUNTY PUBLIC LIBRARY,* PO Box 166, 69121-0166. SAN 309-3832. Tel: 308-764-2219. FAX: 308-764-2216. *Librn*, Twylia Cullinan
Founded 1939. Pop 650
Library Holdings: Bk Titles 7,258
Subject Interests: Large type print
Mem of Panhandle Library System
Open Mon-Fri 2-4

ASHLAND

P ASHLAND PUBLIC LIBRARY,* 207 N 15th St, 68003-1816. SAN 309-3840. Tel: 402-944-7830. FAX: 402-944-7430. E-Mail: co01385@navix.net. Web Site: www.co.saunders.ne.us/ashevent.htm. *Librn*, Doris Regner; *Asst Librn*, Clella Franks; *Cat*, Jean Reinke
Founded 1904. Pop 2,276; Circ 17,713
Library Holdings: Bk Titles 14,000; Per Subs 57
Mem of Bellevue Public Library
Open Mon 1-6, Tues 1-5 & 7-9, Thurs 9-12, 2-5 & 7-9, Sat 9-12 & 1-5
Friends of the Library Group

ATKINSON

P ATKINSON TOWNSHIP LIBRARY,* PO Box 938, 68713-0938. SAN 309-3859. Tel: 402-925-2855. FAX: 402-925-2261. *Librn*, Janet Kliment
Founded 1927. Pop 2,127; Circ 24,371
Library Holdings: Bk Vols 21,585; Per Subs 30
Mem of NE Libr Syst
Friends of the Library Group

AUBURN

P AUBURN MEMORIAL LIBRARY,* 1810 Courthouse Ave, 68305-2323. SAN 309-3867. Tel: 402-274-4023. FAX: 402-274-4433. *Dir*, Boni Hathaway; E-Mail: bonijo@yahoo.com
Founded 1914. Pop 8,367; Circ 36,644
Oct 1998-Sep 1999 Income $120,000. Mats Exp $18,750, Books $17,000, Micro $100, AV Equip $1,650. Sal $56,240
Library Holdings: Bk Titles 25,000; Per Subs 80
Special Collections: NRC Repository
Automation Activity & Vendor Info: (Cataloging) Follett; (Circulation) Follett
Database Vendor: OCLC - First Search
Mem of Southeastern Regional Libr Syst
Open Mon, Tues & Thurs 10-8, Wed & Fri 10-5, Sat 10-4
Friends of the Library Group

AURORA

P ALICE M FARR LIBRARY,* 1603 L St, 68818-2307. SAN 309-3875. Tel: 402-694-2272. FAX: 402-694-2273. E-Mail: afl@hamilton.net. *Dir*, Jan Thomsen; *Asst Librn*, Patricia Oswald
Pop 3,810; Circ 67,176
Library Holdings: Bk Vols 43,000; Per Subs 124
Special Collections: Hamilton County History
Partic in Beatrice Pub Libr Syst; Kilgore Memorial York
Special Services for the Deaf - Books on deafness & sign language; Captioned film depository; High interest/low vocabulary books; Special interest periodicals; Videos & decoder
Friends of the Library Group

BANCROFT

P BANCROFT PUBLIC LIBRARY,* 103 Poplar St, PO Box 67, 68004-0067. SAN 309-3891. Tel: 402-648-3350. *Chief Librn*, Judy Meyer; *Asst Librn*, Pat Logeman; *Asst Librn*, Ruthann Bargmann
Founded 1974. Pop 600; Circ 5,831
Library Holdings: Bk Vols 5,786; Per Subs 27
Mem of Bellevue Public Library; Keene Memorial Library
Friends of the Library Group

S NEBRASKA STATE HISTORICAL SOCIETY - BRANCH MUSEUM, John G Neihardt Research Library, John G Neihardt Center Museum, Elm & Washington St PO Box 344, 68004-0344. SAN 309-3905. Tel: 402-648-3388. FAX: 402-648-3388. E-Mail: neihardt@gpcom.net. *Pres*, Charles Trimble; *Dir*, Nancy Gillis; Staff 2 (MLS 1, Non-MLS 1)
Founded 1976
Library Holdings: Bk Vols 300; Bk Titles 200
Special Collections: Bound Nebraska History Coll; Dr John G Neihardt Coll, bks, mss, critiques
Open Mon-Fri 9-5

BARTLEY

P BARTLEY PUBLIC LIBRARY, 411 Commercial St, PO Box 194, 69020-0194. SAN 309-3913. Tel: 308-692-3313. E-Mail: barplib@swnebr.net. *Dir, Librn*, Janet McNerny; Tel: 308-692-3490, E-Mail: jan@swnebr.net
Pop 342; Circ 1,127
Oct 1999-Sep 2000 Income $631. Mats Exp $900, Books $700, AV Equip $200
Library Holdings: Bk Vols 5,143; Per Subs 16
Mem of Republican Valley Libr Syst
Partic in NE Libr Asn
Resource - Information Center at Kearney, NE

BASSETT

P ROCK COUNTY PUBLIC LIBRARY,* 400 State St, PO Box 465, 68714-0465. SAN 309-3921. Tel: 402-684-3800. FAX: 402-684-3830. E-Mail: rockcolib@huntel.net. Web Site: www.huntel.net/rockcolib. *Dir*, Evelyn Ost; *Asst Dir*, Carol Yaw
Founded 1929. Pop 2,019; Circ 22,181
1998-1999 Income $40,000. Mats Exp $6,600. Sal $21,615
Library Holdings: Bk Vols 18,500; Per Subs 23
Mem of Meridian Libr Syst
Friends of the Library Group

BATTLE CREEK

P BATTLE CREEK PUBLIC LIBRARY,* 103 E Main, PO Box D, 68715. SAN 309-393X. Tel: 402-675-6934. FAX: 402-675-6934. E-Mail: battlecreeklibrary@cableone.net. *Librn*, Kathy Ageton
Pop 998; Circ 30,009 Sal $24,977
Library Holdings: Bk Titles 18,894; Per Subs 54
Mem of NE Libr Syst

BAYARD

P BAYARD PUBLIC LIBRARY,* 509 Avenue A, PO Box B, 69334-0676. SAN 309-3948. Tel: 308-586-1144. FAX: 308-586-1061. *Dir*, Sharon Ulbrich
Founded 1921. Pop 1,435
Library Holdings: Bk Vols 14,365; Per Subs 64
Mem of Panhandle Library System

BEATRICE

P BEATRICE PUBLIC LIBRARY,* 100 N 16th St, 68310-3996. SAN 309-3956. Tel: 402-223-3584. FAX: 402-223-3913. *Dir*, Laureen Riedesel; *Ch Servs*, Carolyn Baker; Staff 2 (MLS 2)
Founded 1893. Pop 12,354; Circ 113,189
Library Holdings: Bk Vols 64,072
Special Collections: Nebraska State Genealogical Society Coll
Member Libraries: Deshler Public Library; Hebron Secrest Library; John G Smith Memorial Public Library; Lydia Bruun Woods Memorial Library; Struckman-Baatz Memorial Library; Talmage Public Library; Wymore Public Library
Open Mon-Thurs 9-8, Fri & Sat 9-6, Sun 2-5
Friends of the Library Group

S BEATRICE STATE DEVELOPMENTAL CENTER, Media Resource Center, 3000 Lincoln Blvd, 68310. SAN 321-5563. Tel: 402-223-6175. FAX: 402-223-7546. *Librn*, Jane Harms; E-Mail: jane.harms@hhss.state.ne.us; Staff 1 (Non-MLS 1)
Founded 1981
Library Holdings: Bk Titles 7,075; Per Subs 80
Subject Interests: Early hist of this institution, Mental retardation
Special Collections: Materials appropriate for persons with mental retardation
Automation Activity & Vendor Info: (Acquisitions) Follett; (Cataloging) Follett; (Circulation) Follett
Database Vendor: OCLC - First Search
Publications: Bibliography
Function: ILL available
Mem of SE Nebr Libr Syst
Partic in NEBASE; Nebr Librns Asn; OCLC Online Computer Library Center, Inc

J SOUTHEAST COMMUNITY COLLEGE LIBRARY,* 4771 W Scott Rd, 68310-7042. Tel: 402-228-3468. FAX: 402-228-2218. *Dir*, Catherine Barringer; E-Mail: cabarrin@sccm.cc.ne.us
Founded 1986. Enrl 1,000
Jul 1998-Jun 1999 Mats Exp $54,595, Books $14,700, Per/Ser (Incl. Access Fees) $28,650, AV Equip $8,597. Sal $99,685
Library Holdings: Bk Vols 15,000
Partic in OCLC Online Computer Library Center, Inc

S US NATIONAL PARK SERVICE HOMESTEAD NATIONAL MONUMENT OF AMERICA, Research Library, 8523 W State Hwy 4, 68310. SAN 370-2944. Tel: 402-223-3514. FAX: 402-228-4231. E-Mail: home ranger activities@nps.gov. Web Site: www.nps.gov/home. *In Charge*, Beverly Albrecht
Library Holdings: Bk Vols 1,000; Per Subs 15
Restriction: Open to public for reference only

BEAVER CITY

P BEAVER CITY PUBLIC LIBRARY,* 408 Tenth St, PO Box 431, 68926-0431. SAN 309-3964. Tel: 308-268-4115. E-Mail: bvrcity@swnebr.net. *Librn*, Betty Oliver; *Asst Librn*, Maxine Parrish
Founded 1922. Circ 7,000
Library Holdings: Bk Vols 7,827; Bk Titles 10,000; Per Subs 41
Mem of Republican Valley Libr Syst

GL FURNAS COUNTY LAW LIBRARY,* Courthouse, 912 R St, PO Box 373, 68926-0373. SAN 374-8294. Tel: 308-268-4025. FAX: 308-268-2345. *In Charge*, Marjory Lambert
Library Holdings: Bk Vols 1,000; Per Subs 10

BEEMER

P KARLEN MEMORIAL LIBRARY,* 215 Blaine St, PO Box 248, 68716. SAN 309-3972. Tel: 402-528-3476. FAX: 402-528-3476. *Librn*, Tammy Lorenz
Founded 1923. Pop 853; Circ 14,104
Library Holdings: Bk Vols 11,847
Friends of the Library Group

BELLEVUE

P BELLEVUE PUBLIC LIBRARY,* 1003 Lincoln Rd, 68005-3199. SAN 309-3999. Tel: 402-293-3157. FAX: 402-293-3163. *Dir*, Guadalupe J Mier; *Ch Servs*, Judy Andrews; *Tech Servs*, William D Owens III; *Ad Servs*, Cindy Williams; Tel: 505-599-0248, E-Mail: williamsc@sjc.cc.nm.us; *Asst Dir, Coll Develop, Ref*, Beverly Lusey; Staff 7 (MLS 4, Non-MLS 3)
Founded 1929. Pop 39,240; Circ 291,682
Library Holdings: Bk Vols 117,000; Bk Titles 106,000; Per Subs 264
Subject Interests: Local history
Publications: Bellevue Library Times (bi-monthly)
Member Libraries: Ashland Public Library; Bancroft Public Library; John Rogers Memorial Public Library; Mead Public Library; Valparaiso Public Library; Waterloo Public Library; Wisner Public Library
Partic in NEBASE
Friends of the Library Group

C BELLEVUE UNIVERSITY, Freeman-Lozier Library, 1000 Galvin Rd S, 68005. SAN 309-3980. Tel: 402-293-3785. Toll Free Tel: 800-756-7920. FAX: 402-291-9265. E-Mail: library@bellevue.edu. Web Site: www.bellevue.edu/Library/library.htm. *Dir*, Robin R Bernstein; Tel: 402-293-2011, E-Mail: robin@bellevue.edu; *Assoc Dir*, Steven Scheuler; Tel: 402-293-2017, E-Mail: steves@bellevue.edu; *Circ, ILL*, D Barbara Haney; Tel: 402-293-2022, E-Mail: dbh@bellevue.edu; *Outreach Serv*, Arra Bailey; Tel: 402-293-2068, E-Mail: abailey@bellevue.edu; *Ref Serv*, Ann Moore; Tel: 402-293-2084, E-Mail: amoore@bellevue.edu; *Tech Servs*, Jeff Tangeman; Tel: 402-293-3786, E-Mail: jeffreyt@bellevue.edu; Staff 6 (MLS 5, Non-MLS 1)
Founded 1966. Highest Degree: Master
Jul 1999-Jun 2000 Mats Exp $275,829, Books $76,911, Per/Ser (Incl. Access Fees) $35,312, Presv $2,318, Micro $21,587, AV Equip $7,805, Electronic Ref Mat (Incl. Access Fees) $82,628. Sal $205,614 (Prof $134,335)
Library Holdings: Bk Vols 131,400; Bk Titles 111,955; Per Subs 2,790
Automation Activity & Vendor Info: (Acquisitions) SIRSI; (Cataloging) SIRSI; (Circulation) SIRSI; (Course Reserve) SIRSI; (ILL) SIRSI; (Media Booking) SIRSI; (OPAC) SIRSI; (Serials) SIRSI
Database Vendor: Ebsco - EbscoHost, OCLC - First Search
Publications: More Than Books (quarterly); Periodical holdings list (rev 2000); Periodical holdings list (rev 98)
Partic in NEBASE; Nebr Independent Col Libr Consortium; OCLC Online Computer Library Center, Inc

S FONTENELLE NATURE ASSOCIATION, 1111 N Bellevue Blvd, 68005-4000. SAN 327-2206. Tel: 402-731-3140. FAX: 402-731-2403. E-Mail: info@fontenelleforest.org. Web Site: www.fontenelleforest.org. *Pub Relations*, Lynn Griffif; E-Mail: lgriffif@natureomaha.com
Founded 1913
Library Holdings: Bk Titles 917; Per Subs 10
Subject Interests: Natural history
Branches:
NEALE WOODS NATURE CENTER, 14323 Edith Marie Ave, Omaha, 68112. SAN 327-8352. Tel: 402-453-5615. FAX: 402-453-0724. *Dir*, Karen Seymour
Library Holdings: Bk Titles 175
Subject Interests: Natural history

BELVIDERE

S THAYER COUNTY MUSEUM, Historical & Genealogical Library,* PO Box 387, 68315. SAN 373-3726. Tel: 402-768-2147. *Curator*, Jacqueline (Jackie) J Williamson
Library Holdings: Bk Vols 14,000
Subject Interests: Genealogy, Local history

BENNINGTON

P BENNINGTON PUBLIC LIBRARY, 15505 Warehouse St, PO Box 32, 68007. SAN 309-4006. Tel: 402-238-2201. FAX: 402-238-2218. E-Mail: benlib@novia.net. *Dir*, Leola Ann Bonge; *Asst Dir*, Darlene Clark; *Circ*, Janiece Coe; *Circ Ch*, Sally Hanson; Staff 4 (Non-MLS 4)
Founded 1948. Pop 1,436; Circ 8,525
Oct 1999-Sep 2000 Income $47,696, City $33,371, Federal $1,015, County $13,310. Mats Exp $9,450, Books $9,000, Per/Ser (Incl. Access Fees) $450. Sal $22,106
Library Holdings: Bk Vols 16,898; Per Subs 27
Special Collections: Cake Pans Coll
Automation Activity & Vendor Info: (Cataloging) Follett; (Circulation) Follett; (OPAC) Follett
Database Vendor: OCLC - First Search, Wilson - Wilson Web
Mem of Eastern Libr Syst
Friends of the Library Group

BIG SPRINGS

P BIG SPRINGS PUBLIC LIBRARY,* 400 Pine St, PO Box 192, 69122. SAN 309-4022. Tel: 308-889-3482. *Librn*, Mary Beth Heidemann
Founded 1927. Pop 505; Circ 1,605
Library Holdings: Bk Vols 5,738; Per Subs 16

BLAIR

P BLAIR PUBLIC LIBRARY, 210 S 17th St, 68008. SAN 309-4030. Tel: 402-426-3617. E-Mail: library@huntel.net. Web Site: www.blairpubliclibrary.com. *Dir*, Ruth Peterson; *Ch Servs*, Corey Goettsche; Staff 4 (MLS 1, Non-MLS 3)
Founded 1915. Pop 6,860; Circ 57,023
Library Holdings: Bk Titles 31,709; Per Subs 106
Automation Activity & Vendor Info: (Cataloging) Follett; (Circulation) Follett
Mem of Eastern Libr Syst
Friends of the Library Group

C DANA COLLEGE, C A Dana-Life Library, 2848 College Dr, 68008-1099. SAN 309-4049. Tel: 402-426-7300. Reference Tel: 402-426-7912. FAX: 402-426-7332. E-Mail: library@acad2.dana.edu. Web Site: www.dana.edu/Academics/library.htm. *Dir Libr Serv*, James Edward Corbly; Tel: 402-426-7301, E-Mail: jcorbly@acad2.dana.edu; *Asst Dir*, Sharon Jensen; Tel: 402-426-7303, E-Mail: sjensen@acad2.dana.edu; *Asst Dir*, Thomas Nielsen; Tel: 402-426-7912, E-Mail: tnielsen@acad2.dana.edu; Staff 5 (MLS 3, Non-MLS 2)
Founded 1884. Enrl 600; Fac 42; Highest Degree: Bachelor
2000-2001 Income Parent Institution $113,600. Mats Exp $86,000, Books $37,500, Per/Ser (Incl. Access Fees) $36,500, Electronic Ref Mat (Incl. Access Fees) $12,000. Sal $130,871 (Prof $105,901)
Library Holdings: Bk Vols 197,421; Bk Titles 109,042; Per Subs 280
Subject Interests: Education
Special Collections: Danish Immigrant Archive; Danish Literature & History; Opera (Lauritz Melchior Memorial Coll)
Automation Activity & Vendor Info: (Cataloging) SIRSI; (Circulation) SIRSI; (Course Reserve) SIRSI; (OPAC) SIRSI
Database Vendor: Ebsco - EbscoHost, IAC - Info Trac, OCLC - First Search
Partic in Nebr Independent Col Libr Consortium

BLOOMFIELD

P BLOOMFIELD PUBLIC LIBRARY,* 121 S Broadway, PO Box 548, 68718-0548. SAN 309-4057. Tel: 402-373-4588. FAX: 402-373-2601. E-Mail: plibrary@beenet.bloom.exi1.K12.ne.us. *Dir*, Dr Marge Stottler; *Asst Librn*, Norma Koertje

Pop 1,393; Circ 8,821
Library Holdings: Bk Titles 6,191; Per Subs 60
Mem of NE Libr Syst
Partic in Northeast Library System
Friends of the Library Group

BLUE HILL

P BLUE HILL PUBLIC LIBRARY,* 317 Gage, PO Box 278, 68930-0278. SAN 309-4065. Tel: 402-756-2701. FAX: 402-756-2702. *Librn*, Judy Grandstaff
Founded 1929. Pop 883; Circ 3,945
Library Holdings: Bk Vols 6,500; Per Subs 31
Open Mon & Sat 9-12, Wed 1-5
Friends of the Library Group

BOYS TOWN

S BOYS TOWN LIBRARY SERVICES, 13727 Flanagan, 68010. SAN 309-4073. Interlibrary Loan Service Tel: 402-498-3292. FAX: 402-498-3294. E-Mail: libraryservices@boystown.org. *In Charge*, Betty J Ackerson; Staff 1 (MLS 1)
Founded 1975
Library Holdings: Bk Titles 3,500; Per Subs 45
Partic in Bibliographical Center For Research, Rocky Mountain Region, Inc; Dialog Corporation; OCLC Online Computer Library Center, Inc

BRIDGEPORT

P BRIDGEPORT PUBLIC LIBRARY,* 722 Main, PO Box 940, 69336-0940. SAN 309-4081. Tel: 308-262-0326. FAX: 308-262-1412. E-Mail: bplb26@hamilton.net. *Librn*, Donna D Nelson
Pop 1,650; Circ 15,507
Library Holdings: Bk Titles 12,000; Per Subs 41
Mem of Panhandle Library System
Open Tues 1:30-7, Wed-Fri 1:30-5:30, Sat 10-1

BROKEN BOW

P BROKEN BOW PUBLIC LIBRARY,* 626 South D St, 68822. SAN 309-4103. Tel: 308-872-2927. FAX: 308-872-2927. E-Mail: bb12849@alltel.net. *Librn*, K Joan Birnie
Founded 1885. Pop 3,979; Circ 53,869
1997-1998 Income $98,494, State $940, Other $4,044. Mats Exp $20,070. Sal $59,500
Library Holdings: Bk Vols 28,118
Subject Interests: Genealogy, Local history
Special Collections: DAR Holdings; Local Newspapers from 1882, bound; Nebraska History & Authors
Mem of Meridian Libr Syst
Friends of the Library Group

L CUSTER COUNTY LAW LIBRARY, Courthouse, 431 S Tenth, 68822. SAN 375-1287. Tel: 308-872-2121. FAX: 308-872-5826.
Library Holdings: Bk Titles 1,000

BRUNING

P BRUNING PUBLIC LIBRARY,* 141 Main, 68322-0250. (Mail add: PO Box 250, 68322-0250), SAN 328-0233. *Librn*, Cathy Otto
Founded 1922. Pop 330; Circ 95
Library Holdings: Bk Titles 5,600
Mem of Southeastern Regional Libr Syst

BRUNSWICK

P BRUNSWICK PUBLIC LIBRARY,* 400 S Hamilton, PO Box 11, 68720. SAN 377-0966. Tel: 402-842-2105. *Librn*, Joan Masat
Library Holdings: Bk Vols 3,200; Per Subs 24
Partic in Antelope County Asn

BURWELL

P GARFIELD COUNTY LIBRARY, 110 S Seventh St, 68823-0307. SAN 309-412X. Tel: 308-346-4711. FAX: 308-346-5109. E-Mail: gcl@nctc.net. *Librn*, Joy Lee
Pop 2,363; Circ 14,154
Library Holdings: Bk Vols 15,399; Per Subs 37
Mem of Meridian Libr Syst
Open Mon-Wed 2-5 & 7-9, Fri 2-5, Sat 9-noon
Friends of the Library Group

BYRON

P BYRON PUBLIC LIBRARY, Kansas Ave, PO Box 91, 68325. SAN 309-4146. Tel: 402-236-8752. *Librn*, Mrs Vernon Grauerholz; *Asst Librn*, Laveta Wit
Founded 1964. Pop 300; Circ 3,000
Library Holdings: Bk Vols 9,605

CALLAWAY

P NIGEL SPROUSE MEMORIAL LIBRARY,* 102 E Kimball, PO Box 277, 68825-0277. SAN 309-4154. Tel: 308-836-2610. *Dir*, Beverly Stivers
Pop 1,052; Circ 4,508
Library Holdings: Bk Vols 11,404; Per Subs 6
Mem of Meridian Libr Syst

CAMBRIDGE

P BUTLER MEMORIAL LIBRARY,* 621 Penn, PO Box 448, 69022-0448. SAN 309-4162. Tel: 308-697-3836. E-Mail: bumemlib@swinber.net. *Librn*, Debra Young; *Asst Librn*, Patricia Young
Founded 1951. Pop 1,107; Circ 16,246 Sal $16,000
Library Holdings: Bk Vols 13,485; Per Subs 17

CAMPBELL

P CAMPBELL PUBLIC LIBRARY,* Main St, PO Box 101, 68932. SAN 377-1814. Tel: 402-756-8850.
Library Holdings: Bk Vols 15,000

CARROLL

P CARROLL PUBLIC LIBRARY,* PO Box 215, 68723-0215. SAN 309-4197. Tel: 402-585-4586. *Dir*, Charlene Jones
Library Holdings: Bk Vols 800; Per Subs 10

CEDAR RAPIDS

P CEDAR RAPIDS PUBLIC LIBRARY,* 423 W Main St, PO Box 344, 68627. SAN 309-4200. Tel: 308-358-0603. FAX: 308-358-0117. *Dir*, Marilyn Jo Schuele; *Asst Librn*, Mary Pat Boesch
Founded 1914. Pop 447; Circ 8,500
Oct 1999-Sep 2000 Income $12,639, State $639, City $10,000, County $2,000. Mats Exp $3,050, Books $2,900, Per/Ser (Incl. Access Fees) $150. Sal $4,700
Library Holdings: Bk Vols 12,300; Per Subs 11
Mem of NE Libr Syst
Friends of the Library Group

CENTRAL CITY

P CENTRAL CITY PUBLIC LIBRARY, 1604 15th Ave, 68826. SAN 309-4219. Tel: 308-946-2512. FAX: 308-946-3290. E-Mail: library@cconline.net. Web Site: www.cconline.net/library.htm. *Dir*, Lynn Manhart; *Asst Librn*, Shirley Higgins; *Ch Servs*, Judy Marco
Founded 1895. Pop 2,868; Circ 68,004
Library Holdings: Bk Vols 31,000; Per Subs 75
Subject Interests: Genealogy, Music
Partic in Northeast Library System

CERESCO

P CERESCO COMMUNITY LIBRARY, 425 S Second St, PO Box 158, 68017-0158. SAN 309-4227. Tel: 402-665-2112. FAX: 402-665-2036. E-Mail: ceresco@inetnebr.com. Web Site: www.co.saunders.ne.us/cerelib.htm. *Librn*, Wylene Twombly
Founded 1977. Pop 1,001
Oct 1998-Jul 1999 Income $12,689, State $764, City $9,125, County $1,000, Locally Generated Income $1,800. Mats Exp $2,780, Books $2,200, Per/Ser (Incl. Access Fees) $240, Electronic Ref Mat (Incl. Access Fees) $340. Sal $6,240
Library Holdings: Bk Titles 6,226; Per Subs 27
Automation Activity & Vendor Info: (Cataloging) Follett; (Circulation) Follett; (OPAC) Follett
Mem of Eastern Libr Syst
Open Tues & Thurs 9-12 & 3:30-8, Wed & Sat 9-12
Friends of the Library Group

CHADRON

P CHADRON PUBLIC LIBRARY,* 507 Bordeaux, 69337. SAN 309-4235. Tel: 308-432-0531. FAX: 308-432-0534. E-Mail: deweycpl@panhandle.net. *Librn*, Imogene Horse; *Asst Librn, Tech Servs*, Dena Crews; *Ch Servs*, Brenda Morford; Staff 4 (MLS 3, Non-MLS 1)

Founded 1911. Pop 5,933; Circ 73,000
Library Holdings: Bk Vols 30,000; Per Subs 82
Publications: Annual Special Library Edition: 1989, A 100-year History
Mem of Panhandle Library System
Friends of the Library Group

C CHADRON STATE COLLEGE, Reta E King Library, 300 E 12th St, 69337. SAN 309-4243. Tel: 308-432-6271. Web Site: www.csc.edu. *Dir*, Terrence Brennan; *Spec Coll*, Ed Hughes; *Acq, Cat, Tech Servs*, Sally Zahn; *YA Servs*, Barbara Carson; *Circ, Ser*, Glenda Gamby; *Publ Servs*, Jim Soester; Staff 9 (MLS 6, Non-MLS 3)
Founded 1911. Fac 109; Highest Degree: Master
1999-2000 Mats Exp $284,000
Library Holdings: Bk Vols 204,388; Per Subs 997
Special Collections: Farrar, Hulm, Madrid Photography Coll; Graves Photography Colls
Database Vendor: Innovative Interfaces INN - View
Mem of Panhandle Library System
Partic in Bibliographical Center For Research, Rocky Mountain Region, Inc; OCLC Online Computer Library Center, Inc

CHAPPELL

P CHAPPELL MEMORIAL LIBRARY & ART GALLERY,* 289 Babcock Ave, PO Box 248, 69129-0248. SAN 309-4251. Tel: 308-874-2626. *Librn*, Dixie Riley
Pop 1,095; Circ 7,823
Library Holdings: Bk Vols 11,500; Per Subs 29
Mem of Panhandle Library System
Open Tues & Thurs 1-5 & 7-9, Sat 2-5

CLARKS

P CLARKSVILLE TOWNSHIP PUBLIC LIBRARY,* PO Box 223, 68628-0223. SAN 377-1830. Tel: 308-548-2864. E-Mail: clarkslibrary@clarks.net.
Library Holdings: Bk Vols 6,500; Per Subs 23
Partic in NE Nebr Libr Asn
Friends of the Library Group

CLARKSON

P CLARKSON PUBLIC LIBRARY,* 318 Pine St, 68629-0017. SAN 309-4278. Tel: 402-892-3235. FAX: 402-892-3235. E-Mail: clarlib@megavision.com. *Librn*, Debra Nadrchal
Pop 817; Circ 3,643
Library Holdings: Bk Vols 8,000; Per Subs 27
Special Collections: Czechoslavakian Language Coll
Partic in Northeast Library System
Open Mon & Fri 9-11, Tues & Thurs 3-7, Wed 9-11 & 7-9, Sat 9-11 & 3-7

CLAY CENTER

P CLAY CENTER PUBLIC LIBRARY,* 117 W Edgar St, 68933. SAN 309-4286. Tel: 402-762-3861. Interlibrary Loan Service Tel: 800-445-7425. FAX: 402-762-3861. E-Mail: cl45824@netal/tel.net. Web Site: www.ci.clay-center.ne.us. *Librn*, Laura Cundiff
Founded 1912. Pop 1,000; Circ 10,931
1998-1999 Income $28,592, State $670, City $21,410, Other $700. Mats Exp $12,972, Other Print Mats $9,400. Sal $12,269
Library Holdings: Bk Vols 16,500; Per Subs 84
Automation Activity & Vendor Info: (Cataloging) Follett; (Circulation) Follett
Mem of Republican Valley Libr Syst
Friends of the Library Group

G ROMAN L HRUSKA US MEAT ANIMAL RESEARCH CENTER, PO Box 166, 68933-0166. SAN 325-030X. Tel: 402-762-3241. FAX: 402-762-4148.
Founded 1975
Library Holdings: Bk Titles 2,545; Per Subs 150
Partic in Dialog Corporation; OCLC Online Computer Library Center, Inc

CLEARWATER

P CLEARWATER PUBLIC LIBRARY, 625 Main St, PO Box 143, 68726-0143. SAN 309-4294. Tel: 402-485-2365. *Librn*, Carolyn M Tuttle
Pop 409; Circ 3,077
Library Holdings: Bk Vols 9,042; Per Subs 25
Mem of NE Libr Syst

COLUMBUS

J CENTRAL COMMUNITY COLLEGE, Platte Campus,* 4500 63rd St, 68601. (Mail add: PO Box 1027, 68601), SAN 309-4316. Tel: 402-562-1275. FAX: 402-562-1227. E-Mail: burplrc@cccadm.cccneb.edu. Web Site: www.cccneb.edu. *In Charge*, Dr Nell Burnham; E-Mail: nburnham@cccneb.edu
Founded 1969. Enrl 770
1997-1998 Mats Exp $100,000, Books $23,000, Per/Ser (Incl. Access Fees) $8,000, AV Equip $8,500, Other Print Mats $14,000. Sal $89,180 (Prof $40,000)
Library Holdings: Bk Vols 31,330

P COLUMBUS PUBLIC LIBRARY, 2504 14th St, 68601-4988. SAN 309-4308. Tel: 402-564-7116. FAX: 402-563-3378. Web Site: www.megavision.net/library. *Dir*, R T Trautwein; *Ref*, Amy VonSeggern; *Cat*, RoJean Lambrecht; *Circ*, Peggy Engel; *Ch Servs*, Glee Nelson; Staff 16 (MLS 3, Non-MLS 13)
Founded 1900. Pop 31,000; Circ 241,560
Oct 1999-Sep 2000 Income $632,799, State $7,658, City $482,319, County $137,722, Other $5,100. Mats Exp $92,500, Books $80,000, Per/Ser (Incl. Access Fees) $6,000, Electronic Ref Mat (Incl. Access Fees) $6,500. Sal $366,672 (Prof $100,000)
Library Holdings: Bk Vols 87,188; Per Subs 181
Special Collections: Play & Theatre Coll
Automation Activity & Vendor Info: (Acquisitions) epixtech, inc.; (Cataloging) epixtech, inc.; (Circulation) epixtech, inc.; (OPAC) epixtech, inc.; (Serials) epixtech, inc.
Mem of NE Libr Syst
Library has an art gallery & a strong literary & ABE Program
Bookmobiles: 1

COZAD

P WILSON PUBLIC LIBRARY,* 910 Meridian, 69130-1755. SAN 309-4340. Tel: 308-784-2019. E-Mail: wpublib@nque.com. *Librn*, Mary Neben
Pop 3,828; Circ 51,286
1998-1999 Income $172,579. Mats Exp $34,500, Per/Ser (Incl. Access Fees) $1,200. Sal $81,992
Library Holdings: Bk Vols 27,800; Per Subs 61
Subject Interests: Local history
Mem of Meridian Libr Syst; Nebr Libr Asn

CRAWFORD

P CRAWFORD PUBLIC LIBRARY,* 601 Second St, 69339-1151. SAN 309-4367. Tel: 308-665-1780. FAX: 308-665-1780. *Librn*, Janet Dodd
Founded 1916. Circ 26,889
Library Holdings: Bk Vols 14,000; Per Subs 30
Mem of Panhandle Library System
Open Mon & Sat 1-6, Wed 9-11 & 1-6, Thurs 6-8, Fri 3-5
Friends of the Library Group

CREIGHTON

P CREIGHTON PUBLIC LIBRARY,* 701 State St, PO Box 158, 68729. SAN 309-4375. Tel: 402-358-5115. FAX: 402-358-5115. E-Mail: crpulib@bloomnet.com. *Librn*, Karen Costello
Founded 1914. Pop 1,223; Circ 18,416
Library Holdings: Bk Vols 13,000; Bk Titles 12,000; Per Subs 52
Special Collections: Old West; Second World War Coll
Mem of NE Nebr Libr Syst
Special Services for the Deaf - High interest/low vocabulary books; Special interest periodicals

CRETE

P CRETE PUBLIC LIBRARY,* 305 E 13th, PO Box 156, 68333-0156. SAN 309-4383. Tel: 402-826-3809. FAX: 402-826-4199. E-Mail: crete1lb@ink.org. *Dir*, Lisa Maddox; *ILL*, Marilyn Beute
Founded 1878. Pop 4,841; Circ 39,722
Library Holdings: Bk Vols 30,000
Special Collections: Czechoslovakian Coll; Nebraska Coll
Mem of Southeastern Regional Libr Syst
Friends of the Library Group

C DOANE COLLEGE, Perkins Library, 1014 Doane Dr, 68333-2495. SAN 309-4391. Tel: 402-826-8565. Circulation Tel: 402-826-8287. FAX: 402-826-8199. Web Site: www.doane.edu. *Bibliog Instr, Dir*, Peggy Brooks Smith; E-Mail: psmith@doane.edu; *Asst Dir, Bibliog Instr, Publ Servs*, Donna Jurena; *Acq*, Janis Mitchell; *Bibliog Instr, Coll Develop*, Jackie K Friedrich; *Cat, Tech Servs*, Mickey Van Dyke; *Per*, Judy Bespalec; Staff 3 (MLS 3)
Founded 1872. Enrl 1,794; Fac 104; Highest Degree: Master
Library Holdings: Bk Vols 78,878; Per Subs 3,165
Special Collections: Doane College Archives Coll; Rall Art Gallery; Rossman Historiography; United Church of Christ Coll
Automation Activity & Vendor Info: (Acquisitions) SIRSI
Publications: Accessions List
Partic in NICLC; OCLC Online Computer Library Center, Inc; PICKLE; SE Libr Network

CROFTON

P EASTERN TOWNSHIP PUBLIC LIBRARY,* 206 W Main St, 68730-0254. SAN 377-5380. Tel: 402-388-4915. FAX: 402-388-4905. *Dir*, Diane Limoges
Jul 1996-Jun 1997 Income $9,000
Library Holdings: Bk Titles 6,000
Mem of NE Libr Syst

CULBERTSON

P CULBERTSON PUBLIC LIBRARY, New York Ave, PO Box 327, 69024-0327. SAN 309-4405. Tel: 308-278-2135. FAX: 308-278-2123. *Librn*, Kelly Tirrill
Founded 1908. Pop 795; Circ 2,898
Library Holdings: Bk Vols 10,430
Special Collections: Art Prints; Old Books; Old History of Hitchcock County (Otis Rogers Coll), clippings & pictures
Mem of Republican Valley Libr Syst
Open Wed 2-8, Fri 9-1, Sat 1-5

CURTIS

P KLYTE BURT MEMORIAL PUBLIC LIBRARY,* 316 Center Ave, PO Box 29, 69025-0029. SAN 309-4413. Tel: 308-367-4148. E-Mail: kbmlib@curtis-ne.com. *Dir*, Marcia Wortman
Founded 1940. Pop 3,416; Circ 10,800
Library Holdings: Bk Titles 12,450; Per Subs 30
Special Collections: County Genealogy Coll; Nebraska Coll
Mem of Republican Valley Libr Syst

C NEBRASKA COLLEGE OF TECHNICAL AGRICULTURE LIBRARY,* 404 E Seventh St, RR 3 Box 23A, 69025-0069. SAN 371-702X. Tel: 308-367-4124. FAX: 308-367-5209. Web Site: www.ncta.unl.edu. *Librn*, Mo Khamouna; E-Mail: m.khamouna.1@unl.edu; Staff 1 (MLS 1)
Enrl 180; Fac 25
1997-1998 Income $15,000. Mats Exp $11,335, Books $4,900, Per/Ser (Incl. Access Fees) $4,700, Micro $580. Sal $30,770 (Prof $27,098)
Library Holdings: Bk Vols 2,600; Bk Titles 2,500; Per Subs 240

DAKOTA CITY

P DAKOTA CITY PUBLIC LIBRARY,* 1710 Broadway, PO Box 189, 68731-0189. SAN 309-4421. Tel: 402-987-3778. FAX: 402-987-3778. *Librn*, Janette Hackney
Pop 1,440; Circ 5,726
Library Holdings: Bk Vols 7,835; Per Subs 26
Special Collections: Library of America Classics; War of the Rebellion Coll
Mem of NE Libr Syst
Friends of the Library Group

DALTON

P DALTON PUBLIC LIBRARY,* 306 Main St, PO Box 206, 69131. SAN 309-443X. Tel: 308-377-2413. *Librn*, Joan Panas
Pop 568; Circ 2,247
Library Holdings: Bk Titles 2,500
Mem of Sidney Pub Libr Syst
Open Wed 9-11, Fri 3-5

DAVENPORT

P DAVENPORT PUBLIC LIBRARY, PO Box 236, 68335. SAN 309-4448. Tel: 402-364-2147. *Librn*, Stacey Hesman
Pop 445; Circ 19,624
Library Holdings: Bk Vols 12,000; Per Subs 17

DAVID CITY

P ROMAN L & VICTORIA E HRUSKA MEMORIAL PUBLIC LIBRARY, 399 Fifth St, 68632. SAN 309-4456. Tel: 402-367-3100. FAX: 402-367-3105. E-Mail: hruskalibrary@navix.net. *Dir*, Kay Schmid
Founded 1891. Pop 2,514; Circ 60,000
Library Holdings: Bk Vols 22,306; Per Subs 68
Subject Interests: County hist
Automation Activity & Vendor Info: (Cataloging) Follett; (Circulation) Follett
Mem of NE Libr Syst
Friends of the Library Group

DAWSON

P JOHN G SMITH MEMORIAL PUBLIC LIBRARY,* 517 Ridge St, 68337. SAN 309-4464. Tel: 402-883-2085. *Librn*, Carol Kean
Founded 1946. Pop 5,298
Library Holdings: Bk Vols 8,000; Per Subs 10
Mem of Beatrice Public Library

DESHLER

P DESHLER PUBLIC LIBRARY,* 310 E Pearl, PO Box 520, 68340-0520. SAN 309-4472. Tel: 402-365-4107. *Librn*, Joyce Schmidt; *Librn*, Mrs Melvin Schoenfeld
Pop 997; Circ 7,865
Library Holdings: Bk Vols 15,100; Per Subs 13
Mem of Beatrice Public Library

DODGE

P JOHN ROGERS MEMORIAL PUBLIC LIBRARY,* 703 Second St, PO Box 187, 68633-0187. SAN 309-4502. Tel: 402-693-2512. E-Mail: joroli01@tvsonline.net. *Librn*, Mary Mandel
Pop 815; Circ 5,500
Library Holdings: Bk Vols 6,500; Per Subs 22
Mem of Bellevue Public Library

DORCHESTER

P DORCHESTER PUBLIC LIBRARY,* Sixth & Washington, PO Box 268, 68343-0268. SAN 377-2489. Tel: 402-946-6061. *Dir*, Kim Dinker
Library Holdings: Bk Vols 5,000
Open Wed 3-5 & Sat 9:30-11:30
Friends of the Library Group

DOUGLAS

P DOUGLAS PUBLIC LIBRARY,* Rte 1, Box 56, 68344. SAN 377-1873. Tel: 402-799-3175. *In Charge*, Ardys Brugman
Library Holdings: Bk Vols 800

ELGIN

P ELGIN PUBLIC LIBRARY,* 503 S 2nd St, PO Box 239, 68636-0239. SAN 309-4529. Tel: 402-843-2460. *Librn*, Mary Miller
Pop 807; Circ 6,291
Library Holdings: Bk Titles 11,260; Per Subs 19
Mem of NE Libr Syst
Friends of the Library Group

ELKHORN

P BESS JOHNSON ELKHORN PUBLIC LIBRARY,* 100 Reading Rd, PO Box 674, 68022. SAN 309-4537. Tel: 402-289-4367. FAX: 402-289-0420. Web Site: www.top.net/alcorn/page6.html. *Dir*, Wendy Anderson; *Circ*, Kathy Polter-Gehl; *Cat*, Janet McGuire; *Circ*, Pam Ruppert; *Circ*, Sue Adamson; *Circ*, Jacqueline Anderson; *Circ*, Michelle Hoffman; *Ch Servs*, Pat Headley
Founded 1925. Pop 1,398; Circ 41,485
Oct 1998-Sep 1999 Income $234,000. Mats Exp $89,000. Sal $117,960
Library Holdings: Bk Vols 27,000
Mem of Eastern Nebr Libr Syst
Friends of the Library Group

ELM CREEK

P ELM CREEK PUBLIC LIBRARY,* 241 N Tyler St, PO Box 489, 68836-0487. SAN 377-189X. Tel: 308-856-4394. *Dir*, Jane Walker
Library Holdings: Bk Vols 10,200; Per Subs 16

ELMWOOD

P ELMWOOD PUBLIC LIBRARY,* 124 W D, PO Box 283, 68349. SAN 309-4545. Tel: 402-994-4125. *Dir*, Virginia Hoyt
Founded 1917. Pop 600; Circ 4,636
Library Holdings: Bk Vols 12,150; Per Subs 96
Special Collections: Autographed Books (Bess Streeter Aldrich Coll)

ELWOOD

P ELWOOD PUBLIC LIBRARY,* 505 Ripley St, PO Box 327, 68937-0327. SAN 309-4553. Tel: 308-785-2035. FAX: 308-785-2035. *Dir*, Jane Hilton
Pop 2,140; Circ 18,492
Library Holdings: Bk Vols 18,226; Per Subs 45
Mem of Republican Valley Libr Syst

EMERSON

P EMERSON PUBLIC LIBRARY,* 110 Main St, PO Box 160, 68733. SAN 309-4561. Tel: 402-695-2449. E-Mail: emlib@bloomnet.com. *Librn*, Marlene Winbolt
Founded 1930. Pop 874; Circ 7,001
Library Holdings: Bk Titles 10,000; Per Subs 26
Mem of NE Nebr Libr Syst
Open Mon & Fri 9-5, Wed 1-8, Sat 8:30-2:30

EUSTIS

P EUSTIS PUBLIC LIBRARY,* 108 N Morton St, PO Box 68, 69028. SAN 309-457X. Tel: 308-486-2651. *Librn*, Eva Searls; *Asst Librn*, Ruth Kugler
Founded 1935. Pop 500; Circ 2,280
Library Holdings: Bk Vols 8,526
Mem of Republican Valley Libr Syst

EWING

P EWING TOWNSHIP LIBRARY,* PO Box 55, 68735. SAN 309-4588. Tel: 402-626-7348. *Librn*, Idella Tuttle
Founded 1926. Pop 520; Circ 1,500
Library Holdings: Bk Titles 3,183
Partic in Nebr Network

EXETER

P EXETER PUBLIC LIBRARY,* 202 S Exeter Ave, 68351-0096. (Mail add: PO Box 96, 68351-0096), SAN 309-4596. Tel: 402-266-3051. FAX: 402-266-3061. E-Mail: epublib@hotmail.com. *Librn*, Nina Bartu; Staff 2 (Non-MLS 2)
Pop 807; Circ 9,895
Library Holdings: Bk Titles 12,853; Per Subs 12
Automation Activity & Vendor Info: (Circulation) Follett
Mem of Southeastern Regional Libr Syst
Partic in Nebr Libr Asn
Open Mon, Wed & Fri 8-12 & 1-5, Sat 11-2

FAIRBURY

P FAIRBURY PUBLIC LIBRARY,* 601 Seventh St, 68352. SAN 309-460X. Tel: 402-729-2843. FAX: 402-729-2880. E-Mail: fp44241@navix.net. *Dir*, Mary Rabenberg; *Ch Servs*, Jean Naiman; Staff 4 (MLS 1, Non-MLS 3)
Founded 1909. Pop 4,335; Circ 24,392
Sep 1999-Oct 2000 Income $86,927, State $1,000, City $100,659, Other $2,500. Mats Exp $103,822, Books $13,620, Per/Ser (Incl. Access Fees) $3,005. Sal $71,712
Library Holdings: Bk Vols 29,045; Bk Titles 19,683; Per Subs 55
Automation Activity & Vendor Info: (Cataloging) Follett; (Circulation) Follett
Partic in NEBASE

FAIRFIELD

P FAIRFIELD PUBLIC LIBRARY,* 412 N "D" St, PO Box 278, 68938-0278. SAN 309-4626. Tel: 402-726-2220. *Librn*, Betty Katen
Circ 2,699
Library Holdings: Bk Vols 4,996; Per Subs 13
Friends of the Library Group

FAIRMONT

P FAIRMONT PUBLIC LIBRARY,* 600 F St, 68354. (Mail add: PO Box 428, 68354), SAN 309-4634. Tel: 402-268-6081. FAX: 402-268-6081. *Librn*, Wanda Marget; *Asst Librn*, Mary Berggren
Founded 1916
Library Holdings: Bk Vols 7,829; Per Subs 42
Mem of Southeastern Regional Libr Syst

FALLS CITY

P LYDIA BRUUN WOODS MEMORIAL LIBRARY,* 120 E 18th St, 68355-2199. SAN 309-4642. Tel: 402-245-2913. FAX: 402-245-3031. Web Site: www.scentco.net/subscribers/fclib. *Dir*, Hope Schawang; *Ch Servs*, Eleanor Last; *Ch Servs*, Susan Weinerman; *Circ*, Diann Merz; *Cat*, Kellie Wiers
Pop 5,043; Circ 39,077
Library Holdings: Bk Vols 39,077; Per Subs 60
Special Collections: Cakepan Coll; Local Artists Coll, paintings
Mem of Beatrice Public Library
Friends of the Library Group

FARNAM

P FARNAM PUBLIC LIBRARY, 313 Main St, PO Box 186, 69029-0186. SAN 309-4650. Tel: 308-569-2346. *Dir*, Jan Steuerwald
Pop 220; Circ 3,663
Library Holdings: Bk Vols 9,463
Mem of Meridian Libr Syst
Open Tues 2-5, Sat 1-6

FORT CALHOUN

S WASHINGTON COUNTY HISTORICAL ASSOCIATION, Museum Library, 14th & Monroe Sts, 68023. (Mail add: PO Box 25, 68023), SAN 326-5811. Tel: 402-468-5740. E-Mail: info@newashcohist.org. Web Site: www.newashcohist.org.
1998-1999 Mats Exp $250
Special Collections: Books with Copyright Date from 1850's to 1950's & Histories Principly Midwest/Nebraska
Publications: 1876 History of Washington, with index
Restriction: Non-circulating to the public

FRANKLIN

P FRANKLIN PUBLIC LIBRARY,* 1502 P St, 68939-1542. SAN 309-4669. Tel: 308-425-3162. E-Mail: frklnlbry@gtmc.net. *Librn*, Linda Gooder
Pop 1,067; Circ 11,500
Library Holdings: Bk Titles 12,000
Mem of Republican Valley Libr Syst
Friends of the Library Group

FREMONT

S DODGE COUNTY HISTORICAL SOCIETY, May Museum Library, 1643 N Nye, 68025. SAN 327-2265. Tel: 402-721-4515. FAX: 402-721-8354. E-Mail: maymuseum@juno.com. Web Site: www.connectfremont.org. *Dir*, Patty Manhart
Library Holdings: Bk Titles 1,000

S EASTERN NEBRASKA GENEALOGICAL SOCIETY LIBRARY, PO Box 541, 68026. SAN 370-8551. Tel: 402-721-9553. Web Site: www.connectfremont.org/club/engs.htm.
Founded 1972
Library Holdings: Bk Vols 400; Per Subs 200
Publications: Newsletter (quarterly)

P KEENE MEMORIAL LIBRARY, Fremont Public Library, 1030 N Broad St, 68025-4199. SAN 309-4677. Tel: 402-727-2694. FAX: 402-727-2693. Web Site: www.keene.lib.ne.us. *Dir*, Ann E Stephens; E-Mail: stephens@keene.lib.ne.us; *Ch Servs*, Joan Chesley; *Circ, Ref*, Barbara Bandlow; *ILL*, Myrtle Nygren; Staff 4 (MLS 2, Non-MLS 2)
Founded 1901. Pop 23,680; Circ 194,654
Oct 1999-Sep 2000 Income $564,114, State $4,973, City $539,641, Locally Generated Income $19,500. Mats Exp $98,900, Books $60,500, Per/Ser (Incl. Access Fees) $10,000, AV Equip $16,000, Other Print Mats $2,400, Electronic Ref Mat (Incl. Access Fees) $10,000. Sal $357,560 (Prof $141,762)
Library Holdings: Bk Vols 76,000; Bk Titles 71,000; Per Subs 235
Special Collections: Classics (Taylor)
Automation Activity & Vendor Info: (Acquisitions) epixtech, inc.; (Cataloging) epixtech, inc.; (Circulation) epixtech, inc.; (OPAC) epixtech, inc.; (Serials) epixtech, inc.
Database Vendor: OCLC - First Search
Member Libraries: Bancroft Public Library
Partic in NEBASE; OCLC Online Computer Library Center, Inc
Friends of the Library Group

CR MIDLAND LUTHERAN COLLEGE, Luther Library, 900 N Clarkson, 68025. SAN 309-4685. Tel: 402-721-5480, Ext 6250. FAX: 402-727-6223. Web Site: www.campus.mlc.edu. *Dir*, Thomas Boyle; E-Mail: boyle@campus.mic.edu; *Ref*, Steve Cox; E-Mail: cox@campus.mlc.edu; *Media Spec*, Barbara Dean; Staff 2 (MLS 2)
Founded 1883. Enrl 1,040; Fac 59; Highest Degree: Bachelor
2000-2001 Income $290,000. Mats Exp $106,662, Books $48,000, Per/Ser (Incl. Access Fees) $35,200, Micro $6,500, AV Equip $3,200, Other Print Mats $7,762, Electronic Ref Mat (Incl. Access Fees) $6,000. Sal $159,900 (Prof $77,400)
Library Holdings: Bk Vols 108,000; Bk Titles 102,000
Special Collections: Biblical Literature
Automation Activity & Vendor Info: (Acquisitions) SIRSI; (Cataloging) SIRSI; (Circulation) SIRSI; (Course Reserve) SIRSI; (Media Booking) SIRSI; (OPAC) SIRSI; (Serials) SIRSI
Database Vendor: Ebsco - EbscoHost, OCLC - First Search
Partic in NEBASE; Nebr Independent Col Libr Consortium; OCLC Online Computer Library Center, Inc

FRIEND

P GILBERT MEMORIAL LIBRARY, 628 Second St, 68359-1308. SAN 309-4693. Tel: 402-947-5081. *Asst Librn*, Dorothy Kelso
Founded 1916. Circ 3,046
Library Holdings: Bk Vols 10,558; Per Subs 35

FULLERTON

P FULLERTON PUBLIC LIBRARY,* 903 Broadway, PO Box 578, 68638. SAN 309-4707. Tel: 308-536-2382. E-Mail: fpl@hamilton.net. *Dir*, Joyce Anderson
Founded 1913. Pop 1,452; Circ 12,008
Oct 1999-Sep 2000 Income $33,600. Mats Exp Books $8,500. Sal $13,100
Library Holdings: Bk Vols 13,000; Per Subs 38
Mem of NE Libr Syst
Friends of the Library Group

GENEVA

P GENEVA PUBLIC LIBRARY, 1043 G St, 68361. SAN 309-4715. Tel: 402-759-3416. FAX: 402-759-3416. *Librn*, Donna Shearer
Pop 3,032; Circ 35,510
2000-2001 Income $65,009, State $860, City $52,739, Other $11,410
Library Holdings: Bk Vols 20,284; Per Subs 51

GENOA

P GENOA PUBLIC LIBRARY,* 421 Willard Ave, PO Box 279, 68640-0279. SAN 309-4723. Tel: 402-993-2943. E-Mail: glibry@megavision.com. Web Site: www.megavision.com/glbry. *Librn*, Tammy Johnson
Pop 1,090; Circ 8,015
Library Holdings: Bk Vols 8,597; Per Subs 22

GERING

P GERING PUBLIC LIBRARY,* 1055 P St, 69341-2826. SAN 309-4731. Tel: 308-436-7433. FAX: 308-436-6869. Web Site: www.gering.org/library. *Dir*, Nadine de'Bacco
Founded 1895. Pop 7,886; Circ 81,000
Library Holdings: Bk Titles 40,000
Mem of Panhandle Library System
Friends of the Library Group

S NATIONAL PARK SERVICE, Scotts Bluff National Monument, Oregon Trail Museum Library, PO Box 27, 69341-0027. SAN 309-474X. Tel: 308-436-4340. FAX: 308-436-7611. Web Site: www.nps.gov/scbl. *In Charge*, Dean Knudsen
Library Holdings: Bk Vols 1,300
Restriction: In-house use for visitors

GIBBON

P GIBBON PUBLIC LIBRARY,* 116 LaBarre, PO Box 309, 68840-0309. SAN 309-4758. Tel: 308-468-5889. FAX: 308-468-5501. E-Mail: gibbonpublibrary@nctc.net. *Dir*, Darlene Catlin
Founded 1909. Pop 1,531; Circ 17,046
Library Holdings: Bk Vols 9,625; Per Subs 61
Friends of the Library Group

GILTNER

P GILTNER PUBLIC LIBRARY,* 355 N Pelham Ave, 68841. SAN 377-1903. Tel: 402-849-2942. *Dir*, Beulah Wagner
Library Holdings: Bk Vols 2,000
Open Tues 3-5

GORDON

P GORDON CITY LIBRARY,* 101 W Fifth St, 69343. SAN 309-4766. Tel: 308-282-1198. FAX: 308-282-1431. E-Mail: gorcitli@gpcom.net. Web Site: www.gordoncitylibrary.org. *Dir, Librn*, Maria Kling
Founded 1922. Pop 1,924
Library Holdings: Bk Titles 11,500; Per Subs 58
Subject Interests: History, Literary criticism
Special Collections: Gordon Journal Coll from 1894, micro; Interpreter's Bible; Large Print Coll; Nebraska History Coll
Mem of Panhandle Library System
Friends of the Library Group

GOTHENBURG

P GOTHENBURG PUBLIC LIBRARY,* 1104 Lake Ave, 69138-1903. SAN 309-4774. Tel: 308-537-2591. FAX: 308-537-3667. *Dir*, Lisa Geiken
Founded 1915. Pop 3,480; Circ 25,209
Library Holdings: Bk Vols 20,000; Per Subs 77
Mem of Kearney Pub Libr

GRAND ISLAND

P EDITH ABBOTT MEMORIAL LIBRARY, Grand Island Public Library,* 211 N Washington, 68801-5855. SAN 309-4782. Tel: 308-385-5333. FAX: 308-385-5339. E-Mail: refdesk@gi.lib.ne.us. *Dir*, Steve Fosselman; E-Mail: sf@gi.lib.ne.us; *Cat*, Bobbie Lawrey; E-Mail: ral@gi.lib.ne.us; *Ad Servs*, Ella Rathod; E-Mail: er@gi.lib.ne.us; *Ch Servs*, Merry VonSeggern; E-Mail: mv@gi.lib.ne.us; *ILL*, Gerianne Pickering; *Ref Servs YA*, Faye Friesen; E-Mail: faf@gi.lib.ne.us; Staff 23 (MLS 3, Non-MLS 20)
Founded 1884. Pop 48,000; Circ 244,363
Library Holdings: Bk Vols 107,336; Per Subs 208
Special Collections: Genealogy (Lue R Spencer State DAR Coll & Ella Sprague Coll)
Database Vendor: Ebsco - EbscoHost, epixtech, inc., OCLC - First Search, Wilson - Wilson Web
Member Libraries: Maltman Memorial Public Library
Friends of the Library Group

J CENTRAL COMMUNITY COLLEGE LIBRARY,* 3134 W Hwy 34, 68802-4903. (Mail add: PO Box 4903, 68802-4903), SAN 377-1741. Tel: 308-389-6395. FAX: 308-389-6397, 308-389-7397. Web Site: www.cccneb.edu. *Librn*, Linda Bowden; E-Mail: lbowde.@cccneb.edu
1997-1998 Mats Exp $80,000
Library Holdings: Bk Vols 3,500; Per Subs 70
Partic in OCLC Online Computer Library Center, Inc

GM DEPARTMENT OF VETERANS AFFAIRS MEDICAL CENTER, Library Service,* 2201 N Broadwell Ave, 68803-2196. SAN 309-4804. Tel: 308-382-3660. FAX: 308-389-5148.
Founded 1950
Oct 1997-Sep 1998 Income $24,000. Mats Exp $24,000
Library Holdings: Bk Vols 3,395; Per Subs 125
Special Collections: Talking Books
Partic in Medline; Nat Libr of Med

S STUHR MUSEUM OF THE PRAIRIE PIONEER, Research Library, 3133 W Hwy 34, 68801-7280. SAN 309-4790. Tel: 308-385-5316. FAX: 308-385-5028. *Asst Curator*, Karen Keehr; Staff 2 (Non-MLS 2)
Founded 1967
Library Holdings: Bk Titles 10,000; Per Subs 10
Special Collections: Arthur F Bentley Coll; Judge Bayard H Paine Coll
Publications: Bartenbach Opera House, fourth publication; Prairie Pioneer Press, first publication; Schimmer's Sand Krog-Resort on the Platte; Sheep King, third publication; Townbuilders, second publication

GRANT

P HASTINGS MEMORIAL LIBRARY, Grant City Library, 246 Central Ave, 69140-0786. SAN 309-4812. Tel: 308-352-4894. E-Mail: booksrus@gpcom.net. *Librn*, Sally Borowski
Pop 1,270; Circ 13,299
Library Holdings: Bk Vols 15,000
Mem of Republican Valley Libr Syst
Open Mon-Wed 2-5 & Sat 10-12 & 1-5

GREELEY

P GREELEY PUBLIC LIBRARY,* Rte 1, Box 8, 68842. SAN 309-4820. Tel: 308-428-2545. *Librn*, Helen Sullivan
Pop 597; Circ 2,392
Library Holdings: Bk Vols 6,080
Open Wed & Sat 3-5pm

GREENWOOD

P GREENWOOD PUBLIC LIBRARY,* 619 Main St, PO Box 29, 68366-0029. SAN 309-4839. Tel: 402-789-2301. FAX: 402-789-2300. E-Mail: libpatron@aol.com. *Dir*, Lesa Cameron; *Asst Librn*, Arnetta Carpenter
Pop 587; Circ 2,663
1997-1998 Income $23,248, State $438, Locally Generated Income $250. Mats Exp $3,150, Books $1,800, Per/Ser (Incl. Access Fees) $450, Other Print Mats $900. Sal $12,000
Library Holdings: Bk Titles 12,000
Mem of Southeastern Regional Libr Syst
Friends of the Library Group

GRESHAM

P GRESHAM PUBLIC LIBRARY,* 424 Elm St, PO Box 148, 68367-0148. SAN 309-4847. *Librn*, Julie Dey
Founded 1904. Pop 400; Circ 2,500
Library Holdings: Bk Vols 8,500
Friends of the Library Group

GRETNA

P GRETNA PUBLIC LIBRARY,* 736 South St, 68028. SAN 309-4855. Tel: 402-332-4480. FAX: 402-332-2506. *Librn*, Sylvia Allen; *Asst Librn*, Diane Bergman; Staff 4 (Non-MLS 4)
Founded 1929. Pop 2,900
Oct 1998-Sep 1999 Income $61,800, State $800, City $55,000, Locally Generated Income $6,000. Mats Exp $8,900, Books $7,500, Per/Ser (Incl. Access Fees) $1,200, Electronic Ref Mat (Incl. Access Fees) $200. Sal $24,195
Library Holdings: Bk Vols 17,311; Bk Titles 14,347; Per Subs 44
Mem of Eastern Libr Syst

GUIDE ROCK

P AULD-DOUDNA PUBLIC LIBRARY, PO Box 126, 68942-0126. SAN 309-4863. *Librn*, Wanda Langer
Founded 1918. Pop 290; Circ 1,559
1998-1999 Income $4,574, City $3,977, Other $597. Mats Exp $709, Books $655, Other Print Mats $54. Sal $1,875
Library Holdings: Bk Vols 10,430
Mem of Republican Valley Libr Syst

HARTINGTON

P HARTINGTON PUBLIC LIBRARY,* 106 S Broadway, PO Box 458, 68739. SAN 309-4871. Tel: 402-254-6245. *Librn*, Lee Rose; *Asst Librn*, Joyce Rossiter
Founded 1914. Pop 1,730; Circ 27,000
Library Holdings: Bk Vols 20,000; Per Subs 55
Friends of the Library Group

HARVARD

P HARVARD PUBLIC LIBRARY,* 309 N Clay Ave, PO Box 130, 68944-0130. SAN 309-488X. Tel: 402-772-7131. E-Mail: hpl@inebraska.com. *Librn*, Mae Morgan
Founded 1915. Pop 976; Circ 4,416
Library Holdings: Bk Vols 6,560; Per Subs 32
Mem of Republican Valley Libr Syst
Friends of the Library Group

HASTINGS

S ADAMS COUNTY HISTORICAL SOCIETY ARCHIVES, 1330 N Burlington Ave, PO Box 102, 68902. SAN 309-4898. Tel: 402-463-5838. E-Mail: achs@inebraska.com. Web Site: www.adamshistory.org. *In Charge*, Catherine Renschler
Founded 1965
Library Holdings: Bk Vols 150
Subject Interests: Genealogy
Special Collections: Adams County Archives; Adams County Newspapers, micro; Church Records Coll; Dust Bowl Years, oral hist; Friborg Architectural Coll, drawings; Probate Records; School Records Coll
Publications: Historical News (bi-monthly)
Restriction: Non-circulating to the public

J CENTRAL COMMUNITY COLLEGE, Nuckolls Library, E Hwy 6, PO Box 1024, 68902. SAN 309-4901. Tel: 402-461-2538. FAX: 402-460-2135. *Dean*, Dr Sandra Block; *Tech Servs*, Denise Harder; E-Mail: dharders@cccneb.edu; Staff 2 (Non-MLS 2)
Founded 1970. Enrl 1,420; Fac 135
Library Holdings: Bk Vols 4,112; Bk Titles 3,939; Per Subs 53
Database Vendor: OCLC - First Search, Wilson - Wilson Web
Partic in Nebr Libr Com

R FIRST PRESBYTERIAN CHURCH LIBRARY, 621 N Lincoln, 68901. SAN 309-491X. Tel: 402-462-5147. FAX: 402-462-6818. E-Mail: fpc@tcgcs.com. *Librn*, Susan Nedderman; Staff 1 (MLS 1)
Founded 1950
Jan 1999-Dec 1999 Income Parent Institution $1,500. Mats Exp Books $1,500
Library Holdings: Bk Titles 5,000; Per Subs 11
Subject Interests: Philosophy, Religion
Special Collections: Large Print Coll

C HASTINGS COLLEGE, Perkins Library, 800 N Turner Ave, 68901-7695. SAN 309-4928. Tel: 402-461-7330. FAX: 402-461-7480. Web Site: www.hastings.edu/resource/library/perkins.htm. *Coll Develop, Dir*, Robert Nedderman; *Media Spec, Ref*, Dee Yost; *Tech Servs*, Patrice Hughes
Founded 1882. Enrl 1,118; Fac 67; Highest Degree: Master
Library Holdings: Bk Vols 123,512; Bk Titles 90,000; Per Subs 583
Special Collections: Holcomb Lewis & Clark Coll; Plains & Western History (Brown Coll)
Partic in NEBASE; Nebr Independent Col Libr Consortium; OCLC Online Computer Library Center, Inc
Friends of the Library Group

S HASTINGS CORRECTIONAL CENTER LIBRARY,* PO Box 2048, 68902-2048. SAN 377-1768. Tel: 402-462-1947. FAX: 402-462-1957. *Dir*, Brandon Bejaraivo
Library Holdings: Bk Vols 1,200; Per Subs 15

S HASTINGS MUSEUM OF NATURAL & CULTURAL HISTORY LIBRARY, 1330 N Burlington, 68901-3099. (Mail add: PO Box 1286, 68902-1286), Tel: 402-461-2399. FAX: 402-461-2379. E-Mail: hmcollections@alltel.net. *Dir*, Terry Hunter
Library Holdings: Bk Vols 1,000; Per Subs 15
Special Collections: Bureau of American Ethnology Reports: Smithsonian Institution, 1880 to 1930; Official Records of the Union & Confederate Armies, Washington, 1881; War of the Rebellion
Restriction: Non-circulating to the public

P HASTINGS PUBLIC LIBRARY, 517 W Fourth St, 68901. (Mail add: PO Box 849, 68902-0849), SAN 309-4944. Tel: 402-461-2346. TDD: 402-461-2357. FAX: 402-461-2359. E-Mail: staff@hastings.lib.ne.us. Web Site: www.hastings.lib.ne.us. *Dir*, Linda M Rea; E-Mail: lrea@hastings.lib.ne.us; *Asst Dir*, Pam P Bohmfalk; E-Mail: pbohmfal@hastings.lib.ne.us; *Ch Servs*, Kathy Schultz; E-Mail: kschultz@hastings.lib.ne.us; Staff 23 (MLS 5, Non-MLS 18)
Founded 1903. Pop 29,625; Circ 280,069
Oct 1999-Sep 2000 Income $780,210, State $8,015, City $635,213, Federal $5,504, County $155,177, Locally Generated Income $26,990, Other $1,600. Mats Exp $152,122, Books $120,779, Electronic Ref Mat (Incl. Access Fees) $31,343. Sal $505,908
Library Holdings: Bk Vols 136,962; Per Subs 276
Special Collections: Toys, Puppets
Automation Activity & Vendor Info: (Acquisitions) epixtech, inc.; (Cataloging) epixtech, inc.; (Circulation) epixtech, inc.; (Serials) epixtech, inc.
Database Vendor: Ebsco - EbscoHost, OCLC - First Search
Publications: Friends News (Newsletter)
Mem of Republican Valley Libr Syst
Special Services for the Deaf - Staff with knowledge of sign language; TDD
Friends of the Library Group

M HASTINGS REGIONAL CENTER, Medical Center Library,* PO Box 579, 68902. SAN 350-1213. Tel: 402-462-1971, Ext 3342. FAX: 402-460-3100. *Dir*, Ruth Swingle
Founded 1938
Jul 1996-Jun 1997 Income $54,401. Mats Exp $1,900, Books $500, Per/Ser (Incl. Access Fees) $1,200, Other Print Mats $200. Sal $40,500 (Prof $28,000)
Library Holdings: Bk Vols 6,400; Per Subs 30
Subject Interests: Nursing, Psychiatry, Psychology
Special Collections: Hastings Regional Center Archives
Branches:
PATIENTS Tel: 402-463-2471, Ext 391. *In Charge*, Ruth Swingle
Special Collections: Nebraska History

HAYES CENTER

P HAYES CENTER PUBLIC LIBRARY,* 402 Troth St, PO Box 174, 69032-0174. SAN 309-4960. Tel: 308-286-3411. *Librn*, Phyllis Fellker
Pop 231; Circ 2,010
Library Holdings: Bk Vols 6,000
Mem of Republican Valley Libr Syst
Open Tues-Fri 1-5pm

HEBRON

P HEBRON SECREST LIBRARY, PO Box 125, 68370. SAN 309-4979. Tel: 402-768-6701. *Librn*, Janice A Rihn; *Asst Librn*, Judy Kassebaum
Founded 1921. Pop 1,907; Circ 10,666
Library Holdings: Bk Vols 11,052; Per Subs 27
Subject Interests: Church history
Special Collections: Local Memorabilia
Publications: Library Folder for 60th Anniversary, 1921-81
Mem of Beatrice Public Library

HEMINGFORD

P HEMINGFORD PUBLIC LIBRARY,* PO Box 6, 69348. SAN 309-4987. Tel: 308-487-3454. E-Mail: hpl@bbc.net. *Librn*, Sheryl Roberts
Pop 1,023; Circ 2,058
Library Holdings: Bk Vols 8,500; Per Subs 26

HENDERSON

SR BETHESDA MENNONITE CHURCH LIBRARY, PO Box 115, 68371. SAN 309-4995. Tel: 402-723-4562. FAX: 402-723-4567. *Librn*, Velma Friesen
Feb 1998-Jan 1999 Income $1,000. Mats Exp $1,228, Books $1,026, Per/Ser (Incl. Access Fees) $100, Micro $102
Library Holdings: Bk Vols 4,500
Special Collections: Children's & Christian Literature Coll

HILDRETH

P HILDRETH PUBLIC LIBRARY,* 248 Commercial Ave, PO Box 112, 68947-0112. SAN 309-5002. Tel: 308-938-2471. FAX: 308-938-2545. E-Mail: hpl@gtmc.net. *Librn*, Vicki Casper
Pop 394; Circ 4,286
Library Holdings: Bk Vols 8,000; Per Subs 12
Mem of Holdrege Public Library System
Friends of the Library Group

HOLDREGE

P HOLDREGE PUBLIC LIBRARY SYSTEM,* 604 East Ave, 68949. SAN 309-5029. Tel: 308-995-6556. FAX: 308-995-5732. E-Mail: holdr1lb@ink.org. Web Site: www.ci.holdrege.ne.us/libindex.htm. *Dir*, Jeff A Gilderson-Duwe; *Circ, Ref*, Linda Davey; *Cat*, Phyllis Exstrom; *Ch Servs*, Cinthia Gitt; Staff 12 (MLS 1, Non-MLS 11)
Founded 1895. Pop 14,553; Circ 112,445
Jul 1997-Jun 1998 Income $320,006, State $3,286, City $146,214, County $89,707, Other $80,799. Mats Exp $305,419, Books $15,420, Per/Ser (Incl. Access Fees) $8,326. Sal $193,899
Library Holdings: Bk Vols 65,000; Bk Titles 60,000; Per Subs 160
Automation Activity & Vendor Info: (Cataloging) Follett; (Circulation) Follett
Member Libraries: Arapahoe Public Library; Axtell Public Library; Hildreth Public Library
Partic in NEBASE; Nebr Telecommunications Network
Friends of the Library Group

S NEBRASKA PRAIRIE MUSEUM, (Formerly Phelps County Historical Society Library), Don O Lindgren Library, N Hwy 183, PO Box 164, 68949-0164. SAN 325-2256. Tel: 308-995-5015. E-Mail: rs55453@navix.net.; Staff 1 (Non-MLS 1)
Founded 1972
Library Holdings: Bk Vols 4,200
Subject Interests: Genealogy, Local history, Nebraska hist, Phelps County

HOOPER

P HOOPER PUBLIC LIBRARY,* 201 N Main, PO Box 45, 68031. SAN 309-5037. Tel: 402-654-3833. *Dir*, Lylas Guthrie
Library Holdings: Bk Vols 10,169; Per Subs 10
Partic in Eastern Nebr Libr Asn; Nebr Libr Asn
Open Tues & Thurs 9-5:30, Sat 9-1

HOWELLS

P HOWELLS PUBLIC LIBRARY,* 130 N Third St, PO Box 337, 68641. SAN 309-5045. Tel: 402-986-1666. FAX: 402-986-1666. *Librn*, Lorraine Gall; *Asst Librn*, Marlene Hegemann
Pop 615; Circ 7,020
Library Holdings: Bk Vols 6,784; Per Subs 58
Publications: Booklist; Library Journal
Partic in Northeast Library System
Friends of the Library Group

HUMBOLDT

P BRUUN MEMORIAL PUBLIC LIBRARY,* 730 Third St, PO Box 368, 68376-0368. SAN 309-5053. Tel: 402-862-2914. E-Mail: bruunlib@navix.net. *Chief Librn*, Carol Glathar
Founded 1885. Pop 1,173; Circ 23,524
Library Holdings: Bk Titles 22,000; Per Subs 67
Mem of Southeastern Regional Libr Syst
Open Mon 2-8:30, Tues & Wed 10-12 & 2-5:30, Thurs & Fri 2-5:30, Sat 9-12
Friends of the Library Group

HUMPHREY

P HUMPHREY PUBLIC LIBRARY, 309 Main St, PO Box 266, 68642-0266. SAN 309-5061. Tel: 402-923-0957. FAX: 402-923-0957. E-Mail: hplibry@megavision.com. *Librn*, Michele Hastreiter; *Asst Librn*, Betty Sueper
Founded 1938. Circ 6,958
Oct 1999-Sep 2000 Income $38,850, City $31,850, Federal $2,000, County $5,000. Mats Exp Books $10,000. Sal $15,000
Library Holdings: Bk Vols 12,572; Per Subs 60
Automation Activity & Vendor Info: (Circulation) Follett
Mem of NE Libr Syst

HYANNIS

P GRANT COUNTY LIBRARY,* PO Box 328, 69350-0328. SAN 309-507X. Tel: 308-458-2218. FAX: 308-458-2485. *Librn*, Rhonda Manning
Founded 1929. Pop 877; Circ 18,896
Library Holdings: Bk Vols 8,000; Per Subs 48
Mem of Panhandle Library System
Open Mon, Wed & Fri 9-12 & 1-5

IMPERIAL

P IMPERIAL PUBLIC LIBRARY,* 703 Broadway, PO Box 728, 69033-0728. SAN 309-5088. Tel: 308-882-4754. FAX: 308-882-4754. E-Mail: library@chase3000.com. *Coll Develop, Dir*, Norma Dannatt
Pop 6,761; Circ 59,026
1998-1999 Income $88,950
Library Holdings: Per Subs 63
Automation Activity & Vendor Info: (Circulation) Follett
Mem of Republican Valley Libr Syst
Friends of the Library Group

KEARNEY

P KEARNEY PUBLIC LIBRARY & INFORMATION CENTER,* 2020 First Ave, 68847. SAN 309-510X. Tel: 308-233-3282. FAX: 308-233-3291. E-Mail: secretary@kpl.kearneylib.org. Web Site: www.kearneylib.org. *Dir*, Jeanne Saathoff; *Ad Servs, Asst Dir, Bkmobile Coordr*, Carol Reed; Tel: 308-233-3283, E-Mail: assistdir@kpl.kearneylib.org; *Ch Servs*, Shawna Linder; Tel: 308-233-3284, E-Mail: youthserv@kpl.kearneylib.org; *Tech Servs*, Mike Marchand
Founded 1890. Pop 37,447; Circ 384,418
Oct 1998-Sep 1999 Income $868,991, City $731,764, County $137,227. Mats Exp $113,669, Books $102,180, Per/Ser (Incl. Access Fees) $6,596, Electronic Ref Mat (Incl. Access Fees) $4,893. Sal $389,289 (Prof $176,936)
Library Holdings: Bk Vols 100,210; Bk Titles 75,026; Per Subs 157
Subject Interests: Genealogy
Special Collections: Kearney Coll, VF
Automation Activity & Vendor Info: (Acquisitions) epixtech, inc.; (Cataloging) epixtech, inc.; (Circulation) epixtech, inc.; (OPAC) epixtech, inc.; (Serials) epixtech, inc.
Database Vendor: OCLC - First Search
Mem of Meridian Libr Syst
Friends of the Library Group
Bookmobiles: 1

UNIVERSITY OF NEBRASKA AT KEARNEY

C CALVIN T RYAN LIBRARY, 2508 11th Ave, 68849-2240. Tel: 308-865-8535. Interlibrary Loan Service Tel: 308-865-8594. Circulation Tel: 308-865-8599. Reference Tel: 308-865-8586. Toll Free Tel: 800-856-5155. FAX: 308-865-8722. Web Site: www.unk.edu/acad/library/home.html. *Dir*, Mike Herbison; *Govt Doc*, Diana Keith; *Online Servs*, Greg Anderson; *Head, Cat*, Sharon Mason; *Ref*, Trudy de Goede; *Archivist, Ref*, John Lillis; *Head, Ser Acq*, James Rowling; *Ref Servs Ch, Ref Servs YA*, Janet Wilke; *Head Ref*, Mary Barton; *Access Serv*, Dee Goedert; *ILL*, Sheryl Heidenreich; Staff 11 (MLS 10, Non-MLS 1)
Founded 1906. Enrl 7,500; Fac 325
Jul 1998-Jun 1999 Income $2,061,962, State $1,890,381, Locally Generated Income $135,060, Parent Institution $36,521. Mats Exp $584,812, Books $126,111, Per/Ser (Incl. Access Fees) $401,475, Presv $15,967, Micro $22,742, Electronic Ref Mat (Incl. Access Fees) $18,517. Sal $895,087 (Prof $526,037)
Library Holdings: Bk Vols 306,307; Bk Titles 192,333; Per Subs 1,657
Subject Interests: Education, Psychology
Automation Activity & Vendor Info: (Acquisitions) Innovative Interfaces Inc.; (Cataloging) Innovative Interfaces Inc.; (Circulation) Innovative Interfaces Inc.
Partic in Dialog Corporation; NEBASE; OCLC Online Computer Library Center, Inc

S VOCATIONAL CURRICULUM RESOURCE CENTER, WSTC E212, 68849. SAN 377-6247. Tel: 308-865-8669. FAX: 308-865-8669. E-Mail: nvcrc@unk.edu. *Dir*, Mary Jo Klesath; Tel: 308-865-8462, E-Mail: klesathmj@unk.edu; Staff 2 (Non-MLS 2)
Founded 1974

Jul 2000-Jun 2001 Income (Main Library Only) State $55,000
Library Holdings: Bk Vols 12,000; Bk Titles 10,000; Spec Interest Per Sub 10,000
Subject Interests: Post-secondary educ, Secondary educ, Vocational education
Special Collections: Applied Academics/Integrated Education; Software; Tech Prep; Vocational Special Needs
Mem of Meridian Libr Syst
Partic in NE Libr Asn

S YOUTH REHABILITATION & TREATMENT CENTER LIBRARY, 2802 30th Ave, 68847-9599. SAN 377-1806. Tel: 308-865-5313. FAX: 308-865-5323. *Librn*, Susan Divan; E-Mail: sdivan@esv10.org
Founded 1881
Library Holdings: Bk Vols 7,300; Per Subs 50
Automation Activity & Vendor Info: (Cataloging) Follett; (Circulation) Follett
Mem of Meridian Libr Syst

KIMBALL

P KIMBALL PUBLIC LIBRARY,* 208 S Walnut St, 69145. SAN 309-5126. Tel: 308-235-4523. FAX: 308-235-2971. E-Mail: kplib@megavision.com. *Dir, Librn*, Carolyn Brown
Pop 4,792; Circ 28,440
Library Holdings: Bk Vols 26,000; Per Subs 60
Special Collections: Kimball County History Coll, newsp clippings, photog
Mem of Panhandle Library System
Partic in Panhandle Library Access Network
Friends of the Library Group

LA VISTA

P LA VISTA PUBLIC LIBRARY,* 9110 Giles Rd, 68128. SAN 309-5134. Tel: 402-537-3900. FAX: 402-537-3902. *Librn*, Sharon McAnulty; *Asst Librn*, Cathy D'Agosta; Staff 2 (MLS 1, Non-MLS 1)
Founded 1972. Pop 10,140; Circ 45,358
Library Holdings: Bk Vols 36,000; Bk Titles 30,784; Per Subs 97
Partic in Bellevue Pub Libr Syst

LEIGH

P LEIGH PUBLIC LIBRARY,* 156 Main St, PO Box 158, 68643-0158. SAN 309-5142. Tel: 402-487-2507. FAX: 402-487-2507. E-Mail: leilib@megavision.com. *Dir*, Lori Welsch
Pop 509; Circ 2,742
Library Holdings: Bk Vols 5,000; Per Subs 30
Mem of NE Libr Syst
Open Tues 2-5, Wed 2-6, Thurs 5-8 & Sat 9-11 & 2-5

LEWELLEN

P LEWELLEN PUBLIC LIBRARY,* PO Box 104, 69147-0104. SAN 309-5150. Tel: 308-778-5421. *Librn*, Peggy Rohlfing
Founded 1920. Pop 368; Circ 3,868
Library Holdings: Bk Vols 4,500

LEXINGTON

P LEXINGTON PUBLIC LIBRARY,* 103 E Tenth St, PO Box 778, 68850-0778. SAN 309-5169. Tel: 308-324-2151. FAX: 308-324-2140. *Dir*, Ruth Seward; *Asst Dir*, Elberta Brummet; *Assoc Librn*, Edna Schultz
Pop 8,544; Circ 73,019
Library Holdings: Bk Titles 25,286; Per Subs 81
Mem of Meridian Libr Syst
Friends of the Library Group

LINCOLN

S AMERICAN HISTORICAL SOCIETY OF GERMANS FROM RUSSIA, Archives & Historical Library,* 631 D St, 68502-1199. SAN 328-0454. Tel: 402-474-3363. FAX: 402-474-7229. E-Mail: ahsgr@aol.com. Web Site: pixel.cs.vt.edu/library, www.ahsgr.org. *Librn*, Jan Traci Roth
Founded 1968
Library Holdings: Bk Vols 3,400; Bk Titles 2,820; Per Subs 179
Special Collections: Germans from Russia
Publications: Annotated Bibliography; Family History List
Mem of SE Nebr Libr Syst
Partic in NEBASE

SR BACK TO THE BIBLE, Broadcast Library,* 6400 Cornhusker Hwy, 68507-3160. SAN 377-3795. Tel: 402-474-4567. FAX: 402-464-7474. Web Site: www.backtothebible.org.
Library Holdings: Bk Vols 800; Per Subs 25

M BRYAN LGH MEDICAL CENTER EAST, Helene Fuld Learning Resource Center, 1600 S 48th St, 68506. SAN 327-2281. Tel: 402-481-3908. FAX: 402-481-8404, 402-481-8421. *Librn*, Susan P Echols; Staff 3 (MLS 1, Non-MLS 2)
Library Holdings: Bk Titles 5,000; Per Subs 300
Subject Interests: Nursing
Automation Activity & Vendor Info: (Acquisitions) Athena; (Cataloging) Athena; (Circulation) Athena; (Course Reserve) Athena
Database Vendor: Silverplatter Information Inc.
Restriction: Open to public for reference only

M BRYAN LGH MEDICAL CENTER WEST, Medical Library, 2300 S 16th St, 68502. SAN 324-6256. Tel: 402-481-5637. *Librn*, Carmen Jirovec
Library Holdings: Bk Vols 1,000; Bk Titles 800; Per Subs 100
Subject Interests: Oncology, Orthopedics, Psychiatry
Special Collections: Orthopedics (Winnett Orr Coll), bks, journals
Partic in Docline; Lincoln Health Sciences Library Group; Medline

R CHRIST UNITED METHODIST CHURCH LIBRARY,* 4530 A St, 68510. SAN 309-5185. Tel: 402-489-9618. FAX: 402-489-9619. *Librn*, Cheryl Pope
Library Holdings: Bk Vols 4,550

S CHRISTIAN RECORD SERVICES, Lending Library, 4444 S 52nd St, 68516. SAN 327-6058. Tel: 402-488-0981. FAX: 402-488-7582. E-Mail: crsnet@compuserv.com. Web Site: www.ChristianRecord.org. *Dir*, Jerry Stevens
Library Holdings: Bk Titles 2,156

S CHURCH OF JESUS CHRIST OF LATTER-DAY SAINTS, Family History Center, 3100 Old Cheney Rd, 68516-2775. (Mail add: PO Box 82244, 68501-2244), SAN 377-3825. Tel: 402-423-4561. *Dir*, Susan Randall
Library Holdings: Bk Vols 350

GM DEPARTMENT OF VETERANS AFFAIRS, Library Service,* 600 S 70th St, 68510. SAN 309-5320. Tel: 402-489-3802, Ext 6380. FAX: 402-486-7868.
Founded 1930
Library Holdings: Bk Vols 4,577; Per Subs 307
Subject Interests: Allied health, Medicine
Special Collections: Patient health education
Mem of Southeastern Regional Libr Syst
Partic in Lincoln Health Sciences Library Group

P LINCOLN CITY LIBRARIES, Bennett Martin Library, 136 S 14th St, 68508-1899. SAN 350-1272. Tel: 402-441-8500. TDD: 402-441-8589. FAX: 402-441-8586. E-Mail: library@rand.lcl.lib.ne.us. Web Site: www.lcl.lib.ne.us. *Dir*, Carol J Connor; Tel: 402-441-8510, E-Mail: cjc@rand.lcl.lib.ne.us; *Asst Dir*, John F Dale; *Automation Syst Coordr*, John Felton; *Ch Servs*, Pat Leach; *Tech Servs*, Cindy Cochran; *Res*, Suzan Connell; Staff 134 (MLS 26, Non-MLS 108)
Founded 1877. Pop 213,000; Circ 2,260,728
Sep 1998-Aug 1999 Income (Main Library and Branch Library) $4,716,475, State $44,864, City $3,784,433, Federal $33,831, County $391,132, Other $462,215. Mats Exp $440,725, Books $354,725, Per/Ser (Incl. Access Fees) $86,000. Sal $3,400,662
Library Holdings: Bk Vols 657,047; Bk Titles 278,422; Per Subs 1,984
Special Collections: Nebraska Authors
Automation Activity & Vendor Info: (Cataloging) epixtech, inc.; (Circulation) epixtech, inc.; (OPAC) epixtech, inc.
Database Vendor: Ebsco - EbscoHost, epixtech, inc., IAC - Info Trac, OCLC - First Search
Function: ILL available
Partic in OCLC Online Computer Library Center, Inc
Friends of the Library Group
Branches: 6
ARNOLD HEIGHTS, 3815 NW 54th St, 68524. SAN 350-1337. Tel: 402-441-8580. FAX: 402-441-8582.
BELMONT, 1234 Judson, 68521. SAN 350-1361. Tel: 402-441-8590. FAX: 402-441-8592.
BETHANY, 1810 N Cotner Blvd, 68505. SAN 350-1396. Tel: 402-441-8550. FAX: 402-441-8552.
Friends of the Library Group
CHARLES H GERE BRANCH, 2400 S 56th St, 68506-3599. SAN 350-1426. Tel: 402-441-8560. FAX: 402-441-8563.
SOUTH, 27th & South Sts, 68502-3099. SAN 350-1485. Tel: 402-441-8570. FAX: 402-441-8572.
VICTOR E ANDERSON BRANCH, 3635 Touzalin Ave, 68507-1698. SAN 350-1302. Tel: 402-441-8540. FAX: 402-441-8543.
Bookmobiles: 1

S LINCOLN CORRECTIONAL CENTER, Diagnostic & Evaluation Center Library,* PO Box 22800, 68502. SAN 377-1695. Tel: 402-471-2861. FAX: 402-479-6368. *Librn*, Sandra Elcon
1998-1999 Mats Exp $6,500, Books $5,000, Per/Ser (Incl. Access Fees) $1,000
Library Holdings: Bk Vols 4,750; Per Subs 50

S LINCOLN CORRECTIONAL CENTER LIBRARY,* 3216 W Van Dorn, PO Box 22800, 68542-2800. SAN 377-1601. Tel: 402-471-2861, Ext 6137. FAX: 402-479-6100. *Librn*, Sandra Elton
Library Holdings: Bk Vols 10,000; Per Subs 43
Partic in Nebr Libr Asn

S LINCOLN FAMILY PRACTICE PROGRAM LIBRARY, 4600 Valley Rd, Ste 210, 68510-4892. SAN 377-1563. Tel: 402-483-4591. FAX: 402-483-5079. E-Mail: lincfamprac@medline.com. *Librn*, Geri Herrera
Library Holdings: Bk Vols 300; Per Subs 16
Partic in Lincoln Libr Group

S LINCOLN JOURNAL-STAR LIBRARY, 926 P St, 68508. (Mail add: PO Box 81709, 68501), SAN 309-5223. Tel: 402-473-7295. Toll Free Tel: 800-742-7315, Ext 7295. FAX: 402-473-7291. E-Mail: library@journalstar.com. Web Site: www.journalstar.com. *Librn*, Patricia Sloan; Staff 3 (MLS 1, Non-MLS 2)
Founded 1951
Library Holdings: Bk Titles 4,000; Per Subs 50
Special Collections: Charles Starkweather Coll, clippings & micro; Newspapers (Lincoln Journal & Lincoln Star), micro 1867-to-date, pictures, wire photos & clippings
Limited public access for a fee

LINCOLN REGIONAL CENTER
M MEDICAL LIBRARY, W Prospector Pl & Folsom, PO Box 94949, 68509-4949. SAN 350-154X. Tel: 402-471-4444. FAX: 402-479-5460. E-Mail: lrclib1@mail.state.ne.us. *Librn*, Tom Schmitz
Library Holdings: Bk Vols 1,000; Per Subs 40
Subject Interests: Psychiatry, Psychology
Database Vendor: OCLC - First Search
Function: ILL available, Reference services available
Mem of Lincoln Health Sci Libr Group

S PATIENTS' LIBRARY, W Prospector Pl & Folsom, PO Box 94949, 68509-4949. SAN 350-1574. Tel: 402-479-5475. FAX: 402-479-5460. E-Mail: lrclib1@mail.state.ne.us. *Librn*, Tom Schmitz
Library Holdings: Bk Vols 9,344; Per Subs 21
Mem of Southeastern Regional Libr Syst

S LINCOLN SCHOOL OF COMMERCE LIBRARY,* 1821 K St, 68508. SAN 377-158X. Tel: 402-474-5315. FAX: 402-474-5302. Web Site: www.lsc.advantage.com. *Librn*, Kathy Griffin
Library Holdings: Bk Vols 11,000; Per Subs 40
Mem of SE Nebr Libr Syst
Partic in Nebr Libr Asn

SR LITURGY LIBRARY,* 8000 Hickory Lane, 68510-4458. SAN 326-4475. Tel: 402-488-1668. *Dir*, Judy Hartfield Barrick
Founded 1975
Jan 1997-Dec 1998 Income $3,000. Mats Exp $875, Books $600, Other Print Mats $250
Library Holdings: Bk Vols 6,500; Bk Titles 6,200
Special Collections: Arts in Worship; Choral Music
Partic in SE Lib Sys of Nebr
Special Services for the Deaf - Books on deafness & sign language

M MADONNA REHABILITATION HOSPITAL, Medical Library, 5401 South St, 68506-2134. SAN 327-6074. Tel: 402-489-7102. Interlibrary Loan Service Tel: 402-483-9406. FAX: 402-486-8381. *Librn*, Carrie Zimmer; E-Mail: cczimmer@madonna.org
Library Holdings: Bk Titles 600
Restriction: Not open to public
Partic in Docline; Lincoln Health Sciences Library Group

S NATIONAL PARK SERVICE, Midwest Archeological Center Library, Federal Bldg, Rm 474, 100 Centennial Mall N, 68508. SAN 309-5231. Tel: 402-437-5392, Ext 223. FAX: 402-437-5098. Web Site: www.emwas.mps.gov. *In Charge*, Jay Sturdevant
Founded 1969
Library Holdings: Bk Titles 23,830; Per Subs 45
Subject Interests: Archaeology, History
Special Collections: Archeology Coll, mss
Limited distribution of published reports

GL NEBRASKA DEPARTMENT OF CORRECTIONAL SERVICES LIBRARY, Folsom & W Prospector Pl, PO Box 94661, 68509. SAN 377-1679. Tel: 402-471-2654. FAX: 402-479-5119. E-Mail: joa41@aol.com. *Coordr*, John Arnold; Staff 9 (MLS 1, Non-MLS 8)
Library Holdings: Bk Vols 2,000
Database Vendor: OCLC - First Search, Wilson - Wilson Web
Mem of Southeastern Regional Libr Syst
Partic in Nebr Libr Asn

G NEBRASKA DEPARTMENT OF ECONOMIC DEVELOPMENT, Research Division,* 301 Centennial Mall S, PO Box 94666, 68509-4666. SAN 370-6443. Tel: 402-471-3111, 402-471-3801. Toll Free Tel: 800-426-6505. FAX: 402-471-3778. Web Site: www.ded.state.ne.us/index.html, www.neded.org. *Res*, Thomas R Doering
Library Holdings: Per Subs 70

G NEBRASKA DEPARTMENT OF ROADS, Resource Library, 1500 Nebraska Hwy 2, PO Box 94759, 68509. SAN 377-1628. Tel: 402-479-4316. FAX: 402-479-3989. *Librn*, Don Robertson; E-Mail: droberts@dor.state.ne.us; Staff 1 (MLS 1)
1998-1999 Mats Exp $1,000, Books $200, Per/Ser (Incl. Access Fees) $800. Sal $27,000
Library Holdings: Bk Vols 18,000; Per Subs 300
Subject Interests: Transportation
Partic in Chinese Am Libr Asn; Nebr Libr Asn

G NEBRASKA ETHANOL BOARD LIBRARY, 301 Centennial Mall S, 4th flr, PO Box 94922, 68509-4922. SAN 321-8848. Tel: 402-471-2941. FAX: 402-471-2470. Web Site: www.ne-ethanol.org. *Librn*, Gerri Monahan
Library Holdings: Bk Titles 3,500

G NEBRASKA GAME & PARKS COMMISSION LIBRARY,* 2200 N 33rd St, PO Box 30370, 68503. SAN 327-6090. Tel: 402-471-0641. FAX: 402-471-5528. *Librn*, Barbara Voeltz
Library Holdings: Bk Vols 5,000; Per Subs 200
Restriction: By appointment only

M NEBRASKA HEALTH CARE ASSOCIATION LIBRARY,* 421 S Ninth St, Ste 137, 68508. SAN 375-6750. Tel: 402-435-3551. FAX: 402-435-4829.
Library Holdings: Bk Vols 920; Bk Titles 900; Per Subs 25

G NEBRASKA LEGISLATIVE COUNCIL, Legislative Reference Library,* State Capitol Rm 1201, 68509-4945. (Mail add: PO Box 94945, 68509-4945), SAN 328-1760. Tel: 402-471-2221. FAX: 402-479-0967. *Librn*, Anne Christensen; *Librn*, Mary Rasmussen; Staff 2 (MLS 1, Non-MLS 1)
Founded 1980
Library Holdings: Bk Titles 11,500; Per Subs 300
Publications: Acquisitions List (monthly); Annotated Periodicals List
Partic in Dialog Corporation

P NEBRASKA LIBRARY COMMISSION, The Atrium, 1200 N St Ste 120, 68508-2023. SAN 350-1604. Tel: 402-471-2045. Toll Free Tel: 800-307-2665. FAX: 402-471-2083. E-Mail: ready@neon.nlc.state.ne.us. Web Site: www.nlc.state.ne.us. *Dir*, Rod Wagner; *Dep Dir*, Nancy Busch; *Acq, Ref*, Lisa Brawner; *Online Servs*, Jo Budler; Staff 33 (MLS 17, Non-MLS 16)
Founded 1901. Pop 1,711,263
Jul 1999-Jun 2000 Income $4,956,485, State $3,567,553, Federal $1,252,545, Locally Generated Income $136,387. Mats Exp $96,981. Sal $1,369,947
Library Holdings: Bk Titles 29,000; Per Subs 615
Automation Activity & Vendor Info: (Circulation) Sydney; (OPAC) Sydney
Database Vendor: OCLC - First Search, Wilson - Wilson Web
Publications: Interchange; Magazine in Special Format; N3-Nebraska Library Commission Network Services News; NCompass; Nebraska Cassette Books; NLCommunicator; What's Up Doc
Partic in OCLC Online Computer Library Center, Inc
Special Services for the Blind - Braille; Talking Books
Branches: 1
TALKING BOOK & BRAILLE SERVICE
See Separate Entry

P NEBRASKA LIBRARY COMMISSION, Talking Book & Braille Service, 1200 N St, Ste 120, 68508-2023. SAN 309-5258. Tel: 402-471-4038. Toll Free Tel: 800-742-7691. FAX: 402-471-2083. E-Mail: tbbs@nlc.state.ne.us. Web Site: www.nlc.state.ne.us/tbbs/. *Dir*, David L Oertli; E-Mail: doertli@neon.nlc.state.ne.us
Founded 1952
Library Holdings: Bk Vols 169,000; Bk Titles 47,000
Special Collections: Children's Braille; Nebraska Coll, cassette bks
Publications: Interchange (newsletter)

G NEBRASKA NATURAL RESOURCES COMMISSION LIBRARY,* State Office Bldg, 4th flr, PO Box 94876, 68509-4876. SAN 377-371X. Tel: 402-471-2081. FAX: 402-471-3132. *Librn*, Dan Kloch
Library Holdings: Bk Vols 1,000; Per Subs 30

S NEBRASKA STATE HISTORICAL SOCIETY LIBRARY, Division of Library-Archives, 1500 R St, 68508. (Mail add: PO Box 82554, 68501), SAN 309-5266. Tel: 402-471-4751. FAX: 402-471-8922. E-Mail: nshs@nebraskahistory.org. Web Site: www@nebraskahistory.org. *Archivist, Assoc Dir*, Andrea Faling; *Tech Servs*, Cindy S Drake; Tel: 402-471-4786, E-Mail: nshs05@nebraskahistory.org; *Ref*, Ann Billesbach; Staff 10 (MLS 1, Non-MLS 9)
Founded 1878
Jul 1999-Jun 2000 Income $835,700, State $720,000, Federal $6,700, Locally Generated Income $109,000. Mats Exp $49,500, Books $8,000, Per/Ser (Incl. Access Fees) $3,500, Micro $35,000, Manuscripts & Archives $2,000. Sal $598,900 (Prof $315,000)
Library Holdings: Bk Vols 80,000; Per Subs 116
Subject Interests: Genealogy, Nebr hist
Automation Activity & Vendor Info: (OPAC) Athena
Restriction: Non-circulating

GL NEBRASKA STATE LIBRARY, State Capitol, 3rd Flr S, 68509. SAN 309-5274. Tel: 402-471-3189. FAX: 402-471-1011. E-Mail: lawlib@nsc.state.ne.us. Web Site: www.court.nol.org.
Founded 1854
Library Holdings: Bk Titles 127,000
Subject Interests: Law

S NEBRASKA STATE PENITENTIARY LIBRARY,* PO Box 2500, Sta B, 68502. SAN 377-3922. Tel: 402-471-3161. FAX: 402-471-4326. *Dir*, Jo Gray
Library Holdings: Bk Vols 16,000; Per Subs 30
Partic in SE Nebr Libr Asn

R NEBRASKA UNITED METHODIST HISTORICAL CENTER,* Nebraska Wesleyan Univ, 5000 St Paul Ave, 68504-2796. SAN 309-5215. Tel: 402-465-2175. FAX: 402-464-6203. *Curator*, Maureen Vetter; E-Mail: mvetter@umcneb.org
Founded 1942
1998-1999 Mats Exp Books $100. Sal $9,470
Library Holdings: Bk Titles 6,000; Per Subs 14
Special Collections: Nebraska Conference Minutes 1856-1999 (includes Methodist, Evangelical, United Brethren & United Methodist)

C NEBRASKA WESLEYAN UNIVERSITY, Cochrane-Woods Library, 50th & St Paul, 68504. SAN 309-5282. Tel: 402-465-2400. FAX: 402-465-2189. E-Mail: library@nebrwesleyan.edu. Web Site: www.nebrwesleyan.edu. *Dir*, John Montag; *Online Servs, Publ Servs*, Janet Lu; *Tech Coordr*, Barbara Cornelius; Staff 4 (MLS 4)
Founded 1888. Enrl 1,460; Fac 114; Highest Degree: Bachelor
Library Holdings: Bk Vols 200,000; Per Subs 1,596
Subject Interests: Methodism, relig
Special Collections: Mignon G Eberhart Coll; Publications of Faculty, bks, mss; Rare Books/College Archives
Publications: Newsletter
Partic in Lincoln Health Sciences Library Group; NEBASE; Nebr Independent Col Libr Consortium; Nebr Libr Com; OCLC Online Computer Library Center, Inc

M NOVARTIS CONSUMER HEALTH LIBRARY,* 10401 Hwy 6, 68517. SAN 377-1717. Tel: 402-464-6311. *Librn*, Cheryl Hendrickson
Library Holdings: Bk Vols 2,000; Per Subs 25

M SAINT ELIZABETH REGIONAL MEDICAL CENTER, Medical Library,* 555 S 70th St, 68510. SAN 309-5290. Tel: 402-486-7306. FAX: 402-486-8973. E-Mail: library@stez.org. *Coordr*, Maria Ford; Staff 1 (MLS 1)
Founded 1928
Library Holdings: Bk Vols 2,579; Per Subs 97
Subject Interests: Burn therapy, Family practice, Neonatal med, Ob-gyn, Pediatrics
Special Collections: Allied Health; Medical; Nursing
Automation Activity & Vendor Info: (Cataloging) Sagebrush Corporation
Publications: AV Catalog
Partic in Lincoln Health Sciences Library Group; National Network Of Libraries Of Medicine - Midcontinental Region

C SOUTHEAST COMMUNITY COLLEGE-LINCOLN CAMPUS, Learning Resource Center, 8800 O St, 68520. SAN 350-1663. Tel: 402-437-2585. FAX: 402-437-2593. *In Charge*, Jo Schimmin; E-Mail: jcshimmi@sccm.cc.ne.us; *Ser*, Jeannette Bean; Staff 5 (MLS 3, Non-MLS 2)
Founded 1972
Library Holdings: Bk Vols 12,500; Bk Titles 12,700; Per Subs 300
Subject Interests: Career educ, Vocational education
Automation Activity & Vendor Info: (OPAC) SIRSI
Database Vendor: Ebsco - EbscoHost, IAC - Info Trac, OCLC - First Search, ProQuest, Wilson - Wilson Web

R TIFERETH ISRAEL SYNAGOGUE LIBRARY,* 3219 Sheridan Blvd, 68502. SAN 309-5312. Tel: 402-423-8569.
Founded 1955
Library Holdings: Bk Titles 2,500; Per Subs 20
Subject Interests: Hebrew lang, Judaica, Yiddish (Language)

C UNION COLLEGE LIBRARY,* 3800 S 48th St, 68506-4386. SAN 350-1728. Tel: 402-486-2514. FAX: 402-486-2678. Web Site: www.ucollege.edu/library/library. *Dir*, Chloe Foutz; E-Mail: chfoutz@ucollege.edu; *Publ Servs*, E Deforest Nesmith; *Cat*, Melanie Show; *Tech Servs*, Karla Britain; *Per*, Mitzi Wiggle; Staff 5 (MLS 3, Non-MLS 2)
Founded 1891. Enrl 636
Jun 1999-May 2000 Income Parent Institution $334,269. Mats Exp $106,802, Books $39,411, Per/Ser (Incl. Access Fees) $53,583, Electronic Ref Mat (Incl. Access Fees) $7,545. Sal $206,965 (Prof $112,750)
Library Holdings: Bk Vols 105,100; Per Subs 692
Subject Interests: Genealogy, Seventh-Day Adventists
Special Collections: College Archives; E N Dick Coll; Heritage Room
Partic in NEBASE; NICLC; OCLC Online Computer Library Center, Inc

UNIVERSITY OF NEBRASKA-LINCOLN

C C Y THOMPSON LIBRARY, East Campus, 38th & Holdrege Sts, 68583-0717. SAN 350-1841. Tel: 402-472-4407. Interlibrary Loan Service Tel: 402-472-4406. Circulation Tel: 402-472-4401. Reference Tel: 402-472-4407. FAX: 402-472-7005. E-Mail: cytref@unlnotes.unl.edu. Web Site: iris.unl.edu. *Head of Libr*, Rebecca Bernthal; Tel: 402-472-4404; Staff 10 (MLS 5, Non-MLS 5)
Library Holdings: Bk Vols 361,000; Per Subs 4,700; Bks on Deafness & Sign Lang 20,800
Subject Interests: Agriculture, Animal sci, Biochemistry, Communication disorders, Dentistry, Entomology, Food sci, Home econ, Natural resources, Nutrition, Plant sci, Special education, Textiles, Vet sci
Automation Activity & Vendor Info: (Acquisitions) Innovative Interfaces Inc.; (Cataloging) Innovative Interfaces Inc.; (Circulation) Innovative Interfaces Inc.; (OPAC) Innovative Interfaces Inc.
Friends of the Library Group

CL MARVIN & VIRGINIA SCHMID LAW LIBRARY, 40 Fair St, 68583. Tel: 402-472-3547. FAX: 402-472-8260. Web Site: www.unl.edu/lawcoll/library. *Coll Develop, Dir*, Sally Wise; *Assoc Dir, Publ Servs*, Don Arndt; *Tech Servs*, Brian D Striman; *Ref*, Mike Matis; *Ref*, Beth Smith; Staff 6 (MLS 6)
Founded 1891. Enrl 420; Fac 28; Highest Degree: Doctorate
Library Holdings: Bk Vols 199,473; Bk Titles 48,041; Per Subs 2,858
Special Collections: Anglo-American Law Coll; Tax Law Coll
Partic in NEBASE

C UNIVERSITY LIBRARIES, 13th & R St, 68588-0410. (Mail add: PO Box 880410, 68588-0410), Tel: 402-472-2526. Interlibrary Loan Service Tel: 402-472-2522. Circulation Tel: 402-472-2556. Reference Tel: 402-472-2848. Interlibrary Loan Service FAX: 402-472-5131. Web Site: iris.unl.edu. *Dean of Libr*, Joan R Giesecke; Fax: 402-472-5181, E-Mail: jgiesecke1@unl.edu; *ILL*, Debra Pearson; *Acq*, Judy Johnson; *Coll Develop*, Agnes Adams; *Archivist*, Mary Ellen Ducey; *Spec Coll*, Katherine Walter; Staff 45 (MLS 45)
Founded 1869. Fac 1,200; Highest Degree: Doctorate
Jul 1999-Jun 2000 Income $10,736,800. Mats Exp $4,709,881. Sal $4,750,736 (Prof $1,887,717)
Library Holdings: Bk Vols 2,398,140; Per Subs 20,057
Special Collections: 20th Century Russian Coll; Agriculture Coll; Botany Coll; Czechoslovakia Colls; Folklore Coll; Latvian Coll; Military History Coll; Natural History; Nebraska Literature (Mari Sandoz & Willa Cather); Plains Materials (Sandoz Coll & Cather Coll); University Archives; UNL Alumni; Women in Community Service
Automation Activity & Vendor Info: (Acquisitions) Innovative Interfaces Inc.; (Cataloging) Innovative Interfaces Inc.; (Circulation) Innovative Interfaces Inc.; (Course Reserve) Innovative Interfaces Inc.; (OPAC) Innovative Interfaces Inc.; (Serials) Innovative Interfaces Inc.
Publications: The Link: Newsletter of the University of Nebraska-Lincoln Libraries
Partic in OCLC Online Computer Library Center, Inc
Friends of the Library Group

LITCHFIELD

P LITCHFIELD PUBLIC LIBRARY, PO Box 79, 68852-0079. SAN 309-5355. Tel: 308-446-2268. *Librn*, Bess Schweitzer
Library Holdings: Bk Vols 5,000
Open Tues, Wed & Sat 3-5

LODGEPOLE

P NANCY FAWCETT MEMORIAL LIBRARY, 724 Oberfelder St, PO Box 318, 69149. SAN 309-5363. Tel: 308-483-5714. FAX: 308-483-5715. *Pres*, Dixie Kripal; *Librn*, Norma Michelman
Founded 1930. Pop 410; Circ 2,330
Oct 1998-Sep 1999 Income $13,017. Mats Exp $1,658. Sal $4,992
Library Holdings: Bk Vols 5,985; Per Subs 16
Mem of Panhandle Library System

LOUISVILLE

P LOUISVILLE PUBLIC LIBRARY,* 217 Main St, PO Box 39, 68037-0039. SAN 309-5371. Tel: 402-234-6265. *Librn*, Ruth Ann Hlavac
Pop 1,120; Circ 5,988
Library Holdings: Bk Titles 12,000; Per Subs 7

LOUP CITY

P LOUP CITY PUBLIC LIBRARY,* 880 N Eighth St, PO Box 505, 68853-0505. SAN 309-538X. Tel: 308-745-0548. E-Mail: lcpublibrary@hotmail.com, lcpublibrary929@hotmail.com. *Librn*, Lillian Kaslon
Founded 1917. Pop 4,500; Circ 13,000
Library Holdings: Bk Vols 27,000; Bk Titles 25,000; Per Subs 60
Mem of Grand Island Libr Syst; Meridian Libr Syst
Partic in Am Libr Asn
Friends of the Library Group

LYMAN

P LYMAN PUBLIC LIBRARY,* 313 Jeffers St, PO Box 301, 69352-0301. SAN 309-5398. Tel: 308-787-1366. *Librn*, Stephanie Steiner
Pop 551; Circ 3,552
Library Holdings: Bk Titles 7,000; Per Subs 10
Mem of Panhandle Library System
Open Mon-Thurs 2-5, Fri 9-12, Sat 9-11

LYNCH

P LYNCH PUBLIC LIBRARY,* PO Box 385, 68746. SAN 377-208X. Tel: 402-569-3491. *Librn*, Mariene Rosicky
Library Holdings: Bk Vols 10,000

LYONS

P LYONS PUBLIC LIBRARY,* 335 Main, PO Box 198, 68038. SAN 309-5401. Tel: 402-687-2895. E-Mail: lyonspublib@genisisnet.net. *Librn*, Mary Fritts
Pop 1,214; Circ 4,322
Library Holdings: Bk Vols 7,197; Per Subs 12
Mem of Eastern Libr Syst
Open Mon, Wed & Fri 2-5, Tues & Thurs 6-8, Sat 9-12 & 1-5
Friends of the Library Group

MACY

J NEBRASKA INDIAN COMMUNITY COLLEGE, Tribal Library,* PO Box 428, 68039. SAN 377-1733. Tel: 402-837-5078. FAX: 402-837-4183. *Dir*, Linda Robinson
Library Holdings: Bk Vols 3,000; Per Subs 50
Partic in Nebr Libr Com

MADISON

P MADISON PUBLIC LIBRARY,* 208 W Third St, PO Box 387, 68748-0387. SAN 309-5444. Tel: 402-454-3500. FAX: 402-454-3498. *Librn*, Evelyn Kurpgeweit
Pop 2,100; Circ 14,382
Library Holdings: Bk Titles 18,121; Per Subs 30
Mem of NE Pub Libr Syst
Friends of the Library Group

MASON CITY

P SUNSHINE TOWNSHIP LIBRARY, Main St, PO Box 12, 68855. SAN 309-5452. Tel: 308-732-3269. *Librn*, Joan Cox
Founded 1926. Pop 320; Circ 1,463
Jul 1999-Jun 2000 Income $2,076, Locally Generated Income $2,051, Other $25. Mats Exp Books $650. Sal $1,000
Library Holdings: Bk Titles 5,433
Special Collections: Central Nebraska Authors; History Books of Area Towns
Partic in Meridian Library System

MC COOK

S HIGH PLAINS MUSEUM LIBRARY,* 413 Norris Ave, 69001. SAN 309-541X. Tel: 308-345-3661. *Dir*, Marilyn Hawkins
Founded 1961
Library Holdings: Bk Vols 2,050
Subject Interests: Cooking, Veterinary medicine
Special Collections: Frank Lloyd Wright Coll; German Bibles & School Books; Men & Women Fashion Catalogues; Old Medical Books & Equipment

P MC COOK PUBLIC LIBRARY,* 802 Norris Ave, 69001-3143. SAN 309-5436. Tel: 308-345-1906. FAX: 308-345-1461. *Librn*, Patrick Tolle; *Cat*, Patricia Hall; *Circ, Ref*, Laurel Goin; *Ch Servs*, Kathy Schaaf; Staff 1 (MLS 1)
Founded 1902. Circ 117,000
Library Holdings: Bk Vols 55,000; Per Subs 145

J MCCOOK COMMUNITY COLLEGE, Von Riesen Library, 1205 E Third, 69001-2631. SAN 309-5428. Tel: 308-345-6303. FAX: 308-345-6767. Web Site: www.mcc.mccook.cc.ne.us. *Dir*, Pat Bonge; E-Mail: bongep@mpcca.cc.ne.us; Staff 2 (MLS 2)
Founded 1926. Enrl 801; Fac 44
Library Holdings: Bk Titles 25,000; Per Subs 240
Subject Interests: Genealogy, Law
Publications: Periodical & Microfilm Holdings
Mem of Republican Valley Libr Syst
Partic in CMS; NEBASE; OCLC Online Computer Library Center, Inc

MEAD

P MEAD PUBLIC LIBRARY,* 316 S Vine, 68041. SAN 309-5460. Tel: 402-624-6605. FAX: 402-624-6695. E-Mail: mp84556@alltel.net. *Librn*, Vera Kuhr
Pop 506
Library Holdings: Bk Vols 4,100
Mem of Bellevue Public Library; East Libr Syst
Friends of the Library Group

MEADOW GROVE

P MEADOW GROVE PUBLIC LIBRARY, 205 Main St, PO Box 198, 68752-0198. Tel: 402-634-2266. *Dir*, Beverly Raulston; Staff 2 (MLS 2)
Founded 1926. Pop 400; Circ 5,200
2000-2001 Income $9,000
Library Holdings: Bk Vols 4,200
Mem of NE Libr Syst
Open Mon 9-12, Tues 2-5:30, Wed 4:30-8:30, Thurs 2-5:30, Sat 9-12
Friends of the Library Group

MERNA

P BRENIZER PUBLIC LIBRARY, 430 W Center Ave, PO Box 8, 68856-0008. SAN 309-5487. Tel: 308-643-2268. *Librn*, Vickie Burnett; *Asst Librn*, Carol Squier
Founded 1916. Pop 1,000; Circ 7,720
1999-2000 Income $11,672, State $661, Other $9,500. Mats Exp $2,260, Books $1,578. Sal $4,691
Library Holdings: Bk Titles 12,600; Per Subs 36
Mem of Meridian Libr Syst
Open Tues & Thurs 12:30-5, Sat 12:30-5:30

MILFORD

J SOUTHEAST COMMUNITY COLLEGE - MILFORD, Stanley A Matzke Learning Resource Center,* 600 State St, 68405. SAN 309-5495. Tel: 402-761-2131, Ext 8245. FAX: 402-761-2324. Web Site: www.college.sccm.ca.ac.us. *Coordr*, Arden Mohrman
Founded 1975. Enrl 1,000; Fac 82
Library Holdings: Bk Titles 12,000; Per Subs 350
Special Collections: Vocational/Technical
Learning Resource Center includes the instructional media production center

P WEBERMEIER MEMORIAL PUBLIC LIBRARY,* 617 C St, PO Box 705, 68405. SAN 309-5509. Tel: 402-761-2937. *Librn*, Edna Riedl; *Asst Librn*, Lucy Honig
Founded 1930. Pop 2,110; Circ 15,513
Library Holdings: Bk Vols 17,940; Per Subs 51
Mem of Southeastern Regional Libr Syst
Open Mon & Tues 12:30-5 & 7-9, Wed 10-5 & 7-9, Sat 10-5
Friends of the Library Group

MILLIGAN

P MILLIGAN PUBLIC LIBRARY,* PO Box 324, 68406-9752. SAN 309-5517. Tel: 402-629-4527. *Librn*, Beatrice Vavra
Library Holdings: Bk Vols 2,000; Bk Titles 1,500
Open Wed 3-5 & Sat 9-11

MINATARE

P MINATARE PUBLIC LIBRARY,* 309 Main St, PO Box 483, 69356-0483. SAN 309-5525. Tel: 308-783-1414. *In Charge*, Lillian Covalt
Pop 1,100; Circ 5,761
Library Holdings: Bk Vols 7,278
Open Mon, Wed & Fri 9-12 & 1:30-4:30

MINDEN

P JENSEN MEMORIAL LIBRARY,* 443 N Kearney, PO Box 264, 68959. SAN 309-5533. Tel: 308-832-2648. FAX: 308-832-1642. *Dir*, Ellen Burchell
Founded 1907. Pop 2,939; Circ 29,814
Library Holdings: Bk Vols 18,000; Per Subs 57
Special Collections: Genealogy Reference Coll
Mem of Republican Valley Libr Syst
Friends of the Library Group

MITCHELL

P MITCHELL PUBLIC LIBRARY,* 1449 Center Ave, 69357. SAN 309-5541. Tel: 308-623-2222. E-Mail: mipl@prairieweb.com. *Dir*, Maryruth Reed
Founded 1920. Pop 1,743; Circ 20,271
Oct 1998-Sep 1999 Income $42,550. Mats Exp $9,198, Books $7,805. Sal $25,179

Library Holdings: Bk Titles 14,884; Per Subs 20
Subject Interests: Nebr hist
Automation Activity & Vendor Info: (Cataloging) Follett; (Circulation) Follett; (OPAC) Follett
Database Vendor: OCLC - First Search
Mem of Panhandle Library System
Friends of the Library Group

MORRILL

P MORRILL PUBLIC LIBRARY,* 119 E Webster, PO Box 402, 69358-0402. SAN 309-555X. Tel: 308-247-2611. FAX: 308-247-2309. E-Mail: mpl@prairieweb.com. *Coll Develop, Dir*, Judy Engebretsen
Founded 1916. Pop 1,140; Circ 5,410
1998-1999 Income $15,199, State $688, City $2,113, Locally Generated Income $126, Other $272. Mats Exp $12,811, Books $1,692, Per/Ser (Incl. Access Fees) $316. Sal $5,559 (Prof $5,128)
Library Holdings: Bk Vols 7,812; Per Subs 24
Mem of Panhandle Library System
Open Mon-Wed & Fri 1-5, Thurs 5-8, Sat 9-12
Friends of the Library Group

MULLEN

P HOOKER COUNTY LIBRARY, PO Box 479, 69152-0479. SAN 309-5568. Tel: 308-546-2240. *Librn*, Julie Pfeiffer
Pop 977; Circ 16,630
Library Holdings: Bk Vols 17,222; Per Subs 26
Mem of Valentine Public Library

NEBRASKA CITY

P MORTON-JAMES PUBLIC LIBRARY,* 923 First Corso, 68410. SAN 309-5576. Tel: 402-873-5609. FAX: 402-873-5601. E-Mail: mjpl@alltel.net. *Dir*, Kathleen Griepenstroh
Founded 1896. Pop 6,639; Circ 88,090
Library Holdings: Bk Vols 46,000; Per Subs 80
Friends of the Library Group

P NEBRASKA SCHOOL FOR THE VISUALLY HANDICAPPED LIBRARY,* 824 Tenth Ave, 68410. SAN 377-0982. Tel: 402-873-5513. FAX: 402-873-3463. *Librn*, Jean Gotschall
Library Holdings: Bk Vols 15,000; Per Subs 40
Mem of Southeastern Regional Libr Syst
Partic in Nebr Libr Asn; Spec Libr Asn

NELIGH

P NELIGH PUBLIC LIBRARY, 710 Main St, 68756-1246. SAN 309-5584. Tel: 402-887-5140. FAX: 402-887-4530. E-Mail: nelighpub@bloomnet.com. *Dir*, Ruth Strassler; *Ch Servs*, Fae Bitney; *Asst Librn*, Crystal Legate; Staff 3 (Non-MLS 3)
Founded 1904. Pop 1,893; Circ 22,000
Oct 1998-Sep 1999 Income $49,273, State $817, City $45,681, Federal $900, County $1,875. Mats Exp $10,400, Books $9,000, Per/Ser (Incl. Access Fees) $1,000, Micro $400. Sal $22,400
Library Holdings: Bk Vols 14,170; Per Subs 55
Special Collections: Nebraska
Database Vendor: OCLC - First Search
Mem of NE Libr Syst

NELSON

P NELSON PUBLIC LIBRARY, 10 W Third St, PO Box 322, 68961-0322. SAN 309-5592. Tel: 402-225-7111. *Librn*, Mary Statz
Founded 1917. Circ 2,854
Library Holdings: Bk Vols 6,051
Mem of Republican Valley Libr Syst
Take books to the local Good Samaritan Nursing Home every 2 weeks
Friends of the Library Group

NEWMAN GROVE

P NEWMAN GROVE PUBLIC LIBRARY, 615 Hale Ave, PO Box 430, 68758-0430. SAN 309-5606. Tel: 402-447-2331. FAX: 402-447-2331. *Librn*, Ardis Von Seggern; Staff 3 (MLS 1, Non-MLS 2)
Founded 1922. Pop 930; Circ 9,341
Library Holdings: Bk Titles 12,579; Per Subs 45
Special Collections: Local Newspaper, micro
Automation Activity & Vendor Info: (Cataloging) Follett
Database Vendor: Ebsco - EbscoHost
Mem of NE Libr Syst

NIOBRARA

J NEBRASKA INDIAN COMMUNITY COLLEGE LIBRARY,* 425 Frazier Ave N Ste 1, 68760. SAN 377-3590. Tel: 402-857-2434. FAX: 402-857-2543. *Librn*, Julia Sage
Library Holdings: Bk Vols 5,500; Per Subs 13
Partic in Nebr Libr Com

P NIOBRARA PUBLIC LIBRARY,* 254-14 Park Ave, PO Box 227, 68760-0227. SAN 309-5614. Tel: 402-857-3565. FAX: 402-857-3824. E-Mail: niolib@bloomnet.com. *Librn*, Linda Leader
Pop 419
Library Holdings: Bk Vols 8,000; Per Subs 15
Subject Interests: Native Am hist, Santee Sioux hist
Special Collections: Niobrara Nebraska Centennial History Coll
Mem of NE Libr Syst

NORFOLK

CR NEBRASKA CHRISTIAN COLLEGE, Loren T & Melva M Swedburg Library, 1800 Syracuse Ave, 68701-2458. SAN 309-5622. Tel: 402-379-5014. FAX: 402-379-5100. *Librn*, Linda Lu Lloyd; E-Mail: llloyd@nechristian.edu; Staff 1 (MLS 1)
Founded 1945
Library Holdings: Bk Vols 25,486; Per Subs 173
Subject Interests: Christian church, Relig studies, Restoration hist
Special Collections: Rare Bibles
Partic in OCLC Online Computer Library Center, Inc

P NORFOLK PUBLIC LIBRARY, 308 Prospect Ave, 68701-4138. SAN 309-5630. Tel: 402-644-8711. FAX: 402-370-3260. Web Site: www.ci.norfolk.ne.us/library. *Dir*, Ted J Smith; E-Mail: tsmith@ci.norfolk.ne.us; *Cat*, Sally Stahlecker; E-Mail: sstahlec@ci.norfolk.ne.us; *Ref*, Judy Hilkemann; E-Mail: jhilkema@ci.norfolk.ne.us; *ILL*, Marci Retzlaff; E-Mail: mretzlaf@ci.norfolk.ne.us; *YA Servs*, Karen Drevo; E-Mail: kdrevo@ci.norfolk.ne.us; Staff 5 (MLS 2, Non-MLS 3)
Founded 1906. Pop 26,000
Oct 2000-Sep 2001 Income $1,080,674, State $5,942, City $1,074,732. Mats Exp $127,680, Books $93,929, Per/Ser (Incl. Access Fees) $13,751, Presv $2,000, AV Equip $8,000, Electronic Ref Mat (Incl. Access Fees) $10,000. Sal $610,145
Library Holdings: Bk Titles 84,076; Per Subs 191
Subject Interests: Genealogy, Nebr hist, Poetry
Database Vendor: epixtech, inc.
Mem of NE Libr Syst

NORFOLK REGIONAL CENTER
M RESIDENT LIBRARY, 1700 N Victory Rd, PO Box 1209, 68702-1209. SAN 350-1930. Tel: 402-370-3400, Ext 3354. FAX: 402-370-3194. E-Mail: nregcntr@sufia.net. *Librn*, Susan Kohlhof
Library Holdings: Bk Titles 3,000; Per Subs 20
Subject Interests: Education, Recreation
M STAFF LIBRARY, 1700 N Victory Rd, PO Box 1209, 68702. SAN 350-1906. Tel: 402-370-3400, Ext 3354. FAX: 402-370-3194. E-Mail: nregcntr@sufia.net. *Librn*, Susan Kohlhof
Founded 1967
Library Holdings: Bk Vols 1,500; Per Subs 15
Subject Interests: Psychiatry
Partic in Midcontinental Regional Med Libr Program

J NORTHEAST COMMUNITY COLLEGE, Library Resource Center, 801 E Benjamin Ave, PO Box 469, 68702-0469. SAN 309-5649. Tel: 402-644-0515. FAX: 402-644-0555. E-Mail: librarian@alpha.necc.cc.ne.us. Web Site: www.northeastcollege.com. *Dir Libr Serv*, Debora Robertson; Staff 5 (MLS 1, Non-MLS 4)
Founded 1928. Enrl 3,200; Fac 113
Library Holdings: Bk Titles 28,250; Per Subs 290
Automation Activity & Vendor Info: (Acquisitions) EOS; (Cataloging) EOS; (Circulation) EOS; (OPAC) EOS
Database Vendor: IAC - SearchBank, OVID Technologies, Wilson - Wilson Web
Partic in NEBASE

S PREVENTION PATHWAYS-PARENT CONNECTION, (Formerly Project Access Library), Resource Center, 110 N Seventh St, 68701. SAN 377-2365. Tel: 402-370-3113. FAX: 402-370-3444. E-Mail: prevpath@conpoint.com. Web Site: www.preventionpathways.org. *Librn*, Kimberly Black
Library Holdings: Bk Vols 1,000

NORTH BEND

P NORTH BEND PUBLIC LIBRARY,* 140 E Eighth St, PO Box 279, 68649. SAN 309-5657. Tel: 402-652-8356. E-Mail: nbpublib@dtmspeed.net. *Dir*, Evla Saalfeld
Pop 1,368; Circ 14,970
Library Holdings: Bk Vols 9,500; Per Subs 20
Mem of Eastern Libr Syst

NORTH LOUP

P NORTH LOUP PUBLIC LIBRARY, Corner Second & B Sts, PO Box 157, 68859-0157. SAN 309-5665. Tel: 308-496-4230. E-Mail: nlpl@nctc.net.
Librn, Muriel Tolfa; Tel: 308-496-4741
Founded 1925. Pop 563; Circ 1,433
Library Holdings: Bk Vols 6,044; Per Subs 12
Special Collections: North Loup Newspapers, 1887-1942, microfilm & reader printer
Mem of Meridian Libr Syst
Special Services for the Blind - Bks on tape; Large print bks

NORTH PLATTE

J MID-PLAINS COMMUNITY COLLEGE, Learning Resource Center,* 601 W State Farm Rd, 69101. SAN 309-5673. Tel: 308-532-8980. FAX: 308-532-8590. *Dir*, Keith Saathoff
Founded 1965. Enrl 500; Fac 65
Library Holdings: Bk Vols 25,000; Per Subs 120

P NORTH PLATTE PUBLIC LIBRARY, 120 W Fourth St, 69101-3993. SAN 309-5681. Tel: 308-535-8036. FAX: 308-535-8296. *Dir*, Cecelia C Lawrence; E-Mail: claw@nque.com; *Asst Dir*, Sara Aden; E-Mail: saden@kdsi.net; *Acq, Tech Servs*, Brenda Behsman; *Ch Servs*, Mitzi Mueller; *Circ*, Diane Nelsen; *Instr, Web Coordr*, Carolyn Clark; *ILL, Ref*, Sharon Lohoefener; *Ser*, Barbara Yonkey; *Tech Servs*, Dianne Jensen. Subject Specialists: *Technology*, Sara Aden; Staff 15 (MLS 2, Non-MLS 13)
Founded 1907. Pop 34,000; Circ 173,821
Oct 1999-Sep 2000 Income $815,000, State $5,700, City $783,300, County $26,000. Mats Exp $103,000, Books $88,000, Per/Ser (Incl. Access Fees) $2,000, Other Print Mats $11,000, Electronic Ref Mat (Incl. Access Fees) $2,000. Sal $435,000 (Prof $224,000)
Library Holdings: Bk Vols 93,684; Per Subs 211
Subject Interests: Genealogy, Local history, Nebraska, Western Americana
Special Collections: CD-ROMS; Circulating Original Art Coll; music on CD Coll
Automation Activity & Vendor Info: (Cataloging) epixtech, inc.; (Circulation) epixtech, inc.; (OPAC) epixtech, inc.; (Serials) epixtech, inc.
Database Vendor: CARL, OCLC - First Search
Mem of Republican Valley Libr Syst
Partic in NEBASE; OCLC Online Computer Library Center, Inc
Friends of the Library Group

OAKDALE

P OAKDALE PUBLIC LIBRARY,* PO Box 187, 68761-0187. SAN 309-569X. Tel: 402-776-2602. FAX: 402-776-2602. E-Mail: libra@gpcom.net.
Librn, Gloria Roth
Pop 350; Circ 7,273
1997-1998 Income $9,300. Mats Exp $3,895. Sal $3,642
Library Holdings: Bk Titles 4,294; Per Subs 54
Special Collections: Back issues of Oakdale Sentinel newspaper, 1887-1960; Large Print Book Coll
Mem of NE Libr Syst
Friends of the Library Group

OAKLAND

P OAKLAND PUBLIC LIBRARY,* 110 E Third St, 68045-1356. SAN 309-5703. Tel: 402-685-5113.
Pop 1,393; Circ 10,049
1997-1998 Income $6,382, State $715, County $1,000, Locally Generated Income $527, Other $4,125. Mats Exp $5,634, Books $4,392, Per/Ser (Incl. Access Fees) $1,242. Sal $8,728
Library Holdings: Bk Vols 15,000; Per Subs 42
Partic in Eastern Library System

OFFUTT AFB

UNITED STATES AIR FORCE
A OFFUTT AIR FORCE BASE LIBRARY FL4600, 55 SVS/SVMG, 510 Custer Dr Ste 101, 68113-2150. SAN 350-199X. Tel: 402-294-2533. FAX: 402-294-7124. *Librn*, Rebecca Sims
Library Holdings: Bk Vols 54,000; Per Subs 100
Partic in OCLC Online Computer Library Center, Inc

OGALLALA

P GOODALL CITY LIBRARY, 203 West A St, 69153. SAN 309-5711. Tel: 308-284-4354. *Dir*, Charlotte Kumor
Founded 1913. Pop 8,800; Circ 69,000
Library Holdings: Bk Vols 24,000; Per Subs 80
Special Collections: Nebraska History & Western Culture
Automation Activity & Vendor Info: (Acquisitions) Follett; (Cataloging) Follett; (Circulation) Follett; (OPAC) Follett
Database Vendor: Ebsco - EbscoHost, OCLC - First Search
Mem of Panhandle Library System
Friends of the Library Group

OMAHA

M ALEGENT HEALTH BERGAN MERCY MEDICAL CENTER, John D Hartigan Medical Library, 7500 Mercy Rd, 68124-9832. SAN 325-3228. Tel: 402-398-6092. FAX: 402-398-6923. *Librn*, Ken Oyer; E-Mail: koyer@alegent.org; Staff 1 (MLS 1)
Founded 1975
Jul 1998-Jun 1999 Income Parent Institution $127,000. Mats Exp $85,000, Books $8,000, Per/Ser (Incl. Access Fees) $73,000, Micro $4,000. Sal $46,000 (Prof $40,000)
Library Holdings: Bk Vols 1,800; Bk Titles 1,500; Per Subs 180
Partic in Info Consortium; Medical Libr Asn

M BOY'S TOWN NATIONAL RESEARCH HOSPITAL, Information Resources Center, 555 N 30th St, 68131. SAN 377-435X. Tel: 402-498-6760. FAX: 402-498-6343. *Librn*, Dean Janssen
Library Holdings: Bk Vols 200
Partic in Info Consortium; Mid-Continental Regional Med Librs Asn

M CLARKSON COLLEGE LIBRARY,* 101 S 42nd St, 68131-2739. SAN 327-4764. Tel: 402-552-3387. FAX: 402-552-2899. E-Mail: library@clrkcol.crhsnet.edu, vison@clrkcol.crhsnet.edu. *Actg Dir*, Larry Vinson; *Tech Servs*, Jonice Rogers; *Tech Servs*, Terri Hartwiger; *Cat*, Debra Mangano; *ILL*, Kimberly Madrigal
Jul 1997-Jun 1998 Income $333,461. Mats Exp $79,277, Books $13,443, Per/Ser (Incl. Access Fees) $61,676, Micro $2,283. Sal $118,200 (Prof $33,000)
Library Holdings: Bk Vols 13,749; Per Subs 282
Automation Activity & Vendor Info: (Cataloging) Sydney; (Circulation) Sydney
Partic in Docline; ICON; LVIS

JR COLLEGE OF SAINT MARY LIBRARY, 1901 S 72nd St, 68124-2377. SAN 309-572X. Tel: 402-399-2466. FAX: 402-399-2686. Web Site: www.csm.edu. *Dir*, Sara C Martin; Tel: 402-399-2467; *ILL*, Sister Judith P Healy; Tel: 402-399-2471, E-Mail: jhealy@csm.edu; *AV, Coordr*, Mary McClary; Tel: 402-399-2470, E-Mail: mmcclary@csm.edu; *Admin Assoc*, Rose Crowley; E-Mail: rcrowley@csm.edu; Staff 6 (MLS 3, Non-MLS 3)
Founded 1923. Enrl 1,056; Fac 73; Highest Degree: Bachelor
Jul 1999-Jun 2000 Income Parent Institution $305,000. Mats Exp $154,414, Books $52,500, Per/Ser (Incl. Access Fees) $39,083, Presv $445, Micro $360, AV Equip $2,500, Other Print Mats $100, Manuscripts & Archives $300, Electronic Ref Mat (Incl. Access Fees) $17,900. Sal $150,922
Library Holdings: Bk Vols 70,846; Bk Titles 57,566; Per Subs 416
Subject Interests: Women's studies
Database Vendor: Dialog, Ebsco - EbscoHost, OVID Technologies
Function: ILL available
Partic in ICON; NEBASE; Nebr Independent Col Libr Consortium; OCLC Online Computer Library Center, Inc; PICKLE

C CREIGHTON UNIVERSITY, Reinert-Alumni Memorial Library, 2500 California Plaza, 68178. SAN 350-2023. Tel: 402-280-2705. Interlibrary Loan Service Tel: 402-280-2219. Circulation Tel: 402-280-2260. Reference Tel: 402-280-2227. FAX: 402-280-2435. Web Site: reinert.creighton.edu. *Dir*, Michael J LaCroix; Tel: 402-280-2217, E-Mail: lacroix@creighton.edu; *ILL*, Lynn Schneiderman; E-Mail: lynns@creighton.edu; *Coll Develop, Tech Servs*, Lauralee Grabe; Tel: 402-280-2216, E-Mail: lgrabe@creighton.edu; *Ref*, Mary Nash; Tel: 402-280-2226, E-Mail: mdnash@creighton.edu; *Online Servs*, Chris LeBeau; Tel: 402-280-1757, E-Mail: clbeau@creighton.edu; *Archivist*, Marge Wannarka; Tel: 402-280-2746, E-Mail: margew@creighton.edu; Staff 10 (MLS 10)
Founded 1878. Enrl 4,635; Fac 227; Highest Degree: Doctorate
Jul 1999-Jun 2000 Income (Main Library Only) $1,956,554, Locally Generated Income $61,636, Parent Institution $1,890,082, Other $4,836. Mats Exp $887,356, Books $215,975, Per/Ser (Incl. Access Fees) $405,592, Presv $18,684, Micro $34,462, AV Equip $34,405, Other Print Mats $106,581, Electronic Ref Mat (Incl. Access Fees) $71,657. Sal $674,783 (Prof $411,970)
Library Holdings: Bk Vols 416,307; Per Subs 1,719
Subject Interests: Physics, Theology
Special Collections: Early Christian Writings, bks, micro; Fables of Aesop & la Fontaine
Automation Activity & Vendor Info: (Acquisitions) SIRSI; (Cataloging) SIRSI; (Circulation) SIRSI; (Course Reserve) SIRSI; (OPAC) SIRSI; (Serials) SIRSI
Database Vendor: Dialog, Ebsco - EbscoHost, Lexis-Nexis, Silverplatter Information Inc., Wilson - Wilson Web
Publications: Creighton Cornerstone (Newsletter)
Partic in LVIS; NEBASE; OCLC Online Computer Library Center, Inc
Departmental Libraries:
CM HEALTH SCIENCES LIBRARY, 2500 California Plaza, 68178. SAN 350-2058. Tel: 402-280-5108. Circulation Tel: 402-280-5109. Reference Tel: 408-280-5138. FAX: 402-280-5134. E-Mail: jbothmer@creighton.edu. Web

Site: hsl.creighton.edu. *Dir*, A James Bothmer; E-Mail: jbothmer@creighton.educ; *Head Tech Servs*, Nannette Bedrosky; E-Mail: bedrosky@creighton.edu; *Head, Circ*, Patricia Meeves; E-Mail: meeves@creighton.edu; *Coll Develop, Head Ref*, Richard Jizba; E-Mail: rjizba@creighton.edu; *AV*, Jane Stehlik-Romack; E-Mail: jromack@creighton.edu; Staff 21 (MLS 8, Non-MLS 13)
Founded 1977. Enrl 6,237; Fac 641; Highest Degree: Doctorate
Jul 1999-Jun 2000 Income $1,448,604, Locally Generated Income $232,214, Parent Institution $1,216,390. Mats Exp $675,934, Books $41,940, Per/Ser (Incl. Access Fees) $539,115, Presv $14,056, Micro $8,769, AV Equip $24,850, Electronic Ref Mat (Incl. Access Fees) $47,204. Sal $625,660 (Prof $427,346)
Library Holdings: Bk Vols 227,331; Bk Titles 45,537; Per Subs 1,592
Subject Interests: Allied health, Dentistry, Medicine, Nursing, Pharm
Special Collections: NFL Autism Coll
Automation Activity & Vendor Info: (Acquisitions) SIRSI; (Cataloging) SIRSI; (Media Booking) SIRSI; (OPAC) SIRSI; (Serials) SIRSI
Database Vendor: Silverplatter Information Inc.
Publications: Acquisitions List; Bic-Informer; Newsletter
Function: Reference services available
Partic in Dialog Corporation; ICON; Metro Omaha Health Info Consortium; OCLC Online Computer Library Center, Inc

CL KLUTZNICK LAW LIBRARY - MCGRATH, NORTH LEGAL RESEARCH CENTER, School of Law, 2500 California Plaza, 68178-0340. SAN 350-2082. Tel: 402-280-2251, 402-280-2875. FAX: 402-280-2244. Web Site: www.creighton.edu/culaw/lawlib/lawlib.htm, www.culaw.creighton.edu/lawlib/lawlib.shtm/. *Dir*, Kay L Andrus; *Assoc Dir*, Ann C Kitchel; *Ref*, Patrick Charles; *Cat, Ref*, Hua Li; *Acq, Ser*, Heather Buckwalter; *Automation Syst Coordr, Ref*, Ana Marie Hinman; Staff 14 (MLS 6, Non-MLS 8)
Founded 1904. Enrl 470; Fac 26
Library Holdings: Bk Vols 254,585
Subject Interests: Jury instructions
Special Collections: History of Anglo-American Law (Te Poel Coll); US Supreme Court Coll, briefs & rec
Publications: Acquisitions list (monthly)
Partic in NEBASE; OCLC Online Computer Library Center, Inc; Westlaw

GL DOUGLAS COUNTY DISTRICT COURT, Law Library, Hall of Justice, 1701 Farnam St, 1st flr, 68183. SAN 309-5738. Tel: 402-444-7174. FAX: 402-444-3927. *Librn*, Ann Borer; E-Mail: aborer@co.douglas.ne.us; Staff 2 (MLS 1, Non-MLS 1)
Founded 1905
Library Holdings: Bk Vols 25,000
Publications: Nebraska Bankruptcy Service
Restriction: Members only
Function: Research library
Partic in LOIS
Friends of the Library Group

S DOUGLAS COUNTY YOUTH CENTER LIBRARY, 1301 S 41st St, 68105. SAN 377-5658. Tel: 402-444-4054, 402-444-7492. FAX: 402-444-4252. *Librn*, Sharon Hurley
Library Holdings: Bk Vols 2,000

SR FIRST CHRISTIAN CHURCH (DISCIPLES OF CHRIST) LIBRARY,* 6630 Dodge St, 68132-2742. SAN 328-5626. Tel: 402-558-1939. FAX: 402-558-1941.
Library Holdings: Bk Vols 1,500; Per Subs 10

CR GRACE UNIVERSITY LIBRARY, 823 Worthington, 68108-3642. (Mail add: 1311 S Ninth St, 68108-3629), SAN 309-5754. Tel: 402-449-2893. FAX: 402-449-2919. Web Site: www.graceuniversary.edu/library. *Dir*, Gary R Shook; E-Mail: gshook@mail.grace.edu; *Asst Librn*, Steve Reid; E-Mail: sreid@mail.graceu.edu. Subject Specialists: *Theology*, Steve Reid; Staff 2 (MLS 1, Non-MLS 1)
Founded 1943. Enrl 474; Fac 26; Highest Degree: Master
Jul 1999-Jun 2000 Income Parent Institution $153,807. Mats Exp $153,807, Books $21,373, Per/Ser (Incl. Access Fees) $6,654, Presv $531, AV Equip $510, Electronic Ref Mat (Incl. Access Fees) $4,200. Sal $95,090
Library Holdings: Bk Vols 42,912; Bk Titles 32,459; Per Subs 187
Subject Interests: Biblical studies, Counseling, Theology
Database Vendor: Ebsco - EbscoHost, OCLC - First Search
Partic in Nebr Independent Col Libr Consortium

S GREAT PLAINS BLACK HISTORY MUSEUM LIBRARY,* 2213 Lake St, 68110. SAN 371-1439. Tel: 402-345-2212. FAX: 402-345-2256. *Dir*, Jim Calloway
Library Holdings: Bk Vols 5,500; Per Subs 19
Restriction: Non-circulating to the public
African American history resource library

S HISTORICAL SOCIETY OF DOUGLAS COUNTY, Library Archives Center,* 5730 N 30th St Bldg 11B, 68111-1657. SAN 328-3178. Tel: 402-451-1013. FAX: 402-451-1394. E-Mail: hsdc-lac@radiks.net. *Exec Dir*, Betty J Davis; *Dir*, Jeffrey S Spencer; *Archivist, Librn*, Deirdre Roult
Library Holdings: Bk Vols 600; Bk Titles 2,000
Subject Interests: Local history
Special Collections: Company & Individual Official Archives of Douglas County: Documents to early 1800; Omaha World-Herald Newspaper Clipping Coll (5 million)
Publications: History lectures; Local Historical Works; Newsletter, Oral interviews

M IMMANUEL MEDICAL CENTER, Professional Library,* 6901 N 72nd St, 68122. SAN 325-3767. Tel: 402-572-2345. FAX: 402-572-2797. *Librn*, Joy A Winkler
Library Holdings: Bk Titles 750; Per Subs 225
Restriction: Staff use only

S JOSLYN ART MUSEUM, Milton R & Pauline S Abrahams Library, 2200 Dodge St, 68102-1296. SAN 309-5770. Tel: 402-342-3300, Ext 208. FAX: 402-342-2376. E-Mail: info@joslyn.org. *Head Librn*, Kathryn L Corcoran; Tel: 402-342-3300, Ext 239, E-Mail: kcorcoran@joslyn.org; *Ref*, Christine Jorgensen; Staff 3 (MLS 2, Non-MLS 1)
Founded 1931
Library Holdings: Bk Vols 27,000; Per Subs 50
Subject Interests: Art, Native Am art
Special Collections: Artists' Clipping Files; Publications of the Metropolitan Museum of Art, microfich set; Western Americana: Frontier History of the Trans-Mississippi West, microfilm set
Automation Activity & Vendor Info: (Cataloging) TLC; (Circulation) TLC; (OPAC) TLC
Restriction: Not a lending library
Partic in LVIS; NEBASE; OCLC Online Computer Library Center, Inc

R KRIPKE JEWISH FEDERATION LIBRARY, (Formerly Jewish Federation Of Omaha Library), 333 S 132nd St, 68154. SAN 309-5762. Tel: 402-334-6461. Circulation Tel: 402-334-6462. Reference Tel: 402-334-6462. FAX: 402-334-6464. E-Mail: jewishlibrary@jewishomaha.org. Web Site: www.jewishomaha.org. *Dir*, Finkelstein Harris; *Asst Librn*, Janette Shaffer; Tel: 402-334-6462, Fax: 402-334-6464, E-Mail: janetteshaffer@aol.com; Staff 6 (MLS 1, Non-MLS 5)
Founded 1945
Library Holdings: Bk Titles 39,000; Per Subs 75
Subject Interests: Archeology, Bible, Comparative relig, Holocaust, Israel, Judaica, Middle East
Automation Activity & Vendor Info: (Cataloging) Sagebrush Corporation; (Circulation) Sagebrush Corporation
Database Vendor: IAC - SearchBank
Publications: Index to the Omaha Jewish Press
Friends of the Library Group

L KUTAK ROCK, Law Library,* 1650 Farnam St, 68102-2186. SAN 327-490X. Tel: 402-346-6000. FAX: 402-346-1148. *Librn*, Avis Forsman; E-Mail: avis.forsman@kutakrock.com
Library Holdings: Bk Vols 25,000; Per Subs 150
Restriction: By appointment only

L LAMSON, DUGAN & MURRAY LLP, Law Library, 10306 Regency Pkwy Dr, 68114. SAN 377-3868. Tel: 402-397-7300. FAX: 402-397-7824. Web Site: www.ldm.com. *Librn*, Evelyn Owens
Library Holdings: Bk Vols 20,000; Per Subs 50

R METROPOLITAN AREA PLANNING AGENCY, MAPA Regional Library, 2222 Cuming St, 68102-4328. SAN 329-076X. Tel: 402-444-6866. FAX: 402-342-0949. E-Mail: mapa@mapacog.org. Web Site: www.mapacog.org. *Info Specialist*, Patricia Jesse
Library Holdings: Bk Vols 200

J METROPOLITAN COMMUNITY COLLEGE LIBRARY, 30th & Fort Sts, 68103. (Mail add: PO Box 3777, 68103-0777), Tel: 402-457-2524. TDD: 402-457-2705. FAX: 402-457-2768. Web Site: www.mccneb.edu/library. *Br Coordr*, Kathryn E Hershey; Tel: 402-457-2763, E-Mail: khershey@metropo.mccneb.edu; *Librn*, Scott Mahoney; Tel: 402-738-4737, Fax: 402-738-4738, E-Mail: smahoney@metropo.mccneb.edu; *Librn*, Patricia McGinnis; Tel: 402-289-1324, Fax: 402-289-1286, E-Mail: pmcginnis@metropo.mccneb.edu; *Librn*, Ann Wills; Tel: 402-457-2630, Fax: 402-457-2633, E-Mail: awills@metropo.mccneb.edu; *Acq*, Dorothy Mittlieder; Tel: 402-457-2762, E-Mail: dmittlieder@metropo.mccneb.edu; *ILL*, Pam Neseth; Tel: 402-457-2760, E-Mail: pneseth@metropo.mccneb.edu; *Cat*, Diane Schram; Tel: 402-457-2761, E-Mail: dschram@metropo.mccneb.edu; Staff 18 (MLS 2, Non-MLS 16)
Founded 1974. Pop 619,000; Enrl 11,668; Fac 160; Highest Degree: Associate
Jul 1999-Jun 2000 Income (Main Library and Branch Library) Parent Institution $1,075,891. Mats Exp $335,689, Books $114,792, Per/Ser (Incl. Access Fees) $220,897. Sal $478,551 (Prof $131,105)
Library Holdings: Bk Vols 56,343; Bk Titles 40,928; Per Subs 931; High Interest/Low Vocabulary Bk Vols 317; Bks on Deafness & Sign Lang 129
Automation Activity & Vendor Info: (Acquisitions) GEAC; (Cataloging) GEAC; (Circulation) GEAC; (OPAC) GEAC; (Serials) GEAC
Database Vendor: Ebsco - EbscoHost, GaleNet, Lexis-Nexis, OCLC - First Search, ProQuest, Wilson - Wilson Web
Partic in NEBASE
Special Services for the Deaf - Books on deafness & sign language; TDD

Departmental Libraries:
ELKHORN VALLEY CAMPUS, PO Box 3777, 68103-0777. SAN 350-2201. Tel: 402-289-1206. FAX: 402-289-1286. *Librn*, Patricia McGinnis
FORT OMAHA CAMPUS, 30th & Fort Sts, PO Box 3777, 68103-0777. SAN 350-2147. Tel: 402-457-2306. FAX: 402-457-2633. *Librn*, Pat McGinnis
SOUTH OMAHA CAMPUS, 27th & Q Sts, PO Box 3777, 68103-0777. SAN 350-2171. Tel: 402-738-4506. FAX: 402-738-4738. *Librn*, Scott Mahoney

S NATIONAL PARK SERVICE, Midwest Regional Library, 1709 Jackson St, 68102-2571. SAN 309-5797. Tel: 402-221-3471. *Dir*, Verne Haselwood
Founded 1938
Library Holdings: Bk Titles 7,500; Per Subs 5
Subject Interests: Archaeology, Botany, Ethnology, Geology, Resources mgt, Western Americana, Zoology
Special Collections: Early Western Travels; Pacific Railroad Surveys; Westerners Brand Book
Publications: National Park Service Reports on the Midwest Region
Restriction: Restricted public use

M NEBRASKA METHODIST COLLEGE, John Moritz Library, 8303 Dodge St, 68114. SAN 327-4888. Tel: 402-354-4694. FAX: 402-354-3155.; Staff 7 (MLS 1, Non-MLS 6)
Library Holdings: Bk Vols 15,176; Per Subs 374
Mem of Eastern Libr Syst
Partic in ICON; Metro Omaha Health Info Consortium; National Network Of Libraries Of Medicine - Midcontinental Region

S OMAHA CORRECTIONAL CENTER LIBRARY,* 2323 East Ave J, 68111. SAN 377-4511. Tel: 402-595-3964. FAX: 402-595-2227. *Dir*, Bill Pserros
Library Holdings: Bk Vols 8,000; Per Subs 25
Partic in Nebr Inst Librs; Nebr Libr Asn

S OMAHA HOME FOR BOYS LIBRARY,* 4343 N 52nd St, 68104. SAN 322-8207. Tel: 402-457-7000, Ext 7157. FAX: 402-457-7162. *Chief Librn*, Karen Brooks
Founded 1963. Pop 100; Circ 25; Enrl 74; Fac 1
Library Holdings: Bk Vols 6,000; Per Subs 64
Subject Interests: History
Special Services for the Deaf - Books on deafness & sign language; High interest/low vocabulary books

P OMAHA PUBLIC LIBRARY, W Dale Clark Library, 215 S 15th St, 68102-1629. SAN 350-2295. Tel: 402-444-4800. Interlibrary Loan Service Tel: 402-444-4857. TDD: 402-444-3825. FAX: 402-444-4504. E-Mail: webdesk@omaha.lib.ne.us. Web Site: www.omaha.lib.ne.us. *Dir*, Ronald R Heezen; Tel: 402-444-4834, E-Mail: rheezen@omaha.lib.ne.us; *Asst Dir*, Verda H Bialac; Tel: 402-444-4843, E-Mail: vbialac@omaha.lib.ne.us; *Commun Relations*, Linda S Trout; Tel: 402-444-4838, E-Mail: ltrout@omaha.lib.ne.us; *Publ Servs*, Lillian R Wunsch; Tel: 402-444-4807, E-Mail: lwunsch@omaha.lib.ne.us; *Cat*, Mary Marchio; Tel: 402-444-4997, E-Mail: mmarchio@omaha.lib.ne.us; *Coll Develop*, Mary T Griffin; Tel: 402-444-4854, E-Mail: mgriffin@omaha.lib.ne.us; *Ch Servs, YA Servs*, Sarah Watson; Tel: 402-444-4808, E-Mail: swatson@omaha.lib.ne.us; *Tech Coordr*, Janet Davenport; Tel: 402-444-4836, E-Mail: janetd@omaha.lib.ne.us; Staff 62 (MLS 53, Non-MLS 9)
Founded 1872. Pop 432,492; Circ 2,422,390
Jan 1999-Dec 1999 Income (Main Library and Branch Library) $9,541,212, State $86,970, City $7,931,865, Federal $73,446, County $1,329,431, Other $119,500. Mats Exp $1,657,795, Books $1,179,556, Per/Ser (Incl. Access Fees) $140,097, Presv $5,167, Micro $20,004, AV Equip $296,220, Electronic Ref Mat (Incl. Access Fees) $16,751. Sal $4,784,974 (Prof $2,405,413)
Library Holdings: Bk Vols 963,001; Bk Titles 297,605; Per Subs 2,369
Subject Interests: Black history, Foreign Language, Genealogy, Local history
Automation Activity & Vendor Info: (Acquisitions) epixtech, inc.; (Circulation) epixtech, inc.; (OPAC) epixtech, inc.
Database Vendor: Ebsco - EbscoHost, epixtech, inc., GaleNet, IAC - Info Trac, OCLC - First Search, OVID Technologies
Publications: BST Bulletin; Large Print Notes; Omaha Public Library Connection
Special Services for the Deaf - TDD
Friends of the Library Group
Branches: 9
BENSON, 2918 N 60th, 68104. SAN 350-2325. Tel: 402-444-4846. FAX: 402-444-6595. Web Site: www.omaha.lib.ne.us. *Librn*, Carolyn McDougle
Library Holdings: Bk Vols 53,730
CHARLES B WASHINGTON BRANCH, 2868 Ames, 68111. SAN 350-2473. Tel: 402-444-4849. FAX: 402-444-6658. Web Site: www.omaha.lib.ne.us. *Librn*, John Bernardi
Library Holdings: Bk Vols 55,472
Subject Interests: Black history
FLORENCE, 2920 Bondesson, 68112. SAN 350-2384. Tel: 402-444-5299. FAX: 402-444-6607. Web Site: www.omaha.lib.ne.us. *Librn*, Michael Wolfe
Library Holdings: Bk Vols 46,753
MILLARD, 13214 Westwood Lane, 68144. SAN 350-2449. Tel: 402-444-4848. FAX: 402-444-6623. Web Site: www.omaha.lib.ne.us. *Librn*, Lucille Lewis
Library Holdings: Bk Vols 131,153
MILTON R ABRAHAMS BRANCH, 5111 N 90th St, 68134. SAN 329-6032. Tel: 402-444-6284. FAX: 402-444-6590. Web Site: www.omaha.lib.ne.us. *Librn*, Gloria Sorensen
Library Holdings: Bk Vols 124,947
SORENSEN, 4808 Cass St, 68132. SAN 350-2503. Tel: 402-444-5274. FAX: 402-444-6592. Web Site: www.omaha.lib.ne.us. *Librn*, Patricia Scott
Library Holdings: Bk Vols 46,583
SOUTH, 2302 M St, 68107. SAN 350-2538. Tel: 402-444-4850. FAX: 402-444-6644. Web Site: www.omaha.lib.ne.us. *Librn*, Susan Thornton
Library Holdings: Bk Vols 53,315
SWANSON, 9101 W Dodge Rd, 68114. SAN 350-2562. Tel: 402-444-4852. FAX: 402-444-6651. Web Site: www.omaha.lib.ne.us. *Librn*, Marsha Greenhill
Library Holdings: Bk Vols 135,730
Friends of the Library Group
WILLA CATHER BRANCH, 1905 S 44th St, 68105-2807. SAN 350-235X. Tel: 402-444-4851. FAX: 402-444-6662. Web Site: www.omaha.lib.ne.us. *Librn*, Virginia Kavvadias
Library Holdings: Bk Vols 64,885

S OMAHA WORLD-HERALD LIBRARY,* 1334 Dodge St, 68102. SAN 325-0938. Tel: 402-444-1000, Ext 2560. FAX: 402-345-0183. *Librn*, Jeanne Hauser; Staff 5 (Non-MLS 5)
Founded 1900
Library Holdings: Bk Vols 400; Bk Titles 150
Partic in Spec Libr Asn

UNITED STATES ARMY
A CORPS OF ENGINEERS, OMAHA DISTRICT, 215 N 17th St, 68102-4978. SAN 309-5827. Tel: 402-221-3229. FAX: 402-221-4886. Web Site: www.nwo.usace.army.mil/html/im-c/lib/hp.htm. *Librn*, Karen L Stefero; E-Mail: karen.l.stefero@usace.army.mil
Library Holdings: Bk Titles 13,000; Per Subs 131
Subject Interests: Engineering, Law
Special Collections: Engineering Design Memo; Sediment Series
Partic in Dialog Corporation; Fedlink; NEBASE; OCLC Online Computer Library Center, Inc

G UNITED STATES COURT OF APPEALS, Branch Library, 111 S 18th Plaza, Ste 4104, 68102-1322. SAN 325-4321. Tel: 402-661-7590. FAX: 402-661-7591. *Librn*, Angela Lange
Library Holdings: Bk Vols 14,000

C UNIVERSITY OF NEBRASKA AT OMAHA, University Library, 6001 Dodge St, 68182-0237. SAN 309-5835. Tel: 402-554-2640. Interlibrary Loan Service Tel: 402-554-3209. Circulation Tel: 402-554-3206. Reference Tel: 402-554-2661. FAX: 402-554-3215. Web Site: www.library.unomaha.edu/. *Actg Dean*, Janice S Boyer; *Assoc Dean*, Janice S Boyer; *Access Serv*, Ella Jane Bailey; *Coll Develop, Spec Coll*, Robert Nash; *Coll Develop, Ref*, John Reidelbach; Staff 54 (MLS 16, Non-MLS 38)
Founded 1908. Enrl 14,000; Fac 450; Highest Degree: Doctorate
Jul 1999-Jun 2000 Income $4,090,671, State $3,963,360, Locally Generated Income $127,311. Mats Exp $1,863,812, Books $625,275, Per/Ser (Incl. Access Fees) $1,205,802, Presv $32,735. Sal $1,901,536 (Prof $832,578)
Library Holdings: Bk Vols 602,704; Bk Titles 600,466
Special Collections: Arthur Paul Afghanistan Coll; Icarian Community Coll; Mary L Richmond - Cummings Press Coll; Nebraska Authors & History; Omaha Federal Writers Project Papers (WPA)
Automation Activity & Vendor Info: (Acquisitions) Innovative Interfaces Inc.; (Cataloging) Innovative Interfaces Inc.; (Circulation) Innovative Interfaces Inc.; (OPAC) Innovative Interfaces Inc.; (Serials) Innovative Interfaces Inc.
Database Vendor: OCLC - First Search
Publications: The Library User (published 3 times per year)
Partic in Dialog Corporation; NEBASE; OCLC Online Computer Library Center, Inc
Friends of the Library Group

CM UNIVERSITY OF NEBRASKA MEDICAL CENTER, McGoogan Library of Medicine, 600 S 42nd St, 68198-6705. (Mail add: University of Nebraska Medical Center, 986705 Nebraska Medical Center, 68198-6705), SAN 350-2597. Tel: 402-559-4407, 402-559-7078, 402-559-7085 (Interlibrary Loan Service Tel No.). FAX: 402-559-5498. *Dir*, Nancy N Woelfl; E-Mail: nwoelfl@unmc.edu; *Assoc Dir*, Marie Reidelbach; *Assoc Dir*, Mary E Helms; *Assoc Dir*, K Sutterwaite; *Cat*, Helen K Yam; Tel: 402-559-7091, E-Mail: hyam@unmc.edu; *Tech Servs*, Thomas F Gensichen; Tel: 402-559-8119, E-Mail: tgenisch@unmc.edu; *Ref Servs YA*, Roxanne C Byrd; Tel: 402-559-7228, E-Mail: rcox@unmc.edu; *Media Spec Ad*, Stuart K Dayton; Tel: 402-559-6334, E-Mail: sdayton@unmc.edu; *Coll Develop*, Rose Schinker; Tel: 402-559-5418, E-Mail: rschinke@unmc.edu; Staff 47 (MLS 17, Non-MLS 30)
Founded 1902. Enrl 2,113; Fac 940; Highest Degree: Doctorate
Jun 1998-Jun 1999 Income $3,197,156, State $2,436,016, Federal $468,903,

Locally Generated Income $151,412, Other $140,825. Mats Exp $841,706, Books $93,780, Per/Ser (Incl. Access Fees) $601,888, Presv $23,070, Electronic Ref Mat (Incl. Access Fees) $122,968. Sal $1,594,703 (Prof $872,728)
Library Holdings: Bk Vols 247,186; Bk Titles 64,753; Per Subs 1,859
Subject Interests: Allied health, Medicine
Special Collections: Consumer Health Information Resource Services Coll, bks, journals; History of Medicine, bks, memorabilia; Obstetrics & Gynecology (Moon Coll); Surgery & Related Subjects (H Winnett Orr Coll & American College of Surgeons Coll), bks, memorabilia
Automation Activity & Vendor Info: (Cataloging) LS 2000; (Circulation) Innovative Interfaces Inc.; (Course Reserve) LS 2000; (ILL) epixtech, inc.; (Media Booking) Innovative Interfaces Inc.; (OPAC) Innovative Interfaces Inc.
Database Vendor: OCLC - First Search, Silverplatter Information Inc.
Publications: Point of Access (quarterly)
Partic in Nat Libr of Med; National Network Of Libraries Of Medicine - Midcontinental Region
Open Mon-Thurs 7:30am-12am, Fri 7:30am-9pm, Sat 9-5, Sun 1pm-12am
Friends of the Library Group

GM VETERANS AFFAIRS, Medical Library,* 4101 Woolworth Ave, 68105. SAN 309-5843. Tel: 402-346-8800, Ext 3531. FAX: 402-449-0692.; Staff 1 (MLS 1)
Founded 1950
Library Holdings: Bk Titles 1,261; Per Subs 266
Subject Interests: Allied health, Bus, Medicine, Mgt
Partic in Medline; Vets Admin Libr Network

O'NEILL

P O'NEILL PUBLIC LIBRARY,* 601 E Douglas, 68763. SAN 309-586X. Tel: 402-336-3110. FAX: 402-336-3268. *Dir*, Patricia Hering
Founded 1913. Pop 4,490; Circ 31,000
Library Holdings: Bk Vols 23,000; Per Subs 138
Mem of NE Libr Syst
Partic in OCLC Online Computer Library Center, Inc
Friends of the Library Group

ORCHARD

P ORCHARD PUBLIC LIBRARY,* 232 Windom, PO Box 317, 68764. SAN 309-5878. Tel: 402-893-4606. E-Mail: orchpl@bloomnet.com. *Librn*, Linda Risinger
Founded 1902. Pop 942; Circ 14,726
Library Holdings: Bk Titles 13,000; Per Subs 20
Special Collections: Orchard News, 1902-to-date, 1903-1983 on micro-film
Mem of NE Libr Syst
Have Local Genealogical Index
Friends of the Library Group

ORD

P ORD TOWNSHIP LIBRARY,* 1718 M St, PO Box 206, 68862. SAN 309-5886. Tel: 308-728-3012. FAX: 308-728-3126. E-Mail: ordlibr@cornhusker.net. *Librn*, Sally Wagner
Pop 3,000; Circ 18,000
Library Holdings: Bk Titles 15,000; Per Subs 82
Mem of Meridian Libr Syst
Partic in OCLC Online Computer Library Center, Inc

ORLEANS

P CORDELIA B PRESTON MEMORIAL LIBRARY, PO Box 430, 68966-0430. SAN 309-5894. Tel: 308-473-3425. FAX: 308-473-3425. E-Mail: olibry@megavision.com. *Librn*, Raylene Stephens
Founded 1917. Pop 490; Circ 6,355
Library Holdings: Bk Vols 11,900; Per Subs 15
Special Collections: Civil War (War of Rebellion)
Friends of the Library Group

OSCEOLA

P OSCEOLA PUBLIC LIBRARY, 131 N Main, PO Box 448, 68651. SAN 309-5908. Tel: 402-747-4301. Interlibrary Loan Service Tel: 800-334-4538. E-Mail: ol83424@alltel.net. *Librn*, Paula E Johnson; *Asst Librn*, Lola Urban
Founded 1949. Pop 879; Circ 6,424
Oct 1999-Sep 2000 Income $33,000
Library Holdings: Bk Titles 10,314; Per Subs 27
Automation Activity & Vendor Info: (Acquisitions) Follett
Mem of NE Pub Libr Syst
Open Mon & Fri 12:30-5:30, Wed 12:30-8 & Sat 10-3
Friends of the Library Group

OSHKOSH

P OSHKOSH PUBLIC LIBRARY,* 307 W First St, PO Box 140, 69154-0140. SAN 309-5916. Tel: 308-772-4554. FAX: 308-772-4492. E-Mail: oshpublib@lakemac.net. *Dir*, Ruby Chryst; *Librn*, Carol Kyser
Pop 1,057; Circ 10,920
Library Holdings: Bk Vols 7,509; Per Subs 37
Special Collections: Cake Pan Coll
Mem of Panhandle Library System
Friends of the Library Group

OSMOND

P OSMOND PUBLIC LIBRARY, 412 N State St, PO Box 478, 68765-0478. SAN 309-5924. Tel: 402-748-3382. FAX: 402-748-3382. E-Mail: ospuli@huntel.net. *Dir*, Don Weinand; Tel: 402-748-3345
Pop 774; Circ 1,623
Sep 1998-Oct 1999 Income $33,550, State $800, City $29,300, Federal $900, County $2,550. Mats Exp $15,200, Books $12,000, Per/Ser (Incl. Access Fees) $1,200, AV Equip $1,000, Other Print Mats $1,000. Sal $13,000 (Prof $10,537)
Library Holdings: Bk Vols 16,000; Per Subs 35; Bks on Deafness & Sign Lang 10
Mem of NE Libr Syst
Friends of the Library Group

OVERTON

P OVERTON COMMUNITY LIBRARY,* 407 Hwy 30, PO Box 117, 68863. SAN 309-5932. Tel: 308-987-2543. *Dir*, Nancy Purinton
Pop 660; Circ 3,238
Library Holdings: Bk Vols 5,232
Open Mon 1-4, Fri 2-5

OXFORD

P OXFORD MUNICIPAL LIBRARY,* 411 Ogden St, PO Box 156, 68967-0156. SAN 309-5940. Tel: 308-824-3381. *Librn*, Karen Johnston; *Asst Librn*, Eleanor Hays
Founded 1941. Pop 1,109
Library Holdings: Bk Vols 11,000; Per Subs 23
Special Collections: American Heritage, History of the United States; Bess Streeter Aldrich; Civil War; Encyclopedia of Collectibles; Lexicon Universal - World Book; Louisa May Alcott; Mari Sandoz; Mark Twain; Nebraska Authors; The Old West; Time-Life, History of World War II; Vietnam, encyclopedia; Willa Cather; Winston Churchill; World War II; Zane Gray
Mem of Republican Valley Libr Syst

PALISADE

P PALISADE PUBLIC LIBRARY,* 124 N Main St, PO Box 308, 69040. SAN 309-5959. Tel: 308-285-3525. *Librn*, Debra Alberts
Pop 401; Circ 3,820
Library Holdings: Bk Vols 7,960

PALMER

P PALMER PUBLIC LIBRARY,* W Commercial St, PO Box 248, 68864. SAN 309-5967. Tel: 308-894-5305. FAX: 308-894-8245. *Dir*, Debra Brakke
Library Holdings: Bk Vols 12,000; Per Subs 20

PALMYRA

P PALMYRA MEMORIAL LIBRARY,* 535 Illinois Ave, 68418-9755. SAN 322-6816. Tel: 402-780-5344. FAX: 402-780-5344. E-Mail: pl53541@alltel.net. *Librn*, Mickie Schrader
Pop 510; Circ 1,725
Library Holdings: Bk Titles 5,096
Mem of Southeastern Regional Libr Syst
Open Mon-Fri 1-5, Sat 1-3
Friends of the Library Group

PAPILLION

P PAPILLION PUBLIC LIBRARY, 222 N Jefferson, 68046. SAN 309-5975. Tel: 402-597-2040. FAX: 402-339-8019. Web Site: www.papillion.ne.us. *Dir*, Sally Payne; E-Mail: spayne@monarch.papillion.ne.us; *Ch Servs*, Sharon Wiegert; Staff 5 (Non-MLS 5)
Founded 1921. Pop 15,700
Oct 2000-Sep 2001 Mats Exp $83,150, Books $57,750, Per/Ser (Incl. Access Fees) $4,800, Micro $100, AV Equip $8,000, Electronic Ref Mat (Incl. Access Fees) $12,500. Sal $307,287
Library Holdings: Bk Titles 47,378; Per Subs 163
Automation Activity & Vendor Info: (Cataloging) Follett; (Circulation)

Follett; (OPAC) Follett
Database Vendor: OCLC - First Search
Mem of Eastern Libr Syst
Partic in OCLC Online Computer Library Center, Inc
Special Services for the Blind - Kurzweil Reader
Friends of the Library Group

PAWNEE CITY

P PAWNEE CITY (CARNEGIE) PUBLIC LIBRARY, 730 G St, PO Box 311, 68420-0311. SAN 309-5983. Tel: 402-852-2118. *Librn*, Mary Friedly; *Asst Librn*, Carol Glathar; Staff 2 (Non-MLS 2)
Founded 1907. Pop 1,003; Circ 14,562
Oct 2000-Sep 2001 Income $46,621, State $691, City $38,280, Other $7,650. Mats Exp $6,118, Books $5,000, Per/Ser (Incl. Access Fees) $624, Electronic Ref Mat (Incl. Access Fees) $494. Sal $23,487
Library Holdings: Bk Titles 12,930; Per Subs 33
Subject Interests: Adult fiction, Children's fiction
Special Collections: Harold Lloyd Coll
Automation Activity & Vendor Info: (Circulation) Follett
Mem of Southeastern Regional Libr Syst
Partic in Southeast Nebraska Library System
Storytime for pre-schoolers every Fri Jan-May

PAXTON

P PAXTON PUBLIC LIBRARY, 108 N Oak St, 69155. (Mail add: PO Box 278, 69155-0278), SAN 309-5991. Tel: 308-239-4763. E-Mail: plibrary@esu16.esu.16.k12.us. *Librn*, Carol Murray; Staff 1 (MLS 1)
Founded 1932. Pop 1,175; Circ 3,678
Oct 1998-Sep 1999 Income $12,367, City $11,072, County $900, Locally Generated Income $35, Other $360. Mats Exp $1,446, Books $1,275, Per/Ser (Incl. Access Fees) $171. Sal $4,830
Library Holdings: Bk Vols 8,250; Per Subs 18
Subject Interests: Local history, Nebraska
Mem of Panhandle Library System
Friends of the Library Group

PENDER

P HOUSE MEMORIAL PUBLIC LIBRARY,* 220 Thurston Ave, 68047-0509. (Mail add: PO Box 509, 68047-0509), SAN 309-6009. Tel: 402-385-2521. *Librn*, Donna McQuistan
Pop 1,318; Circ 18,298
Oct 1998-Sep 1999 Income $41,709, State $709, City $41,000. Mats Exp $7,226, Books $5,000, Per/Ser (Incl. Access Fees) $2,000, Other Print Mats $226. Sal $37,000
Library Holdings: Bk Titles 14,000; Per Subs 59
Mem of NE Libr Syst

PERU

C PERU STATE COLLEGE LIBRARY,* Park Ave, 68421. SAN 309-6017. Tel: 402-872-2218. FAX: 402-872-2298. Web Site: www.peru.edu/library. *Dir*, Margaret O'Rourke; Tel: 402-872-2360, E-Mail: porourke@oakmail.peru.edu; *Ref*, Barbara Robb; E-Mail: robb@bobcat.peru.edu; Staff 6 (MLS 3, Non-MLS 3)
Founded 1867. Enrl 1,183; Fac 47; Highest Degree: Master
Library Holdings: Bk Vols 105,615; Bk Titles 71,408
Special Collections: Marion Marsh Brown Coll
Publications: Newsletter
Partic in NEBASE; OCLC Online Computer Library Center, Inc
Open Mon-Thurs 7:30am-10pm, Fri 7:30-5, Sat 2-5 & Sun 5-10

PETERSBURG

P PETERSBURG PUBLIC LIBRARY,* 103 S Second St, PO Box 60, 68652-0060. SAN 325-2582. Tel: 402-386-5755. *Librn*, Bel Esau
Founded 1984. Pop 380; Circ 917
Library Holdings: Bk Titles 5,000; Per Subs 40
Mem of NE Libr Syst
Open Mon, Wed & Thurs 3-5:30

PIERCE

P PIERCE PUBLIC LIBRARY, 207 W Court, PO Box 39, 68767. SAN 309-6025. Tel: 402-329-6324. FAX: 402-329-6324. E-Mail: pplib@ptcnet.net. *Dir*, Kathy Bretschneider; Staff 3 (Non-MLS 3)
Founded 1911. Pop 1,560; Circ 8,731
Oct 2000-Sep 2001 Income $28,850, City $26,100, County $2,750
Library Holdings: Bk Vols 11,500; Per Subs 40
Automation Activity & Vendor Info: (Circulation) Follett
Database Vendor: OCLC - First Search
Mem of NE Libr Syst
Open Mon & Wed 1-5:30 & 7-9, Tues, Thurs & Fri 2:30-5:30 & Sat 1-5
Friends of the Library Group

PILGER

P PILGER PUBLIC LIBRARY,* PO Box 54, 68768-0054. SAN 309-6033. Tel: 402-396-3550. *Librn*, Charlene Clemens
Founded 1934. Pop 361; Circ 5,515
Aug 1996-Jul 1997 Income $16,876, State $1,338, City $1,800, County $1,250, Locally Generated Income $9,238, Other $3,250. Mats Exp $3,147, Books $2,847, Per/Ser (Incl. Access Fees) $250. Sal $4,000
Library Holdings: Bk Vols 6,350; Per Subs 11
Mem of NE Libr Syst

PLAINVIEW

P PLAINVIEW CARNEGIE PUBLIC LIBRARY,* Main St, PO Box 728, 68769-0728. SAN 309-6041. Tel: 402-582-4507. FAX: 402-582-4813. *Librn*, Loydell Swan
Pop 1,483; Circ 14,592
Library Holdings: Bk Vols 16,000; Bk Titles 13,000; Per Subs 87
Mem of NE Libr Syst
Partic in Nebr Libr Asn

PLATTSMOUTH

P PLATTSMOUTH PUBLIC LIBRARY, 401 Ave A, 68048. SAN 309-605X. Tel: 402-296-4154. FAX: 402-296-4712. *Librn*, Cheryl Grimshaw; Staff 1 (MLS 1)
Founded 1885. Pop 6,412; Circ 46,963
Library Holdings: Bk Vols 40,897; Per Subs 85
Special Collections: Local & Nebraska History
Mem of Southeastern Regional Libr Syst
Friends of the Library Group

POLK

P POLK PUBLIC LIBRARY, 180 N Main St, PO Box 49, 68654. SAN 309-6068. Tel: 402-765-6471. *Librn*, Jane Nyberg; *Tech Servs*, Marie Brown
Pop 675; Circ 4,549
Oct 2000-Sep 2001 Income $14,526, State $690, City $10,248, County $1,000, Locally Generated Income $2,588. Mats Exp Books $3,005
Library Holdings: Bk Vols 7,000; Per Subs 38; High Interest/Low Vocabulary Bk Vols 25
Subject Interests: Nebraska
Mem of NE Libr Syst

PONCA

P PONCA PUBLIC LIBRARY, 203 Second St, PO Box 368, 68770-0368. SAN 309-6084. Tel: 402-755-2739. FAX: 402-755-2739. *Librn*, Carol Plowman; Staff 3 (Non-MLS 3)
Founded 1913. Pop 982; Circ 9,104
Oct 1999-Sep 2000 Income City $25,000
Library Holdings: Bk Titles 11,886
Subject Interests: Genealogy
Special Collections: Census on Microfilm, 1860-1920 (Dixon County, Nebraska); Lewis & Clark materials; Micro Film Newsp (1884-1996)
Automation Activity & Vendor Info: (Cataloging) Follett; (Circulation) Follett
Mem of NE Libr Syst
Partic in Northeast Library System
Open Tues, Wed & Fri 1-6, Sat 10-4
Friends of the Library Group

POTTER

P POTTER PUBLIC LIBRARY, 333 Chestnut, PO Box 317, 69156-0317. SAN 377-192X. Tel: 308-879-4345. *Dir*, Donna Aurich
Library Holdings: Bk Vols 7,000; Per Subs 10

PRIMROSE

P PRIMROSE PUBLIC LIBRARY,* 230 Commercial St, PO Box 5, 68655. SAN 377-1946. Tel: 308-396-1527. *Dir*, Sue McIntyre
Library Holdings: Bk Vols 1,500

RALSTON

P HOLLIS & HELEN BARIGHT PUBLIC LIBRARY,* 5555 S 77th St, 68127-2899. SAN 309-6092. Tel: 402-331-7636. FAX: 402-331-1168. *Dir*, Jan Gorman; *Ch Servs*, Dorothy Daugherty; Staff 1 (Non-MLS 1)

Founded 1920. Pop 25,000; Circ 62,343
Library Holdings: Bk Vols 30,000; Bk Titles 27,500; Per Subs 85
Special Collections: Northeast Scottish Society Coll
Mem of Eastern Libr Syst

RANDOLPH

P RANDOLPH PUBLIC LIBRARY,* PO Box 307, 68771-0307. SAN 309-6106. Tel: 402-337-0046. *Dir*, Eileen Leise; *Ch Servs*, Joan Steffen; *Ch Servs*, Nancy Granfield
Founded 1919. Pop 1,106; Circ 10,229
Library Holdings: Bk Vols 16,000; Per Subs 48
Subject Interests: Agriculture, History
Open Tues-Thurs 1:30-6, Sat 9:30-11:30 & 1:30-6

RAVENNA

P RAVENNA PUBLIC LIBRARY,* 121 W Seneca St, 68869-1362. SAN 309-6114. Tel: 308-452-4213. *Librn*, Jennifer Hanifch; *Asst Librn*, Erin Groeteke
Circ 9,181
Library Holdings: Bk Vols 9,616; Bk Titles 9,014
Open Tues 9:45-10:45 (storytime), Tues-Fri 2-5:30, Wed 6:30pm-8pm & Sat 9-12:30
Friends of the Library Group

RED CLOUD

P AULD PUBLIC LIBRARY,* 537 N Webster St, 68970. SAN 309-6122. Tel: 402-746-3352. E-Mail: aupuili01@nol.org. *Librn*, Donna Lammers; *Asst Librn*, Teresa Young
Founded 1917. Pop 1,204; Circ 7,015
Library Holdings: Bk Vols 9,604; Per Subs 32
Mem of Republican Valley Libr Syst

S WILLA CATHER PIONEER MEMORIAL & EDUCATION FOUNDATION LIBRARY, 326 N Webster, 68970. SAN 309-6130. Tel: 402-746-2653. FAX: 402-746-2652. Web Site: www.willacather.org. *Dir*, Dr Steven Ryan; E-Mail: sryan@gpcom.net
Founded 1955
Library Holdings: Bk Vols 400; Bk Titles 300
Subject Interests: Webster County, Willa Cather
Special Collections: Willa Cather Pioneer Memorial & Educational Foundation Coll
A branch of the Nebraska State Historical Society managed by The Willa Cather Pioneer Memorial

S WEBSTER COUNTY HISTORICAL MUSEUM LIBRARY, 721 W Fourth St, 68970. (Mail add: PO Box 464, 68970), SAN 377-1474. Tel: 402-746-2444. *Dir*, Helen Mathew
Library Holdings: Bk Vols 300
Partic in Nebr Libr Asn

RISING CITY

P RISING CITY COMMUNITY LIBRARY, 675 Main St, PO Box 190, 68658. SAN 309-6149. Tel: 402-542-2344. *Librn*, Diane Dunker
Founded 1963. Pop 450; Circ 2,300
Library Holdings: Bk Vols 5,500
Special Collections: Zane Grey Series
Mem of NE Libr Syst
Friends of the Library Group

ROYAL

P ROYAL PUBLIC LIBRARY, Third & Ryan St, PO Box 38, 68773. SAN 377-3884. *Dir*, Lois Colson; Tel: 402-893-3486
Library Holdings: Bk Vols 1,600
Partic in Antelope County Libr Comn
Open Tues 6:30-8:30, Wed & Sat 1:30-4

RUSHVILLE

P RUSHVILLE PUBLIC LIBRARY,* 207 Sprague, PO Box 389, 69360. SAN 309-6157. Tel: 308-327-2740. *Librn*, Christine Plantz; E-Mail: chrisplantz@hotmail.com
Pop 1,220; Circ 8,300
Library Holdings: Bk Vols 10,900; Per Subs 22
Special Collections: Native American History & Literature
Mem of Panhandle Library System

S SHERIDAN COUNTY HISTORICAL SOCIETY, INC, Benschoter Memorial Library, Hwy 20 & Nelson Ave, 69360. (Mail add: PO Box 291, 69347-0291), SAN 371-6627. Tel: 308-638-7643. *Curator*, David Perkins; E-Mail: dsperkins@gpcom.net; Staff 1 (Non-MLS 1)
Founded 1960
Library Holdings: Bk Titles 700
Special Collections: Camp Sheridan Nebraska 1874-1881, bks, micro, monographs
Restriction: Non-circulating to the public

RUSKIN

P RUSKIN PUBLIC LIBRARY, Main St, PO Box 87, 68974. SAN 309-6165. Tel: 402-226-2311. *Librn*, Amy Mrosko
Founded 1920. Pop 224; Circ 809
1998-1999 Income $2,765, City $2,565. Mats Exp $1,205, Books $955, Per/Ser (Incl. Access Fees) $37. Sal $1,248
Library Holdings: Bk Vols 3,856
Subject Interests: Local history
Mem of Republican Valley Libr Syst
Partic in Republican Libr Systs

SAINT EDWARD

P SAINT EDWARD PUBLIC LIBRARY,* 307 Beaver, PO Box 249, 68660-0249. SAN 309-6173. Tel: 402-678-2204. E-Mail: stedpl@sherwood.net. Web Site: www.ci.saint-edward.ne.us. *Librn*, Sandy Zurovski
Pop 2,074; Circ 5,948
Library Holdings: Bk Vols 11,000; Per Subs 10
Open Mon 12-6, Wed 12-8, Thurs & Sat 9-12
Friends of the Library Group

SAINT PAUL

P SAINT PAUL LIBRARY,* 1301 Howard Ave, 68873-2021. SAN 309-6181. Tel: 308-754-5223. FAX: 308-754-5374. *Dir, Librn*, Laura Martinsen
Pop 2,094; Circ 21,011
Library Holdings: Bk Vols 17,076; Per Subs 67
Mem of Meridian Libr Syst

SARGENT

P SARGENT TOWNSHIP LIBRARY,* 504 Main, PO Box 476, 68874-0476. SAN 309-6203. Tel: 308-527-4241. *Librn*, Janice Unruh
Founded 1928. Pop 1,060; Circ 2,741
Library Holdings: Bk Vols 7,792; Bk Titles 6,485; Per Subs 27
Mem of Valentine Public Library
Partic in Nebr Libr Network

SCHUYLER

P SCHUYLER PUBLIC LIBRARY,* 1123 A St, 68661-1929. SAN 309-6211. Tel: 402-352-2221. FAX: 402-352-5377. E-Mail: sp81844@navix.net. *Dir*, Douglas Stutzman
Founded 1909. Pop 6,370
Oct 1998-Sep 1999 Income $85,865, State $1,501, City $70,393, County $6,552, Locally Generated Income $5,947, Other $1,472. Mats Exp $10,772, Books $7,789, Per/Ser (Incl. Access Fees) $2,177. Sal $60,791
Library Holdings: Bk Titles 20,611; Per Subs 85
Mem of NE Libr Syst
Friends of the Library Group

SCOTIA

P SCOTIA PUBLIC LIBRARY,* PO Box 188, 68875. SAN 309-622X. Tel: 308-245-3350. *Librn*, Pam Sweley; *Asst Librn*, Magdalene Sautter
Pop 349; Circ 5,094
Library Holdings: Bk Vols 10,388; Per Subs 10
Subject Interests: Agriculture, Education, History, Music
Special Collections: Pioneer
Mem of Valentine Public Library
Open Wed & Sat 2-5

SCOTTSBLUFF

P PANHANDLE LIBRARY SYSTEM,* 1517 Broadway, Ste 129, 69361. SAN 377-1962. Tel: 308-632-1350. FAX: 308-632-3978.
Library Holdings: Bk Vols 300
Member Libraries: Alliance Public Library; Arthur County Public Library; Bayard Public Library; Bridgeport Public Library; Chadron Public Library; Chadron State College; Chappell Memorial Library & Art Gallery; Crawford Public Library; Gering Public Library; Goodall City Library; Gordon City Library; Grant County Library; Holmes County Library; Kimball Public Library; Kootenai-Shoshone Areas Library; Lyman Public Library; Mitchell Public Library; Morrill Public Library; Nancy Fawcett Memorial Library; Oshkosh Public Library; Paxton Public Library; Rushville Public Library;

Scottsbluff Public Library; Sidney Public Library; Washington County Library; Western Nebraska Community College
Partic in Am Libr Asn; Mountain Plains Libr Asn; Nebr Libr Asn

R PLATTE VALLEY BIBLE COLLEGE LIBRARY, 305 E 16th St, PO Box 1227, 69363. SAN 309-6246. Tel: 308-632-6933. FAX: 308-632-8599. *Librn*, Evie Hopper
Founded 1952. Enrl 70
Library Holdings: Bk Vols 17,000; Per Subs 25

M REGIONAL WEST MEDICAL CENTER LIBRARY,* 4021 Ave B, 69361. SAN 377-1458. Tel: 308-630-1368. FAX: 308-630-1721. E-Mail: rwme@hannibal.wncc.cc.ne.us. *Librn*, Michelle Parks
Library Holdings: Bk Vols 3,300; Per Subs 250
Partic in Mid-Continental Regional Med Librs Asn

P SCOTTSBLUFF PUBLIC LIBRARY, 1809 Third Ave, 69361-2493. SAN 309-6254. Tel: 308-630-6250. Interlibrary Loan Service Tel: 308-630-6252. TDD: 308-630-6287. FAX: 308-630-6293. Web Site: city.scottsbluff.net/library. *Dir*, Beverly Kay Russell; Tel: 308-630-6251, E-Mail: brussell@city.scottsbluff.net; *Tech Servs*, Judith Oltmanns; Tel: 308-630-6252, E-Mail: judyo@city.scottsbluff.net; *Ad Servs*, LaVern Allbaugh; E-Mail: laverna@city.scottsbluff.new; *YA Servs*, Trudy Frank; E-Mail: tfrank@city.scottsbluff.net; *ILL*, Nancy Escamilla; Tel: 308-630-6252, E-Mail: nancyk@city.scottsbluff.net; *Ch Servs*, Debra Carlson; Tel: 308-630-6284, E-Mail: dcarlson@city.scottsbluff.net. Subject Specialists: *American history*, Beverly Kay Russell; Staff 15 (MLS 2, Non-MLS 13)
Founded 1917. Pop 14,304; Circ 191,749
Oct 2000-Sep 2001 Income $477,996, State $6,800, City $468,516, Other $2,680. Mats Exp $151,934, Books $30,000, Per/Ser (Incl. Access Fees) $17,700, Micro $890, AV Equip $10,922, Electronic Ref Mat (Incl. Access Fees) $600. Sal $260,731 (Prof $177,739)
Library Holdings: Bk Vols 64,702; Bk Titles 60,446; Per Subs 159
Special Collections: Western Americana (Western History Coll)
Automation Activity & Vendor Info: (Acquisitions) epixtech, inc.; (Cataloging) epixtech, inc.; (Circulation) epixtech, inc.; (OPAC) epixtech, inc.; (Serials) epixtech, inc.
Database Vendor: epixtech, inc., OCLC - First Search
Function: ILL available
Mem of Panhandle Library System
Partic in NEBASE
Special Services for the Deaf - Captioned film depository; TDD; Videos & decoder
Special Services for the Blind - Audiobooks
Friends of the Library Group

J WESTERN NEBRASKA COMMUNITY COLLEGE, Information Services,* 1601 E 27th NE, 69361-1899. SAN 309-6238. Tel: 308-635-6040. FAX: 308-635-6086. Web Site: www.wncc.net/library. *Dir*, Valetta Schneider; E-Mail: vschneid@hannibal.wncc.cc.ne.us; *Tech Servs*, Jill Ellis; *Publ Servs*, Connie Hariman; *Acq*, Betty Black
Founded 1926. Enrl 1,398; Fac 43
Library Holdings: Bk Vols 34,000; Per Subs 180
Automation Activity & Vendor Info: (Cataloging) Follett
Mem of Panhandle Library System
Partic in NEBASE; OCLC Online Computer Library Center, Inc
Departmental Libraries:
SIDNEY CAMPUS, 371 College Dr, Sidney, 69162. SAN 374-5287. Tel: 308-254-7541. *In Charge*, Marcia Miller

S WESTERN NEBRASKA VETERANS HOME LIBRARY,* 1102 W 42nd St, 69361-4713. SAN 377-3779. Tel: 308-632-0300. FAX: 308-632-1384. *Librn*, Laura Singleton
Library Holdings: Bk Vols 1,000; Per Subs 15

SCRIBNER

P SCRIBNER PUBLIC LIBRARY, PO Box M, 68057. SAN 309-6262. Tel: 402-664-3540. FAX: 402-664-3009. E-Mail: stories@tvsonline.net. *Dir*, Jeanette Groppe; *Librn*, Margaret Alt
Founded 1902. Pop 950; Circ 10,000
Library Holdings: Bk Titles 8,000; Per Subs 30
Mem of Eastern Libr Syst

SEWARD

C CONCORDIA UNIVERSITY, Link Library, 800 N Columbia Ave, 68434-1595. SAN 309-6270. Tel: 402-643-7254. Interlibrary Loan Service Tel: 402-643-7255. Reference Tel: 402-643-7256. FAX: 402-643-4218. E-Mail: library@seward.cune.edu. Web Site: www.cune.edu/library/. *Dir*, Myron Boettcher; Tel: 402-643-7358, Fax: 402-643-4218; *Ref*, Tymmi Woods; *Media Spec*, Raymond Huebschman; *ILL*, Lois Mannigel; *Tech Servs*, Glenn Ohlmann; Staff 8 (MLS 4, Non-MLS 4)
Founded 1912. Enrl 1,130; Fac 85; Highest Degree: Master
Jul 1997-Jun 1998 Income $325,000. Mats Exp $158,000, Books $40,000, Per/Ser (Incl. Access Fees) $30,000. Sal $238,000 (Prof $145,000)
Library Holdings: Bk Vols 192,500; Per Subs 565
Subject Interests: Education, Relig studies
Special Collections: Children's Literature; Curriculum
Database Vendor: Ebsco - EbscoHost, GaleNet, OCLC - First Search, Wilson - Wilson Web
Partic in NEBASE; OCLC Online Computer Library Center, Inc

P SEWARD PUBLIC LIBRARY, 204 S Fifth, 68434. SAN 309-6289. Tel: 402-643-3318. Web Site: www.sewardpubliclibrary.org. *Dir*, Becky Baker; Staff 8 (Non-MLS 8)
Founded 1888. Pop 5,700; Circ 97,002
Library Holdings: Bk Titles 25,000; Per Subs 99
Subject Interests: Large print, Nebraska
Friends of the Library Group

SHELBY

P SHELBY PUBLIC LIBRARY, 255 Walnut, PO Box 146, 68662-0236. SAN 377-1989. Tel: 402-527-5181. FAX: 402-527-5181. E-Mail: sl12430@alltel.net. *Dir*, Laura Alt
Library Holdings: Bk Vols 6,000
Partic in Am Libr Asn; Nebr Libr Asn
Open Tues-Thurs 12:30-5:30, Sat 9-12
Friends of the Library Group

SHELTON

P SHELTON TOWNSHIP LIBRARY,* PO Box 10, 68876. SAN 309-6297. Tel: 308-647-5182. *Librn*, Clair McKibben
Founded 1914. Pop 1,254
Library Holdings: Bk Vols 8,500; Per Subs 33
Friends of the Library Group

SHICKLEY

P VIRGIL BIEGERT PUBLIC LIBRARY, 214 N Market, PO Box 412, 68436-0412. SAN 309-6300. Tel: 402-627-3365. E-Mail: library@inebraska.com. *Librn*, Carolyn K Schlegel
Pop 360; Circ 10,526
Oct 1999-Sep 2000 Income $24,739, State $815, City $22,424, Other $1,500. Mats Exp $4,906, Books $2,629, Per/Ser (Incl. Access Fees) $1,890, AV Equip $387. Sal $8,404 (Prof $7,592)
Library Holdings: Bk Vols 12,879; Per Subs 65
Automation Activity & Vendor Info: (Cataloging) Sagebrush Corporation
Friends of the Library Group

SHUBERT

P SHUBERT PUBLIC LIBRARY, 313 Main St, PO Box 148, 68437-0148. SAN 377-2004. Tel: 402-883-2593. *Dir, Librn*, Connie Shafer
Library Holdings: Bk Vols 3,500; Per Subs 38
Open Tues 1-5, Fri 10-12 & 1-4

SIDNEY

P SIDNEY PUBLIC LIBRARY,* 1112 12th Ave, 69162. SAN 309-6319. Tel: 308-254-3110. FAX: 308-254-3710. *Dir*, Thomas Stark
Pop 8,425; Circ 68,095
Library Holdings: Bk Vols 40,404; Bk Titles 39,186; Per Subs 134
Subject Interests: Local history, Nebr authors
Mem of Panhandle Library System

SILVER CREEK

P TOWNSHIP LIBRARY OF SILVER CREEK, 309 Vine St, 68663-0249. (Mail add: PO Box 249, 68663-0249), SAN 309-6327. Tel: 308-773-2594. *Librn*, Elissia Vanek
Founded 1934. Pop 709; Circ 1,715
Jul 1999-Jun 2000 Income $8,000. Mats Exp $425, Books $350, Per/Ser (Incl. Access Fees) $75. Sal $2,500
Library Holdings: Bk Vols 6,000
Mem of NE Libr Syst
Open Mon-Fri 2-5

SNYDER

P SNYDER PUBLIC LIBRARY,* 203 Ash St, PO Box 26, 68664-0026. SAN 309-6335. Tel: 402-568-2570. FAX: 402-568-2688. *Librn*, Laura Hamata
Pop 390; Circ 9,022
Library Holdings: Bk Vols 3,489

SOUTH SIOUX CITY

P SOUTH SIOUX CITY PUBLIC LIBRARY,* 2219 Dakota Ave, 68776. SAN 309-6343. Tel: 402-494-7545. FAX: 402-494-7546. Web Site: www.sscdc.net/library. *Dir*, William E Kendra; E-Mail: wkendra@sscdc.net
Founded 1920. Pop 9,677; Circ 44,096
1997-1998 Income $101,063. Mats Exp Books $21,600. Sal $56,000 (Prof $28,500)
Library Holdings: Bk Vols 24,344; Per Subs 98
Special Collections: Nebraska Coll, large print
Mem of NE Libr Syst
Friends of the Library Group

SPALDING

P SPALDING PUBLIC LIBRARY,* Main St, PO Box 101, 68665. SAN 309-6351. Tel: 308-428-2545, 308-497-2695. *Dir*, Helen Langer
Library Holdings: Bk Vols 7,000
Open Tues 9-12 & 1-5:30, Sat 9-11:30

SPENCER

P SPENCER TOWNSHIP LIBRARY,* PO Box 189, 68777-0189. SAN 309-636X. Tel: 402-589-1131. E-Mail: spnlib@inetnebr.com. *Librn*, Paulette Blaire
Pop 596; Circ 67,590
Library Holdings: Bk Vols 6,355; Per Subs 15
Open Mon, Wed & Sat 1:30-5

SPRINGFIELD

P SPRINGFIELD PUBLIC LIBRARY,* 170 N Third St, PO Box 40, 68059-0040. SAN 309-6378. Tel: 402-253-2797. FAX: 402-253-2797. E-Mail: spl@cyberpage.net. *Dir*, Charlene Harding
Pop 1,426; Circ 13,694
1997-1998 Income $24,885, State $728, City $21,723, Locally Generated Income $1,099, Other $1,335. Mats Exp $6,377. Sal $12,300
Library Holdings: Bk Vols 17,790; Per Subs 45
Mem of Eastern Libr Syst
Friends of the Library Group

STANTON

P STANTON PUBLIC LIBRARY,* PO Box 497, 68779. SAN 309-6386. Tel: 402-439-2230. FAX: 402-439-2230. E-Mail: spl@stanton.net. *Dir*, Carol Armbruster; *Asst Librn*, Laura Hess
Founded 1886. Pop 1,549; Circ 11,542
Oct 1997-Sep 1998 Income $74,931, City $40,245, County $1,500, Locally Generated Income $1,872, Other $30,000. Mats Exp $4,739, Books $2,705, Per/Ser (Incl. Access Fees) $1,092, Other Print Mats $942. Sal $25,675
Library Holdings: Bk Titles 11,979; Per Subs 42
Subject Interests: Games
Mem of NE Libr Syst

STAPLETON

P LOGAN COUNTY LIBRARY,* 317 Main St, PO Box 8, 69163-0245. SAN 309-6394. Tel: 308-636-2343. *Librn*, Mary Keslar
Pop 340; Circ 3,400
Library Holdings: Bk Titles 6,688; Per Subs 16
Mem of Republican Valley Libr Syst
Open Tues, Thurs & Sat 1-5

STELLA

P STELLA COMMUNITY LIBRARY,* Third & Main St, 68442. SAN 321-2408. Tel: 402-883-2232. FAX: 402-883-2435. *Librn*, Elizabeth S Ketner; E-Mail: gwketn@sentco.net
Founded 1908. Pop 280
Library Holdings: Bk Vols 2,244
Partic in Nebr Libr Com; SE Libr Network
Open Wed 3-5:30, Sat 9-11:30am

STERLING

P STERLING PUBLIC LIBRARY,* PO Box 57, 68443. SAN 309-6408. Tel: 402-866-2056. E-Mail: skw8754@excite.com. *Librn*, Susan Wilken
Pop 510; Circ 5,759
Library Holdings: Bk Titles 9,955; Per Subs 35
Mem of Southeastern Regional Libr Syst
Open Tues-Thurs 2-5 & Sat 8-12

STRATTON

P STRATTON PUBLIC LIBRARY,* 502 Bailey St, PO Box 182, 69043-0182. SAN 309-6416. Tel: 308-276-2472. *Dir*, Beverly Henderson
Library Holdings: Bk Vols 5,000

STROMSBURG

P STROMSBURG PUBLIC LIBRARY, 113 E Fifth, PO Box 366, 68666. SAN 309-6424. Tel: 402-764-7681. FAX: 402-764-7681. E-Mail: stromsburglibrary@alltel.net. *Dir*, Diana Johnson
Founded 1918. Pop 1,241; Circ 14,084
Oct 1999-Sep 2000 Income $43,259, State $801, City $17,093, County $1,000, Locally Generated Income $1,022, Other $441. Mats Exp Books $8,150. Sal $20,380
Library Holdings: Bk Vols 15,650; Per Subs 53
Automation Activity & Vendor Info: (Cataloging) Follett; (Circulation) Follett
Mem of NE Libr Syst

STUART

P STUART TOWNSHIP LIBRARY,* PO Box 207, 68780-0207. SAN 309-6432. Tel: 402-924-3242. E-Mail: library@elkhorn.net. *Librn*, Angie Olberding
Pop 1,102; Circ 2,066
Library Holdings: Bk Vols 4,897; Per Subs 13
Mem of NE Libr Syst

SUPERIOR

P SUPERIOR PUBLIC LIBRARY,* 449 N Kansas, 68978-1852. SAN 309-6440. Tel: 402-879-4200. FAX: 402-879-4002. *Dir*, Vicki Perrie; *Asst Librn*, Peggie Lipker
Founded 1901. Pop 2,502; Circ 24,282
Library Holdings: Bk Vols 20,000; Per Subs 40
Mem of Republican Valley Libr Syst

SUTHERLAND

P SUTHERLAND PUBLIC LIBRARY,* 900 Second St, PO Box 275, 69165-0275. SAN 309-6459. Tel: 308-386-2228. *Dir*, Patsy Marrs
Library Holdings: Bk Vols 15,000
Open Tues-Wed 10-12, 1-5:30 & 7-9, Thurs & Sat 10-12 & 1-5:30

SUTTON

P SUTTON MEMORIAL LIBRARY, 201 S Saunders, PO Box 433, 68979-0433. SAN 309-6467. Tel: 402-773-5259. E-Mail: co52133@alltel.net. *Librn*, Gertie Schmer
Pop 1,353; Circ 15,238
Oct 1999-Sep 2000 Income $27,417, State $994, City $12,423, Other $14,000. Mats Exp $6,700, Books $6,000, Electronic Ref Mat (Incl. Access Fees) $700. Sal $12,956
Library Holdings: Bk Vols 15,247; Per Subs 43
Automation Activity & Vendor Info: (Circulation) Follett
Mem of Republican Valley Libr Syst
Friends of the Library Group

SYRACUSE

P SYRACUSE PUBLIC LIBRARY,* 469 Sixth St, PO Box 8, 68446-0008. SAN 309-6475. Tel: 402-269-2336. *Librn*, Sue Antes
Pop 1,638; Circ 17,917
Library Holdings: Bk Titles 18,000; Per Subs 27
Partic in SE Libr Network
Friends of the Library Group

TABLE ROCK

P TABLE ROCK PUBLIC LIBRARY,* Luzerne St, Box 86, 68447. SAN 309-6483. *Librn*, Carol Glathar
Pop 308
Library Holdings: Bk Vols 5,700
Open Thurs 11:30-4:30

TALMAGE

P TALMAGE PUBLIC LIBRARY,* 213 Main, PO Box 7, 68448-0007. SAN 309-6491. Tel: 402-264-3715. FAX: 402-264-4725.
Founded 1904. Pop 246; Circ 1,564
Library Holdings: Bk Vols 5,000; Per Subs 14

Mem of Beatrice Public Library
Special Services for the Deaf - Captioned film depository
Open Mon, Tues, Fri & Sat 8-12, Wed 1:30-6:30

TAYLOR

P TAYLOR PUBLIC LIBRARY, PO Box 206, 68879. SAN 309-6505. Tel: 308-942-6125. *Librn*, Leola M Brodine
Pop 683; Circ 2,714
Library Holdings: Bk Vols 5,152
Function: ILL available
Mem of Meridian Libr Syst
Partic in Meridian Library System

TECUMSEH

P TECUMSEH PUBLIC LIBRARY, 170 Branch St, 68450. SAN 309-6513. Tel: 402-335-2060. FAX: 402-335-2069. E-Mail: tecpublib@navix.net. *Librn*, Ruby Meister; *Asst Librn*, Susie Kerner
Founded 1907. Pop 1,702; Circ 16,014
Oct 1998-Sep 1999 Income City $45,000. Mats Exp $21,000, Books $13,000, Per/Ser (Incl. Access Fees) $900. Sal $13,000
Library Holdings: Bk Titles 11,258; Per Subs 33
Automation Activity & Vendor Info: (Cataloging) Follett; (Circulation) Follett
Database Vendor: OCLC - First Search
Mem of Southeastern Regional Libr Syst

TEKAMAH

S BURT COUNTY MUSEUM, INC LIBRARY, 319 N 13th St, PO Box 125, 68061-0125. SAN 372-6088. Tel: 402-374-1505. *Curator*, Bonnie Newell
Founded 1967
Library Holdings: Bk Vols 780; Bk Titles 530; Per Subs 250
Subject Interests: Genealogy
Special Collections: History of Bunt County 1929; Tekamah Book 1904; Tekamah Centennial Book 1854-1954
Friends of the Library Group

P TEKAMAH PUBLIC LIBRARY, 204 S 13th St, 68061-1304. SAN 309-6521. Tel: 402-374-2453. FAX: 402-374-2521. *Dir*, Mary E King
Founded 1916. Pop 3,409; Circ 27,000
Library Holdings: Bk Titles 13,551; Per Subs 54
Mem of Eastern Libr Syst
Partic in Nebr Librns Asn
Friends of the Library Group

THEDFORD

P THOMAS COUNTY LIBRARY,* 501 Main St, PO Box 228, 69166-0228. SAN 350-2686. Tel: 308-645-2237. *Librn*, Ronda Haumann; *Asst Librn*, Rosalee Hamilton; *Bkmobile Coordr*, Melissa Holt
Founded 1958. Pop 3,079; Circ 38,006
Library Holdings: Bk Vols 21,107; Per Subs 37
Subject Interests: Architecture, Art, Education, Natural science
Special Collections: Indians of North America; Libr of American Literature Coll; Western History (especially Nebraska)
Mem of Meridian Libr Syst
Partic in Nebr Libr Asn
Open Mon 7pm-9pm, Tues-Thurs 2-6, Fri 2-5

TILDEN

P TILDEN PUBLIC LIBRARY,* 108 E Second St, PO Box 457, 68781-0457. SAN 309-653X. Tel: 402-368-5306. FAX: 402-368-5306. E-Mail: tildenpl@ncfcomm.com. Web Site: www.users.ncfcomm.com/tildenpl. *Librn*, Dixie Kucera
Founded 1923. Pop 1,525; Circ 16,628
Library Holdings: Bk Vols 12,000; Per Subs 45
Subject Interests: Dinosaurs, Internet
Mem of NE Libr Syst
Partic in Madison County Libr Asn; telope Libr Asn
Friends of the Library Group

TOBIAS

P TOBIAS PUBLIC LIBRARY,* Main St, PO Box 97, 68453-0097. SAN 309-6548. Tel: 402-243-2219. *Dir*, Mary Ann Kronhofman
Library Holdings: Bk Vols 2,000
Open Wed 1-3, Sat 8:30-10:30am

TRENTON

P TRENTON PUBLIC LIBRARY,* E First St, PO Box 307, 69044-0307. SAN 309-6556. Tel: 308-334-5413. *Librn*, Helen Campbell; *Asst Librn*, Twyla Steinbrink
Pop 656; Circ 7,813
Library Holdings: Bk Vols 7,728

ULYSSES

P ULYSSES TOWNSHIP LIBRARY,* 410 C St, PO Box 217, 68669. SAN 309-6564. Tel: 402-549-2451. E-Mail: ulysseslib@clarks.net. *Librn*, Glenna Mashek; *Asst Librn*, Cindy Kadavy
Founded 1914. Pop 504; Circ 3,540
Library Holdings: Bk Vols 8,000; Per Subs 32
Friends of the Library Group

VALENTINE

S CHERRY COUNTY HISTORICAL SOCIETY LIBRARY,* Box 284, 69201. SAN 377-4295. Tel: 402-376-2015. *Curator, Dir*, Diane Rathman
Library Holdings: Bk Vols 1,500

SR PRESBYTERIAN CHURCH LIBRARY,* 325 N Victoria St, 69201. SAN 373-8159. Tel: 402-376-1305. *Actg Librn*, Kristi Benson
Founded 1977
Library Holdings: Bk Vols 1,382; Bk Titles 1,211

SR SAINT JOHNS EPISCOPAL CHURCH LIBRARY,* 372 N Main, PO Box 261, 69201. SAN 373-8205. Tel: 402-376-1723. *Actg Librn*, Solveig Perrett
Founded 1993
Library Holdings: Bk Vols 668; Bk Titles 575
Special Collections: Episcopal Church Holdings Coll

SR UNITED METHODIST CHURCH LIBRARY,* 804 E Fifth St, 69201-1613. Tel: 402-376-3473.
Founded 1963
1997-1998 Income $700. Mats Exp $700, Books $625, Other Print Mats $75
Library Holdings: Bk Titles 1,756
Special Collections: United Methodist Church Holdings Coll

P VALENTINE PUBLIC LIBRARY,* 324 N Main, 69201. SAN 309-6572. Tel: 402-376-3160. *Dir*, Joyce Mann; *Asst Librn*, Marie Wiley
Founded 1921. Pop 6,846; Circ 53,672
Library Holdings: Bk Vols 37,222; Per Subs 57
Special Collections: Mari Sandoz American Indian Coll
Member Libraries: Hooker County Library; Sargent Township Library; Scotia Public Library

VALLEY

S VALLEY HISTORICAL MUSEUM LIBRARY, 218 W Alexander St, 68064. (Mail add: PO Box 685, 68064), SAN 377-1377. Tel: 402-359-2678. *Pres*, Marianne Nielsen
Founded 1966
Library Holdings: Bk Vols 250
Special Collections: Collection of Valley area newspapers from the 1915s
Open May-Sept Sun 2-4 or by appointment all year long

P VALLEY PUBLIC LIBRARY,* 210 N Locust, PO Box 353, 68064-0353. SAN 309-6580. Tel: 402-359-9924. FAX: 402-359-9924. *Librn*, Dr Nina Little; E-Mail: nlittle@radikx.net
Founded 1902. Pop 1,775; Circ 9,026
1998-1999 Income $24,503, State $794, City $14,427, County $9,282. Mats Exp $5,400, Books $5,200, Per/Ser (Incl. Access Fees) $200. Sal $13,951
Library Holdings: Bk Vols 9,174; Per Subs 25
Mem of Eastern Libr Syst
Friends of the Library Group

VALPARAISO

P VALPARAISO PUBLIC LIBRARY, 300 W Second, PO Box 440, 68065-0440. SAN 309-6599. Tel: 402-784-6141. FAX: 402-784-6141. *Dir*, Mary Rittenburg; Staff 1 (MLS 1)
Pop 484
Library Holdings: Bk Vols 5,000
Mem of Bellevue Public Library
Open Wed 5-8:30, Sat 12-4:30
Friends of the Library Group

VERDIGRE

P VERDIGRE PUBLIC LIBRARY,* 301 S Main St, PO Box 40, 68783. SAN 309-6602. Tel: 402-668-2677. E-Mail: vplibr@bloomnet.com. *Dir*, Linda Bower; *Librn*, Kathy Farnik

Pop 617; Circ 10,491
Library Holdings: Bk Vols 15,000
Mem of NE Libr Syst
Friends of the Library Group

WAHOO

P WAHOO PUBLIC LIBRARY,* 627 N Broadway St, 68066-1607. SAN 309-6610. Tel: 402-443-3871. FAX: 402-443-3871. E-Mail: wahoojudy@hotmail.com. *Librn*, Judy Coday
Founded 1923. Circ 41,361
Library Holdings: Bk Vols 30,000; Per Subs 70
Mem of Eastern Libr Syst

WAKEFIELD

P GRAVES PUBLIC LIBRARY, 206 W Third St, PO Box 150, 68784. SAN 309-6629. Tel: 402-287-2334. FAX: 402-287-2334. *Librn*, Nancy Frederickson
Founded 1915
Library Holdings: Bk Titles 12,741; Per Subs 46
Special Collections: Antique Guns; Indian Artifacts
Mem of NE Libr Syst
Friends of the Library Group

WALTHILL

P WALTHILL PUBLIC LIBRARY, PO Box 466, 68067. SAN 309-6637. Tel: 402-846-5051. *Librn*, Judy Davis
Pop 847
Library Holdings: Bk Vols 6,300
Open Thurs 12-4 & Sat 10-1

WATERLOO

P WATERLOO PUBLIC LIBRARY,* 205 Washington, PO Box 188, 68069. SAN 309-6645. Tel: 402-779-4171. FAX: 402-779-4369. E-Mail: wpl205@aol.com. *Dir*, Linda Oyster
Pop 450; Circ 2,478
Library Holdings: Bk Vols 7,000
Mem of Bellevue Public Library; Eastern Libr Syst

WAUNETA

P WAUNETA PUBLIC LIBRARY, 319 N Tecumseh, 69045. SAN 309-6653. Tel: 308-394-5243. *Librn*, Ruth Hohl
Pop 675; Circ 5,690
Oct 2000-Sep 2001 Mats Exp Books $2,000
Library Holdings: Bk Vols 5,690

WAUSA

P LINCOLN TOWNSHIP LIBRARY,* PO Box H, 68786-0319. SAN 309-6661. Tel: 402-586-2454. FAX: 402-586-2454. E-Mail: linctnlb@bloomnet.com. *Dir*, Virginia Lindquist
Pop 900; Circ 3,921
Library Holdings: Bk Vols 20,000; Per Subs 74
Mem of NE Libr Syst

WAYNE

P WAYNE PUBLIC LIBRARY,* Robert B & Mary Y Benthack Library-Senior Ctr, 410 Pearl St, 68787. SAN 309-667X. Tel: 402-375-3135. FAX: 402-375-5772. *Dir*, Jolene Klein; E-Mail: jklein@wayne.esu1.k12.ne.us; Staff 1 (Non-MLS 1)
Founded 1899. Pop 5,142; Circ 48,523
Oct 1999-Sep 2000 Income $105,722, State $1,080, City $104,642. Mats Exp $18,772, Books $15,992, Per/Ser (Incl. Access Fees) $2,700, Micro $80. Sal $72,476 (Prof $37,205)
Library Holdings: Bk Vols 20,898; Bk Titles 20,000; Per Subs 100
Subject Interests: Large print, Nebraska
Special Collections: Nebraska Coll, video, book on tape, art reproduction
Automation Activity & Vendor Info: (Circulation) Follett
Database Vendor: Ebsco - EbscoHost, OCLC - First Search
Mem of Nebr Libr Asn

C WAYNE STATE COLLEGE, Conn Library, 1111 Main St, 68787. SAN 309-6688. Tel: 402-375-7257. Circulation Tel: 402-375-7258. Reference Tel: 402-375-7263. Toll Free Tel: 800-311-3990. FAX: 402-375-7538. E-Mail: library@wscgate.wsc.edu. Web Site: www.wsc.edu/academic/conn/. *Dir*, Dr Stan Gardner; E-Mail: sgardner@wsc.edu; *Ref*, Maria Johnson; *Publ Servs, Syst Coordr*, Jan Brumm; *Bibliog Instr, Doc*, Gayle Poirier; *Electronic Resources*, David Graber; *Coll Develop*, Marcus Schlichter; *Head Tech Servs*, Marilyn Liedorff; Staff 16 (MLS 7, Non-MLS 9)
Founded 1892. Enrl 2,915; Fac 160; Highest Degree: Master
Jul 1999-Jun 2000 Income $753,434, State $738,369, Other $15,065. Mats Exp $189,631, Books $93,089, Per/Ser (Incl. Access Fees) $61,094, Presv $3,000, AV Equip $10,932, Other Print Mats $5,600, Electronic Ref Mat (Incl. Access Fees) $19,516. Sal $612,171 (Prof $255,883)
Library Holdings: Bk Vols 162,140; Bk Titles 140,754; Per Subs 620; High Interest/Low Vocabulary Bk Vols 3,470
Special Collections: Instructional Resources; Juvenile & Young Adults; Kessler Art Coll; Musical Score Coll; Val Peterson Archives
Automation Activity & Vendor Info: (Acquisitions) Innovative Interfaces Inc.; (Cataloging) Innovative Interfaces Inc.; (Circulation) Innovative Interfaces Inc.; (OPAC) Innovative Interfaces Inc.; (Serials) Innovative Interfaces Inc.
Database Vendor: OCLC - First Search
Publications: Children/Young Adults Materials Review
Partic in Nebr Libr Com; Nebr State Col Syst; Northeast Library System; OCLC Online Computer Library Center, Inc

WEEPING WATER

P WEEPING WATER PUBLIC LIBRARY,* 206 West H St, PO Box 425, 68463-0425. SAN 309-6696. Tel: 402-267-3050. *Librn*, Nancy Behrns
Founded 1914. Pop 1,100; Circ 9,741
Library Holdings: Bk Vols 10,615; Bk Titles 15,000; Per Subs 10
Mem of SE Network of Nebr

WEST POINT

P JOHN A STAHL LIBRARY, 330 N Colfax St, PO Box 258, 68788. SAN 309-670X. Tel: 402-372-3831. FAX: 402-372-5931. E-Mail: sj42353@alltel.net. *Librn*, Mary Jo Mack
Circ 37,717
Library Holdings: Bk Vols 28,000; Per Subs 86
Special Collections: Education Information Center
Mem of Eastern Libr Syst

WESTERN

P STRUCKMAN-BAATZ MEMORIAL LIBRARY, 104 NW Ave, PO Box 338, 68464-0338. SAN 309-6718. Tel: 402-433-2177. *Dir*, Barbara J Schwisow
Pop 344; Circ 1,682
Library Holdings: Bk Titles 6,027; Per Subs 12
Mem of Beatrice Public Library

WILBER

P DVORACEK MEMORIAL LIBRARY, 419 W Third, PO Box 803, 68465-0803. SAN 309-6726. Tel: 402-821-2832. E-Mail: dvoraceklib@ispchannel.com. *Dir*, Betty Skrdla; *Asst Librn*, Nancy Vacek; *Asst Librn*, Susie Homolka
Founded 1968. Pop 1,517; Circ 15,952
Oct 2000-Sep 2001 Income $82,000. Mats Exp $8,900, Books $8,000, Per/Ser (Incl. Access Fees) $900. Sal $43,000
Library Holdings: Bk Titles 14,500; Per Subs 31
Special Collections: Czech Materials, bks
Automation Activity & Vendor Info: (Circulation) Follett
Mem of Southeastern Regional Libr Syst

WILCOX

P WILCOX PUBLIC LIBRARY,* PO Box 37, 68982-0037. SAN 377-4627. Tel: 308-478-5544. *Librn*, Donna Johnson
Library Holdings: Bk Vols 3,000

WILSONVILLE

P WILSONVILLE PUBLIC LIBRARY,* 706 Main St, PO Box 100, 69046-0278. SAN 309-6734. Tel: 308-349-4367. *Dir*, Laurie Love
Pop 189; Circ 3,729
Library Holdings: Bk Vols 6,128
Special Collections: Memorials
Mem of Republican Valley Libr Syst
Open Mon 5:30-7:30, Wed & Fri 8:30-12

WINSIDE

P WINSIDE PUBLIC LIBRARY, 420 Main St, PO Box 217, 68790-0217. SAN 309-6750. Tel: 402-286-4422. *Librn*, JoAnn V Field; Staff 1 (Non-MLS 1)
Founded 1911. Pop 434; Circ 5,394
Oct 1999-Sep 2000 Income $10,194, City $9,412, Other $782. Mats Exp $2,783, Books $2,571, Per/Ser (Incl. Access Fees) $212. Sal $5,201
Library Holdings: Bk Titles 6,719; Per Subs 30
Mem of NE Libr Syst

WISNER

P WISNER PUBLIC LIBRARY,* PO Box 547, 68791-9999. SAN 309-6769. Tel: 402-529-6018. E-Mail: wisnrlib@gpcom.net. *Dir*, Carol Duncan
Pop 1,253; Circ 13,999
Library Holdings: Bk Vols 8,645; Per Subs 20
Automation Activity & Vendor Info: (Cataloging) Follett; (Circulation) Follett
Mem of Bellevue Public Library

WOLBACH

P WOLBACH PUBLIC LIBRARY,* PO Box 97, 68882. SAN 309-6777. Tel: 308-246-5278. *Dir*, Maria Shepard
Pop 301; Circ 380
1999-2000 Income Locally Generated Income $1,500. Mats Exp Books $500
Library Holdings: Bk Vols 2,288; Bk Titles 1,700
Open Sat 10-1

WOOD RIVER

P MALTMAN MEMORIAL PUBLIC LIBRARY,* 910 Main St, PO Box 10, 68883. SAN 309-6785. Tel: 308-583-2349. *Dir*, Nancy Jack
Founded 1905. Pop 1,150; Circ 8,826
Library Holdings: Bk Titles 16,220; Per Subs 34
Mem of Edith Abbott Memorial Library
Open Mon 3-6, Wed 2-5 & 7-9, Thurs 1-5, Sat 9-12

WYMORE

P WYMORE PUBLIC LIBRARY,* 116 West F St, 68466. SAN 309-6793. Tel: 402-645-3787. E-Mail: co73107@alltel.net. *Librn*, Jackie Nicholson
Founded 1917. Pop 1,841; Circ 16,494
Library Holdings: Bk Titles 13,000; Per Subs 50
Mem of Beatrice Public Library
Partic in SE Nebr Libr Network
Friends of the Library Group

YORK

S NEBRASKA CORRECTIONAL CENTER FOR WOMEN LIBRARY, 1107 Recharge Rd, 68467-8003. SAN 377-1334. Tel: 402-362-3317. FAX: 402-362-3892. *Dir*, Janice Axdahl; Staff 6 (Non-MLS 6)
Jul 1998-Jun 1999 Income Parent Institution $1,115. Mats Exp $1,115, Per/Ser (Incl. Access Fees) $815
Library Holdings: Bk Vols 6,522; Per Subs 36; High Interest/Low Vocabulary Bk Vols 35
Subject Interests: Black culture, Law, Native Americans, Spanish lang mat
Mem of Southeastern Regional Libr Syst
Partic in Nebr Institutional Asn for Libs

J YORK COLLEGE, Levitt Library Learning Center,* 1125 E Eighth, 68467-2699. SAN 309-6807. Tel: 402-363-5704. FAX: 402-363-5685. Web Site: www.york.edu/library/. *Dir*, Todd Mountjoy; E-Mail: Todd.mountjoy@york.edu; *Archivist, Librn*, Leo Miller; Tel: 402-363-5706, E-Mail: Leo.miller@york.edu; *Acq, Cat*, Ruth Carlock; Tel: 402-363-5703, E-Mail: Rmcarlock@york.edu; *Per*, Terry Law; Tel: 402-363-5708, E-Mail: Terri.law@york.edu; Staff 5 (MLS 1, Non-MLS 4)
Founded 1956. Enrl 512; Fac 36; Highest Degree: Bachelor
Jul 1998-Jun 1999 Income $198,557. Mats Exp $49,179, Books $18,464, Per/Ser (Incl. Access Fees) $27,718, Electronic Ref Mat (Incl. Access Fees) $2,997. Sal $103,096 (Prof $64,784)
Library Holdings: Bk Vols 41,503; Bk Titles 34,442; Per Subs 285; Bks on Deafness & Sign Lang 16
Special Collections: Church History (Restoration Movement); Missions; Yorkana
Database Vendor: Ebsco - EbscoHost, OCLC - First Search
Partic in NEBASE; OCLC Online Computer Library Center, Inc
Friends of the Library Group

P YORK PUBLIC LIBRARY, Kilgore Memorial Library, 520 Nebraska Ave, 68467-3095. SAN 309-6815. Tel: 402-363-2620. FAX: 402-363-2627. E-Mail: co51537@navix.net. *Dir*, Stan Schulz; *Ch Servs*, Bernice Mason; Staff 5 (MLS 1, Non-MLS 4)
Founded 1885. Pop 7,884; Circ 78,490
Oct 1999-Sep 2000 Income $270,038, State $3,000, County $32,500. Mats Exp $52,000. Sal $114,231
Library Holdings: Bk Vols 47,306; Bk Titles 45,544; Per Subs 100
Automation Activity & Vendor Info: (Acquisitions) epixtech, inc.; (Cataloging) epixtech, inc.; (Circulation) epixtech, inc.; (OPAC) epixtech, inc.; (Serials) epixtech, inc.
Friends of the Library Group

YUTAN

P YUTAN PUBLIC LIBRARY,* 502 Third St, 68073. SAN 309-6823. Tel: 402-625-2111. FAX: 402-625-2111. E-Mail: yutanpubliclibrary@alltel.com. *Librn*, Sophie Dolinski; *Librn*, Debby Rupp
Founded 1966. Pop 1,350; Circ 5,179
Library Holdings: Bk Vols 6,698
Mem of Eastern Libr Syst

NEVADA

Date of Statistics: 2000
Population, 1999 Census: 1,965,660
Population Served by Public Libraries: 1,974,812
Total Holdings in Public Libraries: 4,194,430
Holdings Per Capita: 2.12
Total Public Library Circulation: 8,105,517
Circulation Per Capita: 4.10
Total Public Library Operating Expenditures (including Grants-in-Aid): $45,471,669
Source of Income: Local Funds, State grants, federal LSTA
Expenditure Per Capita: $23.03
Number of County & Regional Libraries: 12 County, 9 Districts, 2 City
Number of Bookmobiles in State: 3
Grants-in-Aid to Public Libraries:
State Grants: $836,518

AMARGOSA VALLEY

P AMARGOSA VALLEY COMMUNITY LIBRARY,* HCR 69, Box 401-T, 89020-9701. SAN 320-488X. Tel: 702-372-5340. FAX: 702-372-1188. *Librn*, Diane Brigham; Staff 1 (MLS 1)
Founded 1977. Pop 1,400
Jul 1997-Jun 1998 Income $118,000, State $8,000, Federal $500, Locally Generated Income $1,800. Mats Exp $18,000, AV Equip $75. Sal $49,000
Library Holdings: Bk Vols 18,000; Per Subs 55
Subject Interests: Local history
Automation Activity & Vendor Info: (Cataloging) Gaylord; (Circulation) Gaylord
Partic in Nev Rural Librs Coop
Friends of the Library Group

BEATTY

P BEATTY LIBRARY DISTRICT, 400 N Fourth St, PO Box 129, 89003. SAN 309-684X. Tel: 775-553-2257. FAX: 775-553-2257. *Actg Librn*, Kathryn Tolleson; E-Mail: ktolleson50@hotmail.com; *Cat*, Dianna Smith; Staff 2 (Non-MLS 2)
Founded 1966. Pop 1,600; Circ 32,786
Jul 1999-Jun 2000 Income $86,144. Mats Exp $80,548
Library Holdings: Bk Vols 13,000; Bk Titles 17,295; Per Subs 22
Subject Interests: Civil War, Lincoln war, Local history, Nevada
Automation Activity & Vendor Info: (Serials) Sagebrush Corporation
Function: ILL available
Mem of Southern Nev Libr Servs
Partic in Coop Librs Automated Network

BOULDER CITY

P BOULDER CITY LIBRARY,* 813 Arizona St, 89005-2697. SAN 309-6858. Tel: 702-293-1281. FAX: 702-293-0239. Web Site: www.accessnv.com/bclibrary/. *Electronic Resources, Ref*, Deanna Duffy; *Dir*, Duncan R McCoy; E-Mail: duncan@accessnv.com; *Publ Servs*, Mary Alice Watrous; *Tech Servs*, Anne Karr; *Ch Servs*, Stephanie Miller
Founded 1933. Pop 15,000; Circ 155,000
Jul 1999-Jun 2000 Income $626,495. Mats Exp $157,920, Books $140,920, Per/Ser (Incl. Access Fees) $11,000, Micro $5,000, AV Equip $1,000. Sal $293,098 (Prof $146,420)
Library Holdings: Bk Vols 65,000; Bk Titles 63,000; Per Subs 250
Subject Interests: Local history
Automation Activity & Vendor Info: (Circulation) DRA

S LAKE MEAD NATIONAL RECREATION AREA LIBRARY,* Allan Bible Visitor Ctr, 601 Nevada Hwy, 89005. SAN 309-6874. Tel: 702-293-8990. FAX: 702-293-8029.
Founded 1962
Library Holdings: Bk Titles 1,650
Subject Interests: Amphibians, Archaeology, Botany, Geology, History, Indians, Interpretation, National Park Serv, Natural history, Palentology, Reptiles, Water resources
Restriction: Open to public for reference only

CARSON CITY

P CARSON CITY LIBRARY, 900 N Roop St, 89701. SAN 309-6963. Tel: 775-887-2244. FAX: 775-887-2273. E-Mail: cclb@ci.carson-city-nv.us. Web Site: www.clan.lib.nv.uc/docs/nsla/clan/clan.htm. *Dir*, Sally Edwards; *Ref*, Susan Antipa; *Publ Servs*, Jan Bachman; *Ch Servs, YA Servs*, Cory King; Staff 20 (MLS 5, Non-MLS 15)
Founded 1966. Pop 75,000; Circ 350,000
Jul 1998-Jun 1999 Income $1,163,476, State $48,333, City $1,105,538, Other $9,605. Mats Exp $187,715, Books $165,215, Per/Ser (Incl. Access Fees) $15,000, Presv $995, Micro $1,000, Other Print Mats $5,505. Sal $853,314
Library Holdings: Bk Vols 101,000; Per Subs 206
Subject Interests: Large print, Nevada
Automation Activity & Vendor Info: (Acquisitions) Gaylord; (Cataloging) Gaylord; (Circulation) Gaylord; (ILL) Gaylord; (OPAC) Gaylord; (Serials) Gaylord
Partic in Coop Librs Automated Network
Friends of the Library Group

M CARSON-TAHOE HOSPITAL, Lahontan Basin Medical Library, 775 Fleischmann Way, PO Box 2168, 89702-2168. SAN 309-6912. Tel: 775-885-4358. FAX: 775-883-5063. *Librn*, Richard Bickel; Staff 1 (Non-MLS 1)
Founded 1972
Library Holdings: Bk Vols 1,000; Per Subs 200
Subject Interests: Consumer health, Medicine, Nursing
Special Collections: Core Coll of Clinical Medicine & Nursing Materials
Partic in Dialog Corporation; Medline; Pac NW Regional Med Libr Serv
Physicians contribute to a memorial fund which is used for database charges, ILL, books & journals

S EXPERIMENTAL AIRCRAFT ASSOCIATION, Reference & Lending Library,* 2500 E College Parkway, 89706. Tel: 775-883-3627. *Pres*, Michae Digangi
Library Holdings: Bk Titles 1,000; Per Subs 25

S LEGISLATIVE COUNSEL BUREAU RESEARCH LIBRARY, 401 S Carson St, 89701-4747. Tel: 775-684-6827. Web Site: www.leg.state.nev.us/lcb/research/library. *Chief Librn*, Nan Bowers; Staff 4 (MLS 2, Non-MLS 2)
Founded 1971
Library Holdings: Bk Vols 10,500; Bk Titles 10,000; Per Subs 250
Automation Activity & Vendor Info: (Acquisitions) Inmagic, Inc.; (Cataloging) Inmagic, Inc.; (OPAC) Inmagic, Inc.
Restriction: Circulation limited

P NEVADA STATE LIBRARY & ARCHIVES,* 100 N Stewart St, 89701-4285. SAN 350-2740. Tel: 775-684-3313 (Admin). Reference Tel: 775-684-3360. Toll Free Tel: 800-922-2880. FAX: 775-684-3311 (Admin). Interlibrary Loan Service FAX: 775-684-3330. E-Mail: mhightow@

clan.ib.nv.us. Web Site: www.clan.lib.nv.us. *Dir*, Joan G Kerschner; *State Librn*, Monteria Hightower; Tel: 775-684-3315; *Coll Develop, Publ Servs*, Susan Kendall; Tel: 775-684-3303, E-Mail: slkendal@clan.lib.nv.us; *Cat*, Ann Sanford; Tel: 775-684-3308, E-Mail: asanford@clan.lib.nv.us; *Tech Servs*, Ann Brinkmeyer; Tel: 775-684-3309, E-Mail: acbrinkm@clan.lib.nv.us; *Coll Develop*, Bonnie Buckley; Tel: 775-684-3324, E-Mail: bjbuckle@clan.lib.nv.us
Founded 1859
1999-2000 Mats Exp $188,411, Books $94,684, Per/Ser (Incl. Access Fees) $56,708, Micro $37,019
Library Holdings: Bk Vols 59,297; Per Subs 483
Subject Interests: Bus, Govt affairs, Libr sci, Nevada, Pub admin, Pub affairs, Statistics
Special Collections: Nevada Coll; Nevada Newspaper Coll (microform, retrospective); US Bureau of the Census Data Center
Automation Activity & Vendor Info: (Acquisitions) Gaylord; (Cataloging) Gaylord; (Circulation) Gaylord; (ILL) Gaylord; (Media Booking) Gaylord; (OPAC) Gaylord; (Serials) Gaylord
Database Vendor: Dialog, OCLC - First Search
Publications: Nevada Library Directory & Statistics; Nevada Official Publications; Nevada Records; Silver Lining (Talking Books); State Data Center Report
Mem of Coop Libr Automated Network
Partic in Bibliographical Center For Research, Rocky Mountain Region, Inc; Cooperating Libraries Automated Network (CLAN); Information Nevada; OCLC Online Computer Library Center, Inc; RLIN
Library & archival services to state government; statewide library development
Friends of the Library Group
Branches: 1
ARCHIVES & RECORDS, 100 N Stewart St, 89701-4285. Tel: 775-684-3310. FAX: 775-684-3311. Web Site: www.clan.lib.nv.us. *Archivist*, Guy Louis Rocha
Founded 1965
Library Holdings: Bk Titles 500
Subject Interests: Local government, State government
Special Collections: 1862-1875 Territorial & State Censuses, micro; Bureau of Indian Affairs, micro; Nevada History
Publications: Preserving Nevada's Documentary Heritage; The History of the Capitol Building & Governor's Mansion
Restriction: Restricted access
Partic in RLIN

P NEVADA STATE LIBRARY & ARCHIVES, Regional Library for the Blind & Physically Handicapped,* 100 N Stewart St, 89701-4285. SAN 309-6939. Tel: 775-684-3354. Toll Free Tel: 800-922-9334. TDD: 775-687-8338. FAX: 775-684-3311. Web Site: www.clan.lib.nv.us, www.dmla.clan.lib.nv.us/docs/nsla/tbooks. *Librn*, Kerin E Putnam; E-Mail: keputnam@clan.lib.nv.us; Staff 5 (MLS 1, Non-MLS 4)
Founded 1968. Pop 1,907,815
Library Holdings: Bk Vols 76,445; Bk Titles 42,292
Subject Interests: Gen fiction, Nonfiction
Special Collections: Nevada Authors; Nevada Titles
Publications: Silver Lining (newsletter)
Open Mon-Fri 8-5

S NEVADA STATE MUSEUM, Capitol Complex Library, 600 N Carson St, 89701-4004. SAN 327-4624. Tel: 775-687-4810, Ext 239. FAX: 775-687-4168. *Curator*, Robert Nylen
Library Holdings: Bk Vols 6,000
Subject Interests: Nev hist
Function: Reference only

GL NEVADA SUPREME COURT LIBRARY, Supreme Court Bldg, 201 S Carson St Rm 100, 89701-4702. SAN 309-6955. Tel: 775-684-1640. TDD: 775-684-1665. FAX: 775-684-1662. E-Mail: sasouth@clan.lib.nv.us. Web Site: www.clan.lib.nv.us/polpac/nsc/nscl.htm. *Librn*, Susan Southwick; Tel: 775-684-1670, E-Mail: southwick@nvcourts.state.nv.us; *Asst Librn, Coll Develop*, Kathleen Harrington; *Cat*, Ann Whitney; *Doc*, Charlyn Lewis; Staff 4 (MLS 2, Non-MLS 2)
Founded 1973
Jul 1999-Jun 2000 Income $1,099,383, State $1,075,606, Federal $3,559, Locally Generated Income $11,968, Other $8,250. Mats Exp $418,607, Books $326,187, Per/Ser (Incl. Access Fees) $9,678, Presv $3,450, Micro $3,451, Electronic Ref Mat (Incl. Access Fees) $75,841. Sal $342,572 (Prof $262,505)
Library Holdings: Bk Vols 115,442; Bk Titles 9,347; Per Subs 267
Special Collections: American & English Law
Automation Activity & Vendor Info: (Cataloging) Gaylord; (OPAC) Gaylord
Database Vendor: GaleNet, Lexis-Nexis
Publications: New Titles List
Partic in Coop Librs Automated Network

J WESTERN NEVADA COMMUNITY COLLEGE, Library & Media Services,* 2201 W College Pkwy, 89703. SAN 350-2805. Tel: 775-887-3070. FAX: 775-887-3087. E-Mail: wnclrc@scs.unr.edu. Web Site: www.library.wncc.nevada.edu. *Dir*, Ken Sullivan; *Ref*, Danna Stern; *Ref*, Valerie Andersen; *Media Spec*, Mike Batesel; *Tech Servs*, Kristic Gangestad; *AV*, Howard Collett; *Circ*, Susan Ikehara; Staff 12 (MLS 4, Non-MLS 8)
Founded 1972. Enrl 1,869; Fac 82 Sal $414,496 (Prof $181,963)
Library Holdings: Bk Vols 33,354; Per Subs 168
Departmental Libraries:
BECK LIBRARY & MEDIA SERVICES (FALLON CAMPUS), 160 Campus Way, Fallon, 89406. SAN 372-8420. Tel: 775-423-5330. FAX: 775-423-8029. Web Site: www.wnec.nevada.edu. *Asst Dir*, Rita Mazur; E-Mail: rmazur@wncc.nevada.edu; *Media Spec*, Ray Sprinkle
Library Holdings: Bk Vols 6,700; Per Subs 42
THE DOUGLAS CENTER, 1680 Bently Pkwy, Minden, 89423. SAN 378-1550. Tel: 775-782-2413, Ext 5234. FAX: 775-782-2415. *Librn*, Larry Calkins; E-Mail: calkins@wncc.nevada.edu

DYER

P FISH LAKE LIBRARY,* PO Box 250, 89010. SAN 309-703X. Tel: 702-572-3311. FAX: 702-572-3311. *Librn*, Mary Lou Hunter; E-Mail: mlhunter@.clan.lib.nv.us
Circ 8,900
Library Holdings: Bk Vols 6,000
Subject Interests: Bilingual, Nev local hist, Spanish
Open Wed-Fri 9-4, Sat 9-1

ELKO

P ELKO-LANDER-EUREKA COUNTY LIBRARY SYSTEM, 720 Court St, 89801-3397. SAN 350-283X. Tel: 775-738-3066. FAX: 775-738-8262. *Dir*, Sara F Jones; E-Mail: sfjones@clan.lib.nv.us; *Br Coordr*, Laura Oki; E-Mail: ljoki@clan.lib.nv.us; *ILL*, Jennie Meyer; E-Mail: jmeyer@clan.lib.nv.us; *Ch Servs*, Jeannette Moore; E-Mail: jmoore@clan.lib.nv.us; *Circ*, Mercedes Macpherson; E-Mail: mmmacphe@clan.lib.nv.us; *Cat*, Mary Gibson; E-Mail: megibson@clan.lib.nv.us; *Bkmobile Coordr*, Julia Doren; E-Mail: jdoren@clan.lib.nv.us; Staff 38 (MLS 3, Non-MLS 35)
Founded 1922. Pop 59,000; Circ 250,000
1999-2000 Income (Main Library and Branch Library) $1,160,000, State $100,000, Federal $50,000, County $1,000,000, Locally Generated Income $10,000. Mats Exp $160,000, Books $120,000, Per/Ser (Incl. Access Fees) $15,000, Micro $15,000, Electronic Ref Mat (Incl. Access Fees) $10,000. Sal $520,000 (Prof $170,000)
Library Holdings: Bk Titles 155,000; Per Subs 151
Subject Interests: Mining, Nevada
Automation Activity & Vendor Info: (Cataloging) Gaylord; (Circulation) Gaylord; (ILL) Gaylord; (OPAC) Gaylord
Database Vendor: Ebsco - EbscoHost, IAC - Info Trac, IAC - SearchBank, OCLC - First Search
Function: ILL available
Partic in Cooperating Libraries Automated Network (CLAN)
Open Mon-Thurs 9-8, Fri & Sat 9-5
Friends of the Library Group
Branches: 9
AUSTIN BRANCH, Austin, 89310. SAN 350-2864. Tel: 702-964-2428. *Asst Librn*, Virginia Richardson
Library Holdings: Bk Vols 3,500
Open Mon 1-5, Wed 1-6 & Fri 2-5
Friends of the Library Group
BATTLE MOUNTAIN BRANCH, PO Box 141, Battle Mountain, 89820. SAN 350-2899. Tel: 702-635-2534. *Asst Librn*, Lynn Chambliss
Library Holdings: Bk Vols 5,000
Open Mon 11-5, Tues 12-6, Wed 2-6, Thurs 4-8, Fri 12-4 & Sat 10-2
BEOWAWE BRANCH, HC 66, Unit 1, Box 3, Beowawe, 89821. SAN 350-2929. Tel: 702-468-2103. *Asst Librn*, Pat Tarkelson
Library Holdings: Bk Vols 2,000
Open Mon 10-2:30 & Thurs 1-5:30
CARLIN BRANCH, 811 Main St, PO Box 1120, Carlin, 89822. SAN 373-8558. Tel: 775-754-6766. FAX: 775-754-6621. *Asst Librn*, Wendy House
Library Holdings: Bk Vols 2,500
Open Tues, Thurs & Fri 12-5, Wed 4-8
Friends of the Library Group
CRESCENT VALLEY, HC 66, Unit 1, Box 3, Beowawe, 89821. SAN 377-757X. Tel: 702-468-0249.
Open Tues & Wed 10-2:30
EUREKA BRANCH, PO Box 293, Eureka, 89316. SAN 350-2953. Tel: 702-237-5307. *Asst Librn*, Robin Evans
Library Holdings: Bk Vols 6,000
Open Mon & Wed 12-5, Tues & Thurs 1-5, Fri 12-4
TUSCARORA BRANCH, Tuscarora, 89834. SAN 350-2988. Tel: 702-756-6597. *Asst Librn*, Julie Parks
Library Holdings: Bk Vols 500
Open Mon-Fri 8-2
WELLS BRANCH, 208 Baker St, PO Box 691, Wells, 89835. SAN 350-3011. Tel: 775-752-3856. *Asst Librn*, Earlene Larsen
Library Holdings: Bk Vols 12,000

Open Mon, Tues, Wed, Fri 11-5, Thurs 1-5 & 7-9
WEST WENDOVER BRANCH, 590 Camper Dr, PO Box 5040, West Wendover, 89883. SAN 329-059X. Tel: 775-664-2226. FAX: 775-664-2226. *Asst Librn*, Carla Loncar
Library Holdings: Bk Vols 5,500
Open Mon & Wed 12-6, Tues 1-5 & 6-8, Thurs & Fri 12-5
Bookmobiles: 1

J GREAT BASIN COLLEGE, Learning Resources Center, 1500 College Pkwy, 89801. SAN 309-7005. Tel: 775-753-2222. Circulation Tel: 775-753-2222. Reference Tel: 775-753-2280. FAX: 702-753-2296. Web Site: www.gbcnv.edu/library/. *Dir*, Juanita R Karr; Tel: 775-753-2221, E-Mail: karr@gbcnv.edu; *Doc Delivery*, Sallie Knowles; Tel: 775-753-2183, E-Mail: sknowles@gbcnv.edu; *Ref*, Gary Avent; Tel: 775-753-2280, Fax: 775-753-2296, E-Mail: gba@gbcnv.edu; *Ref*, Karen Dannehl; Tel: 775-753-2300, E-Mail: dannehl@gbcnv.edu; *Govt Doc, ILL*, Patricia Loper; Tel: 775-753-2223, E-Mail: loper@gbcnv.edu; *Circ*, Joanne Forsythe; Tel: 775-753-2281, E-Mail: forsythe@gbcnv.edu; *Media Spec*, Edward Wright; Tel: 775-753-2172, E-Mail: ewright@gbcnv.edu. Subject Specialists: *Business*, Gary Avent; *Education*, Karen Dannehl; *Health*, Karen Dannehl; *Social sciences*, Gary Avent; Staff 7 (MLS 3, Non-MLS 4)
Founded 1967. Enrl 930; Fac 45; Highest Degree: Bachelor
Jul 1999-Jun 2000 Income State $423,451. Mats Exp $118,006, Books $32,555, Per/Ser (Incl. Access Fees) $15,800, AV Equip $551, Electronic Ref Mat (Incl. Access Fees) $69,100. Sal $302,698 (Prof $165,099)
Library Holdings: Bk Vols 30,304; Bk Titles 25,507; Per Subs 250
Subject Interests: Juv lit
Special Collections: American Indian; Basque; Federal Deposit Depository; Nevada
Database Vendor: Ebsco - EbscoHost, GaleNet, IAC - SearchBank, Innovative Interfaces INN - View, ProQuest

S NEVADA YOUTH TRAINING CENTER, 100 Youth Center Rd, 89801. (Mail add: PO Box 459, 89803-5907), Tel: 775-738-5907, Ext 244. *Librn*, Ida McBride
Library Holdings: Bk Titles 11,070; Per Subs 52

S NORTHEASTERN NEVADA HISTORICAL SOCIETY, Museum Research Library,* 1515 Idaho St, 89801. SAN 309-6998. Tel: 775-738-3418. FAX: 775-778-9318. *Dir*, Lisa Seymour
Founded 1968
Library Holdings: Bk Titles 2,500
Subject Interests: Anthropology, History, Natural history, Northeast Nevada hist
Special Collections: Area Newspaper Coll (1869 - present), bd, micro; Elko Coll; Jarbidge, Lamoille, Wells, Metropolis & Area Railroads Coll, pioneer vehicles; Tuscarora Coll
Publications: Northeastern Nevada Historical Society Quarterly

G UNITED STATES BUREAU OF LAND MANAGEMENT, Elko District Office Library,* 3900 E Idaho St, 89801. SAN 309-6971. Tel: 702-753-0200, Ext 250. FAX: 702-753-0255.
Library Holdings: Bk Titles 350; Per Subs 32
Subject Interests: Burros, Cadastral surveys, Environmental analysis (water), Fire rehabilitation, Found section corners, Gas hist index plat for townships in dist, Geology, Geothermal, Hist of dist, Land use, Mineral, MT plates, Oil hist index plat for townships in dist, Range mgt, Recreation statistics, Topographic maps, Well logs, Wild horses, Wildlife
Special Collections: Aerial Photos covering Elko District Bureau of Land Management Lands, photog; Game Harvests for over; thirteen years, published by Nevada Fish & Game

ELY

P WHITE PINE COUNTY LIBRARY, 950 Campton, 89301. SAN 350-3046. Tel: 775-289-3737. FAX: 775-289-1555. *Dir*, Lori Romero
Founded 1961. Pop 10,600; Circ 51,680
Jul 2000-Jun 2001 Income County $226,812
Library Holdings: Bk Vols 39,020; Per Subs 71
Special Collections: Local History (White Pine County Historical Society), photog; Nevada Materials
Automation Activity & Vendor Info: (Circulation) Gaylord
Partic in CLAN; Information Nevada
Friends of the Library Group

FALLON

M CHURCHILL COMMUNITY HOSPITAL, Health Science Library, 801 E William Ave, 89406. Tel: 775-423-3151, Ext 2047. FAX: 775-423-5122. *Dir*, Doris Wight
Library Holdings: Bk Titles 30

P CHURCHILL COUNTY LIBRARY,* 553 S Maine St, 89406-3387. SAN 309-7021. Tel: 775-423-7581. FAX: 775-423-7766. Web Site: www.clan.lib.nv.us/polpac/library/clan/churchill.htm. *Dir*, Barbara Mathews; E-Mail: blmathew@clan.lib.nv.us
Founded 1932. Pop 22,580; Circ 141,556
Library Holdings: Bk Vols 74,000; Per Subs 75
Special Collections: Nevada History
Publications: Footnotes (semi-annual newsletter)
Partic in Cooperating Libraries Automated Network (CLAN)
Friends of the Library Group

S CHURCHILL COUNTY MUSEUM & ARCHIVES, 1050 S Maine St, 89406. SAN 373-2401. Tel: 702-423-3677. FAX: 702-423-3662. E-Mail: ccmuseum@phonewave.net. Web Site: www.cccom.net/museum. *Dir*, Jane Pieplow
Library Holdings: Bk Vols 800
Subject Interests: Local history

UNITED STATES NAVY
A NAS FALLON STATION LIBRARY, 4755 Pasture Rd, 89496-5000. SAN 350-3100. Tel: 775-426-2599. FAX: 775-426-2839. *Head Librn*, Sarah J Hurley; E-Mail: hurley@phonewave.net; *Asst Librn*, Sylvia B Mumey
Founded 1942. Pop 6,000
Oct 1999-Sep 2000 Income $105,000, Federal $40,000, Other $65,000. Mats Exp $39,000, Books $35,000, Per/Ser (Incl. Access Fees) $4,000. Sal $51,900
Library Holdings: Bk Vols 25,000; Per Subs 62
Subject Interests: Fiction, Mil, Naval aviation, Technology
Special Collections: World War II
Automation Activity & Vendor Info: (Cataloging) Brodart; (Circulation) Sagebrush Corporation; (OPAC) Sagebrush Corporation
Database Vendor: Ebsco - EbscoHost

GABBS

P GABBS COMMUNITY LIBRARY,* PO Box 206, 89409. SAN 377-3434. Tel: 775-285-2686. FAX: 775-285-2301. *Librn*, Myrna Lumsden; *Asst Librn*, Nancy Howerton
Library Holdings: Bk Vols 25,000; Bk Titles 20,000; Per Subs 15
Partic in Information Nevada
Open Tues 9-3 & 7-9, Wed & Thurs 9-3
Friends of the Library Group

GOLDFIELD

P GOLDFIELD PUBLIC LIBRARY,* PO Box 430, 89013. SAN 309-7048. Tel: 775-485-3236. FAX: 775-485-3236. *Librn*, Diane Shimp
Founded 1976. Pop 558
Jul 1997-Jun 1998 Income $5,000
Library Holdings: Bk Vols 15,000

HAWTHORNE

P MINERAL COUNTY PUBLIC LIBRARY,* First & A Sts, PO Box 1390, 89415. SAN 350-3135. Tel: 775-945-2778. FAX: 775-945-0703. *Dir*, Steve Schlatter; *Asst Dir*, Antonia Dellamonica; *Circ*, Jasmin Odom
Founded 1955. Pop 7,051; Circ 30,234
Library Holdings: Bk Vols 26,000; Per Subs 39
Special Collections: State of Nevada History Coll
Friends of the Library Group
Branches: 1
MINA-LUNING COMMUNITY, PO Box 143, Mina, 89422. SAN 350-316X. Tel: 775-573-2505. *In Charge*, Linda Mansfield
Library Holdings: Bk Vols 8,500
Special Collections: State of Nevada History Coll

HENDERSON

P HENDERSON DISTRICT PUBLIC LIBRARIES, James I Gibson Library, 280 Water St, 89015. SAN 309-7056. Tel: 702-565-8402. Reference Tel: 702-564-9261. FAX: 702-565-8832. Web Site: www.hdpl.org. *Asst Dir, Mgr*, Gayle Hornaday; E-Mail: gmhornaday@hdpl.org; *Circ*, Vicki Rudolph; E-Mail: vlrudolph@hdpl.org; Staff 37 (MLS 14, Non-MLS 23)
Founded 1953. Pop 170,000; Circ 209,857
1998-1999 Income (Main Library and Branch Library) $3,500,000. Mats Exp $515,000, Books $500,000, Per/Ser (Incl. Access Fees) $15,000
Library Holdings: Bk Vols 170,607; Per Subs 250
Subject Interests: Small bus admin, SW regional hist
Special Collections: Nevada History
Automation Activity & Vendor Info: (Acquisitions) DRA; (Cataloging) DRA; (Circulation) DRA; (OPAC) DRA
Database Vendor: DRA, IAC - Info Trac, OCLC - First Search
Publications: Subject bibliographies; subject bibliographies
Branches: 1
LYDIA MALCOLM BRANCH, 80 N Pecos, 89014. SAN 375-4235. Tel: 702-263-7522. FAX: 702-263-7402. Web Site: www.hdpl.org. *Branch Mgr*, Marjorie Kern; E-Mail: mmkern@hdpl.org; *Ch Servs*, Elizabeth Johnson
Library Holdings: Bk Vols 42,000; Per Subs 60

Automation Activity & Vendor Info: (Acquisitions) DRA; (Cataloging) DRA; (Circulation) DRA; (OPAC) DRA
Database Vendor: OCLC - First Search
Friends of the Library Group

S TITANIUM METALS CORPORATION OF AMERICA, Henderson Technical Library, PO Box 2128, 89009. SAN 323-4371. Tel: 702-564-2544, Ext 403. FAX: 702-564-9038. *Librn*, Lynn Mooso
Library Holdings: Bk Titles 20,000; Per Subs 75
Restriction: Not open to public

INCLINE VILLAGE

C SIERRA NEVADA COLLEGE, MacLean Library, 591 Village Blvd, 89450. (Mail add: 999 Tahoe Blvd, 89451), SAN 309-7064. Tel: 775-831-1314, Ext 5052. Toll Free Tel: 800-332-8666. FAX: 702-832-6134. E-Mail: library@sierranevada.edu. Web Site: sierranevada.edu/academic/library/home. *Info Res, Res*, Wayne H Cole; Tel: 775-831-1314, Ext 5033, E-Mail: wcole@sierranevada.edu; Staff 2 (MLS 1, Non-MLS 1)
Founded 1969. Enrl 600; Fac 22; Highest Degree: Bachelor
Jul 2000-Jun 2001 Mats Exp $40,000, Books $20,000, Per/Ser (Incl. Access Fees) $10,000, Electronic Ref Mat (Incl. Access Fees) $10,000
Library Holdings: Bk Vols 19,959; Bk Titles 19,740; Per Subs 174
Subject Interests: California, Computer science, Environmental studies, Hospitality indust, International studies, Music, Nevada, Nursing, Resort mgt, Sierra maps, Teacher educ, Visual arts
Automation Activity & Vendor Info: (Cataloging) Gaylord; (Circulation) Gaylord; (OPAC) Gaylord
Database Vendor: Ebsco - EbscoHost, Lexis-Nexis, OCLC - First Search
Function: ILL available
Partic in Cooperating Libraries Automated Network (CLAN); Information Nevada

LAS VEGAS

GL CLARK COUNTY LAW LIBRARY, 309 S Third St, Ste 400, PO Box 557340, 89155-7340. SAN 309-7099. Tel: 702-455-4696. FAX: 702-455-5120. Web Site: www.co.clark.nv.us/lawlibry/lawlibix.htm. *Dir*, Kevin Clanton; Staff 7 (MLS 1, Non-MLS 6)
Founded 1923
Library Holdings: Bk Vols 68,000; Per Subs 420
Subject Interests: Cases, Formbks, Regulations, Statutes, Treatises
Special Collections: Nevada Coll, Statutes of each state
Automation Activity & Vendor Info: (OPAC) Sagebrush Corporation
Publications: News & Notes
Partic in Westlaw
Friends of the Library Group

C COMMUNITY COLLEGE OF SOUTHERN NEVADA, Department of Libraries, 6375 W Charleston Blvd, 89146. SAN 309-7188. Tel: 702-651-5716. FAX: 702-651-5718. E-Mail: irving@nevada.edu. Web Site: www.ccsn.nevada.edu/library. *Chairperson*, Rose Ellis; Tel: 702-651-5530, Fax: 702-651-5003, E-Mail: rose_ellis@ccsn.nevada.edu; *Librn*, Virginia Kozarich; Tel: 702-651-5710, Fax: 702-651-5003, E-Mail: virginia_kozarich@ccsn.nevada.edu; *Ref*, Marcia Arado; Tel: 702-651-7437, Fax: 702-651-5003, E-Mail: mgarado@nevada.edu; *Ref*, Lynn Best; Tel: 702-651-4494, Fax: 702-643-8103, E-Mail: lynn_best@ccsn.nevada.edu; *Ref*, Clarissa Erwin; Tel: 702-651-4690, Fax: 702-643-8103, E-Mail: clarissa_erwin@ccsn.nevada.edu; *Ref*, Christine Janssen; Tel: 702-651-3112, Fax: 702-651-3531, E-Mail: christine_janssen@ccsn.nevada.edu; *Ref*, Laura Moskowitz; Tel: 702-651-5709, Fax: 702-651-5003, E-Mail: moskowil@ccsn.nevada.edu; *Ref*, Ken Schott; Tel: 702-651-3314, Fax: 702-651-3513, E-Mail: schott@ccsn.nevada.edu; Staff 23 (MLS 8, Non-MLS 15)
Founded 1972. Enrl 17,500; Highest Degree: Associate
Jul 1999-Jun 2000 Income (Main Library and Branch Library) $587,000, State $465,000, Parent Institution $100,000, Other $22,000. Mats Exp $515,000, Books $326,000, Per/Ser (Incl. Access Fees) $89,000, Electronic Ref Mat (Incl. Access Fees) $100,000. Sal $355,409
Library Holdings: Bk Vols 58,000; Bk Titles 56,000; Per Subs 540
Subject Interests: Computer science, Criminal justice, Culinary arts, Dental hygiene, Electronics, Fire science, Gaming, Horticulture, Nursing, Resorts
Automation Activity & Vendor Info: (Acquisitions) Innovative Interfaces Inc.; (Circulation) Innovative Interfaces Inc.; (ILL) Innovative Interfaces Inc.; (Serials) Innovative Interfaces Inc.
Database Vendor: Dialog, GaleNet, IAC - Info Trac, IAC - SearchBank, Lexis-Nexis, OCLC - First Search, OVID Technologies
Function: Reference services available
Partic in BCR
Departmental Libraries:
CHEYENNE CAMPUS, 3200 E Cheyenne Ave, North Las Vegas, 89030. SAN 376-8805. Tel: 702-651-4419. Interlibrary Loan Service Tel: 702-651-4441. FAX: 702-643-8103. Web Site: www.ccsn.nevada.edu/library. *Librn*, Clarrissa Erwin; *Librn*, Marcia Arado
HENDERSON CAMPUS, 700 S College Dr, Henderson, 89015-8419. SAN 321-6071. Tel: 702-564-7484, Ext 231. FAX: 702-564-7708. Web Site: www.ccsn.nevada.edu/library. *Librn*, Ken Schott
WEST CHARLESTON CAMPUS, 6375 W Charleston Blvd, W16, 89146. SAN 372-5065. Tel: 702-651-5729. FAX: 702-651-5718. E-Mail: irving@nevada.edu. Web Site: www.ccsn.nevada.edu/library.; Staff 16 (MLS 6, Non-MLS 10)
Library Holdings: Bk Vols 6,095; Bk Titles 5,721; Per Subs 104
Publications: Get the Facts

SR JEWISH FEDERATION OF LAS VEGAS, Holocaust Studies Library, 3909 S Maryland Pkwy, Ste 400, 89119. SAN 375-7757. Tel: 702-732-0556. FAX: 702-732-3228. *Chair*, Edythe Katz
Library Holdings: Bk Titles 3,000
Friends of the Library Group

S LAS VEGAS FAMILY HISTORY CENTER, Genealogical Library,* 509 S Ninth, 89101. SAN 309-7080. Tel: 702-382-9695. FAX: 702-382-1597. *Dir*, Deon J Sanders; *Assoc Dir*, Alice Myers; *Assoc Dir*, Melvin Sommers
Founded 1966
Library Holdings: Bk Vols 7,500
Subject Interests: Family hist, Genealogical res
Special Collections: Local Histories (Nevada); State & County History (US & Canada)
For main library, see Salt Lake City

LAS VEGAS MUNICIPAL COURT LIBRARY, (Formerly City of Las Vegas Municipal Court Library), Alternative Sentencing & Education Division Library, City Hall, Plaza Level, 400 Stewart Ave, 89101-2986. (Mail add: 416 N 7th St, 89101-3010), SAN 321-1665. Tel: 702-229-6874. TDD: 702-386-9108. FAX: 702-382-1783. E-Mail: dortiz@ci.las-vegas.nv.us. Web Site: www.ci.las-vegas.nv.us.; Staff 1 (MLS 1)
Founded 1980
Library Holdings: Bk Titles 1,200; Per Subs 27
Subject Interests: Criminal justice planning, Legal ref
Special Collections: Misdemeanor Diversionary Programs & Curriculum Materials
Restriction: Non-circulating
Function: Reference only

P LAS VEGAS-CLARK COUNTY LIBRARY DISTRICT, 833 Las Vegas Blvd N, 89101. SAN 350-3194. Tel: 702-382-3493. FAX: 702-474-7138. Web Site: www.lvccld.org. *Exec Dir*, Daniel L Walters; *Dep Dir*, Nancy Ledeboer; *Dep Dir*, Kay Godbey; *Assoc Dir*, Bud Pierce; *Assoc Dir*, Michael Zomlefer; Staff 573 (MLS 102, Non-MLS 471)
Founded 1985. Pop 1,290,571; Circ 5,252,780
Jul 1999-Jun 2000 Income (Main Library and Branch Library) $30,683,471, State $12,067,269, Federal $208,759, Locally Generated Income $18,407,443. Mats Exp $4,740,572. Sal $13,481,084
Library Holdings: Bk Vols 2,439,592; Per Subs 4,178
Subject Interests: Building constr, Entertainment, Fine arts, Gaming, Grants, Health science, Hospitality indust, Hotels, Local history, Nev hist, Patents-trademarks, Southwest
Special Collections: Nevada Coll; Nevada State Data Center; State Publication Distribution Center
Automation Activity & Vendor Info: (Acquisitions) DRA; (Cataloging) DRA; (Circulation) DRA; (Course Reserve) DRA; (ILL) DRA; (OPAC) DRA; (Serials) DRA
Database Vendor: Dialog, Ebsco - EbscoHost, GaleNet, OCLC - First Search
Publications: Nevada Foundations Directory
Function: ILL available, Outside services via phone, cable & mail, Photocopies available, Reference services available
Partic in Information Nevada; OCLC Online Computer Library Center, Inc
Friends of the Library Group
Branches: 25
BLUE DIAMOND BRANCH, PO Box 40, Blue Diamond, 89004. SAN 350-3259. Tel: 702-875-4295. FAX: 702-875-4095. Web Site: www.lvccld.org. *In Charge*, Nina Mata; Staff 2 (Non-MLS 2)
Founded 1969. Pop 319; Circ 4,017
Automation Activity & Vendor Info: (Acquisitions) DRA; (Cataloging) DRA; (Circulation) DRA; (ILL) DRA; (OPAC) DRA; (Serials) DRA
Database Vendor: Dialog, Ebsco - EbscoHost, GaleNet, OCLC - First Search
BUNKERVILLE BRANCH, 150 W Virgin St, PO Box 7208, Bunkerville, 89007. SAN 350-3283. Tel: 702-346-5238. FAX: 702-346-5784. Web Site: www.lvccld.org. *In Charge*, Carolynn Leavitt; Staff 2 (Non-MLS 2)
Founded 1973. Pop 880; Circ 12,136
Automation Activity & Vendor Info: (Acquisitions) DRA; (Cataloging) DRA; (Circulation) DRA; (ILL) DRA; (OPAC) DRA; (Serials) DRA
Database Vendor: Dialog, Ebsco - EbscoHost, GaleNet, OCLC - First Search
CLARK COUNTY REGIONAL, 1401 E Flamingo Rd, 89119. SAN 350-3348. Tel: 702-733-7810. FAX: 702-733-1567. Web Site: www.lvccld.org. *Adminr*, Laura Gollod; Staff 83 (MLS 17, Non-MLS 66)
Founded 1966. Pop 96,135; Circ 595,298
Subject Interests: Patents-trademarks
Special Collections: Jean Ford Coll; Nevada Coll
Automation Activity & Vendor Info: (Acquisitions) DRA; (Cataloging) DRA; (Circulation) DRA; (ILL) DRA; (OPAC) DRA; (Serials) DRA

Database Vendor: Dialog, Ebsco - EbscoHost, GaleNet, OCLC - First Search

ENTERPRISE, 25 E Shelbourne Ave, 89123. SAN 377-6565. Tel: 702-269-3000. FAX: 702-269-8030. Web Site: www.lvccld.org. *Adminr*, Judith Gray; Staff 19 (MLS 4, Non-MLS 15)
Founded 1996. Pop 46,325; Circ 234,147
Subject Interests: Building constr
Automation Activity & Vendor Info: (Cataloging) DRA; (Circulation) DRA; (ILL) DRA; (OPAC) DRA; (Serials) DRA
Database Vendor: Dialog, Ebsco - EbscoHost, GaleNet, OCLC - First Search

GOODSPRINGS BRANCH, 365 San Pedro Ave, PO Box 667, Goodsprings, 89019. SAN 350-3372. Tel: 702-874-1366. FAX: 702-874-1335. Web Site: www.lvccld.org. *In Charge*, Peggy Stephens; Staff 2 (Non-MLS 2)
Founded 1968. Pop 184; Circ 3,057
Automation Activity & Vendor Info: (Acquisitions) DRA; (Cataloging) DRA; (Circulation) DRA; (ILL) DRA; (OPAC) DRA; (Serials) DRA
Database Vendor: Dialog, Ebsco - EbscoHost, GaleNet, OCLC - First Search

GREEN VALLEY, 2797 N Green Valley Pkwy, Henderson, 89014. SAN 325-4224. Tel: 702-435-1840. FAX: 702-435-3481. Web Site: www.lvccld.org. *Adminr*, Sally Feldman; Staff 26 (MLS 5, Non-MLS 21)
Founded 1989. Pop 112,516; Circ 481,987
Automation Activity & Vendor Info: (Acquisitions) DRA; (Cataloging) DRA; (Circulation) DRA; (ILL) DRA; (OPAC) DRA; (Serials) DRA
Database Vendor: Dialog, Ebsco - EbscoHost, GaleNet, OCLC - First Search

INDIAN SPRINGS BRANCH, 715 Gretta Lane, PO Box 628, Indian Springs, 89018. SAN 350-3402. Tel: 702-879-3845. FAX: 702-879-5227. Web Site: www.lvccld.org. *In Charge*, Dodie Patrick; Staff 2 (Non-MLS 2)
Founded 1969. Pop 1,380; Circ 9,009
Automation Activity & Vendor Info: (Acquisitions) DRA; (Cataloging) DRA; (Circulation) DRA; (ILL) DRA; (OPAC) DRA; (Serials) DRA
Database Vendor: Dialog, Ebsco - EbscoHost, GaleNet, OCLC - First Search

LAS VEGAS REGIONAL, 833 Las Vegas Blvd N, 89101. SAN 350-3437. Tel: 702-382-3493. FAX: 702-382-1280. Web Site: www.lvccld.org. *Adminr*, Toby V Sulenski; Staff 43 (MLS 10, Non-MLS 33)
Founded 1973. Pop 127,801; Circ 247,247
Subject Interests: Gaming, Local history
Special Collections: Nevada Data Center; State Publication Distribution Center
Automation Activity & Vendor Info: (Acquisitions) DRA; (Cataloging) DRA; (Circulation) DRA; (ILL) DRA; (OPAC) DRA; (Serials) DRA
Database Vendor: Dialog, Ebsco - EbscoHost, GaleNet, OCLC - First Search

LAUGHLIN LIBRARY, 2840S Needles Hwy, Laughlin, 89029. (Mail add: PO Box 32225, Laughlin, 89028-2225), Tel: 702-298-1081. FAX: 702-298-3940. Web Site: www.lvccld.org. *Adminr*, Joyce Pipkin; Staff 9 (MLS 2, Non-MLS 7)
Founded 1987. Pop 8,100; Circ 94,295
Automation Activity & Vendor Info: (Acquisitions) DRA; (Cataloging) DRA; (Circulation) DRA; (ILL) DRA; (OPAC) DRA; (Serials) DRA
Database Vendor: Dialog, Ebsco - EbscoHost, GaleNet, OCLC - First Search
Friends of the Library Group

MEADOWS VILLAGE LIBRARY & HOMEWORK CENTER, 300 W Boston Ave, 89102. SAN 378-1755. Tel: 702-474-0023. Web Site: www.lvccld.org. *Adminr*, Toby Sulenski; Staff 3 (MLS 1, Non-MLS 2)
Founded 1994
Subject Interests: Spanish lang
Automation Activity & Vendor Info: (Acquisitions) DRA; (Cataloging) DRA; (Circulation) DRA; (ILL) DRA; (OPAC) DRA; (Serials) DRA
Database Vendor: Dialog, Ebsco - EbscoHost, GaleNet, OCLC - First Search

MESQUITE BRANCH, 121 W First North St, Mesquite, 89027. SAN 350-3550. Tel: 702-346-5224. FAX: 702-346-5788. Web Site: www.lvccld.org. *In Charge*, Geraldine Zarate; Staff 7 (Non-MLS 7)
Founded 1973. Pop 15,000; Circ 54,104
Automation Activity & Vendor Info: (Acquisitions) DRA; (Cataloging) DRA; (Circulation) DRA; (ILL) DRA; (OPAC) DRA; (Serials) DRA
Database Vendor: Dialog, Ebsco - EbscoHost, GaleNet, OCLC - First Search

METRO JAIL, 833 Las Vegas Blvd N, 89101. SAN 350-3453. Tel: 702-384-4887. FAX: 702-455-3971. Web Site: www.lvccld.org. *Librn*, Elaine Wing; Staff 3 (MLS 1, Non-MLS 2)
1999-2000 Income (Main Library Only) $281,200, City $26,690, County $254,510. Sal $207,635
Subject Interests: Circulating paperbacks, Fed law bk vols, Nevada
Automation Activity & Vendor Info: (Acquisitions) DRA; (Cataloging) DRA; (Circulation) DRA; (ILL) DRA; (OPAC) DRA; (Serials) DRA

MOAPA TOWN BRANCH, 1340 E Hwy 168, PO Box 250, Moapa, 89025. SAN 374-4132. Tel: 702-864-2438. FAX: 702-864-2467. Web Site: www.lvccld.org. *In Charge*, Jan Johnson; Staff 2 (Non-MLS 2)
Founded 1988. Pop 550; Circ 12,230
Automation Activity & Vendor Info: (Acquisitions) DRA; (Cataloging) DRA; (Circulation) DRA; (ILL) DRA; (OPAC) DRA; (Serials) DRA
Database Vendor: Dialog, Ebsco - EbscoHost, GaleNet, OCLC - First Search

MOAPA VALLEY, 350 N Moapa Valley Blvd, PO Box 397, Overton, 89040. SAN 350-3461. Tel: 702-397-2690. FAX: 702-397-2698. Web Site: www.lvccld.org. *In Charge*, Debra Hamilton; Staff 5 (Non-MLS 5)
Founded 1967. Pop 5,820; Circ 53,952
Automation Activity & Vendor Info: (Acquisitions) DRA; (Cataloging) DRA; (Circulation) DRA; (ILL) DRA; (OPAC) DRA; (Serials) DRA
Database Vendor: Dialog, Ebsco - EbscoHost, GaleNet, OCLC - First Search

MOUNT CHARLESTON, 1252 Aspen Ave, HCR 38, Box 269, 89124. SAN 350-347X. Tel: 702-872-5585. FAX: 702-872-5631. Web Site: www.lvccld.org. *In Charge*, Sandra Gibson; Staff 2 (Non-MLS 2)
Founded 1980. Pop 1,053; Circ 4,855
Automation Activity & Vendor Info: (Acquisitions) DRA; (Cataloging) DRA; (Circulation) DRA; (ILL) DRA; (OPAC) DRA; (Serials) DRA
Database Vendor: Dialog, Ebsco - EbscoHost, GaleNet, OCLC - First Search

RAINBOW, 3510 N Buffalo, 89128. SAN 325-4240. Tel: 702-243-7323. FAX: 702-243-7300. Web Site: www.lvccld.org. *Adminr*, Jane Richardson; Staff 38 (MLS 7, Non-MLS 31)
Founded 1985. Pop 156,991; Circ 603,610
Automation Activity & Vendor Info: (Acquisitions) DRA; (Cataloging) DRA; (Circulation) DRA; (ILL) DRA; (OPAC) DRA; (Serials) DRA
Database Vendor: Dialog, Ebsco - EbscoHost, GaleNet, OCLC - First Search

SAHARA WEST REGIONAL, 9600 W Sahara Ave, 89117. SAN 373-8213. Tel: 702-228-1940. FAX: 702-228-3730. Web Site: www.lvccld.org. *Adminr*, Robb Morss; Staff 52 (MLS 14, Non-MLS 38)
Founded 1992. Pop 137,811; Circ 559,357
Subject Interests: Fine arts
Automation Activity & Vendor Info: (Acquisitions) DRA; (Cataloging) DRA; (Circulation) DRA; (ILL) DRA; (OPAC) DRA; (Serials) DRA
Database Vendor: Dialog, Ebsco - EbscoHost, GaleNet, OCLC - First Search

SANDY VALLEY BRANCH, 650 W Quartz Ave, HCR 31 Box 77, Sandy Valley, 89019. SAN 322-5828. Tel: 702-723-5333. FAX: 702-723-1010. Web Site: www.lvccld.org. *In Charge*, Gwen Doty; Staff 2 (Non-MLS 2)
Founded 1984. Pop 1,315; Circ 20,923
Automation Activity & Vendor Info: (Acquisitions) DRA; (Cataloging) DRA; (Circulation) DRA; (ILL) DRA; (OPAC) DRA; (Serials) DRA
Database Vendor: Dialog, Ebsco - EbscoHost, GaleNet, OCLC - First Search

SEARCHLIGHT BRANCH, 200 Michael Wendell Way, PO Box 98, Searchlight, 89046. SAN 350-3496. Tel: 702-297-1442. FAX: 702-297-1782. Web Site: www.lvccld.org. *In Charge*, Lynn Rhodes; Staff 2 (Non-MLS 2)
Founded 1969. Pop 756; Circ 14,481
Automation Activity & Vendor Info: (Acquisitions) DRA; (Cataloging) DRA; (Circulation) DRA; (ILL) DRA; (OPAC) DRA; (Serials) DRA
Database Vendor: Dialog, Ebsco - EbscoHost, GaleNet, OCLC - First Search

SPRING VALLEY, 4280 S Jones Blvd, 89103. SAN 325-4208. Tel: 702-368-4411. FAX: 702-368-2586. Web Site: www.lvccld.org. *Adminr*, Marsha Cutler; Staff 25 (MLS 5, Non-MLS 20)
Founded 1985. Pop 106,989; Circ 362,700
Subject Interests: Asian studies
Automation Activity & Vendor Info: (Acquisitions) DRA; (Cataloging) DRA; (Circulation) DRA; (ILL) DRA; (OPAC) DRA; (Serials) DRA
Database Vendor: Dialog, Ebsco - EbscoHost, GaleNet, OCLC - First Search

SUMMERLIN LIBRARY & PERFORMING ARTS CENTER, 1771 Inner Circle Dr, 89134. SAN 374-4140. Tel: 702-256-5111. FAX: 702-256-7228. Web Site: www.lvccld.org. *Adminr*, Kelly Richards; Staff 25 (MLS 5, Non-MLS 20)
Founded 1993. Pop 94,255; Circ 350,282
Automation Activity & Vendor Info: (Acquisitions) DRA; (Cataloging) DRA; (Circulation) DRA; (ILL) DRA; (OPAC) DRA; (Serials) DRA
Database Vendor: Dialog, Ebsco - EbscoHost, GaleNet, OCLC - First Search

SUNRISE, 5400 Harris Ave, 89110. SAN 350-3526. Tel: 702-453-1104. FAX: 702-438-2296. Web Site: www.lvccld.org. *Adminr*, Beryl Andrus-Fundel; Staff 27 (MLS 6, Non-MLS 21)
Founded 1987. Pop 106,402; Circ 386,088
Automation Activity & Vendor Info: (Acquisitions) DRA; (Cataloging) DRA; (Circulation) DRA; (ILL) DRA; (OPAC) DRA; (Serials) DRA
Database Vendor: Dialog, Ebsco - EbscoHost, GaleNet, OCLC - First Search

WEST CHARLESTON, 6301 W Charleston Blvd, 89102. SAN 350-3313. Tel: 702-878-3682. FAX: 702-877-0620. Web Site: www.lvccld.org. *Adminr*, Kim Clanton-Green; Staff 41 (MLS 10, Non-MLS 31)
Founded 1973. Pop 104,608; Circ 421,781
Subject Interests: Health science, Medicine
Automation Activity & Vendor Info: (Acquisitions) DRA; (Cataloging) DRA; (Circulation) DRA; (Course Reserve) DRA; (ILL) DRA; (OPAC) DRA; (Serials) DRA
Database Vendor: Dialog, Ebsco - EbscoHost, GaleNet, OCLC - First

Search
WEST LAS VEGAS, 951 E Lake Mead Blvd, 89106. SAN 350-3585. Tel: 702-647-2117. FAX: 702-646-5664. Web Site: www.lvccld.org. *Adminr*, Felton Thomas; Staff 22 (MLS 5, Non-MLS 17)
Founded 1973. Pop 67,893; Circ 100,704
Special Collections: African American Experience
Automation Activity & Vendor Info: (Acquisitions) DRA; (Cataloging) DRA; (Circulation) DRA; (ILL) DRA; (OPAC) DRA; (Serials) DRA
Database Vendor: Dialog, Ebsco - EbscoHost, GaleNet, OCLC - First Search
WHITNEY, 5175 E Tropicana Ave, 89122. SAN 370-9280. Tel: 702-454-4575. FAX: 702-454-3161. Web Site: www.lvccld.org. *Adminr*, Barb Carey; Staff 22 (MLS 5, Non-MLS 17)
Founded 1994. Pop 65,953; Circ 293,422
Subject Interests: Southwest
Automation Activity & Vendor Info: (Acquisitions) DRA; (Cataloging) DRA; (Circulation) DRA; (ILL) DRA; (OPAC) DRA; (Serials) DRA
Database Vendor: Dialog, Ebsco - EbscoHost, GaleNet, OCLC - First Search
Friends of the Library Group

S NEVADA POWER COMPANY LIBRARY,* 6226 W Sahara Ave, 89146. SAN 377-2330. Tel: 702-367-5055. FAX: 702-227-2023. *Dir*, Linda Backstrom; *Librn*, Vicki Snyder; E-Mail: snyder@nevp.com
Library Holdings: Bk Titles 1,300; Per Subs 200

P NEVADA STATE LIBRARY & ARCHIVES, Subregional Library for the Blind & Physically Handicapped,* 1401 E Flamingo Rd, 89119. Tel: 702-733-1925. *In Charge*, MaryAnne Morton
Publications: SilverLining (Newsletter)
Special Services for the Blind - Bks on cassette; Books on computer floppy disk; Braille; Large print bks; Magazines & books recorded
Delivers Talking Books services for Clark, Lincoln, Nye & Esmeralda counties

S NEVADA STATE MUSEUM, Historical Society Library, 700 Twin Lakes Dr, 89107. Tel: 702-486-5205. *In Charge*, David Millman
Library Holdings: Bk Vols 1,950; Bk Titles 1,000; Per Subs 48

S REVIEW JOURNAL NEWSPAPER LIBRARY,* 1111 W Bonanza, 89106. SAN 329-1812. Tel: 702-383-0264, 702-383-0269. FAX: 702-383-4676. *Librn*, Padmini P Pai; *Asst Librn*, Pamela Busse; Staff 1 (Non-MLS 1)
Library Holdings: Bk Titles 100
Restriction: Staff use only

R SALVATION ARMY CHURCH LIBRARY, 2900 Palamino Lane, 89107. SAN 309-7137. Tel: 702-870-4430. FAX: 702-870-4087. *Librn*, Carol Williams
Founded 1970
Subject Interests: Christian lit, Fiction, Non-fiction
Special Collections: Salvation Army Literature
Publications: Newsletter

M SUNRISE HOSPITAL & MEDICAL CENTER, Medical Library Office of Continuing Medical Education, 3186 S Maryland Pkwy, 89109. SAN 309-7153. Tel: 702-731-8210. FAX: 702-731-8674. Web Site: www.sunrisehospital.com. *Dir*, Allan A Froman; E-Mail: aafroman@vegas.infi.net; Staff 1 (MLS 1)
Founded 1975
Library Holdings: Bk Titles 1,000; Per Subs 250
Subject Interests: Clinical medicine, Health care admin
Special Collections: Ciba slides
Partic in Nat Libr of Med; National Network Of Libraries Of Medicine - Pacific Northwest Region; Nevada Medical Library Group

G UNITED STATES BUREAU OF LAND MANAGEMENT, Las Vegas District Office Library,* 4765 W Vegas Dr, 89108. SAN 309-7072. Tel: 702-647-5000. FAX: 702-647-5023. *In Charge*, Karen Tucker
Library Holdings: Bk Vols 100; Per Subs 50

G UNITED STATES DEPARTMENT OF ENERGY, Nevada Operations Office Techinal Information Resource Center (TIRC),* PO Box 98518, 89193-8518. SAN 309-7161. Tel: 702-295-1826. FAX: 702-295-0109.
Founded 1969
Library Holdings: Bk Titles 4,000; Per Subs 1,500
Subject Interests: Alternate energy sources, Environ restoration, Geology, Hydrol, Nuclear explosions, Radiation bioenviron effects, Radioactive waste storage, Waste mgt
Special Collections: Peaceful Uses of Nuclear Explosions
Publications: Doe Standards List; Fact Sheets; Quarterly Accessions List
Partic in Dialog Corporation; Doe-ITIS

G UNITED STATES ENVIRONMENTAL PROTECTION AGENCY, National Exposure Research Laboratory-Characterization Research Division Technical Reference Center, 944 E Harmon Ave, 89119-6794. (Mail add: PO Box 93478, 89193-3478), SAN 371-9073. Tel: 702-798-2648. Interlibrary Loan Service Tel: 702-798-2540. FAX: 702-798-2622. E-Mail: library-lv@epamail.epa.gov. Web Site: www.epa.gov/crdlvweb/library/home6.htm. *Info Specialist*, Jessie Choate; E-Mail: choate.jessie@epa.gov; *Info Specialist*, Sandra Isaacson; E-Mail: isaacson.sandra@epa.gov; Staff 3 (MLS 1, Non-MLS 2)
Founded 1966
1999-2000 Income $384,000. Mats Exp $137,200, Books $5,000, Per/Ser (Incl. Access Fees) $86,000, Micro $1,200, Electronic Ref Mat (Incl. Access Fees) $45,000. Sal $129,000 (Prof $63,211)
Library Holdings: Bk Titles 9,700; Per Subs 60
Subject Interests: Radiation effects
Special Collections: National Estuary Surveys; OSWER Directives
Publications: Internet Addressbook: Environment; New from the EMSL-LV Library
Restriction: Restricted public use
Partic in BRC Colleage

M UNIVERSITY MEDICAL CENTER OF SOUTHERN NEVADA, Medical Library, 2040 W Charleston Blvd, Ste 500, 89102. SAN 309-7145. Tel: 702-383-2368. FAX: 702-383-2369. *Dir*, Bonnie Stuenkel; Staff 5 (MLS 1, Non-MLS 4)
Founded 1960
Jul 1999-Jun 2000 Income Parent Institution $131,000. Mats Exp $74,000, Books $16,000, Per/Ser (Incl. Access Fees) $45,000, Electronic Ref Mat (Incl. Access Fees) $13,000. Sal $55,000 (Prof $45,000)
Library Holdings: Bk Vols 18,000; Bk Titles 2,000; Per Subs 175
Subject Interests: Health sciences, Medicine
Function: For research purposes
Partic in Nev Libr Asn

C UNIVERSITY OF NEVADA, LAS VEGAS, Lied Library, 4505 Maryland Pkwy, Box 457001, 89154-7001. SAN 350-3615. Tel: 702-895-2286. Interlibrary Loan Service Tel: 702-895-3864. Circulation Tel: 702-895-2111. Reference Tel: 702-895-2100. FAX: 702-895-1207. Interlibrary Loan Service FAX: 702-895-3050. Web Site: www.library.nevada.edu. *Dean of Libr*, Kenneth E Marks; Fax: 702-895-2287, E-Mail: kmarks@ccmail.nevada.edu; *Asst Dean*, Myoung-ja Lee Kwon; E-Mail: kwon@ccmail.nevada.edu; *Assoc Dean*, Gail Munde; Tel: 702-895-2232, E-Mail: gmunde@ccmail.nevada.edu; *Branch Mgr*, Jeanne Brown; Tel: 702-895-4369, E-Mail: jeanneb@nevada.edu; *Branch Mgr*, Stephen Fitt; Tel: 702-895-0983, Fax: 702-895-3528; *Acq*, Xiaoyin Zhang; Tel: 702-895-2199, E-Mail: xzhang@nevada.edu; *AV*, Joan Rozzi; Tel: 702-895-2165, E-Mail: rossi@nevada.edu; *Bibliog Instr*, Diane VanderPol; Tel: 702-895-2126, E-Mail: vanderpd@nevada.edu; *Cat*, Brad Eden; *Circ*, Maria White; Tel: 702-895-2117, E-Mail: mwhite@nevada.edu; *Coll Develop*, Chris Sugnet; Tel: 702-895-2135, E-Mail: sugnet@nevada.edu; *ILL*, Vicky Hart; Tel: 702-895-2145, E-Mail: hartv@nevada.edu; *Music*, Cheryl Taranto; Tel: 702-893-2130, E-Mail: tarantoc@nevada.edu; *Publ Servs*, Wendy M Starkweather; E-Mail: starkw@nevada.edu; *Res*, Shelley Heaton; Tel: 702-895-2140, E-Mail: shelley@neveda.edu; *Spec Coll*, Peter Michel; Tel: 702-895-2243, E-Mail: michelp@nevada.edu; *Tech Servs*, Kenneth J Bierman; Tel: 702-895-2210, E-Mail: biermank@nevada.edu. Subject Specialists: *Architecture*, Jeanne Brown; *Curriculum mat*, Stephen Fitt; Staff 90 (MLS 33, Non-MLS 57)
Founded 1957. Enrl 15,318; Fac 632
Jul 1999-Jun 2000 Income (Main Library and Branch Library) $8,625,000, State $8,274,199, Other $165,328. Mats Exp $3,475,451, Books $965,903, Per/Ser (Incl. Access Fees) $1,884,283, Presv $106,668, Micro $104,332, AV Equip $57,951, Electronic Ref Mat (Incl. Access Fees) $356,314. Sal $4,557,026 (Prof $1,981,507)
Library Holdings: Bk Vols 1,240,347; Per Subs 8,335
Special Collections: Architectural Drawings (Martin Stern Coll); Gaming; Union Pacific Railroad Coll; Urban & Regional Historical Coll
Automation Activity & Vendor Info: (Cataloging) Innovative Interfaces Inc.; (Circulation) Innovative Interfaces Inc.; (Course Reserve) Innovative Interfaces Inc.; (ILL) Innovative Interfaces Inc.; (OPAC) Innovative Interfaces Inc.; (Serials) Innovative Interfaces Inc.
Database Vendor: Ebsco - EbscoHost, Innovative Interfaces INN - View, OCLC - First Search, Silverplatter Information Inc.
Publications: Communications; Ex Libris (Newsletter); TechNotes
Function: Research library
Partic in Amigos Library Services, Inc
Departmental Libraries:
ARCHITECTURE STUDIES Tel: 702-895-1959. FAX: 702-895-1975. *Librn*, Jeanne Brown
CURRICULUM MATERIALS LIBRARY Tel: 702-895-3593. FAX: 702-895-3528. *Librn*, Stephen Fitt
Subject Interests: Children's literature

LOGANDALE

S AMERICAN INSTITUTE FOR ADVANCED STUDIES, INC LIBRARY, PO Box 542, 89021. SAN 374-969X. Tel: 702-398-3222. FAX: 702-398-3700. Web Site: www.benifitcapital.com, www.tbcci.com. *Dir, Librn*, M T Smiley
Library Holdings: Bk Vols 9,941; Per Subs 156

LOVELOCK

P PERSHING COUNTY LIBRARY, 1125 Central, 89419. (Mail add: PO Box 781, 89419), SAN 350-3674. Tel: 775-273-2216. FAX: 775-273-0421. Web Site: ahontan.clan.lib.nv.us/polpac/html_client/default.asp. *Dir*, Jeanne Munk
Founded 1930. Pop 7,460; Circ 23,148
Jul 1998-Jun 1999 Income $212,800, State $7,280, County $204,958, Other $562. Mats Exp $212,800, Books $26,451, Per/Ser (Incl. Access Fees) $2,015, Micro $180. Sal $106,099
Library Holdings: Bk Vols 26,013; Per Subs 61
Subject Interests: Art, Cooking, Handicrafts, History, Nevada
Automation Activity & Vendor Info: (Acquisitions) Gaylord; (Circulation) Gaylord; (ILL) Gaylord; (OPAC) Gaylord; (Serials) Gaylord
Database Vendor: IAC - Info Trac, OCLC - First Search
Partic in Cooperating Libraries Automated Network (CLAN); OCLC Online Computer Library Center, Inc
Friends of the Library Group

MINDEN

P DOUGLAS COUNTY PUBLIC LIBRARY, 1625 Library Lane, 89423-4420. (Mail add: PO Box 337, 89423), SAN 350-3739. Tel: 775-782-9841. FAX: 775-782-6766. Web Site: www.douglas.lib.nv.us. *Dir*, Linda L Deacy; E-Mail: ldeacy@douglas.lib.nv.us; *Acq*, Constance Alexander; E-Mail: clalexan@clan.lib.nv.us; *Ch Servs*, Carol Slavik; *Publ Servs*, Linda Wilson; Tel: 775-782-6841, E-Mail: lawilson@clan.lib.nv.us; *Ser*, Patty Timmens; E-Mail: pstimmen@clan.lib.nv.us; Staff 19 (MLS 3, Non-MLS 16)
Founded 1967. Pop 41,420; Circ 128,502
Jul 2000-Jun 2001 Income (Main Library and Branch Library) $1,091,000, State $54,000, Federal $27,000, County $995,000, Locally Generated Income $15,000. Mats Exp $132,850, Books $83,850, Per/Ser (Incl. Access Fees) $20,000, AV Equip $15,000, Electronic Ref Mat (Incl. Access Fees) $14,000. Sal $346,000 (Prof $277,200)
Library Holdings: Bk Vols 125,266; Bk Titles 81,000; Per Subs 140
Special Collections: Carson Valley History (Van Sickle Coll), mss, micro; Nevada Historical Society
Automation Activity & Vendor Info: (Acquisitions) Gaylord; (Cataloging) Gaylord; (Circulation) Gaylord; (OPAC) Gaylord; (Serials) Gaylord
Database Vendor: Ebsco - EbscoHost, Wilson - Wilson Web
Publications: Douglas County's Architectural Heritage
Partic in CLAN
Friends of the Library Group
Branches: 1
LAKE TAHOE, 233 Warrior Way, Zephyr Cove, 89448. (Mail add: PO Box 4770, Stateline, 89449-4770), SAN 350-3763. Tel: 775-588-6411. FAX: 775-588-6464. *Dir*, Linda L Deacy; E-Mail: ldeacy@douglas.lib.nv.ux; *Librn*, Patty Timmens
Library Holdings: Bk Vols 32,696

NELLIS AFB

UNITED STATES AIR FORCE
A NELLIS AIR FORCE BASE LIBRARY FL4852, 99 SVS/SVMG, 4311 N Washington Blvd Ste 101, 89191-7064. SAN 350-3798. Tel: 702-652-9210. FAX: 702-652-8188. *Dir*, Mary P Petty; *Librn*, Michael Newman; Tel: 702-652-5072; Staff 9 (MLS 2, Non-MLS 7)
Founded 1942
Library Holdings: Bk Vols 46,000; Per Subs 365
Subject Interests: Aeronautics, Bus, Mgt, Military history
Automation Activity & Vendor Info: (Circulation) DRA
Database Vendor: Dialog, Ebsco - EbscoHost, Lexis-Nexis, OCLC - First Search, ProQuest
Mem of Clark County Libr District
Partic in Dialog Corporation; OCLC Online Computer Library Center, Inc

NORTH LAS VEGAS

S BECHTEL NV, Coordination & Information Center, 2621 Losee Rd, 89030-4129. (Mail add: PO Box 98521, Mail Stop NLV 040, 89193-8521), SAN 373-4684. Tel: 702-295-1623. FAX: 702-295-1624. E-Mail: cic@nv.doe.gov. Web Site: www.nv.doe.gov. *Librn*, Jeff Gordon
Founded 1981
Library Holdings: Bk Vols 345,000

P NORTH LAS VEGAS LIBRARY DISTRICT, 2300 Civic Center Dr, 89030. SAN 309-7196. Tel: 702-633-1070. FAX: 702-649-2576. *Dir*, Anita Laruy
Founded 1962. Pop 117,250
Jul 1999-Jun 2000 Income $1,353,772. Mats Exp $153,193, Books $141,292, Per/Ser (Incl. Access Fees) $7,401, Electronic Ref Mat (Incl. Access Fees) $4,500. Sal $692,129
Library Holdings: Bk Vols 87,652; Per Subs 102
Subject Interests: Auto repair manuals
Special Collections: Kiel Ranch Coll; Nevada Coll
Automation Activity & Vendor Info: (Circulation) DRA
Friends of the Library Group

OWYHEE

M OWYHEE COMMUNITY HOSPITAL, Nevada Hwy 225, 89832. (Mail add: PO Box 130, 89832-0130), Tel: 775-757-2415. FAX: 775-757-2066. *Admin Dir*, Warden Towsend

PAHRUMP

P PAHRUMP COMMUNITY LIBRARY,* 2101 E Calvada Blvd, PO Box 578, 89041. SAN 309-720X. Tel: 775-727-5930. FAX: 775-727-6209. *Dir*, Charlene Board; *ILL*, Mandy Caffeo; *Ch Servs, YA Servs*, Brenda Gibbons; *Ref*, Amanda Johnson
Pop 21,022; Circ 86,338
Jul 1996-Jun 1997 Income $187,084. Mats Exp $21,930. Sal $73,064
Library Holdings: Bk Titles 45,000; Per Subs 30
Subject Interests: Nev Coll
Open Tues-Thurs 9-7, Fri 9-5, Sat 11-5, closed Sun & Mon
Friends of the Library Group

PIOCHE

P LINCOLN COUNTY LIBRARY,* PO Box 330, 89043. SAN 309-7218. Tel: 775-962-5244. FAX: 775-962-5244. *Librn*, Peggy Draper; E-Mail: psdraper@clan.lib.nv.us
Pop 4,130; Circ 20,000
Library Holdings: Bk Titles 18,955
Partic in Nev Libr Asn
Branches: 2
ALAMO BRANCH, 100 South First W, Alamo, 89001. (Mail add: PO Box 239, Alamo, 89001), Tel: 702-725-3343. FAX: 702-725-3343. *Librn*, Catherine Stewart; E-Mail: cstewart@clan.lib.nv.us
Library Holdings: Bk Vols 11,687
CALIENTE BRANCH, PO Box 306, Caliente, 89008. SAN 324-1084. Tel: 702-726-3104. FAX: 702-726-3104. *Librn*, Carolyn Wilcox; E-Mail: crwilcox@clan.lib.nv.us
Library Holdings: Bk Vols 10,226

RENO

S CHURCH OF JESUS CHRIST OF LATTER-DAY SAINTS, Reno Family History Center, 4751 Neil Rd. (Mail add: 2931 Randolph Ct, 89502), SAN 370-6656. Tel: 775-826-1130. *Dir*, Loren Spencer; *Coll Develop*, LaRene Spencer
Library Holdings: Bk Titles 3,500
Special Collections: Genealogy, bks, CD-ROM, fiche, flm
Open Tues-Thurs 10-9. For main library, see Salt Lake City, UT

GM DEPARTMENT OF VETERANS AFFAIRS, Medical Center Library,* 1000 Locust St, 89520. SAN 309-7285. Tel: 702-328-1470. FAX: 702-328-1732. *Chief Librn*, Christine Simpson; E-Mail: simpsonc@equinox.unr.edu
Nov 1996-Oct 1997 Income $123,277. Mats Exp $111,465
Library Holdings: Bk Titles 1,836; Per Subs 249
Subject Interests: Clinical medicine, Geriatrics, Nursing
Partic in Valnet

L LIBRARY OF THE US COURTS, 400 S Virginia St Rm 1001, 89501. SAN 372-3410. Tel: 775-686-5776. FAX: 775-686-5779. *Librn*, Cheryl Kidd
Library Holdings: Bk Vols 18,865; Bk Titles 1,102; Per Subs 20
Open Mon-Fri 8-1, 1:30-4:30

S MERIDIAN GOLD COMPANY LIBRARY,* 9670 Gateway Dr Ste 200, 89511. SAN 301-8377. Tel: 775-850-3777. FAX: 775-850-3733. Web Site: www.meridangold.com.
Library Holdings: Bk Vols 100; Per Subs 23
Restriction: Staff use only

C MORRISON UNIVERSITY LIBRARY, 140 Washington St, 89503. SAN 326-0305. Tel: 775-323-4145. FAX: 775-323-8495. Web Site: www.morrison.edu. *Librn*, Usha Mehta; E-Mail: ushamehta@homemail.com
Enrl 300; Fac 25
Library Holdings: Bk Vols 3,035; Bk Titles 2,625; Per Subs 40
Database Vendor: Lexis-Nexis
Partic in Am Libr Asn; Nev Libr Asn

S NATIONAL AUTOMOBILE MUSEUM, (Formerly William F Harrah Foundation), Harrah Collection, 10 Lake St S, 89501. SAN 327-4462. Tel: 775-333-9300. FAX: 775-333-9309. E-Mail: info@automuseum.org. Web Site: www.automuseum.org. *Exec Dir*, Jackie L Frady
Library Holdings: Bk Titles 1,000
Special Collections: 1908 New York to Paris Race; Automotive Literature Coll, cat, club publications, film, owner & shop manuals, per, photogs, postcards, prints, sales brochures, tech data
Restriction: Not open to public

CL NATIONAL JUDICIAL COLLEGE, Law Library,* Judicial College Bldg, Univ of Nev, 89557. SAN 309-7242. Tel: 775-327-8278. FAX: 775-784-8057. *Librn*, Clara S Kelly

Founded 1966
Library Holdings: Bk Vols 83,000
Subject Interests: Mat relating to courts
Special Collections: Benchbooks; Court Administration; Dispute Resolution; Evidence; Jury Instructions; Sentencing; SJI Products (Judicial Education)
Partic in RLIN; Westlaw

S NEVADA HISTORICAL SOCIETY, Museum-Research Library, 1650 N Virginia St, 89503. SAN 309-7250. Tel: 775-688-1191. FAX: 775-688-2917. Web Site: www.clan.lib.nv.us. *Dir*, Peter L Bandurraga; Staff 8 (MLS 8)
Founded 1904
Library Holdings: Bk Titles 30,000; Per Subs 260
Subject Interests: Communication in Nev, Gambling, Lumber, Mining, Transportation, Water, Western US
Special Collections: Nevada History Coll, mss, photogs
Publications: A Guide to the George Wingfield Collection; Eureka's Yesterdays; Growing Up in Company Town; This was Nevada, A Guide to the Willim Stewart Papers

S RENO GAZETTE JOURNAL, Information Resource Center, 955 Kuenzli St, 89520. (Mail add: PO Box 22000, 89520), SAN 377-4457. Tel: 775-788-6200. FAX: 775-788-6458. Web Site: www.rgsi.com. *Librn*, J R Rasmussen
Library Holdings: Bk Titles 200; Per Subs 12
Restriction: Staff use only

M SAINT MARY'S REGIONAL MEDICAL CENTER, Max C Fleischmann Medical Library, 235 W Sixth St, 89520-0108. SAN 309-7269. Tel: 775-770-3108. FAX: 775-770-3685. *Coordr*, Donna M Alexander
Founded 1956
Library Holdings: Bk Vols 1,600; Per Subs 120
Subject Interests: Allied health, Medicine, Mgt, Nursing
Restriction: Staff use only
Partic in Nevada Medical Library Group; Northern California & Nevada Medical Library Group; Pac SW Regional Med Libr

J TRUCKEE MEADOWS COMMUNITY COLLEGE, Elizabeth Sturm Library, 7000 Dandini Blvd, 89512-3999. SAN 320-6947. Tel: 702-673-7000. FAX: 702-673-7273. Web Site: www.tmcc.edu/library/index.html. *Dir*, Lorin Lindsay; *Librn*, Susan Jimenez-Anderson; *Librn*, John Fitzsimmons; *Librn*, Nadine Phinney; *Librn*, Neil Siegal; Staff 13 (MLS 5, Non-MLS 8)
Jul 2000-Jun 2001 Income State $586,552. Mats Exp $123,000, Books $85,000, Per/Ser (Incl. Access Fees) $8,000, Electronic Ref Mat (Incl. Access Fees) $30,000. Sal $328,644 (Prof $179,063)
Library Holdings: Bk Vols 35,307; Bk Titles 37,450; Per Subs 105
Subject Interests: Career educ, Folklore, Health educ, Indust, Tech fields

C UNIVERSITY & COMMUNITY COLLEGE SYSTEM OF NEVADA, Desert Research Institute Library,* 2215 Raggio Pkwy, 89512. SAN 309-7323. Tel: 775-674-7041. FAX: 775-674-7183. Web Site: www.dri.edu/library. *Dir Libr Serv*, Melanie Scott; Tel: 702-895-0405, Fax: 702-895-0542, E-Mail: melanie@dri.edu; Staff 2 (MLS 1, Non-MLS 1)
Founded 1977
Library Holdings: Bk Vols 13,350
Subject Interests: Atmospheric sci, Environ sci
Database Vendor: CARL, Dialog, Ebsco - EbscoHost, OCLC - First Search, ProQuest
Publications: New Books; newsletter
Function: For research purposes
Departmental Libraries:
DRI SNSC LIBRARY, 755 E Flamingo Rd, Las Vegas, 89119. SAN 375-3964. Tel: 702-895-0405. FAX: 702-859-0542. Web Site: www.dri.edu/library.

C UNIVERSITY OF NEVADA-RENO, Noble H Getchell Library, 1664 N Virginia St, Mailstop 322, 89557-0044. SAN 350-3828. Tel: 775-784-6500. FAX: 775-784-1751. Web Site: www.library.unr.edu. *Dean of Libr*, Steven D Zink; Tel: 775-784-6500, Ext 252, Fax: 775-784-4529, E-Mail: stevenz@unr.edu; *Librn*, Janita Jobe; Tel: 775-784-6500, Ext 246, Fax: 775-784-4529, E-Mail: jobe@unr.eud; *Circ*, Marsheilah Lyons; *Automation Syst Coordr, Tech Servs*, Carol A Parkhurst; Tel: 775-784-1540, Ext 266, Fax: 775-784-4050, E-Mail: carolp@unr.edu; *Govt Doc*, Duncan Aldrich; Tel: 775-784-6500, Ext 256, Fax: 775-784-4398, E-Mail: duncan@unr.edu; *Acq*, Michele Y Moore; *Archivist*, Karen E Gash; *Cat*, Lou Amestoy; *Cat*, Elizabeth Icenhower; *Cat*, Virginia M Scheschy; *Ref Serv*, Michael F Simons; *ILL*, Millie Syring; Tel: 775-784-6500, Ext 289, E-Mail: mlsyring@unr.edu; *Res*, Donnelyn Curtis; Tel: 775-784-6500, Ext 285, Fax: 775-784-4529, E-Mail: dcurtis@unr.edu; *Publ Servs*, Michael Simons; Tel: 775-784-6500, Ext 311, E-Mail: simons@unr.edu; *Ser*, Rick Anderson; Tel: 775-784-6500, Ext 273, Fax: 775-784-1328; *Commun Relations*, Michele Basta; Tel: 775-784-6500, Ext 265, Fax: 775-784-4529, E-Mail: basta@unr.edu; *Spec Coll*, Robert E Blesse; Tel: 775-784-6500, Ext 317, Fax: 775-784-4529, E-Mail: blesse@unr.edu; Staff 75 (MLS 23, Non-MLS 52)
Founded 1886. Enrl 12,303; Fac 795; Highest Degree: Doctorate
Jul 1998-Jun 1999 Income (Main and Other College/University Libraries) $7,657,875. Mats Exp $3,615,107, Books $1,094,330, Per/Ser (Incl. Access Fees) $1,802,630, Presv $70,667, Electronic Ref Mat (Incl. Access Fees) $647,480. Sal $3,329,526 (Prof $1,575,408)
Library Holdings: Bk Vols 999,806; Per Subs 5,496
Special Collections: Army Map Serv & US Patent; Basque Studies; Modern English & American Authors; Nevada & the Great Basin; Women in the West
Automation Activity & Vendor Info: (ILL) Innovative Interfaces Inc.; (OPAC) Innovative Interfaces Inc.; (Serials) Innovative Interfaces Inc.
Database Vendor: Ebsco - EbscoHost, GaleNet, IAC - Info Trac, Lexis-Nexis, OCLC - First Search, ProQuest, Silverplatter Information Inc., Wilson - Wilson Web
Publications: Faculty newsletter (4 issues/yr); Friends of the University Library Newsletter (2 issues/yr); IRTeam (2 issues/yr); Memo to the Staff of the University of Nevada, Reno, Library (monthly)
Partic in Coop Libr Agency for Syst & Servs; OCLC Online Computer Library Center, Inc
Friends of the Library Group
Departmental Libraries:
DE LA MARE LIBRARY, 1664 N Virginia St, 89357. (Mail add: MS 262, 89357), Tel: 775-784-6945. FAX: 775-784-6949. Web Site: www.delamare.unr.edu. *Librn*, Glee Willis; E-Mail: willis@unr.edu.
Subject Specialists: *Geography*, Linda Newman; *Maps*, Linda Newman; *Science*, Linda Newman
Library Holdings: Bk Vols 37,346; Per Subs 738
Subject Interests: Civil, Computer science, Electrical, Math eng
Friends of the Library Group
S LIFE & HEALTH SCIENCES Tel: 775-784-6616. FAX: 775-784-1046. *Librn*, Amy Shannon; E-Mail: ashannon@unr.edu
Library Holdings: Bk Vols 44,000; Per Subs 800
Special Collections: Great Basin & Eastern Sierra
Friends of the Library Group
PHYSICAL SCIENCES Tel: 775-784-6716. FAX: 775-784-1720. *Librn*, Maggie Ressel; E-Mail: ressel@admin.unr.edu
Library Holdings: Bk Vols 35,000; Per Subs 300
Subject Interests: Chemistry, Physics
Friends of the Library Group

CM SAVITT MEDICAL LIBRARY, 1664 N Virginia St, Mail Stop 306, 89557-0046. SAN 350-3976. Tel: 702-784-4625. FAX: 702-784-4489. Web Site: med.unr.edu/medlib. *Dir*, Joan Zenan; E-Mail: joanz@unr.edu; *Acq*, Debby O'Brien; *Cat*, Jeannine Funk; *Circ*, Robert Boyd; *ILL*, Norman Huckle; *Online Servs, Ref*, Terry Henner; *Ref, Ser*, Rosalyn Casey; Staff 2 (MLS 2)
Founded 1978
Library Holdings: Bk Vols 47,749; Per Subs 376
Subject Interests: Audiology, Basic sci, Medicine, Speech pathology
Special Collections: Nevada Medical Archives; Sons of Italy Birth Defects & Genetics Coll
Partic in National Network Of Libraries Of Medicine - South Central Region; OCLC Online Computer Library Center, Inc

GL WASHOE COUNTY LAW LIBRARY,* Courthouse, PO Box 11130, 89520-0027. SAN 309-7293. Tel: 702-328-3250. FAX: 702-328-3441. Web Site: www.co.washoe.ny.us/lawlib/. *Dir*, Sandra Marz; E-Mail: smarz@mail.co.washoe.nv.us; *Tech Servs*, Kent Milunovich; *Ref*, D J Morrison; Staff 6 (MLS 3, Non-MLS 3)
Founded 1915
Jul 1997-Jun 1998 Income $690,220, County $647,100, Locally Generated Income $43,120. Mats Exp $272,935, Books $241,545, Per/Ser (Incl. Access Fees) $14,085, Presv $3,140, Micro $1,350. Sal $272,440 (Prof $158,755)
Library Holdings: Bk Vols 40,960; Bk Titles 6,168; Per Subs 315
Special Collections: General Law Library (Nevada Law, California Law Coll)
Automation Activity & Vendor Info: (Cataloging) epixtech, inc.
Publications: Library Acquisitions Lists
Partic in Nev Educ Online Network; RLIN; Westlaw
Friends of the Library Group

P WASHOE COUNTY LIBRARY SYSTEM, Downtown Reno Library, 301 S Center St, 89501. SAN 350-4069. Tel: 775-327-8300. FAX: 775-327-8390. E-Mail: info@washoe.lib.nv.us. Web Site: www.washoe.lib.nv.us. *Dir*, Nancy Cummings; *Assoc Dir*, Chuck Manley; *ILL*, Sharon Campbell; *Commun Relations*, Susie Kapahee; Tel: 775-785-4085
Founded 1902. Pop 305,792; Circ 1,452,989
Jul 1998-Jun 1999 Income (Main Library and Branch Library) $8,003,306, Federal $171,960, County $7,577,831, Other $253,515. Mats Exp $1,086,122, Books $739,193, Per/Ser (Incl. Access Fees) $338,114, AV Equip $8,815. Sal $3,917,548
Library Holdings: Bk Vols 640,045; Per Subs 1,270
Special Collections: Gambling; Literacy; Nevada History
Automation Activity & Vendor Info: (Circulation) epixtech, inc.
Publications: Annual Report; branch monthly calendars (two); pocket listing of branches
Partic in Coop Libr Agency for Syst & Servs; Information Nevada
Special Services for the Deaf - High interest/low vocabulary books; Staff with knowledge of sign language
Friends of the Library Group
Branches: 12
BILLINGHURST, 6685 Chesterfield Lane, 89503. SAN 376-8562. Tel: 702-746-5858. FAX: 702-746-5869. Web Site: www.washoe.lib.nv.us. *Mgr*, Janet Elcano
Library Holdings: Bk Vols 25,067

Friends of the Library Group
DUNCAN-TRANER, 1650 Carville Dr, 89512. SAN 374-7131. Tel: 775-333-5134. FAX: 775-333-5076. Web Site: www.washoe.lib.nv.us. *Mgr*, Marian Moses
Library Holdings: Bk Vols 20,192
Friends of the Library Group
GALENA, 3600 Butch Cassidy Way, 89511. SAN 373-5001. Tel: 702-851-5639. FAX: 702-851-5636. Web Site: www.washoe.lib.nv.us. *Librn*, Debbie Dahlstrom
Library Holdings: Bk Vols 26,802
Friends of the Library Group
GERLACH BRANCH, 555 E Sunset Blvd, Gerlach, 89412. SAN 371-9782. Tel: 775-557-2447. FAX: 775-557-2450. Web Site: www.washoe.lib.nv.us. *Mgr*, Sherry Anderson
Library Holdings: Bk Vols 6,462
INCLINE VILLAGE BRANCH, 846 Tahoe Blvd, Incline Village, 89451. SAN 350-4093. Tel: 775-832-4130. FAX: 775-832-4145. Web Site: www.washoe.lib.nv.us. *Mgr*, Marguerite Kelnhofer
Library Holdings: Bk Vols 46,598
Special Collections: Lake Tahoe Coll
Friends of the Library Group
MENDIVE, 1900 Whitewood Dr, Sparks, 89434. SAN 376-8570. Tel: 702-353-5989. FAX: 702-353-5988. Web Site: www.washoe.lib.nv.us. *Mgr*, Mary Claire Hutchinson
Library Holdings: Bk Vols 24,477
Friends of the Library Group
NORTH VALLEYS, 1075 N Hills Blvd, No 340, 89506. SAN 350-4158. Tel: 702-972-0281. FAX: 702-972-6810. Web Site: www.washoe.lib.nv.us. *Mgr*, Janet Pozarski
Library Holdings: Bk Vols 51,080
Friends of the Library Group
NORTHWEST RENO, 2325 Robb Dr, 89523. (Mail add: PO Box 2151, 89505), SAN 374-7123. Tel: 775-787-4100. FAX: 775-787-4127. Web Site: www.washoe.lib.nv.us. *Mgr*, Dianne Varnon
Library Holdings: Bk Vols 184,751
Subject Interests: Nevada
Friends of the Library Group
SENIOR CITIZENS CENTER, 1155 E Ninth St, 89512. SAN 350-4115. Tel: 702-328-2586. FAX: 702-785-4610. Web Site: www.washoe.lib.nv.us. *Mgr*, Ginger Traut
Friends of the Library Group
SIERRA VIEW, 4001 S Virginia St, 89502. SAN 329-6385. Tel: 775-827-3232. FAX: 775-827-8792. Web Site: www.washoe.lib.nv.us. *Mgr*, Martha Greene; Tel: 775-827-0327, E-Mail: mgreene@mail.co.washoe.nv.us; Staff 18 (MLS 2, Non-MLS 16)
Founded 1987
Library Holdings: Bk Vols 106,000; Bk Titles 84,000; Per Subs 221
Special Collections: New Adult Readers
Database Vendor: epixtech, inc., IAC - SearchBank, OVID Technologies
Friends of the Library Group
SPARKS BRANCH, 1125 12th St, Sparks, 89431. SAN 350-4123. Tel: 775-352-3200. Reference Tel: 775-352-3205. FAX: 775-352-3207. Web Site: www.washoe.lib.nv.us. *Mgr*, Randy Bledsoe; Tel: 775-352-3204
Founded 1932. Pop 65,000
Library Holdings: Bk Vols 156,056
Special Services for the Blind - Talking book center
Friends of the Library Group
VERDI, 250 Bridge St, Verdi, 89439. SAN 371-9790. Tel: 775-345-8104. FAX: 775-345-7277. Web Site: www.washoe.lib.nv.us. *Mgr*, Debby Dahlstrom
Library Holdings: Bk Vols 11,251
Friends of the Library Group
Bookmobiles: 1

M WASHOE HEALTH SYSTEM, Washoe Medical Center Library, 77 Pringle Way, 89502-1474. SAN 309-7307. Tel: 775-982-5693. FAX: 775-982-5735. *Librn*, Sherry A McGee; E-Mail: smcgee@washoehealth.com; Staff 2 (MLS 1, Non-MLS 1)
Founded 1941
Jul 2000-Jun 2001 Income Parent Institution $136,382. Mats Exp $48,600, Books $9,000, Per/Ser (Incl. Access Fees) $39,600. Sal $71,500 (Prof $53,100)
Library Holdings: Bk Titles 2,150; Per Subs 268
Subject Interests: Health admin, Medicine, Nursing, Paramedical
Automation Activity & Vendor Info: (Cataloging) EOS; (Circulation) EOS; (Serials) EOS
Partic in Docline; NCNMLG; Pacific Southwest Regional Med Libr Serv

ROUND MOUNTAIN

P ROUND MOUNTAIN PUBLIC LIBRARY, Hadley Circle,* PO Box 1265, 89045. Tel: 775-377-2215. *Dir*, Diane Canfield
Library Holdings: Bk Vols 22,000; Bk Titles 20,000; Per Subs 300

SPARKS

M NEVADA MENTAL HEALTH INSTITUTE LIBRARY,* 480 Galletti Way, 89431-5574. SAN 309-7315. Tel: 702-688-2001, 702-688-2055. FAX: 702-688-2192. *Librn*, Pat Merrill
Founded 1968
1997-1998 Income $2,000. Mats Exp $2,000
Library Holdings: Bk Vols 2,250
Subject Interests: Mental health, Psychiatric nursing, Psychiatry, Psychology

TONOPAH

S CENTRAL NEVADA HISTORICAL SOCIETY MUSEUM LIBRARY, Logan Field Rd, PO Box 326, 89049. SAN 373-241X. Tel: 775-482-9676. FAX: 775-482-5423. E-Mail: cnmuseum@sierra.net. Web Site: www.tonopahnevada.com. *Dir*, William J Metscher; Tel: 775-482-2336; Staff 3 (Non-MLS 3)
Founded 1980. Pop 10,000
Jul 1998-Jul 1999 Mats Exp $5,470, Books $1,750, Per/Ser (Incl. Access Fees) $220, Presv $2,000, AV Equip $1,000, Electronic Ref Mat (Incl. Access Fees) $500
Library Holdings: Bk Vols 2,000; Bk Titles 2,000
Special Collections: Mining History Central Nevada; Repository for Obsolete Nye County Records
Restriction: Non-circulating to the public

L NYE COUNTY LAW LIBRARY, 101 Radar Rd, 89049. (Mail add: PO Box 153, 89049), SAN 373-0794. Tel: 775-482-8103. FAX: 775-482-8198. *Librn*, Justina Fyfe; E-Mail: jdfyfe@sierra.net
Library Holdings: Bk Vols 9,500
Partic in Westlaw

VIRGINIA CITY

P STOREY COUNTY PUBLIC LIBRARY, 95 South R St, PO Box 14, 89440-0014. SAN 329-157X. Tel: 775-847-0956. FAX: 775-847-0996. Web Site: www.clan.lib.nv.us. *Dir*, Lucy W Bouldin; E-Mail: lwbouldi@clan.lib.nv.us; Staff 1 (Non-MLS 1)
Founded 1985. Pop 3,620
Jul 1999-Jun 2000 Income $75,190, State $3,681, County $71,509
Library Holdings: Bk Titles 8,476
Database Vendor: IAC - SearchBank
Partic in Cooperating Libraries Automated Network (CLAN)
Friends of the Library Group

WINNEMUCCA

G BUREAU OF LAND MANAGEMENT LIBRARY,* 5100 E Winnemucca Blvd, 89445. SAN 309-734X. Tel: 702-623-1500. FAX: 702-623-1503.
Library Holdings: Bk Vols 2,200
Subject Interests: Burros, Cultural res, Minerals, Range, Recreation, Wild horses, Wildlife
Special Collections: Land Use Reference Material Coll
Restriction: Open to public for reference only

P HUMBOLDT COUNTY LIBRARY,* 85 E Fifth St, 89445. SAN 350-4182. Tel: 775-623-6388. FAX: 775-623-6438. *Dir*, Sharon Allen; *Asst Dir*, Jeff Marcinik; *YA Servs*, Leanne Autry; *Circ*, Lawana Ferier; *ILL*, Connie Side; *Bkmobile Coordr*, Patty Glovach; *Tech Servs*, Dede McCoy; *Tech Servs*, Nellie Schofield
Founded 1923. Pop 16,500; Circ 160,000
Library Holdings: Bk Vols 55,000; Per Subs 171
Subject Interests: Local history, Nevada
Branches: 2
DENIO Tel: 775-941-0330. *In Charge*, Duncan Sherrie
Library Holdings: Bk Vols 2,000
MCDERMITT Tel: 775-532-8014. FAX: 775-532-8018. *Librn*, Vicky Easterday
Library Holdings: Bk Vols 8,500
Bookmobiles: 1

S NORTH CENTRAL NEVADA HISTORICAL SOCIETY, Humboldt Museum Research Department,* Maple Ave & Jungo Rd, PO Box 819, 89446. SAN 373-2428. Tel: 775-623-2912. FAX: 775-623-5640. *Curator*, Pansilee Larson
Library Holdings: Bk Vols 5,000
Publications: The Humboldt Historian

YERINGTON

P LYON COUNTY LIBRARY SYSTEM,* 20 Nevin Way, 89447. SAN 350-4271. Tel: 775-463-6645. FAX: 775-463-6646. *Coll Develop, Dir*, Christiane Freer-Parsons; E-Mail: cdfreer@lahonton.clan.lib.nv.us; *Mgr*, Lenora McCarty; *Ch Servs*, Jeanne Stockman; *Tech Servs*, Dora Page; *ILL*, Robyn Holderman

Pop 26,680; Circ 101,716
Library Holdings: Bk Vols 81,000; Per Subs 65
Partic in Coop Libr Syst Region II; Cooperating Libraries Automated Network (CLAN)
Friends of the Library Group
Branches: 4
DAYTON VALLEY BRANCH, 321 (Old) Dayton Valley Rd, Dayton, 89403. SAN 377-0257. Tel: 775-246-6212. FAX: 775-246-6213. *Mgr*, Pat Allen
Friends of the Library Group
FERNLEY BRANCH, 575 Silver Lace Blvd, Fernley, 89408. SAN 350-4301. Tel: 775-575-3366. FAX: 775-575-3368. *Mgr*, Patricia Zdunich
Circ 14,891
Friends of the Library Group
IDA COMPSTON, 32 Day Lane, Smith, 89430. SAN 377-0273. Tel: 775-465-2369. FAX: 775-465-2309. *Mgr*, Mary Jane Bettencourt
Friends of the Library Group
SILVER-STAGE BRANCH, 3905 Hwy 50 W, Silver Springs, 89429. SAN 350-428X. Tel: 702-577-5015. FAX: 702-577-5013. *Branch Mgr*, Donna Roelle; E-Mail: dkroell@clan.lib.nv.us
Friends of the Library Group

NEW HAMPSHIRE

Date of Statistics: 1999
Population, 1990 Census: 1,109,117
Population Served by Public Libraries: 1,201,134
Total Volumes in Public Libraries: 5,073,844
Volumes Per Capita: 4.22
Total Public Library Circulation: 8,4521,547
Circulation Per Capita: 7.04
Total Public Library Income (not including Grants-in-Aid): $30,402,786
Income Per Capita: $25.313
Source of Income: Mainly public funds (2/3 public, 1/3 endowment)
Expenditures Per Capita: $32.49

ACWORTH

P ACWORTH SILSBY LIBRARY,* PO Box 179, 03601. SAN 324-3729. Tel: 603-835-2150. E-Mail: acworthlibrary@sugar-river.net. *In Charge*, Devik Hemmings
Founded 1891. Pop 620; Circ 2,546
Library Holdings: Bk Vols 8,000; Per Subs 15
Subject Interests: NH hist
Publications: Library & Town newsletter
Building on National Register of Historic Places
Friends of the Library Group

ALEXANDRIA

P HAYNES MEMORIAL PUBLIC LIBRARY,* 567 Washburn Rd, 03222-6532. SAN 320-4898. Tel: 603-744-6529. *Librn*, Nancy Butler
Founded 1885. Circ 1,218
Library Holdings: Bk Vols 6,940
Subject Interests: Local history

ALLENSTOWN

P ALLENSTOWN PUBLIC LIBRARY,* 59 Main St, 03275-1716. SAN 309-7358. Tel: 603-485-7651. E-Mail: allentownslibrary@juno.com. *Librn*, Georgette S Plourde; *Asst Librn*, Bettye Richard
Pop 5,000; Circ 5,784
Library Holdings: Bk Vols 12,000; Per Subs 28
Subject Interests: Historic maps, Town hist
Mem of Cent Libr District
Friends of the Library Group

ALSTEAD

P SHEDD-PORTER MEMORIAL LIBRARY, Main St, PO Box 209, 03602. SAN 309-7366. Tel: 603-835-6661. *Librn*, Julia Cunniff; Staff 1 (Non-MLS 1)
Founded 1910. Pop 1,463; Circ 20,000
Library Holdings: Bk Vols 20,000; Per Subs 14
Open Wed 12-4 & 6-8, Thurs & Fri 12-6

ALTON

P GILMAN PUBLIC LIBRARY,* Main St, 03809-0960. (Mail add: PO Box 960, 03809-0960), SAN 309-7374. Tel: 603-875-2550. E-Mail: gilman@worldpath.net. *Librn*, Holly Brown; *Asst Librn*, Cindy Miller
Founded 1951. Pop 3,800; Circ 23,426
Library Holdings: Bk Titles 18,000; Per Subs 42
Mem of Cent Libr District
Friends of the Library Group

AMHERST

P AMHERST TOWN LIBRARY, 14 Main St, 03031. SAN 309-7382. Tel: 603-673-2288. FAX: 603-672-6063. E-Mail: library@amherst.lib.nh.us. Web Site: www.amherst.lib.nh.us. *Dir*, Mary Ann List; E-Mail: mlist@amherst.lib.nh.us; *Ch Servs*, Erna Johnson; E-Mail: ejohnson@amherst.lib.nh.us; *Ref*, Francesca Denton; *Ref*, Roslyn Vear; Staff 21 (MLS 4, Non-MLS 17)
Founded 1891. Pop 10,000; Circ 143,891
Jul 1999-Jun 2000 Income $428,063, City $392,184, Locally Generated Income $18,331, Other $17,548. Mats Exp $92,365, Books $61,594, Per/Ser (Incl. Access Fees) $4,195, Electronic Ref Mat (Incl. Access Fees) $11,576. Sal $282,136
Library Holdings: Bk Vols 66,442; Bk Titles 51,498; Per Subs 136
Automation Activity & Vendor Info: (Cataloging) epixtech, inc.; (Circulation) epixtech, inc.; (OPAC) epixtech, inc.; (Serials) epixtech, inc.
Database Vendor: Dialog, Ebsco - EbscoHost, IAC - SearchBank, OCLC - First Search, ProQuest
Partic in GMILCS
Special Services for the Blind - Magnifiers; Screen enlargement software for people with visual disabilities; Talking Books
Friends of the Library Group

ANDOVER

P ANDOVER PUBLIC LIBRARY,* 86 Main St, 03216. SAN 309-7390. Tel: 603-735-5333. FAX: 603-735-6975. *Librn*, Ann Clark; E-Mail: tayclark@tds.net
Pop 1,584; Circ 10,328
Library Holdings: Bk Vols 11,000; Per Subs 33
Mem of Cent Libr District

ANTRIM

P JAMES A TUTTLE LIBRARY,* 45 Main St, 03440. (Mail add: PO Box 235, 03440), SAN 309-7412. Tel: 603-588-6786. E-Mail: tuttle@conknet.com. *Librn*, Kathryn Chisholm
Pop 2,203; Circ 20,698
Jan 1997-Dec 1998 Income $60,447, City $43,920, Parent Institution $16,199. Mats Exp $16,199, Books $6,000, Per/Ser (Incl. Access Fees) $1,000, AV Equip $4,000. Sal $43,416 (Prof $22,000)
Library Holdings: Bk Vols 15,000; Per Subs 22
Subject Interests: Genealogy, NH hist
Open Mon & Wed 2-6, Tues & Thurs 2-8, Fri 9-12, Sat 10-4
Friends of the Library Group

ASHLAND

P ASHLAND TOWN LIBRARY,* Main St, 03217-0660. (Mail add: PO Box 660, 03217-0660), SAN 309-7420. Tel: 603-968-7928. FAX: 603-968-7928.
Pop 1,915; Circ 4,777

Library Holdings: Bk Titles 18,000; Per Subs 28
Mem of North Country District
Open Mon, Tues & Thurs 2-8, Sat 10-2

S HYDROSOURCE ASSOCIATES LIBRARY,* 26 Winter St, PO Box 609, 03217. SAN 324-6914. Tel: 603-284-6171. FAX: 603-968-7605. *Librn*, Rosemarie de Mars; Staff 2 (MLS 1, Non-MLS 1)
Founded 1980
Library Holdings: Bk Titles 1,000
Subject Interests: Computer software, Geology, Hydrol, Remote sensing

ATKINSON

P KIMBALL PUBLIC LIBRARY,* 3 Academy Ave, 03811-2202. SAN 309-7439. Tel: 603-362-5234. *Head Librn*, Mitchell Perlow
Pop 5,600; Circ 66,000
1997-1998 Income $124,071. Mats Exp $23,275, Books $15,000, Per/Ser (Incl. Access Fees) $2,400, Presv $200, Micro $1,000, AV Equip $4,000, Other Print Mats $675. Sal $81,500
Library Holdings: Bk Vols 35,000; Per Subs 30
Subject Interests: Local history
Special Collections: New England, audio, bks, large-print bks
Automation Activity & Vendor Info: (Circulation) Sagebrush Corporation
Partic in Merri-Hill-Rock Library Cooperative; WinnShare Libr Coop
Friends of the Library Group

AUBURN

P GRIFFIN FREE PUBLIC LIBRARY,* 22 Hooksett Rd, PO Box 308, 03032-0308. SAN 309-7447. Tel: 603-483-5374. FAX: 603-483-0483. *Dir*, Edith B Cummings
Pop 4,200
Library Holdings: Bk Vols 16,500
Mem of SE Libr District
Open Tues & Fri 10-5, Wed & Thurs 12:30-8 & Sat 10-1
Friends of the Library Group

BARRINGTON

P BARRINGTON PUBLIC LIBRARY, 39 Province Lane, 03825. SAN 309-7463. Tel: 603-664-9715. FAX: 603-664-9715. E-Mail: bpl@nh.ultranet.com. Web Site: www.nh.ultranet.com/~bpl. *Librn*, Amy Richards; *Asst Librn*, Virginia Schonwald; *Asst Librn*, Wendy Rowe; Staff 4 (Non-MLS 4)
Founded 1795. Pop 6,500; Circ 26,000
2000-2001 Income City $70,088. Mats Exp $13,900, Books $11,500, Per/Ser (Incl. Access Fees) $1,000, Presv $400, AV Equip $1,000. Sal $46,679 (Prof $23,003)
Library Holdings: Bk Vols 21,000; Per Subs 22; Bks on Deafness & Sign Lang 10
Subject Interests: Genealogy, Local area histories
Special Collections: Local Historical Society, bks & doc
Automation Activity & Vendor Info: (Circulation) Athena; (OPAC) Athena
Database Vendor: ProQuest
Function: ILL available, Photocopies available, Some telephone reference
Friends of the Library Group

BARTLETT

P BARTLETT PUBLIC LIBRARY,* Main St, PO Box 366, 03812-0366. SAN 309-7471. Tel: 603-374-2755. *Librn*, Jean Garland
Jan 1999-Dec 1999 Income $20,000
Library Holdings: Bk Titles 13,500; Per Subs 60
Partic in Carroll County Library Cooperative

BATH

P BATH PUBLIC LIBRARY,* Rte 302, Town Hall, PO Box 5, 03740. SAN 309-748X. Tel: 603-747-3372. FAX: 603-747-3372. E-Mail: bathlibrary@connriver.net, brit@together.net. *Librn*, Bernie Prochnik
Pop 790; Circ 2,900
1998-1999 Income $8,000. Mats Exp $2,300, Books $2,000, Per/Ser (Incl. Access Fees) $300. Sal $4,800
Library Holdings: Bk Vols 13,385
Mem of North Country District

BEDFORD

P BEDFORD PUBLIC LIBRARY,* 3 Meetinghouse Rd, 03110. SAN 309-7498. Tel: 603-472-2300, 603-472-3023. FAX: 603-472-2978. E-Mail: bedpl@mv.mv.com. Web Site: www.bedford.lib.nh.us. *Dir*, Frances M Wiggin; *Ch Servs*, Luci Albertson; *Ref*, Susan Rotch; *Tech Servs*, Joanna Baqqi
Founded 1789. Pop 15,000; Circ 118,933
Jan 1998-Dec 1998 Income $656,372. Mats Exp $70,000. Sal $235,684
Library Holdings: Bk Vols 54,376; Per Subs 215
Special Collections: Sheet Music Coll
Publications: Town Directory & Friends Newsletter
Open Mon, Wed & Thurs 9-8, Tues 7-8, Fri 9-5, Sat 10-3, Sun 12-2
Friends of the Library Group

S NORMANDEAU ASSOCIATES, INC LIBRARY,* 25 Nashua Rd, 03110. SAN 309-7501. Tel: 603-472-5191. FAX: 603-472-7052. *Librn*, Denise Morin
Founded 1970
Library Holdings: Bk Vols 5,000
Subject Interests: Environ

BELMONT

P BELMONT PUBLIC LIBRARY,* 146 Main St, 03220-0308. (Mail add: PO Box 308, 03220-0308), SAN 309-751X. Tel: 603-267-8331. E-Mail: bpl@worldpath.net. *Librn*, Joanne Ricard
Founded 1928. Pop 5,000; Circ 9,144
Library Holdings: Bk Vols 14,000; Per Subs 25
Open Mon & Wed 1-5, Thurs 11-6, Sat 9-12 (except July & Aug)

BENNINGTON

P GEP DODGE LIBRARY, 2 Main St, 03442-4109. (Mail add: PO Box 129, 03442-0129), SAN 309-7528. Tel: 603-588-6585. FAX: 603-588-6585. E-Mail: dodgelibrary@conknet.com. *Librn*, Leslie McGregor
Pop 1,183; Circ 11,544
Library Holdings: Bk Vols 14,000; Per Subs 36
Mem of SW Libr District
Friends of the Library Group

BERLIN

M ANDROSCOGGIN VALLEY HOSPITAL, Medical Library,* 59 Page Hill Rd, 03570. SAN 327-747X. Tel: 603-752-2200, Ext 385. FAX: 603-752-2376. *Librn*, Joyce Leclere
Library Holdings: Bk Titles 200; Per Subs 75

P BERLIN PUBLIC LIBRARY, 270 Main St, 03570. SAN 309-7536. Tel: 603-752-5210. FAX: 603-752-8568. *Librn*, Yvonne Thomas
Founded 1893. Pop 11,900; Circ 79,344
2000-2001 Income $160,000. Mats Exp $27,600, Books $25,000, Per/Ser (Incl. Access Fees) $2,600
Library Holdings: Bk Titles 39,562; Per Subs 180
Special Collections: French Fiction Coll
Mem of North Country District
Partic in NHAIS

J NEW HAMPSHIRE COMMUNITY TECHNICAL COLLEGE, Berlin Fortier Library, 2020 Riverside Dr, 03570-3799. SAN 309-7552. Tel: 603-752-1113. FAX: 603-752-6335. E-Mail: berlinlibary@tec.nh.us, berlinlibrary@tec.nh.us. Web Site: comet.berl.tec.nh.us/services/library.html. *In Charge*, Katherine M Doherty; E-Mail: kdoherty@tec.nh.us; Staff 2 (MLS 1, Non-MLS 1)
Founded 1970. Enrl 500; Fac 50
Library Holdings: Bk Vols 10,000; Per Subs 165
Automation Activity & Vendor Info: (Cataloging) TLC; (OPAC) TLC
Publications: CINAHL; ESCOHOST
Partic in Docline

BETHLEHEM

P BETHLEHEM PUBLIC LIBRARY,* 2155 Main St, 03574-0250. (Mail add: PO Box 250, 03574-0250), SAN 309-7560. Tel: 603-869-2409. *Librn*, Mrs Floyd S Brown
Pop 2,000; Circ 11,936
Jan 1997-Dec 1998 Income $27,700. Mats Exp $25,700
Library Holdings: Bk Vols 12,500; Per Subs 65
Mem of North Country District

BOSCAWEN

P BOSCAWEN PUBLIC LIBRARY,* King St, PO Box 3099, 03303. SAN 350-4336. Tel: 603-796-2442. *Librn*, Barbara Keegan
Founded 1797. Pop 3,419; Circ 7,500
Library Holdings: Bk Vols 13,000; Per Subs 15
Special Collections: Local History Coll; New Hampshire Law Books Coll; Town Records Coll
Partic in NH Trust Asn
Friends of the Library Group
Branches: 1
BOSCAWEN BRANCH LIBRARY, 73 N Main St, 03303. Tel: 603-753-8576. *Librn*, Barbara Keegan
Open Mon 2:30-6:30 & Wed 2:30-7

BOW

P BAKER FREE LIBRARY, 509 South St, 03304-3413. SAN 309-7579. Tel: 603-224-7113. FAX: 603-224-2063. E-Mail: hshw@lilac.nhsl.lib.nh.us. Web Site: www.people.ne.mediaone.net/bowbakerfreelibrary. *Head Librn*, Linda Kling; *Ch Servs*, Jennifer Ericsson; Staff 2 (MLS 1, Non-MLS 1)
Founded 1914. Pop 6,500; Circ 60,970
Jan 2000-Dec 2000 Income Locally Generated Income $205,363. Mats Exp $42,600, Books $35,600, Per/Ser (Incl. Access Fees) $5,000, Presv $2,000. Sal $108,467
Library Holdings: Bk Vols 33,251; Per Subs 118
Automation Activity & Vendor Info: (Circulation) Sagebrush Corporation
Mem of Cent Libr District
Friends of the Library Group

BRADFORD

P BROWN MEMORIAL LIBRARY,* 78 W Main St, PO Box 437, 03221. SAN 309-7587. Tel: 603-938-5562. *Librn*, Margaret Ainslie; *Asst Librn*, Elsa Weir
Pop 1,118; Circ 11,445
Library Holdings: Bk Vols 11,000; Per Subs 15
Mem of Cent Libr District
Friends of the Library Group

BRENTWOOD

P MARY E BARTLETT MEMORIAL LIBRARY, 22 Dalton Rd, 03833. SAN 309-7595. Tel: 603-642-3355. FAX: 603-642-3383. E-Mail: bartlettlibrary@pop.ne.mediaone.net. Web Site: people.ne.mediaone.net/bartlettlibrary/indexhtml. *Head Librn*, Marilyn Morehead; *Asst Librn*, Joyce Miller
Founded 1893. Pop 3,010
2000-2001 Income $72,577, City $70,011, Federal $159, Locally Generated Income $2,407. Mats Exp $14,387, Books $11,466, Per/Ser (Incl. Access Fees) $1,349, AV Equip $752, Other Print Mats $820. Sal $38,643
Library Holdings: Bk Vols 18,036; Per Subs 57
Automation Activity & Vendor Info: (Cataloging) Sagebrush Corporation; (Circulation) Sagebrush Corporation
Mem of SE Libr District
Partic in NHAIS
Friends of the Library Group

BRISTOL

P MINOT-SLEEPER LIBRARY,* 35 Pleasant St, 03222-1407. SAN 309-7609. Tel: 603-744-3352. *Librn*, Doreen Powden
Pop 2,279; Circ 12,556
Library Holdings: Bk Vols 12,000; Per Subs 35
Special Collections: Stuffed Bird Coll
Mem of Cent Libr District

BROOKLINE

P BROOKLINE PUBLIC LIBRARY,* 16 Main St, PO Box 157, 03033. SAN 309-7617. Tel: 603-673-3330. FAX: 603-673-0735. E-Mail: brpl@ma.ultranet.com. *Librn*, Claudette M Gill; *Asst Librn*, Dianna Boyle
Pop 2,600; Circ 26,000
Library Holdings: Bk Vols 20,000
Friends of the Library Group

CAMPTON

P CAMPTON PUBLIC LIBRARY,* Box 1212, RR 1, 03223. SAN 376-5113. Tel: 603-726-4877. E-Mail: cpl@cyberport.net. *Librn*, Corinna Kern-Arroyo
Jan 1998-Dec 1998 Income $17,000
Library Holdings: Bk Titles 12,000; Per Subs 10
Partic in Scrooge & Marley Cooperative

CANAAN

P CANAAN TOWN LIBRARY, Main St, PO Box 368, 03741-0368. SAN 309-7633. Tel: 603-523-9650. FAX: 603-523-9092. E-Mail: canaantownlibrary@hotmail.com. Web Site: town.canaan.nh.us/library.htm. *Librn*, Amy Thurber; Staff 5 (Non-MLS 5)
Founded 1804. Pop 2,464; Circ 20,211
Library Holdings: Bk Vols 40,000; Per Subs 65
Automation Activity & Vendor Info: (Circulation) Follett
Open Mon 6-9, Tues & Thurs 1-5, Wed 1-9, Fri 9-12, Sat 9-3
Friends of the Library Group

CANDIA

P SMYTH PUBLIC LIBRARY, 194 High St, 03034. SAN 309-880X. Tel: 603-483-8245. FAX: 603-483-5217. Web Site: www.smythpl.org. *Librn*, Jon R Godfrey; Staff 3 (Non-MLS 3)
Founded 1888. Pop 3,800; Circ 21,800
2000-2001 Income Locally Generated Income $80,000. Mats Exp Books $13,000. Sal $39,500
Library Holdings: Bk Vols 18,000; Bk Titles 18,000; Per Subs 40
Subject Interests: Local history
Automation Activity & Vendor Info: (Circulation) Sagebrush Corporation
Publications: Booklist/ALA

CANTERBURY

P ELKINS PUBLIC LIBRARY, One Baptist Rd, PO Box 300, 03224-2401. SAN 309-7641. Tel: 603-783-4386. *Librn*, Susan Holmes; *Asst Librn*, Elaine DeStefano
Pop 1,800; Circ 14,732
Mar 2001-Feb 2002 Income City $40,168. Mats Exp Books $6,183. Sal $20,728
Library Holdings: Bk Titles 11,400; Per Subs 12
Special Collections: Shaker Coll
Mem of Cent Libr District
Partic in NHAIS
Friends of the Library Group

CARROL

P TWIN MOUNTAIN PUBLIC LIBRARY,* School St, PO Box 163, 03595. SAN 309-765X. Tel: 603-846-5818. *Librn*, Mary-Lew Chevalier
Pop 722; Circ 900
Library Holdings: Bk Titles 6,000
Special Collections: White Mountain & Surrounding Region Material Coll (1800's), bks, pictures
Mem of North Country District
Open Mon 6:30-8:30, Wed & Sat 1-4
Friends of the Library Group

CENTER BARNSTEAD

P OSCAR FOSS MEMORIAL LIBRARY,* Main St, Rte 126, PO Box 219, 03225-0219. SAN 309-7455. Tel: 603-269-3900. *Librn*, Susan Conrad; *Asst Librn*, Bonnie Brannigan
Pop 3,000; Circ 8,655
Library Holdings: Bk Vols 10,000; Per Subs 25
Mem of Cent District Libr Syst
Open Mon & Tues 2-8pm, Wed 10am-5pm, Thurs 7am-9pm, Fri 2-5pm & Sat 9am-2pm
Friends of the Library Group

CENTER HARBOR

P JAMES E NICHOLS MEMORIAL LIBRARY,* Main St, PO Box 1339, 03226-1339. SAN 309-7668. Tel: 603-253-6950. *Librn*, Sandra S Pickel; Staff 2 (MLS 1, Non-MLS 1)
Founded 1910. Pop 1,018; Circ 10,833
Jan 1999-Dec 1999 Income $43,900, City $37,987, Other $5,913. Mats Exp $7,520, Books $6,778, Per/Ser (Incl. Access Fees) $167, Other Print Mats $575. Sal $25,504
Library Holdings: Bk Vols 14,453; Per Subs 45

CENTER OSSIPEE

P OSSIPEE PUBLIC LIBRARY,* 74 Main St, PO Box 638, 03814. SAN 309-9210. Tel: 603-539-6390. FAX: 603-539-5758. E-Mail: opl@worldpath.net. *Dir*, Marvelene Beach; Tel: 732-346-6200, Ext 883, E-Mail: beach_m@oceancounty.lib.nj.us
Pop 3,300; Circ 17,000
1997-1998 Income $67,000. Mats Exp $7,800, Books $7,250, Per/Ser (Incl. Access Fees) $350. Sal $46,012
Library Holdings: Bk Vols 18,000; Per Subs 25
Subject Interests: NH hist
Friends of the Library Group

CENTER SANDWICH

P SAMUEL H WENTWORTH LIBRARY,* 35 Main St, 03227. SAN 309-9482. Tel: 603-284-6665. FAX: 603-284-6577. E-Mail: wentworthlib@cyberportal.net. *Librn*, John Perkins
Pop 1,100; Circ 24,000
Library Holdings: Bk Vols 21,000; Per Subs 40

Subject Interests: Local history
Publications: Library History
Mem of Cent District Libr Syst
Friends of the Library Group

CENTER STRAFFORD

P HILL LIBRARY,* Rte 126, Box 130, 03815-0130. SAN 376-656X. Tel: 603-664-2800. *Librn*, Kathryn Steward
Mar 1998-Feb 1999 Income $25,000
Library Holdings: Bk Vols 13,500; Bk Titles 13,000; Per Subs 15
Friends of the Library Group

CENTER TUFTONBORO

P TUFTONBORO FREE LIBRARY, 221 Middle Rd, 03816. (Mail add: Box 73, 03816), SAN 309-9733. Tel: 603-569-4256. FAX: 603-569-5885. E-Mail: tborolib@conknet.com. Web Site: www.conknet/~tborolib. *Dir*, Christie V Sarles; *Dir*, Lindalee M Lambert; *Asst Librn*, Mary E Bagg
Founded 1839. Pop 2,189; Circ 10,172
Library Holdings: Bk Vols 17,819; Per Subs 28
Subject Interests: Country living, Local history, Nature
Automation Activity & Vendor Info: (Circulation) Sagebrush Corporation
Partic in NHAIS
Friends of the Library Group

CHARLESTOWN

SR FOUNDATION FOR BIBLICAL RESEARCH LIBRARY, 43 Paris Ave, PO Box 373, 03603-0373. SAN 377-2691. Tel: 603-826-7751. FAX: 603-826-4304. E-Mail: biblefdn@cyberportal.net. Web Site: www.thefoundation.org. *Dir*, Helen Mathis
Founded 1956
Library Holdings: Bk Titles 4,000; Per Subs 25

P SILSBY FREE PUBLIC LIBRARY, 226 Main St, PO Box 307, 03603-0307. SAN 309-7676. Tel: 603-826-7793. FAX: 603-826-7793. E-Mail: silsby@fmis.net. *Librn*, Elisabeth Wilterdink; Staff 2 (MLS 1, Non-MLS 1)
Founded 1896. Pop 4,680; Circ 21,717
Library Holdings: Bk Vols 21,724; Per Subs 80
Subject Interests: Local genealogical mat, Local history
Partic in Librarians of the Upper Valley Coop

CHESTER

P CHESTER PUBLIC LIBRARY,* 3 Chester St, PO Box 277, 03036-0277. SAN 309-7684. Tel: 603-887-3404. FAX: 603-887-6622. *Dir*, Judy Balk
Pop 2,158; Circ 49,500
1997-1998 Income $80,400, City $49,900, Locally Generated Income $500, Parent Institution $30,000. Mats Exp $16,000, Books $13,000, Per/Ser (Incl. Access Fees) $1,000. Sal $30,000 (Prof $11,000)
Library Holdings: Bk Vols 28,900; Per Subs 42
Subject Interests: New England
Mem of SE District
Partic in Merry-Hill Rock Libr Coop
Friends of the Library Group

J WHITE PINES COLLEGE, Wadleigh Library, 40 Chester St, 03036-4301. SAN 309-7692. Tel: 603-887-7425. FAX: 603-887-1777. Web Site: www.whitepinescollege.edu. *Librn*, Loretta Kandress; E-Mail: lkandress@whitepinescollege.edu; Staff 1 (MLS 1)
Founded 1965. Enrl 76; Fac 13
Library Holdings: Bk Vols 23,691; Bk Titles 19,162; Per Subs 75
Subject Interests: Art, Graphic design, Photography, Writing
Publications: Acquisitions list (monthly)

CHESTERFIELD

P CHESTERFIELD PUBLIC LIBRARY,* 524 Rte 63, PO Box 158, 03443-0158. SAN 309-7706. Tel: 603-363-4621. FAX: 603-363-4958. *Librn*, Jane Anderson; *Asst Librn*, Leona Taft
Founded 1939. Pop 3,119; Circ 14,300
Jan 1998-Dec 1998 Income $45,585, City $43,085, Locally Generated Income $600, Other $1,900. Mats Exp $9,300, Books $8,700, Per/Ser (Incl. Access Fees) $300, Micro $300. Sal $25,000
Library Holdings: Bk Titles 20,276; Per Subs 81
Subject Interests: Biographies, Cooking, Crafts, History, Large print, Mysteries, Natural science, New Eng hist, Relig studies, Sci-tech
Publications: Adult Newsletter; Children's Book reviews
Mem of Southwest District
Friends of the Library Group

CHICHESTER

P CHICHESTER TOWN LIBRARY, 161 Main St, 03234. SAN 309-7714. Tel: 603-798-5613. FAX: 603-798-5439. E-Mail: chichesterlibrary@hotmail.com. *Librn*, Harold Arey
Founded 1899. Pop 2,000; Circ 15,000
Jan 2000-Dec 2000 Income Locally Generated Income $24,000. Mats Exp $5,700, Books $2,500, Per/Ser (Incl. Access Fees) $500, Presv $700, AV Equip $900, Other Print Mats $1,100. Sal $11,400
Library Holdings: Bk Vols 13,000; Bk Titles 12,000; Per Subs 20
Database Vendor: Ebsco - EbscoHost, ProQuest
Function: ILL available, Literary searches, Mail loans to members, Outside services via phone, cable & mail, Photocopies available, Reference services available, Some telephone reference
Mem of Cent District Libr Syst

CHOCORUA

P CHOCORUA PUBLIC LIBRARY,* 125 Deerhill Rd, 03817. (Mail add: PO Box 128, 03817), SAN 309-7722. Tel: 603-323-8610. FAX: 603-323-7107. E-Mail: hrah@lilac.nhsl.lib.nh.us. *Librn*, Putnam Smith
Pop 1,663; Circ 6,987
Library Holdings: Bk Vols 15,150; Per Subs 30
Mem of North Country District
Open Mon 6-9, Thurs 1-6, Sat 1-5

CLAREMONT

P FISKE FREE LIBRARY,* 108 Broad St, 03743-2673. SAN 309-7730. Tel: 603-542-7017. FAX: 603-542-7029. *Librn*, Marilyn Nagy; *Ad Servs, Asst Librn*, Marta Smith; *Cat*, Sandra Perron; *Ch Servs*, Brenda Tripodes
Founded 1873. Pop 13,902; Circ 121,852
Jan 1997-Dec 1998 Income $265,855, City $214,236, Other $4,000. Mats Exp $55,685, Books $48,500, Per/Ser (Incl. Access Fees) $3,800, Presv $2,135, Micro $1,250. Sal $188,113
Library Holdings: Bk Vols 52,000; Per Subs 112
Subject Interests: Local genealogy, Local history
Automation Activity & Vendor Info: (Acquisitions) Sagebrush Corporation
Publications: Bibliography; Genealogy & Local History
Friends of the Library Group

J NEW HAMPSHIRE COMMUNITY TECHNICAL COLLEGE LIBRARY,* One College Dr, 03743. SAN 309-7749. Tel: 603-542-7744. FAX: 603-543-1844. Web Site: www.claremont.tec.nh.us. *Dir*, Phil Prever; E-Mail: p_prever@tec.nh.us
Founded 1969
Library Holdings: Bk Titles 11,000; Per Subs 90
Subject Interests: Allied health educg, Nursing
Special Collections: Deaf Education; New Hampshire Local History
Special Services for the Deaf - Books on deafness & sign language; Special interest periodicals; Staff with knowledge of sign language

M VALLEY REGIONAL HOSPITAL, Medical Library,* 243 Elm St, 03743. SAN 373-2436. Tel: 603-542-1839. FAX: 603-542-1814. E-Mail: educat@varh.org.
Library Holdings: Bk Vols 1,000; Per Subs 120

COLEBROOK

P COLEBROOK PUBLIC LIBRARY,* 149 Main St, PO Box 58, 03576-1010. SAN 309-7757. Tel: 603-237-4808. *Dir*, Julie Colby; *Ch Servs*, Teresa Hebert
Founded 1928. Pop 2,744; Circ 26,350
Library Holdings: Bk Vols 18,900; Per Subs 40

S NUMISMATICS INTERNATIONAL, Book Library, 30 Pleasant St, 03576-1120. SAN 372-7033. Tel: 603-237-4039. *Librn*, Granvyl G Hulse, Jr; E-Mail: ghulse@ncia.net
Library Holdings: Bk Vols 3,641; Bk Titles 2,500
Restriction: Members only
Branches:
PERIODICAL LIBRARY, PO Box 305, White River Junction, 05001. SAN 372-705X. Tel: 802-295-3998. *Librn*, Jim Haley
Library Holdings: Bk Vols 3,000

CONCORD

S AUDUBON SOCIETY OF NEW HAMPSHIRE, Francis Beach White Library, 3 Silk Farm Rd, 03301-8200. SAN 323-8296. Tel: 603-224-9909. FAX: 603-226-0902. E-Mail: nhaudubon@igc.apc.org.
Founded 1972
Library Holdings: Bk Titles 3,000; Per Subs 56
Subject Interests: Ecology, Natural history, Ornithology
Open Thurs 10-4, or by appointment for research

G BUREAU OF SUBSTANCE ABUSE SERVICES LIBRARY,* State Office Park S, 105 Pleasant St, 03301. SAN 327-7496. Tel: 603-271-6100. FAX: 603-271-6116. *Dir*, Tim Hartnett

SR CHURCH MEDIA CENTER, 63 Green St, 03301. SAN 375-2798. Tel: 603-224-7020. FAX: 603-225-7884. E-Mail: chmediactr@aol.com. *Dir*, Doris M Dunbar
Founded 1976
Jan 2000-Dec 2000 Income Locally Generated Income $39,031. Mats Exp $5,400, Books $4,000, Per/Ser (Incl. Access Fees) $400, AV Equip $1,000. Sal $25,481
Library Holdings: Bk Vols 700; Per Subs 12

P CONCORD PUBLIC LIBRARY,* 45 Green St, 03301. SAN 350-4395. Tel: 603-225-8670. FAX: 603-225-8688. *Dir*, Louis Ungarelli; E-Mail: lungarelli@ci.concord.nh.us; *Ad Servs*, Patricia A Immen; *Ch Servs*, Carol Berry; *Tech Servs*, Christine Wanta; Staff 9 (MLS 9)
Founded 1855. Pop 37,160; Circ 326,720
Jul 1997-Jun 1998 Income $1,239,020, City $1,070,380, Locally Generated Income $56,750, Other $111,890. Mats Exp $181,500, Books $136,300, Per/Ser (Incl. Access Fees) $20,000, Presv $1,400. Sal $916,780 (Prof $470,170)
Library Holdings: Bk Vols 160,000; Per Subs 400
Special Collections: Concord Historical Coll
Friends of the Library Group
Branches: 1
PENACOOK BRANCH, 3 Merrimack St, PO Box 97, Penacook, 03303. SAN 350-4425. Tel: 603-753-4441. *Librn*, Mary Joan MacArthur
Library Holdings: Bk Vols 10,977; Per Subs 16
Friends of the Library Group
Bookmobiles: 1

GL NEW HAMPSHIRE DEPARTMENT OF JUSTICE, Office of the Attorney General Library,* 33 Capitol St, 03301-6397. SAN 377-2713. Tel: 603-271-3658. FAX: 603-271-2110. *Librn*, Ellen Webb
Library Holdings: Bk Vols 10,000

G NEW HAMPSHIRE DEPARTMENT OF TRANSPORTATION (NH DOT) LIBRARY,* PO Box 483, 03302-0483. SAN 309-7773. Tel: 603-271-3344, Ext 3344. FAX: 603-271-3914. *Librn*, Robert Lyford
Founded 1959
Library Holdings: Bk Titles 1,000
Subject Interests: Enforcement, Highways, Law, Spec transportation rpts, State codes, Traffic control

S NEW HAMPSHIRE HISTORICAL SOCIETY LIBRARY, 30 Park St, 03301-6384. SAN 309-7781. Tel: 603-225-3381, Ext 11. FAX: 603-224-0463. Web Site: www.nhhistory.org. *Librn*, William N Copeley; E-Mail: bcopeley@nhhistory.org; Staff 4 (MLS 2, Non-MLS 2)
Founded 1823
Oct 1999-Sep 2000 Income $93,000, Locally Generated Income $25,000, Parent Institution $68,000. Mats Exp $45,000, Books $10,000, Per/Ser (Incl. Access Fees) $2,000, Presv $15,000, Micro $2,000, AV Equip $7,000, Other Print Mats $4,000, Manuscripts & Archives $5,000
Library Holdings: Bk Vols 50,000; Bk Titles 40,000; Per Subs 150
Subject Interests: Architecture, Decorative arts, Genealogy, History of New Hampshire, Local history, Ref coll in American fine
Special Collections: New Hampshire Church Records, 1700-1900, ms vols; New Hampshire Maps 1700-1900; New Hampshire Newspapers, 1790-1900, microfilm; New Hampshire Photographs, 1850-1990; New Hampshire Provincial Deeds, 1640-1770, micro
Partic in NHAIS; OCLC Online Computer Library Center, Inc

M NEW HAMPSHIRE HOSPITAL, Dorothy M Breene Memorial Library, 36 Clinton St, 03301-3861. SAN 309-779X. Tel: 603-271-5420. Web Site: www.state.nh.us/nhssl. *Coll Develop, Librn*, Allen Marion; E-Mail: mallen@dhhs.state.nh.us; Staff 2 (MLS 1, Non-MLS 1)
Founded 1880
Jul 2000-Jun 2001 Income State $81,832. Mats Exp $68,000, Books $20,058, Per/Ser (Incl. Access Fees) $30,000, Micro $210. Sal $27,924
Library Holdings: Bk Titles 4,000
Subject Interests: Behavior sci, Commun mental health, Geriatrics, Neurology, Nursing, Occupational, Psychiatry, Psychology, Recreational therapy, Soc sci, Soc work
Partic in Nat Network of Libraries of Med - Region 3

L NEW HAMPSHIRE LAW LIBRARY, Supreme Court Bldg, One Noble Dr, 03301-6160. SAN 350-4514. Tel: 603-271-3777. FAX: 603-271-2168. *Librn*, Christine H Swan; Staff 4 (MLS 2, Non-MLS 2)
Founded 1819
Jul 2000-Jun 2001 Mats Exp $169,000, Books $160,000, Per/Ser (Incl. Access Fees) $9,000. Sal $118,000
Library Holdings: Bk Vols 91,000; Per Subs 110
Subject Interests: Anglo-Am law
Special Collections: Laws & Court Reports; New Hampshire Material
Restriction: Circulation limited

G NEW HAMPSHIRE PUBLIC UTILITIES COMMISSION LIBRARY,* 8 Old Suncook Rd, 03301-5185. SAN 327-7593. Tel: 603-271-2431. FAX: 603-271-3878. *Librn*, Adele Leighton
Library Holdings: Bk Vols 3,000; Per Subs 55
Special Collections: New Hampshire Public Utilities Commission Reports; Utility Regulations Particular to New Hampshire Utility Regulation

G NEW HAMPSHIRE STATE FISH & GAME DEPARTMENT, Management & Research Div Library,* 2 Hazen Dr, 03301. SAN 327-7534. Tel: 603-271-2461. FAX: 603-271-1438.
Library Holdings: Bk Titles 600

P NEW HAMPSHIRE STATE LIBRARY, 20 Park St, 03301-6314. SAN 350-445X. Tel: 603-271-2392. Interlibrary Loan Service Tel: 603-271-2144. FAX: 603-271-2205, 603-271-6826. Web Site: www.state.nh.us/nhsl. *State Librn*, Michael York; Tel: 603-271-2397, E-Mail: myork@finch.nhsl.lib.nh.us; *Coll Develop, Ref*, John McCormick; Tel: 603-271-2060, E-Mail: mccormick@finch.nhsl.lib.nh.us; *Tech Servs*, Eleanor O'Donnell; Tel: 603-271-2429, E-Mail: odonnell@finch.nhsl.lib.nh.us; *Adminr*, Janet Eklund; E-Mail: jeklund@finch.nhsl.lib.nh.us; Staff 21 (MLS 21)
Founded 1716. Pop 1,201,134
Jul 1999-Jun 2000 Income (Main Library Only) $2,915,049, State $1,935,329, Federal $847,343, Other $132,377. Mats Exp $148,500. Sal $1,150,907
Library Holdings: Bk Vols 536,788; Per Subs 264
Subject Interests: Biog, Genealogy, Info sci, Law, Libr sci, Pub admin, Soc sci
Special Collections: Historical Children's Books; New Hampshire Authors; New Hampshire Government & History; New Hampshire Imprints; New Hampshire Maps
Automation Activity & Vendor Info: (Cataloging) Gaylord; (ILL) Gaylord; (OPAC) Gaylord
Database Vendor: OCLC - First Search, ProQuest
Publications: Checklist of New Hampshire State Departments' Publications (biennial); Granite Bits (irregularly); Granite State Libraries (bi-monthly newsletter); New Hampshire Libraries (annual directory); New Hampshire Library Statistics (annual)
Function: Archival collection, ILL available, Reference only
Partic in Nelinet, Inc
Branches: 1
NORTH COUNTRY OFFICE, 244 Main St, Lancaster, 03584-3038. Tel: 603-788-5187. Toll Free Tel: 800-462-1726. FAX: 603-788-5125. *Coordr*, Tom Ladd; E-Mail: tladd@finch.nhsl.lib.nh.us; *Coordr*, Susan Palmatier; E-Mail: spalmatier@finch.nhsl.lib.nh.us; Staff 2 (MLS 2)
Library Holdings: Bk Vols 500
Restriction: Not a lending library
Function: Some telephone reference

P NEW HAMPSHIRE STATE LIBRARY, SERVICES TO PERSONS WITH DISABILITIES, 117 Pleasant St, 03301-3852. SAN 309-7803. Tel: 603-271-1498, 603-271-2417, 603-271-3429. Toll Free Tel: 800-491-4200. FAX: 603-271-8370. Web Site: www.state.nh.us/nhsl. *Dir*, Eileen Keim; Staff 1 (MLS 1)
Founded 1970
Library Holdings: Bk Vols 80,000; Bk Titles 40,000; Per Subs 24
Publications: Granite Bits (newsletter)
Special Services for the Blind - Braille; Talking Books

S NEW HAMPSHIRE STATE PRISON LIBRARY,* 281 N State St, PO Box 14, 03301. SAN 309-7811. Tel: 603-271-1929. E-Mail: prison@chi.tds.net. *Coll Develop, Librn*, Cathy Dawson
Founded 1918
1997-1998 Mats Exp $38,000, Per/Ser (Incl. Access Fees) $2,500. Sal $26,000
Library Holdings: Bk Vols 12,000; Per Subs 20
Subject Interests: Hobby craft, Law, Penology, Recreational
Publications: HRBC

J NEW HAMPSHIRE TECHNICAL INSTITUTE LIBRARY, 11 Institute Dr, 03301-7412. SAN 309-782X. Tel: 603-271-7186. FAX: 603-271-7189. Web Site: www.nhti.net/library/farnum.htm. *Dir*, Wm John Hare; E-Mail: jhare@tec.nh.us; *Librn*, Steven P Ambra; E-Mail: sambra@tec.nh.us; *Circ*, Joan Malfait; E-Mail: j_malfai@tec.nh.us; *AV*, Debra Smith; *Tech Servs*, Charlotte Green; E-Mail: c_green@tec.nh.us; *Circ*, Claudette Welch; Staff 2 (MLS 2)
Founded 1965. Enrl 2,000; Fac 150; Highest Degree: Associate
Jul 2000-Jun 2001 Income $103,013, State $100,013, Federal $3,000. Mats Exp $103,000, Books $36,000, Per/Ser (Incl. Access Fees) $40,000, Micro $1,000, AV Equip $12,000, Electronic Ref Mat (Incl. Access Fees) $14,000. Sal $169,000 (Prof $77,000)
Library Holdings: Bk Vols 30,000; Bk Titles 28,000; Per Subs 425
Subject Interests: Alcoholism counseling, Architectural eng tech, Architecture, Autism, Bus, Computer info systs, Dental hygiene, Diagnostic ultrasound, Early childhood educ, Electronic, Emergency med care, Landscape architecture, Mechanical, Mental health, Mgt, Nursing, Radiologic tech
Special Collections: College Archives; Novels about Nurses; Photos of Concord, NH
Database Vendor: Ebsco - EbscoHost
Publications: Acquisitions List; Bibliographies; Page Notes
Restriction: Non-circulating
Reference & periodicals (non-circulating)

L ORR & RENO LAW LIBRARY,* One Eagle Sq, PO Box 3550, 03302-3550. SAN 323-7419. Tel: 603-224-2381. FAX: 603-224-2301, 603-224-2318. *Res*, C Elisabeth Carey; Tel: 603-224-9105, E-Mail: cecarey@orr-reno.com; *Asst Librn*, Rebecca Gerlack; Staff 2 (MLS 1, Non-MLS 1)
Library Holdings: Bk Titles 500; Per Subs 45
Subject Interests: Environmental law, International trade
Automation Activity & Vendor Info: (Acquisitions) Inmagic, Inc.; (Cataloging) Inmagic, Inc.; (Circulation) Inmagic, Inc.; (Serials) Inmagic, Inc.
Database Vendor: Dialog, Lexis-Nexis
Restriction: Staff use only

L FRANKLIN PIERCE LAW CENTER LIBRARY, 2 White St, 03301. SAN 309-7838. Tel: 603-228-1541, Ext 1130. Interlibrary Loan Service Tel: 603-228-1541, Ext 1133. Circulation Tel: 603-228-1541, Ext 1130. FAX: 603-228-0388. Web Site: www.fplc.edu. *Dir*, Judith A Gire; Tel: 603-228-1541, Ext 1129, E-Mail: jgire@fplc.edu; *Coll Develop*, Cynthia Landau; Tel: 603-228-1541, Ext 1132, E-Mail: clandau@fplc.edu; *Cat*, Mary Cogswell; Tel: 603-228-1541, Ext 1201, E-Mail: mcogswell@fplc.edu; *Res*, Cynthia Lewis; Tel: 603-228-1541, Ext 1193, E-Mail: clewis@fplc.edu; *Spec Coll*, Jon R Cavicchi; Tel: 603-228-1541, Ext 1139, E-Mail: jcavicchi@fplc.edu; *Tech Servs*, Melanie Cornell; Tel: 603-228-1541, Ext 1135, E-Mail: mcornell@fplc.edu; Staff 13 (MLS 7, Non-MLS 6)
Founded 1973. Pop 450; Enrl 450; Fac 20; Highest Degree: Doctorate
Jul 2000-Jun 2001 Income Parent Institution $1,026,428. Mats Exp $587,911, Books $64,080, Per/Ser (Incl. Access Fees) $457,121, Presv $5,991, AV Equip $4,503, Electronic Ref Mat (Incl. Access Fees) $60,674. Sal $372,107 (Prof $245,383)
Library Holdings: Bk Vols 221,745; Bk Titles 53,224; Per Subs 3,044
Subject Interests: Intellectual property
Automation Activity & Vendor Info: (Acquisitions) Innovative Interfaces Inc.; (Cataloging) Innovative Interfaces Inc.; (Circulation) Innovative Interfaces Inc.; (Course Reserve) Innovative Interfaces Inc.; (OPAC) Innovative Interfaces Inc.; (Serials) Innovative Interfaces Inc.
Database Vendor: Dialog, IAC - Info Trac, Innovative Interfaces INN - View, Lexis-Nexis, OCLC - First Search
Publications: Newsletter (bi-monthly)
Restriction: Access at librarian's discretion
Function: ILL available
Partic in Innopac; Nelinet, Inc; Nellco

G STATE OF NEW HAMPSHIRE, DEPARTMENT OF STATE, New Hampshire Records & Archives Library, 71 S Fruit St, 03301-2410. SAN 326-081X. Tel: 603-271-2236. TDD: 800-735-2964. FAX: 603-271-2272. Web Site: www.state.nh.us/state/archives.htm. *Archivist*, Frank C Mevers; E-Mail: fmevers@sos.state.nh.us; Staff 3 (MLS 2, Non-MLS 1)
Founded 1961
Jul 2000-Jun 2001 Income $253,000

CONTOOCOOK

P HOPKINTON TOWN LIBRARY,* PO Box 266, 03229. SAN 309-8494. Tel: 603-746-3663. FAX: 603-746-6799. E-Mail: hsea@lilac.nhsl.lib.nh.us or hoplib@conknet.com. *Librn*, Elizabeth Schulz
Founded 1871. Pop 3,930; Circ 9,795
Jan 1997-Dec 1998 Income $93,000
Open Tues, Wed & Thurs 10-8, Fri 10-5 & Sat 10-3
Friends of the Library Group

CONWAY

P CONWAY PUBLIC LIBRARY, PO Box 2100, 03818. SAN 350-4662. Tel: 603-447-5552. FAX: 603-447-6921. E-Mail: info@conway.lib.nh.us. Web Site: www.conway.lib.nh.us. *Dir*, Margaret Marschner; *Ch Servs*, Olga Morrill
Founded 1900. Pop 9,000; Circ 70,000
Library Holdings: Bk Vols 31,000; Per Subs 95
Subject Interests: Local history
Automation Activity & Vendor Info: (Circulation) Sagebrush Corporation; (OPAC) Sagebrush Corporation
Partic in Carroll County Library Cooperative
Friends of the Library Group

CORNISH

S SAINT-GAUDENS NATIONAL HISTORIC SITE LIBRARY,* National Park Service, RR 3, Box 73, 03745. SAN 309-7846. Tel: 603-675-2175. FAX: 603-675-2701. E-Mail: saga@valley.net. Web Site: www.sgnhs.org. *Curator*, John H Dryfhout
Founded 1919
1998-1999 Mats Exp $800
Library Holdings: Bk Vols 1,400
Subject Interests: Art, Photog, Sculpture
Special Collections: Cornish Art Colony Coll 1885-1935

CORNISH FLAT

P GEORGE H STOWELL FREE LIBRARY, School St, PO Box 360, 03746. SAN 309-7854. Tel: 603-543-3644. *Librn*, Emily Cromwell; *Librn*, Kate Freeland
Pop 1,500; Circ 3,800
Jan 1999-Dec 1999 Income $12,918, City $10,095, Locally Generated Income $2,823. Mats Exp $4,830, Books $3,500, Per/Ser (Incl. Access Fees) $400, AV Equip $450, Electronic Ref Mat (Incl. Access Fees) $480. Sal $5,199 (Prof $4,628)
Library Holdings: Bk Vols 10,000; Bk Titles 9,750; Per Subs 15; High Interest/Low Vocabulary Bk Vols 50; Bks on Deafness & Sign Lang 10
Subject Interests: Cornish hist
Mem of Southwest District
Open Mon & Wed 3-5 & 6:30-8:30, Fri 6:30-8:30, Sat 10-12

DALTON

P DALTON PUBLIC LIBRARY,* Unit 2, 741 Dalton Rd, 03598. SAN 309-7870. Tel: 603-837-2751. FAX: 603-837-2273. E-Mail: dpl@connrivers.net. *Librn*, Doris Mitton
Pop 664; Circ 1,221
Library Holdings: Bk Vols 7,000; Per Subs 14
Mem of North Country District
Partic in North Country Library Cooperative
Friends of the Library Group

DANBURY

P GEORGE GAMBLE LIBRARY, Rte 104, Main St, 03230. (Mail add: PO Box 209, 03230-0209), SAN 309-7889. Tel: 603-768-3765. *Librn*, Janet McGonigle
Founded 1911. Pop 613; Circ 1,525
Library Holdings: Bk Vols 5,200
Mem of Cent District Libr Syst
Special Services for the Blind - Audio-cassettes

DANVILLE

P COLBY MEMORIAL LIBRARY,* 7 Colby Rd, PO Box 10, 03819-5104. SAN 309-7897. Tel: 603-382-6733. FAX: 603-382-0487. *Dir*, Dorothy Billbrough
Founded 1892. Pop 2,200; Circ 4,000
Jan 1997-Dec 1998 Income $30,130, State $150. Mats Exp $7,739, Books $6,999, Per/Ser (Incl. Access Fees) $400, AV Equip $340. Sal $19,000
Library Holdings: Bk Titles 14,500; Per Subs 47
Partic in Merri-Hill-Rock Library Cooperative
Friends of the Library Group

DEERFIELD

P PHILBRICK-JAMES LIBRARY, 4 Old Center Rd S, 03037-1410. SAN 309-7919. Tel: 603-463-7187. *Librn*, Evelyn F Cronyn
Pop 3,242; Circ 12,692
Jan 1999-Dec 1999 Income $15,400. Mats Exp $15,915, Books $9,722, Per/Ser (Incl. Access Fees) $450. Sal $18,517
Library Holdings: Bk Titles 16,637; Per Subs 30
Friends of the Library Group

DERRY

P DERRY PUBLIC LIBRARY,* 64 E Broadway, 03038-2412. SAN 309-7935. Tel: 603-432-6140. TDD: 603-432-6756. FAX: 603-432-6128. Web Site: www.derry.nh.us/library/derrypl.html. *Ch Servs*, Adele Boeske; *Ch Servs*, Kelly Richie; *Ad Servs*, Cheryl Lynch; *Cat*, Kathy O'Connell; *Circ*, Cathy Goldthwaite; *Reader Servs*, Stephen Bahre; *Reader Servs*, Marilyn Dent; Staff 15 (MLS 6, Non-MLS 9)
Founded 1905. Pop 33,500; Circ 185,768
1998-1999 Income $769,000, City $739,000, Locally Generated Income $30,000. Mats Exp $114,000, Books $84,000, Per/Ser (Incl. Access Fees) $8,500, Micro $4,500. Sal $413,000 (Prof $227,000)
Library Holdings: Bk Vols 83,602; Per Subs 228
Special Collections: Houses of Derry (Harriet Newell Coll); Robert Frost material; Tasha Tudor Drawings
Special Services for the Deaf - Staff with knowledge of sign language; TDD
Friends of the Library Group

M PARKLAND MEDICAL CENTER, Medical Library, One Parkland Dr, 03038. SAN 323-6889. Tel: 603-432-1500, Ext 3367. FAX: 603-421-2166.
Library Holdings: Bk Titles 230; Per Subs 120
Restriction: Staff use only

DOVER

P DOVER PUBLIC LIBRARY,* 73 Locust St, 03820-3785. SAN 309-796X. Tel: 603-743-6050. FAX: 603-743-6053. Web Site: www.dover.lib.nh.us. *Dir*, Cathleen C Beaudoin; E-Mail: cathy.beaudoin@dover.lib.nh.us
Founded 1883. Pop 26,000; Circ 281,261
Jul 1999-Jun 2000 Income $829,000, City $805,000, Locally Generated Income $24,000. Mats Exp $81,000, Books $64,800, Per/Ser (Incl. Access Fees) $9,000, AV Equip $4,000, Electronic Ref Mat (Incl. Access Fees) $3,200. Sal $441,200
Library Holdings: Bk Vols 96,000; Bk Titles 83,000; Per Subs 270
Special Collections: New Hampshire & New England Historical & Genealogical Materials
Automation Activity & Vendor Info: (Acquisitions) epixtech, inc.; (Cataloging) epixtech, inc.; (Circulation) epixtech, inc.; (OPAC) epixtech, inc.; (Serials) epixtech, inc.
Friends of the Library Group

J MCINTOSH COLLEGE LIBRARY, 23 Cataract Ave, 03820-3990. SAN 309-7978. Tel: 603-742-1234. Reference Tel: 603-742-1234, Ext 110. FAX: 603-743-0060. Web Site: www.cecybrary.com. *Dir*, Barbara Bolko; E-Mail: bbolko@mcintoshcollege.com; Staff 2 (MLS 1, Non-MLS 1)
Founded 1896. Fac 25; Highest Degree: Doctorate
Library Holdings: Bk Vols 12,000; Per Subs 220
Subject Interests: Bus, Criminal law, Law libr, Med assisting
Special Collections: Law Library
Automation Activity & Vendor Info: (Cataloging) Sagebrush Corporation; (Circulation) Sagebrush Corporation
Database Vendor: Ebsco - EbscoHost
Partic in New England Libr Asn

M WENTWORTH-DOUGLASS HOSPITAL LIBRARY,* 789 Central Ave, 03820. SAN 377-9866. Tel: 603-740-2881. FAX: 603-740-2249. E-Mail: mlkl@wdhospital.com. *Dir*, Karen Lambert
Library Holdings: Bk Vols 200; Per Subs 100

DUBLIN

P DUBLIN PUBLIC LIBRARY,* Main St, PO Box 442, 03444-0442. SAN 309-7986. Tel: 603-563-8658. FAX: 603-563-8751. E-Mail: dpl@sau1.mv.com. *Librn*, Elizabeth McIntyre
Pop 1,400; Circ 7,500
Library Holdings: Bk Vols 18,000; Per Subs 40
Mem of SW Libr District
Friends of the Library Group

DUNBARTON

P DUNBARTON PUBLIC LIBRARY,* 10004 School St, 03045-4816. SAN 309-8001. Tel: 603-774-3546. FAX: 603-774-5563. E-Mail: mail@dunlib.mv.com. Web Site: www.mv.com/org/dunlib. *Dir*, Andrea Douglas; *Librn*, Nancy C Lang
Pop 1,805; Circ 7,621
Library Holdings: Bk Vols 11,500; Per Subs 30
Special Collections: Dunbarton History
Automation Activity & Vendor Info: (Cataloging) Sagebrush Corporation; (Circulation) Sagebrush Corporation
Mem of Cent Libr District
Partic in Hillstown Cooperative
Open Tues & Thurs 2-8, Wed & Fri 10-4, Sat 10-2

DURHAM

P DURHAM PUBLIC LIBRARY, 7-H Mill Rd Plaza, 03824. (Mail add: PO Box 954, 03824-0954), SAN 377-5372. Tel: 603-868-6699. FAX: 603-868-9944. E-Mail: dplib@nh.ultranet.com. Web Site: www.nh.ultranet.com/~dplib. *Dir*, R W Hedden; Staff 2 (MLS 1, Non-MLS 1)
Founded 1997. Pop 8,000; Circ 15,000
Library Holdings: Bk Vols 30,000

C UNIVERSITY OF NEW HAMPSHIRE LIBRARY, 18 Library Way, 03824. SAN 350-4727. Tel: 603-862-1540. Circulation Tel: 603-862-1535. Reference Tel: 603-862-1544. FAX: 603-862-1173. Web Site: www.library.unh.edu. *Head Librn*, Linda Johnson; Tel: 603-862-2453, Fax: 603-862-3403, E-Mail: linda@cisunix.unh.edu; *Librn*, Dr Claudia Morner; Tel: 603-862-1506, Fax: 603-862-0247, E-Mail: cjmorner@cisunix.unh.edu; *Assoc Librn*, Diane Tebbetts; Tel: 603-862-1509, Fax: 603-862-0247, E-Mail: drt@cisunix.unh.edu; *Web Coordr*, Barry Hennessey; Tel: 603-862-1459, Fax: 603-862-0085, E-Mail: barry.hennessey@cisunix.unh.edu; *Spec Coll*, William E Ross; Tel: 603-862-0346, Fax: 603-862-2956, E-Mail: wer@cisunix.unh.edu; *ILL*, Karen Fagerberg; Tel: 603-862-1173, Fax: 603-862-0247, E-Mail: kkf@cisunix.unh.edu; *Ref*, Deborah Watson; Tel: 603-862-3800, Fax: 603-862-2637, E-Mail: dewatson@cisunix.unh.edu; *Coll Develop*, Melinda Dolan; Tel: 603-832-4049, Fax: 603-862-2907, E-Mail: mpdolan@cisunix.unh.edu; *Coll Develop*, Jake Viebrock; Staff 83 (MLS 23, Non-MLS 60)
Founded 1868. Enrl 12,454; Fac 564; Highest Degree: Doctorate
Jul 1998-Jun 1999 Income (Main Library and Branch Library) $6,838,840. Mats Exp $2,888,965, Books $578,662, Per/Ser (Incl. Access Fees) $2,245,863, Presv $64,440. Sal $2,398,333 (Prof $873,927)
Library Holdings: Bk Vols 1,628,341; Per Subs 4,953
Special Collections: Amy Beach Papers; Angling (Milne Coll); Contra Dance & Folk Music (Ralph Page Coll); Donald Hall Coll; Frost Archives; Galway Kinnell Coll; Senator McIntyre Papers; Senator Norris Cotton Papers; US Patent Doc
Function: Document delivery services
Partic in Nelinet, Inc; New Hampshire College & University Council; OCLC Online Computer Library Center, Inc
Friends of the Library Group
Departmental Libraries:
BIOLOGICAL SCIENCES, Kendall Hall, 129 Main St, 03824-3590. SAN 350-4751. Tel: 603-862-1018. FAX: 603-862-2789. *Librn*, David Lane
Friends of the Library Group
CHEMISTRY, Parsons Hall, 23 College Rd, 03824-3598. SAN 350-4816. Tel: 603-862-1083. *Librn*, Emily LeViness-Poworoznek
Friends of the Library Group
ENGINEERING-MATHEMATICS - COMPUTER SCIENCE, Kingsbury Hall, 33 College Rd, 03824-3591. SAN 350-4840. Tel: 603-862-1196. FAX: 603-862-4112. *Librn*, Emily LeViness-Poworoznek
Friends of the Library Group
PHYSICS, DeMeritt Hall, 9 Library Way, 03824-3568. SAN 350-4875. Tel: 603-862-2348.
Friends of the Library Group

EAST ANDOVER

P WILLIAM ADAMS BACHELDER LIBRARY,* PO Box 128, 03231. SAN 309-801X. Tel: 603-735-5333. E-Mail: hsei@lilac.nhsl.lib.nh.us. *Librn*, Pauline Richards
Pop 1,584; Circ 2,817
Library Holdings: Bk Titles 6,000
Mem of Cent Libr District

EAST DERRY

P TAYLOR LIBRARY,* 49 E Derry Rd, PO Box 110, 03041-0110. SAN 309-7943. Tel: 603-432-7186. FAX: 603-432-0985. Web Site: www.derry.nh.us/library/derrypl.htm. *Librn*, Marjorie Palmer; *Asst Librn*, Linda Merrill
Founded 1878. Pop 8,000
Library Holdings: Bk Vols 17,435

EAST KINGSTON

P EAST KINGSTON PUBLIC LIBRARY,* 41 Depot Rd, PO Box 9, 03827. SAN 320-8443. Tel: 603-642-8333. E-Mail: ekpublib@nh.ultranet.com. *Librn*, Tracey Waldron
Pop 1,352; Circ 7,194
Library Holdings: Bk Vols 9,500; Per Subs 30
Friends of the Library Group

EAST LEMPSTER

P MINER MEMORIAL LIBRARY, Three Second New Hampshire Turnpike, PO Box 131, 03605. SAN 321-0448. Tel: 603-863-0051. *Librn*, Susan Fratus
Founded 1893. Pop 1,000; Circ 4,000
Library Holdings: Bk Titles 9,000
Open Mon & Wed 3-8
Friends of the Library Group

EFFINGHAM

P EFFINGHAM PUBLIC LIBRARY,* Center Ossipee, RR 1, Box 406, 03814. SAN 309-8036. Tel: 603-539-2227. *Librn*, Joyce Van Tassel
Pop 600
Jan 1997-Dec 1998 Income $2,000. Mats Exp $1,500. Sal $624
Library Holdings: Bk Vols 8,000
Subject Interests: Local history, Northern Indians (New England), State hist
Mem of Cent Libr District
Open Thurs 7-9 (will open by phone call appointment)

ENFIELD

S DIETRICH COLLECTION, W Farms Rd, RR 1, Box 335, 03748. SAN 326-5676. Tel: 603-632-7156. *Dir*, Dr R Krystyna Dietrich; Staff 1 (MLS 1)
Founded 1962
Library Holdings: Bk Vols 15,000
Subject Interests: Art, Polish (language)
Special Collections: American books & periodicals with information about A Orlowski; American Literature in Poland; Art Coll, 1400 works of art; Etchings of Daniel Chodowiecki, 1726-1801; Etchings of Jean Pierre Norblin de la Gourdaine, 1745-1830; Paintings, drawings & graphics of Alexander Orlowski, 1777-1832; Polish translations of American Literature,

1790-1960
Publications: Alexander Orlowski in America; Alexander Orlowski in America (a bibliography); Dartmouth Exhibition Catalog of A Orlowski in the Dietrich Coll; special catalogs: Daniel Chodowiecki in the collection (bibliography); US Literature in Poland (bibliography); US Literature in Poland, 1790-1960
Restriction: By appointment only
This is the largest American collection of works by and about Orlowski, as well as the only collection of American literature in Polish in the US

P ENFIELD FREE PUBLIC LIBRARY, 23 Main St, 03748. (Mail add: PO Box 1030, 03748-1030), SAN 309-8044. Tel: 603-632-7145. FAX: 603-632-7145. E-Mail: enfield.public.library@valley.net. *Librn*, Marjorie Carr
Founded 1893. Pop 4,222; Circ 30,003
Jan 1999-Dec 1999 Income $79,261. Mats Exp $24,149, Books $22,299, Electronic Ref Mat (Incl. Access Fees) $1,850. Sal $47,821
Library Holdings: Bk Vols 25,881; Per Subs 45

EPPING

P HARVEY-MITCHELL MEMORIAL LIBRARY, 152 Main St, 03042. SAN 309-8052. Tel: 603-679-5944. FAX: 603-679-5944. E-Mail: hmml@nh.ultranet.com. *Dir*, Duane Schaffer
Pop 6,000; Circ 15,000
Library Holdings: Bk Vols 22,000; Per Subs 65
Special Collections: New Hampshire Coll
Mem of SE Libr District
Friends of the Library Group

EPSOM

P EPSOM PUBLIC LIBRARY,* 1775 Dover Rd, 03234. SAN 309-8060. Tel: 603-736-9920. FAX: 603-736-4955. E-Mail: epl@tdsnet.com. *Librn*, Nancy Claris
Pop 3,300
Library Holdings: Bk Vols 15,000; Per Subs 32
Mem of Cent Libr District
Open Mon 10-7, Tues 4-7, Wed 10-7, Thur 10-5 & Sat 10-1
Friends of the Library Group

ERROL

P ERROL PUBLIC LIBRARY,* 69 Main St, PO Box 7, 03579-0007. SAN 309-8079. Tel: 603-482-7720. *Librn*, Carol Norman
Pop 292; Circ 8,523
Library Holdings: Bk Vols 6,288
Subject Interests: Christian living, Fiction, Handicrafts, Local history
Mem of Area Library Forum I
Friends of the Library Group

ETNA

P HANOVER TOWN LIBRARY,* 130 Etne Rd, PO Box 207, 03750-0207. SAN 309-8346. Tel: 603-643-3116. E-Mail: etna.library@valley.net. *Dir*, Patricia Hardenberg; Staff 2 (Non-MLS 2)
Founded 1905. Pop 9,212
Jul 1998-Jun 1999 Income $31,145. Mats Exp $3,118, Books $2,545, Per/Ser (Incl. Access Fees) $550, Presv $23. Sal $18,314
Library Holdings: Bk Titles 6,000; Per Subs 26
Subject Interests: Local history
Database Vendor: Innovative Interfaces INN - View
Open Mon & Wed 2-7, Thurs & Fri 10-2, Sat 10-12

EXETER

S AMERICAN INDEPENDENCE MUSEUM LIBRARY, One Governor's Lane, 03833. SAN 373-2843. Tel: 603-772-2622. FAX: 603-772-0861. E-Mail: aim@nh.ultranet.com. Web Site: www.independencemuseum.org. *Dir*, Carol Walker Aten; *Librn*, Sylvia Fitts Getchell
Founded 1902
Library Holdings: Bk Vols 950; Bk Titles 920
Special Collections: NH & US History of 18th Century, bks, docs & pamphlets; Original 18th & 19th Century Documents, Maps & Letters
Restriction: Staff use only
Open Mon-Fri 8-4

M EXETER HOSPITAL INC, Health Sciences Library, 10 Buzzell Ave, 03833. SAN 377-9556. Tel: 603-778-7311, Ext 6226. FAX: 603-773-4926. *Librn*, Alice Reed; E-Mail: areed@ehr.org; Staff 1 (MLS 1)
Oct 2000-Sep 2001 Mats Exp $27,370, Books $6,000, Per/Ser (Incl. Access Fees) $18,600, Electronic Ref Mat (Incl. Access Fees) $2,770
Library Holdings: Bk Titles 500; Per Subs 100
Subject Interests: Medicine, Nursing
Database Vendor: OVID Technologies
Restriction: Open to others by appointment, Staff use only
Function: ILL available
Partic in Health Science Libraries Of New Hampshire & Vermont; Medical Libr Asn; National Network of Libraries of Medicine - Greater Midwest Region; North Atlantic Health Sciences Libraries, Inc

P EXETER PUBLIC LIBRARY, Founders Park, 03833. SAN 309-8087. Tel: 603-772-3101, 603-772-6036. FAX: 603-772-7548. Web Site: www.nh.ultranet.com/~dewey. *Dir*, Hope Godino
Founded 1853. Pop 13,000; Circ 211,013
Library Holdings: Bk Vols 75,000; Per Subs 194
Special Collections: NE Antiquities Research Association; New Hampshire; Rockingham County Genealogical Coll
Partic in Seacoast Coop Libraries
Friends of the Library Group

S ROCKINGHAM SOCIETY OF GENEALOGISTS, Exeter Public Library, PO Box 81, 03833-0081. SAN 323-858X. Tel: 603-436-5824.
Founded 1980
Our library is a part of the Exeter Public Library & is composed of donated materials for the use of those hunting their ancestors

FARMINGTON

P GOODWIN LIBRARY,* 9 S Main St, 03835-1519. SAN 309-8095. Tel: 603-755-2944. E-Mail: goodwin@worldpath.net. Web Site: www.goodwin-library.net. *Librn*, Melody Laroche
Pop 5,800; Circ 26,000
Library Holdings: Bk Vols 14,654; Per Subs 50
Mem of Cent Libr District

FITZWILLIAM

P FITZWILLIAM TOWN LIBRARY,* 11 Templeton Tpke, 03447. SAN 309-8109. Tel: 603-585-6503. FAX: 603-585-6738. E-Mail: fitzlib@top.monad.net. *Librn*, Susan Massin; Staff 3 (MLS 1, Non-MLS 2)
Pop 2,011; Circ 20,000
Jan 1999-Dec 1999 Income $75,000. Mats Exp $8,500, Books $6,000, Per/Ser (Incl. Access Fees) $1,000, AV Equip $1,500. Sal $40,000 (Prof $29,000)
Library Holdings: Bk Titles 14,000; Per Subs 35
Automation Activity & Vendor Info: (Cataloging) Sagebrush Corporation; (Circulation) Sagebrush Corporation
Friends of the Library Group

FRANCESTOWN

P GEORGE HOLMES BIXBY MEMORIAL LIBRARY, 52 Main St, 03043-3025. (Mail add: PO Box 69, 03043-0069), SAN 309-8117. Tel: 603-547-2730. *Librn*, Joan E Hanchett; *Ch Servs*, Nancy Houlihan
Founded 1827. Pop 1,300; Circ 10,099
Library Holdings: Bk Vols 11,550; Per Subs 40
Publications: Conservation Letter; Monthly Calendar
Mem of SW Libr District

FRANCONIA

P ABBIE GREENLEAF LIBRARY, Main St, 03580. (Mail add: PO Box 787, 03580), SAN 309-8125. Tel: 603-823-8424. FAX: 603-823-5581. *Dir*, Amy W Bahr; Staff 1 (MLS 1)
Founded 1892. Pop 1,000; Circ 22,044
Jan 1999-Dec 1999 Income $65,500, City $50,000, Locally Generated Income $15,500. Sal $49,000
Library Holdings: Bk Titles 20,000; Per Subs 26
Subject Interests: New Hampshire-Franconia Region
Special Collections: Franconia Coll; New Hampshire Coll
Friends of the Library Group

FRANKLIN

P FRANKLIN PUBLIC LIBRARY, 310 Central St, 03235. SAN 309-8133. Tel: 603-934-2911. FAX: 603-934-7413. E-Mail: library@fcgnetworks.net. Web Site: www.franklinpubliclibrary.org. *Dir*, Randy Brough; *Ch Servs*, Jo Darling; *ILL*, Susan Lovering; *Cat*, Ruth Niven; *Circ*, Gloria Nash; Staff 5 (MLS 1, Non-MLS 4)
Founded 1907. Pop 8,300; Circ 65,000
Jul 1998-Jun 1999 Income $195,000, City $179,000, Locally Generated Income $8,500, Other $7,500. Mats Exp $35,000, Books $25,000, Per/Ser (Incl. Access Fees) $4,300. Sal $112,000 (Prof $35,000)
Library Holdings: Bk Titles 30,000; Per Subs 100
Special Collections: Daniel Webster Materials, clippings.; New Hampshire History, (Franklin Newspapers), bks & microfilm; photog, bks; World War I bks
Partic in Five Rivers Area Libr Network

FREEDOM

P FREEDOM PUBLIC LIBRARY,* Portland Rd, PO Box 159, 03836-0159. SAN 309-8141. Tel: 603-539-5176. FAX: 603-539-5176. *Librn*, Eleanor Thurston
Pop 831; Circ 4,592
Library Holdings: Bk Vols 10,400
Special Collections: N Hampshire
Mem of Cent District Libr Syst
Friends of the Library Group

FREMONT

P FREMONT PUBLIC LIBRARY,* 8 Beede Hill Rd, 03044. SAN 309-815X. Tel: 603-895-9543. *Librn*, Barbara Bassett
Founded 1894. Pop 2,500; Circ 5,047
Library Holdings: Bk Titles 7,100
Mem of SE Libr District

GILFORD

P GILFORD PUBLIC LIBRARY, 2 Belknap Mountain Rd, 03249-6807. SAN 309-8168. Tel: 603-524-6042. FAX: 603-524-1218. E-Mail: gplnh@worldpath.net. *Dir*, Katherine Dormody; E-Mail: kdormody@gilfordnh.org; *Librn*, Diane Mitton; Staff 4 (MLS 1, Non-MLS 3)
Founded 1926. Pop 5,900
Jan 1999-Dec 1999 Income $146,169
Library Holdings: Bk Vols 30,000; Per Subs 40
Subject Interests: New Hampshire
Automation Activity & Vendor Info: (OPAC) Sagebrush Corporation
Database Vendor: ProQuest
Friends of the Library Group

GILMANTON

GL CALIFORNIA DEPARTMENT OF JUSTICE, Attorney General's Law Library,* The Iron Works, PO Box 299, 03837-0299. SAN 309-8184. Tel: 916-324-5314. FAX: 916-323-5342. *Librn*, John Hoffman
Subject Interests: California

P GILMANTON CORNER PUBLIC LIBRARY,* RR 2, Box 40, 03237-8011. SAN 309-8176. Tel: 603-267-5957.
Founded 1912. Pop 1,200
Library Holdings: Bk Titles 5,000
Mem of Central Regional Libr Syst

GILMANTON IRON WORKS

P GILMANTON IRON WORKS PUBLIC LIBRARY,* PO Box 299, 03837-0299. Tel: 603-527-1007. *Librn*, Alice Bean
Pop 2,111
Library Holdings: Bk Vols 3,500
Mem of Cent Libr District

GILSUM

P GILSUM PUBLIC LIBRARY,* PO Box 57, 03448-0057. SAN 309-8206. Tel: 603-352-0832. *Librn*, Gail Bardwell
Founded 1892. Pop 600; Circ 4,555
Library Holdings: Bk Vols 10,800; Per Subs 23

GOFFSTOWN

P GOFFSTOWN PUBLIC LIBRARY, 2 High St, 03045-1910. SAN 309-8214. Tel: 603-497-2102. FAX: 603-497-8437. E-Mail: goflib@goffstown.lib.nh.us. Web Site: www.goffstown.lib.nh.us. *Dir*, Diane Hathaway; E-Mail: dianneh@goffstown.lib.nh.us; *Asst Dir*, Amy Lapointe; E-Mail: amy@goffstown.lib.nh.us; *Ch Servs*, Marsha Ciardullo; E-Mail: marshac@goffstown.lib.nh.us; Staff 13 (MLS 2, Non-MLS 11)
Founded 1888. Pop 15,951; Circ 52,000
Jan 2000-Dec 2000 Income Locally Generated Income $358,129. Mats Exp $41,302, Books $25,102, Per/Ser (Incl. Access Fees) $3,200, Electronic Ref Mat (Incl. Access Fees) $13,000. Sal $232,869 (Prof $78,122)
Library Holdings: Bk Vols 30,000; Bk Titles 37,000; Per Subs 125
Automation Activity & Vendor Info: (Acquisitions) epixtech, inc.; (Cataloging) epixtech, inc.; (Circulation) epixtech, inc.; (OPAC) epixtech, inc.
Database Vendor: OCLC - First Search, ProQuest
Mem of Greater Manchester Integrated Libr Coop
Friends of the Library Group

GORHAM

P GORHAM PUBLIC LIBRARY, 35 Railroad St, 03581. SAN 309-8222. Tel: 603-466-2525. *Librn*, Ida Bagley; *Asst Librn*, Valerie La Pointe
Founded 1895. Pop 3,600; Circ 24,856
Jan 1998-Dec 1999 Income $68,357. Mats Exp $14,200. Sal $35,660
Library Holdings: Bk Vols 70,871; Per Subs 50
Special Collections: New Hampshire Books Coll
Mem of North Country District
Open Mon-Fri 1-9

GOSHEN

P OLIVE G PETTIS LIBRARY, Mill Village Rd, PO Box 521, 03752-0742. SAN 309-8230. Tel: 603-863-6921. FAX: 603-863-7936. *Librn*, Ethel Nilsen
Pop 742; Circ 1,050
1999-2000 Income $7,462. Mats Exp $1,500, Books $1,350, Per/Ser (Incl. Access Fees) $150. Sal $4,680
Library Holdings: Bk Vols 1,400
Subject Interests: Local history
Special Collections: John Gunnison
Partic in SW Libr District
Friends of the Library Group

GRAFTON

P GRAFTON FREE PUBLIC LIBRARY, Library Rd, 03240-9720. (Mail add: 805 Williams Hill Rd, 03240-9720), SAN 309-8249. Tel: 603-523-7865. *Librn*, Mary L Gove
Pop 998; Circ 2,355
Library Holdings: Bk Vols 6,000; Per Subs 10
Mem of SW Libr District

GRANTHAM

P DUNBAR FREE LIBRARY,* 401 Rt 10 S, 03753-1580. (Mail add: Box 1580, 03753-1580), SAN 309-8257. Tel: 603-863-2172. FAX: 603-863-2172. *Librn*, Sally Allen
Pop 1,600
Library Holdings: Bk Vols 13,000
Open Mon, Wed & Thurs 9-5, Mon & Wed evenings 6:30-8:30, Fri & Sat 10-12
Friends of the Library Group

GREENFIELD

P STEPHENSON MEMORIAL LIBRARY, Greenfield Library, 761 Forest Rd, 03047-0127. SAN 309-8265. Tel: 603-547-2790. E-Mail: smemlib@tellink.net. *Librn*, Velma G Stone
Library Holdings: Bk Vols 15,000; Per Subs 25
Special Collections: American Anthology of Music, recs; Greenfield (Town & Local Events), photogs
Publications: New Town History
Friends of the Library Group

GREENLAND

P WEEKS PUBLIC LIBRARY,* 36 Post Rd, PO Box 430, 03840-2312. SAN 309-8273. Tel: 603-436-8548. FAX: 603-436-1422. E-Mail: weekspl@nh.ultranet.com. *Dir*, Bonnie K Gardner; *Ch Servs*, Susan MacDonald
Founded 1897. Pop 2,750; Circ 16,000
Jan 1998-Dec 1998 Income $73,820. Mats Exp $11,750, Books $10,300, Per/Ser (Incl. Access Fees) $1,450. Sal $44,089
Library Holdings: Bk Vols 15,009
Subject Interests: New Hampshire
Open Mon 10-8, Tues, Wed & Fri 10-6, Sat 10-2
Friends of the Library Group

GREENVILLE

P CHAMBERLIN FREE PUBLIC LIBRARY, 46 Main St, PO Box 499, 03048-0499. SAN 309-8281. Tel: 603-878-1105. FAX: 603-878-4092. E-Mail: staff@cpl.mv.com. Web Site: www.mv.com/ipusers/mct/chamberlin/library.htm. *ILL*, Brenda Cassidy
Founded 1876. Pop 2,200; Circ 13,255
Library Holdings: Bk Vols 12,000; Per Subs 90
Special Collections: Cook Book Coll; Gardening Coll; Occult Coll
Mem of SE Libr District
Partic in Hillstown Cooperative

HAMPSTEAD

P HAMPSTEAD PUBLIC LIBRARY, Mary E Clark Dr, PO Box 190, 03841-2035. SAN 309-829X. Tel: 603-329-6411. FAX: 603-329-6036. Web Site: www.hampstead.lib.nh.us. *Dir*, Judith L Crowley; E-Mail: jcrowley@hampstead.lib.nh.us; Staff 9 (MLS 2, Non-MLS 7)
Founded 1898. Pop 7,700; Circ 66,000
Library Holdings: Bk Titles 29,000; Per Subs 93
Special Collections: Civil War Coll
Partic in Merri-Hill-Rock Library Cooperative
Friends of the Library Group

HAMPTON

S HAMPTON HISTORICAL SOCIETY, Tuck Museum Library, 40 Park Ave, PO Box 1601, 03842. SAN 373-2444. Tel: 603-929-0781. E-Mail: hhs@ultranet.com. Web Site: www.nh.ultranet.com/~hhs/hhshome.htm. *Pres*, Paul T Corbett
Library Holdings: Bk Vols 500
Subject Interests: Education, Genealogy
Special Collections: Local History, Genealogy & NH Town Histories, postcards, photos of Hampton area
Restriction: By appointment only

P LANE MEMORIAL LIBRARY,* 2 Academy Ave, 03842. SAN 309-8303. Tel: 603-926-3368. FAX: 603-926-1348. Web Site: www.hampton.lib.nh.us. *Dir*, Catherine M Redden; E-Mail: credden@hampton.lib.nh.us; *Ch Servs*, Beverly A Vetter; Tel: 603-926-4729; *Asst Dir*, William H Teschek
Founded 1881. Pop 12,300; Circ 152,186
Subject Interests: Hampton, New Hampshire
Special Collections: New Adult Readers
Publications: Newsletter (periodically)
Partic in Seacoast Coop Libraries

HAMPTON FALLS

P HAMPTON FALLS FREE PUBLIC LIBRARY, 45 Exeter Rd, 03844-2004. SAN 309-8311. Tel: 603-926-3682. FAX: 603-926-0170. E-Mail: hfpublib@nh.ultranet.com. *Librn*, Judith Haskell
Pop 1,500; Circ 13,500
1999-2000 Mats Exp Books $11,000. Sal $31,000 (Prof $18,000)
Library Holdings: Bk Vols 12,000; Per Subs 35
Mem of SE Libr District
Friends of the Library Group

HANCOCK

P HANCOCK TOWN LIBRARY,* 25 Main St, PO Box 130, 03449. SAN 309-832X. Tel: 603-525-4411. E-Mail: hancocklibrary@monad.net. *Dir*, Marsha Zaccone
Pop 1,627; Circ 27,082
1998-1999 Income $55,370, City $25,400, Other $11,620. Mats Exp $11,100, Books $9,900, Per/Ser (Incl. Access Fees) $1,200. Sal $25,700
Library Holdings: Bk Titles 18,000; Per Subs 55
Subject Interests: Town hist
Mem of SW Libr District

HANOVER

S CREARE, INC, Technical Information Center,* Etna Rd, PO Box 71, 03755. SAN 309-8338. Tel: 603-643-3800. FAX: 603-643-1816. E-Mail: library@creare.com. *Mgr*, Margaret F Ackerson; *Asst Librn*, Rebecca Torrey; *Res*, Dale Copps; Staff 3 (MLS 1, Non-MLS 2)
Founded 1961
Library Holdings: Bk Titles 1,000; Per Subs 250
Subject Interests: Aeronautics, Boundary layers, Compressors, Computers, Cryogenics, Data proc, Energy sources, Fluid machinery, Fluids, Heat transfer, Multi-phase flow, Pumps, Turbines
Special Collections: Computer Library; Nuclear Safety (loss of coolant accident file)
Restriction: Staff use only
Partic in Dialog Corporation

C DARTMOUTH COLLEGE LIBRARY, 6025 Baker Library, Rm 115, 03755-3525. SAN 350-493X. Tel: 603-646-2236. FAX: 603-646-3702. E-Mail: dartmouth.college.library@dartmouth.edu. Web Site: www.dartmouth.edu/~library/thelibs.html. *Librn*, Richard Lucier; *Admin Dir*, John G Crane; *Coll Develop*, John R James; *Publ Servs*, Cynthia Pawlek; *Acq*, Ann McHugo; *Cat*, Mary Davis; *Cat*, Cecilia Tittemore; Staff 180 (MLS 53, Non-MLS 127)
Founded 1769. Enrl 5,328; Fac 932; Highest Degree: Doctorate
Library Holdings: Bk Vols 2,355,700; Per Subs 20,679
Publications: Dartmouth College Library Bulletin
Partic in OCLC Online Computer Library Center, Inc; Research Libraries Group, Inc
Friends of the Library Group

Departmental Libraries:

BAKER-BERRY LIBRARY Tel: 603-646-2560. Interlibrary Loan Service Tel: 603-646-2596. Reference Tel: 603-646-2704. FAX: 603-646-2167. E-Mail: baker.library.reference@dartmouth.edu. Web Site: www.dartmouth.edu/~lbaker/baker.html. *Humanities and Soc Sci, Librn*, William S Moran; *Access Serv*, Pamela Ploeger; *ILL*, Patricia Carter; Staff 42 (MLS 12, Non-MLS 30)
Founded 1928
Library Holdings: Bk Vols 1,516,959; Per Subs 11,925

CM BIOMEDICAL LIBRARIES (DANA BIOMEDICAL LIBRARY & MATTHEWS-FULLER HEALTH SCIENCES LIBRARY-MFHSL), 6168 Dana Biomedical Library, 03755-3880. SAN 350-4964. Interlibrary Loan Service Tel: 603-650-1656. Circulation Tel: 603-650-1658 (Dana Biomedical), 603-650-7658 (Matthews-Fuller). Reference Tel: 603-650-1660 (Dana Biomedical), 603-650-7660 (Matthews-Fuller). FAX: 603-650-1354. E-Mail: biomedical.libraries.reference@dartmouth.edu. Web Site: www.dartmouth.edu/~biomed/. *Dir*, William Garrity; Tel: 603-650-1662; *AV*, David Izzo; Tel: 603-650-1663; *Coll Develop*, Margaret Sleeth; Tel: 603-650-1635; Staff 30 (MLS 14, Non-MLS 16)
Library Holdings: Bk Vols 300,512; Per Subs 2,510

COOK MATHEMATICS LIBRARY, 6188 Bradley Hall, 03755-3551. SAN 350-5049. Tel: 603-646-2766. FAX: 603-646-3681. E-Mail: cook.library.reference@dartmouth.edu. Web Site: www.dartmouth.edu/~krescook/cookhome.shtml. *In Charge*, Joy Weale; Staff 1 (Non-MLS 1)
Library Holdings: Bk Vols 36,991; Per Subs 564

FELDBERG BUSINESS ADMINISTRATION & ENGINEERING LIBRARY, 6193 Murdough Ctr, 03755-3560. SAN 350-4999. Tel: 603-646-2191. FAX: 603-646-2384. E-Mail: feldberg.reference@dartmouth.edu. Web Site: www.dartmouth.edu/~feldberg. *Librn*, James R Fries; E-Mail: james.r.fries@dartmouth.edu; *ILL*, Amanda Merk; Tel: 603-646-2354, E-Mail: amanda.merk@dartmouth.edu; Staff 10 (MLS 5, Non-MLS 5)
Founded 1973. Highest Degree: Doctorate
Library Holdings: Bk Vols 115,325; Bk Titles 45,325; Per Subs 2,474

KRESGE PHYSICAL SCIENCES LIBRARY, 6115 Fairchild Ctr, 03755-3571. SAN 350-5022. Tel: 603-646-3563. FAX: 603-646-3681. E-Mail: kresge.library.reference@dartmouth.edu. Web Site: www.dartmouth.edu/~krescook/home.shtml. *Librn*, Barbara DeFelice; *ILL*, Sean Padgett; Staff 6 (MLS 3, Non-MLS 3)
Library Holdings: Bk Vols 129,634; Per Subs 1,533

PADDOCK MUSIC LIBRARY, 6187 Hopkins Center, Dartmouth Col, 03755. Tel: 603-646-3234. Interlibrary Loan Service Tel: 603-646-3234. Circulation Tel: 603-646-3234. FAX: 603-646-1219. E-Mail: paddock.music.library@dartmouth.edu. Web Site: www.dartmouth.edu/~paddock/. *Coll Develop, Librn*, Patricia B Fisken; Tel: 603-646-3120, E-Mail: patricia.fisken@dartmouth.edu; *ILL*, Helmut Baer; E-Mail: helmut.baer@dartmouth.edu; Staff 4 (MLS 1, Non-MLS 3)
Library Holdings: Bk Vols 85,711; Per Subs 308
Subject Interests: Music

S RAUNER SPECIAL COLLECTIONS LIBRARY, Dartmouth College, 6065 Webster Hall, 03755-3519. SAN 378-0546. Tel: 603-646-2037. E-Mail: rauner.special.collections.reference@dartmouth.edu. Web Site: www.dartmouth.edu/~speccoll/. *Curator, Spec Coll*, Philip Cronenwett; *Archivist*, Anne Ostendarp; *Curator, Rare Bks*, Stanley Brown; Staff 17 (MLS 4, Non-MLS 13)
Special Collections: American Calligraphy; Bookplates; Dartmouth Archives; Don Quixote; George Ticknor Library; German & English Plays (Barrett Clark Coll); Horace (Barlow Coll); New England Early Illustrated Books (1926 Memorial); New Hampshire History & Imprints; Polar Regions (Stefansson Coll); Private Presses; Railroads (Chase Streeter Coll); Robert Frost Coll; Shakespeare (Hickmott Coll); Spanish Civilization (Bryant Coll); Spanish Plays; White Mountains

SANBORN ENGLISH LIBRARY, Dartmouth Col, HB6025, 03755-3525. Tel: 603-646-2312. FAX: 603-646-2159. E-Mail: sanborn.library@dartmouth.edu. Web Site: www.dartmouth.edu/~library/thelibs/sanborn.html. *In Charge*, Bonnie Nallin. Subject Specialists: *American literature*, Bonnie Nallin; *English literature*, Bonnie Nallin; Staff 2 (Non-MLS 2)
Founded 1928. Enrl 5,700; Highest Degree: Doctorate
Library Holdings: Bk Vols 8,373; Per Subs 40
Subject Interests: Am lit, Eng lit
Special Collections: Poetry Chapbooks
Database Vendor: OCLC - First Search
Friends of the Library Group

SHERMAN ART LIBRARY, 6033 Carpenter Hall, 03755-3570. SAN 350-5081. Tel: 603-646-2305. FAX: 603-646-1218. E-Mail: sherman.library.reference@dartmouth.edu. Web Site: www.dartmouth.edu/~library/thelibs/sherman.html. *Librn*, Barbara E Reed; *ILL*, Susan Jorgensen
Library Holdings: Bk Vols 110,000; Per Subs 600
Subject Interests: Architecture, Photography
Special Collections: Artists Books

P HOWE LIBRARY, 13 E South St, 03755. SAN 309-8354. Tel: 603-643-4120. FAX: 603-643-0725. E-Mail: howe.library@valley.net. Web Site: www.thehowe.org. *Dir*, Marlene F McGonigle; *Ch Servs*, Denise Reitsma; *Asst Dir*, Ellen Lynch; *Tech Servs*, Pam Smith; *ILL, Ref*, Mary Hardy; *Circ*, Kristina Burnett; Staff 6 (MLS 6)

Founded 1900. Pop 9,218; Circ 214,000
Jul 1999-Jun 2000 Income $856,032, City $638,115, Other $217,917. Mats Exp $85,903. Sal $468,025
Library Holdings: Per Subs 212
Automation Activity & Vendor Info: (Acquisitions) Innovative Interfaces Inc.; (Cataloging) Innovative Interfaces Inc.; (Circulation) Innovative Interfaces Inc.; (OPAC) Innovative Interfaces Inc.; (Serials) Innovative Interfaces Inc.
Database Vendor: ProQuest

S SPECTRA, INC, Technical Information Center,* PO Box 68-C, 03755. SAN 321-4389. Tel: 603-643-4390.; Staff 1 (MLS 1)
Founded 1976
Library Holdings: Bk Vols 1,500; Bk Titles 1,250; Per Subs 150
Subject Interests: Computer display tech, Electromechanical eng, Indust automation
Special Collections: Patents Coll
Restriction: Staff use only
Partic in Dialog Corporation; Dow Jones News Retrieval; Orbit; Reuters Textline; STN

UNITED STATES ARMY
A COLD REGIONS RESEARCH & ENGINEERING LABORATORY LIBRARY, 72 Lyme Rd, 03755-1290. SAN 350-5111. Tel: 603-646-4221, 603-646-4238. FAX: 603-646-4712. Web Site: www.usace.army.mil/library. *Dir*, Nancy C Liston; E-Mail: nliston@crrel.usace.army.mil; *Librn*, Elizabeth Hoffmeister; Tel: 603-646-4039; *Librn*, Elisabeth Smallidge; Staff 5 (MLS 3, Non-MLS 2)
Founded 1952
Library Holdings: Bk Titles 28,000; Per Subs 501
Subject Interests: Engineering, Geology, Hydrology, Mathematics, Meteorology, Physics
Special Collections: Cold Regions Science & Technology Bibliography
Publications: Bibliography of Cold Regions Science & Technology
Partic in Dialog Corporation; Fedlink; Nelinet, Inc; OCLC Online Computer Library Center, Inc; Orbit

HARRISVILLE

S BOSTON ORGAN CLUB LIBRARY,* 55 Nelson Rd, PO Box 104, 03450-0104. SAN 373-014X. Tel: 603-827-3055. FAX: 603-827-3750.
Founded 1965
Library Holdings: Bk Titles 682; Per Subs 17
Special Collections: US Pipe Organ History, bks, doc, ephemera
Open by appt only

P HARRISVILLE PUBLIC LIBRARY,* Island St, PO Box 248, 03450. SAN 309-8362. Tel: 603-827-2918. FAX: 603-827-2917. *Librn*, Constance Boyd
Pop 885; Circ 7,332
Library Holdings: Bk Vols 5,500; Per Subs 18
Mem of SW Libr District
Open Mon 6-8:30, Wed 2-5, Fri 3-6:30, Sat 9-12

HAVERHILL

P HAVERHILL LIBRARY ASSOCIATION, Court St, 03765-0117. (Mail add: PO Box 117, 03765-0117), SAN 309-8370. Tel: 603-989-5578. E-Mail: hla@conniver.net. *Librn*, Paula Kent; *Ch Servs*, Anne Marie Ballam
Founded 1880. Pop 350; Circ 7,850
Library Holdings: Bk Vols 14,000; Per Subs 27
Mem of North Country District
Open Wed 2-5 & 6-9 & Sat 9-1

HEBRON

P HEBRON PUBLIC LIBRARY,* Church Lane, PO Box 90, 03241. SAN 309-8419. Tel: 603-744-7998. *Librn*, Donna Esty
Pop 342; Circ 3,533
Library Holdings: Bk Vols 7,200; Per Subs 12
Mem of North County Libr Syst
Open Mon & Wed 9-12

HENNIKER

C NEW ENGLAND COLLEGE, H Raymond Danforth Library, 28 Bridge St, 03242-3298. SAN 350-5146. Tel: 603-428-2344. FAX: 603-428-4273. *Acq, Coll Develop, Dir*, Joseph D Considine; *Cat*, Russell Rattray; *Publ Servs*, Katherine Van Weelden; *Ref*, Karen Penrod; Staff 5 (MLS 4, Non-MLS 1)
Founded 1946. Enrl 700; Fac 48; Highest Degree: Master
Library Holdings: Bk Vols 110,000; Per Subs 700
Special Collections: College Archives & Art Coll; New Hampshiriana; Shakespeare Coll (Adams Col)
Automation Activity & Vendor Info: (Acquisitions) EOS; (Cataloging) EOS; (Circulation) EOS; (OPAC) EOS; (Serials) EOS
Database Vendor: Ebsco - EbscoHost
Partic in Dialog Corporation; Nelinet, Inc; New Hampshire College & University Council; Wilsonline
Friends of the Library Group

P TUCKER FREE LIBRARY, 11 Western Ave, PO Box 688, 03242. SAN 309-8427. Tel: 603-428-3471. FAX: 603-428-7106. *Librn*, Peggy Ward
Founded 1903. Pop 4,200; Circ 40,000
Library Holdings: Bk Vols 28,000; Per Subs 42
Special Collections: Francis Childs Coll, papers
Friends of the Library Group

HILL

P HILL PUBLIC LIBRARY,* Crescent St, 03243. SAN 309-8435. Tel: 603-934-9712. *Librn*, Ann Clement
Pop 694; Circ 5,026
Library Holdings: Bk Titles 7,000
Mem of Cent Libr District
Friends of the Library Group

HILLSBORO

P DEERING PUBLIC LIBRARY,* RR 1 Box 227B, 03244. SAN 309-7927. *In Charge*, Susan MacLeod
Pop 1,700
Library Holdings: Bk Vols 2,500
Mem of Cent District Libr Syst
Open Summer Only Wed 10-12 & 1-3, Sat 10-12

P FULLER PUBLIC LIBRARY,* 29 School St, 03244-0043. (Mail add: PO Box 43, 03244-0043), SAN 309-8443. Tel: 603-464-3595. FAX: 603-464-4572. *Chief Librn*, Tamara McClure; *Asst Librn*, Robin Sweetser; *Ch Servs*, Susan Bearor
Founded 1877. Pop 3,000; Circ 14,737
Library Holdings: Bk Vols 20,000; Per Subs 50
Mem of Cent Libr District
Friends of the Library Group

HINSDALE

P HINSDALE PUBLIC LIBRARY,* Main & Depot Sts, PO Box 6, 03451. SAN 309-8451. Tel: 603-336-5713. *Librn*, Mary Major; *Asst Librn*, Marjorie Johnson
Pop 4,000; Circ 6,193
Library Holdings: Bk Vols 20,000
Mem of SW Libr District
Friends of the Library Group

HOLDERNESS

P HOLDERNESS FREE LIBRARY, Main St, PO Box L, 03245-0712. SAN 309-846X. Tel: 603-968-7066. E-Mail: holdrnes@worldpath.net. *Dir*, Mary DeLashmit; Staff 1 (Non-MLS 1)
Founded 1878. Pop 1,700; Circ 13,900
Jan 2000-Dec 2000 Income $38,400, City $35,900, Locally Generated Income $2,500. Mats Exp $6,200, Books $5,500, Presv $200, AV Equip $500. Sal $23,000 (Prof $21,250)
Library Holdings: Bk Vols 15,533; Per Subs 56
Special Collections: New Hampshire Special Coll, bks, pamphlets
Automation Activity & Vendor Info: (Cataloging) Sagebrush Corporation; (Circulation) Sagebrush Corporation; (OPAC) Sagebrush Corporation
Database Vendor: Ebsco - EbscoHost, GaleNet, Wilson - Wilson Web
Partic in MUM Coop; NH Automated Info Systs
Open Mon 1-8, Wed, Fri & Sat 10-5
Friends of the Library Group

HOLLIS

P HOLLIS SOCIAL LIBRARY, 2 Monument Sq, 03049. (Mail add: PO Box 659, 03049), SAN 309-8478. Tel: 603-465-7721. Circulation Tel: 603-465-7721. Reference Tel: 603-465-7721. FAX: 603-465-3507. E-Mail: hollis@hollis.lib.nh.us. Web Site: www.hollis.nh.us/library. *Dir*, Steve Russo; *Ch Servs*, Jenn Costas; Staff 2 (MLS 1, Non-MLS 1)
Founded 1799. Pop 6,800; Circ 47,659
Jan 2000-Dec 2000 Income $126,957, City $108,957, Other $18,000
Library Holdings: Bk Vols 25,161; Per Subs 59
Subject Interests: Local history
Partic in Hillstown Cooperative; NHAIS
Friends of the Library Group

HOOKSETT

P HOOKSETT PUBLIC LIBRARY,* 1701B Hooksett Rd, 03106-1852. SAN 309-8486. Tel: 603-485-6092. FAX: 603-485-6193. E-Mail: hplbooks@hooksett.lib.nh.us. Web Site: www.hooksett.lib.nh.us. *Librn*, Frances Hebert; *Asst Librn*, Patrica Cate; *Automation Syst Coordr*, Jeffrey Scott; Staff 6 (MLS 6)
Founded 1909. Pop 8,000; Circ 54,000
Jul 1997-Jun 1998 Income $242,116. Mats Exp $202,373, Books $26,307. Sal $110,869
Library Holdings: Bk Titles 43,000; Per Subs 112
Subject Interests: Arts, Crafts
Automation Activity & Vendor Info: (Cataloging) epixtech, inc.; (Circulation) epixtech, inc.
Partic in GMILCS
Friends of the Library Group

HOPKINTON

S NEW HAMPSHIRE ANTIQUARIAN SOCIETY LIBRARY, 300 Main St, 03229. SAN 326-0836. Tel: 603-746-3825. *Exec Dir*, Elaine Loft
Library Holdings: Bk Vols 14,000
Special Collections: Primitive Portraits Costume Coll
Open Thurs & Fri 10-5, Sat 10-2

HUDSON

P HILLS MEMORIAL LIBRARY, 18 Library St, 03051-4244. SAN 309-8508. Tel: 603-886-6030. FAX: 603-595-2850. Web Site: www.hillsml.lib.nh.us. *Tech Coordr*, Brian Hewey; Tel: 603-886-6030, Ext 30, E-Mail: bhewey@mail.hillsml.lib.nh.us; *Dir*, Mary P Weller; Tel: 603-886-6030, Ext 22, E-Mail: tweller@mail.hillsml.lib.nh.us; *Media Spec Ch*, Connie Vandervort; Tel: 603-886-6030, Ext 24, E-Mail: cvandervort@mail.hillsml.lib.nh.us; *Head Ref*, Gayle St Cyr; Tel: 603-886-6030, Ext 21, E-Mail: gstcyr@mail.hillsml.lib.nh.us; *Head Tech Servs*, Gerald Rice; Tel: 603-886-6030, Ext 29, E-Mail: jrice@mail.hillsml.lib.nh.us; *Ad Servs, Bkmobile Coordr, Head, Circ, Ser*, Carol Ann Razewski; Tel: 603-886-6030, Ext 26, E-Mail: crazewski@mail.hillsml.lib.nh.us; Staff 5 (MLS 3, Non-MLS 2)
Founded 1908. Pop 22,000; Circ 92,000
Library Holdings: Bk Vols 55,000; Per Subs 127
Subject Interests: Local genealogy
Special Collections: Zylonis Lithuanian Heritage Coll
Automation Activity & Vendor Info: (Circulation) Sagebrush Corporation; (OPAC) Sagebrush Corporation
Database Vendor: Ebsco - EbscoHost, ProQuest
Mem of Merri-Hill-Rock Coop
Open Mon-Thurs 9:30-9, Fri & Sat 9:30-5, Sun 1-5
Friends of the Library Group
Bookmobiles: 1. Bluebird

JACKSON

P JACKSON PUBLIC LIBRARY,* Main St, PO Box 276, 03846-0276. SAN 309-8524. Tel: 603-383-9731. FAX: 603-383-9731. E-Mail: jplib@worldpath.net. *Librn*, Susan Dunker-Bendigo
Founded 1879. Pop 650; Circ 4,576
Library Holdings: Bk Vols 11,000
Friends of the Library Group

JAFFREY

P JAFFREY PUBLIC LIBRARY, 38 Main St, 03452-1196. SAN 309-8532. Tel: 603-532-7301. FAX: 603-532-7301. E-Mail: jaffreylibs1@monad.net. *Dir*, Joan Knight; *Asst Dir*, Christine Tarrio; *ILL*, Marilyn Simmons; *ILL*, Sheila Vanderhorst; Staff 3 (MLS 1, Non-MLS 2)
Pop 5,434; Circ 37,804
Jan 1999-Dec 1999 Income $170,144, City $128,820, Other $40,000. Mats Exp $27,676, Books $20,000, Per/Ser (Incl. Access Fees) $3,600, AV Equip $1,500, Electronic Ref Mat (Incl. Access Fees) $2,576. Sal $98,603
Library Holdings: Bk Vols 25,000; Per Subs 100
Special Collections: Amos Fortune Historical Coll
Partic in Nubanusit Library Cooperative
Friends of the Library Group

JEFFERSON

P JEFFERSON PUBLIC LIBRARY,* Rte 2, 03583. (Mail add: PO Box 27, 03583), SAN 309-8540. Tel: 603-586-7791. E-Mail: lookitup@nci.net. *Dir*, Sue Crafton
Pop 802; Circ 2,544
Library Holdings: Bk Vols 4,300
Subject Interests: Town hist
Mem of North Country District
Open Tues & Thurs 1-4 & 6-8, Sat 10-12
Friends of the Library Group

KEENE

C ANTIOCH NEW ENGLAND GRADUATE SCHOOL,* 40 Avon St, 03431-3516. SAN 309-8559. Tel: 603-357-3122. FAX: 603-357-7345. E-Mail: library@antiochne.edu. Web Site: 204.97.19.238/libpage/libhome.html. *Asst Librn*, Marcia Leversee; *Ref, Tech Servs*, Charlotte Greenhalgh
Library Holdings: Bk Vols 28,000; Per Subs 742
Subject Interests: Counseling psychology, Dance movement therapy, Doctoral programs in psychology, Education, Environmental studies, Experienced educators program, Family therapy, Marriage, Mgt, Organization, Psychology, Substance abuse, Waldorf educ
Publications: ExLibris (newsletter)

M CHESHIRE HOSPITAL, Medical Library,* 580 Court St, 03431. SAN 309-8567. Tel: 603-352-4111. FAX: 603-357-2905. *Librn*, Jean Slepian
Founded 1956
Library Holdings: Bk Vols 700; Per Subs 260
Subject Interests: Consumer health

S HISTORICAL SOCIETY OF CHESHIRE COUNTY, 246 Main St, PO Box 803, 03431. SAN 323-9675. Tel: 603-352-1895. FAX: 603-352-9226. E-Mail: hscc@cheshire.net. *Dir*, Alan Rumrill; *Asst Librn*, Roxanne Roy; Staff 1 (MLS 1)
Founded 1927
Jan 2000-Dec 2000 Income $148,000. Mats Exp $148,000. (Prof $41,000)
Library Holdings: Bk Titles 11,000; Spec Interest Per Sub 15
Special Collections: Cheshire County History, bks, mss, photog; New England Genealogy & Local History Coll
Publications: Newsletter

P KEENE PUBLIC LIBRARY,* 60 Winter St, 03431-3360. SAN 309-8575. Tel: 603-352-0157. FAX: 603-352-1101. Web Site: www.ci.keene.nh.us/library/. *Dir*, Nancy Vincent; E-Mail: nvincent@ci.keene.nh.us; *Coll Develop*, B J Wahl; *Commun Relations*, Charlotte Lesser; E-Mail: clesser@ci.keene.nh.us; *Tech Servs*, Jennifer Bone; E-Mail: jbone@ci.keene.nh.us; *Ref*, David Howlett; E-Mail: dhowlett@ci.keene.nh.us; *Coll Develop, Electronic Resources*, B J Wahl; E-Mail: bjwahl@ci.keene.nh.us
Founded 1857. Pop 23,000
Jul 1997-Jun 1998 Income City $844,000. Mats Exp $112,000. Sal $431,000
Library Holdings: Bk Vols 95,000; Per Subs 243
Subject Interests: Local history, New Hampshire
Database Vendor: Innovative Interfaces INN - View
Friends of the Library Group

C KEENE STATE COLLEGE, Wallace E Mason Library, 229 Main St, 03435-3201. SAN 309-8583. Tel: 603-358-2711. Interlibrary Loan Service Tel: 603-358-2715. Reference Tel: 603-358-2710. FAX: 603-358-2745. Web Site: www.keene.edu/library. *Actg Dir*, Thomas Warger; Tel: 603-358-2736, E-Mail: twarger@keene.edu; *Asst Dir*, Peggie Partello; *Acq*, C Christopher Pratt; Tel: 603-358-2728, E-Mail: cpratt@keene.edu; *Ref*, Peg Barrett; Tel: 603-358-2714, E-Mail: pbarrett@keene.edu; *Ref*, Robert J Madden; Tel: 603-358-2717, E-Mail: rmadden@keene.edu; *Ref*, Patrick O'Brien; Tel: 603-358-2713, E-Mail: pobrien@keene.edu; *Tech Servs*, Lois Merry; Tel: 603-358-2738, E-Mail: lmerry@keene.edu; *Publ Servs*, Judith M Hildebrandt; Tel: 603-358-2749, E-Mail: jhildebr@keene.edu; *Circ*, Anne Ames; Tel: 603-358-2712, E-Mail: aames@keene.edu; *Syst Coordr*, Markham Woodford; Tel: 603-358-2716, E-Mail: mwoodfor@keene.edu. Subject Specialists: *Archives*, Anne Ames; *Preservation*, Anne Ames; Staff 18 (MLS 6, Non-MLS 12)
Founded 1909. Enrl 4,700; Fac 178; Highest Degree: Master
Jul 2000-Jun 2001 Income $1,590,729. Mats Exp $415,000. Sal $547,311
Library Holdings: Bk Vols 300,000; Per Subs 1,000
Subject Interests: Curriculum related materials for K - 12, Education, State hist
Special Collections: Center for Holocaust Studies; ERIC; New Hampshire History
Automation Activity & Vendor Info: (Cataloging) Innovative Interfaces Inc.; (Circulation) Innovative Interfaces Inc.; (OPAC) Innovative Interfaces Inc.; (Serials) Innovative Interfaces Inc.
Database Vendor: Ebsco - EbscoHost, OCLC - First Search, Silverplatter Information Inc., Wilson - Wilson Web
Partic in Nelinet, Inc; New Hampshire College & University Council; NH Automated Info Systs; OCLC Online Computer Library Center, Inc

KENSINGTON

P KENSINGTON SOCIAL & PUBLIC LIBRARY,* 126 Amesbury Rd, 03833-5621. SAN 309-8605. Tel: 603-772-5022. FAX: 603-778-2953. *Dir*, Cheryl Saunders; *Ch Servs*, Lisa Vlasich
Pop 1,319; Circ 13,848
Jan 1997-Dec 1998 Income $41,435. Mats Exp $6,300. Sal $25,000

Library Holdings: Bk Vols 13,000; Per Subs 49
Special Collections: Antiques & Art Coll
Open Tues & Thurs 6-8, Sat 10-1
Friends of the Library Group

KINGSTON

P NICHOLS MEMORIAL LIBRARY,* 169 Main St, PO Box 128, 03848-0128. SAN 309-8613. Tel: 603-642-3521. FAX: 603-642-3135. Web Site: www.nichols.lib.nh.us. *Dir*, Natasha Leonard; E-Mail: nleonard@nichols.lib.nh.us
Founded 1898. Circ 42,140
Jan 1998-Dec 1998 Income $89,350, Locally Generated Income $2,500. Mats Exp $14,500, Books $7,200, Per/Ser (Incl. Access Fees) $1,400, Micro $1,500, Other Print Mats $4,400. Sal $54,000
Library Holdings: Bk Vols 20,000; Per Subs 68
Subject Interests: History, New Hampshire hist

LACONIA

P LACONIA PUBLIC LIBRARY,* 695 Main St, 03246-2780. SAN 350-5170. Tel: 603-524-4775. FAX: 603-527-1277. *Dir*, Carol S Sykes
Founded 1878. Pop 15,579; Circ 100,573
Library Holdings: Bk Vols 50,000; Per Subs 35
Partic in Urban Libr Consortia
Friends of the Library Group
Branches: 1
LAKEPORT (OSSIAN WILBUR GOSS READING ROOM), 188 Elm St, 03246. SAN 350-5200. Tel: 603-524-3808. *Librn*, Susan Laramie

M LAKES REGION GENERAL HOSPITAL, Jessup Library, 80 Highland St, 03246-3298. SAN 377-2462. Tel: 603-527-2837. FAX: 603-527-7197. *Librn*, Norma Phillips; E-Mail: nphillips@lrgh.org
Library Holdings: Bk Titles 700; Per Subs 130

J NEW HAMPSHIRE COMMUNITY TECHNICAL COLLEGE BENNET LIBRARY,* 379 New Prescott Hill Rd, 03246. SAN 309-8621. Tel: 603-524-3207. FAX: 603-524-8084. *Dir*, Patty Miller; E-Mail: p_miller@tec.nh.us
Founded 1968. Enrl 1,097; Fac 26
1998-1999 Income $16,000. Mats Exp $8,000, Books $4,000, Per/Ser (Incl. Access Fees) $4,000. Sal $44,413 (Prof $34,646)
Library Holdings: Bk Titles 9,815; Per Subs 125
Subject Interests: Accounting, Automotive, Bus, Computers, Early childhood, Electrical, Fire science, Graphic arts, Human servs, Paralegal
Publications: Current Acquisitions

LANCASTER

M WEEKS MEMORIAL HOSPITAL, Medical Library,* 173 Middle St, 03584. SAN 323-6706. Tel: 603-788-4911. FAX: 603-788-5027. *Librn*, Peggy Deyette
Partic in Docline

P WILLIAM D WEEKS MEMORIAL LIBRARY,* 128 Main St, 03584-3031. SAN 309-863X. Tel: 603-788-3352. FAX: 603-788-3203. E-Mail: weekslib@ncia.net. *Librn*, Barbara R Robarts
Pop 3,500; Circ 45,000
Jan 1999-Dec 1999 Income $108,857, City $104,857, Locally Generated Income $4,000. Mats Exp $17,500, Books $15,500, Per/Ser (Incl. Access Fees) $1,600. Sal $47,484 (Prof $25,000)
Library Holdings: Bk Vols 32,000
Subject Interests: New Hampshire
Friends of the Library Group

LEBANON

P LEBANON PUBLIC LIBRARY,* 9 E Park St, 03766. SAN 350-5235. Tel: 603-448-2459. FAX: 603-448-0696. E-Mail: library@lebcity.com. Web Site: www.valley.net:80/~lebanon/library1.html. *Dir*, Susanne Robb; *Ch Servs*, Joanne Scobie; *Asst Dir*, Olive MacGregor
Founded 1909. Pop 13,000; Circ 102,126
Jan 1997-Dec 1998 Income $474,479, City $385,479, Other $89,000. Mats Exp $54,600, Books $41,000, Per/Ser (Incl. Access Fees) $5,500, Micro $250, Other Print Mats $1,500. Sal $289,659
Library Holdings: Bk Vols 62,000; Per Subs 137
Subject Interests: Local history
Friends of the Library Group
Branches: 1
WEST LEBANON BRANCH, 57 Main St, West Lebanon, 03784. SAN 350-526X. Tel: 603-298-8544. *Librn*, Steven Bailey

LEE

P LEE PUBLIC LIBRARY, 7 Mast Rd, 03824. SAN 309-8648. Tel: 603-659-2626. FAX: 603-659-2986. E-Mail: leelibrary@mediaone.net. Web Site: www.ultranet.com/~leepl. *Dir*, Linda Morrill
Founded 1892. Pop 4,500; Circ 109,000
1999-2000 Income $85,887. Mats Exp $28,317, Books $19,200, Other Print Mats $1,400. Sal $57,570 (Prof $28,000)
Library Holdings: Bk Titles 26,580; Per Subs 71; Bks on Deafness & Sign Lang 10
Mem of Central Regional Libr Syst
Open Mon & Wed 12-8, Tues 3-8, Thurs & Fri 10-5, Sat 10-3
Friends of the Library Group

LINCOLN

P LINCOLN PUBLIC LIBRARY,* Church St, PO Box 98, 03251. SAN 309-8656. Tel: 603-745-8159. FAX: 603-745-2037. E-Mail: library@linwoodnet.com. *Librn*, Carol Reiley
Pop 1,100; Circ 11,000
Library Holdings: Bk Vols 10,000
Subject Interests: New Hampshire
Mem of North Country District

LISBON

P LISBON PUBLIC LIBRARY,* 45 School St, 03585. SAN 309-8664. Tel: 603-838-6615. E-Mail: lisbonlib@anothcabove.com. *Dir*, Karla O Speetjens; Fax: 603-838-6790; *Librn*, Selena M Cate
Founded 1864. Pop 1,543; Circ 9,200
Library Holdings: Bk Vols 8,900
Special Collections: Local Culture & History (New Hampshire Coll)
Partic in North Country Library Cooperative
Friends of the Library Group

LITCHFIELD

P AARON CUTLER MEMORIAL LIBRARY,* 269 Charles Bancroft Hwy, 03052. SAN 309-8516. Tel: 603-424-4044. E-Mail: aml1@juno.com. *Librn*, Cheryl Brigham; *Librn*, Florence Hamilton
Pop 4,510
Library Holdings: Bk Vols 24,900; Per Subs 44
Special Collections: New Hampshire History (Special New Hampshire Coll)
Friends of the Library Group

LITTLETON

P LITTLETON PUBLIC LIBRARY, 92 Main St, 03561-1238. SAN 309-8672. Tel: 603-444-5741. FAX: 603-444-1706. E-Mail: litt_lib@ncia.net. Web Site: www.ncia.net/library/littleton/. *Dir*, Jeanne Dickerman; *ILL*, Ellen Morrow; *Ch Servs*, Steffaney Highland; Staff 4 (Non-MLS 4)
Founded 1890. Pop 6,061; Circ 65,987
Jan 2000-Dec 2000 Income $202,046, City $172,777
Library Holdings: Bk Vols 43,688; Per Subs 77
Special Collections: Kilburn Stereoptic Views Coll; NH History and Genealogy Coll
Function: ILL available
Partic in Five Rivers Area Libr Network; North Country Library Cooperative
Special Services for the Blind - Optelek 20/20 video magnification system
Open Mon-Fri 10-7, Sat 10-2

M LITTLETON REGIONAL HOSPITAL, Gale Medical Library, 600 St Johnsbury Rd, 03561. SAN 377-273X. Tel: 603-444-7739, Ext 164. *Librn*, Linda Ford
Library Holdings: Bk Vols 500; Bk Titles 400; Per Subs 125

LONDONDERRY

P LEACH LIBRARY, 276 Mammoth Rd, 03053-3097. SAN 309-8680. Tel: 603-432-1132. FAX: 603-437-6610. Web Site: www.londonderry.org. *Dir*, Shirley Barron; E-Mail: sbarron@londonderry.org; *Tech Servs*, Ellen Knowlton; *Ref*, Diane Arrato Gavrish; *Circ*, Sally Nelson; Staff 14 (MLS 6, Non-MLS 8)
Founded 1880. Pop 24,000; Circ 184,454
Jul 2000-Jun 2001 Income $715,804. Mats Exp $118,000, Books $105,000, Per/Ser (Incl. Access Fees) $6,000, Electronic Ref Mat (Incl. Access Fees) $7,000. Sal $398,086 (Prof $211,860)
Library Holdings: Bk Vols 52,000; Per Subs 150
Subject Interests: Local history
Automation Activity & Vendor Info: (Cataloging) Sagebrush Corporation; (Circulation) Sagebrush Corporation; (ILL) Gaylord; (OPAC) Sagebrush Corporation
Database Vendor: Ebsco - EbscoHost, ProQuest

Publications: Children's Room News; Leach Library News
Mem of Merri-Hill-Rock Coop
Partic in Urban Pub Libr Consortium

LOUDON

P MAXFIELD PUBLIC LIBRARY,* 8 Rte 129, 03307. SAN 309-8699. Tel: 603-798-5153. FAX: 603-798-5232. *Librn*, Nancy Hendy
Pop 3,519; Circ 4,883
Jan 1997-Dec 1998 Income $61,195. Mats Exp $6,100, Books $2,500, Per/Ser (Incl. Access Fees) $800, Other Print Mats $2,800. Sal $37,200 (Prof $20,995)
Library Holdings: Bk Vols 13,597; Per Subs 42
Publications: Newsletter (bi-annual)
Mem of Cent District Libr Syst
Friends of the Library Group

LYME

P LYME TOWN LIBRARY, 38 Union St, 03768-9702. SAN 350-5294. Tel: 603-795-4622. E-Mail: lyme_library@valley.net. *Librn*, Betsy Eaton
Pop 1,700; Circ 15,932
Library Holdings: Bk Vols 20,000; Per Subs 33
Friends of the Library Group

LYNDEBOROUGH

P J A TARBELL LIBRARY, Forest Rd, PO Box 54, 03082-0054. SAN 376-5075. Tel: 603-654-6790. FAX: 603-654-6790. *Librn*, Brenda Cassidy
Library Holdings: Bk Vols 8,500; Bk Titles 7,500; Per Subs 29
Partic in Hillstown Cooperative
Friends of the Library Group

MADISON

P MADISON LIBRARY,* Rte 113, Box 240, 03849-0240. SAN 309-8702. Tel: 603-367-8545. FAX: 603-367-4479. *Librn*, John Kinnaman; *Asst Librn*, Kathy Barrett
Founded 1893. Pop 2,000; Circ 8,950
Library Holdings: Bk Vols 10,000
Friends of the Library Group

MANCHESTER

SR AMERICAN - CANADIAN GENEALOGICAL SOCIETY LIBRARY,* PO Box 6478, 03108-6478. SAN 326-212X. Tel: 603-622-1554. Web Site: ourworld.compuserve.com/homepages/acgs. *Pres*, Albert W Hamel; *VPres*, Ron Marchand
Founded 1973
Library Holdings: Bk Vols 8,000; Bk Titles 4,000
Special Collections: ACA Coll; Canadian Marriage Records; Diocese of Moncton, microfilm; Drouin Index; Loiselle, microfilm & fiche; Manchester, New Hampshire Vitals; N B Records; State of New Hampshire Vitals; State of Vermont Vitals
Publications: American-Canadian Genealogist (quarterly); Repertoires of the Marriages of Several New England Catholic Churches

SR BROOKSIDE CONGREGATIONAL CHURCH LIBRARY,* 2013 Elm St, 03104. SAN 373-4706. Tel: 603-669-2807. *Librn*, Evelyn Graf
1997-1998 Mats Exp $100
Library Holdings: Bk Vols 500

M CATHOLIC MEDICAL CENTER, Health Science Library,* 100 McGregor St, 03102-3770. SAN 309-8710. Tel: 603-626-2520. FAX: 603-668-5348. *Dir*, Samuel King; Staff 3 (MLS 1, Non-MLS 2)
Founded 1978
Library Holdings: Bk Vols 3,081; Per Subs 408
Subject Interests: Cardiac, Geriatrics, Hospital mgt, Orthopedics, Psychiatry
Partic in Greater NE Regional Med Libr Serv; Medline

S CURRIER GALLERY OF ART, Art Reference Library, 201 Myrtle Way, 03104. SAN 377-2446. Tel: 603-669-6144. FAX: 603-626-4166. Web Site: www.currier.org. *Librn*, Kathy Ritter; Staff 1 (MLS 1)
Founded 1929
Library Holdings: Bk Vols 15,000; Per Subs 25
Subject Interests: American painting, Decorative arts, Photography
Restriction: Non-circulating to the public

GM DEPARTMENT OF VETERANS AFFAIRS MEDICAL CENTER LIBRARY, 718 Smyth Rd, 03104. SAN 309-8818. Tel: 603-624-4366, Ext 6030. FAX: 603-626-6503. *Mgr*, Martha Roberts; E-Mail: martha.roberts@med.va.gov; Staff 1 (Non-MLS 1)
Founded 1950
Library Holdings: Bk Vols 1,200; Bk Titles 2,000; Per Subs 190
Subject Interests: Dentistry, Medicine, Nursing
Restriction: Restricted public use, Staff use only
Partic in Health Science Libraries Of New Hampshire & Vermont; Medline; Valnet

L DEVINE MILLIMET & BRANCH LIBRARY, 111 Amherst St, 03101. SAN 371-571X. Tel: 603-695-8669. FAX: 603-669-8547. *Librn*, Betsy Swan; E-Mail: easwan@dmb.com. Subject Specialists: *Law*, Betsy Swan; Staff 2 (Non-MLS 2)
Founded 1947
Library Holdings: Bk Vols 9,000; Bk Titles 4,000; Per Subs 50
Database Vendor: CARL, Lexis-Nexis

M ELLIOT HOSPITAL, Health Sciences Library, 1 Elliot Way, 03103-3599. Tel: 603-628-2334. FAX: 603-628-3507. *Dir*, Samuel King; Tel: 603-628-4208, E-Mail: sking@optima.org; Staff 3 (MLS 1, Non-MLS 2)
Library Holdings: Bk Titles 4,000; Per Subs 200

C HESSER COLLEGE, Kenneth W Galeucia Memorial Library, 3 Sundial Ave, 03103. SAN 321-5814. Tel: 603-668-6660, Ext 2127. FAX: 603-666-4722. E-Mail: library@hesser.edu. *Dir*, Rob Halbeck; E-Mail: rhalbeck@hesser.edu; Staff 5 (MLS 3, Non-MLS 2)
Library Holdings: Bk Vols 30,000; Per Subs 250
Subject Interests: Criminal justice, Info tech, Interior design, Physical therapy, Real estate, Tourism
Partic in OCLC Online Computer Library Center, Inc

L HILLSBOROUGH COUNTY LAW LIBRARY, 300 Chestnut St, 03101. SAN 372-445X. Tel: 603-627-5629. *In Charge*, William Beaupre
Library Holdings: Bk Vols 10,800

S INSTITUT CANADO-AMERICAIN BIBLIOTHEQUE, 52 Concord St, PO Box 989, 03101-0989. SAN 309-8729. Tel: 603-625-8577. FAX: 603-625-1214. *Librn*, Sr Alice Aube
Founded 1918
Library Holdings: Bk Titles 40,000
Subject Interests: Acadians, Franco-Americans, French, Louisiana, Quebecois
Special Collections: 250 museum pieces; Rare Books; Record Coll; sculptures, paintings, photos, old newsp published in French in the US, archives, rare books.

P MANCHESTER CITY LIBRARY, Carpenter Memorial Bldg, 405 Pine St, 03104-6199. SAN 309-8737. Tel: 603-624-6550. FAX: 603-624-6559. Web Site: www.manchester.lib.nh.us. *Dir*, John Brisbin; E-Mail: jbrisbin@ci.manchester.nh.us; *Dep Dir*, Greg Sauer; E-Mail: gsauer@ci.manchester.nh.us; *Ref*, Dee Santoso; Fax: 603-628-6289, E-Mail: dsantoso@ci.manchester.nh.us; *Circ*, Claudia Mayer; E-Mail: cmayer@ci.manchester.nh.us; *Tech Servs*, Denise Van Zanten; Fax: 603-628-6018, E-Mail: dvanzant@ci.manchester.nh.us; *Ch Servs*, Kathryn Urie; E-Mail: kurie@ci.manchester.nh.us; *Automation Syst Coordr*, Susan Deschenes; E-Mail: sdeschen@ci.manchester.nh.us; *Br Coordr*, Susan Dufault; Fax: 603-628-6216, E-Mail: sdufault@ci.manchester.nh.us
Founded 1854
Jul 1999-Jun 2000 Income $1,950,027, City $1,868,796, Other $81,231. Mats Exp $284,933, Books $216,813, Per/Ser (Incl. Access Fees) $24,692, Presv $3,094, Micro $24,849, AV Equip $14,601, Other Print Mats $884
Library Holdings: Bk Vols 275,131; Per Subs 401
Special Collections: New Hampshire Coll
Automation Activity & Vendor Info: (Acquisitions) epixtech, inc.; (Cataloging) epixtech, inc.; (Circulation) epixtech, inc.; (OPAC) epixtech, inc.; (Serials) epixtech, inc.
Partic in GMILCS
Friends of the Library Group
Branches: 1
WEST SIDE COMMUNITY, 76 N Main St, 03102-4084. SAN 377-029X. Tel: 603-624-6560. FAX: 603-628-6216. Web Site: www.manchester.lib.nh.us. *Librn*, Susan Dufault
Library Holdings: Bk Vols 17,764
Friends of the Library Group

S MANCHESTER HISTORIC ASSOCIATION LIBRARY, 129 Amherst St, 03101. SAN 309-8745. Tel: 603-622-7531. FAX: 603-622-0822. E-Mail: history@mha.mv.com. Web Site: www.manchesterhistoric.org. *Curator*, Eileen O'Brien; *Asst Librn*, Arlene Crossett
Founded 1896
Library Holdings: Bk Vols 3,500
Subject Interests: Amoskeag industries, Amoskeag Manufacturing Co (Textiles), History of Manchester, Inc (Real Estate Develop)
Special Collections: Correspondence, notes & reports; Personal Files (F C Dumaine Coll); Photographs - 19th Century & early 20th; Textile Design (SMYRL), graphs & notes
Publications: Guide to Amoskeag Manufacturing Company Collections in the Manchester Historic Association

S MCLANE, GRAF, RAULERSON & MIDDLETON, Law Library, 900 Elm St, Ste 900, 03101-2007. (Mail add: PO Box 326, 03105-0326), SAN 323-7133. Tel: 603-628-1444. FAX: 603-625-6464. E-Mail: library@mclane.com. *Dir, Info Res*, Lesley R Duncan; Tel: 603-628-1445, E-Mail: lesley.duncan@

mclane.com; *Asst Librn*, Cynthia L M David; E-Mail: cynthia.david@mclane.com; *Asst Librn*, Jennifer M Finch; Tel: 603-628-1428, E-Mail: jennifer.finch@mclane.com
Jan 2001-Dec 2001 Income $220,000. Mats Exp $220,000
Library Holdings: Bk Vols 12,000; Bk Titles 2,250; Per Subs 100
Special Collections: New Hampshire legal, legislative, regulatory and historical information
Automation Activity & Vendor Info: (Cataloging) Inmagic, Inc.; (Circulation) Inmagic, Inc.; (OPAC) Inmagic, Inc.; (Serials) Inmagic, Inc.
Database Vendor: Dialog, Lexis-Nexis
Restriction: Not open to public, Private library
Function: ILL limited
Partic in Dialog Corporation; Nelinet, Inc; Weslaw

C NEW HAMPSHIRE COLLEGE, Shapiro Library, 2500 N River Rd, 03106-1045. SAN 309-8753. Tel: 603-645-9605. FAX: 603-645-9685. Web Site: www.nhc.edu/academic/library.htm. *Per*, Ed Daniels; Tel: 605-645-9605, Ext 2163, E-Mail: danieled@nhc.edu; *Cat, Tech Servs*, Deborah Wilcox; Tel: 603-645-9605, Ext 2168, Fax: 603-645-9729, E-Mail: wilcoxde@nhc.edu; *Govt Doc, Ref*, Patricia Beaton; Tel: 603-645-9605, Ext 2166, E-Mail: beatonpa@nhc.edu; *Circ*, Kevin Coakley-Welch; Tel: 603-645-9605, Ext 2225, E-Mail: coakleke@nhc.edu; *Network Services*, Carol West; Tel: 603-645-9605, Ext 2159, E-Mail: westca@nhc.edu; Staff 14 (MLS 6, Non-MLS 8)
Founded 1963. Enrl 5,363; Fac 147; Highest Degree: Doctorate
Jul 1999-Jun 2000 Mats Exp $312,969, Books $119,610, Per/Ser (Incl. Access Fees) $63,428, Presv $91, Micro $23,028, Electronic Ref Mat (Incl. Access Fees) $106,812. Sal $483,671 (Prof $283,208)
Library Holdings: Bk Vols 78,628; Bk Titles 61,349; Per Subs 621
Subject Interests: Accounting, Behav sci, Bus, Computers, Econ, Education, Hotels, Humanities, Indust, Mgt, Soc sci, Tourism
Special Collections: AMEX & NYSE 10K & Annual Reports, fiche; Business History Coll, micro; Business Teacher Education (BTE Coll); Social Science & History (Library of American Civilization), fiche
Automation Activity & Vendor Info: (Acquisitions) epixtech, inc.; (Cataloging) epixtech, inc.; (Circulation) epixtech, inc.; (Course Reserve) epixtech, inc.; (OPAC) epixtech, inc.; (Serials) epixtech, inc.
Publications: Accession List (monthly); Periodical List; Periodical Subject List
Mem of Greater Manchester Integrated Libr Coop
Partic in Nelinet, Inc; New Hampshire College & University Council

C NEW HAMPSHIRE COMMUNITY TECHNICAL COLLEGE, Learning Resources Center, 1066 Front St, 03102. SAN 309-8761. Tel: 603-668-6706. FAX: 603-668-5354. *Dir*, Dr Mary T Marks; Tel: 603-668-6706, Ext 259, E-Mail: mmarks@tec.nh.us; *Circ*, Mark McShane; Tel: 603-668-6706, Ext 239, E-Mail: mmshane@tec.nh.us; *Tech Servs*, Vandana Dhakar; Tel: 603-668-6706, Ext 212, E-Mail: vdhakar@tec.nh.us
Founded 1968. Enrl 1,595; Fac 77
Library Holdings: Bk Vols 16,400; Bk Titles 16,000; Per Subs 170
Subject Interests: Nursing, Technologies
Special Collections: Alternative Energies
Automation Activity & Vendor Info: (Acquisitions) TLC
Database Vendor: Ebsco - EbscoHost
Publications: Research Procedure; Standardized Term Paper Guidelines
Special Services - Satellite Teleconferencing Down-Linking capability & t/v projecting auditorium. 2 multimedia workstations, 6 wordprocessing workstations, 10 PC workstations with wordprocessing programs & internet access. Bookwise Scanning equipment for visually impaired & students with learning disabilities

S NEW HAMPSHIRE YOUTH DEVELOPMENT CENTER LIBRARY, 1056 N River Rd, 03104. SAN 371-7283. Tel: 603-625-5471. FAX: 603-665-9381. E-Mail: ydclib@seresc.k12.nh.us. *Librn*, Lynn N Dermott
Library Holdings: Bk Titles 9,400; Per Subs 85
Automation Activity & Vendor Info: (Cataloging) Follett; (Circulation) Follett

C NOTRE DAME COLLEGE, Paul Harvey Library, 2321 Elm St, 03104. SAN 309-877X. Tel: 603-222-7300. Circulation Tel: 603-222-7300. Reference Tel: 603-222-7301. FAX: 603-222-7307. Web Site: www.notredame.edu. *Dir*, Marie Lasher; Tel: 603-222-7303, E-Mail: mlasher@notredame.edu; *Publ Servs*, Eileen Whittle; *Circ, ILL*, David Ogden; *Tech Servs*, Ann Carle; Tel: 603-222-7302; Staff 6 (MLS 3, Non-MLS 3)
Founded 1950. Enrl 1,200; Fac 67; Highest Degree: Master
Jul 1999-Jun 2000 Income Parent Institution $270,000. Mats Exp $142,000, Books $25,000, Per/Ser (Incl. Access Fees) $67,000, Presv $5,000, Micro $15,000, AV Equip $2,000, Electronic Ref Mat (Incl. Access Fees) $25,000. (Prof $66,000)
Library Holdings: Bk Vols 54,000; Bk Titles 45,000; Per Subs 600
Subject Interests: Education, Health sciences, Psychology, Theology
Special Collections: College Archives; Sisters of Holy Cross American Publications
Database Vendor: Ebsco - EbscoHost, GaleNet, OCLC - First Search, ProQuest, Silverplatter Information Inc.
Publications: Acquisitions List (monthly)
Partic in Health Science Libraries Of New Hampshire & Vermont; Nelinet, Inc; New Hampshire College & University Council; OCLC Online Computer Library Center, Inc

C SAINT ANSELM COLLEGE, Geisel Library, 100 Saint Anselm Dr, 03102-1310. SAN 309-8796. Tel: 603-641-7300. FAX: 603-641-7345. Web Site: www.anselm.edu. *Librn*, Joseph W Constance, Jr; *Acq*, Suzanne Bailey; *Cat*, John Dillon; *ILL*, Susan Gagnon; *Coll Develop*, Elizabeth Holmes; Staff 16 (MLS 16)
Founded 1889. Enrl 2,000; Fac 146; Highest Degree: Bachelor
Jul 1998-Jun 1999 Income $1,200,000. Mats Exp $333,000. Sal $555,840 (Prof $240,000)
Library Holdings: Bk Vols 214,000; Bk Titles 160,120; Per Subs 1,923
Subject Interests: History, New Eng hist, Nursing, Theology
Special Collections: Archives of College; New England History
Publications: Monthly Accession List
Partic in Nelinet, Inc; New Hampshire College & University Council; OCLC Online Computer Library Center, Inc
Friends of the Library Group

L SHEEHAN, PHINNEY, BASS & GREEN LIBRARY, 1000 Elm St, PO Box 3701, 03105. SAN 371-568X. Tel: 603-668-0300. FAX: 603-627-8121. E-Mail: postmaster@sheehan.com. Web Site: www.sheehan.com.; Staff 3 (MLS 1, Non-MLS 2)
Library Holdings: Bk Vols 10,000

C UNIVERSITY OF NEW HAMPSHIRE AT MANCHESTER LIBRARY, 400 Commercial St, 03101. SAN 320-6955. Tel: 603-641-4173. Interlibrary Loan Service Tel: 603-641-4172. FAX: 603-641-4124. E-Mail: unhmlibrary@unh.edu. Web Site: www.unh.edu/unhm/library.html. *Dir*, Ann E Donahue; Tel: 603-641-4123, E-Mail: adonahue@cisunix.unh.edu; Staff 5 (MLS 3, Non-MLS 2)
Founded 1967. Enrl 900; Fac 40; Highest Degree: Master
Jul 1999-Jun 2000 Income $285,582. Mats Exp $89,643, Books $18,300, Per/Ser (Incl. Access Fees) $50,400, AV Equip $900, Electronic Ref Mat (Incl. Access Fees) $20,043. Sal $131,710 (Prof $101,210)
Library Holdings: Bk Vols 25,000; Per Subs 300
Subject Interests: Deafness, Early New Hampshire newspapers, Sign lang
Special Collections: Twentieth Century European Intellectual Thought
Automation Activity & Vendor Info: (Cataloging) Innovative Interfaces Inc.; (Circulation) Innovative Interfaces Inc.; (Course Reserve) Innovative Interfaces Inc.; (OPAC) Innovative Interfaces Inc.; (Serials) Innovative Interfaces Inc.
Database Vendor: Ebsco - EbscoHost, Wilson - Wilson Web
Publications: Handbook; Library Research Guides
Partic in Nelinet, Inc; New Hampshire College & University Council
Special Services for the Deaf - TTY machine
Special Services for the Blind - Braille

MARLBOROUGH

P FROST FREE LIBRARY,* 28 S Main St, PO Box 416, 03455. SAN 309-8826. Tel: 603-876-4479. E-Mail: frostfreelib@monad.net. *Dir*, Lisa R Bearce; *Asst Librn*, Dolores Biron
Founded 1865. Pop 2,025; Circ 12,818
Library Holdings: Bk Vols 16,000; Per Subs 47
Publications: Bemis History of Marlborough
Mem of New England Libr Asn
Friends of the Library Group

MARLOW

P MARLOW TOWN LIBRARY,* Church St, 03456-0417. (Mail add: PO Box 417, 03456-0417), SAN 309-8834. Tel: 603-446-3466. *Librn*, Patricia Strickland
Library Holdings: Bk Vols 11,000; Per Subs 15
Partic in Nubanusit Library Cooperative

MASON

P MASON PUBLIC LIBRARY, 16 Darling Hill Rd, 03048. SAN 309-8842. Tel: 603-878-3867. FAX: 603-878-6146. E-Mail: masonlib@monad.net. Web Site: www.top.monad.net/~masonlib/. *Dir*, Susanne V Wolpert
Pop 1,270; Circ 8,858
Library Holdings: Bk Vols 10,571; Per Subs 22
Special Collections: Video Classics Project Coll
Database Vendor: ProQuest
Publications: Booklist

MEREDITH

P MEREDITH PUBLIC LIBRARY, Benjamin M Smith Memorial Library, 91 Main St, PO Box 808, 03253-0808. SAN 309-8850. Tel: 603-279-4303. FAX: 603-279-5352. *Dir, Librn*, Lydia M Torr; *Asst Librn*, Marilyn E Rushton; Staff 7 (MLS 2, Non-MLS 5)

Founded 1882. Pop 4,636; Circ 115,201
Jan 2000-Dec 2000 Income $315,099. Mats Exp $60,570. Sal $226,646
Library Holdings: Bk Vols 31,797; Per Subs 72
Automation Activity & Vendor Info: (Circulation) Sagebrush Corporation

MERIDEN

P MERIDEN LIBRARY, 22 Bean Rd, 03770-0128. (Mail add: PO Box 128, 03770-0128), SAN 309-8869. Tel: 603-469-3252. E-Mail: meriden.library@valley.net. *Librn*, Bettyann Dole
Founded 1797. Pop 2,200; Circ 6,413
Jan 1999-Dec 1999 Income $22,641. Mats Exp $6,201. Sal $14,064
Library Holdings: Bk Vols 16,640; Per Subs 86
Subject Interests: Artifacts, History
Special Collections: Boyd's History (Plainfield) 4 vols; Meriden Bird Club; Plainfield Oral History, 4 vols
Open Mon 2-8, Tues & Thurs 10-12 & 2-6, Sat 10-1

MERRIMACK

S KOLLSMAN LIBRARY,* 220 Daniel Webster Hwy, 03054-4809. SAN 309-8877. Tel: 603-889-2500. *Mgr*, Bill Wagner
Founded 1939
Subject Interests: Aeronautical instrumentation, Electro-optics
Partic in Nelinet, Inc

P MERRIMACK PUBLIC LIBRARY, 470 Daniel Webster Hwy, 03054-3694. SAN 309-8885. Tel: 603-424-5021. FAX: 603-424-7312. E-Mail: mmkpl@merrimack.lib.nh.us. Web Site: www.merrimack.lib.nh.us. *Dir*, Janet Angus; *Asst Dir*, Debra Covell; *Ad Servs*, Sue Jefferson; *Ch Servs*, Beverly Little; *Ref*, Katie Martin; *Tech Servs*, Shannon Tennant; Staff 29 (MLS 6, Non-MLS 23)
Founded 1892. Pop 23,340; Circ 247,341 Sal $452,738 (Prof $168,468)
Library Holdings: Bk Titles 78,000; Per Subs 200
Automation Activity & Vendor Info: (Acquisitions) Brodart
Publications: Library Link
Friends of the Library Group

S THOMAS MORE COLLEGE OF LIBERAL ARTS, Warren Memorial Library, 6 Manchester St, 03054-4805. SAN 373-0816. Tel: 603-880-8308. FAX: 603-880-9280. Web Site: www.thomasmorecollege.edu. *Dir*, Mary K Mumbach
Enrl 70; Fac 8; Highest Degree: Bachelor
Library Holdings: Bk Vols 35,000; Bk Titles 28,000
Subject Interests: History, Literature, Philosophy, Religion

MILAN

P MILAN PUBLIC LIBRARY,* Bridge St, 03588. SAN 309-8893. Tel: 603-449-7307. E-Mail: milanlib@ncia.com. *Dir*, Lois Alger; *Librn*, Fern Stiles
Pop 1,088
Library Holdings: Bk Vols 1,841
Subject Interests: Local history
Open Mon 6-8, Tues, Wed & Thurs 1:30-4:30, Sat 2:30-4:30

MILFORD

P WADLEIGH MEMORIAL LIBRARY, 49 Nashua St, 03055-3753. SAN 309-8907. Tel: 603-673-2408. FAX: 603-672-6064. E-Mail: wadleigh@wadleigh.lib.nh.us. Web Site: www.wadleigh.lib.nh.us. *Dir*, Arthur L Bryan; E-Mail: artbryan@wadleigh.lib.nh.us; *Ref*, Debra Spratt; E-Mail: dspratt@wadleigh.lib.nh.us; *Ch Servs*, Stephanie Minteer; Staff 9 (MLS 3, Non-MLS 6)
Founded 1868. Pop 13,100; Circ 165,000
Jan 2000-Dec 2000 Income $529,472, City $478,972, Locally Generated Income $28,000, Other $22,500. Mats Exp $73,000, Books $43,300, Per/Ser (Incl. Access Fees) $7,100, Micro $600, AV Equip $6,000, Electronic Ref Mat (Incl. Access Fees) $16,000. Sal $338,794 (Prof $115,609)
Library Holdings: Bk Vols 61,934; Per Subs 185
Subject Interests: Ch storytelling, Fairy tales
Special Collections: Hutchinson Family (singers); Local History; Rothovius (scholarly research)
Automation Activity & Vendor Info: (Acquisitions) epixtech, inc.; (Cataloging) epixtech, inc.; (Circulation) epixtech, inc.; (OPAC) epixtech, inc.; (Serials) epixtech, inc.
Database Vendor: Ebsco - EbscoHost, IAC - Info Trac, OCLC - First Search, ProQuest
Partic in GMILCS; Hillstown Cooperative
Friends of the Library Group

MILTON

P NUTE LIBRARY,* PO Box 697, 03851. SAN 350-5359. Tel: 603-652-7829. FAX: 603-652-4793. *Librn*, Barbara Loiselle; *Asst Librn*, Karen Brown
Pop 4,000; Circ 15,069
Library Holdings: Bk Vols 15,500; Per Subs 78
Subject Interests: Local history
Mem of Cent Libr District

MILTON MILLS

P MILTON FREE PUBLIC LIBRARY, 13 Main St, PO Box 127, 03852-0127. Tel: 603-473-8535. *Admin Dir, Dir*, Debora J Banks; *Asst Librn*, Victoria E Kelly; Staff 1 (Non-MLS 1)
Founded 1916. Circ 2,149
1999-2000 Income $18,327, City $17,800, Locally Generated Income $527. Mats Exp $2,100, Books $2,000, Per/Ser (Incl. Access Fees) $100. Sal $11,076
Library Holdings: Bk Vols 9,671

MONROE

P MONROE PUBLIC LIBRARY,* Plains Rd, PO Box 67, 03771-0067. SAN 309-8915. Tel: 603-638-4736. *Librn*, Beverly Everett; *Asst Dir*, Becky Gibson
Pop 618; Circ 17,887
Library Holdings: Bk Titles 19,000; Per Subs 56

MONT VERNON

P DALAND MEMORIAL LIBRARY, Main St, PO Box 335, 03057-0335. SAN 309-8923. Tel: 603-673-7888. FAX: 603-673-7888. E-Mail: daland@nh.ultranet.com. *Librn*, Edith March; *Ch Servs*, Karen MacDonald
Founded 1892. Pop 2,000
Library Holdings: Bk Vols 12,000
Mem of Hillstown Coop District; SE Libr District
Friends of the Library Group

MOULTONBORO

P MOULTONBORO PUBLIC LIBRARY, 4 Holland St, 03254. (Mail add: PO Box 150, 03254-0150), SAN 309-8931. Tel: 603-476-8895. FAX: 603-476-5262. *Librn*, Nancy McCue
Founded 1890. Pop 3,500; Circ 61,725
Library Holdings: Bk Vols 30,000; Per Subs 50
Subject Interests: Drama, Local history
Automation Activity & Vendor Info: (Cataloging) Sagebrush Corporation; (Circulation) Sagebrush Corporation
Mem of Cent Libr District
Friends of the Library Group

NASHUA

C DANIEL WEBSTER COLLEGE, Anne Bridge Baddour Library, 20 University Dr, 03063-1300. SAN 309-8966. Tel: 603-577-6559. FAX: 603-577-6199. Web Site: www.dwc.edu/library. *Dir*, Irene M H Herold; Tel: 603-577-6540, E-Mail: herold@dwc.edu; *Head Tech Servs*, Jennifer Diffin; Tel: 603-577-6543, E-Mail: diffin@dwc.edu; *Head, Circ*, Marilyn Frankland; Tel: 603-577-6542, E-Mail: franklan@dwc.edu; *Head, Info Serv*, Keith Martin; Tel: 603-577-6541, E-Mail: martink@dwc.edu; *Ser*, Glenna Rosenstein; Tel: 603-577-6541, E-Mail: rosenstein@dwc.edu; *Ref*, Barbara Boucher; Tel: 603-577-6544; *Ref*, Becky Schulz; Tel: 603-577-6544, E-Mail: schulz@dwc.edu; *Cat*, Maureen Meagher; Tel: 603-577-6544, E-Mail: meagher@dwc.edu; *Media Spec*, Jennifer Darrow; Tel: 603-577-6144, E-Mail: darrow@dwc.edu; *Acq*, Nicole Karlsson; Tel: 603-577-6546, E-Mail: nkarlsson@dwc.edu. Subject Specialists: *Administration*, Irene M H Herold; Staff 10 (MLS 5, Non-MLS 5)
Founded 1965. Enrl 1,099; Highest Degree: Bachelor
Jul 1999-Jun 2000 Mats Exp $156,000, Books $56,000, Per/Ser (Incl. Access Fees) $49,590, AV Equip $2,000, Electronic Ref Mat (Incl. Access Fees) $19,770. Sal $222,000 (Prof $130,000)
Library Holdings: Bk Vols 35,443; Bk Titles 31,244; Per Subs 336
Subject Interests: Aviation, Bus mgt, Computer science, Engineering, Sport mgt
Special Collections: Advisory Circulars; Aviation materials
Automation Activity & Vendor Info: (Acquisitions) MultiLIS; (Cataloging) MultiLIS; (Circulation) MultiLIS; (OPAC) MultiLIS; (Serials) MultiLIS
Database Vendor: Ebsco - EbscoHost, OCLC - First Search
Function: Research library
Partic in Nelinet, Inc; New Hampshire College & University Council

S NASHUA CORP, Information Center,* 11 Trafalgar Square, 2nd Flr, 03063-1995. SAN 309-8958. Tel: 603-880-2618. FAX: 603-880-2541. *Ref*, Jerry O'Connor; E-Mail: joconnor@corprdz.mv.com
Founded 1918
Library Holdings: Bk Vols 5,500; Per Subs 95

Subject Interests: Chemistry, Coating tech, Discrete particle tech, Physics, Reprography
Special Collections: Patents, Technical Reports & Laboratory Notebooks Coll

P NASHUA PUBLIC LIBRARY,* 2 Court St, 03060. SAN 350-5413. Tel: 603-594-3412. FAX: 603-594-3457. *Dir*, Clarke S Davis; *Asst Dir*, Robert C Frost; *Ad Servs, Online Servs, Ref*, Nancy Grant; *Ch Servs*, Kathy E Bolton; *Media Spec*, Ann R Warren; *Acq*, Helen Bonenfant; *Cat*, Margaret Gleeson; *Circ*, Sharon A Woodman; *ILL*, Cathy Lukasik; *Bkmobile Coordr*, Eugene Dunn; *Publ Servs*, Trudy Wheatley
Founded 1867. Pop 78,000; Circ 636,989
Library Holdings: Bk Vols 206,000; Per Subs 1,500
Subject Interests: Architecture, Art, Bus, Music
Special Collections: Local & State Histories (Hunt Room Coll)
Publications: Nashua Experience: History in the making, 1673-1978
Partic in Dialog Corporation; NY Times Info Bank
Branches: 1
CHANDLER MEMORIAL - ETHNIC CENTER, 257 Main St, 03060. SAN 350-5448. Tel: 603-594-3415. *Coordr*, Margaret Merrigan
Library Holdings: Bk Vols 11,000
Special Collections: Foreign Language, bks, mags
Bookmobiles: 1

J NEW HAMPSHIRE COMMUNITY TECHNICAL COLLEGE, Learning Resource Center, 505 Amherst St, PO Box 2052, 03061-2052. SAN 309-8974. Tel: 603-882-6923. FAX: 603-882-8690. *Dir*, William A McIntyre; *Librn*, Rownak Hussain; Staff 4 (MLS 2, Non-MLS 2)
Founded 1971. Enrl 1,000; Fac 40; Highest Degree: Associate
Library Holdings: Bk Titles 12,500; Per Subs 250
Subject Interests: Automotive, Bus, Computer, Drafting, Electronics tech, Machining, Mat sci
Publications: Handbook (user's guide); PR materials; reference guides

R PILGRIM CONGREGATIONAL CHURCH, Goodhue Memorial Library, 4 Watson St, 03060. SAN 309-8982. Tel: 603-882-1801. FAX: 603-882-1801. *In Charge*, Virginia Hart
Library Holdings: Bk Vols 2,100
Subject Interests: Children's, Congregational info, Fiction

CR RIVIER COLLEGE, Regina Library, 420 Main St, 03060-5086. SAN 309-8990. Tel: 603-897-8256. FAX: 603-897-8889. E-Mail: library@rivier.edu. Web Site: www.rivier.edu. *Dir*, Marilyn Smith Bregoli; Tel: 603-897-8576, E-Mail: mbregoli@rivier.edu; *Assoc Dir*, Elizabeth Donnelly; Tel: 603-897-8601, E-Mail: edonnelly@rivier.edu; *Asst Dir*, Donna Page; Tel: 603-897-8563, E-Mail: dpage@rivier.edu; *Cat*, Amy DeBrower; Tel: 603-897-8671, E-Mail: adebrower@rivier.edu; *Acq*, Cynthia Garside; Tel: 603-897-8535; *Librn*, Rownak Hussain; *Coll Develop*, Sister Arlene Callahan; *Syst Coordr*, Elaine Bean; Tel: 603-897-8672, E-Mail: ebean@simmons.edu; Staff 15 (MLS 7, Non-MLS 8)
Founded 1933. Enrl 1,685; Highest Degree: Master
Jul 2000-Jun 2001 Income $349,500. Mats Exp $180,860, Books $109,000, Per/Ser (Incl. Access Fees) $60,000, Micro $10,660, AV Equip $1,200, Electronic Ref Mat (Incl. Access Fees) $39,000. Sal $305,000 (Prof $205,000)
Library Holdings: Bk Titles 78,000; Per Subs 512
Subject Interests: Bus, Education, Law, Nursing
Special Collections: Franco-American Literary Criticism (Rocheleau-Rouleau Coll); Patristics (Gilbert Coll)
Automation Activity & Vendor Info: (Cataloging) Innovative Interfaces Inc.; (Circulation) Innovative Interfaces Inc.; (OPAC) Innovative Interfaces Inc.; (Serials) Innovative Interfaces Inc.
Database Vendor: Ebsco - EbscoHost, Lexis-Nexis, Silverplatter Information Inc., Wilson - Wilson Web
Function: ILL available
Partic in New Hampshire College & University Council

M ST JOSEPH HOSPITAL, Health Science Library,* 172 Kinsley St, 03061. SAN 377-9572. Tel: 603-595-3143. FAX: 603-889-1508. E-Mail: sjhlib@aol.com. *Librn*, Cindy Sloan
Library Holdings: Bk Titles 400; Per Subs 150
Partic in Basic Health Sciences Library Network; Health Science Libraries Of New Hampshire & Vermont; National Network of Libraries of Medicine - Greater Midwest Region; North Atlantic Health Sciences Libraries, Inc; UCMP

S SANDERS A LOCKHEED MARTIN CO, Technical Information Center, 95 Canal St, PO Box 868, 03061-0868. SAN 309-9008. Tel: 603-885-2671, 603-885-4144. FAX: 603-885-2919, 603-885-4143. *In Charge*, James A Cirillo; E-Mail: james.a.cirillo@lmco.com
Founded 1955
Library Holdings: Bk Vols 25,000; Per Subs 500
Subject Interests: Computer science, Electronics, Engineering, Mathematics, Microwave, Physics, Telecommunications
Restriction: Not open to public
Partic in Lockheed Info Syst Network

M SOUTHERN NEW HAMPSHIRE REGIONAL MEDICAL CENTER, Health Sciences Library,* PO Box 2014, 03061-2014. SAN 327-3962. Tel: 603-886-3211, Ext 2750. *Librn*, Janis Silver
Library Holdings: Bk Titles 850; Per Subs 100
Restriction: By appointment only
Partic in Docline

NELSON

P OLIVIA RODHAM MEMORIAL LIBRARY,* HCR 33 Box 656, 03457. SAN 324-2862. Tel: 603-847-3214. E-Mail: oliviar@top.monad.net. Web Site: www.top.monad.net/~oliviar/index.htm. *Librn*, Kristine Finnegan; E-Mail: finnegan@dublinschool.org
Library Holdings: Bk Vols 6,077; Bk Titles 4,000; Per Subs 25
Partic in Nubanusit Library Cooperative
Open Mon 3-6, Tues & Thurs 5-8, Wed 2-5 & Sat 9-12
Friends of the Library Group

NEW BOSTON

P WHIPPLE FREE LIBRARY, Central Sq, PO Box 237, 03070=0237. SAN 309-9016. Tel: 603-487-3391. FAX: 603-487-2886. E-Mail: wflb@grolen.com. *Librn*, Sarah Chapman
Pop 4,000
2000-2001 Mats Exp Books $12,000
Library Holdings: Bk Vols 18,000; Per Subs 70
Friends of the Library Group

NEW CASTLE

P NEW CASTLE PUBLIC LIBRARY,* Wentworth Rd, PO Box 329, 03854-0329. SAN 309-9024. Tel: 603-431-6773. FAX: 603-431-6773. *Librn*, Jane E Barrett
Pop 964; Circ 6,500
Library Holdings: Bk Vols 10,000
Subject Interests: Genealogy, Local history, Popular new fiction
Special Collections: Local History, bks, prints
Mem of SE Libr District
Friends of the Library Group

NEW DURHAM

P NEW DURHAM PUBLIC LIBRARY,* 2 Old Bay Rd, PO Box 400, 03855-0400. SAN 309-9032. Tel: 603-859-2201. FAX: 603-859-2201 (Call first). E-Mail: ndpl@worldpath.net. Web Site: www.worldpath.net/~ndpl. *Librn*, Rozalind Benoit; *Asst Librn*, Peggy Ferlend
Pop 2,000; Circ 7,500
Jan 1998-Dec 1998 Income $36,000. Mats Exp $7,800. Sal $22,000
Library Holdings: Bk Titles 12,000; Per Subs 32
Subject Interests: Local genealogy, Local history

NEW HAMPTON

P GORDON-NASH LIBRARY, 69 Main St, 03256-0549. (Mail add: PO Box 549, 03256-0549), SAN 309-9040. Tel: 603-744-8061. FAX: 603-744-6555. *Dir*, Linda Dowal; *Asst Dir*, Diane Gilson; *Ch Servs*, Betsey Martel; Staff 3 (Non-MLS 3)
Founded 1895. Pop 1,723; Circ 44,000
1998-1999 Income $387,627. Mats Exp $23,823, Books $13,125, Per/Ser (Incl. Access Fees) $4,386, Presv $349, AV Equip $4,359, Other Print Mats $1,604. Sal $109,466 (Prof $28,960)
Library Holdings: Bk Vols 40,096; Bk Titles 39,484; Per Subs 113
Subject Interests: NH Shakers
Friends of the Library Group

NEW LONDON

C COLBY-SAWYER COLLEGE, Susan Colgate Cleveland Library & Learning Center, 100 Main St, 03257-4648. SAN 309-9067. Tel: 603-526-3685. FAX: 603-526-3777. E-Mail: library@colby-sawyer.edu. Web Site: www.colby-sawyer.edu/information/index.html. *Librn*, Carrie P Thomas; Tel: 603-526-3686, E-Mail: cathomas@colby-sawyer.edu; *Cat*, Jane Graham; Tel: 603-526-3688, E-Mail: jgraham@colby-sawyer.edu; *Acq*, Nancy Langley; Tel: 603-526-3684, E-Mail: nlangley@colby-sawyer.edu; *Archivist, Ref*, Lianne Hanson; Tel: 603-526-3687, E-Mail: lhanson@colby-sawyer.edu; *Circ*, Lisa Eaton; E-Mail: leaton@colby-sawyer.edu
Founded 1837. Enrl 880; Fac 69; Highest Degree: Bachelor
Jul 1998-Jun 1999 Income $420,000. Mats Exp $124,600, Books $65,000, Per/Ser (Incl. Access Fees) $55,000, Presv $600, Micro $4,000. Sal $195,000 (Prof $85,000)
Library Holdings: Bk Vols 80,000; Per Subs 800
Automation Activity & Vendor Info: (Cataloging) epixtech, inc.; (Circulation) epixtech, inc.; (OPAC) epixtech, inc.

Database Vendor: Ebsco - EbscoHost, OCLC - First Search, Silverplatter Information Inc., Wilson - Wilson Web
Partic in Nelinet, Inc; New Hampshire College & University Council
Friends of the Library Group

M NEW LONDON HOSPITAL, Medical Library,* 270 County Rd, 03257. SAN 378-0201. Tel: 603-526-2911, Ext 5226. FAX: 603-526-2990. *Librn*, Marion Allen
Library Holdings: Bk Titles 2,500; Per Subs 30
Partic in Basic Health Sciences Library Network; Health Science Libraries Of New Hampshire & Vermont; New England Libr Asn; North Atlantic Health Sciences Libraries, Inc

P TRACY MEMORIAL LIBRARY,* Main St, PO Box 1919, 03257. SAN 309-9075. Tel: 603-526-4656. FAX: 603-526-8035. Web Site: www.cyberportal.net/traceymemlib2. *Librn*, Virginia Foose
Pop 3,168; Circ 94,444
Jan 1998-Dec 1998 Income $248,803, City $164,182, Locally Generated Income $21,937, Other $20,453. Mats Exp $25,421, Books $20,506, Per/Ser (Incl. Access Fees) $3,715, Presv $200, AV Equip $1,000. Sal $167,398 (Prof $70,424)
Library Holdings: Bk Vols 27,000; Per Subs 123
Publications: Tracings (newsletter)
Partic in Area Forum Two
Friends of the Library Group

NEWBURY

P NEWBURY PUBLIC LIBRARY, 933 Rte 103, 03255-5803. (Mail add: PO Box 245, 03242-0245), SAN 309-9083. Tel: 603-763-5803. FAX: 603-763-5803. Web Site: www.town.newbury.nh.us/library. *Librn*, Alan Brown; E-Mail: alanb@sugar-river.net; *Asst Librn*, Alice Lynn; Staff 2 (MLS 1, Non-MLS 1)
Founded 1893
Library Holdings: Bk Titles 9,200; Per Subs 40
Mem of W of the Merrimack

NEWFIELDS

P NEWFIELDS PUBLIC LIBRARY, 76 Main St, PO Box 200, 03856-0200. SAN 309-9091. Tel: 603-778-8169. *Librn*, Doris Goerner; *Asst Librn*, Dottie Evans
Founded 1893. Pop 1,300; Circ 4,600
Jan 1999-Dec 1999 Income $13,257, Locally Generated Income $2,362, Other $8,620. Mats Exp $3,709, Books $3,528, Per/Ser (Incl. Access Fees) $181. Sal $4,517 (Prof $3,779)
Library Holdings: Bk Vols 10,000; Per Subs 16
Subject Interests: Newfields hist
Mem of SE Libr District
Open Tues 1-6, Wed & Thurs 9:30-11:30 & 2:30-6:30, Fri 1-4 & 6:30-8:30
Friends of the Library Group

NEWINGTON

P LANGDON PUBLIC LIBRARY,* Nimble Hill Rd, Rte 151, 03801. SAN 309-9105. Tel: 603-436-5154. E-Mail: langdon@nh.ulternet.com. *Librn*, Duane Shaffer
Founded 1892. Pop 716; Circ 7,839
Library Holdings: Bk Titles 17,000; Per Subs 36
Special Collections: Historical Records & Photographs Coll
Publications: Newington Neighbor (quarterly newsletter)

NEWMARKET

S NEWMARKET HISTORICAL SOCIETY, Stone School Museum Collections Library, Granite St, 03857. (Mail add: 51 N Main St, 03857), SAN 371-6686. Tel: 603-659-3652. *Curator, Librn*, Sylvia Fitts Getchell
Founded 1966
Library Holdings: Bk Vols 300
Subject Interests: Local history
Special Collections: Newmarket & Area of Seacoast New Hampshire, deeds, letters, mss & photogs

P NEWMARKET PUBLIC LIBRARY,* One Elm St, 03857-1201. SAN 309-9113. Tel: 603-659-5311. FAX: 603-659-8506. *Librn*, Sharon Kidney
Pop 4,292; Circ 10,517
Library Holdings: Bk Vols 27,000; Per Subs 60
Subject Interests: Town hist
Mem of SE Libr District
Friends of the Library Group

NEWPORT

P RICHARDS FREE LIBRARY, 58 N Main St, 03773-1597. SAN 309-9121. Tel: 603-863-3430. FAX: 603-863-3022. E-Mail: rfl@newport.lib.nh.us. Web Site: www.newport.lib.nh.us. *Dir*, Andrea Thorpe; E-Mail: athorpe@newport.lib.nh.us; Staff 7 (MLS 1, Non-MLS 6)
Founded 1888. Pop 6,110
1999-2000 Income $191,135, City $154,035, Other $37,100. Mats Exp $20,950. Sal $120,281
Library Holdings: Bk Vols 32,786; Per Subs 96
Special Collections: Kenneth Andler N H Hist Coll; Local Newspapers (Argus Champion 1878 to present), micro; Sarah Josepha Hale Coll
Automation Activity & Vendor Info: (Circulation) Sagebrush Corporation; (OPAC) Sagebrush Corporation
Friends of the Library Group

P UNITY FREE PUBLIC LIBRARY, HCR 66 Box 176, 03773. SAN 309-9741. Tel: 603-543-3253. FAX: 603-542-9736. E-Mail: unitylibrary@fcgnetworks.net. *Librn*, Mary Ellen Bellimer
Pop 1,300; Circ 3,086
Library Holdings: Bk Vols 4,200; Per Subs 30
Special Collections: Film Strip Coll; government publications; rare books, town history
Mem of SW Libr District
Friends of the Library Group

NEWTON

P GALE LIBRARY, 16 S Main St, 03858-3310. (Mail add: PO Box 329, 03858-0329), SAN 309-913X. Tel: 603-382-4691. FAX: 603-382-2528. E-Mail: gale@ttlc.net. Web Site: members.ttlc.net/~gale. *Dir*, Andrea Ange; Staff 6 (Non-MLS 6)
Pop 4,000; Circ 24,000
Jan 1998-Dec 1999 Income $73,000. Mats Exp $17,000. Sal $41,000
Library Holdings: Bk Vols 23,000; Per Subs 50
Special Collections: New Hampshire Coll
Mem of SE Libr District
Partic in Merri-Hill-Rock Library Cooperative
Open Mon & Wed 12-8, Tues & Sat 10-2 & Fri 10-6
Friends of the Library Group

NORTH CONWAY

M MEMORIAL HOSPITAL, Health Sciences Library,* PO Box 5001, 03860. SAN 377-9513. Tel: 603-356-5461. FAX: 503-356-9048. *Mgr*, Diane Betz
Library Holdings: Bk Titles 150; Per Subs 25
Partic in Health Science Libraries Of New Hampshire & Vermont; National Network of Libraries of Medicine - Greater Midwest Region; North Atlantic Health Sciences Libraries, Inc

S MOUNT WASHINGTON OBSERVATORY, Gladys Brooks Memorial Library, 2936 Main St, PO Box 2310, 03860-2310. SAN 371-2370. Tel: 603-356-2137. FAX: 603-356-0307. Web Site: www.mountwashington.org. *Dir*, Peter Crane
Library Holdings: Bk Vols 1,400
Subject Interests: Polar regions, White Mountains
Open Thurs 10-5, other times by appt

P NORTH CONWAY PUBLIC LIBRARY,* 2719 Main St, PO Box 409, 03860-0409. SAN 376-5083. Tel: 603-356-2961. FAX: 603-356-2961. E-Mail: ncpl@landmarknet.net. *Librn*, Carrie Gleason
Jan 1998-Dec 1999 Income $40,000
Library Holdings: Bk Vols 21,000; Per Subs 85
Partic in Northern Carroll County Coop

NORTH HAMPTON

P NORTH HAMPTON PUBLIC LIBRARY, 237A Atlantic Ave, 03862-0628. SAN 309-9148. Tel: 603-964-6326. FAX: 603-964-1107. E-Mail: nhpl@nh.ultranet.com. Web Site: www.nh.ultranet.com/~nhpl. *Dir*, Pamela Schwotzer; *Asst Dir, Ch Servs*, Lorreen Keating; *Circ*, Martha Jones; Staff 5 (MLS 1, Non-MLS 4)
Founded 1892. Pop 4,200; Circ 38,914
Jul 1999-Jun 2000 Income $220,955, City $204,715, Other $16,240. Mats Exp $34,924, Books $28,793, Per/Ser (Incl. Access Fees) $3,116, AV Equip $1,652, Electronic Ref Mat (Incl. Access Fees) $302. Sal $143,867 (Prof $88,995)
Library Holdings: Bk Titles 26,533; Per Subs 83
Automation Activity & Vendor Info: (Cataloging) Athena; (Circulation) Athena
Database Vendor: OCLC - First Search, ProQuest
Friends of the Library Group

NORTH HAVERHILL

P NORTH HAVERHILL LIBRARY,* PO Box 55, 03774-9740. SAN 309-8389. Tel: 603-787-6152. *Librn*, Marilyn Spooner
Pop 1,200; Circ 7,000
Library Holdings: Bk Vols 20,000; Per Subs 50
Mem of North Country District

NORTH WOODSTOCK

P MOOSILAUKE PUBLIC LIBRARY, Lost River Rd, PO Box 21, 03262. SAN 309-9156. Tel: 603-745-9971. *Librn*, William D Goyette; Staff 2 (MLS 1, Non-MLS 1)
Pop 1,167; Circ 2,911
1999-2000 Mats Exp $7,500
Library Holdings: Bk Vols 9,555; Per Subs 30
Special Collections: White Mountains & Local History

NORTHFIELD

P HALL MEMORIAL LIBRARY, 18 Park St, 03276. SAN 309-9717. Tel: 603-286-8971. FAX: 603-286-2278. E-Mail: hallmemo@worldpath.net. *Librn*, Mary Ahlgren
Founded 1887. Pop 8,500; Circ 34,700
Jan 2000-Dec 2000 Income $199,575, City $77,000, Locally Generated Income $118,675, Other $3,900. Mats Exp $20,560, Books $16,000, Per/Ser (Incl. Access Fees) $2,160, AV Equip $2,000, Electronic Ref Mat (Incl. Access Fees) $400. Sal $68,950 (Prof $31,000)
Library Holdings: Bk Vols 17,000; Per Subs 42; High Interest/Low Vocabulary Bk Vols 60
Special Collections: 19th Century; Northfield History, bks, illustrations, town rpts & tax lists
Partic in Scrooge & Marley Cooperative

NORTHWOOD

P CHESLEY MEMORIAL LIBRARY, 8 Mountain Ave, PO Box 157, 03261-0157. SAN 309-9172. Tel: 603-942-5472. FAX: 603-942-5132. E-Mail: chesley1@worldpath.net. *Librn*, Donna Bunker; Staff 1 (Non-MLS 1)
Pop 3,240; Circ 22,898
2000-2001 Income City $84,807. Mats Exp $13,500, Books $12,000, Per/Ser (Incl. Access Fees) $1,000, Other Print Mats $500. Sal $45,503 (Prof $24,752)
Library Holdings: Bk Vols 16,000; Per Subs 30
Friends of the Library Group

NOTTINGHAM

P BLAISDELL MEMORIAL LIBRARY, Rte 152, Box 115, 03290-0115. SAN 320-8451. Tel: 603-679-8484. E-Mail: blaisdel@ultranet.com. *Librn*, Rhoda Capron
Pop 2,500; Circ 14,200
Library Holdings: Bk Vols 12,000; Per Subs 10
Friends of the Library Group

ORFORD

P ORFORD FREE LIBRARY,* PO Box 186, 03777. SAN 309-9199. Tel: 603-353-9166. E-Mail: orfordfreelibrary@connriver.net. *Librn*, Gina Donegan
Founded 1893. Pop 926; Circ 2,211
Library Holdings: Bk Vols 5,000; Per Subs 10
Special Collections: Clothing; Old Snapshots
Mem of North Country Library System
Friends of the Library Group

P ORFORD SOCIAL LIBRARY,* Main St, PO Box 189, 03777. SAN 309-9202. Tel: 603-353-9756. *Librn*, Sarah Putnam
Pop 926; Circ 1,778
Library Holdings: Bk Vols 5,800; Per Subs 15
Mem of North Country District
Friends of the Library Group

PELHAM

P PELHAM PUBLIC LIBRARY,* 5 Main St, 03076. SAN 309-9229. Tel: 603-635-7581. FAX: 603-635-6952. E-Mail: library@pelham-nh.com. *Dir*, Betty Kelley; Staff 1 (MLS 1)
Founded 1896. Pop 9,000
Library Holdings: Bk Vols 30,000; Per Subs 95
Partic in Area Libr Forum VI; Merri-Hill-Rock Library Cooperative
Friends of the Library Group

PEMBROKE

P PEMBROKE TOWN LIBRARY,* 261 Pembroke St, 03275. SAN 309-9237. Tel: 603-485-7851. FAX: 603-485-3351. Web Site: www.people.ne.mediaone.net/pembrokelibrary. *Coll Develop, Librn*, Melinda Baxter
Pop 6,619; Circ 23,000
1997-1998 Income $66,279, City $43,831, Other $260. Mats Exp $20,775, Books $10,000, Per/Ser (Incl. Access Fees) $2,000. Sal $45,504 (Prof $26,000)
Library Holdings: Bk Vols 16,000; Per Subs 78
Open Mon & Thurs 1-8:30, Tues 10-5, Wed & Fri 1-5, Sat 10-2

PETERBOROUGH

M MONADNOCK COMMUNITY HOSPITAL, Thomas Eckfeldt Memorial Medical Library, 452 Old Street Rd, 03458. SAN 323-6277. Tel: 603-924-7191, Ext 1100. *Librn*, Jean Slepian; Staff 1 (MLS 1)
Founded 1970
Library Holdings: Bk Titles 200; Per Subs 35

S PETERBOROUGH HISTORICAL SOCIETY LIBRARY, 19 Grove St, 03458. (Mail add: PO Box 58, 03458), SAN 328-1442. Tel: 603-924-3235. FAX: 603-924-3200. E-Mail: office.phs@webryders.com. *Exec Dir*, Ellen S Derby; Staff 1 (Non-MLS 1)
1998-1999 Income $69,000
Library Holdings: Bk Vols 200
Subject Interests: Genealogy, Local history
Special Collections: Mills Records Coll (1796-1920); Peterborough 1796-1873 (Dr Albert Smith Coll), letters

P PETERBOROUGH TOWN LIBRARY, 2 Concord St, 03458. SAN 309-9245. Tel: 603-924-8040. FAX: 603-924-8041. E-Mail: petertlib@monad.net. Web Site: www.townofpeterborough.com/library. *Dir*, Michael Price; E-Mail: mprice@ptl.monad.net; *Asst Dir, Cat*, Linda Tiernan Kepner; *Ch Servs*, Joan Butler; E-Mail: jbutler@ptl.monad.net; *ILL, Ref*, Brian Hackert; E-Mail: peterboroughtownlibrary@hotmail.com; Staff 7 (MLS 3, Non-MLS 4)
Founded 1833. Pop 5,239; Circ 93,073
1998-1999 Income $254,708, City $201,708, Locally Generated Income $53,000. Mats Exp $39,500. Sal $199,358
Library Holdings: Bk Vols 44,030; Per Subs 172
Subject Interests: Local history, Original art photog, State hist, Town hist
Special Collections: Town Histories (McGilvray Coll)
Automation Activity & Vendor Info: (Cataloging) EOS; (Circulation) EOS; (OPAC) EOS
Publications: History of the First Free Tax-Supported Library in the World-Peterborough
Partic in OCLC Online Computer Library Center, Inc
Friends of the Library Group

PIERMONT

P PIERMONT PUBLIC LIBRARY,* 130 Rt 10, 03779. (Mail add: PO Box 6, 03779), SAN 309-9253. Tel: 603-272-4967. E-Mail: pvl@connriver.net. *Librn*, Maureen Byrne
Pop 624; Circ 12,016
Library Holdings: Bk Vols 15,000; Per Subs 20

PIKE

P PIKE LIBRARY ASSOCIATION, Rte 25, PO Box 268, 03780. SAN 309-8397. Tel: 603-989-9847. *Librn*, Betty Conrad
Circ 1,632
Library Holdings: Bk Vols 5,241
Mem of North Country District

PITTSBURG

P BREMER POND MEMORIAL LIBRARY, Main St, PO Box 98, 03592. SAN 309-9261. Tel: 603-538-7032. *Librn*, Bill Stebbins
Pop 1,000; Circ 1,300
Library Holdings: Bk Vols 20,000
Mem of North Country Library System

PITTSFIELD

P CARPENTER MEMORIAL LIBRARY,* 41 Main St, 03263. SAN 309-927X. Tel: 603-435-8406. E-Mail: carplib@worldpath.net. *Librn*, Joan Wadleigh
Founded 1901. Pop 3,800; Circ 9,000
Library Holdings: Bk Vols 12,668; Per Subs 35
Subject Interests: Town hist
Publications: Newsletter
Open Mon & Thurs 2-8, Wed 2-5, Fri 10-5 & Sat 10-12

PLAINFIELD

P PHILIP READ MEMORIAL LIBRARY, 1088 Rte 12A, 03781. SAN 309-9288. Tel: 603-675-6866. E-Mail: plfdlib@cyberportal.net. Web Site: www.cyberportal.net/plfdlib. *Librn*, Nancy Norwalk; Staff 1 (Non-MLS 1)
Founded 1920. Pop 2,254; Circ 11,700
Jan 2000-Dec 2000 Income $29,427, City $25,407, Locally Generated Income $1,400, Other $2,620. Mats Exp $6,350, Books $6,150, Presv $200.

Sal $14,911 (Prof $13,900)
Library Holdings: Bk Vols 19,200; Per Subs 95
Subject Interests: Local author coll, Local history, Oral hist tapes
Special Collections: Local Author Book & Magazine Coll; Video Coll
Publications: Newsletter
Partic in Librarians of the Upper Valley Coop; MUM Coop
Friends of the Library Group

PLAISTOW

P PLAISTOW PUBLIC LIBRARY, 85 Main St, 03865. SAN 309-9296. Tel: 603-382-6011. FAX: 603-382-0202. E-Mail: plaistowlibrary@mediaone.net. *Dir*, Laurie Houlihan; Staff 8 (MLS 1, Non-MLS 7)
Founded 1897
Library Holdings: Bk Vols 29,000; Per Subs 62
Open Mon-Thurs 9-8:30, Fri 9-5, Sat 9-2
Friends of the Library Group

PLYMOUTH

P THE PEASE PUBLIC LIBRARY,* One Russell St, 03264-1414. SAN 309-930X. Tel: 603-536-2616. FAX: 603-536-2369. E-Mail: pease@worldpath.net. Web Site: www.worldpath.net/~pease/home.htm. *Dir*, Katherine Hillier
Founded 1876. Pop 5,800; Circ 43,621 Sal $70,465
Library Holdings: Bk Vols 23,000; Per Subs 90
Subject Interests: Children's literature
Special Collections: History-Genealogy (Eva A Speare Coll)
Partic in Statewide Libr Network
Friends of the Library Group

C PLYMOUTH STATE COLLEGE, Herbert H Lamson Library, Highland Ave, 03264-1595. SAN 309-9318. Tel: 603-535-2258. FAX: 603-535-2445. Web Site: www.plymouth.edu/psc/library. *Dir*, Todd Trevorrow; *Librn*, Elaine Allard; *Ref*, Gary McCool; *Tech Servs*, Gaynell Zimmerman; *Bibliog Instr*, Robert Fitzpatrick; *Bibliog Instr*, Lissa Zinfon; *Per*, William Kietzman; Staff 8 (MLS 8)
Founded 1871. Enrl 4,381; Fac 224; Highest Degree: Master
Jul 1999-Jun 2000 Income $1,431,266. Mats Exp $379,300, Books $132,339, Per/Ser (Incl. Access Fees) $141,584, Presv $3,169, Other Print Mats $43,833. Sal $704,080 (Prof $428,840)
Library Holdings: Per Subs 1,100
Special Collections: Robert Frost (George H Brown Coll)
Automation Activity & Vendor Info: (Acquisitions) Innovative Interfaces Inc.; (Cataloging) Innovative Interfaces Inc.; (Circulation) Innovative Interfaces Inc.; (Course Reserve) Innovative Interfaces Inc.; (OPAC) Innovative Interfaces Inc.; (Serials) Innovative Interfaces Inc.
Database Vendor: OCLC - First Search
Publications: BI Publications; Bibliographies; CAI; Guide to Information Resources; Handouts; Users' Guides
Partic in Nelinet, Inc; NHCUC; OCLC Online Computer Library Center, Inc

PORTSMOUTH

S PORTSMOUTH ATHENAEUM, Library-Museum, 9 Market Sq, PO Box 848, 03821-0848. SAN 320-2038. Tel: 603-431-2538. FAX: 603-431-7180. E-Mail: athenaeum@juno.com. *In Charge*, Jane Porter; *Coll Develop, Librn*, Lynn Aber; *Asst Librn, Cat*, Robin Silva; *Ref*, Marcia Jebb; Staff 4 (MLS 2, Non-MLS 2)
Founded 1817
Library Holdings: Bk Titles 40,000; Per Subs 18
Subject Interests: Genealogy, Local, Maine, Marine, Naval, New England, NH hist, Ships
Special Collections: church, institutional, business & family papers; Langdon Papers Coll; Larkin Papers Coll, docs; Manuscripts; NH Gazette Coll; NNH Fire & Marine Insurance Company Papers, docs; Pierce Papers, docs; Wendell Family Papers, photographs
Exhibit cats. available for each exhibit held here; call for titles

P PORTSMOUTH PUBLIC LIBRARY, 8 Islington St, 03801-4261. SAN 309-9334. Tel: 603-427-1540. FAX: 603-433-0981. Web Site: www.cityofportsmouth.com/library. *Dir*, Sherman Pridham; E-Mail: scpridham@lib.cityofportsmouth.com; *Asst Dir*, Susan McCann; E-Mail: sfmccann@lib.cityofportsmouth.com; *Ch Servs*, Susan Brough; E-Mail: slbrough@lib.cityofportsmouth.com; *Cat*, Patricia Palmer; E-Mail: papalmer@lib.cityofportsmouth.com; *Ref*, Michael Huxtable; E-Mail: mjhuxtable@lib.cityofportsmouth.com; *Circ*, Leslie Inglis; E-Mail: ltinglis@lib.cityofportsmouth.com; *Spec Coll*, Nicole Luongo; E-Mail: nnluongo@lib.cityofportsmouth.com; Staff 19 (MLS 7, Non-MLS 12)
Founded 1896. Pop 27,966; Circ 348,334
Jul 1998-Jun 1999 Income $1,113,010, City $1,029,378, Locally Generated Income $56,830, Other $26,802. Mats Exp $222,224, Books $126,339, Per/Ser (Incl. Access Fees) $16,731, Micro $26,674, AV Equip $29,723, Other Print Mats $1,770, Manuscripts & Archives $1,268, Electronic Ref Mat (Incl. Access Fees) $19,719. Sal $585,369
Library Holdings: Bk Vols 123,158; Bk Titles 118,976; Per Subs 400
Subject Interests: Local history
Special Collections: Isles of Shoals
Automation Activity & Vendor Info: (Acquisitions) Innovative Interfaces Inc.; (Cataloging) Innovative Interfaces Inc.; (Circulation) Innovative Interfaces Inc.; (OPAC) Innovative Interfaces Inc.; (Serials) Innovative Interfaces Inc.
Friends of the Library Group

M PORTSMOUTH REGIONAL HOSPITAL, Health Science Library,* 333 Borthwick Ave, PO Box 7004, 03802-7004. SAN 377-9394. Tel: 603-433-4094. FAX: 603-433-5245. *Librn*, Chris Beairsto; E-Mail: christople.beairsto@columbia.net
Library Holdings: Bk Titles 500; Per Subs 125
Partic in Basic Health Sciences Library Network; Health Science Libraries Of New Hampshire & Vermont; North Atlantic Health Sciences Libraries, Inc

S STRAWBERY BANKE, INC, Thayer Cumings Library & Archives,* 454 Court St, 03802. SAN 309-9342. Tel: 603-422-7502. FAX: 603-433-1115. *Archivist, Librn*, Roberta Ransley; E-Mail: rransley@juno.com
Founded 1970
Library Holdings: Bk Vols 8,000; Bk Titles 7,000; Per Subs 48
Subject Interests: Archaeology, Architecture, Art, Decorative arts, Horticulture, Local history, Presv
Special Collections: Manuscript Coll; Portsmouth Photo Coll, 1870-1970
Publications: A Guide to the Cumings Library & Archives (pamphlet); Official Strawbery Banke Guide Book
Open by appt to the public Tues 10-1 & Thurs 1-4

UNITED STATES NAVY
A PORTSMOUTH NAVAL SHIPYARD LIBRARY, Code 822, Bldg 22, Portsmouth Naval Shipyard, 03804-5000. SAN 350-5502. Tel: 207-438-2769. FAX: 207-438-2722. *Librn*, Deirdre Bissell; E-Mail: bisselldg@mail.ports.navy.mil
Founded 1913
Library Holdings: Bk Vols 7,000; Per Subs 100
Subject Interests: Computers, Electronics eng, Military, Security, Submarines

S JAMES E WHALLEY MUSEUM & LIBRARY,* 351 Middle St, 03801. SAN 328-0217. Tel: 603-436-3712. *Dir*, Lynn J Sanderson
Founded 1962
Library Holdings: Bk Vols 3,600; Bk Titles 3,500; Per Subs 2,200
Open Wed 8am-noon or by appt

RAYMOND

P DUDLEY-TUCKER LIBRARY,* 6 Epping St, 03077-0909. (Mail add: PO Box 909, 03077-0909), SAN 309-9350. Tel: 603-895-2633. FAX: 603-895-0904. E-Mail: dudleytucker@mediadne.net. Web Site: www.raymond-nh.com. *Librn*, Sherry Brox; *Asst Librn*, Linda Hoelzel
Founded 1894. Pop 9,000; Circ 22,398
Library Holdings: Bk Vols 23,000; Per Subs 100
Open Mon & Thurs 1-8:30, Wed 10-5
Friends of the Library Group

RICHMOND

P RICHMOND PUBLIC LIBRARY,* 19 Winchester Rd, 03470. SAN 309-9369. Tel: 603-239-6164. FAX: 603-239-7332. *Coll Develop, Librn*, Sara D Jacobson
Pop 980; Circ 5,352
Library Holdings: Bk Vols 11,800; Per Subs 20
Mem of SW District Libr Syst
Friends of the Library Group

RINDGE

C FRANKLIN PIERCE COLLEGE LIBRARY, College Rd, PO Box 60, 03461. SAN 309-9377. Tel: 603-899-4140. Reference Tel: 603-899-4149. FAX: 603-899-4375. E-Mail: library@fpc.edu. Web Site: library.fpc.edu. *Dir Libr Serv*, Mary Ledoux; Tel: 603-899-4142, E-Mail: ledouxm@fpc.edu; *Tech Servs*, Melissa Stearns; Tel: 603-899-4143, E-Mail: stearnmm@fpc.edu; *Ref*, Anthony Krier; E-Mail: kriert@fpc.edu; *Circ*, Jill Wixom; Tel: 603-899-4144, E-Mail: wixombj@fpc.edu; *Media Spec*, Michael McNerney; Tel: 603-899-4141, E-Mail: mcnerneym@fpc.edu; Staff 4 (MLS 4)
Founded 1962. Enrl 2,348; Fac 78; Highest Degree: Master
Jul 2000-Jun 2001 Income $629,756. Mats Exp $256,764, Books $101,264, Per/Ser (Incl. Access Fees) $129,000, Presv $5,500, AV Equip $21,000. Sal $311,072 (Prof $145,750)
Library Holdings: Bk Titles 120,000
Subject Interests: Ecology, Graphic arts, Mass communications
Automation Activity & Vendor Info: (Acquisitions) Endeavor; (Cataloging) Endeavor; (Circulation) Endeavor; (Course Reserve) Endeavor; (Media Booking) Endeavor; (OPAC) Endeavor
Database Vendor: Ebsco - EbscoHost
Partic in Nelinet, Inc; New Hampshire College & University Council

P INGALLS MEMORIAL LIBRARY, 252 Main St, 03461. SAN 309-9385. Tel: 603-899-3303. FAX: 603-899-5797. E-Mail: ingallslibrary@top.monad.net. *Dir*, Diane Gardenour; E-Mail: ingallslibrary@top.monad.net
Founded 1894. Pop 5,358; Circ 32,096
Jan 1999-Dec 1999 Income $82,241, State $101, City $70,604, Other $11,536. Mats Exp $13,285, Books $12,285, Per/Ser (Incl. Access Fees) $1,000. Sal $45,197
Library Holdings: Bk Vols 21,172; Per Subs 75
Subject Interests: Humanities, New Hampshire
Automation Activity & Vendor Info: (Cataloging) Sagebrush Corporation; (Circulation) Sagebrush Corporation; (OPAC) Sagebrush Corporation
Partic in Nubanusit Library Cooperative
Friends of the Library Group

ROCHESTER

P EAST ROCHESTER PUBLIC LIBRARY,* 57 Main St, PO Box 6006, 03868-6006. SAN 309-9393. Tel: 603-332-8013. E-Mail: lyslnsan@cybertours.com. *Librn*, Sandy Burrows
Pop 2,500
Library Holdings: Bk Vols 6,000
Mem of Cent Libr District
Open Tues & Thurs 2-5
Friends of the Library Group

M FRISBIE MEMORIAL HOSPITAL, Medical Library,* 11 Whitehall Rd, 03867. SAN 377-953X. Tel: 603-335-8419. FAX: 603-332-2699. *Librn*, Margaret Robak
Library Holdings: Bk Titles 450; Per Subs 70
Partic in Health Science Libraries Of New Hampshire & Vermont; Medical Libr Asn; National Network of Libraries of Medicine - Greater Midwest Region

P ROCHESTER PUBLIC LIBRARY, 65 S Main St, 03867-2707. SAN 309-9407. Tel: 603-332-1428. FAX: 603-335-7582. Web Site: www.rpl.lib.nh.us. *Dir*, Cynthia Scott; *Ch Servs*, Katherine Wright; *Tech Servs*, Dorinda Howard; *Circ*, Celina Houlne; *ILL*, Marie Lejcune; Staff 18 (MLS 5, Non-MLS 13)
Founded 1893. Pop 28,000; Circ 160,776
Jul 1999-Jun 2000 Income $1,040,527, City $1,000,291, Locally Generated Income $33,172, Other $7,064. Mats Exp $68,551, Books $58,969, Micro $1,731, AV Equip $7,851. Sal $439,014
Library Holdings: Bk Titles 74,745; Per Subs 167
Special Collections: French Coll (Notre Heritage Coll); Rochester Courier Coll, 1864 to 1992, 1864-1952 on microfilm
Friends of the Library Group

ROLLINSFORD

S ROLLINSFORD SCHOOL LIBRARY, 487 Locust St, 03869. SAN 374-5449. Tel: 603-742-2351. FAX: 603-749-5629. E-Mail: dmnt_hom@harry.mv.com. *Librn*, Mary Stumhofer
Enrl 206
Jul 2000-Jun 2001 Mats Exp $5,300
Library Holdings: Bk Vols 10,160; Bk Titles 9,535; Per Subs 29

RUMNEY

P BYRON G MERRILL LIBRARY, 10 Buffalo Rd, 03266. SAN 309-9415. Tel: 603-786-9520. *Librn*, Muriel Kenneson; Staff 2 (Non-MLS 2)
Pop 1,466; Circ 9,416
Jan 1999-Dec 1999 Income $21,288. Mats Exp $2,500. Sal $10,983
Library Holdings: Bk Vols 20,000; Per Subs 50
Mem of North Country Library System

RYE

P RYE PUBLIC LIBRARY, 581 Washington Rd, 03870. SAN 309-9423. Tel: 603-964-8401. FAX: 603-964-7065. E-Mail: ryepl@nh.ultranet.com. Web Site: www.nh.ultranet.com/~ryepl. *Dir*, Sherry Evans; E-Mail: sevans@rye.lib.nh.us; *Ad Servs, ILL*, Patricia Quinn; E-Mail: tricia@rye.lib.nh.us; *Ad Servs*, Randall O'Brien; E-Mail: randall.obrien@rye.lib.nh.us; *Ch Servs*, Julie Doherty; E-Mail: jdoherty@rye.lib.nh.us; *YA Servs*, Sharon Macdonald; E-Mail: sharon@rye.lib.nh.us; *Computer Services*, Jonathan Ramsay; E-Mail: jramsay@rye.lib.nh.us; Staff 7 (MLS 1, Non-MLS 6)
Founded 1911. Pop 4,738; Circ 80,000
Jan 2000-Dec 2000 Income $410,165, City $394,671, Locally Generated Income $994, Other $14,500. Mats Exp $52,000, Books $38,850, Per/Ser (Incl. Access Fees) $6,300, AV Equip $6,000, Electronic Ref Mat (Incl. Access Fees) $840. Sal $195,874 (Prof $41,200)
Library Holdings: Bk Vols 50,685; Bk Titles 44,240; Per Subs 279
Subject Interests: Rye hist
Automation Activity & Vendor Info: (Cataloging) TLC; (Circulation) TLC; (OPAC) TLC
Database Vendor: OCLC - First Search
Publications: Off the Shelf (Newsletter)
Mem of Nelinet
Partic in Seacoast Coop Libraries
Special Services for the Blind - Bks on tape
Friends of the Library Group

SALEM

P KELLEY LIBRARY, Salem Public Library, 234 Main St, 03079-3190. SAN 309-944X. Tel: 603-898-7064. FAX: 603-898-8583. E-Mail: kelleylb@salem.lib.nh.us. Web Site: www.salem.lib.nh.us. *Dir*, Eleanor Strang; *Asst Dir*, Jean Williams; *Cat, Tech Servs*, Margaret Kuehn; *Ad Servs*, Natalie Ducharme; *ILL*, Paul Giblin; *Ch Servs*, Sheila Murray; *YA Servs*, Coralyn Chicknas; *Ref*, Deborah Berlin
Founded 1893. Pop 27,378; Circ 247,327
Library Holdings: Bk Vols 106,158; Per Subs 354
Subject Interests: Bus, Career, Col, Consumer, Health
Database Vendor: epixtech, inc.
Publications: Salem Community Information Directory (now available on website)
Partic in GMILCS

SALISBURY

P SALISBURY FREE LIBRARY,* PO Box 205, 03268. SAN 309-9458. Tel: 603-648-2278. *Librn*, Gail Clukay
Pop 1,063; Circ 5,000
1998-1999 Income $10,000. Mats Exp $5,000
Library Holdings: Bk Vols 5,750
Special Collections: Antique History Coll
Open Tues 1-5, Thurs 9-12 & 3-6, Fri 6-8, Sat 1-4
Friends of the Library Group

SANBORNTON

P SANBORNTON PUBLIC LIBRARY, 27 Meeting House Hill, PO Box 88, 03269-0088. SAN 309-9466. Tel: 603-286-8288. E-Mail: spl@worldpath.net. *Librn*, Priscilla A Bodwell; *Asst Librn*, Kathleen Lebel; Staff 4 (MLS 3, Non-MLS 1)
Pop 2,200; Circ 16,500
Jan 2000-Dec 2000 Income $66,728. Mats Exp $6,000. Sal $49,178
Library Holdings: Bk Vols 16,000; Per Subs 30; Bks on Deafness & Sign Lang 10
Subject Interests: New Hampshire
Database Vendor: ProQuest
Mem of Cent District Libr Syst
Partic in Scrooge & Marley Cooperative

SANBORNVILLE

P GAFNEY LIBRARY, INC, 14 High St, PO Box 517, 03872-0517. SAN 309-975X. Tel: 603-522-3401. FAX: 602-522-8469. E-Mail: gafney@worldpath.net. *Librn*, Beryl Donovan; Staff 2 (Non-MLS 2)
Founded 1925. Pop 3,200; Circ 18,316
Jan 2000-Dec 2000 Income $109,170. Mats Exp Books $5,000. Sal $26,100
Library Holdings: Bk Vols 12,000
Friends of the Library Group

P WAKEFIELD LIBRARY ASSOCIATION,* PO Box 904, 03872-0904. SAN 309-9768. Tel: 603-522-3032. *Librn*, Margaret Harvey
Founded 1895. Pop 2,600
Library Holdings: Bk Vols 11,682
Mem of Cent Libr District
Open Wed 1-4, Sat's in July & Aug
Friends of the Library Group

SANDOWN

P SANDOWN PUBLIC LIBRARY, 305 Main St, 03873. (Mail add: PO Box 580, 03873), SAN 309-9474. Tel: 603-887-3428. FAX: 603-887-0590. E-Mail: sandownlibrary@gsi.net. Web Site: gsinet.net/~sandownlibrary/index.html. *Dir*, Heidi B Traeger; Staff 8 (Non-MLS 8)
Founded 1892. Pop 4,750; Circ 28,686
Jan 1999-Dec 1999 Income $99,168, City $96,668, Other $2,500. Mats Exp $21,575, Books $14,400, Per/Ser (Incl. Access Fees) $1,325, Electronic Ref Mat (Incl. Access Fees) $3,350. Sal $58,868
Library Holdings: Bk Vols 21,000; Per Subs 39
Automation Activity & Vendor Info: (Circulation) Sagebrush Corporation
Database Vendor: ProQuest
Function: ILL available
Partic in Merri-Hill-Rock Library Cooperative
Friends of the Library Group

SEABROOK

P SEABROOK LIBRARY,* 101 Centennial St, 03874-4506. SAN 309-9490. Tel: 603-474-2044. FAX: 603-474-1835. E-Mail: ocean@sealib.org. *Dir*, Elizabeth G Heath; *Ch Servs*, Anne M Ferreira; *Circ, ILL*, Suzanne Weinreich; *Ser, Tech Servs*, Sharon L Rafferty; *YA Servs*, Lesley K Gaudreau; *Ref*, Bill Thayer
Pop 6,616; Circ 28,748
Library Holdings: Bk Vols 30,000
Subject Interests: New Age, Occult
Partic in Seacoast Coop Libraries
Friends of the Library Group

SHELBURNE

P SHELBURNE PUBLIC LIBRARY,* 397 North Rd, 03581-3106. SAN 309-9504. Tel: 603-466-3986. *Librn*, Kathleen Judge
Pop 320; Circ 562
Library Holdings: Bk Vols 3,255
Subject Interests: Local history
Mem of North Country Library System

SOMERSWORTH

P SOMERSWORTH PUBLIC LIBRARY, 25 Main St, 03878-3198. SAN 309-9512. Tel: 603-692-4587. FAX: 603-692-9110. E-Mail: sompl@nh.ultranet.com. Web Site: www.somersworth.com. *Librn*, Debora Longo; *Ch Servs*, Nancy Polito; *Asst Librn*, Dr Kathleen Dill; Staff 3 (MLS 1, Non-MLS 2)
Founded 1899. Pop 11,650
Jul 1999-Jun 2000 Income $216,895, City $212,695, Locally Generated Income $4,200. Mats Exp $37,913, Books $30,413, Per/Ser (Incl. Access Fees) $4,500, AV Equip $3,000. Sal $143,553 (Prof $88,810)
Library Holdings: Bk Titles 43,000; Per Subs 115
Special Collections: Somersworth Historical Coll
Partic in Rochester Regional Library Council
Friends of the Library Group

SOUTH HAMPTON

P SOUTH HAMPTON FREE PUBLIC LIBRARY,* 3-1 Hilldale Ave, 03827. SAN 309-9520. Tel: 603-394-7319. *Librn*, Shirley Reid
Pop 790; Circ 7,440
Library Holdings: Bk Vols 8,330; Per Subs 20
Special Collections: Al Capp Coll; Memorial Coll; New Hampshire History
Partic in Seacoast Coop Libraries
Friends of the Library Group

SPRINGFIELD

P LIBBIE A CASS MEMORIAL LIBRARY,* 757 Main St, PO Box 89, 03284-0089. SAN 309-9539. Tel: 603-763-4381. FAX: 603-763-4381. E-Mail: spfldlibrary@cyberportal.net. *Librn*, Steve Klein
Founded 1893. Pop 820; Circ 4,025
1998-1999 Income $8,149, City $5,600, Locally Generated Income $186, Other $162. Mats Exp $4,274, Books $3,935, Per/Ser (Incl. Access Fees) $99, Other Print Mats $240
Library Holdings: Bk Vols 15,000
Partic in Librarians of the Upper Valley Coop
Friends of the Library Group

STARK

P STARK PUBLIC LIBRARY,* c/o Stark Town Hall, 03582. SAN 309-9547. Tel: 603-636-2076. FAX: 603-636-6199. *Librn*, Cecile Eich
Pop 462; Circ 1,307
Library Holdings: Bk Vols 5,150

STODDARD

P DAVIS PUBLIC LIBRARY,* HCR 32, Rte 123 N, Box 244, 03464. SAN 309-9571. Tel: 603-446-6251. *Librn*, Frances Rumrill
Pop 447; Circ 1,433
Library Holdings: Bk Vols 5,271
Mem of SW Libr District

STRATHAM

J NEW HAMPSHIRE COMMUNITY TECHNICAL COLLEGE, Library & Media Services,* 277 Portsmouth Ave, 03885-2297. SAN 309-9326. Tel: 603-772-1194. FAX: 603-772-1198. *Dir*, Rebecca Clerkin; Staff 2 (MLS 1, Non-MLS 1)
Founded 1970. Enrl 1,200; Fac 35
Library Holdings: Bk Vols 10,400; Per Subs 128
Automation Activity & Vendor Info: (Acquisitions) TLC
Publications: Handbook

P WIGGIN MEMORIAL LIBRARY, 10 Bunker Hill Ave, 03885. SAN 309-9601. Tel: 603-772-4346. FAX: 603-772-4071. E-Mail: wigginml@mediaone.net, wigginml@nh.ultranet.com. *Librn*, Lesley Gaudreau
Founded 1891. Pop 6,000; Circ 46,971
Library Holdings: Bk Vols 35,000
Subject Interests: New Hampshire
Partic in MUM Coop

SUGAR HILL

P RICHARDSON MEMORIAL LIBRARY,* PO Box 622, 03585-6000. SAN 309-961X. Tel: 603-823-7001. *Librn*, Sharyn McGuigan
Pop 450; Circ 2,335
Library Holdings: Bk Vols 4,900; Per Subs 10
Mem of North Country District
Partic in North Country Library Cooperative

SULLIVAN

P SULLIVAN PUBLIC LIBRARY, 436 Centre St, PO Box 92, 03445-0092. SAN 376-7698. Tel: 603-847-3458. FAX: 603-847-9154 (Town Hall). E-Mail: spl@webryders.com. *Librn*, Denise McFarland
Library Holdings: Bk Titles 10,503; Per Subs 20
Friends of the Library Group

SUNAPEE

P ABBOTT LIBRARY, 542 Rte 11, Box 314, 03782-0314. SAN 309-9636. Tel: 603-763-5513. FAX: 603-763-8765. E-Mail: hsv9@lilac.nhsl.lib.nh.us. Web Site: abbott.sugar-river.net. *Dir*, Patricia Hand; E-Mail: phand@turbont.net; *Asst Librn*, Sharon Montambeault
Founded 1926. Pop 3,500; Circ 44,524
Jan 1999-Dec 1999 Income $118,161. Mats Exp $21,000, Books $13,500, Per/Ser (Incl. Access Fees) $3,000, Other Print Mats $4,500. Sal $61,169
Library Holdings: Bk Vols 28,454
Automation Activity & Vendor Info: (Cataloging) Follett; (Circulation) Follett
Friends of the Library Group

SURRY

P REED FREE LIBRARY,* 8 Village Rd, 03431-8314. SAN 309-9644. Tel: 603-352-1761. E-Mail: surrylibrary@monad.com. *Librn*, Irene Metivier
Pop 662; Circ 2,207
Library Holdings: Bk Vols 8,000
Mem of SW Libr District

SUTTON MILLS

P SUTTON FREE LIBRARY,* Main St, PO Box 91, 03221. SAN 309-9652. Tel: 603-927-4927. *Librn*, Jeanette Couch
Pop 1,086; Circ 11,369
Library Holdings: Bk Vols 9,207
Mem of SW Libr District
Open Mon 1:30-4, Wed 1-4 & 6:30-9, Fri 7-9 & Sat 1-4

SWANZEY

P MOUNT CAESAR UNION LIBRARY, 628 Old Homestead Hwy, 03446. SAN 309-9660. Tel: 603-357-0456. E-Mail: mtcaesarlib@cheshire.net. *Librn*, Susan MacPhail; *Asst Librn*, Robin Armstrong
Founded 1880. Pop 5,341; Circ 18,354
Jan 2000-Dec 2000 Mats Exp $7,800, Books $6,200, Per/Ser (Incl. Access Fees) $700, AV Equip $900
Library Holdings: Bk Vols 21,000; Per Subs 25
Subject Interests: Genealogy, Local history
Automation Activity & Vendor Info: (Circulation) Sagebrush Corporation
Publications: Newsletter

TAMWORTH

P COOK MEMORIAL LIBRARY, 93 Main St, PO Box 249, 03886. SAN 309-9687. Tel: 603-323-8510. FAX: 603-323-2077. E-Mail: cooklib@ncia.net. Web Site: www.tamworth.lib.nh.us. *Librn*, Jay Rancourt
Founded 1892. Pop 2,300; Circ 14,061
Jan 1999-Dec 1999 Income $56,536, City $45,943, Other $10,593. Mats Exp $7,238, Books $5,165, Per/Ser (Incl. Access Fees) $382, AV Equip $599, Other Print Mats $1,092. Sal $28,809

Library Holdings: Bk Vols 14,000
Special Collections: Index card file on vital statistics (1777-1890); Remnants of Tamworth Social Library Coll (26 vols)
Publications: Booklist; Hornbook; Library Journal; School Library Journal
Friends of the Library Group

TEMPLE

P MANSFIELD PUBLIC LIBRARY,* Sen Tobey Hwy, PO Box 210, 03084-0210. SAN 309-9695. Tel: 603-878-3100. E-Mail: mansfield@tellink.net. *Dir*, Priscilla Weston
Founded 1890. Pop 1,300; Circ 8,609
Jan 1998-Dec 1998 Income $23,960. Mats Exp $4,498, Books $3,430, Per/Ser (Incl. Access Fees) $908, Electronic Ref Mat (Incl. Access Fees) $160. Sal $12,959
Library Holdings: Bk Vols 13,838; Per Subs 17
Friends of the Library Group

THORNTON

P THORNTON PUBLIC LIBRARY, Rte 175, RFD 1, 03223. SAN 309-9709. Tel: 603-726-8981. FAX: 603-726-3801. E-Mail: thorntonlibrary@visto.com. *Librn*, Kathy-Jean Uhlman
Founded 1899. Pop 1,700; Circ 2,900
Library Holdings: Bk Titles 6,500; Per Subs 14
Open Mon-Fri 8:30-3:30

TROY

P GAY-KIMBALL LIBRARY, 10 S Main St, PO Box 837, 03465-0837. SAN 309-9725. Tel: 603-242-7743. FAX: 603-242-7743. E-Mail: troylibrary@monad.net. *Dir*, Sandra Licks; Staff 3 (MLS 1, Non-MLS 2)
Founded 1824. Pop 2,137; Circ 16,043
Jan 2000-Dec 2000 Income $60,104, City $48,084, Locally Generated Income $10,020, Other $2,000. Mats Exp $8,600, Books $8,000, Per/Ser (Incl. Access Fees) $600. Sal $35,969 (Prof $25,000)
Library Holdings: Bk Vols 18,806; Per Subs 50
Special Collections: Local Area (New England Coll), bk & pamphlet; Troy Mills Business Coll
Function: ILL available, Photocopies available, Reference services available

UNION

P UNION VILLAGE LIBRARY,* Maple St, PO Box 203, 03887-0203. SAN 325-2515. *Librn*, Kathie Damen
Founded 1900. Pop 800; Circ 1,000
1997-1998 Income $5,000. Mats Exp $1,500. Sal $780
Library Holdings: Bk Titles 4,500
Open Mon & Wed 7-9, Sat 2-4
Friends of the Library Group

WALPOLE

P WALPOLE TOWN LIBRARY,* Main St, PO Box 487, 03608-0487. SAN 350-5626. Tel: 603-756-9806. *Librn*, Frances Knibb; *Asst Librn*, Fran Moses; *Asst Librn*, Mary Farrell; *Asst Librn*, Michael Kreck; Staff 4 (MLS 1, Non-MLS 3)
Founded 1795. Pop 3,178; Circ 20,663
Jan 1998-Dec 1998 Income $61,620. Mats Exp $13,495. Sal $33,627
Library Holdings: Bk Vols 20,000; Per Subs 12
Mem of SW Libr District
Partic in Nubanusit Library Cooperative
Friends of the Library Group
Branches: 1
NORTH WALPOLE, 70 Church St, North Walpole, 03609. SAN 350-5650. Tel: 603-445-5153. *Librn*, Rose Werden
Library Holdings: Bk Vols 9,406; Bk Titles 4,000

WARNER

C MAGDALEN COLLEGE LIBRARY, 511 Kearsarge Mountain Rd, 03278. SAN 321-7337. Tel: 603-456-2656. FAX: 603-456-2660. E-Mail: magdalen_lib@conknet.com. *Dir*, Dr David Hayes
Founded 1973. Enrl 74; Fac 9; Highest Degree: Master
Library Holdings: Bk Vols 26,000; Bk Titles 20,000; Per Subs 20
Subject Interests: Catholic studies, Liberal arts, Religion

P PILLSBURY FREE LIBRARY, 18 E Main St, PO Box 299, 03278-0299. SAN 309-9776. Tel: 603-456-2289. FAX: 603-456-3177. E-Mail: pillsburylib@conknet.com. Web Site: www.conknet.com/~pillsburylib/. *Librn*, Nancy Ladd; *Asst Librn*, Mary McDonough; Staff 3 (MLS 1, Non-MLS 2)
Founded 1891. Pop 2,500; Circ 19,000
Jan 2000-Dec 2000 Income $84,000, Locally Generated Income $78,000, Other $6,000. Mats Exp $11,000, Books $8,500, Per/Ser (Incl. Access Fees) $1,900, Presv $200, Electronic Ref Mat (Incl. Access Fees) $400. Sal $35,000
Library Holdings: Bk Vols 20,000; Per Subs 74; Bks on Deafness & Sign Lang 10
Subject Interests: Town hist
Automation Activity & Vendor Info: (Circulation) Sagebrush Corporation; (OPAC) Sagebrush Corporation
Partic in NHAIS
Friends of the Library Group

WARREN

P JOSEPH PATCH LIBRARY,* S Main St, 03279-9716. SAN 309-9784. Tel: 603-764-9072. *Librn*, Julie Noury
Pop 820; Circ 4,096
Library Holdings: Bk Vols 6,000; Per Subs 25

WASHINGTON

P SHEDD FREE LIBRARY,* 46 N Main, 03280. (Mail add: PO Box 288, 03280), SAN 309-9792. Tel: 603-495-3592. FAX: 603-495-3410. *Dir*, JoEllen Wright
Founded 1869. Pop 800; Circ 5,314
Library Holdings: Bk Vols 7,000; Per Subs 33
Subject Interests: Large print
Friends of the Library Group

WATERVILLE VALLEY

P OSCEOLA LIBRARY,* W Branch Rd, PO Box 367, 03215-0367. SAN 321-1029. Tel: 603-236-9113. FAX: 603-236-2056. *Librn*, Betty Rathman
Founded 1888. Pop 264; Circ 1,250
1997-1998 Income $2,000
Library Holdings: Bk Titles 3,500
Subject Interests: New Hampshire hist, White Mountains
Special Collections: Recreational bks
Open Tues & Thurs 1-3

WEARE

P WEARE PUBLIC LIBRARY, 10 Paige Memorial Lane, PO Box 227, 03281-0227. SAN 309-9806. Tel: 603-529-2044. Web Site: www.ultranet.com/~wearepl. *Dir*, Christine Hague; *Asst Librn*, Dino Quimby; *Ch Servs*, Cora Jo Ciampi; Staff 6 (Non-MLS 6)
Pop 6,800; Circ 36,325
Jan 2000-Dec 2000 Income $112,061, City $104,159, Locally Generated Income $2,902, Other $5,000. Mats Exp $15,920, Books $14,746, Per/Ser (Incl. Access Fees) $1,174. Sal $79,688
Library Holdings: Bk Vols 19,214; Per Subs 84; Bks on Deafness & Sign Lang 11

WEBSTER

P WEBSTER FREE PUBLIC LIBRARY,* 947 Battle St, 03303. SAN 309-9814. Tel: 603-648-2706. *Librn*, Cathryn Clark-Dawe
Pop 1,405; Circ 9,300
Jan 1999-Dec 1999 Income $13,000. Mats Exp $4,800. Sal $6,760
Library Holdings: Bk Vols 10,000; Per Subs 10
Mem of Cent Libr District

WENTWORTH

P WEBSTER MEMORIAL LIBRARY,* PO Box 105, 03282-0105. SAN 309-9822. Tel: 603-764-5818. *Dir*, Donna L Herlihy; Staff 2 (Non-MLS 2)
Founded 1917. Pop 620; Circ 7,025
Library Holdings: Bk Vols 14,707; Per Subs 53
Partic in Baker River Audio-Visual Ctr

WEST STEWARTSTOWN

P DENNIS JOOS MEMORIAL LIBRARY,* Washington St, PO Box 360, 03597. SAN 309-9563. Tel: 603-246-3329. *Librn*, Donna Allen
Pop 950
Library Holdings: Bk Vols 3,349
Mem of North Country District

WEST SWANZEY

P STRATTON FREE LIBRARY,* 9 Main St, PO Box 578, 03469. SAN 309-9679. Tel: 603-352-9391. *Librn*, Evelyn Fortner
Pop 2,800
Library Holdings: Bk Vols 7,000; Per Subs 10
Subject Interests: Local history

WESTMORELAND

P WESTMORELAND PUBLIC LIBRARY, 33 S Village Rd, 03467. SAN 309-9830. Tel: 603-399-7750. Web Site: westmorelandpl@monad.net. *Librn*, Mary Crowther
Founded 1888. Pop 1,650; Circ 5,938
Library Holdings: Bk Titles 11,000; Per Subs 10
Open Mon 11-8, Thurs 9-6 & Sat 9-1

WHITEFIELD

P WHITEFIELD PUBLIC LIBRARY, 8 Lancaster Rd, 03598. SAN 309-9849. Tel: 603-837-2030. E-Mail: wpl@connriver.net. *Librn*, Sandra Holz
Founded 1893. Pop 1,724; Circ 13,680
Jan 2000-Dec 2000 Income $25,075. Mats Exp $8,850, Books $8,000, Per/Ser (Incl. Access Fees) $850. Sal $10,000
Library Holdings: Bk Vols 12,000; Per Subs 40
Partic in North Country Library Cooperative

WILMOT

P WILMOT PUBLIC LIBRARY,* N Wilmot Rd, PO Box 133, 03287-0133. SAN 309-9857. Tel: 603-526-6804. FAX: 603-526-6804. E-Mail: wplib@sugar-river.net. *Librn*, Kathryn L Donovan
Pop 800; Circ 3,000
Library Holdings: Bk Vols 7,000
Mem of SW Libr District
Friends of the Library Group

WILTON

P WILTON PUBLIC & GREGG FREE LIBRARY,* 7 Forest Rd, 03086. SAN 309-9865. Tel: 603-654-2581. FAX: 603-654-2581. E-Mail: wpl@tellink.net. Web Site: www.wiltonlibrarynh.org. *Dir*, Carol R Roberts; Staff 4 (MLS 1, Non-MLS 3)
Founded 1908. Pop 3,250; Circ 28,153
1998-1999 Income $103,910. Mats Exp $14,000. Sal $65,200
Library Holdings: Bk Vols 18,578; Per Subs 70
Mem of SE Libr District
Open Mon, Wed & Fri 2-5, Tues & Thurs 9-12 & 2-8, Sat 9-12
Friends of the Library Group

WINCHESTER

P CONANT PUBLIC LIBRARY,* PO Box 6, 03470. SAN 309-9873. Tel: 603-239-4331. FAX: 603-239-4331. E-Mail: conantlibrary@cheshire.net. Web Site: adam.cheshire.net/~conantlibrary/home.htm. *Librn*, Louise E Reason
Pop 4,038; Circ 31,514
Jul 1997-Jun 1998 Income $54,000, City $40,000, Other $14,000. Mats Exp $15,000, Books $13,000, Per/Ser (Incl. Access Fees) $2,000. Sal $31,837
Library Holdings: Bk Vols 33,000
Special Collections: microfilm of Town Records 1733-1800; Winchester Star, 1895-1917
Mem of SW Libr District

P THAYER PUBLIC LIBRARY,* 3 Main St, 03441. (Mail add: PO Box 49, 03441-0049), Tel: 603-239-4099. *Librn*, Shannon Lake
Pop 3,440
Library Holdings: Bk Vols 4,070
Open Tues & Fri 1-8

WINDHAM

P NESMITH LIBRARY,* 8 Fellows Rd, PO Box 60, 03087. SAN 309-989X. Tel: 603-432-7154. FAX: 603-537-0097. Web Site: www.ultranet.com/~nesmith. *Dir*, Kathleen D Hutchins; E-Mail: khutchins@library.windham.nh.us; *Ch Servs*, Diane Mayr; *Ref*, Lois Freeston; *Cat*, Alberta Corvi; Staff 11 (MLS 3, Non-MLS 8)
Founded 1871. Pop 12,000; Circ 82,000
Jan 1999-Dec 1999 Income $380,865, City $371,910, Locally Generated Income $8,955. Mats Exp $61,470, Books $46,000, Per/Ser (Incl. Access Fees) $12,980, Micro $400, Electronic Ref Mat (Incl. Access Fees) $2,090. Sal $240,700 (Prof $138,900)
Library Holdings: Bk Vols 44,865; Bk Titles 42,674; Per Subs 115; Bks on Deafness & Sign Lang 13
Subject Interests: NH hist
Automation Activity & Vendor Info: (Cataloging) Follett; (Circulation) Follett; (OPAC) Follett
Database Vendor: Ebsco - EbscoHost, OCLC - First Search
Publications: Newsletter
Friends of the Library Group

WOLFEBORO

M HUGGINS HOSPITAL LIBRARY,* 240 S Main St, PO Box 912, 03894-0912. SAN 323-682X. Tel: 603-569-2150. FAX: 603-569-7509. *Librn*, Ann Robinson
Library Holdings: Bk Titles 380; Per Subs 32
Subject Interests: Medicine, Nursing
Publications: Acquisition List

S WOLFEBORO HISTORICAL SOCIETY LIBRARY,* S Main St, PO Box 1066, 03894. SAN 326-2987. Tel: 603-569-4842, 603-569-6768. *Librn*, Chris Fipphen; *Librn*, Dorothy Tarr; Staff 1 (Non-MLS 1)
Subject Interests: Genealogy, History
Special Collections: Local Pictures & Photographs
Restriction: By appointment only
Open 10-4 (July 4-Labor Day)

P WOLFEBORO PUBLIC LIBRARY, 259 S Main St, PO Box 710, 03894. SAN 309-9903. Tel: 603-569-2428. FAX: 603-569-8180. E-Mail: wolfelib@worldpath.net. Web Site: worldpath.net/~wolfelib. *Dir*, Louise A Gehman; Staff 7 (MLS 1, Non-MLS 6)
Founded 1900. Pop 5,188
Jan 2000-Dec 2000 Income $260,827, City $254,927, Locally Generated Income $5,900. Mats Exp $34,100, Books $20,600, Per/Ser (Incl. Access Fees) $8,000, Manuscripts & Archives $2,315. Sal $137,251 (Prof $62,780)
Library Holdings: Bk Titles 42,192; Per Subs 177
Automation Activity & Vendor Info: (Cataloging) Sagebrush Corporation; (Circulation) Sagebrush Corporation
Database Vendor: IAC - SearchBank
Function: ILL available
Friends of the Library Group

WOODSVILLE

M COTTAGE HOSPITAL, Medical Library,* Sulftuater Rd, PO Box 2001, 03785-2001. SAN 377-9416. Tel: 603-747-2761. FAX: 603-747-3310.
Library Holdings: Bk Vols 15; Bk Titles 400

P WOODSVILLE FREE PUBLIC LIBRARY, 14 School St, 03785. SAN 309-8400. Tel: 603-747-3483. FAX: 603-787-6507. *Librn*, Dawn Langley; E-Mail: dlangley@together.net; *Asst Librn*, Diann Noyes
Pop 3,444; Circ 23,111
Library Holdings: Bk Vols 35,860; Per Subs 54
Subject Interests: Town hist
Publications: Local Paper
Open Mon, Wed & Fri 1-8

NEW JERSEY

Date of Statistics: Calendar 1999
Population, 1990 Census: 7,730,188
Population Served by Public Libraries: 8,041,454
  Unserved: 59,285
Total Volumes in Public Libraries: 28,773,804
  Volumes Per Capita: 3.58
Total Public Library Income: $283,661,047
  Average Income Per Library: $981,526
  Source of Income: Mainly public funds
Expenditures Per Capita: $34.29 (statewide)
Number of County Libraries: 14
Grants-in-Aid to Public Libraries (fiscal 1999): $4,747,093
  Federal: $2,644,305
  State Aid: $8,358,894

ABSECON

P ABSECON PUBLIC LIBRARY, 305 New Jersey Ave, 08201. SAN 309-9911. Tel: 609-646-2228. FAX: 609-383-8992. *Dir*, Barbara Wilson; *Librn*, Ruth Mufferi
Founded 1937. Pop 7,000; Circ 20,429
Library Holdings: Bk Vols 25,000; Per Subs 50

ALLAIRE

S ALLAIRE VILLAGE INC., Research Library, Allaire State Park, Rte 524, PO Box 220, 07727. Tel: 732-919-3500. FAX: 732-938-3302. E-Mail: allairevillage@bytheshore.com. Web Site: www.allairevillage.org. *Exec Dir*, John Curtis
Library Holdings: Bk Vols 300
Special Collections: James P Allaire Coll, letters, ledgers, business records
Restriction: By appointment only

ALLENDALE

P LEE MEMORIAL LIBRARY, Allendale Public Library, 500 W Crescent Ave, 07401-1799. SAN 309-992X. Tel: 201-327-4338. FAX: 201-327-5838. E-Mail: aldl1@bccls.org. Web Site: www.bccls.org/allendale/. *Dir*, Melissa Hughes; E-Mail: hughes@bccls.org; *Ch Servs*, Elaine Moustakas; *Ad Servs*, Martha Urbiel; Staff 7 (MLS 3, Non-MLS 4)
Founded 1923. Pop 6,500; Circ 104,490
Jan 2000-Dec 2000 Income $353,614, State $6,333, City $306,748, Other $40,533. Mats Exp $68,904, Books $52,904, Per/Ser (Incl. Access Fees) $6,500, AV Equip $9,500. Sal $168,749 (Prof $99,766)
Library Holdings: Bk Vols 48,172; Bk Titles 44,808; Per Subs 100
Partic in Bergen County Cooperative Library System
Friends of the Library Group

ALPHA

P W H WALTERS FREE PUBLIC LIBRARY,* 1001 East Blvd, 08865. SAN 376-0650. Tel: 908-454-1445. *Librn*, Myrna Minardi
Library Holdings: Bk Titles 16,000
Open Mon, Wed & Fri 9-5, Tues & Thurs 9-8

ANCORA

ANCORA PSYCHIATRIC HOSPITAL
M HEALTH SCIENCES LIBRARY, 202 Spring Garden Rd, 08037. SAN 350-7696. Tel: 609-561-1700. FAX: 609-561-2509.
Founded 1954
Library Holdings: Bk Vols 3,000; Per Subs 35
Subject Interests: Medicine, Neurology, Nursing, Psychiatry, Psychology
Special Collections: Psychiatry (Specialty Coll), bks & tapes
Restriction: Open to public for reference only
Mem of SE Regional Network of NJ

S RESIDENTS' LIBRARY, 202 Spring Garden Rd, 08037-9699. SAN 350-7750. Tel: 609-561-1700, Ext 7497. FAX: 609-561-2509. *In Charge*, Ed Force
Library Holdings: Bk Vols 10,000; Per Subs 50

ANNANDALE

S EXXON RESEARCH & ENGINEERING CO, Clinton Information Center, Clinton Township, Rte 22 E, 08801. SAN 375-9180. Tel: 908-730-2755. FAX: 908-730-3021. *In Charge*, Marie Latino
Library Holdings: Bk Vols 15,000

M EXXONMOBIL BIOMEDICAL SCIENCES, Corporate Library, 1545 Rte 22-E, PO Box 971, 08801-0971. SAN 350-8293. Tel: 908-730-1145. Reference Tel: 908-730-1010. FAX: 908-730-1110. *Head Ref*, Andrea Holladay; E-Mail: acholla@erenj.com. Subject Specialists: *Chemistry*, Andrea Holladay; Staff 4 (MLS 1, Non-MLS 3)
Founded 1952
Library Holdings: Bk Vols 6,000; Bk Titles 4,000; Per Subs 200
Subject Interests: Toxicology

S MOUNTAIN VIEW YOUTH CORRECTIONAL FACILITY LIBRARY, Main Compound, 31 Petticoat Lane, 08801-4097. (Mail add: PO Box 994, 08801-0994), SAN 375-7463. Tel: 908-638-6191, Ext 7326. *Librn*, Krishan D Sharma; Tel: 908-638-6191, Ext 7316
Library Holdings: Bk Vols 5,500; Per Subs 35
Automation Activity & Vendor Info: (Cataloging) Sagebrush Corporation; (Circulation) Sagebrush Corporation
Branches:
MINIMUM UNIT, 31 Petticoat Lane, 08801-4097. (Mail add: PO Box 994, 08801-0994), Tel: 908-638-6191, Ext 7326. *Librn*, Craig Merrick; Tel: 908-638-6191, Ext 7384
Library Holdings: Bk Vols 400

ASBURY PARK

P ASBURY PARK FREE PUBLIC LIBRARY, 500 First Ave, 07712. SAN 309-9938. Tel: 732-774-4221. FAX: 732-988-6101. E-Mail: info@asburypark.lib.nj.us. *Dir*, Robert W Stewart
Founded 1878. Circ 47,469
Library Holdings: Bk Vols 95,600; Bk Titles 86,200; Per Subs 350
Mem of NJ Regional Libr Coop

ATCO

P WATERFORD TOWNSHIP PUBLIC LIBRARY, 2204 Atco Ave, 08004. SAN 309-9954. Tel: 856-767-7727. FAX: 856-753-8998. E-Mail: wtpl@camden.lib.nj.us. *Ch Servs, Dir*, Eva Lynch; E-Mail: elynch@camden.lib.nj.us; *Circ*, Elizabeth Diaz; *Ref*, Margaret Haggerty; Staff 9 (MLS 1, Non-MLS 8)
Founded 1964. Pop 11,000
Jan 1999-Dec 1999 Income $189,749, State $22,461, City $143,400, Locally

Generated Income $23,888. Mats Exp $29,362, Books $25,000, Per/Ser (Incl. Access Fees) $3,500, Electronic Ref Mat (Incl. Access Fees) $862. Sal $114,155
Library Holdings: Bk Vols 24,684; Per Subs 131
Subject Interests: Parenting
Automation Activity & Vendor Info: (Circulation) Sagebrush Corporation
Friends of the Library Group

ATLANTIC CITY

P ATLANTIC CITY FREE PUBLIC LIBRARY, One N Tennessee Ave, 08401. SAN 350-5685. Tel: 609-345-2269. FAX: 609-345-5570. Web Site: www.acfpl.org. *Dir*, Maureen Sherr Frank; *Ch Servs*, Constance L Swanson; *Ref*, Julie Senack; *Asst Dir, Tech Servs*, Robert Rynkiewicz; Staff 37 (MLS 9, Non-MLS 28)
Founded 1902. Pop 37,986; Circ 182,521
Library Holdings: Bk Vols 129,999; Bk Titles 104,200; Per Subs 350
Special Collections: Casino Gambling; Genealogy & Atlantic City History (Heston Coll)
Automation Activity & Vendor Info: (Acquisitions) epixtech, inc.; (Cataloging) epixtech, inc.; (Circulation) epixtech, inc.
Publications: Atlantic City News Index; Clubs & Organizations Directory
Mem of S Jersey Regional Libr Coop
Partic in OCLC Online Computer Library Center, Inc
Branches: 1
RICHMOND AVENUE SCHOOL, Windsor & Ventnor Aves, 08401. SAN 350-574X. Tel: 609-347-1902. Web Site: www.acfpl.org. *In Charge*, Bradley Theda
Library Holdings: Bk Vols 5,000

M ATLANTIC CITY MEDICAL CENTER, Medical Library, 1925 Pacific Ave, 08401. SAN 309-9962. Tel: 609-344-4081. FAX: 609-441-2137. *Librn*, John P Doesburgh
Library Holdings: Bk Vols 3,500; Per Subs 200
Subject Interests: Nursing, Public health

G FEDERAL AVIATION ADMINISTRATION, Wm J Hughes Technical Center Library Act-71A,* Atlantic City International Airport, 08405. SAN 309-9970. Tel: 609-485-5124. FAX: 609-485-4329. E-Mail: actlibrary@admin.tc.faa.gov. Web Site: www.tc.faa.gov.
Founded 1958
Library Holdings: Bk Vols 12,000; Per Subs 400
Subject Interests: Aeronautics, Air traffic control, Airports, Aviation safety, Communications, Elec, Navigation, Radar
Partic in OCLC Online Computer Library Center, Inc

S PRINCETON ANTIQUES BOOKSERVICE, Art Marketing Reference Library,* 2915-17 Atlantic Ave, 08401-6395. SAN 309-9989. Tel: 609-344-1943. FAX: 609-344-1944. E-Mail: princetn@earthlink.net. Web Site: princetonantiques.com. *Curator*, Christine Albertson; Staff 2 (MLS 1, Non-MLS 1)
Founded 1974
Library Holdings: Bk Titles 150,000; Per Subs 15
Subject Interests: Antiques, Bk market, Function in US of art, Gambling, Price info hist from 1900
Special Collections: Post Card Photo Library Information Bank Coll (1900-1950)

ATLANTIC HIGHLANDS

P ATLANTIC HIGHLANDS PUBLIC LIBRARY ASSOCIATION, 100 First Ave, 07716. SAN 309-9997. Tel: 732-291-1956. FAX: 732-291-2044. *Dir*, Marilyn C Scherfen; Staff 1 (MLS 1)
Founded 1926. Pop 4,895; Circ 21,611
Library Holdings: Bk Titles 20,000; Per Subs 50
Mem of Monmouth County Library
Open Tues-Sat 10-11:30 & Mon 1-5
Friends of the Library Group

AUDUBON

P FREE PUBLIC LIBRARY OF AUDUBON, (FPLA), 239 Oakland Ave, 08106-1598. SAN 310-0006. Tel: 856-547-8686. FAX: 856-547-0277.; Staff 7 (MLS 1, Non-MLS 6)
Pop 9,205; Circ 39,751
Library Holdings: Bk Vols 45,000; Bk Titles 38,594; Per Subs 102
Publications: Newsletter
Partic in South Jersey Regional Library Cooperative

AVENEL

S WOODBRIDGE DIAGNOSTIC CENTER LIBRARY,* 15 Paddock St, 07001. SAN 375-7447. Tel: 732-499-5070. FAX: 732-815-4874. *Dir*, William B Falvo
Library Holdings: Per Subs 34
Open Mon-Thurs 5:30-8

AVON BY THE SEA

P AVON PUBLIC LIBRARY,* Garfield & Fifth Ave, 07717. SAN 310-0014. Tel: 732-502-4525. FAX: 732-775-8430. E-Mail: apl@shore.co.monmouth.nj.us. *Dir, Librn*, Sheila Watson
Founded 1916. Pop 2,163; Circ 25,174
Library Holdings: Bk Vols 18,273; Per Subs 61
Mem of State Libr Syst
Open Mon, Wed & Thurs 12-7, Tues & Fri 1-5, Sat 10-2

BASKING RIDGE

P BERNARDS TOWNSHIP LIBRARY, 32 S Maple Ave, 07920-1216. SAN 310-0049. Tel: 908-204-3031. FAX: 908-766-1580. Web Site: www.bernards.org/library. *Dir*, Anne Meany; E-Mail: ameany@bernards.org; *Ch Servs*, Antonette D'Orazio; *Circ*, Karen Choie; *Ref*, Ruth Lufkin; E-Mail: lufkin@main.morris.org; *Tech Servs*, Nancy Widmer; Staff 34 (MLS 8, Non-MLS 26)
Founded 1898. Pop 26,000
Library Holdings: Bk Vols 95,000; Per Subs 290
Subject Interests: Local history, Performing arts
Automation Activity & Vendor Info: (Cataloging) DRA; (Circulation) DRA; (OPAC) DRA
Publications: History of the Library in Basking Ridge; Newsletter
Partic in Morris-Union Federation
Friends of the Library Group

S PASSAIC RIVER COALITION, Environmental Library,* 246 Madisonville Rd, 07920. SAN 329-0409. Tel: 908-766-7550. FAX: 908-766-7550. *Adminr*, Ella F Filippone; *Acq, Circ, Publ Servs*, Ralph Zimmerman
Founded 1971
Library Holdings: Bk Vols 5,000; Per Subs 140
Publications: Special Studies

G SOMERSET COUNTY PARK COMMISSION, (EEC), Environmental Education Center Library, 190 Lord Stirling Rd, 07920. SAN 321-043X. Tel: 908-766-2489. FAX: 908-766-2687. Web Site: www.park.co.somerset.nj.us. *In Charge*, Catherine Schrein; Tel: 908-766-2489, Ext 324, E-Mail: cschrein@parks.co.somerset.nj.us. Subject Specialists: *Environmental studies*, Catherine Schrein; Staff 15 (Non-MLS 15)
Founded 1972
Jan 1999-Dec 1999 Income $2,900. Mats Exp $2,900, Books $1,200, Per/Ser (Incl. Access Fees) $1,700
Library Holdings: Bk Titles 5,000; Per Subs 30
Subject Interests: Environmental studies, Mushroom culture, Natural history
Restriction: Restricted loan policy

BAYONNE

M BAYONNE HOSPITAL, Medical Library, 29 E 29th St, 07002. SAN 377-3620. Tel: 201-858-5304. FAX: 201-858-7322.
Library Holdings: Bk Vols 175; Bk Titles 150; Per Subs 40
Partic in Consortium Biomed Libr Asn; Medical Libr Asn

P FREE PUBLIC LIBRARY OF BAYONNE, 697 Avenue C, 07002. SAN 350-5774. Tel: 201-858-6970. Interlibrary Loan Service Tel: 201-858-6980. FAX: 201-437-6928. Web Site: www.library.bayonne.net. *Dir*, Sneh P Bains; E-Mail: sbains@bccls.org; *Music*, Adele Puccio; *Govt Doc*, Pat Payette; *Ch Servs*, Paula Micalizzi; Tel: 201-858-6975, E-Mail: micalizzi@bccls.org; Staff 21 (MLS 8, Non-MLS 13)
Founded 1893. Pop 65,000; Circ 190,503
Jul 1999-Jun 2000 Income (Main Library and Branch Library) $1,679,225, State $79,159, City $1,600,066. Mats Exp $158,500, Books $140,000, Per/Ser (Incl. Access Fees) $18,500. Sal $925,549 (Prof $240,000)
Library Holdings: Bk Vols 264,623; Per Subs 526
Subject Interests: Architecture, Art, Bus, Indust, Mgt, Music, Sci-tech
Special Collections: Local History, (New Jersey & Bayonneana)
Automation Activity & Vendor Info: (Cataloging) DRA; (Circulation) DRA; (OPAC) DRA
Database Vendor: Ebsco - EbscoHost
Publications: Newsletter (quarterly)
Partic in Bergen County Cooperative Library System; Infolink Eastern New Jersey Regional Library Cooperative, Inc
Friends of the Library Group
Branches: 2
BRANCH II, 1055 Avenue C, 07002. SAN 350-5839. Tel: 201-858-6977. Web Site: www.library.bayonne.net. *In Charge*, Susan Humenic
Pop 61,000
Library Holdings: Bk Titles 8,922
Subject Interests: Arts, City hist, Music
Automation Activity & Vendor Info: (Cataloging) DRA; (Circulation) DRA; (OPAC) DRA
Friends of the Library Group
STORY COURT, Story Ct & Fourth St, 07002. SAN 350-5863. Tel: 201-858-6979. Web Site: www.library.bayonne.net. *In Charge*, Marie Smith

Library Holdings: Bk Titles 16,091
Automation Activity & Vendor Info: (Cataloging) DRA; (Circulation) DRA; (OPAC) DRA
Friends of the Library Group

BEACH HAVEN

P BEACH HAVEN FREE PUBLIC LIBRARY, 247 N Beach Ave & Third St, 08008-1865. SAN 310-0073. Tel: 609-492-7081. E-Mail: bhpubliclibrary@worldnet.att.net. *Dir*, Jeanne Bonnell; *Asst Librn*, Eileen Mitchell
Founded 1924. Pop 2,400; Circ 25,924
Library Holdings: Bk Vols 25,000; Per Subs 60
Subject Interests: Local history, Regional hist

BEDMINSTER

P CLARENCE DILLON PUBLIC LIBRARY, 2336 Lamington Rd, 07921. SAN 310-009X. Tel: 908-234-2325. FAX: 908-781-9402. Web Site: www.somersethills.com/cdpl. *Dir*, Patricia K Anderson; *Assoc Dir*, Diana Simon; *Ch Servs*, Helen Petersen
Pop 8,000; Circ 91,000
Library Holdings: Bk Vols 75,000
Subject Interests: Civil War
Special Collections: Local History (Anne O'Brien Coll)
Partic in Highlands Regional Library Cooperative; Raritan Valley Fedn of Librs; Somerset Hills Libr Consortium
Homebound delivery system for infirmed or elderly
Friends of the Library Group

BELLE MEAD

M CARRIER CLINIC, Nolan DC Lewis Library, PO Box 147, 08502. SAN 327-9421. Tel: 908-281-1411. FAX: 908-281-1672. Web Site: www.carrier.org. *Dir*, Lynne Cohn; E-Mail: lcohn@carrierclinic.com
Library Holdings: Bk Titles 5,000; Per Subs 164
Subject Interests: Mental health, Psychiatry, Psychotherapy
Special Collections: Nolan D C Lewis Coll

BELLEVILLE

P BELLEVILLE PUBLIC LIBRARY & INFORMATION CENTER, 221 Washington Ave, 07109-3189. SAN 310-0103. Tel: 973-450-3434. FAX: 973-450-7931, 973-759-6731. Web Site: www.bellepl.org. *Dir*, Joan Barbara Taub; Fax: 973-450-9518, E-Mail: jtaub@infolink.org; *Br Coordr*, Frederick Lewis; *Acq, Head Ref*, Cindy LaRue; *Ch Servs*, Melissa Kopecky; *Head Tech Servs*, Mary Spina; *Circ*, Caroline Stahl; Staff 13 (MLS 5, Non-MLS 8)
Founded 1902. Pop 34,213; Circ 115,248
Library Holdings: Bk Vols 90,937; Bk Titles 72,873; Per Subs 142
Subject Interests: Career, City hist, State hist
Automation Activity & Vendor Info: (Cataloging) Gaylord
Database Vendor: Ebsco - EbscoHost, IAC - Info Trac
Publications: Belleville Public Library Newsletter (quarterly)
Partic in Infolink
Friends of the Library Group

P BELLEVILLE PUBLIC LIBRARY & INFORMATION CENTER, Mrs Richard A Shafter Branch, 30 Magnolia St, 07109. SAN 376-0472. Tel: 973-450-3438. FAX: 973-450-3164. Web Site: www.intac.com/~bplibn/. *Librn*, Frederick Lewis
Founded 1965
Library Holdings: Bk Titles 10,000
Subject Interests: Fiction
Open Mon-Fri 1-5, summer (July & Aug) Mon-Fri 9-1
Friends of the Library Group

M CEREBRAL PALSY OF ESSEX & WEST HUDSON, Dr Charles I Nadel Library, 7 Sanford Ave, 07109. SAN 375-9989. Tel: 973-751-0200. FAX: 973-751-4635. E-Mail: cpcpb@intac.com. *Exec Dir*, Peter Kurtz
Library Holdings: Bk Titles 112; Per Subs 205

M CLARA MAASS MEDICAL CENTER, (Formerly St Barnabas Health Care System), Medical Library, One Clara Maass Dr, 07109. SAN 327-3601. Tel: 973-450-2294. FAX: 973-450-1936. *Librn*, Arlene Mangino; E-Mail: amangino@sbhcs.com; Staff 1 (MLS 1)
Library Holdings: Bk Titles 1,050; Per Subs 124
Subject Interests: Medicine, Nursing
Publications: What's New in the Library
Partic in BHSL; Infolink Eastern New Jersey Regional Library Cooperative, Inc; National Network Of Libraries Of Medicine - South Central Region; New Jersey Health Sciences Library Network

BELMAR

P BELMAR PUBLIC LIBRARY, 517 Tenth Ave, 07719. SAN 310-012X. Tel: 732-681-0775. FAX: 732-681-8419. *Dir*, Lois T Gallagher; *Asst Librn*, Natalie M Hurley; Staff 2 (MLS 2)
Founded 1913. Pop 6,000; Circ 16,902
Library Holdings: Bk Vols 21,000; Bk Titles 19,000; Per Subs 60
Friends of the Library Group

BELVIDERE

P BELVIDERE FREE PUBLIC LIBRARY, 301 Second St, 07823-1517. SAN 310-0138. Tel: 908-475-3941. FAX: 908-475-3893. E-Mail: bellib@epicsnet. *Dir*, Theresa Aicher
Circ 275
Library Holdings: Bk Vols 22,000; Per Subs 38
Mem of Phillipsburg Pub Libr
Open Mon, Wed & Fri 11-5, Tues & Thurs 1-8, Sat 11-3
Friends of the Library Group

S WARREN COUNTY HISTORICAL SOCIETY, Resource Room,* 313 Mansfield St, PO Box 313, 07823-0313. SAN 375-7374. Tel: 908-475-4246. *Pres*, Gladys Eggler
Library Holdings: Bk Vols 300
Open Sun 2-4 except holidays & by appointment

P WARREN COUNTY LIBRARY,* Court House Annex, 199 Hardwick St, 07823. SAN 350-5898. Tel: 908-475-6322. *Dir*, Thomas L Carney; *Ref*, Asha Bhargava; *Acq, AV*, Richard Moore; *Cat*, Joseph Szeplaki; *ILL*, Earline Ziech; *Bkmobile Coordr*, Angela Lundgren; Staff 6 (MLS 6)
Founded 1931. Pop 57,000; Circ 189,278
Library Holdings: Bk Titles 116,606; Per Subs 225
Special Collections: Local History (Warren County Reference), bks, pamphlets
Special Services for the Deaf - Books on deafness & sign language
Friends of the Library Group
Branches: 3
CATHERINE DICKSON HOFMAN LIBRARY, Four Lambert Rd, Blairstown, 07825. SAN 310-0227. Tel: 908-362-8335. FAX: 908-362-7775. *In Charge*, Marilyn Grandin
Founded 1941. Pop 10,300; Circ 19,710
Library Holdings: Bk Vols 20,000
Database Vendor: epixtech, inc.
Friends of the Library Group
FRANKLIN BRANCH, 1502 Rte 57, Washington, 07882. SAN 376-2580. Tel: 908-689-7922. FAX: 908-689-8265. *Br Coordr*, Christina Reedell; *Publ Servs*, Virginia Peterlin; *Cat*, Anne Sottile; *Circ*, Karen Hahn; *ILL*, Cynthia Seelig
Founded 1989. Pop 6,798; Circ 135,098
Library Holdings: Bk Vols 40,000
Partic in Highlands Regional Library Cooperative
Friends of the Library Group
NORTHEAST, 63 US Hwy 46, Hackettstown, 07840. SAN 377-7774. Tel: 908-813-3858. FAX: 908-813-3813. *Mgr*, Patricia Opitz
Library Holdings: Bk Titles 35,000; Per Subs 70
Database Vendor: epixtech, inc.
Friends of the Library Group
Bookmobiles: 3

BERGENFIELD

P BERGENFIELD FREE PUBLIC LIBRARY & INFORMATION CENTER, 50 W Clinton Ave, 07621-2799. SAN 310-0146. Tel: 201-387-4040. Circulation Tel: 201-387-4040, Ext 840. Reference Tel: 201-387-4040, Ext 832. FAX: 201-387-9004. E-Mail: BFLD1@BCCLS.org. Web Site: www.BCCLS.org/Bergenfield/. *Dir*, Robert Pawson; Tel: 201-387-4040, Ext 829, E-Mail: pawson@bccls.org; *Asst Dir*, Tina Painter; Tel: 201-387-4040, Ext 844, E-Mail: painter@bbcls.org; *Head, Circ*, Betty Costello; Tel: 201-387-4040, Ext 824; *Ch Servs*, Louise Moroses; Tel: 201-387-4040, Ext 896, E-Mail: bookwoman15@yahoo.com; *Head Ref*, Mary Ellen Henitz; Tel: 201-387-4040, Ext 830, E-Mail: henitz@bccls.org; Staff 37 (MLS 8, Non-MLS 29)
Founded 1920. Pop 24,827; Circ 284,877
Jan 1999-Dec 1999 Income $1,326,478, State $31,505, City $1,236,850, Locally Generated Income $58,123. Mats Exp $110,315, Books $76,771, Per/Ser (Incl. Access Fees) $19,952, Presv $245, AV Equip $10,940, Electronic Ref Mat (Incl. Access Fees) $2,407. Sal $734,298 (Prof $291,984)
Library Holdings: Bk Vols 124,997; Bk Titles 117,857; Per Subs 350
Subject Interests: Education
Special Collections: ESL Coll, New Jersey
Automation Activity & Vendor Info: (Circulation) DRA
Database Vendor: DRA, Ebsco - EbscoHost
Publications: Shelf-Wise
Mem of Bergen County Co-op Libr Syst
Partic in Bergen County Coop Libr Computer Consortium
Friends of the Library Group

BERKELEY HEIGHTS

P BERKELEY HEIGHTS FREE PUBLIC LIBRARY, 290 Plainfield Ave, 07922. SAN 310-0154. Tel: 908-464-9333. FAX: 908-464-7098. E-Mail: bhplreference@hotmail.com. Web Site: www.bhs.k1-2.nj.us/bhpl. *Dir*, Stephanie Bakos; *Head Ref*, Bridgett Brambilla; *ILL*, Lynn Thompson; *Cat*, Lois Williams; *Ch Servs*, Laura Fuhro; Staff 5 (MLS 5)
Founded 1953. Pop 11,980; Circ 136,719
Library Holdings: Bk Vols 68,208; Bk Titles 57,924; Per Subs 210
Subject Interests: Architecture, Art
Friends of the Library Group

S OAKITE PRODUCTS, INC, Technical Library,* 50 Valley Rd, 07922. SAN 310-0162. Tel: 908-464-6900. FAX: 908-464-4658. *Pres*, William Wenhold
Library Holdings: Bk Titles 3,500
Restriction: Staff use only

M RUNNELLS SPECIALIZED HOSPITAL, Watson B Morris Library,* 40 Watchung Way, 07922. SAN 375-9296. Tel: 908-771-5922. FAX: 908-771-5820. *In Charge*, Monique Blackman
Library Holdings: Bk Vols 660; Per Subs 40

BERLIN

P MARIE FLECHE MEMORIAL LIBRARY,* 49 S White Horse Pike, 08009. SAN 310-0170. Tel: 856-767-2448. FAX: 856-768-7421. *Dir*, Mary Rencic
Founded 1957. Pop 6,000; Circ 22,470
Library Holdings: Bk Vols 20,209; Bk Titles 16,820; Per Subs 55
Mem of Camden County Library System

BERNARDSVILLE

P BERNARDSVILLE PUBLIC LIBRARY, One Anderson Hill Rd, 07924. SAN 310-0189. Tel: 908-766-0118. FAX: 908-766-2464. Web Site: www.bernardsville.org. *Dir*, Jane Kennedy; E-Mail: jkennedy@hublib.lib.nj.us; *Ch Servs*, Michaele Casey; *Tech Servs*, Rosalie Baker; *Circ*, Thomas Kenney; Staff 13 (MLS 3, Non-MLS 10)
Founded 1902. Pop 7,500; Circ 188,373
Jan 1999-Dec 1999 Income $545,559, State $7,082, City $448,000, Federal $5,000, Other $85,477. Mats Exp $92,847, Books $64,707, Per/Ser (Incl. Access Fees) $18,986, AV Equip $9,154. Sal $265,980
Library Holdings: Bk Vols 68,758; Bk Titles 59,091; Per Subs 132
Special Collections: Local History (Spinning Coll), bks & microfilm
Automation Activity & Vendor Info: (Circulation) Gaylord
Publications: Bernardsville Library Times (newsletter-bimonthly)
Partic in NW Regional Libr Coop
Friends of the Library Group

S GEOSCIENCE SERVICES, Technical Library,* 25 Claremont Rd, 07924. SAN 323-4118. Tel: 908-221-9332. FAX: 908-221-0406. E-Mail: geoserv@hotmail.com. *In Charge*, Joseph J Fischer
Library Holdings: Bk Vols 2,000

BEVERLY

P BEVERLY FREE LIBRARY, 441 Cooper St, 08010. (Mail add: 1025 Detwiler Ave, 08010), SAN 310-0197. Tel: 609-387-1259. FAX: 609-387-1259. *Dir*, Margaret Lowden; Staff 1 (MLS 1)
Founded 1929. Pop 13,000
Library Holdings: Bk Titles 11,500; Per Subs 3
Subject Interests: New Jersey
Mem of Burlington County Library
Open Mon, Wed &Thurs 2-5pm, Tues & Fri 7-9pm Sat 11am-3pm
Friends of the Library Group

BLACKWOOD

J CAMDEN COUNTY COLLEGE LIBRARY, Charles Wolverton Learning Resource Center, Little Gloucester Rd, PO Box 200, 08012. SAN 310-0200. Tel: 856-227-7200, Ext 4406. Interlibrary Loan Service Tel: 856-227-7200, Ext 4401. Circulation Tel: 856-227-7200, Ext 4404. Reference Tel: 856-227-7200, Ext 4408. FAX: 856-374-4897. Web Site: www.camdencc.edu/library. *Dir*, Joan Getaz; E-Mail: jgetaz@camdencc.edu; *Tech Servs*, Lorraine Baggett-Heuser; Tel: 856-227-7200, Ext 4417, E-Mail: LBaggett@camdencc.edu; *Ref*, Alfred A Fry; Tel: 856-227-7200, Ext 4405, E-Mail: AFry@camdencc.edu; *Ref*, Miriam Mlynarski; Tel: 856-227-7200, Ext 4615, E-Mail: MMlynarski@camdencc.edu; *AV*, David Maloney; Tel: 856-227-7200, Ext 4422, Fax: 856-374-5014, E-Mail: DMaloney@camdencc.edu; *Coll Develop*, Patricia Fazio; Tel: 856-227-7200, Ext 4402, E-Mail: PFazio@camdencc.edu; Staff 15 (MLS 7, Non-MLS 8)
Founded 1967. Enrl 11,000; Fac 600; Highest Degree: Associate
Jul 1999-Jun 2000 Income $844,200, Locally Generated Income $3,500, Parent Institution $840,700. Mats Exp $228,800, Presv $3,300. Sal $615,400
Library Holdings: Bk Vols 101,870; Bk Titles 71,500; Per Subs 400; Bks on Deafness & Sign Lang 250
Subject Interests: Art, Judaica, Real estate
Automation Activity & Vendor Info: (Cataloging) DRA; (Circulation) DRA; (OPAC) DRA
Database Vendor: Lexis-Nexis, OCLC - First Search
Partic in PALINET & Union Library Catalogue of Pennsylvania; South Jersey Regional Library Cooperative

M HELENE FULD SCHOOL OF NURSING IN CAMDEN COUNTY LIBRARY,* College Dr, Bldg 26, PO Box 1669, 08012. SAN 327-3660. Tel: 609-374-0100. FAX: 609-374-0712. *Librn*, Beth DeGeorge; E-Mail: bdegeorg@wjhs.org; Staff 2 (MLS 1, Non-MLS 1)
Library Holdings: Bk Vols 2,200; Bk Titles 1,800; Per Subs 115
Subject Interests: Allied health, Nursing
Special Collections: 130 Periodicals; Archives, NLN & ANA
Partic in Basic Health Sciences Library Network; Health Sciences Library Association Of New Jersey; South Jersey Regional Library Cooperative; SW NJ Consortium

BLOOMFIELD

S ABB LUMMUS GLOBAL, INC, Lummus Technology Division Library, 1515 Broad St, 07003. SAN 310-0251. Tel: 973-893-2251. Interlibrary Loan Service Tel: 973-893-2253. FAX: 973-893-2119. *Librn*, Elizabeth A Schefler; E-Mail: elizabeth.a.schefler@us.abb.com; Staff 2 (MLS 1, Non-MLS 1)
Founded 1930
Library Holdings: Bk Vols 10,500; Per Subs 200
Subject Interests: Chemical engineering, Petrochemicals, Petroleum refining
Special Collections: Crude Oil, bks & pamphlets
Database Vendor: Dialog, Lexis-Nexis
Partic in New Jersey Library Network

C BLOOMFIELD COLLEGE LIBRARY, 467 Franklin St, 07003. SAN 310-0235. Tel: 973-748-9000, Ext 337. FAX: 973-743-3998. Web Site: www.bloomfield.edu. *Dir*, Danilo H Figueredo; *Acq, Per*, Stanley Porteur; Tel: 973-748-9000, Ext 335; *Cat, Ref Serv, Syst Programmer*, Ying Shen; Tel: 973-748-9000, Ext 336; *ILL, Online Servs, Ref Serv*, Mark Jackson; Tel: 973-748-9000, Ext 714; *Media Spec*, Barbara Isacson; Tel: 973-748-9000, Ext 370; *Head, Circ*, Annmarie Battista; Tel: 973-748-9000, Ext 332; Staff 4 (MLS 4)
Founded 1869. Enrl 2,000; Fac 170; Highest Degree: Bachelor
Library Holdings: Bk Titles 64,000; Per Subs 375
Subject Interests: Education, Multicultural diversity
Mem of Essex-Hudson Regional Libr Coop
Partic in BRS; Dialog Corporation; OCLC Online Computer Library Center, Inc; PALINET & Union Library Catalogue of Pennsylvania

P BLOOMFIELD PUBLIC LIBRARY, 90 Broad St, 07003. SAN 310-0243. Tel: 973-566-6200. FAX: 973-566-6217. Reference FAX: 973-566-6206. Web Site: www.bloomfieldtwpnj.com/library.htm. *Dir*, Joyce Jollimore; Fax: 973-566-6217; *ILL*, Lisa Cohn; Tel: 973-566-6210; *Librn*, Linda Pendergrass; *Ch Servs*, Lisa Miklus; Tel: 973-566-6222; *AV, Per*, Barinderjit Bal; Tel: 973-566-6208; *Ad Servs*, Carol Steen; Tel: 973-566-6207; *Cat, Tech Servs*, Harold Smead; Tel: 973-566-6212; *Govt Doc*, Donald Carlo; *Reader Servs*, Linda Esler; Tel: 973-566-6210; Staff 23 (MLS 8, Non-MLS 15)
Founded 1924. Pop 48,000; Circ 201,941
Jan 1999-Dec 1999 Mats Exp $129,838, Books $110,000, Per/Ser (Incl. Access Fees) $19,838. Sal $653,232 (Prof $234,855)
Library Holdings: Bk Vols 181,063
Subject Interests: Bus, Labor, Music
Special Collections: Business & Labor Coll, bk, per, micro; Local History; Music Coll
Automation Activity & Vendor Info: (Circulation) GEAC
Database Vendor: Ebsco - EbscoHost, OCLC - First Search
Partic in Dialog Corporation; Essex-Hudson Regional Libr Coop; OCLC Online Computer Library Center, Inc; PALINET & Union Library Catalogue of Pennsylvania
Friends of the Library Group

BLOOMINGDALE

P BLOOMINGDALE FREE PUBLIC LIBRARY, Municipal Bldg, 101 Hamburg Tpk, 07403-1297. SAN 310-0278. Tel: 973-838-0077. FAX: 973-838-2482. *Dir*, Theresa J Rubin; *Asst Dir*, Patti Perugino
Founded 1926. Pop 7,530; Circ 31,034
Library Holdings: Bk Vols 23,057; Bk Titles 21,609; Per Subs 65
Subject Interests: Bloomingdale hist
Automation Activity & Vendor Info: (Cataloging) Sagebrush Corporation; (Circulation) Sagebrush Corporation; (OPAC) Sagebrush Corporation
Mem of Bergen - Passaic Regional Libr Syst; Passaic County Libr Syst
Friends of the Library Group

BOGOTA

P BOGOTA PUBLIC LIBRARY, 375 Larch Ave, 07603. SAN 310-0286. Tel: 201-488-7185. FAX: 201-342-0574. E-Mail: bogt1@bccls.org. Web Site: www.bccls.org. *Dir*, Eileen Mackesy-Karpoff

Founded 1915. Circ 41,000
1998-1999 Income $137,000. Mats Exp $21,500, Books $20,000, Per/Ser (Incl. Access Fees) $1,500. Sal $90,000 (Prof $40,000)
Library Holdings: Bk Vols 40,000; Per Subs 82
Partic in NJ Regional Libr Coop, Region 2
Friends of the Library Group

BOONTON

P THE BOONTON HOLMES PUBLIC LIBRARY, 621 Main St, 07005. SAN 310-0308. Tel: 973-334-2980. FAX: 973-334-3917. Web Site: www.boonton.org/library/index.htm. *Dir*, Sandra Rightmyer; E-Mail: rightmyer@main.morris.org; *Ch Servs*, Lesley Karczewski; E-Mail: karczewski@main.morris.org; Staff 2 (MLS 2)
Founded 1893. Pop 8,500; Circ 60,000
Jan 2000-Dec 2000 Income $221,986, State $8,986, City $205,000, Locally Generated Income $8,000. Mats Exp $37,700, Books $34,000, Per/Ser (Incl. Access Fees) $3,700. Sal $144,287 (Prof $75,700)
Library Holdings: Bk Vols 38,000; Bk Titles 35,000; Per Subs 105
Subject Interests: Collectibles, Local history, NJ hist, Travel
Special Collections: Boonton Newspaper Coll, microfiche; Boonton postcards
Publications: Boonton Library Newsletter
Partic in Highlands Regional Network; Morris Automated Information Network
Special Services for the Blind - Homebound delivery
Friends of the Library Group

BORDENTOWN

S ALBERT C WAGNER YOUTH CORRECTIONAL FACILITY LIBRARY,* 500 Ward Ave, PO Box 500, 08505. Tel: 609-298-0500, Ext 1535. FAX: 609-298-3639. *Adminr*, Joseph Butler; *Librn*, Prem Sinha
Library Holdings: Bk Titles 14,300

BOUND BROOK

P BOUND BROOK MEMORIAL LIBRARY, 402 E High St, 08805. SAN 310-0340. Tel: 732-356-0043. FAX: 732-356-1379. E-Mail: bbmlibrary@hotmail.com. Web Site: www.boundbrooklibrary.org. *Ch Servs*, Margaret Draghi; *Cat*, Mary Nelson; *Ad Servs, ILL, Ref*, Margaret McKay; Staff 4 (MLS 4)
Founded 1897. Pop 13,845; Circ 83,782
Jan 2000-Dec 2000 Income $358,477. Mats Exp $62,375, Books $41,000, Per/Ser (Incl. Access Fees) $9,650, Micro $3,725, AV Equip $7,000, Manuscripts & Archives $1,000. Sal $261,912 (Prof $126,000)
Library Holdings: Bk Vols 70,125; Bk Titles 66,571; Per Subs 163
Subject Interests: Antiques, History, Local history, Mysteries
Automation Activity & Vendor Info: (Circulation) Gaylord; (OPAC) Gaylord
Publications: Newsletter (bi-monthly)
Partic in Raritan Valley Fedn of Librs
Friends of the Library Group

BRADLEY BEACH

P BRADLEY BEACH PUBLIC LIBRARY, 511 Fourth Ave, 07720. SAN 310-0367. Tel: 732-776-2995. FAX: 732-774-4591. *Dir*, Karen Klapperstuck; Staff 4 (MLS 1, Non-MLS 3)
Founded 1927. Pop 4,700; Circ 19,177
1999-2000 Income $97,263. Mats Exp $12,760, Books $8,000, Per/Ser (Incl. Access Fees) $1,660, AV Equip $3,100. Sal $42,414 (Prof $33,785)
Library Holdings: Bk Vols 33,942; Per Subs 38
Subject Interests: Baseball
Partic in Central Jersey Regional Library Cooperative
Hours (Winter) Mon 12-5, Tues & Thurs 12-8, Wed & Fri 9-5, Sat 9-12
Friends of the Library Group

BRICK

M THE MEDICAL CENTER OF OCEAN COUNTY, Information Resource Center,* 425 Jack Martin Blvd, 08724. SAN 329-9198. Tel: 732-840-3343. FAX: 732-206-8052. E-Mail: pistolakiss@meridianhealth.com. *Librn*, Susan Pistolakis
Library Holdings: Bk Vols 1,800; Bk Titles 1,650; Per Subs 173
Subject Interests: Medicine
Mem of NJ Regional Libr Coop

BRIDGETON

P BRIDGETON FREE PUBLIC LIBRARY, 150 E Commerce St, 08302-2684. SAN 310-0375. Tel: 856-451-2620. Web Site: www.clueslibs.com. *Dir*, Gail S Robinson; Staff 10 (MLS 2, Non-MLS 8)
Founded 1811. Pop 18,750; Circ 40,000
Jul 1999-Jun 2000 Income $325,790. Mats Exp $28,000, Books $24,000, Per/Ser (Incl. Access Fees) $4,000. Sal $238,500 (Prof $89,000)
Library Holdings: Bk Vols 62,800; Bk Titles 60,000; Per Subs 105
Subject Interests: Genealogy
Special Collections: American Indians (Lenni-Lenapes); South Jersey History
Automation Activity & Vendor Info: (Cataloging) Inlex; (Circulation) Inlex; (OPAC) Inlex
Mem of Cumberland Libr United Elec Syst

S CUMBERLAND COUNTY JUVENILE DETENTION CENTER LIBRARY, 135 Sunny Slope Lane, 08302. SAN 375-734X. Tel: 856-455-0717. FAX: 856-455-4927. *Librn*, Susan Widjeskog
Library Holdings: Bk Vols 600; Per Subs 20

L CUMBERLAND COUNTY LAW LIBRARY,* Cumberland County Courthouse, Broad & Fayette Sts, 08302. SAN 328-1515. Tel: 856-451-8000. FAX: 856-455-9490. *Acq, Tech Servs*, Maria Buono; *Librn*, Diane Frank
Founded 1909
Library Holdings: Bk Vols 6,000; Bk Titles 1,500; Per Subs 30

P CUMBERLAND COUNTY LIBRARY, 800 E Commerce St, 08302-2295. SAN 310-0383. Tel: 856-453-2210. FAX: 856-451-1940. E-Mail: ref@clueslibs.org. Web Site: www.clueslibs.org. *Dir*, Nancy Forester; Tel: 856-453-2210, Ext 13, E-Mail: nancyfo@clueslibs.org; *Asst Dir*, Jean Edwards; Tel: 856-453-2210, Ext 14, E-Mail: jeaned@clueslibs.org; *ILL*, Margaret Allen; Tel: 856-453-2210, Ext 15, E-Mail: margaretal@clueslibs.org; *Ref*, Myron Estelle; Tel: 856-453-2210, Ext 11, E-Mail: myrones@clueslibs.org; *Syst Coordr*, Susan D'Ottavio; Tel: 856-453-2210, Ext 17, E-Mail: susando@clueslibs.org; *Tech Servs*, Frances A Jervis; Tel: 856-453-2210, Ext 19, E-Mail: francesje@clueslibs.org; Staff 6 (MLS 6)
Founded 1963. Pop 138,053; Circ 84,306
Library Holdings: Bk Vols 164,125; Bk Titles 130,466; Per Subs 197
Special Collections: Adult Basic Education materials
Automation Activity & Vendor Info: (Cataloging) DRA; (Circulation) DRA; (OPAC) DRA
Database Vendor: DRA
Member Libraries: Cedarville Public Library; Penns Grove-Carney's Point Public Library; Pennsville Public Library; Salem Free Public Library; Vineland Free Public Library; Woodstown-Pilesgrove Public Library
Partic in OCLC Online Computer Library Center, Inc
Special Services for the Deaf - TTY machine
Bookmobiles: 1

M SOUTH JERSEY HOSPITAL, Health Sciences Library, 333 Irving Ave, 08302. SAN 375-9288. Tel: 856-575-4536. FAX: 856-451-0335. *In Charge*, Eileen Niedzialek
Library Holdings: Per Subs 60

BRIDGEWATER

M AVENTIS PHARMACEUTICALS INC, (Formerly Hoechst Marion Roussel, Inc), Information & Library Services-United States, Rte 202-206, 08807-0800. SAN 310-5067. Tel: 908-231-2560. FAX: 908-231-2802. *Dir*, June Strupczewski; E-Mail: june.strupczewski@aventis.com; *Librn*, Sharon Srodin; Tel: 908-231-2625, E-Mail: sharon.srodia@aventis.com; Staff 6 (MLS 4, Non-MLS 2)
Founded 1970
Library Holdings: Bk Vols 3,000; Per Subs 600
Subject Interests: Anti-infectives, Bone diseases, Cardiovasular, Chemistry, Indust mgt, Medicine, Neuroscience, Oncology, Pharmacology, Respiratory, Rheumatology
Restriction: By appointment only

S COURIER-NEWS LIBRARY, 1201 US Hwy 22, 08807. SAN 310-0391. Tel: 908-722-8800. FAX: 908-707-3252. *Librn*, Brad Wadlow
Founded 1920
Library Holdings: Bk Vols 200
Subject Interests: Local history
Restriction: By appointment only

S HOECHST MARION ROUSSEL, INC, Library Services,* 1041 Rte 202-206 N, 08807. SAN 313-2838. Tel: 908-231-3013. FAX: 908-231-4774. *Tech Servs*, Lin Chang; Staff 5 (MLS 3, Non-MLS 2)
Founded 1922
Library Holdings: Bk Vols 6,037; Per Subs 554
Subject Interests: Chemistry, Medicine, Pharmacy
Publications: Acquisitions list (quarterly)

S KVAERNER PROCESS LIBRARY,* 440 Rte 22 E, Box 6884, 08807-6884. SAN 320-1295. Tel: 908-429-4996, Ext 3515. FAX: 908-429-9010. *Librn*, Rosemarie Riley
Founded 1977
Library Holdings: Bk Vols 1,500; Bk Titles 1,000; Per Subs 30
Subject Interests: Alcohol and drugs, Chemical engineering, Technology
Publications: Monthly engineering newsletter
Restriction: Staff use only, Use of others with permission of librarian
Partic in Dialog Corporation; Univ Halifax

S NATIONAL STARCH & CHEMICAL CORP, Information Resource Center,* 10 Finderne Ave, Rm 2214, 08807. SAN 310-0405. Tel: 908-685-5081. FAX: 908-685-7037. *Info Specialist*, Barbara Groff; Tel: 908-685-5233, E-Mail: barbara.groff@nstarch.com. Subject Specialists: *Chemical*, Barbara Groff
Founded 1954
Subject Interests: Chemistry

S SOMERSET COUNTY HISTORICAL SOCIETY, Colonel Van Horn Library,* 9 Van Veghten Dr, 08807-3259. SAN 375-507X. Tel: 908-218-1281. *Librn*, George Bebbington
Founded 1971
Library Holdings: Bk Vols 1,000; Bk Titles 900
Special Collections: Somerset County History, genealogical family rec, newsp articles, photos, unbd hist doc

P SOMERSET COUNTY LIBRARY,* One Vogt Dr, PO Box 6700, 08807-0700. SAN 351-3661. Tel: 908-526-4016. FAX: 908-526-5221. Web Site: www.somerset.lib.nj.us. *Dir*, James M Hecht; Fax: 908-707-8324, E-Mail: jhecht@rvcc.raritanval.edu; *Assoc Dir*, Kathleen Jones Harris; Fax: 908-707-8324, E-Mail: kharris@rvcc.raritanval.edu; *Ch Servs*, Susan Barancik; E-Mail: sbaranci@rvcc.raritanval.edu; *Automation Syst Coordr*, Wendy Clarkson; E-Mail: clarkson@rvcc.raritanval.edu; *Tech Servs*, Adele Barree; E-Mail: abarree@rvcc.raritanval.edu; *Ser*, Mun-Hwa Liu; E-Mail: mliu@rvcc.raritanval.edu; *AV*, Linda DeCastro; E-Mail: ldecastr@rvcc.raritanval.edu; *Ad Servs*, Anne Parkison; E-Mail: aparkiso@rvcc.raritanval.edu; *Tech Coordr*, Kevin Whalen; E-Mail: kwhalen@rvcc.raritanval.edu; *Spec Coll*, Susan Feibush; E-Mail: sfeibush@rvcc.raritanval.edu; *Res*, Elizabeth Griesbach; E-Mail: egriesba@rvcc.raritanval.edu; Staff 200 (MLS 45, Non-MLS 155)
Founded 1930. Pop 143,000; Circ 1,466,603
Jan 1999-Dec 1999 Income (Main Library and Branch Library) $6,670,288, State $123,639, County $6,383,149, Other $163,500. Mats Exp $1,649,900, Books $725,000, Per/Ser (Incl. Access Fees) $128,000, Micro $53,000, AV Equip $108,500, Electronic Ref Mat (Incl. Access Fees) $131,125. Sal $4,175,000 (Prof $2,063,000)
Library Holdings: Bk Vols 605,000; Bk Titles 335,000; Per Subs 710
Special Collections: The New Jersey Room, bks, pamphlets, maps, micro
Automation Activity & Vendor Info: (Acquisitions) epixtech, inc.; (Cataloging) epixtech, inc.; (Circulation) epixtech, inc.; (OPAC) epixtech, inc.; (Serials) epixtech, inc.
Publications: Staff newsletter
Function: ILL available
Partic in Highlands Regional Library Cooperative; OCLC Online Computer Library Center, Inc; PALINET & Union Library Catalogue of Pennsylvania
Special Services for the Blind - Electronic magnifier available; Talking books (cassettes & rec)
Friends of the Library Group
Branches: 7
HILLSBOROUGH BRANCH, Hillsborough Municipal Complex, 379 S Branch Rd, Hillsborough, 08844. SAN 351-3696. Tel: 908-369-2200. FAX: 908-369-8242. *Branch Mgr*, Virginia Parks; Tel: 908-369-2200, Ext 18, E-Mail: vparks@hublib.lib.nj.us; *Ch Servs*, Laura Mellor; *Ad Servs*, Paula Carlson; Staff 27 (MLS 9, Non-MLS 18)
Founded 1966. Pop 34,000; Circ 291,000
Library Holdings: Bk Titles 98,900
Database Vendor: Ebsco - EbscoHost, epixtech, inc., ProQuest
Partic in Highlands Regional Library Cooperative
Friends of the Library Group
MARY JACOBS MEMORIAL, 64 Washington St, Rocky Hill, 08553. SAN 351-3726. Tel: 908-924-7073. FAX: 908-924-7668. *Librn*, Helen Morris
Circ 186,270
Library Holdings: Bk Vols 46,994
Friends of the Library Group
NORTH PLAINFIELD MEMORIAL, 6 Rockview Ave, North Plainfield, 07060. SAN 351-3750. Tel: 908-755-7909. FAX: 908-755-8177. *Librn*, Richard Stevens
Pop 22,464; Circ 168,452
Library Holdings: Bk Vols 93,693
Friends of the Library Group
PEAPACK-GLADSTONE PUBLIC, School St, Peapack, 07977. SAN 310-1819. Tel: 908-234-0598. FAX: 908-719-2236. *Librn*, Janet Castelpietra; Staff 6 (MLS 2, Non-MLS 4)
Pop 2,111; Circ 31,000
Jan 1999-Dec 1999 Mats Exp $14,100, Books $10,500, AV Equip $3,600
Library Holdings: Bk Vols 30,000; Per Subs 83
Friends of the Library Group
WARREN TOWNSHIP, 42 Mountain Blvd, Warren, 07059. SAN 351-3777. Tel: 908-754-5554. FAX: 908-754-2899. Web Site: scls.lib.nj.us. *Librn*, Elaine Whiting
Circ 154,787
Library Holdings: Bk Vols 73,263
Friends of the Library Group
WASHINGTON VALLEY, PO Box 577, Martinsville, 08836. SAN 310-2734. Tel: 732-356-2363.
Founded 1950. Pop 3,400; Circ 4,533
Library Holdings: Bk Vols 4,800
Friends of the Library Group
WATCHUNG PUBLIC, 12 Stirling Rd, Watchung, 07060. SAN 310-5814. Tel: 908-561-0117. FAX: 908-769-1145. *Librn*, Douglas Poswencyk
Circ 85,715
Library Holdings: Bk Vols 36,595
Friends of the Library Group

S SOMERSET YOUTH SHELTER LIBRARY,* 49 Brahma Ave, 08807. SAN 376-0561. Tel: 908-526-6605. FAX: 908-526-4433. *Librn*, Amy Badger
Library Holdings: Bk Vols 800

BRIELLE

P BRIELLE PUBLIC LIBRARY, 610 South St, 08730-1494. SAN 310-0413. Tel: 732-528-9381. FAX: 732-223-0346. Web Site: www.cybercomm.net/~tensen/brielle. *Dir*, Richard A Bidnick; E-Mail: rbidnick@hawkmail.monmouth.edu
Founded 1954. Pop 4,406; Circ 58,000
Jan 1999-Dec 1999 Income $140,156, State $5,156, City $98,000, Parent Institution $37,000. Mats Exp $20,800, Books $15,000, Per/Ser (Incl. Access Fees) $3,000, Micro $2,800. Sal $93,000
Library Holdings: Bk Vols 25,000; Per Subs 70
Subject Interests: New Jersey
Mem of Regional Libr Coop Region 5
Friends of the Library Group

BROWNS MILLS

M DEBORAH HEART & LUNG CENTER, Edith & Jack Tobin Medical Library, 200 Trenton Rd, 08015. SAN 310-043X. Tel: 609-893-6611, Ext 397. FAX: 609-893-1566. Web Site: www.deborah.org. *Librn*, Carol A Harris; Tel: 609-893-6611, Ext 398, E-Mail: harris@deborah.org
Founded 1971
Library Holdings: Bk Vols 3,000; Bk Titles 2,200; Per Subs 210
Subject Interests: Cardio-pulmonary diseases
Partic in Mid-Eastern Regional Med Libr Serv

BUDD LAKE

P MOUNT OLIVE PUBLIC LIBRARY, Wolfe Rd, 07828. SAN 310-0448. Tel: 973-691-8686. FAX: 973-691-8542. Web Site: www.users.gti.net/molivepl. *Dir*, Rita L Hilbert; E-Mail: hilbert@main.morris.org; *Librn*, Timothy Gilbert; E-Mail: gilbert@main.morris.org; *Librn*, Wendy Sanford; E-Mail: sanford@main.morris.org; *Librn*, Ilene Lefkowitz; E-Mail: ilefkowitz@main.morris.org. Subject Specialists: *Electronic*, Timothy Gilbert; *Reference*, Wendy Sanford; Staff 25 (MLS 8, Non-MLS 17)
Founded 1976. Pop 24,000; Circ 240,000
2000-2001 Income $707,000
Library Holdings: Bk Vols 67,000; Per Subs 138
Special Collections: New Jersey History; Mt Olive History
Automation Activity & Vendor Info: (Circulation) DRA; (ILL) DRA; (OPAC) DRA
Database Vendor: DRA, Ebsco - EbscoHost, ProQuest
Partic in Highlands Regional Library Cooperative; Morris Automated Information Network
Friends of the Library Group

BUENA

S NEW KUBAN EDUCATION & WELFARE ASSOCIATION, (NKEWA), Historical Museum & Library, 228 Don Rd, 08310. (Mail add: 521 Weymouth Rd, 08310), SAN 371-9286. Tel: 856-697-2255. E-Mail: nkewainc@aol.com. *Librn*, Nina Sienczenko
Library Holdings: Bk Titles 2,000
Special Collections: Cossack History & Culture, Russian & Ukrainian Coll Archival Library

BURLINGTON

S BURLINGTON COUNTY HISTORICAL SOCIETY, Delia Biddle Pugh Library, 457 High St, 08016. SAN 310-0456. Tel: 609-386-4773. FAX: 609-386-4828. *Librn*, Joan Lanphear
Library Holdings: Bk Vols 3,000; Per Subs 10
Subject Interests: Genealogy, Local history
Special Collections: James Fenimore Cooper Coll
Restriction: Non-circulating to the public

P BURLINGTON LIBRARY CO, 23 W Union St, 08016. SAN 310-0464. Tel: 609-386-1273. FAX: 609-386-1273. *Librn*, Michelle Stricker; Staff 3 (MLS 1, Non-MLS 2)
Founded 1757. Pop 20,000; Circ 23,000
Library Holdings: Bk Titles 40,800; Per Subs 91
Subject Interests: NJ hist
Special Collections: Early 18th Century Vols
Mem of Burlington County Library
Open Mon, Tues & Thurs 2-8, Wed 11-7, Sat 10-3

BUTLER

P BUTLER PUBLIC LIBRARY, One Ace Rd, 07405. SAN 310-0480. Tel: 973-838-3262. FAX: 973-838-9436. *Dir*, Ronald Rizio
Founded 1924. Pop 7,600; Circ 37,000
Jan 2000-Dec 2000 Income $180,000. Mats Exp $25,000. Sal $92,000
Library Holdings: Bk Vols 44,000; Bk Titles 43,000; Per Subs 90
Partic in Associated Librs of Morris County; NW Libr Network
Friends of the Library Group

CALDWELL

C CALDWELL COLLEGE, Jennings Library, 9 Ryerson Ave, 07006-6195. SAN 310-0499. Tel: 973-618-3312. Interlibrary Loan Service Tel: 973-618-3502. FAX: 973-618-3360. Web Site: jenningslibrary.caldwell.edu. *Cat, Exec Dir*, Lynn Randall; *ILL*, Joan Reamer; Staff 13 (MLS 5, Non-MLS 8)
Founded 1939
Library Holdings: Bk Vols 122,757; Bk Titles 110,692; Per Subs 841
Subject Interests: Architecture, Art, Educ curric, History, Literature, Relig studies, Women's studies
Special Collections: Grover Cleveland Coll of American History
Publications: General Information Brochure; Monthly New Acquisitions List; Newsletter (occasionally)
Partic in Essex County Coop Librs; Infolink Eastern New Jersey Regional Library Cooperative, Inc; OCLC Online Computer Library Center, Inc; PALINET & Union Library Catalogue of Pennsylvania

P CALDWELL FREE PUBLIC LIBRARY, 268 Bloomfield Ave, 07006-5198. SAN 310-0502. Tel: 973-226-2837. FAX: 973-403-8606. *Dir*, Lori Ann Barnes; Tel: 973-403-4649, E-Mail: lbarnes@nplhub.org; *Ch Servs*, Evelyn Klaus; Tel: 973-226-1636, E-Mail: eklaus@nplhub.org; *ILL*, Norine Slajchert; Tel: 973-403-4648, E-Mail: nslajchert@nplhub.org; Staff 10 (MLS 2, Non-MLS 8)
Founded 1907. Pop 7,315; Circ 67,478
Jan 1999-Dec 1999 Income $321,747, State $9,724, City $248,945, Other $14,421. Mats Exp $35,507, Books $25,071, Per/Ser (Incl. Access Fees) $3,061, AV Equip $4,375, Electronic Ref Mat (Incl. Access Fees) $3,000. Sal $164,471 (Prof $40,000)
Library Holdings: Bk Vols 35,637; Bk Titles 33,699; Per Subs 70
Subject Interests: Local history
Automation Activity & Vendor Info: (Cataloging) Sagebrush Corporation; (Circulation) Sagebrush Corporation
Database Vendor: Ebsco - EbscoHost
Function: ILL available
Partic in Essex County Coop Librs; Infolink
Friends of the Library Group

CAMDEN

S CAMDEN COUNTY HISTORICAL SOCIETY, Charles S Boyer Memorial Library, Park Blvd & Euclid Ave, 08103. (Mail add: PO Box 378, 08108-0378), SAN 310-0529. Tel: 856-964-3333. FAX: 856-964-0378. E-Mail: cchsnj@cchsnj.org. Web Site: www.cchsnj.org. *Dir*, John R Seitter; *Librn*, Linda Cope
Founded 1899
Library Holdings: Bk Titles 20,000; Per Subs 15
Subject Interests: Delaware, Genealogical rec for Camden County, New Jersey, New York hist, Pennsylvania
Special Collections: Dorwart Papers & other manuscripts; History (Boyer Coll & Morgan Coll), newsp, bd & micro vols
Publications: Bulletin (semi-annually); newsletter (quarterly)
Open Tues-Thurs 12:30-4:30, Sun 1-5

P CAMDEN FREE PUBLIC LIBRARY, (CFPL), 418 Federal St, 08103. SAN 350-5987. Tel: 856-757-7640. FAX: 856-757-7631. *Publ Servs*, Linda Diner; *Dir*, Theresa Gorman; *Cat*, Patricia Dillenschneider; *Ref*, Robert Sorrentino; *Ch Servs*, Starr Kirkland; *Circ*, Judy Johnson
Founded 1904. Pop 87,000
Library Holdings: Bk Vols 73,646; Per Subs 155
Subject Interests: City hist, NJ hist, Spanish language
Special Collections: Black History & Culture
Branches: 3
COOPER, Sixth & Erie Sts, 08102. SAN 350-6010. Tel: 856-757-7418. *In Charge*, Gaynell Burch
FAIRVIEW, 1503 Collings Rd, 08104. SAN 350-607X. Tel: 856-962-6669. *In Charge*, Barbara Park
ISABEL MILLER BRANCH, Eighth & Van Hook Sts, 08103. SAN 350-6118. Tel: 856-757-7469. *In Charge*, Keyhana Morton
Bookmobiles: 1. Also have 1 van

M COOPER HEALTH SYSTEM, Reuben L Sharp Health Science Library, One Cooper Plaza, 08103. SAN 310-0545. Tel: 856-342-2525. FAX: 856-342-9588. Web Site: www.4.umdnj.edu/chlibweb/. *Dir*, Barbara Miller; E-Mail: bmiller@umdnj.edu; Staff 7 (MLS 3, Non-MLS 4)
Founded 1971
Library Holdings: Bk Vols 6,000; Per Subs 300
Subject Interests: Allied health, Health admin, Medicine, Nursing, Patient information
Automation Activity & Vendor Info: (Cataloging) Endeavor; (Circulation) Endeavor; (OPAC) Endeavor
Publications: Acquisitions list (monthly), Current Awareness Service for Hospital Managers (monthly)
Restriction: Non-circulating to the public
Partic in Nat Libr of Med; S Jersey Regional Libr Consortium; SW NJ Consortium

S L-3 COMMUNICATIONS, Communications Systems East Library,* One Federal St, Bldg AE-2C, 08102. SAN 377-2314. Tel: 609-338-3000, 856-338-2742. FAX: 856-338-3152. *Librn*, Sandra Franchi; E-Mail: sandra.b.franchi@l-3com.com
Library Holdings: Bk Vols 5,000; Per Subs 200

OUR LADY OF LOURDES

M MEDICAL CENTER LIBRARY, 1600 Haddon Ave, 08103. SAN 350-6134. Tel: 856-757-3548. FAX: 856-757-3215. *Dir*, Frederick Kafes; Staff 1 (MLS 1)
Founded 1973
Jan 2000-Dec 2000 Mats Exp $48,660, Books $8,400, Per/Ser (Incl. Access Fees) $40,260
Library Holdings: Bk Titles 650; Per Subs 250
Subject Interests: Clinical health sci
Special Collections: Hospital Archives
Partic in Medical Library Center Of New York; New Jersey Health Sciences Library Network; Regional Libr Med Network; South Jersey Regional Library Cooperative; SW NJ Consortium

M SCHOOL OF NURSING LIBRARY, 1565 Vesper Blvd, 08103. SAN 350-6169. Tel: 856-757-3722. FAX: 856-968-2593. *Librn*, Kimberly Auger Fogle; E-Mail: foglek@lourdesnet.org
Founded 1961. Enrl 170; Fac 15
Library Holdings: Bk Vols 1,810; Per Subs 83
Subject Interests: Nursing educ
Automation Activity & Vendor Info: (Cataloging) Sagebrush Corporation; (Circulation) Sagebrush Corporation
Database Vendor: Ebsco - EbscoHost
Partic in Basic Health Sciences Library Network; Health Sciences Library Association Of New Jersey; National Network Of Libraries Of Medicine - South Central Region; New Jersey Health Sciences Library Network; S Jersey Regional Libr Consortium

RUTGERS, THE STATE UNIVERSITY OF NEW JERSEY

CL CAMDEN LAW LIBRARY, 217 N Fifth, 08102-1203. SAN 350-6223. Tel: 856-225-6172. FAX: 856-225-6488. Web Site: www.libraries.rutgers.edu/rul/libs/law_camden-lib/law_camden.shtml. *Dir*, Anne Dalesandro; *Circ*, John Jorgensen; *Govt Doc*, A Hays Butler; *ILL*, Susan King; *Tech Servs*, Gloria Chao; Staff 21 (MLS 6, Non-MLS 15)
Founded 1926
Library Holdings: Bk Vols 400,000; Per Subs 1,337
Mem of Asn of Research Libraries
Partic in RLIN

C PAUL ROBESON LIBRARY, CAMDEN, 300 N Fourth St, 08102-1404. SAN 350-6193. Tel: 856-225-6036. FAX: 856-225-6428. Web Site: www.libraries.rutgers.edu/rul/libs/robeson_lib/robeson_lib.shtml. *Dir*, Gary A Golden; E-Mail: ggolden@crab.rutgers.edu; *Circ, Doc*, John Maxymuk; *Coll Develop*, James Nettleman; *ILL*, Theo Haynes; *Publ Servs, Ref*, Susan J Beck; *Ref*, Ann M Scholz-Crane; *Ref*, Julie Still; Staff 22 (MLS 7, Non-MLS 15)
Founded 1951. Enrl 5,520; Fac 235; Highest Degree: Master
Library Holdings: Bk Vols 245,625; Per Subs 1,976
Mem of Asn of Research Libraries
Partic in OCLC Online Computer Library Center, Inc; Research Libraries Group, Inc; South Jersey Regional Library Cooperative
Friends of the Library Group

G UNITED STATES COURT OF APPEALS, James Hunter III Memorial Library, One J F Gerry Plaza, Fourth & Cooper, 08101. (Mail add: PO Box 1988, 08101), SAN 377-2055. Tel: 856-968-4859. FAX: 856-968-4871. *Librn*, Robin Kershaw; E-Mail: robin_kershaw@ca3.uscourts.gov
Library Holdings: Bk Vols 10,000
Automation Activity & Vendor Info: (Cataloging) SIRSI

M UNIVERSITY OF MEDICINE & DENTISTRY OF NEW JERSEY, UMDNJ & Coriell Research Library,* 401 Haddon Ave, 08103. SAN 370-7482. Tel: 609-757-7740. FAX: 609-757-7713. E-Mail: camlbweb@umdnj.edu. *Librn*, Betty Jean Swartz; *ILL*, Alisha Crawford; Staff 2 (MLS 1, Non-MLS 1)
Founded 1967
Library Holdings: Bk Vols 9,400; Bk Titles 1,700; Per Subs 112
Subject Interests: Cancer, Genetics, Immunology
Partic in Dialog Corporation; Health Sciences Library Association Of New Jersey; National Network Of Libraries Of Medicine - South Central Region; Pinelands Consortium for Health Info; South Jersey Regional Library Cooperative

S WALT WHITMAN HOUSE LIBRARY,* 326 Mickle Blvd, 08103. SAN 329-2665. Tel: 609-964-5383. E-Mail: whitmanhse@aol.com. *Dir*, Margaret O'Neil
Founded 1984. Pop 1,000
Library Holdings: Bk Titles 600; Per Subs 10
Friends of the Library Group

CAPE MAY

P CAPE MAY CITY LIBRARY, 110 Ocean St, 08204. SAN 310-0596. Tel: 609-884-9568. *Dir*, Linda Smith; *Asst Librn*, Mercedes Gaines
Circ 221,769
Library Holdings: Bk Vols 42,000; Per Subs 32
Mem of Cape May County Library

CAPE MAY COURT HOUSE

M BURDETTE TOMLIN MEMORIAL HOSPITAL, Professional Library, Stone Harbor Blvd, 08210. SAN 375-8435. Tel: 609-463-2049. FAX: 609-463-2787. Web Site: www.bthosp.com. *Librn*, Emma Merkel; E-Mail: emerkel@bthosp.com
Library Holdings: Bk Titles 1,000; Per Subs 90

S CAPE MAY COUNTY HISTORICAL & GENEALOGICAL SOCIETY LIBRARY, 504 Rte 9 N, 08210-3090. SAN 329-8663. Tel: 609-465-3535. FAX: 609-465-4274. *Librn*, Ione E Williams
Library Holdings: Bk Vols 800
Subject Interests: Genealogy

GL CAPE MAY COUNTY LAW LIBRARY, Main St, PO Box 425, 08210. SAN 373-2878. Tel: 609-463-0323. FAX: 609-463-1656. *Dir*, Jean Jenkins
Founded 1993
Library Holdings: Bk Titles 7,000; Per Subs 15
Special Collections: Casino Control Commission Hearings; NJ Legislative History
Partic in Westlaw

P CAPE MAY COUNTY LIBRARY, 30 W Mechanic St, 08210. SAN 350-6258. Tel: 609-463-6350. Reference Tel: 609-463-6352. FAX: 609-465-3895. Web Site: www.cape-may.county.lib.nj.us. *Dir*, Andrew Martin; E-Mail: andrewm@mail.cape-may.county.lib.nj.us; *ILL*, Linda Hayes; *Asst Dir*, Deborah Poillon; *Ch Servs*, Mary E James; *Tech Servs*, Hsiu-hsiang Hsu; *Ref*, Leonard Szymanski; Staff 64 (MLS 20, Non-MLS 44)
Founded 1925. Pop 92,250; Circ 424,634
Jan 1999-Dec 1999 Income (Main Library and Branch Library) $4,266,289. Mats Exp $3,468,596
Library Holdings: Bk Vols 358,842; Bk Titles 180,000; Per Subs 700
Subject Interests: Environmental studies, Marine sciences
Automation Activity & Vendor Info: (Acquisitions) epixtech, inc.; (Cataloging) epixtech, inc.; (Circulation) epixtech, inc.; (Course Reserve) epixtech, inc.
Member Libraries: Cape May City Library
Partic in South Jersey Regional Library Cooperative
Special Services for the Deaf - High interest/low vocabulary books; Staff with knowledge of sign language
Branches: 6
AVALON BRANCH, 26 25th St, Avalon, 08202. SAN 350-6282. Tel: 609-967-4010. *Branch Mgr*, Joan Costello
Library Holdings: Bk Titles 10,000
CAPE MAY CITY BRANCH, Ocean & Hughes St, Cape May, 08204. SAN 375-5142. Tel: 609-884-9569. *Branch Mgr*, Linda Smith
LOWER CAPE, 2600 Bayshore Rd, Villas, 08251. SAN 350-6290. Tel: 609-886-8999. *Librn*, Edward Carson; Staff 9 (MLS 2, Non-MLS 7)
Library Holdings: Bk Titles 35,000
SEA ISLE CITY BRANCH, 125 John F Kennedy Blvd, Sea Isle City, 08243. SAN 350-6304. Tel: 609-263-8485. *Branch Mgr*, Donna MacBride
Library Holdings: Bk Titles 8,000
STONE HARBOR BRANCH, 95th & Second Ave, Stone Harbor, 08247. SAN 350-6312. Tel: 609-368-6809. *Branch Mgr*, Mary Ann Samuel
Library Holdings: Bk Titles 6,000
Friends of the Library Group
UPPER CAPE, PO Box 555, Tuckahoe, 08250. SAN 325-4267. Tel: 609-628-2607. *Librn*, Donna Soffe; Staff 8 (MLS 2, Non-MLS 6)
Bookmobiles: 1

CARLSTADT

P WILLIAM E DERMODY FREE PUBLIC LIBRARY, 420 Hackensack St, 07072. SAN 310-060X. Tel: 201-438-8866. FAX: 201-438-2733. E-Mail: carl1@bccls.org. Web Site: www.bccls.org. *Dir*, Pilar Odenheim; Tel: 201-438-4659, E-Mail: odenheim@bccls.org; *Ch Servs*, J Bos; Staff 1 (MLS 1)
Founded 1936. Pop 5,510; Circ 32,076
Jan 1999-Dec 1999 Income $374,826, State $5,992, City $368,834. Mats Exp $70,352, Books $35,000, Per/Ser (Incl. Access Fees) $5,591, Micro $5,361, Other Print Mats $400, Electronic Ref Mat (Incl. Access Fees) $24,000. Sal $168,849 (Prof $53,210)
Library Holdings: Bk Vols 31,777; Per Subs 145
Subject Interests: Local history
Special Collections: Carlstadt Freie Press Newspaper (1873-1926 & 1936-present), microfilm
Automation Activity & Vendor Info: (Circulation) DRA; (ILL) DRA
Database Vendor: Ebsco - EbscoHost, GaleNet
Publications: Newsletter
Partic in Am Libr Asn; Bergen County Cooperative Library System; NJ Libr Asn
Friends of the Library Group

CARNEYS POINT

J SALEM COMMUNITY COLLEGE LIBRARY, 460 Hollywood Ave, 08069. SAN 321-6233. Tel: 856-299-2100, Ext 653. FAX: 856-351-2748. Web Site: www.salemcc.org. *Coordr*, Joan Oliver; Tel: 856-351-2652, E-Mail: oliver@salemcc.org; *AV*, Geoffrey Worrall; Staff 4 (MLS 1, Non-MLS 3)
Founded 1972. Enrl 872; Fac 22
Library Holdings: Bk Vols 26,000; Per Subs 200
Subject Interests: Glassblowing
Special Collections: Glassblowing
Automation Activity & Vendor Info: (Cataloging) SIRSI; (Circulation) SIRSI; (OPAC) SIRSI
Publications: Nursing Handbook; Student Handbook
Partic in South Jersey Regional Library Cooperative

CARTERET

P CARTERET PUBLIC LIBRARY, 100 Cook Ave, 07008. SAN 310-0626. Tel: 732-541-3830. FAX: 732-541-6948. *Dir*, Veronica Chan
Founded 1931. Pop 20,598; Circ 39,440
Library Holdings: Bk Vols 64,197; Bk Titles 57,728; Per Subs 140
Automation Activity & Vendor Info: (Cataloging) epixtech, inc.; (Circulation) epixtech, inc.; (OPAC) epixtech, inc.
Database Vendor: Ebsco - EbscoHost
Mem of Woodbridge Pub Libr Syst
Partic in Librs of Middlesex Automation Consortium

CEDAR GROVE

P CEDAR GROVE FREE PUBLIC LIBRARY, One Municipal Plaza, 07009. SAN 310-0642. Tel: 973-239-1447. FAX: 973-239-1275. E-Mail: cgpl@nplhub.org. *Dir*, Patricia Heyer; E-Mail: pheyer@nplhub.org; *Mgr Libr*, Usha Thampi-Lukose; *Cat*, Caterina Chi; Staff 10 (MLS 2, Non-MLS 8)
Founded 1954. Pop 11,789; Circ 91,062
Jan 1999-Dec 1999 Income $452,882, State $15,526, City $437,356. Mats Exp $65,555, Books $42,600, Per/Ser (Incl. Access Fees) $10,313. Sal $263,828
Library Holdings: Bk Vols 42,600; Bk Titles 41,819; Per Subs 102
Automation Activity & Vendor Info: (Cataloging) Gaylord; (Circulation) Gaylord; (Media Booking) Gaylord
Database Vendor: Ebsco - EbscoHost
Function: ILL available
Partic in Infolink

M ESSEX COUNTY HOSPITAL CENTER, Hamilton Memorial Library, 125 Fairview Ave, 07009. SAN 310-0650. Tel: 973-228-8000, 973-228-8001. Interlibrary Loan Service Tel: 973-228-8002. FAX: 973-228-0674. *Dir*, Janet Treamont
Founded 1958
Library Holdings: Bk Titles 4,000; Per Subs 115
Subject Interests: Psychiatry, Psychology, Social serv
Publications: Acquisitions (quarterly)
Restriction: Restricted public use
Partic in NY & NJ Regional Med Libr

CEDAR KNOLLS

M SAINT CLARE'S HEALTH SERVICES, (Formerly Saint Clares Hospital), American Self-Help Clearinghouse, 100 E Hanover Ave, Ste 202, 07927-2020. SAN 373-4714. Tel: 973-326-6789. FAX: 973-326-9467. E-Mail: ashc@cybernex.net. Web Site: www.selfhelpgroups.org. *Dir*, Edward J Madara; *Coordr*, Barbara White
Library Holdings: Bk Vols 2,100
Publications: Self-Help Sourcebook

CHATHAM

L BLUME, GOLDFADEN, BERKOWITZ, DONNELLY, FRIED & FORTE, Law Library, One Main St, 07928. SAN 371-716X. Tel: 973-635-5400, Ext 149. FAX: 973-635-9339. *Librn*, Judith T Schlissel; E-Mail: jschliss@njatty.com; Staff 1 (MLS 1)
Founded 1975
Library Holdings: Bk Vols 3,000; Bk Titles 3,000; Per Subs 58

Subject Interests: Obstetrics and gynecology
Special Collections: Exhibits of Skulls, Hands, Feet & Other Anatomy
Partic in Highlands Regional Library Cooperative; NJLLA

P JOINT FREE PUBLIC LIBRARY OF THE CHATHAMS, 214 Main St, 07928. SAN 310-0693. Tel: 973-635-0603. FAX: 973-635-7827. *Dir*, Diane R O'Brien; *Ad Servs*, Deborah R Fitzgerald; *Ref*, Joan Hipp; *Ch Servs*, Jay Chaterjee; *Cat*, Rosalind Libbey; Staff 8 (MLS 8)
Founded 1907. Pop 18,260; Circ 172,631
Library Holdings: Bk Titles 82,526; Per Subs 251
Subject Interests: Consumer health, Earth science, Health, Medicine, Psychology
Database Vendor: DRA
Mem of Morris Automated Info Network; Morris-Union Fedn
Partic in Highlands Regional Library Cooperative
Friends of the Library Group

M PHARMACO-MEDICAL DOCUMENTATION, INC, Research Library,* PO Box 429, 07928. SAN 310-0707. Tel: 973-822-9200. FAX: 973-765-0722. *Librn*, Borka Stiffler
Library Holdings: Bk Vols 1,500; Per Subs 120
Subject Interests: Drug mkt, Med chem, Pharmacology

SR PRESBYTERIAN CHURCH OF CHATHAM TOWNSHIP LIBRARY, 240 Southern Blvd, 07928. SAN 371-7178. Tel: 973-635-2340. FAX: 973-635-2447. *Librn*, Janice Wanggaard; E-Mail: jwanggaa@drew.edu; *Tech Servs*, Marion Strack
Jan 2000-Dec 2000 Income $1,000. Mats Exp $1,000, Books $900, Per/Ser (Incl. Access Fees) $50, AV Equip $50
Library Holdings: Bk Titles 2,800

CHATSWORTH

G PINELANDS RESIDENTIAL GROUP CENTER LIBRARY,* 3016 Rte 563, 08019. SAN 375-9970. Tel: 609-726-1525. FAX: 609-726-9678.
Library Holdings: Bk Titles 449; Per Subs 14

CHERRY HILL

L BLANK, ROME, COMISKY & MCCAULEY, Law Library, 210 Lake Dr E, Woodland Falls Corp Pk, Ste 200, 08002. SAN 323-8555. Tel: 856-779-3633. FAX: 856-779-7647. Web Site: www.blankrome.com. *Librn*, Mary S Newman; E-Mail: newman-ms@blankrome.com
Library Holdings: Bk Vols 5,000; Per Subs 50
Automation Activity & Vendor Info: (Cataloging) Sydney
Restriction: Staff use only
Mem of S Jersey Regional Libr Coop

P CHERRY HILL PUBLIC LIBRARY, 1100 Kings Hwy N, 08034-1970. SAN 310-0715. Tel: 856-667-0300. FAX: 856-667-4937. Web Site: www.cherryhill.lib.nj.us. *Dir*, Barbara Shapiro; *Asst Dir*, Martha Oxley; *Ref*, Susan Lyons; *Ad Servs*, Thomas Clapham; *Ser, Tech Servs*, Kei Kawano; *Ch Servs*, Linda Meuse
Founded 1957. Pop 75,000; Circ 371,478
Library Holdings: Bk Vols 149,560; Bk Titles 131,298; Per Subs 566
Subject Interests: Bus, Computers, Foreign trade, Investing, Local history
Special Collections: New Jersey; Telephone Directories Coll
Publications: Cherry Hill Area Organizations and Agencies
Partic in OCLC Online Computer Library Center, Inc; PALINET & Union Library Catalogue of Pennsylvania
Friends of the Library Group

M KENNEDY MEMORIAL HOSPITALS-UNIVERSITY MEDICAL CENTER, CHERRY HILL DIVISION, Dr Barney A Slotkin Memorial Library, 2201 Chapel Ave W, 08002-2048. SAN 320-3948. Tel: 609-488-6865. FAX: 609-488-6606. *Dir*, Sharon G S Sobel; Staff 1 (MLS 1)
Founded 1974
Library Holdings: Bk Titles 1,000; Per Subs 140
Subject Interests: Medicine, Nursing, Osteopathy, Psychiatry
Partic in Basic Health Sciences Library Network; Health Sciences Library Association Of New Jersey; Pinelands Consortium for Health Info

R TEMPLE BETH SHOLOM, Adele & Terry Uhr Memorial Library, 1901 Kresson Rd, 08003. SAN 310-1967. Tel: 856-751-6663. FAX: 856-751-2369. Web Site: www.tbsonline.org. *Librn*, Judy Brookover
Founded 1948
Library Holdings: Bk Titles 3,000

R TEMPLE EMANUEL LIBRARY, 1101 Springdale Rd, 08003. SAN 310-0723. Tel: 856-489-0035, Ext 18. FAX: 609-489-0032. *Head of Libr*, Bonnie Slobodien; E-Mail: bonnies@templeemanuel.org; *Actg Librn*, Anne S Bressman; Fax: 856-489-8656; Staff 1 (Non-MLS 1)
Founded 1971
Library Holdings: Bk Vols 3,000; Per Subs 30
Subject Interests: Holocaust, Judaica

R TRINITY PRESBYTERIAN CHURCH LIBRARY, 499 Rte 70E, 08034. SAN 310-0731. Tel: 856-428-2050. *Librn*, Bernice Ahlquist
Founded 1962
Library Holdings: Bk Titles 3,500
Subject Interests: Bible study, Christian educ

CHESTER

P CHESTER LIBRARY, 250 W Main St, 07930. SAN 310-074X. Tel: 908-879-7612. FAX: 908-879-8695. Web Site: chester-library.gti.net. *Dir*, Susan Persak; E-Mail: persak@main.morris.org
Founded 1911. Pop 7,172; Circ 157,924
Jan 2000-Dec 2000 Income $414,827, State $7,699, City $393,278, Locally Generated Income $11,850. Mats Exp $88,613, Books $69,913, Per/Ser (Incl. Access Fees) $6,200, AV Equip $10,000, Electronic Ref Mat (Incl. Access Fees) $2,500. Sal $222,900 (Prof $113,000)
Library Holdings: Bk Vols 42,462; Bk Titles 40,301; Per Subs 137
Automation Activity & Vendor Info: (Circulation) DRA
Database Vendor: DRA, Ebsco - EbscoHost, GaleNet, ProQuest, Wilson - Wilson Web
Partic in Highlands Regional Library Cooperative; Morris Automated Information Network
Friends of the Library Group

CINNAMINSON

R JACK BALABAN MEMORIAL LIBRARY OF TEMPLE SINAI, 2101 New Albany Rd, 08077-3536. SAN 310-0766. Tel: 856-829-0658. FAX: 856-829-0310. E-Mail: tsoffice@snip.net. *Librn*, Paula Pappas
Founded 1963
Library Holdings: Bk Titles 1,450
Subject Interests: Jewish authors, Jewish content
Special Collections: Encyclopaedia Judaica; Yiddish Coll

S HOEGANAES CORP LIBRARY, 1001 Taylors Lane, 08077. SAN 310-4818. Tel: 856-829-2220, Ext 3371. FAX: 856-786-1872. *Librn*, Dorothy Armstrong; E-Mail: dotarm@aol.com. Subject Specialists: *Metallurgy*, Dorothy Armstrong
Library Holdings: Bk Vols 2,000
Subject Interests: Chemistry, Metallurgy

CLARK

P CLARK PUBLIC LIBRARY, (CLP), 303 Westfield Ave, 07066. SAN 310-0774. Tel: 732-388-5999. FAX: 732-388-7866. E-Mail: frontdesk@clarklibrary.org. Web Site: www.clarklibrary.org. *Dir*, Meg Kolaya; E-Mail: mkolaya@clark.njpublib.org; *Ch Servs*, Melinda Gauld-Elichko; E-Mail: mgauldelichko@clark.njpublic.org; *Ad Servs*, Melissa Schabel; E-Mail: mschabel@clark.njpublic.org; Staff 3 (MLS 3)
Founded 1961. Pop 14,629; Circ 79,922
Jan 1999-Dec 1999 Income $570,000
Library Holdings: Bk Titles 53,223; Per Subs 190
Automation Activity & Vendor Info: (Cataloging) TLC; (Circulation) TLC; (ILL) TLC; (OPAC) TLC
Partic in Infolink Eastern New Jersey Regional Library Cooperative, Inc; Mural
Friends of the Library Group

CLEMENTON

P CLEMENTON COMMUNITY CENTER & MEMORIAL LIBRARY, 165 Gibbsboro Rd, 08021. SAN 310-0790. Tel: 856-783-2322. Web Site: www.clementon.com/gov/library.htm. *Librn*, Thelma Ralston
Circ 7,278
Library Holdings: Bk Vols 13,100
Mem of Camden County Library System

CLIFFSIDE PARK

P CLIFFSIDE PARK FREE PUBLIC LIBRARY, 505 Palisades Ave, 07010. SAN 310-0804. Tel: 201-945-2867. FAX: 201-945-1016. E-Mail: clpk1@bccls.org. Web Site: www.bergen.bccls.org/cliffsidepark. *Dir*, Ana R Chelariu; *Asst Libr Dir*, Michele Skowronski; E-Mail: skowronski@bccls.org; *Ch Servs*, Brian Cazanave; *Ref Servs YA*, Sherri Kendrick; E-Mail: clkpref@bccls.org; Staff 9 (MLS 3, Non-MLS 6)
Founded 1999. Pop 21,141; Circ 75,000
Jan 1999-Dec 1999 Income $502,759, State $21,892, City $451,879, Locally Generated Income $20,400. Mats Exp $92,700, Books $54,600, Per/Ser (Incl. Access Fees) $4,500, Micro $3,500, Electronic Ref Mat (Incl. Access Fees) $21,900. Sal $307,000 (Prof $124,000)
Library Holdings: Bk Vols 60,402; Bk Titles 55,149; Per Subs 161
Automation Activity & Vendor Info: (Cataloging) DRA; (OPAC) DRA; (Serials) Gateway
Database Vendor: Ebsco - EbscoHost, IAC - SearchBank

Function: Reference services available
Mem of Bergen County Co-op Libr Syst
Partic in BCCLS Computer Consortium
Friends of the Library Group

CLIFTON

P CLIFTON PUBLIC LIBRARY, 292 Piaget Ave, 07011. SAN 350-6347. Tel: 973-772-5500. FAX: 973-772-2926. Web Site: www.palsplus.org/cliftonpl. *Dir*, Christine Zembicki; E-Mail: zembicki@palsplus.org; *Ref*, Dale Bedford; *Ch Servs*, Patricia Vasilik; *Ad Servs*, Pat John Ferro; Staff 40 (MLS 9, Non-MLS 31)
Founded 1920. Pop 71,742; Circ 340,061
Jan 1999-Dec 1999 Income (Main Library and Branch Library) $2,185,005, State $77,011, City $2,043,063, Federal $48,931, Locally Generated Income $86,000. Mats Exp $232,783, Books $163,884, Per/Ser (Incl. Access Fees) $18,606, Micro $24,415, AV Equip $15,421, Electronic Ref Mat (Incl. Access Fees) $10,457. Sal $1,252,694
Library Holdings: Bk Vols 167,694; Bk Titles 104,539; Per Subs 319
Subject Interests: Local history
Automation Activity & Vendor Info: (Cataloging) DRA; (Circulation) DRA; (OPAC) DRA
Database Vendor: Ebsco - EbscoHost, ProQuest
Partic in Highlands Regional Library Cooperative
Special Services for the Deaf - TTY machine
Friends of the Library Group
Branches: 1
ALLWOOD BRANCH, 44 Lyall Rd, 07012. SAN 350-6371. Tel: 973-471-0555. FAX: 973-471-2984. *Librn*, Christine Zembicki
Bookmobiles: 1

S ITT INDUSTRIES, AV ACD Technical Library, 100 Kingsland Rd, MS 8545, 07014. SAN 310-3730. Tel: 973-284-3810. FAX: 973-284-4141.; Staff 1 (MLS 1)
Subject Interests: Electronics
Restriction: Not open to public

S SCHER CHEMICALS, INC LIBRARY,* Industrial West, 07012. SAN 310-0863. Tel: 973-471-1300. FAX: 973-471-3783. *Tech Servs*, Janie Woo
Library Holdings: Bk Vols 1,000; Per Subs 15
Subject Interests: Chemical engineering, Organic chemistry
Restriction: Staff use only

CLINTON

S CORRECTIONAL INSTITUTION FOR WOMEN, Edna Mahan Hall Library, PO Box 4004, 08809. SAN 310-0898. Tel: 908-735-7111, Ext 3262. FAX: 908-735-0108. *In Charge*, Celia Love; Staff 3 (MLS 1, Non-MLS 2)
Pop 450
Library Holdings: Bk Vols 8,600; Per Subs 40
Subject Interests: Law
Special Collections: Criminal Law; Women in Prison
Distribution point for books donated monthly from various publishers; all correctional agencies are eligible to participate in this program
Branches:
C-COTTAGE, PO Box 4004, 08809. Tel: 908-735-7111, Ext 3262. *In Charge*, Celia Love
NORTH HALL, PO Box 4004, 08809. Tel: 908-735-7111, Ext 3262. FAX: 908-735-0108. *In Charge*, Celia Love

P GRANDIN LIBRARY ASSOCIATION,* 6 Leigh St, 08809. SAN 310-0871. Tel: 908-735-4812. *Dir*, Marjorie Schaefer Goff
Founded 1896. Pop 1,910
Library Holdings: Bk Titles 25,000; Per Subs 65
Subject Interests: Local history
Special Collections: Picture file
Publications: Newsletter
Mem of Hunterdon County Library
Partic in Morris County Film Libr; Region I - NW Regional Libr Coop

S HUNTERDON DEVELOPMENTAL CENTER LIBRARY,* PO Box 4003, 08809-4003. SAN 325-7584. Tel: 908-735-4031, Ext 1038. FAX: 908-730-1311. *Dir*, Roger Schumacher; *Librn*, Diane Di Lullo
Library Holdings: Bk Vols 4,500

S HUNTERDON HISTORICAL MUSEUM LIBRARY, 56 Main St, PO Box 5005, 08809. SAN 321-5970. Tel: 908-735-4101. FAX: 908-735-0914. *Exec Dir*, Dr Charles F Speierl; *Coll Develop*, Jean Daly
Library Holdings: Bk Vols 399; Bk Titles 365
Subject Interests: Antiques, Local history
Special Collections: Antique Textbooks; Daybooks
Restriction: By appointment only

CLOSTER

P FREE PUBLIC LIBRARY OF CLOSTER, 280 High St, 07624-1898. SAN 310-0901. Tel: 201-768-4197. FAX: 201-768-4220. E-Mail: cltr@bccls.org. Web Site: www.bccls.org/closter. *Dir*, Ruth Rando; E-Mail: rando@bccls.org; *Ch Servs*, Beth Jonus; E-Mail: jonus@bccls.org; *Ad Servs*, Janet Fleck; Staff 3 (MLS 2, Non-MLS 1)
Founded 1956. Pop 8,094; Circ 84,200
Jan 2000-Dec 2000 Income Locally Generated Income $348,000. Mats Exp $78,300, Books $69,000, Per/Ser (Incl. Access Fees) $6,500, AV Equip $2,800. Sal $166,000 (Prof $125,000)
Library Holdings: Bk Vols 47,200; Bk Titles 45,194; Per Subs 120
Subject Interests: Closter hist, New Jersey
Automation Activity & Vendor Info: (OPAC) DRA
Database Vendor: DRA, Ebsco - EbscoHost, IAC - SearchBank, ProQuest
Mem of Bergen County Co-op Libr Syst
Partic in Bergen County Cooperative Library System
Friends of the Library Group

COLLINGSWOOD

P COLLINGSWOOD FREE PUBLIC LIBRARY, 771 Haddon Ave, 08108-3714. SAN 310-091X. Tel: 856-858-0649. FAX: 856-858-5016. *Dir*, Peter P Childs; E-Mail: pchilds@camden.lib.nj.us; *Ch Servs*, Dorothy Garabedian; E-Mail: ggarabed@camden.lib.nl.us; *Ref*, Kathleen Liu; *Tech Servs*, Jackie Jungclaus; *ILL*, Maureen Sambuco; E-Mail: msambuco@camden.lib.nl.us
Founded 1910. Pop 14,500; Circ 70,000
2000-2001 Income $320,000, State $20,000, City $300,000. Mats Exp $42,500, Books $34,000, Per/Ser (Incl. Access Fees) $8,500. Sal $230,000
Library Holdings: Bk Vols 64,000; Bk Titles 58,900; Per Subs 125
Special Collections: Southern New Jersey Coll, bks, blue prints, engravings, maps, trade cat, photog
Publications: Friends of the Library (newsletter)
Mem of SJ Regional Libr Coop
Friends of the Library Group

COLTS NECK

UNITED STATES NAVY
A NAVAL WEAPONS STATIONS EARLE LIBRARY, WPNSTA Earle, 201 Hwy 34 S, 07722-5020. SAN 350-6401. Tel: 732-866-2103. FAX: 732-866-1042.
Pop 4,088
Library Holdings: Bk Vols 2,500

CRANBURY

M CARTER-WALLACE, INC LIBRARY, Half Acre Rd, 08512. SAN 310-0952. Tel: 609-655-6297, Ext 6302. FAX: 609-655-6298. *Librn*, Paul Chagnon
Founded 1957
Library Holdings: Bk Vols 4,500; Per Subs 60
Subject Interests: Cent nervous syst acting drugs such as propanediol dicarbonates (infection), Diagnostic agents, Hypersensitivity, Immunity, Pet products, Toiletries

P CRANBURY PUBLIC LIBRARY, 23 N Main St, 08512. SAN 310-0979. Tel: 609-655-0555. FAX: 609-655-2858. *Dir*, Howard Zogott
Founded 1906. Pop 2,500; Circ 33,692
Library Holdings: Bk Vols 16,060; Per Subs 176
Subject Interests: Local history
Special Collections: Teen Corner
Cranbury Public Library & Cranbury School Library share merged collections & facilities
Friends of the Library Group

S RHODIA NORTH AMERICAN LIBRARY, (Formerly Rhodia Inc Research Library), Bldg B, 259 Prospect Plains Rd, 08512-7500. SAN 327-5906. Tel: 609-860-4465. Reference Tel: 609-860-4436. FAX: 609-860-0165. *Mgr Libr Serv*, Scott C Boito; E-Mail: scott.boito@us.rhodia.com. Subject Specialists: *Chemistry*, Scott C Boito; Staff 2 (MLS 1, Non-MLS 1)
Founded 1990
Library Holdings: Bk Titles 5,000; Per Subs 120
Subject Interests: Chemistry
Special Collections: Technical Reports (internal)
Database Vendor: Dialog, Ebsco - EbscoHost
Function: For research purposes
Partic in Dialog Corporation

CRANFORD

S CHARLES E STEVENS AMERICAN ATHEIST LIBRARY & ARCHIVES, INC, (CESAALA), 225 Cristiani Street, 07016-3214. (Mail add: PO Box 5733, 07054-6733), E-Mail: ej@atheist.org. Web Site: www.atheists.org. *Pres*, Ellen Johnson; Staff 2 (Non-MLS 2)
Founded 1968

Library Holdings: Bk Titles 55,000
Subject Interests: Anarchism, Atheism, Church-state, Religion
Special Collections: Haldeman-Julius publications; Ingersoll Coll; McCabe Coll; Robertson Coll
Restriction: By appointment only

P CRANFORD FREE PUBLIC LIBRARY, (Formerly Cranford Public Library), 224 Walnut Ave, PO Box 400, 07016. SAN 310-0987. Tel: 908-709-7272. FAX: 908-709-1658. E-Mail: cranlib@cranford.njpublib.org. Web Site: cranford.com/library. *Dir*, John Malar; E-Mail: jmalar@cranford.njpublib.org; *Asst Dir*, Judith Klimowicz; E-Mail: jklimowicz@cranford.njpublib.org; *Ref*, Robert Salmon; E-Mail: rsalmon@cranford.njpublib.org; Staff 10 (MLS 4, Non-MLS 6)
Founded 1908. Pop 22,000; Circ 209,947
Library Holdings: Bk Vols 112,000; Bk Titles 96,815; Per Subs 130
Automation Activity & Vendor Info: (Cataloging) Gaylord; (Circulation) Gaylord; (OPAC) Gaylord
Database Vendor: Ebsco - EbscoHost, IAC - SearchBank
Publications: Newsletter (bi-monthly)
Function: ILL available
Partic in Infolink Eastern New Jersey Regional Library Cooperative, Inc
Friends of the Library Group

R CRANFORD UNITED METHODIST CHURCH LIBRARY, 201 Lincoln Ave E, 07016. SAN 310-0995. Tel: 908-276-0936. *Librn*, Robin Hoy
Library Holdings: Bk Vols 3,300; Per Subs 11
Subject Interests: Children's bks, History, Relig studies

R FIRST PRESBYTERIAN CHURCH, Betty Pethick Memorial Library, 11 Springfield Ave, 07016. SAN 310-1010. Tel: 908-276-8440. FAX: 908-276-8441. Web Site: www.cranfordnj.com/fpc. *Librn*, Mildred Nary
Library Holdings: Bk Vols 2,000

J UNION COUNTY COLLEGE LIBRARIES, MacKay Library,* 1033 Springfield Ave, 07016. SAN 310-1029. Tel: 908-709-7623, Ext 7019 (Dir). FAX: 908-709-1827. *Dir*, Corinne Smith; *Asst Dir*, Andrea MacRitche; *Tech Servs*, Pamela Holmes; *Ref*, Susan Bissett; Staff 10 (MLS 10)
Founded 1933. Enrl 7,263; Fac 175
Library Holdings: Bk Vols 126,486; Bk Titles 117,783; Per Subs 913
Subject Interests: Eng as a second language, Nursing
Publications: Bibliographies; Handbook Guides; Newsletter
Partic in Infolink Eastern New Jersey Regional Library Cooperative, Inc; Librs of Union County Consortium; OCLC Online Computer Library Center, Inc; PALINET & Union Library Catalogue of Pennsylvania
Special Services for the Deaf - TDD; TTY machine

CRESSKILL

P CRESSKILL PUBLIC LIBRARY, 53 Union Ave, 07626. SAN 310-1037. Tel: 201-567-3521. FAX: 201-567-5067. E-Mail: cres1@bccls.org. *Dir*, Alice Chi; E-Mail: chi@bccls.org; *Asst Dir*, Margaret M Churley; E-Mail: churley@bccls.org; Staff 4 (MLS 3, Non-MLS 1)
Founded 1930. Pop 7,609; Circ 105,475
Library Holdings: Bk Titles 64,776; Per Subs 200
Database Vendor: DRA, Ebsco - EbscoHost, IAC - Info Trac, ProQuest
Mem of Bergen County Co-op Libr Syst

CROSSWICKS

P CROSSWICKS PUBLIC LIBRARY, 483 Main St, 08515. SAN 321-0537. Tel: 609-298-6271. *Librn*, Alice N Bumbera
Founded 1817. Pop 4,000
Library Holdings: Bk Vols 13,800; Bk Titles 12,346
Subject Interests: Antiques, Local history, NJ hist, Quaker info
Mem of Burlington County Library

DEEPWATER

S DUPONT COMPANY, Jackson Laboratory Library, Chambers Works, 08023. SAN 336-6278. Tel: 856-540-2851. FAX: 856-540-2344. *Info Res*, Mike Hennessy
Founded 1918
Library Holdings: Bk Titles 10,000; Per Subs 120
Subject Interests: Chemical engineering, Petroleum
Publications: Library Notes (additions list)
Partic in OCLC Online Computer Library Center, Inc

DELANCO

P DELANCO PUBLIC LIBRARY,* M Joan Pearson School, 1303 Burlington Ave, 08075. SAN 310-1053. Tel: 856-461-6850. *Dir*, Patricia Krell; *Asst Dir*, Catherine Cheyne
Founded 1865. Pop 3,361; Circ 10,732
Library Holdings: Bk Titles 39,534; Per Subs 30
Mem of Burlington County Library
Special Services for the Deaf - Books on deafness & sign language; High interest/low vocabulary books; Special interest periodicals

DELMONT

S SOUTHERN STATE CORRECTION FACILITY LIBRARY,* Rte 47, Box 150, 08314. SAN 376-2017. Tel: 856-785-1300. *Librn*, Pat Gruccio
Library Holdings: Bk Vols 11,000; Per Subs 45

DEMAREST

P DEMAREST PUBLIC LIBRARY, 90 Hardenburgh Ave, 07627-2197. SAN 310-1061. Tel: 201-768-8714. FAX: 201-767-8094. E-Mail: dema1@bccls.org. Web Site: bccls.org. *Dir*, Edna Ortega
Founded 1965. Pop 4,950; Circ 32,494
1998-1999 Income $117,463, State $1,800, City $64,363, Other $51,300. Mats Exp $22,790, Books $20,616, Per/Ser (Incl. Access Fees) $2,164. Sal $49,234
Library Holdings: Bk Vols 28,357; Bk Titles 27,526; Per Subs 50
Special Collections: Literary Criticisms Coll
Mem of Bergen - Passaic Regional Libr Syst

DENVILLE

P DENVILLE FREE PUBLIC LIBRARY, 121 Diamond Spring Rd, 07834. SAN 310-107X. Tel: 973-627-6555. FAX: 973-627-1913. Web Site: www.denvillenj.org. *Dir*, Elizabeth L Kanouse; *Ad Servs, ILL, Ref*, Jeanne Notestein; *Cat, Tech Servs*, Vita Ferlanti; *Ch Servs, YA Servs*, Carol Hsia; Staff 5 (MLS 5)
Founded 1921. Pop 13,812; Circ 125,881
Jan 1999-Dec 1999 Income $561,582, State $14,827, City $512,118, Other $34,637. Mats Exp $59,083, Books $49,531, Per/Ser (Incl. Access Fees) $8,181, Presv $916, Electronic Ref Mat (Incl. Access Fees) $455. Sal $354,566
Library Holdings: Bk Vols 70,450; Bk Titles 64,884; Per Subs 162
Database Vendor: DRA
Partic in Morris Automated Information Network
Friends of the Library Group

M ST CLARE'S HEALTH SERVICES, Medical Library, 25 Pocono Rd, 07834. SAN 376-0545. Tel: 973-625-6547. FAX: 973-625-6678. *Dir*, Joann Connor
Library Holdings: Bk Vols 500; Per Subs 80

DEPTFORD

P JAMES H JOHNSON MEMORIAL LIBRARY, 670 Ward Dr, 08096. SAN 310-1088. Tel: 609-848-9149. FAX: 609-848-1813. *Dir*, Arn Ellsworth Winter; E-Mail: awinter@gloucester.lib.nj.us; *Ch Servs*, Susann Kaback; *Publ Servs, Ref*, Marie Scholding; Staff 12 (MLS 3, Non-MLS 9)
Founded 1961. Circ 64,152
1998-1999 Income $500,000. Mats Exp $55,000
Library Holdings: Bk Vols 49,856; Bk Titles 44,285; Per Subs 190
Subject Interests: Antiques, Deptford hist, Hearing impaired
Partic in Georgia Online Database
Special Services for the Deaf - Books on deafness & sign language
Friends of the Library Group

DOVER

P DOVER FREE PUBLIC LIBRARY, 32 E Clinton St, 07801. SAN 310-1096. Tel: 973-366-0172. FAX: 973-366-0175. *Dir*, Lawrence Huss; Staff 8 (MLS 2, Non-MLS 6)
Founded 1978. Pop 15,000; Circ 61,000
Library Holdings: Bk Vols 47,000; Bk Titles 45,000; Per Subs 120
Subject Interests: Spanish
Partic in Morris Automated Information Network
Friends of the Library Group

UNITED STATES ARMY
A ARMAMENT R, D&E CENTER (ARDEC), INFORMATION RESEARCH CENTER, Bldg 59, Phipps Rd, Picatinny Arsenal, 07806-5000. SAN 350-6460. Tel: 973-724-5898. Interlibrary Loan Service Tel: 973-724-4712. Circulation Tel: 973-724-4712. Reference Tel: 973-724-3757. FAX: 973-724-3044. Web Site: w3.pica.army.mil/irc. *Automation Syst Coordr, Doc*, Patricia Ays; E-Mail: pays@pica.army.mil; *ILL*, Cathy Allen; *Chief Librn*, Suseela Chandrasekar; E-Mail: chandras@pica.army.mil; *Info Specialist*, Janet DePreter; Tel: 973-724-5738, E-Mail: depreter@pica.army.mil; *Info Specialist*, Mimi Ng; Tel: 973-724-4750; *Chief Librn*, Suseela Chandrasekar; E-Mail: chandras@pica.army.mil; Staff 4 (MLS 2, Non-MLS 2)
Founded 1929
Oct 1999-Sep 2000 Income Federal $500,000. Mats Exp $26,000, Books $10,000, Per/Ser (Incl. Access Fees) $5,000, Manuscripts & Archives $1,000, Electronic Ref Mat (Incl. Access Fees) $10,000. Sal $325,000

(Prof $250,000)
Library Holdings: Bk Vols 66,552; Bk Titles 41,703; Per Subs 20
Subject Interests: Ammunition, Armament, Explosives, Plastics, Propellants, Pyrotechnics, Weapons
Special Collections: Archives for Picatinny Arsenal (NJ); Frankford Arsenal (PA)
Automation Activity & Vendor Info: (Circulation) SIRSI; (OPAC) SIRSI
Database Vendor: OCLC - First Search
Restriction: Circulation limited, Open to others by appointment
Function: Archival collection, ILL available, Reference services available, Research fees apply
Partic in Defense Technical Information Center; Dialog Corporation; Fedlink; NW Libr Network

DUMONT

P DIXON HOMESTEAD LIBRARY, 180 Washington Ave, 07628. SAN 310-1118. Tel: 201-384-2030. FAX: 201-384-5878. *Dir*, Elizabeth M A Stewart; *Cat, Ref*, Kathy McGrath; *Tech Servs*, Leyla Korzelius; *Ch Servs*, Carol Heinz; Staff 12 (MLS 2, Non-MLS 10)
Founded 1925. Pop 17,000; Circ 99,164
Library Holdings: Bk Vols 49,398; Bk Titles 45,809; Per Subs 128
Special Collections: American Theatre
Database Vendor: DRA
Mem of Bergen County Co-op Libr Syst
Partic in Bergen Passaic Health Sciences Library Consortium
Friends of the Library Group

DUNELLEN

P DUNELLEN FREE PUBLIC LIBRARY,* New Market Rd, 08812. SAN 310-1134. Tel: 732-968-4585. FAX: 732-424-1370. *Dir*, William M Robins; E-Mail: wrobins123@cs.com
Founded 1911. Pop 6,500; Circ 56,000
1997-1998 Income $165,265, State $8,409, City $120,000. Mats Exp $19,930, Books $13,000, Per/Ser (Incl. Access Fees) $4,200. Sal $110,000
Library Holdings: Bk Vols 33,514; Per Subs 107
Mem of Libraries of Middlesex
Friends of the Library Group

EAST BRUNSWICK

P EAST BRUNSWICK PUBLIC LIBRARY, 2 Civic Ctr, 08816-3599. SAN 350-6525. Tel: 732-390-6950. Reference Tel: 732-390-6767. TDD: 732-390-6776. FAX: 732-390-6869 (Admin). Reference FAX: 732-390-6796. Web Site: www.ebpl.org. *Dir*, Jason R Stone; Tel: 732-390-6761, E-Mail: jstone@ebpl.org; *Asst Dir*, Cheryl O'Connor; E-Mail: cheryloconnor@ebpl.org; *Mgr*, Patricia Irons; E-Mail: prions@ebpl.org; *Ad Servs*, Kathryn Smith; Tel: 732-390-6772, E-Mail: ksmith@ebpl.org; *Ch Servs*, Carol Phillips; Tel: 732-390-6789, Fax: 732-390-6796, E-Mail: cphillips@ebpl.org; *AV*, Susan Sclar; Tel: 732-390-6777, E-Mail: ssclar@ebpl.org; *Circ*, Katherine Hoener; E-Mail: khoener@ebpl.org; *Ref Serv Ad*, Susan Kheel; Fax: 732-390-6796, E-Mail: skheel@ebpl.org; *Per*, Martha Hess; *Doc*, Ann Grice; *Info Tech, Mgr Libr Serv*, Dianne Hall; E-Mail: dhall@ebpl.org; Staff 95 (MLS 24, Non-MLS 71)
Founded 1967. Pop 43,548; Circ 841,917
Jan 1999-Dec 1999 Income $4,138,357, State $367,439, City $2,848,057, Federal $34,020, Locally Generated Income $350,509, Other $507,142. Mats Exp $421,851, Books $267,050, Per/Ser (Incl. Access Fees) $33,698, Other Print Mats $2,131. Sal $2,239,727
Library Holdings: Bk Vols 174,200; Bk Titles 131,204; Per Subs 668
Subject Interests: Chinese Language, Holocaust
Special Collections: Indian Languages Fiction Coll; Mystery Classics
Automation Activity & Vendor Info: (Acquisitions) epixtech, inc.; (Cataloging) epixtech, inc.; (Circulation) epixtech, inc.; (Media Booking) epixtech, inc.
Publications: Library Lines
Partic in Libr of Middlesex
Special Services for the Deaf - TDD
Friends of the Library Group

S HOME NEWS TRIBUNE, 35 Kennedy Blvd, PO Box 1049, 08816. SAN 310-3323. Tel: 732-246-5500, Ext 7351. Web Site: www.ithnt.com. *Librn*, Winnie Zagariello
Special Collections: Photograph Coll

R TEMPLE B'NAI SHALOM LIBRARY,* PO Box 957, 08816. SAN 310-1142. Tel: 732-251-4300. FAX: 732-251-4940. *Dir*, Miriam Eichler
Library Holdings: Bk Vols 1,100

R TRINITY PRESBYTERIAN CHURCH, Media Center Library,* 367 Cranberry Rd, 08816. SAN 310-1150. Tel: 732-257-6636. *Librn*, Doris Marsh
Founded 1971
Library Holdings: Bk Vols 500; Per Subs 30
Subject Interests: Family life, Presbyterian hist, Self help

EAST HANOVER

P EAST HANOVER TOWNSHIP FREE PUBLIC LIBRARY, 415 Ridgedale Ave, 07936. SAN 310-1169. Tel: 973-428-3075. FAX: 973-428-7253. *Dir*, Gayle B Carlson
Founded 1959. Pop 9,976
Jan 1999-Dec 1999 Income $592,919. Mats Exp $67,700, Books $61,000, Per/Ser (Incl. Access Fees) $6,700. Sal $238,300
Library Holdings: Bk Vols 56,600; Per Subs 107
Partic in Morris Automated Information Network
Friends of the Library Group

S NABISCO BRANDS, INC LIBRARY,* 200 DeForest Ave, 07936-1944. SAN 310-1525. Tel: 973-503-2000, Ext 2769. FAX: 973-428-8950. *Chief Librn*, Karen Ferradin; Staff 3 (MLS 2, Non-MLS 1)
Founded 1957
Library Holdings: Bk Titles 9,000; Per Subs 480
Automation Activity & Vendor Info: (Cataloging) Sydney; (Circulation) Sydney
Publications: Guide to Current Technical Literature; Library Bulletin
Restriction: By appointment only

EAST ORANGE

GM DEPARTMENT OF VETERANS AFFAIRS MEDICAL CENTER LIBRARY,* 385 Tremont Ave, 07018-1095. SAN 310-1207. Tel: 973-676-1000, Ext 1388. FAX: 973-414-9253. *Librn*, Sophie Winston
Founded 1955
Library Holdings: Bk Vols 12,300; Per Subs 425
Subject Interests: Alcoholism, Clinical needs in med, Drug rehab, Neurology, Nursing, Psychiatry, Psychology, Social work
Restriction: Non-circulating to the public
Partic in BRS; Dialog Corporation; Medline

M EAST ORANGE GENERAL HOSPITAL MEDICAL LIBRARY,* 300 Central Ave, 07019. SAN 350-6584. Tel: 973-266-8519. FAX: 973-266-8469.
Library Holdings: Bk Titles 700; Per Subs 100
Subject Interests: Allied health, Medicine, Nursing
Mem of Regional Med Libr Network
Partic in Biomed Libr Prog; Regional Med Libr - Region 1

P EAST ORANGE PUBLIC LIBRARY, 21 S Arlington Ave, 07018-3892. SAN 350-6649. Tel: 973-266-5600. FAX: 973-674-1991. *Dir*, Carolyn Ryan Reed; Tel: 973-266-5607, Fax: 973-675-6128, E-Mail: eopl05@earthlink.net; *ILL*, Aleyamma Mathai; *Ad Servs*, Sally E Rice; *Ch Servs*, Rita Roque; *Media Spec*, Alfred Buckley; *Acq, Cat, Tech Servs*, Jenny Tong; *Ref*, Robin Starkey; Staff 13 (MLS 13)
Founded 1900. Pop 73,552; Circ 231,534
Jul 1999-Jun 2000 Income (Main Library and Branch Library) $2,919,237
Library Holdings: Bk Vols 393,585; Bk Titles 256,713; Per Subs 802
Subject Interests: Ethnic studies
Special Collections: New Jerseyana
Database Vendor: Dialog, IAC - SearchBank, Innovative Interfaces INN - View, OCLC - First Search
Partic in Infolink
Special Services for the Deaf - High interest/low vocabulary books; Staff with knowledge of sign language
Friends of the Library Group
Branches: 3
AMPERE, 39 Ampere Plaza, 07017. SAN 350-6673. Tel: 973-266-7047. FAX: 973-674-1991. *Librn*, Sally E Rice
Library Holdings: Bk Vols 29,298
ELMWOOD, 317 S Clinton St, 07018. SAN 350-6703. Tel: 973-266-7050. FAX: 973-674-1991. *Librn*, Sally Rice
Library Holdings: Bk Vols 22,654
FRANKLIN, 192 Dodd St, 07017. SAN 350-6738. Tel: 973-266-7053. FAX: 973-674-1991. *Librn*, Sally Rice
Library Holdings: Bk Vols 14,796

EAST RUTHERFORD

P EAST RUTHERFORD MEMORIAL LIBRARY,* 143 Boiling Springs Ave, 07073. SAN 310-1215. Tel: 201-939-3930. FAX: 201-939-3930. E-Mail: erut1@bccls.org. *Dir*, Karen Di Nardo
Pop 7,902; Circ 24,870
Jan 1997-Dec 1998 Income $198,635, State $3,018, City $157,499, Other $3,084
Library Holdings: Bk Vols 30,327; Per Subs 78
Mem of Bergen County Co-op Libr Syst

EATONTOWN

P EATONTOWN PUBLIC LIBRARY,* 33 Broad St, 07724-1594. SAN 310-124X. Tel: 732-389-2665. E-Mail: eatontow@shore.co.monmouth.nj.us. *Dir*, Cindy Williams; Tel: 505-599-0248

Founded 1902. Pop 13,800; Circ 39,193
Library Holdings: Bk Vols 17,631; Per Subs 43
Mem of Monmouth County Library
Friends of the Library Group

EDGEWATER

P EDGEWATER FREE PUBLIC LIBRARY,* 49 Hudson Ave, 07020. SAN 310-1258. Tel: 201-224-6144. FAX: 201-886-3395. *Librn*, Harris M Richard; Tel: 505-599-0289, E-Mail: richard@sjc.cc.nm.us; *Ch Servs*, Susan Merfe
Founded 1906. Pop 5,000; Circ 18,557
Library Holdings: Bk Vols 25,000; Bk Titles 18,631; Per Subs 80
Special Collections: US Presidents Coll
Mem of Bergen County Co-op Libr Syst; Johnson Free Public Library

S UNILEVER RESEARCH US, Information Services, 45 River Rd, 07020. SAN 310-1266. Tel: 201-943-7100, Ext 2453. FAX: 201-840-8287. *Librn*, Anne McDermott; Staff 1 (Non-MLS 1)
Library Holdings: Bk Titles 6,000; Per Subs 225
Subject Interests: Biology, Chemical technology, Chemistry, Engineering
Automation Activity & Vendor Info: (Cataloging) epixtech, inc.; (Circulation) epixtech, inc.; (OPAC) epixtech, inc.; (Serials) epixtech, inc.
Restriction: Staff use only
Partic in Dialog Corporation; New Jersey Library Network

EDISON

P EDISON TOWNSHIP FREE PUBLIC LIBRARY, 340 Plainfield Ave, 08817. SAN 350-6762. Reference Tel: 732-287-2298, Ext 226, 227. TDD: 732-777-7813. FAX: 732-819-9134. Circulation FAX: 732-287-2298, Ext 221. Web Site: www.lmxac.org/edisonlib. *Dir*, Susan Krieger; *Branch Mgr*, Penny Vellucci; *Asst Dir*, Molly Davis-Bright; *Br Coordr, Head of Libr*, Judith Mansbach; *Librn*, Margaret Vellucci; *Acq*, Barbara Espenschied; *Bkmobile Coordr*, Sharon Giniger; *Ch Servs*, Carolyn Cullum; *Ch Servs*, Dolores Chupela; *Media Spec*, Francine Everson; Staff 80 (MLS 17, Non-MLS 63)
Founded 1928. Pop 100,000; Circ 415,806
Jul 2000-Jun 2001 Income (Main Library and Branch Library) $3,306,629, State $95,198, City $2,925,000, Other $286,431. Mats Exp $357,949, Books $240,749, Per/Ser (Incl. Access Fees) $29,914, Other Print Mats $11,286, Electronic Ref Mat (Incl. Access Fees) $76,000. Sal $1,656,000 (Prof $726,382)
Library Holdings: Bk Vols 256,842; Per Subs 440
Subject Interests: Local history
Database Vendor: CARL
Publications: "Library Letter"—Edison Township Public Library Newsletter
Partic in Librs of Middlesex Automation Consortium
Special Services for the Deaf - TTY machine
Friends of the Library Group
Branches: 2
CLARA BARTON BRANCH, 141 Hoover Ave, 08817. SAN 350-6797. Tel: 908-738-0096. FAX: 908-738-8325. Web Site: www.mxac.org/edisonlib. *Branch Mgr*, Margaret Vellucci
Library Holdings: Bk Titles 45,894
Friends of the Library Group
NORTH EDISON, 777 Grove Ave, 08820. SAN 350-6827. Tel: 908-548-3045. FAX: 908-549-5171. Web Site: www.lmxac.org/edisonlib. *Asst Dir, Branch Mgr*, Molly Davis-Bright; Staff 24 (MLS 7, Non-MLS 17)
Library Holdings: Bk Vols 87,749; Per Subs 113
Database Vendor: CARL
Friends of the Library Group
Bookmobiles: 1

M JFK MEDICAL CENTER, Medical Library, 65 James St, 08818-3059. SAN 320-6971. Tel: 732-321-7181. FAX: 732-632-1623. *Dir*, Lena Feld
Founded 1976
Library Holdings: Bk Titles 3,000; Per Subs 300
Subject Interests: Family practice, Rehabilitation
Publications: Library News; Library Update (acquisitions list)
Partic in Med Resources Consortium of Cent NJ

L LEVINSON, AXELROD, WHEATON & GRAYZEL LIBRARY,* Levinson Plaza, 2 Lincoln Hwy, PO Box 2095, 08818-2905. SAN 375-7323. Tel: 732-494-2727. FAX: 732-494-2712. E-Mail: levinson@njlawyers.com. Web Site: www.njlawyers.com. *Dir*, Sandra Helewa; Staff 1 (MLS 1)
Database Vendor: Lexis-Nexis
Restriction: Not open to public
Partic in Infolink

J MIDDLESEX COUNTY COLLEGE LIBRARY,* 2600 Woodbridge Ave, 08818. SAN 310-1282. Tel: 732-906-2561. FAX: 732-906-4159. *Dir*, Lewis Ostar; Tel: 732-906-4252, E-Mail: lostar@pilot.njin.net
Founded 1967
Jul 1999-Jun 2000 Mats Exp $158,610, Books $94,211, Per/Ser (Incl. Access Fees) $66,033, Presv $2,000, Micro $15,000, AV Equip $5,000, Other Print Mats $2,500. Sal $410,742 (Prof $283,000)
Library Holdings: Bk Vols 81,000; Per Subs 752
Subject Interests: Bus, Nursing, Paralegal
Publications: Fact Sheets; Pathfinders
Partic in Colorado Alliance Of Research Libraries; Dialog Corporation; Infolink Eastern New Jersey Regional Library Cooperative, Inc; LMX Automation Consortium; New Jersey Library Network; OCLC Online Computer Library Center, Inc; PALINET & Union Library Catalogue of Pennsylvania

M NEW JERSEY VETERANS MEMORIAL HOME AT MENLO PARK,* 132 Evergreen Rd, 08818. SAN 375-8494. Tel: 732-603-3000, Ext 3112. FAX: 732-603-3016.
Library Holdings: Per Subs 16

S REVLON RESEARCH CENTER LIBRARY,* 2121 Rte 27, 08818. SAN 310-9178. Tel: 732-287-1400. FAX: 732-287-7650. *Librn*, Ann Van Dine
Founded 1955
Library Holdings: Bk Titles 11,000; Per Subs 75
Subject Interests: Cosmetics, Dermatology, Dyes, Microbiology, Perfumery, Pharmacology, Toxicology
Open Mon-Thurs 9-2

G UNITED STATES ENVIRONMENTAL PROTECTION AGENCY, Region II Field Office Library,* 2890 Woodbridge Ave, 08837-3679. SAN 376-0618. Tel: 732-321-6762. Interlibrary Loan Service Tel: 732-321-6762. FAX: 732-321-6613. E-Mail: library-ed@epamail.epa.gov. *Tech Servs*, Margaret Esser
Library Holdings: Bk Titles 3,000; Per Subs 60

ELIZABETH

P FREE PUBLIC LIBRARY OF ELIZABETH,* 11 S Broad St, 07202. SAN 350-6851. Tel: 908-354-6060. FAX: 908-354-5845. Web Site: www.njpublib.org. *Dir*, Joseph J Keenan, Jr; E-Mail: jkeenan@epl.njpublib.org; *Ref*, Charles K Boll; *Ad Servs*, Andy Merkovsky; *Ch Servs*, Carolyn Geeding; *Tech Servs*, Carol Pristasch; Staff 13 (MLS 13)
Founded 1908. Pop 110,000; Circ 21,653
Library Holdings: Bk Vols 300,000; Bk Titles 200,000; Per Subs 587
Special Collections: Elizabethtown Room Coll
Automation Activity & Vendor Info: (Cataloging) DRA; (Circulation) DRA; (OPAC) DRA
Publications: Union List of Periodicals
Partic in LUCC; MURAL
Friends of the Library Group
Branches: 1
LACORTE, 408 Palmer St, 07202. SAN 377-5895. Tel: 908-820-0200, Ext 4. *Librn*, Kristi Miller
Library Holdings: Bk Vols 8,500; Bk Titles 8,000; Per Subs 16

R JEWISH EDUCATIONAL CENTER LIBRARY,* 330 Elmora Ave, 07208. SAN 310-1347. Tel: 908-353-4446. FAX: 908-289-5245. *In Charge*, Mrs Dvorah Preil
Library Holdings: Bk Vols 4,500; Per Subs 6

M SAINT ELIZABETH HOSPITAL, Health Sciences Library,* 225 Williamson St, 07207. SAN 310-1355. Tel: 908-527-5371. FAX: 908-820-0554. *Librn*, Sonal Chulka
Founded 1930
Library Holdings: Bk Vols 1,000; Per Subs 120
Subject Interests: Cardiology, Medicine, Nursing
Special Collections: History of Nursing; Medical Ethics
Partic in Health Sciences Library Association Of New Jersey; National Network Of Libraries Of Medicine - South Central Region; New Jersey Library Network
Affiliate of Seton Hall University Graduate Medical Education program & University of Medicine & Dentistry

M TRINITAS HOSPITAL, (Formerly Elizabeth General Medical Center), Charles H Schlichter, MD Health Science Library, 925 E Jersey St, 07201. SAN 310-1339. Tel: 908-629-8092. FAX: 908-629-8974. *Librn*, Jessica Brown
Library Holdings: Bk Vols 3,744; Bk Titles 3,374
Subject Interests: Medicine, Nursing
Partic in Basic Health Sciences Library Network; New Jersey Health Sciences Library Network; NJ Regional Libr Coop; OCLC Online Computer Library Center, Inc

UNION COUNTY COLLEGE
See Cranford

GL UNION COUNTY LAW LIBRARY, Union County Courthouse, 2 Broad St, 07207. SAN 310-138X. Tel: 908-659-4166. *In Charge*, Nicholas Tomich; Staff 1 (MLS 1)

ELMER

P ELMER PUBLIC LIBRARY,* 116 S Main St, 08318. SAN 375-7382. Tel: 856-358-2014. *Librn*, Stephanie Donovan
Library Holdings: Bk Vols 10,000

ELMWOOD PARK

S AMERICAN INSTITUTE OF FOOD DISTRIBUTION INC, Information & Research Center, One Broadway, 2nd flr, 07407. SAN 374-891X. Tel: 201-791-5570, Ext 19. FAX: 201-791-5222. E-Mail: food1@foodinstitute.com. Web Site: www.foodinstitute.com. *Dir*, Mary Ann Rizzitello
Library Holdings: Bk Titles 150; Per Subs 10

P ELMWOOD PARK PUBLIC LIBRARY, 210 Lee St, 07407-2799. SAN 310-1401. Tel: 201-796-2299. Interlibrary Loan Service Tel: 201-796-2497. Circulation Tel: 201-796-8888. Reference Tel: 201-796-2443. FAX: 201-703-1425. E-Mail: elpk1@bccls.org. Web Site: www.bccls.org/members/elpk.html. *Dir*, M K Kuriakose; E-Mail: kuriakose@bccls.org; *Ch Servs*, Darlene Bowman; Tel: 201-796-2323; *Circ*, Andrew Marrone; Tel: 201-796-2584; *ILL*, Evelyn Hornyak; Tel: 201-796-2497; Staff 22 (MLS 4, Non-MLS 18)
Founded 1953. Pop 17,721; Circ 90,721
Jan 2000-Dec 2000 Income $603,003, State $18,917, City $491,000, Locally Generated Income $49,022, Other $44,064. Mats Exp $117,400, Books $80,000, Per/Ser (Incl. Access Fees) $4,700, Micro $1,000, AV Equip $8,100, Electronic Ref Mat (Incl. Access Fees) $23,600. Sal $398,290 (Prof $127,993)
Library Holdings: Bk Vols 63,087; Bk Titles 55,083; Per Subs 117
Automation Activity & Vendor Info: (Circulation) DRA; (ILL) DRA; (OPAC) DRA
Database Vendor: DRA, IAC - Info Trac, ProQuest
Function: ILL available
Mem of Bergen County Co-op Libr Syst
Partic in BCCLS Computer Consortium
Friends of the Library Group

EMERSON

P EMERSON PUBLIC LIBRARY, 20 Palisade Ave, 07630. SAN 310-141X. Tel: 201-261-5604. FAX: 201-262-7999. E-Mail: emer1@bccls.org.. *Dir*, Patricia Ann Hannon; Staff 2 (MLS 1, Non-MLS 1)
Founded 1958. Pop 7,000; Circ 30,400
Jan 2000-Dec 2000 Income $249,190, State $7,460, City $232,000, Locally Generated Income $7,930, Other $1,800. Mats Exp $29,300, Books $22,100, Per/Ser (Incl. Access Fees) $2,400, AV Equip $4,300, Electronic Ref Mat (Incl. Access Fees) $500. Sal $133,000 (Prof $50,000)
Library Holdings: Bk Vols 29,700; Per Subs 56
Automation Activity & Vendor Info: (Circulation) DRA; (OPAC) DRA
Database Vendor: DRA, Ebsco - EbscoHost, IAC - Info Trac, ProQuest
Partic in Bergen County Cooperative Library System; Highlands Regional Library Cooperative
Friends of the Library Group

ENGLEWOOD

M ENGLEWOOD HOSPITAL & MEDICAL CENTER, Dr Walter Phillips Health Sciences Library, 350 Engle St, 07631. SAN 310-1436. Tel: 201-894-3070. FAX: 201-894-9049. Web Site: www.englewoodhospital.com. *Dir*, Katherine Lindner; Tel: 201-894-3071, E-Mail: kathy.lindner@chmc.com; *Librn*, Lice Sabbagh; Tel: 201-894-3069, E-Mail: lice.sabbagh@chmc.com; Staff 2 (MLS 2)
Founded 1943
Library Holdings: Bk Titles 3,000; Per Subs 250
Subject Interests: Commun health, Internal medicine, Ophthalmology, Otolaryngology, Patient educ, Psychiatry, Surgery
Special Collections: Consumer Health; Videosurgery Coll
Partic in Bergen-Passaic Med Libr Consortium; Docline; Health Sci Libr Asn of NJ; Medline

P ENGLEWOOD PUBLIC LIBRARY, 31 Engle St, 07631. SAN 310-1444. Tel: 201-568-2215. FAX: 201-568-6895. Web Site: www.englewoodlibrary.org. *Dir*, Donald Jacobsen; Tel: 201-568-2215, Ext 222, E-Mail: jacobsen@bccls.org; *ILL*, Jean Grushkin; *Circ*, Arlene Wargo; *Ch Servs*, Donna-Lynn Cooper; *Tech Servs*, Rose Koa; *Ref*, Ann Sparanese; Tel: 201-568-2215, Ext 229, E-Mail: sparanese@englewoodlibrary.org; Staff 20 (MLS 9, Non-MLS 11)
Founded 1901. Pop 25,148; Circ 217,031
Jan 1999-Dec 1999 Income $1,972,902, State $56,510, City $1,620,481, Other $82,584. Mats Exp $188,611, Books $141,587, Per/Ser (Incl. Access Fees) $14,902, Presv $1,520, Micro $6,172, Electronic Ref Mat (Incl. Access Fees) $1,959. Sal $1,052,802
Library Holdings: Bk Vols 119,886; Bk Titles 103,014; Per Subs 265
Subject Interests: Afro-American studies, Careers, Judaica, Local history
Automation Activity & Vendor Info: (Circulation) DRA; (Circulation) DRA
Database Vendor: DRA, Ebsco - EbscoHost, IAC - Info Trac, ProQuest
Publications: Newsletter (quarterly)
Mem of Bergen County Co-op Libr Syst
Friends of the Library Group

ENGLEWOOD CLIFFS

S LIPTON LIBRARY-INFORMATION CENTER,* 800 Sylvan Ave, 07632. SAN 310-1460. Tel: 201-894-7568. FAX: 201-871-8149. *Mgr*, Teris W Binder; *Info Specialist*, Diane Y Cassatly
Founded 1942
Library Holdings: Bk Vols 6,500; Per Subs 200
Subject Interests: Food indust, Food sci, Nutrition
Special Collections: Tea
Publications: KWAC Index to Tea Publications (1965-96)
Partic in Dialog Corporation; Dow Jones News Retrieval; Medline

EWING

S EWING TOWNSHIP HISTORICAL PRESERVATION SOCIETY LIBRARY,* 27 Federal City Rd, 08638. SAN 376-0715. Tel: 609-530-1220.
Library Holdings: Bk Vols 300

C THE COLLEGE OF NEW JERSEY, Roscoe L West Library, 2000 Pennington Rd, 08628-1104. (Mail add: PO Box 7718, 08628-0718), SAN 310-5520. Tel: 609-771-2311, 609-771-2332. Interlibrary Loan Service Tel: 609-771-2028. FAX: 609-637-5177. Web Site: www.tcnj.edu/~library. *Assoc Dean*, Philip Tramdack; *Asst Dir*, Mary Mallery; *Cat*, Kay Yu; *Coll Develop*, Eleanor Fogarty; *Head Ref*, Patricia A Beaber; Tel: 609-771-2405; *Ch Servs, YA Servs*, Janice Kisthardt; *Science*, Maureen Gorman; *Music*, Taras Pavlovsky; *Electronic Resources*, Joanne Zangara. Subject Specialists: *Art*, Joanne Zangara; *Business and management*, Eleanor Fogarty; *Economics*, Eleanor Fogarty; *Electronic*, Joanne Zangara; *Humanities*, Marc Meola; *Literacy*, Deborah Sheesley; *Media*, Taras Pavlovsky; *Social sciences and issues*, Karen Hartman
Founded 1855. Enrl 7,500
Library Holdings: Bk Vols 580,200; Per Subs 1,365
Special Collections: History of American Education, Historical Textbooks & Historical Children's Books; History of New Jersey; History of the American Revolution
Automation Activity & Vendor Info: (Acquisitions) Endeavor; (Cataloging) Endeavor; (Circulation) Endeavor; (OPAC) Endeavor; (Serials) Endeavor
Partic in OCLC Online Computer Library Center, Inc; PALINET & Union Library Catalogue of Pennsylvania
Friends of the Library Group

FAIR HAVEN

P FAIR HAVEN PUBLIC LIBRARY,* 748 River Rd, 07704. SAN 310-1495. Tel: 732-747-5031. *Dir*, Gloria Price
Founded 1933. Pop 6,000; Circ 51,000
Library Holdings: Bk Vols 20,000; Bk Titles 20,000
Mem of Monmouth County Library

FAIR LAWN

P MAURICE M PINE FREE PUBLIC LIBRARY, 10-01 Fair Lawn Ave, 07410. SAN 310-1533. Tel: 201-796-3400. FAX: 201-794-6344. E-Mail: fair1@bccls.org. Web Site: www.bccls.org/fairlawn. *Dir*, Timothy H Murphy; *Asst Dir*, Penelope Kaplan; *Ch Servs*, Kate Nafz; *Circ*, Barbara Wilson; *Ref*, Gail Zimmer; *Tech Servs*, Nancy Fezell; Staff 8 (MLS 8)
Founded 1933. Pop 32,229; Circ 375,921
Jan 1999-Dec 1999 Income $1,584,000, State $39,350, City $1,460,300. Mats Exp $162,072, Books $147,672, Per/Ser (Incl. Access Fees) $14,400. Sal $1,045,018
Library Holdings: Bk Vols 177,194; Per Subs 450
Subject Interests: Art
Automation Activity & Vendor Info: (Cataloging) DRA; (Circulation) DRA; (OPAC) DRA
Database Vendor: GaleNet
Partic in Bergen County Cooperative Library System
Friends of the Library Group

FAIRFIELD

P FAIRFIELD PUBLIC LIBRARY, Anthony Pio Costa Memorial Library, 261 Hollywood Ave, 07004. SAN 310-155X. Tel: 973-227-3575. FAX: 973-227-7305. E-Mail: ffpl@nplhub.org. *Dir*, John Helle; Staff 2 (MLS 1, Non-MLS 1)
Founded 1968. Pop 7,615; Circ 63,320
Library Holdings: Bk Vols 60,600; Per Subs 134
Partic in Infolink Eastern New Jersey Regional Library Cooperative, Inc

S PAT GUIDA ASSOCIATES LIBRARY,* 24 Spielman Rd, 07004-3412. SAN 327-8476. Tel: 973-227-7418, 973-729-8176. *Pres*, Pat Guida
Library Holdings: Bk Vols 2,500; Per Subs 50
Subject Interests: Nutrition, Toxicology

FAIRVIEW

P FAIRVIEW FREE PUBLIC LIBRARY, 213 Anderson Ave, 07022. SAN 310-1568. Tel: 201-943-6244. FAX: 201-943-5289. E-Mail: favw1@bccls.org. Web Site: www.bccls.org/fairview. *Dir*, Arlene Sahraie; E-Mail: sahraie@bccls.org; Staff 11 (MLS 1, Non-MLS 10)
Founded 1944. Pop 10,733; Circ 42,951
1999-2000 Income $300,100, State $11,100, City $289,000. Mats Exp $33,000, Books $30,000, Per/Ser (Incl. Access Fees) $3,000. Sal $200,000 (Prof $58,000)
Library Holdings: Bk Titles 23,190; Per Subs 199
Partic in Bergen County Cooperative Library System; Highlands Regional Library Cooperative
Friends of the Library Group

FANWOOD

P FANWOOD MEMORIAL LIBRARY, North Ave & Tillotson Rd, 07023-1399. SAN 310-1576. Tel: 908-322-6400. FAX: 908-322-5590. E-Mail: fanwdlib@lmxac.org. Web Site: www.lmxac.org/fanwood. *Dir*, Dan Weiss; E-Mail: dweiss@lmxac.org; *Circ*, Gloria Rusnak; *Ch Servs*, Susan Staub; *Tech Servs*, Ruth Ahnert; Staff 2 (MLS 2)
Founded 1903. Pop 7,000; Circ 57,000
Library Holdings: Bk Vols 37,500; Bk Titles 28,000; Per Subs 108
Subject Interests: Local history
Automation Activity & Vendor Info: (OPAC) CARL
Database Vendor: CARL
Partic in Infolink Regional Libr Coop; LMX Automation Consortium
Friends of the Library Group

FAR HILLS

S UNITED STATES GOLF ASSOCIATION MUSEUM & LIBRARY,* Golf House, PO Box 708, 07931-0708. SAN 310-1584. Tel: 908-234-2300. FAX: 908-470-5012. Web Site: www.usga.org.
Founded 1936
Library Holdings: Bk Vols 20,000; Per Subs 25
Special Collections: Rare bks

FARMINGDALE

M ARTHUR BRISBANE CHILD TREATMENT CENTER LIBRARY, Allaire Rd, PO Box 625, 07727. SAN 310-1592. Tel: 732-938-5061. FAX: 732-938-9202. *Dir*, Raymond Grimaldi; *Librn*, Mary Nash
Library Holdings: Bk Vols 4,500; Per Subs 12

FLEMINGTON

P FLEMINGTON FREE PUBLIC LIBRARY,* 118 Main St, 08822. SAN 310-1606. Tel: 908-782-5733. FAX: 908-782-3875. E-Mail: ffpl@hvglib.hb.nj.us. Web Site: www.ffpl.hvglib.hb.nj.us. *Dir*, Janis E Schroeder
Founded 1799. Pop 4,344; Circ 35,838
Library Holdings: Bk Vols 40,000; Per Subs 50
Subject Interests: Humanities

S HIRAM E DEATS MEMORIAL LIBRARY, Hunterdon County Historical Society,* 114 Main St, 08822. SAN 325-9307. Tel: 908-782-1091. *Librn*, Roxanne Carkhuff
Library Holdings: Bk Vols 5,000
Subject Interests: Genealogy, Local history
Open Thurs 1-3 & 7-9, other times by appointment

L HUNTERDON COUNTY LAW LIBRARY,* 65 Park Ave, 08822. SAN 325-7606. Tel: 908-788-1240. FAX: 908-788-1284.
Jul 1997-Jun 1998 Mats Exp $27,000. Sal $31,200
Library Holdings: Bk Vols 9,000

P HUNTERDON COUNTY LIBRARY, 314 State Rte 12, 08822. SAN 310-1614. Tel: 908-788-1444. Reference Tel: 908-788-1434. FAX: 908-806-4862. E-Mail: library@hclibr.eclipse.net. Web Site: www.hunterdon.lib.nj.us. *Dir*, Janet S Friend; *Acq, Asst Dir*, Floyd Saums; *Ch Servs*, Patricia Strickland; *Tech Servs*, Kristin Momberg; *Librn for Blind, Ref*, Amanda Philipp; *AV*, Leslie Moore; Staff 54 (MLS 16, Non-MLS 38)
Founded 1928. Pop 115,000; Circ 500,000
Library Holdings: Bk Titles 176,564
Special Collections: New Jersey (Jerseyana)
Automation Activity & Vendor Info: (Acquisitions) epixtech, inc.; (Cataloging) epixtech, inc.; (Circulation) epixtech, inc.
Database Vendor: Ebsco - EbscoHost, ProQuest
Publications: HCL Pulse
Function: ILL available, Mail loans to members, Reference services available
Member Libraries: Frenchtown Public Library; Grandin Library Association; High Bridge Public Library; Holland Alexandria Free Public Library; Newark Public Library; Tewksbury Township Public Library
Partic in Highlands Regional Library Cooperative
Friends of the Library Group
Bookmobiles: 1

M HUNTERDON MEDICAL CENTER LIBRARY,* 2100 Wescott Dr, 6th flr, 08822. SAN 310-1622. Tel: 908-788-6100, Ext 3220. FAX: 908-788-2537. *Librn*, Jeanne Dutka
Founded 1954
Library Holdings: Bk Vols 1,000; Per Subs 100
Mem of Regional Libr Coop, Region 1
Partic in Health Sci Libr Asn of NJ; Med Resources Consortium of Cent NJ

FLORHAM PARK

S AT&T, Shannon Laboratory Library, 180 Park Ave, Bldg 103, 07932-0971. Tel: 973-360-8160. FAX: 973-360-8020. E-Mail: library@research.att.com. *Chief Librn, Dir*, Laurinda Jean Alcorn; Tel: 973-360-8162, E-Mail: laurinda@research.att.com; *Cat*, Jane Ma
Founded 1997
Library Holdings: Per Subs 500
Subject Interests: Computer science, Mathematics, Networks, Signal processing, Speech, Statistics, Telephony
Automation Activity & Vendor Info: (Cataloging) VTLS; (Circulation) VTLS
Database Vendor: Dialog, GaleNet
Partic in Highlands Regional Library Cooperative

L DRINKER BIDDLE & SHANLEY, (Formerly Shanley & Fisher), Law Library, 500 Campus Dr, 07932. SAN 310-3587. Tel: 973-360-1100. FAX: 973-360-9831. Web Site: www.dbr.com. *Librn*, Kate Zuhusky; E-Mail: kzuhusky@dbr.com
Library Holdings: Bk Vols 20,000; Per Subs 40
Special Collections: Law Coll
Partic in Dialog Corporation; Westlaw

P FLORHAM PARK PUBLIC LIBRARY, 107 Ridgedale Ave, 07932. SAN 310-1665. Tel: 973-377-2694. FAX: 973-377-2085. Web Site: www.gti.net/flpklib. *Dir*, Barbara M McConville; E-Mail: mcconville@main.morris.org
Founded 1965. Pop 9,000; Circ 84,000
Jan 1999-Dec 1999 Income $494,982. Mats Exp $88,146, Books $51,365, Per/Ser (Incl. Access Fees) $15,103, AV Equip $4,936, Electronic Ref Mat (Incl. Access Fees) $12,767. Sal $214,842 (Prof $90,000)
Library Holdings: Bk Vols 39,089; Per Subs 175
Subject Interests: Art
Automation Activity & Vendor Info: (Cataloging) DRA; (Circulation) DRA; (ILL) DRA; (OPAC) DRA
Database Vendor: Ebsco - EbscoHost, GaleNet, ProQuest
Publications: Newsletter (bimonthly)
Function: ILL available, Photocopies available, Some telephone reference
Partic in Morris Automated Information Network
Friends of the Library Group

L PITNEY, HARDIN, KIPP & SZUCH LLP, Law Library, 200 Campus Dr, 07932. (Mail add: PO Box 1945, 07962), SAN 310-3153. Tel: 201-966-6300, Ext 7340. FAX: 201-966-1550. Web Site: www.phks.com. *Dir*, Julie L von Schrader; E-Mail: jvonschrader@phks.com; Staff 4 (MLS 2, Non-MLS 2)
Founded 1902
1999-2000 Income $530,000. Mats Exp $530,000, Books $526,500, Per/Ser (Incl. Access Fees) $2,000, Presv $1,500
Library Holdings: Bk Vols 33,000; Bk Titles 5,800; Per Subs 100
Subject Interests: NJ law
Database Vendor: Dialog, Lexis-Nexis
Restriction: Staff use only
Partic in CDB Infotek; CourtLink; Dun & Bradstreet Info Servs; Highlands Regional Library Cooperative; Pacer; Superior Info; Westlaw

S TROY CORPORATION, Corporate Library, 8 Vreeland Rd, 07932-0955. SAN 378-2190. Tel: 973-443-4200. FAX: 973-443-0258. Web Site: www.troycorp.com.
1998-1999 Mats Exp $125,000, Books $12,000, Per/Ser (Incl. Access Fees) $18,225. Sal $50,000
Library Holdings: Bk Vols 5,000; Per Subs 198
Subject Interests: Chemistry
Special Collections: Chemical Publications in English, German, French & Japanese from 1868

FORKED RIVER

S AMERGEN ENERGY, (Formerly GPU Nuclear), Oyster Creek Technical Library, US Hwy 9 S, PO Box 388, 08731. SAN 320-9911. Tel: 609-971-4000, Ext 4043. FAX: 609-971-2266. Web Site: www.amergenenergy.com. *In Charge*, Mark Orski; Staff 1 (MLS 1)
Founded 1981
Library Holdings: Bk Titles 1,300

Subject Interests: Nuclear power
Special Collections: EPRI Reports; Industry Standards; Institute for Nuclear Power Reports
Restriction: Not open to public
Partic in Dialog Corporation

FORT DIX

UNITED STATES AIR FORCE AT FORT DIX
AM WALSON AIR FORCE CLINIC LIBRARY, Bldg 5250, New Jersey Ave, 08640-5017. SAN 350-7033. Tel: 609-562-9506. FAX: 609-562-9065.
Founded 1960
Library Holdings: Bk Vols 1,100; Per Subs 26
Subject Interests: Dentistry, Medicine, Nursing, Surgery

A UNITED STATES ARMY AT FORT DIX, General Library,* Bldg 5403, First & Delaware St, 08640-5332. SAN 350-7009. Tel: 609-562-5228. FAX: 609-562-3554. *Librn*, Judy Neff; Tel: 515-281-3569
Founded 1917
Library Holdings: Bk Titles 30,000; Per Subs 14
Publications: New book lists; periodical lists; subject bibliographies
Partic in Dialog Corporation; OCLC Online Computer Library Center, Inc

FORT LEE

P FREE PUBLIC LIBRARY OF THE BOROUGH OF FORT LEE, 320 Main St, 07024. SAN 310-1673. Tel: 201-592-3614. Interlibrary Loan Service Tel: 201-592-3629. Reference Tel: 201-592-3629. FAX: 201-585-0375. E-Mail: ftle1@bccls.org. Web Site: www.bccls.org/fortlee. *Dir*, Rita Altomara; *Ch Servs*, Diana Chen; Tel: 201-592-3620; *Asst Dir*, Lucy Haskell; *YA Servs*, Carole Watson; *Tech Servs*, Joan Kafes; Staff 7 (MLS 7)
Founded 1930. Pop 32,367; Circ 246,560
Jan 2000-Dec 2000 Income $1,333,892, State $39,996, City $1,200,000, Locally Generated Income $93,896. Mats Exp $186,000, Books $150,000, Per/Ser (Incl. Access Fees) $16,000, Micro $6,000, AV Equip $4,000, Electronic Ref Mat (Incl. Access Fees) $10,000. Sal $820,769 (Prof $332,464)
Library Holdings: Bk Vols 132,936; Bk Titles 130,930; Per Subs 315
Subject Interests: Feminism
Special Collections: Books in Japanese & Korean
Automation Activity & Vendor Info: (Circulation) DRA; (OPAC) DRA
Publications: Library Looking Glass (newsletter)
Partic in Bergen County Cooperative Library System; Highlands Regional Library Cooperative
Friends of the Library Group

FORT MONMOUTH

UNITED STATES ARMY
A COMMUNICATIONS-ELECTRONICS COMMAND R&D TECHNICAL LIBRARY, AMSEL-IM-BM-I-L-R, Bldg 2700, 07703-5703. SAN 350-7122. Tel: 732-427-2553. FAX: 732-427-2313. E-Mail: amsel-im-bm-i-l-r@mail1.monmouth.army.mil. *Librn*, Henry J McAteer; Tel: 732-427-2235, E-Mail: james.mcateer@mail1.monmouth.army.mil; *Info Specialist*, Lawrence W Goldberg; Tel: 732-427-2328; Staff 2 (MLS 1, Non-MLS 1)
Founded 1941
Library Holdings: Bk Titles 43,339; Per Subs 300
Subject Interests: Applied sci, Communications, Computer science, Electrochem, Electronics, Pure sci, Radar
Restriction: Not open to public
Partic in Fedlink; OCLC Online Computer Library Center, Inc
A COMMUNICATIONS-ELECTRONICS MUSEUM LIBRARY, Bldg 275, Kaplan Hall, 07703. SAN 350-7092. Tel: 732-532-1682. FAX: 732-532-2440. *Dir*, Mindy Rosewitz
Founded 1954
Subject Interests: Develop in communications, Res in communications
Special Collections: Extensive Coll of US Army Technical Manuals dealing with Communications Equipment, as well as photographs dealing with both the History of Fort Monmouth & the Equipment
A VAN DEUSEN POST LIBRARY, Bldg 502, 07703-5117. SAN 350-7068. Tel: 732-532-3172. FAX: 732-532-4766. *Dir*, Carol Z Rippetoe; *Tech Servs*, Mary Ann Holland; *Tech Servs*, Catherine Fitzgerald; *Tech Servs*, Mary R Sandilos; Staff 4 (MLS 1, Non-MLS 3)
Founded 1917
Library Holdings: Bk Vols 53,000; Per Subs 98
Subject Interests: Mil art, Mil sci
Partic in Fedlink; NJ Region 5 Libr Coop

FRANKLIN LAKES

S BECTON, DICKINSON & CO, Information Resource Centers, One Becton Dr, 07417-1884. SAN 310-4893. Tel: 201-847-7230. FAX: 201-847-5377. *Mgr*, Faina Menzul
Library Holdings: Bk Vols 8,000; Per Subs 400
Subject Interests: Biomed, Bus, Engineering, Law, Medicine, Plastics
Special Collections: Medical Devices Coll
Publications: InfoFocus (bi-monthly)
Partic in Dialog Corporation; OCLC Online Computer Library Center, Inc

P FRANKLIN LAKES FREE PUBLIC LIBRARY, 470 Dekorte Dr, 07417. SAN 310-1681. Tel: 201-891-2224. FAX: 201-891-5102. Web Site: www.franklinlakes.org. *Ad Servs*, Lillian Brunetti; *Ad Servs*, Catherine Dodwell; *Ch Servs*, Gerry McMahon; Staff 25 (MLS 6, Non-MLS 19)
Founded 1968. Pop 10,000
Jan 2000-Dec 2000 Income $798,731, State $10,500, City $721,331, Other $66,900. Mats Exp $152,000, Books $104,000, Per/Ser (Incl. Access Fees) $12,000, AV Equip $24,000, Electronic Ref Mat (Incl. Access Fees) $12,000. Sal $541,600
Library Holdings: Bk Vols 80,000; Per Subs 255
Automation Activity & Vendor Info: (Cataloging) DRA; (Circulation) DRA; (OPAC) DRA
Database Vendor: DRA
Partic in Bergen County Cooperative Library System; Highlands Regional Library Cooperative
Friends of the Library Group

FRANKLINVILLE

P FRANKLIN TOWNSHIP PUBLIC LIBRARY, 1549 Delsea Dr, 08322. SAN 350-8625. Tel: 856-694-2833. FAX: 856-694-1708. E-Mail: ftpl@yahoo.com. *Dir*, Denise Saia; Staff 10 (MLS 1, Non-MLS 9)
Founded 1966. Pop 16,000
1999-2000 Income $219,000, State $15,546, Locally Generated Income $13,000. Mats Exp $51,000, Books $34,700, Per/Ser (Incl. Access Fees) $4,800, Presv $300, AV Equip $12,000, Electronic Ref Mat (Incl. Access Fees) $2,000. Sal $110,000 (Prof $35,600)
Library Holdings: Bk Vols 25,000; Bk Titles 24,000; Per Subs 100
Automation Activity & Vendor Info: (Circulation) SIRSI; (OPAC) SIRSI
Database Vendor: OCLC - First Search
Friends of the Library Group

FREEHOLD

M CENTRASTATE MEDICAL CENTER LIBRARY, 901 W Main St, 07728. SAN 375-5088. Tel: 732-294-2668. FAX: 732-294-2589. *Librn*, Robin Siegel; E-Mail: rsiegel@centrastate.com; Staff 1 (MLS 1)
Library Holdings: Bk Vols 1,500; Per Subs 125
Partic in BHSL; Docline; Health Sciences Library Association Of New Jersey; Monmouth-Ocean Biomedical Information Consortium; OCLC Online Computer Library Center, Inc

P FREEHOLD PUBLIC LIBRARY, 28 1/2 E Main St, 07728-2202. SAN 310-1703. Tel: 732-462-5135. FAX: 732-577-9598. E-Mail: fplib@yahoo.com. *Dir*, Barbara Greenberg; E-Mail: bglib@yahoo.com; Staff 8 (MLS 1, Non-MLS 7)
Founded 1903. Pop 10,742; Circ 29,914
Library Holdings: Bk Vols 23,506; Per Subs 78
Subject Interests: Local history
Special Collections: Books on Cassette; Large Print Books
Publications: Patron brochure
Mem of Central Jersey Regional Libr Coop
Friends of the Library Group

S MONMOUTH COUNTY HISTORICAL ASSOCIATION LIBRARY & ARCHIVES,* 70 Court St, 07728. SAN 310-172X. Tel: 732-462-1466. FAX: 732-462-8346. E-Mail: mchalib@cjrlc.org. Web Site: www.cjrlc.org/~mchalib. *Archivist, Librn*, Carla Tobias; *Asst Librn*, Megan Springate
Founded 1898
Library Holdings: Bk Titles 8,000; Per Subs 15
Special Collections: Allaire Papers (Howell Works); Battle of Monmouth; Mott Family Papers; North American Phalanx; Philip Freneau
Publications: A Guide to Resources in the Monmouth County Historical Association Library; Directory of Historical Societies, Monmouth County, New Jersey. (1995)
Restriction: Non-circulating to the public

GL SUPERIOR COURT LAW LIBRARY, Courthouse, 71 Monument Park, 07728. SAN 370-1646. Tel: 732-431-7079. *Librn*, Maureen Burgess
Library Holdings: Bk Titles 1,170; Per Subs 100

FRENCHTOWN

P FRENCHTOWN PUBLIC LIBRARY,* Boro Hall, Second St, 08825. SAN 310-1746. Tel: 908-996-4788. *Librn*, Sara Heil
Circ 21,514
Library Holdings: Bk Vols 16,310; Per Subs 20
Mem of Hunterdon County Library
Friends of the Library Group

GARFIELD

P GARFIELD FREE PUBLIC LIBRARY,* 500 Midland Ave, 07026. SAN 310-1754. Tel: 973-478-3800. FAX: 973-478-7162. Web Site: www.bccls.org/garfield. *Dir*, I MacArthur Nickles; *Ch Servs*, Patricia Gelinski; *Ref*, Kathleen Zalenski; Staff 13 (MLS 3, Non-MLS 10)
Founded 1923. Pop 26,803; Circ 71,406
Library Holdings: Bk Vols 85,000; Bk Titles 75,000; Per Subs 147
Special Collections: Black History-Literature (Black History), bks; Persian Art
Mem of Bergen County Co-op Libr Syst; Johnson Free Public Library

GARWOOD

P GARWOOD FREE PUBLIC LIBRARY,* 223 Walnut St, 07027. SAN 310-1789. Tel: 908-789-1670. FAX: 908-317-8146. E-Mail: garwoodlibrary@home.com. *Dir*, Carol A Lombardo; Staff 4 (MLS 1, Non-MLS 3)
Founded 1933. Pop 4,724; Circ 7,096
Library Holdings: Bk Vols 28,000; Per Subs 43
Special Collections: New Jersey Coll
Partic in Infolink

GLASSBORO

C ROWAN UNIVERSITY LIBRARY,* 201 Mullica Hill Rd, 08028-1701. SAN 350-7572. Tel: 856-256-4800. Interlibrary Loan Service Tel: 856-256-4803. FAX: 856-256-4924. Web Site: www.rowan.edu/library. *Dean of Libr*, Marilyn J Martin; E-Mail: martin@rowan.edu; *Assoc Dean*, Gregory C Potter; E-Mail: potter@rowan.edu; *Asst Dean*, Nicholas Yovnello; *Archivist, Spec Coll*, William A Garrabrant; *ILL*, Cynthia Mullens; *Cat*, Carol M Clark; *Per*, Judith Holmes; *Acq*, Jacquelyn Gryckiewicz; *Circ*, Laverne Hines; Staff 57 (MLS 18, Non-MLS 39)
Founded 1923. Enrl 8,588; Fac 363; Highest Degree: Doctorate
Jul 1998-Jun 1999 Income (Main and Other College/University Libraries) $3,348,892. Mats Exp $1,079,236, Books $366,382, Per/Ser (Incl. Access Fees) $249,688, Presv $33,619, Micro $22,743, AV Equip $5,000, Other Print Mats $113,585, Manuscripts & Archives $2,000, Electronic Ref Mat (Incl. Access Fees) $286,219. Sal $1,959,198 (Prof $1,194,543)
Library Holdings: Bk Vols 415,989; Bk Titles 308,942; Per Subs 1,580
Subject Interests: Education, Engineering
Special Collections: United States, New Jersey & Delaware Valley History (Stewart Coll), bks, deeds, genealogical mat, mss, papers
Automation Activity & Vendor Info: (Acquisitions) DRA; (Cataloging) DRA; (Circulation) DRA
Publications: Library Reports (newsletter)
Partic in South Jersey Regional Library Cooperative; Tri-State College Library Cooperative (TCLC)
Friends of the Library Group
Departmental Libraries:
WILSON MUSIC LIBRARY, Main Campus, Rte 322, 08028. SAN 350-7602. Tel: 609-256-3542. Web Site: www.rowan.edu. *Librn*, Marjorie Morris; Tel: 856-256-4500, Ext 3542, Fax: 856-256-4924; Staff 3 (MLS 2, Non-MLS 1)
Enrl 175; Highest Degree: Master
Jul 1999-Jun 2000 Income $31,353. Mats Exp $34,959, Books $10,500, Per/Ser (Incl. Access Fees) $5,393, Presv $11,000, AV Equip $1,000, Other Print Mats $3,066, Electronic Ref Mat (Incl. Access Fees) $4,000. Sal $105,000 (Prof $70,000)
Library Holdings: Bk Vols 18,000; Per Subs 65
Special Collections: Musical Scores; Reference Books; Sound & Video Recordings
Database Vendor: OCLC - First Search
Restriction: Circulation limited
Friends of the Library Group

GLEN RIDGE

P GLEN RIDGE FREE PUBLIC LIBRARY, 240 Ridgewood Ave, 07028. SAN 310-1843. Tel: 973-748-5482. E-Mail: jstinik@infolink.org. *Dir*, John A Sitnik; *Asst Dir*, Helen V Beckert; Staff 10 (MLS 2, Non-MLS 8)
Founded 1912. Pop 7,076; Circ 68,228
Jan 1999-Dec 1999 Income $405,788, State $9,115, City $361,586, Locally Generated Income $35,087. Mats Exp $52,324, Books $36,003, Per/Ser (Incl. Access Fees) $4,697, Micro $250, AV Equip $8,154, Electronic Ref Mat (Incl. Access Fees) $3,220. Sal $250,783
Library Holdings: Bk Vols 50,796; Bk Titles 48,436; Per Subs 205
Special Collections: Glen Ridge History Coll, pictures, slides, clippings, memorabilia
Publications: Sunscripts (Friends of the Library Newsletter)
Partic in Infolink Eastern New Jersey Regional Library Cooperative, Inc
Friends of the Library Group

GLEN ROCK

S GIFTED CHILD SOCIETY LIBRARY,* 190 Rock Rd, 07452-1736. SAN 377-2772. Tel: 201-444-6530. FAX: 201-444-9099. Web Site: www.gifted.org. *Exec Dir*, Gina Ginsberg Riggs
Library Holdings: Bk Vols 250; Bk Titles 200

P GLEN ROCK PUBLIC LIBRARY,* 315 Rock Rd, 07452-1795. SAN 310-1851. Tel: 201-670-3970. FAX: 201-445-0872. E-Mail: glrk1@bccls.org. *Dir*, Gerald J Fadlalla; *Ad Servs*, Anita Giannella; *Ch Servs*, Monique Reynolds; *Cat*, Rita Becker; Staff 16 (MLS 4, Non-MLS 12)
Founded 1922. Pop 10,885; Circ 142,246
Library Holdings: Bk Vols 84,750; Bk Titles 80,000; Per Subs 187
Mem of Bergen - Passaic Regional Libr Syst; Bergen County Co-op Libr Syst
Friends of the Library Group

GLOUCESTER CITY

P GLOUCESTER CITY LIBRARY, 50 N Railroad Ave, 08030. SAN 310-186X. Tel: 856-456-4181. FAX: 856-456-6724. E-Mail: gc@camden.lib.nj.us. Web Site: www.gloucester.camden.lib.nj.us. *Dir*, Elizabeth J Egan; *Ch Servs, ILL, Ref*, Deena Worrell; *Ref*, Illene Rubin; Staff 10 (MLS 4, Non-MLS 6)
Founded 1925. Pop 12,700; Circ 50,000
Library Holdings: Bk Vols 61,000; Bk Titles 65,000; Per Subs 113
Special Collections: How-to-do-it & Mechanics
Automation Activity & Vendor Info: (Cataloging) TLC; (Circulation) TLC; (OPAC) TLC
Database Vendor: Ebsco - EbscoHost, IAC - Info Trac
Publications: Gloucester City Library (Newsletter, monthly)
Partic in South Jersey Regional Library Cooperative

GREENWICH

S CUMBERLAND COUNTY HISTORICAL SOCIETY LIBRARY, PO Box 16, 08323. SAN 375-8427. Tel: 856-455-4055, 856-455-8580. *Dir*, Warren Adams; *Librn*, Jonathon Woods
Library Holdings: Bk Vols 1,000
Subject Interests: Genealogy
Open first Wed of the month 10-4, Fri 1-4, Sun 2-5

GREYSTONE PARK

GM GREYSTONE PARK PSYCHIATRIC HOSPITAL, Health Science Library, Central Ave/MBC, 07950. SAN 310-1886. Tel: 973-538-1800, Ext 4591. FAX: 973-538-9544. *Librn*, Jeanette Hodelin; *Librn*, Mary O Walker; E-Mail: mowalker@dhs.state.nj.us. Subject Specialists: *Medicine*, Mary O Walker; *Psychiatry*, Mary O Walker; Staff 1 (MLS 1)
Founded 1930
Library Holdings: Bk Vols 1,650; Bk Titles 1,600; Per Subs 94; Spec Interest Per Sub 94; Bks on Deafness & Sign Lang 10
Subject Interests: Medicine, Nursing, Psychiatric rehabilitation, Psychiatry, Psychology
Restriction: Open to department staff only, Open to others by appointment
Function: ILL by photocopy only
Partic in Basic Health Sciences Library Network; Cosmopolitan Biomedical Library Consortium

HACKENSACK

GL BERGEN COUNTY LAW LIBRARY, Justice Center Bldg, 10 Main St, Rm 107, 07601. SAN 310-1894. Tel: 201-646-2056. FAX: 201-646-2598. *Librn*, Henry Gozdz
Library Holdings: Bk Vols 36,000; Per Subs 10

S BERGEN RECORD CORP LIBRARY, (Formerly Bergen Evening Record Corp Library), 150 River St, 07601. SAN 375-748X. Tel: 201-646-4090. Reference Tel: 201-646-4541. FAX: 201-646-4737. E-Mail: library@bergen.com. *Mgr Libr Serv*, Paul Schulman; Tel: 201-646-4518, E-Mail: schulman@bergen.com; *Librn*, Donna Blair; E-Mail: blair@bergen.com; *Librn*, Dorothy Fersch; Tel: 201-646-4579, E-Mail: fersch@bergen.com; *Librn*, Maggie Hutchinson; Tel: 201-646-4089, E-Mail: hutchinson@bergen.com; *Librn*, Leonard Iannaccone; Tel: 201-646-4132, E-Mail: iannaccone@bergen.com; *Librn*, David Mammone; Tel: 201-646-4137, E-Mail: mammone@bergen.com; *Librn*, Paul Wilder; E-Mail: wilder@bergen.com. Subject Specialists: *Photos*, David Mammone; Staff 10 (MLS 2, Non-MLS 8)
Library Holdings: Bk Titles 5,000; Per Subs 150
Special Collections: The Record clippings from 1960-1986
Database Vendor: Dialog, GaleNet, Lexis-Nexis
Restriction: Not open to public
Function: Newspaper reference library
Partic in Highlands Regional Library Cooperative
Open Mon-Thurs 7-12, Fri 7-7, Sun 2-10

M HACKENSACK UNIVERSITY MEDICAL CENTER LIBRARY,* 30 Prospect Ave, 07601. SAN 310-1916. Tel: 201-996-2326. FAX: 201-996-2467. *Librn*, Duressa Pujat
Library Holdings: Bk Titles 3,500; Per Subs 312
Special Collections: History Coll
Partic in Bergen Passaic Health Sciences Library Consortium; Health Sciences Library Association Of New Jersey

P JOHNSON FREE PUBLIC LIBRARY,* 274 Main St, 07601-5797. SAN 350-7637. Tel: 201-343-4169. Reference Tel: 201-343-4781. FAX: 201-343-1395. *Dir*, Maureen Taffe; *Asst Dir*, Corey Faver; *ILL*, Elma W Hall; *Ch Servs*, Marilyn Olson; *Ref*, Valerie Clark; *Circ*, Isaac Annan; *Per*, Deborah Bock; *Govt Doc*, Sunil D Mehta. Subject Specialists: *Music*, Marceil Jackson; Staff 12 (MLS 12)
Founded 1901. Pop 37,049; Circ 135,108
Library Holdings: Bk Vols 157,853; Per Subs 488
Subject Interests: Art, Careers, Law, Music
Special Collections: Bergen County Historical Society Coll; New Jersey History Coll, bks, microfilm, per, pictures
Member Libraries: Edgewater Free Public Library; Garfield Free Public Library

HACKETTSTOWN

C CENTENARY COLLEGE, Taylor Memorial Learning Resource Center, 400 Jefferson St, 07840. SAN 310-1932. Tel: 908-852-1400, Ext 2345. FAX: 908-850-9528. *Dir*, Nancy Madacsi; *Asst Dir*, Jane Endrizzi; *Acq*, Susan Nicol; *Tech Servs*, Maryanne Fegan; Staff 8 (MLS 3, Non-MLS 5)
Founded 1867. Enrl 580; Fac 37
Library Holdings: Bk Vols 73,000; Bk Titles 69,300; Per Subs 254
Subject Interests: Interior design
Special Collections: Centenary College Historical Coll; Lancey Coll on Lincoln
Publications: Acquisitions List; Bibliographies; Guides; Handbook for the Taylor Memorial LRC
Partic in Dialog Corporation; NW NJ Regional Libr Coop; OCLC Online Computer Library Center, Inc

M HACKETTSTOWN COMMUNITY HOSPITAL, Medical Staff Library,* 651 Willow Grove St, 07840. SAN 373-2479. Tel: 908-852-7743. FAX: 908-850-6815. *Librn*, Margaret Gesuale
Library Holdings: Bk Vols 1,300; Per Subs 50

P HACKETTSTOWN FREE PUBLIC LIBRARY, 110 Church St, 07840. SAN 310-1940. Tel: 908-852-4936. FAX: 908-852-7850. E-Mail: hfplinfo@goes.com. Web Site: www.goes.com/hfplinfo. *Dir*, J Rona Mosler; Staff 5 (MLS 1, Non-MLS 4)
Founded 1913. Pop 8,120; Circ 49,808
Jan 2000-Dec 2000 Income $256,481, State $8,717, City $234,939, Locally Generated Income $12,825. Mats Exp $25,125, Books $17,435, Per/Ser (Incl. Access Fees) $4,200, AV Equip $3,490. Sal $165,044 (Prof $53,000)
Library Holdings: Bk Vols 33,403; Bk Titles 33,124; Per Subs 66
Subject Interests: Local history
Automation Activity & Vendor Info: (Circulation) epixtech, inc.; (OPAC) epixtech, inc.
Partic in Highlands Regional Library Cooperative; New Jersey Library Network

HADDON HEIGHTS

S CHI RESEARCH LIBRARY, 10 White Horse Pike, 08035. SAN 325-7568. Tel: 856-546-0600. FAX: 856-546-9633. E-Mail: info@chiresearch.com. Web Site: www.chiresearch.com.
Library Holdings: Bk Vols 1,000
Subject Interests: Patents

P HADDON HEIGHTS PUBLIC LIBRARY,* 608 Station Ave, PO Box 240, 08035. SAN 310-1959. Tel: 856-547-7132. FAX: 856-547-2867. *Dir*, Robert J Hunter; *Ch Servs, ILL*, Kathleen Bernardi; *Tech Servs*, Lynne Clarke
Founded 1902. Pop 8,500; Circ 42,000
1997-1998 Income $195,000. Mats Exp $27,000
Library Holdings: Bk Vols 46,000; Bk Titles 43,500; Per Subs 91
Subject Interests: Drama, Local history

HADDONFIELD

S ARCHER & GREINER LIBRARY, One Centennial Sq, 08033-0968. SAN 325-7681. Tel: 856-795-2121. FAX: 856-795-0574. *Librn*, Elizabeth Olson; E-Mail: lolson@archerlaw.com; Staff 4 (MLS 1, Non-MLS 3)
Library Holdings: Bk Vols 12,000
Subject Interests: Law

P HADDONFIELD PUBLIC LIBRARY, 60 Haddon Ave, 08033-2422. SAN 310-1975. Tel: 856-429-1304. FAX: 856-429-3760. Web Site: haddonfield.lib.nj.us. *Dir*, Douglas B Rauschenberger; E-Mail: dbr@camden.lib.nj.us; *Tech Servs*, Anne Frontino; *Ref*, Jo-Ann Pure; E-Mail: jkp@camden.lib.nj.us; *Ch Servs*, Dorothy Peppard; *Circ*, Nancy Baash-Schweizer; E-Mail: nbaasc@camden.lib.nj.us; Staff 12 (MLS 4, Non-MLS 8)
Founded 1803. Pop 11,628; Circ 160,800
Jan 2000-Dec 2000 Income $714,979, State $14,979, City $685,000, Locally Generated Income $15,000. Mats Exp $103,090, Books $75,250, Per/Ser (Incl. Access Fees) $14,225, Electronic Ref Mat (Incl. Access Fees) $4,500. Sal $465,800 (Prof $244,633)
Library Holdings: Bk Vols 71,000; Bk Titles 63,000; Per Subs 204
Subject Interests: Local history
Automation Activity & Vendor Info: (Cataloging) Gaylord; (Circulation) Gaylord; (OPAC) Gaylord
Database Vendor: Ebsco - EbscoHost, GaleNet
Friends of the Library Group

S HISTORICAL SOCIETY OF HADDONFIELD LIBRARY, 343 King's Hwy E, 08033. SAN 325-7703. Tel: 856-429-7375. E-Mail: hadhistlib@aol.com. *Librn*, Kathy Mansfield Tassini; Tel: 856-429-2462. Subject Specialists: *Local history*, Kathy Mansfield Tassini; Staff 1 (MLS 1)
Founded 1914
2000-2001 Mats Exp Presv $4,000
Library Holdings: Bk Vols 750; Bk Titles 500
Subject Interests: Local history
Special Collections: Family Papers including Gill, Hinchman, Hopkins, Rowand, Rhoads, Tatem-Moore-Brigham, and Cuthbert-Ogden
Restriction: Non-circulating to the public
Function: Archival collection

S KC PUBLISHING INC, 51 Kings Hwy W, 08033-2114. SAN 373-4641. Tel: 856-354-5034. Toll Free Tel: 800-878-7855. FAX: 856-354-5147. E-Mail: kcpublishing@earthlink.net. Web Site: www.flowerandgardenmag.com. *In Charge*, Carol A Prebich
Subject Interests: Gardening, Horticulture
Special Collections: Published Periodicals (past issues)
Publications: Flower & Garden Magazine

HALEDON

P HALEDON FREE PUBLIC LIBRARY, 404 Morrissee Ave, 07508-1396. SAN 310-1991. Tel: 973-790-3808. FAX: 973-790-7662. E-Mail: sulc@exchg1.palsplus.org. *Dir*, Linda T Sulc; Staff 5 (Non-MLS 5)
Founded 1958. Pop 7,000; Circ 28,000
Jan 2000-Dec 2000 Income $140,000, State $9,000, City $110,000, Locally Generated Income $9,000. Mats Exp $25,500, Books $21,000, Per/Ser (Incl. Access Fees) $3,500, Electronic Ref Mat (Incl. Access Fees) $1,000. Sal $70,000 (Prof $39,000)
Library Holdings: Bk Vols 20,000; Bk Titles 19,000; Per Subs 65
Automation Activity & Vendor Info: (Cataloging) Brodart; (Circulation) Brodart
Database Vendor: Ebsco - EbscoHost
Mem of Passaic County Libr Syst
Partic in Cross County Libr Consortium; Highlands Regional Library Cooperative

HAMILTON

S ROBERT WOOD JOHNSON UNIVERSITY HOSPITAL AT HAMILTON, Medical Library,* One Hamilton Health Pl, 08690-3599. SAN 327-845X. Tel: 609-584-6473. FAX: 609-586-6419. *Librn*, Ahnde Lin; E-Mail: alin@pluto.njcc.com
Library Holdings: Bk Vols 445
Subject Interests: Medicine, Nursing

P TOWNSHIP OF HAMILTON FREE PUBLIC LIBRARY,* One Municipal Dr, 08619-3895. SAN 351-4862. Tel: 609-581-4060. FAX: 609-581-4067. E-Mail: hamiltonlib@hslc.org. *Dir*, Frank Coleman; *ILL, Per, Ref*, Sally Chen; *Ch Servs*, Susan Brozena; *Tech Servs*, Brenda Eberst; *Ref*, Linda Cardaciotto; Staff 9 (MLS 9)
Founded 1923. Pop 87,375
Jan 1998-Dec 1998 Income $2,720,896, State $111,491, City $1,769,735, Locally Generated Income $128,229, Other $711,441. Mats Exp $304,968, Books $228,692, Per/Ser (Incl. Access Fees) $26,924, Presv $3,818, AV Equip $19,969, Electronic Ref Mat (Incl. Access Fees) $25,565. Sal $1,179,783
Library Holdings: Bk Vols 251,000; Per Subs 414
Subject Interests: Local history
Automation Activity & Vendor Info: (Acquisitions) DRA; (Acquisitions) Inlex; (Cataloging) DRA; (Cataloging) Inlex; (Circulation) DRA; (Circulation) Inlex; (OPAC) DRA; (OPAC) Inlex
Database Vendor: OCLC - First Search
Mem of Central Jersey Regional Libr Coop
Partic in OCLC Online Computer Library Center, Inc; PALINET & Union Library Catalogue of Pennsylvania
Special Services for the Deaf - Books on deafness & sign language; High interest/low vocabulary books; Staff with knowledge of sign language; TTY machine
Adult Basic Reading Program
Friends of the Library Group

HAMMONTON

M WILLIAM B KESSLER MEMORIAL HOSPITAL, Medical Staff Library,* 600 S White Horse Pike, 08037. SAN 377-3051. Tel: 609-561-6700. FAX: 609-567-3942.
Library Holdings: Bk Titles 200

HANCOCKS BRIDGE

S PUBLIC SERVICE ELECTRIC & GAS COMPANY, Nuclear Information Resource Center, Nuclear Admin Bldg, End of Alloyway Creek Neck Rd, 08038. (Mail add: PSE&G Nuclear IRC N02, PO Box 236, 08038), Tel: 856-339-1135. FAX: 856-339-1136. E-Mail: virginia.swichel@pseg.com. *Info Res, Mgr*, Virginia L Swichel; Staff 4 (MLS 2, Non-MLS 2)
Founded 1983
Library Holdings: Bk Vols 20,000; Per Subs 80
Subject Interests: Nuclear
Database Vendor: Dialog, Lexis-Nexis
Restriction: Not open to public
Partic in OCLC, Inc through Palinet; South Jersey Regional Library Cooperative

HARRINGTON PARK

P HARRINGTON PARK PUBLIC LIBRARY,* 10 Herring St, 07640. SAN 310-2017. Tel: 201-768-5675. FAX: 201-768-7495. *Librn*, Judith Heldman
Founded 1964. Pop 5,000; Circ 25,251
Library Holdings: Bk Vols 23,000; Per Subs 63
Mem of Bergen County Co-op Libr Syst
Friends of the Library Group

HARRISON

S CASSIDY CATALOGUING SERVICES, INC, 111 Frank E Rodgers Blvd S, 07029. SAN 323-7079. Tel: 973-481-0900. FAX: 973-481-9110. Web Site: www.cassidycat.com. *Pres, Tech Servs*, Joni L Cassidy; E-Mail: joni@cassidycat.com; *VPres*, Michael J Cassidy; Staff 9 (MLS 9)
Founded 1985
Subject Interests: Law, Technology

P HARRISON PUBLIC LIBRARY, 415 Harrison Ave, 07029. SAN 310-2025. Tel: 973-483-2366. FAX: 973-483-1052. *Dir*, Ellen Lucas; E-Mail: elucas@harrison.k12.nj.us
Founded 1911. Circ 70,000
Library Holdings: Bk Vols 40,000; Per Subs 70
Automation Activity & Vendor Info: (Cataloging) CASPR; (Circulation) CASPR; (OPAC) CASPR
Mem of Essex-Hudson Regional Libr Coop
Partic in New Jersey Library Network

HASBROUCK HEIGHTS

S FREE PUBLIC LIBRARY OF HASBROUCK HEIGHTS,* 301 Division Ave, 07604. SAN 310-2033. Tel: 201-288-0488. FAX: 201-288-6653. E-Mail: hash1@bccls.org, maiullo@bccls.org. Web Site: www.bccls.org. *Dir*, Michele Maiullo; *Ch Servs*, Rosalie Nickles; Staff 5 (MLS 5)
Founded 1916. Pop 11,527; Circ 101,143
Library Holdings: Bk Vols 49,303; Bk Titles 45,834; Per Subs 137
Subject Interests: Local history
Publications: Hasbrouck Heights: A History
Partic in Bergen County Cooperative Library System
Friends of the Library Group

HAWORTH

P HAWORTH MUNICIPAL LIBRARY, 300 Haworth Ave, 07641. SAN 310-2041. Tel: 201-384-1020. FAX: 201-385-7750. Web Site: www.bccls.org/haworth. *Dir*, Elizabeth Rosenberg; E-Mail: rosenberg@bccls.org
Circ 36,663
Library Holdings: Bk Vols 28,146; Per Subs 85
Subject Interests: Local history
Automation Activity & Vendor Info: (Circulation) DRA
Mem of Regional Libr Coop Region 2
Friends of the Library Group

HAWTHORNE

P LOUIS BAY 2ND LIBRARY & COMMUNITY CENTER, Hawthorne Public Library, 345 Lafayette Ave, 07506-2599. SAN 310-205X. Tel: 973-427-5745. FAX: 973-427-5269. Web Site: www.bccls.org/hawthorne. *Dir*, Andrew M Wentink; Tel: 973-427-5745, Ext 102, E-Mail: andy@bccls.org; *Tech Servs*, Joanne Van Lenten; Tel: 973-427-5745, Ext 108, E-Mail: vanlenten@bccls.org; *Ad Servs*, Kathleen Lehmann; Tel: 973-427-5745, Ext 107; *Ref Servs YA*, Jean Begue; Tel: 973-427-5745, Ext 101; *Ch Servs*, Wendy Hollis; Tel: 973-427-5745, Ext 104; *Circ*, Marilyn Rees; Tel: 973-427-5745, Ext 106; *Commun Relations*, Clara Caldarone; Tel: 973-427-5745, Ext 113; *Coordr*, Diane Brown; Tel: 973-427-5745, Ext 100; *Coordr*, Janice Judge; Tel: 973-427-5745, Ext 100; Staff 25 (MLS 3, Non-MLS 22)
Founded 1913. Pop 18,000; Circ 191,132
Jan 1999-Dec 1999 Income $717,624, State $22,000, City $680,524, Locally Generated Income $15,100. Mats Exp $95,250, Books $59,000, Per/Ser (Incl. Access Fees) $8,000, Presv $1,250, AV Equip $12,500, Electronic Ref Mat (Incl. Access Fees) $14,500. Sal $450,524 (Prof $126,386)
Library Holdings: Bk Vols 80,000; Per Subs 194; High Interest/Low Vocabulary Bk Vols 250; Spec Interest Per Sub 15; Bks on Deafness & Sign Lang 115
Subject Interests: Cinema, History, Quilting
Special Collections: Deafness & Sign Language; Early Childhood & Parenting; Hawthorne & Passaic County Local History; Literacy; Seniors; Video
Automation Activity & Vendor Info: (Cataloging) DRA; (Circulation) DRA; (OPAC) DRA
Database Vendor: DRA, IAC - Info Trac, IAC - SearchBank, ProQuest
Function: ILL available
Mem of Bergen County Co-op Libr Syst; Passaic County Libr Syst
Partic in Bergen County Cooperative Library System; Highlands Regional Library Cooperative
Friends of the Library Group

HEWITT

S CITIZEN'S ENERGY COUNCIL LIBRARY, PO Box U, 07421. SAN 375-7986. Tel: 973-728-7835. FAX: 973-728-7664. *Dir*, Karin Westdyk
Library Holdings: Bk Titles 420
Special Collections: Larry Bogart Archives
Friends of the Library Group

S NATIONAL INSTITUTE FOR REHABILITATION ENGINEERING, Engineering Library, PO Box T, 07421. SAN 326-4947. Tel: 973-853-6585. Toll Free Tel: 800-736-2216. E-Mail: nire@theoffice.net. Web Site: www.theoffice.net/nire. *Librn*, Donald Selwyn
Library Holdings: Bk Vols 2,500; Per Subs 75
Special Services for the Blind - Adapted computers & special software with speech output to assist learning disabled, mentally retarded & uneducated; Low vision aids & talking readers; Low-cost screen magnifier software utilities for PCs
Special Services - Bookstands & page turning machine for the paralyzed, cerebral palsied & dexterity impaired

HIGH BRIDGE

P HIGH BRIDGE PUBLIC LIBRARY,* 71 Main St, 08829. SAN 310-2068. Tel: 908-638-8231. E-Mail: hbplib@eclipse.net. *Librn*, Judith Garey
Founded 1914. Pop 4,000; Circ 10,304
Library Holdings: Bk Vols 12,056; Per Subs 30
Mem of Hunterdon County Library

HIGHLAND PARK

P HIGHLAND PARK PUBLIC LIBRARY, 31 N Fifth Ave, 08904. SAN 310-2076. Tel: 732-572-2750. FAX: 732-819-9046. Web Site: www.hppl.nj.org. *Dir*, Jane Stanley; *Ch Servs*, Frances Lee; *Ref*, Jeanne Gallo; *Automation Syst Coordr*, Margaret Auguste; Staff 4 (MLS 4)
Founded 1922. Pop 13,396; Circ 169,259
2000-2000 Income $704,540, State $15,817, City $645,695, Locally Generated Income $26,163, Other $16,865. Mats Exp $118,324, Books $87,824, Per/Ser (Incl. Access Fees) $6,500, Micro $6,000, Electronic Ref Mat (Incl. Access Fees) $18,000. Sal $382,000 (Prof $202,240)
Library Holdings: Bk Vols 56,169; Per Subs 168
Subject Interests: Drama
Database Vendor: epixtech, inc.
Publications: Directory of Community Organizations; flyers
Friends of the Library Group

HIGHLANDS

G NOAA, NATIONAL MARINE FISHERIES SERVICE, Lionel A Walford Library, Northeast Fisheries Science Ctr, 74 McGruder Rd, 07732. SAN 310-2084. Tel: 732-872-3034, 732-872-3035. FAX: 732-872-3088. Web Site: www.sh.nmfs.gov. *Librn*, Claire Steimle; *Tech Servs*, Judith D Berrien
Library Holdings: Bk Titles 4,000; Per Subs 72
Subject Interests: Biology, Chemistry, Environmental studies, Oceanography
Special Collections: NJ Sea Grant Coll
Database Vendor: OCLC - First Search
Publications: Annual staff publications list
Partic in Fedlink; OCLC Online Computer Library Center, Inc

HIGHTSTOWN

S DAVIS CONSULTANTS LIBRARY,* 179 Voelbel Rd, 08520. SAN 370-2049. Tel: 609-448-0161. *Dir*, W F Davis
Subject Interests: Engineering, History
Restriction: Not open to public

HILLSBOROUGH

S DEPARTMENT OF HUMAN SERVICES REGIONAL SCHOOL, Somerset Campus Library, 1600 Brooks Blvd, 08844. SAN 375-8486. Tel: 908-704-3060. FAX: 908-704-3067.
Library Holdings: Bk Vols 100

HILLSDALE

P HILLSDALE FREE PUBLIC LIBRARY,* 509 Hillsdale Ave, 07642. SAN 310-2106. Tel: 201-358-5072. FAX: 201-358-5074. *Dir*, Jean M Scott; E-Mail: jscott@bccls.org; *Ref*, Rita Browning; Staff 5 (MLS 3, Non-MLS 2)
Founded 1935. Pop 10,222; Circ 92,000
Library Holdings: Bk Vols 55,742; Per Subs 150
Subject Interests: Fiction, Literary criticism, Literature
Mem of Region 2 Bergen-Passaic Counties
Partic in Bergen County Computer Consortium
Friends of the Library Group

HILLSIDE

S BRISTOL-MYERS PRODUCTS, Strategic Information & Analysis Center, 1350 Liberty Ave, 07205. SAN 310-2114. Tel: 908-851-6235. FAX: 908-851-6073. *Dir*, Ann C Swist
Founded 1946
Library Holdings: Bk Titles 9,000; Per Subs 225
Subject Interests: Medicine, Microbiology, Pharmaceutical science, Pharmacology
Restriction: Company library
Partic in Dialog Corporation; Nat Libr of Med; PALINET & Union Library Catalogue of Pennsylvania

P HILLSIDE FREE PUBLIC LIBRARY,* John F Kennedy Plaza, 07205-1893. SAN 310-2122. Tel: 973-923-4413. FAX: 973-923-0506. *Dir*, Eugene Krautblatt; *Ch Servs*, Joyce Goldberg; *Ref*, Susan Lipstein; Staff 19 (MLS 4, Non-MLS 15)
Founded 1947. Pop 21,800
Library Holdings: Bk Vols 95,871; Per Subs 150
Mem of Linx
Friends of the Library Group

HOBOKEN

P HOBOKEN PUBLIC LIBRARY, 500 Park Ave, 07030. SAN 310-2157. Tel: 201-420-2346. Interlibrary Loan Service Tel: 201-420-2280. Circulation Tel: 201-420-2280. Reference Tel: 201-420-2347. FAX: 201-420-2299. E-Mail: hobk1@bccls.org. Web Site: www.bccls.org/hoboken. *Ad Servs*, Rosary Van Ingen; *Ch Servs*, Rosalie Brereton; Staff 19 (MLS 4, Non-MLS 15)
Founded 1890. Pop 33,363; Circ 56,466
1999-2000 Income $821,400, State $28,000, City $793,400. Mats Exp $104,500, Books $75,000, Per/Ser (Incl. Access Fees) $12,000, Presv $4,000, AV Equip $3,500, Electronic Ref Mat (Incl. Access Fees) $10,000. Sal $525,265 (Prof $211,745)
Library Holdings: Bk Vols 121,015; Bk Titles 55,366; Per Subs 166
Special Collections: Hoboken History Coll
Automation Activity & Vendor Info: (Circulation) DRA; (ILL) DRA
Database Vendor: DRA
Function: ILL available
Partic in Bergen County Cooperative Library System; Infolink
Friends of the Library Group

M SAINT MARY HOSPITAL, Medical Library, 308 Willow Ave, 07030. SAN 375-8443. Tel: 201-418-1075. FAX: 201-418-1078. *Librn*, Modesta M Piedra; *Mgr Libr Serv*, Michelle Harmon; E-Mail: mharmon@fhsnj.org; Staff 1 (MLS 1)
Library Holdings: Bk Vols 800
Automation Activity & Vendor Info: (OPAC) Inmagic, Inc.
Database Vendor: Ebsco - EbscoHost
Restriction: Medical staff only
Function: ILL to other special libraries

C STEVENS INSTITUTE OF TECHNOLOGY, Samuel C Williams Library, Castle Point on Hudson, 07030. SAN 310-2165. Tel: 201-216-5200. Interlibrary Loan Service Tel: 201-216-5420. Circulation Tel: 201-216-5327. Reference Tel: 201-216-5419. FAX: 201-216-8319. Web Site: www.lib.stevens-tech.edu. *Dir*, Richard P Widdicombe; E-Mail: rpw@stevens-tech.edu; *Dep Dir*, Ourida Oubraham; E-Mail: oubraha@stevens-tech.edu; *Circ*, John Cruz; *ILL*, Leah Kaufman; *ILL*, Carol Perkins; *Asst Curator*, Nydia Cruz; *Tech Servs*, Lisa Cacciola; Tel: 201-216-5382; *Distance Educ*, Lesley Butler; Tel: 201-216-8297; *Ref*, Linda Scanlon; *Ref*, Scott Smith; Tel: 201-216-5412; Staff 8 (MLS 4, Non-MLS 4)
Founded 1870. Highest Degree: Doctorate
Jul 1999-Jun 2000 Income $931,339. Mats Exp $235,154, Books $73,100, Per/Ser (Incl. Access Fees) $29,633, Micro $5,678, Electronic Ref Mat (Incl. Access Fees) $126,743. Sal $539,340 (Prof $289,603)
Library Holdings: Bk Vols 111,607; Bk Titles 59,489; Per Subs 138
Subject Interests: Applied sci, Engineering, Natural science
Special Collections: Art (Leonardo da Vinci Coll), bks, drawings, micro; History (Stevens Family Archives), bks, micro; Industrial Management (Frederick Winslow Taylor Coll), bks, micro
Automation Activity & Vendor Info: (Cataloging) SIRSI; (Circulation) SIRSI; (Course Reserve) SIRSI; (OPAC) SIRSI; (Serials) SIRSI
Partic in Metro NY Libr Coun; OCLC Online Computer Library Center, Inc
Friends of the Library Group

HO-HO-KUS

P WORTH PINKHAM MEMORIAL LIBRARY,* 91 Warren Ave, 07423. SAN 310-2130. Tel: 201-445-8078. E-Mail: hoho1@bccls.org. *Dir*, Mildred Thurklsen
Founded 1938. Pop 4,358; Circ 21,609
Library Holdings: Bk Vols 27,000; Per Subs 60
Partic in Bergen County Cooperative Library System; Dialog Corporation; New Jersey Academic Library Network

HOLMDEL

M BAYSHORE COMMUNITY HOSPITAL, Medical Library, 727 N Beers St, 07733. SAN 376-0596. Tel: 732-888-7377. FAX: 732-888-7330.
Library Holdings: Bk Vols 240; Per Subs 50
Open Mon-Fri 9:30-4:00

HOPEWELL

S HOPEWELL MUSEUM LIBRARY,* 28 E Broad St, 08525. SAN 373-2487. Tel: 609-466-0103. *Curator*, Beverly Weidl
Library Holdings: Bk Vols 200

P HOPEWELL PUBLIC LIBRARY, 13 E Broad St, 08525. SAN 310-2203. Tel: 609-466-1625. *Dir*, Beth Miko; E-Mail: bmiko@njstatelib.org; *Asst Librn*, Barbara Orr; *Asst Librn*, Linda Wood; *Ch Servs*, Janet Payne
Circ 17,500
Library Holdings: Bk Titles 20,000; Per Subs 48
Mem of Trenton Area Libr Syst
Friends of the Library Group

HURFFVILLE

P MARGARET E HEGGAN FREE PUBLIC LIBRARY OF THE TOWNSHIP OF WASHINGTON, 208 E Holly Ave, 08080. SAN 310-5555. Tel: 856-589-3334. FAX: 856-582-2042. E-Mail: meheggan lib@gloucester.lib.nj.us. Web Site: www.snj.com/mhlibrary. *Dir*, Linda H Snyder; *Coll Develop*, T R Salvadori; *Ch Servs*, Theresa Doyle; *Ref*, Linda Rogers. Subject Specialists: *Soc and behav sci*, Theresa Doyle
Founded 1965. Pop 45,262; Circ 238,295
Jan 2000-Dec 2000 Income $848,697, State $45,044, Locally Generated Income $743,153, Other $60,500. Mats Exp $156,539, Books $121,325, Per/Ser (Incl. Access Fees) $5,175, Micro $8,500, Electronic Ref Mat (Incl. Access Fees) $21,539. Sal $363,622
Library Holdings: Bk Vols 65,655; Per Subs 124
Subject Interests: New Jersey
Automation Activity & Vendor Info: (Cataloging) TLC; (Circulation) Sagebrush Corporation
Partic in South Jersey Regional Library Cooperative
Friends of the Library Group

IRVINGTON

P IRVINGTON PUBLIC LIBRARY, Civic Sq, 07111-2498. SAN 350-7785. Tel: 973-372-6400. FAX: 973-372-6860. Web Site: ipl@nplhub.org. *Ref*, Joan Weiss; *Dir*, Allan Kleiman; Staff 31 (MLS 7, Non-MLS 24)
Founded 1914. Pop 61,018; Circ 73,242
Library Holdings: Bk Vols 203,062; Per Subs 160
Special Collections: Adult Literacy; Local History & Photographs
Partic in Infolink Eastern New Jersey Regional Library Cooperative, Inc

ISELIN

S ENGELHARD CORP, Technical Information Center, 101 Wood Ave S, 08830. SAN 310-1274. Tel: 732-205-5271. FAX: 732-205-6900. *Mgr*, Maurica Fedors; E-Mail: maurica.fedors@engelhard.com; *Info Specialist*, Arda Agulian; E-Mail: arda.agulian@engelhard.com
Library Holdings: Bk Titles 40,000
Subject Interests: Clay products, Incl refining, Indust applications, Koalin

products, Mineral separation, Ores, Properties
Special Collections: Nonmetallic Minerals, Raolin, & Clays; Precious Metals
Automation Activity & Vendor Info: (Cataloging) EOS; (Circulation) EOS

L GREENBAUM, ROWE, SMITH, RAVIN, DAVIS & HIMMEL LLP, Law Library,* 99 Wood Ave S, 08830. SAN 323-6684. Tel: 732-549-5600. FAX: 732-549-1881. *Librn*, Leigh DeProspo; *Asst Librn*, Carolyn Rogers; *Asst Librn*, Kathy Bruno; Staff 4 (MLS 1, Non-MLS 3)
Library Holdings: Bk Vols 13,000
Subject Interests: Real estate
Partic in Westlaw

JAMESBURG

P JAMESBURG PUBLIC LIBRARY,* 229 Gatzmer Ave, 08831. SAN 310-222X. Tel: 732-521-0440. FAX: 732-521-6136. Web Site: www.lmxac.org/jamesburgpl. *Dir*, C Yasher; *Librn*, Andrea Wellet; *Librn*, Marlene Bilcik
Founded 1930. Pop 5,200; Circ 20,000
Jan 1997-Dec 1998 Income $93,000, State $10,000, City $75,000, Other $8,000. Mats Exp $13,452, Books $10,257, Per/Ser (Incl. Access Fees) $2,000
Library Holdings: Bk Vols 18,000; Per Subs 58
Partic in Infolink Eastern New Jersey Regional Library Cooperative, Inc; Librs of Middlesex
Open Mon, Wed & Thurs 10-8:30; Tues & Fri 10-5; Sat 10-3
Friends of the Library Group

JERSEY CITY

S BLOCK DRUG COMPANY, Research & Development Library, 257 Cornelison Ave, 07302. SAN 310-2238. Tel: 201-434-3000, Ext 1440. Web Site: www.blockdrugco.com.; Staff 2 (MLS 1, Non-MLS 1)
Founded 1960
Library Holdings: Bk Vols 5,000; Per Subs 240
Subject Interests: Dentistry, Dermatology, Medicine, Pharmacology
Special Collections: Neilson Reports Coll; US & Foreign Patents Coll
Automation Activity & Vendor Info: (Serials) EOS
Partic in Data Star; Dialog Corporation; Nat Libr of Med; STN

M CHRIST HOSPITAL, Learning Resource Center Library, 169 Palisade Ave, 07306. SAN 375-6904. Tel: 201-418-7044. FAX: 201-795-8737. *Librn*, Katherine Vargo; Fax: 201-795-8737, E-Mail: kvargo@christhospital.org; Staff 1 (MLS 1)
Library Holdings: Bk Vols 1,100; Per Subs 120
Subject Interests: Nursing
Database Vendor: IAC - SearchBank
Friends of the Library Group

J HUDSON COUNTY COMMUNITY COLLEGE LIBRARY,* 25 Journal Square, 07306-4302. SAN 371-9928. Tel: 201-714-2229. FAX: 201-963-0789. Web Site: www.hudson.cc.nj.us. *Coll Develop, Dir*, Grace Patterson; E-Mail: gpatterson@mail.hudson.cc.nj.us; *Ref*, Ellen Renaud; *Circ*, Sara H Davis; *Per*, Milena Moscoso; *Tech Servs*, Compton Hubbard; *Tech Servs*, Mei Xie; Staff 6 (MLS 3, Non-MLS 3)
Enrl 3,800; Fac 60
Jul 1997-Jun 1998 Income $597,000. Mats Exp $200,000. Sal $275,044
Library Holdings: Bk Titles 20,000; Per Subs 250
Special Collections: ESL Reading Coll, Faculty/Staff Development Coll, HCCC Archives
Automation Activity & Vendor Info: (Circulation) SIRSI
Publications: Audio Visual Technology Services; Electronic Searching; Faculty Facts; How to Find Information; Library Services at Hudson County Community College; Periodical Directory; Term Paper Tips; Video tapes in the Library LRC
Partic in Infolink; OCLC Online Computer Library Center, Inc

GL HUDSON COUNTY LAW LIBRARY,* Hudson County Admin Bldg, 595 Newark Ave, 07306. SAN 310-2246. Tel: 201-795-6629. FAX: 201-795-6603. *Librn*, Theresa Banks
Library Holdings: Bk Vols 19,000

M JERSEY CITY MEDICAL CENTER LIBRARY,* 24 Baldwin Ave, 07304. SAN 373-2495. Tel: 201-915-2000, Ext 3006. FAX: 201-915-2006. *Mgr*, Judith Wilkinson
Library Holdings: Bk Vols 800; Per Subs 180

P JERSEY CITY PUBLIC LIBRARY,* 472 Jersey Ave, 07302-3499. SAN 350-7874. Tel: 201-547-4500. FAX: 201-547-4584. *Dir*, Dennis Hayes; Tel: 201-547-4508, Fax: 201-547-5207; *Chief Librn*, Joan Lovero; *Ch Servs, Coordr*, Aida Claveria; *Doc*, Sharron Tucker; Tel: 201-547-4517
Founded 1889. Pop 223,000; Circ 451,757
1998-1998 Income $6,448,978, State $341,798, City $6,060,000, Federal $47,180. Mats Exp $557,887, Books $427,544, Per/Ser (Incl. Access Fees) $81,197, Electronic Ref Mat (Incl. Access Fees) $49,146. Sal $5,111,695
Library Holdings: Bk Vols 374,616; Bk Titles 243,551; Per Subs 783
Special Collections: New Jersey Coll
Partic in OCLC Online Computer Library Center, Inc
Special Services for the Deaf - Staff with knowledge of sign language
Special Services for the Blind - Kurzweil Reading Machine
Branches: 12
CLAREMONT, 291 Martin Luther King Dr, 07305. SAN 350-7939. Tel: 201-547-4555. *Librn*, Sellisteen Prince-Steward
FIVE CORNERS, 678 Newark Ave, 07306. SAN 350-7963. Tel: 201-547-4543. *Librn*, Spencer Brown
GREENVILLE, 1841 Kennedy Blvd, 07305. SAN 350-7998. Tel: 201-547-4553. *Librn*, Mary Quinn
HUDSON CITY, 14 Zabriskie St, 07307. SAN 350-8021. Tel: 201-547-4556.
LAFAYETTE, 307 Pacific Ave, 07304. SAN 350-8056. Tel: 201-547-5017. *Librn*, Louvenia Best
MARION, 1017 West Side Ave, 07306. SAN 350-8080. Tel: 201-547-4552. *Librn*, Mary Powell
MILLER, 489 Bergen Ave, 07304. SAN 350-8110. Tel: 201-547-4551. *Librn*, Priscilla Gardner
PAVONIA, 326 Eighth St, 07302. SAN 350-8145. Tel: 201-547-4808. *Librn*, Chris Arroyo
PEARSALL, 104 Pearsall Ave, 07305. SAN 350-8153. Tel: 201-547-6557. *Librn*, Rose Barnes
PERFECTO OYOLA BIBLIOTECA & CULTURAL CENTER, 280 First Ave, 07302. SAN 350-7904. Tel: 201-547-4541. *Librn*, Nellie Flores
WATTERS MEDIA ARTS DEPT, 678 Newark Ave, 07306. SAN 329-5737. Tel: 201-547-4546. *Librn*, Kenny Uko
WEST BERGEN, 476 West Side Ave, 07304. SAN 350-817X. Tel: 201-547-4554. *Librn*, Florence Cherico
Bookmobiles: 1

C NEW JERSEY CITY UNIVERSITY, Congressman Frank J Guarini L ibrary, 2039 Kennedy Blvd, 07305-1597. SAN 310-2254. Tel: 201-200-3030. Interlibrary Loan Service Tel: 201-200-2183. Reference Tel: 201-200-3033. FAX: 201-200-2330, 201-200-2331. *Dir*, Grace F Bulaong; Tel: 201-200-3027, E-Mail: gbulaong@njcu.edu; *Assoc Dir*, Roger F Krentz; Tel: 201-200-3042, E-Mail: rkrentz@njcu.edu; *Doc, Per*, Maryann Rentko; Tel: 201-200-3518, E-Mail: mrentko@njcu.edu; *Ref*, Fred Smith; Tel: 201-200-3474, E-Mail: fsmith@njcu.edu; *Cat*, Anne Trattner; Tel: 201-200-2372, E-Mail: atrattner@njcu.edu; *Circ*, Gary Peacock; Tel: 201-200-2211, E-Mail: gpeacock@njcu.edu; Staff 13 (MLS 13)
Founded 1927. Circ 18,264; Enrl 10,000; Fac 240; Highest Degree: Master
Library Holdings: Bk Vols 209,148; Per Subs 1,260
Subject Interests: Art, Education, Fire science, History, Music, Nursing
Special Collections: Anthropology (Human Relations Area Files), fiche; Eric Coll; McCarthy Memorial Coll of Alcohol Literature, fiche
Publications: Guide to the Library
Partic in Dialog Corporation; Infolink Eastern New Jersey Regional Library Cooperative, Inc; New Jersey Academic Library Network

CR O'TOOLE LIBRARY, (Formerly Saint Peter's College Library), 99 Glenwood Ave, 07306. (Mail add: 2641 Kennedy Blvd, 07306), SAN 350-820X. Tel: 201-915-9387. Circulation Tel: 201-915-9396. Reference Tel: 201-915-9392. FAX: 201-432-4117. E-Mail: libdept@spc.edu. Web Site: www.spc.edu/library. *Dir*, Frederick N Nesta; E-Mail: nesta_f@spcvxa.spc.edu; *Head Ref*, Thomas J Kenny; E-Mail: kenny_t@spc.edu; *Head Tech Servs*, David Hardgrove; E-Mail: hardgrove_d@spc.edu; Staff 12 (MLS 11, Non-MLS 1)
Founded 1872. Enrl 3,512; Fac 114; Highest Degree: Master
Jul 2000-Jun 2001 Income (Main Library Only) $1,191,523. Mats Exp $486,670, Books $67,215, Per/Ser (Incl. Access Fees) $254,505, Presv $16,950, Micro $15,000, Other Print Mats $45,000, Manuscripts & Archives $3,000, Electronic Ref Mat (Incl. Access Fees) $85,000. Sal $694,100 (Prof $434,893)
Library Holdings: Bk Vols 228,013; Bk Titles 181,938; Per Subs 1,500
Subject Interests: Biology, Nursing, Philosophy, Theology
Database Vendor: Ebsco - EbscoHost, epixtech, inc., GaleNet, IAC - SearchBank, OCLC - First Search, ProQuest, Silverplatter Information Inc.
Publications: Library Scene
Mem of Essex-Hudson Regional Libr Coop
Partic in Infolink; New York Metrop Ref & Res Libr Agency; PALINET & Union Library Catalogue of Pennsylvania
Friends of the Library Group

S PERSHING & CO, INC, Research Library,* One Pershing Plaza, 07399. SAN 311-9955. Tel: 201-413-2000. FAX: 201-432-7998. *Dir, Res*, Andy Gray
Founded 1957
Library Holdings: Bk Vols 146; Bk Titles 100; Per Subs 26
Subject Interests: Bus, Finance, Mgt
Special Collections: Financial Information (Conference Board Record, Wall Street Journal, National Stock Summary, Moody's; Industrial Manual, Moody's Bank & Finance, Fortune Magazine, Financial Analyst Journal, Arthur D; Little), rpt, micro, bks, mag, mag rpt

S PRICEWATERHOUSECOOPERS LLP, (Formerly Coopers Price Waterhouse National Library), National Library, 101 Hudson St, 25th Flr, 07302. SAN 311-709X. Tel: 201-521-4278. FAX: 201-521-3523. *Mgr*, Kathy Porta

Founded 1959
Library Holdings: Bk Vols 13,000; Per Subs 500
Subject Interests: Accounting, Security docs
Restriction: Not open to public

M SAINT FRANCIS SCHOOL OF NURSING LIBRARY, One McWilliams Pl, 07302. SAN 376-0499. Tel: 201-418-2209. FAX: 201-418-2208. *Mgr Libr Serv*, Michelle Harmon; E-Mail: mharmon@fhsnj.org; Staff 1 (MLS 1)
Library Holdings: Bk Vols 2,000
Automation Activity & Vendor Info: (OPAC) Inmagic, Inc.
Database Vendor: Ebsco - EbscoHost
Restriction: Not open to public
Function: ILL to other special libraries

S SOCIETY OF NAVAL ARCHITECTS & MARINE ENGINEERS LIBRARY, 601 Pavonia Ave, 07306. SAN 375-0744. Tel: 201-798-4800. FAX: 201-798-4975. Web Site: www.sname.org. *Librn*, Alan Rowan; Tel: 201-798-4800, Ext 3031, E-Mail: arowen@sname.org
Library Holdings: Bk Vols 1,000

KEARNY

P KEARNY PUBLIC LIBRARY,* 318 Kearny Ave, 07032. SAN 310-2270. Tel: 201-998-2666. FAX: 201-998-1141. *Dir*, Gail Colure; *Ref*, Nancy Smith; *Ch Servs*, Joanne Friedman
Founded 1906. Pop 34,874
Library Holdings: Bk Vols 70,000; Per Subs 147
Subject Interests: Local history
Partic in Infolink Eastern New Jersey Regional Library Cooperative, Inc
Branches: 1
KEARNY BRANCH, 759 Kearny Ave, 07032. SAN 376-2513. Tel: 201-991-2116. *In Charge*, Deborah Nalbach
Library Holdings: Bk Titles 5,200; Per Subs 15

KENILWORTH

P KENILWORTH PUBLIC LIBRARY,* 548 Boulevard, 07033. SAN 310-2297. Tel: 908-276-2451. FAX: 908-276-7897. *Dir*, Dale Spindel; E-Mail: dale@lmxac.org
Founded 1931. Pop 7,574; Circ 29,996
Jan 1998-Dec 1998 Income $322,807, State $7,231, City $259,513. Mats Exp $26,453, Books $21,598, Per/Ser (Incl. Access Fees) $4,237. Sal $147,021
Library Holdings: Bk Vols 30,000; Per Subs 82
Partic in Infolink Eastern New Jersey Regional Library Cooperative, Inc
Friends of the Library Group

S SCHERING-PLOUGH RESEARCH INSTITUTE, Library Information Center, 2015 Galloping Hill Rd, 07033. SAN 310-2319. Tel: 908-740-7390. FAX: 908-740-7015. *Dir*, Stephen Heiber; Tel: 908-740-7385, E-Mail: stephen.heiber@spcorp.com; *Head Tech Servs*, Monica McKenzie; Tel: 908-740-3591, Fax: 908-740-3592, E-Mail: monica.mckenzie@spcorp.com; *Head Ref*, Allison Warzala; Tel: 908-740-4770, E-Mail: allisonwarzala@spcop.com; *Head, Info Serv*, Barbara Maletz; Tel: 908-740-3594, E-Mail: barbara.maletz@spcorp.com
Founded 1940
Library Holdings: Bk Vols 10,000; Bk Titles 8,000; Per Subs 1,500
Subject Interests: Biology, Chemistry, Medicine, Patents
Special Collections: Scholar-Proprietary Company Product Database
Publications: In the News; New Titles
Restriction: Staff use only
Partic in Dialog Corporation; Infolink Eastern New Jersey Regional Library Cooperative, Inc; OCLC Online Computer Library Center, Inc

KEYPORT

P KEYPORT FREE PUBLIC LIBRARY,* 109 Broad St, 07735-1202. SAN 310-2327. Tel: 732-264-0543. FAX: 732-264-0875. E-Mail: keyportlib@nae.net. *Librn*, Jackie Lapolla
Founded 1914. Pop 7,500; Circ 22,000
1997-1998 Income $196,225, State $5,800, Locally Generated Income $1,375, Other $86,150. Mats Exp $23,480, Books $19,120, Per/Ser (Incl. Access Fees) $2,140, Other Print Mats $1,300. Sal $46,608
Library Holdings: Bk Vols 54,000; Per Subs 80
Special Collections: War of the Rebellion: A Compilation of the Official Records of the Union & Confederate Armies

KINNELON

P KINNELON PUBLIC LIBRARY,* 132 Kinnelon Rd, 07405-2393. SAN 310-2335. Tel: 973-838-1321. FAX: 973-838-0741. *Dir*, Roslyn Pelcyger; *Tech Servs*, Barbara Owens; E-Mail: owens@main.morris.org; *Ref*, Mary Ann O'Goorman; *AV*, Carol Gordon; E-Mail: gordon@main.morris.org; *Ch Servs*, Ann Job; E-Mail: job@main.morris.org; *Circ*, Kate Wolthoff; E-Mail: wolthoff@main.morris.org; Staff 11 (MLS 2, Non-MLS 9)
Founded 1962. Pop 8,500; Circ 89,000
Jan 2000-Dec 2000 Income $421,000, State $11,000, City $400,000, Other $10,000
Library Holdings: Bk Vols 66,000; Bk Titles 55,000; Per Subs 150
Automation Activity & Vendor Info: (Cataloging) DRA; (Circulation) DRA; (OPAC) DRA
Database Vendor: DRA, Ebsco - EbscoHost, GaleNet, ProQuest, Wilson - Wilson Web
Publications: Bookmarks (bi-monthly newsletter); Kinnelon Service Directory
Partic in Morris Automated Information Network; Northwest Regional Union Libr Syst
Closed through January 2001
Friends of the Library Group

LAKEHURST

UNITED STATES NAVY
A NAVAL AIR WARFARE CENTER, AIR CRAFT DIVISION TECHNICAL LIBRARY, Code 7244 Mail Stop 149-3, 08733-5042. SAN 350-8234. Tel: 732-323-2893. FAX: 732-323-1965.
Founded 1917
Library Holdings: Bk Titles 7,500; Per Subs 75
Subject Interests: Cryogenics

LAKEWOOD

CR GEORGIAN COURT COLLEGE, (Formerly S Mary Joseph Cunningham Library), S Mary Joseph Cunningham Library, 900 Lakewood Ave, 08701-2697. SAN 310-2351. Tel: 732-364-2200, Ext 419. Reference Tel: 732-364-2200, Ext 422. FAX: 732-364-2215. Interlibrary Loan Service FAX: 732-364-2200, Ext 480. Web Site: www.georgian.edu/library/library.htm. *Dir*, Barbara J Hutchinson; Tel: 732-364-2200, Ext 421, E-Mail: bhutchinson@georgian.edu; *Librn*, Laura Gewissler; Tel: 732-364-2200, Ext 431, E-Mail: gewissler@georgian.edu; *Librn*, Barbara Herbert; Tel: 732-364-2200, Ext 428, E-Mail: herbert@georgian.edu; *Librn*, Mary Meola; Tel: 732-364-2200, Ext 427, E-Mail: mmeola@georigian.edu; *Librn*, Sister Barbara Williams; Tel: 732-364-2200, Ext 426; *Info Tech*, Pamela Dong; Tel: 732-364-2200, Ext 429, E-Mail: pdong@georgian.edu; *Tech Servs*, Reya Maxymuk; Tel: 732-364-2200, Ext 435. Subject Specialists: *Behavior sci*, Barbara Herbert; *Humanities*, Mary Meola; *Mathematics*, Sister Barbara Williams; *Science*, Sister Barbara Williams; *Social sciences*, Laura Gewissler; Staff 7 (MLS 7)
Founded 1908. Enrl 2,409; Fac 182; Highest Degree: Master
Jul 1999-Jun 2000 Income $1,168,738. Mats Exp $530,930, Books $133,943, Per/Ser (Incl. Access Fees) $225,893, Presv $5,932, Micro $3,973, AV Equip $8,429, Electronic Ref Mat (Incl. Access Fees) $53,459. Sal $597,168 (Prof $326,140)
Library Holdings: Bk Vols 109,823; Bk Titles 104,352; Per Subs 1,430
Subject Interests: Education, Religious studies
Special Collections: Georgian Court College Archives
Automation Activity & Vendor Info: (Acquisitions) SIRSI; (Cataloging) SIRSI; (Circulation) SIRSI; (Course Reserve) SIRSI; (OPAC) SIRSI; (Serials) SIRSI
Database Vendor: Lexis-Nexis, OCLC - First Search, Silverplatter Information Inc., Wilson - Wilson Web
Publications: LibraryLines (Newsletter)
Partic in New Jersey Library Network; OCLC Online Computer Library Center, Inc; PALINET & Union Library Catalogue of Pennsylvania
Friends of the Library Group

M KIMBALL MEDICAL CENTER, Medical Library,* 600 River Ave, 08701. SAN 375-7315. Tel: 732-886-4462. FAX: 732-886-4898. *Librn*, Mary Ann Sandusky
Library Holdings: Bk Vols 488

M WORTHINGTON BIOCHEMICAL CORP LIBRARY,* 730 Vassar Ave, 08701. SAN 375-7455. Tel: 732-942-1660. FAX: 732-942-9270. *Librn*, Nancy Worthington; E-Mail: nancyw@worthington-biochem.com
Library Holdings: Per Subs 20

LAMBERTVILLE

P LAMBERTVILLE FREE PUBLIC LIBRARY, (LFPL), 6 Lilly St, 08530-1805. SAN 310-2378. Tel: 609-397-0275. FAX: 609-397-1784. *Dir*, Helen Kosowski; E-Mail: hkosowski@njstatelib.org; *Ch Servs*, Martha Kubik
Founded 1881. Pop 4,000; Circ 34,000
Jan 2000-Dec 2000 Income $116,000, State $4,000, Provincial $109,000, Locally Generated Income $1,000, Other $2,000. Mats Exp $16,700, Books $15,000, Per/Ser (Incl. Access Fees) $1,700. Sal $66,000
Library Holdings: Bk Vols 12,000; Bk Titles 14,000; Per Subs 70
Subject Interests: Regional hist
Special Collections: Art
Partic in Highlands Regional Library Cooperative

LAWRENCEVILLE

P MERCER COUNTY LIBRARY,* 2751 Brunswick Pike, 08648-4132. SAN 351-4536. Tel: 609-882-9246. Interlibrary Loan Service Tel: 609-989-6923. Reference Tel: 609-989-6922. FAX: 609-538-1208. Web Site: www.mcl.org. *Dir*, Martin P Winar; *Head of Libr*, Richard J Cavallo; Tel: 609-989-6918, Fax: 609-538-1206, E-Mail: rcavallo@mcl.org; *Librn*, Susan Steele; *ILL*, Erlene Jones; *Cat*, Janice Rockmore; *Ref*, Ann Kerr. Subject Specialists: *Finance*, Richard J Cavallo; Staff 47 (MLS 7, Non-MLS 40)
Founded 1929. Pop 130,000; Circ 1,450,000
Jan 1999-Dec 1999 Income (Main Library and Branch Library) $7,813,036, State $135,000, County $7,400,836, Locally Generated Income $277,200. Mats Exp $878,800. Sal $4,296,430
Library Holdings: Bk Titles 359,468; Per Subs 357
Special Collections: New Jersey History; Spanish & Chinese Coll
Database Vendor: epixtech, inc.
Function: Research library
Mem of Central Jersey Regional Libr Coop
Partic in OCLC Online Computer Library Center, Inc; PALINET & Union Library Catalogue of Pennsylvania
Friends of the Library Group
Branches: 9
EWING BRANCH, 61 Scotch Rd, Trenton, 08628. SAN 351-4595. Tel: 609-882-3130. FAX: 609-538-0212. Web Site: www.mcl.org. *Librn*, Jackie Huff
Library Holdings: Bk Vols 103,401
Friends of the Library Group
HICKORY CORNER BRANCH, 138 Hickory Corner Rd, East Windsor, 08520. SAN 351-4560. Tel: 609-448-1330. FAX: 609-490-0189. Web Site: www.mcl.org. *Branch Mgr*, Kathleen Devonshire; *Ref*, Ann Zigrand; *YA Servs*, Carolyn Gishlick; Staff 8 (MLS 3, Non-MLS 5)
Library Holdings: Bk Vols 46,554
Friends of the Library Group
HIGHTSTOWN MEMORIAL, 114 Franklin St, Hightstown, 08520. SAN 351-4625. Tel: 609-448-1474. FAX: 609-490-0279. Web Site: www.mcl.org. *Librn*, Sandra Johnson; Staff 5 (MLS 2, Non-MLS 3)
Library Holdings: Bk Vols 29,916
Friends of the Library Group
HOLLOWBROOK COMMUNITY CENTER, 320 Hollowbrook Dr, 08638. SAN 328-8021. Tel: 609-883-5914. Web Site: www.mcl.org. *Librn*, Sonya Brockington
Library Holdings: Bk Vols 11,832
HOPEWELL TOWNSHIP, Pennington Titusville Rd, Rte 31, Pennington, 08534. SAN 351-4633. Tel: 609-737-2610. FAX: 609-737-7419. Web Site: www.mcl.org. *Librn*, Edward Hoag
Library Holdings: Bk Vols 59,103
Friends of the Library Group
LAWRENCE HEADQUARTERS, 2751 Brunswick Pike, 08648. SAN 351-465X. Tel: 609-989-6920. FAX: 609-538-1208. Web Site: www.mcl.org. *Librn*, Ellen Brown
Library Holdings: Bk Vols 144,891
Friends of the Library Group
TWIN RIVERS BRANCH, 276A Abbington Dr, Twin Rivers, 08520. SAN 351-4684. Tel: 609-443-1880. FAX: 609-490-0186. Web Site: www.mcl.org. *Librn*, Elissa Pearlman
Library Holdings: Bk Vols 50,119
Friends of the Library Group
WASHINGTON, 42 Robbinsville/Allentown Rd, Robbinsville, 08691. SAN 351-4714. Tel: 609-259-2150. FAX: 609-259-1411. Web Site: www.mcl.org. *Librn*, Ruth Greenberg
Library Holdings: Bk Vols 33,752
Friends of the Library Group
WEST WINDSOR, 333 N Post Rd, Princeton Junction, 08550. SAN 351-4749. Tel: 609-799-0462. FAX: 609-936-9511. Web Site: www.mcl.org. *Librn*, Kaija Greenberg
Library Holdings: Bk Vols 82,079
Friends of the Library Group

C RIDER UNIVERSITY, Franklin F Moore Library, 2083 Lawrenceville Rd, 08648-3099. SAN 310-2394. Tel: 609-896-5000, Ext 7222. Reference Tel: 609-896-5115. FAX: 609-896-8029. Web Site: library.rider.edu. *Dean of Libr*, Dr Elizabeth S Smith; Tel: 609-896-5111; *Chair, Coll Develop*, John Buschman; *Librn*, Dorothy Warner; *Librn*, Sharon Young; *Doc Delivery, ILL*, Carol Beane; *Bibliog Instr*, Robert Lackie; *Archivist*, Lynn Livingston; *Acq, Electronic Resources*, Kathy Holden; *Ref Serv*, Sam Weigh; *Cat*, Marilyn Quinn; Staff 14 (MLS 14)
Founded 1865. Enrl 5,000; Fac 250; Highest Degree: Master
Library Holdings: Bk Vols 905,083; Bk Titles 434,489; Per Subs 3,031
Special Collections: Delaware Valley Newspapers (from Colonial Times to present); Dispatches of United States Envoys in Britain & France During Civil War Period, micro; Early Shorthand Works (Kendrick C Hill Coll), per; Historical Shorthand Materials (Leslie Coll); Typewriting History (Alan Lloyd Coll)
Automation Activity & Vendor Info: (Acquisitions) Endeavor; (Cataloging) Endeavor; (Circulation) Endeavor; (OPAC) Endeavor; (Serials) Endeavor
Mem of NJ Regional Libr Coop
Partic in Dialog Corporation; Dow Jones News Retrieval; OCLC Online Computer Library Center, Inc; PALINET & Union Library Catalogue of Pennsylvania
Departmental Libraries:
WESTMINSTER CHOIR COLLEGE, TALBOTT LIBRARY, 101 Walnut Lane, Princeton, 08540-3899. SAN 351-3181. Tel: 609-921-7100, Ext 237. FAX: 609-497-0243. *Chair*, John Buschman; *Archivist, Reader Servs, Ref, Spec Coll*, Nancy Wicklund; *Cat*, Jeanette Jacobson; *Cat*, Jane Nowakowski; *Acq*, Mi-Hye Chyun; *Coll Develop*, Devin Mariman; *Circ*, Rena Blakeslee; Staff 5 (MLS 5)
Subject Interests: Music
Special Collections: Hymnology (Routley Coll); Music Education Resource Center; Organ Historical Society Archives
Automation Activity & Vendor Info: (Acquisitions) Endeavor; (Cataloging) Endeavor; (Circulation) Endeavor; (OPAC) Endeavor; (Serials) Endeavor
Partic in OCLC Online Computer Library Center, Inc; PALINET & Union Library Catalogue of Pennsylvania
Friends of the Library Group

LEESBURG

S BAYSIDE STATE PRISON LIBRARY, 08327. SAN 376-0464. Tel: 856-785-0040, Ext 5408. FAX: 856-785-2463. *Librn*, Isac George
Library Holdings: Bk Titles 42,000; Per Subs 37
Restriction: Not open to public

LEONIA

P LEONIA PUBLIC LIBRARY,* 227 Ft Lee Rd, 07605. SAN 310-2408. Tel: 201-592-5770. FAX: 201-592-5775. E-Mail: leon1@bccls.org. Web Site: www.bccls.org/leonia. *Dir*, Harold A Ficke; *Asst Dir*, Debra Bigelow; *Ch Servs*, Jennifer Holan; *Media Spec*, Maureen Cohn; *Ref*, Teresa Wyman
Founded 1923. Pop 8,300; Circ 105,140
Library Holdings: Bk Vols 60,000; Bk Titles 57,775; Per Subs 135
Friends of the Library Group

LINCOLN PARK

P LINCOLN PARK PUBLIC LIBRARY,* 12 Boonton Tpk, 07035. SAN 310-2416. Tel: 973-694-8283. FAX: 973-694-5515. Web Site: www.gti.net/main/lp. *Dir*, Francis Kaiser; E-Mail: kaiser@main.morris.org
Founded 1922. Pop 10,978; Circ 65,702
Library Holdings: Bk Vols 51,188; Per Subs 129
Special Collections: New Jersey Coll
Partic in Morris Automated Information Network
Friends of the Library Group

LINCROFT

J BROOKDALE COMMUNITY COLLEGE LIBRARY, 765 Newman Springs Rd, 07738-1597. SAN 310-2424. Tel: 732-224-2706. FAX: 732-224-2982. Web Site: bcc-library.brookdale.cc.nj.us. *Dir*, David Murray; *Ref*, Susan Rosenberg; Staff 10 (MLS 10)
Founded 1969. Enrl 13,000; Fac 200
Jul 1999-Jun 2000 Mats Exp $257,020. Sal $1,200,204 (Prof $506,258)
Library Holdings: Bk Vols 74,800; Bk Titles 55,954; Per Subs 821
Special Collections: New Jersey Coll
Automation Activity & Vendor Info: (Circulation) Innovative Interfaces Inc.
Mem of NJ Regional Libr Coop
Partic in OCLC Online Computer Library Center, Inc

LINDEN

S EXXON CHEMICAL COMPANY, Linden Information Center,* 1900 E Linden Ave, PO Box 536, 07036. SAN 375-9172. Tel: 908-474-3842. FAX: 908-474-2020. *Librn*, Judith F Krieg; Staff 1 (MLS 1)
Founded 1920
Library Holdings: Bk Vols 17,000; Bk Titles 15,000; Per Subs 125
Subject Interests: Patents
Automation Activity & Vendor Info: (Cataloging) Sydney
Restriction: Not open to public

P LINDEN FREE PUBLIC LIBRARY, 31 E Henry St, 07036. SAN 350-8323. Tel: 908-298-3830. FAX: 908-486-2636. *Dir*, Rick Neff; E-Mail: lssi@njpublib.org; *Br Coordr*, Robert Kelly; *Br Coordr*, Elizabeth Piskorik; *Cat*, Elizabeth Hwang; E-Mail: ehwang@njpublib.org; *Ch Servs*, Catherine Chodack; *ILL, Ref*, Dennis Purves; *Ref*, Linda Klein; *Ref*, Robert Van Bergen; Staff 28 (MLS 9, Non-MLS 19)
Founded 1925. Pop 37,000; Circ 143,539
Jan 1999-Dec 1999 Income (Main Library and Branch Library) $1,804,175, State $47,275, City $1,717,900, Other $39,000. Mats Exp $149,410, Books $121,160, Per/Ser (Incl. Access Fees) $18,745, Electronic Ref Mat (Incl.

Access Fees) $4,200. Sal $1,378,441
Library Holdings: Bk Vols 128,221; Bk Titles 94,082; Per Subs 227
Subject Interests: Local history
Automation Activity & Vendor Info: (Cataloging) epixtech, inc.; (Circulation) epixtech, inc.; (OPAC) epixtech, inc.
Publications: Library Lineup
Partic in Infolink Eastern New Jersey Regional Library Cooperative, Inc
Friends of the Library Group
Branches: 2
EAST, 1425 Dill Ave, 07036. SAN 350-8358. Tel: 908-298-3829. *Librn*, Betty Piskorik; Staff 3 (MLS 1, Non-MLS 2)
Circ 7,753
Library Holdings: Bk Vols 25,467
Friends of the Library Group
SUNNYSIDE, 100 Edgewood Rd, 07036. SAN 350-8447. Tel: 908-298-3839. *Librn*, Robert Kelly; Staff 3 (MLS 1, Non-MLS 2)
Circ 20,988
Library Holdings: Bk Vols 28,072
Friends of the Library Group

LINDENWOLD

P LINDENWOLD PUBLIC LIBRARY, 310 E Linden Ave, 08021. SAN 310-2467. Tel: 856-784-5602. FAX: 856-784-3276. E-Mail: library@lindenwold.net. Web Site: www.lindenwold.net. *Librn*, Doris Shull
Pop 18,000
Library Holdings: Bk Vols 10,000; Per Subs 37
Mem of Camden County Library System
Friends of the Library Group

LINWOOD

P LINWOOD PUBLIC LIBRARY,* 301 Davis Ave, 08221. SAN 310-2475. Tel: 609-926-7991. FAX: 609-927-6147. *Dir*, Maria Moss; *Asst Dir*, Mary Ann Branciforti
Founded 1926. Pop 6,144; Circ 31,190
Library Holdings: Bk Vols 25,000; Per Subs 68
Special Collections: New Jersey Coll
Mem of NJ Regional Libr Coop
Friends of the Library Group

LITTLE FALLS

P LITTLE FALLS FREE PUBLIC LIBRARY, 8 Warren St, 07424. SAN 310-2483. Tel: 973-256-2784. FAX: 973-256-6312. *Dir*, Patricia Pelak; E-Mail: pelak@exchg1.palsplus.org; *ILL, Ref*, Michael Griffith; *Ch Servs*, Mary Louise Helwig-Rodriguez; Staff 1 (MLS 1)
Founded 1905. Pop 11,400; Circ 50,773
Jan 1999-Dec 1999 Income $328,164, State $12,123, City $302,373, Locally Generated Income $13,668. Mats Exp $63,088, Books $40,550, Per/Ser (Incl. Access Fees) $7,428, Electronic Ref Mat (Incl. Access Fees) $15,110. Sal $161,912
Library Holdings: Bk Vols 47,100; Per Subs 130
Special Collections: New Jersey Coll
Partic in Highlands Regional Library Cooperative; Passaic County Libr Syst

LITTLE FERRY

P LITTLE FERRY FREE PUBLIC LIBRARY, 239 Liberty St, 07643. SAN 310-2491. Tel: 201-641-3721. FAX: 201-641-8575. E-Mail: lify@bccls.org. *Dir*, Ellen Yamrick
Founded 1929. Pop 10,000
Library Holdings: Bk Vols 31,703; Bk Titles 30,238; Per Subs 73
Special Collections: United States Cinema History
Partic in Bergen County Cooperative Library System
Special Services for the Blind - Large print bks; Talking book center
Friends of the Library Group

LITTLE SILVER

P LITTLE SILVER PUBLIC LIBRARY, 484 Prospect Ave, 07739. SAN 310-2505. Tel: 732-747-9649. E-Mail: littlesi@shore.co.monmouth.nj.us. *Dir*, Susan M Edwards; *Asst Librn*, Lorraine Ayres; Staff 4 (MLS 1, Non-MLS 3)
Founded 1926. Pop 5,721
Jan 1999-Dec 1999 Income $107,525, State $2,524, Provincial $95,401, Other $9,600. Mats Exp $13,100, Books $10,300, Per/Ser (Incl. Access Fees) $2,800. Sal $86,526 (Prof $41,000)
Library Holdings: Bk Vols 26,400; Bk Titles 25,000; Per Subs 63
Automation Activity & Vendor Info: (Cataloging) SIRSI; (Circulation) SIRSI
Mem of Monmouth County Library.
Partic in Central Jersey Regional Library Cooperative
Open Mon 10-8:30, Tues 9-5:30, Wed-Thurs 10-5:30, Fri 10-8:30, Sat 10-12
Friends of the Library Group

S SOCIETY FOR THE INVESTIGATION OF THE UNEXPLAINED LIBRARY,* PO Box 265, 07739. SAN 375-2437. Tel: 732-842-5229. *Pres*, Robert Warth
Library Holdings: Per Subs 40

LIVINGSTON

S SEYMOUR S BODNER PE COLLECTION LIBRARY, 27 Shadowlawn Dr, 07039. SAN 377-3450. Tel: 973-994-3472. FAX: 973-994-3472. *In Charge*, Seymour S Bodner
Library Holdings: Bk Vols 1,500; Bk Titles 1,000
Subject Interests: Safety

L CIT GROUP INC, Law Library, 650 CIT Dr, 07039. SAN 373-0832. Tel: 973-740-5439. FAX: 973-740-5595. Web Site: www.cit.com. *Admin Assoc*, Susan August; E-Mail: susan.august@cit.com
Library Holdings: Per Subs 30

S MOTION PICTURE SERVICES LIBRARY, PO Box 252, 07039-0252. SAN 320-3956. Tel: 973-992-8194. E-Mail: mopicserv@aol.com. *Dir*, Gloria Mankowitz; Staff 4 (MLS 2, Non-MLS 2)
Founded 1960. Pop 14,000
Subject Interests: Accident prevention, History, Human relations, Safety, Transportation
Publications: Film brochures

P RUTH L ROCKWOOD MEMORIAL LIBRARY, Public Library of Livingston,* 10 Robert H Harp Dr, 07039-3986. SAN 310-2513. Tel: 973-992-4600. TDD: 973-992-4654. FAX: 973-994-2346. *Dir*, Barbara Jean Sikora; *Ref*, Arlene Boland; *Ch Servs*, Grace Chen; *Reader Servs*, Tamar Strauss; *YA Servs*, George King; Staff 51 (MLS 10, Non-MLS 41)
Founded 1911. Pop 27,000; Circ 301,187
Library Holdings: Bk Vols 129,411; Bk Titles 115,000; Per Subs 370
Subject Interests: Art, Holocaust
Special Collections: Bibliography of Dr Lyndon A Peer; Large Print Coll; New Jerseyana
Automation Activity & Vendor Info: (Cataloging) Inlex; (Circulation) Inlex
Publications: Annual Report; Archival Holdings for the Township of Livingston; Footnotes (monthly newsletter); Livingston Local Business Directory
Partic in Infolink Eastern New Jersey Regional Library Cooperative, Inc
Special Services for the Deaf - TDD
Special Services - Monthly program for perceptually impaired adults, monthly Senior Happening, bi-weekly Writer's Group, monthly art exhibits, book delivery for homebound, YA advisory board. Book & author series/tax counseling for seniors. Elevator access & bathrooms for handicapped
Friends of the Library Group

M SAINT BARNABAS HEALTH SCIENCES, Medical Library, Old Short Hills Rd, 07039. SAN 320-3964. Tel: 973-322-5050. FAX: 973-533-5279. *Dir*, Christine Connor; Tel: 973-322-5052, E-Mail: cconnor@sbhcs.com; Staff 4 (MLS 1, Non-MLS 3)
Library Holdings: Bk Titles 5,000; Per Subs 410
Subject Interests: Medicine, Plastic surgery, Surgery
Database Vendor: OVID Technologies
Partic in Medical Library Center Of New York

LODI

S BERGEN COUNTY HISTORICAL SOCIETY LIBRARY, c/o Felician College Library, 262 Main St, 07644. (Mail add: PO Box 55, 07661-0055), Tel: 201-343-9492. Web Site: www.carroll.com/bchs. *In Charge*, Robert D Griffin; Tel: 201-816-0585, Fax: 201-816-0585, E-Mail: bhb@cybernex.net
Founded 1902
Library Holdings: Bk Vols 3,000; Bk Titles 2,500
Subject Interests: Colonial hist, Revolutionary war
Restriction: By appointment only

C FELICIAN COLLEGE LIBRARY, 262 S Main St, 07644-2198. SAN 310-253X. Tel: 201-559-6071. FAX: 973-777-3917. E-Mail: gatline@inet.felician.edu. Web Site: www.felician.edu/library/index.htm. *Dir*, Dr Stephen Karetzky; Tel: 201-559-6070, E-Mail: karetzkys@inet.felician.edu; *Librn*, Sister Mary Carmeline; Tel: 201-559-3187, Fax: 201-559-3604, E-Mail: kowalskic@inet.felician.edu; *Ser*, Sister Mary Lucretia; Tel: 201-559-6132; *AV*, Joe Greenberg; Tel: 201-559-6100, Fax: 201-559-6188, E-Mail: greenberg@inet.felician.edu; *Tech Servs*, Joanne Karetzky; Tel: 201-559-6133, E-Mail: karetzkyj@inet.felician.edu; *Ref*, Elisabeth Gatlin; Tel: 201-559-6125, E-Mail: gatline@inet.felician.edu; Staff 15 (MLS 6, Non-MLS 9)
Founded 1942. Enrl 1,500; Fac 152; Highest Degree: Master
Jul 2000-Jun 2001 Mats Exp $255,000, Books $115,000, Per/Ser (Incl. Access Fees) $85,000, Presv $7,000, Micro $13,000, AV Equip $5,000, Electronic Ref Mat (Incl. Access Fees) $30,000
Library Holdings: Bk Vols 116,200; Bk Titles 108,095; Per Subs 815
Subject Interests: Education, Humanities, Natural science, Nursing, Religion, Soc sci

Special Collections: Audio Visual; Education
Automation Activity & Vendor Info: (Cataloging) SIRSI; (Circulation) SIRSI; (OPAC) SIRSI
Database Vendor: OCLC - First Search
Publications: Faculty Library Guide; Guide to Felicians Online Resources; Library Handbook
Partic in Dialog Corporation; New Jersey Library Network; OCLC Online Computer Library Center, Inc; PALINET & Union Library Catalogue of Pennsylvania

P LODI MEMORIAL LIBRARY, (LML), One Memorial Dr, 07644-1692. SAN 310-2548. Tel: 973-365-4044. FAX: 973-365-0172. Web Site: www.bccls.org/lodi. *Dir*, Anthony P Taormina; E-Mail: taormina@bccls.org; Staff 3 (MLS 3)
Founded 1924. Pop 23,956; Circ 80,000
Jul 1999-Jun 2000 Income $725,970, State $39,020, City $677,485, Other $9,465. Mats Exp $104,986, Books $72,337, Per/Ser (Incl. Access Fees) $10,282, Micro $3,939, AV Equip $13,384, Electronic Ref Mat (Incl. Access Fees) $5,044. Sal $479,043
Library Holdings: Bk Vols 92,281; Bk Titles 89,374; Per Subs 328; High Interest/Low Vocabulary Bk Vols 500; Bks on Deafness & Sign Lang 50
Automation Activity & Vendor Info: (Cataloging) DRA; (Circulation) DRA; (ILL) DRA; (OPAC) DRA
Database Vendor: DRA
Partic in Bergen County Cooperative Library System; Highlands Regional Library Cooperative
Friends of the Library Group

LONG BRANCH

P LONG BRANCH FREE PUBLIC LIBRARY,* 328 Broadway, 07740. SAN 310-2564. Tel: 732-222-3900. FAX: 732-222-3799. Web Site: www.lmxac.org/longbranch. *Dir*, Ingrid Bruck; E-Mail: ibruck@lmxac.org; *Ch Servs, Head of Libr*, Dennis Stranz; E-Mail: dstranz@lmxac.org; *Tech Servs*, Francine Silverman; E-Mail: fsilverma@lmxac.org; *Circ*, Barbara Williams; E-Mail: bwilliam@lmxac.org; *Ad Servs, YA Servs*, Janet Birckhead; E-Mail: jbirckhe@lmaxac.org; *Ref*, Beatrice Priestly; E-Mail: bpriestl@lmxac.org
Founded 1916. Pop 29,819; Circ 105,512
Jan 1999-Dec 1999 Income (Main Library and Branch Library) $667,763, State $30,764, City $595,835, Federal $15,000, Locally Generated Income $19,000, Other $32,000. Mats Exp $667,763, Books $65,651, Per/Ser (Incl. Access Fees) $7,683, Micro $4,600, Other Print Mats $4,401, Electronic Ref Mat (Incl. Access Fees) $3,500. Sal $340,888 (Prof $138,343)
Library Holdings: Bk Vols 76,883; Bk Titles 66,370; Per Subs 110
Special Collections: Books on Tape; Long Branch Historical Coll, scrapbooks, photos, bks, pictures & maps; Spanish & Portuguese Coll
Automation Activity & Vendor Info: (Circulation) CARL; (OPAC) CARL
Publications: Open to the Public (newsp column)
Partic in Cent Jersey Regional Libr Coop; LMX Automation Consortium
Friends of the Library Group
Branches: 1
ELBERON BRANCH, 168 Lincoln Ave, Elberon, 07740. SAN 310-1312. Tel: 908-870-1776. *In Charge*, Dennis Stranz
Library Holdings: Bk Vols 13,835
Friends of the Library Group

M MONMOUTH MEDICAL CENTER, Altschul Medical Library, 300 Second Ave, 07740. SAN 310-2572. Tel: 732-923-6646. FAX: 732-222-3742. *Dir*, Frederic C Pachman; E-Mail: frederic.c.pachman@drexel.edu; Staff 3 (MLS 1, Non-MLS 2)
Founded 1959
Library Holdings: Bk Vols 3,000; Bk Titles 3,100; Per Subs 400
Subject Interests: Medicine, Nursing, Pediatrics
Publications: Acquisitions List (quarterly); Newsletter (quarterly)
Mem of Regional Libr Coop 5 Cent Jersey
Partic in National Network Of Libraries Of Medicine - South Central Region

LONG VALLEY

S WASHINGTON TOWNSHIP HISTORICAL SOCIETY LIBRARY, 6 Fairview Ave, PO Box 189, 07853. SAN 373-2509. Tel: 908-876-9696.
Subject Interests: Genealogy, Local history
Special Collections: Local Cemetery Listings; Local church records; New Jersey History by Henry Charlton Beck; original newspaper articles; Schooley's Mountain Springs Coll

P WASHINGTON TOWNSHIP PUBLIC LIBRARY, (WTPL), 37 E Springtown Rd, 07853. SAN 310-2580. Tel: 908-876-3596. FAX: 908-876-3541. Web Site: www.gti.net/washtwp. *Librn*, Virginia Scarlatelli; E-Mail: scarlalelli@main.morris.org; Staff 16 (MLS 4, Non-MLS 12)
Founded 1968. Pop 17,000; Circ 136,000
Jan 2000-Dec 2000 Income $543,637, State $16,700, City $495,037, Locally Generated Income $31,900. Mats Exp $98,531, Books $76,000, Per/Ser (Incl. Access Fees) $6,000, AV Equip $10,000, Electronic Ref Mat (Incl. Access Fees) $6,531. Sal $315,875 (Prof $133,167)
Library Holdings: Bk Vols 46,876; Per Subs 95
Automation Activity & Vendor Info: (Cataloging) DRA; (Circulation) DRA; (OPAC) DRA
Database Vendor: DRA
Partic in Highlands Regional Library Cooperative; Morris Automated Information Network
Friends of the Library Group

LYNDHURST

P LYNDHURST FREE PUBLIC LIBRARY, 355 Valley Brook Ave, 07071. SAN 310-2599. Tel: 201-804-2478. Reference Tel: 201-804-2479. FAX: 201-939-7677. E-Mail: lynd1@bccls.org. Web Site: www.bccls.org/lyndhurst/. *Dir*, Charles F Sieger; Tel: 201-804-2486, E-Mail: sieger@bccls.org; *Ref*, Nancy Barnhouse; E-Mail: lyndref@bccls.org; *Ch Servs*, Denise Yanosey; Tel: 201-804-2480; *Tech Servs*, Elizabeth Hughes; Tel: 201-804-2480; *Circ*, Diane McDonald; Tel: 201-804-7478; Staff 10 (MLS 3, Non-MLS 7)
Founded 1914. Pop 18,500; Circ 70,000
Jul 1999-Jul 2000 Income $579,000, City $555,000, Locally Generated Income $24,000. Mats Exp $105,000, Books $57,000, Per/Ser (Incl. Access Fees) $13,000, Micro $10,000, Electronic Ref Mat (Incl. Access Fees) $15,000. Sal $350,000 (Prof $115,000)
Library Holdings: Bk Vols 65,000; Bk Titles 57,500; Per Subs 114
Special Collections: Local History Coll, slides tapes; New Jerseyana Col, bks, photog, a-tapes, slides
Automation Activity & Vendor Info: (Cataloging) DRA; (Circulation) DRA; (OPAC) DRA
Database Vendor: DRA, Ebsco - EbscoHost, GaleNet, IAC - Info Trac, ProQuest
Partic in Bergen County Cooperative Library System

LYONS

DEPARTMENT OF VETERANS AFFAIRS
GM MEDICAL LIBRARY, 551 Knollcroft Rd, 07939. SAN 350-8501. Tel: 908-647-0180, Ext 4410. FAX: 908-604-5837. *Librn*, James Delo; *ILL*, Lynn Fellows
Founded 1931
Oct 1997-Sep 1998 Income $98,000
Library Holdings: Bk Titles 4,200; Per Subs 350
Subject Interests: Medicine, Nursing, Psychiatry, Psychology
Special Collections: Patient Health Education
Partic in BRS; Medline
Friends of the Library Group
G PATIENT'S LIBRARY, 551 Knollcroft Rd, 07939. SAN 350-8536. Tel: 908-647-0180, Ext 6420. FAX: 908-604-5837.
Oct 1997-Sep 1998 Income $15,000. Mats Exp Books $6,000
Library Holdings: Bk Titles 5,000; Per Subs 110
Mem of NW Regional Libr Coop

MADISON

C DREW UNIVERSITY LIBRARY, 36 Madison Ave, 07940. SAN 310-2602. Tel: 973-408-3125. Interlibrary Loan Service Tel: 973-408-3478. FAX: 973-408-3770. Web Site: www.depts.drew.edu/lib/. *Dir*, Andrew Scrimgeour; *Assoc Dir*, Jean Schoenthaler; Tel: 973-408-3473, E-Mail: jschoent@drew.edu; *Librn*, Kenneth Rowe; *Librn*, Suzanne Selinger; *Ref*, Jody Caldwell; *Cat*, Lessie Culmer-Nier; *Coll Develop*, Linda Connors; *ILL*, Josie Cook; *Govt Doc*, Jan Wanggaard. Subject Specialists: *Conservation*, Masato Okinaka; *Methodistica*, Kenneth Rowe; *Theology*, Suzanne Selinger; Staff 40 (MLS 11, Non-MLS 29)
Founded 1867. Enrl 1,939; Highest Degree: Doctorate
Jul 1999-Jun 2000 Income $2,691,843. Mats Exp $965,388, Books $435,184, Per/Ser (Incl. Access Fees) $341,531, Presv $30,147, Micro $45,052, Electronic Ref Mat (Incl. Access Fees) $113,474. Sal $1,262,363 (Prof $649,486)
Library Holdings: Bk Vols 487,562; Per Subs 3,066
Subject Interests: Methodistica, Slavery
Special Collections: Hymnology (David A Creamer Coll); Kohler Coll (Reformation Church Hist); Theology Coll, bks, mss; Tipple Coll, bks, prints, mss; United Nations Coll, bks, doc
Automation Activity & Vendor Info: (Acquisitions) DRA; (Cataloging) DRA
Database Vendor: CARL, Dialog, DRA, Ebsco - EbscoHost, Lexis-Nexis, OCLC - First Search, OVID Technologies, ProQuest
Publications: The Methodist Union Catalog; Visions
Partic in Center For Research Libraries; Highlands Regional Library Cooperative; OCLC Online Computer Library Center, Inc; PALINET & Union Library Catalogue of Pennsylvania
Drew University provides library services to the General Commission on Archives & History of the United Methodist Church located at Drew University
Friends of the Library Group

C FAIRLEIGH DICKINSON UNIVERSITY, Florham-Madison Campus Library, 285 Madison Ave, 07940. SAN 350-8595. Tel: 973-443-8515. Reference Tel: 973-443-8516. FAX: 973-443-8525. Web Site: www.fdu.edu.

Actg Dir, Publ Servs, Maria Webb; E-Mail: webb@alpha.fdu.edu; *Acq*, Jane Wenneis; Tel: 973-443-8530; *Media Spec*, Ursula Sommer; Tel: 973-443-8517; *Ref*, Eleanor Friedl; *Ref Serv*, Robert Richlan; Staff 8 (MLS 4, Non-MLS 4)
Founded 1958. Circ 3,800; Enrl 2,800; Fac 130; Highest Degree: Master
1999-2000 Income $454,217, Locally Generated Income $1,800, Parent Institution $447,417, Other $5,000. Mats Exp $210,500, Books $52,000, Per/Ser (Incl. Access Fees) $106,000, Presv $2,000, Micro $20,000, AV Equip $500, Electronic Ref Mat (Incl. Access Fees) $30,000. Sal $382,015 (Prof $151,000)
Library Holdings: Bk Vols 191,000; Bk Titles 173,000; Per Subs 840; Bks on Deafness & Sign Lang 64
Special Collections: Comic Art & Illustration (Chesler Coll), bks, drawings, mss; Douglas Kahn Photo & Film History; Lloyd Haberly Book Arts Coll, bks
Automation Activity & Vendor Info: (Acquisitions) epixtech, inc.; (Cataloging) epixtech, inc.; (Circulation) epixtech, inc.; (ILL) epixtech, inc.; (OPAC) epixtech, inc.; (Serials) epixtech, inc.
Database Vendor: IAC - Info Trac, Lexis-Nexis, OCLC - First Search, ProQuest, Silverplatter Information Inc., Wilson - Wilson Web
Restriction: Public use on premises
Function: Research library
Partic in Highlands Regional Library Cooperative; OCLC Online Computer Library Center, Inc
Must have card
Friends of the Library Group

P MADISON PUBLIC LIBRARY, 39 Keep St, 07940. SAN 310-2610. Tel: 973-377-0722. FAX: 973-377-3142. Web Site: www.rosenet.org/library/. *Dir*, Nancy S Adamczyk; E-Mail: adamczykn@mpl.rosenet.org; *Ad Servs*, Adrienne Tawil; *Ch Servs*, Bonnie McDonald; E-Mail: McDonald@main.morris.org; *Circ*, Helene Corlett; *Tech Servs*, Pauline Lang; E-Mail: lang@main.morris.org; Staff 32 (MLS 9, Non-MLS 23)
Founded 1900. Pop 15,850; Circ 159,506
Jan 1999-Dec 1999 Income $1,133,807, State $20,418, City $876,740, Locally Generated Income $236,649. Mats Exp $135,837, Books $96,149, Per/Ser (Incl. Access Fees) $18,575, Micro $7,020, Electronic Ref Mat (Incl. Access Fees) $14,093. Sal $608,509
Library Holdings: Bk Vols 121,394; Per Subs 394
Subject Interests: American literature, British lit
Special Collections: Golden Hind Press publications; Madison History
Automation Activity & Vendor Info: (Circulation) DRA; (ILL) DRA; (OPAC) DRA
Database Vendor: DRA, Ebsco - EbscoHost, GaleNet, ProQuest, Silverplatter Information Inc.
Publications: Newsletter (bimonthly)
Mem of Morris Automated Info Network
Partic in Morris Automated Information Network; Morris-Union Federation
Friends of the Library Group

S MUSEUM OF EARLY TRADES & CRAFTS LIBRARY, Main St & Green Village Rd, 07940. SAN 377-483X. Tel: 973-377-2982. FAX: 973-377-7358. E-Mail: metc@msn.com. Web Site: www.rosenet.org/metc. *Dir*, Sheila Marines
Library Holdings: Bk Titles 200

R UNITED METHODIST CHURCH, General Commission on Archives & History Library, 36 Madison Ave, 07940. SAN 312-8997. Tel: 973-408-3590. FAX: 973-408-3836. Web Site: www.gcah.org. *Librn*, Kenneth E Rowe; E-Mail: krowe@drew.edu
Founded 1968
Library Holdings: Bk Vols 50,000; Bk Titles 40,000; Per Subs 600
Subject Interests: Antecedent bodies, United Methodist Church
Automation Activity & Vendor Info: (Acquisitions) DRA; (Cataloging) DRA; (Circulation) DRA; (OPAC) DRA; (Serials) DRA
Partic in PALINET & Union Library Catalogue of Pennsylvania
Friends of the Library Group

S WHITEHALL-ROBINS, Information Center & Library, 5 Giralda Farms, 07940-0871. SAN 370-7628. Tel: 973-660-5231. FAX: 973-660-5731. *Dir*, Mimi Golob; Tel: 973-660-5587, E-Mail: golobm@ahp.com; *Senior Info Specialist*, Rose Araya; *ILL*, Leah Baptiste; *Mgr*, Marygrace Record; Staff 7 (MLS 3, Non-MLS 4)
Founded 1988
Library Holdings: Bk Titles 4,000; Per Subs 400
Subject Interests: Arthritis, Dietary supplements, Medicine, Pharmaceutical industry, Pharmacology
Database Vendor: Dialog, IAC - Info Trac, Lexis-Nexis
Restriction: Staff use only
Partic in Manhattan-Bronx Health Sciences Libraries Group; Medical Library Center Of New York; New York Metrop Ref & Res Libr Agency

MAHWAH

P MAHWAH PUBLIC LIBRARY, 100 Ridge Rd, 07430. SAN 310-2645. Tel: 201-529-READ. FAX: 201-529-9027. E-Mail: mahw@bccls.org. Web Site: www.bccls.org/mahwah. *Dir*, Kenneth W Giaimo; Tel: 201-529-2972, E-Mail: giaimo@bccls.org/; *Head Librn*, Delores Bostrom; *Ref Serv Ad*, Silvestra Praino; *Ch Servs*, Margaret Kistinger; *Ch Servs*, Marianne Stein; *Circ*, Marilee Dardenne; *Tech Servs*, Linda Straut; *Commun Servs*, Denise Laude; Staff 31 (MLS 7, Non-MLS 24)
Founded 1912. Pop 20,527; Circ 176,000
Jan 2000-Dec 2000 Income $1,185,914, State $15,377, City $1,010,521, Locally Generated Income $26,950, Other $133,066. Mats Exp $172,200, Books $115,000, Per/Ser (Incl. Access Fees) $12,000, Micro $1,000, AV Equip $30,500, Electronic Ref Mat (Incl. Access Fees) $13,700. Sal $619,196 (Prof $268,048)
Library Holdings: Bk Vols 79,622; Bk Titles 76,286; Per Subs 278
Subject Interests: Poetry, Theatre
Special Collections: Business Directories; Videocassette Coll
Database Vendor: DRA, IAC - SearchBank, ProQuest
Publications: Monthly newsletter; Web Page
Mem of Bergen County Co-op Libr Syst
Partic in Bergen County Cooperative Library System; Highlands Regional Library Cooperative
Friends of the Library Group

C RAMAPO COLLEGE OF NEW JERSEY, George T Potter Library, 505 Ramapo Valley Rd, 07430. SAN 310-2661. Tel: 201-684-7574. Interlibrary Loan Service Tel: 201-684-7579. Circulation Tel: 201-684-7575. Interlibrary Loan Service FAX: 201-684-6741. Web Site: www.ramapo.edu/. *Dean of Libr*, Dr Pauline Rothstein; Tel: 201-684-7569, E-Mail: prothste@ramapo.edu; *Assoc Dir*, George F Heise; *Bibliog Instr*, Judith E Jeney; Tel: 201-684-7581, E-Mail: jjeney@ramapo.edu; *Cat*, Robert Dilly; Tel: 201-684-7580, E-Mail: rdilly@ramapo.edu; *Coll Develop*, Elaine Risch; Tel: 201-684-7570, E-Mail: erisch@ramapo.edu; *Govt Doc*, Shirley Knight; Tel: 201-684-7315, E-Mail: skmight@ramapo.edu; *Circ*, Irene Kuchta; E-Mail: ikuchta@ramapo.edu; *Ref*, DelRitta Hornbuckle; Tel: 201-684-7316, E-Mail: dhornbuc@ramapo.edu; *Ref*, Susan Kurzmann; Tel: 201-684-7199, E-Mail: skurzman@ramapo.edu; Staff 25 (MLS 8, Non-MLS 17)
Founded 1968. Enrl 5,195; Fac 162; Highest Degree: Master
Jul 1999-Jun 2000 Income $1,663,516. Mats Exp $462,621, Books $164,531, Per/Ser (Incl. Access Fees) $133,604, Presv $4,004, Micro $18,519, Other Print Mats $69,810, Electronic Ref Mat (Incl. Access Fees) $72,153. Sal $958,383
Library Holdings: Bk Vols 145,413; Bk Titles 109,844; Per Subs 672
Automation Activity & Vendor Info: (Circulation) Endeavor
Database Vendor: CARL, DRA, Ebsco - EbscoHost, GaleNet, IAC - Info Trac, OCLC - First Search, ProQuest, Silverplatter Information Inc., Wilson - Wilson Web
Partic in Highlands Regional Library Cooperative; NJ Col & Univ Libr Coun

MANAHAWKIN

M SOUTHERN OCEAN COUNTY HOSPITAL, Health Sciences Library,* 1140 Rte 72 W, 08050. Tel: 609-597-6011. FAX: 609-978-8940. *Librn*, Reina Reisler
Library Holdings: Bk Vols 500; Per Subs 70

MANALAPAN

P MONMOUTH COUNTY LIBRARY,* 125 Symmes Dr, 07726. SAN 350-7181. Tel: 732-431-7220. FAX: 732-409-2556. *Dir*, Ken Sheinbaum; *Asst Dir*, Margaret Field; *Ch Servs, YA Servs*, Constance Lyons; *Publ Servs*, Flora Higgins; *Acq, Cat, Tech Servs*, John Smothers; *Online Servs*, Jacqueline Cochran; Staff 50 (MLS 50)
Founded 1922. Pop 390,000; Circ 2,492,474
1997-1998 Income $8,927,288, State $263,000, Federal $247,000, County $8,380,288. Mats Exp $2,011,351, Books $1,550,000, Per/Ser (Incl. Access Fees) $332,851. Sal $4,257,226
Subject Interests: Civil War, Law, Local history, Medicine
Special Collections: Monmouth County; Official records of the union & confederate armies
Publications: Children's Newsletter; Monthly Calendar; Municipal Government Newsletter
Member Libraries: Atlantic Highlands Public Library Association; Eatontown Public Library; Fair Haven Public Library; Little Silver Public Library; Manasquan Public Library; Tinton Falls Public Library; Union Beach Memorial Library; West Long Branch Public Library
Partic in OCLC Online Computer Library Center, Inc
Friends of the Library Group
Branches: 10
ALLENTOWN BRANCH, Main St, Allentown, 08501. SAN 350-7211. Tel: 609-259-7565. FAX: 609-259-9620. *Librn*, Nancy Stein
Library Holdings: Bk Vols 20,350
COLTS NECK BRANCH, Heyers Mills Rd, Colts Neck, 07722. SAN 350-722X. Tel: 732-431-5656. *Librn*, Mary Lindsay
Library Holdings: Bk Vols 28,450
EASTERN, Rte 35, Shrewsbury, 07702. SAN 350-7246. Tel: 732-842-5995. FAX: 732-219-0140. *Librn*, Janet Kranis
Library Holdings: Bk Vols 145,000
Subject Interests: Art, Education, Law, Music

Special Collections: Monmouth County
HAZLET BRANCH, 251 Middle Rd, Hazlet, 07730. SAN 350-7270. Tel: 732-264-7164. *Librn*, Kim Avagliano
Library Holdings: Bk Vols 54,000
Special Collections: Hazlet History
HOLMDEL BRANCH, 1300 N Main St, Holmdel, 07733. SAN 350-7300. Tel: 732-946-4118. *Librn*, Deborah Bagchi
Library Holdings: Bk Vols 38,000
Special Collections: Township History
HOWELL BRANCH, Old Tavern Rd, PO Box 577, Howell, 07731. SAN 350-7335. Tel: 732-938-2300. *Librn*, Ellen Deeble
Library Holdings: Bk Vols 46,000
Special Collections: Township History
MARLBORO BRANCH, One Library Ct, Marlboro, 07746-1102. SAN 350-7394. Tel: 732-536-9406. *Librn*, Jennifer King
Library Holdings: Bk Vols 79,000
Subject Interests: Local history
OCEANPORT BRANCH, Monmouth Blvd & Myrtle Ave, Oceanport, 07757. SAN 350-7424. Tel: 732-229-2626. *Librn*, Michele Dorsey
Library Holdings: Bk Vols 20,350
TOWNSHIP OF OCEAN, Monmouth & Deal Rds, Oakhurst, 07755. SAN 350-7459. Tel: 732-531-5092. *Librn*, Linda Cusanelli
Library Holdings: Bk Vols 64,000
Subject Interests: Local history
WALL, 2700 Allaire Rd, Wall, 07719. SAN 350-7483. Tel: 732-449-8877. *Librn*, Louise Parr
Library Holdings: Bk Vols 64,000
Special Collections: Local History; Women's Studies
Bookmobiles: 2

MANASQUAN

P MANASQUAN PUBLIC LIBRARY,* 55 Broad St, 08736. SAN 310-2688. Tel: 732-223-1503. *Dir*, Margo L Petersen
Founded 1915. Pop 5,364; Circ 32,936
Library Holdings: Bk Titles 25,842; Per Subs 50
Mem of Monmouth County Library
Friends of the Library Group

MANVILLE

P MANVILLE PUBLIC LIBRARY, 100 S Tenth Ave, 08835. SAN 310-2696. Tel: 908-722-9722. FAX: 908-722-0631. Web Site: www.manvillembpa.com. *Dir*, Ed Smith; E-Mail: edsmith@lmxac.org; *Asst Dir*, Ruth Bielanski; Staff 8 (MLS 1, Non-MLS 7)
Founded 1960. Pop 10,567; Circ 27,301
Jan 1999-Dec 2000 Income $249,153, State $11,343, City $222,452, Locally Generated Income $15,358. Mats Exp $27,600, Books $24,600, Per/Ser (Incl. Access Fees) $3,000. Sal $133,312
Library Holdings: Bk Vols 32,000; Bk Titles 85; Per Subs 85
Subject Interests: Coal
Database Vendor: CARL
Publications: Monthly calendar; Newsletter (quarterly)
Partic in LMX Automation Consortium; Raritan Valley Fedn of Librs

MAPLE SHADE

P MAPLE SHADE PUBLIC LIBRARY,* 200 Stiles Ave, 08052. SAN 310-270X. Tel: 856-779-9767. FAX: 856-779-2524. *Dir*, Carmella Hirnickel
Library Holdings: Bk Vols 50,000; Per Subs 85

MAPLEWOOD

P MAPLEWOOD MEMORIAL LIBRARY,* 51 Baker St, 07040-2618. SAN 350-8684. Tel: 973-762-1622. FAX: 973-762-0762. Web Site: www.infolink.org/maplewoodlibrary. *Dir*, Rowland Bennett; *Ad Servs*, Ruth Greenwald; *Ch Servs*, Jane Folger; *Media Spec*, Susan F Murphy; *Tech Servs*, Katharine Patton; Staff 7 (MLS 7)
Founded 1913. Pop 22,950; Circ 263,432
Jan 1999-Dec 1999 Income $1,223,000. Mats Exp $132,435, Books $92,335, Per/Ser (Incl. Access Fees) $14,000, Micro $1,800, Manuscripts & Archives $300. Sal $853,000
Library Holdings: Bk Vols 106,000; Bk Titles 75,000; Per Subs 304
Special Collections: Local History (Durand Room Coll), bks, clippings, photog, especially Asher B Durand, 1796-1886 & James A Ricalton, 1844-1929
Publications: Maplewood Library News (co-published with Friends)
Partic in Eastern NJ Regional Libr Coop; Infolink; ReBL
Friends of the Library Group
Branches: 1
HILTON, 1688 Springfield Ave, 07040-2923. SAN 350-8714. Tel: 973-762-1688. Web Site: www.infolink.org/maplewoodlibrary. *Librn*, Kris Hammond
Founded 1882
Library Holdings: Bk Vols 25,000; Bk Titles 21,000

SR MORROW MEMORIAL CHURCH LIBRARY & MEDIA CENTER,* 600 Ridgewood Rd, 07040-1228. SAN 326-2359. Tel: 973-763-7676. FAX: 973-763-6798. *Librn*, Kathy Finch; *Media Spec*, Althea MacWhorter; Staff 3 (MLS 1, Non-MLS 2)
Pop 861
Library Holdings: Bk Vols 1,450; Bk Titles 1,400
Subject Interests: Art, Church history, Fiction, History
Special Collections: National Geographic Magazines Coll

MARGATE CITY

P MARGATE CITY PUBLIC LIBRARY, 8100 Atlantic Ave, 08402. SAN 310-2726. Tel: 609-822-4700. FAX: 609-823-0064. Web Site: www.margatelibrary.org. *Dir*, James J Cahill, Jr; Staff 1 (MLS 1)
Founded 1972. Pop 9,200
Library Holdings: Bk Titles 36,593; Per Subs 120
Automation Activity & Vendor Info: (Cataloging) epixtech, inc.; (Circulation) epixtech, inc.
Database Vendor: Ebsco - EbscoHost, epixtech, inc., GaleNet
Partic in South Jersey Regional Library Cooperative
Friends of the Library Group

MATAWAN

S MADISON TOWNSHIP HISTORICAL SOCIETY, Thomas Warne Historical Museum & Library, Old Bridge Township, 4216 Rte 516, 07747. SAN 325-7746. Tel: 732-566-2108. FAX: 732-566-6943. *Curator*, Alvia Martin; Tel: 732-566-0348
Founded 1964
Library Holdings: Bk Vols 1,300
Special Collections: 19th Century Tools; Handcrafts; Local History & Genealogy; Newspaper Coll, Early 1800s; Old School, bks, related items; Photograph Coll, Early 19th Century, vf ref
Publications: At the Headwaters of Cheesequake Creek (local history book); From Groaning Board Cooks
Restriction: Not a lending library

P MATAWAN-ABERDEEN PUBLIC LIBRARY, 165 Main St, 07747. SAN 310-2742. Tel: 732-583-9100. FAX: 732-583-9360. Web Site: www.imxac.org/mata/index.html. *Dir*, Susan Pike; E-Mail: spike@imxac.org; *ILL*, Virginia Moshen; *Ch Servs*, Daina Lucs; E-Mail: dlucs@imxac.org; *Ad Servs*, Nancy Shamod; E-Mail: nshamod@imxac.org; Staff 14 (MLS 4, Non-MLS 10)
Founded 1903. Pop 26,308; Circ 163,549
Jan 2000-Dec 2000 Income $537,714, State $28,382, City $458,701, Locally Generated Income $20,000, Other $30,631. Mats Exp $77,902, Books $58,702, Per/Ser (Incl. Access Fees) $14,200, Micro $5,000. Sal $300,302
Library Holdings: Bk Titles 77,712; Per Subs 153
Automation Activity & Vendor Info: (Circulation) CARL
Friends of the Library Group

MAYS LANDING

J ATLANTIC CAPE COMMUNITY COLLEGE, William Spangler Library, 5100 Blackhorse Pike, 08330. SAN 310-2750. Tel: 609-343-4952. FAX: 609-343-4957. Web Site: www.atlantic.edu/library/library.html. *Dir*, Paul Rigby; E-Mail: rigby@atlantic.edu; *Ref*, Grant Wilinski; Staff 2 (MLS 2)
Founded 1966
Jul 1999-Jun 2000 Income $327,000. Mats Exp $327,000
Library Holdings: Bk Vols 78,000; Bk Titles 76,500; Per Subs 250
Subject Interests: Culinary arts
Special Collections: Southern New Jersey History
Automation Activity & Vendor Info: (Cataloging) epixtech, inc.; (Circulation) epixtech, inc.; (OPAC) epixtech, inc.
Partic in Med Libr & Info Consortium; OCLC Online Computer Library Center, Inc; South Jersey Regional Library Cooperative

P ATLANTIC COUNTY LIBRARY, 40 Farragut Ave, 08330-1750. SAN 310-4346. Tel: 609-625-2776. FAX: 609-625-8143. Web Site: www.aclink.org. *Dir*, Alyce Bowers; *Asst Dir*, William Paullin; *Mgr*, Brian Tomlinson; *Bkmobile Coordr*, Gloria Donelson; *Ref*, Edwina Cahill; *Tech Servs*, Susan Vance; *ILL*, Clare Bebbington; *Commun Relations*, Beverly Bird; Staff 24 (MLS 24)
Founded 1926. Pop 163,739; Circ 732,468
Library Holdings: Bk Vols 338,135; Bk Titles 172,913
Special Collections: Afro-America Coll; Jerseyana; Music Coll
Automation Activity & Vendor Info: (Acquisitions) epixtech, inc.; (Cataloging) epixtech, inc.; (Circulation) epixtech, inc.; (OPAC) epixtech, inc.; (Serials) epixtech, inc.
Publications: Wavelength (newsletter)
Member Libraries: Atlantic County Library
Partic in South Jersey Regional Library Cooperative
Friends of the Library Group
Branches: 9
BRIGANTINE BRANCH, 201 15th St, Brigantine, 08203. SAN 321-8198.

Tel: 609-266-0110. FAX: 609-266-0040. *Librn*, Susan Wick
EGG HARBOR TOWNSHIP, One Swift Dr, Egg Harbor Township, 08234. SAN 320-9962. Tel: 609-927-8664. FAX: 609-927-4683. *Librn*, Jean MacPherson
GALLOWAY BRANCH, 306 E Jimmie Leeds Rd, Absecon, 08201. SAN 328-6754. Tel: 609-652-2352. FAX: 609-652-3613. *Librn*, Catherine Ostrum
HAMMONTON BRANCH, 451 Egg Harbor Rd, Hammonton, 08037. SAN 320-3603. Tel: 609-561-2264. FAX: 609-561-1816. *Librn*, David Munn
LONGPORT BRANCH, 2305 Atlantic Ave, Longport, 08403. SAN 373-1901. Tel: 609-487-0272. FAX: 609-487-9521. *Librn*, Sarah Cochran
MAYS LANDING BRANCH, 40 Farragut Ave, 08330. SAN 321-818X. Tel: 609-625-2776. FAX: 609-625-8143. *Librn*, Julie Reist
PLEASANTVILLE BRANCH, 132 W Washington Ave, Pleasantville, 08232. SAN 322-6018. Tel: 609-641-1778. FAX: 609-641-0771. *Librn*, Pam Saunders; Staff 8 (MLS 2, Non-MLS 6)
Founded 1955
Mem of Atlantic County Library
Partic in South Jersey Regional Library Cooperative
SOMERS POINT BRANCH, 747 Shore Rd, Somers Point, 08244. SAN 310-5040. Tel: 609-927-7113. FAX: 609-926-3062. *Coordr*, Mary Jane Bolden
VENTNOR BRANCH, 6500 Atlantic Ave, Ventnor, 08406. SAN 320-3611. Tel: 609-823-4614. FAX: 609-823-2639. *Librn*, Ellen Eisen
Bookmobiles: 1

MAYWOOD

P MAYWOOD PUBLIC LIBRARY, 459 Maywood Ave, 07607-1909. SAN 310-2777. Tel: 201-845-2915. FAX: 201-845-7387. E-Mail: mayw1@bccls.org. Web Site: www.bccls.org/maywood. *Dir*, Diane Rhodes; E-Mail: rhodes@bccls.org
Founded 1951. Pop 9,800; Circ 72,851
Jan 1999-Dec 1999 Income $413,155. Mats Exp Books $55,000. Sal $199,765
Library Holdings: Bk Vols 60,302; Bk Titles 59,269; Per Subs 79
Subject Interests: Automobile manuals
Automation Activity & Vendor Info: (Cataloging) DRA; (Circulation) DRA
Database Vendor: DRA
Publications: Library guide (flyer)
Partic in Bergen County Cooperative Library System
Friends of the Library Group

MC GUIRE AFB

UNITED STATES AIR FORCE
A MC GUIRE AIR FORCE BASE LIBRARY FL4484, 305 SVS/SVRL, 2603 Tuskegee Airmen Ave, 08641-5016. SAN 350-8560. Tel: 609-724-2079. FAX: 609-724-5108. E-Mail: baselib@x1.mcguire.af.mil. *In Charge*, Tracey Hunter Hayes; Staff 7 (MLS 1, Non-MLS 6)
Library Holdings: Bk Vols 36,000; Per Subs 200
Subject Interests: Aviation, Military history
Special Collections: Air Force History Coll
Partic in South Jersey Regional Library Cooperative

MENDHAM

CR ASSUMPTION COLLEGE FOR SISTERS LIBRARY, Mallinckrodt Convent, 350 Bernardsville Rd, 07945. SAN 310-2793. Tel: 973-543-6528. FAX: 973-543-9459. E-Mail: socc@nac.net. *Coll Develop, Dir*, Sister Edmund Joseph Reif; *Per*, Catherine Laboure Hutt; Staff 4 (MLS 1, Non-MLS 3)
Founded 1961. Enrl 50; Fac 21; Highest Degree: Associate
Jul 2000-Jun 2001 Income $10,800. Mats Exp $11,000, Books $5,000, Per/Ser (Incl. Access Fees) $3,000, Micro $1,000, AV Equip $2,000
Library Holdings: Bk Vols 28,300; Bk Titles 27,892; Per Subs 91
Subject Interests: German lang, Philosophy, Theology
Publications: New Books Listing (monthly)
Restriction: Open to others by appointment, Open to students
Function: Outside services via phone, cable & mail, Reference services available

P MENDHAM FREE PUBLIC LIBRARY,* 10 Hilltop Rd, 07945. SAN 321-4931. Tel: 973-543-4152. FAX: 973-543-9096. *Dir*, Karen Yannetta; Staff 5 (MLS 1, Non-MLS 4)
Founded 1912. Pop 5,000
Library Holdings: Bk Titles 32,000; Per Subs 55
Special Collections: Local History Coll
Publications: Legacy through the Lens (local archit hist); Library Notes (quarterly newsletter); Mendham Poets (irregular)
Friends of the Library Group

MENDHAM TOWNSHIP

P MENDHAM TOWNSHIP LIBRARY, Cherry Lane, 07926. (Mail add: Cherry Lane, Box 500, 07926-0500), SAN 310-0421. Tel: 973-543-4018. FAX: 973-543-5472. Web Site: www.gti.net/main/ment/. *Dir*, Eileen Burnash; E-Mail: eburnash2000@yahoo.com; Staff 6 (MLS 1, Non-MLS 5)
Pop 4,900; Circ 60,000
Library Holdings: Bk Titles 32,000; Per Subs 70
Subject Interests: Bks on tape, Gardening, Local history, Mysteries
Database Vendor: CARL, Ebsco - EbscoHost
Publications: Newsletter
Mem of Morris County Free Libr
Partic in Morris Automated Information Network
Special Services for the Blind - Bks on tape
Friends of the Library Group

MERCHANTVILLE

P MERCHANTVILLE SCHOOL & PUBLIC LIBRARY,* 130 S Centre St, 08109-2201. SAN 310-2823. Tel: 856-663-1091, Ext 22. FAX: 856-486-9755. *Librn*, Diane Edmonds; Staff 1 (MLS 1)
Library Holdings: Bk Titles 18,280; Per Subs 62
Special Collections: Children's Materials; Local History
Mem of Camden County Library System
Friends of the Library Group

METUCHEN

S LIBRA TECHNOLOGIES INC LIBRARY,* 101 Liberty St, 08840-1215. SAN 374-9215. Tel: 732-321-5200. FAX: 732-321-5203. *Librn*, Trean K Blumenthal
Library Holdings: Bk Vols 500; Per Subs 20
Subject Interests: Analytical chemistry, Chemistry

P METUCHEN PUBLIC LIBRARY,* 480 Middlesex Ave, 08840. SAN 310-2831. Tel: 732-632-8526. FAX: 732-632-8535. *Dir*, Melody B Kokola; *Ref*, Hsi Hsi Chung; *Ad Servs*, John McBride; *Ch Servs*, Glynis Brookens
Founded 1870. Pop 12,804; Circ 131,592
Jan 1998-Dec 1999 Income $574,705, State $14,669, City $512,885, Locally Generated Income $47,151. Mats Exp $83,506, Books $66,175, Per/Ser (Incl. Access Fees) $8,276, Micro $3,500, AV Equip $3,000. Sal $329,527 (Prof $167,869)
Library Holdings: Bk Vols 75,911; Bk Titles 72,500; Per Subs 121
Subject Interests: Biography, Genealogy, Literacy, Mystery
Special Collections: Chinese Language Coll; Large Print
Partic in Infolink Eastern New Jersey Regional Library Cooperative, Inc; Librs of Middlesex Automation Consortium
Special Services for the Deaf - Deaf publications; Staff with knowledge of sign language
Friends of the Library Group

MICKLETON

P EAST GREENWICH LIBRARY,* 535 Kings Hwy, PO Box 26, 08056. SAN 376-0634. Tel: 856-423-1149. FAX: 856-423-3036. E-Mail: eastgreenwichlib@yahoo.com. *Dir*, Carol Baughman
Library Holdings: Bk Titles 13,000; Per Subs 53
Open Mon, Tues & Thurs 9-12:45 & 6-8:45, Wed 9-12:45 & 3-8:45, Sat 9-3:45

MIDDLESEX

P MIDDLESEX PUBLIC LIBRARY, 1300 Mountain Ave, 08846. SAN 310-284X. Tel: 732-356-6602. FAX: 732-356-8420. *Dir*, Carole Chellis; E-Mail: cchellis@lmxac.org; Staff 14 (MLS 5, Non-MLS 9)
Founded 1963. Pop 13,055; Circ 74,282
Jan 2000-Dec 2000 Income $377,006, State $14,015, City $357,991, Locally Generated Income $5,000
Library Holdings: Bk Titles 58,000; Per Subs 147
Database Vendor: CARL
Partic in Librs of Middlesex Automation Consortium
Friends of the Library Group

MIDDLETOWN

P MIDDLETOWN TOWNSHIP PUBLIC LIBRARY, 55 New Monmouth Rd, 07748. SAN 350-8749. Tel: 732-671-3700. FAX: 732-671-5839. Web Site: www.middletown.lib.nj.us. *Dir*, Susan O'Neal; *Ch Servs*, Laurie Mason; *Tech Servs*, Shan An; *Circ*, Pamela Curchin; *Ref*, Joann Strano; Staff 11 (MLS 11)
Founded 1921. Pop 68,355; Circ 510,330
Jan 1999-Dec 1999 Income $2,379,726, State $73,194, City $1,950,140, Federal $25,000, Locally Generated Income $60,550. Mats Exp $352,773, Books $266,000, Per/Ser (Incl. Access Fees) $35,203, Micro $20,870, AV Equip $30,700. Sal $1,325,653

Library Holdings: Bk Vols 199,792; Bk Titles 150,181; Per Subs 292
Subject Interests: NJ mat
Automation Activity & Vendor Info: (Acquisitions) epixtech, inc.; (Cataloging) epixtech, inc.; (Circulation) epixtech, inc.; (Course Reserve) epixtech, inc.; (OPAC) epixtech, inc.; (Serials) epixtech, inc.
Database Vendor: epixtech, inc.
Friends of the Library Group
Branches: 3
BAYSHORE, 168 Main St, Port Monmouth, 07758. SAN 350-8773. Tel: 732-787-1568. *Branch Mgr*, Eileen McGrath
Library Holdings: Bk Titles 15,507
Friends of the Library Group
LINCROFT BRANCH, 722 Newman Springs Rd, Lincroft, 07738. SAN 350-8803. Tel: 732-747-1140. *Branch Mgr*, Dorothea Hand; Tel: 732-747-1140
Library Holdings: Bk Titles 18,279
Friends of the Library Group
NAVESINK BRANCH, Monmouth Ave, Navesink, 07752. SAN 350-8838. Tel: 732-291-1120. *Branch Mgr*, Lois Juccarone
Library Holdings: Bk Titles 14,554
Friends of the Library Group

S MONMOUTH COUNTY PARK SYSTEM, Elvin McDonald Horticultural Library, 352 Red Hill Rd, 07748. (Mail add: 805 Newman Springs Rd, 07738), SAN 323-6021. Tel: 732-671-6050. *Librn*, Mae H Fisher
Founded 1979
Library Holdings: Bk Titles 5,500; Per Subs 30

MIDLAND PARK

P MIDLAND PARK MEMORIAL LIBRARY,* 250 Godwin Ave, 07432. SAN 310-2858. Tel: 201-444-2390. FAX: 201-444-2813. E-Mail: mipk1@bccls.org. *Dir*, Elaine Lowell; Staff 6 (MLS 3, Non-MLS 3)
Founded 1937. Pop 7,047
Jan 1997-Dec 1998 Income $285,000. Mats Exp $60,000. Sal $173,000
Library Holdings: Bk Vols 55,000; Per Subs 155
Subject Interests: Local history
Mem of Bergen County Co-op Libr Syst; Highlands Regional Libr Coop
Friends of the Library Group

MILFORD

P HOLLAND ALEXANDRIA FREE PUBLIC LIBRARY, (Formerly Holland Alexandria Township Free Public Library), 129 Spring Mills Rd, 08848. SAN 310-2866. Tel: 908-995-4767. FAX: 908-995-4767. E-Mail: htlibrary@eclipse.net. Web Site: www.eclipse.net/~htlibrary. *Dir*, Sylvia Gidwani
Founded 1965. Pop 9,300; Circ 22,024
1998-1999 Income $52,612, State $612, Locally Generated Income $13,000, Other $4,000. Mats Exp $2,335, Books $2,200, Per/Ser (Incl. Access Fees) $135. Sal $23,500
Library Holdings: Bk Vols 22,958; Per Subs 46
Subject Interests: Large print
Automation Activity & Vendor Info: (Cataloging) epixtech, inc.; (Circulation) epixtech, inc.; (OPAC) epixtech, inc.
Publications: Library Links
Mem of Hunterdon County Library
Open Mon-Fri 9-12 & 3-8, Sat 9-3

P MILFORD PUBLIC LIBRARY,* PO Box F, 08848. SAN 310-2874. Tel: 908-995-4072. *Librn*, Nancy Beisel
Circ 13,423
Library Holdings: Bk Vols 19,500; Per Subs 34

MILLBURN

R CONGREGATION B'NAI ISRAEL, Gruenewald Library, 160 Millburn Ave, 07041. SAN 310-2890. Tel: 973-379-3811. FAX: 973-379-1941. E-Mail: cbi160@aol.com. Web Site: www.cbi-nj.org.
Founded 1952
Library Holdings: Bk Vols 3,640; Bk Titles 3,600; Per Subs 15
Subject Interests: Judaica

P MILLBURN FREE PUBLIC LIBRARY, 200 Glen Ave, 07041. SAN 310-2912. Tel: 973-376-1006. FAX: 973-376-0104. Web Site: www.millburn.lib.nj.us. *Dir*, William Swinson; Tel: 973-376-1006, Ext 26, E-Mail: bswinson@millburn.lib.nj.us; *Ref*, Susan Pober; Tel: 973-376-1006, Ext 17, E-Mail: susan@millburn.lib.nj.us; *Tech Servs*, Luisa Porcella; Tel: 973-376-1006, Ext 21, E-Mail: luisa@millburn.lib.nj.us; Staff 9 (MLS 9)
Founded 1938. Pop 17,962; Circ 264,491
Jan 1999-Dec 1999 Income $1,818,263, State $19,999, City $1,667,200, Federal $38,500, Locally Generated Income $92,564. Mats Exp $1,795,064, Books $114,634, Per/Ser (Incl. Access Fees) $13,520, AV Equip $12,983, Electronic Ref Mat (Incl. Access Fees) $60,653. Sal $917,745 (Prof $548,395)
Library Holdings: Bk Vols 103,165; Bk Titles 91,838; Per Subs 326
Automation Activity & Vendor Info: (Cataloging) DRA; (Circulation) DRA; (OPAC) DRA
Database Vendor: OCLC - First Search
Partic in Infolink
Friends of the Library Group

MILLTOWN

P MILLTOWN PUBLIC LIBRARY,* 20 W Church St, 08850. SAN 310-2920. Tel: 732-247-2270. FAX: 732-745-9493. Web Site: www.imxac.org/milltown. *Dir*, Christine Reed; Staff 1 (MLS 1)
Founded 1896. Pop 7,099; Circ 53,000
Library Holdings: Bk Vols 43,000; Per Subs 120
Friends of the Library Group

MILLVILLE

P MILLVILLE PUBLIC LIBRARY,* 210 Buck St, 08332. SAN 310-2939. Tel: 856-825-7087. Interlibrary Loan Service Tel: 856-827-7087. FAX: 856-327-8572. Web Site: www.cumberland.county.lib.nj.us. *Ch Servs*, Richard King; *Cat*, Bernadette Conover; *Dir*, Lorraine O'Dell
Founded 1864. Pop 26,000; Circ 67,000
Jul 1997-Jun 1998 Income $557,545, State $29,778, City $501,909, Locally Generated Income $24,028, Other $1,830. Mats Exp $65,210, Books $49,262, Per/Ser (Incl. Access Fees) $5,490, Micro $3,602. Sal $248,929 (Prof $114,050)
Library Holdings: Bk Vols 70,386; Bk Titles 61,524; Per Subs 180
Special Collections: Career & College Center; New Jersey Coll
Mem of S Jersey Regional Libr Coop

S MUSEUM OF AMERICAN GLASS, Research Library, Wheaton Village, 1501 Glasstown Rd, 08332. SAN 370-3002. Tel: 856-825-6800, Ext 2746. FAX: 856-825-2410. E-Mail: mail@wheatonvillage.org. Web Site: www.wheatonvillage.org. *Curator*, Gay LeCleire Taylor; *Librn*, Dianne Wood
Library Holdings: Bk Vols 2,000
Subject Interests: Antiques
Special Collections: Charles B Gardner Coll; Glass Related; Historical Document & Photos
Restriction: By appointment only

MONMOUTH BEACH

P MONMOUTH BEACH LIBRARY,* 18 Willow Ave, 07750. SAN 310-2947. Tel: 732-229-1187. E-Mail: monmouth@shore.monmouth.us.gov. *Dir*, Nancy Leporatti; *Asst Librn*, Judith Bakos
Circ 25,000
Library Holdings: Bk Vols 45,000; Per Subs 20
Friends of the Library Group

MONMOUTH JUNCTION

S AMERICAN HOME PRODUCTS CORP, Wyeth-Ayerst Research Library, 865 Ridge Rd, 08852. (Mail add: CN 8000, 08543-8000), Tel: 732-274-4268. FAX: 732-274-4733. E-Mail: ptnlib@war.wyeth.com. *Mgr Libr Serv*, Janet Cooper Weiss; E-Mail: weissj2@war.wyeth.com; Staff 4 (MLS 2, Non-MLS 2)
Founded 1984
Library Holdings: Bk Vols 25,000; Bk Titles 6,000; Per Subs 400
Subject Interests: Biochemistry, Chemistry, Molecular biology, Neurosciences, Pharmacology
Database Vendor: Dialog, OVID Technologies, Silverplatter Information Inc.
Partic in Infolink; PALINET & Union Library Catalogue of Pennsylvania

P SOUTH BRUNSWICK PUBLIC LIBRARY, 110 Kingston Lane, 08852. SAN 310-2955. Tel: 732-329-4000, Ext 280. Reference Tel: 732-329-4000, Ext 286. FAX: 732-329-0573. Web Site: www.lmac.org/sobr. *Dir*, Lorraine Jackson; Tel: 732-329-4000, Ext 282; *Asst Dir*, Carl Heffington; Tel: 732-329-4000, Ext 287, E-Mail: hefngton@lmac.org; *YA Servs*, Judy Pietrobono; Tel: 732-329-4000, Ext 286; *Ref*, Chris Carbone; Tel: 732-329-4000, Ext 286; *Ch Servs*, Virginia McKee; Tel: 732-329-4000, Ext 285; Staff 11 (MLS 11)
Founded 1967. Pop 25,792; Circ 363,399
Jan 1999-Dec 1999 Income $1,953,787, State $33,225, City $1,732,855, Federal $27,259, Locally Generated Income $77,136. Mats Exp $231,117, Books $174,900, Per/Ser (Incl. Access Fees) $30,921, Presv $1,180, AV Equip $19,439, Electronic Ref Mat (Incl. Access Fees) $17,435. Sal $1,088,509
Library Holdings: Bk Vols 124,018; Per Subs 500
Subject Interests: Adult basic reading, Arabic language, Chinese, ESL-English as a second language, Local history, NJ hist, Spanish
Automation Activity & Vendor Info: (Circulation) CARL
Database Vendor: CARL
Publications: Calendar of Events; Check It Out; Echo

Partic in Libr of Middlesex
South Brunswick Public Library Foundation established in 1996
Friends of the Library Group
Bookmobiles: 1

MONROE TOWNSHIP

P MONROE TOWNSHIP PUBLIC LIBRARY, 4 Municipal Plaza, 08831. SAN 375-5061. Tel: 732-521-5000. FAX: 732-521-4766. Web Site: www.monroetwp.com. *Dir*, Irene Goldberg; Tel: 732-521-5000, Ext 107, E-Mail: igoldber@lmxac.org; *Asst Dir, Ch Servs*, Leah Wagner; Tel: 732-521-5000, Ext 108, E-Mail: lwagner@lmxac.org; *Ch Servs*, Joan Henry; Tel: 732-521-5000, Ext 117, E-Mail: jhenry@lmxac.org; *Tech Servs*, Tracy Lau; *Circ*, MaryAnn Reiner; Tel: 732-521-5000, Ext 101, E-Mail: mreiner@lmxac.org; *Ref*, Sean Garvey; Tel: 732-521-5000, Ext 163, E-Mail: sgarvey@lmxac.org; *Ref*, Sharon Goldschneider; Tel: 732-521-5000, Ext 165; *Ref*, Susan Grotyohann; Tel: 732-521-5000, Ext 153; *Ref*, Betty Lau; Tel: 732-521-5000, Ext 105, E-Mail: blau@lmxac.org; *Ref*, JoAnn Jesson Post; Tel: 732-521-5000, Ext 106; Staff 24 (MLS 8, Non-MLS 16)
Founded 1989. Pop 28,000; Circ 200,000
Jan 2000-Dec 2000 Income $950,393, State $21,893, City $928,500. Mats Exp $200,000, Books $150,000, Per/Ser (Incl. Access Fees) $15,000. Sal $583,279
Library Holdings: Bk Vols 78,320; Bk Titles 67,790; Per Subs 155
Special Collections: Holocaust (Henry Ricklis Memorial Coll), bks, AV
Automation Activity & Vendor Info: (Circulation) CARL
Partic in LMX Automation Consortium
Special Services for the Deaf - Books on deafness & sign language; High interest/low vocabulary books; Staff with knowledge of sign language; TTY machine
Special Services for the Blind - Large screen microcomputer monitor with software; Optelek; Reading edge system
Friends of the Library Group

MONTCLAIR

J GIBBS COLLEGE LIBRARY, 22 S Park St, 07042. SAN 321-4729. Tel: 973-509-0902. FAX: 973-744-8096. *Librn*, Dawn Quinn; Staff 3 (MLS 2, Non-MLS 1)
Enrl 1,000; Highest Degree: Associate
Library Holdings: Bk Vols 8,600; Bk Titles 8,300; Per Subs 89
Subject Interests: Secretarial arts
Special Collections: Katharine Gibbs Schools Archives
Function: ILL available, Reference services available
Partic in ReBL

S MONTCLAIR ART MUSEUM, Le Brun Library, 3 S Mountain Ave, 07042-1747. SAN 310-2963. Tel: 973-746-5555. FAX: 973-746-9118. E-Mail: library@montclair-art.org. Web Site: montclair-art.org. *Librn*, Susanna Sabolcsi
Founded 1924
Library Holdings: Bk Titles 14,000; Per Subs 50
Subject Interests: Am art, Am Indian, Hist of art
Special Collections: 1993 Kaleidoscopic Views Bookplates Coll; Artist' Five Coll; Book Plate Coll; Bookplate Work of David McNeely Stauffer, 1990; Exhibris (selected Bookplates of Arthur Nelson Macdonald)
Open Wed-Fri 9:30-4:30, closed Aug
Friends of the Library Group

M MONTCLAIR COMMUNITY HOSPITAL, Medical Library,* 120 Harrison Ave, 07042. SAN 375-7021. Tel: 973-744-7300. FAX: 973-509-6103.
Library Holdings: Bk Titles 250

P MONTCLAIR FREE PUBLIC LIBRARY,* 50 S Fullerton Ave, 07042. SAN 350-8927. Tel: 973-744-0500. FAX: 973-744-2349. Web Site: www.montlib.com. *Dir*, Michael L Connell; *Asst Dir*, Carol Robinson; *Ad Servs*, Mary L Cass; *Ch Servs*, Mary Riskind
Founded 1893. Pop 35,911; Circ 289,945
1999-2000 Income (Main Library and Branch Library) $3,062,800, State $48,600, City $2,724,200, Other $290,000. Mats Exp $201,639, Books $144,282, Per/Ser (Incl. Access Fees) $20,581, AV Equip $14,208, Other Print Mats $8,750, Electronic Ref Mat (Incl. Access Fees) $13,818. Sal $2,215,445 (Prof $38,523)
Library Holdings: Bk Vols 182,046; Bk Titles 153,760; Per Subs 1,009
Subject Interests: Architecture, Art, Bus, Ethnic studies, Feminism, Folkland fairy tales, Humanities, Mgt, Music
Special Collections: Art & Music, bks, mss, repro & rec; College & Career; Delahinty Irish; Folk Arts; Howard Vogt Music; Montclair History, pictures & micro; Newberry & Caldecott
Automation Activity & Vendor Info: (Circulation) CLSI LIBS
Partic in Infolink
Special Services for the Deaf - Books on deafness & sign language; Staff with knowledge of sign language; TTY machine
Friends of the Library Group
Branches: 1
BELLEVUE, 185 Bellevue Ave, Upper Montclair, 07043. SAN 350-8951. Tel: 973-744-2468. FAX: 973-744-3712.
Founded 1914
Library Holdings: Bk Vols 19,000; Per Subs 71
Friends of the Library Group

MOUNTAINSIDE HOSPITAL
M FRANK A ASSMANN HEALTH SCIENCE LIBRARY, One Bay Ave, 07042-4898. SAN 350-8986. Tel: 973-429-6240. FAX: 973-680-7850. Web Site: ilalpha.infolink.org/ahslibraries. *Dir*, Patricia Regenberg; E-Mail: pat.regenberg@ahsys.org; Staff 2 (MLS 1, Non-MLS 1)
1998-1999 Income $200,000. Mats Exp $183,212, Books $12,000, Per/Ser (Incl. Access Fees) $55,000, Micro $8,000. Sal $96,500 (Prof $62,000)
Library Holdings: Bk Titles 3,000; Per Subs 306
Subject Interests: Hosp admin, Medicine, Psychology
Partic in Basic Health Sciences Library Network; Infolink Eastern New Jersey Regional Library Cooperative, Inc; New Jersey Health Sciences Library Network

M LOUISE A MERSHON LIBRARY, School of Nursing, Bay & Highland Ave, 07042. SAN 350-901X. Tel: 973-429-6063. FAX: 973-429-6068. Web Site: atlantichealth.org. *Librn*, Juliette Ratner; E-Mail: juliette.ratner@ahsys.org
Founded 1895. Enrl 110; Fac 16
1999-2000 Income $13,500. Mats Exp $13,500, Books $2,000, Per/Ser (Incl. Access Fees) $8,000, Micro $3,500
Library Holdings: Bk Vols 1,800; Per Subs 120
Subject Interests: Nursing
Special Collections: History of Nursing
Restriction: By appointment only
Partic in Basic Health Sciences Library Network; New Jersey Health Sciences Library Network

MONTVALE

S INSTITUTE OF MANAGEMENT ACCOUNTANTS MCLEOD INFORMATION CENTER, 10 Paragon Dr, 07645-1760. SAN 311-9122. Tel: 201-573-9000, Ext 235. FAX: 201-573-9795. E-Mail: library@imanet.org. Web Site: www.imanet.org/content/Benefits_and_Services/information_Center/infocntr.htm. *Dir*, Kathleen Muldowney. Subject Specialists: *Accounting*, Kathleen Muldowney; *Management*, Kathleen Muldowney; Staff 2 (MLS 1, Non-MLS 1)
Founded 1919
Library Holdings: Bk Vols 10,000; Bk Titles 5,000; Per Subs 300
Subject Interests: Accounting, Data proc, Financial mgt, Mgt
Database Vendor: ProQuest
Publications: Bibliographies (activity based corting, internal auditing, environmental accounting, etc) (Bibliographies)
Restriction: Members only
Function: For research purposes
Partic in Highlands Regional Library Cooperative

M MEDICAL ECONOMICS CO LIBRARY,* 5 Paragon Dr, 07645-1742. SAN 328-3097. Tel: 201-358-7200. FAX: 201-722-2799. *Librn*, Sheila Fitzgibbon
Library Holdings: Bk Vols 1,000; Per Subs 700
Special Collections: State Medical Journals
Partic in Medical Libr Asn

P MONTVALE FREE PUBLIC LIBRARY,* E Grand Ave, 07645. SAN 310-298X. Tel: 201-391-5090. FAX: 201-307-5647. E-Mail: movl1@bccls.org. Web Site: www.bccls.org/montvale. *Dir*, Susan J Ruttenber; *Librn*, David Franz; Staff 2 (MLS 2)
Founded 1975. Pop 6,946
Library Holdings: Bk Titles 38,700; Per Subs 150
Partic in Highlands Regional Library Cooperative
Friends of the Library Group

S RECKITT & COLMAN INC, Information Center,* One Philips Pkwy, 07645-1810. SAN 310-2998. Tel: 201-573-6031. FAX: 201-573-6017.
Library Holdings: Bk Vols 1,500; Per Subs 100
Subject Interests: Bus, Chemistry, Finishes, Marketing, Mgt, Microbiology, Surfactants, Waxes
Partic in HRLC

MONTVILLE

M BERLEX LABORATORIES LIBRARY, 340 Changebridge Rd, PO Box 1000, 07045-1000. SAN 310-0669. Tel: 973-276-3702. FAX: 973-276-2014. *Librn*, Anne Little; *Librn*, Kathleen Millington; *Librn*, Patricia Rodgers; Staff 4 (MLS 2, Non-MLS 2)
Founded 1972
Library Holdings: Bk Vols 300; Per Subs 200
Subject Interests: Bus, Medicine, Pharmaceutical indust, Radiology, Statistics, Toxicology
Automation Activity & Vendor Info: (Acquisitions) Inmagic, Inc.; (Cataloging) Inmagic, Inc.; (Circulation) Inmagic, Inc.; (Course Reserve) Inmagic, Inc.; (ILL) Inmagic, Inc.; (Media Booking) Inmagic, Inc.; (OPAC)

Inmagic, Inc.; (Serials) Inmagic, Inc.
Publications: Berlex Library News; Serials Holding List
Restriction: Not open to public

P MONTVILLE TOWNSHIP PUBLIC LIBRARY,* 90 Horseneck Rd, 07045-9626. SAN 310-3005. Tel: 973-402-0900. FAX: 973-402-0592. Web Site: www.montvillelib.org. *Dir*, Diana Smartt; *Ch Servs*, Patti Farmer; *Ref*, Elaine Reise; Staff 23 (MLS 3, Non-MLS 20)
Founded 1921. Pop 20,105; Circ 200,000
Jan 1998-Dec 1998 Income $804,792. Mats Exp $125,500, Books $117,000, Per/Ser (Incl. Access Fees) $6,000, Micro $2,500. Sal $365,931 (Prof $157,156)
Library Holdings: Bk Vols 65,000; Bk Titles 60,000
Automation Activity & Vendor Info: (Acquisitions) DRA; (Cataloging) DRA; (Circulation) DRA; (Course Reserve) DRA; (ILL) DRA; (OPAC) DRA
Partic in Highlands Regional Library Cooperative; Morris Automated Information Network; New Jersey Library Network
Friends of the Library Group

MOORESTOWN

S HISTORICAL SOCIETY OF MOORESTOWN LIBRARY, 12 High St, PO Box 477, 08057. SAN 372-6762. Tel: 856-235-0353. E-Mail: historical@moorestown.com. Web Site: www.moorestown.com/community/history/index.html. *Librn*, Jeannie Roulet Minchak
Founded 1969
Library Holdings: Bk Vols 550; Bk Titles 500
Subject Interests: Manuscripts, Maps, Photos
Special Collections: Historic Buildings & House Index; Moorestown History & Genealogy
Restriction: Non-circulating
Function: Photocopies available

S LOCKHEED MARTIN, Naval Electronics & Surveillance Systems Engineering Library, 199 Borton Landing Rd, 08057-3054. (Mail add: PO Box 1027, 08057-0927), SAN 310-303X. Tel: 856-722-3394. FAX: 856-273-5249. *Senior Librn*, Natalie J Mamchur; E-Mail: natalie.j.mamchur@lmco.com; *Assoc Librn*, Elisa Valenzuela
Founded 1953
Library Holdings: Bk Titles 30,000; Per Subs 150
Subject Interests: Associated electronics, Bus sci, Computer science, Electronics, Engineering, Mathematics, Mil strategy, Physics, Radar electronics
Automation Activity & Vendor Info: (Cataloging) TechLIB; (Circulation) TechLIB; (OPAC) TechLIB
Restriction: By appointment only
Partic in Dialog Corporation

P MOORESTOWN FREE PUBLIC LIBRARY, 111 W Second St, 08057-2481. SAN 310-3021. Tel: 856-234-0333. FAX: 856-778-9536. Web Site: www.moorestown.lib.nj.us. *Dir*, Deborah Ellis Dennis; Tel: 856-234-0333, Ext 3029, E-Mail: debbie@burlnet.org; *Ad Servs*, Maria Esche; *Ch Servs*, Melanie Crotty; *Tech Servs*, Joseph Galbraith; Staff 18 (MLS 5, Non-MLS 13)
Founded 1853. Pop 17,000; Circ 170,000
Jan 2000-Dec 2000 Income $1,000,947, State $20,975, City $931,020, Locally Generated Income $48,952. Mats Exp $115,000, Books $89,000, Per/Ser (Incl. Access Fees) $16,000, Micro $3,000, Electronic Ref Mat (Incl. Access Fees) $7,000. Sal $575,990 (Prof $262,278)
Library Holdings: Bk Vols 116,000; Bk Titles 108,000; Per Subs 270
Automation Activity & Vendor Info: (Acquisitions) Innovative Interfaces Inc.; (Cataloging) Innovative Interfaces Inc.; (Circulation) Innovative Interfaces Inc.; (OPAC) Innovative Interfaces Inc.
Database Vendor: Ebsco - EbscoHost, GaleNet
Partic in South Jersey Regional Library Cooperative
Friends of the Library Group

MORRIS PLAINS

P MORRIS PLAINS LIBRARY,* 77 Glenbrook Rd, 07950. SAN 310-3048. Tel: 973-538-2599. FAX: 973-538-8974. *Dir*, Charlot Lamm
Founded 1881. Pop 5,700; Circ 32,947
Library Holdings: Bk Vols 19,586; Per Subs 40
Mem of Morris County Free Libr
Friends of the Library Group

S OLI SYSTEMS, INC LIBRARY, 108 American Rd, 07950. SAN 375-846X. Tel: 973-539-4996. FAX: 973-539-5922. E-Mail: olisys@worldnet.att.net. *Pres*, Marshall Rafal; *Librn, Per*, Peiming Wang; *Asst Librn*, Margaret Lencka
Founded 1990
Feb 1998-Jan 1999 Mats Exp $33,500, Books $20,000, Per/Ser (Incl. Access Fees) $5,000, AV Equip $6,500, Other Print Mats $2,000. Sal $75,000
Library Holdings: Bk Titles 1,000; Per Subs 40
Subject Interests: Chemistry

M PFIZER INC, (Formerly Warner-Lambert Company), Information Center, 182 Tabor Rd, 07950. SAN 310-3056. Tel: 973-385-2875. FAX: 973-385-4756. *Mgr*, Ellen Callanan; Staff 4 (MLS 3, Non-MLS 1)
Library Holdings: Bk Vols 15,000; Per Subs 400
Subject Interests: Bus, Confectionery, Medicine, Mgt, Microbiology, Pharmaceuticals
Restriction: Company library

MORRISTOWN

ALLIED-SIGNAL, INC
S TECHNICAL INFORMATION SERVICES, 101 Columbia Rd, CRL-3 Bldg, 07962-1021. SAN 350-9044. Tel: 973-455-2000. FAX: 973-455-5295. *Librn*, Linda Morgan; Staff 4 (MLS 4)
Founded 1965
Library Holdings: Bk Titles 30,000; Per Subs 650
Subject Interests: Bus as related to the chem, Chemistry, Econ as related to the chem, Energy indust, Environ health, Immunology, Mat sci, Medicine, Occupational health, Physics, Polymers, Toxicology
Special Collections: Annual Reports; Consultants Reports
Partic in Dialog Corporation; Nat Libr of Med

S CANAL SOCIETY OF NEW JERSEY, Museum & Library, PO Box 737, 07963-0737. SAN 375-2607. Tel: 908-722-9556. FAX: 908-722-9556. Web Site: www.canalsocietynj.org. *Pres*, Robert Barth; Tel: 908-722-7428, E-Mail: bobandlindabarth@worldnet.att.net; *Librn*, Myra Snook
Founded 1969
Library Holdings: Bk Vols 400
Restriction: By appointment only

C COLLEGE OF SAINT ELIZABETH, Mahoney Library, 2 Convent Rd, 07960-6989. SAN 310-0936. Tel: 973-290-4237. Interlibrary Loan Service Tel: 973-290-4240. FAX: 973-290-4226. Web Site: www.st-elizabeth.edu. *Dir*, Bro Paul Chervenie; Tel: 973-290-4233; *Ref*, Renita Krasnodebski; Tel: 973-290-4239; *Per*, Mark Ferguson; *Per*, Nolan Ledet; Tel: 973-290-4238; *Cat*, Lois Ann Griglak; *Admin Assoc*, Barbara Giordano
Founded 1899. Highest Degree: Master
Jul 1999-Jun 2000 Mats Exp $132,379, Books $49,198, Per/Ser (Incl. Access Fees) $79,297, Presv $3,884
Library Holdings: Bk Vols 110,230; Bk Titles 104,805; Per Subs 830
Subject Interests: Bus, Econ, Education, Literature, Nursing, Nutrition, Theology
Special Collections: Atlases (Phillips Coll); History of Chemistry (Florence E Wall Coll); World War I (Henry C & Ann Fox Wolfe Coll), literary first & signed editions
Database Vendor: Ebsco - EbscoHost, GaleNet, Lexis-Nexis, OCLC - First Search, Silverplatter Information Inc.
Partic in OCLC Online Computer Library Center, Inc; PALINET & Union Library Catalogue of Pennsylvania

S FINANCIAL EXECUTIVES RESEARCH FOUNDATION LIBRARY,* 10 Madison Ave, PO Box 1938, 07962-1938. SAN 311-7650. Tel: 973-898-4605. FAX: 973-898-6636. *Librn*, Victoria Wollny
Founded 1944
Subject Interests: Acctg mgt, Financial
Restriction: Members only

S IRISH-AMERICAN CULTURAL INSTITUTE LIBRARY, (Formerly Irish-American Cultural Association Library), One Lackawanna Pl, 07960. SAN 376-1592. Tel: 973-605-1991. FAX: 973-605-8875. E-Mail: irishwaynj@aol.com. Web Site: www.irishaci.org. *Librn*, Ann Hennessey
Library Holdings: Bk Vols 2,100
Subject Interests: Culture, Irish, Irish hist, Politics, Sociology
Restriction: Non-circulating to the public
Function: Research library

P JOINT FREE PUBLIC LIBRARY OF MORRISTOWN & MORRIS TOWNSHIP, One Miller Rd, 07960. SAN 310-3099. Tel: 973-538-6161. FAX: 973-267-4064. Web Site: www.jfpl.com. *Dir*, Susan H Gulick; E-Mail: sgulick@ushwy1.com; *Asst Dir*, Maria Norton; *Ch Servs*, Arlene Sprague; *Circ*, Ruth Bensley; *Per*, Tim Lynch; *Ref*, Polly Lacey; *Tech Servs*, Diana Cheng
Founded 1917. Pop 39,000; Circ 270,000
Library Holdings: Bk Vols 180,000; Per Subs 573
Subject Interests: Arts, Astronomy, Genealogy, Local NJ hist, Rare children's bks
Publications: Early Printing in Morristown, New Jersey; In Lights & Shadows: Morristown in three centuries; Men from Morris County New Jersey who served in the American Revolution; Morris Township, New Jersey: A Glimpse into the past; Setting up our own City, '93
Friends of the Library Group
Branches: 1
NEW JERSEY HISTORY & GENEALOGY DEPARTMENT, One Miller Rd, 07960. Tel: 973-538-3473. *Head of Libr*, Korin Rosenkraus; *Archivist*, Chrys Jochem
Partic in Morris Automated Information Network
Friends of the Library Group
Bookmobiles: 1

S MACCULLOCH HALL HISTORICAL MUSEUM, Archives, 45 Macculloch Ave, 07960. SAN 373-2525. Tel: 973-538-2404. FAX: 973-538-9428. E-Mail: macchall@aol.com. Web Site: www.machall.org. *Curator*, Lisa Roush; E-Mail: ldroush@aol.com; Staff 2 (MLS 1, Non-MLS 1)
Library Holdings: Bk Vols 1,439

S MORRIS COUNTY HISTORICAL SOCIETY, 68 Morris Ave, 07960-4212. SAN 327-6333. Tel: 973-267-3465. FAX: 973-267-8773. *Dir*, Bonnie-Lynn Nadzeika; *Librn*, Learned T Bulman
Library Holdings: Bk Vols 2,500

GL MORRIS COUNTY LAW LIBRARY,* Court House, PO Box 910, 07963-0910. SAN 310-3110. Tel: 973-285-6371. FAX: 973-538-7664. *Librn*, Peter DeLucia
Founded 1970
Library Holdings: Bk Vols 31,000; Per Subs 35
Special Collections: Pilch Library (Henry Pilch Family Coll); West's National Reporter System Coll, ultrafiche
Partic in Westlaw

R MORRISTOWN JEWISH CENTER LIBRARY, 177 Speedwell Ave, 07960-3891. SAN 310-3137. Tel: 973-538-9292. Interlibrary Loan Service Tel: 973-538-9293. FAX: 973-538-3229.
Founded 1967
Library Holdings: Bk Titles 6,800
Subject Interests: Art, Biographies, History, Holocaust, Israel, Judaica, Lang, Relig studies
Partic in NJ NW Regional Libr Coop
Friends of the Library Group

M MORRISTOWN MEMORIAL HOSPITAL, Lathrope Health Sciences Library, 100 Madison Ave, 07962. (Mail add: PO Box 1956, 07962-1956), SAN 320-3972. Tel: 973-971-8926. FAX: 973-290-7045. E-Mail: library@ahsys.org. Web Site: www.infolink.org/ahslibraries. *Mgr*, Mary K Joyce; Staff 3 (MLS 2, Non-MLS 1)
Founded 1952
1999-2000 Income $330,000. Mats Exp $125,000, Books $20,000, Per/Ser (Incl. Access Fees) $105,000. Sal $100,000 (Prof $80,000)
Library Holdings: Bk Titles 5,000; Per Subs 400
Subject Interests: Dentistry, Medicine, Nursing
Special Collections: Consumer Health
Automation Activity & Vendor Info: (Cataloging) Inmagic, Inc.; (Circulation) Inmagic, Inc.
Mem of Highlands Regional Libr Coop
Partic in Basic Health Sciences Library Network; Cosmopolitan Biomedical Library Consortium; Health Sci Libr Asn of NJ; Highlands Regional Library Cooperative

S MORRISTOWN NATIONAL HISTORICAL PARK LIBRARY,* 30 Washington Pl, 07960. SAN 310-3145. Tel: 973-539-2017. FAX: 973-539-8361. E-Mail: morr_library@nps.gov. Web Site: www.nps.gov/morr/. *Archivist*, David Vecchioli
Founded 1933
Library Holdings: Bk Vols 45,000; Bk Titles 16,000; Per Subs 83
Subject Interests: 18th Century Am life, 18th Century culture, Am Revolutionary War, George Washington
Special Collections: Ford Papers, mss; Hessian Paper Coll; Lloyd W Smith Coll; Park Coll, mss; Washington Assoc of NJ Papers, mss
Publications: Bibliographies & MSS Guides: A Guide to the Manuscript Coll of Morristown National Historical Park; Guide to Hessian Papers of the American Revolution 1776-1783; Morristown National Historical Park Library, brochure
Partic in New Jersey Library Network
Friends of the Library Group

L PORZIO, BROMBERG & NEWMAN LIBRARY, 100 Southgate Pkwy, 07962-1997. SAN 372-4360. Tel: 973-538-4006. FAX: 973-538-5146. *Librn*, Janice Schouten; *Asst Librn*, Susan Ticker; Tel: 973-889-4311, E-Mail: slticker@pbnlaw.com
Library Holdings: Bk Vols 10,000; Per Subs 100

C RABBINICAL COLLEGE OF AMERICA, Hoffman Memorial Library,* 226 Sussex Ave, 07960. SAN 375-8478. Tel: 973-267-9404. FAX: 973-267-5208. *Adminr*, Rabbi Israel Gordon
Library Holdings: Bk Vols 67,000
Subject Interests: Hebrew

L RIKER, DANZIG, SCHERER, HYLAND & PERRETTI, Law Library, Headquarters Plaza, One Speedwell Ave, 07962. SAN 372-476X. Tel: 973-538-0800. FAX: 973-538-1984. *Librn*, Karen Brunner; E-Mail: kbrunner@riker.com; *Ref*, Josaine Royster
Library Holdings: Bk Vols 10,000

S TELCORDIA TECHNOLOGIES INC, Library & Information Services Network, 445 South St, 07960-6438. SAN 310-4206. Tel: 973-829-4603. FAX: 973-829-5891. *Dir Libr Serv*, Anne N Kneller; Staff 15 (MLS 11, Non-MLS 4)
Founded 1984
Automation Activity & Vendor Info: (Circulation) epixtech, inc.

Branches:
MORRIS RESEARCH & ENGINEERING CENTER, 445 South St, 07960-6438. SAN 328-9052. Tel: 973-829-4601. FAX: 973-829-5891. *Res*, Martha Broad; Staff 1 (MLS 1)
Library Holdings: Bk Vols 10,000; Per Subs 300
Subject Interests: Engineering, Finance, Marketing, Mathematics, Statistics, Telecommunications
Partic in New Jersey Library Network
NAVESINK RESEARCH & ENGINEERING CENTER LIBRARY, 331 Newman Springs Rd, Red Bank, 07701-5699. SAN 328-8498. Tel: 732-758-2407. FAX: 732-758-4333. *Res*, Cecilia Fiscus; Staff 1 (MLS 1)
Library Holdings: Bk Titles 14,000; Per Subs 300
Subject Interests: Chemistry, Computer science, Engineering, Mathematics, Physics, Psychology, Telecommunications
Partic in New Jersey Library Network
RARITAN RIVER SOFTWARE SYSTEMS CENTER LIBRARY, 444 Hoes Lane RRC 1D124, Piscataway, 08854-4182. SAN 328-8552. Tel: 732-699-2290. FAX: 732-336-2940. E-Mail: skaplan@telcordia.com. *Mgr*, Susan J Kaplan; Tel: 732-699-2283, Fax: 732-336-2625; *Res*, Carol Abatelli; Staff 5 (MLS 3, Non-MLS 2)
Library Holdings: Bk Titles 14,000; Per Subs 300
Subject Interests: Telecommunications
Database Vendor: Dialog, epixtech, inc., OCLC - First Search, ProQuest
Partic in NJ Regional Libr Coop

MOUNT ARLINGTON

P MOUNT ARLINGTON PUBLIC LIBRARY,* 404 Howard Blvd, 07856-1196. SAN 310-317X. Tel: 973-398-1516. FAX: 973-398-0171. Web Site: www.gti.net/mountarlington/. *Dir*, James Garland; Staff 2 (Non-MLS 2)
Founded 1968. Pop 3,630; Circ 19,845
Library Holdings: Bk Vols 20,803; Per Subs 50
Friends of the Library Group

MOUNT EPHRAIM

P MOUNT EPHRAIM PUBLIC LIBRARY,* 130 Bell Rd, 08059. SAN 310-3188. Tel: 856-931-6606. *Librn*, Gloria Marsh-Junkowski
Pop 4,500
Library Holdings: Bk Vols 6,341; Per Subs 4
Open summer hours: Mon 9-10, Tues, Thurs & Fri 9-12:30, Wed 5-8, winter hours: Mon, Thurs & Fri 1-4:30, Tues 9-1, Wed 5-8
Friends of the Library Group

MOUNT HOLLY

P MOUNT HOLLY PUBLIC LIBRARY,* 307 High St, 08060. SAN 310-3196. Tel: 609-267-7111. *Dir*, Marge Dennison; Staff 8 (MLS 2, Non-MLS 6)
Founded 1765. Pop 12,713; Circ 28,000
Library Holdings: Bk Titles 35,000; Per Subs 10
Subject Interests: Children's bks, County hist, Humanities, Local history
Special Collections: Burlington County Lyceum; Genealogical Papers (Nathan Dunn Coll), rare bks & archives; Historical Materials (Bridgeton Coll); Indians of North America Coll (William Slaughter Coll), bks & rec; King George III 1765 Charter; Local History (Shinn Coll), bks, letters, photo, personal papers; Robert Mills' Architectural Plans for Burlington Jail and Treatise on Prison Reform
Mem of Burlington County Library
Library Board established Langstaff Foundation to assist in financing Mt Holly Library/Lyceum
Friends of the Library Group

M VIRTUA MEMORIAL HOSPITAL OF BURLINGTON COUNTY, L B Reagan Health Sciences Library, 175 Madison Ave, 08060. SAN 310-320X. Tel: 609-267-0700, Ext 43021. FAX: 609-267-8073. *Librn*, Karen Quinn; E-Mail: kquinn@virtua.org
Founded 1958
Library Holdings: Bk Vols 3,000; Per Subs 150
Subject Interests: Allied health, Clinical medicine, Hosp admin, Nursing
Partic in Health Sciences Library Association Of New Jersey; South Jersey Regional Library Cooperative

MOUNT LAUREL

R ADATH EMANU-EL LIBRARY, 205 Elbow Lane, 08054. SAN 310-6144. Tel: 856-608-1200. FAX: 856-608-1218. E-Mail: adath205@aol.com. Web Site: www.adathemanuel.com. *Librn*, Rosalie Mittelman
Library Holdings: Bk Vols 1,000

L CAPEHART & SCATCHARD, PA LIBRARY, 8000 Midlantic Dr, Ste 300, 08054. SAN 323-6498. Tel: 856-234-6800, Ext 2151. FAX: 856-235-2786. Web Site: www.capehart.com. *Librn*, Francine Viden
Library Holdings: Bk Vols 8,600; Bk Titles 367; Per Subs 32
Mem of Regional Libr Coop 6

P MOUNT LAUREL LIBRARY, 100 Walt Whitman Ave, 08054. SAN 310-3218. Tel: 856-234-7319. FAX: 856-234-6916. E-Mail: ref@mtlaurel.lib.nj.us. Web Site: www.mtlaurel.lib.nj.us. *Dir*, Joan E Bernstein; E-Mail: jeb@mtlaurel.lib.nj.us; *Asst Dir*, Stephen Wolownik; *Tech Servs*, Becky Boydston; E-Mail: becky@mtlaurel.lib.nj.us; *Ch Servs*, Karen Wright; E-Mail: wright@mtlaurel.lib.nj.us; *Ad Servs*, Timothy Watters; *YA Servs*, Lisa Whitley; E-Mail: lwhitley@mtlaurel.lib.nj.us; *Circ*, Angelika Kuntz; E-Mail: angel@mtlaurel.lib.nj.us; Staff 23 (MLS 9, Non-MLS 14)
Founded 1970. Pop 40,000; Circ 200,000
Jan 2000-Dec 2000 Income $1,120,680, State $32,500, City $1,000,000, Locally Generated Income $88,180, Other $35,000. Mats Exp $105,600, Books $76,000, Per/Ser (Incl. Access Fees) $13,200, AV Equip $10,400, Electronic Ref Mat (Incl. Access Fees) $6,000. Sal $617,700 (Prof $381,997)
Library Holdings: Bk Vols 97,000; Per Subs 300
Special Collections: Adult New Reader; Alice Paul Coll
Automation Activity & Vendor Info: (Acquisitions) epixtech, inc.; (Cataloging) epixtech, inc.; (Circulation) epixtech, inc.; (OPAC) epixtech, inc.
Database Vendor: epixtech, inc.
Publications: Newsletter
Partic in South Jersey Regional Library Cooperative
Friends of the Library Group

MOUNT OLIVE

S BASF CORPORATION, Business Information Center, 3000 Continental Dr N, 07828. SAN 370-8403. Tel: 973-426-2600. FAX: 973-426-2885. *In Charge*, Rosemary Matthews; Tel: 973-426-2801
Library Holdings: Bk Vols 1,500; Per Subs 200

M KNOLL PHARMACEUTICALS, InteliQuest Library, 3000 Continental Dr N, 07828-1234. SAN 310-608X. Tel: 973-426-5562. FAX: 973-426-5569. *Dir*, Joanne Lustig; E-Mail: lustigj@knoll-pharma.com; Staff 12 (MLS 8, Non-MLS 4)
Founded 1938
Library Holdings: Bk Vols 5,000; Bk Titles 2,000; Per Subs 500
Subject Interests: Drug info, Medicine, Pharmaceutical indust
Publications: Daily News; Electronic Current Awareness; Electronic Current Awareness Bulletin
Partic in Health Sci Libr Asn of NJ; Highlands Regional Library Cooperative

MOUNTAIN LAKES

P MOUNTAIN LAKES PUBLIC LIBRARY,* 3 Elm Rd, 07046. SAN 310-3226. Tel: 973-334-5095. FAX: 973-299-1622. Web Site: www.mtlnlakes.org. *Dir*, Peggy Bulfer
Pop 3,835; Circ 49,890
Library Holdings: Bk Vols 34,305; Per Subs 62
Partic in Morris Automated Information Network
Friends of the Library Group

MOUNTAINSIDE

M CHILDREN'S SPECIALIZED HOSPITAL, Medical Library, 150 New Providence Rd, 07092. SAN 375-6955. Tel: 908-233-3720, Ext 5227. FAX: 908-301-5576. Web Site: www.csh-children.org. *Librn*, Elaine Brogan
Library Holdings: Bk Vols 3,000; Per Subs 75
Subject Interests: Neurology, Orthopedics
Partic in Health Sciences Library Association Of New Jersey

P MOUNTAINSIDE PUBLIC LIBRARY,* Constitution Plaza, 07092. SAN 310-3234. Tel: 908-233-0115. FAX: 908-232-7311. E-Mail: mtnlib@~.net. *Dir*, Miriam Bein; Staff 10 (MLS 3, Non-MLS 7)
Founded 1934. Pop 6,657; Circ 63,638
Jan 1998-Dec 1998 Income $357,642, State $7,146, City $322,234, Other $28,262. Mats Exp $63,332, Books $37,840, Per/Ser (Incl. Access Fees) $10,237, AV Equip $6,488, Electronic Ref Mat (Incl. Access Fees) $8,767. Sal $189,650 (Prof $96,613)
Library Holdings: Bk Vols 51,634; Bk Titles 48,456; Per Subs 120
Automation Activity & Vendor Info: (Cataloging) epixtech, inc.; (Circulation) epixtech, inc.; (OPAC) epixtech, inc.
Publications: Friend's Newsletter
Partic in Infolink; Union-Middlesex Regional Libr Coop, Inc
Friends of the Library Group

MULLICA HILL

P GLOUCESTER COUNTY LIBRARY SYSTEM,* 389 Wolfert Station Rd, 08062. SAN 321-0820. Tel: 856-223-6000. FAX: 856-223-6039. E-Mail: gloucester@gloucester.lib.nj.us. Web Site: www.gloucester.lib.nj.us. *Dir*, Victoria Rosch; *Tech Servs*, Barbara Rosas; *Coll Develop*, Alice Bronstein; Staff 62 (MLS 11, Non-MLS 51)
Founded 1976. Pop 80,000
Jan 1999-Dec 1999 Income (Main Library and Branch Library) $2,054,906, County $1,664,097. Mats Exp $414,890. Sal $1,186,622
Library Holdings: Bk Vols 245,860; Bk Titles 183,088; Per Subs 162
Automation Activity & Vendor Info: (Acquisitions) epixtech, inc.; (Cataloging) epixtech, inc.; (Circulation) epixtech, inc.; (OPAC) epixtech, inc.; (Serials) epixtech, inc.
Mem of NJ Regional Libr Coop
Homebound Program - Video, audio & large print circuits
Friends of the Library Group
Branches: 3
GLASSBORO PUBLIC LIBRARY, 2 Center St, Glassboro, 08028-1995. SAN 350-7513. Tel: 856-881-0001, 856-881-5571. FAX: 856-881-9338. E-Mail: gloucester@gloucester.lib.nj.us. Web Site: www.gloucester.lib.nj.us. *Mgr*, Carol Wolf; *Ch Servs*, Janet Ralston; Staff 16 (MLS 2, Non-MLS 14)
Founded 1956. Pop 18,800; Circ 96,216
Library Holdings: Bk Vols 47,000; Bk Titles 33,791; Per Subs 400
Special Collections: African-Am Coll
Partic in Gloucester County Libr Syst; South Jersey Regional Library Cooperative
GREENWICH BRANCH, 415 Swedesboro Rd, Gibbstown, 08027. SAN 310-1800. Tel: 856-423-0684. FAX: 856-423-1201. *Branch Mgr*, Patricia Woodruff
Pop 5,333; Circ 12,341
Library Holdings: Bk Vols 16,000; Per Subs 51
LOGAN TOWNSHIP, 101 Beckett Rd, Swedesboro, 08085. SAN 376-9313. Tel: 609-241-0202. FAX: 609-241-0491. Web Site: www.gloucester.lib.nj.us. *Librn*, Joan Chaika
Friends of the Library Group
Bookmobiles: 1

MURRAY HILL

S BOC GROUP, INC, Information Center, 100 Mountain Ave, 07974. SAN 310-3242. Reference Tel: 908-771-6498. FAX: 908-771-6182. Web Site: www.boc.com. *Acq, Ref*, Barbara Sinnott; *Online Servs*, Doris Wang; Staff 6 (MLS 3, Non-MLS 3)
Founded 1918
Library Holdings: Bk Titles 10,000; Per Subs 61
Subject Interests: Anesthesiology, Cryogenics, Health care, Indust gases, Metallurgy
Automation Activity & Vendor Info: (Cataloging) Sydney
Partic in Dialog Corporation

S LUCENT TECHNOLOGIES, Advanced Information Management, 600 Mountain Ave, 07974-2070. SAN 350-9435. Tel: 908-582-4636, 908-582-4840. FAX: 908-582-7591. E-Mail: libnet@library.lucent.com. *Dir, Mgr*, Audrey C Harvey; Tel: 908-582-6532, E-Mail: acharvey@lucent.com; *Librn*, Nancy J Miller; Tel: 908-582-6880
Founded 1925. Pop 60,000; Circ 88,000
Library Holdings: Bk Vols 253,965; Bk Titles 144,480; Per Subs 6,000
Subject Interests: Chemistry, Electrical engineering, Electronics, Marketing, Mathematics, Metallurgy, Mgt, Physics, Statistics, Telecommunications
Special Collections: Bell Laboratories Authored Book & Historical Coll
Publications: Acquisitions list; Announcement Bulletins; Bibliographies; Business Bulletins; Current Computing Information; Current Management Information; Current Technical Papers; Current Telecommunications Information; Mercury Abstract Bulletin; Pathfinders; Serial Catalog
Restriction: Private library
Function: Research library
Partic in BRS; Cas; CIS; Dialog Corporation; Dow Jones News Retrieval; ISI; Nat Libr of Med; Newsnet; OCLC Online Computer Library Center, Inc; SDC Info Servs; Termium; Vutext
Branches:
ALLENTOWN LIBRARY, 555 Union Blvd, Allentown, 18103-1285. SAN 350-9796. Tel: 610-712-6773. FAX: 610-712-6073. *Ref*, Jeri Scott
CRAWFORD HILL LIBRARY, Holmdel-Keyport Rd, Holmdel, 07733. SAN 329-7152. Tel: 732-888-7001. FAX: 732-949-9333. *Mgr*, M E Brennan; Tel: 732-949-5967, E-Mail: mollyb@lucent.com; *Librn*, Audrey Robertson
ENGINEERING RESEARCH & TECHNICAL INFORMATION CENTER, Carter Rd, Hopewell Twp, PO Box 900, Princeton, 08542. SAN 350-9702. Tel: 609-639-2385. FAX: 609-639-3065.
HOLMDEL LIBRARY, 101 Crawfords Corner Rd, Holmdel, 07733-3030. SAN 350-9613. Tel: 732-949-3913. FAX: 732-949-9333. *Mgr*, M E Brennan; Tel: 732-949-5967, E-Mail: mollyb@lucent.com; *Ref*, Ann Hutcheson; Staff 7 (MLS 2, Non-MLS 5)
Subject Interests: Business, Computer science, Engineering, Telecommunications
MERRIMACK VALLEY, 1600 Osgood St, North Andover, 01845. SAN 350-9583. Tel: 978-960-6750. FAX: 978-960-1211.
MURRAY HILL LIBRARY, 600 Mountain Ave Rm 6A-2000, 07974-2070. SAN 350-9648. Tel: 908-582-4636. FAX: 908-582-7591. *Mgr*, Audrey C Harvey; Tel: 908-582-6532, E-Mail: acharvey@lucent.com; *Librn*, Karen T Parry; Tel: 908-582-2526, E-Mail: kparry@lucent.com; Staff 8 (MLS 2, Non-MLS 6)
Founded 1925. Pop 4,500; Circ 10,000
Library Holdings: Bk Vols 71,301; Bk Titles 69,184; Per Subs 1,000

Restriction: Private library
Function: Research library
NAPERVILLE-LISLE LIBRARY, 2000 N Naperville Rd, Naperville, 60566. SAN 350-9508. Tel: 630-979-2551. *Mgr*, Audrey Harvey; *Ref*, Ruby Chu
OPTOELECTRONICS, 9999 Hamilton Blvd, Rm 25-135, Breingville, 18031. SAN 378-2301. Tel: 610-939-6392. *Mgr*, Betty Kaufman; *Ref*, Katie Stapleford
READING LIBRARY, 2525 N 12th St, Reading, 19612-3566. SAN 350-9826. Reference Tel: 610-939-6392. *Ref*, Katie Stapleford
WHIPPANY LIBRARY, Whippany Rd, Whippany, 07981-0903. SAN 350-9737. Reference Tel: 973-386-2037. FAX: 973-952-3647. *Mgr*, M E Brennan; *Ref*, Paula Nier

NEPTUNE

S ASBURY PARK PRESS NEWS LIBRARY, 3601 Hwy 66, 07754-2694. (Mail add: PO Box 1550, 07754-1550), SAN 309-9946. Tel: 732-922-6000, Ext 4550. FAX: 732-922-4818. *Librn*, Mollie F Graham; Staff 1 (MLS 1)
Founded 1879
Library Holdings: Bk Vols 400

M JERSEY SHORE MEDICAL CENTER, Health Sciences Library,* 1945 Rte 33, 07754-0397. SAN 310-3269. Tel: 732-776-4265. FAX: 732-776-4530. E-Mail: jsmclib@monmouth.com.; Staff 2 (MLS 1, Non-MLS 1)
Jan 1999-Dec 1999 Mats Exp $131,521, Books $21,000, Per/Ser (Incl. Access Fees) $69,880, Micro $19,000. Sal $90,893 (Prof $55,726)
Library Holdings: Bk Vols 5,000; Per Subs 500
Subject Interests: Medicine, Nursing
Special Collections: ANA Publications; NLN Publications
Publications: Acquisitions List (monthly); Journal Holdings List; Library brochure
Partic in Basic Health Sciences Library Network; Central Jersey Regional Library Cooperative; National Network Of Libraries Of Medicine - South Central Region; New Jersey Health Sciences Library Network

P NEPTUNE PUBLIC LIBRARY, 25 Neptune Blvd, 07753-1125. SAN 310-3277. Tel: 732-775-8241. FAX: 732-774-1132. E-Mail: heinlein@neptunetownship.org. Web Site: www.neptunetownship.org. *Dir*, Alan Randolph Heinlein; *Ch Servs*, Donna Donelon; *Syst Coordr*, Marian Bauman; *Cat*, Sandra Ostroski; *Ref*, Sandra Michlich; *Ch Servs*, Cheryl Otten
Founded 1924. Pop 28,500; Circ 150,000
1999-2000 Income $1,066,290. Mats Exp $106,125. Sal $520,000
Library Holdings: Bk Vols 71,000
Automation Activity & Vendor Info: (Cataloging) SIRSI; (Circulation) SIRSI; (OPAC) SIRSI
Partic in Central Jersey Regional Library Cooperative

NESHANIC STATION

S EXTRUSION ENGINEERS LIBRARY, 858 Princeton Ct, 08853-9686. SAN 373-4978. Tel: 908-369-7260. *Pres*, David W Riley; E-Mail: drdriley@aol.com; *Admin Assoc*, Barbara Riley
Library Holdings: Bk Vols 400; Per Subs 50
Subject Interests: Engineering

NEW BRUNSWICK

S BRISTOL-MYERS SQUIBB CO, Pharmaceutical Research Institute Library, Rte 1 & One Squibb Dr, 08903-9990. SAN 310-3366. Tel: 732-519-2269. FAX: 732-519-1055. Web Site: www.bms.com. *Science*, Donna Gibson; Staff 5 (MLS 3, Non-MLS 2)
Library Holdings: Bk Vols 4,500; Per Subs 410
Subject Interests: Chemistry, Pharmaceutical, Pharmacology
Partic in Dialog Corporation; OCLC Online Computer Library Center, Inc; PALINET & Union Library Catalogue of Pennsylvania
Branches:
PLAINSBORO BRANCH, 777 Scudders Mill Rd, Plainsboro, 08536. SAN 378-3871. Tel: 609-897-2215. FAX: 609-897-6797. *Librn*, Sarah Brown; Tel: 609-897-3983
Library Holdings: Bk Vols 2,548; Per Subs 234

M INTERFERON SCIENCES INC, Research Library,* 783 Jersey Ave, 08901. SAN 375-698X. Tel: 732-249-3250, Ext 513. E-Mail: library@interferonsciences.com.
Library Holdings: Bk Titles 500
Subject Interests: Medicine, Patents

S JEWISH HISTORICAL SOCIETY OF CENTRAL JERSEY LIBRARY, 228 Livingston Ave, 08901. SAN 376-0529. Tel: 732-249-4894. FAX: 732-249-4894. E-Mail: jhscj@cs.com. Web Site: www.jewishgen.org/jhscj/. *In Charge*, Rachel Weintraub
Founded 1977
Library Holdings: Bk Vols 609
Subject Interests: Jewish hist
Restriction: Not a lending library
Open Mon-Thurs 10-2, Fri 9-12

S JOHNSON & JOHNSON, Corporate Communications Library, One Johnson & Johnson Plaza, 08933. SAN 375-6947. Tel: 732-524-3545. FAX: 732-524-3564. *In Charge*, Elisabeth S King; E-Mail: eking@corus.jnj.com
Library Holdings: Bk Vols 400

S MIDDLESEX COUNTY CULTURAL & HERITAGE COMMISSION, Resource & Reference Library,* 703 Jersey Ave, 08901. SAN 375-6998. Tel: 732-745-4489. FAX: 732-745-4524. E-Mail: mechcpr@cultureheritage.org. Web Site: www.cultureheritage.org. *Exec Dir*, Anna Aschkenes
Library Holdings: Bk Titles 600
Subject Interests: Archaeology, Architecture
Special Services for the Deaf - TDD

GL MIDDLESEX COUNTY LAW LIBRARY,* One Kennedy Sq, 08901. SAN 310-3293. Tel: 732-981-3099. FAX: 732-981-3233. *Dir*, Betty Agin
Library Holdings: Bk Vols 22,500

G MIDDLESEX COUNTY PLANNING BOARD LIBRARY,* 40 Livingston Ave, 08901. SAN 310-3307. Tel: 732-745-3062. FAX: 732-745-3201.
Founded 1972
Library Holdings: Bk Vols 4,000; Per Subs 12

P NEW BRUNSWICK FREE PUBLIC LIBRARY, 60 Livingston Ave, 08901-2597. SAN 310-3315. Tel: 732-745-5108. FAX: 732-846-0226. Web Site: www.lmxac.org/nbfpl. *Dir*, Robert Belvin; Tel: 732-745-5721, Fax: 732-846-0243, E-Mail: bbelvin@lmxac.org; *Asst Dir*, Dorothy Key; Tel: 732-745-5110; *Ch Servs*, Laura Malmen; Staff 8 (MLS 8)
Founded 1883. Pop 41,711; Circ 84,000
Jan 2000-Dec 2000 Income $1,381,855, State $54,287, City $898,477, Locally Generated Income $37,203, Other $89,600. Mats Exp $142,368, Books $95,357, Per/Ser (Incl. Access Fees) $25,694, AV Equip $11,101, Electronic Ref Mat (Incl. Access Fees) $8,428. Sal $716,822
Library Holdings: Bk Titles 80,000; Per Subs 254
Subject Interests: Hungarian, Local history
Automation Activity & Vendor Info: (Circulation) CARL; (OPAC) CARL
Database Vendor: CARL
Partic in Libr of Middlesex
Friends of the Library Group

R NEW BRUNSWICK THEOLOGICAL SEMINARY, Gardner A Sage Library, 21 Seminary Pl, 08901-1159. SAN 310-3331. Tel: 908-247-5243. Toll Free Tel: 800-445-6287. FAX: 908-247-1356. E-Mail: rsh@nbts.edu. Web Site: www.nbts.edu. *Coll Develop, Dir*, Renee House; *ILL*, So-Ae Lee; *Cat, Tech Servs*, Lynn Berg; *Acq*, Gwen Greenberg; *Ref*, Marsha Blake; Staff 4 (MLS 3, Non-MLS 1)
Founded 1784. Enrl 211; Fac 11; Highest Degree: Master
Jul 1998-Jun 1999 Mats Exp $55,700, Books $37,643, Per/Ser (Incl. Access Fees) $16,423, Presv $250. Sal $116,138
Library Holdings: Bk Vols 151,824; Per Subs 319
Subject Interests: Biblical studies, Classics, Dutch church hist, Theol disciplines
Special Collections: Archives of Reformed Church in America; Leiby Coll
Partic in NY Area Theol Libr Asn; RLIN; Southeastern Pennsylvania Theological Library Association; Union-Middlesex Counties

S PROCEDYNE CORPORATION LIBRARY,* 11 Industrial Dr, 08901. SAN 329-983X. Tel: 732-249-8347. FAX: 732-249-7220.
Library Holdings: Bk Vols 300; Per Subs 18
Subject Interests: Chemical engineering

C RUTGERS, THE STATE UNIVERSITY OF NEW JERSEY, 169 College Ave, 08901-1163. SAN 350-9850. Tel: 732-932-7505. Interlibrary Loan Service Tel: 732-932-8345. FAX: 732-932-7637. Web Site: www.libraries.rutgers.edu. *Librn*, Marianne Gaunt; *Admin Assoc*, Linda York; E-Mail: lyork@rci.rutgers.edu; *Assoc Librn, Publ Servs*, Jeanne Boyle; *Assoc Librn, Coll Develop, Mgr*, Robert Sewell; *Assoc Librn*, Samson Soong; Staff 305 (MLS 90, Non-MLS 215)
Founded 1766. Enrl 49,465; Fac 2,520; Highest Degree: Doctorate
Jul 1999-Jun 2000 Mats Exp $16,240,686, Books $7,425,644, Per/Ser (Incl. Access Fees) $4,465,146, Micro $4,349,896. Sal $14,332,381
Library Holdings: Bk Vols 3,295,373; Per Subs 22,686
Automation Activity & Vendor Info: (Acquisitions) SIRSI; (Circulation) SIRSI; (Serials) SIRSI
Publications: Collection Guides; Instructional & Informational Material; Journal of the Rutgers University Libraries; RUL Report, Agenda
Mem of Asn of Research Libraries
Partic in New York Metrop Ref & Res Libr Agency; PALINET & Union Library Catalogue of Pennsylvania; Research Libraries Group, Inc; RLIN
Rutgers University Libraries includes central library administration operations, six major libraries & a number of branches located in Camden, Newark & New Brunswick
Friends of the Library Group
Departmental Libraries:
ACKERSON LAW LIBRARY

See Rutgers, Ackerson Law Library, Newark
ARCHIBALD STEVENS ALEXANDER LIBRARY, College Avenue Campus, 169 College Ave, 08901-1163. SAN 350-9885. Tel: 732-932-7129. FAX: 732-932-1101, 732-932-6808. Web Site: www.libraries.rutgers.edu/rul/libs/alex_lib/alex_lib.shtml. *Dir*, Ryoko Toyama; *Assoc Dir*, Francoise Puniello; *Coll Develop*, Myoung C Wilson; *Ref*, Emily Fabiano; Staff 45 (MLS 16, Non-MLS 29)
Library Holdings: Bk Vols 1,075,820; Per Subs 8,681
Friends of the Library Group
ART, Voorhees Hall, College Ave Campus, 08901-1248. SAN 350-9974. Tel: 732-932-7739. FAX: 732-932-6743. Web Site: www.libraries.rutgers.edu/rul/libs/art_lib/art_lib.shtml. *Librn*, Halina Rusak; Staff 2 (MLS 2)
Library Holdings: Bk Vols 60,342; Per Subs 111
Subject Interests: Architecture, Art history, Landscape architecture, Mus studies
Friends of the Library Group
BLANCHE & IRVING LAURIE MUSIC LIBRARY, Chapel Dr, PO Box 270, 08903-2700. SAN 351-0255. Tel: 732-932-9783, 732-932-9786. FAX: 732-932-6777. Web Site: www.libraries.rutgers.edu/rul/libs/music_lib/music_lib.shtml. *Coll Develop, Ref*, Roger Tarman; Staff 3 (MLS 1, Non-MLS 2)
Library Holdings: Bk Vols 51,774; Per Subs 260
Subject Interests: Music
Friends of the Library Group
CENTER FOR THE AMERICAN WOMAN & POLITICS LIBRARY, EATELTON INSTITUTE OF POLITICS, Wood Lawn, 191 Ryders Lane, 08901. SAN 326-6532. Tel: 732-932-9384. FAX: 732-932-6778. Web Site: www.rci.rutgers.edu/~cawp. *Actg Dir*, Debbie Walsh
Library Holdings: Bk Titles 1,000; Per Subs 20
Subject Interests: Women in politics
Special Collections: Photos of Women in American politics; Unpublished Academic Papers; Vertical Files of Clippings
CENTER OF ALCOHOL STUDIES, Busch Campus, Smithers Hall, 607 Allison Rd, Piscataway, 08854-8001. SAN 350-994X. Tel: 732-445-4442. FAX: 732-445-5944. Web Site: www.libraries.rutgers.edu/rul/libs/alcohol/alcohol.shtml. *Librn*, Valerie Mead; *Librn*, Penny Page; E-Mail: ppage@rci.rutgers.edu; Staff 6 (MLS 2, Non-MLS 4)
Library Holdings: Bk Vols 14,100; Per Subs 215
Subject Interests: Alcohol-drug abuse
Special Collections: Alcohol History Coll of Temperance & Prohibition Materials; Connor Alcohol Research Reference Files (500 survey instruments); McCarthy Memorial Coll of 50,000 alcohol research documents
Automation Activity & Vendor Info: (Cataloging) SIRSI; (Circulation) SIRSI; (OPAC) SIRSI
Database Vendor: Ebsco - EbscoHost, OVID Technologies
Publications: Alcohol Bibliography Series
Partic in NJ State Libr Network
Friends of the Library Group
CHEMISTRY, Busch Campus, Piscataway, Wright-Chemistry Bldg, 610 Taylor Rd, 08854. SAN 351-0069. Tel: 732-445-2625. FAX: 732-445-3255. Web Site: www.libraries.rutgers.edu/rul/libs/chem_lib/chem_lib.shtml. *Librn*, Howard M Dess; E-Mail: dess@rci.rutgers.edu; *Assoc Librn*, Mary Gadek; *Admin Assoc*, Linda York; Tel: 732-932-7505, Fax: 732-932-7637, E-Mail: lyork@rci.rutgers.edu
Library Holdings: Bk Vols 12,313; Per Subs 244
Subject Interests: Chemistry
Friends of the Library Group
JOHN COTTON DANA LIBRARY
See Separate Entry in Newark
EAST ASIAN LIBRARY, Alexander Library, 2nd Flr, New Wing, College Ave Campus, 08903. SAN 329-3491. Tel: 732-932-7161. FAX: 732-932-6808. Web Site: www.libraries.rutgers.edu/rul/libs/east_asia_lib/east_asia_lib.shtml. *Librn*, Nelson Chou; Staff 2 (MLS 1, Non-MLS 1)
Library Holdings: Bk Vols 101,316; Per Subs 327
Friends of the Library Group
INSTITUTE OF JAZZ STUDIES
See Separate Entry in Newark
CM LIBRARY OF SCIENCE & MEDICINE, Busch Campus, Piscataway, 165 Bevier Rd, 08854-8009. SAN 351-2169. Tel: 732-445-3850. FAX: 732-445-5703. Web Site: www.libraries.rutgers.edu/rul/libs/lsm_lib/lsm_lib.shtml. *Dir*, Ryoko Toyama; *Coll Develop*, Howard Dess; Staff 28 (MLS 9, Non-MLS 19)
Founded 1970
Library Holdings: Bk Vols 252,792; Per Subs 3,019
Subject Interests: Agriculture, Biology, Earth science, Engineering, Environ, Medicine, Pharm sci, Psychology
Friends of the Library Group
LIVINGSTON COLLEGE LIBRARY, Livingston Campus, Kilmer Area Library, 75 Avenue E, Piscataway, 08854. SAN 351-2134. Tel: 732-445-3610. FAX: 732-445-3472. Web Site: www.libraries.rutgers.edu/rul/libs/kilmer_lib/kilmer_lib.shtml. *Publ Servs*, Judith Gardner; Staff 12 (MLS 7, Non-MLS 5)
Founded 1969
Library Holdings: Bk Vols 142,652; Per Subs 349
Subject Interests: Bus
Friends of the Library Group
MABEL SMITH DOUGLASS LIBRARY, Mabel Smith Douglass Library, Douglass Campus, 8 Chapel Dr, 08903. SAN 351-0123. Tel: 732-932-9411. FAX: 732-932-6777. Web Site: www.libraries.rutgers.edu/rul/libs/douglass_lib/douglass_lib.shtml.; Staff 15 (MLS 6, Non-MLS 9)
Founded 1918. Enrl 6,194; Highest Degree: Bachelor
Library Holdings: Bk Vols 217,297; Per Subs 524
Subject Interests: Agriculture, Environ, Fine arts, Sci, Women's studies
Special Collections: Elizabeth Cady Stanton Papers
Friends of the Library Group
MATHEMATICAL SCIENCES, Hill Center for Math Science, 110 Frelinghuysen Rd, Piscataway, 08854-8019. SAN 351-0212. Tel: 732-445-3735. FAX: 732-445-3064. Web Site: www.libraries.rutgers.edu/rul/libs/math_lib/math_lib.shtml. *Librn*, Sylvia Walsh; Staff 3 (MLS 1, Non-MLS 2)
Library Holdings: Bk Vols 38,551; Per Subs 633
Subject Interests: Computer science, Mathematics, Statistics
Special Collections: Technical Reports
Friends of the Library Group
PAUL ROBESON LIBRARY
See Separate Entry in Camden
PHYSICS, Busch Campus, Piscataway, Serin Physics Laboratories, 126 Frelinghuysen Rd, 08854. SAN 351-0301. Tel: 732-445-2500. FAX: 732-445-4964. Web Site: www.libraries.rutgers.edu/rul/libs/physics_lib/physics_lib.shtml. *Librn*, Howard M Dess; *Assoc Librn*, Pathmosothy Padmanathan
Library Holdings: Bk Vols 14,816; Per Subs 183
Subject Interests: Astronomy, Physics
Special Collections: Preprint Coll
Friends of the Library Group
SCHOOL OF MANAGEMENT & LABOR RELATIONS LIBRARY, Cook Campus, Labor Educ Ctr, Ryders Lane & Clifton Ave, 08903. SAN 351-0182. Tel: 908-932-9513. FAX: 908-932-4699. Web Site: www.libraries.rutgers.edu/rul/libs/smlr/smlr.shtml. *Dir*, George Kanzler; *Librn*, Jeffrey Katz; E-Mail: jefkatz@rci.rutgers.edu; Staff 4 (MLS 2, Non-MLS 2)
Library Holdings: Bk Vols 6,288; Per Subs 447
Subject Interests: Human res, Indust relations, Labor mgt
Special Collections: New Jersey Public Sector Collective Bargaining Contracts
Publications: Acquisitions List (monthly)
Friends of the Library Group
SPECIAL COLLECTIONS & UNIVERSITY ARCHIVES, Alexander Library, 169 College Ave, 08901-1163. SAN 323-5696. Tel: 732-932-7006. FAX: 732-932-7012. Web Site: www.libraries.rutgers.edu/rul/libs/special_coll/special_coll.shtml. *Head of Libr*, Ronald L Becker; E-Mail: rbecker@rci.rutgers.edu; *Admin Assoc*, Linda York; E-Mail: lyork@rci.rutgers.edu; *Archivist*, Thomas Frusciano; E-Mail: fruscian@rci.rutgers.edu; *Archivist*, Ruth J Simmons; Tel: 732-932-7001, E-Mail: rsimmens@rci.rutgers.edu; *Bibliogr*, Bonita Grant; E-Mail: craftg@rci.rutgers.edu; Staff 13 (MLS 8, Non-MLS 5)
Founded 1946
Library Holdings: Bk Vols 152,000; Bk Titles 150,000; Per Subs 340
Subject Interests: City planning, Cookbooks, Genealogy, Hist of sci and tech, Maps, NJ state local hist, Regional planning, Women's hist
Special Collections: British & American Literature (18th & 19th centuries); Diaries; Dictionaries; History of Business & Labor; Rare Book Coll (17th & 18th Century British & American Writers); University Archives; Westerners in Japan
Automation Activity & Vendor Info: (Acquisitions) SIRSI; (Cataloging) SIRSI; (OPAC) SIRSI
Publications: Bibliographies
Friends of the Library Group

M ST PETER'S MEDICAL CENTER LIBRARY, 254 Easton Ave, 08903. SAN 310-3358. Tel: 732-745-8545. FAX: 732-937-6091. E-Mail: info@stpeterslibrary.com. Web Site: www.stpeterslibrary.com. *Mgr*, Wumin Si; *Librn*, Debbie Berowitz; Staff 5 (MLS 2, Non-MLS 3)
Founded 1907
Library Holdings: Bk Vols 25,000; Per Subs 450
Subject Interests: Gynecology, Medicine, Nursing, Obstetrics, Pediatrics
Special Collections: History of Medicine
Automation Activity & Vendor Info: (Cataloging) Sagebrush Corporation
Publications: Library Notes (newsletter); New Acquisitions
Partic in Health Sciences Library Association Of New Jersey
Affiliated with University of Medicine & Dentistry of New Jersey

M UNIVERSITY OF MEDICINE & DENTISTRY OF NEW JERSEY, Robert Wood Johnson Library of Health Sciences, PO Box 19, 08903. SAN 320-3980. Tel: 732-235-7606. Interlibrary Loan Service Tel: 732-235-7610. FAX: 732-235-7826. Web Site: www2.umdnj.edu/rwjlbweb. *Dir*, Kerry O'Rourke; *Syst Coordr*, Robert Gessner; *Ref*, Donald J Miller; *Ref*, Cathy Weglarz; Staff 9 (MLS 4, Non-MLS 5)
Library Holdings: Bk Vols 25,155; Bk Titles 6,604; Per Subs 507
Subject Interests: Clinical medicine, Hospital administration, Nursing
Automation Activity & Vendor Info: (Acquisitions) Endeavor; (Cataloging) Endeavor; (Circulation) Endeavor; (OPAC) Endeavor; (Serials) Endeavor

Publications: Library Rounds (quarterly)
Partic in Health Sciences Library Association Of New Jersey; New Jersey Library Network
Library is operated by the University of Medicine & Dentistry, Robert Wood Johnson Medical School

NEW MILFORD

P NEW MILFORD PUBLIC LIBRARY,* 200 Dahlia Ave, 07646-1812. SAN 310-3374. Tel: 201-262-1221. FAX: 201-262-5639. E-Mail: nmil@bccls.org. *Dir*, Phyllis Palley; E-Mail: palley@bccls.org; *Ad Servs, Ref*, Brian Leddy; *Ch Servs, YA Servs*, Mary Koob; E-Mail: koob@bccls.org; *Circ*, Lori Ricci
Founded 1936. Pop 16,054; Circ 103,205
Jan 1999-Dec 1999 Income $410,597, State $20,597, City $390,000. Mats Exp $52,542, Books $38,032, Per/Ser (Incl. Access Fees) $9,834, Micro $552, AV Equip $2,623, Electronic Ref Mat (Incl. Access Fees) $1,501. Sal $322,335
Library Holdings: Bk Vols 66,369; Per Subs 153
Subject Interests: Consumer info
Automation Activity & Vendor Info: (Circulation) DRA; (OPAC) DRA
Partic in Bergen County Cooperative Library System; Highlands Regional Library Cooperative; N Jersey Video Circuit
Friends of the Library Group

NEW PROVIDENCE

S MCNEIL & FOSTER MEMORIAL LIBRARY, Resource Center, 121 Chanlon Rd, 07974. SAN 330-0366. Tel: 908-665-2846. FAX: 908-771-7704. *Dir*, Susan Anne Jones; *Asst Dir*, Betty Blue; *Librn*, Elizabeth Button
1997-1998 Mats Exp $15,000
Library Holdings: Bk Vols 1,000; Bk Titles 1,800
Friends of the Library Group

S NEW PROVIDENCE HISTORICAL SOCIETY LIBRARY, c/o Memorial Library, 377 Elkwood Ave, 07974. SAN 323-4673. Tel: 908-665-1065. *Pres*, Ann Chovan
Library Holdings: Bk Vols 100

P NEW PROVIDENCE MEMORIAL LIBRARY, 377 Elkwood Ave, 07974. SAN 310-3382. Tel: 908-665-0311. FAX: 908-665-2319. *Dir*, Ann M Oster; E-Mail: aoster@juno.com; *Head Ref*, Colleen Byrne; *Ch Servs*, Lore Reinhart; *Head, Cat*, Donna Gulino; Staff 15 (MLS 4, Non-MLS 11)
Founded 1921. Pop 11,459; Circ 109,206
Jan 1999-Dec 1999 Income $508,198, State $11,566, City $485,231, Other $11,401. Mats Exp $75,137, Books $57,235, Per/Ser (Incl. Access Fees) $11,622, Micro $3,280, Electronic Ref Mat (Incl. Access Fees) $3,000. Sal $289,149
Library Holdings: Bk Vols 82,076; Bk Titles 80,770; Per Subs 140
Automation Activity & Vendor Info: (Cataloging) Follett; (Circulation) Follett; (OPAC) Follett
Database Vendor: Ebsco - EbscoHost, IAC - SearchBank
Mem of Morris-Union Fedn
Partic in Infolink; LUCC; Morris-Union Federation; MURAL
Friends of the Library Group

S REED ELSEVIER-NEW PROVIDENCE LIBRARY, 121 Chanlon Rd, 07974. SAN 372-4778. Tel: 908-665-6761. FAX: 908-508-7668. *Mgr Libr Serv*, Nancy Upham
Library Holdings: Bk Vols 12,000; Per Subs 450
Restriction: Staff use only
Branches:
MARQUIS WHO'S WHO Tel: 908-464-6800, Ext 4627. FAX: 908-771-8618. *Librn*, Oscar Maldonado
Restriction: Staff use only

NEWARK

L CARPENTER, BENNETT & MORRISSEY, Law Library, 3 Gateway Ctr, 100 Mulberry St, 07102. SAN 372-4794. Tel: 973-622-7711, Ext 2300. FAX: 973-622-5314. *Librn*, Jeff Cohan
Library Holdings: Bk Vols 13,000
Restriction: Not open to public

M COLUMBUS HOSPITAL, Medical Library, 495 N 13th St, 07107. SAN 376-0553. Tel: 973-268-1400, Ext 2074. FAX: 973-268-4865. *Librn*, Joan Cataldo
Library Holdings: Bk Vols 700
Open Mon-Fri 9-5

J ESSEX COUNTY COLLEGE LIBRARY, 303 University Ave, 07102. SAN 351-0395. Tel: 973-877-3238. Interlibrary Loan Service Tel: 973-877-3241. Reference Tel: 973-877-3239. FAX: 973-623-6449. Web Site: www.essex.edu/librar. *Assoc Dean*, Gwendolyn C Slaton; Tel: 973-877-3233, E-Mail: slaton@essex.edu; *Cat*, Sangyol Kim; Tel: 973-877-3235, E-Mail: kim@essex.edu; *Asst Prof*, William Hulzenga; Tel: 973-403-2546, Fax: 973-228-6181, E-Mail: hulzenga@essex.edu; *Per*, Katherine Wilson; Tel: 973-877-3239, E-Mail: kwilson@essex.edu; *Ref Serv Ad*, Leola Taylor; Tel: 973-877-3241, E-Mail: ltaylor@essex.edu; *Circ*, Rita Willis; Tel: 973-877-3028, E-Mail: rwillis@essex.edu; *Acq*, Natalie Elder; Tel: 973-877-3242, E-Mail: elder@essex.edu. Subject Specialists: *Allied health*, Natalie Elder; *Art*, Rita Willis; *Bilingual*, Katherine Wilson; *Biology*, Leola Taylor; *Business*, Katherine Wilson; *Chemistry*, Leola Taylor; *Education*, Gwendolyn C Slaton; *Engr*, Leola Taylor; *History*, Rita Willis; *Humanities*, Rita Willis; *Law*, Gwendolyn C Slaton; *Music*, Rita Willis; *Nursing*, Natalie Elder; *Social sciences*, Sangyol Kim; Staff 13 (MLS 6, Non-MLS 7)
Founded 1968. Enrl 8,000; Fac 150
Jul 1999-Jun 2000 Income $1,516,455. Mats Exp $561,525, Books $110,145, Micro $10,648, AV Equip $13,300, Electronic Ref Mat (Incl. Access Fees) $11,271. Sal $615,287 (Prof $450,953)
Library Holdings: Bk Vols 103,423; Bk Titles 94,115; Per Subs 436; High Interest/Low Vocabulary Bk Vols 1,328; Spec Interest Per Sub 35; Bks on Deafness & Sign Lang 11
Subject Interests: Nursing
Automation Activity & Vendor Info: (Cataloging) Innovative Interfaces Inc.; (Circulation) Innovative Interfaces Inc.; (ILL) Innovative Interfaces Inc.; (Serials) Innovative Interfaces Inc.
Database Vendor: Ebsco - EbscoHost, Innovative Interfaces INN - View, OCLC - First Search, ProQuest, Silverplatter Information Inc., Wilson - Wilson Web
Publications: Subject Bibliographies
Function: ILL available
Partic in Eastern NJ Regional Libr Coop; Infolink; ReBL
Departmental Libraries:
J BRANCH CAMPUS, 730 Bloomfield Ave, West Caldwell, 07007. SAN 370-0259. Tel: 973-403-2546. FAX: 973-228-6181. Web Site: www.essex.edu/library. *Assoc Dean*, Slaton C. Gwendolyn; Tel: 973-877-3233, E-Mail: slaton@essex.edu; *Librn*, William Hulzenga; E-Mail: hulzenga@essex.edu; Staff 2 (MLS 1, Non-MLS 1)
Library Holdings: Bk Vols 12,416; Bk Titles 111,000; Per Subs 180
Database Vendor: Ebsco - EbscoHost

GL ESSEX COUNTY LAW LIBRARY, 50 W Market St, Rm 512, 07102. SAN 310-3420. Tel: 973-693-5723. *Librn*, Debra Womeck; *Asst Librn*, Patricia Sherwood
Founded 1907
Library Holdings: Per Subs 25
Special Collections: American & English Law Reports; Legal Periodicals; Legal Treatises & Texts

L GIBBONS, DEL DEO, DOLAN, GRIFFINGER & VECCHIONE, Law Library, One Riverfront Plaza, 07102. SAN 371-5272. Tel: 973-596-4500. FAX: 973-596-0545. Web Site: www.gibbonslaw.com. *Mgr*, Karen Wojan; E-Mail: kwojan@gibbonslaw.com; *Librn*, Rita Bronnenkant; *Librn*, Wendi Taylor
Library Holdings: Bk Vols 35,000; Bk Titles 4,000
Restriction: Private library
Mem of Infolink Regional Library Coop

L MCCARTER & ENGLISH, Law Library, 4 Gateway Ctr, 100 Mulberry St, 07102. SAN 310-3447. Tel: 973-622-4444, Ext 2288. FAX: 973-624-7070. Web Site: www.mccarter.com. *Dir*, Mary Ellen Kaas
Library Holdings: Bk Vols 29,000; Per Subs 200
Restriction: Staff use only

L NEW JERSEY BOARD OF PUBLIC UTILITIES, Law Library,* 2 Gateway Ctr, 07102. SAN 375-7366. Tel: 973-648-2015. FAX: 973-648-4298. *Librn*, Emma Williams
Library Holdings: Bk Vols 971

S NEW JERSEY HISTORICAL SOCIETY LIBRARY, 52 Park Pl, 07102. SAN 310-348X. Tel: 973-596-8500, Ext 249. *Dir*, James Kaser; Staff 6 (MLS 3, Non-MLS 3)
Founded 1845
Library Holdings: Bk Vols 65,000; Per Subs 50
Subject Interests: Am art, Am hist, Antiques, Genealogy, NJ hist
Special Collections: Manuscripts; Rare books
Publications: Selected Acquisitions (quarterly)
Restriction: Non-circulating to the public
Mem of Essex-Hudson Regional Libr Coop
Partic in New Jersey Library Network; OCLC Online Computer Library Center, Inc; PALINET & Union Library Catalogue of Pennsylvania

C NEW JERSEY INSTITUTE OF TECHNOLOGY, Robert W Van Houten Library, University Heights, 07102-1982. SAN 310-3498. Tel: 973-596-3206. Interlibrary Loan Service Tel: 973-596-3204. FAX: 973-643-5601. E-Mail: lib_ref@admin.njit.edu. Web Site: www.library.njit.edu. *Mgr*, Doreen Mettle; *Librn*, Richard T Sweeney; *Asst Librn*, Derry Juneja; Staff 10 (MLS 10)
Founded 1881. Enrl 7,670; Fac 349; Highest Degree: Doctorate
Library Holdings: Bk Vols 207,973; Per Subs 995
Subject Interests: Architecture, Computer science, Engineering, Mgt, Sci, Technology
Special Collections: Weston History of Science & Technology Coll
Automation Activity & Vendor Info: (Acquisitions) DRA; (Cataloging) DRA; (Circulation) DRA; (OPAC) DRA; (Serials) DRA

Publications: Nineer Tutorial; Pathfinder
Partic in New Jersey Academic Library Network; OCLC Online Computer Library Center, Inc; PALINET & Union Library Catalogue of Pennsylvania
Departmental Libraries:
BARBARA & LEONARD LITTMAN LIBRARY - ARCHITECTURE, University Heights, 07102-1982. Tel: 973-596-3083. FAX: 973-643-5601. Web Site: www.njit.edu/library/archlib. *Dir*, James Robertson; E-Mail: james.c.robertson@njit.edu
Library Holdings: Bk Vols 10,500; Per Subs 3,000
Automation Activity & Vendor Info: (Acquisitions) DRA; (Cataloging) DRA; (Circulation) DRA; (OPAC) DRA; (Serials) DRA

L NEW JERSEY OFFICE OF THE PUBLIC DEFENDER, Newark Branch,* 31 Clinton St 9th flr, 07102. (Mail add: PO Box 46004, 07102), SAN 373-0840. Tel: 973-877-1264. FAX: 973-877-1239. *Librn*, Kevin M Hale
Library Holdings: Bk Vols 10,000; Per Subs 25

M NEWARK BETH ISRAEL MEDICAL CENTER, Dr. Victor Parsonnet Memorial Library, 201 Lyons Ave, 07112. SAN 310-3501. Tel: 973-926-7441. FAX: 973-923-4280. *Dir Libr Serv*, Ellen T Morris; E-Mail: emorris@sbhcs.com; *Asst Librn*, Laverne Davis
Founded 1900
Library Holdings: Bk Titles 2,000; Per Subs 220
Special Collections: Dr Aaron Parsonnet Coll, bks
Partic in Infolink Eastern New Jersey Regional Library Cooperative, Inc; New Jersey Library Network

S NEWARK MUSEUM LIBRARY, 49 Washington St, PO Box 540, 07101-0540. SAN 310-3536. Tel: 973-596-6625. FAX: 973-642-0459. E-Mail: library@newarkmuseum.org. *Librn*, William A Peniston; E-Mail: wpeniston@newarkmuseum.org; Staff 2 (MLS 1, Non-MLS 1)
Founded 1926
Jan 2000-Dec 2000 Mats Exp $44,500, Books $30,000, Per/Ser (Incl. Access Fees) $10,000, Presv $4,500. (Prof $40,000)
Library Holdings: Bk Titles 30,000; Per Subs 300
Subject Interests: African art, Am art, Asian art, Decorative arts, Natural science, Numismatics
Special Collections: History of the Newark Museum, (Dana Coll); Tibet Coll
Partic in Essex-Hudson Regional Libr Coop

P NEWARK PUBLIC LIBRARY, 5 Washington St, PO Box 630, 07101-0630. SAN 351-045X. Tel: 973-733-7784, 973-733-7793, 973-733-7800. Interlibrary Loan Service Tel: 973-733-7767. FAX: 973-733-5648. Web Site: www.npl.org. *Dir*, Dr Alex Boyd; E-Mail: aboyd@npl.org; *Asst Dir*, Marianne K Avery; E-Mail: mavery@npl.org; *Asst Dir*, Joseph Casale; E-Mail: jcasale@npl.org; *Asst Dir, Spec Coll*, Charles F Cummings; E-Mail: ccummings@npl.org; *Asst Dir*, Gerald Fitzhugh; E-Mail: gfitzhugh@npl.org; *Access Serv, Asst Dir*, Bruce Ford; E-Mail: bford@npl.org; *Asst Dir, Commun Servs*, Wilma J Grey; E-Mail: wgrey@npl.org; *Asst Dir*, Paul Stelhorn; E-Mail: pstellhorn@npl.org; *Senior Librn*, Margaret Orimogunje; E-Mail: morimogunje@npl.org; *Govt Doc, Senior Librn*, Laura Saurs; E-Mail: lsaurs@npl.org; *Acq*, Donald Lewis; E-Mail: dlewis@npl.org; *ILL*, Carolyn A Deodene; E-Mail: cdeodene@npl.org; *Cat*, Penelope Jabido; E-Mail: pjabido@npl.org; *Spec Coll*, William Dane; E-Mail: wdane@npl.org. Subject Specialists: *Art*, Leslie Kahn; *Arts*, George Hawley; *Business*, James E Capuano; *Business*, Maureen Ritter; *Hispanic*, Ingrid Betancourt; *Humanities*, Leslie Kahn; *Humanities*, George Hawley; *Multilingual*, Ingrid Betancourt; *New Jersey*, Charles F Cummings; *Science/technology*, James E Capuano; *Science/technology*, Maureen Ritter; *Technology*, Paul Pattwell; *Training*, Paul Pattwell; Staff 184 (MLS 61, Non-MLS 123)
Founded 1888. Pop 275,000; Circ 450,000
Jan 1999-Dec 1999 Income (Main Library and Branch Library) $11,651,837, State $354,540, City $10,004,361, Federal $204,525, County $5,000, Locally Generated Income $78,000, Other $845,411. Mats Exp $694,986, Books $439,735, Per/Ser (Incl. Access Fees) $81,181, Micro $32,000, Electronic Ref Mat (Incl. Access Fees) $142,070. Sal $8,607,875
Library Holdings: Bk Vols 1,530,117; Bk Titles 552,349; Per Subs 980
Subject Interests: Art, Bus, Doc, Music, New Jersey, Patents, US govt
Special Collections: Art (Pictures, Prints & Popular Sheet Music); Children's Books 18th, 19th & Early 20th Century (Wilbur Macy Stone Coll); Fine Printing (R C Jenkins Coll); New Jersey Rare Books; Newark Evening News Morgue; Puerto Rican Reference Coll; US Patent Coll
Automation Activity & Vendor Info: (Acquisitions) epixtech, inc.; (Cataloging) epixtech, inc.; (Circulation) epixtech, inc.; (ILL) epixtech, inc.; (OPAC) epixtech, inc.; (Serials) epixtech, inc.
Publications: Second Century (newsletter)
Partic in Dialog Corporation; Infolink Eastern New Jersey Regional Library Cooperative, Inc; New Jersey Library Network; Wilsonline
Friends of the Library Group
Branches: 10
BRANCH BROOK, 235 Clifton Ave, 07104. SAN 351-0484. Tel: 973-733-7760. FAX: 973-733-6388. *Librn*, Paula Harris; E-Mail: pharris@npl.org; *Librn*, Barbara Sullivan; E-Mail: bsullivan@npl.org
Library Holdings: Bk Vols 38,700
CLINTON, 739 Bergen St, 07108. SAN 351-0514. Tel: 973-733-7754, 973-733-7757. FAX: 973-733-7757. *Librn*, Deloris Moses; E-Mail: dmoses@npl.org; *Librn*, Wilhelmina Person; E-Mail: wperson@npl.org
Library Holdings: Bk Vols 36,000
Mem of Hunterdon County Library
FIRST AVENUE, 282 First Ave, 07107. SAN 351-0522. Tel: 973-733-8091. FAX: 973-733-8091. *Librn*, Juanita Egoavil; E-Mail: jegoavil@npl.org
MADISON AREA, 790 Clinton Ave, 07108. SAN 351-0557. Tel: 973-733-8090. FAX: 973-733-8090. *Librn*, Patricia Dozier; E-Mail: pdozier@npl.org
NORTH END, 722 Summer Ave, 07104. SAN 351-0549. Tel: 973-733-7766. FAX: 973-733-7683. *Librn*, Paula Baratta; E-Mail: pbaratta@npl.org; *Librn*, Heather Rivera; E-Mail: hrivera@npl.org
Library Holdings: Bk Vols 30,000
ROSEVILLE, 99 N Fifth St, 07107. SAN 351-0573. Tel: 973-733-7770. FAX: 973-733-6883. *Librn*, Luqueen Lee-Jackson; E-Mail: ljackson@npl.org
Library Holdings: Bk Vols 20,000
SPRINGFIELD, 50 Hayes St, 07103. SAN 351-0603. Tel: 973-733-7736. FAX: 973-733-7819. *Librn*, William Stockton; E-Mail: wstockton@npl.org; *Librn*, Clara Wilson; E-Mail: cwilson@npl.org
Library Holdings: Bk Vols 33,520
VAILSBURG, 75 Alexander St, 07106. SAN 351-0638. Tel: 973-733-7755. *Librn*, Edward H Small; E-Mail: esmall@npl.org; *Librn*, Merilyn Thomas; E-Mail: mthomas@npl.org
Library Holdings: Bk Vols 35,000
VAN BUREN, 140 Van Buren St, 07105. SAN 351-0662. Tel: 973-733-7750. FAX: 973-733-3897. Web Site: www.vanburen.org. *Librn*, Susan Blake; E-Mail: sblake@npl.org; *Librn*, Fran Poteet; E-Mail: fpoteet@npl.org
Library Holdings: Bk Vols 39,000
WEEQUAHIC, 355 Osborne Terrace, 07112. SAN 351-0697. Tel: 973-733-7751. FAX: 973-733-7752. *Librn*, Funmi Songonuga; E-Mail: fsongonuga@npl.org; *Librn*, Delores Whitehead; E-Mail: dwhitehead@npl.org
Library Holdings: Bk Vols 49,000

S NEWARK PUBLIC LIBRARY, Business, Science & Technology Center,* 5 Washington St, PO Box 630, 07101-0630. SAN 310-351X. Tel: 973-733-7779. FAX: 973-733-5648. Web Site: www.npl.org.; Staff 7 (MLS 2, Non-MLS 5)
Subject Interests: Accounting, Advertising, Banking, Bus conditions, Bus hist, Insurance, Investments, Marketing, Money, Salesmanship
Partic in Data Time; Dialog Corporation
Friends of the Library Group

S NORTHERN STATE PRISON LIBRARY, (NSPL), 168 Frontage Rd, 07114-3794. (Mail add: PO Box 2300, 07114-0300), SAN 371-5574. Tel: 973-465-0068, Ext 4521. FAX: 973-589-7454. *Librn*, Gail Gillespie; Staff 1 (MLS 1)
Founded 1987
Library Holdings: Bk Titles 8,100; Per Subs 84
Publications: Infolink
Partic in Infolink

PRUDENTIAL INSURANCE COMPANY OF AMERICA
S BUSINESS LIBRARY, 16 Prudential Plaza, 751 Broad St, 07102-3777. SAN 351-0727. Tel: 973-802-7583. FAX: 973-367-8149. *Res*, Barbara A Ciccone; Staff 3 (MLS 2, Non-MLS 1)
Library Holdings: Per Subs 157
Subject Interests: Bus, Ins, Mgt, Personnel
Special Collections: Insurance (Life, Group, Health, Social)
Publications: Capsules
Restriction: Staff use only
Partic in BRS; Human Res Info Network; Texline; Utex; Washington Alert
S FINANCIAL RESEARCH LIBRARY, 100 Mulberry St, 8GC4, 07102. SAN 376-2254. Tel: 973-802-6513. FAX: 973-802-2237. *Dir*, Mary Beck
Library Holdings: Bk Titles 500; Per Subs 15
L LAW LIBRARY, 22 Plaza, 751 Broad St, 07102-3777. SAN 351-0751. Tel: 973-802-9255. FAX: 973-802-2298. E-Mail: refdesk@prudential.com. *Dir Libr Serv*, Johanna C Bizub; Tel: 973-367-3175, E-Mail: jbizub@prudential.com; *Asst Librn, Res, Tech Servs*, Sarah Connell; Tel: 973-802-6802, E-Mail: sarah.connell@prudential.com; *Asst Librn, Ref, Res*, Magali Velez; Tel: 973-802-6811, E-Mail: magil.velez@prudential.com; Staff 5 (MLS 2, Non-MLS 3)
Library Holdings: Bk Vols 7,500; Bk Titles 1,000; Per Subs 100
Subject Interests: Ins, Law, Real estate, Securities
Database Vendor: Dialog, Lexis-Nexis

S PUBLIC SERVICE ELECTRIC & GAS COMPANY, Corporate Library,* 80 Park Plaza, Mailcode P3C, 07101. SAN 310-3552. Tel: 973-430-7333. Interlibrary Loan Service Tel: 973-430-7336. FAX: 973-624-1551. *Ref*, Lisa Holland; Staff 16 (MLS 10, Non-MLS 6)
Founded 1911
Library Holdings: Bk Titles 27,140; Per Subs 775
Subject Interests: Bus, Electric power, Environmental studies, Mgt, Natural gas, Nuclear energy, Synthetic gas
Publications: InfoConnection
Restriction: Staff use only

Partic in Dialog Corporation; Dow Jones News Retrieval; Dunsnet; Nat Libr of Med; OCLC Online Computer Library Center, Inc; Orbit; PALINET & Union Library Catalogue of Pennsylvania; Vutext; Westlaw; Wilsonline
Branches:
NUCLEAR INFORMATION RESOURCE CENTER, MC N02, PO Box 236, Hancocks Bridge, 08038. SAN 324-2714. Tel: 609-339-7109. FAX: 609-339-1136. E-Mail: virginia.swichel@pseg.com.; Staff 4 (MLS 2, Non-MLS 2)
Library Holdings: Bk Titles 20,000; Per Subs 80
Subject Interests: Nuclear engineering, Nuclear power
Special Collections: Industry Standards; Vendor Catalogs
Partic in Dialog Corporation; OCLC Online Computer Library Center, Inc; PALINET & Union Library Catalogue of Pennsylvania; South Jersey Regional Library Cooperative; Westlaw

RUTGERS, THE STATE UNIVERSITY OF NEW JERSEY
CL ACKERSON LAW LIBRARY, Samuel I Newhouse Law Ctr, 15 Washington St, 07102-3192. SAN 351-0816. Tel: 973-353-1720. FAX: 973-353-1356. Web Site: www.libraries.rutgers.edu/rul/libs/law_newark_lib/law_newark.shtml. *Dir*, Carol A Roehrenbeck; *Acq*, Shannon Engelman; *Circ, ILL*, Dan Campbell; *Coll Develop*, Paul Axel-Lute; *Govt Doc*, Helen Leskovac; *Publ Servs*, Steven C Perkins; *Tech Servs*, Marjorie Crawford; Staff 25 (MLS 6, Non-MLS 19)
Founded 1946. Enrl 733
Library Holdings: Bk Titles 103,429
Special Collections: Law Library of US Supreme Court Justice Bradley (Bradley Coll)
Mem of Asn of Research Libraries
Partic in Research Libraries Group, Inc; RLIN

C CRIMINAL JUSTICE NCCD COLLECTION, 15 Washington St, 4th flr, 07102. SAN 327-9499. Tel: 973-353-5522. FAX: 873-353-1275.
1998-1999 Mats Exp $34,455, Books $26,303, Per/Ser (Incl. Access Fees) $5,553, Presv $1,805, Other Print Mats $794. Sal $57,130
Library Holdings: Bk Titles 18,388; Per Subs 253
Publications: Acquisitions List (bi-monthly)
Mem of Asn of Research Libraries
Friends of the Library Group

INSTITUTE OF JAZZ STUDIES, 185 University Ave, 4th flr, 07102. SAN 351-0808. Tel: 973-353-5595. FAX: 973-353-5944. Web Site: www.libraries.rutgers.edu/rul/libs/jazz/jazz.shtml. *Dir*, Dan Morgenstern; *Asst Dir*, Edward Berger; Staff 6 (MLS 1, Non-MLS 5)
Founded 1952
Library Holdings: Bk Vols 10,000; Per Subs 150
Special Collections: Jazz Archive Coll; Memorabilia; Realia
Publications: Annual Review of Jazz Studies; IJS Jazz Register & Indexes; Studies in Jazz
Mem of Asn of Research Libraries
Partic in RLIN
Friends of the Library Group

C JOHN COTTON DANA LIBRARY, 185 University Ave, 07102. SAN 351-0786. Tel: 973-353-5222. Interlibrary Loan Service Tel: 973-353-5902. FAX: 973-353-5257. Web Site: www.libraries.rutger.edu/rul/librs/dana_lib/dana_lib.shtml. *Dir*, Lynn S Mullins; *Bibliog Instr*, Roberta Tipton; *Circ*, Ann Watkins; *Govt Doc*, Wen-Hua Ren; *Publ Servs*, Natalie Borisovets. Subject Specialists: *Business and management*, Ka-Neng Au; *Business and management*, Roberta Tipton; *Criminal law and justice*, Phyllis Schultze; *Science/technology*, Veronica Calderhead; Staff 31 (MLS 3, Non-MLS 28)
Founded 1927. Enrl 10,000; Fac 500; Highest Degree: Doctorate
Library Holdings: Bk Vols 369,730; Per Subs 3,528
Subject Interests: Humanities, Nursing
Automation Activity & Vendor Info: (Circulation) SIRSI
Publications: Library Guide Series, Library News Release
Mem of Asn of Research Libraries
Partic in BRS; Center For Research Libraries; Dialog Corporation; Medline; New York Metrop Ref & Res Libr Agency; Research Libraries Group, Inc; RLIN; SDC
See New Brunswick entry for budget figures for the University's library system
Friends of the Library Group

M SAINT JAMES HOSPITAL OF NEWARK LIBRARY,* 155 Jefferson St, 07105. SAN 376-0510. Tel: 973-465-2744. FAX: 973-465-2861. *In Charge*, Larry Bormer
Library Holdings: Bk Vols 200

L ST JOHN & WAYNE, Law Library,* 2 Penn Plaza E, 07105. SAN 323-8334. Tel: 973-491-3300. FAX: 973-491-3555. *Librn*, Thomas Miller; Staff 1 (MLS 1)
Founded 1971
Library Holdings: Bk Vols 8,000
Restriction: Staff use only

M SAINT MICHAEL MEDICAL CENTER, Aquinas Medical Library, 268 Dr Martin Luther King Jr Blvd, 07102. SAN 310-3560. Tel: 973-877-5471. FAX: 973-877-5378. *Dir*, Larry Dormer; E-Mail: larryd@cathedralhealth.org
Founded 1939
Library Holdings: Bk Vols 1,200; Per Subs 141
Subject Interests: Cardiology, Medicine, Podiatry, Surgery
Partic in Cosmopolitan Biomedical Library Consortium; Health Sciences Library Association Of New Jersey; Infolink Eastern New Jersey Regional Library Cooperative, Inc

CL SETON HALL UNIVERSITY, Peter W Rodino Jr Law Library, One Newark Ctr, 07102. SAN 310-3579. Tel: 973-642-8720. FAX: 973-642-8748. Web Site: www.shu.edu/law/. *Dir*, Deborah D Herrera; Tel: 973-642-8766; *Cat*, Johanna Nolan; *Archivist, Cat*, Diane West; *Ref*, Jeanne O'Connor; *Reader Servs*, Eileen Denner; *Ref*, Kathleen McCarthy; *Ref*, Maja Basioli; *Ser*, Dianne Oster; *Tech Servs*, Barbara Mol; Staff 23 (MLS 10, Non-MLS 13)
Founded 1950. Enrl 1,281; Fac 45; Highest Degree: Doctorate
Library Holdings: Bk Vols 412,100; Per Subs 6,517
Automation Activity & Vendor Info: (Acquisitions) Innovative Interfaces Inc.; (Cataloging) Innovative Interfaces Inc.; (Circulation) Innovative Interfaces Inc.; (OPAC) Innovative Interfaces Inc.; (Serials) Innovative Interfaces Inc.
Partic in OCLC Online Computer Library Center, Inc; PALINET & Union Library Catalogue of Pennsylvania; Westlaw

L SILLS, CUMMIS, ET AL LAW LIBRARY,* One Riverfront Plaza, 07102-5400. SAN 323-6161. Tel: 973-643-7000. FAX: 973-643-6500. *Dir*, Lynne Cruz; E-Mail: lcruz@sillscummis.com; Staff 4 (MLS 1, Non-MLS 3)
Library Holdings: Bk Vols 25,000; Bk Titles 15,000; Per Subs 500
Restriction: Staff use only
Partic in Dialog Corporation; Dow Jones News Retrieval; Westlaw

S STAR-LEDGER LIBRARY, One Star-Ledger Plaza, 07102. SAN 377-239X. Tel: 973-877-1710. FAX: 973-877-5845. E-Mail: moose@starledger.com. Web Site: www.nj.com/archive. *Info Specialist*, M J Crowley
Library Holdings: Bk Vols 2,000; Per Subs 30
Partic in Data Time; Dow Jones News Retrieval

L STRYKER, TAMS & DILL, Law Library,* 2 Penn Plaza E, 07105. SAN 372-4786. Tel: 973-491-9500. FAX: 973-491-9692. Web Site: www.stryker.com. *Librn*, Kelly Bowdin
Library Holdings: Bk Vols 14,000; Per Subs 35

L TOMPKINS, MCGUIRE, WACHENFELD & BARRY, (Formerly Tompkins, McGuire & Wachenfeld), Law Library, 4 Gateway Ctr, 100 Mulberry St, 07102. SAN 375-0663. Tel: 973-622-3000. FAX: 973-623-7780. *Librn*, Mary Beth Guenther; Tel: 973-623-7120, E-Mail: mguenther@tompkinsmcguire.com
Library Holdings: Bk Vols 1,400; Per Subs 20

GL UNITED STATES ATTORNEY'S OFFICE LIBRARY, 970 Broad St, Rm 700, 07102. SAN 310-3595. Tel: 973-645-2700. *Librn*, Roberta Klotz; *Asst Librn*, Ihsia Hu; Staff 4 (MLS 2, Non-MLS 2)
Restriction: Not open to public
Mem of New Jersey State Library
Branches:
CAMDEN BRANCH, Cohen Court House, Fourth & Cooper Sts, Rm 2070, Camden, 08101. SAN 321-4982. Tel: 973-645-2700.
Library Holdings: Bk Vols 4,000
TRENTON BRANCH, 402 E State St, Trenton, 08608. SAN 321-4990. Tel: 973-645-2700.
Library Holdings: Bk Vols 5,000

GL UNITED STATES COURT OF APPEALS LIBRARY, King Courthouse, Rm 5007, 50 Walnut St, 07102. (Mail add: PO Box 1068, 02101-1068), SAN 325-7762. Tel: 973-645-3034. *Librn*, Andrea Battel; *Asst Librn*, Dorothy Cordo; Staff 2 (MLS 2)
Library Holdings: Bk Vols 23,000; Per Subs 70
Subject Interests: Law
Automation Activity & Vendor Info: (Acquisitions) SIRSI
Database Vendor: Lexis-Nexis
Restriction: Circulates for staff only

CM UNIVERSITY OF MEDICINE & DENTISTRY OF NEW JERSEY, George F Smith Library of the Health Sciences,* 30 12th Ave, 07103-2706. SAN 310-3412. Tel: 973-972-4580. Interlibrary Loan Service Tel: 973-972-5319. FAX: 973-972-6949. Web Site: www.umdnj.edu/librweb/newarklib/index.htm. *Dir*, Judith S Cohn; *Librn*, Victor A Basile; *ILL*, Robert Cupryk; *Media Spec*, Laura Barrett; *Acq*, Beth Lapow; *Tech Servs*, Barbara Packard-Spencer; *Cat*, Daria Gorman; *Circ*, Melvin White; *Ser*, Ela Susnowska; Staff 36 (MLS 17, Non-MLS 19)
Founded 1956. Enrl 1,719; Fac 450; Highest Degree: Doctorate
Library Holdings: Bk Vols 146,653; Bk Titles 63,809; Per Subs 1,452
Subject Interests: Dentistry, Medicine
Special Collections: Historical Medicine Coll; Medicine (Morris H Saffron Coll)
Publications: acquisitions list; George F Smith Library Annual Report; newsletter
Partic in BRS; Greater NE Regional Med Libr Program; Medical Library Center Of New York; PALINET & Union Library Catalogue of Pennsylvania

NEWFIELD

P NEWFIELD PUBLIC LIBRARY, 115 Catawba Ave, 08344-9511. (Mail add: PO Box 37, 08344-0037), SAN 310-3617. Tel: 856-697-0415. FAX: 856-697-1544. E-Mail: newfieldlibrary@usa.net. *Dir*, Susan Mounier; Staff 3 (Non-MLS 3)
Founded 1876
Jan 1999-Dec 1999 Income $32,769, State $6,865, City $16,367, Other $9,537. Mats Exp $1,996, Books $1,049, Per/Ser (Incl. Access Fees) $736, AV Equip $188, Other Print Mats $23. Sal $16,495
Library Holdings: Bk Vols 18,062; Bk Titles 17,629; Per Subs 32
Automation Activity & Vendor Info: (Acquisitions) epixtech, inc.; (Cataloging) epixtech, inc.; (Circulation) epixtech, inc.
Partic in Gloucester County Libr Syst; South Jersey Regional Library Cooperative

S UNEXPECTED WILDLIFE REFUGE LIBRARY,* Unexpected Rd, PO Box 765, 08344. SAN 371-4551. Tel: 856-697-3541. *Librn*, Hope Sawyer Buyukmihci
Library Holdings: Bk Titles 320

NEWTON

M NEWTON MEMORIAL HOSPITAL LIBRARY,* 175 High St, 07860. SAN 375-9156. Tel: 973-383-2121, Ext 2334. FAX: 973-383-4559. E-Mail: nallmang@ptdprolog.net. *Librn*, Nancy Allmang
Library Holdings: Bk Vols 275
Partic in BRS; Highlands Regional Library Cooperative

J SUSSEX COUNTY COMMUNITY COLLEGE, Learning Resource Center, College Hill, 07860. SAN 375-7439. Tel: 973-300-2162. Reference Tel: 973-300-2164. FAX: 973-300-2276. Web Site: www.sussex.cc.nj.us. *Dir*, Dr Peter Panos; *Circ*, Lauren Kildoft; *Coll Develop*, *Ref*, Angela Camack; E-Mail: angelatalk@excite.com; Staff 3 (MLS 2, Non-MLS 1)
Founded 1989. Enrl 2,700; Fac 38; Highest Degree: Associate
Library Holdings: Bk Titles 28,120; Per Subs 205; Bks on Deafness & Sign Lang 54
Subject Interests: Juv, Law
Automation Activity & Vendor Info: (Acquisitions) SIRSI; (Cataloging) SIRSI; (Circulation) SIRSI; (Course Reserve) SIRSI; (OPAC) SIRSI
Database Vendor: ProQuest
Restriction: Non-circulating to the public, Open to student, faculty & staff
Partic in Highlands Regional Library Cooperative; PALINET & Union Library Catalogue of Pennsylvania
Special Services for the Deaf - Staff with knowledge of sign language
Special Services for the Blind - Magnifiers
Open Mon-Thurs 8:30-8, Fri 8:30-4:30, Sat 10-2

S SUSSEX COUNTY HISTORICAL SOCIETY LIBRARY,* 82 Main St, 07860. (Mail add: PO Box 913, 07860), SAN 328-1868. Tel: 973-383-6010. Web Site: www.sussexcountyhistory.com. *Pres*, Robert Langcore

L SUSSEX COUNTY LAW LIBRARY,* 4347 High St, 07860. SAN 327-9456. Tel: 973-579-0702. FAX: 973-579-0679. *Asst Librn*, *Tech Servs*, Barbara Mattingly
Library Holdings: Bk Titles 9,000

P SUSSEX COUNTY LIBRARY SYSTEM, Sussex County Area Reference Library, 125 Morris Tpk, 07860-0076. SAN 351-0905. Tel: 973-948-3660. FAX: 973-948-2071. *Dir*, Harold Neuschafer; E-Mail: neuschfr@hublib.lib.nj.us; *Spec Coll*, Judy Gessel; *Ch Servs*, Jean VanOrden; *Tech Servs*, Tim Thacker; *Coordr*, Marsha Labovitz; Staff 64 (MLS 13, Non-MLS 51)
Founded 1942. Pop 119,416; Circ 558,237
Jan 1997-Dec 1998 Income $3,579,373, State $110,243. Mats Exp $398,079, Books $313,195, Per/Ser (Incl. Access Fees) $53,730. Sal $1,608,757
Library Holdings: Bk Vols 307,168; Bk Titles 147,054; Per Subs 529
Special Collections: County History; Delaware Water Gap National Recreation Area (Tocks Island Regional Advisory Council Library); Sussex
Automation Activity & Vendor Info: (Circulation) epixtech, inc.
Database Vendor: epixtech, inc.
Partic in Highlands Regional Library Cooperative
Branches: 5
DOROTHY E HENRY MEMORIAL LIBRARY (VERNON-NORTHEASTERN DISTRICT), 66 Rte 94, Vernon, 07462. SAN 351-1081. Tel: 973-827-8095.
Friends of the Library Group
E LOUISE CHILDS MEMORIAL LIBRARY (HOPATCONG-SOUTHERN DISTRICT), 21 Sparta Rd, Stanhope, 07874. SAN 351-1022. Tel: 973-770-1000. *Librn*, Vici Larson
FRANKLIN (EASTERN DISTRICT), 103 Main St, Franklin, 07416. SAN 351-0999. Tel: 973-827-6555. *Librn*, Elizabeth Dewey
NEWTON-DENNIS MEMORIAL (CENTRAL DISTRICT), 101 Main St, 07860. SAN 351-0964. Tel: 973-383-4810. *Librn*, Deborah L Mole
SUSSEX-WANTAGE (NORTHERN DISTRICT), 27 Bank St, Sussex, 07461. SAN 351-1057. Tel: 973-875-1336, 973-875-3940. *Chief Librn*, Nancy L Helmer; Staff 1 (MLS 1)
Pop 11,000; Circ 25,000
Library Holdings: Bk Titles 15,000; Per Subs 50
Friends of the Library Group
Bookmobiles: 2

NORTH ARLINGTON

P NORTH ARLINGTON FREE PUBLIC LIBRARY, 210 Ridge Rd, 07031. SAN 310-3633. Tel: 201-955-5640. FAX: 201-991-7850. E-Mail: noari@bccls.org. Web Site: www.bccls.org/northarlington. *Dir*, Maria Puszkar; *Ref*, Kate Landis
Founded 1939. Pop 14,000; Circ 70,000
Jan 2000-Dec 2000 Income $496,510, State $15,939, City $456,081, Locally Generated Income $10,711. Mats Exp $82,333, Books $60,081, Per/Ser (Incl. Access Fees) $7,850, Micro $2,750, AV Equip $2,500, Other Print Mats $3,550. Sal $340,000
Library Holdings: Bk Vols 95,000; Bk Titles 90,000; Per Subs 60
Automation Activity & Vendor Info: (Cataloging) DRA; (Circulation) DRA; (OPAC) DRA
Mem of Bergen - Passaic Regional Libr Syst; Bergen County Co-op Libr Syst
Partic in BCCLS Computer Consortium
Friends of the Library Group

NORTH BERGEN

P NORTH BERGEN FREE PUBLIC LIBRARY, 8411 Bergenline Ave, 07047-5097. SAN 351-1111. Tel: 201-869-4715. FAX: 201-868-0968. Web Site: www.bccls.org. *Dir*, Sai Rao; E-Mail: rao@bccls.org; *Business*, Sherie Habermann; Staff 27 (MLS 6, Non-MLS 21)
Founded 1951. Pop 48,414; Circ 101,000
Library Holdings: Bk Vols 156,663; Bk Titles 153,914; Per Subs 226
Subject Interests: Foreign Language, Literature
Special Collections: Large Print; New Jerseyiana
Automation Activity & Vendor Info: (Cataloging) DRA; (Circulation) DRA; (OPAC) DRA
Database Vendor: Ebsco - EbscoHost
Mem of Bergen County Co-op Libr Syst
Partic in Infolink Eastern New Jersey Regional Library Cooperative, Inc
Friends of the Library Group

NORTH BRUNSWICK

C DEVRY INSTITUTE LIBRARY, 630 US Hwy One, 08902. Tel: 732-435-4880. FAX: 732-435-4865. Toll Free FAX: 732-435-4864. Web Site: www.nj.devry.edu/library. *Dir*, Jacquelin Maresch; Tel: 732-435-4880, Ext 3847, E-Mail: jmaresch@admin.nj.devry.edu; *Librn*, Joseph Louderback; *Librn*, Tami Sandberg; *Automation Syst Coordr*, Ann Liu; *Tech Servs*, Edgar Ortiz; Staff 6 (MLS 4, Non-MLS 2)
Enrl 3,700; Fac 160; Highest Degree: Bachelor
Jul 1999-Jun 2000 Mats Exp $228,000, Books $150,000, Per/Ser (Incl. Access Fees) $18,000, Electronic Ref Mat (Incl. Access Fees) $60,000. Sal $200,000 (Prof $166,000)
Library Holdings: Bk Vols 33,100; Bk Titles 32,670; Per Subs 96
Automation Activity & Vendor Info: (Cataloging) Endeavor
Database Vendor: Dialog, Ebsco - EbscoHost, Lexis-Nexis, ProQuest
Partic in Infolink; PALINET & Union Library Catalogue of Pennsylvania

P NORTH BRUNSWICK FREE PUBLIC LIBRARY, 880 Hermann Rd, 08902. SAN 310-3668. Tel: 732-246-3545. FAX: 732-246-1341. Web Site: www.imxac.org/northbrunswick/index.html. *Dir*, Maureen Rees; E-Mail: meodrees@lmxac.org; *Librn*, Christopher Grippo; *Ch Servs*, Hilary Mirrer; *Ref*, Radha Dhanyamraju; *Ref*, Jennifer Gerridge; *Ref*, Jean Ruch; Staff 16 (MLS 5, Non-MLS 11)
Founded 1966. Pop 35,000; Circ 227,931
Jan 2000-Dec 2000 Income $828,121, State $32,000, City $796,121. Mats Exp Books $160,000. Sal $487,940 (Prof $190,000)
Library Holdings: Bk Vols 101,000; Bk Titles 99,913
Subject Interests: Antiques
Special Collections: Adult Basic Reading for Literacy Program
Database Vendor: DRA, IAC - Info Trac
Partic in Librs of Middlesex Automation Consortium
Friends of the Library Group

S STARK INFORMATION SPECIALISTS LIBRARY,* 4 Vetter Ct, 08902. SAN 377-2373. Tel: 732-422-1969. FAX: 732-422-4330.
Library Holdings: Bk Vols 175; Bk Titles 150; Per Subs 12
Partic in Highlands Regional Library Cooperative

NORTH HALEDON

P FREE PUBLIC LIBRARY OF THE BOROUGH OF NORTH HALEDON, 129 Overlook Ave, 07508-2533. SAN 310-3676. Tel: 973-427-6213. FAX: 973-427-1826. Web Site: www.palsplus.org/nhfpl. *Dir*, Susan Serico; Staff 1 (MLS 1)
Founded 1929. Pop 7,987; Circ 39,420

Jan 1999-Dec 1999 Income $228,640, State $11,195, City $188,912, Locally Generated Income $6,961, Other $21,572. Mats Exp $32,696, Books $23,738, Per/Ser (Incl. Access Fees) $1,963, AV Equip $4,700, Electronic Ref Mat (Incl. Access Fees) $2,295. Sal $101,475 (Prof $42,639)
Library Holdings: Bk Vols 24,922; Bk Titles 22,795; Per Subs 59
Database Vendor: DRA
Partic in Highlands Regional Library Cooperative; Pals; Passaic County Libr Syst
Friends of the Library Group

NORTHFIELD

P OTTO BRUYNS PUBLIC LIBRARY OF NORTHFIELD, 241 W Mill Rd, 08225. SAN 310-3684. Tel: 609-646-4476. FAX: 609-484-9006. *Dir*, Margaret Derascavage; Staff 1 (Non-MLS 1)
Founded 1926. Pop 7,875; Circ 37,082
Library Holdings: Bk Titles 23,566; Per Subs 76
Special Collections: History of Northfield, monographs
Automation Activity & Vendor Info: (Circulation) Sagebrush Corporation; (Media Booking) Sagebrush Corporation
Friends of the Library Group

NORTHVALE

S GLOBTEK LABORATORIES, INC LIBRARY,* 186 Veterans Dr, 07647. SAN 323-4037. Tel: 201-784-1000. FAX: 201-784-0111. E-Mail: globtek1@chelsea.ios.com.
Library Holdings: Bk Vols 1,000
Restriction: Not open to public

P NORTHVALE LIBRARY ASSOCIATION,* 116 Paris Ave, 07647. SAN 310-3706. Tel: 201-768-4784. E-Mail: novl1@bccls.org. *Dir*, Viginia Beckman
Founded 1957. Circ 36,813
Library Holdings: Bk Vols 32,000; Per Subs 64
Special Collections: Biography
Mem of Bergen County Co-op Libr Syst

NORWOOD

P NORWOOD PUBLIC LIBRARY,* 198 Summit St, 07648-1835. SAN 310-3722. Tel: 201-768-9555. FAX: 201-767-2176. *Acq, Cat, Coll Develop, Dir*, David Beckman; *Circ*, Eleanor Falkenstern; *Circ*, Constance Seter; *Circ*, Ellen Nordquist; *Ch Servs*, Brieana Choinski; *Circ*, Linda Grove; *Circ*, Slobhan Kelly
Founded 1936. Pop 4,600; Circ 14,035
Jan 1998-Dec 1999 Income $123,000. Mats Exp $17,000, Books $12,000, Per/Ser (Incl. Access Fees) $2,000, Micro $3,000. Sal $75,500 (Prof $37,500)
Library Holdings: Bk Titles 18,143; Per Subs 60
Special Collections: Birds (Melvin Quackenbush Coll)
Mem of Bergen - Passaic Regional Libr Syst; Bergen County Co-op Libr Syst

NUTLEY

S HOFFMANN-LA ROCHE, INC LIBRARY, 340 Kingsland St, 07110-1199. SAN 351-1200. Tel: 973-235-3092. FAX: 973-235-5477. *Mgr*, Peter Borgulya; Tel: 973-235-2066, E-Mail: peter.borgulya@roche.com; *Librn*, Marian Koob; Tel: 973-235-2060, E-Mail: marian.koob@roche.com; *Asst Librn*, Sandra J DiGiacomo; Tel: 973-235-3092, E-Mail: sandra.digiacomo@roche.com; *Asst Librn*, Christine Green; Tel: 973-235-3094, E-Mail: chris.green@roche.com; *Ref*, Pat Williams; Tel: 973-235-2586, E-Mail: pat.williams@roche.com; Staff 5 (MLS 1, Non-MLS 4)
Library Holdings: Bk Titles 16,000; Per Subs 200
Subject Interests: Bus, Marketing, Medicinal chem, Pharmaceutical industry, Pharmacology, Vitamins
Publications: Periodicals & Serials List
Restriction: By appointment only, Company library
Function: Research library
Partic in Dialog Corporation; OCLC Online Computer Library Center, Inc

P NUTLEY FREE PUBLIC LIBRARY, 93 Booth Dr, 07110-2782. SAN 310-3749. Tel: 973-667-0405. FAX: 973-667-0408, 973-667-4673. E-Mail: nutl@bccls.org. Web Site: www.bccls.org/nutley. *Dir*, JoAnn A Tropiano; E-Mail: tropiano@bccls.org; *Ref, Senior Librn, Tech Servs*, Patel Kiran; *Reader Servs, Senior Librn*, Mark Sannino; *Ch Servs, YA Servs*, Jean Ellen Roberts; *Ref*, Min Zhang; Staff 18 (MLS 5, Non-MLS 13)
Founded 1913. Pop 25,604; Circ 146,337
Jan 1999-Dec 1999 Income $1,015,494, State $49,909, City $928,678, Federal $500, Other $36,407. Mats Exp $133,675, Books $94,822, Per/Ser (Incl. Access Fees) $28,981, Presv $417, Micro $150, Electronic Ref Mat (Incl. Access Fees) $9,305. Sal $686,591
Library Holdings: Bk Vols 103,299; Bk Titles 95,851; Per Subs 250
Subject Interests: Local history
Special Collections: Hoeber Collection; Index for Nutley Sun
Automation Activity & Vendor Info: (Cataloging) DRA; (Circulation) DRA; (OPAC) DRA
Database Vendor: DRA
Partic in Bergen County Cooperative Library System; Essex County Coop Librs; Infolink Eastern New Jersey Regional Library Cooperative, Inc
Special Services for the Blind - Audio-cassettes; Large print bks; Printed text enlargers
First floor computer center - adults & students with high school & up I.D.; Second floor computer center - children with parents; Book discussion groups; Concert series.
Friends of the Library Group

S NUTLEY HISTORICAL SOCIETY, Alice J Bickers Library, 65 Church St, 07110. SAN 326-6400. Tel: 973-667-1528. *Pres*, Richard O'Connor
Founded 1945. Pop 30,000
Library Holdings: Bk Vols 200; Bk Titles 175
Special Collections: Geneology of Nutley Coll; Nutley Authors; Old Account Books of Nutley
Restriction: By appointment only

OAK RIDGE

P JEFFERSON TOWNSHIP PUBLIC LIBRARY,* 1031 Weldon Rd, 07438. SAN 320-2046. Tel: 973-208-6115. FAX: 973-697-7051. Web Site: www.hicom.net/~jefferson. *Dir*, Seth Stephens; *Asst Librn*, Caroline Johnson; Staff 8 (MLS 1, Non-MLS 7)
Founded 1960. Pop 20,000
Library Holdings: Bk Titles 52,000; Per Subs 97
Publications: annual report; Bookmarks
Partic in Highlands Regional Library Cooperative; Morris Automated Information Network
Friends of the Library Group

OAKHURST

S OCEAN TOWNSHIP HISTORICAL MUSEUM LIBRARY, 163 Monmouth Rd, 07755. SAN 377-5011. Tel: 732-531-2136. *Pres*, Virginia Richmond
Library Holdings: Bk Vols 200

S SUBSTANCE ABUSE RESOURCES, Prevention & Education Resource Center, 1806 State Hwy 35, 07755. SAN 377-533X. Tel: 732-663-1800. TDD: 732-663-0080. FAX: 732-663-1698. E-Mail: info@sarnj.com. Web Site: www.sarnj.com. *Coordr*, Barbara Sprechman
Library Holdings: Bk Titles 450
Partic in Central Jersey Regional Library Cooperative
Special Services for the Deaf - TDD

OAKLAND

P FREE PUBLIC LIBRARY OF OAKLAND,* Municipal Plaza, 07436. SAN 310-3773. Tel: 201-337-3742. FAX: 201-337-0261. E-Mail: oakpl@bcels.org. Web Site: www.bccls.org/oakland/. *Dir*, Unda Brechtel; *Cat, Ref*, Rose Marie Kollar; *Ch Servs*, Debbie Pfeuffer; *Circ*, Margaret Farley; Staff 16 (MLS 3, Non-MLS 13)
Founded 1910. Pop 11,997; Circ 95,029
Jan 1999-Dec 1999 Income $575,674. Mats Exp $123,778, Books $65,000, Per/Ser (Incl. Access Fees) $7,600. Sal $329,896
Library Holdings: Bk Vols 57,973
Automation Activity & Vendor Info: (OPAC) DRA
Mem of Bergen County Co-op Libr Syst
Partic in Highlands Regional Library Cooperative
Friends of the Library Group

S RELAY SPECIALTIES, INC LIBRARY,* 17 Raritan Rd, 07436. (Mail add: PO Box 7000, 07436), SAN 328-2961. Tel: 201-337-1000. FAX: 201-337-1862. E-Mail: sales@relayspec.com. *In Charge*, Joan Giglio
Subject Interests: Electronics

OAKLYN

P OAKLYN MEMORIAL LIBRARY,* 602 Newton Ave, 08107. SAN 310-3803. Tel: 856-858-8226. FAX: 856-858-3007. *Dir*, Kathleen Anderson; *Asst Librn*, Doris Ahearn; *Asst Librn*, Eleanore Kirsh-Gassner; *Asst Librn*, Grace Vassalotti
Founded 1927. Pop 5,000; Circ 15,789
Library Holdings: Bk Vols 17,421; Bk Titles 16,776; Per Subs 32
Subject Interests: Local history
Special Collections: Manuscript
Mem of Camden County Library System

OCEAN CITY

P OCEAN CITY FREE PUBLIC LIBRARY,* 1735 Simpson Ave, 08226-3071. SAN 310-382X. Tel: 609-399-2434. FAX: 609-398-8944. E-Mail: oclib@acy.digex.net. Web Site: www.acy.digex.net/~oclib/. *Dir*, Karen G Mahar; *Ref*, Chris Maloney; *Ch Servs*, Leslie E Diaz; *Senior Librn*, Robert

N Baggs; *Tech Servs*, Bob Rynkiewicz
Pop 15,512; Circ 114,082
Library Holdings: Bk Vols 90,000; Per Subs 250
Subject Interests: Local history
Partic in South Jersey Regional Library Cooperative
Volunteers program
Friends of the Library Group

S OCEAN CITY HISTORICAL MUSEUM RESEARCH LIBRARY, (Formerly Ocean City Historical Museum Library), 1735 Simpson Ave, 08226. SAN 373-2533. Tel: 609-399-1801. FAX: 609-399-0544. E-Mail: ocnjhistmuseum@aol.com. Web Site: www.ocnjmuseum.org.
Founded 1964
Library Holdings: Bk Vols 200; Per Subs 10
Subject Interests: Local history
Restriction: By appointment only
Function: Research library

OCEAN GROVE

S HISTORICAL SOCIETY OF OCEAN GROVE LIBRARY & ARCHIVES, 50 Pitman Ave, PO Box 446, 07756. SAN 329-2991. Tel: 732-774-1869. Web Site: www.oceangrovehistory.org. *Archivist, Librn*, Frederic C Pachman
Founded 1970. Pop 29,000
Library Holdings: Bk Vols 250
Publications: Bibliographies; newsletters

OLD BRIDGE

P OLD BRIDGE PUBLIC LIBRARY, One Old Bridge Plaza, 08857-2498. SAN 351-1235. Tel: 732-721-5600, Ext 5013. Interlibrary Loan Service Tel: 732-721-5600, Ext 5030. Circulation Tel: 732-721-5600, Ext 5010. Reference Tel: 732-721-5600, Ext 5033. FAX: 732-679-0556. Web Site: www.oldbridge.com. *Dir*, Ed Troike; Tel: 732-721-5600, Ext 5014, E-Mail: edtroike@lmxac.org; *Asst Dir*, Barbara A Ketterer; Tel: 732-721-5600, Ext 5015, E-Mail: ketterer@lmxac.org; *Ch Servs*, Shirley Zuk; Tel: 732-721-5600, Ext 5021, E-Mail: shirlzuk@lmxac.org; *Circ*, Mary Garcia; Tel: 732-721-5600, Ext 5012, E-Mail: mgarcia@lmxac.org; *Ref*, Dennis Schaub; Tel: 732-721-5600, Ext 5019, E-Mail: dschaub@lmxac.org; *Electronic Resources*, Barbara Elieff; Tel: 732-721-5600, Ext 5039, E-Mail: belieff@lmxac.org; *Ad Servs*, Wendi Smolowitz; Tel: 732-721-5600, Ext 2313, E-Mail: wens@lmxac.org; Staff 15 (MLS 15)
Founded 1970. Pop 58,000; Circ 345,000
Library Holdings: Bk Vols 167,596; Bk Titles 110,000; Per Subs 538
Special Collections: Circulating AV Equipment; Information & Referral Service; Municipal Reference Coll
Automation Activity & Vendor Info: (Circulation) CARL; (ILL) CARL; (OPAC) CARL
Database Vendor: CARL, Ebsco - EbscoHost, IAC - SearchBank
Publications: Bookends (bi-monthly newsletter)
Partic in Infolink Eastern New Jersey Regional Library Cooperative, Inc; LMX Automation Consortium
Friends of the Library Group
Branches: 1
LAURENCE HARBOR BRANCH, 277 Shoreland Circle, Laurence Harbor, 08879. SAN 351-126X. Tel: 732-566-2227. *In Charge*, Rose Layer

OLD TAPPAN

P OLD TAPPAN FREE PUBLIC LIBRARY,* 56 Russell Ave, 07675. SAN 310-3854. Tel: 201-664-3499. FAX: 201-664-5999. E-Mail: ottn1@bccls.org. *Dir*, Susan Meeske
Founded 1943. Pop 4,300; Circ 25,400
Library Holdings: Bk Vols 35,000; Per Subs 55
Mem of Bergen - Passaic Regional Libr Syst; Bergen County Co-op Libr Syst
Friends of the Library Group

OLDWICK

P TEWKSBURY TOWNSHIP PUBLIC LIBRARY,* 31 Old Turnpike Rd, PO Box 49, 08858. SAN 310-3862. Tel: 908-439-3761. FAX: 908-439-2326. *Coll Develop, Dir*, April Kane
Circ 23,677
Jan 1997-Dec 1998 Income $66,115, State $111, County $18,690, Locally Generated Income $5,762, Other $24,052. Mats Exp $18,690, Books $15,690, Per/Ser (Incl. Access Fees) $3,000. Sal $25,725
Library Holdings: Bk Vols 18,000; Per Subs 67
Subject Interests: Art, Gardening, History
Special Collections: Art
Mem of Hunterdon County Library
Open Mon 1-9, Tues & Thurs 2-6, Wed 10-6, Sat 9-2
Friends of the Library Group

ORADELL

S BURNS & ROE ENTERPRISES, INC, Technical Library, 800 Kinderkamack Rd, 07649. SAN 310-3870. Tel: 201-265-2000, Ext 4224. FAX: 201-986-4210. *Librn*, Pat Bernstein
Founded 1961
Library Holdings: Bk Vols 2,000
Subject Interests: Architecture, Engineering
Special Collections: Safety Analysis Reports for Nuclear Power Plants; Technical Reports

P ORADELL FREE PUBLIC LIBRARY, 375 Kinderkamack Rd, 07649-2122. SAN 310-3889. Tel: 201-262-2613. FAX: 201-262-9112. Web Site: web2.bccls.org/members/orad.html. *Dir*, George W Cooke; E-Mail: cooke@bccls.org; *Ch Servs*, Ruth Camins; Staff 24 (MLS 1, Non-MLS 23)
Founded 1913. Pop 8,314; Circ 151,955
Jan 2000-Dec 2000 Income $556,211, State $9,027, City $345,559, Other $36,221. Mats Exp $105,026, Books $78,000, Per/Ser (Incl. Access Fees) $9,800, Presv $1,500, Other Print Mats $726, Electronic Ref Mat (Incl. Access Fees) $15,000. Sal $373,735 (Prof $61,000)
Library Holdings: Bk Vols 80,000; Per Subs 190; Bks on Deafness & Sign Lang 15
Subject Interests: Bks, Local history, Paper, Photogs
Special Collections: Books Illustrated by Charles Livingston Bull
Database Vendor: DRA
Publications: Newsletter
Mem of Region 2 Bergen-Passaic Counties
Partic in Bergen County Cooperative Library System

ORANGE

P ORANGE PUBLIC LIBRARY,* 348 Main St, 07050-2794. SAN 310-3897. Tel: 973-673-0153. FAX: 973-673-1847. *Dir*, Doris Walker; *Ch Servs*, Deborah Ferraro; *ILL, Ref*, Alice McMillan; Staff 4 (MLS 4)
Founded 1884. Pop 29,925; Circ 98,781
Jul 1997-Jun 1998 Income $743,874, State $34,284, City $611,420, Federal $2,375, Other $95,795. Mats Exp $54,809, Books $41,351, Per/Ser (Incl. Access Fees) $7,309. Sal $569,448 (Prof $156,000)
Library Holdings: Bk Vols 190,355; Bk Titles 125,676; Per Subs 135
Special Collections: Black Literature & History; Orangeana
Partic in Essex County Coop Librs; Infolink Eastern New Jersey Regional Library Cooperative, Inc

OXFORD

P OXFORD PUBLIC LIBRARY,* 42 Washington Ave, 07863. SAN 376-0480. Tel: 908-453-2625. *Dir*, Helen Lynch
Founded 1921
Library Holdings: Bk Titles 1,800
Open Tues & Thurs 2-7
Friends of the Library Group

S WARREN COUNTY CULTURAL & HERITAGE COMMISSION LIBRARY,* Shippen Manor, 8 Belvidere Ave, 07863. SAN 376-0626. Tel: 908-453-4381. FAX: 908-453-4981. E-Mail: wcchc@nac.net. Web Site: www.wcchc.org. *Chair*, Susan Morgan; *Coordr*, Dennis Austin
Library Holdings: Bk Titles 1,500

PALISADES PARK

P PALISADES PARK FREE PUBLIC LIBRARY,* 257 Second St, 07650. SAN 310-3935. Tel: 201-585-4150. FAX: 201-585-2151. E-Mail: palp1@bccls.org. Web Site: www.bergen.bccls.org/palisadespark/. *Dir*, Ana R Chelariu; Staff 1 (MLS 1)
Founded 1922. Pop 14,530; Circ 58,534
1998-1999 Income $340,000, State $15,600, Locally Generated Income $2,600. Mats Exp $11,700, Books $7,800, Per/Ser (Incl. Access Fees) $3,900. Sal $200,000
Library Holdings: Bk Vols 45,316; Per Subs 95
Subject Interests: Mythology
Special Collections: Cookery Coll
Mem of Bergen County Co-op Libr Syst

PARAMUS

S ARMENIAN MISSIONARY ASSOCIATION OF AMERICA LIBRARY, 31 W Century Rd, 07652. Tel: 201-265-2607. FAX: 201-265-6015. *Dir*, Dikran Youmshakian
Library Holdings: Bk Vols 20,000; Bk Titles 20,000; Per Subs 16

J BERGEN COMMUNITY COLLEGE, Sidney Silverman Library & LRC, 400 Paramus Rd, 07652-1595. SAN 310-3943. Tel: 201-447-7970. FAX: 201-444-7036. Web Site: www.bergen.cc.nj.us/library/. *Dir*, N J Wolfe; Tel: 201-447-7130, E-Mail: njwolfe@bergen.cc.nj.us; *Asst Dir*, Patricia Denholm; Tel: 201-447-7447, E-Mail: pdenholm@bergen.cc.nj.us; *Head Tech Servs*, Martha Lewicky; E-Mail: mlewicky@bergen.cc.nj.us; *Ref*, Barbara Alper;

E-Mail: balper@bergen.cc.nj.us; *Ser*, Joan G Cohen; E-Mail: jcohen@bergen.cc.nj.us; *Bibliog Instr*, Vivian Brown-Carman; *Ref*, Paula Williams; E-Mail: pwilliams@bergen.cc.nj.us; *Coll Develop*, Edith Sirianni; E-Mail: esirianni@bergen.cc.nj.us; *Ref*, Barbara Walcott; Staff 30 (MLS 12, Non-MLS 18)
Founded 1965. Enrl 11,812; Fac 253; Highest Degree: Associate
Jul 2000-Jun 2001 Income $2,617,877. Mats Exp $384,000, Books $225,000, Per/Ser (Incl. Access Fees) $67,000, Micro $14,000, Electronic Ref Mat (Incl. Access Fees) $78,000. Sal $2,000,000 (Prof $18,000)
Library Holdings: Bk Vols 142,746; Per Subs 838
Subject Interests: Allied health, Deaf educ, Nursing
Automation Activity & Vendor Info: (Acquisitions) Innovative Interfaces Inc.; (Cataloging) Innovative Interfaces Inc.; (Circulation) Innovative Interfaces Inc.; (Course Reserve) Innovative Interfaces Inc.; (ILL) Innovative Interfaces Inc.; (OPAC) Innovative Interfaces Inc.; (Serials) Innovative Interfaces Inc.
Database Vendor: Ebsco - EbscoHost, IAC - Info Trac, IAC - SearchBank, Lexis-Nexis, ProQuest
Partic in Bergen County Cooperative Library System; Bergen Passaic Health Sciences Library Consortium; Highlands Regional Library Cooperative; OCLC Online Computer Library Center, Inc

M BERGEN REGIONAL MEDICAL LIBRARY, 230 E Ridgewood Ave, 07652. SAN 310-3951. Tel: 201-967-4163. *In Charge*, B Jan Hudgens
Founded 1952
Library Holdings: Bk Titles 2,500; Per Subs 135
Subject Interests: Clinical medicine
Restriction: Staff use only
Partic in NY & NJ Regional Med Libr

P PARAMUS PUBLIC LIBRARY, E 116 Century Rd, 07652-4398. SAN 351-1324. Tel: 201-599-1300. Circulation Tel: 201-599-1302. Reference Tel: 201-599-1305. FAX: 201-599-0059. E-Mail: paral@bccls.org, paramus@bccls.org. Web Site: www.bccls.org/paramus. *Dir*, Leonard LoPinto; *Ch Servs*, Dolores Murphy; *Ref*, Sylvia Gaddi; *Circ*, Jane Uber; *Br Coordr*, Cathy Eng; *Coll Develop*, Hanna Blatt; Staff 39 (MLS 8, Non-MLS 31)
Founded 1954. Pop 26,474; Circ 336,334
Jan 2000-Dec 2000 Income (Main Library and Branch Library) $1,532,020, State $27,000, City $1,428,709, Locally Generated Income $70,000, Other $6,311. Mats Exp $140,814, Books $109,000, Per/Ser (Incl. Access Fees) $19,814, Micro $12,000. Sal $1,255,285
Library Holdings: Bk Vols 101,838
Special Collections: Anita W Lipsett (fine & performing arts videos)
Partic in Highlands Regional Library Cooperative
Friends of the Library Group
Branches: 1
CHARLES E REID BRANCH, W 239 Midland Ave, 07652. SAN 351-1359. Tel: 201-444-4911.
Friends of the Library Group

PARK RIDGE

S JOHN E ALLEN INC, Motion Picture Archives, 116 North Ave, 07656. SAN 329-207X. Tel: 201-391-3299. FAX: 201-391-6335.
Founded 1951
Subject Interests: Education, Indust, Transportation, World War I, World War II
Special Collections: Actuality Stock Footage, flms & dramatic; General Motion Picture Coll, bks, flms, posters, still photogs

P PARK RIDGE PUBLIC LIBRARY, 51 Park Ave, 07656. SAN 310-3978. Tel: 201-391-5151. FAX: 201-391-2739. E-Mail: pkrdl@bccls.org. Web Site: www.bccls.org/members.shtml. *Dir*, Julie Linnavuori; Staff 10 (MLS 2, Non-MLS 8)
Pop 8,102; Circ 35,590
Library Holdings: Bk Titles 38,400; Per Subs 79
Subject Interests: Local history
Automation Activity & Vendor Info: (Circulation) DRA; (OPAC) DRA
Publications: Library Lines
Partic in Bergen County Cooperative Library System
Friends of the Library Group

PARLIN

P SAYREVILLE PUBLIC LIBRARY, 1050 Washington Rd, 08859. SAN 310-3994. Tel: 732-727-0212. FAX: 732-553-0775. *Actg Dir*, Liza Scherff-Nesarikar; *Ch Servs*, Grace Horetsky; *Per*, Joanne Kaluzny; *Ref*, Sylvia Borsuk; Staff 3 (MLS 3)
Founded 1931. Pop 35,000; Circ 105,594
Library Holdings: Bk Vols 93,800; Bk Titles 90,000; Per Subs 170
Friends of the Library Group

PARSIPPANY

S AQUILA EAST COAST GENERATION INC, (Formerly GPU Nuclear Corporation Library), One Upper Pond Rd, 07054. SAN 351-1383. Tel: 973-263-6590. Web Site: www.aquila.com.
Founded 1971
Library Holdings: Bk Titles 3,000; Per Subs 250
Subject Interests: Mechanical engineering, Nuclear power
Special Collections: Historical Engineering Standards; Nuclear Regulatory Commission Reports
Publications: New Titles
Restriction: Not open to public
Partic in Dialog Corporation

S CONVERSE CONSULTANTS EAST LIBRARY, 3 Century Dr, 07054-0265. SAN 310-0510. Tel: 973-605-5200. FAX: 973-605-8145. E-Mail: convers@mail.idt.net. Web Site: www.converseconsultants.com. *Librn*, Phyllis Palombini
Library Holdings: Bk Vols 2,000; Per Subs 20
Subject Interests: Foundation eng, Related topics, Soils

P PARSIPPANY-TROY HILLS FREE PUBLIC LIBRARY, 292 Parsippany Rd, 07054. SAN 351-1448. Tel: 973-887-5150. FAX: 973-887-0062. Web Site: www.users.nac.net/ptlib. *Dir*, Jayne Beline; E-Mail: beline@main.morris.org; *Ch Servs*, Paula Lefkowitz; *Tech Servs*, Bill Harrison; *AV, Circ*, Marion Perry; *Ref*, Judith Kron
Founded 1968
2000-2001 Income $1,907,346, State $62,000, City $1,775,346, Locally Generated Income $70,000. Mats Exp $243,287, Books $216,485, Per/Ser (Incl. Access Fees) $26,802. Sal $991,720 (Prof $386,990)
Library Holdings: Bk Vols 204,422; Bk Titles 96,752; Per Subs 201
Automation Activity & Vendor Info: (Acquisitions) DRA; (Cataloging) DRA; (Circulation) DRA; (OPAC) DRA
Database Vendor: DRA
Partic in Highlands Regional Library Cooperative; Morris Automated Information Network
Friends of the Library Group
Branches: 2
LAKE HIAWATHA BRANCH, 39 Nokomis Ave, Lake Hiawatha, 07034. SAN 351-1472. Tel: 973-335-0952. FAX: 973-335-8610. Web Site: www.users.nac.net/ptlib. *Branch Mgr*, Judy Weinstein; *Ch Servs*, Aida Courtney
Database Vendor: DRA
Friends of the Library Group
MOUNT TABOR BRANCH, 31 Trinity Park, Mount Tabor, 07878. SAN 351-1502. Tel: 973-627-9508. *Head of Libr*, Debra Insetta
Friends of the Library Group

S SCOTT FORESMAN DIVISION OF PEARSON EDUCATION,* 299 Jefferson Rd, 07054. SAN 310-3161. Tel: 973-739-8416. FAX: 973-739-8595.
Founded 1885
Library Holdings: Bk Titles 10,000; Per Subs 100
Subject Interests: Computer educ
Special Collections: Silver Burdett Publications from 1885
Restriction: Staff use only
Partic in Morris County Libr Network

S SMITHKLINE BEECHAM CONSUMER HEALTHCARE, Research Library,* 1500 Littleton Rd, 07054. SAN 310-4001. Tel: 973-889-2231. FAX: 973-889-2397. *In Charge*, Kathleen Morris; Staff 5 (MLS 4, Non-MLS 1)
Founded 1978
Library Holdings: Bk Titles 3,000; Per Subs 150
Publications: Information Bulletin
Restriction: Not open to public
Partic in NY & NJ Regional Med Libr; OCLC Online Computer Library Center, Inc

PASSAIC

P PASSAIC PUBLIC LIBRARY, Julius Forstmann Library, 195 Gregory Ave, 07055. SAN 351-1561. Tel: 973-779-0474. FAX: 973-779-0889. E-Mail: pasc1@bccls.org. *Dir*, Laurie Sansone; *Asst Dir*, Kathleen Mollica; *Ch Servs*, Arlene Sauer; *Ref*, Jean Ellis; *Ref*, Luba Furtock; Staff 30 (MLS 7, Non-MLS 23)
Founded 1887. Pop 58,041; Circ 122,675
Jul 1998-Jun 1999 Income (Main Library and Branch Library) $1,346,774, State $74,764, City $1,219,869, Federal $13,750, Locally Generated Income $38,391. Mats Exp $127,549, Books $126,507, Per/Ser (Incl. Access Fees) $18,696, Micro $375. Sal $739,255
Library Holdings: Bk Vols 141,769; Bk Titles 91,186; Per Subs 294
Subject Interests: Art, Cooking, Jewish studies, Literacy
Special Collections: Local History (Passaic Coll), bks, mss, clippings, photog
Automation Activity & Vendor Info: (Cataloging) DRA; (Circulation) DRA
Database Vendor: DRA
Partic in Bergen County Cooperative Library System; Highland Regional Libr Syst; Passaic County Libr Syst

Branches: 1
REID MEMORIAL BRANCH, 80 Third St, 07055. SAN 351-1626. Tel: 973-777-6044.; Staff 2 (Non-MLS 2)
Library Holdings: Bk Vols 26,900; Per Subs 34
Automation Activity & Vendor Info: (Circulation) DRA
Bookmobiles: 1

M ST MARY'S HOSPITAL, Resource Center, 211 Pennington Ave, 07055. SAN 325-7789. Tel: 973-470-3055. FAX: 973-470-3499. *Dir*, Sister Gertrude Doremus; E-Mail: doremusg@smh-passaic.org
Library Holdings: Bk Vols 2,000; Bk Titles 400; Per Subs 100

PATERSON

J PASSAIC COUNTY COMMUNITY COLLEGE, Library & Learning Resources Center, One College Blvd, 07505. SAN 310-4028. Tel: 973-684-5896. Interlibrary Loan Service Tel: 973-684-6918. Circulation Tel: 973-684-5877. Reference Tel: 973-684-8007. FAX: 973-684-6675. Web Site: www.pccc.cc.nj.us/library. *Dir*, Gregory Fallon; E-Mail: gfallon@pccc.cc.nj.us; *Librn*, Hugh Holden; Tel: 973-684-5880, E-Mail: hholden@pccc.cc.nj.us; *Librn*, Ken Karol; E-Mail: kkarol@pccc.cc.nj.us; *Ref*, Ruth Hamman; Tel: 973-684-5880, E-Mail: rhamann@pccc.cc.nj.us; *Tech Servs*, Mibong La; Tel: 973-684-5885, E-Mail: mla@pccc.cc.nj.us; Staff 4 (MLS 4)
Founded 1971. Enrl 2,162; Fac 102; Highest Degree: Associate
Library Holdings: Bk Vols 44,605; Bk Titles 37,990
Special Collections: Passaic County Poetry Center
Automation Activity & Vendor Info: (Cataloging) DRA; (Circulation) DRA; (Course Reserve) DRA; (ILL) DRA; (OPAC) DRA
Database Vendor: DRA, OCLC - First Search
Publications: LRC Handbook; LRC News
Partic in OCLC, Inc through Palinet

S PASSAIC COUNTY HISTORICAL SOCIETY, Edward B Haines Local History Library, Lambert Castle, Valley Rd, 07503-2932. SAN 310-4036. Tel: 973-881-2761. FAX: 973-357-1070. *Dir*, Andrew Shick; Staff 1 (Non-MLS 1)
Founded 1926
Library Holdings: Bk Titles 10,000
Special Collections: Derrom Family Coll; Haines Family Coll; Hewitt Coll; Hobart Family Coll; Industrial History (Society for Establishing Useful Manufactures Papers), mss; New Jersey (John Reid Photo Coll), photos; Passaic General Hospital Coll; Paterson Orphans Asylum Records; Wright Aeronautical Coll
Publications: Castle Genie (Newsletter); The Castle Light (Newsletter)
Restriction: Non-circulating
Function: Archival collection, Photocopies available, Research fees apply, Research library

L PASSAIC COUNTY LAW LIBRARY,* 77 Hamilton St, 07505-2096. SAN 310-4044. Tel: 973-247-8013. FAX: 973-881-2832. *Actg Librn*, Tami Lowe; Staff 1 (MLS 1)
Founded 1930
Jul 1997-Jun 1998 Income $125,000. Mats Exp $126,000, Books $123,500, Per/Ser (Incl. Access Fees) $2,500. Sal $41,281 (Prof $25,780)
Library Holdings: Bk Vols 57,220

P THE PATERSON FREE PUBLIC LIBRARY, Danforth Memorial Library, 250 Broadway, 07501. SAN 351-1685. Tel: 973-357-3000. Interlibrary Loan Service Tel: 973-357-3001. Reference Tel: 973-357-3005. Interlibrary Loan Service FAX: 973-881-8338. Reference FAX: 973-754-1797. E-Mail: danforth2@interactive.net. Web Site: www.paterson.k12.nj.us/~publiclibrary. *Dir*, Cynthia Czesak; Tel: 973-357-3013, Fax: 973-523-5540, E-Mail: czesak@palsplus.org; *Cat, Tech Servs*, Diana Springfield; Tel: 973-357-3007; *ILL*, Joan Petricca; *Ch Servs*, Mabel Ajala; Tel: 973-357-3002; *Ad Servs*, Bryna Fox; *Ref*, Bruce Barkarik; *Coll Develop*, Damaris N Ganga; Staff 5 (MLS 5)
Founded 1885. Pop 150,000
Jan 1999-Dec 1999 Income (Main Library and Branch Library) $2,360,454, State $127,047, City $1,847,105, Federal $36,018, Locally Generated Income $7,077, Other $343,207. Mats Exp $255,073, Books $193,759, Per/Ser (Incl. Access Fees) $24,531, AV Equip $10,999, Electronic Ref Mat (Incl. Access Fees) $35,784. Sal $1,445,568 (Prof $417,097)
Library Holdings: Bk Vols 333,868; Bk Titles 181,986; Per Subs 469
Subject Interests: Genealogy, Local history, Spanish
Special Collections: Arabic/Islamic Coll
Mem of Passaic County Libr Syst
Partic in Highlands Regional Library Cooperative
Friends of the Library Group
Branches: 3
FIRST WARD, 56 N Main St, 07522. SAN 351-174X. Tel: 973-357-3021. Web Site: www.paterson.k12.nj.us/~publiclibrary.
Pop 150,000
Library Holdings: Bk Vols 26,562
Friends of the Library Group
SOUTH PATERSON, 930 Main St, 07503. SAN 351-1863. Tel: 973-357-3020. FAX: 973-279-4814. Web Site: www.paterson.k12.nj.us/~publiclibrary.
Circ 150,000
Library Holdings: Bk Vols 30,609
Special Collections: Arabic/Islamic Coll
Friends of the Library Group
TOTOWA, 405 Union Ave, 07512. SAN 351-1898. Tel: 973-357-3022. Web Site: www.paterson.k12.nj.us/~publiclibrary.
Library Holdings: Bk Vols 30,366
Friends of the Library Group

M SAINT JOSEPH'S HOSPITAL & MEDICAL CENTER, Health Sciences Library,* 703 Main St, 07503. SAN 320-5835. Tel: 973-754-2000. FAX: 973-754-3593. *Dir*, Patrica May
Founded 1932
Library Holdings: Bk Vols 5,000; Per Subs 280

PAULSBORO

P GILL MEMORIAL LIBRARY, 145 E Broad St, 08066. SAN 310-4079. Tel: 856-423-5155. FAX: 856-423-9162. E-Mail: staff@paulsboro.k12.nj.us. *Dir*, Violet Jean Valentin; E-Mail: wvalenti@paulsboro.k12.nj.us; *Asst Librn*, Curtis Banks; E-Mail: cbanks@paulsboro.k12.nj.us
Founded 1951. Pop 6,500
Jan 1999-Dec 1999 Income $112,509, State $2,259, City $102,115, Other $8,135. Mats Exp $18,763, Books $13,722, Per/Ser (Incl. Access Fees) $2,249, Micro $2,520, AV Equip $272. Sal $32,062
Library Holdings: Bk Vols 17,636; Bk Titles 16,416; Per Subs 52
Special Collections: Microfilm of Local Newspapers; New Jersey Archives; New Jersey Museum Room with Local History
Automation Activity & Vendor Info: (Cataloging) Sagebrush Corporation; (Circulation) Sagebrush Corporation
Open Tues & Thurs 12-7, Wed 12-5, Sat 10-3

S MOBIL TECHNOLOGY COMPANY, Information Resources Center,* PO Box 300, 08066. SAN 310-4087. Tel: 609-224-3143. FAX: 609-224-3621. *Librn, Online Servs*, Jane Bitter
Founded 1931
Library Holdings: Bk Titles 18,000; Per Subs 400
Subject Interests: Chemistry, Engineering, Technology
Partic in Dialog Corporation; OCLC Online Computer Library Center, Inc; Questal Orbit; STN

PEMBERTON

J BURLINGTON COUNTY COLLEGE LIBRARY, Pemberton Browns Mills Rd, 08068. SAN 310-4095. Tel: 609-894-9311, Ext 7306. FAX: 609-894-4189. Web Site: www.bcc.edu.. *Dir*, Judith M Olsen; Tel: 609-894-9311, Ext 7222, E-Mail: jolsen@bcc.edu; *Asst Dir*, Ann Hiros; Tel: 609-894-9311, Ext 7265, E-Mail: ahiros@bcc.edu; *Info Specialist, Per*, Patricia Dawson; E-Mail: pdawson@bcc.edu; *Cat*, Hung-yi Chang; Tel: 609-894-9311, Ext 7269; Staff 4 (MLS 4)
Founded 1969. Enrl 7,200; Fac 93; Highest Degree: Associate
Library Holdings: Bk Vols 92,000; Per Subs 340
Special Collections: Cinema Coll; Geneology & Local History (Pinelands Coll)
Automation Activity & Vendor Info: (Acquisitions) epixtech, inc.; (Cataloging) epixtech, inc.; (Circulation) epixtech, inc.; (Course Reserve) epixtech, inc.; (ILL) epixtech, inc.; (Media Booking) epixtech, inc.
Database Vendor: OCLC - First Search
Partic in NJULS; OCLC Online Computer Library Center, Inc; PALINET & Union Library Catalogue of Pennsylvania; S Jersey Regional Libr Network

PENNINGTON

P PENNINGTON PUBLIC LIBRARY, 30 N Main St, 08534. SAN 310-4109. Tel: 609-737-0404. FAX: 609-737-9780. *Dir*, Patricia Butcher; Staff 2 (MLS 1, Non-MLS 1)
Pop 2,106; Circ 27,000
Jan 1999-Dec 1999 Income $84,000, State $2,700, City $73,000, Locally Generated Income $8,300. Mats Exp $18,400, Books $12,000, Per/Ser (Incl. Access Fees) $3,200, AV Equip $1,100. Sal $48,000 (Prof $36,000)
Library Holdings: Bk Vols 22,000; Per Subs 48
Special Collections: Pennington Newspaper, 1897-present
Partic in Region C Libr Coop of NJ
Friends of the Library Group

SR UNITED METHODIST CHURCH, SOUTHERN NEW JERSEY CONFERENCE, Commission on Archives & History Library,* c/o Bishop Johnson, The Pennington School, 112 W Delaware Ave, 08534. SAN 375-068X. Tel: 609-737-3940. FAX: 609-737-6962.
Library Holdings: Bk Vols 1,000

PENNS GROVE

P PENNS GROVE-CARNEY'S POINT PUBLIC LIBRARY, 222 S Broad St, 08069. SAN 310-4117. Tel: 856-299-4255. FAX: 856-299-4552. *Dir*, Barbara Hunt; E-Mail: barbarhu@clueslibs.org
Pop 13,285; Circ 51,000

Library Holdings: Bk Vols 24,000; Per Subs 50
Automation Activity & Vendor Info: (Cataloging) Sagebrush Corporation; (Circulation) Sagebrush Corporation; (OPAC) Sagebrush Corporation
Mem of Cumberland County Library
Partic in South Jersey Regional Library Cooperative

PENNSAUKEN

S DATA SYSTEMS ANALYSTS, Technical Library,* 4300 Haddonfield Rd, Ste 200, 08109. SAN 310-4133. Tel: 609-665-6088. FAX: 609-665-6672. *Mgr*, Lynn Pincosy
Founded 1963
Library Holdings: Bk Titles 3,550; Per Subs 125
Subject Interests: Telecommunications

P PENNSAUKEN FREE PUBLIC LIBRARY, 5605 Crescent Blvd, 08110. SAN 310-4141. Tel: 856-665-5959. Circulation Tel: 856-665-5959, Ext 3. Reference Tel: 856-665-5959, Ext 4. FAX: 856-486-0142. *Dir*, Susan Briant; Tel: 856-665-5959, Ext 5, E-Mail: sbriant384@aol.com; *Ch Servs*, Ellen Eifert; Tel: 856-665-5959, Ext 6; *Ref*, Stephanie A D'Angelico; Tel: 856-665-5959, Ext 18; *Ref*, Gerald Simon; Staff 20 (MLS 4, Non-MLS 16)
Founded 1959. Pop 34,738; Circ 149,735
Jan 1999-Dec 1999 Income $728,829, State $52,290, City $587,000, Locally Generated Income $45,868, Other $3,660. Mats Exp $106,273, Books $61,495, Per/Ser (Incl. Access Fees) $21,397, AV Equip $16,220, Electronic Ref Mat (Incl. Access Fees) $6,514. Sal $469,874
Library Holdings: Bk Vols 101,751; Bk Titles 94,781; Per Subs 211
Automation Activity & Vendor Info: (Acquisitions) Innovative Interfaces Inc.; (Cataloging) Innovative Interfaces Inc.; (Circulation) Innovative Interfaces Inc.; (OPAC) Innovative Interfaces Inc.; (Serials) Innovative Interfaces Inc.
Partic in Cap Area Libr Network Inc
Friends of the Library Group

PENNSVILLE

P PENNSVILLE PUBLIC LIBRARY, (PPL), 190 S Broadway, 08070. SAN 310-415X. Tel: 856-678-5473. FAX: 856-678-8121. *Coll Develop, Dir*, Richard Blocksom; *Coll Develop*, Debra Ecret; *Admin Assoc*, Nancy Whitesell; Staff 7 (MLS 1, Non-MLS 6)
Founded 1937. Pop 13,784; Circ 25,953
Jan 1999-Dec 1999 Income $153,386, State $6,219, City $132,150, Other $10,017. Mats Exp $25,735, Books $14,659, Per/Ser (Incl. Access Fees) $3,692, AV Equip $7,384. Sal $75,272 (Prof $8,400)
Library Holdings: Bk Vols 51,658; Bk Titles 50,421; Per Subs 122
Subject Interests: New Jersey
Automation Activity & Vendor Info: (Circulation) Follett
Database Vendor: Ebsco - EbscoHost
Mem of Cumberland County Library; New Jersey State Library
Friends of the Library Group

S PENNSVILLE TOWNSHIP HISTORICAL SOCIETY LIBRARY,* 86 Church Landing Rd, 08070. SAN 375-7412. Tel: 856-678-4453, 856-678-5994. *Pres*, Lee Horn
Founded 1987
Library Holdings: Bk Titles 150
Special Collections: Early Craftsman; Genealogy Coll; History of Pennsville
Open Sun & Wed 12-4

PERTH AMBOY

P PERTH AMBOY FREE PUBLIC LIBRARY, 196 Jefferson St, 08861. SAN 351-2010. Tel: 732-826-2600. FAX: 732-324-8079. E-Mail: herschel@lmxac.org. *Dir*, Patricia Gandy; E-Mail: patricia@lmxac.org; Staff 9 (MLS 2, Non-MLS 7)
Founded 1903. Pop 41,967; Circ 91,579
Library Holdings: Bk Vols 176,236; Per Subs 444
Subject Interests: Large print bks, Local history, Spanish (language)
Mem of Regional Libr Coop Region 4
Partic in LMX Automation Consortium

M RARITAN BAY MEDICAL CENTER LIBRARY, 530 New Brunswick Ave, 08861. SAN 310-4176. Tel: 732-324-5087. FAX: 732-324-4676. *Dir*, Catherine Hilman; E-Mail: chilman@rbmc.org; Staff 3 (MLS 1, Non-MLS 2)
Library Holdings: Bk Vols 3,100; Per Subs 144
Subject Interests: Medicine, Nursing

PHILLIPSBURG

S INGERSOLL-RAND CO, Corporate Technical Library,* 942 Memorial Pkwy, 08865. SAN 324-3648. Tel: 908-859-7754. FAX: 908-859-7758. *Librn*, Sharon L Shiner; E-Mail: sharon_shiner@ingerrand.com; Staff 1 (MLS 1)
Founded 1950
Library Holdings: Bk Titles 6,000; Per Subs 250
Subject Interests: Bus, Mechanical, Metallurgical eng, Welding eng
Special Collections: Ingersoll-Rand Company Documents; Military Standards & Specifications Coll
Publications: Audio Cassette & Video Listing; Library Bulletin
Restriction: Company library
Partic in Dialog Corporation
This library also serves as the military document center for all military & industrial standards for the Ingersoll-Rand Co

S MALLINCKRODT BAKER INC, The Library Center, 600 N Broad St, 08865. SAN 310-4184. Tel: 908-859-2151, Ext 9615. FAX: 908-859-9454. *Mgr*, Patti Otani; E-Mail: patrice.otani@mkg.com
Founded 1945
Library Holdings: Bk Vols 12,500; Per Subs 100
Subject Interests: Analytical chemistry, Biochemistry
Partic in Highlands Regional Library Cooperative

P PHILLIPSBURG FREE PUBLIC LIBRARY, 200 Frost Ave, 08865. SAN 310-4192. Tel: 908-454-3712. FAX: 908-854-3222. E-Mail: lawson@hublib.lib.nj.us. Web Site: www.pburglib.com. *Dir*, Patricia Lawson; *Ch Servs*, Beverly Moon; *Ref*, Beverly Rose; Staff 20 (MLS 6, Non-MLS 14)
Founded 1923. Pop 15,733; Circ 152,619
Jan 1999-Dec 1999 Income $503,280, State $20,298, City $482,982. Mats Exp $214,124, Books $150,274, Per/Ser (Incl. Access Fees) $27,063, Electronic Ref Mat (Incl. Access Fees) $21,504. Sal $522,887
Library Holdings: Bk Vols 86,419; Bk Titles 78,558; Per Subs 279; High Interest/Low Vocabulary Bk Vols 150
Subject Interests: Education
Special Collections: ERIC repts on microfiche
Automation Activity & Vendor Info: (Acquisitions) Gaylord; (Cataloging) Gaylord; (Circulation) Gaylord; (OPAC) Gaylord
Partic in Highlands Regional Library Cooperative
Special Services for the Blind - CCTV for print enlargement
Friends of the Library Group

M WARREN HOSPITAL, Medical Library, 185 Roseberry St, 08865. SAN 325-7274. Tel: 908-859-6700, Ext 2012. FAX: 908-859-6831. *Librn*, June Roberts; E-Mail: juneroberts@warrenhospital.org; Staff 1 (MLS 1)
Library Holdings: Bk Vols 700; Bk Titles 800; Per Subs 75
Subject Interests: Medicine
Database Vendor: Ebsco - EbscoHost

PISCATAWAY

S COLGATE-PALMOLIVE CO, (TIC), Technology Information Center, 909 River Rd, 08855. SAN 310-4230. Tel: 732-878-7574. FAX: 732-878-7128. *Res*, Miranda Scott; E-Mail: miranda_scott@colpal.com; Staff 5 (MLS 1, Non-MLS 4)
Founded 1898
Library Holdings: Bk Vols 25,000; Per Subs 400
Subject Interests: Chemistry, Dental, Environmental studies, Medicine, Toxicology
Database Vendor: Dialog
Publications: Current Technical Bulletin, Category Bulletins
Restriction: Not open to public
Partic in Dialog Corporation; Dow Jones News Retrieval; Nat Libr of Med; Sci & Tech Info Network

S DEGUSSA, INC LIBRARY, (Formerly Creanova, Inc Library), PO Box 365, 08855-0365. SAN 310-4257. Tel: 732-981-5253. FAX: 732-981-5033. *Mgr*, Joan A Carnahan; Staff 2 (MLS 1, Non-MLS 1)
Founded 1935
Library Holdings: Bk Titles 5,000; Per Subs 60
Subject Interests: Microbiology, Organic chemistry
Automation Activity & Vendor Info: (Cataloging) Athena
Restriction: Staff use only
Partic in Dialog Corporation; Eastern NJ Regional Libr Coop; Medline

S ENZON INC LIBRARY, 20 Kingsbridge Rd, 08854-3998. SAN 328-0586. Tel: 732-980-4500. FAX: 732-980-5911. Web Site: www.enzon.com. *Librn*, Joann Polgar
Founded 1982
Library Holdings: Bk Vols 2,000; Bk Titles 1,500; Per Subs 100
Subject Interests: Genetics, Molecular biology
Publications: Acquisitions List; Serials Holding List
Restriction: Staff use only
Partic in BRS; Dialog Corporation; Gen Bank; Nat Libr of Med

P PISCATAWAY TOWNSHIP FREE PUBLIC LIBRARY, John F Kennedy Memorial Library, 500 Hoes Lane, 08854. SAN 351-207X. Tel: 732-463-1633. FAX: 732-463-9022. Web Site: www.lmxac.org/piscataway, www.lmxac.org/piscataway. *Dir Libr Serv*, Anne Roman; E-Mail: aroman@lmxac.org; *Asst Dir*, Molly Newling; E-Mail: mnewling@lmxac.org; *Ch Servs*, Margaret Serpico; E-Mail: mserpico@lmxac.org; *Tech Servs*, Jack Xi; Tel: 732-752-1166, E-Mail: jackxi@lmxac.org; *Ad Servs*, Joan Dellecave; E-Mail: joandc@lmxac.org; Staff 53 (MLS 16, Non-MLS 37)
Founded 1961. Pop 52,000; Circ 428,231
Jul 1999-Jun 2000 Income (Main Library and Branch Library) $3,036,872.

Mats Exp $285,836, Books $183,531, Per/Ser (Incl. Access Fees) $30,009, Electronic Ref Mat (Incl. Access Fees) $26,243. Sal $1,203,259
Library Holdings: Bk Vols 143,700; Per Subs 407
Subject Interests: Local history
Special Collections: Art Books (Silkotch Coll); Local History Coll
Automation Activity & Vendor Info: (Circulation) CARL; (OPAC) CARL
Publications: News & Events Newsletter (Bimonthly)
Partic in Infolink; LMX Automation Consortium
Special Services for the Deaf - TTY machine
Friends of the Library Group
Branches: 1
JOHANNA W WESTERGARD LIBRARY, 20 Murray Ave, 08854. SAN 351-210X. Tel: 732-752-1166. FAX: 732-752-1951. Web Site: www.lmxac.org/piscataway.
Friends of the Library Group
Bookmobiles: 1

S RESEARCH & EDUCATION ASSOCIATION LIBRARY,* 61 Ethel Rd W, 08854. SAN 312-0287. Tel: 732-819-8880. FAX: 732-819-8808. Web Site: www.rea.com. *Librn*, Carl Fuchs; E-Mail: c.fuchs@rea.com; Staff 3 (MLS 1, Non-MLS 2)
Founded 1959
Library Holdings: Bk Titles 1,000
Restriction: Staff use only

S UNION CARBIDE CORPORATION, (IRC), R&D Site Services Information Resources Center, Library - 200, 141 Baekeland Ave, 08854. (Mail add: PO Box 670, 08805-0670), SAN 376-589X. Tel: 732-563-5731. FAX: 732-563-5599. *Mgr*, Catherine Misner. Subject Specialists: *Chemistry*, Catherine Misner
Library Holdings: Bk Vols 11,000; Per Subs 210
Subject Interests: Chemistry, Polymers
Publications: Users Guide
Restriction: Not open to public

PITMAN

P MCCOWAN MEMORIAL LIBRARY, 15 Pitman Ave, 08071. SAN 310-4265. Tel: 856-589-1656. FAX: 856-582-4982. E-Mail: mccowanlibrary@yahoo.com. Web Site: www.pitman.org/library.htm. *Dir*, Linda Anderson; *Mgr*, Marie Flaherty; *Ch Servs*, Elizabeth Mears; *ILL*, Margaret Ware; Staff 11 (MLS 1, Non-MLS 10)
Founded 1919. Pop 9,170; Circ 75,052
Library Holdings: Bk Vols 33,709; Per Subs 42
Partic in New Jersey Library Network; South Jersey Regional Library Cooperative
Friends of the Library Group

PLAINFIELD

M MUHLENBERG REGIONAL MEDICAL CENTER, E Gordon Glass MD Memorial Library, Park Ave & Randolph Rd, 07061. SAN 310-429X. Tel: 908-668-2005. *Librn*, Lana Strazhnik
Founded 1963
Library Holdings: Bk Vols 4,452; Bk Titles 4,300; Per Subs 138
Subject Interests: Hosp admin, Medicine, Nursing
Partic in Docline

P PLAINFIELD FREE PUBLIC LIBRARY,* Eighth St at Park Ave, 07060-2594. SAN 310-4303. Tel: 908-757-1111. FAX: 908-754-0063. *Dir*, Joseph Hugh DaRold; *Ch Servs*, Khana Chakraborty; *Circ*, Vivian Bose
Founded 1881. Pop 48,000; Circ 88,750
Library Holdings: Bk Vols 190,060; Bk Titles 136,062; Per Subs 609
Subject Interests: 19th Century per, NJ hist, US hist
Special Collections: Architectural Plans from 1896 of Plainfield area; Music Scores
Partic in Infolink Eastern New Jersey Regional Library Cooperative, Inc
Friends of the Library Group

UNION COUNTY COLLEGE
See Cranford , .

PLAINSBORO

P PLAINSBORO FREE PUBLIC LIBRARY, 641 Plainsboro Rd, 08536-0278. SAN 326-3924. Circulation Tel: 609-275-2897. FAX: 609-799-5883. *Dir*, Virginia Baeckler; E-Mail: baeckler@lmxac.org; *Ch Servs*, Rachel Camporeale; *Circ*, Wei Gao; *Ref*, Regan Tuerff; *Tech Servs*, Kyung Kim; Staff 4 (MLS 4)
Founded 1964. Pop 17,500; Circ 220,000
Jan 2000-Dec 2000 Income $850,000, State $12,000, City $776,000, Locally Generated Income $61,200. Mats Exp $139,700, Books $85,000, Per/Ser (Incl. Access Fees) $16,700, Micro $6,000, Electronic Ref Mat (Incl. Access Fees) $32,000. Sal $508,000
Library Holdings: Bk Vols 67,000; Per Subs 115
Special Collections: Chinese Cultural Exchange; German Coll; JFK Coll; Large Print Coll
Automation Activity & Vendor Info: (Cataloging) CARL; (Circulation) CARL; (OPAC) CARL
Publications: Annual Report Newsletter; Plainsboro Community Directory
Mem of Libraries of Middlesex
Partic in Infolink Eastern New Jersey Regional Library Cooperative, Inc; OCLC Online Computer Library Center, Inc
Friends of the Library Group

R ST JOSEPH'S SEMINARY, Mary Immaculate Library, 72 Mapleton Rd, PO Box 808, 08536-0808. SAN 314-8300. Tel: 609-716-4214. Web Site: www.mil.library.net. *Coll Develop, Librn*, Joseph P McClain; E-Mail: mcclainj@vincentianfamilycenter.com; *Cat*, Mary Ellen Cser; Staff 2 (MLS 1, Non-MLS 1)
Founded 1939. Enrl 25; Highest Degree: Master
Library Holdings: Bk Vols 62,000; Bk Titles 54,625; Per Subs 204
Subject Interests: Catholic theol, Med ethics, Relig studies
Special Collections: Vincentian Fathers Coll
Automation Activity & Vendor Info: (Cataloging) TLC
Partic in Southeastern Pennsylvania Theological Library Association

POMONA

M ATLANTIC CITY MEDICAL CENTER, Health Science Library Mainland Division, Jim Leeds Rd, 08240. SAN 376-1517. Tel: 609-652-1000, Ext 2764. FAX: 609-652-3504. *Asst Librn*, Jeanne Jarensky
Library Holdings: Bk Vols 500

M BACHARACH INSTITUTE FOR REHABILITATION, Medical-Clinical Staff Library, 61 W Jim Leeds Rd, PO Box 723, 08240-0723. SAN 373-2541. Tel: 609-748-5392. FAX: 609-748-6869. *Dir Libr Serv*, Margaret Grunow; E-Mail: margeg@bacharach.org
Library Holdings: Bk Vols 2,300; Per Subs 114

C RICHARD STOCKTON COLLEGE OF NEW JERSEY LIBRARY,* PO Box 195, 08240-0195. SAN 310-4362. Tel: 609-652-4343. FAX: 609-652-4964. E-Mail: iaprod110@pollux.stockton.edu. Web Site: loki.stockton.edu/~millerr/libhome.htm. *Dir*, Gerald O'Sullivan; *Tech Servs*, William Bearden
Founded 1971. Enrl 5,200; Fac 180; Highest Degree: Master
Jul 1997-Jun 1998 Income $1,849,994. Mats Exp $798,483, Books $257,239, Per/Ser (Incl. Access Fees) $312,794, Presv $21,837, Micro $39,523, AV Equip $42,000. Sal $1,043,547 (Prof $471,332)
Library Holdings: Bk Vols 287,730; Bk Titles 241,713; Per Subs 3,169
Special Collections: New Jersey Pine Barrens
Automation Activity & Vendor Info: (Acquisitions) DRA; (Cataloging) DRA; (Circulation) DRA; (OPAC) DRA; (Serials) DRA
Database Vendor: DRA
Publications: Newsletter (Wordsworth)
Partic in New Jersey Academic Library Network; PALINET & Union Library Catalogue of Pennsylvania; South Jersey Regional Library Cooperative

POMPTON LAKES

P THE FREE PUBLIC LIBRARY OF THE BOROUGH OF POMPTON LAKES, 333 Wanaque Ave, 07442. SAN 310-4370. Tel: 973-835-0482. FAX: 973-835-4767. Web Site: www.palsplus.org/pomptonlakes. *Dir*, Margaret M Freathy; E-Mail: freathy@palsplus.org; *Ch Servs*, Eileen Unger
Founded 1912. Pop 10,508; Circ 34,638
Jan 1999-Dec 1999 Income $217,500, State $10,000. Mats Exp $21,500, Books $18,000, Per/Ser (Incl. Access Fees) $3,500. Sal $144,065
Library Holdings: Bk Vols 37,041; Per Subs 99
Special Collections: Albert Payson Terhune Coll; New Jersey History (Van Orden Coll)
Automation Activity & Vendor Info: (Cataloging) DRA; (Circulation) DRA; (OPAC) DRA
Database Vendor: DRA
Partic in Highlands Regional Library Cooperative; Pals

POMPTON PLAINS

M CHILTON MEMORIAL HOSPITAL, Medical Library, 97 West Pkwy, 07444. SAN 325-9404. Tel: 973-831-5058. FAX: 973-831-5041. *Librn*, Charlene Taylor
Library Holdings: Bk Vols 1,500

P PEQUANNOCK TOWNSHIP PUBLIC LIBRARY,* 477 Turnpike, 07444. SAN 351-2223. Tel: 973-835-7460. FAX: 973-835-1928. *Dir*, Rosemary Garwood; *Asst Dir*, Maureen Bartolicci; *Ref*, Romilly Liloia; *Acq*, Julie Reeves; Staff 4 (MLS 4)
Founded 1962. Pop 12,000; Circ 144,348
Library Holdings: Bk Titles 71,000; Per Subs 254
Subject Interests: Local history
Special Collections: Landsberger Holocaust Coll
Automation Activity & Vendor Info: (Circulation) DRA
Publications: Quarterly Program Brochure
Partic in Morris Automated Information Network
Friends of the Library Group

PRINCETON

S BASF CO, (Formerly American Cyanamid Co), Agriculture Products Research Division Library, Clarksville Rd, PO Box 400, 08543-0400. SAN 310-4400. Tel: 609-716-2514. FAX: 609-275-3576. *Assoc Dir*, Dr David S Saari; Tel: 609-716-2512, E-Mail: saarid@pt.cyanamid.com; *Librn*, Pat Bartiling; Staff 15 (MLS 7, Non-MLS 8)
Founded 1947
Library Holdings: Bk Titles 10,000; Per Subs 650
Subject Interests: Agrichemicals, Agriculture, Biology, Biotechnology, Chemistry, Veterinary medicine
Publications: Current Awareness Bulletins
Restriction: Staff use only
Partic in OCLC Online Computer Library Center, Inc; PALINET & Union Library Catalogue of Pennsylvania

M BRISTOL-MYERS SQUIBB PHARMACEUTICAL RESEARCH INSTITUTE LIBRARY, Rte 206 & Provence Line Rd, PO Box 4000, 08543-4000. SAN 310-4575. Tel: 609-252-4925. FAX: 609-252-6280. *Info Specialist*, Kathy Anderegg
Founded 1925
Library Holdings: Bk Vols 112,000; Per Subs 1,100
Subject Interests: Biology, Chemistry, Medicine, Pharmacology
Publications: Index Squibicus; Library Bulletin
Partic in Dialog Corporation; Medline; New Jersey Library Network; SDC Search Serv

S CUH2A INC LIBRARY, 211 Carnegie Ctr, 08540-6298. SAN 375-4634. Tel: 609-452-1212. FAX: 609-419-8137. E-Mail: smoss@cuh2a.com.
Library Holdings: Bk Vols 800; Bk Titles 600; Per Subs 137
Subject Interests: Architecture
Partic in Central Jersey Regional Library Cooperative

L DRINKER, BIDDLE & SHANLEY LIBRARY, 105 College Rd E, 08542. SAN 377-5593. Tel: 609-716-6500. FAX: 609-799-7000. Web Site: www.dbr.com. *Librn*, Ann McCarron; E-Mail: mccarrac@dbr.com
Library Holdings: Bk Vols 50,000

S EDUCATIONAL TESTING SERVICE, Carl Campbell Brigham Library & Test Collection, Rosedale Rd, 08541. SAN 310-4419. Tel: 609-734-5667. FAX: 609-683-7186. E-Mail: library@ets.org. *Dir*, Janet L Williams; E-Mail: jwilliams@ets.org; Staff 9 (MLS 5, Non-MLS 4)
Founded 1961
Library Holdings: Bk Vols 18,000; Per Subs 300
Subject Interests: Artificial intelligence, Behav sci, Cognitive sci, Education, Expert systs, Internet, Measurements, Psychology, Soc sci, Statistics
Special Collections: Tests
Automation Activity & Vendor Info: (Circulation) Sydney
Database Vendor: Dialog, Ebsco - EbscoHost, OCLC - First Search, ProQuest
Publications: Cummulative Index to Tests in Microfiche, 1975-98; Tests in Microfiche
Partic in Central Jersey Regional Library Cooperative; Dialog Corporation; OCLC Online Computer Library Center, Inc; PALINET & Union Library Catalogue of Pennsylvania

S FOUNDATION FOR STUDENT COMMUNICATION, Library & Resource Center, 305 Aaron Burr Hall, 08544. SAN 325-9420. Tel: 609-258-1111. FAX: 609-258-1222. Web Site: www.businesstoday.org. *Pres*, Nate Faust; *Librn*, John Taylor
Library Holdings: Bk Vols 3,500
Restriction: Staff use only
Friends of the Library Group

S HISTORICAL SOCIETY OF PRINCETON LIBRARY,* 158 Nassau St, 08542. SAN 310-4443. Tel: 609-921-6748. FAX: 609-921-6939. Web Site: www.princetonol.com/groups/histsoc. *Curator, Dir*, Maureen M Smyth
Founded 1938
Library Holdings: Bk Titles 1,500
Subject Interests: Local history, Princeton hist
Publications: Guide to Manuscripts
Open Tues & Sat 1-4

S INSTITUTE FOR ADVANCED STUDY LIBRARIES, Einstein Dr, 08540. SAN 310-4451. Tel: 609-734-8371. FAX: 609-951-4515. E-Mail: hslib@ias.edu, mnlib@ias.edu. Web Site: www.admin.ias.edu/hslib/ls.htm. *Librn*, Momota Ganguli; Tel: 609-734-8181, E-Mail: mg@ias.edu; *Librn*, Marcia Tucker; Tel: 609-734-8276, E-Mail: tucker@ias.edu; *Asst Librn*, Kayo Denda; *Asst Librn*, Dana Van Meter; Tel: 609-734-8376, E-Mail: vanmeter@ias.edu; *ILL*, Karen Downing; Tel: 609-734-8371, E-Mail: kd@ias.edu. Subject Specialists: *Mathematics*, Momota Ganguli; *Natural scis*, Momota Ganguli; *Social sciences*, Marcia Tucker; Staff 9 (MLS 3, Non-MLS 6)
Founded 1940. Fac 31
Library Holdings: Bk Vols 130,000; Per Subs 1,000
Subject Interests: Art, Classical archaeol, Classical studies, History, Mathematics, Natural science, Soc sci
Special Collections: History of Science (Rosenwald Coll)
Automation Activity & Vendor Info: (Acquisitions) epixtech, inc.; (Cataloging) epixtech, inc.; (OPAC) epixtech, inc.; (Serials) epixtech, inc.
Database Vendor: Dialog, Ebsco - EbscoHost, epixtech, inc., Lexis-Nexis, OCLC - First Search
Function: Research library

S INSTITUTE FOR DEFENSE ANALYSIS LIBRARY,* 29 Thanet Rd, 08540. SAN 310-446X. Tel: 609-924-4600. FAX: 609-924-3061. *Mgr*, Barbara Hamilton; E-Mail: hamilton@ccr-p.ida.org; Staff 2 (MLS 1, Non-MLS 1)
Founded 1959
Library Holdings: Bk Vols 13,500; Per Subs 350
Subject Interests: Computer science, Electrical engineering, Linguistics, Mathematics
Publications: Acquisitions list (twice yearly); Journals List; Print Catalog of Book Holdings; staff publications list
Restriction: Staff use only
Partic in Data Star; Dialog Corporation

S THE LIPOSOME RESEARCH LIBRARY,* Princeton Forrestal Ctr, One Research Way, 08540. SAN 328-1744. Tel: 609-951-5411. FAX: 609-520-8250. E-Mail: ressecy@lipo.com. *In Charge*, Michele Moscatello; Staff 2 (MLS 1, Non-MLS 1)
Library Holdings: Bk Vols 700; Per Subs 50
Partic in New Jersey Library Network

S MATHEMATICA POLICY RESEARCH INC LIBRARY,* 600 Alexander Park, 08543. SAN 376-0537. Tel: 609-275-2334. FAX: 609-799-1654. Web Site: www.mathematica-mpr.com. *Librn*, Jan Watterworth; E-Mail: jwatterworth@mathematica-mpr.com; *Assoc Librn*, Stephanie Golding; Staff 3 (MLS 1, Non-MLS 2)
Library Holdings: Bk Vols 40,000
Open Mon-Fri 8:30-5:30

M MEDICAL CENTER AT PRINCETON, Medical Center Library,* 253 Witherspoon St, 08540. SAN 326-2405. Tel: 609-497-4487, 609-497-4488. FAX: 609-497-4998. Web Site: www.tripod.members.com/~Medical_Library or www.mcp.org. *Librn*, Louise M Yorke; E-Mail: yorkel.mcp@worldnet.att.net; Staff 3 (MLS 1, Non-MLS 2)
Founded 1953
Library Holdings: Bk Vols 3,000; Bk Titles 2,800; Per Subs 200
Subject Interests: Allied health, Medicine, Nursing, Psychiatry, Surgery
Special Collections: Plastic Surgery (Anna K Snyderman Coll), bks; Psychology (Morris Parmet Coll), bks, slides
Publications: AV Catalogue; Guide to the Library; Newsletter, Staff In Print; Pamphlet file; Serial holdings
Partic in Central Jersey Health Science Libraries Association; Health Sciences Library Association Of New Jersey; Medcore; Medical Libr Asn

S METAL POWDER INDUSTRIES FEDERATION - AMERICAN POWDER METALLURGY INSTITUTE, Technical Information Center,* 105 College Rd E, 08540-6692. SAN 371-9421. Tel: 609-452-7700. FAX: 609-987-8523. E-Mail: info@mpif.org. Web Site: www.mpif.org/mpif.; Staff 2 (MLS 1, Non-MLS 1)
Library Holdings: Bk Titles 7,500; Per Subs 25

G NATIONAL OCEANIC & ATMOSPHERIC ADMINISTRATION, Geophysical Fluid Dynamics Laboratory Library,* Forrestal Campus, US Rte 1. (Mail add: PO Box 308, 08542), SAN 310-4524. Tel: 609-452-6550. FAX: 609-987-5063. E-Mail: gth@gfdl.gov. *Librn*, Gail T Haller
Founded 1968
Library Holdings: Bk Vols 10,000; Bk Titles 8,000; Per Subs 130
Subject Interests: Applied math, Meteorology, Oceanography, Sci-tech
Partic in Dialog Corporation; OCLC Online Computer Library Center, Inc

M NEW JERSEY HOSPITAL ASSOCIATION, J Harold Johnston Memorial Library, 760 Alexander Rd, 08543. (Mail add: PO Box 1, 08543-0001), SAN 320-4545. Tel: 609-275-4230. FAX: 609-275-4107. Web Site: www.njha.com. *Dir*, Michelle Volesko; E-Mail: mvolesko@njha.com; Staff 1 (MLS 1)
Founded 1965
Library Holdings: Bk Titles 4,186; Per Subs 716
Subject Interests: Health care admin, Health systs, Hospital
Special Collections: New Jersey Hospital files, prints; NJHA Data Coll
Publications: Annual NJ Healthcare CEO Conference Bibliography
Partic in Dialog Corporation; New Jersey Health Sciences Library Network; New Jersey Library Network
Compiled Critical Pathways in New Jersey Database

M NOVA NORDISK PHARMACEUTICALS, INC, Medical Library,* 100 College Rd W, 08540-6604. SAN 377-2357. Tel: 609-987-5800. FAX: 609-987-3092. E-Mail: subl@novo.dk. *Librn*, Susan Bales
Library Holdings: Bk Vols 250; Bk Titles 200; Per Subs 150
Partic in Spec Libr Asn

P PRINCETON PUBLIC LIBRARY,* 65 Witherspoon St, 08542-3267. SAN 310-4540. Tel: 609-924-8822 (Admin), 609-924-9529. FAX: 609-924-7937. Reference FAX: 609-924-6109. Web Site: www.princeton.lib.nj.us. *Dir*, Leslie Burger; *Asst Dir*, Eric Greenfeldt; *ILL*, Jane Brown; *Ad Servs*,

Barbara Silberstein; *Online Servs, Ref*, Elba Barzellato; *Ref*, Mary Louise Hartman; *Coll Develop*, Jane Clinton; Staff 14 (MLS 14)
Founded 1909. Pop 27,000; Circ 330,000
Library Holdings: Bk Vols 144,339; Bk Titles 118,386; Per Subs 479
Subject Interests: Bus, Consumer health
Special Collections: Princeton History
Automation Activity & Vendor Info: (Circulation) CLSI LIBS
Publications: Friends Newsletter
Mem of Regional Libr Coop 5 - Mercer-Monmouth, Ocean Counties
Partic in OCLC Online Computer Library Center, Inc; PALINET & Union Library Catalogue of Pennsylvania

R PRINCETON THEOLOGICAL SEMINARY, Speer Library, Mercer St & Library Pl, PO Box 111, 08542-0111. SAN 310-4559. Tel: 609-497-7940. FAX: 609-497-1826. Web Site: www.library1.ptsem.edu. *Dir*, Stephen Crocco; E-Mail: stephen.crocco@ptsem.edu; *Archivist*, William O Harris; *Ref*, Katherine Skrebutenas; *Coll Develop*, Donald M Vorp
Founded 1812. Highest Degree: Doctorate
Library Holdings: Bk Vols 587,000
Special Collections: Baptist Controversy; Early American Theological Pamphlets (Sprague Coll); Hymnology (Benson Coll); Puritan Literature, bks, pamphlets
Automation Activity & Vendor Info: (Acquisitions) Endeavor; (Cataloging) Endeavor; (Circulation) Endeavor; (OPAC) Endeavor; (Serials) Endeavor
Partic in OCLC Online Computer Library Center, Inc

C PRINCETON UNIVERSITY, Firestone Library, One Washington Rd, 08544-2089. SAN 351-2282. Tel: 609-258-4820. Interlibrary Loan Service Tel: 609-258-3272. Circulation Tel: 609-258-3202. Reference Tel: 609-258-5964. FAX: 609-258-4105. Web Site: www.libweb.princeton.edu:2003/. *Librn, Selection of Ref Mat Humanities*, Mary George; E-Mail: mwgeorge@princeton.edu; *Librn*, Janice J Powell; *Asst Librn, Syst Coordr*, Marvin F Bielawski; *Admin Assoc*, Dorothy Pearson; *Bibliogr*, John Logan; *Bibliogr*, Peter Johnson; *Cat*, Donald Thornbury; *Circ*, Paula Clancy; *ILL*, Susanne McNatt; *Rare Bks, Spec Coll*, Ben Primer; *Rare Bks*, Stephen Ferguson; *Selection of Ref Mat Sci*, Kevin Barry; *Tech Servs*, Richard Schulz. Subject Specialists: *Art*, Janice J Powell; *Near East*, James Weinberger; *Social sciences*, Kevin Barry; Staff 327 (MLS 121, Non-MLS 206)
Enrl 6,340; Fac 716; Highest Degree: Doctorate
Library Holdings: Bk Vols 5,315,332; Per Subs 37,629
Subject Interests: Ancient history, Behav sci, China, Classics hist, Econ, History, Humanities, International law, Japan, Languages, Literature, Music, Natural science, Near East, Relations, Sci-tech, Soc sci
Special Collections: Aeronautics Coll; Ainsworth, Barrie, the Brontes, Bulwer-Lytton, Collins, Mrs Craik, Dickens, Disraeli, Dogson, George Eliot, Mrs Gaskell, Hardy, Hughes, Kingsley, Lever, Reade, Stevenson, Thackeray, Trollope (Parrish Coll of Victorian Novelists); American Historical Manuscripts Coll; American Woodcut Illustrated Books Coll; Americana Coll; Arts; Chateaubriand Coll; Chess Coll; Civil Rights Coll; Coins; Emblem Books; Emily Dickinson Coll; English Restoration Drama; European Historical Manuscripts; European Legal Documents (11th to 19th Century); Fishing & Angling; Graphic; Halliburton, Handel, Hemingway, Horace, Leigh Hunt, Laurence Hutton, Otto H Kahn, George Keenan, Kierkegaard, Ivy Lee, C G Leland, Lilienthal, George McAneny, Thomas Mann, E L Masters, Harold R Medina, Montaigne, W V Moody, O'Neill, Coventry Patmore, H L Piozzi, Pound, Rabelais, Rowlandson, Richard Rush, Ruskin, Schweitzer, William Seymour, Shellabarger, H Alexander Smith, Samuel Southard, Adlai Stevenson, Julian Street, Symons, Tarkington, Allen Tate, Ridgeley Torrence, Carl Van Doren, Henry Van Dyke, Vergil, Viele-Griffin, Woodrow Wilson; History of Women.; Horace Coll; Incunabula; Individual Collections: Louis Adamic, Elmer Adler, American Civil Liberties Union, Audubon, Bernard Baruch, Beardsley, Beauharnais (Administration of Italy & War Claims, Archives of Prince Eugene De Beauharnais), Blake, Boker, Boudinot Family, Aaron Burr Sr, M S Burt, F A R De Chateaubriand, William Cowper, J G Cozzens, Cruishank, John Davidson, Allan Dulles, J F Duells, Jonathan Edwards, Faulkner, F S Fitzgerald, Forrestal, Goethe,; Islamic Manuscripts; John Foster Dulles Project; Latin America (Spanish & English Language Documents, 16th to 19th Century); Manuscripts & Maps Coll; Medieval & Renaissance Manuscripts; Middle East Manuscripts; Montaigne Coll; Mormon History; Mountaineering; New Jersey History & Imprints; Papyrus Manuscripts; Publishers & Publishing (Doubleday, Harper, Holt, John Day, Scribner), papers; Rowlandson Coll; Sporting Books Coll; Story Magazine; Theater Coll; United Nations; Vergil Coll; Western Americana Coll
Publications: The Princeton University Library Chronicle
Mem of Asn of Research Libraries
Partic in RLIN
Founded as college of New Jersey, Elizabeth in 1746; the University Library's principal building is the Harvey S Firestone Memorial Library, constructed in 1948
Friends of the Library Group
Departmental Libraries:
AFRICAN-AMERICAN STUDIES COLLECTION Tel: 609-258-5547. *Curator*, Emily Belcher; Staff 1 (MLS 1)
Library Holdings: Bk Vols 3,089
ART & ARCHAEOLOGY, Marquand Library, 08544. SAN 351-2371. Tel: 609-258-3783. FAX: 609-258-0103. *Dir*, Janice Powell
Library Holdings: Bk Vols 214,130
ASTROPHYSICS Tel: 609-258-3820. *Librn*, Jane Holmquist
Library Holdings: Bk Vols 19,043
BIOLOGY Tel: 609-258-3235. *Librn*, David Goodman
Library Holdings: Bk Vols 60,108
CHEMISTRY Tel: 609-258-3238. *Librn*, Juliette Arnheim
Library Holdings: Bk Vols 54,836
DEPARTMENT OF RARE BOOKS Tel: 609-258-3184. *Rare Bks*, Stephen Ferguson
Library Holdings: Bk Vols 162,556
ENGINEERING Tel: 609-258-3200. *Librn*, Edward Wladas
Library Holdings: Bk Vols 114,925
GEOSCIENCES & MAPS Tel: 609-258-3267. *Librn*, Patricia Gaspari-Bridges
Library Holdings: Bk Vols 75,245
GEST ORIENTAL LIBRARY & EAST ASIAN COLLECTION Tel: 609-258-3182. FAX: 609-258-4573. *Curator*, Dorothy Pearson
Library Holdings: Bk Vols 394,510
GRAPHIC ARTS COLLECTION Tel: 609-258-3197.
Library Holdings: Bk Vols 29,743
INDUSTRIAL RELATIONS Tel: 609-258-3701. *Librn*, Kevin Barry
Library Holdings: Bk Vols 7,451
MATHEMATICS & PHYSICS Tel: 609-258-3187. *In Charge*, Mitchell Brown
Library Holdings: Bk Vols 116,559
MICROFORMS Tel: 609-258-3252. *Librn*, Sooni Johnson
SEELEY G MUDD MANUSCRIPT LIBRARY Tel: 609-258-6345. FAX: 609-258-3385. *Curator*, Ben Primer
NEAR EAST COLLECTIONS Tel: 609-258-3266. *In Charge*, James Weinberger
Library Holdings: Bk Vols 125,087
PLASMA PHYSICS Tel: 609-243-3567.
Library Holdings: Bk Vols 15,975
PLINY-FISK LIBRARY OF ECONOMICS & FINANCE Tel: 609-258-3211. *Librn*, Bobray Bordelon
Library Holdings: Bk Vols 4,279
PSYCHOLOGY, Green Hall, 08544-1010. Tel: 609-258-3239. *Librn*, Mary Chaikin
Library Holdings: Bk Vols 35,859
PUBLIC & INTERNATIONAL AFFAIRS & POPULATION RESEARCH LIBRARY Tel: 609-258-5455. FAX: 609-258-6844. *Actg Librn*, Jacqueline Druery
Library Holdings: Bk Vols 15,535; Per Subs 250
PUBLIC ADMINISTRATION Tel: 609-258-3209. *Librn*, Rosemary Little
Library Holdings: Bk Vols 18,559
SCHEIDE MUSIC LIBRARY, Woolworth Center of Musical Studies, 08544. Tel: 609-258-3230. FAX: 609-258-4105. *Librn*, Paula Matthews
SCHOOL OF ARCHITECTURE LIBRARIES Tel: 609-258-3256. *Librn*, Frances Chen
Library Holdings: Bk Vols 30,808
UNIVERSITY ARCHIVES Tel: 609-258-5879. FAX: 609-258-3385. *Archivist*, Ben Primer

S RECORDING FOR THE BLIND DYSLEXIC, INC, Library & Customer Services,* 20 Roszel Rd, 08540. SAN 312-0228. Tel: 609-452-0606. Toll Free Tel: 800-221-4792. FAX: 609-987-8116. E-Mail: info@rfbd.org. Web Site: www.rfbd.org. *Dir, Mgr*, Pamela Johnson; *Cat*, Wen Qi Wang; *Acq*, Anne McArthur; *Ref*, Elizabeth Kline; *Asst Librn*, Linda Paciotti; *Cat*, Kathy Cannata; *Cat*, Mei-Yu Tsai; *Coll Develop*, Doris Kelly; Staff 20 (MLS 6, Non-MLS 14)
Founded 1948
Jul 1998-Jun 1999 Income $3,265,911. Mats Exp $1,753,288, Books $66,890. Sal $1,522,623 (Prof $347,762)
Library Holdings: Bk Titles 80,000
Publications: Catalog & Bibliographies
Partic in OCLC Online Computer Library Center, Inc; PALINET & Union Library Catalogue of Pennsylvania
Books on computer floppy disk for nonprofit sale; consumer products including tape recorders; accessible catalogs & library & reference services

S ROPER STARCH WORLDWIDE, Information Resource Center, 1060 State Rd, 08542-0158. (Mail add: PO Box 158, 08542-0158), SAN 326-3592. Tel: 609-921-3333. FAX: 609-921-2611. E-Mail: afrihart@roper.com. Web Site: www.roper.com. *In Charge*, Anne R Frihart; Staff 1 (MLS 1)
Founded 1979
Library Holdings: Bk Titles 1,200; Per Subs 120
Subject Interests: Market res
Special Collections: Annual Report Coll, reports; Corporate Information
Database Vendor: Dialog
Publications: Book Rac (Acquisitions List & Newsletter)
Partic in Highlands Regional Library Cooperative

S SARNOFF CORPORATION LIBRARY, 201 Washington Rd, 08540. (Mail add: CN5300, 08543-5300), SAN 351-3157. Tel: 609-734-2850. FAX: 609-734-2339. *In Charge*, Larry Eubank; E-Mail: leubank@sarnoff.com; Staff 2 (MLS 1, Non-MLS 1)
Founded 1942
Library Holdings: Bk Vols 25,000; Per Subs 350

Subject Interests: Electronics
Restriction: Non-circulating to the public
Partic in Dialog Corporation; DTIC; Profound; Sci & Tech Info Network

S SIEMENS CORPORATE RESEARCH, INC, Research Library, 755 College Rd E, 08540. SAN 375-6440. Tel: 609-734-6506. FAX: 609-734-6565. E-Mail: rhw@scr.siemens.com. *Librn*, Ruth Weitzenfeld; Staff 1 (MLS 1)
Library Holdings: Bk Vols 8,500; Bk Titles 8,000; Per Subs 150
Subject Interests: Computer science
Automation Activity & Vendor Info: (Cataloging) EOS; (Circulation) EOS; (OPAC) EOS; (Serials) EOS
Partic in PALINET & Union Library Catalogue of Pennsylvania

L STARK & STARK, Law Library,* PO Box 5315, 08543. SAN 372-4743. Tel: 609-896-9060. *Librn*, Ann Roberts
Library Holdings: Bk Vols 5,000; Per Subs 30

S TAKEDA AMERICA INC LIBRARY,* 104 Carnegie Ctr, Ste 201, 08540-6232. SAN 377-2039. Tel: 609-734-4413. FAX: 609-452-1218. *Librn*, Lynn Siegelman; E-Mail: siegel@takeda-america.com; Staff 1 (MLS 1)
Library Holdings: Bk Titles 160; Per Subs 50

S TOBACCO MERCHANTS ASSOCIATION OF THE UNITED STATES, Howard S Cullman Library,* 231 Clarkville Rd, PO Box 8019, 08543-8019. SAN 312-0929. Tel: 609-275-4900. FAX: 609-275-8379. *Pres*, Farrell Delman; *VPres*, Darryl Jayson; *Librn*, Judith Mathus; E-Mail: judith@tma.org; Staff 3 (MLS 1, Non-MLS 2)
Founded 1915
Library Holdings: Bk Vols 2,000; Per Subs 125
Special Collections: Tobacco & Products (Trademark & Brand Files)
Publications: Newsletters

RAHWAY

S EAST JERSEY STATE PRISON LIBRARY,* Lock Bag R, Woodbridge Ave, 07065. SAN 375-8451. Tel: 732-499-5449. FAX: 732-815-4925. *Librn*, Rick Liss
Library Holdings: Bk Vols 10,000

M MERCK & COMPANY, INC, Library Rahway, LR86,* R86-230, PO Box 2000, 07065. SAN 351-3270. Tel: 732-594-3747. FAX: 732-594-4172. *Actg Librn*, Susan Budavari; *Coll Develop*, Diana Komanesky; Staff 10 (MLS 5, Non-MLS 5)
Founded 1953
Library Holdings: Bk Vols 45,000; Per Subs 1,500
Subject Interests: Chemistry, Computer science, Genetics, Medicine, Pharmacology
Partic in OCLC Online Computer Library Center, Inc; PALINET & Union Library Catalogue of Pennsylvania
Branches:
LR80W, R80W-118, PO Box 2000, 07065. SAN 351-3289. Tel: 732-594-7528. FAX: 732-594-7422. *In Charge*, Rita Nacchio-Wells
Founded 1980
Library Holdings: Bk Titles 800; Per Subs 150
Subject Interests: Biochemistry, Immunology
Partic in OCLC Online Computer Library Center, Inc; PALINET & Union Library Catalogue of Pennsylvania
LR80Y, R80Y-365, PO Box 2000, 07065. SAN 373-5524. Tel: 732-594-6249. FAX: 732-594-6232. *In Charge*, Rita Nacchio-Wells
Founded 1986
Library Holdings: Bk Vols 75; Per Subs 153
Subject Interests: Chemistry, Microbiology
LR50, RY50-200, PO Box 2000, 07065. SAN 373-7179. Tel: 732-594-7211. FAX: 732-594-7900. *In Charge*, Rita Nacchio-Wells
Founded 1993
Library Holdings: Bk Vols 200; Per Subs 40
Subject Interests: Chemistry
LR121, R121-115, PO Box 2000, 07065. Tel: 732-594-5516. FAX: 732-594-1626. *In Charge*, Rita Nacchio-Wells
Founded 1992
Library Holdings: Bk Vols 240; Per Subs 39
Subject Interests: Chemistry

P RAHWAY PUBLIC LIBRARY, 75 E Cherry St, 07065. SAN 310-4648. Tel: 732-388-0761, 732-388-6058. FAX: 732-388-4865. E-Mail: rahlib@lmxac.org. Web Site: www.lmxac.org/rahway. *Dir*, Harry R Williams, III; *Coll Develop*, Carol Marlowe; Staff 23 (MLS 6, Non-MLS 17)
Founded 1858. Pop 25,760; Circ 125,341
Jul 1998-Jun 1999 Income $880,060, State $32,660, City $800,400, Locally Generated Income $21,000. Mats Exp $116,800, Books $94,220, Per/Ser (Incl. Access Fees) $10,680, Presv $1,000. Sal $485,849 (Prof $194,787)
Library Holdings: Bk Vols 78,000; Bk Titles 64,266; Per Subs 210
Subject Interests: Local history, New Jersey
Publications: Annual Report
Partic in Infolink

RAMSEY

P RAMSEY FREE PUBLIC LIBRARY,* 30 Wyckoff Ave, 07446. SAN 310-4656. Tel: 201-327-1445. FAX: 201-327-3687. E-Mail: rams1@bccls.org, ramsfer@bccls.org. Web Site: www.nic.com/~/rfpl. *Dir*, Thomas J Coyle; *Asst Dir*, Anita Palladino; *Ch Servs*, Laura Neske; *Ref*, Kathy Elwell
Founded 1921. Pop 14,500; Circ 116,263
Library Holdings: Bk Vols 95,000
Subject Interests: Large print, NJ hist
Publications: Library Lines
Mem of Bergen - Passaic Regional Libr Syst
Friends of the Library Group

RANDOLPH

J COUNTY COLLEGE OF MORRIS, Sherman H Masten Learning Resource Center, 214 Center Grove Rd, 07869-2086. SAN 310-4672. Tel: 973-328-5282. Interlibrary Loan Service Tel: 973-328-5307. FAX: 973-328-2370. Web Site: www.ccm.edu/library/. *Dir*, John M Cohn; E-Mail: jcohn@ccm.edu; *Assoc Dir*, Ann L Kelsey; *Media Spec*, Bonnie Murphy; *Bibliog Instr*, Lynee Richel; *ILL, Ref*, Diane Davenport; *Ref*, Heather Craven; *Online Servs*, Geetali Basu; *Cat*, Virginia Chang; *Cat*, David E Jones; *AV*, Ethan D Shapiro; *AV*, Richard Watt; Staff 15 (MLS 10, Non-MLS 5)
Founded 1968. Enrl 8,000; Fac 466; Highest Degree: Associate
Jul 1999-Jun 2000 Income $1,627,612
Library Holdings: Bk Vols 94,019; Bk Titles 82,595; Per Subs 819
Automation Activity & Vendor Info: (Acquisitions) Gaylord; (Cataloging) Gaylord; (Circulation) Gaylord; (Course Reserve) Gaylord; (ILL) Gaylord; (OPAC) Gaylord; (Serials) Gaylord
Publications: Bibliographies; In-house Catalogs
Partic in Highlands Regional Library Cooperative; OCLC Online Computer Library Center, Inc; PALINET & Union Library Catalogue of Pennsylvania

P RANDOLPH TOWNSHIP FREE PUBLIC LIBRARY, 28 Calais Rd, 07869. SAN 310-4664. Tel: 973-895-3556. FAX: 973-895-4946. Web Site: www.gti.net/randolph/library. *Dir*, Anita S Freeman; E-Mail: freeman@main.morris.org; *Asst Dir*, Leanna Povilaitis; *Ch Servs*, Linda Breder; Staff 5 (MLS 5)
Founded 1964. Pop 23,000; Circ 206,435
Jan 2000-Dec 2000 Income $734,772, State $20,000, Locally Generated Income $54,000. Mats Exp $127,000, Books $103,000, Per/Ser (Incl. Access Fees) $6,000, AV Equip $18,000. Sal $373,160
Library Holdings: Bk Titles 93,000; Per Subs 395
Subject Interests: Handicapped, Learning disabilities, Special educ
Automation Activity & Vendor Info: (Circulation) DRA
Mem of NJ Regional Libr Coop
Partic in Morris Automated Information Network

RARITAN

S R W JOHNSON PHARMACEUTICAL RESEARCH INSTITUTE, Hartman Library, 1000 Rte 202, Box 300, 08869-0602. SAN 310-4699. Tel: 908-704-4919. FAX: 908-707-9860. *Mgr*, June Bente; *Tech Servs*, Kathleen Amberg; *Bibliog Instr*, Elizabeth Walker; Staff 6 (MLS 2, Non-MLS 4)
Founded 1944
Library Holdings: Bk Vols 8,000; Per Subs 700
Subject Interests: Biology, Chemistry, Medicine
Automation Activity & Vendor Info: (OPAC) DRA
Database Vendor: DRA
Restriction: By appointment only
Function: Archival collection, Document delivery services
Partic in Dialog Corporation; MLA; PALINET & Union Library Catalogue of Pennsylvania; SDC Info Servs; SLA

M ORTHO DIAGNOSTIC SYSTEMS RESEARCH LIBRARY,* 1001 US Hwy 202, 08869-0606. SAN 310-4680. Tel: 908-218-8163. FAX: 908-704-3933. *Mgr*, Mary Ann Adams
Founded 1976
Subject Interests: Biomed, Clinical chem, Hematology, Immunology
Publications: Research Library Information Center Users Guide, Periodicals List

P RARITAN PUBLIC LIBRARY,* 54 E Somerset St, 08869. SAN 310-4702. Tel: 908-725-0413. FAX: 908-725-1832. *Dir*, Jackie Widows
Founded 1961. Pop 5,798; Circ 39,000
Jan 1997-Dec 1998 Income $221,044, State $5,044, City $178,000, Locally Generated Income $38,000. Mats Exp $28,000, Books $20,000, Per/Ser (Incl. Access Fees) $6,000. Sal $115,000 (Prof $62,000)
Library Holdings: Bk Vols 39,000; Per Subs 100
Special Collections: Basilone Congressional Record, Tribute & Citation; Basilone History Coll; Frelinghuysen Portraits Coll
Publications: Raritan Library News
Partic in NW Regional Libr Coop; Raritan Valley Fedn of Librs
Friends of the Library Group

RED BANK

P RED BANK PUBLIC LIBRARY, Eisner Memorial Library, 84 W Front St, 07701. SAN 310-4710. Tel: 732-842-0690. FAX: 732-842-4191. *Dir*, Debra Griffin-Sadel; *Ad Servs, Ref*, Jane Eigenrauch; *Ch Servs*, Marianne Schumann; Staff 3 (MLS 3)
Founded 1878. Pop 10,636; Circ 62,928
Library Holdings: Bk Vols 52,676; Per Subs 184
Subject Interests: NJ hist
Automation Activity & Vendor Info: (Cataloging) CARL; (Circulation) CARL; (OPAC) CARL
Open Mon, Wed & Thurs 9am - 8pm, Tues, Fri & Sat 9am - 5pm

M RIVERVIEW MEDICAL CENTER, Clinical Library,* One Riverview Plaza, 07701. SAN 310-4729. Tel: 732-530-2275. FAX: 732-530-2394. *Librn*, Joanne Papanicolaou
Founded 1968
Library Holdings: Bk Vols 2,500; Per Subs 277
Subject Interests: Clinical medicine, Nursing
Mem of NJ Regional Libr Coop
Partic in Monmouth Consortium; OCLC Online Computer Library Center, Inc

RIDGEFIELD

P RIDGEFIELD PUBLIC LIBRARY, 527 Morse Ave, 07657. SAN 310-4745. Tel: 201-941-0192. FAX: 201-941-3424. E-Mail: rfld1@bccls.org. *Dir*, Carolyn R Stefani; E-Mail: stefani@bccls.ort; *Ch Servs*, Jane Forte; E-Mail: rfldjuv@bccls.org; *Ref*, Yilin Sheng; E-Mail: rfldref@bccls.org; Staff 3 (MLS 3)
Founded 1930. Pop 9,996; Circ 69,082
Library Holdings: Bk Vols 61,000
Special Collections: Ridgefield History Coll
Automation Activity & Vendor Info: (Cataloging) DRA; (Circulation) DRA; (ILL) DRA; (OPAC) DRA
Database Vendor: DRA
Partic in Bergen County Cooperative Library System; Highlands Regional Library Cooperative
Friends of the Library Group

RIDGEFIELD PARK

P RIDGEFIELD PARK FREE PUBLIC LIBRARY,* 107 Cedar St, 07660. SAN 310-4753. Tel: 201-641-0689. E-Mail: rfpk1@bccls.org. Web Site: www.ci,ridgefield-park.nj.us. *Dir*, Caroline Fannin; *Ad Servs*, Ellen Kovarik; *Ch Servs*, Margaret Astolfi
Founded 1890. Pop 12,854; Circ 69,561
1997-1998 Income $407,731, State $11,890. Mats Exp $30,393, Books $23,064, Per/Ser (Incl. Access Fees) $6,292. Sal $282,321
Library Holdings: Bk Vols 80,495; Per Subs 95
Partic in Bergen County Cooperative Library System
Friends of the Library Group

S SAMSUNG ELECTRONICS, Information Center, 105 Challenger Rd, 07660. SAN 377-4406. Tel: 201-229-7075. FAX: 201-229-7079. *In Charge*, Tony Litwinowicz; E-Mail: anthonyl@sna.samsung.com; Staff 3 (MLS 1, Non-MLS 2)
Library Holdings: Bk Vols 200; Per Subs 100
Partic in Am Libr Asn

RIDGEWOOD

P RIDGEWOOD PUBLIC LIBRARY, 125 N Maple Ave, 07450-3288. SAN 351-336X. Tel: 201-670-5600. FAX: 201-670-0293. E-Mail: rgwd1@bccls.org. Web Site: www.lib.ridgewood.nj.us. *Dir*, Nancy K Greene; *Asst Dir*, Nancy Blasberg; *Ch Servs*, Lois Brodie; *YA Servs*, Gina Mitgang; *ILL*, Michael Schinn; *Tech Servs*, Nancy Haab; *Ref*, Eileen Colyer; Staff 13 (MLS 13)
Founded 1923. Pop 24,152; Circ 340,000
Jan 2000-Dec 2000 Income $1,819,000, State $31,113, City $1,595,000. Mats Exp $240,620. Sal $1,113,128
Library Holdings: Bk Vols 110,000
Subject Interests: Art, Bus, History, Literature, Local history, Mgt, Music, Technology
Publications: Annual Report
Partic in Bergen County Cooperative Library System; Highlands Regional Library Cooperative
Friends of the Library Group

M VALLEY HOSPITAL, Medical Library, 223 N Van Dien Ave, 07450. SAN 322-9122. Tel: 201-447-8285. FAX: 201-447-8602. Web Site: www.valleyhealth.com. *Librn*, Claudia Allocco; E-Mail: callocc@valleyhealth.com; Staff 2 (MLS 1, Non-MLS 1)
Library Holdings: Bk Vols 2,000; Per Subs 200
Database Vendor: Ebsco - EbscoHost

RINGWOOD

P RINGWOOD PUBLIC LIBRARY,* 30 Cannici Dr, 07456. SAN 310-477X. Interlibrary Loan Service Tel: 973-962-6256. FAX: 973-962-7799. Web Site: www.palsplus.org/rpl. *Dir*, Andrea R Cahoon; *Ad Servs*, Ellen Munn; *Ch Servs*, Ann Marie Solch; Staff 4 (MLS 1, Non-MLS 3)
Founded 1960. Pop 12,623; Circ 56,000
Jan 1998-Dec 1998 Mats Exp $290,392, Books $25,512, Per/Ser (Incl. Access Fees) $3,548, Micro $4,465, Electronic Ref Mat (Incl. Access Fees) $4,627. Sal $182,006
Library Holdings: Bk Vols 37,000; Bk Titles 34,306; Per Subs 110
Special Collections: Ringwood History Coll, microfiche, clippings, bks & pamphlets
Automation Activity & Vendor Info: (Cataloging) Brodart; (Circulation) Brodart; (OPAC) Brodart
Partic in Highlands Regional Library Cooperative; New Jersey Library Network
Friends of the Library Group

RIVER EDGE

L PECKAR & ABRAMSON, Law Library,* 70 Grand Ave, 07661. SAN 372-4298. Tel: 201-343-3434. FAX: 201-343-6306. *Librn*, Edmund Dabkowski; E-Mail: dabkowe@pecklaw.com
Library Holdings: Bk Vols 5,000; Per Subs 70

P RIVER EDGE FREE PUBLIC LIBRARY,* Elm & Tenney Aves, 07661. SAN 310-4788. Tel: 201-261-1663. FAX: 201-986-0214. Web Site: www.bccls.org/riveredge. *Dir*, Jane Galgoci; *Ch Servs*, Susan Mengers; *Ref*, Mary Disanza; *Ad Servs*, Brietta Savoie
Founded 1953
Library Holdings: Bk Vols 90,946; Bk Titles 88,490; Per Subs 200
Special Collections: Language Coll
Mem of Bergen County Co-op Libr Syst
Friends of the Library Group

RIVER VALE

P RIVER VALE FREE PUBLIC LIBRARY,* 412 Rivervale Rd, 07675. SAN 310-4796. Tel: 201-391-2323. FAX: 201-391-6599. E-Mail: rivl1@bccls.org. *Dir*, Andrea Ouida; E-Mail: ouida@bccls.org; *Asst Dir, Ref*, Kathryn Hatfield; E-Mail: hatfield@bccls.org; *Ch Servs*, Mary Anne Ketabchi
Founded 1964. Pop 10,012; Circ 108,285
Jan 1998-Dec 1998 Income $424,846, State $13,426, City $380,991, Locally Generated Income $30,429. Mats Exp $66,268, Books $52,688, Per/Ser (Incl. Access Fees) $9,335, Electronic Ref Mat (Incl. Access Fees) $4,245. Sal $243,091
Library Holdings: Bk Vols 50,078; Per Subs 147
Database Vendor: DRA
Partic in Bergen County Cooperative Library System; Highlands Regional Library Cooperative
Friends of the Library Group

RIVERDALE

P RIVERDALE PUBLIC LIBRARY,* 56 Post Lane, 07457. SAN 376-057X. Tel: 973-835-4320. *Dir*, Nancy Stiehl; *Asst Librn*, Mercedes Swanson
Library Holdings: Bk Vols 10,000; Per Subs 30
Open Mon & Wed 9-4 & 6-9, Tues & Thurs 9-11 & 12-5, Fri 9-3

RIVERSIDE

P RIVERSIDE PUBLIC LIBRARY ASSOCIATION, INC,* 10 Franklin St, 08075. SAN 310-480X. Tel: 856-461-6922. *Dir*, Jean Bowker; Staff 3 (Non-MLS 3)
Founded 1922. Pop 7,941; Circ 22,630
Library Holdings: Bk Titles 37,000; Per Subs 5
Mem of Burlington County Library

RIVERTON

P RIVERTON FREE LIBRARY,* 306 Main St, 08077. SAN 310-4826. Tel: 856-829-2476. FAX: 856-829-4790. *Dir*, Michael Robinson; E-Mail: mrobinso@mail.burlco.lib.nj.us; *Asst Librn*, Jean Markovitz
Founded 1899. Circ 21,944
Library Holdings: Bk Vols 17,000; Per Subs 40
Mem of Coop with Burlington County Libr
Friends of the Library Group

ROCKAWAY

P ROCKAWAY FREE PUBLIC LIBRARY,* 82 E Main St, 07866. SAN 371-5388. Tel: 973-627-5709. FAX: 973-627-5796. E-Mail: rcbill@main.morris.org. Web Site: www.rockboro.gti.net, www.uscis.nac.net/rockboro. *Dir*, Edna Puleo; *Circ, ILL*, Theresa Tironi; *Ch Servs*, Jennifer

Boyle; Staff 9 (MLS 1, Non-MLS 8)
Founded 1914. Pop 6,500
Library Holdings: Bk Vols 35,000; Bk Titles 30,000
Publications: Rockaway Borough Library Newsletter
Partic in Morris Automated Information Network
Special Services for the Blind - Magnifiers
Library houses a museum of national, state & local historical papers & artifacts
Friends of the Library Group

P ROCKAWAY TOWNSHIP FREE PUBLIC LIBRARY,* 61 Mount Hope Rd, 07866. SAN 351-3424. Tel: 973-627-2344. FAX: 973-627-7658. E-Mail: rocktwp@gti.net. Web Site: www.gti.net/rocktwp. *Dir*, Jeanette Cohn; *Ad Servs*, Ann Weissenburger; *Ch Servs*, Marilyn Heckler; *Ref*, Doreen Szymczak
Founded 1966. Pop 20,000
Jan 1999-Dec 1999 Income $822,500, State $21,009. Mats Exp $107,500, Books $85,000, Per/Ser (Incl. Access Fees) $8,000, AV Equip $5,500, Other Print Mats $2,000, Electronic Ref Mat (Incl. Access Fees) $7,000. Sal $440,600
Library Holdings: Bk Vols 112,000; Per Subs 160
Subject Interests: Bus
Partic in Morris Automated Information Network; OCLC Online Computer Library Center, Inc
Friends of the Library Group
Branches: 1
HIBERNIA BRANCH, Green Pond Rd, Hibernia, 07842. SAN 351-3459. Tel: 973-627-6872. Web Site: www.gti.net/rocktwp. *Dir*, Jeanette Cohn
Library Holdings: Bk Vols 12,000
Friends of the Library Group

ROEBLING

P FLORENCE TOWNSHIP PUBLIC LIBRARY,* 1350 Hornberger Ave, 08554. SAN 310-4842. Tel: 609-499-0143. FAX: 609-499-0551. *Librn*, Marion Huebler
Circ 12,000
Library Holdings: Bk Vols 26,000; Per Subs 29
Mem of Burlington County Library

ROSELAND

§L CONNELL FOLEY LAW LIBRARY, 85 Livingston Ave, 07068-1765. Tel: 973-535-0500. FAX: 973-535-9217. Web Site: www.connellfoley.com. *Dir*, Tae Yoo; E-Mail: tyoo@connellfoley.com; *Asst Librn*, Anne Ramaglin
Library Holdings: Bk Vols 13,000
Subject Interests: Banking, Corporate, Estates, NJ law, Tax, Trusts
Restriction: Private library, Restricted access
Partic in Infolink Eastern New Jersey Regional Library Cooperative, Inc

L FRIEDMAN SIEGELBAUM, Law Library,* 7 Becker Farm Rd, 07068-1757. SAN 371-7461. Tel: 973-992-1990, Ext 199. FAX: 973-992-4643. Web Site: www.fslaw.com. *Librn*, Brian Haley; E-Mail: bhaley@fslaw.com
Library Holdings: Bk Vols 3,500; Per Subs 53
Publications: Brief Bank; Corp File; Holdings List
Partic in Dialog Corporation; Dow Jones News Retrieval; Westlaw
Special Services for the Deaf - Staff with knowledge of sign language

L HANNOCH WEISMAN, Law Library,* 4 Becker Farm Rd, 07068. SAN 372-4808. Tel: 973-535-5300. FAX: 973-994-7198. *Librn*, Sandra L Willis; E-Mail: swillis@hannock.com; *Asst Librn*, Rita Bronnenkant
Library Holdings: Bk Vols 12,000
Restriction: Private library
Partic in NJ Infolink

L LOWENSTEIN SANDLER PC-CAPITOL LIBRARY, 65 Livingston Ave, 07068. SAN 376-0707. Tel: 973-597-2500. FAX: 973-597-2400. *Dir Libr Serv*, Beth Petruska; Tel: 973-597-6122, Fax: 973-597-6123, E-Mail: bpetruska@lowenstein.com; *Electronic Resources*, Kathleen Taggart; Tel: 973-522-6442, Fax: 973-522-6423, E-Mail: ktaggart@lowenstein.com
Library Holdings: Bk Vols 25,000

L LUM, HOENS, CONANT, DANZIS & KLEINBERG, Law Library,* 103 Eisenhower Pkwy, 07068-1049. SAN 310-3439. Tel: 973-403-9000. FAX: 973-403-9021. *Dir*, Annette Davis
Founded 1869
Library Holdings: Bk Vols 19,500
Subject Interests: Banking, Corporate, Estates, Securities, Tax, Trusts
Partic in Dialog Corporation; Westlaw

P ROSELAND FREE PUBLIC LIBRARY, 20 Roseland Ave, 07068. SAN 310-4850. Tel: 973-226-8636. FAX: 973-226-6429. Web Site: www.roselandnj.org. *Dir*, Judith Yankielun Lind; E-Mail: jlind@nplhvb.org; *Ref*, Reina Jacobowitz; *Ch Servs*, Joelle Mellon
Founded 1961. Pop 5,200; Circ 75,000
Library Holdings: Bk Vols 46,000; Bk Titles 42,000; Per Subs 125
Subject Interests: Local history, Railroadiana
Automation Activity & Vendor Info: (ILL) Gaylord

L WOLFF & SAMSON, Law Library, 5 Becker Farm Rd, 07068. SAN 372-414X. Tel: 201-740-0500. FAX: 201-740-1407. *Librn*, Rosemary Walton; E-Mail: rwalton@wolffsamson.com
Library Holdings: Bk Vols 12,000

ROSELLE

P ROSELLE FREE PUBLIC LIBRARY,* 104 W Fourth Ave, 07203. SAN 310-4869. Tel: 908-245-5809. FAX: 908-298-8881. *Dir*, Terence Blackburn; *Acq*, Patricia O'Connell; *Ch Servs*, Paul Volpe; *Circ*, Virginia Drewniany; Staff 11 (MLS 2, Non-MLS 9)
Founded 1917. Pop 20,314; Circ 66,408
Library Holdings: Bk Vols 52,926; Bk Titles 50,153; Per Subs 96
Subject Interests: Ethnic studies, NJ hist
Mem of Linx

ROSELLE PARK

P ROSELLE PARK, (RVP), Veterans Memorial Library, 404 Chestnut St, 07204-1506. SAN 310-4877. Tel: 908-245-2456. FAX: 908-245-9204. Web Site: www.roselle.park.nj.us. *Dir*, Barbara E Shallit; E-Mail: bshallit@rvp.nj.publib.org; *Ch Servs*, Judith Love-Fischer; *Circ, ILL*, Deborah Heiss; *Tech Servs*, Judith Gibbons; *Ref Serv*, Harriet Gruber; Staff 3 (MLS 3)
Founded 1920. Pop 12,687; Circ 57,722
Jan 2000-Dec 2000 Income $304,990. Mats Exp Books $41,300. Sal $247,400 (Prof $89,350)
Library Holdings: Bk Vols 52,000; Bk Titles 51,800; Per Subs 132
Special Collections: Jones Memorial Science Coll; Weissman Coll (decorating)
Automation Activity & Vendor Info: (Cataloging) Gaylord; (Circulation) Gaylord; (OPAC) Gaylord
Database Vendor: Ebsco - EbscoHost
Partic in Infolink
Friends of the Library Group

RUMSON

P OCEANIC FREE LIBRARY,* Avenue of Two Rivers & Ridge Rd, 07760. SAN 310-4885. Tel: 732-842-2692. FAX: 732-842-2692. *Dir*, Anne Wissel
Founded 1920. Pop 7,000; Circ 43,000
Library Holdings: Bk Vols 28,000; Per Subs 60
Special Collections: Opera Libretti, autographed bks

RUNNEMEDE

P RUNNEMEDE FREE PUBLIC LIBRARY, Broadway & Black Horse Pike, 08078. (Mail add: PO Box 119, 08078-0119), SAN 320-491X. Tel: 856-939-4688. E-Mail: runnemedelibrary@home.com. *Dir*, Mrs Kathleen Ann Vasinda; *Librn*, Mrs Ann Korpan; *Asst Librn*, Joyce Bergman; Staff 2 (Non-MLS 2)
Founded 1975. Pop 9,042; Circ 14,361
Library Holdings: Bk Titles 22,000; Per Subs 59
Database Vendor: epixtech, inc.

RUTHERFORD

P RUTHERFORD FREE PUBLIC LIBRARY, 150 Park Ave, 07070. SAN 310-4907. Tel: 201-939-8600. FAX: 201-939-4108. E-Mail: ruth1@bccls.org. Web Site: bccls.org/rutherford. *Dir*, Miriam Sawyer; *Asst Dir*, Joan Velez; *YA Servs*, Barbara Snyder; *Ref*, Mary Kate Cullinan; *Per*, Judy Manzo; *Ch Servs*, Jane Tarantino; Staff 18 (MLS 5, Non-MLS 13)
Founded 1894. Pop 19,068
1999-2000 Income $775,300, State $25,300, City $700,000, Locally Generated Income $50,000. Mats Exp $102,600, Books $98,000, Per/Ser (Incl. Access Fees) $3,300, Presv $1,300. Sal $510,000 (Prof $280,000)
Library Holdings: Bk Vols 103,000; Per Subs 230
Special Collections: William Carlos Williams Coll
Database Vendor: DRA
Partic in Bergen County Cooperative Library System; Highlands Regional Library Cooperative
Friends of the Library Group

SADDLE BROOK

S FAST PULSE TECHNOLOGY, INC LIBRARY,* 220 Midland Ave, 07663. SAN 323-4584. Tel: 973-478-5757. FAX: 973-478-6115. *In Charge*, Robert Goldstein
Library Holdings: Bk Vols 1,100; Per Subs 12

P SADDLE BROOK FREE PUBLIC LIBRARY, 340 Mayhill St, 07663. SAN 310-4915. Tel: 201-843-3287. FAX: 201-843-5512, 201-843-7888. *Dir*, Jack C Bury; Staff 3 (MLS 2, Non-MLS 1)

Founded 1945. Circ 95,000
Library Holdings: Bk Vols 52,000; Per Subs 125
Partic in Bergen County Cooperative Library System; Highlands Regional Library Cooperative

SALEM

S SALEM COUNTY HISTORICAL SOCIETY, Josephine Jaquett Memorial Library, 79-83 Market St, 08079. SAN 310-4923. Tel: 856-935-5004. FAX: 856-935-0728. E-Mail: schistorical@willie.salem.cc.nj.us. Web Site: www.salemcounty.com/schs/index.html. *Dir*, Dr James F Turk; *Librn*, Alice Boggs
Founded 1884
Library Holdings: Bk Vols 1,000; Per Subs 10
Subject Interests: Genealogy, History
Special Collections: Family Bibles Coll; Unrecorded Deed Coll
Publications: Quarterly Newsletter (Newsletter)

G SALEM COUNTY LIBRARY COMMISSION-BOOKMOBILE, 112 W Broadway, 08079-1302. Tel: 856-935-3767. FAX: 856-935-5110. E-Mail: splbkm@clueslibs.org. *Coll Develop, Coordr*, Margaret Ellyn Masserini; Tel: 856-935-3767, Fax: 856-935-5110, E-Mail: splbkm@clueslibs.org; Staff 3 (Non-MLS 3)
Founded 1981
Jan 1998-Dec 1998 Income $36,000, County $29,000, Locally Generated Income $7,000. Mats Exp Books $7,000. Sal $21,000 (Prof $11,000)
Library Holdings: Bk Vols 18,000; Bk Titles 18,250; High Interest/Low Vocabulary Bk Vols 100; Bks on Deafness & Sign Lang 10
Partic in South Jersey Regional Library Cooperative
Special Services for the Blind - Book tables; Large print bks; Magnifying glasses/lamps
Special Services - Home delivery
Bookmobiles: 1

P SALEM FREE PUBLIC LIBRARY, 112 W Broadway, 08079-1302. SAN 310-4931. Tel: 856-935-0526. FAX: 856-935-5110. E-Mail: salemlib@cumberland.county.lib.nj.us. *Coll Develop, Dir*, Pamela Nelson; Fax: 856-935-0526; *Ch Servs*, C Odessa Nokes; *ILL*, Paula Pew; *Ref*, Arleen Maiden; *Tech Servs*, Sharon Thomas
Founded 1920. Pop 6,883; Circ 12,861
Jan 2000-Dec 2000 Income $130,336, State $14,017, City $85,000, Federal $1,136, Locally Generated Income $30,183. Mats Exp $17,630, Books $14,704, Per/Ser (Incl. Access Fees) $1,012, Other Print Mats $740, Electronic Ref Mat (Incl. Access Fees) $1,174. Sal $85,560
Library Holdings: Bk Vols 46,473; Bk Titles 42,644; Per Subs 84
Special Collections: Local History (Granville S Thomas Coll), bks, pamphlets; PSEG Salem Nuclear Generating Station
Mem of Cumberland County Library
Partic in South Jersey Regional Library Cooperative
Friends of the Library Group

M THE MEMORIAL HOSPITAL OF SALEM COUNTY, David W Green Medical Library, 310 Woodstown Rd, 08079. SAN 375-7005. Tel: 856-935-1000. FAX: 856-935-5420.
Library Holdings: Bk Vols 357; Per Subs 32

SCOTCH PLAINS

P SCOTCH PLAINS PUBLIC LIBRARY, 1927 Bartle Ave, 07076-1299. SAN 310-494X. Tel: 908-322-5007. FAX: 908-322-0490. Web Site: www.njpublib.org/scotchplains. *Dir*, Norbert Bernstein; *Circ, Ref Serv*, Mary Czarnomski; *Cat*, Vivian Marek; *Ch Servs*, Ann Luerssen; Staff 2 (MLS 2)
Founded 1888. Pop 21,160; Circ 95,160
Jan 1999-Dec 1999 Income $747,461, State $22,714, City $724,747. Mats Exp $58,631, Books $43,195, Per/Ser (Incl. Access Fees) $7,424, Presv $557, AV Equip $2,326. Sal $439,303 (Prof $131,515)
Library Holdings: Bk Vols 71,102; Bk Titles 64,984; Per Subs 196; Bks on Deafness & Sign Lang 30
Subject Interests: Cookbks
Special Collections: Local & State Hist (New Jersey); Poetry & Prose (Robert Frost)
Database Vendor: epixtech, inc.
Partic in Infolink Eastern New Jersey Regional Library Cooperative, Inc; Librs of Union County Consortium
Friends of the Library Group

SEA BRIGHT

S MOSS ARCHIVES, PO Box 3336, 07760-3336. SAN 374-9975. Tel: 732-842-0336. *Archivist*, George H Moss, Jr. Subject Specialists: *Local history*, George H Moss, Jr
Library Holdings: Bk Titles 200
Subject Interests: Monmouth County hist

SEA GIRT

L NEW JERSEY STATE POLICE TRAINING BUREAU LIBRARY,* Training Center, 08750. SAN 375-8419. Tel: 732-449-5200, Ext 5203. FAX: 732-449-8763.
Library Holdings: Bk Titles 18,000

SECAUCUS

M MEADOWLANDS HOSPITAL MEDICAL CENTER, Health Science Library,* Meadowlands Pkwy, 07096-1580. SAN 375-703X. Tel: 201-348-9300, Ext 3217. FAX: 201-392-3270. *Librn*, Eleanor Cohen
Library Holdings: Per Subs 50

S PHYSICIANS WORLD - THOMSON HEALTHCARE, (Formerly Physicians World Communications Group), Medical Library & Knowledge Management, 400 Plaza Dr, 07094. SAN 370-5072. Tel: 201-271-6105. FAX: 201-865-9247. Web Site: www.pwcg.com. *Dir*, Maria Vee Kwonn; E-Mail: mkwonn@pwcg.com; Staff 3 (MLS 2, Non-MLS 1)
Founded 1983
Library Holdings: Bk Vols 3,000; Bk Titles 2,000; Per Subs 200
Subject Interests: Cardiology
Automation Activity & Vendor Info: (OPAC) Sydney
Database Vendor: Dialog, OCLC - First Search, OVID Technologies
Restriction: Staff use only
Function: Research library
Partic in New Jersey Library Network

P SECAUCUS FREE PUBLIC LIBRARY,* Plaza Ctr, 07094. SAN 310-4974. Tel: 201-330-2083. FAX: 201-330-1741. E-Mail: seca1@bccls.org. Web Site: www.bccls.org/secaucus. *Dir*, Kathy Steffens; Staff 2 (MLS 2)
Founded 1957. Pop 13,500; Circ 87,367
Library Holdings: Bk Vols 57,500; Per Subs 82
Subject Interests: Arts, Crafts, Sci
Mem of Jersey City Free Pub Libr; Region III Library Coop Serv
Friends of the Library Group

SEWELL

S EDUCATIONAL INFORMATION & RESOURCE CENTER, 606 Delsea Dr, 08080-9199. SAN 375-3409. Tel: 856-582-7000, Ext 140. FAX: 856-582-4206. E-Mail: info@eirc.org. Web Site: www.eirc.org. *Dir, Res*, Patricia Bruder; Staff 4 (Non-MLS 4)
Founded 1969
Library Holdings: Per Subs 90
Special Collections: ERIC Coll from 1975-98, microfiche
Database Vendor: Ebsco - EbscoHost
Restriction: Open to faculty, students & qualified researchers
Partic in South Jersey Regional Library Cooperative

J GLOUCESTER COUNTY COLLEGE, Library-Media Center,* 1400 Tanyard Rd, 08080. SAN 310-4982. Tel: 856-468-5000, Ext 320. Interlibrary Loan Service Tel: 856-468-5000, Ext 321. FAX: 856-464-1695. *Dir*, Jane Lopes-Crocker; *Media Spec*, Howard Silverman; *Ref*, Linda DeFelice; *ILL*, Patricia Hirsekorn; *Per*, Anna Kehnast; Staff 4 (MLS 4)
Founded 1968. Enrl 3,351; Fac 93
Library Holdings: Bk Vols 50,000; Per Subs 479
Subject Interests: Art, Bus, Nursing
Publications: Info-Depot
Partic in South Jersey Regional Library Cooperative

SHREWSBURY

S ROBERT A STANGER COMPANY LIBRARY,* 1129 Broad St, 07702. SAN 328-4824. Tel: 732-389-3600, Ext 253. FAX: 732-389-1751. *Librn, Mgr*, Bella Dodds
Library Holdings: Per Subs 100

SKILLMAN

S JOHNSON & JOHNSON CONSUMER PRODUCTS INC, Business & Technical Information Center Library,* Grandview Rd, 08558. SAN 325-9447. Tel: 908-874-1439. FAX: 908-874-1255. *Mgr*, Marilyn Faulkner
Library Holdings: Bk Vols 1,800; Per Subs 210
Subject Interests: Dentistry

SOMERDALE

P SOMERDALE PUBLIC LIBRARY,* 125 S Hilltop Ave, 08083. SAN 310-5024. Tel: 856-783-4344. *Dir*, Marie Hughes
Pop 7,000; Circ 9,086
Library Holdings: Bk Vols 10,000
Mem of Camden County Library System

SOMERS POINT

S ATLANTIC COUNTY HISTORICAL SOCIETY LIBRARY, 907 Shore Rd, 08244-2335. (Mail add: PO Box 301, 08244-0301), SAN 310-5032. Tel: 609-927-5218.
Founded 1913
Library Holdings: Bk Titles 6,000
Subject Interests: Genealogy, Local history
Special Collections: Atlantic County, diaries, deeds, genealogy, letters, mss; Family Bible; New Jersey History & Genealogy, rare & out of print bks; old maps, photographs, lantern slides & glass plate negatives of Atlantic County
Publications: Annual Year Book; Quarterly Newsletter

SOMERSET

P FRANKLIN TOWNSHIP FREE PUBLIC LIBRARY, 485 DeMott Lane, 08873. SAN 351-3572. Tel: 732-873-8700. FAX: 732-873-0746. Web Site: www.franklintwp.org. *Dir*, January Adams; *YA Servs*, Anne Lemay; *Tech Servs*, Marcie Wybraniec; *Circ*, Greta Elfe; *Ad Servs*, William Brahms; *Tech Servs*, Helen Imre; Staff 14 (MLS 6, Non-MLS 8)
Founded 1957. Pop 49,000
Jul 2000-Jun 2001 Income $1,200,000. Sal $767,159
Library Holdings: Bk Vols 111,000; Bk Titles 101,000
Special Collections: African-Am, collectibles
Automation Activity & Vendor Info: (Acquisitions) MultiLIS; (Cataloging) MultiLIS; (Circulation) MultiLIS; (OPAC) MultiLIS
Partic in Highlands Regional Network
Friends of the Library Group

S UNILEVER BESTFOODS, (Formerly Bestfoods), Information Center, 150 Pierce St, 08873. SAN 310-5563. Tel: 732-627-8500. *Mgr*, Les Van Alstine; Tel: 732-627-8725, Fax: 732-627-8506, E-Mail: leslie.van.alstine@na.bestfoods.com; *Senior Info Specialist*, Beth Currie; Tel: 732-627-8608, Fax: 732-627-8506, E-Mail: beth.currie@na.bestfoods.com; *Syst Coordr*, Na Lin; Tel: 732-627-8607, Fax: 732-627-8506, E-Mail: na.lin@na.bestfoods.com; Staff 4 (MLS 2, Non-MLS 2)
Founded 1970
Library Holdings: Bk Vols 7,000; Bk Titles 6,000; Per Subs 300
Subject Interests: Food sci, Nutrition, Technology
Automation Activity & Vendor Info: (Acquisitions) Inmagic, Inc.; (Cataloging) Inmagic, Inc.; (Circulation) Inmagic, Inc.; (OPAC) Inmagic, Inc.; (Serials) Inmagic, Inc.
Database Vendor: Dialog
Publications: Journals Holdings List; New Titles (Acquisitions list)
Restriction: Circulates for staff only, Company library, Private library
Partic in Dialog Corporation; STN

S UNION CARBIDE CORP, Information Resource Center, One Riverview Dr, 08875. SAN 375-9962. Tel: 732-271-2060. Circulation Tel: 732-271-7944. FAX: 732-271-7873. *Branch Mgr*, Jean Eldridge Raper; E-Mail: raperje@ucarb.com. Subject Specialists: *Polymer chemistry*, Jean Eldridge Raper; Staff 2 (MLS 1, Non-MLS 1)
Library Holdings: Bk Titles 3,000; Per Subs 60
Subject Interests: Polymer chemistry
Database Vendor: Dialog, Ebsco - EbscoHost

SOMERVILLE

S ETHICON, INC, Scientific Information Services, US Rte 22, 08876. SAN 320-4553. Tel: 908-218-3259. FAX: 908-218-3558. *Librn*, Norma Bregen; *Info Specialist*, Sharon Ma
Founded 1956
Library Holdings: Bk Titles 9,000; Per Subs 375
Subject Interests: Biomat, Polymer chemistry, Surgery, Toxicology
Publications: Scientific Information Reports
Partic in Dialog Corporation; New Jersey Library Network
Friends of the Library Group

J EVELYN S FIELD LIBRARY, (Formerly Raritan Valley Community College), Raritan Valley Community College, Rte 28 & Lamington Rd, 08876. (Mail add: PO Box 3300, 08876), Tel: 908-526-1200, Ext 8865. Circulation Tel: 908-526-1200, Ext 8423. Reference Tel: 908-526-1200, Ext 8350. FAX: 908-526-2985. Web Site: library.raritanval.edu. *Dean*, Chuck Chulvick; *Chair, Librn*, Birte Nebeker; E-Mail: bnebeker@raritanval.edu; *Circ*, Debbie Dulepski; E-Mail: ddulepsk@raritanval.edu; *Bibliog Instr, Ref*, Mary Ann Ryer; E-Mail: mryer@raritanval.edu; Staff 12 (MLS 4, Non-MLS 8)
Founded 1968. Enrl 1,495
1999-2000 Mats Exp $242,000, Books $100,000, Per/Ser (Incl. Access Fees) $72,000, Micro $20,000, Electronic Ref Mat (Incl. Access Fees) $50,000. Sal $535,000 (Prof $201,000)
Library Holdings: Bk Vols 80,000; Bk Titles 65,000; Per Subs 550
Subject Interests: Acad index, Bus, Gen sci, Holocaust, Humanities, Nursing, Soc sci
Special Collections: Art Coll, slides; Local Authors Collection
Automation Activity & Vendor Info: (Cataloging) epixtech, inc.; (Circulation) epixtech, inc.; (Course Reserve) epixtech, inc.; (OPAC) epixtech, inc.; (Serials) epixtech, inc.
Database Vendor: epixtech, inc., Lexis-Nexis, ProQuest, Silverplatter Information Inc., Wilson - Wilson Web
Publications: Acquisitions List (quarterly)
Restriction: Circulation limited
Function: For research purposes
Mem of NJ Regional Libr Coop
Partic in Dialog Corporation; OCLC Online Computer Library Center, Inc; PALINET & Union Library Catalogue of Pennsylvania

L NORRIS, MCLAUGHLIN & MARCUS, Law Library, 721 Rte 202-206 N, PO Box 1018, 08876-1018. SAN 372-4824. Tel: 908-722-0700. FAX: 908-722-0755. *Librn*, Janice S Lustiger; E-Mail: jslustiger@nmmlaw.com; Staff 2 (MLS 1, Non-MLS 1)
Library Holdings: Bk Vols 10,000
Restriction: Not open to public

GL SOMERSET COUNTY LAW LIBRARY, 20 N Bridge St, PO Box 3000, 08876-1262. SAN 321-9747. Tel: 908-231-7612. FAX: 908-707-9112. *Librn*, Robert Schriek; Staff 1 (MLS 1)
Library Holdings: Bk Vols 20,000
Subject Interests: Fed law, State law
Restriction: Open to public for reference only
Partic in Westlaw

M SOMERSET MEDICAL CENTER LIBRARY, 110 Rehill Ave, 08876. SAN 320-698X. Tel: 908-685-2423. FAX: 908-685-2869. *Librn*, Kenneth Whitmore; E-Mail: kenwhitmore@somerset-healthcare.com
Library Holdings: Bk Titles 2,000; Per Subs 155
Partic in Medcore

P SOMERVILLE PUBLIC LIBRARY, 35 West End Ave, 08876. SAN 310-5091. Tel: 908-725-1336, 908-725-1781. Interlibrary Loan Service Tel: 908-725-1336, Ext 41. Reference Tel: 908-725-1336, Ext 41. FAX: 908-231-0608. E-Mail: somref@lmxac.org. Web Site: www.mindpulse.com/users/spl. *Dir*, Stan Pollakoff; E-Mail: spollako@lmxac.org; *Cat*, Miryam Block; E-Mail: miryam@lmxa.org; *Ch Servs*, Nancy Lepionka; E-Mail: nancyl@lmxac.org; *Circ*, Donna d'Anunciacao; E-Mail: donnad@lmxac.org; *Purchasing*, Kathy Repole; E-Mail: kathyre@lmxac.org; *Ref*, James Laing Sommerville, III; E-Mail: jims@lmxac.org; *Res*, Martha Sullivan; E-Mail: marthas@lmxac.org; *Tech Servs*, Winona Manello; Tel: wmanello@lmxac.org; Staff 12 (MLS 5, Non-MLS 7)
Founded 1871. Pop 11,323; Circ 65,000
Jan 1999-Dec 1999 Income $491,838, State $14,983, City $476,855. Mats Exp $78,501, Books $31,766, Per/Ser (Incl. Access Fees) $9,300, AV Equip $6,435, Other Print Mats $31,000. Sal $231,778 (Prof $102,000)
Library Holdings: Bk Vols 55,470; Bk Titles 55,348; Per Subs 116; High Interest/Low Vocabulary Bk Vols 200; Bks on Deafness & Sign Lang 24
Subject Interests: Local history, New Jersey, Somerset County hist, Somerville County hist
Special Collections: New Jersey Archives holdings; Paul Robeson-iana; Somerville, Somerset County, New Jersey genealogical material
Automation Activity & Vendor Info: (Cataloging) CARL; (Circulation) CARL; (ILL) CARL; (OPAC) CARL
Database Vendor: CARL, IAC - SearchBank, ProQuest
Function: Professional lending library
Partic in Librs of Middlesex
Friends of the Library Group

SOUTH AMBOY

P DOWDELL LIBRARY OF SOUTH AMBOY, 100 Hoffman Plaza, 08879. SAN 310-5105. Tel: 732-721-6060. FAX: 732-721-1054. E-Mail: comments@dowdell.org. Web Site: www.dowdell.org. *Dir*, Philip Israel; Tel: 732-721-6061, E-Mail: pisrael@dowdell.org; *Publ Servs*, Janet Simeone; E-Mail: jsimeone@dowdell.org; *Ch Servs*, Eleanore Westerholm; E-Mail: eleanore64@yahoo.com; Staff 8 (MLS 1, Non-MLS 7)
Founded 1917. Pop 7,830; Circ 49,000
Jul 2000-Jun 2001 Income $276,742, State $10,136, City $238,000, Locally Generated Income $28,606. Mats Exp $51,285, Books $33,540, Per/Ser (Incl. Access Fees) $3,920, Presv $200, Micro $250, AV Equip $4,285, Electronic Ref Mat (Incl. Access Fees) $9,090. Sal $159,110 (Prof $48,643)
Library Holdings: Bk Vols 44,391; Bk Titles 40,550; Per Subs 100
Subject Interests: NJ hist, Railroads, South Amboy hist
Automation Activity & Vendor Info: (Circulation) Sagebrush Corporation
Database Vendor: Ebsco - EbscoHost
Publications: Annual Report, History of Dowdell Library
Restriction: Residents only
Function: ILL limited, Photocopies available, Some telephone reference
Friends of the Library Group

SOUTH ORANGE

S ARCHAEOLOGICAL SOCIETY OF NEW JERSEY LIBRARY, Fahy Hall, Rm 8, Seton Hall Univ, 07079. SAN 374-910X. Tel: 973-761-9543. FAX: 973-761-9596. *In Charge*, John Kraft
Library Holdings: Bk Titles 1,000; Per Subs 15

R IMMACULATE CONCEPTION SEMINARY LIBRARY, (ICSL), Seton Hall University, 400 S Orange Ave, 07079. SAN 310-1045. Tel: 973-761-9198, 973-761-9584. FAX: 973-761-9577. Web Site: www.shu.edu/. *Dir*, James C Turro; *Librn*, Sister Concetta Russo
Founded 1858. Enrl 215; Fac 35; Highest Degree: Master
Jun 1999-May 2000 Mats Exp $55,800, Books $41,706, AV Equip $6,000, Other Print Mats $8,094. Sal $62,563
Library Holdings: Bk Vols 63,760; Per Subs 475
Subject Interests: Biblical, Catechism, Christian ethics, Church history, Church ministries, Liturgy, Philosophy, Theology
Database Vendor: Ebsco - EbscoHost
Restriction: Open to students, Use of others with permission of librarian

CR SETON HALL UNIVERSITY LIBRARY, Walsh Library Bldg, 400 S Orange Ave, 07079. SAN 310-5113. Tel: 973-761-9435. Interlibrary Loan Service Tel: 973-761-9441. Reference Tel: 973-761-9437. FAX: 973-761-9432. Web Site: library.shu.edu. *Dir*, James Turro; Tel: 973-761-9263, E-Mail: TurroJam@shu.edu; *Dean of Libr*, Arthur W Hafner; E-Mail: HafnerAW@shu.edu; *Publ Servs*, Sr Anita Talar; Tel: 973-761-9795, Fax: 973-275-2119, E-Mail: TalarAni@shu.edu; *Cat*, Teresa Yang; Tel: 973-275-2047, 761-9436, Fax: 973-275-2119, E-Mail: YangTere@shu.edu; *ILL*, Barbara Ward; *Spec Coll*, William Noe Field; Tel: 973-761-9126, Fax: 973-761-9550, E-Mail: FieldWil@shu.edu; *Publ Servs*, Xue-Ming Bao; Tel: 973-275-2399, E-Mail: BaoXuemi@shu.edu; *Publ Servs*, Beth Bloom; Tel: 973-275-2035, Fax: 973-275-2119, E-Mail: BloomBet@shu.edu; *Publ Servs*, Declan J Cunniff; Tel: 973-275-2224, E-Mail: CunnifDe@shu.edu; *Publ Servs*, Natalia Milszyn; Tel: 973-761-9796, Fax: 972-275-2119, E-Mail: MilszyNa@shu.edu; *Publ Servs*, Richard E Stern; Tel: 973-275-2046, Fax: 973-275-2119, E-Mail: SternRic@shu.edu; *Acq*, Sulekha Kalyan; Tel: 973-761-9438, Fax: 973-275-2119, E-Mail: KalyanSu@shu.edu; *Archivist*, Alan Bernard Delozier; Tel: 973-275-2223, Fax: 973-761-9550, E-Mail: DeloziAl@shu.edu; *Cat*, Marta M Deyrup; Tel: 973-275-2223, E-Mail: DeyrupMa@shu.edu; *Publ Servs*, Anthony Lee; Tel: 973-761-9440, Fax: 973-275-2119, E-Mail: LeeAntho@shu.edu; *Dean*, Paul C Chao; Tel: 973-761-9445, E-Mail: ChaoPaul@shu.edu; *Tech Coordr*, Zi-Yu Lin; Tel: 973-275-2058, 761-7698, Fax: 973-275-2119, E-Mail: LinZiyu@shu.edu; *Publ Servs*, Katalin Mandelker; Tel: 973-761-9444, Fax: 973-275-2119, E-Mail: MandellKa@shu.edu; *Publ Servs*, Charles Yen; Tel: 973-275-2059, Fax: 973-275-2119, E-Mail: YenCharl@shu.edu; *Spec Coll*, JoAnn Cotz; Tel: 973-275-2033, Fax: 973-761-9550, E-Mail: CotzJoan@shu.edu; *Circ*, Mabel Wong; Tel: 973-761-9443, E-Mail: WongMabe@shu.edu; *Ser*, Carol Earrusso; Tel: 973-761-9439, E-Mail: EarrusCa@shu.edu; *Coll Develop*, Lucy Manto; Tel: 973-761-9027, E-Mail: MantoLuc@shu.edu; *Coll Develop*, Lori Anderson; Tel: 973-275-2786, E-Mail: AndersLo@shu.edu; *Media Spec Ad*, Ronald Myzie; Tel: 973-761-9429, Fax: 973-761-7942, E-Mail: MyzieRon@shu.edu. Subject Specialists: *Accounting*, Richard E Stern; *Adult education*, Beth Bloom; *Archeology*, Paul C Chao; *Art*, Alan Bernard Delozier; *Asian studies*, JoAnn Cotz; *Biology*, Natalia Milszyn; *Business*, Arthur W Hafner; *Business*, Richard E Stern; *Catholic studies*, William Noe Field; *Chemistry*, Natalia Milszyn; *Classical*, Anthony Lee; *Communications*, JoAnn Cotz; *Criminal justice*, Charles Yen; *Diplomacy*, Charles Yen; *Economics*, Richard E Stern; *Education*, Sr Anita Talar; *English*, Paul C Chao; *Govt publications*, Charles Yen; *History*, Marta M Deyrup; *Info tech*, Katalin Mandelker; *Italian*, Sr Anita Talar; *Libr sci*, Arthur W Hafner; *Libr sci*, JoAnn Cotz; *Mathematics*, Arthur W Hafner; *Medicine*, Natalia Milszyn; *Middle East*, Sr Anita Talar; *Mil sci*, Declan J Cunniff; *Modern lang*, Anthony Lee; *Mus studies*, Mabel Wong; *Music*, Alan Bernard Delozier; *Nursing*, Alan Bernard Delozier; *Philosophy*, Marta M Deyrup; *Religious studies*, Declan J Cunniff; *Religious studies*, William Noe Field; *Theology*, Declan J Cunniff; *Theology*, William Noe Field; Staff 49 (MLS 14, Non-MLS 35)
Founded 1856. Highest Degree: Doctorate
Library Holdings: Bk Vols 493,335; Bk Titles 409,975; Per Subs 1,872
Special Collections: Civil War (Gerald Murphy Coll); Irish Literature & History (McManus Coll); Seton Hall Univ & Archdiocesan Archives
Automation Activity & Vendor Info: (Cataloging) Endeavor
Database Vendor: Ebsco - EbscoHost, GaleNet, Lexis-Nexis, ProQuest, Silverplatter Information Inc.
Restriction: Not open to public
Function: ILL available
Partic in BRS; Dialog Corporation; OCLC Online Computer Library Center, Inc; PALINET & Union Library Catalogue of Pennsylvania
Special Services for the Blind - Adapted computers & special software with speech output to assist learning disabled, mentally retarded & uneducated
Friends of the Library Group

P SOUTH ORANGE PUBLIC LIBRARY,* 65 Scotland Rd, 07079. SAN 310-5121. Tel: 973-762-0230. FAX: 973-762-1469. *Dir*, Elaine M Clark; E-Mail: emclark@infolink.org; *Ref*, Catherine Sullivan; E-Mail: csulliva@infolink.org; *Ch Servs*, Karen Lyons; E-Mail: klyons@infolink.org; *Tech Servs*, Ellen Columbus; E-Mail: ecolumbu@infolink.org
Founded 1864. Pop 15,864
Jan 1999-Dec 1999 Income $747,577, State $21,000, City $708,577, Locally Generated Income $18,000. Mats Exp $75,850, Books $52,000, Per/Ser (Incl. Access Fees) $16,000. Sal $565,528
Library Holdings: Bk Vols 96,744; Bk Titles 88,205; Per Subs 300
Partic in Infolink Regional Libr Coop
Friends of the Library Group

R TEMPLE SHAREY TEFILO-ISRAEL, Abelson Echikson Ehrenkrantz Memorial Library, 432 Scotland Rd, 07079. SAN 325-948X. Tel: 973-763-4116. FAX: 973-763-3941. E-Mail: tefiloisrael@aol.com. *Librn*, Sunny Seglin
Library Holdings: Bk Vols 5,000
Partic in Asn of Jewish Librs

SOUTH PLAINFIELD

P SOUTH PLAINFIELD FREE PUBLIC LIBRARY,* 2484 Plainfield Ave, 07080. SAN 310-5156. Tel: 908-754-7885. FAX: 908-753-3846. *Dir*, Sundra L Fenn; *ILL, Ref*, Mae H Chu; *Librn*, Debra L Messling; *Circ*, Robert Hermbrecht
Founded 1935. Pop 21,152; Circ 86,274
1997-1998 Income $614,110, State $22,061, City $561,226, Locally Generated Income $30,823. Mats Exp $56,858, Books $38,799, Per/Ser (Incl. Access Fees) $6,672, Presv $21, Micro $8,049. Sal $273,928 (Prof $132,836)
Library Holdings: Bk Vols 51,537; Per Subs 185
Mem of NJ Regional Libr Coop
Partic in LMX Automation Consortium
Friends of the Library Group

SOUTH RIVER

P SOUTH RIVER PUBLIC LIBRARY,* 55 Appleby Ave, 08882-2499. SAN 310-5164. Tel: 732-254-2488. FAX: 732-254-4116. *Dir*, Andrea Lodensky; E-Mail: alodens@lmxac.org; *Ch Servs*, Dawn Bladzinski; *Tech Servs*, Irene Malinowski; Staff 6 (MLS 2, Non-MLS 4)
Founded 1920. Pop 14,360; Circ 66,648
Library Holdings: Bk Vols 41,000; Per Subs 145
Special Collections: ABR (Literacy Coll); Hungarian, Polish, Portuguese, Russian Coll; Job Opportunities; Large Print Books; Parenting
Database Vendor: CARL
Publications: Newsletter
Partic in LMX Automation Consortium
Friends of the Library Group

SPARTA

P SPARTA PUBLIC LIBRARY,* 22 Woodport Rd, 07871. SAN 310-5172. Tel: 973-729-3101. FAX: 973-729-1755. E-Mail: spartapl@hublib.lib.nj.us. Web Site: www.spartan.lib.nj.us. *Dir*, Carol Boutilier; *Asst Dir, Coll Develop*, Diane Lapsley; *Ch Servs*, Cynthia Banner; *Ref*, Suzanne Blecker; Staff 16 (MLS 3, Non-MLS 13)
Founded 1841. Circ 175,535
Jan 1998-Dec 1998 Income $495,745, State $14,911, City $480,834. Mats Exp $103,806, Books $86,500, Per/Ser (Incl. Access Fees) $9,500, Presv $640, Micro $4,796, AV Equip $1,770, Other Print Mats $400, Manuscripts & Archives $200. Sal $311,337 (Prof $129,757)
Library Holdings: Bk Vols 68,111; Per Subs 100
Special Collections: Local History: Sparta & Lake Mohawk New Jersey
Publications: Newsletter (quarterly)
Partic in New Jersey Library Network

SPOTSWOOD

P SPOTSWOOD PUBLIC LIBRARY,* 548 Main St, 08884. SAN 310-5180. Tel: 732-251-1515. FAX: 732-251-8151. E-Mail: spotswood@skyweb.net. Web Site: spotswoodboro.com/library.htm. *Dir*, Mary Faith Chmiel; E-Mail: mfchmiel@lmxac.org; Staff 9 (MLS 1, Non-MLS 8)
Founded 1965. Pop 7,983
Jan 1999-Dec 1999 Income $205,000, State $8,570, City $189,000, Locally Generated Income $8,200. Sal $113,000
Library Holdings: Bk Vols 28,000; Per Subs 70
Subject Interests: Antiques, Civil War
Special Collections: Civil War Coll; New Jersey Coll
Automation Activity & Vendor Info: (Circulation) CARL
Database Vendor: CARL
Function: ILL available
Partic in LMX Automation Consortium; Middlesex County Libr Consortium
Friends of the Library Group

SPRING LAKE

P SPRING LAKE PUBLIC LIBRARY,* 1501 Third Ave, 07762. SAN 310-5199. Tel: 732-449-6654. E-Mail: splklib@bellatlantic.net. Web Site: www.springlake.org/. *Dir*, Kater Quinn
Founded 1920. Circ 28,000
Jan 1997-Dec 1998 Income $256,557. Mats Exp $30,000, Books $23,000, Per/Ser (Incl. Access Fees) $1,000. Sal $189,749 (Prof $35,800)
Library Holdings: Bk Vols 56,000; Per Subs 50
Special Collections: Large Print Coll
Open Mon & Wed 10-5, 7-9, Tues 10-5, Fri 10-5, Sat 10-3
Friends of the Library Group

SPRINGFIELD

P SPRINGFIELD FREE PUBLIC LIBRARY,* 66 Mountain Ave, 07081-1786. SAN 310-5202. Tel: 973-376-4930, Ext 27. FAX: 973-376-1334. *Ch Servs*, Kathleen Percoco; *Dir*, Susan Permahos; E-Mail: spermahos@springfield.nj.publib.org; *Tech Servs*, Bettye Barcan; *Ref*, Henriann Robins; Staff 15 (MLS 6, Non-MLS 9)
Founded 1931. Pop 13,955; Circ 122,688
Library Holdings: Bk Vols 80,000; Bk Titles 66,000; Per Subs 229
Special Collections: Local History (Sarah Bailey); Local History Artifacts (Donald B Palmer Museum)
Publications: Newsletter (quarterly)
Partic in Infolink Eastern New Jersey Regional Library Cooperative, Inc
Friends of the Library Group

S SPRINGFIELD HISTORICAL SOCIETY LIBRARY,* 126 Morris Ave, 07081. SAN 371-4365. Tel: 973-912-4464. *Pres*, Margaret Grambowski
Library Holdings: Bk Vols 246; Bk Titles 200
Restriction: By appointment only

S TALBOT ASSOCIATES, INC LIBRARY,* 11 Cleveland Pl, 07081. SAN 370-4211. Tel: 973-376-9570. FAX: 973-376-7617. *Pres*, Duncan Talbot; E-Mail: duncan@metalbot.com
Library Holdings: Bk Vols 280

STIRLING

P LONG HILL TOWNSHIP FREE PUBLIC LIBRARY, 91 Central Ave, 07980. SAN 310-5210. Tel: 908-647-2088. Toll Free Tel: 908-647-2098. FAX: 908-647-2098. Web Site: www.gti.net/lhtlib. *Dir*, Arline Most; E-Mail: most@main.morris.org; *Ch Servs*, Meredith McGuire; *Ch Servs*, Debbie Sievering; E-Mail: sievering@main.morris.org; *Ref Servs YA*, Robert Nelson; E-Mail: rnelson@main.morris.org; Staff 10 (MLS 4, Non-MLS 6)
Founded 1957. Pop 9,500; Circ 105,000
Jan 2000-Dec 2000 Income $373,769, State $8,000, City $341,769, Other $24,000. Mats Exp $71,183, Books $52,183, Per/Ser (Incl. Access Fees) $9,000, AV Equip $5,000, Electronic Ref Mat (Incl. Access Fees) $5,000. Sal $220,688
Library Holdings: Bk Vols 48,200; Bk Titles 47,000; Per Subs 140
Subject Interests: Cooking, Gardening, Large print, Parenting
Database Vendor: DRA, Ebsco - EbscoHost, IAC - Info Trac, ProQuest
Publications: newsletter
Mem of Morris Automated Info Network
Partic in Highlands Regional Library Cooperative; Morris Automated Information Network
Friends of the Library Group

STONE HARBOR

S WETLANDS INSTITUTE, Herbert Mills Memorial Library, 1075 Stone Harbor Blvd, 08247. SAN 372-6754. Tel: 609-368-1211. FAX: 609-368-3871. E-Mail: wetlands@cybernet.net. Web Site: www.wetlands.org. *Librn*, Dr Albert Wood; *Asst Librn*, Irene McCullough; Staff 2 (MLS 1, Non-MLS 1)
Founded 1969
Library Holdings: Bk Vols 1,000
Special Collections: Coastal Ecology
Publications: Teacher Guides
Restriction: Members only
Function: Reference services available
Friends of the Library Group

STRATFORD

P FREE PUBLIC LIBRARY OF STRATFORD,* 303 Union Ave, 08084. SAN 310-5229. Tel: 609-783-0602. FAX: 609-435-8757. *Dir*, Ruth C Roderick; *Acq, Cat*, Marguerite Arentzen
Founded 1923. Pop 9,000; Circ 30,000
1997-1998 Income $110,629, State $4,367. Mats Exp $23,188, Books $14,397, Per/Ser (Incl. Access Fees) $1,589, Micro $1,396, AV Equip $5,806. Sal $17,200
Library Holdings: Bk Vols 34,556; Per Subs 50
Automation Activity & Vendor Info: (Cataloging) Gaylord; (Circulation) Sagebrush Corporation
Partic in South Jersey Regional Library Cooperative
Friends of the Library Group

M UNIVERSITY OF MEDICINE & DENTISTRY OF NEW JERSEY, (Formerly University Of Medicine & Dentistry Of New Jersey-School Of Osteopathic Medicine), Health Science Library, Academic Ctr, One Medical Ctr Dr, 08084. SAN 320-6998. Tel: 856-566-6800. FAX: 856-566-6380. Web Site: www.umdnj.edu/librweb/stratlib. *Dir*, Jan Skica; E-Mail: skica@umdnj.edu; *Publ Servs*, Cynthia McClellan; *ILL*, Thomas Walker; *Ser*, David Kaczorowski; *ILL*, Elaine Mayweather; Staff 4 (MLS 4)
Founded 1970
Library Holdings: Bk Vols 30,000; Per Subs 615
Subject Interests: Basic scis, Clinical medicine, Health care admin, Nursing
Special Collections: History of Osteopathy
Publications: The Library File (quarterly newsletter)
Partic in Dialog Corporation

SUCCASUNNA

P ROXBURY PUBLIC LIBRARY, 103 Main St, 07876. SAN 310-5237. Tel: 973-584-2400. FAX: 973-584-5484. E-Mail: romance@main.morris.org. Web Site: www.roxburylibrary.gti.net. *Dir*, Mary Romance Whalen; *Asst Dir*, Patricia Wayne; *Tech Servs*, Susan Collins; *Ref, Tech Coordr*, Janice Perrier
Founded 1960. Pop 23,924; Circ 188,251
Library Holdings: Bk Vols 70,482; Per Subs 217
Special Collections: Children's Historical Fiction (Mary Wolfe Thompson Coll); Historical Reference (New Jersey)
Automation Activity & Vendor Info: (Circulation) DRA
Partic in Highlands Regional Library Cooperative; Morris Automated Information Network
Friends of the Library Group

SUMMIT

P FREE PUBLIC LIBRARY OF SUMMIT,* 75 Maple St, 07901-9984. SAN 310-5261. Tel: 908-273-0350. FAX: 908-273-0031. *Dir*, Glenn E Devitt; *Ch Servs*, Patricia Obst; *Ref*, Robin Carroll-Mann
Founded 1874. Pop 19,600; Circ 278,291
Library Holdings: Bk Vols 118,000
Subject Interests: Bus, Mgt
Mem of NJ Libr Network
Partic in Infolink Eastern New Jersey Regional Library Cooperative, Inc; Morris-Union Federation
Friends of the Library Group

S HOECHST CELANESE RESEARCH DIVISION, Technical Information Center,* 86 Morris Ave, 07901. SAN 310-5245. Tel: 908-522-5700. FAX: 908-522-3902.; Staff 5 (MLS 4, Non-MLS 1)
Founded 1966
Library Holdings: Bk Vols 12,000; Per Subs 300
Subject Interests: Ceramics, Chemical engineering, Chemistry, Optics, Plastics, Polymer chemistry
Restriction: By appointment only

S NETTER LIBRARY, (Formerly Novartis), 556 Morris Ave, 07901. SAN 310-1177. Tel: 908-277-5544. Circulation Tel: 908-277-5544. Reference Tel: 908-277-5547. FAX: 908-277-7999. *Mgr*, Binu Chaudhuri; Tel: 908-277-7114, E-Mail: binu.chaudhuri@pharma.novartis.com; *Assoc Dir*, Deborah Juterbock; Staff 19 (MLS 11, Non-MLS 8)
Founded 1984
Library Holdings: Bk Titles 14,500; Per Subs 987
Subject Interests: Biology, Medicine, Organic chemistry, Pharm, Toxicology
Automation Activity & Vendor Info: (OPAC) Sydney
Database Vendor: Dialog, Lexis-Nexis, OCLC - First Search, OVID Technologies
Publications: Library bulletin
Restriction: By appointment only
Function: For research purposes

S NOVARTIS PHARMACEUTICALS, Netter Library,* 566 Morris Ave, 07901. SAN 310-5253. Tel: 908-277-5000, 908-277-5544. FAX: 908-277-7999. E-Mail: lcs@ussu.ciba.com.; Staff 10 (MLS 8, Non-MLS 2)
Founded 1938
Library Holdings: Bk Vols 12,000; Bk Titles 5,000; Per Subs 900
Subject Interests: Biochemistry, Bus, Chemistry, Mgmt, Mktg, Pharm, Pharmacology, Toxicology
Publications: Current Awareness Service
Partic in Dialog Corporation; OCLC Online Computer Library Center, Inc; PALINET & Union Library Catalogue of Pennsylvania; Sci & Tech Info Network

M OVERLOOK HOSPITAL, Health Sciences Library,* 99 Beauvoir Ave, 07901-0220. SAN 370-1891. Tel: 908-522-2119. FAX: 908-522-2274. Web Site: www.infolink.org/overlooklibrary/. *Dir*, Kathleen A Moeller
Library Holdings: Bk Titles 6,000; Per Subs 510
Subject Interests: Consumer health, Medicine

SWEDESBORO

P SWEDESBORO PUBLIC LIBRARY,* 442 Kings Hwy, 08085. SAN 310-527X. Tel: 856-467-0111. FAX: 856-241-0594. *Librn*, Marge Dombrosky
Pop 2,000; Circ 12,578
Library Holdings: Bk Vols 15,000; Per Subs 44
Subject Interests: Local history
Mem of NJ Regional Libr Coop

TEANECK

C FAIRLEIGH DICKINSON UNIVERSITY, Weiner Library, 1000 River Rd, 07666-1914. SAN 351-3785. Interlibrary Loan Service Tel: 201-692-2279. FAX: 201-692-9815. *Librn*, Dr Ruth Schwartz; Tel: 201-692-2276, E-Mail: schwartz@alpha.fdu.edu; *Per*, K Stein; Tel: 201-692-2289, E-Mail: stein@mailbox.fdu.edu; *Bibliog Instr, Online Servs, Ref*, Judith Katz; Tel: 201-692-2100, E-Mail: judith@alpha.fdu.edu; *Tech Servs*, Steven Gromatzky; Tel: 201-692-2452, E-Mail: gromatzky@mailbox.fdu.edu; *Govt Doc*, R Goerner; Tel: 201-692-2290, E-Mail: goerner@alpha.fdu.edu; *Circ*, P Murray; Tel: 201-692-2278, E-Mail: murray@fdusvrtl.fdu.edu; Staff 9 (MLS 9)
Founded 1954. Enrl 5,032; Fac 365; Highest Degree: Doctorate
1998-1999 Mats Exp $1,029,655, Books $129,000, Per/Ser (Incl. Access Fees) $171,800. Sal $649,581 (Prof $376,299)
Library Holdings: Bk Vols 481,310; Bk Titles 435,673; Per Subs 1,284
Special Collections: Lincoln, Mf Coll Presidential Papers
Database Vendor: Ebsco - EbscoHost
Publications: Newsletter
Partic in BRS; OCLC Online Computer Library Center, Inc; PALINET & Union Library Catalogue of Pennsylvania
Friends of the Library Group
Departmental Libraries:
NEW COLLEGE LIBRARY, 150 Kotte Pl, Hackensack, 07601. SAN 351-384X. Tel: 201-692-2673. FAX: 201-692-2503. *In Charge*, Della H O'Malley; E-Mail: della@fdusvrtl.fdu.edu
Library Holdings: Bk Vols 11,000; Bk Titles 10,000; Per Subs 63
Friends of the Library Group

M HOLY NAME HOSPITAL LIBRARY, 718 Teaneck Rd, 07666. SAN 310-5288. Tel: 201-833-3395. FAX: 201-833-3006. Web Site: www.holyname.org. *Dir*, Jesse Caudill; E-Mail: caudill@holyname.org; Staff 2 (MLS 1, Non-MLS 1)
Founded 1925
1999-2000 Mats Exp $47,000, Books $15,000, Per/Ser (Incl. Access Fees) $30,000, AV Equip $2,000. Sal $75,000 (Prof $44,000)
Library Holdings: Bk Titles 5,000; Per Subs 152
Subject Interests: Medicine, Nursing
Database Vendor: Ebsco - EbscoHost, OVID Technologies
Partic in Bergen Passaic Health Sciences Library Consortium; Nat Libr of Med; New Jersey Library Network

S PRICE WATERHOUSE, COOPERS & UNIFI NETWORK LIBRARY, (Formerly Price Waterhouse, Coopers & Kwasha Library), Glenpointe Centre West, 500 Frank W Burr Blvd, 07666. SAN 325-7649. Tel: 201-530-2026. FAX: 201-530-2314. Web Site: www.pricewaterhousecoopers.com, www.unifi.com. *Mgr*, Mary Seaman; E-Mail: mary.seaman@unifi.com; *Asst Librn*, Cynthia Boykin
Library Holdings: Bk Titles 350; Per Subs 70
Subject Interests: Employee benefits

P TEANECK PUBLIC LIBRARY, 840 Teaneck Rd, 07666. SAN 310-5296. Tel: 201-837-4171. FAX: 201-837-0410. E-Mail: teanl@bccls.org. Web Site: www.teaneck.org. *Dir*, Michael McCue; *Ref*, Lucille Bertram; *Circ*, Cathe Quirke; *Tech Servs*, Carol Anderson; *Ch Servs*, Yvonne Van Lith; Staff 26 (MLS 7, Non-MLS 19)
Founded 1922. Pop 38,000; Circ 435,000
Jan 1999-Dec 1999 Income $1,799,000, State $44,000, City $1,705,000, Other $50,000. Mats Exp $274,200, Books $248,000, Per/Ser (Incl. Access Fees) $19,000, Micro $3,200, Electronic Ref Mat (Incl. Access Fees) $4,000. Sal $1,105,000 (Prof $424,000)
Library Holdings: Bk Vols 129,500; Per Subs 395
Subject Interests: Black studies, Judaica
Automation Activity & Vendor Info: (Cataloging) DRA; (Circulation) DRA; (OPAC) DRA
Partic in Bergen County Cooperative Library System
Friends of the Library Group

TENAFLY

SR JEWISH COMMUNITY CENTER ON THE PALISADES, Judaica Library, 411 E Clinton Ave, 07670. SAN 310-1452. Tel: 201-569-7900, Ext 234. FAX: 201-569-7448. *Dir*, Debra Turitz; *Librn*, Freida Harris
Library Holdings: Bk Vols 3,000; Per Subs 10
Restriction: Members only

P TENAFLY PUBLIC LIBRARY, 100 River Edge Rd, 07670-2087. SAN 310-5318. Tel: 201-568-8680. FAX: 201-568-5475. E-Mail: tenfl@bccls.org. Web Site: www.bccls.org. *Dir*, Stephen R Wechtler; E-Mail: wechtler@bccls.org; *Asst Dir, ILL*, Soon Juhng; *Acq, Ad Servs, Tech Servs*, Etelka Halasz; *Ch Servs*, Latricia Batchelor; *Ref*, Agnes Kolben; Staff 4 (MLS 4)
Founded 1920. Pop 13,500; Circ 127,000
Jan 1999-Dec 1999 Income $687,305, State $14,305, City $640,000, Other $33,000. Mats Exp $124,753, Books $115,253, Per/Ser (Incl. Access Fees) $8,000, Electronic Ref Mat (Incl. Access Fees) $1,500. Sal $426,000 (Prof $196,000)
Library Holdings: Bk Vols 72,186; Bk Vols 66,000; Per Subs 186
Special Collections: East Asian Culture; Gardening; Local History Coll, bks, photos, postcards, two hist local newsp on microfilm; Mitchell Young Adult Fiction Coll; Music Coll, compact discs, sheet music (librettos)
Automation Activity & Vendor Info: (Circulation) DRA; (OPAC) DRA
Mem of Bergen County Co-op Libr Syst; Highlands Regional Libr Coop
Friends of the Library Group

TETERBORO

S AVIATION HALL OF FAME & MUSEUM LIBRARY OF NEW JERSEY, Teterboro Airport, 400 Fred Wehran Dr, 07608. SAN 375-7285. Tel: 201-288-6345. FAX: 201-288-5666. E-Mail: info@njahof.org. Web Site: www.njahof.org. *Exec Dir*, Pat Reilly
Library Holdings: Bk Titles 3,000

S HONEYWELL DEFENSE & AVIONICS SYSTEMS, (ELTET), (Formerly Allied-Signal Aerospace), Engineering Library, Guidance & Control Systems, 699 Rte 46, 07608-1171. SAN 351-3874. Tel: 201-393-3190. FAX: 201-393-6776. Web Site: www.telb.allied.com/ds/resource/lib. *Librn*, Nicholas Patton; E-Mail: pattonn@alliedsignal.com; Staff 1 (MLS 1)
Founded 1940
Library Holdings: Bk Vols 6,000; Bk Titles 11,000; Per Subs 220
Subject Interests: Aeronautics, Computer science, Electronics, Mathematics, Physics
Special Collections: Bendix (Teterboro) Historical Collection; Government Reports (DOD NASA); Military Standards & Specifications
Automation Activity & Vendor Info: (Cataloging) Inmagic, Inc.; (Circulation) Inmagic, Inc.
Partic in Dialog Corporation

THOROFARE

P WEST DEPTFORD PUBLIC LIBRARY,* 420 Crown Point Rd, 08086-9598. SAN 310-5326. Tel: 856-845-5593. FAX: 856-848-3689. Web Site: www.westdeptford.lib.nj.us. *Dir*, Christine Keresztury; E-Mail: ckeresztury@westdeptford.lib.nj.us; *Ch Servs*, Marie Downes; *Tech Servs*, Geraldine Schwebel; *Ref*, Cheryl Rheiner; *Circ*, Florence Dubosque; *YA Servs*, Carol Murphy; Staff 32 (MLS 4, Non-MLS 28)
Founded 1966. Pop 19,700; Circ 130,000
Jan 1997-Dec 1998 Income $645,431, State $24,731, City $584,000, Locally Generated Income $9,000, Other $24,200. Mats Exp $54,500, Books $28,000, Per/Ser (Incl. Access Fees) $16,500, AV Equip $7,000. Sal $370,000 (Prof $155,000)
Library Holdings: Bk Titles 65,000; Per Subs 175
Subject Interests: Environ, Health, Nutrition
Special Collections: S Jersey Environ Info Ctr; UN Environ Prog
Automation Activity & Vendor Info: (Circulation) epixtech, inc.
Publications: Newsletters; Patron Brochures
Mem of CBG Video Circuit
Partic in South Jersey Regional Library Cooperative
Special Services for the Deaf - Staff with knowledge of sign language
Notary Public - Head of Reference, South Jersey Environmental Information Center; special services for the disabled
Friends of the Library Group

TINTON FALLS

P TINTON FALLS PUBLIC LIBRARY, 664 Tinton Ave, 07724. SAN 310-5342. Tel: 732-542-3110. FAX: 732-542-6755. E-Mail: tintonfa@shore.co.monmouth.nj.us. *Pres*, Linda Cicalese; Staff 5 (Non-MLS 5)
Founded 1959. Pop 16,000; Circ 65,000
Jan 1999-Dec 1999 Income $65,802, City $55,800, Locally Generated Income $10,002. Mats Exp $11,222, Books $7,300, Per/Ser (Incl. Access Fees) $802, AV Equip $1,860, Electronic Ref Mat (Incl. Access Fees) $1,260. Sal $44,812
Library Holdings: Bk Vols 29,850; Per Subs 100
Mem of Monmouth County Library
Four preschool programs for ages 2-5
Friends of the Library Group

TITUSVILLE

S JANSSEN RESEARCH FOUNDATION, Research Information Services,* 1125 Trenton-Harbourton Rd, CN 500, 08560-0500. SAN 375-7307. Tel: 609-730-3099. FAX: 609-730-3134. *Dir*, Dona Haura
Library Holdings: Bk Vols 4,000; Bk Titles 300; Per Subs 250

TOMS RIVER

M COMMUNITY MEDICAL CENTER, Medical Library, 99 Hwy 37 W, 08755. SAN 375-6912. Tel: 732-557-8117. FAX: 732-557-8354. *Dir*, Reina Reisler; E-Mail: rreisler@sbhcs.com
Subject Interests: Medicine

J OCEAN COUNTY COLLEGE LIBRARY, College Dr, PO Box 2001, 08754-2001. SAN 310-5350. Tel: 732-255-0392. FAX: 732-255-0421. Web Site: www.lib.ocean.cc.nj.us. *Dean of Libr*, Mary K Dobbs; E-Mail:

mdobbs@ocean.cc.nj.us; *Ref*, Torris Andersen; *Ref*, Yvonne T Huacuja; *Ref*, Tracey Hershey; Staff 14 (MLS 5, Non-MLS 9)
Founded 1966. Enrl 7,458; Fac 227
Jul 1999-Jun 2000 Income $742,759. Mats Exp $113,658, Books $70,226, Per/Ser (Incl. Access Fees) $31,523, Electronic Ref Mat (Incl. Access Fees) $11,909. Sal $398,591 (Prof $287,099)
Library Holdings: Bk Vols 80,783; Per Subs 491
Subject Interests: Computer science, Fine arts, Humanities, Sci, Soc scis
Automation Activity & Vendor Info: (Acquisitions) DRA; (Cataloging) DRA; (Circulation) DRA; (Course Reserve) DRA; (OPAC) DRA
Publications: CJRLC; OCLC Online Computer Libr Ctr, Inc; Palinet & Union Libr Catalogue of Pa
Special Services for the Blind - Adapted computers & special software with speech output to assist learning disabled, mentally retarded & uneducated

S OCEAN COUNTY HISTORICAL SOCIETY, Richard Lee Strickler Research Center, PO Box 2191, 08754-2191. SAN 371-6252. Tel: 732-341-1880. FAX: 732-341-4372. Web Site: www.hawkmail.monmouth.edu'~ochs. *Librn*, Richard L Strickler; *Asst Librn*, Nancy Klebold. Subject Specialists: *Genealogy*, Richard L Strickler; *New Jersey*, Richard L Strickler
Founded 1980
Library Holdings: Bk Vols 16,000; Bk Titles 9,000
Subject Interests: Genealogy, History
Restriction: Non-circulating

P OCEAN COUNTY LIBRARY, 101 Washington St, 08753. SAN 351-3998. Tel: 732-349-6200. FAX: 732-341-6698. Reference FAX: 732-349-0478. Web Site: www.oceancountylibrary.org. *Dir*, Elaine McConnell; Tel: 732-349-6200, Ext 813, E-Mail: mcconnell_e@oceancounty.lib.nj.us; *Asst Dir*, James Wudzki; Tel: 732-349-6200, Ext 857, E-Mail: wudzki_j@oceancounty.lib.nj.us; *Publ Servs*, Marvelene Beach; Tel: 732-349-6200, Ext 883, E-Mail: beach_m@oceancounty.lib.nj.us; *Publ Servs*, Mary Malagiere; Tel: 732-349-6200, Ext 815, E-Mail: malagiere_m@oceancounty.lib.nj.us; *Spec Coll*, Elizabeth Richman-Scott; *Tech Coordr*, Christine E Matteo; Staff 325 (MLS 86, Non-MLS 239)
Founded 1925. Pop 478,682; Circ 3,859,812
Jan 2000-Dec 2000 Income (Main Library and Branch Library) $17,700,534, State $418,184, County $16,682,350, Locally Generated Income $600,000. Mats Exp $2,670,000, Books $2,466,000, Per/Ser (Incl. Access Fees) $204,000. Sal $9,819,961
Library Holdings: Bk Vols 997,741; Bk Titles 249,313; Per Subs 2,149
Special Collections: Local History (New Jersey Coll)
Automation Activity & Vendor Info: (Acquisitions) epixtech, inc.; (Cataloging) epixtech, inc.; (Circulation) epixtech, inc.; (Serials) epixtech, inc.
Database Vendor: OCLC - First Search
Publications: Clubs & Organizations of Ocean County; How to Start a Small Business in Ocean County; Ocean County Resource Directory; various bibliographies
Partic in Central Jersey Regional Library Cooperative; New Jersey Library Network; OCLC Online Computer Library Center, Inc; PALINET & Union Library Catalogue of Pennsylvania
Special Services for the Deaf - Captioned media; Staff with knowledge of sign language; TTY machine
Special Services for the Blind - ADA terminals for visually impaired
Open Mon-Thurs 9-9, Fri & Sat 9-5, Sun 1-5
Friends of the Library Group
Branches: 19
BARNEGAT BRANCH, 112 Burr St, Barnegat, 08005. SAN 351-4005. Tel: 609-698-3331. FAX: 609-698-9592. *Librn*, Lydia Lloyd
Library Holdings: Bk Vols 30,393
Open Mon & Thurs-Sat 10-5, Tues & Wed 10-9
Friends of the Library Group
BAY HEAD READING CENTER, 136 Meadow Ave, Bay Head, 08742-5080. SAN 371-4713. Tel: 732-892-0662.
Library Holdings: Bk Vols 3,802
Open Mon & Wed 1-5, Thurs 1-5 & 7-9, Sat 10-1
BEACHWOOD BRANCH, 126 Beachwood Blvd, Beachwood, 08722-2810. SAN 351-4021. Tel: 732-244-4573. FAX: 732-736-1025. *Librn*, Kathy Erikson
Library Holdings: Bk Vols 9,092
Open Mon 10-5 & 7-9, Tues & Fri 1-5, Wed & Thurs 10-5, Sat 10-1
Friends of the Library Group
BERKELEY, 30 Station Rd, Bayville, 08721-2198. SAN 351-403X. Tel: 732-269-2144. FAX: 732-237-2955. *Librn*, Suzanne Scro
Library Holdings: Bk Vols 42,958
Open Mon-Thurs 10-9, Fri & Sat 10-5
Friends of the Library Group
BRICK BRANCH, 301 Chambers Bridge Rd, Brick, 08723-2803. SAN 351-4056. Tel: 732-477-4513. FAX: 732-920-9314. *Librn*, Eleanor Clarke
Library Holdings: Bk Vols 98,986
Open Mon-Thurs 9-9, Fri & Sat 9-5
Friends of the Library Group
ISLAND HEIGHTS BRANCH, Summit & Central Aves, Island Heights, 08732. SAN 351-4080. Tel: 732-270-6266. FAX: 732-270-0308. *Librn*, Pat Hockenjos
Library Holdings: Bk Vols 12,130
Open Mon 1-5 & 7-9, Tues-Fri 10-12 & 1-5, Sat 10-1
Friends of the Library Group
JACKSON TOWNSHIP, Don Connor Blvd, Jackson, 08527-3601. SAN 351-4145. Tel: 732-928-4400. FAX: 732-833-0615. *Librn*, Paul Zubritzky
Library Holdings: Bk Vols 47,250
Open Mon-Thurs 10-9, Fri & Sat 10-5
Friends of the Library Group
LACEY TOWNSHIP, 10 Lacey Rd, Forked River, 08731-3626. SAN 351-4110. Tel: 609-693-8566. FAX: 609-971-8973. *Librn*, Kathlyn Lanzim
Library Holdings: Bk Vols 52,564
Open Mon-Thurs 10-9, Fri & Sat 10-5
Friends of the Library Group
LAKEWOOD BRANCH, 301 Lexington Ave, Lakewood, 08701. SAN 310-236X. Tel: 732-363-1435. FAX: 732-363-1438. *Mgr*, Valerie Bell; *Ref*, Linda Adams; *Ch Servs*, Lucinda Heinlein
Founded 1872
Library Holdings: Bk Vols 113,392; Per Subs 372
Mem of NJ Regional Libr Coop
Friends of the Library Group
LITTLE EGG HARBOR BRANCH, 290 Mathistown Rd, Little Egg Harbor, 08087. SAN 376-8317. Tel: 609-294-1197. FAX: 609-294-1302.
Library Holdings: Bk Vols 30,326
Open Mon, Wed, Fri & Sat 10-5, Tues & Thurs 10-9
Friends of the Library Group
LONG BEACH ISLAND, 217 S Central Ave, Surf City, 08008-4800. SAN 351-417X. Tel: 609-494-2480. FAX: 609-494-7850. *Librn*, Elise Weber
Library Holdings: Bk Vols 23,088
Open Mon & Wed 10-9, Tues & Thurs-Sat 10-5
Friends of the Library Group
MANCHESTER TOWNSHIP, 21 Colonial Dr, Lakehurst, 08733-3801. SAN 370-4475. Tel: 732-657-7600. FAX: 732-323-9246. *Librn*, Shermon Howard
Library Holdings: Bk Vols 57,553
Open Mon-Thurs 9-9, Fri & Sat 9-5
Friends of the Library Group
PLUMSTED, 10 Evergreen Rd, New Egypt, 08533. SAN 351-420X. Tel: 609-758-7888. FAX: 609-758-6997. *Librn*, Barbara Rothlein
Library Holdings: Bk Vols 14,091
Open Mon & Thurs 10-5 & 7-9, Tues & Fri 10-5, Wed 1-5, Sat 10-1
Friends of the Library Group
POINT PLEASANT BEACH BRANCH, 710 McLean Ave, Point Pleasant Beach, 08742-2522. SAN 370-4483. Tel: 732-892-4575. FAX: 732-701-1941. *Librn*, Terry Alberts
Library Holdings: Bk Vols 20,573
Open Mon, Wed & Thurs 10-5, Tues 1-9, Fri 1-5, Sat 10-1
Friends of the Library Group
POINT PLEASANT BRANCH, 834 Beaver Dam Rd, Point Pleasant, 08742-3853. Tel: 732-295-1555. FAX: 732-714-1578. *Librn*, Barbara Kaden
Library Holdings: Bk Vols 42,522
Open Mon, Wed & Thurs 10-9, Tues, Fri & Sat 10-5
Friends of the Library Group
STAFFORD, 129 N Main St, Manahawkin, 08050-2933. SAN 351-4250. Tel: 609-597-3381. FAX: 609-978-0770. *Librn*, Sharon Osborn
Library Holdings: Bk Vols 34,007
Open Mon & Thurs 10-9, Tues, Wed, Fri & Sat 10-5
Friends of the Library Group
TUCKERTON BRANCH, 380 Bay Ave, Tuckerton, 08087-2557. SAN 351-4269. Tel: 609-296-1470. FAX: 609-296-6487. *Librn*, Rita Oakes
Library Holdings: Bk Vols 19,364
Open Mon & Wed 1-5 & 7-9, Tues & Thurs 10-5, Fri 1-5, Sat 10-1
Friends of the Library Group
UPPER SHORES, 112 Jersey City Ave, Lavallette, 08735. SAN 376-8325. Tel: 732-793-3996. FAX: 732-793-4942. Web Site: www.oceancounty.lib.nj.us. *Librn*, Gail Bourque
Library Holdings: Bk Vols 22,098
Open Mon & Thurs 10-5, Tues & Wed 1-9, Fri 1-5, Sat 10-1
Friends of the Library Group
WARETOWN BRANCH, 112 Main St, Waretown, 08758-9252. SAN 351-4277. Tel: 609-693-5133. FAX: 609-242-8784.
Library Holdings: Bk Vols 11,037
Open Mon & Wed 1-5 & 7-9, Tues & Thurs 10-5, Fri 1-5, Sat 10-1
Friends of the Library Group
Bookmobiles: 1

L OCEAN VICINAGE LAW LIBRARY,* Ocean County Justice Complex, 120 Hooper Ave, 08753. SAN 325-9110. Tel: 732-506-5026. *Librn*, Barbara J Woods
Library Holdings: Bk Vols 13,500
Mem of Ocean County Libr Syst

TOTOWA

P DWIGHT D EISENHOWER PUBLIC LIBRARY,* 537 Totowa Rd, 07512-1699. SAN 310-5377. Tel: 973-790-3265. FAX: 973-790-0306. *Dir*, Joan A Krautheim; *Asst Librn*, Anne Marie Shapiola
Founded 1957. Pop 11,697; Circ 31,629
Library Holdings: Bk Vols 37,373; Bk Titles 34,847; Per Subs 130

Subject Interests: Literature
Special Collections: Library of America (60 vol set)
Mem of Wayne Area Libr Syst - Bergen-Passaic Region II
Special Services for the Deaf - Books on deafness & sign language; Staff with knowledge of sign language
Friends of the Library Group

TRENTON

M CAPITAL HEALTH SYSTEM AT FULD MEDICAL CENTER, Medical Library, 750 Brunswick Ave, 08638. SAN 310-5407. Tel: 609-394-6065. FAX: 609-278-1882. Web Site: www.members.tripod.com/~chs_library/. *Librn*, Theresa Cuddy; Staff 2 (MLS 1, Non-MLS 1)
Library Holdings: Bk Titles 3,500; Per Subs 250
Subject Interests: Allied health, Medicine, Nursing
Special Collections: Hist of Hospital & Nursing School
Database Vendor: OVID Technologies
Restriction: Open to student, faculty & staff, Public use on premises
Partic in Dialog Corporation; Docline; Nat Libr of Med

M CAPITAL HEALTH SYSTEM AT MERCER, Health Sciences Library, 446 Bellevue Ave, 08607. SAN 310-5423. Tel: 609-394-4125. FAX: 609-394-4131. *Dir*, Catherine Marchok; *Librn*, Erica Moncrief; Staff 2 (MLS 2)
Founded 1947
Library Holdings: Bk Titles 4,000; Per Subs 200
Special Collections: 19th Century Medical Books
Restriction: Staff use only
Partic in BHSL; Cent Jersey Health Libr Asn; New Jersey Health Sciences Library Network
Friends of the Library Group

S CONGOLEUM CORPORATION, Technical Research Library, 861 Sloan Ave, PO Box 3127, 08619. SAN 310-5385. Tel: 609-584-3264. FAX: 609-584-3305. *Librn*, Carrie Jones
Founded 1920
Library Holdings: Bk Vols 1,000; Per Subs 38
Subject Interests: Chemistry, Coatings, Engineering, Floor coverings, Paper, Patents, Physics, Plastics, Polymer chemistry, Tech ref

S DEMAG DELAVAI TURBO MACHINERY, Technical Operations Library,* 840 Nottingham Way, 08638. SAN 310-5393. Tel: 609-890-5274. FAX: 609-890-6326. *Librn*, Barbara Lupkes
Founded 1946
Library Holdings: Bk Vols 1,700
Subject Interests: Compressers, Gears, Marine eng, Mechanical engineering, Naval archit, Pumps, Turbine

J MERCER COUNTY COMMUNITY COLLEGE LIBRARY, 1200 Old Trenton Rd, 08690. SAN 351-4471. Tel: 609-586-4800, Ext 3554. FAX: 609-588-3778. E-Mail: library@mccc.edu. *Dir*, Pamela A Price; E-Mail: pprice@mccc.edu; *Ref Serv*, Frank G Butorac; *Ref Serv*, Denise Niclas; *AV, Circ*, Josephine Schaible; *Access Serv, Bibliog Instr, Cat*, Laura Ingersoll; *Acq*, Carolyn DelMonte; *ILL*, Eugenio Lopez; Staff 7 (MLS 4, Non-MLS 3)
Founded 1947. Enrl 6,500; Fac 150; Highest Degree: Associate
Jul 1999-Jun 2000 Income $512,000. Mats Exp $127,875, Books $57,725, Per/Ser (Incl. Access Fees) $52,000, Presv $150, Micro $11,000, AV Equip $100. Sal $387,898 (Prof $224,540)
Library Holdings: Bk Titles 54,559; Per Subs 537
Subject Interests: Gen acad libr res
Special Collections: Mortuary Sci, floppy disks & videocassettes
Automation Activity & Vendor Info: (Acquisitions) epixtech, inc.; (Circulation) epixtech, inc.; (OPAC) epixtech, inc.
Database Vendor: Ebsco - EbscoHost, Lexis-Nexis, Wilson - Wilson Web
Publications: Faculty & Staff Handbook of the Library; Library Handbook; Library Resources Guides; Library Student Workers Handbook; Periodicals Directory; Title & Subject Video Catalog
Partic in Cent Jersey Regional Libr Coop; PALINET & Union Library Catalogue of Pennsylvania
Departmental Libraries:
JAMES KERNEY CAMPUS, N Broad & Academy Sts, 08690. SAN 351-4501. Tel: 609-586-4800, Ext 6679. FAX: 609-394-8167. *In Charge*, Rebecca Sar; Staff 1 (Non-MLS 1)
Founded 1975. Enrl 2,000; Fac 22; Highest Degree: Associate
Library Holdings: Bk Titles 5,601; Per Subs 63
Subject Interests: Gen acad, High sch level res
Special Collections: African Art Books; Literacy
Restriction: Open to student, faculty & staff, Public use on premises
Partic in PALINET & Union Library Catalogue of Pennsylvania

S MERCER COUNTY CORRECTION CENTER LIBRARY,* PO Box 8068, 08650-0068. SAN 375-7013. Tel: 609-989-6901. FAX: 609-583-3563.
Library Holdings: Bk Titles 7,000
Restriction: Not open to public

S NEW JERSEY DEPARTMENT OF ENVIRONMENTAL PROTECTION, Information Resource Center,* PO-409, 08625-0409. SAN 325-9323. Tel: 609-984-2249. FAX: 609-292-3298. Web Site: www.state.nj.us/dep/dsr/irc.html. *Mgr*, Maria Baratta; E-Mail: mbaratta@dep.state.nj.us; *Librn*, Dorothy Alibrando
Jul 1998-Jun 1999 Income $172,000. Mats Exp $70,200, Books $2,000, Per/Ser (Incl. Access Fees) $42,000, Other Print Mats $1,400. Sal $103,000
Library Holdings: Bk Vols 6,500; Per Subs 125
Subject Interests: Water resources
Special Collections: EPA Documents; IARC Monographs; NJ DEP Documents; WHO Environmental Health Criteria
Publications: Acquisitions List
Partic in Dialog Corporation; Nat Libr of Med; OCLC Online Computer Library Center, Inc

G NEW JERSEY DEPARTMENT OF HEALTH, Occupational-Environmental Health Information Center,* Health/Agriculture Blvd, Box 360, 08625. SAN 310-5482. Tel: 609-984-1863. FAX: 609-292-5677. Web Site: www.state.nj.us.health-eoh-odisweb-odishome.
Library Holdings: Bk Vols 600; Per Subs 12

G NEW JERSEY DEPARTMENT OF LABOR LIBRARY,* John Fitch Plaza, 5th flr, PO Box 943, 08625-0943. SAN 310-544X. Tel: 609-292-2035. FAX: 609-984-6833. *Librn*, Jannifer McAdoo; E-Mail: jmcadoo@dol.state.nj.us; *Asst Librn*, Shirley Yenner; *Librn*, Fengzhi Fan; Staff 2 (MLS 1, Non-MLS 1)
Founded 1966
Library Holdings: Bk Vols 4,500; Bk Titles 3,500; Per Subs 350
Subject Interests: Census, Disability ins, Employment, Labor law practices, Labor market info, Training, Unemployment ins, Vocational rehabilitation
Special Collections: Labor Law Reports.
Publications: Selected New Titles

G NEW JERSEY GEOLOGICAL SURVEY, Information Center,* 29 Arctic Pkwy, 08625. (Mail add: PO Box 427, 08625), SAN 374-9924. Tel: 609-292-2576. FAX: 609-633-1004. Web Site: www.state.nj.us/dep/njgs.
Library Holdings: Bk Titles 1,000

S NEW JERSEY RAILROAD & TRANSPORTATION MUSEUM LIBRARY,* c/o Friends of NJ Railroad & Transportation Museum, PO Box 8301, 08650-8301. SAN 375-6963. Tel: 908-464-9335. FAX: 908-464-9335. Web Site: www.tburgonline.com/tburgrte. *Pres*, William McKelvey; *Purchasing*, Thomas Hellyer; *Coll Develop*, Robert Hooper
Library Holdings: Bk Titles 600; Per Subs 50
Publications: New Jersey Transport Heritage
Friends of the Library Group

GL NEW JERSEY STATE DEPARTMENT OF LAW & PUBLIC SAFETY, (AGL), Attorney General's Library, Hughes Justice Complex 25 Market St, 08625. (Mail add: PO Box 115, 08625-0115), SAN 310-5490. Tel: 609-292-4958. FAX: 609-633-6555. E-Mail: lpalibr@smtp.lps.state.nj.us. *Librn*, Tamar Pritchard; *Librn*, Larry Wolford; *Mgr*, Maria Baratta; Staff 6 (MLS 3, Non-MLS 3)
Library Holdings: Bk Vols 47,000; Per Subs 300
Subject Interests: Administrative law, Criminology
Special Collections: Legal Memoranda Coll; New Jersey Legislative Material Coll
Restriction: Staff use only

G NEW JERSEY STATE LEAGUE OF MUNICIPALITIES, Bureau of Municipal Information,* 407 W State St, 08618. SAN 323-4266. Tel: 609-695-3481. FAX: 609-695-0151. *Res*, Michael Cerra
Special Collections: Ordinances

P NEW JERSEY STATE LIBRARY, 185 W State St, PO Box 520, 08625-0520. SAN 351-4773. Tel: 609-292-6200, 609-292-6230 (Law Ref), 609-292-6294 (NJ Ref). Interlibrary Loan Service Tel: 609-633-0556. Reference Tel: 609-292-6220. FAX: 609-984-7900, 984-7898. Web Site: www.njstatelib.org. *State Librn*, Norma Blake; *Adminr*, Brian Goldsmith; Tel: 609-984-6714, E-Mail: bgoldsmith@njstatelib.org; *Assoc Librn*, Colleen Daze; Tel: 609-292-6211, E-Mail: cdaze@njstatelib.org; *Info Tech*, Alan Jacobowitz; E-Mail: ajacobowitz@njstatelib.org
Founded 1796
Jul 1999-Jun 2000 Income $7,637,254, State $2,993,268, Federal $4,606,986, Locally Generated Income $37,000. Mats Exp $912,988, Books $738,936, Per/Ser (Incl. Access Fees) $105,000, Presv $1,200, Electronic Ref Mat (Incl. Access Fees) $67,852. Sal $3,902,340 (Prof $1,990,193)
Library Holdings: Bk Vols 1,959,000; Per Subs 1,460
Subject Interests: Education, Found grantsmanship, Government, Law, Libr sci
Special Collections: Jerseyana: New Jersey History, Genealogy, Political, Social & Economic Affairs; NY, Calif, partial for many states, & foundation center
Automation Activity & Vendor Info: (Acquisitions) epixtech, inc.; (Cataloging) epixtech, inc.; (Circulation) epixtech, inc.; (ILL) epixtech, inc.; (OPAC) epixtech, inc.; (Serials) epixtech, inc.
Database Vendor: epixtech, inc.
Publications: Analyses of New Jersey Public Library Statistics; Checklist of Official New Jersey Publications; Grants Bulletin; Impressions (newsletter); Library Grant Programs (catalog); New Books Lists; New Jersey Library Laws; New Jersey Public Library Statistics; Shipping List of NJ Documents; Special Bibliographies

Member Libraries: Pennsville Public Library; United States Attorney's Office Library
Partic in New Jersey Library Network
Administers New Jersey documents depository system
Friends of the Library Group
Branches: 1

P LIBRARY FOR THE BLIND & HANDICAPPED, 2300 Stuyvesant Ave, 08618. (Mail add: PO Box 501, 08625-0501), SAN 329-0131. Tel: 609-530-4000. Toll Free Tel: 800-792-8322. TDD: 877-882-5593. FAX: 609-530-6384. Web Site: www.state.nj.us/statelibrary/njlbh.htm. *Head of Libr*, Deborah Rutledge; E-Mail: njlbh@njstate.lib.org; *Ad Servs*, Christine Lisiocki; *Ch Servs*, Karen Messick; *Librn for Deaf*, Peggy Klotz; Staff 4 (MLS 3, Non-MLS 1)
Jul 1998-Jun 1999 Income $1,282,816, State $148,170, Federal $1,125,146, Locally Generated Income $9,500. Mats Exp Books $14,817. Sal $883,165 (Prof $238,146)
Library Holdings: Bk Titles 60,000; Bks on Deafness & Sign Lang 50
Special Services for the Deaf - TDD; TTY machine
Special Services for the Blind - Braille
Friends of the Library Group

S NEW JERSEY STATE MUSEUM LIBRARY,* 205 W State St, 08625. (Mail add: PO Box 530, 08625), SAN 323-5122. Tel: 609-292-6308. FAX: 609-599-4098. *Dir*, Leah P Sloshberg
Library Holdings: Bk Vols 4,000; Per Subs 12
Subject Interests: Fine arts, Natural history

S NEW JERSEY STATE PRISON LIBRARY,* PO Box 861, 08625. SAN 310-5539. Tel: 609-292-9700. FAX: 609-392-3433. *Librn*, Patricia Singleton
Founded 1900
Library Holdings: Bk Vols 2,000
Subject Interests: Fiction, Non-fiction, Philosophy, Psychology

M SAINT FRANCIS MEDICAL CENTER, Health Sciences Library,* 601 Hamilton Ave, 08629-1986. SAN 310-5504. Tel: 609-599-5068. FAX: 609-599-5773. *Dir*, Donna Barlow; Staff 1 (MLS 1)
Founded 1930
Library Holdings: Bk Vols 8,000; Per Subs 325
Subject Interests: Allied health, Health servs admin, Medicine, Nursing, Patient education
Publications: Journal Holdings List; Library Bulletin

G STATE OF NEW JERSEY - DEPARTMENT OF BANKING & INSURANCE, Roebling Building Library,* 20 W State St, PO Box 325, 08625. SAN 371-7887. Tel: 609-984-1666. FAX: 609-633-3601.
Founded 1978
1997-1998 Mats Exp Books $10,000
Library Holdings: Bk Vols 1,000; Bk Titles 300; Per Subs 150
Special Collections: New Jersey Department of Higher Education; New Jersey Law
Publications: Checklist of Publications
Mem of Regional Libr Coop 5 Cent Jersey
Partic in Dialog Corporation

S THE TIMES LIBRARY (TRENTON),* 500 Perry St, 08618. SAN 329-0832. Tel: 609-989-5454. FAX: 609-394-2819. E-Mail: news@njtimes.com. Web Site: www.nj.com/times. *Librn*, Diana Groden; *Asst Librn*, Lisa Belknap
Library Holdings: Bk Titles 100; Per Subs 18
Subject Interests: Local history, Mercer Co soc hist
Restriction: Staff use only
Mem of Regional Libr Coop Region 5

P TRENTON PUBLIC LIBRARY, 120 Academy St, 08608. SAN 351-4293. Tel: 609-392-7188. FAX: 609-396-7655. Web Site: www.trenton.lib.nj.us. *Dir*, Robert E Coumbe; *Asst Dir*, Joyce Willis; *Head, Cat*, James Kisthardt; *Ref*, Cathy Stout; *Ch Servs*, Joyce Bagnall; *Spec Coll*, Cathy Stout; *Circ*, Cecelia Mulryne; *Per*, Sharon Ward. Subject Specialists: *Business and management*, Richard Rebecca; *Labor*, Richard Rebecca; Staff 47 (MLS 16, Non-MLS 31)
Founded 1750. Pop 85,000; Circ 160,000
Jul 2000-Jun 2001 Income (Main Library and Branch Library) $2,952,463, State $115,000, City $2,758,963, Locally Generated Income $78,500. Mats Exp $327,750, Books $221,000, Per/Ser (Incl. Access Fees) $56,000, Presv $4,000, Micro $25,000, AV Equip $13,750, Other Print Mats $3,000, Manuscripts & Archives $5,000. Sal $2,054,996
Library Holdings: Bk Vols 375,000; Bk Titles 300,000; Per Subs 770
Special Collections: Art & Music, bks, CDs, prints, recs, scores; Trentoniana Coll, bks, pamphlets, photogs, docs
Automation Activity & Vendor Info: (Acquisitions) DRA; (Cataloging) DRA; (Circulation) DRA; (Course Reserve) DRA; (ILL) DRA; (Media Booking) DRA; (OPAC) DRA; (Serials) DRA
Database Vendor: DRA
Publications: Acquisitions List (monthly); Friends (newsletter); Union List of Serials
Mem of Central Jersey Regional Libr Coop
Friends of the Library Group
Branches: 4
BRIGGS, 1115 Greenwood Ave, 08609. SAN 351-4323. Tel: 609-392-7856. *Librn*, Deirdre Hindley; Staff 4 (MLS 1, Non-MLS 3)
Database Vendor: DRA
CADWALADER, 200 N Hermitage Ave, 08618. SAN 351-4358. Tel: 609-392-7886. *Librn*, Frances O'Brien; Staff 8 (MLS 1, Non-MLS 7)
Library Holdings: Bk Vols 40,000; Bk Titles 37,000; Per Subs 300; High Interest/Low Vocabulary Bk Vols 5,000
Database Vendor: DRA
Mem of Central Jersey Regional Libr Coop
Friends of the Library Group
EAST TRENTON, N Clinton Ave at Girard, 08638. SAN 351-4382. Tel: 609-392-7866. *Librn*, Pearl Blagg; Staff 4 (MLS 1, Non-MLS 3)
Database Vendor: DRA
SKELTON, S Broad St at Malone, 08611. SAN 351-4447. Tel: 609-392-7876. *Librn*, Deirdre Hindley; Staff 7 (MLS 1, Non-MLS 6)
Database Vendor: DRA

GL US COURTS LIBRARY, 402 E State St, 08608. SAN 377-3647. Tel: 609-989-2345. FAX: 609-989-0485. *Librn*, Tom Fasching
Library Holdings: Bk Vols 8,000; Bk Titles 5,000
Open Mon-Fri 8:30-4:30

TURNERSVILLE

M KENNEDY MEMORIAL HOSPITALS-UNIVERSITY MEDICAL CENTER, Paul Barsky Memorial Library Washington Township Campus, 435 Hurffville-Cross Keys Rd, 08012. SAN 326-1239. Tel: 856-582-2675. FAX: 856-582-3190. Web Site: www.kennedyheath.org. *Librn*, Elaine Mayweather; E-Mail: e.mayweather@kennedyhealth.org; Staff 1 (MLS 1)
Library Holdings: Bk Vols 300; Bk Titles 200; Per Subs 119
Partic in Basic Health Sciences Library Network; New Jersey Health Sciences Library Network; Pinelands Consortium for Health Info

UNION

S GLOBAL LEARNING, INC, Global Learning Resource Center, 1018 Stuyvesant Ave, 07083. SAN 328-4336. Tel: 908-964-1114. FAX: 908-964-6335. E-Mail: globallearning@att.net. Web Site: community.nj.com/cc/sustainableschools, www.ala.org/sustainablecommunities, www.globallearningng.org. *Exec Dir*, Jeffrey Brown
Library Holdings: Bk Vols 1,000
Special Collections: Conflict Resolution & Mediation; Sustainable Development
Publications: A Sustainable Development Curriculum Framework for World History & Cultures; Local Libraries: Global Awareness-A Librarian's Guide to Global Programming for a Sustainable Future; Making Global Connections in the Middle School; Middle School Lessons on Sustainable Agriculture & Farmland Preservation; Sustaining the Future; Where Are the Gardens in the Garden State?

S HAMMOND WORLD ATLAS CORP, Editorial Division Library, 95 Progress St, 07083. SAN 310-2718. Tel: 908-206-1300. FAX: 908-206-1102. Web Site: www.hammondmap.com. *Info Res*, Harry Morin; E-Mail: harry@hammondmap.com
Library Holdings: Bk Vols 50,000
Subject Interests: Archaeology, Atlases, Demography, Earth science, Gen statistics, Geography, Geology, History, Maps, Natural history, Oceanography
Special Collections: International Census Reports
Restriction: Not open to public

C KEAN UNIVERSITY, Nancy Thompson Library, 1000 Morris Ave, 07083. SAN 310-558X. Tel: 908-527-2017. FAX: 908-527-2365. Web Site: www.library.kean.edu. *Dir*, Barbara Simpson; *Assoc Dir*, Mark Ferrara; *Assoc Dir*, Hui-Min Kuo; *Assoc Dir, Tech Servs*, Eleanor McKnight; *Librn*, Craig Anderson; *Librn*, Kimberly Fraone; *Access Serv, Librn*, Shirley Horbatt; *Librn*, Gene Rhie; *Librn*, Kenneth Riccardi; *Librn*, Kim Frazne; *Librn*, Raymon Davis; *Cat*, Sue Sun; Staff 11 (MLS 11)
Founded 1914. Enrl 13,000; Fac 550; Highest Degree: Master
2000-2001 Mats Exp $591,000
Library Holdings: Bk Vols 270,000; Bk Titles 265,000; Per Subs 1,365
Subject Interests: Allied health, Bus, Computer science, Econ, Education, English, Occupational therapy
Special Collections: History (New Jerseyiana), bks, pamphlets; Political Science (Dwyer Papers)
Automation Activity & Vendor Info: (Acquisitions) Endeavor; (Cataloging) Endeavor; (Circulation) Endeavor; (Course Reserve) Endeavor; (OPAC) Endeavor; (Serials) Endeavor
Publications: Library User's Guide
Partic in Consortium of E Jersey; Dialog Corporation; New Jersey Academic Library Network; OCLC Online Computer Library Center, Inc; PALINET & Union Library Catalogue of Pennsylvania; SDC Info Servs

M UNION HOSPITAL, Schering-Plough Library of Science & Medicine,* 1000 Galloping Hill Rd, 07083. SAN 322-7235. Tel: 908-851-7234. FAX: 908-851-5850.

1997-1998 Mats Exp $45,000, Presv $2,500
Library Holdings: Bk Titles 2,200; Per Subs 150
Special Collections: Osteopathic Literature - Thanatology Library
Partic in BSHL; Cosmopolitan Biomedical Library Consortium; National Network Of Libraries Of Medicine - South Central Region; New Jersey Library Network

P UNION TOWNSHIP PUBLIC LIBRARY, 1980 Morris Ave, 07083-3578. SAN 351-5079. Tel: 908-851-5450. Reference Tel: 908-851-5452. FAX: 908-851-4671. E-Mail: unionpl@infolink.org, unionpl@upl.njpublib.org. Web Site: www.njpublib.org/union. *Dir*, Janet W Wheeler; Tel: 908-851-5453, E-Mail: jwheeler@upl.njpublib.org; Staff 31 (MLS 9, Non-MLS 22)
Founded 1927. Pop 50,000; Circ 203,725
Jan 2000-Dec 2000 Income (Main Library and Branch Library) $1,630,032, State $52,000, City $1,548,032, Locally Generated Income $30,000. Mats Exp $214,350, Books $117,000, Per/Ser (Incl. Access Fees) $11,000, Presv $350, Micro $11,000, AV Equip $40,000, Electronic Ref Mat (Incl. Access Fees) $35,000. Sal $767,000
Library Holdings: Bk Vols 136,429; Bk Titles 109,818; Per Subs 211
Database Vendor: DRA
Partic in Infolink; NJ State Libr Network
Friends of the Library Group
Branches: 1
VAUX HALL BRANCH, Russell St & Hilton Ave, Vaux Hall, 07088. SAN 351-5133. Tel: 908-851-5451. FAX: 908-810-7072. E-Mail: vauxhall@upl.njpublib.org.
Library Holdings: Bk Vols 24,000

UNION BEACH

S INTERNATIONAL FLAVORS & FRAGRANCES, INC, IFF Technical Information Center, 1515 Hwy 36, 07735. SAN 310-5598. Tel: 732-335-2435. FAX: 732-335-2657. *Librn*, Bernard J Mayers; *Info Specialist*, Susan Joseph; Tel: 732-335-2687, E-Mail: susan.joseph@iff.com; *Info Specialist*, Shin-Shyong Tseng; Tel: 732-335-2521, E-Mail: shinshyong.tseng@iff.com. Subject Specialists: *Business*, Susan Joseph; *Chemistry*, Shin-Shyong Tseng; *Patents*, Susan Joseph; *Trademarks*, Susan Joseph; Staff 3 (MLS 1, Non-MLS 2)
Founded 1967
Jan 2000-Dec 2000 Mats Exp $143,000, Books $35,000, Per/Ser (Incl. Access Fees) $83,000, Micro $20,000, Electronic Ref Mat (Incl. Access Fees) $5,000
Library Holdings: Bk Vols 11,000; Bk Titles 2,200; Per Subs 200
Subject Interests: Essential oils, Flavor, Food tech, Fragrance chem, Microbiology, Organic chemistry, Sensory sci, Synthetic perfumes, Toxicology
Special Collections: Complete Sets of American Chemical Society Journal, Biological Abstracts, Chemical Abstracts & US Chemical Patents (1966 to present), micro
Database Vendor: Dialog
Partic in Central Jersey Regional Library Cooperative

P UNION BEACH MEMORIAL LIBRARY,* 810 Union Ave, 07735. SAN 310-5601. Tel: 732-264-3792. *Librn*, Audrey Harvey
Library Holdings: Bk Titles 31,000; Per Subs 38
Mem of Monmouth County Library

UNION CITY

P UNION CITY FREE PUBLIC LIBRARY, 324 43rd St, 07087-5008. SAN 351-5168. Tel: 201-866-7500. FAX: 201-866-0962. Web Site: www.uclibrary.org. *Dir*, William Otis Breedlove, II; E-Mail: wbreedlove@union-city.k12.nj.us; *Ch Servs*, Rudolfo Robles; Staff 7 (MLS 1, Non-MLS 6)
Founded 1905. Pop 58,212
Jan 1999-Dec 1999 Income (Main Library and Branch Library) $608,821, City $481,098, Locally Generated Income $100,000, Other $364. Mats Exp $23,564, Books $12,487, Per/Ser (Incl. Access Fees) $8,355, Micro $2,200, AV Equip $522. Sal $366,635 (Prof $223,981)
Library Holdings: Bk Vols 84,550; Bk Titles 63,166; Per Subs 117
Subject Interests: Am lit, Bus, English literature, Film, Mgt, Spanish lang
Automation Activity & Vendor Info: (Cataloging) Follett; (Circulation) Follett; (OPAC) Follett
Database Vendor: Ebsco - EbscoHost
Partic in Infolink
Friends of the Library Group
Branches: 1
FIFTEENTH STREET, 420 15th St, 07087-4320. SAN 351-5192. Tel: 201-866-7503. FAX: 201-866-0962. Web Site: www.uclibrary.org. *Dir*, William O Breedlove, II; Tel: 201-866-7500, Fax: 201-866-7503, E-Mail: wbreedlove@union-city.k12.nj.us; *Branch Mgr*, Nolan Ledet, Jr; E-Mail: ledet@union-city.k12.nj.us; Staff 5 (MLS 1, Non-MLS 4)
Pop 58,212
Library Holdings: Bk Vols 65,250
Automation Activity & Vendor Info: (Circulation) Follett; (OPAC) Follett
Database Vendor: Ebsco - EbscoHost
Partic in Infolink

UPPER MONTCLAIR

C MONTCLAIR STATE UNIVERSITY, Harry A Sprague Library,* Normal Ave, 07043-1699. SAN 310-5628. Tel: 973-655-4301. FAX: 973-655-7780. Web Site: www.montclair.edu/pages/library/library.html. *Dean*, Dr Judith Lin Hunt; E-Mail: huntjl@mail.montclair.edu; *Assoc Dir, Publ Servs*, Luis Rodriguez; *Acq, Coll Develop*, Norman Stock; *Cat*, Kathleen Hughes; *Doc*, Joyce Schaffer; *ILL*, Kevin Prendergast; *Media Spec*, Karen Venturella; *Per*, Eduardo Gil; *Ref*, Patricia Sanders; Staff 16 (MLS 16)
Founded 1908. Enrl 12,686; Fac 433; Highest Degree: Master
Library Holdings: Bk Vols 428,784; Per Subs 2,593
Subject Interests: Bus, Communications, Modern poetry, Music, Philosophy, Speech, Teacher educ
Database Vendor: DRA
Partic in Dialog Corporation; New Jersey Academic Library Network; OCLC Online Computer Library Center, Inc; PALINET & Union Library Catalogue of Pennsylvania

R UNION CONGREGATIONAL CHURCH, Schneidewind Library, 176 Cooper Ave, 07043. SAN 310-5636. Tel: 973-744-7424. FAX: 973-744-1364. E-Mail: infoucc@unioncong.org. Web Site: www.unioncong.org. *Librn*, Chandler Grannis
Founded 1958
Library Holdings: Bk Vols 3,000
Subject Interests: Art, Biblical hist, Christian educ, Current affairs, Ecology, Mental health, Philosophy, Relig hist, Relig symbolism, Soc ethics, Theology

UPPER SADDLE RIVER

P UPPER SADDLE RIVER PUBLIC LIBRARY, 245 Lake St, 07458. SAN 310-5644. Tel: 201-327-2583. FAX: 201-327-3966. E-Mail: usdri@bccls.org. Web Site: www.uppersaddleriver.org. *Dir*, Barbara Newmark-Kruger
Founded 1960. Pop 7,500; Circ 107,000
1998-1999 Income $499,000, State $6,880, City $422,000. Mats Exp $44,000, Books $10,000, Per/Ser (Incl. Access Fees) $14,000. Sal $300,000
Library Holdings: Bk Titles 60,000; Per Subs 175
Automation Activity & Vendor Info: (Circulation) DRA
Publications: Business & Residents Local Directory
Partic in Bergen County Cooperative Library System
Friends of the Library Group

VERONA

P FREE PUBLIC LIBRARY OF VERONA, 17 Gould St, 07044-1928. SAN 310-5679. Tel: 973-857-4848. FAX: 973-857-4851. E-Mail: veronalibrary@veronaonline.com. Web Site: www.veronaonline.com/vpl. *Dir*, James A Thomas; *Ch Servs*, Rebecca Burkhart; *Tech Servs*, William Trafton; *Ref*, Kathleen Ligon
Founded 1912. Pop 13,552; Circ 91,145
Library Holdings: Bk Vols 60,000; Bk Titles 55,000; Per Subs 175
Automation Activity & Vendor Info: (Cataloging) Gaylord; (Circulation) Gaylord; (OPAC) Gaylord
Library operates cable access TV station
Friends of the Library Group

VINCENTOWN

P SALLY STRETCH KEEN MEMORIAL LIBRARY,* 94 Main St, 08088. SAN 310-5687. Tel: 609-859-3598. FAX: 609-859-4029. *Dir*, Teresa Gower
Founded 1923. Pop 10,000
1997-1998 Income $62,000. Mats Exp $5,151, Books $3,242, Per/Ser (Incl. Access Fees) $1,412. Sal $39,745
Library Holdings: Bk Vols 38,000; Per Subs 78
Subject Interests: Civil War
Mem of Burlington County Library
Partic in South Jersey Regional Library Cooperative

VINELAND

R BETH ISRAEL SYNAGOGUE, Beth Israel Community Library, 1015 E Park Ave, 08360. SAN 310-5695. Tel: 609-691-0852. FAX: 609-692-1957. *Dir*, Ruth Greenblatt; *Cat*, Phyllis Zislin; *Circ*, Helen Wolf; *Tech Servs*, Shirley K Paull
Founded 1926
Aug 1999-Jul 2000 Income $9,674. Mats Exp $4,200, Books $2,300, Per/Ser (Incl. Access Fees) $350, AV Equip $500. Sal $7,200
Library Holdings: Bk Titles 6,788; Per Subs 25

Subject Interests: Judaica
Special Collections: Hitler Period (Holocaust Literature)
Publications: Column in Beth Israel Scroll - 10 year
Friends of the Library Group

J CUMBERLAND COUNTY COLLEGE LIBRARY, College Dr, 08360. SAN 310-5709. Tel: 856-691-8600, Ext 261. FAX: 856-691-1969. E-Mail: paschmid@cccnj.net. Web Site: www.cccnj.net. *Head Librn*, Patti Schmid; *Librn*, Paul Krivonak; *Librn*, James Luther; Staff 3 (MLS 3)
Founded 1966. Enrl 2,433; Fac 47
Library Holdings: Bk Vols 37,000; Bk Titles 30,520; Per Subs 93
Subject Interests: Holistic health, Law, Mythology, Nursing
Special Collections: Jerseyanna
Automation Activity & Vendor Info: (Cataloging) DRA; (Circulation) DRA; (OPAC) DRA
Database Vendor: Ebsco - EbscoHost, ProQuest, Wilson - Wilson Web
Publications: Student Handbook
Partic in OCLC Online Computer Library Center, Inc

M VINELAND DEVELOPMENTAL CENTER HOSPITAL LIBRARY,* 1676 E Landis Ave, 08360. SAN 376-060X. Tel: 609-696-6585.
Library Holdings: Bk Titles 750; Per Subs 36
Partic in South Jersey Regional Library Cooperative

P VINELAND FREE PUBLIC LIBRARY, 1058 E Landis Ave, 08360. SAN 310-5717. Tel: 856-794-4244. FAX: 856-691-0366. Web Site: www.vineland.lib.nj.us. *Dir*, Jeannie Robbana; *Ch Servs*, Helen Cowan; *Ref*, Holly Rogerson; Tel: 856-794-4244, Ext 4737, E-Mail: hrogerson@vineland.lib.nj.us
Founded 1901. Pop 54,780; Circ 215,537
Library Holdings: Bk Vols 105,600; Bk Titles 102,131; Per Subs 110
Mem of Cumberland County Library
Partic in South Jersey Regional Library Cooperative
Friends of the Library Group

S VINELAND HISTORICAL & ANTIQUARIAN SOCIETY LIBRARY,* 108 S Seventh St, PO Box 35, 08362. SAN 325-8998. Tel: 856-691-1111. FAX: 856-691-1111. *Pres*, Barbara Sheftall
Library Holdings: Bk Vols 8,000; Per Subs 200
Subject Interests: Genealogy, History
Special Collections: Autographs 1750-1900
Friends of the Library Group

VOORHEES

P CAMDEN COUNTY LIBRARY SYSTEM, 203 Laurel Rd, 08043. SAN 351-5222. Tel: 856-772-1636. Reference Tel: 856-772-1636, Ext 3311. FAX: 856-772-6105, 772-6128. E-Mail: ref@camden.lib.nj.us. Web Site: www.camden.lib.nj.us. *Dir*, Claudia B Sumler; *Asst Dir*, Karen Avenick; *Chief Librn*, Robert Flanagan; *Media Spec*, Barbara Capoferri; *Ref*, Peter Bromberg; *ILL*, Stefanie Corda; E-Mail: ill@camden.lib.nj.us; *Tech Servs*, Lisa Derfler; *Automation Syst Coordr*, Janice Masvd; Staff 36 (MLS 31, Non-MLS 5)
Founded 1922. Pop 250,000; Circ 1,068,665
1999-2000 Income $5,786,376, State $238,461, County $4,387,804, Locally Generated Income $152,985, Other $1,007,126. Mats Exp $729,000, Books $333,153, Per/Ser (Incl. Access Fees) $80,710, AV Equip $48,800, Electronic Ref Mat (Incl. Access Fees) $34,000. Sal $3,620,969
Library Holdings: Bk Vols 301,682; Bk Titles 183,803; Per Subs 828
Subject Interests: New Jersey
Automation Activity & Vendor Info: (Circulation) DRA
Member Libraries: Berlin Township Library; Clementon Community Center & Memorial Library; Lindenwold Public Library; Magnolia Public School; Marie Fleche Memorial Library; Merchantville School & Public Library; Oaklyn Memorial Library; Somerdale Public Library; Westville Public Library
Partic in Dialog Corporation; OCLC Online Computer Library Center, Inc; PALINET & Union Library Catalogue of Pennsylvania; Vutext
Friends of the Library Group
Branches: 4
BELLMAWR TOWNSHIP, 35 E Browning Rd, Bellmawr, 08031. SAN 378-1542. Tel: 856-931-1400. FAX: 856-931-5538. *Branch Mgr*, Debbie Stefano; Staff 2 (MLS 2)
Pop 22,074
Automation Activity & Vendor Info: (OPAC) DRA
GLOUCESTER TOWNSHIP, 15 S Black Horse Pike, Blackwood, 08012. SAN 351-5257. Tel: 856-228-0022. FAX: 856-228-9085. *Branch Mgr*, Anne Ackroyd; Staff 2 (MLS 2)
Pop 68,282
Library Holdings: Bk Titles 43,000
Automation Activity & Vendor Info: (OPAC) DRA
Friends of the Library Group
HADDON TOWNSHIP, 15 McArthur Blvd, Westmont, 08108. SAN 351-5281. Tel: 856-854-2752. FAX: 856-854-8825. *Branch Mgr*, Nan Rosenthal; Staff 2 (MLS 2)
Pop 29,681
Library Holdings: Bk Titles 30,000
Automation Activity & Vendor Info: (OPAC) DRA
Friends of the Library Group
SOUTH COUNTY REGIONAL BRANCH, 35 Coopers Folly Rd, Atco, 08004. SAN 351-5311. *Branch Mgr*, Arthur Wolk; Staff 29 (MLS 8, Non-MLS 21)
Library Holdings: Bk Titles 26,725
Friends of the Library Group

M VIRTUA HEALTH SYSTEM, VOORHEES DIVISION, (Formerly West Jersey Health System, Voorhees Division), Staff Medical Library, 101 Carnie Blvd, 08043. SAN 351-5346. Tel: 609-325-3207. FAX: 609-325-3222. Web Site: www.virtua.org. *Dir*, Susan Cleveland; E-Mail: scleveland@virtua.org; Staff 1 (MLS 1)
Founded 1976
Library Holdings: Bk Titles 2,100; Per Subs 165
Subject Interests: Hospital administration, Medicine, Nursing, Patient educ
Partic in Basic Health Sciences Library Network; Health Sciences Library Association Of New Jersey; South Jersey Regional Library Cooperative; SW NJ Consortium
Branches:

WALDWICK

P WALDWICK PUBLIC LIBRARY,* 19 E Prospect St, 07463-2099. SAN 310-5733. Tel: 201-652-5104. FAX: 201-652-6233. E-Mail: wald1@bccls.org. Web Site: www.bccls.org/wald/. *Dir*, J David Kamykoski; *Ch Servs*, Monica Fernandes; Staff 2 (MLS 2)
Founded 1954. Pop 9,712; Circ 122,124
1997-1998 Income $341,788, State $9,327, Locally Generated Income $32,461. Mats Exp $42,733, Books $36,233, Per/Ser (Incl. Access Fees) $3,500. Sal $203,258 (Prof $84,000)
Library Holdings: Bk Titles 42,500; Per Subs 93
Special Collections: Drugs, bks, pamphlets; Local History, pamphlets
Partic in Bergen County Cooperative Library System; Bergen County Cooperative Library System
Friends of the Library Group

WALL

S NEW JERSEY NATURAL GAS COMPANY LIBRARY,* 1415 Wyckoff Rd, 07719. SAN 375-6939. Tel: 732-938-1000. FAX: 732-938-2134. *In Charge*, Wendy Waltsak
Library Holdings: Bk Vols 200

WALLINGTON

P JOHN F KENNEDY MEMORIAL LIBRARY,* 92 Hathaway St, 07057. SAN 310-5741. Tel: 973-471-1692. FAX: 973-471-1387. *Dir*, Marie E Plucinsky; *Circ*, Susan Kowalski; Staff 4 (MLS 1, Non-MLS 3)
Pop 10,741; Circ 29,000
Library Holdings: Bk Titles 40,000; Per Subs 146

WANAQUE

P WANAQUE BOROUGH FREE PUBLIC LIBRARY, 616 Ringwood Ave, 07465. SAN 310-575X. Tel: 973-839-4434. FAX: 973-839-8904. E-Mail: wancirc@palsplus.org. Web Site: www.palsplus.org/wanaque. *Dir*, Richard Louis Mariconda; E-Mail: mariconda@palsplus.org; *Ch Servs*, Fran Alala; Tel: 973-839-4434, Ext 12, E-Mail: falala@lakeland.k12.nj.us; *Ad Servs*, Grace Alessio; Tel: 973-839-4434, Ext 11, E-Mail: alessio@lakeland.k12.nj.us; *Circ*, Lori McCracken; Tel: 973-839-4434, Ext 11, E-Mail: wancirc@palsplus.org; Staff 9 (MLS 1, Non-MLS 8)
Founded 1968. Pop 10,520; Circ 35,000
Jan 2000-Dec 2000 Income $268,425, State $10,425, City $258,000. Mats Exp $28,800, Books $24,500, Per/Ser (Incl. Access Fees) $3,700, Electronic Ref Mat (Incl. Access Fees) $600. Sal $153,850 (Prof $40,000)
Library Holdings: Bk Vols 30,000; Bk Titles 29,027; Per Subs 83
Automation Activity & Vendor Info: (Acquisitions) ComPanion Corp; (Cataloging) DRA; (Circulation) DRA; (OPAC) DRA
Database Vendor: DRA, Ebsco - EbscoHost
Publications: Booklist; Library Journal; School Library Journal
Partic in Highlands Regional Library Cooperative; Pals; Passaic County Libr Syst

WARREN

L CHUBB & SON, INC, Law & Business Library, 15 Mountain View Rd, 07059. SAN 372-4263. Tel: 908-903-2000. FAX: 908-903-3820.
Library Holdings: Bk Vols 15,000

WASHINGTON

J WARREN COUNTY COMMUNITY COLLEGE, Library-Learning Resources Center,* 475 Rte 57 W, 07882-4343. SAN 371-9170. Tel: 908-689-7614, 908-835-2336. FAX: 908-835-1283. *Coll Develop, Dir*, Lynea Anderman; E-Mail: anderman@mail.warren.cc.nj.us; *ILL, Ref*, Paula Hering;

Circ, ILL, Linda Rowan; Staff 3 (MLS 2, Non-MLS 1)
Founded 1984. Enrl 1,300; Fac 40
Library Holdings: Bk Vols 32,126; Bk Titles 30,000; Per Subs 442
Subject Interests: Humanities, Law, Nursing
Special Collections: New Reader; Small Business, av & bks; WCCC archives
Publications: Acquisitions List; Bibliographies; Video Holding Catalog
Partic in NJ State Libr Network; OCLC Online Computer Library Center, Inc
Special Services for the Deaf - Videos & decoder
Serves as resource library for Skylands Small Business Development Center

P WASHINGTON PUBLIC LIBRARY, 20 W Carlton Ave, 07882. SAN 310-5792. Tel: 908-689-0201. FAX: 908-835-0803. Web Site: www.wpl.hublib.lib.nj.us. *Dir*, Barbara Carroll; Staff 8 (MLS 1, Non-MLS 7)
Pop 6,447; Circ 43,124
Jan 1997-Dec 1998 Income $215,473, State $12,854, City $184,613, Locally Generated Income $17,406. Mats Exp $26,681, Books $13,691, Per/Ser (Incl. Access Fees) $3,524, Presv $500, Micro $200, AV Equip $6,054. Sal $125,372 (Prof $40,469)
Library Holdings: Bk Vols 40,913; Bk Titles 40,513; Per Subs 150
Subject Interests: Local history
Special Collections: Star Gazette, newspaper archive
Automation Activity & Vendor Info: (Cataloging) Sagebrush Corporation; (Circulation) Sagebrush Corporation
Database Vendor: Ebsco - EbscoHost
Publications: 10 Year Anniversary Pamphlet
Partic in Highlands Regional Library Cooperative; New Jersey Library Network
Friends of the Library Group

WAYNE

S ISP MANAGEMENT CO, INC, Technical Information Services Library, 1361 Alps Rd, 07470. SAN 310-5830. Tel: 973-628-3234. FAX: 973-628-3404. *Tech Servs*, Phyllis Bronson; Staff 3 (MLS 3)
Founded 1972
Library Holdings: Bk Titles 11,000; Per Subs 165
Subject Interests: Acetylene chem, Bldg mat, Organic chemistry, Specialty chemicals
Restriction: Staff use only
Partic in BRS; Dialog Corporation; Medline; STM Chemical Abstracts

S KEARFOTT GUIDANCE & NAVIGATION CORP, Technical Information Center Library,* 150 Totowa Rd, MS HQB33, 07474-0946. SAN 310-5849. Tel: 973-785-6481. FAX: 973-785-6121. *Mgr*, Ed Hellmuth
Founded 1954
Library Holdings: Bk Vols 27,000; Per Subs 110
Subject Interests: Aerospace eng, Computer software, Electrical engineering, Hardware, Mat, Mathematics, Mech eng
Special Collections: Patents; Symposia; Technical Reports
Mem of Regional Libr Coop Region 2
Partic in Dialog Corporation

SR PACKANACK COMMUNITY CHURCH LIBRARY,* 120 Lake Dr E, 07470. SAN 328-3739. Tel: 973-694-0608. FAX: 973-694-7161. Web Site: www.forministry.com/07470pcc.
Library Holdings: Bk Titles 2,200
Subject Interests: Psychology

S URS GREINER WOODWARD-CLYDE CONSULTANTS LIBRARY, 201 Willowbrook Blvd, 07470-0290. SAN 326-1859. Tel: 973-785-0700, Ext 358, 973-812-3100. FAX: 973-785-0023. Toll Free FAX: 877-565-8519. *Librn*, Mitra Purkayastha
Library Holdings: Bk Vols 14,000; Bk Titles 9,000; Per Subs 120
Subject Interests: Architectural eng tech, Civil engineering, Environmental studies, Geology, Metallurgy
Restriction: Staff use only
Mem of NJ Libr Network
Partic in Dialog Corporation; Highlands Regional Library Cooperative

P WAYNE PUBLIC LIBRARY, 461 Valley Rd, 07470. SAN 351-5494. Tel: 973-694-4272. Circulation Tel: 973-694-4272, Ext 5210. Reference Tel: 973-694-4272, Ext 5401. FAX: 973-692-0637. E-Mail: waynepl@exchg1.palsplus.org. Web Site: www.waynetownship.com/library. *Dir*, Barbara Pickell; E-Mail: pickell@exchg1.palsplus.org; *Asst Dir*, Judy Treadway; E-Mail: treadway@exchg1.palsplus.org; *Ch Servs*, Susan Pirozzi; E-Mail: pirozzi@exchg1.palsplus.org; *Ref*, Doreen Shoba; E-Mail: shoba@exchg1.palsplus.org; *Circ*, Gail Kantor; E-Mail: kantor@exchg1.palsplus.org; *Tech Servs*, William Wilkinson; E-Mail: wilkinson@exchg1.palsplus.org; *Br Coordr*, Patricia McLoone; E-Mail: kell@exchg1.palsplus.org; Staff 18 (MLS 15, Non-MLS 3)
Founded 1922. Pop 54,000; Circ 266,136
Jan 2000-Dec 2000 Income (Main Library and Branch Library) $2,274,937, State $93,870, City $2,043,259, Other $47,154. Mats Exp $215,098, Books $163,728, Per/Ser (Incl. Access Fees) $25,840, Presv $400, Micro $10,000, Electronic Ref Mat (Incl. Access Fees) $15,130. Sal $1,483,943 (Prof $700,666)
Library Holdings: Bk Vols 157,362; Bk Titles 95,020; Per Subs 329
Subject Interests: Bus ref, NJ docs
Special Collections: Business Reference; New Jersey History (Lockett Coll)
Automation Activity & Vendor Info: (Cataloging) epixtech, inc.; (Circulation) epixtech, inc.; (OPAC) epixtech, inc.
Partic in Highlands Regional Library Cooperative; Pals
Friends of the Library Group
Branches: 1
PREAKNESS, Wayne Civic Ctr, 1006 Hamburg Tpk, 07470. SAN 351-5559. Tel: 973-694-7110. FAX: 973-694-8415. *Librn*, Patricia McLoone
Library Holdings: Bk Vols 36,495; Bk Titles 34,209
Automation Activity & Vendor Info: (Cataloging) epixtech, inc.; (Circulation) epixtech, inc.; (OPAC) epixtech, inc.
Partic in Highlands Regional Library Cooperative; Pals
Friends of the Library Group

C WILLIAM PATERSON UNIVERSITY OF NEW JERSEY, Sarah Byrd Askew Library, 300 Pompton Rd, 07470. SAN 310-5865. Tel: 973-720-2541. Interlibrary Loan Service Tel: 973-720-2567. FAX: 973-720-2585. E-Mail: refdesk@wpunj.edu. Web Site: www.wpunj.edu/library. *Actg Dir*, Anne Ciliberti; *Bibliog Instr*, Judy Matthew; *Coll Develop*, Anne Ciliberti; *ILL*, Jackie Hill; *Media Spec*, Jane Hutchison; *Online Servs*, Jane Bambrick; *Ref*, Kathleen Malanga; *Spec Coll*, Robert Wolk; *Tech Servs*, Amy Job; Staff 24 (MLS 22, Non-MLS 2)
Founded 1855. Enrl 9,700; Fac 310; Highest Degree: Master
Jul 1999-Jun 2000 Mats Exp $997,100, Books $225,000, Per/Ser (Incl. Access Fees) $589,700, Presv $8,400, AV Equip $17,000, Electronic Ref Mat (Incl. Access Fees) $157,000
Library Holdings: Bk Vols 343,153; Bk Titles 294,341; Per Subs 1,700
Subject Interests: Business, Education, Law, Psychology
Special Collections: First & Limited Editions of 19th & 20th Century American & British Authors; New Jerseyiana; Personal Papers of William Paterson (1745-1806)
Automation Activity & Vendor Info: (Acquisitions) DRA; (Cataloging) DRA; (Circulation) DRA; (OPAC) DRA; (Serials) DRA
Database Vendor: OCLC - First Search
Publications: Bibliographic Series; Collection Development Policy; Information Series; Instruction Bulletins; Newsletter
Partic in OCLC Online Computer Library Center, Inc; PALINET & Union Library Catalogue of Pennsylvania
Friends of the Library Group

WEEHAWKEN

P WEEHAWKEN FREE PUBLIC LIBRARY, Multimedia Center,* 49 Hauxhurst Ave, 07087. SAN 310-5873. Tel: 201-863-7823. FAX: 201-863-7958. Web Site: www.bccls.org. *Dir*, Phillip R Greco
Founded 1942. Pop 13,400; Circ 42,200
Jan 1997-Dec 1998 Income $270,000. Mats Exp $36,200, Books $35,000, Per/Ser (Incl. Access Fees) $1,200. Sal $172,000
Library Holdings: Bk Vols 45,000
Mem of Jersey City Free Pub Libr

WENONAH

P WENONAH FREE PUBLIC LIBRARY,* 101 E Mantua Ave, 08090-1950. SAN 310-5881. Tel: 856-468-6323. *Dir*, Carol Wiltsee; *Dir*, Meta O'Connor
Circ 7,239
Library Holdings: Bk Vols 10,000
Mem of S Jersey Regional Libr Coop
Open Mon-Thurs 3-5 & 7-9, Sat 1-5

WEST BERLIN

P BERLIN TOWNSHIP LIBRARY, 201 Veteran's Lane, 08091. SAN 310-589X. Tel: 856-767-0439. FAX: 856-753-6729. *Librn*, Mary Holt
Founded 1965. Pop 5,400; Circ 8,000
Library Holdings: Bk Vols 8,250; Per Subs 42
Mem of Camden County Library System
Open Mon & Wed 2-5pm, Tues & Thurs 1-7pm

WEST CALDWELL

S INTERNATIONAL UNION OF OPERATING ENGINEERS TRAINING CENTER, Local 68, 68A, 68B Library,* 14 Fairfield Pl, PO Box 534, 07006. SAN 325-9013. Tel: 973-227-6426. FAX: 973-227-8373.
Library Holdings: Bk Vols 1,000

P WEST CALDWELL PUBLIC LIBRARY, 30 Clinton Rd, 07006. SAN 310-5903. Tel: 973-226-5441. FAX: 973-228-7572. E-Mail: judge@bccls.org. *Dir*, April L Judge; *Acq*, Joan Lui; *Cat, Tech Servs*, Carolyn Blowers; *Ch Servs*, Holly Belli; *Circ*, Karen Kelly; *ILL*, Karen Freda; Staff 15 (MLS 7, Non-MLS 8)
Founded 1915. Pop 9,768; Circ 276,476
Jan 2000-Dec 2000 Income $882,725, State $13,425, City $740,274, Locally

Generated Income $129,026. Mats Exp $101,000. Sal $509,540
Library Holdings: Bk Vols 58,899; Bk Titles 36,190; Per Subs 214
Automation Activity & Vendor Info: (Cataloging) DRA; (Circulation) DRA
Database Vendor: DRA
Mem of Bergen County Co-op Libr Syst
Partic in Infolink Eastern New Jersey Regional Library Cooperative, Inc; New Jersey Library Network
Friends of the Library Group

WEST LONG BRANCH

C MONMOUTH UNIVERSITY, Guggenheim Memorial Library, 400 Cedar Ave, 07764. SAN 310-592X. Tel: 732-571-3450. FAX: 732-263-5124. Web Site: www.monmouth.edu/irs/library/library/html. *Dean of Libr*, Dr Terry Webb; *Circ*, Sandra Epstein; *Doc, ILL*, Linda Silverstein; *Bibliog Instr*, Rachel M Gardner; *Bibliogr*, Aurora S Ioanid; *Coll Develop*, Susan Kuykendall; Staff 9 (MLS 9)
Founded 1933. Enrl 5,200; Fac 188; Highest Degree: Master
Library Holdings: Bk Vols 255,701; Bk Titles 190,673; Per Subs 1,318
Special Collections: Lewis Mumford Coll; New Jersey History Coll
Automation Activity & Vendor Info: (Acquisitions) Innovative Interfaces Inc.; (Cataloging) Innovative Interfaces Inc.; (Circulation) Innovative Interfaces Inc.; (OPAC) Innovative Interfaces Inc.; (Serials) Innovative Interfaces Inc.
Database Vendor: OCLC - First Search
Publications: Bibliographies; Current periodicals holdings
Mem of Central Jersey Regional Libr Coop
Partic in NJ Union List of Serials; OCLC Online Computer Library Center, Inc; PALINET & Union Library Catalogue of Pennsylvania
Friends of the Library Group

P WEST LONG BRANCH PUBLIC LIBRARY, 95 Poplar Ave, 07764. SAN 310-5938. Tel: 732-222-5993. FAX: 732-229-5138. Web Site: www.monmouth.lib.nj.us/wlb/. *Dir*, Elsalyn Palmisano; E-Mail: epalmisa@hawkmail.monmouth.edu; *Admin Assoc*, Cindy Cioffi; E-Mail: cindycioffi@hotmail.com; Staff 2 (MLS 1, Non-MLS 1)
Founded 1927. Pop 7,800; Circ 40,470
Jan 1999-Dec 1999 Income $194,316. Mats Exp $53,553, Books $10,353, Per/Ser (Incl. Access Fees) $4,200, Micro $1,000, AV Equip $600. Sal $140,763
Library Holdings: Bk Vols 35,000; Per Subs 125
Subject Interests: Art, Monmouth County hist, New Jersey
Special Collections: book & cassettes; New Jersey Coll; video tape & compact disc
Automation Activity & Vendor Info: (Acquisitions) SIRSI; (Cataloging) SIRSI; (Circulation) SIRSI; (OPAC) SIRSI; (Serials) SIRSI
Database Vendor: Ebsco - EbscoHost
Publications: Acquisitions List; Newsletter
Mem of Monmouth County Library
Partic in Central Jersey Regional Library Cooperative
Friends of the Library Group

WEST MILFORD

P WEST MILFORD TOWNSHIP LIBRARY,* 1490 Union Valley Rd, 07480. SAN 310-5946. Tel: 973-728-2820. FAX: 973-728-2106. *Dir*, Barbara Ann Cordaro; Tel: 973-728-2824, E-Mail: cordaro@palsplus.org; *Asst Dir*, Christine O'Brien; *Assoc Dir*, Kim Hill; Tel: 973-728-2981, E-Mail: Hill@palsplus.org; *Ad Servs*, Lauren Angle; *Ad Servs*, Mary Warren; *Ref Servs YA*, Sandy Schlosser; Tel: 973-728-2822, E-Mail: Schlosser@palsplus.org; *Ch Servs*, Richard Bryce; Tel: 973-728-2823, E-Mail: Bryce@palsplus.org; Staff 25 (MLS 11, Non-MLS 14)
Founded 1954. Pop 28,560; Circ 155,000
Jan 2000-Dec 2000 Income $800,000, State $30,000, City $750,000, Locally Generated Income $20,000. Mats Exp $123,000, Books $62,000, Per/Ser (Incl. Access Fees) $6,000, Electronic Ref Mat (Incl. Access Fees) $55,000. Sal $450,000 (Prof $200,000)
Library Holdings: Bk Vols 37,000; Bk Titles 35,000; Per Subs 90
Automation Activity & Vendor Info: (Circulation) DRA; (OPAC) DRA
Database Vendor: DRA, IAC - Info Trac, Wilson - Wilson Web
Friends of the Library Group

WEST NEW YORK

P WEST NEW YORK PUBLIC LIBRARY, 425 60th St, 07093-2211. SAN 310-5954. Tel: 201-295-5135. FAX: 201-662-1473. E-Mail: wnypl@nplhub.org. *Dir*, Weiliang Lai; *Acq, Cat, Tech Servs*, Nina Rhodes; *Ref*, Estela Longo-Salvador; Staff 3 (MLS 3)
Founded 1916. Pop 38,125
Jul 2000-Jun 2001 Income $585,420, State $25,000, City $555,100, Other $5,000. Mats Exp $68,000, Books $55,000, Per/Ser (Incl. Access Fees) $5,000, AV Equip $5,000, Electronic Ref Mat (Incl. Access Fees) $3,000. Sal $392,358 (Prof $105,000)
Library Holdings: Bk Vols 65,000; Bk Titles 61,000; Per Subs 125
Subject Interests: Family literacy, Jerseyana, Large print, Local history, Parenting, Spanish
Automation Activity & Vendor Info: (Acquisitions) Gaylord; (Cataloging) Gaylord; (Circulation) Gaylord; (OPAC) Gaylord; (Serials) Gaylord
Database Vendor: Ebsco - EbscoHost, ProQuest
Mem of Menla-NJ Libr Network
Partic in Infolink
Friends of the Library Group

WEST ORANGE

P EDISON NATIONAL HISTORIC SITE FRIENDS OF LIBRARY,* 342 Main St, 07052. SAN 375-7331. Tel: 973-736-2916. FAX: 973-736-8496. *Curator*, Roger S Durham; *Librn*, Mary Anne Gerbauckas
Library Holdings: Bk Vols 10,000
Restriction: By appointment only

M KMRREC, Medical Library & Patient Resource Center, 1199 Pleasant Valley Way, 07052-1499. SAN 375-7358. Tel: 973-731-3900, Ext 2396. Toll Free Tel: 800-248-3221, Ext 2396. FAX: 973-243-6835. *Librn for Blind, Mgr*, Robert T Mackes; E-Mail: rmackes@kmrrec.org; *Asst Librn*, Marita F Demonico; Staff 1 (MLS 1)
Founded 1948
Jan 2000-Dec 2000 Income $125,000
Library Holdings: Bk Titles 1,500; Per Subs 150
Automation Activity & Vendor Info: (Acquisitions) CASPR; (Cataloging) CASPR; (Circulation) CLSI LIBS; (OPAC) CASPR; (Serials) CASPR
Database Vendor: Ebsco - EbscoHost, OVID Technologies
Restriction: Internal circulation only
Function: For research purposes
Partic in Basic Health Sciences Library Network; New Jersey Health Sciences Library Network

L LAMPF, LIPKIND, PRUPIS, PETIGROW & LABUE, Law Library,* 80 Main St, 07052-5482. SAN 372-4654. Tel: 973-325-2100, Ext 325. FAX: 243-0964, 973-325-2839. *Librn*, Lucille Field
Library Holdings: Bk Vols 10,000; Per Subs 75

S UNITED STATES DEPARTMENT OF THE INTERIOR-NATIONAL PARK SERVICE, Edison National Historic Site Library,* Main St & Lakeside Ave, 07052-5515. SAN 375-9997. Tel: 973-736-0550, Ext 13. FAX: 973-736-8496. E-Mail: edis_archives@nps.gov. Web Site: www.nps.gov/edis/. *Curator*, Roger Durham
Library Holdings: Bk Vols 15,000
Friends of the Library Group

P WEST ORANGE FREE PUBLIC LIBRARY,* 46 Mount Pleasant Ave, 07052. SAN 351-5583. Tel: 973-736-0198. FAX: 973-736-1655. Web Site: www.wopl.lib.nj.us. *Dir*, Cynthia Chamberlin; *Asst Dir*, Renee Riczker; *Ref*, Juan Almodovar; *Ref*, David Cohen; *ILL, Ref*, Marilyn Force; *Ch Servs*, Linda Simpfendorfer; *Tech Servs*, Barbara Railo; Staff 8 (MLS 8)
Founded 1948. Pop 39,532; Circ 368,207
Library Holdings: Bk Vols 151,000; Bk Titles 120,000; Per Subs 412
Partic in Infolink
Branches: 1
TORY CORNER, 252 Main St, 07052. SAN 351-5613. Tel: 973-736-0452. *Librn*, Yvonne Crum

WEST PATERSON

P ALFRED H BAUMANN FREE PUBLIC LIBRARY, 7 Brophy Lane, 07424-2733. SAN 310-5989. Tel: 973-345-8120. FAX: 973-345-8196. *Dir*, Robert E Lindsley; Staff 1 (MLS 1)
Founded 1962. Pop 11,400; Circ 30,834
1998-1999 Income $318,252, State $8,252, City $310,000. Mats Exp $46,100, Books $29,000, Per/Ser (Incl. Access Fees) $6,500, Presv $1,000, Micro $600, Other Print Mats $2,500, Electronic Ref Mat (Incl. Access Fees) $6,500. Sal $109,000
Library Holdings: Bk Vols 43,000; Bk Titles 37,000; Per Subs 95
Automation Activity & Vendor Info: (OPAC) Brodart
Mem of Highlands Regional Libr Coop

J BERKELEY COLLEGE, Walter A Brower Library, 44 Rifle Camp Rd, 07424. SAN 325-5573. Tel: 973-278-5400, Ext 230. FAX: 973-278-2242. E-Mail: md@berkeleycollege.edu. Web Site: www.berkeleycollege.edu/library. *Dir*, Marlene J Doty; *Librn*, Mary Bludnicki; *Librn*, Nancy Weiner; Staff 3 (MLS 3)
Founded 1931. Enrl 640; Fac 25
Library Holdings: Bk Vols 50,000; Bk Titles 33,000; Per Subs 196
Subject Interests: Bus, Computers, Fashion, Marketing, Secretarial sci
Automation Activity & Vendor Info: (Cataloging) TLC; (Circulation) TLC; (OPAC) TLC
Publications: Handbook
Mem of Passaic County Libr Syst
Partic in Highlands Regional Library Cooperative; OCLC Online Computer Library Center, Inc

Departmental Libraries:
BERGEN CAMPUS, 100 W Prospect St, Waldwick, 07463. SAN 370-6958. Tel: 201-652-0388. FAX: 201-652-1536, 201-652-2366. E-Mail: bgcampus@berkeleycollege.edu. Web Site: www.berkeleycollege.edu/campuses/bncampus.htm. *Librn*, Katherine Lynch; Fax: 201-652-0589, E-Mail: kjl@berkeleycollege.edu
Library Holdings: Bk Vols 50,000
Subject Interests: Interior design
Mem of Regional Libr Coop Region 2
MIDDLESEX CAMPUS, 430 Rahway Ave, Woodbridge, 07095. SAN 370-6966. Tel: 732-750-1800, Ext 2200. FAX: 732-726-9286. *Librn*, Bess Twaskas
Library Holdings: Bk Vols 50,000

WEST TRENTON

S DELAWARE RIVER BASIN COMMISSION LIBRARY, 25 State Police Dr, PO Box 7360, 08628-0360. SAN 310-5997. Tel: 609-883-9500, Ext 263. FAX: 609-883-9522. Web Site: www.state.nj.us/drbc. *Librn*, Judith L Strong; E-Mail: jstrong@drbc.state.nj.us; Staff 1 (MLS 1)
Founded 1962
Subject Interests: Aquatic biol, Delaware River, Flood control, Geology, Hydrology, Water pollution, Water resources
Database Vendor: GaleNet
Publications: Bibliographies
Restriction: By appointment only
Partic in Central Jersey Regional Library Cooperative

WESTAMPTON

P BURLINGTON COUNTY LIBRARY, 5 Pioneer Blvd, 08060. SAN 350-9281. Tel: 609-267-9660. FAX: 609-267-4091. Web Site: www.burlco.lib.nj.us. *Dir*, Gail Sweet; *Asst Dir*, Molly Connor; *Coordr, Tech Servs*, Lynn Crawford; *ILL*, Vicky Kolo; Staff 156 (MLS 39, Non-MLS 117)
Founded 1921. Pop 390,000; Circ 1,650,000
Jan 1998-Dec 1999 Income $8,023,620, State $271,406, County $5,061,000. Mats Exp $817,645. Sal $3,872,001
Library Holdings: Bk Vols 726,000; Per Subs 565
Subject Interests: Architecture, Art, Genealogy, Local history
Special Collections: Local Newspapers from 1835, bd & microflm; New Jersey, multi-media; Sight Saving & Talking Books
Automation Activity & Vendor Info: (Cataloging) epixtech, inc.
Publications: Union List of Periodicals
Member Libraries: Beverly Free Library; Burlington Library Co; Crosswicks Public Library; Delanco Public Library; Florence Township Public Library; Mount Holly Public Library; Riverside Public Library Association, Inc; Sally Stretch Keen Memorial Library
Friends of the Library Group
Branches: 6
BORDENTOWN BRANCH, 18 E Union St, Bordentown, 08505. SAN 350-9311. Tel: 609-298-0622. FAX: 609-298-3682. *In Charge*, Regina Reay
Library Holdings: Bk Vols 40,131
Friends of the Library Group
BROWNS MILLS BRANCH, 348 Lakehurst Rd, Browns Mills, 08015. SAN 328-9281. Tel: 609-893-8262. FAX: 609-893-5459. *Librn*, Marie Mento
Library Holdings: Bk Vols 61,000
Friends of the Library Group
CINNAMINSON BRANCH, 1619 Riverton Rd, Cinnaminson, 08077. SAN 350-9346. Tel: 856-829-9340. FAX: 856-829-2243. *Branch Mgr*, Isabelle K Addis
Library Holdings: Bk Vols 82,537
Friends of the Library Group
EVESHAM, 984 Tuckerton Rd, Marlton, 08053. SAN 350-9370. Tel: 856-983-1444. FAX: 856-983-4939. *Dir*, Susan Szymanik; *Senior Librn*, Ranjana Das; *Librn*, Laurie Bowden
Library Holdings: Bk Vols 85,000
Friends of the Library Group
PEMBERTON BRANCH, 51 Egbert St, Pemberton, 08068. SAN 378-1941. Tel: 609-894-2516. FAX: 609-894-2560. *Librn*, Marie Mento
PINELANDS, 39 Allen Ave, Medford, 08055. SAN 350-9400. Tel: 609-654-6113. FAX: 609-953-2142. *Librn*, Judy Aley
Library Holdings: Bk Vols 72,000
Friends of the Library Group
Bookmobiles: 1

WESTFIELD

R PRESBYTERIAN CHURCH LIBRARY,* 140 Mountain Ave, 07090. SAN 310-6004. Tel: 908-233-0301. FAX: 908-317-9218. *Librn*, Dorothy Hulsart; Tel: 908-232-0274; Staff 3 (MLS 2, Non-MLS 1)
Founded 1960
Library Holdings: Bk Titles 4,500; Per Subs 10
Friends of the Library Group

P WESTFIELD MEMORIAL LIBRARY, 550 E Broad St, 07090. SAN 310-6012. Tel: 908-789-4090. FAX: 908-789-0921. Web Site: www.infolink.org/wml. *Dir*, Barbara Thiele; *Asst Dir*, Carol Wilson; *ILL*, Sally Hanford; *Tech Servs*, Eileen Haigh; *Ref*, Miriam Kornblatt; Staff 19 (MLS 7, Non-MLS 12)
Founded 1872. Pop 28,870
Jan 1999-Dec 1999 Income $1,296,417, State $30,990, City $1,153,500, Other $111,927. Mats Exp $173,937, Books $150,387, Per/Ser (Incl. Access Fees) $16,200, Presv $350, Micro $1,000, Electronic Ref Mat (Incl. Access Fees) $6,000. Sal $680,594
Library Holdings: Bk Vols 130,860; Bk Titles 111,601; Per Subs 254
Subject Interests: Local history
Automation Activity & Vendor Info: (Circulation) epixtech, inc.; (OPAC) epixtech, inc.
Database Vendor: Ebsco - EbscoHost
Publications: Take Note (newsletter)
Partic in Infolink Eastern New Jersey Regional Library Cooperative, Inc
Friends of the Library Group

WESTVILLE

P WESTVILLE PUBLIC LIBRARY,* 1035 Broadway, 08093. SAN 310-6020. Tel: 856-456-0357. FAX: 609-742-8190. E-Mail: westvillelibrary@home.com. *Dir*, Lin Eastlack; *Publ Servs, Tech Servs*, Mary Ward
Founded 1924. Pop 4,823
Library Holdings: Bk Titles 20,000; Per Subs 54
Publications: Newsletter (bi-yearly)
Mem of Camden County Library System
Partic in OCLC Online Computer Library Center, Inc
Friends of the Library Group

WESTWOOD

M PASCACK VALLEY HOSPITAL, David Goldberg Memorial Medical Library, Old Hook Rd, 07675. SAN 325-304X. Tel: 201-358-3240. FAX: 201-358-6215. *Librn*, Elaine Goldman
Library Holdings: Bk Titles 2,000; Per Subs 220
Subject Interests: Allied health, Medicine, Nursing
Special Collections: Cardiac Rehabilitation Coll; Sports Medicine Coll, bks
Publications: AV Holdings; Book Marks; Journal Holdings; Library Holdings
Restriction: By appointment only
Mem of Regional Libr Coop, Region 1
Partic in Health Sci Libr Asn of NJ

P TOWNSHIP OF WASHINGTON PUBLIC LIBRARY,* 144 Woodfield Rd, 07675. SAN 310-6047. Tel: 201-664-4586. FAX: 201-664-7331. E-Mail: wash1@bccls.org. Web Site: www.bccls.org/washingtontwp. *Dir*, Juliette Sobon; *Ch Servs*, Maria Halzack; *Ref*, Patricia Boyd; Staff 2 (MLS 2)
Founded 1963. Pop 9,245; Circ 77,100
Library Holdings: Bk Vols 41,238; Bk Titles 38,770; Per Subs 114
Subject Interests: Cooking, Japanese culture, Mysteries, Travel
Special Collections: Books on Cassette; Careers; Large Print Bks
Partic in Bergen County Cooperative Library System
Friends of the Library Group

P WESTWOOD FREE PUBLIC LIBRARY, 49 Park Ave, 07675. SAN 310-6055. Tel: 201-664-0583. FAX: 201-664-6088. E-Mail: wewdl@bccls.org. Web Site: www.bccls.org/wewd1/index.html. *Circ*, Valerie Danhart; *Dir*, Phyllis Palley; *Ch Servs*, Dorothy Lagrimas; *Cat*, Linda Salib; *Ref*, Susan Sampietro; Staff 3 (MLS 3)
Founded 1919. Pop 10,315
Library Holdings: Bk Vols 50,000; Bk Titles 40,000; Per Subs 150
Special Collections: Health & Popular Medicine Coll; Literacy Program Coll
Mem of Bergen County Co-op Libr Syst
Partic in BCCLS Computer Consortium; Bergen County Cooperative Library System
Friends of the Library Group

WHARTON

P WHARTON PUBLIC LIBRARY,* 15 S Main St, 07885. SAN 310-6063. Tel: 973-361-1333. FAX: 973-361-2893. *Coll Develop, Dir*, Susan Calentone
Founded 1891. Pop 5,405; Circ 25,694
1998-1999 Income $130,150. Mats Exp $18,850, Books $16,500, Per/Ser (Incl. Access Fees) $1,850. Sal $58,800 (Prof $30,800)
Library Holdings: Bk Vols 31,040; Bk Titles 30,736; Per Subs 75
Partic in ALMC; CORE; Morris Automated Information Network; Sails, Inc
Friends of the Library Group

WHIPPANY

P MORRIS COUNTY LIBRARY, 30 E Hanover Ave, 07981. SAN 310-6098. Tel: 973-285-6930. Interlibrary Loan Service Tel: 973-285-6961. Reference Tel: 973-285-6969. TDD: 973-285-6942. FAX: 973-285-6962. Interlibrary Loan Service FAX: 973-285-6965. Reference FAX: 973-285-6982. E-Mail:

morris@main.morris.org. Web Site: www.gti.net/mocolibl/mcl.html. *Dir*, Knute E Seebohm; Tel: 973-285-6934, E-Mail: seebohm@main.morris.org; *Librn*, Marie Heagney; Tel: 973-285-6974, E-Mail: heagney@main.morris.org; *Reader Servs*, John P Menzel; Tel: 973-285-6972, E-Mail: menzel@main.morris.org; *Automation Syst Coordr*, Pat Hodges; Tel: 973-285-6951, E-Mail: hodges@main.morris.org; *ILL*, Janet Bone; E-Mail: bone@main.morris.org; *Media Spec*, Elaine Gaber; Tel: 973-285-6975, E-Mail: gaber@main.morris.org; *Tech Servs*, Brenda Adams; Tel: 973-285-6955, E-Mail: badams@main.morris.org; *Ref*, Joanne Kares; Tel: 973-285-6967, E-Mail: kares@main.morris.org; *Ch Servs*, Princess Thomas; Tel: 973-285-6981, E-Mail: thomas@main.morris.org; Staff 31 (MLS 31)
Founded 1922. Circ 314,640
Jan 1999-Dec 1999 Income $3,609,736, Federal $175,241, County $3,434,495. Mats Exp $429,582, Books $352,641, Per/Ser (Incl. Access Fees) $54,579, Micro $22,362. Sal $2,351,928 (Prof $1,104,424)
Library Holdings: Bk Vols 209,757; Bk Titles 180,622; Per Subs 1,008; High Interest/Low Vocabulary Bk Vols 400; Spec Interest Per Sub 55; Bks on Deafness & Sign Lang 150
Subject Interests: Business, Music
Special Collections: Books on Tape; Mysteries; New Adult Readers; New Jersey History; Original art; Sheet music
Automation Activity & Vendor Info: (Cataloging) DRA; (Circulation) DRA; (OPAC) DRA
Database Vendor: Ebsco - EbscoHost, IAC - Info Trac, ProQuest
Function: ILL available, Reference services available
Partic in ELN; Highlands Regional Library Cooperative; Morris Automated Information Network
Special Services for the Deaf - TDD; TTY machine; Videos & decoder
Special Services for the Blind - Special programs

S UNITED JEWISH FEDERATION OF METROWEST, Jewish Historical Society Of Metrowest Library, 901 Rte 10 E, 07981-1156. SAN 375-3123. Tel: 973-884-4800, Ext 565. FAX: 973-428-8237. Web Site: www.jhsmw.org. *Archivist*, Joseph A Settanni; Staff 1 (MLS 1)
Founded 1990
Jul 1998-Jun 1999 Income $75,000, Locally Generated Income $30,000, Parent Institution $45,000. Mats Exp $9,500, Presv $3,000, AV Equip $30, Other Print Mats $500, Manuscripts & Archives $3,000. Sal $45,000
Library Holdings: Bk Titles 90; Per Subs 20
Publications: Newsletter; technical leaflets
Special Services - Speakers Bureau; internship program; exhibitions
Friends of the Library Group

P WHIPPANONG LIBRARY, 1000 Rte 10, 07981. SAN 310-6101. Tel: 973-428-2460. FAX: 973-515-4769. E-Mail: das@main.morris.org. Web Site: www.whippanong.org. *Dir*, Sulekha Das
Founded 1957. Pop 13,000; Circ 61,503
Jan 1999-Dec 1999 Income $271,124, State $9,909, City $245,673, Locally Generated Income $5,792, Other $9,750. Mats Exp $39,600, Books $30,000, AV Equip $3,000, Electronic Ref Mat (Incl. Access Fees) $6,600. Sal $165,276 (Prof $114,365)
Library Holdings: Bk Vols 39,800; Bk Titles 38,833; Per Subs 80
Subject Interests: Gardening
Special Collections: Cookbooks
Automation Activity & Vendor Info: (Cataloging) DRA; (Circulation) DRA; (ILL) DRA; (OPAC) DRA; (Serials) DRA
Partic in Morris Info Network

WHITEHOUSE STATION

L MERCK & CO, INC, Law Library, One Merck Dr, 08889. SAN 351-3246. Tel: 908-423-5805. FAX: 908-735-1147. *Mgr*, Elizabeth Arnold; E-Mail: elizabeth_arnold@merck.com; Staff 4 (MLS 2, Non-MLS 2)
Founded 1959
Library Holdings: Per Subs 272
Restriction: Staff use only
Mem of NJ Regional Libr Coop

WILDWOOD

S GEORGE F BOYER MUSEUM LIBRARY, 3907 Pacific Ave, 08260. SAN 374-8715. Tel: 609-523-0277. *Mgr*, Robert Bright
Library Holdings: Bk Vols 250

WILDWOOD CREST

S WILDWOOD CREST PUBLIC LIBRARY, 6301 Ocean Ave, 08260. SAN 310-611X. Tel: 609-522-0564. *Dir*, William M Smith; *Asst Librn*, Elise Gallagher; *Asst Librn*, Alice Harrison
Founded 1972. Circ 34,000
Library Holdings: Bk Vols 23,000; Per Subs 20
Open Mon-Fri 10-5, Sat 1-5

WILLIAMSTOWN

P FREE PUBLIC LIBRARY OF MONROE TOWNSHIP,* 306 S Main St, 08094. SAN 310-6128. Tel: 856-629-1212. FAX: 856-875-0191. E-Mail: mtlibrary@buyrite.com. Web Site: www.buyrite.com/monroetownship/library. *Ad Servs, Ref*, Ieva Hartman; Fax: 856-875-0191, E-Mail: ihartman@buyrite.com; *Dir*, Nana E Bogis; Fax: 856-629-5967, E-Mail: nbogis@buyrite.com; *Cat*, Lynn Harpool; E-Mail: lharpool@buyrite.com; *Ch Servs*, Elizabeth L Lillie; E-Mail: elillie@buyrite.com; Staff 11 (MLS 4, Non-MLS 7)
Founded 1969. Pop 29,608; Circ 121,400
Jan 1998-Dec 1998 Income $631,137, State $34,399, City $566,738, Locally Generated Income $30,000. Mats Exp $31,500, Per/Ser (Incl. Access Fees) $15,450, Micro $2,500, AV Equip $6,550, Electronic Ref Mat (Incl. Access Fees) $7,000. Sal $448,802 (Prof $185,168)
Library Holdings: Bk Vols 61,424; Bk Titles 52,995; Per Subs 152
Subject Interests: Motion pictures
Automation Activity & Vendor Info: (Circulation) Sagebrush Corporation
Publications: Library Lines
Mem of S Jersey Regional Libr Coop
Friends of the Library Group

WILLINGBORO

S BURLINGTON COUNTY TIMES LIBRARY, 4284 Rte 130 N, 08046-1482. SAN 310-6136. Tel: 609-871-8082. FAX: 609-871-0490. E-Mail: bctimes@bctimes.com. *Librn*, Annette Parker
Founded 1965
Library Holdings: Bk Vols 155; Bk Titles 125
Subject Interests: Burlington County, Nat subjects, State subjects
Special Collections: Local Newspaper Coll

M RANCOCAS HOSPITAL, Grantham Memorial Library,* 218A Sunset Rd, 08046. SAN 373-4765. Tel: 609-835-2900, Ext 4140. FAX: 609-835-5470. Web Site: www.cyberenet.net/~rancocas. *Librn*, Celeste Hodges; E-Mail: chodges@cyberenet.net
Library Holdings: Bk Vols 250; Per Subs 60

P WILLINGBORO PUBLIC LIBRARY, One Salem Rd, 08046. SAN 310-6152. Tel: 609-877-6668. FAX: 609-835-1699. E-Mail: wipl@willingboro.org. Web Site: www.willingboro.org. *Dir*, Christine H King; Fax: 609-877-7941; *Head Ref*, Janet Cheeseman; E-Mail: jcheesem@willingboro.org; *Ch Servs*, Christine Hill; E-Mail: chill@willingboro.org; *Ad Servs*, Taifa Jengaji-El; E-Mail: tjengaji@willingboro.org; *Tech Servs*, Eugene Rifkind; E-Mail: erifkind@willingboro.org; *Librn*, Dorothy Leverett; *Circ*, Linda Bowker; Staff 22 (MLS 7, Non-MLS 15)
Founded 1960. Pop 37,000; Circ 107,000
Jan 1999-Dec 1999 Income $946,633, State $46,815, City $870,235, Locally Generated Income $29,583. Mats Exp $96,000, Books $62,000, Per/Ser (Incl. Access Fees) $15,600, Micro $6,200, Other Print Mats $10,100, Electronic Ref Mat (Incl. Access Fees) $8,700. Sal $534,500 (Prof $225,650)
Library Holdings: Bk Vols 70,653; Bk Titles 61,391; Per Subs 199
Special Collections: African American History Coll; History (Sanford Soren Spanish Civil War History Coll)
Automation Activity & Vendor Info: (Circulation) epixtech, inc.
Database Vendor: Ebsco - EbscoHost, IAC - Info Trac
Function: Some telephone reference
Friends of the Library Group

WOODBRIDGE

P FREE PUBLIC LIBRARY OF WOODBRIDGE, George Frederick Plaza, 07095. SAN 351-5648. Tel: 732-634-4450. TDD: 732-634-1841. FAX: 732-634-7610. Web Site: www.woodbridge.lib.nj.us. *Dir*, John Hurley; E-Mail: jhurley@lmxac.org; *Br Coordr*, Ellen Peterson; Tel: 732-634-4450, Ext 243; *Tech Servs*, Lynne Merz; *Ad Servs*, Nancy Slater; *Coordr*, Linda Cooper; *Automation Syst Coordr*, Irwin Pashkin; *Ch Servs*, Sharon Gill; Staff 24 (MLS 24)
Founded 1964. Pop 93,086; Circ 562,506
Jul 1999-Jun 2000 Income $4,651,647, State $119,906, City $4,226,566, Locally Generated Income $176,175, Other $129,500. Mats Exp $665,768, Books $410,000, Per/Ser (Incl. Access Fees) $50,000, Micro $17,000. Sal $3,669,331 (Prof $1,455,662)
Library Holdings: Bk Vols 378,312; Bk Titles 213,337; Per Subs 623; High Interest/Low Vocabulary Bk Vols 120
Subject Interests: Education, Law
Automation Activity & Vendor Info: (Acquisitions) epixtech, inc.; (Cataloging) epixtech, inc.; (Circulation) epixtech, inc.
Partic in OCLC Online Computer Library Center, Inc; PALINET & Union Library Catalogue of Pennsylvania
Special Services for the Deaf - TDD
Special Services for the Blind - Talking book center
Friends of the Library Group
Branches: 3
FORDS BRANCH, 211 Ford Ave, Fords, 08863. SAN 351-5737. Tel: 732-738-0250. FAX: 732-738-5875. *Librn*, Anne Taylor

Library Holdings: Bk Vols 52,752
HENRY INMAN BRANCH, 607 Inman Ave, Colonia, 07067. SAN 351-5761. Tel: 732-382-5090. FAX: 732-382-8367. *Librn*, Louise Cangelosi
Library Holdings: Bk Vols 42,672
ISELIN BRANCH, 1081 Green St, Iselin, 08830. SAN 351-5826. Tel: 732-283-1200. FAX: 732-283-1502. *Librn*, Karen Haase-Gray
Library Holdings: Bk Vols 46,723

L WILENTZ, GOLDMAN & SPITZER, Law Library, 90 Woodbridge Center Dr, 07095. SAN 372-4646. Tel: 732-855-6160. FAX: 732-855-6117. Web Site: www.newjerseylaw.com. *Librn*, Scott L Fisher
Library Holdings: Bk Vols 20,000; Per Subs 110

WOODBURY

S GLOUCESTER COUNTY HISTORICAL SOCIETY LIBRARY, 17 Hunter St, 08096-4605. SAN 310-6187. Tel: 856-845-4771. FAX: 856-845-0131. E-Mail: gchs@gate-net.com. Web Site: www.rootsweb.com/~njglouce/gchs. *Dir*, Edith Hoelle
Founded 1903
Library Holdings: Bk Titles 7,800; Per Subs 12
Subject Interests: Genealogy of the Del Valley-South Jersey area, History
Special Collections: Genealogical Coll, doc, mss, typescripts, vital statistics; History of Gloucester County (Gloucester County Documents 1686-1900); South Jersey Church, local records; US Navy in Early Nineteenth Century (Richard Somers Coll), doc
Restriction: Non-circulating

S GLOUCESTER COUNTY TIMES LIBRARY,* 309 S Broad St, 08096. SAN 375-7293. Tel: 609-845-3300. FAX: 609-845-5480. *Librn*, Sally Ethier

M UNDERWOOD MEMORIAL HOSPITAL, Medical Library, 509 N Broad St, 08096. SAN 320-7005. Tel: 856-845-0100, Ext 2901. FAX: 856-848-5752. *Librn*, Laurie Neblock; E-Mail: neblockl@umhospital.org. Subject Specialists: *Medical*, Laurie Neblock; Staff 1 (MLS 1)
Founded 1965
Library Holdings: Bk Titles 500; Per Subs 95
Database Vendor: Ebsco - EbscoHost
Restriction: Open to public with supervision only
Function: ILL to other special libraries
Mem of SJ Regional Libr Coop
Partic in BHSL; Health Science Library Asn of NJ & Med Libr Asn
Affiliate of Thomas Jefferson University

P WOODBURY PUBLIC LIBRARY,* 33 Delaware St, 08096. SAN 310-6209. Tel: 856-845-2611. FAX: 856-845-5280. E-Mail: wod@jersey.net. *Dir*, Jean Wipf; *Ref*, Florence Meyer; *Ref*, Roxanne Long
Founded 1790. Pop 10,350; Circ 37,884
Library Holdings: Bk Vols 45,000; Per Subs 100
Friends of the Library Group

WOOD-RIDGE

P WOOD-RIDGE MEMORIAL LIBRARY, 231 Hackensack St, 07075. SAN 310-6179. Tel: 201-438-2455. FAX: 201-438-8399. E-Mail: wrdgl@bccls.org.; Staff 2 (MLS 2)
Founded 1931. Pop 7,802; Circ 48,878
Library Holdings: Bk Vols 39,926; Per Subs 95
Special Collections: Local History Coll, (Wood-Ridge)
Automation Activity & Vendor Info: (Cataloging) DRA
Partic in Bergen County Cooperative Library System; Highlands Regional Library Cooperative
Friends of the Library Group

WOODSTOWN

P WOODSTOWN-PILESGROVE PUBLIC LIBRARY,* 14 School Lane, 08098. SAN 310-6217. Tel: 609-769-0098. FAX: 609-769-3658. *Librn*, Ruth T Fritz
Founded 1810. Pop 5,995; Circ 16,455
Library Holdings: Bk Vols 28,900
Special Collections: New Jersey Historical Books
Mem of Cumberland County Library
Partic in S Jersey Regional Libr Network

WRIGHTSTOWN

S MID STATE CORRECTIONAL FACILITY LIBRARY,* Range Rd, PO Box 866, 08562. SAN 375-7048. Tel: 609-723-4221, Ext 8415. FAX: 609-723-8271. *Librn*, Emma Pervall
Library Holdings: Bk Vols 8,701; Bk Titles 4,018; Per Subs 62

WYCKOFF

M CHRISTIAN HEALTH CARE CENTER, Peter Carras Library, 301 Sicomac Ave, 07481. SAN 375-2704. Tel: 201-848-5782. FAX: 201-848-5212. Web Site: www.chcc.org. *In Charge*, Faye Ann Kershen
Library Holdings: Bk Vols 500
Friends of the Library Group

P WYCKOFF PUBLIC LIBRARY, 200 Woodland Ave, 07481. SAN 310-6225. Tel: 201-891-4866. FAX: 201-891-3892. Web Site: www.wyckoff-nj-com. *Dir*, Judy Schmitt; E-Mail: schmitt@bccls.org; *Ch Servs*, Maggie Shoemaker; *Ad Servs*, Linda Fleming; *Ad Servs*, Mary Vallely; *Ref*, Ellen Zamir; Staff 19 (MLS 5, Non-MLS 14)
Founded 1921. Pop 15,372; Circ 237,889
Jan 2000-Dec 2000 Income $818,588, State $16,500, City $792,088, Locally Generated Income $10,000. Mats Exp $187,000, Books $120,000, Per/Ser (Incl. Access Fees) $12,000, AV Equip $40,000, Electronic Ref Mat (Incl. Access Fees) $15,000. Sal $426,021 (Prof $217,097)
Library Holdings: Bk Vols 75,000; Per Subs 90
Subject Interests: Local history
Mem of Bergen County Co-op Libr Syst
Friends of the Library Group

YARDVILLE

S GARDEN STATE YOUTH CORRECTIONAL FACILITY LIBRARY, PO Box 11401, 08620. SAN 375-7471. Tel: 609-298-6300, Ext 2574. FAX: 609-298-3135. *Librn*, Rayford L Johnson
Library Holdings: Bk Vols 15,000; Per Subs 48

NEW MEXICO

Date of Statistics: Fiscal 1998-99
Population, 1997 Census: 1,715,000
Population Served by Public Libraries: 1,434,052
  Unserved: 280,948
Total Volumes in Public Libraries: 4,029,595
  Volumes Per Capita: 2.35 (state population), 2.80 (served population)
Total Public Library Circulation: 8,028,536
  Circulation Per Capita: 4.68 (state population), 5.59 (served population)
Total Public Library Income: $25,395,637
  Source of Income: Public funds: 15.3% county, 76.8% municipal, less than 1% federal, 6% other
  Expenditures Per Capita: $17.70 (served population), $14.80 (state population)
Number of Bookmobiles in State: 5
Grants-in-Aid to Public Libraries: $350,000
  Formula for Apportionment: 95% for library materials, 5% competitive application & per-capita.

ABIQUIU

SR GHOST RANCH CONFERENCE CENTER LIBRARY, HC 77, Box 11, 87510-9601. SAN 310-6233. Tel: 505-685-4333, Ext 109. FAX: 505-685-4519. *Librn*, Edgar Davy; E-Mail: edavy@cybermesa.com; Staff 2 (MLS 1, Non-MLS 1)
Founded 1955
1998-1999 Income $15,990, Locally Generated Income $600, Parent Institution $15,390. Mats Exp $5,500, Books $4,500, Per/Ser (Incl. Access Fees) $1,000
Library Holdings: Bk Titles 20,000; Per Subs 35
Subject Interests: Archaeology, Art, Geology, Religion
Special Collections: Southwest
Automation Activity & Vendor Info: (Cataloging) TLC
Ghost Ranch is a Program Center of the Presbyterian Church (USA)
Friends of the Library Group

ALAMOGORDO

P ALAMOGORDO PUBLIC LIBRARY, 920 Oregon Ave, 88310. SAN 310-6241. Tel: 505-439-4140. Reference Tel: 505-439-4148, Ext 17. FAX: 505-439-4108. E-Mail: alamopl@wazoo.com. Web Site: www.ci.alamogordo.nm.us/library/coalibrary.html. *Dir*, Jim Preston; *ILL*, Annie Tyrrell; Tel: 505-439-4140, Ext 21; *Cat*, Betty Haydu; E-Mail: bhaydu@ci.alamogordo.nm.us; *Ref*, Mary Leslie Schmitt; E-Mail: mschmitt@ci.alamogordo.nm.us; *Ch Servs*, Kathleen Manes; E-Mail: kmanes@ci.alamagordo.nm.us; *Admin Assoc, Syst Coordr*, Mannie Salgado; E-Mail: msalgado@ci.alamagordo.nm.us; *Circ*, Bonnie Meagher; Staff 4 (MLS 4)
Founded 1899. Pop 55,000; Circ 254,000
Jul 1999-Jun 2000 Income $640,405, State $3,866, City $543,233, County $37,300, Other $56,006. Mats Exp $140,678, Books $122,611, Micro $475, Electronic Ref Mat (Incl. Access Fees) $17,592. Sal $309,014
Library Holdings: Bk Vols 89,692; Bk Titles 75,795; Per Subs 250
Subject Interests: Literature, SW hist
Special Collections: Eugene M Rhodes Coll, bks & mss; Mother Goose Editions (Lillian Maddox Coll)
Automation Activity & Vendor Info: (Acquisitions) epixtech, inc.; (Cataloging) epixtech, inc.; (Circulation) epixtech, inc.; (OPAC) epixtech, inc.
Database Vendor: epixtech, inc., OCLC - First Search, ProQuest
Partic in Amigos Library Services, Inc; OCLC Online Computer Library Center, Inc
Friends of the Library Group

S NEW MEXICO SCHOOL FOR THE VISUALLY HANDICAPPED LIBRARY,* 1900 N White Sands Blvd, 88310. SAN 320-2062. Tel: 505-437-3505. FAX: 505-439-4411. *In Charge*, Pam Briggs; Staff 3 (MLS 1, Non-MLS 2)
Enrl 100
1997-1998 Mats Exp $30,000
Library Holdings: Bk Titles 16,500; Per Subs 100
Subject Interests: Gen K-12 fiction, Gen K-12 nonfiction
Special Collections: Blindness; Professional Shelf; Visually Impaired & Multi Handicapped
Library has separate depository collection of textbooks & instructional materials which are disseminated statewide to schools & agencies

J NEW MEXICO STATE UNIVERSITY AT ALAMOGORDO, David H Townsend Library, 2400 N Scenic Dr, 88310. SAN 310-625X. Tel: 505-439-3650. FAX: 505-439-3657. Web Site: www.alamo.nmsu.edu/~library. *Asst Dir*, Jean Strader; E-Mail: jeans@nmsua.nmsu.edu; Staff 6 (MLS 2, Non-MLS 4)
Founded 1975
Library Holdings: Bk Vols 45,000; Per Subs 400
Subject Interests: Allied health, Art, New Mexico, Nursing
Automation Activity & Vendor Info: (Acquisitions) Endeavor; (Cataloging) Endeavor; (Circulation) Endeavor; (Course Reserve) Endeavor; (ILL) Endeavor; (Media Booking) Endeavor; (OPAC) Endeavor; (Serials) Endeavor
Partic in Amigos Library Services, Inc; OCLC Online Computer Library Center, Inc

ALBUQUERQUE

S ALBUQUERQUE JOURNAL-TRIBUNE LIBRARY,* 7777 Jefferson NE, PO Drawer J-T, 87103. SAN 329-1820. Tel: 505-823-3493. *Librn*, Judy Pence; *Publ Servs*, Pat Seligman; Staff 6 (MLS 1, Non-MLS 5)
Founded 1960
Library Holdings: Bk Vols 500; Bk Titles 300; Per Subs 117
Special Collections: New Mexico Current Events & Politics

S THE ALBUQUERQUE MUSEUM OF ART & HISTORY, Reference Library, 2000 Mountain Rd NW, 87104. SAN 320-8664. Tel: 505-243-7255. FAX: 505-764-6546. Web Site: www.cabq.gov/museum. *Dir*, James C Moore
Founded 1967
Library Holdings: Bk Vols 1,600; Per Subs 15
Subject Interests: History, Middle Rio Grande valley, Southwest art

J ALBUQUERQUE TECHNICAL-VOCATIONAL INSTITUTE LIBRARIES, Main Library, 2000 Coal SE, 87106. (Mail add: 525 Buena Vista SE, 87106), SAN 320-4561. Circulation Tel: 505-224-3274. Reference Tel: 505-224-3285. FAX: 505-224-3300. Web Site: planet.tvi.cc.nm.us/library. *Dir*, Shirlene K Gordon; Tel: 505-224-3281, Fax: 505-224-3293, E-Mail: shirlene@tvi.cc.nm.us; *Tech Servs*, Ruth Krug; Tel: 505-224-3278, E-Mail: alinda@tvi.cc.nm.us; *Tech Servs*, Barbara Lovato-Gassman; Tel: 505-224-3279, E-Mail: bgassman@tvi.cc.nm.us; *Electronic Resources*, Paulita Aguilar; Tel: 505-224-3286, E-Mail: paguilar@tvi.cc.nm.us; *Ser*, Clorie Salazar; Tel: 505-224-3283, E-Mail: closal19@tvi.cc.nm.us; *Ref*, Polly Trump; Tel: 505-224-3276, E-Mail: ptrump@tvi.cc.nm.us; *Media Spec*, Wynn Harris; Tel: 505-224-3284, E-Mail: wharris@tvi.cc.nm.us; *Circ*, Ann Johnson; Tel: 505-224-3301, E-Mail: annj@tvi.cc.nm.us; *Syst Coordr*, Pei Pei; Tel: 505-224-3299, E-Mail: ppei@tvi.cc.nm.us; Staff 11 (MLS 4, Non-MLS 7)

Founded 1965. Enrl 15,000; Fac 700
Jul 1999-Jun 2000 Mats Exp $141,529, Books $48,029, Per/Ser (Incl. Access Fees) $40,000, Micro $7,000, Electronic Ref Mat (Incl. Access Fees) $46,500. Sal $420,951 (Prof $216,330)
Library Holdings: Bk Titles 59,508; Per Subs 584
Subject Interests: Air conditioning, Alternative energy, Auto repair, Carpentry, Creativity, Culinary arts, Data proc, Electronics, Health occupations, Hospitality, Laser optics, Law enforcement, Plumbing, Robotics, Secy sci, Sheet metal, Tourism, Use of tools, Welding
Automation Activity & Vendor Info: (Cataloging) TLC; (Circulation) TLC; (OPAC) TLC
Database Vendor: Ebsco - EbscoHost, GaleNet, IAC - Info Trac, OCLC - First Search, ProQuest
Partic in Amigos Library Services, Inc; New Mexico Consortium Of Academic Libraries; New Mexico Consortium Of Biomedical & Hospital Libraries
Departmental Libraries:
MONTOYA CAMPUS, 4700 Morris NE, 87111. SAN 320-9598. Circulation Tel: 505-224-5721. Reference Tel: 505-224-5730. FAX: 505-224-5727. Web Site: planet.tvi.cc.nm.us/library. *Assoc Dir*, Sally A Lindsey; Tel: 505-224-5729, E-Mail: slindsey@tvi.cc.nm.us; *Circ*, Gloria Ortiz; Tel: 505-224-5724, E-Mail: gortiz@tvi.cc.nm.us; *Publ Servs*, Pam Blocker; Tel: 505-224-5723, E-Mail: pbik@tvi.cc.nm.us; *Ser*, Allyson James-Vigil; Tel: 505-224-5731, E-Mail: allyson@tvi.cc.nm.us. Subject Specialists: *Business*, Allyson James-Vigil; *Graphics*, Pam Blocker; *Humanities*, Sally A Lindsey; *Humanities*, Gloria Ortiz; *Technology*, Pam Blocker; Staff 6 (MLS 1, Non-MLS 5)
Founded 1981
Subject Interests: Laser optics
Function: For research purposes

P ALBUQUERQUE-BERNALILLO COUNTY LIBRARY SYSTEM, 501 Copper Ave NW, 87102. SAN 351-5915. Tel: 505-768-5100 (Admin), 505-768-5140 (Info). Interlibrary Loan Service Tel: 505-768-5145. FAX: 505-768-5191. Web Site: www.cabq.gov/rgvls. *Dir*, Eileen Longsworth; *Asst Dir*, Julia Clark; *Asst Dir*, John Godfrey; *Asst Dir*, Ida Mazzoni; *Asst Dir*, Kirsten Shield; *Acq*, Anne Lefkofsky
Founded 1891. Pop 545,493; Circ 2,521,376
Jul 1999-Jun 2000 Income $9,289,200, State $56,002, County $976,349. Mats Exp $2,100,000. Sal $5,151,189
Library Holdings: Bk Vols 1,235,211; Per Subs 1,565
Automation Activity & Vendor Info: (Acquisitions) Innovative Interfaces Inc.
Partic in Amigos Library Services, Inc; OCLC Online Computer Library Center, Inc
Friends of the Library Group
Branches: 17
WESTGATE, 1300 Delgado Dr SW, 87121. Tel: 505-833-6984. *Librn*, Victoria Fee; Tel: 505-833-6985
Library Holdings: Bk Vols 22,934
WYOMING, 8205 Apache Ave NE, 87110. SAN 351-6067. Tel: 505-291-6264. FAX: 505-291-6275. *Mgr*, Cindy Earhart; Tel: 505-291-6266
Library Holdings: Bk Vols 134,326
EAST MOUNTAIN, Hwy 333, Tijeras, 87059. SAN 374-7115. Tel: 505-281-8508. FAX: 505-281-8510. *Librn*, Ellanie Sampson; Tel: 503-281-8509
Library Holdings: Bk Vols 59,185
ESPERANZA, 5600 Esperanza Dr NW, 87105. SAN 351-5974. Tel: 505-836-0684. FAX: 505-876-8779. *Librn*, Elizabeth Haskett; Tel: 505-836-0685
Library Holdings: Bk Vols 42,329
ERNA FERGUSSON BRANCH, 3700 San Mateo Blvd NE, 87110-1246. SAN 351-6008. Tel: 505-888-8100. FAX: 505-888-8109. *Branch Mgr*, Victoria Fee; Tel: 505-888-8101
Library Holdings: Per Subs 25
Automation Activity & Vendor Info: (Serials) Innovative Interfaces Inc.
Special Services for the Blind - Talking books (cassettes & rec)
Friends of the Library Group
LOMAS-TRAMWAY, 908 Eastridge NE, 87123. SAN 329-689X. Tel: 505-291-6295. FAX: 505-291-6299. *In Charge*, Leslie Bihn; Tel: 605-291-6296
Library Holdings: Bk Vols 82,823
LOS GRIEGOS, 1000 Griegos Rd NW, 87107. SAN 351-6032. Tel: 505-761-4020. FAX: 505-761-4014. *Librn*, Annie Morningstar; Tel: 505-761-4021
Library Holdings: Bk Vols 68,638
MAIN LIBRARY, 501 Copper Ave NW, 87102. SAN 351-594X. Tel: 505-768-5100, 505-768-5141. FAX: 505-768-5182. *Librn*, Joseph Sabatini; Tel: 505-768-5174, E-Mail: jsabatin@albug.rgv.lib.nm.us; *Mgr*, Ida Mazzoni; Tel: 505-768-5152, E-Mail: imazzoni@abq.gov; *Ref*, Steve Roehling
Library Holdings: Bk Vols 319,762
NORTH VALLEY, 7704 Second St NW, 87104. SAN 374-7107. Tel: 505-897-8823, 505-897-8824. FAX: 505-897-8825.
Founded 1994
Library Holdings: Bk Vols 63,427
ERNIE PYLE BRANCH, 900 Girard Blvd SE, 87106. SAN 351-6091. Tel: 505-256-2065. FAX: 505-256-2069. *Mgr*, Elaine Shannon; Tel: 505-256-2066
Library Holdings: Bk Vols 17,776
SAN PEDRO BRANCH, 5600 Trumbull Ave SE, 87108. SAN 351-6121. Tel: 505-256-2067. FAX: 505-256-2064. *Mgr*, Pat Martinez; Tel: 505-256-2068
Library Holdings: Bk Vols 45,026
SOUTH BROADWAY, 1025 Broadway Blvd SE, 87102. SAN 373-9309. Tel: 505-764-1742. FAX: 505-764-1783. *Librn*, Elaine Shannon; Tel: 505-764-1769
Library Holdings: Bk Vols 57,205
SOUTH VALLEY, 3904 Isleta Blvd SW, 87105. SAN 329-6938. Tel: 505-877-5170. FAX: 505-877-6639. *Librn*, Jacquelen Rubin; Tel: 505-873-6638; *Br Coordr*, Steven Roehling; E-Mail: sroeh@earthlink.net; Staff 6 (MLS 3, Non-MLS 3)
Library Holdings: Bk Vols 43,159; Per Subs 50
Database Vendor: Innovative Interfaces INN - View
Friends of the Library Group
SPECIAL COLLECTIONS, 423 Central Ave NE, 87102. SAN 351-6156. Tel: 505-848-1376. FAX: 505-833-6989. *Mgr*, Joe Sabatini; Tel: 505-848-1377
Library Holdings: Bk Vols 24,268
Special Collections: Genealogy; Southwest Reference
JUAN TABO BRANCH, 3407 Juan Tabo Blvd NE, 87111. SAN 351-6164. Tel: 505-291-6260. FAX: 505-291-6225. *Librn*, Joan Murphy; Tel: 505-291-6261
Library Holdings: Bk Vols 85,855
TAYLOR RANCH, 5700 Bogart NW, 87120. SAN 329-6911. Tel: 505-897-8816. FAX: 505-897-8813. *Mgr*, Elizabeth Haskett; Tel: 505-897-8817
Library Holdings: Bk Vols 84,207
Bookmobiles: 1. Coordr, Joseph Sabatini. Tel.: 505-768-5127. Bk Vols 1986

G BUREAU OF LAND MANAGEMENT LIBRARY,* 435 Montano Rd NE, 87107-4935. SAN 310-6306. Tel: 505-761-8700. *Librn*, George Moore
Library Holdings: Bk Vols 3,750; Per Subs 55
Subject Interests: Environ, Land, Minerals, Wildlife habitat mgt
Special Collections: Cultural & Archeological Resource Inventories; Environmental Impact Statements

S CENTER FOR ANTHROPOLOGICAL STUDIES LIBRARY, 1517 Figueroa NE 87112, PO Box 14576, 87191. SAN 310-6314. Tel: 505-296-6336. *Dir*, A E Ward
Founded 1976
Library Holdings: Bk Titles 2,450; Per Subs 20
Subject Interests: Archaeology, History, Southwestern anthrop
Special Collections: Wetherill Family Archives

SR CENTRAL UNITED METHODIST CHURCH LIBRARY, 1615 Cooper NE, 87106-4596. SAN 371-8476. Tel: 505-243-7834. FAX: 505-242-6986. *Librn*, Rex Allender
Special Collections: Bible, bk & AV; Methodist History, bks & AV
Publications: Acquisitions List; Bibliographies; Guides

SR CHURCH OF JESUS CHRIST OF LATTER-DAY SAINTS, Albuquerque South State Family History Center Library,* 4708 Ponderosa NE, 87110. SAN 323-4797. Tel: 505-266-4867. *Dir*, Cecile Hawk; *Dir*, John Hawk
Library Holdings: Bk Vols 1,475; Per Subs 40
Subject Interests: Genealogy
Open Mon & Sat 9-3, Tues-Thurs 9-3 & 6-9

R CONGREGATION B'NAI ISRAEL, Isidore & Rose Bloch Memorial Library, 4401 Indian School Rd NE, 87110. SAN 310-6322. Tel: 505-266-0155. FAX: 505-268-6136. *Librn*, Elinor Sherry; *Librn*, Leon Sherry
Library Holdings: Bk Vols 3,800
Special Collections: Judaica Coll

GM DEPARTMENT OF VETERANS AFFAIRS, General & Medical Library (142D), 1501 San Pedro SE, 87108. SAN 310-6489. Tel: 505-256-2786. FAX: 505-256-2870. *Dir Libr Serv*, Phyllis Kregstein; E-Mail: phyllis.kregstein@med.va.gov; Staff 3 (MLS 2, Non-MLS 1)
Founded 1932
Library Holdings: Bk Vols 2,202; Per Subs 280
Subject Interests: General med, Geriatrics, Gerontology, Nursing, Psychiatry, Psychology, Surgery
Restriction: Not open to public
Partic in N Mex Consortium of Biomedical & Hospital Libr; Nat Libr of Med; Vets Admin Libr Network
Special Services for the Blind - Talking book center
Library also serves Kirtland AFB

SR FIRST BAPTIST CHURCH LIBRARY,* 101 Broadway NE, PO Box 26446, 87125-6446. SAN 326-2243. Tel: 505-247-3611. FAX: 505-247-0345. *Acq, Librn*, Mahote Bowen; *Asst Librn*, Bobbie Cloud; *Asst Librn*, Katy Boyd; *Asst Librn*, Betty Wilson; *Asst Librn*, Emma Dale Daniel
Founded 1937
Apr 1996-Mar 1997 Mats Exp $3,200, Books $1,450, Per/Ser (Incl. Access Fees) $100, AV Equip $700
Library Holdings: Bk Vols 11,000
Subject Interests: Fiction
Special Collections: Publication for archives

R FIRST PRESBYTERIAN CHURCH LIBRARY, 215 Locust NE, 87102. SAN 310-6349. Tel: 505-764-2900. FAX: 505-764-2940. *Librn*, Lucille Katzenberger; Staff 12 (MLS 3, Non-MLS 9)
Founded 1955. Circ 1,000
Library Holdings: Bk Vols 7,000; Bk Titles 6,000; Per Subs 30
Subject Interests: Personal help, Religion
Special Collections: Local History & Culture, bks, flms
Publications: Column in monthly newsletter
Friends of the Library Group

S HISPANIC CULTURE FOUNDATION RESOURCE LIBRARY,* 600 Central SW Ste 201, 87102. (Mail add: PO Box 7279, 87194), SAN 370-6516. Tel: 505-766-9858. FAX: 505-766-9665. E-Mail: info@hcfoundation.org. Web Site: www.hcfoundation.org.; Staff 1 (MLS 1)
Founded 1986
Library Holdings: Bk Titles 350
Publications: El Puente (newsletter); Flow of the River: Corre el Rio (also video); New Mexico Directory of Hispanic Culture

R HOFFMANTOWN BAPTIST CHURCH LIBRARY,* 8888 Harper Dr NE, 87111. SAN 322-6581. Tel: 505-828-2600. FAX: 505-821-5398. *Dir*, Jeanne Mayerhoffer; Staff 8 (MLS 3, Non-MLS 5)
Founded 1965. Circ 3,000
Library Holdings: Bk Vols 8,100; Bk Titles 8,000
Subject Interests: Bible studies, Religion

R LA MESA PRESBYTERIAN CHURCH LIBRARY, 7401 Copper Ave NE, 87108. SAN 310-6357. Tel: 505-255-8095. FAX: 505-265-5102. *In Charge*, Lila Roger
Library Holdings: Bk Titles 1,700
Special Collections: Cambridge Bible for Schools & Colleges (1890-1899 edition) Coll; Christian religion, bks

M LOVELACE HEALTH SYSTEMS, Lassetter Foster Memorial Library, 5400 Gibson Blvd SE, 87108. SAN 310-6365. Tel: 505-262-7158. FAX: 505-262-7897. Web Site: www.lovelace.com. *Chief Librn*, Linda Morgan Davis; E-Mail: linda.davis@lovelace.com; Staff 3 (MLS 1, Non-MLS 2)
Founded 1947
Jan 1999-Dec 1999 Mats Exp $75,000, Books $9,000, Per/Ser (Incl. Access Fees) $52,000, AV Equip $5,000, Electronic Ref Mat (Incl. Access Fees) $9,000. Sal $72,500
Library Holdings: Bk Vols 7,500; Per Subs 210
Subject Interests: Clinical medicine, Herbals, Native Am med
Special Collections: Native American Collection
Automation Activity & Vendor Info: (Circulation) Inmagic, Inc.; (OPAC) Inmagic, Inc.; (Serials) Inmagic, Inc.
Database Vendor: Ebsco - EbscoHost, OCLC - First Search
Partic in Medline; New Mexico Consortium Of Biomedical & Hospital Libraries; OCLC Online Computer Library Center, Inc; S Cent Regional Med Libr Program

S LOVELACE RESPIRATORY RESEARCH INSTITUTE, Inhalation Toxicology Research Institute Library,* PO Box 5890, 87185. SAN 310-6810. Tel: 505-845-1048. FAX: 505-845-1233. Web Site: www.lrri.org. *Dir*, Sandy Spurlock; Staff 2 (MLS 1, Non-MLS 1)
Founded 1974
Library Holdings: Bk Vols 12,309; Bk Titles 11,709; Per Subs 200
Subject Interests: Aerosol physics, Fossil fuels effluents, Radiation effects, Respiratory syst, Toxicology, Veterinary medicine
Partic in Dialog Corporation; Nat Libr of Med; New Mexico Consortium Of Biomedical & Hospital Libraries; S Cent Regional Libr Prog; SDC Info Servs

S MAXWELL MUSEUM ASSOCIATION, Clark Field Archives,* University of New Mexico, 87131. SAN 377-3280. Tel: 505-277-8675. *Dir*, Garth Bawden; *Head of Libr*, Allen Shallette
Library Holdings: Bk Titles 9,000; Per Subs 24

S MENAUL HISTORICAL LIBRARY OF THE SOUTHWEST, (MHL), 301 Menaul Blvd NE, 87107. SAN 371-2249. Tel: 505-343-7480. *Adminr*, Nona Browne
Founded 1974
Jan 2000-Dec 2000 Income $7,300. Mats Exp $7,300, Books $300, Per/Ser (Incl. Access Fees) $20, Presv $3,000, Micro $500, AV Equip $2,500
Library Holdings: Bk Vols 21,000; Spec Interest Per Sub 20
Subject Interests: Presbyterian churches of the Southern US
Function: Research library

L MILLER, STRATVERT & TORGERSON, Law Library, 500 Marquette NW, Ste 1100, PO Box 25687, 87102. SAN 372-4387. Tel: 505-842-1950. FAX: 505-243-4408. Web Site: www.mstlaw.com. *Librn*, Diana Busbey; E-Mail: dbusbey@mstlaw.com
Founded 1978
Library Holdings: Bk Vols 5,000; Per Subs 20

L MODRALL, SPERLING, ROEHL, HARRIS & SISK, Law Library,* PO Box 2168, 87103. SAN 372-4255. Tel: 505-848-1800. FAX: 505-848-1891. *Librn*, Miriam Greenwood
Library Holdings: Bk Vols 10,000; Per Subs 40
Friends of the Library Group

SR MONTE VISTA CHRISTIAN CHURCH, Pearce Memorial Library-Media Center, 3501 Campus Blvd NE, 87106. SAN 371-8514. Tel: 505-268-3365. *Librn*, Elizabeth C Bundy; *Asst Librn*, Pat White
Jan 2000-Dec 2000 Income Parent Institution $600. Mats Exp $625, Books $600, Per/Ser (Incl. Access Fees) $25
Library Holdings: Bk Titles 6,150
Special Collections: Religious & Interpersonal; Southwest
Friends of the Library Group

S NATIONAL ATOMIC MUSEUM LIBRARY, Sandia National Lab, PO Box 5800, 87185-1490. SAN 310-6829. Tel: 505-284-3234. FAX: 505-284-3244. *In Charge*, Arlene Lucero
Founded 1969
Library Holdings: Bk Titles 2,050
Subject Interests: Aircraft, Fighting ships, Manhattan Project, Nuclear hist, Nuclear science, Nuclear weapons, Space, World War II hist
Special Collections: Historic Books on the Nuclear Age
Database Vendor: epixtech, inc.
Restriction: Non-circulating to the public

S NATIONAL INFORMATION CENTER FOR EDUCATIONAL MEDIA (NICEM) LIBRARY,* 131 Adams St NE, PO Box 8640, 87198. SAN 325-5093. Tel: 505-265-3591. Toll Free Tel: 800-926-8328. FAX: 505-256-1080. E-Mail: nicem@nicem.com. Web Site: www.nicem.com. *Exec Dir*, Roy Morgan
Subject Interests: AV media, Nonprint mat
Special Collections: Catalogs of Audiovisual producers & distributors
Publications: Audio Cassette & Compact Disc Finder; AV Online CD-ROM: Film & Video Finder; Filmstrip & Slide Set Finder; Index to AV Producers & Distributors; International Directory of Educational Audiovisuals

G NEW MEXICO INSTITUTE OF MINING & TECHNOLOGY, Environmental Evaluation Group Library,* 7007 Wyoming Blvd NE, Ste F-2, 87109. SAN 370-5420. Tel: 505-828-1003. FAX: 505-828-1062. Web Site: www.rt66.com/~eeg/home_frames.htm. *Librn*, Linda Kennedy; E-Mail: lindak@eeg.org; Staff 1 (MLS 1)
Founded 1978
Library Holdings: Bk Titles 10,000; Per Subs 25
Special Collections: Rad Waste Disposal, Bks, docs
Publications: EEG reports

S NEW MEXICO YOUTH DIAGNOSTIC CENTER, Forrester Library, 4000 Edith NE, 87107. SAN 325-8300. Tel: 505-841-4239. FAX: 505-841-4247. *Librn*, Christina Tullar
Founded 1916
Library Holdings: Bk Titles 8,000; Per Subs 32
Special Collections: Educational; Professional

M PRESBYTERIAN HOSPITAL, Robert Shafer Memorial Library, 1100 Central SE, PO Box 26666, 87125-6666. SAN 310-6411. Tel: 505-841-1516. FAX: 505-841-1067. *Librn*, Frankie Ewing; Staff 2 (MLS 2)
Founded 1962
Library Holdings: Bk Titles 1,200; Per Subs 160
Subject Interests: Medicine
Partic in New Mexico Consortium Of Biomedical & Hospital Libraries
Friends of the Library Group

S RODEY, DICKASON, SLOAN, AKIN & ROBB, PA LIBRARY,* 201 Third St NW Ste 2200, 87102. (Mail add: PO Box 1888, 87103), SAN 371-1366. Tel: 505-765-5900. FAX: 505-768-7395. *Librn*, Pamela M Dempsey
Library Holdings: Bk Vols 20,000; Per Subs 238

R SAINT JOHN'S EPISCOPAL CATHEDRAL, Kadey Memorial Library, 318 Silver SW, 87102. SAN 310-642X. Tel: 505-247-1581. FAX: 505-247-3377. E-Mail: StJohnsABQ@aol.com. *Librn*, Catharine Musgrave
Founded 1975
Library Holdings: Bk Titles 1,000
Subject Interests: Biblical lit, Devotional, Devotional psychol, Liturgy, Philosophy, Relig studies, Theology

S SAINT JOSEPH MEDICAL CENTER, Medical Library,* PO Box 25555, 87125. SAN 325-9153. Tel: 505-727-8291. FAX: 505-727-8190. E-Mail: mclib@sjhs.org. *In Charge*, Leigh Turner; Staff 1 (MLS 1)
Library Holdings: Bk Titles 400; Per Subs 65
Partic in New Mexico Consortium Of Biomedical & Hospital Libraries; South Central Academic Medical Libraries Consortium

SR SAINT PAUL'S UNITED METHODIST CHURCH LIBRARY, 9500 Constitution Rd NE, 87112. SAN 371-1218. Tel: 505-298-5596. FAX: 505-275-8066.
Library Holdings: Bk Vols 200

SR ST STEPHEN'S UNITED METHODIST CHURCH LIBRARY, 4601 Juan Tabo NE, 87111. SAN 325-2523. Tel: 505-293-9673. FAX: 505-294-6243. E-Mail: ssumc@nmia.com. Web Site: www.ssumc.com. *Librn*, Jeanette Baker
Library Holdings: Bk Titles 3,350
Subject Interests: Christianity, Religion

R SANDIA BAPTIST CHURCH, Media Library, 9429 Constitution NE, 87112. SAN 325-0814. Tel: 505-292-2713, 505-292-2717, 505-299-2130. FAX: 505-296-3009. E-Mail: sandiabaptist@/wo/.com. *Librn*, Saundra A Morris
Founded 1963
Library Holdings: Bk Vols 7,100

S SANDIA NATIONAL LABORATORIES, Technical Library, PO Box 5800, MS 0899, 87185-0899. SAN 310-6438. Tel: 505-845-8287. Web Site: www.sandia.gov/library.htm. *Dir*, Herbert Pitts; *Mgr, Ref Serv*, Susan Stinchcomb; *Circ*, Georgia Teller; *Coll Develop*, Lynn Kaczor; *Mgr, Tech Servs*, Sally Landenberger; Staff 37 (MLS 14, Non-MLS 23)
Founded 1948
Library Holdings: Bk Titles 70,000; Per Subs 1,100
Subject Interests: Aerodynamics, Electronics, Energy res, Explosives, Mats, Nuclear safety, Nuclear waste mgt, Nuclear weapons, Ordinance, Security, Solid-state physics
Special Collections: Sandia Technical Reports
Automation Activity & Vendor Info: (Acquisitions) epixtech, inc.; (Cataloging) epixtech, inc.; (Circulation) epixtech, inc.; (OPAC) epixtech, inc.; (Serials) epixtech, inc.
Publications: New Books and Unclassified Reports Acquisitions
Restriction: Staff use only
Partic in Amigos Library Services, Inc; Horizon Users Group

S SCIENTECH, INC-REDDY CORPORATION INTERNATIONAL, Information Resource Center, 4501 Indian School Blvd, Ste 200, 87110. (Mail add: PO Box 3209, 87190-3209), SAN 302-1548. Tel: 505-244-7600. Toll Free Tel: 888-972-8676. FAX: 505-244-7658. E-Mail: research@scientech.com. Web Site: www.scientech.com. *Senior Info Specialist*, Phyllis Morgan; E-Mail: pmorgan@scientech.com
Library Holdings: Bk Vols 1,550; Per Subs 450
Subject Interests: Elec utilities, Energy, Indust
Restriction: Not open to public

S SOUTHWEST RESEARCH & INFORMATION CENTER LIBRARY, 105 Stanford SE, 87106-3537. (Mail add: PO Box 4524, 87106-4524), SAN 326-0089. Tel: 505-262-1862. FAX: 505-262-1864. Web Site: www.sric.org. *Librn*, Don Hancock; E-Mail: sricdon@earthlink.net; Staff 1 (Non-MLS 1)
Founded 1971
Library Holdings: Bk Titles 10,000; Per Subs 450
Restriction: Open to public for reference only
Function: Photocopies available, Reference only

J SOUTHWESTERN INDIAN POLYTECHNIC INSTITUTE LIBRARIES,* 9169 Coors Rd NW, 87120. SAN 310-6454. Tel: 505-346-2352. FAX: 505-346-2381. E-Mail: library@sipi.bia.edu. Web Site: www.native.sipi.bia.edu. *Librn*, Paula M Smith
Library Holdings: Bk Vols 30,000; Per Subs 150
Subject Interests: Acct electronics, Bus, Data proc, Eng tech, Food tech, Marketing, Natural resources, Secretarial
Special Collections: Indian Coll, mat, tech bks

L SUTIN, THAYER & BROWNE, Law Library, 2 Park Square Bldg, 10th flr, 6565 Americas Pkwy NE, 87110. SAN 372-4379. Tel: 505-883-2500. FAX: 505-888-6565. E-Mail: rpm@sutinfirm.com. Web Site: www.sutinfirm.com.
Library Holdings: Bk Vols 10,000; Per Subs 100

S THE LLOYD SHAW DANCE ARCHIVES, 5506 Coal SE, 87108. (Mail add: 1620 Los Alamos SW, 87104), SAN 329-0255. Tel: 505-247-3921, 505-255-2661. Web Site: www.lsda.org. *Dir*, Dr William M Litchman; E-Mail: litchman@unm.edu
Founded 1977. Pop 6,000,000
Sep 1999-Aug 2000 Income Parent Institution $1,500
Library Holdings: Bk Titles 2,500; Per Subs 50; Spec Interest Per Sub 50
Subject Interests: Dance, Folk
Special Collections: Brundage Coll; Clossin Coll; Shaw Coll (Dorothy & Lloyd Shaw, mss, printed); Walsh Coll
Automation Activity & Vendor Info: (Cataloging) Sagebrush Corporation
Publications: Bibliography of American Country Dance; Catalog of Dance; Catalog of Dance Videos; Dissertations
Friends of the Library Group

M CARRIE TINGLEY HOSPITAL MEDICAL LIBRARY,* 1127 University Blvd NE, 87102. SAN 310-740X. Tel: 505-272-5200.
Library Holdings: Bk Vols 3,050; Per Subs 20
Special Collections: Mainly general orthopaedic & pediatric orthopaedic books & journals.

UNITED STATES ARMY

A CORPS OF ENGINEERS, ALBUQUERQUE DISTRICT, 4101 Jefferson Plaza NE, 87109-3435. SAN 351-6180. Tel: 505-342-3169. FAX: 505-342-3198. *In Charge*, Sue Hill; E-Mail: susan.e.hill@spa02.usace.army.mil
Founded 1974
Subject Interests: Civil engineering, Dams, Environmental studies, Flood operations, Leadership develop, Parks, Recreation
Function: Reference services available
Partic in OCLC Online Computer Library Center, Inc

L UNITED STATES COURTS LIBRARY,* 333 Lomas Blvd NW Ste 360, 87102. SAN 372-428X. Tel: 505-348-2135. FAX: 505-348-2795. *Librn*, Gregory L Townsend; E-Mail: gtownsend@nmcourt.fad.us; *Tech Servs*, Greg Surratt
Library Holdings: Bk Vols 18,000; Per Subs 50

C UNIVERSITY OF NEW MEXICO, General Library, 87131-1466. SAN 351-6210. Tel: 505-277-4241. Interlibrary Loan Service Tel: 505-277-5617. Circulation Tel: 505-277-5057. Reference Tel: 505-277-5761. FAX: 505-277-6019. Web Site: elibrary.unm.edu. *Dean of Libr*, Robert Migneault; *Assoc Dean*, Fran Wilkinson; *Tech Servs*, Nancy Dennis; *Circ*, Edward Padilla; *Ref*, Dan Barkley; *ILL*, Randall Moorehead; *Cat*, Claire-Lise Benaud; *Acq, Ser*, Carol Rentro; *Govt Doc*, Dan Barkley; *Coordr*, R Davidson; *Dir*, Johann van Reenen; *Dir*, Dave Baldwin; *Coll Develop*, Linda K Lewis. Subject Specialists: *Education*, M E Hanson; *Humanities*, N Pistorius; *Science/technology*, B Neville; *Social sciences and issues*, S Bordeianu; Staff 181 (MLS 39, Non-MLS 142)
Founded 1892. Enrl 18,923; Fac 862; Highest Degree: Doctorate
Jul 1999-Jun 2000 Income (Main and Other College/University Libraries) $14,083,821. Mats Exp $4,648,931, Books $1,438,471, Per/Ser (Incl. Access Fees) $2,695,642, Presv $113,937, Other Print Mats $103,178. Sal $7,163,244 (Prof $2,045,913)
Library Holdings: Bk Vols 1,926,945; Per Subs 12,698
Subject Interests: Hist of photog, Ibero-Am mat, Southwestern archit
Special Collections: 19th & 20th Century Oaxaca, Mexico Pamphlet & Regional History; 19th Century Latin American Travel Narratives; Indian Affairs (Glenn Leonidas Emmons & Michael Steck Coll), papers; Indians (Doris Duke Foundation Coll AIM archives); John Donald Robb Archive of Southwestern Music, A-tapes; Land Records (Maxwell Land Grant Company, United States Soil Conservation Service Reports); Latin American Agrarian History, Agricultural Economics & Rural Sociology (T Lynn Smith Coll); Literary Manuscripts (Erna Fergusson Papers, Frank Waters Papers, Papers of Regional Hispanic Writers; New Mexicana; Papers of Public Figures (Thomas B Catron, Albert Bacon Fall, Miguel Antonio Otero, United States Senators: Dennis Chavez, Pete V Domenici, Joseph M Montoya, Harrison H Schmitt, Congressman Manuel J Lujan); Photocopies Spanish, Mexican, & New Mexican Archives; Pioneers Foundation Coll (Anglos); Popular Culture Coll (Day Science Fiction periodicals, dime novels); Puppetry (McPharlin Coll), bks, realia; Regional Historical Manuscripts: Business Records (Bell Ranch-Red River Valley Company, Charles Ilfeld Mercantile Company, First National Bank of Santa Fe); Regional Historical Photographs (William Henry Cobb, Charles Fletcher Lummis, Henry Schmidt Coll); Southwestern Americana; Southwestern Historical Architectural Documents (John Gaw Meem Coll); US Patent Dept
Publications: Information Express; Lexicon UNM General Library Newsletter; University of New Mexico General Library Handbook for Faculty; University of New Mexico General Library Official Bulletin; University of New Mexico General Library Sources Series; UNM General Library Annual Report
Mem of Asn of Research Libraries
Partic in Amigos Library Services, Inc; New Mexico Consortium Of Academic Libraries
Special Services for the Deaf - Books on deafness & sign language; High interest/low vocabulary books; Special interest periodicals; TTY machine
Special Services for the Blind - Braille printing of screens from OPAC; Braille Webster's Dictionary; Compressed speech cassette players; Kurzweil Reading Machine; Opticon; Telesensory screen enlarger & speech synthesis interface to the OPAC; VisualTek text enlargers; World Book Encyclopedia on cassette
Friends of the Library Group
Departmental Libraries:
CENTENNIAL SCIENCE & ENGINEERING LIBRARY, 87131. Tel: 505-277-4858. FAX: 505-277-0702. Web Site: www.unm.edu/~csel/. *Dir*, Johann vanReenen; E-Mail: jreenen@unm.edu
Special Collections: Map Room; United States Patents
Friends of the Library Group
FINE ARTS Tel: 505-277-2357. FAX: 505-277-7134. Web Site: www.unm.edu/fal/ref. *Dir*, David Baldwin
Friends of the Library Group
CM HEALTH SCIENCES CENTER LIBRARY Tel: 505- 272-0654. Interlibrary Loan Service Tel: 505-272-0654. FAX: 505-272-5350, 505-272-8254. E-Mail: hsclref@salud.unm.edu. Web Site: www.caliban.unm.edu, www.hfc.unm.edu/library/. *Dir*, Holly Shipp Buchanan; *Access Serv*, Deborah L Graham; *Coll Develop*, Jon Eldredge; *Info Tech*, Greg Gaillard; *Instrul Serv*, Janis Teal; *Online Servs*, Richard Saavedra; *Ref*, Christee King; *Tech Servs*, Ruth Morris; *Tech Servs*, Ruth Morris; Staff 37 (MLS 11, Non-MLS 26)
Founded 1963. Enrl 1,650; Fac 624; Highest Degree: Doctorate

Jul 1997-Jun 1998 Income $2,375,620. Mats Exp $1,081,063, Books $66,971, Per/Ser (Incl. Access Fees) $610,676, Presv $24,359, AV Equip $6,428. Sal $1,136,012 (Prof $564,251)
Library Holdings: Bk Vols 59,993; Bk Titles 59,280; Per Subs 1,716
Subject Interests: Allied health, Dent hygiene, Med hist, Medicine, Native American health, Nursing, Pharm
Special Collections: Consumer Health Information; Indian Health Services Research; Southwest & New Mexico Medicine, media; UNM Health Sciences Center Archives; World Health Organization Publications
Publications: Adobe Medicus; Selected Bibliographies
Partic in Amigos Library Services, Inc; National Network Of Libraries Of Medicine - South Central Region; OCLC Online Computer Library Center, Inc; South Central Academic Medical Libraries Consortium
Friends of the Library Group

CL LAW LIBRARY, 1117 Stanford Dr NE, 87131-1441. SAN 351-627X. Tel: 505-277-6236. FAX: 505-277-0068. Web Site: www.lawschool.unm.edu/library/. *Dir*, Marsha Baum; *Access Serv*, Lisa Peters; *Coll Develop*, Lorraine Lester; *Tech Servs*, Eileen Cohen
Founded 1948. Enrl 320; Fac 30; Highest Degree: Doctorate
Library Holdings: Bk Vols 202,469; Bk Titles 75,194; Per Subs 3,168
Special Collections: Alternative Dispute Resolution; American Indian Law Coll; Land Grant Law Coll; Mexican Law Coll
Publications: New Acquisitions-Selected Titles
Partic in Amigos Library Services, Inc; New Mexico Consortium Of Academic Libraries; Westlaw
Friends of the Library Group

BUSINESS & ECONOMICS-WILLIAM J PARISH MEMORIAL, 87131-1496. Tel: 505-277-5912. FAX: 505-277-9813. Web Site: elibrary.unm.edu/pmleref. *Dir, Librn*, Susan C Awe
Subject Interests: Bus, Econ
Special Collections: Foreign Corporate Annual Reports; US Corporate Annual Reports
Friends of the Library Group

S UNIVERSITY OF NEW MEXICO, (Formerly Data Bank Bureau Of Business & Economic Research), Data Bank Bureau of Business & Economic Research, University of New Mexico, 1920 Lomas NE, 87131-6021. SAN 310-6330. Tel: 505-277-6626. FAX: 505-277-2773. E-Mail: dbinfo@unm.edu. Web Site: www.unm.edu/~bber.; Staff 3 (Non-MLS 3)
Founded 1945
Library Holdings: Bk Vols 16,000; Per Subs 40
Subject Interests: Econ develop, New Mexico demographics
Special Collections: New Mexico Social Statistics (1970, 1980 & 1990 Census Summary Tapes Coll); New Mexico Statistics (New Mexico State & Local Government Agency Publications Coll, 1950-present); New Mexico's Economy Coll
Publications: Census in New Mexico; Economic Census-New Mexico; New Mexico Business-Current Economic Report
Restriction: Open to public for reference only

ANTHONY

P VALLEY COMMUNITY LIBRARY,* 735 Church St, PO Box 1297, 88021-1297. SAN 375-3379. Tel: 505-882-7982. FAX: 505-524-4318. E-Mail: valleycl@nm-us.campus.mci.net. *Dir*, Erma Sanchez Adler; *Librn*, Jay Foster Kanitz; Staff 3 (MLS 3)
Founded 1989. Pop 5,160
Jul 1996-Jun 1997 Income $20,071, State $14,029, County $2,000, Locally Generated Income $2,042. Mats Exp $12,800, Books $11,852, Per/Ser (Incl. Access Fees) $73, Micro $437. Sal $6,948 (Prof $6,629)
Library Holdings: Bk Vols 15,000; Per Subs 12
Special Collections: Southwest Coll
Friends of the Library Group

ARTESIA

S ARTESIA HISTORICAL MUSEUM & ART CENTER, Research Facility, 505 W Richardson Ave, 88210. SAN 373-4773. Tel: 505-748-2390. FAX: 505-746-3886. E-Mail: ahmac@putnetworks.net. *Dir*, Nancy Dunn
Founded 1970
Library Holdings: Bk Vols 500
Subject Interests: Genealogy, Local history
Special Collections: City of Artesia Archives

P ARTESIA PUBLIC LIBRARY,* 306 W Richardson Ave, 88210-2499. SAN 310-6500. Tel: 505-746-4252, 505-746-4692. FAX: 505-746-3886. *Librn*, Pamela Castle; *Ch Servs*, Sally Carrera
Founded 1902. Pop 14,000; Circ 77,627
Library Holdings: Bk Titles 60,000; Per Subs 166
Partic in Amigos Library Services, Inc

AZTEC

P AZTEC PUBLIC LIBRARY,* 201 W Chaco, 87410-1996. SAN 310-6519. Tel: 505-334-7658. FAX: 505-334-7609. E-Mail: aztecpl@cyberport.com. *Librn*, Leanne Hathcock; Staff 1 (MLS 1)
Founded 1908
Library Holdings: Bk Vols 28,559
Subject Interests: Aztec ruins, Chaco Canyon, Large print, Mesa Verde areas
Special Collections: Audio/Video Coll (Adult & Juvenile); Southwest Coll
Friends of the Library Group

G NATIONAL PARK SERVICE, Aztec Ruins National Monument Library, 84 County Rd 2900, 87410. SAN 329-0697. Tel: 505-334-6174. FAX: 505-334-6372. E-Mail: azsu_front_desk@nps.gov. Web Site: www.nps.gov/azsu. *In Charge*, Tracy Bodnar
Founded 1923
Library Holdings: Bk Vols 500; Bk Titles 500
Subject Interests: Archaeology

BELEN

P BELEN PUBLIC LIBRARY, (BPL), 333 Becker Ave, 87002. SAN 310-6527. Tel: 505-864-7522, 505-864-7797. FAX: 505-864-7798. *Dir*, Beverly McFarland; Staff 6 (MLS 1, Non-MLS 5)
Founded 1966. Pop 18,000; Circ 58,676
Jul 1999-Jun 2000 Income City $160,000. Mats Exp $15,400, Books $12,000, Per/Ser (Incl. Access Fees) $1,400, Electronic Ref Mat (Incl. Access Fees) $2,000
Library Holdings: Bk Vols 37,000; Per Subs 54
Subject Interests: Southwest
Automation Activity & Vendor Info: (Cataloging) TLC; (Circulation) TLC; (OPAC) TLC
Partic in Rio Abajo Libr Coop
Friends of the Library Group

BERNALILLO

P TOWN OF BERNALILLO PUBLIC LIBRARY,* 134 Calle Malinche, PO Box 10, 87004-0638. SAN 310-6535. Tel: 505-867-1440. FAX: 505-867-8040. *Librn*, Juanita Montano
Founded 1965. Pop 7,000
Library Holdings: Bk Vols 17,500; Per Subs 20
Special Collections: Historical Coll of Southwest
Partic in NMex Libr Asn
Friends of the Library Group

BLOOMFIELD

P BLOOMFIELD PUBLIC LIBRARY, 333 S First St, 87413-6221. SAN 375-5207. Tel: 505-632-8315. FAX: 505-632-0876. E-Mail: bpl@cyberport.com. *Librn*, Jeannette Lassell; *Asst Librn*, Anna Gwinn; Staff 2 (Non-MLS 2)
Founded 1990. Pop 5,600; Circ 22,007
Jul 1998-Jun 1999 Income $200,000, State $2,500, City $85,000, County $2,500. Mats Exp $99,500. Sal $69,600
Library Holdings: Bk Vols 17,000; Per Subs 50
Automation Activity & Vendor Info: (Cataloging) Follett; (Circulation) Follett
Special Services for the Deaf - Books on deafness & sign language; High interest/low vocabulary books
Special Services for the Blind - Talking Books
Friends of the Library Group

S SAN JUAN COUNTY ARCHAEOLOGICAL RESEARCH CENTER, Salmon Ruin Museum Library, PO Box 125, 87413. SAN 326-2480. Tel: 505-632-2013. FAX: 505-632-1707. *Exec Dir*, Larry Baker; *Coordr*, Karen Sandefur
Founded 1973
1998-1999 Mats Exp $500
Library Holdings: Bk Titles 3,300; Per Subs 2,960
Subject Interests: Local history
Special Collections: Native Plants (Wynhoff Coll); Rock Art (Hadlock & Rothrock Coll); Salmon Ruin Excavation Records (Salmon Coll); San Juan Episcopal Mission Records (Turbull Coll); San Juan Historical File

BOSQUE FARMS

P BOSQUE FARMS PUBLIC LIBRARY,* 1455 W Bosque Loop, 87068. SAN 373-8167. Tel: 505-869-2227. FAX: 505-869-3342. E-Mail: bfpublib@yahoo.com. *Dir*, Lorena Solano
Founded 1985. Pop 4,700; Circ 26,541
Jul 1998-Jun 1999 Income $57,043, State $2,218, City $54,825. Mats Exp $5,718, Books $5,218, Per/Ser (Incl. Access Fees) $500. Sal $32,105
Library Holdings: Bk Titles 21,157
Automation Activity & Vendor Info: (Cataloging) Follett; (Circulation) Follett; (OPAC) Follett
Friends of the Library Group

CANNON AFB

UNITED STATES AIR FORCE

A CANNON AIR FORCE BASE LIBRARY FL4855, 27 SVS/SVMG, 107 Trident Ave Bldg 75, 88103-5211. SAN 351-6393. Tel: 505-784-2786. FAX: 505-784-6929. *Mgr*, Melissa Haraughty; E-Mail: melissa.haraughty@cannon.al.mil; *Ref*, Jan McCullough; Staff 5 (MLS 2, Non-MLS 3) Sal $197,600
Library Holdings: Bk Vols 35,000; Per Subs 160
Automation Activity & Vendor Info: (Acquisitions) SIRSI; (Cataloging) SIRSI; (Circulation) SIRSI; (Serials) SIRSI
Partic in Amigos Library Services, Inc; Fedlink

CAPULIN

G US NATIONAL PARK SERVICE, Capulin Volcano National Monument Library, PO Box 40, 88414. SAN 325-917X. Tel: 505-278-2201, Ext 231. FAX: 505-278-2211. Web Site: www.nps.gov/cavo/. *In Charge*, Ruben Andrade
Library Holdings: Bk Vols 1,500; Bk Titles 1,455

CARLSBAD

S CARLSBAD CAVERNS NATIONAL PARK LIBRARY, 3225 National Parks Hwy, 88220. SAN 370-3126. Tel: 505-785-2232, Ext 438. FAX: 505-785-2302. *In Charge*, Robert J Hoff; E-Mail: bob_hoff@nps.gov; Staff 2 (Non-MLS 2)
Founded 1930
Library Holdings: Bk Vols 4,000; Per Subs 125
Subject Interests: Geology, Local history
Special Collections: Caves Archival Coll
Restriction: Open to public for reference only
Library located at park Visitor Center near entrance to Carlsbad Caverns

M CARLSBAD MEDICAL CENTER, Medical Staff Library,* 2430 W Pierce St, 88220. SAN 321-8821. Tel: 505-887-4100. FAX: 505-887-4384. *Dir*, Tom Edwards
Library Holdings: Bk Titles 2,500; Per Subs 50
Partic in University of NM

P CARLSBAD PUBLIC LIBRARY, 101 S Halagueno St, 88220. SAN 310-6543. Tel: 505-885-0731. FAX: 505-885-8809. E-Mail: library@carlsbad.net. Web Site: www.carlsbad.net/library. *Ad Servs, Asst Dir*, Jeanne Houghtaling; *Ch Servs*, Cassandra Arnold; *Publ Servs*, Sybisl Walter-Schied; Staff 5 (MLS 5)
Founded 1897. Pop 35,000; Circ 119,000
Jul 1996-Jun 1997 Income $481,240, State $2,969, City $478,271. Mats Exp $35,000, Books $25,000, Per/Ser (Incl. Access Fees) $5,000, AV Equip $2,000. Sal $372,900 (Prof $182,721)
Library Holdings: Bk Titles 50,000; Per Subs 225
Subject Interests: Family hist, Local history
Special Collections: Family History; New Mexico History; Waste Isolation Pilot Project (WIPP)
Publications: Friends of the Library Newletter
Friends of the Library Group

J NEW MEXICO STATE UNIVERSITY AT CARLSBAD, Library & Media Center, 1500 University Dr, 88220. SAN 310-6551. Tel: 505-234-9330. FAX: 505-885-4951. E-Mail: library@cavern.nmsu.edu. Web Site: cavern.nmsu.edu/library. *Librn*, Julia White; E-Mail: jwhite@cavern.nmsu.edu; Staff 1 (MLS 1)

S WESTINGHOUSE GESC COMPANY, WIPP Technical Library, 4021 National Parks Hwy, 88220. (Mail add: PO Box 2078, 88221), Tel: 505-234-7618, 505-234-7631, 505-234-8062. FAX: 505-234-7076. *Mgr*, Jay Lees; *Librn*, Lata Desai; E-Mail: desail@wipp.carlsbad.nm.us; Staff 2 (Non-MLS 2)
Library Holdings: Bk Titles 11,000; Per Subs 275
Subject Interests: Waste mgt
Database Vendor: Lexis-Nexis
Partic in Dialog Corporation

CHAMA

P ELEANOR DAGGETT MEMORIAL PUBLIC LIBRARY, 299 Fourth St, PO Box 795, 87520-0786. SAN 310-6578. Tel: 505-756-2388. FAX: 505-756-2412. E-Mail: chamalib@yahoo.com. *Librn*, Margaret Palmer; *Asst Librn*, Margaret Martinez
Founded 1973. Pop 3,000; Circ 16,500
Library Holdings: Bk Vols 9,700; Per Subs 47
Special Collections: Southwest Coll
Partic in NMex Info Systs

CIMARRON

P NEW MEXICO STATE LIBRARY, (NER), Rural Bookmobile Northeast, Ninth & Lincoln, PO Box 97, 87714. SAN 310-6586. Tel: 505-376-2474. FAX: 505-376-2433. E-Mail: rbnenmus@cimarron.springercoop.com. *Librn*, Edward Montoya; *Assoc Librn*, Tim Martinez; *Assoc Librn*, Betty Palmer; Staff 3 (MLS 1, Non-MLS 2)
Founded 1957. Circ 61,000
Library Holdings: Bk Vols 22,000
Special Collections: Southwest Coll
Partic in Amigos Library Services, Inc; OCLC Online Computer Library Center, Inc
Bookmobiles: 1

S PHILMONT MUSEUM & SETON MEMORIAL LIBRARY,* Philmont Scout Ranch & Explorer Base, Rte 1, Box 35, 87714. SAN 310-6594. Tel: 505-376-2281, Ext 257. FAX: 505-376-2281, Ext 284. *Librn*, Annette Carlisle
Pop 35,000
Library Holdings: Bk Vols 7,500; Per Subs 12
Subject Interests: Am Indians, SW hist
Special Collections: Artifacts & Jewelry (Indian Coll); Natural History (Boy Scout Coll)

CLAYTON

P CLAYTON PUBLIC LIBRARY, Albert W Thompson Memorial Library, 17 Chestnut St, 88415. SAN 310-6608. Tel: 505-374-9423. FAX: 505-374-8420. E-Mail: awtml@plateautel.net. *Librn*, Lacie Cook; *Asst Librn*, Sylvia Vigil; Staff 1 (MLS 1)
Founded 1920. Pop 4,500; Circ 13,000
Jul 1999-Jun 2000 Income Other $7,000. Mats Exp Books $7,000. (Prof $12,600)
Library Holdings: Bk Vols 16,000; Bk Titles 14,500; Per Subs 30
Special Collections: New Mexico & Southwest, bks & filmstrips
Partic in NMex Info Systs

CLOVIS

C CLOVIS COMMUNITY COLLEGE, Clovis Campus Library, 417 Schepps Blvd, 88101. SAN 310-6624. Tel: 505-769-4080. FAX: 505-769-4190. E-Mail: ccclib@clovis.cc.nm.us. Web Site: www.clovis.cc.nm.us. *Dir*, Deborah McBeth Anderson; *Media Spec*, Rex Regnier; *Circ*, Karen Jones; *Ref*, Kelly Gray; *Acq*, Sharon Crain; Staff 3 (MLS 3)
Founded 1969. Enrl 1,900; Fac 60
Jul 1998-Jun 1999 Income $300,000. Mats Exp $107,000, Books $65,000, Per/Ser (Incl. Access Fees) $30,000, Micro $7,000, Other Print Mats $5,000. Sal $180,000 (Prof $85,000)
Library Holdings: Bk Vols 46,000; Per Subs 350
Subject Interests: SW Am
Special Collections: Rare Books (some autographed); Southwest
Automation Activity & Vendor Info: (Cataloging) Gaylord; (Circulation) Gaylord
Publications: Bibliographies (in-house)
Partic in Leann

P CLOVIS-CARVER PUBLIC LIBRARY,* 701 Main, 88101. SAN 310-6616. Tel: 505-769-7840. FAX: 505-769-7842. *Librn, Tech Servs*, Marilyn Belcher; *YA Servs*, Lora Harlan; *Ref*, Janette Paiz; Staff 14 (MLS 10, Non-MLS 4)
Founded 1949. Pop 34,300; Circ 189,553
Jul 1998-Jun 1999 Income $508,540, State $3,444, City $458,332, County $15,000, Other $31,764. Mats Exp $67,035, Books $44,938, Per/Ser (Incl. Access Fees) $5,073, Micro $209, AV Equip $2,119, Other Print Mats $3,443, Electronic Ref Mat (Incl. Access Fees) $11,253. Sal $260,634
Library Holdings: Bk Vols 79,434; Per Subs 127
Subject Interests: Southwest
Special Collections: New Mexico Documents
Automation Activity & Vendor Info: (Cataloging) Gaylord; (OPAC) Gaylord
Database Vendor: OCLC - First Search
Publications: Monthly Flyer
Partic in NMex Info Systs; OCLC Online Computer Library Center, Inc
Friends of the Library Group

COCHITI

P PUEBLO DE COCHITI COMMUNITY LIBRARY,* PO Box 70, 87072. SAN 321-7515. Tel: 505-465-2885. FAX: 505-465-2203. *Librn*, Nellie Pachcco
Founded 1977
Library Holdings: Bk Titles 3,200; Per Subs 20
Special Collections: Cochiti History; Cochiti Pueblo Past & Present, photogs
Friends of the Library Group

COCHITI LAKE

§P COCHITI LAKE COMMUNITY LIBRARY, 6515 Hoochaneetsa Blvd, 87083. SAN 375-4359. Tel: 505-465-2561. FAX: 505-465-1205. E-Mail: library@cochitilake.org. *Dir*, Clare Gearhart
Jul 2000-Jun 2001 Income $33,000

Library Holdings: Bk Vols 6,500
Subject Interests: Arizona, Colorado, New Mexico, Southwest, Texas, Utah
Automation Activity & Vendor Info: (Cataloging) Sagebrush Corporation

CORRALES

P CORRALES COMMUNITY LIBRARY,* PO Drawer 1868, 87048-1868. SAN 310-6632. Tel: 505-897-0733. FAX: 505-897-0596. *Dir, Librn*, Carla Spencer
Founded 1957. Pop 7,000
Library Holdings: Bk Vols 22,500; Per Subs 70
Special Collections: Southwest Coll
Mem of Tri-West Libr
Friends of the Library Group

CUBA

P CUBA COMMUNITY LIBRARY,* PO Box 426, 87013. SAN 321-4680. Tel: 505-289-3100. FAX: 505-289-3769. *Librn*, Fabiola Morales
Founded 1962. Pop 623; Circ 3,111
Jul 1997-Jun 1998 Income $10,000. Mats Exp $2,034, Books $2,000, Per/Ser (Incl. Access Fees) $34
Library Holdings: Bk Titles 9,000; Per Subs 30

DEMING

P MARSHALL MEMORIAL LIBRARY,* 301 S Tin Ave, 88030-3698. SAN 310-6640. Tel: 505-546-9202. FAX: 505-546-9649. E-Mail: demingpl@zianet.com. Web Site: www.zianet.com/demingpl/. *Dir*, Margaret Becker; Tel: 505-546-8408; *Asst Dir*, Pat Turner; *YA Servs*, Rayanne Jayne; *Circ*, Barbara Dominguez
Founded 1917. Pop 18,000; Circ 164,402
Jul 1998-Jun 1999 Income $233,878, State $31,597, City $160,000, County $31,500, Locally Generated Income $10,781. Mats Exp $94,314, Books $55,477, Micro $939, AV Equip $5,000, Other Print Mats $32,898. Sal $112,523 (Prof $30,000)
Library Holdings: Bk Vols 51,126; Per Subs 150
Subject Interests: Nonfiction, SW US fiction
Special Collections: Southwest Coll
Publications: Information brochure
Partic in OCLC Online Computer Library Center, Inc
Friends of the Library Group

EDGEWOOD

P EDGEWOOD COMMUNITY LIBRARY,* 1950B Pioneer Park Rd, PO Box 1134, 87015-1134. SAN 375-5029. Tel: 505-281-0138. FAX: 505-281-0138. E-Mail: edgewoodcl@nm-us.campus.mci.net. Web Site: www.users.uswest.net/~jsuda/library.htm. *Librn*, Anne Dacey-Lucas; Tel: 505-281-2018; Staff 1 (MLS 1)
Founded 1991. Pop 5,000; Circ 10,246
Library Holdings: Bk Titles 10,580
Automation Activity & Vendor Info: (Cataloging) Sagebrush Corporation; (Circulation) Sagebrush Corporation
Friends of the Library Group

ELIDA

P TOWN OF ELIDA, Ruth McCowen Public Library, PO Box 208, 88116. SAN 320-4928. *Librn*, Peggy Patterson
Founded 1945. Pop 500; Circ 3,500
Library Holdings: Bk Titles 8,000
Open Thurs 1:30-4

ESPANOLA

P ESPANOLA PUBLIC LIBRARY, 314-A Onate St, 87532. SAN 310-6659. Tel: 505-747-6087. FAX: 505-753-5543. E-Mail: espanolapl@nnm.cc.nm.us. *Dir*, Marilyn Reeves; Staff 5 (MLS 1, Non-MLS 4)
Founded 1969. Pop 14,000; Circ 40,707
Jul 1998-Jun 1999 Income $245,494, State $2,756, City $225,003, Locally Generated Income $2,132, Other $15,603. Mats Exp $41,415, Books $30,836, Per/Ser (Incl. Access Fees) $2,675, Electronic Ref Mat (Incl. Access Fees) $7,904. Sal $121,303 (Prof $38,002)
Library Holdings: Bk Vols 56,777; Per Subs 105
Special Collections: Southwest Coll
Automation Activity & Vendor Info: (Cataloging) TLC
Publications: Library Journal & Booklist
Partic in NMex Info Systs
Friends of the Library Group

J NORTHERN NEW MEXICO COMMUNITY COLLEGE, Learning Resource Center,* 921 Paseo de Unare, 87532. SAN 310-7108. Tel: 505-747-2241. FAX: 505-747-2245. *Coll Develop, Dir*, Isabel Rodarte
Founded 1973. Enrl 1,800
Jul 1997-Jun 1998 Income $117,500. Mats Exp $45,400, Books $25,000, Per/Ser (Incl. Access Fees) $11,000, Presv $800, Micro $1,600, AV Equip $7,000
Library Holdings: Bk Titles 20,000; Per Subs 250
Special Collections: Local History

P SANTA CLARA PUBLIC COMMUNITY LIBRARY,* PO Box 580, 87532. SAN 310-6667. Tel: 505-753-7326. FAX: 505-753-8988. *Librn*, Teresa Naranjo
Circ 6,984
Library Holdings: Bk Vols 8,535; Bk Titles 7,000; Per Subs 60
Subject Interests: Native Am
Special Collections: Southwest Indian Special Coll
Partic in New Mexico Libr Asn Round Table

ESTANCIA

P ESTANCIA PUBLIC LIBRARY,* Tenth & Highland, PO Box 167, 87016. SAN 373-837X. Tel: 505-384-9655. FAX: 505-384-2267. E-Mail: estanciapl@nm-us.campus.mci.net. *Librn*, Dee Crownover; Staff 1 (MLS 1)
Pop 10,000; Circ 9,857
Library Holdings: Bk Vols 9,473; Bk Titles 9,124; Per Subs 10
Special Collections: New Mexico & the Southwest (Southwest Coll)
Automation Activity & Vendor Info: (Cataloging) Follett

EUNICE

P EUNICE PUBLIC LIBRARY,* Corner Tenth & N St, PO Box 1629, 88231-1629. SAN 310-6675. Tel: 505-394-2336. FAX: 505-394-3601. E-Mail: eunplib@gte.net. *Librn*, Peggy Suter; *Ch Servs*, Tara Parker; *Asst Librn*, Georgia Hahn
Pop 3,100; Circ 25,638
Library Holdings: Bk Vols 27,040; Bk Titles 26,341; Per Subs 52
Subject Interests: Livestock, Oil field, SW
Publications: Book Charger
Partic in ALA; Lea County Asn; NMex Libr Asn
Special Services for the Blind - Talking Books

FARMINGTON

P FARMINGTON PUBLIC LIBRARY, 100 W Broadway, 87401. SAN 310-6683. Tel: 505-599-1270. Reference Tel: 505-599-1272. FAX: 505-599-1257. E-Mail: sysop@infoway.lib.nm.us. Web Site: www.infoway.lib.nm.us. *Admin Dir*, Karen McPheeters; E-Mail: kmcpheet@infoway.lib.nm.us; *Admin Assoc*, Kathy Wilson; E-Mail: kwilson@infoway.lib.nm.us; *Tech Servs*, Sharon BlueEyes; *Head Ref*, Mary Lee Smith; E-Mail: mismith@infoway.lib.nm.us; *Ref*, Mary Brewster; *Tech Coordr*, Cowan Bowman; Tel: 505-599-1256, E-Mail: cowan@infoway.lib.nm.us; *Ch Servs*, Flo Trujillo; Staff 37 (MLS 2, Non-MLS 35)
Founded 1921. Pop 80,000; Circ 296,606
1999-2000 Income (Main Library and Branch Library) $1,474,038, State $7,128, City $1,367,122, Other $99,787. Mats Exp $461,580, Books $352,738, Electronic Ref Mat (Incl. Access Fees) $56,105. Sal $666,323
Library Holdings: Bk Titles 176,329; Per Subs 307
Subject Interests: Am Indians, Southwest
Special Collections: NM State, US and UN depository; Southwest Coll
Database Vendor: OCLC - First Search, ProQuest
Publications: Bookshelf (Newsletter)
Partic in Amigos Library Services, Inc; OCLC Online Computer Library Center, Inc
Friends of the Library Group
Branches: 1
FARMINGTON LIBRARY EAST, 2702 E 22nd, 87402. SAN 377-0311. Tel: 505-599-1291. *Assoc Librn*, Kathy Wilson
Friends of the Library Group

J SAN JUAN COLLEGE LIBRARY, 4601 College Blvd, 87402. SAN 310-6691. Tel: 505-599-0249. FAX: 505-566-3381. Web Site: www.sjc.cc.nm.us. *Dir Libr Serv*, Louise Bolton; Tel: 505-566-3449, E-Mail: boltonl@sjc.cc.nm.us; *Tech Servs*, Harris M Richard; Tel: 505-566-3289, E-Mail: richard@sjc.cc.nm.us; *Acq*, Cindy Williams; Tel: 505-566-3248, E-Mail: williams_c@sjc.cc.nm.us; *Ref*, Margaret Sartin; Tel: 505-566-3256, E-Mail: sartinm@sjc.cc.nm.us; *Tech Servs*, Gayle Sanders; E-Mail: sanders_g@sjc.cc.nm.us; *ILL*, Charlotte Collins; Tel: 505-566-3288, E-Mail: collins_c@sjc.cc.nm.us; Staff 8 (MLS 3, Non-MLS 5)
Founded 1964. Circ 48,324; Enrl 2,981; Fac 85; Highest Degree: Associate
Jul 2000-Jun 2001 Income Parent Institution $554,721. Mats Exp $167,902, Books $99,800, Per/Ser (Incl. Access Fees) $38,100, Micro $10,222, Electronic Ref Mat (Incl. Access Fees) $19,780. Sal $285,204 (Prof $134,512)
Library Holdings: Bk Vols 56,903; Per Subs 458
Special Collections: Southwestern Americana, bks, maps, rpts; Tom Carter Petroleum Geological Coll
Automation Activity & Vendor Info: (Acquisitions) DRA; (Cataloging) DRA; (Circulation) DRA; (OPAC) DRA; (Serials) DRA

Database Vendor: GaleNet, OCLC - First Search, ProQuest
Publications: Information Brochures
Partic in Amigos Library Services, Inc; Llano Estacado Info Access Network; New Mexico Consortium Of Academic Libraries; OCLC Online Computer Library Center, Inc

FORT BAYARD

P RURAL BOOKMOBILE SOUTHWEST,* PO Box 36669, 88036. SAN 310-7302. Tel: 505-537-5121. FAX: 505-537-2730. E-Mail: swbmnm@nm_us.campus.mci.net. *Dir*, Fred Barraza
Circ 64,212
1997-1998 Income $146,650, Federal $140,000, County $6,650. Mats Exp $7,100, Books $6,650, Per/Ser (Incl. Access Fees) $450. Sal $72,453
Library Holdings: Bk Vols 22,763; Per Subs 16

FORT SUMNER

P FORT SUMNER PUBLIC LIBRARY,* 300 Sumner, PO Drawer D, 88119. SAN 310-6713. Tel: 505-355-2832. FAX: 505-355-7732. E-Mail: fspl@plateautel.net. *Librn*, Karla Hunt
Pop 2,615; Circ 25,200
Library Holdings: Bk Vols 14,000; Per Subs 32
Friends of the Library Group

GALLUP

M GALLUP INDIAN MEDICAL CENTER, Medical Library,* PO Box 1337, 87301. SAN 321-4575. Tel: 505-722-1119. FAX: 505-722-1554. *Librn*, Pat Bradley
Founded 1960
Library Holdings: Bk Titles 1,100; Per Subs 80
Subject Interests: Medicine, Nursing
Publications: A 100-year collection of Navajo Health Studies

P OCTAVIA FELLIN PUBLIC LIBRARY, 115 W Hill Ave, 87301. SAN 351-6423. Tel: 505-863-1291. FAX: 505-863-1286. Web Site: www.ci.gallup.nm.us. *Dir*, Mary Browder; *Asst Librn*, Debbie Macias; *Ch Servs*, Eloise Symonds; *Info Specialist*, Stephanie West; Staff 4 (MLS 2, Non-MLS 2)
Founded 1928
2000-2001 Income $591,520, State $5,700, City $580,820, County $5,000. Mats Exp $92,000, Books $69,000, Per/Ser (Incl. Access Fees) $8,900, Micro $4,300. Sal $248,240
Library Holdings: Bk Vols 139,000; Spec Interest Per Sub 165
Subject Interests: Alcoholism, Art, Local history, SW
Special Collections: Alcohol Abuse Video Coll; Memorial Book Coll; Southwest Coll, slides
Publications: Community Resource Directory: An Information & Reference Service, 1978
Partic in NMex Info Systs

C UNIVERSITY OF NEW MEXICO-ZOLLINGER LIBRARY,* 200 College Rd, 87301. SAN 310-6721. Tel: 505-863-7608. FAX: 505-863-7624. *Coll Develop, Dir*, Katherine S Larason; E-Mail: larason@gallup.unm.edu
Founded 1970. Enrl 1,600; Fac 80
Library Holdings: Bk Vols 35,000; Bk Titles 29,000; Per Subs 142
Subject Interests: Educ K-12, Health careers, Native Americans
Partic in New Mexico Consortium Of Academic Libraries

GRANTS

P MOTHER WHITESIDE MEMORIAL LIBRARY,* 525 W High, 87020-2526. SAN 310-673X. Tel: 505-287-7927 ((main)). FAX: 505-287-4793. *Librn*, Jae Luree King; Staff 2 (MLS 1, Non-MLS 1)
Founded 1949. Pop 23,794
Library Holdings: Bk Vols 23,150
Subject Interests: Local history
Special Collections: Large Print; Southwest

S NEW MEXICO DEPARTMENT OF CORRECTIONS, Western New Mexico Correctional Facility Library, Lobo Canyon, PO Drawer 250, 87020. SAN 375-4731. Tel: 505-876-8318. FAX: 505-289-7015. *Asst Librn*, Jim Kaufman; *Asst Librn*, Pilar S Lorenzo; Staff 2 (MLS 1, Non-MLS 1)
Founded 1975
Library Holdings: Bk Titles 6,000; Per Subs 40
Automation Activity & Vendor Info: (Acquisitions) Sagebrush Corporation; (Cataloging) Sagebrush Corporation; (Circulation) Sagebrush Corporation
Special Services for the Deaf - Books on deafness & sign language; High interest/low vocabulary books; Staff with knowledge of sign language

J NEW MEXICO STATE UNIVERSITY, Grants Branch Library,* 1500 Third St, 87020. SAN 310-6748. Tel: 505-287-6637. FAX: 505-287-6676. Web Site: www.grants.nmsu.edu. *Librn*, Frederic H Wilding-White; E-Mail: fwilding@grants.nmsu.edu; *Asst Librn*, Sharon Ziemann
Founded 1968. Enrl 600; Fac 55
Jul 1996-Jun 1997 Income $96,290. Mats Exp $16,253, Books $9,198, Per/Ser (Incl. Access Fees) $4,205, Presv $400, Micro $2,000, AV Equip $450. Sal $68,922 (Prof $34,960)
Library Holdings: Bk Vols 34,000; Per Subs 68
Special Collections: New Mexico History
Partic in New Mexico Consortium Of Academic Libraries
The 13th Judicial Court County Law Library is also housed within the walls of our library. It is not included in the above statistical figures

HATCH

P HATCH PUBLIC LIBRARY,* PO Box 289, 87937-0289. SAN 310-6756. Tel: 505-267-5132. *Librn*, Rita Sue Medina; *Asst Librn*, Gloria Hernandez
Founded 1946. Circ 16,006
Library Holdings: Bk Vols 11,000; Per Subs 15

HOBBS

C COLLEGE OF THE SOUTHWEST, Scarborough Memorial Library, 6610 Lovington Hwy, 88240. SAN 310-6764. Tel: 505-392-6561, Ext 1066. FAX: 505-392-6006. Web Site: www.csw.edu. *Dir*, John McCance; E-Mail: jmccance@csw.edu; *Ref*, Jerri Erickson; Tel: 505-391-6561, Ext 1071, E-Mail: jerickson@csw.edu; *Cat*, Cyndi Garrison; Tel: 505-392-6561, Ext 1067, E-Mail: cgarrison@csw.edu
Founded 1962. Enrl 682; Fac 75; Highest Degree: Master
Jun 1998-May 1999 Income Parent Institution $41,131. Mats Exp $41,131, Per/Ser (Incl. Access Fees) $32,579, Micro $3,039, Electronic Ref Mat (Incl. Access Fees) $1,741
Library Holdings: Bk Vols 65,877; Bk Titles 54,898; Per Subs 300
Subject Interests: Folklore, Free market econ, Literature, SW hist
Special Collections: Hatton W Sumners Coll; New Mexico Textbook Adoption Center; Southwest Heritage Room (Thelma A Webber Coll); Southwestern History & Art Literature
Automation Activity & Vendor Info: (Acquisitions) SIRSI; (Cataloging) SIRSI; (Circulation) SIRSI; (Course Reserve) SIRSI; (Serials) SIRSI
Database Vendor: OCLC - First Search, ProQuest
Partic in Amigos Library Services, Inc; New Mexico Consortium Of Academic Libraries

P HOBBS PUBLIC LIBRARY, 509 N Shipp, 88240. SAN 310-6772. Tel: 505-397-9328. FAX: 505-397-1508. E-Mail: hobbspubliclibrary@leaco.net. Web Site: hobbspublib.leaco.net. *Dir Libr Serv*, Cristine Marie Adams; E-Mail: cris6@juno.com; *Asst Libr Dir*, Doris Camp; *Ref*, Heidi Hoecker; E-Mail: hhoecker@elin.lib.nm.us; *Circ*, Sharon L Bailey; *Ch Servs*, Celesta Stewart; *Ch Servs*, Celesta Stewart; *Tech Servs*, Donna Lee; Staff 19 (MLS 3, Non-MLS 16)
Founded 1939. Pop 58,000; Circ 155,805
Jul 1999-Jun 2000 Income $780,850, State $6,758, City $689,092, County $80,000, Other $5,000. Mats Exp $92,557, Books $79,908, Per/Ser (Incl. Access Fees) $11,149, Presv $1,000, Micro $500. Sal $474,848 (Prof $125,580)
Library Holdings: Bk Vols 98,864; Bk Titles 93,000; Per Subs 204; Bks on Deafness & Sign Lang 56
Subject Interests: Audio bks, Large print bks, Petroleum, Southwest, Video cassettes
Special Collections: Petroleum; Southwest
Automation Activity & Vendor Info: (Acquisitions) SIRSI; (Cataloging) SIRSI; (Circulation) SIRSI; (OPAC) SIRSI
Database Vendor: Ebsco - EbscoHost, OCLC - First Search, ProQuest
Partic in Amigos Library Services, Inc; OCLC Online Computer Library Center, Inc

J NEW MEXICO JUNIOR COLLEGE, Pannell Library & Information Resources Center, 5317 Lovington Hwy, 88240. SAN 310-6780. Tel: 505-392-5473. FAX: 505-392-3668. E-Mail: library@nmjc.cc.nm.us. Web Site: nmjc.cc.nm.us/library. *Dir*, Sharon D Jenkins; E-Mail: sjenkins@nmjc.cc.nm.us; *Ref*, Vicki Gann; *Circ*, Janell Babb; *Circ*, Cheri West; *Cat*, Gail Drennan; *Ser*, Patricia Sanderson; *Govt Doc*, Earl Dye; *AV*, Jason Anderson; Staff 8 (MLS 1, Non-MLS 7)
Founded 1965. Enrl 3,000; Fac 175; Highest Degree: Associate
Jul 2000-Jun 2001 Income $452,000. Mats Exp $190,000, Books $45,000, Per/Ser (Incl. Access Fees) $23,000, Presv $2,000, Micro $25,000, AV Equip $2,000. Sal $350,000 (Prof $73,000)
Library Holdings: Bk Vols 88,000; Per Subs 343
Subject Interests: Automotive, Bus, Humanities, Nursing, Paralegal, Petroleum, Physical educ
Special Collections: Waste Isolation Pilot Plant Depository
Automation Activity & Vendor Info: (Cataloging) SIRSI; (Circulation) SIRSI; (Course Reserve) SIRSI; (OPAC) SIRSI; (Serials) SIRSI
Database Vendor: Ebsco - EbscoHost, IAC - Info Trac, OCLC - First Search, ProQuest
Publications: Newsletter
Partic in Amigos Library Services, Inc
Friends of the Library Group

HOLLOMAN AFB

UNITED STATES AIR FORCE

A HOLLOMAN AIR FORCE BASE LIBRARY, FL 4801, 596 Fourth St, 88330-8038. SAN 351-6482. Tel: 505-572-3939. Reference Tel: 505-572-5075. FAX: 505-572-5340. E-Mail: library@hollomaneducation.org. *Dir*, Cora Ahrens; Tel: 505-572-3501, E-Mail: ahrens.cora@hollomaneducation.org; *Ref*, Marsha Buffin; Tel: 505-572-5075, E-Mail: buffin.marsha@hollomaneducation.org; *Syst Coordr*, Jason Leppaluoto; Tel: 505-572-7290, E-Mail: leppaluoto.jason@hollomaneducation.org; Staff 9 (MLS 3, Non-MLS 6)
Library Holdings: Bk Vols 30,000; Bk Titles 33,766; Per Subs 160
Subject Interests: Aerospace, Bus, Foreign relations, Mgt, Mil studies, SW
Special Collections: Mil Studies, Foreign Relations and Mgt
Database Vendor: Ebsco - EbscoHost, GaleNet, OCLC - First Search, ProQuest
Partic in OCLC Online Computer Library Center, Inc
Department of Defense Affiliate

JAL

P WOOLWORTH COMMUNITY LIBRARY, Third & Utah, 88252. (Mail add: PO Box 1249, 88252-1249), SAN 310-6802. Tel: 505-395-3268. Toll Free Tel: 800-748-2138. FAX: 505-395-2138. *Actg Dir*, Donnie Fuller; *Librn*, Dorothy Brame; *Librn*, Joyce Pittam
Founded 1978. Pop 1,576; Circ 26,996
Library Holdings: Bk Vols 37,108
Subject Interests: Large print, Local history, Spanish lang, SW hist

JEMEZ SPRINGS

P JEMEZ SPRINGS PUBLIC LIBRARY, 30 Jemez Plaza, PO Box 247, 87025-0247. SAN 320-4936. Tel: 505-829-9155. FAX: 505-829-3339. E-Mail: library@sulphurcanyon.com. *Dir*, Judith Isaacs; *Asst Librn*, Carol Meine; *Coordr*, Christine Barton; Staff 3 (Non-MLS 3)
Pop 1,700; Circ 2,800
Library Holdings: Bk Titles 9,000; Per Subs 10
Friends of the Library Group

KIRTLAND AFB

S ITT INDUSTRIES - ADVANCED ENGINEERING & SCIENCES DIVISION, DTRIAC, 1680 Texas St SE, 87117-5669. SAN 301-5483. Tel: 505-846-9448. FAX: 505-846-9454. *Doc*, Connie Salus; E-Mail: connie.salus@ao.dtra.mil; *Media Spec*, Sharon Theobald
Library Holdings: Bk Vols 150,000
Special Collections: Technical Reports & Test Data Files on the Subject of Nuclear Weapons Effects
Restriction: Not open to public

UNITED STATES AIR FORCE

A KIRTLAND AIR FORCE BASE LIBRARY FL4469, 377 SVS/SVMG, 2050-B Second St SE Bldg 20204, 87117-5525. SAN 351-6547. Tel: 505-846-1071. FAX: 505-846-6674. *Asst Librn*, Robert C Matthews
Founded 1945
Oct 1997-Sep 1998 Income $209,266. Mats Exp $52,785, Books $17,655, Per/Ser (Incl. Access Fees) $31,034. Sal $126,144
Library Holdings: Bk Vols 46,571; Per Subs 311
Subject Interests: Mil arts, Sci, Southwest
Special Collections: Military Art & Science; United States History (Southwest Coll)
Automation Activity & Vendor Info: (Circulation) SIRSI

A PHILLIPS SITE TECHNICAL LIBRARY FL2809, AFRL/PSTL, 3550 Aberdeen Ave SE Bldg 419, 87117-5776. SAN 351-6571. Tel: 505-846-4767. FAX: 505-846-4790. Web Site: library.plk.af.mil. *Coll Develop, Librn*, Bryan C Stoneburner; Staff 11 (MLS 6, Non-MLS 5)
Founded 1947
Library Holdings: Bk Vols 38,000; Per Subs 800
Subject Interests: Eng with applications in advanced weapons, Physical sci
Partic in Fedlink; NMex Libr Servs Alliance

LAS CRUCES

P THOMAS BRANIGAN MEMORIAL LIBRARY, Las Cruces Public Library, 200 E Picacho Ave, 88001-3499. SAN 310-6837. Tel: 505-528-4000. Interlibrary Loan Service Tel: 505-528-4024. Reference Tel: 505-528-4004. TDD: 505-528-4008. FAX: 505-528-4030. E-Mail: rdeford@las-cruces.org. Web Site: library.las-cruces.org. *Bkmobile Coordr, Ref*, Mark Pendleton; Tel: 505-528-4001, E-Mail: mpendleton@las-cruces.org; *Spec Coll, Tech Servs*, Lori Grumet; Tel: 505-528-4025, E-Mail: lgrumet@las-cruces.org; *Per*, Lee Waugh; Tel: 505-528-4017, E-Mail: lwaugh@las-cruces.org; *ILL*, Patricia McAdams; Tel: 505-528-4024, E-Mail: pmcadams@las-cruces.org; *Circ*, Nancy Harmeson; Tel: 505-528-4009, E-Mail: nharmeson@las-cruces.org; *YA Servs*, Debbie McWilliams; Tel: 505-528-4011, E-Mail: dmcwilliams@las-cruces.org; *Syst Coordr*, Rima Deford; Tel: 505-528-4034, E-Mail: rdeford@las-cruces.org; *Media Spec*, Elise Vidal; *Ch Servs*, Sandy VanLandingham; Tel: 505-528-4225, E-Mail: svanlandingham@las-cruces.org; Staff 34 (MLS 8, Non-MLS 26)
Founded 1935. Pop 165,000; Circ 375,957
Jul 1998-Jun 1999 Income $1,411,266, State $9,414, City $1,363,852, County $38,000. Mats Exp $443,659, Books $147,049, Per/Ser (Incl. Access Fees) $18,002. Sal $950,945 (Prof $272,410)
Library Holdings: Bk Vols 221,250; Bk Titles 177,000; Per Subs 489; Bks on Deafness & Sign Lang 50
Subject Interests: Architecture, Art, History
Special Collections: Arts & Crafts; Cats (Eunice Mannen Coll); Cookbooks (Louise Garrett Coll); Humane Society (Alicia Melgaard Coll); Movies (John White Coll); New Mexico & Southwestern History (Helen P Caffey Coll); Railroads (John Sharer Coll); Theatre (Max Freudenthal Coll)
Automation Activity & Vendor Info: (Acquisitions) Innovative Interfaces Inc.; (Cataloging) Innovative Interfaces Inc.; (Circulation) Innovative Interfaces Inc.; (Course Reserve) Innovative Interfaces Inc.; (ILL) Innovative Interfaces Inc.; (Media Booking) Innovative Interfaces Inc.; (OPAC) Innovative Interfaces Inc.; (Serials) Innovative Interfaces Inc.
Publications: TBML Newsletter
Partic in Amigos Library Services, Inc; NMex Info Systs; OCLC Online Computer Library Center, Inc
Special Services for the Deaf - TTY machine
Special Services for the Blind - Braille printer & software
Open Mon-Thurs 10-9 & Fri-Sat 10-6; Sun 1-5 (Augt-May only)
Friends of the Library Group
Bookmobiles: 1

S INSTITUTE OF HISTORICAL SURVEY FOUNDATION LIBRARY, (IHS), 3035 S Main, 88005. (Mail add: PO Box 36, 88047), SAN 377-8223. Tel: 505-525-3035. FAX: 505-525-0106. E-Mail: ihsf@zianet.com. *Librn*, Anne Morgan; E-Mail: anmorgan@zianet.com; *Pres*, Dr Evan Davies
Founded 1970
Library Holdings: Bk Vols 25,000; Bk Titles 20,000
Subject Interests: Art, Geography, Philosophy, Theater

M MEMORIAL MEDICAL CENTER LIBRARY,* 2450 S Telshor, 88011-5076. SAN 325-1276. Tel: 505-521-2234. FAX: 505-521-5450. *Librn*, Sharon Dalton
Library Holdings: Bk Titles 500; Per Subs 65
Partic in Medline

G NASA, White Sands Test Facility Technical Library, PO Box 20, 88004-0020. SAN 328-0969. Tel: 505-524-5293. FAX: 505-524-5544. Web Site: www.wstf.nasa.gov/enable/editing/librarysvc.htm. *Librn*, Jose G Beltran; E-Mail: jbeltran@wstf.nasa.gov; *Librn*, Lurlene Ford; Staff 2 (MLS 1, Non-MLS 1)
Circ 500
Library Holdings: Bk Titles 2,000
Partic in Defense Technical Information Center; Dialog Corporation; Nasa Libraries Information System - Nasa Galaxie; OCLC Online Computer Library Center, Inc; STN

C NEW MEXICO STATE UNIVERSITY LIBRARY, MSC 3475, 88003-8006. SAN 351-6636. Tel: 505-646-1508. Circulation Tel: 505-646-6910. Reference Tel: 505-646-5791. FAX: 505-646-6940. Web Site: www.lib.nmsu.edu. *Dean of Libr*, Elizabeth A Titus; *Assoc Dean*, Gwen Gregory; *Circ*, Holly Reynolds; *Spec Coll*, Cheryl Wilson; *Access Serv*, Karen Stabler; *Archivist*, Austin Hoover; *Ref*, Susan Beck; *Ref*, Sylvia Ortiz; *Coll Develop*, Kennith Slagle; *Syst Coordr*, Carol Boyce; Staff 83 (MLS 30, Non-MLS 53)
Founded 1888. Enrl 15,500; Fac 629; Highest Degree: Doctorate
Jul 1999-Jun 2000 Income $6,134,909, State $5,848,256, Other $286,653. Mats Exp $2,691,469, Books $613,877, Per/Ser (Incl. Access Fees) $1,432,864, Presv $78,293, Other Print Mats $71,635, Electronic Ref Mat (Incl. Access Fees) $494,800. Sal $2,537,290 (Prof $1,275,963)
Library Holdings: Bk Vols 1,057,887; Bk Titles 628,218; Per Subs 6,762
Special Collections: Rio Grande Historical Coll; Southwest Border Research Center Coll
Automation Activity & Vendor Info: (OPAC) Endeavor; (Serials) Endeavor
Database Vendor: IAC - Info Trac, Lexis-Nexis, OCLC - First Search, OVID Technologies, ProQuest, Silverplatter Information Inc.
Publications: New Mexico State University Library Newsletter; Rio Grande History
Partic in Amigos Library Services, Inc; Big Twelve Plus Libr Consortium

R SAINT PAUL'S UNITED METHODIST CHURCH, Ralph Johnson Memorial Library, PO Box 696, 88004. SAN 328-1272. Tel: 505-526-6689. FAX: 505-524-7660. *Adminr*, Mark Ewing
Founded 1961
Library Holdings: Bk Vols 6,017
Publications: History of Church

G UNITED STATES DEPARTMENT OF INTERIOR, BUREAU OF LAND MANAGEMENT, Las Cruces District Office Library,* 1800 Marquess, 88005. SAN 310-6845. Tel: 505-525-4300. FAX: 505-525-4412.
Library Holdings: Bk Vols 3,500; Per Subs 20

R UNIVERSITY UNITED METHODIST CHURCH LIBRARY, S 2000 Locust St, 88001. SAN 325-2833. Tel: 505-522-8220. *Librn*, Peg Dickinson
Founded 1967
Library Holdings: Bk Titles 3,900

S WILDLIFE INFORMATION SERVICE LIBRARY,* 409 Baca Rd, 88005-6021. SAN 370-6877. Tel: 505-527-2547. E-Mail: wildlife@greatwhite.com. Web Site: www.greatwhite.com/~wildlife. *Librn*, Julie L Moore; Staff 1 (MLS 1)
Library Holdings: Bk Vols 2,148; Per Subs 10

LAS VEGAS

P CARNEGIE PUBLIC LIBRARY,* 500 National Ave, 87701. SAN 310-6853. Tel: 505-454-1401, Ext 272, 505-454-1401, Ext 273, 505-454-1447 (Weekends). FAX: 505-425-0193. *Dir*, JoAnn Castillo; *Asst Dir*, Darleen Martinez
Founded 1904. Circ 84,557
Library Holdings: Bk Vols 62,000
Subject Interests: Southwest
Special Collections: Local history; Southwest Collection
Partic in Amigos Library Services, Inc; OCLC Online Computer Library Center, Inc
Friends of the Library Group

GM LAS VEGAS MEDICAL CENTER (STATE HOSPITAL), Medical Library,* PO Box 1388, 87701-1388. SAN 310-6861. Tel: 505-454-2108. FAX: 505-454-2136. *Librn*, Victor Sandoval
Founded 1970
Library Holdings: Bk Titles 7,000
Subject Interests: Gen med, Long-term care, Mgt, Nursing
Special Collections: Psychiatry; Psychology; Social Work
Partic in National Network Of Libraries Of Medicine - South Central Region

C NEW MEXICO HIGHLANDS UNIVERSITY, Thomas C Donnelly Library, 901 University Ave, 87701-4073. SAN 310-687X. Tel: 505-454-3332. FAX: 505-454-0026. Web Site: donnelly.nmhu.edu. *Dir*, Ruben F Aragon; *Circ, Ref*, Kathleen Kroll; *Circ*, Rita Arellanes; *ILL*, Phyllis Schmitz; *Per*, Agnes Ludi; *Cat*, Edith Landau; *Tech Servs*, Allen Schwartz; *Archivist*, Michael Olsen; Staff 20 (MLS 5, Non-MLS 15)
Founded 1893. Enrl 2,818; Fac 179; Highest Degree: Master
1999-2000 Income $1,352,746. Mats Exp $480,000, Books $115,000, Per/Ser (Incl. Access Fees) $290,000, Micro $25,000, AV Equip $5,000. Sal $523,619 (Prof $199,685)
Library Holdings: Bk Vols 178,794; Bk Titles 143,035; Per Subs 728
Special Collections: Census Data Center; Fort Union Archives, mss; Government Documents Coll; Southwest History (Arrott Coll)
Automation Activity & Vendor Info: (Acquisitions) DRA; (Cataloging) DRA; (Circulation) DRA; (OPAC) DRA; (Serials) DRA
Partic in Amigos Library Services, Inc; Dialog Corporation; ProQuest

LORDSBURG

P LORDSBURG-HIDALGO LIBRARY, 208 E Third St, 88045. SAN 310-6888. Tel: 505-542-9646. FAX: 505-542-9646. E-Mail: lhpldir@hotmail.com. *Dir*, Marlene Siepel; *Ch Servs*, Rita Morris
Founded 1919. Pop 5,000; Circ 23,247
Jul 1999-Jun 2000 Income $62,000
Library Holdings: Bk Vols 24,000; Per Subs 60

LOS ALAMOS

SR FIRST UNITED METHODIST CHURCH LIBRARY,* 715 Diamond Dr, 87544. SAN 373-479X. Tel: 505-662-6277. FAX: 505-662-4879. *Librn*, Terri Morris
Library Holdings: Bk Vols 250
Subject Interests: Theology

SR IMMACULATE HEART OF MARY PARISH LIBRARY,* 3700 Canyon Rd, 87544. SAN 310-690X. Tel: 505-662-6193, 505-662-7720. FAX: 505-662-5191. *Librn*, Marcella Backsen
Founded 1961
Library Holdings: Bk Titles 5,000; Per Subs 20
Subject Interests: Family, Marriage, Philosophy, Psychology, Religion, Religious education, Socioecon concerns, Theology

P LOS ALAMOS COUNTY LIBRARY SYSTEM,* 2400 Central Ave, 87544. SAN 370-4602. Tel: 505-662-8240. FAX: 505-662-8245. *Dir*, Patricia Scharinger; *Circ*, Rita Carpenter; *Tech Servs*, Margaret Weaver; *ILL*, Jan Sinclair; Staff 21 (MLS 7, Non-MLS 14)
Founded 1943. Pop 18,366; Circ 345,286
Jul 1998-Jun 1999 Income (Main Library and Branch Library) $1,318,446, State $5,000, County $1,303,446, Other $10,000. Mats Exp $151,527, Books $111,627, Per/Ser (Incl. Access Fees) $19,600, Micro $10,000, Other Print Mats $1,300, Electronic Ref Mat (Incl. Access Fees) $9,000. Sal $824,299 (Prof $276,905)
Library Holdings: Bk Vols 130,881; Per Subs 551
Special Collections: Southwest Americana Regional Coll bk, video
Automation Activity & Vendor Info: (Acquisitions) epixtech, inc.; (Cataloging) epixtech, inc.; (Circulation) epixtech, inc.
Partic in Amigos Library Services, Inc
Friends of the Library Group
Branches: 2
MESA PUBLIC LIBRARY, 2400 Central Ave, 87544. SAN 310-6918. Tel: 505-662-8240. Interlibrary Loan Service Tel: 505-662-8255. FAX: 505-662-8246. Web Site: www.trail.com/~lac/. *Dir*, Mary Pat Kraemer; *Tech Servs*, Margeret Weaver; *Circ*, Rita Carpenter
Founded 1943. Pop 19,000; Circ 386,871
Friends of the Library Group
WHITE ROCK, 133 Long View Dr, 87544. SAN 370-7563. Tel: 505-662-8265. FAX: 505-672-0334. *Mgr*, Carol-Lee McKenna
Friends of the Library Group

S LOS ALAMOS HISTORICAL MUSEUM ARCHIVES, 1921 Juniper St, PO Box 43, 87544. SAN 325-903X. Tel: 505-662-6272. FAX: 505-662-6312. E-Mail: historicalsociety@losalamos.com. Web Site: losalamos.com/historicalsociety. *Curator*, Mariane Mortonson; *Dir*, Hedy Dunn; *Archivist*, Rebecca Collinsworth
Founded 1968
Library Holdings: Bk Vols 1,000; Per Subs 100
Special Collections: Laura Gilpin Photographs Coll; T H Parkhurst Photographs Coll
Partic in Am Asn for State & Local Hist; Am Asn of Museums; Soc of Am Archivists
Los Alamos Historical Society Memberships available

S LOS ALAMOS NATIONAL LABORATORY, Research Library, MS-P362, PO Box 1663, 87544-7113. SAN 351-6695. Tel: 505-667-4448. Interlibrary Loan Service Tel: 505-667-5809. FAX: 505-665-6452. E-Mail: library@lanl.gov. Web Site: lib-www.lanl.gov. *Dir*, Richard E Luce; *Assoc Dir*, Jacqueline Stack; Staff 49 (MLS 22, Non-MLS 27)
Founded 1943
Library Holdings: Bk Vols 131,500; Per Subs 1,600
Subject Interests: Sci-tech
Special Collections: AEC period publications; Electronic Reports; LANL Technical Reports

S LOS ALAMOS TECHNICAL ASSOCIATES LIBRARY,* PO Box 410, 87544. SAN 323-4282. Tel: 505-662-9080. FAX: 505-662-1757. *Librn*, Ellynn McCleary
Library Holdings: Per Subs 60

R UNITED CHURCH OF LOS ALAMOS LIBRARY,* 2525 Canyon Rd, 87544. SAN 310-6926. Tel: 505-662-2971. FAX: 505-662-5927. *Librn*, Jan Sinclair
Founded 1966
Library Holdings: Bk Vols 3,350; Per Subs 10
Subject Interests: Family life, Health, Psychology, Religion, Social problems

C UNIVERSITY OF NEW MEXICO-LOS ALAMOS CAMPUS LIBRARY, 4000 University Dr, 87544. SAN 326-1476. Tel: 505-662-0343. FAX: 505-662-0344. E-Mail: libhelp@chicoma.la.unm.edu. Web Site: www.la.unm.edu/~lalib/lib-home.html. *Dir*, Dennis Davies-Wilson; E-Mail: davies@chicoma.la.unm.edu; Staff 4 (MLS 2, Non-MLS 2)
Jul 1999-Jun 2000 Income State $158,082. Mats Exp $50,771, Books $25,534, Per/Ser (Incl. Access Fees) $5,878, AV Equip $2,000, Electronic Ref Mat (Incl. Access Fees) $900. Sal $107,311 (Prof $69,493)
Library Holdings: Bk Titles 13,000; Per Subs 102
Subject Interests: Art, Southwest
Special Collections: Southwest Collection
Automation Activity & Vendor Info: (Cataloging) Innovative Interfaces Inc.; (Circulation) Innovative Interfaces Inc.; (Course Reserve) Innovative Interfaces Inc.; (OPAC) Innovative Interfaces Inc.
Database Vendor: CARL, OCLC - First Search, ProQuest
Partic in Amigos Library Services, Inc; New Mexico Consortium Of Academic Libraries; OCLC Online Computer Library Center, Inc

LOS LUNAS

P LOS LUNAS PUBLIC LIBRARY,* 460 Main St NE, 87031-8305. (Mail add: PO Box 1209, 87031-8305), SAN 310-6934. Tel: 505-865-6779. FAX: 505-865-1541. Web Site: www.angelfire.com/nm/LosLunasPL/. *Librn*, Carmen Jaramillo-Campos; *Asst Librn*, Cynthia Shetter
Circ 34,000
Library Holdings: Bk Vols 24,093
Open Tues 10-7, Wed & Fri 9-5, Thurs 9-7

LOVINGTON

P LOVINGTON PUBLIC LIBRARY,* 115 Main St, 88260. SAN 310-6950. Tel: 505-396-3144, 505-396-6900. FAX: 505-396-7189. E-Mail: lovingtonpl@nm-us.campus.mci.net. *Librn*, Tuoreida McBride

Founded 1931. Pop 9,322; Circ 96,105
Library Holdings: Bk Vols 55,599; Per Subs 45
Subject Interests: Genealogy
Friends of the Library Group

MOUNTAINAIR

G NATIONAL PARK SERVICE, Salinas Pueblo Missions Research Library, Corner of Broadway & Ripley, PO Box 517, 87036-0517. SAN 374-5538. Tel: 505-847-2585. FAX: 505-847-2441. *Librn*, Loretta Moseley; E-Mail: loretta_moseley@nps.gov; Staff 1 (Non-MLS 1)
Founded 1930
Library Holdings: Bk Titles 1,500
Special Collections: Archaeology; Prehistory & History
Partic in OCLC Online Computer Library Center, Inc

NAGEEZI

G USDI NATIONAL PARK SERVICE, Chaco Culture National Historical Park, PO Box 220, 87037. SAN 323-9691. Tel: 505-786-7014. FAX: 505-786-7061. Web Site: www.nps.gov/chcu. *In Charge*, Russ Bodnar
Library Holdings: Bk Titles 5,000

PORTALES

C EASTERN NEW MEXICO UNIVERSITY, Golden Library, 1300 S Ave K, Sta 32, 88130-7402. SAN 351-675X. Tel: 505-562-2624. Circulation Tel: 505-562-2634. Reference Tel: 505-562-2638. FAX: 505-562-2647. Web Site: www.enmu.edu/golden.html. *Coll Develop, Dir*, Melveta Walker; E-Mail: melveta.walker@enmu.edu; *Spec Coll*, Gene Bundy; Tel: 505-562-2636, E-Mail: gene.bundy@enmu.edu; *Ser*, James Akins; Tel: 505-562-2629, E-Mail: james.akins@enmu.edu; *Govt Doc*, Linda McCreight; Tel: 505-562-2650, E-Mail: linda.mccreight@enmu.edu; *AV*, Wanda Graham; Tel: 505-562-2776, E-Mail: wanda.graham@enmu.edu; *Ref*, Brackston William Taylor; Tel: 505-562-2646, E-Mail: brackston.taylor@enmu.edu; *Syst Coordr*, Lilah Gainey; Tel: 505-562-2640, E-Mail: lilah.gainey@enmu.edu; *Cat*, Ellen Jeane; Tel: 505-562-2300, E-Mail: ellen.jeane@enmu.edu; *ILL*, Michele Wood; Tel: 505-562-2644, E-Mail: michele.wood@enmu.edu; Staff 19 (MLS 8, Non-MLS 11)
Founded 1934. Enrl 3,650; Fac 173; Highest Degree: Master
Jul 1999-Jun 2000 Income $1,826,864. Mats Exp $1,082,256, Books $613,500, Per/Ser (Incl. Access Fees) $235,855, Presv $8,000, AV Equip $145,901, Electronic Ref Mat (Incl. Access Fees) $79,000. Sal $610,816 (Prof $303,380)
Library Holdings: Bk Vols 232,395; Per Subs 1,663
Subject Interests: Bus, Education, Fine arts, Liberal arts
Special Collections: Harold Runnels Coll; Lyric Theatre & Dance Coll; NMex; Textbook Review Center; Williamson Science Fiction Coll
Partic in Amigos Library Services, Inc; Llano Estacado Info Access Network; New Mexico Consortium Of Academic Libraries

P PORTALES PUBLIC LIBRARY,* 218 S Avenue B, 88130. SAN 310-6985. Tel: 505-356-3940. FAX: 505-356-3964. E-Mail: ppl@yucca.net. *Dir*, Denise Burnett; *Cat*, Danielle Swopes; *Ch Servs*, Liz Garcia; Staff 3 (MLS 3)
Founded 1934. Pop 15,695; Circ 68,639
Library Holdings: Bk Vols 40,000; Per Subs 85
Subject Interests: Genealogy
Friends of the Library Group

RATON

P ARTHUR JOHNSON MEMORIAL LIBRARY,* 244 Cook Ave, 87740. SAN 310-6993. Tel: 505-445-9711. *Librn*, Thayla Wright
Founded 1912. Pop 12,925; Circ 79,732
Library Holdings: Bk Vols 44,000; Per Subs 90
Special Collections: Southwest & Local History, audio, CD, file mat, pictures, tapes, video
Partic in Amigos Library Services, Inc; NMex Info Systs; OCLC Online Computer Library Center, Inc
Friends of the Library Group

RIO RANCHO

P RIO RANCHO PUBLIC LIBRARY, (RRPL), 950 Pinetree Rd SE, 87124. (Mail add: PO Box 15670, 87124), SAN 321-7671. Tel: 505-891-5013. Circulation Tel: 505-891-5013, Ext 3059. Reference Tel: 505-891-5013, Ext 3030. FAX: 505-891-7246. Web Site: www.ci.rio-rancho.nm.us/library.htm. *Dir*, Antoinette L Beatty; Tel: 505-896-8817, E-Mail: tbeatty@ci.rio-rancho.nm.us; *Ch Servs*, Vaunda Nelson; E-Mail: tbeatty@ci.rio-rancho.nm.us; *Coll Develop, Ref*, Marilyn Schroeder; *Tech Servs*, Rhen Busch; Staff 11 (MLS 7, Non-MLS 4)
Founded 1974. Pop 54,000; Circ 370,000
Jul 1999-Jun 2000 Income $1,516,812, State $31,053, City $587,716, County $828,979, Locally Generated Income $69,064. Mats Exp $195,443, Books $173,994, Per/Ser (Incl. Access Fees) $4,800, Presv $3,600, Electronic Ref Mat (Incl. Access Fees) $13,049. Sal $402,298 (Prof $324,134)
Library Holdings: Bk Vols 110,000; Per Subs 130
Subject Interests: Southwest
Automation Activity & Vendor Info: (Acquisitions) Innovative Interfaces Inc.; (Circulation) Innovative Interfaces Inc.; (OPAC) Innovative Interfaces Inc.; (Serials) Innovative Interfaces Inc.
Database Vendor: Ebsco - EbscoHost, OCLC - First Search
Publications: Booklist; Library Journal; School Library Journal
Mem of Rio Grande Valley Libr Syst
Special Services for the Blind - Bks on tape
Friends of the Library Group

ROSWELL

SR BETHEL BAPTIST CHURCH, Media Library,* 2420 N Garden, 88201. SAN 373-4803. Tel: 505-622-8182. FAX: 505-622-4419.
Library Holdings: Bk Vols 1,000

GL CHAVES COUNTY DISTRICT COURT LIBRARY,* PO Box 1776, 88202. SAN 310-7019. Tel: 505-622-2565. FAX: 505-624-9506.
Library Holdings: Bk Vols 10,000
Partic in Westlaw

M EASTERN NEW MEXICO MEDICAL CENTER, Physician's Library,* 405 W Country Club Rd, 88201. SAN 329-2886. Tel: 505-622-8170, Ext 4014. FAX: 505-627-4141. *In Charge*, Patricia Cox
Pop 400
Library Holdings: Bk Vols 250; Per Subs 10

J EASTERN NEW MEXICO UNIVERSITY - ROSWELL, Learning Resource Center,* PO Box 6000, 88202-6000. SAN 310-7027. Tel: 505-624-7282. FAX: 505-624-7119. Web Site: www.enmu.edu/roswell/buchanaj/enmru-r/homepage. *Dir*, Rollah Aston; E-Mail: aston@lib.enmuros.cc.nm.us; *Tech Servs*, Diane Pearse; Staff 2 (MLS 2)
Founded 1959. Enrl 2,140; Fac 150
Jul 1997-Jun 1998 Income $300,000. Mats Exp $81,200, Books $35,000, Per/Ser (Incl. Access Fees) $10,800, Presv $1,000, Micro $9,700, AV Equip $3,000. Sal $140,000
Library Holdings: Bk Vols 45,000; Per Subs 235
Automation Activity & Vendor Info: (Acquisitions) Gaylord
Partic in Amigos Library Services, Inc

J NEW MEXICO MILITARY INSTITUTE, (NMM), Paul Horgan Library - Tole's Learning Center, Toles Learning Ctr, 101 W College, 88201-5173. SAN 310-7051. Tel: 505-624-8380. Circulation Tel: 505-624-8394. FAX: 505-624-8390. Web Site: www.nmmi.cc.nm.us/toles/learning.htmlx. *Dir*, Jerry Klopfer; Tel: 505-624-8381; *Librn*, Linda Rasmussen; Tel: 505-624-8382; *Media Spec*, June Aubrey; Tel: 505-624-8384; Staff 7 (MLS 3, Non-MLS 4)
Founded 1902. Enrl 980; Fac 70; Highest Degree: Associate
Jul 1998-Jun 1999 Income $300,000, Federal $3,000, Locally Generated Income $250,000. Mats Exp $77,000, Books $24,000, Per/Ser (Incl. Access Fees) $20,000, Presv $2,000, Micro $7,000, AV Equip $20,000, Electronic Ref Mat (Incl. Access Fees) $4,000. Sal $230,000 (Prof $126,000)
Library Holdings: Bk Vols 60,000; Bk Titles 42,000; Per Subs 231
Subject Interests: History, Humanities, Natural science
Special Collections: Henry David Thoreau; Military History; Napoleonic History; Paul Horgan Writings; Southwestern History
Automation Activity & Vendor Info: (Cataloging) Gaylord; (Circulation) Gaylord; (OPAC) Gaylord
Database Vendor: OCLC - First Search, ProQuest
Partic in Amigos Library Services, Inc; New Mexico Consortium Of Academic Libraries

S NEW MEXICO REHABILITATION CENTER LIBRARY,* 31 Gail Harris Ave, 88201. SAN 310-706X. Tel: 505-347-3400. FAX: 505-347-5177. *Librn*, Winnie Blount; Tel: 505-347-3467
Library Holdings: Bk Vols 105; Per Subs 19

S ROSWELL MUSEUM & ART CENTER LIBRARY,* 100 W 11th St, 88201. SAN 310-7078. Tel: 505-624-6744. FAX: 505-624-6765. *Dir*, Laurie Rufe; *Librn*, Candace Jordan
Library Holdings: Bk Vols 10,000; Per Subs 47
Subject Interests: Artists, SW art
Special Collections: Native American Indian Art; Southwestern Archaeology

P ROSWELL PUBLIC LIBRARY, 301 N Pennsylvania Ave, 88201. SAN 310-7086. Tel: 505-622-7101. FAX: 505-622-7107. *Dir*, Betty Long; *Ad Servs*, Barbara Harris; *Ch Servs*, Mary Stickford; *AV*, Lorena Blanco; *Circ*, Robert Kerwick; *Ref*, Loretta Clark; *ILL, Per*, Rosemarie Klopfer; Staff 6 (MLS 3, Non-MLS 3)
Founded 1906. Pop 55,000; Circ 479,387
Jul 1999-Jun 2000 Income $985,426, State $5,491, City $955,832, County $4,000, Other $20,103. Mats Exp $176,818, Books $154,199, Per/Ser (Incl. Access Fees) $10,148, Micro $12,471. Sal $469,866
Library Holdings: Bk Vols 149,238; Per Subs 192
Subject Interests: Genealogy

Special Collections: Southwest Coll
Automation Activity & Vendor Info: (Circulation) SIRSI; (OPAC) SIRSI
Database Vendor: OCLC - First Search
Publications: Discover New Mexico (reading list)
Partic in Amigos Library Services, Inc; NMex Info Systs
Friends of the Library Group

G UNITED STATES BUREAU OF LAND MANAGEMENT, Roswell District Office Library,* 2909 W Second St, 88201-2019. SAN 310-7000. Tel: 505-627-0272. FAX: 505-627-0276. *Librn*, Carol Hines
Library Holdings: Bk Vols 2,000

RUIDOSO

P RUIDOSO PUBLIC LIBRARY, 107 Kansas City Rd, 88345. SAN 310-7094. Tel: 505-258-3704. FAX: 505-258-4619. *Dir*, Nancy Osterberg
Founded 1950. Pop 15,000; Circ 49,500
Library Holdings: Bk Vols 50,000
Publications: Newsletter
Friends of the Library Group

SAN LORENZO

S PINHOLE RESOURCE LIBRARY,* Star Rte 15, Box 1355, 88041. SAN 326-288X. Tel: 505-536-9942. Web Site: www.pinholeresource.com. *Dir*, Nancy Spencer; *Librn*, Eric Renner
Library Holdings: Bk Titles 400
Publications: Bibliography of Pinhole Optics; Bibliography of Pinhole Photography; Pinhole Journal
Partic in Soc for Photog Educ

SANTA FE

S ANTHROPOLOGY FILM CENTER LIBRARY,* 1626 Upper Canyon Rd, 87501. SAN 371-456X. Tel: 505-983-4127. E-Mail: anthrofilm@nets.com. Web Site: www.nets.com/anthrofilm. *Exec Dir*, Carroll Williams
Library Holdings: Bk Vols 4,000; Per Subs 40

R CHURCH OF THE HOLY FAITH, EPISCOPAL, Parish Library,* 311 E Palace Ave, 87501. SAN 310-7124. Tel: 505-982-4447. FAX: 505-992-8843. *Librn*, Mary Lou Stark
Founded 1949
Library Holdings: Bk Titles 4,600; Per Subs 20
Subject Interests: Altar, Arts, Biblical studies, Biog, Children's literature, Church history, Comparative faiths, Healing, Missions, Music, Personal relig, Symbolism, Theology
Publications: Monthly parish magazine; weekly bulletin
Friends of the Library Group

C COLLEGE OF SANTA FE, Fogelson Library Center, 1600 St Michael's Dr, 87505-7615. SAN 310-7132. Tel: 505-473-6569. Reference Tel: 505-473-6594. FAX: 505-473-6593. E-Mail: reference@csf.edu. Web Site: www.library.csf.edu. *Acq, Ser*, Hariret Meiklejohn; Tel: 505-473-6592, E-Mail: hmeiklej@csf.edu; *Circ*, Daria Carson; Tel: 505-473-6572, E-Mail: dcarson@csf.edu; *Circ*, Matt Clinton; Tel: 505-473-6597, E-Mail: mclinton@csf.edu; *Circ*, Gwen Kalavaza; Tel: 505-473-6597, E-Mail: gkalavaza@csf.edu; *ILL*, Ali Aran; Tel: 505-473-6598, E-Mail: ali@csf.edu; *Music*, James Benefiel; Tel: 505-473-6569; *Music*, Robert Pierson; Tel: 505-473-6569; *Publ Servs*, Margaret Johnson; Tel: 505-473-6570, E-Mail: pjohnson@csf.edu; *Tech Servs*, Peggy Rudberg; Tel: 505-473-6575, E-Mail: prudberg@csf.edu. Subject Specialists: *Art*, Allison Colborne; Staff 8 (MLS 4, Non-MLS 4)
Founded 1874. Enrl 1,425; Fac 73; Highest Degree: Master
Jul 1999-Jun 2000 Income Parent Institution $457,686. Mats Exp $115,000, Books $33,000, Per/Ser (Incl. Access Fees) $24,000, Presv $500, Micro $5,000, Electronic Ref Mat (Incl. Access Fees) $23,919. Sal $307,777 (Prof $216,098)
Library Holdings: Bk Vols 150,000; Bk Titles 145,000; Per Subs 495
Subject Interests: Education, Fine arts, Moving image arts, Performing arts
Special Collections: Beaumont Newhall & Nancy Newhall/James Enyeart & Roxanne Malone (History of Photography) Library; Chase Art History Library; Extensive Collection of 33 1/3 LP Records; Fogelson Library Special Coll; Southwest & New Mexico History Coll; State of New Mexico Department of Education Curriculum Library; Thaw Art History Coll
Automation Activity & Vendor Info: (Cataloging) SIRSI; (Circulation) SIRSI; (Course Reserve) SIRSI; (OPAC) SIRSI
Database Vendor: Dialog, OCLC - First Search, ProQuest
Partic in Amigos Library Services, Inc; New Mexico Consortium Of Academic Libraries
Friends of the Library Group

G COMMISSION OF PUBLIC RECORDS, New Mexico State Record Center & Archives,* 1205 Camino Carlos Rey, 87505. SAN 328-3232. Tel: 505-476-7900. FAX: 505-476-7901. E-Mail: asd@rain.state.nm.us. Web Site: www.state.nm.us/cpr. *In Charge*, Elaine Olah
Special Collections: Land Grant Documents; Mexican Archives (1821-1846); Spanish Archives of New Mexico (1621-1821); Territorial Archives (1846-1912)

J INSTITUTE OF AMERICAN INDIAN ARTS LIBRARY, 83 Avan Nu Po Rd, 87505. SAN 310-7167. Tel: 505-424-2398. FAX: 505-424-3131. E-Mail: library_info@iaiancad.org. Web Site: www.iaiancad.org/library. *Dir*, Allen Schwartz; Tel: 505-424-2397, E-Mail: aschwartz@iaiancad.org; *Librn*, Jennifer James; *Asst Librn*, Grace Nuvayesteya; Staff 3 (MLS 2, Non-MLS 1)
Founded 1962. Enrl 200
Oct 1997-Sep 1998 Income $200,000. Mats Exp $35,000, Books $30,000, Per/Ser (Incl. Access Fees) $5,000. Sal $95,000 (Prof $68,000)
Library Holdings: Bk Vols 20,000; Per Subs 200
Subject Interests: Am Indian culture, Fine art, History
Special Collections: Art Coll; Indian Coll; Indian Music Coll, cassettes, tapes, records; Indian Photos Coll; Smithsonian Indian Photos Coll

G INTERMOUNTAIN SUPPORT OFFICE, National Park Service, 2968 Rodeo Park Dr W, 87505. (Mail add: PO Box 728, 87504-0728), Tel: 505-988-6840. Circulation Tel: 505-988-6712. FAX: 505-988-6876. Web Site: www.library.nps.gov. *Curator*, Virginia Salazar; Tel: 505-988-6813, E-Mail: virginia_salazar@nps.gov; Staff 2 (Non-MLS 2)
Founded 1978
Subject Interests: Anthropology, Archaeology, Ethnography, Geography, Geology, Hist of the NPS, Res mgt
Special Collections: Park Service Southwest region, notes, maps, mss
Restriction: Staff use only
Function: ILL available

G LEGISLATIVE COUNCIL SERVICE LIBRARY, 411 State Capitol, 87501. SAN 310-7183. Tel: 505-986-4600. FAX: 505-986-4610. *Librn*, Tracey Kimball; *Assoc Librn*, Susan Lilley; Staff 2 (MLS 2)
Founded 1951
Library Holdings: Bk Vols 4,000; Bk Titles 2,350; Per Subs 25
Subject Interests: Government, Indian gaming, Pub finance, Taxation
Special Collections: Legislative Rpts

L MONTGOMERY & ANDREWS, Law Library,* 325 Paseo de Pralta, 87501. SAN 372-4271. Tel: 505-982-3873. FAX: 505-982-4289. *Librn*, Bertha Trujillo
Library Holdings: Bk Vols 15,000
Subject Interests: Commercial law

MUSEUM OF NEW MEXICO

G FRAY ANGILICO CHAVEZ HISTORY LIBRARY, 120 Washington Ave, PO Box 2087, 87504-2087. SAN 351-6814. Tel: 505-476-5090. FAX: 505-476-5104. E-Mail: histlib@mnm.state.nm.us. Web Site: www.palaceofthegovernors.org. *Curator*, Thomas Jaehn; Fax: 505-476-5053, E-Mail: tjaehn@mnm.state.nm.us; *Cat*, Hazel Romero; Staff 2 (Non-MLS 2)
Founded 1885
Library Holdings: Bk Vols 15,000; Per Subs 42
Subject Interests: New Mexico, Southwest, Western Americana
Special Collections: Manuscript Coll; Maps; Newspapers; Oral Histories; Photographs; Prints; Rare Books; New Mexico, maps & mss, newsp, rare bks; Southwest (Photo Archives), prints
Publications: El Palacio
Restriction: Open to public for reference only
Open Mon-Fri 1-5

S MUSEUM OF FINE ARTS LIBRARY, 107 W Palace Ave, PO Box 2087, 87504-2087. SAN 351-6873. Tel: 505-476-5061. FAX: 505-476-5076. E-Mail: mfalib@nm-us.campus.mci.net. *Librn*, Mary Jebsen
Founded 1917
Library Holdings: Bk Titles 7,000; Per Subs 35
Special Collections: Artist Biographies; Exchange Exhibition, cats; New Mexican & Southwestern Art Coll
Subscribes to New Mexico Press Clipping Service

S MUSEUM OF INDIAN ARTS & CULTURE, 708 Camino Lejo, 87505. (Mail add: Laboratory of Anthropology, PO Box 2087, 87504-2087), Tel: 505-476-1263. FAX: 505-476-1330. Web Site: www.miaclab.org. *Librn*, Laura Holt; E-Mail: lholt@miaclab.org; *Librn*, Mara Yarbrough; Tel: 505-476-1264, E-Mail: myarbrough@miaclab.org; Staff 2 (MLS 2)
Founded 1929
Library Holdings: Bk Vols 25,000; Per Subs 210
Subject Interests: Native Americans, SW anthrop
Special Collections: Meso American Archaeology & Ethnohistory Coll (Sylvanus G Morley Library)
Automation Activity & Vendor Info: (OPAC) Inmagic, Inc.
Database Vendor: OCLC - First Search
Publications: List of Serials Holdings
Restriction: In-house use for visitors, Open to public for reference only

S MUSEUM OF INTERNATIONAL FOLK ART LIBRARY, PO Box 2087, 87504-2087. SAN 351-6903. Tel: 505-827-6357, Ext 623. FAX: 505-827-6349.
Founded 1953
Library Holdings: Bk Titles 13,000; Per Subs 145

Subject Interests: Costumes, Folk art, Hispanic folklife, New Mexico, Spanish colonial art, Textiles
Partic in OCLC Online Computer Library Center, Inc

S PHOTOGRAPHIC ARCHIVES LIBRARY, 120 Washington Ave, PO Box 2087, 87504. SAN 351-6938. Tel: 505-476-5092. FAX: 505-476-5104. *Archivist*, Arthur Olivas; *Curator*, Richard Rudisill; Staff 2 (Non-MLS 2)
Founded 1960
Jul 1998-Jun 1999 Income $108,500, State $70,000, Locally Generated Income $35,000, Other $3,500
Library Holdings: Bk Titles 3,000
Subject Interests: Agriculture, Anthropology, Archaeology, Australia, China, Ethnology, Hist of NMex, India, Indians, Japan, Latin America, Middle East, Mining, New Zealand, Philippines, Railroads
Special Collections: Photograph Coll 1850-present
Publications: Collection Guides; Photog Catalogs; Reprint Series
Restriction: Not a lending library
Open Mon-Fri 1-5

S NEW MEXICO CORRECTIONS DEPARTMENT, Education Bureau, PO Box 27116, 87502. SAN 310-723X. Tel: 505-827-8682. FAX: 505-827-8548. *In Charge*, Gail Oliver; E-Mail: gail.oliver@state.nm.us; *Coordr*, Sandra Yeffa; E-Mail: sandra.yeffa@state.nm.us; Staff 15 (MLS 3, Non-MLS 12)
Enrl 1,600; Fac 98; Highest Degree: Master Sal $264,000 (Prof $190,000)
Library Holdings: Bk Vols 115,000; Per Subs 210
Subject Interests: Corrections, Law
Special Collections: Criminal Justice Coll, AV, bk training kits; National Criminal Justice Training Center
Special Services for the Deaf - Captioned film depository; High interest/low vocabulary books

G NEW MEXICO ECONOMIC DEVELOPMENT DEPARTMENT, Technology Enterprise Div Library,* Joseph M Montoya Bldg, Rm 1079, 1100 S Saint Francis Dr, 87503. SAN 326-2928. Tel: 505-827-0265. FAX: 505-827-0588. *Librn*, Marsha Oldakowski; Staff 1 (MLS 1)
Special Collections: Economic (bks & reports); Energy Research & Development (bks & reports)
Publications: NMERDI Bibliography
Restriction: Staff use only

G NEW MEXICO ENVIRONMENT DEPARTMENT, Environment Library, 1190 Saint Francis Dr, 87502. SAN 321-4923. Tel: 505-827-2633. FAX: 505-827-2836.
Founded 1980
Jul 1999-Jun 2000 Income $6,000. Mats Exp $6,000, Per/Ser (Incl. Access Fees) $4,000
Library Holdings: Bk Titles 450; Per Subs 55
Subject Interests: Air pollution, Public health, Radiation, Waste disposal
Publications: Library Guide; Library News (monthly); Publication List; Subscription List

S NEW MEXICO SCHOOL FOR THE DEAF LIBRARY,* 1060 Cerrillos Rd, 87503. SAN 310-7191. Tel: 505-827-6743. FAX: 505-827-6684. E-Mail: jdn@nmsd.k12.nm.us. *Media Spec*, Jill Naumann
Library Holdings: Bk Vols 16,000; Per Subs 46
Subject Interests: Deaf culture, Deaf educ, Deafness, Sign lang
Special Collections: Captioned Film Depository

P NEW MEXICO STATE LIBRARY,* 1209 Camino Carlos Rey, 87505. SAN 351-6962. Tel: 505-476-9700. Interlibrary Loan Service Tel: 800-477-4401. FAX: 505-476-9701. Web Site: www.stlib.state.nm.us. *State Librn*, Benjamin P Wakashige; *Tech Servs*, Harold Bogart; *Pub Relations*, Robert Upton; *Bkmobile Coordr*, Dan Monrreal; *Head, Info Serv*, Devon Steele; Staff 22 (MLS 22)
Founded 1929. Pop 1,515,069
Jul 1997-Jun 1998 Income $4,490,600. Mats Exp Per/Ser (Incl. Access Fees) $298,700. Sal $2,482,200
Library Holdings: Bk Vols 300,000; Per Subs 700
Subject Interests: Government, Pub policy
Special Collections: Southwest Resources, bks, doc & per
Automation Activity & Vendor Info: (Circulation) epixtech, inc.
Publications: Annual Statistical Reports; Hitchhiker; Library Directory
Partic in OCLC Online Computer Library Center, Inc
Branches: 1

P , 1209 Camino Carlos Rey, 87505. SAN 310-7213. Tel: 505-476-9770. Toll Free Tel: 800-456-5515. FAX: 505-476-9701. E-Mail: talkingbooks@stlib.state.nm.us. Web Site: www.stlib.state.nm.us. *Librn*, John Brewster; E-Mail: jbrewstr@stlib.state.nm.us; Staff 7 (MLS 1, Non-MLS 6)
Founded 1967
Library Holdings: Bk Vols 250,000; Bk Titles 45,000
Subject Interests: New Mexico, SW
Publications: Newsletter
Special Services for the Blind - Braille & recorded books
Friends of the Library Group
Bookmobiles: 4. Centers located at Belen, Cimarron, Silver City & Tucumcari

GL NEW MEXICO STATE SUPREME COURT LAW LIBRARY, 237 Don Gaspar, 87501. (Mail add: PO Drawer L, 87504), SAN 310-7221. Tel: 505-827-4850. FAX: 505-827-4852. E-Mail: libref@jidmail.nmcourts.com. Web Site: www.fscll.org. *Dir*, Thaddeus Bejnar; *Assoc Librn*, Kevin Lancaster; *Assoc Librn*, Michael Poulson; Staff 8 (MLS 3, Non-MLS 5)
Founded 1853
Jul 2000-Jun 2001 Income $1,235,500. Mats Exp $613,000, Books $25,000, Per/Ser (Incl. Access Fees) $121,000, Presv $15,000, Micro $1,000, Other Print Mats $240,000, Electronic Ref Mat (Incl. Access Fees) $210,000. Sal $440,300 (Prof $230,000)
Library Holdings: Bk Vols 185,000; Per Subs 412
Subject Interests: Anglo-American law, Pre-1850 Mexican Law
Automation Activity & Vendor Info: (Cataloging) EOS; (Circulation) EOS; (OPAC) EOS
Friends of the Library Group

C SAINT JOHN'S COLLEGE, Meem Library, 1160 Camino Cruz Blanca, 87501. SAN 310-7248. Tel: 505-984-6041, 505-984-6042. FAX: 505-984-6004. Web Site: www.sjcsf.edu. *Dir*, Inga Waite; E-Mail: iwaite@mail.sjcsf.edu; *Acq, Ser*, Masao Imamara; *Cat, Tech Coordr*, Heather McLean; *Publ Servs*, Laura Cooley
Founded 1964. Enrl 450; Fac 64; Highest Degree: Master
Library Holdings: Bk Vols 70,000; Bk Titles 35,000; Per Subs 138
Subject Interests: Classics, Music, Philosophy
Special Collections: Hunt Coll; Music (Grumman, Holzman, Schmidt & White)
Automation Activity & Vendor Info: (Acquisitions) VTLS
Partic in Amigos Library Services, Inc; New Mexico Consortium Of Academic Libraries; OCLC Online Computer Library Center, Inc
Friends of the Library Group

M ST VINCENT HOSPITAL LIBRARY, 455 St Michael's Dr, 87505. SAN 375-1929. Tel: 505-820-5218. *Librn*, Beth Saltzman; E-Mail: beth.saltzman@stvin.org
Library Holdings: Bk Vols 2,000; Per Subs 150

S SANTA FE INSTITUTE LIBRARY,* 1399 Hyde Park Rd, 87501. SAN 375-359X. Tel: 505-984-8800. FAX: 505-982-0565. E-Mail: mba@santafe.edu. Web Site: www.santafe.edu. *Librn*, Margaret Alexander
Founded 1984. Fac 25
Jan 1998-Dec 1998 Income $80,000. Mats Exp $40,000, Books $25,000, Per/Ser (Incl. Access Fees) $15,000
Library Holdings: Bk Vols 6,000; Per Subs 50
Subject Interests: Mathematics
Restriction: Non-circulating to the public
Partic in Amigos Library Services, Inc; OCLC Online Computer Library Center, Inc

P SANTA FE PUBLIC LIBRARY, 145 Washington Ave, 87501. SAN 351-7020. Tel: 505-955-6780. Interlibrary Loan Service Tel: 505-955-6720. Circulation Tel: 505-955-6782. Reference Tel: 505-955-6781. TDD: 505-984-6715. FAX: 505-955-6676. E-Mail: library@ci.santa-fe.nm.us. Web Site: www.ci.santa-fe.nm.us/sfpl/. *Dir*, Joanne Werger; Tel: 505-955-6788; *Dir Libr Serv*, Valerie Brooker; Tel: 505-955-6791; *Dir, Tech Serv*, Mary Grathwol; Tel: 505-955-6786; Staff 21 (MLS 12, Non-MLS 9)
Founded 1896. Pop 62,514; Circ 101,087
Jul 1999-Jun 2000 Income (Main Library and Branch Library) $2,237,457, State $14,246, City $2,142,780, Locally Generated Income $80,431. Mats Exp $294,409. Sal $1,742,445
Library Holdings: Bk Vols 258,614; Per Subs 380
Special Collections: New Mexico & Santa Fe
Automation Activity & Vendor Info: (Acquisitions) Innovative Interfaces Inc.; (Cataloging) Innovative Interfaces Inc.; (Circulation) Innovative Interfaces Inc.; (OPAC) Innovative Interfaces Inc.
Database Vendor: Ebsco - EbscoHost, Innovative Interfaces INN - View, ProQuest
Partic in Amigos Library Services, Inc; OCLC Online Computer Library Center, Inc
Friends of the Library Group
Branches: 2
LIBRARY BOOKSTOP, Villa Linda Mall, 87505-9718. SAN 370-1050. Tel: 505-955-2980. FAX: 505-955-2981.; Staff 2 (MLS 1, Non-MLS 1)
Founded 1988
Library Holdings: Bk Vols 17,657
OLIVER LA FARGE, 1730 Llano, 87505-5460. SAN 351-7101. Tel: 505-955-4860. Reference Tel: 505-955-4862. FAX: 505-955-4861. *Dir Libr Serv*, Susan Sonflietn; Tel: 505-955-4866; Staff 5 (MLS 3, Non-MLS 2)
Founded 1978
Library Holdings: Bk Vols 97,114
Friends of the Library Group

S SCHOOL OF AMERICAN RESEARCH LIBRARY, 660 Garcia St, PO Box 2188, 87504-2188. SAN 310-7256. Tel: 505-954-7202. FAX: 505-954-7214. *Librn*, Lee Goodwin; E-Mail: goodwin@sarsf.org; *Asst Librn*, Shirley Girard; Staff 1 (MLS 1)
Founded 1907
Library Holdings: Bk Titles 8,000; Per Subs 52
Subject Interests: Res in anthrop

Special Collections: Advanced Seminar Series; Archaeology of the Grand Canyon Series; Arroyo Hondo Archaeological Series; Monograph Series; Southwestern Indian Arts Series

C SOUTHWESTERN COLLEGE, Quimby Memorial Library, San Felipe at Airport Rd, Rte 20, Box 29-D, 87502-4788. (Mail add: PO Box 4788, 87502), SAN 375-3166. Tel: 505-471-5756, Ext 23. FAX: 505-471-4071. E-Mail: circul1@swc.edu. Web Site: www.swc.edu. *Librn*, Sondra Hareld; Staff 3 (MLS 1, Non-MLS 2)
Highest Degree: Master
Library Holdings: Bk Vols 15,000; Bk Titles 11,000; Per Subs 57
Automation Activity & Vendor Info: (Acquisitions) Athena; (Cataloging) Athena; (Circulation) Athena; (Serials) Athena
Partic in New Mexico Consortium Of Academic Libraries; OCLC Online Computer Library Center, Inc

G US INTERNATIONAL TRADE ADMINISTRATION, US Commercial Service Office Library, Economic Development Department, 1100 Saint Francis Dr, 87503. SAN 375-6319. Tel: 505-827-0350. FAX: 505-827-0263. Web Site: www.usatrade.gov. *Dir*, Sandra Necessary
Subject Interests: International trade

S WHEELWRIGHT MUSEUM OF THE AMERICAN INDIAN, Mary Cabot Wheelwright Research Library, 704 Camino Lejo, 87505. (Mail add: PO Box 5153, 87502-9990), SAN 310-7264. Tel: 505-982-4636. FAX: 505-989-7386. E-Mail: wheelwright@wheelwright.org. *Dir*, Jonathan Batkin; *Curator*, Cheri Falkenstein-Doyle
Founded 1937
Library Holdings: Bk Vols 4,000
Subject Interests: Culture of Navajo Indians, Indians of NAm

SANTA ROSA

P MOISE MEMORIAL LIBRARY,* 208 Fifth St, 88435. SAN 310-7272. Tel: 505-472-3101. FAX: 505-472-3101. E-Mail: moiselibrary@plateantel.net. *Dir*, Joan Chavez
Founded 1932. Pop 2,469; Circ 29,144
1998-1999 Income $89,094. Mats Exp $10,908. Sal $33,469
Library Holdings: Bk Vols 14,000; Per Subs 32
Special Collections: Municipal
Special Services for the Deaf - Special interest periodicals

SHIPROCK

J DINE COLLEGE, Shiprock Campus Library,* 1228 Yucca St, 87420. (Mail add: PO Box 580, 87420), SAN 310-7280. Tel: 505-368-3543. FAX: 505-368-3519. Web Site: www.dclib.ncc.cc.nm.us. *Dir Libr Serv*, Eleanor Kuhl; E-Mail: erkuhl@shiprock.ncc.cc.nm.us
Aug 1998-Jul 1999 Income $147,855. Mats Exp $39,000, Books $20,000, Per/Ser (Incl. Access Fees) $9,000, AV Equip $10,000. Sal $68,657 (Prof $34,847)
Library Holdings: Bk Vols 28,000; Bk Titles 18,000; Per Subs 140
Subject Interests: Geol of western US
Special Collections: American Indian Culture With Special Navajo Coll

SILVER CITY

P THE PUBLIC LIBRARY, 515 W College Ave, 88061. SAN 310-7299. Tel: 505-388-3757, 505-538-3672. FAX: 505-388-3757. E-Mail: silvercitypl@zianet.com. *Dir*, Bonnie Taylor; *Asst Dir*, Cheryl Ward; Staff 5 (MLS 1, Non-MLS 4)
Founded 1952. Pop 23,000; Circ 135,548
Jul 1999-Jun 2000 Income $332,997, State $5,640, City $314,638, Other $12,719. Mats Exp $39,401, Books $32,890, Per/Ser (Incl. Access Fees) $2,750, AV Equip $482, Electronic Ref Mat (Incl. Access Fees) $3,279. Sal $170,125 (Prof $32,000)
Library Holdings: Bk Vols 51,956; Bk Titles 50,822; Per Subs 77; High Interest/Low Vocabulary Bk Vols 122; Bks on Deafness & Sign Lang 20
Subject Interests: Local history, SW mat
Special Collections: Local History Coll
Automation Activity & Vendor Info: (Cataloging) Follett; (Circulation) Follett; (OPAC) Follett
Partic in New Mexico Consortium Of Academic Libraries
Friends of the Library Group

G UNITED STATES FOREST SERVICE DEPARTMENT OF AGRICULTURE, Gila Cliff Dwellings National Monument Library, Rte 100, HC 68, Box 100, 88061-9352. SAN 323-9713. Tel: 505-536-9461. FAX: 505-536-9461. E-Mail: glcl/administration@nps.gov. Web Site: nps.gov.gicl/index.htm. *Librn*, Marie Williams
Founded 1950
Library Holdings: Bk Titles 453
Special Services for the Deaf - TTY machine

C WESTERN NEW MEXICO UNIVERSITY, Miller Library, 1000 W College, PO Box 680, 88062. SAN 310-7310. Tel: 505-538-6350. Interlibrary Loan Service Tel: 505-538-6409. FAX: 505-538-6178. Web Site: millerlibrary.wnmu.edu/miller.htm.; Staff 14 (MLS 4, Non-MLS 10)
Founded 1893. Enrl 2,600; Fac 80; Highest Degree: Master
Jul 1999-Jun 2000 Income State $683,027. Mats Exp $302,000, Books $52,000, Per/Ser (Incl. Access Fees) $184,000, Presv $2,000, Micro $43,000, Electronic Ref Mat (Incl. Access Fees) $21,000. Sal $307,924 (Prof $139,650)
Library Holdings: Bk Vols 135,000; Bk Titles 120,000; Per Subs 950; Bks on Deafness & Sign Lang 45
Subject Interests: Culture, History, Southwest
Special Collections: Education (ERIC), fiche; History (Library of American Civilization, Indian Claims Commission, Contemporary Newspapers of the North American Indian & Western Americana History), fiche & film; Music (Musicache Coll), fiche Local Newspapers from 1886
Automation Activity & Vendor Info: (Acquisitions) Endeavor; (Cataloging) Endeavor; (Circulation) Endeavor; (Course Reserve) Endeavor; (ILL) Endeavor; (Media Booking) Endeavor; (OPAC) Endeavor; (Serials) Endeavor
Partic in Amigos Library Services, Inc; OCLC Online Computer Library Center, Inc
Special Services for the Deaf - TTY machine
Friends of the Library Group

SOCORRO

C NEW MEXICO INSTITUTE OF MINING & TECHNOLOGY, New Mexico Tech Library, 801 Leroy Pl, 87801. (Mail add: Campus Sta, 87801-4682), Tel: 505-835-5614. Interlibrary Loan Service Tel: 505-835-5173. FAX: 505-835-5754. Web Site: www.nmt.edu/~nmtlib. *Dir*, Kay Krehbiel; Tel: 505-835-5615, E-Mail: kkrehbie@nmt.edu; *Tech Servs*, Brigitte Schimek; Tel: 505-835-5766, E-Mail: bschimek@nmt.edu; *ILL*, Sandra Licata; Tel: 505-835-5173, E-Mail: illdept@admin.nmt.edu; Staff 13 (MLS 2, Non-MLS 11)
Founded 1895. Enrl 1,550; Fac 110; Highest Degree: Doctorate
Jun 2000-Jul 2001 Income Parent Institution $1,001,989. Mats Exp $750,000, Books $100,000, Per/Ser (Incl. Access Fees) $507,000, Presv $5,000, Micro $7,000, AV Equip $1,000, Electronic Ref Mat (Incl. Access Fees) $114,000. Sal $397,256 (Prof $89,437)
Library Holdings: Bk Vols 306,950; Bk Titles 88,000; Per Subs 650
Subject Interests: Computer science, Electrical engineering, Environ sci, Environmental engineering, Geology, Hydrology, Petroleum engineering
Special Collections: Geology (US Geological Survey Publications), print & microfiche; Theses & Dissertations; US Bureau of Mines Publications; US Geological Survey Publications
Automation Activity & Vendor Info: (Cataloging) Innovative Interfaces Inc.; (Circulation) Innovative Interfaces Inc.; (ILL) Innovative Interfaces Inc.
Database Vendor: Ebsco - EbscoHost, OCLC - First Search, ProQuest
Partic in New Mexico Consortium Of Academic Libraries

P SOCORRO PUBLIC LIBRARY,* 401 Park St, 87801-4544. SAN 310-7345. Tel: 505-835-1114. FAX: 505-835-1182. E-Mail: library@sdc.org. Web Site: www.sdc.org/~library. *Ad Servs*, Paula Mertz; *Ch Servs*, Jeanne Griffen
Founded 1924. Pop 18,000; Circ 65,351
Jul 1997-Jun 1998 Income $350,137. Mats Exp $35,067, Books $20,000, Per/Ser (Incl. Access Fees) $2,600. Sal $161,959 (Prof $73,698)
Library Holdings: Bk Vols 37,000; Per Subs 100
Subject Interests: Adult basic reading, Local history, SW hist
Publications: Friends of the Socorro Public Library newsletter
Partic in NMex Info Systs; Rio Abajo Libr Coop
Friends of the Library Group

SPRINGER

P FRED MACARON LIBRARY,* 600 Colbert, 87747-0726. (Mail add: PO Box 726, 87747-0726), SAN 310-7353. Tel: 505-483-2848. FAX: 505-483-2670. E-Mail: springerlib@yahoo.com. *Librn*, Ruth Blevins
Circ 7,453
Library Holdings: Bk Vols 10,000; Per Subs 14

SUNSPOT

S NATIONAL SOLAR OBSERVATORY, Technical Library,* 88349. SAN 310-7361. Tel: 505-434-7024. FAX: 505-434-7029. E-Mail: library@sunspot.noao.edu. Web Site: www.sunspot.noao.edu/library. *Librn*, John Cornett
Founded 1953
Library Holdings: Bk Vols 4,500; Bk Titles 3,900; Per Subs 80
Subject Interests: Astronomy, Computer science, Optics, Solar physics
Special Collections: Other Observatory Publications (foreign & US); Publications of National Solar Observatory; Solar Spectral Atlases
Publications: Book Acquisitions; NSO, quarterly
Partic in Dialog Corporation; Fedlink; OCLC Online Computer Library Center, Inc

TAOS

S MILLICENT ROGERS MUSEUM LIBRARY,* 1504 Museum Rd, PO Box A, 87571. SAN 327-5035. Tel: 505-758-2462. FAX: 505-758-5751. E-Mail: mrm@laplaza.taos.nm.us. *Dir*, William Ebie
Library Holdings: Bk Vols 3,000; Per Subs 20
Subject Interests: Archaeology, Art, Ethnology
Special Collections: Directory of Hispanic Artists; Directory of Native American Artists
Friends of the Library Group

P TAOS PUBLIC LIBRARY, 402 Camino de La Placita, 87571. SAN 310-7388. Tel: 505-758-3063. Interlibrary Loan Service Tel: 505-737-2592. Circulation Tel: 505-737-2591. Reference Tel: 505-737-2590. FAX: 505-737-2586. Web Site: www.taoslibrary.org. *Dir*, Laurie Macrae; Tel: 505-737-2587, E-Mail: laurimac@laplaza.org
Founded 1923. Pop 25,000
Jul 2000-Jun 2001 Income $421,474, State $3,965, City $400,009, Locally Generated Income $17,500. Mats Exp Books $32,147. Sal $299,331
Library Holdings: Bk Vols 55,000; Bk Titles 45,000; Per Subs 100
Subject Interests: Fine arts, Southwest
Special Collections: D H Lawrence Coll; Frank Waters Coll; Scottish Clan Macleod Coll; Taos-specific Coll
Automation Activity & Vendor Info: (Cataloging) Follett; (Circulation) Follett; (OPAC) Follett
Database Vendor: Ebsco - EbscoHost, ProQuest
Publications: Newsletter (quarterly)
Partic in New Mexico Libr Asn Round Table
Special Services for the Blind - Magnifiers
Friends of the Library Group

TATUM

P TATUM COMMUNITY LIBRARY, 216 E Broadway, 88267. (Mail add: PO Box 156, 88267-0156), SAN 310-7396. Tel: 505-398-4822. E-Mail: library@leaco.net. *Librn*, Carol Glover
Founded 1964. Pop 1,000; Circ 4,299
2000-2001 Income $6,300, State $3,800, Locally Generated Income $2,500. Mats Exp Books $6,300
Library Holdings: Bk Titles 5,200

TRUTH OR CONSEQUENCES

P TRUTH OR CONSEQUENCES PUBLIC LIBRARY,* 325 Library Lane, 87901-2375. SAN 310-7418. Tel: 505-894-3027. FAX: 505-894-2068. E-Mail: torcpl@riolink.com. Web Site: www.globaldrum.com/rulakeside/library. *Dir*, Pat O'Hanlon
Founded 1933. Circ 100,000
Library Holdings: Bk Titles 50,000; Per Subs 180
Subject Interests: Southwest
Partic in Amigos Library Services, Inc; NMex Info Systs; OCLC Online Computer Library Center, Inc
Friends of the Library Group

TUCUMCARI

P RURAL BOOKMOBILE EAST,* 423 W Nobles, PO Box 1163, 88401. SAN 310-7426. Tel: 505-461-1206. FAX: 505-461-1824. *Dir*, Paula White
Founded 1961. Pop 28,000
Library Holdings: Bk Titles 12,000; Per Subs 15

P SCHLIENTZ MEMORIAL LIBRARY,* 602 S Second, 88401-2899. SAN 310-7434. Tel: 505-461-0295. FAX: 505-461-0297. *Librn*, Clara Rey
Founded 1927. Pop 10,577; Circ 44,402
Library Holdings: Bk Vols 29,732; Per Subs 90
Friends of the Library Group

WHITE SANDS MISSILE RANGE

UNITED STATES ARMY

A CONSOLIDATED LIBRARY, Bldg 464, 88002-5039. SAN 351-711X. Tel: 505-678-1556, 505-678-5820. FAX: 505-678-2270. E-Mail: postlib@wsmr.army.mil. *Chief Librn*, Larry Castleman; E-Mail: castlemanll@wsmr.army.mil; *Doc*, Kathleen Hogan; Staff 2 (MLS 2)
Founded 1950
Library Holdings: Bk Titles 52,300; Per Subs 45
Subject Interests: Engineering, SW, US mil
Special Collections: Military Science; Southwest Coll
Automation Activity & Vendor Info: (Cataloging) EOS; (Circulation) EOS; (OPAC) EOS
Database Vendor: OCLC - First Search
Partic in Fedlink; OCLC Online Computer Library Center, Inc

A TRADOC ANALYSIS CTR TECHNICAL RESEARCH CENTER, USA TRAC-WSMR Attn: ATRC-WSS-R, 88002-5502. SAN 351-7195. Tel: 505-678-1467, 505-678-3135. FAX: 505-678-5104. *In Charge*, Maria M Feliu; Tel: 505-678-3135, E-Mail: felium@trac.wsmr.army.mil; Staff 1 (Non-MLS 1)
Founded 1977
Library Holdings: Bk Vols 5,500; Bk Titles 5,000; Per Subs 215
Subject Interests: Computer modeling, Computer science, Mathematics, Mil, Operations res
Special Collections: DMA Map Coll
Publications: New Acquisitions; Periodical Holdings List
Partic in Faxon; Fedlink; OCLC Online Computer Library Center, Inc; Tralinet

ZUNI

S ZUNI HERITAGE & HISTORIC PRESERVATION OFFICE LIBRARY,* PO Box 339, 87327. SAN 375-1791. Tel: 505-782-4113. FAX: 505-782-4119. E-Mail: zcre@nm.net. *Coordr*, Loren Panteah; *Librn*, Georgia Hughte
Library Holdings: Bk Titles 3,000

NEW YORK

Date of Statistics: 1999-2000
Population, 1990 Census: 17,990,764
Population Served by Public Libraries: 17,990,764
Total Materials in Public Libraries: 124,880,145
Materials Per Capita:6.94
Total Volumes in Public Libraries: 73,738,769
Volumes Per Capita: 4.09
Total Public Library Circulation: 122,780,288
Circulation Per Capita: 6.82
Total Public Library Income (including Capital & Grant-in-Aid): $814,464,640
Source of Income: Mainly public funds
Expenditure Per Capita: $42.39
Number of County or Multi-county (Regional) Libraries: 23
Counties Served: 62
Number of Bookmobiles in State: 15
Grants-in-Aid to Public Libraries:
Federal (Library Services & Construction Act) Titles I & III: $3,179,687
State Aid: $77,107,190
Formula for Apportionment Intent: Formation of Library System to serve given area. Operation: Payment on basis of population, service, and square mileage (includes fixed annual grant)
State Library's Share from Federal Sources: $4,088,273

ADAMS

P ADAMS FREE LIBRARY, 2 N Main St, 13605. SAN 376-3102. Tel: 315-232-2265. FAX: 315-232-2265. *Dir*, Frances Sischo
Founded 1902. Pop 1,750; Circ 2,989
Jan 1999-Dec 1999 Income $21,000. Mats Exp $21,000, Books $3,000. Sal $8,900
Library Holdings: Bk Vols 9,793; Per Subs 18
Mem of North Country Library System

ADAMS CENTER

P ADAMS CENTER FREE LIBRARY,* 18267 NYS RT 177, 13606. SAN 310-7442. Tel: 315-583-5501. FAX: 315-583-5501. Web Site: www.nc3r.org/adc. *Librn*, Constance A Holberg; E-Mail: cholberg@northnet.org
Library Holdings: Bk Vols 4,500
Mem of North Country Library System
Open Mon & Wed 2-7, Fri 2-8

ADDISON

P ADDISON PUBLIC LIBRARY,* 6 South St, 14801. SAN 310-7450. Tel: 607-359-3888. FAX: 607-359-3611.
Founded 1893. Pop 2,734; Circ 19,077
Library Holdings: Bk Vols 16,500; Per Subs 52
Mem of Southern Tier Library System
Open Mon & Wed 5-8, Tues & Thurs 9-1 & 2-6

AFTON

P AFTON FREE LIBRARY,* 105A Main St, 13730. SAN 310-7469. Tel: 607-639-1212. FAX: 607-639-1557. E-Mail: aw_ill@4cty.org. *Librn*, Ramona Bogart
Founded 1933. Pop 2,728; Circ 12,597
Library Holdings: Bk Vols 11,834; Per Subs 31
Mem of Four County Library System

AKRON

P DENIO MEMORIAL LIBRARY, Akron Library, 50 John St, 14001-1020. SAN 310-7477. Tel: 716-542-2327. FAX: 716-542-2327. Web Site: www.buffalolib.org. *Dir*, Kristine Sutton; E-Mail: suttonk@buffalolib.org; Staff 3 (MLS 1, Non-MLS 2)
Founded 1942. Pop 7,440; Circ 32,507
Jan 1999-Dec 1999 Mats Exp $13,000, Books $9,000, Per/Ser (Incl. Access Fees) $2,500, AV Equip $1,500
Library Holdings: Bk Titles 13,000; Per Subs 99
Mem of Buffalo & Erie County Public Library System
Friends of the Library Group

ALBANY

CM ALBANY COLLEGE OF PHARMACY, George & Leona Lewis Library, 106 New Scotland Ave, 12208. SAN 324-7503. Tel: 518-445-7270. FAX: 518-445-7300. Web Site: www.acp.edu. *Librn*, Debra Locascio; *Asst Librn*, Sue Iwanowicz; Staff 4 (MLS 2, Non-MLS 2)
Founded 1960. Enrl 690; Fac 37; Highest Degree: Doctorate
Library Holdings: Bk Titles 5,745; Per Subs 199
Subject Interests: Pharm
Automation Activity & Vendor Info: (Cataloging) SIRSI; (Circulation) SIRSI; (Course Reserve) SIRSI; (OPAC) SIRSI
Database Vendor: OCLC - First Search
Partic in CDLC; National Network of Libraries of Medicine - Greater Midwest Region; WALDO

S ALBANY INSTITUTE OF HISTORY & ART, 125 Washington Ave, 12210-2296. SAN 310-7493. Tel: 518-463-4478. FAX: 518-463-5506. Web Site: albanyinstitute.org. *Chief Librn*, Sandra Markham; E-Mail: markhams@albanyinstitute.org; Staff 2 (MLS 2)
Library Holdings: Bk Vols 14,000; Per Subs 50
Subject Interests: American painting, Art, Decorative art, History, Local history, Upper Hudson valleys
Special Collections: Albany imprints, almanacs, maps, photographs, manuscripts, broadsides, archives, architectural drawings, ephemera, scrapbooks; Albany Social, Political & Business History, 18th & 19th Centuries, maps, mss, photog; American Painters & Sculptors, manuscripts, photog; Broadsides (including The DeWitt Clinton Collection of 18th & Early 19th Century; Dutch in The Upper Hudson Valley, 17th & 18th Centuries, maps, mss; Political Broadsides)
Automation Activity & Vendor Info: (OPAC) Sagebrush Corporation
Database Vendor: Ebsco - EbscoHost
Partic in Capital District Library Council for Reference & Research Resources
Written research requests are accepted

CL ALBANY LAW SCHOOL, Schaffer Law Library,* 80 New Scotland Ave, 12208. SAN 310-7507. Tel: 518-445-2340. Interlibrary Loan Service Tel: 518-445-2338. FAX: 518-472-5842. Web Site: www.als.edu/lib/. *Dir*, Robert T Begg; *Asst Dir, Coll Develop*, Robert Emery; *Tech Servs*, Elizabeth Duncan; *Circ, ILL, Publ Servs*, Mary Wood; *Doc, Ref*, Nancy Lenahan; *AV*, Robert Eaton; *Cat*, Ellen Rappaport; *Ref*, Marcel LaJoy; Staff 8 (MLS 8)
Founded 1851. Enrl 750; Fac 41; Highest Degree: Doctorate
Jul 1997-Jun 1998 Income $1,642,093, State $5,100, Parent Institution $1,636,993. Mats Exp $911,000, Books $89,000, Per/Ser (Incl. Access Fees) $79,000, Presv $11,500, Micro $99,500, Other Print Mats $505,000. Sal $731,087
Library Holdings: Bk Vols 230,813; Bk Titles 60,000; Per Subs 1,194
Publications: Faculty & staff publications
Partic in Cap District Libr Coun for Ref & Res Resources; Nellco; New England Law Library Consortium, Inc; OCLC Online Computer Library Center, Inc; Westlaw

CM ALBANY MEDICAL COLLEGE, Schaffer Library of Health Sciences, 47 New Scotland Ave, 12208. SAN 351-7985. Tel: 518-262-5586. Interlibrary Loan Service Tel: 518-262-5538. Reference Tel: 518-262-5532. FAX: 518-262-5820. E-Mail: library@mail.amc.edu. Web Site: www.amc.edu/Academic/Library/library.html. *Dir*, Sherry A Hartman; *ILL*, Andy Krzystiniak; *Tech Servs*, Enid Geyer; *Media Spec*, Gwen Weldy; *Coll Develop*, Gail Botta; *Ref Serv*, Sue Lahey; *Publ Servs*, Elizabeth Irish; *Access Serv, Circ*, Veronica Cunningham; Staff 10 (MLS 10)
Founded 1928. Enrl 1,490; Fac 417; Highest Degree: Doctorate
Jan 1999-Dec 1999 Income $1,660,001, State $5,480, Parent Institution $1,654,521. Sal $730,401 (Prof $370,884)
Library Holdings: Bk Vols 140,434; Bk Titles 38,620; Per Subs 1,000
Subject Interests: Med sci
Special Collections: Archives of Albany Medical College
Automation Activity & Vendor Info: (Circulation) SIRSI
Database Vendor: CARL, Dialog, Ebsco - EbscoHost, OVID Technologies, ProQuest
Publications: Fact Sheets
Partic in Cap District Libr Coun for Ref & Res Resources; Nat Libr of Med; OCLC Online Computer Library Center, Inc

P ALBANY PUBLIC LIBRARY,* 161 Washington Ave, 12210. SAN 351-7209. Tel: 518-427-4300. FAX: 518-427-4321. *Dir*, Jeffrey Cannell; *Ad Servs, Ref*, James Hobin; *ILL*, John Cirrin; Staff 31 (MLS 31)
Founded 1833. Circ 647,225
Library Holdings: Bk Vols 400,000; Per Subs 6,200
Subject Interests: Bus, Mgt
Special Collections: History (Albany City & County History), bks, clippings, microflm
Automation Activity & Vendor Info: (Circulation) CLSI LIBS
Mem of Upper Hudson Library System
Partic in OCLC Online Computer Library Center, Inc
Special Services for the Blind - Kurzweil Reading Machine; Micro computer access & training
Friends of the Library Group
Branches: 4
DELAWARE, 485 Delaware Ave, 12209. SAN 351-7268. Tel: 518-463-0254. *Librn*, Eileen Purcell
JOHN HOWE LIBRARY, Schuyler & Broad Sts, 12202. SAN 351-7292. Tel: 518-472-9485. *Librn*, Ethel LaPier
NEW SCOTLAND, 369 New Scotland Ave, 12208. SAN 351-7322. Tel: 518-482-6661. *Librn*, Eileen Purcell
PINE HILLS, 517 Western Ave, 12203. SAN 351-7357. Tel: 518-482-7911. *Librn*, Ethel LaPier

J BRYANT & STRATTON BUSINESS INSTITUTE LIBRARY,* 1259 Central Ave, 12205. SAN 310-7485. Tel: 518-437-1802. FAX: 518-437-1048. Web Site: www.bryantstratton.edu. *Dir*, David Titus
Founded 1961. Enrl 500; Fac 35
Library Holdings: Bk Vols 4,900; Bk Titles 4,700; Per Subs 40
Subject Interests: Bus, Data processing, Econ, Law, Marketing, Med assisting, Mgt, Off procedures, Travel
Publications: F Y I
Partic in Cap District Libr Coun for Ref & Res Resources

S CENTER FOR THE STUDY OF AGING LIBRARY,* 706 Madison Ave, 12208-3604. SAN 328-1612. Tel: 518-465-6927. FAX: 518-462-1339. E-Mail: iapaas@aol.com. Web Site: www.members.aol.com/iapaas/. *Dir*, Sara Harris
Library Holdings: Bk Titles 4,000; Per Subs 45
Subject Interests: Aging, Housing, Mental health, Nutrition, Psychiatry, Psychology
Publications: Annotated bibliographics lists by subject and/or category; Environment & Aging; Physical Activity, Aging & Sports (Vols I-IV); Safe Therapeutic Exercise for the Frail Elderly: An Introduction; Senior Citizen School Volunteer Program (manual); Who? Me? Exercise? Safe Exercise for People Over 50
Restriction: By appointment only

C COLLEGE OF SAINT ROSE, Neil Hellman Library, 392-396 Western Ave, 12203. SAN 310-7515. Tel: 518-454-5180. Interlibrary Loan Service Tel: 518-454-2155. Circulation Tel: 518-454-5180. Reference Tel: 518-454-5182. FAX: 518-454-2897. E-Mail: refdesk@rosnet.strose.edu. Web Site: www.strose.edu/library/li_hp.htm. *Dir*, Peter Koonz; E-Mail: koonzp@mail.strose.edu; *Cat, Tech Servs*, Carl Cording; Tel: 518-458-5382, E-Mail: cordingc@mail.strose.edu; *Ref, Ser*, Steve Black; Tel: 518-458-5494, E-Mail: blacks@mail.strose.edu; *Circ, ILL, Ref*, Kate Moss; Tel: 518-454-2154, E-Mail: mossk@mail.strose.edu; *Archivist, Spec Coll*, Jean Root Mahalov; Tel: 518-454-5190, E-Mail: mahalovj@mail.strose.edu; *Electronic Resources*, Peter Osterhoudt; Tel: 518-454-2026, E-Mail: osterhop@mail.strose.edu; Staff 17 (MLS 7, Non-MLS 10)
Founded 1920. Enrl 3,145; Fac 172; Highest Degree: Master
Jul 1999-Jun 2000 Income $825,334, State $8,118, Parent Institution $817,216. Mats Exp $262,877, Books $83,478, Per/Ser (Incl. Access Fees) $134,061, Micro $8,609, Electronic Ref Mat (Incl. Access Fees) $36,729. Sal $457,539 (Prof $251,401)
Library Holdings: Bk Vols 200,987; Per Subs 945
Subject Interests: Education, Special educ
Special Collections: Col archives; Curriculum Library
Automation Activity & Vendor Info: (Cataloging) epixtech, inc.; (Circulation) epixtech, inc.; (OPAC) epixtech, inc.; (Serials) epixtech, inc.
Database Vendor: Dialog, Ebsco - EbscoHost, IAC - Info Trac, Lexis-Nexis, OCLC - First Search, Silverplatter Information Inc.
Publications: Guide to the Neil Hellman Libr
Partic in Capital District Library Council for Reference & Research Resources; OCLC Online Computer Library Center, Inc

R CONGREGATION BETH EMETH, Judaica Library, 100 Academy Rd, 12208. SAN 310-7523. Tel: 518-436-9761. FAX: 518-436-0476. E-Mail: cbemeth@aol.com. Web Site: www.bethemeth.org.
Founded 1930
Library Holdings: Bk Titles 3,500; Per Subs 12
Special Collections: Judaica Periodicals

S EARTH TECH, Information Services,* 12 Metro Park Rd, 12205. SAN 329-0395. Tel: 518-458-1313. FAX: 518-458-2472.; Staff 4 (MLS 2, Non-MLS 2)
Founded 1987
Library Holdings: Bk Titles 8,500; Per Subs 120
Subject Interests: Geology
Special Collections: New York State Geology, hydrology
Automation Activity & Vendor Info: (Cataloging) Inmagic, Inc.
Partic in Dialog Corporation; Westlaw

S FIRST UNITARIAN UNIVERSALIST SOCIETY OF ALBANY, Charles R Joy Library, 405 Washington Ave, 12206. SAN 323-5459. Tel: 518-463-7135. *In Charge*, Jack Atwater
Library Holdings: Bk Titles 1,300
Special Collections: First Unitarian Society of Albany Archives
Restriction: By appointment only
Open Sun 9-12

S LEAGUE OF WOMEN VOTERS OF NEW YORK STATE EDUCATION FOUNDATION INC, Anna Lord Strauss Library,* 35 Maiden Lane, 12207-2712. SAN 327-1854. Tel: 518-465-4162. FAX: 518-465-0812. E-Mail: lwvny@lwvny.org. *Exec Dir*, Lee F Serravillo
Library Holdings: Bk Vols 500
Other holdings: Citizens Info Service, Info NY State Govt

J MARIA COLLEGE OF ALBANY LIBRARY, 700 New Scotland Ave, 12208. SAN 310-7574. Tel: 518-438-3111. FAX: 518-438-7170. Web Site: www.mariacollege.org. *Dir*, Sister Rose Hobbs; E-Mail: roseh@mariacollege.org
Founded 1958. Enrl 700
Library Holdings: Bk Vols 55,000; Per Subs 225
Subject Interests: Allied health, Early childhood
Partic in Capital District Library Council for Reference & Research Resources

L MCNAMEE, LOCHNER, TITUS & WILLIAMS, Law Library, 75 State St, 12201-0459. (Mail add: PO Box 459, 12201-0459), SAN 372-4638. Tel: 518-447-3200. FAX: 518-426-4260. *Librn*, Dana Rogers; E-Mail: danar@mltw.com
Library Holdings: Bk Vols 12,000
Restriction: Staff use only
Open Mon-Fri 9-5

M MEMORIAL HOSPITAL, Health Sciences Library,* 600 Northern Blvd, 12204. SAN 310-7582. Tel: 518-471-3264. FAX: 518-447-3559. *Librn*, Mary Beth Farr; Staff 3 (MLS 1, Non-MLS 2)
Founded 1960
Library Holdings: Bk Vols 3,500; Bk Titles 3,200; Per Subs 90
Subject Interests: Nursing, Obstetrics, Surgery
Mem of Cap District Libr Coun for Ref & Res Resources

GL NEW YORK STATE COURT OF APPEALS LIBRARY,* 20 Eagle St, 12207-1905. SAN 310-7604. Tel: 518-455-7770. *Librn*, Elizabeth F Murray
Founded 1870
Library Holdings: Bk Vols 80,000; Bk Titles 1,200; Per Subs 100
Subject Interests: Law
Restriction: Staff use only
Partic in Westlaw

S NEW YORK STATE DEPARTMENT OF CORRECTIONAL SERVICES, Office of the Counsel,* State Campus, Bldg 2, Library Services, 1220 Washington Ave, 12226-2050. SAN 323-9772. Tel: 518-485-7109. FAX: 518-485-9629. *Librn*, Jean Clancy Botta

G NEW YORK STATE DEPARTMENT OF ECONOMIC DEVELOPMENT, Empire State Development Library, 30 S Pearl St, 12245. SAN 310-7639. Tel: 518-292-5238. FAX: 518-292-5805. *Dir Libr Serv*, Barbara S Beverley; E-Mail: bbeverley@empire.state.ny.us; Staff 4 (MLS 1, Non-MLS 3)
Founded 1944
Apr 2000-Mar 2001 Income $150,000
Library Holdings: Bk Vols 20,000; Per Subs 800
Subject Interests: Business, Econ develop, International trade
Automation Activity & Vendor Info: (Cataloging) Inmagic, Inc.; (OPAC)

Inmagic, Inc.
Database Vendor: Dialog, Lexis-Nexis
Restriction: By appointment only
Function: ILL available
Partic in Cap District Libr Coun for Ref & Res Resources; New York State Interlibrary Loan Network

G NEW YORK STATE DEPARTMENT OF FAMILY ASSISTANCE LIBRARY,* Dept Lib 1 CP Rm 725, 40 N Pearl St, 12243. SAN 310-768X. Tel: 518-473-8072. FAX: 518-486-3434. *Librn*, Madeline Raciti; E-Mail: ay6350@dfa.state.ny.us; Staff 1 (MLS 1)
Founded 1937
Library Holdings: Bk Vols 6,000; Bk Titles 6,000; Per Subs 320
Subject Interests: Child welfare, Pub welfare, Soc servs
Open Mon-Fri 8:30-5, public by appointment

GM NEW YORK STATE DEPARTMENT OF HEALTH, Dickerman Library, Wadsworth Center, Empire State Plaza, Box 509, 12201-0509. SAN 310-7655. Tel: 518-474-6172. FAX: 518-474-3933. Web Site: dickerman.wadsworth.org. *Dir, Online Servs*, Thomas Flynn; E-Mail: flynn@wadsworth.org; *Ref, Ser*, Cynthia Yochym; *Cat*, Rae Clark; Staff 8 (MLS 3, Non-MLS 5)
Founded 1914
Library Holdings: Bk Vols 40,000; Per Subs 1,100
Subject Interests: Clinical labs, Environ health, Epidemiology, Health policy, Infectious diseases, Molecular biology, Molecular genetics, Public health, Radiol health, Toxicology, Veterinary medicine
Automation Activity & Vendor Info: (OPAC) Innovative Interfaces Inc.; (Serials) Innovative Interfaces Inc.
Database Vendor: OVID Technologies
Partic in OCLC Online Computer Library Center, Inc

G NEW YORK STATE DEPARTMENT OF LABOR, Research Library, Bldg 12, Rm 480, State Office Bldg Campus, 12240. SAN 310-7663. Tel: 518-457-1292. *Senior Librn*, R Ashley Hibbard; Fax: 518-457-6199, E-Mail: usbrah@labor.state.ny.us; Staff 1 (MLS 1)
Founded 1907
Oct 2000-Sep 2001 Mats Exp $22,000, Books $5,000, Per/Ser (Incl. Access Fees) $5,000, Electronic Ref Mat (Incl. Access Fees) $12,000
Library Holdings: Bk Titles 1,500; Per Subs 160
Subject Interests: Demographics, Labor market info, Vocational guidance
Special Collections: New York State Department of Labor Publications
Database Vendor: Dialog, Ebsco - EbscoHost, OCLC - First Search
Publications: Selected Additions List
Function: Research library

GL NEW YORK STATE DEPARTMENT OF LAW LIBRARY,* The Capitol, 12224. SAN 351-7381. Tel: 518-474-3840. FAX: 518-473-1822. *Chief Librn*, Judith A Brown; E-Mail: judith.brown@oag.state.ny.us; *Librn*, Franette Sheinwald; Tel: 212-416-8012, Fax: 212-416-6130; *Librn*, Patricia Partello; *Librn*, Christina Marie Rovelli; *Librn*, Barbara Ost; *Assoc Librn*, Sarah P Browne; Staff 14 (MLS 6, Non-MLS 8)
Founded 1944
Library Holdings: Bk Vols 125,000; Per Subs 556
Special Collections: New York State Law Department Records & Briefs
Publications: Check It Out (quarterly newsletter)
Partic in Westlaw

G NEW YORK STATE DEPARTMENT OF TAXATION & FINANCE LIBRARY,* Bureau of Tax Policy Analysis, W A Harriman Campus, Bldg 9, Rm 280, 12227. SAN 310-7701. Tel: 518-457-3512. FAX: 518-485-1365. *Librn*, Michael Craig
Founded 1946
Library Holdings: Bk Vols 14,500; Per Subs 60
Open Mon-Fri 7am-5pm

G NEW YORK STATE DEPARTMENT OF TRANSPORTATION & DEVELOPMENT, Planning Data & Analysis,* State Campus Bldg, 7A Rm 600, 1220 Washington, 12232-0869. SAN 310-771X. Tel: 518-457-2967, 518-485-2077. FAX: 518-457-7535. *Dir*, Ron Tweedie
Founded 1962
Library Holdings: Bk Vols 1,500; Per Subs 30
Subject Interests: Econ, Energy, Environ policy, Highway eng, Legislation, Planning
Restriction: Open to public for reference only
Friends of the Library Group

G NEW YORK STATE LEGISLATIVE LIBRARY, State Capitol, Rm 337, 12224-0345. SAN 372-431X. Tel: 518-455-4000. FAX: 518-463-0218. *Librn*, Kate Balassie; *Librn*, Ellen Breslin; *Librn*, James Giliberto; *Librn*, Heather Redlich; *Librn*, Barbara Van-Nortwick; Staff 11 (MLS 5, Non-MLS 6)
Library Holdings: Bk Vols 100,000; Per Subs 100
Subject Interests: Law, Legislation
Special Collections: History of New York Laws; Legislative Reports; New York State Agency Reports
Partic in Dialog Corporation; Westlaw

P NEW YORK STATE LIBRARY, Talking Book & Braille Library, Empire State Plaza, Cultural Education Ctr Basement, 12230. SAN 310-7744. Tel: 518-474-5935. Toll Free Tel: 800-342-3688. FAX: 518-474-5786. E-Mail: tbbl@mail.nysed.gov. *Dir*, Jane Somers; Staff 26 (MLS 5, Non-MLS 21)
Founded 1896. Pop 39,000; Circ 600,000
Library Holdings: Bk Vols 730,000
Publications: Bibliographies; newsletters
Special Services for the Blind - Braille & recorded books; Kurzweil Reading Machine; Printed text enlargers; Talking Books
Friends of the Library Group

P NEW YORK STATE LIBRARY, State Education Department, Cultural Education Center, Empire State Plaza, 12230. SAN 351-756X. Tel: 518-474-5355. FAX: 518-474-5786. Web Site: www.nysl.nysed.gov. *Dir*, Liz Lane; Tel: 518-473-1189; *Adminr*, Beth Closson; Tel: 518-474-4660; *Assoc Librn*, Soumaya Baaklini; *Ref*, Sally Lebendre; *Spec Coll*, Kathi Stanley; Tel: 518-474-5963; *Syst Coordr*, J Van der Veer Judd; Tel: 518-474-5955; *Ref*, Mary Redmond; Tel: 518-486-5755; *Coll Develop*, Liza Duncan; Tel: 518-474-5946. Subject Specialists: *Manuscripts*, Kathi Stanley; Staff 65 (MLS 62, Non-MLS 3)
Founded 1818. Circ 44,100
Apr 1998-Mar 1999 Income (Main Library Only) $11,079,942, State $8,141,507, Federal $2,938,435. Mats Exp $2,408,106, Books $690,577, Per/Ser (Incl. Access Fees) $1,678,672, Presv $38,857. Sal $6,314,184
Library Holdings: Bk Vols 2,441,437; Per Subs 15,247
Special Collections: Dutch Colonial Records; New York State Political & Social History; Shaker Coll
Automation Activity & Vendor Info: (Acquisitions) SIRSI; (Cataloging) SIRSI; (Circulation) SIRSI; (Course Reserve) SIRSI; (ILL) SIRSI; (OPAC) SIRSI; (Serials) SIRSI
Database Vendor: Dialog, Ebsco - EbscoHost, IAC - SearchBank, Lexis-Nexis, OCLC - First Search, ProQuest
Publications: Checklist of Official Publications of the State of New York
Mem of Asn of Research Libraries
Partic in New York State Interlibrary Loan Network; OCLC Online Computer Library Center, Inc; RLIN
Special Services for the Blind - Kurzweil Reading Machine
Friends of the Library Group
Branches: 1
TALKING BOOK & BRAILLE LIBRARY
See Separate Entry

GM NEW YORK STATE OFFICE OF MENTAL HEALTH LIBRARY,* 44 Holland Ave, 12229. SAN 310-7671. Tel: 518-474-7167. FAX: 518-474-7361. *Chief Librn*, Paul Hillengas
Founded 1969
Library Holdings: Bk Vols 5,300; Bk Titles 5,200; Per Subs 50
Subject Interests: Gerontology, Hosp admin, Mental health, Neurology, Nursing, Personnel admin, Psychiatry, Psychology, Psychotherapy, Social, Statistics
Special Collections: Annual Reports of the Department
Restriction: Open to public for reference only
Partic in Capital District Library Council for Reference & Research Resources
Open Mon-Fri 8:30-4:30

G NEW YORK STATE OFFICE OF THE STATE COMPTROLLER LIBRARY, Alfred E Smith Off Bldg, 12236. SAN 310-7612. Tel: 518-473-4206, 518-473-5960. FAX: 518-473-1900. *Librn*, Rosemary A Del Vecchio; E-Mail: rdelvecchio@osc.state.ny.us; Staff 2 (MLS 1, Non-MLS 1)
Library Holdings: Bk Vols 7,700; Per Subs 135
Subject Interests: Econ, Government, Municipal law
Open Mon-Fri 8-4:30

G NEW YORK STATE WORKER'S COMPENSATION BOARD LIBRARY,* 20 Park St, 12207. SAN 371-411X. Tel: 518-486-7676. FAX: 518-473-2233. *In Charge*, Peter Molinaro
Library Holdings: Bk Vols 1,500; Per Subs 44

GL NEW YORK SUPREME COURT APPELLATE DIVISION, Third Department Library,* Justice Bldg, Empire State Plaza, 12223. SAN 310-7752. Tel: 518-432-3473. *In Charge*, Ronald J Milkins
Library Holdings: Bk Vols 75,000

S NYS SBDC RESEARCH NETWORK, SUNY Plaza, 41 State St, 12246-0001. SAN 377-5763. Tel: 518-443-5265. FAX: 518-443-5275. E-Mail: sbdcrn@nyssbdc.org. Web Site: www.nyssbdc.org. *Dir*, Mary Hoffman; Staff 4 (MLS 4)
Founded 1991
Library Holdings: Bk Vols 800; Per Subs 35
Restriction: By appointment only
Partic in Am Libr Asn; Dialog Corporation; Dow Jones News Retrieval

J THE SAGE COLLEGES, Albany Campus Library, 140 New Scotland Ave, 12208. SAN 310-7787. Tel: 518-292-1721. Interlibrary Loan Service Tel: 518-292-1742. Reference Tel: 518-292-1945. FAX: 518-292-1904. E-Mail: libref@sage.edu. Web Site: www.sage.edu. *Dir*, Kingsley W Greene; Tel: 518-244-2346, Fax: 518-244-2400, E-Mail: greenk@sage.edu; *Assoc Dir*,

Lynne King; E-Mail: kingl@sage.edu; *ILL*, Doris Robinson; Tel: 518-292-1784, E-Mail: robind@sage.edu; *Electronic Resources*, Margaret Lanoue; Tel: 518-292-1959, E-Mail: lanoum@sage.edu; *Publ Servs*, Sheldon Wein; Tel: 518-292-8635, E-Mail: weins@sage.edu; Staff 10 (MLS 4, Non-MLS 6)
Founded 1957. Enrl 2,407; Fac 161; Highest Degree: Master
May 1999-Apr 2000 Income Parent Institution $475,541. Mats Exp $153,552, Books $37,218, Per/Ser (Incl. Access Fees) $49,556, Presv $6,225, AV Equip $4,245, Electronic Ref Mat (Incl. Access Fees) $28,883. Sal $294,334 (Prof $167,890)
Library Holdings: Bk Vols 82,102; Bk Titles 65,323; Per Subs 250
Subject Interests: Graphic arts
Automation Activity & Vendor Info: (Circulation) SIRSI; (Course Reserve) SIRSI; (OPAC) SIRSI
Database Vendor: Ebsco - EbscoHost, GaleNet, Lexis-Nexis, OCLC - First Search, ProQuest, Silverplatter Information Inc.
Publications: Library Handbook; Newsletter; Serials & Full-Text Lists
Partic in Cap District Libr Coun for Ref & Res Resources; OCLC Online Computer Library Center, Inc; WALDO

M SAINT PETER'S HOSPITAL, Health Sciences Library, 315 S Manning Blvd, 12208. SAN 310-7795. Tel: 518-525-1490. FAX: 518-525-1670. *Dir*, Phyllis Miyauchi; E-Mail: pmiyauchi@stpetershealthcare.org; Staff 1 (MLS 1)
Founded 1950
Library Holdings: Bk Titles 1,300; Per Subs 160
Subject Interests: Internal medicine, Pediatrics, Surgery
Database Vendor: OVID Technologies
Publications: Library Guide
Restriction: Staff use only
Partic in BHSL; Capital District Library Council for Reference & Research Resources; Medline; Nat Libr of Med

C UNIVERSITY AT ALBANY, STATE UNIVERSITY OF NEW YORK, University Libraries, 1400 Washington Ave, 12222-0001. SAN 351-7896. Tel: 518-442-3568. Interlibrary Loan Service Tel: 518-442-3613. FAX: 518-442-3567. E-Mail: mb801@csc.albany.edu. Web Site: library.albany.edu/. *Dir*, Meredith A Butler; *Syst Coordr, Tech Servs*, Heather Miller; *Online Servs*, Sara Knapp; *Archivist*, Geoffrey Williams; *Spec Coll*, Dorothy E Christiansen
Founded 1844. Enrl 17,000; Fac 920; Highest Degree: Doctorate
Jul 1999-Jun 2000 Mats Exp $4,797,115, Books $1,242,857, Per/Ser (Incl. Access Fees) $2,851,478, Presv $214,700, Micro $47,080, AV Equip $250,000, Electronic Ref Mat (Incl. Access Fees) $191,000. Sal $5,300,561
Library Holdings: Bk Vols 1,976,374; Per Subs 5,286
Subject Interests: Criminal justice, Education, Public affairs, Soc sci
Special Collections: Archives for Public Affairs and Policy; Children's Historical Lit Coll; German Intellectual Emigre Coll
Automation Activity & Vendor Info: (Circulation) GEAC
Publications: Fact Sheet series; Guide to Resources & Services; Library Update (bi-annual newsletter); University Libraries Strategic Plan, 1995-2000 & Annual Progress reports
Partic in Asn of Research Libraries; Cap District Libr Coun for Ref & Res Resources; Center For Research Libraries; New York State Interlibrary Loan Network; OCLC Online Computer Library Center, Inc; Research Libraries Group, Inc
Special Services for the Blind - Kurzweil Reading Machine
Friends of the Library Group
Departmental Libraries:
GOVERNOR THOMAS E DEWEY GRADUATE LIBRARY FOR PUBLIC AFFAIRS & POLICY, 135 Western Ave, 12222. SAN 370-3320. Tel: 518-442-3693. FAX: 518-442-3474. *Head of Libr*, Barbara Via
Library Holdings: Bk Vols 127,834
Subject Interests: Criminal justice, Info sci, Libr sci, Pub admin, Soc welfare
Friends of the Library Group
SCIENCE LIBRARY, 1400 Washington Ave, 12222. Tel: 518-437-3948. Reference Tel: 518-437-3945. FAX: 518-437-3952. Web Site: library.albany.edu/. *Head of Libr*, Gregg Sapp

P UPPER HUDSON LIBRARY SYSTEM, 28 Essex St, 12206. SAN 310-7817. Tel: 518-437-9880. FAX: 518-437-9884. E-Mail: uhls@uhls.lib.ny.us. Web Site: www.uhls.org/uhls. *Dir*, Philip Ritter; Tel: 518-437-9880, Ext 222, E-Mail: phil@uhls.lib.ny.us; *Ad Servs, Info Specialist*, Rachel R Baum; Tel: 518-437-9880, Ext 225, E-Mail: rachel@uhls.lib.ny.us; *Dep Dir*, Sara Dallas; Tel: 518-437-9880, Ext 227, E-Mail: sara@uhls.lib.ny.us; Staff 12 (MLS 7, Non-MLS 5)
Founded 1960. Pop 447,222; Circ 2,619,121
Library Holdings: Bk Vols 114,000
Automation Activity & Vendor Info: (Circulation) DRA
Database Vendor: DRA
Publications: Annual reports; newsletter (monthly)
Member Libraries: Albany Public Library; Altamont Free Library; Arvilla E Diver Memorial Library; Berlin Free Town Library; Bethlehem Public Library; Castleton Public Library; Cheney Library; Cohoes Public Library; East Greenbush Community Library; Guilderland Public Library; Menands Public Library; Nassau Free Library; North Greenbush Public Library; Petersburg Public Library; RCS Community Library; Rensselaer Public Library; Rensselaerville Library; Sand Lake Town Library; Stephentown Memorial Library; The William K Sanford Town Library; Town Of Berne Free Library; Troy Public Library; Valley Falls Free Library; Voorheesville Public Library; Watervliet Public Library; Westerlo Public Library
Partic in Capital District Library Council for Reference & Research Resources

GM VA HEALTHCARE NETWORK - UPSTATE NEW YORK, Samuel S Stratton VA Medical Center, 113 Holland Ave, 142D, 12208. SAN 310-7825. Tel: 518-462-3311, Ext 2349. FAX: 518-462-5457. Web Site: www.va.gov/visns/visn02/alb_nf.html. *Dir Libr Serv*, Halyna L Korhun; E-Mail: halyna.korhun@med.va.gov; Staff 2 (MLS 2)
Founded 1951
Library Holdings: Bk Titles 2,500; Per Subs 275
Subject Interests: Allied health, Medicine, Patient educ
Publications: AV List; Journal Holdings List; New Media List; Patient Pamphlet List
Partic in BHSL; CDLC; Docline; Medline; Vets Admin Libr Network
Open Mon-Fri 8-4

S VAN RENSSELEAR - RANKIN FAMILY HISTORIC CHERRY HILL MUSEUM & LIBRARY,* 523 1/2 S Pearl St, 12202. SAN 327-7461. Tel: 518-434-4791. FAX: 518-434-4806. *Dir*, Liselle LaFrance
Library Holdings: Bk Vols 5,000
Open Tues-Sat 10-4

ALBERTSON

S NATIONAL CENTER FOR DISABILITY SERVICES, National Business & Disability Council, 201 I U Willetts Rd, 11507-1599. SAN 310-7833. Tel: 516-465-1515 (Helpline), 516-747-5400. FAX: 516-465-3730. *In Charge*, Laura Francis
Founded 1961
Library Holdings: Bk Vols 2,500; Per Subs 250
Subject Interests: Adjustment, Independent living for disabled personnel, Special educ, Technology, Vocational rehabilitation, Work evaluation
Partic in BRS; Dialog Corporation; Long Island Library Resources Council
Open Mon-Fri 8:30-4:30

P SHELTER ROCK PUBLIC LIBRARY,* 165 Searingtown Rd, 11507. SAN 310-7841. Tel: 516-248-7343. FAX: 516-248-4897. E-Mail: shelter@nassaulibrary.org. *Dir*, Frances M Conrad; *Ad Servs, Asst Dir*, Andrea Meluskey; *Per*, Ronnie Axelrod; *YA Servs*, Cathy Loechner
Founded 1962. Pop 25,585; Circ 276,000
Library Holdings: Bk Vols 133,000; Bk Titles 119,000; Per Subs 472
Automation Activity & Vendor Info: (Circulation) CLSI LIBS
Publications: The Scene (quarterly newsletter)
Mem of Nassau Library System

ALBION

S NEW YORK STATE DEPARTMENT OF CORRECTIONAL SERVICES, Albion Correctional Facility General Library, 3595 State School Rd, 14411. SAN 327-1129. Tel: 716-589-5511, Ext 4600. FAX: 716-589-5511, Ext 2099, 716-589-5511, Ext 3299. *Librn*, Eugene S Veress; E-Mail: evere@nioga.org; Staff 2 (MLS 1, Non-MLS 1)
Apr 2000-Mar 2001 Income $29,000, State $17,000, Other $12,000. Mats Exp $25,000, Books $15,000, Per/Ser (Incl. Access Fees) $4,841, AV Equip $5,000. Sal $60,000 (Prof $49,000)
Library Holdings: Bk Titles 9,205; Per Subs 48
Subject Interests: Adult education, Women's studies
Automation Activity & Vendor Info: (Cataloging) Follett; (Circulation) Follett
Mem of Nioga Library System

S ORLEANS CORRECTIONAL FACILITY LIBRARY,* 3531 Gaines Basin Rd, 14411. SAN 327-2478. Tel: 716-589-6820, Ext 4600. FAX: 716-589-6835. *Librn*, Douglas Bauer; Staff 1 (MLS 1)
Library Holdings: Bk Vols 14,000; Per Subs 80
Mem of Nioga Library System

P SWAN LIBRARY,* 4 N Main St, 14411. SAN 310-785X. Tel: 716-589-4246. FAX: 716-589-2473. *Dir*, Susan Rudnicky; *Ch Servs*, Mary Bailey; *Ch Servs*, Michelle Watt; *Ref*, Cheryle Mowatt; *Coll Develop*, Evelyn L Lyman
Founded 1899. Pop 15,000; Circ 41,335
Library Holdings: Bk Vols 47,108; Per Subs 76
Subject Interests: Genealogy
Special Collections: Lillian Achilles Doll Coll; Local History, bks, pamphlets, photogs; Rare Books; Stuart Flintham Egg Coll; William G Curtis Civil War Library
Publications: Annual Report Brochure; Books & Money; History of Swan Library; Hours & Services, Welcome to Swan Library; Swan Library News (weekly)
Mem of Nioga Library System
Partic in Western New York Library Resources Council
Friends of the Library Group

ALDEN

P ALDEN-EWELL FREE LIBRARY,* 13280 Broadway, 14004. SAN 310-7868. Tel: 716-937-7082. *Librn*, Jane H Burke; *Asst Librn*, Jamie Craft
Founded 1902. Pop 10,000; Circ 25,000
Library Holdings: Bk Vols 17,000; Per Subs 52
Function: Photocopies available
Open Mon 12:30-5 & 7-9, Tues & Thurs 9-12, 12:30-5 & 7-9, Sat 12:30-5

S WENDE CORRECTIONAL FACILITY LIBRARY,* 3622 Wende Rd, PO Box 1187, 14004-1187. SAN 327-2346. Tel: 716-937-4000. FAX: 716-937-0206. *Librn*, William Smith
Library Holdings: Bk Vols 12,000; Per Subs 50
Mem of Buffalo & Erie County Public Library System

ALEXANDRIA BAY

P MACSHERRY LIBRARY,* 112 Walton St, 13607. SAN 310-7876. Tel: 315-482-2241. FAX: 315-482-3500. E-Mail: alblib@northnet.org. *Librn*, Lil Purpura
Pop 1,265; Circ 18,874
Library Holdings: Bk Vols 15,000; Bk Titles 14,000; Per Subs 18
Mem of North Country Library System
Open winter hours: Tues, Wed & Fri 2-5 & 7-9, Sat 2-5; summer hours: Mon-Wed & Sat 2-5 & 7-9, Thurs 10-12 & 2-5 & Fri 10-12, 2-5 & 7-9

ALFRED

ALFRED UNIVERSITY

C HERRICK MEMORIAL LIBRARY, Saxon Dr, 14802. SAN 351-8043. Tel: 607-871-2184. Reference Tel: 607-871-2994. FAX: 607-871-2992. Web Site: www.herr.alfred.edu. *Dir*, Steve Crandall; Tel: 607-871-2987, E-Mail: fcrandall@alfred.edu; *Archivist*, Laurie McFadden; Tel: 607-871-2385, E-Mail: fmcfadden@alfred.edu; *Coll Develop*, Toni Olshan; Tel: 607-871-2244, E-Mail: folshant@alfred.edu; *ILL*, Rima O'Connor; Tel: 607-871-2370, E-Mail: oconnorr@alfred.edu; *Head Ref*, Frank McBride; Tel: 607-871-2629, E-Mail: fmcbride@alfred.edu; *Res*, Pamela Lakin; Tel: 607-871-2231, E-Mail: flakin@alfred.edu; *Syst Coordr*, Gary Roberts; Tel: 607-871-2991, E-Mail: roberts@alfred.edu; Staff 17 (MLS 7, Non-MLS 10)
Founded 1857. Enrl 2,258; Fac 201; Highest Degree: Doctorate
Jul 1999-Jun 2000 Income (Main Library Only) Parent Institution $942,775. Mats Exp $220,593, Books $31,673, Per/Ser (Incl. Access Fees) $143,800, Presv $2,120, Micro $23,000, Electronic Ref Mat (Incl. Access Fees) $20,000. Sal $471,843
Library Holdings: Bk Vols 251,586; Bk Titles 150,343; Per Subs 778
Subject Interests: Am hist, Behav sci, Soc sci
Special Collections: British Literature & History (Openhym Coll); Nazi Germany (Waid Coll); William Dean Howells (Howells-Frechette Coll)
Automation Activity & Vendor Info: (Cataloging) MultiLIS; (Circulation) MultiLIS; (Course Reserve) MultiLIS; (OPAC) MultiLIS
Database Vendor: CARL, Dialog, Lexis-Nexis, OCLC - First Search, ProQuest, Silverplatter Information Inc., Wilson - Wilson Web
Publications: Research Guides
Restriction: In-house use for visitors
Partic in OCLC Online Computer Library Center, Inc; S Cent Res Libr Coun
Friends of the Library Group

C SCHOLES LIBRARY OF CERAMICS, 2 Pine St, 14802. SAN 351-8078. Tel: 607-871-2492. Reference Tel: 607-871-2950. FAX: 607-871-2022. Web Site: scholes.alfred.edu. *Dir*, Carl C Johnson; Tel: 607-871-2945, Fax: 607-871-2349, E-Mail: ccjohnson@alfred.edu; *Head Tech Servs*, Elizabeth Gulacsy; Tel: 607-871-2948, Fax: 607-871-2349, E-Mail: gulacsy@alfred.edu; *AV*, Mandy Economus; Tel: 607-871-2944, E-Mail: economms@alfred.edu; *Asst Librn*, Patricia LaCourse; Tel: 607-871-2943, Fax: 607-871-2349, E-Mail: lacourpc@alfred.edu; *Syst Coordr*, Mart A Smith; Tel: 607-871-2942, Fax: 607-871-2349, E-Mail: msmith@alfred.edu; *Tech Servs*, Laurie Fiegl; Tel: 607-871-2496, E-Mail: lfiegl@alfred.edu. Subject Specialists: *Art*, Elizabeth Gulacsy; *Engineering*, Patricia LaCourse; *Science*, Patricia LaCourse; Staff 12 (MLS 5, Non-MLS 7)
Founded 1947. Enrl 797; Fac 58; Highest Degree: Doctorate
Jul 1999-Jun 2000 Income $747,695, State $654,663, Locally Generated Income $8,740, Parent Institution $84,292. Mats Exp $255,356, Books $34,645, Per/Ser (Incl. Access Fees) $191,123, Presv $10,470, Micro $360, AV Equip $4,131, Other Print Mats $1,123, Electronic Ref Mat (Incl. Access Fees) $13,504. Sal $415,705 (Prof $257,863)
Library Holdings: Bk Vols 100,562; Bk Titles 84,886; Per Subs 711
Subject Interests: Ceramic eng, Electrical engineering, Industrial engineering, Mat sci, Mechanical engineering, Pottery, Sculpture
Special Collections: Building Materials (McBurney Coll); Ceramic Art (NCECA Archives); Ceramics (Barringer Coll); Charles F Binns Papers; Glass (Hostetter, Silverman, & Shand Coll); John & Mae McMahom memorabilia; Metals & Materials (Spretnak Coll)
Automation Activity & Vendor Info: (Cataloging) MultiLIS; (OPAC) MultiLIS; (Serials) MultiLIS
Database Vendor: CARL, Dialog, DRA, OCLC - First Search
Publications: Research Guides; Scholes Library Bulletin
Function: ILL available
Partic in OCLC Online Computer Library Center, Inc; S Cent Res Libr Coun

C STATE UNIVERSITY OF NEW YORK, COLLEGE OF TECHNOLOGY, Walter C Hinkle Memorial Library, 14802. SAN 351-8108. Tel: 607-587-4313. FAX: 607-587-4351. Web Site: www.web.alfredstate.edu/library/library.htm. *Chair*, David G Haggstrom; E-Mail: haggstdg@alfredstate.edu; *Automation Syst Coordr*, Ellen Ehrig; E-Mail: ehrigeh@alfredstate.edu; *Bibliog Instr*, Barbara Greil; E-Mail: greilbj@alfredstate.edu; *Circ*, Diana Hovorka; E-Mail: hovorkdh@alfredstate.edu; *Tech Servs*, Joseph Petrick; E-Mail: petricja@alfredstate.edu; Staff 9 (MLS 5, Non-MLS 4)
Founded 1911. Enrl 2,793; Highest Degree: Bachelor
Jul 1999-Jun 2000 Income (Main Library and Branch Library) State $407,234. Mats Exp $117,820, Books $20,052, Per/Ser (Incl. Access Fees) $57,806, Presv $2,975, Micro $19,282, AV Equip $9,332, Electronic Ref Mat (Incl. Access Fees) $8,373. Sal $272,493 (Prof $170,305)
Library Holdings: Bk Vols 61,846; Bk Titles 44,708; Per Subs 703
Subject Interests: Agriculture, Allied health, Bus, Engineering, Vocational
Special Collections: Western New York State Historical Coll, bks, maps, artifacts
Automation Activity & Vendor Info: (Circulation) MultiLIS
Database Vendor: Dialog, GaleNet, IAC - Info Trac, Lexis-Nexis, OCLC - First Search, ProQuest, Wilson - Wilson Web
Publications: Film & Video Guide; Hinkle Memorial Library Periodicals List (title & subject)
Function: ILL available
Partic in S Cent Res Libr Coun
Departmental Libraries:
VOCATIONAL DIV, Brooklyn St, Wellsville, 14895. SAN 351-8132. Tel: 716-593-6270. FAX: 607-587-3120.
Library Holdings: Bk Vols 3,156
Subject Interests: Automotive, Bldg, Construction trades, Culinary trades

ALLEGANY

P ALLEGANY PUBLIC LIBRARY,* 90 W Main St, 14706-1204. SAN 310-7884. Tel: 716-373-1056. FAX: 716-373-1056. E-Mail: alleycat@easynet.net. Web Site: www.cclslib.org/alle/alle.html. *Dir*, June Bernas
Founded 1965. Pop 2,078
Library Holdings: Bk Titles 20,950; Per Subs 104
Special Collections: Freedom Shrine
Mem of Chautauqua-Cattaraugus Library System
Partic in OCLC Online Computer Library Center, Inc

ALMOND

P TWENTIETH CENTURY CLUB LIBRARY, Main St, PO Box D, 14804-0504. SAN 310-7892. Tel: 607-276-6311. FAX: 607-276-2753. *Dir*, Marilyn Holmes; *Asst Dir*, Velma Sherman
Circ 9,530
Library Holdings: Bk Vols 13,000; Per Subs 25
Subject Interests: Local history, Quilting
Special Collections: Children's Coll
Mem of Chemung-Southern Tier Libr Syst; Southern Tier Library System
Open Tues & Thurs 2-7pm & Sat 9:30-12:30

ALTAMONT

P ALTAMONT FREE LIBRARY, Park St, PO Box 662, 12009-0662. SAN 310-7906. Tel: 518-861-7239. FAX: 518-861-7239. E-Mail: altm@uhls.lib.ny.us. *Librn*, Helen King; Staff 2 (MLS 1, Non-MLS 1)
Founded 1916. Pop 1,519; Circ 24,120
Jan 2000-Dec 2000 Income $68,400, State $1,500, City $55,000, Locally Generated Income $8,900, Other $3,000. Mats Exp $11,020, Books $8,400, Per/Ser (Incl. Access Fees) $700, AV Equip $600, Electronic Ref Mat (Incl. Access Fees) $1,320. Sal $42,300 (Prof $31,000)
Library Holdings: Bk Vols 11,000; Bk Titles 10,900; Per Subs 50; High Interest/Low Vocabulary Bk Vols 60
Automation Activity & Vendor Info: (Circulation) DRA
Database Vendor: DRA
Mem of Upper Hudson Library System
Friends of the Library Group

ALTONA

S NEW YORK STATE DEPARTMENT OF CORRECTIONAL SERVICES, Altona Correctional Facility Library, 555 Devil Den Rd, 12910. SAN 328-0144. Tel: 518-236-7841.
Library Holdings: Bk Titles 5,000; Per Subs 44
Mem of Clinton-Essex-Franklin Library System

AMAGANSETT

P AMAGANSETT FREE LIBRARY,* 215 Main St, PO Box 2550, 11930-2550. SAN 310-7922. Tel: 516-267-3810. FAX: 516-267-0087. *Librn*, Carleton Kelsey
Pop 3,000; Circ 20,000
Library Holdings: Bk Vols 32,191; Per Subs 55
Mem of Suffolk Cooperative Library System

AMENIA

P AMENIA FREE LIBRARY,* 3309 Rte 343, PO Box 27, 12501. SAN 310-7930. Tel: 914-373-8273. E-Mail: amenialib@netscape.net. *Dir*, Miriam Devine
Library Holdings: Bk Vols 7,934; Bk Titles 7,225; Per Subs 35
Mem of Mid-Hudson Library System

AMHERST

S ACRES INTERNATIONAL LIBRARY,* 140 John James Audubon Pkwy, 14228-1180. SAN 310-9569. Tel: 716-689-3737. FAX: 716-689-3749. *Librn*, Shawn Shumway
Founded 1970
Library Holdings: Bk Vols 8,250; Per Subs 53
Subject Interests: Engineering, Environmental studies, Geotechnical, Hazardous waste, Hydroelectric, Indust, Waste treatment
Partic in Western New York Library Resources Council
Open Mon-Fri 8-5

S AMHERST ARCHIVES & RESEARCH CENTER,* 5178 Main St, 14221. SAN 371-4594. Tel: 716-631-7010, 716-631-7125. FAX: 716-631-7126. *In Charge*, Susan K Jaros
Library Holdings: Bk Vols 1,000
Special Collections: Local Government records; photo coll; Rezoning & subdivision files; Supvs Subject files

P AMHERST PUBLIC LIBRARY,* 350 John James Audubon Pkwy, 14228. SAN 354-4117. Tel: 716-688-4919, 716-689-4922. FAX: 716-689-6116. *Dir*, Mary F Bobinski; E-Mail: bobinskim@buffalolib.org
Founded 1842. Pop 111,711; Circ 1,581,567
Library Holdings: Bk Vols 254,373; Per Subs 4,147
Special Collections: Library Limelight, weekly TV show over int cable, videotapes
Mem of Buffalo & Erie County Public Library System
Friends of the Library Group
Branches: 4
AMHERST MAIN LIBRARY AT AUDUBON Tel: 716-689-4922. FAX: 716-688-0281. E-Mail: aud@buffalolib.org. *Branch Mgr*, Mary Jane Kibby
Library Holdings: Bk Vols 88,128
Friends of the Library Group
CLEARFIELD, 770 Hopkins Rd, Williamsville, 14221. SAN 354-4141. Tel: 716-688-4955. FAX: 716-688-0281. E-Mail: cfd@buffalolib.org. *Branch Mgr*, Lynne Nothum
Library Holdings: Bk Vols 73,649
Friends of the Library Group
EGGERTSVILLE-SNYDER, 4622 Main St, 14226. SAN 354-4176. Tel: 716-839-0700. E-Mail: egg@buffalolib.org. *Librn*, Judy Lopez-del Morel
Library Holdings: Bk Vols 52,035
Friends of the Library Group
WILLIAMSVILLE, 5571 Main St, 14221. SAN 354-4206. Tel: 716-632-6176. E-Mail: wil@buffalolib.org. *Librn*, Mary O'Ponnell
Library Holdings: Bk Vols 40,561
Friends of the Library Group

S ATSI, INC, Technical Library, 415 Commerce Dr, 14228. SAN 311-0427. Tel: 716-691-9200. FAX: 716-691-7221. Web Site: www.atsiinc.com, www.atsiinc.com. *Librn*, Anita Bonito; E-Mail: bonito@atsiinc.com
Library Holdings: Bk Vols 125; Per Subs 18
Subject Interests: Steel industry
Restriction: Staff use only

C DAEMEN COLLEGE, Marian Library, 4380 Main St, 14226-3592. SAN 351-8167. Tel: 716-839-8243. FAX: 716-839-8475. E-Mail: library@daeman.edu. Web Site: www.daemen.edu. *Librn*, Glenn V Woike; E-Mail: gwoike@daemen.edu; *Syst Coordr*, Frank Carey; E-Mail: fcarey@daemen.edu; *Ref*, Randolph Chojecki; E-Mail: rchojeck@daemen.edu; Staff 4 (MLS 4)
Founded 1948. Enrl 1,800; Fac 120; Highest Degree: Master
Jun 2000-May 2001 Income $541,684, State $6,108, Parent Institution $535,576. Mats Exp $281,310, Books $88,000, Per/Ser (Incl. Access Fees) $149,000, Presv $6,800, Electronic Ref Mat (Incl. Access Fees) $37,510. Sal $208,271 (Prof $131,000)
Library Holdings: Bk Vols 123,523; Bk Titles 91,216; Per Subs 957
Subject Interests: Bus, Fine art, Health sci, Humanities, Liberal arts, Nursing, Physical therapy, Physician asst, Social sci
Automation Activity & Vendor Info: (Cataloging) Innovative Interfaces Inc.; (Circulation) Innovative Interfaces Inc.; (Course Reserve) Innovative Interfaces Inc.; (OPAC) Innovative Interfaces Inc.; (Serials) Innovative Interfaces Inc.
Database Vendor: Dialog, OCLC - First Search, ProQuest
Publications: Periodical Holdings: Complete Listing
Partic in OCLC Online Computer Library Center, Inc; Western New York Library Resources Council
Friends of the Library Group
Departmental Libraries:
TEACHING RESOURCES CENTER Tel: 716-839-8350.
Subject Interests: Elem, Secondary textbooks, Teaching aids

SR TEMPLE SHAAREY ZEDEK, Rabbi Isaac Kline Library, 621 Getzville Rd, 14226. SAN 327-4632. Tel: 716-838-3232. FAX: 716-835-6154. *Librn*, Judy Carrel
Library Holdings: Bk Vols 7,799; Per Subs 13

AMITYVILLE

P AMITYVILLE PUBLIC LIBRARY,* Oak & John Sts, 11701. SAN 310-7949. Tel: 516-264-0567. FAX: 516-264-2006. *Dir*, Nora Schual; *Ch Servs*, Celine Lieffrig; *Coll Develop*, Susan Benard Handler; *Tech Servs*, Joan Traugott; *YA Servs*, Linda Ferraro
Founded 1906. Pop 24,262; Circ 144,008
Jul 1998-Jun 1999 Income $1,262,420. Mats Exp $175,250, Books $116,250, Per/Ser (Incl. Access Fees) $15,000, Presv $800. Sal $678,908 (Prof $241,392)
Library Holdings: Bk Vols 100,000; Bk Titles 87,000; Per Subs 255
Publications: Library Browser (quarterly)
Mem of Suffolk Cooperative Library System

AMSTERDAM

P AMSTERDAM FREE LIBRARY,* 28 Church St, 12010. SAN 310-7973. Tel: 518-842-1080. FAX: 518-842-1169. E-Mail: amslib@telenet.net. *Dir*, Esther M Dean; *Coll Develop*, Patrice Mei-Scholl; *Ch Servs*, Sally Romano; *Circ, ILL*, Mrs Barbara Miller; Staff 13 (MLS 1, Non-MLS 12)
Founded 1891. Pop 20,714; Circ 60,485
Jan 1999-Dec 1999 Income $203,125, City $97,500, Locally Generated Income $14,500, Other $47,500. Mats Exp $213,808, Books $34,000, Per/Ser (Incl. Access Fees) $5,700, AV Equip $1,500, Manuscripts & Archives $1,200. Sal $117,000 (Prof $33,000)
Library Holdings: Bk Titles 36,000; Per Subs 80
Subject Interests: Job info, Local history, Spanish lang
Special Collections: Kirk Douglas memorabilia coll
Automation Activity & Vendor Info: (Circulation) Sagebrush Corporation
Publications: Friends of the Library Newsletter (Quarterly)
Mem of Mohawk Valley Library Association
Friends of the Library Group

S WALTER ELWOOD MUSEUM LIBRARY,* 300 Guy Park Ave, 12010-2228. SAN 329-1863. Tel: 518-843-5151. FAX: 518-843-6098. *Dir*, Mary Margaret Gage; *Librn*, Grace Fedreres; Staff 3 (MLS 1, Non-MLS 2)
Founded 1945
1998-1999 Income $500, Locally Generated Income $500. Mats Exp $1,000, Books $400, Per/Ser (Incl. Access Fees) $100, Presv $300, Other Print Mats $100
Library Holdings: Bk Titles 2,000
Special Collections: Bibles & other religious tracts; Mohawk Valley & New York State; Natural History, old school books
Restriction: Open to public for reference only

ANDES

P ANDES PUBLIC LIBRARY, 242 Main St, PO Box 116, 13731-0116. SAN 310-799X. Tel: 845-676-3333. *Librn*, Vera Mattews-Ward
Founded 1922. Pop 372; Circ 1,200
Library Holdings: Bk Vols 5,600; Per Subs 14
Mem of Four County Library System
Friends of the Library Group

ANDOVER

P ANDOVER FREE LIBRARY,* Main St, PO Box 751, 14806. SAN 310-8007. Tel: 607-478-8442. FAX: 607-478-5056. *Dir*, Evelyn Smith; *Ch Servs*, Mary Alice Richardson
Circ 11,673
Library Holdings: Bk Vols 14,249; Per Subs 20
Mem of Southern Tier Library System
Friends of the Library Group

ANGELICA

P ANGELICA FREE LIBRARY,* 55 W Main St, 14709-0128. SAN 310-8015. Tel: 716-466-7860. *Librn*, Doris Feldbauer
Library Holdings: Bk Vols 15,000; Per Subs 58
Mem of Southern Tier Library System

ANGOLA

P ANGOLA PUBLIC LIBRARY, 34 N Main St, 14006. SAN 310-8023. Tel: 716-549-1271. FAX: 716-549-3954. *Dir*, Mary Truby
Founded 1924. Pop 2,693; Circ 54,851
Library Holdings: Bk Vols 20,337; Per Subs 45
Mem of Buffalo & Erie County Public Library System
Open Mon 12-8, Tues 12-6, Thurs 2-8, Fri 10-8, Sat 12-5; Sat 10-3 June, July, Aug
Friends of the Library Group

ANNANDALE-ON-HUDSON

C BARD COLLEGE, Stevenson Library, 1 Library Rd, 12504. SAN 310-8031. Tel: 845-758-7501. Interlibrary Loan Service Tel: 845-758-7502. Circulation Tel: 845-758-7359. FAX: 845-758-5801. Interlibrary Loan Service FAX: 845-758-5701. Web Site: www.bard.edu/library. *Dean*, Jeffrey Katz; E-Mail: katz@bard.edu; *ILL*, Jane Hryshko; E-Mail: hryshko@bard.edu; *Cat*, Bonnie S Sgarro; Tel: 845-758-7619, E-Mail: sgarro@bard.edu; *Curator*, Susan Leonard; Tel: 845-758-7567, E-Mail: sleonard@bard.edu; *Acq*, Elizabeth Cawley; Tel: 845-758-7617, E-Mail: cawley@bard.edu; *Coll Develop*, Jane Dougall; Tel: 845-758-7620, E-Mail: dougall@bard.edu; Staff 19 (MLS 8, Non-MLS 11)
Founded 1860. Enrl 1,100; Fac 140; Highest Degree: Master
Jul 2000-Jun 2001 Income $1,075,110, State $5,620, Parent Institution $1,069,490. Mats Exp $458,390, Books $201,040, Per/Ser (Incl. Access Fees) $135,000, Presv $21,250, Micro $11,500, AV Equip $20,000, Electronic Ref Mat (Incl. Access Fees) $30,004. Sal $518,350 (Prof $317,512)
Library Holdings: Bk Vols 270,000; Bk Titles 155,770; Per Subs 1,060
Special Collections: Bardiana, publications by Bard faculty & alumnae; Hannah Arendt & Heinrich Bluecher Coll; Hudson Valley History
Database Vendor: GaleNet, Innovative Interfaces INN - View, Lexis-Nexis, OCLC - First Search, OVID Technologies, ProQuest, Silverplatter Information Inc., Wilson - Wilson Web
Restriction: Internal circulation only, Members only, Open to student, faculty & staff
Partic in Southeastern New York Library Resources Council
Affiliated with Simon's Rock of Bard College, Great Barrington, Mass; Bard Graduate Center for Studies in the Decorative Arts, New York City. Open Mon-Thurs 8:30-1am, Fri 8:30am-10pm, Sat 10-10 & Sun 10am-1am

ANTWERP

P CROSBY PUBLIC LIBRARY, Main St, PO Box 120, 13608-0120. SAN 310-804X. Tel: 315-659-8564. FAX: 315-659-8564. E-Mail: crosbylib2@hotmail.com. *Dir*, Charee Cook
Founded 1917. Pop 1,856; Circ 4,148
Jan 1999-Dec 1999 Income $16,978, State $3,000, County $2,694, Locally Generated Income $7,000, Other $4,284. Mats Exp $954, Books $569, Per/Ser (Incl. Access Fees) $385. Sal $8,870
Library Holdings: Bk Titles 6,595; Per Subs 33
Mem of North Country Library System
Partic in OCLC Online Computer Library Center, Inc

ARCADE

P ARCADE FREE LIBRARY, 365 W Main St, 14009. SAN 310-8058. Tel: 716-492-1297. FAX: 716-492-3305. Web Site: www.arcade.pls-net.org. *Dir*, Joanne Usatch; E-Mail: jusatch@pls-net.org; *Ch Servs*, Jennifer VonIstein; Staff 6 (MLS 1, Non-MLS 5)
Founded 1912. Pop 3,938; Circ 55,623
Library Holdings: Bk Vols 27,100; Bk Titles 25,950; Per Subs 75
Special Collections: Lone Ranger Coll
Database Vendor: IAC - SearchBank, OVID Technologies
Mem of Pioneer Library System
Open Mon 1-5pm & 7-9pm, Tues & Thurs 1-9pm, Wed 9am-1pm, Fri 11am-5pm & Sat 10am-2pm
Friends of the Library Group

ARDSLEY

P ARDSLEY PUBLIC LIBRARY,* 9 American Legion Dr, 10502. SAN 310-8066. Tel: 914-693-6636. FAX: 914-693-6837. Web Site: www.wls.lib.ny.us/libs/ardsley/. *Dir*, Angela Groth; E-Mail: agroth@wls.lib.ny.us; Staff 7 (MLS 2, Non-MLS 5)
Founded 1972. Pop 4,272
1997-1998 Income $289,495, Other $8,762. Mats Exp $33,444, Books $29,000, Per/Ser (Incl. Access Fees) $4,444. Sal $121,045 (Prof $74,873)
Library Holdings: Bk Vols 40,000; Per Subs 70
Subject Interests: Best sellers, Computers, Cooking, Local history, Parenting, Travel
Mem of Westchester Library System
Open Mon-Wed 10-5:30, Thurs 1-8, Fri & Sat 10-5:30
Friends of the Library Group

P WESTCHESTER LIBRARY SYSTEM,* 410 Saw Mill River Rd Ste 1000, 10502. SAN 311-2942. Tel: 914-674-3600. FAX: 914-674-4185. Web Site: www.wls.lib.ny.us. *Dir*, Dr Maurice J Freedman; Tel: 914-674-3600, Ext 223, E-Mail: freedman@wls.lib.ny.us; *Ad Servs, Outreach Serv*, Robin Osborne; Tel: 914-674-3600, Ext 237, E-Mail: rosborne@wls.lib.ny.us; *YA Servs*, Judith Rovenger; Tel: 914-674-3600, Ext 236, E-Mail: rovenger@wls.lib.ny.us; *ILL*, Teresa Fox; Tel: 914-674-3600, Ext 258, Fax: 914-674-4186, E-Mail: tfox@wls.lib.ny.us; *Cat, ILL*, Heeja Chung; Tel: 914-674-3600, Ext 247, Fax: 914-674-4186, E-Mail: hchung@wls.lib.ny.us; *Tech Coordr*, Wayne Hay; Tel: 914-674-3600, Ext 228, E-Mail: hay@wls.lib.ny.us
Founded 1958. Circ 7,094,611
Library Holdings: Per Subs 35
Automation Activity & Vendor Info: (Acquisitions) epixtech, inc.; (Cataloging) TLC; (Circulation) epixtech, inc.; (OPAC) epixtech, inc.; (Serials) epixtech, inc.
Database Vendor: CARL, Dialog, Ebsco - EbscoHost, IAC - Info Trac
Publications: assorted bookmarks & brochures describing specific services & bibliographies; Calendar of Events (monthly); Childrens Services Newsletter; WLS Annual Report; WLS Fact Sheet; WLS Members Directory; WLS Members Library Statistics (annual); WLS Salary Survey
Member Libraries: Ardsley Public Library; Bedford Free Library; Bedford Hills Library; Briarcliff Manor Public Library; Chappaqua Central School District Public Library; Croton Free Library; Dobbs Ferry Public Library; Eastchester Public Library; Field Library Of Peekskill; Greenburgh Public Library; Harrison Public Library; Hastings-On-Hudson Public Library; Hendrick Hudson Free Library; Hiram Halle Memorial Library; Irvington Public Library; John C Hart Memorial Library; Katonah Village Library; Larchmont Public Library; Mamaroneck Public Library District; Mount Kisco Public Library; Mount Pleasant Public Library; Mount Vernon Public Library; New Rochelle Public Library; North Castle Public Library; North Salem Free Library; Ossining Public Library; Port Chester Public Library; Purchase Free Library; Rye Free Reading Room; Scarsdale Public Library; Somers Library; South Salem Library; Town Of Pelham Public Library; Tuckahoe Public Library; Warner Library; White Plains Public Library; Yonkers Public Library
Partic in Coop Libr Agency for Syst & Servs; Metro NY Libr Coun; New York Metrop Ref & Res Libr Agency; New York State Interlibrary Loan Network; OCLC Online Computer Library Center, Inc

ARGYLE

P ARGYLE FREE LIBRARY,* 21 Sheridan St, PO Box 238, 12809. SAN 310-8082. Tel: 518-638-8911. FAX: 518-638-8911. *Dir*, Joy Hanchett
Founded 1920. Pop 2,850; Circ 14,010
Library Holdings: Bk Vols 9,000; Per Subs 25
Mem of Southern Adirondack Library System
Friends of the Library Group

ARMONK

P NORTH CASTLE PUBLIC LIBRARY,* 19 Whippoorwill Rd E, 10504. SAN 310-8104. Tel: 914-273-3887. FAX: 914-273-5572. Web Site: www.wls.lib.ny.us.libs/armonk/amk.html. *Dir*, M Cristina Ansnes; *Circ*, Terry Strelec; *Br Coordr*, Teresa Conde; *Coll Develop*, Debby Kleinberg; Staff 6 (MLS 6)
Founded 1938. Pop 10,061; Circ 140,858
Jan 1998-Dec 1998 Income $923,935. Mats Exp $129,400, Books $79,048, Per/Ser (Incl. Access Fees) $7,559, Micro $11,745, Other Print Mats $2,200. Sal $624,941 (Prof $236,805)
Library Holdings: Bk Vols 63,663; Bk Titles 61,988; Per Subs 2,029
Mem of Westchester Library System
Friends of the Library Group

ASHVILLE

P ASHVILLE FREE LIBRARY,* 2200 N Maple St, PO Box 397, 14710. SAN 310-8112. Tel: 716-763-9906. E-Mail: ashvilib@madbbs.com. *Librn*, Tabitha Butler
Founded 1914. Pop 2,400; Circ 11,733
Library Holdings: Bk Titles 7,431; Per Subs 33
Special Collections: Local History; New York State, bks, pamphlets
Mem of Chautauqua-Cattaraugus Library System

ATHENS

P D R EVARTS LIBRARY, 80 Second St, 12015. SAN 310-8120. Tel: 518-945-1417. FAX: 518-945-1417. Web Site: www.evarts.athens.lib.ny.us. *Dir*, Mary Lou Becker
Founded 1907. Pop 3,700; Circ 5,976
Library Holdings: Bk Vols 12,000
Mem of Mid-Hudson Library System
Friends of the Library Group

ATLANTA

P E J COTTRELL MEMORIAL LIBRARY,* 30 Main St, 14808-0192. SAN 310-8139. Tel: 716-534-5030. *Librn*, Shirley Bidlack
Circ 3,568
Library Holdings: Bk Titles 5,336
Mem of Chemung-Southern Tier Libr Syst; Southern Tier Library System

ATTICA

S ATTICA CORRECTIONAL FACILITY, School Library,* Exchange St, 14011-0149. (Mail add: PO Box 149, 14011-0149), SAN 325-1950. Tel: 716-591-2000, Ext 4504. *Librn*, Edward O'Mara
Apr 1998-Mar 1999 Income $12,500. Mats Exp $12,500, Books $7,148, Per/Ser (Incl. Access Fees) $5,342
Library Holdings: Bk Vols 11,232; Per Subs 63
Open Mon-Fri 8-4

P STEVENS MEMORIAL LIBRARY,* 146 Main St, 14011. SAN 310-8147. Tel: 716-591-2733. FAX: 716-591-2630. *Dir*, Beth Wargo; Staff 6 (MLS 1, Non-MLS 5)
Founded 1893. Pop 2,500; Circ 83,682
Library Holdings: Bk Titles 34,000; Per Subs 26
Subject Interests: Local history, NY hist
Mem of Pioneer Library System
Open Mon, Wed & Fri 1-9, Tues & Thurs 10-5
Friends of the Library Group

S WYOMING CORRECTIONAL FACILITY LIBRARY,* PO Box 501, 14011. SAN 327-2516. Tel: 716-591-1010, Ext 4600. E-Mail: eddo788@aol.com. *Librn*, Ed Omara
Library Holdings: Bk Vols 12,000; Per Subs 70

AU SABLE FORKS

P AU SABLE FORKS FREE LIBRARY, 9 West Church St, 12912. (Mail add: PO Box 179, 12912), SAN 310-8155. Tel: 518-647-5596. FAX: 518-647-5753. E-Mail: afbooks@kvvi.net. *Dir*, Carole Miller Osborne; Staff 2 (Non-MLS 2)
Founded 1962. Pop 2,100; Circ 22,000
Library Holdings: Bk Vols 22,000; Bk Titles 20,000; Per Subs 25
Special Collections: The Adirondack Collection
Function: ILL available
Mem of Clinton-Essex-Franklin Library System
Friends of the Library Group

AUBURN

S AUBURN CORRECTIONAL FACILITY LIBRARY,* 135 State St, PO Box 618, 13024. SAN 328-5065. Tel: 315-253-8401, Ext 4650. FAX: 315-253-8401, Ext 2099. *Librn*, Andrea Abbott; Staff 1 (MLS 1)
Apr 1997-Mar 1998 Mats Exp $18,240, Books $9,240, Per/Ser (Incl. Access Fees) $8,000. Sal $46,000 (Prof $39,000)
Subject Interests: Law
Mem of Finger Lakes Library System

M AUBURN MEMORIAL HOSPITAL, Medical Library, 17 Lansing St, 13021. SAN 310-8163. Tel: 315-255-7231. FAX: 315-255-7012. *Librn*, Anne Costello Tomlin; E-Mail: atomlin@dreamscape.com; atomlin@lakenet.org; Staff 1 (MLS 1)
Founded 1951
Jan 2000-Dec 2000 Income $65,768, State $3,100, Parent Institution $55,318, Other $7,350. Mats Exp $21,908, Books $3,600, Per/Ser (Incl. Access Fees) $13,906, Other Print Mats $250. Sal $33,410
Library Holdings: Bk Titles 1,757; Per Subs 72
Subject Interests: Health sci, Medicine, Nursing
Special Collections: Hospital Archives
Mem of S Cent Res Libr
Partic in NY & NJ Regional Med Libr; OCLC Online Computer Library Center, Inc
Special Services for the Deaf - Books on deafness & sign language

J CAYUGA COMMUNITY COLLEGE, Norman F Bourke Memorial Library Learning Resources Center, 197 Franklin St, 13021. SAN 310-8171. Tel: 315-255-1743, Ext 296. FAX: 315-255-2050. Web Site: www.cayuga-cc.edu/library. *Dir*, Douglas O Michael; E-Mail: michaeld@cayuga-cc.edu; *Tech Servs*, Martha J Lollis; E-Mail: lollismj@cayuga-cc.edu; *Bibliog Instr, Ref*, Kathleen J Long; E-Mail: longkj@cayuga-cc.edu; *AV*, James Vivenzio; E-Mail: vivenjioj@cayuga-cc.edu; *Per*, Nona Moore; E-Mail: mooren@cayuga-cc.edu; *Acq, Coll Develop*, Margaret Devereaux; E-Mail: deverema@cayuga-cc.edu; *Circ*, Rosanne Bourke; E-Mail: bourker@cayuga-cc.edu; Staff 7 (MLS 5, Non-MLS 2)
Founded 1953. Enrl 2,882; Fac 138; Highest Degree: Associate
Sep 1999-Aug 2000 Income $801,634, State $6,352, Parent Institution $794,182, Other $1,100. Mats Exp $232,186, Books $71,982, Per/Ser (Incl. Access Fees) $32,437, Presv $1,144, Micro $13,639, AV Equip $12,598, Electronic Ref Mat (Incl. Access Fees) $5,440. Sal $584,518 (Prof $362,391)
Library Holdings: Bk Vols 81,490; Bk Titles 66,339; Per Subs 527
Subject Interests: Criminal justice, Local history, Telecommunications
Special Collections: Auburn Imprints
Automation Activity & Vendor Info: (Circulation) MultiLIS; (OPAC) MultiLIS; (Serials) MultiLIS
Publications: Cayuga Pathfinder Series
Partic in OCLC Online Computer Library Center, Inc; South Central Regional Library Council
Open Mon-Thurs 8-9:30, Fri 8-4:30 & Sun 1-7:30

G CAYUGA COUNTY LEGISLATURE HISTORIAN'S OFFICE, Research Library, Historic Old Post Off Bldg, 157 Genesee St, 13021-3490. SAN 371-5469. Tel: 315-253-1300. *Archivist*, Malcolm Goodelle. Subject Specialists: *History*, Thomas Eldred
Founded 1969
Library Holdings: Bk Titles 1,000; Per Subs 20
Subject Interests: Local hist archives
Special Collections: County; Newspapers 1811-2000
Restriction: Not a lending library
Function: Research library

S CAYUGA MUSEUM LIBRARY, 203 Genesee St, 13021. SAN 310-818X. Tel: 315-253-8051. FAX: 315-253-9829. *Dir*, Eileen McHugh; *Curator*, Gina Stankivitz; *Publ Servs*, Beth Henson; Staff 4 (Non-MLS 4)
Founded 1936
Subject Interests: Cayuga County hist, Iroquois, Sound flm
Special Collections: Archival Coll of Local Hist; Auburn Theological Seminary; Case Research Laboratory Coll, sound motion pictures; Native American (Clark Coll)
Restriction: Non-circulating to the public, Open to others by appointment

S FOUNDATION HISTORICAL ASSOCIATION, INC LIBRARY,* Seward House, 33 South St, 13021. SAN 310-8198. Tel: 315-252-1283. *Curator*, Betty Mae Lewis
Founded 1955
Subject Interests: Alaska, Civil War, Genealogy, Local history
Open Tues-Sat 1-4

GL NEW YORK SUPREME COURT LAW LIBRARY, Cayuga County Court House, 15L Genesee St, 13021. SAN 310-8201. Tel: 315-255-4310. FAX: 315-255-4322. *In Charge*, Jill Fandrich; E-Mail: jfandric@courts.state.ny.us; Staff 1 (Non-MLS 1)
Library Holdings: Bk Vols 7,500; Bk Titles 115; Per Subs 12
Automation Activity & Vendor Info: (Acquisitions) epixtech, inc.; (Cataloging) epixtech, inc.; (Circulation) epixtech, inc.

P SEYMOUR PUBLIC LIBRARY DISTRICT, 176 Genesee St, 13021. SAN 310-821X. Tel: 315-252-2571. FAX: 315-252-7985. E-Mail: seymourlib@relex.com. Web Site: www.flls.org/seymour. *Dir*, Stephen C Erskine; *ILL*, Catherine M Piccirillo; *Ch Servs*, Corrinne M Needham; *Ref*, Danette Davis. Subject Specialists: *Genealogy*, Mary Gilmore; *Local history*, Mary Gilmore; Staff 28 (MLS 5, Non-MLS 23)
Founded 1876. Pop 36,008; Circ 165,200
Jan 1999-Dec 1999 Income $539,321, State $11,125, County $11,500, Locally Generated Income $316,000, Parent Institution $118,000, Other $82,696. Mats Exp $234,255, Books $85,520, Per/Ser (Incl. Access Fees) $13,901, Presv $2,438, AV Equip $9,943, Other Print Mats $3,000. Sal $263,242
Library Holdings: Bk Titles 103,549; Per Subs 359
Special Collections: Auburn Imprints; Auburn Prison; Harriet Tubman Coll, bks, newsp
Publications: From the Bookshelf (semi-annual)
Mem of Finger Lakes Library System
Partic in OCLC Online Computer Library Center, Inc
Friends of the Library Group

AURORA

P AURORA FREE LIBRARY, 370 Main St, PO Box 85, 13026. SAN 376-303X. Tel: 315-364-8074. FAX: 315-364-8074. E-Mail: auroralib@relex.com. *Librn*, Sandy Groth; *Asst Librn*, Sara Miller
Pop 637
Jan 1999-Dec 1999 Income $19,500, State $1,600, City $900, County $5,000, Locally Generated Income $2,000, Other $10,000. Mats Exp $6,140, Books $6,000, Per/Ser (Incl. Access Fees) $40, Electronic Ref Mat (Incl. Access Fees) $100. Sal $8,675
Library Holdings: Bk Vols 6,800
Mem of Finger Lakes Library System

C WELLS COLLEGE, Louis Jefferson Long Library, Main St, 13026-0500. SAN 310-8228. Tel: 315-364-3351, Ext 3356. FAX: 315-364-3412. Web Site: www.wells.edu/library/. *Librn*, Jeri L Vargo; E-Mail: jvargo@wells.edu; *Ser, Syst Coordr*, Muriel Godbout; *Cat, Circ*, Elsie Torres; *ILL, Ref*, Louise Rossmann; *Acq*, Kelly Steele; Staff 4 (MLS 4)
Founded 1868. Enrl 425; Fac 55; Highest Degree: Bachelor
Library Holdings: Bk Vols 250,893; Per Subs 384
Special Collections: Chemistry-Physics; Economics (Weld Coll); Fine Arts

(Morgan Coll); History (Lowe Coll); Philosophy (Lowenberg Coll); Pierce W Gaines Americana Coll; Wells Fargo Express Co, CA 1825-80, mss, personal papers
Partic in OCLC Online Computer Library Center, Inc; S Cent Res Libr Coun

AVERILL

P SAND LAKE TOWN LIBRARY, 8428 Miller Hill Rd, 12018. Tel: 518-674-5050. FAX: 518-674-5050. *Dir*, Jane Minotti
Jan 2000-Dec 2000 Income $144,000, City $98,000, County $1,550. Mats Exp $25,100. Sal $71,000 (Prof $31,350)
Library Holdings: Bk Vols 22,000; Bk Titles 20,000; Per Subs 54
Database Vendor: DRA
Mem of Upper Hudson Library System
Open Mon-Thurs 11-8, Fri 11-6, Sat 11-2, Sun 1-4 (Sept-May)
Friends of the Library Group

AVOCA

P AVOCA FREE LIBRARY,* 5 Griswold St, PO Box S, 14809-0519. SAN 376-3056. Tel: 607-566-9279. FAX: 607-566-9279. E-Mail: avoco-lib@linkny.com. *Dir*, Dorothy V Spaulding; *Asst Librn*, Sandy Feager
Library Holdings: Bk Vols 17,000; Per Subs 53
Mem of Southern Tier Library System

AVON

P AVON FREE LIBRARY,* 143 Genesee St, 14414. SAN 310-8244. Tel: 716-226-8461. FAX: 716-226-6615. *Dir*, Jeanna Ruter; *Ch Servs*, Marcia Veeder
Pop 6,185; Circ 43,416
Library Holdings: Bk Vols 32,000; Bk Titles 30,850; Per Subs 50
Mem of Pioneer Library System
Friends of the Library Group

BABYLON

P BABYLON PUBLIC LIBRARY, 24 S Carll Ave, 11702. SAN 310-8260. Tel: 631-669-1624. TDD: 631-422-0548. FAX: 631-669-7826. E-Mail: babllib@suffolk.lib.ny.us. Web Site: www.suffolk.lib.ny.us/libraries/babl. *Dir*, Robert Lusak; *Ch Servs*, Ann Burke; *Ref*, Patricia LaWare; *YA Servs*, Alison McDermott; Staff 39 (MLS 12, Non-MLS 27)
Founded 1895. Pop 11,572; Circ 153,159
Jul 2000-Jun 2001 Income Locally Generated Income $1,273,755. Mats Exp $180,000, Books $67,000, Per/Ser (Incl. Access Fees) $39,000, Micro $17,000, AV Equip $27,000, Other Print Mats $15,000, Electronic Ref Mat (Incl. Access Fees) $15,000. Sal $645,000
Library Holdings: Bk Vols 57,387; Per Subs 2,075
Subject Interests: Babylon hist
Special Collections: Large Print; Long Island History; Parenting
Automation Activity & Vendor Info: (Acquisitions) Innovative Interfaces Inc.; (Cataloging) Innovative Interfaces Inc.; (Circulation) Innovative Interfaces Inc.; (ILL) Innovative Interfaces Inc.; (OPAC) Innovative Interfaces Inc.
Publications: Small Talk (Newsletter); The Anchor (Newsletter)
Mem of Suffolk Cooperative Library System
Partic in Partnership of Automated Librs in Suffolk
Special Services for the Deaf - TTY machine
Friends of the Library Group

BAINBRIDGE

P BAINBRIDGE FREE LIBRARY,* 13 N Main, 13733. SAN 310-8279. Tel: 607-967-5305. FAX: 607-967-5305. *Dir*, Beverly Fox
Founded 1908. Pop 3,331; Circ 9,048
Library Holdings: Bk Vols 15,510; Per Subs 24
Mem of Four County Library System
Open Mon & Thurs 1-5 & 6:30-9, Tues 9-12 & 1-5, Sat 9-12

BALDWIN

P BALDWIN PUBLIC LIBRARY, 2385 Grand Ave, 11510-3289. SAN 310-8287. Tel: 516-223-6228. FAX: 516-623-7991. E-Mail: bapl3@lilrc.org. Web Site: www.macroserve.com/bpl/home.htm. *Dir*, Barbara Hopkins; *Ad Servs, Coll Develop, Ref*, Helen Gittleman; *Ch Servs*, Wendy Kappelmier; *Media Spec*, Gail Baselice; *Cat, Per*, Edward Daly; *ILL*, Frances Carey; *Automation Syst Coordr*, Catherine Overton; Staff 12 (MLS 11, Non-MLS 1)
Founded 1922. Pop 31,615; Circ 355,124
Jul 2000-Jun 2001 Income $2,083,495, State $22,359, Locally Generated Income $117,986, Other $1,943,150. Mats Exp $311,907, Books $222,348, Per/Ser (Incl. Access Fees) $28,811, AV Equip $21,150, Other Print Mats $1,715, Electronic Ref Mat (Incl. Access Fees) $37,883. Sal $1,240,096 (Prof $408,355)
Library Holdings: Bk Vols 137,404; Per Subs 2,700
Subject Interests: Special educ
Special Collections: Baldwin History; Long Island Coll
Automation Activity & Vendor Info: (Circulation) DRA; (OPAC) DRA
Database Vendor: Ebsco - EbscoHost, GaleNet, ProQuest
Publications: Piper (6 every year)
Mem of Nassau Library System
Partic in Long Island Library Resources Council
Special Services for the Blind - Magnifiers
Open Oct-May Mon-Fri 9-9, Sat 9-5 & Sun 1-5; June-Sept Fri 9-5 & Sat 9-1

BALDWIN PLACE

S GEORGE KURIAN REFERENCE BOOKS, Editorial Library, PO Box 519, 10505-0519. SAN 322-6573. Tel: 914-962-3287. FAX: 914-962-3287. *Librn*, Sarah Claudine
Jan 1999-Dec 1999 Income $52,000, Parent Institution $7,000. Mats Exp $21,000, Books $15,500, Per/Ser (Incl. Access Fees) $4,500, Presv $500, Other Print Mats $500. Sal $31,000 (Prof $18,000)
Library Holdings: Bk Vols 22,900
Subject Interests: Education, History, Humanities, Law

BALDWINSVILLE

P BALDWINSVILLE PUBLIC LIBRARY,* 33 E Genesee St, 13027-2575. SAN 310-8295. Tel: 315-635-5631. FAX: 315-635-6760. E-Mail: info@bville.lib.ny.us. Web Site: www.bville.lib.ny.us. *Dir*, Marilyn R Laubacher; E-Mail: marilyn@bville.lib.ny.us; *Tech Coordr*, Margaret Bye; E-Mail: peggyb@bville.lib.ny.us; *Ad Servs*, Valerie Chism; E-Mail: valc@bville.lib.ny.us; *Ref Serv Ad*, Margaret A Van Patten; E-Mail: megv@bville.lib.ny.us; *Ch Servs*, Elizabeth Stillwell; E-Mail: bettys@bville.lib.ny.us; *Ref Servs YA*, Pamela Dano; E-Mail: pamd@bville.lib.ny.us; *Ch Servs*, Victoria Gaworecki; E-Mail: vickyg@bville.lib.ny.us; Staff 37 (MLS 9, Non-MLS 28)
Founded 1948. Pop 29,923; Circ 300,616
Jan 1999-Dec 1999 Income $869,469, State $9,276, Locally Generated Income $792,749, Other $67,444. Mats Exp $126,649, Books $78,474, Per/Ser (Incl. Access Fees) $10,562, Presv $798, AV Equip $13,655, Electronic Ref Mat (Incl. Access Fees) $22,887. Sal $469,522 (Prof $222,260)
Library Holdings: Bk Vols 68,138; Per Subs 769
Subject Interests: Local history
Special Collections: Newspaper Coll (1846-present), micro
Automation Activity & Vendor Info: (Circulation) epixtech, inc.; (ILL) epixtech, inc.; (OPAC) epixtech, inc.
Database Vendor: epixtech, inc., GaleNet, Innovative Interfaces INN - View, OVID Technologies, Wilson - Wilson Web
Publications: Annual report; Reference bibliography (quarterly)
Mem of Onondaga County Public Library
Special Services for the Blind - Magnifiers
Friends of the Library Group

BALLSTON SPA

P BALLSTON SPA PUBLIC LIBRARY,* 21 Milton Ave, 12020. SAN 310-8309. Tel: 518-885-5022. FAX: 518-885-5022 (with permission only). Web Site: www.ballston.sals.edu. *Dir, Librn*, Virginia Humphrey; E-Mail: bal_humph@sals.edu; Staff 7 (MLS 2, Non-MLS 5)
Founded 1893. Pop 4,937; Circ 81,565
Jan 1998-Dec 1998 Income $138,593, State $2,407, County $1,542, Locally Generated Income $134,644. Mats Exp $25,591, Books $16,745, Per/Ser (Incl. Access Fees) $2,657, AV Equip $5,214, Electronic Ref Mat (Incl. Access Fees) $975. Sal $70,409 (Prof $38,141)
Library Holdings: Bk Vols 39,097; Per Subs 75
Special Collections: Literacy Center; Parenting Center; Resource Center for the Handicapped; Saratoga County (Bruce M Manzer Coll), bks, per
Mem of Southern Adirondack Library System
Friends of the Library Group

BARKER

P BARKER FREE LIBRARY,* 8706 Main St, PO Box 261, 14012. SAN 310-8317. Tel: 716-795-3344. FAX: 716-795-3344. *Dir*, Nancy S Millard; Staff 3 (MLS 1, Non-MLS 2)
Founded 1935. Pop 2,655; Circ 12,159
Jan 1998-Dec 1998 Income $39,726, State $6,741, County $4,866, Locally Generated Income $14,700, Other $13,419. Mats Exp $7,360
Library Holdings: Bk Vols 15,300; Per Subs 15; High Interest/Low Vocabulary Bk Vols 34
Subject Interests: Adult literacy, GED programs, Local history
Mem of Nioga Library System
Special Services for the Blind - Bks on tape
Open Tues 9-5 & 7-9, Wed 7-9, Fri 12-5 & Sat 9-5
Friends of the Library Group

BARNEVELD

P BARNEVELD FREE LIBRARY ASSOCIATION,* Boon St, PO Box 306, 13304. SAN 310-8325. Tel: 315-896-2096. *Librn*, Greta Madore
Pop 2,499; Circ 7,556
Library Holdings: Bk Vols 9,500; Per Subs 26
Mem of Mid-York Library System

BATAVIA

J GENESEE COMMUNITY COLLEGE, Alfred C O'Connell Library, One College Rd, 14020-9704. SAN 310-8333. Tel: 716-343-0055, Ext 6350. Circulation Tel: 716-345-6834. Reference Tel: 716-343-0055, Ext 6419. FAX: 716-343-0433. Web Site: www.genesee.suny.edu/library.default.htm. *Dean*, Robert G Knipe; Tel: 716-343-0055, Ext 6595, E-Mail: rgknipe@genesee.suny.edu; *Circ, Dir Libr Serv*, Judith A Sikora; Tel: 716-343-0055, Ext 6414, E-Mail: jasikora@genesee.suny.edu; *Bibliog Instr, Distance Educ, Ref*, Adrienne L Furness; Tel: 716-343-0055, Ext 6418, E-Mail: alfurness@genesee.suny.edu; *Electronic Resources, Syst Coordr, Web Coordr*, Nina T Warren; Tel: 716-343-0055, Ext 6256, E-Mail: ntwarren@genesee.suny.edu; *Cat, Coll Develop*, Patricia S Jones; Tel: 716-343-0055, Ext 6231, E-Mail: psjones@genesee.suny.edu; Staff 7 (MLS 4, Non-MLS 3)
Founded 1966. Enrl 2,656; Fac 71
Sep 1999-Aug 2000 Income $546,881, State $16,773, Federal $7,547. Mats Exp $105,923, Books $53,660, Per/Ser (Incl. Access Fees) $45,701, Presv $46, Electronic Ref Mat (Incl. Access Fees) $6,516. Sal $300,100 (Prof $185,963)
Library Holdings: Bk Vols 71,629; Bk Titles 65,232; Per Subs 332; Bks on Deafness & Sign Lang 64
Automation Activity & Vendor Info: (Cataloging) DRA; (Circulation) DRA; (OPAC) DRA
Database Vendor: Dialog, DRA, GaleNet, IAC - Info Trac, IAC - SearchBank, OCLC - First Search
Publications: A Guide to Learning Resources; Library Handbook; New Acquisitions; Periodical Holdings
Partic in Western New York Library Resources Council
Special Services for the Blind - VisualTek

S GENESEE COUNTY HISTORY DEPARTMENT, Research Library, 3 W Main St, 14020-2021. SAN 326-2626. Tel: 716-344-2550, Ext 2613. FAX: 716-344-8558. E-Mail: history@co.genesee.ny.us. Web Site: www.co.genesee.ny.us. *In Charge*, Susan Conklin; Staff 1 (MLS 1)
Jan 2000-Dec 2000 Income $127,004, County $125,744, Locally Generated Income $1,260. Mats Exp $650, Books $400, Presv $250. Sal $93,135
Library Holdings: Bk Titles 2,000
Special Collections: County; Genealogy, bks & files; Local Hist, bks & files
Restriction: Non-circulating
Open Mon-Fri 8:30-4:30; County government agency
Friends of the Library Group

P RICHMOND MEMORIAL LIBRARY,* 19 Ross St, 14020. SAN 310-8341. Tel: 716-343-9550. FAX: 716-344-4651. *Dir*, Martha Spinnegan; *ILL*, Jane Bedle; *Ad Servs*, Kathleen Facer; *Ch Servs*, Sandra A Gillard; *Outreach Serv, Ref*, Paula Meyer; *Ref*, Rita McCormack; Staff 5 (MLS 5)
Founded 1889. Pop 19,145; Circ 243,996
Library Holdings: Bk Titles 98,000; Per Subs 177
Subject Interests: Genealogy, Local history
Mem of Nioga Library System
Friends of the Library Group

M UNITED MEMORIAL MEDICAL CENTER, (Formerly Genesee Memorial Hospital), Medical Library, 127 North St, 14020-1697. SAN 326-5374. Tel: 716-343-6030, 716-344-5273, Ext 5273. FAX: 716-343-8413. E-Mail: gmhlib@eznet.net. *Mgr*, Esther Marone
Founded 1958
Library Holdings: Bk Vols 500; Bk Titles 450; Per Subs 80
Partic in Ref & Research Resource of New York
Open Mon-Fri 9-3

M UNITED MEMORIAL MEDICAL CENTER LIBRARY, (Formerly Gennessee Mercy Healthcare-Bank Street), 127 North St, 14020. SAN 320-7013. Tel: 716-344-5273. FAX: 716-343-8413. *Mgr*, Esther Marone
Library Holdings: Bk Titles 350; Per Subs 80
Subject Interests: Internal medicine, Nursing, Surgery
Partic in Western New York Library Resources Council

BATH

GM DEPARTMENT OF VETERANS AFFAIRS, Library Service (142D),* 76 Veterans Ave, 14810. SAN 310-8384. Tel: 607-776-2111, Ext 1224. FAX: 607-776-2111, Ext 1809.; Staff 2 (MLS 1, Non-MLS 1)
Library Holdings: Per Subs 175
Subject Interests: Bioethics, Geriatrics, Medicine, Nursing, Patient education
Partic in S Cent Res Libr Coun; Vets Admin Libr Network

P DORMANN LIBRARY,* 101 W Morris St, 14810. SAN 310-8368. Tel: 607-776-4613. FAX: 607-776-6693. *Dir*, Deborah M Stahr
Founded 1869. Pop 5,801; Circ 42,916
Library Holdings: Bk Vols 16,700; Per Subs 30
Special Collections: Local History
Mem of Chemung-Southern Tier Libr Syst; Southern Tier Library System
Friends of the Library Group

GL NEW YORK SUPREME COURT, Seventh Judicial District Law Library,* 3 Pulteney Sq, 14810. SAN 310-8376. Tel: 607-776-9631, Ext 2099. FAX: 607-776-7715.
Library Holdings: Bk Vols 3,000
Subject Interests: Agriculture, Bankruptcy, NYS statutes

BAY SHORE

M SOUTHSIDE HOSPITAL, Medical Library, 301 E Main St, 11706-8458. SAN 310-8392. Tel: 631-968-3026. FAX: 631-968-3978. *Librn*, Freddie Borock; E-Mail: fborockl@southsidehospital.org; Staff 1 (MLS 1)
Founded 1962
2000-2001 Mats Exp $25,000, Books $5,000, Per/Ser (Incl. Access Fees) $20,000
Library Holdings: Bk Vols 600; Per Subs 150
Subject Interests: Allied health, Medicine, Nursing
Restriction: Medical staff only
Function: ILL available, Literary searches, Photocopies available, Reference services available
Partic in BHSL; Long Island Library Resources Council; Medical & Scientific Libraries of Long Island
Open Mon, Wed & Fri 8-4

BAYSIDE

J QUEENSBOROUGH COMMUNITY COLLEGE, Kurt R Schmeller Library, 222-05 56th Ave, 11364-1497. SAN 310-8414. Tel: 718-631-6226. Interlibrary Loan Service Tel: 718-631-6241. Circulation Tel: 718-631-6227. Reference Tel: 718-631-6241. TDD: 718-281-5169. FAX: 718-281-5012. *Chief Librn*, Kyu Hugh Kim; E-Mail: kkim@qcc.cuny.edu; *Circ, Per*, Constance Williams; E-Mail: cwilliams@qcc.cuny.edu; *Acq, Archivist, Coll Develop*, Maxine Genn; E-Mail: mgenn@qcc.cuny.edu; *Cat, ILL*, Devin Feldman; E-Mail: dfeldman@qcc.cuny.edu; *Ref*, Sandra Marcus; E-Mail: smarcus@qcc.cuny.edu; *Instrul Serv, Ref*, Christine Bruzzese; E-Mail: cbruzzese@qcc.cuny.edu; *Media Spec*, Jia Jeffrey; Tel: 718-631-6225. Subject Specialists: *Education*, Constance Williams; *Music*, Devin Feldman; *Psychology*, Constance Williams; *Religion*, Constance Williams; Staff 15 (MLS 15)
Founded 1960. Enrl 8,000; Fac 500; Highest Degree: Associate
Jul 1998-Jun 1999 Mats Exp $158,410, Books $86,607, Per/Ser (Incl. Access Fees) $70,726, Electronic Ref Mat (Incl. Access Fees) $1,077. Sal $979,698 (Prof $694,513)
Library Holdings: Bk Vols 141,289; Bk Titles 123,068; Per Subs 581
Publications: How to Guides; Library Letter (newsletter); QCC Periodicals Listing; Student Library Handbook; Subject Bibliographies
Partic in Metropolitan New York Library Council; State University Of New York-NYLINK
Friends of the Library Group

BAYVILLE

P BAYVILLE FREE LIBRARY,* 34 School St, 11709. SAN 310-8422. Tel: 516-628-2765. FAX: 516-628-2738. Web Site: www.nassaulibrary.org/bayville/. *Dir*, Richard Rapecis
Circ 71,351
Jun 1998-May 1999 Income $215,200, State $2,000, Locally Generated Income $10,800. Mats Exp $41,206, Books $31,850, Per/Ser (Incl. Access Fees) $4,100. Sal $128,973 (Prof $50,775)
Library Holdings: Bk Vols 55,872; Per Subs 70
Automation Activity & Vendor Info: (Circulation) Follett
Publications: Bayville Bookmark
Mem of Nassau Library System
Friends of the Library Group

BEACON

M FISHKILL CORRECTIONAL FACILITY LIBRARY,* Bldg 13, PO Box 307, 12508. SAN 310-8430. Tel: 914-831-4800, Ext 2496. FAX: 914-831-3199. *Librn*, Nancy Maicovski
Pop 1,728
Library Holdings: Bk Vols 12,000
Subject Interests: Black studies, Criminology, Spanish language
Mem of Mid-Hudson Library System; SE NY Libr Resources Coun

P HOWLAND PUBLIC LIBRARY,* 313 Main St, 12508. SAN 310-8449. Tel: 914-831-1134. FAX: 914-831-1165. E-Mail: beacon@sebridge.org. *Dir*, Peter Wessley; *Ch Servs*, Ginny Figlia; *Ref*, Peter McGivney
Founded 1872. Pop 24,000

Jul 1999-Jun 2000 Income $455,716, State $7,700, City $396,570, County $13,800, Locally Generated Income $37,646. Mats Exp $71,161, Books $42,500, Per/Ser (Incl. Access Fees) $10,600, AV Equip $6,061, Electronic Ref Mat (Incl. Access Fees) $12,000. Sal $237,038
Library Holdings: Bk Titles 33,490; Per Subs 106
Subject Interests: Ethnic studies, Local history
Special Collections: Handicapped Coll, bks, kits, VF; Spanish Language (Libros Coll), bks, rec
Mem of Mid-Hudson Library System

BEAR MOUNTAIN

S BEAR MOUNTAIN TRAILSIDE MUSEUMS LIBRARY,* Bear Mountain State Park, 10911-0427. SAN 371-2095. Tel: 914-786-2701, Ext 278. FAX: 914-786-1876.
Library Holdings: Bk Vols 500
Restriction: Staff use only
Open Mon-Fri 9-5

BEAVER FALLS

P BEAVER FALLS LIBRARY,* Lewis St, PO Box 75, 13305. SAN 310-8473. Tel: 315-346-6216. FAX: 315-346-6216. *Librn*, Carol Jackson
Founded 1920. Pop 700; Circ 9,818
Library Holdings: Bk Vols 4,000; Per Subs 20
Mem of North Country Library System
Open Mon 10:30-4 & 5:30-8, Thurs 12-4, Fri 4-8 & Sat 10-2

BEDFORD

P BEDFORD FREE LIBRARY,* Village Green, Box 375, 10506. SAN 310-8481. Tel: 914-234-3570. FAX: 914-234-0546. Web Site: www.bedfordny.com. *Dir*, Paula Desperito
Founded 1903. Pop 4,100; Circ 39,494
Library Holdings: Bk Vols 28,963; Bk Titles 22,284; Per Subs 38
Subject Interests: Biog, Local history
Mem of Westchester Library System
Open Mon 11-7, Tues-Fri 11-6 & Sat 10-1
Friends of the Library Group

BEDFORD HILLS

S BEDFORD HILLS CORRECTIONAL FACILITY LIBRARY, 247 Harris Rd, 10507-2499. SAN 327-1218. Tel: 914-241-3100, Ext 4540. FAX: 914-241-3100, Ext 3199. *Librn*, Robert A McMahon; E-Mail: mcmahon@britannica.com
2000-2001 Mats Exp Books $14,000
Library Holdings: Bk Vols 10,000; Per Subs 50

P BEDFORD HILLS LIBRARY,* 26 Main St, 10507-1832. SAN 310-849X. Tel: 914-666-6472. FAX: 914-666-6473. Web Site: www.bedfordny.com. *Dir*, Rhoda M Gushue; *Coll Develop*, Eileen Baer
Founded 1915. Pop 5,410; Circ 72,026
Library Holdings: Bk Vols 42,350; Bk Titles 41,102; Per Subs 124
Mem of Westchester Library System

BELFAST

P BELFAST PUBLIC LIBRARY,* 75 S Main St, PO Box 455, 14711-0455. SAN 310-8503. Tel: 716-365-2072. FAX: 716-365-2072. *Librn*, Judith Barber
Pop 1,300; Circ 10,000
Library Holdings: Bk Vols 9,060; Per Subs 30
Mem of Southern Tier Library System
Friends of the Library Group

BELLEROSE

M QUEENS CHILDREN'S PSYCHIATRIC CENTER, Lauretta Bender Staff Resource Center, Bldg 55, 74-03 Commonwealth Blvd, 11426. SAN 320-4901. Tel: 718-264-4518. FAX: 718-264-4965.
Founded 1969
Library Holdings: Bk Titles 4,000; Per Subs 69
Subject Interests: Child develop, Child psychiat, Learning disabilities, Soc work
Special Collections: L Bender Coll, bks & reprint articles

BELLEVILLE

P BELLEVILLE PUBLIC LIBRARY, Philomathean Free Library, 2404 Academy St, PO Box 27, 13611. SAN 310-8511. Tel: 315-846-5103. FAX: 315-846-5107. *Librn*, Lydia Miller
Circ 7,375
Library Holdings: Bk Vols 3,000
Mem of North Country Library System
Open winter hours: Mon 7-9, Wed 1-5 & 7-9, Fri 5-9

BELLMORE

P BELLMORE MEMORIAL LIBRARY,* 2288 Bedford Ave, 11710. SAN 310-852X. Tel: 516-785-2990. FAX: 516-783-8550. *Dir*, Steven Bregman; *Asst Dir*, P Furlong; *Ch Servs*, D Rosenthal; *Ad Servs*, P Paris; *Ref*, M Zuckerman; *YA Servs*, P Gleiberman; *Tech Servs*, C Schuler; Staff 8 (MLS 8)
Founded 1948. Pop 15,000
Library Holdings: Bk Vols 92,429; Bk Titles 80,857; Per Subs 284
Publications: Bellmore Memorial Library Newsletter
Mem of Nassau Library System

BELLPORT

P SOUTH COUNTRY LIBRARY, 22 Station Rd, 11713. SAN 310-8538. Tel: 631-286-0818. FAX: 631-286-4873. E-Mail: sctylib@suffolk.lib.ny.us. Web Site: sctylib.suffolk.lib.ny.us. *Dir*, Patricia Campbell; *Ref*, Nan Bunce; *Ch Servs*, B Allison Gray; *ILL*, Kate Thomlinson; *YA Servs*, Lia Vasquez; Staff 48 (MLS 10, Non-MLS 38)
Founded 1921. Pop 25,200; Circ 300,000
Jul 2000-Jun 2001 Income $1,618,669, Locally Generated Income $1,510,669, Other $108,000. Mats Exp $168,000, Books $148,000, Electronic Ref Mat (Incl. Access Fees) $20,000. Sal $935,596 (Prof $428,400)
Library Holdings: Bk Titles 83,000; Per Subs 772
Subject Interests: Boating, Gardening, Long Island hist
Publications: Newsletter (bi-monthly)
Mem of Suffolk Cooperative Library System
Partic in Pals
Friends of the Library Group

P SUFFOLK COOPERATIVE LIBRARY SYSTEM, 627 N Sunrise Service Rd, 11713-1540. SAN 351-837X. Tel: 631-286-1600. FAX: 631-286-1647. E-Mail: staffmember@suffolk.lib.ny.us. Web Site: www.suffolk.lib.ny.us. *Dir*, Gerald D Nichols; *Asst Dir*, Florence Denny; *Ch Servs*, Marie Orlando; *ILL*, Kristina Farmer; Staff 67 (MLS 15, Non-MLS 52)
Founded 1961. Pop 1,321,864; Circ 14,922,368
Jan 1999-Dec 1999 Income (Main Library and Branch Library) $5,308,115, State $3,976,700, Federal $91,451, Locally Generated Income $957,310, Other $282,654. Mats Exp $96,803, Books $8,086, Per/Ser (Incl. Access Fees) $24,777, Other Print Mats $31,424, Electronic Ref Mat (Incl. Access Fees) $30,686. Sal $2,305,855 (Prof $817,078)
Library Holdings: Bk Vols 15,000,000; Bks on Deafness & Sign Lang 49
Special Collections: Adult New Readers (literacy); Auto & Home Appliance Repair Manuals; County Coll; Disability Reference Coll; Last Copy Center; Multi- Language Coll; Talking Books
Automation Activity & Vendor Info: (Acquisitions) Innovative Interfaces Inc.; (Cataloging) Innovative Interfaces Inc.; (Circulation) Innovative Interfaces Inc.; (ILL) Innovative Interfaces Inc.; (OPAC) Innovative Interfaces Inc.; (Serials) Innovative Interfaces Inc.
Database Vendor: Wilson - Wilson Web
Member Libraries: Amagansett Free Library; Amityville Public Library; Babylon Public Library; Baiting Hollow Free Library; Bay Shore-Brightwaters Public Library; Bayport-Blue Point Public Library; Brentwood Public Library; Brookhaven Free Library; Center Moriches Free Public Library; Central Islip Public Library; Cold Spring Harbor Library; Commack Public Library; Comsewogue Public Library; Connetquot Public Library; Copiague Memorial Public Library; Cutchogue-New Suffolk Free Library; Deer Park Public Library; East Hampton Library; East Islip Public Library; Emma S Clark Memorial Library; Fishers Island Library; Floyd Memorial Library; Half Hollow Hills Community Library; Hampton Bays Public Library; Hampton Library in Bridgehampton; Harborfields Public Library; Huntington Public Library; Islip Public Library; John Jermain Memorial Library; Lindenhurst Memorial Library; Longwood Public Library; Mastics-Moriches-Shirley Community Library; Mattituck-Laurel Library; Middle Country Public Library; Montauk Library; North Babylon Public Library; North Shore Public Library; Northport-East Northport Public Library; Patchogue-Medford Library; Port Jefferson Free Library; Quogue Library, Inc; Riverhead Free Library; Rogers Memorial Library; Sachem Public Library; Sayville Library; Shelter Island Public Library; Smithtown Library; South Country Library; South Huntington Public Library; Southold Free Library; West Babylon Public Library; West Islip Public Library; Westhampton Free Library; Wyandanch Public Library
Special Services for the Deaf - TTY machine
Branches: 1

P TALKING BOOKS PLUS, 627 N Sunrise Service Rd, 11713. SAN 351-840X. Tel: 516-286-1600. TDD: 516-286-4546. FAX: 516-286-1647. Web Site: www.suffolk.lib.ny.us/tbp. *Librn*, Julie Klauber; Staff 2 (MLS 2)
Founded 1972
Special Collections: Blindness & Other Disabilities Reference Materials; Inkprint Signed English Books; Print-Braille Books for Children
Publications: Fast Forward Newsletter (large print & cassette)
Special Services for the Deaf - TDD

Special Services for the Blind - Closed circuit television magnifier; Kurzweil Personal Reader
Aids & devices for disabled; volunteer recording service; Assistive Device Center

BELMONT

S ALLEGANY COUNTY HISTORICAL MUSEUM LIBRARY, Courthouse, Court St, 14813-1089. SAN 310-8546. Tel: 716-268-9293. FAX: 716-268-9446. E-Mail: historian@alleganyco.com. *In Charge*, Craig Braack
Founded 1972
Library Holdings: Bk Titles 1,000
Subject Interests: 19th Century Allegany County genealogical records, 20th Century Allegany County genealogical records, Land records
Special Collections: Philip Church Records (1500 original deeds, maps & mortgages by Philip Church & Moses Van Campen for the 100,000-acre church tract in Allegany County)

P BELMONT LITERARY & HISTORICAL SOCIETY FREE LIBRARY,* 2 Willets Ave, 14813. SAN 310-8554. Tel: 716-268-5308. FAX: 716-268-5081. *Dir*, Virginia I Cook; Tel: 516-663-2280
Founded 1885
Library Holdings: Bk Titles 16,500; Per Subs 30
Special Collections: Local Newspaper Coll
Mem of Southern Tier Library System
Open Tues & Fri 1-5 & 7-9, Sat 1-3
Friends of the Library Group

BEMUS POINT

P BEMUS POINT PUBLIC LIBRARY,* 13 Main St, 14712. SAN 310-8562. Tel: 716-386-2274. FAX: 716-386-2176. *Dir*, Mary Jane Stahley
Founded 1908. Pop 444; Circ 28,279
Library Holdings: Bk Vols 13,882
Subject Interests: Local history
Mem of Chautauqua-Cattaraugus Library System
Friends of the Library Group

BERGEN

P BYRON-BERGEN PUBLIC LIBRARY,* 13 S Lake Ave, PO Box 430, 14416-0430. SAN 370-6435. Tel: 716-494-1120. FAX: 716-494-2339. *Librn*, Virginia B Adams; Staff 3 (Non-MLS 3)
Founded 1962. Pop 5,000; Circ 25,000
Library Holdings: Bk Vols 6,914; Bk Titles 6,672; Per Subs 47
Subject Interests: Local history
Mem of Nioga Library System
Special Services for the Deaf - Books on deafness & sign language
Friends of the Library Group

BERKSHIRE

P BERKSHIRE FREE LIBRARY,* Main St, PO Box 151, 13736. SAN 310-8570. Tel: 607-657-4418. FAX: 607-657-4418. *Dir*, Christopher Sharp
Founded 1926. Pop 1,335; Circ 7,717
Library Holdings: Bk Titles 5,800
Mem of Finger Lakes Library System
Open: Tues 12:30-5, Wed 8:30-12, Thurs 1-5 & Fri 5-8

BERLIN

P BERLIN FREE TOWN LIBRARY,* 47 Main St, 12022. (Mail add: Whitehouse Memorial Bldg, PO Box 466, 12022-0466), SAN 310-8589. Tel: 518-658-2231. *Dir*, Ruth Coughtry
Founded 1895. Pop 1,929; Circ 19,616
Library Holdings: Bk Vols 10,235; Bk Titles 9,946; Per Subs 32
Subject Interests: History
Special Collections: Civil War
Mem of Upper Hudson Library System

BERNE

P TOWN OF BERNE FREE LIBRARY, Helderberg Trail, PO Box 209, 12023. SAN 310-8597. Tel: 518-872-1246. FAX: 518-872-9024. *Dir*, J Maria Dostis; E-Mail: jmdostis@nyoap.rr.com; *Librn*, Frieda Saddlemire
Founded 1962. Pop 2,037; Circ 25,291
Library Holdings: Bk Vols 12,000; Per Subs 20
Mem of Upper Hudson Library System

BETHPAGE

P BETHPAGE PUBLIC LIBRARY,* 47 Powell Ave, 11714. SAN 310-8600. Tel: 516-931-3907. FAX: 516-932-8639. *Dir*, Toby Hyman; *Ad Servs, Asst Dir*, Karen Gruskin; *Ch Servs*, Carol Shapiro; *YA Servs*, Janet Steiniger; *Tech Servs*, Marie Rehill; *Ref*, Lois Lovislo; Staff 5 (MLS 5)
Founded 1927. Pop 24,730; Circ 196,376
Library Holdings: Bk Vols 105,000; Per Subs 400
Publications: Newsletter (monthly)
Mem of Nassau Library System
Partic in Long Island Library Resources Council
Friends of the Library Group

J BRIARCLIFFE COLLEGE LIBRARY, 1055 Stewart Ave, 11714. SAN 371-8190. Tel: 516-918-3628. FAX: 516-470-6020. Web Site: www.briarcliffe.edu. *Dir Libr Serv*, Irene Kossowsky; E-Mail: ikossows@bcl.edu; Staff 3 (MLS 3)
Enrl 1,243; Fac 44
Jul 1998-Jun 1999 Mats Exp $29,000, Books $20,000, Per/Ser (Incl. Access Fees) $9,000. Sal $85,000 (Prof $60,000)
Library Holdings: Bk Vols 17,000; Bk Titles 13,000; Per Subs 125
Subject Interests: Bus, Computer, Graphic design, Technology
Special Collections: Business Technology & Career Development
Automation Activity & Vendor Info: (Acquisitions) Brodart
Publications: Bibliographies: Career Guide & Paralegal Profession
Partic in Long Island Library Resources Council
Departmental Libraries:
LYNBROOK CAMPUS, 10 Peninsula Blvd, Lynbrook, 11563. SAN 371-831X. FAX: 516-596-1394.; Staff 2 (MLS 1, Non-MLS 1)
Library Holdings: Bk Vols 4,200; Per Subs 31
PATCHOGUE CAMPUS, 10 Lake St, Patchogue, 11772. SAN 371-8328. Tel: 516-918-3907. FAX: 631-654-5082. Web Site: www.briarcliffe.edu. *Librn*, Linda Myers; Staff 3 (MLS 1, Non-MLS 2)
Library Holdings: Bk Vols 4,000; Per Subs 52

S NORTHROP GRUMMAN AEROSPACE CORP, Advanced Technology & Development Center Technical Library,* LO 1-14, 11714. SAN 310-8619. Interlibrary Loan Service Tel: 516-575-3912. FAX: 516-346-2147. *Chief Librn*, Mary L Westerling
Founded 1955
Library Holdings: Bk Vols 20,000; Per Subs 525
Subject Interests: Aerospace tech, Bus, Electrical engineering, Electronics, Mathematics, Mgt, Physics
Publications: Acquisition Bulletin; Newsletter
Restriction: Company library
Partic in Aerospace Online; BRS; Dialog Corporation; Dow Jones Interactive; DRI; DTIC; Dun & Bradstreet Info Servs; Nasa Libraries Information System - Nasa Galaxie; Pergamon Infoline; US Naval Inst Database; Vutext

BINGHAMTON

M BINGHAMTON GENERAL HOSPITAL, Stuart B Blakely Memorial Library, 10-42 Mitchell Ave, 13903. SAN 310-8627. Tel: 607-762-2110. FAX: 607-762-2903. E-Mail: medical_library@uhs.org. *Librn*, Kathy Mols; E-Mail: kathy_mols@uhs.org. Subject Specialists: *Health sciences*, Kathy Mols; Staff 2 (MLS 1, Non-MLS 1)
Founded 1940
Library Holdings: Bk Vols 2,560; Per Subs 132
Subject Interests: Healthcare admin, Medicine, Nursing
Publications: Newsletter
Restriction: Open to public for reference only
Partic in South Central Regional Library Council
Open Mon-Fri 8-4:30

BINGHAMTON PSYCHIATRIC CENTER
M LIBRARY SERVICES DEPARTMENT, 425 Robinson St, 13901-4199. SAN 351-8434. Tel: 607-773-4308. FAX: 607-773-4411. *Librn*, Martha A Mason; E-Mail: bpcmason@atdial.net. Subject Specialists: *Mental health*, Martha A Mason; Staff 1 (MLS 1)
Library Holdings: Bk Titles 3,700; Per Subs 45
Subject Interests: Medicine, Mental health, Nursing, Psychology, Quality improvement
Special Collections: History of Mental Health Department; State Hospital History Coll
Database Vendor: Ebsco - EbscoHost, OCLC - First Search
Partic in Basic Health Sciences Library Network; Docline; S Cent Res Libr Coun; State University Of New York-NYLINK
Library participates in Work-For-Pay program in which patient workers assist in clerical & typing duties as part of treatment & on-the-job training. Part of a sheltered workshop program. Separate area for patients & separate area for staff. Open Mon-Fri 8-4

J BROOME COMMUNITY COLLEGE, Cecil C Tyrrell Learning Resources Center,* PO Box 1017, 13902. SAN 310-8635. Tel: 607-778-5020. Interlibrary Loan Service Tel: 607-778-5238. FAX: 607-778-5108. Web Site: www.sunybroome.edu. *Dir*, Andrew Lakie; *Tech Servs*, Jane Rawoof; *Ref*, Deborah Spanfelner; *Ref*, Beverly Long; *Ref*, Karen Pitcher; Staff 6 (MLS 6)
Founded 1947. Enrl 5,500; Fac 215
Library Holdings: Bk Vols 67,000; Per Subs 377
Subject Interests: Bus, Eng tech, Health sci, Liberal arts
Special Collections: Community Col Educ
Partic in Dialog Corporation; OCLC Online Computer Library Center, Inc
Open Mon-Thurs 7:30-10, Fri 7:30-5, Sat 12-5, Sun 4-10

S BROOME COUNTY HISTORICAL SOCIETY LIBRARY,* Roberson Mus & Sci Ctr, 30 Front St, 13905. SAN 310-8643. Tel: 607-772-0660. FAX: 607-771-8905. *Mgr*, Charles J Browne; Staff 1 (Non-MLS 1)
Founded 1919
1998-1999 Income $55,000, County $35,000, Locally Generated Income $20,000. Mats Exp $9,500, Books $2,000, Per/Ser (Incl. Access Fees) $500, Presv $3,000, Other Print Mats $1,000, Manuscripts & Archives $3,000. Sal $6,000
Library Holdings: Bk Vols 2,500
Subject Interests: Architecture, Broome County culture, Decorative arts, Genealogy, Histories of NY, History, New England, Pennsylvania, William Bingham
Special Collections: Civil War (Mattoon Coll), mss; Daniel S Dickinson, mss; Photographic Coll (25,000); Stillson Coll; Uriah Gregory Coll; Whitney Family, papers & mss; William Bingham, mss; William L Ford Coll, 1850-1870
Open Tue-Fri 10-4

P BROOME COUNTY PUBLIC LIBRARY,* 78 Exchange St, 13901-3489. SAN 351-8493. Tel: 607-778-6400. FAX: 607-778-1441. E-Mail: bcpl@pronetisp.net. Web Site: www.tier.net/bcpl. *Dir*, Donna Riegel; *Asst Dir*, Lisa Wise; *Automation Syst Coordr*, Lavinia Adler; *Circ, ILL*, Andrea Gaska; *Ch Servs*, Mary Ann Karre; *AV*, George Schuter; *Ref*, Mary Brigiotta
Founded 1902. Pop 212,160; Circ 504,000
Jan 1998-Dec 1998 Income $2,078,862, State $172,635, City $797,765, County $847,587, Locally Generated Income $139,686, Parent Institution $121,189. Mats Exp $222,000, Books $185,793, Per/Ser (Incl. Access Fees) $32,707, Presv $3,500. Sal $966,600
Library Holdings: Bk Vols 176,642
Special Collections: Local History Memorabilia with Emphasis on Early Medicine (Dr Putnam Coll); Rare or Unusual Editions
Automation Activity & Vendor Info: (Acquisitions) epixtech, inc.; (Circulation) epixtech, inc.
Publications: Bibliographies; Calendar of Events; Contents (newsletter)
Mem of Four County Library System; S Cent Res Libr
Partic in OCLC Online Computer Library Center, Inc
Special Services for the Blind - Extensive large print collection
Friends of the Library Group
Branches: 4
BENJAMIN FRANKLIN BRANCH, 307 Conklin Ave, 13903. SAN 351-8582. Tel: 607-778-6455. FAX: 607-778-6455. *Librn*, Jennifer Burgher
Library Holdings: Bk Vols 6,919
Friends of the Library Group
EAST, 167 E Frederick St, 13904. SAN 351-8558. Tel: 607-778-6457. FAX: 607-778-6457. *Librn*, Kathleen Smith
Library Holdings: Bk Vols 17,762
Friends of the Library Group
FOUNDRY PLAZA, 10 Glenwood Ave, Ste 10, 13905. SAN 351-8523. Tel: 607-763-4437. FAX: 607-763-4437. *Librn*, Steve Steflik
Library Holdings: Bk Vols 19,937
Friends of the Library Group
SOUTH, 1123 Vestal Ave, 13903. SAN 351-8612. Tel: 607-778-6458. FAX: 607-778-6458. *Librn*, Kathleen Smith
Library Holdings: Bk Vols 16,625
Friends of the Library Group

S BROOME DEVELOPMENTAL DISABILITIES SERVICES OFFICE LIBRARY,* 249 Glenwood Rd, 13905-1695. SAN 325-0237. Tel: 607-770-0410. FAX: 607-770-0392. *Librn*, Mary Jeanne Perlmutter; E-Mail: mary.jeanne.perlmutter@omr.state.ny.us; Staff 1 (MLS 1)
Founded 1975
Apr 1997-Mar 1998 Income $61,837. Mats Exp $12,776, Books $855, Per/Ser (Incl. Access Fees) $6,259, AV Equip $5,662. Sal $46,532 (Prof $22,747)
Library Holdings: Bk Vols 12,242; Per Subs 100
Subject Interests: Developmental disabilities, Mental retardation
Publications: The Quill & Shutter
Mem of S Cent Res Libr
Partic in OCLC Online Computer Library Center, Inc

P FENTON FREE LIBRARY,* Moody Memorial Library Bldg, 1062 Chenango St, 13901. SAN 310-8651. Tel: 607-724-8649. *Dir*, Pam Klesse
Founded 1936. Pop 7,040; Circ 74,948
Library Holdings: Bk Vols 17,769
Publications: Dictionary Guide to Services Offered at the Moody Memorial Library; What's New (newsletter)
Mem of Four County Library System
Friends of the Library Group

S GANNETT NEWSPAPERS, Press Sun-Bulletin Library,* Vestal Pkwy E, PO Box 1270, 13902-1270. SAN 310-8686. Tel: 607-798-1159. FAX: 607-798-1113. Web Site: www.pressconnects.com. *Dir*, Shulamis Landesman; Staff 4 (MLS 1, Non-MLS 3)
Founded 1942
Library Holdings: Bk Titles 300
Subject Interests: Binghamton County hist, Broome County hist

S HAWORTH PRESS, INC, Editorial Department Archive,* 10 Alice St, 13904-1580. SAN 329-8493. Tel: 607-722-5857, Ext 322. FAX: 607-722-6362. E-Mail: getinfo@haworth.com. Web Site: www.haworthpress.nc.com. *Dir*, Christine Miner
Library Holdings: Bk Titles 400; Per Subs 700
Subject Interests: Alcoholism, Mental health, Soc work, Substance abuse
Open Mon-Thurs 8:30-5 & Fri 8-2

S INSTITUTE FOR DEVELOPMENT ANTHROPOLOGY LIBRARY,* 99 Collier St, Ste 302, PO Box 2207, 13902-2207. SAN 326-1840. Tel: 607-772-6244. FAX: 607-773-8993. E-Mail: devanth@binghamton.edu. *Assoc Librn*, Stephanie R Horowitz
Founded 1976
Library Holdings: Bk Titles 1,600; Per Subs 41
Publications: Development Anthropologist; Instititute for Development Anthropology Working Papers
Restriction: Non-circulating to the public

S NEW YORK STATE ELECTRIC & GAS CORP, Corporate Library, Corporate Dr, Kirkwood Industrial Park, 13902-5224. (Mail add: PO Box 5224, 13902-5224), SAN 310-8694. Tel: 607-762-7434. FAX: 607-762-8432. *Librn, Res*, Michelle Budney; E-Mail: mibudney@nyseg.com; Staff 1 (MLS 1)
Founded 1954
Subject Interests: Elec utilities, Natural gas
Publications: Library News
Restriction: Restricted public use
Partic in S Cent Res Libr Coun

GL NEW YORK STATE SUPREME COURT LIBRARY, 92 Court St, Broome County Courthouse, Rm 107, 13901-3313. SAN 310-8716. Tel: 607-778-2119. FAX: 607-772-8331. *Dir*, Judy A Lauer; E-Mail: jlauer@courts.state.ny.us; Staff 3 (MLS 1, Non-MLS 2)
Founded 1859
Library Holdings: Bk Vols 60,000; Bk Titles 7,500; Per Subs 270
Subject Interests: Bankruptcy, Criminology, Domestic relations, Gen practice, New York, Statute law
Database Vendor: epixtech, inc.
Mem of S Cent Res Libr
Partic in South Central Regional Library Council

M OUR LADY OF LOURDES MEMORIAL HOSPITAL LIBRARY,* 169 Riverside Dr, 13905. SAN 373-5990. Tel: 607-798-5290. FAX: 607-798-5989. Web Site: www.lourdes.com. *Librn*, Susan Bretscher; E-Mail: sbretscher@lourdes.com
Library Holdings: Bk Titles 3,500; Per Subs 275
Partic in Basic Health Sciences Library Network; LVIS; Nat Network of Librs of Med, S Cent Res Libr Coun

C STATE UNIVERSITY OF NEW YORK AT BINGHAMTON, University Libraries, Vestal Pkwy E, PO Box 6012, 13902-6012. SAN 351-8671. Tel: 607-777-4841. Interlibrary Loan Service Tel: 607-777-4985. Circulation Tel: 607-777-2194. Reference Tel: 607-777-2345. FAX: 607-777-4848. Web Site: library.lib.binghamton.edu. *Dir*, Eleanor L Heishman; Tel: 607-777-2346, E-Mail: eheishma@binghamton.edu; *Assoc Dir*, Roe Keith; Tel: 607-777-4385, E-Mail: kroe@binghamton.edu; *Access Serv*, Ronnie Goldberg; Tel: 607-777-2325, E-Mail: rgoldberg@binghamton.edu; *Spec Coll*, Jeanne Eichelberger; E-Mail: jeichelb@binghamton.edu; *Ser*, Kay Glasgow; Tel: 607-777-4931, E-Mail: kglasgow@binghamton.edu; *Syst Coordr*, Andrew Perry; Tel: 607-777-4331, E-Mail: aperry@binghamton.edu; *Tech Servs*, Frank Mols; Tel: 607-777-2368, E-Mail: fmols@binghamton.edu
Founded 1946. Enrl 12,473; Fac 785; Highest Degree: Doctorate
Jul 1999-Jun 2000 Income (Main and Other College/University Libraries) $9,364,567, State $9,049,111, Locally Generated Income $315,456. Mats Exp $3,967,863, Books $1,056,349, Per/Ser (Incl. Access Fees) $2,135,043, Presv $71,719, Micro $134,127, AV Equip $20,382, Electronic Ref Mat (Incl. Access Fees) $550,243. Sal $4,329,614
Library Holdings: Bk Vols 1,704,380; Per Subs 7,097
Special Collections: French Colonial History (William J Haggerty Coll); Link Coll; Local History Coll; Max Reinhardt Archive; Music (Frances R Conole Archive)
Automation Activity & Vendor Info: (Acquisitions) NOTIS; (Cataloging) NOTIS; (Circulation) NOTIS; (OPAC) NOTIS; (Serials) NOTIS
Partic in CRL; Research Libraries Group, Inc; South Central Regional Library Council; State University Of New York-NYLINK
Friends of the Library Group
Departmental Libraries:
SCIENCE, Vestal Pkwy E, 13902. SAN 351-8760. Tel: 607-777-2218. FAX: 607-777-2274. *Science*, Charlotte Skuster; Tel: 607-777-4122, E-Mail: skuster@binghamton.edu

SR UNITARIAN UNIVERSALIST CONGREGATION, Margaret Jackson Memorial Library, 183 Riverside Dr, 13905. SAN 310-8724. Tel: 607-729-1641. FAX: 607-729-1899. E-Mail: uubinghamton@tier.net. *Chairperson*, Toby Anderson; *Chairperson*, Janice Fiore
Founded 1891
Library Holdings: Bk Vols 3,000
Subject Interests: Philosophy, Sociology, Theology

Special Collections: 19th Century Universalism & Unitarianism; Church Archives; Unitarian Universalist Sermons
Open Sun 11-12 & upon request

BLACK RIVER

P BLACK RIVER FREE LIBRARY,* 102-104 Maple St, PO Box 253, 13612. SAN 310-8732. Tel: 315-773-5163. FAX: 315-773-5163. *Librn*, Sandra Lamb
Founded 1915. Pop 1,349; Circ 23,247
Library Holdings: Bk Vols 6,519; Bk Titles 5,929
Mem of North Country Library System

BLAUVELT

P BLAUVELT FREE LIBRARY, 541 Western Hwy, 10913. SAN 310-8740. Tel: 914-359-2811. FAX: 914-398-0017. E-Mail: blv@rcls.org. Web Site: www.rcls.org/blv. *Dir*, Mary E Behringer; *Ch Servs, YA Servs*, Bessie Sobel; *ILL*, Irene Schutz; Staff 12 (MLS 3, Non-MLS 9)
Founded 1909. Pop 4,838; Circ 47,708
Library Holdings: Bk Titles 57,514; Per Subs 288
Special Collections: Area History; Blauvelt Family History; Genealogy (Blauvelt); Local History (Budke Coll)
Mem of Ramapo Catskill Library System
Open Mon-Thurs 10-9, Fri 10-5, Sat 11-5, Sun 2-5
Friends of the Library Group

C DOMINICAN COLLEGE LIBRARY,* 492 Western Hwy, 10913-2099. SAN 310-8759. Tel: 914-359-8188. FAX: 914-359-2313. *Coll Develop, Librn*, John Barrie; *Tech Servs*, Maureen O'Keeffe; *Per, Ref*, Virginia Dunne; Staff 5 (MLS 5)
Founded 1957. Enrl 1,214; Fac 78; Highest Degree: Bachelor
Library Holdings: Bk Vols 103,500; Bk Titles 94,500; Per Subs 644
Partic in Southeastern New York Library Resources Council

BLISS

P EAGLE FREE LIBRARY,* 3413 School St, 14024. SAN 310-8767. Tel: 716-322-7701. FAX: 716-322-7701. *Dir*, Linda Lavery
Pop 1,211; Circ 8,375
Library Holdings: Bk Vols 7,004
Mem of Pioneer Library System
Open Wed 7-9, Thurs 1-5, Fri 4-7, Sat 9:30-1:30

BLOOMFIELD

P ALLENS HILL FREE LIBRARY,* 3818 Allens Hill Rd, 14469. SAN 311-3191. Tel: 716-229-5636. FAX: 716-229-2460. *Dir*, Linda Mollnow
Founded 1883. Pop 265; Circ 11,608
Library Holdings: Bk Titles 6,000; Per Subs 28
Mem of Pioneer Library System
Open Mon, Tues & Thurs 3-5:30, Wed 5:30-7:30 & Sat 2-4:30

BLOOMINGBURG

P BLOOMINGBURG FREE LIBRARY,* 5 North Rd, PO Box 384, 12721. SAN 310-8775. Tel: 914-733-4993. FAX: 914-733-4993. *Librn*, Margaret Nye
Circ 13,172
Library Holdings: Bk Vols 19,000
Mem of Ramapo Catskill Library System
Friends of the Library Group
Branches: 1
WURTSBORO BRANCH, Sullivan St, Wurtsboro, 12790. SAN 370-3576. Tel: 914-888-2111. *Librn*, Carol Lubin
Friends of the Library Group

BLUE MOUNTAIN LAKE

S ADIRONDACK MUSEUM LIBRARY,* 12812. SAN 310-8783. Tel: 518-352-7311. FAX: 518-352-7653. *Librn*, Jerold Pepper; E-Mail: pepper@northnet.org
Founded 1956
Library Holdings: Bk Titles 9,000; Per Subs 95
Subject Interests: Art, Conservation, Early 20th Centuries, Ecology, Econ life, Emphasis on 19th centuries, Lumbering, Park, Recreation, Soc
Special Collections: Adirondack Park Agency Coll; Association for the Protection of the Adirondacks Archives; Augustus D Shephard Architectural Plans & Drawings; Emporium Co Forestry Coll; McIntyre Iron Co Papers; Photographs Coll; W/H H Adirondack Murray Papers
Partic in North Country Reference & Research Resources Council

BLUE POINT

P BAYPORT-BLUE POINT PUBLIC LIBRARY,* 203 Blue Point Ave, 11715-1217. SAN 310-8791. Tel: 631-363-6133. FAX: 631-363-6133. E-Mail: bprtlib@suffolklib.ny.us. Web Site: www.suffolk.lib.ny.us/libraries/bprt/. *Dir*, John O'Hare; *Ref*, Jocelyn McIntee; *Ch Servs*, Mary Jo Cohan; Staff 11 (MLS 10, Non-MLS 1)
Founded 1938. Pop 12,516; Circ 131,895
Jul 1999-Jun 2000 Income $1,151,062, State $3,504. Mats Exp $178,500, Books $106,000, Per/Ser (Incl. Access Fees) $31,000, Presv $1,500, AV Equip $40,000. Sal $683,184 (Prof $295,205)
Library Holdings: Bk Vols 110,416; Per Subs 242
Subject Interests: Local history
Database Vendor: Innovative Interfaces INN - View
Publications: Newsletter (bi-monthly)
Mem of Suffolk Cooperative Library System
Friends of the Library Group

BOHEMIA

P CONNETQUOT PUBLIC LIBRARY, 760 Ocean Ave, 11716. SAN 310-8805. Tel: 631-567-5079. FAX: 631-567-5137. Web Site: www.connetquot.lib.ny.us. *Dir*, Joan Zaleski; Staff 103 (MLS 40, Non-MLS 63)
Founded 1974. Pop 40,189; Circ 633,546
Jul 1999-Jun 2000 Income $3,751,757. Mats Exp $445,750, Books $412,000, Per/Ser (Incl. Access Fees) $33,250, Presv $500. Sal $2,209,713
Library Holdings: Bk Vols 172,866; Per Subs 689
Special Collections: Standalone Gaylord Galaxy
Publications: Newsletter (quarterly)
Mem of Suffolk Cooperative Library System

BOLIVAR

P BOLIVAR FREE LIBRARY,* 390 Main St, 14715-0512. SAN 310-8813. Tel: 716-928-2015. FAX: 716-928-2015. E-Mail: redrover93@yahoo.com. *Librn*, Betty Cornelius
Founded 1911. Circ 15,000
Library Holdings: Bk Vols 17,482; Per Subs 31
Special Collections: 19th Century New York & Pennsylvania Oilfield Histories; Local Newspaper, 1892-1965
Mem of Chemung-Southern Tier Libr Syst; Southern Tier Library System
Open Mon & Thurs 6-9, Tues & Fri 12:30-4:30, Sat 12:30-3:30

BOLTON LANDING

P BOLTON FREE LIBRARY,* Lake Shore Dr, 12814. (Mail add: PO Box 389, 12814), SAN 310-8821. Tel: 518-644-2233. FAX: 518-644-2233. E-Mail: bfl@netheaven.com. *Dir*, Megan W Baker
Founded 1899. Pop 1,800; Circ 18,234
Library Holdings: Bk Titles 16,896; Per Subs 31
Special Collections: Adirondack; American Riflemen (complete set); New York Conservationst (complete set)
Mem of Southern Adirondack Library System
Open Mon, Fri & Sat 10-5, Tues & Thurs 2-9
Friends of the Library Group

BOONVILLE

P ERWIN LIBRARY & INSTITUTE,* Schuyler St, 13309. SAN 310-883X. Tel: 315-942-4834. *Dir*, Donna Ripp; *Dir*, LeeAnn Riley
Founded 1885. Pop 5,000; Circ 31,541
Library Holdings: Bk Titles 15,181; Per Subs 59
Special Collections: Edmund Wilson Children's Books; Edmund Wilson Puppet Coll; Walter D Edmond's Film & Book Coll
Mem of Mid-York Library System
Special Services for the Deaf - Staff with knowledge of sign language
Friends of the Library Group

BOSTON

P BOSTON FREE LIBRARY,* 9475 Boston State Rd, PO Box 200, 14025. SAN 310-8848. Tel: 716-941-3516. Web Site: www.buffalolib.org/nl_bos.html. *Librn*, Laura McLeod
Pop 7,000; Circ 28,000
Library Holdings: Bk Vols 14,000; Per Subs 67
Mem of Buffalo & Erie County Public Library System

BOVINA CENTER

P BOVINA LIBRARY ASSOCIATION,* 13740. SAN 310-8856. Tel: 607-832-4884. *Librn*, Avis Adams
Founded 1918. Pop 550; Circ 3,938
Library Holdings: Bk Vols 4,922; Per Subs 25
Mem of Four County Library System

BRANCHPORT

P BRANCHPORT FREE LIBRARY,* 29 West Lake Rd, Rte 54A, Box 239, 14418. SAN 310-8864. Tel: 315-595-2899. *Dir*, Jo Graves
Founded 1913. Pop 3,908; Circ 7,353
Library Holdings: Bk Vols 10,479; Bk Titles 10,000
Mem of Southern Tier Library System

BRANT LAKE

P HORICON FREE PUBLIC LIBRARY, 6615 State Rte 8, 12815-1901. (Mail add: PO Box 185, 12815-0185), SAN 376-3153. Tel: 518-494-4189. FAX: 518-494-4189. E-Mail: bllib@netheaven.com. *Dir*, Linda Hoyt
Library Holdings: Bk Vols 6,771; Bk Titles 6,666
Special Collections: Adirondacks
Mem of Southern Adirondack Library System
Open Mon & Thurs 2-8, Tues 12-5 & Sat 10-1

BRENTWOOD

P BRENTWOOD PUBLIC LIBRARY,* Second Ave & Fourth St, 11717. SAN 310-8872. Tel: 516-273-7883. FAX: 516-273-7896. E-Mail: brenlib@suffolk.lib.ny.us. Web Site: www.suffolk.lib.ny.us/libraries/bren. *Dir*, Doris Lewis Sargeant
Founded 1937. Pop 70,000
Jul 1997-Jun 1998 Income $3,749,848, State $20,075. Mats Exp $376,558, Books $330,002, Per/Ser (Incl. Access Fees) $25,505, Presv $1,007, Micro $18,365, Other Print Mats $1,679. Sal $1,712,107 (Prof $864,164)
Library Holdings: Bk Vols 226,038; Per Subs 794
Special Collections: Brentwood History (Verne Dyson Historical Coll), bks, mss, photogs
Publications: Newsletter
Mem of Suffolk Cooperative Library System
Special Services for the Deaf - High interest/low vocabulary books; TTY machine
Friends of the Library Group

C LONG ISLAND UNIVERSITY, Brentwood Campus Library, 100 Second Ave, 11717. SAN 351-8795. Tel: 631-273-5112. FAX: 631-273-5198. *Coll Develop, Dir*, Joong Suk Kim; Tel: 631-273-5112, Ext 34, E-Mail: joong.kim@liu.edu; *Per*, Ellen McCartney; E-Mail: ellen.mccartney@liu.edu; *ILL*, Joann Jantzen; E-Mail: joanjantzen@liu.edu; Staff 5 (MLS 2, Non-MLS 3)
Founded 1972. Highest Degree: Master
Sep 1999-Aug 2000 Income $318,864, State $5,064, Parent Institution $313,800. Mats Exp $114,300, Books $40,000, Per/Ser (Incl. Access Fees) $40,000, Micro $30,000, Other Print Mats $2,800, Electronic Ref Mat (Incl. Access Fees) $1,500. Sal $199,500 (Prof $145,000)
Library Holdings: Bk Vols 55,543; Per Subs 285
Subject Interests: Accounting, Bus, Criminal justice, Education, Pub admin
Database Vendor: Dialog, GaleNet, IAC - Info Trac, OCLC - First Search, ProQuest, Silverplatter Information Inc., Wilson - Wilson Web
Publications: Acquisitions list; bibliographies; ERIC Documents Holdings Index; Periodicals List
Restriction: In-house use for visitors
Function: ILL available, ILL by photocopy only, ILL limited, ILL to other special libraries, Literary searches, Newspaper reference library, Outside services via phone, cable & mail, Photocopies available, Professional lending library, Reference services available, Referrals accepted, Research fees apply
Mem of Long Island Libr Resources Coun, Inc
Partic in Long Island Library Resources Council

J SUFFOLK COUNTY COMMUNITY COLLEGE, Western Campus Library,* 1001 Crooked Hill Rd, 11717. SAN 351-8825. Tel: 516-851-6740. Interlibrary Loan Service Tel: 516-434-6504. FAX: 516-851-6509. Web Site: www.sunysuffolk.edu/web/central/library. *Head of Libr*, David J Quinn; E-Mail: quinnd@sunysuffolk.edu; *Circ, ILL, Reader Servs*, Joyce Gabriele; *Reader Servs, Ref*, Gerald Reminick; *Per*, Francis Parrella; *AV*, Kevin Peterman; Staff 6 (MLS 6)
Founded 1974. Enrl 6,100; Fac 100
Sep 1997-Aug 1998 Income $720,000. Mats Exp $87,336, Books $30,000, Per/Ser (Incl. Access Fees) $43,000, Presv $800, Micro $6,800, AV Equip $3,736, Other Print Mats $1,500. Sal $524,363 (Prof $375,000)
Library Holdings: Bk Vols 41,000; Bk Titles 39,385; Per Subs 300
Publications: Faculty handbook, newsletter, student handbook
Partic in Long Island Library Resources Council; New York State Interlibrary Loan Network

BREWSTER

P BREWSTER PUBLIC LIBRARY, 79 Main St, 10509. SAN 310-8899. Tel: 914-279-6421. FAX: 914-279-0043. E-Mail: brewster@sebridge.org. Web Site: www.brewsterlibrary.com. *Dir*, Patricia Bowen
Pop 15,000; Circ 80,000
Library Holdings: Bk Vols 30,000; Per Subs 50
Mem of Mid-Hudson Library System
Friends of the Library Group

BRIARCLIFF MANOR

P BRIARCLIFF MANOR PUBLIC LIBRARY,* Library Rd, 10510. SAN 310-8910. Tel: 914-941-7072. FAX: 914-941-7091. *Dir*, Geraldine Baldwin; Tel: 914-941-0755, E-Mail: greenbean65@hotmail.com; *Ch Servs*, Edith Crawford
Founded 1959. Pop 7,070; Circ 60,000
May 1999-Jun 2000 Income $300,000. Mats Exp $47,500, Books $35,000, Per/Ser (Incl. Access Fees) $5,000, Electronic Ref Mat (Incl. Access Fees) $7,500. Sal $115,000 (Prof $60,000)
Library Holdings: Bk Titles 29,000; Per Subs 72
Subject Interests: Art
Database Vendor: epixtech, inc.
Mem of Westchester Library System
Friends of the Library Group

S PHILIPS ELECTRONICS NORTH AMERICA CORP, Philips Research-A Daniels Library, 345 Scarborough Rd, 10510. SAN 310-8937. Tel: 914-945-6195. FAX: 914-945-6553. E-Mail: library@philabs.research.philips.com. *Librn*, Betsy McIlvaine
Founded 1945
Library Holdings: Bk Vols 6,000; Per Subs 300
Subject Interests: Computer software
Special Collections: (Advanced digital television, projection display systems, power electronics for lighting & consumer electronic & IC design);

BRIDGEHAMPTON

P HAMPTON LIBRARY IN BRIDGEHAMPTON, 2478 Main St, PO Box 3025, 11932. SAN 310-8945. Tel: 631-537-0015. FAX: 631-537-7229. E-Mail: bridlib@suffolk.lib.ny.us. Web Site: www.hamptonlibrary.org. *Dir*, Debra L Engelhardt; E-Mail: dengelha@suffolk.lib.ny.us; *Circ*, Christine King; *Ch Servs*, Robyn LeGrand; *Tech Servs*, Kathy Cassidy; Staff 6 (MLS 1, Non-MLS 5)
Founded 1877. Circ 29,667
Library Holdings: Bk Vols 34,500; Per Subs 56
Special Collections: Long Island Coll
Automation Activity & Vendor Info: (Cataloging) Follett; (Circulation) Follett
Database Vendor: GaleNet, IAC - SearchBank, Wilson - Wilson Web
Mem of Suffolk Cooperative Library System
Friends of the Library Group

BRIDGEWATER

P BRIDGEWATER FREE LIBRARY,* Pritchard Ave, Box 372, 13313. SAN 310-8953. Tel: 315-822-6475. *Librn, Mgr*, Janet Tilby
Pop 940; Circ 5,600
Library Holdings: Bk Vols 2,100
Mem of Mid-York Library System
Friends of the Library Group

BRIGHTWATERS

P BAY SHORE-BRIGHTWATERS PUBLIC LIBRARY,* One S Country Rd, 11718-1517. SAN 310-8961. Tel: 631-665-4350. FAX: 631-665-4958. E-Mail: bsbwlib@suffolk.lib.ny.us. Web Site: www.bsbw.suffolk.lib.ny.us. *Dir*, Eileen J Kavanagh; *Asst Dir*, Rodney Marve; *Ad Servs*, Colleen Smisek; *Ch Servs*, Linda J Clark; Staff 10 (MLS 10)
Founded 1901. Pop 29,247; Circ 205,374
Jul 1999-Jun 2000 Income $1,877,544. Mats Exp $227,000. Sal $1,032,814
Library Holdings: Bk Vols 135,777; Bk Titles 106,818; Per Subs 526
Subject Interests: Compact discs, Music scores, Videos
Special Collections: Long Island, ESL Coll
Automation Activity & Vendor Info: (Acquisitions) Gaylord; (Cataloging) Gaylord; (Circulation) Gaylord; (Course Reserve) Gaylord; (ILL) Gaylord; (Media Booking) Gaylord; (OPAC) Gaylord; (Serials) Gaylord
Mem of Suffolk Cooperative Library System
Special Services for the Blind - Bks on cassette
Friends of the Library Group

BROCKPORT

P SEYMOUR LIBRARY,* 161 East Ave, 14420-1987. SAN 310-8996. Tel: 716-637-1050. FAX: 716-637-1051. *Ad Servs, Dir*, Mark Jaccarino; *YA Servs*, Cathy Mangant; *Ch Servs*, Ellen Zinni
Circ 266,578
Library Holdings: Bk Vols 52,000; Bk Titles 45,000; Per Subs 85
Special Collections: Books on the Erie Canal; Census Coll, micro

Automation Activity & Vendor Info: (Acquisitions) Brodart; (Circulation) CARL
Mem of Monroe County Library System
Friends of the Library Group

C STATE UNIVERSITY OF NEW YORK COLLEGE AT BROCKPORT, Drake Memorial Library, 350 New Campus Dr, 14420-2995. SAN 351-885X. Tel: 716-395-2140. Interlibrary Loan Service Tel: 716-395-2727. FAX: 716-395-5651. Web Site: www.brockport.edu/~library 5/first.htm/. *Dir*, Raj Madan; E-Mail: rmadan@brockport.edu; *Asst Librn*, Mary Jo Gigliotti; *Asst Librn*, Eileen O'Hara; *Asst Librn*, Jennifer Quigley; *Asst Librn*, Natalie Sommerville; *Asst Librn*, Gregory Toth; *Ser*, Carolyn McBryde; *Ref*, Charles Kowling; *Assoc Librn*, Debra Ames; *Doc*, Betty Chan; *Ref*, Lori Lampert; *ILL*, Robert Gilliam; *Coll Develop*, Sally Petty; Staff 14 (MLS 14)
Founded 1860. Enrl 8,492; Fac 301; Highest Degree: Master Sal $1,086,540 (Prof $465,493)
Library Holdings: Bk Vols 565,000; Bk Titles 400,000; Per Subs 1,365
Subject Interests: Am lit, Dance, Education, English literature, History
Special Collections: Early American Imprints, 1639-1800-Readex, micro-opaque; Early English Books, 1475-1700, microfilm; Library of American Civilization, ultrafiche; Library of English Literature, ultrafiche; Early English Books, 1475-1700, microflm; Library of American Civilization, ultrafiche
Automation Activity & Vendor Info: (Acquisitions) epixtech, inc.; (Circulation) epixtech, inc.
Publications: Drake Library Review
Partic in OCLC Online Computer Library Center, Inc; Rochester Regional Library Council

BROCTON

P AHIRA HALL MEMORIAL LIBRARY,* 37 W Main, PO Box Q, 14716. SAN 310-9003. Tel: 716-792-9418. FAX: 716-792-7334. *Dir*, Ruth Dorogi
Founded 1903. Circ 23,600
Library Holdings: Bk Vols 15,000
Mem of Chautauqua-Cattaraugus Library System

BRONX

M BETH ABRAHAM HOSPITAL, Patient Library,* 612 Allerton Ave, 10467. SAN 327-7542. Tel: 718-519-5959.
Library Holdings: Bk Titles 2,000

CM ALBERT EINSTEIN COLLEGE OF MEDICINE, D Samuel Gottesman Library, 1300 Morris Park Ave, 10461. SAN 351-8884. Tel: 718-430-3108. FAX: 718-430-8795. Web Site: www.library.aecom.yu.edu. *Dir*, Judie Malamud; *Asst Dir*, Florence Schreibstein; *Cat*, Karen Laul; *Online Servs, Ref*, Debbie Stern; *Archivist*, Norma Nelson; *Publ Servs*, Racheline Habousha; Staff 26 (MLS 9, Non-MLS 17)
Founded 1955. Enrl 900; Highest Degree: Doctorate
Jul 1999-Jun 2000 Mats Exp $1,194,923, Books $102,974, Per/Ser (Incl. Access Fees) $988,358, Electronic Ref Mat (Incl. Access Fees) $103,591. Sal $1,050,885 (Prof $467,808)
Library Holdings: Bk Vols 220,075; Bk Titles 86,689; Per Subs 2,275
Subject Interests: Behav sci, Medicine, Psychology
Automation Activity & Vendor Info: (Acquisitions) VTLS; (Cataloging) VTLS; (Circulation) VTLS; (Course Reserve) VTLS; (OPAC) VTLS; (Serials) VTLS
Partic in Medical Library Center Of New York; Metro NY Libr Coun; National Network of Libraries of Medicine - Greater Midwest Region; OCLC Online Computer Library Center, Inc

J BRONX COMMUNITY COLLEGE LIBRARY & LEARNING CENTER,* W 181st St & University Ave, 10453. SAN 310-902X. Tel: 718-289-5439. FAX: 718-289-6063. Web Site: www.bcc.cuny.edu/~lilbrary/. *Dir*, Mark Padnos; E-Mail: mark.padnos@bcc.cuny.edu; *Librn, Prof, Tech Servs*, Julie Skurdenis; *Bibliog Instr, ILL, Ref*, David Koenigstein; *Media Spec*, LaRoi Lawton; *Coll Develop*, Julianne Skurdenis; Staff 5 (MLS 5)
Founded 1958. Enrl 8,000; Fac 200
1998-1999 Income $865,016. Mats Exp $125,222, Books $55,465, Per/Ser (Incl. Access Fees) $23,901, Micro $8,787. Sal $593,758 (Prof $306,279)
Library Holdings: Bk Vols 106,761; Per Subs 440
Publications: Ethinic Bibliography Series; Focus on the Library (newsletter); Here's Help Series; Learning Center Guide; Periodicals Guide
Partic in Metropolitan New York Library Council; OCLC Online Computer Library Center, Inc

L BRONX COUNTY BAR ASSOCIATION, Law Library,* 851 Grand Concourse, Rm 124, 10451. SAN 310-9038. Tel: 718-293-5600. FAX: 718-681-0098. *Exec Dir*, Mary Conlan
Founded 1902
Library Holdings: Bk Vols 10,000

S BRONX COUNTY HISTORICAL SOCIETY, Research Library & Archives, 3309 Bainbridge Ave, 10467. SAN 310-9127. Tel: 718-881-8900. FAX: 718-881-4827. Web Site: www.bronxhistoricalsociety.org. *Exec Dir*, Dr Gary Hermalyn; *Librn*, Laura Tossi; *Archivist*, Dr Peter Derrick
Founded 1955
Library Holdings: Bk Titles 5,000; Per Subs 150
Subject Interests: Bronx hist, Communities, Life
Special Collections: Birds of the Bronx; Bronx Congressmen Records, Bronx Chamber of Commerce Records; Bronx Cookbooks; Bronx County Archives (Chamber of Commerce Records); Bronx Home News 1907-1948, micro; Edgar Allan Poe Coll; Local Newspaper (all current); Maps & Atlases (1000); Photograph Coll (45,000 images)
Publications: Bicentennial of the United States Constitution Commemorative Issue; Birds of the Bronx; Bronx Cookbooks; Edgar Allan Poe at Fordham Teachers Guide & Workbook; Edgar Allen Poe: A Short Biography; Elected Public Officials of the Bronx Since 1898; Genealogy of the Bronx: An Annotated Guide to Sources of Information; History in Asphalt: The Origin of Bronx Street & Place Names; History of the Morris Park Racecourse & the Morris Family; Landmarks of the Bronx; Legacy of the Revolution: The Valentine-Varian House; Morris High School & the Creation of the New York City Public High School System; Poems of Edgar Allan Poe at Fordham; Presidents of the United States; The Beautiful Bronx, 1920-1950; The Bronx County Historical Society Journal; The Bronx in Print: An Annotated Catalogue of Books & Pamphlets About the Bronx; The Bronx in the Frontier Era; The Bronx in the Innocent Years, 1890-1925; The Bronx It Was Only Yesterday, 1935-1965; The Bronx Triangle: A Portrait of Norwood

M BRONX-LEBANON HOSPITAL, Concourse Division Medical Library,* 1650 Selwyn Ave, 10457. SAN 351-9007. Tel: 718-590-1800, Ext 1298. *Librn*, Geraldo Gomez; *Asst Librn*, Laura Villanueva
Library Holdings: Bk Vols 6,000; Per Subs 146
Partic in Medical Library Center Of New York

CALVARY HOSPITAL
M MEDICAL LIBRARY, 1740 Eastchester Rd, 10461. SAN 351-9066. Tel: 718-518-2229. FAX: 718-518-2686. E-Mail: calvary1@metgate.metro.org. *Librn*, Irina Pulatova; Staff 2 (MLS 1, Non-MLS 1)
Founded 1966
Library Holdings: Bk Vols 1,300; Per Subs 283
Subject Interests: Cancer, Medicine, Nursing, Nutrition, Oncology
Restriction: Staff use only
Partic in Medical Library Center Of New York; Nat Libr of Med; New York Metrop Ref & Res Libr Agency

C CITY UNIVERSITY OF NEW YORK (CUNY), Lehman College Library, 250 Bedford Park Blvd W, 10468-1589. SAN 310-9089. Tel: 718-960-7766. Interlibrary Loan Service Tel: 718-960-7762. Circulation Tel: 718-960-8576. Reference Tel: 718-960-8577. FAX: 718-960-8090. Web Site: www.lehman.cuny.edu/library/library2.htm. *Chief Librn*, Rona Ostrow; E-Mail: rostrow@lehman.cuny.edu; *Dep Dir*, Harold Diamond; E-Mail: hjdlc@cunyvm.cuny.edu; *Coll Develop, Ref*, Michael O Shannon; E-Mail: shannon@alpha.lehman.cuny.edu; *Acq, Circ*, Carol Gee; E-Mail: kcglc@cunyvm.cuny.edu; *Per*, Edwin Wallace; E-Mail: edwlc@cunyvm.cuny.edu; *Bibliog Instr*, Susan Voge; E-Mail: savlc@cunyvm.cuny.edu; *ILL*, Muriel Knobloch; E-Mail: mrklc@cunyvm.cuny.edu; *Tech Coordr*, James Watson; E-Mail: jamesw@alpha.lehman.cuny.edu; *Info Tech*, Wayne Halliday; E-Mail: wayne@alpha.lehman.cuny.edu; *Spec Coll*, Janet Butler Munch; E-Mail: jbmlc@cunyvm.cuny.edu. Subject Specialists: *Art*, Harold Diamond; *Communication*, Rona Ostrow; *Education*, Sandrea DeMinco; *English literature*, Rona Ostrow; *Music*, Harold Diamond; Staff 49 (MLS 12, Non-MLS 37)
Founded 1968. Enrl 9,074; Fac 667; Highest Degree: Master
Jul 1999-Jun 2000 Mats Exp $618,935, Books $171,551, Per/Ser (Incl. Access Fees) $380,927, Presv $12,000, Micro $25,038, AV Equip $7,147, Other Print Mats $15,192, Electronic Ref Mat (Incl. Access Fees) $7,080. Sal $1,332,172 (Prof $748,448)
Library Holdings: Bk Vols 556,274; Bk Titles 394,110; Per Subs 1,513
Subject Interests: Botanical sci, Ethnic studies, Health sci
Special Collections: Basic Liberal Arts Coll; Bronx History; City
Automation Activity & Vendor Info: (Acquisitions) epixtech, inc.; (Cataloging) epixtech, inc.; (Circulation) epixtech, inc.; (Course Reserve) epixtech, inc.; (Serials) epixtech, inc.
Database Vendor: epixtech, inc., OCLC - First Search
Partic in Dialog Corporation; New York Metrop Ref & Res Libr Agency; New York State Interlibrary Loan Network; Westlaw
Friends of the Library Group

C COLLEGE OF MOUNT SAINT VINCENT, Elizabeth Seton Library, 6301 Riverdale Ave, 10471. SAN 310-9054. Tel: 718-405-3395. FAX: 718-601-2091. Web Site: www.cmsv.edu/library/index. *Dir*, Dr Edward O'Hara; *Ref*, Eric Darko; *Cat*, Margaret Hsu; *Cat*, Sister Helen Wade; *Cat*, Lina Ip; *Tech Servs*, Steve Feyl
Founded 1910. Highest Degree: Master
Library Holdings: Bk Vols 200,000; Per Subs 800
Subject Interests: Biology, Communications, Irish hist, Literature, Nursing
Publications: Discover Resources Bulletins; Library Guides; Library Lines
Partic in New York Metrop Ref & Res Libr Agency; OCLC Online Computer Library Center, Inc; WALDO

G CRIMINAL COURT OF THE CITY OF NEW YORK LIBRARY,* 215 E 161st St, Rm 9-5A, 10451. (Mail add: 100 Centre St, 10013), SAN 372-770X. Tel: 718-590-2931. FAX: 718-590-7297. E-Mail: lbotsford@courts.state.ny.us. *Librn*, Lisa Botsford; Staff 4 (MLS 2, Non-MLS 2)
Library Holdings: Bk Vols 17,000; Bk Titles 782; Per Subs 106
Subject Interests: Criminal law

GM DEPARTMENT OF VETERANS AFFAIRS, Medical Center Library,* 130 W Kingsbridge Rd, 10468. SAN 310-9194. Tel: 718-584-9000, Ext 6924. FAX: 718-579-3338. *Dir*, Sumitte DeSoyza; Tel: 718-579-1631; *ILL*, Edward Wallace; Staff 3 (MLS 2, Non-MLS 1)
Library Holdings: Bk Titles 6,000; Per Subs 375
Subject Interests: Cancer, Clinical, Dietetics, Nuclear medicine, Rehabilitation, Spinal cord injury
Partic in BRS; Medical Library Center Of New York; Medline; New York Metrop Ref & Res Libr Agency; Valnet

C FORDHAM UNIVERSITY LIBRARIES,* 441 E Fordham Rd, 10458-5151. SAN 351-9120. Tel: 718-817-3570. FAX: 718-817-3582. Web Site: www.library.fordham.edu. *Dir*, James P McCabe; *Acq, ILL*, Elizabeth Garity; *Syst Coordr, Tech Servs*, Michael Wares; *Circ*, Edmund P Maloney; *Cat*, Eileen Mcardle; *Archivist, Spec Coll*, Patrice Kane; *Online Servs*, Jan Kelsey; *Bibliog Instr*, Peter Patton; Staff 34 (MLS 34)
Founded 1841. Fac 525; Highest Degree: Doctorate
Jul 1997-Jun 1998 Income $6,102,287, State $18,000. Mats Exp $7,276,852, Books $1,058,273, Per/Ser (Incl. Access Fees) $1,187,153, Presv $121,578, Micro $82,108. Sal $2,766,117 (Prof $1,372,011)
Library Holdings: Bk Vols 1,700,000; Per Subs 13,000
Subject Interests: Behav sci, Bus admin, Education, Humanities, Natural science, Soc
Special Collections: American Revolution & Early Federal Americana (Charles Allen Munn Coll); Arts & Architecture (Gambosville Coll); Arts & Architecture: (Gambosville Coll); Crimes & Criminals (McGarry Coll); French Revolution (Joseph Givernaud Coll); Gaelic (McGuire-McLees Coll); The Jesuits (Jesuitica Coll); Vatican (Barberini Coll), microfilm; William Cobbett Coll
Automation Activity & Vendor Info: (Acquisitions) DRA; (Circulation) DRA; (Serials) DRA
Publications: Fordham University Library Handbook; Inside Fordham Libraries (semi-annual)
Partic in New York Metrop Ref & Res Libr Agency; OCLC Online Computer Library Center, Inc; Westchester Acad Libr Dir Orgn
Special Services for the Handicapped

J HOSTOS COMMUNITY COLLEGE LIBRARY,* 475 Grand Concourse, 10451. SAN 310-9097. Tel: 718-518-4211. FAX: 718-518-4206. E-Mail: dadho@mail.hostos.cuny.edu. Web Site; www.cuny.hostos.edu. *Ref*, Jose Diaz; *Ref*, Liu Ching-Leou; *ILL, Publ Servs*, Peijun Jia; Staff 8 (MLS 8)
Founded 1968. Enrl 4,500; Fac 40
Library Holdings: Bk Vols 54,451; Bk Titles 42,743
Subject Interests: Ethnic studies, Sci-tech
Special Collections: Allied Health; Black Studies; College Archives; Spanish American Literature
Publications: Dental Hygiene Bibliography; newsletter; Recent Acquisitions
Partic in New York Metrop Ref & Res Libr Agency; OCLC Online Computer Library Center, Inc

S HUNTINGTON FREE LIBRARY, 9 Westchester Sq, 10461. SAN 310-9135. Tel: 718-829-7770. FAX: 718-829-4875. E-Mail: hflib1@metgate.rmi.net. Web Site: www.binc.org/hfl. *Dir*, Mary B Davis; Staff 4 (MLS 1, Non-MLS 3)
Founded 1892
Library Holdings: Bk Vols 23,000; Per Subs 203
Subject Interests: Anthropology, Archaeology, Art, Current affairs, Ethnology, History, Indians of the entire Western Hemisphere, Lang
Special Collections: Bronx History; Indian Lang Dictionaries; Native American (Indian) Coll, newsp
Restriction: By appointment only
Partic in New York Metrop Ref & Res Libr Agency

M LINCOLN MEDICAL CENTER, Health Sciences Library, 234 E 149th St, 10451. SAN 327-4659. Tel: 718-579-5745. FAX: 718-579-5170. *Dir*, Inna Lipnitskaya
Founded 1971
Library Holdings: Bk Vols 13,000; Bk Titles 2,000; Per Subs 200
Subject Interests: Health sciences
Restriction: Staff use only
Partic in Medical Library Center Of New York

C MANHATTAN COLLEGE, Cardinal Hayes Library, 4513 Manhattan College Pkwy, 10471. SAN 351-9244. Tel: 718-862-7166. FAX: 718-862-7995. Web Site: www.manhattan.edu/library. *Dir*, Harry E Welsh; E-Mail: hwelsh@manhattan.edu; *Tech Servs*, Maire I Duchon; *Publ Servs*, Bro Thomas F O'Connor; *ILL, Ref*, Karen Vanterpool; *Per*, Catherine M Shanley; *Cat*, Bernadette F Lopez-Fitzsimmons; *Electronic Resources*, Stacy Pober. Subject Specialists: *Engineering*, John Gormley; Staff 27 (MLS 8, Non-MLS 19)
Founded 1853. Enrl 2,710; Fac 150; Highest Degree: Master
Jul 1999-Jun 2000 Mats Exp $542,757, Books $201,169, Per/Ser (Incl. Access Fees) $303,648, Presv $15,630, Micro $18,210, Electronic Ref Mat (Incl. Access Fees) $4,100. Sal $751,460 (Prof $287,120)
Library Holdings: Bk Vols 206,481; Bk Titles 159,999; Per Subs 1,329
Special Collections: American Culture (Library of American Civilization), micros; English Literature (Library of English Literature), micro; First Editions (Fales Coll); Lydia Cabrera Coll (Spanish); micro
Automation Activity & Vendor Info: (Circulation) PALS; (OPAC) PALS
Database Vendor: Dialog, Ebsco - EbscoHost, GaleNet, Lexis-Nexis, OCLC - First Search, ProQuest, Silverplatter Information Inc., Wilson - Wilson Web
Publications: Library Locator; Manhattan College Libraries Bulletin; Periodicals in the Libraries of Manhattan College & College of Mt St Vincent
Restriction: In-house use for visitors
Partic in MNSCU/PALS; New York Metrop Ref & Res Libr Agency; OCLC Online Computer Library Center, Inc; WALDO
Departmental Libraries:
CHEMISTRY, Hayden Hall, 10471. SAN 351-9309. Tel: 718-862-7206. Web Site: www.manhattan.edu/library.
Library Holdings: Per Subs 31
ENGINEERING, Corlear Ave & 238th St, 10463. SAN 351-9333. Tel: 718-862-7295. FAX: 718-601-1992. *Librn*, John Gormley
Library Holdings: Bk Vols 24,284; Bk Titles 19,777; Per Subs 277
SONNTAG LIBRARY, Engineering Bldg, Corlear Ave & 238th St, 10463. SAN 351-9368. Tel: 718-862-7266.
Library Holdings: Per Subs 40
Special Collections: Plant Morphogenesis

§C MONROE COLLEGE, Thomas P Schnitzler Library, 2468 Jerome Ave, 10468. Tel: 718-933-6700. FAX: 718-584-4242. Web Site: www.monroecoll.edu/contents.html. *Dir*, Peter Whalley; E-Mail: pwhalley@monroecoll.edu; *Asst Librn*, Shawn Kaba; *Librn*, George Diez
Library Holdings: Bk Titles 40,000; Per Subs 215
Automation Activity & Vendor Info: (Cataloging) PALS; (Circulation) PALS; (OPAC) PALS
Partic in WALDO

MONTEFIORE MEDICAL CENTER
M MOSES DIVISION - TISHMAN LEARNING CENTER HEALTH SCIENCES LIBRARY, 111 E 210th St, 10467. SAN 351-9457. Tel: 718-920-4666. FAX: 718-920-4658. *Dir*, Josefina P Lim; *Assoc Dir*, Sheila Smalling; E-Mail: smalling@aecom.yu.edu; *Circ*, Heather Barnabas
Founded 1926
Library Holdings: Bk Vols 25,000; Bk Titles 12,000; Per Subs 600
Publications: Medical Library News
Partic in Medical Library Center Of New York; New York Metrop Ref & Res Libr Agency

S NEW YORK BOTANICAL GARDEN, The LuEsther T Mertz Library, 200th St & Southern Blvd, 10458-5126. SAN 310-9143. Tel: 718-817-8728. Circulation Tel: 718-817-8560. Reference Tel: 718-817-8604. FAX: 718-817-8956. Web Site: www.nybg.org/bsci/libr. *Dir*, John F Reed; Tel: 718-817-8729, E-Mail: jfreed@nybg.org; *Head, Info Serv*, Susan Fraser; Tel: 718-817-8879, E-Mail: sfraser@nybg.org; *Ser*, Marianne Block; Tel: 718-817-8761, E-Mail: mblock@nybg.org; *Cat*, Eun Hee Cho; Tel: 718-817-8618, E-Mail: echo@nybg.org; *Acq*, Don Wheeler; Tel: 718-817-8752, E-Mail: dwheeler@nybg.org; *Tech Servs*, Harry Chapman; Tel: 718-817-8621, E-Mail: hchapman@nybg.org; *ILL*, Rose Meade; Tel: 718-817-8980, E-Mail: rmeade@nybg.org; *Ref*, Marie Long; E-Mail: mlong@nyby.org; *Ref*, Stephen Sinon; Tel: 718-817-8550, E-Mail: ssinon@nybg.org; *Info Specialist*, Dorie Rosen; Tel: 718-817-8681, E-Mail: drosen@nybg.org; *Spec Coll & Archives*, Olga Marder; Tel: 718-817-8754, E-Mail: omarder@nybg.org. Subject Specialists: *Archives*, Susan Fraser; *Reference*, Susan Fraser; Staff 21 (MLS 8, Non-MLS 13)
Founded 1899
Jul 2000-Jun 2001 Income $1,479,700, State $19,700, Federal $110,000, Parent Institution $1,350,000. Mats Exp $304,730, Books $91,597, Per/Ser (Incl. Access Fees) $187,133, Presv $7,000, Electronic Ref Mat (Incl. Access Fees) $19,000. Sal $713,247 (Prof $572,828)
Library Holdings: Bk Vols 251,302; Bk Titles 106,700; Per Subs 1,920
Subject Interests: Botany, Forestry, Horticulture, Lanscape design, Plant ecology
Special Collections: Botanical Art; Darwiniana (Charles F Cox Coll), mss & archives, Rosaceae (Jean Gordon Coll), artifacts; Lord & Burnham Co, drawings & correspondence; NYBG Archives; Scientific Reprints; Seed & Nursery Catalogs
Automation Activity & Vendor Info: (Acquisitions) Innovative Interfaces Inc.; (Cataloging) Innovative Interfaces Inc.; (Circulation) Innovative Interfaces Inc.; (OPAC) Innovative Interfaces Inc.; (Serials) Innovative Interfaces Inc.
Database Vendor: OCLC - First Search, ProQuest, Silverplatter Information Inc.
Publications: Bibliographies; Guide to Archives & Manuscript Coll (1983); Library Materials Preservation Manual (1982)
Restriction: Non-circulating to the public
Function: Research library

Partic in Council On Botanical Horticultural Libraries; Medical Library Center Of New York; Metro NY Libr Coun; Metrop Regional Res & Ref Libs; OCLC Online Computer Library Center, Inc

M OUR LADY OF MERCY MEDICAL CENTER MEDICAL LIBRARY, 600 E 233rd St, Rm B-11, 10466. SAN 351-9392. Tel: 718-920-9869. FAX: 718-920-9407. *In Charge*, Subiatu Deen
Founded 1958
Library Holdings: Bk Vols 9,738
Partic in Medical Library Center Of New York; New York Metrop Ref & Res Libr Agency

M SAINT BARNABAS HOSPITAL, Medical Library,* Third Ave & 83rd St, 10457-2594. SAN 351-9511. Tel: 718-960-6113. FAX: 718-960-3050. *Dir Libr Serv*, Deborah Bonelli
Library Holdings: Per Subs 295
Publications: Quarterly Newsletter
Partic in BRS; Docline; Nat Libr of Med

C STATE UNIVERSITY OF NEW YORK MARITIME COLLEGE, Stephen B Luce Library, 6 Pennyfield Ave, Fort Schyler, 10465. SAN 310-9186. Tel: 718-409-7231. Reference Tel: 718-409-7230. FAX: 718-409-7256. E-Mail: library@sunymaritime.edu. Web Site: www.sunymaritime.edu. *Librn*, Richard H Corson; Tel: 718-409-7236, E-Mail: rhcorson@sunymaritime.edu; *Head Tech Servs*, Jane Brodsky Fitzpatrick; Tel: 718-409-7229, E-Mail: jfitzpatrick@sunymaritime.edu; *Reader Servs*, John J Lee; E-Mail: jlee@sunymaritime.edu; *Cat*, Elizabeth Leschinsky; Tel: 718-409-7232, E-Mail: eleschinsky@sunymaritime.edu; Staff 9 (MLS 5, Non-MLS 4)
Founded 1946. Enrl 752; Highest Degree: Master
Jul 1999-Jun 2000 Income $113,756, Locally Generated Income $4,118, Parent Institution $100,395, Other $9,243. Mats Exp $136,255, Books $81,809, Per/Ser (Incl. Access Fees) $29,477, Micro $9,228, Electronic Ref Mat (Incl. Access Fees) $15,741. Sal $341,149 (Prof $233,168)
Library Holdings: Bk Vols 82,402
Subject Interests: Marine eng, Merchant marine, Nautical sci, Naval archit, Navigation, Shipping, Ships, Transportation mgt
Special Collections: Marine Casualty Reports; Maritime History; Maritime Research, Technical Reports
Automation Activity & Vendor Info: (Cataloging) MultiLIS; (Circulation) MultiLIS; (OPAC) MultiLIS; (Serials) MultiLIS
Database Vendor: Dialog, GaleNet, IAC - SearchBank, OCLC - First Search
Publications: New Accessions
Function: Archival collection
Partic in Metropolitan New York Library Council; State University Of New York-NYLINK
Friends of the Library Group

S WILDLIFE CONSERVATION SOCIETY, Bronx Zoo, 2300 Southern Blvd, 10460. SAN 310-916X. Tel: 718-220-6874. FAX: 718-220-7114. E-Mail: library@wcs.org. *Tech Servs*, Steven P Johnson; E-Mail: sjohnson@wcs.org; *ILL*, Dale Boles; E-Mail: dboles@wcs.org; Staff 4 (MLS 2, Non-MLS 2)
Founded 1908
Jul 1999-Jun 2000 Income $250,000, State $17,500. Mats Exp $41,000, Books $5,000, Per/Ser (Incl. Access Fees) $36,000
Library Holdings: Bk Vols 10,000; Bk Titles 8,000; Per Subs 200
Subject Interests: Allied sci, Conservation, Mgt of wild animals, Zoo biol
Special Collections: Archival Materials
Automation Activity & Vendor Info: (Acquisitions) CASPR; (Cataloging) CASPR; (Circulation) CASPR; (OPAC) CASPR; (Serials) CASPR
Database Vendor: CARL
Publications: Guide the Archives of the New York Zoological Society
Function: ILL available
Partic in Metro NY Libr Coun; OCLC Online Computer Library Center, Inc

BRONXVILLE

P BRONXVILLE PUBLIC LIBRARY, 201 Pondfield Rd, 10708. SAN 310-9208. Tel: 914-337-7680. FAX: 914-337-0332. *Dir*, Roxane Reese Campagna; *Head Ref*, Vivien Shieh; *Ch Servs*, Kelly Joan; *Ref Servs YA*, Patricia Root; Staff 7 (MLS 3, Non-MLS 4)
Founded 1906. Pop 6,032; Circ 132,047
Jun 2000-May 2001 Income $687,354, State $3,000, City $687,354, Locally Generated Income $5,650. Mats Exp $76,750, Books $32,250, Per/Ser (Incl. Access Fees) $13,000, AV Equip $8,000, Electronic Ref Mat (Incl. Access Fees) $23,500. Sal $195,724
Library Holdings: Bk Vols 65,000; Per Subs 135
Special Collections: Bronxville History Coll; Fine Arts & Japanese Coll, paintings; Local History (Burnett Coll)
Automation Activity & Vendor Info: (Acquisitions) epixtech, inc.; (Circulation) epixtech, inc.; (ILL) epixtech, inc.
Database Vendor: Dialog, Ebsco - EbscoHost, epixtech, inc.
Publications: Friends of the Bronxville Library (newsletter)
Friends of the Library Group

C CONCORDIA COLLEGE, Scheele Memorial Library, 171 White Plains Rd, 10708. SAN 310-9216. Tel: 914-337-9300, Ext 2202. FAX: 914-395-4893. Web Site: www.concordia-ny.edu/scheele.html. *Dir Libr Serv*, Kurt A Bodling; *ILL*, Susan Pfeister; *Librn*, William Clifford; *Media Spec*, Henry Joerz; *Ser*, Fred Gervat; Staff 8 (MLS 4, Non-MLS 4)
Founded 1881. Enrl 531; Fac 45; Highest Degree: Bachelor
Library Holdings: Bk Vols 66,247; Per Subs 460
Subject Interests: Religion, Teacher educ
Special Collections: Library of American Civilization, ultrafiche; Library of English Literature Part I, ultrafiche
Publications: Acquisitions List (monthly)
Partic in State University Of New York-NYLINK

M LAWRENCE HOSPITAL CENTER, Ashley Baker Morrill Health Sciences Library, 55 Palmer Ave, 10708-3491. SAN 310-9224. Tel: 914-787-3014. FAX: 914-787-3309. *Librn*, Virgil C Larkin; E-Mail: vlarkin@healthstar.org; Staff 1 (MLS 1)
Library Holdings: Bk Vols 1,003; Bk Titles 999; Per Subs 137
Subject Interests: Gen med, Hospital administration, Nursing, Surgery, Total quality mgt
Publications: Accessions List (biannually)
Partic in Basic Health Sciences Library Network; Health Info Librs of Westchester; New York Metrop Ref & Res Libr Agency; Westchester Libr Asn

C SARAH LAWRENCE COLLEGE, Esther Raushenbush Library, One Mead Way, 10708. SAN 351-9570. Interlibrary Loan Service Tel: 914-395-2479. Reference Tel: 914-395-2474. FAX: 914-395-2473. E-Mail: library@mail.slc.edu. Web Site: www.slc.edu/library/. *Dir*, Charling Chang Fagan; Tel: 914-395-2471; *Assoc Dir, Coll Develop*, Judith Kicinski; *Access Serv, Govt Doc*, Janet Alexander; *ILL*, Barbara Smolow; *Tech Servs*, David Nicholls; *Circ*, Ann Auriemmo. Subject Specialists: *Music*, Barbara Walzer
Founded 1926. Enrl 1,483; Fac 196; Highest Degree: Master
Jun 1999-May 2000 Income (Main Library Only) $1,397,373. Mats Exp $398,350. Sal $741,687
Library Holdings: Bk Vols 213,860; Per Subs 1,042
Subject Interests: Art, Human genetics, Music, Psychology, Women's hist
Special Collections: Bessie Schoenberg Dance Coll; Sarah Lawrence College Faculty Coll
Automation Activity & Vendor Info: (Acquisitions) PALS; (Cataloging) PALS; (Circulation) PALS; (Course Reserve) PALS; (OPAC) PALS; (Serials) PALS
Partic in New York Metrop Ref & Res Libr Agency; OCLC Online Computer Library Center, Inc; Westchester Acad Libr Dir Orgn
Friends of the Library Group
Departmental Libraries:
MUSIC Tel: 914-395-2375. *Librn*, Barbara Walzer

BROOKHAVEN

P BROOKHAVEN FREE LIBRARY, 273 Beaver Dam Rd, 11719. SAN 310-9232. Tel: 631-286-1923. FAX: 631-286-1923. Web Site: www.suffolk.lib.ny.us/libraries/broo. *Dir*, Elizabeth Burns; Fax: 631-286-0120, E-Mail: eburns@suffolk.lib.ny.us; *Ch Servs*, Deb Domingos; *Tech Servs*, Sheila Otten; *Circ*, Kelli Edwards; Staff 12 (MLS 1, Non-MLS 11)
Founded 1912. Pop 25,010
Jul 2000-Jun 2001 Income $405,441. Mats Exp $35,500, Books $26,200, Per/Ser (Incl. Access Fees) $4,300, Electronic Ref Mat (Incl. Access Fees) $5,000. Sal $233,200 (Prof $48,000)
Library Holdings: Bk Vols 29,623; Bk Titles 27,441; Per Subs 138
Special Collections: Long Island History; Nautical (Bolt Coll)
Automation Activity & Vendor Info: (Cataloging) Innovative Interfaces Inc.; (Circulation) Innovative Interfaces Inc.; (ILL) Innovative Interfaces Inc.; (OPAC) Innovative Interfaces Inc.
Database Vendor: GaleNet, IAC - Info Trac, ProQuest, Wilson - Wilson Web
Publications: Brookhaven Free Library News
Mem of Suffolk Cooperative Library System
Partic in Pals
Homebound delivery service
Friends of the Library Group

BROOKLYN

S ANTIQUE PHONOGRAPH MONTHLY, Library of Recorded Sound,* 502 E 17th St, 11226-6606. SAN 310-9259. Tel: 718-941-6835. FAX: 718-941-1408. Web Site: www.members.aol.com/allenamet/PhonoBooks.html. *Dir*, Allen Koenigsberg
Founded 1968
Library Holdings: Bk Titles 500; Per Subs 10
Subject Interests: 1877-1929, Develop of the phonograph, Early advertising, Electric recording, Growth of Am popular music, Hist of invention of acoustic
Special Collections: APM Cylinder Record Archive (5000 Records); History of Recorded Sound (Antique Phonograph Monthly & APM Monograph Series)
Publications: Newsletter
Restriction: By appointment only
Database & hard copy for The Patent History of the Phonograph

C BORICUA COLLEGE, Special Collections Library,* 186 N Sixth St, 11211. SAN 375-2348. Tel: 718-782-2200. FAX: 718-782-2050. *Dir*, Liza Rivera
Library Holdings: Bk Vols 15,000; Per Subs 50
Special Collections: Special Puerto Rico Coll

M BROOKDALE UNIVERSITY HOSPITAL MEDICAL CENTER, Marie S Schwartz Medical Library, One Brookdale Plaza, 11212. SAN 328-5642. Tel: 718-240-5312. FAX: 718-240-5030. *Dir*, Carol Cave-Davis; E-Mail: ccdavis@brookdale.edu; Staff 3 (MLS 2, Non-MLS 1)
Library Holdings: Bk Titles 2,400; Per Subs 410
Subject Interests: Medicine, Nursing
Partic in Basic Health Sciences Library Network; Brooklyn-Queens-Staten Island Health Sciences Librarians; Health Science Library Information Consortium; Medical Library Center Of New York; New York Metrop Ref & Res Libr Agency

L BROOKLYN BAR ASSOCIATION FOUNDATION INC LIBRARY,* 123 Remsen St, 2nd flr, 11201-4212. SAN 310-9283. Tel: 718-624-0868. FAX: 718-797-1713.
Founded 1872
Library Holdings: Bk Vols 15,000
Subject Interests: Law related govt publications

S BROOKLYN BOTANIC GARDEN LIBRARY, 1000 Washington Ave, 11225. SAN 310-9291. Tel: 718-623-7302. Reference Tel: 718-623-7270. E-Mail: grc@bbg.org (Gardener's Resource Center), library@bbg.org. Web Site: www.bbg.org/library. *Dir*, Patricia Jonas; Tel: 718-623-7271, E-Mail: patjonas@bbg.org; *Info Specialist*, Joan McDonald; Tel: 718-623-7272, E-Mail: joanmcdonald@bbg.org; *ILL*, Atiba Alexander; E-Mail: atibaalexander@bbg.org; *Tech Servs*, Juanmin Wang; Tel: 718-623-7303, E-Mail: jennywang@bbg.org; Staff 3 (MLS 1, Non-MLS 2)
Founded 1911
Library Holdings: Bk Vols 30,000; Bk Titles 25,000; Per Subs 435
Subject Interests: Botany, Ecology, Gardening, Horticulture, Landscape design, Landscaping
Automation Activity & Vendor Info: (Cataloging) Sydney; (Circulation) Sydney; (OPAC) Sydney; (Serials) Sydney
Database Vendor: OCLC - First Search, Silverplatter Information Inc.
Partic in New York Metrop Ref & Res Libr Agency; OCLC Online Computer Library Center, Inc

S BROOKLYN CHILDREN'S MUSEUM, Children's Resource Library, 145 Brooklyn Ave, 11213. SAN 351-9635. Tel: 718-735-4427. FAX: 718-604-7442. *Librn*, Dina Sherman; E-Mail: dsherman@brooklynkids.org
Founded 1899
Library Holdings: Bk Vols 5,000; Per Subs 50
Subject Interests: Anthropology, History, Mus educ, Natural science
Special Collections: Brooklyn Children's Museum Archives, 1899-photog, clippings; Leon Kofod Ethnographic Slide Coll
Partic in New York Metrop Ref & Res Libr Agency

C BROOKLYN COLLEGE LIBRARY,* 2900 Bedford Ave, 11210-2889. SAN 351-9694. Tel: 718-951-5000, Ext 5335, 718-951-5342. Interlibrary Loan Service Tel: 718-951-4414. FAX: 718-951-4557. E-Mail: illbc@cunyvm.cuny.edu. Web Site: www.academics.cuny.edu/library. *Chief Librn*, Barbara Buckner Higginbotham; *Tech Servs*, Judith Wild; *Bibliog Instr*, Frederick Bogin; *Spec Coll*, Anthony Cucchiara; *Syst Coordr*, Howard Spivak; *Assoc Librn, Res*, Miriam Deutsch; *Assoc Librn, Coll Develop*, Susan Vaughn; *Acq*, Bertha Bendelstein; Staff 22 (MLS 22)
Founded 1930. Circ 172,386; Highest Degree: Master
Library Holdings: Bk Vols 1,246,791; Bk Titles 841,065; Per Subs 5,000
Special Collections: Academic Freedom; Brooklyn College Archives (including student publications); Brooklyniana; Colonial, Ethiopian & Somalian History
Automation Activity & Vendor Info: (Acquisitions) NOTIS; (Circulation) NOTIS; (Serials) NOTIS
Partic in Academic Libraries of Brooklyn; New York Metrop Ref & Res Libr Agency; OCLC Online Computer Library Center, Inc
Friends of the Library Group
Departmental Libraries:
MUSIC, Gershwin Hall, 2900 Bedford Ave, 11210-2889. SAN 351-9724. Tel: 718-951-5844. E-Mail: rahbc@cunyvm.cuny.edu. Web Site: www.academics.cuny.edu/library. *Librn*, Honora Raphael
Friends of the Library Group

S BROOKLYN HISTORICAL SOCIETY LIBRARY, 2 Metrotech Center, Ste 4200, 4th Flr, 11201. SAN 310-9402. Tel: 718-254-9830. FAX: 718-254-9869.
Founded 1863
Library Holdings: Bk Vols 150,000
Special Collections: 19th Century Furniture and Artifacts; 19th Century Paintings & Prints Coll; Brooklyn & Long Island History; Decorative Arts; Family History; Genealogy; Newspaper Clipping Index; Photographs & Postcards
Publications: Newsletters; Past Publication List
Partic in New York Metrop Ref & Res Libr Agency; OCLC Online Computer Library Center, Inc

M BROOKLYN HOSPITAL CENTER, Medical Library, 121 DeKalb Ave, 11201. SAN 310-9313. Tel: 718-250-6943, 718-250-6944. FAX: 718-250-6428. E-Mail: bhc1@metgate.metro.org. *Librn*, Narciso Rodriguez
Founded 1928
Library Holdings: Bk Vols 3,300; Bk Titles 1,500; Per Subs 130
Subject Interests: Health sci
Restriction: Not open to public
Partic in Docline; Medline

CL BROOKLYN LAW SCHOOL LIBRARY, 250 Joralemon St, 11201. SAN 310-9321. Tel: 718-780-7973. Reference Tel: 718-780-7567. FAX: 718-780-0369. Web Site: brkl.brooklaw.edu. *Dir*, Sara Robbins; Tel: 718-780-7980, E-Mail: srobbins@brooklaw.edu; *Assoc Librn*, Linda Holmes; Tel: 718-780-7974, E-Mail: lhomes@brooklaw.edu; *Head, Ser Acq*, H C Singh; Tel: 718-780-7976, E-Mail: hsingh@brooklaw.edu; *Head, Cat*, George Prager; Tel: 718-780-7978, E-Mail: gprager@brooklaw.edu; *Cat*, Maria Okonska; Tel: 718-780-7977, E-Mail: mokonaska@brooklaw.edu; *Govt Doc*, Rosemary Campagna; Tel: 718-780-7580, E-Mail: rcampag@brooklaw.edu; *Ref*, Jean Davis; Tel: 718-780-7534, E-Mail: jdavis@brooklaw.edu; *Ref*, James Murphy; Tel: 718-780-7544, E-Mail: jmurphy@brooklaw.edu; *Ref*, Deborah Paulus; Tel: 718-780-7981, E-Mail: dpaulus@brooklaw.edu; *Info Specialist*, Victoria Szymczak; Tel: 718-780-7975, E-Mail: vszymc@brooklaw.edu; *Info Tech*, Hainan Yu; Tel: 718-780-7910, E-Mail: hyu@brooklaw.edu; Staff 21 (MLS 11, Non-MLS 10)
Founded 1904. Enrl 1,480; Fac 65; Highest Degree: Doctorate
Library Holdings: Bk Vols 236,567; Bk Titles 60,043; Per Subs 2,789
Subject Interests: Am law, Comparative law, Foreign law, International law
Special Collections: International Law; Women & the Law
Automation Activity & Vendor Info: (Acquisitions) Innovative Interfaces Inc.; (Cataloging) Innovative Interfaces Inc.; (Circulation) Innovative Interfaces Inc.; (Course Reserve) Innovative Interfaces Inc.; (OPAC) Innovative Interfaces Inc.; (Serials) Innovative Interfaces Inc.
Database Vendor: Dialog, IAC - SearchBank, Lexis-Nexis, OCLC - First Search
Publications: Brooklyn Law School Library Guide (Library handbook)
Function: Research library
Partic in OCLC Online Computer Library Center, Inc

BROOKLYN MUSEUM OF ART

S LIBRARIES & ARCHIVES, 200 Eastern Pkwy, 11238. SAN 351-9759. Tel: 718-638-5000, Ext 308. FAX: 718-638-5080. *Librn*, Deirdre E Lawrence; Staff 8 (MLS 3, Non-MLS 5)
Founded 1823
2000-2001 Mats Exp Books $50,000
Library Holdings: Bk Vols 200,000; Per Subs 2,000
Subject Interests: African, American painting, Americas, Archaeology, Asian art, Costumes, Decorative arts, Drawings, European painting, Islamic art, Pacific, Prints, Sculpture, Textiles
Special Collections: Artists Books; Documentary Photographs; Museum Archives; Original Costume & Fashion Sketches (1900-1950)
Restriction: By appointment only
Partic in Research Libraries Group, Inc; RLIN

S WILBOUR LIBRARY OF EGYPTOLOGY, 200 Eastern Pkwy, 11238. SAN 351-9783. Tel: 718-638-5000, Ext 215. FAX: 718-638-5080.; Staff 2 (MLS 1, Non-MLS 1)
Founded 1934
Subject Interests: Archaeology, Art, Egypt, Geography, Geology, Nubiology, Philology, Religion, Travel
Special Collections: Egyptology (Seyffarth Coll), mss
Restriction: By appointment only
Partic in RLIN

P BROOKLYN PUBLIC LIBRARY, Grand Army Plaza, 11238-5698. SAN 351-9813. Tel: 718-230-2100. Interlibrary Loan Service Tel: 718-230-2187. FAX: 718-398-3947. Web Site: www.brooklynpubliclibrary.org. *Exec Dir*, Martin Gomez; Tel: 718-230-2403; *Publ Servs*, Sofia Sequenzia; Tel: 718-230-2408; *Info Tech*, Selvon Smith; Tel: 718-230-2493; *Coll Develop*, Barbara Genco; Tel: 718-230-2138; *Planning Services*, Elisabeth Martin; Tel: 718-230-2166
Founded 1897. Pop 2,300,664; Circ 10,916,696
Jul 1999-Jun 2000 Income (Main Library and Branch Library) $75,700,000, State $7,100,000, City $63,200,000, Federal $400,000, Locally Generated Income $3,400,000, Other $1,600,000. Mats Exp $10,000,000, Books $8,405,442, Per/Ser (Incl. Access Fees) $533,108, Presv $50,000, Micro $95,000, AV Equip $109,450, Electronic Ref Mat (Incl. Access Fees) $807,000. Sal $53,200,000
Library Holdings: Bk Vols 6,970,900
Special Collections: Brooklyn Coll
Partic in OCLC Online Computer Library Center, Inc
Friends of the Library Group
Branches: 60
ARLINGTON, 203 Arlington Ave, 11207. SAN 351-9872. Tel: 718-277-6105. FAX: 718-277-6177. Web Site: www.brooklynpubliclibrary.org. *Librn*, William Lewnes
Library Holdings: Bk Vols 72,950
Friends of the Library Group
BAY RIDGE BRANCH, 7223 Ridge Blvd, 11209. SAN 351-9902. Tel: 718-748-5709. FAX: 718-748-7226. Web Site: www.brooklynpubliclibrary.org.

Librn, Helen Belmonte
Library Holdings: Bk Vols 52,791
Friends of the Library Group
BEDFORD BRANCH, 496 Franklin Ave, 11238. SAN 351-9937. Tel: 718-623-0012. FAX: 718-623-0036. Web Site: www.brooklynpubliclibrary.org. *Librn*, Robert Nerboso
Library Holdings: Bk Vols 58,802
BOROUGH PARK BRANCH, 1265 43rd St, 11219. SAN 351-9961. Tel: 718-437-4085. FAX: 718-437-3021. Web Site: www.brooklynpubliclibrary.org. *Librn*, Catherine Gray
Library Holdings: Bk Vols 115,794
BRIGHTON BEACH BRANCH, 16 Brighton First Rd, 11235. SAN 351-9996. Tel: 718-946-2917. FAX: 718-946-6176. Web Site: www.brooklynpubliclibrary.org. *Librn*, Elizabeth Acerra
Library Holdings: Bk Vols 85,390
Friends of the Library Group
BROOKLYN HEIGHTS BRANCH, 280 Cadman Plaza W, 11201. SAN 352-0021. Tel: 718-623-7100. FAX: 718-222-5681. Web Site: www.brooklynpubliclibrary.org. *Librn*, Mady Kiner
Library Holdings: Bk Vols 74,732
Friends of the Library Group
BROWER PARK BRANCH, 725 Saint Marks Ave, 11216. SAN 352-0056. Tel: 718-773-7208. FAX: 718-773-7838. Web Site: www.brooklynpubliclibrary.org. *Librn*, Sharon Lahey
Library Holdings: Bk Vols 54,525
Friends of the Library Group
BROWNSVILLE BRANCH, 61 Glenmore Ave, 11212. SAN 352-0080. Tel: 718-498-9721. FAX: 718-498-4071. Web Site: www.brooklynpubliclibrary.org. *Librn*, Linda Cohen
Library Holdings: Bk Vols 43,892
Friends of the Library Group
BUSHWICK BRANCH, 340 Bushwick Ave, 11206. SAN 352-0110. Tel: 718-602-1348. FAX: 718-602-1352. Web Site: www.brooklynpubliclibrary.org. *Librn*, Thomas Brogan
Library Holdings: Bk Vols 72,060
BUSINESS, 280 Cadman Plaza W, 11201. SAN 352-0145. Tel: 718-623-7000. FAX: 718-222-5679. Web Site: www.brooklynpubliclibrary.org. *Librn*, Susan Phillis
Library Holdings: Bk Vols 139,276
Friends of the Library Group
CANARSIE BRANCH, 1580 Rockaway Pkwy, 11236. SAN 352-017X. Tel: 718-257-6547. FAX: 718-257-6557. Web Site: www.brooklynpubliclibrary.org. *Librn*, Sharon Owens
Library Holdings: Bk Vols 70,131
Friends of the Library Group
CARROLL GARDENS BRANCH, 396 Clinton St, 11231. SAN 352-020X. Tel: 718-596-6972. FAX: 718-596-0370. Web Site: www.brooklynpubliclibrary.org. *Librn*, Uldis Skrodelis
Library Holdings: Bk Vols 59,763
Friends of the Library Group
CLARENDON, 2035 Nostrand Ave, 11210. SAN 352-0234. Tel: 718-421-1159. FAX: 718-421-1244. Web Site: www.brooklynpubliclibrary.org. *Librn*, Nanella Warren
Library Holdings: Bk Vols 63,749
Friends of the Library Group
CLINTON HILL, 380 Washington Ave, 11238. SAN 352-0269. Tel: 718-398-8713. FAX: 718-398-8715. Web Site: www.brooklynpubliclibrary.org. *Librn*, Michael McKegney
Library Holdings: Bk Vols 68,130
Friends of the Library Group
CONEY ISLAND, 1901 Mermaid Ave, 11224. SAN 352-0293. Tel: 718-265-3220. FAX: 718-265-5026. Web Site: www.brooklynpubliclibrary.org. *Librn*, Sharon Resen
Library Holdings: Bk Vols 58,602
CORTELYOU, 1305 Cortelyou Rd, 11226. SAN 352-0315. Tel: 718-693-7763. FAX: 718-693-7874. Web Site: www.brooklynpubliclibrary.org. *Librn*, Mary Jo Cullinan
Library Holdings: Bk Vols 60,000
Friends of the Library Group
CROWN HEIGHTS, 560 New York Ave, 11225. SAN 352-0323. Tel: 718-773-1180. FAX: 718-773-0144. Web Site: www.brooklynpubliclibrary.org. *Librn*, Ronglin Wan
Library Holdings: Bk Vols 37,473
CYPRESS HILLS, 1197 Sutter Ave, 11208. SAN 352-0358. Tel: 718-277-6004. FAX: 718-277-6009. Web Site: www.brooklynpubliclibrary.org. *Librn*, Eleanore Kilpatrick
Library Holdings: Bk Vols 71,965
Friends of the Library Group
DE KALB, 790 Bushwick Ave, 11221. SAN 352-0382. Tel: 718-455-3898. FAX: 718-455-4071. Web Site: www.brooklynpubliclibrary.org. *Librn*, Zezlie Blyden
Library Holdings: Bk Vols 78,970
Friends of the Library Group
DYKER, 8202 13th Ave, 11228. SAN 352-0412. Tel: 718-748-6261. FAX: 718-748-6370. Web Site: www.brooklynpubliclibrary.org. *Librn*, Ali Huang
Library Holdings: Bk Vols 62,724
EAST FLATBUSH, 9612 Church Ave, 11212. SAN 352-0447. Tel: 718-922-0927. FAX: 718-922-2394. Web Site: www.brooklynpubliclibrary.org. *Librn*, Sylvia Scofield
Library Holdings: Bk Vols 64,142
EASTERN PARKWAY, 1044 Eastern Pkwy, 11213. SAN 352-0471. Tel: 718-953-4225. FAX: 718-953-3970. Web Site: www.brooklynpubliclibrary.org. *Librn*, Sheila Eastmond
Library Holdings: Bk Vols 44,395
FLATBUSH, 22 Linden Blvd, 11226. SAN 352-0501. Tel: 718-856-0813. FAX: 718-856-0899. Web Site: www.brooklynpubliclibrary.org. *Librn*, Negla Ross-Parris
Library Holdings: Bk Vols 54,210
Friends of the Library Group
FLATLANDS, 2065 Flatbush Ave, 11234. SAN 352-0536. Tel: 718-253-4409. FAX: 718-253-5018. Web Site: www.brooklynpubliclibrary.org. *Librn*, Antoinette Vasile
Library Holdings: Bk Vols 73,675
FORT HAMILTON, 9424 Fourth Ave, 11209. SAN 352-0560. Tel: 718-748-6919. FAX: 718-748-7335. Web Site: www.brooklynpubliclibrary.org. *Librn*, Soe Soe Win
Library Holdings: Bk Vols 56,000
Friends of the Library Group
GERRITSEN BEACH, 2808 Gerritsen Ave, 11229. SAN 352-0595. Tel: 718-368-1435. FAX: 718-368-1506. Web Site: www.brooklynpubliclibrary.org. *Librn*, Edward Flanagan
Library Holdings: Bk Vols 70,851
Friends of the Library Group
GRAVESEND, 303 Avenue X, 11223. SAN 352-0625. Tel: 718-302-5792. FAX: 718-627-2426. Web Site: www.brooklynpubliclibrary.org. *Librn*, Barry Ernst
Library Holdings: Bk Vols 64,390
GREENPOINT, 107 Norman Ave, 11223. SAN 352-065X. Tel: 718-349-8504. FAX: 718-349-8790. Web Site: www.brooklynpubliclibrary.org. *Librn*, David Mills
Library Holdings: Bk Vols 39,000
Friends of the Library Group
HIGHLAWN, 1664 W 13th St, 11223. SAN 352-0684. Tel: 718-234-7208. FAX: 718-234-7238. Web Site: www.brooklynpubliclibrary.org. *Librn*, Eileen Kassab
Library Holdings: Bk Vols 65,481
HOMECREST, 2525 Coney Island Ave, 11223. SAN 352-0714. Tel: 718-382-5924. FAX: 718-382-5955. Web Site: www.brooklynpubliclibrary.org. *Librn*, Rita Kuenstler
Library Holdings: Bk Vols 71,206
JAMAICA BAY BRANCH, 9727 Seaview Ave, 11236. SAN 352-0749. Tel: 718-241-3571. FAX: 718-241-1981. Web Site: www.brooklynpubliclibrary.org. *Librn*, Shirley Hall
Library Holdings: Bk Vols 60,112
Friends of the Library Group
KENSINGTON BRANCH, 410 Ditmas Ave, 11218. SAN 352-0773. Tel: 718-435-9431. FAX: 718-435-9491. Web Site: www.brooklynpubliclibrary.org. *Librn*, George Conwell
Library Holdings: Bk Vols 37,207
Friends of the Library Group
KINGS BAY, 3650 Nostrand Ave, 11229. SAN 352-0803. Tel: 718-368-1709. FAX: 718-368-1410. Web Site: www.brooklynpubliclibrary.org. *Librn*, Rosemary Mesh
Library Holdings: Bk Vols 117,495
KINGS HIGHWAY, 2115 Ocean Ave, 11229. SAN 352-0811. Tel: 718-375-3037. FAX: 718-376-3111. Web Site: www.brooklynpubliclibrary.org. *Librn*, Judy Susser
Library Holdings: Bk Vols 130,601
LEONARD, 81 Devoe St, 11211. SAN 352-0838. Tel: 718-486-3365. FAX: 718-486-3370. Web Site: www.brooklynpubliclibrary.org. *Librn*, Leslie Ogan
Library Holdings: Bk Vols 28,819
MACON, 361 Lewis Ave, 11233. SAN 352-0897. Tel: 718-573-5651. FAX: 718-573-5817. Web Site: www.brooklynpubliclibrary.org. *Librn*, Shirley Gaines
Library Holdings: Bk Vols 53,572
Friends of the Library Group
MAPLETON, 1702 60th St, 11204. SAN 352-0927. Tel: 718-256-2117. FAX: 718-256-2215. Web Site: www.brooklynpubliclibrary.org. *Librn*, Gaetano Verdini
Library Holdings: Bk Vols 88,708
Friends of the Library Group
MARCY, 617 DeKalb Ave, 11216. SAN 352-0951. Tel: 718-935-0032. FAX: 718-935-0045. Web Site: www.brooklynpubliclibrary.org. *Librn*, Dionne Mack
Library Holdings: Bk Vols 62,379
Friends of the Library Group
MCKINLEY PARK, 6802 Fort Hamilton Pkwy, 11219. SAN 352-0862. Tel: 718-748-8001. FAX: 718-748-7746. Web Site: www.brooklynpubliclibrary.org. *Librn*, William Senneck
Library Holdings: Bk Vols 71,450

Friends of the Library Group
MIDWOOD, 975 E 16th St, 11230. SAN 352-0986. Tel: 718-252-0967. FAX: 718-252-1263. Web Site: www.brooklynpubliclibrary.org. *Librn*, Rosita McCleavey
Library Holdings: Bk Vols 97,217
Friends of the Library Group
MILL BASIN, 2385 Ralph Ave, 11234. SAN 352-101X. Tel: 718-241-3973. FAX: 718-241-1957. Web Site: www.brooklynpubliclibrary.org. *Librn*, Steven Rosenberg
Library Holdings: Bk Vols 70,011
Friends of the Library Group
NEW LOTS, 665 New Lots Ave, 11207. SAN 352-1044. Tel: 718-649-0311. FAX: 718-649-0719. Web Site: www.brooklynpubliclibrary.org. *Librn*, John Schwab
Library Holdings: Bk Vols 81,629
Friends of the Library Group
NEW UTRECHT, 1743 86th St, 11214. SAN 352-1079. Tel: 718-236-4086. FAX: 718-234-7702. Web Site: www.brooklynpubliclibrary.org. *Librn*, Edward Jelen
Library Holdings: Bk Vols 99,207
Friends of the Library Group
PACIFIC, 25 Fourth Ave, 11217. SAN 352-1109. Tel: 718-638-5180. FAX: 718-638-1580. Web Site: www.brooklynpubliclibrary.org. *Librn*, Julia Mah
Library Holdings: Bk Vols 33,209
Friends of the Library Group
PAERDEGAT, 850 E 59th St, 11234. SAN 352-1133. Tel: 718-241-3994. FAX: 718-241-1335. Web Site: www.brooklynpubliclibrary.org. *Librn*, Ianthee Williams
Library Holdings: Bk Vols 71,357
PARK SLOPE, 431 Sixth Ave, 11215. SAN 352-1168. Tel: 718-832-1853. FAX: 718-832-9024. Web Site: www.brooklynpubliclibrary.org. *Librn*, Ann Kalkhoff
Library Holdings: Bk Vols 79,537
Friends of the Library Group
RED HOOK, 7 Wolcott St, 11231. SAN 352-1192. Tel: 718-935-0203. FAX: 718-935-0160. Web Site: www.brooklynpubliclibrary.org. *Librn*, Paul Van Linden Tol
Library Holdings: Bk Vols 47,169
Friends of the Library Group
RUGBY, 1000 Utica Ave, 11203. SAN 352-1222. Tel: 718-566-0054. FAX: 718-566-0059. Web Site: www.brooklynpubliclibrary.org. *Librn*, Chandra Anthey
Library Holdings: Bk Vols 67,819
Friends of the Library Group
RYDER, 5902 23rd Ave, 11204. SAN 352-1257. Tel: 718-331-2962. FAX: 718-331-3445. Web Site: www.brooklynpubliclibrary.org. *Librn*, Donna Hubbard
Library Holdings: Bk Vols 41,264
Friends of the Library Group
SARATOGA, 8 Thomas S Boyland St, 11233. SAN 352-1281. Tel: 718-573-5224. FAX: 718-573-5402. Web Site: www.brooklynpubliclibrary.org. *Librn*, Lijia Lin
Library Holdings: Bk Vols 81,628
Friends of the Library Group
SERVICE TO THE AGING, 2115 Ocean Ave, 11229. SAN 352-1273. Tel: 718-376-6185. FAX: 718-376-3222. Web Site: www.brooklynpubliclibrary.org. *Librn*, Jo Ann Radioli
SHEEPSHEAD BAY, 2636 E 14th St, 11235. SAN 352-1311. Tel: 718-368-1815. FAX: 718-368-1872. Web Site: www.brooklynpubliclibrary.org. *Librn*, Yelena Litinskaya
Library Holdings: Bk Vols 79,008
SPRING CREEK, 12143 Flatlands Ave, 11207. SAN 352-1346. Tel: 718-257-6571. FAX: 718-257-6588. Web Site: www.brooklynpubliclibrary.org. *Librn*, Gerald Radioli
Library Holdings: Bk Vols 55,072
STONE AVENUE, 581 Stone Ave, 11212. SAN 352-1370. Tel: 718-485-8347. FAX: 718-485-8731. Web Site: www.brooklynpubliclibrary.org. *Librn*, Anthony Murray
Library Holdings: Bk Vols 71,164
Friends of the Library Group
SUNSET PARK, 5108 Fourth Ave, 11220. SAN 352-1400. Tel: 718-567-2806. FAX: 718-567-2810. Web Site: www.brooklynpubliclibrary.org. *Librn*, Opal Brown-Lindsay
Library Holdings: Bk Vols 81,816
Friends of the Library Group
ULMER PARK, 2602 Bath Ave, 11214. SAN 352-1435. Tel: 718-265-3443. FAX: 718-265-5115. Web Site: www.brooklynpubliclibrary.org. *Librn*, Yvonne Zhou
Library Holdings: Bk Vols 62,000
WALT WHITMAN BRANCH, 93 Saint Edwards St, 11205. SAN 352-146X. Tel: 718-935-0244. FAX: 718-935-0284. Web Site: www.brooklynpubliclibrary.org. *Librn*, William Knapp
Library Holdings: Bk Vols 39,635
Friends of the Library Group
WASHINGTON IRVING BRANCH, 360 Irving Ave, 11237. SAN 352-1494. Tel: 718-628-8378. FAX: 718-628-8439. Web Site: www.brooklynpubliclibrary.org. *Librn*, Phyllis Lu
Library Holdings: Bk Vols 71,624
WILLIAMSBURGH, 240 Division Ave, 11211. SAN 352-1524. Tel: 718-302-3485. FAX: 718-302-3499. Web Site: www.brooklynpubliclibrary.org. *Librn*, Joyce Jackson
Library Holdings: Bk Vols 62,883
WINDSOR TERRACE, 160 E Fifth St, 11218. SAN 352-1559. Tel: 718-686-9707. FAX: 718-686-0162. Web Site: www.brooklynpubliclibrary.org. *Librn*, Lyubov Klavansky
Library Holdings: Bk Vols 56,556
Friends of the Library Group

M CONEY ISLAND HOSPITAL, Harold Fink Memorial Library, 2601 Ocean Pkwy, 11235. SAN 352-1583. Tel: 718-616-3000, 718-616-4158. FAX: 718-616-4178. *Dir*, Munir U Din; *Asst Librn*, Rose Delgaudio; Staff 1 (MLS 1)
Library Holdings: Bk Vols 8,100; Bk Titles 6,300; Per Subs 325
Subject Interests: Gynecology, Med hospital admin, Medicine, Nursing, Obstetrics, Pediatrics, Pharm, Podiatry, Surgery
Publications: Journal Holdings; Library News
Restriction: Staff use only
Partic in Basic Health Sciences Library Network; Brooklyn-Queens-Staten Island Health Sciences Librarians; National Network Of Libraries Of Medicine - South Central Region; New York Metrop Ref & Res Libr Agency

GM DEPARTMENT OF VETERANS AFFAIRS, Medical Center Library Service (142D),* 800 Poly Pl, 11209. SAN 310-9534. Tel: 718-836-6600, Ext 3559. FAX: 718-630-3573. *Chief Librn*, Francine Tidona; *Librn*, Robert Hall; Staff 4 (MLS 2, Non-MLS 2)
Library Holdings: Per Subs 318
Subject Interests: Allied health, Health admin, Medicine, Nursing, Patient educ, Psychology, Surgery
Partic in Dialog Corporation; Medical Library Center Of New York; Medline; Metro Atlanta Library Association; New York State Interlibrary Loan Network; Veterans Affairs Library Network

S DIVISION OF BILINGUAL EDUCATION, Resource Library,* 131 Livingston St, Rm 204, 11201. SAN 327-4691. Tel: 718-935-3905. FAX: 718-935-4901. *Librn*, Carmen Gloria Burgos

S DOMINO SUGAR CORP, Research & Development Library,* 266 Kent Ave, 11211. SAN 327-7526. Tel: 718-387-6800, Ext 3370. FAX: 718-486-4492. *Librn*, Paulette Meltzer
Library Holdings: Bk Titles 6,000; Per Subs 1,000
Subject Interests: Microbiology
Special Collections: Research Reports Database (in-house)

INTERFAITH MEDICAL CENTER
M ATLANTIC AVE MEDICAL LIBRARY, 1545 Atlantic Ave, 11213. SAN 310-9348. Tel: 718-604-6030. FAX: 718-604-6033. *Librn*, Jacqueline Heller; *Asst Librn*, Joyce Evans
Founded 1952
Library Holdings: Bk Titles 2,500; Per Subs 102
Subject Interests: Gynecology, Obstetrics, Pediatrics
Partic in Brooklyn-Queens-Staten Island Health Sciences Librarians; Greater NE Regional Med Libr Program; Medical Libr Asn; Nat Libr of Med
M PROSPECT PLACE MEDICAL & NURSING LIBRARY, 555 Prospect Pl, 11238. SAN 352-1672. Tel: 718-935-7085. FAX: 718-935-7019. E-Mail: imclib2@metgate.metro.org. *Librn*, Jacqueline Heller; Staff 3 (MLS 1, Non-MLS 2)
Founded 1896
Library Holdings: Bk Titles 4,906; Per Subs 210
Subject Interests: Allied sci, Med sci

J KINGSBOROUGH COMMUNITY COLLEGE, Robert J Kibbee Library, 2001 Oriental Blvd, 11235. SAN 310-9372. Tel: 718-368-5632. Interlibrary Loan Service Tel: 718-368-5639. Circulation Tel: 718-368-5637. FAX: 718-368-5482. Interlibrary Loan Service FAX: 718-368-5481. Web Site: www.kbcc.cuny.edu/library/library.htm. *Prof*, Coleridge Orr; Tel: 718-368-5444, E-Mail: corr@kbcc.cuny.edu; *ILL, Per, Ser*, Sharad Karkhanis; E-Mail: skarkhanis@kbcc.cuny.edu; *Archivist, Cat, Tech Servs*, Roberta Pike; Tel: 718-368-5471, E-Mail: tepkb@cunyvm.cuny.edu; *Acq, Coll Develop*, Jeanne Galvin; Tel: 718-368-5429, E-Mail: jdgalvin@prodigy.net; *Circ*, Josephine Murphy; Tel: 718-368-5438, E-Mail: jmurphy@kbcc.cuny.edu; *Ref*, Angelo Tripicchio; Tel: 718-368-5428, E-Mail: atripicchio@kbcc.cuny.edu; Staff 10 (MLS 9, Non-MLS 1)
Founded 1964. Enrl 14,400; Fac 293; Highest Degree: Associate
Jul 1998-Jun 1999 Mats Exp $288,221, Books $205,165, Presv $4,830, Micro $74,103, AV Equip $4,123. Sal $860,063 (Prof $579,863)
Library Holdings: Bk Vols 142,921; Bk Titles 118,217; Per Subs 471
Subject Interests: Broadcasting tech, Fisheries and marine tech, Judaica, Nursing, Puppetry, Travel and tourism
Special Collections: Coney Island Chamber of Commerce Coll; Kingsborough Community College Administrative Reports, College Catalogs, Yearbooks; Kingsborough Historical Society Coll, bks, memorabilia, music, newsp & photogs; Manhattan Beach (Herman Field Coll), photogs
Publications: Bibliographic Instruction Sheets; Faculty Library Handbook;

Guide to Kingsborough Community College Library; Using CUNY+ & Finding Books in CUNY+
Partic in New York Metrop Ref & Res Libr Agency; State University Of New York-NYLINK

M KINGSBROOK JEWISH MEDICAL CENTER, Medical Library,* 585 Schenectady Ave, 11203. SAN 310-9399. Tel: 718-604-5689. FAX: 718-604-5539. *Librn*, Mary Buchheit
Founded 1925
Library Holdings: Bk Titles 2,458; Per Subs 410
Subject Interests: Clinical medicine, Neurology, Orthopedics
Restriction: Not open to public
Partic in Basic Health Sciences Library Network; Brooklyn-Queens-Staten Island Health Sciences Librarians

S THE KURDISH LIBRARY, 144 Underhill Ave. (Mail add: 345 Park Pl, 11238), SAN 329-2096. Tel: 718-783-7930. FAX: 718-398-4365. E-Mail: kurdishlib@aol.com. *Dir*, Vera Beaudin Saeedpour
Founded 1986
Library Holdings: Bk Vols 1,500; Bk Titles 2,500
Special Collections: Archibald Roosevelt Jr, pamphlets, newspapers from Mahabad Republic, 1946; Dana Adams Schmidt Photographic Coll on Iraqi Kurdistan 1965; Kurd & US Foreign Policy Coll
Publications: Kurdish Life (quarterly update of news & views); Kurdish Proverbs; The International Journal of Kurdish Studies (semi-annual journal)
Function: Research library

M LONG ISLAND COLLEGE HOSPITAL, Morgan Health Sciences Library, 339 Hicks St, 11201. SAN 327-4675. Tel: 718-780-1077. FAX: 718-780-1608. E-Mail: lich1@rmi.net. *Dir*, George A Wahlert; Staff 4 (MLS 1, Non-MLS 3)
Library Holdings: Bk Titles 3,500; Per Subs 370

C LONG ISLAND UNIVERSITY, Brooklyn Library, One University Plaza, 11201-9926. SAN 352-1737. Tel: 718-488-1081. Circulation Tel: 718-488-1338. Reference Tel: 718-780-4513. FAX: 718-780-4057. Web Site: www.liu.edu/cwis/bklyn/library/home2.htm. *Dean of Libr*, Dr Constance Woo; E-Mail: constance.woo@liu.edu; *Publ Servs*, Peter Salber; Tel: 718-780-4180, E-Mail: peter.salber@liu.edu; *Coll Develop*, Zary Mostashari; Tel: 718-488-1036, E-Mail: zary.mostashari@liu.edu; *Acq*, Paolina Taglienti; Tel: 718-780-4581, E-Mail: paolina.taglienti@liu.edu; *Bibliog Instr*, Annmarie Singh; Tel: 718-780-4067, E-Mail: annmarie.singh@liu.edu; *Cat*, Ari Cohen; Tel: 718-488-1309, E-Mail: ari.cohen@liu.edu; *Ref*, Denise Millman; Tel: 718-488-1315, E-Mail: denise.millman@liu.edu; *Media Spec*, Andrea Slonosky; Tel: 718-488-1311, E-Mail: andrea.slonosky@liu.edu; *Info Tech*, Songqian Lu; Tel: 718-246-6352, E-Mail: songqian.lu@liu.edu; Staff 34 (MLS 17, Non-MLS 17)
Founded 1927. Enrl 5,881; Fac 484; Highest Degree: Doctorate
Sep 2000-Aug 2001 Income $2,985,600, State $12,000, Parent Institution $2,973,600. Mats Exp $1,094,000. Sal $1,879,600
Library Holdings: Bk Vols 240,490; Bk Titles 157,806; Per Subs 2,404
Special Collections: 19th & 20th Century Black Social & Economic Documents (Eato Aid Society Coll, William Hamilton Relief Society Coll & New York African Society for Mutual Relief Coll); Urban Architecture & City Planning (Robert Weinberg Coll), bks, correspondence, drawings, papers, artists' bks
Automation Activity & Vendor Info: (Acquisitions) epixtech, inc.; (Cataloging) epixtech, inc.; (Circulation) epixtech, inc.; (OPAC) epixtech, inc.; (Serials) epixtech, inc.
Database Vendor: epixtech, inc., GaleNet, OCLC - First Search
Publications: Library Leaves (Newsletter)
Partic in Academic Libraries of Brooklyn; Dialog Corporation; New York Metrop Ref & Res Libr Agency; OCLC Online Computer Library Center, Inc; Westchester Acad Libr Dir Orgn

M LUTHERAN MEDICAL CENTER, Medical Library,* 150 55th St, 11220. SAN 310-9410. Tel: 718-630-7200. FAX: 718-630-8918. *Dir*, Jenny Kakleas; Staff 1 (MLS 1)
Founded 1893
Library Holdings: Bk Titles 6,250; Per Subs 232
Subject Interests: Dentistry, Family practice, Internal medicine, Nursing, Obstetrics and gynecology, Pathology, Pediatrics, Radiology, Surgery
Partic in BHSL; BQSI; Medline

M MAIMONIDES MEDICAL CENTER, Medical Library, 4802 Tenth Ave, 11219. SAN 310-9429. Tel: 718-283-7406. FAX: 718-283-7063. *Dir*, Lydia Friedman
Founded 1952
1999-2000 Mats Exp $106,000, Books $26,000, Per/Ser (Incl. Access Fees) $80,000
Library Holdings: Bk Titles 4,711; Per Subs 302
Subject Interests: Anesthesiology, Dentistry, Medicine, Nursing, Obstetrics and gynecology, Pediatrics, Psychiatry, Surgery
Special Collections: Judaica Collection
Database Vendor: OVID Technologies
Restriction: Staff use only
Function: Professional lending library
Partic in BHSL; BQSI; Metropolitan New York Library Council

C MEDGAR EVERS COLLEGE OF THE CITY OF NEW YORK LIBRARY,* 1650 Bedford Ave, 11225. SAN 310-9437. Tel: 718-270-4873. FAX: 718-270-5147. Interlibrary Loan Service FAX: 718-270-4890. Web Site: www.mec.cuny.edu/library.html. *In Charge*, Dr John P Martin; Tel: 718-270-4881, Fax: 718-270-5182, E-Mail: jmartin@mec.cuny.edu; *Bibliog Instr*, Yvonne S Bennett; *AV*, Danesh Yazdani; *Chief Librn*, Vanrea Thomas; *Acq, Coll Develop, Ser*, Ching Chang; *Automation Syst Coordr*, Dr Fred Korn; Staff 14 (MLS 14)
Founded 1971. Enrl 5,116; Fac 210; Highest Degree: Bachelor
1997-1998 Income $982,761. Mats Exp $160,734, Books $59,298, Per/Ser (Incl. Access Fees) $60,221, Micro $16,537. Sal $736,312 (Prof $509,054)
Library Holdings: Bk Vols 109,000; Bk Titles 96,000; Per Subs 550
Subject Interests: Afro-American studies, Bus, Caribbean studies, Health sci, Literature, Women's studies
Special Collections: American Civilization; American Culture Series (PCMI Coll), ultrafiche; American Fiction Series; American Periodicals Series; Black History & Culture (Arthur A Schomburg Coll Series I), microfilm; Library of American Civilization Coll, microfiche; Social Science; Southern Africa Coll
Publications: Acquisitions list; catalog of motion picture films; index to periodicals; Library handbook; mediographies
Partic in Academic Libraries of Brooklyn; New York Metrop Ref & Res Libr Agency; State University Of New York-NYLINK
Friends of the Library Group

GL MTA-NEW YORK CITY TRANSIT, Law Library, 130 Livingston St, 12th flr, 11201. SAN 327-4853. Tel: 718-694-3886. FAX: 718-694-5727. *Dir*, Sandra Gore
Library Holdings: Bk Vols 20,000

S NEW YORK AQUARIUM, (Formerly Aquarium For Wildlife Conservation), Osborn Laboratories of Marine Science, W Eighth St & Surf Ave, 11224. SAN 310-9461. Tel: 718-265-3431, 718-265-3437. FAX: 718-265-3420. Web Site: www.wcs.org. *Dir*, Louis Garabaldi; E-Mail: loiselle@idt.net; *Librn*, Mary Messing; E-Mail: messing@idt.net
Founded 1967
Library Holdings: Bk Vols 4,600; Bk Titles 3,500; Per Subs 56
Subject Interests: Marine biology
Publications: Wildlife Conservation
Restriction: Open to others by appointment, Staff use only

J NEW YORK CITY TECHNICAL COLLEGE, Ursula C Schwerin Library, 300 Jay St, 11201. SAN 352-1885. Tel: 718-260-5470. Interlibrary Loan Service Tel: 718-260-5484. FAX: 718-260-5631. E-Mail: refny@cunyvm.cuny.edu. Web Site: library.nyck.cuny.edu/library.html. *Dir*, Darrow Wood; *ILL*, Bonnie Hack; *Ref*, Joan Grassano; *Tech Servs*, Sharon Swacker; Staff 12 (MLS 12)
Founded 1946. Enrl 8,606; Fac 265
Library Holdings: Bk Vols 180,000; Bk Titles 132,000; Per Subs 600
Subject Interests: Dental hygiene, Eng tech, Hotel mgt, Ophthalmic dispensing, Radiologic tech, Restaurant mgt
Special Collections: College Archives; Hotel & Restaurant Management (Menu File)
Automation Activity & Vendor Info: (Cataloging) NOTIS
Publications: Library Notes
Partic in Academic Libraries of Brooklyn; New York Metrop Ref & Res Libr Agency; OCLC Online Computer Library Center, Inc

M NEW YORK METHODIST HOSPITAL, Health Sciences Library, 506 Sixth St, 11215. SAN 352-1796. Tel: 718-780-5197. FAX: 718-780-7357. *Dir*, Elizabeth R Franck
Library Holdings: Bk Titles 3,000; Per Subs 250
Subject Interests: Medicine, Nursing, Surgery
Special Collections: History of Methodist Hospital; Methodist Hospital Annual Reports
Publications: Library News
Partic in Brooklyn-Queens-Staten Island Health Sciences Librarians; Medical Library Center Of New York; Nat Libr of Med Regional Med Libr Prog; New York Metrop Ref & Res Libr Agency; New York State Interlibrary Loan Network
Open only to employees of New York Methodist Hosptial

GL NEW YORK STATE SUPREME COURT, Appellate Division Second Department Library,* 45 Monroe Pl, 11201. SAN 310-9267. Tel: 718-722-6356. FAX: 718-722-6302.; Staff 2 (MLS 1, Non-MLS 1)
Library Holdings: Bk Vols 35,000
Subject Interests: New York State law
Special Collections: Law Coll

GL NEW YORK STATE SUPREME COURT LIBRARY, BROOKLYN,* Supreme Court Bldg, Rm 349, 360 Adams St, 11201. SAN 310-9488. Tel: 718-643-8080. FAX: 718-643-2412. *Librn*, Brenda E Pantell
Founded 1850
Library Holdings: Bk Vols 250,000
Subject Interests: Criminal law, Medical law
Special Collections: Records & Briefs of the Four Appellate Courts, the Court of Appeals of the State of New York

C POLYTECHNIC UNIVERSITY, Bern Dibner Library of Science & Technology,* 5 Metrotech Ctr, 11201-3840. SAN 352-1915. Tel: 718-260-3530. FAX: 718-260-3756. E-Mail: blibrary@poly.edu. Web Site: dibner.poly.edu. *Dir*, Jana Stevens Richman; *Asst Dir*, Jun Zhang; *Assoc Dir*, James Jarman; Staff 16 (MLS 10, Non-MLS 6)
Founded 1854. Highest Degree: Doctorate
Library Holdings: Bk Vols 195,261; Bk Titles 154,805; Per Subs 601
Subject Interests: Bus, Environmental studies, Mgt, Sci-tech
Special Collections: History of Science & Technology; Paint & Surface Coatings (Mathiello Memorial Coll)
Partic in Academic Libraries of Brooklyn; New York Metrop Ref & Res Libr Agency; OCLC Online Computer Library Center, Inc
Open Mon-Thurs 9-10, Fri 9-6, Sat & Sun 12-6

C PRATT INSTITUTE LIBRARY, 200 Willoughby Ave, 11205-3897. SAN 352-194X. Tel: 718-636-3684. Interlibrary Loan Service Tel: 718-636-3680. FAX: 718-399-4401. Web Site: lib.pratt.edu/public/, www.pratt.edu. *Dean*, F William Chidkering; E-Mail: chick@pratt.edu; *Chairperson*, Sydney Starr; Tel: 718-636-3545, E-Mail: sstarr@pratt.edu; *ILL, Ref*, Margot Karp; E-Mail: mkarp@pratt.edu; *Tech Servs*, Roger E Cartmill; Tel: 718-636-3659, E-Mail: cartmill@pratt.edu; *Cat*, Steven Cohen; Tel: 718-636-3704, E-Mail: scohen@pratt.edu; *Publ Servs*, Anne Leonard; Tel: 718-399-4564, E-Mail: aleonar2@pratt.edu; *Ref*, Robet Fabbro; Tel: 718-636-3686, E-Mail: rfabbro@pratt.edu. Subject Specialists: *Architecture*, Joy Kestenbaum; *Art*, Yvette Cortes; *Library and information science*, Margot Karp
Founded 1887. Enrl 4,200; Fac 400; Highest Degree: Master
Sep 1999-Aug 2000 Income (Main Library and Branch Library) State $8,000. Mats Exp $217,000, Books $98,000, Per/Ser (Incl. Access Fees) $80,000, Presv $5,000, AV Equip $10,000, Electronic Ref Mat (Incl. Access Fees) $24,000. Sal $631,068 (Prof $262,817)
Library Holdings: Bk Vols 177,000; Bk Titles 108,160; Per Subs 660
Subject Interests: Architecture, Art, Libr sci
Special Collections: Fine Printing
Automation Activity & Vendor Info: (Acquisitions) epixtech, inc.; (Cataloging) epixtech, inc.; (Circulation) epixtech, inc.; (Course Reserve) epixtech, inc.; (ILL) epixtech, inc.; (Media Booking) epixtech, inc.; (OPAC) epixtech, inc.; (Serials) epixtech, inc.
Database Vendor: Lexis-Nexis, OCLC - First Search, Wilson - Wilson Web
Restriction: Open to student, faculty & staff
Partic in Academic Libraries of Brooklyn; New York Metrop Ref & Res Libr Agency; OCLC Online Computer Library Center, Inc
Friends of the Library Group
Departmental Libraries:
MULTI-MEDIA CENTER Tel: 718-636-3456. FAX: 718-399-4332. Web Site: lib.pratt.edu/public/, www.pratt.edu. *Dir*, Russell Abell; Tel: 718-636-4437, E-Mail: rabell@pratt.edu
Friends of the Library Group
PRATT MANHATTAN CENTER, Puck Bldg, 295 Lafayette St, New York, 10012. SAN 373-501X. Tel: 212-461-6025. FAX: 212-461-6025. *Coordr*, Jean Hines; E-Mail: jhines@rand.pratt.edu
Library Holdings: Bk Vols 800
Automation Activity & Vendor Info: (Acquisitions) epixtech, inc.; (Cataloging) epixtech, inc.; (Circulation) epixtech, inc.; (Course Reserve) epixtech, inc.; (ILL) epixtech, inc.; (Media Booking) epixtech, inc.; (OPAC) epixtech, inc.; (Serials) epixtech, inc.

C SAINT FRANCIS COLLEGE, McGarry Library, 180 Remsen St, 11201. SAN 352-1974. Circulation Tel: 718-489-5205. Reference Tel: 718-489-5307. FAX: 718-522-1274. E-Mail: library@stfranciscollege.edu. Web Site: www.stfranciscollege.edu. *Head Librn*, Wendell A Guy; Tel: 718-489-5306, E-Mail: wguy@stfranciscollege.edu; *Asst Dir*, Daniel Marshall; Tel: 718-489-5307, E-Mail: dmarshall@stfranciscollege.edu; *Cat*, Janice Syedullah; Tel: 718-489-5206, E-Mail: jsyedullah@stfranciscollege.edu; *Per*, Nora T Donegan; Tel: 718-489-5222, E-Mail: ndonegan@stfranciscollege.edu; *Ref*, Sal Russo; Tel: 718-489-5305, E-Mail: srusso@stfranciscollege.edu; Staff 8 (MLS 5, Non-MLS 3)
Founded 1884. Enrl 1,934; Fac 121; Highest Degree: Bachelor
Jul 1999-Jun 2000 Income $554,083, State $6,357, Parent Institution $547,726. Mats Exp $222,873, Books $91,466, Per/Ser (Incl. Access Fees) $73,284, Presv $5,474, Micro $22,129, AV Equip $8,000, Electronic Ref Mat (Incl. Access Fees) $22,520. Sal $293,335 (Prof $198,221)
Library Holdings: Bk Titles 125,999; Per Subs 573
Subject Interests: Aviation, Behav sci, Econ, Education, English literature, Health mgt, Mgt, Philosophy, Religion, Sci, Soc sci
Special Collections: Archives; Curriculum Library; Kennedy Coll
Automation Activity & Vendor Info: (Cataloging) PALS; (OPAC) PALS
Publications: Library User Manual (Library handbook)
Restriction: In-house use for visitors
Function: ILL available
Partic in Academic Libraries of Brooklyn; New York Metrop Ref & Res Libr Agency; OCLC Online Computer Library Center, Inc; WALDO

C SAINT JOSEPH'S COLLEGE, (SJC), McEntegart Hall Library, 222 Clinton Ave, 11205-3697. SAN 352-2032. Tel: 718-636-6858. Interlibrary Loan Service Tel: 718-636-6860. Reference Tel: 718-636-6860. FAX: 718-636-7250. E-Mail: blib@sjcny.edu. *Dir*, Teresa Ryan; E-Mail: tryan@sjcny.edu; *Bibliog Instr, Ref*, Catherine Cunningham; Staff 15 (MLS 4, Non-MLS 11)
Founded 1916. Circ 30,000; Enrl 1,300; Highest Degree: Master
Jul 1999-Jun 2000 Mats Exp $110,547, Books $39,213, Per/Ser (Incl. Access Fees) $51,936, Presv $4,071, Micro $5,299, AV Equip $767, Electronic Ref Mat (Incl. Access Fees) $9,261. Sal $288,537 (Prof $132,874)
Library Holdings: Bk Vols 103,550; Bk Titles 85,000; Per Subs 440; Bks on Deafness & Sign Lang 450
Subject Interests: Accounting, Bus, Child study, Commun health, Education, Health admin, Liberal arts, Nursing
Special Collections: Local New York History
Automation Activity & Vendor Info: (Acquisitions) Endeavor; (Cataloging) Endeavor; (Circulation) Endeavor; (Course Reserve) Endeavor; (OPAC) Endeavor; (Serials) Endeavor
Publications: Academic Libraries of Brooklyn (ALB) Periodicals; Library News; New Acquisitions Quarterly; Periodical Holdings - 1996-1997
Restriction: Open to faculty, students & qualified researchers, Use of others with permission of librarian
Partic in Academic Libraries of Brooklyn; New York Metrop Ref & Res Libr Agency; OCLC Online Computer Library Center, Inc

C STATE UNIVERSITY OF NEW YORK, Brooklyn Educational Opportunity Center,* 111 Livingston St, Ste 306, 11201. SAN 310-950X. Tel: 718-488-9840. FAX: 718-246-2062. *Librn*, Jacinth Hanson
Founded 1968. Circ 11,000
Library Holdings: Bk Vols 10,500; Per Subs 25
Subject Interests: Black hist

CM STATE UNIVERSITY OF NEW YORK HEALTH SCIENCE CENTER AT BROOKLYN, Medical Research Library of Brooklyn, 450 Clarkson Ave, PO Box 14, 11203. SAN 322-855X. Tel: 718-270-7400. FAX: 718-270-7413, 718-270-7468. Web Site: library.downstate.edu. *Dean*, Richard M Winant; *Actg Dir*, Mohamed Hussain; Tel: 718-270-7014; *Bibliog Instr, Online Servs, Ref*, Mary Doherty; *Cat*, Violet Evans; *Coll Develop, ILL*, Ross Ljungquist; *Archivist*, Jack Termine; *Ref Serv*, Thomas Angelo; *Ref Serv*, Joy Dunkley; *Web Coordr*, Christopher Stewart; Staff 15 (MLS 15)
Founded 1860. Enrl 1,963; Fac 306; Highest Degree: Doctorate
Library Holdings: Bk Vols 57,657; Bk Titles 54,252; Per Subs 1,500
Subject Interests: Allied health, Medicine, Nursing
Special Collections: The History of Medicine in the County of Kings
Automation Activity & Vendor Info: (Acquisitions) DRA; (Circulation) DRA
Publications: Newsletter
Partic in Medical Library Center Of New York; Metrop Regional Res & Ref Librs; OCLC Online Computer Library Center, Inc

UNITED STATES ARMY
A POST LIBRARY, 404 Pershing Loop, 11252-5100. SAN 352-2091. Tel: 718-630-4875. FAX: 718-630-4875. E-Mail: fthmltnlib@yahoo.com. *Dir*, Michael Gerard Plumley; E-Mail: plumleym@hamilton-emh1.army.mil; Staff 1 (MLS 1)
Founded 1942
Jan 1999-Dec 1999 Income Federal $6,505. Mats Exp $6,505, Books $4,140, Per/Ser (Incl. Access Fees) $730, Presv $597, AV Equip $1,038. Sal $35,000
Library Holdings: Bk Vols 26,000; Bk Titles 26,000; Per Subs 42
Subject Interests: Military history, Sci, Tactics
Special Collections: Black history; NY State & NY City Coll
Restriction: Circulation limited, Circulation to military employees only
Function: ILL limited
Open Tues, Wed & Thurs 12-7, Fri 11-6, Sat 10-5

GL UNITED STATES COURTS LIBRARY, Eastern District of New York Library,* 225 Cadman Plaza E, 11201. SAN 310-9526. Tel: 718-260-2320. FAX: 718-330-1754. *Chief Librn, Coll Develop*, John Saiz
Founded 1865
Library Holdings: Bk Vols 36,000
Subject Interests: Fed law, State law
Partic in Dialog Corporation; Westlaw

M VICTORY MEMORIAL HOSPITAL, Medical Library, 699 92nd St, 11228. SAN 374-4426. Tel: 718-567-1037. FAX: 718-567-1038. *Coll Develop, Librn*, Irina Meyman; Staff 1 (MLS 1)
Founded 1982
Library Holdings: Bk Titles 170; Per Subs 47
Subject Interests: Internal medicine, Nursing, Obstetrics and gynecology, Surgery
Restriction: Medical staff only

SR WATCHTOWER BIBLE SCHOOL OF GILEAD LIBRARY, 25 Columbia Heights, 11201-2483. SAN 310-9542. Tel: 718-560-5000. Web Site: www.watchtower.org. *Librn*, M G Smalley; *Librn*, Sarah Hall
Library Holdings: Bk Vols 25,000; Per Subs 30
Subject Interests: Relig matters

M WOODHULL MEDICAL & MENTAL HEALTH CENTER, Health Sciences Library,* 760 Broadway, 11206. SAN 352-1702. Tel: 718-963-8275, 718-963-8397. FAX: 718-963-8888.
Founded 1982
Library Holdings: Bk Vols 2,400; Bk Titles 1,300; Per Subs 185
Partic in BHSL; BQSI; Metro Atlanta Library Association; NY NJ-MLA

S WORLD JEWISH GENEALOGY ORGANIZATION LIBRARY,* PO Box 190420, 11219-0009. SAN 326-095X. Tel: 718-435-4400. FAX: 718-633-7050.
Library Holdings: Bk Vols 25,000

M WYCKOFF HEIGHTS MEDICAL CENTER LIBRARY,* 374 Stockholm St, 11237. SAN 329-8000. Tel: 718-963-7198. FAX: 718-497-7649. E-Mail: wyckoffl@metgate.metro.org. *Dir*, Rimma Perelman; E-Mail: riy9001@nyp.org; Staff 2 (MLS 1, Non-MLS 1)
Founded 1965. Pop 3,000; Circ 4,500
Jan 1998-Dec 1998 Income $98,700, State $3,700, Parent Institution $90,000, Other $5,000
Library Holdings: Bk Titles 2,000; Per Subs 200
Subject Interests: Dentistry, History of medicine, Internal medicine, Nursing, Plastic surgery, Podiatry, Surgery
Partic in Basic Health Sciences Library Network; Brooklyn-Queens-Staten Island Health Sciences Librarians; New York Metrop Ref & Res Libr Agency
Friends of the Library Group

BROOKVILLE

C LONG ISLAND UNIVERSITY - C W POST CAMPUS, B Davis Schwartz Memorial Library, 720 Northern Blvd, 11548. SAN 311-2756. Tel: 516-299-2305, 516-299-2307. FAX: 516-299-4169. Web Site: www.liu.edu/cwis/cwp/library/libhome.htm. *Dean of Libr*, Donald L Ungarelli; *Acq*, Mellissa Hinton; *Circ*, Nancy Menton; *Ref*, Jackie Elsas; E-Mail: reference@liu.edu; *Cat*, Bill Tornow; *Media Spec*, Manju Prasad; *Rare Bks, Spec Coll*, Conrad Schoeffling; *Govt Doc*, Masako Yukawa; *Per*, Melvin Sylvester; *Bibliog Instr*, Laura Manzari; E-Mail: lis@liu.edu; *Online Servs*, Wendy Roberts
Founded 1955. Fac 355; Highest Degree: Doctorate
Library Holdings: Per Subs 5,332
Subject Interests: Tax
Special Collections: Auction Catalogs; Eugene & Carlotta O'Neill Private Library; Henry James First Editions 1900-50 Children's Fiction; Lord Collection of Sporting Books; Theodore Roosevelt Association Coll
Publications: Library Handbooks; New Serial Titles; Post Library Association Report
Partic in Long Island Library Resources Council
Friends of the Library Group
Departmental Libraries:
CENTER FOR BUSINESS RESEARCH LIBRARY, 720 Northern Blvd - 25-A, 11548. SAN 326-5269. Tel: 516-299-2832. FAX: 516-299-4170. Web Site: www.liunet.edu/cwis/cwp/library/cbr/cbrhome.htm.; Staff 7 (MLS 2, Non-MLS 5)
Founded 1978
Library Holdings: Per Subs 613
Subject Interests: Accounting, Bus, Long Island, Tax
Publications: Business Alert
Partic in Dialog Corporation

BROWNVILLE

P BROWNVILLE-GLEN PARK LIBRARY,* 216 Brown Blvd, 13615. SAN 310-9550. Tel: 315-788-7889. *Librn*, Ellen Lapoint; *Asst Librn*, Jennifer Constance
Pop 1,600; Circ 7,951
Library Holdings: Bk Vols 5,219; Per Subs 27
Special Collections: Local Historical materials
Mem of North Country Library System

BUFFALO

S ALBRIGHT-KNOX ART GALLERY, G Robert Strauss Jr Memorial Library, 1285 Elmwood Ave, 14222. SAN 310-9577. Tel: 716-882-8700, Ext 8225. FAX: 716-882-6213. Web Site: www.albrightknox.org. *Head Librn*, Janice Lurie; E-Mail: jlurie@albrightknox.org; Staff 4 (MLS 3, Non-MLS 1)
Founded 1905
Library Holdings: Bk Titles 31,000; Per Subs 100
Subject Interests: Am art, Artists bks, Contemporary art, Illustrated bks, Modern art
Publications: Guide to the Archives
Partic in Western New York Library Resources Council

S BRISTOL-MYERS SQUIBB COMPANY PHARMACEUTICAL RESEARCH INSTITUTE, Scientific Information Dept,* 100 Forest Ave, 14213. SAN 320-7056. Tel: 716-887-3750. FAX: 716-887-7662.
Library Holdings: Bk Titles 4,000; Per Subs 400
Subject Interests: Biology, Chemistry, Dermatology, Medicine, Pharmaceutical
Special Collections: Dermatology Coll
Partic in OCLC Online Computer Library Center, Inc; Western New York Library Resources Council

J BRYANT & STRATTON BUSINESS INSTITUTE, Library Learning Center, 465 Main St, Ste 400, 14203. SAN 310-9607. Tel: 716-884-9120, Ext 261. FAX: 716-884-0091. Web Site: www.bryantstratton.org. *Dir*, Colleen M Anthony; Tel: 716-884-9120, Ext 261; *Asst Librn*, Tom Sommerville; Tel: 716-884-9120, Ext 262; Staff 11 (MLS 2, Non-MLS 9)
Founded 1867. Enrl 350
Jan 2000-Dec 2000 Income Parent Institution $40,000. Mats Exp $30,700, Books $19,000, Per/Ser (Incl. Access Fees) $8,000, Presv $500, Electronic Ref Mat (Incl. Access Fees) $3,200. Sal $60,000 (Prof $45,000)
Library Holdings: Bk Vols 3,900; Bk Titles 3,702; Per Subs 130
Subject Interests: Accounting, Bus, Info tech, Med assisting
Special Collections: Bryant & Stratton historical materials
Database Vendor: Dialog, IAC - Info Trac, OCLC - First Search
Publications: Echo (Newsletter)
Function: Research library

S BUFFALO & ERIE COUNTY HISTORICAL SOCIETY RESEARCH LIBRARY,* 25 Nottingham Ct, 14216-3199. SAN 310-9615. Tel: 716-873-9612. FAX: 716-873-8754. Web Site: www.bechs.com. *Librn*, Mary F Bell
Founded 1862
Subject Interests: Local history
Special Collections: Iconographic Coll, 1000 linear ft; Manuscripts Coll, 5000 linear ft; Western New York Newspaper Coll
Restriction: Non-circulating to the public
Partic in OCLC Online Computer Library Center, Inc; Western New York Library Resources Council

P BUFFALO & ERIE COUNTY PUBLIC LIBRARY SYSTEM, One Lafayette Sq, 14203-1887. SAN 352-2180. Tel: 716-858-8900. FAX: 716-858-6211. Web Site: www.buffalolib.org/. *Dir*, Diane J Chrisman; E-Mail: chrismand@buffalolib.org; *Dep Dir*, Michael C Mahaney; E-Mail: mahaneym@buffalolib.org; *Dep Dir*, Kenneth H Stone; E-Mail: stonek@buffalolib.org; *Dep Dir*, Shirley P Whelan; E-Mail: whelans@buffalolib.org; *Exten Serv*, William A Miles; E-Mail: milesw@buffalolib.org; *Publ Servs*, Ruth A Collins; E-Mail: collinsr@buffalolib.org; *ILL*, Diane Golding; E-Mail: goldingd@buffalolib.org; *Acq*, Judylee Loos; E-Mail: loosj@buffalolib.org; *Ch Servs*, Carol Batt; E-Mail: battc@buffalolib.org; *Rare Bks*, William H Loos; E-Mail: loosw@buffalolib.org; *Spec Coll*, Elaine Barone; E-Mail: baronee@buffalolib.org; *Cat*, Gini Prince; E-Mail: princeg@buffalolib.org; *Commun Relations*, Ami Savigny; E-Mail: savignya@buffalolib.org; Staff 178 (MLS 171, Non-MLS 7)
Founded 1836. Pop 968,584; Circ 8,369,027
Jan 2000-Dec 2000 Income (Main Library and Branch Library) $30,745,951, State $2,889,985, County $26,393,455, Other $1,462,511. Mats Exp $4,223,016. Sal $17,998,374
Library Holdings: Bk Vols 3,128,818; Per Subs 73,839
Subject Interests: Art, Business, Foundations, Genealogy, History, Literature, Local history, Maps, Music, Natural science, Patents, Sci-tech, Sheet music
Special Collections: foundations; genealogy; local history; maps; Mark Twain Coll; Niagara Falls prints; patents; sheet music; World War I & II posters
Automation Activity & Vendor Info: (Acquisitions) DRA; (Cataloging) DRA; (Circulation) DRA; (OPAC) DRA; (Serials) DRA
Publications: Annual Report of Director; Buffalo & Erie County Public Library Bulletin
Member Libraries: Amherst Public Library; Angola Public Library; Aurora Town Public Library; Boston Free Library; Cheektowaga Public Library; Clarence Public Library; Collins Correctional Facility Library; Collins Public Library; Denio Memorial Library; Eden Library; Elma Public Library; Grand Island Memorial Library; Hamburg Public Library; Hulbert Public Library Of The Town Of Concord; Lackawanna Public Library; Lancaster Public Library; Marilla Free Library; Orchard Park Public Library; Tonawanda City Public Library; Town of North Collins Public Library; Town Of Tonawanda Public Library; Wende Correctional Facility Library; West Seneca Public Library
Partic in New York State Interlibrary Loan Network; OCLC Online Computer Library Center, Inc; Western New York Library Resources Council
Special Services for the Deaf - Books on deafness & sign language; Captioned film depository; High interest/low vocabulary books; Special interest periodicals; Staff with knowledge of sign language; TTY machine
Special Services for the Blind - Kurzweil Reading Machine; Perkins Brailler & VisualTek; Radio reading receivers; Talking Books
Branches: 18
CAZENOVIA, 155 Cazenovia, 14210-2407. SAN 352-2210. Tel: 716-822-2436. FAX: 716-822-2436. E-Mail: caz@buffalolib.org. Web Site: www.buffalolib.org. *Librn*, Laurel Guess
Circ 90,346
Library Holdings: Bk Vols 19,317; Per Subs 964
Friends of the Library Group
CRANE, 633 Elmwood, 14222-1801. SAN 352-2245. Tel: 716-883-6651. FAX: 716-883-6651. E-Mail: cra@buffalolib.org. Web Site: www.buffalolib.org. *Librn*, Susan LoPatriello
Circ 136,634
Library Holdings: Bk Vols 19,778; Per Subs 913
Friends of the Library Group
DUDLEY, 2010 S Park, 14220-1894. SAN 352-227X. Tel: 716-823-1854. FAX: 716-823-1854. E-Mail: dud@buffalolib.org. Web Site: www.buffalolib.org. *Librn*, James Stelzle

Circ 77,085
Library Holdings: Bk Vols 17,170; Per Subs 937
Friends of the Library Group
EAST CLINTON, 1929 Clinton, 14206-3214. SAN 352-230X. Tel: 716-823-5626. FAX: 716-823-5626. E-Mail: ecl@buffalolib.org. Web Site: www.buffalolib.org. *Librn*, Kathryn Galvin
Circ 57,031
Library Holdings: Bk Vols 13,659; Per Subs 947
Friends of the Library Group
EAST DELAVAN, 1187 E Delavan, 14215-3801. SAN 352-2334. Tel: 716-896-4433. FAX: 716-896-4433. E-Mail: edl@buffalolib.org. Web Site: www.buffalolib.org. *Librn*, Patricia Covley
Circ 29,893
Library Holdings: Bk Vols 13,094; Per Subs 913
Friends of the Library Group
ERIE COUNTY CORRECTIONAL FACILITY, 11581 Walden Ave, Alden, 14004-0300. SAN 352-2318. Tel: 716-858-7160. *In Charge*, William Miles; E-Mail: milesw@buffalolib.org
Circ 105,281
Library Holdings: Bk Vols 21,385; Per Subs 69
ERIE COUNTY HOLDING CENTER, 40 Delaware Ave, 14202-3999. SAN 352-2342. Tel: 716-858-7161. *In Charge*, William Miles; E-Mail: milesw@buffalolib.org
Circ 79,889
Library Holdings: Bk Vols 10,215; Per Subs 139
ERIE COUNTY HOME, 11580 Walden Ave, Alden, 14004-9716. SAN 352-2350. Tel: 716-858-7161. *In Charge*, William Miles; E-Mail: milesw@buffalolib.org
Circ 41,030
Library Holdings: Bk Vols 14,219; Per Subs 94
FAIRFIELD, 1659 Amherst, 14214-2001. SAN 352-2369. Tel: 716-834-7500. FAX: 716-834-7500. E-Mail: ffd@buffalolib.org. Web Site: www.buffalolib.org. *Librn*, Doreen Bonds
Circ 99,658
Library Holdings: Bk Vols 16,246; Per Subs 965
Friends of the Library Group
FRONCZAK, 1080 Broadway, 14212-1457. SAN 352-2393. Tel: 716-892-3941. FAX: 716-892-3941. E-Mail: fro@buffalolib.org. Web Site: www.buffalolib.org. *Librn*, Kathy Smith
Circ 29,266
Library Holdings: Bk Vols 16,841; Per Subs 940
Special Collections: Polish Language
Friends of the Library Group
KENSINGTON, 22 Westminster, 14215-1614. SAN 352-2458. Tel: 716-833-7278. FAX: 716-833-7278. E-Mail: kns@buffalolib.org. Web Site: www.buffalolib.org. *Librn*, Joe Ermer
Circ 33,769
Library Holdings: Bk Vols 13,929; Per Subs 911
Friends of the Library Group
MARTIN LUTHER KING BRANCH, 451 William, 14204-1893. SAN 352-2512. Tel: 716-854-2070. FAX: 716-854-2070. E-Mail: kin@buffalolib.org. Web Site: www.buffalolib.org. *Librn*, Dorinda Hayes
Circ 17,843
Library Holdings: Bk Vols 10,298; Per Subs 881
Friends of the Library Group
MEAD, 126 Ludington, 14206-1319. SAN 352-2547. Tel: 716-892-4525. FAX: 716-892-4525. E-Mail: mea@buffalolib.org. Web Site: www.buffalolib.org. *Librn*, Dorinda Hayes
Circ 27,877
Library Holdings: Bk Vols 11,149; Per Subs 890
Friends of the Library Group
NIAGARA, 280 Porter, 14201-1030. SAN 352-2601. Tel: 716-882-1537. FAX: 716-882-1537. E-Mail: nia@buffalolib.org. Web Site: www.buffalolib.org. *Librn*, Margaret Guiher
Circ 50,429
Library Holdings: Bk Vols 16,335; Per Subs 954
Subject Interests: Spanish lang
Friends of the Library Group
NORTH JEFFERSON, 332 E Utica, 14208-2129. SAN 352-2636. Tel: 716-883-4418. FAX: 716-883-4418. E-Mail: njf@buffalolib.org. Web Site: www.buffalolib.org. *Librn*, Sandra Bush
Circ 21,019
Library Holdings: Bk Vols 20,060; Per Subs 960
Special Collections: Black History Reference
Friends of the Library Group
NORTH PARK, 2351 Delaware, 14216-2201. SAN 352-2660. Tel: 716-875-3748. FAX: 716-875-3748. E-Mail: npk@buffalolib.org. Web Site: www.buffalolib.org. *Librn*, Kathy Goodrich
Circ 66,487
Library Holdings: Bk Vols 17,041; Per Subs 901
Friends of the Library Group
NORTHWEST, 271 Grant, 14213-1496. SAN 352-2695. Tel: 716-885-8345. FAX: 716-885-8345. E-Mail: nwe@buffalolib.org. Web Site: www.buffalolib.org. *Librn*, Tim Galvin
Circ 45,044
Library Holdings: Bk Vols 14,112; Per Subs 941
Friends of the Library Group
RIVERSIDE, 820 Tonawanda, 14207-1448. SAN 352-2725. Tel: 716-875-0562. FAX: 716-875-0562. E-Mail: riv@buffalolib.org. Web Site: www.buffalolib.org. *Librn*, Judith Rivard
Circ 56,864
Library Holdings: Bk Vols 17,245; Per Subs 913
Friends of the Library Group
Bookmobiles: 2. Book vols 64413

BUFFALO GENERAL HEALTH SYSTEM
M AH AARON HEALTH SCIENCES LIBRARY, 100 High St, 14203. SAN 352-2784. Tel: 716-859-2878. FAX: 716-859-1527. *Dir*, Ms Wentsing Liu; *Librn*, Barbara Ciambor
Founded 1920
Jan 1997-Dec 1998 Income $294,700. Mats Exp $90,000. Sal $165,000
Library Holdings: Bk Vols 22,145; Per Subs 360
Subject Interests: Allied health, Hospital administration, Medicine, Nursing
Mem of Libr Consortium of Health Inst in Buffalo; Western NY Libr Res Coun

S BUFFALO MUSEUM OF SCIENCE, Research Library, 1020 Humboldt Pkwy, 14211-1293. SAN 310-964X. Tel: 716-896-5200, Ext 320. FAX: 716-897-6723. E-Mail: reslib@buffnet.net. Web Site: www.sciencebuff.org. *Librn*, Rachel Brew; Tel: 716-896-5200, Ext 321, E-Mail: rbrew@sciencebuff.org; *Librn*, Lisa A Seivert; Staff 1 (MLS 1)
Founded 1861
Jan 1999-Dec 1999 Income $55,000. Mats Exp $10,500, Books $1,000, Per/Ser (Incl. Access Fees) $9,500
Library Holdings: Bk Vols 45,000; Bk Titles 15,000; Per Subs 500
Subject Interests: Anthropology, Astronomy, Botany, Far Eastern archaeol, Far Eastern art, Geology, Invertebrate zool, Mineralogy, Mycology, Near Eastern archaeol, Near Eastern art, Paleontology, Vertebrate zool
Special Collections: Oriental Art & Archaelogy (Elizabeth W Hamlin Coll); Tifft Farm Oral History Coll
Publications: Milestones of Science
Restriction: By appointment only
Partic in State University Of New York-NYLINK; Western New York Library Resources Council

S BUFFALO NEWS LIBRARY,* One News Plaza, PO Box 100, 14240. SAN 310-9631. Tel: 716-849-4401. FAX: 716-856-5150. *Dir*, David Valenzuela
Founded 1920
Library Holdings: Bk Vols 2,000; Bk Titles 500
Subject Interests: Local history

BUFFALO PSYCHIATRIC CENTER
S STAFF LIBRARY, 400 Forest Ave, 14213. SAN 352-2849. Tel: 716-885-2261, Ext 2691. FAX: 716-885-4852. *Librn*, Mark Wudyka
Founded 1947
Library Holdings: Bk Vols 525
Restriction: Staff use only
Partic in Western New York Library Resources Council

C BUFFALO STATE COLLEGE, Burchfield-Penney Art Center-Archives & Research Library, Rockwell Hall, 1300 Elmwood Ave, 14222-1095. SAN 375-2321. Tel: 716-878-4143. FAX: 716-878-6003. E-Mail: weeklyns@bscmail.buffalostate.edu. Web Site: www.burchfield-penney.org. *Curator*, Nancy Weekly; Staff 2 (Non-MLS 2)
Founded 1966
Library Holdings: Bk Vols 2,500
Special Collections: Charles E Burchfield & Western New York Art; Charles E Burchfield Archives; Rehn Gallery Archives
Restriction: Not a lending library
Function: Research library

S BUFFALO TESTING LABORATORIES, INC LIBRARY,* 68 Fowler Ave, 14217-1502. SAN 310-9658. Tel: 716-873-2302. FAX: 716-873-9914. *Dir*, Edward J Kris; *Librn*, Peggy Crawley
Founded 1927
Library Holdings: Bk Titles 300
Subject Interests: Biology, Chemistry, Engineering, Metallurgy
Publications: ACS, Analytical Chemistry
Open Mon-Fri 8-4:30

C CANISIUS COLLEGE, Andrew L Bouwhuis Library, 2001 Main St, 14208-1098. SAN 310-9674. Tel: 716-888-2901. FAX: 716-888-2887. Web Site: www.canisius.edu/. *Dir*, Dr Joel A Cohen; E-Mail: cohen@canisius.edu; *Syst Coordr*, George Emery; *Cat*, Theresa Dombrowski; *Online Servs, Ref*, Camilla B Baker; *Per*, Thomas W Evans; *Coll Develop*, Barbara Boehnke; Staff 10 (MLS 10)
Founded 1870. Enrl 4,589; Fac 191; Highest Degree: Master
Library Holdings: Bk Vols 258,538; Bk Titles 206,340; Per Subs 1,182
Subject Interests: Bus, Culture, Education, English lang, English literature, History
Special Collections: Jesuitica Coll
Publications: CI Quarterly (newsletter)
Partic in State University Of New York-NYLINK; WALDO; Western New York Library Resources Council

M CHILDREN'S HOSPITAL OF BUFFALO, Health Sciences Library, 118 Hodge Ave, 14222. SAN 310-9682. Tel: 716-878-7304. FAX: 716-878-7547. *Dir*, Elaine C Mosher; Tel: 716-878-7614, E-Mail: emosher@kaleidahealth.org; Staff 4 (MLS 2, Non-MLS 2)
Founded 1912
Library Holdings: Bk Vols 10,000; Bk Titles 1,200; Per Subs 200
Subject Interests: Consumer health, Gynecology, Obstetrics, Pediatrics
Automation Activity & Vendor Info: (OPAC) SIRSI
Partic in Nat Libr of Med

S COLLECTOR CAR APPRAISERS ASSOCIATION LIBRARY,* 25 Myrtle Ave, 14204. SAN 322-757X. Tel: 716-855-1931. *Librn*, Mary Ann Sandoro
Library Holdings: Bk Vols 2,100; Bk Titles 1,970; Per Subs 125
Subject Interests: Autos, Bikes, Motorcycles
Publications: Value Guide to Older Cars
Restriction: By appointment only

C D'YOUVILLE COLLEGE, Library Resources Center,* 320 Porter Ave, 14201-1084. SAN 310-9690. Circulation Tel: 716-881-7618. FAX: 716-881-7770. Web Site: www.dyc.edu/library. *Dir*, Leon Shkolnik; Tel: 716-881-7616, E-Mail: shkolnld@dyc.edu; *Acq*, Grace Kammerer; *Cat*, Rosemarie Spyra; *Per, Ref*, Jill Church; *Archivist*, Sr Mary Kathleen Duggan; *ILL, Ref*, Ava Ehde; *Ref*, Heather Kazinski; *Ref*, Cheryl Lajos; *Ref*, Anita Mitchell; *Ref*, Sharmagne Solis; Staff 8 (MLS 8)
Founded 1908. Enrl 1,904; Highest Degree: Master
Jun 1997-Jul 1998 Income $358,334, State $5,920, Locally Generated Income $2,568, Parent Institution $345,360. Mats Exp $258,786, Books $96,301, Per/Ser (Incl. Access Fees) $134,182, Presv $2,520, Micro $2,600
Library Holdings: Bk Vols 90,163; Per Subs 726
Subject Interests: Education, Nursing, Occupational therapy, Physical therapy
Special Collections: Education Coll (Curriculum Library)
Publications: guides; newsletter; periodicals list; What's New (quarterly)
Partic in National Network Of Libraries Of Medicine - South Central Region; OCLC Online Computer Library Center, Inc; Western New York Library Resources Council

GM DVA-WNY HEALTHCARE SYSTEM, Library Service, 3495 Bailey Ave, 14215. SAN 310-9909. Tel: 716-862-3343. Interlibrary Loan Service Tel: 716-862-8840. FAX: 716-862-8839. *Librn*, James Mendola; E-Mail: mendola.jim@forum.va.gov; Staff 2 (MLS 2)
Founded 1950
Library Holdings: Bk Vols 14,100; Bk Titles 2,100; Per Subs 425
Subject Interests: Medicine
Publications: Journals Holdings List
Partic in Greater NE Regional Med Libr Program; Nat Libr of Med; Vets Admin Libr Network; Western New York Library Resources Council

J ERIE COMMUNITY COLLEGE-CITY CAMPUS, Library Resource Center,* 121 Ellicott St, 14203. SAN 320-0558. Tel: 716-851-1076. FAX: 716-851-1129. Web Site: www.ecc.edu. *Librn*, Jane Ashwill; Staff 5 (MLS 5)
Founded 1971
Library Holdings: Bk Vols 25,000; Per Subs 245
Partic in OCLC Online Computer Library Center, Inc; Western New York Library Resources Council

M ERIE COUNTY MEDICAL CENTER, W Yerby Jones Memorial Library, 462 Grider St, 14215. SAN 310-9720. Tel: 716-898-3939. FAX: 716-898-3291. *Senior Librn*, Edward J Leisner; E-Mail: eleisner@ecmc.edu; *Librn*, Sharon Klug; E-Mail: sklug@ecmc.edu; Staff 3 (MLS 2, Non-MLS 1)
Founded 1921
Jan 2000-Dec 2000 Income $165,000, Parent Institution $141,000, Other $24,000. Mats Exp $137,500, Books $27,000, Per/Ser (Incl. Access Fees) $81,500
Library Holdings: Bk Titles 2,400; Per Subs 304
Subject Interests: Burns, Kidney transplant, Medicine, Nursing, Surgery, Trauma
Automation Activity & Vendor Info: (Acquisitions) SIRSI; (Cataloging) SIRSI; (Circulation) SIRSI; (OPAC) SIRSI; (Serials) SIRSI
Database Vendor: OVID Technologies
Restriction: Staff use only
Partic in Library Consortium Of Health Institutions In Buffalo; OCLC Online Computer Library Center, Inc; Western New York Library Resources Council

S EVERYWOMAN OPPORTUNITY CENTER, INC LIBRARY,* 237 Main St, Ste 330, 14203. SAN 370-2359. Tel: 716-847-1120. FAX: 716-847-1550. E-Mail: ewocbuf@everywoman.org. *Librn*, Marcia Hillock
Library Holdings: Bk Vols 350
Subject Interests: Career guidance, Vocational guidance
Restriction: Not open to public

M MILLARD FILLMORE HEALTH SYSTEM, Kidney Health Sciences Library,* 3 Gates Circle, 14209. SAN 310-9747. Tel: 716-887-4848. FAX: 716-887-4347. E-Mail: library@mfhs.edu. Web Site: www.mfhs.edu/library/.; Staff 2 (MLS 2)
Founded 1948
Library Holdings: Bk Vols 4,280; Bk Titles 3,970; Per Subs 504
Subject Interests: Allied health, Clinical medicine, Health care admin, Nursing
Partic in Library Consortium Of Health Institutions In Buffalo
Open Mon-Fri 8:30-4:30

S HAUPTMAN-WOODWARD MEDICAL RESEARCH INSTITUTE, Biophysics & Biochemistry Library, 73 High St, 14203. SAN 329-2681. Tel: 716-856-9600. FAX: 716-852-6086. *Librn*, Vivian Cody; E-Mail: cody@hwi.buffalo.edu
Library Holdings: Bk Titles 2,000
Subject Interests: Crystallography, Endocrinology
Restriction: Staff use only

L HODGSON, RUSS, ANDREWS, WOODS & GOODYEAR, Law Library,* 1800 One M&T Plaza, 14203. SAN 372-4158. Tel: 716-848-1282. FAX: 716-849-0349. *Librn*, Joan T White; E-Mail: jwhite@hodgsonruss.com
Library Holdings: Bk Vols 18,000
Open Mon-Fri 9-5

S HONEYWELL INTERNATIONAL, (Formerly AlliedSignal Inc), Performance Polymers & Chemical Information Center, 20 Peabody St, 14210-1599. SAN 310-9585. Tel: 716-827-6229. FAX: 716-827-6221. *In Charge*, Janice Hood; E-Mail: janice.hood@honeywell.com
Founded 1880
Jan 2000-Dec 2000 Income $225,000. Mats Exp $202,000, Books $20,000, Per/Ser (Incl. Access Fees) $150,000, Presv $15,000, Other Print Mats $7,000, Manuscripts & Archives $10,000
Library Holdings: Bk Titles 7,000; Per Subs 165
Subject Interests: Chemistry, Fluorine, Polymers
Special Collections: Chemical Abstracts; US Patents, CD-ROM
Publications: Technical newsletter
Partic in Western New York Library Resources Council

C MEDAILLE COLLEGE LIBRARY,* 18 Agassiz Circle, 14214. SAN 310-9771. Tel: 716-884-3281, Ext 283. FAX: 716-884-9638. Web Site: www.medaille.edu/library/library.html. *Dir*, Ilona Middleton; *Librn*, Debbie Cepagglia; *Circ*, Barbara Donovan
Founded 1925. Enrl 1,000; Highest Degree: Master
Library Holdings: Bk Vols 49,866; Per Subs 387
Subject Interests: Bus mgt systs, Human serv, Media
Special Collections: Animal Health Technology; Elementary Education Coll; Rare Books on Buffalo History Coll
Partic in Western New York Library Resources Council

M MERCY HOSPITAL, Health Sciences Library,* 565 Abbott Rd, 14220. SAN 310-978X. Tel: 716-828-2161. FAX: 716-828-2716. *Librn*, Linda Karch; E-Mail: lkarch@acsu.buffalo.edu; Staff 2 (MLS 1, Non-MLS 1)
Founded 1943
Library Holdings: Bk Titles 1,500
Subject Interests: Medicine, Pre-clinical sci
Restriction: Staff use only
Partic in Basic Health Sciences Library Network; Library Consortium Of Health Institutions In Buffalo; Western New York Library Resources Council

S MULTIDISCIPLINARY CENTER FOR EARTHQUAKE ENGINEERING RESEARCH, MCEER Information Service, 304 Capen Hall, State University of New York at Buffalo, 14260-2200. SAN 370-7059. Tel: 716-645-3377. FAX: 716-645-3379. Web Site: mceer.buffalo.edu. *Mgr*, Dorothy S Tao; *Librn*, Marsha Flett; *Librn*, Michael Kukla; *Librn*, Laura Taddeo; Staff 6 (MLS 4, Non-MLS 2)
Library Holdings: Bk Vols 44,000; Bk Titles 30,000; Per Subs 80
Special Collections: Earthquake Engineering & Natural Hazards Mitigation, various formats
Publications: MCEER Information Service News
Partic in OCLC Online Computer Library Center, Inc; Western New York Library Resources Council

S NATIONAL ASSOCIATION FOR INDUSTRY-EDUCATION COOPERATION LIBRARY, 235 Hendricks Blvd, 14226-3304. SAN 374-9940. Tel: 716-834-7047. FAX: 716-834-7047. E-Mail: naiec@pcom.net. Web Site: www.2.pcom.net/naiec. *Pres*, Dr Donald M Clark
Founded 1964. Enrl 748
Library Holdings: Bk Titles 615; Per Subs 900

GL NEW YORK SUPREME COURT, Eighth Judicial District Library,* 92 Franklin St, 4th flr, 14202. SAN 310-981X. Tel: 716-852-0712. FAX: 716-852-3454. *Dir*, James R Sahlem; Staff 7 (MLS 2, Non-MLS 5)
Founded 1863
Library Holdings: Bk Vols 350,000; Per Subs 226
Subject Interests: Law
Special Collections: Court of Appeals Records & Briefs; Law Reports (Old English & Canadian Reports Coll); New York Nominatives; NYCRR Backfile
Partic in LRS; OCLC Online Computer Library Center, Inc

L PHILLIPS, LYTLE, HITCHCOCK, BLAINE & HUBER LIBRARY,* 3400 HSBC Ctr, 14203. SAN 310-9836. Tel: 716-847-7086. FAX: 716-852-6100.; Staff 7 (MLS 3, Non-MLS 4)

Library Holdings: Bk Titles 25,000; Per Subs 120
Subject Interests: Law, Legislation
Partic in Dialog Corporation; Westlaw

S RESEARCH INSTITUTE ON ADDICTIONS, Research Library,* 1021 Main St, 14203-1016. SAN 320-2070. Tel: 716-887-2511. FAX: 716-887-2490. *Chief Librn*, Ann Mina Sawusch; Staff 2 (Non-MLS 2)
Founded 1974
Library Holdings: Bk Vols 7,400; Per Subs 130
Subject Interests: Alcohol abuse, Drug abuse
Partic in Library Consortium Of Health Institutions In Buffalo; Western New York Library Resources Council
Open Mon-Fri 8:30am-noon & 1-4:30pm

GM ROSWELL PARK CANCER INSTITUTE, Dr Edwin A Mirand Library, Elm & Carlton Sts, 14263. SAN 310-9844. Tel: 716-845-5966. FAX: 716-845-8699. E-Mail: library@roswellpark.org. Web Site: roswellpark.org. *Dir*, Nancy A Cunningham; Staff 10 (MLS 3, Non-MLS 7)
Founded 1898
Library Holdings: Bk Vols 92,000; Per Subs 1,000
Subject Interests: Biology, Chemistry, Neoplasms, Nursing
Automation Activity & Vendor Info: (Cataloging) SIRSI; (Circulation) SIRSI; (OPAC) SIRSI; (Serials) SIRSI
Partic in Library Consortium Of Health Institutions In Buffalo; Medical Library Center Of New York; Nat Libr of Med; Western New York Library Resources Council

S SAINT MARY'S SCHOOL FOR THE DEAF, Library Information Center, 2253 Main St, 14214. SAN 310-9852. Tel: 716-834-7200, Ext 152. FAX: 716-837-2080. *Media Spec Ch*, Jean Odien; E-Mail: jmodien@smsdk12.org
Founded 1964
Library Holdings: Bk Titles 18,000; Per Subs 90
Subject Interests: Audiology, Deaf, Spec educ with emphasis on deafness
Partic in Western New York Library Resources Council

L SAPERSTON & DAY PC, Law Library, 1100 M&T Ctr, Three Fountain Plaza, 14203. SAN 372-4603. Tel: 716-856-5400. FAX: 716-856-0139. Web Site: www.saperstonday.com. *Librn*, Jay J Deveau; E-Mail: jdeveau@saperstonday.com
Library Holdings: Bk Vols 10,000; Per Subs 75

M SHEEHAN MEMORIAL HOSPITAL, Medical Library,* 425 Michigan Ave, 14203. SAN 320-7048. Tel: 716-848-2345. FAX: 716-848-2140. *Librn*, Grace Di Virgilio
Library Holdings: Bk Vols 150; Per Subs 35
Subject Interests: Podiatry
Partic in Western New York Library Resources Council

S SIERRA TECHNOLOGIES, INC, Sierra Research Div,* 485 Cayuga Rd, PO Box 222, 14225. SAN 311-0435. Tel: 716-631-6200. FAX: 716-631-7849.
Founded 1960
Library Holdings: Bk Vols 2,500
Subject Interests: Electronics

M SISTERS OF CHARITY HOSPITAL, Medical Staff Library,* 2157 Main St, 14214. SAN 310-9860. Tel: 716-862-1256. FAX: 716-862-1883. *Librn*, Lisa A Nolan; E-Mail: lnolan@acsu.buffalo.edu; Staff 2 (MLS 1, Non-MLS 1)
Founded 1948
Library Holdings: Bk Vols 6,650; Bk Titles 80
Special Collections: Spiritual Care
Open Mon-Fri 8-4

SR SISTERS OF SAINT MARY RESEARCH CENTER LIBRARY,* 257 Layfette Ave, 14213. SAN 325-1462. Tel: 716-885-6252. *Librn*, Sr Mary Thompson; *Librn*, Sr Mary Helen Oates
Founded 1970
Library Holdings: Bk Titles 6,500; Per Subs 25
Subject Interests: Biblical references, Spiritual life
Special Collections: Photograph Coll

C STATE UNIVERSITY OF NEW YORK COLLEGE AT BUFFALO, E H Butler Library, 1300 Elmwood Ave, 14222-1095. SAN 310-9879. Tel: 716-878-6314. Circulation Tel: 716-878-6303. Reference Tel: 716-878-6313. FAX: 716-878-3134. E-Mail: watson@buffalostate.edu. Web Site: www.buffalostate.edu/~library. *Dir*, Maryruth F Glogowski; Tel: 716-878-6314, E-Mail: glogowmf@buffalostate.edu; *Assoc Dir*, Carol Richards; Tel: 716-878-5623, E-Mail: richarcj@buffalostate.edu; *Tech Servs*, Gail M Marinaccio; Tel: 716-878-6311, Fax: 716-878-4316, E-Mail: marinagm@buffalostate.edu; *Web Coordr*, Donna J Davidoff; Tel: 716-878-6301, Fax: 716-878-3134, E-Mail: davidodj@buffalostate.edu; *Acq, Bibliog Instr*, Gail Ellmann; *ILL*, Marjorie Lord; Tel: 716-878-6310, Fax: 716-878-3163, E-Mail: lordml@buffalostate.edu; *Archivist, Spec Coll*, Mary Delmont; *Electronic Resources*, Maureen A Lindstrom; Tel: 716-878-6301, Fax: 716-878-3134, E-Mail: lindstma@buffalostate.edu; *Bibliogr*, Eleanor Munn; *Head, Circ*, Bonita J Percival; Tel: 716-878-6236, E-Mail: percivbj@buffalostate.edu; *Bibliog Instr*, David W Sawicki; Tel: 716-878-6312, Fax: 716-878-3163, E-Mail: sawickdw@buffalostate.edu; *Assoc Librn*, Amy D Rockwell; Tel: 716-878-6321, Fax: 716-878-3134, E-Mail: rockwead@buffalostate.edu; *Media Spec*, Andrew Dutcher; *Head Ref, Librn for Blind*, Hilary I Sternberg; Tel: 716-878-6305, Fax: 716-878-3163, E-Mail: sternbhi@buffalostate.edu. Subject Specialists: *Curriculum mat*, Amy D Rockwell; Staff 52 (MLS 22, Non-MLS 30)
Founded 1910. Enrl 11,162; Fac 410; Highest Degree: Master
Jul 1999-Jun 2000 Income $2,369,384. Mats Exp $926,652, Books $182,000, Per/Ser (Incl. Access Fees) $553,625, Presv $20,539, Micro $69,488, Electronic Ref Mat (Incl. Access Fees) $101,000. Sal $1,554,084 (Prof $975,386)
Library Holdings: Bk Vols 523,448; Bk Titles 399,132; Per Subs 1,801
Subject Interests: African, Afro-American, Am lit, Applied arts, Criminal justice, Education, Exceptional children educ, Fine arts, Local history
Special Collections: Children's Author (Lois Lenski Coll), bk & illustrations; Courier Express Coll; Creative Education (Creative Studies Coll), bks & microfilm; Elementary & Secondary Curriculum; Historical Children's Books (Hertha Ganey Coll); Historical Textbook (Kempke-Root Coll); Isaac Klein Papers; Jazz (William H Talmadge Coll); Local Polish Community Coll (Fronczak Coll); Selig Adler Jewish Archives Coll; Tom Fontana Coll
Automation Activity & Vendor Info: (Acquisitions) Innovative Interfaces Inc.; (Cataloging) Innovative Interfaces Inc.; (Circulation) Innovative Interfaces Inc.; (ILL) Innovative Interfaces Inc.; (Media Booking) Innovative Interfaces Inc.; (OPAC) Innovative Interfaces Inc.; (Serials) Innovative Interfaces Inc.
Database Vendor: Dialog, Ebsco - EbscoHost, GaleNet, IAC - Info Trac, IAC - SearchBank, Lexis-Nexis, OCLC - First Search, Silverplatter Information Inc., Wilson - Wilson Web
Publications: Francis E Fronczak Coll Inventory (Collection catalog); Lois Lenski Children's Collection (booklet)
Function: Reference services available
Partic in OCLC Online Computer Library Center, Inc; Western New York Library Resources Council
Special Services for the Blind - Assistive Technology Center for Persons who are blind or physically handicapped
Friends of the Library Group

R TEMPLE BETH ZION LIBRARY, 805 Delaware Ave, 14209. SAN 352-3292. Tel: 716-886-7150. FAX: 716-886-7152. E-Mail: phoenix@buffnet.net. *Librn*, Madeline Davis
Founded 1915
Library Holdings: Bk Vols 14,000; Per Subs 35
Subject Interests: Judaica
Special Collections: Children's Judaica (Religious School Library)
Publications: American Jewish Odyssey, annotated bibliography of the Jewish experience in America; Jewish Children's Literature, annotated bibliography of books on Judaism & Jewish history; Lest We Forget, a selected annotated list of books on the Holocaust
Branches:
SUBURBAN LIBRARY, 700 Sweet Home Rd, Amherst, 14226. SAN 352-3322. Tel: 716-836-6565. FAX: 716-836-1194.
Special Collections: Children's Judaica (Religious School Library)

R TEMPLE SINAI, Dr Alex Morrison Library, 50 Alberta Dr, 14226. SAN 328-591X. Tel: 716-834-0708. FAX: 716-838-2597. *Librn*, Marianne Goldstein

J TROCAIRE COLLEGE LIBRARY,* 360 Choate Ave, 14220. SAN 310-9887. Tel: 716-827-2434. FAX: 716-828-6102. E-Mail: trocaire@pce.net. *Dir*, Tamara Butler; Staff 3 (MLS 2, Non-MLS 1)
Founded 1957
Library Holdings: Bk Titles 20,000; Per Subs 250
Special Collections: Nursing (Helene Fuld Coll), cassettes, fs, V-tapes
Partic in OCLC Online Computer Library Center, Inc; Western New York Library Resources Council

UNITED STATES ARMY
A CORPS OF ENGINEERS, BUFFALO DISTRICT TECHNICAL LIBRARY, 1776 Niagara St, 14207-3199. SAN 352-3357. Tel: 716-879-4114. FAX: 716-879-4310. *Bibliog Instr, Librn, Online Servs*, Thomas Van Wart; E-Mail: thomas.l.vanwart@usace.army.mil
Founded 1976
Library Holdings: Bk Titles 15,000; Per Subs 70
Subject Interests: Chemistry, Construction, Econ, Engineering, Environmental studies, Geology, Hydrol, Water res develop
Special Collections: Aerial Photography; Government Documents; Great Lakes Research; Microcomputer Software Bank; Nuclear Waste Disposal; Radioactive Waste Isolation
Publications: Buffalo District Technical Library (pamphlet)
Partic in Dialog Corporation; Fedlink; OCLC Online Computer Library Center, Inc; Western New York Library Resources Council

C UNIVERSITY AT BUFFALO-STATE UNIVERSITY OF NEW YORK, University Libraries, 433 Capen Hall, 14260-1625. SAN 352-2903. Tel: 716-645-2967. FAX: 716-645-3721. Web Site: ublib.buffalo.edu/libraries. *Assoc Dir*, Stephen Roberts; *Tech Servs*, John A Edens; *Acq*, David Nuzzo; *Cat*, Marilyn Kramer; *Archivist*, Christopher Densmore; *Curator, Rare Bks*, Robert Bertholf. Subject Specialists: *Poetry*, Robert Bertholf; Staff 74 (MLS

74)
Founded 1922. Enrl 24,257; Highest Degree: Doctorate
Jul 1999-Jun 2000 Income (Main and Other College/University Libraries) $15,178,748, State $14,378,748, Locally Generated Income $800,000. Mats Exp $5,772,474, Books $1,113,972, Per/Ser (Incl. Access Fees) $3,808,226, Presv $128,338, Micro $86,750, Electronic Ref Mat (Incl. Access Fees) $635,188. Sal $7,919,914 (Prof $5,269,320)
Library Holdings: Bk Vols 3,213,870; Per Subs 26,444
Special Collections: 20th-Century; 20th-Century English & American Literature-First Editions, R L Stevenson Library, Katherine Cornell; American Popular Literature; Archives (University Archives & Manuscript Coll); Can; Coll, Private Presses, J Frank Dobie Texas Coll, NY State Governors Autographs); Graves, Dylan Thomas, Wyndham Lewis-Carlow Coll, William Carlos Williams); Health Sciences (History of Medicine Coll & Gottlieb Coll); Lockwood Polish Coll & Orcatha Coll; Poetry Coll; Poetry in English-First Editions & Manuscript Coll (James Joyce-Wickser & Sylvia Beach Coll, Robert; Rare Books (19th & 20th century); Science & Engineering (Brennan Coll of Metallurgy & Early Chemistry)
Automation Activity & Vendor Info: (Circulation) NOTIS
Publications: Annual Report
Mem of Asn of Research Libraries
Partic in OCLC Online Computer Library Center, Inc; State Univ of NY-Region I; Western New York Library Resources Council
Friends of the Library Group
Departmental Libraries:
ARCHITECTURE & PLANNING, Hayes Hall, 14214-3087. SAN 352-2938. Tel: 716-829-3505. FAX: 716-829-2780. E-Mail: uldboehn@ ubvm.cc.buffalo.edu 528. Web Site: ublib.buffalo.edu/libraries/units/apl/. Friends of the Library Group
CHARLES B SEARS LAW LIBRARY, John Lord O'Brian Hall, 14260-1110. SAN 352-2962. Tel: 716-645-6765. FAX: 716-645-3860. E-Mail: asklaw@acsu.buffalo.edu. Web Site: ublib.buffalo.edu/libraries/units/law. *Dir*, James Milles; *Assoc Dir*, Mary Miller; *Media Spec*, Terrence McCormack; *Doc*, Susan Dow; *Ref*, Marcia Zubrow; *ILL*, John Mondo; Staff 12 (MLS 12)
Founded 1887. Enrl 797; Fac 45; Highest Degree: Doctorate
Jul 1999-Jun 2000 Income $2,143,145, State $2,133,145, Locally Generated Income $10,000. Mats Exp $924,924, Books $50,730, Per/Ser (Incl. Access Fees) $771,036, Presv $22,000, Micro $13,779, Electronic Ref Mat (Incl. Access Fees) $67,379. Sal $862,394 (Prof $563,317)
Library Holdings: Bk Vols 296,657; Per Subs 6,767
Subject Interests: Law
Special Collections: Law (John Lord O'Brian Coll), papers, bks
Automation Activity & Vendor Info: (Cataloging) NOTIS; (Circulation) NOTIS
Partic in New York State Interlibrary Loan Network; OCLC Online Computer Library Center, Inc; RLIN; Western New York Library Resources Council

CM HEALTH SCIENCES LIBRARY, Abbott Hall, 14214-3002. SAN 352-2997. Tel: 716-829-3900, Ext 102. FAX: 716-829-2211. E-Mail: askhsl@ acsu.buffalo.edu. Web Site: ublib.buffalo.edu/libraries/units/hsl. *Dir*, Gary Byrd; *Assoc Dir*, Amy Lyons; *Circ*, Evelyn Hufford; *ILL*, Cynthia Bertuca; *Ref*, Sharon Gray; *Cat*, Pamela Rose; *Curator*, Linda Lohr; *Acq, Cat, Ser*, Cindy Hepfer; *Media Spec*, L Widzinski; *Coll Develop*, Renee Bush; *Info Specialist*, Stewart Brower. Subject Specialists: *Education*, Stewart Brower; *History of medicine*, Linda Lohr; *Management*, Stewart Brower; Staff 18 (MLS 18)
Founded 1846. Enrl 3,574; Fac 948; Highest Degree: Doctorate
Jul 1999-Jun 2000 Income $2,715,114, State $2,465,114, Locally Generated Income $250,000. Mats Exp $1,153,129, Books $148,317, Per/Ser (Incl. Access Fees) $957,357, Presv $30,000, Micro $17,455. Sal $1,153,129 (Prof $800,641)
Library Holdings: Bk Vols 335,117; Per Subs 2,223
Subject Interests: Dentistry, Health related professions, Medicine, Nursing, Pharm
Special Collections: History of Medicine Coll; Media Resources Center; Media Resources Center
Publications: Annual Progress Report; Library Guide; Serial Holdings List
Partic in Library Consortium Of Health Institutions In Buffalo; National Network Of Libraries Of Medicine - South Central Region; New York State Interlibrary Loan Network; OCLC Online Computer Library Center, Inc; State Univ of NY at Buffalo; Western New York Library Resources Council
Friends of the Library Group
LOCKWOOD LIBRARY, Lockwood Libr Bldg, 14260-2200. SAN 352-3055. Tel: 716-645-2816. FAX: 716-645-3721. E-Mail: unlock@ acsu.buffalo.edu. *Dir*, Judith Adams-Volpe; *Business, Govt Doc*, Karen Smith; *Coll Develop*, Charles D'Aniello
MUSIC, Baird Hall, 14260-4700. SAN 352-311X. Tel: 716-645-2923. FAX: 716-645-3906. E-Mail: musique@acsu.buffalo.edu. Web Site: ublib.buffalo.edu/libraries/units/music/. *Head of Libr*, Nancy Nuzzo
OSCAR A SILVERMAN UNDERGRADUATE, 107 Capen Hall, 14260-2200. SAN 352-3233. Tel: 716-645-2944. FAX: 716-645-3721. E-Mail: askugl@acsu.buffalo.edu. Web Site: ublib.buffalo.edu/libraries/units/ugl. *Dir*, Margaret R Wells; *Coll Develop*, Glendora Johnson-Cooper; Staff 11 (MLS 5, Non-MLS 6)
POETRY-RARE BOOKS COLLECTION, 420 Capen Hall, 14260-2200. SAN 352-3179. Tel: 716-645-2917. FAX: 716-645-3714. Web Site: ublib.buffalo.edu/libraries/units/pl/. *Curator*, R Bertholf
SCIENCE & ENGINEERING, Capen Hall, 2nd & 3rd flrs, 14260-2200. SAN 352-3209. Tel: 716-645-2946. FAX: 716-645-3721. E-Mail: asksel@ acsu.buffalo.edu. Web Site: ublib.buffalo.edu/libraries/units/sel/. *Actg Dir*, Stephen Roberts
Partic in OCLC Online Computer Library Center, Inc; Western New York Library Resources Council
UNIVERSITY ARCHIVES, 420 Capen Hall, 14260-2200. SAN 352-3268. Tel: 716-645-2916. FAX: 716-645-3714. E-Mail: ub-archives@buffalo.edu. Web Site: ublib.buffalo.edu/libraries/units/archives/. *Archivist*, C Densmore

S VERIDIAN ENGINEERING, (VIC), Veridian Information Center, 4455 Genesee St, PO Box 400, 14225. SAN 310-9666. Tel: 716-631-6833. FAX: 716-631-4119. E-Mail: library@buffalo.veridian.com. *Librn*, Susan Doughtie; Staff 3 (MLS 1, Non-MLS 2)
Founded 1946
Library Holdings: Bk Vols 850,000; Bk Titles 22,000; Per Subs 170
Subject Interests: Aerodynamics, Aeronautics, Applied physics, Astronautics, Automobiles, Competitive intelligence, Defense, Defense procurement, Electronics, Intelligent transportation, Space science, Technology, Transportation
Special Collections: Government Research (NTIS Technical Reports), microfiche, all except DOE

S VERIDION ENGINEERING, Veridion Information Center, 4455 Genesee St, 14225. SAN 321-3471. Tel: 716-631-6833, 716-631-6837. FAX: 716-631-4119. *Mgr*, Sue Doughtie; *Tech Servs*, Nancy Herdic; Staff 4 (MLS 1, Non-MLS 3)
Founded 1975
Library Holdings: Bk Vols 20,000; Per Subs 50
Publications: Acquisitions list
Restriction: Staff use only
Partic in Dialog Corporation; Michigan Library Consortium; Western New York Library Resources Council

JR VILLA MARIA COLLEGE LIBRARY, 240 Pine Ridge Rd, 14225-3999. SAN 310-9917. Tel: 716-896-0700. FAX: 716-891-9020. E-Mail: library@ villa.edu. Web Site: www.villa.edu. *Dir*, Sister Anna Falbo; E-Mail: falbo@ villa.edu; *AV*, Barbara Wetzel; E-Mail: wetzel@villa.edu; *Cat*, Sister M Terenita Dobrzynski; *Bibliog Instr*, Cindy Ehlers; *Bibliog Instr*, William Piekarski; E-Mail: piekarskib@villa.edu; Staff 5 (MLS 3, Non-MLS 2)
Founded 1961. Enrl 343; Fac 30; Highest Degree: Associate
Library Holdings: Bk Titles 33,000; Per Subs 198
Subject Interests: Art, Children's literature, Early childhood, Graphics, Interior design, Photog, Poland, Relig studies
Automation Activity & Vendor Info: (Cataloging) Sagebrush Corporation; (Circulation) Sagebrush Corporation; (OPAC) Sagebrush Corporation
Database Vendor: CARL, Ebsco - EbscoHost, IAC - Info Trac, OCLC - First Search, ProQuest, Wilson - Wilson Web
Publications: Acquisition List; Audiovisual/Media Subject Index; Library News & Views; Subject Bibliographies
Mem of Western NY Libr Res Coun
Partic in Western New York Library Resources Council

BURNT HILLS

P TOWN OF BALLSTON COMMUNITY LIBRARY, (Formerly Burnt Hills-Ballston Lake Community Library), 2 Lawmar Lane, 12027. SAN 310-9933. Tel: 518-399-8174. FAX: 518-399-8187. E-Mail: bur_abara@sals.edu. Web Site: burnthills.sals.edu. *Dir*, Anna Jane Abaray; *Ch Servs*, Maureen M Borgeest; E-Mail: bur_broge@sals.edu; Staff 12 (MLS 2, Non-MLS 10)
Founded 1952. Pop 8,200; Circ 121,040
Jan 1999-Dec 1999 Income $258,968, State $2,992, City $225,869, Federal $620, County $2,245, Locally Generated Income $19,242. Mats Exp $252,900, Books $42,778, Per/Ser (Incl. Access Fees) $7,044, AV Equip $3,111, Other Print Mats $1,248, Electronic Ref Mat (Incl. Access Fees) $5,191. (Prof $131,368)
Library Holdings: Bk Vols 47,119; Per Subs 165
Subject Interests: Local history
Special Collections: History (Town of Ballston), software
Automation Activity & Vendor Info: (Circulation) DRA; (OPAC) DRA
Database Vendor: Dialog, DRA, GaleNet
Publications: Annual Report
Mem of Southern Adirondack Library System
Partic in Capital District Library Council for Reference & Research Resources
Special Services - Monthly exhibits
Friends of the Library Group

CAIRO

P CAIRO PUBLIC LIBRARY,* Main St, PO Box 720, 12413. SAN 310-995X. Tel: 518-622-9864. FAX: 518-622-9874. E-Mail: cairobox@ francomm.com. *Librn*, Lisa Areford

Founded 1963. Circ 30,104
Library Holdings: Bk Vols 18,990; Per Subs 26
Subject Interests: Local history
Mem of Mid-Hudson Library System
Friends of the Library Group

CALEDONIA

P CALEDONIA PUBLIC LIBRARY,* 3108 Main St, 14423. SAN 310-9968. Tel: 716-538-4512. FAX: 716-538-4978. *Librn*, Kathleen Hartness
Pop 4,030; Circ 24,000
Library Holdings: Bk Vols 20,000
Mem of Pioneer Library System
Open Mon & Thurs 2-5:30 & 7-9, Tues 10-1 & 2-5:30, Fri 2-5:30, Sat 10-2

CALLICOON

P DELAWARE FREE LIBRARY,* 133 Main St, 12723. SAN 310-9976. Tel: 914-887-4040. FAX: 914-887-4040. E-Mail: delfl@catskill.net. *Dir*, Lynn Nalven
Founded 1951. Circ 12,492
Jan 1997-Dec 1998 Income $55,791. Mats Exp $11,081. Sal $24,036
Library Holdings: Bk Vols 20,100; Bk Titles 19,500
Subject Interests: Children's, Local history, Mysteries
Mem of Ramapo Catskill Library System
Open Mon 1-5, Tues & Fri 7-9, Wed & Thurs 9-12 & 1-5 & Sat 1-4

CALVERTON

P BAITING HOLLOW FREE LIBRARY,* 4 Warner Dr, 11933. SAN 310-9984. Tel: 516-727-8765. *Librn*, Jeanette Robinson
Founded 1903. Pop 475; Circ 1,392
1997-1998 Income $10,315. Mats Exp Books $1,800. Sal $3,900
Library Holdings: Bk Vols 4,800
Subject Interests: Long Island hist
Mem of Suffolk Cooperative Library System

CAMBRIDGE

P CAMBRIDGE PUBLIC LIBRARY,* W Main St, 12816. SAN 311-0001. Tel: 518-677-2443. FAX: 518-677-2443. *Librn*, Judy B Center
Pop 1,906; Circ 31,005
Library Holdings: Bk Vols 13,193; Per Subs 38
Mem of Southern Adirondack Library System
Open Mon, Wed & Fri 6:30-9, Tues & Thurs 1-5, Sat 10-5
Friends of the Library Group

CAMDEN

P CAMDEN PUBLIC LIBRARY,* 57 Second St, 13316. SAN 311-001X. Tel: 315-245-1980. E-Mail: ca_dial@midyork.lib.ny.us. *Dir*, Linda Frenzel; Staff 4 (Non-MLS 4)
Founded 1890. Pop 2,667; Circ 45,000
Jan 1999-Jan 2000 Mats Exp $19,457, Books $16,540, Per/Ser (Incl. Access Fees) $1,099, AV Equip $1,418, Electronic Ref Mat (Incl. Access Fees) $400. Sal $40,000
Library Holdings: Bk Titles 19,000; Per Subs 46
Special Collections: News (Camden Advance Journal Coll)
Publications: Queen Central News
Mem of Mid-York Library System

CAMILLUS

P MAXWELL MEMORIAL LIBRARY, 14 Genesee St, 13031. SAN 311-0036. Tel: 315-672-3661. FAX: 315-672-5514. *Dir*, Sandra M Mirabelli
Founded 1918. Pop 18,146; Circ 74,145
Jan 1999-Dec 1999 Income $141,825. Mats Exp $29,000, Books $19,000, Per/Ser (Incl. Access Fees) $3,000, AV Equip $4,000, Electronic Ref Mat (Incl. Access Fees) $3,000. Sal $79,175 (Prof $34,000)
Library Holdings: Bk Vols 25,825; Per Subs 98
Automation Activity & Vendor Info: (Cataloging) epixtech, inc.; (Circulation) epixtech, inc.
Mem of Onondaga County Public Library
Friends of the Library Group

CANAJOHARIE

S BEECH-NUT NUTRITION CORP LIBRARY,* 102 Church St, 13317. SAN 311-0044. Tel: 518-673-3251, Ext 2470. FAX: 518-673-3259. *Librn*, Virginia A San Fanandre-Russo
Library Holdings: Bk Vols 900; Per Subs 40
Subject Interests: Bacteriology, Chemistry, Food tech, Infant feeding, Nutrition
Open Mon-Fri 8-4:30

P CANAJOHARIE LIBRARY & ART GALLERY,* 2 Erie Blvd, 13317. SAN 311-0052. Tel: 518-673-2314. FAX: 518-673-5243. E-Mail: can_traha@sals.edu. Web Site: www.clay.org. *Dir*, Eric Trahan; *Curator*, James Crawford
Founded 1914. Pop 3,287; Circ 40,000
Jan 1999-Dec 2000 Income $274,665, State $28,076, City $1,750, Locally Generated Income $22,068, Other $222,771. Mats Exp $20,364, Books $17,176, Per/Ser (Incl. Access Fees) $3,188. Sal $114,412 (Prof $32,500)
Library Holdings: Bk Vols 40,836; Per Subs 132
Subject Interests: Architecture, Art, Local indust hist
Special Collections: American Art Originals, Colonial Times to Present; Art (Gilbert Stuart, Georgia O'Keefe, Winslow Homer)
Publications: Fire (History of Local Volunteer Fire Department); Masterpieces of American Art (brochure); The Permanent Collection (catalog); Walking Tour of Canajoharie (brochure)
Mem of Mohawk Valley Library Association
Partic in Cap District Libr Coun for Ref & Res Resources; OCLC Online Computer Library Center, Inc

CANANDAIGUA

P BRISTOL LIBRARY,* 6750 County Rd 32, 14424. SAN 310-897X. Tel: 716-229-5862. FAX: 716-229-5862. *Dir*, Grace Simones; E-Mail: gsimone@plf.landnet.org
Pop 1,802; Circ 5,700
Library Holdings: Bk Vols 6,000; Per Subs 35
Mem of Ont Coop Libr Syst NY List; Pioneer Library System
Open Mon 1-5 & 6:30-8:30, Tues 6:30-8:30, Wed 2:30-4:30 & 6:30-8:30, Thurs-Sat 6:30-8:30
Friends of the Library Group

J FINGER LAKES COMMUNITY COLLEGE, Charles J Meder Library, 4355 Lakeshore Dr, 14424-8395. SAN 311-0060. Tel: 716-394-3500, Ext 371. FAX: 716-394-8826. Web Site: www.library.flcc.edu. *Dir*, Frank Queener; *Ref*, Charlotte Cooper; *Ref*, Sharon Malecki; *Tech Servs*, Michelle Eichelberger; *ILL, Media Spec*, Susan Clayton; *Circ*, Karen Clement
Founded 1968. Enrl 4,098; Fac 95
Library Holdings: Bk Vols 78,316; Bk Titles 56,322; Per Subs 398
Subject Interests: Environ conserv, Horticulture, Nursing, Tourism, Travel
Special Collections: Canandaigua Lake Pure Waters Assoc archives
Automation Activity & Vendor Info: (Circulation) MultiLIS
Publications: Media Programs; orientation & bibliographic instruction workbook; Periodicals Guide; subject bibliographies
Partic in OCLC Online Computer Library Center, Inc; Rochester Regional Library Council; State University Of New York-NYLINK
Special Services for the Deaf - Captioned film depository
Special Services for the Blind - Integrated Library/Media services; Textbooks on audiocassettes, variable speed cassette players

S ONTARIO COUNTY HISTORICAL SOCIETY LIBRARY, 55 N Main St, 14424. SAN 311-0079. Tel: 716-394-4975. FAX: 716-394-9351. E-Mail: ochs@eznet.net. Web Site: www.ochs.org. *Dir*, Edward Varno; *Curator*, Wilma Townsend; *Res*, Linda McIlveen; Staff 9 (MLS 6, Non-MLS 3)
Founded 1902
Library Holdings: Bk Titles 3,500
Subject Interests: Ont county hist
Special Collections: Civil War Library of Major Charles Richardson NY126 Vol; Western New York Land Sales (Oliver Phelps Coll), mss
Publications: An Illustrated History of the LISK Manufacturing Co; Forgotten Stories of the Finger Lakes; Golden; Photographic History of the City of Canandaigua
Restriction: Non-circulating to the public

P PIONEER LIBRARY SYSTEM, 4595 Rte 21 N, 14424. SAN 312-1593. Tel: 716-394-8260. FAX: 716-394-1935. Web Site: www.pls-net.org. *Exec Dir*, Jennifer Morris; E-Mail: jmorris@pls-net.org; *Asst Dir*, Patricia Stocker; E-Mail: pstocker@pls-net.org; *Ad Servs*, Ellen Reynolds; *Automation Syst Coordr*, Betsy Morris; *Ch Servs*, Roxane Chadwick; *Commun Relations*, Marilyn Longhouse; *Instrul Serv*, Louise Smith; Staff 18 (MLS 7, Non-MLS 11)
Founded 1990. Pop 289,103
Jan 2001-Dec 2001 Income $1,819,583, State $1,447,535, Federal $19,813, County $270,000, Locally Generated Income $40,235, Other $42,000. Mats Exp $71,646. Sal $561,155 (Prof $302,588)
Library Holdings: Bk Vols 12,369; Per Subs 91
Publications: Pioneer Pathfinder (quarterly newsletter); Union Lists & Directories
Member Libraries: Allens Hill Free Library; Arcade Free Library; Avon Free Library; Bell Memorial Library; Bloomfield Public Library; Bristol Library; Caledonia Public Library; Clifton Springs Library; Clyde-Savannah Public Library; Cordelia A Greene Library; Dansville Public Library; Eagle Free Library; Eastern Oregon University; Geneva Free Library; Gorham Free Library; Honeoye Public Library; Lima Public Library; Livonia Public Library; Lyons School District Public Library; Macedon Public Library; Marion Public Library; Mount Morris Library; Naples Library; Newark Public Library; Ontario Public Library; Palmyra King's Daughters' Free Library Inc; Perry Public Library; Phelps Community Memorial Library;

Pike Library; Red Creek Free Library; Rose Free Library; Sodus Free Library; Stevens Memorial Library; Town Of Gainesville Public Library; Victor Free Library; Wadsworth Library; Walworth-Seely Public Library; Warsaw Public Library; Williamson Free Public Library; Wolcott Civic Free Library; Wood Library; Wyoming Free Circulating Library
Partic in Rochester Regional Library Council

GM VETERANS ADMINISTRATION MEDICAL CENTER, Medical Library, Ft Hill Ave, 14424. SAN 311-0087. Tel: 716-393-7995. FAX: 716-393-8356. *Tech Servs*, Sandy Baxter; E-Mail: sandy.baxter@med.va.gov; Staff 2 (Non-MLS 2)
Oct 1999-Sep 2000 Income $93,000. Mats Exp $72,000, Books $17,000, Per/Ser (Incl. Access Fees) $55,000
Library Holdings: Bk Titles 3,600
Subject Interests: Agingl, Alcohol-drug abuse, Medicine, Nursing, Psychiatry, Psychology
Automation Activity & Vendor Info: (Cataloging) Sagebrush Corporation; (Circulation) Sagebrush Corporation
Publications: Medical Library newsletter
Partic in Rochester Regional Library Council; Vets Admin Libr Network
Open Mon-Fri 8-4:30

P WOOD LIBRARY,* 134 N Main St, 14424-1295. SAN 311-0095. Tel: 716-394-1381. FAX: 716-394-2954. *Actg Dir*, Carol R Shama; Tel: 716-394-1404, E-Mail: cshama@pls-net.org; *Ch Servs*, Mary Ferris; *Tech Servs*, Pat Mincer; *Ref, YA Servs*, Carol Shama
Founded 1857. Pop 21,768; Circ 228,648
Jan 1999-Dec 1999 Income $426,960, State $9,091, City $125,120, County $7,864, Locally Generated Income $131,790. Mats Exp $58,000, Books $42,770, Per/Ser (Incl. Access Fees) $2,000. Sal $252,310 (Prof $119,785)
Library Holdings: Bk Titles 66,009; Per Subs 135
Publications: Annual Report & Annual Plan of Service
Mem of Pioneer Library System
Open Mon-Thurs 10-9, Fri & Sat 10-5
Friends of the Library Group

CANASTOTA

P CANASTOTA PUBLIC LIBRARY, 102 W Center St, 13032. SAN 311-0117. Tel: 315-697-7030. FAX: 315-697-8653. Web Site: www.canastotalibrary.org. *Dir*, Elizabeth Metzger; Staff 3 (MLS 2, Non-MLS 1)
Founded 1896. Pop 9,257; Circ 85,000
2000-2001 Income $287,996. Mats Exp $52,000, Books $41,000, Per/Ser (Incl. Access Fees) $11,000
Library Holdings: Bk Titles 58,044; Per Subs 150
Special Collections: Children's Books for Parents (Dorothy Canfield Fisher Award Coll)
Mem of Mid-York Library System
Friends of the Library Group

CANDOR

P CANDOR FREE LIBRARY, 2 Bank St, PO Box 104, 13743-0104. SAN 311-0125. Tel: 607-659-7258. FAX: 607-659-7500. *Librn*, Fran Howe; E-Mail: fhowe@lakenet.org
Founded 1931. Pop 869; Circ 17,529
Library Holdings: Bk Vols 18,440; Per Subs 29
Subject Interests: Adult fiction, History, Mystery, Science fiction, Western, Young adult
Automation Activity & Vendor Info: (Cataloging) Brodart; (Circulation) Brodart
Mem of Finger Lakes Library System
Open Mon, Wed & Fri 2-5, Tues & Thurs 10-12 & 2-5, Sat 2-4 & 6-8
Friends of the Library Group

CANISTEO

P WIMODAUGHSIAN FREE LIBRARY,* 19 W Main St, 14823. SAN 311-0133. Tel: 607-698-4445. FAX: 607-698-2712. *Dir*, Kim Lindsey
Founded 1898. Pop 3,600; Circ 25,714
Library Holdings: Bk Vols 14,900; Bk Titles 14,200; Per Subs 55
Subject Interests: Crafts, Gardening, Railroad hist
Special Collections: History (Steuben County Coll), bk, doc, clippings, pamphlets
Mem of Southern Tier Library System
Open Mon, Wed & Fri 1-5pm, Tues & Thurs 6-9pm & Sat 10am-noon

CANTON

P CANTON FREE LIBRARY,* 8 Park St, 13617. (Mail add: PO Box 150, 13617-0150), SAN 311-0141. Tel: 315-386-3712. FAX: 315-386-4131. E-Mail: canton@northnet.org. Web Site: www.nc3r.org/canlib/. *Dir*, Carolyn J Swafford; E-Mail: swafford@northnet.org; *Assoc Dir*, Carole Berard; E-Mail: berard@northnet.org; *Ch Servs*, Beverly Ewart; Staff 12 (MLS 1, Non-MLS 11)
Founded 1896. Pop 11,120; Circ 60,362
Jan 1998-Dec 1998 Income (Main Library Only) $228,630, City $77,660, County $8,694, Locally Generated Income $25,000, Other $111,175. Mats Exp $183,980, Books $18,940, Per/Ser (Incl. Access Fees) $9,048, Electronic Ref Mat (Incl. Access Fees) $10,202. Sal $100,785 (Prof $25,000)
Library Holdings: Bk Vols 53,872; Per Subs 115
Subject Interests: Local history
Special Collections: Adirondacks (Menard); Frederic Remington's Paintings; Hazel Tyrell's Bird Carvings; Tyrell Handcarved Birds Coll
Database Vendor: OCLC - First Search
Function: Mail loans to members
Mem of North County Libr Syst
Friends of the Library Group
Branches: 2
MORLEY, 7230 County Rte 27, 13617. SAN 321-138X. Tel: 317-379-0066. *Mgr*, Joan Seavey
Library Holdings: Bk Vols 3,248; Per Subs 18
Friends of the Library Group
RENSSELAER FALLS BRANCH, Rensselaer St, PO Box 237, Rensselaer Falls, 13680. Tel: 315-344-7406. *Mgr*, Tim Connolly
Function: Photocopies available
Special Services for the Blind - Braille & recorded books; Large print bks

S SAINT LAWRENCE COUNTY HISTORICAL ASSOCIATION ARCHIVES, 3 E Main St, PO Box 8, 13617-0008. SAN 311-015X. Tel: 315-386-8133. FAX: 315-386-8134. E-Mail: slcha@northnet.org. Web Site: www.slcha.org.; Staff 2 (Non-MLS 2)
Founded 1944
Library Holdings: Bk Titles 2,000; Per Subs 24
Subject Interests: County hist, Genealogy, Northern NY hist, St Lawrence County hist
Special Collections: Silas Wright (Governor Silas Wright & Family Coll), bks, docs, letters & transcripts
Publications: The Quarterly
Restriction: Non-circulating to the public
Partic in North Country Reference & Research Resources Council

C ST LAWRENCE UNIVERSITY, Owen D Young Library, Park St, 13617. SAN 311-0168. Tel: 315-229-5451. Interlibrary Loan Service Tel: 315-229-5485. Reference Tel: 315-229-5477. FAX: 315-229-5729. Web Site: www.web.stlawu.edu/library/. *Librn*, Bart M Harloe; Tel: 315-229-5424, Fax: 315-229-7446, E-Mail: bharloe@stlawu.edu; *Acq, Coll Develop*, William H Walters; Tel: 315-229-5331, Fax: 315-229-7447, E-Mail: whwalters@stlawu.edu; *Syst Coordr*, Michael G Alzo; Tel: 315-229-5316, Fax: 315-229-7434, E-Mail: malzo@stlaw.edu; *Instrul Serv, Ref*, Joan A Larsen; Tel: 315-229-5473, E-Mail: jlarsen@stlawu.edu; *Archivist, Spec Coll*, Mark C McMurray; Tel: 315-229-5476, Fax: 315-229-7446, E-Mail: mcm@stlawu.edu; *Science*, Eric R Williams-Bergen; Tel: 315-229-5405, Fax: 315-229-7291, E-Mail: ewilliamsbergen@stlawu.edu; *Govt Doc, Ser*, Robin H Hutchinson; Tel: 315-229-5486, E-Mail: rhutchinson@stlawu.edu; *Electronic Resources*, Paul A Doty; Tel: 315-229-5483, E-Mail: pdoty@stlawu.edu; *Cat, Tech Servs*, Jean A Thompson; Tel: 315-229-5834, Fax: 315-229-7447, E-Mail: jtompson@stlawu.edu; Staff 10 (MLS 10)
Founded 1856. Enrl 2,000; Highest Degree: Master
Jul 1999-Jun 2000 Income $2,475,021. Mats Exp $1,066,507, Books $282,861, Per/Ser (Incl. Access Fees) $621,319, Presv $23,349, Micro $30,000, Electronic Ref Mat (Incl. Access Fees) $108,978. Sal $843,831 (Prof $408,400)
Library Holdings: Bk Vols 509,348; Per Subs 2,000
Special Collections: David Parish & Family, papers & letters; Edwin Arlington Robinson Coll; Frederic Remington Coll, bks, letters & prints; Irving Bacheller Coll; Nathaniel Hawthorne (Milburn Coll), bks & letters; Northern New York History, bks, letters, maps & doc; Owen D Young Papers; Poetry (Benet Coll); Rabbi Dr Syemour Siegel Coll, bks, writings; Robert Frost Coll
Publications: Bulletin of the Friends of Owen D Young Library; Odyssey: A Newsletter of the SLU Libraries
Partic in North Country Reference & Research Resources Council; OCLC Online Computer Library Center, Inc
Friends of the Library Group
Departmental Libraries:
LAUNDERS SCIENCE, Park St, 13617. Tel: 315-229-5400. *Librn*, Eric Williams-Bergen; Staff 2 (MLS 1, Non-MLS 1)

J STATE UNIVERSITY OF NEW YORK COLLEGE OF TECHNOLOGY, Southworth Library, Cornell Dr, 13617-1098. SAN 311-0176. Tel: 315-386-7228. FAX: 315-386-7931. Web Site: www.canton.edu/library/main.htm. *Dir*, S Farid ul Haq; *Librn*, Mary Bucher; *Coll Develop, Librn*, Kathleen Horton; *Asst Librn*, Douglas Welch; Staff 4 (MLS 4)
Founded 1948
Jul 1999-Jun 2000 Income $379,973, State $6,313, Locally Generated Income $2,106, Parent Institution $371,554. Mats Exp $93,832, Books $24,078, Per/Ser (Incl. Access Fees) $43,124, Presv $98, Micro $13,626, AV Equip $6,040, Electronic Ref Mat (Incl. Access Fees) $6,866. Sal $249,531 (Prof $196,464)
Library Holdings: Bk Vols 60,493; Bk Titles 51,996; Per Subs 338
Automation Activity & Vendor Info: (Acquisitions) DRA; (Acquisitions)

MultiLIS; (Cataloging) MultiLIS; (Cataloging) DRA; (Circulation) DRA; (Circulation) MultiLIS; (Course Reserve) DRA; (Course Reserve) MultiLIS; (OPAC) DRA; (OPAC) MultiLIS; (Serials) DRA; (Serials) MultiLIS
Partic in Associated Colleges of the Saint Lawrence Valley; North Country Reference & Research Resources Council
Open Mon-Thurs 8am-10pm, Fri 8am-5pm & Sun 2-10 pm

CAPE VINCENT

P CAPE VINCENT COMMUNITY LIBRARY,* Real St, PO Box 283, 13618. SAN 311-0184. Tel: 315-654-2132. FAX: 315-654-2132. *Librn*, Linda Voorhees
Pop 1,600; Circ 16,026
Library Holdings: Bk Vols 20,000; Per Subs 35
Mem of North Country Library System
Open Tues 9-5, Wed 5-8, Thurs & Fri 1-5, Sat 10-2

CARMEL

SR INSTITUTE FOR ADVANCED STUDIES OF WORLD RELIGIONS LIBRARY, 2020 Rte 301, 10512. SAN 324-3478. Tel: 854-225-1445. FAX: 854-225-1485. E-Mail: iaswr@aol.com. *Dir*, Lena Lee Yang; Staff 3 (MLS 1, Non-MLS 2)
Founded 1972
Library Holdings: Bk Vols 74,723; Per Subs 471
Subject Interests: Buddhism, Confucianism, Hinduism, Islam, Jainism, Other Asian relig systems, Shinto, Sikhism, Taoism, Zoroastrianism
Special Collections: Asian Philosophy & Comparative Literature (Galen Eugene Sargent Coll); Buddhism & Related Studies (Richard A Gard Coll); Buddhist Manuscripts from Nepal; Buddhist Philosophy & Chinese Art (Richard Hu See-yee Chi Coll); Chinese Buddhist Texts (Ming Southern Edition Coll); Chinese Buddhist Texts (Ngiam Hoo-pang Coll); Chinese Manuscripts from Tun-huang Coll, micro; Pastoral Theology (A Crescenzo Coll); Tibetan Books Printed in India, Nepal & Bhutan (P L 480/SFC Coll)
Publications: Classified Catalogues of Chinese Books
Restriction: Open to public for reference only
Partic in NY Area Theol Libr Asn; OCLC Online Computer Library Center, Inc

P KENT PUBLIC LIBRARY,* 264 Rte 52, 10512. SAN 311-0192. Tel: 914-225-8585. FAX: 914-225-8549. E-Mail: kent@ulysses.sebridge.org. *Dir*, Dona Boyer; *Ch Servs*, Marjorie Seegmuller
Circ 51,000
Library Holdings: Bk Vols 23,000; Per Subs 70
Mem of Mid-Hudson Library System
Open Mon & Wed 10-8, Tues, Thurs & Fri 10-5 & Sat 10-3
Friends of the Library Group

P REED MEMORIAL LIBRARY,* 1733 Rte 6, 10512. SAN 311-0206. Tel: 914-225-2439. FAX: 914-225-2439. *Dir*, Marilyn A Schlansky
Founded 1914. Pop 8,150; Circ 50,000
1997-1998 Mats Exp $20,000, Books $15,000, Per/Ser (Incl. Access Fees) $4,000
Library Holdings: Bk Vols 20,000; Per Subs 75
Subject Interests: Local history
Mem of Mid-Hudson Library System
Open Mon, Wed & Fri 10am-5pm, Tues & Thurs 10am-8pm & Sat 10am-3pm

CARTHAGE

P CARTHAGE FREE LIBRARY,* 412 Budd St, 13619. SAN 352-3381. Tel: 315-493-2620. FAX: 315-493-2620. E-Mail: +car+@aldus.northnet.org. *Librn*, Jerry Anderson; Staff 1 (MLS 1)
Founded 1910. Pop 5,936; Circ 30,999
Library Holdings: Bk Vols 12,708; Per Subs 48
Special Collections: Local History (New York State History Coll), mss, monographs
Mem of North County Libr Syst
Friends of the Library Group

CASTILE

P CORDELIA A GREENE LIBRARY, 11 S Main St, PO Box 208, 14427. SAN 311-0214. Tel: 716-493-5466. FAX: 716-493-5782. E-Mail: caslib@pls-net.org. Web Site: www.castile.pls-net.org, www.catile.pls-net.org. *Admin Dir*, Jacqueline Evadnie Hoyt; E-Mail: jhoyt@pls-net.org; Staff 2 (Non-MLS 2)
Founded 1897. Pop 3,042; Circ 19,000
Jan 2000-Dec 2000 Income $39,600, State $2,000, Locally Generated Income $29,400, Parent Institution $3,700, Other $4,500. Mats Exp $15,000, Books $11,000, Per/Ser (Incl. Access Fees) $2,000, AV Equip $1,000, Electronic Ref Mat (Incl. Access Fees) $1,000. Sal $18,000 (Prof $14,000)
Library Holdings: Bk Vols 17,000; Per Subs 55
Subject Interests: Local history
Special Collections: Dr Cordelia A Greene Coll; Frances Willard Coll
Function: Reference services available
Mem of Pioneer Library System
Open Mon, Tues & Thurs 3-9, Wed & Sat 10-4
Friends of the Library Group

CASTLE POINT

GM VA HUDSON VALLEY HEALTH CARE SYSTEM, Library Service, Rte 90, 12511. SAN 311-0222. Tel: 914-831-2000, Ext 5142. FAX: 914-838-5246. *Chief Librn*, Jeffrey Nicholas; Staff 1 (MLS 1)
Library Holdings: Bk Vols 14,000; Bk Titles 2,400; Per Subs 124
Subject Interests: Dental, Nursing, Sci
Mem of SE NY Libr Resources Coun
Partic in Vets Admin Libr Network
Open Mon-Fri 8-4:30

CASTLETON-ON-HUDSON

P CASTLETON PUBLIC LIBRARY,* 85 S Main St, 12033. SAN 373-8353. Tel: 518-732-2211. FAX: 518-732-1550. *Dir*, Candace Lind; *Asst Librn*, Darlene Miller; Staff 1 (Non-MLS 1)
Library Holdings: Bk Vols 8,586; Bk Titles 8,143; Per Subs 19
Special Collections: Castleton-on-Hudson, bks & photogs
Mem of Upper Hudson Library System
Special Services for the Deaf - Books on deafness & sign language; High interest/low vocabulary books; Special interest periodicals

CATO

P STEWART B LANG MEMORIAL LIBRARY,* E Main St, 13033. SAN 311-0249. Tel: 315-626-2101. FAX: 315-626-3249. E-Mail: sblmenlib@relex.com. *Librn*, Elizabeth Messina
Circ 22,000
1998-1999 Income $44,000, County $5,000, Other $14,000. Mats Exp $12,325, Books $9,500, Per/Ser (Incl. Access Fees) $925, AV Equip $1,000. Sal $22,230 (Prof $14,400)
Library Holdings: Bk Vols 10,000; Per Subs 28
Subject Interests: Cayuga County hist
Publications: Booklist
Mem of Finger Lakes Library System
Open Mon, Wed & Fri 1-5, Tues & Thurs 9:30-11:30, 1-8:30 & Sat 11-3

CATSKILL

P CATSKILL PUBLIC LIBRARY,* One Franklin St, 12414-1496. SAN 352-3470. Tel: 518-943-4230. FAX: 518-943-1439. E-Mail: catskill@francomm.com. *Dir*, Andrew Dancer; Staff 1 (MLS 1)
Founded 1893. Pop 12,608; Circ 35,012
Nov 1996-Oct 1997 Income $197,416, State $2,224, County $4,984, Locally Generated Income $5,883, Other $172,000. Mats Exp $27,231, Books $16,655, Other Print Mats $9,319. Sal $96,350 (Prof $34,019)
Library Holdings: Bk Vols 41,131
Special Collections: Hudson River Steamboats (Saunders Coll), micro
Mem of Mid-Hudson Library System
Friends of the Library Group
Branches: 1
PALENVILLE BRANCH, Maple Grove HCR1, Box 640, Palenville, 12463-0119. SAN 352-3500. Tel: 518-678-3357. FAX: 518-943-1439. *Librn*, Barbara Spataro
Library Holdings: Bk Vols 6,257; Per Subs 18
Friends of the Library Group

L NEW YORK STATE SUPREME COURT, Emory A Chase Memorial Law Library, Greene County Courthouse, 320 Main St, 12414. SAN 311-0257. Tel: 518-943-3130. FAX: 518-943-7763. *Librn*, Eric Maurer; E-Mail: emauer@courts.state.ny.us
Founded 1908
Library Holdings: Bk Vols 14,000
Subject Interests: NY state law
Special Collections: Van Orden Survey Coll
Partic in Southeastern New York Library Resources Council

CATTARAUGUS

P CATTARAUGUS FREE LIBRARY,* 21 Main St, 14719. SAN 311-0265. Tel: 716-257-9500. FAX: 716-257-9500. *Librn*, Deloris Erhart
Founded 1926. Circ 21,238
Library Holdings: Bk Vols 12,384; Per Subs 16
Mem of Chautauqua-Cattaraugus Library System
Open Mon 2-5pm, Tues & Fri 2-5pm & 7-9pm & Thurs & Sat 1:30-5:30pm

CAZENOVIA

J CAZENOVIA COLLEGE, Daniel W Terry Library, Lincklean St, 13035. SAN 311-0273. Tel: 315-655-7132. Circulation Tel: 315-655-7204. Reference Tel: 315-655-7282. FAX: 315-655-8675. Web Site: www.cazcollege.edu/library/library.htm. *Dir*, Stanley J Kozaczka; E-Mail: skozaczka@cazcollege.edu; *Cat*, Sharon Collins; Tel: 315-655-7364, E-Mail: scollins@cazcollege.edu; *ILL, Ref*, Anne Nassar; E-Mail: anassar@cazcollege.edu; Staff 12 (MLS 3, Non-MLS 9)
Founded 1824. Highest Degree: Bachelor
Jul 1999-Jun 2000 Income $408,677, State $5,123, Parent Institution $403,554. Mats Exp $188,747, Books $113,799, Per/Ser (Incl. Access Fees) $61,985, Micro $12,963. Sal $161,986
Library Holdings: Bk Vols 64,128; Bk Titles 55,380; Per Subs 501
Subject Interests: Women's studies
Automation Activity & Vendor Info: (Acquisitions) Innovative Interfaces Inc.; (Cataloging) Innovative Interfaces Inc.; (Circulation) Innovative Interfaces Inc.; (ILL) Innovative Interfaces Inc.; (OPAC) Innovative Interfaces Inc.; (Serials) Innovative Interfaces Inc.
Database Vendor: Lexis-Nexis, OCLC - First Search, ProQuest
Publications: Acquisition Lists; Annual Report
Partic in Central New York Library Resources Council; OCLC Online Computer Library Center, Inc

P CAZENOVIA PUBLIC LIBRARY SOCIETY, INC, 100 Albany St, 13035. SAN 311-0281. Tel: 315-655-9322. FAX: 315-655-5935. E-Mail: cz_circ@midyork.lib.ny.us. Web Site: www.midyork.org/cazenovia. *Librn*, Elizabeth Kennedy; *Asst Librn*, Mary Herbert; Staff 9 (MLS 3, Non-MLS 6)
Founded 1886. Pop 6,514; Circ 160,546
Jan 1999-Dec 1999 Income $250,417, State $2,019, County $13,101, Locally Generated Income $199,034. Mats Exp $34,139, Books $27,920, Per/Ser (Incl. Access Fees) $2,399, AV Equip $3,780, Electronic Ref Mat (Incl. Access Fees) $40. Sal $34,533 (Prof $32,500)
Library Holdings: Bk Vols 41,455; Per Subs 70
Subject Interests: Local history
Automation Activity & Vendor Info: (Acquisitions) DRA; (Cataloging) DRA; (Circulation) DRA; (Course Reserve) DRA; (ILL) DRA; (Media Booking) DRA; (OPAC) DRA; (Serials) DRA
Database Vendor: DRA
Mem of Mid-York Library System
Friends of the Library Group

S NEW YORK STATE DIVISION FOR HISTORIC PRESERVATION, Lorenzo State Historic Site Archives & Library, 17 Rippleton Rd, 13035. SAN 311-029X. Tel: 315-655-3200. FAX: 315-655-4304. E-Mail: lincklaen@juno.com. *In Charge*, Russell A Grills
Founded 1968
Library Holdings: Bk Vols 4,000
Subject Interests: Allied families, Doc hist of Cazenovia, Holland Land Co, Lincklaen-Ledyard, Third great Western Turnpike
Special Collections: Cazenovia & Barneveld, NY, land company material from Amsterdam, Municipal Archives, microfilm; Cazenovia Newspapers, 1800-1960, microfilm; Hubbard, Burr & Allied Family Papers & Photographs; Perry G Childs, Sidney F Fairchild & Charles Stebbins Family Papers (Helen Kennard Coll); Personal & Land Accounts of John Lincklaen & Successors (Lorenzo Library Coll), bks, doc & microfilm; Store Records & Correspondence (Samuel S Forman Papers Coll), doc & microfilm

CENTER MORICHES

P CENTER MORICHES FREE PUBLIC LIBRARY,* 235 Main St, 11934. SAN 311-0303. Tel: 516-878-0940. *Dir*, Nan Peel; *Ref*, Carolyn Locke; *Ch Servs*, Brenda Carter; *Ref*, Braden Singer; Staff 16 (MLS 6, Non-MLS 10)
Founded 1920. Circ 91,092
Library Holdings: Bk Titles 60,000; Per Subs 5,604
Special Collections: Local History (LI Coll) bks, records & tapes
Publications: Index to Moriches Bay Tide 1955 to date (local newspaper); Index to the Center Moriches Record; The Library (newsletter)
Mem of Suffolk Cooperative Library System
Open Mon-Fri 9:30-5, Tues, Wed & Thurs 9:30-8:30, Sat 9:30-5 & open on Sun 1-5 from Sept-May
Friends of the Library Group

CENTEREACH

P MIDDLE COUNTRY PUBLIC LIBRARY, 101 Eastwood Blvd, 11720. SAN 352-3535. Tel: 631-585-9393. FAX: 631-585-6541. Web Site: www.mcpl.lib.ny.us. *Dir*, Sandra Feinberg; Tel: 631-585-9393, Ext 200, E-Mail: feinberg@mcpl.lib.ny.us; *Asst Libr Dir*, Barbara Jordan; Tel: 631-585-9393, Ext 224, E-Mail: jordan@mcpl.lib.ny.us; *Asst Libr Dir*, Rochelle Lipkind; Tel: 631-585-9393, Ext 201, E-Mail: lipkind@mcpl.lib.ny.us; *Ad Servs*, Judith Berry; Tel: 631-585-9393, Ext 218; *Ad Servs*, Ilena Betcher; *Ad Servs*, Mary Frayne; *Ad Servs*, Carol Gray; Tel: 631-585-9393, Ext 217; *Ad Servs*, Nina Kramer; *Ad Servs*, Virginia Lammers; *Ad Servs*, Susan Mille; *Ad Servs*, Lorraine Paesano; *Ad Servs*, Sophia Serlis-McPhillips; *Ad Servs*, Lorraine Squires; *Ad Servs*, Paul Stemke; *Ad Servs*, Luise Weiss; *Ch Servs*, Sharon Breen; Tel: 631-585-9393, Ext 227; *Ch Servs*, Nancy Fazio; *Ch Servs*, Louise Hug; *Ch Servs*, Patricia Kochnower; *Ch Servs*, Frances Murphy; *Ch Servs*, Mary Schumacher; *Ch Servs*, Noreen Stackpole; *Tech Servs*, Joyce Bogin; Tel: 631-585-9393, Ext 229; Staff 33 (MLS 33)
Founded 1960. Pop 58,000; Circ 985,000
Jul 1999-Jun 2000 Income (Main Library and Branch Library) $7,843,158, Locally Generated Income $7,309,400, Other $533,758. Mats Exp Books $430,193. Sal $4,134,874 (Prof $2,214,051)
Library Holdings: Bk Titles 386,405; Per Subs 139,818
Special Collections: Business & Finance Coll; Career Information Center Services & Coll; Children's Braille; Children's Foreign Language Coll; Civil Service Manuals; College Catalogs; Dual Vision & Sign Language Coll; Family Education Professional Materials, Large Print Books, Adult Reader Coll (High Interest/Low Vocabulary); Health & Medical Coll; Law Coll; Local History (including Video Tape Coll); Museum Corner; Out of Town Newspapers; Parents Center; Parents Coll; Serials on Microfilm; Tax Services; Telephone Directories; WISE Center (World of Information for Seniors & the Elderly)
Automation Activity & Vendor Info: (Acquisitions) Innovative Interfaces Inc.; (Circulation) Innovative Interfaces Inc.; (Serials) Innovative Interfaces Inc.
Database Vendor: CARL, Dialog, Ebsco - EbscoHost, GaleNet, IAC - Info Trac, IAC - SearchBank, Innovative Interfaces INN - View, OCLC - First Search, ProQuest, Silverplatter Information Inc., Wilson - Wilson Web
Publications: Adult Services: Middle Country Public Library Directory; Caught in the Web: Mystery Books; Child Care Directory for Suffolk County; Children's Services; Dyslexia: An Annotated Bibliography; Hamlet of Selden; Italian-American Bibliography; Just Getting Started: Books for the Preschool Child; Long Island Bibliography; Menu for Mealtime; On the Go: A List of Local Places to Visit and Activities to do with Preschool Children; Parentips: A Bi-Monthly Newsletter for Parents; Program Calendar-Bi-Monthly; Reflections on 1788: Long Island and the Constitution; Teen Parents: An Annotated Bibliography; The College Bound Selection Process: A Handbook for Students, Parents & Educators; The Learning Disabled Adolescent: An Annotated Bibliography for Parents, Teachers & Students; The Parent/Child Workshop: A Program Handbook; Updates: A Quarterly Newsletter for the Career Information Center; Vocational Sourcefinder, 4 vols
Mem of Suffolk Cooperative Library System
Special Services for the Deaf - Books on deafness & sign language
Special Services for the Blind - Children's Braille, Books on Cassette; Suffolk Family Education Clearinghouse; Talking books for the Blind
Open Mon-Fri 9:30-9, Sat 9:30-5, Sun (Sept-May) 12-5
Friends of the Library Group
Branches: 1
MIDDLE COUNTRY CULTURAL CENTER, 575 Middle Country Rd, Selden, 11784. SAN 352-356X. Tel: 516-585-9393. FAX: 516-732-5002.
Open Mon-Thurs 9:30-9, Fri & Sat 9:30-5
Friends of the Library Group

CENTERPORT

S SUFFOLK COUNTY VANDERBILT MUSEUM LIBRARY,* 180 Little Neck Rd, Box 0605, 17721. SAN 373-7381. Tel: 516-854-5508. FAX: 516-854-5527. *Archivist, Curator*, Florance Ogg
Founded 1950
Special Collections: W K Vanderbilt II Coll, bks, photo albums & scrapbks

CENTRAL ISLIP

P CENTRAL ISLIP PUBLIC LIBRARY,* 33 Hawthorne Ave, 11722. SAN 311-0311. Tel: 631-234-9333. FAX: 631-234-9386. E-Mail: cisplib@suffolk.lib.ny.us. Web Site: www.suffolk.lib.ny.us/libraries/cisp/. *Dir*, Anne Pavlak; *Ch Servs*, Marilyn Miller; *Ch Servs*, Nina Busse; *Ad Servs, Ref*, Paul Facchianno; Staff 29 (MLS 9, Non-MLS 20)
Founded 1952. Pop 29,920; Circ 292,722
Jul 1997-Jun 1998 Income $1,314,104, State $9,297, County $79,445, Locally Generated Income $76,314, Other $1,149,048. Mats Exp $1,582,844. Sal $683,326 (Prof $328,336)
Library Holdings: Bk Vols 156,080; Per Subs 356
Automation Activity & Vendor Info: (Cataloging) Innovative Interfaces Inc.; (Circulation) Innovative Interfaces Inc.
Mem of Suffolk Cooperative Library System
Partic in Pals
Open Mon-Fri 10-9, Sat 10-5, Sun 1-5
Friends of the Library Group

C NEW YORK INSTITUTE OF TECHNOLOGY LIBRARY, Sunburst Center, PO Box 9029, 11722-9029. SAN 372-4972. Tel: 516-348-3090. FAX: 516-348-3094. Web Site: www.nyit.edu/library. *Coll Develop, Librn*, Rosemary Feeney; Tel: 631-348-3093; *Ref*, Joan Lauri; *Ref*, Nancy McCaffrey; *Ref*, Nancy Nelson; *Per*, Nicole DiMichele
Library Holdings: Bk Vols 40,000; Per Subs 445
Subject Interests: Architecture, Culinary
Automation Activity & Vendor Info: (OPAC) DRA
Partic in Long Island Library Resources Council

CENTRAL SQUARE

P CENTRAL SQUARE LIBRARY,* 637 S Main St, PO Box 513, 13036. SAN 311-032X. Tel: 315-668-6104. FAX: 315-668-6104. *Dir*, Mary Last
Pop 1,418; Circ 33,718
Library Holdings: Bk Vols 24,000; Per Subs 45
Mem of North Country Library System
Open Mon, Wed & Fri 12-8, Thurs 9-12:30 & Sat 10-1 (closed Sat in July & Aug)
Friends of the Library Group

CHAMPLAIN

P CHAMPLAIN MEMORIAL LIBRARY, 148 Elm St, 12919. (Mail add: PO Box 397, 12919), Tel: 518-298-8620. FAX: 518-298-8620. *Dir*, Sheila Marie Babbie; E-Mail: sbabbie1@primelink1.net; Staff 1 (MLS 1)
Founded 1925. Pop 1,273; Circ 12,291
Library Holdings: Bk Vols 9,500
Mem of Clinton-Essex-Franklin Library System
Open Mon 1-7, Wed 12-5, Thurs 4-8, Sat 9-2
Friends of the Library Group

CHAPPAQUA

P CHAPPAQUA CENTRAL SCHOOL DISTRICT PUBLIC LIBRARY, 195 S Greeley Ave, 10514. SAN 311-0362. Tel: 914-238-4779. FAX: 914-238-3597. E-Mail: chappaqu@wls.lib.ny.us. Web Site: www.chappaqualibrary.org. *Dir*, Mark Paul Hasskarl; Tel: 914-238-4779, Ext 108, E-Mail: mhasskar@wls.lib.ny.us; *Tech Servs*, Paula Peyraud; Tel: 917-238-4779, Ext 107, E-Mail: ppeyraud@wls.lib.ny.us; *Automation Syst Coordr, Ref, Tech Servs*, Carolyn Jones; *YA Servs*, Michele Capozzella; Tel: 914-238-4779, Ext 114, E-Mail: msnyder@wls.lib.ny.us; *Ref*, Martha Alcott; Tel: 914-238-4779, Ext 103, E-Mail: malcott@wls.lib.ny.us; *Ref*, Maryanne Eaton; Tel: 914-238-4779, Ext 106, E-Mail: meaton@wls.lib.ny.us; *Ref*, Carolyn Reznick; Tel: 914-238-4779, Ext 103, E-Mail: creznick@wls.lib.ny.us; *Ch Servs*, Shara Alpern; Tel: 914-238-4779, Ext 104; *Ch Servs*, Carol Birch; Tel: 914-238-4779, Ext 104, E-Mail: cbirch@wls.lib.ny.us; *Ch Servs*, Miriam Budin; E-Mail: mbudin@wls.lib.ny.us; *Ch Servs*, Teresa Bueti; E-Mail: tbueti@wls.lib.ny.us; *Ch Servs*, Susan Preece; Tel: 914-238-4779, Ext 105, E-Mail: spreece@wls.lib.ny.us; Staff 54 (MLS 11, Non-MLS 43)
Founded 1922. Pop 14,783; Circ 278,583
Jul 2000-Jun 2001 Income $163,375, State $5,648, Locally Generated Income $1,919,174. Mats Exp $144,521, Books $115,286, Per/Ser (Incl. Access Fees) $15,617, Micro $8,657, Electronic Ref Mat (Incl. Access Fees) $4,961. Sal $1,018,099 (Prof $431,295)
Library Holdings: Bk Vols 116,535; Per Subs 329
Subject Interests: Spec edc
Special Collections: Horace Greeley
Automation Activity & Vendor Info: (Circulation) epixtech, inc.; (OPAC) epixtech, inc.
Database Vendor: Dialog, Ebsco - EbscoHost, epixtech, inc., GaleNet, IAC - Info Trac
Publications: Annual Report; Community Organizations; Library Newsletter; Program Calendar; Quarterly Program Calendar; Welcome Brochure
Mem of Westchester Library System
Partic in Westlynx
Friends of the Library Group

CHATEAUGAY

P CHATEAUGAY MEMORIAL LIBRARY, Main St, PO Box 10, 12920-0010. SAN 311-0370. Tel: 518-497-6931. FAX: 518-497-3126. Web Site: www.chatmeml.org. *Dir*, Jeanette Hotchkiss
Founded 1946. Pop 3,204; Circ 9,497
Jan 1999-Dec 1999 Income $31,446, State $2,400, City $5,300, Locally Generated Income $6,642, Other $17,104. Mats Exp $3,358, Books $2,535, Per/Ser (Incl. Access Fees) $112, Presv $200, AV Equip $85, Electronic Ref Mat (Incl. Access Fees) $426. Sal $9,600
Library Holdings: Bk Vols 7,445; Bk Titles 7,011; Per Subs 10
Subject Interests: Adirondacks
Special Collections: American Indian Coll; North Country History; Wilder, Laura Ingalls & Almonzo Coll
Function: Reference services available
Mem of Clinton-Essex-Franklin Library System

CHATHAM

P CHATHAM PUBLIC LIBRARY,* Woodbridge Ave, 12037-1307. SAN 311-0389. Tel: 518-392-3666. FAX: 518-392-1546. *Dir, Librn*, Wendy Fuller; E-Mail: wfuller@taconic.net
Founded 1884. Pop 8,841; Circ 84,986
Jan 1997-Dec 1998 Income $385,278, State $2,577, County $4,166, Locally Generated Income $3,016, Parent Institution $375,519. Mats Exp $46,163, Books $39,249, Per/Ser (Incl. Access Fees) $5,180. Sal $242,604 (Prof $166,377)
Library Holdings: Bk Vols 64,163; Per Subs 199
Subject Interests: Local history
Mem of Mid-Hudson Library System
Friends of the Library Group
Branches: 1
CANAAN BRANCH, Canaan, 12029. SAN 325-3430. Tel: 518-781-3392. *Librn*, Betty Gaupman
Friends of the Library Group

CHAUMONT

P LYME FREE LIBRARY,* Main St, 13622-9603. SAN 311-0397. Tel: 315-649-5454. *Librn*, Patti Hughes
Founded 1923. Pop 1,695
1997-1998 Income $25,427. Mats Exp $12,638. Sal $8,767
Library Holdings: Bk Vols 6,110; Per Subs 17
Special Collections: Viet Nam (John La Comb Coll)
Mem of North Country Library System
Open Tues & Fri 12-8, Sat 10-4
Friends of the Library Group

CHAUTAUQUA

P SMITH MEMORIAL LIBRARY, Chautauqua Institution Library, 21 Miller Ave, PO Box 1093, 14722. SAN 311-0400. Tel: 716-357-6296. FAX: 716-357-3657. Web Site: www.smithlibrary.org. *Dir*, Helene Yurth; E-Mail: hyurth@hotmail.com; Staff 4 (MLS 1, Non-MLS 3)
Founded 1907. Pop 2,000; Circ 42,047
Library Holdings: Bk Vols 30,332; Per Subs 105
Subject Interests: Victorian era
Special Collections: History of Chautauqua Institution (Chautauqua Institution Archives), multi-media
Database Vendor: IAC - Info Trac, ProQuest
Mem of Chautauqua-Cattaraugus Library System
Open Sept 1-July 14: Mon 9:30-5, Wed 9:30-8, Fri 9:30-5, Sat 9:30-3, Sun 12-3; June 15-Aug 31: Mon-Sat 9-5, Sun 12-3
Friends of the Library Group

CHAZY

P CHAZY PUBLIC LIBRARY, 9633 Rte 9, PO Box 88, 12921-0088. SAN 311-0419. Tel: 518-846-7676. FAX: 518-846-7676. E-Mail: chazypl@northnet.com. *Librn*, Frances Fairchild
Founded 1901. Pop 2,777; Circ 5,020
1999-2000 Income $23,039, Locally Generated Income $13,966. Mats Exp Books $2,260. Sal $7,500
Library Holdings: Bk Vols 4,949; Per Subs 19
Subject Interests: History
Mem of Clinton-Essex-Franklin Library System
Friends of the Library Group

C WILLIAM H MINER AGRICULTURAL RESEARCH INSTITUTE, James A Fitzpatrick Library, 596 Ridge Rd, PO Box 100, 12921. SAN 326-4386. Tel: 518-846-8020. FAX: 518-846-7774. Web Site: www.whminer.com. *Librn*, Linda J Masters; Staff 1 (MLS 1)
Library Holdings: Bk Vols 5,300; Bk Titles 3,700; Per Subs 76
Subject Interests: Agriculture
Automation Activity & Vendor Info: (OPAC) Athena
Mem of N Country Ref & Res Resources Coun

CHEEKTOWAGA

P CHEEKTOWAGA PUBLIC LIBRARY, Julia Boyer-Reinstein Library, 1030 Losson Rd, 14227. SAN 376-8694. Tel: 716-668-4991. FAX: 716-668-4806. *Dir*, Elaine Mahaney; *Branch Mgr*, John Nowak; Staff 8 (MLS 8)
Founded 1938. Pop 109,442; Circ 596,521
Library Holdings: Bk Vols 170,189; Bk Titles 115,000; Per Subs 1,282
Special Collections: Local History (Anna M Reinstein Special Local History Reference Coll)
Automation Activity & Vendor Info: (Circulation) DRA
Mem of Buffalo & Erie County Public Library System
Branches: 3
NORTH, 735 Maryvale Dr, 14225. SAN 352-3683. Tel: 716-634-4424. FAX: 716-634-9266. *Librn*, Nancy Mueller
Library Holdings: Bk Vols 42,316; Bk Titles 42,050
REINSTEIN MEMORIAL, 2580 Harlem Rd, 14225. SAN 328-9915. Tel: 716-892-8089. FAX: 716-892-3370. *Branch Mgr*, Christine Bazan
Library Holdings: Bk Vols 57,651
SOUTH, 2660 William St, 14227. SAN 352-3713. Tel: 716-896-1272. FAX: 716-896-4861. *Librn*, Linda Rizzo
Library Holdings: Bk Vols 37,827; Bk Titles 34,826

M SAINT JOSEPH HOSPITAL, Medical Staff Library, 2605 Harlem Rd, 14225. SAN 320-3999. Tel: 716-891-2500. FAX: 716-891-2616. Web Site: www.sjh.org. *Librn*, Tracy Kulick

Founded 1960
1998-1999 Mats Exp $3,500, Books $1,500, Per/Ser (Incl. Access Fees) $2,000. Sal $6,100
Library Holdings: Bk Titles 1,053; Per Subs 20

CHERRY VALLEY

P CHERRY VALLEY MEMORIAL LIBRARY,* 61 Main St, PO Box 25, 13320-0025. SAN 311-0443. Tel: 607-264-8214. FAX: 607-264-8214. E-Mail: cv_ill@4cty.org. Web Site: lib.4cty.org. *Dir*, Claire Ottman
Pop 1,210; Circ 6,988
Jan 1998-Dec 1998 Income $17,186, Locally Generated Income $7,500, Other $9,686. Mats Exp $2,524, Books $2,123, Per/Ser (Incl. Access Fees) $313, Electronic Ref Mat (Incl. Access Fees) $88. Sal $8,270
Library Holdings: Bk Vols 7,355
Mem of Four County Library System

CHESTER

P CHESTER PUBLIC LIBRARY,* 1784 Kings Hwy, 10918. SAN 311-046X. Tel: 914-469-4252. FAX: 914-469-7583. *Dir*, Lynn Coppers; E-Mail: lcoppers@rcls.org; *Ch Servs*, Maureen Jagos; Staff 9 (MLS 1, Non-MLS 8)
Pop 9,138; Circ 77,000
Library Holdings: Bk Vols 41,450; Per Subs 67
Subject Interests: Am hist, Cookery, Local history
Automation Activity & Vendor Info: (Cataloging) epixtech, inc.; (Circulation) epixtech, inc.
Mem of Ramapo Catskill Library System
Friends of the Library Group

CHITTENANGO

P SULLIVAN FREE LIBRARY, Chittenango Public Library,* 519 McDonnell St, PO Box 310, 13037. SAN 352-3748. Tel: 315-687-6331. FAX: 315-687-6512. E-Mail: ch_circ@midyork.lib.ny.us. *Dir*, Karen Traynor
Founded 1947. Pop 14,622; Circ 75,213
Library Holdings: Bk Titles 42,000; Per Subs 42
Mem of Mid-York Library System
Friends of the Library Group
Branches: 1
BRIDGEPORT BRANCH, North Rd, PO Box 477, Bridgeport, 13030. SAN 352-3772. Tel: 315-633-2253. FAX: 315-633-2945. E-Mail: bp_circ@midyork.lib.ny.us.
Friends of the Library Group

CHURCHVILLE

P NEWMAN RIGA, One Village Park, 14428. SAN 311-0486. Tel: 716-293-2009. FAX: 716-293-0932. Web Site: www.rochester.lib.ny.us/towns/riga.html. *Dir*, Donna L Haire; Staff 1 (MLS 1)
Founded 1921. Pop 5,000; Circ 28,000
Library Holdings: Bk Vols 15,000; Bk Titles 15,000; Per Subs 20
Mem of Monroe County Library System

CINCINNATUS

P KELLOGG FREE LIBRARY,* 5681 Telephone Rd Exten, PO Box 150, 13040-0150. SAN 311-0508. Tel: 607-863-4300. FAX: 607-863-3430. *Librn*, Jean White; *Ch Servs*, Patricia Eaton
Founded 1930. Pop 1,151; Circ 20,376
Library Holdings: Bk Titles 13,779; Per Subs 82
Mem of Finger Lakes Library System

CLARENCE

P CLARENCE PUBLIC LIBRARY,* 9655 Main St, 14031. SAN 311-0524. Tel: 716-759-6651. *Dir*, Marie-Therese Robillard; *Asst Librn*, Christopher P Gregoire
Founded 1933. Circ 200,000
Jan 1997-Dec 1998 Income $242,000. Mats Exp $28,000, Books $20,400, Per/Ser (Incl. Access Fees) $7,600. Sal $186,000
Library Holdings: Bk Vols 36,044; Bk Titles 30,000
Mem of Buffalo & Erie County Public Library System
Friends of the Library Group

CLAVERACK

P CLAVERACK FREE LIBRARY,* 1 Rte 9H & 23B, Box 417, 12513. SAN 311-0532. Tel: 518-851-7120. FAX: 518-851-7120. *Dir*, Sally Alderdice
Circ 13,092
Library Holdings: Bk Vols 11,340
Mem of Mid-Hudson Library System

CLAYTON

S ANTIQUE BOAT MUSEUM, Gilbart Mercier Memorial Library, 750 Mary St, 13624. SAN 327-6473. Tel: 315-686-4104. Reference Tel: 315-686-4104, Ext 33. FAX: 315-686-2775. E-Mail: abm@gisco.net. *Librn, Res*, Phoebe Tritton; Staff 1 (Non-MLS 1)
Founded 1983
Library Holdings: Bk Vols 1,600; Bk Titles 1,500; Per Subs 5,250; Spec Interest Per Sub 25
Special Collections: Fresh Water Nautical Coll, boats, mechanical artifacts, charts, maps, boat plans, photos, boat & engine catalogs & manuals; Local Boat Builders
Publications: Gazette & Gazette Annual (Museum News to Membership)
Restriction: By appointment only, Non-circulating to the public
Function: Outside services via phone, cable & mail, Photocopies available, Research fees apply, Research library
Mem of N Country Ref & Res Resources Coun

P HAWN MEMORIAL LIBRARY,* 220 John St, 13624-1107. SAN 311-0540. Tel: 315-686-3762. Interlibrary Loan Service Tel: 315-782-5540. FAX: 315-686-6028. *Librn*, Alice Barton
Founded 1904. Pop 4,225; Circ 36,120
Library Holdings: Bk Vols 19,097
Subject Interests: Local history
Mem of North Country Library System
Friends of the Library Group

CLAYVILLE

P CLAYVILLE LIBRARY ASSOCIATION, Oneida St, PO Box 282, 13322. SAN 376-3021. Tel: 315-839-5893. FAX: 315-839-5070. *Librn*, Allison Fiegl
Library Holdings: Bk Vols 2,800; Per Subs 20
Mem of Mid-York Library System
Friends of the Library Group

CLIFTON PARK

P SHENENDEHOWA PUBLIC LIBRARY, 47 Clifton Country Rd, 12065-3894. SAN 311-0567. Tel: 518-371-8622. FAX: 518-371-3799. E-Mail: she_pirac@sals.edu. Web Site: www.shenpublib.org. *Dir*, Josephine L Piracci; Staff 14 (MLS 14)
Founded 1969. Pop 45,000; Circ 357,633
Jan 2000-Dec 2000 Income $1,388,225, State $9,850, City $9,288, County $6,400, Locally Generated Income $53,400, Other $1,309,287. Mats Exp $174,551, Books $131,551, Per/Ser (Incl. Access Fees) $43,000. Sal $825,299 (Prof $333,022)
Library Holdings: Bk Vols 100,000; Per Subs 264
Special Collections: Job, Business & Finance Information; Local History (Howard I Becker Memorial Coll)
Automation Activity & Vendor Info: (Acquisitions) DRA; (Cataloging) DRA; (Circulation) DRA; (ILL) DRA
Publications: Annual report; Newsletter (quarterly)
Mem of Southern Adirondack Library System
Also have computer instruction program - Terminals 8
Friends of the Library Group

CLIFTON SPRINGS

M CLIFTON SPRINGS HOSPITAL & CLINIC, Medical Library,* 2 Coulter Rd, 14432. SAN 311-0575. Tel: 315-462-9561, Ext 0307. FAX: 315-462-6058. *Dir*, Diane Grey; *Circ*, Lana Rudy
Founded 1914
Library Holdings: Bk Vols 130; Per Subs 12

P CLIFTON SPRINGS LIBRARY,* 4 Railroad Ave, 14432. SAN 311-0583. Tel: 315-462-7371. FAX: 315-462-2131. *Dir*, Maryann Marchitell; E-Mail: mmarchitell@pls-net.org
Founded 1895. Pop 2,500; Circ 40,830
Library Holdings: Bk Vols 18,719; Per Subs 65
Mem of Pioneer Library System
Friends of the Library Group

CLINTON

C HAMILTON COLLEGE, Burke Library, 198 College Hill Rd, 13323-1299. SAN 352-3802. Tel: 315-859-4475. Interlibrary Loan Service Tel: 315-859-4484. FAX: 315-859-4185. Web Site: www.hamilton.edu/library/. *Dir*, Randall Ericson; *Circ, Publ Servs, Ref*, Sharon Britton; *Tech Servs*, Teresa Strozik; *ILL*, Joan T Wolek; *AV*, Tim Hicks; *Acq*, Abigail Morton; *Cat*, Jean Williams; *Curator*, Frank K Lorenz; *Ser*, Ruth Melvin; Staff 11 (MLS 11)
Founded 1812. Enrl 1,716; Fac 171; Highest Degree: Bachelor
Library Holdings: Bk Vols 570,000; Per Subs 2,000
Subject Interests: Contemporary poetry, Feminism, Government, History, Relig studies
Special Collections: Book Arts; Communal Societies; Cruickshankiana; Ezra

Pound Coll, bk & mss; Hamiltoniana (Hamilton & Alumni Coll), bks, mss; Kirklandiana, bk, mss; Lesser Antilles (Beinecke Coll), bk & mss; Provencal; Women (McIntosh Coll)
Automation Activity & Vendor Info: (Serials) VTLS
Partic in Central New York Library Resources Council; OCLC Online Computer Library Center, Inc
Departmental Libraries:
MEDIA, Christian Johnson Bldg, 135 College St, 13323-1299. Tel: 315-859-4923. FAX: 315-859-4923. Web Site: www.library.hamilton.edu. *In Charge*, Jeanne G Marki
RECORD MUSIC, McEwen Hall, 13323-1299. Tel: 315-859-4349. FAX: 315-859-4185. Web Site: www.library.hamilton.edu. *Librn*, Kathryn Stenstrom
SCIENCE, Science Bldg, 13323-1299. Tel: 315-859-4714. FAX: 315-859-4714. *In Charge*, Joan Clair

P KIRKLAND TOWN LIBRARY, 55 1/2 College St, 13323. SAN 311-0605. Tel: 315-853-2038. FAX: 315-853-1785. E-Mail: cl_circ@midyork.lib.ny.us. Web Site: www.borg.com/~kirkland. *Dir*, Lois Marie Lemmer
Founded 1901. Pop 10,000; Circ 103,000
Jan 1999-Dec 1999 Income $203,000, State $3,000, City $160,000, County $20,000, Locally Generated Income $20,000. Mats Exp $47,500, Books $35,000, Per/Ser (Incl. Access Fees) $4,000, AV Equip $8,000, Electronic Ref Mat (Incl. Access Fees) $500. Sal $90,000 (Prof $50,000)
Library Holdings: Bk Vols 33,000; Bk Titles 32,000; Per Subs 130
Subject Interests: NY hist
Automation Activity & Vendor Info: (Circulation) DRA; (OPAC) DRA
Mem of Mid-York Library System
Friends of the Library Group

CLYDE

P CLYDE-SAVANNAH PUBLIC LIBRARY,* 204 Glasgow St, 14433. SAN 311-0613. Tel: 315-923-7767. FAX: 315-923-9315. *Dir*, Susan Ayers
Founded 1931. Pop 6,500; Circ 75,000
1997-1998 Income $118,000, County $9,388, Locally Generated Income $9,000, Other $91,000. Mats Exp $32,150, Books $25,300, Per/Ser (Incl. Access Fees) $1,250. Sal $31,000
Library Holdings: Bk Vols 40,000
Mem of Pioneer Library System
Friends of the Library Group

CLYMER

P CLYMER-FRENCH CREEK FREE LIBRARY,* 1564 N Center St, PO Box 68, 14724. SAN 311-0621. Tel: 716-355-8823. FAX: 716-355-8823. *Librn*, Diane Heslink
Circ 8,745
Library Holdings: Bk Titles 9,025; Per Subs 32
Mem of Chautauqua-Cattaraugus Library System
Open Mon 1-5, Wed & Fri 1-7, Sat 10-2
Friends of the Library Group

COBLESKILL

P COBLESKILL PUBLIC LIBRARY,* Union St, 12043. SAN 311-063X. Tel: 518-234-7897. FAX: 518-234-1163. E-Mail: coblib@telenet.net. *Dir, Librn*, Christine A Dickerson
Founded 1921. Pop 7,048; Circ 35,000
Library Holdings: Bk Vols 18,000; Bk Titles 17,500; Per Subs 43
Subject Interests: Local history
Mem of Mohawk Valley Library Association
Friends of the Library Group

J STATE UNIVERSITY OF NEW YORK COLLEGE OF AGRICULTURE & TECHNOLOGY, Van Wagenen Library, W Main St, 12043. SAN 311-0648. Tel: 518-234-5841. FAX: 518-255-5843. Web Site: www.cobleskill.edu/lrc. *Dir*, Nancy Van Deusen; E-Mail: vandeun@cobleskill.edu; *ILL*, Nancy Niles; *Publ Servs*, Patricia Hults; *Instr*, Francine Apollo; Tel: 518-255-5858; *Cat*, Colleen Smith; Tel: 518-255-5887; Staff 13 (MLS 5, Non-MLS 8)
Founded 1920. Enrl 2,762; Fac 141
Library Holdings: Bk Vols 65,000; Per Subs 300
Subject Interests: Agr sci, Agriculture, Early childhood educ, Local history, Sci
Special Collections: County History; Historical Material Related to Agriculture & Food Service
Automation Activity & Vendor Info: (Circulation) MultiLIS
Database Vendor: IAC - Info Trac, IAC - SearchBank, Lexis-Nexis, OCLC - First Search
Publications: LRC Information Series
Partic in Cap District Libr Coun for Ref & Res Resources; SUNY/OCLC
Open Mon-Thurs 8-10, Fri 8-5 & Sat 11-3; Sun 2-10 (Sept-May only)

COHOES

P COHOES PUBLIC LIBRARY, 169 Mohawk, 12047. SAN 311-0656. Tel: 518-235-2570. FAX: 518-237-4195.; Staff 4 (MLS 1, Non-MLS 3)
Founded 1969. Pop 16,000; Circ 49,484
Library Holdings: Bk Vols 39,236; Bk Titles 36,782; Per Subs 99
Special Collections: History of Cohoes & Environment
Database Vendor: DRA
Mem of Upper Hudson Library System
Friends of the Library Group

COLD SPRING

P JULIA L BUTTERFIELD MEMORIAL LIBRARY,* Morris Ave, 10516. SAN 311-0664. Tel: 914-265-3040. FAX: 914-265-4852. E-Mail: cospring@sebridge.org. *Dir, Librn*, Karen Shea
Pop 2,583; Circ 17,300
1997-1998 Income $90,000, County $18,407. Mats Exp $5,500, Books $4,000, Per/Ser (Incl. Access Fees) $1,000. Sal $30,000
Library Holdings: Bk Vols 12,500; Per Subs 30
Subject Interests: Local history
Mem of Mid-Hudson Library System
Open Mon & Wed 2-8, Tues & Thurs 11-5, Fri 2-5, Sat 11-2

S PUTNAM COUNTY HISTORICAL SOCIETY & FOUNDRY SCHOOL MUSEUM LIBRARY, Research Facilities, 63 Chestnut St, 10516. SAN 311-0672. Tel: 845-265-4010. FAX: 845-265-2884. E-Mail: pchs@highlands.com. *Exec Dir*, Doris Shaw; *Curator*, Charlotte Eaton
Founded 1906. Enrl 725; Fac 2; Highest Degree: Bachelor
1998-1999 Mats Exp $784, Books $180, Per/Ser (Incl. Access Fees) $60, Presv $514, Other Print Mats $30
Library Holdings: Bk Vols 1,550; Bk Titles 1,000
Subject Interests: Local history
Special Collections: Genealogy (Haida Davenport & Nelson Warren Coll), scrapbooks; Local Newspapers 1867-1913, microfilm
Function: Research library
Open Tues & Wed 10-4, Thurs 1-4, Sat & Sun 2-5; Research facilities closed Sat & Sun

COLD SPRING HARBOR

S COLD SPRING HARBOR LABORATORY LIBRARIES,* One Bungtown Rd, 11724-2203. SAN 311-0680. Tel: 516-367-8352. FAX: 516-367-6843. Web Site: www.cshl.org/library. *Dir*, Margaret Henderson; E-Mail: henderso@cshl.org; *ILL*, Wanda Stolen; *Tech Servs*, Ellen De Bruin; Staff 6 (MLS 1, Non-MLS 5)
Founded 1890
Jan 1997-Dec 1998 Income $707,350. Mats Exp $247,000, Books $13,000, Per/Ser (Incl. Access Fees) $232,000, Manuscripts & Archives $1,000. Sal $268,900
Library Holdings: Bk Titles 14,000; Per Subs 500
Subject Interests: Biochemistry, Cancer res, Cell biol, Genetics, Molecular biology, Neurobiol, Plant genetics, Virology
Special Collections: Historical Genetics-Eugenics Coll; History of Cold Spring Harbor Science
Publications: Bibliographies, Newsletter
Restriction: By appointment only
Partic in Dialog Corporation; Long Island Library Resources Council; Medical & Scientific Libraries of Long Island; OCLC Online Computer Library Center, Inc

P COLD SPRING HARBOR LIBRARY, 75 Goose Hill Rd, 11724-1315. SAN 311-0699. Tel: 631-692-6820. FAX: 631-692-6827. E-Mail: cshrlib@suffolk.lib.ny.us. Web Site: www.suffolk.lib.ny.us/libraries/cshr. *Dir*, Helen M Crosson; *Ch Servs*, Susan Holden; *Circ*, Margaret Koziol; *Ref Serv*, Marie T Horney; Staff 22 (MLS 10, Non-MLS 12)
Founded 1886. Pop 8,016; Circ 120,000
Jul 1999-Jun 2000 Income $665,140, Locally Generated Income $35,656. Mats Exp $68,707, Books $48,505, Per/Ser (Incl. Access Fees) $15,202, Electronic Ref Mat (Incl. Access Fees) $5,000. Sal $276,528 (Prof $201,634)
Library Holdings: Bk Vols 50,000; Bk Titles 46,000; Per Subs 130
Subject Interests: Local history
Automation Activity & Vendor Info: (Acquisitions) Innovative Interfaces Inc.; (Cataloging) Innovative Interfaces Inc.; (Circulation) Innovative Interfaces Inc.; (ILL) Innovative Interfaces Inc.; (OPAC) Innovative Interfaces Inc.
Publications: Whales Tale (newsletter)
Restriction: Residents only
Mem of Suffolk Cooperative Library System
Friends of the Library Group

S COLD SPRING HARBOR WHALING MUSEUM LIBRARY, Main St, PO Box 25, 11724. SAN 327-6511. Tel: 631-367-3418. FAX: 631-692-7037. E-Mail: cshwmuseum@aol.com. Web Site: www.cshwhalingmuseum.org. *Exec Dir*, Ann M Gill

Library Holdings: Bk Vols 1,200
Subject Interests: Local history, Maritime history
Special Collections: Whale Conservation; Whales

COLLINS

S COLLINS CORRECTIONAL FACILITY LIBRARY,* PO Box 490, 14034-0490. SAN 327-2419. Tel: 716-532-4588. FAX: 532-458-2099. *Librn*, Mary Metzger; Staff 1 (MLS 1)
Library Holdings: Bk Vols 14,700; Per Subs 66
Mem of Buffalo & Erie County Public Library System
Open Mon-Fri after 2pm

P COLLINS PUBLIC LIBRARY,* Mill St, PO Box 470, 14034. SAN 311-0729. Tel: 716-532-5129. *Librn*, Karen Koch
Pop 6,400; Circ 34,350
Library Holdings: Bk Vols 12,000; Per Subs 40
Mem of Buffalo & Erie County Public Library System

COLTON

P COLTON HEPBURN LIBRARY,* PO Box 7, 13625. SAN 311-0737. Tel: 315-262-2310. Interlibrary Loan Service Tel: 315-782-5540. FAX: 315-262-2182. *Librn*, Nancy McCarthy
Circ 19,378
Library Holdings: Bk Vols 8,433
Mem of North Country Library System
Friends of the Library Group

COMMACK

S BUSINESS TREND ANALYSIS LIBRARY,* 2171 Jericho Turnpike Ste 200, 11725-2900. SAN 373-482X. Tel: 631-462-5454. FAX: 631-462-1842. E-Mail: bta@li.net. Web Site: www.businesstrendanalysts.com. *VPres*, Charles J Ritchie; *Dir*, Donna Priani; *Librn*, Jackie Marquardt; *Commun Relations*, Robert S Travis
Library Holdings: Bk Vols 15,000; Per Subs 1,000
Function: For research purposes
Open Mon-Fri 9-5

P COMMACK PUBLIC LIBRARY, 18 Hauppauge Rd, 11725-4498. SAN 311-0745. Tel: 631-499-0888. FAX: 631-499-0591. E-Mail: cmmklib@suffolk.lib.ny.us. Web Site: www.suffolk.lib.ny.us/libraries/cmmk. *Dir*, Laurie Pastore; E-Mail: lpastore@suffolk.lib.ny.us; Staff 50 (MLS 10, Non-MLS 40)
Founded 1969. Pop 15,782
Library Holdings: Bk Titles 191,185; Per Subs 609
Automation Activity & Vendor Info: (Acquisitions) Innovative Interfaces Inc.; (Cataloging) Innovative Interfaces Inc.; (Circulation) Innovative Interfaces Inc.; (OPAC) Innovative Interfaces Inc.
Publications: Colophon (Newsletter); Internet Gazette (Newsletter)
Mem of Long Island Libr Resources Coun, Inc; Suffolk Cooperative Library System
Friends of the Library Group

SR PRESBYTERY OF LONG ISLAND, Resource Center,* 42 Hauppauge Rd, 11725. SAN 327-6538. Tel: 516-499-7171. FAX: 516-499-7063. *Librn*, Marie Zupka-Ludder
Library Holdings: Bk Vols 2,000; Per Subs 50
Open Mon-Fri 9-5

COMSTOCK

S GREAT MEADOW CORRECTIONAL FACILITY LIBRARY, PO Box 51, Rte 22, 12821. SAN 311-0761. Tel: 518-639-5516, Ext 4601. *Senior Librn*, Stephen M Almasi; Staff 1 (MLS 1)
Founded 1971
Apr 2000-Mar 2001 Mats Exp $13,000, Books $8,000, Per/Ser (Incl. Access Fees) $4,000, AV Equip $1,000. Sal $40,000
Library Holdings: Bk Vols 11,895; Bk Titles 8,250; Per Subs 50; High Interest/Low Vocabulary Bk Vols 300
Subject Interests: Black studies, Spanish lang
Automation Activity & Vendor Info: (Circulation) Follett
Database Vendor: Ebsco - EbscoHost
Mem of Southern Adirondack Library System
Provides services for 1650+ inmates of which 575 are registered library patrons

S WASHINGTON CORRECTIONAL FACILITY LIBRARY,* PO Box 180, 12821-0180. SAN 327-2494. Tel: 518-639-4486. FAX: 518-639-3299. *Librn*, D Cartmell
Mem of Southern Adirondack Library System

CONSTABLEVILLE

P CONSTABLEVILLE VILLAGE LIBRARY,* 3038 Main St, PO Box 376, 13325. SAN 311-077X. Tel: 315-397-2801. FAX: 315-397-2801. E-Mail: cnstbvl@northnet.org. *Librn*, Nancy Seelman
Circ 5,985
Library Holdings: Bk Vols 2,451; Per Subs 26
Mem of North Country Library System
Open Mon 1-5, Wed 3-5, Thurs 7-9, Fri 1-5 & 7-9
Friends of the Library Group

COOPERSTOWN

M BASSETT HEALTHCARE, New York Center for Agricultural Medicine & Health Library, One Atwell Rd, 13326. SAN 374-4965. Tel: 607-547-6023. FAX: 607-547-6087. E-Mail: nycamh@lakenet.org. Web Site: www.nycamh.org. *Librn*, Bernadette Hodge; E-Mail: bhodge@lakenet.org; Staff 1 (MLS 1)
Founded 1989
Library Holdings: Bk Titles 900; Per Subs 35
Subject Interests: Occupational health
Restriction: By appointment only
Mem of S Cent Res Libr

M MARY IMOGENE BASSETT HOSPITAL, Medical Library,* Atwell Rd, 13326. SAN 311-0788. Tel: 607-547-3115. FAX: 607-547-3006. *Librn*, Linda Muehl; *Asst Librn*, Robin Phillips
Founded 1936
Library Holdings: Bk Titles 5,000; Per Subs 600
Subject Interests: Clinical medicine, Pure sci, Transplantation
Special Collections: Gastrointestinal Surgery, bks & pamphlets
Partic in Dialog Corporation; Greater NE Regional Med Libr Program; New York State Interlibrary Loan Network

S NATIONAL BASEBALL HALL OF FAME & MUSEUM, INC, Library & Archives, 25 Main St, 13326-0590. SAN 311-080X. Tel: 607-547-0330. FAX: 607-547-4094. Web Site: www.baseballhalloffame.org. *Dir*, Jim Gates; *AV*, Jeremy Jones; *Ref*, Tim Wiles; *Coll Develop*, Anne McFarland; Staff 17 (MLS 5, Non-MLS 12)
Founded 1939
Library Holdings: Bk Titles 10,000; Per Subs 150
Subject Interests: Baseball, Economics, Sociology of baseball, Sports history
Special Collections: American League & National League Performance Statistics; Archives; Box Scores (1876-present); Schedules
Automation Activity & Vendor Info: (Cataloging) Innovative Interfaces Inc.
Publications: Hall of Fame Yearbook
Partic in S Cent Res Libr Coun

S NEW YORK STATE HISTORICAL ASSOCIATION RESEARCH LIBRARY, Lake Rd, PO Box 800, 13326. SAN 311-0818. Tel: 607-547-1470. FAX: 607-547-1405. E-Mail: library@nysha.org. Web Site: www.nysha.org/research.htm. *Assoc Dir*, Wayne Wright; Staff 5 (MLS 2, Non-MLS 3)
Founded 1899
Library Holdings: Bk Vols 85,000; Per Subs 320
Subject Interests: Am cultural hist, Am social, Decorative arts, Folk arts, Mus studies, N Am Indian art, NY genealogy, NY hist
Special Collections: New York State & Local History Coll, mss
Partic in S Cent Res Libr Coun

P VILLAGE LIBRARY OF COOPERSTOWN, 22 Main St, 13326-1331. SAN 311-0826. Tel: 607-547-8344. Interlibrary Loan Service Tel: 607-723-8236. FAX: 607-547-5487. *Dir*, David Kent
Pop 2,180; Circ 45,123
Library Holdings: Bk Vols 22,000; Per Subs 35
Special Collections: Job & Citizen Information Center
Mem of Four County Library System
Open Mon, Tues, Thurs & Fri 9-5, Wed 9-8, Sat 10-2
Friends of the Library Group

COPIAGUE

P COPIAGUE MEMORIAL PUBLIC LIBRARY, 50 Deauville Blvd, 11726-4100. SAN 311-0834. Tel: 631-691-1111. FAX: 631-691-1111. E-Mail: copglib@suffolk.lib.ny.us. Web Site: www.copiaguelibrary.org. *Dir*, Alicja Feitzinger; Fax: 631-691-5098, E-Mail: afeitzing@suffolk.lib.ny.us; Staff 59 (MLS 6, Non-MLS 53)
Founded 1961. Pop 25,758; Circ 239,857
Library Holdings: Bk Vols 116,507; Per Subs 8,500
Special Collections: Foreign Language
Database Vendor: Innovative Interfaces INN - View
Publications: Newsletter (bi-monthly)
Mem of Suffolk Cooperative Library System
Partic in CLSI Consortium; Long Island Library Resources Council
Friends of the Library Group

CORAM

S US GEOLOGICAL SURVEY WATER RESOURCES DIVISION, New York Sub-District Library, Bldg 4 2045 Rte 112, 11727. SAN 370-2731. Tel: 631-736-0783. FAX: 631-736-4283. *In Charge*, Joann Pitts
Library Holdings: Bk Vols 7,000
Subject Interests: Climatology, Geochemistry, Geology
Restriction: By appointment only

CORFU

P CORFU FREE LIBRARY, 7 Maple Ave, 14036. (Mail add: PO Box 419, 14036-0419), Tel: 716-599-3321. FAX: 716-599-3321. *Dir*, Kelly A March; E-Mail: kmarc@nioga.org; *Asst Librn*, Suzane Schauf; Staff 3 (Non-MLS 3)
Founded 1920. Pop 755; Circ 14,451
Library Holdings: Bk Titles 20,401; Per Subs 10
Function: ILL limited
Mem of Nioga Library System
Open Mon & Thurs 6pm-9pm, Tues & Fri 1pm-8pm, Wed & Sat 10am-1pm
Friends of the Library Group

CORINTH

P CORINTH FREE LIBRARY,* 89 Main St, 12822. SAN 311-0869. Tel: 518-654-6913. FAX: 518-654-6913. E-Mail: corlib@netheaven.com. *Librn*, Rebecca Fasulo
Founded 1926. Pop 5,442; Circ 27,314
1997-1998 Income $38,846, County $657, Locally Generated Income $7,424. Mats Exp $7,100, Books $6,500, Per/Ser (Incl. Access Fees) $600. Sal $23,601
Library Holdings: Bk Vols 20,664; Bk Titles 15,000; Per Subs 16
Mem of Southern Adirondack Library System
Open Mon, Tues & Thurs 11-5 & 7-8:30, Fri 9:30-4, Sat 10-4
Friends of the Library Group

CORNING

P CORNING AREA PUBLIC LIBRARY,* 300 Civic Plaza, 14830. SAN 311-0915. Tel: 607-936-3713. FAX: 607-936-3715. *Dir*, Toni Rorapaugh; *Acq, Ref*, Julia Lon Grimsman; Staff 3 (MLS 3)
Founded 1969. Pop 34,141; Circ 168,604
Library Holdings: Bk Vols 95,114; Bk Titles 100,556; Per Subs 175
Subject Interests: Glass, Local history
Special Collections: Caldecott & Newbery Winners & Honors
Open Mon 9:30-8:30, Tues & Thurs 1-8:30, Wed 9:30-5:30, Fri & Sat 9:30-12:30
Friends of the Library Group

J CORNING COMMUNITY COLLEGE, Arthur A Houghton, Jr Library, One Academic Dr, 14830. SAN 311-0885. Tel: 607-962-9251. Reference Tel: 607-962-9484. Toll Free Tel: 800-358-7171. FAX: 607-962-9466. E-Mail: manheim@corning-cc.edu. Web Site: www.corning-cc.edu/library/. *Dir*, Barbara Hornick-Lockard; E-Mail: lockarbh@corning-cc.edu; *ILL*, Margaret Nyberg; E-Mail: nyberg@corning-cc.edu; *Syst Coordr*, Susan Gloss; E-Mail: roy@corning-cc.edu; *Cat*, Rosanne Darcangelo; E-Mail: darcanrm@corning-cc.edu; *Archivist, Coll Develop, Ref*, Cindy Maier; E-Mail: maiercc@corning-cc.edu; *Govt Doc*, Alexis Manheim; E-Mail: manheim@corning-cc.edu; Staff 6 (MLS 4, Non-MLS 2)
Founded 1957. Enrl 2,900; Fac 116; Highest Degree: Associate
Sep 1998-Aug 1999 Income $545,295, State $7,745. Mats Exp $153,000, Books $20,644, Per/Ser (Incl. Access Fees) $25,025, Presv $3,600, Micro $2,038, AV Equip $5,000. Sal $460,626
Library Holdings: Bk Vols 70,397; Per Subs 958
Special Collections: Local History; Rare Books
Automation Activity & Vendor Info: (Cataloging) DRA; (Cataloging) MultiLIS; (Circulation) MultiLIS; (Circulation) DRA; (OPAC) DRA; (OPAC) MultiLIS; (OPAC) MultiLIS; (Serials) DRA; (Serials) MultiLIS; (Serials) MultiLIS
Database Vendor: OCLC - First Search
Partic in SUNY/OCLC
Special Services for the Deaf - Captioned media
Special Services for the Blind - Adapted computers & special software with speech output to assist learning disabled, mentally retarded & uneducated
Open Mon-Thurs 8-6 & Fri 8-4
Friends of the Library Group

S CORNING INCORPORATED, Technical Information Center,* Sullivan Park, 14831. SAN 311-0893. Tel: 607-974-3359. FAX: 607-974-2406.; Staff 2 (MLS 2)
Founded 1936
Library Holdings: Bk Vols 22,000; Per Subs 320
Subject Interests: Ceramics, Chemistry, Glass, Physics
Automation Activity & Vendor Info: (Cataloging) TechLIB; (Circulation) TechLIB

S CORNING MUSEUM OF GLASS, Rakow Research Library, Five Museum Way, 14830. SAN 311-0907. Tel: 607-974-8166. FAX: 607-974-8677. E-Mail: rakow@cmog.org. Web Site: www.cmog.org. *Librn*, Patricia Rogers; *Asst Librn*, Lori Fuller; E-Mail: fullerla@cmog.org; Staff 10 (MLS 3, Non-MLS 7)
Founded 1951
Library Holdings: Bk Vols 70,000; Bk Titles 45,000; Per Subs 900
Subject Interests: Archaeology, Glass art, Glassware, Hist of glass, Manufacturing of glass before 1930
Special Collections: Antiquarian & Rare Books, bks & microfiche; Trade catalogs, slides
Partic in OCLC Online Computer Library Center, Inc

CORNWALL

P CORNWALL PUBLIC LIBRARY, 395 Hudson St, 12518-1552. SAN 352-4108. Tel: 914-534-8282. FAX: 914-534-3827. *Dir*, Carol M Connell; *Ref*, Vivian Milczarski; Staff 3 (MLS 3)
Pop 14,289; Circ 112,000
Jul 2000-Jun 2001 Income $560,435, City $542,435, Other $18,000. Mats Exp $71,791, Books $40,582, Per/Ser (Incl. Access Fees) $20,309, Presv $500, Micro $400, Electronic Ref Mat (Incl. Access Fees) $10,000. Sal $338,511 (Prof $122,431)
Library Holdings: Bk Vols 34,797
Special Collections: Biography & Literature (Local Authors Coll); Local History, bks, cassettes, mss, maps, micro, pamphlets, slides
Automation Activity & Vendor Info: (Circulation) epixtech, inc.
Publications: Friends of the Cornwall Public Library (newsletter); Library Newsletter
Mem of Ramapo Catskill Library System
Special Services - Homebound library service; Deposit collection at meals site
Friends of the Library Group

CORTLAND

S CORTLAND COUNTY HISTORICAL SOCIETY'S KELLOGG MEMORIAL RESEARCH LIBRARY, 25 Homer Ave, 13045. SAN 311-094X. Tel: 607-756-6071. *Dir*, Mary Ann Kane
Founded 1925
Library Holdings: Bk Titles 3,000
Special Collections: Genealogy & History of Cortland County, mss
Open Tues-Sat 1-5

P CORTLAND FREE LIBRARY,* 32 Church St, 13045. SAN 311-0958. Tel: 607-753-1042. FAX: 607-758-7329. E-Mail: cortland@lakenet.org. *Dir*, Warren S Eddy; Staff 1 (MLS 1)
Founded 1886. Pop 26,761; Circ 104,229
Jan 1999-Dec 1999 Income $321,285, State $10,950, City $239,975, Locally Generated Income $26,160, Other $44,200. Mats Exp $80,120, Books $49,400, Per/Ser (Incl. Access Fees) $21,400, Presv $2,020, Micro $7,000, Other Print Mats $300. Sal $157,645
Library Holdings: Bk Vols 107,933; Bk Titles 86,000; Per Subs 388
Affiliation with Finger Lakes Library System

C STATE UNIVERSITY OF NEW YORK COLLEGE, Memorial Library, 81 Prospect Terrace, 13045. (Mail add: PO Box 2000, 13045), SAN 352-4221. Tel: 607-753-2526. FAX: 607-753-5669. E-Mail: www.library@snycorva.cortland.edu. Web Site: www.library.cortland.edu. *Dir*, Gail Wood; *Automation Syst Coordr*, Dave Ritchie; *Bibliogr*, Thomas Bonn; *Bibliogr*, Gretchen Herrmann; *Bibliogr*, David Kreh; *Bibliogr*, Ellen McCabe; *Cat*, Lorraine Melita; *Info Tech*, Anita Stoner; *ILL*, Ellen Paterson; *Coll Develop*, Charles Bernholz; Staff 31 (MLS 14, Non-MLS 17)
Founded 1868. Enrl 6,306; Fac 428; Highest Degree: Master
Jul 1999-Jun 2000 Income (Main Library Only) $1,725,473. Mats Exp $423,637, Books $93,777, Per/Ser (Incl. Access Fees) $216,784, Presv $12,036, Electronic Ref Mat (Incl. Access Fees) $101,040. Sal $1,143,831
Library Holdings: Bk Vols 400,274; Bk Titles 303,616; Per Subs 1,216
Subject Interests: Education, Health educ, Phys educ, Recreation
Automation Activity & Vendor Info: (Cataloging) MultiLIS; (Circulation) MultiLIS; (OPAC) MultiLIS
Publications: bibliographies & research guides
Partic in OCLC Online Computer Library Center, Inc; S Cent Res Libr Coun
Departmental Libraries:
ART SLIDE, Fine Arts Bldg, 13045. SAN 352-4256. Tel: 607-753-5519. *Curator*, Lisa Joyce
Special Collections: Rousey Arts in Sports Coll
MUSIC, Fine Arts Bldg, 13045. SAN 352-4310. Tel: 607-753-2812. FAX: 607-753-5728. *Chairperson*, Karen Bals

G UNITED STATES GEOLOGICAL SURVEY, Tunison Laboratory of Aquatic Science Library, 3075 Gracie Rd, 13045-9357. SAN 311-0982. Tel: 607-753-9391. FAX: 607-753-0259. *Dir*, Jim Johnson; *Librn*, Janet Potts; E-Mail: janet_potts@usgs.gov
Founded 1932
Library Holdings: Bk Vols 700

Subject Interests: Ecology, Fish diseases, Fish nutrition, Fish physiology, Restoration
This library is part of the USGS Biological Res Div, Technical Information Service, Great Lakes Science Center, Ann Arbor, MI

COXSACKIE

S COXSACKIE CORRECTIONAL FACILITY LIBRARY,* PO Box 200, 12051-0200. SAN 327-1323. Tel: 518-731-2781. FAX: 518-731-2099. *Librn*, Elizabeth Becht
Library Holdings: Bk Titles 3,300; Per Subs 50
Mem of Mid-Hudson Library System
Open 8-4

S GREENE CORRECTIONAL FACILITY LIBRARY,* PO Box 8, 12051-0008. SAN 327-2532. Tel: 518-731-2741, Ext 4600. FAX: 518-731-2741, Ext 2099.
Library Holdings: Bk Titles 5,000; Per Subs 70
Mem of Mid-Hudson Library System

S GREENE COUNTY HISTORICAL SOCIETY, Vedder Memorial Library, 90 County Rd 42, 12051-3022. SAN 311-0990. Tel: 518-731-1033, 518-731-6822. Web Site: www.gchistory.org. *Librn*, Raymond Beecher
Library Holdings: Bk Titles 7,803; Per Subs 20; Spec Interest Per Sub 20
Subject Interests: Catskills, Greene County, Mid-Hudson valley
Special Collections: County Maps; County Newspapers from 1790; Family Papers; Genealogy Coll; Greene County Surrogate Court Records; Postcards; Scrapbooks
Publications: Quarterly journal - indexed each five years

P HEERMANCE MEMORIAL LIBRARY,* One Ely St, 12051. SAN 311-1008. Tel: 518-731-8084. FAX: 518-731-8264. E-Mail: heermlib@mhonline.net. Web Site: www.hml.lib.ny.us. *Dir*, Debbie Scott; Staff 1 (MLS 1)
Pop 6,018; Circ 23,000
Library Holdings: Bk Vols 35,000; Per Subs 20
Subject Interests: Local history, Rare books
Special Collections: Heermance Coll, maps, mss & docs
Mem of Mid-Hudson Library System
Open Tues & Wed 10-5 & 6-8 & Sat 10-1
Friends of the Library Group

CRAGSMOOR

P CRAGSMOOR FREE LIBRARY,* PO Box 410, 12420-0410. SAN 311-1016. Tel: 914-647-4611. FAX: 914-647-4611. E-Mail: zelacom.com@cragsmoor.com. *Dir*, Eileen Kolaitis
Founded 1913. Pop 750; Circ 5,655
Library Holdings: Bk Titles 10,693; Per Subs 62
Special Collections: Local History Coll, including art colony (1880s-1930s)
Publications: Art Show Catalogs; Cragsmoor: A Historical Sketch
Mem of Ramapo Catskill Library System
Open Mon & Thurs 9:30-5, Sat 9:30-2:30
Friends of the Library Group

CRANBERRY LAKE

P CLIFTON COMMUNITY LIBRARY,* SR 3, PO Box 678, 12927. SAN 311-1024. Tel: 315-848-3256. FAX: 315-848-3554. *Librn*, Bethany Rathman
Founded 1975. Pop 1,005
Library Holdings: Bk Vols 10,229; Per Subs 13
Subject Interests: Adirondack, Local history
Special Collections: Adirondack Memorial Coll
Mem of North Country Library System
Open Mon, Wed, Fri & Sat 10-1, Mon-Wed 6:30-9pm Oct-Apr, Mon, Wed, Fri & Sat 10-2, 6-9pm May-Sept
Friends of the Library Group

CROGHAN

P CROGHAN FREE LIBRARY,* Main St, PO Box 8, 13327. SAN 311-1032. Tel: 315-346-6521. *Librn*, Rose Buckingham
Circ 8,694
Library Holdings: Bk Vols 5,309; Per Subs 32
Mem of North Country Library System
Open Mon, Wed & Fri 12:30-4:30, Fri 7-9

CROSS RIVER

G WESTCHESTER COUNTY DEPARTMENT OF PARKS RECREATION & CONSERVATION, Delaware Indian Resource Center, Trailside Nature Museum,* Ward Pound Ridge Reservation, 10518. SAN 328-2325. Tel: 914-763-3993. FAX: 914-763-2429. E-Mail: trailsid@bestweb.net. *Curator*, Beth Herr
Library Holdings: Bk Titles 4,000
Subject Interests: Native Americans
Special Collections: Bureau of Ethnology, annual publications 1879-1940
Friends of the Library Group

CROTON-ON-HUDSON

P CROTON FREE LIBRARY, (CFL), 171 Cleveland Dr, 10520. SAN 311-1040. Tel: 914-271-6612. FAX: 914-271-0931. *Dir*, Mary C Donnery; E-Mail: mdonnery@wis.lib.ny.us; *AV, Ref*, Martha Campbell; *Ch Servs*, Martha Taylor; *Circ*, Sally West; *Circ*, Alice Rothrock; *Tech Servs*, Lori Phillips; Staff 35 (MLS 7, Non-MLS 28)
Founded 1937. Pop 8,685; Circ 121,000
Jul 2000-Jun 2001 Income $630,000. Sal $312,450 (Prof $163,320)
Library Holdings: Bk Titles 86,779
Special Collections: Railroad Coll
Database Vendor: epixtech, inc.
Mem of Westchester Library System

CROWN POINT

P HAMMOND LIBRARY OF CROWN POINT NY, Main St, 12928. (Mail add: PO Box 245, 12928), SAN 311-1075. Tel: 518-597-3616. FAX: 518-597-3066. E-Mail: hlibrary@cptelco.net. *Pres*, Elaine Monroe; *VPres*, Diane Kahler; Staff 1 (MLS 1)
Founded 1899. Circ 10,901
Library Holdings: Bk Vols 6,590; Per Subs 30
Mem of Clinton-Essex-Franklin Library System
Open Tues, Wed & Thurs 12-4, Fri & Sat 9-1, closed Mon
Friends of the Library Group

CUBA

P CUBA CIRCULATING LIBRARY, 39 E Main St, 14727. SAN 311-1083. Tel: 716-968-1668. FAX: 716-968-3004. E-Mail: cuba@stls.org. Web Site: www.stls.org/cuba. *Dir*, Cynthia Dutton; E-Mail: cub_cindy@chstls.org
Circ 44,048
Jan 1999-Dec 1999 Mats Exp $82,056, Books $10,000, Per/Ser (Incl. Access Fees) $1,018. Sal $50,924
Library Holdings: Bk Vols 17,058; Per Subs 57; High Interest/Low Vocabulary Bk Vols 50
Subject Interests: Allegany County, Cuba hist, Genealogy
Automation Activity & Vendor Info: (Circulation) DRA; (OPAC) DRA
Mem of Southern Tier Library System
Open Mon & Tues 9-12, 2-5 & 7- 9, Wed & Thurs 2-5 & 7-9, Fri 2-5, Sat 10-12 & 2-5
Friends of the Library Group

CUTCHOGUE

P CUTCHOGUE-NEW SUFFOLK FREE LIBRARY, (Formerly Cutchogue Free Library), Main Rd, PO Box 935, 11935-0935. SAN 311-1091. Tel: 516-734-6360. FAX: 516-734-7010. E-Mail: cutclib@suffolk.lib.ny.us. Web Site: www.northfork.net/library/cutchogue. *Dir*, Jane Minerva; Staff 13 (MLS 3, Non-MLS 10)
Founded 1841. Pop 3,230; Circ 129,241
Jan 1999-Dec 1999 Income $664,234. Mats Exp $51,587, Books $25,667, Per/Ser (Incl. Access Fees) $6,084. Sal $385,186 (Prof $137,337)
Library Holdings: Bk Titles 30,231; Per Subs 380
Subject Interests: Local history
Mem of Suffolk Cooperative Library System
Friends of the Library Group

DANNEMORA

S CLINTON CORRECTIONAL FACILITY LIBRARY,* PO Box 2000, 12929-2000. SAN 328-7955. Tel: 518-492-2511. FAX: 518-492-2099. *Librn*, Mary Armstrong
1997-1998 Income $20,000, Federal $10,000. Mats Exp $30,200, Books $20,000, Per/Ser (Incl. Access Fees) $10,000, Micro $200
Open Mon-Fri 8-4

P DANNEMORA FREE LIBRARY,* Town Hall Bldg, Cook St, PO Box 326, 12929. SAN 352-4345. Tel: 518-492-7005. *Dir*, Judy Harris; Tel: 518-492-7115
Founded 1940. Pop 2,006; Circ 22,943
Library Holdings: Bk Vols 15,855; Per Subs 31
Mem of Clinton-Essex-Franklin Library System
Partic in OCLC Online Computer Library Center, Inc
Open Tues & Fri 1-5pm & 7-9pm

DANSVILLE

P DANSVILLE PUBLIC LIBRARY, Shepard Memorial Library, 200 Main St, 14437. SAN 311-1105. Tel: 716-335-6720. FAX: 716-335-6133. E-Mail: dpl@servtech.com. Web Site: dansville.lib.ny.us. *Dir*, Teresa A Dearing; Staff 1 (MLS 1)
Founded 1874. Pop 10,423; Circ 47,327
Jul 1999-Jun 2000 Income $193,220, State $8,686, County $7,752, Locally Generated Income $121,493, Other $55,289. Mats Exp $24,140, Books $14,830, Per/Ser (Incl. Access Fees) $2,319, Presv $643, AV Equip $6,303, Other Print Mats $45. Sal $98,156 (Prof $38,213)
Library Holdings: Bk Vols 24,507; Bk Titles 23,500; Per Subs 109
Subject Interests: Local history
Mem of Pioneer Library System
Open Mon & Wed 10am-8:30pm, Tues, Thurs & Fri 1-8:30pm, Sat noon-4pm
Friends of the Library Group

DE RUYTER

P DERUYTER FREE LIBRARY,* PO Box 399, 13052. SAN 325-1543. Tel: 315-852-6262. E-Mail: dr_circ@midyork.lib.ny.os. *Librn*, Nancy Nivison
Pop 1,458; Circ 25,000
1998-1999 Income $30,000, State $1,000, Provincial $11,000, City $3,000, County $2,000. Mats Exp $8,500, Books $7,000, Per/Ser (Incl. Access Fees) $500, Micro $1,000. Sal $10,500
Library Holdings: Bk Titles 18,000
Mem of Mid-York Library System
Friends of the Library Group

DE WITT

P DE WITT COMMUNITY LIBRARY,* Shoppingtown Mall, 3649 Erie Blvd E, 13214. SAN 311-1229. Tel: 315-446-3578. FAX: 315-446-1955. E-Mail: dcl@transit.nyser.net. *Actg Dir*, Susan Rekhow
Founded 1962. Pop 15,546; Circ 186,000
Library Holdings: Bk Vols 47,285; Bk Titles 46,440; Per Subs 234
Subject Interests: Bus marketing, Holocaust, Literary criticism, Stock marketing
Special Collections: Closed-Caption Videos
Automation Activity & Vendor Info: (Circulation) Gaylord
Publications: Dewitt Community Library Newsletter
Mem of Onondaga County Public Library
Open Mon-Thurs 10-9, Fri & Sat 10-5, Sun 12-5

DEER PARK

S AIL SYSTEMS, INC, MS DI Library, Commack Rd, 11729-4591. SAN 373-1790. Tel: 631-595-5430. FAX: 631-595-3592. *Librn*, Roberta Elliiot
Library Holdings: Bk Vols 40,000; Per Subs 25
Subject Interests: Electronics, Space science
Database Vendor: OCLC - First Search

P DEER PARK PUBLIC LIBRARY, 44 Lake Ave, 11729-6047. SAN 311-113X. Tel: 516-586-3000. FAX: 516-586-3006. *Dir*, Dina M Reilly; *Ref*, Lisa Shumicky; *Ch Servs*, Dawn Gaudy
Founded 1964. Pop 26,000; Circ 200,000
Library Holdings: Bk Vols 100,100; Per Subs 410
Publications: Newsletter
Mem of Suffolk Cooperative Library System
Open Mon-Thurs 9-9, Fri 9-6, Sat 9-5

DELEVAN

P DELEVAN-YORKSHIRE PUBLIC LIBRARY, 28 School St, PO Box 185, 14042. SAN 311-1148. Tel: 716-492-1961. FAX: 716-492-3398. *Librn*, Peggy Richardson; Staff 4 (MLS 1, Non-MLS 3)
Circ 19,336
Library Holdings: Bk Vols 15,000
Mem of Chautauqua-Cattaraugus Library System

DELHI

P CANNON FREE LIBRARY,* 40 Elm St, 13753. SAN 311-1156. Tel: 607-746-2662. FAX: 607-746-2662. *Librn*, Cathy Johnson
Founded 1918. Pop 5,015; Circ 71,708
Library Holdings: Bk Vols 30,000; Per Subs 78
Special Collections: Delaware County Hist Coll
Mem of Four County Library System

GL DELAWARE SUPREME COURT LIBRARY,* 3 Court St, 13753-9990. SAN 311-1164. Tel: 607-746-3959. FAX: 607-746-3253.
Founded 1880
Library Holdings: Bk Vols 8,500

M O'CONNOR HOSPITAL DIVISION LIBRARY,* HC 74 Box 205A, 13753. SAN 328-2724. Tel: 607-746-0300. FAX: 607-746-0347. *In Charge*, Barbara Green
Library Holdings: Bk Vols 75; Per Subs 27

J STATE UNIVERSITY OF NEW YORK COLLEGE OF TECHNOLOGY, Resnick Library, Main St, 13753-1190. SAN 311-1172. Tel: 607-746-4635. FAX: 607-746-4327. E-Mail: library@delhi.edu. Web Site: wc.delhi.edu/library. *Dir*, Pamela J Peters; *Doc, Online Servs, Publ Servs*, Kate Majewski; Staff 3 (MLS 3)
Founded 1915. Enrl 2,330; Fac 139
1998-1999 Income $100,000, State $59,000. Mats Exp $65,000
Library Holdings: Bk Vols 50,000; Bk Titles 49,000; Per Subs 330
Subject Interests: Architecture, Horticulture, Hospitality, Local history, Nursing, Technology, Turf, Vet sci
Special Collections: Travel File, pamphlet
Publications: Library Instruction Materials; library rules & regulations; Pathfinders; staff hand books; student handbook
Mem of S Cent Res Libr
Partic in Dialog Corporation; South Central Regional Library Council; State University Of New York-NYLINK

DELMAR

P BETHLEHEM PUBLIC LIBRARY, 451 Delaware Ave, 12054-3042. SAN 311-1180. Tel: 518-439-9314. TDD: TTY/ 518-439-9314. FAX: 518-478-0901. E-Mail: bpl@uhls.org/bethlehem. Web Site: www.uhls.org/bethlehem. *Dir*, Nancy L Pieri; E-Mail: pierin@uhls.lib.ny.us; *Asst Dir*, Jeanne M Biggins; *AV*, Michael V Farley; *Head, Circ, Tech Servs*, Geoffrey Kirkpatrick; *Ad Servs, Head Ref*, Sherry D Haluska; *YA Servs*, Beverly Provest; Staff 68 (MLS 23, Non-MLS 45)
Founded 1913. Pop 24,000; Circ 530,176
Jul 2000-Jun 2001 Income $2,854,443, State $25,000, Locally Generated Income $386,000, Other $2,443,443. Mats Exp $245,600, Books $184,100, Per/Ser (Incl. Access Fees) $22,000, Presv $1,500, AV Equip $28,000, Electronic Ref Mat (Incl. Access Fees) $10,000. Sal $1,628,187 (Prof $831,794)
Library Holdings: Bk Titles 138,652; Per Subs 382
Special Collections: Career Resources Coll; Local History & Genealogy Book Coll; Small Business Coll
Automation Activity & Vendor Info: (Circulation) DRA; (OPAC) DRA
Publications: Footnotes
Mem of Upper Hudson Library System
Partic in Cap District Libr Coun for Ref & Res Resources
Special Services for the Deaf - TDD; TTY machine; Videos & decoder
Friends of the Library Group

DEPAUVILLE

P DEPAUVILLE FREE LIBRARY,* PO Box 239, 13632. SAN 311-1199. Tel: 315-686-3299. *Librn*, Connie Haver
Circ 4,370
Library Holdings: Bk Vols 1,387
Mem of North Country Library System
Open Mon 6-8, Tues & Thurs 11:30-4:30

DEPOSIT

P DEPOSIT FREE LIBRARY, 159 Front St, 13754. SAN 311-1202. Tel: 607-467-2577. *Librn*, Anne Parsons
Pop 4,427; Circ 17,522
Library Holdings: Bk Vols 12,583; Per Subs 50
Mem of Four County Library System
Open Tues & Thurs 12:30-5 & 7-9, Fri & Sat 10-12 & 1-5

DEXTER

P DEXTER FREE LIBRARY,* 120 Kirby St, 13634. SAN 311-1237. Tel: 315-639-6785. E-Mail: plusdexplus@northnet.org. *Librn*, Suzette Cumoletti
Founded 1924. Pop 1,200; Circ 80,000
Library Holdings: Bk Vols 8,200; Per Subs 30
Mem of North Country Library System
Open Tues & Thurs 12-5, Sat 12-4
Friends of the Library Group

DIX HILLS

S DIX HILLS JEWISH CENTER LIBRARY, 555 Vanderbilt Pkwy, 11746. SAN 323-6137. Tel: 631-499-6644. *Librn*, Leslie Schotz; Staff 1 (MLS 1)
Library Holdings: Bk Vols 1,000; Per Subs 16
Restriction: Members only
Open Sun 9:30-12:30 & Wed 5:30-8:30

C FIVE TOWNS COLLEGE LIBRARY, 305 N Service Rd, 11746. SAN 311-4899. Tel: 631-424-7000, Ext 138. FAX: 631-424-7008. *Dir*, Phyllis Z Singer; Tel: 631-424-7000, Ext 133, E-Mail: psinger@ftc.edu; *Asst Librn*,

Tracy Ann Smith; E-Mail: tsmith@ftc.edu; *Music*, Gwen Kowalik; E-Mail: gkowalik@ftc.edu. Subject Specialists: *Computers*, Tracy Ann Smith; *Film*, Phyllis Z Singer; *Music*, Gwen Kowalik; *Popular music*, Phyllis Z Singer; *Psychology*, Tracy Ann Smith; *Reference*, Phyllis Z Singer; Staff 6 (MLS 3, Non-MLS 3)
Founded 1972. Enrl 900; Fac 104; Highest Degree: Master
Jun 2000-Jun 2001 Income $100,000. Mats Exp $100,000. Sal $95,000
Library Holdings: Bk Titles 30,000; Per Subs 550; Spec Interest Per Sub 550; Bks on Deafness & Sign Lang 10
Subject Interests: Business, Music, Theatre, Video
Special Collections: Music sheet music, popular and classic songbooks
Automation Activity & Vendor Info: (Circulation) Athena; (OPAC) Sagebrush Corporation
Database Vendor: Ebsco - EbscoHost, OCLC - First Search, ProQuest
Publications: Newsletter (Accession list)
Function: ILL available
Mem of Suffolk County Libr Syst
Partic in Long Island Library Resources Council
Open 8-6:30

P HALF HOLLOW HILLS COMMUNITY LIBRARY, 55 Vanderbilt Pkwy, 11746. SAN 352-440X. Tel: 516-421-4530. FAX: 516-421-0730. E-Mail: hhhllib@suffolk.lib.ny.us. Web Site: hhhl.suffolk.lib.ny.us. *Dir*, Mary Jane Schmidt; E-Mail: mlaronde@suffolk.lib.ny.us; *Librn*, Johanna Fiske; Tel: 631-421-4535, Fax: 631421-3715; Staff 160 (MLS 30, Non-MLS 130)
Founded 1959. Pop 41,745; Circ 323,744
Jul 1998-Jun 1999 Income (Main Library and Branch Library) $4,571,680, Locally Generated Income $188,261. Mats Exp $525,765, Books $356,188, Per/Ser (Incl. Access Fees) $39,662, Micro $13,861, AV Equip $20,957, Other Print Mats $23,617, Electronic Ref Mat (Incl. Access Fees) $71,480. Sal $2,737,718 (Prof $1,153,178)
Library Holdings: Bk Vols 304,943
Subject Interests: Bus, Econ, Mgt, Relig studies
Publications: The First R
Mem of Suffolk Cooperative Library System
Partic in Long Island Library Resources Council
Branches: 1
MELVILLE BRANCH, 510 Sweet Hollow Rd, Melville, 11747. SAN 352-4434. Tel: 516-421-4535. FAX: 631-421-3715. *Librn*, Johanna Fiske; E-Mail: jfiske@suffolk.lib.ny.us

DOBBS FERRY

S AKZO NOBEL CHEMICALS, INC, Research Library,* One Livingstone Ave, 10522-3401. SAN 329-7624. Tel: 914-674-5000. FAX: 914-693-5840. *Asst Librn*, Edwin Santos
Founded 1965
Library Holdings: Bk Vols 14,422
Subject Interests: Biochemistry, Ceramics
Publications: Information Services Bulletin (monthly)
Partic in Dialog Corporation; Easylink; Orbit; State University Of New York-NYLINK
Open 8am-4pm, with restrictions; guard after hours, ext 5516

P DOBBS FERRY PUBLIC LIBRARY, 153 Main St, 10522. SAN 311-1253. Tel: 914-693-6614. FAX: 914-693-4671. Web Site: www.wls.lib.ny.us. *Dir, Ref Serv Ad*, Jeffrey Ault; *Ch Servs, Librn*, Cheryl Matthews
Founded 1890. Pop 10,000; Circ 48,000
Jun 1998-May 1999 Income $278,000. Mats Exp $37,750, Books $24,000, Per/Ser (Incl. Access Fees) $13,750. Sal $160,900 (Prof $89,400)
Library Holdings: Bk Titles 36,000; Per Subs 100
Database Vendor: epixtech, inc.
Publications: Friends Bimonthly Newsletter
Mem of Westchester Library System
Friends of the Library Group

C MERCY COLLEGE LIBRARIES, 555 Broadway, 10522. SAN 311-1261. Tel: 914-674-7600, Ext 7256. Circulation Tel: 914-674-7256. Reference Tel: 914-674-7257. FAX: 914-674-7581. E-Mail: libref@mercynet.edu. Web Site: www.mercynet.edu/library/. *Dir*, W Bruce Fulton; *Automation Syst Coordr, Tech Servs*, Nina Lee; *Coll Develop, Publ Servs*, Donald Ray; *Bibliog Instr*, Susan Gaskin-Noel; *Bibliog Instr*, Judith Liebman; *Bibliog Instr*, Kristine Wycisk; *ILL*, Heather Blenkinsopp; *Librn*, Margaret Gough; Staff 25 (MLS 12, Non-MLS 13)
Founded 1960. Enrl 5,100; Fac 166; Highest Degree: Master
1998-1999 Income $2,061,226. Mats Exp $651,715. Sal $1,310,186 (Prof $617,231)
Library Holdings: Bk Vols 180,000; Per Subs 1,400
Special Collections: Eric doc; Library of American Civilization; Library of English Literature; Vanderpoel Print Coll
Publications: MCL Newsletter
Partic in New York Metrop Ref & Res Libr Agency; State University Of New York-NYLINK
Departmental Libraries:
BRONX CAMPUS, 50 Antin Pl, Bronx, 10462. SAN 310-9100. Tel: 718-518-7710. FAX: 718-518-7879. E-Mail: libref@mercynet.edu. Web Site: www.mercynet.edu/library/. *Librn*, Addie Armstrong; *Librn*, Michele Lee
Library Holdings: Bk Vols 18,088
WHITE PLAINS CAMPUS, 277 Martine Ave & S Broadway, White Plains, 10601. SAN 312-6862. Tel: 914-948-3666. FAX: 914-686-1858. E-Mail: libref@mercynet.edu. Web Site: www.mercynet.edu/library/. *Librn*, Srivalli Rao
Library Holdings: Bk Vols 11,376; Per Subs 60
YORKTOWN CAMPUS, 2651 Strang Blvd, Yorktown Heights, 10598. SAN 312-7214. Tel: 914-245-6100. FAX: 914-962-1042. E-Mail: libref@mercynet.edu. Web Site: www.mercynet.edu/library/. *Librn*, Agnes Cameron
Library Holdings: Bk Vols 36,243

DOLGEVILLE

P DOLGEVILLE-MANHEIM PUBLIC LIBRARY, 20 N Main St, 13329. SAN 311-1288. Tel: 315-429-3421. E-Mail: do.diao@midyork.lib.ny.us. *Dir*, Sharon Trodler; E-Mail: trodler@midyork.lib.ny.us; Staff 2 (Non-MLS 2)
Founded 1890. Pop 3,527; Circ 21,937
Library Holdings: Bk Vols 11,283; Per Subs 12
Mem of Mid-York Library System
Open Mon-Fri 12-5

DOUGLASTON

S ALLEY POND ENVIRONMENTAL CENTER, INC LIBRARY,* 228-06 Northern Blvd, 11363. SAN 377-368X. Tel: 718-229-4000. FAX: 718-229-0376. *Exec Dir*, Irene V Scheid
Library Holdings: Bk Titles 200

C FRANCIS X MCDERMOTT DIOCESAN RELIGIOUS STUDIES LIBRARY AT THE IMMACULATE CONCEPTION CENTER,* 7200 Douglaston Pkwy, 11362-1997. SAN 311-1296. Tel: 718-229-8001, Ext 256. *Dir*, Charles C Lindner; Staff 3 (MLS 3)
Founded 1967
Library Holdings: Bk Titles 60,000; Per Subs 235
Subject Interests: Church history, Philosophy, Relig studies, Theology
Special Collections: Augustinian Bibliography, 9 reels microfilm; Dictionary Catalog of the Library of the Pontificial Medieval Institute, 11 reels microfilm
Partic in Dialog Corporation
Friends of the Library Group

DOVER PLAINS

P DOVER PLAINS LIBRARY, Tabor Wing House 3128 Rt 22, PO Box 604, 12522-0604. SAN 311-130X. Tel: 845-877-6805. FAX: 845-877-3873. E-Mail: dover_2@hotmail.com. Web Site: dover.lib.ny.us. *Librn*, Gail O'Brien; Staff 1 (MLS 1)
Founded 1904. Pop 7,778; Circ 23,000
Jan 1999-Dec 1999 Income $95,525, City $77,500, County $4,688, Other $13,337. Mats Exp $12,609, Books $10,857, Per/Ser (Incl. Access Fees) $792, AV Equip $610, Electronic Ref Mat (Incl. Access Fees) $350. Sal $50,223 (Prof $28,964)
Library Holdings: Bk Titles 13,193
Automation Activity & Vendor Info: (Circulation) GEAC
Database Vendor: CARL
Mem of Mid-Hudson Library System
Friends of the Library Group

DRYDEN

P SOUTHWORTH LIBRARY ASSOCIATION, 24 W Main St, PO Box 45, 13053-0045. SAN 311-1318. Tel: 607-844-4782. FAX: 607-844-4782. E-Mail: drylib@clarityconnect.com. *Dir*, Gail Park
Founded 1884. Pop 12,156; Circ 32,000
Library Holdings: Bk Titles 23,000
Subject Interests: Local history, Rare books
Special Collections: Rare Books (John Dryden)
Mem of Finger Lakes Library System
Open Mon, Tues & Wed 2-7:30, Thurs 11-4:30, Fri & Sat 10-3

J TOMPKINS-CORTLAND COMMUNITY COLLEGE, Gerald A Barry Memorial Library, 170 North St, PO Box 139, 13053-0139. SAN 311-1326. Tel: 607-844-8222. FAX: 607-844-6540. Web Site: www.sunytccc.edu/library.htm. *Info Res, Instrul Serv*, William Demo; Tel: 607-844-8222, Ext. 4354, E-Mail: demow@sunytccc.edu; *ILL, Syst Coordr*, Linda Frank; Tel: 607-844-8222, Ext. 4394, E-Mail: frankl@sunytccc.edu; *Tech Servs*, David Lewis; Tel: 607-844-8222, Ext. 4387, E-Mail: lewis@sunytccc.edu; *Coll Develop, Ref*, Ann Sullivan; Tel: 607-844-8222, Ext. 4395, E-Mail: sulliva@sunytccc.edu; Staff 6 (MLS 6)
Founded 1968. Circ 21,930; Enrl 2,100; Fac 70; Highest Degree: Associate
Sep 1998-Aug 1999 Income $760,793, Parent Institution $754,576. Mats Exp $98,038, Books $29,507, Per/Ser (Incl. Access Fees) $46,891, Presv $519, Micro $10,747, AV Equip $542, Other Print Mats $6,217, Electronic Ref Mat (Incl. Access Fees) $3,615. Sal $441,702 (Prof $286,198)

Library Holdings: Bk Vols 40,513; Per Subs 515
Subject Interests: Allied health, Bus computing, Nursing
Partic in OCLC Online Computer Library Center, Inc; S Cent Res Libr Coun; State Univ of NY LAIP

DUNDEE

P DUNDEE LIBRARY, 32 Water St, 14837. SAN 311-1334. Tel: 607-243-5938. FAX: 607-243-7733. E-Mail: dundee@stls.org. Web Site: www.linkny.com/~dun_lib, www.stls.org. *Librn*, Mary Geo Tomion; *Ch Servs*, Mary Lamb; Staff 3 (MLS 1, Non-MLS 2)
Founded 1908. Pop 5,626; Circ 29,000
Jan 2000-Dec 2000 Income $62,650, State $1,600, Locally Generated Income $61,050. Mats Exp $11,650, Books $10,000, Per/Ser (Incl. Access Fees) $700, Presv $100, Electronic Ref Mat (Incl. Access Fees) $850. Sal $24,700 (Prof $14,000)
Library Holdings: Bk Vols 21,688; Bk Titles 21,592; Per Subs 53; High Interest/Low Vocabulary Bk Vols 200; Bks on Deafness & Sign Lang 20
Subject Interests: Local history, Trains
Special Collections: Monroe Railroad Collection
Automation Activity & Vendor Info: (Acquisitions) DRA; (Cataloging) DRA; (Circulation) DRA; (Course Reserve) DRA; (ILL) DRA; (Media Booking) DRA; (OPAC) DRA; (Serials) DRA
Database Vendor: DRA
Function: ILL available, Photocopies available, Reference services available, Some telephone reference
Mem of Southern Tier Library System
Special Services for the Blind - Books available with recordings
Friends of the Library Group

DUNKIRK

P DUNKIRK FREE LIBRARY,* 536 Central Ave, 14048. SAN 311-1342. Tel: 716-366-2511. FAX: 716-366-8517. E-Mail: dkklib@netsync.net. *Dir*, Mary Jane Covley-Walker; Staff 1 (MLS 1)
Founded 1904. Pop 15,310; Circ 136,208
Library Holdings: Bk Vols 50,000; Bk Titles 41,770; Per Subs 114
Mem of Chautauqua-Cattaraugus Library System
Special Services for the Blind - Brailling & large print projects
Friends of the Library Group

EARLVILLE

P EARLVILLE FREE LIBRARY,* N Main St, 13332. SAN 311-1350. Tel: 315-691-5931. E-Mail: er_circ@midyork.lib.newyork.us. *Librn*, Nanette Wilcox
Founded 1927. Pop 980; Circ 33,360
Library Holdings: Bk Vols 23,318; Per Subs 50
Special Collections: New York Indian Heroes (Ologan Coll); Wood Artifacts (Conger Coll)
Mem of Mid-York Library System

EAST AURORA

S AURORA HISTORICAL SOCIETY, Elbert Hubbard-Roycroft Museum, 363 Oakwood Ave, 14052. (Mail add: PO Box 472, 14052), SAN 320-2089. Tel: 716-652-4735. *Curator*, Bruce Bland; Tel: 716-634-1231; *Curator*, Marion Fisher; *Curator*, Maryann Myers; Tel: 716-655-1321; *Curator*, Genevieve Steffen; Tel: 716-652-1524
Founded 1962
Library Holdings: Bk Vols 1,100; Bk Titles 900
Subject Interests: Arts and crafts
Special Collections: Elbert Hubbard & Roy Crofters Coll
Open Wed, Sat & Sun 2-4 (June to Oct 15). Also by special appointment

P AURORA TOWN PUBLIC LIBRARY,* 550 Main St, 14052. SAN 351-8280. Tel: 716-652-4440. FAX: 716-655-5875. *Dir*, Lee Ainsworth-Mahaney; *Ch Servs*, Joan M Elevich
Jan 1999-Dec 1999 Mats Exp $60,000. Sal $239,799 (Prof $112,782)
Library Holdings: Bk Vols 44,800
Subject Interests: Roycroft Craft Movement
Mem of Buffalo & Erie County Public Library System
Partic in Western New York Library Resources Council
Open Mon-Thurs 1-9, Tues 10-9, Wed 1-5 & Fri & Sat 10-5
Friends of the Library Group
Branches: 1
WEST FALLS, Davis Rd, West Falls, 14170. SAN 351-8345. Tel: 716-652-5544. *Mgr*, Joan Badding

R CHRIST THE KING SEMINARY LIBRARY, 711 Knox Rd, PO Box 607, 14052-0607. SAN 311-1369. Tel: 716-652-8959. FAX: 716-652-8903. *Acq, Bibliog Instr, Coll Develop, Dir*, Bonaventure Hayes; Tel: 716-652-8940; *Cat, Online Servs*, Teresa Lubienecki; Tel: 716-655-7098; *Tech Servs*, Catherine Hall; Tel: 716-655-7098; *Circ, ILL*, Sister Tiburtia Gorecki; Staff 4 (MLS 3, Non-MLS 1)
Founded 1951. Circ 9,072; Enrl 75; Fac 9; Highest Degree: Master
Jun 1999-May 2000 Income Parent Institution $247,113. Mats Exp $114,835, Books $90,003, Per/Ser (Incl. Access Fees) $17,286, Presv $4,881, Electronic Ref Mat (Incl. Access Fees) $2,665. Sal $110,094
Library Holdings: Bk Vols 149,799; Per Subs 430
Subject Interests: Philosophy, Religion, Theology
Special Collections: Early French Canadian & Niagara Frontier History (Msgr James Bray)
Mem of Western NY Libr Res Coun
Partic in OCLC Online Computer Library Center, Inc; Western New York Library Resources Council
Open 9am-11pm, everyday, when school is in session

EAST BLOOMFIELD

P BLOOMFIELD PUBLIC LIBRARY, 9 Church St, 14443. (Mail add: PO Box 158, 14443), SAN 311-1385. Tel: 716-657-6264. FAX: 716-657-6038. E-Mail: bloomfield@pls-net.org. Web Site: www.bloom.pls-net.org. *Dir*, Marilyn Graham
Founded 1968
Library Holdings: Bk Vols 16,000; Per Subs 50
Mem of Pioneer Library System

EAST DURHAM

S DURHAM CENTER MUSEUM, INC, Research Library,* PO Box 192, 12423. SAN 311-1393. Tel: 518-239-8461, 518-797-3125. *Curator*, Dan Clifton
Founded 1960
Library Holdings: Bk Titles 1,500; Per Subs 12
Subject Interests: Catskill-Canajoharie RR
Special Collections: Bible Records; Genealogical Records (Rossi); records of businesses, organizations, schools, and churches dating from 1790-1900
Open Sun, Wed & Thurs 1-4 (June-Aug)

EAST ELMHURST

J COLLEGE OF AERONAUTICS LIBRARY, 8601 23rd Ave, 11369. SAN 311-1407. Tel: 718-429-6600, Ext 184. FAX: 718-429-0256. Web Site: www.aero.edu. *Dir*, JoAnn Jayne; *Asst Dir*, Xigang Zhou; Staff 2 (MLS 2)
Founded 1932. Enrl 1,500; Fac 100
Library Holdings: Bk Titles 34,000; Per Subs 314
Subject Interests: Aeronautics, Avionics, Electronics
Special Collections: Aircraft Maintenance Manuals; NACA & Other Annual Reports, bd vols; NASA Reports; SAE Reports
Publications: Library handbook
Partic in Wilsonline

EAST HAMPTON

P EAST HAMPTON LIBRARY, 159 Main St, 11937. SAN 311-1415. Tel: 516-324-0222, 516-324-0243. FAX: 516-329-5947. E-Mail: ehamlib@suffolk.lib.ny.us. *Dir*, Beth Gray; Staff 4 (MLS 4)
Founded 1897. Circ 136,000
Jan 1999-Dec 1999 Income $720,197, Locally Generated Income $400,230, Other $319,967. Mats Exp $102,341, Books $60,231, Per/Ser (Incl. Access Fees) $10,530, Presv $3,418, Micro $2,400, Other Print Mats $8,290, Electronic Ref Mat (Incl. Access Fees) $10,000. Sal $331,836 (Prof $126,743)
Library Holdings: Bk Vols 63,719; Bk Titles 59,000; Per Subs 96; High Interest/Low Vocabulary Bk Vols 100; Bks on Deafness & Sign Lang 10
Special Collections: Long Island History, Biography & Genealogy (Pennypacker Coll), bks, microflm, memorabilia; Thomas Moran Biographical Art Coll
Automation Activity & Vendor Info: (Circulation) Follett
Mem of Suffolk Cooperative Library System
Open Mon, Wed & Fri 10-7 & Tues, Thurs & Sat 10-5

EAST ISLIP

P EAST ISLIP PUBLIC LIBRARY, 381 E Main St, 11730-2896. SAN 311-1423. Tel: 516-581-9200. FAX: 516-581-2245. E-Mail: eisplib@suffolk.lib.ny.us. Web Site: www.suffolk.lib.ny.us/libraries/eipl. *Dir*, Guy P Edwards; Tel: 631-581-9200, Ext 3, E-Mail: edwardsg@suffolk.lib.ny.us; *ILL*, Isabelle Chicarelli; *Ch Servs*, Ruth Kaplan; *Ref Servs YA*, Jo-Ann Carhart; *Tech Servs*, Annamae Peterson; Staff 60 (MLS 18, Non-MLS 42)
Founded 1960. Pop 25,596; Circ 250,704
Jul 2000-Jun 2001 Income $1,969,800, State $7,935, Locally Generated Income $1,877,365, Other $84,500. Mats Exp $242,500, Books $169,500, Per/Ser (Incl. Access Fees) $27,000, AV Equip $20,500, Other Print Mats $1,000, Electronic Ref Mat (Incl. Access Fees) $24,500. Sal $1,232,000 (Prof $573,000)
Library Holdings: Bk Titles 144,463; Per Subs 745
Special Collections: Art Originals; Local History.
Database Vendor: IAC - SearchBank
Publications: East of Islip (Local History); Librafax; Little Librafax

Function: Reference services available
Mem of Suffolk Cooperative Library System
Partic in Long Island Library Resources Council; Partnership of Automated Librs in Suffolk
Special Services for the Blind - Low vision aids & talking readers
Friends of the Library Group

EAST MEADOW

P EAST MEADOW PUBLIC LIBRARY,* 1886 Front St, 11554-1700. SAN 311-1431. Tel: 516-794-2570. FAX: 516-794-1272. E-Mail: emeadow@nassaulibrary.org, empl@transit.nyser.net. Web Site: www.nassaulibrary.org. *Dir*, John F Franzen; *Ad Servs*, Marcia Blackman; *Selection of Gen Ref Mat*, Susan Newson; *Dep Dir*, Harriet Edwards; *Tech Coordr*, Rocco Cassano; *Ch Servs*, Kathleen McCabe; *Ref Servs YA*, Frances Jackson; *Media Spec Ad*, Patricia Thomson; Staff 67 (MLS 19, Non-MLS 48)
Founded 1955. Pop 51,094; Circ 604,152
Jul 1998-Jun 1999 Income $4,556,221, State $236,902, Locally Generated Income $3,579,357, Other $156,761. Mats Exp $520,193, Books $214,477, Per/Ser (Incl. Access Fees) $200,163, Micro $12,660, Other Print Mats $48,056, Electronic Ref Mat (Incl. Access Fees) $24,537. Sal $2,420,206 (Prof $1,094,897)
Library Holdings: Bk Vols 358,800; Per Subs 1,323
Subject Interests: Behav sci, Civil serv, Relig studies, Repair manuals, Repair per, Soc sci
Special Collections: Literary Criticism; Long Island History
Automation Activity & Vendor Info: (Cataloging) DRA; (Circulation) DRA; (ILL) DRA; (OPAC) DRA
Database Vendor: CARL, Dialog, DRA, Ebsco - EbscoHost, GaleNet, IAC - Info Trac, IAC - SearchBank, Lexis-Nexis, OCLC - First Search, ProQuest
Publications: East Meadow: Past & Present; Who's Who in East Meadow
Mem of Nassau Library System
Partic in Dialog Corporation; Long Island Library Resources Council
Friends of the Library Group

GM NASSAU COUNTY MEDICAL CENTER, Health Sciences Library,* 2201 Hempstead Tpk, 11554. SAN 311-144X. Tel: 516-572-8742. Interlibrary Loan Service Tel: 516-572-8741. FAX: 516-572-5788. *Dir*, William F Casey; Staff 3 (MLS 2, Non-MLS 1)
Library Holdings: Bk Titles 8,500; Per Subs 950
Subject Interests: Health sciences, Path, Radiology
Publications: Med Lib News
Partic in Long Island Library Resources Council; Medical & Scientific Libraries of Long Island; Medical Library Center Of New York

EAST ROCHESTER

P EAST ROCHESTER PUBLIC LIBRARY,* 111 W Elm St, 14445. SAN 311-1466. Tel: 716-586-8302. *Librn*, Martha Hieber
Pop 6,932; Circ 85,000
Library Holdings: Bk Vols 47,655; Per Subs 60
Subject Interests: Italian lang
Mem of Monroe County Library System
Open (summer) Mon-Thurs 10-9, Fri 10-5, (winter) Mon-Thurs 10-9, Fri 10-5, Sat 10-4
Friends of the Library Group

EAST ROCKAWAY

P EAST ROCKAWAY PUBLIC LIBRARY,* 477 Atlantic Ave, 11518. SAN 311-1474. Tel: 516-599-1664. FAX: 516-596-0154. E-Mail: erl@lilrc.org. Web Site: www.nassaulibrary.org/eastrock. *Dir*, Ellen Rockmuller; *Ch Servs*, Betty Charvat; *Ref*, Susan Blank
Pop 10,152; Circ 91,684
Jun 1998-May 1999 Income $490,786, Locally Generated Income $23,300. Sal $277,000
Library Holdings: Bk Vols 50,707; Per Subs 95
Special Collections: Special Needs Parent Coll
Mem of Nassau Library System
Friends of the Library Group

EAST SYRACUSE

S BRISTOL-MYERS SQUIBB CO, Pharmaceutical Research Institute Library,* Syracuse Site, 6000 Thompson Rd, 13057-5050. SAN 312-5270. Tel: 315-432-2231. FAX: 315-432-2235. *Coll Develop, Mgr*, John Silvin; E-Mail: jsilvin@usccmail.uscc.bms.com
Founded 1946
Library Holdings: Bk Vols 18,800; Per Subs 290
Subject Interests: Biotech, Chemistry, Engineering, Pharm, Toxicology
Publications: Information digest; library bulletin
Partic in Central New York Library Resources Council

P EAST SYRACUSE FREE LIBRARY, 4990 James St, 13057. SAN 311-1490. Tel: 315-437-4841. FAX: 315-437-5982. E-Mail: easylibrary@usa.net. *Dir*, D L Hobert; Staff 7 (MLS 1, Non-MLS 6)
Founded 1924. Pop 21,000; Circ 138,000
Library Holdings: Bk Titles 23,800; Per Subs 189; Bks on Deafness & Sign Lang 18
Subject Interests: Cooking, Local history, Railroad
Automation Activity & Vendor Info: (Circulation) epixtech, inc.
Database Vendor: OVID Technologies
Mem of Onondaga County Public Library
Special Services for the Deaf - Staff with knowledge of sign language
Friends of the Library Group

S O'BRIEN & GERE ENGINEERS, INC LIBRARY, 5000 Brittonfield Pkwy, 13057. (Mail add: PO Box 4873, 13221), SAN 328-5995. Tel: 315-437-6100. FAX: 315-463-7554. Web Site: www.obg.com. *Librn*, Susan Macleod; E-Mail: macleosd@obg.com; *Asst Librn*, Sharon Miele
Library Holdings: Bk Titles 5,000; Per Subs 200
Subject Interests: Engineering
Open Mon-Fri 7-5

EAST WILLISTON

P EAST WILLISTON PUBLIC LIBRARY, 2 Prospect St, 11596. SAN 311-1504. Tel: 516-741-1213. Web Site: www.nassaulibrary.org/eastwill/. *Dir*, Judith Ruth Loeb; Staff 8 (MLS 1, Non-MLS 7)
Founded 1937. Pop 2,515; Circ 20,000
Library Holdings: Bk Vols 23,000; Per Subs 20
Subject Interests: Local history
Database Vendor: DRA
Publications: East Williston Library (Newsletter); East Willston Library (Newsletter)
Mem of Nassau Library System

EASTCHESTER

S EASTCHESTER HISTORICAL SOCIETY, Angelo H Bianchi Library, PO Box 37, 10709. SAN 327-9588. Tel: 914-793-1900. *Librn*, Madeline D Schaeffer
Library Holdings: Bk Vols 6,010; Per Subs 15
Special Collections: Nineteenth Century Juvenile Literature Coll
Restriction: By appointment only

P EASTCHESTER PUBLIC LIBRARY, 11 Oak Ridge Pl, 10709. SAN 311-1512. Tel: 914-793-5055. FAX: 914-793-5055. Web Site: www.wls.lib.ny.us. *Dir*, Catherine L McDowell; E-Mail: mcdowell@wls.lib.ny.us; *Head Ref*, Tracy Wright; *Ch Servs*, Mary Feldhaus; *Head Tech Servs*, Elizabeth Sachs; *Ref Serv Ad*, Mary Elizabeth Enos; Staff 19 (MLS 5, Non-MLS 14)
Founded 1947. Pop 18,537; Circ 248,135
Jan 1999-Dec 1999 Income $1,210,880, City $1,093,080, Other $10,394. Mats Exp $122,778, Books $55,770, Per/Ser (Incl. Access Fees) $15,609, Presv $1,770, Micro $3,164, AV Equip $9,140, Electronic Ref Mat (Incl. Access Fees) $37,325. Sal $717,493 (Prof $280,792)
Library Holdings: Bk Vols 93,465; Per Subs 3,010
Subject Interests: Architecture, Art, Motion picture hist, Music, Mystery novels, Video cassettes
Automation Activity & Vendor Info: (Cataloging) epixtech, inc.; (Circulation) epixtech, inc.; (OPAC) epixtech, inc.
Database Vendor: Dialog, Ebsco - EbscoHost, epixtech, inc., GaleNet, IAC - Info Trac, IAC - SearchBank
Function: Reference services available
Mem of Westchester Library System
Friends of the Library Group

EDEN

P EDEN LIBRARY,* 2901 E Church St, 14057. SAN 311-1520. Tel: 716-992-4028. Interlibrary Loan Service Tel: 716-858-7225. *Librn*, Susan C Minekime; *Asst Librn*, Eileen Jacobi
Founded 1912. Pop 7,450; Circ 63,374
Library Holdings: Bk Vols 20,000; Per Subs 78
Mem of Buffalo & Erie County Public Library System
Open Mon & Wed 10-1 & 4-8, Tues & Fri 10-5, Sat 10-2

EDMESTON

S EDMESTON FREE LIBRARY & MUSEUM, Six West St, 13335. SAN 311-1539. Tel: 607-965-8208. *Librn*, Dorothy Blackman
1999-2000 Income $16,757. Mats Exp Books $2,200. Sal $8,700
Library Holdings: Bk Vols 15,469
Mem of Four County Library System
Open Tues 3-9, Wed & Thurs 1-6 & Sat 9-1

EDWARDS

P HEPBURN LIBRARY OF EDWARDS,* Main St, PO Box 9, 13635. SAN 311-1547. Tel: 315-562-3521. *Librn*, Elaine Archer
Circ 11,669

Library Holdings: Bk Vols 6,171; Bk Titles 6,088; Per Subs 31
Mem of North Country Library System
Open Mon, Tues & Thurs 1:30-5 & 6:30-8:30, Wed 9-12 & Fri 1:30-5
Friends of the Library Group

ELBRIDGE

P ELBRIDGE FREE LIBRARY,* E Main St, 13060. SAN 311-1555. Tel: 315-689-7111. FAX: 315-689-9448. *Librn*, Karen P White
Founded 1922. Pop 1,098; Circ 28,500
Library Holdings: Bk Vols 19,685; Per Subs 65
Special Collections: Local Newspaper (Advocate)
Mem of Onondaga County Public Library
Open Mon, Thurs & Fri 1:30-5:30, Tues & Wed 1:30-5:30, 7-9, Sat 2-4
Friends of the Library Group

ELDRED

P SUNSHINE HALL FREE LIBRARY,* 14 Proctor Rd, PO Box 157, 12732. SAN 311-1563. Tel: 914-557-6258. FAX: 914-557-6258. E-Mail: shfl@warwick.net. *Dir*, Kay Carlton
Founded 1916. Circ 14,158
1997-1998 Income $20,888, Locally Generated Income $4,000, Other $10,500. Mats Exp $3,000, Books $2,700, Per/Ser (Incl. Access Fees) $300. Sal $8,000
Library Holdings: Bk Vols 20,000; Per Subs 20
Mem of Ramapo Catskill Library System
Open Mon & Tues 12-4:30, Thurs 3-8, Fri 10-3:30, Sat 10-2 (summer); Wed 12-4:30, Thurs 3-8, Fri 10-3:30, Sat 10-2 (winter)
Friends of the Library Group

ELIZABETHTOWN

P ELIZABETHTOWN LIBRARY ASSOCIATION,* River St, PO Box 7, 12932. SAN 311-1571. Tel: 518-873-2670. FAX: 518-873-2670. *Dir*, Susan Hughes
Library Holdings: Bk Vols 5,249; Per Subs 20
Mem of Clinton-Essex-Franklin Library System

S ESSEX COUNTY HISTORICAL SOCIETY, Brewster Library, Court St, PO Box 428, 12932. SAN 311-158X. Tel: 518-873-6466. *Dir*, Margaret Gibbs; E-Mail: echs@northnet.org; *Dir*, Reid S Larson; Staff 5 (Non-MLS 5)
Founded 1956
Library Holdings: Bk Vols 8,143; Bk Titles 1,693; Per Subs 75
Special Collections: Essex County NY Cemetery Records, cards & mss; Essex County Place Names, cards; Genealogical Family Files; History of Essex County Towns (Smith Archive), mss transcripts & pamphlets; Newspaper Articles, cards; North Country Index, cards; North County (pamphlets); North County Index, local bks; Photograph File
Publications: Index to a History of Westport, Essex County, NY (a compendium of local history of Essex County, NY)
Mem of Clinton-Essex-Franklin Library System

ELLENVILLE

P ELLENVILLE PUBLIC LIBRARY & MUSEUM, 40 Center St, 12428-1396. SAN 311-1598. Tel: 845-647-5530. FAX: 845-647-3554. E-Mail: epl@rcls.org. Web Site: www.rcls.org/epl/. *Dir*, Pamela Stocking; Staff 4 (MLS 2, Non-MLS 2)
Founded 1893. Pop 13,000
Jan 2000-Dec 2000 Income $589,700, Locally Generated Income $574,700, Parent Institution $15,000
Library Holdings: Bk Vols 50,990; Per Subs 99
Subject Interests: Local history
Publications: Napanoch; Remembering Clayton's; Sampler of Old Houses
Mem of Ramapo Catskill Library System
Open Mon-Thurs 10-8, Fri 10-5 & Sat 10-3
Friends of the Library Group

ELLICOTTVILLE

P ELLICOTTVILLE MEMORIAL LIBRARY, One Washington, 14731. (Mail add: P.O. Box 1226, 14731-1226), SAN 311-1601. Tel: 716-699-2842. FAX: 716-699-5597. E-Mail: evml@eznet.net. *Dir*, Diane Althans
Pop 1,600; Circ 12,000
Library Holdings: Bk Vols 10,816; Per Subs 30
Mem of Chautauqua-Cattaraugus Library System

ELLINGTON

P FARMAN FREE LIBRARY,* 748 Park St, PO Box 26, 14732. SAN 311-161X. Tel: 716-287-2945. FAX: 716-287-2945. E-Mail: farmanfreelib@alltel.net. Web Site: www.cclslib.org/elling/elling.htm. *Librn*, Karen Nowalk
Circ 14,388
Library Holdings: Bk Vols 13,500
Mem of Chautauqua-Cattaraugus Library System
Open Tues 10-2 & 6-8, Wed & Thurs 6-8, Sat 10-1

ELLISBURG

P ELLISBURG FREE LIBRARY,* PO Box 115, 13636. SAN 311-1628. Tel: 315-846-5087. FAX: 315-846-5087. *Dir*, Sheila Bettinger
Library Holdings: Bk Vols 4,500; Per Subs 25
Mem of North Country Library System

ELMA

P ELMA PUBLIC LIBRARY,* 1860 Bowen Rd, 14059. SAN 311-1636. Tel: 716-652-2719. FAX: 716-652-0381. *Dir*, Karen Korpanty; *Ch Servs, Librn*, Debra Slomba; Staff 2 (MLS 2)
Pop 10,355; Circ 183,322
Jan 1998-Dec 1999 Income $215,214. Mats Exp $35,526, Books $29,626, Per/Ser (Incl. Access Fees) $5,900. Sal $166,820 (Prof $89,366)
Library Holdings: Bk Vols 42,171; Per Subs 593
Mem of Buffalo & Erie County Public Library System
Open Mon, Wed & Fri 1-9pm, Tues & Thurs 10am-6pm & Sat 10am-5pm (winter)

ELMHURST

M ELMHURST HOSPITAL CENTER, Medical Library,* 79-01 Broadway, 11373. SAN 311-1644. Tel: 718-334-2040. FAX: 718-334-5690.
Founded 1965
Library Holdings: Per Subs 200
Subject Interests: Basic sci, Education, Health sci, Medicine
Restriction: Staff use only

NEW YORK CITY CORRECTIONAL INSTITUTION FOR MEN LIBRARY
S LAW LIBRARY, 10-10 Hazen St, East Elmhurst, 11370. SAN 352-4523. Tel: 718-546-5745.
Library Holdings: Bk Vols 2,100

ELMIRA

M ARNOT OGDEN MEDICAL CENTER, Wey Memorial Library, 600 Roe Ave, 14905-1676. SAN 311-1660. Tel: 607-737-4101. FAX: 607-737-4207. *Librn*, David Lester; E-Mail: dlester@aomc.org
Founded 1934
Library Holdings: Bk Vols 5,000; Bk Titles 4,000; Per Subs 310
Subject Interests: Allied health, Medicine, Nursing
Partic in National Network Of Libraries Of Medicine New England Region

GL CHARLES B SWARTWOOD SUPREME COURT LIBRARY, 203-205 Lake St, 14901. SAN 311-1733. Tel: 607-737-2983. FAX: 607-733-9863. *Librn*, Laurie A Hubbard; E-Mail: lhubbard@courts.state.ny.us
Founded 1895
Apr 1999-Mar 2000 Income $133,701. Mats Exp Books $121,000
Library Holdings: Bk Titles 15,000
Subject Interests: NY fed law, NY state
Partic in Am Asn of Law Librs; OCLC Online Computer Library Center, Inc; S Cent Res Libr Coun

S CHEMUNG COUNTY HISTORICAL SOCIETY, INC, Mrs Arthur W Booth Library, 415 E Water St, 14901. SAN 326-2154. Tel: 607-734-4167. FAX: 607-734-1565. *Dir*, Constance Barone; Staff 1 (Non-MLS 1)
Founded 1956
1998-1999 Mats Exp $300
Library Holdings: Bk Vols 1,800
Subject Interests: Genealogy, Local history, Military history
Partic in OCLC Online Computer Library Center, Inc

C ELMIRA COLLEGE, Gannett-Tripp Library, One Park Pl, 14901. SAN 311-1679. Tel: 607-735-1862. Interlibrary Loan Service Tel: 607-735-1868. Reference Tel: 607-735-1864. FAX: 607-735-1712. Web Site: www.elmira.edu. *Dir*, James D Gray; Tel: 607-735-1865, E-Mail: jgray@elmira.edu; *Acq*, Doreen Lawrence; E-Mail: dlawrence@elmira.edu; *AV*, Rodney Denson; Tel: 607-735-1871, E-Mail: rdenson@elmira.edu; *Circ*, Cara Pucci; E-Mail: cpucci@elmira.edu; *Doc*, Laura Schiefer; E-Mail: lschiefer@elmira.edu; *Govt Doc*, Sarah Maximiek; Tel: 607-735-1866, E-Mail: smaximiek@elmira.edu; *ILL*, Katy Galvin; E-Mail: kgalvin@elmira.edu; *Media Spec*, Beth Woodard; E-Mail: bwoodard@elmira.edu; *Per*, Pauline Emery; E-Mail: pemery@elmira.edu; *Publ Servs*, Julia Schult; Tel: 607-735-1867, E-Mail: jschult@elmira.edu; *Tech Servs*, Mark Woodhouse; Tel: 607-735-1869, E-Mail: mwoodhouse@elmira.edu; Staff 16 (MLS 5, Non-MLS 11)
Founded 1855. Enrl 1,200; Fac 96; Highest Degree: Master
Jul 1999-Jun 2000 Income $739,304, State $6,000, Parent Institution $733,304. Mats Exp $232,637, Books $91,108, Per/Ser (Incl. Access Fees) $76,477, Presv $5,736, Micro $24,116, AV Equip $16,496, Other Print Mats

$3,261, Electronic Ref Mat (Incl. Access Fees) $15,443. Sal $420,864 (Prof $103,828)
Library Holdings: Bk Vols 252,934; Bk Titles 137,130; Per Subs 855
Subject Interests: Bus, Criminal justice, NY state hist, Women's studies
Special Collections: (Tomlinson Griffes), papers, mss & bks; American & English Rare Books (Lande); American Literature (Mark Twain Archives), bks, mss, photog, letters on microfilm, artifacts, mixed media; American Music (Charles; Elmira College Regional History (Elmira College Archives), bks, photog; New York State Local History (Julia Boyer Reinstein Coll); New York State Women's History (New York Federation of Women's Clubs), papers, bks; Women's Education
Automation Activity & Vendor Info: (Circulation) Innovative Interfaces Inc.; (OPAC) Innovative Interfaces Inc.; (Serials) Innovative Interfaces Inc.
Database Vendor: CARL, Dialog, Ebsco - EbscoHost, IAC - SearchBank, Lexis-Nexis, OCLC - First Search
Publications: The Gannett-Tripp Library Handbook
Partic in S Cent Res Libr Coun

M ELMIRA PSYCHIATRIC CENTER, Professional Library,* 100 Washington St, 14902-2898. SAN 311-1687. Tel: 607-737-4861. FAX: 607-727-9080. E-Mail: eletnls@gw.omh.state.ny.us. *In Charge*, Nancy Sando
Founded 1971
Library Holdings: Bk Vols 2,200; Per Subs 50
Subject Interests: Mental health
Partic in S Cent Res Libr Coun

S ELMIRA STAR GAZETTE LIBRARY,* 201 Baldwin St, PO Box 285, 14902-9976. SAN 375-1074. Tel: 607-734-5151. FAX: 607-733-4408. *Librn*, Peggy Ridosh
Library Holdings: Bk Titles 50
Restriction: Restricted access

S NATIONAL SOARING MUSEUM, Joseph C Lincoln Memorial Library & Ralph S Barnaby Archives, Harris Hill, 51 Soaring Hills Dr, 14903-9204. SAN 373-4838. Tel: 607-734-3128. FAX: 607-732-6745. E-Mail: nsm@soaringmuseum.org. *Curator*, Erik A Pearson
Library Holdings: Bk Vols 1,000; Per Subs 20
Special Collections: Archives of Soaring Society of America, Elmira Area Soaring Club & Harris Hill Soaring Corp; Avionic Instrument Coll; Joseph C Lincoln Coll; Monographs of Motorless Flight & Meteorology; Mountain Wave Projects, mss; Newsletters (1930-present); Original Aircraft; Papers & archives of other soaring pioneers & luminaries; Paul A Schweizer Coll; Periodical Coll (1930-present); Photos; Ralph S Barnaby Coll; Sailplanes & gliders, drawings, blueprints; Wolfgang Klemperer Coll
Restriction: By appointment only

S NEW YORK STATE DEPARTMENT OF CORRECTIONAL SERVICES, Elmira Correctional Facility Library, 1879 Davis St, 14902-0500. (Mail add: PO Box 500, 14902), SAN 321-0014. Tel: 607-734-3901. *Librn*, J A Doyle; Staff 3 (MLS 1, Non-MLS 2)
Founded 1860
Library Holdings: Bk Titles 6,000; Per Subs 100; High Interest/Low Vocabulary Bk Vols 200
Subject Interests: African Amer, Fiction, Gen fiction, Nonfiction, Spanish language
Special Collections: Law Library, bks, fs; Vocational Guidance Coll, A-tapes, bks, fs
Automation Activity & Vendor Info: (Cataloging) Follett; (Circulation) Follett; (OPAC) Follett
Publications: Summary: A Penitentiary Periodical Newsletter

M SAINT JOSEPH'S HOSPITAL LIBRARY, 555 E Market St, 14902. SAN 311-1709. Tel: 607-733-6541, Ext 375. FAX: 607-733-3946. *Librn*, Arlene C Pien; E-Mail: apien@lakenet.org
Founded 1938
Library Holdings: Bk Vols 6,000; Bk Titles 2,500; Per Subs 69
Subject Interests: Allied health, Medicine, Nursing
Publications: Library bulletin
Restriction: Staff use only
Partic in State University Of New York-NYLINK; UCMP

P STEELE MEMORIAL LIBRARY, 101 E Church St, 14901-2799. SAN 311-1725. Tel: 607-733-8607. Interlibrary Loan Service Tel: 607-733-8603. Circulation Tel: 607-733-9173. Reference Tel: 607-733-9175. FAX: 607-733-9176. E-Mail: sml_ref@stls.org. Web Site: www.steele.lib.ny.us. *Dir*, James G Sleeth; Tel: 607-733-8611, E-Mail: sml_jim@stls.org; *Pub Relations*, Ann Brouse; *Ref*, Phyllis Rogan; *Circ*, Christine Harbison; *ILL*, Owen Frank; *Br Coordr*, Eleanore Shepson; *Ad Servs*, Sylvia Tuller
Founded 1893. Pop 97,656; Circ 584,660
Jan 1999-Dec 1999 Income $2,476,249, State $307,709, County $1,700,222, Locally Generated Income $76,776, Other $391,542. Mats Exp $263,445, Books $212,591, Per/Ser (Incl. Access Fees) $14,130, AV Equip $1,000, Other Print Mats $36,724. Sal $1,001,705 (Prof $526,688)
Library Holdings: Bk Vols 332,015; Bk Titles 195,000; Per Subs 300
Subject Interests: Art, Census, Genealogy, Large print
Automation Activity & Vendor Info: (Cataloging) DRA; (Circulation) DRA
Publications: Newsletter
Mem of Southern Tier Library System
Partic in S Cent Res Libr Coun
Also offer Books on Wheels; Outreach Service, Online Services Available.
Open Mon-Thurs 9am-9pm, Fri-Sat 9am-5pm & Sun 1-5pm
Friends of the Library Group
Branches: 5
BIG FLATS BRANCH, Canal St, Big Flats, 14814. SAN 378-1305. Tel: 607-562-3300. FAX: 607-733-9176. *Br Coordr*, Eleanore Shepson
ELMIRA HEIGHTS BRANCH, 266 E 14th St, Elmira Heights, 14903-1320. SAN 378-1321. Tel: 607-733-3457. FAX: 607-733-9176. *Br Coordr*, Eleanore Shepson
SOUTHSIDE-OUTREACH CENTER, 378 S Main St, 14904-1343. SAN 378-1348. Tel: 607-733-4147. *Br Coordr*, Eleanore Shepson
VAN ETTEN LIBRARY, Van Etten, 14889. SAN 374-812X. Tel: 607-589-4435. *Head of Libr*, Bonnie Mallen
WEST ELMIRA LIBRARY, 1231 W Water St, 14905-1996. SAN 378-1364. Tel: 607-733-0541. *Br Coordr*, Eleanore Shepson
Bookmobiles: 1

ELMONT

P ELMONT PUBLIC LIBRARY, 1735 Hempstead Turnpike, 11003-1896. SAN 352-4582. Tel: 516-354-5280. FAX: 516-354-3276. Web Site: www.nassaulibrary.org/elmont. *Dir*, Janis A Schoen; E-Mail: jschoen@epl.lib.ny.us; *Tech Servs*, Connie Thorpe; *Circ*, Sharon Roberts; *Ch Servs*, Carol Freitag; *Ch Servs*, Carol D Miller; *Coll Develop*, Lee Gorray; Staff 8 (MLS 8)
Founded 1939. Pop 44,964; Circ 241,041
Jul 2000-Jun 2001 Mats Exp $267,826, Books $148,000, Per/Ser (Incl. Access Fees) $23,710, Micro $12,611, Electronic Ref Mat (Incl. Access Fees) $54,000. Sal $1,050,081 (Prof $440,529)
Library Holdings: Bk Vols 190,964; Bk Titles 137,498; Per Subs 299
Subject Interests: Local history
Mem of Nassau Library System
Branches: 2
ALDEN MANOR, 799 Elmont Rd, 11003. SAN 352-4612. Tel: 516-285-8000. FAX: 516-285-1219. *In Charge*, Carol DiLeo
Library Holdings: Bk Vols 15,994
STEWART MANOR BRANCH, 100 Covert Ave, Stewart Manor, 11530. SAN 352-4647. Tel: 516-354-8026. FAX: 516-358-1962. *In Charge*, Barbara Alston
Library Holdings: Bk Vols 12,500

ELMSFORD

P GREENBURGH PUBLIC LIBRARY, 300 Tarrytown Rd, 10523. SAN 311-175X. Tel: 914-993-1600. Circulation Tel: 914-993-1607. Reference Tel: 914-993-1602. FAX: 914-993-1613. Web Site: www.greenburghlibrary.org/. *Dir*, Demita A Gerber; Tel: 914-993-1608, E-Mail: gerber@wls.lib.ny.us; *Asst Dir*, Susan Riley; Tel: 914-993-1610, E-Mail: sriley@wls.lib.ny.us; *Ch Servs*, Kate Colquitt; Tel: 914-993-1605; *Ch Servs*, Gail Fell; Tel: 914-993-1605; *Ch Servs*, Mary Slamin; Tel: 914-993-1605; *YA Servs*, Mandy Colgan; *Ad Servs*, Nancy Larrabee; Tel: 914-993-1612; *Business, Ref Serv Ad*, Suzanne Ford; Tel: 914-993-1609; *Head, Info Serv*, Joanne Weinberg; Tel: 914-993-1612; *Head, Circ*, Marilyn Greiner; Tel: 914-993-1607; *Automation Syst Coordr*, Eugenie Contrata; Tel: 914-993-1622, E-Mail: eugenie@cloud9.net; *Commun Relations*, Margo Hart; Tel: 914-993-1651, E-Mail: mhart@wls.lib.ny.us; *Media Spec*, Pamela H Bernstein; Tel: 914-993-1614; *Ref Servs YA*, Elisabeth Story; Tel: 914-993-1613. Subject Specialists: *Local history*, Joanne Weinberg; Staff 30 (MLS 13, Non-MLS 17)
Founded 1962. Pop 45,579; Circ 354,124
Jan 1999-Dec 1999 Income $2,419,865, State $14,742, City $2,123,199, Locally Generated Income $145,470, Other $136,454. Mats Exp $349,853, Books $197,182, Per/Ser (Incl. Access Fees) $20,323, Micro $7,869, AV Equip $61,013, Electronic Ref Mat (Incl. Access Fees) $63,466. Sal $1,302,493 (Prof $648,095)
Library Holdings: Bk Vols 169,070; Per Subs 3,004
Subject Interests: Local history
Automation Activity & Vendor Info: (Circulation) epixtech, inc.
Database Vendor: GaleNet, IAC - Info Trac, IAC - SearchBank
Publications: Calendar of events (monthly)
Mem of Westchester Library System
Partic in Westlynx
Friends of the Library Group

S WESTCHESTER COUNTY HISTORICAL SOCIETY LIBRARY,* 2199 Saw Mill River Rd, 10523. SAN 312-584X. Tel: 914-592-4323. FAX: 914-592-6481. *Librn*, Elizabeth G Fuller
Founded 1874
Library Holdings: Bk Titles 7,000
Subject Interests: Genealogy, Westchester County hist
Special Collections: Westchester County Historical Materials, almhouse ledgers, bks, docs, files, ledgers, maps, photogs
Publications: The Westchester Historian

ENDICOTT

P GEORGE F JOHNSON MEMORIAL LIBRARY, 1001 Park St, 13760. SAN 311-1784. Tel: 607-757-5350. FAX: 607-757-2491. Web Site: www.lib.4cty.org/endicott.html. *YA Servs*, Lee Anne Bryant; *Dir*, Maria A Dixson; Tel: 607-757-2415, E-Mail: en_maria@4cty.org; *Ch Servs*, Eleanor Henricks; *Ad Servs*, Edward A Dunscombe; *YA Servs*, Cathy Seary; *ILL*, Deanna Pipher
Founded 1915. Pop 13,571; Circ 375,000
Jun 1998-May 1999 Income $596,000, State $6,000, Federal $5,000, County $395,000, Locally Generated Income $190,000
Library Holdings: Bk Vols 91,967; Per Subs 271
Special Collections: George F Johnson memorabilia; Local historical photog
Automation Activity & Vendor Info: (Circulation) DRA
Mem of Four County Library System
Open Mon 10-5, Tues 1-9, Wed & Thurs 10-9, Fri 10-6 & Sat 12-4
Friends of the Library Group

S IBM CORP, Endicott Site Technology Library, 1701 North St, 13760. SAN 311-1776. Tel: 607-757-1487. FAX: 607-757-1489. *Librn*, Eileen Deemie; E-Mail: emdeemie@us.ibm.com
Founded 1933
Library Holdings: Bk Vols 12,500; Per Subs 275
Subject Interests: Bus mgt, Chemistry, Computers, Electronics, Engineering, Mathematics
Automation Activity & Vendor Info: (Circulation) epixtech, inc.
Partic in IBM Tech Info Retrieval Ctr; South Central Regional Library Council

ESSEX

P BELDON-NOBLE MEMORIAL LIBRARY,* Main St, Rte 22, 12936. SAN 311-1806. Tel: 518-963-8079. E-Mail: beldennoble@willex.com. *Librn*, Karen East
Circ 4,221
Library Holdings: Bk Vols 5,000
Mem of Clinton-Essex-Franklin Library System
Open Mon-Sat 2-5

EVANS MILLS

P EVANS MILLS PUBLIC LIBRARY,* PO Box 240, 13637. SAN 311-1814. Tel: 315-629-4483. *Librn*, Helen Tooley
Founded 1956. Circ 7,880
Library Holdings: Bk Vols 2,000
Mem of North Country Library System

FAIR HAVEN

P FAIR HAVEN PUBLIC LIBRARY, 14426 S Richmond Ave, 13064. (Mail add: PO Box 602, 13064), SAN 320-4952. Tel: 315-947-5851. FAX: 315-947-5851. E-Mail: fairhave@twcny.rr.com. Web Site: www.fairhavenlibrary.org. *Mgr Libr*, Michelle Parry
Founded 1976. Pop 900
Jan 2000-Dec 2000 Income $22,620, State $1,500, City $8,500, County $9,500, Locally Generated Income $1,500, Other $1,620. Mats Exp $11,958, Books $6,658, Per/Ser (Incl. Access Fees) $500, AV Equip $300, Electronic Ref Mat (Incl. Access Fees) $4,500. Sal $4,500
Library Holdings: Bk Vols 7,100; Bk Titles 6,700; Per Subs 10
Subject Interests: Ecology, Environ conserv, Local history, Photogs, Sailing, Water sports
Mem of Finger Lakes Library System

FAIRPORT

P FAIRPORT PUBLIC LIBRARY,* One Village Landing, 14450. SAN 311-1822. Tel: 716-223-9091. FAX: 716-223-3998. Web Site: www.rochester.lib.ny.us/fairport. *Dir*, Raymond F Buchanan; *Asst Dir, AV*, Phyllis Parsons; *Ad Servs*, Sarah B Foster; *Ch Servs*, Margaret Hagen; *Ch Servs*, Robin Benoit; *Ref, YA Servs*, Linda Macholz
Founded 1906. Pop 37,179; Circ 500,589
1997-1998 Income $1,524,011, County $14,588, Parent Institution $151,112. Mats Exp $238,400, Books $178,400, Per/Ser (Incl. Access Fees) $19,000, Presv $500. Sal $751,611 (Prof $356,000)
Library Holdings: Bk Vols 107,895; Per Subs 1,109
Mem of Monroe County Library System
Friends of the Library Group

S SAATCHI & SAATCHI BUSINESS COMMUNICATIONS LIBRARY,* 255 Woodcliff Dr Ste 200, 14450. SAN 312-3758. Tel: 716-249-6100. FAX: 716-272-6161.
Library Holdings: Bk Vols 2,000
Subject Interests: Advertising, Marketing info
Restriction: Staff use only
Partic in Rochester Regional Library Council

FALCONER

P FALCONER PUBLIC LIBRARY, 101 W Main St, 14733. SAN 311-1830. Tel: 716-665-3504. FAX: 716-665-9203. *Librn*, Sue Seamans
Founded 1921. Pop 2,735; Circ 81,000
1999-2000 Income Locally Generated Income $66,248. Mats Exp $80,000, Books $7,000. Sal $61,140
Library Holdings: Bk Vols 15,700; Per Subs 63
Mem of Chautauqua-Cattaraugus Library System
Open Mon-Thurs 9-5 & 6:30-8:30, Fri 9-5, Sat 10-4

FALLSBURG

S SULLIVAN CORRECTIONAL FACILITY LIBRARY,* PO Box AG, 12733. SAN 327-3245. Tel: 914-434-2080. FAX: 914-434-2080, Ext 2099. *Librn*, Charles Gramlich
Library Holdings: Bk Titles 5,750; Per Subs 100
Mem of Ramapo Catskill Library System

FAR ROCKAWAY

M PENINSULA HOSPITAL CENTER, Medical Library,* 51-15 Beach Channel Dr, 11691-1074. SAN 311-1849. Tel: 718-734-2887. FAX: 718-734-2234. E-Mail: phlib1@metgate.metro.org. *Coll Develop, Dir*, Lyudmila Bunyatova; E-Mail: phlibl@metgate.metro.org; Staff 1 (MLS 1)
Founded 1970
Dec 1999-Nov 2000 Income $36,000. Mats Exp $30,000, Books $10,000, Per/Ser (Incl. Access Fees) $18,000, AV Equip $1,000, Other Print Mats $1,000. Sal $33,179
Library Holdings: Bk Titles 1,000; Per Subs 75
Subject Interests: Cardiology, Dentistry, Family practice, Nursing, Orthopedics, Podiatry, Surgery
Partic in BHSL; Brooklyn-Queens-Staten Island Health Sciences Librarians; EFTS; Medical & Scientific Libraries of Long Island; New York Metrop Ref & Res Libr Agency
Friends of the Library Group

M SAINT JOHN'S EPISCOPAL HOSPITAL-SOUTH SHORE DIVISION, Medical Library, 327 Beach 19th St, 11691. SAN 311-1857. Tel: 718-869-7699. FAX: 718-869-8528. E-Mail: sjeh2@metgate.metro.org. *Librn*, Kalpana Desai; E-Mail: kdesai48@hotmail.com; *Asst Librn*, Curtis Carson
Library Holdings: Bk Vols 3,000; Per Subs 170
Subject Interests: Gynecology, Medicine, Nursing, Obstetrics, Psychiatry
Partic in BHSL; Brooklyn-Queens-Staten Island Health Sciences Librarians; Medical & Scientific Libraries of Long Island; Metro NY Libr Coun

FARMINGDALE

P FARMINGDALE PUBLIC LIBRARY, 116 Merritts Rd, 11735. SAN 311-1881. Tel: 516-249-9090. FAX: 516-694-9697. E-Mail: falmail@nls.lib.ny.us. Web Site: www.nassaulibrary.org/farmingd/index.html. *Dir*, Carol A Probeyahn; Staff 65 (MLS 19, Non-MLS 46)
Founded 1923. Pop 40,000; Circ 401,262
Jul 2000-Jun 2001 Income $2,747,229. Mats Exp $478,600, Books $320,000, Per/Ser (Incl. Access Fees) $27,000, Micro $20,000, Electronic Ref Mat (Incl. Access Fees) $25,000. Sal $1,837,879 (Prof $615,684)
Library Holdings: Bk Vols 201,000; Per Subs 381
Subject Interests: Bus, Local history
Automation Activity & Vendor Info: (Cataloging) DRA; (Circulation) DRA; (Course Reserve) DRA; (OPAC) DRA
Publications: Community Directory; Inside Your Library
Mem of Nassau Library System
Friends of the Library Group

S FARMINGDALE PUBLIC SCHOOLS, Professional Library,* 150 Lincoln St, 11735. SAN 328-6010. Tel: 516-752-6553. FAX: 516-752-9866. *AV, Coordr*, Barbara Pandolfo; E-Mail: bpandolf@villagenet.com
Library Holdings: Bk Vols 950; Per Subs 44

C POLYTECHNIC UNIVERSITY, Long Island Campus Library,* Rte 110, 11735-3995. SAN 352-4671. Tel: 516-755-4320. FAX: 516-755-4379. Web Site: www.dibner.poly.edu. *Mgr*, James A Jarman
Founded 1961. Enrl 800; Fac 70; Highest Degree: Doctorate
Library Holdings: Bk Vols 35,000; Bk Titles 25,000; Per Subs 300
Subject Interests: Aerospace, Computer science, Electrical engineering, Mathematics
Partic in Long Island Library Resources Council

C SUNY AT FARMINGDALE, Thomas D Greenley Library, Rte 110, 11735-1021. SAN 311-1903. Tel: 631-420-2040. FAX: 631-420-2473. Web Site: www.farmingdale.edu/library/. *Dir*, Michael G Knauth; *Librn*, Tara Gelles; *Circ*, George Lo Presti; *Cat, Tech Servs*, Carol Greenholz; *Acq*, Judith C Bird; *Ref*, James Macinick; *Per*, Azadeh Mirzadeh; Staff 13 (MLS 13)
Founded 1912. Enrl 12,500; Fac 650
Library Holdings: Bk Vols 140,000; Bk Titles 125,000; Per Subs 675

Subject Interests: Amlit, Biology, Engineering, English literature, Horticulture, Nursing
Publications: Bibliographies; Newsletter; Research Guide
Partic in OCLC Online Computer Library Center, Inc

FAYETTEVILLE

P FAYETTEVILLE FREE LIBRARY, 111 E Genesee St, 13066-1386. SAN 311-1911. Tel: 315-637-6374. Reference Tel: 315-637-4636. FAX: 315-637-2306. E-Mail: faylib@ocpl.lib.ny.us. Web Site: www.fayettevilleny.com/library. *Dir*, Ann L Moore; Staff 8 (MLS 5, Non-MLS 3)
Founded 1906
Jan 2000-Dec 2000 Income $418,000. Mats Exp $86,800, Books $72,000, Per/Ser (Incl. Access Fees) $4,800, Electronic Ref Mat (Incl. Access Fees) $10,000. Sal $199,200
Library Holdings: Bk Titles 22,394; Per Subs 101; Bks on Deafness & Sign Lang 20
Subject Interests: 19th Century women's hist
Special Collections: American Popular Sheet Music Coll; Local History Coll (titles from 1860)
Automation Activity & Vendor Info: (Cataloging) epixtech, inc.
Mem of Onondaga County Public Library
Partic in OCLC Online Computer Library Center, Inc
Friends of the Library Group

FILLMORE

P WIDE-AWAKE CLUB LIBRARY,* Main St, PO Box 199, 14735. SAN 311-1938. Tel: 716-567-8301. *Librn*, Joan Tavernier
Circ 22,699
Library Holdings: Bk Vols 11,000
Mem of Southern Tier Library System
Partic in Southern Tier Libr Syst
Open Mon-Thurs 9-5, Fri 9-7 & Sat 9-12

FISHERS ISLAND

P FISHERS ISLAND LIBRARY, Oriental Ave, PO Box 366, 06390. SAN 311-1946. Tel: 516-788-7362. *Dir*, Ann Banks
Circ 7,966
Library Holdings: Bk Vols 24,611
Mem of Suffolk Cooperative Library System

FISHKILL

P BLODGETT MEMORIAL LIBRARY,* 37 Broad St, 12524-1836. SAN 311-1954. Tel: 914-896-9215. FAX: 914-896-9243. Web Site: www.midhudson.org. *Dir Libr Serv*, Susan Blackshear; Staff 2 (MLS 2)
Founded 1934. Pop 15,506; Circ 80,749
Library Holdings: Bk Vols 32,174; Bk Titles 32,000; Per Subs 83
Subject Interests: Local history
Mem of Mid-Hudson Library System
Open Mon, Tues & Thurs 10-8, Wed 12-8, Fri 12-5 & Sat 11-4

S FISHKILL HISTORICAL SOCIETY, Van Wyck Homestead Museum Library, 504 Rte 9, 12524-2248. (Mail add: PO Box 133, 12524-0133), SAN 328-3623. Tel: 845-896-9560. *Pres*, Roy Jorgensen; Tel: 845-897-4348, E-Mail: royjorg@aol.com; *Librn*, Patricia McGurk
Founded 1962
Library Holdings: Bk Titles 700
Subject Interests: Dutchess County, Fishkill, Hudson Valley, NY state
Special Collections: Donated Family Genealogies, etc
Publications: Journal of Cornelia Van Wick (Fishkill Historical Society Publication, 11/97)

G NEW YORK STATE DEPARTMENT OF CORRECTIONAL SERVICES, Downstate Correctional Facility,* Red Schoolhouse Rd, 12524-0445. (Mail add: PO Box 445, 12524-0445), SAN 328-1434. Tel: 914-831-6600, Ext 461. FAX: 914-831-6600, Ext 2099. *Librn*, Larry Collins; Staff 1 (MLS 1)
Founded 1979
Library Holdings: Bk Vols 20,817; Bk Titles 15,314; Per Subs 262
Subject Interests: Law
Special Collections: bks & per; Law Coll
Mem of Mid-Hudson Library System
Open Mon-Fri 9-3

FLEISCHMANNS

P SKENE MEMORIAL LIBRARY, 1017 Main St, 12430. SAN 311-1962. Tel: 845-254-4581. FAX: 845-254-4022. E-Mail: skenelib@catskill.net. Web Site: www.skenelib.org/dpq. *Dir*, Carol Love; Staff 1 (Non-MLS 1)
Founded 1901. Pop 434; Circ 13,532
Library Holdings: Bk Vols 17,000
Mem of Four County Library System
Open Mon & Thurs 11-5, Fri & Sat 11-3 in sum Sun 11-3

FLORAL PARK

P FLORAL PARK PUBLIC LIBRARY, Tulip Ave & Caroline Pl, 11002. SAN 311-1970. Tel: 516-326-6330. FAX: 516-437-6959. E-Mail: floralpk@lilrc.org. *Coll Develop, Dir*, H Maria Sysak; *ILL*, Joseph DiPaola; *Ch Servs, YA Servs*, Jeanette Newman; *Ref*, Beverly DiGuilio; Staff 8 (MLS 8)
Founded 1923
Jun 2000-May 2001 Income State $3,000. Mats Exp $127,950, Books $99,000, Per/Ser (Incl. Access Fees) $22,950, Other Print Mats $6,000. Sal $541,369
Library Holdings: Bk Titles 86,955; Per Subs 150
Subject Interests: Local history
Automation Activity & Vendor Info: (Circulation) DRA; (OPAC) DRA
Publications: Monthly Calendar of Events
Mem of Nassau Library System
Friends of the Library Group

FLORIDA

P FLORIDA PUBLIC LIBRARY,* 4 Cohen Circle, PO Box 628, 10921. SAN 311-1989. Tel: 914-651-7659. FAX: 914-651-7689. *Dir*, Madelyn Folino
Founded 1958. Pop 4,724; Circ 7,621
Library Holdings: Bk Vols 5,000
Mem of Ramapo Catskill Library System
Open Mon, Tues, Wed & Fri 1-5, Thurs 1-7, Sat 11-3

FLUSHING

S ATLAS TRAFFIC CONSULTANTS CORPORATION, Tariff Department Library, 1842 College Point Blvd, 11356-2221. SAN 327-7569. Tel: 718-461-0555. FAX: 718-461-0657. Web Site: www.atlastraffic.com. *Librn*, Diana Lee
Library Holdings: Bk Vols 5,000

M FLUSHING HOSPITAL MEDICAL CENTER, Medical Library, 4500 Parsons Blvd, 11355. SAN 311-2020. Tel: 718-670-5653. FAX: 718-670-3089. E-Mail: fhmc@rmi.net. *Dir*, Robin L Dornbaum; Staff 1 (MLS 1)
Founded 1942
Library Holdings: Bk Vols 5,124; Per Subs 180
Subject Interests: Gynecology, Internal medicine, Obstetrics, Pediatrics, Surgery
Partic in Brooklyn-Queens-Staten Island Health Sciences Librarians

M THE NEW YORK HOSPITAL MEDICAL CENTER OF QUEENS, Health Education Library,* 56-45 Main St, 11355. SAN 311-1997. Tel: 718-670-1118. FAX: 718-358-4216. *Dir*, Rita S Maier; Staff 6 (MLS 2, Non-MLS 4)
Founded 1961
Library Holdings: Bk Titles 10,600; Per Subs 450
Subject Interests: Dentistry, Medicine, Nursing, Surgery
Publications: FYI
Partic in Brooklyn-Queens-Staten Island Health Sciences Librarians; Medical Library Center Of New York; Metronet

C QUEENS COLLEGE, Benjamin S Rosenthal Library, 65-30 Kissena Blvd, 11367-0904. SAN 311-2039. Tel: 718-997-3700. Reference Tel: 718-997-3799. FAX: 718-997-3753. Interlibrary Loan Service FAX: 718-997-3758. E-Mail: lib@qc.edu, libqc@cunyvm.cuny.edu. Web Site: www.qc.edu/Library/index.html. *Chief Librn*, Sharon Bonk; *Assoc Librn*, Shoshana Kaufmann; *Acq*, Nancy Macomber; *ILL*, Evelyn Silverman; *Bibliog Instr*, Alexandra de Luise; *Ref*, Manuel Sanudo; *Access Serv*, Amy Beth; *Bibliog Instr*, Belinda Chiang; *Syst Coordr*, A Ben Chitty; *Electronic Resources*, Rolf Swensen; *Coll Develop*, Richard Wall. Subject Specialists: *Art*, Suzanna Simor; *Music*, Joseph Ponte; *Science*, Subash Gandhi; Staff 53 (MLS 22, Non-MLS 31)
Founded 1937. Enrl 15,686; Fac 1,103; Highest Degree: Master
Jul 1999-Jun 2000 Income $898,556. Mats Exp $760,492, Books $151,592, Per/Ser (Incl. Access Fees) $509,849, Presv $30,228, Electronic Ref Mat (Incl. Access Fees) $68,823. Sal $2,509,660 (Prof $1,402,530)
Library Holdings: Bk Vols 752,894; Bk Titles 503,312; Per Subs 3,260
Special Collections: Louis Armstrong archives, mss, personal papers, photographs, recordings, scrapbks, tapes & recordings; Theater & Film Coll (through 1960), posters, programs, scrapbks, scripts, stills
Automation Activity & Vendor Info: (Acquisitions) NOTIS; (Cataloging) NOTIS; (Circulation) NOTIS; (OPAC) NOTIS; (Serials) NOTIS
Publications: PageDown (newsletter)
Partic in New York Metrop Ref & Res Libr Agency; OCLC Online Computer Library Center, Inc
Special Services for the Blind - Assistive Technology Center for Persons who are blind or physically handicapped
Open Mon-Thurs 9am-10pm, Fri 9-5 & Sat-Sun 12-6
Friends of the Library Group

FONDA

P FROTHINGHAM FREE LIBRARY,* 28 W Main St, PO Box 746, 12068. SAN 311-2071. Tel: 518-853-3016. FAX: 518-853-3016. E-Mail: frothham@hotmail.com. Web Site: www2.telenet/community/mula/frot/index.html. *Dir*,

Donna Franklin
Founded 1942. Pop 1,007; Circ 24,475
1998-1999 Income $33,382, Locally Generated Income $12,244, Parent Institution $5,500, Other $2,338. Mats Exp $4,800, Books $4,188, Per/Ser (Incl. Access Fees) $235, Micro $377. Sal $16,948
Library Holdings: Bk Vols 17,232; Per Subs 536
Mem of Mohawk Valley Library Association
Open Mon 12-4:30, Tues 10-7, Wed 12-7, Fri 12-4:30 & Sat 9-1

G MONTGOMERY COUNTY DEPARTMENT OF HISTORY & ARCHIVES, Research Library, Old Court House, PO Box 1500, 12068-1500. SAN 325-5336. Tel: 518-853-8187. FAX: 518-853-8392. E-Mail: histarch@superior.net.; Staff 2 (Non-MLS 2)
Founded 1934
Library Holdings: Bk Titles 8,500
Subject Interests: Genealogy, Local history
Special Collections: Archival Records (1772-present); Extensive Genealogical Coll
Open Mon-Fri 8:30-4, (July-Aug) Mon-Fri 9-4
Friends of the Library Group

FOREST HILLS

S BRAMSON ORT COLLEGE, Library-Learning Resource Center, 69-30 Austin St, 11375. SAN 311-6522. Tel: 718-261-5800. FAX: 718-575-5118. *Librn*, Rivka Burkos; E-Mail: rburkos@bramsonort.org; Staff 2 (MLS 1, Non-MLS 1)
Founded 1977. Enrl 350
Library Holdings: Bk Titles 12,000; Per Subs 105
Subject Interests: Bus admin, Computer prog, Electronics, English as a second lang, Jewish studies
Special Collections: Judaica
Partic in New York Metrop Ref & Res Libr Agency

S ESTONIAN MUSIC CENTER USA, Musical Library,* 68-50 Juno St, 11375-5728. SAN 370-6494. Tel: 718-261-9618. *Librn*, Juta Kurman; Staff 2 (MLS 1, Non-MLS 1)
Founded 1956
Special Collections: Biographies-Estonia Composers & Interpreters, cassettes, rec
Publications: Free Estonian Word (newsletter)
Restriction: By appointment only
Friends of the Library Group

S NORTH SHORE UNIVERSITY HOSPITAL AT FOREST HILLS, Health Sciences Library, 102-01 66 Rd, 11375. SAN 373-1200. Tel: 718-830-4000. FAX: 718-830-1280. *Dir*, Paula Green; E-Mail: pgreen@nshs.edu
Library Holdings: Bk Vols 1,500; Per Subs 160
Partic in Basic Health Sciences Library Network; Brooklyn-Queens-Staten Island Health Sciences Librarians

FORT EDWARD

P FORT EDWARD FREE LIBRARY,* 23 East St, 12828. SAN 311-211X. Tel: 518-747-6743. FAX: 518-747-6743. *Librn*, Victoria Plude
Founded 1914. Pop 3,561; Circ 6,396
Library Holdings: Bk Vols 5,874; Per Subs 34
Mem of Southern Adirondack Library System
Open Mon & Wed 1:30-5, & 7-9, Tues 7-9, Thurs 1:30-5, Fri 3-5

FORT HUNTER

P FORT HUNTER FREE LIBRARY,* Main St, 12069. SAN 311-2128. Tel: 518-829-7248. FAX: 518-829-7248. *Dir*, Shirley Auspelmyer
Library Holdings: Bk Titles 6,728
Mem of Mohawk Valley Library Association

FORT PLAIN

P FORT PLAIN FREE LIBRARY,* 19 Willett St, 13339-1130. SAN 311-2136. Tel: 518-993-4646. FAX: 518-993-2455. Web Site: ww2.telenet.net/community/mvla/ftpl.index.html. *Dir*, Laura Flynn
Founded 1894. Circ 27,670
Jan 1997-Dec 1998 Income $94,028, State $1,732, Locally Generated Income $59,378, Other $25,000. Mats Exp $19,772, Books $16,311, Per/Ser (Incl. Access Fees) $1,172, Other Print Mats $461. Sal $40,928 (Prof $26,763)
Library Holdings: Bk Vols 34,046; Per Subs 50
Subject Interests: Local history
Mem of Mohawk Valley Library Association

FRANKFORT

P FRANKFORT FREE LIBRARY,* 123 Frankfort St, 13340. SAN 311-2144. Tel: 315-894-9611. *Dir*, Margaret Fillingeri; *Librn*, Ann Burton; *Librn*, Kristine Russell
Pop 7,200; Circ 15,281
Library Holdings: Bk Vols 9,200; Per Subs 24
Mem of Mid-York Library System
Open Mon-Thurs 2-8, Fri 2-6, Sat 9-12

FRANKLIN

P FRANKLIN FREE LIBRARY, 66 Main St, PO Box 947, 13775. SAN 311-2152. Tel: 607-829-2941. FAX: 607-829-5017. E-Mail: fr_ill@4cty.org. *Dir*, Linda Burkhart
Founded 1827. Pop 2,440; Circ 8,000
Library Holdings: Bk Vols 6,500; Per Subs 35
Special Collections: 200 Historic Scrapbooks (indexed); Civil War Coll; Local Newspapers on Microfilm 1857-1952; Town & Village Board Meetings 1792 -
Mem of Four County Library System
Open Tues 9-12 & 1-5, Apr-Dec Tues 7-9, Thurs 1:30-5:30, Sat 9-5
Friends of the Library Group

FRANKLIN SQUARE

P FRANKLIN SQUARE PUBLIC LIBRARY, 19 Lincoln Rd, 11010. SAN 311-2160. Tel: 516-488-3444. FAX: 516-354-3368. E-Mail: esplahw@lilrc.org. Web Site: www.nassaulibrary.org. *Dir*, Alice Wolfteich; *Asst Dir, Commun Servs*, Margaret K Smith; *ILL, Ref*, Diane Bolte; *Circ*, Sandra Montenora; *Acq*, Barbara Kelly; *Ad Servs, Ref, YA Servs*, Mary La Rosa; *Ch Servs*, Faye Lieberman; *Per*, Lori Seveneant; *Tech Servs*, Pat Bifolco; Staff 5 (MLS 5)
Founded 1938. Pop 29,000; Circ 205,003
Jul 1999-Jun 2000 Income $1,059,331, State $15,000, Locally Generated Income $1,044,331. Mats Exp $1,027,715, Books $133,058, Per/Ser (Incl. Access Fees) $8,023, AV Equip $14,098, Electronic Ref Mat (Incl. Access Fees) $18,595. Sal $460,000 (Prof $258,206)
Library Holdings: Bk Vols 105,824; Per Subs 198
Automation Activity & Vendor Info: (Circulation) DRA; (OPAC) DRA
Publications: Community Directory; Newsletter
Mem of Nassau Library System
Friends of the Library Group

FRANKLINVILLE

P BLOUNT LIBRARY, INC,* 5 N Main St, 14737. SAN 311-2179. Tel: 716-676-5715. FAX: 716-676-5715. *Librn*, Barbara Scalise
Founded 1899. Pop 4,340; Circ 17,246
1998-1999 Income $28,166, City $6,000, Locally Generated Income $2,243, Other $10,513. Mats Exp $10,305, Books $9,018, Per/Ser (Incl. Access Fees) $1,287. Sal $9,267
Library Holdings: Bk Vols 13,428; Per Subs 51
Subject Interests: Local history
Mem of Chautauqua-Cattaraugus Library System
Open Mon 7-9, Tues 9-5, Wed 7-9, Thurs 9-5:30 & Sat 9-12:30

FREDONIA

P DARWIN R BARKER LIBRARY,* 7 Day St, 14063. SAN 311-2187. Tel: 716-672-8051. FAX: 716-679-3547. E-Mail: barker@netsync.net. *Librn*, Joy Harper; *Asst Librn*, Juanita Ball
Pop 11,101; Circ 127,492
Library Holdings: Bk Vols 55,000; Per Subs 180
Publications: Dr Barker Library Newsletter (quarterly)
Mem of Chautauqua-Cattaraugus Library System
Open Mon, Tues & Thurs 10-9, Wed, Fri & Sat 10-5
Friends of the Library Group

C STATE UNIVERSITY OF NEW YORK COLLEGE, Daniel A Reed Library, 280 Central Ave, 14063. SAN 311-2195. Tel: 716-673-3184. FAX: 716-673-3185. Web Site: www.fredonia.edu/library. *Dir Libr Serv*, Randy Gadikian; Tel: 716-673-3181, E-Mail: gadikian@fredonia.edu; *Instrul Serv, Ref*, Marianne Eimer; Tel: 716-673-3180, E-Mail: eimer@fredonia.edu; *Music*, Kevin Michki; Tel: 716-673-3117, E-Mail: michki@fredonia.edu; *ILL*, Barbara Kittle; Tel: 716-673-3199, E-Mail: kittle@fredonia.edu; *Spec Coll*, Jack Ericson; E-Mail: ericson@fredonia.edu; *Acq*, Tesfai Kflu; Tel: 716-673-3182, E-Mail: kflu@fredonia.edu; *Cat*, Vince Courtney; Tel: 716-673-3192, E-Mail: courtney@fredonia.edu; *Syst Coordr*, Katy Loomis; Tel: 716-673-3192, E-Mail: loomis@fredonia.edu. Subject Specialists: *Bus admin*, Marianne Eimer; *Chemistry*, Vince Courtney; *Communications*, Marianne Eimer; *Computer science*, Kevin Michki; *Dance*, Vince Courtney; *Education*, Barbara Kittle; *Geosciences*, Vince Courtney; *Health*, Barbara Kittle; *Mathematics*, Kevin Michki; *Media*, Marianne Eimer; *Music*, Kevin Michki; *Physics*, Tesfai Kflu; *Political science*, Tesfai Kflu; *Psychology*, Tesfai Kflu; *Recreation*, Barbara Kittle; Staff 11 (MLS 9, Non-MLS 2)
Founded 1826. Enrl 4,850; Fac 250; Highest Degree: Master
Jul 1998-Jun 1999 Income State $1,409,192. Mats Exp $1,230,799, Books $947,940, Per/Ser (Incl. Access Fees) $247,618, Presv $13,318, Micro $19,999, Electronic Ref Mat (Incl. Access Fees) $1,924. Sal $960,899 (Prof $453,949)

Library Holdings: Bk Vols 404,460; Bk Titles 281,977; Per Subs 1,200
Special Collections: Chautauqua & Cattaraugus Counties' History, bks, mss, micro; Holland Land Company Coll; Seneca/Iroquois History, bks, mss, micro; Stephan Zweig Coll, bks, mss, micro
Automation Activity & Vendor Info: (Cataloging) EX Libris; (Circulation) EX Libris; (Serials) EX Libris
Database Vendor: CARL, Dialog, GaleNet, IAC - Info Trac, Lexis-Nexis, OCLC - First Search
Publications: Annual report
Function: Reference services available
Partic in Western New York Library Resources Council
Friends of the Library Group

FREEPORT

P FREEPORT MEMORIAL LIBRARY,* 144 W Merrick Rd & S Ocean Ave, 11520. SAN 311-2209. Tel: 516-379-3274. FAX: 516-868-9741. *Dir*, Dave Opatow
Founded 1884. Pop 37,377; Circ 372,223
Library Holdings: Bk Vols 209,955; Per Subs 592
Subject Interests: Careers, Ethnic studies, Investment lit
Special Collections: Long Island history; Vocational & careers
Automation Activity & Vendor Info: (Circulation) CLSI LIBS
Publications: Monthly newsletter
Mem of Nassau Library System
Open Mon, Tues, Thurs & Fri 9-9, Wed 10-9, Sat 9-1, winter hours Sat 9-5 & Sun 1-5
Friends of the Library Group

FREWSBURG

P MYERS MEMORIAL LIBRARY, Ivory St, 14738. (Mail add: PO Box 559, 14738), SAN 311-2217. Tel: 716-569-5515. FAX: 716-569-2605. *Librn*, Sally Koehler-Burns; Staff 1 (Non-MLS 1)
Founded 1923. Pop 3,500; Circ 30,000
Jan 1999-Dec 1999 Income $43,565. Mats Exp $6,800, Books $5,000, Per/Ser (Incl. Access Fees) $900, Electronic Ref Mat (Incl. Access Fees) $900. Sal $32,487 (Prof $18,000)
Library Holdings: Bk Titles 18,000; Per Subs 50; Bks on Deafness & Sign Lang 10
Special Collections: History (Robert H Jackson Coll), bks, letters; J J Myers Coll, bks
Function: Internet access, Photocopies available
Mem of Chautauqua-Cattaraugus Library System
Open Mon-Wed 2-8, Thurs 10-5, Fri 2-5 & Sat 10-12

FRIENDSHIP

P FRIENDSHIP FREE LIBRARY,* 40 W Main St, 14739. SAN 311-2225. Tel: 716-973-7724. *Asst Librn*, Regina Grastorf
Founded 1898. Circ 7,518
Library Holdings: Bk Vols 9,998; Bk Titles 11,008; Per Subs 24
Publications: Newsletter (quarterly)
Mem of Chemung-Southern Tier Libr Syst; Southern Tier Library System
Friends of the Library Group

FULTON

P FULTON PUBLIC LIBRARY, 160 S First St, 13069. SAN 311-2233. Tel: 315-592-5159. FAX: 315-592-4504. *Dir*, Joyce H Cook; Tel: 315-592-5981; Staff 1 (MLS 1)
Founded 1895. Pop 12,929
Jan 1999-Dec 1999 Income $246,963, State $14,563, City $170,008, County $14,644, Locally Generated Income $5,945, Other $41,803. Mats Exp $32,207, Books $25,453, Per/Ser (Incl. Access Fees) $4,074, AV Equip $972, Electronic Ref Mat (Incl. Access Fees) $1,708. Sal $161,999 (Prof $31,741)
Library Holdings: Bk Vols 46,053; Per Subs 95
Subject Interests: Local history
Partic in North Country Library Cooperative
Open Mon 10-5, Tues-Thurs 10-8 & Fri-Sat 10-5
Friends of the Library Group

GARDEN CITY

C ADELPHI UNIVERSITY LIBRARIES, Swirbul Library,* South Ave, 11530. SAN 352-4701. Tel: 516-877-3570. Reference Tel: 516-877-3580. FAX: 516-877-3592. Web Site: www.adelphi.edu/discover/library. *Dean of Libr*, Eugene T Neely; E-Mail: neely@adlibv.adelphi.edu; *Asst Dean*, Ann Minutella; *Asst Dean*, James P Smith; *Spec Coll*, Gary Cantrell; *Bibliog Instr*, Valerie Feinman; *Coordr, Govt Doc*, Victor Oliva. Subject Specialists: *Afro-American*, Gloria Grant Roberson; *Performing arts*, Gary Cantrell; *Science/technology*, Aditi Bandyopadhyay; Staff 23 (MLS 23)
Founded 1896. Enrl 4,684; Fac 501; Highest Degree: Doctorate
Sep 1997-Aug 1998 Income $3,350,975, State $10,741, Parent Institution $3,329,733, Other $10,501. Mats Exp $872,625, Books $463,000, Per/Ser (Incl. Access Fees) $194,130, Presv $1,322, Micro $11,615. Sal $1,752,931 (Prof $1,017,740)
Library Holdings: Per Subs 1,983
Special Collections: Adelphi University Archives; Aimee Ornstein Memorial Library of Banking & Money Management; Christopher Morley Coll; Cuala Press; Expatriate American Writers of the 1920's & 1930's; Gerhardt Hauptmann (Siegfried Muller Memorial Coll), bks & mss; Gerrit Smith Coll; Musical Instruments (Stoelzer Coll); New York State, New York City & Long Island Region; Political & Presidential Letters & Memorabilia (Robert R McMillan Coll); Robert R McMillan Collection of Political & Presidential Letters & Memorabilia; Source Materials in American History to the Civil War; Spanish Civil War Papers, mss, pictures & other; University Art Coll; William Blake (Hugo & Florentina Leipniker Memorial Coll), rare bks; William Cobbett (C Rexford Davis Coll), mss, rare bks; William Hone
Publications: Aspects of Book Collecting; Catalogs of Libraries Special Collections & Exhibits: Mind & Hand, Selections from the Adelphi University Art Collection; Data in Berlin; Eighty-Five Florins, Favorite Books Selected by Christopher Morley; Footnotes (newsletter); Hand Bookbinding; Library Guide Series; The Stoelzer Coll at Adelphi University; The William Cobbett Coll; various subject bibliographies; William Blake, The Painter as Poet
Partic in BRS; Dialog Corporation; Long Island Library Resources Council; OCLC Online Computer Library Center, Inc
Special Services for the Deaf - Books on deafness & sign language; Special interest periodicals
Friends of the Library Group
Departmental Libraries:
SCIENCE LIBRARY - GARDEN CITY CAMPUS, South Ave, 11530. SAN 352-4736. Tel: 516-877-4166. FAX: 516-877-3674. Web Site: www.adelphi.edu/discover/library. *Librn*, Aditi Bandyopadhyay; Staff 1 (MLS 1)

P GARDEN CITY PUBLIC LIBRARY,* 60 Seventh St, 11530-2891. SAN 311-2276. Tel: 516-742-8405. FAX: 516-294-6207. E-Mail: gcplref@lilrc.org. Web Site: www.nassaulibrary.org/gardenc. *Dir*, Alan Roeckel; *Tech Servs*, Joseph Agolia; *Tech Servs*, Nancy Sherwood; *AV, Ref*, Laura Flanagan; *Ch Servs*, Joann Van Meter; *Ch Servs*, Nancy Pirodsky; *AV*, Mary Jo Scala; *YA Servs*, Laura Hoffman; *Reader Servs, Ref*, Martin Bowe; Staff 9 (MLS 9)
Founded 1952. Pop 22,927; Circ 306,000
Jun 1998-May 1999 Income $2,688,141, State $6,000, City $2,386,161, Federal $12,600, Locally Generated Income $128,850. Mats Exp $347,325. Sal $1,617,560
Library Holdings: Bk Vols 152,698; Per Subs 280
Special Collections: Garden City Archives; Long Island History
Automation Activity & Vendor Info: (Circulation) DRA; (OPAC) DRA
Publications: Newsletter
Mem of Nassau Library System
Partic in Long Island Library Resources Council
Open Mon-Thurs 9:30-9, Fri 9:30-5:30, Sat 9-5 & Sun 1-5
Friends of the Library Group

CR GEORGE MERCER JR SCHOOL OF THEOLOGY, Mercer Theological Library, 65 Fourth St, 11530. SAN 311-2284. Tel: 516-248-4800, Ext 39. FAX: 516-248-4883. E-Mail: mercer@ix.net.com. Web Site: www.mercertheoschool.org. *Librn*, Marilyn Hulland; Staff 2 (MLS 1, Non-MLS 1)
Founded 1966. Enrl 50; Fac 20
2000-2001 Mats Exp $20,500, Books $13,000, Per/Ser (Incl. Access Fees) $7,500
Library Holdings: Bk Titles 28,000; Per Subs 140
Subject Interests: Church history, Religious education, Theology
Mem of Long Island Libr Resources Coun, Inc; Nassau Library System

M NASSAU ACADEMY OF MEDICINE, John N Shell Library, 1200 Stewart Ave, 11530. SAN 311-2292. Tel: 516-832-2320. Interlibrary Loan Service Tel: 516-832-2300, Ext 24, 516-832-2300, Ext 25. FAX: 516-832-8183. *Librn*, Teresa Milone
Founded 1964
Library Holdings: Bk Vols 10,500; Bk Titles 10,000; Per Subs 250
Subject Interests: Medicine, Nursing, Psychiatry
Partic in Medline
Open Mon-Fri 9-4
Friends of the Library Group

J NASSAU COMMUNITY COLLEGE, A Holly Patterson Library, One Education Dr, 11530-6793. SAN 311-2306. Tel: 516-572-7400. Interlibrary Loan Service Tel: 516-572-7845. FAX: 516-572-7846. Web Site: www.sunynassau.edu. *Chair*, Nancy Williamson; *Circ*, Richard Erben; *Media Spec*, Ken Bellafiore; *Media Spec*, Richard Delbango; *Media Spec*, Gerald Leibowitz; *Per*, Linda Breitfeller; *Cat*, Katrina Frazier; *Cat*, Cynthia Powers; *Ref*, David Cugnola; *Doc, Ref*, Charles Owusu; *ILL, Ref*, Marilyn Rosenthal; *Ref*, Donna Seidl; *Ref*, Marsha Spiegelman; *Ref*, Bellinda Wise; *Instrul Serv*, John Day; *Acq*, Sharon Russin; Staff 14 (MLS 11, Non-MLS 3)
Founded 1959. Enrl 20,000; Fac 700
Library Holdings: Bk Vols 171,000; Bk Titles 153,000; Per Subs 700
Subject Interests: Fashion, LI hist

Special Collections: Dozenal Society; G Wilson Knight Interdisciplinary Society
Publications: From the Stacks; Library Newsletter
Partic in Long Island Library Resources Council; SUNY/OCLC
Special Services for the Blind - Computers with Voice Synthesizer; VisualTek

GARDINER

P GARDINER LIBRARY,* PO Box 223, 12525. SAN 376-3145. Tel: 914-255-1255. *Dir*, Peggy Lotvin
1997-1998 Income $56,352
Library Holdings: Bk Titles 11,500; Per Subs 25
Mem of Ramapo Catskill Library System
Open Thurs 2-9, Fri 2-5:30
Friends of the Library Group

GARRISON

S ALICE CURTIS DESMOND & HAMILTON FISH LIBRARY, Rte 9D & 403, Box 265, 10524. SAN 322-7286. Tel: 914-424-3020. FAX: 914-424-4061. E-Mail: dfldirector@highlands.com. Web Site: www.highlands.com/libraries/dfl.html. *Librn*, Caroline H Donick; E-Mail: donick@highlands.com
Founded 1977. Pop 6,900; Circ 42,586
2000-2001 Mats Exp Books $28,000
Library Holdings: Bk Vols 32,000; Per Subs 100
Special Collections: Hudson River School Art Reference Coll, slides
Mem of Mid-Hudson Library System
Open Mon, Wed & Fri 10-5, Tues & Thurs 2-9, Sat 10-4, Sun 1-5
Friends of the Library Group

R GRAYMOOR FRIARY LIBRARY,* Graymoor, Rte 9, Box 300, 10524-0300. SAN 352-4795. Tel: 914-424-3671. *Dir*, Fr Jim Gardner; *Actg Librn*, Br Thomas Orians
Founded 1960
Library Holdings: Bk Vols 88,500; Bk Titles 51,000; Per Subs 88
Subject Interests: Anglicanism, English reformation, N Am ecumenical hist, N Am ecumenical theol, Spirituality
Special Collections: History of the Atonement Friars (Paul Watson Research Center), bks, doc
Publications: Ecumenical Trends

S HASTINGS CENTER, Robert S Morison Memorial Library, 21 Malcolm Gordon Dr, 10524-5555. SAN 326-1530. Tel: 845-424-4040. FAX: 845-424-4545. E-Mail: mail@thehastingscenter.org. Web Site: www.thehastingscenter.org. *Librn, Web Coordr*, Chris McKee; Tel: 845-424-4040, Ext 226, E-Mail: cmckee@thehastingscenter.org; Staff 1 (MLS 1)
Founded 1969
Library Holdings: Bk Titles 8,000; Per Subs 220
Subject Interests: Environ med, Ethic studies, Medicine
Automation Activity & Vendor Info: (OPAC) Inmagic, Inc.
Publications: Hastings Center Report; Hastings Center Studies in Ethics; IRB: A Review of Human Subjects Research
Restriction: Open to others by appointment, Staff use only
Partic in Southeastern New York Library Resources Council

GENESEO

C STATE UNIVERSITY OF NEW YORK COLLEGE AT GENESEO, Milne Library,* One College Circle, 14454. SAN 352-4825. Tel: 716-245-5591, 716-245-5594. Interlibrary Loan Service Tel: 716-245-5589. FAX: 716-245-5003. Web Site: www.geneseo.edu/~library. *Dir*, Edwin Rivenburgh; *Cat*, Joan Cottone; *Circ, Govt Doc*, Paul MacLean; *Ser*, Diane Johnson; *ILL*, Sonja Landes; *Bibliog Instr, Coordr*, Ann Pollot; Staff 14 (MLS 14)
Founded 1871. Highest Degree: Master
1998-1999 Income $1,826,965. Mats Exp $541,178. Sal $826,093
Library Holdings: Bk Vols 492,236
Subject Interests: Education, Music
Special Collections: Aldous Huxley; American Architecture (Carl F Schmidt Coll), mss, bd; Children's Literature (Juvenile & Young Adult Coll); Regional History (Genesee Valley Historical Coll) bk, mss; State University of New York College at Geneseo Archives, mss, bk; Wadsworth Family (Wadsworth Homestead Papers, 1800-1950), mss
Automation Activity & Vendor Info: (Cataloging) MultiLIS; (Circulation) MultiLIS; (Serials) MultiLIS
Publications: Guide to the College Libraries, newsletter, subject lists; Serials Holdings List (computer printout)
Partic in Dialog Corporation; OCLC Online Computer Library Center, Inc; Rochester Regional Library Council

P WADSWORTH LIBRARY,* 24 Center St, 14454. SAN 311-2349. Tel: 716-243-0440. FAX: 716-243-0429. *Dir*, Leslie DeLooze
Founded 1843. Circ 54,072
Library Holdings: Bk Vols 30,000; Per Subs 105
Special Collections: Job Information Center
Mem of Pioneer Library System

GENEVA

P GENEVA FREE LIBRARY,* 244 Main St, 14456-2370. SAN 311-2365. Tel: 315-789-5303. FAX: 315-789-9835. *Dir*, Lindsay Ruth; *Ch Servs*, Susan Reding; *Automation Syst Coordr*, Kimberly Iraci; *Ref*, Deborah Scheffler; Staff 4 (MLS 4)
Founded 1905. Pop 17,500; Circ 133,060
Jan 1997-Dec 1998 Income $510,000, State $163,125, City $115,000, County $10,672, Locally Generated Income $80,369, Other $8,000. Mats Exp $79,500, Books $64,000, Per/Ser (Incl. Access Fees) $10,000. Sal $251,000 (Prof $122,500)
Library Holdings: Bk Titles 68,000; Per Subs 137
Subject Interests: Local history
Mem of Pioneer Library System
Open Mon-Thurs 10-8, Fri 10-6, Sat 10-5
Friends of the Library Group

S GENEVA HISTORICAL SOCIETY, James D Luckett Memorial Archives, 543 S Main St, 14456. SAN 311-2373. Tel: 315-789-5151. FAX: 315-789-0314. E-Mail: genevhst@flare.net. *Curator*, John Marks; *Archivist*, Sharon Barnes
Founded 1961
Library Holdings: Bk Vols 2,300
Subject Interests: Antiques, Architecture, Area hist, Art, Furniture, Genealogy, Local history, Newspaper items, Photog
Open Tues-Fri 1:30-4:30pm

C HOBART & WILLIAM SMITH COLLEGES, Warren Hunting Smith Library, 334 Pulteney St, 14456. SAN 311-2381. Tel: 315-781-3550. Circulation Tel: 315-781-3550. Reference Tel: 315-781-3552. FAX: 315-781-3560. Web Site: www.hws.edu/aca/library/erc.html. *Head Tech Servs*, Sara Greenleaf; Staff 34 (MLS 6, Non-MLS 28)
Founded 1824. Enrl 1,822; Fac 147; Highest Degree: Bachelor
1998-1999 Income Parent Institution $1,452,950. Mats Exp $601,669, Books $220,553, Per/Ser (Incl. Access Fees) $343,635, Presv $20,803, Micro $16,678, Other Print Mats $109,301. Sal $529,843 (Prof $290,385)
Library Holdings: Bk Vols 359,000; Per Subs 3,200; High Interest/Low Vocabulary Bk Vols 4,000; Spec Interest Per Sub 36
Subject Interests: Am lit, Behav sci, English literature, Feminism, History, Local history, Soc sci
Special Collections: Adaline Glasheen Coll; Alexander Campbell Coll, readings; Arch Merrill Coll; David Bates Douglass Coll; E E Griffith Coll; George M B Hawley Coll; Leo Srole Coll
Database Vendor: Dialog, Lexis-Nexis, OCLC - First Search, ProQuest, Silverplatter Information Inc., Wilson - Wilson Web
Publications: Library Associates Newsletter
Partic in OCLC Online Computer Library Center, Inc; Rochester Regional Library Council
Open Mon-Thurs 8am-1pm, Fri 8am-noon, Sat 9am-noon & Sun 9am-1pm
Friends of the Library Group

GERMANTOWN

P GERMANTOWN LIBRARY, 50 Palatine Park Rd, 12526-5309. SAN 376-5830. Tel: 518-537-5800. FAX: 518-537-5928. E-Mail: palatine@valstar.net. Web Site: midhudson.org/member/german.html. *Dir*, Marjorie C Metzler; Staff 2 (MLS 1, Non-MLS 1)
Founded 1948. Pop 2,010
Jan 1999-Dec 1999 Income $28,763, County $4,166, Locally Generated Income $4,000, Other $12,370. Mats Exp $23,384, Books $5,430, Per/Ser (Incl. Access Fees) $660, Electronic Ref Mat (Incl. Access Fees) $415. Sal $8,896 (Prof $5,681)
Library Holdings: Bk Titles 17,304; Per Subs 52
Subject Interests: Cookbooks, Crafts, Gardening, Local history, Medical
Database Vendor: ProQuest
Function: ILL available, Photocopies available
Mem of Mid-Hudson Library System

GETZVILLE

BUREAU OF JEWISH EDUCATION, Milton Plesur Memorial Library, 2640 N Forest Rd, 14068. SAN 320-8990. Tel: 716-689-8844. FAX: 716-689-8862. *Exec Dir*, Mark Cantor Horowitz; *Librn*, Lora Keister
Founded 1928
Library Holdings: Bk Vols 15,000; Per Subs 30
Subject Interests: Education, Hebraica, Israel, Judaica, Philosophy
Special Collections: Jewish Heritage Video Coll
Publications: Video Catalog
Partic in Western New York Library Resources Council
Open Mon, Tues, Thurs 10-2, Wed 11-2, Sun 10-12

GHENT

S ANTHROPOSOPHICAL SOCIETY IN AMERICA, Rudolf Steiner Library, 65 Fern Hill Rd, 12075. SAN 373-1197. Tel: 518-672-7690. FAX: 518-672-5827. *Librn*, Fred Paddock; *Asst Librn*, Jude Limberger
Library Holdings: Bk Vols 25,000; Per Subs 20

GILBERTSVILLE

P GILBERTSVILLE FREE LIBRARY, 19 Commercial St, 13776. (Mail add: PO Box 332, 13776-0332), SAN 311-239X. Tel: 607-783-2832. *Dir*, Irma Ruston
Founded 1889. Pop 388
Library Holdings: Bk Titles 8,000; Per Subs 50
Subject Interests: Local history
Mem of Four County Library System

GLEN COVE

P GLEN COVE PUBLIC LIBRARY, 4 Glen Cove Ave, 11542-2885. SAN 311-242X. Tel: 516-676-2130. FAX: 516-676-2788. E-Mail: glencove@lilrc.org. Web Site: www.nassaulibrary.org/glencove. *Dir*, John P McKay; *Asst Dir, Tech Servs*, Maija Sperauskas; *Ad Servs*, Antonia Petrash; *Ch Servs*, Mary Beth Coco; *Ref*, Michael Freedman; *Automation Syst Coordr*, Alexander Bellos; Staff 40 (MLS 14, Non-MLS 26)
Founded 1894. Pop 24,618; Circ 158,935
Jan 2000-Dec 2000 Income City $1,660,798. Mats Exp $435,300. Sal $1,225,498 (Prof $566,850)
Library Holdings: Bk Vols 149,587; Per Subs 300
Special Collections: Long Island History (Glen Cove)
Automation Activity & Vendor Info: (Circulation) DRA; (OPAC) DRA
Publications: Newsletter (bi-monthly)
Mem of Nassau Library System
Open Mon-Thurs 9-9, Fri & Sat 9-5; Sun 1-5 (Oct-May only); Sat 9-1 (Summer)
Friends of the Library Group

S HOLOCAUST MEMORIAL & EDUCATIONAL CENTER OF NASSAU COUNTY, Louis Posner Memorial Library, Welwyn Preserve, 100 Crescent Beach Rd, 11542. SAN 377-2071. Tel: 516-571-8040. FAX: 516-571-8041. *Dir*, Marcia Posner; E-Mail: MarTV19@aol.com; Staff 6 (MLS 6)
Founded 1994
Jan 2000-Dec 2000 Income Parent Institution $10,000. Mats Exp $8,850, Books $6,000, Per/Ser (Incl. Access Fees) $250, AV Equip $500, Other Print Mats $100, Electronic Ref Mat (Incl. Access Fees) $2,000
Library Holdings: Bk Titles 4,002
Subject Interests: Holocaust
Special Collections: Holocaust Curricula & Graphics
Automation Activity & Vendor Info: (Acquisitions) Sagebrush Corporation; (Cataloging) Sagebrush Corporation; (Circulation) Sagebrush Corporation; (Course Reserve) Sagebrush Corporation; (ILL) Sagebrush Corporation; (Media Booking) Sagebrush Corporation; (OPAC) Sagebrush Corporation; (Serials) Sagebrush Corporation
Restriction: Circulation limited

M NORTH SHORE UNIVERSITY HOSPITAL AT GLEN COVE, Medical Library,* 101 Saint Andrews Lane, 11542. SAN 311-2411. Tel: 516-674-7300. FAX: 516-676-9039. *Librn*, James Redman
Founded 1958
Library Holdings: Per Subs 96
Subject Interests: Medicine, Nursing, Psychiatry, Rehabilitation med

C WEBB INSTITUTE, Livingston Library, 298 Crescent Beach Rd, 11542. SAN 311-2446. Tel: 516-671-0439. FAX: 516-674-9838. *Dir*, Patricia M Prescott; E-Mail: pprescot@webb-institute.edu; Staff 1 (MLS 1)
Founded 1932. Enrl 83; Fac 14; Highest Degree: Master
Library Holdings: Bk Titles 43,621; Per Subs 255
Subject Interests: Sci-tech
Special Collections: Marine Engineering; Marine History; Naval Architecture
Publications: Acquisitions List
Partic in Long Island Library Resources Council; OCLC Online Computer Library Center, Inc

GLENS FALLS

P CRANDALL PUBLIC LIBRARY,* 251 Glen St, 12801-3593. SAN 311-2470. Tel: 518-792-6508. FAX: 518-792-5251. *Dir*, Christine McDonald; *Ch Servs, YA Servs*, Pamela Frazier; *Ad Servs*, Andrea Herman. Subject Specialists: *Health*, Jo-Ann Benedetti; Staff 33 (MLS 10, Non-MLS 23)
Founded 1892. Pop 50,675
Library Holdings: Bk Vols 173,470; Per Subs 1,227
Subject Interests: Architecture, Art
Special Collections: Americana; Folklife & Local History of Northern New York Adirondacks & Upper Hudson Valley, bks, clippings, genealogy, mss, photogs & serials
Publications: Newsletter, Ref Desk Notes
Mem of Southern Adirondack Library System
Special Services for the Deaf - High interest/low vocabulary books
Family focus center relating to parenting, prenatal, infant & toddler care with special emphasis on developmental disabilities. Programs on music, storytelling, lectures, reading discussions, exhibits, folklife workshops; film/video program of independent & foreign films. Open Mon-Wed 9-9, Thurs-Fri 9-6 & Sat 9-5; Sun 1-5 (Jan-June & Sept-Dec)
Friends of the Library Group

S GLENS FALLS-QUEENSBURY HISTORICAL ASSOCIATION, Chapman Historical Museum Library, 348 Glen St, 12801. SAN 327-7178. Tel: 518-793-2826. FAX: 518-793-2831. *Exec Dir*, Timothy Weidner; *Curator*, Rebecca Gereau Pelchar
Library Holdings: Bk Vols 30,000
Subject Interests: Genealogy, Local history
Special Collections: Seneca Ray Stoddard Coll (1864-1917), photos

S HYDE COLLECTION LIBRARY, 161 Warren St, 12801. SAN 311-2489. Tel: 518-792-1761. FAX: 518-792-9197. Web Site: www.hydeartmuseum.org. *Dir*, Randall Suffolk; E-Mail: rand@hydeartmuseum.org
Founded 1963
Subject Interests: Art, First edition, Rare books

GLOVERSVILLE

P GLOVERSVILLE FREE LIBRARY, 58 E Fulton St, 12078. SAN 311-2519. Tel: 518-725-2819. FAX: 518-773-0292. E-Mail: gfl@superior.net. Web Site: www.superior.net/~gfl. *Coll Develop, Dir*, Ann Martin Streit; *Ch Servs*, Paul Weil; *ILL*, Deborah Bucholtz; *Per*, Sherry Teetz; Staff 10 (MLS 2, Non-MLS 8)
Founded 1880. Pop 16,656; Circ 105,013
Library Holdings: Bk Vols 56,705; Bk Titles 52,819; Per Subs 105
Subject Interests: Agriculture, Health, Local history, Music, Parent educ, Small bus ctr
Special Collections: English as a Second Language; Job Information Center; Library Family Center; Wellness Information Center
Publications: Fulton County Day Care & Preschool Directory; Help I'm a Parent - parent educ bibliography
Mem of Mohawk Valley Library Association
Friends of the Library Group

R KNESSETH ISRAEL SYNAGOGUE LIBRARY, 34 E Fulton St, 12078. SAN 311-2527. Tel: 518-725-0649. FAX: 518-725-0640. Web Site: www.knessethisrael.org. *Librn*, Esther Tasner
Founded 1975
Library Holdings: Bk Titles 685; Per Subs 14
Subject Interests: Judaica
Open Mon-Fri 8-4

GORHAM

P GORHAM FREE LIBRARY,* Main St, PO Box 211, 14461. SAN 311-2535. Tel: 716-526-6655. FAX: 716-526-6995. *Librn*, Roberta Zerrahn; E-Mail: rzerrahn@pls-net.org
Founded 1914. Pop 3,598; Circ 14,739
Library Holdings: Bk Vols 9,561; Bk Titles 9,355; Per Subs 18
Mem of Ontario Library Service North; Pioneer Library System

GOSHEN

P GOSHEN PUBLIC LIBRARY & HISTORICAL SOCIETY,* 203 Main St, 10924. SAN 311-2551. Tel: 914-294-6606. FAX: 914-294-7158. E-Mail: gplhs@rcls.org. Web Site: purl.oclc.org/gplhs. *Dir*, Pauline Kehoe; E-Mail: pkehoe@rcls.org
Founded 1894. Pop 15,000; Circ 135,757
Jul 1998-Jun 1999 Income $509,657, Locally Generated Income $452,979, Other $56,678. Mats Exp $65,654, Books $52,541, Per/Ser (Incl. Access Fees) $12,381, Presv $732. Sal $305,963
Library Holdings: Bk Vols 36,014; Per Subs 985
Subject Interests: Local history
Database Vendor: epixtech, inc.
Publications: A Guide to the Manuscript Collection of the Goshen Library & Historical Society; History of the Goshen Public Library
Mem of Ramapo Catskill Library System
Friends of the Library Group

S HARNESS RACING MUSEUM & HALL OF FAME, Peter D Haughton Memorial Library, 240 Main St, PO Box 590, 10924. SAN 311-256X. Tel: 845-294-6330. FAX: 845-294-3463. Web Site: www.harnessmuseum.com. *Dir*, Gail Cunard
Founded 1951
Library Holdings: Bk Vols 400; Per Subs 12
Subject Interests: Art of the Am trotting horse breed, Harness racing, Hist of the Am trotting horse breed

Special Collections: Currier & Ives Travelling Exhibit; History & collections of standard bred horse & harness racing
Restriction: By appointment only
Friends of the Library Group

L NYS SUPREME COURT, Law Library of Orange County, Orange County Government Center, 255-275 Main St, 10924. SAN 311-2578. Tel: 914-291-3138. FAX: 212-401-9144. *Librn*, Margaret S O'Loughlin; E-Mail: moloughl@courts.state.ny.us. Subject Specialists: *Law*, Margaret S O'Loughlin; Staff 1 (MLS 1)
Apr 1999-Mar 2000 Mats Exp $110,000
Library Holdings: Bk Vols 24,000; Bk Titles 350; Per Subs 10
Automation Activity & Vendor Info: (OPAC) epixtech, inc.
Database Vendor: Lexis-Nexis
Restriction: Not a lending library
Function: For research purposes

GOUVERNEUR

P READING ROOM ASSOCIATION OF GOUVERNEUR,* 60 Church St, 13642. SAN 311-2594. Tel: 315-287-0191. *Dir*, Charlotte Garofalo; E-Mail: garofalo@northnet.org
Founded 1885. Pop 6,985; Circ 27,458
Library Holdings: Bk Titles 19,282; Per Subs 36
Mem of North Country Library System
Open Mon, Tues & Thurs 6:30-8:30, Wed 9-11
Friends of the Library Group

GOWANDA

P GOWANDA FREE LIBRARY, 56 W Main St, 14070-1390. SAN 311-2608. Tel: 716-532-3451. *Mgr*, Jeanne Glende
Circ 40,261
Jan 1999-Dec 1999 Income $2,700, County $200, Locally Generated Income $2,500. Mats Exp $6,943, Books $6,643, Per/Ser (Incl. Access Fees) $300
Library Holdings: Bk Vols 15,738
Open Mon, Tues & Thurs 2-5:30 & 7-9, Fri 12-5:30 & Sat 10-1

GRAFTON

P GRAFTON COMMUNITY LIBRARY,* 2455 NY2 PO Box H, 12082. SAN 311-2616. Tel: 518-279-0580. FAX: 518-279-0580. *Dir*, Carolyn Durnin
Circ 5,808
Jan 1997-Dec 1998 Income $19,069. Mats Exp $3,045. Sal $9,595
Library Holdings: Bk Vols 6,748; Per Subs 161

GRAHAMSVILLE

P DANIEL PIERCE LIBRARY,* 328 Main St, PO Box 268, 12740. SAN 311-2624. Tel: 914-985-7233. FAX: 914-985-0135. E-Mail: dpl@rcls.org. *Dir*, Joann Gallagher
Founded 1898. Pop 2,800; Circ 7,441
Library Holdings: Bk Vols 21,000; Per Subs 70
Mem of Ramapo Catskill Library System
Open Tues & Thurs 12-5 & 7-9, Wed & Fri 12-5, Sat 10-3

GRAND ISLAND

P GRAND ISLAND MEMORIAL LIBRARY,* 1715 Bedell Rd, 14072. SAN 311-2632. Tel: 716-773-7124. FAX: 716-774-1146. *Dir*, Lynn Alan Konovitz
Pop 17,561; Circ 207,228
1999-2000 Income $282,934. Mats Exp $37,389, Books $27,489, Per/Ser (Incl. Access Fees) $9,900. Sal $216,894
Library Holdings: Bk Vols 57,000; Per Subs 133
Mem of Buffalo & Erie County Public Library System
Friends of the Library Group

S MOORE NORTH AMERICA, Research Center Library, 300 Lang Blvd, 14072-1697. SAN 311-2659. Interlibrary Loan Service Tel: 716-773-0556. FAX: 716-773-0277. Web Site: www.moore.com. *Senior Librn*, Tanis J Toponak; E-Mail: toponak@research.moore.com. Subject Specialists: *Business*, Tanis J Toponak; Staff 1 (Non-MLS 1)
Founded 1969
Library Holdings: Bk Titles 4,000; Per Subs 500
Subject Interests: Bus forms, Chemistry, Computers, Cost, Electronic printing, Electronics printing, Marketing, Paperproducts, Pricing, Related products
Automation Activity & Vendor Info: (Circulation) Inmagic, Inc.
Database Vendor: Dialog, Ebsco - EbscoHost, OCLC - First Search
Restriction: By appointment only
Partic in Western New York Library Resources Council

S OCCIDENTAL CHEMICAL CORPORATION, Technical Information Center, 2801 Long Rd, 14072. SAN 311-2640. Tel: 716-773-8531. FAX: 716-773-8487.; Staff 1 (MLS 1)
Founded 1916
Library Holdings: Bk Vols 25,000; Per Subs 250
Subject Interests: Bus, Chemistry
Special Collections: Beilstein; Chemical Abstracts; Houben-Weil
Restriction: By appointment only
Partic in OCLC Online Computer Library Center, Inc; Western New York Library Resources Council

GRANVILLE

P PEMBER LIBRARY & MUSEUM, 33 W Main St, 12832. SAN 311-2667. Tel: 518-642-2525. E-Mail: pemberlib@adelphia.net. *Dir*, Kathy Long; Tel: 518-642-0704. Subject Specialists: *Libr sci*, Kathy Long; Staff 2 (MLS 1, Non-MLS 1)
Founded 1909. Pop 3,500; Circ 23,367
Library Holdings: Bk Vols 21,000; Per Subs 44
Special Collections: Local History
Mem of Southern Adirondack Library System
Open Tues 9am-5pm, Wed & Thurs 1-8:30pm, Fri 1-5pm & Sat 10am-3pm; Closed Mon
Friends of the Library Group

GREAT NECK

P GREAT NECK LIBRARY, 159 Bayview Ave, 11023-1938. SAN 352-4884. Tel: 516-466-8055. FAX: 516-829-8297. Web Site: www.nassaulibrary.org/gneck. *Dir*, Christine Salita; *Ch Servs*, Lisa Paulo; *Coll Develop, Tech Servs*, Arlene Nevens; *Mgr*, Neil Zitofsky; *Ref*, Leila Mattson; *Publ Servs*, Muriel Turk; *Circ, Online Servs*, Janet Fine; *Tech Coordr*, Joseph J Latin; Staff 30 (MLS 30)
Founded 1889. Pop 42,428; Circ 722,204
Jan 1999-Dec 1999 Income (Main Library and Branch Library) $6,119,834, State $400, Locally Generated Income $12,827, Other $6,106,607. Mats Exp $6,039,406, Books $463,855, Per/Ser (Incl. Access Fees) $44,561, Micro $15,061, AV Equip $7,083, Electronic Ref Mat (Incl. Access Fees) $51,650. Sal $3,675,286 (Prof $1,410,564)
Library Holdings: Bk Vols 349,464; Bk Titles 197,442; Per Subs 1,211
Subject Interests: Architecture, Art, Behav sci, Soc sci
Automation Activity & Vendor Info: (Acquisitions) Innovative Interfaces Inc.; (Cataloging) Innovative Interfaces Inc.; (Circulation) Innovative Interfaces Inc.; (OPAC) Innovative Interfaces Inc.; (Serials) Innovative Interfaces Inc.
Database Vendor: Ebsco - EbscoHost, IAC - Info Trac, OCLC - First Search
Publications: Bimonthly newsletter
Mem of Nassau Library System
Branches: 3
LAKEVILLE, 475 Great Neck Rd, 11021. SAN 352-4914. Tel: 516-466-8055, Ext 231. FAX: 516-466-7863. *Librn*, Ruth Klement
Library Holdings: Bk Vols 21,700
PARKVILLE, 10 Campbell St, New Hyde Park, 11040. SAN 352-4949. Tel: 516-466-8055, Ext 234. FAX: 516-437-1929. *Librn*, Jayne Alexander
Library Holdings: Bk Vols 21,300
STATION, 40-B Great Neck Rd, 11021. SAN 352-4973. Tel: 516-466-8055, Ext 232. FAX: 516-466-4917.

R TEMPLE BETH EL, Arnold & Marie Schwartz & Hattie & Albert Grauer Library, 5 Old Mill Rd, 11023. SAN 311-2675. Tel: 516-487-0900, Ext 225. FAX: 516-487-6941. Web Site: members.aol.com/tbepage. *Librn*, Margaret Fincsilver
Founded 1950
Library Holdings: Bk Vols 10,000; Per Subs 15
Subject Interests: Judaica

GREENE

P MOORE MEMORIAL LIBRARY, 59 Genesee St, 13778-1298. SAN 311-2691. Tel: 607-656-9349. FAX: 607-656-9349. E-Mail: gr_ill@4cty.org. Web Site: lib.4cls.org/gr/greene.html. *Librn*, Mary King; Staff 1 (Non-MLS 1)
Founded 1902. Pop 6,053; Circ 54,978
Jan 1999-Dec 1999 Income $113,122, State $1,976, Locally Generated Income $40,500, Other $68,284. Mats Exp $18,636, Books $15,000, Per/Ser (Incl. Access Fees) $2,636, Electronic Ref Mat (Incl. Access Fees) $1,000. Sal $50,834 (Prof $24,000)
Library Holdings: Bk Vols 24,212; Per Subs 30
Special Collections: Cemetery Records; Chenango American 1855-present
Database Vendor: DRA
Mem of Four County Library System
Friends of the Library Group

GREENLAWN

S BAE SYSTEMS, Technical Information Center, MS 1-40, One Hazeltine Way, 11740. SAN 373-4846. Tel: 631-262-8276. FAX: 631-262-8285. *Librn*, Connie Muscolino
Library Holdings: Bk Vols 1,400; Per Subs 50

Subject Interests: Engineering, Technology
Restriction: Staff use only
Partic in Long Island Library Resources Council
Open Mon-Fri 8-5

P HARBORFIELDS PUBLIC LIBRARY,* 31 Broadway, 11740-1382. SAN 311-2705. Tel: 516-757-4200. FAX: 516-757-7216. E-Mail: harblib@suffolk.lib.ny.us. Web Site: www.harb.suffolk.lib.ny.us. *Dir*, Paul Elsener; E-Mail: pelsener@suffolk.lib.ny.us; *Tech Coordr*, Joan Clemens; E-Mail: jclemens@suffolk.lib.ny.us; *Ch Servs*, Carol Albano; E-Mail: calbano@suffolk.lib.ny.us; *Selection of Gen Ref Mat*, Elaine Tolle; E-Mail: etolle@suffolk.lib.ny.us; *Ref Servs YA*, Susan Holden; E-Mail: sholden@suffolk.lib.ny.us; *Ad Servs*, Carol Bloomgarden; E-Mail: cbloomga@suffolk.lib.ny.us; *Cat*, Della Bucher; E-Mail: mbucher@suffolk.lib.ny.us; *Circ*, Donna Wickers; E-Mail: dwickers@suffolk.lib.ny.us; Staff 15 (MLS 14, Non-MLS 1)
Founded 1970. Pop 18,197; Circ 278,735
Jul 1998-Jun 1999 Income $2,275,300, State $6,659. Mats Exp $283,847, Books $205,950, Per/Ser (Incl. Access Fees) $36,025, Presv $500, Micro $30,553, AV Equip $3,679, Electronic Ref Mat (Incl. Access Fees) $7,140. Sal $1,233,364 (Prof $591,641)
Library Holdings: Bk Vols 196,208; Per Subs 1,138
Subject Interests: Bus, Career, Consumer info, Health, Parenting, Teacher, Travel
Automation Activity & Vendor Info: (Cataloging) Innovative Interfaces Inc.; (Circulation) Innovative Interfaces Inc.; (ILL) Innovative Interfaces Inc.; (OPAC) Innovative Interfaces Inc.; (Serials) Innovative Interfaces Inc.
Database Vendor: IAC - SearchBank, OCLC - First Search
Publications: Monthly newsletter
Mem of Suffolk Cooperative Library System
Partic in Partnership of Automated Librs in Suffolk
Special Services for the Deaf - Captioned media
Special Services for the Blind - Descriptive videos
Friends of the Library Group

GREENPORT

M EASTERN LONG ISLAND HOSPITAL, Medical Library,* 201 Manor Pl, 11944. SAN 377-3701. Tel: 516-477-1000, Ext 273. FAX: 516-477-1746.
Library Holdings: Per Subs 12

P FLOYD MEMORIAL LIBRARY, 539 First St, 11944-1399. SAN 311-273X. Tel: 631-477-0660. FAX: 631-477-2647. E-Mail: flydlib@suffolk.lib.ny.us. Web Site: www.northfork.net/library/floyd. *Dir*, Lisa Richland; E-Mail: lrichlan@suffolk.lib.ny.us; *Asst Dir*, Priscilla Poppy Johnson; E-Mail: pjohnson@suffolk.lib.ny.us; *Ch Servs, Ref*, April Brazill; E-Mail: abrazill@suffolk.lib.ny.us; Staff 9 (MLS 3, Non-MLS 6)
Founded 1904. Pop 5,300; Circ 80,000
Jan 1999-Dec 1999 Income $495,808, Locally Generated Income $469,808, Other $26,000. Mats Exp $39,000, Books $25,000, Per/Ser (Incl. Access Fees) $4,000, AV Equip $4,500, Other Print Mats $2,000, Electronic Ref Mat (Incl. Access Fees) $3,500. Sal $175,000 (Prof $110,000)
Library Holdings: Bk Vols 36,241; Bk Titles 35,766; Per Subs 110; High Interest/Low Vocabulary Bk Vols 40; Bks on Deafness & Sign Lang 15
Subject Interests: Boating, Local history, Shakespeare
Special Collections: Shakespeare Coll
Automation Activity & Vendor Info: (Cataloging) Follett; (Circulation) Follett
Database Vendor: IAC - SearchBank, ProQuest, Wilson - Wilson Web
Publications: Newsletter
Function: Reference services available
Mem of Suffolk Cooperative Library System
Special Services for the Blind - Bks on cassette
Friends of the Library Group

G PLUM ISLAND ANIMAL DISEASE CENTER,* PO Box 848, 11944. SAN 311-2748. Tel: 516-323-2500, Ext 475. FAX: 516-323-9790. E-Mail: hmcilva@rama.poly.edu. *Librn*, Honore' McIlvain
Founded 1954
Library Holdings: Per Subs 125
Subject Interests: Exotic foreign animal diseases to USA
Special Collections: African Swine Fever Coll; Foot & Mouth Disease Coll
Partic in Dialog Corporation; Fedlink; OCLC Online Computer Library Center, Inc

GREENVILLE

P GREENVILLE PUBLIC LIBRARY,* North St, Rte 32, PO Box 8, 12083. SAN 311-2764. Tel: 518-966-8205. FAX: 518-966-4108. *Dir*, Barbara Flach
Founded 1928. Pop 5,000; Circ 23,644
Library Holdings: Bk Titles 14,535; Per Subs 23
Subject Interests: Cassette bks, Large print, Mystery
Special Collections: Rotating Art Coll
Mem of Mid-Hudson Library System

GREENWICH

P EASTON LIBRARY, 1074 State Rte 40, 12834. SAN 312-1844. Tel: 518-692-2253. FAX: 518-692-2253. E-Mail: easton@netheaven.com. Web Site: easton.sals.edu. *Dir*, Helen C Brownell
Founded 1879. Circ 9,680
Jan 1999-Dec 1999 Income $25,683, Locally Generated Income $16,055, Other $10,100. Mats Exp $26,168, Books $5,167, Per/Ser (Incl. Access Fees) $718, Manuscripts & Archives $4,000. Sal $8,054
Library Holdings: Bk Vols 12,394; Per Subs 24
Subject Interests: Local history
Mem of Southern Adirondack Library System
Open Mon, Tues & Thurs 7pm-9pm, Wed 2-5 & Sat 10-4
Friends of the Library Group

P GREENWICH FREE LIBRARY,* Main St & Academy St, 12834. SAN 311-2772. Tel: 518-692-7157. FAX: 518-692-7157. *Librn*, Claudia Blackler
Founded 1902. Pop 6,500; Circ 33,818
Library Holdings: Bk Vols 30,367; Per Subs 14
Mem of Southern Adirondack Library System
Partic in OCLC Online Computer Library Center, Inc
Open Tues & Thurs 1-5 & 7-9, Wed 10-5, Fri 2-5 & Sat 10-3
Friends of the Library Group

GREENWOOD LAKE

P GREENWOOD LAKE PUBLIC LIBRARY,* 79 Waterstone Rd, PO Box 1139, 10925. SAN 311-2780. Tel: 914-477-8377. FAX: 914-477-8397. Web Site: gwllibrary.org. *Dir*, Stephanie Thiel
Founded 1932. Circ 32,676
Jul 1997-Jun 1998 Income $375,000, Locally Generated Income $1,500, Other $3,000. Mats Exp $74,000, Books $60,000, Per/Ser (Incl. Access Fees) $9,000, AV Equip $5,000. Sal $165,300 (Prof $35,000)
Library Holdings: Bk Vols 24,080; Bk Titles 23,180; Per Subs 122
Mem of Ramapo Catskill Library System
Friends of the Library Group

GREYSTONE

S PSYCHOLOGICAL MOTIVATIONS, INC LIBRARY, 1052 Worburton Ave, 10701. SAN 329-9988. Tel: 914-377-1920. FAX: 914-377-1976. E-Mail: psymot@aol.com. *Pres*, Jeffrey Halvorsen
Library Holdings: Bk Vols 11,500; Per Subs 15

GRIFFISS AFB

UNITED STATES AIR FORCE
A AIR FORCE RESEARCH LABORATORY-INFORMATION DIRECTORATE TECHNICAL LIBRARY, 26 Electronics Pkwy Bldg 106, w 262, Rome, 13441-4514. SAN 352-5031. Tel: 315-330-7600. Reference Tel: 315-330-7607. FAX: 315-330-3086. E-Mail: ifoil@rl.af.mil. Web Site: www.rl.af.mil. *Chief Librn*, Rodney M Heines; E-Mail: mike.heines@rl.af.mil; *Ref*, Jane Sylvestor; *Purchasing*, Eileen Goodell; Staff 5 (MLS 2, Non-MLS 3)
Founded 1952. Pop 1,500
Library Holdings: Bk Vols 23,000; Per Subs 250
Subject Interests: Computer science, Electronics, Mathematics, Radar
Database Vendor: Dialog, GaleNet, OVID Technologies
Publications: Accessions lists - open literature & documents
Restriction: Staff use only
Function: Research library
Partic in Air Force Res Lab Virtual Libr Team; Central New York Library Resources Council
Friends of the Library Group

GROTON

P GROTON PUBLIC LIBRARY,* 112 E Cortland St, 13073. SAN 311-2799. Tel: 607-898-5055. FAX: 607-898-5055. *Librn*, Susan Robey; Staff 10 (MLS 9, Non-MLS 1)
Founded 1896. Pop 5,200; Circ 41,120
Library Holdings: Bk Vols 30,046; Per Subs 50
Subject Interests: Parenting resources
Automation Activity & Vendor Info: (Circulation) epixtech, inc.
Mem of Finger Lakes Library System

GUILDERLAND

P GUILDERLAND PUBLIC LIBRARY, 2228 Western Ave, 12084-9701. SAN 310-754X. Tel: 518-456-2400. FAX: 518-456-0923. E-Mail: guilgen@uhls.lib.ny.us. Web Site: www.family.knick.net/guildlib. *Dir*, Carol J Hamblin; *Asst Dir*, Barbara Nichols Randall; *Head Ref*, Margaret Garrett; *Coll Develop*, Margaret Garnett; Staff 48 (MLS 18, Non-MLS 30)
Founded 1957. Pop 30,000; Circ 380,428
2000-2001 Income $1,457,723, State $8,890, Locally Generated Income

$1,316,440, Other $132,393. Mats Exp $316,456, Books $227,849, Per/Ser (Incl. Access Fees) $18,987, Micro $9,672, AV Equip $41,139, Electronic Ref Mat (Incl. Access Fees) $18,809. Sal $798,535 (Prof $307,388)
Library Holdings: Bk Vols 97,622; Per Subs 270
Special Collections: Altamont Enterprise microfilm, 1892 current
Publications: Newsletter, adult & children's
Mem of Upper Hudson Library System
Partic in CDLC; OCLC Online Computer Library Center, Inc
Friends of the Library Group

HAINES FALLS

P HAINES FALLS FREE LIBRARY,* County Rte 18, Box 397, 12436. SAN 311-2810. Tel: 518-589-5707. FAX: 518-589-0311. E-Mail: haines@sebridge.org. *Dir*, Constance M Carter
Founded 1900. Pop 1,358; Circ 17,156
Library Holdings: Per Subs 70
Subject Interests: Local history
Publications: Library Cookbook
Mem of Mid-Hudson Library System
Open Tues & Thurs 11-5, Wed 1-5, Sat 9:30-1:30

HAMBURG

P HAMBURG PUBLIC LIBRARY, 102 Buffalo St, 14075-5097. SAN 352-5066. Tel: 716-649-4415. FAX: 716-649-4160. Web Site: www.buffalolib.org/nl_ham.html. *Dir*, Jane Rosenfeld; Tel: 716-649-4836, E-Mail: rosenfeldj@buffalolib.org; *Branch Mgr*, John Edson; E-Mail: edsonj@buffalolib.org; Staff 6 (MLS 6)
Founded 1897. Pop 53,735; Circ 252,792
Jan 2000-Dec 2000 Income (Main Library and Branch Library) $686,136, State $16,658, County $669,171. Mats Exp $100,664. Sal $552,828 (Prof $297,054)
Library Holdings: Bk Titles 51,276; Per Subs 150
Subject Interests: Antiques, Art
Special Collections: Art Coll, reprod, videos
Automation Activity & Vendor Info: (Acquisitions) DRA; (Circulation) DRA; (OPAC) DRA
Mem of Buffalo & Erie County Public Library System
Friends of the Library Group
Branches: 2
BLASDELL BRANCH, 54 Madison Ave, Blasdell, 14219. SAN 352-5090. Tel: 716-823-4220. Web Site: www.buffalolib.org/nl_bla.html. *Branch Mgr*, Karen McClure; E-Mail: mcclurek@buffalolib.org
Circ 58,991
Library Holdings: Bk Titles 18,124
Friends of the Library Group
LAKE SHORE, 4857 Lake Shore Rd, 14075. SAN 352-5120. Tel: 716-627-3017. Web Site: www.buffalolib.org/nl_lsh.html. *Branch Mgr*, Richard Moesch; E-Mail: moeschr@buffalolib.org
Library Holdings: Bk Titles 36,302
Friends of the Library Group

C HILBERT COLLEGE, McGrath Library, 5200 S Park Ave, 14075. SAN 311-2829. Tel: 716-649-7900, Ext 361. FAX: 716-648-6530. Web Site: www.hilbert.edu/resources/library.asp. *Dir*, Barbara Bonanno; Tel: 716-649-7900, Ext 238, E-Mail: bonanno@hilbert.edu; *Publ Servs*, Suzette Hino
Founded 1955
Library Holdings: Bk Vols 40,302; Bk Titles 32,949; Per Subs 337
Subject Interests: Am lit, Bus mgt, Criminal justice, English literature, Human servs, Law, Philosophy, Psychology
Special Collections: Polish Language
Automation Activity & Vendor Info: (Cataloging) TLC; (Circulation) TLC; (OPAC) TLC
Database Vendor: Ebsco - EbscoHost, Lexis-Nexis, OCLC - First Search, ProQuest, Wilson - Wilson Web
Publications: Acquisitions List; AV Catalog; Periodical Holdings Catalog; Student Handbook; Subject Bibliographies; Video Catalog
Partic in Western New York Library Resources Council

HAMILTON

C COLGATE UNIVERSITY, Everett Needham Case Library, 13 Oak Dr, 13346-1398. SAN 311-2845. Tel: 315-228-7300. Interlibrary Loan Service Tel: 315-228-7597. FAX: 315-228-7934. Web Site: exlibris.colgate.edu. *Dir*, Judith Gibson Noyes; E-Mail: jnoyes@mail.colgate.edu; *Cat*, Ann Kebabian; *ILL*, Ellen Bolland; *Acq, Coll Develop*, Emily Hutton; *Ref*, David Hughes; *Doc*, Mary Jane Walsh; *Rare Bks*, Carl Peterson; *Bibliog Instr*, Mary Jane Petrowski; *Science*, Deborah Huerta; Staff 32 (MLS 13, Non-MLS 19)
Founded 1819. Enrl 2,820; Highest Degree: Master
Jun 1999-May 2000 Income (Main Library and Branch Library) $3,840,788. Mats Exp $1,798,676, Books $671,439, Per/Ser (Incl. Access Fees) $999,529, Presv $36,934, Micro $60,813, Electronic Ref Mat (Incl. Access Fees) $26,444. Sal $1,116,443 (Prof $666,801)
Library Holdings: Bk Vols 634,874
Special Collections: 17th Century British Religious & Political Tracts; 19th-20th Century American & British Literature; Edward Stone Coll of Photography; George Bernard Shaw Coll; Gertrude Stein Coll; James Joyce Coll; John Masefield Coll; Joseph Conrad Coll; Private Press & Fine Printing, incunabula; T S Eliot Coll; University Archives; World War I & II Posters
Automation Activity & Vendor Info: (Acquisitions) Innovative Interfaces Inc.; (Cataloging) Innovative Interfaces Inc.; (Circulation) Innovative Interfaces Inc.; (Course Reserve) Innovative Interfaces Inc.; (ILL) Innovative Interfaces Inc.; (Media Booking) Innovative Interfaces Inc.; (OPAC) Innovative Interfaces Inc.; (Serials) Innovative Interfaces Inc.
Publications: Philobiblon
Partic in Central New York Library Resources Council; New York State Interlibrary Loan Network; OCLC Online Computer Library Center, Inc
Friends of the Library Group
Departmental Libraries:
GEORGE R COOLEY SCIENCE LIBRARY Tel: 315-228-7312. *Librn*, Deborah Huerta; *Asst Librn*, Peter Tagtmeyer

P HAMILTON PUBLIC LIBRARY, 13 Broad St, 13346. SAN 311-2853. Tel: 315-824-3060. E-Mail: ha_circ@midyork.lib.ny.us. *Dir*, Barbara Coger
Founded 1903. Pop 4,000; Circ 96,019
Library Holdings: Bk Vols 33,853
Subject Interests: Architecture, Cookery, Crafts, Gardening, History, Natural science
Special Collections: Biographical Review of Madison County; History of Chenango & Madison Counties, 1784-1880 (James H; Madison County Cemetery Records (Genealogical Records Committee of the James Madison Chapter; of the Daughters of the American Revolution, 1801-1900); Smith Coll)
Mem of Mid-York Library System
Friends of the Library Group

HAMMOND

P HAMMOND FREE LIBRARY,* Main St, 13646. SAN 311-2861. Tel: 315-324-5139. *Librn*, Sherrie Moquin
Founded 1922. Circ 7,944
Library Holdings: Bk Vols 3,409
Mem of North Country Library System

HAMMONDSPORT

S GLENN H CURTISS MUSEUM OF LOCAL HISTORY, Minor Swarthout Memorial Library, 8419 Rte 54, 14840-0326. SAN 326-0356. Tel: 607-569-2160. FAX: 607-569-2040. Web Site: www.linkny.com/CurtissMuseum. *Dir*, Kirk House; *Mgr*, Chris Geiselmann; Staff 6 (Non-MLS 6)
Founded 1992
Library Holdings: Bk Titles 3,000; Per Subs 32
Subject Interests: Aviation, Local history
Function: Research library

P HAMMONDSPORT PUBLIC LIBRARY, 41 Lake St, PO Box 395, 14840. SAN 311-287X. Tel: 607-569-2045. FAX: 607-569-2045. E-Mail: hml_rachel@stls.org. Web Site: www.stls.org/hammondsport/default.htm. *Dir*, Rachel Brown; *Circ*, Marilyn Conklin; *Ch Servs*, Lisa Treichler
Founded 1876. Pop 2,807; Circ 27,798
Library Holdings: Bk Vols 19,000; Per Subs 30
Subject Interests: Local history
Special Collections: Aircraft Coll, bks & pictures
Mem of Chemung-Southern Tier Libr Syst; Southern Tier Library System

HAMPTON BAYS

P HAMPTON BAYS PUBLIC LIBRARY,* Ponquogue Ave, 11946-0207. SAN 311-2888. Tel: 516-728-6241. FAX: 516-728-0166. *Dir*, Joseph Pirz; Staff 3 (MLS 2, Non-MLS 1)
Founded 1960. Pop 9,319; Circ 103,816
Library Holdings: Bk Vols 37,062; Per Subs 743
Subject Interests: Architecture, Art
Special Collections: Long Island History
Mem of Suffolk Cooperative Library System
Friends of the Library Group

HANCOCK

P LOUISE ADELIA READ MEMORIAL LIBRARY,* 12 Read St, 13783. SAN 311-2896. Tel: 607-637-2519. FAX: 607-637-3377. E-Mail: ha_ill@4cty.org. *Librn*, Jeannine F Decker
Founded 1955. Pop 4,100; Circ 20,000
Library Holdings: Bk Vols 16,000
Mem of Four County Library System

HANNIBAL

P HANNIBAL FREE LIBRARY,* Oswego St, PO Box 174, 13074. SAN 311-2918. Tel: 315-564-5471. FAX: 315-564-5471. *Dir, Librn*, Marlene Sutcliffe; *Asst Librn*, Karen Eckersley
Pop 4,027; Circ 12,000
Library Holdings: Bk Vols 6,414; Per Subs 23
Subject Interests: Large print

HARRISON

P HARRISON PUBLIC LIBRARY, Bruce Ave, 10528. SAN 352-5155. Tel: 914-835-0324. FAX: 914-835-1564. Web Site: www.wls.lib.ny.us/. *Dir*, Virginia Weimer Vogl; *Ad Servs, AV*, Carole Meehan; *Ch Servs*, Carol Katz; *Acq, Cat, Tech Servs*, Jennie Kong; *Circ*, Joan Rosa
Founded 1905. Pop 23,046; Circ 178,000
2000-2001 Income $1,344,236. Sal $826,901 (Prof $425,645)
Library Holdings: Bk Vols 112,339
Special Collections: Italian & Japanese Language Coll
Automation Activity & Vendor Info: (Cataloging) epixtech, inc.; (Circulation) epixtech, inc.; (OPAC) epixtech, inc.
Mem of Westchester Library System
Friends of the Library Group
Branches: 1
WEST HARRISON BRANCH, 2 E Madison St, West Harrison, 10604. SAN 352-518X. Tel: 914-948-2092. FAX: 914-948-4350. Web Site: www.wls.lib.ny.us/. *Librn*, Karen Baker; *Ch Servs*, Aldona Pilmanis
Special Collections: Italian Language Coll
Friends of the Library Group

M SAINT VINCENT'S HOSPITAL & MEDICAL CENTER OF NEW YORK-WESTCHESTER, Medical Library, 275 North St, 10528. SAN 327-5094. Tel: 914-925-5337, Ext 5337. FAX: 914-925-5158. *Librn*, Ethel Eisenberg
Library Holdings: Bk Vols 7,000; Per Subs 100

HARRISVILLE

P HARRISVILLE FREE LIBRARY, PO Box 207, 13648. SAN 311-2934. Tel: 315-543-2442, 315-543-2577. E-Mail: bward@northnet.org. *Dir*, Barbara Ward
Circ 10,565
1998-1999 Income $16,226. Mats Exp $2,799, Books $2,339, Per/Ser (Incl. Access Fees) $410. Sal $6,114
Library Holdings: Bk Vols 5,410
Mem of North Country Library System
Friends of the Library Group

HARTSDALE

S GRAPHIC COMMUNICATIONS WORLD LIBRARY,* PO Box 727, 10530-0727. SAN 374-8642. Tel: 914-472-3051. FAX: 914-472-3880. *Pres*, John R Werner

HARTWICK

P KINNEY MEMORIAL LIBRARY,* 3140 Ct Hwy 11, PO Box 176, 13348. SAN 311-2950. Tel: 607-293-6600. FAX: 607-293-6600. E-Mail: kinymlib@telenet.net. *Dir Libr Serv*, Barbara Ann Potter; E-Mail: quilterb@telenet.net
Founded 1961. Pop 3,255; Circ 12,976
Library Holdings: Bk Titles 12,976; Per Subs 22
Special Collections: Genealogy; Historical Artifacts; Historical Books; Historical Photos
Mem of Four County Library System
Friends of the Library Group

HASTINGS-ON-HUDSON

P HASTINGS-ON-HUDSON PUBLIC LIBRARY,* 7 Maple Ave, 10706. SAN 311-2969. Tel: 914-478-3307. FAX: 914-478-4813. E-Mail: hastings@wls.lib.ny.us. Web Site: www.wls.lib.ny.us. *Dir*, Susan Feir; *Ad Servs*, Janet Murphy; *Ch Servs*, Joan Vaillancourt
Founded 1913. Pop 8,000; Circ 105,000
Library Holdings: Bk Titles 51,000; Per Subs 152
Mem of Westchester Library System
Open (Winter Hrs) Mon-Wed 9:30am-8:30pm, Thurs 9:30am-6pm, Sat 9:30am-2pm & Sun 1-5pm, closed Fri; (Summer Hrs) Mon-Wed 9:30-8:30, Tues 9:30-6, Sat 9:30-2, closed Fri & Sun
Friends of the Library Group

HAUPPAUGE

S ATLANTIC ULTRAVIOLET CORPORATION LIBRARY, 375 Marcus Blvd, 11788-8001. SAN 329-949X. Tel: 631-273-0500. FAX: 631-273-0771. E-Mail: auv@atlanticuv.com. Web Site: www.atlanticuv.com. *Librn*, Ann Wysocki
Library Holdings: Bk Vols 200
Open Mon-Fri 8:30-5

HAVERSTRAW

P HAVERSTRAW KINGS DAUGHTERS PUBLIC LIBRARY, 85 Main St, 10927. SAN 352-521X. Tel: 914-429-3445. FAX: 914-429-7313. E-Mail: kingslibadmin@spyral.net. *Dir*, Joanne Ginsburg; *Asst Dir, Ref*, Donna Sopalsky; Staff 19 (MLS 19)
Founded 1895. Pop 28,942; Circ 212,900
Jul 1998-Jun 1999 Income (Main Library and Branch Library) $1,619,069. Mats Exp $261,084, Books $145,214, Per/Ser (Incl. Access Fees) $12,000, Presv $750, Micro $8,200, Other Print Mats $750, Electronic Ref Mat (Incl. Access Fees) $13,000. Sal $975,872 (Prof $510,444)
Library Holdings: Bk Titles 94,763; Per Subs 239
Subject Interests: Careers, Local history, Spanish lang
Special Collections: Haverstraw Bay Photo Archives; North Rockland History
Automation Activity & Vendor Info: (Circulation) epixtech, inc.
Publications: Bibliographies; Bookmarks; Computer orientation booklet
Mem of Ramapo Catskill Library System
Branches: 1
THIELLS BRANCH, One Rosman Rd, Garnerville, 10923. SAN 352-5244. Tel: 914-786-3800. FAX: 914-786-3712. E-Mail: kingslibadmin@spyral.net. *Asst Dir*, Donna Sopalsky
Subject Interests: Careers, Computer software

HEMPSTEAD

P HEMPSTEAD PUBLIC LIBRARY, 115 Nichols Ct, 11550-3199. SAN 311-2993. Tel: 516-481-6990. FAX: 516-481-6719. E-Mail: hemplib@linet. Web Site: www.nassaulibrary.org/hempstd. *Dir*, Irene A Duszkiewicz; *Ref*, Patricia Sullivan; *Ch Servs, YA Servs*, Trina Reed; *Ad Servs*, Grace DiMaria; *Coll Develop*, Susan Alessi; *Archivist*, Carol Clarke. Subject Specialists: *Foreign Language*, Grace DiMaria; *Literacy*, Caren Cramer; Staff 60 (MLS 20, Non-MLS 40)
Founded 1889. Pop 47,093; Circ 265,268
Jun 2000-May 2001 Income $2,041,022. Mats Exp $595,141, Books $220,000, Per/Ser (Incl. Access Fees) $16,000. Sal $1,117,041
Library Holdings: Bk Vols 212,368; Per Subs 331
Subject Interests: Ethnic studies, History
Special Collections: Adult Multi-Media; Black Studies Coll; Early American Textbooks; Foreign Language Coll for Adults & Children; Hispanic Studies Coll; Job & Education Information Center; LI Photography Coll; Literacy Materials; Long Island Coll; Walt Whitman Coll
Database Vendor: Dialog, DRA, Ebsco - EbscoHost, IAC - Info Trac, OCLC - First Search
Publications: ALC Resources Bibliography; Black Studies Bibliography; Community Directory; Foreign Language Bibliography; Hispanic Studies Bibliography; Newsletter
Mem of Nassau Library System
Partic in Dialog Corporation; Libraries Online, Inc; Long Island Library Resources Council; Vutext
Job Education & Infomation Center; Adult Learning Center; Literacy Program

C HOFSTRA UNIVERSITY, Joan & Donald E Axinn Library, 123 Hofstra University, 11549. SAN 352-5279. Tel: 516-463-5940. Circulation Tel: 516-463-5952. Reference Tel: 516-463-5962. FAX: 516-463-6387. Web Site: www.hofstra.edu/library/axinn. *Dean of Libr*, Daniel Rubey; E-Mail: rgraber@hplsck.org; *Asst Dean*, Reta Graber; E-Mail: rgraber@hplsck.org; *Asst Dean*, Howard Graves; *Asst Dean*, Randall O'Brien; E-Mail: lebobr@nh.ultranet.com; *Mgr*, Carol Sasso; Tel: 516-463-5943, E-Mail: Libprcas@Hofstra.edu; *Archivist*, Geri Solomon; *Coll Develop*, Christine Wondolowski; *Coll Develop*, Vivian Wood; Tel: 516-463-6431, E-Mail: libaqvfw@hofstra.edu; *Media Spec*, David Dapogny; *Online Servs*, Jonathan Ramsay; E-Mail: jramsay@rye.lib.nh.us; *Ser*, Patricia Quinn; *Spec Coll*, Julie Doherty; E-Mail: jdoherty@rye.lib.nh.us; *Tech Servs*, Melanie Freese. Subject Specialists: *Business and management*, Domenica Barbuto; *Science/technology*, Jonathan Ramsay; Staff 98 (MLS 31, Non-MLS 67)
Founded 1935
Sep 1999-Aug 2000 Income Parent Institution $5,609,010. Mats Exp $1,425,478, Books $428,759, Per/Ser (Incl. Access Fees) $568,000, Presv $56,050, Micro $230,000, AV Equip $26,565, Manuscripts & Archives $2,646, Electronic Ref Mat (Incl. Access Fees) $113,458. Sal $2,715,342 (Prof $1,072,073)
Library Holdings: Bk Vols 1,466,750; Bk Titles 648,148; Per Subs 2,200
Special Collections: Authors Collections of Late 19th & Early 20th Century; William Blake Facsimiles; Collection of Books About Books & Early Printed Books; Georgian Poets; Henry Kroul Collection of Nazi Culture & Propaganda; Private Press Coll; Nila Banton Smith Reading Coll;

Utopian Communities; Weingrow Coll of Avant-Garde Art & Literature
Automation Activity & Vendor Info: (Acquisitions) DRA
Database Vendor: CARL, Dialog, DRA, Ebsco - EbscoHost, Lexis-Nexis, OCLC - First Search, ProQuest, Silverplatter Information Inc.

S HELEN KELLER SERVICES FOR THE BLIND LIBRARY,* One Helen Keller Way, 11550. SAN 327-5116. Tel: 516-485-1234, Ext 243. FAX: 516-538-6785. *Dir*, Geralyn Zuzze; *Librn*, Edith Magee
Library Holdings: Bk Titles 10,000
Restriction: Not open to public
Open Mon-Fri 9-4:30

S NASSAU COUNTY MUSEUM, Long Island Studies Institute Library at Hostra Univ, 619 Fulton Ave, 11550-4575. SAN 311-1458. Tel: 516-463-6417. FAX: 516-463-6441. *Curator*, Dr Mildred DeRiggi; *Asst Dir*, Gary Hammond; Tel: 516-463-6418
Founded 1962
Library Holdings: Bk Vols 7,300; Bk Titles 7,100; Per Subs 125
Subject Interests: Genealogy, Long Island hist, Nassau County hist, Suffolk County
Special Collections: Long Island Photographs; Queens County Deeds; Queens County Estate Inventories; Queens, Nassau & Suffolk Censuses
Restriction: Open to public for reference only
Function: Archival collection
Partic in Long Island Library Resources Council

HENDERSON

P HENDERSON FREE LIBRARY,* PO Box 302, 13650. SAN 311-3019. Tel: 315-938-5032. FAX: 315-938-7038. *Dir*, Cheryl Shutts
Founded 1951. Pop 1,330; Circ 11,600
Library Holdings: Bk Vols 10,661; Per Subs 57
Special Collections: Town History (Historical Society)
Open Mon & Wed 1-5 & 7-9, Sat 9-1

HERKIMER

P FRANK J BASLOE LIBRARY OF HERKIMER NEW YORK,* 245 N Main St, 13350. SAN 311-3027. Tel: 315-866-1733. FAX: 315-866-1733. E-Mail: he_circ@midyork.lib.ny.us. *Dir*, Heidi L Moody
Founded 1895. Pop 7,945; Circ 101,422
Library Holdings: Bk Vols 38,682; Per Subs 89
Special Collections: Genealogy; NYS Coll
Mem of Mid-York Library System
Open Mon-Thurs 9-8, Fri 9-5 & Sat 9-3
Friends of the Library Group

J HERKIMER COUNTY COMMUNITY COLLEGE LIBRARY, Reservoir Rd, 13350. SAN 311-3035. Tel: 315-866-0300, Ext 270. Circulation Tel: 315-866-0300, Ext 272. Reference Tel: 315-866-0300, Ext 394. FAX: 315-866-1806. E-Mail: library@hccc.suny.edu. Web Site: www.hccc.ntcnet.com. *Dir Libr Serv*, Scott DiMarco; *Tech Servs*, Valerie Prescott; Staff 4 (MLS 4)
Founded 1967. Enrl 2,400; Fac 83; Highest Degree: Associate
Library Holdings: Bk Titles 69,511; Per Subs 302
Subject Interests: Architecture, Art, Behav sci, Bus, Education, Law, Mgt, Soc sci, Technology, Tourism, Travel
Automation Activity & Vendor Info: (Cataloging) MultiLIS; (Circulation) MultiLIS; (OPAC) MultiLIS; (Serials) MultiLIS
Database Vendor: Dialog, GaleNet, IAC - SearchBank, OCLC - First Search
Publications: Faculty library handbook; Library handbook; Monthly acquisitions list; Periodicals holdings list
Partic in Central New York Library Resources Council; OCLC Online Computer Library Center, Inc
Open Mon-Thurs 7:30-9, Fri 7:30-4:30, Sun 5-9

S HERKIMER COUNTY HISTORICAL SOCIETY LIBRARY, A Walter Suiter Memorial Bldg, 400 N Main St, 13350. SAN 311-3043. Tel: 315-866-6413. E-Mail: hchs@mvip.net. Web Site: www.herkimerhistory.com. *Dir*, Susan R Perkins
Founded 1896
Library Holdings: Bk Vols 4,000
Subject Interests: Herkimer
Special Collections: Herkimer County New York Artifacts
Publications: Local genealogy; Local history
Open Mon-Fri 10-4

GL HERKIMER COUNTY LAW LIBRARY,* 320 N Main St, 13350-1949. SAN 311-3051. Tel: 315-867-1172. FAX: 315-866-7991. E-Mail: herklaw@pppmail.appliedtherory.com, ocali22@transit.nyser.net. *Asst Librn*, Constance Zogby
Founded 1941
Library Holdings: Bk Vols 14,000; Bk Titles 500
Special Collections: Legal Reference Coll

HERMON

P HEPBURN LIBRARY OF HERMON,* Main St, PO Box A, 13652. SAN 311-306X. Tel: 315-347-2285. FAX: 315-347-2285. *Librn*, Bonnie Hayden
Pop 1,080; Circ 25,333
Library Holdings: Bk Vols 14,000; Per Subs 41
Mem of North Country Library System
Open Mon 1-5, Tues 9-12, 2-5, Wed 2-7, Thurs 1-5, Fri 1-5 & Sat 10-2
Friends of the Library Group

HEUVELTON

P HEUVELTON FREE LIBRARY, 57 State St, PO Box 346, 13654. SAN 311-3078. Tel: 315-344-6550. *Dir*, Mary Vassmer; E-Mail: blood@northnet.org
Founded 1912. Pop 777; Circ 17,947
Library Holdings: Bk Vols 5,183; Bk Titles 4,729; Per Subs 62
Mem of North Country Library System
Open Mon & Wed 7-9, Tues 1-5, Fri 1-5 & 7-9 & Sat 2-5
Friends of the Library Group

HEWLETT

P HEWLETT-WOODMERE PUBLIC LIBRARY,* 1125 Broadway, 11557-2336. SAN 311-3086. Tel: 516-374-1967. FAX: 516-569-1229. Web Site: www.nassaulibrary.org/hewlett.index.html. *Dir*, Susan O deSciora; *Asst Dir*, Babette Gurwitz; *Ad Servs, Publ Servs*, Alice F Golbert; *Ch Servs*, Diane Mason; *AV*, Helene Hertzlinger; *Ref*, Charles Buckley; *Circ*, K Fitzgerald; *Tech Servs*, Eleanor Arnost; *Ref*, Florence Funicello; Tel: 516-766-2360, Ext 309, E-Mail: floroberts@yahoo.com. Subject Specialists: *Art*, Nancy Delin; *Music*, Millicent Vollono
Founded 1947. Pop 19,661; Circ 341,000
Library Holdings: Bk Vols 163,635; Per Subs 527
Subject Interests: Art, Music
Special Collections: Art Coll, bks, slides, flm; Music Coll, bks, scores, rec, tapes, cassettes, song indexes
Automation Activity & Vendor Info: (Circulation) DRA
Publications: Index to Art Reproductions in Books; Music & Art Catalogs; Overleaf (newsletter); Overleaf, Jr (children's newsletter)
Mem of Nassau Library System
Partic in Long Island Library Resources Council
Friends of the Library Group

HICKSVILLE

P HICKSVILLE PUBLIC LIBRARY, 169 Jerusalem Ave, 11801. SAN 311-3108. Tel: 516-931-1417. FAX: 516-822-5672. E-Mail: hilmail@alis.nls.lib.ny.us. Web Site: www.nassaulibrary.org/hicksv. *Dir*, Celeste Watman; Staff 10 (MLS 10)
Founded 1926. Pop 41,000; Circ 269,500
Jul 2000-Jun 2001 Income $2,940,748, Mats Exp $351,500, Books $255,938, Per/Ser (Incl. Access Fees) $61,512. Sal $1,236,724 (Prof $511,898)
Library Holdings: Bk Vols 236,020; Per Subs 638
Subject Interests: Local history
Database Vendor: DRA
Mem of Nassau Library System
Partic in Long Island Library Resources Council
Special Services for the Deaf - TDD

HIGHLAND

P HIGHLAND PUBLIC LIBRARY, 30 Church St, 12528. SAN 311-3124. Tel: 845-691-2275. FAX: 845-691-6302. E-Mail: circulation@highlandlibrary.org. Web Site: www.highlandlibrary.org/hplhome.htm. *Dir*, Julie Knutsen; E-Mail: jknutsen@highlandlibrary.org; Staff 8 (MLS 2, Non-MLS 6)
Founded 1915. Pop 11,075; Circ 45,810
Jun 1999-May 2000 Income (Main Library and Branch Library) $216,179, State $3,414, County $10,305, Locally Generated Income $199,255, Other $3,205. Mats Exp $30,962, Books $22,765, Per/Ser (Incl. Access Fees) $1,982, AV Equip $3,715, Electronic Ref Mat (Incl. Access Fees) $2,500. Sal $110,185 (Prof $34,612)
Library Holdings: Bk Titles 26,581; Per Subs 51
Publications: Highland Public Library Events
Mem of Mid-Hudson Library System
Friends of the Library Group
Branches: 1
CLINTONDALE BRANCH, Crescent at Maple, Clintondale, 12515. (Mail add: PO Box 481, Clintondale, 12515), SAN 372-560X. Tel: 845-883-5015. *In Charge*, Arlene McMahon
Library Holdings: Bk Vols 602

HIGHLAND FALLS

P HIGHLAND FALLS LIBRARY,* 298 Main St, 10928. SAN 352-5392. Tel: 914-446-3113. FAX: 914-446-1109. *Dir*, Suzanne Brahm; Staff 1 (MLS 1)
Founded 1884. Pop 5,947; Circ 28,091
Library Holdings: Bk Vols 36,000; Bk Titles 34,000; Per Subs 50
Subject Interests: Local authors, Local history
Mem of Ramapo Catskill Library System
Open Mon, Wed, Thurs & Fri 10-5, Tues 10-7 & Sat 10-2
Friends of the Library Group
Branches: 1
FRANCES TRACY MORGAN MEMORIAL, Fort Montgomery, 10922. SAN 352-5422. Tel: 914-446-5220. *Librn*, Suzanne Brahm
Library Holdings: Bk Vols 3,000
Friends of the Library Group

HIGHLAND MILLS

P WOODBURY PUBLIC LIBRARY, Rushmore Memorial Branch,* County Rte 105, 10930. SAN 311-3140. Tel: 914-928-6162. FAX: 914-928-3079. *Dir*, Martha LaVallee; Staff 2 (MLS 1, Non-MLS 1)
Founded 1923. Pop 8,236
Library Holdings: Bk Vols 29,250; Per Subs 190
Special Collections: Historical Coll-Town of Woodbury
Mem of Ramapo Catskill Library System
Friends of the Library Group
Branches: 2
IDA CORNELL BRANCH, Smith Clove Rd, Central Valley, 10917. SAN 373-7047. Tel: 914-928-2114. FAX: 914-928-8867. *Librn*, Martha LaVallee
RUSHMORE HISTORICAL BRANCH, Rte 32, 10930. SAN 373-7055. Tel: 914-928-6770.

HILLSDALE

P HILLSDALE PUBLIC LIBRARY ASSOCIATION, INC, 2609 Rte 23, PO Box 669, 12529. SAN 311-3159. Tel: 518-325-4101. FAX: 518-325-4101. E-Mail: hllsdle@taconic.net. Web Site: hillsdalepubliclibrary.org. *Dir*, Carol Briggs
Founded 1913. Pop 1,793; Circ 17,962
Library Holdings: Bk Titles 16,146; Per Subs 31
Mem of Mid-Hudson Library System
Friends of the Library Group

HILTON

P PARMA PUBLIC LIBRARY,* 7 West Ave, PO Box 785, 14468. SAN 311-3167. Tel: 716-392-8350. FAX: 716-392-9870. *Dir*, Susan E Henderson
Founded 1885. Pop 13,873; Circ 299,078
Library Holdings: Bk Titles 54,804; Per Subs 147
Subject Interests: Local history
Database Vendor: CARL
Mem of Monroe County Library System
Friends of the Library Group

HOGANSBURG

S AKWESASNE LIBRARY & CULTURE CENTER,* RR Box 14C, 13655. SAN 311-3175. Tel: 518-358-2240. FAX: 518-358-2649. *Dir*, Carol White; E-Mail: white@northnet.org; *Librn*, Corinne White; *Librn*, Valerie Garrow; *Librn*, Janice Brown
Library Holdings: Bk Vols 29,000; Per Subs 51
Special Collections: American Indian Coll
Publications: Ka-Ri-Wen-Ha-Wi (monthly newsletter)
Mem of Clinton-Essex-Franklin Library System; Ontario Library Service North
Partic in North Country Reference & Research Resources Council
Open Mon-Thurs 8-8:30, Fri 8-4 & Sat 11-3

HOLBROOK

P SACHEM PUBLIC LIBRARY,* 150 Holbrook Rd, 11741. SAN 311-3183. Tel: 516-588-5024. FAX: 516-588-5064. E-Mail: sachlib@suffolk.lib.ny.us. Web Site: www.suffolk.lib.us/libraries/sach. *Dir*, Judy Willner; Staff 105 (MLS 26, Non-MLS 79)
Founded 1961. Pop 77,544; Circ 823,190
Jul 1997-Jun 1998 Income $340,142, State $22,236, Locally Generated Income $113,122. Mats Exp $460,432, Books $272,523, Per/Ser (Incl. Access Fees) $34,168, Presv $1,825. Sal $1,979,983 (Prof $966,413)
Library Holdings: Bk Titles 319,502; Per Subs 1,710
Subject Interests: Business
Publications: Local Directory; Newsletter; Periodicals List
Mem of Long Island Libr Resources Coun, Inc; Suffolk Cooperative Library System
Friends of the Library Group

HOLLAND PATENT

P HOLLAND PATENT FREE LIBRARY,* Main St, PO Box 187, 13354-0187. SAN 311-3205. Tel: 315-865-5034. E-Mail: hp_dial@midyork.lib.ny.us. *Dir, Librn*, Cindy McVoy
Circ 26,565
Library Holdings: Bk Vols 13,000; Per Subs 30
Mem of Mid-York Library System
Open Mon, Tues & Fri 6-9, Wed & Thurs 2-5, Sat 10-1
Friends of the Library Group

HOLLEY

P COMMUNITY FREE LIBRARY,* 86 Public Sq, 14470. SAN 311-3213. Tel: 716-638-6987. Interlibrary Loan Service Tel: 716-434-6167. FAX: 716-638-7436. Web Site: www.nioga.org/holley/.
Pop 7,626; Circ 36,920
1997-1998 Income $87,049, State $2,187, County $6,809, Locally Generated Income $51,786, Parent Institution $1,900. Mats Exp $14,854, Books $12,478, Per/Ser (Incl. Access Fees) $1,706. Sal $42,789 (Prof $22,000)
Library Holdings: Bk Vols 21,835; Per Subs 72
Special Collections: Local History
Mem of Nioga Library System

HOMER

P PHILLIPS FREE LIBRARY,* 37 S Main St, 13077-0007. SAN 311-3221. Tel: 607-749-4616. FAX: 607-749-4616. *Dir, Librn*, Nancy Harbison
Founded 1902. Circ 25,000
1997-1998 Income $79,000. Mats Exp $9,000. Sal $40,000
Library Holdings: Bk Vols 15,000
Mem of Finger Lakes Library System
Friends of the Library Group

HONEOYE

P HONEOYE PUBLIC LIBRARY,* E Main St, PO Box 70, 14471-0070. SAN 311-323X. Tel: 716-229-5020. FAX: 716-229-5881. *Dir*, Wendy M Krause; E-Mail: wkrause@pls-net.org
Circ 32,200
Library Holdings: Bk Vols 13,352
Mem of Pioneer Library System
Open Mon & Thurs 2:30-8:30, Tues 10-6 & Sat 10-1

HONEOYE FALLS

P TOWN OF MENDON PUBLIC LIBRARY, 15 Monroe St, 14472. SAN 311-3248. Tel: 716-624-6067. FAX: 716-624-4255. *Dir*, Lory Gunther; Staff 1 (MLS 1)
Pop 6,480; Circ 77,000
1999-2000 Income $181,000. Mats Exp $32,000. Sal $100,000
Library Holdings: Bk Vols 28,600; Per Subs 38
Mem of Monroe County Library System
Open Mon-Thurs 10-9, Fri 10-5, Sat 1-4
Friends of the Library Group

HOOSICK FALLS

P CHENEY LIBRARY, 77 Classic St, 12090-1326. (Mail add: PO Box 177, 12090-0177), SAN 311-3256. Tel: 518-686-9401. FAX: 518-686-9401. *Dir*, Carol Gaillard; E-Mail: gaillarc@uhls.lib.ny.us
Founded 1926. Circ 23,576
Library Holdings: Bk Vols 14,262; Per Subs 46
Mem of Upper Hudson Library System
Friends of the Library Group

HOPEWELL JUNCTION

P E FISHKILL COMMUNITY LIBRARY,* 380 Rte 376, 12533. SAN 312-6269. Tel: 914-221-9943. FAX: 914-226-1404. E-Mail: eastfish@sebridge.org. *Dir*, Adeline Cross; *Asst Dir*, Janet Huen
Founded 1935. Circ 84,050
Library Holdings: Bk Vols 56,000; Bk Titles 52,000
Mem of Mid-Hudson Library System

S IBM MICROELECTRONICS, East Fishkill Site Library Z 402, 2070 Rte 52, 12533. SAN 311-3272. Tel: 845-894-3198. FAX: 845-892-6399. *Librn*, Maris Kristapsons; E-Mail: maris@vnet.ibm.com
Founded 1964
Library Holdings: Bk Vols 15,000; Bk Titles 13,000; Per Subs 350
Subject Interests: Bus, Computer tech, Electronics, Manufacturing, Metallurgy, Polymer chemistry, Programming, Semiconductors, Solid state

physics
Restriction: Not open to public
Partic in Dialog Corporation; Dow Jones News Retrieval; New York State Interlibrary Loan Network

HORNELL

P HORNELL PUBLIC LIBRARY, 64 Genesee St, 14843-1651. SAN 311-3280. Tel: 607-324-1210. FAX: 607-324-2570. E-Mail: hol@stls.org. *Dir*, Alice Taychert; Staff 2 (MLS 2)
Founded 1868. Pop 9,877; Circ 69,000
Library Holdings: Bk Vols 57,707; Per Subs 100
Subject Interests: Local history, Railroads
Mem of Southern Tier Library System
Friends of the Library Group

P HOWARD PUBLIC LIBRARY, 3607 County Rd 70A, Village of Howard, 14843. SAN 310-8236. Tel: 607-566-2412. FAX: 607-566-3679. Web Site: www.stls.org/howard. *Dir*, Sondra Lewis; E-Mail: hwl_sondra@stls.org
Founded 1911. Pop 1,331; Circ 4,894
Library Holdings: Bk Vols 11,000
Mem of Southern Tier Library System
Open Mon 5-9, Tues 2-9, Thurs 9-12 & 2-7, Sat 9-12

HORSEHEADS

P HORSEHEADS FREE LIBRARY, Ruth B Leet Library, 405 S Main St, 14845. SAN 311-3299. Tel: 607-739-4581. FAX: 607-739-4592. *Librn*, Maureen Ferrell; *Ch Servs*, Sherrill Collins; Staff 2 (MLS 2)
Founded 1958. Pop 28,022; Circ 113,451
Library Holdings: Bk Vols 52,975; Per Subs 561
Mem of Southern Tier Library System
Open Mon & Tues 9-9, Wed 12-9, Thurs & Fri 9-5:30, Sat 9-5
Friends of the Library Group

HOUGHTON

C HOUGHTON COLLEGE, Willard J Houghton Memorial Library, One Willard Ave, 14744. SAN 352-5457. Tel: 716-567-9242. FAX: 716-567-9248. Web Site: www.houghton.edu/library/tlib_overview.htm. *Dir*, George E Bennett; Tel: 716-567-9241, E-Mail: gbennett@houghton.edu; *Coordr, Ser, Tech Servs*, Betty Bunt; *ILL*, Laura Wardwell; *Ref*, Glen Avery. Subject Specialists: *Music*, Brad Wilber; Staff 11 (MLS 5, Non-MLS 6)
Founded 1883. Enrl 1,325; Highest Degree: Bachelor
Jun 1999-Jun 2000 Income $604,410. Mats Exp $165,400. Sal $292,764
Library Holdings: Bk Vols 225,000; Bk Titles 175,418; Per Subs 463
Special Collections: John Wesley & Methodism; Science & Christian Faith
Automation Activity & Vendor Info: (Acquisitions) VTLS; (Cataloging) VTLS; (Circulation) VTLS; (Course Reserve) VTLS; (ILL) VTLS; (Media Booking) VTLS; (OPAC) VTLS; (Serials) VTLS
Database Vendor: OCLC - First Search, OVID Technologies, ProQuest
Partic in OCLC Online Computer Library Center, Inc; S Cent Res Libr Coun

HOWES CAVE

S IROQUOIS INDIAN MUSEUM LIBRARY,* PO Box 7, 12092-0007. SAN 376-2025. Tel: 518-296-8949. FAX: 518-296-8955. Web Site: www.iroquoimuseum.org. *Dir*, Tom Elliott
Library Holdings: Bk Vols 1,000
Subject Interests: Local history

HUDSON

M COLUMBIA MEMORIAL HOSPITAL, Medical Library,* Columbia Memorial Hospital, 71 Prospect Ave, 12534. SAN 311-3329. Tel: 518-828-7601, 518-828-8305. FAX: 518-828-8520. E-Mail: cmhdocs@epix.net.; Staff 3 (MLS 1, Non-MLS 2)
Library Holdings: Bk Vols 150; Per Subs 17
Subject Interests: Medicine, Nursing
Partic in NY & NJ Regional Med Libr; Southeastern New York Library Resources Council

J COLUMBIA-GREENE COMMUNITY COLLEGE LIBRARY,* 4400 Rte 23, 12534. SAN 311-3310. Tel: 518-828-4181. FAX: 518-828-4396. Web Site: albweb2.sunyconnect.suny.edu/colgr. *Dir*, Harold J Ettelt; *ILL*, Lynn Erceg; *Acq*, Eric VanDeusen; *Ref*, Gera;umm Demarest; Staff 2 (MLS 2)
Founded 1969. Enrl 1,500; Fac 44
Sep 1997-Aug 1998 Income $407,466. Mats Exp $123,900, Books $58,800, Per/Ser (Incl. Access Fees) $26,250, Micro $38,850. Sal $187,583 (Prof $106,529)
Library Holdings: Bk Titles 51,247; Per Subs 662
Partic in Southeastern New York Library Resources Council

P HUDSON AREA ASSOCIATION LIBRARY,* 400 State St, 12534. SAN 311-3337. Tel: 518-828-1792. FAX: 518-822-0567. E-Mail: haal@taconic.net. *Dir*, Frank Rees; Staff 1 (MLS 1)
Founded 1959. Pop 12,135; Circ 23,544
Library Holdings: Bk Titles 29,301; Per Subs 51
Subject Interests: Bus, Local history
Mem of Mid-Hudson Library System

S HUDSON CORRECTIONAL FACILITY LIBRARY,* E Court St, PO Box 576, 12534-0576. SAN 327-1579. Tel: 518-828-4311, Ext 379. FAX: 518-828-5559. *Librn*, Bob Rummer
Library Holdings: Bk Titles 9,000; Per Subs 55
Mem of Mid-Hudson Library System
Friends of the Library Group

HUDSON FALLS

P HUDSON FALLS FREE LIBRARY, 220 Main St, 12839. SAN 311-3345. Tel: 518-747-6406. Web Site: hudsonfalls.sals.edu. *Dir*, Marie L Gandron; Staff 1 (MLS 1)
Founded 1910. Pop 12,000; Circ 48,848
Jan 1999-Dec 1999 Income $174,499, Provincial $17,000, City $19,000, Federal $20,962, County $3,458, Locally Generated Income $21,543. Mats Exp $14,457, Books $13,289, Per/Ser (Incl. Access Fees) $1,168. Sal $52,245 (Prof $29,600)
Library Holdings: Bk Vols 32,385; Per Subs 30; Bks on Deafness & Sign Lang 10
Subject Interests: Fiction, Local history
Publications: Monthly Newsletters
Mem of Southern Adirondack Library System
Open Mon, Tues & Thurs 1:30-5 & 6:30-8, Wed & Fri 10-12:30 & 1:30-5, Sat 10-4:30

HUNTER

P HUNTER PUBLIC LIBRARY, 6361 Main St, PO Box 376, 12442-0376. SAN 311-3353. Tel: 518-263-4655. FAX: 518-263-4655. E-Mail: hunter@francomm.com. *Librn*, June Bain
Circ 12,175
Library Holdings: Bk Vols 11,881
Mem of Mid-Hudson Library System
Special Services for the Blind - Talking Books
Open Wed-Sat 10am-4pm

HUNTINGTON

S HECKSCHER MUSEUM OF ART LIBRARY,* 2 Prime Ave, 11743-7702. SAN 321-6624. Tel: 516-351-3250. FAX: 516-423-2145. E-Mail: library@heckscher.org. Web Site: www.heckscher.org.
Founded 1981
Library Holdings: Bk Titles 3,127
Special Collections: European & American Art (Western Art Coll); Museum, Gallery & Dealer Exhibition Catalogues

S HUNTINGTON HISTORICAL SOCIETY LIBRARY, Research Center Library, 209 Main St, 11743. SAN 311-337X. Tel: 631-427-7045. FAX: 631-427-7056. *Archivist*, Karen Martin
Founded 1903
Library Holdings: Bk Titles 5,000; Per Subs 19
Subject Interests: Am decorative arts, Crafts, Genealogies of Huntington, Local hist of town, Long Island, Long Island families
Special Collections: Genealogy (Nellie Ritch Scudder Coll of Long Island Genealogical Records & Scudder Family Association Coll), bks, rec, mss, bus rec, church rec, family papers, photogs; New York State Census (Kings, Queens, Nassau & Suffolk Counties, 1915-1925), microfilm; US Federal Census (Suffolk County, 1790-1880), microfilm
Open by appointment Wed-Fri 1-4
Friends of the Library Group

M HUNTINGTON HOSPITAL, Medical Library, 270 Park Ave, 11743. SAN 311-3388. Tel: 631-351-2283. FAX: 631-351-2586.
Founded 1961
Library Holdings: Bk Vols 800; Per Subs 262
Partic in Medline

P HUNTINGTON PUBLIC LIBRARY,* 338 Main St, 11743. SAN 352-5481. Tel: 516-427-5165. Web Site: www.suffolk.lib.ny.us/libraries.hunt. *Dir*, Carroll Ann Kelly; *Acq, Cat*, Nancy Freeman; *Ch Servs*, Michael Bogin; Staff 17 (MLS 17)
Founded 1875. Pop 32,000; Circ 408,181
Library Holdings: Bk Titles 184,391; Per Subs 610
Subject Interests: Bus, Mgt
Special Collections: Long Island History; Walt Whitman Coll
Automation Activity & Vendor Info: (Circulation) epixtech, inc.
Publications: Highlights
Mem of Suffolk Cooperative Library System
Friends of the Library Group

Branches: 1
HUNTINGTON STATION BRANCH, 1335 New York Ave, Huntington Station, 11746. SAN 352-5511.
Friends of the Library Group

R SEMINARY OF THE IMMACULATE CONCEPTION LIBRARY, 440 W Neck Rd, 11743. SAN 373-1189. Tel: 516-423-0483, Ext 141. FAX: 516-423-2346. E-Mail: libnet@aol.com. *Dir*, Jiri (George) Lipa; Staff 2 (MLS 1, Non-MLS 1)
Library Holdings: Bk Vols 46,277; Per Subs 368
Subject Interests: Christianity, Theology
Partic in Long Island Library Resources Council

C TOURO COLLEGE, Jacob D Fuchsberg Law Center Library, 300 Nassau Rd, 11743. SAN 326-7334. Tel: 516-421-2320, Ext 329. FAX: 516-421-5386. Web Site: www.tourolaw.edu. *Head Librn*, Daniel Jordan; E-Mail: danj@tourolaw.edu; *Head Tech Servs*, Carol Shapiro Joseph; *Acq*, Eleanor Frank; *Publ Servs*, Beth Mobley; *Ref*, Gerard Giannattasio; *Ref*, Sophia Martins; *Ref*, Jill Selden; *Publ Servs*, Marge Hudson; *Ser*, Kristina Sembler; *Circ*, Beth Chamberlain; Staff 18 (MLS 9, Non-MLS 9)
Enrl 650; Fac 35
Jul 2000-Jun 2001 Income $1,800,000. Mats Exp $1,800,000
Library Holdings: Bk Vols 410,000; Bk Titles 55,000; Per Subs 1,300
Special Collections: Foreign & International Law; Jewish Law (bks)
Database Vendor: Innovative Interfaces INN - View
Restriction: Not open to public
Partic in Law Libr Microfilm Consortium; Long Island Library Resources Council; OCLC Online Computer Library Center, Inc
Friends of the Library Group

HUNTINGTON STATION

C ADELPHI UNIVERSITY-HUNTINGTON, Huntington Center Library,* 165 Pidgeon Hill Rd, 11746-4560. SAN 352-4779. Tel: 516-547-5115. FAX: 516-423-8644. Web Site: www.adelphi.edu/discover/library. *Librn*, Susan S Chen; Tel: 516-547-5114, E-Mail: chen@adlibr.adelphi.edu; Staff 1 (MLS 1)
Library Holdings: Bk Vols 3,716; Per Subs 42
Subject Interests: Education
Mem of Long Island Libr Resources Coun, Inc
Friends of the Library Group

S KLD ASSOCIATES, INC LIBRARY, 300 Broadway, 11746. SAN 311-340X. Tel: 631-549-9803. FAX: 631-351-7190. E-Mail: kldhunt@aol.com. Web Site: www.kldassociates.com. *Mgr*, Lynn Faulkner
Library Holdings: Bk Vols 270; Per Subs 31
Subject Interests: Traffic eng, Transportation
Partic in Long Island Library Resources Council

P SOUTH HUNTINGTON PUBLIC LIBRARY,* 2 Melville Rd, 11746. SAN 311-3426. Tel: 631-549-4411. FAX: 631-549-6832. E-Mail: shunlib@suffolk.ny.us. *Dir*, Kenneth Weil; *AV, Ref*, Mary Koferl; *Ch Servs*, Lynn Vitters; *Ad Servs, AV*, Leslie Knirien; *Cat, Tech Servs*, Sheila Almansi; *Ad Servs, ILL*, Carol Leach; *Ch Servs*, Stephanie Knepper; *Ad Servs*, Teresa Kruger; Staff 11 (MLS 11)
Founded 1961. Pop 39,149
Library Holdings: Bk Vols 215,876; Per Subs 403
Subject Interests: Education
Publications: Newsletter
Mem of Suffolk Cooperative Library System
Friends of the Library Group

S WALT WHITMAN BIRTHPLACE ASSOCIATION, Research Library,* 246 Old Walt Whitman Rd, 11746-4148. SAN 311-3434. Tel: 516-427-5240. FAX: 516-427-5247. Web Site: www.hysparks.com. *Exec Dir*, Barbara M Bart
Founded 1951
Library Holdings: Bk Vols 380
Special Collections: Foreign Language Translations; Walt Whitman Coll, biog, studies, hist, editions of poetry, collected writings
Open 3rd week in June until Labor Day, 11-4; after Labor Day - Wed, Thurs, Fri 1-4, Sat & Sun 11-4; closed holidays
Friends of the Library Group

HURLEY

P HURLEY LIBRARY ASSOCIATION,* Main St, 12443. (Mail add: PO Box 99, 12443), SAN 311-3442. Tel: 914-338-2092. *Dir*, Alstadt Barbara
Founded 1958. Pop 2,774; Circ 11,500
Library Holdings: Bk Vols 12,752
Subject Interests: Local history
Mem of Mid-Hudson Library System
Open Mon 10-12, Tues, Wed, Thurs 1-5 & 7-8:30pm & Fri 1-5
Friends of the Library Group

HYDE PARK

S CULINARY INSTITUTE OF AMERICA, Conrad N Hilton Library, 1946 Campus Dr, 12538-1499. SAN 311-3450. Tel: 845-451-1270. Reference Tel: 845-451-1322. FAX: 845-451-1092. Web Site: www.ciachef.edu. *Dir*, Eileen de Vries; *Tech Servs*, Michelle Sprague; *Ref*, Gert Trani; Staff 10 (MLS 4, Non-MLS 6)
Founded 1973. Enrl 2,131; Highest Degree: Bachelor
Library Holdings: Bk Vols 61,000; Bk Titles 42,300; Per Subs 310
Subject Interests: Cookery, Culinary arts, Rare books, Restaurant mgt, Spirits, Wines
Special Collections: Menus
Database Vendor: CARL, Dialog, IAC - SearchBank, OCLC - First Search, ProQuest, Silverplatter Information Inc.
Partic in Southeastern New York Library Resources Council
Friends of the Library Group

S NATIONAL ARCHIVES & RECORDS ADMINISTRATION, Franklin D Roosevelt Library, 4079 Albany Post Rd, 12538. SAN 311-3469. Tel: 845-229-8114. FAX: 845-229-0872. E-Mail: library@roosevelt.nara.gov. Web Site: www.fdrlibrary.marist.edu. *Dir*, Cynthia M Koch; *Archivist, AV*, Mark Renovitch; *Archivist*, Raymond Teichman
Founded 1939
Library Holdings: Bk Vols 45,000; Bk Titles 30,000; Per Subs 15
Subject Interests: Am hist, Eleanor Roosevelt, Franklin Roosevelt, Hudson River Valley hist, NY colonial hist, Politics from 1913-1945, US Naval hist
Special Collections: Early Juveniles Coll; Hudson River Valley History Coll; US Naval Hist Coll
Publications: Franklin D Roosevelt & Foreign Affairs, 1935-39 (seventeen volumes); Historical Materials in the Franklin D Roosevelt Library; The Era of Franklin D Roosevelt: A Selected Bibliography of Periodicals, Essays & Dissertation Literature, 1945-1971
Partic in Southeastern New York Library Resources Council

ILANDIA

S FLEXBAR MACHINE, Corporate Library,* 250 Gibbs Rd, 11722. SAN 323-4541. Tel: 631-582-8440. FAX: 631-582-8487. E-Mail: sales@flexbar.com. Web Site: www.flexbar.com. *Pres*, John Adler
Library Holdings: Bk Vols 100
Subject Interests: Machinery, Med devices

ILION

P ILION FREE PUBLIC LIBRARY,* 78 West St, 13357-1797. SAN 311-3485. Tel: 315-894-5028. FAX: 315-894-9980. E-Mail: il_civc@midyork.lib.ny.us. *Dir*, Christine Lozoski; *Ch Servs*, Thomasine Z Jennings; Staff 7 (MLS 2, Non-MLS 5)
Founded 1893. Pop 8,888; Circ 90,000
Jun 1998-May 1999 Income $182,500, State $2,500, City $144,200, County $8,000, Locally Generated Income $20,800, Other $7,000. Mats Exp $15,000, Books $7,654, Per/Ser (Incl. Access Fees) $3,500. Sal $110,950 (Prof $52,100)
Library Holdings: Bk Titles 40,000; Per Subs 98
Special Collections: Ilion, New York (Seamans Coll), photog, slides
Automation Activity & Vendor Info: (Cataloging) DRA; (Circulation) DRA; (OPAC) DRA
Mem of Mid-York Library System
Friends of the Library Group

INDIAN LAKE

P TOWN OF INDIAN LAKE PUBLIC LIBRARY,* Pelon Rd, 12842-0778. SAN 311-3493. Tel: 518-648-5444. FAX: 518-648-6227. *Dir*, Nancy Berkowitz
Pop 1,410; Circ 28,407
1998-1999 Income $80,000. Mats Exp $15,485, Books $11,900, Per/Ser (Incl. Access Fees) $1,220. Sal $53,900 (Prof $21,200)
Library Holdings: Bk Vols 18,000; Per Subs 55
Mem of Southern Adirondack Library System

INTERLAKEN

P INTERLAKEN PUBLIC LIBRARY,* 8390 Main St, PO Box 317, 14847-0317. SAN 311-3507. Tel: 607-532-4341. FAX: 607-532-4341. E-Mail: inlklibr@fltg.net. Web Site: www.inlaklib.epix.net. *Librn*, Pat Moore
Founded 1907. Pop 1,000; Circ 7,500
1997-1998 Income $24,000, County $1,000, Other $5,601. Mats Exp $7,129, Books $6,000, Per/Ser (Incl. Access Fees) $786, Other Print Mats $343. Sal $4,150
Library Holdings: Bk Vols 7,000; Per Subs 14
Subject Interests: History of the town of Interlaken, Local family histories, Seneca County
Mem of Finger Lakes Library System
Open Mon 10-12, Tues & Thurs 2-5 & 7-8:30, Wed 9-12 & Sat 9-12
Friends of the Library Group

IRVING

S SENECA NATION LIBRARY,* 1490 Rte 438, 14081. SAN 375-166X. Tel: 716-532-9449. FAX: 716-532-6115. *Dir*, Ann John
Library Holdings: Bk Vols 18,000; Per Subs 374
Special Collections: Native American Materials

IRVINGTON

S FOUNDATION FOR ECONOMIC EDUCATION LIBRARY,* 30 S Broadway, 10533. SAN 311-3515. Tel: 914-591-7230. FAX: 914-591-8910. Web Site: www.fee.org. *Librn*, Bettina Bien Greaves; Staff 2 (MLS 1, Non-MLS 1)
Founded 1946
Library Holdings: Bk Titles 7,250; Per Subs 50
Subject Interests: Free market econ, Limited govt philos, Relig philos of natural law, US Constitution, US hist
Special Collections: Austrian School of Economics, bks & pamphlets; Henry Hazlitt Coll
Publications: The Freeman

P IRVINGTON PUBLIC LIBRARY, Guiteau Foundation Library, 125 S Astor St, 10533. SAN 311-3523. Tel: 914-591-7840. FAX: 914-591-0347. *Dir*, Agnes Sinko; E-Mail: asinko@wls.lib.ny.us; *Ch Servs*, Pam Perricone
Founded 1866. Pop 6,348; Circ 72,401
Library Holdings: Bk Vols 37,000; Bk Titles 33,000; Per Subs 85
Subject Interests: Local history
Mem of Westchester Library System
Friends of the Library Group

ISLAND PARK

P ISLAND PARK PUBLIC LIBRARY,* 99 Radcliffe Rd, 11558-1498. SAN 311-3531. Tel: 516-432-0122. FAX: 516-889-2393. E-Mail: ilandpk@lilrc.org. Web Site: www.516web.com/library/ip/menu.htm. *Dir*, Jackie Malone; Staff 10 (MLS 4, Non-MLS 6)
Founded 1938. Pop 8,857; Circ 43,466
Jan 1997-Dec 1998 Income $578,541. Mats Exp $60,765. Sal $253,637 (Prof $150,471)
Library Holdings: Bk Vols 60,083; Per Subs 126
Mem of Nassau Library System
Friends of the Library Group

ISLAND TREES

P ISLAND TREES PUBLIC LIBRARY, 38 Farmedge Rd, 11756-5200. SAN 311-4201. Tel: 516-731-2211. FAX: 516-731-2395. *Coll Develop, Dir*, Dennis W King
Founded 1967. Pop 16,000; Circ 62,304
Library Holdings: Bk Titles 62,000; Per Subs 188
Special Collections: Child Psychology (Carol Cass Memorial Coll)
Publications: Island Trees Newsletter (quarterly)
Mem of Nassau Library System

ISLANDIA

S COMPUTER ASSOCIATES INTERNATIONAL LIBRARY,* One Computer Associates Plaza, 11788. SAN 375-104X. Tel: 516-342-5224. FAX: 516-342-5734.
Library Holdings: Bk Titles 250; Per Subs 150

ISLIP

P ISLIP PUBLIC LIBRARY,* 71 Monell Ave, 11751-3999. SAN 311-354X. Tel: 516-581-5933. FAX: 516-581-2431. Web Site: www.suffolk.lib.ny.us/libraries/islip/index.htm. *Dir*, Mary Schubart; E-Mail: mschubar@suffolk.lib.ny.us; *Ref*, Carol Scibilia; *Ref*, Laurie Aitken; *Ch Servs*, Jodi Dolman; *Ch Servs*, Carmela Carman; *Ch Servs*, Vikki Terrile; Staff 32 (MLS 9, Non-MLS 23)
Founded 1924. Pop 19,432; Circ 210,512
Jul 1997-Jun 1998 Income $1,546,239. Mats Exp $217,786, Books $148,195, Per/Ser (Incl. Access Fees) $19,337, AV Equip $10,629, Other Print Mats $17,973, Electronic Ref Mat (Incl. Access Fees) $21,652. Sal $789,805 (Prof $407,941)
Library Holdings: Bk Titles 147,430; Per Subs 469
Database Vendor: Innovative Interfaces INN - View
Publications: The Mariner (Newsletter)
Mem of Suffolk Cooperative Library System
Friends of the Library Group

ITHACA

S BOYCE THOMPSON INSTITUTE FOR PLANT RESEARCH LIBRARY, Cornell University, Tower Rd, 14853. SAN 320-8885. Tel: 607-254-1250. FAX: 607-254-1242. E-Mail: kpk3@cornell.edu. Web Site: bti.cornell.edu/. *Librn*, Kathleen Kramer; Staff 2 (MLS 1, Non-MLS 1)
Jan 2000-Dec 2000 Income $220,000. Mats Exp $149,000, Books $4,500, Per/Ser (Incl. Access Fees) $144,500. Sal $45,750
Library Holdings: Bk Titles 1,200; Per Subs 200
Subject Interests: Plant sci
Restriction: In-house use for visitors
Partic in South Central Regional Library Council

GM CAYUGA MEDICAL CENTER AT ITHACA, Robert Broad Medical Library, 101 Dates Dr, 14850. SAN 327-6953. Tel: 607-274-4407. FAX: 607-274-4214. *Librn*, Sally Van Idistine; E-Mail: svanidistine@cayugamed.org
Library Holdings: Bk Vols 500; Per Subs 80

S CLARITAS CORP LIBRARY,* 53 Brown Rd, 14850. SAN 372-8676. Tel: 607-257-5757. FAX: 607-266-0425.
Library Holdings: Bk Vols 600; Per Subs 17
Restriction: Staff use only

C CORNELL UNIVERSITY LIBRARY, 201 Olin Library, 14853-5301. SAN 352-5546. Tel: 607-255-3393. Interlibrary Loan Service Tel: 607-255-5293. Reference Tel: 607-255-4144. FAX: 607-255-6788. Web Site: www.library.cornell.edu/. *Assoc Librn*, Janet McCue; Tel: 607-255-2285, Fax: 607-255-0318, E-Mail: jam7@cornell.edu; *Librn*, Sarah E Thomas; Tel: 607-255-3689, E-Mail: set9@cornell.edu; *Adminr*, Ross Atkinson; Tel: 607-255-5181, E-Mail: ra13@cornell.edu; *Assoc Librn*, David Corson; Tel: 607-255-5068, Fax: 607-25-2493, E-Mail: dwc1@cornell.edu; *Assoc Librn*, Thomas H Hickerson; Tel: 607-255-9965, Fax: 607-254-5419, E-Mail: hth2@cornell.edu; *Assoc Librn*, Jean Poland; Tel: 607-255-4016, Fax: 607-255-5288, E-Mail: jp126@cornell.edu; Staff 470 (MLS 120, Non-MLS 350)
Founded 1868. Enrl 19,660; Fac 3,037; Highest Degree: Doctorate
Jul 1999-Jun 2000 Mats Exp $12,981,127. Sal $22,121,938
Library Holdings: Bk Vols 6,777,105; Per Subs 63,798
Publications: Guide to Cornell University Library
Partic in Center For Research Libraries; OCLC Online Computer Library Center, Inc; Research Libraries Group, Inc; S Cent Res Libr Coun
Statistics reported include the Medical College in New York City
Friends of the Library Group
Departmental Libraries:
ALBERT R MANN LIBRARY, 14853. Tel: 607-255-5406. Interlibrary Loan Service Tel: 607-255-7754. Circulation Tel: 607-255-3296. Reference Tel: 607-255-5406. FAX: 607-255-0318, 607-255-0850. E-Mail: mann-ref@cornell.edu. Web Site: www.mannlib.cornell.edu. *Dir*, Janet McCue; Tel: 607-255-2285, Fax: 607-255-0318, E-Mail: jam7@cornell.edu; Staff 32 (MLS 21, Non-MLS 11)
Jul 1999-Jun 2000 Mats Exp $1,561,849, Books $220,764, Per/Ser (Incl. Access Fees) $1,130,934, Presv $49,218, Electronic Ref Mat (Incl. Access Fees) $160,933. Sal $2,585,443 (Prof $1,465,697)
Library Holdings: Bk Vols 737,564; Per Subs 7,845
Subject Interests: Agriculture, Biological sci, Education, Human ecology, Nutrition, Psychology
Special Collections: Beekeeping (Everett Franklin Phillips Coll); James E Rice Poultry Library; Lace & Lacemaking (Elizabeth C Kackenmeister Coll); Language of Flowers
Publications: Catalogs & Indexes
Restriction: Open to students, Residents only
Includes Entomology Library data
ANNE CARRY DURLAND MEMORIAL ALTERNATIVES LIBRARY, Anabel Taylor Hall Rm 127, 14853. SAN 352-5589. Tel: 607-255-6486. FAX: 607-255-9985. E-Mail: alt-lib@cornell.edu. Web Site: instruct1.cit.cornell.edu/courses/altlib. *Dir*, Lynn Andersen; *Asst Dir*, Gary Fine; *Librn*, Irene Zahava; Staff 3 (MLS 1, Non-MLS 2)
Founded 1973
Jul 1999-Jun 2000 Income $122,000, Locally Generated Income $2,000, Other $120,000. Mats Exp $23,500, Books $14,000, Per/Ser (Incl. Access Fees) $4,500, AV Equip $5,000. Sal $50,232
Library Holdings: Bk Vols 8,000; Per Subs 320
Subject Interests: Culture, Ecology, Human rights, Politics, Psychology, Sexuality
Special Collections: Native American Archives-Contemporary Culture
Materials also available through the Finger Lakes Library System & OCLC
S ARECIBO OBSERVATORY - NATIONAL ASTRONOMY & IONOSPHERE CENTER LIBRARY, Carretera 625 Final, Arecibo, 00612. (Mail add: HC3 Box 53995, Arecibo, 00612), SAN 352-583X. Tel: 787-878-2612. FAX: 787-878-1861, 787-879-3007. E-Mail: csegarra@naic.edu. Web Site: www.naic.edu.
Founded 1963
Jul 2000-Jun 2001 Mats Exp Presv $2,500. Sal $25,000
Library Holdings: Bk Vols 6,190; Bk Titles 5,175; Per Subs 58
Subject Interests: Astronomy, Astrophysics, Computer science, Electronics, Engineering
Special Collections: Arecibo Observatory Reports; Palomar Sky Atlas; Theses Coll
Database Vendor: Dialog
AUDIO-VISUAL RESOURCE CENTER LIBRARY, 8 Business & Technology Park, 14850. SAN 352-5856. Tel: 607-255-2090, 607-255-2091. FAX: 607-255-9946. E-Mail: rhg2@cornell.edu. Web Site:

www.cce.cornell.edu/publications/catalog.html. *Coordr*, Richard Gray; *AV*, G Kalk
Founded 1948
Publications: Brochures; Catalogs
Partic in Consortium of College & University Media Centers
Department facility library - not part of the Cornell University Library System.

L H BAILEY HORTORIUM LIBRARY, Mann Library, Rm 481, 14853-4301. SAN 352-5929. Tel: 607-255-7781. FAX: 607-255-7979. E-Mail: pf13@cornell.edu. Web Site: www.bio.cornell.edu/hortorium/hortlibe.html. *Librn*, P R Fraissinet; *Coll Develop*, J I Davis
Library Holdings: Bk Vols 30,000
Subject Interests: Horticulture
Special Collections: Sources for Plant Materials, card file; Worldwide Coll of Seed & Plant Lists & Catalogs from Both Botanical Gardens & Commercial Sources
Library serves the NY State College of Agriculture & Life Sciences at Cornell

JOHN HENRIK CLARKE AFRICANA STUDIES, 310 Triphammer Rd, 14850-2599. SAN 352-5821. Tel: 607-255-3822. FAX: 607-255-0784. Web Site: www.library.cornell.edu/africana. *Librn*, Thomas Weissinger Sal $113,210
Library Holdings: Bk Vols 17,378
Internal database: Black studies periodical citations

COMSTOCK MEMORIAL LIBRARY OF ENTOMOLOGY, Comstock Hall, 14853-2601. SAN 352-5600. Tel: 607-255-3265. FAX: 607-255-0439. E-Mail: entomologylib@cornell.edu. Web Site: entomology.library.cornell.edu. *Librn*, Martin Schlabach; E-Mail: mls5@cornell.edu; Staff 3 (MLS 2, Non-MLS 1)

CORNELL CENTER FOR THE ENVIRONMENT, 302 Rice Hall, 14853-3501. SAN 352-6046. Tel: 607-255-0800. FAX: 607-255-4662. E-Mail: emb6@cornell.edu. Web Site: www.cfc.cornell.edu/iris.
Special Collections: New York State Agricultural District Maps; New York State Land Use & Natural Resources Inventory Coll; New York State Wetlands National Inventory

CORNELL INSTITUTE FOR SOCIAL & ECONOMIC RESEARCH (CISER DATA ARCHIVE), 201 Caldwell Hall, 14853. SAN 352-5643. Tel: 607-255-4801. FAX: 607-255-9353. Web Site: www.ciser.cornell.edu/datamenu.html. *Archivist*, Pam Baxter
Special Collections: New York Statistical Data

CORNELL LABORATORY OF ORNITHOLOGY; MACAULEY LIBRARY OF NATURAL SOUNDS, 159 Sapsucker Woods Rd, 14850-1999. SAN 352-6011. Tel: 607-254-2404. FAX: 607-254-2439. E-Mail: libnatsounds@cornell.edu. Web Site: birds.cornell.edu. *Dir*, Jack W Bradbury; *Curator*, Greg Budney; Staff 15 (Non-MLS 15)
Publications: Catalogs & Indexes
Restriction: By appointment only

EDNA MCCONNELL CLARK PHYSICAL SCIENCES LIBRARY, Clark Hall, 14853-2501. SAN 352-5759. Tel: 607-255-4016. FAX: 607-255-5288. E-Mail: pslref@cornell.edu. Web Site: www.library.cornell.edu/psl/. *Librn*, Jean Poland; E-Mail: jp126@cornell.edu
Library Holdings: Bk Vols 107,317
Subject Interests: Astronomy, Bio-chem, Biochemistry, Biophysics, Crystallography, Electron microscopy, Optics, Organic chemistry, Theoretical physics
Special Collections: Indexes of Texas A&M Thermodynamics Research Center & Sadtler Research; Special Indexes of Sadtler Research Lab, American Petroleum Institute & Thermodynamics Research Center; X-ray Powder Diffraction Cards of American Society for Testing & Materials

ENGINEERING LIBRARY, Carpenter Hall, 14853-2201. SAN 352-5872. Tel: 607-255-5933. FAX: 607-255-0278. E-Mail: engrlib@cornell.edu. Web Site: www.englib.cornell.edu. *Librn*, John Saylor
1998-1999 Mats Exp $1,132,410. Sal $444,428
Library Holdings: Bk Vols 366,099
Subject Interests: Computer science, Earth science, Geology, Water resources
Special Collections: NASA & DOE Technical Reports; NTIS Microfiche, 1978-present

FINE ARTS LIBRARY, Sibley Hall, 14853-6701. SAN 352-5902. Tel: 607-255-3710. FAX: 607-255-6718. Web Site: library.cornell.edu/finearts.
Jul 1999-Jun 2000 Mats Exp $132,746. Sal $197,737
Library Holdings: Bk Vols 179,642
Subject Interests: Art and architecture, Art history, City planning, Landscape architecture, Regional planning

CM FLOWER-SPRECHER VETERINARY LIBRARY, S2160 Veterinary Education Ctr, 14853-6401. SAN 352-602X. Tel: 607-253-3510. FAX: 607-253-3080. E-Mail: vet_library@cornell.edu. Web Site: www.vet.connell.edu/extension/information. *Dir*, Erla P Heyns; Tel: 607-253-3515, E-Mail: eph8@cornell.edu; Staff 8 (MLS 3, Non-MLS 5)
Founded 1897. Enrl 321; Fac 172; Highest Degree: Doctorate
Jan 2000-Dec 2000 Mats Exp $468,297. Sal $253,086
Library Holdings: Bk Vols 96,100
Subject Interests: Human med, Immunology, Microbiology, Parasitology, Pharmacology, Physiology, Veterinary medicine
Publications: Newsletter (quarterly)
Friends of the Library Group

JOHNSON GRADUATE SCHOOL OF MANAGEMENT LIBRARY, 101 Sage Hall, 14853. SAN 352-5848. Tel: 607-255-3389. FAX: 607-255-8633. Web Site: www.library.cornell.edu/jgsm. *Librn*, Donald Schnedeker; Staff 4 (MLS 3, Non-MLS 1)
Jul 1999-Jun 2000 Mats Exp $300,443. Sal $371,075
Library Holdings: Bk Vols 156,991; Per Subs 700
Subject Interests: Accounting, Commerce, Marketing
Special Collections: Corporation Reports; United States & Foreign Corporation Reports

HERBERT F JOHNSON MUSEUM OF ART LIBRARY Tel: 607-255-6464. FAX: 607-255-9940. E-Mail: museum@cornell.edu. Web Site: www.museum.cornell.edu/. *Curator*, Nancy Green
Founded 1953
Library Holdings: Per Subs 15
Subject Interests: Art history, Museology
Publications: Catalogue Raisonnes; Exhibition Catalogs
Restriction: Non-circulating

CM KROCH LIBRARY RARE & MANUSCRIPT DIVISION, 26 Kroch Library. SAN 377-810X. Tel: 607-255-3530. FAX: 607-255-9524. Web Site: rmc.library.cornell.edu. *Dir*, H Thomas Hickerson; *Archivist*, Elaine Engst Sal $220,562
Library Holdings: Bk Vols 212,554
Special Collections: Fiske Icelandic Coll, Dante Coll as well as colls relating to Petrarch; witchcraft, Wordsworth, American history, Anglo-American literature, 18th & 19th century French history and human sexuality
This division also houses the Cornell University Archives
Friends of the Library Group

LABORATORY OF ORNITHOLOGY LIBRARY, 159 Sapsucker Woods Rd, 14850-1999. SAN 352-6003. Tel: 607-254-2440. FAX: 607-254-2415. Web Site: www.birds.cornell.edu.
Library Holdings: Bk Vols 4,200; Per Subs 100
Subject Interests: Ornithology
Special Collections: Books Illustrated by Louis A Fuertes; Falconry

CL LAW SCHOOL LIBRARY, Myron Taylor Hall, 14853-4901. SAN 352-5996. Tel: 607-255-7236. Interlibrary Loan Service Tel: 607-255-5750. Reference Tel: 607-255-9577. FAX: 607-255-1357. E-Mail: lawlib@cornell.edu. Web Site: www.lawschool.cornell.edu/library. *In Charge*, Claire M Germain; *Head Tech Servs*, Jean Pajerek; *Adminr, Publ Servs*, Patricia Court; Staff 9 (MLS 7, Non-MLS 2)
Founded 1887. Enrl 610; Fac 37; Highest Degree: Doctorate
Jul 1999-Jun 2000 Income (Main and Other College/University Libraries) $1,020,140. Mats Exp $1,020,139, Books $91,863, Per/Ser (Incl. Access Fees) $842,759, Presv $24,591, Electronic Ref Mat (Incl. Access Fees) $60,926. Sal $1,149,452 (Prof $417,843)
Library Holdings: Bk Vols 483,388; Bk Titles 182,005; Per Subs 6,349
Subject Interests: Foreign law, International law, Law, Rare books
Special Collections: 19th Century Trials; Bennett Coll of Statutory Materials
Automation Activity & Vendor Info: (Acquisitions) NOTIS; (Cataloging) NOTIS
Publications: Cornell Law Library Newsletter
Partic in Nellco; New York State Interlibrary Loan Network; Research Libraries Group, Inc; RLIN; S Cent Res Libr Coun

LENZ LIBRARY - SCHOOL OF INDUSTRIAL AND LABOR RELATIONS, 16 E 34th St, New York, 10016. SAN 378-3855. Tel: 212-340-2845. FAX: 212-340-2822. Web Site: www.ilr.cornell.edu/extension. *Dir*, Donna Schulman; E-Mail: dls30@cornell.edu
Library Holdings: Bk Vols 6,000; Per Subs 120
Automation Activity & Vendor Info: (OPAC) EOS

MARTIN P CATHERWOOD INDUSTRIAL & LABOR RELATIONS LIBRARY, 521 Ives Hall, 14853-3901. SAN 352-5961. Tel: 607-255-5435. Circulation Tel: 607-255-2277. Reference Tel: 607-254-5370. FAX: 607-255-2741. E-Mail: sar3@cornell.edu. Web Site: www.ilr.cornell.edu/library/. *Librn*, Gordon Law
Founded 1945. Enrl 825; Fac 51; Highest Degree: Doctorate
Library Holdings: Bk Vols 200,063
Publications: Acquisition List (monthly)

MATHEMATICS LIBRARY, Malott Hall, 14853-4201. SAN 352-5694. Tel: 607-255-5076. FAX: 607-254-5023. Web Site: www.math.cornell.edu/~library. *Librn*, Steven Rockey; Tel: 607-255-5268, E-Mail: swri@cornell.edu. Subject Specialists: *Mathematics*, Steven Rockey
1999-2000 Mats Exp $240,687. Sal $141,460
Library Holdings: Bk Vols 53,320

NESTLE HOTEL LIBRARY, Statler Hall, 14853-6901. SAN 352-5937. Tel: 607-255-3673. Reference Tel: 607-255-9992. FAX: 607-255-0021. E-Mail: sha_library@cornell.edu. Web Site: www.nestlelib.connell.edu. *Librn*, Katherine Margolis
Founded 1921. Enrl 900; Fac 60; Highest Degree: Doctorate
Jul 1999-Jun 2000 Income Parent Institution $1,059,934. Mats Exp $369,401, Books $187,411, Per/Ser (Incl. Access Fees) $117,244, Micro $11,300, Electronic Ref Mat (Incl. Access Fees) $53,446. Sal $545,970 (Prof $175,181)
Library Holdings: Bk Vols 27,754; Per Subs 1,554
Subject Interests: Accounting, Hotel administration, Marketing, Real estate, Restaurant mgt

Special Collections: American Antiquarian Society Menu Coll; Food & Beverage (Herndon & Vehling College); Oscar of the Waldorf, bks, menus; Other Menus
Restriction: Open to students
Originates Hostline, a fee based ref serv, for practitioners in the hotel industry. Nestle Hotels Library is the library of the Cornell School of Hotel Administration.

NEW YORK STATE AGRICULTURAL EXPERIMENT STATION, FRANK A LEE LIBRARY, W North St, Geneva, 14456-0462. SAN 311-2357. Tel: 315-787-2214. FAX: 315-787-2276. E-Mail: lib@nysaes.cornell.edu. Web Site: www.nysaes.cornell.edu/library/index_.html. *Dir*, Martin Schlabach; E-Mail: mls5@cornell.edu; Staff 2 (MLS 1, Non-MLS 1)
Founded 1882
Library Holdings: Bk Vols 47,007
Subject Interests: Entomology, Food sci, Horticulture, Plant pathology
Special Collections: Wine & Wine Making
Publications: New in the Library (monthly)

OLIN-KROCH-URIS LIBRARY Tel: 607-255-5068. E-Mail: olinref@cornell.edu. Web Site: www.library.cornell.edu/okuref/oku/okuhome.html. *Dir*, David Corson; *Dep Dir*, Patricia Schafer
Library Holdings: Bk Vols 3,512,915
Subject Interests: Government, Linguistics, Literature, Philosophy, Political science, Religion
Publications: Newsletter (quarterly)
Friends of the Library Group

S POPULATION & DEVELOPMENT PROGRAM RESEARCH & REFERENCE LIBRARY, B12 Warren Hall, 14853-7801. SAN 352-5651. Tel: 607-255-4924. FAX: 607-254-2896. E-Mail: jv13@cornell.edu. Web Site: www.einaudi_cornell.edu/pdp/. *Librn*, Josephine Velez
Library Holdings: Bk Vols 15,000; Per Subs 100
Subject Interests: Sociology
Restriction: Not open to public

CM SAMUEL J WOOD LIBRARY & C V STARR BIOMEDICAL INFORMATION CENTER, C V Starr Biomed Information Ctr, 1300 York Ave, New York, 10021-4896. SAN 311-7111. Tel: 212-746-6068 (Admin.). Interlibrary Loan Service Tel: 212-746-6051. Circulation Tel: 212-746-6050. Reference Tel: 212-746-6055. FAX: 212-746-6494. E-Mail: infodesk@med.cornell.edu. Web Site: library.med.cornell.edu. *Dir*, Robert M Braude; E-Mail: bbraud@med.cornell.edu; *Assoc Dir*, Carolyn Anne Reid; E-Mail: careid@med.cornell.edu; *ILL*, Stephen Bright; *Ref*, Kristine M Alpi; *Ref*, Helen-Ann Brown; *Ref*, Daniel Cleary; *Ref*, Patricia Tomasulo; *Archivist*, Adele Lerner; *Cat*, Mira Myhre; *Circ*, Loretta Merlo; *Coll Develop*, Mark E Funk; *Computer Services*, Octavio Morales; Staff 15 (MLS 8, Non-MLS 7)
Founded 1899. Highest Degree: Doctorate
Jul 1999-Jun 2000 Income $3,019,516. Mats Exp $1,157,967, Books $111,266, Per/Ser (Incl. Access Fees) $1,014,830, Other Print Mats $31,871. Sal $1,442,150 (Prof $558,257)
Library Holdings: Bk Vols 168,348; Per Subs 1,708
Subject Interests: Bio-med, Nursing, Psychiatry
Automation Activity & Vendor Info: (Acquisitions) Innovative Interfaces Inc.; (Cataloging) Innovative Interfaces Inc.; (Circulation) Innovative Interfaces Inc.; (OPAC) Innovative Interfaces Inc.; (Serials) Innovative Interfaces Inc.
Publications: Lib Notes (list serv)
Restriction: Private library, Restricted access
Partic in Metropolitan New York Library Council; Middle Atlantic Region National Network Of Libraries Of Medicine; MLCNY
Friends of the Library Group

SIDNEY COX LIBRARY OF MUSIC & DANCE, Lincoln Hall, 14853-4101. SAN 352-5724. Tel: 607-255-4011. FAX: 607-254-2877. Web Site: www.library.cornell.edu/music. *Librn*, Lenore Coral
Library Holdings: Bk Vols 127,349
Subject Interests: Dance, Music
Special Collections: 18th Century Chamber Music; 18th-20th Century American Vocal Music; 19th Century Opera; A Scarlatti Operas; Archive of Field Recordings; Early 16th Century Music

S DEWITT HISTORICAL SOCIETY OF TOMPKINS COUNTY LIBRARY & ARCHIVE, 401 E State St, 14850. SAN 321-0839. Tel: 607-273-8284. FAX: 607-273-6107. E-Mail: dhs@lakenet.org. Web Site: www.lakenet.org_dewitt. *Dir*, Matthew Brawn
Founded 1935
Library Holdings: Bk Titles 4,000
Subject Interests: Genealogy, Tompkins County hist
Special Collections: Local History (Ithaca Imprints), photos

P FINGER LAKES LIBRARY SYSTEM, 119 E Green St, 14850. SAN 311-3566. Tel: 607-273-4074. TDD: 607-273-4074. FAX: 607-273-3618. E-Mail: aweeks@lakenet.org. Web Site: www.flls.org. *Exec Dir*, Karen Creenan; E-Mail: kcreenan@flls.org; *ILL*, *Ref*, Kathleen Parkhurst; E-Mail: kparkh@lakenet.org; *Tech Servs*, Robert McLaughlin; E-Mail: rmclaugh@lakenet.org; *Automation Syst Coordr*, Rex Helwig; E-Mail: rhelwig@lakenet.org; *Outreach Serv*, Melanie Hemingway; E-Mail: mheming@lakenet.org; *Ad Servs*, Marisa Iacobucci; Staff 21 (MLS 6, Non-MLS 15)
Founded 1958. Pop 311,393
Library Holdings: Bk Vols 124,227; Per Subs 15
Automation Activity & Vendor Info: (Cataloging) epixtech, inc.; (Circulation) epixtech, inc.
Publications: Directory (annual); newsletter (quarterly)
Member Libraries: Auburn Correctional Facility Library; Aurora Free Library; Berkshire Free Library; Candor Free Library; Coburn Free Library; Edith B Ford Memorial Library; Fair Haven Public Library; George P & Susan Platt Cady Library; Groton Public Library; Hazard Library Association; Interlaken Public Library; Kellogg Free Library; Lamont Memorial Free Library; Lodi Whittier Library; Mynderse Library; Newfield Public Library; Peck Memorial Library; Phillips Free Library; Powers Library; Seymour Public Library District; Southworth Library Association; Spencer Library; Springport Free Library; Stewart B Lang Memorial Library; Tappan-Spaulding Memorial Library; Tompkins County Public Library; Ulysses Philomathic Library; Waterloo Library & Historical Society; Waverly Free Library; Weedsport Free Library
Partic in OCLC Online Computer Library Center, Inc; S Cent Res Libr Coun
Special Services for the Deaf - TDD
Books-by-Mail Program

C ITHACA COLLEGE LIBRARY,* 1201 Gannet Center, 14850-7060. SAN 311-3574. Tel: 607-274-3182. FAX: 607-274-1539. Web Site: www.ithaca.edu. *Dir*, Margaret Johnson; *Cat*, John Hickey; *Publ Servs*, Gale Stevenson; *Coll Develop*, Kanushalya Sharma; Staff 13 (MLS 13)
Founded 1932. Enrl 5,000; Fac 345; Highest Degree: Master
Library Holdings: Bk Vols 375,000; Bk Titles 300,000; Per Subs 2,500
Subject Interests: Architecture, Art, Behav sci, Music, Paramed, Physical educ, Soc sci
Special Collections: Music Archives (Gustave Haenschen, Donald Voorhees & Robert Peters), scores & records
Partic in OCLC Online Computer Library Center, Inc; S Cent Libr Res Coun

S PALEONTOLOGICAL RESEARCH INSTITUTION LIBRARY, 1259 Trumansburg Rd, 14850. SAN 311-3582. Tel: 607-273-6623. Interlibrary Loan Service Tel: 607-273-6623, Ext 14. FAX: 607-273-6620. Web Site: www.priweb.org. *Dir*, Dr Warren Allmon; E-Mail: wda1@cornell.edu. Subject Specialists: *Earth science*, Dr Warren Allmon; *Paleontology*, Dr Warren Allmon
Founded 1932
Library Holdings: Bk Vols 60,145; Bk Titles 60,000; Per Subs 13
Subject Interests: Geology, Natural history, Paleontology (invertebrate), Taxonomy
Publications: Library Serials List
Partic in S Cent Res Libr Coun
Open Mon-Fri 9-5

S SOUTH AMERICAN EXPLORERS LIBRARY, 126 Indian Creek Rd, 14850. SAN 370-7016. Tel: 607-277-0488. FAX: 607-277-6122. E-Mail: explorer@samexplo.org. Web Site: www.samexplo.org. *Dir*, Don Montague
Founded 1977
Library Holdings: Bk Titles 3,500; Per Subs 27

P TOMPKINS COUNTY PUBLIC LIBRARY,* 312 N Cayuga St, 14850-4295. SAN 311-3590. Tel: 607-272-4557. TDD: 607-272-7545. FAX: 607-272-8111. Web Site: www.lakenet.org/tcpl/home.html. *Dir*, Janet Steiner; E-Mail: jsteiner@mail.co.tompkins.ny.us; *Asst Dir*, Karen Creenan; E-Mail: kcreenan@mail.co.tompkins.ny.us; *Head Ref*, Rosemarie Rice; E-Mail: rrice@mail.co.tompkins.ny.us; *YA Servs*, Shelley Garvey; E-Mail: sgarvey@mail.co.tompkins.ny.us; *Coll Develop*, Amy Hanger; E-Mail: ahanger@mail.co.tompkins.ny.us; Staff 15 (MLS 13, Non-MLS 2)
Founded 1864. Pop 94,097; Circ 800,000
Jan 1999-Dec 1999 Income $1,779,159, State $143,140, City $7,879, County $1,278,577, Locally Generated Income $167,835, Other $181,728. Mats Exp $1,767,248, Books $140,717, Per/Ser (Incl. Access Fees) $10,638, Presv $1,493, Electronic Ref Mat (Incl. Access Fees) $27,015. Sal $1,096,720 (Prof $403,671)
Library Holdings: Bk Vols 218,153; Per Subs 278
Special Collections: Central Book Aid Coll (Finger Lakes Library System)
Automation Activity & Vendor Info: (Circulation) epixtech, inc.
Publications: The Library Connection
Mem of Finger Lakes Library System
Friends of the Library Group

JACKSON HEIGHTS

S LEXINGTON SCHOOL FOR THE DEAF, Library Computer Center,* 30th Ave & 75th St, 11370. SAN 327-697X. Tel: 718-899-8800, Ext 245. FAX: 718-898-5788.; Staff 3 (MLS 1, Non-MLS 2)
Enrl 380; Highest Degree: Doctorate
Library Holdings: Bk Vols 17,153; Bk Titles 12,236; Per Subs 55
Subject Interests: Women's studies
Special Collections: Archives related to deafness, education of the deaf & history of Lexington School

Automation Activity & Vendor Info: (Circulation) Follett
Restriction: Open to faculty, students & qualified researchers
Special Services for the Deaf - Staff with knowledge of sign language; TTY machine; Videos & decoder

JAMAICA

M JAMAICA HOSPITAL MEDICAL CENTER, Medical Library, 8900 Van Wyck Expressway, 11418-2832. SAN 311-3639. Tel: 718-206-8451. Interlibrary Loan Service Tel: 718-206-8450. FAX: 718-206-8460. E-Mail: jamhsp2@rmi.net. *Dir*, Carolyn Mansbach
Founded 1963
Library Holdings: Bk Titles 4,500; Per Subs 285
Restriction: Medical staff only
Partic in Basic Health Sciences Library Network; Brooklyn-Queens-Staten Island Health Sciences Librarians; Docline; Medical & Scientific Libraries of Long Island; New York Metrop Ref & Res Libr Agency

M MOUNT SINAI SERVICES-QUEENS HOSPITAL CENTER AFFILIATION, Health Sciences Library,* 82-68 164th St, 11432. SAN 325-1500. Tel: 718-883-4021. FAX: 718-883-6125. *Dir*, Ruth Hoffenberg; *Asst Librn*, Timothy O'Mara; Staff 3 (MLS 2, Non-MLS 1)
Founded 1960
Library Holdings: Bk Vols 18,000; Per Subs 425
Mem of NY/NJ Med Libr Syst
Partic in BQSI; BRS; MLC; Nat Libr of Med

R PASSIONIST MONASTERY LIBRARY,* 86-45 Edgerton Blvd, 11432-0024. SAN 311-3620. Tel: 718-739-6502. FAX: 718-657-0578. *Dir*, Jack Douglas; E-Mail: jdougcp@aol.com; Staff 3 (MLS 1, Non-MLS 2)
Founded 1930
Library Holdings: Bk Titles 40,000; Per Subs 27
Subject Interests: Hist of US, NY City, Philosophy, Preaching, Scripture liturgy, Spirituality, Theology
Special Collections: Italian Encyclopedia; Patrologiae; Spanish Encyclopedia

P QUEENS BOROUGH PUBLIC LIBRARY, Central Library,* 89-11 Merrick Blvd, 11432. SAN 352-6054. Tel: 718-990-0700. FAX: 718-658-8342. Web Site: www.queens.lib.ny.us. *Dir*, Gary E Strong; *Dir*, Dr Sherman Tang; *Dep Dir*, Carol Sheffer; *Publ Servs*, Joseph Catrambone; *Tech Servs*, Charles McMorran; *Purchasing*, Victor Cintron; *Coll Develop*, Kathleen Cotter
Founded 1896. Pop 1,951,598; Circ 16,065,177
Jul 1997-Jun 1998 Income $79,041,000, State $6,340,000, City $67,175,000, Federal $107,000, Locally Generated Income $5,419,000. Mats Exp $10,230,871, Books $9,062,217, Per/Ser (Incl. Access Fees) $1,168,654. Sal $39,485,000
Library Holdings: Bk Vols 10,036,143
Subject Interests: Behav sci, Bus, Costumes, Ethnic studies, Mgt, Sci-tech, Soc sci
Special Collections: Long Island History
Automation Activity & Vendor Info: (Acquisitions) DRA; (Circulation) DRA; (Serials) DRA
Publications: Library Matters
Partic in BRS; Dialog Corporation; New York Metrop Ref & Res Libr Agency; OCLC Online Computer Library Center, Inc; Vutext
Special Services for the Deaf - Books on deafness & sign language; High interest/low vocabulary books; Special interest periodicals; TTY machine
Special Services for the Blind - Closed circuit print enlarger; Kurzweil Reading Machine; Volunteer readers
Open Mon-Fri 10-9 & Sat 10-5:30; Sun 12-5 (mid-Sept to June only)
Friends of the Library Group
Branches: 70
ARVERNE BRANCH, 312 Beach 54th St, Arverne, 11692. SAN 352-6119. Tel: 718-634-4784. *Mgr*, Carol Freitag
Library Holdings: Bk Vols 74,856
ASTORIA, 14-01 Astoria Blvd, Long Island City, 11102. SAN 352-6143. Tel: 718-278-2220. *In Charge*, Jack Stevenson
Library Holdings: Bk Vols 61,020
AUBURNDALE-CLEARVIEW, 25-55 Francis Lewis Blvd, Flushing, 11358. SAN 352-6178. Tel: 718-352-2027. *In Charge*, Paul Wai Tan
Library Holdings: Bk Vols 168,241
BAISLEY PARK, 117-11 Sutphin Blvd, 11436. SAN 352-6208. Tel: 718-529-1590. *In Charge*, Paula Groings
Library Holdings: Bk Vols 91,361
BAY TERRACE, 18-36 Bell Blvd, Bayside, 11360. SAN 352-6240. Tel: 718-423-7004. *In Charge*, Eve Hammer
Library Holdings: Bk Vols 118,283
BAYSIDE BRANCH, 214-20 Northern Blvd, Bayside, 11361. SAN 352-6232. Tel: 718-229-1834. *In Charge*, Janice Chan
Library Holdings: Bk Vols 170,810
BELLEROSE BRANCH, 250-06 Hillside Ave, Bellerose, 11426. SAN 352-6267. Tel: 718-831-8644. *In Charge*, I-Mei Lee
Library Holdings: Bk Vols 122,130
BRIARWOOD BRANCH, 85-12 Main St, Briarwood, 11435. SAN 352-6291. Tel: 718-658-1680. *In Charge*, Bradford Martin
Library Holdings: Bk Vols 126,647
BROAD CHANNEL BRANCH, 16-26 Cross Bay Blvd, Broad Channel, 11693. SAN 372-0268. Tel: 718-318-4943. *In Charge*, Linda Urban
Library Holdings: Bk Vols 33,595
BROADWAY, 40-20 Broadway, Long Island City, 11103. SAN 352-6321. Tel: 718-721-2462. *In Charge*, Roslyn Rubinstein
Library Holdings: Bk Vols 213,332
BUSINESS, SCIENCE & TECHNOLOGY DIV Tel: 718-990-0852. Web Site: web.queens.lib.ny.us/allinone.html, www.queens.lib.ny.us. *Mgr*, Daniel Cleary
Library Holdings: Bk Vols 256,280; Per Subs 1,000
Subject Interests: Automobile manuals, Bus, Engineering, Home econ, Medicine, Schematics, Sci, Technology
Publications: We're open for business (brochure)
CAMBRIA HEIGHTS BRANCH, 220-20 Linden Blvd, Cambria Heights, 11411. SAN 352-6356. Tel: 718-528-3535. *In Charge*, Dorothy Forde
Library Holdings: Bk Vols 86,227
CENTRAL CIRCULATION SERVICES DIV Tel: 718-990-0846. FAX: 718-658-8342. Web Site: web.queens.lib.ny.us/allinone.html, www.queens.lib.ny.us.
CORONA BRANCH, 38-23 104th St, Corona, 11368. SAN 352-6380. Tel: 718-426-2844. *In Charge*, Diane Vitale
Library Holdings: Bk Vols 111,735
COURT SQUARE, 25-01 Jackson Ave, Long Island City, 11101. SAN 370-0895. Tel: 718-937-2790. *In Charge*, Donna Avant
Library Holdings: Bk Vols 44,474
DOUGLASTON-LITTLE NECK BRANCH, 249-01 Northern Blvd, Little Neck, 11363. SAN 352-6410. Tel: 718-225-8414. FAX: 718-631-8829. *In Charge*, Zhi Hu
Library Holdings: Bk Vols 89,830
EAST ELMHURST BRANCH, 95-06 Astoria Blvd, East Elmhurst, 11369. SAN 352-6445. Tel: 718-424-2619. *In Charge*, Johnnie Dent
Library Holdings: Bk Vols 100,468
EAST FLUSHING BRANCH, 196-36 Northern Blvd, Flushing, 11358. SAN 352-650X. Tel: 718-357-6643. *Mgr*, Alice Norris
Library Holdings: Bk Vols 115,620
ELMHURST BRANCH, 86-01 Broadway, Elmhurst, 11373. SAN 352-647X. Tel: 718-271-1020. *In Charge*, Linna Yu
Library Holdings: Bk Vols 240,412
FAR ROCKAWAY BRANCH, 1637 Central Ave, Far Rockaway, 11691. SAN 352-6534. Tel: 718-327-2549. *In Charge*, Monica Rhodd
Library Holdings: Bk Vols 126,210
FINE ARTS & RECREATION DIV Tel: 718-990-0755. Web Site: web.queens.lib.ny.us/allinone.html, www.queens.lib.ny.us. *Mgr*, Esther Lee
Library Holdings: Bk Vols 130,000; Per Subs 430
Subject Interests: Architecture, Art, Games, Graphic novels, Handicrafts, Performing arts, Photog, Sports
Special Collections: WPA Print Coll
FLUSHING BRANCH, 41-17 Main St, Flushing, 11354. SAN 352-6569. Tel: 718-661-1200. FAX: 718-445-0860. *In Charge*, Ruth Herzberg
Library Holdings: Bk Vols 463,269
FOREST HILLS BRANCH, 108-19 71st Ave, Forest Hills, 11375. SAN 352-6593. Tel: 718-268-7934. *In Charge*, Richard Forest
Library Holdings: Bk Vols 213,274
FRESH MEADOWS BRANCH, 193-20 Horace Harding Expressway, Fresh Meadows, 11365. SAN 352-6623. Tel: 718-454-7272. *In Charge*, Karen Vermut
Library Holdings: Bk Vols 170,629
GLEN OAKS BRANCH, 256-04 Union Tpk, Glen Oaks, 11004. SAN 352-6658. Tel: 718-831-8636. FAX: 718-343-0536. *In Charge*, Jeffrey Berger
Library Holdings: Bk Vols 102,559
GLENDALE BRANCH, 78-60 73rd Pl, Glendale, 11385. SAN 352-6682. Tel: 718-821-4980. FAX: 718-821-7160. *In Charge*, Roz Matzner
Library Holdings: Bk Vols 105,072
HILLCREST, 187-05 Union Tpk, Flushing, 11366. SAN 352-6704. Tel: 718-454-2786. *In Charge*, Bernadine Byer
Library Holdings: Bk Vols 171,202
HOLLIS BRANCH, 202-05 Hillside Ave, Hollis, 11423. SAN 352-6712. Tel: 718-465-7355. *In Charge*, Thomas Witt
Library Holdings: Bk Vols 107,496
HOWARD BEACH BRANCH, 92-06 156th Ave, Howard Beach, 11414. SAN 352-6747. Tel: 718-641-7086. *In Charge*, Diane Manheim
Library Holdings: Bk Vols 114,251
INFORMATION SERVICES DIV Tel: 718-990-0778. Reference Tel: 718-990-0714. FAX: 718-658-8312, 718-658-8344. Web Site: web.queens.lib.ny.us/allinone.html, www.queens.lib.ny.us. *Mgr*, Lorna Rudder
Library Holdings: Bk Vols 2,204; Per Subs 115
Partic in Dialog Corporation
JACKSON HEIGHTS BRANCH, 35-51 81st St, Jackson Heights, 11372. SAN 352-6771. Tel: 718-899-2500. FAX: 718-899-7003. *In Charge*, Harriet Benjamin
Library Holdings: Bk Vols 292,314
KEW GARDENS HILLS, 72-33 Vleigh Pl, Flushing, 11367. SAN 352-7581. Tel: 718-261-6654. *In Charge*, Margaret Susser

Library Holdings: Bk Vols 179,230
LANGSTON HUGHES, 102-09 Northern Blvd, Corona, 11368. SAN 329-6458. Tel: 718-651-1100. FAX: 718-651-6258. *In Charge*, Andrew Jackson
Library Holdings: Bk Vols 79,884
LAURELTON BRANCH, 134-26 225th St, Laurelton, 11413. SAN 352-6801. Tel: 718-528-2822. FAX: 718-723-6837. *In Charge*, Priscilla Johnson
Library Holdings: Bk Vols 114,816
LEFFERTS, 103-34 Lefferts Blvd, Richmond Hill, 11419. SAN 352-6836. Tel: 718-843-5950. *In Charge*, Bernadine Byer
Library Holdings: Bk Vols 167,689
LEFRAK CITY, 98-25 Horace Harding Expressway, Corona, 11368. SAN 352-6860. Tel: 718-592-7677. *In Charge*, Timothy McDonough
Library Holdings: Bk Vols 120,072
LITERATURE & LANGUAGES DIVISION Tel: 718-990-0851. *In Charge*, Paul Bunten
Library Holdings: Bk Vols 378,196; Per Subs 4,851
Subject Interests: Drama, Linguistics, Lit criticism, Non-English lang instruction, Poetry
Special Collections: African-American Literature Coll
LONG ISLAND DIV Tel: 718-990-8633. FAX: 718-658-8312. *Mgr*, Judith Box
Library Holdings: Bk Vols 15,390; Per Subs 202
Special Collections: Long Island History & Culture, mss, maps, newsp & photogs
MASPETH BRANCH, 69-70 Grand Ave, Maspeth, 11378. SAN 352-6925. Tel: 718-639-5228. *In Charge*, Leora Jenkins
Library Holdings: Bk Vols 123,548
MCGOLDRICK, 155-06 Roosevelt Ave, Flushing, 11354. SAN 352-6895. Tel: 718-461-1616. *In Charge*, Frances Shieh
Library Holdings: Bk Vols 145,302
MIDDLE VILLAGE BRANCH, 72-31 Metropolitan Ave, Middle Village, 11379. SAN 352-695X. Tel: 718-326-1390. *Mgr*, Steve Nobel
Library Holdings: Bk Vols 81,685
MITCHELL-LINDEN, 29-42 Union St, Flushing, 11354. SAN 352-6984. Tel: 718-539-2330. *In Charge*, Gan Mar
Library Holdings: Bk Vols 88,843
NORTH FOREST PARK, 98-27 Metropolitan Ave, Forest Hills, 11375. SAN 352-700X. Tel: 718-261-5512. *In Charge*, Margaret Birnstiel
Library Holdings: Bk Vols 99,944
NORTH HILLS, 57-04 Marathon Pkwy, Little Neck, 11362. SAN 352-7018. Tel: 718-225-3550. *In Charge*, Carolyn Luppino
Library Holdings: Bk Vols 80,862
OZONE PARK BRANCH, 92-24 Rockaway Blvd, Ozone Park, 11417. SAN 352-7042. Tel: 718-845-3127. FAX: 718-848-1080. *In Charge*, Mildred Zimmerman
Library Holdings: Bk Vols 117,226
PENINSULA, 92-25 Rockaway Beach Blvd, Rockaway Beach, 11693. SAN 352-7077. Tel: 718-634-1110. FAX: 718-318-5253. *In Charge*, Kriparani Raghaven
Library Holdings: Bk Vols 114,475
POMONOK, 158-21 Jewel Ave, Flushing, 11365. SAN 352-7107. Tel: 718-591-4343. *In Charge*, Thomas Piezzo
Library Holdings: Bk Vols 111,779
POPPENHUSEN, 121-23 14th Ave, College Point, 11356. SAN 352-7131. Tel: 718-359-1102. FAX: 718-353-8894. *In Charge*, Michelle Chan
Library Holdings: Bk Vols 82,563
QUEENS VILLAGE BRANCH, 94-11 217th St, Queens Village, 11428. SAN 352-7190. Tel: 718-776-6800. FAX: 718-479-4609. *In Charge*, Clifton Seale
Library Holdings: Bk Vols 169,927
QUEENSBORO HILL, 60-05 Main St, Flushing, 11355. SAN 352-714X. Tel: 718-359-8332. *In Charge*, Chin-Chu (Jean) Lee
Library Holdings: Bk Vols 152,131
QUEENSBRIDGE, 10-43 41st Ave, Long Island City, 11101. SAN 352-7166. Tel: 718-937-6266. *In Charge*, Judith Anderson
Library Holdings: Bk Vols 73,843
RAVENSWOOD, 35-32 21st St, Long Island City, 11106. SAN 352-7220. Tel: 718-784-2112. *In Charge*, Grace Tang
Library Holdings: Bk Vols 86,792
REGO PARK BRANCH, 91-41 63rd Dr, Rego Park, 11374. SAN 352-7255. Tel: 718-459-5140. *In Charge*, Ramona Rendon
Library Holdings: Bk Vols 177,588
RICHMOND HILL BRANCH, 118-14 Hillside Ave, Richmond Hill, 11418. SAN 352-728X. Tel: 718-849-7150. *In Charge*, Susan Wetjen
Library Holdings: Bk Vols 130,724
RIDGEWOOD BRANCH, 20-12 Madison St, Ridgewood, 11385. SAN 352-731X. Tel: 718-821-4770. FAX: 718-628-6263. *In Charge*, Nicholas Buron
Library Holdings: Bk Vols 150,967
ROCHDALE VILLAGE, 169-09 137th Ave, 11434. SAN 352-7344. Tel: 718-723-4440. *In Charge*, Ann Marie Josephs
Library Holdings: Bk Vols 84,308
ROSEDALE BRANCH, 144-20 243rd St, Rosedale, 11422. SAN 352-7379. Tel: 718-528-8490.
Library Holdings: Bk Vols 94,456
SAINT ALBANS BRANCH, 191-05 Linden Blvd, Saint Albans, 11412. SAN 352-7409. Tel: 718-528-8196. *Mgr*, Thomas Piezzo
Library Holdings: Bk Vols 98,053
SEASIDE, 116-15 Rockaway Beach Blvd, Rockaway Park, 11694. SAN 352-7425. Tel: 718-634-1876. FAX: 718-634-8711. *In Charge*, Sheila Sherwood
Library Holdings: Bk Vols 101,447
SOCIAL SCIENCES DIV Tel: 718-990-0761, 718-990-0762 (Hist, 718-Travel. *Mgr*, Beatrice Daly
Library Holdings: Bk Vols 500,000; Per Subs 510
Subject Interests: Biog, Education, History, Law, Libr sci, Philosophy, Political science, Religion, Travel
Special Collections: African-American History & Life (Carter G Woodson Coll); ERIC Documents, microfiche; Federal Law (statutes & cases); New York City Civil Service Test; New York City Department of Education Curriculum Guides; New York Law (statutes & cases); New York Times Microfilm, 1851-present; Road Maps (US Cities & World Cities)
SOUTH HOLLIS BRANCH, 204-01 Hollis Ave, South Hollis, 11412. SAN 352-7433. Tel: 718-465-6779.
Library Holdings: Bk Vols 86,038
SOUTH JAMAICA BRANCH, 110-36 Guy R Brewer Blvd, 11433. SAN 352-7468. Tel: 718-739-4088. *In Charge*, Ellen Stipo
Library Holdings: Bk Vols 65,971
SOUTH OZONE PARK BRANCH, 128-16 Rockaway Blvd, South Ozone Park, 11420. SAN 352-7492. Tel: 718-529-1660. *In Charge*, Paul Tremblay
Library Holdings: Bk Vols 105,544
STEINWAY, 21-45 31st St, Long Island City, 11105. SAN 352-7522. Tel: 718-728-1965. FAX: 718-956-3575. *In Charge*, Eva Mae Babalis
Library Holdings: Bk Vols 143,159
SUNNYSIDE, 43-06 Greenpoint Ave, Long Island City, 11104. SAN 352-7557. Tel: 718-784-3033. *In Charge*, Christine Gina
Library Holdings: Bk Vols 136,998
WHITESTONE BRANCH, 151-10 14th Rd, Whitestone, 11357. SAN 352-7611. Tel: 718-767-8010. *In Charge*, Eileen Ragone
Library Holdings: Bk Vols 104,845
WINDSOR PARK, 79-50 Bell Blvd, Bayside, 11364. SAN 352-7646. Tel: 718-486-8300. *In Charge*, Heather Tsang
Library Holdings: Bk Vols 111,987
WOODHAVEN BRANCH, 85-41 Forest Pkwy, Woodhaven, 11421. SAN 352-7662. Tel: 718-849-1010. *In Charge*, Sheila Stein
Library Holdings: Bk Vols 94,054
WOODSIDE BRANCH, 54-22 Skillman Ave, Woodside, 11377. SAN 352-7670. Tel: 718-429-4700.
Library Holdings: Bk Vols 124,464
YOUTH SERVICES DIVISION Tel: 718-990-0767 (Ch), 718-990-0768 (YA). *Mgr*, Lynn Gonen
Library Holdings: Bk Vols 211,614; Per Subs 71
Subject Interests: Career info, Children's literature, Col, Graphic novels, Parenting, Picture bks, Sci projects, Spanish lang, Study guides, Young adult literature
Special Collections: African American Culture, History & Biography; Augusta Baker Reference Coll

GL QUEENS COUNTY SUPREME COURT LIBRARY, General Court House, 88-11 Sutphin Blvd, 11435. SAN 311-3655. Tel: 718-520-3140. Interlibrary Loan Service Tel: 718-520-3172. FAX: 718-520-3589. E-Mail: law_library_queens@courts.state.ny.us. Web Site: www.courts.state.ny.us/queenslib/queens.htm. *In Charge*, Andrew Tschinkel; E-Mail: atschink@courts.state.ny.us; *Cat*, J Butler; Staff 4 (MLS 4)
Founded 1911
Apr 1998-Mar 1999 Income $717,000. Mats Exp $385,000, Presv $5,300. Sal $332,000
Library Holdings: Bk Vols 125,000; Bk Titles 10,000; Per Subs 100
Subject Interests: New York City, State law
Restriction: Open to public for reference only
Partic in OCLC Online Computer Library Center, Inc; Westlaw
Branches:
KEW GARDENS BRANCH, 125-01 Queens Blvd, 7th flr, Kew Gardens, 11415. SAN 321-4214. Tel: 718-520-3541. FAX: 718-520-4661. Web Site: ucs.ljx.com/queenslib/queens.htm. *Librn*, Robert Cambridge
Library Holdings: Bk Vols 25,000
Subject Interests: Criminal law of New York

C SAINT JOHN'S UNIVERSITY LIBRARY,* 8000 Utopia Pkwy, 11439. SAN 352-7700. Tel: 718-990-6735. FAX: 718-990-2059. Web Site: www.stjohns.edu/library. *Dean of Libr*, James Benson; *Publ Servs*, Julie Cunningham; *Syst Coordr*, Teresa Edwards; *Cat*, Cynthia Chambers; *Online Servs, Ref*, Charles Livermore; *Rare Bks, Spec Coll*, Szilvia Szmuk; *Acq, Coll Develop*, Andrew Sankowski; *Bibliog Instr*, Joan D'Andrea; *Circ*, Patricia Schuettich; *Media Spec*, Barbara Appleby; *Ser*, William Keogan; *ILL*, Roberta Pessah. Subject Specialists: *Government publications*, Shu Fang Lin; *Science/technology*, Barbara Charton; Staff 32 (MLS 32)
Founded 1870. Enrl 15,000; Fac 600; Highest Degree: Doctorate
Jul 1997-Jun 1998 Income $7,119,577. Mats Exp $7,119,577, Books $323,764, Per/Ser (Incl. Access Fees) $1,069,197, Micro $7,994, AV Equip $22,864, Other Print Mats $252,464. Sal $4,768,118 (Prof $1,681,235)
Library Holdings: Bk Vols 606,086; Per Subs 4,441
Subject Interests: Bus, Humanities, Mgt, Natural science, Pharm, Relig

studies
Special Collections: 19th Century Catholic Periodicals Coll; American Friends of Irish Neutrality (1938-1941), VF; Art Exhibition Catalog Coll; Asian Coll; Hugh L Carey Coll; John E Baxter Coll; Northern Ireland Disturbances (1970-77), VF; Paul O'Dwyer Coll, VF; Saul Heller Coll; Senatorial Papers (James L Buckley Coll), VF; Tennis (Wm M Fischer Lawn Coll); Undivided Ireland (1947-63), VF
Publications: Library Guides; Library Handbook
Partic in New York Metrop Ref & Res Libr Agency
Friends of the Library Group
Departmental Libraries:
LORETTO MEMORIAL
See Separate Entry under Saint John's University, Staten Island, NY
RITTENBERG LAW LIBRARY, 8000 Utopia Pkwy, 11439. SAN 352-776X. Tel: 718-990-6651. FAX: 718-990-6649. Web Site: www.law.stjohns.edu. *Dir*, Linda Ryan; Tel: 718-990-1578, E-Mail: lryan@sjulawfac.stjohns.edu; *Res*, William Manz; Tel: 718-990-6655; *Tech Servs*, Joseph Hinger; Tel: 718-990-1582; *Access Serv, Circ*, Toni Aiello; Tel: 718-990-5894; *Ref*, Aru Satkalhmi; Tel: 718-990-6769; *Ref*, Barbara G Traub; Tel: 718-990-1668; *ILL*, Adrienne Graham; Tel: 718-990-2012; Staff 9 (MLS 9)
Founded 1925. Enrl 950; Fac 50; Highest Degree: Master
Library Holdings: Bk Vols 300,000; Bk Titles 56,000; Per Subs 5,413
Special Collections: NY State Law Libr; St Thomas More Coll, bks & per
Automation Activity & Vendor Info: (Acquisitions) Innovative Interfaces Inc.; (Cataloging) Innovative Interfaces Inc.; (Circulation) Innovative Interfaces Inc.; (Course Reserve) Innovative Interfaces Inc.; (ILL) Innovative Interfaces Inc.; (Media Booking) Innovative Interfaces Inc.; (OPAC) Innovative Interfaces Inc.; (Serials) Innovative Interfaces Inc.
Publications: Acquisitions list; Law Library Guide; Periodicals Guide
Restriction: Open to student, faculty & staff

M ST VINCENT'S, CATHOLIC MEDICAL CENTER, Woods Health Sciences Library, 88-25 153rd St, 11432. SAN 311-3604. Tel: 718-558-7230. FAX: 718-558-7233. *Dir*, Joan A Napolitano; E-Mail: jnapolit@cmcny.com; *ILL*, Indrajeet Chauhan
Founded 1969
Library Holdings: Bk Vols 3,200; Per Subs 250
Subject Interests: Allied health, Medicine, Nursing
Publications: Monthly newsletter

C YORK COLLEGE LIBRARY,* 94-20 Guy Brewer Blvd, 11451. SAN 311-3671. Tel: 718-262-2025, 718-262-2034. FAX: 718-262-2027. Web Site: www.sun3.york.cuny.edu/~lib/main.html. *Chief Librn*, Robert Machalow; *Acq, Chief Librn, Coll Develop*, J Kevin Barry; *Circ*, Njoki Kenyatyi; Staff 6 (MLS 6)
Founded 1966. Enrl 5,122; Fac 254; Highest Degree: Bachelor
Library Holdings: Bk Vols 175,860; Bk Titles 172,630; Per Subs 900
Special Collections: American History & Literature (Library of American Civilization), ultrafiche; Anthropology, Soc Sci; Papers of the NAACP, flm; Papers of the United Negro College Fund, fiche; Special American & Foreign Newspaper Coll, film; United States Department of Interior Geological Survey Coll, maps; Urban Affairs (Newbank), fiche
Publications: Alcohol - Its Use and Abuse (bibliography); The American Indian, Then and Now (bibliography); The Drug Scene (bibliography); York College Library Handbook
Partic in OCLC Online Computer Library Center, Inc

JAMESTOWN

P CHAUTAUQUA-CATTARAUGUS LIBRARY SYSTEM, 106 W Fifth St, 14702-0730. SAN 311-368X. Tel: 716-484-7135. FAX: 716-483-6880. E-Mail: cway@cclslib.org. Web Site: www.cclslib.org. *Dir*, Murray L Bob; E-Mail: mbob@cclslib.org; *Asst Dir*, Catherine Way; E-Mail: cway@cclslib.org; *ILL*, Patricia Johnson; E-Mail: pjohnson@cclslib.org; *Tech Servs*, Martin Swalboski; E-Mail: mswalboski@cclslib.org; *Exten Serv*, Helen Bolton; E-Mail: hbolton@cclslib.org; *Ch Servs*, Camille Guinnane; E-Mail: cguinnane@cclslib.org
Founded 1960. Pop 226,129; Circ 2,181,255
Jan 2000-Dec 2000 Income $1,749,774, State $1,164,139, Federal $49,712, County $196,775, Locally Generated Income $40,000, Other $299,148. Mats Exp $303,762, Books $242,267, Per/Ser (Incl. Access Fees) $7,800, Other Print Mats $23,695, Electronic Ref Mat (Incl. Access Fees) $30,000. Sal $609,225 (Prof $246,996)
Library Holdings: Bk Vols 168,534; Per Subs 3,361
Automation Activity & Vendor Info: (Circulation) Inlex; (OPAC) Inlex
Database Vendor: OCLC - First Search
Publications: Newsletter
Member Libraries: Ahira Hall Memorial Library; Allegany Public Library; Anderson-Lee Library; Ashville Free Library; Bemus Point Public Library; Blount Library, Inc; Cattaraugus Free Library; Clymer-French Creek Free Library; Darwin R Barker Library; Delevan-Yorkshire Public Library; Dunkirk Free Library; Ellicottville Memorial Library; Falconer Public Library; Farman Free Library; Fluvanna Free Library; Hazeltine Public Library; James Prendergast Library Association; Kennedy Free Library; King Memorial Library; Lakewood Memorial Library; Mary E Seymour Memorial Free Library; Mayville Library; Memorial Library Of Little Valley; Minerva Free Library; Myers Memorial Library; Olean Public Library; Patterson Library; Portville Free Library; Randolph Free Library; Ripley Free Library; Salamanca Public Library; Sinclairville Free Library; Smith Memorial Library
Bookmobiles: 1. 1999 Thomas Built Customized by Matthew Specialty Vehicles

S FENTON HISTORICAL SOCIETY, Historical Center Library,* 67 Washington St, 14701-6697. SAN 311-3698. Tel: 716-664-6256. FAX: 716-483-7524. *Dir*, Christin Stein; *Librn*, Karen Livsey
Founded 1964
Library Holdings: Bk Titles 5,300; Per Subs 27
Subject Interests: Civil War period, Genealogy, Local history, Reuben E Fenton
Special Collections: Census Reports Coll; Genealogy (Newspaper Deaths & Marriages & CBS; Genealogy File), card file; Local History (Manuscript Coll); Local Newspapers

P FLUVANNA FREE LIBRARY,* 3532 Fluvanna, 14701. SAN 311-2063. Tel: 716-487-1773. FAX: 716-487-2311. Web Site: www.eclslib.org.
Pop 2,250; Circ 16,000
1999-2000 Income Locally Generated Income $7,700. Mats Exp $4,414, Books $4,000, Per/Ser (Incl. Access Fees) $414. Sal $8,320
Library Holdings: Bk Vols 14,530
Subject Interests: Encyclopedias, Local genealogy
Mem of Chautauqua-Cattaraugus Library System
Open Mon 6-9, Tues, 12:30-6, Wed & Fri 6-9, Thurs 12:30-9, Sat 10-3

P HAZELTINE PUBLIC LIBRARY, 891 Busti-Sugar Grove Rd, 14701-9510. SAN 310-9941. Tel: 716-487-1281. FAX: 716-487-0760. E-Mail: hazeltine@madbbs.com. Web Site: www.cclslib.org/busti.html. *Dir*, Taphna Blood
Founded 1924. Pop 4,486; Circ 51,687
Jan 1999-Dec 1999 Income $42,662, Locally Generated Income $35,500, Other $7,162. Mats Exp $11,957, Books $7,691, Per/Ser (Incl. Access Fees) $1,663, AV Equip $1,526, Other Print Mats $29, Electronic Ref Mat (Incl. Access Fees) $1,048. Sal $14,731
Library Holdings: Bk Titles 14,034; Per Subs 81
Subject Interests: Antiques, Crafts
Mem of Chautauqua-Cattaraugus Library System
Open Mon, Wed & Fri 1-5 & 6:30-8:30, Tues & Thurs 9-5, Sat 9-1

J JAMESTOWN COMMUNITY COLLEGE, Hultquist Library, 525 Falconer St, 14702-0020. SAN 311-3701. Tel: 716-665-5220. FAX: 716-665-5518. Web Site: www.sunyjcc.edu. *Dir*, Daniel Sell; *Ref*, Kathleen Barkham; Staff 5 (MLS 2, Non-MLS 3)
Founded 1950. Enrl 2,600; Fac 50; Highest Degree: Associate
Sep 1999-Aug 2000 Income $399,514, State $155,832, County $150,000, Other $94,000. Mats Exp $121,900, Books $49,000, Per/Ser (Incl. Access Fees) $29,000, Presv $500, Micro $4,000, Electronic Ref Mat (Incl. Access Fees) $39,400. Sal $299,000 (Prof $91,645)
Library Holdings: Bk Titles 59,000; Per Subs 395
Subject Interests: Criminal justice, Human services, Nursing
Special Collections: Scandinavian Studies
Automation Activity & Vendor Info: (Cataloging) DRA; (Circulation) DRA; (OPAC) DRA
Publications: Acquisitions List; Bibliographies; Guide to Staff & Services; Library Skills Workbook; Newsletter; STV Alert (satellite monthly); Subject & Descriptive Guide to Periodicals; TV Alert (monthly per)
Partic in OCLC Online Computer Library Center, Inc; Western New York Library Resources Council
Departmental Libraries:
CATTARAUGUS COUNTY, 312 Barry St, Olean, 14760. SAN 329-3521. Tel: 716-372-1661. FAX: 716-372-0169. Web Site: www.synyjcc.edu. *Librn*, Mary Jermann; Staff 2 (MLS 1, Non-MLS 1)
Enrl 900; Fac 20; Highest Degree: Associate
Sep 2000-Aug 2001 Income (Main Library Only) $148,306, State $58,922, County $48,209, Other $41,000. Mats Exp $45,500, Books $22,000, Per/Ser (Incl. Access Fees) $13,000, Presv $500, Electronic Ref Mat (Incl. Access Fees) $10,000. Sal $65,000 (Prof $34,000)
Library Holdings: Bk Titles 20,000; Per Subs 160
Automation Activity & Vendor Info: (Circulation) DRA; (OPAC) DRA

P JAMES PRENDERGAST LIBRARY ASSOCIATION, 509 Cherry St, 14701. SAN 311-371X. Tel: 716-484-7135. FAX: 716-487-1148. Web Site: www.cclslib.org/prendergast. *Dir*, Murray L Bob; E-Mail: mbob@cclslib.org; *Asst Dir*, Catherine Way; E-Mail: cway@cclslib.org; *Ch Servs*, Camille Guinnane; E-Mail: cguinnane@cclslib.org; *Ref*, Cheryl Johnson; E-Mail: cjohnson@cclslib.org; Staff 28 (MLS 8, Non-MLS 20)
Founded 1880. Pop 34,681; Circ 684,100
Jan 2000-Dec 2000 Income $1,223,968, State $106,390, City $384,948, Federal $24,313, Locally Generated Income $708,317. Mats Exp $205,100, Books $124,100, Per/Ser (Incl. Access Fees) $25,900, Presv $5,500, Micro $14,000, Electronic Ref Mat (Incl. Access Fees) $24,000. Sal $687,499 (Prof $343,712)
Library Holdings: Bk Vols 331,180; Per Subs 4,398
Subject Interests: Art, Art history, Behav sci, Bus and mgt, Sci-tech, Soc sci

Special Collections: Art Gallery
Automation Activity & Vendor Info: (Circulation) Inlex; (OPAC) Inlex
Publications: Catalog of the Paintings of the James Prendergast Library
Mem of Chautauqua-Cattaraugus Library System

M WOMEN'S CHRISTIAN ASSOCIATION HOSPITAL, WCA Health Sciences Library, 207 Foote Ave, 14701-9975. SAN 375-3204. Tel: 716-664-8124. FAX: 716-484-1089. *Librn*, Carole S Colter; *Asst Librn*, Bonnie Engberg; *Tech Servs*, Irene Swanson
Library Holdings: Bk Vols 1,500; Bk Titles 1,200; Per Subs 125
Partic in Western New York Library Resources Council

JASPER

P JASPER FREE LIBRARY,* 3807 Preacher St, PO Box 53, 14855-0053. SAN 311-3728. Tel: 607-792-3576. *Dir*, Debbie Stephens
Library Holdings: Bk Vols 4,000; Per Subs 25
Mem of Southern Tier Library System

JEFFERSONVILLE

P JEFFERSONVILLE PUBLIC LIBRARY,* Center St, PO Box 737, 12748. SAN 376-6950. Tel: 914-482-4350. FAX: 914-482-3092. Web Site: www.rcls.org/jeffpl. *Dir*, James M Gallagher; *Assoc Dir*, Kristine Bellino; *Asst Dir*, Michelle Musetti; Staff 4 (MLS 1, Non-MLS 3)
Jul 1999-Jun 2000 Income $113,372, State $1,400, Locally Generated Income $9,150. Mats Exp $13,050, Books $6,500, Per/Ser (Incl. Access Fees) $500. Sal $57,580 (Prof $30,000)
Library Holdings: Bk Vols 17,578; Per Subs 35
Mem of Ramapo Catskill Library System

JERICHO

P JERICHO PUBLIC LIBRARY,* One Merry Lane, 11753. SAN 311-3736. Tel: 516-935-6790. FAX: 516-433-9581. E-Mail: merry2@lilrc.org. Web Site: www.nassaulibrary.org/jericho/index.htm. *Dir*, Mary E Donor; *ILL*, Elizabeth Sheehan; *Ref*, Barbara Kessler; *Ch Servs*, Patricia Callahan; *Tech Servs*, Deborah Neuman; Staff 10 (MLS 10)
Founded 1964. Pop 17,367; Circ 257,192
Jul 1998-Jun 1999 Income $2,426,568, Locally Generated Income $147,641. Mats Exp $312,224, Books $232,104, Per/Ser (Incl. Access Fees) $21,747, Micro $7,613, Electronic Ref Mat (Incl. Access Fees) $50,760. Sal $1,316,364 (Prof $661,245)
Library Holdings: Bk Vols 92,500
Special Collections: Local History Coll, multi-media
Automation Activity & Vendor Info: (Circulation) DRA
Publications: Community Directory (annual); Newsletter (monthly)
Mem of Nassau Library System

JOHNSON CITY

M UNITED HEALTH SERVICES - WILSON REGIONAL MEDICAL CENTER, Medical Library, 33-57 Harrison St, 13790. SAN 311-3744. Tel: 607-763-6030. FAX: 607-763-6079. E-Mail: medical_library@uhs.org. *Mgr*, Terry Clift; E-Mail: terry_clift@uhs.org; *Librn*, Kathy Mols; E-Mail: kathy_mols@uhs.org; *Ref*, Carol Beyer; E-Mail: carol_beyer@uhs.org; Staff 2 (MLS 1, Non-MLS 1)
Founded 1935
Library Holdings: Bk Vols 6,700; Per Subs 388
Subject Interests: Healthcare admin, Medicine, Nursing
Restriction: Open to public for reference only
Partic in South Central Regional Library Council

P YOUR HOME PUBLIC LIBRARY,* 107 Main St, 13790. SAN 311-3752. Tel: 607-797-4816. *Dir*, Janet A Ottman; *Ad Servs, ILL*, Sharon Dunscombe; Staff 8 (MLS 3, Non-MLS 5)
Founded 1917. Pop 17,126; Circ 145,490
Library Holdings: Bk Vols 54,000
Mem of Four County Library System

JOHNSTOWN

J FULTON-MONTGOMERY COMMUNITY COLLEGE LIBRARY, The Evans Library, 2805 State Hwy 67, 12095-3790. SAN 311-3760. Tel: 518-762-4651, Ext 5600. FAX: 518-762-3834. Web Site: fmcc.suny.edu/library. *Dir*, Mary Donohue; E-Mail: mhartvig@fmcc.suny.edu; *Assoc Librn*, Mary Andolina; *Asst Librn*, Peter Betz; Staff 3 (MLS 3)
Founded 1964. Enrl 1,330; Fac 157
Library Holdings: Bk Vols 53,000; Per Subs 150
Subject Interests: Applied sci, Human servs, Regional hist
Publications: Handbook
Partic in OCLC Online Computer Library Center, Inc

P JOHNSTOWN PUBLIC LIBRARY,* 38 S Market St, 12095. SAN 311-3779. Tel: 518-762-8317. FAX: 518-762-9776. E-Mail: joh_germa@sals.edu. *Dir*, Barbara L Germain
Founded 1901. Pop 9,058; Circ 67,491
Jan 1998-Dec 1999 Income $217,892, State $11,715, City $162,708, Federal $1,508, County $4,800, Locally Generated Income $5,943, Other $22,156. Mats Exp $30,101, Books $24,488, Per/Ser (Incl. Access Fees) $5,479. Sal $135,196 (Prof $40,000)
Library Holdings: Bk Vols 40,698; Per Subs 155
Subject Interests: Genealogy, NY local hist
Publications: Friends of the Library Newsletter (quarterly)
Mem of Mohawk Valley Library Association
Library serves as education, job information & small business information center. Open Mon & Thurs 1-8, Tues & Wed 10-8, Fri 10-5, Sat 10-1 & Sun 1-4
Friends of the Library Group

JORDAN

P JORDAN BRAMLEY FREE LIBRARY,* Whiteley Memorial Bldg, 15 Mechanic St, PO Box 923, 13080-0923. SAN 311-3787. Tel: 315-689-3296. FAX: 315-689-1231. *Dir*, Mildred Simmons
Circ 25,000
Jan 1998-Dec 1999 Income $40,000. Mats Exp $7,520, Books $3,500, Per/Ser (Incl. Access Fees) $450. Sal $20,000
Library Holdings: Bk Vols 31,000
Mem of Onondaga County Public Library
Open Mon & Fri 1-5, Tues & Thurs 1-8, Wed 9-5, Sat 9-12
Friends of the Library Group

JORDANVILLE

R HOLY TRINITY ORTHODOX SEMINARY & MONASTERY LIBRARY,* PO Box 36, 13361-0036. SAN 311-3795. Tel: 315-858-0940. FAX: 315-858-0505. *Librn*, Father John
Library Holdings: Bk Vols 36,000
Subject Interests: Education, Humanities, Russian Orthodox relig

P JORDANVILLE PUBLIC LIBRARY, 2425 Jordanville Rd, PO Box 44, 13361. SAN 311-3809. Tel: 315-858-2874. *Dir*, Inga Rudd
Circ 9,612
Library Holdings: Bk Vols 4,068; Per Subs 10
Special Collections: Roosevelt Robinson NY State Coll
Publications: Historical Booklet
Mem of Mid-York Library System
Open Mon & Fri 12:30-5:30, Wed 12:30-8, Sat 12:30-3
Friends of the Library Group

KATONAH

M FOUR WINDS HOSPITAL, Education Center Library,* 800 Cross River Rd, 10536. SAN 370-5242. Tel: 914-763-8151, Ext 2333. FAX: 914-763-6407. *Dir*, Barbara Kurian
Library Holdings: Bk Vols 970; Per Subs 41
Subject Interests: Psychiatry

S JOHN JAY HOMESTEAD STATE HISTORIC SITE LIBRARY, 400 Rte 22, PO Box 832, 10536. SAN 311-3817. Tel: 914-232-5651. FAX: 914-232-8085.
Founded 1958
Library Holdings: Bk Titles 4,000
Special Collections: Papers of Ancestors & Descendants of John Jay, 1697-1950
Restriction: By appointment only
Open Wed-Sat 10-4, Sun 12-4
Friends of the Library Group

P KATONAH VILLAGE LIBRARY, 26 Bedford Rd, 10536-2121. SAN 311-3833. Tel: 914-232-3508. FAX: 914-232-0415. Web Site: wls.lib.ny.us. *Dir*, Susan Benton; *Asst Dir, Ref*, Van Kozelka; *Tech Servs*, Virginia Fetscher; *Ch Servs*, Vicki Ingrassia; Staff 4 (MLS 3, Non-MLS 1)
Founded 1880. Pop 6,424; Circ 110,300
Jan 2000-Dec 2000 Income $615,797, State $4,108, City $504,489, Other $2,336. Mats Exp $607,244, Books $50,863, Per/Ser (Incl. Access Fees) $8,500, Micro $4,000, AV Equip $5,000, Other Print Mats $604, Electronic Ref Mat (Incl. Access Fees) $30,000. Sal $352,466 (Prof $193,680)
Library Holdings: Bk Vols 70,000; Bk Titles 65,000; Per Subs 196
Subject Interests: Art, Fishing, Literature, Poetry
Mem of Westchester Library System
Friends of the Library Group

KEENE

P KEENE PUBLIC LIBRARY,* Main St, PO Box 206, 12942. SAN 311-3841. Tel: 518-576-2200. *Librn*, Marcy LeClair
Pop 920; Circ 9,044
Library Holdings: Bk Vols 10,000; Per Subs 13
Mem of Clinton-Essex-Franklin Library System

KEENE VALLEY

P KEENE VALLEY LIBRARY ASSOCIATION, Main St, PO Box 86, 12943. SAN 311-385X. Tel: 518-576-4335. FAX: 518-576-4693. E-Mail: library@kvvi.net. Web Site: www.kvvi.net/~library/. *Dir, Librn*, Lesley A Paul; *Archivist*, Patricia Galeski; *Archivist*, Dorothy Irving; Staff 2 (MLS 2)
Founded 1888. Pop 350; Circ 11,000
1999-2000 Income $40,500, State $1,500, City $5,000, Locally Generated Income $20,000, Other $14,000. Mats Exp $10,960, Books $8,500, Per/Ser (Incl. Access Fees) $1,700, Manuscripts & Archives $100, Electronic Ref Mat (Incl. Access Fees) $660. Sal $35,800 (Prof $27,400)
Library Holdings: Bk Titles 27,000; Per Subs 72
Subject Interests: Art, Mountaineering
Special Collections: Fishing (Pickard Coll); Local History (Loomis Room Coll); Mountain (Alpine Coll)
Mem of Clinton-Essex-Franklin Library System
Friends of the Library Group

KEESEVILLE

P KEESEVILLE FREE LIBRARY,* 1721 Front St, 12944. SAN 311-3868. Tel: 518-834-9054. FAX: 518-834-9054. *Dir*, Ann Garcia
Founded 1935. Pop 2,000; Circ 17,000
Library Holdings: Bk Titles 8,000; Per Subs 25
Mem of Clinton-Essex-Franklin Library System
Open Mon, Wed, Fri & Sat 1-5

KENMORE

P TOWN OF TONAWANDA PUBLIC LIBRARY,* 160 Delaware Rd, 14217. SAN 352-7824. Tel: 716-873-2861. FAX: 716-873-8416. *Dir*, Jeffrey P Mahaney
Founded 1925. Pop 82,000; Circ 967,880
Library Holdings: Bk Vols 178,970
Subject Interests: Large print
Special Collections: Newspapers, micro
Mem of Buffalo & Erie County Public Library System
Friends of the Library Group
Branches: 5
BRIGHTON, 999 Brighton Rd, Tonawanda, 14150. SAN 352-7859. Tel: 716-832-7931. FAX: 716-832-4096. *Librn*, Kristin Nazaret
Library Holdings: Bk Vols 25,794
GREENHAVEN, 350 Greenhaven Terrace, Tonawanda, 14150. SAN 352-7883. Tel: 716-694-2111. *Librn*, Michael Walter
Library Holdings: Bk Vols 27,565
KENILWORTH, 318 Montrose Ave, Buffalo, 14223. SAN 352-7913. Tel: 716-834-7657. FAX: 716-834-4695. *Librn*, Melvin Watkins
Library Holdings: Bk Vols 21,847
KENMORE, 160 Delaware Rd, 14217. SAN 352-7948. Tel: 716-873-2843. FAX: 716-873-2842, 716-873-8416. *Librn*, William Rott
Library Holdings: Bk Vols 55,000
SHERIDAN PARKSIDE, 169 Sheridan Parkside Dr, Tonawanda, 14150. SAN 352-7972. Tel: 716-876-6929. *Librn*, LindaBarbara Rizzo
Library Holdings: Bk Vols 9,728

KENNEDY

P KENNEDY FREE LIBRARY,* Church St, PO Box 8, 14747. SAN 311-3876. Tel: 716-267-4265. FAX: 716-267-2049. *Librn*, Linda Bish
Pop 2,639; Circ 9,383
Library Holdings: Bk Vols 9,000; Per Subs 33
Mem of Chautauqua-Cattaraugus Library System
Open Mon & Thurs 1-4 & 6-8, Tues & Sat 10-2 & Wed 10-4
Friends of the Library Group

KEUKA PARK

C KEUKA COLLEGE, Lightner Library, 14478-0038. SAN 311-3884. Tel: 315-279-5224. FAX: 315-279-5334. E-Mail: library@keuka.edu. Web Site: www.keuka.edu/library.html. *Dir*, Deborah Coover; Tel: 315-279-5208, E-Mail: dcoover@mail.keuka.edu; *Ref*, Linda Clark Benedict; E-Mail: lbenedic@mail.keuka.edu; *Tech Servs*, Hilda Mannato; E-Mail: hmannato@mail.keuka.edu; Staff 6 (MLS 3, Non-MLS 3)
Founded 1890. Enrl 880; Fac 52; Highest Degree: Bachelor
Library Holdings: Bk Vols 95,000; Per Subs 1,100
Subject Interests: Behav sci, Biology, Criminal justice, Elementary educ, Local history, Nursing, Occupational therapy, Psychology, Secondary educ, Sign lang, Soc sci, Soc serv
Publications: Journal Holdings List; Keuka Library Handbook
Partic in OCLC Online Computer Library Center, Inc; S Cent Res Libr Coun
Friends of the Library Group

KINDERHOOK

S COLUMBIA COUNTY HISTORICAL SOCIETY LIBRARY, Columbia County Museum, 5 Albany Ave, 12106. SAN 311-3892. Tel: 518-758-9265. FAX: 518-758-2499. *Dir*, Sharon S Palmer; *Curator*, Helen McLallen
Founded 1924
Library Holdings: Bk Vols 3,000
Subject Interests: County, Genealogy, Regional hist
Special Collections: Family History & Genealogies Coll; New York Colonial History Coll; Town History Material Coll
Open Mon-Fri 10-4, please call for winter hrs

P KINDERHOOK MEMORIAL LIBRARY, 18 Hudson St, 12106-2003. (Mail add: PO Box 293, 12106-0293), SAN 311-3906. Tel: 518-758-6192. FAX: 518-758-6055. E-Mail: oklibrary@berk.com. Web Site: www.oklibrary.org. *Dir*, Monica Seebode; *Asst Dir*, Julie Johnson; Staff 1 (MLS 1)
Founded 1928. Pop 4,400; Circ 28,765
Library Holdings: Bk Titles 20,200
Special Collections: Columbia County & Kinderhook; Gardening; Handicrafts
Mem of Mid-Hudson Library System
Open Tues-Thurs 12-8, Fri 12-5, Sat 10-4, Sun 1-3

KINGS POINT

C UNITED STATES MERCHANT MARINE ACADEMY, Schuyler Otis Bland Memorial Library, 11024-1699. SAN 311-3922. Tel: 516-773-5864. Interlibrary Loan Service Tel: 516-773-5503. FAX: 516-773-5502. Web Site: www.usmma.edu. *Dir*, Dr George J Billy; *Reader Servs*, Donald Gill; *Tech Servs*, Marilyn Stern; *Ref*, Ann Wenger; *Ref*, Christine Wang; *Acq*, Laura Cody; *Circ*, Nahid Aminfard
Founded 1942. Enrl 857; Fac 80; Highest Degree: Bachelor
Library Holdings: Bk Vols 235,709; Bk Titles 196,178; Per Subs 985
Subject Interests: Merchant marine
Special Collections: Marad Technical Report Coll; Nuclear Ship Savannah Coll; One-Dot Coll
Publications: Acquisitions List; Bibliography Series; Library Handbook; Newsletter; Periodicals Holdings List
Partic in Dialog Corporation; Long Island Library Resources Council; OCLC Online Computer Library Center, Inc

KINGSTON

P KINGSTON AREA LIBRARY,* 55 Franklin St, 12401. SAN 311-3957. Tel: 914-331-0507, 914-339-4260. Reference Tel: 914-331-0988. FAX: 914-331-7981. E-Mail: kingston@mhv.net, kingston@ulysses.sebridge.org. Web Site: www.kingstonlibrary.org. *Dir*, George R Allen; Tel: 914-339-4260, E-Mail: GAllen9788@aol.com; *Mgr*, Lena Brochetti; Tel: 914-339-4260; *Ref*, Christine Nielsen; *Ref*, Joy Fish; *Coll Develop*, Sharon Morris; Tel: 914-331-0988; *ILL*, Dorothea Warren; *Tech Servs*, Mary Lou Decker; Tel: 914-339-4260; *Ch Servs*, Donna Luxemburg; *Circ*, Marion Tinsley; *Publ Servs*, Stephanie Morgan; *Publ Servs*, Elizabeth Strickland; Staff 12 (MLS 1, Non-MLS 11)
Founded 1899. Pop 23,095; Circ 84,000
Jan 1998-Dec 1998 Income $500,542, State $20,395, City $200,000, Federal $15,989, County $34,817, Locally Generated Income $88,859, Other $24,000. Mats Exp $53,189, Books $25,249, Per/Ser (Incl. Access Fees) $18,350, Micro $3,000, AV Equip $6,383, Electronic Ref Mat (Incl. Access Fees) $3,207. Sal $274,805 (Prof $55,000)
Library Holdings: Bk Vols 74,728; Bk Titles 76,835; Per Subs 95
Subject Interests: Local history
Special Collections: Local History
Automation Activity & Vendor Info: (Cataloging) GEAC; (Circulation) GEAC; (OPAC) GEAC
Database Vendor: CARL, IAC - SearchBank, ProQuest
Mem of Mid-Hudson Library System
Partic in Mid-Hudson Libr Syst; Southeastern New York Library Resources Council
Friends of the Library Group

M KINGSTON HOSPITAL LIBRARY,* 396 Broadway, 12401. SAN 311-3965. Tel: 914-331-3131, Ext 2286. FAX: 914-338-0527. *Librn*, Ann Blish
Founded 1956
Library Holdings: Bk Vols 900; Bk Titles 1,378; Per Subs 138
Subject Interests: Hospital administration, Medicine, Nursing, Surgery
Restriction: Staff use only
Partic in Basic Health Sciences Library Network; Greater NE Regional Med Libr Program; Health Info Librs of Westchester; Nat Libr of Med; Southeastern New York Library Resources Council

G NEW YORK STATE OFFICE OF PARKS RECREATION & HISTORIC PRESERVATION, Senate House State Historic Site - Library & Archives, 296 Fair St, 12401. SAN 311-3973. Tel: 845-338-2786. FAX: 845-334-8173.
Founded 1927
Library Holdings: Bk Vols 1,200; Bk Titles 1,000
Subject Interests: New York from 17th through mid-20th centuries

Special Collections: DeWitt Family Correspondence, mss; Ulster County Coll, doc; Van Gaasbeek Family Papers, mss; Vanderlyn Correspondence, mss
Restriction: By appointment only
Open Apr-Oct, Wed-Sun 10-5

GL NEW YORK STATE SUPREME COURT, Third Judicial District Law Library, 285 Wall St, 12401. SAN 311-3981. Tel: 914-340-3053. FAX: 914-340-3773. *Librn*, Michael Birzenieks
Library Holdings: Bk Vols 17,000

P TOWN OF ULSTER PUBLIC LIBRARY,* 985 Morton Blvd, 12401. SAN 312-5726. Tel: 914-336-5767. FAX: 914-336-5799. *Librn*, Laurie Sheddrick; Staff 7 (MLS 1, Non-MLS 6)
Founded 1962
Library Holdings: Bk Vols 44,000; Bk Titles 43,000; Per Subs 57
Subject Interests: Large print, Local history
Publications: Quarterly newsletter
Mem of Mid-Hudson Library System
Open Mon, Wed & Fri 10-5, Tues & Thurs 12-8, Sat 10-3
Friends of the Library Group

G ULSTER COUNTY PLANNING BOARD LIBRARY,* County Office Bldg, 244 Fair St, 12402. SAN 327-6996. Tel: 914-340-3340. FAX: 914-340-3429.
Library Holdings: Bk Vols 120
Restriction: Open to public for reference only

LA FARGEVILLE

P ORLEANS PUBLIC LIBRARY,* Sunrise Ave, PO Box 139, 13656. SAN 311-399X. Tel: 315-658-2271. *Librn*, Kelly Orvis
Founded 1942. Circ 9,200
Library Holdings: Bk Vols 7,000; Per Subs 12
Mem of North Country Library System

LACKAWANNA

P LACKAWANNA PUBLIC LIBRARY, 560 Ridge Rd, 14218. SAN 311-4007. Tel: 716-823-0630. FAX: 716-827-1997. Web Site: www.buffalolib.org. *Dir*, Salvatore Bordonaro; E-Mail: bordonaros@buffalolib.org; *Ch Servs*, Jennifer Hoffman
Founded 1922. Pop 20,585; Circ 70,770
Jan 1999-Dec 1999 Income $247,389, State $6,381, City $10,000, County $213,794, Locally Generated Income $8,217. Mats Exp $19,777, Books $16,377, Per/Ser (Incl. Access Fees) $3,400. Sal $182,041 (Prof $97,557)
Library Holdings: Bk Titles 27,263
Automation Activity & Vendor Info: (Circulation) DRA; (OPAC) DRA
Mem of Buffalo & Erie County Public Library System
Special Services for the Blind - Talking book center
Open Mon & Wed 1-9, Tues & Thurs-Sat 10-5; Summer hrs Mon & Wed 1-9, Tues, Thurs & Fri 9-5, closed Sat; Library houses a local history & steel plant museum
Friends of the Library Group

M OUR LADY OF VICTORY HOSPITAL, Hospital Library,* 55 Melroy at Ridge Rd, 14218. SAN 320-7110. Tel: 716-825-8000, Ext 309. FAX: 716-825-7271.
Founded 1960
Library Holdings: Bk Vols 622; Per Subs 70
Subject Interests: Allied health, Head trauma rehab, Medicine, Surgery
Restriction: Not open to public
Partic in Western New York Library Resources Council

LAFAYETTE

P LAFAYETTE PUBLIC LIBRARY,* Rte 11 N, 13084. SAN 311-4015. Tel: 315-677-3782. FAX: 315-677-0211. *Dir*, Cara Burton; Staff 1 (MLS 1)
Pop 5,105; Circ 40,015
1998-1999 Income $91,500
Library Holdings: Bk Titles 23,625; Per Subs 85
Mem of Onondaga County Public Library
Partic in OCLC Online Computer Library Center, Inc
Open Mon & Tues 10-8, Wed & Fri 10-5, Thurs 12-8, Sat 10-2

LAKE GEORGE

P CALDWELL-LAKE GEORGE LIBRARY, 336 Canada St, 12845-1118. SAN 325-5824. Tel: 518-668-2528. FAX: 518-668-2528. Web Site: www.caldwell.lakegeorge.sals.edu. *Dir*, Marie Ellsworth; Staff 2 (Non-MLS 2)
Founded 1906. Pop 933
Library Holdings: Bk Vols 16,917; Per Subs 56
Mem of Southern Adirondack Library System

P MOUNTAINSIDE FREE LIBRARY,* 3090 Rte 9L, 12845. SAN 311-4031. Tel: 518-798-1555 (Home). FAX: 518-745-1125. *Dir*, Lena Chambers
Library Holdings: Bk Titles 12,000; Per Subs 56
Mem of Southern Adirondack Library System

GL SUPREME COURT LIBRARY,* Warren County Municipal Ctr, 1340 State Rte 9, 12845-9803. SAN 311-404X. Tel: 518-761-6442. FAX: 518-761-6586.
Library Holdings: Per Subs 19

LAKE LUZERNE

P HADLEY-LUZERNE PUBLIC LIBRARY, 19 Main St, PO Box 400, 12846-0400. SAN 311-4058. Tel: 518-696-3423. FAX: 518-696-3423. Web Site: hadluz.sals.edu. *Dir*, Sarah Kimball Andrews; E-Mail: sandrews15@juno.com. Subject Specialists: *Arts*, Sarah Kimball Andrews; *Music*, Sarah Kimball Andrews; Staff 3 (MLS 1, Non-MLS 2)
Founded 1969. Pop 4,444; Circ 23,725
Jan 2000-Dec 2000 Mats Exp $9,800, Books $8,000, Per/Ser (Incl. Access Fees) $1,000, AV Equip $800
Library Holdings: Bk Vols 17,487; Per Subs 48; High Interest/Low Vocabulary Bk Vols 200; Spec Interest Per Sub 24
Mem of Southern Adirondack Library System
Partic in Capital District Library Council for Reference & Research Resources
Special Services for the Blind - Large print bks
Open Mon, Wed, Fri & Sat 9-2, Tues & Thurs 1-7
Friends of the Library Group

LAKE PLACID

S CENTER FOR BEAD RESEARCH LIBRARY,* 4 Essex St, 12946. SAN 326-2022. Tel: 518-523-1794. Web Site: www.thebeadsite.com. *Librn*, Peter Francis, Jr; E-Mail: pfjr@northnet.org; *Asst Librn*, Virginia LePichon; Staff 2 (MLS 1, Non-MLS 1)
Founded 1985
Library Holdings: Bk Titles 890; Per Subs 35
Special Collections: Beads (Francis Research Notes) & (Study Coll), beads & tools
Publications: Beads & People Series; Contribution of Center for Bead Research; Margaretologist; Occasional Papers of the Center for Bead Research; World of Beads Monograph Series
Restriction: By appointment only
Function: Research library

P LAKE PLACID PUBLIC LIBRARY,* 67 Main St, 12946. SAN 311-4074. Tel: 518-523-3200. FAX: 518-523-3200. *Librn*, Therese Patnode; *Asst Librn*, Linda Blair
Pop 5,000; Circ 28,884
Library Holdings: Bk Vols 20,000; Per Subs 20
Subject Interests: Local history
Special Collections: Adirondack & Olympic Coll
Mem of Clinton-Essex-Franklin Library System
Open Mon-Fri 10-5:30 & Sat 10-4

LAKE SUCCESS

GM MEDICAL SOCIETY OF THE STATE OF NEW YORK, Albion O Bernstein Library, 420 Lakeville Rd, 11042. SAN 325-3465. Tel: 516-488-6100, Ext 388. FAX: 516-488-1267. *Dir*, Ella Abney; E-Mail: eabney@mssny.org
Founded 1975
Library Holdings: Per Subs 85
Special Collections: Clinical Medicine Coll; Socio-Economics Coll
Partic in Long Island Library Resources Council

LAKEWOOD

P LAKEWOOD MEMORIAL LIBRARY, 12 W Summit St, 14750. SAN 311-4120. Tel: 716-763-6234. FAX: 716-763-3624. E-Mail: lakewoodmemorial@hotmail.com. *Librn*, Judith L Koch; Staff 4 (MLS 2, Non-MLS 2)
Founded 1960. Pop 8,050; Circ 58,945
Library Holdings: Bk Vols 31,800; Per Subs 80
Subject Interests: Local history
Mem of Chautauqua-Cattaraugus Library System
Friends of the Library Group

LANCASTER

S ECOLOGY & ENVIRONMENT INC, LIBRARY,* 368 Pleasantview Dr, 14086-1316. SAN 310-9704. Tel: 716-684-8060. FAX: 716-684-0844. *Librn*, Theresa L Wolfe
Founded 1971
Library Holdings: Bk Vols 7,000; Per Subs 250
Subject Interests: Hazardous mat mgt
Partic in OCLC Online Computer Library Center, Inc

P LANCASTER PUBLIC LIBRARY,* 5466 Broadway, 14086. SAN 352-8006. Tel: 716-683-1120. FAX: 716-686-0749. *Dir*, Ann Kling; *Br Coordr*, Amy Christman; *Ch Servs, YA Servs*, Sylvia Barry
Founded 1895. Circ 309,621
Library Holdings: Bk Vols 77,901
Special Collections: Parenting Resource Center
Mem of Buffalo & Erie County Public Library System
Open Mon & Thurs 10-9, Tues 1-9, Wed & Fri 10-6, Sat 10-5 & Sun 1-5
Friends of the Library Group
Branches: 1
DEPEW, 321 Columbia Ave, 14043. SAN 352-8030. *Head of Libr*, Roseanne Butler-Smith; *Ch Servs*, Susan PeTherick
Friends of the Library Group

LARCHMONT

P LARCHMONT PUBLIC LIBRARY, 121 Larchmont Ave, 10538. SAN 311-4139. Tel: 914-834-2281. FAX: 914-834-0351. Web Site: www.larchmontlibrary.org. *Dir*, Diane Courtney; E-Mail: courtney@wls.lib.ny.us; *ILL*, Jacquelyn Anderson; E-Mail: janderson@wls.lib.ny.us; *Ch Servs*, Ray Messing; E-Mail: rmessing@wls.lib.ny.us; *YA Servs*, Ellen Fentas; E-Mail: efentas@wls.lib.ny.us; *Ref*, June Hesler; E-Mail: jhesler@wls.lib.ny.us; *Ref*, Vincent Munch; E-Mail: vmunch@wls.lib.ny.us; *Commun Servs*, Nancy Donovan; E-Mail: ndonovan@wls.lib.ny.us; Staff 5 (MLS 5)
Founded 1926. Pop 17,815; Circ 201,416
Jun 2000-May 2001 Income $1,192,984, State $5,399, Locally Generated Income $1,187,585. Mats Exp $125,165, Books $72,165, Per/Ser (Incl. Access Fees) $36,000, Presv $500, AV Equip $5,500, Electronic Ref Mat (Incl. Access Fees) $11,000. Sal $690,319 (Prof $317,547)
Library Holdings: Bk Vols 90,421; Bk Titles 90,000; Per Subs 231
Subject Interests: Local history
Automation Activity & Vendor Info: (Circulation) epixtech, inc.; (ILL) epixtech, inc.
Database Vendor: CARL, Dialog, Ebsco - EbscoHost, GaleNet
Publications: Friends of Larchmont Public Library Newsletter
Mem of Westchester Library System
Special Services for the Blind - Closed circuit television magnifier
Friends of the Library Group

LATHAM

S NEW YORK STATE NURSES ASSOCIATION LIBRARY, 11 Cornell Rd, 12110. SAN 311-2802. Tel: 518-782-9400, Ext 266. FAX: 518-782-9532. E-Mail: library@nysna.org. *Dir*, Warren Hawkes; Staff 4 (MLS 2, Non-MLS 2)
Founded 1972
Apr 2000-Mar 2001 Income $45,000
Library Holdings: Bk Titles 9,000; Per Subs 245
Subject Interests: Allied health, Labor relations, Nursing, Nursing hist
Publications: NY State Nurses Association Library Guide to Resources & Services
Partic in Capital District Library Council for Reference & Research Resources

LAWRENCE

P PENINSULA PUBLIC LIBRARY, 280 Central Ave, 11559. SAN 311-4155. Tel: 516-239-3262. FAX: 516-239-8425. E-Mail: peninsula@nassaulibrary.org. Web Site: www.nassaulibrary.org/peninsula. *Dir*, Arleen J Reo; *Asst Dir*, Joan Lepelstat; *Bkmobile Coordr*, Jos Squieteri; *Ch Servs*, Priscilla Kesten; *Circ*, Darleen Rodgers; *ILL*, Louisa Delia; *Media Spec*, Mary Harrow; *Ref*, Richard Cooper; *YA Servs*, Geri Krim; Staff 13 (MLS 10, Non-MLS 3)
Founded 1951. Pop 33,988; Circ 290,508
Library Holdings: Bk Vols 120,000; Bk Titles 100,000; Per Subs 12,000
Special Collections: Sign English for Children
Automation Activity & Vendor Info: (Circulation) DRA
Publications: Peninsula Public Library Newsletter
Mem of Nassau Library System
Special Services for the Deaf - Books on deafness & sign language; High interest/low vocabulary books; Staff with knowledge of sign language
Bookmobiles: 1

R TEMPLE ISRAEL LIBRARY,* 140 Central Ave, 11559. SAN 311-4163. Tel: 516-239-1140, 516-239-9213. FAX: 516-239-0859. *Librn*, Geri Krim; Staff 7 (MLS 1, Non-MLS 6)
Founded 1949
Library Holdings: Bk Vols 5,500; Per Subs 10
Subject Interests: Judaica
Restriction: By appointment only

LEROY

S LEROY HISTORICAL SOCIETY LIBRARY, 23 E Main St, PO Box 176, 14482. SAN 327-7011. Tel: 716-768-7433. *Curator, Dir*, Lynne Belluscio
Founded 1940
Library Holdings: Bk Vols 4,000
Subject Interests: Genealogy
Special Collections: Ingham University Archives; Lampson Papers

P WOODWARD MEMORIAL LIBRARY,* 7 Wolcott St, 14482. SAN 311-4198. Tel: 716-768-8300. FAX: 716-768-4768. E-Mail: wmlib@iinc.com. *Dir*, Sue Border; *Librn*, Carol Mast; *YA Servs*, Kevin Conklin; *Ch Servs*, Cindy Frisch
Library Holdings: Bk Vols 50,159; Per Subs 97
Special Collections: Literature (Woodward Coll)
Mem of Nioga Library System

LEVITTOWN

P LEVITTOWN PUBLIC LIBRARY, One Bluegrass Lane, 11756-1292. SAN 311-421X. Tel: 516-731-5728. TDD: 516-579-8585. FAX: 516-735-3168. E-Mail: levtown@nassaulibrary.org. Web Site: www.nassaulibrary.org/levtown/index.html. *Dir*, P W Martin; *Asst Libr Dir*, Margaret Cincotta; Fax: 516-735-8585; *Ad Servs*, John Bosco; *Automation Syst Coordr*, Marie Andreski; *Ch Servs*, Margaret Kapinos; *Circ*, Catherine Lang; *YA Servs*, Lorraine Lopez; *Spec Coll & Archives*, Ann Glorioso; *Tech Servs*, Louis Palumbo; *Ref*, Helene Hertzlinger; Staff 15 (MLS 14, Non-MLS 1)
Founded 1950. Pop 47,871; Circ 390,853
Jul 2000-Jun 2001 Income $3,666,073, State $161,800, Locally Generated Income $3,504,265. Mats Exp $240,470, Books $171,720, Per/Ser (Incl. Access Fees) $27,000, Presv $1,000, Micro $6,750, Electronic Ref Mat (Incl. Access Fees) $34,000. Sal $2,299,492 (Prof $833,337)
Library Holdings: Bk Vols 260,925; Bk Titles 248,742; Per Subs 561
Subject Interests: History, Natural science
Special Collections: Levittown History, misc
Automation Activity & Vendor Info: (Cataloging) DRA; (Circulation) DRA; (OPAC) DRA
Database Vendor: CARL, Dialog, DRA, Ebsco - EbscoHost, GaleNet, IAC - Info Trac, IAC - SearchBank, OCLC - First Search, Silverplatter Information Inc., Wilson - Wilson Web
Publications: Directory of Community Organizations; Going On: Calendar of Events
Mem of Nassau Library System
Special Services for the Deaf - TDD; TTY machine

LEWISTON

P LEWISTON PUBLIC LIBRARY, 305 S Eighth St, 14092. SAN 311-4228. Tel: 716-754-4720. FAX: 716-754-7386. *Dir*, Lisa A Seivert; E-Mail: lseiv@nioga.org; Staff 3 (MLS 3)
Founded 1902. Pop 16,000; Circ 122,000
Jan 2000-Dec 2000 Income $437,200, State $2,200, City $381,000, County $33,000, Locally Generated Income $17,000, Other $4,000. Mats Exp $94,000, Books $66,500, Per/Ser (Incl. Access Fees) $15,000, Micro $1,200, Other Print Mats $4,000. Sal $264,000 (Prof $76,000)
Library Holdings: Bk Titles 58,000; Per Subs 130
Special Collections: Early Lewiston Houses (Bjorne Klaussen Coll), original acrylic & oil paintings; Old Village History
Publications: Lewiston - A Self-Guided Tour
Mem of Nioga Library System
Friends of the Library Group

LIMA

P LIMA PUBLIC LIBRARY,* 1872 Genesee St, PO Box 58A, 14485-0858. SAN 311-4244. Tel: 716-582-1311. FAX: 716-582-1701. E-Mail: lim@pls_net.org. *Dir*, Barbara Wilcox; Staff 2 (Non-MLS 2)
Founded 1910. Pop 4,187
Library Holdings: Bk Vols 25,300; Bk Titles 24,532; Per Subs 63
Special Collections: Local History, articles, bks, pamphlets
Automation Activity & Vendor Info: (Circulation) Follett
Mem of Pioneer Library System
Open Mon, Tues & Thurs 1-5 & 7-9, Wed 10-12 & 1-5, Fri 1-5 & Sat 9-1
Friends of the Library Group

LINDENHURST

P LINDENHURST MEMORIAL LIBRARY, One Lee Ave, 11757-5399. SAN 311-4252. Tel: 631-957-7755. FAX: 631-957-7114. *Dir*, Carol Simpson; *Ch Servs*, Lisa Smith; *Cat, Coll Develop, Ref*, Eileen Feynman; *Ad Servs, Circ*, Paula Bornstein; *YA Servs*, Lynn Odom; *AV*, Carrie Guarria; *Publ Servs*, Patricia Leary; Staff 12 (MLS 12)
Founded 1946. Pop 41,580; Circ 310,000
Jul 1999-Jun 2000 Income $2,643,850, Locally Generated Income $2,344,050, Other $299,800. Mats Exp Books $312,500
Library Holdings: Bk Vols 185,563; Bk Titles 151,539; Per Subs 436
Special Collections: History of Lindenhurst
Automation Activity & Vendor Info: (Acquisitions) Innovative Interfaces Inc.; (Cataloging) Innovative Interfaces Inc.; (Circulation) Innovative

Interfaces Inc.; (OPAC) Innovative Interfaces Inc.
Publications: Newsletter
Mem of Suffolk Cooperative Library System
Special Services for the Deaf - Books on deafness & sign language

LISBON

P HEPBURN LIBRARY OF LISBON,* PO Box 86, 13658. SAN 311-4260. Tel: 315-393-0111. *Librn*, Sylvia Armstrong
Founded 1920. Pop 3,746; Circ 14,841
Library Holdings: Bk Vols 10,440; Per Subs 51
Special Collections: Local History; News Scrapbooks; Yearbooks of Local High School
Mem of North County Libr Coop

LISLE

P LISLE FREE LIBRARY,* Main St, 13797-0032. SAN 311-4279. Tel: 607-692-3115. FAX: 607-692-7947. E-Mail: li_ill@4cty.org. *Librn*, Deborah Sturdevant
Founded 1922. Pop 2,039
1997-1998 Mats Exp $5,000
Library Holdings: Bk Vols 8,000; Per Subs 20
Mem of Four County Library System

LITTLE FALLS

P LITTLE FALLS PUBLIC LIBRARY,* 10 Waverly Pl, 13365. SAN 311-4287. Tel: 315-823-1542. FAX: 315-823-2995. E-Mail: if_circ@midyork.lib.ny.us. *Dir, Librn*, Jeffrey R Singer
Founded 1911. Pop 5,929; Circ 88,572
Library Holdings: Bk Titles 25,285; Per Subs 75
Mem of Mid-York Library System

LITTLE GENESEE

P GENESEE PUBLIC LIBRARY,* 8351 Main St, PO Box 10, 14754. SAN 311-4295. Tel: 716-928-1915. FAX: 716-928-1915. *Librn*, Carolyn Sherman
Circ 1,787
Library Holdings: Bk Vols 1,000
Special Collections: Criminal Law; Game Hunters; Local History, atlases, bks, surveys, Maps, Indina (Resource), Town Cook Book
Mem of Chemung-Southern Tier Libr Syst; Southern Tier Library System
Youth Reading Program
Friends of the Library Group

LITTLE VALLEY

G CATTARAUGUS COUNTY MEMORIAL & HISTORICAL MUSEUM LIBRARY, Court St, 14755. SAN 326-2030. Tel: 716-938-9111, Ext 2440. *Curator*, Lorna Spencer; Staff 2 (Non-MLS 2)
Founded 1914. Pop 86,000
1999-2000 Income $23,900. Mats Exp $2,100, Books $1,500, Micro $600. Sal $8,000
Library Holdings: Bk Vols 500
Subject Interests: Local history
Special Collections: County

P MEMORIAL LIBRARY OF LITTLE VALLEY, 110 Rock City St, 14755. SAN 311-4309. Tel: 716-938-6301. FAX: 716-938-6837. *Dir*, Gretchen Taft; Staff 1 (Non-MLS 1)
Founded 1923. Pop 1,830; Circ 12,750
Library Holdings: Bk Vols 14,048
Subject Interests: Local history
Function: ILL available, Photocopies available, Some telephone reference
Mem of Chautauqua-Cattaraugus Library System
Open Mon 10-4:30 & 7-9pm, Tues 12-4:30 & 7-9pm, Thurs 10-6, Fri 10-4:30, Sat 10-noon (July-Aug, closed Sat)

LIVERPOOL

P LIVERPOOL PUBLIC LIBRARY, 310 Tulip St, 13088-4997. SAN 311-4317. Tel: 315-457-0310. Interlibrary Loan Service Tel: 315-435-1800. FAX: 315-453-7867. E-Mail: webmaster@lpl.org. Web Site: www.lpl.org. *Dir*, Sharon Nottingham; *Head Tech Servs*, Judith Rossoff; *Tech Coordr*, Elaine R Lyon; Tel: 315-457-0310, Ext 104, E-Mail: lyon@mailbox.lpl.org; *Publ Servs*, Elizabeth Dailey; *Head, Info Serv*, Regina Fredericks; *Info Specialist*, Annette Friedrichs; *Info Specialist*, David Fulton; *Outreach Serv*, Susan Smith; *Ad Servs*, Rita Ben-Simon; *Ch Servs*, Rosemary Laguzza; *Ch Servs*, Linda Meyer; *Ch Servs*, Renee Romance; *Ch Servs*, Anne Royer; *Ch Servs*, Laurel Sharp; *Cat*, Leanne Cook; *Ref*, Jeanne Biggins; *YA Servs*, Wanda Abrams; *Coll Develop*, Karen Ingeman. Subject Specialists: *Support servs*, Elaine R Lyon; *Technology*, Elaine R Lyon; Staff 16 (MLS 16)
Founded 1893. Pop 55,000; Circ 507,395
Jul 2000-Jun 2001 Income $3,061,608, Locally Generated Income $2,732,708, Other $392,200. Mats Exp $358,400, Books $158,500, Per/Ser (Incl. Access Fees) $65,000, Presv $2,000, Micro $23,000, AV Equip $7,000, Electronic Ref Mat (Incl. Access Fees) $25,000. Sal $1,855,708 (Prof $679,365)
Library Holdings: Bk Vols 83,033; Per Subs 450
Subject Interests: Local history
Special Collections: Local History Video Coll; Software
Automation Activity & Vendor Info: (OPAC) epixtech, inc.
Database Vendor: GaleNet
Mem of Onondaga County Public Library
Friends of the Library Group

LIVINGSTON

P LIVINGSTON FREE LIBRARY,* Old Post Rd, PO Box 105, 12541. SAN 311-4325. Tel: 518-851-2270. *Librn*, Michelle Arnone
Founded 1906. Circ 1,460
Library Holdings: Bk Vols 2,900; Per Subs 15
Mem of Mid-Hudson Library System
Open Mon & Fri 7-8:30, Wed 2-5

LIVINGSTON MANOR

P LIVINGSTON MANOR FREE LIBRARY,* Main St, PO Box 999, 12758. SAN 311-4333. Tel: 914-439-5440. FAX: 914-439-3141. *Dir*, Marilynn Fredenburg
Founded 1938. Pop 3,645; Circ 15,184
1998-1999 Income $67,190, City $2,500, Locally Generated Income $8,286, Parent Institution $40,000. Mats Exp $23,612, Books $23,091, Per/Ser (Incl. Access Fees) $521. Sal $19,732
Library Holdings: Bk Vols 13,294
Mem of Ramapo Catskill Library System

LIVONIA

P LIVONIA PUBLIC LIBRARY, 2 Washington St, 14487-9738. (Mail add: PO Box 107, 14487-0107), SAN 311-4341. Tel: 716-346-3450. FAX: 716-346-5911. Web Site: www.livonia.pls-net.org. *Dir*, Karen A Deutsch; E-Mail: kdeutsch@pls-net.org; *Asst Librn*, Nancy Krause; Staff 4 (MLS 1, Non-MLS 3)
Founded 1917. Pop 6,804; Circ 47,377
Jan 1999-Dec 1999 Income $139,784, State $2,564, City $121,881, Federal $619, County $7,203, Locally Generated Income $7,517. Mats Exp $29,962, Books $21,343, Per/Ser (Incl. Access Fees) $2,891, Presv $47, AV Equip $3,919, Electronic Ref Mat (Incl. Access Fees) $1,762. Sal $64,738 (Prof $23,700)
Library Holdings: Bk Vols 23,000; Bk Titles 21,733; Per Subs 85
Special Collections: Livonia Hist Coll
Automation Activity & Vendor Info: (Acquisitions) Brodart; (Circulation) Sagebrush Corporation; (ILL) TLC; (OPAC) Sagebrush Corporation; (Serials) Sagebrush Corporation
Mem of Pioneer Library System
Open Mon, Tues, Thurs & Fri 10:30-5:30, Sat 10:30-3:30
Friends of the Library Group

LOCH SHELDRAKE

J SULLIVAN COUNTY COMMUNITY COLLEGE, Hermann Memorial Library, 112 College Rd, 12759-5108. SAN 311-435X. Tel: 845-434-5750, Ext 4223. FAX: 845-434-0839. E-Mail: library@sullivan.suny.edu. Web Site: www.sullivan.suny.edu. *Dir*, Jerome Gittleman; Tel: 845-434-5750, Ext 4208, E-Mail: gittlman@sullivan.sunny.edu; *Cat, Tech Servs*, Phyllis Jones; Tel: 845-434-5750, Ext 4226, E-Mail: jonespr@sullivan.sunny.edu; *ILL*, Diana Hovorka; *Ref*, Richard Arnold; Tel: 845-434-5750, Ext 4227, E-Mail: rarnold@sullivan.sunny.edu; Staff 3 (MLS 3)
Founded 1964. Enrl 1,350; Fac 45; Highest Degree: Associate
Sep 2000-Aug 2001 Income $390,000. Mats Exp $130,328, Books $45,000, Per/Ser (Incl. Access Fees) $44,478, Micro $21,000, Electronic Ref Mat (Incl. Access Fees) $19,850. Sal $243,648 (Prof $170,015)
Library Holdings: Bk Vols 65,000; Bk Titles 63,500; Per Subs 400
Subject Interests: Hotel tech
Publications: Newsletter; Subject Bibliographies
Partic in Southeastern New York Library Resources Council

LOCKPORT

S HISTORICAL SOCIETY, Niagara County Genealogical Society Library, 215 Niagara St, 14094-2605. SAN 326-131X. Tel: 716-433-1033.
Library Holdings: Bk Vols 1,200; Bk Titles 1,000
Subject Interests: Genealogy, Local history, Music scores
Publications: Newsletter (quarterly)
Restriction: Non-circulating to the public
Friends of the Library Group

P LOCKPORT PUBLIC LIBRARY, 23 East Ave, PO Box 475, 14095. SAN 311-4376. Tel: 716-433-5935. FAX: 716-439-0198. Web Site: www.lockportlibrary.org. *Dir*, Margaret W Lynch
Founded 1897. Pop 34,964; Circ 348,489
Jul 1999-Jun 2000 Income $1,063,605. Mats Exp $1,014,390, Books $124,117, Per/Ser (Incl. Access Fees) $29,877, Electronic Ref Mat (Incl. Access Fees) $13,612. Sal $581,384 (Prof $264,601)
Library Holdings: Bk Vols 132,708; Per Subs 238
Special Collections: Freemasonry & Anti-Masonic, bks, micro
Automation Activity & Vendor Info: (Cataloging) epixtech, inc.; (Circulation) epixtech, inc.; (ILL) epixtech, inc.; (OPAC) epixtech, inc.
Mem of Nioga Library System
Friends of the Library Group

P NIOGA LIBRARY SYSTEM,* 6575 Wheeler Rd, 14094. SAN 311-4384. Tel: 716-434-6167. FAX: 716-434-8231. Web Site: www.nioga.org. *Exec Dir*, Mary L Brink; Tel: 716-434-6167, Ext 14, E-Mail: mbrin@nioga.org; *Asst Dir*, Thomas C Bindeman; Tel: 716-434-6167, Ext 24, E-Mail: tbind@nioga.org; *Ch Servs*, Marie K Bindeman; Tel: 716-434-6167, Ext 31, E-Mail: mbind@nioga.org; *Automation Syst Coordr*, Joseph C Umhauer; Tel: 716-434-6167, Ext 18, E-Mail: jumha@nioga.org; *AV*, Carol J Milazzo; Tel: 716-434-6167, Ext 29, E-Mail: cmila@nioga.org; *Business*, Mary Ruth Davis; Tel: 716-434-6167, Ext 15, E-Mail: mdavi@nioga.org; *Syst Coordr*, Justin Genter; Tel: 716-434-6167, Ext 11, E-Mail: jgent@nioga.org
Founded 1959. Pop 322,662
Jan 1998-Dec 1998 Income $1,646,475, State $1,415,831, Federal $44,850, County $5,729, Other $180,065. Mats Exp $131,143, Books $59,928, Per/Ser (Incl. Access Fees) $34,328, Other Print Mats $2,398, Electronic Ref Mat (Incl. Access Fees) $34,489. Sal $583,384 (Prof $248,804)
Library Holdings: Bk Vols 225,956; Per Subs 64
Database Vendor: epixtech, inc.
Publications: Nioga News; Reach Out
Member Libraries: Barker Free Library; Byron-Bergen Public Library; Community Free Library; Corfu Free Library; Lee-Whedon Memorial Library; Lewiston Public Library; Lockport Public Library; Middleport Free Library; New York State Department of Correctional Services; Newfane Free Library; Niagara Falls Public Library; North Tonawanda Public Library; Oakfield Public Library; Orleans Correctional Facility Library; Pavilion Public Library; Ransomville Free Library; Richmond Memorial Library; Sanborn-Pekin Free Library; Swan Library; Wilson Free Library; Woodward Memorial Library; Yates Community Library; Youngstown Free Library
Partic in OCLC Online Computer Library Center, Inc; Western New York Library Resources Council

S ORLEANS-NIAGARA BOCES SCHOOL LIBRARY SYSTEM,* 195 Baettie Ave, 14094. SAN 323-4126. Tel: 716-439-4325. FAX: 716-439-4319. *Dir*, Molly Thomson
Library Holdings: Bk Titles 200,000; Per Subs 450

LOCUST VALLEY

P LOCUST VALLEY LIBRARY, 170 Buckram Rd, 11560-1999. SAN 311-4392. Tel: 516-671-1837. FAX: 516-676-8164. *Dir*, Phyllis Kelly; *Asst Dir*, Salvatore Marino; *Ch Servs*, Kristine Piana; *Ref, YA Servs*, Kathy Ray; *Ref*, David Polinski; Staff 7 (MLS 5, Non-MLS 2)
Founded 1910. Pop 8,917; Circ 77,000
Library Holdings: Bk Vols 60,359; Bk Titles 57,500; Per Subs 152
Subject Interests: Local history
Special Collections: Parenting (Carol Tilliston Holmboe Coll)
Automation Activity & Vendor Info: (Circulation) DRA
Publications: Library Letter (quarterly newsletter)
Mem of Nassau Library System
Friends of the Library Group

LODI

P LODI WHITTIER LIBRARY,* E Seneca St, 14860. SAN 311-4406. Tel: 607-582-6218. FAX: 607-582-6218. E-Mail: b31732@epix.net. *Dir*, Debbie Mulford
Circ 3,035
Library Holdings: Bk Vols 8,250; Per Subs 20
Mem of Finger Lakes Library System
Open Tues 9-11 & 1:30-5, Sat 9-12

LONG BEACH

M LONG BEACH MEDICAL CENTER-MEDICAL LIBRARY,* 455 E Bay Dr, 11561. SAN 374-9223. Tel: 516-897-1012. FAX: 516-897-1341. *Librn*, Ruth Lebowitz
Library Holdings: Bk Titles 400; Per Subs 55

P LONG BEACH PUBLIC LIBRARY, 111 W Park Ave, 11561-3326. SAN 352-8065. Tel: 516-432-7201. FAX: 516-889-4641. E-Mail: lblibrary@yahoo.com. Web Site: www.nassaulibrary.org/longbeach. *Dir*, George Trepp; E-Mail: directorll@nassau.nls.lib.ny.us; *Ad Servs, Asst Dir*, Laura Weir; *Ch Servs*, Jennifer Firth; *ILL*, Delores Sardo; *Ref*, Judith Menges; *Tech Servs*, Faye Hett; *AV*, Richard Fox; *Ad Servs*, Mary Aileen Buss; *Web Coordr*, Eileen Pollis. Subject Specialists: *Foreign Language*, Eileen Pollis; Staff 13 (MLS 9, Non-MLS 4)
Founded 1928. Pop 40,378; Circ 375,539
Jul 1998-Jun 1999 Income (Main Library and Branch Library) $1,888,351, State $45,317, Locally Generated Income $92,505, Parent Institution $1,736,010, Other $14,519. Mats Exp $283,840, Books $196,731, Per/Ser (Incl. Access Fees) $30,917, Electronic Ref Mat (Incl. Access Fees) $17,102. Sal $1,167,609 (Prof $548,168)
Library Holdings: Bk Vols 108,693; Bk Titles 62,378; Per Subs 312
Subject Interests: Holocaust, Local history
Special Collections: Congressman Allard K Lowenstein Memorabilia Coll; Foreign Language (Hebrew, Spanish, Yiddish, French, Italian); Long Beach Historical Coll, bks, clippings, prints; Long Beach Photographs
Automation Activity & Vendor Info: (Cataloging) DRA; (Circulation) DRA; (OPAC) DRA
Publications: Monthly Calendar of Events; Senior Citizen Directory
Mem of Nassau Library System
Special Services for the Blind - Magnifiers
Branches: 2
POINT LOOKOUT BRANCH, 26B Lido Blvd, Point Lookout, 11569. SAN 352-809X. Tel: 516-432-3409. Web Site: www.nassaulibrary.org/longhead. *In Charge*, Alice Platt
Founded 1967
Library Holdings: Bk Vols 5,418; Bk Titles 5,040
Automation Activity & Vendor Info: (Circulation) DRA; (OPAC) DRA
WEST END, 868 W Beech St, 11561. SAN 352-812X. Tel: 516-432-2704. Web Site: www.nassaulibrorg/longhead. *In Charge*, Sheryl Kutsmeda
Founded 1968
Library Holdings: Bk Titles 6,119
Automation Activity & Vendor Info: (Circulation) DRA; (OPAC) DRA

R TEMPLE EMANUEL, Sonabend Family Library, 455 Neptune Blvd, 11561. SAN 311-4414. Tel: 516-431-4060. FAX: 516-432-5194. *Librn*, Bennett Hermann
Founded 1960
Library Holdings: Bk Titles 5,950
Subject Interests: Current events, Judaica, Relig studies

LONG ISLAND CITY

S CONSOLIDATED EDISON LIBRARY, Corporate Library,* 43-82 Vernon Blvd, 11101-6912. SAN 311-7057. Tel: 718-472-6054. FAX: 718-349-1076. Web Site: www.coned.com/tlc/home.htm. *Librn*, Hyrum C Smith
Founded 1906
Library Holdings: Bk Titles 10,000; Per Subs 100
Subject Interests: Company hist
Restriction: Open to public upon request

§J DEVRY INSTITUTE OF TECHNOLOGY LIBRARY, 30-20 Thompson Ave, 11101. SAN 375-4200. Tel: 718-269-4240. FAX: 718-472-9774. E-Mail: athatcher@ny.devry.edu. Web Site: ny.devry.edu/library. *In Charge*, Sandra Roldan; Staff 2 (MLS 1, Non-MLS 1)
Jul 2000-Jun 2001 Income $170,000. Mats Exp $100,000. Sal $70,000
Library Holdings: Bk Vols 11,000; Per Subs 150
Subject Interests: Bus mgt, Computer info systs, Electronics, Technology, Telecommunications
Automation Activity & Vendor Info: (Cataloging) Endeavor; (Circulation) Endeavor

J FIORELLO H LAGUARDIA COMMUNITY COLLEGE LIBRARY,* 31-10 Thomson Ave, 11101. SAN 311-4422. Tel: 718-482-5421. FAX: 718-482-5444. Web Site: www.lagcc.cuny.edu/library. *Librn*, Mrs Ngozi Agbim; *Circ*, Louise Fluk; *Ref*, Kenneth Peeples; *Acq*, Christine Stenstrom; *Archivist*, Kenneth Riccardi; *Per*, Jan Devine
Enrl 9,400
Library Holdings: Bk Vols 80,000; Per Subs 700
Subject Interests: Coop educ, Deaf educ, Nursing, Nutrition, Occupational therapy, Veterinary medicine
Special Collections: Eric Educational Reports; Government Documents; New York Times on microfilm
Publications: faculty publications list; Library newsletter; periodical list
Partic in OCLC Online Computer Library Center, Inc; Utlas

LOUDONVILLE

P THE WILLIAM K SANFORD TOWN LIBRARY, 629 Albany Shaker Rd, 12211-1196. SAN 311-4449. Tel: 518-458-9274. FAX: 518-438-0988. E-Mail: wkslibry@uhls.lib.ny.us. Web Site: www.colonie.org/library. *Dir*, Robert L Jaquay; *Asst Dir*, Richard Naylor; *Coll Develop, YA Servs*, David Cole; *Ref*, William Leone; *Acq, Tech Servs*, Peggy Mello; *ILL*, Ann Close; *Circ, Outreach Serv*, Joseph Nash; *Info Tech*, Maureen Laughter; Staff 52 (MLS 10, Non-MLS 42)
Founded 1963. Pop 76,497; Circ 522,203
Jan 2000-Dec 2000 Income $1,810,612, State $416, Locally Generated Income $1,622,000, Other $188,196. Mats Exp $236,844, Books $174,132, Per/Ser (Incl. Access Fees) $20,587, Presv $2,686, Micro $12,641, AV Equip $26,798. Sal $1,084,290 (Prof $324,992)

Library Holdings: Bk Titles 161,138; Per Subs 335
Special Collections: Basic Education & English as a Second Language Coll; Business & Finance Coll; Job Education Coll; Large Print; Local History; National & Local Telephone Books; NYS Job Bank Outlet; Parent/Teacher
Publications: Annual Report; Bibliographies; Calendar (monthly); Community Contacts Directory; Preschool Directory; Town of Colonie Dept Directory
Mem of Upper Hudson Library System

C SIENA COLLEGE, J Spencer & Patricia Standish Library, 515 Loudon Rd, 12211-9998. SAN 311-4457. Tel: 518-783-2545. Interlibrary Loan Service Tel: 518-783-2518. Circulation Tel: 518-782-6717. Reference Tel: 518-783-2988. FAX: 518-783-2570. E-Mail: sienalibrary@siena.edu. Web Site: www.siena.edu/library. *Dir*, Gary B Thompson; E-Mail: thompson@siena.edu; *Coll Develop*, William Kanalley; Tel: 518-783-2522, E-Mail: kanalley@siena.edu; *Cat*, John Vallely; Tel: 518-783-2591, E-Mail: vallely@siena.edu; *ILL*, Patricia Markley; Tel: 518-783-4196, E-Mail: markley@siena.edu; *Ref Serv*, Sean Maloney; Tel: 518-783-2588, E-Mail: maloney@siena.edu; *Ser*, Catherine Crohan; Tel: 518-782-6731, E-Mail: crohan@siena.edu; *Publ Servs*, Timothy Burke; Tel: 518-783-2539, E-Mail: burke@siena.edu; Staff 8 (MLS 7, Non-MLS 1)
Founded 1937. Enrl 2,728; Fac 200; Highest Degree: Bachelor
Jun 1999-May 2000 Income State $7,201. Mats Exp $485,040, Books $150,000, Per/Ser (Incl. Access Fees) $264,340, Presv $28,000, AV Equip $11,000, Electronic Ref Mat (Incl. Access Fees) $31,700. Sal $526,247 (Prof $359,915)
Library Holdings: Bk Vols 299,918; Bk Titles 200,000; Per Subs 1,243
Subject Interests: Multicultural studies
Special Collections: Franciscana Coll; Medieval & Early Modern Studies (Convivium Coll)
Automation Activity & Vendor Info: (Acquisitions) Innovative Interfaces Inc.; (Cataloging) Innovative Interfaces Inc.; (Circulation) Innovative Interfaces Inc.; (OPAC) Innovative Interfaces Inc.; (Serials) Innovative Interfaces Inc.
Database Vendor: Dialog, GaleNet, Innovative Interfaces INN - View, Lexis-Nexis, OCLC - First Search, ProQuest, Silverplatter Information Inc.
Restriction: Open to student, faculty & staff
Function: Archival collection, Document delivery services, ILL available, Reference services available, Some telephone reference
Partic in Cap District Libr Coun for Ref & Res Resources

LOWVILLE

P LOWVILLE FREE LIBRARY, 5387 Dayan St, 13367. SAN 311-4465. Tel: 315-376-2131. FAX: 315-376-2131. Web Site: www.nc3r.org/lowlibrary. *Dir*, Sally Brown; E-Mail: browns@northnet.org
Founded 1903. Pop 4,849; Circ 32,458
1998-1999 Income $52,441, State $2,000, City $8,000, County $12,517, Locally Generated Income $15,574, Other $11,600. Mats Exp $12,797, Books $9,981, Per/Ser (Incl. Access Fees) $1,231, Other Print Mats $730. Sal $31,666
Library Holdings: Bk Titles 11,494
Subject Interests: Genealogy, Local history
Mem of North Country Library System
Friends of the Library Group

LYNBROOK

P LYNBROOK PUBLIC LIBRARY, Eldert St & Carpenter Ave, 11563. SAN 311-4473. Tel: 516-599-8630. FAX: 516-596-1312. E-Mail: lynbrook@nassaulibrary.org. *Dir, Tech Servs*, Natalie Lapp; *Ad Servs, Asst Dir, Ref*, Judith Opatow; *Ch Servs*, Elizabeth Huschle; *Pub Relations*, Simon Traley; Staff 5 (MLS 5)
Founded 1929. Pop 19,208; Circ 127,707
Jun 1998-May 1999 Income $759,274, State $6,054, City $669,482, Locally Generated Income $20,741, Other $62,997. Mats Exp $109,135, Books $81,989, Per/Ser (Incl. Access Fees) $7,730, Presv $228, Micro $4,200, Electronic Ref Mat (Incl. Access Fees) $14,988. Sal $453,489 (Prof $208,605)
Library Holdings: Bk Vols 80,929; Per Subs 165
Database Vendor: DRA
Publications: Newsletter (quarterly)
Mem of Nassau Library System
Friends of the Library Group

R TEMPLE EMANUEL OF LYNBROOK, Malcolm Eisman Memorial Library, One Saperstein Plaza, 11563. SAN 311-4481. Tel: 516-593-4004. FAX: 516-593-2739.
Library Holdings: Bk Vols 5,000; Per Subs 12
Subject Interests: Jewish bks
Special Collections: Holocaust

LYNDONVILLE

P YATES COMMUNITY LIBRARY,* 15 N Main St, 14098. SAN 311-449X. Tel: 716-765-9041. FAX: 716-765-9041. *Dir*, Margaret N Burtwell; E-Mail: mburt@nioga.org
Founded 1949. Pop 2,371; Circ 16,371
Library Holdings: Bk Vols 16,500; Bk Titles 15,000; Per Subs 55
Special Collections: Lyndonville Enterprise Newspaper 1906-1962, micro
Mem of Nioga Library System
Open Mon & Tues 2-5 & 7-9, Thurs 10-12, 2-5 & 7-9, Fri 2-5, Sat 10-5

LYONS

P LYONS SCHOOL DISTRICT PUBLIC LIBRARY,* 67 Canal St, 14489. SAN 311-4503. Tel: 315-946-9262. FAX: 315-946-3320. *Dir*, Theresa Streb
Founded 1956. Pop 6,934; Circ 40,000
Library Holdings: Bk Titles 21,000; Per Subs 93
Subject Interests: Antiques, Fiction, Local history
Mem of Pioneer Library System; Pioneerland Library System
Open Mon-Wed 10-5 & 7-9, Tues & Thurs 12-5 & 7-9, Fri 10-5 & Sat 9-1

S WAYNE COUNTY HISTORICAL SOCIETY MUSEUM LIBRARY, 21 Butternut St, 14489. SAN 328-3666. Tel: 315-946-4943. FAX: 315-946-0069. E-Mail: wchs4943@aol.com. Web Site: members.aol.com/wchs4943. *Dir*, Andrea Evangelist
Library Holdings: Bk Titles 3,119
Open Tues-Fri 10-4, Sat & Sun by appointment

LYONS FALLS

P LYONS FALLS FREE LIBRARY,* High St, 13368. SAN 311-4511. Tel: 315-348-8633. *Librn*, Esther Houck
Founded 1923. Pop 755; Circ 9,495
Library Holdings: Bk Vols 7,500; Per Subs 35
Subject Interests: Education, Environmental studies, Indust
Mem of North Country Library System

MACEDON

P MACEDON PUBLIC LIBRARY,* 30 Main St, 14502. SAN 311-452X. Tel: 315-986-4755. FAX: 315-986-2952. *Mgr*, Darlene Virkler; Staff 11 (Non-MLS 11)
Circ 60,000
Library Holdings: Bk Vols 24,293; Per Subs 82
Special Collections: Bullis Family Library Coll
Mem of Pioneer Library System
Open Mon-Tues 10-9, Wed-Thurs 12-9, Fri 1-5 & Sat 10-3

S MOBIL CHEMICAL COMPANY, Information Center,* 729 Pittsford-Palmyra, 14502. SAN 311-4538. Tel: 315-986-5027. FAX: 315-986-5214. *Librn*, Candice Johnson; Staff 1 (MLS 1)
Library Holdings: Bk Titles 3,000; Per Subs 200
Subject Interests: Bus, Engineering, Mgt, Polymer sci
Publications: Bulletin; Management News Summary
Partic in New York State Interlibrary Loan Network; Rochester Regional Library Council

MACHIAS

P KING MEMORIAL LIBRARY,* Town Hall, Maple Ave, PO Box 509, 14101. SAN 311-4554. Tel: 716-353-9915. *Dir*, Angela Gonzalez
Founded 1941. Pop 2,052; Circ 10,918
Library Holdings: Bk Vols 10,185
Mem of Chautauqua-Cattaraugus Library System

MADRID

P HEPBURN LIBRARY OF MADRID, 11 Church St, 13660. (Mail add: PO Box 40, 13660), SAN 311-4562. Tel: 315-322-5673. *Dir*, Richard Tabor
Founded 1917. Pop 1,852; Circ 10,587
Library Holdings: Bk Vols 8,086; Per Subs 28
Mem of North Country Library System

MAHOPAC

P MAHOPAC LIBRARY, 668 Rt 6, 10541. SAN 311-4570. Tel: 845-628-2009. FAX: 845-628-0672. E-Mail: library@mahopaclibrary.org. Web Site: www.mahopaclibrary.org. *Dir*, Patricia Kaufman; E-Mail: pkaufman@mahopaclibrary.org; Staff 16 (MLS 5, Non-MLS 11)
Founded 1952. Pop 28,816; Circ 151,475
Jul 1999-Dec 2000 Income $627,517, State $6,938, City $17,000, County $62,088, Locally Generated Income $471,913, Other $69,578. Mats Exp $78,401, Books $64,860, Per/Ser (Incl. Access Fees) $6,896, AV Equip $2,893, Electronic Ref Mat (Incl. Access Fees) $3,752. Sal $289,395 (Prof $127,501)

Library Holdings: Bk Vols 74,331; Per Subs 257; High Interest/Low Vocabulary Bk Vols 18; Bks on Deafness & Sign Lang 24
Special Collections: Foundation Center; Parenting Coll; Putnam County Reference Center
Automation Activity & Vendor Info: (Cataloging) GEAC; (Circulation) GEAC; (OPAC) GEAC
Publications: Children's Calendar (5 per year); Monthly Calendar
Mem of Mid-Hudson Library System
Partic in Southeastern New York Library Resources Council
Special Services for the Deaf - TDD
Special Services for the Blind - Talking Books
Special services for visually impaired - (3) Ednalites
Friends of the Library Group

MALONE

M ALICE HYDE HOSPITAL, Medical Library,* 115 Park St, 12953. SAN 328-3194. Tel: 518-483-3000. FAX: 518-483-0860. Web Site: www.alicehyde.com. *In Charge*, Bill McCall
Library Holdings: Bk Titles 300
Subject Interests: Medicine
Mem of N Country Ref & Res Resources Coun

P WEAD LIBRARY, Malone Central School District Public Library, 64 Elm St, 12953-1594. SAN 311-4589. Tel: 518-483-5251. FAX: 581-483-5251. *Dir*, D W Minnich; E-Mail: minnich@slic.com; *Ch Servs*, Susan Wool; Staff 2 (MLS 2)
Founded 1881. Pop 17,307; Circ 70,800
Jul 2000-Jun 2001 Income $330,434. Mats Exp $49,000, Books $35,500, Per/Ser (Incl. Access Fees) $3,500, Presv $1,000, Micro $3,500, AV Equip $2,000, Electronic Ref Mat (Incl. Access Fees) $3,500. Sal $176,400
Library Holdings: Bk Vols 43,000; Per Subs 99
Subject Interests: Genealogy, Local, State hist
Mem of Clinton-Essex-Franklin Library System
Partic in North Country Reference & Research Resources Council

MALVERNE

P MALVERNE PUBLIC LIBRARY,* 61 Saint Thomas Pl, 11565. SAN 311-4597. Tel: 516-599-0750. FAX: 516-599-3320. E-Mail: malverne@lilrc.org. *Dir*, Joan Kelleher; *Ch Servs, Ref*, Karin Briller
Founded 1928. Pop 9,054; Circ 78,000
May 1997-Apr 1998 Income $378,000. Mats Exp Books $32,000. Sal $262,000
Library Holdings: Bk Vols 44,000; Per Subs 107
Mem of Nassau Library System

MAMARONECK

P MAMARONECK PUBLIC LIBRARY DISTRICT,* 136 Prospect Ave, 10543. SAN 311-4600. Tel: 914-698-1250. Web Site: www.wls.lib.ny.us/mamaroneck/. *Dir*, Joan Grott; *Asst Dir*, Delys DeZwaan; *Ch Servs*, Marcia Hupp
Founded 1922. Pop 17,325; Circ 158,750
Jun 1999-May 2000 Income $1,105,300. Mats Exp $1,105,300, Books $73,000, Per/Ser (Incl. Access Fees) $16,000. Sal $627,000
Library Holdings: Bk Vols 100,000
Database Vendor: epixtech, inc.
Mem of Westchester Library System
Friends of the Library Group

MANHASSET

P MANHASSET PUBLIC LIBRARY, 30 Onderdonk Ave, 11030. SAN 311-4619. Tel: 516-627-2300. FAX: 516-627-4339. E-Mail: manhlib2@lilrc.org. Web Site: www.nassaulibrary.org/manhass. *Dir*, Marian P Robertson; *Ref*, Ann Marie Moore; *Ch Servs*, Nancy Bocarde; *YA Servs*, Marcia Shapiro; *Tech Servs*, Carolyn Ayers; Staff 34 (MLS 12, Non-MLS 22)
Founded 1945. Pop 16,275; Circ 185,779
Jul 2000-Jun 2001 Income $2,463,453, Locally Generated Income $29,500. Mats Exp $245,987, Books $171,500, Per/Ser (Incl. Access Fees) $33,287, Presv $200, Micro $32,500, AV Equip $5,000, Other Print Mats $1,000, Electronic Ref Mat (Incl. Access Fees) $2,500. Sal $1,439,766 (Prof $712,197)
Library Holdings: Bk Vols 130,219; Per Subs 379
Special Collections: Benedetto/Rainone Puppet Coll; Books for the Bibliophile; Career Center; Frances Hodgson Burnett archival Coll; Japanese Corner; Long Island Coll; Manhasset Authors (local oral archives); New York Coll; Poetry for Children (Kelly Miscall Coll)
Automation Activity & Vendor Info: (Cataloging) DRA; (Circulation) DRA; (ILL) DRA; (OPAC) DRA
Publications: Quarterly newsletter
Mem of Nassau Library System
Friends of the Library Group

M NORTH SHORE UNIVERSITY HOSPITAL, Daniel Carroll Payson Medical Library, 300 Community Dr, 11030. SAN 311-4627. Tel: 516-562-4324. FAX: 516-562-2865. *Dir*, Debra Eisenberg; Staff 5 (MLS 3, Non-MLS 2)
Founded 1954
Library Holdings: Bk Titles 5,300; Per Subs 750
Subject Interests: Clinical medicine, History of medicine, Laboratory med, Nursing
Partic in Michigan Library Consortium

MANLIUS

P MANLIUS LIBRARY,* One Elmbrook Dr W, 13104. SAN 311-4635. Tel: 315-682-6400. FAX: 315-682-4490. *Dir*, Patricia W Infantine; *YA Servs*, Helen Vecchio; *AV*, Victoria McClure; Staff 15 (MLS 8, Non-MLS 7)
Founded 1915. Pop 14,000; Circ 210,000
Jan 1999-Dec 1999 Income $526,000, State $2,500, City $107,000, Locally Generated Income $66,500, Other $350,000. Mats Exp $73,000, Books $63,000, Per/Ser (Incl. Access Fees) $4,000, Electronic Ref Mat (Incl. Access Fees) $6,000. Sal $237,000 (Prof $140,000)
Library Holdings: Bk Vols 38,000; Bk Titles 29,000; Per Subs 180; Bks on Deafness & Sign Lang 31
Automation Activity & Vendor Info: (Circulation) epixtech, inc.; (OPAC) epixtech, inc.
Database Vendor: epixtech, inc., IAC - SearchBank, OCLC - First Search, ProQuest
Mem of Onondaga County Public Library

MANNSVILLE

P MANNSVILLE FREE LIBRARY,* 106 Lilac Park Dr, 13661. SAN 311-4643. Tel: 315-465-4049. FAX: 315-465-5115. *Dir, Librn*, Mary E Tingfah
Circ 6,595
Library Holdings: Bk Vols 5,750; Per Subs 30
Mem of North Country Library System
Open Mon, Tues & Wed 3-5, Thurs 3-5 & 6-8, Fri 9-11 & 2-5

MARATHON

P PECK MEMORIAL LIBRARY,* 28 E Main St, PO Box 325, 13803. SAN 311-466X. Tel: 607-849-6135. FAX: 607-849-3799. *Dir, Librn*, Mary Frank
Founded 1895. Pop 1,246; Circ 12,519
Library Holdings: Bk Vols 16,000; Per Subs 24
Mem of Finger Lakes Library System
Open Mon 3-7, Tues 9-12 & 1-4, Wed 6-9, Thurs & Fri 1-4, Sat 9-11, closed Sat in July & Aug

MARCELLUS

P MARCELLUS FREE LIBRARY, 2 Slocombe St, 13108. SAN 311-4678. Tel: 315-673-3221. FAX: 315-673-0148. *Dir*, Marion L MacDonald; E-Mail: macdonml@clrc.org; Staff 3 (Non-MLS 3)
Founded 1913. Pop 6,465; Circ 50,705
Jan 2000-Dec 2000 Income $121,234, State $4,598, City $25,000, Federal $7,000, Locally Generated Income $13,473, Parent Institution $15,000, Other $37,163. Mats Exp $15,256, Books $10,843, Per/Ser (Incl. Access Fees) $1,302, Micro $115, AV Equip $1,675, Other Print Mats $179, Electronic Ref Mat (Incl. Access Fees) $1,142. Sal $43,664 (Prof $25,000)
Library Holdings: Bk Vols 26,598; Per Subs 58
Subject Interests: Chorale music, Local history
Special Collections: Chorale Music (Marcellus Chorale Coll), sheets
Automation Activity & Vendor Info: (Circulation) epixtech, inc.
Publications: Penny Sketches (monthly acquisition list)
Function: ILL available, Photocopies available, Reference services available, Some telephone reference
Mem of Onondaga County Public Library
Friends of the Library Group

MARCY

S MID-STATE CORRECTIONAL FACILITY LIBRARY,* PO Box 216, 13403-0216. SAN 327-2435. Tel: 315-768-8581. FAX: 315-768-8581, Ext 2099. *Librn*, Charles L Youmans III; Staff 1 (MLS 1)
Library Holdings: Bk Vols 12,000; Per Subs 53
Partic in Mid-York Libr Syst
Serves approximately 1600 inmates
Branches:
FACILITY LAW LIBRARY, PO Box 216, 13403-0216. Tel: 315-768-8581.
Library Holdings: Bk Titles 7,000

MARGARETVILLE

P FAIRVIEW PUBLIC LIBRARY, 43 Walnut St, PO Box 609, 12455-0609. SAN 310-8090. Tel: 845-586-3791. FAX: 845-586-2083. E-Mail: fairview@catskill.net. *Librn*, Naomi Weiss

Pop 3,200; Circ 10,800
Library Holdings: Bk Vols 6,567
Mem of Four County Library System
Open Mon 12:30-5, Tues & Thurs 3-5, Wed 12:30-8, Fri 10-5, Sat 10-2:30

MARILLA

P MARILLA FREE LIBRARY,* 11637 Bullis Rd, PO Box 96, 14102. SAN 311-4686. Tel: 716-652-7449. E-Mail: marilla@buffalolib.org. *Librn*, Linda Pautler; *Asst Librn*, Delores Wagener
Pop 4,864; Circ 24,878
Library Holdings: Bk Vols 14,533; Per Subs 92
Mem of Buffalo & Erie County Public Library System
Open Tues-Thurs 10:30-5 & 7-9, Sat 12-5

MARION

P MARION PUBLIC LIBRARY,* 3827 N Main St, PO Box 30, 14505-0030. SAN 311-4694. Tel: 315-926-4933. FAX: 315-926-7038. *Librn*, Pamela Wolfanger; *Asst Librn*, Lonella Levan
Founded 1910. Circ 46,615
1998-1999 Income $86,500. Mats Exp $17,000
Library Holdings: Bk Vols 12,000; Per Subs 50
Mem of Pioneer Library System; Wayne County Libr Syst
Open Mon & Wed 10-8, Tues, Thurs & Fri 2-6, Sat 9-12
Friends of the Library Group

MARLBORO

P MARLBORO FREE LIBRARY, 1251 Rte 9W, 12542-5411. (Mail add: PO Box 780, 12542-0780), SAN 311-4708. Tel: 914-236-7272. FAX: 914-236-7635. Web Site: www.marlborolibrary.org. *Dir*, Elizabeth S Manion; Staff 3 (MLS 2, Non-MLS 1)
Founded 1911. Pop 10,613
Jul 2000-Jun 2001 Income $460,810. Mats Exp $44,107, Books $26,932, Per/Ser (Incl. Access Fees) $4,388, Micro $8,275, Electronic Ref Mat (Incl. Access Fees) $4,512. Sal $239,818 (Prof $116,235)
Library Holdings: Bk Titles 33,832; Per Subs 172
Subject Interests: Local history, Ref
Special Collections: Frederick W Goudy Coll
Publications: Marlboro Library Grapevine (monthly newsletter)
Mem of Mid-Hudson Library System
Friends of the Library Group

MARTINSBURG

P WILLIAM H BUSH MEMORIAL LIBRARY,* Whitaker Rd, PO Box 141, 13404. SAN 311-4716. Tel: 315-376-7490. *Librn*, Dawn E Manzer
Founded 1913. Pop 350; Circ 8,393
Library Holdings: Bk Vols 15,660; Per Subs 52
Subject Interests: History
Special Collections: Local Scrapbooks & Diaries
Publications: Library Journal
Mem of North Country Library System

MARYKNOLL

S CATHOLIC FOREIGN MISSION SOCIETY OF AMERICA, Maryknoll Photo Library, Walsh Bldg, 75 Ryder Rd, 10545. (Mail add: PO Box 308, 10545-0308), SAN 329-1200. Tel: 914-941-7590, Ext 2481. FAX: 914-945-0670. Web Site: www.maryknoll.org. *Librn*, Penny Ann Sandoval; E-Mail: psandoval@maryknoll.org
1998-1999 Mats Exp $2,000, Per/Ser (Incl. Access Fees) $600
Subject Interests: Missions hist
Special Collections: China (early 1900's); History of Mkl Society, photogs
Publications: Maryknoll-Revista Maryknoll; Orbis Books

SR MARYKNOLL SOCIETY LIBRARY,* PO Box 305, 10545-0305. SAN 311-4724. Tel: 914-941-7590, Ext 2309. FAX: 914-941-5753. *Coll Develop, Librn*, Leonard Viggiano; *Assoc Librn*, Zay Green
Founded 1928. Enrl 120
Jan 1998-Dec 1999 Income $270,800. Mats Exp $50,000, Books $20,000, Per/Ser (Incl. Access Fees) $30,000. Sal $153,329 (Prof $85,533)
Library Holdings: Bk Vols 83,697; Per Subs 500
Subject Interests: Biblical studies, Missions, Philosophy, Theology
Special Collections: Area Studies (Africa, Asia, China, Japan, Latin America, Philippines); Foreign Missions
Publications: Library News & Reviews
Partic in OCLC Online Computer Library Center, Inc; Westchester Acad Libr Dir Orgn

MASSAPEQUA

P MASSAPEQUA PUBLIC LIBRARY, 523 Central Ave, 11758. SAN 352-8154. Tel: 516-798-4607. FAX: 516-798-2804. E-Mail: mpl1@lilrc.org. Web Site: www.nassaulibrary.org/nassapq/index.html. *Dir*, William P Serynek; *Ad Servs, Asst Dir, Ref*, Patricia Page; *Acq*, Angela Wrynn; *Ad Servs, Ref*, Carolynn Wiplich; *Ch Servs*, Connie Smith; *Ch Servs*, Germaine Booth; *ILL, YA Servs*, Liz Reitz; *Media Spec*, Nancy Downey; Staff 18 (MLS 18)
Founded 1952. Pop 48,682; Circ 564,627
Library Holdings: Bk Vols 250,000; Per Subs 350
Database Vendor: DRA
Publications: Monthly calendar; Quarterly newsletter
Mem of Nassau Library System
Branches: 1
BAR HARBOUR, 40 Harbor Lane, Massapequa Park, 11762. SAN 352-8189. Tel: 516-799-0770. FAX: 516-541-2648. E-Mail: mpl2@lilrc.org. Web Site: www.nassaulibrary.org. *Asst Dir*, Patricia Page
Bookmobiles: 1

P PLAINEDGE PUBLIC LIBRARY, 1060 Hicksville Rd, 11758. SAN 311-4759. Tel: 516-735-4133. FAX: 516-735-4192. E-Mail: pplained@nassau.cv.net. Web Site: www.nassaulibrary.org/plnedge. *Dir*, Joseph Eisner; *Ad Servs*, Carol Minov; *Ch Servs*, Joan Schein; Staff 14 (MLS 14)
Founded 1963. Pop 22,097; Circ 150,127
Jul 1999-Jun 2000 Income Locally Generated Income $1,695,303. Mats Exp $177,756, Books $130,544, Per/Ser (Incl. Access Fees) $21,454, Micro $9,795, AV Equip $15,963. Sal $909,631 (Prof $313,495)
Library Holdings: Bk Vols 121,329; Per Subs 446
Database Vendor: DRA, Ebsco - EbscoHost, IAC - SearchBank, OCLC - First Search
Publications: Community Courier (local news and info - quarterly); Discovery (quarterly for senior citizens); News for the Consumer (tri-weekly); Newsletter (6 times per yr); Parent Cues (6 times per yr); Tot Talks (for parents of preschoolers & toddlers - 6 times per yr)
Function: ILL available, Photocopies available, Reference services available
Mem of Nassau Library System

MASSENA

M MASSENA MEMORIAL HOSPITAL LIBRARY,* One Hospital Dr, 13662. SAN 328-428X. Tel: 315-764-1711. FAX: 315-769-4660. *Librn*, Harriet Gushea
Library Holdings: Bk Vols 306

P MASSENA PUBLIC LIBRARY, Warren Memorial Library, 41 Glenn St, 13662. SAN 311-4767. Tel: 315-769-9914. FAX: 315-769-5978. Web Site: www.northnet.org/massenalibrary/mpl.htm. *Dir*, Paul L Schaffer; *Ref*, Joan Woodward; Staff 11 (MLS 3, Non-MLS 8)
Founded 1897. Pop 14,000; Circ 125,000
Jan 2000-Dec 2000 Income $558,000, State $18,000, Locally Generated Income $487,000, Other $53,000. Mats Exp $68,000, Books $58,000, Per/Ser (Incl. Access Fees) $5,000, Micro $4,000, Electronic Ref Mat (Incl. Access Fees) $1,000. Sal $249,000
Library Holdings: Bk Vols 62,280; Bk Titles 61,000; Per Subs 140
Automation Activity & Vendor Info: (Circulation) DRA; (OPAC) DRA
Publications: Books & Beyond (bimonthly library activities) (Newsletter)
Mem of North Country Library System
Partic in North Country Reference & Research Resources Council
Friends of the Library Group

MATTITUCK

P MATTITUCK-LAUREL LIBRARY, 13900 Main Rd, PO Box 1437, 11952. SAN 311-4775. Tel: 631-298-4134. FAX: 631-298-4764. Web Site: www.suffolk.lib.ny.us/libraries/matt/. *Dir*, Kay Zegel; Staff 4 (MLS 4)
Pop 5,093; Circ 110,291
Jan 1999-Dec 1999 Income $666,339. Mats Exp $93,100. Sal $305,855 (Prof $136,682)
Library Holdings: Bk Vols 54,321
Mem of Suffolk Cooperative Library System
Friends of the Library Group

MATTYDALE

P SALINA FREE LIBRARY, 100 Belmont St, 13211. SAN 311-4783. FAX: 315-454-3466. E-Mail: info@salinalibrary.org. Web Site: www.salinalibrary.org. *Dir*, Jeannine Chubon; Tel: 315-454-4524, E-Mail: jchubon@salinalibrary.org; Staff 8 (MLS 1, Non-MLS 7)
Founded 1942. Pop 12,097; Circ 62,742
Library Holdings: Bk Vols 26,625
Automation Activity & Vendor Info: (Circulation) epixtech, inc.; (OPAC) epixtech, inc.
Database Vendor: IAC - SearchBank, OCLC - First Search, ProQuest
Mem of Onondaga County Public Library
Open Mon & Wed 10-8, Tues & Thurs 1-8, Fri 1-5, Sat 1-5
Friends of the Library Group

MAYVILLE

GL CHAUTAUQUA COUNTY LAW LIBRARY, Gerace Office Bldg, 3 N Erie St, 14757. SAN 327-5183. Tel: 716-753-4247. FAX: 716-753-4129.
Library Holdings: Bk Vols 12,800
Subject Interests: Air pollution, Education, Fed govt, Labor, Local government, Real estate, State government
Special Collections: Chautauqua County History
Open Mon-Fri 9-5

P MAYVILLE LIBRARY,* 92 S Erie St, 14757. SAN 311-4791. Tel: 716-753-7362. FAX: 716-753-7360. *Dir*, Margaret Fitzgibbon
Circ 19,219
Library Holdings: Bk Vols 19,466; Per Subs 93
Mem of Chautauqua-Cattaraugus Library System
Open Mon 12-8, Tues & Thurs 10-1, Fri 12-6, Sat & Sun 1-4
Friends of the Library Group

MC GRAW

P LAMONT MEMORIAL FREE LIBRARY,* 5 Main St, PO Box 559, 13101-0559. SAN 311-4546. Tel: 607-836-6767. FAX: 607-836-6767. *Dir, Librn*, Julie Widger; Staff 2 (Non-MLS 2)
Founded 1906. Pop 1,208; Circ 28,674
Library Holdings: Bk Vols 14,622; Bk Titles 14,257; Per Subs 55
Subject Interests: Genealogy, History
Mem of Finger Lakes Library System
Open Mon, Tues & Thurs 2-5 & 7-9, Fri 10-12 & 2-5, Sat 9-12, closed Wed

MECHANICVILLE

P MECHANICVILLE DISTRICT PUBLIC LIBRARY,* 190 N Main St, 12118. SAN 311-4805. Tel: 518-664-4646. FAX: 518-664-8641. *Dir*, Ann Marie Renzi; Staff 1 (MLS 1)
Founded 1966. Pop 8,183; Circ 32,840
Library Holdings: Bk Vols 18,608
Subject Interests: Local history
Special Collections: Ellsworth Coll
Mem of Southern Adirondack Library System

MEDINA

P LEE-WHEDON MEMORIAL LIBRARY, 620 West Ave, 14103. SAN 311-4813. Tel: 716-798-3430. FAX: 716-798-4398. *Dir*, Mary G Zangerle; E-Mail: mzang@nioga.org
Founded 1928. Pop 12,461; Circ 102,000
Jul 1999-Jun 2000 Income $378,466, State $3,300, County $10,104, Locally Generated Income $22,500, Other $342,562. Mats Exp $76,000, Books $70,000, Per/Ser (Incl. Access Fees) $6,000. Sal $183,000
Library Holdings: Bk Titles 43,300; Per Subs 115
Mem of Nioga Library System
Friends of the Library Group

M MEDINA MEMORIAL HOSPITAL, Medical Library, 200 Ohio St, 14103. SAN 375-8206. Tel: 716-798-8127. FAX: 716-798-8003.
Library Holdings: Bk Titles 500; Per Subs 24
Mem of Western NY Libr Res Coun

MELVILLE

S ESTEE LAUDER, INC, Research Library,* 125 Pinelawn Rd, 11747. SAN 328-0977. Tel: 516-531-1175. FAX: 516-531-1604. *Res*, Vincent Notarstefano; *Librn*, Rita Intal; Staff 2 (MLS 1, Non-MLS 1)
Founded 1983
Library Holdings: Bk Vols 6,000; Per Subs 350
Subject Interests: Biology, Chemistry, Dermatology, Engineering, Mathematics
Partic in Cooperative Information Network; Dialog Corporation; OCLC Online Computer Library Center, Inc
Friends of the Library Group

S HOLZMACHER, MCLENDON & MURRELL LIBRARY, H2M Group Library, 575 Broad Hollow Rd, 11747. SAN 311-4848. Tel: 631-756-8000, Ext 1740. FAX: 631-694-4122. E-Mail: h2m_lib@h2m.com. Web Site: www.h2m.com. *Librn*, Joan S Newlin; Staff 1 (MLS 1)
Library Holdings: Bk Vols 14,300; Per Subs 240
Subject Interests: Architecture, Civil engineering, Environmental engineering, Hydrogeology
Automation Activity & Vendor Info: (Cataloging) Inmagic, Inc.
Partic in Long Island Library Resources Council

S NEWSDAY, INC LIBRARY, 235 Pinelawn Rd, 11747-4250. SAN 311-2314. Tel: 631-843-2333. FAX: 631-843-2342. Web Site: www.newsday.com. *Chief Librn*, Dorothy Levin; E-Mail: dorothy.guadagno@newsday.com; Staff 27 (MLS 11, Non-MLS 16)
Founded 1940
Library Holdings: Bk Titles 6,000; Per Subs 150
Special Collections: Newsday Clipping & Photo File, 1940-to present
Restriction: Staff use only, Use of others with permission of librarian
Mem of Long Island Libr Resources Coun, Inc
Partic in Dialog Corporation

S NORTHROP GRUMMAN NORDEN SYSTEMS, Information Services, 65 Marcus Dr, 11747. SAN 311-483X. Tel: 516-719-4841. FAX: 516-719-4640. *In Charge*, Maureen Ward
Founded 1981
Library Holdings: Bk Vols 2,500; Per Subs 75
Subject Interests: Electronics, Software engineering
Restriction: Not open to public

MENANDS

P MENANDS PUBLIC LIBRARY, 4 N Lyons Ave, 12204. SAN 311-4880. Tel: 518-463-4035. FAX: 518-449-3863. E-Mail: mend1@uhls.lib.ny.us. *Dir*, Leonard J Zapala; *Librn*, Isabelle Sanford; *Asst Librn*, Marion Kirby; Staff 1 (MLS 1)
Founded 1923. Pop 4,500
Library Holdings: Bk Vols 7,450; Per Subs 43
Database Vendor: DRA
Mem of Upper Hudson Library System
Open Mon & Wed 12-4:30 & 5:30-8, Tues & Thurs 5:30-8:30 & Fri 1-4

MERRICK

P MERRICK LIBRARY,* 2279 Merrick Ave, 11566-4398. SAN 311-4902. Tel: 516-379-3476. FAX: 516-868-6230. E-Mail: mkl@lilrc.org. Web Site: www.lilrc.org/~mkl. *Dir*, Michael Hodgson; *Dep Dir*, Sonyan Minkoff; *Circ, ILL*, Maureen Garvey; *YA Servs*, Marjorie Shuster; *Coll Develop*, Robert Ludemann; *AV*, Marcia Ratcliff; Staff 8 (MLS 8)
Founded 1891. Pop 21,832; Circ 322,526
Jul 1998-Jun 1999 Income $1,520,667, State $26,610, County $1,393,000, Locally Generated Income $101,057. Mats Exp $245,390, Books $160,000, Per/Ser (Incl. Access Fees) $27,740, Presv $100, Micro $5,500, Other Print Mats $1,050, Manuscripts & Archives $6,000, Electronic Ref Mat (Incl. Access Fees) $45,000. Sal $897,000 (Prof $442,000)
Library Holdings: Bk Vols 78,140; Per Subs 233
Subject Interests: Local history
Special Collections: Center for Intellectual Freedom & Censorship Materials
Automation Activity & Vendor Info: (Circulation) DRA
Publications: Children's Newsletter; Library Newsletter; Senior Newsletter
Mem of Nassau Library System
Partic in Long Island Library Resources Council
Friends of the Library Group

MEXICO

P MEXICO PUBLIC LIBRARY,* 3269 Main St, PO Box 479, 13114. SAN 311-4910. Tel: 315-963-3012. FAX: 315-963-7317. *Dir*, Janice Howard
Library Holdings: Bk Titles 8,880; Per Subs 15
Mem of North Country Library System
Friends of the Library Group

MIDDLE ISLAND

P LONGWOOD PUBLIC LIBRARY,* 800 Middle Country Rd, 11953. SAN 311-4929. Tel: 631-924-6400. FAX: 631-924-7538. Web Site: www.suffolk.lib.ny.us/libraries/long/lpl12.html. *Dir*, David Clemens; E-Mail: dclemens@suffolk.lib.ny.us; *Asst Dir*, Suzanne Johnson; *Ch Servs*, Dianne Roberts; Staff 20 (MLS 20)
Founded 1953. Pop 50,858; Circ 641,936
Jul 1997-Jun 1998 Income $3,233,035. Mats Exp $435,700, Books $295,000, Per/Ser (Incl. Access Fees) $15,000, Micro $15,700. Sal $1,667,211
Library Holdings: Bk Vols 221,000; Bk Titles 120,367; Per Subs 324
Special Collections: Thomas R Bayles Historical Coll
Automation Activity & Vendor Info: (Circulation) Gaylord
Publications: Newsletter
Mem of Suffolk Cooperative Library System
Friends of the Library Group

MIDDLE VILLAGE

S COUNCIL ON NATIONAL LITERATURES, International Conference Center, 68-02 Metropolitan Ave, 11379. (Mail add: PO Box 468, 19977), SAN 373-1146. Tel: 718-821-3916. Circulation Tel: 302-659-1318. *Exec Dir, Pres*, Anne Paolucci
1999-2000 Income $25,000, State $10,000, Other $15,000. Mats Exp $25,000, Books $10,000, Per/Ser (Incl. Access Fees) $5,000, Other Print Mats $10,000
Library Holdings: Bk Vols 7,000; Bk Titles 72

MIDDLEBURGH

P MIDDLEBURGH LIBRARY ASSOCIATION,* 7 Wells Ave, 12122. SAN 311-4937. Tel: 518-827-5142. *Librn*, Mary France; Staff 3 (MLS 1, Non-MLS 2)
Pop 2,980; Circ 24,404
Library Holdings: Bk Titles 13,952; Per Subs 55
Special Collections: Genealogy (Frances B Spencer Coll)
Mem of Mohawk Valley Library Association
Friends of the Library Group

MIDDLEPORT

P MIDDLEPORT FREE LIBRARY,* 9 Vernon St, 14105. SAN 311-4953. Tel: 716-735-3281. FAX: 716-735-3281. *Librn*, Marilyn F Greenwell; Staff 1 (MLS 1)
Founded 1930. Pop 1,995; Circ 32,000
Library Holdings: Bk Vols 17,000; Bk Titles 15,500; Per Subs 50
Special Collections: Local History (Middleport Coll), bks, pamphlets
Mem of Nioga Library System
Open Mon 1-5 & 7-8:30, Tues & Thurs 11-5 & 7-8:30, Wed 1-5, Sat 11-5

MIDDLETOWN

M HORTON MEDICAL CENTER LIBRARY, 60 Prospect Ave, 10940. SAN 311-497X. Tel: 845-342-7651. FAX: 845-342-7650. E-Mail: hrt@warwick.net. Web Site: www.hortonmd.org. *Librn*, Sue Ben-Dor; Staff 2 (MLS 1, Non-MLS 1)
Library Holdings: Bk Vols 1,600; Bk Titles 700; Per Subs 225
Partic in BHSL; Hilow; Southeastern New York Library Resources Council

M MIDDLETOWN PSYCHIATRIC CENTER, Medical Professional Library, 122 Dorothea Dix Dr, 10940. SAN 325-6901. Tel: 845-342-5511, Ext 3539. FAX: 914-342-5078. E-Mail: midpsyc@sebridge.org. *Librn*, Judith A McGrath
Library Holdings: Bk Vols 5,500; Per Subs 47
Subject Interests: Homeopathy, Nursing, Psychiatry, Psychology
Database Vendor: OCLC - First Search, OVID Technologies
Publications: Overdue News (quarterly newsletter)
Mem of SE NY Libr Resources Coun
Partic in Basic Health Sciences Library Network; Health Info Librs of Westchester; Southeastern New York Library Resources Council

P MIDDLETOWN THRALL LIBRARY, 11-19 Depot St, 10940. SAN 311-5003. Tel: 845-341-5454. FAX: 845-341-5480. E-Mail: thrall7@warwick.net. Web Site: www.thrall.org. *Dir*, Kevin Gallagher; *Coll Develop*, Linda Aumick; *Coll Develop*, Mary Susan Flannery-Climes; Staff 25 (MLS 8, Non-MLS 17)
Founded 1901. Circ 280,566
Jul 2000-Jun 2001 Mats Exp $353,775, Books $229,775, Per/Ser (Incl. Access Fees) $80,000, Presv $4,000, Micro $7,000, AV Equip $5,000, Electronic Ref Mat (Incl. Access Fees) $28,000. Sal $970,141 (Prof $448,700)
Library Holdings: Bk Vols 167,800; Bk Titles 143,000; Per Subs 667
Special Collections: Orange County History Coll
Automation Activity & Vendor Info: (Acquisitions) epixtech, inc.; (Cataloging) epixtech, inc.; (Circulation) epixtech, inc.; (Course Reserve) epixtech, inc.; (ILL) epixtech, inc.; (Media Booking) epixtech, inc.; (OPAC) epixtech, inc.; (Serials) epixtech, inc.
Publications: Newsletter (quarterly)
Mem of Ramapo Catskill Library System
Partic in Southeastern New York Library Resources Council
Friends of the Library Group

J ORANGE COUNTY COMMUNITY COLLEGE, Learning Resource Center, 115 South St, 10940. SAN 311-4996. Tel: 845-341-4855. Reference Tel: 845-341-4620. FAX: 845-341-4424. Web Site: www.sunyorange.edu. *Dir*, Susan Parry; Tel: 914-341-4251, E-Mail: sparryjo@sunyorange.edu; *Librn*, Porter Barber; Tel: 914-562-4542; *Asst Prof, Cat*, Peter Staats; Tel: 914-341-4256, E-Mail: pstaats@sunyorange.edu; *Asst Prof, Circ, Per*, Diane Swenson; Tel: 914-341-4255, E-Mail: dlswenso@sunyorange.edu; *Assoc Prof, Ref*, Sarah Vasse; Tel: 914-341-4253, E-Mail: sjvasse@sunyorange.edu; *Asst Prof, Coll Develop*, Mary Ann Van Benschoten; Tel: 914-341-4258, E-Mail: mavanben@sunyorange.edu; Staff 21 (MLS 6, Non-MLS 15)
Founded 1950. Enrl 5,823; Fac 149; Highest Degree: Associate
Sep 2000-Aug 2001 Income $763,101. Mats Exp $131,350, Books $59,650, Per/Ser (Incl. Access Fees) $45,900, Presv $5,800, Electronic Ref Mat (Incl. Access Fees) $20,000. Sal $479,015 (Prof $292,439)
Library Holdings: Bk Vols 98,171; Per Subs 250
Special Collections: Orange County History & Heritage
Automation Activity & Vendor Info: (Cataloging) DRA; (OPAC) DRA
Database Vendor: CARL, Dialog, DRA, GaleNet, IAC - Info Trac, OCLC - First Search, ProQuest, Silverplatter Information Inc.
Publications: The LRC at OCCC: News in Views
Mem of SE NY Libr Resources Coun
Partic in OCLC Online Computer Library Center, Inc; Southeastern New York Library Resources Council

P RAMAPO CATSKILL LIBRARY SYSTEM, 619 Rte 17M, 10940-4395. SAN 352-8219. Tel: 845-343-1131. FAX: 845-343-1205. Web Site: www.rcls.org. *Dir*, Robert Hubsher; Tel: 845-343-1131, Ext 242, E-Mail: rhubsher@rcls.org; *Publ Servs*, Leslie S W Riley; *Ch Servs*, Randall Enos; *ILL, Tech Servs*, Linda J Hendon; *Automation Syst Coordr*, Stan Ploszaj; *Electronic Resources*, Jerry Kuntz; *Admin Assoc*, Ruth Daubenspeck; Tel: 845-343-1131 Ext 222, E-Mail: ruth@rcls.org; Staff 35 (MLS 6, Non-MLS 29)
Founded 1959. Circ 43,009
Jan 1999-Dec 1999 Income $2,852,314, State $2,392,543, Federal $49,245, Locally Generated Income $410,526. Mats Exp $247,357, Per/Ser (Incl. Access Fees) $22,405, AV Equip $90,215, Electronic Ref Mat (Incl. Access Fees) $134,737. Sal $1,114,838 (Prof $370,445)
Library Holdings: Bk Vols 15,084; Per Subs 2,218
Subject Interests: Electronic databases, Prof libr sci mgt
Automation Activity & Vendor Info: (Cataloging) epixtech, inc.; (Circulation) epixtech, inc.; (ILL) epixtech, inc.; (Media Booking) epixtech, inc.; (OPAC) epixtech, inc.; (Serials) epixtech, inc.
Database Vendor: Ebsco - EbscoHost
Publications: RCLS Outreach Newsletter; RCLS Weekly Memo; Trustee FYI
Member Libraries: Albert Wisner Public Library; Blauvelt Free Library; Bloomingburg Free Library; Chester Public Library; Cornwall Public Library; Cragsmoor Free Library; Daniel Pierce Library; Delaware Free Library; Ellenville Public Library & Museum; Ethelbert B Crawford Public Library; Finkelstein Memorial Library; Florida Public Library; Gardiner Library; Goshen Public Library & Historical Society; Greenwood Lake Public Library; Haverstraw Kings Daughters Public Library; Highland Falls Library; Jeffersonville Public Library; Josephine-Louise Public Library; Livingston Manor Free Library; Middletown Thrall Library; Moffat Library; Monroe Free Library; Montgomery Free Library; Nanuet Public Library; New City Library; Newburgh Free Library; Nyack College Library; Orangeburg Library; Palisades Free Library; Pearl River Public Library; Piermont Public Library; Port Jervis Free Library; Roscoe Free Library; Rose Memorial Library; Sloatsburg Public Library; Suffern Free Library; Sullivan Correctional Facility Library; Sunshine Hall Free Library; Tappan Library; Tomkins Cove Public Library; Town Of Crawford Free Library; Tusten-Cochecton Library; Tuxedo Park Library; Valley Cottage Free Library; Wallkill Public Library; West Nyack Free Library; Woodbury Public Library

MIDDLEVILLE

P MIDDLEVILLE FREE LIBRARY, One S Main St, PO Box 155, 13406. SAN 311-5011. Tel: 315-891-3655. E-Mail: mvlfrlib@ntcnet.com. *Mgr Libr*, Sandra Zaffarano
Founded 1915. Pop 670; Circ 8,000
Library Holdings: Bk Vols 10,000
Mem of Mid-York Library System

MILFORD

P MILFORD FREE LIBRARY,* S Main St, 13807. (Mail add: PO Box 118, 13807), SAN 311-502X. Tel: 607-286-9076. *Dir*, Barbara Campbell
Founded 1923. Circ 8,900
Library Holdings: Bk Vols 7,010
Subject Interests: Local history
Mem of Four County Library System

MILLBROOK

S INSTITUTE OF ECOSYSTEM STUDIES LIBRARY, PO Box AB, Route 44A, 12545. SAN 311-5046. Tel: 845-677-7600, Ext 164. FAX: 914-677-5976. *Mgr Libr Serv*, Chloe M Keefer; E-Mail: keeferc@ecostudies.org; *Librn*, Annette Frank; E-Mail: franka@ecostudies.org; Staff 3 (MLS 2, Non-MLS 1)
Founded 1985
Library Holdings: Bk Titles 10,000; Per Subs 127
Subject Interests: Ecology, Nutrient cycling, Plant-animal interactions, Wildlife mgt
Database Vendor: Dialog, Ebsco - EbscoHost, OCLC - First Search, OVID Technologies
Function: Research library
Partic in Southeastern New York Library Resources Council

P MILLBROOK LIBRARY,* Franklin Ave & Friendly Lane, PO Box 286, 12545-0286. SAN 311-5038. Tel: 914-677-3611. FAX: 914-677-5127. *Dir*, Muriel Ver DiBello; Staff 5 (MLS 1, Non-MLS 4)
Founded 1901. Pop 4,254; Circ 57,941
Library Holdings: Bk Vols 42,000; Bk Titles 40,000; Per Subs 67
Mem of Mid-Hudson Library System

MILLERTON

P NORTHEAST-MILLERTON LIBRARY, 75 Main St, 12546-5172. (Mail add: PO Box 786, 12546-0786), SAN 311-5054. Tel: 518-789-3340. FAX: 518-789-6802. E-Mail: nem.lib@taconic.net. Web Site: www.nemillertonlibrary.org. *Dir*, Margaret Quick; *Asst Librn*, Roger Cohn; Staff 2 (Non-MLS 2)
Founded 1927. Pop 2,900; Circ 14,000
Library Holdings: Bk Titles 20,000; Per Subs 30
Mem of Mid-Hudson Library System
Open Tues-Sun
Friends of the Library Group

MILLWOOD

S PROBE ECONOMICS INC LIBRARY,* 358 Saw Mill River Rd, PO Box 660, 10546-0660. SAN 372-803X. Tel: 914-923-4505. FAX: 914-923-4508. E-Mail: info@probeeconomics.com. *Mgr*, Harriett Golden
Library Holdings: Bk Titles 500; Per Subs 22

MILTON

P SARAH HULL HALLOCK FREE LIBRARY,* 56 Main St, PO Box 802, 12547-0802. SAN 311-5062. Tel: 914-795-2200. FAX: 914-795-1005. *Librn*, Amy Raff; *Coordr*, Marilyn Fino
Founded 1887. Circ 8,305
Library Holdings: Bk Vols 8,740
Mem of Mid-Hudson Library System

MINEOLA

L MEYER, SUOZZI, ENGLISH & KLEIN, Law Library,* 1505 Kellum Pl, 11501-4824. SAN 372-4344. Tel: 516-741-6565. FAX: 516-741-6706. *Librn*, Linda Caliendo
Library Holdings: Bk Vols 10,000
Restriction: Not open to public

P MINEOLA PUBLIC LIBRARY,* 195 Marcellus Rd, 11501. SAN 311-5089. Tel: 516-746-8488. FAX: 516-294-6459. *Actg Dir*, Carol Ahrens; *AV, Ref, YA Servs*, Charles Sleefe; *Ch Servs*, Anne Marie Stabile
Pop 20,757; Circ 77,219
Library Holdings: Bk Vols 85,000; Per Subs 150
Mem of Nassau Library System

S NASSAU COUNTY PLANNING COMMISSION LIBRARY,* 400 County Seat Dr, 11501. SAN 327-0661. Tel: 516-571-5953. FAX: 516-571-3839. *Dir*, Paul F Ponessa; *Librn*, Robert Gaiser
Subject Interests: Census, Transportation

GL NASSAU COUNTY SUPREME COURT, Law Library,* 100 Supreme Court Dr, 11501. SAN 352-8243. Tel: 516-571-3883. FAX: 516-571-0752. *Chief Librn*, James J Lodato; Tel: 516-571-3884, E-Mail: jlodato@courts.state.ny.us; *Librn*, Barbara Oberlander
Founded 1902
Apr 1997-Mar 1998 Income $949,789. Mats Exp $598,958, Books $598,358, Per/Ser (Incl. Access Fees) $600. Sal $353,866
Library Holdings: Bk Vols 312,113; Per Subs 1,559
Publications: Ex Librris in the Nassau Lawyer/Nassua County Bar Association (monthly journal)
Restriction: Lending to staff only
Partic in OCLC Online Computer Library Center, Inc
Branches:
LAW LIBRARY, 262 Old Country Rd, 11501. SAN 352-8278. Tel: 516-571-3418.

L RUSKIN, MOSCOU, EVANS & FALTISCHEK PC, Law Library,* 170 Old Country Rd, 11501. SAN 374-4868. Tel: 516-663-6525. FAX: 516-663-6601. E-Mail: rmeflib@msn.com. *Librn*, Sue Meringolo
Founded 1968
1998-1999 Mats Exp $150,000
Library Holdings: Bk Vols 5,500; Bk Titles 500; Per Subs 50

M WINTHROP-UNIVERSITY HOSPITAL, Hollis Health Sciences Library, 259 First St, 11501. SAN 311-5100. Tel: 516-663-2802. FAX: 516-663-8171. Web Site: www.winthrop.org. *Dir*, Virginia I Cook; Tel: 516-663-2280, E-Mail: vcook@winthrop.org; *Asst Librn*, Barbara Elish; Tel: 516-663-2783, E-Mail: belish@winthrop.org. Subject Specialists: *Systs*, Barbara Elish; *Technology*, Barbara Elish; Staff 6 (MLS 3, Non-MLS 3)
Founded 1925
Library Holdings: Bk Titles 5,000; Per Subs 485
Subject Interests: Allied health, Computer instruction, Medicine, Nursing, Surgery
Automation Activity & Vendor Info: (OPAC) SIRSI
Database Vendor: OCLC - First Search, OVID Technologies
Publications: Acquisition List (quarterly)
Restriction: Staff use only
Partic in Long Island Library Resources Council; Medical Library Center Of New York

MINOA

P MINOA LIBRARY,* 112 Willard St, 13116. SAN 311-5119. Tel: 315-656-7401. FAX: 315-656-7401. *Dir*, Barbara Young
Founded 1936. Pop 3,640; Circ 38,569
Library Holdings: Bk Vols 16,325; Bk Titles 15,318; Per Subs 55
Mem of Onondaga County Public Library

MODENA

P PLATTEKILL LIBRARY, 2047 Rte 32, 12548. SAN 376-6977. Tel: 845-883-7286. FAX: 845-883-7295. E-Mail: plattekill@vh.net, plattekill_ub@hotmail.com. Web Site: plattekill.lib.ny.us. *Dir*, John Georghiou; Staff 5 (MLS 1, Non-MLS 4)
Founded 1973. Pop 9,981
Jan 2000-Dec 2000 Income $112,000. Mats Exp $90,000, Books $10,000, Per/Ser (Incl. Access Fees) $550, Electronic Ref Mat (Incl. Access Fees) $875. Sal $67,180 (Prof $33,075)
Library Holdings: Bk Titles 16,143; Per Subs 21; Bks on Deafness & Sign Lang 15
Subject Interests: Regional, Spanish language
Mem of Mid-Hudson Library System
Bill & Melinda Gates Foundation Grant recipient, six public access pc's & satellite internet access
Friends of the Library Group

MOHAWK

P WELLER PUBLIC LIBRARY,* 41 W Main St, 13407. SAN 311-5127. Tel: 315-866-2983. *Librn*, Maxine Kublick
Circ 22,295
Library Holdings: Bk Vols 30,000; Per Subs 26
Mem of Mid-York Library System

MONROE

P MONROE FREE LIBRARY, 44 Millpond Pkwy, 10950. SAN 311-5135. Tel: 845-783-4411. FAX: 845-782-4707. E-Mail: mfl@rcls.org, mmcintos@rcls.org. Web Site: www.monroelibrary.org, www.rcls.org/mfl. *Dir*, Marilyn McIntosh; *Asst Dir*, Suzanne Skeels; *Automation Syst Coordr*, Carol Bezkorowajny; *Ref*, Karen LaRocca; *Ch Servs*, Rebecca Lyn
Founded 1908. Pop 23,035; Circ 115,000
Jan 2000-Dec 2000 Income $431,922, Locally Generated Income $53,900, Other $378,022. Mats Exp $70,000. Sal $231,602
Library Holdings: Bk Vols 46,000; Per Subs 129
Special Collections: Local History
Publications: Annual Report; Calendar of events (monthly); Newsletter (quarterly)
Mem of Ramapo Catskill Library System
Friends of the Library Group

MONTAUK

P MONTAUK LIBRARY, 871 Montauk Hwy, PO Box 700, 11954-0500. SAN 325-5204. Tel: 631-668-3377. FAX: 631-668-3468. E-Mail: mntk@suffolk.lib.ny.us. *Dir*, Karen A Rade; E-Mail: karade@suffolk.lib.ny.us
Founded 1980. Pop 3,001; Circ 41,479
Jul 1999-Jun 2000 Income $275,363, State $1,500, City $259,420, Locally Generated Income $14,443. Mats Exp $28,957, Books $14,810, Per/Ser (Incl. Access Fees) $2,465, AV Equip $436, Other Print Mats $969, Electronic Ref Mat (Incl. Access Fees) $10,277. Sal $118,049
Library Holdings: Bk Vols 24,070; Per Subs 81
Special Collections: Long Island Coll; Shakespeare Coll
Mem of Suffolk Cooperative Library System
Friends of the Library Group

MONTGOMERY

P MONTGOMERY FREE LIBRARY,* 133 Clinton St, 12549. SAN 311-5151. Tel: 914-457-5616. FAX: 914-457-5616. *Dir*, Betsy Comizio; *Asst Dir*, Barbara Meyer
Founded 1911. Pop 2,318; Circ 17,219
Library Holdings: Bk Vols 15,265; Per Subs 38
Mem of Ramapo Catskill Library System

MONTICELLO

P ETHELBERT B CRAWFORD PUBLIC LIBRARY, 187-189 Broadway, 12701. SAN 311-516X. Tel: 914-794-4660. FAX: 914-794-4602. *Dir*, Alan Barrish; E-Mail: abarrish@rcls.org; Staff 6 (MLS 1, Non-MLS 5)
Pop 16,350; Circ 70,000
Jan 2000-Dec 2000 Income $308,242. Mats Exp $64,000, Books $50,000, Per/Ser (Incl. Access Fees) $5,000. Sal $138,752 (Prof $47,500)
Library Holdings: Bk Vols 20,170; Bk Titles 18,210; Per Subs 88
Mem of Ramapo Catskill Library System

MONTOUR FALLS

P MONTOUR FALLS MEMORIAL LIBRARY,* 406 Main St, 14865. SAN 376-3048. Tel: 607-535-7489. FAX: 607-535-5517. *Dir*, Amy Mosher
Library Holdings: Bk Vols 3,000; Per Subs 40
Mem of Southern Tier Library System
Friends of the Library Group

G NEW YORK STATE DEPARTMENT OF STATE - OFFICE OF FIRE PREVENTION & CONTROL, New York State Academy of Fire Science Library, 600 College Ave, 14865. SAN 321-1851. Tel: 607-535-7136, Ext 605. FAX: 607-535-4841. Web Site: www.dos.state.ny.us/fire/firewww.html, www.fire.lakenet.org. *Librn*, Diana Robinson; E-Mail: drobins@lakenet.org; Staff 2 (MLS 1, Non-MLS 1)
Founded 1970
Library Holdings: Bk Titles 5,400; Per Subs 125
Subject Interests: Fire science
Special Collections: Fire Prevention & Training (Film Library Coll)
Publications: Acquisitions list
Partic in New York State Interlibrary Loan Network; S Cent Res Libr Coun
Academy also runs film library of an additional 150 videotape titles mostly on fire prevention

S SCHUYLER COUNTY HISTORICAL SOCIETY, Gray Brick Tavern Museum,* PO Box 651, 14865. SAN 327-5175. Tel: 607-535-9741. *Dir*, Doris S Gauvin
Library Holdings: Bk Vols 300; Per Subs 4
Subject Interests: Local history

MONTROSE

P HENDRICK HUDSON FREE LIBRARY, 185 Kings Ferry Rd, 10548. SAN 311-5186. Tel: 914-739-5654. FAX: 914-739-5659. Web Site: www.wls.lib.ny.us/libs/hendrickhudson. *Dir*, Constance Dyckman; E-Mail: cdyckman@wls.lib.ny.us; *Ch Servs*, Laura Giangrande; Staff 8 (MLS 5, Non-MLS 3)
Founded 1937. Pop 14,906; Circ 130,907
Jul 1999-Jun 2000 Income $752,000. Mats Exp $60,765, Books $53,159, Per/Ser (Incl. Access Fees) $7,606. Sal $337,346
Library Holdings: Bk Vols 44,055; Per Subs 159
Automation Activity & Vendor Info: (Cataloging) epixtech, inc.; (Circulation) epixtech, inc.; (ILL) epixtech, inc.; (OPAC) epixtech, inc.
Database Vendor: epixtech, inc.
Publications: Newsletter
Mem of Westchester Library System

GM VA HUDSON VALLEY HEALTH CARE SYSTEM, Castle Point & Franklin Delano Roosevelt Medical Center Libraries, PO Box 100, 10548. SAN 311-5194. Tel: 914-737-4400, Ext 2360. FAX: 914-737-4400, Ext 2754. *Chief Librn*, Jeffrey Nicholas
Library Holdings: Bk Titles 2,000; Per Subs 120
Subject Interests: AIDS, Alzheimers disease, Geriatrics, Geropshychiat, Medicine, Nursing, Post-traumatic stress, Psychiatry, Psychology, Soc work
Publications: Medical Library News
Partic in Nat Libr of Med; Veterans Affairs Library Network

MOOERS

P MOOERS FREE LIBRARY,* PO Box 286, 12958. SAN 311-5208. Tel: 518-236-7744. FAX: 518-236-7744. *Dir*, Edie Morelock
Founded 1917. Circ 6,911
Jan 1997-Dec 1998 Income $13,875. Mats Exp $10,233, Books $1,600, Per/Ser (Incl. Access Fees) $600. Sal $8,300
Library Holdings: Bk Vols 9,046
Subject Interests: Antiques
Mem of Clinton-Essex-Franklin Library System
Friends of the Library Group

MORAVIA

P POWERS LIBRARY,* 29 Church St, 13118. SAN 311-5216. Tel: 315-497-1955. *Dir*, Dolores D Fleckenstein
Founded 1880. Circ 18,219
Library Holdings: Bk Vols 14,500; Per Subs 56
Mem of Finger Lakes Library System

MORRIS

P VILLAGE LIBRARY OF MORRIS, 22 E Main St, 13808. SAN 311-5224. Tel: 607-263-2080. FAX: 607-263-2080. E-Mail: mo@ill.org. *Librn*, Audree Lamb
Founded 1919. Pop 1,787; Circ 7,943
Library Holdings: Bk Vols 7,500; Bk Titles 7,100; Per Subs 24
Subject Interests: Local history
Mem of Four County Library System

MORRISVILLE

P MORRISVILLE LIBRARY, 87 E Main St, 13408. (Mail add: PO Box 37, 13408), SAN 311-5240. Tel: 315-684-9130. FAX: 315-684-7007. E-Mail: mo_dial@midyork.lib.ny.us. *Dir*, Traci Schuster; E-Mail: schuster@midyork.lib.ny.us
Founded 1903. Pop 2,700; Circ 10,414
Library Holdings: Bk Vols 11,374; Per Subs 23
Mem of Mid-York Library System
Friends of the Library Group

J STATE UNIVERSITY OF NEW YORK, College of Agriculture & Technology Library, 13408-0902. SAN 311-5259. Tel: 315-684-6055. FAX: 315-684-6115. E-Mail: hildebm@morrisville.edu. Web Site: www.morrisville.edu/pages/library. *Acq, Dir*, Marion Hildebrand; *Syst Coordr*, Wilfred Drew; *Cat*, Susanne Greenhagen; *Bibliog Instr*, Angela Weiler; *Ser*, Kay Benjamin; Staff 5 (MLS 5)
Founded 1908. Enrl 2,600; Fac 144
Library Holdings: Bk Vols 93,000; Bk Titles 80,600; Per Subs 486
Subject Interests: Agriculture, Animal husbandry-horses, Aquaculture, Automotive tech, Bus, Electrical tech, Environmental studies, Horticulture, Journalism, Mgt, Nursing
Special Collections: Food Service Historical Coll; New York State Historical Coll
Publications: Library Guide; Periodicals Received Currently
Partic in Central New York Library Resources Council; OCLC Online Computer Library Center, Inc

MOUNT KISCO

P MOUNT KISCO PUBLIC LIBRARY, 100 Main St, 10549. SAN 311-5267. Tel: 914-666-8041. FAX: 914-666-3899. Web Site: www.westchesterlibraries.org. *Dir*, Wendy B Bloom; E-Mail: wbloom@wls.lib.ny.us; *Ch Servs*, Ellen Tannenbaum; E-Mail: mtkkids@playful.com; *Ad Servs*, Mary Ayers; E-Mail: mayers@wls.lib.ny.us; Staff 5 (MLS 5)
Founded 1913. Pop 9,108
Jun 2000-May 2001 Income Parent Institution $503,965. Mats Exp $63,200, Books $46,350, Per/Ser (Incl. Access Fees) $10,800, Presv $1,250, Micro $4,800. Sal $350,600 (Prof $163,270)
Library Holdings: Bk Vols 57,054; Bk Titles 57,000; Per Subs 163
Subject Interests: Job info, Large print, Local history
Automation Activity & Vendor Info: (Circulation) epixtech, inc.; (OPAC) epixtech, inc.
Mem of Westchester Library System
Friends of the Library Group

M NORTHERN WESTCHESTER HOSPITAL CENTER, Health Sciences Library, 400 E Main St, 10549-0802. SAN 311-5275. Tel: 914-666-1259. FAX: 914-666-1940. Web Site: www.nwhc.net/health_sciences_library.htm. *Dir*, Joanna Faraday; E-Mail: jfaraday@healthstar.org; Staff 1 (MLS 1)
Founded 1960
Library Holdings: Bk Vols 2,000; Bk Titles 1,950; Per Subs 120
Subject Interests: Clinical medicine, Medical library
Partic in Basic Health Sciences Library Network; Health Info Librs of Westchester; Metro NY Libr Coun

MOUNT MORRIS

P MOUNT MORRIS LIBRARY,* 121 Main St, 14510-1596. SAN 311-5283. Tel: 716-658-4412. FAX: 716-658-3642. *Librn*, Sharon Stanley
Founded 1910. Pop 4,478; Circ 25,412
Library Holdings: Bk Vols 17,600; Bk Titles 17,923; Per Subs 24
Subject Interests: English as a second lang
Mem of Pioneer Library System

MOUNT VERNON

M MOUNT VERNON HOSPITAL, Library & Information Services,* 12 N Seventh Ave, 10550-2026. SAN 311-5305. Tel: 914-664-8000, Ext 3218. FAX: 914-664-1709. E-Mail: mtvern1@metgate.metro.org.; Staff 1 (MLS 1)
1999-2000 Mats Exp $20,000, Books $3,000, Per/Ser (Incl. Access Fees) $7,000, AV Equip $2,000, Other Print Mats $1,000, Electronic Ref Mat (Incl. Access Fees) $7,000. Sal $23,000

Library Holdings: Bk Vols 3,400; Per Subs 121
Subject Interests: Health sciences, Medicine, Nursing
Restriction: Staff use only
Partic in Metronet

P MOUNT VERNON PUBLIC LIBRARY,* 28 S First Ave, 10550. SAN 311-5313. Tel: 914-668-1840. FAX: 914-668-1018. Web Site: www.wls.lib.ny.us/ubs/mount-vernon/mtv.html. *Tech Servs*, Regina Abrams; *Ref*, Gary Newman; *Online Servs*, Rachel Charny; *YA Servs*, Joanne Israel; Staff 13 (MLS 13)
Founded 1854. Pop 67,153; Circ 239,186
1997-1998 Income $2,572,912, State $19,256, City $2,375,920, Locally Generated Income $56,679. Mats Exp $186,362, Books $121,476, Per/Ser (Incl. Access Fees) $54,493, Micro $10,393. Sal $1,638,793 (Prof $715,448)
Library Holdings: Bk Vols 515,382; Per Subs 22,560
Subject Interests: Behav sci, Black hist, Foreign Language, Law, Music, Soc sci
Special Collections: Large Print Coll; Local History; Mills Law Coll
Database Vendor: CARL
Mem of Westchester Library System
Friends of the Library Group

NANUET

P NANUET PUBLIC LIBRARY,* 149 Church St, 10954. SAN 311-5364. Tel: 914-623-4281. FAX: 914-623-2415. *Dir*, Patricia Brunsman; *Ch Servs*, Gretchen Bell; *Ad Servs*, Richard Piatelli; *Ad Servs*, Ann Borsuk; *Tech Servs*, Vivian Maisey
Founded 1894. Pop 14,000; Circ 152,000
Library Holdings: Bk Titles 100,241; Per Subs 200
Mem of Ramapo Catskill Library System

NAPANOCH

S EASTERN CORRECTIONAL FACILITY LIBRARY, PO Box 338, 12458-0338. SAN 325-8955. Tel: 914-647-7400. FAX: 914-647-7400, Ext 2099. *Librn*, Pauline Lewis; Staff 2 (Non-MLS 2)
Apr 1999-Mar 2000 Income $20,000, State $9,000, Parent Institution $11,000. Mats Exp $23,600, Books $9,600, Per/Ser (Incl. Access Fees) $10,000, Electronic Ref Mat (Incl. Access Fees) $4,000
Library Holdings: Bk Vols 11,000; Per Subs 88
Partic in Ramapo Catskill Libr Syst

NAPLES

P NAPLES LIBRARY, 118 S Main, 14512. SAN 311-5372. Tel: 716-374-2757. FAX: 716-374-6493. *Dir*, Blanche Warner; E-Mail: bwarner@pls-net.org; *Asst Dir*, Georgeanne Scalzo
Founded 1962. Pop 3,563; Circ 17,367
Library Holdings: Bk Titles 17,000; Per Subs 50
Mem of Pioneer Library System
Open Mon-Thurs 2-7, Fri 10-8, Sat 10-2
Friends of the Library Group

NARROWSBURG

P TUSTEN-COCHECTON LIBRARY,* 198 Bridge St, PO Box 129, 12764. SAN 376-6985. Tel: 914-252-3360. FAX: 914-252-3331. E-Mail: tclib@ezacess.net. *Mgr*, Mary Paige Lang-Clouse
Jan 1998-Dec 1998 Income $50,392, Locally Generated Income $9,170, Other $5,555. Mats Exp $7,884, Presv $2,703. Sal $10,200
Library Holdings: Bk Vols 13,700; Per Subs 30
Subject Interests: Local history
Mem of Ramapo Catskill Library System

NASSAU

P NASSAU FREE LIBRARY,* 18 Church St, PO Box 436, 12123. SAN 311-5380. Tel: 518-766-2715. FAX: 518-766-3854. *Librn*, Patricia Sahr; *Asst Librn*, Jane Visconti
Circ 19,249
Library Holdings: Bk Vols 16,133
Mem of Upper Hudson Library System
Open Mon 1-5, Thurs 10-12 & 7-9, Fri 1-5 & Sat 10-12
Friends of the Library Group

NEW BERLIN

P NEW BERLIN LIBRARY, 15 S Main St, 13411-2905. (Mail add: PO Box J, 13411-0610), SAN 311-5399. Tel: 607-847-8564. FAX: 607-847-9732. *Dir*, Darlene LaBrie
Founded 1896. Pop 4,519; Circ 24,362
Library Holdings: Bk Vols 16,000; Per Subs 82
Subject Interests: Genealogy, Local history
Special Collections: Literacy Service Center Museum; New Berlin Gazettes, microfilm; Oral History Project
Mem of Four County Library System

NEW CITY

S HISTORICAL SOCIETY OF ROCKLAND COUNTY LIBRARY, 20 Zukor Rd, 10956. SAN 328-4271. Tel: 845-634-9629. FAX: 845-634-8690. E-Mail: hsrockland@aol.com. *Dir*, Sarah Henrich
Library Holdings: Bk Titles 550
Open Tues 1-5 or by appointment

P NEW CITY LIBRARY, 220 N Main St, 10956. SAN 311-5402. Tel: 845-634-4997. Circulation Tel: 845-634-4997, Ext 124. Reference Tel: 845-634-4997, Ext 126. FAX: 845-634-0173. E-Mail: ncl@newcitylibrary.org. Web Site: www.newcitylibrary.org. *Dir*, Richard Treleven; Tel: 845-634-4997, Ext 111, E-Mail: rtreleven@rcls.org; *Ad Servs, Per, Selection of Elec Mat*, Maureen Shields; Tel: 845-634-4997, Ext 128, E-Mail: rook@mail.creativeonline.com; *Commun Relations*, Robert Devino; Tel: 845-634-4997, Ext 139, E-Mail: bdevino@rcls.org; *Head Ref*, Kathleen Preston; Tel: 845-634-4997, Ext 115, E-Mail: kpreston@rcls.org; *Head, Circ*, Gail Seidenfrau; Tel: 845-634-4997, Ext 101, E-Mail: gseidenf@rcls.org; *Ch Servs*, Joanne Warren; Tel: 845-634-4997, Ext 133, E-Mail: jwarren@rcls.org; *Spec Coll & Archives*, Sally Pellegrini; Tel: 845-634-4997, Ext 137, E-Mail: spelleg@rcls.org; *Head Tech Servs*, Arlene Olszewski; Tel: 845-634-4997, Ext 118, E-Mail: aolszews@rcls.org; *Business*, Ellen Ellis; Tel: 845-634-4997, Ext 113, E-Mail: epellis@rmailcity.com; *YA Servs*, Mary Phillips; Tel: 845-634-4997, Ext 114, E-Mail: mphillip@rcls.org; *AV*, Harriet Wollenberg; Tel: 845-634-4997, Ext 120, E-Mail: hwollenb@rcls.org; *Ch Servs*, Arlene Sandner; Tel: 845-634-4997, Ext 122, E-Mail: asandner@rcls.org; *Coll Develop*, Naomi Honor; Tel: 845-634-4997, Ext 140, E-Mail: nhonor@rcknet.com; *Ch Servs*, Marie McDermott; Tel: 845-634-4997, Ext 141, E-Mail: mmcdermo@rcls.org. Subject Specialists: *Adult literature*, Naomi Honor; *New York hist*, Sally Pellegrini; Staff 50 (MLS 18, Non-MLS 32)
Founded 1933. Pop 41,676; Circ 471,910
Jul 1998-Jun 1999 Income $3,416,294, Locally Generated Income $198,560, Other $3,217,734. Mats Exp $330,291, Books $221,358, Per/Ser (Incl. Access Fees) $32,373, Presv $1,061, Micro $11,900, AV Equip $10,000, Electronic Ref Mat (Incl. Access Fees) $44,945. Sal $1,643,614 (Prof $803,944)
Library Holdings: Bk Vols 176,090; Bk Titles 143,039; Per Subs 2,939
Subject Interests: Bus, Consumer info, Health, Local history
Special Collections: Rockland County (NY) information & genealogy
Automation Activity & Vendor Info: (Circulation) epixtech, inc.; (OPAC) epixtech, inc.
Database Vendor: Ebsco - EbscoHost, GaleNet, IAC - Info Trac, IAC - SearchBank, ProQuest
Publications: New City Library (Newsletter)
Mem of Ramapo Catskill Library System

NEW HAMPTON

G MID-HUDSON FORENSIC PSYCHIATRIC CENTER LIBRARY,* Rte 17M, Box 158, 10958. SAN 327-8700. Tel: 914-374-3171, Ext 3625. FAX: 914-374-7500. *Librn*, Elizabeth Horvath
Apr 1997-Mar 1998 Income $60,000. Mats Exp $14,500, Books $3,500, Per/Ser (Incl. Access Fees) $11,000. Sal $46,000
Library Holdings: Bk Vols 9,000; Per Subs 250
Publications: Outlook (newsletter)
Mem of SE NY Libr Resources Coun

NEW HARTFORD

P NEW HARTFORD PUBLIC LIBRARY, 2 Library Lane, 13413-2815. SAN 326-5358. Tel: 315-733-1535. FAX: 315-733-0795. E-Mail: nh-circ@midyork.lib.ny.us. *Dir*, Hans J Plambeck; E-Mail: plambeck@midyork.lib.ny.us; *Reader Servs*, Gene Schreiner; *Ch Servs*, Ruth Cook; *Circ*, Bernice Costner; Staff 20 (MLS 2, Non-MLS 18)
Founded 1976. Pop 21,640; Circ 139,604
Jan 1999-Dec 1999 Income $286,055, State $6,205, County $25,000, Locally Generated Income $25,000, Other $229,850. Mats Exp $46,500, Per/Ser (Incl. Access Fees) $6,500, Other Print Mats $40,000. Sal $150,000
Library Holdings: Bk Vols 32,946
Database Vendor: DRA, Ebsco - EbscoHost
Publications: Footnotes; Friends (newsletter)
Mem of Mid-York Library System
Friends of the Library Group

S SPECIAL METALS CORP, Technical Library-Information Center,* 4317 Middle Settlement Rd, 13413-5392. SAN 311-5429. Tel: 315-798-2900. FAX: 315-798-2001. *Librn*, Barbara Donahoe; E-Mail: donahoeb@circ.org
Founded 1957
Library Holdings: Per Subs 125
Subject Interests: Bus, Ceramics, Govt reports, Medicine, Metallurgy, Mgt,

Sci-tech
Special Collections: Acta Metallurgica; AIME Transactions; ASM Transactions; Journal of the Institute of Metals; Journal of Vacuum Science & Technology; Scripta Metallurgica

L UTICA MUTUAL INSURANCE CO, Reference & Law Library,* 180 Genesee St, 13413. SAN 311-5437. Tel: 315-734-2000, 315-734-2531. FAX: 315-734-2680. *Dir, Res*, Steve Barry
Library Holdings: Bk Vols 9,200

NEW HYDE PARK

P HILLSIDE PUBLIC LIBRARY, 1950 Hillside Ave, 11040. SAN 311-5453. Tel: 516-488-3316. FAX: 516-437-8010. E-Mail: hs@lilrc.org. Web Site: www.nassaulibrary.org/hillside/index.htm. *Dir*, Stanley L Itkin; Staff 32 (MLS 4, Non-MLS 28)
Founded 1962. Pop 20,000; Circ 124,135
Jul 2000-Jun 2001 Income $992,925, State $7,000, City $944,475, Locally Generated Income $41,450. Mats Exp $151,000, Books $90,000, Per/Ser (Incl. Access Fees) $10,000, AV Equip $6,000, Electronic Ref Mat (Incl. Access Fees) $45,000. Sal $568,353 (Prof $170,000)
Library Holdings: Bk Titles 65,000; Per Subs 90
Special Collections: Cooking; Crafts
Mem of Nassau Library System

M LONG ISLAND JEWISH MEDICAL CENTER, Health Sciences Library, 270-05 76th Ave, 11040. SAN 311-5461. Tel: 718-470-7070. FAX: 718-470-6150. Web Site: url: www.lij.edu/library. *Dir*, Debra C Rand; E-Mail: rand@lij.edu; *Assoc Dir, Tech Servs*, Shifra Atik; E-Mail: atik@lij.edu; *Asst Dir*, Mary Shanahan; Staff 4 (MLS 4)
Founded 1954
Library Holdings: Bk Vols 23,000; Bk Titles 9,000; Per Subs 600
Subject Interests: Dentistry, Geriatrics, Health care admin, Medicine, Nursing, Pharm
Automation Activity & Vendor Info: (Cataloging) SIRSI; (Circulation) SIRSI; (OPAC) SIRSI; (Serials) SIRSI
Database Vendor: OVID Technologies
Partic in Medical Library Center Of New York; New York Metrop Ref & Res Libr Agency
Branches:
HILLSIDE HOSPITAL DIVISION, 75-59 263rd St, Glen Oaks, 11004. SAN 311-2454. Tel: 718-470-8090. FAX: 718-962-1718. *Circ, ILL*, Lee Letterman; *Circ, ILL*, Lillian Buller
Library Holdings: Bk Titles 10,000; Per Subs 175
Subject Interests: Psychiatry, Psychoanalysis, Psychology, Social work
Automation Activity & Vendor Info: (Circulation) SIRSI; (OPAC) SIRSI

P NEW HYDE PARK PUBLIC LIBRARY,* 1420 Jericho Tpk, 11040. SAN 311-547X. Tel: 516-354-1350, 516-354-1413. FAX: 516-437-8119. *Librn for Deaf, Publ Servs*, Nylah Scheider; *Tech Servs*, Kathy Ferrara
Founded 1936. Pop 9,801
Library Holdings: Bk Vols 60,500; Bk Titles 59,000; Per Subs 405
Subject Interests: Culinary skills, NY hist
Publications: New Hyde Park Newsletter
Mem of Nassau Library System

NEW LEBANON

P NEW LEBANON LIBRARY,* Tilden Rd, Rte 20 & 22 Box 295, 12125. SAN 311-418X. Tel: 518-794-8844. FAX: 518-794-9688. E-Mail: leb@taconic.net. Web Site: www.taconic.net/newlebanon. *Dir*, Anne Just
Founded 1804. Pop 2,271; Circ 9,000
Jan 1998-Dec 1998 Income $67,617, City $6,000, County $4,166, Locally Generated Income $5,270, Other $10,772. Mats Exp $5,560, Books $2,584, Per/Ser (Incl. Access Fees) $302. Sal $12,500
Library Holdings: Bk Titles 12,620; Per Subs 35
Subject Interests: Local history, Shakers
Mem of Mid-Hudson Library System
Open Mon, Tues, Thurs & Fri 2:30-4:30, Wed 2:30-8, Sat 9-3
Friends of the Library Group

NEW PALTZ

P ELTING MEMORIAL LIBRARY, 93 Main St, 12561-1593. SAN 311-5488. Tel: 845-255-5030. E-Mail: elting@sebridge.org. *Dir*, John A Giralico
Founded 1909. Pop 11,500; Circ 55,000
Library Holdings: Bk Titles 40,000
Special Collections: Mid-Hudson History (Haviland-Heidgerd Coll)
Mem of Mid-Hudson Library System
Open Mon 1-5:30pm & 7-9pm, Tues & Thurs 1-5:30pm, Wed & Fri 10am-5:30pm & 7-9pm & Sat 10am-4pm
Friends of the Library Group

S HUGUENOT HISTORICAL SOCIETY LIBRARY, 88 Huguenot St, 12561. SAN 311-5496. Tel: 845-255-6738. FAX: 845-255-0376. E-Mail: hhslib@ix.netcom.com. Web Site: www.hhs-newpaltz.org. *Archivist, Librn*, Eric J Roth; *Asst Librn*, Byron Preston; *Asst Librn*, Kristin E Raab; Staff 3 (MLS 1, Non-MLS 2)
Founded 1965
Library Holdings: Bk Vols 5,000
Subject Interests: Dutch hist, Genealogy, Huguenot hist, Immigration to Am, 17th-19th centuries, Local history, NY state hist
Special Collections: Bible Coll; Biographies; County Documents); Genealogical Chart Coll; Map Coll; Personal & Family Papers Coll; Photograph Coll; Rare Books Coll
Open Wed-Sat 10-4 (May-Oct), Wed-Fri 10-4 (Nov-May) & by appointment; special collections available by appointment only
Friends of the Library Group

C STATE UNIVERSITY OF NEW YORK COLLEGE AT NEW PALTZ, Sojourner Truth Library, 75 S Manheim Blvd, 12561-2493. SAN 311-550X. Tel: 845-257-3719. Interlibrary Loan Service Tel: 845-257-3680. FAX: 845-257-3718. Interlibrary Loan Service FAX: 845-257-3670. E-Mail: leec@newpaltz.edu. Web Site: www.lib.newpaltz.edu. *Dir*, Chui-chun Lee; E-Mail: leec@newpaltz.edu; *Coordr, Instrul Serv, Ref Serv*, Michael Stafford; Tel: 845-257-3729, Fax: 845-257-3712, E-Mail: stafform@newpaltz.edu; *Ref*, Susan Kratt; Tel: 845-257-3705, E-Mail: kratts@newpaltz.edu; *Circ*, Nancy Nielson; Tel: 845-257-3715, Fax: 845-257-3712, E-Mail: nielsonn@newpaltz.edu; *Ser*, Michael Zackheim; Tel: 845-257-3662, Fax: 845-257-3888, E-Mail: zackheim@newpaltz.edu; *Coll Develop*, Gerlinde Barley; Tel: 845-257-3731, Fax: 845-257-3712, E-Mail: barleyg@newpaltz.edu; *ILL*, Corinne Nyquist; Tel: 845-257-3681, Fax: 845-257-3670, E-Mail: nyquistc@newpaltz.edu; Staff 34 (MLS 13, Non-MLS 21)
Founded 1886. Enrl 6,069; Highest Degree: Master
Jul 1998-Jun 1999 Income $2,036,438, State $2,020,705. Mats Exp $642,561, Books $223,748, Per/Ser (Incl. Access Fees) $308,038, Presv $6,842, Micro $48,316, Electronic Ref Mat (Incl. Access Fees) $55,617. Sal $1,167,601 (Prof $561,630)
Library Holdings: Bk Vols 491,778; Per Subs 1,463
Subject Interests: Bus, Communications, Computer science, Education, Engineering, Film, Fine arts, Non-western studies, Nursing
Automation Activity & Vendor Info: (Acquisitions) epixtech, inc.; (Cataloging) epixtech, inc.; (Circulation) epixtech, inc.; (Course Reserve) epixtech, inc.; (OPAC) epixtech, inc.; (Serials) epixtech, inc.
Database Vendor: CARL, Dialog, epixtech, inc., GaleNet, IAC - Info Trac, IAC - SearchBank, Lexis-Nexis, OCLC - First Search, OVID Technologies, ProQuest, Silverplatter Information Inc.
Publications: The Newsletter of Sojourner Truth Library
Partic in Southeastern New York Library Resources Council; State University Of New York-NYLINK
Friends of the Library Group

NEW ROCHELLE

C COLLEGE OF NEW ROCHELLE, Gill Library, Castle Pl, 10805-2308. SAN 311-5518. Tel: 914-632-5300, Ext 5340. FAX: 914-654-5884. E-Mail: cnrrefdesk@cnr.edu. Web Site: cnr.edu/library.htm. *Dean*, Dr James T Schleifer; *Assoc Dean, Tech Servs*, Frances Martin; *Coordr*, Patricia Smith-Freeman; *Coll Develop, Tech Servs*, Margaret Lynn; *ILL, Ref*, Yvonne Carmicheal; *Ref*, Mark Haber; *Ref, Ser*, Shannon Weidemann; *Syst Coordr*, Susan Acampora; Staff 16 (MLS 14, Non-MLS 2)
Founded 1904. Enrl 5,503; Fac 787; Highest Degree: Master
Jul 1999-Jun 2000 Income $1,630,300, State $11,248. Mats Exp $436,000, Books $89,700, Per/Ser (Incl. Access Fees) $178,150, Presv $4,000, Micro $28,100, Manuscripts & Archives $500. Sal $1,194,300 (Prof $576,300)
Library Holdings: Bk Vols 143,800; Per Subs 1,257
Subject Interests: Education, Health science, Psychology
Special Collections: Early English Text Society; English Literature (Thomas More); James Joyce; Religious History (Ursuline Coll)
Automation Activity & Vendor Info: (Acquisitions) Innovative Interfaces Inc.; (Circulation) Innovative Interfaces Inc.; (Course Reserve) Innovative Interfaces Inc.; (OPAC) Innovative Interfaces Inc.; (Serials) Innovative Interfaces Inc.
Database Vendor: CARL, Dialog, Ebsco - EbscoHost, GaleNet, OCLC - First Search, ProQuest, Silverplatter Information Inc., Wilson - Wilson Web
Publications: Acquisition list; Notes from Gill
Partic in Innopac; New York Metrop Ref & Res Libr Agency; OCLC Online Computer Library Center, Inc; WALDO; Webpals
Friends of the Library Group

C IONA COLLEGE, Ryan Library, 715 North Ave, 10801. SAN 311-5534. Tel: 914-633-2350. FAX: 914-633-2136. E-Mail: library@iona.edu. Web Site: www.iona.edu/library/library.htm. *Dir*, Joy S Collins; Tel: 914-633-2351, E-Mail: jcollins@iona.edu; *Asst Dir*, Richard Palladino; Tel: 914-633-2220, E-Mail: rpalladino@iona.edu; *Bibliog Instr, Ref*, Adrienne Franco; Tel: 914-633-2348, E-Mail: afranco@iona.edu; *Coll Develop, Coordr, Tech Servs*, Diana Kiel; Tel: 914-633-2417, E-Mail: dkiel@iona.edu; *Media Spec*, Kevin Fitzgerald; Tel: 914-633-2353, E-Mail: kfitzgerald@iona.edu; *Circ*, Kathleen Pascuzzi; Tel: 914-633-2343, E-Mail: kpascuzzi@iona.edu; *Acq*, Anthony Mastantuoni; Tel: 914-633-2028, E-Mail: amastantuoni@iona.edu; *Bibliog Instr*, Gabriela Cipollone; Tel: 914-633-2347, E-Mail: gcipollone@iona.edu; Staff 15 (MLS 8, Non-MLS 7)
Founded 1940. Enrl 4,469; Fac 169; Highest Degree: Master
Jul 1999-Jun 2000 Income (Main and Other College/University Libraries)

$1,298,493, State $8,937, Parent Institution $1,289,556. Mats Exp $350,518, Books $158,041, Per/Ser (Incl. Access Fees) $112,658, Micro $19,437, AV Equip $781, Electronic Ref Mat (Incl. Access Fees) $59,601. Sal $829,222 (Prof $510,438)
Library Holdings: Bk Vols 225,505; Per Subs 679
Subject Interests: Bus, Culture, History, Irish lang, Literature, Relig studies
Special Collections: Brother Edmund Rice Coll; Committee on the Art of Teaching Coll; Sean McBride Coll
Publications: ICL NewsFLASH; Ryan Library Bulletin
Partic in OCLC Online Computer Library Center, Inc; WALDO
Departmental Libraries:
HELEN T ARRIGONI LIBRARY-TECHNOLOGY CENTER Tel: 914-633-2608. FAX: 914-633-2136. *Coordr*, Michele Melia; Tel: 914-633-2000, Ext 4248, Fax: 914-633-2136, E-Mail: mmelia@ion.edu; Staff 3 (MLS 2, Non-MLS 1)
Library Holdings: Bk Vols 13,809
Subject Interests: Computer science, Education, Mass communications
MANHATTAN, 350 E 56th St, New York, 10022. SAN 375-5452. Tel: 212-753-3224. *Dir*, Patricia Toney; Tel: 212-688-1545, E-Mail: ptoney@iona.edu; *Librn*, Jane Mollyneaux; Tel: 212-688-1545, E-Mail: jmollyneaux@iona.edu; Staff 3 (MLS 2, Non-MLS 1)
Library Holdings: Bk Vols 1,843; Per Subs 84
Subject Interests: Behav sci, Health care admin
ROCKLAND, One Dutch Hill Rd, Orangeburg, 10962. SAN 375-5460. Tel: 914-359-2252. *Librn*, Kathleen Sullivan; Fax: 914-359-2261, E-Mail: ksullivan@iona.edu; Staff 1 (MLS 1)
Library Holdings: Bk Vols 5,751; Per Subs 40
Subject Interests: Bus, Communication arts, Computer science, Education

M MEDICAL LETTER INC LIBRARY,* 1000 Main St, 10801. SAN 311-5542. Tel: 914-235-0500. FAX: 914-235-5079. *Librn*, Arthe Kelly; E-Mail: arthe@themedicalletter.org
Founded 1959
Library Holdings: Bk Titles 300; Per Subs 204
Subject Interests: Pharmacology, Therapeutics
Partic in Health Info Librs of Westchester

P NEW ROCHELLE PUBLIC LIBRARY, One Library Plaza, 10801. SAN 352-8308. Tel: 914-632-7878. Circulation Tel: 914-632-7878, Ext 17. Reference Tel: 914-632-7878, Ext 20. FAX: 914-632-0262. Web Site: www.nrpl.org. *Dir*, Patricia Anderson; *Commun Relations*, Billie Tucker; *Ref Serv*, Beth Mills; *Ad Servs*, Daniel Ogyiri; *Ch Servs*, Kathleen Cronin; *Ch Servs*, Mary Thompson; *Tech Servs*, Pamela Thornton; *Librn*, Sandra DeCarle; Staff 40 (MLS 12, Non-MLS 28)
Founded 1894. Pop 67,265; Circ 446,557
Jan 1999-Dec 1999 Income (Main Library and Branch Library) $776,000, City $557,000, Federal $19,000, Other $200,000. Mats Exp $333,000, Books $238,000, Per/Ser (Incl. Access Fees) $87,000, Micro $8,000. Sal $990,500
Library Holdings: Bk Vols 270,989; Per Subs 3,055
Special Collections: Art Slides; Fine Art Books (Retrospective); Libretti Scores; Local History Coll; Local Newspapers from 1861; Opera; Picture Coll
Automation Activity & Vendor Info: (Cataloging) epixtech, inc.; (Circulation) epixtech, inc.; (OPAC) epixtech, inc.; (Serials) epixtech, inc.
Database Vendor: Ebsco - EbscoHost, GaleNet, IAC - SearchBank
Publications: Monthly Calendar
Mem of Westchester Library System
Friends of the Library Group
Branches: 1
HUGUENOT CHILDREN'S, 794 North Ave, 10801. SAN 377-6484. Tel: 914-632-8954. *Br Coordr*, Lynn Sheeran; Staff 2 (MLS 1, Non-MLS 1)
2000-2001 Mats Exp Books $10,000
Library Holdings: Bk Vols 4,400; Bk Titles 4,000
Database Vendor: epixtech, inc.
Friends of the Library Group

M SOUND SHORE MEDICAL CENTER OF WESTCHESTER, Health Science Library,* 16 Guion Pl, 10802. SAN 311-5550. Tel: 914-632-5000, Ext 3566. FAX: 914-576-4028. *AV*, Rachod Krumsoongnoen
Founded 1950
Library Holdings: Bk Vols 3,000; Per Subs 270
Subject Interests: Archives, AV, Hosp, Medicine, Nursing
Publications: Newsletter (quarterly)
Partic in Medical Library Center Of New York; Medline; NLM; Regional Med Libr

R TEMPLE ISRAEL OF NEW ROCHELLE, Handleman Library, 1000 Pinebrook Blvd, 10804. SAN 311-5569. Tel: 914-235-1800. FAX: 914-235-1854. *Librn*, Karen Grayson; Staff 1 (MLS 1)
Library Holdings: Bk Vols 6,500
Special Collections: Judaica
Open Wed
Friends of the Library Group

NEW WOODSTOCK

P NEW WOODSTOCK FREE LIBRARY,* Main St, 13122-0340. SAN 311-5577. Tel: 315-662-3134. *Dir*, Norm Parry
Founded 1939. Pop 900; Circ 20,236
Library Holdings: Bk Titles 15,000; Per Subs 40
Subject Interests: Local history
Mem of Mid-York Library System
Open Mon & Wed 1-5 & 7-9

NEW YORK

C ADELPHI UNIVERSITY, Manhattan Center Library,* 75 Varick St, 10013. SAN 352-4787. Tel: 212-965-8366. FAX: 212-965-8367. Web Site: www.adelphi.edu/library/branches.html. *Librn*, Michael Margolis; Staff 1 (MLS 1)
1997-1998 Income $83,246. Mats Exp $36,385, Books $15,625, Per/Ser (Incl. Access Fees) $18,755, Presv $1,005. Sal $49,286 (Prof $22,545)
Library Holdings: Bk Vols 7,451; Per Subs 117
Subject Interests: Counseling, Education, Psychology
Partic in New York Metrop Ref & Res Libr Agency

S ADVERTISING RESEARCH FOUNDATION LIBRARY,* 641 Lexington Ave, 10022. SAN 311-5593. Tel: 212-751-5656. FAX: 212-319-5265.
Founded 1936
Library Holdings: Bk Titles 3,500; Per Subs 150
Publications: Journal of Advertising Research
Restriction: Members only

AESTHETIC REALISM FOUNDATION
S AESTHETIC REALISM FOUNDATION LIBRARY, 141 Greene St, 10012-3201. SAN 328-8706. Tel: 212-777-4490. FAX: 212-777-4426. Web Site: www.aestheticrealism.org. *Librn*, Richita Anderson; Staff 1 (Non-MLS 1)
Founded 1973
Library Holdings: Bk Vols 4,800
Subject Interests: Aesthetics, Art, Drama, Literature, Physical sci, Poetry, Soc sci
Special Collections: Books & periodicals containing poems, essays, lectures by Eli Siegel & works by Aesthetic Realism consultants
Publications: Aesthetic Realism Foundation Publication: The Right of Aesthetic Realism to Be Known, Ellen Reiss, Editor (weekly per)
Restriction: Open to faculty, students & qualified researchers
The Aesthetic Realism Foundation is a not-for-profit educational foundation, teaching the philosophy Aesthetic Realism through public seminars & dramatic presentations, classes & individual consultations. Aesthetic Realism, founded by the American poet & critic Eli Siegel, is based on his historic principle: "The world, art, and self explain each other: each is the aesthetic oneness of opposites"
S ELI SIEGEL COLLECTION, 141 Greene St, 10012-3201. SAN 328-8722. Tel: 212-777-4490. FAX: 212-777-4426. Web Site: www.aestheticrealism.org. *Librn*, Richita Anderson; *Librn*, Leila Rosen; *Librn*, Meryl Simon; Staff 3 (Non-MLS 3)
Founded 1982
Library Holdings: Bk Vols 25,000; Per Subs 500
Subject Interests: Art, Economics, History, Labor, Literary criticism, Philosophy, Poetry, Sciences
Special Collections: 19th Century Periodical Literature; British & American Poetry; Early American History; French, German & Spanish Literature; Lessons & lectures by Eli Siegel, founder of Aesthetic Realism; Poetry & prose of Eli Siegel, original mss, holograph
Restriction: Open to faculty, students & qualified researchers

S AMERICAN ACADEMY OF ARTS & LETTERS LIBRARY,* 633 W 155th St, 10032. SAN 311-564X. Tel: 212-368-6361. FAX: 212-491-4615. *Dir*, Virginia Dajani; Staff 111 (MLS 111)
Library Holdings: Bk Vols 24,000
Subject Interests: Art, Literature, Manuscripts, Memorabilia, Music
Database Vendor: DRA
Restriction: By appointment only, Not open to public

S AMERICAN ACADEMY OF DRAMATIC ARTS LIBRARY,* 120 Madison Ave, 10016. SAN 311-5658. Tel: 212-686-9244, Ext 337. FAX: 212-545-7934. *Librn*, Deborah Picone; Staff 1 (MLS 1)
Founded 1978. Enrl 486
Library Holdings: Bk Titles 7,300
Subject Interests: Acting, Theater
Partic in New York Metrop Ref & Res Libr Agency

S AMERICAN ARBITRATION ASSOCIATION, Library & Information Center on The Resolution of Disputes, 1633 Broadway, Flr 10, 10019-6708. SAN 311-5682. Tel: 212-484-4127. FAX: 212-245-9572. E-Mail: referencedesk@adr.org. Web Site: www.adr.org/. *Dir*, Laura Ferris Brown; Tel: 212-484-4129; *Ref*, Steven Simpson; Staff 3 (MLS 2, Non-MLS 1)
Founded 1954
Library Holdings: Bk Vols 21,000; Per Subs 475
Subject Interests: Arbitration, Conciliation, Democratic election as it relates to bus, Domestic relations, Fact-finding, Health indust, Ins, Int political relations, Int trade disputes, Investments, Labor, Mediation

Special Collections: Arbitration Awards; Archival Coll, rpt, letters, photog, pamphlets; State, Federal & Foreign ADR Statutes; Trade Association & ADR Institution Rules
Publications: Bibliographies; The Library: Recent Acquisitions (Published quarterly in The Dispute Resolution Journal)
Partic in Dialog Corporation

S AMERICAN ASSOCIATION FOR THE INTERNATIONAL COMMISSION OF JURISTS LIBRARY,* 777 United Nations Plaza, 9th flr, 10017. SAN 370-9779. Tel: 212-972-0883. *Pres*, William J Butler
Library Holdings: Bk Vols 300; Per Subs 19

S AMERICAN ASSOCIATION OF ADVERTISING AGENCIES, Member Information Service, 405 Lexington, 18th flr, 10174. SAN 311-5690. Tel: 212-682-2500. *Mgr*, Marge Morris; *Mgr*, Koichi Tasa; *Online Servs*, Julie Zilavy; *Senior Info Specialist*, Rhonda Kleiman; *Senior Info Specialist*, Harvey Wiener; *Head Tech Servs*, Edith Ziffer; Staff 18 (MLS 12, Non-MLS 6)
Founded 1938
Library Holdings: Bk Vols 2,000; Bk Titles 1,800; Per Subs 400
Subject Interests: Advertising, Advertising agency bus, Marketing
Publications: Index to AAAA Bulletins, Newsletters & Press Releases

S AMERICAN BANKER & BOND BUYER, Editorial Library,* One State Street Plaza, 10004. SAN 311-5704. Tel: 212-803-8371. FAX: 212-843-9613. *Chief Librn*, Viki Goldman; *Librn*, James Petrassi
Library Holdings: Bk Vols 2,000; Per Subs 125
Subject Interests: Banking

SR AMERICAN BIBLE SOCIETY LIBRARY,* 1865 Broadway, 10023-9980. SAN 311-5712. Tel: 212-408-1203. FAX: 212-408-1526. E-Mail: library@americanbible.org. *Dir*, Mary Jane Ballou; Tel: 212-408-1495, E-Mail: mballou@americanbible.org; *Assoc Dir*, Jacquelyn Sapiie; E-Mail: jsapiie@americanbible.org; *Curator*, Liana Lupas; Tel: 212-408-1204, E-Mail: llupas@americanbible.org; *Cat*, Anca Giurescu; Tel: 212-408-1297, E-Mail: agiurescu@americanbible.org; *Archivist*, Orley Jones; Tel: 212-408-1445, E-Mail: ojones@americanbible.org; *Archivist*, Mary Cordato; Tel: 212-408-1258, E-Mail: mcordato@americanbible.org; *Archivist*, Maria Deptula; Tel: 212-408-1504, E-Mail: mdeptula@americanbible.org. Subject Specialists: *Preservation*, Dorothea Colligan
Founded 1816
1999-2000 Income Parent Institution $800,000
Library Holdings: Bk Vols 70,000; Per Subs 300
Subject Interests: Bible, Publishing, Relig hist, Relig in Am, Translation
Special Collections: Book Volumes in 2150 Languages (Historic Bibles Coll); The Bible and/or Its Parts (Chicago Bible Society Scripture Coll)
Publications: A Concise History of the English Bible; English Bible in America; Portraits: An American Bible Society Catalog; Scriptures of the World; The Book of a Thousand Tongues
Restriction: Open to public for reference only
Partic in OCLC Online Computer Library Center, Inc

S AMERICAN BROADCASTING CO, INC, ABC News Research Center, 47 W 66th St, 10023. SAN 311-5720. Tel: 212-456-3796. FAX: 212-456-2450. E-Mail: nrc@abc.com. *Dir*, C B Hayden; E-Mail: haydenc@abc.com; *Online Servs*, Candace Stuart; Staff 18 (MLS 11, Non-MLS 7)
Founded 1982
Library Holdings: Bk Titles 35,000; Per Subs 600
Subject Interests: Current events, International relations, Media
Automation Activity & Vendor Info: (Acquisitions) Sydney; (Cataloging) Sydney; (Circulation) Sydney; (Course Reserve) Sydney; (ILL) Sydney; (Media Booking) Sydney; (OPAC) Sydney; (Serials) Sydney
Restriction: Not open to public

S AMERICAN CRAFT COUNCIL LIBRARY, 72 Spring St, 6th flr, 10012-4019. SAN 311-5755. Tel: 212-274-0630. FAX: 212-274-0650. E-Mail: library@craftcouncil.org. Web Site: www.craftcouncil.org. *Dir*, Mary B Davis; Staff 4 (MLS 1, Non-MLS 3)
Founded 1956
Oct 1998-Sep 1999 Income $25,000
Library Holdings: Bk Titles 10,000; Per Subs 250
Subject Interests: Contemporary Am crafts
Special Collections: ACM Slide Study Coll; American Craft Council Archives; American Craft Museum Exhibition & Photograph Archives until 1990; Craft artist database & files documenting the work of ACC award winners & artists featured in American Craft magazine
Automation Activity & Vendor Info: (OPAC) Inmagic, Inc.
Publications: Bibliographic Research Guides (Research guide)
Function: Reference only, Research library
Partic in Metropolitan New York Library Council
Open Mon, Wed, Thurs, Fri 1-5, Tues 1-7

S AMERICAN FEDERATION OF JEWS FROM CENTRAL EUROPE, Research Foundation for Jewish Immigration, Inc Library, 570 Seventh Ave, 11th flr, 10018. SAN 326-3460. Tel: 212-921-3871. FAX: 212-575-1918. *Archivist, Librn*, Dennis E Rohrbaugh
Library Holdings: Bk Titles 150
Special Collections: Biographical data on German-speaking emigres from Central Europe worldwide, 1933-1945 (Archival Coll), bks, published materials, questionnaires; Jewish-German-speaking emigres in US (Oral Hist Coll), bks, transcribed taped interviews

S AMERICAN FEDERATION OF STATE, COUNTY & MUNICIPAL EMPLOYEES (DISTRICT COUNCIL 37), Dept of Research & Negotiations Library,* District Council 37, 125 Barclay St, 10007. SAN 311-578X. Tel: 212-815-1470. FAX: 212-815-1402. *Dir*, Dennis Sullivan; *Assoc Dir*, Evelyn Seinfeld
Founded 1974
Library Holdings: Bk Titles 3,800; Per Subs 150
Subject Interests: Econ, Pub sector labor relations, Trade unions, Urban affairs, With major emphasis on New York City
Special Collections: Annual Reports & Audit Reports of New York City & Agencies; Area Wage Surveys, Bureau of Labor; District Council 37 Contracts with the City of New York; Financial Reports of the City of New York; Personnel Orders & Labor; Relations Orders; Statistics, Job Specifications for the City of New York

R AMERICAN FORUM FOR GLOBAL EDUCATION LIBRARY, 120 Wall St, Ste 2600, 10005-4001. SAN 311-9505. Tel: 212-624-1300. FAX: 212-624-1412. E-Mail: globed120@aol.com. Web Site: www.globaled.org. *Pres*, Andrew Smith
Founded 1970
Library Holdings: Bk Titles 1,000; Per Subs 200
Subject Interests: Col educ, Cross-culture studies, Develop issues, Education, Elem, Environ educ, Global issues, Interdependence, International relations, Secondary, Soc change, Soc res
Publications: Issues in Global Ed (Newsletter)
Restriction: By appointment only

S AMERICAN FOUNDATION FOR THE BLIND, M Migel C Memorial Library & Information Center,* 11 Penn Plaza 300, 10001. SAN 311-5798. Tel: 212-502-7661. FAX: 212-502-7771. E-Mail: info@afb.org. Web Site: www.afb.org. *Dir*, Regina Genwright; *Mgr*, Jessica Matheson; Staff 5 (MLS 3, Non-MLS 2)
Founded 1929
Library Holdings: Bk Titles 125,000
Subject Interests: Blindness, Visual impairment
Special Collections: Helen Keller Archives
Publications: Bibliographies; fact sheets
Partic in Metropolitan New York Library Council

S AMERICAN HERITAGE MAGAZINE, A DIVISION OF FORBES INC, 60 Fifth Ave, 10011. SAN 311-5801. Tel: 212-206-5107. FAX: 212-367-3150. *Librn*, Jeanette Baik
Founded 1955
Library Holdings: Bk Vols 11,000; Per Subs 45
Subject Interests: Illustration, Photos

S AMERICAN HUNGARIAN LIBRARY & HISTORICAL SOCIETY,* 215 E 82nd St, 10028. SAN 375-7277. Tel: 212-744-5298. *In Charge*, Elizabeth Mauthner
1998-1999 Income $6,000. Mats Exp $1,200
Library Holdings: Bk Titles 4,000
Open on Thursday only

S AMERICAN INSURANCE SERVICES GROUP, Engineering & Safety Dept Information Center, 26 Broadway Tenth flr, 10004-1898. SAN 329-8310. Tel: 212-558-2016. FAX: 212-558-2110. Web Site: www.iso.com/aisg/es/es.html.
Founded 1866
Library Holdings: Bk Vols 6,000; Per Subs 110
Subject Interests: Construction safety, Fire protection, Industrial hygiene, Occupational safety, Product liability, Technology
Database Vendor: Dialog, Lexis-Nexis
Function: Research library

S AMERICAN INTERNATIONAL GROUP, Corporate Information Center Library,* 70 Pine St, 56th Fl, 10270. SAN 370-727X. Tel: 212-770-7912. FAX: 212-742-0949.
Founded 1977
Library Holdings: Bk Vols 5,000; Per Subs 300

S AMERICAN IRISH HISTORICAL SOCIETY LIBRARY,* 991 Fifth Ave, 10028. SAN 311-5860. Tel: 212-288-2263. FAX: 212-628-7927. E-Mail: amerirish@earthlink.net. Web Site: www.aihs.org. *Dir*, William Corbert; *Librn*, Phyllis Brugnolotti; E-Mail: amerirish@earthlink.net
Founded 1897
Library Holdings: Bk Vols 10,000
Subject Interests: American Irish, Gaelic lit, Irish hist, Literature
Special Collections: Daniel Cohalan Papers; Friends of Irish Freedom Papers
Publications: Newsletter (quarterly); The Recorder (semi-annual)
Open Mon-Fri 10:30-5:00

CR AMERICAN JEWISH COMMITTEE, Blaustein Library, 165 E 56th St, 10022. SAN 311-5879. Tel: 212-751-4000. FAX: 212-751-4017. E-Mail: library@ajc.org. *Dir*, Cyma M Horowitz; *Asst Librn*, Michele J Anish

Founded 1939
Library Holdings: Bk Titles 35,000; Per Subs 650
Subject Interests: Anti-Semitism, Archives, Contemporary Jewish problems, Israel

R AMERICAN JEWISH CONGRESS, Shad Polier Memorial Library, 15 E 84th St, 10028-0458. SAN 326-2332. Tel: 212-879-4500. Interlibrary Loan Service Tel: 212-360-1549. Reference Tel: 212-360-1549. FAX: 212-249-3672. *Librn*, Sarah Witt; Staff 1 (MLS 1)
Founded 1977
Library Holdings: Bk Titles 1,000; Per Subs 40
Subject Interests: Civil rights
Special Collections: AJ Congress court briefs; Commission on Law & Social Action Archives
Restriction: Staff use only
Partic in Westlaw

S AMERICAN KENNEL CLUB INC LIBRARY, 260 Madison Ave 4th flr, 10016. SAN 311-5895. Tel: 212-696-8245, 212-696-8348. FAX: 212-696-8281. E-Mail: library@akc.org. Web Site: www.akc.org/insideakc/depts.library.cfm. *Librn*, Barbara Kolk; Staff 3 (MLS 1, Non-MLS 2)
Founded 1934
Library Holdings: Bk Vols 17,000; Per Subs 300
Subject Interests: Art about dogs, Breeding, Care, Domestic, Foreign stud bks, Training of dogs
Restriction: Open to public for reference only
Partic in Metropolitan New York Library Council

S AMERICAN MERCHANT MARINE LIBRARY ASSOCIATION,* One World Trade Ctr, Ste 2161, 10048. SAN 311-5917. Tel: 212-775-1038. FAX: 212-432-5492. E-Mail: ussammla@ix.netcom.com. Web Site: www.uss-ammla.com. *Exec Dir*, Roger T Korner
Founded 1921
Jan 1998-Dec 1998 Income $124,155. Sal $36,780
Subject Interests: Admiralty law, Astronomy, Marine eng, Marine ins, Maritime history, Meteorology, Nautical lit, Navigation, Oceanography, Seamanship, Shipping, Travel
Special Collections: William P Bollman Nautical Library
This library is the only public library chartered to provide library service on ships

S AMERICAN MIME THEATRE LIBRARY, 61 Fourth Ave, 2nd Flr, 10003. SAN 370-9744. Tel: 212-777-1710. E-Mail: ammime@aol.com. Web Site: www.americanmime.org.. *Dir*, Paul J Curtis
Library Holdings: Bk Vols 425; Per Subs 27

S AMERICAN MUSEUM OF NATURAL HISTORY LIBRARY,* 79th St & Central Park W, 10024-5192. SAN 352-8510. Tel: 212-769-5400. FAX: 212-769-5009. E-Mail: libref@anmh.org. Web Site: nimidi.amnh.org. *Dir*, Tom Moritz; Tel: 212-769-5417; *Coll Develop*, Priscilla Watson; *Librn*, Sandra Kitt; Staff 26 (MLS 11, Non-MLS 15)
Founded 1869
Library Holdings: Bk Vols 487,000; Bk Titles 153,000; Per Subs 4,004
Subject Interests: Anthropology, Astronomy, Biology, Expedition, Geology, History of science, Mineralogy, Museology, Paleontology, Travel, Zoology
Special Collections: Art & Memorabilia; Natural History Film Archives; Photograph & Archives Coll; Rare Books & Manuscripts Coll
Publications: Anthropological Papers; Bull of the American Museum of Natural History Library; James Arthur Lecture Series; Novitates, Natural History
Partic in Med Libr Consortium; OCLC Online Computer Library Center, Inc
Friends of the Library Group
Branches:
DEAN MEMORIAL LIBRARY, DEPARTMENT OF ICHTHYOLOGY, 79th St at Central Park W. SAN 352-857X. Tel: 212-769-5798. FAX: 212-769-5642. *Curator*, Melanie Stiassyn
Subject Interests: Biol of fishes
OSBORN LIBRARY, 79th St & Central Park W, 10024. SAN 352-8545. Tel: 212-769-5803. *Librn*, Charlotte P Holton
Library Holdings: Bk Vols 12,000
Subject Interests: Vertebrate paleontology

S AMERICAN MUSIC CENTER, INC LIBRARY,* 30 W 26th St, Ste 1001, 10010-2011. SAN 311-5925. Tel: 212-366-5260, Ext 11. FAX: 212-366-5265. E-Mail: center@amc.net. Web Site: www.amc.net/amc/.; Staff 5 (MLS 2, Non-MLS 3)
Founded 1940
Subject Interests: Contemporary Am music
Special Collections: National Endowment for the Arts (Composer/Librettish Coll)
Publications: American Music Center Membership Directory; Opportunities in New Music
Mem of NY Pub Libr Syst
Open Mon-Fri 12:30-5:30

S AMERICAN NUMISMATIC SOCIETY LIBRARY,* Broadway at 155th St, 10032. SAN 311-5941. Tel: 212-234-3130, Ext 2. FAX: 212-234-3381. Web Site: www.amnumsoc2.org. *Librn*, Francis D Campbell; E-Mail: campbell@amnumsoc.org; *Assoc Librn*, Tamara Fultz
Founded 1858
Library Holdings: Bk Titles 100,000; Per Subs 228
Special Collections: Auction catalogs; Numismatics
Open Tues-Sun 9-4:30
Friends of the Library Group

S AMERICAN SOCIETY FOR PSYCHICAL RESEARCH INC LIBRARY,* 5 W 73rd St, 10023. SAN 311-5984. Tel: 212-799-5050. FAX: 212-496-2497. E-Mail: aspr@aspr.com. Web Site: www.aspr.com.
Founded 1885
Library Holdings: Bk Vols 8,500; Bk Titles 7,500; Per Subs 110
Subject Interests: Alternative med, Parapsychol, Philosophy, Psychology, Psys res, Relig studies, Spiritualism
Special Collections: Shaker Books & Manuscripts
Automation Activity & Vendor Info: (Cataloging) Inmagic, Inc.; (Circulation) Inmagic, Inc.
Partic in Dialog Corporation
Open Mon-Fri 10am-6pm

S AMERICAN STANDARDS TESTING BUREAU, INC, Sam Tour Memorial Library, 40 Water St, 10004-2672. (Mail add: PO Box 583, 10274-0583), SAN 311-5992. Tel: 212-943-3160. FAX: 212-825-2250. E-Mail: worldteck@aol.com. *Dir*, Dr Charles Coleman
Founded 1916
Library Holdings: Bk Titles 25,000; Per Subs 300
Subject Interests: Applied sci, Applied sci manual, Engineering, Forensic eng, Govt standards, Indust, Texts
Special Collections: National & International Standards
Restriction: Staff use only

S AMERICAN STOCK EXCHANGE, INC, Martin J Keena Memorial Library, 86 Trinity Pl, 10006-1872. SAN 311-600X. Tel: 212-306-1292. FAX: 212-306-5433. *Dir*, Sue Trowbridge; Tel: 212-306-1291, E-Mail: strowbridge@amex.com; Staff 1 (Non-MLS 1)
Founded 1966
Subject Interests: Bus, Derivatives, Finance, Options, Securities
Special Collections: Corporation Records; Fiche; Prices of all Equities & Options Listed on Amex

S ANALYTICAL PSYCHOLOGY CLUB OF NEW YORK, Kristine Mann Library, C G Jung Center of New York, 28 E 39th St, 10016. SAN 311-6018. Tel: 212-697-7877. FAX: 212-986-1743. *Dir*, Michele McKee; *Asst Librn*, David Ward; *Circ*, Steven O'Neill; Staff 3 (MLS 1, Non-MLS 2)
Founded 1945
Library Holdings: Bk Vols 20,000; Per Subs 40
Subject Interests: Analytical psychology, Jungian psychol, Mythology, Occult, Religion, Symbolism
Special Collections: Carl Gustav Jung (Jung Press Archive), photostats of press clippings
Restriction: Subscription library
Function: Research library
Open Mon 10:15-8:45, Tues & Wed 10:15-6:45; borrowing membership by subscription

S ARTHUR ANDERSEN BUSINESS INFORMATION CENTER,* 1345 Avenue of the Americas, Rm 338, 10105. SAN 311-6034. Tel: 212-708-3600. FAX: 212-708-4512. *Dir*, Lucy Lettis
Founded 1922
Library Holdings: Bk Vols 5,000; Per Subs 300
Subject Interests: Accounting
Special Collections: Finance (Moody's Manuals)
Partic in Dialog Corporation

M ANDERSON, KILL & OLICK, Law Library,* 1251 Avenue of the Americas, 10020-1182. SAN 325-5026. Tel: 212-278-1790. FAX: 212-278-1733. E-Mail: ako@andersonkill.com. *Librn*, Alina Alvarez-Lenda; *Asst Librn*, Timothy Baran
Library Holdings: Bk Vols 20,100; Bk Titles 2,500; Per Subs 150
Publications: Newsletter
Partic in Dialog Corporation; Dow Jones News Retrieval; Westlaw

S ANDREW W MELLON FOUNDATION, Nathan Marsh Pusey Library, 140 E 62nd St, 10021. SAN 375-7188. Tel: 212-838-8400. FAX: 212-888-4172. Web Site: www.mellon.org. *Dir*, Susanne Pichler; E-Mail: scp@mellon.org
Library Holdings: Bk Titles 5,230; Per Subs 233

M ANIMAL MEDICAL CENTER LIBRARY,* 510 E 62nd St, 10021. SAN 311-6042. Tel: 212-838-8100, Ext 265. FAX: 212-832-9630. E-Mail: amclibra@60@panix. *Librn*, John Lyons
Library Holdings: Bk Vols 1,000; Per Subs 75
Subject Interests: Human med, Veterinary medicine
Partic in Nat Libr of Med

S ANTHOLOGY FILM ARCHIVES, Jerome Hill Reference Library, 32 Second Ave, 10003. SAN 321-9003. Tel: 212-505-5181. FAX: 212-477-2714. *Dir*, Robert Haller; Staff 1 (MLS 1)
Founded 1970
1998-1999 Income $1,020. Mats Exp Books $250

Library Holdings: Bk Titles 7,000; Per Subs 400
Subject Interests: Avant garde film, Avant garde video
Publications: Legend of Maya Deren
Restriction: By appointment only

S ANTI-DEFAMATION LEAGUE OF B'NAI B'RITH, Rita & Leo Greenland Library & Research Center, 823 United Nations Plaza, 10017. SAN 311-6050. Tel: 212-490-2525. FAX: 212-867-7690. *Librn*, Barbara Ehrlich; Staff 4 (MLS 1, Non-MLS 3)
Founded 1939
Library Holdings: Per Subs 300
Subject Interests: Anti-Semitism, Civil rights, Discrimination, Human relations, Intergroup relations, Political extremism

S ARCHIVE OF CONTEMPORARY MUSIC,* 54 White St, 10013. SAN 371-9219. Tel: 212-226-6967. FAX: 212-226-6540. E-Mail: arcmusic@inch.com. Web Site: www.arcmusic.org. *Dir*, Robert George; *Librn*, Jason Williams; Staff 2 (MLS 2)
Founded 1986
1997-1998 Income $150,000. Mats Exp $25,000
Library Holdings: Bk Titles 7,500; Per Subs 60
Special Collections: Audio work by visual artists; Punk (New wave 7 inch singles) international
Publications: Newsletter

SR ARMENIAN APOSTOLIC CHURCH OF AMERICA, Saint Nerses Shnorhali Library, 138 E 39th St, 10016. SAN 371-5663. Tel: 212-689-7810. FAX: 212-689-7168. *Librn*, Houri Ghougassian
Founded 1975
Library Holdings: Bk Vols 8,000; Per Subs 30

S ARNHOLD & S BLEICHROEDER INC LIBRARY,* 1345 Avenue of Americas, 10105. SAN 374-9630. Tel: 212-698-3000. FAX: 212-299-4300.
Library Holdings: Bk Vols 50; Per Subs 20

S ART STUDENTS LEAGUE OF NEW YORK LIBRARY,* 215 W 57th St, 10019. SAN 311-6093. Tel: 212-247-4510. FAX: 212-541-7024. *Librn*, Belle Weinberg; *Librn*, Betty Elmann; *Librn*, Ellen Hett
Library Holdings: Bk Vols 4,500
Subject Interests: Art

S ARTISTS SPACE, Artists File Library, 38 Green St, 3rd Fl, 10013. SAN 377-5275. Tel: 212-226-3970. FAX: 212-966-1434. E-Mail: artfile@artistsspace.org. Web Site: www.artistsspace.org. *Dir*, Barbara Hunt

S ASSOCIATED PRESS, News & Information Research Center,* 50 Rockefeller Plaza, 10020-1605. SAN 374-9649. Tel: 212-621-1580. FAX: 212-621-6956.
Library Holdings: Bk Vols 200; Per Subs 15

L ASSOCIATION OF THE BAR OF THE CITY OF NEW YORK LIBRARY,* 42 W 44th St, 10036. SAN 311-6166. Tel: 212-382-6666. FAX: 212-302-8219. Web Site: www.abcny.org. *Dir*, Elizabeth H Klampert; E-Mail: eklampert@abony.org
Founded 1870
Library Holdings: Bk Vols 600,000; Bk Titles 200,000; Per Subs 2,500
Special Collections: Major collection of legal materials including appellate court records & briefs, domestic law, early Am session laws, foreign & int law
Restriction: Members only

S AUSTRIAN CULTURAL INSTITUTE LIBRARY,* 950 Third Ave, 20th flr, 10022. SAN 311-6204. Tel: 212-759-5165. FAX: 212-319-9636. E-Mail: desk@aci.org. Web Site: www.austriaculture.net. *Librn*, Friederike Zeitlhofer
Founded 1962
Library Holdings: Bk Vols 10,000; Per Subs 22
Subject Interests: Architecture, Art, Education, History, Literature, Music, Performing arts
Special Collections: Austriaca Coll

S AVSC INTERNATIONAL LIBRARY, 440 Ninth Ave, 10001. SAN 324-2870. Tel: 212-561-8000. FAX: 212-561-8068. E-Mail: infoctr@avsc.org. *Librn, Mgr*, Harriett Schick; E-Mail: hschick@avsc.org; Staff 2 (MLS 1, Non-MLS 1)
Library Holdings: Bk Vols 1,400; Per Subs 85
Subject Interests: Health, Tech assistance
Restriction: By appointment only
Partic in APLIC International Census Network; Nat Libr of Med; New York Metrop Ref & Res Libr Agency

S N W AYER & PARTNERS INC, Information Center,* 825 Eighth Ave, 10019. SAN 311-6220. Tel: 212-474-5181. FAX: 212-474-5038. *Mgr*, John Lovari
Library Holdings: Per Subs 250
Subject Interests: Advertising, Bus info, Marketing

L BAER, MARKS & UPHAM, Law Library,* 805 Third Ave, 10022. SAN 372-4441. Tel: 212-702-5931. FAX: 212-702-5941. *Librn*, Erenia Domingquez; E-Mail: domingquez@baermarks.com
Library Holdings: Bk Vols 7,500; Per Subs 120

L BAKER & MCKENZIE LIBRARY,* 805 Third Ave, 10022. SAN 311-6263. Tel: 212-891-3990. FAX: 212-759-9133. *Dir Libr Serv*, Janice E Henderson; Tel: 212-891-3967, E-Mail: janice.e.henderson@bakernet.com; *Ref*, Joanne Camejo; Tel: 212-891-3529, E-Mail: susan.chesser@bakernet.com
Founded 1971
1999-2000 Mats Exp $350,000, Books $330,000, Per/Ser (Incl. Access Fees) $10,000, Presv $10,000. Sal $199,000 (Prof $145,000)
Library Holdings: Bk Vols 25,000; Bk Titles 4,500; Per Subs 75
Subject Interests: Arbitration, Banking, Captive ins, Finance, Intellectual property, International law, Latin, S Am law, Securities, Tax
Automation Activity & Vendor Info: (Acquisitions) Sydney; (Cataloging) Sydney; (Circulation) Sydney; (OPAC) Sydney; (Serials) Sydney
Partic in CDB Infotek; CourtLink; Dialog Corporation; Dow Jones News Retrieval; Dun & Bradstreet Info Servs; Westlaw

S BANK OF NEW YORK, Information Research Department,* One Wall St, 10286. SAN 353-1392. Tel: 212-635-1599. FAX: 212-635-1568. E-Mail: reicherter@bony.com. *Mgr*, Joan M Reicherter
Founded 1920
Library Holdings: Per Subs 160
Subject Interests: Banking, Banks, Econ, Finance

C BANK STREET COLLEGE OF EDUCATION LIBRARY, 610 W 112th St, 5th Flr, 10025. SAN 311-628X. Tel: 212-875-4455. Reference Tel: 212-875-4456. FAX: 212-875-4558. Web Site: www.streetcat.bnkst.edu. *Dir Libr Serv*, Linda Greengrass; Tel: 212-875-4450, E-Mail: lindag@bnkst.edu; *Tech Servs*, Kristin Freda; Tel: 212-875-4458, E-Mail: kfreda@bnkst.edu; *Acq of New Ser*, Nora Gaines; Tel: 212-875-4457, E-Mail: ngaines@bnkst.edu; *Web Coordr*, Stacie Renfro; E-Mail: srenfro@bnkst.edu; *Ch Servs*, Lisa Von Drasek; Tel: 212-875-4452, E-Mail: lisav@bnkst.edu. Subject Specialists: *Children's literature*, Linda Greengrass; *Children's literature*, Lisa Von Drasek; *Education*, Kristin Freda; *Education*, Nora Gaines; *Education*, Stacie Renfro; Staff 10 (MLS 5, Non-MLS 5)
Founded 1916. Enrl 1,007; Fac 125; Highest Degree: Master
Jul 1999-Jun 2000 Income $601,500, State $6,000, City $2,000, Locally Generated Income $22,000, Parent Institution $563,000, Other $8,500. Mats Exp $106,300, Books $48,500, Per/Ser (Incl. Access Fees) $37,000, Presv $2,500, Micro $2,600, Electronic Ref Mat (Incl. Access Fees) $15,700. Sal $336,000 (Prof $191,000)
Library Holdings: Bk Vols 122,426; Bk Titles 80,123; Per Subs 472
Subject Interests: Adolescence, Bilingual Education, Children's literature, Early childhood educ, Education, Elementary education, Math methods, Sci educ, Soc sci, Special education
Automation Activity & Vendor Info: (Cataloging) epixtech, inc.; (Circulation) epixtech, inc.
Database Vendor: Dialog, Ebsco - EbscoHost, Lexis-Nexis, OCLC - First Search, ProQuest, Wilson - Wilson Web
Publications: Multicultural Education: A Bibliographic Essay & AIDS Education
Restriction: In-house use for visitors, Open to others by appointment
Partic in Metro NY Libr Coun; State University Of New York-NYLINK

C BARD COLLEGE, Bard Graduate Center for Studies in the Decorative Arts, Culture & Design Library, 38 W 86th St, 10024. SAN 374-5848. Tel: 212-501-3000. FAX: 212-501-3098. Web Site: www.bgc.bard.edu/library/. *Chief Librn*, Greta K Earnest; Tel: 212-501-3035, E-Mail: gearnest@bgc.bard.edu; *Reader Servs*, Stephanie Sueppel; Tel: 212-501-3036, E-Mail: topcik@bgc.bard.edu; *Tech Servs*, Erin Elliott; Tel: 212-501-3037, E-Mail: elliott@bgc.bard.edu; Staff 4 (MLS 3, Non-MLS 1)
Founded 1992. Enrl 50; Highest Degree: Doctorate
Jul 2001-Jun 2002 Mats Exp $161,000, Books $100,000, Per/Ser (Incl. Access Fees) $30,000, Micro $15,000, Electronic Ref Mat (Incl. Access Fees) $16,000. Sal $133,000
Library Holdings: Bk Titles 35,000; Per Subs 190
Subject Interests: Decorative arts, Design, Gardens, Landscaping, Material culture
Automation Activity & Vendor Info: (Acquisitions) Innovative Interfaces Inc.; (Cataloging) Innovative Interfaces Inc.; (Course Reserve) Innovative Interfaces Inc.; (OPAC) Innovative Interfaces Inc.; (Serials) Innovative Interfaces Inc.
Database Vendor: OCLC - First Search, Silverplatter Information Inc., Wilson - Wilson Web
Publications: Exhibition Catalogs
Restriction: By appointment only
Function: Research library
Partic in New York Metrop Ref & Res Libr Agency

C BARNARD COLLEGE, Wollman Library, 3009 Broadway, 10027-6598. SAN 353-037X. Tel: 212-854-3846. Interlibrary Loan Service Tel: 212-854-3953. FAX: 212-854-3766. E-Mail: refdesk@barnard.edu. Web Site: www.barnard.edu/library. *Dean of Libr*, Carol Falcione; E-Mail: cfalcione@barnard.edu; *Media Spec*, Christina Bickford; E-Mail: cbickford@barnard.edu; *Electronic Resources*, Mary Ellen Tucker; E-Mail: mtucker@barnard.edu; *Ref*, Lois Coleman; E-Mail: lcoleman@barnard.edu; *Ref*, Cynthia Johnson; E-Mail: cjohnson@barnard.edu; *Ref*, Karen Dobrusky; E-Mail: kdobrusky@barnard.edu; *Tech Servs*, Michael Elmore; E-Mail: melmore@barnard.edu; *Access Serv*, Tatiana Keis; E-Mail: tkeis@

barnard.edu; *Archivist*, Donald Glassman; E-Mail: dglassman@barnard.edu; Staff 10 (MLS 10)
Founded 1889. Enrl 2,290; Fac 201; Highest Degree: Bachelor
Jul 1999-Jun 2000 Income $1,686,055. Mats Exp $334,805, Books $163,455, Per/Ser (Incl. Access Fees) $79,792, Presv $12,920, Micro $5,036, AV Equip $19,117, Electronic Ref Mat (Incl. Access Fees) $23,110. Sal $1,001,572 (Prof $516,989)
Library Holdings: Bk Vols 194,445; Bk Titles 141,055; Per Subs 548
Special Collections: American Women Writers (Overbury Coll); Gabriela Mistral Library
Automation Activity & Vendor Info: (Cataloging) NOTIS; (Circulation) NOTIS; (OPAC) NOTIS
Publications: Catalog of Gabriela Mistral Library
Partic in Metro NY Libr Coun; New York State Interlibrary Loan Network; Research Libraries Group, Inc
Departmental Libraries:

C BARUCH COLLEGE/CUNY, (Formerly Bernard M Baruch College), William & Anita Newman Library, 151 E 25th St, 10010. (Mail add: 17 Lexington Ave Box H-0520, 10010), SAN 311-6395. Tel: 212-802-2420. FAX: 212-802-2393. Web Site: newman.baruch.cuny.edu. *Chief Librn*, Arthur Downing; Tel: 212-802-2391, E-Mail: adowning@baruch.cuny.edu; *Dep Dir*, Bliss Siman; Tel: 212-802-2394; *Coll Develop*, Douglas Duchin; Tel: 212-802-2361; *Access Serv*, Eric Neubacher; Tel: 212-802-2445; *Ref*, Bobbie Pollard; Tel: 212-802-2417; *Ref*, Mario Charles; Tel: 212-802-2434; Staff 41 (MLS 20, Non-MLS 21)
Founded 1968. Enrl 16,400; Fac 450; Highest Degree: Doctorate
Library Holdings: Bk Vols 415,621; Bk Titles 248,909; Per Subs 4,161
Subject Interests: Bus, Financial, Tax servs
Database Vendor: Dialog, Ebsco - EbscoHost, GaleNet, IAC - SearchBank, Lexis-Nexis, OCLC - First Search, ProQuest, Silverplatter Information Inc., Wilson - Wilson Web
Mem of CUNY Plus Intergrated Libr Syst
Partic in New York Metrop Ref & Res Libr Agency
Special Services for the Blind - Assistive Technology Center for Persons who are blind or physically handicapped
Friends of the Library Group
Departmental Libraries:
ELIAS LIEBERMAN HIGHER EDUCATION CONTRACT LIBRARY, Nat Ctr for Study of Collective Bargaining in Higher Educ & the Professions, 17 Lexington Ave, Box F-1228, 10010. SAN 324-6728. Tel: 212-802-6751. FAX: 212-802-5903. E-Mail: frabb@cunyum.cuny.edu. *Dir*, Victor Gotbaum
Founded 1973
Library Holdings: Bk Vols 650; Bk Titles 600; Per Subs 35
Subject Interests: Acad freedom, Collective bargaining, Discrimination, Higher educ, Professions, Retrenchment, Tenure, Unions
Special Collections: Collective bargaining agreements
Publications: Directory of Faculty Contracts (annual)

S BATES USA, Information Center, 498 Seventh Ave, Rm 2039, 10018. SAN 311-631X. Reference Tel: 212-297-8484. *Mgr*, Erika Gill; Tel: 212-297-8741, Fax: 212-297-7940, E-Mail: egill@batesww.com; Staff 5 (MLS 1, Non-MLS 4)
Founded 1940
Library Holdings: Per Subs 250
Subject Interests: Advertising, Marketing
Database Vendor: Dialog, IAC - Info Trac, Lexis-Nexis
Restriction: Company staff only
Function: For research purposes

S BAYVIEW CORRECTIONAL FACILITY LIBRARY,* 550 W 20th St, 10011-2878. SAN 327-1455. Tel: 212-255-7590. FAX: 212-255-7590. *Dir*, Edna Crespo
Library Holdings: Bk Vols 6,000
Partic in NY Pub Libr Syst
Serves 188 inmates

S BBDO, INC, Information Resource Center, 1285 Avenue of the Americas, 10019. SAN 311-6328. Tel: 212-459-5103. FAX: 212-459-6417. *Assoc Dir*, Sylvia Wachtel
Founded 1965
Library Holdings: Bk Titles 1,200; Per Subs 500
Subject Interests: Advertising, Gen bus, Marketing, Marketing research

S BEAR STEARNS & CO INC LIBRARY,* 245 Park Ave, 14th flr, 10167. SAN 329-9252. Tel: 212-272-2607. FAX: 212-272-3083. *Dir*, Robin Sanders; *Circ*, Brigitta Anderson-Crumb; Staff 6 (MLS 4, Non-MLS 2)
Library Holdings: Bk Vols 3,000; Bk Titles 1,200; Per Subs 250
Special Collections: Corporate Reports
Automation Activity & Vendor Info: (Acquisitions) Innovative Interfaces Inc.
Restriction: Staff use only

S BEHRE DOLBEAR & COMPANY LIBRARY,* 275 Madison Ave, Ste 2301, 10016. SAN 370-8446. Tel: 212-684-4150. FAX: 212-684-4438.
Library Holdings: Bk Vols 5,000; Per Subs 20

M BELLEVUE HOSPITAL CENTER, Clarence E de la Chapelle Medical Library, First Ave & 27th St, 10016. SAN 352-8812. Tel: 212-562-6535. FAX: 212-562-3506. *Dir Libr Serv*, Martha Lynch
Founded 1941
Library Holdings: Bk Titles 3,000; Per Subs 306
Subject Interests: Allied health, Medicine, Nursing
Restriction: Medical staff only
Partic in Basic Health Sciences Library Network; Manhattan-Bronx Health Sciences Libraries Group
Branches:
PATIENTS LIBRARY Tel: 212-562-3833. *Librn*, Imma Palmieri
Library Holdings: Bk Vols 5,000; Per Subs 50

S MATTHEW BENDER & COMPANY INC LIBRARY,* 2 Park Ave, 10016-5675. SAN 325-7479. Tel: 212-448-2000. FAX: 212-532-5737. E-Mail: nyo.library@bender.com. Web Site: www.bender.com. *Mgr Libr*, Marilyn Kahn; Staff 3 (MLS 2, Non-MLS 1)

J THE BERKELEY COLLEGE LIBRARY, New York Branch,* 3 E 43rd St, 10017. SAN 329-9260. Tel: 212-986-4343, Ext 172. FAX: 212-697-3371. Web Site: www.berkeleycollege.edu. *Dir*, Corazon C Estavillo; *Asst Librn*, Georgette Coffey; Staff 2 (MLS 2)
Fac 33
Library Holdings: Bk Vols 12,000; Bk Titles 10,041; Per Subs 125
Partic in OCLC Online Computer Library Center, Inc; PALINET & Union Library Catalogue of Pennsylvania

S BESSEMER TRUST COMPANY, Investment Library-Information Center, 630 Fifth Ave, 38th flr, 10111. SAN 326-3835. Tel: 212-708-9184. FAX: 212-265-5826. *Chief Librn, Dir Info Resources & Res*, Louise Stoops; E-Mail: stoops@bessemer.com; *Ref Serv Ad*, Jeffrey Liss; Tel: 212-708-9185, E-Mail: liss@bessemer.com; Staff 2 (MLS 2)
Founded 1980
Library Holdings: Bk Vols 150; Bk Titles 100; Per Subs 110
Database Vendor: Ebsco - EbscoHost, Lexis-Nexis
Restriction: Staff use only

M BETH ISRAEL MEDICAL CENTER, Seymour J Phillips Health Sciences Library, First Ave at 16th St, 10003. SAN 311-6417. Tel: 212-420-2855. FAX: 212-420-4640. *Dir*, Maria Astifidis; Staff 8 (MLS 5, Non-MLS 3)
Founded 1946
Library Holdings: Bk Vols 13,500; Bk Titles 19,000; Per Subs 600
Subject Interests: Alcohol, Allied health sci, Behav sci, Drug, Medicine, Nursing, Nursing educ, Psychiatry, Psychology, Soc sci, Surgery
Restriction: Staff use only
Partic in Medical Library Center Of New York; OCLC Online Computer Library Center, Inc; Regional Med Libr

M BETH ISRAEL MEDICAL CENTER, NORTH DIVISION, Dutka Advanced Learning Center, 170 E End Ave at 87th St, 10128. SAN 329-918X. Tel: 212-870-9470. FAX: 212-870-9482. Web Site: www.bethisraelny.org. *Librn*, Marsha Handel; E-Mail: mhandel@bethisraelny.org; *Librn*, Robert Lasner; E-Mail: rlasner@bethisraelny.org; Staff 1 (MLS 1)
Library Holdings: Bk Vols 700; Per Subs 88
Subject Interests: Medicine, Neurology, Nursing, Orthopedics
Restriction: Staff use only
Mem of NY Metrop Ref & Res Libr Agency, Inc
Partic in Manhattan-Bronx Health Sciences Libraries Group
A member of the Beth Israel Health Care System

L BIGHAM, ENGLAR, JONES & HOUSTON, Law Library,* 40 Wall St, 10005. SAN 311-6425. Tel: 212-269-5500. FAX: 212-269-4030, 212-269-4031. *Librn*, Maria Cucarese
Library Holdings: Bk Vols 10,000; Per Subs 10
Subject Interests: Ins, Maritime law

L BINGHAM, DANA & MURASE, Law Library,* 399 Park Ave, 10022. SAN 312-1305. Tel: 212-318-7838. FAX: 212-752-5378. *In Charge*, Stuart L Jacobs; E-Mail: jacobssl@bingham.com
Founded 1966
Library Holdings: Bk Vols 15,000; Per Subs 75
Special Collections: International & Japanese Law Coll; Taxation Coll

L BLANK, ROME, COMISKY & MCCAULEY LLP LIBRARY, (Formerly Tenzer, Greenblatt LLP Library), Chrysler Bldg, 405 Lexington Ave, 10174. SAN 371-5361. Tel: 212-885-5000. FAX: 212-885-5001. Web Site: www.blankrome.com. *Librn*, Preston Marshall; E-Mail: pmarshall@tenzerllp.com; Staff 3 (MLS 2, Non-MLS 1)
Library Holdings: Bk Vols 20,000; Bk Titles 3,000; Per Subs 800
Publications: Newsletter

S BOOZ, ALLEN & HAMILTON, INC, Research Services,* 101 Park Ave, 10178. SAN 311-6476. Tel: 212-697-1900, Ext 460. Interlibrary Loan Service Tel: 212-551-6450. FAX: 212-551-6732. *In Charge*, Brian Reed; Staff 12 (MLS 8, Non-MLS 4)
Founded 1945
Library Holdings: Bk Titles 3,000; Per Subs 350
Subject Interests: Bus, Corp rec, Mgt, Mgt consult, Technology

Automation Activity & Vendor Info: (Acquisitions) Inmagic, Inc.; (Cataloging) Inmagic, Inc.
Restriction: Staff use only
Partic in BRS; Compuserv; Dialog Corporation

J BOROUGH OF MANHATTAN COMMUNITY COLLEGE LIBRARY, A Philip Randolph Memorial Library, 199 Chambers St, 10007. SAN 311-6484. Tel: 212-346-8600. Interlibrary Loan Service Tel: 212-346-8605. Reference Tel: 212-346-8616. FAX: 212-346-8627. E-Mail: libbm@cunyvm.cuny.edu. Web Site: www.bmcc.cuny.edu/lib/index.html. *Chief Librn, Syst Coordr*, Sidney Eng; Tel: 212-346-8602; *Circ*, Leo Theinert; *Coll Develop*, Joanna Bevecqua; Tel: 212-346-8618; *Coll Develop*, Wanbui Mbugua; Tel: 212-346-8611; *Archivist, Per*, Evelyn Hisz; Tel: 212-346-8614; *Bibliog Instr*, Vicente Revilla; Tel: 212-346-8604; *Tech Servs*, Zhao Taian; *ILL, Tech Servs*, Taian Zhoa; *Ref Serv*, Barbara Linton; Tel: 212-346-8603; *Media Spec*, Bruce Salen; Tel: 212-346-8613; Staff 9 (MLS 9)
Founded 1964. Enrl 16,285; Fac 425; Highest Degree: Associate
1999-2000 Income $276,000. Sal $920,000
Library Holdings: Bk Vols 96,000; Per Subs 714
Subject Interests: Allied health, Bus, Computer info syst, Ethnic studies, Medicine, Mgt, Nursing
Automation Activity & Vendor Info: (Acquisitions) NOTIS; (Cataloging) NOTIS; (Circulation) NOTIS; (Course Reserve) NOTIS; (ILL) NOTIS; (OPAC) NOTIS; (Serials) NOTIS
Publications: Library Handbook; Media List; Newsletter; Periodical Holdings (irreg); Selected Bibliographies
Partic in City University of New York Film Consortia; New York Metrop Ref & Res Libr Agency
Special Services for the Blind - Closed circuit television

S BOYS' CLUB OF NEW YORK LIBRARY,* 321 E 111th St, 10029. SAN 311-6506. Tel: 212-534-2661. FAX: 212-722-9087. *Dir*, Ron Williams
Founded 1927
Library Holdings: Bk Vols 3,506; Per Subs 15

S BOZELL, INC, Media & Research Libraries,* 40 W 23th St, 10010. SAN 311-8495. Tel: 212-727-5304. FAX: 212-727-5137. *Head of Libr*, Rachel Belton
Library Holdings: Bk Vols 700; Per Subs 250
Subject Interests: Advertising, Marketing
Restriction: Staff use only

S BRANT PUBLICATIONS, INC, The Magazine Antiques Library, 575 Broadway, 5th Flr, 10012. SAN 327-6317. Tel: 212-941-2800. FAX: 212-941-2819. *In Charge*, Allison Eckardt Ledes
Library Holdings: Bk Vols 5,500

L BRIGER & ASSOCIATES LIBRARY,* 300 Park Ave, 24th flr, 10022. SAN 329-8469. Tel: 212-758-4000. FAX: 212-888-7587. *Librn*, Erika Soldano
Library Holdings: Bk Vols 4,000

S BRITISH INFORMATION SERVICES LIBRARY, 845 Third Ave, 10022-6691. SAN 311-6565. Tel: 212-745-0277. FAX: 212-758-5395. E-Mail: media.enquiries@newyork.mail.fco.gov.uk. Web Site: www.britainusa.com. *Dir*, Leslie Slocum; Tel: 212-745-0258, E-Mail: leslie.slocum@newyork.mail.fco.gov.uk; Staff 5 (MLS 1, Non-MLS 4)
Founded 1942
Library Holdings: Bk Titles 3,000; Per Subs 50
Subject Interests: United Kingdom
Special Collections: British Government Publications (HMSO)
Automation Activity & Vendor Info: (Acquisitions) EOS; (Cataloging) EOS; (Serials) EOS

L BROWN & WOOD LLP LIBRARY,* One World Trade Ctr, 10048. SAN 311-6581. Tel: 212-839-5444. FAX: 212-839-5599. *Librn*, Connie L Kluever; E-Mail: ckluever@brownwoodlaw.com
Library Holdings: Bk Vols 20,000

S BRUNDAGE, STORY & ROSE, Investment Counsel Library,* One Broadway 5th flr, 10004. SAN 311-659X. Tel: 212-530-0760. FAX: 212-425-4286. *Librn*, Kathleen M Halston; Staff 2 (MLS 1, Non-MLS 1)
Founded 1932
Library Holdings: Bk Titles 1,100; Per Subs 225
Subject Interests: Agr-zinc, Econ, Investing
Special Collections: Corporate Records; Wall Street Journal (1942 to date), micro

S BURSON-MARSTELLER, Knowledge Center,* 230 Park Ave S, 10003. SAN 311-8851. Tel: 212-614-4255. Interlibrary Loan Service Tel: 212-614-4257. FAX: 212-598-5581. *Mgr*, Chris Florez
Founded 1955
Library Holdings: Bk Titles 1,000; Per Subs 114
Subject Interests: Advertising, Consumer marketing, Indust, Pub relations
Partic in Corporate Profound; Data Time; Dialog Corporation; Dow Jones News Retrieval; Investext

S BUTTENWIESER LIBRARY, 92nd Street Young Men's & Young Women's Hebrew Association, 1395 Lexington Ave, 10128-1612. SAN 311-6638. Tel: 212-415-5542. FAX: 212-427-6119. E-Mail: library@92ndst.org. *Librn*, Lynn Feinman; Tel: 212-415-5543, E-Mail: ifeinman@92ndsty.org; Staff 5 (MLS 2, Non-MLS 3)
Founded 1874
Library Holdings: Bk Titles 30,000; Per Subs 90
Subject Interests: Judaica, Poetry
Special Collections: Archives of parent institution
Restriction: Open to public for reference only
Function: Archival collection
Special Services for the Blind - Videos on blindness & physical handicaps

S BUTTERICK PATTERNS ARCHIVES LIBRARY,* 161 Sixth Ave, 10013. SAN 311-6646. Tel: 212-620-2790. FAX: 212-620-2562. *Archivist, Mgr*, Sherry Onna Handlin
Founded 1968
Library Holdings: Bk Titles 5,000; Per Subs 25
Subject Interests: Fashion, Graphic arts
Special Collections: Fashion Art
Restriction: By appointment only
Function: For research purposes

M CABRINI MEDICAL CENTER, Dr Massimo Bazzini Memorial Library, 227 E 19th St, 10003. SAN 311-6662. Tel: 212-995-6630. FAX: 212-995-6639. *Librn*, Dorothy Schwartz; Staff 1 (MLS 1)
Founded 1930
Library Holdings: Bk Vols 3,500; Per Subs 210
Subject Interests: Medicine, Nursing, Surgery
Publications: Acquisitions List; AV List; Library Guide (annually) Periodical List
Restriction: By appointment only
Partic in Medical Library Center Of New York; Nat Libr of Med; New York Metrop Ref & Res Libr Agency

L CADWALADER, WICKERSHAM & TAFT LIBRARY, 100 Maiden Lane, 10038. SAN 311-6670. Tel: 212-504-6000. Interlibrary Loan Service Tel: 212-504-6767. FAX: 212-412-7041. Web Site: www.cadwalder.com. *Librn*, Rissa Peckar; *Ref*, Catherine Backes; *Ref*, Joseph L Biagiotti; *Ref*, Melissa Bopp; *Ref*, Lisa Fricker; *Ref*, Kathryn McRae; *Ref*, Sarah Mitchell; Staff 14 (MLS 6, Non-MLS 8)
Library Holdings: Bk Titles 40,000
Subject Interests: Acquisitions, Banking, Commodities, Gen corp, Healthcare, Insolvency, Litigation, Mergers, Project finance, Real estate, Securities, Tax
Publications: Associates Manual; Check It Out (newsletter); Internet Ink
Partic in D&B

S CAHILL GORDON & REINDEL LIBRARY, 80 Pine St, 10005. SAN 311-6689. Tel: 212-701-3542. FAX: 212-269-5420. *Librn*, Margaret J Davenport; Staff 11 (MLS 2, Non-MLS 9)
Library Holdings: Bk Vols 55,000; Per Subs 478
Subject Interests: Antitrust, Corporate, Securities, Tax law
Special Collections: Legislative Histories & Law Reports Coll
Partic in Data Time; Dialog Corporation; Dow Jones News Retrieval; Newsnet; Vutext

S CAHNERS PUBLISHING CO, Frederic G Melcher Library, 245 W 17th St, 10011. SAN 311-6492. Tel: 212-463-6850. *Librn*, Jean Peters
Founded 1962
Library Holdings: Bk Vols 8,000; Per Subs 300
Subject Interests: Book trade, Libr sci
Special Collections: Books About Books

S CANADIAN CONSULATE GENERAL LIBRARY,* 1251 Avenue of the Americas, 10020-1175. SAN 311-6700. Tel: 212-596-1628. FAX: 212-596-1792. E-Mail: cngnylib@pipeline.com. Web Site: canada-ny.org. *Dir*, Curtis Field
Founded 1945
Library Holdings: Bk Vols 6,000; Per Subs 220
Subject Interests: Bus, Cultural affairs, Econ, Geography, Government, History, Indust, Law, Politics, Trade
Special Collections: Can; Statistics Canada, Annual Reports of Canadian Companies
Restriction: By appointment only
Partic in Dialog Corporation; Dow Jones News Retrieval; Info Globe; Infomart

S CARIBBEAN CULTURE CENTER LIBRARY,* 408 W 58th St, 10019. SAN 371-2419. Tel: 212-307-7420. FAX: 212-315-1086. *Asst Dir*, Melody Capote
Library Holdings: Bk Vols 1,075

S CARNEGIE CORPORATION OF NEW YORK LIBRARY, 437 Madison Ave, 10022. SAN 323-5432. Tel: 212-371-3200. FAX: 212-754-4073. E-Mail: rs@carnegie.org. Web Site: www.carnegie.org. *Librn*, Ron Sexton; Staff 3 (MLS 1, Non-MLS 2)
Founded 1911
Library Holdings: Bk Titles 4,502; Per Subs 200
Restriction: Not open to public
Corporation's archives housed at the Rare Book & Manuscript Library, Columbia University, New York, NY. Tel: 212-854-8937

S GUY CARPENTER & CO, INC, Library & Information Services, 2 World Trade Ctr, 10048. SAN 324-7872. Tel: 212-323-1800. FAX: 212-313-4972. *Chief Librn*, Valerie Logan; Staff 5 (MLS 2, Non-MLS 3)
Founded 1980
Library Holdings: Bk Vols 3,000; Per Subs 125
Subject Interests: Casualty ins, Property ins, Reinsurance

L CARTER, LEDYARD & MILBURN LIBRARY,* 2 Wall St, 10005. SAN 311-6727. Tel: 212-238-8746. FAX: 212-732-3232. *Librn*, Julius M Pomerantz; *Asst Librn*, Emily Moog
Library Holdings: Bk Vols 19,500; Per Subs 27

SR CATHEDRAL CHURCH OF SAINT JOHN THE DIVINE LIBRARY, 1047 Amsterdam Ave, 10025. SAN 311-6743. Tel: 212-316-7495. *Librn*, Madeleine L'Engle Franklin; *Asst Librn*, Charlotte Jones
Founded 1957
Library Holdings: Bk Vols 15,000; Per Subs 1,000
Subject Interests: Architecture, Art, Behav sci, Biblical studies, Biog, Philosophy, Prayer books, Soc sci, Theology
Special Collections: Barbara Simonds Coll; Canon Edward West Coll; William Reed Huntington Coll

S CBS, News Reference Library, 524 W 57th St, 10019. SAN 311-6654. Tel: 212-975-2877. FAX: 212-975-7766. *Dir*, Laura B Kapnick; *Mgr*, Cryder Bankes; *Mgr*, Leslie Kuizema; *Mgr*, Carole D Parnes; *Librn*, Jean Stevenson; Staff 9 (MLS 6, Non-MLS 3)
Founded 1940
Library Holdings: Bk Vols 31,000; Bk Titles 24,000; Per Subs 250
Subject Interests: Biography, Broadcasting, Current events, Government, History, Politics
Special Collections: CBS News Broadcasts Coll (transcripts)
Automation Activity & Vendor Info: (Acquisitions) Sydney; (Cataloging) Sydney; (Circulation) Sydney; (ILL) Sydney; (OPAC) Sydney; (Serials) Sydney
Restriction: By appointment only

L CBS BROADCASTING NETWORK, Law Department Library, 51 W 52nd St, 36th flr, 10019. SAN 372-4557. Tel: 212-975-4260. FAX: 212-975-5721. *Librn*, Marilee Martel; E-Mail: mnmartel@cbs.com
Library Holdings: Bk Vols 9,000; Per Subs 40

S CENTER FOR CUBAN STUDIES LIBRARY, Lourdes Casal Library, 124 W 23rd St, 10011. SAN 311-676X. Tel: 212-242-0559. FAX: 212-242-1937. E-Mail: cubanctr@igc.org. Web Site: cubanartspace.net, www.cubanartuspace.net. *Librn*, Jerome Nickel
Library Holdings: Bk Vols 6,000; Per Subs 30
Subject Interests: Cuban hist, Culture, International relations, Literature, Soc

M CENTER FOR MEDICAL CONSUMERS & HEALTH INFORMATION LIBRARY,* 237 Thompson St, 10012. SAN 329-9236. Tel: 212-674-7105. FAX: 212-674-7100. E-Mail: medconsumers@earthlink.net. Web Site: www.medicalconsumers.org. *Exec Dir*, Arthur Levin
Founded 1976
Library Holdings: Bk Titles 2,000; Per Subs 25
Subject Interests: AIDS, Breast cancer, Cancer treatment, Med consumerism, Nutrition
Publications: HealthFacts (monthly)

M CENTER FOR MODERN PSYCHOANALYTIC STUDIES LIBRARY,* 16 W Tenth St, 10011. SAN 320-2119. Tel: 212-260-7050. FAX: 212-228-6410.
Founded 1972. Enrl 260; Fac 40
Library Holdings: Bk Vols 5,000; Bk Titles 4,500; Per Subs 10
Subject Interests: Psychiatry, Psychoanalysis, Psychology, Sociology
Special Collections: Psychoanalysts Research Projects Coll
Friends of the Library Group

S CENTER FOR THE STUDY OF THE PRESIDENCY LIBRARY,* 208 E 75th St, 10021. SAN 320-7161. Tel: 212-249-1200. FAX: 212-628-9503. E-Mail: csp@aol.com. *In Charge*, Dr R Gordon Hoxie
Library Holdings: Bk Vols 3,000; Per Subs 15
Special Collections: Benjamin Franklin Coll, bks; Complete George Washington Papers Coll, microfilm; Foreign-Policy Coll
Publications: Presidential Studies Quarterly

S CENTRO DE ESTUDIOS PUERTORRIQUENOS, Center for Puerto Rican Studies,* Hunter College, E 1429, 14th flr, 695 Park Ave, Box 548, 10021. SAN 325-7533. Tel: 212-772-4197. FAX: 212-650-3628. *Librn*, Amilcar Tirado; *Librn*, Nelida Perez
Library Holdings: Bk Vols 10,000
Special Collections: Puerto Rican Dissertation Coll

S THE CENTURY ASSOCIATION LIBRARY, 7 W 43rd St, 10036. SAN 311-6778. Tel: 212-944-0090. FAX: 212-840-3609. E-Mail: calib1@rmi.net. *Librn*, W Gregory Gallagher; Staff 2 (MLS 2)
Founded 1847
Library Holdings: Bk Titles 23,000
Special Collections: Charles A Platt Library
Publications: Newsletter
Restriction: Members only
Partic in Metro NY Libr Coun

L CHADBOURNE & PARKE LIBRARY,* 30 Rockefeller Plaza, 33rd flr, 10112. SAN 311-6786. Tel: 212-408-1035 (Interlibrary Loan Services Tel No), 212-408-5286. FAX: 212-765-6923. *Dir*, Lillian Arcuri; E-Mail: arcuri@way.com; *Asst Dir*, Michael B Roth; *Assoc Librn, Tech Servs*, Anna Smallen; Staff 12 (MLS 6, Non-MLS 6)
Library Holdings: Bk Vols 70,000; Bk Titles 8,000
Subject Interests: Corp proj finance estates trust litigation, Ins, Labor, Real estate, Taxation
Publications: Newsletter (bi-monthly)
Partic in RLIN

CHASE MANHATTAN BANK

L LEGAL RESEARCH & INFORMATION SERVICES UNIT, One Chase Manhattan Plaza, 25th flr, 10081. SAN 321-3765. Tel: 212-552-2499, 212-552-7820. FAX: 212-383-0252. *In Charge*, Tamar Raum; E-Mail: tammy.raum@chase.com
Library Holdings: Bk Vols 35,000; Per Subs 250
Subject Interests: Banking law
Special Collections: Legislative Histories, microforms
Publications: Newsletters
Friends of the Library Group

S CHILDREN'S BOOK COUNCIL LIBRARY, 12 W 37th St, 2nd Flr, 10018-7480. SAN 311-6840. Tel: 212-966-1990. FAX: 212-966-2073. E-Mail: staff@cbcbooks.org. Web Site: www.cbcbooks.org. *Pres*, Paula Quint; *Online Servs*, Stephen Christensen
Founded 1945
Library Holdings: Bk Titles 6,500; Per Subs 45
Subject Interests: Bibliog, Bks about children's bks, Current children's trade bks, Selected prize winning children's bks
Special Collections: National Children's Book Week Posters 1919-2001
Publications: CBC Features (Newsletter)

S CHINESE INFORMATION & CULTURE CENTER LIBRARY,* 1230 Avenue of the Americas 2nd flr, 10020-1513. SAN 373-1081. Tel: 212-373-1834. FAX: 212-373-1866. E-Mail: roctaiwan@taipei.org. Web Site: www.taipei.org. *Dir*, Yu Yuh-Chao; *Coll Develop, Librn*, Verna Tang
Library Holdings: Bk Vols 40,000; Per Subs 250
Subject Interests: China
Special Collections: Government Documents of Taiwan
Publications: CICC Currents
Partic in RLIN

S CIBC WORLD MARKETS CORP, Information Center, CIBC Oppenheimer Tower, One World Financial Ctr, 8th flr, 10281. SAN 327-9324. Tel: 212-667-7890. FAX: 212-667-5792. *Dir*, Marilyn H Adamo
Library Holdings: Bk Titles 4,200; Per Subs 1,200
Subject Interests: Finance
Special Collections: SEC Filings, 1982-present
Publications: Library News
Restriction: Not open to public

L CITICORP, Law Library,* 425 Park Ave, 2nd flr, 10043. SAN 321-785X. Tel: 212-559-8990. FAX: 212-793-4400. *Librn*, Amparo Reyes; Staff 2 (MLS 1, Non-MLS 1)
Founded 1977
Library Holdings: Bk Vols 10,000; Bk Titles 600; Per Subs 40
Subject Interests: Banking, Compliance, Intellectual property, Securities, Telecommunications
Special Collections: Legal Memos
Publications: Library Information Bulletin; Library Newsletter; Recent Additions List
Restriction: Staff use only

G CITIZENS UNION FOUNDATION LIBRARY, 198 Broadway, 10038. SAN 323-6013. Tel: 212-227-0342. FAX: 212-227-0345. E-Mail: citizens@citizensunion.org. *Exec Dir*, Stone-Davidoff Linda; *Admin Dir*, Jasper Niblock
Founded 1948
Library Holdings: Bk Vols 1,000; Bk Titles 400
Special Collections: NY City Charter Revision Commission
Restriction: By appointment only
Files on past & present elected local officials of New York City & state legislative issues

C CITY COLLEGE OF THE CITY UNIVERSITY OF NEW YORK, Morris Raphael Cohen Library, North Academic Ctr, 138th St & Convent Ave, 10031. SAN 352-9177. Tel: 212-650-7155. Interlibrary Loan Service Tel: 212-650-7616. Reference Tel: 212-650-7611, 212-650-7612. FAX: 212-650-7604. E-Mail: illcc@cunyvm.cuny.edu. Web Site: www.ccny.cuny.edu/library. *Chief Librn*, Pamela Gillespie; Tel: 212-650-7271, E-Mail: prgcc@scisun.sci.cuny.edu; *Archivist*, Sydney Van Nort; Tel: 212-650-7609, E-Mail: ccacc@cunyvm.cuny.edu; *Publ Servs*, Richard Uttich; Tel: 212-650-7267, E-Mail: rmucc@cunyvm.cuny.edu; *Acq*, Jacqueline Gill; Tel: 212-650-7151,

Fax: 212-650-7618, E-Mail: jaccc@cunyvm.cuny.edu; *Cat*, Laurel Franklin; Tel: 212-650-7623, E-Mail: lifcc@cunyvm.cuny.edu; *ILL*, Evelyn Bodden; Fax: 212-650-7648, E-Mail: illcc@cunyvm.cuny.edu; *Tech Servs*, Charles Stewart; Tel: 212-650-5369, E-Mail: chscc@cunyvm.cuny.edu; *Ref*, Robert Laurich; Tel: 212-650-7153, E-Mail: roblaurich@aol.com; *Instrul Serv*, Jeffrey Clapp; Tel: 212-650-6708, Fax: 212-650-5924, E-Mail: jeffrey@ccny.cuny.edu; Staff 37 (MLS 19, Non-MLS 18)
Founded 1849. Enrl 14,157; Fac 470; Highest Degree: Master
Library Holdings: Bk Vols 1,366,006; Bk Titles 766,064; Per Subs 2,853
Subject Interests: Am archit, Animal behavior, Art, Biochemistry, Black studies, Chemistry, Ecology, History, Law, Organic, Physics, Solid state, Spectroscopy, Urban planning
Special Collections: (Russell Sage Coll); 18th & Early 19th Century Plays; Astronomy (Newcomb Coll); Costume Coll; English Civil War Pamphlets; Metropolitan Applied Research Center (MARC) Archives; Poetry (Library of Contemporary Poets: Readings From 1932-1941), rec; Social Welfare & Related Fields; Socio-Economic Broadsides before 1800 on microfilm (Gitelson Coll)
Automation Activity & Vendor Info: (Acquisitions) NOTIS; (Cataloging) NOTIS; (Circulation) NOTIS; (Course Reserve) NOTIS; (ILL) NOTIS; (Media Booking) NOTIS; (OPAC) NOTIS; (Serials) NOTIS
Database Vendor: Dialog, Ebsco - EbscoHost, IAC - Info Trac, Lexis-Nexis, OCLC - First Search, ProQuest, Silverplatter Information Inc., Wilson - Wilson Web
Publications: Circumspice; Library Handbook
Function: Archival collection, Document delivery services, ILL available, ILL to other special libraries, Literary searches, Outside services via phone, cable & mail, Photocopies available, Reference services available, Referrals accepted, Research library, Some telephone reference
Partic in New York Metrop Ref & Res Libr Agency; OCLC Online Computer Library Center, Inc
Friends of the Library Group
Departmental Libraries:
ARCHITECTURE, Shepard Hall, Rm 408, 138th St & Convent Ave, 10031. SAN 352-9207. Tel: 212-650-8767. FAX: 212-650-7214. Web Site: www.ccny.cuny.edu/library/divisions/architecture/index.html. *Librn*, Judith Connorton; E-Mail: jmccc@cunyvm.cuny.edu. Subject Specialists: *Art and architecture*, Judith Connorton; Staff 2 (MLS 1, Non-MLS 1)
Subject Interests: Architecture, Art, Urban landscape planning, Urban planning
COLLEGE ARCHIVES & SPECIAL COLLECTIONS, North Academic Ctr-Cohen Library, 138th St & Convent Ave, 10031. SAN 352-9231. Tel: 212-650-7609. FAX: 212-650-7604. E-Mail: ccacc@cunyvm.cuny.edu. Web Site: www.ccny.cuny.edu/library/divisions/archives/index.html. *Archivist*, Sydney Van Nort; E-Mail: sunnyv57@hotmail.com; Staff 1 (MLS 1)
Special Collections: First Editions & Rare Books; Papers of Cleveland Abbe, R R Bowker, Townsend Harris, J H Finley, Waldemar Kaempffert, L F Mott, Edward M Shepard, Alexander Webb & Everett Wheeler; Source material relating to free higher education in New York since 1847; William Butler Yeats, printed editions
MUSIC, Shepard Hall, Rm 160, 138th & Convent Ave, 10031. SAN 352-9355. Tel: 212-650-7174. FAX: 212-650-7231. Web Site: www.ccny.cuny.edu/library/divisions/music/index.html. *Librn*, Ruth Henderson; Tel: 212-650-7120, E-Mail: ruhcc@cunyvm.cuny.edu. Subject Specialists: *Music*, Ruth Henderson; Staff 2 (MLS 1, Non-MLS 1)
SCIENCE-ENGINEERING, Marshak Bldg, Rm 29, 138th St & Convent Ave, 10031. SAN 352-938X. Tel: 212-650-8246. Reference Tel: 212-650-5712. FAX: 212-650-7626. Web Site: www.ccny.cuny.edu/library/divisions/science/index.html. *Librn*, Philip Barnett; Tel: 212-650-8243, E-Mail: phbcc@cunyvm.cuny.edu; *Librn*, Claudia Lascar; Tel: 212-650-6826, E-Mail: claudialascar@hotmail.com. Subject Specialists: *Sci-eng*, Mendelsohn Loren; Staff 5 (MLS 3, Non-MLS 2)
Friends of the Library Group

C CITY UNIVERSITY OF NEW YORK, Mina Rees Library of Graduate School & University Center, 365 Fifth Ave, 10016-4309. SAN 311-6883. Tel: 212-817-7040. Circulation Tel: 212-817-7083. Reference Tel: 212-817-7077. FAX: 212-817-1604. E-Mail: mrlgc@cunyvm.cuny.edu. Web Site: web.gc.cuny.edu/library. *Chief Librn*, Susan T Newman; Tel: 212-817-7060, E-Mail: snewman@gc.cuny.edu; *Head Tech Servs, Ser*, Minna C Saxe; Tel: 212-817-7075, E-Mail: msaxe@gc.cuny.edu; *Head Ref*, Marilyn Geels; Tel: 212-817-7059, E-Mail: mgeels@gc.cuny.edu; *Acq*, Ofelia Rabassa; *Cat*, Men-Sze Butt; Tel: 212-817-7072, E-Mail: mbutt@gc.cuny.edu; *Cat*, Neil Jacobowitz; Tel: 212-817-7067, E-Mail: njacobowitz@gc.cuny.edu; *Web Coordr*, James Michael Adams; Tel: 212-817-7055, E-Mail: madams@gc.cuny.edu; *Music*, David Gilbert; Tel: 212-817-7056, E-Mail: dgilbert@gc.cuny.edu; *ILL*, Beth Posner; Tel: 212-817-7051, E-Mail: bposner@gc.cuny.edu; *Syst Coordr*, Saad Abulhab; Staff 19 (MLS 9, Non-MLS 10)
Founded 1964. Enrl 4,000; Highest Degree: Doctorate
Jul 1999-Jun 2000 Mats Exp $427,587, Books $98,432, Per/Ser (Incl. Access Fees) $252,377, Presv $3,000, Other Print Mats $2,399, Electronic Ref Mat (Incl. Access Fees) $71,379
Library Holdings: Bk Vols 275,808; Per Subs 1,640
Special Collections: American History (US Presidential Papers), microfilm; City University of New York; Old York Library (Seymour Durst Coll)
Automation Activity & Vendor Info: (Acquisitions) NOTIS; (Cataloging) NOTIS; (Circulation) NOTIS; (OPAC) NOTIS; (Serials) NOTIS
Database Vendor: Ebsco - EbscoHost, GaleNet, IAC - Info Trac, Lexis-Nexis, ProQuest, Silverplatter Information Inc., Wilson - Wilson Web
Restriction: Open to student, faculty & staff
Partic in Metropolitan New York Library Council; New York Metrop Ref & Res Libr Agency
Friends of the Library Group

GL CIVIL COURT OF THE CITY OF NEW YORK LIBRARY,* 111 Centre St, Rm 1034, 10013. SAN 311-6891. Tel: 212-374-6250, 212-374-8043. FAX: 212-748-5171. *Librn*, Jacob Chacko
Founded 1962
Library Holdings: Bk Vols 60,000
Subject Interests: Commercial law, Procedures, Real property, Torts

L CLEARY, GOTTLIEB, STEEN & HAMILTON LIBRARY,* One Liberty Plaza, 10006. SAN 311-6913. Tel: 212-225-3444. FAX: 212-225-3449. *Dir Libr Serv*, Karol M Sokol; Staff 12 (MLS 6, Non-MLS 6)
Library Holdings: Bk Titles 25,000
Subject Interests: Foreign, Int taxation, International law

L CLIFFORD CHANCE ROGERS & WELLS LIBRARY, 200 Park Ave, 51st flr, 10166. SAN 312-0368. Tel: 212-878-8095, 212-878-8210. Reference Tel: 212-878-8211. FAX: 212-878-3474, 212-878-8375. Web Site: www.cliffordchance.com. *Dir Libr Serv*, Shireen Kumar; *Coordr, Tech Servs*, Josephine Pascual; Tel: 212-878-3241, E-Mail: josephine.pascual@cliffordchance.com; Staff 10 (MLS 6, Non-MLS 4)
Founded 1871
Library Holdings: Bk Vols 25,000; Per Subs 300

S AUDREY COHEN COLLEGE LIBRARY, 75 Varick St, 12th Flr, 10013. SAN 311-6956. Tel: 212-343-1234, Ext 5007. Circulation Tel: 212-343-1234, Ext 2001. Reference Tel: 212-343-1234, Ext 2010. FAX: 212-343-7398. E-Mail: library@audreycohen.edu. Web Site: www.audreycohen.edu/htm/body_libinfo.html. *Dir*, Robert J Dorn; Tel: 212-343-1234, Ext 2011, E-Mail: dornr@audreycohen.edu; *Branch Mgr*, Nirmala Bhattacharya; Tel: 718-886-9462, E-Mail: bhattacharyan@audreycohen.edu; *Branch Mgr*, Stephanie Cimino; Tel: 718-420-0157, Ext 11, E-Mail: ciminos@audreycohen.edu; *Branch Mgr*, Robert Erler; Tel: 718-993-8426, E-Mail: erlerr@audreycohen.edu; *Publ Servs*, Gregory Lewis; Tel: 212-343-1234, Ext 2007, E-Mail: lewisg@audreycohen.edu; *ILL*, Jane Kingsland; Tel: 212-343-1234, Ext 2014, E-Mail: kingslandj@audreycohen.edu; *Syst Coordr*, Barbara Breiman; Tel: 212-343-1234, Ext 2008, E-Mail: breimanb@audreycohen.edu; *Tech Servs*, Linda Wadas; Tel: 212-343-1234, Ext 2005, E-Mail: wadasl@audreycohen.edu; *Tech Servs*, Linda Wadas; Tel: 212-343-1234, Ext 2005, E-Mail: wadasl@audreycohen.edu; *Ref*, Jane Kingsland; Tel: 212-343-1234, Ext 2014, E-Mail: kingslandj@audreycohen.edu; *Head, Circ*, Sandra Greene; Tel: 212-343-1234, Ext 2003, E-Mail: greenes@audreycohen.edu; *Circ*, Blondel Brown; Tel: 212-343-1234, Ext 2002, E-Mail: brownb@audreycohen.edu. Subject Specialists: *Admin*, Robert J Dorn; *Human resources*, Jane Kingsland; *Management*, Jane Kingsland; *Ref*, Jane Kingsland; *Ref*, Robert Erler; *Reference*, Gregory Lewis; Staff 21 (MLS 13, Non-MLS 8)
Founded 1966
Jan 2000-Dec 2000 Income $23,950, State $5,800, Locally Generated Income $18,150. Mats Exp $239,050, Books $128,500, Per/Ser (Incl. Access Fees) $23,000, Electronic Ref Mat (Incl. Access Fees) $15,000. Sal $469,000 (Prof $326,000)
Library Holdings: Bk Vols 29,580; Bk Titles 25,200; Per Subs 268
Subject Interests: Human services, Management, Med mgt, Res mgt
Special Collections: Audrey Cohen Archives
Automation Activity & Vendor Info: (Circulation) SIRSI; (Course Reserve) SIRSI; (OPAC) SIRSI; (Serials) SIRSI
Database Vendor: Dialog, Ebsco - EbscoHost, Lexis-Nexis, OCLC - First Search, Silverplatter Information Inc., Wilson - Wilson Web
Publications: Library Matters (Newsletter)
Function: For research purposes
Partic in Metro NY Libr Coun; OCLC Online Computer Library Center, Inc; WALDO

M COLER MEMORIAL HOSPITAL, Medical Library,* Roosevelt Island, 10044. SAN 311-693X. Tel: 212-318-4375, 212-318-4800, 212-848-6070. FAX: 212-848-6945. *Dir*, Dr Martin M Leibovici
Founded 1964
Library Holdings: Bk Vols 3,140; Per Subs 210
Subject Interests: Chronic disease gen med, Geriatrics, Hearing, Psychiatry, Rehab med, Speech

S COLLECTORS CLUB LIBRARY,* 22 E 35th St, 10016-3806. SAN 311-6948. Tel: 212-683-0559. FAX: 212-481-1269. *Chairperson*, Robert Mitchell; *In Charge*, Irene Bromberg
Founded 1896
Jan 1998-Dec 1998 Income $3,850, Locally Generated Income $250, Parent Institution $3,600. Mats Exp $6,500, Books $1,500, Per/Ser (Incl. Access Fees) $5,000
Library Holdings: Bk Titles 30,000; Per Subs 30
Subject Interests: Philately, Postal history
Publications: Collectors Club Philatelist
The Collectors Club Library is currently installing a computerized

information retrieval system in conjunction with the American Philatelic Research Library in State College, Pennsylvania. The system will allow members & other researchers at this library to access information on holdings of both libraries so that items not available at one institution may be accessible at the other; due to limited staff, we cannot honor requests to furnish research information; the public is asked not to address letters to the librarian asking for research information

C COLLEGE OF INSURANCE LIBRARY,* 101 Murray St, 10007. SAN 311-6964. Tel: 212-815-9263. FAX: 212-815-9272. Web Site: www.tci.edu/library. *Coll Develop, Dir*, Barbie E Keiser; Staff 6 (MLS 5, Non-MLS 1)
Founded 1901
May 1998-Apr 1999 Income $77,936, State $4,690, Other $73,246. Mats Exp $251,262, Books $124,615, Per/Ser (Incl. Access Fees) $48,434, Presv $842, AV Equip $919, Electronic Ref Mat (Incl. Access Fees) $76,452. Sal $233,308 (Prof $24,707)
Library Holdings: Bk Vols 100,706; Bk Titles 91,830; Per Subs 436
Subject Interests: Actuarial sci, Ins (all kinds), Risk mgt, Workers comp
Special Collections: Earthquake (Heber B Churchill Coll); Insurance (Winter Coll); Marine; Marine Insurance Law (Association of Average Adjusters of the United States)
Automation Activity & Vendor Info: (Acquisitions) epixtech, inc.; (Cataloging) epixtech, inc.; (Circulation) epixtech, inc.; (Course Reserve) epixtech, inc.; (OPAC) epixtech, inc.; (Serials) epixtech, inc.
Publications: (monthly) (Acquisition list); The Insurance Connection! (Newsletter)
Partic in New York Metrop Ref & Res Libr Agency
Friends of the Library Group

C COLUMBIA UNIVERSITY, National Center for Children in Poverty Library, Joseph L Mailman Sch of Pub Health of Columbia Univ, 154 Haven Ave, 10032. SAN 373-9163. Tel: 212-304-7100. FAX: 212-544-4200. E-Mail: nccp@columbia.edu. Web Site: www.nccp.org. *Librn*, Elizabeth Siecke; Tel: 212-304-7119, Fax: 212-544-4201, E-Mail: ejs22@columbia.edu; Staff 1 (MLS 1)
Founded 1987
Library Holdings: Bk Titles 12,000; Per Subs 100
Publications: Bibliographies; Fact Sheets; Thesauri/Bibliography of Young Children in Poverty
Restriction: Non-circulating to the public

C COLUMBIA UNIVERSITY, University Libraries,* Butler Library Rm 518, 535 W 114th St, 10027. SAN 352-941X. Tel: 212-854-2247. Interlibrary Loan Service Tel: 212-854-3542. FAX: 212-854-9099. *Librn*, Elaine Sloan; *Assoc Librn*, Anthony Ferguson; *Asst Librn*, Karin Ngai-Crim; Staff 168 (MLS 168)
Founded 1761. Enrl 20,249; Fac 2,639; Highest Degree: Doctorate
Library Holdings: Bk Vols 7,018,408
Automation Activity & Vendor Info: (Acquisitions) NOTIS; (Cataloging) NOTIS; (Circulation) NOTIS
Publications: Books & Bytes; Columbia Library Columns
Mem of Asn of Research Libraries
Partic in New York Metrop Ref & Res Libr Agency; New York State Interlibrary Loan Network; Research Libraries Group, Inc; State University Of New York-NYLINK
Friends of the Library Group
Departmental Libraries:
ACCESS SERVICES, Butler Library 207 C, 535 W 114th St, 10027. Tel: 212-854-2245. Circulation Tel: 212-854-2235. FAX: 212-854-0089. *Dir*, Curtis Kendrick; E-Mail: kendrick@columbia.edu; Staff 5 (MLS 2, Non-MLS 3)
Friends of the Library Group
ACCESS SERVICES SCIENCE LIBRARY, 601 Fairchild, 10027. Tel: 212-854-6768. FAX: 212-854-8972. *Dir*, Alena Ptak-Danchak
Friends of the Library Group
AFRICAN STUDIES, 308 International Affairs Bldg, 420 W 118th St, 10027. SAN 377-0044. Tel: 212-854-8045. FAX: 212-854-3834. E-Mail: africa@libraries.col.columbia.edu. Web Site: www.columbia.edu/cu/libraries/indiv/africa. *Librn*, Joseph Caruso
Friends of the Library Group
ANGLO-AMERICAN, 309 Butler Library, 10027. (Mail add: 535 W 114th St, 10027), SAN 376-2467. Tel: 212-854-4356. *Bibliogr*, John Tofanelli
Friends of the Library Group
AVERY ARCHITECTURAL & FINE ARTS LIBRARY Tel: 212-854-3068. FAX: 212-854-8904. *Librn*, Angela Giral
Library Holdings: Bk Vols 318,000
Friends of the Library Group
BARNARD COLLEGE
See Separate Entry
BIOLOGICAL SCIENCES LIBRARY, 601 Fairchild, 10027. SAN 352-9746. Tel: 212-854-4182. *Coll Develop*, Kathleen Kehoe
Library Holdings: Bk Vols 57,691
Friends of the Library Group
BUTLER LIBRARY REFERENCE DEPARTMENT, 301 Butler Library, 10027. (Mail add: 535 W 114th St, 10027), SAN 352-9568. Tel: 212-854-5477. Reference Tel: 212-854-2241. FAX: 212-854-9099. E-Mail: www.reference@columbia.edu. *Head of Libr*, Eileen McIlvaine; E-Mail: mcilvain@columbia.edu; Staff 6 (MLS 6)
Library Holdings: Bk Vols 57,981
Friends of the Library Group
CHEMISTRY LIBRARY, 454 Chandler, 10027. SAN 352-9770. Tel: 212-854-5778. *Librn*, Jayashri Nagaraja
Library Holdings: Bk Vols 54,534
Friends of the Library Group
COLUMBIANA, 210 Low Library, MC 4316, 535 W 116th St, New York City, 10027. SAN 353-0191. Tel: 212-854-3786. FAX: 212-854-7320. E-Mail: archives-columbiana@columbia.edu. Web Site: www.columbia.edu/cu/columbiana/. *Curator*, Hollee Haswell; *Dir*, Marilyn H Pettit; Tel: 212-854-1331, E-Mail: mhp74@columbia.edu; *Asst Dir*, Stephen H Urgola; Tel: 212-854-4290, E-Mail: shu7@columbia.edu; *Archivist*, Mae Pan; Tel: 212-854-4051, E-Mail: mp834@columbia.edu; *Archivist*, Jpcelyn K Wilk; Tel: 212-854-1338, E-Mail: jkw19@columbia.edu; Staff 4 (MLS 1, Non-MLS 3)
Founded 1883
Library Holdings: Bk Vols 44,638
Function: Archival collection
Friends of the Library Group
DIAMOND LAW LIBRARY, 435 W 116th St, 10027. SAN 353-0256. Tel: 212-854-3737. Circulation Tel: 212-854-3922. Reference Tel: 212-854-3743. FAX: 212-854-3295. Web Site: www.library.law.columbia.edu. *Dir*, Kent McKeever; Tel: 212-854-4228, E-Mail: mckeever@law.columbia.edu; Staff 47 (MLS 17, Non-MLS 30)
Library Holdings: Bk Vols 795,000; Bk Titles 328,000; Per Subs 7,350
Subject Interests: Foreign law, International law
Partic in Nellco; RLG
Friends of the Library Group
EARTH OBSERVATORY, 601 Schermerhorn, 10027. SAN 352-9835. Tel: 212-854-4713. *Librn*, Elizabeth Fish
Library Holdings: Bk Vols 96,021
Friends of the Library Group
EAST ASIAN LIBRARY, 305M Kent, 10027. SAN 353-0132. Tel: 212-854-1508. FAX: 212-662-6286. *Librn*, Amy Heinrich
Library Holdings: Bk Vols 665,732
Subject Interests: Humanities, Lang, Literature, Soc sci
Friends of the Library Group
ENGINEERING, 422 SW Mudd, 10027. SAN 352-9800. Tel: 212-854-8338. FAX: 212-854-3323. *Librn*, Ujwal Ranadive
Library Holdings: Bk Vols 232,930
Special Collections: Technical Reports
Friends of the Library Group
GIFTS & EXCHANGE DEPARTMENT, 108 Butler Library, 10027. SAN 352-9452. Tel: 212-854-3532. FAX: 212-854-3290. *Head of Libr*, John McNees
Friends of the Library Group

CM HEALTH SCIENCES LIBRARY, 701 W 168th St, 10032. SAN 353-0221. Tel: 212-305-3688. FAX: 212-305-8388.
Library Holdings: Bk Vols 510,730
Special Collections: Anatomy (Huntington Coll); Cancer Research; Physiology (Curtis Coll); Plastic Surgery (Jerome P Webster Coll)
Friends of the Library Group
INTERLIBRARY LOAN DEPARTMENT, 505 Butler Library, 10027. SAN 352-9592. Tel: 212-854-2533. FAX: 212-854-3313. *Head of Libr*, Kathleen Davis
Friends of the Library Group
LAMONT-DOHERTY GEOSCIENCE LIBRARY, Palisades, 10964. SAN 352-986X. Tel: 914-365-8808. *Librn*, Elizabeth Fish
Library Holdings: Bk Vols 32,587
Friends of the Library Group
LATIN AMERICAN & IBERIAN STUDIES, 307 International Affairs Bldg, 420 W 118th St, 10027. SAN 377-0060. Tel: 212-854-3630. FAX: 212-854-3834. E-Mail: latam@libraries.col.columbia.edu. Web Site: www.columbia.edu/cu/libraries/indiv/latam. *Librn*, Pamela Graham
Friends of the Library Group
LEHMAN LIBRARY, 328 International Affairs Bldg, 10027. SAN 377-0125. Tel: 212-854-7768. *Librn*, Jane Winland; Tel: 212-854-5588, Fax: 212-854-2495, E-Mail: winland@columbia.edu
Founded 1971
Friends of the Library Group
LIBRARY INFORMATION OFFICE, 201 Butler Library, 10027. SAN 352-9606. Tel: 212-854-4734. FAX: 212-854-5082. E-Mail: lio@columbia.edu. *Head, Circ*, Trevor Dawes; Staff 1 (MLS 1)
Friends of the Library Group
MATHEMATICS-SCIENCE LIBRARY, 303 Mathematics, 10027. SAN 352-9894. Tel: 212-854-8833.
Library Holdings: Bk Vols 123,390
Friends of the Library Group
MIDDLE EAST & JEWISH STUDIES, 303 International Affairs Bldg, 420 W 118th St, 10027. SAN 377-0087. Tel: 212-854-3995. FAX: 212-854-3834. E-Mail: mideast@libraries.col.columbia.edu. Web Site: www.columbia.edu/cu/libraries/indiv/mideast. *Librn*, Frank Unlandherm
Friends of the Library Group
MONOGRAPH ACQUISITIONS DEPARTMENT, 106 Butler Library, 10027. SAN 352-9436. Tel: 212-854-3530. FAX: 212-854-3290. *Head of Libr*, Alan Schaplowsky

Friends of the Library Group
MONOGRAPH PROCESSING SERVICES, 101 Butler Library, 10027. SAN 352-9517. Tel: 212-854-5042. *Head of Libr*, Ilona Bicsak
Friends of the Library Group
MONOGRAPHIC RECON PROJECTS, 606 Butler Library, 10027. SAN 375-1457. Tel: 212-854-5722. *Head of Libr*, Michaela Harnick
Friends of the Library Group
MUSIC & ARTS LIBRARY, 2960 Broadway, 7th flr, 10027. SAN 352-9657. Tel: 212-854-4711. FAX: 212-854-4748. Web Site: www.columbia.edu/cu/libraries/indiv/music. *Librn*, Elizabeth Davis; Tel: 212-854-7604, E-Mail: davise@columbia.edu
Library Holdings: Bk Vols 73,405
Friends of the Library Group
ORIGINAL & SPECIAL MATERIALS CATALOGING, 102 Butler Library, 10027. SAN 352-9487. Tel: 212-854-2237. *In Charge*, Rick Block
Friends of the Library Group
PHILIP L MILSTEIN FAMILY COLLEGE LIBRARY, Butler Library, 535 W 114th St, 10027. SAN 352-9479. Tel: 212-854-5327. FAX: 212-854-9099. Web Site: www.columbia.edu/ca/lweb/indiv/under.; Staff 4 (MLS 3, Non-MLS 1)
Founded 1998
Library Holdings: Bk Vols 125,000
Friends of the Library Group
PHYSICS-ASTRONOMY LIBRARY, 810 Pupin, 10027. SAN 352-9924. Tel: 212-854-8447. *Librn*, Kathleen Kehoe
Library Holdings: Bk Vols 40,946
Friends of the Library Group
PSYCHOLOGY LIBRARY, 409 Schermerhorn, 10027. SAN 352-9959. Tel: 212-854-5658. FAX: 212-854-5660. *Librn*, Vivian Sukenik
Library Holdings: Bk Vols 36,009
Friends of the Library Group
RARE BOOK & MANUSCRIPT LIBRARY, Butler Library, 6th flr E, 10027. SAN 353-0167. Tel: 212-854-2232. FAX: 212-854-1365. *Librn*, Jean Ashton
Special Collections: Murray Kempton Papers
Friends of the Library Group
RUSSIAN, EURASIAN & EAST EUROPEAN STUDIES, 306 International Affairs Bldg, 420 W 118th St, 10027. SAN 377-0109. Tel: 212-854-4701. FAX: 212-854-3834. E-Mail: slavic@libraries.col.columbia.edu. Web Site: www.columbia.edu/cu/libraries/indiv/slavic. *Librn*, Jared Ingersoll
Friends of the Library Group
SERIALS ACQUISITIONS DEPARTMENT, 101 H Butler Library, 10027. SAN 376-2459. Tel: 212-854-3540. *Head of Libr*, Jeff Carroll
Friends of the Library Group
SOUTH & SOUTHEAST ASIA STUDIES, 304 International Affairs Bldg, 420 W 118th St, 10027. SAN 377-0141. Tel: 212-854-8046. FAX: 212-854-3834. E-Mail: southasia@libraries.col.columbia.edu. Web Site: www.columbia.edu/cu/libraries/indiv/southasia. *Librn*, David Magier
Friends of the Library Group
TEACHERS COLLEGE - COLUMBIA UNIVERSITY
See Separate Entry
WATSON LIBRARY OF BUSINESS AND ECONOMICS, 130 Uris Hall, 3022 Broadway, MC 9163, 10027. SAN 352-9983. Tel: 212-854-4000. Circulation Tel: 212-854-7804. Reference Tel: 212-854-3383. FAX: 212-854-5723. *Librn*, Jill Parchuck; Tel: 212-854-7803, E-Mail: parchuck@columbia.edu; Staff 23 (MLS 5, Non-MLS 18)
Highest Degree: Doctorate
Library Holdings: Bk Vols 370,000
Subject Interests: Business, Economics
Automation Activity & Vendor Info: (OPAC) NOTIS
Database Vendor: CARL, Lexis-Nexis, OCLC - First Search, ProQuest
Restriction: Open to public upon request, Residents only
Function: Research library
Partic in RLG
WEST EUROPEAN, 309 Butler Library, 10027. (Mail add: 535 W 114th St, 10027), SAN 377-0168. Tel: 212-854-1341. *Bibliogr*, Andrew Carricker
Friends of the Library Group
WHITNEY M YOUNG JR MEMORIAL LIBRARY OF SOCIAL WORK, 328 International Affairs Bldg, 420 W 118th St, 10027. SAN 353-0078. Tel: 212-854-4170. Circulation Tel: 212-854-4170. Reference Tel: 212-854-5087. FAX: 212-854-2495. E-Mail: socwk@libraries.cul.columbia.edu. Web Site: www.columbia.edu/cu/libraries/indiv/socwk/. *Librn*, Jane Winland
Library Holdings: Bk Vols 149,791
Friends of the Library Group

S CONDE NAST PUBLICATIONS LIBRARY,* 4 Times Square, 10036. SAN 311-7022. Tel: 212-286-2860. *Librn*, Cynthia Cathcart; *Librn*, Linda Sweeney; *Librn*, Donald Osterweil; *Librn*, Stanford Friedman
Founded 1935
Library Holdings: Bk Vols 5,500; Bk Titles 500; Per Subs 114
Subject Interests: Fashion, Photog
Restriction: By appointment only
Library maintains file & cross reference on original art work appearing in Conde Nast publications; special index for Vogue Magazine. All European editions available for view

S CONDON & FORSYTH LIBRARY,* 685 Third Ave, 10017. SAN 326-1875. Tel: 212-490-9100. FAX: 212-370-4453. Web Site: www.condonlaw.com. *Librn*, Antonietta Tatta
Founded 1922
Library Holdings: Bk Vols 13,000; Per Subs 76
Subject Interests: Aviation
Restriction: Staff use only

S CONFERENCE BOARD, INC, Information Service, 845 Third Ave, 10022. SAN 320-2658. Tel: 212-759-0900. FAX: 212-836-9750. E-Mail: info@conference-board.org. Web Site: www.conference-board.org. *Dir*, Ellen Ackerman; *Assoc Dir*, Carol Estoppey; Staff 8 (MLS 8)
Founded 1916
Library Holdings: Bk Titles 6,000; Per Subs 400
Subject Interests: Bus, Econ, Human resource mgt, Mgt
Publications: Cumulative Index; periodicals list; price list
Restriction: Members only

R CONGREGATION EMANU-EL, Ivan M Stettenheim Library, One E 65th St, 10021-6596. SAN 312-0864. Tel: 212-744-1400. Circulation Tel: 212-744-1400, Ext 361. FAX: 212-570-0826. E-Mail: establer@redconnect.net.; Staff 1 (MLS 1)
Founded 1906
Jun 2000-May 2001 Income $58,100. Mats Exp $18,500, Books $10,000, Per/Ser (Incl. Access Fees) $2,000, AV Equip $3,000, Electronic Ref Mat (Incl. Access Fees) $3,500. Sal $45,000 (Prof $45,000)
Library Holdings: Bk Vols 20,000; Bk Titles 10,000; Per Subs 45; Spec Interest Per Sub 45
Subject Interests: Judaica
Automation Activity & Vendor Info: (Acquisitions) SIRSI; (Cataloging) SIRSI; (Circulation) SIRSI; (Course Reserve) SIRSI; (Media Booking) SIRSI; (OPAC) SIRSI; (Serials) SIRSI
Restriction: Non-circulating to the public

S CONGREGATION SHEARITH ISRAEL ARCHIVES LIBRARY,* 8 W 70th St, 10023. SAN 327-2362. Tel: 212-873-0300. FAX: 212-724-6165. *Archivist*, Susan Tobin
Founded 1840
Library Holdings: Bk Vols 5,000; Per Subs 10

L CONNER & CHOPNICK LIBRARY,* 500 Fifth, Ste 740, 10110. SAN 311-7049. Tel: 212-696-1050. FAX: 212-768-0919.
Library Holdings: Bk Vols 4,000; Per Subs 20

S CONSULATE GENERAL OF INDIA, Information Service of India Library,* 3 E 64th St, 10021. SAN 311-8185. Tel: 212-774-0600, Ext 612.
Founded 1958
Library Holdings: Bk Vols 6,636; Per Subs 40
Subject Interests: Humanities, Indian affairs (polit and soc)

S CONSULATE GENERAL OF IRELAND LIBRARY,* 345 Park Ave & 51st St, 17 flr, 10154-0037. SAN 375-1023. Tel: 212-319-2555. FAX: 212-980-9475.
Library Holdings: Bk Titles 300; Per Subs 10
Restriction: Restricted public use

G CONSULATE GENERAL OF ISRAEL, David Tamia Library & Reading Room,* 800 Second Ave, 14th flr, 10017. SAN 370-856X. Tel: 212-499-5300. FAX: 212-499-5425. *Publ Servs*, Evelyn Musher
Library Holdings: Bk Vols 3,000
Open Mon-Fri 9:15-12 by appointment

C COOPER UNION FOR ADVANCEMENT OF SCIENCE & ART LIBRARY, 7 E Seventh St, 10003-8001. SAN 311-7081. Tel: 212-353-4186. Interlibrary Loan Service Tel: 212-353-4189. Circulation Tel: 212-353-4188. FAX: 212-353-4017. Web Site: www.cooper.edu/facilities/library/library.html. *Dir*, Ulla Volk; E-Mail: volk@cooper.edu; *ILL*, Claire Gunning; E-Mail: gunning@cooper.edu; *Electronic Resources*, Julie Castelluzzo; E-Mail: juliec@cooper.edu; *Archivist, Science*, Carol Salomon; E-Mail: salomo@cooper.edu. Subject Specialists: *Architecture*, Claire Gunning; *Art*, Claire Gunning; *Computer science*, Julie Castelluzzo; *Electrical engineering*, Julie Castelluzzo; *Eng-tech*, Carol Salomon; *Engineering*, Carol Salomon; Staff 9 (MLS 5, Non-MLS 4)
Founded 1859. Enrl 925; Fac 60; Highest Degree: Master
Library Holdings: Bk Vols 84,100; Per Subs 374
Subject Interests: Architecture, Art, Engineering
Special Collections: Cooperana, bk & mss
Automation Activity & Vendor Info: (Circulation) GEAC; (Course Reserve) GEAC; (OPAC) GEAC
Database Vendor: OCLC - First Search
Publications: Acquisitions Lists; Databases List; Faculty Guide
Partic in Asn of S Manhattan; Metropolitan New York Library Council

S COPPER DEVELOPMENT ASSOCIATION, INC, Copper Data Center, 260 Madison Ave, 10016. SAN 311-7103. Tel: 212-251-7200. FAX: 212-251-7234. Web Site: www.csa.com/copperdata.

Founded 1963
Subject Interests: Copper, Copper alloy tech
Publications: Accessions; Bulletin; Patent Brief; Thesaurus of Terms on Copper Technology

S CORBIS BETTMANN ARCHIVES,* 902 Broadway, 5th flr, 10010. SAN 324-4148. Tel: 212-777-6200. FAX: 212-477-2683. E-Mail: amyt@corbis.com. Web Site: www.corbis.com. *VPres*, Leslie Hughes; *Assoc Dir*, Justin Burke; *Mgr*, Ken Johnston
Subject Interests: History, Photo journalism, Sports
Special Collections: Agency France Presse; Bettmann Archive; Bracklow Coll; Jazz (Frank Driggs Coll); Lynn Goldsmith Collection; New York Daily Mirror; Penguin & John Springer Coll; Reuters Coll; Springer Collection Film Stills; Sygma Coll; Underwood & Underwood Coll; United Press International Photo Library
Publications: Bettmann Portable Archive; Brochure
Restriction: By appointment only
Function: Archival collection

L COUDERT BROTHERS LIBRARY,* 1114 Avenue of the Americas, 10036-7703. SAN 311-712X. Tel: 212-626-4796. FAX: 212-626-4120. *In Charge*, Jane C Rubens
Library Holdings: Bk Vols 30,000; Per Subs 70
Subject Interests: International law

S COUNCIL OF STATE GOVERNMENTS LIBRARY,* 5 World Trade Ctr, Ste 9241, 10048. SAN 311-7146. Tel: 212-912-0128. FAX: 212-912-0549.
Library Holdings: Bk Vols 150
Subject Interests: Intergovernmental relations, Proceedings of governors' conferences

S COUNCIL ON FOREIGN RELATIONS LIBRARY,* 58 E 68th St, 10021. SAN 311-7154. Tel: 212-434-9400. FAX: 212-861-3524. *Dir Libr Serv*, Lilita Gusts; Staff 5 (MLS 3, Non-MLS 2)
Founded 1930
Library Holdings: Bk Titles 20,000; Per Subs 324
Subject Interests: Econ, History, International law, International relations, Political science
Special Collections: European Communities
Partic in Consortium Of Foundation Libraries; New York Metrop Ref & Res Libr Agency; OCLC Online Computer Library Center, Inc

L CRAVATH, SWAINE & MOORE, Law Library, 825 Eighth Ave, 10019. SAN 311-7162. Tel: 212-474-3500. FAX: 212-474-3556. *Dir Libr Serv*, Elsbeth Moller; E-Mail: emoller@cravath.com; Staff 23 (MLS 9, Non-MLS 14)
Founded 1819
Library Holdings: Bk Vols 50,000
Subject Interests: Antitrust, Corporate, Litigation, Tax

S CREDIT SUISSE FIRST BOSTON CORP LIBRARY,* 11 Madison Ave, 28th flr, 10010. SAN 311-7677. Tel: 212-325-4000. FAX: 212-325-8271. *Mgr*, Pamela C Rollo; Staff 24 (MLS 12, Non-MLS 12)
Founded 1963
Library Holdings: Bk Titles 2,500
Subject Interests: Corporate mat, Econ, Finance
Automation Activity & Vendor Info: (Acquisitions) Sydney; (Cataloging) Sydney
Publications: New acquisitions (Monthly bulletin)
Partic in OCLC Online Computer Library Center, Inc

S CREDIT SWISS ASSET MANAGEMENT, Library - Information Center, 466 Lexington Ave, 13th Flr, 10017. SAN 370-842X. Tel: 212-832-2626. FAX: 212-355-1662, 646-658-0741. *Librn*, Darren Johnston; E-Mail: darren.johnston@csam.com
Library Holdings: Bk Vols 329; Per Subs 250

S CULVER PICTURES, INC LIBRARY,* 150 W 22nd St, Ste 300, 10011-2421. SAN 325-9315. Tel: 212-645-1672. FAX: 212-627-9112. *Pres*, Harriet Culver
Library Holdings: Bk Vols 1,050; Per Subs 514
Restriction: Staff use only

L CURTIS, MALLET-PREVOST, COLT & MOSLE LIBRARY,* 101 Park Ave, 10178-0061. SAN 311-7197. Tel: 212-696-6138. FAX: 212-697-1559. *Librn*, Gary J Jaskula; E-Mail: gjaskula@cm-p.com
Founded 1900
Library Holdings: Bk Vols 50,000; Per Subs 120
Subject Interests: Cent, S Am law
Special Collections: Central & South American Law
Partic in Lexis, Solinet, Westlaw

S DANCE NOTATION BUREAU LIBRARY,* 151 W 30th St Ste 202, 10001. SAN 324-8054. Tel: 212-564-0985. FAX: 212-904-1426. E-Mail: notation@mindspring.com. Web Site: www.dancenotation.org/. *Librn*, Robert B Shapiro; Staff 1 (MLS 1)
Founded 1940
Library Holdings: Bk Titles 720
Special Collections: Audiotapes for Notated Dances; Benesh Notation Scores; Isaac Archive (Original pencil Labanotation Scores); Music Scores & Supplementary Items for Individual Dances; Technical papers on Labanotation
Publications: Notated Theatrical Dances: A Listing of Theatrical Dance Scores Housed at the Dance Notation Bureau (free catalogue)
The Dance Notation Bureau has an Extension Library which is a part of the Special Coll, Ohio State University Librs

L DAVIS POLK & WARDWELL LIBRARY,* 450 Lexington Ave, 10017. SAN 311-7235. Tel: 212-450-4266. FAX: 212-450-5522. *Librn*, Daniel J Hanson; E-Mail: hanson@dpw.com; *Tech Servs*, Lauie Wilson; *Online Servs*, Hope Bernard
Founded 1891
Library Holdings: Bk Vols 70,000; Per Subs 1,400
Subject Interests: Antitrust, Banking, Securities, Taxation
Special Collections: International Law; Legislature
Publications: Electronic bulletin (bi-weekly)
Partic in Dialog Corporation; Dow Jones News Retrieval; OCLC Online Computer Library Center, Inc; Westlaw

L DAVIS, SCOTT, WEBBER & EDWARDS LAW LIBRARY,* 100 Park Ave, 32nd flr, 10017. SAN 326-1212. Tel: 212-685-5885, Ext 240. FAX: 212-889-4515. *Librn*, Carrie-Ann Philp
Founded 1980
Library Holdings: Bk Vols 6,500; Bk Titles 400; Per Subs 27

S DDB WORLDWIDE, Information Center, 437 Madison Ave, 10022. SAN 311-7391. Tel: 212-415-2546. *Dir*, Alice Bromley
Founded 1958
Library Holdings: Bk Vols 6,000; Per Subs 300
Subject Interests: Advertising, Marketing

S DEAN WITTER REYNOLDS, INC,* 2 World Trade Ctr, 10048. SAN 312-1429. Tel: 212-392-2745. FAX: 212-392-4524. Web Site: cybrary-info.com.
Founded 1971
Library Holdings: Bk Vols 2,500; Per Subs 400
Subject Interests: Bus, Corp rec, Econ, Finance, Investment, Mgt

L DEBEVOISE & PLIMPTON, Law Library,* 875 Third Ave, 10022. SAN 311-7251. Tel: 212-909-6275. FAX: 212-909-1025. *Dir Libr Serv*, Denis R O'Connor; Tel: 212-909-6278
Library Holdings: Bk Vols 40,000; Per Subs 100
Subject Interests: Aviation, Corp law, Litigation, Real estate, Securities, Taxation law
Automation Activity & Vendor Info: (Cataloging) epixtech, inc.; (Circulation) epixtech, inc.; (Course Reserve) epixtech, inc.; (OPAC) epixtech, inc.; (Serials) epixtech, inc.
Database Vendor: Dialog, Lexis-Nexis
Restriction: Staff use only
Function: For research purposes

L DECHERT LAW LIBRARY, (Formerly Dechert, Price & Rhoads), 30 Rockefeller Plaza 22nd flr, 10112. SAN 372-4549. Tel: 212-698-3500. FAX: 212-698-3599. *Librn*, John Davey
Library Holdings: Bk Vols 20,000; Per Subs 300
Subject Interests: Corporate securities

S DELOITTE & TOUCHE INFORMATION SERVICES GROUP,* 2 World Financial Ctr, 10281. SAN 324-606X. Tel: 212-436-2419. FAX: 212-436-7008. *Mgr*, Rhea Tabakin; Staff 9 (MLS 4, Non-MLS 5)
Library Holdings: Bk Vols 500
Subject Interests: Accounting, Mgt consulting
Restriction: Staff use only

GM DEPARTMENT OF VETERANS AFFAIRS, NEW YORK HARBOR HEALTHCARE SYSTEM, New York Campus Library, 423 E 23rd St, 10010. SAN 353-829X. Tel: 212-686-7500, Ext 7682. FAX: 212-951-3367. *Chief Librn*, Karin Wiseman; E-Mail: wiseman.karin@forum.va.gov; *Ser*, Judy Steever; *Coll Develop*, Judy Steever; *Coll Develop*, Tom Waugh; Staff 6 (MLS 3, Non-MLS 3)
Founded 1956
Library Holdings: Bk Titles 8,000; Per Subs 430
Subject Interests: Patient health educ
Automation Activity & Vendor Info: (Cataloging) EOS; (Circulation) EOS; (OPAC) EOS
Partic in Medical Library Center Of New York; New York Metrop Ref & Res Libr Agency
Special Services for the Blind - Kurzweil Reader; Talking Books

S DEUTSCHE BANK, Business Information Services, 130 Liberty St, 2nd Flr, MS2028, 10006. SAN 323-5149. Tel: 212-250-5353. FAX: 212-669-0796. *VPres*, Mark Biles; *VPres*, Madeline J Kiely-Eng; *Per*, Hibert Sealy. Subject Specialists: *Research*, Madeline J Kiely-Eng
Library Holdings: Bk Vols 1,000
Subject Interests: Economics, Finance

S DEUTSCHE BANK SECURITIES, Information Research,* 31 W 52nd St, 10019. SAN 311-8568. Tel: 212-469-5661. FAX: 212-469-5485.
Founded 1994
Library Holdings: Per Subs 350
Subject Interests: Bus, Corp rec, Econ, Finance, Mgt

L DEWEY BALLANTINE LLP, Law Library, 1301 Avenue of the Americas, 10019. SAN 311-7286. Tel: 212-259-6000. FAX: 212-259-6333. Web Site: www.deweyballantine.com. *Dir Libr Serv*, Gitelle Seer; E-Mail: gseer@deweyballantine.com; Staff 16 (MLS 8, Non-MLS 8)
Founded 1915
Library Holdings: Bk Vols 55,000; Per Subs 300
Subject Interests: Antitrust, Corp, Environment, Securities, Tax
Special Collections: Legislative Histories
Automation Activity & Vendor Info: (Acquisitions) Sydney; (Cataloging) Sydney; (Circulation) Sydney; (Course Reserve) Sydney; (ILL) Sydney; (Media Booking) Sydney; (OPAC) Sydney; (Serials) Sydney

S DIRECT MARKETING ASSOCIATION, Library Resource Center,* 1120 Avenue of the Americas, 10036-7600. SAN 311-7332. Tel: 212-768-7277, Ext 1930. FAX: 212-398-6725. Web Site: www.the-dma.org. *Mgr*, Nilda Castillo
Founded 1960
Library Holdings: Bk Titles 300
Special Collections: Award Winning Direct Marketing Campaigns, Catalog coll, Coll of Direct Marketing Studies & Surveys (Microfiche)

S DONALDSON, LUFKIN & JENRETTE, INC, Corporate Information Center,* 277 Park Ave, 10072. SAN 311-7359. Tel: 212-892-3000. FAX: 212-892-7247. *Dir*, Susan W Littin; *Ref*, Mitchell Feir; *Ref*, Richard Redmond; *Ref*, Laura Ripin; Staff 5 (MLS 5)
Founded 1962
Library Holdings: Bk Titles 3,500; Per Subs 330
Subject Interests: Bus, Bus statistics, Corp, Econ, Finance, Investment, Mgt, Pensions
Special Collections: Americana (Financial History of the American Revolution)
Restriction: Staff use only

S DOW JONES & CO, INC, Wall Street Journal Library, 200 Liberty St, 10281. SAN 312-1240. Tel: 212-416-2000. *Chief Librn*, Lottie Lindberg; Staff 5 (MLS 2, Non-MLS 3)
Founded 1903
Library Holdings: Bk Vols 2,000
Subject Interests: Finance
Partic in Dow Jones Interactive

S DREYFUS CORP LIBRARY, 200 Park Ave, 7th flr, 10166. SAN 311-7405. Tel: 212-922-6084. FAX: 212-922-6093. *Dir*, Cytheria Theodos; *Librn*, Sharon Laurie; *Librn*, Clara Keriotis; Staff 7 (MLS 3, Non-MLS 4)
Founded 1962
Library Holdings: Bk Titles 300; Per Subs 400
Subject Interests: Corp bus, Econ, Finance, Invest co
Special Collections: Investment Companies
Automation Activity & Vendor Info: (Serials) EOS
Database Vendor: Dialog, Lexis-Nexis
Restriction: Staff use only
Function: Research library

S EAST-WEST INSTITUTE LIBRARY, 700 Broadway, 2nd flr, 10003. SAN 325-4623. Tel: 212-824-4100. FAX: 212-824-4149. Toll Free FAX: 800-824-4100. E-Mail: iews@iews.org. Web Site: www.iews.org. *Librn*, Althea Herlock
Library Holdings: Per Subs 150
Subject Interests: Arms control, East-West relations, Economic issues, Int politics, International relations, Politics, Security issues, US-Soviet relations
Special Collections: Eastern Europe; Economic Coll; Soviet Newspapers
Publications: Library New Acquisition List (bimonthly)

S ECONOMIST INTELLIGENCE UNIT RESEARCH LIBRARY, 111 W 57th St, 10019-2211. SAN 311-662X. Tel: 212-554-0600. FAX: 212-586-1181. *Mgr*, Beth Kilmer
Founded 1954
Subject Interests: Bus, Financial res, Int econ
Special Collections: Multinational Corporations, bks, files & papers; United Nations & International Organizations statistical data

S EDITOR & PUBLISHER INFORMATION SERVICES DEPARTMENT, 770 Broadway, 7th Flr, 10003-9595. SAN 311-7464. FAX: 646-654-5352.
Founded 1912
Library Holdings: Bk Vols 500; Per Subs 100
Subject Interests: Advertising, Journalism
Special Collections: Historical Reference Material on Newsmen, Newspaper Activities, Newspapers, Journalism

S EDUCATIONAL BROADCASTING CORP, Thirteen WNET Reference Library, 450 W 33rd St, 10001. SAN 311-7472. Tel: 212-560-8080. FAX: 212-560-3199. *Dir*, Leslie Rosen; Tel: 215-560-3065, E-Mail: rosenl@wnet.org; *Mgr*, Jessica Topper; Tel: 215-560-3063, E-Mail: topper@thirteen.org; *Librn*, Harriett Obus; Tel: 212-560-3064, E-Mail: obus@thirteen.org; *Archivist*, Daisy Pommer; Tel: 212-560-2058, E-Mail: pommer@thirteen.org; Staff 7 (MLS 3, Non-MLS 4)
Founded 1972
Library Holdings: Bk Vols 1,000; Per Subs 175
Subject Interests: Art, Culture, Current events, New York City, Public affairs
Special Collections: Thirteen Program Guides
Automation Activity & Vendor Info: (Cataloging) Inmagic, Inc.
Database Vendor: Dialog, Ebsco - EbscoHost, Lexis-Nexis, ProQuest

M EMPIRE HEALTH CHOICE INC, (Formerly Empire Blue Cross & Blue Shield), Corporate Library, One World Trade Ctr, 28th Flr, 10048-0682. Tel: 212-476-3277. FAX: 212-476-3071. *Librn*, Charlene Ciego; E-Mail: charlene.ciego@empirehealthcare.com; Staff 1 (MLS 1)
Founded 1966
Library Holdings: Bk Titles 1,000; Per Subs 50
Subject Interests: Bus, Health care financing, Ins, Medicine
Special Collections: Health Care History Archives
Database Vendor: Dialog, Lexis-Nexis
Publications: Journal List; New Book List; Newsclips
Mem of NY Metrop Ref & Res Libr Agency, Inc

S ENGLISH-SPEAKING UNION, Ruth M Shellens Memorial Library, 16 E 69th St, 10021. SAN 311-7510. Tel: 212-879-6800. FAX: 212-772-2886. E-Mail: info@english-speakingunion.org. Web Site: www.english-speakingunion.org. *Exec Dir*, Alice Boyne
Founded 1944
Library Holdings: Bk Titles 7,500
Subject Interests: Britain, United Kingdom
Special Collections: Ambassador Book Awards Winners; Biographies & Autobiographies of British & American Authors, 1900-1964 (Winifred Nerney Coll)
Restriction: Members only

S ENVIRONMENTAL ACTION COALITION LIBRARY,* 29 Broadway, Rm 1100, 10006-3201. SAN 321-754X. Tel: 212-677-1601. FAX: 212-505-8613. *Mgr*, Maria S Rivera-Maulucci
Founded 1972
Library Holdings: Bk Vols 500
Subject Interests: Energy, Environ, Health, Pop, Waste, Water
Publications: Eco-Facts (brochure)

G ENVIRONMENTAL PROTECTION AGENCY, Region II Library, 290 Broadway, Rm 1660, 10007. SAN 311-7529. Tel: 212-637-3185. FAX: 212-637-3086. E-Mail: library.reg.2@epamail.epa.gov.; Staff 5 (MLS 4, Non-MLS 1)
Founded 1965
Library Holdings: Bk Titles 13,000; Per Subs 100
Subject Interests: Chem risk assessment, Drinking water, Environmental law, Groundwater protection, Hazardous waste, Pesticides, Quality, Superfund, Toxic substance, Wetlands
Special Collections: Hazardous Waste Coll
Publications: Environmental Grants; Environmental Law; Graduate Studies; Internet
Partic in Dialog Corporation; Fedlink; OCLC Online Computer Library Center, Inc

L EPSTEIN, BECKER & GREEN, Law Library, 250 Park Ave 12th flr, 10177. SAN 372-2414. Tel: 212-351-4695. FAX: 212-661-0989. E-Mail: egan@ebglaw.com. Web Site: www.ebglaw.com. *Dir Libr Serv*, Elaine Egan; *Ref*, Mike Fillinger
1998-1999 Mats Exp $205,000, Books $40,000, Per/Ser (Incl. Access Fees) $165,000. Sal $180,000
Library Holdings: Bk Vols 8,000; Per Subs 120
Publications: Library Focus (bimonthly)

L EQUITABLE LIFE ASSURANCE SOCIETY OF THE UNITED STATES LIBRARY,* Law Library 12th flr, 1290 Avenue of Americas, 10104. SAN 372-4301. Tel: 212-314-3820. FAX: 212-707-7858. *Librn*, Katherine Camesas
Library Holdings: Bk Vols 40,000
Subject Interests: Corporate law
Restriction: Not open to public

S ERNST & YOUNG, Center for Business Knowledge, 787 Seventh Ave, 10019. SAN 353-8710. Tel: 212-773-5330. Interlibrary Loan Service Tel: 212-773-5964. Toll Free Tel: 877-392-8773. FAX: 212-489-1745. *Mgr*, Myron Menewitzh; Tel: 212-773-5950, Fax: 212-489-1745, E-Mail: myron.menewitch@ey.com; *Res*, Judith Albert; Tel: 212-773-6230. Subject Specialists: *Accounting*, Diane Lee; *Consumer info*, Richard Reid; *Financial servs*, Roni Pidala; *Insurance*, Emily Kranis; *Tax*, Edith Hwang; Staff 9 (MLS 6, Non-MLS 3)
Founded 1953
Library Holdings: Bk Titles 2,000; Per Subs 275
Subject Interests: Accounting, Auditing, Corp finance, Mgt servs, Taxation
Function: ILL to other special libraries
Partic in Dialog Corporation; Dow Jones News Retrieval; SDC Info Servs

C FASHION INSTITUTE OF TECHNOLOGY, Gladys Marcus Library, Seventh Ave at 27th St, 10001-5992. SAN 311-7596. Tel: 212-217-5590. FAX: 212-217-5268. Web Site: www.fitnyc.suny.edu. *Dir*, Howard Dillon; Tel: 212-217-5889, E-Mail: dillhow@fitsuny.edu; *Ref, Syst Coordr*, Lorraine Weberg; *Ref*, Beryl Rentof; *Ref, Spec Coll*, Joshua Waller; *Circ, ILL, Ref*, Stephen Rosenberger; *Coll Develop*, Judith Wood; *Acq*, Judy Wood; *Cat*, Janette Rozene
Enrl 8,466; Fac 386; Highest Degree: Master
Library Holdings: Bk Vols 138,000; Bk Titles 92,806; Per Subs 487
Subject Interests: Bus, Fashion design, Fine arts, Gallery, Merchandising, Mgt, Mus studies, Retail art admin, Technology
Special Collections: 123 Interviews of Members of the Fashion Industry; Fashion (Sketch bks of fashion designs)
Publications: Acquisitions list; bibliographies; brochures/pathfinders; faculty handbook; Library News & Notes; subject heading brochures
Partic in Metropolitan New York Library Council; RLIN

FEDERAL RESERVE BANK OF NEW YORK
S COMPUTER SCIENCE LIBRARY, 59 Maiden Lane, 24th flr, 10038-4502. SAN 325-3457. Tel: 212-720-1337. FAX: 212-720-1298. *Librn*, Amy L Boggess
Library Holdings: Bk Titles 1,500; Per Subs 200
Restriction: Staff use only
Partic in Fedlink
S RESEARCH LIBRARY, 33 Liberty St, Federal Reserve PO Sta, 10045. SAN 353-0701. Tel: 212-720-5670. FAX: 212-720-1372.; Staff 11 (MLS 5, Non-MLS 6)
Founded 1916
Library Holdings: Per Subs 2,000
Subject Interests: Banking, Bus conditions, Cent banking, Credit, Econ, Fed Reserve Syst, Gold, Govt finance, Int monetary affairs, Money
Publications: Library News of Recent Acquisitions
Partic in Fedlink; OCLC Online Computer Library Center, Inc

L FERDINAND GALLOZZI CUSTOMS LIBRARY, 6 World Trade Ctr, Rm 708, 10048. SAN 312-0236. Tel: 212-637-7040. *Librn*, Ellen Berg; *Assoc Librn*, Michael Horne
Founded 1960
Library Holdings: Bk Vols 12,000; Per Subs 90
Subject Interests: Customs law
Restriction: Staff use only

S FIDUCIARY TRUST CO INTERNATIONAL, Research Library,* 2 World Trade Ctr, 94th flr, 10048. SAN 311-7642. Tel: 212-466-4100. FAX: 212-313-2551. E-Mail: s.fair@ftci.com.; Staff 1 (MLS 1)
Founded 1933
Library Holdings: Bk Vols 2,000; Per Subs 180
Subject Interests: Banking finance, Corp records, Investment
Publications: Index to Research Department Publications; Research Library Bulletin

S FIND-SVP INC, LIBRARY, 625 Avenue of the Americas, 2nd flr, 10011. SAN 320-4014. Tel: 212-645-4500. FAX: 212-645-7681.; Staff 13 (MLS 3, Non-MLS 10)
Founded 1970
Library Holdings: Bk Vols 5,000; Per Subs 4,000
Publications: The Information Catalog
Partic in BRS; Data Time; Dow Jones News Retrieval; Infoline; Nat Libr of Med; Newsnet; Pergamon; Pergamon Orbit; Texline; Vutext

S FISH & NEAVE LIBRARY,* 1251 Avenue of the Americas, 10020. SAN 371-0467. Tel: 212-596-9200. FAX: 212-596-9090. *Dir*, Janet M Stark; *Tech Servs*, Louise E Studer
Library Holdings: Bk Vols 15,500; Per Subs 78

S FORBES, INC, Information Center,* 60 Fifth Ave, Mezzanine, 10011. SAN 311-7693. Tel: 212-620-2200. FAX: 212-620-1811.
Founded 1956
Library Holdings: Bk Vols 5,000
Subject Interests: Bus conditions, Corp records, Corporate finance, Econ, Investment co, Stock exchanges

S FORD FOUNDATION LIBRARY, 320 E 43rd St, 10017. Tel: 212-573-5157. Interlibrary Loan Service Tel: 212-573-5158. Circulation Tel: 212-573-5158. Reference Tel: 212-573-5156. FAX: 212-351-3679. *Librn*, Victoria A Dawson; E-Mail: v.dawson@fordfound.org; Staff 4 (MLS 2, Non-MLS 2)
Founded 1953
Library Holdings: Bk Titles 2,000; Per Subs 150
Subject Interests: Econ assistance, Education, Human rights, Philanthropy, Urban affairs
Restriction: Staff use only, Use of others with permission of librarian
Partic in Metro NY Libr Coun
Branches:
S INVESTMENT RESEARCH LIBRARY, 320 E 43rd St, 10017. SAN 321-6713. Tel: 212-573-4798. FAX: 212-351-3684.
Founded 1971
Library Holdings: Bk Titles 1,050; Per Subs 240
Subject Interests: Corp rec, Endowment funds, Pension funds, Securities, US int investments
Restriction: Staff use only
Partic in Consortium for Found Librs; Data Time; Dialog Corporation; Dow Jones News Retrieval

C FORDHAM UNIVERSITY LIBRARY AT LINCOLN CENTER, Quinn Library, Leon Lowenstein Bldg, 113 W 60th St, 10023-7480. SAN 311-7731. Tel: 212-636-6000, Ext 6055. FAX: 212-636-6766. Web Site: www.library.fordham.edu. *Dir*, Dr James McCabe; Tel: 718-817-3570; *Librn*, Linda LoSchiavo; *Head Ref*, Allan Halpern; *Ref*, Dale Chapman; *Ref*, Kathryn Trotter; *Ref*, David Vassar; *Ref*, Roger Harris; *Head, Circ*, Robert Allen; Staff 7 (MLS 7)
Founded 1969. Enrl 6,841; Fac 262; Highest Degree: Doctorate
Library Holdings: Bk Vols 400,000; Per Subs 1,500
Subject Interests: Business, Education, Social work
Special Collections: Education (ERIC Documents), microfiche; Holocaust
Automation Activity & Vendor Info: (Circulation) DRA
Publications: Inside Fordham Libraries (quarterly)
Partic in New York Metrop Ref & Res Libr Agency

CL FORDHAM UNIVERSITY SCHOOL OF LAW, Leo T Kissam Memorial Library, 140 W 62nd St, 10023. SAN 311-7723. Tel: 212-636-6900. Interlibrary Loan Service Tel: 212-636-6909. Reference Tel: 212-636-6908. FAX: 212-636-7357. E-Mail: refdesk@mail.lawnet.fordham.edu. Web Site: lawpac.fordham.edu. *Dir*, Janet R Tracy; Tel: 212-636-6906, E-Mail: jtracy@mail.lawnet.fordham.edu; *Assoc Librn*, Kristine R Kreilick; Tel: 212-636-6904, E-Mail: kkreilick@mail.lawnet.fordham.edu; *Assoc Librn, Tech Servs*, Mary McKee; Tel: 212-636-6903, E-Mail: mmckee@mail.lawnet.fordham.edu; *Assoc Librn, Publ Servs*, Kathleen McLeod; Tel: 212-636-7968, E-Mail: kmcleod@mail.lawnet.fordham.edu; *Doc, Ref*, Janice Greer; Tel: 212-636-6915, E-Mail: jgreer@mail.lawnet.fordham.edu; *Ref*, Yvette LeRoy; Tel: 212-636-6901, E-Mail: yleroy@mail.lawnet.fordham.edu; *Ref*, Jorene Robbie; Tel: 212-636-7005, E-Mail: jrobbie@mail.lawnet.fordham.edu; *Acq*, Kurtie Sannon; Tel: 212-636-6751, E-Mail: ksannon@mail.lawnet.fordham.edu; *Cat*, Yael Mandelstam; Tel: 212-636-7971; *ILL*, Joyce Dindayal; E-Mail: jdindayal@mail.lawnet.fordham.edu. Subject Specialists: *International law*, Victor Essien; Staff 17 (MLS 10, Non-MLS 7)
Founded 1905. Enrl 1,500; Fac 60; Highest Degree: Master
Jul 1999-Jun 2000 Income Parent Institution $3,167,481. Mats Exp $1,569,143, Books $240,521, Per/Ser (Incl. Access Fees) $960,817, Presv $23,015. Sal $1,598,338 (Prof $1,127,122)
Library Holdings: Bk Vols 346,228; Bk Titles 181,652; Per Subs 6,212
Subject Interests: European Econ Commun (EEC) law
Automation Activity & Vendor Info: (Acquisitions) Innovative Interfaces Inc.; (Cataloging) Innovative Interfaces Inc.; (Circulation) Innovative Interfaces Inc.; (Course Reserve) Innovative Interfaces Inc.; (OPAC) Innovative Interfaces Inc.; (Serials) Innovative Interfaces Inc.
Database Vendor: Lexis-Nexis
Publications: Acquisitions List; FULL Story; Law Library Guide; Learned Handy Research Guides
Partic in Asn Jesuit & Univs; Nellco; OCLC Online Computer Library Center, Inc; RLIN

S FOUNDATION CENTER LIBRARY,* 79 Fifth Ave, 10003-3076. SAN 311-774X. Tel: 212-620-4230. Toll Free Tel: 800-424-9836. FAX: 212-691-1828. E-Mail: jm@fdncenter.org. Web Site: fdncenter.org. *Publ Servs, VPres*, Judi Margolin; *Dir*, Sarah Collins; *Coll Develop*, Shahi Sarentz; Staff 16 (MLS 8, Non-MLS 8)
Founded 1956
Library Holdings: Bk Vols 5,000; Bk Titles 3,800; Per Subs 100
Subject Interests: Corporate grants, Found grants, Fund raising, Nonprofit mgt, Philanthropy, Pvt founds
Special Collections: Foundation Annual Reports; IRS Information Returns on aperture cards for private foundations
Publications: A Nonprofit Organization Operating Manual; America's Voluntary Spirit; America's Wealthy & the Future of Foundations; Corporate Foundation Profiles; Foundation 1000; Foundation Directory; Foundation Directory Part II; Foundation Fundamentals; Foundation Giving; Foundation Grants Index; Foundation Grants Index (quarterly); Foundation Grants to Individuals; Grant Guides; Guide to US Foundation their Trustees Officers & Donors; Literature of the Nonprofit Sector; Managing for Profit in the Nonprofit World; National Directory of Corporate Giving; New York State Foundations; Philanthropy & Volunteerism; Philanthropy in Action; Promoting Issues & Ideas; Securing Your Organization's Future; The Board Members Book; The Foundation Center's Guide to Proposal Writing; The Foundation Center's User-Friendly Guide; The Twenty-First Century Nonprofit
Partic in Consortium Of Foundation Libraries; Dialog Corporation
Public services - Orientations to foundation research; special programs & workshops

S FPG INTERNATIONAL CORP, 32 Union Sq E, 10003. SAN 311-7766. Tel: 212-777-4210. FAX: 212-995-9652. Web Site: www.fpg.com. *Dir*, Kimber VanRy; E-Mail: kimberv@fpg.com; Staff 33 (MLS 1, Non-MLS 32)
Founded 1936
Library Holdings: Bk Vols 300
Subject Interests: Animals, Human interest, Indust, Sports, Technology,

Travel
Special Collections: Alpha Photo Associates; European Picture Service; Henry Miller; Keystone Pictures; Paul Thompson

S FREEDOM HOUSE, Information Center,* 120 Wall St, 10005. SAN 329-8655. Tel: 212-514-8040. FAX: 212-514-8055. E-Mail: fhpres@aol.com. Web Site: www.freedomhouse.org. *Pres*, A Karatnycky; *VPres*, Kendra Zaharescu
Library Holdings: Per Subs 30
Subject Interests: Am heritage, Human rights, International relations, Soc sci
Publications: Annual Survey of Freedom in the World

S FRENCH INSTITUTE-ALLIANCE FRANCAISE LIBRARY, 22 E 60th St, 10022-1077. SAN 311-7774. Tel: 212-355-6100. FAX: 212-935-4119. E-Mail: frinst2@rmi.net. Web Site: www.fiaf.org. *Librn*, Katharine Branning; *Ref*, Mylene Duguay; Tel: 212-355-6100, Ext 216; Staff 5 (MLS 2, Non-MLS 3)
Founded 1911
1998-1999 Income $289,583, Parent Institution $264,667, Other $24,916. Mats Exp $47,000, Books $15,000, Per/Ser (Incl. Access Fees) $12,000, Presv $5,000. Sal $160,000 (Prof $90,000)
Library Holdings: Bk Vols 30,000; Per Subs 110
Subject Interests: Architecture, Art, Behav sci, Civilization, France, French lang, French-speaking countries, History, Literature, Philosophy, Soc sci
Special Collections: Paris Coll
Automation Activity & Vendor Info: (Acquisitions) Bestseller; (Cataloging) Bestseller; (Circulation) Bestseller; (Course Reserve) Bestseller; (ILL) Bestseller; (Media Booking) Bestseller; (OPAC) Bestseller; (Serials) Bestseller
Publications: Acquisitions List; Newsletter; Web Page
Restriction: Open to public for reference only
Partic in New York Metrop Ref & Res Libr Agency
Friends of the Library Group

S FRICK ART REFERENCE LIBRARY, 10 E 71st St, 10021. SAN 311-7782. Tel: 212-288-8700. FAX: 212-879-2091. Web Site: www.frick.org. *Chief Librn*, Patricia Barnett; *Coll Develop, Res*, Inge Reist; Staff 58 (MLS 26, Non-MLS 32)
Founded 1920
Library Holdings: Bk Titles 287,000; Per Subs 700
Subject Interests: Drawing, Hist of painting, Illuminated mss from fourth century AD in Western Europe, Sculpture
Automation Activity & Vendor Info: (Acquisitions) Innovative Interfaces Inc.; (Cataloging) Innovative Interfaces Inc.; (OPAC) Innovative Interfaces Inc.
Publications: Frick Art Reference Library Original Index to Art Periodicals (1983); Frick Art Reference Library Sales Catalogue Index (1992); Spanish Artists from the Fourth to the Twentieth Century, Vol 1 (A-F) (1993); The Story of the Frick Art Reference Library: The Early Years (1979)
Partic in New York Metrop Ref & Res Libr Agency; Research Libraries Group, Inc
Friends of the Library Group

L FRIED, FRANK, HARRIS, SHRIVER & JACOBSON LIBRARY,* One New York Plaza, 10004. SAN 311-7790. Tel: 212-859-8302. FAX: 212-859-8586. *Dir*, Nancy Rine; *Librn*, Warren Gordon; E-Mail: gordowa@ffhsj.com
Founded 1960
Library Holdings: Bk Vols 30,000; Per Subs 110
Subject Interests: Corporate, Fed, Securities, State law

L FULBRIGHT & JAWORSKI LLP LIBRARY, 666 Fifth Ave, 32nd flr, 10103. SAN 312-021X. Tel: 212-318-3257, 212-318-3258. FAX: 212-752-5958. *Mgr*, Millicent Levy
Library Holdings: Bk Titles 20,000; Per Subs 300
Subject Interests: Law, Securities

M HELENE FULD SCHOOL OF NURSING, Learning Center Library,* 1879 Madison Ave, 10035. SAN 327-1919. Tel: 212-423-1000. FAX: 212-427-2453. *Dir*, Helen Leach
Library Holdings: Bk Vols 4,500; Per Subs 101
Mem of NY Metrop Ref & Res Libr Agency, Inc

L FUND FOR MODERN COURTS LIBRARY,* 351 W 54th St, 10019-5101. SAN 329-7934. Tel: 212-575-1577. FAX: 212-869-1133. *Exec Dir*, Steven Zeidman
Library Holdings: Bk Vols 1,250

S GENERAL AMERICAN INVESTORS CO, INC LIBRARY,* 450 Lexington Ave, Ste 3300, 10017. SAN 311-7812. Tel: 212-916-8433. FAX: 212-377-3871. *Librn*, Gay Fahys
Founded 1930
Library Holdings: Bk Vols 1,000; Per Subs 100
Subject Interests: Am Exchange, Econ, Finance, NY stock exchange
Special Collections: Standard & Poors & Moodys Directories
Restriction: By appointment only

S GENERAL SOCIETY OF MECHANICS & TRADESMEN, General Society Library, 20 W 44th St, 10036. SAN 311-7839. Tel: 212-921-1767. FAX: 212-398-4381. Web Site: www.generalsociety.org. *Librn*, Eric Graeber; E-Mail: egraeber@mindspring.com; Staff 2 (MLS 1, Non-MLS 1)
Founded 1820
Library Holdings: Bk Titles 153,000; Per Subs 45
Special Collections: Gilbert & Sullivan (Alma Watson Coll)
Restriction: Subscription library
Partic in New York Metrop Ref & Res Libr Agency; Spec Libr Asn
Friends of the Library Group
Branches:
SMALL PRESS CENTER, 20 W 44th St, 10036. Tel: 212-764-7021. FAX: 212-354-5365. E-Mail: smallpress@aol.com. Web Site: www.smallpress.org. *Dir*, Karin Taylor
Library Holdings: Bk Titles 1,400

SR GENERAL THEOLOGICAL SEMINARY, Saint Mark's Library, 175 Ninth Ave, 10011. SAN 311-7847. Reference Tel: 212-243-5150, Ext 211. FAX: 212-924-6304. *Dir*, David E Green; *Circ*, Sally Denmed; *Ref*, Laura Moore; *Tech Servs*, Thea Pratt; Staff 3 (MLS 3)
Founded 1819. Enrl 120; Fac 20; Highest Degree: Doctorate
Library Holdings: Bk Vols 250,000; Bk Titles 200,000; Per Subs 680
Subject Interests: Anglican, Christian hist, Liturgics, Spirituality, Theology
Special Collections: Clement Clarke Moore Coll; Early English Theology Coll; Episcopal Church History (coll on the Protestant Episcopal Church in the United States), mss; Latin Bible Coll; Liturgics; T S Eliot Coll (Julius Crase Coll)
Partic in New York Metrop Ref & Res Libr Agency; OCLC Online Computer Library Center, Inc

S HENRY GEORGE SCHOOL OF SOCIAL SCIENCE, Research Library,* 121 E 30th St, 10016. SAN 374-5767. Tel: 212-889-8020. FAX: 212-889-8953. *Librn*, Vesa J Nelson
Founded 1937. Enrl 1,500; Fac 15
Library Holdings: Bk Titles 8,000; Per Subs 50
Special Collections: Henry George & Family, bks (incl rare ed), clippings, letters; Land Value Tax/Single Tax (Georgist Authors Coll), bks, journal-art, clippings, theses

S GERMAN INFORMATION CENTER, Federal Republic of Germany Collection,* 871 United Nations Plaza, 10017. SAN 375-7099. Tel: 212-610-9800. FAX: 212-610-9802. E-Mail: gic1@germany-info.org. Web Site: www.germany-info.org. *Librn*, Fay Conway

S GETTY IMAGES, (Formerly Archive Films/Archive Photos), Hulton - Archive, 75 Varick St, 10013. SAN 329-7950. Tel: 212-822-7710. Toll Free Tel: 800-688-5656. FAX: 212-645-2137. E-Mail: sales@archivefilms.com. Web Site: www.archivefilms.com. *Librn*, Anne Loustaunou; Tel: 212-822-7764, E-Mail: aloustaunou@archivephotos.com
Founded 1979
Subject Interests: Geography, Historical recordings, Industry, Lifestyle, Personalities, Transportation
Special Collections: Film footage from 1986-1994, photos & engravings illustrating beginning of time to present day
Restriction: By appointment only
Function: Archival collection
Research & licensing fees charged by the project

J KATHARINE GIBBS SCHOOL LIBRARY,* 200 Park Ave, 10166. SAN 311-8460. Tel: 212-973-4987. *Librn*, Linda Perahia; Staff 2 (MLS 1, Non-MLS 1)
Library Holdings: Bk Vols 3,371; Bk Titles 4,000; Per Subs 71
Subject Interests: Bus
Special Collections: Secretarial Studies Coll
Publications: Acquisitions list (monthly); fact sheet for library users
Partic in New York Metrop Ref & Res Libr Agency

L GIBSON, DUNN & CRUTCHER, 200 Park Ave, 48th Flr, 10166-0193. SAN 323-5688. Tel: 212-351-4005. FAX: 212-351-4035. Web Site: www.gdclaw.com. *Librn*, Steven Raber; E-Mail: sraber@gdclaw.com; Staff 4 (MLS 2, Non-MLS 2)
Founded 1987
Library Holdings: Per Subs 125
Publications: Library Bulletin

S GIRL SCOUTS OF THE USA LIBRARY,* 420 Fifth Ave, 10018-2798. SAN 311-7863. Tel: 212-852-8623. FAX: 212-852-6517. *Librn*, Juana Alers-Quinones
Founded 1974
Library Holdings: Bk Vols 5,000; Bk Titles 4,000; Per Subs 100
Subject Interests: Adolescent develop, Mgt non- profit, Pluralism, Voluntarism, Women's hist
Special Collections: Girl Scout publications, bks, per
Restriction: By appointment only

S GLOBAL EDUCATION ASSOCIATES, Curriculum Resource Library, 475 Riverside Dr, Rm 1848, 10115-0122. SAN 371-1862. Tel: 212-870-3290. FAX: 212-870-2729. E-Mail: globaleduc@earthlink.net. Web Site: www.globaleduc.org. *Librn*, Ann Smith; E-Mail: globaleduc@earthlink.net

Founded 1973
Library Holdings: Bk Vols 2,200; Per Subs 60
Restriction: Not open to public

S GLOBE PHOTOS, INC LIBRARY,* 275 Seventh Ave, 10001. SAN 377-5046. Tel: 212-645-9292. FAX: 212-627-8932. *Librn*, Mary Beth Whelan

S GOETHE-INSTITUT NEW YORK, German Cultural Center Library, 1014 Fifth Ave, 10028. SAN 311-7871. Tel: 212-439-8688. Interlibrary Loan Service Tel: 212-439-8693. FAX: 212-439-8705. E-Mail: library@goethe-newyork.org. Web Site: www.goethe.de/newyork. *Librn*, Freya U Jeschke; Tel: 212-439-8700, 439-8694. Subject Specialists: *Culture*, Freya U Jeschke; *German lang*, Freya U Jeschke; *German lit*, Freya U Jeschke; Staff 3 (MLS 2, Non-MLS 1)
Founded 1957
Library Holdings: Bk Vols 15,000; Per Subs 150
Subject Interests: German (Language)
Automation Activity & Vendor Info: (Cataloging) Inmagic, Inc.
Database Vendor: OCLC - First Search
Function: Professional lending library

M GOLDWATER MEMORIAL HOSPITAL, Health Sciences Library,* Franklin D Roosevelt Island, 10044. SAN 311-7898. Tel: 212-318-8000, Ext 4800. FAX: 212-318-4460. *Dir*, Dr Martin M Leibovici
Founded 1939
Library Holdings: Bk Vols 13,680; Per Subs 386
Subject Interests: Chronic disease, Geriatrics, Hearing, Medicine, Phys, Rehabilitation med, Speech
Publications: Acquisition List
Partic in Medical Library Center Of New York; New York Metrop Ref & Res Libr Agency; OCLC Online Computer Library Center, Inc
New York University Medical Center Affiliate

S GRADUATE SCHOOL & UNIVERSITY CENTER, CITY UNIVERSITY OF NEW YORK, National Self-Help Clearinghouse Library,* 365 Fifth Ave, Ste 3300, 10016-4304. SAN 329-3009. Tel: 212-817-1822. Web Site: www.selfhelpweb.org. *Dir*, Frank Riessman; *Exec Dir*, Audrey Gartner
Founded 1976
Library Holdings: Bk Titles 100; Per Subs 50
Restriction: Non-circulating to the public

L GRAHAM & JAMES, Law Library,* 885 Third Ave 24th flr, 10022. SAN 372-4476. Tel: 212-848-1000. FAX: 212-688-2449. E-Mail: mv@gj.com. *Mgr*, Victor Michele
Library Holdings: Bk Vols 10,000

L GREENBERG, TRAGER, TOPLITZ, & HERBST LIBRARY,* 100 Church St, Ste 1630, 10007. SAN 321-7523. Tel: 212-267-5700. FAX: 212-267-5814.
Library Holdings: Bk Vols 7,000; Per Subs 25
Subject Interests: Construction contract claims
Special Collections: Annotated ALR

S GREY WORLDWIDE INFORMATION CENTER, (Formerly Grey Advertising, Inc), 777 Third Ave, 36th Flr, 10017. SAN 311-7944. Tel: 212-546-2511. FAX: 212-546-2565. *Dir*, Ellen Spross; E-Mail: espross@grey.com; *Info Specialist*, Tanya Kessler; E-Mail: tkessler@grey.com; *Info Specialist*, Norman Tobias; E-Mail: ntobias@grey.com; Staff 3 (MLS 1, Non-MLS 2)
Founded 1948
Library Holdings: Bk Titles 400; Per Subs 110
Subject Interests: Advertising, Consumer behavior, Marketing, Planning
Database Vendor: Dialog, Lexis-Nexis, ProQuest
Restriction: Staff use only
Function: For research purposes

S GROLIER CLUB OF NEW YORK LIBRARY,* 47 E 60th St, 10022. SAN 311-7952. Tel: 212-838-6690. FAX: 212-838-2445. E-Mail: grolier@grolierclub.org. Web Site: www.grolierclub.org. *Dir, Librn*, Eric Holzenberg; E-Mail: ejh@grolierclub.org; *Cat*, Michael North; Staff 6 (MLS 1, Non-MLS 5)
Founded 1884
Library Holdings: Bk Vols 100,000; Per Subs 200
Special Collections: Authors, Printers & Artists; Bibliography; Book Trade & Auction Catalogs; History of Printing & Book Collecting; Inventories of Private Libraries
Partic in RLIN

S GUILD OF BOOK WORKERS LIBRARY, University of Iowa, 521 Fifth Ave, 17th Flr, 10175. SAN 311-7979. Tel: 212-292-4444. FAX: 212-335-5900. *In Charge*, Anna Embree
Founded 1958
Library Holdings: Bk Vols 600
Subject Interests: Bk conserv, Bookbinding, Calligraphy, Crafts, Paper decorating, Paper marbling, Papermaking, Printing
Special Collections: History of Hand Bookbinding
Publications: Acquisitions List
Restriction: Members only

L HAIGHT, GARDNER, HOLLAND & KNIGHT, Law Library, 195 Broadway, 10007. SAN 311-7987. Tel: 212-513-3580. FAX: 212-385-9010. Web Site: www.hklaw.com. *Librn*, Cristina Alvy; E-Mail: calvy@hklaw.com
Library Holdings: Per Subs 60
Subject Interests: Admiralty, Aviation
Restriction: Members only
Partic in Dialog Corporation; Westlaw

S THE HAMPDEN-BOOTH THEATRE LIBRARY AT THE PLAYERS,* 16 Gramercy Park S, 10003. SAN 312-0015. Tel: 212-228-7610. FAX: 212-473-2701. *Librn*, Raymond Wemmlinger
Founded 1957
Library Holdings: Bk Titles 10,000; Per Subs 25
Subject Interests: Hist of Am stage, Hist of English stage, With emphasis on 19th century
Special Collections: (La Mama Experimental Theatre Club Coll), playbills, doc; 18th-19th Century English Playbills (William Henderson Coll); Burlesque (Chuck Callahan Coll); Cabinet; Edwin Booth; Franklin; George M Cohan; Heller; Maurice Evans; Off-Off Broadway Theatre; Photographs; Pipenight; Players; Robert B Mantell; Stage Charities (British Actors Orphanage Fund Coll), correspondence, doc; Union Square Theatre; Walter Hampden

HARLEM HOSPITAL MEDICAL CENTER

M HEALTH SCIENCES LIBRARY, 506 Lenox Ave, KP6108, 10037. SAN 353-1066. Tel: 212-939-1685. FAX: 212-939-1692. E-Mail: jes106@columbia.edu. *Dir*, James Swanton
Founded 1907
Jul 1997-Jun 1998 Income $50,000. Mats Exp $50,000
Library Holdings: Bk Titles 5,000; Per Subs 200
Subject Interests: Medicine, Nursing
Partic in Basic Health Sciences Library Network; Manhattan-Bronx Health Sciences Libraries Group; New York Metrop Ref & Res Libr Agency

S HARRIS INTERACTIVE, Information Services Library, 111 Fifth Ave, 10003. SAN 325-7398. Tel: 212-539-9600. Toll Free Tel: 800-575-4749. FAX: 212-539-9669. Web Site: www.harrisinteractive.com. *Coordr*, Cheryl Lee; Tel: 212-539-9697, E-Mail: clee@harrisinteractive.com
Library Holdings: Bk Vols 500; Per Subs 86
Special Collections: The Harris Poll Columns, since 1963

S HARVARD LIBRARY IN NEW YORK,* 27 W 44th St, 10036. SAN 311-8002. Tel: 212-827-1246. FAX: 212-827-1251, Ext 1246. *Librn*, Adrienne G Fischier
Founded 1978
Library Holdings: Bk Vols 24,000
Special Collections: Harvardiana

R HASHOMER HATZAIR YOUTH MOVEMENT LIBRARY, 114 W 26th St, Ste 1001, 10001. SAN 323-6595. Tel: 212-627-2830. FAX: 212-989-9840.
Founded 1927
Library Holdings: Bk Titles 200

S HATCH-BILLOPS COLLECTION, INC LIBRARY, Archive of Black American Cultural History,* 491 Broadway, 7th flr, 10012. SAN 326-551X. Tel: 212-966-3231. FAX: 212-966-3231. *Archivist*, James Hatch
Library Holdings: Bk Vols 6,000
Publications: Artist & Influence

L HAWKINS, DELAFIELD & WOOD, Law Library, 67 Wall St, 10005. SAN 311-8010. Tel: 212-820-9444. FAX: 212-514-8425. *Librn*, Kathryn McRae; Staff 4 (MLS 1, Non-MLS 3)
Library Holdings: Bk Vols 20,000; Per Subs 125

CR HEBREW UNION COLLEGE-JEWISH INSTITUTE OF RELIGION-BROOKDALE CENTER, Klau Library, One W Fourth St, 10012-1186. SAN 353-1120. Tel: 212-674-5300. FAX: 212-388-1720. *Librn*, Dr Philip E Miller; E-Mail: miller@huc.edu; *Circ*, Louis Massone
Founded 1922
Library Holdings: Bk Titles 130,000
Subject Interests: Hebrew lit, History, Relig studies

S MILTON HELPERN LIBRARY OF LEGAL MEDICINE,* Milton Helpern Institute of Forensic Medicine, 520 First Ave, 10016. SAN 311-8037. Tel: 212-447-2030, 212-447-2343. FAX: 212-447-2744.
Founded 1962
Library Holdings: Bk Titles 4,800; Per Subs 30
Subject Interests: Criminalistics, Forensic aspects of pathology, Medicine, Psychiatry, Serology, Toxicology
Publications: International Microform Journal of Legal Medicine & Forensic Sciences
Restriction: By appointment only

L HILL, BETTS & NASH LIBRARY,* One World Trade Ctr, 52nd flr, Ste 5215, 10048. SAN 325-5441. Tel: 212-839-7161. FAX: 212-466-0514.; Staff 1 (MLS 1)
Library Holdings: Bk Vols 12,000; Bk Titles 1,500; Per Subs 50

Subject Interests: Corporate law, Finance, Maritime law
Publications: Library Bulletin (monthly)
Restriction: Private library
Partic in Dialog Corporation

S HISPANIC SOCIETY OF AMERICA LIBRARY, Broadway between 155th & 156th St. (Mail add: 613 W 155th St, 10032), SAN 311-8061. Tel: 212-926-2234. FAX: 212-690-0743. Web Site: www.hispanicsociety.org. *Curator*, Gerald J MacDonald; *Rare Bks*, John O'Neill; *Per*, Edwin Rolon; Staff 8 (MLS 3, Non-MLS 5)
Founded 1904
Library Holdings: Bk Vols 300,000; Per Subs 142
Subject Interests: Archaeology, Art, Customs, Hispanic, History, Language, Literature
Special Collections: Golden Age Drama Manuscript Coll; Medieval Manuscripts Coll; Rare Book Coll
Publications: Bibliographies, Catalogues
Restriction: Non-circulating to the public
Function: Reference services available, Research library

S BERNARD HODES ADVERTISING, Information Center,* 220 E 42nd St, 16th flr, 10017. SAN 325-7339. Tel: 212-758-2600. FAX: 212-888-7693. Web Site: www.hodes.com.
Library Holdings: Bk Vols 500; Per Subs 35
Subject Interests: Human resources

S HOLLAND SOCIETY OF NEW YORK LIBRARY, 122 E 58th St, 10022. SAN 311-807X. Tel: 212-758-1871. FAX: 212-758-2232. E-Mail: holsoc@aol.com. *Librn*, Linda Rolufs
Founded 1885
Library Holdings: Bk Titles 6,000; Per Subs 20
Subject Interests: Culture, Ethnology, Folkways, Genealogy of Am immigrants in the Dutch settlements, History
Publications: De Halve Maen Journal; New York Historical Manuscripts; Society Publications
Open most Sats 11-4, closed Aug & holidays
Friends of the Library Group

S HORTICULTURAL SOCIETY OF NEW YORK, INC LIBRARY, 128 W 58th St, 10019. SAN 311-810X. Tel: 212-757-0915. FAX: 212-246-1207. Web Site: www.hsny.org. *Librn*, Katherine Powis; E-Mail: kpowis@hsny.org
Founded 1922
Library Holdings: Bk Titles 7,000; Per Subs 120
Subject Interests: Botany, Environ, Flower arranging, Gardening, Horticulture, House plants, Landscape design, Natural history
Restriction: Open to public for reference only
Partic in New York Metrop Ref & Res Libr Agency

M HOSPITAL FOR SPECIAL SURGERY, Kim Barrett Memorial Library, 535 E 70th St, 10021. SAN 311-8126. Tel: 212-606-1000, 212-606-1210. FAX: 212-774-2779. *Librn*, Inga Zhygalo; E-Mail: zhygaloi@hss.edu; Staff 1 (Non-MLS 1)
Founded 1952
Library Holdings: Bk Titles 4,200; Per Subs 98
Subject Interests: Orthopaedic surgery, Orthopedics, Rheumatic diseases
Database Vendor: OVID Technologies
Mem of Metro Coop Libr Syst
Friends of the Library Group

L HUGHES HUBBARD & REED LIBRARY, Law Library, One Battery Park Plaza, 16th Flr, 10004. SAN 311-8142. Tel: 212-837-6666. FAX: 212-422-4726. E-Mail: library@hugheshubbard.com. *Dir Libr Serv*, Patricia E Barbone; Tel: 212-837-6594, E-Mail: barbone@hugheshubbard.com; *Ref*, James H Meece; E-Mail: meece@hugheshubbard.com. Subject Specialists: *Securities*, James H Meece; Staff 6 (MLS 3, Non-MLS 3)
Founded 1942
Library Holdings: Bk Vols 45,000; Bk Titles 5,500; Per Subs 350
Subject Interests: Corporate securities, Insurance, Labor, Litigation, Product liability, Securities law, Tax
Database Vendor: Dialog, OCLC - First Search, OVID Technologies
Restriction: Not open to public
Function: ILL to other special libraries
Partic in RLIN

S HUGUENOT SOCIETY OF AMERICA LIBRARY, 122 E 58th St, 10022. SAN 327-1935. Tel: 212-755-0592. FAX: 212-317-0676. *In Charge*, Dorothy F Kimball
Library Holdings: Bk Vols 3,000
Subject Interests: Genealogy, Manuscripts
Open Tues & Wed 10-4 By Appointment

C HUNTER COLLEGE OF THE CITY UNIVERSITY OF NEW YORK LIBRARY,* 695 Park Ave, 10021. SAN 353-1155. Tel: 212-772-4137, 212-772-4146. Interlibrary Loan Service Tel: 212-772-4192. FAX: 212-772-4142, 212-772-4243. E-Mail: asklib@shiva.hunter.cuny.edu. Web Site: www.library.hunter.cuny.edu. *Chief Librn*, Louise Sherby; *Chief Librn*, Pamela Wonsek; *Online Servs, Publ Servs*, Danise Hoover; *Bibliog Instr*, Patricia Woodard; *Coordr*, Clay Williams; Tel: 212-772-4137, Fax: 212-772-4243, E-Mail: clay.williams@hunter.cuny.edu; *Acq*, Yvonne Webb; *Cat*, Wendy Tan; *Rare Bks, Spec Coll*, Julio Hernandez-Delgado; *Coll Develop*, Elliott Kaback. Subject Specialists: *Music*, Elliott Kaback; Staff 43 (MLS 27, Non-MLS 16)
Founded 1870. Enrl 18,500; Fac 895; Highest Degree: Doctorate
Jul 1997-Jun 1998 Income $1,131,450. Mats Exp $713,133, Books $254,826, Per/Ser (Incl. Access Fees) $370,205, Presv $34,999, Micro $38,083. Sal $1,865,416 (Prof $1,314,657)
Library Holdings: Bk Vols 753,465; Bk Titles 521,740; Per Subs 2,419
Special Collections: Early English Novels (Stonehill Coll); Eileen Cowe Historical Textbooks; Lenox Hill Neighborhood Coll; Women's City Club of NY Coll
Automation Activity & Vendor Info: (Circulation) NOTIS
Partic in New York Metrop Ref & Res Libr Agency; OCLC Online Computer Library Center, Inc
Friends of the Library Group
Departmental Libraries:

CM HEALTH PROFESSIONS, Hunter College Brookdale Campus, 425 E 25th St, 10010. SAN 353-118X. Tel: 212-481-4326. FAX: 212-481-5116. Web Site: www.library.hunter.cuny.edu/hpl. *Librn*, Veronika A Conant
Founded 1909
Library Holdings: Bk Vols 19,000; Per Subs 330
Automation Activity & Vendor Info: (Circulation) NOTIS

SCHOOL OF SOCIAL WORK LIBRARY, 129 E 79th St, 10021. SAN 353-121X. Tel: 212-452-7076. FAX: 212-452-7125. Web Site: www.library.hunter.cuny.edu/ssw/. *Librn*, Philip Swan
Founded 1969
Library Holdings: Bk Vols 41,216; Per Subs 489
Automation Activity & Vendor Info: (Circulation) NOTIS

L HUNTON & WILLIAMS, Law Library, 200 Park Ave, 44th Flr, 10166. SAN 371-8433. Tel: 212-309-1078. Interlibrary Loan Service Tel: 212-309-1077. FAX: 212-309-1100. *Librn*, Alina Alvarez-Lenda; Staff 2 (MLS 2)
Library Holdings: Bk Titles 25,000; Per Subs 5,000

S THE IMAGE BANK LIBRARY,* 111 Fifth Ave, 10003. SAN 323-505X. Tel: 212-539-8300. FAX: 212-539-8391. Web Site: www.theimagebank.com. *Mgr*, Kevin Connelly; E-Mail: kconnelly@theimagebank.com
Subsidiary of Kodak

S INSTITUTES OF RELIGION & HEALTH LIBRARY,* 3 W 29th St, 10001. SAN 311-8258. Tel: 212-725-7850, Ext 317. FAX: 212-689-3212. *Librn*, Mary Pascarello
Founded 1960
Library Holdings: Bk Vols 3,500
Subject Interests: Family therapy, Marital, Pastoral psychotherapy, Psychoanalysis
Publications: The Journal of Religion & Health

S INSTITUTO ITALIANO DI CULTURA, BIBLIOTECA,* 686 Park Ave, 10021-5009. SAN 311-8347. Tel: 212-879-4242, Ext 31. FAX: 212-861-4018. E-Mail: lib@italcultny.org. *Librn*, Paolo Barlera
Founded 1959
Library Holdings: Bk Titles 34,100; Per Subs 110
Subject Interests: Italy

S INSURANCE INFORMATION INSTITUTE LIBRARY,* 110 William St, 10038. SAN 324-6272. Tel: 212-669-9200. FAX: 212-267-9591. Web Site: www.III.org. *Librn*, Maydine Singer; E-Mail: madines@iii.org
Founded 1960
Library Holdings: Bk Vols 1,500; Bk Titles 1,000; Per Subs 130
Subject Interests: Casualty ins, Property ins
Restriction: By appointment only
Maintains a bibliographic database known as the Insurance Information Institute Data Base

J INTERBORO INSTITUTE LIBRARY, 450 W 56th St, 10019. SAN 325-2302. Tel: 212-399-0091. FAX: 212-765-5772. Web Site: www.interboro.com. *Librn*, Elaine Braithwaite; E-Mail: ebraithwaite@interboro.com; Staff 3 (MLS 1, Non-MLS 2)
Founded 1888. Enrl 1,000; Fac 37; Highest Degree: Associate
Library Holdings: Bk Titles 6,020; Per Subs 100
Subject Interests: Business and management, Ophthalmic dispensing, Paralegal studies, Security

SR INTERCHURCH CENTER, Ecumenical Library, 475 Riverside Dr, Rm 900, 10115. SAN 311-8266. Tel: 212-870-3804. FAX: 212-870-2440. Web Site: metro.org/members/icelib.html. *Librn*, Ernest Rubinstein; E-Mail: rubinsteine@interchurch-center.org
Founded 1978
Jan 1999-Dec 1999 Income Parent Institution $89,700. Mats Exp $15,800, Books $11,000, Per/Ser (Incl. Access Fees) $4,000, Presv $500, Electronic Ref Mat (Incl. Access Fees) $300. Sal $56,900 (Prof $51,000)
Library Holdings: Bk Titles 13,600; Per Subs 100
Subject Interests: Church history, Develop, Missions, Religion, Soc problems, Theology
Special Collections: Denominational Yearbooks; Religious Research Projects (H Paul Douglass), micro
Automation Activity & Vendor Info: (OPAC) TLC

Database Vendor: OCLC - First Search
Function: ILL available, Reference services available, Research library
Partic in New York Metrop Ref & Res Libr Agency; NY Area Theol Libr Asn

S INTERNATIONAL CENTER OF PHOTOGRAPHY LIBRARY,* 1133 Avenue of Americas, 10036. SAN 324-1823. Tel: 212-768-4682. FAX: 212-768-4688. *Chief Librn*, Lucia Siskin; Staff 3 (MLS 3)
Founded 1977. Enrl 300; Fac 30
Library Holdings: Bk Titles 4,000; Per Subs 200
Subject Interests: Photog
Publications: Museum Publications
Friends of the Library Group

S INTERNATIONAL COPPER ASSOCIATION LIMITED,* 260 Madison Ave, 10016. SAN 370-8810. Tel: 212-251-7240. FAX: 212-251-7245. E-Mail: ica@copper.org. *Pres*, Jan Smolders
Library Holdings: Bk Titles 500; Per Subs 20

S INTERNATIONAL COUNCIL OF SHOPPING CENTERS, Albert Sussman Library, 1221 Avenue of the Americas, 41st fl, 10020-1099. SAN 324-1696. Tel: 646-728-3800. FAX: 212-589-5555. Web Site: www.icsc.org. *Mgr Libr Serv*, Susan Pistilli; E-Mail: spistilli@icsc.org; *Asst Librn*, Michael Tubridy; E-Mail: mtubridy@icsc.org; Staff 2 (MLS 2)
Library Holdings: Bk Titles 1,700; Per Subs 250
Subject Interests: Mgt of shopping ctrs, Real estate, Retail
Automation Activity & Vendor Info: (Cataloging) Inmagic, Inc.
Database Vendor: Dialog, Lexis-Nexis
Publications: Albert Sussman Library News (Newsletter)
Restriction: Members only
Function: Research library

S INTERNATIONAL LADIES' GARMENT WORKERS' UNION, Research Department Library,* 1710 Broadway, 10019. SAN 311-8274. Tel: 212-265-7000, Ext 207. FAX: 212-489-7238. Web Site: www.uniteunion.org. *Dir*, Nemrod Mitton
Library Holdings: Per Subs 14
Subject Interests: Bus, Garment industry, Labor hist, Mgt

S INTERNATIONAL TRADEMARK ASSOCIATION LIBRARY,* 1133 Avenue of the Americas, 10036. SAN 312-1208. Tel: 212-768-9887. FAX: 768-7796. *Librn*, Charlotte Jones
Founded 1878
Library Holdings: Bk Titles 2,000
Subject Interests: Trademarks

S INTERPUBLIC GROUP OF COMPANIES, Center for Advertising Services,* 1271 Avenue of the Americas 44th flr, 10020. SAN 328-526X. Tel: 212-399-8222. FAX: 212-399-8130. Web Site: www.interpublic.com. *Dir*, Robin Feurstein

L JACKSON, LEWIS, SCHNITZLER & KRUPMAN, Law Library,* 101 Park Ave, 37th flr, 10178-3898. SAN 372-4247. Tel: 212-697-8200, Ext 4033. FAX: 212-687-0228. *Librn*, Catherine M Dillon; E-Mail: dillonc@jacksonlewis.com
Library Holdings: Bk Vols 10,000

S JAPAN SOCIETY LIBRARY,* 333 E 47th St, 10017. SAN 311-8355. Tel: 212-832-1155. FAX: 212-715-1262. Web Site: www.jpmsoc.com. *Dir, Librn*, Reiko Sassa
Library Holdings: Bk Titles 14,000; Per Subs 116
Subject Interests: Architecture, Art, Bus, Econ, History, Language arts, Mgt

S JEWISH BOARD OF FAMILY & CHILDREN SERVICES, Mary & Louis Robinson Library, 120 W 57th St, 10019. SAN 327-1978. Tel: 212-582-9100, Ext 1504. FAX: 212-956-0526. *Librn*, Sue Weiland
Library Holdings: Bk Vols 8,000; Per Subs 60
Subject Interests: Mental health

S JEWISH BRAILLE INSTITUTE, 110 E 30th St, 10016. SAN 327-1994. Tel: 212-889-2525. FAX: 212-689-3692. E-Mail: library@jewishbraille.org. Web Site: www.jewishbraille.org.
Library Holdings: Bk Titles 7,500
Publications: Concert, Lecture & Poetry Series (quarterly on tape); JBI Voice - English Cassette (monthly); Jewish Braille Review - English Braille (monthly)
The mission of the Jewish Braille Institute & its library is to lend parity & dignity to those blind, visually impaired & learning disabled individuals whose participation in Jewish life cycles & other community activities depends upon their ability to gain access to printed Judaic material

S JEWISH DEFENSE ORGANIZATION LIBRARY, PO Box 159, 10150. SAN 370-1417. Tel: 212-252-3383. Web Site: www.jdo.org. *Librn*, Steuart Leben
1999-2000 Mats Exp $4,950, Books $1,000, Per/Ser (Incl. Access Fees) $2,800, Presv $100, AV Equip $300, Other Print Mats $750
Library Holdings: Bk Vols 1,000

R JEWISH EDUCATION SERVICE OF NORTH AMERICA, INC, Resource Center, 111 Eighth Ave, 11th flr, 10011-5201. SAN 327-201X. Tel: 212-284-6898, 212-284-6950. FAX: 212-284-6951. E-Mail: info@jesna.org. Web Site: www.jesna.org. *Dir*, Caren N Levine
Subject Interests: Jewish educ, Technology

S JEWISH GUILD FOR THE BLIND, Guild Cassette Library, 15 W 65th St, 10023. SAN 311-8371. Tel: 212-769-6331. FAX: 212-769-6266. *Dir*, Peter Williamson; Staff 4 (MLS 1, Non-MLS 3)
Founded 1974
Library Holdings: Bk Titles 1,600
Subject Interests: Fiction, Non-fiction, Poetry
Special Collections: People Magazine, WE MEDIA Magazine & Time Magazine monthly on audio cassettes
Publications: Bibliography
Circulates cassette best-sellers to visually & physically handicapped persons worldwide; national magazine circulation

R JEWISH THEOLOGICAL SEMINARY LIBRARY, 3080 Broadway, 10027. SAN 311-8398. Tel: 212-678-8075. Interlibrary Loan Service Tel: 212-678-8963. Circulation Tel: 212-678-8082. Reference Tel: 212-678-8081. FAX: 212-678-8998. E-Mail: library@jtsa.edu. Web Site: www.jtsa.edu/library. *Chief Librn*, Mayer E Rabinowitz; E-Mail: marabinowitz@jtsa.edu; *Librn*, Naom M Steinberger; Tel: 212-678-8982, E-Mail: nsteinberger@jtsa.edu; *Coll Develop*, Rena Borow; Tel: 212-678-8970, E-Mail: reborow@jtsa.edu; *Publ Servs*, Odelia Levanovsky; Tel: 212-678-8079, E-Mail: odlevanovsky@jtsa.edu; *Spec Coll*, Jerry Schwarzbard; Tel: 212-678-8973, E-Mail: jschwarzbard@jtsa.edu; *Tech Servs*, Sara Spiegel; Tel: 212-678-8093, E-Mail: saspiegel@jtsa.edu; Staff 20 (MLS 11, Non-MLS 9)
Founded 1903. Enrl 750; Fac 57; Highest Degree: Doctorate
Jul 2000-Jun 2001 Income $1,770,977. Mats Exp $167,500, Books $115,000, Per/Ser (Incl. Access Fees) $42,500. Sal $1,320,477
Library Holdings: Bk Vols 370,000; Per Subs 788
Subject Interests: Bible, Hebrew lit, Israel, Jewish hist, Judaism, Liturgy, Rabbinics
Special Collections: Bible; Hebrew Incunabula, archives; Hebrew Manuscripts, micro; Liturgical works; Rabbinics; rare bks
Automation Activity & Vendor Info: (Acquisitions) EX Libris; (Cataloging) EX Libris; (Circulation) EX Libris; (Course Reserve) EX Libris; (ILL) EX Libris; (Media Booking) EX Libris; (OPAC) EX Libris; (Serials) EX Libris
Publications: Between the Lines
Partic in New York Metrop Ref & Res Libr Agency; OCLC Online Computer Library Center, Inc; RLG
On-site access with photo ID
Friends of the Library Group

CL JOHN JAY COLLEGE OF CRIMINAL JUSTICE, Lloyd George Sealy Library, 899 Tenth Ave, 10019. SAN 311-8401. Tel: 212-237-8265. FAX: 212-237-8221. E-Mail: lesjj@cunyvm.cuny.edu. Web Site: www.lib.jjay.cuny.edu. *Chief Librn*, Dr Larry E Sullivan; Tel: 212-237-8265; *Assoc Librn*, Bonnie R Nelson; Tel: 212-237-8267, E-Mail: bnelson@jjay.cuny.edu; *Assoc Librn, Publ Servs, Reader Servs*, Janice Dunham; Tel: 212-237-8256, E-Mail: janjj@cunyvm.cuny.edu; *Ser*, Dolores Grande; Tel: 212-237-8235, E-Mail: dmgjj@cunyvm.cuny.edu; *Cat, Tech Servs*, Marlene Kandel; Tel: 212-237-8237, E-Mail: mkkjj@cunyvm.cuny.edu; *ILL*, Nancy Egan; Tel: 212-237-8269, E-Mail: nanjj@cunyvm.cuny.edu; *Ref*, Kathy Killoran; Tel: 212-237-8263, E-Mail: kbkjj@cunyvm.cuny.edu; *Ref*, Marvelous Brooks; Tel: 212-237-8261; *Ref*, Antony E Simpson; Tel: 212-237-8242, E-Mail: asimpson@jjay.cuny.edu; *Ref*, Kiriakova Maria; *Coll Develop*, Jane Davenport; Tel: 212-237-8236, E-Mail: janedavenport@yahoo.com. Subject Specialists: *Info systs*, Bonnie R Nelson; Staff 15 (MLS 13, Non-MLS 2)
Founded 1965. Enrl 8,094; Fac 238; Highest Degree: Doctorate
Library Holdings: Bk Vols 222,423; Bk Titles 150,682; Per Subs 3,031
Subject Interests: Criminal justice, Fire serv admin, Forensic psychol, Pub admin, Sci
Special Collections: Flora R Schreiber, papers; New York Criminal Court Transcripts & Records 1890-1920; NYC Police Dept Blotters, Manhatten 1920-1933; Police Department Annual Reports; Sing Sing Prison, Papers of the Warden (Lewis E Lawes Coll)
Automation Activity & Vendor Info: (Circulation) NOTIS
Publications: Newsletter; research guides; self-guided workbooks
Partic in Criminal Justice Info Exchange; New York Metrop Ref & Res Libr Agency; OCLC Online Computer Library Center, Inc
Friends of the Library Group

S THE JOURNAL OF COMMERCE LIBRARY,* 2 World Trade Ctr, 27th flr, 10048. SAN 329-7837. Tel: 212-837-7116. FAX: 212-837-7079. Web Site: www.joc.com. *Mgr*, Christine Karpevych; Staff 2 (Non-MLS 2)
Founded 1977
Library Holdings: Bk Titles 600; Per Subs 100
Subject Interests: Maritime, Trade, Transportation
Publications: Clues
Partic in BRS; Data Time; Dialog Corporation; Infonautics; Mediastream; Reuters

S JUILLIARD SCHOOL, Lila Acheson Wallace Library, 60 Lincoln Center Plaza, 10023-6588. SAN 311-8436. Tel: 212-799-5000, Ext 265. FAX: 212-769-6421. E-Mail: library@juilliard.edu. Web Site: www.juilliard.edu/library/lib.htm. *Dir, Info Res*, Jane Gottlieb; E-Mail: gottlieb@juilliard.edu; *Archivist*, Jeni Dahmus; Tel: 212-799-5000, Ext 367, E-Mail: jdahmus@juilliard.edu; *Cat*, Robert Sherrane; E-Mail: rsherrane@juilliard.edu; *Cat*, Brien Weiner; E-Mail: bweiner@juilliard.edu; *Cat, Ref*, Patricia Thomson; E-Mail: pthomson@juilliard.edu; *Media Spec Ad*, Sandra Czajkowski; E-Mail: sczajkowski@juilliard.edu; *Tech Servs*, Alan Klein; E-Mail: aklein@juilliard.edu; Staff 13 (MLS 6, Non-MLS 7)
Founded 1905. Enrl 1,769; Fac 300; Highest Degree: Doctorate
Jul 1999-Jun 2000 Income $665,040, State $5,440, Parent Institution $659,600. Mats Exp $191,274, Books $74,669, Per/Ser (Incl. Access Fees) $23,045, Presv $12,000, AV Equip $12,982. Sal $473,766 (Prof $320,680)
Library Holdings: Bk Vols 80,793; Bk Titles 56,978; Per Subs 220
Subject Interests: Dance, Drama, Music
Special Collections: First & Early Editions of Liszt Piano Works; Oboe Coll; Opera Librettos of 19th Century; Opera Piano-Vocal Scores; Soulima & Igor Stravinsky Coll
Automation Activity & Vendor Info: (Acquisitions) Innovative Interfaces Inc.; (Cataloging) Innovative Interfaces Inc.; (Circulation) Innovative Interfaces Inc.; (Course Reserve) Innovative Interfaces Inc.; (ILL) Innovative Interfaces Inc.; (Media Booking) Innovative Interfaces Inc.; (OPAC) Innovative Interfaces Inc.; (Serials) Innovative Interfaces Inc.
Database Vendor: Innovative Interfaces INN - View, OCLC - First Search
Publications: Guide to The Juilliard School Archives
Restriction: Open to researchers by request, Open to student, faculty & staff
Partic in New York Metrop Ref & Res Libr Agency; OCLC Online Computer Library Center, Inc

L JULIEN & SCHLESINGER, PC, Attorneys at Law Library, 150 William St, 19th Flr, 10038. SAN 311-8444. Tel: 212-962-8020. *Dir*, Dina Horowitz
Library Holdings: Bk Vols 6,000; Per Subs 32
Subject Interests: Litigation
Restriction: Not open to public

L KAYE, SCHOLER, FIERMAN, HAYS & HANDLER, LLP, Law Library, 425 Park Ave, 10022. SAN 311-8479. Tel: 212-836-8312. FAX: 212-836-7153. *Dir*, Shabeer Khan; *ILL*, Sabrina Busgith; *Tech Servs*, Lawrence Niculescu; *Ref*, Cassandra Porter; *Ref*, Jada Wong; Staff 13 (MLS 5, Non-MLS 8)
Library Holdings: Bk Vols 80,000; Per Subs 1,137
Subject Interests: Banking, Bankruptcy, Copyright, Corporate, Emerging markets, Estates, Labor, Latin America, Law-antitrust, Real estate, Tax, Trademarks, Wills
Database Vendor: epixtech, inc., Lexis-Nexis, OCLC - First Search, ProQuest
Restriction: By appointment only

L KELLEY, DRYE & WARREN, Law Library,* 101 Park Ave, 10178. SAN 327-2052. Tel: 212-808-7800. FAX: 212-808-7897. Web Site: www.kelleydrye.com. *Chief Librn*, Patricia Renze; E-Mail: prenze@kelleydrye.com; *Asst Librn*, Maureen Cleary; *Ref*, Ann Caufield; *Ref*, Marsha Stuart
Library Holdings: Bk Vols 25,000; Per Subs 75

S KENNEDY GALLERIES INC LIBRARY,* 730 Fifth Ave, 10019-4044. SAN 375-8265. Tel: 212-541-9600. FAX: 212-977-3833. E-Mail: kennedygal@aol.com. Web Site: www.kgny.com. *VPres*, Lillian Brenwasser
Library Holdings: Bk Titles 4,000

L KENYON & KENYON, Law Library,* One Broadway, 10004. SAN 372-4409. Tel: 212-425-7200. FAX: 212-908-6113. *Dir*, Virginia Monterosso; E-Mail: vmonterosso@kenyonlaw.com
Library Holdings: Bk Vols 20,000

S KEYSTONE PRESS AGENCY, INC, Picture Library,* 202 E 42nd St, 4th flr, 10017. SAN 370-145X. Tel: 212-924-8123. FAX: 212-924-8123. *Librn*, Satoko Alpert; E-Mail: balpert@worldnet.att.net

L KIRKLAND & ELLIS, Law Library,* 153 E 53rd St, 10022. SAN 372-2317. Tel: 212-446-4990. FAX: 212-446-4900. Web Site: www.k&e.com. *Librn*, Elaine T Sciolino; *Asst Librn*, Mildred Velazquez
Library Holdings: Bk Vols 5,000; Per Subs 100

S THE KITCHEN, Video Distribution Collection Library,* 512 W 19th St, 10011. SAN 374-7670. Tel: 212-255-5793. FAX: 212-645-4258. E-Mail: kitchen@panix.com. Web Site: www.kitchen.org.

S KNOEDLER ART LIBRARY, 19 E 70th St, 10021. SAN 311-8517. Tel: 212-794-0567. FAX: 212-772-6932. E-Mail: library@knoedlergallery.com. *Librn*, Edye Weissler
Founded 1846
Library Holdings: Bk Vols 60,000
Subject Interests: 19th-20th Centuries, Am painting, Western European
Publications: Exhibition catalogues
Restriction: By appointment only
Function: Research library

S KOREA TRADE PROMOTION CENTER,* 460 Park Ave Rm 402, 10022. SAN 373-1154. Tel: 212-826-0900. FAX: 212-888-4930. Web Site: www.kotra.or.kr. *VPres*, Poong Park
Library Holdings: Bk Vols 1,000; Per Subs 10
Subject Interests: International trade

KPMG LLP

S KNOWLEDGE CENTER, 345 Park Ave, Lexington Level, 10154. SAN 353-7455. Tel: 212-872-3019, 212-872-3251, 212-872-3320. FAX: 212-872-5831. *Dir*, George Mauter; *Librn, Online Servs*, Alison Donald; *Librn, Online Servs*, Karen Neuberg; *Librn, Online Servs*, Marianne Ridout; *Librn*, Ethel Brown; *Librn*, Marlene Augustin
Founded 1952
Subject Interests: Accounting, Mgt consulting, Tax
Partic in Dialog Corporation; Dow Jones News Retrieval; IDD

S TAX LIBRARY, 345 Park Ave, Lexington Level, 10154. SAN 353-748X. Tel: 212-872-6503. FAX: 212-872-5831. *Librn*, Marlene Augustin; E-Mail: maugustin@kpmg.com
Library Holdings: Bk Vols 9,500; Per Subs 100

L KRAMER, LEVIN, NAFTALIS & FRANKEL LLP, Law Library, 919 Third Ave, 10022. SAN 372-4212. Tel: 212-715-9321. FAX: 212-715-8000. Web Site: www.kramerlevin.com. *Librn*, Daniel J Pelletier; *Asst Librn*, Eileen Dolan; *ILL*, Sheldon Snaggs; *Ref*, Brian Boyle; *Ref*, Andre Grgas
Library Holdings: Bk Vols 15,000; Bk Titles 5,000; Per Subs 300
Automation Activity & Vendor Info: (Acquisitions) Sydney; (Cataloging) Sydney; (Circulation) Sydney; (Course Reserve) Sydney; (ILL) Sydney; (Media Booking) Sydney; (OPAC) Sydney; (Serials) Sydney

L KRONISH, LIEB, WEINER & HELLMAN LLP, Law Library, 1114 Avenue of the Americas, 10036. SAN 372-2457. Tel: 212-479-6000. Interlibrary Loan Service Tel: 212-479-6025. Reference Tel: 212-479-6027. FAX: 212-479-6275. *Dir Libr Serv*, Gary Jaskula; E-Mail: gjaskula@klwhllp.com; Staff 3 (MLS 1, Non-MLS 2)
Library Holdings: Bk Vols 15,000; Bk Titles 2,000; Per Subs 100
Automation Activity & Vendor Info: (Acquisitions) Inmagic, Inc.; (Cataloging) Inmagic, Inc.; (Serials) Inmagic, Inc.

S LABAN BARTENIEFF INSTITUTE OF MOVEMENT STUDIES, Library Archives,* 234 Fifth Ave, 10001. SAN 375-5096. Tel: 212-477-4299. FAX: 212-477-3702. Web Site: www.limsonline.org.; Staff 2 (Non-MLS 2)
Founded 1978
Special Collections: Movement Choirs & German Modern Dance (Martin Gluvner Coll), photog, prints

S LABOR RESEARCH ASSOCIATION LIBRARY,* 145 W 28th Ste 6R, 10001-6191. SAN 371-0440. Tel: 212-714-1677. FAX: 212-714-1674. E-Mail: info@lra-ny.com. Web Site: www.laborresearch.org. *Dir*, Greg Tarpinian
Library Holdings: Bk Vols 700

S LABORATORY INSTITUTE OF MERCHANDISING LIBRARY,* 12 E 53rd St, 3rd flr, 10022. SAN 311-855X. Tel: 212-752-1530. FAX: 212-832-6708. *Librn*, George Sanchez
Founded 1939
Library Holdings: Bk Vols 12,000; Per Subs 110
Subject Interests: Advertising, Bus, Current affairs, Econ, Fashion buying, Language arts, Marketing, Mathematics, Mgt, Psychology, Retailing, Visual merchandising
Special Collections: Merchandising (B Earl Puckett Fund for Retail Education)

S LANDAUER ASSOCIATES, INC, Information Center,* 55 E 59th St, 4th Flr, 10122-1112. SAN 371-1730. Tel: 212-621-9500. FAX: 212-621-9582.
Library Holdings: Bk Vols 400; Per Subs 225
Restriction: Staff use only

S LANE & MITTENDORF LLP, Law Library,* 320 Park Ave, 10022. SAN 326-4769. Tel: 212-508-3311. FAX: 212-508-3230. *Librn*, Candi McBride
Library Holdings: Bk Vols 10,000

L LASALLE BANK BUILDING LAW LIBRARY,* One World Trade Ctr 28th Floor, 10048-0682. SAN 311-645X. Tel: 312-558-3135. FAX: 312-558-1929. *Librn*, Sherman Lewis
Library Holdings: Bk Vols 16,000; Per Subs 12
Subject Interests: Law

L LATHAM & WATKINS, Law Library,* 885 Third Ave, Ste 1000, 10022. SAN 372-4522. Tel: 212-906-1200. FAX: 212-751-4864. *Mgr*, Anne Lewis
Library Holdings: Bk Vols 20,000; Per Subs 150

S LAZARD, FRERES & COMPANY LLC LIBRARY,* 30 Rockefeller Plaza, 10020. SAN 325-7436. Tel: 212-632-6333. FAX: 212-632-6051. *Mgr*, Joan Morris; *Ref*, Debra Sherline; *Ref*, Frank Dell'Aquila; *Ref*, Harold Gee
Library Holdings: Bk Vols 500; Bk Titles 300; Per Subs 520
Subject Interests: Finance
Special Collections: Moody's Manual, 1957 - Present, microfiche

S LEBHAR-FRIEDMAN INC, Information Center, 425 Park Ave, 10022. SAN 311-8592. Tel: 212-756-5088. FAX: 212-838-9487. Web Site: www.lf.com. *Mgr*, Heather Harris-Martin; E-Mail: hmartin@lf.com; Staff 1 (MLS 1)
Library Holdings: Bk Vols 300
Subject Interests: Food topics, Mgt, Retailing
Special Collections: Bound Issues of Magazines, 1925-Current

L LEBOEUF, LAMB, GREENE & MACRAE, Law Library,* 125 W 55th St, 10019-5389. SAN 311-8576. Tel: 212-424-8000. FAX: 212-424-8500. *Librn*, Douglas Cinque; *Ref*, Cathy Rice
Founded 1929
Subject Interests: Administrative law, Antitrust, Banking, Corporate, Energy, Environ, Estates, Ins, Municipal law, Pub utilities, Real property, Securities, Tax, Trusts
Special Collections: Federal Energy Regulatory Commission Coll; Insurance Laws; Securities & Exchange Commission Coll; Tax Coll; Water Coll
Partic in Dialog Corporation; Phinet; Vutext; Westlaw

S LEGAL AID SOCIETY CENTRAL LIBRARY & INFORMATION CENTER,* 90 Church St, 10007. SAN 371-1722. Tel: 212-577-3439. FAX: 212-577-3954. Web Site: www.legal-aid.org. *Dir*, Marie H Rothman; *Tech Servs*, John H Williams
Library Holdings: Bk Vols 64,000; Per Subs 80

S LEHMAN BROTHERS, Business Information Services,* 3 World Financial Ctr, American Express Towers, 15th flr, 10285-1500. SAN 311-760X. Tel: 212-526-2783. FAX: 212-526-5370, 619-9457. *Dir, VPres*, Greg Taylor; *Tech Servs*, Tom Fearon; *Ref*, Martin Culler
Founded 1930
Library Holdings: Bk Vols 5,000; Bk Titles 3,000; Per Subs 700
Subject Interests: Bus, Econ, Finance, Industry, Mgt
Partic in Dialog Corporation; Dow Jones News Retrieval

M LENOX HILL HOSPITAL, Jerome S Leopold Health & Sciences Library, 100 E 77th St, 10021. SAN 311-8614. Tel: 212-434-2075. FAX: 212-434-4829. *Dir*, Julia Chai; Staff 4 (MLS 1, Non-MLS 3)
Founded 1925
Library Holdings: Bk Titles 6,452; Per Subs 390
Subject Interests: Dentistry, Hosp admin, Medicine, Nursing
Special Collections: Staff Authored Literature From 1800's
Restriction: Staff use only
Partic in Manhattan-Bronx Health Sciences Libraries Group; Medical Library Center Of New York; Metro Atlanta Library Association; NY & NJ Regional Med Libr
Friends of the Library Group

S LEO BAECK INSTITUTE LIBRARY, 15 W 16 St, 10011-6301. SAN 311-6255. Tel: 212-744-6400. FAX: 212-988-1305. E-Mail: lbi1@lbi.com. Web Site: www.lbi.org. *Coll Develop, Librn*, John Bednarz, Jr; *Ref*, Dr Diane Spielmann; *Archivist*, Dr Frank Mecklenburg
Founded 1955
Library Holdings: Bk Vols 61,000; Per Subs 10,000
Special Collections: Art Coll; Extensive Coll of Literature by Jews in German Language; History & Archives of German-speaking Jewry of Central Europe, 18th-20th Century
Publications: Judischer Almanach des Leo Baeck Instituts; LBI News; Leo Baeck Institute Yearbook; Library & Archives News; Schriftenreihe Wissenschaftlicher Abhandlungen des Leo Baeck Instituts
Partic in New York Metrop Ref & Res Libr Agency
Friends of the Library Group

S LESBIAN HERSTORY ARCHIVES, (Formerly Lesbian Herstory Educational Foundation, Inc), PO Box 1258, 10116. SAN 325-9250. Tel: 718-768-3953. FAX: 718-768-4663. Web Site: www.datalounge.net/network/pages/lha//. *In Charge*, Deborah Edel
Founded 1974
1999-2000 Income Locally Generated Income $40,000. Mats Exp $4,550, Books $250, Per/Ser (Incl. Access Fees) $200, Presv $2,000, AV Equip $100, Other Print Mats $2,000
Library Holdings: Bk Vols 20,000; Bk Titles 20,000; Per Subs 1,500; Spec Interest Per Sub 20
Publications: Lesbian History Archives News
Restriction: Non-circulating to the public

S LIGHTHOUSE INTERNATIONAL, Ruth M Shellens Memorial Library, 111 E 59th St, 10022. SAN 311-9335. Tel: 212-821-9681. FAX: 212-821-9687. Web Site: www.lighthouse.org. *Dir*, Gloria Aks; E-Mail: gaks@lighthouse.org; *Reader Servs*, Rosie Lopez
Founded 1967
Library Holdings: Bk Titles 10,000; Per Subs 50
Subject Interests: Blindness, Computer tech, Employment, Vision res
Special Collections: Braille Loan Library (produced by Lighthouse); fiction and non fiction; Popular Book Cassettes
Publications: Bibliography of books on cassette
Mem of Metro Coop Libr Syst
Partic in New York Metrop Ref & Res Libr Agency
Special Services for the Blind - Adapted computers & special software with speech output to assist learning disabled, mentally retarded & uneducated; Closed circuit television
Library houses deposit collection of cassettes & recorded discs provided by National Library For The Blind & Physically Handcapped

L LINKLATERS & ALLIANCE, Law Library, 1345 Sixth Ave, 10105. SAN 372-4166. Tel: 212-757-6000. FAX: 212-424-9100. Web Site: www.linklaters.com. *Librn*, Sheri Wanamaker; E-Mail: swanamak@linklaters.com
Library Holdings: Bk Titles 1,000; Per Subs 100

M LIPPINCOTT WILLIAMS & WILKINS, Sophia F Palmer Memorial Library, 345 Hudson St, 16th fl, 10014-4502. SAN 311-5887. Tel: 212-886-1354. FAX: 212-886-1206. Web Site: www.nursingcenter.com/resources/sophia.cfm. *Librn*, Yelena Friedman; E-Mail: yfriedma@lww.com; Staff 1 (MLS 1)
Founded 1951
Library Holdings: Bk Titles 11,000; Per Subs 356
Subject Interests: Nursing, Nursing educ
Publications: International Nursing Index
Restriction: By appointment only, Company library, Open to researchers by request, Open to students
Partic in Docline; EFTS; Metro Atlanta Library Association

S CHANCELLOR ROBERT R LIVINGSTON MASONIC LIBRARY,* 71 W 23rd St 14th Floor, 10010-4171. SAN 311-7901. Tel: 212-337-6620. FAX: 212-633-2639. E-Mail: livmalib@pipeline.com. Web Site: www.vpi.edu/~nichot3/masonry/library/index.html. *Dir*, Tom Sevini; *Coll Develop, Librn*, Jennifer Somerwitz
Founded 1865
1997-1998 Income $207,000
Subject Interests: Freemasonry, History, Philosophy
Special Collections: NY City, bibliog, directories & mss; NY City, State & County Hist
Friends of the Library Group

L LOEB & LOEB LLP, Law Library, 345 Park Ave, 18th flr, 10154-0037. SAN 372-2325. Tel: 212-407-4961. FAX: 212-407-4990. E-Mail: ohamelsdorf@loeb.com. Web Site: www.loeb.com. *Librn*, Ora Hamelsdorf
Library Holdings: Bk Vols 10,000; Per Subs 500

M LOWE MCADAMS HEALTHCARE LIBRARY,* 1740 Broadway, 10019. SAN 311-8703. Tel: 212-698-4011. *Mgr*, Jim Hoon; Staff 2 (MLS 1, Non-MLS 1)
Founded 1950
Library Holdings: Bk Titles 2,000; Per Subs 300
Subject Interests: Advertising, Drugs, Medicine, Pharmacology
Restriction: Staff use only

S M ROSENBLATT & SON, INC, Engineering & Research Library,* 350 Broadway, 10013. SAN 329-0387. Tel: 212-431-6900, Ext 216. FAX: 212-334-0837. *Librn*, Alfred Cocchini; E-Mail: cocchini@mrosenblatt.com
Library Holdings: Bk Vols 1,200; Bk Titles 800; Per Subs 22
Special Collections: Naval Auxiliaries; Oceanographic Vessels, prints
Restriction: Staff use only

S MAGAZINE PUBLISHERS OF AMERICA, Information Center, 919 Third Ave, 10022. SAN 311-8754. Tel: 212-872-3700. FAX: 212-888-4217. E-Mail: infocenter@magazine.org. Web Site: www.magazine.org. *Dir*, Debbie Martin; Staff 2 (MLS 1, Non-MLS 1)
Founded 1940
Library Holdings: Bk Titles 850; Per Subs 150
Subject Interests: Advertising, Mag publ, Marketing
Publications: Statistical Fact Sheets on Consumer Magazine Publishing in the US
Restriction: Staff & members only
Function: Research library

M MANHATTAN EYE, EAR & THROAT HOSPITAL, Medical Library,* 210 E 64th St, 10021. SAN 370-5137. Tel: 212-605-3786. FAX: 212-758-7988. E-Mail: meethdds@tiac.net. *Librn*, Dede Silverston; Staff 1 (MLS 1)
Founded 1985
Library Holdings: Bk Titles 2,500; Per Subs 108
Subject Interests: Ophthalmology, Otolaryngology, Plastic surgery
Partic in Association of Vision Science Librarians (AVSL); Manhattan-Bronx Health Sciences Libraries Group

M MANHATTAN PSYCHIATRIC CENTER, Margaret Hornick Memorial Library, Wards Island Complex, 10035. SAN 311-8789. Tel: 212-369-0500. *Librn*, Cindy Kline
Library Holdings: Bk Vols 5,000; Per Subs 130

C MANHATTAN SCHOOL OF MUSIC, Frances Hall Ballard Library, 120 Claremont Ave, 10027. SAN 311-8770. Tel: 212-749-2802, Ext 511. FAX: 212-749-5471. Web Site: www.msmnyc.edu. *Coll Develop, Dir*, Peter Caleb; E-Mail: pcaleb@msmnyc.edu; Staff 6 (MLS 3, Non-MLS 3)
Founded 1925. Enrl 876; Highest Degree: Doctorate
Library Holdings: Bk Vols 70,000; Per Subs 134

Subject Interests: Music
Partic in New York Metrop Ref & Res Libr Agency; OCLC Online Computer Library Center, Inc; State University Of New York-NYLINK

C MANNES COLLEGE OF MUSIC, Harry Scherman Library, 150 W 85th St, 10024-4499. SAN 311-8797. Tel: 212-580-0210, Ext 232. FAX: 212-580-1738. Web Site: www.newschool.edu/library/mannes.htm. *Dir*, Deborah Davis; E-Mail: ddavis@newschool.edu; Staff 3 (MLS 3)
Founded 1954. Enrl 289; Highest Degree: Master
Jul 1998-Jun 1999 Income $213,000. Mats Exp $45,000, Books $23,000, Per/Ser (Incl. Access Fees) $6,000, Presv $6,000, AV Equip $3,000, Electronic Ref Mat (Incl. Access Fees) $7,000. Sal $128,000
Library Holdings: Bk Vols 36,400; Per Subs 74
Special Collections: Leopold Mannes Compositions; Salzedo Harp Coll
Partic in OCLC Online Computer Library Center, Inc; Research Library Association of South Manhattan

S JOHN & MARY R MARKLE FOUNDATION LIBRARY,* 10 Rockefeller Plaza, 16th Flr, 10020-1903. SAN 376-1770. Tel: 212-489-6655. FAX: 212-765-9690. E-Mail: info@markle.org. Web Site: www.markle.org.
Library Holdings: Bk Vols 1,000
Restriction: By appointment only

S MARLBOROUGH GALLERY LIBRARY,* 40 W 57th St, 10019. SAN 373-1162. Tel: 212-541-4900. FAX: 212-541-4948. E-Mail: mny@marlboroughgallery.com. Web Site: www.marlboroughgallery.com. *Archivist*, Elena Gischer; *Archivist*, Hope Svenson
Library Holdings: Bk Vols 10,000

S J MARSH & H MCLENNAN , INC, Information Center,* 1166 Avenue of the Americas, 10036. SAN 311-8835. Tel: 212-345-6000. FAX: 212-345-3776. *Librn*, Margaret Orloske
Founded 1972
Library Holdings: Bk Vols 7,000
Subject Interests: Finance, Property-casualty ins, Risk mgt, Safety

C MARYMOUNT MANHATTAN COLLEGE, Thomas J Shanahan Library, 221 E 71st St, 10021. SAN 311-886X. Tel: 212-774-4806. Reference Tel: 212-774-4808. Web Site: www.marymount.mmm.edu. *Dir*, Donna Hurwitz; Tel: 212-774-4801, Fax: 212-452-8207, E-Mail: dhurwitz@mmm.edu; *Head Ref*, Henry Blanke; E-Mail: hblanke@mmm.edu; *Ref*, Tammy Wofsey; Tel: 212-774-4803, E-Mail: twofsey@mmm.edu; *Media Spec*, Sean Smith; Tel: 212-774-4805, E-Mail: ssmithe@mmm.edu; *Tech Servs*, Amy Wolfe; Tel: 212-774-4802, E-Mail: awolfe@mmm.edu; *Circ Ch*, Rose Lynn Boddie; Tel: 212-774-4804, E-Mail: rboddie@mmm.edu; *Ser*, Christine Wilson; Tel: 212-775-4807, E-Mail: cwilson@mmm.edu. Subject Specialists: *Art*, Christine Wilson; *Arts*, Henry Blanke; *History*, Donna Hurwitz; *Political science*, Henry Blanke; Staff 18 (MLS 6, Non-MLS 12)
Founded 1948. Fac 52; Highest Degree: Bachelor
Library Holdings: Bk Vols 91,000; Bk Titles 75,000; Per Subs 600
Subject Interests: Communications, Theatre, Women's studies
Special Collections: Geraldine A Ferraro Archives; William Harris Coll
Automation Activity & Vendor Info: (Cataloging) epixtech, inc.; (Circulation) epixtech, inc.; (ILL) epixtech, inc.; (OPAC) epixtech, inc.; (Serials) epixtech, inc.
Database Vendor: Dialog, Ebsco - EbscoHost, epixtech, inc., IAC - SearchBank, Lexis-Nexis, OCLC - First Search, OVID Technologies, ProQuest, Silverplatter Information Inc., Wilson - Wilson Web
Publications: bibliographical publications; resource aids & bulletins; Shanahan Library Interface (newsletter)
Partic in OCLC Online Computer Library Center, Inc; WALDO
Special Services for the Deaf - Books on deafness & sign language
Friends of the Library Group

S MCKINSEY & CO, INC, Information Services Department, 55 E 52nd St, 10022. SAN 311-8738. Tel: 212-446-7000, Ext 8926. FAX: 212-446-7030. *Mgr*, Alan Fitzgerald; Staff 70 (MLS 30, Non-MLS 40)
Founded 1937
Library Holdings: Bk Vols 1,000; Bk Titles 550; Per Subs 330
Subject Interests: Corp, Econ, Finance, Industry, Marketing, Mgt, Opers res, Orgn, Personnel admin
Restriction: Not open to public
Partic in State University Of New York-NYLINK

M MEMORIAL SLOAN-KETTERING CANCER CENTER MEDICAL LIBRARY, Nathan Cummings Center, 1275 York Ave, 10021. SAN 311-8886. Tel: 212-639-8487. Interlibrary Loan Service Tel: 212-639-7441. Circulation Tel: 212-639-7439. Reference Tel: 212-639-7443. FAX: 212-717-3048. *Dir*, Katherine Stemmer Frumento; E-Mail: frumentk@mskcc.org; *Tech Servs*, Arsenia Avetria; Staff 13 (MLS 5, Non-MLS 8)
Library Holdings: Per Subs 600
Subject Interests: Oncology
Special Collections: Memorial Sloan-Kettering Cancer Center Archives
Restriction: Staff use only, Use of others with permission of librarian
Partic in Medical Library Center Of New York; New York Metrop Ref & Res Libr Agency; OCLC Online Computer Library Center, Inc

L MENDES & MOUNT, LLP, Law Library, 750 Seventh Ave, 10019-6829. SAN 372-4239. Tel: 212-261-8338. FAX: 212-261-8750. *Librn*, James J Simonelli; E-Mail: james.simonelli@mendes.com
Library Holdings: Bk Vols 10,000

P MERCANTILE LIBRARY ASSOCIATION, 17 E 47th St, 10017. SAN 311-8908. Tel: 212-755-6710. FAX: 212-758-1387. E-Mail: mercantile_library@msn.com. Web Site: www.mercantilelibrary.org. *Dir*, Harold Augenbraum; Staff 2 (MLS 2)
Founded 1820
Jan 1999-Dec 1999 Income $450,000, Federal $24,000. Mats Exp $30,000, Books $28,000, Per/Ser (Incl. Access Fees) $2,000. Sal $207,000
Library Holdings: Bk Vols 150,000; Per Subs 66
Subject Interests: Literature
Special Collections: 19th Century Fiction & Nonfiction
Publications: Newsletter (semi-monthly)
Special Services - Writer's studio

S MERRILL LYNCH & CO, Corporate & Institutional Client Group Library,* 250 Vesey St, 24th flr, 10281-1324. SAN 326-9248. Tel: 212-449-3814. FAX: 212-449-1379. *Tech Servs*, Linda Greenberg; *Ref*, Dorothy Nelsen Gille; *Ref*, Philip Smith; *Ref*, Katherine Hassell; *Ref*, Sue Moy; *Ref*, Chris Lezenby; *Ref*, Jill Weinstein
Library Holdings: Bk Vols 3,000; Per Subs 1,000
Subject Interests: Acquisitions, Bus, Econ, Investment, Mergers, Securities
Restriction: Not open to public

S METROPOLITAN CLUB LIBRARY,* One E 60th St, 10022. SAN 311-8932. Tel: 212-838-7400. FAX: 212-755-3127. *Pres*, Douglas W Brandrup
Founded 1891
Library Holdings: Bk Vols 10,000; Per Subs 20
Subject Interests: Americana, New York City, NY state

METROPOLITAN HOSPITAL CENTER

M FREDERICK M DEARBORN LIBRARY, 1901 First Ave & 97th St, 10029. SAN 353-1694. Tel: 212-423-6055. Interlibrary Loan Service Tel: 212-423-6270. Reference Tel: 212-423-6270. FAX: 212-423-7961. E-Mail: mhc7@rmi.net. *Coordr, Mgr*, Antoinette Drago; Staff 3 (MLS 1, Non-MLS 2)
Founded 1906
Jul 2000-Jun 2001 Mats Exp $56,950, Books $10,000, Per/Ser (Incl. Access Fees) $26,000, Presv $500, Electronic Ref Mat (Incl. Access Fees) $800. Sal $100,000
Library Holdings: Bk Vols 5,000; Bk Titles 4,000; Per Subs 112
Subject Interests: Medicine, Psychiatry, Surgery
Publications: Acquisitions List (quarterly)
Restriction: Medical staff only, Open to others by appointment
Partic in Basic Health Sciences Library Network; Metropolitan New York Library Council; National Library Of Medicine, Medlars

METROPOLITAN LIFE INSURANCE CO

S CORPORATE INFORMATION CENTER & LIBRARY, One Madison Ave, 1M-GH, 10010. SAN 353-1724. Tel: 212-578-3700. Interlibrary Loan Service Tel: 212-578-3907. FAX: 212-689-0926. *Mgr*, Marianne Stolp; Staff 7 (MLS 5, Non-MLS 2)
Founded 1910
Library Holdings: Per Subs 40
Subject Interests: Bus, Econ, Liability ins, Life, Mgt, Property
Special Collections: Metropolitan Life Insurance Company History (Archives), bks, pamphlets, pictures, artifacts
Publications: Library Bulletin (3 times per year); Periodical Holdings List
Partic in New York Metrop Ref & Res Libr Agency; State University Of New York-NYLINK

L LAW LIBRARY, One Madison Ave, 10010. SAN 353-1759. Tel: 212-578-3112. FAX: 212-578-3916. *Dir*, Amy Comeau; Staff 3 (MLS 2, Non-MLS 1)
Founded 1910
Library Holdings: Bk Vols 30,000; Per Subs 30
Subject Interests: Insurance law
Restriction: Staff use only

S METROPOLITAN OPERA ARCHIVES, Lincoln Center Plaza, 10023. SAN 323-5165. Tel: 212-799-3100, Ext 2525. FAX: 212-870-7657. Web Site: www.metopera.org. *Archivist*, Robert Tuggle; *Archivist*, John Pennino; *Archivist*, Jeff McMillan; Staff 3 (MLS 1, Non-MLS 2)
Library Holdings: Per Subs 15
Restriction: By appointment only, Reference only to non-staff

L METROPOLITAN TRANSPORTATION AUTHORITY, Law Library & Corporate Library, 347 Madison Ave, 9th Flr, 10017. SAN 372-4581. Tel: 212-878-7192. FAX: 212-878-0147. *Librn*, Dennis Maffettone; E-Mail: dmaffett@mtahq.org
Library Holdings: Bk Vols 8,000; Per Subs 80

S MIDMARCH ARTS PRESS, Women Artists Archives, 300 Riverside Dr, 10025-5239. SAN 325-0792. Tel: 212-666-6990. *Librn, Per*, Lara Ferb
Founded 1975
Library Holdings: Bk Titles 600; Per Subs 20
Subject Interests: Architecture, Art, Woman artists

Publications: Women Artists News Book Review
Restriction: By appointment only
Friends of the Library Group

MONY LIFE INSURANCE CO
S CORPORATE LIBRARY, 1740 Broadway, 10019. SAN 353-2089. Tel: 212-708-2139. FAX: 212-708-2320. *Mgr*, Jerry Foster
Founded 1943
Library Holdings: Bk Vols 200; Per Subs 75
Subject Interests: Bus, Finance, Ins health, Ins life, Mgt, Pensions
Special Collections: Company History (Mutual of New York Library Historical Coll), print
Partic in Dialog Corporation; Dow Jones News Retrieval
L LAW DEPARTMENT LIBRARY, 1740 Broadway, 10019. SAN 353-2119. Tel: 212-708-2235. FAX: 212-708-2278. *Librn*, Marie Papandrea; E-Mail: mpapandr@mony.com
Library Holdings: Bk Vols 5,000
Subject Interests: Ins law
Restriction: Not open to public
Partic in Westlaw

S MOODY'S INVESTORS SERVICE, INC, Information Center, 99 Church St, 10th Flr, 10007. SAN 311-8975. Tel: 212-553-0300, 212-553-1337. FAX: 212-553-1411. *Res*, Jennifer Bradshaw
Library Holdings: Bk Vols 520
Subject Interests: Corp data, Govt agencies

L MORGAN & FINNEGAN LLP, Library, 345 Park Ave, 22nd flr library, 10154-0053. SAN 325-5174. Tel: 212-415-8569. FAX: 212-303-2656. E-Mail: library@morganfinnegan.com. Web Site: www.morganfinnegan.com. *Dir*, Lucy Curci-Gonzalez; Tel: 212-415-8576, E-Mail: lcurcigonzalez@morganfinnegan.com; *Senior Librn*, Jennifer C Groh; Tel: 212-415-8582, E-Mail: jgroh@morganfinnegan.com; Staff 4 (MLS 2, Non-MLS 2)
Founded 1979
Library Holdings: Bk Titles 5,000
Subject Interests: Patent law
Automation Activity & Vendor Info: (Acquisitions) Inmagic, Inc.
Publications: Newsletter
Partic in OCLC Online Computer Library Center, Inc; RLIN

S J P MORGAN INFORMATION RESOURCE CENTER,* 60 Wall St, 10260. SAN 311-8983. Tel: 212-648-4636. FAX: 212-648-5230. *Mgr*, Heather J May; Staff 21 (MLS 10, Non-MLS 11)
Founded 1989
Library Holdings: Bk Vols 1,500; Bk Titles 750; Per Subs 300
Subject Interests: Banking, Finance
Publications: Brochure
Restriction: Staff use only

S MORGAN STANLEY & CO, INC LIBRARY,* 1585 Broadway, 10036. SAN 311-9009. Tel: 212-761-4701. FAX: 212-761-0244. *VPres*, Sally Jones; Staff 37 (MLS 13, Non-MLS 24)
Founded 1935
Library Holdings: Per Subs 490
Subject Interests: Investment banking
Restriction: Staff use only

L MORRISON & FOERSTER, Law Library,* 1290 Avenue of the Americas 41st flr, 10104. SAN 372-4484. Tel: 212-468-8000. FAX: 212-468-7900. Web Site: www.mofo.com. *Asst Dir*, Carrie Hart; *Librn*, Bobbie Smith
Library Holdings: Bk Vols 1,250

CM MOUNT SINAI SCHOOL OF MEDICINE OF CITY UNIVERSITY OF NEW YORK, Gustave L & Janet W Levy Library, One Gustave L Levy Pl, PO Box 1102, 10029-6574. SAN 311-9033. Tel: 212-241-7892. Interlibrary Loan Service Tel: 212-241-7795. FAX: 212-831-2625. Web Site: www.mssm.edu/library. *Dir*, Lynn Kasner Morgan; E-Mail: lynn.morgan@mssm.edu; *Asst Dir*, Merril Schindler; *Archivist*, Barbara Niss; *ILL*, Celia Soto; *Cat*, Florinda Coral; *Circ*, Henry Stickell; *Ref*, Alan Krissoff; *Ref*, Sussana Markgrer; *Tech Servs*, Daniel Reznick; *Coll Develop*, Dorothy Hill; *Ref*, Lynn Peperone; *Web Coordr*, Dana Lewis; *Tech Servs*, Andrew Pizzimenti; Staff 56 (MLS 21, Non-MLS 35)
Enrl 624; Fac 3,413; Highest Degree: Doctorate
Jul 1998-Jun 1999 Income $4,673,138, Locally Generated Income $307,229, Parent Institution $3,732,808. Mats Exp $1,298,945, Books $90,428, Per/Ser (Incl. Access Fees) $969,191, Presv $37,710, Micro $725, AV Equip $82,536, Other Print Mats $40,811, Manuscripts & Archives $1,789, Electronic Ref Mat (Incl. Access Fees) $75,755. Sal $2,213,713 (Prof $1,522,833)
Library Holdings: Bk Vols 168,602; Bk Titles 52,602; Per Subs 1,801
Subject Interests: Medicine
Special Collections: Archives; Biomedical Audiovisual & Computer software
Automation Activity & Vendor Info: (Acquisitions) SIRSI; (Circulation) SIRSI; (Course Reserve) SIRSI; (OPAC) SIRSI; (Serials) SIRSI
Database Vendor: Silverplatter Information Inc.
Publications: Collection Development Policy; Levy Library News; Library Guides
Restriction: Not open to public
Partic in Health Science Library Information Consortium; Medical Library Center Of New York; New York Metrop Ref & Res Libr Agency; OCLC Online Computer Library Center, Inc

S MOVIE STAR NEWS, Photograph Collections,* 134 W 18th St, 10011. SAN 377-5224. Tel: 212-620-8160. Web Site: www.moviestarnews.com. *Pres*, Ira Kramer; *Mgr*, William Rosa

S MUNICIPAL ART SOCIETY, The Information Exchange, 457 Madison Ave, 10022. SAN 320-4022. Tel: 212-935-3960. FAX: 212-753-1816. E-Mail: tie@mas.org. Web Site: www.mas.org. *Coordr*, Ann Anielewski; *Librn*, Claudia M Gisolfi; Staff 2 (MLS 1, Non-MLS 1)
Founded 1978
Library Holdings: Bk Titles 1,500; Per Subs 110
Subject Interests: Architecture, Historic preservation, Urban planning
Automation Activity & Vendor Info: (Acquisitions) CASPR; (Cataloging) CASPR; (Circulation) CASPR
Library collects clippings from current periodicals & documents relating to Architecture, Historic Preservation, Urban Design, Parks, Waterfronts, Land Use & Development, Neighborhood Conservation, Transit, and Public Art

S MUSEUM OF AMERICAN FOLK ART LIBRARY,* 555 W 57th St, Ste 1300, 10019. SAN 311-905X. Tel: 212-977-7170. FAX: 212-977-8134. *Curator*, Stacy Hollander; Staff 3 (MLS 2, Non-MLS 1)
Founded 1961
Library Holdings: Bk Titles 9,000; Per Subs 60
Subject Interests: Am decorative arts, Am folk art
Publications: Folk Art (magazine)

S MUSEUM OF JEWISH HERITAGE LIBRARY - A LIVING MEMORIAL TO THE HOLOCAUST,* One Battery Park Plaza, 10004-1484. SAN 326-162X. Tel: 212-968-1800. FAX: 212-968-1368. *Librn*, Julia Bock
Library Holdings: Bk Titles 8,000
Subject Interests: World War II
Special Collections: Holocaust, bks, flm, learning ctr, oral history tapes & videotapes

S MUSEUM OF MODERN ART LIBRARY, 11 W 53rd St, 10019-5498. SAN 311-9076. Tel: 212-708-9433. Interlibrary Loan Service Tel: 212-708-9441. FAX: 212-333-1122. E-Mail: library@moma.org. Web Site: library.moma.org. *Chief Librn*, Milan R Hughston; *Tech Servs*, Daniel Starr; *Coll Develop*, Janis Ekdahl; Staff 11 (MLS 5, Non-MLS 6)
Founded 1929
Library Holdings: Per Subs 300
Subject Interests: Architecture, Art, Design, Drawing, Film, Graphic art, Mixed media, Painting, Photog, Sculpture, Video from 1880 to present
Special Collections: Artist Files; Artists' Books; Dada & Surrealism (Eluard-Dausse Coll); Latin American Art; Museum of Modern Art Publications; Political Art Documentation & Distribution (PADD) Archives
Automation Activity & Vendor Info: (Acquisitions) Endeavor; (Cataloging) Endeavor; (Circulation) Endeavor; (OPAC) Endeavor; (Serials) Endeavor
Publications: Annual Bibliography of Modern Art 1986- (ongoing)
Partic in New York Metrop Ref & Res Libr Agency; Research Libraries Group, Inc; RLIN
Friends of the Library Group

S MUSEUM OF TELEVISION & RADIO LIBRARY,* 25 W 52nd St, 10019. SAN 311-9068. Tel: 212-621-6600. FAX: 212-621-6632. Web Site: www.mtr.org. *Dir Libr Serv*, Douglas F Gibbons; *Res*, Jonathan Rosenthal
Founded 1975
Library Holdings: Bk Titles 2,600; Per Subs 67
Subject Interests: Advertising, Comedy, Drama, Music, Presidents, Space program, US hist, Vietnam War, World War II
Special Collections: Broadcast Journalism (Welles Hangen Coll), AV-tapes; Television (1939-present)
Automation Activity & Vendor Info: (Cataloging) Sagebrush Corporation; (Circulation) Sagebrush Corporation
Publications: Exhibition catalogs
Restriction: Non-circulating to the public
The Museum offers a broad range of seminars, screenings, lectures & symposia covering all aspects of the art & technology of radio & TV broadcasting; broadcast study center equipped with 96 consoles for viewing or listening to programs. Second location: 465 N Beverly Dr, Beverly Hills, CA 90210, Tel.: 310-786-1000, Fax: 310-786-1086; broadcast study center with 64 consoles

S MUSEUM OF THE CITY OF NEW YORK, Theatre Collection Library, 1220 Fifth Ave, 10029. SAN 325-7371. Tel: 212-534-1672. FAX: 212-534-5974. E-Mail: mcny@interport.net. *Curator*, Marty Jacobs
Special Collections: New York City Stage Productions & Personalities, correspondence, docs, scripts, scores, clippings, programs, paintings, drawings, photog, memorabilia, props, costumes, set models & designs, costume designs

G NASA, Goddard Institute For Space Studies Library, 2880 Broadway, Rm 710, 10025. SAN 311-9092. Tel: 212-678-5613. FAX: 212-678-5552. *Mgr*, Zoe Wai; *Librn*, Josefina Mora; Staff 1 (MLS 1)
Founded 1961

Subject Interests: Astronomy, Astrophysics, Geophysics, Global warming, Mathematics, Meteorology, Physics, Planetary atmospheres, Remote sensing of environ
Automation Activity & Vendor Info: (Cataloging) SIRSI; (Circulation) SIRSI; (OPAC) SIRSI
Publications: Booklist
Partic in OCLC Online Computer Library Center, Inc

S NATIONAL ACADEMY OF MUSEUM LIBRARY,* 1083 Fifth Ave, 10128. SAN 311-9106. Tel: 212-369-4880. FAX: 212-360-6795. *Dir*, Nancy Cafferty; *Archivist, Curator*, David B Dearinger
Founded 1826
Library Holdings: Bk Vols 4,500
Subject Interests: American art
Special Collections: Archival Material on National Academy of Design (1826 to present)
Restriction: By appointment only

S NATIONAL ACADEMY OF POPULAR MUSIC, Song Writer's Hall of Fame Library, 330 W 58th St, Ste 411, 10019. SAN 375-7943. Tel: 212-957-9230. FAX: 212-957-9227. E-Mail: songwritershalloffame@compuserve.org. Web Site: www.songwritershalloffame.org. *Dir*, April Anderson; *Curator*, Oscar Brand
Special Collections: Lyric Notes: Musical Memorabilia

S NATIONAL ARCHIVES & RECORDS ADMINISTRATION, Northeast Region (New York City), 201 Varick St 12th flr, 10014-4811. SAN 373-1928. Tel: 212-337-1300. FAX: 212-337-1306. E-Mail: newyork.archives@nara.gov. Web Site: www.nara.gov/regional/newyork.html. *Dir*, Robert C Morris; *Asst Dir*, John Celardo; Staff 8 (MLS 4, Non-MLS 4)
Founded 1969
Special Collections: Archival records of Federal agencies & courts in New York, New Jersey, Puerto Rico & the US Virgin Islands

S NATIONAL ASSOCIATION FOR THE ADVANCEMENT OF COLORED PEOPLE, NAACP Legal Defense & Educational Fund Law Library,* 99 Hudson St 16th flr, 10013. SAN 373-1170. Tel: 212-965-2200. FAX: 212-226-7592. *Info Specialist*, Donna Gloeckner; E-Mail: mgloeckn@council.com; *Asst Librn*, Sharmaign Griffin
Library Holdings: Bk Vols 19,000
Subject Interests: Civil rights

S NATIONAL ASSOCIATION FOR VISUALLY HANDICAPPED, Large Print Loan Library, 22 W 21st St, 6th Flr, 10010. SAN 371-7291. Tel: 212-889-3141. FAX: 212-727-2931. E-Mail: staff@navh.org. Web Site: www.navh.org. *Acq, Librn, Publ Servs*, Ann Illuzzi
Founded 1978
1999-2000 Mats Exp $82,312, Books $79,301, Presv $3,011. Sal $28,474
Library Holdings: Bk Vols 12,000; Bk Titles 7,500
Publications: Large Print Loan Library Catalog

NATIONAL BROADCASTING CO
S INFORMATION RESOURCES CENTER, 30 Rockefeller Plaza, Rm 2666E, 10112. SAN 353-2208. Tel: 212-664-5308. FAX: 212-247-8063.; Staff 12 (MLS 10, Non-MLS 2)
Founded 1930
Library Holdings: Bk Titles 9,500; Per Subs 175
Subject Interests: Broadcasting, Current events, Government, Marketing and advertising, Politics
Partic in Dialog Corporation; Dow Jones News Retrieval
L LEGAL DEPT LIBRARY, 30 Rockefeller Plaza, Rm 1022, 10112. SAN 325-3414. Tel: 212-664-5165. FAX: 212-664-2147. *Mgr*, Doreen F Polizzi
Founded 1933
S NEWS ARCHIVES, 30 Rockefeller Plaza, Rm 280E, 10112. SAN 353-2178. Tel: 212-664-3797. FAX: 212-957-8917. E-Mail: footage@nbc.com. Web Site: www.nbcnewsarchives.com. *Dir*, Nancy Cole; Fax: 212-664-4472, E-Mail: nancy.cole@nbc.com; *Mgr*, Chin Yuien; E-Mail: yuien.chin@nbc.com; Staff 24 (MLS 3, Non-MLS 21)
Founded 1950
Library Holdings: Per Subs 11
Subject Interests: Domestic affairs, International relations
Special Collections: NBC Documentaries; Political Material; Space Sciences Library Coll; Today Show & Nightly News Broadcasts

S NATIONAL BUREAU OF ECONOMIC RESEARCH, INC LIBRARY, 365 Fifth Ave 5th flr, 10016-4309. SAN 311-9173. Tel: 212-817-7955. FAX: 212-817-1597. E-Mail: nber@gc.cuny.org. Web Site: www.nber.org. *Librn*, Marinella Moscheni
Founded 1920
Library Holdings: Bk Vols 2,000; Per Subs 35
Subject Interests: Bus cycle, Gen econ

S NATIONAL CHAMBER OF COMMERCE FOR WOMEN LIBRARY, 10 Waterside Plaza, Ste 6H, 10010. SAN 320-8982. Tel: 212-685-3454. *In Charge*, R Wright
Founded 1977
Library Holdings: Bk Vols 1,100; Bk Titles 800; Per Subs 16
Subject Interests: Corporate-commun relations, Home-based bus, Labor-mgt relations, Marketing practices
Restriction: Staff use only

S NATIONAL COFFEE ASSOCIATION LIBRARY,* 15 Maiden Lane Ste 1405, 10038. SAN 311-6921. Tel: 212-766-4007. FAX: 212-766-5815. *In Charge*, Sabrina Velez; E-Mail: svelez@ncausa.org
Founded 1970
Subject Interests: Coffee, Health, Physiological effects of caffeine
Restriction: By appointment only

S NATIONAL COUNCIL ON ECONOMIC EDUCATION LIBRARY,* 1140 Avenue of the Americas, 10036. SAN 311-841X. Tel: 212-730-7007. FAX: 212-730-1793.
Founded 1949
Library Holdings: Bk Titles 1,200; Per Subs 55
Subject Interests: Curric, Econ educ
Restriction: Staff use only

L NATIONAL EMPLOYMENT LAW PROJECT LIBRARY,* 55 John St, 7th flr, 10038. SAN 325-7355. Tel: 212-285-3025, Ext 100. FAX: 212-285-3044. *Librn*, Debra Buchanon-Taylor
Library Holdings: Bk Vols 1,000

S NATIONAL MULTIPLE SCLEROSIS SOCIETY, Information Resource Center & Library,* 733 Third Ave, 10017. SAN 326-5838. Tel: 212-986-3240. FAX: 212-986-7981. E-Mail: info@nmss.org. Web Site: www.nmss.org. *Dir*, Abraham Eastwood; *Coll Develop, Ref*, Ann Palmer; Staff 2 (Non-MLS 2)
1998-1999 Income $688,000. Mats Exp $5,000, Books $2,500, Per/Ser (Incl. Access Fees) $2,500
Library Holdings: Bk Vols 997; Bk Titles 1,300; Per Subs 95
Subject Interests: Neurology, Nursing
Special Collections: Multiple Sclerosis, bks, reprints & pamphlets
Publications: Compendium of MS Information (Online)
Partic in Dialog Corporation
Open Mon-Fri 9-5

S NATIONAL PSYCHOLOGICAL ASSOCIATION FOR PSYCHOANALYSIS, INC, George Lawton Memorial Library, 150 W 13th St, 10011. SAN 311-9254. Tel: 212-924-7440. FAX: 212-989-7543. E-Mail: nber@gc.cuny.org. Web Site: www.nber.org. *In Charge*, Doris Mare
Founded 1958
Library Holdings: Bk Titles 5,000; Per Subs 25

S NATIONAL TRAINING CENTER OF POLYGRAPH SCIENCE LIBRARY,* 200 W 57th St, 10019-3211. SAN 371-2591. Tel: 212-755-5241. *Dir*, Richard O Arther
Library Holdings: Bk Vols 350

S NCI ADVERTISING LIBRARY,* 41 Madison Ave, 27th flr, 10010. SAN 329-921X. Tel: 212-684-0909, Ext 296. FAX: 212-684-5731. *Librn*, Judy Lee; E-Mail: jlee@41mad.com
Founded 1983
Library Holdings: Bk Vols 1,200; Per Subs 500
Special Collections: Business, Health Care, Medical
Partic in Basic Health Sciences Library Network; Coop Libr Agency for Syst & Servs; Manhattan-Bronx Health Sciences Libraries Group; New York Metrop Ref & Res Libr Agency

S NEIGHBORHOOD PLAYHOUSE SCHOOL OF THE THEATRE, Irene Lewisohn Library, 340 E 54th St, 10022. SAN 311-9300. Tel: 212-688-3770. FAX: 212-906-9051. Web Site: www.the-neiplay.org. *Librn*, David Semonin
Founded 1945
Library Holdings: Bk Vols 7,000; Per Subs 12
Subject Interests: Acting, Drama
Special Collections: Neighborhood Playhouse (N P-iana Coll), bks, files, photos

S NEW SCHOOL UNIVERSITY, (Formerly New School for Social Research), Raymond Fogelman Library, 65 Fifth Ave, 10003. SAN 311-9319. Tel: 212-229-5600. Interlibrary Loan Service Tel: 212-229-5303. FAX: 212-229-5306. *Dir*, Gail Persky; *ILL*, Carmen Hendershott; *Ref*, Susan Gilfert; Staff 4 (MLS 4)
Founded 1919. Highest Degree: Doctorate
Library Holdings: Bk Vols 188,000; Per Subs 600
Subject Interests: Behav sci, Econ, Literature, Philosophy, Soc sci
Special Collections: Husserl Archives; NACLA Archive of Latin Americana
Partic in Metro NY Libr Coun; OCLC; RLIN

§S NEW YORK ACADEMY OF ART LIBRARY, 111 Franklin St, 10013-2911. SAN 375-4421. Tel: 212-966-0300. FAX: 212-966-3217. Web Site: www.nyaa.edu. *Librn*, John Thompson; E-Mail: john@nyaa.edu
Founded 1990
Jul 1999- 2000 Income $118,000. Mats Exp $56,000, Books $50,000, Per/Ser (Incl. Access Fees) $4,000, Other Print Mats $2,000. Sal $60,000 (Prof

$35,000)
Library Holdings: Bk Titles 5,071; Per Subs 50
Special Collections: Art history; Drawing; Sculpture; Techniques of painting

M NEW YORK ACADEMY OF MEDICINE LIBRARY, 1216 Fifth Ave, 10029-5293. SAN 311-9327. Tel: 212-822-7300. FAX: 212-722-7650. E-Mail: library@nyam.org. Web Site: www.nyam.org/library/index.shtml. *Dir*, David N King; Tel: 212-822-7301, E-Mail: dking@nyam.org; *Assoc Dir*, Mary Mylenki; Tel: 212-822-7351, Fax: 212-534-7042, E-Mail: mmylenki@nyam.org; *Assoc Dir*, Patrick Newell; Tel: 212-822-7312, E-Mail: pnewell@nyam.org; *Assoc Librn*, Ed Mormon; Tel: 212-822-7314, E-Mail: emormon@nyam.org; *Curator*, Elaine Schlefer; Tel: 212-822-7363, E-Mail: eschlefer@nyam.org; *Tech Servs*, Ying Jia; Tel: 212-822-7334, E-Mail: yjia@nyam.org; *ILL*, Steve Chiaffone; Tel: 212-822-7296, E-Mail: schiaffone@nyam.org; *Rare Bks*, Miriam Mandelbaum; Tel: 212-822-7311, E-Mail: mmandelbaum@nyam.org; Staff 54 (MLS 25, Non-MLS 29)
Founded 1847
Jan 1999-Dec 1999 Income $2,119,186. Mats Exp $478,862, Books $68,033, Per/Ser (Incl. Access Fees) $309,006. Sal $1,415,097
Library Holdings: Bk Vols 700,000; Per Subs 1,501
Subject Interests: AIDS, Epidemiology, Health policy, Medicine, Public health
Special Collections: 16-19th Century Medals (Greenwald Coll), medals; Anatomy & Surgery (Lambert Coll); Cardiology (Levy Coll), bks, mss; Engravings of Medical Men (Ladd Coll), prints; Foods & Cookery (Wilson Coll); Francesco Redi & Contemporaries (Cole Coll); German Psychology & Psychiatry (Harms Coll); Medical; Medical Americana By & About J & W Hunter (Beekman Coll); Medical Economics (Michael Davis Coll), VF; Plague (Neinken Coll), bks, broadsides; Rare Medical Works (Friends of Rare Book Room), bk, mss; Theses-16th-18th Century (Gamble-Cranefield), pamphlets
Automation Activity & Vendor Info: (Cataloging) Innovative Interfaces Inc.; (Circulation) Innovative Interfaces Inc.; (OPAC) Innovative Interfaces Inc.; (Serials) Innovative Interfaces Inc.
Database Vendor: Dialog, IAC - Info Trac, Innovative Interfaces INN - View, Lexis-Nexis, OCLC - First Search, OVID Technologies, Silverplatter Information Inc.
Publications: Author Catalog of the Library & first supplement; Catalog of Biographies in the Library; History of Medicine Series; Illustration Catalog of the Library; Subject Catalog of the Library & first supplement
Function: Research library
Partic in Medical Library Center Of New York
Friends of the Library Group

GM NEW YORK CITY DEPARTMENT OF HEALTH, William Hallock Park Memorial Library, Public Health Laboratories, 455 First Ave, 10016. SAN 311-9378. Tel: 212-447-2676. FAX: 212-532-5241. *Librn*, Shirley Chapin; E-Mail: schapin@phri.nyu.edu
Founded 1900
Library Holdings: Bk Vols 5,200; Per Subs 172
Subject Interests: Bacteriology, Biochemistry, Cytobiology, Genetics, Immunology, Lab diagnosis, Microbiology, Virology

GL NEW YORK CITY LAW DEPARTMENT, Office of Corporation Counsels Law Library,* 100 Church St, Rm 6-310, 10007. SAN 311-9394. Tel: 212-788-1609. FAX: 212-788-1239. *Chief Librn*, Evania A Thompson; *Librn*, James Poteat; *Librn*, Susan Kegg
Founded 1856
Library Holdings: Bk Titles 71,600; Per Subs 3,000
Subject Interests: Legal, Legal per, NY fed case law, Statutes

S NEW YORK CITY MUNICIPAL REFERENCE & RESEARCH CENTER,* 31 Chambers St, Rm 112, 10007. SAN 353-202X. Tel: 212-788-8590. FAX: 212-788-8589. E-Mail: nycmrrc2@metgate.metro.org. *Dir*, Paul C Perkus; Staff 6 (MLS 5, Non-MLS 1)
Founded 1913
Subject Interests: Administration, Civil serv, Consul studies, Hist of New York City, Hosp admin, Legislation, Local government, Municipal mgt, New York City, Politicians, Public health, State doc, Urban affairs
Special Collections: Street Name Origins (Street Name File), cards, serials, bks
Partic in Metro Atlanta Library Association

G NEW YORK CITY PLANNING COMMISSION, Interdepartmental Planning & Housing Library, 22 Reade St, 10007. SAN 311-9408. Tel: 212-720-3300. FAX: 212-720-3495.
Founded 1965
Library Holdings: Bk Vols 1,500
Subject Interests: Architecture, Housing, NY City govt, Planning, Transportation, Urban design

G NEW YORK CITY POLICE DEPARTMENT, Training Resource Unit Library,* 235 E 20th St, Rm 639, 10003. SAN 325-5352. Tel: 212-477-9723. FAX: 212-477-9270.
Library Holdings: Bk Vols 11,000; Per Subs 70
Subject Interests: Commun policing, Criminal justice, Forensic sci, Hist of NYCPD, Law, Police sci, Psychology, Sociology
Publications: New York City Police Department-Management & Training Journal (quarterly)

CM NEW YORK COLLEGE OF PODIATRIC MEDICINE, Sidney Druskin Memorial Library, 53-55 E 124th St, 10035. SAN 311-9416. Tel: 212-410-8019. FAX: 212-876-9426. *Dir*, Tom Walker; E-Mail: twalker@nycpm.edu; Staff 4 (MLS 2, Non-MLS 2)
Founded 1911. Highest Degree: Doctorate
Library Holdings: Bk Vols 13,000; Bk Titles 6,300; Per Subs 260
Subject Interests: Dermatology, Podiatry
Partic in Greater NE Regional Med Libr Program; Medical Library Center Of New York; New York Metrop Ref & Res Libr Agency

GL NEW YORK COUNTY DISTRICT ATTORNEY'S OFFICE LIBRARY, One Hogan Pl, 10013. SAN 311-9424. Tel: 212-335-4292. FAX: 212-385-9789. *Dir Libr Serv*, Mary E Matuszak; Staff 1 (MLS 1)
Library Holdings: Bk Titles 26,970; Per Subs 56
Subject Interests: Criminal law
Restriction: Staff use only
Partic in Westlaw

L NEW YORK COUNTY LAWYERS' ASSOCIATION LIBRARY, 14 Vesey St, 10007. SAN 311-9432. Tel: 212-267-6646. FAX: 212-791-6437. Web Site: www.nycla.org. *Dir Libr Serv*, Alison Alifano; Tel: 212-267-6646, Ext 201, E-Mail: aalifano@mindspring.com; Staff 9 (MLS 3, Non-MLS 6)
Founded 1908
Library Holdings: Bk Titles 200,000; Per Subs 450
Special Collections: American Citizenship Coll
Publications: Acquisition lists (bimonthly); subject bibliographies
Restriction: Members only
Function: Reference only
Partic in OCLC Online Computer Library Center, Inc

GL NEW YORK COUNTY SURROGATE'S COURT, Law Library, 31 Chambers St, Rm 401, 10007. SAN 311-9440. Tel: 212-374-8275. *Librn*, Nadine Dubson
Library Holdings: Per Subs 10
Subject Interests: Estates, Trusts, Wills
Restriction: Not open to public

S NEW YORK DAILY NEWS LIBRARY,* 450 W 33rd St, 10001. SAN 311-9459. Tel: 212-210-1509. FAX: 212-244-4033. Web Site: www.nydailynews.com. *Chief Librn*, Faigi Rosenthal; Staff 9 (MLS 6, Non-MLS 3)
Founded 1919
Library Holdings: Bk Vols 5,000
Database Vendor: Lexis-Nexis, ProQuest
Restriction: Staff use only

M NEW YORK EYE & EAR INFIRMARY, Medical Library,* 310 E 14th St, 10003. SAN 311-9483. Tel: 212-979-4000. FAX: 212-979-4074. *Dir, Librn*, Mary Ann Lach
Founded 1954
Library Holdings: Bk Vols 1,650; Per Subs 68
Subject Interests: Head, Neck surgery, Ophthalmology, Otolaryngology, Plastic surgery
Partic in Manhattan-Bronx Health Sciences Libraries Group

S NEW YORK GENEALOGICAL & BIOGRAPHICAL SOCIETY LIBRARY, 122 E 58th St, 4th flr, 10022-1939. SAN 311-9513. Tel: 212-755-8532. FAX: 212-754-4218. E-Mail: library@nygbs.org. Web Site: www.nygbs.org. *Exec Dir*, William Potter Johns; *Ref*, Catherine M Ellard; *Asst Librn*, Robert F Gibson; *Asst Librn*, Catherine M Ellard; *Admin Assoc*, David Cepil; *Dir*, Joy Rich; E-Mail: joyrich@nygbs.org; Staff 4 (MLS 2, Non-MLS 2)
Founded 1869
1998-1999 Mats Exp $14,950, Books $4,300, Per/Ser (Incl. Access Fees) $1,000
Library Holdings: Bk Vols 75,000; Per Subs 1,320
Subject Interests: Biog, Genealogy, Local history, US hist
Special Collections: Family & Bible Records; New York State Town, Church & Cemetery Records; Professional Genealogists Research Material
Automation Activity & Vendor Info: (Acquisitions) Inmagic, Inc.; (Cataloging) Inmagic, Inc.; (OPAC) Inmagic, Inc.; (Serials) Inmagic, Inc.
Publications: Bibliographies of holdings by ethnicity
Restriction: Members only
Function: Research library

S NEW YORK HISTORICAL SOCIETY LIBRARY, 170 Central Park W, 10024-5194. SAN 311-9521. Tel: 212-873-3400. Interlibrary Loan Service Tel: 212-873-3400, Ext 225. Reference Tel: 212-873-3400, Ext 225. FAX: 212-875-1591. Web Site: www.nyhistory.org. *Coll Develop, Dir*, Margaret Heilbrun; *Publ Servs*, Nina Nazionale; Staff 10 (MLS 8, Non-MLS 2)
Founded 1804
Library Holdings: Bk Titles 650,000
Subject Interests: Am art, Hist of N Am continent, Hist of New York City, Hist of US, Naval hist, NY genealogy, State

Special Collections: 18th & 19th Century New York City & New York State Newspapers; American Almanacs; American Genealogy; American Indian (Accounts of & Captivities); Among the Manuscript Collections: Horatio Gates, Alexander McDougall, Rufus King, American Fur Company, Livingston Family, American Art Union, American Academy of Fine Arts; Circus in America (Leonidas Westervelt); Civil War Regimental Histories & Muster Rolls; Early American; Early American Trials; Early Travels in America; Imprints; Jenny Lind (Leonidas Westervelt); Maps; Military History & Science (Seventh Regiment Military Library); Military History (Military Order of the Loyal Legion of the United States, Commandery of the State of New York); Naval & Marine History (Naval History Society); Slavery & the Civil War; Spanish American War (Harper)
Publications: Catalogs; Indexes; Special Publications
Partic in Bobcat; RLIN
Friends of the Library Group

C NEW YORK INSTITUTE OF TECHNOLOGY, Manhattan Campus, 1855 Broadway, 10023. SAN 353-2291. Tel: 212-261-1526. FAX: 212-261-1681. E-Mail: smarion@nyit.edu. Web Site: www.nyit.edu/library. *Dir*, Elisabete Ferretti; *ILL, Ref*, Jennifer Tsao; Staff 6 (MLS 6)
Founded 1958. Circ 9,719
Library Holdings: Bk Vols 41,664; Per Subs 792
Subject Interests: Architecture, Art, Computer science
Publications: Library News; New Acquisitions
Partic in Long Island Library Resources Council; New York Metrop Ref & Res Libr Agency; WALDO

L NEW YORK LAW INSTITUTE LIBRARY,* 120 Broadway, Rm 932, 10271-0043. SAN 311-9548. Tel: 212-732-8720. *Chief Librn*, Nancy G Joseph; *Ref*, Ralph Caiazzo; Staff 11 (MLS 3, Non-MLS 8)
Founded 1828
Library Holdings: Bk Vols 270,000
Subject Interests: Anglo-Am law, Colonies, Former possessions, Incl British Dominions
Special Collections: Appellate Divisions, 1st, 2nd & 3rd Departments; Records & Briefs for New York Court of Appeals; United States Court of Appeals for Second Circuit; United States Supreme Court, fiche
Automation Activity & Vendor Info: (Serials) Innovative Interfaces Inc.
Publications: Newsletter
Restriction: Members only
Partic in OCLC Online Computer Library Center, Inc

L NEW YORK LAW SCHOOL LIBRARY,* 57 Worth St, 10013. SAN 311-9564. Tel: 212-431-2332. FAX: 212-965-8839. *Librn*, Joyce Saltalamachia; *Assoc Librn*, William Mills
Founded 1891
Library Holdings: Bk Vols 435,000; Per Subs 1,450
Subject Interests: Anglo-Am, International law, New York
Publications: Current Acquisitions (bi-monthly); Table of Contents (weekly)
Partic in Dialog Corporation; New York Metrop Ref & Res Libr Agency; OCLC Online Computer Library Center, Inc; Westlaw

L NEW YORK LEGISLATIVE SERVICE, INC LIBRARY,* 299 Broadway 2nd flr Ste 220, 10007. SAN 372-4328. Tel: 212-962-2826. FAX: 212-962-1420. E-Mail: nylegal@nyxfer.blythe.org. Web Site: www.nyls.org. *Exec Dir*, Laird Ehlert
Library Holdings: Bk Vols 10,000
Special Collections: Governor's Bill Jackets, 1905-present; New York State Legislative Documents
Publications: New York City Legislative Annual; New York State Legislative Annual

NEW YORK LIFE INSURANCE CO
L LAW LIBRARY, 51 Madison Ave, Rm 10-SB, 10010. SAN 353-2321. Tel: 212-576-6458. Interlibrary Loan Service Tel: 212-576-5949. FAX: 212-576-6886. *Librn*, Diana Louros; E-Mail: diana_louros@newyorklife.com
Founded 1946
Library Holdings: Bk Vols 15,000; Per Subs 30
Restriction: Staff use only

M NEW YORK ORTHOPAEDIC HOSPITAL-COLUMBIA UNIVERSITY COLLEGE OF PHYSICIANS & SURGEONS, Russell A Hibbs Memorial Library, 622 W 168th St, PH-11, 10032. SAN 370-5536. Tel: 212-305-3294. FAX: 212-305-6193. E-Mail: is369@columbia.edu. *Librn*, Inna Shpilko; Staff 1 (MLS 1)
Founded 1927
Library Holdings: Bk Titles 4,000; Per Subs 100
Subject Interests: Orthopedics
Special Collections: Rare Books on Orthopaedics
Publications: Newsletter (quarterly)
Partic in Metropolitan New York Library Council

S NEW YORK POST LIBRARY,* 1211 Avenue of the Americas, 10036. SAN 311-9580. Tel: 212-930-8735. FAX: 212-930-8548. *Librn*, Laura Harris; E-Mail: laharris40@aol.com; Staff 8 (MLS 2, Non-MLS 6)
Founded 1920
Library Holdings: Bk Vols 5,000
Subject Interests: Biog info, Current events, New York City hist
Special Collections: New York Post Microfile 1802-present
Restriction: Staff use only

L NEW YORK POWER AUTHORITY, Law Library,* 1633 Broadway, 10019. SAN 371-5558. Tel: 212-468-6192. FAX: 212-468-6272. *Librn*, Elyse Silverstein; E-Mail: silverstein.e@nypa.gov; Staff 2 (MLS 1, Non-MLS 1)
Library Holdings: Bk Vols 10,000

NEW YORK PRESBYTERIAN HOSPITAL-CORNELL MEDICAL CENTER LIBRARIES
S HELEN MITCHELL GRAVES & MARILYN PRESTON MEMORIAL PATIENT LIBRARY, New York Hospital, 525 E 68th St, M-0044, 10021. SAN 353-2232. Tel: 212-746-4398. FAX: 212-746-8283. *Librn*, Nancy Streeter
Founded 1932
Library Holdings: Bk Titles 3,500; Per Subs 52

M NEW YORK PSYCHOANALYTIC INSTITUTE, Abraham A Brill Library, 247 E 82nd St, 10028. SAN 311-9599. Tel: 212-879-6900. FAX: 212-879-0588. Web Site: www.nypsa.org. *Dir*, Matthew von Unwerth
Library Holdings: Bk Titles 30,000; Per Subs 55
Subject Interests: Behav sci, Humanities, Psychiatry, Psychoanalysis, Psychology, Soc sci
Special Collections: Art (Arieti Papers); Freud's Writings in all Editions & Languages (Sigmund Freud Coll); History, Literature &; Languages & Linguistics Coll; Sociology (Ernst Kris Coll); Transcripts of Prominent Psychoanalysis
Partic in Dialog Corporation

P NEW YORK PUBLIC LIBRARY, Astor, Lenox & Tilden Foundations Library, 188 Madison Avenue, 10016. SAN 353-2410. Tel: 212-930-0800. FAX: 212-921-2546. Web Site: www.nypl.org. *Dir*, Norman Holman
Founded 1895
Jul 1998-Jun 1999 Income $203,737,000, State $19,211,000, City $94,282,000, Federal $1,763,000, Other $88,481,000. Mats Exp $22,670,000
Library Holdings: Bk Titles 17,762,034
Publications: Biblion; NYPL News; Various books
Mem of Asn of Research Libraries
Partic in Dialog Corporation; New York State Interlibrary Loan Network; OCLC Online Computer Library Center, Inc; RLIN
Friends of the Library Group
Branches: 126
ACCESS SERVICES, Fifth Ave & 42nd St, 10018. Tel: 212-930-0854. Web Site: www.nypl.org. *Asst Dir*, Helga Borck; E-Mail: hborck@nypl.org
AGUILAR, 174 E 110th St, 10029. SAN 353-4065. Tel: 212-534-2930. FAX: 212-860-4580. *Librn*, Christiana Pinto
ALLERTON, 2740 Barnes Ave, Bronx, 10467. SAN 353-409X. Tel: 718-881-4240. FAX: 718-881-4240. *Librn*, Cesare Passudetti; E-Mail: cpassudetti@nypl.org
P ANDREW HEISKELL LIBRARY FOR THE BLIND & PHYSICALLY HANDICAPPED, 40 W 20th St, 10011-4211. SAN 353-3913. Tel: 212-206-5400. TDD: 212-206-5458. FAX: 212-206-5418. E-Mail: ahlbph@nypl.org. Web Site: www.nypl.org/branch/lb/. *Librn*, Kathleen Rowan
Special Services for the Deaf - TTY machine
Special Services for the Blind - Braille books on tape; Electronic readers; Magazines on cassette; Reading room
Open Mon 10-5, Tues & Fri 12-5, Thurs 12-7, Sat 1-5
Friends of the Library Group
ARENTS COLLECTION, Humanities & Soc Scis Library, Fifth Ave & 42nd St, Rm 324, 10018-2788. SAN 353-3107. Tel: 212-930-0801. FAX: 212-302-4815. E-Mail: rbkref@nypl.org. *Curator*, Virginia Bartow; Staff 3 (MLS 2, Non-MLS 1)
Subject Interests: 16th Century herbals, 19th Century English lit, French, German, Hist of tobacco, Italian, Rare early works in English, Spanish
Special Collections: Books in Parts (over 1200 items preserved in original wrappers) & Autographed Letters Relating to the Books & Their Illustrators, including W H Ainsworth, Wilkie Collins, Charles Dickens, Kate Greenaway, W M Thackeray & Anthony Trollope; Holograph Manuscripts & Original Drawings of Illustrators, including George Cruikshank, John Leech & Thomas Rowlandson; Tobacco Coll (over 10,400 items in 28 languages relating to tobacco, including autographs, bks, drawings, mss, music, pamphlets & prints)
ART COLLECTION, Mid-Manhattan Library, 3rd Flr, 455 Fifth Ave, 40th St at Fifth Ave, 10016. Tel: 212-340-0871. *Librn*, Matthew Tallow
Subject Interests: Architecture, Art history, Art photog, Costume design, Decorative arts, Design, Drawing, Fashion, Graphics, Painting, Sculpture
Open Mon, Wed & Thurs 9-9, Tues 11-7, Fri & Sat 10-6
BAYCHESTER, 2049 Asch Loop N, Bronx, 10475. SAN 353-412X. Tel: 718-379-6700. FAX: 718-671-2836. *Librn*, Stella Shang; E-Mail: sshang@

nypl.org
BLOOMINGDALE, 150 W 100th St, 10025. SAN 353-4189. Tel: 212-222-8030. FAX: 212-932-2421.
BRONX REFERENCE CENTER, 2556 Bainbridge Ave, 10458. SAN 353-4219. Tel: 718-579-4257. FAX: 718-562-1885. *Librn*, Lucidia Gratacos-Arus; E-Mail: larus@nypl.org
CASTLE HILL, 947 Castle Hill Ave, Bronx, 10473. SAN 353-4243. Tel: 718-824-3838. FAX: 718-824-3838. *Librn*, Paushou Chuang; E-Mail: pchuang@nypl.org
CENTRAL CHILDREN'S ROOM, Donnell Library Ctr, 20 W 53rd St, 10019-6185. SAN 353-4308. Tel: 212-621-0636. *Librn*, Jeanne Lamb; Tel: 212-621-0638, Fax: 212-245-5272, E-Mail: jlamb@nypl.org
Subject Interests: Bibliog, Bk reviews, Cassettes, Children's mag, Children's poetry, Fiction, Folklore, Hist of children's lit, Indexes, Juvenile bk illustration, Largest coll of juvenile lit in New York Public Library, Non-print coll of records, Ref
Special Collections: 18th & 19th Century Children's Books; Anne Carroll Moore Coll of First Editions; Erica Davies Coll of Autographed Children's Books; Mary Gould Davis Coll of Folklore; Original Winnie-the-Pooh & Friends Stuffed Toys
Open Mon, Wed & Fri 12-6, Tues 10-6, Thurs 12-8, Sat 12-5, Sun 1-5
CHATHAM SQUARE, 33 E Broadway, 10002. SAN 353-4367. Tel: 212-964-6598. FAX: 212-385-7850. *Librn*, Ronald Chan
CITY ISLAND, 320 City Island Ave, Bronx, 10464. SAN 353-4391. Tel: 718-885-1703. FAX: 718-885-3051. *Librn*, Neal Steinberg; E-Mail: nsteinberg@nypl.org
CLASON'S POINT, 1215 Morrison Ave, Bronx, 10472. SAN 353-4421. Tel: 718-842-1235. FAX: 718-842-1235. *Librn*, Duck-Hi Min; E-Mail: dmin@nypl.org
COLUMBIA, 514 W 113th St, 10025. SAN 353-4456. Tel: 212-864-2530. FAX: 212-665-4692. *Librn*, Dean Smith
COLUMBUS, 742 Tenth Ave, 10019. SAN 353-4480. Tel: 212-586-5098. FAX: 212-459-9066. *Librn*, Jennie Czarny
COOPERATIVE SERVICES DIV, Fifth Ave & 42nd St, 10018. Tel: 212-930-0878. FAX: 212-391-2502. *In Charge*, Daniel Simko
Restriction: Non-circulating to the public
Contact NYPL Express for photocopies (188 Madison Ave, 10016-4314); Tel: 212-592-7206; Fax: 212-592-7215
COUNTEE CULLEN, 104 W 136th St, 10030. SAN 353-4510. Tel: 212-491-2070. FAX: 212-491-6541. *Librn*, Phyllis Mack
DONGAN HILLS, 1617 Richmond Rd, Staten Island, 10304. SAN 353-4545. Tel: 718-351-1444. FAX: 718-987-6883. *Librn*, Mary L Pyrak
DONNELL LIBRARY CENTER, 20 W 53rd St, 10019. SAN 353-3557. Tel: 212-621-0618. Interlibrary Loan Service Tel: 212-621-0601. FAX: 212-245-5272. *Chief Librn*, Anne J Hofmann; Tel: 212-621-0665, E-Mail: ahofmann@nypl.org; *ILL*, Alexandra Lutz; E-Mail: alutz@nypl.org
Special Services for the Deaf - TTY machine
DRAMA & DANCE, Libr for the Performing Arts, 40 Lincoln Center Plaza, 10023-7498. SAN 353-376X. Tel: 212-870-1622. Web Site: www.nypl.org/research/lpa/circ/circ.html. *Librn*, Janice Frank; E-Mail: jfrank@nypl.org; Staff 7 (MLS 5, Non-MLS 2)
Subject Interests: Acting, Arts management, Auditions, Bks, Cinema, Circus, Clippings, Costuming, Dance, Film hist, Film production, Periodicals, Plays, Published plays, Puppetry, Radio-TV, Theatre production, Theatrical hist
EARLY CHILDHOOD RESOURCE & INFORMATION CENTER (ECRIC), 66 Leroy St at Seventh Ave, 10014. SAN 353-4561. Tel: 212-929-0815. FAX: 212-242-8242. *Librn*, Rachel Payne
EASTCHESTER, 1385 E Gun Hill Rd, Bronx, 10469. SAN 353-457X. Tel: 718-653-3292. FAX: 718-653-3292. *Librn*, Joan Aikens; E-Mail: jaikens@nypl.org
EDENWALD, 1255 E 233rd St, Bronx, 10466. SAN 353-460X. Tel: 718-798-3355. FAX: 718-798-3355. *Librn*, Mawusinu C Apreku; E-Mail: capreku@nypl.org
EDUCATION, Mid-Manhattan Library, 2nd Flr, 455 Fifth Ave, 10016. Reference Tel: 212-340-0864. *Librn*, Jean Peterson
Special Collections: Catalogs & Directories of US & International Colleges & Universities; Dissertation Abstracts International; Financial Aid Materials; Microfiche of Materials in the Educational Resources Information Center (ERIC); New York City Continuing Education Catalogs; Non-Traditional Higher Education Program Information; School Pamphlets; Study Manuals for Exams; Vocational & Technical School Directories
Open Mon, Wed & Thurs 9-9, Tues 11-7, Fri & Sat 10-6
BELMONT ENRICO FERMI CULTURAL CENTER, 610 E 186th St, Bronx, 10458. SAN 353-4154. Tel: 718-933-6410. FAX: 718-365-8756. *Librn*, Marisa Parish; E-Mail: mparish@nypl.org
EPIPHANY, 228 E 23rd St, 10010. SAN 353-4634. Tel: 212-679-2645. FAX: 212-779-4624. *Librn*, Amelia Schwartz
FIFTY-EIGHTH STREET, 127 E 58th St, 10022. SAN 353-4669. Tel: 212-759-7358. FAX: 212-758-6858. *Librn*, John Bhagwandin
FORDHAM LIBRARY CENTER, 2556 Bainbridge Ave, Bronx, 10458. SAN 353-3522. Tel: 718-579-4244. FAX: 718-579-4264. *Librn*, Elga Cace; E-Mail: ecace@nypl.org
Special Services for the Deaf - TTY machine
Special Services for the Blind - Kurzweil Reading Machine
FORT WASHINGTON, 535 W 179th St, 10033. SAN 353-4693. Tel: 212-927-3533. FAX: 212-740-8601. *Librn*, Estelle Friedman
FRANCIS MARTIN BRANCH, 2150 University Ave, Bronx, 10453. SAN 353-4723. Tel: 718-295-5287. FAX: 718-365-8979. *Librn*, Patricia Long; E-Mail: plong@nypl.org
GENERAL REFERENCE & ADVISORY SERVICES, Mid-Manhattan Library, 2nd Flr, 455 Fifth Ave, 10016. SAN 353-5282. *Head of Libr*, Wol Sue Lee
Subject Interests: Education, Health info tech
Special Services for the Deaf - TTY machine
Special Services for the Blind - Kurzweil Reading Machine
Open Mon, Wed & Thurs 9-9, Tues 11-7, Fri & Sat 10-6
GENERAL RESEARCH DIV, Rm 315, 10018-2788. SAN 353-2682. Tel: 212-930-0830. FAX: 212-930-0572. E-Mail: grdref@nypl.org. Web Site: www.nypl.org. *Chief Librn*, Elizabeth Diefendorf; *Dir, Tech Serv*, Cynthia Clark
Library Holdings: Bk Vols 3,400,000; Per Subs 11,000
Subject Interests: Am hist, Anthropology, Archaeology, Bibliog, Biog, Drama, Geography, History, Literature, Philology, Philosophy, Popular culture, Printing, Psychology, Sports, Women
Special Collections: Baseball (Spalding Coll); Chess Coll; Folklore of Americas; Literature (Bunyan, Cervantes, Dante, Milton & Shakespeare Colls); Native Americans; Small Press Poetry; Spanish Civil War (David McKelvy White Coll); World Wars I & II
Publications: Bibligraphic Guides
GEORGE BRUCE BRANCH, 518 W 125th St, 10027. SAN 353-4758. Tel: 212-662-9727. FAX: 212-662-0534. *Librn*, Manuel Figueroa
GRAND CONCOURSE, 155 E 173rd St, Bronx, 10457. SAN 353-4782. Tel: 718-583-6611. FAX: 718-583-6611. *Librn*, Getulio Orta-Rosa; E-Mail: gortarosa@nypl.org
GREAT KILLS, 56 Giffords Lane, Staten Island, 10308. SAN 353-4812. Tel: 718-984-6670. FAX: 718-966-1140. *Librn*, Hishi Velardo
HAMILTON FISH PARK, 415 E Houston St, 10002. SAN 353-4847. Tel: 212-673-2290. FAX: 212-673-2290. *Librn*, Jayne Pierce
HAMILTON GRANGE, 503 W 145th St, 10031. SAN 353-4871. Tel: 212-926-2147. FAX: 212-926-2147. *Librn*, Michael Alverez
HARLEM, 9 W 124th St, 10027. SAN 353-4901. Tel: 212-348-5620. FAX: 212-348-5620. *Librn*, Jerome Hammond
HENRY W & ALBERT A BERG COLLECTION OF ENGLISH & AMERICAN LITERATURE, Fifth Ave & 42nd St, Rm 320, 10018-2788. SAN 353-3131. Tel: 212-930-0803. FAX: 212-930-0079. *Curator, Dir*, Rodney Phillips; E-Mail: rphillips@nypl.org; Staff 3 (MLS 2, Non-MLS 1)
Subject Interests: 16th-20th Centuries, with strength from mid-18th century
Special Collections: Literary Colls (including Auden, Auster, Bryant, Clemens, Conrad, Dickens, Dickinson, Doyle, George Eliot, T S Eliot, Gissing, Hawthorne, Irving, Kerouac, Kipling, Koch, Levine, R Lowell, Nabokov, Poe, Roethke, Rukeyser, Sarton, G B Shaw, Synge, Thackeray, Thoreau, Whitman, Wilde, Woolf, Wordsworth & Yeats), autographed letters, first editions, mss & rare bks
HIGH BRIDGE, 78 W 168th St, Bronx, 10452. SAN 353-4936. Tel: 718-293-7800. FAX: 718-293-7800. *Librn*, Margaret Fleesak; E-Mail: mfleesak@nypl.org
HISTORY & SOCIAL SCIENCES, Mid-Manhattan Library, 5th Flr, 455 Fifth Ave, 10016. Tel: 212-340-0887. *Head of Libr*, Edith Ostrowsky
Subject Interests: African-American, Am hist, Crime, Folklore, Journalism, Law, Libr sci, Native Am studies, Philosophy, Psychiatry, Psychology, Puerto Rican studies, Relig studies, Selective govt docs, Soc problems, Sociology, Women's studies, World history
Open Mon, Wed & Thurs 9-9, Tues 11-7, Fri & Sat 10-6
HUDSON PARK, 66 Leroy St, 10014. SAN 353-4960. Tel: 212-243-6876. FAX: 212-242-8242. *Librn*, Jan Klucevsek
HUGUENOT PARK, 830 Huguenot Ave, Staten Island, 10312. SAN 353-4995. Tel: 718-984-4636. FAX: 718-966-9163. *Librn*, Kan Wong Wou
HUMANITIES & SOCIAL SCIENCES LIBRARY, Fifth Ave & 42nd St, 10018. Tel: 212-221-7660 (automated hours), 212-869-8089 (automated exhibition), 212-930-0501 (tour info). *Dir*, Rodney Phillips; *Assoc Dir*, Ann Thornton; *Spec Coll*, H George Fletcher
HUNT'S POINT, 877 Southern Blvd, Bronx, 10459. SAN 353-5029. Tel: 718-617-0338. FAX: 718-893-3491. *Librn*, Margaret Hetley; E-Mail: mhetley@nypl.org
INWOOD, 4790 Broadway, 10034. SAN 353-5053. Tel: 212-942-2445. FAX: 212-304-4666. *Librn*, Tara Johnson
IRMA & PAUL MILSTEIN DIVISION OF US HISTORY, LOCAL HISTORY & GENEALOGY, Humanities & Soc Scis Library, Fifth Ave & 42nd St, Rm 121, 10018-2788. SAN 353-2771. Tel: 212-930-0828. Web Site: www.nypl.org. *In Charge*, Ruth A Carr; Staff 11 (MLS 6, Non-MLS 5)
Library Holdings: Bk Vols 150,000
Subject Interests: European genealogy, Flags, Genealogy of Am families, Heraldry, New York City hist, Origin, Personal names, US hist
Special Collections: 110,000 Photographic Views of New York City, arranged basically by address; Local History; Political Campaign Ephemera, broadsides, candidate postition papers, pamphlets; Postcards &

Scrapbooks of United States Local Views
JEFFERSON MARKET, 425 Avenue of the Americas, 10011. SAN 353-5088. Tel: 212-243-4334. FAX: 212-627-0877. *Librn*, Frank Collerius
JEROME PARK, 118 Eames Pl, Bronx, 10468. SAN 353-5118. Tel: 718-549-5200. FAX: 718-549-5200. *Librn*, Arlene Geller; E-Mail: ageller@nypl.org
JEROME ROBBINS DANCE DIVISION, 40 Lincoln Ctr Plaza, 10023-7498. SAN 353-3344. Tel: 212-870-1657. FAX: 212-870-1869. *Curator*, Madeleine Nichols
Founded 1944
Library Holdings: Bk Vols 35,500; Per Subs 210
Subject Interests: All types of dance, Econ, Education, Religion, Theatrical, Therapeutic
Special Collections: Agnes de Mille Coll; American Ballet Theatre Papers; Asian Dance; Brooklyn Academy of Music Performance Videos; Dallet Russe de Monte Carlo-Serge Denham Coll; Dance Theater Workshop Performance Videos; Denishawn; Doris Humphrey Coll; Gallet Russe de Monte Carlo-Serge Denham Coll; Hanya Holm Coll; Helen Tamiris Coll; Isadora Duncan (Irma Duncan Coll & Craig-Duncan Correspondence); Jose Limon Coll; Les Ballets Russes de Diaghilev (Astruc-Diaghilev Papers); Loie Fuller Coll; Rare Ballet History (Cia Fornaroli Toscanini Coll); Rare Dance History (Lillian Moore & Lincoln Kirstein Colls); Rudolf Nureyev Coll; Ruth Page Coll; Ruth St Denis Coll; Ted Shawn Coll; Vaslav Nijinsky Diary
Publications: Dance on Disc; Dictionary Catalog of the Dance Collection & Annual Supplements; Index to Dance Periodicals
JEWISH DIV, Rm 84, 10018-2788. SAN 353-2747. Tel: 212-930-0601. FAX: 212-642-0141. E-Mail: freidus@nypl.org. Web Site: www.nypl.org/research/chss/jws/jewish.html.
Library Holdings: Bk Vols 308,000
Subject Interests: Jewish studies
Special Collections: Early Hebrew Printing; Jewish Newspapers on Microfilm; Oral Histories of the American Jewish Experience; Yiddish Theater Manuscripts & Ephemera
Publications: A Sign & A Witness: 2000 Years of Hebrew Books & Illuminated Manuscripts (1988)
KINGSBRIDGE, 280 W 231st St, Bronx, 10463. SAN 353-5142. Tel: 718-548-5656. FAX: 718-796-4065. *Librn*, Arnold Hyman; E-Mail: ahyman@nypl.org
KIPS BAY, 446 Third Ave, 10016. SAN 353-5177. Tel: 212-683-2520. FAX: 212-545-8553. *Librn*, Patricia Pardo
LIBRARY FOR THE PERFORMING ARTS, 40 Lincoln Ctr Plaza, 10023-7498. SAN 353-331X. Tel: 212-870-1630. *Actg Dir*, Susan Sommer
Open Mon & Wed 9-9, Tues & Thurs 11-7, Fri & Sat 10-6
LITERATURE & LANGUAGE COLLECTION, Mid-Manhattan Library, 3rd Flr, 455 Fifth Ave, 10016. Tel: 212-340-0873. FAX: 212-576-0048. *Head of Libr*, Lucia Chen; *Librn*, Jay Barksdale
Subject Interests: American literature, Classical literature, English literature, Foreign lit in translation, French lit, Languages, Literary criticism, Per on Am, Spanish lit
Open Mon, Wed & Thurs 9-9, Tues 11-7, Fri & Sat 10-6
MACOMB'S BRIDGE, 2650 Adam Clayton Powell Jr Blvd, 10039. SAN 353-5207. Tel: 212-281-4900. FAX: 212-694-6134.
MANUSCRIPTS & ARCHIVES DIVISION, Humanities & Soc Scis Library, Fifth Ave & 42nd St, Rm 328, 10018-2788. Tel: 212-930-0801. Web Site: www.nypl.org. *Curator*, Mary B Bowling; Staff 7 (MLS 5, Non-MLS 2)
Founded 1895
Subject Interests: American revolution, Science fiction
Special Collections: Alfred W Anthony Coll; Archives of New York World's Fairs, 1939-40 & 1964-65; Babylonica (Wilberforce Eames Coll); Civil War History (United States Sanitary Commission Records); Cuneiform Tablets; DeCoursey Fales Coll; Early Colonial Latin American History (Obadiah Rich Coll - 18th Century Transcripts & Some Originals of the Age of Discovery & Exploration); Founding Fathers (Declaration of Independence, George Washington's Farewell Address); George Bancroft Collection; Gordon Lester Ford Coll; Lee Kohns & David McNeely Stauffer Autograph Colls; Loyalist Transcripts (American Revolutionary Period); Medieval & Renaissance Illuminated Manuscripts (such as the Landevennec Gospels, Lectionarium Evangeliorum & the Towneley Lectionary); Mortimer & Anna Neinken Collection of American Seals; Papers of Edwin Arlington, Truman Capote, Babette Deutsch, Peter Gansevoort, Horation Gates, Philip Schuyler, Richard Rogers Bowker, William Cullen Bryant, Evert Augustus Duyckinck, Richard Watson Gilder, Washington Irving, Robert Underwood Johnson, Edgar Lee Masters, Herman Melville, Henry Louis Mencken, Albert Shaw, Genevieve Taggard, Carl Van Vechten & Noah Webster; Publishers' Archives (Century Co, Crowell-Collier, Macmillan, Alfred A Knopf, Inc, Farrar, Straus & Giroux, Inc & The New Yorker); Samuel Adams, John Bigelow, Henry George, Horace Greeley, James Madison, James Monroe, Robert Morris, Norman Thomas, Frank P. Walsh (American Statesmen); Science Fiction (Carter Burden Coll); Thomas Addis Emmett Collection
MAP DIV, Humanities & Soc Scis Library, Fifth Ave & 42nd St, Rm 117, 10018-2788. SAN 353-2801. Reference Tel: 212-930-0587. FAX: 212-930-0027. E-Mail: mapref@nypl.org. Web Site: www.nypl.org/research/chss/map/map.html. *In Charge*, Alice C Hudson; Staff 5 (MLS 4, Non-MLS 1)
Founded 1898
Library Holdings: Bk Vols 19,310
Subject Interests: Am and other maps from 1700, Atlases, City plans, European maps from 1600, Gazetteers, Large-scale maps of US, Major cartographical, Road maps, Topographical surveys, US real estate maps
Special Collections: Uncataloged US Road Map Coll (1900 to present)
Publications: English Mapping of America (1675-1715)
Partic in OCLC Online Computer Library Center, Inc; RLIN
Friends of the Library Group
MEDIA CENTER, Donnell Library Ctr, 20 W 53rd St, 10019-6185. SAN 353-3646. Tel: 212-621-0609. FAX: 212-245-5272. *Chief Librn*, Marie Nesthus; Tel: 212-621-0663, E-Mail: mnesthus@nypl.org
Special Collections: Film Collection - Animation, Avant Garde, Documentary & Feature, 16 mm sound films for all age levels; Recordings - Classical & Semi-Classical, Folk, Jazz & Popular Music, Instructional Recordings, Literature, Radio Broadcasts & Speeches; Video Collection - Video Art, Documentary, Performance, 3/4 inch & 1/2 inch VHS videotapes, DVD formats
Open Mon, Wed & Fri 10-6, Tues & Thurs 10-8, Sat 10-5, Sun 1-5
MEDIA LIBRARY, Fordham Library Ctr, 2556 Bainbridge Ave, 10458-4698. SAN 353-4030. Tel: 718-579-4248. FAX: 718-579-4264. *In Charge*, Pamela Lieber; E-Mail: plieber@nypl.org
MELROSE, 910 Morris Ave, Bronx, 10451. SAN 353-5231. Tel: 718-588-0110. FAX: 718-588-1432. *Actg Librn*, Linda Jones; E-Mail: ljones@nypl.org
MID-MANHATTAN LIBRARY, 455 Fifth Ave, 10016. SAN 353-5266. Tel: 212-340-0833. FAX: 212-576-0048. *Chief Librn*, Robert Goldstein
Special Services for the Deaf - TTY machine
Open Mon, Wed & Thurs 9-9, Tues 11-7, Fri & Sat 10-6
MIRIAM & IRA D WALLACH DIVISION OF ART, PRINTS & PHOTOGRAPHS, Fifth Ave & 42nd St, 10018. Tel: 212-930-0817 (Print Rm), 212-930-0835 (Art & Archit Coll), 212-930-0837 (Photog Coll). FAX: 212-930-0530. Web Site: www.nypl.org. *Asst Dir*, Robert Rainwater; *Curator*, Paula Baxter; *Curator*, Julia Van Haaften; *Curator*, Roberta Waddell
Library Holdings: Bk Vols 240,000
Subject Interests: Archit design, Bks on graphic artists, Cat of their works, Ceramics, Contemporary Am, Costume, European, Folk arts, Glass, Illustrated bks, Interior decoration, Jewelry, Oriental art, Original fine prints of the past six centuries with special emphasis on 19th century French, Post-Columbian-Am art, Silversmithing, Techniques
Special Collections: American & European Political Cartoons & Caricatures; American Views (Phelps Stokes Coll); Exhibition Catalogs; George Washington Portraits (McAlpin Coll); Individual Artists & Architects, clipping file, over 350,000 items; Japanese Prints (Smith Coll); Milton & Pope Portraits (Beverly Chew Bequest); New York City Views (Eno Coll); Private & Public Collection Catalogs; Sales Catalogs
Friends of the Library Group
MORRISANIA, 610 E 169th St, Bronx, 10456. SAN 353-5479. Tel: 718-589-9268. FAX: 718-861-0394. *Librn*, Colbert Nembhard; E-Mail: cnembhard@nypl.org
MOSHOLU, 285 E 205th St, Bronx, 10467. SAN 353-5509. Tel: 718-882-8239. FAX: 718-882-8239. *Librn*, Ann Alexander; E-Mail: aalexander@nypl.org
MOTT HAVEN, 321 E 140th St, 10454. SAN 353-5533. Tel: 718-665-4878. FAX: 718-585-8059. *Librn*, Ken Giles; E-Mail: kgiles@nypl.org
MUHLENBERG, 209 W 23rd St, 10011. SAN 353-5568. Tel: 212-924-1585. *Librn*, Adele Bellinger
MUSIC, Libr for the Performing Arts, 40 Lincoln Center Plaza, 10023-7498. SAN 353-3794. Tel: 212-870-1675. Web Site: www.nypl.org/research/lpa/circ/circ.html. *Librn*, Josephine Chan Yung; E-Mail: jyung@nypl.org; Staff 6 (MLS 3, Non-MLS 3)
Subject Interests: Bibliographies, Biographies, Bks, Chamber music, Clippings, Instrumental music, Jazz music, Libretti, Music, Music theory, Music therapy, Musical comedy, Musical scores, Opera, Orchestra performance mat, Periodicals, Popular music, Relig scores, Vocal
MUSIC DIVISION, 40 Lincoln Ctr Plaza, 3rd flr, 10023-7498. SAN 353-3379. Tel: 212-870-1650. FAX: 212-870-1794. *In Charge*, Susan Sommer
Library Holdings: Bk Vols 572,400; Per Subs 850
Subject Interests: Am music, Ballet music, Fine prints, Jazz, Manuscripts, Music theory, Opera (especially 19th century), Orchestra, Photog, Ragtime, Scene designs, Spirituals
Special Collections: Beethoven Coll; Drexel Coll; Individual & Corporate Archival Coll (Marcella Sembrich, Arturo Toscanini, Town Hall, the New Music Society & Composers Forum); Joseph Muller Coll, fine prints; Toscanini Memorial Archives, autograph scores of European composers 17th-20th centuries, micro
Partic in Res Librs Local Area Network
NATHAN STRAUS YOUNG ADULT CENTER, Donnell Library Ctr, 20 W 53rd St, 10019-6185. SAN 353-5592. Tel: 212-621-0633. *Librn*, Joanne Rosario; Fax: 212-245-5272, E-Mail: jrosario@nypl.org
Subject Interests: Bks, Largest collection of materials for 7th through 12th grade in the New York Public Library, Talking books
Special Collections: Books in Spanish & Chinese; Historical Teenage Book Coll; Teen Magazines

Open Mon, Wed & Fri 12-6, Tues 10-6, Thurs 12-8, Sat 12-5, Sun 1-5
NEW AMSTERDAM, 9 Murray St, 10007. SAN 371-3423. Tel: 212-732-8186. FAX: 212-732-8815. *Librn*, Lynn Taylor
NEW DORP, 309 New Dorp Lane, Staten Island, 10306. SAN 353-5622. Tel: 718-351-2977. FAX: 718-351-4993. *Librn*, Susan Gitman
NINETY-SIXTH STREET, 112 E 96th St, 10128. SAN 353-5657. Tel: 212-289-0908. FAX: 212-410-4564. *Librn*, William Seufert
ONE HUNDRED & FIFTEENTH STREET, 203 W 115th St, 10026. SAN 353-5681. Tel: 212-666-9393. FAX: 212-531-3149. *Librn*, Bajabulie Masakela
ONE HUNDRED & TWENTY-FIFTH STREET, 224 E 125th St, 10035. SAN 353-5711. Tel: 212-534-5050. FAX: 212-534-4848. *Librn*, James Drumgo
ORIENTAL DIV, Fifth Ave & 42nd St, Rm 219 & 220, 10018-2788. SAN 353-2836. Tel: 212-930-0721. Reference Tel: 212-930-0845. FAX: 212-930-0551. E-Mail: asiaref@nypl.org, orientref@nypl.org. *Chief Librn*, John M Lundquist; Staff 14 (MLS 6, Non-MLS 8)
Founded 1897
Library Holdings: Bk Vols 411,000; Per Subs 1,400
Subject Interests: Archaeology, Armenian, Central Asian langs, East Asia, Exploration, Humanities, Literature, Manchu, Middle East, Oriental religions, Per in all lit langs of Middle East, South Asia, Tibetology, Travelers accounts
Special Collections: Arabic Manuscripts; Bibliographie Papyrologique Index; Chinese Rare Books of Ming & Ching Dynasties from the Personal Library of James Legge, including manuscript copies of his works; Early Imprints (all languages including Arabic, Armenian, Persian, Tibetan); French Revolution Orientalist: Imprints; Languages of India, Manchu; Materials from the Schiff Coll & Manuscripts Coll; Professor Edward A Allworth Central Asian Coll; Scholarly Literature-17th-19th Century (including runs of early Orientalist periodicals); The Mason Coll of Chinese Mohammedan Literature
Publications: Bibliographic Guide to East Asian Studies; Bibliographic Guide to Middle Eastern Studies; The New York Public Library Reference Department Oriental Collection (16 vols, 1960, supplement, 8 vols, 1965); Treasure of the New York Public Library (1988)
OTTENDORFER, 135 Second Ave, 10003. SAN 353-5746. Tel: 212-674-0947. *Librn*, Lawrence Kapture
PARKCHESTER, 1985 Westchester Ave, Bronx, 10462. SAN 353-5770. Tel: 718-829-7830. FAX: 718-518-8375. *Librn*, Renee Kotler; E-Mail: rkotler@nypl.org
PELHAM BAY, 3060 Middletown Rd, Bronx, 10461. SAN 353-5800. Tel: 718-792-6744. FAX: 718-792-6744. *Librn*, Susan Cassel; E-Mail: scassel@nypl.org
PICTURE COLLECTION, Mid-Manhattan Library, 3rd Flr, 455 Fifth Ave, 10016. Tel: 212-340-0878. *Librn*, Constance Novak
Subject Interests: Advertising, Animals, Architecture, Costumes, Decorative arts, Design, Fashion, Personalities, Plants
Open Mon, Wed & Thurs 9-9, Tues 11-7, Fri & Sat 10-6
POPULAR LIBRARY, Mid-Manhattan Library, 1st Flr, 455 Fifth Ave, 10016. Tel: 212-340-0837. *Librn*, Elena Bivona
Subject Interests: Best sellers, Biographies, Bks on tape, Large print bks, Mysteries, Travel info
Open Mon, Wed & Thurs 9-9, Tues 11-7, Fri & Sat 10-6
PORT RICHMOND, 75 Bennett St, Staten Island, 10302. SAN 353-5835. Tel: 718-442-0158. FAX: 718-447-2851.
RARE BOOKS DIVISION, Humanities & Social Sciences Library, Fifth Ave & 42nd St, Rm 328, 10018-2788. SAN 353-3166. Tel: 212-930-0801. FAX: 212-302-4815. E-Mail: rbkref@nypl.org. Web Site: www.nypl.org. *Curator*, Virginia Bartow; Staff 4 (MLS 2, Non-MLS 2)
Founded 1895
Library Holdings: Bk Vols 140,000
Subject Interests: Am Revolution, Econ, Eng in 19th century Am, Lit mat up to 20th century, Magazine publishers, Major emphasis on Am, Medieval, N Am Colonies examples, Records of Am bk, Sci, Spanish, Theatrical hist
Special Collections: 18th Century American Newspapers & Periodicals; Bay Psalm Book (1640); Beadle & Adams Dime Novel Coll; Block Books; Canadian Jesuit Relations; De Bry Prints; Early Americana; Early Bibles, including Gutenberg; Early English Cookbooks (Whitney Coll); English & American First Editions, especially Shakespear, Milton, Walton, Bunyan & Whitman; Examples of the Work of Private & Special Presses; German Literature (Axel Rosin Coll); History of Magnetics & Telegraphy (Wheeler Coll); Kelmscott Press, Ashendene, Doves, Golden Cockerel, Grabhorn, Nonesuch, Vale, Bruce Rogers (Modern Fine Printing Coll); Korean History Coll, 1870-1948; Nucleus of Rarities Originally Collected by James Lenox
RICHMONDTOWN, 200 Clarke Ave, Staten Island, 10306. SAN 377-6891. Tel: 718-668-0413. FAX: 718-668-1889. *Librn*, Nancy Avrin
RIVERDALE, 5540 Mosholu Ave, Bronx, 10471. SAN 353-5894. Tel: 718-549-1212. FAX: 718-549-1212. *Librn*, Mark Consani; E-Mail: mconsani@nypl.org
RIVERSIDE, 127 Amsterdam Ave, 10023. SAN 353-5924. Tel: 212-870-1810. FAX: 212-870-1819. *Librn*, Jutta Zaplinski
RODGERS & HAMMERSTEIN ARCHIVES OF RECORDED SOUND, 40 Lincoln Ctr Plaza, 10023-7498. SAN 353-3360. Tel: 212-870-1663. FAX: 212-870-1720. E-Mail: rha@nypl.org. Web Site: www.nypl.org. *Curator*, Donald McCormick
Library Holdings: Bk Vols 9,500
Subject Interests: Related mat, Sound recordings
Special Collections: Association of German Broadcasters Tapes; Benedict Stambler Memorial Coll of Recorded Jewish Music; Bert Williams Recordings; Jan Holcman Coll of Recorded Piano Music; Kirsten Flagstad Private Tape Coll; Koussevitzky Foundation on Tapes; Mapleson Cylinders of Metropolitan Opera 1900-03; Marian McPartland's Piano Jazz Radio Series; Metropolitan Opera Broadcast Archives; Music & Opera Video Coll; National Orchestra Association Concert & Rehersal Coll; Pre-Glasnost Underground Videos of Russian Rock Groups; Railroad Hour Broadcasts of American Musical Theatre; Rosalyn Tureck Archives; Toscanini Legacy Discs & Tapes; WNYC Archives; Yaddo Music Festival
ROOSEVELT ISLAND, 524 Main St, 10044. SAN 377-6875. Tel: 212-308-6243. FAX: 212-223-9224.
BILLY ROSE THEATRE COLLECTION, 40 Lincoln Ctr Plaza, 10023-7498. SAN 353-3409. Tel: 212-870-1639. FAX: 212-870-1868. *Curator*, Robert Taylor
Subject Interests: Circus, Designers, Drama, Films, Indust shows, Magic, Musical theatre, Performing artists, Producting firms, Puppets, Radio, Stage, Television, Vaudeville
Special Collections: 560 playbills covering Mexican theatre, 1815-1953 (Maria & Campos Coll); Archives & Memorabilia of Brooks Atkinson, Richard Barstow, Frederick Brisson, Harold Clurman, Betty Comden & Adolph Green, Katharine Cornell, Cheryl Crawford, Maurice Evans, Dorothy Fields, Hallie Flanagan, Helen Hayes, Leland Hayward, Joseph George Holman, Burl Ives, Carolyn Leigh, Edwin Justus Mayer, Zero Mostel, Elliott Nugent, Clifford Odets, Molly Picon, Harold Prince, Richard Rodgers, Bernard Sobel; Archives of the Living Theatre, Federal Theatre Project, Chelsea Theatre Center, Alexander H Cohen, Lambs Club, Lawrence & Lee, Repertory Theatre of Lincoln Center & San Francisco Actors' Workshop; British Theatre Between 1672-1932, including 500 portfolios of letters, autographs, leases & documents relating to theatrical litigation; Chamberlain & Lyman Brown Theatrical Coll of Photographs, Scrapbooks & Acting Reviews; Dramatic Scrapbooks, 1000 vols, 2500 portfolios of clippings, holograph letters & unmounted photographs (Robinson Locke Coll); Light plots of Jules Fisher; Material on the Parisian Stage from 18th & 19th Centuries, including Original Drawings for Costumes & Scenery (Henin Coll); Montgomery Clift, Vincent J Donehue, Jules Fisher, Nancy Hamilton, Bert Lahr, Jo Mielziner, Paul Muni & Billy Rose; Original Scenery, Plans & Costume Designs (Boris Aronson, Howard Bay, Aline Bernstein, Bonnie Cashin, George Jenkins, W Robert La Vine, Jo Mielziner, Donald Oenslager; Photographs with Emphasis on Hippodrome Theatre & Musical Comedy Productions on Broadway (R H Burnside Coll); playbills & portraits (Hiram Stead Coll); Prints, Negatives & Key Sheets (Vandamm Coll); Prompt Books; Promptbooks & Holographs of Plays Produced in the United States & England During 18th & 19th Centuries (George Becks Coll); Raymond Sovey); Several Hundred Thousand Photographic Negatives of Actors, Playwrights & Scenes from Plays (White Studio Coll); Stage Productions & Discussions Between Theatrical Personalities (Theatre on Film & Tape Project), filmed records; Theatrical Portraits (Carl Van Vechten Coll); Typescript; Typescripts & Manuscripts of Edward Albee; Typescripts of Samuel Taylor, Israel Horovitz; Typescripts, Photographs, Original Designs & Scrapbooks (David Belasco Coll)
Friends of the Library Group
ST GEORGE LIBRARY CENTER, 5 Central Ave, 10301. SAN 353-4006. Tel: 718-442-8560. FAX: 718-447-2703. *Librn*, Scott Lambin
SCHOMBURG CENTER FOR RESEARCH IN BLACK CULTURE, 515 Malcolm X Blvd, 10037-1801. SAN 353-3468. Tel: 212-491-2200. FAX: 212-491-6760. *Dir*, Howard Dodson
Library Holdings: Bk Vols 85,000
Subject Interests: Africa, Black people throughout the world, with major emphasis on Afro-Am, Caribbean
Special Collections: African Sculpture & Artifacts; Afro-American Paintings, Prints & Sculpture; Harlem On My Mind; Harry A Williamson Library of the Negro in Masonry; Kurt Fisher & Eugene Maximilien Coll of Haitian manuscripts; Manuscripts of W E B DuBois, Langston Hughes, Claude McKay, Arthur Schomburg, George & Philippa Schuyler, Robert C Weaver, Clarence Cameron White, Richard Wright, Piri Thomas & Amiri Baraka; Papers of John E Bruce, Civil Rights Congress, International Labor Defense, Carnegie-Myrdal research memoranda, Alexander Crummell, Oakley Johnson, National Association of Colored Graduate Nurses, National Negro Congress, Phelps-Stokes Fund, Central Africa project, William Pickens, Richard Parrish New York Urban League, Universal Negro Improvement Ass, Paul Robeson, Hugh Smythe & Robert Weaver, 5 million items; Photographs; Rare Books; Tape & Phonograph Records, including Interviews & Music
Publications: Schomburg Center Journal, exhibition catalogs, bibliographies
SCIENCE, INDUSTRY & BUSINESS LIBRARY, 188 Madison Ave, 10016-4314. SAN 371-3415. Tel: 212-592-7000. FAX: 212-592-7082. Web Site: www.nypl.org/research/sibl. *Dir*, Kristin McDonough; Tel: 212-592-7082, E-Mail: kmcdonough@nypl.org
Subject Interests: Advertising, Astronautics, Astronomy, Automobiles, Banking, Beverages, Chemistry, Communications, Computer science, Demography, Earth science, Economics, Electricity, Electronics,

Engineering, Finance, Food tech, Hydrology, Indust relations, Int bus, Labor, Manufacturing, Marketing, Mathematics, Metallurgy, Mgt, Mining, Navigation, Paper, Physics, Plastics, Railroads, Rubber, Sci (hist), Shipbuilding, Small bus, Soc statistics, Tech aspects of transportation, Technology, Textiles
Special Collections: Government Publications (United States, United Nations, European Union, New York State); Patent & Trademark Gazettes (European Patent Office & Patent Cooperation Treaty, United States, British & German Patents)
Special Services for the Deaf - TTY machine
Special Services for the Blind - Adapted computers & special software with speech output to assist learning disabled, mentally retarded & uneducated
Open Mon & Fri 10-6, Tues & Thurs 11-8, Wed 11-7, Sat 12-6
SEDGWICK, 1701 University Ave, Bronx, 10453. SAN 353-5983. Tel: 718-731-2074. FAX: 718-299-2608. *Librn*, Samuel Ansah; E-Mail: sansah@nypl.org
SEWARD PARK, 192 E Broadway, 10002. SAN 353-6017. Tel: 212-477-6770. FAX: 212-477-6770. *Librn*, Susan Singer
SHELBY CULLOM DAVIS MUSEUM, Libr for the Performing Arts, 40 Lincoln Center Plaza, 10023-7498. SAN 353-3883. Tel: 212-870-1608. FAX: 212-873-4156. *Curator*, Barbara Cohen-Stratyner
Special Collections: Exhibitions in Vincent Astor, Amsterdam & Main Galleries of Particular Themes from the Performing Arts
SIXTY-SEVENTH STREET, 328 E 67th St, 10021. SAN 353-6041. Tel: 212-734-1717. FAX: 212-734-3910. *Librn*, Carol Breheny
SLAVIC & BALTIC DIV, Humanities & Soc Scis Library, Fifth Ave & 42nd St, Rm 216-217, 10018-2788. SAN 353-2860. Tel: 212-930-0714. FAX: 212-930-0693. E-Mail: slavicref@nypl.org. Web Site: www.nypl.org/research/chss/slv/slav.balt.html. *In Charge*, Edward Kasinec; E-Mail: ekasinec@nypl.org; Staff 8 (MLS 6, Non-MLS 2)
Founded 1898
Library Holdings: Bk Vols 445,500; Per Subs 1,200
Subject Interests: Baltic philology, Folklore, Former Soviet Union, Genealogy, Govt publ, Hist of lit, Humanities, Linguistics, Publ of learned socs, Ser of Eastern Europe, Slavic, Soc sci
Special Collections: Art Publications; Baltic Slavic Language Monographic & Serial Materials; Bates/Pantuhoff Coll of Russian Imprints & Art; Early Russian Imprints; Glaser Microfilm Coll; Illustrated Books; Rare Books; Russian Imperial Association Copies
Publications: Slavic & Baltic Library Resources in the New York Public Library: A First History & Practical Guide
SOUND RECORDING & VIDEOTAPE COLLECTIONS, Libr for the Performing Arts, 40 Lincoln Center Plaza, 10023-7498. SAN 353-3824. Tel: 212-870-1621. FAX: 212-870-1704. Web Site: www.nypl.org/research/lpa/circ/circ.html. *Librn*, Joseph Boonin; E-Mail: jboonin@nypl.org. Subject Specialists: *Recording*, Joseph Boonin; Staff 6 (MLS 4, Non-MLS 2)
Founded 1965
Subject Interests: Classical music, Comedy, Dance, Drama, Exercise rec, Folk, Jazz, Monologues, Performing arts, Plays, Popular music, Sound effects, Sound tracks, World music
SOUNDVIEW, 660 Soundview Ave, Bronx, 10473. SAN 353-6076. Tel: 718-589-0880. FAX: 718-589-0880. *Librn*, Olive Baker; E-Mail: obaker@nypl.org
SOUTH BEACH, 21-25 Robin Rd, Staten Island, 10305. SAN 353-6106. Tel: 718-816-5834. FAX: 718-816-5936. *Librn*, Louise Lareau
SPENCER COLLECTION, Fifth Ave & 42nd St, Rm 308, 10018-2788. SAN 353-3255. Tel: 212-930-0817. FAX: 212-930-0530. *Curator*, Robert Rainwater
Library Holdings: Bk Vols 9,000
Subject Interests: Fine binding, Finely illustrated bks, Illuminated mss
SPUYTEN DUYVIL, 650 W 235th St, Bronx, 10463. SAN 353-6165. Tel: 718-796-1202. FAX: 718-796-2351. *Librn*, Jennine Porta; E-Mail: jporta@nypl.org
ST AGNES, 444 Amsterdam Ave, 10024. SAN 353-5959. Tel: 212-877-4380. FAX: 212-873-3351. *Librn*, Alene E Moroni
STACK MAINTENANCE & DELIVERY DIV, Fifth Ave & 42nd St, 10018. Tel: 212-930-0018. FAX: 212-930-0017.; Staff 18 (MLS 1, Non-MLS 17)
STAPLETON, 132 Canal St, Staten Island, 10304. SAN 353-619X. Tel: 718-727-0427. FAX: 718-447-3847. *Librn*, Jeffrey Sperber
TERENCE CARDINAL COOKE-CATHEDRAL, 560 Lexington Ave, 10022. SAN 353-4278. Tel: 212-752-3824. FAX: 212-752-3824. *Librn*, Frank Connelly
THE CARL H PFORZHEIMER COLLECTION OF SHELLEY & HIS CIRCLE, Humanities & Soc Svcs Library, Fifth Ave & 42nd St, Rm 319, 10018-2788. SAN 311-9971. Tel: 212-930-0717. FAX: 212-930-0076. *Curator*, Stephen Wagner; E-Mail: swagner@nypl.org; *Bibliogr*, Laura O'Keefe; E-Mail: lokeefe@nypl.org; Staff 2 (MLS 2)
Founded 1957
Library Holdings: Bk Vols 13,000
Special Collections: Outstanding English Literature Material of the Poet Percy Bysshe Shelley & Members of His Circle, including Lord Byron, Leigh Hunt, Thomas Love Peacock, William Godwin, Thomas Moore, Edward Trelawny, T J Hogg, women writers 1790-1840 (Claire Clairmont, Mary Wollstonecraft, Mary Hays & Lady Blessington)
Publications: Shelley & His Circle (1773-1822)
Open Tues-Sat
THE RESEARCH LIBRARIES TECHNICAL SERVICES, Fifth Ave & 42nd St, 10018. Tel: 212-930-9201. *Dir*, Cynthia Clark; *Cat*, Karen Hsu; *Acq*, Natalie Seweryn
THROG'S NECK, 3025 Cross Bronx Expressway Exten, Bronx, 10465. SAN 353-622X. Tel: 718-792-2612. FAX: 718-792-2612. *Librn*, Helen Kotler; E-Mail: hkotler@nypl.org
TODT HILL-WESTERLEIGH, 2550 Victory Blvd, Staten Island, 10314. SAN 353-6254. Tel: 718-494-1642. FAX: 718-370-1219. *Librn*, Michael Loscalzo
TOMPKINS SQUARE, 331 E Tenth St, 10009. SAN 353-6289. Tel: 212-228-4747. FAX: 212-475-4510. *Librn*, Hara Seltzer
TOTTENVILLE, 7430 Amboy Rd, Staten Island, 10307. SAN 353-6319. Tel: 718-984-0945. FAX: 718-967-8817. *Librn*, Donald Laub
TREMONT, 1866 Washington Ave, Bronx, 10457. SAN 353-6343. Tel: 718-299-5177. FAX: 718-299-5177. *Librn*, Richard Sabino; E-Mail: rsabino@nypl.org
VAN CORTLANDT, 3874 Sedgwick Ave, 10463. SAN 353-6378. Tel: 718-543-5150. *Librn*, Horace Harrison; E-Mail: hharrison@nypl.org
VAN NEST, 2147 Barnes Ave, Bronx, 10462. SAN 353-6408. Tel: 718-829-5864. FAX: 718-829-5864. *Librn*, Tim Tureski; E-Mail: ttureski@nypl.org
WAKEFIELD, 4100 Lowerre Pl, Bronx, 10466. SAN 353-6432. Tel: 718-652-4663. FAX: 718-652-0425. *Librn*, Carmine Diodati; E-Mail: cdiodati@nypl.org
WASHINGTON HEIGHTS, 1000 St Nicholas Ave, 10032. SAN 353-6467. Tel: 212-923-6054. FAX: 212-923-6054. *Librn*, John Flood
WEBSTER, 1465 York Ave, 10021. SAN 353-6491. Tel: 212-288-5049. FAX: 212-288-5049. *Librn*, Heather Caines
WEST FARMS, 2085 Honeywell Ave, Bronx, 10460. SAN 353-6521. Tel: 718-367-5376. FAX: 718-220-4262. *Librn*, Lou Della Elliott; E-Mail: lelliot@nypl.org
WEST NEW BRIGHTON, 976 Castleton Ave, Staten Island, 10310. SAN 353-6556. Tel: 718-442-1416. FAX: 718-727-7194. *Librn*, Margaret Ma
WESTCHESTER SQUARE, 2521 Glebe Ave, Bronx, 10461. SAN 353-6580. Tel: 718-863-0436. FAX: 718-863-0436. *Librn*, Aurea Garcia; E-Mail: asgarcia@nypl.org
WOODLAWN HEIGHTS, 4355 Katonah Ave, Bronx, 10470. SAN 353-6610. Tel: 718-324-0791. FAX: 718-324-0791. *Librn*, Sharon Aperto; E-Mail: saperto@nypl.org
WOODSTOCK, 761 E 160th St, Bronx, 10456. SAN 353-6645. Tel: 718-665-6255. FAX: 718-665-6255. *Librn*, Gene Shaw; E-Mail: gshaw@nypl.org
WORLD LANGUAGES COLLECTION, Donnell Library Ctr, 20 W 53rd St, 10019-6185. SAN 353-3670. Tel: 212-621-0641. FAX: 212-245-5272. *Librn*, Bosiljka Stevanovic
Library Holdings: Bk Vols 150,000; Per Subs 65
Subject Interests: Gen, Popular, Strong emphasis on lit of country
Special Collections: Bilingual Dictionaries (over 100 languages); Eighty Languages Represented - Major Collections in Chinese, French, German, Italian, Japanese, Russian & Spanish; Encyclopedias in French, German, Italian, Hebrew & Russian; Large Collections in Czech, Modern Greek, Gujarati, Hebrew, Hungarian & Polish
Open Mon, Wed & Fri 12-6, Tues 10-6, Thurs 12-8, Sat 12-5, Sun 1-5
YORKVILLE, 222 E 79th St, 10021. SAN 353-667X. Tel: 212-744-5824. FAX: 212-744-5929. *Librn*, Sally Speller

S NEW YORK ROAD RUNNERS CLUB, (Formerly New York Road Runners Club-International Running Center), 9 E 89th St, 10128. SAN 326-1379. Tel: 212-860-4455. FAX: 212-423-2271. Web Site: www.nyrrc.org.
Library Holdings: Bk Vols 600
Special Collections: Papers of First President of NY Road Runners Club (Ted Corbitt Archives)

C NEW YORK SCHOOL OF INTERIOR DESIGN LIBRARY, 170 E 70th St, 10021. SAN 321-0545. Tel: 212-472-1500, Ext 214. Reference Tel: 212-472-1500, Ext 216. Toll Free Tel: 800-33NYSID, Ext 214. FAX: 212-472-8175. *Dir*, Paul Glassman; E-Mail: paul@nysid.edu
Founded 1924. Enrl 600; Fac 85; Highest Degree: Master
Jul 1999-Jun 2000 Income Parent Institution $44,000. Mats Exp $40,800, Books $18,000, Per/Ser (Incl. Access Fees) $7,000, Presv $4,000, Manuscripts & Archives $3,000, Electronic Ref Mat (Incl. Access Fees) $8,800. Sal $92,000
Library Holdings: Bk Vols 10,000; Bk Titles 9,000; Per Subs 92
Subject Interests: Architecture, Interior design
Special Collections: Architectural Treatises; Collection of 3500 Slides
Database Vendor: Ebsco - EbscoHost, OCLC - First Search
Restriction: Open to faculty, students & qualified researchers
Function: Photocopies available

S THE NEW YORK SOCIETY LIBRARY, 53 E 79th St, 10021. SAN 311-9602. Tel: 212-288-6900. FAX: 212-744-5832. E-Mail: webmaster@nysoclib.org. Web Site: www.nysoclib.org. *Librn*, Mark Piel; E-Mail: head_librarian@nysoclib.org; *Acq, ILL*, Susan O'Brien; E-Mail: acquisitions@nysoclib.org; *Cat, Syst Coordr*, Steven Baumholtz; E-Mail: steve@nysoclib.org; *Circ*, Jane Goldstein; E-Mail: jane@nysoclib.org; *Web Coordr*, Ingrid Richter; E-Mail: webmaster@nysoclib.org; Staff 13 (MLS 7, Non-MLS 6)

Founded 1754
Jan 1999-Dec 1999 Mats Exp $1,410,000, Books $106,000, Per/Ser (Incl. Access Fees) $6,000, Presv $23,000. Sal $804,000
Library Holdings: Bk Vols 220,000; Per Subs 250
Subject Interests: Americana, Art, Biography, New York City, Travel, WWII
Special Collections: 18th & Early 19th Century Fiction (Hammond Coll); 18th Century Statesman (Goodhue Papers), mss; Alchemy & Chemistry (John Winthrop Library); Early Gothic Fiction; Minerva Press; Rev John Sharpe Collection; Sharaff/Sze Coll.
Publications: Annual report; monthly book list

GL NEW YORK STATE DEPARTMENT OF LAW LIBRARY,* 120 Broadway, Rm 2520, 10271. SAN 311-9610. Tel: 212-416-8012. FAX: 212-416-6130. *Librn*, Fran Sheinwald
Library Holdings: Bk Titles 25,000; Per Subs 50
Subject Interests: Attorney Generals' opinions, NY state law

G NEW YORK STATE DIVISION OF HOUSING & COMMUNITY RENEWAL, Reference Room,* 25 Beaver St, 7th flr, 10004. SAN 311-9637. Tel: 212-480-7403. FAX: 212-480-7416. *Librn*, Dionisio Figueroa
Restriction: Staff use only

GM NEW YORK STATE OFFICE OF MENTAL HEALTH, Psychiatric Institute Research Library,* 1051 Riverside Dr, 10032. SAN 311-9629. Tel: 212-543-5000, 212-543-5672. FAX: 212-543-5673. *Bibliog Instr, Chief Librn, Online Servs*, David T Lane
Founded 1896
Library Holdings: Bk Vols 30,000; Bk Titles 15,000; Per Subs 400
Subject Interests: Neurology, Neuropathology, Psychiatry, Psychoanalysis, Psychology
Publications: Acquisition Newsletter
Partic in Medical Library Center Of New York

NEW YORK STATE SUPREME COURT

L FIRST JUDICIAL DISTRICT CIVIL LAW LIBRARY, 60 Centre St, 10007. SAN 353-6793. Tel: 212-374-8384. FAX: 212-374-8159.
Library Holdings: Bk Vols 75,000
Special Collections: New York City Codes; New York State Statutes; Records & Briefs NY Court of Appeals & Appellate Divisions, 1984-present, micro
Publications: Newsletter (quarterly)

GL FIRST JUDICIAL DISTRICT CRIMINAL LAW LIBRARY, 100 Centre St, 17th Flr, 10013. SAN 353-6769. Tel: 212-374-5615. FAX: 212-748-7908. E-Mail: nyssc1@rmi.net. Web Site: 199.29.31.29/nysscl/nysc_library_homepage.htm. *Librn*, David G Badertscher
Library Holdings: Bk Vols 107,000; Bk Titles 33,000
Subject Interests: Court admin, Criminology, Law, Mgt
Special Collections: Trial Transcripts for New York State, First JD Supreme Court-Criminal Branch
Automation Activity & Vendor Info: (Acquisitions) epixtech, inc.; (Cataloging) epixtech, inc.; (Circulation) epixtech, inc.; (ILL) epixtech, inc.; (OPAC) epixtech, inc.; (Serials) epixtech, inc.
Partic in New York Metrop Ref & Res Libr Agency; OCLC Online Computer Library Center, Inc; Westlaw

S NEW YORK STOCK EXCHANGE, Research Library,* 11 Wall St, 17th flr, 10005. SAN 311-9653. Tel: 212-656-2491. FAX: 212-656-5045. Web Site: www.nyse.com. *Librn*, Bethann Ashfield; E-Mail: bashfield@nyse.com
Founded 1935
Library Holdings: Bk Titles 3,000; Per Subs 241
Subject Interests: Econ, Finance, Investing, Statistics
Restriction: Not open to public

R NEW YORK THEOLOGICAL SEMINARY LIBRARY, 5 W 29th St, 8th flr, 10001. SAN 311-967X. Tel: 212-532-4012, Ext 244. FAX: 212-684-0757. *Dir*, Eleanor Soler; E-Mail: ellie_sol@hotmail.com; Staff 1 (MLS 1)
Founded 1902
1998-1999 Mats Exp $7,800, Books $7,000, Per/Ser (Incl. Access Fees) $800. Sal $75,000
Library Holdings: Bk Titles 23,000; Per Subs 49
Subject Interests: Bible, Church history, Ethnic studies, Feminism, Theology
Automation Activity & Vendor Info: (Circulation) EOS
Restriction: Open to faculty, students & qualified researchers

NEW YORK TIMES

S PHOTO LIBRARY, 229 W 43rd St, 10036. SAN 353-6882. Tel: 212-556-7220. FAX: 212-246-5908. *Dir*, Nancy Lee

S REFERENCE LIBRARY, 229 W 43rd St, 10th flr, 10036. SAN 353-6912. Tel: 212-556-7428. FAX: 212-556-4448. *Res*, Linda Amster
Library Holdings: Bk Vols 65,000; Bk Titles 50,000; Per Subs 350
Subject Interests: Biog, Journalism, Politics

C NEW YORK UNIVERSITY, Elmer Holmes Bobst Library,* 70 Washington Sq S, 10012-1091. SAN 353-6947. Tel: 212-998-2444, 212-998-2505. Interlibrary Loan Service Tel: 212-998-2511. Interlibrary Loan Service FAX: 212-995-4071. Web Site: www.nyu.edu/library/bobst. *Dean of Libr*, Carol A Mandel; *Assoc Dean*, Nancy Kranich; *Tech Servs*, Arno Kastner; *Spec Coll*, Marvin Taylor; *Ref*, Lucinda Covert-Vail; *Electronic Resources, Media Spec*, Gloria Rohmann; *Cat*, Sherman Clarke; *Coll Develop*, Joan Grant. Subject Specialists: *Humanities*, Evelyn Ehrlich; *Science/technology*, Suzanne Fedunok; *Social sciences and issues*, Angela Carreno; Staff 113 (MLS 113)
Founded 1831. Enrl 36,719; Fac 2,380; Highest Degree: Doctorate
Sep 1998-Aug 1999 Mats Exp $7,443,488, Books $3,131,641, Per/Ser (Incl. Access Fees) $2,649,932, Presv $446,222, Other Print Mats $729,948, Electronic Ref Mat (Incl. Access Fees) $485,745. Sal $9,502,750 (Prof $3,209,405)
Library Holdings: Bk Vols 2,987,062; Per Subs 20,015
Special Collections: Alfred C Berol Lewis Carroll Coll, bks, letters, mss, photogs; Erich Maria Remarque Library Coll; Rare Judaica and Hebraica; Robert Frost Library Coll; Tamiment Institute-Ben Josephson Library & Robert F Wagner Labor Archives; Toumlilene Monastery (Morocco) Library of North Africana; Wiet Coll of Islamic Materials
Automation Activity & Vendor Info: (Circulation) GEAC; (Serials) GEAC
Publications: New York Labor Heritage; Progressions, Library Division Newsletter
Partic in New York Metrop Ref & Res Libr Agency; Research Libraries Group, Inc
Friends of the Library Group
Departmental Libraries:

CONSERVATION CENTER LIBRARY, 14 E 78th St, 10021-1706. SAN 353-7110. Tel: 212-772-5854. *In Charge*, Robert Stacy; Tel: 212-772-5825, E-Mail: ros1@is.nyu.edu; Staff 1 (Non-MLS 1)
Library Holdings: Bk Vols 13,839; Per Subs 202
Subject Interests: Art conserv
Partic in RLIN

COURANT INSTITUTE OF MATHEMATICAL SCIENCES, 251 Mercer St 12th Flr, 10012-1185. SAN 353-7129. Tel: 212-998-3315. FAX: 212-995-4808. Web Site: www.nyu.edu/pages/cimslibrary. *Librn*, Carol Hutchins; E-Mail: hutchins@nyu.edu
Founded 1954. Enrl 2,000
Library Holdings: Bk Vols 66,014; Per Subs 250
Subject Interests: Computer science, Fluid mechanics, Mathematics, Robotics
Special Collections: Mathematics (Courant, Bohr & Friedricks Reprints)

FALES COLLECTION, Elmer Holmes Bobst Libr 3rd Flr, 70 Washington Square S, 10012. Tel: 212-998-2596. E-Mail: fales.library@nyu.edu. *Librn*, Marvin Taylor; *Asst Librn*, Mike Kelly; Staff 2 (MLS 2)
Library Holdings: Bk Vols 200,000
Subject Interests: 17th-20th Century English, American fiction
Special Collections: English & American Literature
Publications: Fales Checklist
Restriction: Not a lending library
Function: Archival collection, Research library

JACK BRAUSE LIBRARY & INFORMATION CENTER, 11 W 42nd St, Rm 510, 10036-8002. SAN 353-7080. Tel: 212-790-1325. FAX: 212-790-1684.
Library Holdings: Bk Titles 1,130; Per Subs 166
Subject Interests: NYC real estate
Publications: Reinform
Partic in RLIN

LIBRARY OF THE SCHOOL OF LAW, 40 Washington Sq S, 10012-1099. SAN 353-7218. Tel: 212-998-6300. FAX: 212-995-3477. *Librn*, Kathy Price; *Publ Servs*, Leslie Rich; *Tech Servs*, Mary Chapman; Staff 58 (MLS 21, Non-MLS 37)
Library Holdings: Bk Vols 727,170; Per Subs 5,527
Partic in RLIN

NEW YORK UNIVERSITY ARCHIVES *Archivist*, Nancy Cricco
Subject Interests: NY univ hist

STEPHEN CHAN LIBRARY OF FINE ARTS, Institute of Fine Arts, One E 78th St, 10021. SAN 353-7099. Tel: 212-772-5825. FAX: 212-772-5807. *Dir*, Sharon Chickanzeff; Staff 4 (MLS 4)
Library Holdings: Bk Vols 117,710; Per Subs 508
Subject Interests: Archaeology, Art history, Conservation
Partic in RLIN

TAMIMENT INSTITUTE-BEN JOSEPHSON LIBRARY & ROBERT F WAGNER LABOR ARCHIVES *Librn*, Andrew Lee; *Archivist*, Debra Bernhardt
Library Holdings: Bk Vols 60,502; Per Subs 684
Subject Interests: Labor, Polit, Soc liberalism, Utopianism
Publications: New York Labor Heritage

UNITED NATIONS COLLECTION *Librn*, Ann Snoeyenbos
Library Holdings: Bk Vols 4,000; Per Subs 530

M NEW YORK UNIVERSITY DOWNTOWN HOSPITAL, Elisha Walker Medical Library, 170 William St, 10038. SAN 311-6352. Tel: 212-312-5229. FAX: 212-312-5929. *Mgr*, Xiomara Cruz; E-Mail: xiomara.cruz@library.med.nyu.edu; Staff 1 (Non-MLS 1)
Founded 1944
Library Holdings: Bk Vols 2,469; Per Subs 125
Subject Interests: Medicine, Surgery
Partic in Regional Med Libr

CM NEW YORK UNIVERSITY SCHOOL OF MEDICINE, Frederick L Ehrman Medical Library, New York Univ Sch of Med, 550 First Ave, 10016-6450. SAN 353-7242. Tel: 212-263-5397. Interlibrary Loan Service Tel: 212-263-5397. FAX: 212-263-8196. Web Site: library.med.nyu.edu. *Dir*, Karen Brewer; E-Mail: brewerk01@library.me.nyu.edu; *Coll Develop*, Paul Wrynn; Staff 40 (MLS 14, Non-MLS 26)
Founded 1914. Enrl 650; Fac 3,000; Highest Degree: Doctorate
Sep 1999-Aug 2000 Income (Main and Other College/University Libraries) $3,573,034, Locally Generated Income $235,540, Parent Institution $3,111,520, Other $225,974. Mats Exp $1,159,431, Books $76,582, Per/Ser (Incl. Access Fees) $863,313, Presv $29,160, Other Print Mats $8,408, Electronic Ref Mat (Incl. Access Fees) $181,968. Sal $1,896,539 (Prof $854,046)
Library Holdings: Bk Vols 173,061; Bk Titles 62,822; Per Subs 4,692; Bks on Deafness & Sign Lang 62
Special Collections: History (Heaton Coll)
Automation Activity & Vendor Info: (Acquisitions) Innovative Interfaces Inc.; (Cataloging) Innovative Interfaces Inc.; (Circulation) Innovative Interfaces Inc.; (Course Reserve) Innovative Interfaces Inc.; (OPAC) Innovative Interfaces Inc.; (Serials) Innovative Interfaces Inc.
Database Vendor: CARL, Dialog, Lexis-Nexis, OCLC - First Search, OVID Technologies, ProQuest
Restriction: Not open to public
Function: Archival collection, Document delivery services, ILL to other special libraries, Literary searches, Photocopies available, Reference services available
Partic in Medical Library Center Of New York; National Network Of Libraries Of Medicine - South Central Region; New York Metrop Ref & Res Libr Agency; OCLC Online Computer Library Center, Inc
Friends of the Library Group
Departmental Libraries:
ELISHA WALKER STAFF LIBRARY, NY Univ Downtown Hospital, 170 William St, 10038. SAN 378-0961. Tel: 212-312-5229. FAX: 212-312-5929. *Mgr*, Xiomara Cruz; E-Mail: cruzx01@library.med.nyu.edu
HERMAN ROBBINS MEDICAL LIBRARY, Hospital for Joint Diseases, 301 E 17th St, 10003. Tel: 212-598-6275. FAX: 212-598-6634. *Mgr*, Robert Joven; E-Mail: jovenr01@library.med.nyu.edu
JOHN & BERTHA E WALDMANN MEMORIAL, Dental Library, 345 E 24th St, 10010-4020. SAN 353-7153. Tel: 212-998-9794. FAX: 212-995-3529. Web Site: www.nyu.edu/dental/library. *Dir*, Van B Afes; Staff 11 (MLS 3, Non-MLS 8)
Sep 1999-Aug 2000 Income $650,229, Locally Generated Income $1,440, Parent Institution $648,789. Mats Exp $125,236, Books $27,183, Per/Ser (Incl. Access Fees) $49,589, Presv $13,327, Other Print Mats $2,106. Sal $466,925 (Prof $154,181)
Library Holdings: Bk Vols 38,285; Bk Titles 14,576; Per Subs 562
Subject Interests: Dentistry
Special Collections: History of Dentistry (Blum, Mestel & Weinburger Coll), rare bks
Automation Activity & Vendor Info: (Acquisitions) Innovative Interfaces Inc.; (Cataloging) Innovative Interfaces Inc.; (Circulation) Innovative Interfaces Inc.; (OPAC) Innovative Interfaces Inc.; (Serials) Innovative Interfaces Inc.
Database Vendor: CARL, Lexis-Nexis, OCLC - First Search, OVID Technologies, ProQuest
Publications: Waldmann Letter
Restriction: Not open to public
Function: Archival collection, Research library
Partic in Medical Library Center Of New York; New York Metrop Ref & Res Libr Agency; NYU Affiliates; OCLC Online Computer Library Center, Inc
NELSON INSTITUTE OF ENVIRONMENTAL MEDICINE, Long Meadow Rd, Tuxedo Park, 10987. SAN 312-5106. Tel: 914-351-4232. FAX: 914-351-3492. *Mgr*, Karrie Yarwood; E-Mail: yarwok01@library.med.nyu.edu

S NEWSWEEK, INC, Research Center,* 251 W 57th St, 10019-1894. SAN 353-7366. Tel: 212-445-4680. FAX: 212-445-4131. *Dir*, Madeline Cohen; *Dep Dir*, Dana Gordon; *Acq, Cat, ILL*, Judith Hausler; Staff 13 (MLS 9, Non-MLS 4)
Founded 1933
Library Holdings: Bk Titles 20,000; Per Subs 800
Subject Interests: Current affairs, Politics
Restriction: Staff use only
Partic in New York Metrop Ref & Res Libr Agency; OCLC Online Computer Library Center, Inc

S NORTH AMERICAN CONGRESS ON LATIN AMERICA LIBRARY,* 475 Riverside Dr Rm 454, 10115. SAN 375-6769. Tel: 212-870-3146. FAX: 212-870-3305. E-Mail: nacla@nacla.org. Web Site: www.nacla.org. *In Charge*, Fred Rosen
Library Holdings: Per Subs 250
Subject Interests: Latin America
Special Collections: Latin America Coll, per
Publications: NACLA - Report on the Americas

M NORTH GENERAL HOSPITAL, Medical Library,* 1879 Madison Ave, 10035. SAN 311-8118. Tel: 212-423-4476. FAX: 212-423-4477. *Dir*, Bruce Delman; Staff 2 (MLS 1, Non-MLS 1)
Founded 1957
Subject Interests: Medicine, Podiatry, Surgery
Special Collections: Audiovisual Collection on Medicine, Surgery & Podiatry
Partic in Manhattan-Bronx Health Sciences Libraries Group; National Network Of Libraries Of Medicine - South Central Region; New York Metrop Ref & Res Libr Agency

L O'MELVENY & MYERS LIBRARY, 153 E 53rd St, 10022. SAN 371-6074. Tel: 212-326-2020. Reference Tel: 212-326-2008. FAX: 212-326-2061. *Librn*, Jo Ellen Cooper; E-Mail: jcooper@omm.com; *Tech Servs*, Jill Lanier; E-Mail: jlanier@omm.com; *Branch Mgr*, Heide-Marie Bliss; E-Mail: hbliss@omm.com. Subject Specialists: *Law*, Heide-Marie Bliss; Staff 6 (MLS 3, Non-MLS 3)
Library Holdings: Bk Vols 15,000
Subject Interests: Law
Restriction: Staff use only
Function: ILL limited

L O'SULLIVAN, GRAEV & KARABELL, Law Library,* 30 Rockefeller Plaza, 10112. SAN 372-2449. Tel: 212-408-2435. FAX: 212-408-2467. *Librn*, Joan Fazzari
Library Holdings: Bk Vols 17,000; Per Subs 40
Subject Interests: Corporate law

S OGILVY & MATHER ADVERTISING, Research Library,* 309 W 49th St, 11th flr, 10019. SAN 311-9750. Tel: 212-237-5502. FAX: 212-237-7553. *Librn*, Linda Goldstein
Founded 1955
Library Holdings: Bk Titles 6,500; Per Subs 350
Subject Interests: Advertising, Marketing
Restriction: Not open to public

S OGILVY PUBLIC RELATIONS WORLDWIDE INFORMATION CENTER, 909 Third Ave, 10022-4731. SAN 311-9718. Tel: 212-880-5318. FAX: 212-884-1941, 212-972-6974. Web Site: www.ogilvypr.com. *Dir, VPres*, Jennifer Farrar; E-Mail: jennifer.farrar@ogilvypr.com; Staff 6 (MLS 3, Non-MLS 3)
Founded 1977
Library Holdings: Bk Vols 2,000; Bk Titles 1,800; Per Subs 210
Subject Interests: Bus, Communications, Finance, Health care, Mgt, Mktg, Pub relations, Technology

S ORGANIZATION RESOURCES COUNSELORS, INC, Information Center Library, 1211 Avenue of the Americas, 10036-8701. SAN 311-9807. Tel: 212-719-3400, Ext 360. FAX: 212-398-1358. *Librn*, Sharon Lombardo; Tel: 212-852-0396, E-Mail: sharon.lombardo@orcinc.com; Staff 2 (MLS 1, Non-MLS 1)
Founded 1926
Library Holdings: Bk Vols 1,500; Per Subs 200
Subject Interests: Human resources, Labor relations
Restriction: Company staff only

S ORIGAMI USA LIBRARY,* 15 W 79th St, 10024-5192. SAN 326-2170. Tel: 212-769-5635. FAX: 212-769-5668. *Librn*, Tony Cheng
Library Holdings: Bk Vols 1,000; Per Subs 6
Special Collections: Historical Manuscripts; Original Origami Creations; Unpublished Diagrams
Restriction: Members only

L ORRICK, HERRINGTON & SUTCLIFFE, Law Library,* 666 Fifth Ave, 10103. SAN 372-4425. Tel: 212-506-5343. FAX: 212-506-5151. *Librn*, Janet C Hefferle
Library Holdings: Bk Vols 15,000

S OXFORD UNIVERSITY PRESS, INC LIBRARY,* 198 Madison Ave, 10016. SAN 311-9815. Tel: 212-726-6000, 212-726-6013. FAX: 212-726-6457. *Librn*, Peter Belisle
Library Holdings: Bk Titles 10,000; Per Subs 30
Subject Interests: Am, Architecture, Art, Bibliogs, Biology, English, Foreign lit, History, Law, Mathematics, Medicine, Music, Political science, Reference, Relig studies

C PACE UNIVERSITY LIBRARY, Henry Birnbaum Library, New York Civic Ctr, One Pace Plaza, 10038-1502. SAN 353-7420. Tel: 212-346-1331, 212-346-1366. FAX: 212-346-1615. Web Site: library.pace.edu. *Assoc Dir*, Melvin Isaacson; Staff 9 (MLS 9)
Founded 1934. Highest Degree: Doctorate
Library Holdings: Bk Vols 414,825; Bk Titles 309,240; Per Subs 754
Subject Interests: Accounting, Computer science, Education, Finance, Liberal arts, Marketing, Mgt, Nursing, Real estate, Taxation
Partic in New York Metrop Ref & Res Libr Agency; OCLC Online Computer Library Center, Inc; Westchester Acad Libr Dir Orgn

S PAINE WEBBER INC, LIBRARY,* 1285 Avenue of the Americas, 10019. SAN 311-6468. Tel: 212-713-3673. FAX: 212-713-3078. *VPres*, Barbara A Fody; Staff 14 (MLS 5, Non-MLS 9)
Founded 1967
Library Holdings: Bk Titles 5,000; Per Subs 150
Subject Interests: Banking, Bus conditions, Econ, Finance, Indust, Investing, Money
Automation Activity & Vendor Info: (Acquisitions) EOS; (Cataloging) EOS; (OPAC) EOS; (Serials) EOS
Publications: Monthly bulletin

S PANNELL KERR FORSTER LIBRARY,* 420 Lexington Ave, Ste 2400, 10170. SAN 322-9149. Tel: 212-867-8000. FAX: 212-687-4346. E-Mail: dsu@pkfny.com. *Librn*, Di Su
Library Holdings: Bk Titles 1,500; Per Subs 65
Subject Interests: Accounting, Hotels, Real estate, Restaurants, Tourism

S PARADE PUBLICATIONS, INC LIBRARY, 711 Third Ave, 7th flr, 10017-4014. SAN 311-9858. FAX: 212-450-7283. *Dir*, Stacie G Fenster; *Senior Librn*, Mireille De Vidas; *Librn*, Anita Goss; *Librn*, Louis Leventhal; *Librn*, David A Grzelecki; *Librn*, Sharon Cappelson; Staff 6 (MLS 6)
Founded 1941
Library Holdings: Bk Vols 3,500; Bk Titles 2,000; Per Subs 300
Subject Interests: Biographies, Personalities
Special Collections: Celebrity files; Parade Magazine (1941-present)
Database Vendor: Lexis-Nexis, Wilson - Wilson Web
Publications: Parade Magazine (index)
Restriction: Not open to public

S PARAPSYCHOLOGY FOUNDATION INC, Eileen J Garrett Library, 228 E 71st St, 10021-5136. SAN 311-9866. Tel: 212-628-1550. FAX: 212-628-1559. Web Site: www.parapsychology.org. *Exec Dir*, Lisette Coly; E-Mail: lizettecoly@parapsychology.org
Founded 1951
Library Holdings: Bk Titles 10,000; Per Subs 100
Subject Interests: Parapsychol
Special Collections: Audio-Visual Archive
Publications: Guide to Sources of Information on Parapsychology (revised annually)

R PARK AVENUE SYNAGOGUE, Edmond de Rothschild Library, 50 E 87th St, 10128. SAN 311-9874. Tel: 212-369-2600, Ext 137. FAX: 212-410-7879. E-Mail: library@pasyn.com. *Librn*, Ilana Abend-David
Founded 1956
Library Holdings: Bk Vols 9,000; Per Subs 10
Subject Interests: 15th-20th Century, Bible, Childrens' bks, Fiction, Holocaust, Israel, Jewish cookbooks, Judaica, Judaica novels, Judaica ref, Juv Judaica, Young adult
Special Collections: Judaica Picture Books
Automation Activity & Vendor Info: (Acquisitions) Athena

S PARKER, CHAPIN, FLATTAU & KLIMPL LIBRARY,* 1211 Avenue of the Americas, 10036. SAN 371-4136. Tel: 212-704-6330. FAX: 212-704-6288. *Librn*, Elizabeth Cafferky
Library Holdings: Bk Vols 14,000; Per Subs 77
Subject Interests: Law

L PARKER, DURYEE, ROSOFF & HAFT, Law Library,* 529 Fifth Ave, 10017. SAN 371-5353. Tel: 212-599-0500. FAX: 212-972-9487. *Librn*, Carolyn Cooper; E-Mail: ccooper@parkerduryee.com; Staff 2 (MLS 1, Non-MLS 1)
Founded 1920
Library Holdings: Bk Vols 80,000; Bk Titles 500; Per Subs 24
Subject Interests: Litigation, Real estate, Securities, Tax

C PARSONS SCHOOL OF DESIGN, NEW SCHOOL FOR SOCIAL RESEARCH, Adam & Sophie Gimbel Design Library, 2 W 13th St, 10011. SAN 311-9890. Tel: 212-229-8914. Reference Tel: 212-229-5587. FAX: 212-229-2806. Web Site: www.newschool.edu/. *Dir*, Clayton C Kirking; E-Mail: kirkingc@newschool.edu; *Librn*, Christina Gjertsen; E-Mail: gjertsen@newschool.edu; *Librn*, Linda Marchand; E-Mail: marchanl@newschool.edu; Staff 5 (MLS 4, Non-MLS 1)
Founded 1896. Enrl 240; Fac 675; Highest Degree: Master
Jul 1999-Jun 2000 Income $560,000. Mats Exp $100,700, Books $48,000, Per/Ser (Incl. Access Fees) $20,000, Presv $18,000, AV Equip $6,000, Other Print Mats $3,200, Electronic Ref Mat (Incl. Access Fees) $5,500. Sal $337,000 (Prof $126,000)
Library Holdings: Bk Vols 52,000; Bk Titles 51,000; Per Subs 195
Subject Interests: Architecture, Costume, Crafts, Fashion, Fine arts, Graphic, Indust design, Interior design, Lighting, Photog, Textiles design
Special Collections: Fashion Design (Claire McCardell Coll), sketchbks; Parsons Archives
Automation Activity & Vendor Info: (Acquisitions) GEAC; (Cataloging) GEAC; (Circulation) GEAC; (Course Reserve) GEAC; (Serials) GEAC
Publications: Care for Our Books
Partic in New York Metrop Ref & Res Libr Agency; RLIN

S PARSONS, BRINCKERHOFF, QUADE & DOUGLAS LIBRARY, One Penn Plaza, 10119. SAN 311-9882. Tel: 212-465-5000, Ext 5290. FAX: 212-465-5477. *Librn*, Elizabeth Fox; E-Mail: foxe@pbworld.com; Staff 2 (MLS 1, Non-MLS 1)
Founded 1975
Library Holdings: Bk Titles 5,500; Per Subs 250
Subject Interests: Civil engineering, Energy, Environ planning, Environ tech, Structural engineering, Transportation planning
Database Vendor: Dialog, Lexis-Nexis, OCLC - First Search
Friends of the Library Group

S PATRICOF & CO,* 445 Park Ave, 11th flr, 10022. SAN 374-8782. Tel: 212-753-6300. FAX: 212-319-6155.
Library Holdings: Bk Titles 250; Per Subs 450
Subject Interests: Finance

L PATTERSON, BELKNAP, WEBB & TYLER LLP LIBRARY, 1133 Avenue of the Americas, 10036. SAN 311-9904. Tel: 212-336-2930. Interlibrary Loan Service Tel: 212-336-2325. Reference Tel: 212-336-2103. FAX: 212-336-2222. *Librn*, Christina Senezak; E-Mail: cmsenezak@pbwt.com; *Asst Librn*, Betty Hunter-Beatty; Staff 6 (MLS 2, Non-MLS 4)
Library Holdings: Bk Vols 30,000; Per Subs 200
Subject Interests: Bankruptcy, Corporate, Equal rights amendments, Estates, Intellectual property, Libel, Litigation, Product liability, Tax
Automation Activity & Vendor Info: (Cataloging) EOS; (Circulation) EOS
Partic in CDB Infotek; Dialog Corporation; Dun & Bradstreet Info Servs; Westlaw

L PAUL, WEISS, RIFKIND, WHARTON & GARRISON LIBRARY,* 1285 Avenue of the Americas, 10019-6064. SAN 311-9912. Tel: 212-373-2401. FAX: 212-373-2268. *Librn*, Theresa O'Leary; Staff 19 (MLS 10, Non-MLS 9)
Library Holdings: Bk Vols 80,000
Subject Interests: Law
Partic in RLIN

S PEN & BRUSH, INC LIBRARY, 16 E Tenth St, 10003. SAN 325-7452. Tel: 212-475-3669. FAX: 212-475-6018. *Librn*, Jean Murai
Library Holdings: Bk Vols 3,000; Per Subs 10
Restriction: Members only

L PENNIE & EDMONDS LLP LIBRARY, 1155 Avenue of the Americas, 10036. SAN 311-9947. Tel: 212-790-9090, Ext 6414. FAX: 212-869-9741. E-Mail: library@pennie.com. *Librn*, Mary A Gilligan
Founded 1915
Library Holdings: Bk Titles 4,000; Per Subs 250
Subject Interests: Chemistry, Copyright, Electronics, Metallurgy, Patent law, Trademark law
Database Vendor: Lexis-Nexis
Publications: Bulletin (quarterly); library guide; newsletter (irregular)
Partic in Dialog Corporation; Orbit; STN; Westlaw

S PHILATELIC FOUNDATION, Archives & Library, 501 Fifth Ave, Rm 1901, 10017. SAN 325-9439. Tel: 212-867-3699. FAX: 212-867-3984. *Archivist*, Robert Waterman
Library Holdings: Bk Vols 6,000
Specialized Philatelic & Postal History Library

S PHILIP MORRIS INC, Library Services,* 120 Park Ave, 18th flr, 10017. SAN 374-8812. Tel: 212-880-3862, 212-880-5000. FAX: 212-907-5355. *Ref*, Robin Bertrand
Library Holdings: Bk Titles 2,000; Per Subs 150

S PHOTO RESEARCHERS, INC LIBRARY, Stock Photography Agency,* 60 E 56th St 6th flr, 10022-3238. SAN 370-1913. Tel: 212-758-3420. FAX: 212-355-0731. E-Mail: photorsrch@aol.com. *Pres*, Robert L Zentmaier
Library Holdings: Per Subs 31
Subject Interests: Stock photog
Open Mon-Fri 9-5

S PIERPONT MORGAN LIBRARY, 29 E 36th St, 10016. SAN 311-998X. Tel: 212-590-0311. FAX: 212-481-3484. E-Mail: media@morganlibrary.org. Web Site: www.morganlibrary.org. *Dir*, Charles E Pierce, Jr; Staff 116 (MLS 10, Non-MLS 106)
Founded 1924
Library Holdings: Bk Vols 150,000; Bk Titles 125,000; Per Subs 300
Subject Interests: Autograph mss, Bk bindings, Doc, Early children's bks, Egyptian, Greek, Incunabula, Later printed bks, Letters, Master drawings, Medieval mss, Mesopotamian seals, Mesopotamian tablets, Musical mss, Renaissance mss
Publications: Catalogs of Exhibitions; Report to the Fellows
Partic in RLIN
Friends of the Library Group

S PILSUDSKI INSTITUTE OF AMERICA LIBRARY,* 180 Second Ave, 10003-5778. SAN 325-9358. Tel: 212-505-9077. FAX: 212-505-9052. E-Mail: jozef_pilsudski@msn.com.

1997-1998 Mats Exp $1,500, Books $1,000, Per/Ser (Incl. Access Fees) $500
Library Holdings: Bk Vols 22,000
Open Mon-Fri 10-6:30

L PIPER, MARBURY, RUDNICK & WOLFE LLP, Law Library, 1251 Ave of Americas, 38th Flr, 10020-1104. SAN 372-4395. Tel: 212-835-6135. FAX: 212-835-6001. Web Site: www.piperrudnick.com. *Librn*, Marsha Pront; E-Mail: marshapront@piperrudnick.com; Staff 2 (MLS 1, Non-MLS 1)
Library Holdings: Bk Vols 5,000; Per Subs 100

S PLANNED PARENTHOOD FEDERATION OF AMERICA, INC, Katharine Dexter McCormick Library, 810 Seventh Ave, 10019. SAN 311-9998. Tel: 212-261-4637. FAX: 212-247-6269. E-Mail: library@lppfa.org. Web Site: www.plannedparenthood.org/lib.; Staff 3 (MLS 2, Non-MLS 1)
Founded 1964
Library Holdings: Bk Titles 5,000; Per Subs 125
Subject Interests: Abortion, Artificial insemination, Contraception, Contraceptives, Educ in family planning, Fertility res, Hist of birth control movement, Infertility res, Legal status of family planning subj, Reproductive health, Reproductive rights, Sex educ, Sterilization, Teenage sexualtiy, Training in family planning, US legis
Special Collections: Margaret Sanger Coll
Publications: Family Planning Library Manual
Partic in Metro NY Libr Coun

S POLISH INSTITUTE OF ARTS & SCIENCES IN AMERICA, INC, Research Library, 208 E 30th St, 10016. SAN 312-004X. Tel: 212-686-4164. FAX: 212-545-1130. Web Site: www.piasa.org. *Librn*, Krystyna Baron; *Asst Librn*, Krystyna Swierbutowicz; Staff 5 (MLS 3, Non-MLS 2)
Founded 1942
Library Holdings: Bk Titles 24,000; Per Subs 400
Special Collections: Latin-American Coll; Lechon's Coll; Translators; workshops
Open Mon-Thurs 10-3

S POPULATION COUNCIL LIBRARY, One Dag Hammarskjold Plaza, 10017. SAN 320-4049. Tel: 212-339-0533. FAX: 212-755-6052. Web Site: www.popcouncil.org. *Librn*, H Neil Zimmerman; E-Mail: nzimmerman@popcouncil.org; Staff 2 (MLS 1, Non-MLS 1)
Founded 1953
Library Holdings: Bk Vols 28,000; Bk Titles 25,000; Per Subs 350
Subject Interests: Demography, Develop countries, Development economics, Family planning, Womens' studies
Partic in Asn for Pro-Family Planning Libr & Info Ctrs; Consortium Of Foundation Libraries

PRESBYTERIAN HOSPITAL

S MILBANK LIBRARY, Millstein Bldg, 2nd flr, 177 Fort Washington Ave, 10032. SAN 353-7544. Tel: 212-305-5904.; Staff 1 (MLS 1)
Founded 1928
Library Holdings: Bk Vols 5,000; Per Subs 30
Subject Interests: Consumer health educ, Foreign Language
Special Collections: Talking Books
Partic in ALA; New York Metrop Ref & Res Libr Agency; NYLA

M JOHN M WHEELER LIBRARY, Edward S Harkness Eye Institute, 635 W 165th St, 10032. SAN 353-751X. Tel: 212-305-2916, 212-305-9855. FAX: 212-305-3173. *Dir*, Lijun Tian
Founded 1933
Library Holdings: Bk Titles 14,121; Per Subs 90
Special Collections: Ophthalmology Memorabilia; Rare Book Coll
Partic in Greater NE Regional Group; Med Libr Res Librs Group; Medical Library Center Of New York

S PRINCETON LIBRARY IN NEW YORK, 15 W 43rd St, 5th Flr, 10036. SAN 312-0104. Tel: 212-596-1250. FAX: 212-596-1398. E-Mail: info@princetonclub.com. *Librn*, Betty Dornheim; *Asst Librn*, Doris Humphrey; Staff 2 (Non-MLS 2)
Founded 1962
Library Holdings: Bk Vols 10,000; Per Subs 80
Subject Interests: Histories of NY
Special Collections: Princetoniana
Open Tues-Thurs 11-7:30, Mon & Fri 11-5

S PROGRAM PLANNERS, INC, Library Information Center, 230 W 41st St, 10036. SAN 312-0112. Tel: 212-840-2600, Ext 217. FAX: 212-764-4094. E-Mail: ppi@bway.net. *Dir, Res*, Burt Lazarin; *Librn*, April Ames; Staff 2 (MLS 1, Non-MLS 1)
Founded 1971
Library Holdings: Bk Titles 10,000; Per Subs 180
Subject Interests: Employee benefits, Health, Labor relations, Pensions, Pub finance, Transportation, Urban affairs
Special Collections: Government Finances (Annual Comptroller Reports & Budgets-New York & other major US cities); New York City Financial Control Board, minutes & rpts; New York City Fiscal Crisis, 1974-1982; New York City Municipal Worker Labor Agreements; Pension Systems (ann rpts New York City Employee); Program Planners Inc Research Reports
Partic in New York State Interlibrary Loan Network; NY & NJ Regional Med Libr

S PROJECT FOR PUBLIC SPACES, INC, Media Library, 153 Waverly Pl, 10014. SAN 370-7415. Tel: 212-620-5660. FAX: 212-620-3821. E-Mail: pps@pps.org. Web Site: www.pps.org. *Media Spec*, Norma Smith; Staff 1 (MLS 1)
Founded 1975
Library Holdings: Bk Titles 1,000
Restriction: By appointment only

L PROSKAUER ROSE LLP LIBRARY, 1585 Broadway, 19th Flr, 10036. SAN 312-0139. Tel: 212-969-5001, Ext 5030. FAX: 212-969-2900. Web Site: www.proskauer.com. *Dir*, Kit Hartnett; *Head Ref*, Alma DeJesus; *Circ*, Wesley Beaco; *Ref Serv*, Megan D'Errico; *Ref*, Joanne Doria; *Ref*, Sarah Kagen; *Ref*, Maria Maida; *Ref*, Ruthie McGonagil; Staff 16 (MLS 7, Non-MLS 9)
Founded 1875
Library Holdings: Bk Titles 40,000; Per Subs 400
Subject Interests: Law
Special Collections: Labor Law Coll
Publications: Library Bulletin (quarterly)
Restriction: By appointment only

S PROTAPE, INC LIBRARY,* 370 Seventh Ave, 10001. SAN 371-6465. Tel: 212-244-0500. *Librn*, John Pliny Jr
Founded 1970
Library Holdings: Bk Titles 10,000; Per Subs 1,100
Subject Interests: Accounting, Law, Real estate, Securities, Travel

L PRYOR, CASHMAN, SHERMAN & FLYNN, Law Library,* 410 Park Ave, 10022. SAN 372-4433. Tel: 212-421-4100. FAX: 212-326-0806. *Librn*, Anna Greene
Library Holdings: Bk Vols 10,000

P PUBLIC EDUCATION ASSOCIATION LIBRARY & ARCHIVES,* 28 W 44th St Ste 914, 10036. SAN 325-9498. Tel: 212-868-1640. FAX: 212-302-0088. Web Site: www.pea-online.
Restriction: By appointment only

S PUBLIC RELATIONS SOCIETY OF AMERICA, Information Center,* 33 Irving Pl, 10003-2376. SAN 312-0147. Tel: 212-460-1458. FAX: 212-995-5024. E-Mail: ppc@prsa.org. *Dir*, G Blane Withers
Founded 1956
Library Holdings: Bk Vols 900; Per Subs 14
Subject Interests: Pub relations
Restriction: By appointment only

L PUTNEY, TWOMBLY, HALL & HIRSON, Law Library,* 521 Fifth Ave, 10th flr, 10175. SAN 325-9234. Tel: 212-682-0020. FAX: 212-682-9380. *Librn*, Mary Young
Library Holdings: Bk Vols 40,000; Per Subs 30
Restriction: Staff use only

S RACQUET & TENNIS CLUB LIBRARY, 370 Park Ave, 10022-5968. SAN 312-0171. Tel: 212-753-9700. *Head Librn*, Gerard J Belliveau, Jr; *Asst Librn*, Todd M Thompson; Staff 2 (MLS 2)
Founded 1905
Library Holdings: Bk Titles 19,500; Per Subs 30
Subject Interests: Sports
Special Collections: Court Tennis (Jeu de Paume Coll); Early American Sports; Lawn Tennis
Publications: Annual Report to Members

S RADIO ADVERTISING BUREAU, Marketing Information Center,* 261 Madison Ave 23rd flr, 10016. SAN 353-7579. Tel: 212-681-7200. FAX: 212-681-7223. *In Charge*, Judy Carlough
Founded 1952
Library Holdings: Bk Titles 300; Per Subs 150
Subject Interests: Advertising, Consumer markets, Media, National advertisers, Television
Special Collections: Broadcasting Year Book from 1935; History of Radio
Open Mon-Fri 9am-5pm

S REAL ESTATE BOARD OF NEW YORK, Seymour B Durst Library, 570 Lexington Ave, 2nd flr, 10022. SAN 312-0201. Tel: 212-532-3100. FAX: 212-481-0420. Web Site: www.rebny.com. *Librn*, Carolyn Dunn; E-Mail: cdunn@rebny.com; *Librn*, Jaslyn Fitzpatrick; *VPres*, Carol Trezza; Staff 3 (Non-MLS 3)
Founded 1896
Library Holdings: Bk Titles 850; Per Subs 100
Restriction: Members only

S REFERENCE PICTURES, 900 Broadway, 10003. SAN 324-2889. Tel: 212-254-0008. FAX: 212-353-9152. *Librn*, Doris Denhil
Founded 1960
Restriction: Open to public for reference only

S REHABILITATION INTERNATIONAL, Collection on Disability-Handicap Library, 25 E 21st St, 4th flr, 10010. SAN 329-1359. Tel: 212-420-1500. FAX: 212-505-0871. E-Mail: rehabintl@rehab-international.org. Web Site: www.rehab-international.org. *In Charge*, Barbara Duncan
Founded 1949

Library Holdings: Bk Vols 3,510
Subject Interests: Barrier free designs, Childhood disability in developing countries, Developing countries, Disability, Legis, Soc policy, Soc security disability progs, Technology, Women
Restriction: Members only
Partic in Easylink

S RELIANCE GROUP HOLDINGS, Corporate Library,* Park Ave Plaza, 55 E 52nd Sta, 10055. SAN 324-6485. Tel: 212-909-1888. FAX: 212-909-1864. *Librn*, Laurie Meyers; Staff 1 (MLS 1)
Founded 1979
Library Holdings: Bk Titles 250; Per Subs 150
Subject Interests: Accounting, Bus, Ins, Investing, Mgt

S RESEARCH & DOCUMENTATION CENTER OF THE UKRANIAN INSTITUTE OF AMERICA, Research & Development Center, 2 E 79th St, 10021. SAN 374-7824. Tel: 212-288-8660. FAX: 212-288-2918. *Exec Dir*, Olena Nessin; Tel: 212-288-2917
Library Holdings: Bk Vols 1,000
Subject Interests: Emigration and immigration, Ukrainian hist
Special Collections: Ukranian Engineers Society of America Journal Coll
Restriction: Access at librarian's discretion, Not a lending library, Open to others by appointment, Open to students
Function: Archival collection, For research purposes, Photocopies available, Research library, Some telephone reference

S RESEARCH CENTER FOR MUSICAL ICONOGRAPHY, City University of NY, 365 Fifth Ave, 10016-4309. SAN 312-0295. Tel: 212-817-1992. FAX: 212-817-1569. *Dir*, Zdravko Blazekovic; E-Mail: zblazekovic@gc.cuny.edu
Founded 1971
Library Holdings: Bk Vols 800
Subject Interests: Music in all visual arts
Special Collections: Martin Bernstein Coll, slides; Vienna Gesellschaft der Musikfreunde Portrait Coll, transparencies, Emanuel Winternitz Archive of Photos; Viennese Classical Period: Haydn, Mozart, Beethoven, Schubert Iconography slides & transparencies
Publications: Music in Art (annual); RIdIM/RCMI Inventory of Music Iconography
Restriction: By appointment only

S RESEARCH INSTITUTE FOR THE STUDY OF MAN LIBRARY,* 162 E 78th St, 10021. SAN 312-0309. Tel: 212-535-8448. FAX: 212-535-0084. *Librn*, Judith Selakoff; Staff 1 (MLS 1)
Founded 1955
Library Holdings: Bk Vols 25,000; Per Subs 120
Subject Interests: Behav sci, Soc sci, Soc sci of the Caribbean, Soc sci of the non-Hispanic West Indies
Special Collections: Caribbean, pamphlets, dissertations, govt publ, mss; Historical & Contemporary Newspaper Clippings of Non-Hispanic West Indies, microflm
Publications: Accession list

L RICHARDS & O'NEIL, LLP, Law Library, 885 Third Ave, 10022. SAN 372-4514. Tel: 212-207-1200, 212-207-1389. FAX: 212-750-9022. *Dir, Librn*, Paulette Toth; E-Mail: ptoth@richoneil.com
Library Holdings: Bk Vols 4,000; Per Subs 150

R RIVERSIDE CHURCH LIBRARY, 490 Riverside Dr, 10027. SAN 312-0325. Tel: 212-870-6728. FAX: 212-870-6800. *Chief Librn*, Marie K Wilson; E-Mail: mwilson@theriversidechurchny.org
1998-1999 Income $17,629, Locally Generated Income $500, Parent Institution $17,129. Mats Exp $3,035, Books $2,000, Per/Ser (Incl. Access Fees) $35, AV Equip $1,000. Sal $14,000
Library Holdings: Bk Vols 7,000
Subject Interests: Biography, Environmental studies, Fiction, Fine arts, Philosophy, Psychology, Religion, Sociology
Special Collections: Books by South African Writers; Works of Harry Emerson Fosdick
Partic in CSLA

L ROBINSON, SILVERMAN, PEARCE, ARONSOHN & BERMAN LLP LIBRARY, 1290 Avenue of the Americas, 10104. SAN 324-1157. Tel: 212-541-2166. FAX: 212-541-1465. Web Site: www.robinsonsilverman.com. *Librn*, Christine M Wierzba; Tel: 212-541-2165, E-Mail: wierzba@rspab.com; *Asst Librn*, Roxanne Hamberry; Tel: 212-541-2167, E-Mail: hamberry@rspab.com; *ILL*, Solomon K Crook; E-Mail: crook@rspab.com
Founded 1950
Library Holdings: Bk Vols 10,000; Bk Titles 3,250; Per Subs 300
Subject Interests: Law
Automation Activity & Vendor Info: (Cataloging) Sydney; (Serials) Sydney
Database Vendor: Lexis-Nexis
Partic in Am Asn of Law Librs; Spec Libr Asn

S ROCKEFELLER FOUNDATION RECORDS & LIBRARY SERVICES,* 420 Fifth Ave, 10018-1600. SAN 312-0341. Tel: 212-852-8428. FAX: 212-852-8443. E-Mail: information@rockfound.org. *Mgr*, Meredith S Averill; E-Mail: maverill@rockfound.org; *Librn, Res*, Christopher Bailey; *Senior Librn*, Tracy Friesen; Staff 7 (MLS 4, Non-MLS 3)
Founded 1913
Library Holdings: Bk Titles 10,000; Per Subs 600
Subject Interests: Agriculture, Arts, Behav sci, Biog, Culture, Education, Environ, Global issues, Health sci, Humanities, Inter security, Philanthropy, Pop, Soc sci
Publications: Periodicals Holding List, Acquisitions List
Restriction: Staff use only
Partic in Consortium Of Foundation Libraries; Metropolitan New York Library Council; OCLC Online Computer Library Center, Inc

C ROCKEFELLER UNIVERSITY LIBRARY, 1230 York Ave, PO Box 263, 10021-6399. SAN 312-035X. Tel: 212-327-8904. Circulation Tel: 212-327-8905. Reference Tel: 212-327-8907. Toll Free Tel: 800-980-6922. FAX: 212-327-7840. E-Mail: librequest@rockefeller.edu. Web Site: rockefeller.edu/library/. *Dir*, Patricia Elaine Mackey; Tel: 212-327-8909, E-Mail: mackey@rockefeller.edu; *Ref*, Beverly Gordon; E-Mail: gordonb@rockefeller.edu; *ILL*, Angela Matthews; Tel: 212-327-8916, E-Mail: larkin@rockefeller.edu; *Cat*, Paula Desko; Tel: 212-327-8911, E-Mail: desko@rockefeller.edu; *Cat*, Janet Johnson; Tel: 212-327-8911, E-Mail: johnsoj@rockefeller.edu; *Acq*, Wilma Leona Dowden; Tel: 212-327-8944, E-Mail: jacobsw@rockefeller.edu; *Doc Delivery*, Daemein Chisholm; Tel: 212-327-8957; *Syst Coordr*, Douglas James Many; Tel: 212-327-8906, E-Mail: many@rockefeller.edu; *Per*, James Sanders; Tel: 212-327-8957; *Circ*, Magdelena Rivera; Tel: 212-327-8905, E-Mail: riveram@rockefeller.edu; *Reader Servs*, Matthew McDermott; Tel: 212-327-8221, E-Mail: mcdermm@rockefeller.edu. Subject Specialists: *Biology*, Paula Desko; *Life sciences*, Patricia Elaine Mackey; Staff 11 (MLS 3, Non-MLS 8)
Founded 1906. Enrl 150; Fac 350; Highest Degree: Doctorate
Jul 1999-Jun 2000 Income $1,480,600, State $6,418, Parent Institution $1,474,182. Mats Exp $301,241, Books $49,981, Per/Ser (Incl. Access Fees) $525,921, Micro $680, Electronic Ref Mat (Incl. Access Fees) $250,580. Sal $465,538 (Prof $217,700)
Library Holdings: Bk Vols 54,371; Bk Titles 51,329; Per Subs 375
Subject Interests: Cell biol, Chemistry, History of science, Immunology, Mathematics, Med sci, Microbiology, Neuroscience, Physics
Automation Activity & Vendor Info: (Acquisitions) Innovative Interfaces Inc.; (Cataloging) Innovative Interfaces Inc.; (Circulation) Innovative Interfaces Inc.; (Course Reserve) Innovative Interfaces Inc.; (ILL) Innovative Interfaces Inc.; (Serials) Innovative Interfaces Inc.
Database Vendor: Dialog, Ebsco - EbscoHost, Innovative Interfaces INN - View, OCLC - First Search, OVID Technologies
Function: Research library
Partic in Medical Library Center Of New York; New York Metrop Ref & Res Libr Agency

S ROMANIAN CULTURAL CENTER,* 200 E 38th St, 10016. SAN 320-2143. Tel: 212-687-0181. FAX: 212-687-0181. E-Mail: ro.culture@aol.com. *Dir*, Coriolan Babeti; *Librn*, Mariana Stoian; Staff 5 (MLS 3, Non-MLS 2)
Founded 1969
Library Holdings: Bk Titles 22,000; Per Subs 60
Subject Interests: Romania
Special Collections: Bibliographies (Romanian Topics Coll)

M ROOSEVELT HOSPITAL, Medical Library,* 1000 Tenth Ave, 10019. SAN 312-0376. Tel: 212-523-6100. FAX: 212-523-6108. *Librn*, Paul Barth
Founded 1955
Library Holdings: Bk Titles 1,500; Per Subs 450
Subject Interests: Medicine, Pediatrics, Surgery
Restriction: Staff use only
Partic in Docline; Medical Library Center Of New York; Metrop Consortium

L ROSENMAN & COLIN LLP, Law Library, 575 Madison Ave, 10022. SAN 312-0384. Tel: 212-940-8800. Interlibrary Loan Service Tel: 212-940-6709. Reference Tel: 212-940-8585. FAX: 212-940-8776. Web Site: www.rosenman.com. *Chief Librn*, Rochelle Cheifetz; E-Mail: rcheifet@rosenman.com; *Tech Servs*, Caren Rabinowitz; E-Mail: crabinowitz@rosenman.com; *ILL*, Sheila Marshall; *Ref*, Anthony Burgalassi; E-Mail: ajburgalassi@rosenman.com; Staff 4 (MLS 4)
Founded 1946
Library Holdings: Bk Vols 50,000; Per Subs 700
Automation Activity & Vendor Info: (Acquisitions) Inmagic, Inc.; (Cataloging) Inmagic, Inc.; (Circulation) Inmagic, Inc.; (ILL) Inmagic, Inc.; (Serials) Inmagic, Inc.
Restriction: Staff use only
Partic in Dialog Corporation; Westlaw

S S H & E, INC LIBRARY,* 90 Park Ave, 27th flr, 10016. SAN 312-0600. Tel: 212-682-8455. FAX: 212-986-1825. E-Mail: newyork@sh-e.com. Web Site: www.sh-e.com. *Librn*, Liana Alaverdova; Tel: 212-682-8455, Ext 204, E-Mail: lalaverdova@she.com
Founded 1963
1998-1999 Mats Exp $101,000, Books $60,000, Per/Ser (Incl. Access Fees) $10,000, Other Print Mats $10,000, Manuscripts & Archives $10,000. Sal $64,000
Library Holdings: Bk Titles 7,400
Subject Interests: Aircraft evaluation, Airport planning, Aviation, Econ, Environmental studies, Freight, Marketing, Tourism, Travel

Restriction: Company staff only
Function: Research library
Figures reported include Boston SH&E Library, Cambridge, MA

S SAATCHI & SAATCHI ADVERTISING, Research Library,* 375 Hudson St, 10014. SAN 311-7006. Tel: 212-463-2259. FAX: 212-463-2627. *Librn*, Joyce Melito; Staff 1 (MLS 1)
Library Holdings: Bk Vols 4,000; Per Subs 120
Subject Interests: Advertising, Marketing

S RUSSELL SAGE FOUNDATION LIBRARY, 112 E 64th St, 10021. SAN 324-1815. Tel: 212-752-8641. FAX: 212-688-3398. E-Mail: library@rsage.org. Web Site: www.russellsage.org. *Dir Libr Serv*, Nicole M T Radmore; *Librn*, Michelle C K McKowen; Tel: 212-752-8640; *Librn*, Catherine Winograd; Tel: 212-752-8640; Staff 3 (MLS 2, Non-MLS 1)
Founded 1982
Library Holdings: Bk Titles 1,500; Per Subs 80
Subject Interests: Soc sci
Special Collections: Russell Sage Foundation Publications
Automation Activity & Vendor Info: (OPAC) Inmagic, Inc.
Database Vendor: Dialog, Lexis-Nexis, OCLC - First Search
Restriction: Open to public upon request
Function: ILL available
Partic in Consortium Of Foundation Libraries; New York Metrop Ref & Res Libr Agency; State University Of New York-NYLINK

M SAINT CLARE'S HOSPITAL & HEALTH CENTER, Medical Library, 415 W 51st St, 10019. SAN 353-7722. Tel: 212-586-1500. FAX: 212-459-8784.; Staff 2 (MLS 1, Non-MLS 1)
Founded 1934
Library Holdings: Bk Titles 1,500; Per Subs 80
Subject Interests: AIDS, Nursing, Obstetrics-gynecology, Ophthalmology, Pediatrics, Surgery

M ST LUKE'S-ROOSEVELT HOSPITAL CENTER, Richard Walker Bolling Memorial Medical Library, 1111 Amsterdam Ave, 10025. SAN 312-0422. Tel: 212-523-4315. FAX: 212-523-4313. *Librn*, Dr Nancy Panella; E-Mail: npanella@panix.com; *ILL*, Robert Garrett; *Per*, Carroll Otis
Founded 1876
Library Holdings: Bk Vols 10,000; Per Subs 275
Subject Interests: History of medicine
Special Collections: Photographs & Other Memorabilia; Surgical & Medical Historical Instruments
Restriction: Open to others by appointment, Staff use only
Partic in Medical Library Center Of New York; New York Metrop Ref & Res Libr Agency

S SAINT MATTHEW'S & SAINT TIMOTHY'S NEIGHBORHOOD CENTER, INC LIBRARY, Star Learning Center, 26 W 84th St, 10024. SAN 320-2151. Tel: 212-362-6750. FAX: 212-787-6196. *Dir*, Rita Spano; *Librn*, Beverly Hannum
Founded 1971
Library Holdings: Bk Vols 11,000
Subject Interests: Children's literature, Remedial reading
Friends of the Library Group

M SAINT VINCENT'S HOSPITAL, School of Nursing Library, 27 Christopher St, 10014. SAN 329-4285. Tel: 212-604-7000, 212-604-8484. FAX: 212-604-2064. *Librn*, Marianne Dono
Library Holdings: Bk Titles 3,325
Subject Interests: Medicine, Nursing

M SAINT VINCENT'S HOSPITAL & MEDICAL CENTER, Boller Health Sciences Library, 153 W 11th St, 10011. SAN 312-0457. Tel: 212-604-7811. FAX: 212-366-6067. E-Mail: vince1@rmi.net. *Dir*, Agnes T Frank; Tel: 212-604-7812; *Asst Librn*, Denis Gaffney; Staff 3 (MLS 2, Non-MLS 1)
Founded 1955
Library Holdings: Bk Titles 6,945; Per Subs 281
Subject Interests: Health sciences
Database Vendor: OVID Technologies
Publications: Newsletter
Restriction: Staff use only
Function: ILL available
Partic in Medical Library Center Of New York; Metro Atlanta Library Association; New York Metrop Ref & Res Libr Agency; NY Med Col

S SALMAGUNDI CLUB LIBRARY,* 47 Fifth Ave, 10003. SAN 312-0473. Tel: 212-255-7740. FAX: 212-229-0172. *Librn*, Agnes C Olsson
Founded 1899
Library Holdings: Bk Vols 6,500
Subject Interests: Art, Coronations, Costumes, Uniforms

S SALOMON SMITH BARNEY CORPORATE LIBRARY, 388 Greenwich St 31st flr, 10013. SAN 312-0643. Tel: 212-816-3800. FAX: 212-816-3584. *Mgr, VPres*, Arthur DiMeglio; Tel: 212-816-3837, E-Mail: arthur.j.dimeglio@ssmb.com; *Acq*, Allan Roberts; Tel: 212-816-3812, Fax: 212-816-5264, E-Mail: allan.roberts@ssmb.com; *Res*, Florence Gunther; Tel: 212-816-3838, E-Mail: florence.gunther@ssmb.com; *Res*, Louise Klusek; E-Mail: louise.a.klusek@ssmb.com; *Tech Servs*, Cecelia Scotti; Tel: 212-816-4411, Fax: 212-816-7025, E-Mail: cecelia.b.scotti@ssmb.com; Staff 13 (MLS 6, Non-MLS 7)
Founded 1922
Library Holdings: Bk Vols 1,200; Per Subs 475
Subject Interests: Annual reports, Investment, Securities
Special Collections: International Prospectuses; National Stock & Bond Summaries, 1920-date; Wall Street Journal, from 1920, micro

S SANFORD C BERSTEIN & CO, INC, Research Library, 767 Fifth Ave, 19th fl, 10153. SAN 321-8864. Tel: 212-756-4609. FAX: 212-756-4168. *Info Res*, Melanie Ashmore; *Info Res*, Rita Barkovich
Founded 1968
Library Holdings: Bk Titles 50; Per Subs 150
Subject Interests: Investing

M SANOFI - SYNTHELABO, INC, (Formerly Sanofi Pharmaceuticals, Inc), Library & Information Services, 90 Park Ave, 7th flr, 10016. SAN 312-0767. Tel: 212-551-4105. FAX: 212-551-4908. *Mgr*, Donna Brown; E-Mail: donna.brown@us.sanofi.com
Founded 1927
Library Holdings: Bk Vols 120; Per Subs 120
Subject Interests: Clinical medicine, Drug therapy, Drugs, Pharmaceutical, Pharmacology
Publications: Current News Headlines
Restriction: Staff use only

L SATTERLEE, STEPHENS, BURKE & BURKE, Law Library, 230 Park Ave, 10169. SAN 311-6603. Tel: 212-818-9200. FAX: 212-818-9606. Web Site: www.ssbb.com. *Librn*, Dolores Fusik; E-Mail: dfusik@ssbb.com
Library Holdings: Bk Vols 13,000; Per Subs 25

S SBC WARBURG DILLON READ LIBRARY,* 299 Park Ave, 37th flr, 10171. SAN 311-7324. Tel: 212-821-4646. FAX: 212-821-4840. *Dir*, Nancy J Bowles; Staff 16 (MLS 6, Non-MLS 10)
Founded 1966
Library Holdings: Bk Vols 3,000; Per Subs 900
Subject Interests: Corp finance, Econ, Indust analysis

L SCHNADER, HARRISON, SEGAL & LEWIS, LLP, Law Library, 140 Broadway, 31st Flr, 10005. SAN 372-4417. Tel: 212-973-8127. FAX: 212-972-8798. *Librn*, Anthony Rivetti; E-Mail: anthonyrivetti@shsl.com
Library Holdings: Bk Vols 7,000
Restriction: Staff use only

S SCHOLASTIC, INC LIBRARY,* 555 Broadway, 10012. SAN 312-0511. Tel: 212-343-6176. FAX: 212-343-6185. *Dir Libr Serv*, Bert Schachter; *Senior Librn*, Margaret Stevaralgia; *Librn*, Karen Van Rossen; *Librn*, Debbie Gerber
Founded 1929
Library Holdings: Bk Vols 25,200; Per Subs 250
Subject Interests: Behav sci, Curric mat, Sci, Soc sci
Special Collections: Children's Magazines, bks, per

L SCHULTE ROTH & ZABEL LLP, Law Library, 919 Third Ave, 10022. SAN 372-4573. Tel: 212-756-2302. FAX: 212-593-5955. Web Site: www.srz.com. *Dir Libr Serv*, Carol K Sergis; E-Mail: carol.sergis@srz.com; *Asst Dir*, Linda Wood; Tel: 212-756-2305, E-Mail: linda.wood@srz.com; *Res*, Jeffrey Giles; Tel: 212-756-2304, E-Mail: jeffrey.giles@srz.com; *Res*, Laraine Ginsberg; Tel: 212-756-2309, E-Mail: laraine.ginsburg@srz.com; *Electronic Resources*, Ellyn Freeman; Tel: 212-756-2321, E-Mail: ellyn.freeman@srz.com; Staff 10 (MLS 4, Non-MLS 6)
Founded 1969
Library Holdings: Bk Vols 70,000; Bk Titles 7,500; Per Subs 450
Subject Interests: Corporate law, Human rights, Securities industry
Automation Activity & Vendor Info: (Acquisitions) Sydney; (Cataloging) Sydney; (Circulation) Sydney; (ILL) Sydney; (OPAC) Sydney; (Serials) Sydney
Restriction: Staff use only
Partic in AALL; SLA

L SEAMEN'S CHURCH INSTITUTE OF NEW YORK & NEW JERSEY, Center for Seafarers' Rights, 241 Water St, 10038. SAN 373-3408. Tel: 212-349-9090, Ext 255. FAX: 212-349-8342. E-Mail: csr@seamenschurch.org, sci@seamenschurch.org. *Dir*, Douglas Stevenson
Library Holdings: Bk Titles 500; Per Subs 10
Subject Interests: Maritime law
Open 8:30-4:30

L SERKO & SIMON, Law Library,* One World Trade Ctr, Ste 3371, 10048. SAN 372-2465. Tel: 212-775-0055, 212-839-9102. FAX: 212-839-9103.
Library Holdings: Bk Vols 7,500; Per Subs 25

S SEWARD & KISSEL LIBRARY, One Battery Park Plaza, 10004. SAN 325-9471. Tel: 212-574-1478. FAX: 212-480-8421. *Librn*, Judith Koziara; *Librn*, Robert J Davis
Library Holdings: Bk Vols 18,000; Bk Titles 1,200; Per Subs 215
Subject Interests: Law
Restriction: Staff use only
Partic in Westlaw

S SEYFARTH, SHAW, FAIRWEATHER & GERALDSON LIBRARY,* 1270 Avenue of the Americas, 25th flr, 10020. SAN 327-0211. Tel: 212-218-5500. FAX: 212-218-5526. *Librn*, Anthony Colella
Library Holdings: Bk Vols 10,000; Per Subs 100
Subject Interests: Labor, Securities
Restriction: Staff use only

L SHEARMAN & STERLING LIBRARY, 599 Lexington Ave, 10022-6069. SAN 353-7900. Tel: 212-848-4624. Interlibrary Loan Service Tel: 212-848-5400. FAX: 212-848-5229. *Mgr*, John W Lai; Tel: 212-848-4627, E-Mail: jlai@shearman.com
Founded 1873
Library Holdings: Bk Vols 35,000; Per Subs 700
Subject Interests: Banking law, Labor law, Legislative hist, Securities
Database Vendor: Dialog, Lexis-Nexis
Restriction: Not open to public

S SHEVCHENKO SCIENTIFIC SOCIETY INC, LIBRARY & ARCHIVES, 63 Fourth Ave, 10003. SAN 326-0976. Tel: 212-254-5130. FAX: 212-254-5239. E-Mail: info@shevchenko.org. Web Site: www.brama.com/sss. *Dir*, Svitlana Andrushkiw; Staff 3 (MLS 1, Non-MLS 2)
Founded 1952
Library Holdings: Bk Titles 45,000
Subject Interests: Ukrainian hist, Ukrainian lit
Special Collections: The Immigration of Ukrainians to North & South America, rare bks, archives & docs
Restriction: Access at librarian's discretion, Not a lending library
Function: Archival collection, Photocopies available, Research library
Open Mon-Fri 9-4

L SIDLEY & AUSTIN, Law Library,* 875 Third Ave, 10022. SAN 372-2554. Tel: 212-906-2110, Ext 211. FAX: 212-906-2021. *Ref*, Birgit Berkow
Library Holdings: Bk Vols 20,000; Per Subs 250
Open 9-6

S SIECUS (SEXUALITY INFORMATION & EDUCATION COUNCIL OF THE UNITED STATES), Mary S Calderone Library, 130 W 42nd St, Ste 350, 10036-7802. SAN 326-8756. Tel: 212-819-9770. FAX: 212-819-9776. E-Mail: siecus@siecus.org. Web Site: www.siecus.org.
Founded 1964
Library Holdings: Bk Titles 20,000; Per Subs 30
Subject Interests: Human sexuality, Sex educ
Publications: Series of bibliographies, fact sheets, booklets & reports on sexuality topics

L SIMPSON, THACHER & BARTLETT, Law Library,* 425 Lexington Ave, 10017-3954. SAN 312-0619. Tel: 212-455-2800. FAX: 212-455-3142, 455-2502. *Dir*, Peggy Martin; *Coll Develop*, Michael Bronson; Staff 20 (MLS 7, Non-MLS 13)
Founded 1884
Library Holdings: Bk Vols 50,000
Subject Interests: Antitrust, Banking, Corp, Labor, Taxation
Partic in OCLC Online Computer Library Center, Inc; RLIN

L SKADDEN, ARPS, SLATE, MEAGHER & FLOM LIBRARY, 4 Times Square, 10036. SAN 312-0627. Tel: 212-735-3000. FAX: 212-735-3244. *Dir*, Janet Accardo; *Librn*, Carrie Hirtz; Staff 26 (MLS 8, Non-MLS 18)
Founded 1948
Library Holdings: Bk Vols 75,000
Subject Interests: Law

S SKIDMORE, OWINGS & MERRILL, Information Services,* 14 Wall St, 10005. SAN 327-6937. Tel: 212-298-9300. FAX: 212-298-9500. Web Site: www.som.com. *Librn*, Carlos Martinez
Library Holdings: Bk Vols 3,000; Per Subs 175
Special Collections: Design Reports

S SMITHSONIAN INSTITUTION LIBRARIES, Cooper-Hewitt, National Design Museum Library, 2 E 91st St, 10128-9990. SAN 312-0651. Tel: 212-849-8331. FAX: 212-849-8339. E-Mail: libmail@sil.si.edu. Web Site: www.sil.si.edu. *Librn*, Stephen H VanDyk; *Ref Serv*, Elizabeth Broman; Staff 2 (MLS 2)
Library Holdings: Bk Vols 45,000; Per Subs 160
Subject Interests: Architecture, Decorative arts, Decorative design, Industrial design, Interior design, Rare books, Textiles
Special Collections: 18th & 19th Century Line Engravings (George W Kubler Coll); American & Foreign Auction Catalogs; Donald Deskey Archive; Henry Dreyfuss Archive; Ladislav Sutnar Archive; Pop-Up Book Coll; Therese Bonney Photographs; World's Fair Coll, 1844-1893
Restriction: By appointment only
Mem of Asn of Research Libraries; NY Metrop Ref & Res Libr Agency, Inc
Partic in New York Metrop Ref & Res Libr Agency
Friends of the Library Group

S R M SMYTHE & CO, INC, Inactive & Obsolete Securities Library,* 26 Broadway, Ste 271, 10004. SAN 312-066X. Tel: 212-943-1880. Toll Free Tel: 800-622-1880. FAX: 212-908-4047. E-Mail: info@rm-smythe.com. *Librn*, Diana E Herzog
Founded 1880
Library Holdings: Bk Vols 5,000
Subject Interests: Bonds of the world, Financial hist, Old stocks, Quotations, Stock tickers
Special Collections: Financial History (Antique Stocks & Bonds Certificates Coll - All Countries), autographs, bks, photogs
Publications: Friends of Financial History

S SOCIETY FOR THE ADVANCEMENT OF TRAVEL FOR THE HANDICAPPED LIBRARY,* 347 Fifth Ave, Ste 610, 10016. SAN 371-8735. Tel: 212-447-7284. FAX: 212-725-8253. Web Site: www.sath.org. *Exec Dir*, M T V Shaw-Lawrence
Library Holdings: Bk Titles 300; Per Subs 10

S SOCIETY OF WOMEN ENGINEERS, Information Center,* 120 Wall St, 11th flr, 10005-3902. SAN 375-2488. Tel: 212-509-9577. FAX: 212-509-0224. E-Mail: hq@swe.org. *Exec Dir*, Christine Burke
Library Holdings: Bk Vols 100

L SONNENSCHEIN, NATH & ROSENTHAL, Law Library,* 1221 Avenue of the Americas 24th flr, 10020. SAN 372-2473. Tel: 212-768-6700. FAX: 212-768-6800. *Librn*, Rochelle Malcow
Library Holdings: Bk Vols 4,500; Per Subs 15

S SONS OF THE REVOLUTION IN THE STATE OF NEW YORK LIBRARY, Fraunces Tavern Museum,* 54 Pearl St, 10004. SAN 371-4373. Tel: 212-425-1778, Ext 17. FAX: 212-509-3467. *Dir*, Lauren Kaminsky
Library Holdings: Bk Vols 9,000; Bk Titles 9,000

S SONY MUSIC ENTERTAINMENT, INC, Sony Music Archives,* 550 Madison Ave, 10022. SAN 374-4892. Tel: 212-833-4737. FAX: 212-833-4102. *Coordr, Res*, Nathaniel Brewster

S SOTHEBY'S LIBRARY,* 1334 York Ave, 10021. SAN 312-0694. Tel: 212-606-7265. FAX: 212-606-7499. *Librn*, Judy Israel
Library Holdings: Bk Titles 20,000; Per Subs 200
Subject Interests: Decorative arts, Painting
Special Collections: Auction Sales (American Art Association, Anderson Galleries, Parke Bernet & Sotheby Parke Bernet since 1891)
Restriction: Not open to public

S SOUTH STREET SEAPORT MUSEUM LIBRARY,* 207 Front St, 10038. SAN 312-0708. Tel: 212-748-8648. FAX: 212-748-8610.
Founded 1967
Library Holdings: Bk Vols 20,000; Bk Titles 17,000
Subject Interests: Maritime history, New York City, Shipping
Special Collections: General Shipping (Port of New York), photogs & negatives; ship plans
Open Mon-Fri 10:30-6

S STACKS RARE COIN COMPANY OF NY, Technical Information Center Library, 123 W 57th St, 10019-2280. SAN 327-0270. Tel: 212-582-2580. Toll Free Tel: 800-566-2580. FAX: 212-245-5018. E-Mail: info@stacks.com. Web Site: www.stacks.com. *In Charge*, Scott Mitchell
Founded 1858
Library Holdings: Bk Vols 5,060
Subject Interests: Numismatics

S STANDARD & POOR'S LIBRARY, Central Inquiry Center, 55 Water St, 43rd Flr, 10041. SAN 312-0740. Tel: 212-438-7760. FAX: 212-438-3429. *Info Res*, Milvia Luckenbach; *Info Res*, Bethany Phillip; Staff 24 (MLS 5, Non-MLS 19)
Founded 1917
Library Holdings: Bk Vols 15,500; Bk Titles 7,000; Per Subs 2,000
Special Collections: Corporate File, pamphlets; Corporations; Corporations (Reports from 1968), microfiche; Daily Stock Price Record (NASDAQ, American Stock Exchange, New York Stock Exchange); Finance Securities Investments (Factual Standard & Poor's publications since 1860), bk, per; Financial Chronicles; Historical Pricing & Research; S&P Security Price Index Record
Publications: Newsletter
Restriction: Staff use only

CM STATE UNIVERSITY OF NEW YORK, STATE COLLEGE OF OPTOMETRY, Harold Kohn Vision Science Library, 33 W 42nd St, 10036-8003. SAN 312-0759. Tel: 212-780-5088. Interlibrary Loan Service Tel: 212-780-5087. FAX: 212-780-5094. Web Site: www.sunyopt.edu/library/libhome.html. *Dir*, Elaine Wells; E-Mail: ewells@sunyopt.edu; *Asst Librn, Coll Develop, Tech Servs*, Kadri Niider; E-Mail: kniider@sunyopt.edu; *ILL*, Clementine Perez; E-Mail: perez@sunyopt.edu; Staff 2 (MLS 2)
Founded 1971. Enrl 283; Fac 150; Highest Degree: Doctorate
Library Holdings: Bk Vols 38,251; Bk Titles 20,983; Per Subs 483
Subject Interests: Ophthalmology, Optics, Optometry, Physiological optics
Special Collections: Learning Disabilities & Optometry
Publications: Newsletter
Partic in Docline; New York Metrop Ref & Res Libr Agency; OCLC Online Computer Library Center, Inc

S STEP FAMILY FOUNDATION, INC LIBRARY,* 333 W End Ave, 10023. SAN 327-0297. Tel: 212-877-3244. FAX: 212-362-7030. *Exec Dir*, Jeannette Lofas

SR STEPHEN WISE FREE SYNAGOGUE, Rabbi Edward E Klein Memorial Library, 30 W 68th St, 10023. SAN 371-6260. Tel: 212-877-4050, Ext 38. FAX: 212-787-7108. *Dir, Librn*, Helen Singer; Staff 1 (MLS 1)
Library Holdings: Bk Vols 5,000
Subject Interests: Judaica
Special Collections: Stephen Wise Archives, docs, letters

S STOCK MARKET PHOTO AGENCY,* 360 Park Ave S, 16th flr, 10010. SAN 324-2110. Tel: 212-684-7878. Toll Free Tel: 800-283-0808. FAX: 212-532-6750. Web Site: www.stockmarket.com.
Operate our Network called STOCKNET to develop world wide library of color transparencies

L STROOCK, STROOCK & LAVAN LIBRARY, 180 Maiden Lane, 10038. SAN 312-0791. Tel: 212-806-5700. FAX: 212-806-6006. *Dir*, June Berger; E-Mail: jberger@stroock.com
Library Holdings: Bk Vols 20,000; Per Subs 41
Restriction: Staff use only

L SULLIVAN & CROMWELL, Law Library, 125 Broad St, 10004. SAN 312-0805. Tel: 212-558-3780. FAX: 212-558-3346. E-Mail: library@sullcrom.com. Web Site: www.sullcrom.com. *Dir Libr Serv*, Jennifer G Rish; E-Mail: rishj@sullcrom.com; *Assoc Dir*, Alison Alifanao; E-Mail: alifanoa@sullcrom.com; *Coordr*, Loius Benjamin; E-Mail: benjaminl@sullcrom.com; *Head Tech Servs*, Kan Kin; E-Mail: kink@sullcrom.com; *Head Ref*, Lucy Redmond; E-Mail: redmondl@sullcrom.com; *Res*, Brian Craig; E-Mail: craigb@sullcrom.com; *Res*, Tariq Khwaja; E-Mail: khwajat@sullcrom.com; *Res*, Brian Nolan; E-Mail: nolanb@sullcrom.com; *Res*, Evelyn Seeger; E-Mail: seegere@sullcrom.com; *Res*, Teresa Tully; E-Mail: tullyt@sullcrom.com; Staff 11 (MLS 9, Non-MLS 2)
Library Holdings: Bk Vols 70,000
Database Vendor: Dialog, Lexis-Nexis, OCLC - First Search

S SUPERSTOCK, INC, 381 Park Ave S, 10016. SAN 375-0949. Tel: 212-889-6464. Toll Free Tel: 800-828-4545. FAX: 212-889-9696. Web Site: www.superstock.com. *Dir*, Marie Bouvet
Subject Interests: Stock photog

GL SUPREME COURT, APPELLATE DIVISION, First Dept Law Library, 27 Madison Ave, 10010. SAN 312-0813. Tel: 212-340-0478. *Librn*, Gene Preudhomme; E-Mail: genep@ix.netcom.com
Founded 1901
Library Holdings: Bk Vols 70,000; Per Subs 60

S SWEDISH INFORMATION SERVICE, Reference Library, One Dag Hammarskjold Plaza, 45th Flr, Second Ave at 48th St, 10017-2201. SAN 329-997X. Tel: 212-751-2550. FAX: 212-752-4789. E-Mail: swedinfo@ix.netcom.com. Web Site: www.swedeninfo.com. *Asst Librn*, Elisabeth Halvarsson-Stapen
Library Holdings: Bk Titles 8,000; Per Subs 80
Special Collections: Swedish-American Immigration History

L SWIDLER, BERLIN, SHEREFF, FRIEDMAN, Law Library, 405 Lexington Ave, 10174. SAN 372-249X. Tel: 212-973-0111. FAX: 212-891-9598. *Librn*, Carol Jarema; E-Mail: cjarema@swidlaw.com
Library Holdings: Bk Vols 10,000; Per Subs 50
Restriction: Staff use only

S TAIPEI ECONOMIC & CULTURAL OFFICE, Chinese Information & Culture Center Library, 1230 Avenue of the Americas, 2 Flr, 10020-1513. SAN 325-7517. Tel: 212-373-1800. FAX: 212-373-1866. E-Mail: roctaiwan@taipei.org. Web Site: www.taipei.org. *Dir*, William Yeh; Tel: 212-373-1811; *Librn*, Verna Tang; Tel: 212-373-1836, Fax: 212-373-1867, E-Mail: roctaiwan@taipei.org; Staff 4 (MLS 2, Non-MLS 2)
Founded 1991
Library Holdings: Bk Vols 42,000; Per Subs 199
Subject Interests: Art, Economics, History, Literature, Philosophy, Politics, Religion
Special Collections: Republic of China Government Document Coll
Automation Activity & Vendor Info: (Acquisitions) EOS; (Cataloging) EOS; (Circulation) EOS; (OPAC) EOS; (Serials) EOS
Publications: CICC Currents
Partic in RLIN

S TAYLOR BUSINESS INSTITUTE LIBRARY,* 269 W 40th St, 10018. SAN 327-0335. Tel: 212-302-4000. *Librn*, Mary E Cardwell; Fax: 212-302-2624, E-Mail: cardwellm@tbiglobal.com; Staff 1 (MLS 1)
Enrl 350; Highest Degree: Associate
Library Holdings: Bk Vols 3,000; Bk Titles 2,700; Per Subs 26
Partic in New York Metrop Ref & Res Libr Agency
Open Mon-Thurs 9-8

C TEACHERS COLLEGE - COLUMBIA UNIVERSITY, The Milbank Memorial Library, 525 W 120th St, The Milbank Memorial Library, 10027-6696. SAN 353-0345. Tel: 212-678-3494. Circulation Tel: 212-678-3028. TDD: 212-678-4124. FAX: 212-678-3092. E-Mail: @edunet.tc.columbia.edu. Web Site: lweb.tc.columbia.edu. *Dir*, Jane P Franck; *Assoc Dir*, Maureen E Horgan; Tel: 212-678-3446, E-Mail: maureen@edunet.tc.columbia.edu; *Assoc Dir*, Francis M Webster; Tel: 212-678-3039, E-Mail: frank@edunet.tc.columbia.edu; *Head, Acq*, Janet Pierce; Tel: 212-678-3457, E-Mail: janet@edunet.tc.columbia.edu; *Head, Cat*, Anita Lauer; Tel: 212-678-3424, E-Mail: anita@edunet.tc.columbia.edu; *Head, Circ*, David Donabedian; Tel: 212-678-3027, E-Mail: david@edunet.tc.columbia.edu; *Head Ref*, Allen Foresta; Tel: 212-678-3026, E-Mail: allen@edunet.tc.columbia.edu; *Head, Ser Acq*, Yodit Kebede; Tel: 212-678-3440, E-Mail: yodit@edunet.tc.columbia.edu; *Syst Coordr*, Adolfo Bon; Tel: 212-678-3819, E-Mail: adolfo@edunet.tc.columbia.edu; *Librn*, Hal Grossman; Tel: 212-678-3021, E-Mail: hal@edunet.tc.columbia.edu; *Librn*, Cecile Hastie; Tel: 212-678-3020, E-Mail: cecile@edunet.tc.columbia.edu; *Librn*, Anca Meret; Tel: 212-678-3496, E-Mail: anca@edunet.tc.columbia.edu; *Spec Coll & Archives*, Melanie Martin; Tel: 212-678-3439, E-Mail: melanie@edunet.tc.columbia.edu; *Spec Coll & Archives*, Dr David Ment; Tel: 212-678-4104, E-Mail: david@edunet.tc.columbia.edu; *Spec Coll & Archives*, Bette Weneck; Tel: 212-678-3072, E-Mail: bette@edunet.tc.columbia.edu; *Ch Servs*, Irina Posnansky; Tel: 212-678-3145, E-Mail: irina@edunet.tc.columbia.edu; *Info Tech*, Abdur Raqib; Tel: 212-678-4073, E-Mail: abdur@edunet.tc.columbia.edu; *Per*, Nelson Escobar; Tel: 212-678-3035, E-Mail: nelson@edunet.tc.columbia.edu; *Coll Develop*, Jennifer Govan; Tel: 212-678-3022, E-Mail: jennifer@edunet.tc.columbia.edu; *Circ*, Yaling Li; E-Mail: yaling@edunet.tc.columbia.edu; *Cat*, Nina Erastov; Tel: 212-678-3032, E-Mail: nina@edunet.tc.columbia.edu; *Cat*, Weiyan Meng; Tel: 212-678-3032, E-Mail: weiyan@edunet.tc.columbia.edu; *Cat*, Ellen Stockdale-Wolfe; Staff 43 (MLS 20, Non-MLS 23)
Founded 1887. Circ 85,091; Enrl 5,000; Fac 130; Highest Degree: Doctorate
Sep 1999-Aug 2000 Mats Exp $496,954, Books $218,942, Per/Ser (Incl. Access Fees) $203,543, Presv $39,989, Micro $19,127, Electronic Ref Mat (Incl. Access Fees) $15,353. Sal $1,846,297 (Prof $1,251,329)
Library Holdings: Bk Vols 591,775; Bk Titles 375,489; Per Subs 2,095
Subject Interests: Adult education, Applied linguistics, Art educ, Audiology, Bilingual Education, Clinical psychol, Communications, Computing, Counseling psychology, Curric, Early childhood educ, Econ educ, Educ admin, Educ philos, Education, Educational psychology, Elementary education, English, Evaluation, Health educ, Health sciences, Higher educ, Hist of educ, Int educ, Mathematics, Neurosciences, Nursing, Nutrition, Psychology, Science, Secondary educ, Soc studies, Sociology, Spanish, Spec edc, Speech-lang pathology, Teaching
Special Collections: Annie E. Moore Illustrated Children's Books (18th & 19th Century); Black History Series (Educational Coll) films; Board of Education of the City of New York Records, mss; Children's Village Records, mss; Curriculum Resource Center Coll; Education (Rare Books of 15th-19th Century); Educational Microcomputer Software Coll (K-12); Harvey Darton Collection of English Children's Books (18th & 19th Century); Historical photographs relating to education; Learning Technology Services; Microcomputer Resource Center; National Council of Social Studies Records Coll, mss; National Kindergarten Association Records, mss; Nursing Education (Adelaid Nutting History of Nursing Collection); Papers of Prominent Educators; Resource Center; Teachers College Archives; Textbooks Coll (18th-20th century K-12 texts, both US & foreign)
Automation Activity & Vendor Info: (Acquisitions) Innovative Interfaces Inc.; (Cataloging) Innovative Interfaces Inc.; (Circulation) Innovative Interfaces Inc.; (OPAC) Innovative Interfaces Inc.
Database Vendor: CARL, Dialog, Ebsco - EbscoHost, GaleNet, IAC - Info Trac, IAC - SearchBank, Innovative Interfaces INN - View, Lexis-Nexis, OCLC - First Search, OVID Technologies, ProQuest, Silverplatter Information Inc., Wilson - Wilson Web
Publications: Audiovisual & Video Lab Services; Bulletin of New Titles; Circulation & Borrowing Policies; Collection development policy; David Eugene Smith Mathematics Education Coll; EDUCAT: Searching Basics, Remote Dial-in; Education in; Floor Plan; Library bookmarks for call numbers, locations, Photocopy service, specific collections; Referral guide, Interlibrary Loan Services, Special Services for the Disabled; Research guides on specific subject areas of the TC Collection; Russia & Other Former Soviet Republics; Visitors Guide
Function: For research purposes
Partic in BRS; Dialog Corporation; Metropolitan Library Service Agency; Metropolitan New York Library Council; New York Metrop Ref & Res Libr Agency; Research Libraries Group, Inc; RLIN; Wilsonline
Special Services for the Deaf - Books on deafness & sign language; Special interest periodicals
Special Services for the Blind - Braille printer & software; Compressed speech tape recorder; High powered magnifying glasses; Thermoform Brailon Duplicator
Friends of the Library Group

S TEACHERS INSURANCE & ANNUITY ASSOCIATION OF AMERICA, College Retirement Equities Fund, Business Information & Research Services,* 730 Third Ave, 12th fl, 10017. SAN 353-796X. Tel: 212-490-9000, Ext 2592. FAX: 212-916-5858. *Chief Librn*, Margaret Beirne; *Asst Librn*, Krista Friedman; *Asst Librn*, Mary-Lynne Bancone; *Asst Librn*, Lisa J Koch; *Archivist*, Carolyn Kopp; Staff 9 (MLS 5, Non-MLS 4)
Founded 1959
Library Holdings: Bk Vols 10,000; Bk Titles 10,000; Per Subs 541
Subject Interests: Ins for teachers, Retirement plans
Partic in Dialog Corporation; OCLC Online Computer Library Center, Inc

Branches:
COLLEGE RETIREMENT EQUITIES FUND, RESEARCH LIBRARY, 730 Third Ave, 11th fl, 10017. SAN 353-7994. Tel: 212-916-4007. FAX: 212-916-4582. *Librn*, Linda Bashover; Staff 5 (MLS 1, Non-MLS 4)
Founded 1973
Library Holdings: Bk Titles 800; Per Subs 390
Subject Interests: Bus, Econ, Investing, Mgt

J TECHNICAL CAREER INSTITUTES, INC,* 320 W 31st St, 10001. SAN 325-2752. Tel: 212-594-4000, Ext 279. FAX: 212-629-3937. *Dir*, Mark Lefkowitz; Staff 2 (MLS 1, Non-MLS 1)
Library Holdings: Bk Vols 4,500; Bk Titles 4,350; Per Subs 404
Subject Interests: Electrical engineering, Electronics, Mathematics

L THACHER, PROFFITT & WOOD, Law Library, Two World Trade Ctr, 39th flr, 10048. SAN 312-0880. Tel: 212-912-7743. FAX: 212-912-7751. *Librn*, Liz Tavss Ohman; E-Mail: lohman@thacherproffitt.com; *Asst Librn*, Jeannette Schneider
Library Holdings: Bk Vols 18,500; Per Subs 75

J THE ALFRED ADLER INSTITUTE OF NEW YORK,* 24 E 21st, 8th flr, 10010. SAN 329-241X. Tel: 212-254-1048. *Exec Dir*, Dr Robert Ellenbogen
Founded 1950. Enrl 40
Library Holdings: Bk Titles 300; Per Subs 500
Subject Interests: Counseling, Psychiatry, Psychology, Psychotherapy
Open after 4:30

S THE EXPLORERS CLUB, James B Ford Library, 46 E 70th St, 10021. SAN 311-7553. Tel: 212-628-8383. FAX: 212-717-1584. *Librn*, Janet Baldwin; Staff 1 (MLS 1)
Founded 1905
Library Holdings: Bk Titles 20,000; Per Subs 50
Subject Interests: Ethnology, Exploration, Natural history, Travel
Special Collections: 18th - 20th Century Travel; Arctic Exploration & Studies (Peary Coll)
Function: Reference only
Friends of the Library Group

S THE JAMES BEARD FOUNDATION, Archive & Library, 167 W 12th St, 10011. SAN 323-8490. Tel: 212-675-4984. FAX: 212-645-1438. E-Mail: beardlib@sca.com. *Librn*, Phyllis Isaacson; Staff 1 (MLS 1)
Founded 1987
Library Holdings: Bk Titles 2,300; Per Subs 15
Subject Interests: Cookbooks, Wines
Special Collections: Material by & about James Beard

S THE JEWISH MUSEUM, National Jewish Archive of Broadcasting,* 1109 Fifth Ave, 10128. SAN 326-3274. Tel: 212-423-3234. FAX: 212-423-3232. Web Site: www.thejewishmuseum.org. *Dir*, Aviva Weintraub; *AV, Coordr*, Alessandro Cavadini; *Archivist, Coordr*, Andrew Ingall; Staff 3 (Non-MLS 3)
Founded 1981
1998-1999 Mats Exp $22,750, Books $400, Per/Ser (Incl. Access Fees) $500, Presv $500, AV Equip $21,350
Library Holdings: Bk Titles 4,000
Special Collections: Civilization & the Jews (Heritage Coll), 16mm Outtake footage; Holocaust (Israel State Archives & Eichmann Trial Coll), v-tapes
Publications: A Subject Guide to the Coll of the National Jewish Archive of Broadcasting; Annotated catalogue of selected holdings of the Jewish Museum's National Jewish Archive of Broadcasting; Brochures
Restriction: Non-circulating to the public

THE METROPOLITAN MUSEUM OF ART

S CLOISTERS LIBRARY, Fort Tryon Park, 10040. SAN 353-1848. Tel: 212-923-3700, Ext 154. FAX: 212-795-3640. E-Mail: cloister@interport.net. *Asst Librn*, Paige North
Founded 1938
Library Holdings: Bk Vols 13,000; Per Subs 66
Subject Interests: European medieval art, Medieval archit, Middle ages
Special Collections: Archives of The Cloisters; George Gray Barnard Papers; Harry Bober Papers; Sumner McKnight Crosby Papers
Partic in RLIN

S IRENE LEWISOHN COSTUME REFERENCE LIBRARY, 1000 Fifth Ave, 10028. SAN 353-1961. Tel: 212-879-5500, Ext 3018. FAX: 212-570-3970. Web Site: metmuseum.org. *Librn*, Tatyana Pakhladzhyan; E-Mail: tatyana.pakhladzhyan@metmuseum.org; *Asst Librn*, Stephane Houy-Towner
Founded 1951
Library Holdings: Bk Titles 20,000; Per Subs 75
Subject Interests: Fashion, Hist of costume
Special Collections: Giorgio di Sant 'Angelo Coll; Mainbocher Archive; Norman Norell Coll (scrap bks)

S PHOTOGRAPH & SLIDE LIBRARY, 1000 Fifth Ave, 10028. SAN 353-1996. Tel: 212-650-2262. FAX: 212-396-5050. *Chief Librn*, Priscilla Farah; Staff 23 (MLS 7, Non-MLS 16)
Founded 1907
Subject Interests: Hist of art from prehistoric to present time, With greater coverage of Western arts
Special Collections: William Keighley Color Slide Coll of architecture & other arts of Europe & Asia Minor
Large format color transparencies of objects in Metropolitan Museum of Art available through rental for publication; black & white photographs of the Metropolitan Museum's collections available for purchase through special order

S ROBERT GOLDWATER LIBRARY, 1000 Fifth Ave, 10028-0198. SAN 353-1872. Tel: 212-570-3707. FAX: 212-570-3879. E-Mail: goldwater.library@metmuseum.org. Web Site: library.metmuseum.org. *Head of Libr*, Ross Day; *Librn*, Leslie Preston; Staff 3 (MLS 2, Non-MLS 1)
Founded 1957
Library Holdings: Bk Vols 20,000; Bk Titles 15,000; Per Subs 224
Subject Interests: African, Am Indian, Pacific
Database Vendor: Innovative Interfaces INN - View
Publications: Catalog of The Robert Goldwater Library (Boston, 1982 4 vols)
Partic in RLIN

S ROBERT LEHMAN COLLECTION LIBRARY, 1000 Fifth Ave, 10028. SAN 353-1937. Tel: 212-570-3915. FAX: 212-650-2542. E-Mail: robertlehmancollection@metmuseum.org. Web Site: www.metmuseum.org. *Curator*, Pia Palladino; Staff 2 (MLS 1, Non-MLS 1)
Library Holdings: Bk Vols 18,500
Subject Interests: Decorative arts, Old Master drawings, Renaissance, Western European Arts from the 13th to 20th centuries, With special emphasis on Siena
Special Collections: Archives of bk, mss, reproductions, correspondence; Photograph Coll, photogs, negatives

S THOMAS J WATSON LIBRARY, 1000 Fifth Ave, 10028-0198. SAN 353-1813. Tel: 212-650-2225. Interlibrary Loan Service Tel: 212-650-2504. Circulation Tel: 212-650-2175. FAX: 212-570-3847. E-Mail: metart4@metgate.metro.org. Web Site: www.metmuseum.org/education/er_lib.asp#tho. *Chief Librn*, Kenneth Soehner; Tel: 212-570-3933, E-Mail: ken.soehner@metmuseum.org; *Reader Servs*, Linda Seckelson; Tel: 212-570-3759, E-Mail: linda.seckelson@metmuseum.org; *Acq*, Theresa Boccia; Tel: 212-650-2949, E-Mail: terri.boccia@metmuseum.org; *Ser*, Evalyn Stone; Tel: 212-650-2440, E-Mail: evalyn.stone@metmuseum.org; *ILL*, Heather Topcik; E-Mail: heather.topcik@metmuseum.org; *Electronic Resources*, Carolyn DeLuca; Tel: 212-650-2912, E-Mail: cdeluca@metmuseum.org. Subject Specialists: *Preservation*, Mindell Dubansky; Staff 47 (MLS 17, Non-MLS 30)
Founded 1880
Jul 2000-Jun 2001 Mats Exp $475,000. Sal $1,800,000
Library Holdings: Bk Vols 450,000; Per Subs 2,500
Subject Interests: Archaeology, Architecture, Decorative art, Fine art
Special Collections: Auction-Sale Catalogs; Autograph Letters; Ephemera on Individual Artists; Museum History
Automation Activity & Vendor Info: (Acquisitions) Innovative Interfaces Inc.; (Cataloging) Innovative Interfaces Inc.; (Circulation) Innovative Interfaces Inc.; (OPAC) Innovative Interfaces Inc.; (Serials) Innovative Interfaces Inc.
Publications: Library Catalog of the Metropolitan Museum of Art (2nd ed)
Partic in Metropolitan New York Library Council; Research Libraries Group, Inc; RLIN
Auction catalog holdings are a part of SCIPIO (Sales Catalog Index Project Input Online) & RLIN database
Friends of the Library Group

S URIS LIBRARY & RESOURCE CENTER Tel: 212-570-3788. FAX: 212-570-3972. E-Mail: urislibr@metmuseum.org. Web Site: www.metmuseum.org.
Founded 1941
Library Holdings: Bk Vols 4,060
Subject Interests: Archaeology, Art educ, Art lit, Crafts, Fine arts, Illustrators, Metrop Mus of Art, Mythology, Visual arts
Special Collections: Art & Architecture Coll
Restriction: Open to public for reference only
Partic in RLIN
Teachers Resource Room contains books, periodicals & circulating AV materials available to educators & community groups

S THEATRE COLLECTION OF THE INTERNATIONAL THEATRE INSTITUTE OF THE UNITED STATES, INC, 355 Lexington Ave, 10017-6603. SAN 311-8304. Tel: 212-697-5230. FAX: 212-983-4847. Web Site: www.tcg.org. *Dir*, Louis A Rachow; E-Mail: lrachow@tcg.org; Staff 1 (MLS 1)
Founded 1969
Library Holdings: Bk Vols 6,166; Per Subs 275
Subject Interests: Int performing arts
Special Collections: Collection of 12,905 plays from 97 countries; Contemporary Theatre in 146 countries, brochures, clippings, house organs, newsletters, playbills, schedules, yearbks
Publications: Newsletter

L THELEN, REID & PRIEST LLP LIBRARY, 40 W 57th St, 10019. SAN 312-0252. Tel: 212-603-2265. Reference Tel: 212-603-2266. FAX: 212-603-2001. *Head Librn*, Ruth Ulfrets; E-Mail: rulferts@thelenreid.com; *Res*,

David Byrne; *Res*, Daming Lee; Tel: 212-603-2079; Staff 8 (MLS 3, Non-MLS 5)
Subject Interests: Fed securities, Foreign, Latin America, Pub utility, Taxation
Automation Activity & Vendor Info: (Cataloging) SIRSI; (Serials) SIRSI
Database Vendor: Dialog, Lexis-Nexis
Function: ILL to other special libraries

S J WALTER THOMPSON CO, Knowledge Center, 466 Lexington Ave, 10017. SAN 312-0899. Tel: 212-210-7267. FAX: 212-210-7817. Web Site: www.jwt.com. *Dir*, Carol Simas; Staff 7 (MLS 5, Non-MLS 2)
Founded 1918
Library Holdings: Bk Vols 7,955; Bk Titles 5,441; Per Subs 400
Subject Interests: Advertising, Communications, Indust, Marketing, Markets, Products, Servs
Special Collections: Consumer Print Advertisements; Picture Reference Coll
Publications: Reference Feature
Partic in Dialog Corporation; Dow Jones News Retrieval; Newsnet

TIME WARNER, INC
S RESEARCH CENTER, 1271 Avenue of the Americas, 10020. SAN 353-8028. Tel: 212-522-7033. FAX: 212-522-0224. *Dir*, Lany W McDonald; *Asst Dir*, Lynn Dombek; *Ref*, Patricia Clark; Staff 50 (MLS 31, Non-MLS 19)
Founded 1930
Library Holdings: Bk Titles 60,000; Per Subs 2,300
S SPORTS ILLUSTRATED LIBRARY, 1271 Avenue of the Americas, 10020. SAN 353-8052. Tel: 212-522-3397. FAX: 212-522-1719. *Librn*, Linda Ronan; E-Mail: lronan@si.timeinc.com
Founded 1960
Library Holdings: Bk Titles 5,000; Per Subs 190
Special Collections: College & Professional Team Media Guides; Olympic Games Resource Coll
Publications: Sports Source
Restriction: Staff use only
Partic in Data Time; Dialog Corporation

L TORYS, Law Library, 237 Park Ave, 20th Flr, 10017. SAN 372-4530. Tel: 212-880-6177. FAX: 212-682-0200. Web Site: www.torys.com. *Asst Librn*, Claudette Wellington; *Librn*, Michael B Hoffman; E-Mail: mhoffman@torys.com
Library Holdings: Bk Vols 10,000; Per Subs 50

C TOURO COLLEGE LIBRARIES, 2733 W 23rd St, 10010. SAN 312-0937. Tel: 212-463-0400, Ext 321. FAX: 212-627-9144. Web Site: www.touro.edu/library. *Dir Libr Serv*, Jacqueline A Maxin; Tel: 212-463-0400, Ext 221, Fax: 212-463-0400, Ext 550, E-Mail: maxin@touro.edu; *Chief Librn*, Blanche L Cohn; Tel: 631-665-1600, Ext 224, Fax: 631-665-6263, E-Mail: blanchec@touro.edu; *Chief Librn*, Robert J Kayton; Fax: 212-463-0400, Ext 550, E-Mail: robertjk@touro.edu; *Chief Librn*, Bashe Simon; Tel: 718-252-7800, Ext 226, Fax: 718-338-7732, E-Mail: simonb@touro.edu; *Librn*, Rachel M Dobin; Fax: 212-463-0400, Ext 550, E-Mail: rachelmd@touro.edu; *Librn*, Jerome Goldstein; Tel: 212-722-1575, Ext 171, Fax: 212-426-5544, E-Mail: goldstj@touro.edu; *Librn*, Margaret Hamm; Tel: 718-871-3779, Fax: 718-871-4072, E-Mail: margareh@touro.edu; *Librn*, Leib I Klein; Tel: 718-871-3779, Fax: 718-871-4072, E-Mail: leibk@touro.edu; *Librn*, Myra R Reisman; Tel: 631-665-1600, Ext 224, Fax: 631-665-6263, E-Mail: myrar@touro.edu; *Librn*, Idelle Rudman; Tel: 212-213-2230, Ext 119, Fax: 212-689-3515, E-Mail: rudmani@touro.edu; *Librn*, Roberta Standish; Tel: 718-252-7800, Ext 260, Fax: 212-463-0400, Ext 440, E-Mail: robertas@touro.edu; *Cat*, Howard R Schwartz; Tel: 212-463-0400, Ext 219, Fax: 212-463-0400, Ext 550, E-Mail: howardrs@touro.edu; *Electronic Resources*, Michoel Ronn; Tel: 212-463-0400, Ext 229, Fax: 212-463-0400, Ext 550, E-Mail: michoelr@touro.edu; *Tech Servs*, Evelyn W Behar; Tel: 212-463-0400, Ext 224, Fax: 212-463-0400, Ext 550, E-Mail: evelynb@touro.edu. Subject Specialists: *Judaica*, Idelle Rudman; *Medical*, Blanche L Cohn; *Medical*, Myra R Reisman; Staff 40 (MLS 26, Non-MLS 14)
Library Holdings: Bk Vols 250,000; Per Subs 2,800
Subject Interests: Business, Education, Jewish studies, Psychology
Publications: Newsletter; Pathfinder; Research & Writing
Partic in Long Island Library Resources Council; New York Metrop Ref & Res Libr Agency

SR TRINITY CHURCH ARCHIVES, 74 Trinity Pl, 4th fl, 10006-2088. SAN 320-4405. Tel: 212-602-9676. FAX: 212-602-9675. *In Charge*, Gwynedd Cannon; E-Mail: cgwynedd@trinitywallstreet.org; Staff 2 (MLS 1, Non-MLS 1)
Founded 1980
Library Holdings: Bk Titles 500
Subject Interests: Episcopal church, Theology

S TURKISH TOURIST OFFICE LIBRARY, 821 United Nations Plaza, 4th flr, 10017. SAN 374-7581. Tel: 212-687-2194. FAX: 212-599-7568. E-Mail: ny@tourismturkey.org. Web Site: www.tourismturkey.org. *Dir*, Selami Karaibrahimgil

S TURTLE BAY MUSIC SCHOOL LIBRARY, 244 E 52nd St, 10022-6201. SAN 370-5234. Tel: 212-753-8811. FAX: 212-752-6228. Web Site: www.tbms.org. *Dir*, David Carleton
Founded 1925. Enrl 650; Fac 60
Library Holdings: Bk Titles 1,000
Special Collections: 19th Century & Early 20th Sheet Music; Out of Print Editions of Music

S TWENTIETH CENTURY FUND LIBRARY,* 41 E 70th St, 10021. SAN 327-0378. Tel: 212-535-4441. FAX: 212-535-7534. E-Mail: xxthfund@ix.netcom.com. *Librn*, Rashida Valvassori; E-Mail: valvassori@tcf.org
Library Holdings: Bk Vols 1,000
Restriction: Staff use only

S UNION LEAGUE CLUB LIBRARY, 38 E 37th St, 10016. SAN 312-102X. Tel: 212-685-3800. FAX: 212-685-3675. *Librn*, Arthur Lawrence
Founded 1863
Library Holdings: Bk Titles 25,000; Per Subs 120
Subject Interests: American biography, American hist, Civil War

SR UNION OF AMERICAN HEBREW CONGREGATIONS, Synagogue Architectural & Art Library,* 633 Third Ave, 10017. SAN 375-6378. Tel: 212-249-0100. FAX: 212-650-4239. *Dir*, Dale Glasser; *Publ Servs*, Mary Markowitz
Library Holdings: Bk Titles 125

S UNION OF NEEDLE TRADE INDUSTRIAL & TEXTILE EMPLOYEES, Research Department Library, 1710 Broadway, 10019. SAN 311-5623. Tel: 212-265-7000. FAX: 212-489-7238. *In Charge*, Jeanette Revaro
Founded 1921
Library Holdings: Bk Vols 4,500; Bk Titles 3,000; Per Subs 363
Subject Interests: Earnings, Employment, Int trade in apparel, Labor hist, Labor standards, Labor-mgt relations, Production, Soc ins progs, Textiles
Special Collections: Publications by & about Amalgamated Clothing & Textile Workers; Union & its Predecessors; Union Agreements

R UNION THEOLOGICAL SEMINARY, The Burke Library, 3041 Broadway, 10027. SAN 312-1054. Tel: 212-280-1504. Interlibrary Loan Service Tel: 212-280-1314. FAX: 212-280-1456. E-Mail: refdesk@uts.columbia.edu. *Dir*, Sara J Myers; Staff 12 (MLS 6, Non-MLS 6)
Founded 1836. Enrl 226; Fac 25; Highest Degree: Doctorate
Library Holdings: Bk Vols 584,648
Subject Interests: Art, Bible, Christian ethics, Church history, Communication, Ecumenics
Special Collections: (Hymn Society of America Coll); Americana Coll; Archives; Auburn Coll; Bonhoeffer Coll; British History & Theology (McAlpin Coll); Christian Science Coll; Ecumenics & Church Union (William Adams Brown Coll); Gillett Coll; Hymnology; Missionary Research Library Coll; mss & early printed bks; Reformation Tracts; Thompson; Van Ess Coll
Publications: UTS CATALOG (microfiche)
Partic in New York State Interlibrary Loan Network; OCLC Online Computer Library Center, Inc; Research Libraries Group, Inc; RLIN

S UNITED CEREBRAL PALSY OF NEW YORK, INC LIBRARY,* 120 E 23rd St, 5th flr, 10010. SAN 327-0394. Tel: 212-979-9700. FAX: 212-260-7469.
Library Holdings: Bk Vols 220

S UNITED HOSPITAL FUND OF NEW YORK, Reference Library, 350 Fifth Ave, 23rd flr, 10118. SAN 312-1070. Tel: 212-494-0720. FAX: 212-494-0800. Web Site: www.uhfnyc.org. *Librn*, Rochelle Yates; E-Mail: syates@uhfnyc.org
Founded 1941
1998-1999 Mats Exp $20,000, Books $10,000, Per/Ser (Incl. Access Fees) $10,000. Sal $60,000 (Prof $50,000)
Library Holdings: Per Subs 120
Subject Interests: Fund raising, Health care econ, Health care mgt
Automation Activity & Vendor Info: (OPAC) CASPR
Publications: United Hospital Fund
Restriction: By appointment only
Partic in EFTS; Manhattan-Bronx Health Sciences Libraries Group; New York Metrop Ref & Res Libr Agency

S UNITED LODGE OF THEOSOPHISTS, Theosophy Hall Library, 347 E 72nd St, 10021. SAN 312-1089. Tel: 212-535-2230.
Founded 1922
Library Holdings: Bk Titles 6,800
Subject Interests: Ancient philosophy, Ancient psychol, Comparative mythology, Comparative relig, Modern philosophy, Original writings of H P Blavatsky, Original writings of Wm Q Judge, Parapsychol, Reincarnation research in relig, Reincarnation research in science, Theosophical hist
Restriction: By appointment only

S UNITED NATIONS, Dag Hammarskjold Library, United Nations Plaza, 10017. SAN 353-8176. Reference Tel: 212-963-7394, 212-963-7412. FAX: 212-963-2388. E-Mail: undhl@undp.org. Web Site: www.un.org/depts/dhl/direct.htm. *Head Librn*, Phyllis Dickstein; Tel: 212-963-7443, Fax: 212-963-2388, E-Mail: dickstein@un.org; *Coll Develop*, Elena Drozdova-Christonikos; Tel: 212-963-7399, Fax: 212-263-2608; Staff 101 (MLS 45, Non-MLS 56)
Founded 1946

Jan 2001-Dec 2001 Income $18,331,800. Mats Exp $1,716,000. Sal $16,207,800
Library Holdings: Bk Vols 400,000; Per Subs 8,500
Subject Interests: Disarmament, Econ, Environ, International law, International relations, Legis, Nat law, Peace-keeping, Political science, Sustainable develop, Women
Special Collections: Activities & History of the United Nations; Government Documents of Member States; International Affairs 1918-1945 (Woodrow Wilson Memorial Library); League of Nations Documents; Maps Coll; Official Gazettes of all Countries; Specialized Agencies Documents; United Nations Documents
Publications: Indexes to Proceedings of General Assembly, Economic & Social Council, Security Council; UNBIS-Plus on CD-ROM
Partic in Dialog Corporation
Branches:
LEGAL REFERENCE COLLECTION (Mail add: United Nations Plaza, Rm S-3455, 10017), Tel: 212-963-5372. FAX: 212-963-1770. *Librn*, Rosemary Noona
Library Holdings: Bk Vols 13,000
Special Collections: International Law with Treaty Coll; Legal Periodicals & Yearbooks; New York Legislation & Decisions; United States Federal Legislation & Decisions
Publications: Bibliography, United Nations Juridical Yearbook (annual)
Partic in Dialog Corporation; Westlaw
MAP LIBRARY, United Nations Plaza, Rm L-282, 10017. SAN 377-8614. Tel: 212-963-7425. *Librn*, Brenda Brookes
Library Holdings: Per Subs 36
Subject Interests: Cartography, Geography, Vexillology
Special Collections: Documents of the UN Conference on the Standardization of Geographical Names & the UN regional cartographic conferences; National Flag Specifications; National Hymns
STATISTICAL LIBRARY, United Nations Plaza, Rm DC2-1143, 10017. SAN 353-8230. Tel: 212-963-8727. FAX: 212-963-0479. E-Mail: turabian@un.org. *Librn*, Luz Maria Saavedra
Library Holdings: Bk Vols 65,000
Subject Interests: Demographic, Econ, Energy, Environ, Housing, Intergovt orgns, Nat orgns, Pop censuses statistics, Soc, Statistical publications, Trade, Transport, Women
Partic in Dialog Corporation

S UNITED NATIONS CHILDRENS FUND LIBRARY, 3 UN Plaza, H-12C UNICEF House, 10017. SAN 374-7557. Tel: 212-326-7064. FAX: 212-303-7989. *Librn*, Howard Dale
Library Holdings: Bk Vols 25,000; Per Subs 400
Partic in Consortium Of Foundation Libraries; New York Metrop Ref & Res Libr Agency

S UNITED NATIONS DEVELOPMENT PROGRAM, UNDP Reference Unit,* One United Nations Plaza, Rm DCI 1790, 10017. SAN 371-5647. Tel: 212-906-5332. FAX: 212-906-5337. *Asst Librn, Circ*, Wendy Gadd; Staff 3 (MLS 2, Non-MLS 1)
Founded 1987
Library Holdings: Bk Titles 200; Per Subs 50
Subject Interests: Energy, Natural resources
Special Collections: Energy, bks, docs & per; Environment & Development, bks, docs & per
Publications: UPDATE (quarterly newsletters E & F)
Friends of the Library Group

GL UNITED STATES COURT OF APPEALS LIBRARY, 40 Center St, Rm 2603, 10007-1595. SAN 312-1143. Tel: 212-857-8900. FAX: 212-857-8925. *Librn*, Margaret J Evans; Staff 14 (MLS 10, Non-MLS 4)
Library Holdings: Bk Vols 100,000; Per Subs 973
Subject Interests: Fed law, Judicial admin, US legis hist
Partic in OCLC Online Computer Library Center, Inc; Westlaw

GL UNITED STATES COURT OF INTERNATIONAL TRADE, Court Library, One Federal Plaza, 10278. SAN 312-1151. Tel: 212-264-2816. FAX: 212-264-3242. Web Site: www.uscit.gov. *Dir*, Christina Rattiner; *Dep Dir*, Anna Djirdjirian; *Asst Librn*, Frederick Frankel; *Asst Librn*, Mary Finnegan Hurley; Staff 6 (MLS 4, Non-MLS 2)
Library Holdings: Bk Vols 50,000; Bk Titles 5,000; Per Subs 100
Subject Interests: Customs law, Law
Publications: United States Court of International Trade Reports: Cases Adjudged in the US Court of International Trade (annually)
Partic in Fedlink; OCLC Online Computer Library Center, Inc

G UNITED STATES DEPARTMENT OF LABOR, Bureau of Labor Statistics,* 201 Varick St, Rm 808, 10014. SAN 312-1194. Tel: 212-337-2400. FAX: 212-337-2532. Web Site: stats.bls.gov/ro2home.htm. *In Charge*, Patricia A Bommicino; E-Mail: bommicino_p@bls.gov; Staff 6 (MLS 4, Non-MLS 2)
Founded 1949
Library Holdings: Bk Vols 5,000; Per Subs 10
Subject Interests: Consumer prices, Econ growth, Employment, Occupational health, Occupational outlook, Occupational safety, Producer prices, Productivity, Unemployment, Wages, Working conditions
Visitor Information Center open to public 8:30-5; Telephone hours Mon-Fri 8:30-12:30 & 1:30-4:30

G UNITED STATES TRUST CO, Information Center,* 114 W 47th St, 10036. SAN 371-4578. Tel: 212-852-3641, 212-852-3662. FAX: 212-852-3667.; Staff 4 (MLS 2, Non-MLS 2)

S UNIVERSITY CLUB LIBRARY, One W 54th St, 10019. SAN 312-1224. Tel: 212-572-3418. FAX: 212-572-3452. E-Mail: uclub2@rmi.net. *Curator*, Andrew J Berner; *Assoc Dir*, Jane Reed; *Librn*, Laurie Bolger; *Tech Servs*, Susan Grant. Subject Specialists: *Conservation*, Laurie Bolger; Staff 5 (MLS 4, Non-MLS 1)
Founded 1865
Library Holdings: Bk Vols 90,000; Per Subs 125
Subject Interests: 1st World War, 2nd World War, Am hist, Am lit, Architecture, Art, Biog, Civil War, English literature
Special Collections: Civil War Ante-bellum Southern History (New York Southern Society Coll); Fine Printing & Limited Editions Coll; H Gregory Thomas George Cruikshank Coll; Rare Book Coll; Tinker Coll of Illustrated Books; Whitney Darrow Coll of Publishing History
Automation Activity & Vendor Info: (Cataloging) GEAC; (Circulation) GEAC
Publications: The Illuminator
Partic in New York Metrop Ref & Res Libr Agency
Friends of the Library Group

S VALUE LINE PUBLISHING, INC, Research Department Library, 220 E 42nd St, 10017. SAN 311-6409. Tel: 212-907-1500. FAX: 212-818-9747. *Chief Librn*, Roy De Nunzio
Founded 1951
Library Holdings: Bk Vols 80
Subject Interests: Bus cycles, Econ forecasting, Investment advice
Restriction: Not open to public

S VERIZON, (Formerly Bell Atlantic), Information Access Center, 1095 Avenue of Americas, Rm 100, 10036. SAN 329-7241. Tel: 212-395-1900, 212-395-2121. FAX: 212-597-2834. *Dir*, Suzanne Lamador; *Online Servs*, Linda Lago Margino; Staff 11 (MLS 8, Non-MLS 3)
Library Holdings: Bk Vols 3,700; Bk Titles 3,500; Per Subs 400
Subject Interests: Telecommunications
Publications: Current Awareness; Information Industry Alert; Technical Alert
Partic in Metro Atlanta Library Association; OCLC Online Computer Library Center, Inc

L VERIZON-NEW JERSEY, (Formerly Bell Atlantic-New Jersey), Law Library, 1095 Ave of the Americas, 10036. SAN 310-3463. Tel: 212-395-3931. FAX: 212-354-7348. *Librn*, Jill Sutton
Library Holdings: Bk Vols 10,500; Per Subs 80
Subject Interests: Labor relations, Marketing contracts, Pub utility rpts, Session laws of NJ, Statutes of NJ, Telecommunications

S VILLAGE VOICE LIBRARY,* 36 Cooper Sq, 10003. SAN 376-5881. Tel: 212-475-3300, Ext 2220. FAX: 212-475-8944. *Librn*, Hervay Petion
1997-1998 Income $10,000
Library Holdings: Bk Vols 962
Restriction: Private library

C VISUAL ARTS LIBRARY, SCHOOL OF VISUAL ARTS, 380 Second Ave, 10010. SAN 312-052X. Tel: 212-592-2660. FAX: 212-592-2655. E-Mail: library@adm.schoolofvisualarts.edu. Web Site: www.schoolofvisualarts.edu. *Coll Develop, Dir Libr Serv*, Robert Lobe; *Assoc Dir, Ref*, Beth Kleber; *Per*, Caitlin Kilgallen; *Tech Servs*, Don Spicehandler; *Curator*, Lorraine Gerety; Staff 11 (MLS 5, Non-MLS 6)
Founded 1962. Enrl 2,400; Highest Degree: Master
Library Holdings: Bk Vols 70,000; Per Subs 306
Subject Interests: Architecture, Art, Art history, Computer art, Film, Graphic art, Graphic design, Illustration, Photog
Special Collections: Alumni Book Coll; Picture Coll; Slide Libr
Publications: Acquisitions Lists; Collection guides; Library Handbook; Newsletter
Partic in Metropolitan New York Library Council; OCLC Online Computer Library Center, Inc

L WACHTELL, LIPTON, ROSEN & KATZ, Law Library,* 51 W 52nd St, 10019. SAN 372-2422. Tel: 212-371-9200. FAX: 212-403-2030. *Librn*, Justine M Kalka
Library Holdings: Bk Vols 3,000; Per Subs 500
Subject Interests: Corporate law

S RAOUL WALLENBERG COMMITTEE OF THE UNITED STATES LIBRARY,* 575 Lexington Ave, 7th flr, 10022. SAN 375-1694. Tel: 212-350-4875. FAX: 212-350-4240. *Pres*, Rachel Oestreicher Bernheim
Library Holdings: Bk Vols 200

L WALTER, CONSTON, ALEXANDER & GREEN PC LIBRARY,* 90 Park Ave, 15th flr, 10016. SAN 325-5255. Tel: 212-210-9526. FAX: 212-210-9444. *Dir*, Lydia Wilson; Staff 2 (MLS 1, Non-MLS 1)
Library Holdings: Bk Vols 15,000
Special Collections: German Law Materials
Partic in Dialog Corporation; Westlaw

L WARSHAW, BURSTEIN, COHEN, SCHLESINGER & KUH, Law Library, 555 Fifth Ave, 11th Flr, 10017. SAN 372-4220. Tel: 212-984-7730. FAX: 212-972-9150. Web Site: www.wbcsk.com. *Librn*, Helen Akulich; E-Mail: hakulich@wbcsk.com; Staff 2 (MLS 1, Non-MLS 1)
Library Holdings: Bk Vols 15,000; Bk Titles 1,200; Per Subs 120
Subject Interests: Corporate law, Estates, Litigation, Mergers, Real estate law, Securities law, Tax, Trusts
Partic in Am Asn of Law Librs

L WEIL, GOTSHAL & MANGES LIBRARY,* 767 Fifth Ave, 10153. SAN 312-1283. Tel: 212-310-8626. Interlibrary Loan Service Tel: 212-735-4560. FAX: 212-310-8786. *Mgr*, Deborah G Cinque; E-Mail: deborah.cinque@weil.com; *Ref*, Bonnie Fox Schwartz; *Ref*, Margaret Jones; *Ref*, Fran Fredrick; *Ref*, Philip Barahona; *Ref*, Kathleen McGee; *ILL*, Sylvia Siegel; *Tech Servs*, Rosalie Pisciteui
1998-1999 Mats Exp $6,000,000, Books $800,000, Per/Ser (Incl. Access Fees) $300,000
Library Holdings: Bk Vols 80,000
Subject Interests: Bus, Law
Publications: Access: Library Newsletter
Partic in RLIN

L WELFARE LAW CENTER LIBRARY,* 275 Seventh Ave, Ste 1205, 10001. SAN 325-9544. Tel: 212-633-6967. FAX: 212-633-6371. Web Site: www.welfarelaw.org. *Librn*, Elizabeth Korn; E-Mail: korn@welfarelaw.org
Library Holdings: Bk Vols 2,000; Per Subs 150
Special Collections: Publications & Case Materials on Welfare Law
Publications: Welfare Bulletin (monthly), Welfare News (bimonthly)

S WEST GROUP LEGAL EDITORIAL LIBRARY,* 375 Hudson St, 2nd flr, 10014. SAN 372-4492. Tel: 212-929-7500. FAX: 212-807-6209. *Librn*, Shirley Chan; E-Mail: shirleychan@westgroup.com
Library Holdings: Bk Vols 1,000

L WHITE & CASE, Law Library,* 1155 Avenue of the Americas, 10036. SAN 353-8419. Tel: 212-819-7567, 212-819-8200. Interlibrary Loan Service Tel: 212-819-7569. FAX: 212-354-8113. *Chief Librn*, John J Banta
Founded 1901
Library Holdings: Bk Titles 40,000
Publications: Acquisitions List
Partic in Dialog Corporation; Dow Jones News Retrieval; NY Times Info Bank; Westlaw

S WHITNEY MUSEUM OF AMERICAN ART, Frances Mulhall Achilles Library, 945 Madison Ave, 10021. SAN 312-1380. Tel: 212-570-3648. FAX: 212-570-7729. E-Mail: library@whitney.org. Web Site: www.whitney.org. *Chief Librn*, Carol Rusk; Tel: 215-570-3649, E-Mail: carol_rusk@whitney.org; *Asst Librn*, Zimra Panitz; E-Mail: zimra_panitz@whitney.org; Staff 8 (MLS 4, Non-MLS 4)
Founded 1931
Library Holdings: Bk Vols 33,700; Bk Titles 30,000; Per Subs 100
Subject Interests: 20th Century art, American art, Artists bks, Rare books
Special Collections: American Art Research Council Papers; Museum Archives
Automation Activity & Vendor Info: (OPAC) Endeavor
Database Vendor: Lexis-Nexis, OCLC - First Search, Wilson - Wilson Web
Restriction: By appointment only
Function: Research library

S JOHN WILEY & SONS, INC, Information Center,* 605 Third Ave, 10158. SAN 329-1766. Tel: 212-850-6050. FAX: 212-850-6154. *Librn*, Helen Witsenhausen; E-Mail: hwitsenh@wiley.com; Staff 2 (MLS 1, Non-MLS 1)
Founded 1982
Library Holdings: Bk Vols 500; Per Subs 35
Subject Interests: Bus, Electronic publishing, Higher educ, Publishing
Restriction: Staff use only
Partic in Dialog Corporation; Dow Jones News Retrieval

S WILLIAM M MERCER INC, Information Research Center,* 1166 Avenue of the Americas, 10036. SAN 311-8916. Tel: 212-345-7027. FAX: 212-345-7413. *Dir*, Judi Olstein
Library Holdings: Bk Vols 875; Per Subs 257

L WILLKIE, FARR & GALLAGHER, Law Library,* 787 Seventh Ave, 10019. SAN 312-1399. Tel: 212-728-8700. Interlibrary Loan Service Tel: 212-728-8709. FAX: 212-728-3303. *Dir Libr Serv*, Debra Glessner; E-Mail: dglessner@willkie.com; Staff 16 (MLS 8, Non-MLS 8)
Library Holdings: Bk Titles 50,000; Per Subs 200
Subject Interests: Corporation, Securities law, Taxation
Publications: Bulletin
Partic in Dialog Corporation; Dow Jones News Retrieval; OCLC Online Computer Library Center, Inc; Westlaw

L WILSON, ELSER, MOSKOWITZ, EDELMAN & DICKER, Law Library,* 150 E 42nd St, 10017-5639. SAN 372-2430. Tel: 212-490-3000. FAX: 212-490-3038. *Asst Librn*, Calvin Conyers
Library Holdings: Bk Vols 20,000; Per Subs 30
Partic in Dialog Corporation; Dow Jones News Retrieval; Westlaw

S WINDELS, MARX, DAVIES & IVES LIBRARY,* 156 W 56th St, 10019. SAN 312-1402. Tel: 212-237-1000. FAX: 212-262-1215. *Librn*, Joel Solomon; E-Mail: jlsolomo@sprynet.com
Library Holdings: Bk Vols 26,000; Bk Titles 27,000
Subject Interests: Banking law, Corp law, International law, Litigation

L WINSTON & STRAWN LIBRARY, (Formerly Whitman, Breed, Abbott & Morgan Library), 200 Park Ave, 10166. SAN 312-1356. Tel: 212-294-4648. Interlibrary Loan Service Tel: 212-294-4713. FAX: 212-294-4700. *Librn*, Winston McKenzie; Tel: 212-351-3006, E-Mail: wmckenzie@winston.com; Staff 5 (MLS 2, Non-MLS 3)
Founded 1993
Library Holdings: Bk Vols 100,000; Per Subs 150
Subject Interests: Law
Partic in Dialog Corporation; OCLC; Westlaw

L WINTHROP, STIMSON, PUTNAM & ROBERTS LIBRARY,* One Battery Park Plaza, 10004-1490. SAN 312-1410. Tel: 212-858-1000. FAX: 212-858-1500. *Librn*, Linda Becker; *Ref*, Stanley Conrad; Staff 5 (MLS 3, Non-MLS 2)
Library Holdings: Bk Vols 32,000; Bk Titles 35,000
Subject Interests: Law

S WOOD-TOBE-COBURN SCHOOL LIBRARY,* 8 E 40th St, 10016. SAN 328-5936. Tel: 212-686-9040. FAX: 212-686-9171.
Library Holdings: Bk Vols 800; Per Subs 100

S JONES LANG WOOTTON INFORMATION CENTER,* 101 E 52nd St, 10022. SAN 327-2079. Tel: 212-688-8181. FAX: 212-308-5199. *Chief Librn*, Laura McLaughlin
Library Holdings: Bk Vols 550; Per Subs 150
Publications: Newslink (in house)
Partic in Dialog Corporation; Vutext

S XAVIER SOCIETY FOR THE BLIND, National Catholic Press & Library for the Visually Impaired, 154 E 23rd St, 10010. SAN 328-3577. Tel: 212-473-7800. *Dir*, Alfred E Caruana; *Librn*, Robert Nealon; Staff 4 (MLS 1, Non-MLS 3)
Founded 1900
Library Holdings: Bk Vols 18,362; Bk Titles 1,500; Per Subs 10
Subject Interests: Braille, Catholicism, Inspirational, Large print, Religious, Spirituals
Publications: Braille Calender; Catholic Review; Large Print Calender; Xavier Review; XSB Lending Library Catalog of Braille, Large Print & Audio Cassette Books
Partic in National Library Service For The Blind & Physically Handicapped, Library Of Congress

S YALE CLUB LIBRARY,* 50 Vanderbilt Ave, 10017. SAN 312-1488. Tel: 212-661-2070. FAX: 212-983-3324. *Librn*, Louise Jones
Library Holdings: Bk Vols 45,500
Special Collections: Yale Memorabilia & Publications

C YESHIVA UNIVERSITY LIBRARIES,* 500 W 185th St, 10033. SAN 353-8508. Tel: 212-960-5363. Interlibrary Loan Service Tel: 212-960-5378. FAX: 212-960-0066. E-Mail: unilib@ymail.yu.edu. *Dean of Libr*, Pearl Berger; Staff 29 (MLS 29)
Founded 1897. Highest Degree: Doctorate
Jul 1998-Jun 1999 Income (Main and Other College/University Libraries) $6,696,580, State $44,757. Mats Exp $3,218,062, Books $478,701, Per/Ser (Incl. Access Fees) $1,845,181, Presv $91,554, Micro $58,150. Sal $2,740,123
Library Holdings: Bk Vols 1,090,627
Subject Interests: Archives, Jewish studies, Law, Manuscripts, Medicine, Psychology, Rare books, Soc work
Database Vendor: Innovative Interfaces INN - View
Publications: Rubbinic Manuscripts - Mendel Gottesman Library
Partic in Council Of Archives & Research Libraries In Jewish Studies; Dialog Corporation; New York Metrop Ref & Res Libr Agency; OCLC Online Computer Library Center, Inc; PALINET & Union Library Catalogue of Pennsylvania; Westlaw
Departmental Libraries:
ALBERT EINSTEIN COLLEGE OF MEDICINE
See Separate Entry (Bronx)
Subject Interests: Medicine, Psychology
LILLIAN & REBECCA CHUTICK LAW LIBRARY, Benjamin N Cardozo School of Law, 55 Fifth Ave, 10003-4301. SAN 353-8567. Tel: 212-790-0285. Interlibrary Loan Service Tel: 212-790-0220. FAX: 212-790-0236. E-Mail: lawlib@ymail.yu.edu. Web Site: www.cardozo.yu.edu/library. *Librn*, Lynn Wishart; *Asst Librn*, Norma Feld; *Tech Servs*, Grace Wong; *Tech Servs*, Linda Aschkenasy; *Publ Servs*, Beth Gordon; Staff 7 (MLS 7)
Founded 1976. Enrl 915; Fac 45; Highest Degree: Doctorate
Jul 1998-Jun 1999 Income $1,951,218. Mats Exp $967,405, Books

$78,805, Per/Ser (Incl. Access Fees) $139,983, Micro $38,290, Other Print Mats $619,070, Electronic Ref Mat (Incl. Access Fees) $91,257. Sal $714,924 (Prof $416,543)
Library Holdings: Bk Vols 440,378; Bk Titles 62,841; Per Subs 6,083
Subject Interests: Israeli law
Automation Activity & Vendor Info: (Acquisitions) Innovative Interfaces Inc.; (Cataloging) Innovative Interfaces Inc.; (Circulation) Innovative Interfaces Inc.; (OPAC) Innovative Interfaces Inc.; (Serials) Innovative Interfaces Inc.
Database Vendor: OCLC - First Search
Publications: Current Contents; Research guides
Partic in OCLC Online Computer Library Center, Inc; Westlaw

HEDI STEINBERG LIBRARY, 245 Lexington Ave, 10016. SAN 353-8680. Tel: 212-340-7720. FAX: 212-340-7808. Web Site: www.yu.edu. *Chief Librn*, Edith Lubetski; E-Mail: lubetski@mail.yu.edu; *Per*, Elinor Grumet; *Ref*, Vivian Moskowitz; Staff 3 (MLS 3)
Founded 1954
Jul 1998-Jun 1999 Income $501,652. Mats Exp $251,733, Books $100,424, Per/Ser (Incl. Access Fees) $64,653. Sal $249,919 (Prof $122,825)
Library Holdings: Bk Vols 126,297; Bk Titles 76,791; Per Subs 594
Subject Interests: Hebraica, Judaica
Partic in New York Metrop Ref & Res Libr Agency

CR MENDEL GOTTESMAN LIBRARY OF HEBRAICA-JUDAICA, 2520 Amsterdam Ave, 10033. (Mail add: 500 W 185th St, 10033), Tel: 212-960-5382. FAX: 212-960-0066. Web Site: www.yu.edu. *Librn*, Leah Adler; *Coll Develop*, Zvi Erenyi; *Ref*, Moshe Schapiro; *Per*, Zalman Alpert; Staff 4 (MLS 4)
Founded 1897
Jul 1998-Jun 1999 Income (Main Library Only) $367,556. Mats Exp $183,476, Books $136,526, Per/Ser (Incl. Access Fees) $34,637, Presv $11,293, Micro $1,020. Sal $175,744
Library Holdings: Bk Vols 235,068; Bk Vols 228,931; Per Subs 826
Subject Interests: Bible, Hebrew language, Jewish hist, Jewish lit, Jewish philos, Rabbinics
Special Collections: Hebraica Rare Books & Manuscripts; Sephardic Studies Coll
Automation Activity & Vendor Info: (Cataloging) VTLS; (Circulation) VTLS; (Course Reserve) VTLS; (OPAC) VTLS; (Serials) VTLS
Partic in New York Metrop Ref & Res Libr Agency; OCLC Online Computer Library Center, Inc; RLIN
Serves Yeshiva College, Bernard Revel Graduate School, Stern College for Women & Wuraweiler School of Social Work

POLLACK LIBRARY & LANDOWNE BLOOM COLLECTION, 2520 Amsterdam Ave, 10033. (Mail add: Main Campus, 500 W 185th St, 10033), Tel: 212-960-5379, 212-960-5380. Interlibrary Loan Service Tel: 212-960-5378. FAX: 212-960-0066. Web Site: www.yu.edu/libraries/index.html. *Chief Librn*, John Moryl; *Publ Servs*, Kerry Santoro; *Per*, Marie Center; Staff 3 (MLS 3)
Founded 1938
1998-1999 Income $581,472. Mats Exp $242,840, Books $61,776, Per/Ser (Incl. Access Fees) $136,609, Presv $3,355, Micro $17,100. Sal $371,877
Library Holdings: Bk Vols 327,642; Per Subs 700
Subject Interests: Soc work
Partic in New York Metrop Ref & Res Libr Agency; OCLC Online Computer Library Center, Inc; RLIN

SIMON WIESENTHAL CENTER LIBRARY
See Separate Entry in Los Angeles, CA

S YIVO INSTITUTE FOR JEWISH RESEARCH, Library & Archives, 15 W 16th St, 10011. SAN 312-1496. Tel: 212-246-6080. FAX: 212-292-1892. E-Mail: yivomail@yivo.cjh.org. Web Site: www.yivoinstitute.org. *Dir*, Aviva E Astrinsky; E-Mail: avastrinsky@yivo.cjh.org; *Archivist*, Marek Web; E-Mail: mweb@yivo.cjh.org. Subject Specialists: *East European hist*, Marek Web; Staff 15 (MLS 8, Non-MLS 7)
Founded 1925
Library Holdings: Bk Vols 350,000; Per Subs 200
Subject Interests: Eastern European Jewish hist, Holocaust, Literature, Yiddish (Language)
Special Collections: Hebrew Immigrant Aid Society Coll; Jewish Sheet Music; Jewish Music Coll; Milwitzki Coll of Ladino Literature; Nazi Coll; Jewish Music Coll; Jewish Sheet Music; Manuscript Coll; Milwitzki Coll of Ladino Literature; Nazi Coll; Rabbinics (Vilna Coll); Yiddish Linguistics (Weinreich Library Coll)
Publications: Yivo Bleter (Yiddish); Yivo News
Restriction: Not a lending library
Partic in Asn of Jewish Librs; New York Metrop Ref & Res Libr Agency; RLIN

S YOUNG & RUBICAM, INC LIBRARY,* 285 Madison Ave, 10th flr, 10017. SAN 312-150X. Tel: 212-210-3982. FAX: 212-210-3918. *Dir*, Maureen Pine; *Res*, Shelia Parker; *Res*, Stephen Fleming; *Res*, Gwen Loeffler; *Res*, Nicola Pullen; *Coll Develop*, Donna C Vetere
Founded 1953
Library Holdings: Bk Vols 5,000; Per Subs 220
Subject Interests: Advertising, Marketing

S ZURICH, KEMPER INVESTMENTS LIBRARY, (Formerly Scudder, Kemper Investments Library), 345 Park Ave, 10154. SAN 312-0570. Tel: 212-326-6371. FAX: 212-705-6102. *Librn*, Denise Burton; E-Mail: denise_burton@zurich.com; Staff 2 (MLS 1, Non-MLS 1)
Founded 1926
Library Holdings: Bk Titles 1,500; Per Subs 300
Subject Interests: Investment
Restriction: Staff use only, Use of others with permission of librarian

NEW YORK MILLS

P NEW YORK MILLS PUBLIC LIBRARY,* 399 Main St, 13417. SAN 312-1577. Tel: 315-736-5391. *Librn*, Patricia Urban
Circ 32,949
Library Holdings: Bk Vols 27,891
Open Mon-Fri 12-8 & Sat 10-2
Friends of the Library Group

NEWARK

P NEWARK PUBLIC LIBRARY,* 121 High St, 14513-1492. SAN 312-1585. Tel: 315-331-4370. FAX: 315-331-0552. E-Mail: npl@eznet.net. *Dir*, Elaine B Dawson; *Ch Servs*, Maureen Wroblewski
Founded 1897. Pop 10,017; Circ 200,000
Library Holdings: Bk Vols 42,000; Per Subs 62
Special Collections: Local History Coll
Automation Activity & Vendor Info: (Circulation) MultiLIS
Mem of Pioneer Library System
Partic in OCLC Online Computer Library Center, Inc
Also houses the Hoffman Clock Museum
Friends of the Library Group

NEWARK VALLEY

P TAPPAN-SPAULDING MEMORIAL LIBRARY,* 6 Rock St, PO Box 397, 13811. SAN 312-1615. Tel: 607-642-9960. FAX: 607-642-9960. *Dir*, David Peck
Library Holdings: Bk Vols 14,000; Per Subs 27
Mem of Finger Lakes Library System

NEWBURGH

S EA ENGINEERING SCIENCE & TECHNOLOGY LIBRARY, The Maple Bldg, 3 Washington Ctr, 12550. SAN 311-4961. Tel: 845-565-8100. FAX: 845-565-8203. *Res*, Michelle Predmore
Library Holdings: Bk Vols 1,000; Per Subs 30
Partic in NY Libr Res Coun

S LIBRARY OF HISTORICAL SOCIETY OF NEWBURGH BAY & THE HIGHLANDS, 189 Montgomery St, 12550. SAN 326-579X. Tel: 845-561-2585. FAX: 845-561-0999. *Librn*, Pat Favata; E-Mail: favata@msne.edu
Founded 1951
Library Holdings: Bk Vols 3,000
Special Collections: Art & Architecture; Charitible Organizations; Civil War; Environmental Affairs; Ethnic Groups, English, German, Irish; Local History, Newburgh, NY area; Military; Natural Resources; Revolutionary War; Social Science
Partic in Southeastern New York Library Resources Council
Open Sun 1-4, other times by appt

C MOUNT SAINT MARY COLLEGE, Curtin Memorial Library, 330 Powell Ave, 12550-3494. SAN 312-1623. Tel: 845-569-3241. FAX: 845-561-0999. Web Site: www.msmc..edu/library. *Dir*, Marie Meyer; E-Mail: mmeyer@msmc.edu; *Ref*, Suzanne Christensen; *Acq, Coll Develop*, Sr Estelle McKeever; *Cat, Info Tech*, Deborah Vroman
Founded 1959
Library Holdings: Bk Vols 100,000; Bk Titles 82,556; Per Subs 1,000
Subject Interests: Bus, Grad educ programs, Nursing, Sci
Publications: Faculty Handbook-Student Handbook; Resource Guides
Partic in Southeastern New York Library Resources Council

P NEWBURGH FREE LIBRARY,* 124 Grand St, 12550. SAN 353-880X. Tel: 914-561-1985, 914-561-2497. FAX: 914-561-2401, 914-561-2499. E-Mail: newburgh@sebridge.org. Web Site: www.newburghlibrary.org. *Dir*, Mary Ellen Leimer; *Coll Develop, Ref*, James R Halpin; *Doc*, Heather Henricksen-Georghiou; *Automation Syst Coordr*, Marian DeCaterina; *Ch Servs*, Virginia Nasser; *Circ*, Jeanne Stiller; Staff 83 (MLS 28, Non-MLS 55)
Founded 1852. Pop 58,980; Circ 295,911
Jan 1999-Dec 1999 Income $2,349,685, City $1,931,692, Federal $27,796, Locally Generated Income $135,950, Other $254,247. Mats Exp $357,742, Books $195,596, Per/Ser (Incl. Access Fees) $93,239, Presv $1,238, Micro $12,205, Other Print Mats $546, Electronic Ref Mat (Incl. Access Fees) $54,918. Sal $1,484,789 (Prof $784,510)
Library Holdings: Bk Vols 185,357; Bk Titles 247,856; Per Subs 2,480
Subject Interests: Am hist, Am lit, Applied sci, Bibliographies, Bus, Local history, Micro computer, Parenting coll

Special Collections: Children's Lit Coll; Genealogy, bk, micro
Automation Activity & Vendor Info: (Cataloging) Brodart
Database Vendor: Dialog, epixtech, inc., IAC - Info Trac, IAC - SearchBank, OCLC - First Search
Mem of Ramapo Catskill Library System
Special Services for the Deaf - Books on deafness & sign language; Special interest periodicals
Friends of the Library Group

M SAINT LUKE'S HOSPITAL, Medical Library, 70 Dubois St, 12550-9986. SAN 353-8869. Tel: 845-568-2220. FAX: 845-568-2913. E-Mail: slhlib@senylrc.org. *Librn*, Twyla Snead. Subject Specialists: *Med info*, Twyla Snead
Founded 1957
Library Holdings: Bk Titles 350; Per Subs 130
Subject Interests: Medicine
Partic in EFTS; Hilow; NY Acad of Med; Southeastern New York Library Resources Council
Open Mon-Fri 8-12

G WASHINGTON'S HEADQUARTERS STATE HISTORIC SITE LIBRARY, 84 Liberty St, PO Box 1783, 12551-1476. SAN 326-5404. Tel: 845-562-1195. *Librn*, Mel Johnson
Founded 1850
Library Holdings: Bk Vols 1,000; Bk Titles 800
Special Collections: George Washington Coll, mss, papers; Revolutionary War Colls, mss; Timothy Pickering Coll, mss
Restriction: Non-circulating to the public

NEWFANE

P NEWFANE FREE LIBRARY, 2761 Maple Ave, 14108. SAN 312-164X. Tel: 716-778-9344. FAX: 716-778-9344. Web Site: www.nioga.org/newfane. *Dir*, Kristine DeGlopper
Pop 9,833; Circ 42,431
Library Holdings: Bk Vols 29,452; Per Subs 68
Mem of Nioga Library System
Open Mon-Fri 10-12 & 1:30-5:30, Tues & Thurs 6:30pm-8:30pm, Sat 10-2
Friends of the Library Group

NEWFIELD

P NEWFIELD PUBLIC LIBRARY,* 196 Main St, 14867. SAN 312-1658. Tel: 607-564-3594. Web Site: www.flls.org. *Librn*, Lois Maki
Founded 1882. Circ 13,739
Library Holdings: Bk Vols 10,500; Bk Titles 8,824; Per Subs 35
Mem of Finger Lakes Library System
Open Mon 6-9pm, Tues 2-6pm, Thurs 5-9pm & Sat 12-4

NEWPORT

P NEWPORT FREE LIBRARY, 7390 Main St, 13416-0359. (Mail add: PO Box 359, 13416), SAN 312-1666. Tel: 315-845-8533. E-Mail: ne_dial@midyork.lib.ny.us. *Dir*, Phyllis Fisher
Founded 1923. Pop 3,614; Circ 18,784
Jan 2000-Dec 2000 Income $18,416. Mats Exp $6,400, Books $6,000, Per/Ser (Incl. Access Fees) $400. Sal $9,000
Library Holdings: Bk Titles 18,000; Per Subs 23
Subject Interests: Cooking, Education, Fiction, History
Mem of Mid-York Library System

NIAGARA FALLS

S CARBIDE GRAPHITE GROUP, INC, Technical Library,* 4861 Packard Rd, 14304. SAN 312-1674. Tel: 716-286-0321. FAX: 716-286-0322. *In Charge*, Victoria Scott
Library Holdings: Bk Vols 5,000; Per Subs 25
Subject Interests: Carbon tech, Graphite tech

P NIAGARA FALLS PUBLIC LIBRARY,* 1425 Main St, 14305. SAN 353-8958. Tel: 716-286-4910. FAX: 716-286-4912. *Dir*, Betty Babanoury; E-Mail: betty_babanoury@niagara.k12.ny.us; *Ch Servs*, Diane Palaszynski; *Media Spec*, Donald J Fleischman. Subject Specialists: *Local history*, Maureen Fennie; Staff 11 (MLS 11)
Founded 1838. Pop 61,840; Circ 340,000
1998-1999 Income $2,849,242. Mats Exp $276,435, Books $215,435, Per/Ser (Incl. Access Fees) $25,000, Other Print Mats $6,000. Sal $925,563
Library Holdings: Bk Vols 350,000
Subject Interests: Local history
Publications: Newsletter
Mem of Nioga Library System
Friends of the Library Group
Branches: 1
LASALLE, 8728 Buffalo Ave, 14304. SAN 353-8982. Tel: 716-283-8309. FAX: 716-286-4912. *Librn*, Margaret Stein
Friends of the Library Group

S NIAGARA GAZETTE PUBLISHING CORP ARCHIVES,* 310 Niagara St, 14303-0549. (Mail add: PO Box 549, 14302), SAN 326-0240. Tel: 716-282-2311. FAX: 716-286-3895. *In Charge*, James Neiss
Founded 1915
Restriction: Staff use only

NIAGARA UNIVERSITY

C NIAGARA UNIVERSITY LIBRARY, Lewiston Rd, 14109. SAN 312-1712. Tel: 716-286-8000. Interlibrary Loan Service Tel: 716-286-8013. Circulation Tel: 716-286-8020. Reference Tel: 716-286-8022. FAX: 716-286-8030. E-Mail: reflib@niagara.edu. Web Site: www.niagara.edu/library. *Dir*, David Schoen; *Publ Servs*, Jonathan Coe; *Acq, Per*, Charles Dabkowski; *Cat*, Cindy Woodruff; Tel: 716-286-8015; Staff 8 (MLS 8)
Founded 1856. Enrl 3,500; Fac 198; Highest Degree: Master
Jun 1999-May 2000 Mats Exp $406,000, Books $115,000, Per/Ser (Incl. Access Fees) $215,000, Electronic Ref Mat (Incl. Access Fees) $40,000. Sal $413,000
Library Holdings: Bk Vols 320,000; Bk Titles 212,000; Per Subs 4,500; Bks on Deafness & Sign Lang 50
Special Collections: 15th-17th Century Religious Materials
Automation Activity & Vendor Info: (Circulation) epixtech, inc.
Partic in State University Of New York-NYLINK; Western New York Library Resources Council

NICHOLS

P GEORGE P & SUSAN PLATT CADY LIBRARY, 42 E River St, 13812. SAN 312-1720. Tel: 607-699-3835. FAX: 607-699-3835. E-Mail: cadylibrary@csma.com. *Librn*, Carol Visscher
Circ 13,547
Library Holdings: Bk Vols 9,732
Automation Activity & Vendor Info: (Cataloging) Brodart; (Circulation) Brodart; (ILL) Brodart
Mem of Finger Lakes Library System
Friends of the Library Group

NINEVEH

P NINEVEH PUBLIC LIBRARY OF COLESVILLE TOWNSHIP, 3029 New York Rte 7, 13813. (Mail add: PO Box 124, 13813-0124), SAN 312-1739. Tel: 607-693-1858. FAX: 607-693-2226. E-Mail: ni_ill@4cty.org. *Dir*, Sigrid Gilkeson
Founded 1901. Pop 5,590
Library Holdings: Bk Titles 11,000
Mem of Four County Library System
Open Mon-Thurs 12:30-7:30, Fri 12:30-5:30, Sat 10-2

NISKAYUNA

S GENERAL ELECTRIC CORPORATE RESEARCH & DEVELOPMENT, Whitney Information Services, One Research Circle, 12309. (Mail add: PO Box 8, 12301), SAN 354-1177. Tel: 518-387-7947. Interlibrary Loan Service Tel: 518-387-7539. FAX: 518-387-7593. E-Mail: library@crd.ge.com. *Mgr*, James Lommel; *Librn*, Marian Smith; *Cat*, Diane G Glock; *ILL, Ref*, Louise Macuirles; *Online Servs*, Carolyn Warden; Staff 6 (MLS 4, Non-MLS 2)
Founded 1900
Library Holdings: Bk Titles 26,000; Per Subs 1,100
Subject Interests: Biology, Chemistry, Electronics, Engineering, Finance, Info sci, Mathematics, Metallurgy, Physics
Automation Activity & Vendor Info: (Acquisitions) TechLIB; (Circulation) TechLIB; (OPAC) TechLIB
Publications: Bibliogram; Intranet Web Page
Restriction: Staff use only
Partic in Cap District Libr Coun for Ref & Res Resources; OCLC Online Computer Library Center, Inc

NORFOLK

P HEPBURN LIBRARY OF NORFOLK, One Hepburn St, PO Box 530, 13667. SAN 312-1747. Tel: 315-384-3052. FAX: 315-384-3841. Web Site: www.nc3r.org/norfolk/. *Librn*, Vicky Brothers
Pop 4,258; Circ 13,023
Library Holdings: Per Subs 75
Mem of North Country Library System
Partic in North Country Reference & Research Resources Council
Open Mon-Fri 2-5 & 7-9, Sat 10-12pm
Friends of the Library Group

NORTH BABYLON

P NORTH BABYLON PUBLIC LIBRARY, 815 Deer Park Ave, 11703. SAN 312-1755. Tel: 631-669-4020. TDD: 631-669-4140. FAX: 631-669-3432. E-Mail: nbablib@suffolk.lib.ny.us. Web Site: www.suffolk.lib.ny.us/libraries/nbab/. *Dir*, Marc Horowitz; E-Mail: horowm@suffolk.lib.ny.us; *Asst Dir*,

Melanie Weiss; Tel: 631-669-4050, E-Mail: mweiss@suffolk.lib.ny.us; *Ch Servs*, Gail Francavilla; *Ch Servs*, Debbie Hawkins; *Ad Servs*, Brad Silverman; *Ad Servs*, Kirsten Torgersen; *Ref*, Jeffrey Bavolar; Staff 9 (MLS 9)
Founded 1960. Pop 31,089; Circ 259,591
Library Holdings: Bk Vols 119,239; Bk Titles 116,157; Per Subs 513
Subject Interests: European history, European travel
Special Collections: Newsday on microfilm from 1944
Database Vendor: IAC - Info Trac, IAC - SearchBank, Innovative Interfaces INN - View, Silverplatter Information Inc., Wilson - Wilson Web
Publications: News & Notes (bi-monthly)
Mem of Suffolk Cooperative Library System
Partic in Pals
Open Mon-Fri 9-9, Sat 9-5, Sun 1-9 (Oct - May)

NORTH BELLMORE

P NORTH BELLMORE PUBLIC LIBRARY, 1551 Newbridge Rd, 11710. SAN 312-1763. Tel: 516-785-6260. FAX: 516-826-8092. Web Site: www.nassaulibrary.org. *Dir*, Lois Black; E-Mail: leblack24@aol.com; *Ad Servs*, Theresa Scala; *Ad Servs*, Barbara Shapiro; *Commun Servs, ILL, Ref, YA Servs*, Renee Gewirtz; *YA Servs*, Vivian Kowalewski; *Ch Servs*, Tom Bazzicalupo; *Ch Servs*, Francine Powell; *AV*, Christine Kulakis. Subject Specialists: *Computers*, Vivian Kowalewski; Staff 14 (MLS 14)
Founded 1946. Pop 25,921; Circ 222,032
Jul 1999-Jun 2000 Income $1,549,093. Mats Exp $261,700, Books $196,200, Per/Ser (Incl. Access Fees) $20,000, Micro $8,000, AV Equip $9,000, Electronic Ref Mat (Incl. Access Fees) $28,500. Sal $870,693 (Prof $507,924)
Library Holdings: Bk Vols 107,520; Bk Titles 105,063; Per Subs 417
Automation Activity & Vendor Info: (Circulation) DRA; (OPAC) DRA
Publications: Inklings (monthly newsletter)
Mem of Nassau Library System

NORTH CHATHAM

P NORTH CHATHAM FREE LIBRARY, PO Box 907, 12131. SAN 312-1771. Tel: 518-766-3211. FAX: 518-766-3211. E-Mail: nclibrary@taconic.net. *Dir*, Clai Sommers
Founded 1915. Pop 848; Circ 6,918
Jan 1999-Dec 1999 Income $22,000. Mats Exp $8,000, Books $3,000, Per/Ser (Incl. Access Fees) $300. Sal $10,000
Library Holdings: Bk Titles 11,000; Per Subs 21
Subject Interests: Local history
Mem of Mid-Hudson Library System
Open Tues & Thurs 3-9, Wed 10-12, Sat 10-2 & Sun 2-4

NORTH COLLINS

P TOWN OF NORTH COLLINS PUBLIC LIBRARY, 2095 School St, PO Box 730, 14111. SAN 312-178X. Tel: 716-337-3211. FAX: 716-337-0647. *Dir*, Corinne F Leone; E-Mail: leonec@buffalolib.org
Founded 1878. Circ 18,772
Library Holdings: Bk Vols 8,000; Per Subs 102
Special Collections: Local Historical & Geneological Resources
Mem of Buffalo & Erie County Public Library System
Open Mon, Tues & Wed 2-8, Thurs 4-8, Fri 10-4, Sat 10-12
Friends of the Library Group

NORTH MERRICK

P NORTH MERRICK PUBLIC LIBRARY, 1691 Meadowbrook Rd, 11566. SAN 312-1798. Tel: 516-378-7474. FAX: 516-378-0876. E-Mail: nomerric@lilrc.org. *Head Ref*, Anibal Salazar; E-Mail: salazaralonso@yahoo.com; *Ref*, Judith Jankolovits; *Ref*, Greg Wirszyla; *Ch Servs*, Ilene Leibowitz; Staff 8 (MLS 8)
Founded 1965. Pop 12,972; Circ 123,697
Library Holdings: Bk Vols 89,574; Per Subs 303
Subject Interests: Art, Cookery
Automation Activity & Vendor Info: (Circulation) DRA
Publications: Yesterday in the Merricks (local hist)
Mem of Nassau Library System
Friends of the Library Group

NORTH SALEM

P NORTH SALEM FREE LIBRARY,* 276 Titicus Rd, 10560. SAN 353-9016. Tel: 914-669-5161. FAX: 914-669-5173. Web Site: www.wls.lib.ny.us. *Dir*, Judy Koopmann
Founded 1932. Pop 5,264; Circ 40,317
Library Holdings: Bk Vols 32,131; Bk Titles 30,000
Special Collections: Hellen Whitman Herbal Coll
Publications: Newsletter (bi-annually)
Mem of Westchester Library System

NORTH SYRACUSE

P NORTHERN ONONDAGA PUBLIC LIBRARY,* 100 Trolley Barn Lane, 13212. SAN 377-8398. Tel: 315-699-2534. FAX: 315-699-2301. Web Site: www.nopl.org. *Dir*, John Walter
Founded 1996. Pop 51,000; Circ 244,902
Jan 1997-Dec 1998 Income $482,268, State $14,600, Locally Generated Income $16,400, Other $40,168
Mem of Onondaga County Public Library
Friends of the Library Group
Branches: 3
BREWERTON BRANCH, 5437 Library St, PO Box 624, Brewerton, 13029. SAN 310-8880. Tel: 315-676-7484. FAX: 315-676-7463. Web Site: www.nopl.org. *Dir*, John Walter; *Mgr*, Joyce Brown; E-Mail: brown03@dreamscape.com
Pop 6,000; Circ 26,793
Library Holdings: Bk Titles 23,258; Per Subs 63
Subject Interests: Genealogy, Local history
Friends of the Library Group
CICERO BRANCH, 8686 Knowledge Lane, PO Box 1826, Cicero, 13039. SAN 311-0494. Tel: 315-699-2032. FAX: 315-699-2034. Web Site: www.nopl.org. *Mgr*, Elyse Meltz; E-Mail: emeltz@juno.com
Founded 1924. Pop 7,500; Circ 24,742
Library Holdings: Bk Titles 12,400; Per Subs 62
Friends of the Library Group
NORTH SYRACUSE, 100 Trolley Barne Lane, 13212. SAN 312-181X. Tel: 315-458-6184. FAX: 315-458-7026. Web Site: www.nopl.org. *Mgr*, Nancy Ewanick
Founded 1929. Circ 125,000
Library Holdings: Bk Vols 35,000
Subject Interests: Local history
Special Collections: Antique, Craft & Needlework Books; Cookbook Coll; Mystery Coll; Rare Books
Friends of the Library Group

NORTH TONAWANDA

M DE GRAFF MEMORIAL HOSPITAL, Medical Science & Nursing Library,* 445 Tremont St, 14120. SAN 320-4073. Tel: 716-690-2116, 716-694-4500. FAX: 716-690-2313.
Founded 1979
Library Holdings: Bk Vols 234; Bk Titles 190; Per Subs 26
Subject Interests: Admin, Infection control, Medicine, Nursing, Surgery
Partic in Western New York Library Resources Council

P NORTH TONAWANDA PUBLIC LIBRARY, 505 Meadow Dr, 14120-2888. SAN 312-1836. Tel: 716-693-4132. Reference Tel: 716-693-3009. FAX: 716-693-0719. E-Mail: ntw@ntonawanda.lib.ny.us. Web Site: www.ntonawanda.lib.ny.us. *Dir*, Daniel R Killian; E-Mail: dkill@ntonawanda.lib.ny.us; *Acq, Ref*, Jane Olstad; E-Mail: jolstad@ntonawanda.lib.ny.us; *Ch Servs*, Margaret Waite; E-Mail: pwaite@ntonawanda.lib.ny.us; Staff 20 (MLS 7, Non-MLS 13)
Founded 1893. Pop 34,989; Circ 350,449
Jan 1999-Dec 1999 Income $1,104,262, State $20,369, County $80,124, Locally Generated Income $42,250, Parent Institution $898,930, Other $62,589. Mats Exp $1,720,808, Books $133,489, Per/Ser (Incl. Access Fees) $19,477, Presv $31, AV Equip $24,954, Electronic Ref Mat (Incl. Access Fees) $8,094. Sal $528,484 (Prof $282,714)
Library Holdings: Bk Vols 153,333; Bk Titles 133,750; Per Subs 271
Subject Interests: Antiques, Bus, Handicraft, Local history, Mgt
Special Collections: Carousels
Automation Activity & Vendor Info: (Cataloging) epixtech, inc.; (Circulation) epixtech, inc.
Publications: North Tonawanda Public Library Log (newsletter)
Mem of Nioga Library System
Friends of the Library Group

NORTHPORT

GM DEPARTMENT OF VETERANS AFFAIRS, Medical Library (142D), 79 Middleville Rd, 11768-2290. SAN 312-1852. Tel: 631-261-4400. FAX: 631-754-7992. *Librn*, Kathy Kessel; *Librn*, Robert Toronto
Pop 1,800; Circ 24,085
Library Holdings: Bk Vols 6,262; Per Subs 550
Subject Interests: Allied health, Geriatrics, Hospital administration, Medicine, Psychiatry, Psychology, Surgery
Publications: Library Line (quarterly)
Partic in Long Island Library Resources Council; Vets Admin Libr Network

S NORTHPORT HISTORICAL SOCIETY MUSEUM LIBRARY, 215 Main St, PO Box 545, 11768. SAN 372-5677. Tel: 631-757-9859. FAX: 631-757-9398. E-Mail: info@northporthistorical.org. Web Site: www.northporthistorical.org. *Dir*, Barbra Wells Fitzgerald; *Asst Curator*, George Wallace
Founded 1974. Pop 7,500; Circ 350
Library Holdings: Bk Titles 350

P NORTHPORT-EAST NORTHPORT PUBLIC LIBRARY, 151 Laurel Ave, 11768. SAN 353-9075. Tel: 631-261-6930. FAX: 631-261-6718, 631-754-6613. E-Mail: netwalk@suffolk.lib.ny.us. Web Site: netwalk.suffolk.lib.ny.us. *Dir*, Stephanie Heineman; *Asst Dir, Coll Develop*, Eileen Minogue; *Commun Servs*, Mary Ellen Moll; *Ref Serv*, Nancy Morcerf; *Computer Services*, James Olney; *YA Servs*, Doris Gebel; *YA Servs*, Lisa Herskowitz; *Media Spec*, Dolorita Gillman; *Tech Servs*, Angela Richards; *Circ*, Barbara Dattolico; *Ch Servs*, Patricia Koven; *Coll Develop*, Colette Malik. Subject Specialists: *Career Information Center*, Rochelle Freed; *Health info tech*, Evelyn Degen; *Local history*, Barbara Johnson; Staff 30 (MLS 30)
Founded 1914. Pop 36,499; Circ 515,126
Library Holdings: Bk Vols 220,500; Per Subs 820
Subject Interests: Architecture, Art, Boating
Special Collections: Jack Kerouac Coll; Kerovac-Off the Shelf (Bibliography); Milton E Brasher Portfolio; Rosemary Wells Coll
Automation Activity & Vendor Info: (Acquisitions) Innovative Interfaces Inc.; (Cataloging) Innovative Interfaces Inc.; (Circulation) Innovative Interfaces Inc.; (OPAC) Innovative Interfaces Inc.; (Serials) Innovative Interfaces Inc.
Publications: bibliographies; Book, Bytes & Beyond; booklists; Guide to Northport Library; Internet Quick Start Guides; Library Smarts-A Parent's Guide to Resources; Living in Northport & East Northport; PC Station: Guidelines; Preschooler's Door to Learning; Rosemary Wells Collection; Special Loan Service to Our Schools; The Library (monthly newsletter); Write Now
Mem of Suffolk Cooperative Library System
Special Services for the Deaf - Staff with knowledge of sign language
Friends of the Library Group
Branches: 1
EAST NORTHPORT PUBLIC, 185 Larkfield Rd, East Northport, 11731. SAN 353-9105. Tel: 631-261-2313. FAX: 631-261-3523. Web Site: netwalk.suffolk.lib.ny.us. *Librn*, Margaret Brozek; *YA Servs*, Doris Gebel; *Circ*, Frances Byrne
Library Holdings: Bk Vols 75,000
Friends of the Library Group

NORTHVILLE

P NORTHVILLE PUBLIC LIBRARY,* 341 S Third St, PO Box 1259, 12134. SAN 376-3099. Tel: 518-863-6922. FAX: 518-863-6922. E-Mail: norlib@klink.net. Web Site: www.klink.net/~norlib/fol. *Dir*, Michael Burnett
Circ 24,092
Jul 1997-Jun 1998 Income $92,830, State $1,800, Other $88,930. Mats Exp $15,250, Books $11,500, Per/Ser (Incl. Access Fees) $2,250. Sal $37,418 (Prof $32,865)
Library Holdings: Bk Vols 15,742; Per Subs 77
Mem of Mohawk Valley Library Association
Friends of the Library Group

NORWICH

M CHENANGO MEMORIAL HOSPITAL, Medical Library,* 179 N Broad St, 13815. SAN 312-1860. Tel: 607-337-4111, 607-337-4159. FAX: 607-334-2024. *Librn*, Ann L Slocum
Founded 1972
Library Holdings: Bk Vols 2,000; Per Subs 246
Subject Interests: Clinical medicine, Geriatric nursing, Nursing
Publications: In-house newsletter
Partic in Medline; Nat Libr of Med; OCLC Online Computer Library Center, Inc; S Cent Res Libr Coun

P GUERNSEY MEMORIAL LIBRARY, 3 Court St, 13815. SAN 312-1879. Tel: 607-334-4034. FAX: 607-336-3901. Web Site: lib.4cty.org/norwich.html. *Dir*, Melanie Battoe; E-Mail: no_melanie@4cty.org; *ILL*, Linda Doughty; *Circ*, Sue Morehead. Subject Specialists: *Genealogy*, Kathy Barton
Founded 1908. Pop 14,000; Circ 162,338
Jul 1999-Jun 2000 Income $719,302
Library Holdings: Bk Titles 64,410
Subject Interests: Genealogy, Health, Job info, Local history, Women's issues
Automation Activity & Vendor Info: (OPAC) DRA
Publications: Glance at Guernsey (newspaper column)
Mem of Four County Library System
Friends of the Library Group

GL NEW YORK STATE SUPREME COURT LAW LIBRARY, David L Follett Memorial Library, 5 W Main St, 13815-1899. SAN 312-1887. Tel: 607-334-9463. FAX: 607-334-9236. *Librn*, Lorraine Knapp
Founded 1902
Library Holdings: Bk Vols 13,000
Partic in S Cent Res Libr Coun

S PROCTER & GAMBLE PHARMACEUTICALS, Research Library,* Rt 320, Woods Corners. (Mail add: PO Box 191, 13815), SAN 312-1895. Tel: 607-335-2947. FAX: 607-335-2098. *Librn*, Linda Slentz
Founded 1961
Library Holdings: Bk Vols 10,000; Bk Titles 10,000; Per Subs 500
Subject Interests: Biology, Chemistry, Medicine, Pharm
Special Collections: Pharmacy (Drugs)
Publications: Library accesions List; Various Current Awareness Publications
Partic in BRS; Dialog Corporation; Nat Libr of Med; OCLC Online Computer Library Center, Inc; S Cent Res Libr Coun

NORWOOD

P NORWOOD LIBRARY,* One Morton St, PO Box 206, 13668. SAN 312-1909. Tel: 315-353-6692. *Librn*, Marcia Murray
Founded 1912. Circ 21,120
Library Holdings: Bk Vols 14,490; Per Subs 50
Mem of North Country Library System

NUNDA

P BELL MEMORIAL LIBRARY, 16 East St, PO Box 725, 14517. SAN 312-1917. Tel: 716-468-2266. FAX: 716-468-2266. *Dir*, Patricia Galbraith; E-Mail: pgalbraith@pls-net.org
Pop 5,034; Circ 20,934
Jan 1999-Dec 1999 Income $71,371, State $5,656, Locally Generated Income $42,000, Other $12,616. Mats Exp $9,750, Books $7,500, Per/Ser (Incl. Access Fees) $475, Electronic Ref Mat (Incl. Access Fees) $1,775. Sal $40,158 (Prof $16,230)
Library Holdings: Bk Vols 19,628; Per Subs 32
Mem of Pioneer Library System

NYACK

SR FELLOWSHIP OF RECONCILIATION LIBRARY,* PO Box 271, 10960. SAN 327-2117. Tel: 914-358-4601. FAX: 914-358-4924. E-Mail: forlibrary@igc.org. *In Charge*, Elisa Thayer
Library Holdings: Bk Vols 5,000; Per Subs 20
Restriction: Staff use only

C NYACK COLLEGE LIBRARY, One South Blvd, 10960-3698. SAN 312-1925. Tel: 845-358-1710, Ext 105. Interlibrary Loan Service Tel: 845-358-1710, Ext 325. FAX: 845-353-0817. *Dir*, Linda Poston; E-Mail: postonl@nyack.edu; *Tech Servs*, Georgi Bordner; Tel: 845-358-1710, Ext 104, E-Mail: bordnerg@nyack.edu; *ILL*, Brian Jennings; Tel: 914-358-1710, Ext 325, E-Mail: jenningb@nyack.edu; *Acq*, Julia Guest; Tel: 914-358-1710, Ext 103, E-Mail: guestj@nyack.edu; *Ref*, Dori Nason; Tel: 914-358-1710, Ext 324, E-Mail: nasond@nyack.edu; Staff 5 (MLS 3, Non-MLS 2)
Founded 1882. Enrl 1,900; Fac 88; Highest Degree: Master
Jul 1999-Jun 2000 Income $354,496. Mats Exp $120,100, Books $68,000, Per/Ser (Incl. Access Fees) $40,600, Presv $1,500, Micro $10,000. Sal $153,781
Library Holdings: Bk Vols 70,775; Bk Titles 59,486; Per Subs 521
Subject Interests: Bible, Missions, Theology
Automation Activity & Vendor Info: (OPAC) PALS
Database Vendor: GaleNet, Lexis-Nexis, ProQuest, Silverplatter Information Inc.
Mem of Ramapo Catskill Library System
Partic in OCLC Online Computer Library Center, Inc; Southeastern New York Library Resources Council; WALDO

M NYACK HOSPITAL, Memorial Library, 160 N Midland Ave, 10960. Tel: 914-348-2515. FAX: 914-348-2517. *Dir*, Albert Robinson; E-Mail: robinsona@nyackhospital.org; Staff 4 (MLS 1, Non-MLS 3)
Founded 1960
Library Holdings: Bk Titles 1,250; Per Subs 180
Subject Interests: Medicine, Nursing, Pediatrics
Publications: Acquisitions List
Restriction: Medical staff only
Function: ILL available, Research library
Partic in BHSL; BRS; Hilow; Nat Libr of Med; Southeastern New York Library Resources Council

G ROCKLAND COUNTY GUIDANCE CENTER, Career Information Library,* 83 Main St, 10960-3218. SAN 312-1941. Tel: 914-358-9390. FAX: 914-358-4980. *Dir*, Dr Rita Lieberman
Founded 1966
Library Holdings: Bk Vols 375; Bk Titles 300; Per Subs 18
Subject Interests: Careers, Education, Feminism
Special Collections: Careers in Wide Variety of Subjects, pamphlets, tapes, bks
Publications: 1988 State Adult Education Department Career Counseling Manual (collaboration)

OAK HILL

S STIEFEL LABORATORIES, INC, Stiefel Research Institute Inc Library,* Rte 145, 12460. SAN 312-195X. Tel: 518-239-6901, Ext 3356. FAX: 518-239-8402. *Coordr*, Joanne Fraser
Founded 1967

Library Holdings: Bk Titles 450; Per Subs 27
Subject Interests: Diseases of the skin
Restriction: Staff use only
Partic in NY State Libr

OAKDALE

C DOWLING COLLEGE LIBRARY, Idle Hour Blvd, 11769-1999. SAN 312-1968. Interlibrary Loan Service Tel: 631-244-3488. Circulation Tel: 631-244-3280. Reference Tel: 631-244-3282. FAX: 631-244-3374. E-Mail: reference@dowling.edu. Web Site: www.dowling.edu/library. *Coordr, Electronic Resources*, Francie C Davis; Tel: 631-244-3283, E-Mail: davisf@dowling.edu; *Tech Servs*, Katherine Ryner; Tel: 631-244-3219, E-Mail: rynerk@dowling.edu; *Archivist, Circ, Ser*, David Jank; Tel: 631-244-3081, E-Mail: jankd@dowling.edu; *Govt Doc*, Joyce Renfroe Gotsch; Tel: 631-244-3150, E-Mail: gotschj@dowling.edu; *Ref*, Laura Pope Robbins; Tel: 631-244-5023, E-Mail: pope-rol@dowling.edu; *Coll Develop*, Diane Holliday; Tel: 631-244-3397, E-Mail: hollidad@dowling.edu; *Res*, Marjorie Fusco; Tel: 631-244-3284, E-Mail: fuscom@dowling.edu; *Spec Coll*, Suzanne Terry; Tel: 631-244-3285, E-Mail: gterrys@dowling.edu; *Automation Syst Coordr*, Priscilla Powers; Tel: 631-244-3343, E-Mail: powersp@dowling.edu; Staff 35 (MLS 19, Non-MLS 16)
Founded 1955. Enrl 6,000; Fac 113; Highest Degree: Doctorate
Library Holdings: Bk Vols 182,861; Bk Titles 146,946; Per Subs 1,296
Subject Interests: Aviation, Bus, Education, Transportation
Special Collections: Long Island History; Vanderbilt Family Coll
Automation Activity & Vendor Info: (Cataloging) Innovative Interfaces Inc.; (Circulation) Innovative Interfaces Inc.; (Course Reserve) Innovative Interfaces Inc.; (ILL) Innovative Interfaces Inc.; (OPAC) Innovative Interfaces Inc.; (Serials) Innovative Interfaces Inc.
Database Vendor: Dialog, GaleNet, IAC - Info Trac, Lexis-Nexis, OCLC - First Search, Silverplatter Information Inc.
Function: Reference services available
Partic in Long Island Library Resources Council; OCLC Online Computer Library Center, Inc; SUNY/OCLC; Westchester Acad Libr Dir Orgn
Friends of the Library Group

OAKFIELD

P OAKFIELD PUBLIC LIBRARY, Haxton Memorial Library, 3 N Pearl St, 14125. SAN 312-1976. Tel: 716-948-9900. FAX: 716-948-9900. *Dir*, Brenda Wiedrich; *Ch Servs*, Carol Glor
Founded 1963. Pop 3,500; Circ 29,606
Library Holdings: Bk Vols 38,500; Per Subs 150
Mem of Nioga Library System
Friends of the Library Group

OCEANSIDE

P OCEANSIDE LIBRARY, 30 Davison Ave, 11572-2299. SAN 312-1984. Tel: 516-766-2360. FAX: 516-766-1895. Web Site: www.oceansidelibrary.com. *Dir*, Evelyn Rothschild; E-Mail: erothschild@oceansidelibrary.com; *Asst Dir, Head Ref*, Barbara Markowitz; *Tech Servs*, Robyn Klose; *Ch Servs*, Judy Turbin; *ILL*, Mary Nespeco; *YA Servs*, Margaret Cole
Founded 1938. Pop 38,573; Circ 593,287
Jul 2000-Jun 2001 Income $2,661,090. Mats Exp $294,750, Books $230,000, Per/Ser (Incl. Access Fees) $30,000, Micro $4,750, AV Equip $30,000. Sal $1,297,100
Library Holdings: Bk Vols 161,131
Publications: Prose & Cons (newsletter)
Mem of Nassau Library System
Partic in Long Island Library Resources Council
Special Services for the Blind - Talking Books
Open Mon-Fri 9:30-9, Sat 9:30-5 & Sun 12-5

M SOUTH NASSAU COMMUNITIES HOSPITAL, Jules Redish Memorial Medical Library, 2445 Oceanside Rd, 11572. SAN 312-1992. Tel: 516-763-3452. FAX: 516-766-3857. *Dir*, Claire Joseph; E-Mail: cbjoseph_2000@yahoo.com; Staff 1 (MLS 1)
Founded 1958
Library Holdings: Bk Titles 1,100; Per Subs 120
Subject Interests: Medicine, Nursing, Surgery
Partic in Long Island Library Resources Council

ODESSA

P DUTTON S PETERSON MEMORIAL LIBRARY,* 106 First St, 14869-0046. SAN 376-3064. Tel: 607-594-2791. FAX: 607-594-2791. *Dir*, Gayle Greuber
Library Holdings: Bk Titles 6,000
Mem of Southern Tier Library System

OGDENSBURG

SR DIOCESE OF OGDENSBURG ARCHIVES, 622 Washington St, PO Box 369, 13669. SAN 377-4961. Tel: 315-393-2920. FAX: 315-394-7401. *In Charge*, Terry R LaValley
Special Collections: Parish Historical Listings

M HEPBURN MEDICAL CENTER LIBRARY, 214 King St, 13669. SAN 312-2018. Tel: 315-393-3600, Ext 5180. FAX: 315-393-8506. *Librn*, Dr Lynn H Widrick
Founded 1958
Library Holdings: Bk Vols 800
Subject Interests: Health sci, Medical
Partic in North Country Reference & Research Resources Council

S OGDENSBURG CORRECTIONAL FACILITY GENERAL LIBRARY, One Correction Way, 13669-2288. SAN 327-1870. Tel: 315-393-0281. FAX: 315-393-0281, Ext 3299. *Librn*, Thomas E Lawrence; Staff 1 (MLS 1)
Founded 1982
Jan 1999-Dec 1999 Income $69,440, State $7,354, Parent Institution $62,086. Mats Exp $22,591, Books $9,923, Per/Ser (Incl. Access Fees) $7,327, AV Equip $1,536, Other Print Mats $2,328. Sal $47,086
Library Holdings: Bk Vols 19,006; Per Subs 100; High Interest/Low Vocabulary Bk Vols 827; Spec Interest Per Sub 19
Special Collections: Black culture History & Spanish Language
Automation Activity & Vendor Info: (Cataloging) Follett; (Circulation) Follett; (OPAC) Follett
Mem of North Country Library System
Partic in North Country Reference & Research Resources Council
Inmate patrons, facility staff & volunteers direct access. All others through ILL only

P OGDENSBURG PUBLIC LIBRARY, 312 Washington St, 13669-1599. SAN 312-2034. Tel: 315-393-4325. FAX: 315-393-4344. Web Site: www.nc3r.org/ogdensburg. *Dir*, David A Franz; E-Mail: franz@northnet.org; *Ad Servs*, Marc Boyer; E-Mail: boyer@northnet.org; *Ch Servs*, Bonnie L Wright; Staff 11 (MLS 3, Non-MLS 8)
Founded 1893. Pop 13,521; Circ 82,227
Jan 1999-Dec 1999 Income $476,435, State $73,673, City $326,467, County $11,951, Locally Generated Income $64,344. Mats Exp $91,336, Books $58,014, Per/Ser (Incl. Access Fees) $18,867, Micro $8,558, AV Equip $1,553, Electronic Ref Mat (Incl. Access Fees) $4,344. Sal $312,788 (Prof $107,437)
Library Holdings: Bk Vols 59,003; Per Subs 315
Subject Interests: Local history
Special Collections: General Newton Martin Curtis Civil War Coll; Ogdensburg History (Ogdensburg Archives), bk, mss, flm
Automation Activity & Vendor Info: (Circulation) DRA; (OPAC) DRA
Publications: Informer (irregular newsletter)
Mem of North Country Library System
Friends of the Library Group

CR WADHAMS HALL SEMINARY-COLLEGE LIBRARY, 6866 State Hwy 37, 13669. SAN 312-2050. Tel: 315-393-4231. FAX: 315-393-4249. *Mgr*, Robert Jollett; E-Mail: jollett@northnet.org
Founded 1924. Enrl 19; Highest Degree: Bachelor
Jul 1999-Jun 2000 Income Parent Institution $104,671. Mats Exp $43,222, Books $12,216, Per/Ser (Incl. Access Fees) $19,006, Presv $1,583, Micro $42, AV Equip $64, Other Print Mats $57, Electronic Ref Mat (Incl. Access Fees) $2,883. Sal $59,883 (Prof $32,600)
Library Holdings: Bk Vols 81,294; Bk Titles 67,275; Per Subs 268
Subject Interests: Philosophy, Theology
Special Collections: Patristic Writings
Database Vendor: CARL, OCLC - First Search, ProQuest, Silverplatter Information Inc., Wilson - Wilson Web
Partic in North Country Ref & Res Resources Coun

OLD CHATHAM

SR SHAKER MUSEUM & LIBRARY, Emma B King Library, 88 Shaker Museum Rd, 12136. SAN 312-2069. Tel: 518-794-9100, Ext 111. FAX: 518-794-8621. E-Mail: shakermuseum@library.org. Web Site: www.shakermuseumandlibrary.org. *Librn*, Jerry Grant; Staff 5 (MLS 4, Non-MLS 1)
Founded 1950
Library Holdings: Bk Titles 2,000; Per Subs 12
Subject Interests: Architecture, Art, Furniture, Religion, Shakers, Women
Special Collections: Paper Artifacts, drawings, broadsides, advertising labels, product packages, watercolors; Photograph Coll; Society of Shakers: Their Arts, Crafts, Theology, Philosophy, includes membership rolls, patents, deeds, diaries, account books
Publications: Making His Mark: The World of Shaker Craftsman Orren Haskins; Noble But Plain: The Shaker Meetinghouse at Mount Lebanon; Shaker Adventure; Shaker Museum & Library Broadside (to members); Shakerism & Feminism: Reflections on Women's Religion & the Early Shakers; The Shaker Museum Guide to Shaker Collections & Libraries

OLD FORGE

P OLD FORGE LIBRARY,* Crosby Blvd, PO Box 128, 13420. SAN 312-2077. Tel: 315-369-6008. E-Mail: of-dial@midyork.lib.ny.us, oldforgl@nysernet.org. *Dir*, Isabella P Worthen
Founded 1914. Pop 1,637; Circ 19,326
Library Holdings: Bk Titles 12,898; Per Subs 20
Subject Interests: Adirondack hist
Publications: Adirondack Reflections
Mem of Mid-York Library System
Open Tues-Fri 1-5
Friends of the Library Group

OLD WESTBURY

M NEW YORK COLLEGE OF OSTEOPATHIC MEDICINE, Medical Library,* New York Institute of Technology, 11568. SAN 326-1697. Tel: 516-626-6943. FAX: 516-626-7439. *Librn*, Dr Gerri Flranzraich; Staff 1 (MLS 1)
Founded 1978
Library Holdings: Bk Vols 6,708; Per Subs 334
Special Collections: Osteopathy
Publications: Newsletter
Restriction: Staff use only

C NEW YORK INSTITUTE OF TECHNOLOGY, Wisser Library, PO Box 8000, 11568. SAN 329-1774. Tel: 516-686-7657. FAX: 516-626-2914. Web Site: www.nyit.edu/library. *Coll Develop, Librn*, Gerri Flanzraich; *Cat, Online Servs, Tech Servs*, Clare Cohn; *Per*, Liz Young; Staff 17 (MLS 17)
Founded 1955. Circ 82,270; Enrl 8,555; Fac 734; Highest Degree: Master
Library Holdings: Bk Vols 105,000; Per Subs 1,247
Subject Interests: Architecture, Computer science, Education, Engineering
Special Collections: Architecture; Center for Prejudice Reduction; Culinary Arts; Engineering
Automation Activity & Vendor Info: (Cataloging) DRA
Publications: New Acquisitions; Newsletter; Resource Guides
Partic in OCLC Online Computer Library Center, Inc
Departmental Libraries:
EDUCATION HALL LIBRARY, PO Box 8000, 11568. Tel: 516-686-7579. FAX: 516-686-7921. Web Site: www.nyit.edu/library. *Librn*, Leslie Goldstein
Library Holdings: Bk Vols 30,000; Per Subs 229

C STATE UNIVERSITY OF NEW YORK, College at Old Westbury Library, PO Box 229, 11568-0229. SAN 312-2093. Tel: 516-876-3156. Interlibrary Loan Service Tel: 516-876-3151. FAX: 516-876-3325. Web Site: www.oldwestbury.edu/library.cfm. *Dir*, Dr Paul Frisch; *Bibliog Instr, Ref*, Stephen Kirkpatrick; Tel: 516-876-3152; *Circ, Per*, Barbara Walsh; *ILL, Ref*, Rebecca Perez; *Electronic Resources*, Michael Epstein; Staff 6 (MLS 6)
Founded 1967. Enrl 3,691; Highest Degree: Bachelor
Library Holdings: Bk Vols 204,473; Per Subs 1,059
Subject Interests: Behav sci, Ethnic studies, Feminism, Soc sci
Special Collections: Black Poetry & Literature Coll; Slavery Source Material Coll, (micro); Underground Press Coll, (micro); Women's Studies Coll
Publications: focus bibliographies; library information pamphlets; Recent Acquisitions; research guides; subject list of periodicals
Partic in Long Island Library Resources Council; OCLC Online Computer Library Center, Inc

OLEAN

P OLEAN PUBLIC LIBRARY, 134 N Second St, 14760-2583. SAN 312-2115. Tel: 716-372-0200. FAX: 716-372-8651. E-Mail: info@oleanlibrary.org. Web Site: www.oleanlibrary.org. *Dir*, Lance Chaffee; *Ch Servs*, Kathy Price; *Tech Servs*, Chris Spink; *YA Servs*, Rosemarie Grainer; Staff 3 (MLS 3)
Founded 1871. Pop 38,400
Jan 1999-Dec 1999 Income $860,468, State $99,086, City $676,492, Locally Generated Income $63,915, Other $20,975. Mats Exp $114,185, Books $78,496, Per/Ser (Incl. Access Fees) $19,405, Other Print Mats $745. Sal $458,503
Library Holdings: Bk Vols 92,365; Per Subs 388
Subject Interests: Agriculture, Architecture, Art, Bus, Education, Mgt
Automation Activity & Vendor Info: (Circulation) Gaylord; (OPAC) Gaylord
Mem of Chautauqua-Cattaraugus Library System
Friends of the Library Group

ONEIDA

S MADISON COUNTY HISTORICAL SOCIETY LIBRARY, 435 Main St, PO Box 415, 13421. SAN 325-0741. Tel: 315-363-4136. *Dir*, Sydney Loftus; *Librn*, Mary King; *Curator*, Kimberly Kotary; Staff 6 (MLS 2, Non-MLS 4)
Founded 1895
Library Holdings: Bk Vols 2,000
Subject Interests: City of Oneida, Genealogy, History, Madison County, New York
Special Collections: George W Walter Coll; Gerrit Smith Coll; Henry A Herter Coll; Marshall Hope Coll

P ONEIDA LIBRARY,* 220 Broad St, 13421. SAN 312-2123. Tel: 315-363-3050. E-Mail: on_circ@midyork.lib.ny.us. Web Site: www.dreamscape.com/clare. *Dir*, Carolyn Gerakoupolos
Founded 1924. Pop 15,300; Circ 94,738
Library Holdings: Bk Vols 52,189; Bk Titles 58,000; Per Subs 110
Special Collections: Local History & Genealogy, bks, clippings, Cemetery rec; Madison County History; Oneida Community, bks, newsp; Oneida Indian Nation History
Publications: Life at Oneida Library (quarterly)
Mem of Mid-York Library System
Partic in OCLC Online Computer Library Center, Inc
Friends of the Library Group

ONEONTA

C HARTWICK COLLEGE, Stevens-German Library, 13820. SAN 312-214X. Tel: 607-431-4440. Interlibrary Loan Service Tel: 607-431-4440. FAX: 607-431-4457. E-Mail: library@hartwick.edu. Web Site: hartwick.edu/library/hompage.html. *Dir, Librn*, Marilyn Dunn; Tel: 607-431-4448, E-Mail: dunnm@hartwick.edu; *ILL, Ref*, Sue Stevens; *Tech Servs*, Nancy Chiang; Staff 10 (MLS 7, Non-MLS 3)
Founded 1928. Enrl 1,415; Fac 113; Highest Degree: Bachelor
Jul 1998-Jun 1999 Income $1,157,126, Parent Institution $1,152,126. Mats Exp $414,975, Books $153,996, Per/Ser (Incl. Access Fees) $218,000, Presv $11,179, Manuscripts & Archives $5,300, Electronic Ref Mat (Incl. Access Fees) $26,500. Sal $579,800 (Prof $376,000)
Library Holdings: Bk Vols 299,000; Per Subs 2,300
Subject Interests: N Am Indians
Special Collections: Judge William Cooper Papers, mss; North American Indians (Yager Coll), bk, micro
Publications: Stevens-German Library (newsletter)
Partic in OCLC Online Computer Library Center, Inc; S Cent Res Libr Coun

P HUNTINGTON MEMORIAL LIBRARY, 62 Chestnut, 13820-2498. SAN 312-2158. Tel: 607-432-1980. FAX: 607-432-5623. Web Site: lib.4cty.org. *Dir*, Marie Bruni; Staff 16 (MLS 2, Non-MLS 14)
Founded 1893. Pop 25,000; Circ 285,171
Jan 2000-Dec 2000 Income $540,860, State $16,000, City $283,210, Locally Generated Income $231,350, Other $10,300. Mats Exp $96,700, Books $69,000, Per/Ser (Incl. Access Fees) $8,800, Presv $6,000, Other Print Mats $10,900, Electronic Ref Mat (Incl. Access Fees) $2,000. Sal $312,590 (Prof $86,540)
Library Holdings: Bk Vols 85,000; Per Subs 215
Special Collections: DAR Lineage Coll; Railroads (Beach Coll), pictures
Automation Activity & Vendor Info: (Acquisitions) DRA; (Circulation) DRA; (ILL) DRA; (OPAC) DRA
Mem of Four County Library System
Friends of the Library Group

C STATE UNIVERSITY OF NEW YORK, COLLEGE AT ONEONTA, James M Milne Library, 13820-4014. SAN 312-2166. Tel: 607-436-2723. Interlibrary Loan Service Tel: 607-436-2726. Circulation Tel: 607-436-2720. Reference Tel: 607-436-2025. TDD: 607-436-2025. FAX: 607-436-3081. Web Site: library.oneonta.edu. *Dir Libr Serv*, Janet L Potter; E-Mail: potterjl@oneonta.edu; *Asst Dir*, Christine E Bulson; E-Mail: bulsonce@oneonta.edu; *Asst Dir*, Elaine L Downing; Tel: 607-436-2727, E-Mail: downinel@oneonta.edu; *Circ*, Kathy Croft; E-Mail: croftkc@oneonta.edu; *ILL*, Andrea F Gerberg; E-Mail: gerberaf@oneonta.edu; *Tech Coordr*, Daniel F Kissane; Tel: 607-436-3331, E-Mail: kissandf@oneonta.edu; *Electronic Resources*, Nancy Cannon; E-Mail: cannons@oneonta.edu; Staff 35 (MLS 12, Non-MLS 23)
Founded 1889. Enrl 5,412; Fac 392; Highest Degree: Master
Jul 1999-Jun 2000 Income $2,012,802, State $1,833,216, Locally Generated Income $10,989, Other $168,597. Mats Exp $608,401, Books $271,070, Per/Ser (Incl. Access Fees) $240,431, Presv $14,954, Micro $25,950, Electronic Ref Mat (Incl. Access Fees) $55,996. Sal $1,152,827 (Prof $564,250)
Library Holdings: Bk Vols 546,770; Bk Titles 394,226; Per Subs 2,221
Subject Interests: Education, Home economics
Special Collections: 19th & Early 20th Century Popular Fiction; Early Textbooks & Early Educational Theory; James Fenimore Cooper; New York State History Coll; New York State Verse Coll
Automation Activity & Vendor Info: (Cataloging) MultiLIS; (Circulation) MultiLIS; (OPAC) MultiLIS; (Serials) MultiLIS
Database Vendor: CARL, Dialog, DRA, GaleNet, IAC - SearchBank, Lexis-Nexis, OCLC - First Search, Silverplatter Information Inc., Wilson - Wilson Web
Publications: Grist from the Milne; Milne Library Information Series
Function: ILL limited
Partic in S Cent Res Libr Coun; State University Of New York-NYLINK

Special Services for the Deaf - TTY machine
Reciprocal borrowing privileges with Hartwick College; community borrowing privileges for adults in surrounding 8-county area; SUNY open access

ONTARIO

P ONTARIO PUBLIC LIBRARY,* 1850 Ridge Rd, 14519. SAN 312-2174. Tel: 315-524-8381. FAX: 315-524-5838.
Founded 1914. Pop 8,549; Circ 125,357
Library Holdings: Bk Titles 29,453; Per Subs 150
Mem of Pioneer Library System; Wayne County Libr Syst
Friends of the Library Group

ORANGEBURG

GM NATHAN S KLINE INSTITUTE FOR PSYCHIATRIC RESEARCH, Health Sciences Library, 140 Old Orangeburg Rd, Bldg 35, 10962. SAN 312-2204. Tel: 845-398-6575. FAX: 845-398-5551. Web Site: www.rfmh.org/nki. *Dir*, Stuart Moss; E-Mail: moss@nki.rfmh.org; Staff 3 (MLS 1, Non-MLS 2)
Founded 1952
Apr 2000-Mar 2001 Income $240,000. Mats Exp $140,000, Books $500, Per/Ser (Incl. Access Fees) $108,000, Presv $10,000, Electronic Ref Mat (Incl. Access Fees) $12,500. Sal $100,000 (Prof $50,000)
Library Holdings: Bk Vols 25,000; Bk Titles 10,000; Per Subs 80
Subject Interests: Biochemistry, Mental health, Neuroscience, Psychiatry, Psychology, Psychopharmacology
Special Collections: Family Resource Center
Database Vendor: OVID Technologies
Publications: Bibliographies; staff publications
Restriction: In-house use for visitors, Public use on premises
Function: Archival collection, For research purposes, Photocopies available
Partic in Basic Health Sciences Library Network; Health Info Librs of Westchester; Nat Libr of Med; OCLC Online Computer Library Center, Inc; Southeastern New York Library Resources Council; UCMP

P ORANGEBURG LIBRARY,* 20 Greenbush Rd, 10962-1311. SAN 312-2190. Tel: 914-359-2244. FAX: 914-359-8692. *Dir*, Kevin Rosswurm; *Asst Librn, Ch Servs*, Nancy Wissman; Staff 3 (MLS 3)
Founded 1973. Pop 4,500; Circ 44,509
Library Holdings: Bk Titles 42,691; Per Subs 164
Special Collections: Career & Education Resource Center; Constitutional materials
Publications: Quarterly newsletter
Mem of Ramapo Catskill Library System

ORCHARD PARK

J ERIE COMMUNITY COLLEGE-SOUTH CAMPUS, Library Resources Center, 4041 Southwestern Blvd, 14127. SAN 353-913X. Tel: 716-851-1772. FAX: 716-851-1778. E-Mail: slib@ecc.edu. Web Site: www.nstaff.sunyerie.edu/home/library/index.htm. *Chair*, Judith Geer; Tel: 716-851-1773, E-Mail: geer@ecc.edu; *Acq*, Jill Barrile; Tel: 716-851-1776, E-Mail: barriljc@ecc.edu; *ILL*, Robert Kushin; Tel: 716-851-1775, E-Mail: kushin@ecc.edu; Staff 9 (MLS 5, Non-MLS 4)
Founded 1974. Pop 4,800; Circ 8,000; Enrl 4,800; Fac 106; Highest Degree: Associate
Sep 1999-Aug 2000 Income $586,650. Mats Exp $103,500, Books $54,000, Per/Ser (Incl. Access Fees) $21,000, Presv $500, Micro $9,000, AV Equip $4,000, Electronic Ref Mat (Incl. Access Fees) $15,000. Sal $428,750 (Prof $255,417)
Library Holdings: Bk Vols 52,832; Bk Titles 50,206; Per Subs 321
Special Collections: Henry Louis Mencken; Women Writers of Western New York
Automation Activity & Vendor Info: (Cataloging) MultiLIS
Database Vendor: DRA, GaleNet, IAC - Info Trac, Lexis-Nexis, OCLC - First Search
Publications: LRC News; Periodical Holdings List; Study guides
Partic in Western New York Library Resources Council

P ORCHARD PARK PUBLIC LIBRARY, S-4570 S Buffalo St, 14127. SAN 312-2212. Tel: 716-662-9851. FAX: 716-667-3098. Web Site: www.buffalolib.org. *Dir*, Ann Laubacker; E-Mail: laubackera@buffalolib.org; *Ad Servs*, Patricia Forsberg; E-Mail: forsergp@buffalolib.org; *Ch Servs*, Joyce Maguda; Staff 3 (MLS 3)
Founded 1935. Pop 24,900; Circ 345,773
Library Holdings: Bk Titles 65,873; Per Subs 129
Mem of Buffalo & Erie County Public Library System
Friends of the Library Group

ORIENT

S OYSTERPONDS HISTORICAL SOCIETY LIBRARY,* Village Lane, PO Box 70, 11957. SAN 312-2220. Tel: 631-323-2480. FAX: 631-323-3719. *Chief Librn*, Donald Boerum
Founded 1944
Library Holdings: Bk Vols 450
Subject Interests: 19th Century, Education, Local history, NY state hist, Religion
Special Collections: Art (William Steeple Davis), paintings; Local Historical Research (Clarence Ashton Wood Coll); Photography (William Steeple Davis & Vinton Richard Coll), black & white glass plates
Partic in Am Asn for State & Local Hist; Am Asn of Museums; Asn for Conservation; NY Hist Soc; Suffolk County Hist Soc

ORISKANY

P ORISKANY PUBLIC LIBRARY,* 621 Utica St, 13424. SAN 312-2239. Tel: 315-736-2532. *Librn*, Theda R Bowers
Pop 1,500; Circ 9,960
Library Holdings: Bk Titles 9,000; Per Subs 15
Mem of Mid-York Library System
Friends of the Library Group

ORISKANY FALLS

P CW CLARK MEMORIAL LIBRARY, 160 N Main, 13425. SAN 312-2247. Tel: 315-821-7850. FAX: 315-821-7850. E-Mail: os_circ@midyork.lib.ny.us. *Librn*, Jackie Roys
Pop 1,600; Circ 10,000
Library Holdings: Bk Vols 12,000; Per Subs 40
Mem of Mid-York Library System
Open Mon, Wed & Fri 9:30am-11:30am & 2-5:30, Tues & Thurs 2-8, Sat 9:30-11:30
Friends of the Library Group

ORWELL

P ORWELL LIBRARY, 1999 County Rte 2, PO Box 35, 13426. SAN 312-2255. Tel: 315-298-5563. FAX: 315-298-5563.
Circ 9,926
2000-2001 Mats Exp Books $5,000. Sal $6,760
Library Holdings: Bk Vols 8,075
Mem of North Country Library System

OSSINING

S OSSINING HISTORICAL SOCIETY MUSEUM,* 196 Croton Ave, 10562. SAN 323-4525. Tel: 914-941-0001. *Dir*, Roberta Y Arminio
Library Holdings: Bk Vols 1,100; Per Subs 15

P OSSINING PUBLIC LIBRARY, 53 Croton Ave, 10562-4903. SAN 312-2263. Tel: 914-941-2416. Circulation Tel: 914-941-2416, Ext 301. Reference Tel: 914-941-2416, Ext 304. FAX: 914-941-7464. E-Mail: opl@wls.lib.ny.us. Web Site: ossininglibrary.org. *Dir*, Edward M Falcone; E-Mail: efalcone@wls.lib.ny.us; *Asst Dir*, Joan Hraban; *Ch Servs*, Judith Sagat; *Ch Servs*, Sally Dow; *ILL*, John Hawkins; Tel: 914-941-2416, Ext 307; *Pub Relations*, Jane Clark; *Ref*, Joyce Koyner; *Librn*, Patricia Perito; Tel: 914-941-2416, Ext 305; *YA Servs*, Cheryl Cohen; Tel: 914-941-2416, Ext 308. Subject Specialists: *Edu*, Patricia Perito; *Job info*, Patricia Perito; Staff 34 (MLS 14, Non-MLS 20)
Founded 1898. Pop 31,173; Circ 325,000
Jul 2000-Jun 2001 Income $1,898,837, State $11,000, Locally Generated Income $1,887,837. Mats Exp $217,000, Books $126,000, Per/Ser (Incl. Access Fees) $52,000, AV Equip $39,000. Sal $1,078,872 (Prof $477,000)
Library Holdings: Bk Vols 92,000; Per Subs 307
Special Collections: Job Information Center, bks, per & pamphlets
Automation Activity & Vendor Info: (Circulation) epixtech, inc.
Publications: The Library Byline (monthly)
Mem of Westchester Library System
Friends of the Library Group

S SING SING CORRECTIONAL FACILITY LIBRARY,* 354 Hunter St, 10562. SAN 327-0718. Tel: 914-941-0108. FAX: 914-941-6583. *Librn*, Robert Richter

OSWEGO

S NEW YORK STATE OFFICE OF PARKS, RECREATION & HISTORIC PRESERVATION, Fort Ontario State Historic Site Research Library, One E Fourth St, 13126. SAN 326-324X. Tel: 315-343-4711. FAX: 315-343-1430.
Library Holdings: Bk Titles 1,500; Per Subs 10
Subject Interests: Architecture, History
Restriction: Non-circulating to the public

P OSWEGO CITY LIBRARY,* 120 E Second St, 13126. SAN 312-2271. Tel: 315-341-5867. FAX: 315-342-3206. *Librn*, Carol Ferlito; *Ad Servs*, Martha Lyon
Founded 1854. Pop 19,195; Circ 108,980

Library Holdings: Bk Vols 53,000; Per Subs 1,188
Special Collections: Local Cemetery Records; Oswego County Historical Society Coll, per
Mem of North Country Library System
Friends of the Library Group

C STATE UNIVERSITY OF NEW YORK AT OSWEGO, Penfield Library, SUNY Oswego, 13126-3514. SAN 312-228X. Tel: 315-341-4232. Interlibrary Loan Service Tel: 315-312-4546. Circulation Tel: 315-312-2560. Reference Tel: 315-312-4267. FAX: 315-341-3194. E-Mail: refdesk@oswego.edu. Web Site: www.oswego.edu/library. *Dir*, Mary Beth Bell; E-Mail: mbell@oswego.edu; *Spec Coll & Archives*, Mary Loe; Tel: 315-312-3537, E-Mail: archives@oswego.edu; *Doc*, Mary Bennett; Tel: 315-312-3564; *ILL*, Cathryn Reed; E-Mail: ill@oswego.edu; *Circ*, Nedra L Peterson; E-Mail: circdesk@oswego.edu; *Ref*, Thomas Larson; E-Mail: refdesk@oswego.edu; *Tech Servs*, Deborah Curry; Tel: 315-312-3210; *Syst Coordr*, Natalie Sturr; E-Mail: sturr@oswego.edu; Staff 36 (MLS 16, Non-MLS 20)
Founded 1861. Enrl 8,149; Fac 360; Highest Degree: Master
Jul 1999-Jun 2000 Income $2,060,000. Mats Exp $593,806, Books $146,469, Per/Ser (Incl. Access Fees) $323,063, Presv $16,211, Micro $23,072, AV Equip $13,209, Electronic Ref Mat (Incl. Access Fees) $71,782. Sal $1,207,299 (Prof $660,699)
Library Holdings: Bk Vols 453,390; Bk Titles 291,080; Per Subs 1,802
Subject Interests: Bus admin, Education, Liberal arts, Technology
Special Collections: College Archives; Local & State History (Safe Haven Coll); Local History (Marshall Family Coll); Presidential Papers (Millard Fillmore Coll).
Automation Activity & Vendor Info: (Acquisitions) EX Libris; (Cataloging) EX Libris; (Circulation) EX Libris; (Course Reserve) EX Libris; (OPAC) EX Libris; (Serials) EX Libris
Database Vendor: Dialog, IAC - Info Trac, Lexis-Nexis, OCLC - First Search, Silverplatter Information Inc.
Partic in North Country Reference & Research Resources Council; OCLC Online Computer Library Center, Inc
Friends of the Library Group

OTEGO

P HARRIS MEMORIAL LIBRARY, 69 Main St, 13825. SAN 312-2298. Tel: 607-988-6661. FAX: 607-988-6661. *Librn*, Dawn Rogers; Staff 1 (MLS 1)
Founded 1923. Pop 3,000; Circ 13,000
Library Holdings: Bk Titles 10,000; Per Subs 32
Database Vendor: DRA
Mem of Four County Library System
Open Tues 10-12 & 2-5, Wed 2-5 & 6-9, Thurs 10-12 & 2-5, Fri 2-5 & 6-9, Sat 10-1

OTISVILLE

S OTISVILLE CORRECTIONAL FACILITY LIBRARY,* PO Box 8, 10963-0008. SAN 327-1811. Tel: 914-386-1490. FAX: 914-386-1574. *Librn*, Donald Drewett

OVID

P EDITH B FORD MEMORIAL LIBRARY, 7169 Main St, 14521. SAN 312-2301. Tel: 607-869-3031. FAX: 607-869-3031. *Librn*, Eilene E Moeri
Founded 1899. Pop 660; Circ 18,256
Library Holdings: Bk Titles 34,427; Per Subs 40
Mem of Finger Lakes Library System

OWEGO

P COBURN FREE LIBRARY,* 275 Main St, 13827. SAN 312-231X. Tel: 607-687-3520. FAX: 607-687-5628. *Dir*, Christine Burroughs
Circ 55,204
Library Holdings: Bk Vols 21,640; Bk Titles 17,190
Special Collections: Genealogy (Dr Hyde Room)
Mem of Finger Lakes Library System
Friends of the Library Group

S LOCKHEED MARTIN FEDERAL SYSTEMS, Library & Information Research Center, 1801 State Rte 17C, Maildrop 0127, 13827. SAN 312-2328. Tel: 607-751-2725. FAX: 607-751-5208. *Info Specialist, Librn*, Patricia Ann Puglisi; E-Mail: patricia.puglisi@lmco.com; Staff 2 (MLS 1, Non-MLS 1)
Founded 1955
Library Holdings: Bk Vols 10,000; Per Subs 240
Subject Interests: Aeronautics, Astronautics, Bus, Computers, Electricity, Electronics, Mathematics, Mgt, Undersea (naval)
Automation Activity & Vendor Info: (Cataloging) TechLIB
Database Vendor: Dialog, Ebsco - EbscoHost, Lexis-Nexis, OCLC - First Search
Partic in Dialog Corporation

S TIOGA COUNTY HISTORICAL SOCIETY MUSEUM LIBRARY, 110-112 Front St, 13827. SAN 312-2336. Tel: 607-687-2460. FAX: 607-687-7788. E-Mail: tiogamus@clarityconnect.com. Web Site: www.tioga.history.tier.net.
Founded 1914
Library Holdings: Bk Vols 3,000
Subject Interests: Genealogy, Hist of NY
Special Collections: Local Newspapers on microfilm

OXFORD

G NEW YORK STATE VETERANS HOME LIBRARY,* 4211 St Hwy 220, 13830. SAN 376-0774. Tel: 607-843-3100. FAX: 607-843-3199. *Dir*, Dr Phillip Dzwonczyk
Library Holdings: Bk Vols 700

P OXFORD MEMORIAL LIBRARY,* Fort Hill, PO Box 552, 13830. SAN 312-2344. Tel: 607-843-6146. FAX: 607-843-9157. *Dir*, Nancy Wilcox; E-Mail: ox_nancy@4cty.org
Founded 1900. Pop 5,361; Circ 28,000
1997-1998 Income $78,261, State $1,200. Mats Exp $18,000, Books $17,200, Per/Ser (Incl. Access Fees) $800. Sal $29,800
Library Holdings: Bk Titles 12,500; Per Subs 44
Mem of Four County Library System
Friends of the Library Group

OYSTER BAY

S OYSTER BAY HISTORICAL SOCIETY LIBRARY, 20 Summit St, PO Box 297, 11771-0297. SAN 326-1999. Tel: 516-922-5032. FAX: 516-922-6892. E-Mail: obhistory@aol.com. Web Site: members.aol.com/obhistory. *Librn*, Kate Riley
Founded 1960
Jul 2000-Jun 2001 Income $13,375, Locally Generated Income $1,075, Parent Institution $12,300. Mats Exp $1,100, Books $250, Per/Ser (Incl. Access Fees) $150, Presv $500, Other Print Mats $200. Sal $11,800
Library Holdings: Bk Vols 1,010; Bk Titles 997
Subject Interests: Genealogy, Local history
Special Collections: Early American Tools & Trades (Reichman Coll); Theodore Roosevelt Coll
Publications: Magazine for members (quarterly); The Freeholder
Restriction: Non-circulating to the public

P OYSTER BAY-EAST NORWICH PUBLIC LIBRARY,* 89 E Main St, 11771. SAN 312-2352. Tel: 516-922-1212. FAX: 516-264-8693, 516-922-6453. E-Mail: oysterbay@nassaulibrary.org. Web Site: www.nassaulibrary.org/oysterbay. *Dir*, Suzanne Koch; *Coll Develop, Ref*, Dorothy Moore; *Circ*, Carol Ann Haug; *Librn*, Julie Genovese; *YA Servs*, Jennifer Griffing; *Tech Servs*, Ann Smith; Staff 6 (MLS 6)
Founded 1901. Pop 13,404; Circ 161,183
Library Holdings: Bk Vols 112,000; Per Subs 1,703
Subject Interests: Career develop, Local history
Special Collections: Presidential (Theodore Roosevelt Coll)
Automation Activity & Vendor Info: (Circulation) CLSI LIBS
Publications: Bimonthly Newsletter
Mem of Nassau Library System
Friends of the Library Group

S PLANTING FIELDS ARBORETUM, Garden Library, Planting Filelds Rd, 11771-1302. (Mail add: PO Box 58, 11771-0058), SAN 312-2360. Tel: 516-922-9024. FAX: 516-922-7603. E-Mail: gardenlibrary@prodigy.net. Web Site: www.plantingfields.com. *Librn*, Rosemarie I Papayanopulos. Subject Specialists: *Horticulture*, Rosemarie I Papayanopulos; Staff 8 (MLS 2, Non-MLS 6)
Founded 1975
Library Holdings: Bk Vols 7,000; Bk Titles 6,100; Per Subs 100; Spec Interest Per Sub 150
Subject Interests: Botany, Horticulture
Special Collections: Charles Darwin Coll; L H Bailey Coll; Long Island Nursery Catalogs
Restriction: Staff & members only
Function: Reference services available

S SAGAMORE HILL NATIONAL HISTORIC SITE LIBRARY,* 20 Sagamore Hill Rd, 11771-1899. SAN 324-4393. Tel: 516-922-4788. FAX: 516-922-4792. *Curator*, Amy Verone
Library Holdings: Bk Vols 950; Bk Titles 850
Subject Interests: Nat park area, Sagamore Hill
Special Collections: Theodore Roosevelt Life & Career

PAINTED POST

P SOUTHERN TIER LIBRARY SYSTEM, 580 W Water St, 14870. SAN 352-3861. Tel: 607-962-3141. FAX: 607-962-5356. Web Site: www.stls.org. *Dir*, Ristiina Wigg; *Tech Coordr*, Ken Behn; *Electronic Resources*, Nichola Lerczak; *Tech Servs*, Mary Kay Quiggle; *Ad Servs*, Mary Passage; *YA Servs*, Shawn Brommer; Staff 24 (MLS 4, Non-MLS 20)
Founded 1958. Pop 286,225

Library Holdings: Bk Vols 45,562; Per Subs 60
Subject Interests: NY state county hist
Automation Activity & Vendor Info: (Acquisitions) DRA; (Cataloging) DRA; (Circulation) DRA; (OPAC) DRA
Database Vendor: DRA
Publications: FYI
Member Libraries: Addison Public Library; Andover Free Library; Angelica Free Library; Avoca Free Library; Belfast Public Library; Belmont Literary & Historical Society Free Library; Bolivar Free Library; Branchport Free Library; Colonial Library; Cuba Circulating Library; David A Howe Public Library; Dormann Library; Dundee Library; Dutton S Peterson Memorial Library; E J Cottrell Memorial Library; Essential Club Free Library; Friendship Free Library; Genesee Public Library; Hammondsport Public Library; Hornell Public Library; Horseheads Free Library; Howard Public Library; Jasper Free Library; Montour Falls Memorial Library; Penn Yan Public Library; Prattsburg Library; Pulteney Free Library; Rushford Free Library; Savona Free Library; Scio Free Library; Steele Memorial Library; Twentieth Century Club Library; Watkins Glen Central School District Free Public Library; Wayland Free Library; Wide-Awake Club Library; Wimodaughsian Free Library
Branches: 5
ARKPORT VILLAGE BOOK CENTER, East Ave, Arkport, 14807. SAN 352-3926. Tel: 607-295-7811. Web Site: www.stls.org. *Dir*, Jeanette Clark; Staff 1 (Non-MLS 1)
BOX OF BOOKS READING CENTER, One W University St, Alfred, 14802-1113. SAN 352-3896. Tel: 607-587-9290. FAX: 607-587-9290. Web Site: www.stls.org. *Dir*, Janice Porter; Staff 1 (Non-MLS 1)
ELIZABETH B PERT LIBRARY, Valois-Logan-Hector Fire House, Rte 414, Hector, 14841. (Mail add: PO Box 82, Hector, 14841), SAN 352-4078. Tel: 607-546-2605. Web Site: www.stls.org. *Dir*, Gayle Hatch; Staff 1 (Non-MLS 1)
GREENWOOD READING CENTER, Main St, PO Box 837, Greenwood, 14839-0837. SAN 328-9877. Tel: 607-225-4654. Web Site: www.stls.org. *Dir*, Mary Mullen
MABEL D BLODGETT MEMORIAL, 35 S Main St, Rushville, 14544-9648. SAN 352-3950. Tel: 716-554-3939. Web Site: www.stls.org. *Dir*, Betty Clark; Staff 1 (Non-MLS 1)

PALISADES

P PALISADES FREE LIBRARY, 19 Closter Rd, PO Box 610, 10964. SAN 312-2379. Tel: 845-359-0136. FAX: 845-359-6124. E-Mail: pal@rcls.org. Web Site: www.rcls.org/pal/. *Dir*, Beatrice W Agnew; *Ref*, Johanna Lo; *ILL*, Marie Firestone; Staff 2 (MLS 2)
Founded 1891. Pop 1,282; Circ 18,187
Library Holdings: Bk Vols 20,566; Per Subs 64
Special Collections: Local History, bks, microflm, maps
Mem of Ramapo Catskill Library System
Friends of the Library Group

PALMYRA

P PALMYRA KING'S DAUGHTERS' FREE LIBRARY INC, 127 Cuyler St, 14522. SAN 312-2387. Tel: 315-597-5276. FAX: 315-597-1375. Web Site: www.palmyra.pls-net.org. *Dir*, Patricia Baynes; E-Mail: pbaynes@pls-net.org; *Asst Dir*, Betty O'Neill
Founded 1901. Pop 7,652; Circ 34,147
Library Holdings: Bk Vols 19,412
Subject Interests: Local history
Mem of Pioneer Library System
Friends of the Library Group

PARISH

P PARISH PUBLIC LIBRARY,* Main & Church St, 13131. SAN 312-2395. Tel: 315-625-7130. *Librn*, Bridget Schwartz
Pop 1,700; Circ 7,071
Library Holdings: Bk Titles 10,500; Per Subs 47
Open Mon 9-3 & 7-9, Wed 12-5, Thurs 7-9 & Sat 12-5
Friends of the Library Group

PATCHOGUE

M BROOKHAVEN MEMORIAL HOSPITAL, Dr Joseph D'Agrosa Medical Library, 101 Hospital Rd, 11772-4897. SAN 312-2409. Tel: 516-654-7774. FAX: 516-447-3723.
Founded 1975
Library Holdings: Bk Titles 3,000; Per Subs 200
Subject Interests: Allied health, Medicine, Nursing
Restriction: Members only

C CALLAHAN LIBRARY, SAINT JOSEPH'S COLLEGE, 25 Audubon Ave, 11772-2399. SAN 352-2067. Tel: 631-447-3232. FAX: 631-654-3255. Web Site: www.plib.sjcny.edu. *Dir*, Sister Agnes Meagher; *Ref*, Barbara Koch; *Ref*, Sister Joan Ryan; *Cat*, Ruth Hazzard; Staff 4 (MLS 4)
Founded 1972. Highest Degree: Master
Library Holdings: Bk Vols 90,000; Per Subs 455
Subject Interests: Bus, Child studies, Education, Health sci
Special Collections: Long Island History
Partic in Long Island Library Resources Council; OCLC Online Computer Library Center, Inc

SR CONGREGATIONAL CHURCH OF PATCHOGUE, Stuart VanCott Memorial Library, 95 E Main St, 11772. SAN 371-9405. Tel: 516-475-1235. FAX: 516-475-1235. *Librn*, Gerri Clements; *Asst Librn*, Toni Dean; Staff 6 (MLS 1, Non-MLS 5)
Founded 1967
1998-1999 Mats Exp $750, Books $500, Per/Ser (Incl. Access Fees) $100
Library Holdings: Bk Vols 5,350; Bk Titles 4,530
Subject Interests: Church history, Local history, Religion
Partic in Church & Synagogue Libr Asn

G NATIONAL PARK SERVICE, Fire Island National Seashore Library, 120 Laurel St, 11772. SAN 324-2897. Tel: 516-289-4810, Ext 228. FAX: 516-289-4898. Web Site: www.nps.gov/fiis. *Dir*, Maria Wagenbrenner; E-Mail: maria_wagenbrenner@nps.gov
Library Holdings: Bk Titles 5,000
Subject Interests: Geomorphology, Oceanography
Special Collections: Shipwrecks on Fire Island; US Life-Saving Service Material
Restriction: By appointment only, Open to public for reference only

P PATCHOGUE-MEDFORD LIBRARY, 54-60 E Main St, 11772. SAN 312-2417. Tel: 631-654-4700. Reference Tel: 631-654-4700, Ext 221. FAX: 631-289-3999. E-Mail: ptchlib@suffolk.lib.ny.us. Web Site: pml.suffolk.lib.ny.us. *Dir*, Judith Gibbard; Tel: 631-654-4700, Ext 300; *Asst Dir*, Geraldine Chrils; Tel: 631-654-4700, Ext 301; *Head Ref*, Jean Kaleda; Tel: 631-654-4700, Ext 220; *AV, Ref Servs YA*, Barbara Hoffman; Tel: 631-654-4700, Ext 250; *Ref Serv Ad*, Sally Rein; Tel: 631-654-4700, Ext 235; *Ch Servs*, Sally Ickes; Tel: 631-654-4700, Ext 260; *Coll Develop*, June Cerveny; Tel: 631-654-4700, Ext 231; *ILL, Per*, Toni Raptis; Tel: 631-654-4700, Ext 234; *Head Tech Servs*, Janet Gillen; Tel: 631-654-4700, Ext 280; *Electronic Resources*, Bruce Silverstein; Tel: 631-654-4700, Ext 236; *Tech Coordr*, Rona Dressler; Tel: 631-654-4700, Ext 290; *Cat*, Anne Reissig; Tel: 631-654-4700, Ext 288; *Head, Circ*, Marie Mallon; Tel: 631-654-4700, Ext 215; Staff 101 (MLS 23, Non-MLS 78)
Founded 1900. Pop 47,290; Circ 547,736
Jul 1998-Jun 1999 Income $5,112,081, State $377,585, Locally Generated Income $4,560,366, Other $174,130. Mats Exp $829,608, Books $551,853, Per/Ser (Incl. Access Fees) $126,417, AV Equip $75,413, Other Print Mats $7,115, Electronic Ref Mat (Incl. Access Fees) $68,810. Sal $2,981,410 (Prof $1,444,032)
Library Holdings: Bk Vols 327,751; Bk Titles 252,633; Per Subs 3,243; High Interest/Low Vocabulary Bk Vols 482
Subject Interests: Adult education, Consumer health, Foreign Language, Law, Local genealogies, Local history, Music
Special Collections: Martial Arts (Maccarrone-Kresge Coll); Opera (Sara Courant Coll)
Automation Activity & Vendor Info: (Acquisitions) Innovative Interfaces Inc.; (Cataloging) Innovative Interfaces Inc.; (Circulation) Innovative Interfaces Inc.; (ILL) Innovative Interfaces Inc.; (OPAC) Innovative Interfaces Inc.; (Serials) Innovative Interfaces Inc.
Database Vendor: Dialog, Ebsco - EbscoHost, GaleNet, Lexis-Nexis, OCLC - First Search, Wilson - Wilson Web
Publications: An Index to Selected Popular Song Books; An Index to the Records-Town of Brookhaven up to 1800; Centennial Research Digest; Classical Music Index; Guide to Senior Citizen Services; Newsletter (bi-monthly); Patchogue-Medford Library Community Directory; Songs in Collections; The Library Story: A Patchogue-Medford Library Centennial Story for Children & Parents; The Maccarrone-Kresge Martial Arts Book Collection
Function: ILL available
Mem of Suffolk Cooperative Library System
Special Services for the Blind - CCTV (VisualTex); Magnifiers
Friends of the Library Group

PATTERSON

P PATTERSON LIBRARY ASSOCIATION, Rte 311, PO Box 418, 12563. SAN 312-2425. Tel: 845-878-6121. FAX: 845-878-3116. Web Site: pattersonlibrary.org. *Dir*, Patti Haar
Founded 1947. Pop 12,000; Circ 54,738
Library Holdings: Bk Vols 24,999; Per Subs 45
Special Collections: Maxwell Weaner Music Book Coll
Automation Activity & Vendor Info: (Circulation) GEAC; (OPAC) GEAC
Mem of Mid-Hudson Library System
Open Mon & Wed 10-9, Tues, Thurs & Fri 12-5, Sat 10-4

PAUL SMITHS

J PAUL SMITHS COLLEGE OF ARTS & SCIENCES, Frank L Cubley Library, 12970. SAN 312-2433. Tel: 518-327-6313. FAX: 518-327-6350. Web Site: www.paulsmiths.edu. *Coll Develop, Dir*, Theodore Mack; E-Mail:

mackt@paulsmiths.edu; *Asst Librn*, Sean Conley; *ILL*, Lynn Whalen; Staff 5 (MLS 2, Non-MLS 3)
Founded 1946. Enrl 780; Fac 53; Highest Degree: Bachelor
Library Holdings: Bk Vols 54,000; Per Subs 493
Subject Interests: Culinary arts, Environmental studies, Forestry, Hotel mgt, Outdoor recreation, Restaurant mgt, Surveying, Urban tree mgt, Wastewater treatment
Automation Activity & Vendor Info: (Circulation) SIRSI; (OPAC) SIRSI
Mem of N Country Ref & Res Resources Coun
Partic in North Country Reference & Research Resources Council; OCLC Online Computer Library Center, Inc

PAWLING

S AKIN HALL ASSOCIATION, Akin Free Library,* 238 Quaker Hill Rd, 12564. SAN 371-0165. Tel: 914-855-5099. *Librn*, James Mandracchia; Tel: 860-354-2822
Library Holdings: Bk Vols 10,000
Open Thurs 7-9 & Sun 2-4

P PAWLING FREE LIBRARY,* 11 Broad St, 12564. SAN 312-2441. Tel: 914-855-3444. FAX: 914-855-8138. *Librn*, Pat Dagata
Pop 5,000; Circ 22,000
Library Holdings: Bk Vols 20,500; Per Subs 25
Mem of Mid-Hudson Library System

PEARL RIVER

S LAWLER, MATUSKY & SKELLY ENGINEERS LLP LIBRARY, One Blue Hill Plaza, 10965-3104. SAN 325-4631. Tel: 845-735-8300, Ext 334. FAX: 845-735-7466. *In Charge*, Victoria Galperin; E-Mail: vgalperin@emseng.com; Staff 1 (MLS 1)
Founded 1965
Library Holdings: Bk Vols 10,500; Bk Titles 10,000; Per Subs 150
Database Vendor: GaleNet
Restriction: Staff use only
Partic in Southeastern New York Library Resources Council

S ORANGE & ROCKLAND UTILITIES, INC LIBRARY,* One Blue Hill Plaza, 10965. SAN 321-3854. Tel: 914-577-2680. FAX: 914-577-2730. Web Site: www.oru.com.; Staff 2 (MLS 1, Non-MLS 1)
Founded 1968
Library Holdings: Bk Vols 6,500; Per Subs 200
Subject Interests: Coal, Electric, Energy, Environ, Gas
Restriction: Staff use only
Partic in Dialog Corporation

P PEARL RIVER PUBLIC LIBRARY, 80 Franklin Ave, 10965. SAN 312-2468. Tel: 845-735-4084. FAX: 845-735-4041. E-Mail: pearlriverlibrary@roldirect.com. Web Site: www.pearlriverlibrary.org, www.rcls.org. *Dir*, Carolyn E Johnson
Founded 1935. Pop 14,444; Circ 210,569
Jul 1999-Jun 2000 Income $1,370,504. Mats Exp $436,129. Sal $728,351
Library Holdings: Bk Vols 76,158; Per Subs 269
Subject Interests: Architecture, Art
Automation Activity & Vendor Info: (Acquisitions) epixtech, inc.; (Cataloging) epixtech, inc.; (Circulation) epixtech, inc.; (Course Reserve) epixtech, inc.; (ILL) epixtech, inc.; (Media Booking) epixtech, inc.; (OPAC) epixtech, inc.; (Serials) epixtech, inc.
Database Vendor: epixtech, inc.
Mem of Ramapo Catskill Library System
Friends of the Library Group

S WYETH-AYERST RESEARCH, Subba Row Memorial Library,* 401 N Middletown Rd, 10965-1299. SAN 312-245X. Tel: 914-732-3401. FAX: 914-732-5525. E-Mail: prllib@war.wyeth.com. *Mgr*, Dr Anne T O'Brien; E-Mail: obriena@war.wyeth.com
Founded 1915
Library Holdings: Bk Titles 15,000; Per Subs 900
Subject Interests: Biomed sci, Chemistry, Medicine, Pharmacology, Veterinary medicine
Restriction: Staff use only
Partic in Dialog Corporation; Medical Library Center Of New York; Nat Libr of Med; Nat Tech Info Serv; Southeastern New York Library Resources Council

PEEKSKILL

P FIELD LIBRARY OF PEEKSKILL, 4 Nelson Ave, 10566-2138. SAN 312-2476. Tel: 914-737-1212. FAX: 914-737-0714. Web Site: www.peekskill.org. *Dir*, Sibyl Canaan; E-Mail: scanaan@wls.lib.ny.us; *Asst Dir*, Susan Thaler; E-Mail: sthaler@wls.lib.ny.us; *Ch Servs*, Sara A Bentley; *Tech Servs*, Amy Ubben; Staff 22 (MLS 7, Non-MLS 15)
Founded 1887. Pop 19,000
Library Holdings: Bk Vols 86,000; Per Subs 300
Special Collections: Down Syndrome & Mental Retardation (Marjorie Gibbs Coll); Law Coll; Lincoln Coll; Local History (Peekskill Historical Coll)
Mem of Westchester Library System
Friends of the Library Group

PELHAM

P TOWN OF PELHAM PUBLIC LIBRARY,* 530 Colonial Ave, 10803. SAN 312-1801. Tel: 914-738-1234. FAX: 914-738-0809. E-Mail: ggoverma@wls.lib.ny.us. *Dir*, Gloria W Goverman; *Coll Develop*, Cheryl Berent; *Coll Develop*, Gloria Goverman
Founded 1915. Pop 12,000; Circ 84,000
Library Holdings: Bk Vols 23,500
Special Collections: Mysteries
Mem of Westchester Library System
Friends of the Library Group

PENFIELD

P PENFIELD PUBLIC LIBRARY,* 1985 Baird Rd, 14526. SAN 312-2506. Tel: 716-383-0500. TDD: 716-383-8712. FAX: 716-383-0057. E-Mail: infodesk@mcls.rochester.lib.ny.us. Web Site: www.ggw.org/penlib. *Dir*, Carolyn L Smith
Pop 30,219
Jan 1998-Dec 1998 Income $895,580. Mats Exp $170,900
Library Holdings: Bk Vols 95,400; Per Subs 2,340
Mem of Monroe County Library System
Special Services for the Deaf - TDD
Friends of the Library Group

PENN YAN

P PENN YAN PUBLIC LIBRARY,* 214 Main St, 14527. SAN 312-2514. Tel: 315-536-6114. FAX: 315-536-0131. *Dir*, Lynn Overgaard; *Ref*, John Creamer
Founded 1895. Pop 14,101; Circ 136,067
Jul 1999-Jun 2000 Income $365,000, State $4,000, City $1,000, Other $338,000. Mats Exp $51,600, Books $39,700, Per/Ser (Incl. Access Fees) $4,500, Micro $100, AV Equip $7,300. Sal $215,000
Library Holdings: Bk Titles 55,000; Per Subs 185
Subject Interests: Local history
Automation Activity & Vendor Info: (Acquisitions) Gaylord; (Cataloging) Gaylord; (Circulation) Gaylord; (OPAC) Gaylord
Mem of Southern Tier Library System
Friends of the Library Group

PERRY

P PERRY PUBLIC LIBRARY,* 70 N Main St, 14530-1299. SAN 312-2522. Tel: 716-237-2243. FAX: 716-237-2008. E-Mail: perrypublib@wycol.com. Web Site: www.perry.pls-net.org. *Dir*, Margaret S Parker; *Ch Servs*, Christina B Nolan; Staff 4 (MLS 2, Non-MLS 2)
Founded 1914
Jan 1997-Dec 1998 Income $110,996, State $7,274, Parent Institution $75,000, Other $11,822. Mats Exp $17,650, Books $15,500, Per/Ser (Incl. Access Fees) $1,950. Sal $63,945 (Prof $40,661)
Library Holdings: Bk Vols 30,713; Per Subs 73
Special Collections: Lemuel M Wiles, Artist (Stowell-Wiles Coll), oil paintings; Local History (Henry Page Coll)
Mem of Pioneer Library System
Open Mon-Thurs 2-9, Fri 10-9 & Sat 9-1
Friends of the Library Group

PERU

P PERU FREE LIBRARY,* 3024 N Main St, 12972. SAN 312-2530. Tel: 518-643-8618. FAX: 518-643-8618. *Librn*, Mary Kay Rillahan
Circ 14,119
Library Holdings: Bk Vols 16,000; Per Subs 32
Mem of Clinton-Essex-Franklin Library System
Open Tues-Thurs 11-5 & 7-9 & Sat 9-3
Friends of the Library Group

PETERSBURG

P PETERSBURG PUBLIC LIBRARY,* 69 Main St, PO Box 250, 12138. SAN 312-2549. Tel: 518-658-2927. FAX: 518-658-2927. Web Site: www.uhls.org/petersburgh. *Librn*, Sharon Hodges
Circ 24,000
Library Holdings: Bk Vols 12,000; Per Subs 12
Mem of Upper Hudson Library System
Open Mon 2-5, Wed 7pm-9 & Sat 9:30am-12:30pm

PHELPS

P PHELPS COMMUNITY MEMORIAL LIBRARY, 15 Church St, 14532. SAN 312-2557. Tel: 315-548-3120. FAX: 315-548-5314. *Dir*, Fran De Nardo
Founded 1948. Pop 6,749; Circ 23,723
Jan 1999-Dec 1999 Income $63,943, State $2,092, City $33,000, County $3,083, Locally Generated Income $25,768. Mats Exp $12,256, Books $10,288, Per/Ser (Incl. Access Fees) $1,112, AV Equip $742, Electronic Ref Mat (Incl. Access Fees) $114. Sal $29,749
Library Holdings: Bk Vols 23,239; Per Subs 58
Special Collections: Historical (Bellamy Partridge Coll)
Automation Activity & Vendor Info: (Cataloging) Sagebrush Corporation; (Circulation) Sagebrush Corporation
Mem of Pioneer Library System
Friends of the Library Group

PHILADELPHIA

P BODMAN MEMORIAL LIBRARY,* 8 Aldrich St, 13673. SAN 312-2565. Tel: 315-642-3323. *Librn*, Barbara A Dingle
Circ 10,146
Library Holdings: Bk Vols 11,199
Mem of North Country Library System

PHILMONT

P PHILMONT PUBLIC LIBRARY, 124 Main St, 12565. (Mail add: PO Box II, 12565-0816), SAN 312-2573. Tel: 518-672-5010. FAX: 518-672-5010. E-Mail: library@philmont.org. Web Site: www.philmont.org/. *Dir*, Peggy Alt; Staff 2 (Non-MLS 2)
Founded 1898. Pop 1,650; Circ 8,209
Jun 1999-May 2000 Income $14,000. Mats Exp $6,000, Books $5,600, Per/Ser (Incl. Access Fees) $100, Electronic Ref Mat (Incl. Access Fees) $300. Sal $8,000
Library Holdings: Bk Vols 25,000; High Interest/Low Vocabulary Bk Vols 200
Special Collections: Main Street Coll
Automation Activity & Vendor Info: (Circulation) GEAC
Mem of Mid-Hudson Library System
Special Services for the Deaf - TTY machine
Friends of the Library Group

PHOENICIA

P PHOENICIA LIBRARY,* 48 Main St, PO Box 555, 12464. SAN 312-2581. Tel: 914-688-7811. FAX: 914-688-7811. *Dir*, Hilary Gold; *Asst Librn*, Debby Lepp; *Asst Librn*, Susan Penick
Pop 2,500; Circ 13,000
Library Holdings: Bk Vols 12,000
Mem of Mid-Hudson Library System
Open Tues 10-3, Wed & Fri 1-6, Thurs 2-7 & Sat 10-2

PHOENIX

P PHOENIX PUBLIC LIBRARY,* 34 Elm St, 13135. SAN 312-259X. Tel: 315-695-4355. FAX: 315-695-4355. *Librn*, Joanne M Trask; *Publ Servs*, Rita Hamilton
Founded 1920. Circ 27,659
Library Holdings: Bk Vols 24,100
Subject Interests: Civil War hist, Local history
Mem of North Country Library System
Open Mon-Fri 11-5 & Sat 10-1

PIERMONT

P PIERMONT PUBLIC LIBRARY,* 153 Hudson Terrace, 10968. SAN 312-2603. Tel: 914-359-4595. FAX: 914-365-1423. E-Mail: pml@rcls.org. *Librn*, Grace Meyer
Circ 6,382
Library Holdings: Bk Vols 11,860
Subject Interests: Boating, Local history
Mem of Ramapo Catskill Library System
Friends of the Library Group

PIKE

P PIKE LIBRARY,* 65 Main St, 14130. SAN 312-262X. Tel: 716-493-5900. FAX: 716-493-5900. *Dir*, Doris M Flint
Circ 7,617
Library Holdings: Bk Vols 12,700; Per Subs 42
Mem of Pioneer Library System; Wyo County Libr Syst
Open Mon, Wed & Sat 2-6

PINE BUSH

P TOWN OF CRAWFORD FREE LIBRARY,* Maple Ave, PO Box 63, 12566. SAN 312-2638. Tel: 914-744-3375. FAX: 914-744-3375.
Circ 61,000
Library Holdings: Bk Vols 13,000
Mem of Ramapo Catskill Library System
Friends of the Library Group

PINE HILL

P MORTON MEMORIAL LIBRARY, (Formerly Pine Hill Public Library), 22 Elm St, 12465. SAN 312-2646. Tel: 845-254-4222. FAX: 845-254-4222. E-Mail: morton@catskill.net. *Librn*, Charlis Weiss
Founded 1903. Circ 1,822
Library Holdings: Bk Vols 5,555
Mem of Mid-Hudson Library System
Open Tues, Thurs, Sat 2-6, Wed & Fri 5-9

PINE PLAINS

P PINE PLAINS FREE LIBRARY,* S Main St, PO Box 325, 12567-0325. SAN 312-2654. Tel: 518-398-1927. Web Site: www.ldsl.net/pinelib. *Librn*, Marguerite Hill
Pop 1,792; Circ 111,027
Library Holdings: Bk Vols 6,500; Bk Titles 6,400; Per Subs 28
Mem of Mid-Hudson Library System

PITTSFORD

P PITTSFORD COMMUNITY LIBRARY, 24 State St, 14534. SAN 353-9164. Tel: 716-248-6275. FAX: 716-248-6259. Web Site: www.rochester.lib.ny.us/pittsford. *Dir*, Marjorie Shelly; E-Mail: mshelly@mcls.rochester.lib.ny.us; *Ad Servs, Asst Dir*, Liz Barrett; *AV, Ref*, Mary Kopczynski; *ILL*, Sally Lyddon; *YA Servs*, Linda Bartlett; Staff 5 (MLS 5)
Founded 1920. Pop 24,382; Circ 431,933
Jan 1999-Dec 1999 Income (Main Library and Branch Library) $617,816. Mats Exp $124,498, Books $104,195, Per/Ser (Incl. Access Fees) $18,259, Electronic Ref Mat (Incl. Access Fees) $2,044. Sal $429,060
Library Holdings: Bk Vols 77,489
Automation Activity & Vendor Info: (Circulation) CARL; (OPAC) CARL
Database Vendor: CARL
Mem of Monroe County Library System
Friends of the Library Group
Branches: 1
JANES BRANCH, 200 Fairport Rd, East Rochester, 14445. SAN 353-9199. Tel: 716-248-6244. Web Site: www.rochester.lib.ny.us/janes.html. *Head of Libr*, Ichin Zinn; Staff 2 (MLS 2)
Mem of Monroe County Library System
Friends of the Library Group

PLAINVIEW

M ASSOCIATION FOR CHILDREN WITH DOWN SYNDROME, Resource Library for Down Syndrome, Four Fern Pl, 11803. SAN 373-4811. Tel: 516-933-4700. FAX: 516-933-9524. E-Mail: info@acds.org. Web Site: www.acds.org. *Exec Dir*, Sebastian J Muzio; *Librn*, Dolores Seelig
Founded 1979
Library Holdings: Bk Vols 200; Per Subs 30
Restriction: By appointment only

SR CHURCH OF JESUS CHRIST OF THE LATTER DAY SAINTS, Family History Center,* 160 Washington Ave, 11803. SAN 377-5631. Tel: 516-433-0122. *Dir*, Julia Morano
Library Holdings: Bk Vols 500
Open Tues & Thurs 10-4 & 6:30-9:30, Wed 10-2 & 6:30-9:30, Fri & Sat 10-4

P PLAINVIEW-OLD BETHPAGE PUBLIC LIBRARY, 999 Old Country Rd, 11803-4995. SAN 312-2689. Tel: 516-938-0077, Ext 1232. FAX: 516-433-4645. E-Mail: pvref@worldnet.att.net. Web Site: www.nassaulibrary.org. *Dir*, Rhoda Orenstein; Staff 102 (MLS 24, Non-MLS 78)
Founded 1955. Pop 28,760; Circ 580,144
Jul 1999-Jun 2000 Income $3,755,920, State $8,915, County $3,739,440, Other $7,565. Mats Exp $355,854, Books $278,090, Per/Ser (Incl. Access Fees) $36,406, Presv $606, Micro $8,343, AV Equip $11,370, Other Print Mats $1,570, Electronic Ref Mat (Incl. Access Fees) $19,469. Sal $2,157,100 (Prof $717,415)
Library Holdings: Bk Vols 266,161; Per Subs 2,267; High Interest/Low Vocabulary Bk Vols 94; Bks on Deafness & Sign Lang 58
Subject Interests: Bus info, Career info, College catalogs, Educ opportunities, Employment, Law, Local history, Medicine, Video cassettes
Special Collections: Career; Career-Job Learning; Consumer Information; Law; LI Jewish Genealogical Society Coll; New & Used Automobiles; Plainview Old Bethpage Coll
Automation Activity & Vendor Info: (Circulation) DRA

Publications: Community Calendar (monthly); Library World (bi-monthly)
Mem of Nassau Library System
Partic in Dialog Corporation; OCLC Online Computer Library Center, Inc
Special Services for the Deaf - TTY machine
Special Services - Family Center with 2 Macintosh computers for children
Friends of the Library Group

PLATTSBURGH

M CHAMPLAIN VALLEY PHYSICIANS HOSPITAL MEDICAL CENTER, Medical Library,* 75 Beekman St, 12901. SAN 312-2700. Tel: 518-562-7325. FAX: 518-562-7129. *Librn*, Christina Ransom; E-Mail: cransom@cvph.org; Staff 2 (MLS 2)
Founded 1930
Library Holdings: Bk Titles 1,000; Per Subs 500
Publications: Library Newsletter (quarterly)
Restriction: Open to public for reference only
Partic in Health Sci Libr & Info Consortium; Nat Libr of Med; North Country Reference & Research Resources Council; OCLC Online Computer Library Center, Inc

J CLINTON COMMUNITY COLLEGE, LeRoy M Douglas Learning Resource Center, 136 Clinton Point Dr, 12901-5690. SAN 312-2719. Tel: 518-562-4143. FAX: 518-562-4158. *Dir*, Andrew Hersh-Tudor; *ILL, Ref*, Catherine Figlioli; *Tech Servs*, Patricia Miranda; Staff 9 (MLS 4, Non-MLS 5)
Founded 1969. Enrl 2,200; Fac 42
Library Holdings: Bk Vols 47,073; Bk Titles 43,000; Per Subs 300
Special Collections: Adirondack coll
Database Vendor: IAC - Info Trac, OCLC - First Search, Wilson - Wilson Web
Publications: Second Story (quarterly), The Library Presents (monthly)
Partic in North Country Reference & Research Resources Council; OCLC Online Computer Library Center, Inc

P CLINTON-ESSEX-FRANKLIN LIBRARY SYSTEM, 33 Oak St, 12901-2810. SAN 312-2727. Tel: 518-563-5190. FAX: 518-563-0421. E-Mail: +vzc+@northnet.org. Web Site: www.cefls.org. *Dir*, Mary A Brown; Tel: 518-563-5190, Ext 11, E-Mail: mabrown@northnet.org; *Acq, Coll Develop, ILL*, Elizabeth Rogers; Tel: 518-563-5190, Ext 14, E-Mail: rogers@northnet.org; *Automation Syst Coordr*, Betsy Brooks; Tel: 518-563-5190, Ext 35, E-Mail: brooksb@northnet.org; *Outreach Serv*, Julie Wever; Tel: 518-563-5190, Ext 18, E-Mail: wever@northnet.org; *Ch Servs, YA Servs*, Kathie LaBombard; Tel: 518-563-5190, Ext 21, E-Mail: labombar@northnet.org; Staff 13 (MLS 5, Non-MLS 8)
Founded 1954. Pop 169,661
Jan 2000-Dec 2000 Income $1,244,139, State $18,000, County $67,752. Mats Exp $195,461, Books $112,363, Per/Ser (Incl. Access Fees) $53,223, Other Print Mats $29,875. Sal $464,552 (Prof $220,493)
Library Holdings: Bk Titles 102,911; Per Subs 98
Automation Activity & Vendor Info: (Circulation) DRA; (Circulation) MultiLIS; (OPAC) DRA; (OPAC) MultiLIS
Database Vendor: OCLC - First Search
Member Libraries: Akwesasne Library & Culture Center; Au Sable Forks Free Library; Beldon-Noble Memorial Library; Black Watch Memorial Library; Champlain Memorial Library; Chateaugay Memorial Library; Chazy Public Library; Dannemora Free Library; Dodge Library; Dodge Memorial Library; E M Cooper Memorial Library; Elizabethtown Library Association; Essex County Historical Society; Goff-Nelson Memorial Library; Hammond Library of Crown Point NY; Keene Public Library; Keene Valley Library Association; Keeseville Free Library; Lake Placid Public Library; Mooers Free Library; New York State Department Of Correctional Services; Paine Memorial Free Library; Peru Free Library; Plattsburgh Public Library; Saranac Lake Free Library; Schroon Lake Public Library; Sherman Free Library; Wadhams Free Library; Wead Library; Wells Memorial Library; Westport Library Association
Partic in New York State Interlibrary Loan Network; OCLC Online Computer Library Center, Inc
Bookmobiles: 1

GL NEW YORK STATE SUPREME COURT FOURTH DISTRICT, Law Library,* 72 Clinton St, 12901. SAN 312-2735. Tel: 518-565-4808. FAX: 518-562-1193. *Librn*, Mary E Brewster
Library Holdings: Bk Vols 12,000

P PLATTSBURGH PUBLIC LIBRARY,* 19 Oak St, 12901-2810. SAN 312-2743. Tel: 518-563-0921. FAX: 518-563-1681. *Dir*, Ann Minter O'Donald; *ILL, Online Servs*, Larry Hahn; *Ch Servs*, Sharon Candhold; *Tech Servs*, Colleen Pelletier; Staff 3 (MLS 3)
Founded 1894. Pop 21,074; Circ 123,344
Library Holdings: Bk Vols 62,491; Per Subs 221
Subject Interests: Cookbooks
Special Collections: History (Clinton County & Plattsburgh)
Automation Activity & Vendor Info: (Circulation) MultiLIS
Mem of Clinton-Essex-Franklin Library System
Partic in North Country Reference & Research Resources Council; OCLC Online Computer Library Center, Inc
Friends of the Library Group

C STATE UNIVERSITY OF NEW YORK COLLEGE AT PLATTSBURGH, Benjamin F Feinberg Library, 2 Draper Ave, 12901-2697. SAN 312-2751. Tel: 518-564-5180. Circulation Tel: 518-564-5182. Reference Tel: 518-564-5190. FAX: 518-564-5209. E-Mail: library@plattsburgh.edu. Web Site: www.plattsburgh.edu/library. *Dean of Libr*, Cerise Oberman; *Bibliog Instr*, Carla List; *Online Servs*, Patricia Bentley; *Spec Coll*, Wayne Miller; *Coll Develop, Media Spec*, Carla Hendrix; *Ref*, Dennis Kimmage; *Ref*, Michelle Toth; *Ref*, Ravil Veli; *Ref*, Karen Volkman; Staff 20 (MLS 17, Non-MLS 3)
Founded 1889. Fac 325; Highest Degree: Master
Jul 1999-Jun 2000 Income $1,983,222. Mats Exp $854,212, Per/Ser (Incl. Access Fees) $485,500, Presv $7,500. Sal $1,129,010 (Prof $676,630)
Library Holdings: Bk Vols 378,020; Bk Titles 302,416; Per Subs 1,420
Subject Interests: Adirondack hist, North Country hist
Automation Activity & Vendor Info: (Cataloging) MultiLIS
Publications: Focus on Feinberg; Introduction to Library Research
Partic in New York State Interlibrary Loan Network; North Country Reference & Research Resources Council; State University Of New York-NYLINK
Open Sun 12-11:30, Mon-Thurs 8am-11:30pm, Fri 8-8
Departmental Libraries:

PLEASANT VALLEY

P PLEASANT VALLEY FREE LIBRARY, 1584 Main St, 12569. (Mail add: PO Box 633, 12569), SAN 312-276X. Tel: 845-635-8460. FAX: 845-635-9556. E-Mail: plvalley@ulysses.sebridge.org. Web Site: pleasantvalleylibrary.org. *Dir*, Daniela Pulice; E-Mail: danielapulice@hotmail.com; *Ch Servs*, Julie Poplees; *Cat*, Stephanie Valentine; Staff 5 (MLS 1, Non-MLS 4)
Founded 1903. Pop 8,064; Circ 56,176
1999-2000 Income $209,185, State $2,600, City $180,000, County $5,535, Locally Generated Income $21,050. Mats Exp $39,452, Books $27,035, Per/Ser (Incl. Access Fees) $2,000, AV Equip $10,417. Sal $95,845 (Prof $36,500)
Library Holdings: Bk Titles 27,104; Per Subs 40; High Interest/Low Vocabulary Bk Vols 50
Special Collections: Toys for handicapped children
Automation Activity & Vendor Info: (Cataloging) GEAC; (Circulation) GEAC
Database Vendor: CARL, IAC - Info Trac
Mem of Mid-Hudson Library System
Partic in Mid-Hudson Libr Syst

PLEASANTVILLE

P MOUNT PLEASANT PUBLIC LIBRARY, 350 Bedford Rd, 10570-3099. SAN 353-9253. Tel: 914-769-0548. FAX: 914-769-6149. E-Mail: mt.pleasant.lib@eudoramail.com. Web Site: www.mountpleasantlibrary.org. *Dir*, John Fearon; E-Mail: jfearon@wls.lib.ny.us; *Asst Dir, Br Coordr*, Karen Bucci; *Librn*, Irena Sperauskas; *Ref*, Michael McCoy; *Ch Servs*, Susan Chajes; *Tech Servs*, Tess Epstein; *YA Servs*, Sue Grossman; *Circ*, Matthew Ditomasso; Staff 27 (MLS 9, Non-MLS 18)
Founded 1893. Pop 32,000; Circ 327,000
Jan 2000-Dec 2000 Income (Main Library and Branch Library) $1,456,456. Mats Exp $213,482, Books $131,321, Per/Ser (Incl. Access Fees) $15,779, Presv $668, AV Equip $14,281, Electronic Ref Mat (Incl. Access Fees) $51,433. Sal $851,401 (Prof $360,865)
Library Holdings: Bk Vols 139,783; Per Subs 150
Subject Interests: Art, Humanities, Local history
Special Collections: Lachenbruch Coll (Children's books for Storytellers)
Database Vendor: Ebsco - EbscoHost, epixtech, inc., IAC - SearchBank
Publications: Inklings; quarterly newsletter
Mem of Westchester Library System
Partic in Dynix Consortium
Friends of the Library Group
Branches: 1
MOUNT PLEASANT, 125 Lozza Dr, Valhalla, 10595-1268. SAN 353-9288. Tel: 914-741-0276. FAX: 914-741-0228. *Librn*, Jill Lerner
Library Holdings: Bk Vols 30,000; Per Subs 20
Friends of the Library Group

C PACE UNIVERSITY, Edward & Doris Mortola Library, 861 Bedford Rd, 10570-2799. SAN 353-9318. Tel: 914-773-3380. Interlibrary Loan Service Tel: 914-773-3853. Circulation Tel: 914-773-3380. Reference Tel: 914-773-3381. FAX: 914-773-3508. Web Site: www.library.pace.edu/. *Librn*, William J Murdock; *Asst Librn, Coll Develop*, Nancy Bobrek; *Asst Librn*, Sarah K Burns; Tel: 914-773-3505, E-Mail: sburns@pace.edu; *Asst Librn*, Noreen McGuire; *Assoc Librn*, David T S Leighton; Tel: 914-773-3503, E-Mail: dleighton@pace.edu; *Head Tech Servs*, Wendy Yurt; Tel: 914-773-3852, E-Mail: wyurt@pace.edu; *Res*, Christa J Burns; *Ref*, Christina Conte; Tel: 914-773-3505, E-Mail: cconte@pace.edu; *Ref*, Michelle Lang; Tel: 914-422-4384, E-Mail: mlang@pace.edu; *Ref*, John Lee; Tel: 914-773-3505, E-Mail: jjlee@pace.edu; *Circ*, Nadine MacDonald; Tel: 914-773-3854, E-Mail: nmacdonald@pace.edu; *Cat*, June Pang; Tel: 914-773-3385, E-Mail: jpang@pace.edu; *Doc*, Sheila Hu; Tel: 914-773-3385, E-Mail: shu@pace.edu; *Coll Develop*, Harriet Huang; Tel: 914-773-3505, E-Mail: hhuang@pace.edu;

Bibliog Instr, Karen E M DeSantis; Tel: 914-773-3505, E-Mail: kdesantis@pace.edu; *Purchasing*, Terri Rivera-Pons; Tel: 914-773-3385, E-Mail: trivera@pace.edu; Staff 23 (MLS 15, Non-MLS 8)
Founded 1963. Enrl 3,300; Fac 325; Highest Degree: Master
Sep 1999-Aug 2000 Income $1,086,425, State $8,400, Parent Institution $1,078,025. Mats Exp $240,000. Sal $610,760 (Prof $450,390)
Library Holdings: Bk Vols 208,077; Bk Titles 181,011; Per Subs 566
Subject Interests: Bus, Computer science, Education, Literature, Nursing
Special Collections: Rene Dubos; Saint Joan of Arc
Automation Activity & Vendor Info: (Acquisitions) Innovative Interfaces Inc.; (Cataloging) Innovative Interfaces Inc.; (Circulation) Innovative Interfaces Inc.; (OPAC) Innovative Interfaces Inc.; (Serials) Innovative Interfaces Inc.
Database Vendor: Ebsco - EbscoHost, GaleNet, IAC - Info Trac, Lexis-Nexis, OCLC - First Search, ProQuest, Silverplatter Information Inc.
Publications: Information Edge (Newsletter); Printed & online bibliographic handouts
Partic in New York Metrop Ref & Res Libr Agency; OCLC Online Computer Library Center, Inc; Westchester Acad Libr Dir Orgn

S READER'S DIGEST ASSOCIATION INC LIBRARY, Editorial & Research Libraries, Reader's Digest Rd, 10570-7000. SAN 353-7692. Tel: 914-244-5289. FAX: 914-238-0534. *Librn*, Ann DiCesare; *Per*, Lynne Dolan; *Res*, Susan Doremus; *Res*, Edward Goralski
Library Holdings: Bk Vols 20,000; Per Subs 375
Subject Interests: Current news, Journalism
Restriction: Private library

POLAND

P POLAND PUBLIC LIBRARY,* Main St, PO Box 140, 13431. SAN 312-2786. Tel: 315-826-3112. *Librn*, Paula Johnson
Circ 31,288
Library Holdings: Bk Vols 10,203; Per Subs 28
Mem of Mid-York Library System
Open Tues & Thurs 1-5 & 7-8:30, Fri 1-5, Sat 10:30-2

POPLAR RIDGE

P HAZARD LIBRARY ASSOCIATION,* 2485 Rte 34 B, PO Box 3, 13139-0003. SAN 312-2794. Tel: 315-364-7975. FAX: 315-364-6704. E-Mail: hazardlib@relex.com. Web Site: www.flls.org/poplar/. *Librn*, Sally Otis
Founded 1887. Pop 625; Circ 12,587
Library Holdings: Bk Titles 7,487
Subject Interests: Local history
Special Collections: Quaker Coll, 20 volumes of original 1883 coll
Mem of Finger Lakes Library System

PORT CHESTER

P PORT CHESTER PUBLIC LIBRARY, One Haseco Ave, 10573. SAN 312-2816. Tel: 914-939-6710. FAX: 914-939-4735. Web Site: www.portchesterlibrary.org. *Dir*, Robin Lettieri; *Ad Servs, Ref Serv*, Mark Ross; *Tech Servs*, Jazmin Mendez; *Ch Servs*, Teresa Cotter; *YA Servs*, Stacey Harris; Staff 18 (MLS 8, Non-MLS 10)
Founded 1876. Pop 32,493; Circ 185,229
Jun 1999-Jul 2000 Income $991,367, State $10,073, Provincial $4,669, Locally Generated Income $29,823, Other $34,492. Mats Exp $125,149, Books $52,574, Per/Ser (Incl. Access Fees) $18,476, Micro $264, AV Equip $2,604, Other Print Mats $12,831, Electronic Ref Mat (Incl. Access Fees) $38,400. Sal $495,880 (Prof $201,652)
Library Holdings: Bk Titles 96,651; Per Subs 4,216
Subject Interests: Foreign Language, Large print
Special Collections: Genealogy, bks & original ms; Job Information Center; Local & County History
Mem of Westchester Library System
Special Services - Book-on-tape; Video Cassettes; Shut-in Service; Story Hours; ESL Classes; Internet access; Book Discussion Groups
Friends of the Library Group

PORT EWEN

P TOWN OF ESOPUS PUBLIC LIBRARY, 189 Broadway, PO Box 1167, 12466. SAN 312-2832. Tel: 845-338-5580. FAX: 845-338-5583. E-Mail: esopus@midhudson.org. Web Site: www.esopuslibrary.org. *Dir*, Susan Hauer
Founded 1922. Circ 45,000
Library Holdings: Bk Vols 25,000; Per Subs 75
Subject Interests: Art, Cooking, Crafts, Ecology, Health, Hudson River Valley hist, Local history
Special Collections: John Burrough Coll
Publications: Booklist (weekly)
Mem of Mid-Hudson Library System
Open Mon, Wed, Fri 10-8, Tues & Thurs 12-5:30, Sat 10-4
Friends of the Library Group

PORT HENRY

P SHERMAN FREE LIBRARY,* 4 Church St, 12974-1298. SAN 312-2840. Tel: 518-546-7461. *Dir*, Nancy Tuffield
Circ 7,778
Library Holdings: Bk Vols 10,500
Special Collections: Local History
Mem of Clinton-Essex-Franklin Library System

PORT JEFFERSON

P PORT JEFFERSON FREE LIBRARY, 100 Thompson St, 11777-1897. SAN 312-2867. Tel: 631-473-0022. FAX: 631-473-4765. Web Site: pjfl.suffolk.lib.ny.us. *Dir*, Estherine Bonanno; Fax: 631-473-8661, E-Mail: ebonanno@suffolk.lib.ny.us; *Ch Servs*, Linda Lubell; *Ch Servs*, Joann Muscardin; *Ref*, Barbara Sussman; *Ref*, Robert Maggio; *AV*, Earlene O'Hare; *YA Servs*, Laurie Farr; *Computer Services*, Laura Gallucci
Founded 1908. Pop 8,342; Circ 265,000
Jul 1999-Jun 2000 Income Locally Generated Income $1,798,000. Mats Exp $229,500, Books $154,500, Per/Ser (Incl. Access Fees) $20,000, Micro $14,000, AV Equip $10,000, Other Print Mats $14,000, Electronic Ref Mat (Incl. Access Fees) $17,000. Sal $1,104,980 (Prof $486,235)
Library Holdings: Bk Vols 133,270; Bk Titles 117,367; Per Subs 276; High Interest/Low Vocabulary Bk Vols 500
Automation Activity & Vendor Info: (Cataloging) Innovative Interfaces Inc.; (Circulation) Innovative Interfaces Inc.; (ILL) Innovative Interfaces Inc.; (OPAC) Innovative Interfaces Inc.
Publications: The Yeoman (newsletter)
Mem of Suffolk Cooperative Library System
Special Services for the Blind - Reading edge system
Friends of the Library Group

M SAINT CHARLES HOSPITAL LIBRARY,* 200 Belle Terre Rd, 11777. SAN 312-2875. Tel: 516-474-6000, 516-474-6146. FAX: 516-474-6413.
Library Holdings: Bk Vols 120; Bk Titles 100; Per Subs 52

PORT JEFFERSON STATION

P COMSEWOGUE PUBLIC LIBRARY, 170 Terryville Rd, 11776. SAN 312-2883. Tel: 631-928-1212. FAX: 631-928-6307. *Dir*, Richard Lusak; *Asst Dir*, Brandon Pantorno; *Admin Assoc*, Brenda Fort; *Circ*, Anna DeFigueiredo; *Network Services, Syst Coordr*, Len Frosina; *Ref Serv Ad*, Sheryl Sessa; *Ref Servs Ch*, Carol O'Connell; *Tech Servs*, Dianne Hall
Founded 1966. Pop 20,000; Circ 554,665
Library Holdings: Bk Vols 161,105; Per Subs 400
Special Collections: Video Cassette Titles
Mem of Suffolk Cooperative Library System

PORT JERVIS

S MINISINK VALLEY HISTORICAL SOCIETY LIBRARY,* 138 Pike St, PO Box 659, 12771-0659. SAN 325-4607. Tel: 914-856-2375. FAX: 914-856-1049. E-Mail: muhs1889@magiccarpet.com. Web Site: www.munisink.org. *Exec Dir*, Peter Osborne III; Staff 1 (MLS 1)
Founded 1889
Library Holdings: Bk Vols 31,000; Bk Titles 30,000
Subject Interests: Genealogy, Local history
Publications: Quarterly newsletter
Open Mon-Fri 9-5

P PORT JERVIS FREE LIBRARY,* 138 Pike St, 12771. SAN 312-2891. Tel: 914-856-7313, 914-856-9154. FAX: 914-858-8710. *Dir*, Phyllis Vail; *Ch Servs*, Henrietta Towne; *Asst Librn, Ch Servs*, Rhonda Samarelli; Staff 17 (MLS 1, Non-MLS 16)
Founded 1892. Pop 16,000; Circ 147,646
1998-1999 Income $433,974, State $7,403, City $426,571. Mats Exp $67,914, Books $60,578, Per/Ser (Incl. Access Fees) $3,570. Sal $198,458 (Prof $30,242)
Library Holdings: Bk Titles 40,000; Per Subs 140
Special Collections: Local Newspaper (115 years of the Port Jervis Union Gazette), microflm; Stephen Crane Materials
Publications: Newsletters
Mem of Ramapo Catskill Library System

PORT LEYDEN

P PORT LEYDEN COMMUNITY LIBRARY,* Canal St, 13433. (Mail add: PO Box 97, 13433), SAN 312-2913. Tel: 315-348-6077. FAX: 315-348-4234. E-Mail: +ply+@northnet.org. *Librn*, Lyn Cyr
Founded 1925. Circ 11,751
Jan 1999-Dec 2000 Income $12,729, City $900, County $2,670, Locally Generated Income $850, Other $1,000. Mats Exp $4,630, Books $3,768, Per/Ser (Incl. Access Fees) $592. Sal $11,112
Library Holdings: Bk Titles 7,057
Mem of North Country Library System

PORT WASHINGTON

S PALL CORPORATION LIBRARY,* 25 Harbor Park Dr, 11050. SAN 328-5952. Tel: 516-484-3600, Ext 6163. FAX: 516-484-3646.
Library Holdings: Bk Vols 5,000; Per Subs 300
Subject Interests: Chemistry, Engineering
Mem of Long Island Libr Resources Coun, Inc
Partic in Dialog Corporation

P PORT WASHINGTON PUBLIC LIBRARY, One Library Dr, 11050. SAN 312-2921. Tel: 516-883-4400. FAX: 516-883-7927. E-Mail: library@pwpl.org. Web Site: www.pwpl.org. *Dir*, Nancy Curtin; *Assoc Dir*, Corinne Camarata; E-Mail: camarata@pwpl.org; *Ad Servs*, Cathleen Towey; *Ch Servs*, Rachel Fox; *Circ*, Cindy Verruso; *Media Spec Ad*, Jonathan Guildroy; *Ref Servs YA*, Suzanne Ponzini; *Selection of Gen Ref Mat*, Janet West
Founded 1892. Pop 29,064; Circ 332,539
Jul 2000-Jun 2001 Income $4,749,025. Mats Exp $427,000, Books $304,000, Per/Ser (Incl. Access Fees) $57,000, Micro $22,000, AV Equip $16,000, Other Print Mats $28,000. Sal $2,726,048 (Prof $1,326,485)
Library Holdings: Bk Vols 152,719; Bk Titles 29,553; Per Subs 915
Special Collections: Long Island Coll; Nautical Center Coll; Robert Hamilton Ball Theatre Coll; Sinclair Lewis
Automation Activity & Vendor Info: (Circulation) DRA; (OPAC) DRA
Database Vendor: Dialog, DRA, Ebsco - EbscoHost, GaleNet, IAC - Info Trac, OCLC - First Search, ProQuest
Publications: Flight of Memory: Long Island's Aeronautical Past; It Looks Like Yesterday to Me: Port Washington's Afro-American Heritage; Particles of the Past: Sandmining on Long Island 1870's-1980's; Workers on the Grand Estates of Long Island 1980's-1940's
Mem of Nassau Library System
Partic in OCLC Online Computer Library Center, Inc
Friends of the Library Group

PORTVILLE

P PORTVILLE FREE LIBRARY,* 2 N Main St, 14770. SAN 312-293X. Tel: 716-933-8441. FAX: 716-933-7020. *Dir*, Charles F Bretzin
Founded 1902. Pop 1,140; Circ 40,187
Library Holdings: Bk Vols 42,530; Per Subs 89
Subject Interests: Local history
Special Collections: Dusenbury Coll; Portville Newspaper Coll
Mem of Chautauqua-Cattaraugus Library System
Friends of the Library Group

POTSDAM

S CANTON-POTSDAM HOSPITAL, Medical Library,* 50 Leroy St, 13676. SAN 326-0917. Tel: 315-265-3300, Ext 5402. FAX: 315-265-0562. *Dir*, Michael Pinkerton
Library Holdings: Bk Vols 203; Bk Titles 93
Subject Interests: Internal medicine, Nursing
Restriction: Medical staff only
Partic in North Country Reference & Research Resources Council

C CLARKSON UNIVERSITY, Andrew S Schuler Educational Resources Center, 8 Clarkson Ave, 13699-5590. SAN 312-2948. Tel: 315-268-2292. FAX: 315-268-7655. E-Mail: adminlns@clarkson.edu. Web Site: www.clarkson.edu/library. *Actg Dir, Librn*, J Natalia Stahl; *Cat*, Sylvia Haq; *Publ Servs, Ref*, Gayle C Berry; *Coll Develop, Tech Servs*, Byron V Whitney; Staff 4 (MLS 4)
Founded 1896. Enrl 2,522; Fac 170; Highest Degree: Doctorate
Library Holdings: Bk Vols 110,000; Per Subs 1,149
Subject Interests: Engineering, Mgt, Sci
Partic in OCLC Online Computer Library Center, Inc

P POTSDAM PUBLIC LIBRARY, Civic Center, Two Park St, 13676. SAN 312-2956. Tel: 315-265-7230. FAX: 315-268-0306. E-Mail: potsdam@northnet.org. Web Site: www.northnet.potsdamlib.org. *Dir*, Patricia Musante; E-Mail: musante@northnet.org; Staff 15 (MLS 2, Non-MLS 13)
Founded 1887. Pop 14,829; Circ 80,571
Jun 1998-May 1999 Income $206,445, Locally Generated Income $170,930. Mats Exp $29,208, Books $24,320, Per/Ser (Incl. Access Fees) $4,188, Micro $700. Sal $110,023 (Prof $56,550)
Library Holdings: Bk Vols 57,499; Per Subs 141
Subject Interests: Local history
Special Collections: Employment Information and Micro-Enterprize Coll
Automation Activity & Vendor Info: (OPAC) DRA
Mem of North Country Library System
Partic in North Country Reference & Research Resources Council
Friends of the Library Group
Bookmobiles: 3

C STATE UNIVERSITY OF NEW YORK COLLEGE AT POTSDAM, Frederick W Crumb Memorial Library, 44 Pierrepont Ave, 13676-2294. SAN 353-9342. Tel: 315-267-2482, 315-267-2485. Interlibrary Loan Service Tel: 315-267-2489. FAX: 315-267-2744, 315-267-3318. E-Mail: libcrumb@potsdam.edu. Web Site: www.potsdam.edu/library.html. *Dir*, Rebecca J Thompson; *Automation Syst Coordr*, Keith W Compeau; *Circ, ILL*, Nancy A Alzo; *Acq, Doc*, Marion Blauvelt; *Archivist*, Jane Subramanian; *Ser*, Susan Dresye; *Bibliog Instr, Ref*, David Trithart; Staff 13 (MLS 9, Non-MLS 4)
Founded 1816. Enrl 4,039; Fac 208; Highest Degree: Master
Library Holdings: Bk Vols 398,202; Per Subs 1,367
Subject Interests: Architecture, Art
Special Collections: Archives; Education; St Lawrence Seaway (Bertrand H Snell Papers), bks & mss
Publications: Library Connection; Various bibliographic & instructional guides
Partic in North Country Reference & Research Resources Council; State University Of New York-NYLINK
Departmental Libraries:
JULIA E CRANE MEMORIAL LIBRARY, Crane School of Music, 13676-2294. SAN 353-9377. Tel: 315-267-2451. Web Site: www.potsdam.edu/library.html. *In Charge*, Nancy Alzo; Tel: 315-267-3227
Library Holdings: Bk Vols 40,841
Subject Interests: Music educ, Performance
Special Collections: Helen Hosmer Papers, bks & mss; Music/Music Education (Julia E Crane Papers)

POUGHKEEPSIE

J DUTCHESS COMMUNITY COLLEGE LIBRARY,* 53 Pendell Rd, 12601-1595. SAN 312-2964. Tel: 914-431-8630. FAX: 914-431-8995. Web Site: www.sumidutchess.edu/library. *Acq, Dir*, Barbara Liesenbein; *Tech Servs*, Alice McGovern; *Bibliog Instr, Ref*, Ron Crovisier; *ILL*, Christine Craig; Staff 5 (MLS 5)
Founded 1957. Enrl 4,544; Fac 216 Sal $419,878
Library Holdings: Bk Vols 92,485; Per Subs 316
Publications: Library Handbook (annual); Periodical List (annual); Professional Staff Library Handbook
Partic in Southeastern New York Library Resources Council

S DUTCHESS COUNTY GENEALOGICAL SOCIETY LIBRARY, Spackenkill Rd, 12602. (Mail add: PO Box 708, 12602), SAN 370-2316. Tel: 845-462-2470. *Librn*, Linda C Koehler
Founded 1972
Jul 2000-Jun 2001 Income Parent Institution $600. Mats Exp $600
Library Holdings: Bk Vols 375
Subject Interests: Genealogy, Heraldry, History
Restriction: Not a lending library, Public use on premises
Function: Research library
Open Tues 9-2, Wed 5-9, Thurs 10-1 & 7-9

S DUTCHESS COUNTY MENTAL HEALTH LIBRARY,* 230 North Rd, 12601. SAN 312-2980. Tel: 914-486-2896. FAX: 914-486-2897. *Librn*, Janet Caruso
Founded 1969
Library Holdings: Bk Titles 3,000; Per Subs 50
Subject Interests: Alcoholism, Child psychiat, Child study, Developmental disabilities, Drug abuse, Psychiatry, Psychology, Psychotherapy
Publications: Accessions List; Audio-Visual Catalog; Brochure
Partic in Southeastern New York Library Resources Council

M HUDSON RIVER PSYCHIATRIC CENTER STAFF LIBRARY,* Branch B 373 North Rd, 12601. SAN 312-2999. Tel: 914-452-8000, Ext 7324. FAX: 452-3730, 914-452-7445. *In Charge*, Thomas A Shaw
Library Holdings: Bk Vols 6,055; Per Subs 110
Partic in Southeastern New York Library Resources Council

S IBM CORP, MHV Library, 2455 South Rd, 12601-5400. SAN 312-3006. Tel: 845-435-6029. FAX: 845-432-9442. *Ref*, Gregg Kiehl; *Ref*, Maris Kristapsons; Staff 4 (MLS 2, Non-MLS 2)
Library Holdings: Bk Titles 15,000; Per Subs 400
Subject Interests: Business, Computer software, Engineering, Mgt

P LA GRANGE ASSOCIATION LIBRARY, 488 Freedom Plains Rd, 12603. SAN 376-5849. Tel: 845-452-3141. FAX: 845-452-1974. E-Mail: lagrange@sebridge.org. *Dir*, Lisa LeGloahec
Library Holdings: Bk Titles 34,000; Per Subs 300
Mem of Mid-Hudson Library System
Friends of the Library Group

C MARIST COLLEGE, James A Cannavino Library, 3399 North Rd, 12601-1387. SAN 312-3014. Tel: 845-575-3199. FAX: 845-575-3150. E-Mail: library.reference@marist.edu. Web Site: www.library.marist.edu. *Actg Dir*, Dennis Benamati; E-Mail: dennis.benamati@marist.edu; *Coordr, Tech Servs*, Cathy Carl; E-Mail: cathy.carl@marist.edu; *ILL, Ref*, Charyl Pollard; E-Mail: charyl.pollard@marist.edu; *Coordr, Publ Servs*, Elena Filchagina; E-Mail: elena.filchagina@marist.edu; *Acq, Coll Develop*, Judy Diffenderfer; E-Mail: judy.diffenderfer@marist.edu; *Automation Syst Coordr*, Kathryn Silberger; E-Mail: kathryn.silberger@marist.edu; *Archivist*, John Ansley; E-Mail: john.ansley@marist.edu; Staff 16 (MLS 8, Non-MLS 8)
Founded 1929. Enrl 3,200; Fac 241; Highest Degree: Master
Jul 2000-Jun 2001 Income $1,353,206, State $8,894, Locally Generated Income $10,000, Parent Institution $1,328,542, Other $5,770. Mats Exp $288,000, Books $47,000, Per/Ser (Incl. Access Fees) $150,000, Micro

$10,000, Other Print Mats $45,000, Electronic Ref Mat (Incl. Access Fees) $36,000. Sal $543,209 (Prof $390,404)
Library Holdings: Bk Vols 166,802; Per Subs 6,528
Subject Interests: Hudson Valley Regional studies
Special Collections: Hudson River Environmental Society Coll; John Tillman Newscasts; Lowell Thomas Coll; Maristiana; Rick Whitsell R&B Rec Coll
Automation Activity & Vendor Info: (Acquisitions) Endeavor; (Cataloging) Endeavor; (Circulation) Endeavor; (Course Reserve) Endeavor; (OPAC) Endeavor
Database Vendor: Dialog, IAC - Info Trac, Lexis-Nexis, OCLC - First Search, ProQuest, Silverplatter Information Inc.
Partic in Southeastern New York Library Resources Council; Westchester Acad Libr Dir Orgn

P MID-HUDSON LIBRARY SYSTEM, 103 Market St, 12601-4098. SAN 312-3022. Tel: 845-471-6060. FAX: 845-454-5940. E-Mail: mhls@ulysses.sebridge.org. *Exec Dir*, Joshua Cohen; E-Mail: cohen@sebridge.org; *Ch Servs*, Susan Hausermann; Staff 41 (MLS 8, Non-MLS 33)
Founded 1959. Pop 583,314
Jan 2000-Dec 2000 Income $2,665,984, State $1,719,920, Federal $214,678, Other $731,386. Sal $963,356 (Prof $294,056)
Automation Activity & Vendor Info: (Cataloging) GEAC; (Circulation) GEAC
Publications: Mid-Hudson Library System (bulletin, weekly; multi-media catalog; newsletter, quarterly); NYSAVE; NYSAVE/BOCES; NYSCAT
Member Libraries: Alice Curtis Desmond & Hamilton Fish Library; Amenia Free Library; Beekman Library; Blodgett Memorial Library; Brewster Public Library; Cairo Public Library; Catskill Public Library; Chatham Public Library; Claverack Free Library; Coxsackie Correctional Facility Library; D R Evarts Library; Dover Plains Library; E Fishkill Community Library; Elting Memorial Library; Fishkill Correctional Facility Library; Germantown Library; Green Haven Correctional Facility Library; Greene Correctional Facility Library; Greenville Public Library; Grinnell Library Association; Haines Falls Free Library; Heermance Memorial Library; Highland Public Library; Hillsdale Public Library Association, Inc; Howland Public Library; Hudson Area Association Library; Hudson Correctional Facility Library; Hunter Public Library; Hurley Library Association; Julia L Butterfield Memorial Library; Kent Public Library; Kinderhook Memorial Library; Kingston Area Library; La Grange Association Library; Livingston Free Library; Mahopac Library; Marlboro Free Library; Millbrook Library; Morton Memorial Library; Morton Memorial Library; New Lebanon Library; New York State Department Of Correctional Services; North Chatham Free Library; NorthEast-Millerton Library; Olive Free Library Association; Patterson Library Association; Pawling Free Library; Philmont Public Library; Phoenicia Library; Pine Plains Free Library; Plattekill Library; Pleasant Valley Free Library; Poughkeepsie Public Library District; Putnam Valley Free Library; Red Hook Public Library; Reed Memorial Library; Rosendale Library; Sarah Hull Hallock Free Library; Saugerties Public Library; Shawangunk Correctional Facility Library; Staatsburg Library Society; Stanford Free Library; Starr Library; Stone Ridge Library; Tivoli Free Library; Town of Esopus Public Library; Town Of Ulster Public Library; Valatie Free Library; West Hurley Public Library; Windham Public Library; Woodstock Library
Partic in Southeastern New York Library Resources Council

GL NEW YORK STATE SUPREME COURT, Law Library,* Court House, Ninth Judicial District, 50 Market St, 12601-3203. SAN 312-3030. Tel: 914-486-2215. FAX: 914-486-2216. *In Charge*, Mary Boback; E-Mail: mboback@pppmail.appliedtheory.com
Founded 1904
Library Holdings: Bk Titles 14,500
Subject Interests: Law
Special Collections: Legal Reference Material

G POUGHKEEPSIE PUBLIC LIBRARY DISTRICT, 93 Market St, 12601. SAN 353-9407. Tel: 845-485-3445. Circulation Tel: 845-485-3445, Ext 3000. Reference Tel: 845-485-3445, Ext 3303. FAX: 845-485-3789. E-Mail: info@poklib.org. Web Site: www.poklib.org. *Exec Dir*, Thomas A Lawrence; Tel: 845-485-3445, Ext 3312, E-Mail: tlawrence@poklib.org; *Asst Dir*, Julie Cohen; Tel: 845-485-3445, Ext 3326, E-Mail: jcohen@poklib.org; *Asst Dir*, Lauren Muffs; Tel: 845-485-3445, Ext 3321, E-Mail: lmuffs@poklib.org; *Br Coordr*, Susan Polikoff; Tel: 845-454-9301, E-Mail: spolikoff@poklib.org; *Head Tech Servs*, Janet Huen; Tel: 845-485-3445, Ext 3314, E-Mail: jhuen@poklib.org; *Head, Circ*, Nancy Foster; Tel: 845-485-3445, Ext 3327, E-Mail: nfoster@poklib.org; *Ch Servs*, Barbara Haymann-Diaz; Tel: 845-485-3445, Ext 3315, E-Mail: bhaymann-diaz@poklib.org; Staff 62 (MLS 18, Non-MLS 44)
Founded 1841
Jan 1999-Dec 1999 Income (Main Library and Branch Library) $2,253,700, State $297,048, County $146,986, Locally Generated Income $1,639,818, Other $169,848. Mats Exp $414,072, Books $296,650, Per/Ser (Incl. Access Fees) $43,348, AV Equip $41,891, Electronic Ref Mat (Incl. Access Fees) $32,183. Sal $1,094,750 (Prof $517,455)
Library Holdings: Bk Vols 120,000; Per Subs 460; High Interest/Low Vocabulary Bk Vols 300
Subject Interests: Local history
Special Collections: Foundation Center; Genealogy; Local History
Automation Activity & Vendor Info: (Cataloging) GEAC; (Circulation) GEAC; (ILL) GEAC; (OPAC) GEAC
Database Vendor: CARL, GaleNet, IAC - SearchBank, OCLC - First Search, ProQuest
Mem of Mid-Hudson Library System
Partic in Mid-Hudson Libr Syst; Southeastern New York Library Resources Council
Friends of the Library Group
Branches:
ARLINGTON, 504 Haight Ave, 12603. SAN 353-9466. Tel: 914-454-9301. FAX: 914-454-9308. *In Charge*, Susan Polikoff
Library Holdings: Bk Vols 11,100; Bk Titles 10,800
MAPLEWOOD, 457 Maple St Bldg A, 12601. SAN 322-5909. Tel: 914-485-5741. FAX: 914-485-1290. *In Charge*, Dorothea Thompson
Library Holdings: Bk Vols 6,300; Bk Titles 6,000
Automation Activity & Vendor Info: (Circulation) GEAC

M SAINT FRANCIS HOSPITAL, Health Science Library,* North Rd, 12601. SAN 320-7234. Tel: 914-431-8132. FAX: 914-485-2964. *Librn*, Valerie C Roberts
1998-1999 Mats Exp $50,200, Books $20,000, Per/Ser (Incl. Access Fees) $30,000, AV Equip $200. Sal $38,000
Library Holdings: Bk Vols 600; Bk Titles 1,200; Per Subs 158
Subject Interests: Allied health prof, Medicine
Partic in BRS; NY Libr Res Coun
Base location for Southeastern Health Information Network

M VASSAR BROTHERS HOSPITAL, Medical Library, 45 Reade Pl, 12601. SAN 312-3049. Tel: 845-437-3121. FAX: 845-437-3002. E-Mail: vasshosp@senylrc.org. *Librn*, Mary Jo Russell; Staff 1 (MLS 1)
Founded 1951
Jan 2000-Dec 2000 Income $61,200, Locally Generated Income $200, Parent Institution $61,000. Mats Exp $32,200, Books $6,000, Per/Ser (Incl. Access Fees) $26,000, Presv $200. Sal $33,000
Library Holdings: Bk Titles 360; Per Subs 129
Subject Interests: Cardiology, Internal medicine, Nursing, Oncology, Pediatrics, Surgery
Special Collections: Hospital archives
Automation Activity & Vendor Info: (Cataloging) SIRSI
Database Vendor: Ebsco - EbscoHost, OVID Technologies
Restriction: By appointment only
Partic in Basic Health Sciences Library Network; Health Info Librs of Westchester; Southeastern New York Library Resources Council
Research support for patient care

C VASSAR COLLEGE LIBRARY, 124 Raymond Ave, Maildrop 20, 12604-0020. SAN 312-3057. Tel: 914-437-5760. FAX: 914-437-5864. Web Site: iberia.vassar.edu/vcl/index.html. *Dir*, Sabrina Pape; *Acq, Coll Develop*, Elizabeth Oktay; *Reader Servs*, Shirley Maul; *ILL*, Lucinda Dubinski; *Curator, Rare Bks*, Ronald Patkus; *Doc*, Christine Fitchett; *Cat*, Joan Pirie; Staff 17 (MLS 15, Non-MLS 2)
Founded 1861. Enrl 2,345
Jul 1999-Jun 2000 Mats Exp $1,594,233, Books $493,702, Per/Ser (Incl. Access Fees) $1,002,691, Presv $54,965, Micro $42,875. Sal $1,653,217 (Prof $819,690)
Library Holdings: Bk Vols 803,021
Special Collections: College History & Archives; Early Atlases & Maps; Elizabeth Bishop Papers; Incunabula; John Burroughs Journals; Mark Twain Coll, mss; Mary McCarthy Papers; Robert Owens Coll; Ruth Benedict Papers; Village Press; Women, bks, mss
Partic in Southeastern New York Library Resources Council
Departmental Libraries:
ART LIBRARY, Vassar College, 12604-0022. SAN 321-4230. Tel: 914-437-5790. *Librn*, Thomas E Hill
GEORGE SHERMAN DICKINSON MUSIC LIBRARY, Vassar College, 12604-0038. SAN 320-0507. Tel: 914-437-7492. FAX: 914-437-5864. *Librn*, Sarah Canino

POUGHQUAG

P BEEKMAN LIBRARY,* Rte 55 & Dorn Rd, PO Box 697, 12570. SAN 376-3013. Tel: 914-724-3414. FAX: 914-724-3941. *Dir*, Lee Eaton
Library Holdings: Bk Titles 16,500; Per Subs 35
Mem of Mid-Hudson Library System
Friends of the Library Group

POUND RIDGE

P HIRAM HALLE MEMORIAL LIBRARY,* 271 Westchester Ave, 10576-1714. SAN 312-3065. Tel: 914-764-5085. FAX: 914-764-5319. E-Mail: mtinter@wls.lib.ny.us. Web Site: www.wls.lib.ny.us. *Dir*, Marilyn Tinter
Founded 1953. Pop 4,500; Circ 74,484
Library Holdings: Bk Vols 57,152; Per Subs 62
Special Collections: Art; Phonograph Records
Mem of Westchester Library System

PRATTSBURG

PRATTSBURG LIBRARY, 26 Main St, PO Box 426, 14873-0426. SAN 376-6969. Tel: 607-522-3490. *Dir*, Jack Fermoil; Staff 1 (Non-MLS 1)
Founded 1981
Library Holdings: Bk Titles 4,100
Mem of Southern Tier Library System

PROSPECT

PROSPECT FREE LIBRARY, 915 Trenton Falls St, PO Box 177, 13435. SAN 376-3080. Tel: 315-896-2736. *Dir*, Carol Lynskey
Library Holdings: Bk Vols 5,391; Per Subs 40
Mem of Mid-York Library System
Special Services for the Blind - Bks on tape

PULASKI

PULASKI PUBLIC LIBRARY,* 4917 N Jefferson St, 13142. SAN 312-3073. Tel: 315-298-2717. FAX: 315-298-2717. *Librn*, Margaret Weigel
Circ 22,189
Library Holdings: Bk Vols 22,000; Per Subs 35
Mem of North Country Library System
Friends of the Library Group

PULTENEY

PULTENEY FREE LIBRARY,* 9068 Main St, PO Box 215, 14874-0215. SAN 312-3081. Tel: 607-868-3652. FAX: 607-868-4010. *Dir, Librn*, Barbara Radigan
Founded 1881. Pop 1,274; Circ 13,138
Library Holdings: Bk Vols 13,000; Bk Titles 12,500; Per Subs 20
Mem of Chemung-Southern Tier Libr Syst; Southern Tier Library System
Special Services for the Deaf - Books on deafness & sign language; High interest/low vocabulary books
Open Tues & Thurs 12-8, Wed 12-6 & Sat 9-1
Friends of the Library Group

PURCHASE

C MANHATTANVILLE COLLEGE LIBRARY, 2900 Purchase St, 10577. SAN 312-309X. Tel: 914-323-5275. Reference Tel: 914-323-5282. FAX: 914-323-8139. E-Mail: library@mville.edu. Web Site: www.mville.edu/library/. *Dir*, Rhonna A Goodman; Tel: 914-323-5277, E-Mail: goodmanr@mville.edu; *Asst Dir*, Jeff Rosedale; E-Mail: roosedalej@mville.edu; *Tech Servs*, Lucye Boland; Tel: 914-323-5292, E-Mail: bolandl@mville.edu; *Publ Servs*, Gus Stamatopooulos; Tel: 914-323-3132, E-Mail: stamatopooulosg@mville.edu; *Ref*, Elizabeth Gallagher; Tel: 914-323-3133, E-Mail: gallaghere@mville.edu; *Media Spec*, Tami-Jo Eckley; Tel: 914-323-5274, E-Mail: eckleyt@mville.edu; *Instr*, Paula Moskowitz; E-Mail: moskowitzp@mville.edu; Staff 14 (MLS 9, Non-MLS 5)
Founded 1841. Pop 1,300; Fac 80; Highest Degree: Master
Jul 1999-Jun 2000 Income $815,030, State $12,000, Parent Institution $753,030, Other $50,000. Mats Exp $200,000, Presv $4,000, AV Equip $4,500, Electronic Ref Mat (Incl. Access Fees) $21,285. Sal $5,117,945 (Prof $340,000)
Library Holdings: Bk Vols 245,142; Bk Titles 182,789; Per Subs 1,010
Subject Interests: Architecture, Art, Asian studies, Biog, Education, Music
Special Collections: Alexander Stephens letters; Alexander Stephens, letters; Allain Biography; Buddhism & Hindusin (Zigmund Cerbu)
Automation Activity & Vendor Info: (Media Booking) PALS
Database Vendor: Dialog, Ebsco - EbscoHost, GaleNet, IAC - Info Trac, IAC - SearchBank, Lexis-Nexis, OCLC - First Search, ProQuest, Silverplatter Information Inc., Wilson - Wilson Web
Restriction: Restricted access
Partic in Metropolitan New York Library Council; WALDO
Friends of the Library Group

S PEPSI-COLA COMPANY, Information Center, 700 Anderson Hill Rd, 10577. SAN 372-7815. Tel: 914-253-3186. FAX: 914-253-2229.; Staff 2 (MLS 1, Non-MLS 1)
Founded 1981
Library Holdings: Bk Titles 2,000; Per Subs 300
Restriction: Staff use only
Partic in Dialog Corporation

P PURCHASE FREE LIBRARY, 3093 Purchase St, 10577. SAN 312-3103. Tel: 914-948-0550. FAX: 914-328-3405. *Dir*, Anne Collins; *Librn*, Janet Elmiger
Founded 1928. Pop 4,950; Circ 19,848
Jan 2000-Dec 2000 Income $139,912. Mats Exp $22,300, Books $15,000, Per/Ser (Incl. Access Fees) $1,500, Micro $800, AV Equip $5,000
Library Holdings: Bk Vols 18,000; Bk Titles 17,000; Per Subs 28
Subject Interests: Business mat, Local history
Mem of Westchester Library System
Friends of the Library Group

C STATE UNIVERSITY OF NEW YORK, Purchase College Library, 735 Anderson Hill Rd, 10577-1400. SAN 312-3111. Tel: 914-251-6400. Interlibrary Loan Service Tel: 914-251-6428. Reference Tel: 914-251-6410. FAX: 914-251-6437. Web Site: www.purchase.edu/services/instrfac/library/. *Dir Libr Serv*, Patrick F Callahan; Tel: 914-251-6435, E-Mail: patrick.callahan@purvid.purchase.edu; *Publ Servs*, Richard Arsenty; Tel: 914-251-6415, E-Mail: rarsenty@purvid.purchase.edu; *Circ, ILL*, Martha Smith; Tel: 914-251-6416, E-Mail: martha.smith@purchase.edu; *Tech Servs*, Michael Handis; Tel: 914-251-6433, E-Mail: mhandis@purvid.purchase.edu; *Bibliog Instr*, Rebecca Albrecht; Tel: 914-251-6417, E-Mail: rebecca.albrecht@purchase.edu; *Tech Coordr*, Deborah Amory; Tel: 914-251-6267, E-Mail: deborah.amory@purchase.edu. Subject Specialists: *Art*, Martha Smith; Staff 24 (MLS 7, Non-MLS 17)
Founded 1967. Enrl 3,950; Fac 150; Highest Degree: Master
Jul 1998-Jun 1999 Income State $1,135,475. Mats Exp $334,500, Books $49,000, Per/Ser (Incl. Access Fees) $249,000, Presv $18,000, Micro $18,500. Sal $676,000
Library Holdings: Bk Vols 261,598; Bk Titles 174,307; Per Subs 1,141
Subject Interests: Art, Music, Performing arts
Automation Activity & Vendor Info: (Cataloging) MultiLIS; (Circulation) MultiLIS; (OPAC) MultiLIS; (Serials) MultiLIS
Database Vendor: Ebsco - EbscoHost, GaleNet, IAC - Info Trac, Lexis-Nexis, OCLC - First Search, ProQuest, Silverplatter Information Inc.
Publications: Books & Bytes (newsletter)
Function: ILL available
Partic in New York Metrop Ref & Res Libr Agency; Westchester Acad Libr Dir Orgn

PUTNAM VALLEY

P PUTNAM VALLEY FREE LIBRARY,* 30 Oscawana Lake Rd, PO Box 425, 10579. SAN 312-312X. Tel: 914-528-3242. FAX: 914-528-3297. *Dir*, Kathleen McLoughlin
Founded 1936. Circ 100,040
Library Holdings: Bk Vols 40,700; Bk Titles 30,800
Special Collections: Fine Arts (Harry N Abrams Coll)
Mem of Mid-Hudson Library System

QUEENS VILLAGE

CREEDMOOR PSYCHIATRIC CENTER
S PATIENTS LIBRARY, Bldg 51, 80-45 Winchester Blvd, 11427. SAN 353-9555. Tel: 718-464-7500, Ext 5020.
Founded 1950
Library Holdings: Bk Vols 5,600; Per Subs 25
Subject Interests: Large print

QUEENSBURY

J ADIRONDACK COMMUNITY COLLEGE LIBRARY, Scoville Learning Center, 640 Bay Rd, 12804. SAN 311-2462. Tel: 518-743-2260. FAX: 518-745-1442. Web Site: www.sunyacc.edu. *Dir*, Teresa Ronning; *Media Spec*, David Ofiara; *Ref*, Joyce Miller; *Ref*, Suzanne Delman; *Ref*, Walt Hagen; Staff 11 (MLS 7, Non-MLS 4)
Founded 1961. Enrl 2,300; Fac 100; Highest Degree: Associate
Library Holdings: Bk Vols 56,000; Bk Titles 50,000; Per Subs 350
Subject Interests: Criminal justice, Liberal arts, Nursing
Special Collections: Local History (Hill Coll)
Automation Activity & Vendor Info: (Cataloging) DRA; (Cataloging) MultiLIS; (Circulation) DRA; (Circulation) MultiLIS; (Course Reserve) DRA; (Course Reserve) MultiLIS; (OPAC) DRA
Database Vendor: Dialog, GaleNet, OCLC - First Search, ProQuest
Publications: LR Faculty & Student Handbooks
Function: ILL available, Some telephone reference
Partic in Cap District Libr Coun for Ref & Res Resources; Dialog Corporation; OCLC Online Computer Library Center, Inc

QUOGUE

P QUOGUE LIBRARY, INC,* 90 Quogue St, 11959. SAN 312-3138. Tel: 516-653-4224. FAX: 516-653-6151. E-Mail: quoglib@suffolk.lib.ny.us. *Dir*, Kate Belden
Founded 1897. Circ 15,000
1997-1998 Income $16,000
Library Holdings: Bk Vols 28,000
Mem of Suffolk Cooperative Library System

RANDOLPH

P RANDOLPH FREE LIBRARY,* 26 Jamestown St, 14772. SAN 312-3146. Tel: 716-358-3712. FAX: 716-358-2039. E-Mail: rfl@madbbs.com. *Librn*, Mary Chriest; Staff 2 (Non-MLS 2)
Founded 1909. Pop 1,393; Circ 32,719
1997-1998 Income $90,000
Library Holdings: Bk Vols 22,700; Bk Titles 20,350; Per Subs 40

Subject Interests: Antiques, Local genealogy
Special Collections: Garden Club Coll, bks, pamphlets & per; Local Newspaper 1876-1979, micro
Mem of Chautauqua-Cattaraugus Library System
Open Mon, Tues, Thurs & Fri 1-5 & 7-9, Wed 7-9 & Sat 10-5

RANSOMVILLE

P RANSOMVILLE FREE LIBRARY,* 3733 Ransomville Rd, 14131. SAN 312-3154. Tel: 716-791-4073. FAX: 716-791-4073. *Librn*, Sue Holmes
Circ 32,714
Library Holdings: Bk Titles 25,000; Per Subs 57
Mem of Nioga Library System
Open daily 2-8pm

RAQUETTE LAKE

P RAQUETTE LAKE FREE LIBRARY,* PO Box 129, 13436. SAN 312-3162. Tel: 315-354-4005. FAX: 315-354-4005. *Librn*, Diane Carver
Pop 200; Circ 11,280
Library Holdings: Bk Vols 8,247; Per Subs 47
Subject Interests: Adirondack hist
Special Collections: Adirondack Region
Publications: Winter Newsletter
Mem of Southern Adirondack Library System
Open Mon 6-9, Thurs 12-5 & 7-9 & Sun 1-4 (winter hours), Mon 6-9, Tues 1-5, Wed 7-9, Thurs 12-5 & 7-9, Sun 10-2 (summer hours-July-Oct)
Friends of the Library Group

RAVENA

P RCS COMMUNITY LIBRARY, 15 Mountain Rd, 12143. SAN 312-3170. Tel: 518-756-2053. FAX: 518-756-8595. E-Mail: rcsc1@uhls.lib.ny.us. *Dir*, Judy Felsten; *Coll Develop*, Barbara Goetschius; Staff 2 (MLS 2)
Founded 1994. Pop 14,671; Circ 24,031
Jul 2000-Jun 2001 Income $195,210, State $4,548, Locally Generated Income $178,262, Other $12,400. Mats Exp $18,540, Books $15,000, Per/Ser (Incl. Access Fees) $750, Presv $150, Electronic Ref Mat (Incl. Access Fees) $2,640. Sal $112,613 (Prof $68,186)
Library Holdings: Bk Vols 16,700; Bks on Deafness & Sign Lang 25
Special Collections: Hudson River Valley Coll
Automation Activity & Vendor Info: (Cataloging) DRA; (Circulation) DRA; (ILL) DRA; (OPAC) DRA
Database Vendor: DRA
Publications: Newsletter
Function: ILL available, Photocopies available
Mem of Upper Hudson Library System

RAY BROOK

S ADIRONDACK CORRECTIONAL FACILITY LIBRARY, PO Box 110, 12977. SAN 327-1749. Tel: 518-891-1343. FAX: 518-891-1343, Ext 4599. *In Charge*, Len DeMarse; *Senior Librn*, Sylvia Norton; Staff 1 (MLS 1)
Library Holdings: Bk Vols 6,000; Per Subs 17
Subject Interests: Spanish lang

RED CREEK

P RED CREEK FREE LIBRARY,* 6817 Main St, PO Box 360, 13143. SAN 312-3189. Tel: 315-754-6679. *Librn*, Josephine Mercer
Circ 10,192
Library Holdings: Bk Vols 5,540
Subject Interests: Local history
Mem of Pioneer Library System; Wayne County Libr Syst

RED HOOK

P RED HOOK PUBLIC LIBRARY,* 744 S Broadway, 12571. SAN 312-3197. Tel: 914-758-3241. *Dir*, Theresa Dockerty
Circ 11,524
Library Holdings: Bk Titles 10,000
Mem of Mid-Hudson Library System
Friends of the Library Group

REMSEN

P DIDYMUS THOMAS LIBRARY,* Main St, 13438. SAN 312-3200. Tel: 315-831-5651. E-Mail: re-dial@midyork.lib.n.y.us. *Dir*, Linda Horn
Founded 1899. Pop 518; Circ 10,266
Library Holdings: Bk Titles 13,214
Publications: History of Remsen, by Millard Roberts
Mem of Mid-York Library System

RENSSELAER

P EAST GREENBUSH COMMUNITY LIBRARY,* 225 Columbia Tpk, 12144. SAN 352-4469. Tel: 518-477-7476. FAX: 518-477-6692. *Dir*, Patricia Noramaker; E-Mail: nonamakerp@uhls.lib.ny.us; Staff 6 (MLS 6)
Founded 1948. Pop 15,000; Circ 175,000
Jan 1997-Dec 1998 Income $345,196, State $4,037, Federal $1,250, County $6,500, Locally Generated Income $333,409. Mats Exp $349,914, Books $40,180, Per/Ser (Incl. Access Fees) $11,198. Sal $163,201 (Prof $65,193)
Library Holdings: Bk Vols 41,696; Per Subs 123
Automation Activity & Vendor Info: (Circulation) CLSI LIBS
Publications: Greenbush Bookmark
Mem of Upper Hudson Library System
Special Services - Books with Wheels service to homebound residents
Friends of the Library Group

M HEALTHCARE ASSOCIATION OF NEW YORK STATE-HEALTHCARE EDUCATIONAL & RESEARCH FUND, Lillian R Hayt Memorial Library, One Empire Dr, 12144. SAN 310-7558. Tel: 518-431-7600. FAX: 518-431-7812. *Dir Libr Serv*, Elaine C Rotman; E-Mail: erotman@hanys.org; Staff 1 (MLS 1)
Founded 1965
Library Holdings: Bk Titles 2,500; Per Subs 400
Subject Interests: Economics, Finance, Health administration, Planning
Automation Activity & Vendor Info: (Cataloging) Inmagic, Inc.
Database Vendor: OVID Technologies
Restriction: Employees & their associates
Function: Research library
Partic in Capital District Library Council for Reference & Research Resources

P RENSSELAER PUBLIC LIBRARY,* 810 Broadway, 12144. SAN 312-3227. Tel: 518-462-1193. FAX: 518-462-2819. *Librn*, Kenneth A Ryder
Founded 1920. Pop 9,047; Circ 20,619
Library Holdings: Bk Vols 20,500; Per Subs 55
Special Collections: Civil War; Ecology
Mem of Upper Hudson Library System
Partic in OCLC Online Computer Library Center, Inc

RENSSELAERVILLE

P RENSSELAERVILLE LIBRARY,* Main St, PO Box 188, 12147. SAN 312-3251. Tel: 518-797-3949. *Librn*, Archa Wachowicz; *Asst Librn*, Emily Rauch; *Asst Librn*, Megan Thackeray
Pop 3,500; Circ 12,482
Library Holdings: Bk Vols 23,123; Per Subs 57
Mem of Upper Hudson Library System
Friends of the Library Group

RHINEBECK

S ASTOR HOME FOR CHILDREN, Professional Library,* 36 Mill St, PO Box 5005, 12572-5005. SAN 312-326X. Tel: 914-876-4081, Ext 192. FAX: 914-876-2020. *Librn*, Theresa Brettschneider
Founded 1958
Library Holdings: Bk Vols 2,500; Per Subs 40
Subject Interests: Child psychiat, Child psychology, Family therapy, Mental health, Residential child care, Social work
Special Collections: Bibliotherapy - children & parents
Partic in Southeastern New York Library Resources Council

P STARR LIBRARY,* 68 W Market St, 12572. SAN 312-3278. Tel: 914-876-4030. FAX: 914-876-4030. Web Site: www.midhudson.org. *Librn*, Dona McLaughlin; *Asst Librn*, David Wanzer; *Ch Servs*, Judith Augustine; Staff 3 (MLS 3)
Founded 1915. Pop 6,500; Circ 34,000
Library Holdings: Bk Vols 25,321; Per Subs 35
Special Collections: Constitution Coll; Franklin D Roosevelt Coll; Large Print Coll; Local History (DAR Coll); Rare Book Coll
Mem of Mid-Hudson Library System
Friends of the Library Group

RHINECLIFF

P MORTON MEMORIAL LIBRARY,* 32 Kelly St, PO Box 157, 12574. SAN 312-3286. Tel: 914-876-2903. *Librn*, Joanne A Meyer
Circ 7,643
Library Holdings: Bk Vols 6,600
Mem of Mid-Hudson Library System
Open Thurs - Sat 12-5 (winter)

RICHBURG

P COLONIAL LIBRARY,* 160 Main St, 14774. SAN 312-3294. Tel: 716-928-2694. FAX: 716-928-2694. *Librn*, Christine Shutt
Founded 1913. Pop 1,200

Library Holdings: Bk Titles 19,250; Per Subs 52
Mem of Southern Tier Library System
Open Mon & Thurs 12-5, Wed 6-8

RICHFIELD SPRINGS

P RICHFIELD SPRINGS PUBLIC LIBRARY,* 102 Main St, PO Box 271, 13439-0271. SAN 312-3308. Tel: 315-858-0230. FAX: 315-858-0230. *Librn*, Alice Mahardy; *Asst Librn*, Joyce Urtz
Founded 1909. Pop 1,561; Circ 22,362
Library Holdings: Bk Vols 13,800; Per Subs 63
Special Collections: Microfilm Coll of RS Mercury 1867-1972, (incl Summer Daily 1888-1917)
Mem of Four County Library System
Open Mon 11:30-4:30 & 7pm-9, Tues-Fri 11:30-4:30

RICHVILLE

P RICHVILLE FREE LIBRARY,* 87 Main St, PO Box 55, 13681-0055. SAN 312-3316. Tel: 315-287-1481. *Librn*, Lila Youngs; E-Mail: youngs@northnet.org
Founded 1932. Pop 2,103
Library Holdings: Bk Vols 5,000; Per Subs 30
Special Collections: Adirondack Mountains; St Lawrence County Topographical Maps
Mem of North Country Library System
Open Mon 6-9, Tues & Wed 7-9, Fri 1-3

RIPLEY

P RIPLEY FREE LIBRARY,* 64 W Main St, 14775-0631. SAN 312-3324. Tel: 716-736-3913. FAX: 716-736-3923. *Dir*, Laura Sinden
Founded 1938. Pop 3,181; Circ 29,600
Library Holdings: Bk Vols 10,573; Bk Titles 10,430; Per Subs 47
Mem of Chautauqua-Cattaraugus Library System
Friends of the Library Group

RIVERHEAD

M CENTRAL SUFFOLK HOSPITAL, Medical Library,* 1300 Roanoke Ave, 11901. SAN 312-3332. Tel: 516-548-6000, Ext 6445. FAX: 516-727-8890. *Librn*, Anne Kirsch
Founded 1973
Library Holdings: Bk Titles 850; Per Subs 93
Restriction: Staff use only

P RIVERHEAD FREE LIBRARY, 330 Court St, 11901-2885. SAN 312-3340. Tel: 631-727-3228. FAX: 631-727-4762. Web Site: river.suffolk.lib.ny.us. *Dir*, Kathy Kalanz; E-Mail: kkalanz@suffolk.lib.ny.us; *Asst Dir*, David Troyan; *Ch Servs*, Evelyn Voulgarelis; *Ref*, Susan Frey; *Ad Servs, YA Servs*, Laura LaSita; Staff 70 (MLS 12, Non-MLS 58)
Founded 1896. Pop 27,031; Circ 222,006
Jul 1999-Jun 2000 Income $1,649,068, State $8,380, Locally Generated Income $1,485,668. Mats Exp $233,200, Books $147,000, Per/Ser (Incl. Access Fees) $16,000, Presv $700, Micro $13,000, Other Print Mats $13,000, Electronic Ref Mat (Incl. Access Fees) $28,000. Sal $940,370 (Prof $322,880)
Library Holdings: Bk Vols 155,275
Special Collections: Polish Coll
Automation Activity & Vendor Info: (Circulation) epixtech, inc.
Publications: Newsletter
Mem of Suffolk Cooperative Library System
Special Services for the Deaf - TTY machine
Friends of the Library Group

J SUFFOLK COUNTY COMMUNITY COLLEGE, Riverhead Campus Library,* 121 Speonk Riverhead Rd, 11901-9990. SAN 320-8907. Tel: 516-548-2536. FAX: 516-369-2641. Web Site: www.sunysuffolk.edu. *Librn*, Mary Ann Miller; E-Mail: millerma@sunysuffolk.edu; *Bibliog Instr, Coll Develop*, Carol Longo; *AV*, Jay Schwartz; Staff 11 (MLS 6, Non-MLS 5)
Founded 1977. Enrl 1,446; Fac 46
Library Holdings: Bk Vols 35,912; Bk Titles 31,522; Per Subs 402
Subject Interests: Food servs, Graphic design, Horticulture, Hotel tech, Tourism, Travel
Publications: Bottom Shelf (newsletter); Media News
Partic in Long Island Library Resources Council; New York State Interlibrary Loan Network

S SUFFOLK COUNTY HISTORICAL SOCIETY LIBRARY,* 300 W Main St, 11901-2894. SAN 312-3359. Tel: 516-727-2881. *Librn*, Gerald J Stanonis; Staff 1 (MLS 1)
Founded 1886
Library Holdings: Bk Vols 15,000; Bk Titles 9,000; Per Subs 12
Subject Interests: Agriculture, Genealogy, General Long Island mat, Specifically Suffolk County events, Specifically Suffolk County people
Special Collections: archives objects; bks; Churches; Daughters of the Revolution of 1776; Deeds; Fullerton; Long Island History Coll; micro; Military; photog plate negatives; Shipwrecks; The Talmage Weaving Coll; Towns & Wills Coll; VF
Publications: booklist; Index of the Munsell; Register (quarterly genealogy)

GL TENTH JUDICIAL DISTRICT SUPREME COURT LAW LIBRARY,* Arthur M Cromarty Court Complex, 220 Center Dr, 11901-3312. SAN 353-961X. Tel: 516-852-2419. FAX: 516-852-1782. E-Mail: ocalig@transit.ny.sev.net. *Librn*, Michele M Warner; Staff 6 (MLS 2, Non-MLS 4)
Founded 1909
Library Holdings: Bk Vols 110,000; Per Subs 150
Subject Interests: Fed law, State law
Restriction: Open to public for reference only
Partic in Long Island Library Resources Council; OCLC Online Computer Library Center, Inc; Wesllaw
Branches:
COHALAN SUPREME COURT LIBRARY, 400 Carleton Ave, Central Islip, 11722-9079. SAN 373-9295. Tel: 516-853-7530. FAX: 516-853-7533. *Librn*, Laurie Brentson
SUPREME COURT LAW LIBRARY BRANCH, Court House, Rm 210, Griffing Ave, 11901. SAN 353-9644. Tel: 516-852-1693. FAX: 516-852-1690.

ROCHESTER

SR ALDERSGATE UNITED METHODIST CHURCH LIBRARY,* 4115 Dewey Ave, 14616. SAN 327-0157. Tel: 716-663-3665. FAX: 716-865-8442. *Librn*, Carol Poole
Library Holdings: Bk Vols 3,300
Friends of the Library Group

S ALSTOM SIGNALING, INC, Technical Resource Center, 150 Sawgrass Dr, 14620. SAN 312-3499. Tel: 716-783-2179. FAX: 716-783-2070. *In Charge*, Andro P Gagne; E-Mail: andro.gagne@transport.alstom.com
Founded 1965
Library Holdings: Bk Vols 4,500; Per Subs 79
Subject Interests: Computer science, Electrical engineering, Electronics, Mass transit, Mat sci, Mechanical engineering, Optics, Railroads, Telecommunications

CR AMBROSE SWASEY LIBRARY, 1100 S Goodman St, 14620-2592. SAN 312-3421. Tel: 716-271-1320, Ext 225. FAX: 716-271-2166. Web Site: www.crds.edu/AmbroseSwaseyLibrary.asp. *Librn*, Christine Wenderoth; E-Mail: cwenderoth@crds.edu; *Tech Servs*, Christopher Brennan; *Cat*, Gail McClain; *Publ Servs*, Thomas Haverly; Staff 9 (MLS 6, Non-MLS 3)
Founded 1817. Enrl 109; Fac 21; Highest Degree: Doctorate
Jul 2000-Jun 2001 Income Parent Institution $583,166. Mats Exp $112,699, Books $56,182, Per/Ser (Incl. Access Fees) $41,517, Presv $8,800, Electronic Ref Mat (Incl. Access Fees) $7,200. Sal $378,425 (Prof $252,894)
Library Holdings: Bk Vols 314,974; Per Subs 422
Subject Interests: Behav sci, Relig studies, Soc sci
Special Collections: Bible Coll; Church History; Rare Book Coll in Theology
Automation Activity & Vendor Info: (Cataloging) Endeavor; (Circulation) Endeavor; (Course Reserve) Endeavor; (OPAC) Endeavor; (Serials) Endeavor
Partic in Rochester Regional Library Council
Serves two graduate schools of theology: Colgate Rochester Divinity School-Bexley Hall-Crozer Theological Seminary & St Bernard's Institute

R AMERICAN BAPTIST - SAMUEL COLGATE HISTORICAL LIBRARY, 1106 S Goodman St, 14620-2532. SAN 312-3367. Tel: 716-473-1740. FAX: 716-473-1740. E-Mail: abhs@crds.edu. Web Site: www.crds.edu/abhs/default.htm.; Staff 2 (MLS 1, Non-MLS 1)
Founded 1853
Library Holdings: Bk Titles 60,000
Subject Interests: Baptist hist, Baptist theol, Local Baptist proceedings, Writing about Baptists, Writing by Baptists
Special Collections: American Bible Union Archives; Danish-Norwegian Baptist General Conference of American Archives; Rauschenbusch family papers; Samuel B Colgate (Historical Coll); Seventeenth & Eighteenth Century English Baptist History (Henry S Burrage)
Publications: American Baptist Quarterly; Primary Source; The Associate
Restriction: Not a lending library
Function: Archival collection, Research fees apply

M AMERICAN RED CROSS, Blood Services Library,* 50 Prince St, 14607-1016. SAN 373-6571. Tel: 716-241-4201. FAX: 716-461-5251.
Library Holdings: Bk Titles 700; Per Subs 20
Subject Interests: Hematology
Restriction: Staff use only
Partic in Central New York Library Resources Council; National Network Of Libraries Of Medicine - South Central Region

R ASBURY FIRST UNITED METHODIST CHURCH LIBRARY, 1050 East Ave, 14607. SAN 312-3375. Tel: 716-271-1050. FAX: 716-271-3743. *Librn*, Janice Cygan
Library Holdings: Bk Vols 2,500

R BETHANY PRESBYTERIAN CHURCH LIBRARY, 3000 Dewey Ave, 14616. SAN 312-3391. Tel: 716-663-3000. FAX: 716-663-5325.
Founded 1958
Jan 2000-Dec 2000 Income Parent Institution $250. Mats Exp $150
Library Holdings: Bk Vols 2,016; Bk Titles 1,867; High Interest/Low Vocabulary Bk Vols 457
Restriction: Restricted public use

P BRIGHTON MEMORIAL LIBRARY,* 2300 Elmwood Ave, 14618. SAN 312-3405. Tel: 716-473-5420. TDD: 716-442-5619. FAX: 716-442-3188. E-Mail: brirefl@mcls.rochester.lib.ny.us. Web Site: www.rochester.lib.ny.us/brighton/. *Dir*, Angela Bonazinga; *AV*, Jennifer Lenio; *Ad Servs*, Lizabeth Barrett; *Ch Servs*, Elaine Vitone; *Ref*, Kim Bolan; *YA Servs*, Sally Snow
Founded 1953. Pop 34,455
Jan 1997-Dec 1998 Income $953,376, State $12,403, Locally Generated Income $75,723, Other $29,165. Mats Exp $134,727, Books $111,380, Per/Ser (Incl. Access Fees) $16,942, Presv $240, Micro $6,165. Sal $563,603 (Prof $281,916)
Library Holdings: Bk Vols 105,114
Subject Interests: Brighton local hist, Judaica
Automation Activity & Vendor Info: (Circulation) CARL
Publications: Brighton Directory of Organizations
Mem of Monroe County Library System
Special Services for the Deaf - TDD
Friends of the Library Group

S CAREER DEVELOPMENT SERVICES, Career Information Center,* 706 East Ave, 14607-2105. SAN 325-4569. Tel: 716-244-0750. FAX: 716-244-7115. E-Mail: info@careerdev.org. Web Site: www.careerdev.org. *Dir*, Timothy A Dixon; *Coll Develop*, Karen S Kral
Founded 1975
Library Holdings: Bk Vols 1,100; Bk Titles 1,250; Per Subs 95
Subject Interests: Bus directories, Career planning
Special Collections: Employer information file on Rochester area companies; Vocational guidance, career management & development, bks, pamphlets, articles
Publications: Bibliographies on Careers & Job Search; Guide to Library

S CENTER FOR GOVERNMENTAL RESEARCH, INC LIBRARY,* 37 S Washington St, 14608. SAN 312-3413. Tel: 716-325-6360. FAX: 716-325-2612. Web Site: www.cgr.org. *Librn*, Peter Young; E-Mail: pyoung@cgr.org
Founded 1915
Library Holdings: Bk Titles 6,000; Per Subs 100
Subject Interests: Criminal justice, Demographics, Finance, Human services, Planning, Prog evaluation, Pub admin, Soc indicators
Special Collections: Local Government Documents; New York State Census Data Center; Revenue Sharing
Restriction: Open to public for reference only
Partic in Rochester Regional Library Council

L CHAMBERLAIN, D'AMANDA, OPPENHEIMER & GREENFIELD, Law Library, 1600 Crossroads Bldg, 2 State St, 14614. SAN 372-2392. Tel: 716-232-3730. FAX: 716-232-3882. E-Mail: cab@cdog.com. Web Site: www.cdog.com. *Librn*, Christine Becker
Library Holdings: Bk Vols 8,000; Per Subs 15
Restriction: Internal circulation only, Not open to public, Private library
Function: Reference only, Reference services available

P CHILI PUBLIC LIBRARY, 3333 Chili Ave, 14624-5494. SAN 311-0478. Tel: 716-889-2200. FAX: 716-889-5819. Web Site: www.rochester.lib.ny.us/chili. *Dir*, Bernadette Foster; *Ref*, Jeanne Austin; *YA Servs*, Richard Gegnier; *Ch Servs*, Lee Ann Sperling
Founded 1962. Pop 25,178; Circ 222,236
Library Holdings: Bk Vols 58,681; Bk Titles 54,398; Per Subs 198
Subject Interests: Local history
Automation Activity & Vendor Info: (Circulation) CARL
Mem of Monroe County Library System
Friends of the Library Group

SR CHRIST EPISCOPAL CHURCH, Christ Church Library,* 141 East Ave, 14604. SAN 323-8474. Tel: 716-454-3878. *Librn*, Robert W Barnes
JanDec
Library Holdings: Bk Titles 1,200; Per Subs 33
Subject Interests: Religion
Open Mon-Fri 9-2, Sun 10-12

M CRESTWOOD CHILDREN'S CENTER LIBRARY, 2075 Scottsville Rd, 14623. SAN 312-3448. Tel: 716-436-4442. FAX: 716-436-0169. *Librn*, Jim Montione; Tel: 716-436-4442, Ext 314
Founded 1967
Subject Interests: Child psychiat, Clinical psychol, Community mental health, Mental health of children, Psychiat soc work
Partic in Rochester Regional Library Council
Special Services for the Deaf - Staff with knowledge of sign language

S DEMOCRAT & CHRONICLE LIBRARY, 55 Exchange Blvd, 14614-2001. SAN 312-3472. Tel: 716-258-2506. FAX: 716-258-2265. E-Mail: library@democratandchronicle.com. *Mgr*, Virginia Wheeler
Founded 1929
Special Collections: Life Magazine Coll from 1936-present
Partic in Dialog Corporation

S EASTMAN KODAK CO, Business Information Center,* 343 State St, 14650-1206. SAN 353-9679. Tel: 716-724-3041. Interlibrary Loan Service Tel: 716-477-8884. FAX: 716-724-1985. *Mgr*, Raymond Curtin; Staff 3 (MLS 1, Non-MLS 2)
Founded 1920
Library Holdings: Bk Vols 8,000; Per Subs 200
Subject Interests: Bus, Econ, Marketing, Mgt, Photog, Salesmanship
Special Collections: Company Archives; Financial Reports
Restriction: Not open to public
Branches:
INFOSOURCE B69 RESEARCH LIBRARY, Bldg 67, Mail Code 01861, Kodak Park, 14650-1861. SAN 353-9709. Tel: 716-722-2356. FAX: 716-477-8161.; Staff 2 (MLS 1, Non-MLS 1)
Founded 1948
Library Holdings: Bk Titles 4,400; Per Subs 500
Subject Interests: Bus, Computing, Electronic engineering, Human factors, Imaging sci, Photog tech
Restriction: By appointment only
Partic in OCLC Online Computer Library Center, Inc; Rochester Regional Library Council
INFOSOURCE ENGINEERING & STANDARDS INFORMATION CENTER, Bldg 23, Mail Code 24332, 14652-4332. SAN 377-7391. Tel: 716-722-6263. FAX: 716-722-5636. *Mgr*, Ray Curtin
INFOSOURCE KEMD LIBRARY, 901 Elmgrove Rd, Mail Code 35213, 14653-5213. SAN 353-9768. Tel: 716-726-3418. FAX: 716-726-7307. *Mgr*, Richard Bartl
Founded 1944
Library Holdings: Bk Titles 17,000; Per Subs 400
Subject Interests: Chemistry, Electrical, Electronic engineering, Finishes, Mat, Mechanical, Optics, Photog, Physics, Syst eng
Special Collections: IEEE Coll
Restriction: Not open to public
Partic in OCLC Online Computer Library Center, Inc; Rochester Regional Library Council
INFOSOURCE LIBRARY, Kodak Park Div, B-320, Mail Code 26265, 14652-3615. SAN 353-9733. Tel: 716-588-3619. FAX: 716-588-9705. *Mgr*, Ellen Dietterick; Staff 2 (MLS 1, Non-MLS 1)
Founded 1952
Library Holdings: Bk Vols 8,100; Per Subs 360
Subject Interests: Biomed, Clinical chem, Indust hygiene, Occupational med, Tech safety, Toxicology
Partic in Nat Libr of Med; Rochester Regional Library Council
INFOSOURCE RESEARCH LIBRARY, Research Laboratories, Bldg 83, Mail Code 02224, 1669 Lake Ave, 14650-2224. SAN 353-9822. Tel: 716-722-2723. FAX: 716-477-1909. *Mgr*, Richard Bartl; Staff 6 (MLS 3, Non-MLS 3)
Founded 1912
Library Holdings: Bk Vols 55,000; Bk Titles 30,000; Per Subs 1,500
Subject Interests: Chemistry, Communications, Computer science, Electronics, Engineering, Physics
Partic in OCLC Online Computer Library Center, Inc; Rochester Regional Library Council

S FINGERLAKES DEVELOPMENTAL DISABILITIES SERVICE OFFICE MONROE DEVELOPMENTAL CENTER, Staff Library,* 620 Westfall Rd, 14620-4610. SAN 354-009X. Tel: 716-461-8975. FAX: 716-473-1963. *Coordr*, Steve Jarose
Founded 1974
1997-1998 Mats Exp $3,300, Books $300, Per/Ser (Incl. Access Fees) $3,000. Sal $5,000
Library Holdings: Bk Titles 3,100; Per Subs 30
Subject Interests: Psychology, Special education
Special Collections: History of Mental Retardation; Special Education Curriculum; Training of the Mentally Retarded
Partic in Rochester Regional Library Council

P GATES PUBLIC LIBRARY,* 1605 Buffalo Rd, 14624. SAN 353-9881. Tel: 716-247-6446. FAX: 716-426-5733. Web Site: www.gates.library.org. *Dir*, Susan Swanton; E-Mail: sswanton@mcls.rochester.lib.ny.us; *Asst Dir*, Judy MacKnight; *Ch Servs*, Donna Preasley; *Ch Servs*, Mary Jo Smith; *Ad Servs*, *Coll Develop*, Nancy Blanda; *YA Servs*, Heidi Jung; Staff 50 (MLS 7, Non-MLS 43)
Founded 1960. Pop 28,583; Circ 479,558
Jan 2000-Dec 2000 Income $1,093,679, State $15,980, City $1,009,599, Locally Generated Income $68,100. Mats Exp $142,948, Books $116,582, Per/Ser (Incl. Access Fees) $6,500, Presv $750, Micro $1,300, AV Equip $17,816. Sal $729,171
Library Holdings: Bk Vols 119,683; Per Subs 2,073
Special Collections: Italian Coll, bks

Automation Activity & Vendor Info: (Circulation) CARL; (OPAC) CARL
Publications: Gates Human Services Directory
Mem of Monroe County Library System
Friends of the Library Group

S GAY ALLIANCE OF THE GENESSE VALLEY, INC LIBRARY,* 179 Atlantic Ave, 14607. SAN 375-2526. Tel: 716-244-8640. FAX: 716-244-8246. *Librn*, Tonya Smolinsky
Library Holdings: Bk Vols 1,400; Per Subs 11
Open Mon-Thurs 1-9:30 & Fri 1-6

M GENESEE HOSPITAL, Samuel Stabins Health Sciences,* 224 Alexander St, 14607. SAN 312-3502. Tel: 716-263-6305. FAX: 716-263-2925. Web Site: www.viahealth.org. *Librn*, Sally M Gerling; E-Mail: sgerling@rghnet.edu; Staff 5 (MLS 1, Non-MLS 4)
Library Holdings: Bk Titles 4,000; Per Subs 190
Subject Interests: Cardiology, Gastroenterology, Nursing
Restriction: Staff use only
Partic in OCLC Online Computer Library Center, Inc; Rochester Regional Library Council

S GEORGE EASTMAN HOUSE, Richard & Ronay Menschel Library, 900 East Ave, 14607. SAN 312-3537. Tel: 716-271-3361, Ext 313. FAX: 716-271-3970. Web Site: www.eastman.org. *Librn*, Rachel Stuhlman; E-Mail: rachel@geh.org; *Assoc Librn*, Rebecca Simmons; E-Mail: becky@geh.org; *Tech Servs*, Lenore Rouse
Founded 1947
Library Holdings: Bk Titles 24,000; Per Subs 320
Subject Interests: Motion pictures, Still photog
Special Collections: History, Technology & Aesthetics of Film; History, Technology & Aesthetics of Photography
Partic in OCLC Online Computer Library Center, Inc

S GRAVURE ASSOCIATION OF AMERICA LIBRARY,* 1200-A Scottsville Rd, 14624. SAN 372-5979. Tel: 716-436-2150. FAX: 716-436-7689. *Librn*, Sophia Chatkin
Library Holdings: Bk Titles 500
Special Collections: Gravure Printing, bks & manuals

P GREECE PUBLIC LIBRARY,* 125 Mitchell Rd, 14626. SAN 353-9946. Tel: 716-225-8951. FAX: 716-225-2777. Web Site: 204.97.3.3. *Dir*, June R Shapiro; *Librn*, Donna Mancuso; *Ad Servs*, Ann Patterson; *YA Servs*, Carol Dressing; *Ch Servs*, Nancy Nau; Staff 16 (MLS 16)
Founded 1958. Pop 90,106; Circ 592,145
Jan 1998-Dec 1999 Income $1,504,014, State $28,000, Locally Generated Income $104,000. Mats Exp $193,900, Books $182,000, Per/Ser (Incl. Access Fees) $11,900. Sal $908,413
Library Holdings: Bk Vols 104,454
Mem of Monroe County Library System
Partic in OCLC Online Computer Library Center, Inc
Friends of the Library Group
Branches: 2
BARNARD CROSSING, 2780 Dewey Ave, 14616. SAN 353-9954. Tel: 716-663-3357. FAX: 716-663-5587. Web Site: 204.97.3.3. *Librn*, Bernadette Foster
PADDY HILL, 1785 Latta Rd, 14612. SAN 354-0006. Tel: 716-865-3350. FAX: 716-663-3013. Web Site: 204.97.3.3. *Librn*, Clare Maloney

S HARRIS CORPORATION, RF Communications Div, 1680 University Ave, 14610. SAN 312-3685. Tel: 716-244-5830. Interlibrary Loan Service Tel: 716-242-3665. FAX: 716-242-3217. *Librn*, Holly Weston; E-Mail: hweston@harris.com; Staff 1 (Non-MLS 1)
Founded 1961
Jul 1998-Jun 1999 Mats Exp $30,000
Library Holdings: Bk Titles 1,300; Per Subs 41
Subject Interests: Communications, Electronics, Mechanical engineering
Publications: BSTJ; IEEE Transactions; Military Specifications

L HARRIS, BEACH & WILCOX LLP, Law Library,* 130 E Main St, 14604. SAN 371-5205. Tel: 716-232-4440, Ext 244. FAX: 716-232-1299. Web Site: www.harrisbeach.com. *Dir Libr Serv*, Joan Pedzich; E-Mail: jpedzich@frontiernet.net; *Coll Develop*, Renee He; *Ref*, Cyndi Trembley
1998-1999 Mats Exp $600,000
Library Holdings: Bk Vols 32,000; Per Subs 450
Publications: Harris Beach & Wilcox Library Guide
Restriction: Staff use only

L HARTER, SECREST & EMERY, Law Library, 700 Midtown Tower, 14604. SAN 372-2406. Tel: 716-231-1228. FAX: 716-232-2152. *Dir Info Resources & Res*, Robert Salerno; E-Mail: rsalerno@hselaw.com
1998-1999 Mats Exp $250,000. Sal $55,000 (Prof $52,000)
Library Holdings: Bk Vols 15,000; Per Subs 25
Publications: Library newsletter

P HENRIETTA PUBLIC LIBRARY, 455 Calkins Rd, 14623. SAN 312-3510. Tel: 716-334-3401. Reference Tel: 716-359-7092. FAX: 716-334-6369. Web Site: www.hpl.org. *Dir*, Patricia Bernhard; *AV, Per*, Nancy Maxwell; *YA Servs*, Virginia Cooper; *Ch Servs*, Ellen Xydias; *Ref*, Sara Mathias; *Ad Servs*, Anne Richards; *Ref*, John Funt; Staff 8 (MLS 8)
Founded 1958. Pop 38,000; Circ 375,000
Jan 2000-Dec 2000 Income $856,458, State $12,192, Locally Generated Income $844,266. Mats Exp $138,392, Books $116,892, Per/Ser (Incl. Access Fees) $17,000, Electronic Ref Mat (Incl. Access Fees) $4,500. Sal $525,542
Library Holdings: Bk Vols 104,676; Per Subs 282
Subject Interests: Local history
Database Vendor: CARL
Mem of Monroe County Library System
Special Services for the Deaf - TTY machine
Key operated drive up book-drop for disabled; various in-house assistive devices
Friends of the Library Group

M HIGHLAND HOSPITAL, Williams Health Sciences Library, 1000 South Ave, 14620. SAN 312-3529. Tel: 716-341-6761. FAX: 716-341-8242. E-Mail: hh_library@urmc.rochester.edu. Web Site: www.urmc.rochester.edu/hh/library. *Librn*, Angela Dixon; E-Mail: angela_dixon@urmcrochester.edu; Staff 1 (MLS 1)
Founded 1967
Library Holdings: Bk Titles 1,200; Per Subs 200
Subject Interests: Family med, Geriatrics, Gynecology, Medicine, Obstetrics, Oncology, Women's health
Database Vendor: Ebsco - EbscoHost, OCLC - First Search, OVID Technologies
Restriction: Not open to public
Function: ILL available, Reference services available

P IRONDEQUOIT PUBLIC LIBRARY, Pauline Evans Branch,* 45 Cooper Rd, 14617. SAN 312-3545. Tel: 716-336-6062. FAX: 716-336-6066. Web Site: www.irondequoit.org/library/index.htm. *Actg Dir*, Carla Robbins; *Coll Develop*, Carol Trout; Staff 9 (MLS 9)
Founded 1947. Pop 53,657; Circ 665,000
Jan 1997-Dec 1998 Income $1,449,392, State $61,000, Parent Institution $1,228,708, Other $159,684. Mats Exp $282,710, Books $229,605, Per/Ser (Incl. Access Fees) $18,249. Sal $817,360 (Prof $442,923)
Library Holdings: Bk Vols 137,482
Mem of Monroe County Library System
Friends of the Library Group
Branches: 1
HELEN MCGRAW BRANCH, 2180 Ridge Rd E, 14622. SAN 320-3808. Tel: 716-336-6060. FAX: 716-336-6067. Web Site: www.irondequoit.org/library/index.htm. *Actg Dir*, Carla Robbins; *Librn*, Kathleen Lazar
Friends of the Library Group

R JEWISH COMMUNITY CENTER OF GREATER ROCHESTER, Philip Feinbloom Library, 1200 Edgewood Ave, 14618-5408. SAN 325-6790. Tel: 716-461-2000, Ext 607. FAX: 716-461-0805. Web Site: www.jccrochester.org. *Librn*, Miriam Duman Goldberg; Staff 1 (Non-MLS 1)
Library Holdings: Bk Vols 8,000; Per Subs 20
Subject Interests: Judaica
Special Collections: Dr Saul Moress Peace Coll; Holocaust Coll; Jewish Children Coll; Jewish Genealogy, print microfiche; Jewish Themes, videos, audio cassettes
Friends of the Library Group
Branches:
ISRAEL EMIOT MEMORIAL YIDDISH LIBRARY, 1200 Edgewood Ave, 14618-5408. Tel: 716-461-2000, Ext 607. FAX: 716-461-0805. Web Site: www.jccrochester.org. *Librn*, Miriam Duman Goldberg
Founded 1981
Library Holdings: Bk Vols 1,500
Subject Interests: Yiddish

S LANDMARK SOCIETY OF WESTERN NEW YORK, INC, Wenrich Memorial Library, 133 S Fitzhugh St, 14608-2204. SAN 312-3561. Tel: 716-546-7029. FAX: 716-546-4788. Web Site: www.landmarksociety.org. *Dir*, Ann B Parks; Tel: 716-546-7029, Ext 14, E-Mail: aparks@landmarksociety.org; Staff 1 (Non-MLS 1)
Founded 1970
Jul 1999-Jun 2000 Income Parent Institution $1,500. Mats Exp Books $1,500
Library Holdings: Bk Vols 2,750; Per Subs 236; Spec Interest Per Sub 15
Subject Interests: Bldg techniques, Hist preservation, Hist rehabilitation, Horticulture, Landscape design, Regional archit
Special Collections: Information on Local Architecture; Local Architectural Surveys
Restriction: Non-circulating
Function: Research library
Partic in RLIN
Special Services for the Deaf - Staff with knowledge of sign language

J MONROE COMMUNITY COLLEGE, LeRoy V Good Library, 1000 E Henrietta Rd, PO Box 92810, 14692-8910. SAN 312-3596. Tel: 716-292-2090. Interlibrary Loan Service Tel: 716-292-2318. Reference Tel: 716-292-2319. FAX: 716-424-1402. E-Mail: shr-library@monroecc.edu. Web Site: www.monroecc.edu/depts/library/lvg.htm. *Actg Dir*, Thaddeus J Ciambor; Tel: 716-292-2310, Fax: 716-292-3859, E-Mail: tciambor@monroecc.edu; *Tech Servs*, Deborah Mohr; Tel: 716-292-2316, E-Mail: dmohr@

monroecc.edu; *Tech Servs*, Charlene Rezabek; Tel: 716-292-2330, E-Mail: crezabek@monroecc.edu; *Coll Develop*, Richard Squires; Tel: 716-292-2314, E-Mail: rsquires@monroecc.edu; *Access Serv*, Ellen M Mancuso; Tel: 716-292-2313, E-Mail: emancuso@monroecc.edu; *Res*, Alice Harrington; Tel: 716-292-2304, E-Mail: aharrington@monroecc.edu; *Distance Educ*, Julie Wash; Tel: 716-292-3036, E-Mail: jwash@monroecc.edu; Staff 17 (MLS 9, Non-MLS 8)
Founded 1962. Enrl 15,000; Fac 281; Highest Degree: Associate
Library Holdings: Bk Vols 108,000; Per Subs 1,000
Special Collections: AIDS Resource Library; Holocaust/Genocide Resource Center
Automation Activity & Vendor Info: (Cataloging) MultiLIS; (Circulation) MultiLIS; (OPAC) MultiLIS; (Serials) MultiLIS
Database Vendor: CARL, Dialog, DRA, IAC - SearchBank, OCLC - First Search, Silverplatter Information Inc.
Publications: 25 descriptive brochures
Restriction: In-house use for visitors
Function: Archival collection, Document delivery services, ILL available
Partic in OCLC Online Computer Library Center, Inc; Rochester Regional Library Council
Open Mon-Thurs 8-9, Fri 8-5 during academic semesters

M MONROE COMMUNITY HOSPITAL, T F Williams Health Sciences Library, 435 E Henrietta Rd, 14620. SAN 312-360X. Tel: 716-760-6102. FAX: 716-760-6104. E-Mail: mch@rrlc.rochester.lib.ny.us. *Dir*, Marilyn Rosen
Founded 1970
Library Holdings: Bk Vols 967; Per Subs 114
Subject Interests: Aging, Geriatrics, Gerontology, Long term care, Rehabilitation
Partic in Miraclenet; OCLC Online Computer Library Center, Inc; Rochester Regional Library Council
Open Mon-Fri 9-12:30 pm

S MONROE COUNTY HISTORIAN'S DEPARTMENT LIBRARY, 115 South Ave, 14604. SAN 327-7194. Tel: 716-428-8352. FAX: 716-428-8353. *In Charge*, Carolyn S Vacca; E-Mail: cvacca@mcls.rochester.lib.ny.us; Staff 1 (MLS 1)
Library Holdings: Bk Vols 10,000

P MONROE COUNTY LIBRARY SYSTEM, (MCLS), 115 South Ave, 14604-1896. SAN 312-3626. Tel: 716-428-8046. Interlibrary Loan Service Tel: 716-428-8160. FAX: 716-428-8353. Web Site: www.rochester.lib.ny.us. *Dir*, Richard Panz; E-Mail: rpanz@mcls.rochester.lib.ny.us
Founded 1952. Pop 713,968
1998-1999 Mats Exp $16,563, Books $12,921, Per/Ser (Incl. Access Fees) $3,642
Database Vendor: CARL
Member Libraries: Brighton Memorial Library; Chili Public Library; East Rochester Public Library; Fairport Public Library; Gates Public Library; Greece Public Library; Henrietta Public Library; Irondequoit Public Library; Newman Riga; Ogden Farmer's Library; Parma Public Library; Penfield Public Library; Pittsford Community Library; Pittsford Community Library; Rochester Public Library; Rush Public Library; Scottsville Free Library; Seymour Library; Town Of Mendon Public Library; Webster Public Library
Partic in Colorado Alliance Of Research Libraries

S NATIONAL BRAILLE ASSOCIATION, INC, Braille Book Bank, 3 Townline Cir, 14623-2513. SAN 370-3665. Tel: 716-427-8260. FAX: 716-427-0263. *Exec Dir*, Angela Coffaro
Jan 1999-Dec 1999 Income $39,467. Mats Exp Books $7,177. Sal $41,423
Library Holdings: Bk Titles 2,453
Subject Interests: Col level texts, Music, Tech tables, Vocational mat
Special Collections: Braille College Level Textbooks; Braille Music; Technical Tables
Publications: Catalogs of the Braille Collections (available free in print & braille or on audio cassette)
Restriction: Not a lending library
Special Services for the Blind - Braille; Transcribing service

C NAZARETH COLLEGE OF ROCHESTER LIBRARY, 4245 East Ave, PO Box 18950, 14618-0950. SAN 312-3634. Tel: 716-389-2121. FAX: 716-248-8766. Web Site: www.naz.edu/dept/library. *Dir*, David Chatham; E-Mail: dwchatha@naz.edu; *Assoc Dir*, Sheila A Smyth; Tel: 716-389-2126, E-Mail: sasmyth@naz.edu; *Assoc Dir*, Dr Scott Smith; Tel: 716-389-2123, E-Mail: sssmith@naz.edu; *AV*, Sue Atkins; Tel: 716-389-2134, E-Mail: sqatkins@naz.edu; *Coll Develop*, Janet Smith; Tel: 716-389-2124, E-Mail: jbsmith@naz.edu; *Ser*, Christine Sisak; Tel: 716-389-2184, E-Mail: casisak@naz.edu; Staff 23 (MLS 9, Non-MLS 14)
Founded 1924. Enrl 2,202; Fac 114; Highest Degree: Master
Jul 1999-Jun 2000 Income (Main Library Only) $1,491,597, State $7,070, Parent Institution $1,484,527. Mats Exp $500,723, Books $91,731, Per/Ser (Incl. Access Fees) $287,871, Presv $17,620, Micro $41,679, AV Equip $29,779, Electronic Ref Mat (Incl. Access Fees) $32,043. Sal $779,120 (Prof $440,218)
Library Holdings: Bk Vols 283,810; Bk Titles 205,999; Per Subs 1,941
Special Collections: Belloc Colll; Byrne Coll; Chesterton Coll; Hendrick Papers; Maurice Baring Coll; Sitwells Coll; Thomas Merton Coll
Automation Activity & Vendor Info: (Cataloging) Innovative Interfaces Inc.; (Circulation) Innovative Interfaces Inc.; (Course Reserve) Innovative Interfaces Inc.; (ILL) Innovative Interfaces Inc.; (OPAC) Innovative Interfaces Inc.; (Serials) Innovative Interfaces Inc.
Database Vendor: Dialog, Lexis-Nexis, OCLC - First Search, ProQuest
Publications: Acquisitions List; Periodicals; Special Collections Brochure; Subject Guides
Partic in Rochester Regional Library Council

GL NEW YORK STATE JUDICIAL DEPARTMENT, Appellate Division Law Library, 50 East Ave, Ste 100, 14604. SAN 312-3642. Tel: 716-530-3250. Interlibrary Loan Service Tel: 716-530-3254. Reference Tel: 716-530-3251. FAX: 716-530-3270. Web Site: www.courts.state.ny.us/ad4/. *Dir*, David Voisinet; *Publ Servs*, Betsy Vipperman; *Ref*, Judy Weiner; *Automation Syst Coordr*, Stephen Weiter; *Cat*, Joan Hoolihan; *Librn*, Stephen Weiter; Staff 12 (MLS 5, Non-MLS 7)
Founded 1849
Apr 1999-Mar 2000 Income $1,108,000. Mats Exp $450,000, Books $420,000, Per/Ser (Incl. Access Fees) $30,000. Sal $460,000 (Prof $181,000)
Library Holdings: Bk Vols 275,000; Per Subs 650
Subject Interests: Admin rules, Appeal papers, Citators, Court rpt, Decisions, Digest, Encyclopedias, Indexes, Monographs, Statutes
Special Collections: Pre-1850 Law bks; Regional directories & Plat bks
Mem of Rochester Regional Libr Coun
Partic in Rochester Regional Library Council

L NIXON, HARGRAVE, DEVANS & DOYLE, Information Services Department,* Clinton Sq, PO Box 1051, 14603. SAN 312-3650. Tel: 716-263-1000. FAX: 716-263-1600.
Library Holdings: Bk Vols 15,000; Bk Titles 30,000

S NORTHERN TELECOM, Information Resource Center, 97 Humboldt St, 14609. SAN 373-8000. Tel: 716-654-2412. FAX: 716-654-2700. *Librn*, Rose Carey; E-Mail: rcarey@nortelnetworks.com
Library Holdings: Bk Vols 800; Per Subs 75
Restriction: Staff use only
Mem of Rochester Regional Libr Coun

M PARK RIDGE HOSPITAL LIBRARY,* 1555 Long Pond Rd, 14626. SAN 327-2338. Tel: 716-723-7755. FAX: 716-723-7078. E-Mail: parkrdge@rrlc.rochester.lib.ny.us. *Librn*, Kathleen Martin
Library Holdings: Bk Vols 1,900; Per Subs 140
Restriction: Staff use only
Partic in OCLC Online Computer Library Center, Inc

S PREVENTION PARTNERS RESOURCE CENTER,* One Mustard St, 14609-6925. SAN 374-4027. Tel: 716-288-2800. FAX: 716-288-2847. E-Mail: drugslie@frontiernet.net. Web Site: www.preventionconnection.org.
Founded 1993
Library Holdings: Bk Titles 500; Per Subs 20
Special Collections: Alcohol, Tobacco & Other Drugs, bks, brochures & v-tapes; Community Resources Subject File
Publications: NETWORK (newsletter)
Partic in Rochester Regional Library Council

CR ROBERTS WESLEYAN COLLEGE, Ora A Spraque Library, 2301 Westside Dr, 14624-1997. SAN 312-3693. Tel: 716-594-6280. Reference Tel: 716-594-6499. FAX: 716-594-6543. Web Site: www.roberts.edu/library/. *Dir Libr Serv*, Alfred Krober; Tel: 714-594-6501, E-Mail: krobera@roberts.edu; *Dir, Tech Serv*, Charles H Canon, III; Tel: 716-594-6016, E-Mail: canonc@roberts.edu; *Librn*, Dr Barry Hamilton; E-Mail: hamilton_barry@roberts.edu; *Bibliog Instr*, Sylvia Brown; Tel: 716-594-6044, E-Mail: browns@roberts.edu; *Automation Syst Coordr*, Wendy Sue Saxena; Tel: 716-594-6064, E-Mail: saxenaw@roberts.edu; *ILL*, Annemarie Baldo; Tel: 716-594-6058, E-Mail: baldoa@roberts.edu; *Ref*, Gary Metzenbacher; Tel: 716-594-6499, E-Mail: metzenbacher_gary@roberts.edu. Subject Specialists: *Theology*, Dr Barry Hamilton; Staff 10 (MLS 5, Non-MLS 5)
Founded 1866. Enrl 1,650; Fac 73; Highest Degree: Master
Jul 1999-Jun 2000 Income $594,461, State $7,197, Parent Institution $587,264. Mats Exp $255,640, Books $105,614, Per/Ser (Incl. Access Fees) $87,338, Presv $6,916, Micro $13,081, AV Equip $2,600, Electronic Ref Mat (Incl. Access Fees) $40,092. Sal $236,428 (Prof $136,300)
Library Holdings: Bk Vols 97,467; Bk Titles 85,000; Per Subs 877
Subject Interests: Art, Biblical studies, Bus and mgt, Education, Music, Soc work, Theology
Special Collections: Benjamin Titus Roberts Coll, bks, mss, & photog; Free Methodist Church History, bks, per, photog; Roberts Wesleyan College historical materials
Automation Activity & Vendor Info: (Cataloging) Endeavor; (Circulation) Endeavor; (OPAC) Endeavor
Database Vendor: Ebsco - EbscoHost, IAC - Info Trac, Lexis-Nexis, OCLC - First Search, ProQuest, Silverplatter Information Inc., Wilson - Wilson Web
Partic in Christian Libr Asn; Rochester Regional Library Council
Special Services for the Blind - Kurzweil Reader

ROCHESTER ACADEMY OF MEDICINE LIBRARY,* 1441 East Ave, 14610-1665. SAN 312-3707. Tel: 716-271-1313. FAX: 716-271-4172. *Dir*, William L Craver MD
Founded 1900
Library Holdings: Bk Vols 31,300; Per Subs 70

ROCHESTER BUSINESS INSTITUTE, Betty Cronk Memorial Library, 1630 Portland Ave, 14621. SAN 312-3715. Tel: 716-266-0430, Ext 109. FAX: 716-266-8243. *Librn*, Kyle Daniels; E-Mail: kdaniels@cci.com; Staff 1 (MLS 1)
Founded 1925
Library Holdings: Bk Titles 4,000; Per Subs 21
Subject Interests: Bus, Computer science, Mgt, Rochester Bus Inst sch hist
Special Collections: Annual Report Coll, bklet; College Catalog Coll; Rochester Business Institute School Catalogs Coll, 1860 to date
Publications: Library brochure
Partic in Rochester Regional Library Council
Open Mon-Thurs 8-8, Fri 8-5

ROCHESTER CIVIC GARDEN CENTER, INC LIBRARY, 5 Castle Park, 14620. SAN 312-3480. Tel: 716-473-5130. FAX: 716-473-8136. E-Mail: gardencenter@surfree.com. Web Site: www.rcgc.com. *Coll Develop, Librn*, Carolyn VanNess
Founded 1945
Jan 1999-Dec 1999 Income $2,500, Locally Generated Income $700, Parent Institution $1,200, Other $600. Mats Exp $2,450, Books $1,550, Per/Ser (Incl. Access Fees) $500, Presv $300, Other Print Mats $100
Library Holdings: Bk Vols 4,000; Per Subs 17
Subject Interests: Garden hist, Horticulture, Landscaping, Natural crafts, Related facets incl flower arrangements
Special Collections: 19th Century Garden, bks, cat
Publications: The Garden Center Bulletin
Partic in Rochester Regional Library Council

S ROCHESTER GAS & ELECTRIC CORPORATION, Technical Information Center,* 89 East Ave, 14649. SAN 327-229X. Tel: 716-724-8125. FAX: 716-771-2802.
Library Holdings: Bk Vols 29,887; Per Subs 97
Subject Interests: Energy, Engineering
Special Collections: Nureg & Electricpower Research Institute

M ROCHESTER GENERAL HOSPITAL, Lillie B Werner Health Sciences Library, 1425 Portland Ave, 14621. SAN 312-3723. Tel: 716-338-4743. FAX: 716-544-1504. E-Mail: wellness@viahealth.org. Web Site: www.viahealth.org. *Dir*, Bernie Todd-Smith; Tel: 716-922-4045, E-Mail: bernie.todd-smith@viahealth.org; *Ref*, Mary McVicar-Keim; Tel: 716-922-4723; *Librn*, Tami Hartzell; *Librn*, Mary Ann Howie; *Librn*, Ed Lewek; *Librn*, Lana Rudy. Subject Specialists: *Education*, Ed Lewek; *Wellness*, Mary Ann Howie; Staff 10 (MLS 6, Non-MLS 4)
Founded 1883
Library Holdings: Bk Titles 6,000; Per Subs 391
Special Collections: History of Medicine Coll
Database Vendor: Ebsco - EbscoHost
Publications: Libra Links & Circuit Connection (monthly) (Newsletter)
Partic in OCLC Online Computer Library Center, Inc; Rochester Regional Library Council
Sponsors a Circuit Librarian Program serving seven rural hospitals & employing two librarians
Friends of the Library Group

S ROCHESTER HISTORICAL SOCIETY LIBRARY, 485 East Ave, 14607. SAN 312-3731. Tel: 716-271-2705. Web Site: www.rochesterhistory.org. *Dir*, Ann Salter; *Librn*, Lois Gauch
Library Holdings: Bk Vols 15,000
Special Collections: Rochester & Genesee Valley History Coll, bks, mss, photog; Rochester City Directories; Rochester Historical Society Publications
Restriction: By appointment only, Non-circulating to the public
Function: ILL by photocopy only

C ROCHESTER INSTITUTE OF TECHNOLOGY, Wallace Library, 90 Lomb Memorial Dr, 14623-5604. SAN 354-012X. Tel: 716-475-2411. Interlibrary Loan Service Tel: 716-475-2560. FAX: 716-475-7007. Web Site: wally.rit.edu. *Dir*, Patricia Pitkin; *ILL*, Kerry Hughes; *Media Spec*, Christine Geith; *Archivist*, Kari Horowicz; *Acq, Coll Develop*, Sheila Smokey; *Ref*, Chandra McKenzie; *Science*, John Kester; *Electronic Resources, Head, Info Serv*, Liz Dopp; *Business*, Margaret Bartlett. Subject Specialists: *Art*, Kari Horowicz; *Criminal law and justice*, Linda Coppola; *Economics*, Margaret Bartlett; *Engineering*, John Kester; *Humanities*, Linda Coppola; *Management*, Margaret Bartlett; *Photography*, Kari Horowicz; *Social service (social work)*, Linda Coppola; Staff 14 (MLS 14)
Founded 1829. Enrl 12,600; Fac 1,095; Highest Degree: Doctorate
1999-2000 Mats Exp $1,418,052, Books $307,902, Per/Ser (Incl. Access Fees) $746,717, Presv $45,439, Micro $60,526. Sal $1,437,903 (Prof $885,379)
Library Holdings: Bk Vols 261,134; Bk Titles 255,911; Per Subs 3,430
Subject Interests: Allied health, Applied art, Business, Computer graphics, Computers, Crafts, Deafness, Electronics, Engineering, Graphic arts, Imaging sci, Mat sci, Optics, Photog, Printing
Special Collections: Archives Coll; Deafness Coll; Melbert B Cary Graphic Arts Library
Partic in Rochester Regional Library Council
Special Services for the Deaf - Books on deafness & sign language; Special interest periodicals; Staff with knowledge of sign language; TTY machine
Departmental Libraries:
NATIONAL TECHNICAL INSTITUTE FOR THE DEAF, EDUCATIONAL TECHNOLOGY RESOURCE RM, 52 Lomb Memorial Dr, NTID at RIT, 14623. SAN 354-0170. Tel: 716-475-6823. TDD: 716-475-7588. FAX: 716-475-7588. Web Site: www.rit.edu/~abcnmp/etrr/. *Head Librn*, Jonathan Millis; Tel: 716-475-7913, E-Mail: jjm8789@rit.edu. Subject Specialists: *Deafness*, Jonathan Millis
Oct 2000-Sep 2001 Income (Main Library Only) Parent Institution $75,000. Mats Exp $5,000, Books $3,000, Per/Ser (Incl. Access Fees) $2,000. Sal $20,000
Library Holdings: Bk Vols 5,000; Bk Titles 1,400; Per Subs 25; Spec Interest Per Sub 20; Bks on Deafness & Sign Lang 1,400
Subject Interests: Audiology, Deaf culture, Deaf hist, Deafness, Interpreting, Sign lang
Special Collections: Deaf Video Coll
Database Vendor: Innovative Interfaces INN - View
Publications: Deafness: An Annotated Bibliography & Guide to Basic Materials; Employment of Deaf Persons: An Annotated Bibliography; Perspectives on Deafness: A Selected Bibliography of the Literature
Function: Research library
Special Services for the Deaf - Books on deafness & sign language; Captioned media; Special interest periodicals; Staff with knowledge of sign language; TTY machine

S ROCHESTER MUSEUM & SCIENCE CENTER, Schuyler C Townson Library, 657 East Ave, 14607. SAN 354-0189. Tel: 716-271-4320, Ext 315. FAX: 716-271-2119. *Librn*, Leatrice Kemp
Founded 1914
Library Holdings: Bk Titles 30,000
Subject Interests: Anthropology, Antiques, Archaeology, Costume, Gardening, Local history, Mus techniques, Native Am especially Iroquois, Natural history, Philosophy, Technology
Special Collections: 19th Century Periodicals, Almanacs, Posters, Greeting Cards; Domestic Architecture (Barrows Coll, Thomas Boyd Coll & William H Richardson Coll), architectural drawings; Flour Milling Industry (Moseley & Motley Coll), mss; Rochester Button Company, mss; Rochester History; Stone Coll - Glass Plate Negatives
Restriction: Open to public for reference only
Partic in OCLC Online Computer Library Center, Inc; Rochester Regional Library Council
Branches:
STRASENBURGH PLANETARIUM, TODD LIBRARY Tel: 716-271-4320. *Librn*, Grace Matthews
Founded 1968
Library Holdings: Bk Vols 2,000; Per Subs 34
Subject Interests: Astronautics, Astronomy

M ROCHESTER PSYCHIATRIC CENTER, Professional Library,* 111 Elmwood Ave, 14620-3972. SAN 312-374X. Tel: 716-473-3230, Ext 1471. FAX: 716-473-9187. E-Mail: roetdem@gw.ohm.state.ny.us.
Founded 1937
Library Holdings: Bk Vols 75; Per Subs 31
Subject Interests: Psychiatry, Psychology
Partic in Rochester Regional Library Council

P ROCHESTER PUBLIC LIBRARY,* 115 South Ave, 14604-1896. SAN 354-0243. Tel: 716-428-7300. Interlibrary Loan Service Tel: 716-428-8160. FAX: 716-428-8353. Web Site: www.rochester.lib.ny.us. *Dir*, Richard Panz; E-Mail: rpanz@mcls.rochester.lib.ny.us; *ILL*, Martin Steinhauser; *Acq*, Larry Naukam; *Automation Syst Coordr*, Carole Joyce
Founded 1911. Pop 713,968; Circ 1,638,291
1997-1998 Income $11,785,577, State $605,134, City $2,990,502, County $6,554,549, Locally Generated Income $486,948, Other $1,148,444. Mats Exp $1,026,249, Books $754,264, Per/Ser (Incl. Access Fees) $220,739. Sal $9,210,875 (Prof $4,316,906)
Library Holdings: Bk Vols 1,103,556
Special Collections: Black History (Wheatley Branch Coll); Department Coll, flm; Local History, bks, photogs, newsp; Reynolds Audio Visual
Automation Activity & Vendor Info: (Acquisitions) CARL; (Circulation) CARL; (Serials) CARL
Publications: Directory of Associations in Monroe County; Directory of Clubs in Monroe County; Guide to Grant Markers; Human Services Directory; Neighborhood Associations; Visiting Artists Directory
Mem of Monroe County Library System
Partic in OCLC Online Computer Library Center, Inc; Rochester Regional Library Council
Special Services for the Deaf - Books on deafness & sign language; Captioned film depository; Special interest periodicals; Staff with knowledge of sign language
Friends of the Library Group
Branches: 10
ARNETT, 310 Arnett Blvd, 14619. SAN 354-0278. Tel: 716-235-6583. FAX: 716-328-5294. Web Site: www.rochester.lib.ny.us. *Librn*, Jean Verno

Library Holdings: Bk Vols 58,489
Subject Interests: Black hist
CHARLOTTE, 3615 Lake Ave, 14612. SAN 354-0332. Tel: 716-663-5433. FAX: 716-621-2443. Web Site: www.rochester.lib.ny.us. *Librn*, Maureen Whalen
Library Holdings: Bk Vols 38,140
Subject Interests: Boating, Local history
HIGHLAND, 971 South Ave, 14620. SAN 354-0510. Tel: 716-271-3840. FAX: 716-271-5796. Web Site: www.rochester.lib.ny.us. *Librn*, Lynn Borrie
Library Holdings: Bk Vols 26,739
LINCOLN, 851 Joseph Ave, 14621. SAN 354-0421. Tel: 716-266-6820. FAX: 716-266-2584. Web Site: www.rochester.lib.ny.us. *Librn*, Theresa Bennett
Library Holdings: Bk Vols 44,845
Subject Interests: Black hist, Spanish lang
LYELL, 956 Lyell Ave, 14606. SAN 325-4356. Tel: 716-254-0790. FAX: 716-254-0303. Web Site: www.rochester.lib.ny.us. *Librn*, Tom Blanda
Library Holdings: Bk Vols 23,079
Subject Interests: Ital lang
MAPLEWOOD, 1111 Dewey Ave, 14613. SAN 354-0456. Tel: 716-254-7048. FAX: 716-647-1058. Web Site: www.rochester.lib.ny.us. *Librn*, Kris Smith
Library Holdings: Bk Vols 42,410
MONROE, 809 Monroe Ave, 14607. SAN 354-0480. Tel: 716-271-1957. FAX: 716-271-0136. Web Site: www.rochester.lib.ny.us. *Librn*, Marilyn Olson
Library Holdings: Bk Vols 39,298
SULLY, 939 Bay St, 14609. SAN 354-0545. Tel: 716-288-5615. FAX: 716-288-1318. Web Site: www.rochester.lib.ny.us. *Librn*, Jean McClure
Library Holdings: Bk Vols 34,300
WHEATLEY, 13 Bronson Ave, 14608. SAN 354-057X. Tel: 716-235-3682. FAX: 716-328-5266. Web Site: www.rochester.lib.ny.us. *Librn*, Leatrice Brantley
Library Holdings: Bk Vols 33,720
Subject Interests: African Am hist, Black hist
WINTON, 611 N Winton Rd, 14609. SAN 354-060X. Tel: 716-288-6030. FAX: 716-288-8243. Web Site: www.rochester.lib.ny.us. *Librn*, Maria Lucarelli
Library Holdings: Bk Vols 60,407
Subject Interests: Russian lang
Bookmobiles: 2

S ROCHESTER TIMES-UNION & ROCHESTER DEMOCRAT & CHRONICLE LIBRARY,* 55 Exchange Blvd, 14614. SAN 373-4870. Tel: 716-232-7100. FAX: 716-258-2265. *Mgr*, Virginia Wheeler
Library Holdings: Bk Vols 3,403; Per Subs 75
Special Collections: Life Magazine Coll 1936-present

C SAINT JOHN FISHER COLLEGE, Lavery Library, 3690 East Ave, 14618-3599. SAN 312-2662. Tel: 716-385-8164. Interlibrary Loan Service Tel: 716-385-8140. Circulation Tel: 716-385-8165. Reference Tel: 716-385-8141. FAX: 716-385-8445. Web Site: www.sjfc.edu. *Dir*, Karen Junker; E-Mail: junker@sjfc.edu; *Bibliog Instr, Online Servs, Ref*, Judith Van Buskirk; Tel: 716-385-8139, E-Mail: vanbuski@sjfc.edu; *Ser*, Rob DiFazio; Tel: 716-385-7399, E-Mail: difazio@sjfc.edu; *ILL*, Diane Lucas; Tel: 716-385-7340, E-Mail: lucas@sjfc.edu; *AV, Instrul Serv*, Lori Wagoner; Tel: 716-385-8140, E-Mail: wagoner@sjfc.edu; *Tech Servs*, Mary Throumoulos; Tel: 716-385-8136, E-Mail: throumou@sjfc.edu; *Coll Develop*, Mary Throumoulos; Staff 7 (MLS 7)
Founded 1951. Enrl 2,250; Fac 125; Highest Degree: Master
Jun 1999-May 2000 Income $1,042,398, State $6,000, Parent Institution $1,036,398. Mats Exp $506,222, Books $200,000, Per/Ser (Incl. Access Fees) $235,022, Presv $6,200, Electronic Ref Mat (Incl. Access Fees) $55,000. Sal $454,916 (Prof $242,060)
Library Holdings: Bk Vols 204,424; Bk Titles 147,677; Per Subs 1,388
Subject Interests: Accounting, Bus, Commun, Liberal arts, Nursing
Special Collections: Big Band Recordings (Bill Givens), rec tapes; Book Plates, Early Genesee Country Newspapers; Decker Papers; Dime Novels; Frederick Douglass Anti-Slavery Materials; Grand Army of the Republic Coll; Post Cards
Automation Activity & Vendor Info: (Acquisitions) DRA; (Cataloging) DRA; (Circulation) DRA; (Course Reserve) DRA; (OPAC) DRA; (Serials) DRA
Publications: Ex Libris; New on the Shelves; Using Lavery Library
Partic in Dialog Corporation; OCLC Online Computer Library Center, Inc; Rochester Regional Library Council; WALDO
Special Services for the Blind - Assistive Technology Center for Persons who are blind or physically handicapped

S SEAR BROWN GROUP, Information Center,* 85 Metro Park, 14623. SAN 327-5248. Tel: 716-475-1440, Ext 340. FAX: 716-272-1814.
Library Holdings: Bk Titles 2,000
Subject Interests: Engineering

S SENECA PARK ZOO, Marion C Barry Memorial Library, 2222 St Paul St, 14621-1097. SAN 329-2819. Tel: 716-266-6591. FAX: 716-266-5775. *Dir*, Lawrence J Sorel
Founded 1980
Library Holdings: Bk Titles 2,041; Per Subs 75
Subject Interests: Veterinary medicine, Zoology

S THE STRONG MUSEUM LIBRARY,* One Manhattan Sq, 14607. SAN 312-3790. Tel: 716-263-2700. FAX: 716-263-2493. *Librn*, Carol Sandler; *Cat*, Susan Drexler; Staff 3 (MLS 2, Non-MLS 1)
Founded 1972
Library Holdings: Bk Titles 40,000
Subject Interests: 19th Century Am domestic life bks inc socio-cultural hist, Decorative arts, Early 20th Century Am domestic life bks inc socio-cultural hist, Mat culture
Special Collections: 19th & 20th Century Trade Catalogs; 19th & early 20th Century Children's; Fore-Edge Paintings Coll; Patent Papers for Dolls & Toys; Winslow Homer Coll
Partic in Rochester Regional Library Council; State University Of New York-NYLINK

R TEMPLE B'RITH KODESH LIBRARY, 2131 Elmwood Ave, 14618-1021. SAN 312-3812. Tel: 716-244-7060, Ext 34. FAX: 716-244-0557. *Librn*, Nettie Sheiman
Founded 1962
Library Holdings: Bk Vols 13,000

R TEMPLE BETH EL LIBRARY, 139 Winton Rd S, 14610. SAN 312-3804. Tel: 716-473-1770, Ext 27. FAX: 716-473-2689. *Librn*, Ellen Steinberg; Staff 2 (MLS 1, Non-MLS 1)
Founded 1946
Library Holdings: Bk Vols 10,000; Bk Titles 6,900; Per Subs 29

R TEMPLE SINAI LIBRARY, 363 Penfield Rd, 14625. SAN 312-3820. Tel: 716-381-6890. FAX: 716-381-4921. *Librn*, Randi Kaplan
Founded 1974
Library Holdings: Bk Vols 4,300
Subject Interests: Judaica

L UNDERBERG & KESSLER, Law Library,* 1800 Chase Sq, 14604. SAN 372-252X. Tel: 716-258-2800. FAX: 716-258-2821. *Librn*, Jane Snyder
Library Holdings: Bk Vols 8,000; Per Subs 5

C UNIVERSITY OF ROCHESTER, Rush Rhees Library, Wilson Blvd, 14627-0055. SAN 354-0693. Tel: 716-275-4461. Interlibrary Loan Service Tel: 716-275-4454. FAX: 716-273-5309. Web Site: www.lib.rochester.edu. *Dean of Libr*, Ronald F Dow; *Asst Dean*, Stanley Wilder; *Publ Servs*, Phyllis Andrews; *Ser*, Teresa Evan; *Cat*, Jennifer Bowen; *Ref*, Violanda Burns; *Syst Coordr*, Melinda Stowe; *Rare Bks, Spec Coll*, Peter Dzwonkoski; *Rare Bks, Spec Coll*, Alan Lupack; *Coll Develop*, Helen Anderson; *Acq*, Sharon Briggs. Subject Specialists: *Info syst mgt*, Stanley Wilder; *Preservation*, Richard Peek; Staff 117 (MLS 58, Non-MLS 59)
Founded 1850. Enrl 7,203; Fac 1,226; Highest Degree: Doctorate
Dec 1999-Nov 2000 Income $8,796,195. Mats Exp $3,333,184, Books $638,857, Per/Ser (Incl. Access Fees) $2,641,883, Other Print Mats $52,444. Sal $4,003,119 (Prof $2,425,456)
Library Holdings: Bk Vols 2,515,872; Per Subs 8,858
Special Collections: American Literature: Washington Irving, Henry James, Mark Twain, William Dean Howells, Edward Everett Hale (filmed bks), William Heyen (mss & printed works) filmed books, histroical children's books, Christopher Morley, Adelaide Crapsey (mss & printed works), Henry W Clune, (mss & printed works), Frederick Exley (mss & printed works), John A Williams (mss & printed works), John Gardner (mss & printed works), Jerre Mangione (mss & printed works), Plutzik Library (mss & printed works), Paul Zimmer Papers; Art & Architecture: Claude Bragdon papers, drawings & printed works; Dyrer & Dryer papers; English History & Literature: Eikon Basilike Coll, John Dryden, Restoration drama, John Ruskin, John Masefield, Benjamin Disraeli, Sean O'Casey, Edward Gorey, Nineteenth & Twentieth Century Theatre Mss Coll, Robert Southey (mss & printed works), Arnold Bennett; Leonardo da Vinci Coll; Nineteenth & Twentieth Century Public Affairs: Papers of William Henry Seward, Thurlow Weed, David Jayne Hill, Susan B Anthony, Rev William C Gannett, Thomas E Dewey, Marion Folsom, Kenneth Keating & Frank Horton.; Optical industry Trade Catalogs Coll; Regional History: New York State settlement, land development & local history especially Rochester & Monroe County, Native Americans, early upstate New York printing, manuscript records of Rochester benevolent organizations, businesses & industry; Social & Natural Science: Papers of anthropologist Lewis Henry Morgan & scientists Herman LeRoy Fairchild, Henry A Ward, Carl E Akeley, printed works of Charles Darwin. Nineteenth Century Botany & Horticulture: Ellwanger & Barry Nursery papers & library, Historian Christopher Lasch Archives, Political Scientist William Riker
Publications: Bookmark; University of Rochester Library Bulletin
Mem of Asn of Research Libraries
Partic in Rochester Regional Library Council; State University Of New York-NYLINK
Friends of the Library Group
Departmental Libraries:
ART & MUSIC, Rush Rhees Library, 14627. SAN 354-0723. Tel: 716-275-4476. FAX: 716-273-1032. E-Mail: artlib@rcl.lib.rochester.edu. Web Site: www.lib.rochester.edu/art. *Librn*, Stephanie Frontz

Library Holdings: Bk Vols 60,000; Per Subs 200
Subject Interests: Architecture, Art history, Cultural studies, Fine arts, Mus, Photog, Visual
Special Collections: Robert MacCameron Coll, papers & photos
Friends of the Library Group

CARLSON LIBRARY, Carlson Library, 14627. SAN 327-9138. Tel: 716-275-4465. FAX: 716-273-4656. Web Site: www.lib.rochester.edu/car/. *Dir*, Katie Clark; E-Mail: kclark@rcl.lib.rochester.edu; Staff 15 (MLS 5, Non-MLS 10)
Library Holdings: Bk Vols 160,550; Per Subs 1,200
Subject Interests: Biology, Chemistry, Computer science, Engineering, Geology, Maps, Mathematics, Statistics
Special Collections: USGS Topographic Maps
Friends of the Library Group

CHARLOTTE WHITNEY ALLEN LIBRARY, Memorial Art Gallery, 500 University Ave, 14607. SAN 354-0758. Tel: 716-473-7720, Ext 3022. FAX: 716-473-6266. Web Site: www.rochester.edu/mag/artlib.htm. *Dir Libr Serv, Librn*, Lu Harper; E-Mail: lharper@mag.rochester.edu; *AV*, Susan Nurse; E-Mail: snurse@mag.rochester.edu; Staff 2 (MLS 1, Non-MLS 1)
Founded 1913
Subject Interests: Art history, Decorative art, Museology
Special Collections: Fritz Trautman Coll, papers, MAG Archives
Friends of the Library Group

LABORATORY FOR LASER ENERGETICS LIBRARY, Laboratory For Laser Energetics, 14623. SAN 327-9219. Tel: 716-275-4479. FAX: 716-273-3663. Web Site: www.lib.rochester.edu/lle/. *Librn*, Kenneth Harper; E-Mail: kharper@rcl.lib.rochester.edu
Library Holdings: Bk Vols 2,836; Per Subs 44
Subject Interests: Applied optics, Lasers, Plasma physics, Thermonuclear fusion
Special Collections: DOE Energyfiche
Friends of the Library Group

MANAGEMENT, Rush Rhees Library, 14627. SAN 354-0847. Tel: 716-275-4463. FAX: 716-273-5316. Web Site: www.lib.rochester.edu/mgt/. *Librn*, Brenda Reeb; Staff 4 (MLS 3, Non-MLS 1)
Library Holdings: Bk Vols 2,625; Per Subs 590
Subject Interests: Accounting, Computer science, Econ, Finance, Manufacturing mgt, Marketing, Operations mgt, Operations res
Friends of the Library Group

MULTIMEDIA CENTER, Rush Rhees Library, 14627. SAN 376-2432. Tel: 716-273-5009. FAX: 716-273-1032. E-Mail: mmclib@rcl.lib.rochester.edu. Web Site: www.lib.rochester.edu/mmc. *Head of Libr*, Stephanie Frontz; Tel: 716-875-4476, E-Mail: sfrontz@rel.lib.rochester.edu
Subject Interests: Classics, Compact discs, Langs, Videos
Friends of the Library Group

PHYSICS-OPTICS-ASTRONOMY LIBRARY, Bausch & Lomb Hall, 14627. SAN 327-9197. Tel: 716-275-4469. FAX: 716-273-5321. Toll Free FAX: 716-273-5321. E-Mail: poalib@pas.rochester.edu. Web Site: www.lib.rochester.edu/poa/. *Librn*, Patricia Sulouff
Library Holdings: Bk Vols 35,083; Per Subs 210
Subject Interests: Astronomy, Optics, Physics
Special Collections: History of Optics; Lens Design Patents
Friends of the Library Group

ROSSELL HOPE ROBBINS LIBRARY, Rush Rhees Library, 14627. SAN 372-509X. Tel: 716-275-0110. Web Site: www.lib.rochester.edu/camelot/cphome.stm. *Dir*, Alan Lupack; E-Mail: alupak@rcl.lib.rochester.edu
Founded 1987
Library Holdings: Bk Titles 15,000
Subject Interests: Medieval English lit, Medieval studies
Special Collections: Medieval Literature (Offprint Coll)
Restriction: Non-circulating to the public
Friends of the Library Group

SIBLEY MUSIC LIBRARY, Eastman School of Music, 27 Gibbs St, 14604-2596. SAN 354-0901. Tel: 716-274-1350. FAX: 716-274-1380. E-Mail: sibref@mail.rochester.edu. Web Site: sibley.esm.rochester.edu/. *Publ Servs*, James Farrington; *Rare Bks*, David Coppen; *Tech Servs*, Jennifer Bowen; Staff 9 (MLS 6, Non-MLS 3)
Founded 1904. Enrl 748; Fac 89; Highest Degree: Doctorate
Library Holdings: Bk Vols 326,000; Bk Titles 192,000; Per Subs 650
Subject Interests: Chamber music, Contemporary American music, Hist of music, Libretti, Music theory, Musical theatre, Opera, Solo lit
Special Collections: 17th Century Sacred Music (Olschki Coll); Books & Scores (Oscar Sonneck Library); Chamber Music; Folk Music (Krehbiel Coll); Music Biography, Theatre & Librettos (Pougin Coll); Music Manuscripts (Howard Hanson, Gardner Read, Burrill Philips, Weldon Hart Coll, Karl Weigl & Alec Wilder Colls); Music Publishing (Sengstack Archives); Performers' Coll (Malcolm Frager, Jan DeGaetani & Jacques Gordon Colls)
Publications: Sibley Muse (newsletter)
Partic in OCLC Online Computer Library Center, Inc; RLIN; Rochester Regional Library Council
Friends of the Library Group

M UNIVERSITY OF ROCHESTER MEDICAL CENTER, (Formerly University Of Rochester Medical Center - Eastman Dental Center), Basil G Bibby Library, Eastman Dental Center, 625 Elmwood Ave, 14620. SAN 312-3456. Tel: 716-275-5010. FAX: 716-273-1230. Web Site: www.urmc.rochester.edu/dentistry/bibby/. *Librn*, Christine DeGolyer; E-Mail: christine_degolyer@urmc.rochester.edu; Staff 2 (MLS 1, Non-MLS 1)
Founded 1947
Library Holdings: Bk Vols 3,500; Per Subs 95
Special Collections: Dentistry Coll
Publications: Basil G Bibby Library Gazette (quarterly)
Partic in New York State Interlibrary Loan Network; Rochester Regional Library Council; Univ of Rochester Voyager Syst

S VISUAL STUDIES WORKSHOP, Research Center, 31 Prince St, 14607. SAN 312-3839. Tel: 716-442-8676. FAX: 716-442-1992. *Coordr*, William Johnson; Staff 1 (MLS 1)
Founded 1970
Library Holdings: Bk Titles 19,000; Per Subs 214
Subject Interests: Artists bks, Cultural hist, Media studies, Photography, Social history, Videos
Special Collections: Alice Wells Archive (1960-1970); Barbara Blondeau Archives (1960-1970); Cartes-de-Visites; Contemporary Photographers; Illustrated Book Coll (1964-); Independent Press Archive (1960-); Lejaren a Hiller Archive (1900-1940),photog; Nineteenth Century Photographic Material (Gorsline), prints, bks; Original photographs from all eras (Lantern Slides, 1900); Soibelman Syndicate Collection (1920-1940), Photo, prints, photo albums & scrapbooks; Syl Labrot Archives (1960-1970); VSW Student Trace Coll
Publications: Artist's Books; Critical Anthology & Source Book; The Stereograph in America, a series of historically relevant reprints; video culture
Restriction: Non-circulating
Function: ILL limited
Open Mon-Fri 1-5
Friends of the Library Group

S WINTERS GROUP, Information Center,* 2509 Browncroft Blvd, 14625. SAN 323-4533. Tel: 716-218-9820. FAX: 716-218-9816. *Librn*, Debby Russo
Library Holdings: Bk Titles 100; Per Subs 75
Subject Interests: Marketing

ROCKVILLE CENTRE

P LAKEVIEW PUBLIC LIBRARY, One Tanglewood Rd, 11570. SAN 312-3855. Tel: 516-536-3071. FAX: 516-536-6260. *Dir*, A Blair Cummins; Staff 4 (MLS 4)
Founded 1973. Pop 5,500
Jan 1999-Dec 1999 Income $462,557. Mats Exp $37,000, Books $31,000, Per/Ser (Incl. Access Fees) $6,000. Sal $174,452 (Prof $115,331)
Library Holdings: Bk Vols 40,507; Bk Titles 38,595; Per Subs 232
Special Collections: Black Experience, bks, per, micro
Publications: Community Directory of Community Organizations; Community Library Newsletter
Mem of Nassau Library System
Partic in Long Island Library Resources Council; New York State Interlibrary Loan Network
Friends of the Library Group

M MERCY MEDICAL CENTER, Professional Library Services,* 1000 N Village Ave, 11570-1098. SAN 312-3863. Tel: 516-255-0111. FAX: 516-763-5448. *Librn*, Carol Reid
Founded 1940
Library Holdings: Bk Vols 3,000; Per Subs 180
Subject Interests: Medicine, Nursing
Restriction: By appointment only
Mem of Long Island Libr Resources Coun, Inc
Partic in BRS; NLM; OCLC Online Computer Library Center, Inc

C MOLLOY COLLEGE, James Edward Tobin Library, 1000 Hempstead Ave, 11571-5002. (Mail add: PO Box 5002, 11571-5002), SAN 312-3871. Tel: 516-678-5000, Ext 6236. FAX: 516-678-8908. Web Site: www.molloy.edu/library. *Dir*, Robert D Martin; Tel: 516-678-5000, Ext 6819, E-Mail: rmartin@molloy.edu; *Ref*, Norman Weil; E-Mail: nweil@molloy.edu; *Ref*, Sister Elizabeth Gill; E-Mail: egill@molloy.edu; *Ref*, Wenhui Chen; Tel: 516-678-5000, Ext 6461, E-Mail: wchen@molloy.edu; *Media Spec*, Cori Miller; Tel: 516-678-5000, Ext 6237, E-Mail: clmiller@molloy.edu; Staff 29 (MLS 9, Non-MLS 20)
Founded 1955. Enrl 2,400; Fac 307; Highest Degree: Master
Jul 2000-Jun 2001 Income $657,595. Mats Exp $223,000, Books $45,000, Per/Ser (Incl. Access Fees) $75,000, Presv $1,000, Micro $5,200, AV Equip $11,000, Electronic Ref Mat (Incl. Access Fees) $80,000. Sal $380,212 (Prof $232,707)
Library Holdings: Bk Vols 133,000; Per Subs 702
Special Collections: Microbook of English Literature (3000 books)
Automation Activity & Vendor Info: (Cataloging) Endeavor; (Circulation) Endeavor; (Course Reserve) Endeavor; (ILL) Endeavor; (OPAC) Endeavor; (Serials) Endeavor
Database Vendor: IAC - Info Trac, OCLC - First Search, ProQuest, Silverplatter Information Inc.

Publications: Annual Media Holdings; Annual Periodical Holdings; Library Manual; Monthly Accession Lists
Partic in Long Island Library Resources Council

P ROCKVILLE CENTRE PUBLIC LIBRARY, 221 N Village Ave, 11570. SAN 312-388X. Tel: 516-766-6257. Circulation Tel: 516-766-6257, Ext 10. Reference Tel: 516-766-6257, Ext 5. FAX: 516-766-6090. E-Mail: reference@rvcpl.org. Web Site: www.nassaulibrary.org/rvc. *Dir*, Gretchen Browne; E-Mail: gbrowne@rvcpl.org; *AV*, Frank McGinniss; *YA Servs*, Terry Ain; *Tech Servs*, Ruth Black; *Ch Servs*, Anita La Spina; *Coll Develop*, Laura Hohauser; Staff 65 (MLS 20, Non-MLS 45)
Founded 1882. Pop 24,020; Circ 315,130
Jul 1997-Jun 1998 Income $1,819,765, State $45,718, Locally Generated Income $115,847. Mats Exp $285,955, Books $210,464, Per/Ser (Incl. Access Fees) $12,459, Micro $3,659. Sal $979,251 (Prof $47,600)
Library Holdings: Bk Vols 173,209; Bk Titles 132,851; Per Subs 295
Subject Interests: Education, Feminism, History, Indust
Special Collections: Rockville Centre History, bks, pictures, newsp
Database Vendor: CARL, DRA, Ebsco - EbscoHost, GaleNet, IAC - Info Trac, IAC - SearchBank, OCLC - First Search, ProQuest
Publications: Library Newsletter
Open Mon, Wed & Thurs 9-9, Tues 10-9, Fri 9-6, Sat 9-5 & Sun 1-5; closed Sun, July & Aug only
Friends of the Library Group

RODMAN

P RODMAN PUBLIC LIBRARY,* Town Hall, PO Box B, 13682. SAN 312-3898. Tel: 315-232-2522. FAX: 315-232-2522. *Librn*, Kristin A Benner
Circ 7,000
Library Holdings: Bk Vols 2,700
Mem of North Country Library System
Friends of the Library Group

ROME

S IIT RESEARCH INSTITUTE, RAC AMPTIAC Libraries, 201 Mill St, 13440. SAN 370-8918. Tel: 315-339-7052. FAX: 315-337-9932, 339-7107. Web Site: rome.iitri.org/rac/technical/library/. *Librn*, Perry Onderdonk
Library Holdings: Bk Titles 30,000; Per Subs 50
Subject Interests: Ceramics, Composites, Metals, Plastics, Quality

P JERVIS PUBLIC LIBRARY ASSOCIATION, 613 N Washington St, 13440-4296. SAN 312-3901. Tel: 315-336-4570. FAX: 315-336-2056. E-Mail: jervis@borg.com, ro-ref@midyork.lib.ny.us. Web Site: www.jervislibrary.org. *Dir*, Carole F Fowler; *Ad Servs*, Christopher Zackey; *Ch Servs*, Lorie O'Donnell; *ILL*, Peter Chien; *Media Spec, Ref*, Lori Chien; *Coll Develop*, Joan Pellikka; *Coll Develop*, Lisa Matte; Staff 11 (MLS 9, Non-MLS 2)
Founded 1894. Pop 44,350; Circ 304,000
Jan 2000-Dec 2000 Income $1,293,450, State $33,150, City $541,250, Federal $23,652, County $550,000, Locally Generated Income $103,398, Other $42,000. Mats Exp $169,202, Books $105,400, Per/Ser (Incl. Access Fees) $18,700, Presv $2,500, Micro $1,200, AV Equip $15,000, Other Print Mats $1,402, Electronic Ref Mat (Incl. Access Fees) $25,000. Sal $720,000 (Prof $373,000)
Library Holdings: Bk Vols 147,780; Bk Titles 108,367; Per Subs 357; High Interest/Low Vocabulary Bk Vols 107; Spec Interest Per Sub 32
Special Collections: Civil Engineering Canals, Aqueducts, Railroads (John B Jervis Papers), letters, mss, microfilm, bks; Revolutionary War (Bright-Huntington Coll), mss
Automation Activity & Vendor Info: (Acquisitions) DRA; (Cataloging) DRA; (Circulation) DRA; (Course Reserve) DRA; (ILL) DRA; (Media Booking) DRA; (OPAC) DRA; (Serials) DRA
Database Vendor: DRA
Publications: Newsletter
Mem of Mid-York Library System
Partic in Dialog Corporation
Special Services for the Deaf - Staff with knowledge of sign language
Special Services for the Blind - Braille; Cassette bks; Talking Books
Microcomputer room for the public; handicapped accessible; accessible OPACs

S ROME HISTORICAL SOCIETY, William E & Elaine Scripture Memorial Library, 200 Church St, 13440. SAN 312-391X. Tel: 315-336-5870. FAX: 315-336-5912. *Archivist*, Kathleen Bouska; Staff 2 (Non-MLS 2)
Founded 1936
Library Holdings: Bk Vols 3,500
Subject Interests: Canals and railroads, Civil War, Genealogy, Industrial, Local hist to date, Revolutionary period
Special Collections: Audio-visual presentation - Built of Iron, Copper & Steel: The Industrial Development of Rome; From Portage to Cross Road: The Changing Face of Rome; Journals, letters, ephemery of local heritage; Oral Histories; Our Goodly Heritage, maps, photogs, newsp, prog for schools; Rome Turney Radiator Company Records Coll 1905-33; The Ill-fated Village of Delta
Publications: Annals & Recollections (quarterly); Newsletter; Special Topics Monographs
Teacher in-service programs

ROOSEVELT

SR DIOCESE OF ROCKVILLE CENTRE, The Long Island Catholic Research Library, 200 W Centennial Ave, Ste 201, PO Box 9000, 11575. SAN 325-5069. Tel: 516-594-1000. FAX: 516-594-1092. *Actg Librn*, JoAnne Oleary; Staff 1 (MLS 1)
Founded 1962
Library Holdings: Bk Titles 5,000; Per Subs 35
Subject Interests: Religion
Special Collections: Nat Catholic News Serv releases; newsp clippings; Roman Catholic Church history including Papal Documents & Bishops' statements
Restriction: Not open to public

P ROOSEVELT PUBLIC LIBRARY,* 27 W Fulton, 11575. SAN 354-1029. Tel: 516-378-0207, 516-378-0222. FAX: 516-377-3238. *Dir*, Shawn Dunnom; Staff 3 (MLS 3)
Founded 1934. Pop 15,564
Library Holdings: Bk Vols 60,000; Bk Titles 48,000; Per Subs 156
Special Collections: Black Studies, bks, per
Publications: Four Seasons Library News Bulletin
Mem of Nassau Library System
Branches: 1
CHILDREN'S ROOM, 27 W Fulton Ave, 11575. Tel: 516-378-0222. FAX: 516-377-3238. *Ch Servs, Librn*, Beverly Landers
Library Holdings: Bk Vols 13,074; Bk Titles 12,702
Special Collections: Black Studies & Easy Books Coll

ROSCOE

P ROSCOE FREE LIBRARY, Maple & Highland Ave, 12776. SAN 312-3928. Tel: 607-498-5574. FAX: 607-498-5574. Web Site: www.rcls.org/ros/. *Dir*, Joyce Goff
Founded 1920. Pop 1,200; Circ 15,000
Library Holdings: Bk Vols 15,000; Per Subs 23
Mem of Ramapo Catskill Library System

ROSE

P ROSE FREE LIBRARY,* PO Box 67, 14542-0067. SAN 312-3936. Tel: 315-587-2335. FAX: 315-587-2808. *Dir*, Donna J Norris
Founded 1912. Pop 2,684; Circ 15,325
Library Holdings: Bk Vols 9,323; Bk Titles 9,250; Per Subs 38
Mem of Pioneer Library System; Wayne County Libr Syst

ROSENDALE

P ROSENDALE LIBRARY,* 264 Main St, PO Box 482, 12472. SAN 312-3944. Tel: 914-658-9013. FAX: 914-658-9236. *Dir*, Wendy Alexander
Pop 6,220; Circ 24,461
Library Holdings: Bk Vols 20,161
Mem of Mid-Hudson Library System
Friends of the Library Group

ROSLYN

P BRYANT LIBRARY, 2 Paper Mill Rd, 11576-2193. SAN 312-3952. Tel: 516-621-2240. FAX: 516-621-7211. E-Mail: rnlinfo@lilirc.org. Web Site: www.nassaulibrary.org/bryant. *Dir*, Elizabeth McCloat; *Asst Dir*, Cathleen Mealing; *Tech Servs*, Paulette Palumbo; *Ch Servs*, Barbara Homola; *Ch Servs*, Ann Secter; *Ref*, Barbara Campbell Czekala; *Ref*, Joan Casson Sauer; *AV*, Kathleen Micucci; *YA Servs*, Susan Owens; *Circ*, Barbara Federman; *Archivist*, Myrna Sloam; *Ad Servs*, Marie Courtney; *Pub Relations*, Victor Caputo
Founded 1878. Pop 16,617; Circ 288,865
Jul 2000-Jun 2001 Income $3,181,370. Mats Exp $392,250, Books $255,400, Per/Ser (Incl. Access Fees) $29,600, Presv $400, Micro $9,700, Electronic Ref Mat (Incl. Access Fees) $47,100. Sal $2,137,300
Library Holdings: Bk Vols 245,226; Bk Titles 171,147; Per Subs 325
Special Collections: Christopher Morley Coll; Local History Coll, photog; Roslyn Architecture Coll; William Cullen Bryant Coll
Automation Activity & Vendor Info: (Circulation) DRA; (OPAC) DRA
Publications: Pathways to the Past (videotape & teacher's manual); Regular Newsletter; W C Bryant in Roslyn
Mem of Nassau Library System
Library art exhibits curated by Heckscher Museum of Art (1996-), Gallery space Heckscher Museum of Art at Bryant Library
Friends of the Library Group

M SAINT FRANCIS HOSPITAL, Medical Library, 100 Port Washington Blvd, 11576. SAN 312-3960. Tel: 516-562-6673. FAX: 516-562-6695. *Senior Librn*, Judith Weinstein; E-Mail: jweinstein@sfhmmc.org; *Librn*, Sylvia Horowitz
Founded 1949
2000-2001 Income $36,800, State $800, Parent Institution $36,000. Mats Exp $30,000, Books $9,000, Per/Ser (Incl. Access Fees) $17,000
Library Holdings: Bk Vols 1,200; Per Subs 80
Subject Interests: Cardiology
Publications: New book list; newsletter; periodicals holding list
Mem of Long Island Libr Resources Coun, Inc
Partic in Basic Health Sciences Library Network; National Network Of Libraries Of Medicine - South Central Region

ROSLYN HEIGHTS

R TEMPLE SINAI LIBRARY, 425 Roslyn Rd, 11577. SAN 312-3979. Tel: 516-621-6800. FAX: 516-625-6020. *Librn*, Burnette Groveman
Library Holdings: Bk Vols 10,000
Subject Interests: Judaica

ROUND LAKE

P ROUND LAKE LIBRARY,* 31 Wesley Ave, PO Box 665, 12151. SAN 312-3987. Tel: 518-899-2285. FAX: 518-899-2285. *Librn*, Jo-Anne Patenaude
Pop 2,000; Circ 23,000
Library Holdings: Bk Vols 12,000; Per Subs 20
Special Collections: Round Lake Historical Coll
Mem of Southern Adirondack Library System
Open Wed, Thurs & Fri 10-8, Sat 10-2
Friends of the Library Group

ROUSES POINT

P DODGE MEMORIAL LIBRARY,* 144 Lake St, 12979. SAN 312-4002. Tel: 518-297-6242. FAX: 518-297-6943. *Librn*, Mary Ann Tremblay
Founded 1922. Pop 2,220; Circ 25,667
Library Holdings: Bk Titles 11,000; Per Subs 26
Mem of Clinton-Essex-Franklin Library System
Open Mon & Thurs 7-9, Tues 1-5 & 7-9, Fri 1-5 & Sat 10-12

ROXBURY

P ROXBURY LIBRARY,* Main St, 12474. SAN 312-4010. Tel: 607-326-7901. FAX: 607-326-7901. *Dir, Librn*, Barbara Scudder
Founded 1903. Pop 2,200; Circ 8,036
Library Holdings: Bk Titles 10,848
Subject Interests: Natural science
Special Collections: John Burroughs, bks, pictures; Local History, bks, maps, ledgers
Publications: History of the Town of Roxbury
Mem of Four County Library System
Open Mon & Wed 11-4, Sat 11-2, Thurs (July & Aug) 1-4 & 7-9, (Sept-June) 1-6

RUSH

P RUSH PUBLIC LIBRARY,* 5977 E Henrietta Rd, 14543. SAN 312-4029. Tel: 716-533-1370. FAX: 716-533-1546. *Dir*, Joan C Starkweather; Staff 1 (MLS 1)
Founded 1914. Pop 3,217; Circ 30,461
Library Holdings: Bk Vols 19,427; Per Subs 31
Subject Interests: Architecture, Art, Crafts, History
Mem of Monroe County Library System
Open Mon - Fri 2-9

RUSHFORD

P RUSHFORD FREE LIBRARY,* 9012 Main St, PO Box 8, 14777-0008. SAN 312-4037. Tel: 716-437-2533. FAX: 716-437-9940. Web Site: www.members.aol.com/rushweb. *Librn*, Frances Gilbert; *Ch Servs*, Rebecca Cole
Circ 8,223
Library Holdings: Bk Vols 16,511
Publications: Newsletter (three times a year)
Mem of Southern Tier Library System

RYE

P RYE FREE READING ROOM,* 1061 Boston Post Rd, 10580. SAN 312-4053. Tel: 914-967-0480. FAX: 914-967-5522. E-Mail: rfrr@wls.lib.ny.us. Web Site: www.ryelibrary.org. *Dir*, Betty Gay Teoman; *Coll Develop*, Maria Lagonia
Founded 1884. Pop 14,936; Circ 173,281
1998-1999 Income $836,326, State $12,317, City $601,000, Locally Generated Income $214,259, Other $8,654. Mats Exp $93,094, Books $63,448, Per/Ser (Incl. Access Fees) $15,393, Presv $1,669. Sal $545,739 (Prof $200,311)
Library Holdings: Bk Titles 70,411; Per Subs 231
Subject Interests: Rye hist
Publications: Annual report, Newsletter
Mem of Westchester Library System
Library is a free association library, chartered by NY state

S RYE HISTORICAL SOCIETY LIBRARY, One Purchase St, 10580. SAN 312-4061. Tel: 914-967-7588. FAX: 914-967-6253. *Dir*, Phyllis Dillon
Founded 1964
Library Holdings: Bk Vols 1,100; Bk Titles 920
Subject Interests: Genealogy, Local history
Special Collections: Rye History, photogs, slides (manuscripts 557.25 cu ft)
Publications: Estates of Grace; Father Burke's Dream to Rescue Children of the Inner City: St Benedict's Home, Rye, NY, 1891-1941; One Hundred Years of Health Care: 1889-1989; Read about Rye 1660-1960; Rye in the Twenties; Silent Companions: Dummy Board Figures of the 17th through 19th Centuries; The Art of Lauren Ford

SACKETS HARBOR

P HAY MEMORIAL LIBRARY, Broad & E Main Sts, PO Box 288, 13685-0288. SAN 312-4088. Tel: 315-646-2228. FAX: 315-646-2228. Web Site: www.imcnet.net/~tjspence/library.htm. *Mgr*, Antonette Joan Ellenger; E-Mail: ellinger@northnet.org; Staff 1 (Non-MLS 1)
Founded 1900. Pop 3,089; Circ 10,244
Library Holdings: Bk Vols 5,420; Per Subs 32
Database Vendor: CARL, OCLC - First Search, Wilson - Wilson Web
Mem of North Country Library System
Friends of the Library Group

SAG HARBOR

P JOHN JERMAIN MEMORIAL LIBRARY,* Main St, PO Box 569, 11963-0013. SAN 312-4096. Tel: 516-725-0049. FAX: 516-725-0597. Web Site: www.suffolk.lib.ny.us/libraries/jjer/. *Dir*, James C Ashe
Pop 5,944; Circ 48,000
Library Holdings: Bk Vols 33,163; Per Subs 117
Subject Interests: Whaling
Mem of Suffolk Cooperative Library System
Friends of the Library Group

SAINT BONAVENTURE

C SAINT BONAVENTURE UNIVERSITY, Friedsam Memorial Library, 14778. SAN 312-410X. Tel: 716-375-2323. FAX: 716-375-2389. Web Site: www.sbu.edu/friedsam. *Dir, Rare Bks, Spec Coll*, Paul J Spaeth; *Librn*, Bro Anthony Lobalbo; *Acq*, Martha Drake; *Cat*, Janet Lippert; *ILL, Ref*, Theresa Shaffer; *Govt Doc, Ref*, Michael Spencer; *Computer Services*, Ann Tenglurd
Founded 1858. Enrl 2,300
Library Holdings: Bk Vols 285,000; Bk Titles 225,000; Per Subs 1,650
Special Collections: Franciscan Institute; Jim Bishop Coll, mss; Rare Books, mss & incunabula; Robert Lax Coll, mss; Thomas Merton Coll, mss
Partic in Western New York Library Resources Council

SAINT JOHNSVILLE

P MARGARET REANEY MEMORIAL LIBRARY,* 19 Kingsbury Ave, 13452. SAN 312-4126. Tel: 518-568-7822. FAX: 518-568-7822. *Dir*, Dawn L Capece
Circ 20,436
Library Holdings: Bk Vols 31,200; Bk Titles 31,000; Per Subs 22
Special Collections: Local Hist Coll, genealogies, newspapers, & hist ref
Mem of Mohawk Valley Library Association

SALAMANCA

P SALAMANCA PUBLIC LIBRARY, 155 Wildwood Ave, 14779-1576. SAN 312-4134. Tel: 716-945-1890. FAX: 716-945-2741. Web Site: www.salamancacity.wnyric.org. *Dir*, Thomas L Sharbaugh; E-Mail: tsharbaugh@sccs.wnyric.org; Staff 1 (MLS 1)
Founded 1920. Pop 6,566; Circ 70,734
Apr 2000-Mar 2001 Income $249,504. Mats Exp $42,900, Books $26,800, Per/Ser (Incl. Access Fees) $9,200, Micro $4,400, AV Equip $2,500. Sal $154,036 (Prof $41,800)
Library Holdings: Bk Vols 44,108; Per Subs 118
Special Collections: Iroquois & Seneca Indians (Iroquoia); Salamanca Historical Coll
Automation Activity & Vendor Info: (Circulation) Sagebrush Corporation;

(OPAC) Sagebrush Corporation
Database Vendor: IAC - Info Trac, ProQuest
Mem of Chautauqua-Cattaraugus Library System
Friends of the Library Group

SALEM

P BANCROFT PUBLIC LIBRARY, 181 Main St, 12865. SAN 312-4142. Tel: 518-854-7463. E-Mail: slibrari@nycap.rr.com. *Librn*, Peg Culver; Staff 1 (Non-MLS 1)
Pop 9,877; Circ 13,298
Library Holdings: Bk Vols 12,700; Bk Titles 11,587; Per Subs 10
Mem of Southern Adirondack Library System
Friends of the Library Group

SALISBURY CENTER

P KIRBY FREE LIBRARY OF SALISBURY,* Rte 29A, Rd One, Box 322, 13454. SAN 376-3137. Tel: 315-429-9006. FAX: 315-429-9006. *Librn*, Jane Voorhes
Library Holdings: Bk Vols 8,000
Mem of Mid-York Library System
Open Thurs 1-4, Fri 10-noon

SANBORN

J NIAGARA COUNTY COMMUNITY COLLEGE, Library Learning Center,* 3111 Saunders Settlement Rd, 14132. SAN 312-4150. Tel: 716-614-6222, Ext 6705. FAX: 716-614-7118. Web Site: www.sunyniagara.cc.ny.us/library. *Dir*, Elizabeth Fulwell; *Ref*, Jeanne Tuohey; *Circ*, Cathy Gibbs; *Cat*, Karen Ferington; *Tech Servs*, Nancy Verstreate; Staff 8 (MLS 8)
Founded 1963. Enrl 5,000; Fac 200
Sep 1998-Aug 1999 Income $910,170, State $8,148, Parent Institution $902,022. Mats Exp $220,425, Books $98,800, Per/Ser (Incl. Access Fees) $87,398, Micro $12,567. Sal $605,020
Library Holdings: Bk Vols 86,765
Publications: Pathfinders; Periodicals in the LLC; What's New
Partic in OCLC Online Computer Library Center, Inc; Western New York Library Resources Council

P SANBORN-PEKIN FREE LIBRARY,* 5884 West Ave, 14132. SAN 312-4169. Tel: 716-731-9933. FAX: 716-731-9933. *Librn*, Sallie Ditzel
Pop 4,000; Circ 52,966
Library Holdings: Bk Vols 33,000; Per Subs 92
Mem of Nioga Library System
Open Mon 1-8:30, Tues & Fri 1-5 & 7-8:30, Wed 12-5 & 7-8:30, Thurs 7-8:30

SANDY CREEK

P ANNIE PORTER AINSWORTH MEMORIAL LIBRARY,* 6064 S Main St, PO Box 69, 13145-0069. SAN 312-4177. Tel: 315-387-3732. FAX: 315-387-2005. Web Site: www.hc3r.org/sandycreek. *Librn*, Kay E Dealing
Founded 1928. Pop 3,256; Circ 10,000
Library Holdings: Bk Vols 4,500; Per Subs 10
Special Collections: Abraham Lincoln Coll
Mem of North Country Library System
Friends of the Library Group

SARANAC LAKE

J NORTH COUNTRY COMMUNITY COLLEGE LIBRARY, 20 Winona Ave, PO Box 89, 12983. SAN 312-4185. Tel: 518-891-2915, Ext 218. Web Site: www.nccc.edu. *Bibliog Instr, Coll Develop, Dir*, Patrick F McIntyre; E-Mail: mclntyre@northnet.org; *ILL*, Dianna Trummer; *Acq*, Phil Gallos; Tel: 518-891-2915, Ext 225; Staff 1 (MLS 1)
Founded 1967. Enrl 1,027; Fac 31; Highest Degree: Associate
Sep 1999-Aug 2000 Income $164,787, State $5,230, Parent Institution $159,557. Mats Exp $44,396, Books $15,929, Per/Ser (Incl. Access Fees) $20,335, Micro $6,246. Sal $100,000
Library Holdings: Bk Vols 57,985; Per Subs 168; Bks on Deafness & Sign Lang 47
Subject Interests: Adirondack Mountain hist, Criminal justice, Nursing, Radiologic tech
Special Collections: Adirondack History (Adirondack Coll), bks, maps & prints; Nettie Marie Jones Fine Arts Coll
Automation Activity & Vendor Info: (Circulation) Follett
Database Vendor: IAC - Info Trac, OCLC - First Search, ProQuest
Publications: From the Top of the Hill (newsletter)
Mem of N Country Ref & Res Resources Coun
Partic in North Country Ref & Res Resources Coun; OCLC Online Computer Library Center, Inc; WALDO
Special Services for the Blind - Kurzweil Reader

P SARANAC LAKE FREE LIBRARY,* 100 Main St, 12983. SAN 312-4207. Tel: 518-891-4190. FAX: 518-891-5931. E-Mail: whitefie@northnet.org. *Dir*, Betsy Whitefield
Founded 1907. Circ 66,207
Jan 1997-Dec 1998 Income $136,585, State $3,787, Locally Generated Income $26,000. Mats Exp $18,200, Books $14,000, Per/Ser (Incl. Access Fees) $4,200. Sal $71,000 (Prof $30,800)
Library Holdings: Bk Vols 28,355; Bk Titles 25,000
Special Collections: Adirondack History Coll; Mounted Wildlife Museum
Publications: Newsletter
Mem of Clinton-Essex-Franklin Library System
Friends of the Library Group

M TRUDEAU INSTITUTE LIBRARY,* 100 Alconquin Ave, PO Box 59, 12983. SAN 312-4215. Tel: 518-891-3080. FAX: 518-891-5126. *Librn*, Linda Auclair; E-Mail: auclair@hslc.org
Founded 1964
Library Holdings: Bk Vols 15,000; Per Subs 110
Subject Interests: Immunology, Microbiology

SARATOGA SPRINGS

S ESPEY MANUFACTURING & ELECTRONICS CORPORATION, Component Specifications Library,* 233 Ballston Ave, 12866. SAN 327-2273. Tel: 518-584-4100. FAX: 518-584-4330. *Librn*, Bernard Smith
Library Holdings: Bk Vols 5,000; Per Subs 100

S NATIONAL MUSEUM OF RACING & HALL OF FAME, INC, John A Morris Library, 191 Union Ave, 12866. SAN 312-4231. Tel: 518-584-0400. FAX: 518-584-4574. E-Mail: nmrhof96@race.saratoga.ny.us. *Dir*, Peter Hammell
Library Holdings: Bk Titles 1,500; Per Subs 12
Subject Interests: Horses, Thoroughbred horse racing
Publications: Horses & Members in the National Racing Hall of Fame (set of 2 booklets); The Race Horses of America 1832-1872
Restriction: By appointment only
Partic in OCLC Online Computer Library Center, Inc

M SARATOGA HOSPITAL, Medical Library, 211 Church St, 12866. SAN 328-316X. Tel: 518-583-8301. FAX: 518-583-8310. E-Mail: shlibry@saratogacare.org. *Librn*, Marilynn H Peterson; Staff 10 (MLS 2, Non-MLS 8)
Jan 2000-Dec 2000 Income $17,500, State $2,500, Parent Institution $13,000, Other $2,000. Mats Exp $15,500, Books $4,500, Per/Ser (Incl. Access Fees) $10,500, Electronic Ref Mat (Incl. Access Fees) $500
Library Holdings: Bk Titles 400; Per Subs 45
Database Vendor: Ebsco - EbscoHost
Partic in Capital District Library Council for Reference & Research Resources

P SARATOGA SPRINGS PUBLIC LIBRARY,* 49 Henry St, 12866. SAN 312-424X. Tel: 518-584-7860. FAX: 518-584-7866. E-Mail: sar-dutch@sals.edu. *Dir*, Harry Dutcher; *Asst Dir*, Jean Stamm; *Ch Servs*, Jim Karge; *Ref*, Dan Hubbs; *ILL*, Rita McNamara; Staff 12 (MLS 12)
Founded 1950. Pop 46,000; Circ 630,000
Library Holdings: Bk Vols 155,000; Bk Titles 80,000; Per Subs 187
Special Collections: Balneology; Hydrotherapy; Saratogiana
Publications: Bibliography of Research Materials on Saratoga Springs
Mem of Southern Adirondack Library System
Friends of the Library Group

S SARATOGIAN LIBRARY,* 20 Lake Ave, 12866. SAN 375-4642. Tel: 518-584-4242, Ext 208. FAX: 518-587-7750. E-Mail: saratoga4u@aol.com. *Librn*, Eleanor Brower
Library Holdings: Bk Titles 300
Subject Interests: Local history
Friends of the Library Group

C SKIDMORE COLLEGE, Lucy Scribner Library, 815 N Broadway, 12866. SAN 312-4266. Tel: 518-580-5000. FAX: 518-580-5540. E-Mail: illdesk@skidmore.edu, skidmore@scott.edu. Interlibrary Loan Service E-Mail: illdesk@skidmore.edu. Web Site: www.skidmore.edu/irc/library. *Dir*, Barbara Doyle-Wilch; *ILL*, Amy Syrell; *Tech Servs*, Susan Zappen; *Spec Coll*, Ruth Copans; Staff 8 (MLS 8)
Founded 1911. Enrl 2,385; Fac 173; Highest Degree: Master
Library Holdings: Bk Vols 362,496; Per Subs 2,164
Subject Interests: Art
Special Collections: bks, photogs; College Archives; Edith Wharton Coll; Edna St Vincent Millay Coll; Hebraica-Judaica (Leo Usdan Coll); Late 19th Century Illustrated Books; Max Beerbohm Coll; Saratogiana (Anita P Yates Coll)
Publications: Friends of the Library Newsletter (semi-annual)
Partic in Capital District Library Council for Reference & Research Resources; OCLC Online Computer Library Center, Inc
Friends of the Library Group

SOUTHERN ADIRONDACK LIBRARY SYSTEM, 22 Whitney Pl, 12866-4596. SAN 312-4274. Tel: 518-584-7300. FAX: 518-587-5589. Web Site: www.sals.edu. *Actg Dir*, Miriam Meier; *Ch Servs*, Rebecca Wright-Sedam; *Tech Servs*, Elayne Leonelli; Staff 7 (MLS 7)
Founded 1958. Pop 302,933
Library Holdings: Bk Vols 170,903; Bk Titles 162,116; Per Subs 194
Publications: Newsletter
Member Libraries: Argyle Free Library; Ballston Spa Public Library; Bancroft Public Library; Bolton Free Library; Caldwell-Lake George Library; Cambridge Public Library; Corinth Free Library; Crandall Public Library; Easton Library; Fort Edward Free Library; Great Meadow Correctional Facility Library; Greenwich Free Library; Hadley-Luzerne Public Library; Horicon Free Public Library; Hudson Falls Free Library; Mechanicville District Public Library; Mount McGregor Correctional Facility Library; Mountainside Free Library; Pember Library & Museum; Raquette Lake Free Library; Richards Library; Round Lake Library; Saratoga Springs Public Library; Schuylerville Public Library; Shenendehowa Public Library; Stillwater Free Library; Stony Creek Free Library; Town of Ballston Community Library; Town Of Indian Lake Public Library; Washington Correctional Facility Library; Waterford Public Library
Partic in Capital District Library Council for Reference & Research Resources

GL SUPREME COURT LIBRARY AT SARATOGA SPRINGS, Fourth Judicial District, 474 Broadway, Ste 2, 12866-2297. SAN 312-4282. Tel: 518-584-4862. FAX: 518-581-0966. *In Charge*, Linda Macica
Founded 1866
Library Holdings: Bk Vols 20,000
Subject Interests: Law
Special Collections: Directories of Saratoga Springs (1884-present)

SAUGERTIES

P SAUGERTIES PUBLIC LIBRARY, Washington Ave, 12477. SAN 312-4304. Tel: 914-246-4317. FAX: 914-246-0858. E-Mail: saugerts@ulysses.sebridge.org. Web Site: saugerties.lib.ny.us. *Dir*, Beverly Kane; Staff 8 (MLS 1, Non-MLS 7)
Founded 1894. Pop 19,000; Circ 70,000
Jan 2000-Dec 2000 Income $200,000, State $5,000, County $12,000, Locally Generated Income $171,210. Mats Exp $31,500, Books $24,000, Per/Ser (Incl. Access Fees) $3,500, Micro $4,000. Sal $114,500 (Prof $32,000)
Library Holdings: Bk Vols 38,000; Bk Titles 35,000
Special Collections: Local Newspapers Coll, microfilm; New York State, Ulster County & Local History Coll, bks, newsp, pamphlet
Automation Activity & Vendor Info: (Circulation) GEAC
Mem of Mid-Hudson Library System
Open Mon & Wed 12-8, Tues, Thurs & Fri 10-6 & Sat 10-2
Friends of the Library Group

SAVONA

P SAVONA FREE LIBRARY,* 15 McCoy St, PO Box 475, 14879. SAN 312-4312. Tel: 607-583-4426. FAX: 607-583-4426. *Librn*, Cindy Schamel
Circ 2,571
Library Holdings: Bk Vols 7,300; Bk Titles 5,230; Per Subs 15
Mem of Southern Tier Library System
Friends of the Library Group

SAYVILLE

P SAYVILLE LIBRARY, 11 Collins Ave, 11782-3199. SAN 312-4320. Tel: 631-589-4440. FAX: 631-589-6128. E-Mail: sayvlib@suffolk.lib.ny.us. Web Site: www.sayville.suffold.lib.ny.us. *Dir*, Thomas A Tarantowicz; *Senior Librn*, Stephanie F Rubin; *Automation Syst Coordr*, Wm Olsen; *Ch Servs*, Karen Giambertone; *YA Servs*, Caryn Sinclair; *Ref*, Jonathan Pryer; Staff 15 (MLS 15)
Founded 1914. Pop 18,131; Circ 244,809
Jul 1999-Jun 2000 Income $1,679,981, Locally Generated Income $1,622,153, Other $57,828. Mats Exp $234,360, Books $175,257, Per/Ser (Incl. Access Fees) $23,645, Electronic Ref Mat (Incl. Access Fees) $15,131. Sal $871,433 (Prof $487,319)
Library Holdings: Bk Vols 93,502; Per Subs 250
Special Collections: Local History Coll; Long Island Coll
Mem of Suffolk Cooperative Library System

SCARSDALE

P SCARSDALE PUBLIC LIBRARY, 54 Olmsted Rd, 10583. SAN 312-4339. Tel: 914-722-1300. FAX: 914-722-1305. Web Site: www.scarsdalelibrary.org. *Dir*, Stephanie C Sarnoff; E-Mail: ssarnoff@wls.lib.ny.us; *Asst Dir*, Leni Glauber; *Ch Servs*, Jane Marino; Staff 52 (MLS 25, Non-MLS 27)
Founded 1928. Pop 16,987; Circ 250,000
Jun 2000-May 2001 Income $2,045,975, State $7,485, City $2,038,490. Mats Exp $293,000, Books $202,000, Per/Ser (Incl. Access Fees) $12,500, Presv $1,000, Micro $2,500, AV Equip $8,000, Electronic Ref Mat (Incl. Access Fees) $67,000. Sal $1,256,470 (Prof $787,585)
Library Holdings: Bk Vols 172,500; Per Subs 3,140
Subject Interests: Local history
Special Collections: Local photographs
Automation Activity & Vendor Info: (Acquisitions) epixtech, inc.; (Cataloging) epixtech, inc.; (Circulation) epixtech, inc.
Database Vendor: Dialog, Ebsco - EbscoHost, GaleNet, IAC - SearchBank
Mem of Westchester Library System
Partic in Westlynx
Friends of the Library Group

S WEINBERG NATURE CENTER LIBRARY,* 455 Mamaroneck Rd, 10583. SAN 328-364X. Tel: 914-722-1289. FAX: 914-723-4784. *Exec Dir*, Walter D Terrell, Jr
Library Holdings: Bk Vols 521; Bk Titles 500; Per Subs 12
Subject Interests: Am hist, Environ, Local history, Native Am, Nature
Special Collections: Birds & local mammals Coll; Native American/Woodland Indian Antifacts Coll
Open Wed-Sun 9-5
Friends of the Library Group

R WESTCHESTER REFORM TEMPLE LIBRARY, 255 Mamaroneck Rd, 10583. SAN 312-4347. Tel: 914-723-7727. FAX: 914-723-5946. E-Mail: office@wrtemple.org. *Librn*, Florence Gross
Founded 1960
Library Holdings: Bk Vols 3,080; Bk Titles 3,000; Per Subs 10
Subject Interests: Judaica

S WORK IN AMERICA INSTITUTE LIBRARY,* 700 White Plains Rd, 10583. SAN 327-5264. Tel: 914-472-9600. FAX: 914-472-9606.; Staff 2 (MLS 2)
Library Holdings: Bk Vols 4,000; Per Subs 200
Subject Interests: Personnel management

SCHAGHTICOKE

P ARVILLA E DIVER MEMORIAL LIBRARY,* 136 Main St, 12154. SAN 312-4355. Tel: 518-753-4344. *Librn*, Jane Getty
Circ 5,708
Library Holdings: Bk Vols 7,000; Per Subs 20
Mem of Upper Hudson Library System
Friends of the Library Group

SCHENECTADY

C DUDLEY OBSERVATORY LIBRARY,* 107 Nott Terrace Ste 201, 12308. SAN 354-1509. Tel: 518-382-7583. FAX: 518-382-7584. E-Mail: dudley@union.edu. *Archivist*, Nancy Langford
Founded 1852
Library Holdings: Bk Titles 5,000; Per Subs 10
Subject Interests: Astronomy, Astrophysics, Hist of astronomy, Space science
Special Collections: Archives of Dudley Observatory; Benjamin A Gould Jr Library
Partic in Capital District Library Council for Reference & Research Resources

GL JOSEPH F EGAN MEMORIAL SUPREME COURT LIBRARY, Schenectady County Judicial Bldg, 612 State, 12305. SAN 312-4363. Tel: 518-388-4310. FAX: 518-377-5909. *Senior Librn*, Patricia L Schultz; Staff 3 (MLS 1, Non-MLS 2)
Library Holdings: Bk Vols 27,650

M ELLIS HOSPITAL, Medical-Nursing Library,* 1101 Nott St, 12308. SAN 312-4371. Tel: 518-243-4000, 518-243-4381. FAX: 518-243-4668. *Librn*, Christopher Stater
Founded 1930
Library Holdings: Bk Vols 3,150; Bk Titles 2,815; Per Subs 210
Special Collections: Nursing History
Restriction: Staff use only
Partic in Cap District Libr Coun for Ref & Res Resources; Medline; New York State Interlibrary Loan Network

SR FIRST REFORMED CHURCH OF SCHENECTADY, Norman B Johnson Library, 8 N Church St, 12305-1699. SAN 371-7712. Tel: 518-377-2201. FAX: 518-374-4098. E-Mail: info@frcschdy.org. Web Site: www.frcschdy.org. *Coll Develop, Dir*, Joan W Ipsen; *Cat*, Alice B Reed; Staff 26 (MLS 3, Non-MLS 23)
Founded 1838
Jan 2000-Dec 2000 Income $1,643, Locally Generated Income $43, Parent Institution $1,400, Other $200. Mats Exp $1,380, Books $1,110, Per/Ser (Incl. Access Fees) $150, Presv $120
Library Holdings: Bk Titles 7,600
Subject Interests: Art, History, Literature, Music, Religion
Special Collections: Children's Coll; Christmas Coll
Special Services for the Deaf - Books on deafness & sign language

S KAPL INC LIBRARIES, 2401 River Rd, 12309. (Mail add: PO Box 7400, 12301), SAN 371-0998. Tel: 518-395-4000, 518-395-4317. FAX: 518-395-7761. *Mgr*, Mike Gerard; *Librn*, Patricia Oliver
Library Holdings: Bk Vols 34,000; Bk Titles 500; Per Subs 400

P MOHAWK VALLEY LIBRARY ASSOCIATION,* 858 Duanesburg Rd, 12306-1095. SAN 312-438X. Interlibrary Loan Service Tel: 518-355-2010. FAX: 518-355-0674. E-Mail: mvl_cling@sals.edu. Web Site: www.mvla.org. *Dir*, Carol Clingan; *Ad Servs, Electronic Resources*, Rebekah Tanner; E-Mail: mvl_tanne@sals.edu; *Automation Syst Coordr, ILL*, Valerie Catlin; E-Mail: mvl_rokos@sals.edu; *Ch Servs, YA Servs*, Sue Z Rokos; E-Mail: mvl_rokos@sals.edu; *Outreach Serv*, Lois Gordon; E-Mail: mvl_gordo@sals.edu; Staff 18 (MLS 4, Non-MLS 14)
Founded 1959. Pop 287,316
Library Holdings: Bk Vols 119,177
Publications: MVLA Connection (Newsletter)
Member Libraries: Amsterdam Free Library; Canajoharie Library & Art Gallery; Cobleskill Public Library; Fort Hunter Free Library; Fort Plain Free Library; Frothingham Free Library; Gloversville Free Library; Johnstown Public Library; Margaret Reaney Memorial Library; Middleburgh Library Association; Northville Public Library; Schenectady County Public Library; Schoharie Free Library Association; Sharon Springs Free Library
Partic in Cap District Libr Coun for Ref & Res Resources

S REMOVE INTOXICATED DRIVERS-USA LIBRARY, 1013 Nott St, PO Box 520, 12301. SAN 377-4252. Tel: 518-372-0034. FAX: 518-370-4917. E-Mail: dwi@rid-use.org. Web Site: www.rid-usa.org. *Pres*, Doris Aiken
Library Holdings: Bk Vols 1,000

M ST CLARE'S HOSPITAL, Medical Library, 600 McClellan St, 12304-1090. SAN 312-4398. Tel: 518-382-2000. FAX: 518-347-5520. *Dir Libr Serv*, Laurie Wasniski; E-Mail: wasniski52@hotmail.com
Library Holdings: Bk Vols 1,205; Per Subs 88
Partic in Cap District Libr Coun for Ref & Res Resources

SR SAINT GEORGE'S EPISCOPAL CHURCH, John A Howe Memorial Library, 30 N Ferry St, 12305. SAN 312-4401. Tel: 518-374-3163. FAX: 518-377-2902.
Founded 1959
Library Holdings: Bk Titles 980
Subject Interests: Anglican church hist, Biog, Dogma, Practice of faith

J SCHENECTADY COUNTY COMMUNITY COLLEGE, Begley Library, 78 Washington Ave, 12305. SAN 312-4428. Tel: 518-381-1240. FAX: 518-346-0379, 518-370-4659. Web Site: www.sunysccc.edu/library/index.html. *Dir*, Barbara Walton; *Ref*, Caroline Laier; *Per*, Peter Barvoets; *Tech Servs*, David Moore; Staff 7 (MLS 5, Non-MLS 2)
Founded 1968. Enrl 2,362
Library Holdings: Bk Vols 80,000; Bk Titles 74,000; Per Subs 420; Bks on Deafness & Sign Lang 45
Subject Interests: Culinary arts, Fire science, Hotel tech, Paralegal, Travel and tourism
Special Collections: College Memorabilia Coll
Automation Activity & Vendor Info: (Circulation) DRA; (Course Reserve) DRA; (OPAC) DRA
Database Vendor: OCLC - First Search
Publications: A Guide to Begley Library & the Instructional Technology Center
Partic in Cap District Libr Coun for Ref & Res Resources; OCLC Online Computer Library Center, Inc

S SCHENECTADY COUNTY HISTORICAL SOCIETY, Grems-Doolittle Library, 32 Washington Ave, 12305. SAN 321-0030. Tel: 518-374-0263. FAX: 208-361-5305. E-Mail: librarian@schist.org. Web Site: www.schist.org. *In Charge*, Virginia LaGoy; Staff 1 (MLS 1)
Founded 1905
Library Holdings: Bk Vols 3,500; Per Subs 8
Subject Interests: Genealogy, Local history
Special Collections: Schenectady County Historical Society
Publications: A History of the Schenectady PATENT; The Markers Speak
Restriction: Not a lending library
Function: Research fees apply

P SCHENECTADY COUNTY PUBLIC LIBRARY, 99 Clinton St, 12305-2083. SAN 354-1266. Tel: 518-388-4500. Interlibrary Loan Service Tel: 518-388-4518. FAX: 518-386-2241. Web Site: www.scpl.org/. *Dir*, Ronald L Lagasse; Tel: 518-388-4543, E-Mail: scp_lagas@sals.edu; *Asst Dir, Br Coordr*, Wonja Brucker; *Asst Dir*, Andrew Kulmatiski; Tel: 518-388-4545, E-Mail: scp_kulma@sals.edu; *ILL*, Betsy Rock; *Ch Servs*, Serena Butch; *Ref Servs YA*, JoAnn Adams; *Ref*, Timothy McGowan; *Tech Servs*, Diane E McDougall; *AV*, Kenneth Wagner; Staff 84 (MLS 24, Non-MLS 60)
Founded 1894. Pop 149,285; Circ 857,690
Jan 1999-Dec 1999 Income (Main Library and Branch Library) $4,039,877, State $234,160, Federal $23,624, County $3,607,922, Locally Generated Income $172,470. Mats Exp $564,860, Books $335,138, Per/Ser (Incl. Access Fees) $119,549, Presv $15,000, Micro $18,000, AV Equip $38,942, Other Print Mats $2,512, Electronic Ref Mat (Incl. Access Fees) $16,429. Sal $2,477,980 (Prof $1,362,889)
Library Holdings: Bk Vols 532,237; Bk Titles 169,088; Per Subs 1,710
Automation Activity & Vendor Info: (Cataloging) DRA; (Circulation) DRA
Database Vendor: Ebsco - EbscoHost, IAC - Info Trac
Mem of Mohawk Valley Library Association
Partic in Capital District Library Council for Reference & Research Resources
Friends of the Library Group
Branches: 9
DUANE, 1331 State St, 12304. SAN 354-1290. Tel: 518-386-2242. FAX: 518-386-2242. *Librn*, Eleanor Alger-Monlea
Library Holdings: Bk Vols 18,190
GLENVILLLE, 20 Glenridge Rd, Scotia, 12302. SAN 370-9299. Tel: 518-386-2243. FAX: 518-386-2243. *Librn*, Paula Carosella
Library Holdings: Bk Vols 25,587
HAMILTON HILL Tel: 518-386-2244. *Librn*, Dorothy Neff
Library Holdings: Bk Vols 13,083
MONT PLEASANT, 1026 Crane St, 12306. SAN 354-1320. Tel: 518-386-2245. FAX: 518-386-2245. *Librn*, Ann Moore
Library Holdings: Bk Vols 18,283
NISKAYUNA, 2400 Nott St E, 12309. SAN 370-128X. Tel: 518-386-2249. FAX: 518-386-2249. *Librn*, Ann Moore
Library Holdings: Bk Vols 29,797
QUAKER STREET-DUANESBURG, Quaker St, 12141. SAN 354-1339. Tel: 518-895-2719. FAX: 518-895-2719. *Librn*, Frances Brown
Library Holdings: Bk Vols 19,835
ROTTERDAM, 2558 Guilderland Ave, 12306. SAN 354-138X. Tel: 518-356-3440. FAX: 518-356-3440. *Librn*, Frances Brown
Library Holdings: Bk Vols 31,846
SCOTIA BRANCH, 14 Mohawk Ave, Scotia, 12302. SAN 354-1355. Tel: 518-386-2247. FAX: 518-366-2247. *Librn*, Paula Carosella
Library Holdings: Bk Vols 20,768
WOODLAWN, 2 Sanford St, 12304. SAN 354-141X. Tel: 518-386-2248. FAX: 518-386-2248. *Librn*, Wonja K Brucker
Library Holdings: Bk Vols 23,823

S SCHENECTADY INTERNATIONAL, INC, Henry Howard Wright Research Center Library, 2750 Balltown Rd, 12309-1094. SAN 312-441X. Tel: 518-347-4401. FAX: 518-347-6401. *Mgr, Tech Servs*, Marsha J Shea; E-Mail: marsha.shea@siigroup.com; Staff 2 (MLS 1, Non-MLS 1)
Founded 1968
Library Holdings: Bk Vols 1,610
Subject Interests: Polymer chemistry
Partic in Cap District Libr Coun for Ref & Res Resources

C UNION COLLEGE, Schaffer Library, 807 Union St, 12308. SAN 354-1479. Tel: 518-388-6277. Interlibrary Loan Service Tel: 518-388-6282. Circulation Tel: 518-388-6280. Reference Tel: 518-388-6281. FAX: 388-6619, 518-388-6641. Web Site: www.union.edu/public/library/. *Dir*, Thomas G McFadden; *Tech Servs*, Annette LeClair; Tel: 518-388-6631, E-Mail: leclaira@union.edu; *Coll Develop*, Maribeth Krupezak; Tel: 518-388-6632, E-Mail: krupczam@union.edu; *ILL*, Mary Cahill; Tel: 518-388-6612, E-Mail: cahillm@union.edu; *Publ Servs*, David Gerhan; *Archivist*, Ellen Fladger; Tel: 518-388-6620, E-Mail: fladgere@union.edu; *Bibliog Instr*, Bruce Connolly; *Govt Doc*, Donna Burton; *Access Serv*, Carca Molyneaux; Tel: 518-388-6279, E-Mail: molyneac@union.edu; Staff 26 (MLS 13, Non-MLS 13)
Founded 1795. Enrl 2,308; Fac 189
Jul 1999-Jun 2000 Mats Exp $1,333,847, Books $273,796, Per/Ser (Incl. Access Fees) $797,847, Presv $35,922, Micro $97,916, Electronic Ref Mat (Incl. Access Fees) $128,366. Sal $1,057,569 (Prof $726,732)
Library Holdings: Bk Vols 539,809; Bk Titles 286,503; Per Subs 1,519
Special Collections: 19th Century American Wit & Humor (Bailey Coll); French Civilization to End of 19th Century (John Bigelow Library Coll); Local History (Schenectady Coll); Manuscript Coll; Microscopy (Kellert Coll); Rare Book Coll; Science & Technology (Schenectady Archives of Science & Technology Coll), personal papers of various General Electric Co Scientists; Union College Archives; William J Stillman Coll
Automation Activity & Vendor Info: (Acquisitions) DRA; (Cataloging) DRA; (Circulation) DRA
Database Vendor: Ebsco - EbscoHost, Lexis-Nexis, OCLC - First Search, ProQuest, Silverplatter Information Inc.
Publications: Friends of the Library; Occasional Publications; Union College Faculty Bibliography
Partic in Capital District Library Council for Reference & Research Resources; OCLC Online Computer Library Center, Inc
Friends of the Library Group

SCHOHARIE

S SCHOHARIE COUNTY HISTORICAL SOCIETY, Historical Museum Reference Library, N Main St, RR 2 Box 30A, 12157. SAN 312-4452. Tel: 518-295-7192. FAX: 518-295-7187. *Dir*, Carle Kopecky; *Archivist, Librn*, Christine Palmatier
Founded 1889
Library Holdings: Bk Vols 2,000; Bk Titles 1,600
Subject Interests: Genealogy, Local history, NY state hist
Special Collections: Area Business Papers; Area Town/County/Village

Papers; Civil War Papers; Folklore & Folklife
Publications: Schoharie County Historical Review
Restriction: Not a lending library, Open to public with supervision only

P SCHOHARIE FREE LIBRARY ASSOCIATION, Mary Beatrice Cushing Memorial Library, 119 Knower Ave, 12157-1713. (Mail add: PO Box 519, 12157-0519), SAN 312-4460. Tel: 518-295-7127. FAX: 518-295-7127. E-Mail: sholib@telenet.net. Web Site: www2.telenet.net/community/mvla/scho. *Librn*, Catherine Caiazzo
Pop 1,016; Circ 15,148
Library Holdings: Bk Titles 19,000; Per Subs 42
Mem of Mohawk Valley Library Association
Open Mon 9-12, Tues 12-5:30, Thurs 1-5 & 7-9, Fri 12:30-6, Sat 9-12:30, June-Aug 11-2:30

SCHROON LAKE

P SCHROON LAKE PUBLIC LIBRARY,* South Ave, PO Box 398, 12870. SAN 312-4479. Tel: 518-532-7737. FAX: 518-532-9474. *Librn*, Jane Bouchard
Library Holdings: Bk Vols 30,000; Per Subs 35
Mem of Clinton-Essex-Franklin Library System

SCHUYLERVILLE

P SCHUYLERVILLE PUBLIC LIBRARY, 52 Ferry St, 12871. SAN 312-4487. Tel: 518-695-6641. *Librn*, Jane Rodeheaver
Circ 14,691
Library Holdings: Bk Vols 14,054; Per Subs 177
Mem of Southern Adirondack Library System
Open Mon & Fri 2-5 & 7-9, Wed 7-9, Thurs & Sat 2-5
Friends of the Library Group

SCIO

P SCIO FREE LIBRARY,* PO Box 77, 14880-0075. SAN 312-4495. Tel: 716-593-4816. *Librn*, Betty Chalker; Staff 1 (Non-MLS 1)
Founded 1906. Pop 1,900; Circ 7,500
Library Holdings: Bk Vols 6,100; Per Subs 37
Subject Interests: Civil War, Crafts, Genealogy, Quilting
Mem of Southern Tier Library System
Open Tues & Thurs 1-7, Fri 12-5 & Sat 9-12
Friends of the Library Group

SCOTTSVILLE

P SCOTTSVILLE FREE LIBRARY, 28 Main St, 14546. SAN 312-4509. Tel: 716-889-2023. FAX: 716-889-7938. *Dir*, Jacquelyn DiNolfo
Founded 1917. Pop 5,092; Circ 56,121
Library Holdings: Bk Vols 42,391; Per Subs 51
Mem of Monroe County Library System
Friends of the Library Group

SEA CLIFF

P SEA CLIFF VILLAGE LIBRARY,* Sea Cliff Ave, 11579-0280. SAN 312-4517. Tel: 516-671-4290. FAX: 516-759-6613. *Dir*, Linda Kundla
Circ 39,390
Library Holdings: Bk Vols 35,102; Per Subs 105
Publications: Newsletter
Mem of Nassau Library System

SEAFORD

M MASSAPEQUA GENERAL HOSPITAL, Medical Library,* 750 Hicksville Rd, 11783. SAN 377-2098. Tel: 516-520-3249. FAX: 516-520-6069.

G NASSAU COUNTY MUSEUM, Tackapausha Museum Library, Washington Ave, 11783. SAN 327-2230. Tel: 516-571-7443. E-Mail: tackapausha@yahoo.com. *Curator*, Carole Neidich Ryder
Library Holdings: Bk Vols 1,000
Special Collections: Natural History
Restriction: Staff use only

P SEAFORD PUBLIC LIBRARY, 2234 Jackson Ave, 11783. SAN 312-4525. Tel: 516-221-1334. FAX: 516-826-8133. E-Mail: selcirc@nassau.nls.lib.ny.us. Web Site: www.nassaulibrary.org/seaford. *Dir*, Judith Schimmel; Staff 31 (MLS 9, Non-MLS 22)
Founded 1956. Pop 16,591; Circ 159,592
Jul 1998-Jun 1999 Income $1,164,569, State $4,200. Mats Exp $1,177,110, Books $110,704, Per/Ser (Incl. Access Fees) $25,100, AV Equip $15,404. Sal $634,615 (Prof $347,390)
Library Holdings: Bk Vols 81,583
Automation Activity & Vendor Info: (Acquisitions) DRA; (Cataloging) DRA; (Circulation) DRA; (Course Reserve) DRA; (ILL) DRA; (Media Booking) DRA; (OPAC) DRA; (Serials) DRA
Publications: Newsletter (monthly)
Mem of Nassau Library System
Partic in Long Island Library Resources Council
Friends of the Library Group

SELDEN

SUFFOLK COUNTY COMMUNITY COLLEGE
J AMMERMAN CAMPUS LIBRARY, 533 College Rd, 11784-2899. SAN 354-1568. Tel: 516-451-4177. Interlibrary Loan Service Tel: 516-451-4170. FAX: 516-451-4697. Web Site: www.sunysuffok.edu/webiselden/library/ready/htm. *Circ, ILL*, Carol Gambrell; *Ref*, Tom Phillips; *Per*, Marcia Jefferson; *AV*, Kevin McCoy; *Coll Develop*, Frances Kelly; Staff 7 (MLS 7)
Founded 1960. Enrl 12,870; Fac 300
Library Holdings: Bk Vols 124,610; Bk Titles 105,345; Per Subs 712
Subject Interests: Allied health, Bus, Nursing
Special Collections: Long Island Coll
Publications: Centralized media & periodicals catalog; newsletter; student handbook
Partic in Long Island Library Resources Council

SENECA FALLS

P MYNDERSE LIBRARY, 31 Fall St, 13148. SAN 312-455X. Tel: 315-568-8265. FAX: 315-568-1606. Web Site: www.flls.org. *Librn*, Michael Caraher; E-Mail: mcaraher@lakenet.org
Founded 1888. Pop 7,370; Circ 34,901
1999-2000 Income $80,000
Library Holdings: Bk Vols 25,943; Per Subs 61
Special Collections: DAR Coll; Genealogy Coll
Mem of Finger Lakes Library System
Open Mon & Fri 9-5, Tues-Thurs 2-9, Sat 2-5
Friends of the Library Group

M NEW YORK CHIROPRACTIC COLLEGE LIBRARY,* 2360 State Rte 89, Box 800, 13148-0800. SAN 320-457X. Tel: 315-568-3244. FAX: 315-568-3119. *Dir*, Daniel Kanaley; E-Mail: dkanaley@nycc.edu; Staff 3 (MLS 3)
Founded 1919. Enrl 763
Sep 1997-Aug 1998 Income $705,526, State $5,589, Locally Generated Income $2,012. Mats Exp $110,942, Books $18,776, Per/Ser (Incl. Access Fees) $71,585, Presv $5,158, AV Equip $1,368. Sal $265,831
Library Holdings: Bk Vols 12,826; Bk Titles 11,000; Per Subs 339
Subject Interests: Chiropractic, Chiropractic hist, Health sci
Publications: Acquisition list (monthly); research aids; Shelf Notes (quarterly newsletter)
Partic in Chiropractic Libr Consortium; S Cent Res Libr Coun
Open Mon-Thurs 7:45-1am, Fri 7:45-10pm, Sat 10am-10pm & Sun noon-midnight (hours vary during school year)

S SENECA FALLS HISTORICAL SOCIETY LIBRARY, 55 Cayuga St, 13148. SAN 329-4307. Tel: 315-568-8412. FAX: 315-568-8426. E-Mail: sfhs@flare.net. *Dir*, Lisa Compton; Staff 2 (Non-MLS 2)
Founded 1896
Library Holdings: Bk Titles 1,500; Per Subs 10
Subject Interests: Seneca County hist, Seneca Falls hist, Victorian era
Special Collections: Civil War; Women's Rights
Restriction: In-house use for visitors
Function: Research library
Open Mon-Fri 9-4

SETAUKET

P EMMA S CLARK MEMORIAL LIBRARY,* 120 Main St, 11733-2868. SAN 312-4568. Tel: 516-941-4080. FAX: 516-941-4541. E-Mail: emsclib@suffolk.lib.ny.us. Web Site: emma.suffolk.lib.ny.us. *Dir*, Edward Elenausky; *Ref*, Phyllis Akins; *Circ*, Aileen Clark; *Ch Servs*, Marge Bengston
Founded 1892. Pop 42,168; Circ 593,193
Jan 1999-Dec 1999 Income $2,584,508. Mats Exp $454,000. Sal $1,498,308
Library Holdings: Bk Vols 200,000; Per Subs 436
Subject Interests: Long Island hist
Automation Activity & Vendor Info: (Cataloging) Innovative Interfaces Inc.; (Circulation) Innovative Interfaces Inc.; (ILL) Innovative Interfaces Inc.; (OPAC) Innovative Interfaces Inc.
Mem of Suffolk Cooperative Library System

SHARON SPRINGS

P SHARON SPRINGS FREE LIBRARY,* Main St, PO Box 268, 13459. SAN 312-4576. Tel: 518-284-2625. FAX: 518-284-3126. E-Mail: shalib@telenet.net. *Dir*, Mary Ellen Wolfe
Circ 5,527
1997-1998 Income $11,170, State $1,200, City $700, Locally Generated Income $710, Other $330. Mats Exp Books $2,600. Sal $5,980

Library Holdings: Bk Vols 5,995
Mem of Mohawk Valley Library Association
Open Mon 12-4 & 6-9, Wed 5-9, Fri 12-5 & Sat 9-1

SHELTER ISLAND

P SHELTER ISLAND PUBLIC LIBRARY,* 37 N Ferry Rd, PO Box 2016, 11964-2016. SAN 312-4584. Tel: 516-749-0042. FAX: 516-749-1575. *Dir*, Kathleen Henry
Founded 1885. Circ 23,565
Library Holdings: Bk Vols 21,414; Per Subs 6
Special Collections: Local History Coll
Mem of Suffolk Cooperative Library System
Open Mon, Wed & Fri 11-5, Tues & Thurs 11-8 & Sat 10-4

SHERBURNE

S ROGERS ENVIRONMENTAL EDUCATION CENTER, Hotchkin Memorial Library, 2721 State Hwy 80, 13460. (Mail add: PO Box 932, 13460), SAN 327-2214. Tel: 607-674-4017. FAX: 607-674-2655. Web Site: www.ascent.net/rogers/. *Dir*, Marsha Guzewich
Founded 1968
Library Holdings: Bk Vols 2,100; Per Subs 18
Restriction: Not a lending library
Function: Research library
Friends of the Library Group

P SHERBURNE PUBLIC LIBRARY,* 2 E State St, 13460. SAN 312-4592. Tel: 607-674-4242.
Pop 3,903; Circ 29,384
Library Holdings: Bk Vols 17,000; Per Subs 60
Database Vendor: DRA
Mem of Four County Library System
Open Mon-Wed 1-8:30, Thurs & Fri 10-5 & Sat 10-12
Friends of the Library Group

SHERMAN

P MINERVA FREE LIBRARY, 116 Miller, PO Box 588, 14781-0588. SAN 312-4606. Tel: 716-761-6378. FAX: 716-761-6378. E-Mail: shermlib@cecomet.net. Web Site: www2.cecomet.net/shermlib/. *Librn*, Shellie Williams
Founded 1907. Pop 1,505; Circ 6,738
1998-1999 Income $13,660, Locally Generated Income $252, Other $2,848. Mats Exp $2,903, Books $1,891, Per/Ser (Incl. Access Fees) $839. Sal $5,323
Library Holdings: Bk Vols 13,488; Per Subs 15
Mem of Chautauqua-Cattaraugus Library System
Friends of the Library Group

SHERRILL

P SHERRILL-KENWOOD FREE LIBRARY,* 543 Sherrill Rd, 13461-1263. SAN 312-4614. Tel: 315-363-5980. FAX: 315-363-4133. *Dir*, Bonnie Unsworth; Staff 1 (MLS 1)
Founded 1910. Pop 3,187; Circ 35,360
Library Holdings: Bk Vols 21,000; Bk Titles 20,000; Per Subs 50
Mem of Mid-York Library System

SHIRLEY

P MASTICS-MORICHES-SHIRLEY COMMUNITY LIBRARY, 407 William Floyd Pkwy, 11967. SAN 312-4622. Tel: 631-399-1511. FAX: 631-281-4442. E-Mail: mmshlib@suffolk.lib.ny.us. Web Site: www.communitylibrary.org. *Dir*, William Cicola; E-Mail: wcicola@suffolk.lib.ny.us; *Ad Servs, ILL, Ref*, Laurie Hastings; *Ch Servs*, Kathleen Deerr; *Circ*, Annamay Adams; *YA Servs*, Teri Germano; Staff 20 (MLS 20)
Founded 1974. Pop 44,752; Circ 597,919
Jul 1999-Jun 2000 Income $4,615,849. Mats Exp $427,284, Books $297,457, Per/Ser (Incl. Access Fees) $51,466, Micro $78,361. Sal $2,309,550 (Prof $1,127,245)
Library Holdings: Bk Vols 307,096; Bk Titles 165,000; Per Subs 573
Subject Interests: Italian lang, Large print, Local history, Spanish
Automation Activity & Vendor Info: (Acquisitions) Innovative Interfaces Inc.; (Cataloging) Innovative Interfaces Inc.; (Circulation) Innovative Interfaces Inc.; (ILL) Innovative Interfaces Inc.; (OPAC) Innovative Interfaces Inc.
Publications: Newsletter
Mem of Suffolk Cooperative Library System
Partic in Long Island Library Resources Council

SHOREHAM

P NORTH SHORE PUBLIC LIBRARY, 250 Rte 25A, 11786-9677. SAN 320-4960. Tel: 631-929-4488. FAX: 631-929-4551. E-Mail: nspl@suffolk.lib.ny.us. Web Site: www.nspl.suffolk.lib.ny.us. *Dir*, Elaine Brecha; *Acq*, L Hawrey; *Ch Servs*, L Blend; *Ch Servs*, D Caracciolo; *Circ*, R Barbera; *Circ*, J Tousey; *ILL*, M Sokolski; *Ref*, R Hawkins; *Ref*, J O'Hare; *Ser*, J Gatto; *YA Servs*, K Welch; Staff 34 (MLS 12, Non-MLS 22)
Founded 1975. Pop 22,933; Circ 285,000
Jul 2000-Jun 2001 Income $2,465,200. Mats Exp $403,900, Books $191,500, Per/Ser (Incl. Access Fees) $45,400, Presv $300, AV Equip $86,400, Electronic Ref Mat (Incl. Access Fees) $80,300. Sal $1,229,300 (Prof $705,800)
Library Holdings: Bk Titles 106,472; Per Subs 325
Automation Activity & Vendor Info: (Acquisitions) Innovative Interfaces Inc.; (Cataloging) Innovative Interfaces Inc.; (Circulation) Innovative Interfaces Inc.; (Serials) Innovative Interfaces Inc.
Mem of Suffolk Cooperative Library System
Friends of the Library Group

SHRUB OAK

P JOHN C HART MEMORIAL LIBRARY, 1130 Main St, 10588. SAN 354-1622. Tel: 914-245-5262. FAX: 914-245-2216. Web Site: www.wls.lib.ny.us/lib/yorktown. *Ad Servs*, James Cahill; *Dir*, Patricia Barresi; Tel: 914-245-1598, Fax: 914-245-5936, E-Mail: pbarresi@wls.lib.ny.us; *Ref*, Patricia Hallinan; *Circ*, Sandra Norman; *Ch Servs*, Janet Carlson; *Tech Servs*, Patricia Anton
Founded 1920. Pop 35,000
Jan 2000-Dec 2000 Income $1,300,387. Mats Exp $170,500, Books $95,000, Per/Ser (Incl. Access Fees) $43,300. Sal $738,986 (Prof $442,265)
Library Holdings: Bk Titles 99,276; Per Subs 205
Special Collections: Special Education (Jerome Thaler Weather Coll)
Database Vendor: epixtech, inc.
Mem of Westchester Library System
Open Mon-Thurs 9:30-8, Fri & Sat 9:30-5, Sun 1-5 (Oct-Apr)
Friends of the Library Group

SIDNEY

S AMPHENOL AEROSPACE INC LIBRARY,* 40-60 Delaware St, 13838. SAN 374-907X. Tel: 607-563-5011. FAX: 607-563-5669.
Library Holdings: Bk Titles 300

P SIDNEY MEMORIAL PUBLIC LIBRARY,* 8 River St, 13838. SAN 312-4649. Tel: 607-563-1200, 607-563-8021. FAX: 607-563-7675. Web Site: www.lib.4cty.org/sidney/smpl.htm. *Librn*, Janice Vartuli; E-Mail: si_Janice@4cty.org
Founded 1887. Pop 8,396
Jul 1999-Jun 2000 Income $432,322, State $5,556, Locally Generated Income $426,766. Mats Exp $74,400, Books $39,000, Per/Ser (Incl. Access Fees) $5,800, AV Equip $3,000, Electronic Ref Mat (Incl. Access Fees) $26,600. Sal $262,222
Library Holdings: Bk Vols 55,928; Bk Titles 44,572; Per Subs 206
Subject Interests: Local history
Database Vendor: DRA
Publications: Newsletter
Mem of Four County Library System
Open Mon-Thurs 9-9, Fri 9-6, Sat 9-3 & Sun 1-4

SILVER CREEK

P ANDERSON-LEE LIBRARY,* 43 Main St, 14136. SAN 312-4657. Tel: 716-934-3468. FAX: 716-934-3037. Web Site: www.cclslib.org/silver~l/silver~/.htm. *Librn*, Sandra Apthorpe; Staff 1 (MLS 1)
Founded 1924. Circ 57,028
1998-1999 Income $38,340, City $9,000, Locally Generated Income $6,000, Parent Institution $3,000, Other $3,000. Mats Exp $4,000, Books $3,200, Per/Ser (Incl. Access Fees) $800. Sal $22,700 (Prof $13,700)
Library Holdings: Bk Vols 25,000
Subject Interests: Large print, Local history
Mem of Chautauqua-Cattaraugus Library System
Friends of the Library Group

SILVER SPRINGS

P TOWN OF GAINESVILLE PUBLIC LIBRARY,* 10 Church St, PO Box 321, 14550-0321. SAN 312-4665. Tel: 716-493-2970. FAX: 716-493-2970. *In Charge*, Mary Mann
Circ 12,289
Library Holdings: Bk Vols 12,500
Mem of Pioneer Library System
Open Mon & Fri 2-4:30, Tues & Thurs 2-4:30 & 6-8:30, Sat 9-12

SINCLAIRVILLE

P SINCLAIRVILLE FREE LIBRARY,* Lester St, PO Box 609, 14782-0609. SAN 312-4673. Tel: 716-962-5885. FAX: 716-962-5885. *Librn*, Pat Webb; Staff 2 (MLS 2)
Founded 1870. Pop 772; Circ 29,000

1998-1999 Income $6,173, State $4,102, City $2,071. Mats Exp $11,342. Sal $5,371
Library Holdings: Bk Vols 12,800; Per Subs 35
Subject Interests: Local history
Mem of Chautauqua-Cattaraugus Library System
Open Mon & Thurs 7-9, Tues 10-12, Wed & Sat 1-5, Fri 10-12 & 1-5

SKANEATELES

P SKANEATELES LIBRARY ASSOCIATION, 49 E Genesee, 13152. SAN 312-4681. Tel: 315-685-5135. *Librn*, DeAnn Porter; *Coll Develop*, Elizabeth LaPorte
Founded 1878. Circ 104,946
Jan 1999-Dec 1999 Income Locally Generated Income $50,000. Mats Exp $26,900, Books $21,000, Per/Ser (Incl. Access Fees) $3,400, Micro $2,500. Sal $58,900
Library Holdings: Bk Titles 26,682; Per Subs 90
Subject Interests: Art, Arts, Crafts, Gardening, History, Local history
Special Collections: Barrow Art Gallery (local artist's work late 19th century); Large Print Books Coll; Unabridged Book-on-Tapes
Automation Activity & Vendor Info: (Cataloging) Follett; (Circulation) Follett; (OPAC) Follett

SLOATSBURG

P SLOATSBURG PUBLIC LIBRARY, One Liberty Rock Rd, 10974-2392. SAN 322-8355. Tel: 845-753-2001. FAX: 845-753-2144. Web Site: www.bestweb.net/~slolib. *Dir*, Dot Guerrera; Staff 1 (Non-MLS 1)
Founded 1959. Pop 3,035; Circ 41,000
Jan 2000-Dec 2000 Income $328,610, City $76,000, County $7,500, Locally Generated Income $7,500, Parent Institution $1,500, Other $236,110. Mats Exp $67,000, Books $35,000, Per/Ser (Incl. Access Fees) $5,000, AV Equip $8,000, Other Print Mats $5,000, Electronic Ref Mat (Incl. Access Fees) $14,000. Sal $128,600 (Prof $37,100)
Library Holdings: Bk Vols 31,587; Per Subs 95
Subject Interests: Local history
Automation Activity & Vendor Info: (Circulation) epixtech, inc.
Publications: Books & Beyond (Newsletter)
Mem of Ramapo Catskill Library System
Friends of the Library Group

SMITHTOWN

M SAINT CATHERINE OF SIENA MEDICAL CENTER LIBRARY, 50 Rte 25 A, 11787. SAN 312-4703. Tel: 631-862-3000, 631-862-3186. FAX: 631-862-3576. E-Mail: smmedlib@i-zooo.com. *Librn*, George Gmygeasiewez
Founded 1966
Library Holdings: Bk Titles 400
Subject Interests: Health care admin, Medicine

S SMITHTOWN HISTORICAL SOCIETY LIBRARY,* 5 N Country Rd, 11787. SAN 328-3313. Tel: 516-265-6768. FAX: 516-265-6768. Web Site: www.smithtownhistorical.org. *Dir*, Barbara Lee Moss
Library Holdings: Bk Titles 500
Subject Interests: Genealogy, Local history

P SMITHTOWN LIBRARY,* One N Country Rd, 11787. SAN 354-1657. Tel: 516-265-2072. FAX: 516-265-2044. *Dir*, Peter Ward; *Cat*, Suzanne McManus; *Circ*, Patricia Fisher; *Doc, Ref*, Arlene Lesser; *Per*, Fern Gutman; *Ad Servs*, Gladys Jan-Bicklee; *Ch Servs*, Mary Louis Nicholls; *Rare Bks, Spec Coll*, Richard Hawkins; *Acq*, Anita Lee; *Automation Syst Coordr*, Alice Lepore; *Coll Develop*, Pat Weltsch; Staff 117 (MLS 32, Non-MLS 85)
Founded 1905. Pop 113,406; Circ 991,032
1997-1998 Income $5,830,781, State $35,000, Other $196,500. Mats Exp $247,578, Books $201,193, Per/Ser (Incl. Access Fees) $16,125, Micro $30,260. Sal $3,450,081 (Prof $1,543,242)
Library Holdings: Bk Vols 427,208; Per Subs 975
Subject Interests: Behav sci, Bus, Mgt, Soc sci
Special Collections: Long Island (Richard Handley & Charles E Lawrence Coll), bk, mss, fiche, microflm
Publications: Inside Your Library (monthly)
Mem of Suffolk Cooperative Library System
Friends of the Library Group
Branches: 3
COMMACK BRANCH, 3 Indian Head Rd, Commack, 11725. SAN 354-1681. Tel: 516-543-0998. FAX: 516-543-0661. *Librn*, Joan Guadagno
Library Holdings: Bk Vols 100,000
Friends of the Library Group
KINGS PARK BRANCH, One Church St, Kings Park, 11754. SAN 354-1711. Tel: 516-269-9191. FAX: 516-269-0807.
Library Holdings: Bk Vols 63,000
Friends of the Library Group
NESCONSET BRANCH, 127-20 Smithtown Blvd, Nesconset, 11767. SAN 354-1746. Tel: 516-265-3994. FAX: 516-265-8158. *Librn*, Ina Gravitz
Library Holdings: Bk Vols 68,000
Friends of the Library Group

SMYRNA

P SMYRNA PUBLIC LIBRARY,* 607 Main St, PO Box 202, 13464. SAN 312-472X. Tel: 607-627-6271. *Dir*, Eileen Carson
Pop 1,265; Circ 4,169
Library Holdings: Bk Vols 4,500
Mem of Four County Library System
Open Mon 7-9, Tues 3-5, Wed 1-5, Thurs 3-5 & 7-9, Sat 10-12

SODUS

P SODUS FREE LIBRARY,* 17 Maple Ave, 14551. SAN 312-4738. Tel: 315-483-9292. FAX: 315-483-9616. *Dir*, Carol Garland
Founded 1907. Pop 1,667; Circ 37,300
Library Holdings: Bk Vols 8,000; Per Subs 80
Special Collections: Antique Books & Periodicals of Collectibles; Crocks; Glass (Clyde); Jars (Lyons); Jugs
Mem of Pioneer Library System
Friends of the Library Group

SOLVAY

P SOLVAY PUBLIC LIBRARY,* 615 Woods Rd, 13209-1697. SAN 312-4754. Tel: 315-468-2441. FAX: 315-468-0373. E-Mail: solvaylib@hotmail.com. *Dir*, Geoffrey Socha; Staff 13 (MLS 1, Non-MLS 12)
Founded 1903. Pop 6,717; Circ 95,000
Jun 1998-May 1999 Income $232,530, State $1,900, City $220,000, Locally Generated Income $5,000, Other $5,630. Mats Exp $37,705, Books $31,559, Per/Ser (Incl. Access Fees) $3,400, AV Equip $2,746. Sal $109,139 (Prof $34,500)
Library Holdings: Bk Vols 30,000; Per Subs 75
Special Collections: Local History; Solvay Process Co
Automation Activity & Vendor Info: (Circulation) epixtech, inc.
Mem of Onondaga County Public Library

SOMERS

S SOMERS HISTORICAL SOCIETY LIBRARY, Dr Hugh Grant Rowell Circus Library Collection,* Elephant Hotel, 335 Rte 100, PO Box 336, 10589. SAN 328-333X. Tel: 914-277-4977. FAX: 914-277-4977. *Curator*, Terry Ariano
Library Holdings: Bk Vols 450
Subject Interests: Circus memorabilia, Genealogy

P SOMERS LIBRARY, Reis Park, Rte 139, PO Box 443, 10589. SAN 312-4762. Tel: 914-232-5717. FAX: 914-232-1035. Web Site: www.somerslibrary.org. *Dir*, Pamela Thornton; *Ref, Tech Servs*, Emily Dillon; E-Mail: edillon@wls.lib.ny.us; *Ch Servs*, Cathy Bashaw; *YA Servs*, Paula Clinchy; Staff 20 (MLS 5, Non-MLS 15)
Founded 1876. Pop 16,216; Circ 119,884
Jan 1999-Dec 1999 Income $504,263, State $3,600, City $488,463, Locally Generated Income $11,500, Other $700. Mats Exp $66,968, Books $46,703, Per/Ser (Incl. Access Fees) $15,839, Micro $3,134, Electronic Ref Mat (Incl. Access Fees) $1,292. Sal $281,779 (Prof $106,617)
Library Holdings: Bk Vols 61,920; Per Subs 120
Subject Interests: Circus bks, Somers local hist
Database Vendor: epixtech, inc.
Publications: Somers Library Friends Newsletter
Function: For research purposes
Mem of Westchester Library System
Friends of the Library Group

SONYEA

S GROVELAND CORRECTIONAL FACILITY LIBRARY,* Rte 36, Sonyea Rd, 14556-0001. SAN 327-2354. Tel: 716-658-2871. *Librn*, Doug Petric
Library Holdings: Bk Titles 20,000

SOUTH NEW BERLIN

P SOUTH NEW BERLIN FREE LIBRARY,* Rte 8, 13843-0007. SAN 312-4789. Tel: 607-859-2420. E-Mail: sn_ill@4cty.org. *Librn*, Donna Henderson
Founded 1924. Pop 600; Circ 13,829
Library Holdings: Bk Vols 6,981; Bk Titles 6,899; Per Subs 23
Mem of Four County Library System

SOUTH SALEM

P SOUTH SALEM LIBRARY,* 15 Main St, 10590. (Mail add: PO Box 477, 10590), SAN 312-4797. Tel: 914-763-3857. *Dir*, Dorothy Carr
Founded 1798. Pop 11,313; Circ 86,000
1997-1998 Income $317,240. Mats Exp $43,350, Books $38,000, Per/Ser (Incl. Access Fees) $3,200. Sal $171,000
Library Holdings: Bk Vols 44,000; Per Subs 85
Special Collections: Early Childhood Development (Ethel Horn Memorial

Coll)
Publications: Newsletter (semi-annually)
Mem of Westchester Library System
Partic in OCLC Online Computer Library Center, Inc

SOUTHAMPTON

S PARRISH ART MUSEUM LIBRARY,* 25 Jobs Lane, 11968. SAN 312-4800. Tel: 516-283-2118. FAX: 516-283-7006. *Dir*, Trudy Kramer
Founded 1955
Library Holdings: Bk Titles 5,000
Special Collections: Aline B Saarinen Library Coll; Moses & Ida Soyer Library Coll; William Merritt Chase Archives Coll

P ROGERS MEMORIAL LIBRARY,* 9 Jobs Lane, 11968. SAN 312-4819. Tel: 516-283-0774. FAX: 516-283-3717. *Coll Develop, Dir*, Lyn Ashe; *Ref*, Sue Ann Taylor; *Ch Servs*, Jane Chaleff; *ILL*, Ann Ernst; Staff 3 (MLS 3)
Founded 1895. Pop 11,600; Circ 182,000
Library Holdings: Bk Vols 76,000; Per Subs 263
Special Collections: Long Island Coll
Mem of Suffolk Cooperative Library System
Friends of the Library Group

C SOUTHAMPTON COLLEGE LIBRARY OF LONG ISLAND UNIVERSITY, Long Island University, 239 Montauk Hwy, 11968-9989. SAN 312-4827. Tel: 631-287-8376. Reference Tel: 631-287-8379. FAX: 631-287-4049. E-Mail: shlibrary@southampton.liunet.edu. Web Site: www.southampton.liunet.edu/library/library.htm. *Dir*, Robert Gerbereux; Tel: 631-287-8380, E-Mail: rgerbereux@southampton.liu.edu; *Acq*, Ruth Coleman; Tel: 631-287-8377; *Cat*, Susan Ketcham; Tel: 631-287-8378; *Online Servs, Ref*, William Roberson; Tel: 631-287-8379; *Per*, Robert Battenfeld; *ILL*, Elizabeth Herbert; Staff 5 (MLS 5)
Founded 1963. Enrl 1,200; Fac 65; Highest Degree: Master
Sep 1999-Aug 2000 Income $833,225, State $5,946, Locally Generated Income $33,079, Parent Institution $794,200. Mats Exp $365,225, Books $30,305, Per/Ser (Incl. Access Fees) $228,768, Presv $8,405, Micro $24,938. Sal $468,100 (Prof $252,450)
Library Holdings: Bk Vols 120,000; Per Subs 660
Subject Interests: Marine biology
Special Collections: History of American Theatre
Automation Activity & Vendor Info: (Acquisitions) epixtech, inc.; (Cataloging) epixtech, inc.; (Circulation) epixtech, inc.; (OPAC) epixtech, inc.; (Serials) epixtech, inc.
Database Vendor: OCLC - First Search, ProQuest, Silverplatter Information Inc.
Publications: Library Chronicle; Student & faculty handbooks
Restriction: Public use on premises
Function: ILL available, Photocopies available, Reference services available
Partic in Dialog Corporation; Long Island Library Resources Council; OCLC Online Computer Library Center, Inc
Friends of the Library Group

SOUTHOLD

S INCORPORATED LONG ISLAND CHAPTER OF THE NEW YORK STATE ARCHAEOLOGICAL ASSOCIATION, Stanton Mott Memorial Library, PO Box 268, 11971. SAN 326-274X. Tel: 631-765-5577. FAX: 631-765-5577. Web Site: www.i2.i-2000.com/~skindoc. *Pres*, Walter Smith
Library Holdings: Bk Titles 10,000; Per Subs 2,500
Special Collections: Library of New York State Archaelogic Association
Also known as Southold Indian Museum

P SOUTHOLD FREE LIBRARY, 53705 Main Rd, PO Box 697, 11971-0697. SAN 312-4843. Tel: 631-765-2077. FAX: 631-765-2197. E-Mail: sohdlib@suffolk.library.us. Web Site: www.sohd.suffolk.lib.ny.us. *Dir*, Caroline MacArthur; E-Mail: cmacarth@suffolk.lib.ny.us; Staff 15 (MLS 3, Non-MLS 12)
Founded 1797. Pop 6,000; Circ 93,267
Jan 2000-Dec 2000 Income $490,600, State $1,800, Provincial $10,000, Locally Generated Income $434,000, Other $44,800. Mats Exp $79,080, Books $60,000, Per/Ser (Incl. Access Fees) $4,280, AV Equip $14,800. Sal $266,000 (Prof $107,000)
Library Holdings: Bk Vols 35,000; Bk Titles 38,598; Per Subs 80; High Interest/Low Vocabulary Bk Vols 30
Special Collections: Southold History & Genealogy (Whitaker Coll)
Automation Activity & Vendor Info: (Cataloging) Gaylord; (Circulation) Gaylord; (Course Reserve) Gaylord; (ILL) Gaylord; (Media Booking) Gaylord; (OPAC) Gaylord
Mem of Suffolk Cooperative Library System
Special Services for the Blind - Depository for Braille Inst; Talking Books
Friends of the Library Group

S SOUTHOLD HISTORICAL SOCIETY MUSEUM LIBRARY, 54325 Main Rd, 11971. SAN 327-2192. Tel: 631-765-5500. FAX: 631-765-5500. *Pres*, Gerard Gaughran; *Archivist*, Clara Bjerknes
Founded 1965
Library Holdings: Bk Vols 1,500
Subject Interests: Local history

SPARKILL

C SAINT THOMAS AQUINAS COLLEGE, Lougheed Library, 125 Rte 340, 10976. SAN 312-4851. Tel: 845-398-4219. Reference Tel: 845-398-4218. FAX: 845-359-9537. E-Mail: library@stac.edu. Web Site: www.stac.edu. *Dir*, Suzann M Weekly; Tel: 845-398-4221, E-Mail: sweekly@stac.edu; *Head Tech Servs*, John Barth; Tel: 845-398-4222, E-Mail: jbarth@stac.edu; *Head, Ser Acq*, Nancy Cosgrove; Tel: 845-398-4214, E-Mail: ncosgrov@stac.edu; *Head, Info Serv*, Kenneth Donohue; E-Mail: kdonohue@stac.edu; *Govt Doc*, Virginia Dunnigan; Tel: 845-398-4216, E-Mail: vdunniga@stac.edu; Staff 10 (MLS 5, Non-MLS 5)
Founded 1952. Enrl 1,400; Highest Degree: Master
Jul 1999-Jun 2000 Income State $6,182. Mats Exp $221,100, Books $73,000, Per/Ser (Incl. Access Fees) $38,000, Micro $15,000, AV Equip $8,000, Electronic Ref Mat (Incl. Access Fees) $48,000
Library Holdings: Bk Vols 110,000; Bk Titles 98,978; Per Subs 548
Automation Activity & Vendor Info: (Cataloging) PALS; (Circulation) PALS
Database Vendor: Dialog, Ebsco - EbscoHost, OCLC - First Search, ProQuest, Silverplatter Information Inc., Wilson - Wilson Web
Publications: Library Guide
Function: ILL available
Mem of SE NY Libr Resources Coun
Partic in WALDO

SPENCER

P SPENCER LIBRARY,* N Main St, PO Box 305, 14883-0305. SAN 312-486X. Tel: 607-589-4496. FAX: 607-589-4496. *Librn*, Theresa Barbour
Founded 1915. Circ 22,689
Jan 1997-Dec 1998 Income $21,235, County $737, Locally Generated Income $1,668, Other $2,442. Mats Exp $5,368, Books $5,085, Per/Ser (Incl. Access Fees) $283. Sal $13,781
Library Holdings: Bk Vols 16,427; Per Subs 10
Special Collections: Spencer Needles Coll 1888-1977
Mem of Finger Lakes Library System

SPENCERPORT

P OGDEN FARMER'S LIBRARY, Farmers' Library Company of Ogden, 269 Ogden Center Rd, 14559. SAN 312-4878. Tel: 716-352-2141. FAX: 716-352-3406. Web Site: www.ogdenny.com/Library. *Dir*, Patricia Uttaro; E-Mail: uttaro@ogdenny.com; *Ch Servs*, Anne Nolan; *Ad Servs*, Kate Vreeland; *YA Servs*, Roberta Voelkl; Staff 16 (MLS 3, Non-MLS 13)
Founded 1817. Pop 16,912; Circ 179,579
Jan 1999-Dec 1999 Income $302,202, County $6,709, Locally Generated Income $36,878, Other $258,615. Mats Exp $84,309, Books $65,602, Per/Ser (Incl. Access Fees) $1,964, AV Equip $14,089, Electronic Ref Mat (Incl. Access Fees) $2,654. Sal $158,359 (Prof $82,485)
Library Holdings: Bk Vols 63,648; Per Subs 136
Special Collections: Genealogy Coll; Local History Coll
Automation Activity & Vendor Info: (Circulation) CARL
Database Vendor: CARL, Dialog, IAC - Info Trac, IAC - SearchBank
Mem of Monroe County Library System
Open Mon-Thurs 10-9 & Fri-Sat 10-5, closed Sat during summer
Friends of the Library Group

SPRING VALLEY

P FINKELSTEIN MEMORIAL LIBRARY,* 24 Chestnut St, 10977-5594. SAN 312-4886. Tel: 914-352-5700. FAX: 914-352-2319. Web Site: finkelsteinlibrary.org. *Dir*, Eleanor Kuhns; *Ch Servs*, Ann Letzter; *ILL*, Lorraine McFarland; *Business*, Richard Guarascio; *Tech Servs*, Jessie Scott; *Coordr*, Erica Grodin; *Circ, Media Spec*, Fred Sandner; *Circ*, Goldie Berland; *Coll Develop, Ref*, John Dempsey; *Ad Servs*, Susan M Brown; Staff 45 (MLS 19, Non-MLS 26)
Founded 1917. Pop 80,000; Circ 687,387
Jul 1999-Jun 2000 Income $3,835,097, County $5,000, Locally Generated Income $79,000, Other $67,000. Mats Exp $445,022, Books $410,217, Per/Ser (Incl. Access Fees) $26,902, Other Print Mats $7,903. Sal $2,266,247 (Prof $1,002,606)
Library Holdings: Bk Titles 251,298; Per Subs 536
Subject Interests: Education, Foreign Language, Holocaust, Local history
Publications: ADLIB (quarterly newsletter)
Mem of Ramapo Catskill Library System; SE NY Libr Resources Coun
Friends of the Library Group

SPRINGVILLE

P HULBERT PUBLIC LIBRARY OF THE TOWN OF CONCORD, Concord Public, 18 Chapel St, 14141. SAN 312-4908. Tel: 716-592-7742. Web Site: www.buffalolib.org. *Librn*, Annette Gernatt; E-Mail: gernatta@buffalolib.org; Staff 7 (MLS 1, Non-MLS 6)
Pop 8,171; Circ 98,768
1999-2000 Income $90,000. Mats Exp Books $25,000
Library Holdings: Bk Vols 25,000; Per Subs 52; Bks on Deafness & Sign Lang 15
Subject Interests: Bks on tape, Large print
Special Collections: West Valley Nuclear Coll
Mem of Buffalo & Erie County Public Library System

STAATSBURG

P STAATSBURG LIBRARY SOCIETY,* 70 Old Post Rd, PO Box 397, 12580-0397. SAN 312-4916. Tel: 914-889-4683. Interlibrary Loan Service Tel: 914-471-6060. FAX: 914-889-8414. E-Mail: staats@ulysses.sebridge.org. Web Site: midhudson.org/member/staats.html. *Coll Develop, Dir*, Carol Snyder
Founded 1894. Pop 3,840; Circ 9,550
Library Holdings: Bk Vols 10,291; Bk Titles 10,199; Per Subs 21
Mem of Mid-Hudson Library System
Friends of the Library Group

STAMFORD

P STAMFORD VILLAGE LIBRARY,* 117 Main St, 12167. SAN 312-4924. Tel: 607-652-5001. FAX: 607-652-5001. *Librn*, Janet Kirch Wenner
Founded 1908. Pop 1,286; Circ 18,181
Library Holdings: Bk Vols 18,794
Special Collections: Local Historical Papers & Memorabilia
Mem of Four County Library System

STANFORDVILLE

P STANFORD FREE LIBRARY,* 14 Creamery Rd, 12581. SAN 312-4932. Tel: 914-868-1341. FAX: 914-868-7482. *Librn*, Arlene Christensen
Pop 3,495; Circ 16,601
Library Holdings: Bk Vols 12,000; Per Subs 10
Mem of Mid-Hudson Library System
Open Mon, Wed & Fri 2-5, Tues & Thurs 2-7 & Sat 10-2

STATEN ISLAND

S ARTHURKILL CORRECTIONAL FACILITY LIBRARY, 2911 Arthurkill Rd, 10309. SAN 327-1145. Tel: 718-356-7333, Ext 4600. FAX: 718-356-7333, Ext 2099. *Librn*, Carl Romalis; Staff 1 (MLS 1)
Founded 1976. Pop 980
Apr 1999-Mar 2000 Mats Exp $10,000, Books $6,000, Per/Ser (Incl. Access Fees) $4,000. Sal $50,000 (Prof $48,000)
Library Holdings: Per Subs 40
Restriction: Not open to public
Separate inmate law library maintained with separate budget (not included in budget or statistics)

S CENTER FOR MIGRATION STUDIES LIBRARY, 209 Flagg Pl, 10304. SAN 321-1827. Tel: 718-351-8800. FAX: 718-667-4598. E-Mail: library@cmsny.org. Web Site: http://cmsny.library.net. *Head of Libr*, Diana J Zimmerman
Founded 1964
Library Holdings: Bk Vols 21,000; Bk Titles 18,000; Per Subs 202
Subject Interests: Ethnic studies, Int migration, Refugees
Special Collections: Ethnic Press Coll; Italian American Archives
Publications: Archival Guide Series; Directory of International Migration Study Centers, Research Programs & Library Resources; Refugees: Holdings of the Center of Migrations Studies Library/Archives
Restriction: Non-circulating to the public
Friends of the Library Group

C COLLEGE OF STATEN ISLAND LIBRARY, 2800 Victory Blvd, 10314. SAN 354-1770. Tel: 718-982-4001. Interlibrary Loan Service Tel: 718-982-4014. TDD: 718-982-4096. FAX: 718-982-4002. E-Mail: library@postbox.csi.cuny.edu. Web Site: www.library.csi.cuny.edu. *Dep Dir*, Wilma L Jones; Tel: 718-982-4024, E-Mail: Jones@postbox.csi.cuny.edu; *Chief Librn*, James Marcum; E-Mail: Marcum@postbox.csi.cuny.edu; *Acq*, Linda Roccos; Tel: 718-982-3917, E-Mail: roccos@postbox.cuny.edu; *Cat*, Shen Zuwang; Tel: 718-982-4025, E-Mail: shen@postbox.csi.cuny.edu; *ILL*, Raja Jayatilleke; Tel: 718-982-4016, Fax: 718-982-4015, E-Mail: Jayatilleke@postbox.csi.cuny.edu; Staff 42 (MLS 12, Non-MLS 30)
Founded 1976. Pop 11,000; Enrl 12,400; Fac 301; Highest Degree: Master
Library Holdings: Bk Vols 210,000; Bk Titles 205,000; Per Subs 1,425
Subject Interests: Computer science, Education, Engineering, History, Nursing, Polymer chemistry
Special Collections: Staten Island
Automation Activity & Vendor Info: (Cataloging) NOTIS; (Circulation) NOTIS; (Course Reserve) NOTIS; (Serials) NOTIS
Database Vendor: IAC - Info Trac, Lexis-Nexis, OCLC - First Search, Silverplatter Information Inc., Wilson - Wilson Web
Publications: KWIK list; Periodicals-Serials List; Periodicals-Serials Subject List; Student-Faculty Library Handbook
Partic in New York Metrop Ref & Res Libr Agency; OCLC Online Computer Library Center, Inc
Friends of the Library Group

S GARIBALDI & MEUCCIL MUSEUM, The Italian Research Center, 420 Tompkins Ave, 10305. SAN 326-8772. Tel: 718-442-1608. FAX: 718-442-8635. *Curator, Dir*, Anne Alarcon
Founded 1956
Library Holdings: Bk Vols 1,200
Special Collections: Garibaldi & Meucci in New York (Italian Risorgimento Coll)
Restriction: By appointment only
Partic in Am Asn of Museums; Atlantic Asn of Museums
Open Tues-Sun 1-4:30

SR IMANUEL LUTHERAN CHURCH, (Formerly Holy Trinity Luthern Church), Metro New York Synod Archives, 2018 Richmond Ave, 10314-3916. SAN 328-2988. Tel: 718-761-5133. *Archivist*, William Kirsh-Carr
Library Holdings: Bk Vols 200

R JEWISH COMMUNITY CENTER OF STATEN ISLAND, William Rosenthal Judaica Library, 475 Victory Blvd, 10301. SAN 312-4940. Tel: 718-981-1500. FAX: 718-720-5085. *Actg Dir*, Sheila Lipton; E-Mail: sheilajcc@aol.com
Founded 1968
Library Holdings: Bk Vols 1,600; Bk Titles 1,475
Restriction: Members only

S JACQUES MARCHAIS MUSEUM OF TIBETAN ART LIBRARY,* 338 Lighthouse Ave, PO Box 060198, 10306-1217. SAN 312-4959. Tel: 718-987-3500. FAX: 718-351-0402. Web Site: www.tibetanmuseum.com. *Dir*, Elizabeth Rogers
Founded 1945
1998-1999 Mats Exp $5,000, Books $2,000, Per/Ser (Incl. Access Fees) $500, Presv $1,000, Other Print Mats $500, Manuscripts & Archives $1,000. Sal $200,000
Library Holdings: Bk Vols 1,200
Subject Interests: Architecture, Art, Asia, Ethical philos, Language arts, Moral, Oriental culture, Relig studies, Tibet

GM NEW YORK STATE OFFICE OF MENTAL RETARDATION & DEVELOPMENTAL DISABILITIES, Institute for Basic Research in Developmental Disabilities Library, 1050 Forest Hill Rd, 10314. SAN 312-4967. Tel: 718-494-5119. FAX: 718-494-6660. E-Mail: nyibr1@rmi.net. *Librn*, Lawrence Black; Staff 2 (MLS 1, Non-MLS 1)
Founded 1969
Library Holdings: Bk Vols 6,000; Bk Titles 5,900; Per Subs 150
Subject Interests: Biochemistry, Genetics, Immunology, Neurology, Neuropathology, Physiological psychol, Virology
Partic in Medical Library Center Of New York

C SAINT JOHN'S UNIVERSITY, Loretto Memorial Library, Staten Island Campus, 300 Howard Ave, 10301. SAN 312-4983. Tel: 718-390-4456. Interlibrary Loan Service Tel: 718-390-4362. Circulation Tel: 718-390-4457. Reference Tel: 718-390-4460. FAX: 718-390-4290. Web Site: www.stjohns.edu. *Ref*, Lois Cherepon; Tel: 718-390-4521, E-Mail: cherepol@stjohns.edu; *Ref*, Ann Jusino; Tel: 718-390-4355, E-Mail: jusinoa@stjohns.edu; *Ref*, Andrea McElrath; E-Mail: mcelrata@stjohns.edu; *Ref*, Mark Meng; Tel: 718-390-4363, E-Mail: mengm@stjohns.edu; Staff 4 (MLS 4)
Founded 1972. Enrl 2,500; Highest Degree: Master
Jul 2000-Jun 2001 Income $886,000. Mats Exp $256,648, Books $42,688, Per/Ser (Incl. Access Fees) $118,000, Micro $8,550, Other Print Mats $65,000, Electronic Ref Mat (Incl. Access Fees) $15,057. Sal $630,789 (Prof $192,440)
Library Holdings: Bk Vols 148,254; Per Subs 1,215
Subject Interests: Bus, Education
Partic in New York Metrop Ref & Res Libr Agency; OCLC Online Computer Library Center, Inc; WALDO
Friends of the Library Group

M SAINT VINCENT'S CATHOLIC MEDICAL CENTERS OF NEW YORK, (Formerly Sisters Of Charity Medical Center Library), Dimitrios Fournarakis Medical Library, 355 Bard Ave, 10310-1699. SAN 312-4991. Tel: 718-876-3117. FAX: 718-727-2456. *Librn*, Mary Hicks; E-Mail: mhicks@schsi.org; Staff 4 (MLS 1, Non-MLS 3)
Founded 1925
Library Holdings: Bk Vols 3,500; Per Subs 188
Subject Interests: Cardiology, Gynecology, Internal medicine, Nursing, Obstetrics, Pathology, Pediatrics, Psychiatry, Radiology, Surgery
Database Vendor: OVID Technologies

Restriction: Staff use only
Function: ILL limited, Literary searches
Partic in BHSL; BQSI; New York Metrop Ref & Res Libr Agency

M SAINT VINCENT'S CATHOLIC MEDICAL CENTERS OF NEW YORK-BAYLEY SETON CAMPUS, (Formerly Bayley Seton), Charles Ferguson Medical Library, 75 Vanderbilt Ave, 10304-3850. SAN 312-5068. Tel: 718-354-5525. FAX: 718-354-5524. *Librn*, Mary Hicks; E-Mail: mhicks@schsi.org
Founded 1918
Library Holdings: Bk Vols 2,220; Per Subs 111
Subject Interests: Clinical medicine, Dermatology, Ophthalmology, Psychiatry
Restriction: Staff use only
Function: ILL limited, Literary searches
Partic in BHSL; BQSI; Metro NY Libr Coun; Nat Libr of Med; New York Metrop Ref & Res Libr Agency; OCLC Online Computer Library Center, Inc

M SEA VIEW HOSPITAL & HOME, Health Sciences Library,* 460 Brielle Ave, 10314. SAN 312-5009. Tel: 718-317-3689. FAX: 718-980-7182. *Librn*, George Taylor
Founded 1905
Library Holdings: Bk Vols 5,588
Special Collections: Geriatrics; Media Journals Coll, from 1910
Partic in Regional Med Libr
Friends of the Library Group

S STATEN ISLAND HISTORICAL SOCIETY LIBRARY, (Formerly The Historic Richmond Town Library), 441 Clarke Ave, 10306. SAN 312-5025. Tel: 718-351-1611. FAX: 718-351-6057. *Dir*, Barnett Shepherd
Founded 1933
Library Holdings: Bk Vols 6,000
Subject Interests: Local history
Special Collections: Staten Island Manuscript Coll (1670 to present)
Publications: Staten Island Historian
Restriction: By appointment only, Non-circulating, Not a lending library, Open to public for reference only
Function: Archival collection, Business archives, Photocopies available, Reference only

S STATEN ISLAND INSTITUTE OF ARTS & SCIENCES, Archives & Library, 75 Stuyvesant Pl, 10301. SAN 354-1835. Tel: 718-727-1135. FAX: 718-273-5683. *Archivist*, Vince Sweeney; *Librn*, Mary S De Silva
Founded 1881
Library Holdings: Bk Vols 30,000
Subject Interests: Archaeology, City planning, Conservation of mat, Environ, Local Black hist, Museology, Natural science, Photog, Preservation, Staten Island
Special Collections: Black Community on Staten Island (Crooke Coll & Gravelle Coll); Britton, Desosway & Gratacap Family (Charles G Hine Coll); Conservation History Coll, bks, clippings, letters; Daguerreotypes (H H Cleaves Coll); Davis, Hollick & Anthon Archives; Environmental Coll; Kreischer Family (Chapin Coll); Leng (Harry B Weiss Coll); Manuscript Colls; Staten Island & Environments Coll, docs, maps, photogs, scrapbks; Staten Island Newspaper (Curtis Coll), maps, photogs, print; Staten Island Newspapers from 1828 to 1945, micro; Steele Family (Mabel Abbott Coll); Women's Suffrage (Delvan Coll)
Publications: Proceedings

M STATEN ISLAND UNIVERSITY HOSPITAL, Medical Library,* 475 Seaview Ave, 10305. SAN 312-5033. Tel: 718-226-9545. FAX: 718-226-8582. *Dir*, Jennifer Miller; E-Mail: jennifermiller@juno.com; *Coll Develop*, Mary Lynch
Founded 1938
Library Holdings: Bk Titles 22,000; Per Subs 430

S STATEN ISLAND ZOOLOGICAL SOCIETY LIBRARY,* 614 Broadway, 10310. SAN 312-5041. Tel: 718-442-3174. FAX: 718-981-8711.
Founded 1936
Library Holdings: Bk Vols 1,000
Special Collections: Animal-related (biology, zoology, animal behavior, etc)

GL SUPREME COURT LIBRARY,* Richmond County Court House, 10301. SAN 312-505X. Tel: 718-390-5291. *In Charge*, Philip A Klingle; Staff 1 (MLS 1)
Founded 1920
Apr 1999-Mar 2000 Income $246,241. Mats Exp $139,524, Books $1,200, Per/Ser (Incl. Access Fees) $113,400, Micro $1,300, Electronic Ref Mat (Incl. Access Fees) $23,624. Sal $106,717 (Prof $66,799)
Library Holdings: Bk Vols 75,000; Bk Titles 1,684; Per Subs 281
Partic in OCLC Online Computer Library Center, Inc

C WAGNER COLLEGE, Horrmann Library, One Campus Rd, 10301-4495. SAN 312-5076. Tel: 718-390-3401. Interlibrary Loan Service Tel: 718-390-4110. Circulation Tel: 718-390-3401. Reference Tel: 718-390-3402. FAX: 718-390-3107. Web Site: www.wagner.edu. *Coll Develop, Dean*, Dorothy Davison; E-Mail: ddavison@wagner.edu; *ILL, Media Spec*, Mitchell Dakelman; Tel: 718-420-4110, E-Mail: mdakelma@wagner.edu; *Publ Servs, Ref*, Frank Polizzi; Tel: 718-390-3377, E-Mail: fpolizzi@wagner.edu; *Syst Coordr, Tech Servs*, Yan Ye Lee; Tel: 718-390-3378, E-Mail: ylee@wagner.edu; Staff 14 (MLS 5, Non-MLS 9)
Founded 1889. Enrl 2,049; Fac 181; Highest Degree: Master
Sep 1999-Aug 2000 Income $890,125, State $6,461, Parent Institution $883,664. Mats Exp $286,000, Books $124,000, Per/Ser (Incl. Access Fees) $95,000, AV Equip $31,800, Electronic Ref Mat (Incl. Access Fees) $35,200. Sal $373,232 (Prof $224,432)
Library Holdings: Bk Vols 290,660; Bk Titles 139,200; Per Subs 914
Subject Interests: Bus, Chemistry, Education, Nursing
Special Collections: Literature (Edwin Markham Coll), bks & monographs
Publications: Library Faculty/Administration Handbook; Periodicals Handbook
Partic in Educ Resources Info Ctr; New York Metrop Ref & Res Libr Agency

STEPHENTOWN

P STEPHENTOWN MEMORIAL LIBRARY, 472 NY #43, PO Box 70, 12168. SAN 312-5092. Tel: 518-733-5750. *Dir*, Barbara Kubli; Staff 1 (MLS 1)
Founded 1946. Pop 2,551; Circ 11,215
Library Holdings: Bk Titles 7,086; Per Subs 10
Mem of Upper Hudson Library System

STILLWATER

S NATIONAL PARK SERVICE, Saratoga National Historical Park Library, 648 Rte 32, 12170. SAN 312-5114. Tel: 518-664-9821, Ext 224. FAX: 518-664-3349. Web Site: www.nps.gov/sara.
Founded 1941
Library Holdings: Bk Vols 1,000
Subject Interests: American revolution
Special Collections: Northern Campaign of 1777
Restriction: By appointment only

P STILLWATER FREE LIBRARY, 72 S Hudson Ave, PO Box 485, 12170. SAN 312-5122. Tel: 518-664-6255. FAX: 518-664-6255. Web Site: www.stillwater.sals.edu. *Dir*, Charlotte Anthony; E-Mail: spidersarchorp@netscape.net; Staff 2 (MLS 1, Non-MLS 1)
Founded 1949. Pop 4,523; Circ 20,311
Jan 1998-Dec 1998 Income $50,910, State $11,000, County $710, Locally Generated Income $6,257, Other $32,943. Mats Exp $6,781, Books $6,109, Per/Ser (Incl. Access Fees) $537, Electronic Ref Mat (Incl. Access Fees) $135. Sal $24,154
Library Holdings: Bk Vols 19,354; Per Subs 10
Mem of Southern Adirondack Library System
Friends of the Library Group

STOCKTON

P MARY E SEYMOUR MEMORIAL FREE LIBRARY, 22 N Main St, 14784-0432. SAN 354-1959. Tel: 716-595-3323. FAX: 716-595-3323. E-Mail: casslib@cecomet.net. *Dir*, Judy Yonkers
Founded 1899. Pop 2,301; Circ 17,928
Library Holdings: Bk Vols 18,000; Bk Titles 16,000; Per Subs 25
Special Collections: Local History (Town of Stockton), bks, church records, military records
Mem of Chautauqua-Cattaraugus Library System
Friends of the Library Group
Branches: 1
CASSADAGA BRANCH, 18 Maple Ave, Cassadaga, 14718. SAN 354-1983. Tel: 716-595-3822. FAX: 716-595-3822. *Dir*, Judy Yonkers
Friends of the Library Group

STONE RIDGE

P STONE RIDGE LIBRARY, Rte 209, Box 188, 12484. SAN 312-5130. Tel: 914-687-7023. FAX: 914-687-2044. E-Mail: stonerid@sebridge.org. *Dir*, Jody Ford
Founded 1909. Pop 7,500; Circ 66,718
2000-2001 Income $192,500. Mats Exp Books $22,000
Library Holdings: Bk Vols 30,759; Per Subs 106
Mem of Mid-Hudson Library System

J ULSTER COUNTY COMMUNITY COLLEGE, MacDonald DeWitt Library, 12484. SAN 312-5149. Tel: 845-687-5213. Reference Tel: 845-687-5212. FAX: 845-687-5207. Web Site: www.sunyelster.edu/resources/library.asp. *Dir*, Lawrence Berk; *Asst Dir*, Kari Mack; *Tech Servs*, Karen Carney; *Ref*, Cheri Gerstung; *Info Res*, Robin Walsh; Staff 8 (MLS 5, Non-MLS 3)
Founded 1963. Enrl 2,759
Library Holdings: Bk Vols 78,000; Bk Titles 70,589; Per Subs 551
Subject Interests: Local history, Psychology
Publications: Bibliographies; Handbook of General Information; Periodical

List
Partic in OCLC Online Computer Library Center, Inc; Southeastern New York Library Resources Council

STONY BROOK

C STATE UNIVERSITY OF NEW YORK AT STONY BROOK, Melville Library, 11794-3300. SAN 354-2017. Tel: 631-632-7100. Interlibrary Loan Service Tel: 631-632-7117. FAX: 631-632-9194. Interlibrary Loan Service FAX: 631-632-9194. Web Site: www.sunysb.edu/library. *Actg Dir*, Charles W Simpson; *ILL*, Diane E Englot; E-Mail: denglot@notes.cc.sunysb.edu; *Tech Servs*, Daniel Kinney; *Ref*, Nathan Baum; *Spec Coll*, Mitsuko Collver; *Doc*, Jyoti Pandit; *Ref*, Godlind Johnson; *Bibliog Instr*, Richard Feinberg; *Circ*, David Weiner; Staff 91 (MLS 30, Non-MLS 61)
Founded 1957. Enrl 15,023; Fac 663; Highest Degree: Doctorate
Jul 1997-Jun 1998 Income $8,730,208. Mats Exp $3,706,755. Sal $3,919,357 (Prof $1,723,660)
Library Holdings: Bk Vols 1,756,999; Per Subs 8,331
Subject Interests: Behav sci, Engineering, Environmental studies, Music, Nat sci, Physical sci, Soc sci
Special Collections: 19th Century Children's Books; Current Fine Publishing & Printing (Perishable Press Coll); Ezra Pound Coll; Fielding Dawson; Fielding Dawson Coll; Hispanic Literature & Culture (Jorge Carrera Andrade Coll); Jacob K Javits Papers; Robert Creeley Coll; Robert Payne Coll; William Butler Yeats Papers (microform)
Automation Activity & Vendor Info: (Circulation) NOTIS
Publications: Daily Bulletin (in-house newsletter)
Mem of Asn of Research Libraries
Partic in Long Island Library Resources Council; OCLC Online Computer Library Center, Inc; Research Libraries Group, Inc; RLIN
Special Services for the Deaf - Staff with knowledge of sign language
Special Services for the Blind - Reading edge system
Friends of the Library Group
Departmental Libraries:
BIOLOGICAL SCIENCES Tel: 516-632-7152. FAX: 516-632-8331. *Head of Libr*, Jonathan Nabe
CHEMISTRY Tel: 516-632-7150. FAX: 516-632-9191. Web Site: ws.cc.sunysb.edu/chemlib/. *Librn*, Puiyan Lee
Friends of the Library Group
COMPUTER SCIENCE Tel: 516-632-7628. FAX: 516-632-7401. *Librn*, Donna Albertus

CM HEALTH SCIENCES CENTER LIBRARY, 8034 SUNY Stony Brook, 11794-8034. SAN 354-2165. Tel: 516-444-2512. Interlibrary Loan Service Tel: 516-444-3105. FAX: 516-751-5809. E-Mail: username@hsclib.hsc.sunysb.edu. Web Site: www.informatics.sunysb.edu/hsclib/libhp.html. *Dir*, Spencer Marsh; *Assoc Dir, Coll Develop*, Antonija Prelec; *Syst Coordr*, William Murray; *Ser*, Julitta Jo; Staff 16 (MLS 16)
Founded 1969. Enrl 2,293; Fac 557; Highest Degree: Doctorate
1998-1999 Income $2,481,460. Mats Exp $949,425. Sal $1,250,626 (Prof $667,059)
Library Holdings: Bk Vols 268,374; Per Subs 2,175
Subject Interests: Allied health, Basic health sci, Dentistry, Medicine, Nursing, Soc welfare
Special Collections: History of Medicine, Dentistry & Nursing
Mem of Long Island Libr Resources Coun, Inc; Regional Med Libr Network
Partic in BRS; Dialog Corporation; Nat Libr of Med; OCLC Online Computer Library Center, Inc
MARINE & ATMOSPHERIC SCIENCES INFORMATION CENTER (MASIC) Tel: 516-632-8679. FAX: 516-632-9359. *Head of Libr*, Roger Kelly
MATHEMATICS-PHYSICS Tel: 516-632-7145. FAX: 516-632-9192. *Librn*, Sherry Chang
MUSIC Tel: 516-632-7097. FAX: 516-632-7116. *Librn*, Christine King

THE LONG ISLAND MUSEUM OF AMERICAN ART, HISTORY & CARRIAGES

S GERSTENBURG CARRIAGE REFERENCE LIBRARY, 1200 Rte 25A, 11790-1992. SAN 323-5610. Tel: 631-751-0066, Ext 222. FAX: 631-751-0353. *Curator*, Merri Ferrell; E-Mail: merri.ferrell@yahoo.com
Founded 1950
Library Holdings: Bk Titles 5,000
Subject Interests: Accoutrements, Carriage archives, Carriage decoration, Carriage design, Carriage per, Horse drawn transportation, Horses
Friends of the Library Group

S KATE STRONG HISTORICAL LIBRARY, 1200 Rte 25A, 11790. SAN 312-5157. Tel: 631-751-0066, Ext 201. FAX: 631-751-0353. Web Site: www.longislandmuseum.org. *Librn*, Eva Greguski
Founded 1942
Library Holdings: Bk Titles 4,000
Subject Interests: 19th Cent trade cat, Am art hist, Costumes, Decoys, Hunting, Local Long Island mat
Special Collections: Otto Johs Memorial Library (Decoys)
Restriction: By appointment only

STONY CREEK

P STONY CREEK FREE LIBRARY, 37 Harrisburg Rd, 12878-1622. (Mail add: PO Box 0064, 12878-0064), SAN 312-5165. Tel: 518-696-5911. FAX: 518-696-5911. E-Mail: words@hotmail.com. *Librn*, Norma Hastings; E-Mail: hastings@sals.edu
Founded 1916. Pop 670; Circ 6,763
Jan 1998-Dec 1998 Income $21,792, State $1,900, City $10,000, County $1,605, Locally Generated Income $4,287, Other $4,000. Mats Exp $2,557, Books $1,272, Per/Ser (Incl. Access Fees) $20, AV Equip $861, Electronic Ref Mat (Incl. Access Fees) $404. Sal $10,299
Library Holdings: Bk Vols 7,518
Mem of Southern Adirondack Library System
Open Mon & Wed 5-9, Tues & Thurs 1-5:30, Sat 9-12

STONY POINT

P ROSE MEMORIAL LIBRARY,* 79 E Main St, 10980-1699. SAN 312-5173. Tel: 914-786-2100. FAX: 914-786-6042. E-Mail: stp@rcls.org. *Dir*, Kent C Horner
Founded 1950. Pop 12,838; Circ 29,455
Jan 1999-Dec 1999 Income $172,000, City $94,000. Mats Exp $25,000, Books $19,000, Per/Ser (Incl. Access Fees) $2,000. Sal $71,000 (Prof $10,000)
Library Holdings: Bk Titles 17,203; Per Subs 35
Subject Interests: Local history
Mem of Ramapo Catskill Library System
Friends of the Library Group

STORMVILLE

S GREEN HAVEN CORRECTIONAL FACILITY LIBRARY,* Green Haven Correctional Facility, 12582. SAN 354-2254. Tel: 914-221-2711. FAX: 914-221-2711, Ext 2099. *Librn*, Frances Sandiford; Staff 1 (MLS 1)
Founded 1942
Mar 1998-Feb 1999 Mats Exp $18,000, Books $9,000, Per/Ser (Incl. Access Fees) $9,000. Sal $42,000
Library Holdings: Bk Vols 24,940; Bk Titles 12,000; Per Subs 75; Spec Interest Per Sub 30
Subject Interests: Black studies, Coping skills material, Hispanic studies, Occult, Yoga
Special Collections: Black History; Spanish
Automation Activity & Vendor Info: (Cataloging) Follett
Restriction: Not open to public
Mem of Mid-Hudson Library System
Branches:
GL LAW FAX: 914-221-2711, Ext 2099.
Subject Interests: Crim law

SUFFERN

S AVON PRODUCTS, INC, Research Library, Avon Pl, 10901. SAN 312-5181. Tel: 914-369-2756. FAX: 914-369-2803. *In Charge*, Mary Warren; E-Mail: mary.warren@avon.com; Staff 2 (MLS 1, Non-MLS 1)
Founded 1966
Library Holdings: Bk Titles 7,000; Per Subs 300
Subject Interests: Cosmetics, Dermatology, Perfumery, Toxicology
Publications: Journal List
Mem of SE NY Libr Resources Coun

J ROCKLAND COMMUNITY COLLEGE LIBRARY,* 145 College Rd, 10901. SAN 312-519X. Tel: 914-574-4409. FAX: 914-574-4424. Web Site: www.suny.rockland.edu/library. *Acq, Actg Dir, Cat, Online Servs*, Shi Xi; *Spec Coll*, Mildred Galentine-Steis; Staff 8 (MLS 8)
Founded 1959. Enrl 6,200; Fac 240
Library Holdings: Bk Vols 119,000; Per Subs 250
Subject Interests: Higher educ, Int educ
Special Collections: Art; Elaine Magid Mystery & Detective Coll; Judaica; Rockland County History
Publications: bibliographic instruction aids; Bibliographies
Partic in OCLC Online Computer Library Center, Inc

SR SALVATION ARMY SCHOOL FOR OFFICER TRAINING, Brengle Library, 201 Lafayette Ave, 10901. SAN 312-5203. Tel: 845-368-7228. FAX: 845-357-6644. Web Site: www.sfotusa.org. *Librn*, Robin Rader; E-Mail: rrader@use.salvationarmy.org
Founded 1936
Library Holdings: Bk Vols 22,000; Bk Titles 16,000; Per Subs 225
Special Collections: Salvation Army Publications
Partic in Southeastern New York Library Resources Council

P SUFFERN FREE LIBRARY,* 66 Maple Ave, 10901-5694. SAN 312-5211. Tel: 914-357-1237. FAX: 914-357-3156. Web Site: www.rcls.org/sufpl. *Dir*, Ruth Bolin; *Ad Servs, Coll Develop, Ref*, Patricia Wood; *Asst Dir*, Pauline Brower; *Ch Servs*, Elizabeth Henry
Founded 1926. Pop 25,963; Circ 210,007
Jul 1997-Jun 1998 Income $1,584,790, City $13,000, Locally Generated

Income $70,546. Mats Exp $218,033, Books $117,439, Per/Ser (Incl. Access Fees) $6,000, AV Equip $30,000, Other Print Mats $42,777. Sal $503,767 (Prof $209,133)
Library Holdings: Bk Vols 115,000; Per Subs 430
Subject Interests: Local history
Publications: Newsletter (bi-monthly)
Mem of Ramapo Catskill Library System

SYOSSET

R NORTH SHORE SYNAGOGUE, Charles Cohn Memorial Library, 83 Muttontown Rd, 11791. SAN 312-5246. Tel: 516-921-2282. FAX: 516-921-2393.
Founded 1972
Library Holdings: Bk Titles 4,200; Per Subs 24
Subject Interests: Holocaust, Judaica
Special Collections: Sound Filmstrip Coll

SR ORTHODOX CHURCH IN AMERICA, Department of History & Archives,* Rte 25A, PO Box 675, 11791. SAN 327-2176. Tel: 516-922-0550. FAX: 516-922-0954. *Archivist*, Alexis Liberovsky
Library Holdings: Bk Vols 60
Open Mon-Fri 9-5
Friends of the Library Group

P SYOSSET PUBLIC LIBRARY, 225 S Oyster Bay Rd, 11791-5897. SAN 312-5254. Tel: 516-921-7161. FAX: 516-921-8771. Web Site: www.nassaulibrary.org/syosset. *Dir*, Alice Nayer; E-Mail: acnayer@worldnet.att.net; *Admin Assoc*, Ginny Kowalski; *Circ*, Susanah Kuchenbrod; *Ch Servs*, Merryl Traub; *YA Servs*, Karen Cooper; *Ref*, Isabel Goldenkoff; *Tech Servs*, Rosemarie Germaine; Staff 23 (MLS 22, Non-MLS 1)
Founded 1961. Pop 32,889; Circ 342,818; Highest Degree: Master
Jul 1998-Jun 1999 Income $2,620,815, State $16,226, Locally Generated Income $2,474,696, Other $129,893. Mats Exp $333,178, Books $235,679, Per/Ser (Incl. Access Fees) $32,651, AV Equip $56,082, Electronic Ref Mat (Incl. Access Fees) $8,766. Sal $1,334,428 (Prof $670,058)
Library Holdings: Bk Vols 254,623; Per Subs 2,314
Subject Interests: Bus
Special Collections: Local Hist
Automation Activity & Vendor Info: (Circulation) DRA
Publications: (Newsletter); Monthly Calendar
Mem of Nassau Library System

SYRACUSE

L BOND, SCHOENECK & KING, Law Library,* One Lincoln Ctr, 13202-1355. SAN 372-2384. Tel: 315-422-0121. FAX: 315-422-3598. Web Site: www.bsk.com. *Dir*, Maureen T Kays
Library Holdings: Bk Vols 25,000; Per Subs 100
Partic in Central New York Library Resources Council

G CENTRAL NEW YORK REGIONAL PLANNING & DEVELOPMENT BOARD, Library & Information Center, 100 Clinton Sq, Ste 200, 126 N Salinast, 13202. SAN 327-2370. Tel: 315-422-8276. FAX: 315-422-9051. Web Site: www.cnyrpdb.org. *Dir*, Gary Hayes; *Librn*, Kathleen Bertuch; E-Mail: kbertuch@cnyrpdb.org
Founded 1966
Library Holdings: Bk Titles 3,000; Per Subs 900
Partic in NY State Data Ctr Network

M COMMUNITY-GENERAL HOSPITAL OF GREATER SYRACUSE, Medical Library,* Broad Rd, 13215-2299. SAN 312-5300. Tel: 315-492-5500. FAX: 315-492-5221. *Librn*, Lucy Wrightington; E-Mail: lucywrightington@cgh.org; Staff 1 (Non-MLS 1)
Founded 1968
1998-1999 Mats Exp $49,000, Books $14,000, Per/Ser (Incl. Access Fees) $35,000
Library Holdings: Bk Vols 3,000; Per Subs 310
Subject Interests: Med ethics, Medicine, Nursing
Publications: Library Newsletter
Partic in Central New York Library Resources Council; National Network Of Libraries Of Medicine - South Central Region

M CROUSE HOSPITAL LIBRARY,* 736 Irving Ave, 13210. SAN 312-5327. Tel: 315-470-7380. FAX: 315-470-7443. Web Site: www.crouse.org. *Dir*, Wendy Tarby; *Librn*, Ellen Owens; *Librn*, Kris Hogan; Staff 4 (MLS 4)
Founded 1916. Enrl 325; Fac 10
Library Holdings: Bk Vols 5,000; Bk Titles 3,500; Per Subs 240
Subject Interests: Healthcare, Medicine, Nursing
Special Collections: Nursing Archives
Partic in Nat Libr of Med

S ERIE CANAL MUSEUM RESEARCH LIBRARY,* 318 Erie Blvd E, 13202. SAN 312-5289. Tel: 315-471-0593. FAX: 315-471-7220. *Dir*, Persijs Kolberg
1997-1998 Income $400. Mats Exp $300
Library Holdings: Bk Vols 5,000; Bk Titles 500; Per Subs 50
Subject Interests: New York State canal hist, Social hist
Special Collections: Erie Canal (State Engineers & Surveyors), doc

S EVERSON MUSEUM OF ART LIBRARY, 401 Harrison St, 13202. SAN 312-5335. Tel: 315-474-6064. FAX: 315-474-6943. E-Mail: eversonadmin@everson.org. Web Site: www.everson.org. *Librn*, Mary Iversen
Founded 1896
Library Holdings: Bk Vols 16,200; Per Subs 20
Subject Interests: Am, Ceramics, Exhibition catalogs, Oriental art, Photog
Special Collections: American Ceramics, mss; Archives of Ceramic National Exhibitions, 1932-present

P FAIRMOUNT COMMUNITY LIBRARY, 406 Chapel Dr, 13219. SAN 312-5343. Tel: 315-487-8933. FAX: 315-484-9475. *Librn*, Paul Morrell
Founded 1957. Pop 6,106; Circ 68,551
Library Holdings: Bk Vols 13,946; Per Subs 29
Subject Interests: Adult fiction, Antiques, History
Mem of Onondaga County Public Library
Open Mon & Wed 10-8:30, Tues & Thurs 2-8:30, Fri 10-5, Sat 10-1 (closed Sat, July & Aug)

C NOREEN REALE FALCONE LIBRARY, LeMoyne College, 1419 Salt Springs Rd, 13214-1399. SAN 312-536X. Tel: 315-445-4153. Interlibrary Loan Service Tel: 315-445-4333. Circulation Tel: 315-445-4325. Reference Tel: 315-445-4330. FAX: 315-445-4642. Web Site: www.lemoyne.edu/library. *Dir*, James J Simonis; Tel: 315-445-4321, E-Mail: simonis@mail.lemoyne.edu; *Librn*, Susan D Spence; Tel: 315-445-4627, E-Mail: spencesd@mail.lemoyne.edu; *Business*, Elizabeth A Lukacs; Tel: 315-445-4322, E-Mail: lukacs@mail.lemoyne.edu; *Head Tech Servs*, I-Chene Tai; Tel: 315-445-4331, E-Mail: tai@mail.lemoyne.edu; *Publ Servs, Ref*, Gretchen E Pearson; Tel: 315-445-4154, E-Mail: pearson@mail.lemoyne.edu; *Bibliog Instr*, Inga H Barnello; Tel: 315-445-4326, E-Mail: barnello@mail.lemoyne.edu; *Electronic Resources, Science*, Michael W Poulin; Tel: 315-445-4332, E-Mail: poulinmw@mail.lemoyne.edu. Subject Specialists: *Accounting*, Elizabeth A Lukacs; *Computer science*, Michael W Poulin; *Economics*, Elizabeth A Lukacs; *Education*, Susan D Spence; *English*, Gretchen E Pearson; *Fine arts*, James J Simonis; *Foreign Language*, James J Simonis; *History*, Inga H Barnello; *Mathematics*, Michael W Poulin; *Medical*, Michael W Poulin; *Philosophy*, Gretchen E Pearson; *Political science*, Inga H Barnello; *Psychology*, Susan D Spence; *Religion*, Gretchen E Pearson; *Sociology*, Inga H Barnello; Staff 14 (MLS 7, Non-MLS 7)
Founded 1946. Enrl 2,487; Fac 178; Highest Degree: Master
Jun 1999-May 2000 Income $1,444,252, State $7,419, Federal $42,676, Parent Institution $1,387,806, Other $6,351. Mats Exp $608,382, Books $102,968, Per/Ser (Incl. Access Fees) $213,249, Presv $13,330, Micro $33,546, AV Equip $9,558, Other Print Mats $21,225, Electronic Ref Mat (Incl. Access Fees) $101,182. Sal $726,862 (Prof $406,244)
Library Holdings: Bk Vols 201,752; Bk Titles 157,384; Per Subs 1,494
Subject Interests: Philosophy, Religion
Special Collections: Archives; Danny Biasone Syracuse Nationals Coll; Irish Literature (Father William Noon, S J Coll); Jesuitica (Jesuit History); McGrath Music Coll
Automation Activity & Vendor Info: (Acquisitions) Innovative Interfaces Inc.; (Cataloging) Innovative Interfaces Inc.; (Circulation) Innovative Interfaces Inc.; (Course Reserve) Innovative Interfaces Inc.; (Media Booking) Innovative Interfaces Inc.; (OPAC) Innovative Interfaces Inc.; (Serials) Innovative Interfaces Inc.
Database Vendor: Dialog, IAC - SearchBank, Lexis-Nexis, OCLC - First Search, Silverplatter Information Inc., Wilson - Wilson Web
Publications: AlphaBYTES (newsletter); Bibliography of Le Moyne College Authors (1946-1992); Library Guides (folder of general information); Serials Holdings (complete alphabetical list by title)
Partic in Central New York Library Resources Council

L HANCOCK & ESTABROOK, LLP, Law Library, 1500 MONY Tower One, 13202-2720. (Mail add: PO Box 4976, 13221-4976), SAN 327-5302. Tel: 315-471-3151. FAX: 315-471-3167. Web Site: www.hancocklaw.com. *Librn*, Donna Byrne; Tel: 315-471-3151, Ext 278, E-Mail: dbyrne@hancocklaw.com; Staff 3 (MLS 1, Non-MLS 2)
Founded 1889. Pop 80
Library Holdings: Bk Titles 2,128; Per Subs 50
Subject Interests: Bus, Employment, Environ, Estates, Health law, Intellectual property, Labor, Real estate, Tax, Trial practice law
Automation Activity & Vendor Info: (Acquisitions) Inmagic, Inc.; (Cataloging) Inmagic, Inc.; (Circulation) Inmagic, Inc.
Restriction: Private library
Function: Document delivery services, Reference services available
Open Mon-Fri 9-5

S LAUBACH LITERACY RESOURCE CENTER, 1320 Jamesville Ave, PO Box 131, 13210-0131. SAN 324-2218. Tel: 315-422-9121. FAX: 315-422-6369. *Mgr*, Valerie L Gigliotti; E-Mail: vgigliotti@laubach.org; Staff 1 (MLS 1)
Jun 1998-May 1999 Income $69,412. Sal $59,950
Library Holdings: Bk Titles 6,950; Per Subs 152
Subject Interests: Adult illiteracy, Adult literacy, English second language, Fund raising, Nonprofit mgt, Nontraditional adult basic educ, Publishing for

adult new readers, Reading, Voluntarism
Special Collections: Literacy (Frank Laubach Coll)
Publications: Information-Alert Bulletin (in-house resource newsletter)

LOCKHEED MARTIN CORP
S OCEAN, RADAR & SENSOR SYSTEMS DEPARTMENT
INFORMATION RESOURCE CENTER, Bldg 6, Rm 49, Electronics Park, PO Box 4840, 13221. SAN 375-8176. Tel: 315-456-2269. FAX: 315-456-0099. *Librn*, Lori Scoones; E-Mail: lori.k.scoones@lmco.com
Library Holdings: Bk Titles 5,000; Per Subs 180

L MACKENZIE, SMITH, LEWIS, MICHELL & HUGHES, Law Library,* 600 On Bank Bldg, PO Box 4967, 13221-4967. SAN 312-5378. Tel: 315-474-7571. FAX: 315-474-6409. *Librn*, Cheryl L Wolfe
Library Holdings: Bk Vols 16,500; Per Subs 110
Subject Interests: Civil litigation, Corporate, Estates, Real estate, Tax, Worker compensation
Special Collections: Extensive tax collection
Partic in Dialog Corporation; Westlaw

S MANUFACTURERS ASSOCIATION OF CENTRAL NEW YORK LIBRARY, 1 Webster's Landing, 5th Flr, 13202. SAN 312-5386. Tel: 315-474-4201. FAX: 315-474-0524. *Librn*, Ann Kassel
Library Holdings: Bk Vols 2,100
Subject Interests: Collective bargaining
Open Mon-Fri 8:30-5

S NIAGARA MOHAWK POWER CORP, Technology Resource Center, 300 Erie Blvd W D-M, 13202. SAN 377-5437. Tel: 315-428-6353. FAX: 315-428-5004. Web Site: www.niagaramohawk.com. *Dir*, Barbara J Raymond; E-Mail: raymondb@niagaramohawk.com. Subject Specialists: *Business*, Barbara J Raymond; *Energy*, Barbara J Raymond; Staff 1 (MLS 1)
Founded 1992
Library Holdings: Bk Vols 15,000; Bk Titles 12,000; Per Subs 75
Special Collections: Energy related materials; EPRI, NYSERDA, ESEERCO REPORTS; IEEE journals from 1907; Lighting Research Center materials (both old and new); NM History
Automation Activity & Vendor Info: (Acquisitions) Inmagic, Inc.; (Cataloging) Inmagic, Inc.; (Circulation) Inmagic, Inc.; (ILL) Inmagic, Inc.; (OPAC) Inmagic, Inc.; (Serials) Inmagic, Inc.
Database Vendor: Dialog, OCLC - First Search, ProQuest
Restriction: By appointment only
Function: Research library
Partic in Central New York Library Resources Council

J ONONDAGA COMMUNITY COLLEGE, Sidney B Coulter Library, 4941 Onondaga Rd, 13215. SAN 312-5432. Tel: 315-469-7741, Ext 2334. FAX: 315-469-8247. Web Site: www.sunyocc.edu/library. *Chair*, Frank Doble; E-Mail: doblef@aurora.sunyocc.edu; *Cat, Online Servs, Tech Servs*, Jeff Harr; *Acq, Archivist, Coll Develop, Spec Coll*, Robert O'Boyle; *Reader Servs, Ref*, Gretchen Roberts; Staff 6 (MLS 6)
Founded 1962. Enrl 5,600; Fac 190
Sep 1998-Aug 1999 Income $815,214. Mats Exp $103,500, Books $42,000, Per/Ser (Incl. Access Fees) $45,000, Presv $2,000, Micro $8,000, AV Equip $5,000, Other Print Mats $1,000, Manuscripts & Archives $500. Sal $613,103 (Prof $299,000)
Library Holdings: Bk Vols 96,659; Bk Titles 86,595; Per Subs 450
Subject Interests: Bus, Careers, Health, Humanities, Technologies
Special Collections: Berrigan Brothers Coll; Central New York History; Faculty Authors; Local History Coll; Onondaga Community College Archives
Automation Activity & Vendor Info: (Cataloging) DRA; (Circulation) DRA
Publications: Bibliographies; Film/video catalog; Newsletters; Periodical holdings
Partic in Central New York Library Resources Council; New York State Interlibrary Loan Network; OCLC Online Computer Library Center, Inc
Special Services for the Deaf - Books on deafness & sign language
Special Services for the Blind - Kurzweil Reading Machine

P ONONDAGA COUNTY PUBLIC LIBRARY, 447 S Salina St, 13202-2494. SAN 354-2319. Tel: 315-435-1800. FAX: 315-435-8533. E-Mail: ocpl@ocpl.lib.ny.us. Web Site: www.co.onondaga.ny.us, www.ocpl.lib.ny.us. *Dir*, Lawrence Frank; *Admin Assoc*, Sally Jensen-Darnell; *Circ*, Chris Cox; *Ch Servs*, Roz NaPier; *Spec Coll*, Janet Lomicka; *Publ Servs*, Mary Fran Floreck; *Publ Servs*, Kathryn Whitney; *Syst Coordr*, Robert E Brown; Staff 55 (MLS 55)
Founded 1852. Pop 468,973; Circ 1,873,970
Jan 1999-Dec 1999 Income $10,227,543, State $1,556,685, City $4,450,313, Federal $63,067, County $4,157,478. Mats Exp $897,493. Sal $5,134,035
Library Holdings: Bk Vols 1,500,000
Subject Interests: Literacy, Local history
Special Collections: Foundation Center; Genealogy; Historic Syracuse, microfiche
Database Vendor: epixtech, inc.
Member Libraries: Baldwinsville Public Library; De Witt Community Library; East Syracuse Free Library; Elbridge Free Library; Fairmount Community Library; Fayetteville Free Library; Jordan Bramley Free Library; Lafayette Public Library; Liverpool Public Library; Manlius Library; Marcellus Free Library; Maxwell Memorial Library; Minoa Library; Northern Onondaga Public Library; Onondaga Free Library; Salina Free Library; Solvay Public Library; Tully Free Library
Partic in Central New York Library Resources Council; OCLC Online Computer Library Center, Inc
Special Services for the Deaf - TDD; TTY machine; Videos & decoder
Special Services for the Blind - Kurzweil Reading Machine
Friends of the Library Group
Branches: 13
ADMINISTRATION *Exec Dir*, Lawrence J Frank; *Publ Servs*, Mary F Floreck
BEAUCHAMP, 2111 S Salina St, 13205. SAN 354-2343. Tel: 315-435-3395. FAX: 315-435-2729. *Librn*, Olivia Opello
BETTS, 4862 S Salina St, 13205. SAN 354-2378. Tel: 315-435-1940. FAX: 315-435-1944. *Librn*, Jane Kalkbrenner
CHILDREN'S Tel: 315-435-1800.
HAZARD, 1620 W Genesee St, 13204. SAN 354-2408. Tel: 315-484-1528. FAX: 315-435-3552. *Librn*, Karen Pitoniak
Friends of the Library Group
LOCAL HISTORY
MUNDY, 1204 S Geddes St, 13204. SAN 354-2432. Tel: 315-435-3797. FAX: 315-435-8557. *Librn*, Pamela Crane
Friends of the Library Group
NORTHEAST COMMUNITY CENTER, 716 Hawley Ave, 13203. SAN 354-2580. Tel: 315-472-6343, Ext 8. *Librn*, Lynn Berman
PAINE, 113 Nichols Ave, 13206. SAN 354-2467. Tel: 315-435-5442. FAX: 315-435-3553. *Librn*, Lorraine Mavins
PETIT, 105 Victoria Pl, 13210. SAN 354-2491. Tel: 315-435-3636. FAX: 315-435-2731. *Librn*, Kate McCaffrey
SOULE, 101 Springfield Rd, 13214. SAN 354-2521. Tel: 315-449-4300. FAX: 315-449-4239. *Librn*, Elizabeth Loftus
SOUTHWEST COMMUNITY CENTER, 401 South Ave, 13203. SAN 354-2610. Tel: 315-474-6823, Ext 42. *Librn*, Milena Hansen
WHITE, 763 Butternut St, 13208. SAN 354-2556. Tel: 315-435-3519. FAX: 315-435-3367. *Librn*, Patricia Swanson

P ONONDAGA FREE LIBRARY,* 4840 W Seneca Tpk, 13215. SAN 312-5440. Tel: 315-492-1727. FAX: 315-492-1323. E-Mail: onondagafree@yahoo.com. Web Site: www.admass.com/library. *Dir*, Katherine Chave; *Asst Dir*, Dave D'Ambrosio; *Ch Servs*, Anna Louise Chappell; *Ch Servs*, Holly Hart; Staff 2 (MLS 2)
Founded 1961. Circ 122,655
Library Holdings: Bk Vols 33,107; Per Subs 144
Subject Interests: Local history
Special Collections: Fine Art Originals
Automation Activity & Vendor Info: (Cataloging) epixtech, inc.; (Circulation) epixtech, inc.
Mem of Onondaga County Public Library
Friends of the Library Group

S ONONDAGA HISTORICAL ASSOCIATION LIBRARY, 311 Montgomery St, 13202-2098. SAN 312-5459. Tel: 315-428-1862. FAX: 315-471-2133. *Exec Dir*, Peter Apgar
Founded 1863
Library Holdings: Bk Vols 8,020
Subject Interests: Erie Canal, Onondaga county hist, Railroads, Syracuse hist, Women's suffrage movement
Open Mon-Fri 1-4:30

M SAINT JOSEPH'S HOSPITAL HEALTH CENTER, School of Nursing & Medical Library, 206 Prospect Ave, 13203. SAN 312-5467. Tel: 315-448-5053. FAX: 315-423-6804 (Nursing). Web Site: sjhsyr.org. *Librn*, Ellie Sheldon; E-Mail: ellie.sheldon@sjhsyr.org; Staff 4 (MLS 2, Non-MLS 2)
Founded 1948
Library Holdings: Bk Titles 4,000; Per Subs 200
Subject Interests: Nursing, Nursing hist
Special Collections: Three-Dimensional Models
Database Vendor: Ebsco - EbscoHost
Publications: Accession list (monthly)
Mem of Cent NY Libr Resources Coun

L SCOLARO, SHULMAN, COHEN, LAWLER & BURSTEIN, Law Library, 90 Presidential Plaza, 13202. SAN 372-2376. Tel: 315-471-8111, Ext 238. FAX: 315-425-3638. *Dir*, Rose Marie Romano; E-Mail: rromano@scolaro.com
Library Holdings: Bk Vols 5,000; Per Subs 20
Restriction: Staff use only

S STATE UNIVERSITY OF NEW YORK EDUCATIONAL OPPORTUNITY CENTER, Paul Robeson Library,* 100 New St, 13202. SAN 373-8213. Tel: 315-472-0130, Ext 30. FAX: 315-472-1241. *Librn*, Grace Lai; Staff 1 (MLS 1)
Founded 1969
Library Holdings: Bk Titles 12,000; Per Subs 100
Special Collections: African-American Books (Frazier Library Coll), bks,

slides
Publications: Periodical holdings
Mem of Cent NY Libr Resources Coun

C STATE UNIVERSITY OF NEW YORK, COLLEGE OF ENVIRONMENTAL SCIENCE & FORESTRY, F Franklin Moon Library, One Forestry Dr, 13210. SAN 312-5483. Tel: 315-470-6715. Interlibrary Loan Service Tel: 315-470-6729. FAX: 315-470-6512. Web Site: www.esf.edu/moonlib/. *Dir*, Elizabeth A Elkins; E-Mail: eaelkins@esf.edu; *ILL*, James Williamson; Staff 11 (MLS 6, Non-MLS 5)
Founded 1919. Enrl 1,600; Fac 125; Highest Degree: Doctorate
Library Holdings: Bk Vols 121,000; Per Subs 1,793
Subject Interests: Environmental studies, Forestry, Landscape architecture, Natural resources, Outdoor recreation, Paper sci, Plant pathology, Polymer chemistry, Wildlife mgt
Automation Activity & Vendor Info: (Acquisitions) Endeavor; (Circulation) Endeavor; (Course Reserve) Endeavor; (ILL) Endeavor; (Media Booking) Endeavor; (OPAC) Endeavor; (Serials) Endeavor
Publications: Newsletter, Point of use Guides
Partic in Central New York Library Resources Council; OCLC Online Computer Library Center, Inc
Friends of the Library Group

CM SUNY HEALTH SCIENCE CENTER AT SYRACUSE, Health Sciences Library,* 766 Irving Ave, 13210-1602. SAN 312-5475. Tel: 315-464-4582. Interlibrary Loan Service Tel: 315-464-5116. FAX: 315-464-4584. Interlibrary Loan Service FAX: 315-464-7199. E-Mail: library@vax.cs.hscsyr.edu. Web Site: www.hscsyr.edu/library/. *Dir*, Laurie Thompson; E-Mail: thompsol@vax.cs.hscsyr.edu; *Syst Coordr*, Patricia Onsi; *Tech Servs*, Godfrey Belleh; *Circ*, Carla Godfrey; Tel: 701-252-3467, ext 2432, E-Mail: cgodfrey@jc.edu; *Rare Bks*, Eric Van der Luft; *AV*, Christine Kucharski; *Ref*, Diane Hawkins; *Ref*, James Capodagli; *Ref*, Bette Jean Ingui; *Ref*, Kay Root; *Coll Develop*, Rosemarie Bundy; Staff 13 (MLS 12, Non-MLS 1)
Founded 1912
Library Holdings: Bk Vols 189,999; Bk Titles 60,669; Per Subs 1,472
Subject Interests: Behav sci, Medicine, Pre clinical sci, Sci-tech, Soc sci
Special Collections: Geneva Coll; Medicine (Americana Coll); Rare Books Coll; Stephen Smith Coll
Automation Activity & Vendor Info: (Circulation) DRA; (OPAC) DRA
Database Vendor: CARL, Dialog, OVID Technologies, ProQuest
Publications: alphabetical list of serial titles (bi-annual); subject mediagraphies for slides, NCME videotapes & videotapes (annual); Synapse (quarterly)
Partic in Central New York Library Resources Council; National Network Of Libraries Of Medicine - South Central Region; OCLC Online Computer Library Center, Inc

S SYRACUSE NEWSPAPERS LIBRARY, Clinton Square, PO Box 4915, 13221-4915. SAN 375-0906. Tel: 315-470-2242. FAX: 315-470-2005. Web Site: www.syracuse.com. *Mgr Libr Serv*, Laura Soto-Barra; E-Mail: lsoto-barra@syracuse.com; *Res*, Bonnie Ross; Tel: 315-470-3074, E-Mail: bross@syracuse.com; Staff 3 (MLS 2, Non-MLS 1)
Library Holdings: Bk Vols 200
Restriction: Not open to public
Function: Archival collection, Newspaper reference library
Partic in Mediastream

S SYRACUSE RESEARCH CORP LIBRARY,* 6225 Running Ridge Rd, 13212. SAN 312-5521. Tel: 315-452-8044. FAX: 315-452-8090. *Librn*, Nancy H Hall; E-Mail: hall@syrres.com; *Librn*, Randi Starmer
Founded 1961
Library Holdings: Bk Vols 4,000; Bk Titles 4,370; Per Subs 100
Subject Interests: Aquatic toxicol, Chem hazard assessment, Electrical engineering, Environ sci, Radar systems
Partic in Central New York Library Resources Council; Chemline; New York State Interlibrary Loan Network; NY Libr Res Coun
Chemical Hazard Assessment maintains a separate environmental fate database

GL SYRACUSE SUPREME COURT LAW LIBRARY, 401 Montgomery St, 13202. SAN 312-5424. Tel: 315-671-1150. FAX: 315-671-1160. *Dir*, Colleen Stella; Staff 4 (MLS 4)
Founded 1849
Library Holdings: Bk Vols 165,000; Bk Titles 15,556; Per Subs 1,200
Subject Interests: Extensive New York state, Federal legal materials, Shared federal depository
Database Vendor: epixtech, inc.
Publications: Articles of Interest & Subject Bibliographies; Library Guide; Microform Guide; New Book List; New Doc Topic Finders; Records & Briefs Guide
Partic in NY Cent Libr Resources Coun; State University Of New York-NYLINK
Open Mon-Fri 8:30-5

C SYRACUSE UNIVERSITY LIBRARY, E S Bird Library, 222 Waverly Ave, 13244-2010. SAN 354-2645. Tel: 315-443-2573. Interlibrary Loan Service Tel: 315-443-3725. Interlibrary Loan Service FAX: 315-443-4507. Web Site: web.syr.edu/~libweb. *Librn*, Peter Graham; *Publ Servs*, Carol Parke; *Coll Develop*, Peter McDonald; *ILL*, Dorcas MacDonald; *Media Spec*, George L Abbott; *Ref, Res*, Lisa Moeckel; *Doc Delivery, Electronic Resources*, Pamela McLaughlin; *Ref Serv*, Elaine Coppola; *Circ*, Eileen DeRycke. Subject Specialists: *Fine arts*, Barbara Opar; *Science/technology*, Lee Murray; Staff 196 (MLS 56, Non-MLS 140)
Founded 1871. Enrl 18,535; Fac 1,386; Highest Degree: Doctorate
Library Holdings: Bk Vols 2,764,000; Per Subs 9,015
Special Collections: Albert Schweitzer Papers; Anna Hyatt Huntington Papers; Arna Bontemps Papers; Averill Harriman Gubernatorial Papers; Benjamin Spock Papers; C P Huntington Papers; Cartoonist Coll; Continuing Education Coll; Dorothy Thompson Papers; Earl R Browder Papers; Gerrit & Peter Smith Coll; Grove Press Archive; Leopold Von Ranke Library; Library; Marcel Breuer Coll; Margaret Bourke-White Coll; Mary Walker Papers; Modern American Private Press Books; Novotny Library of Economic History; Oneida Community Coll; Peggy Bacon Papers; Revolution; Rudyard Kipling First Editions; Science Fiction Books & Manuscripts; Shaker Coll; Sol Feinstone Library; Spire Collection on Loyalists in the American; Stephen Crane First Editions & Manuscripts; Street & Smith Archive; William Hobart-Royce Balzac Coll; William Safire Coll
Publications: Courier
Mem of Asn of Research Libraries
Partic in Central New York Library Resources Council; OCLC Online Computer Library Center, Inc; Research Libraries Group, Inc
Special Services for the Deaf - Captioned media
Special Services for the Blind - Talking books for the Blind; Voice synthezier, online text enlargement
Friends of the Library Group
Departmental Libraries:
GEOLOGY, 300 Heroy Geology Bldg, 13244-1070. (Mail add: 300 Heroy Laboratory, 13244-1070), SAN 354-2769. Tel: 315-443-3337. FAX: 315-443-3363. *Librn*, Elizabeth Wallace; Tel: 315-443-2160, Fax: 315-443-5549, E-Mail: eawallac@library.syr.edu; Staff 2 (MLS 1, Non-MLS 1)
Subject Interests: Geology, Hydrogeology, Paleontology
H DOUGLAS BARCLAY LAW LIBRARY, College of Law, E I White Hall, 13244-1030. SAN 354-2793. Tel: 315-443-9560, 315-443-9582. Circulation Tel: 315-443-9570. FAX: 315-443-9567. E-Mail: library@law.syr.edu. Web Site: www.law.syr.edu, www.law.syr.edu/library. *Dir*, Thomas R French; Tel: 315-443-9571, E-Mail: trfrench@law.syr.edu; *Assoc Librn, Publ Servs*, Wendy Scott; E-Mail: wescott@law.syr.edu; *Assoc Librn, Tech Servs*, Jan Fleckenstein; Tel: 315-443-9531, E-Mail: jflecken@law.syr.edu; Staff 19 (MLS 8, Non-MLS 11)
Founded 1899
Library Holdings: Bk Vols 194,152; Bk Titles 50,096; Per Subs 3,261
Subject Interests: Anglo-Am law, Family law, International law, Law mgt, Legal hist, Technology, Trial practice
Automation Activity & Vendor Info: (Cataloging) Endeavor; (Circulation) Endeavor; (Course Reserve) Endeavor; (OPAC) Endeavor; (Serials) Endeavor
Publications: Acquisitions Bulletin; Electronic Newsletter; Law Library Guide; Library Update
Partic in OCLC Online Computer Library Center, Inc
New York State documents information & access center
MATHEMATICS, 308 Carnegie Bldg, 13244-1150. SAN 354-2823. Tel: 315-443-2092. FAX: 315-443-5539. E-Mail: libmmd@suvm.bitnet. *Librn*, Mary DeCarlo; E-Mail: mmdecarl@library.syr.edu
Library Holdings: Bk Vols 27,000; Per Subs 250
PHYSICS, 208 Physics Bldg, 13244-1130. SAN 354-2858. Tel: 315-443-2692. Web Site: web.syr.edu/~jlpease/physlib.html. *Librn*, Janet Pease; Tel: 315-443-2160, Fax: 315-443-5549, E-Mail: jlpease@library.syr.edu; Staff 1 (MLS 1)
Subject Interests: Astronomy, Physics
SCIENCE & TECHNOLOGY, Carnegie Bldg, 13244-2010. Tel: 315-443-2160. FAX: 315-443-5549. *Librn*, Mary DeCarlo; Tel: 315-443-2092, E-Mail: mmdecarl@library.syr.edu; *Librn*, Tom Keays; E-Mail: htkeays@syr.edu; *Librn*, Lee Murray; E-Mail: lmmurray@syr.edu; *Librn*, Janet Pease; E-Mail: jlpease@syr.edu; *Librn*, Elizabeth Wallace; E-Mail: eawallace@library.syr.edu. Subject Specialists: *Biology*, Tom Keays; *Chemistry*, Tom Keays; *Earth science*, Elizabeth Wallace; *Health sciences*, Lee Murray; *Mathematics*, Mary DeCarlo; *Nutrition*, Janet Pease; *Physics*, Janet Pease; Staff 11 (MLS 5, Non-MLS 6)
Enrl 16,000
Subject Interests: Biology, Chemistry, Engineering, Nursing, Nutrition

S UNITED TECH INFO NETWORK,* Carrier Pkwy, PO Box 4808, 13221. SAN 312-5297. Tel: 315-432-3473. FAX: 315-432-7380.
Founded 1942
Library Holdings: Bk Titles 15,000
Subject Interests: Air conditioning, Heating, Ventilating
Publications: Library Bulletin (monthly)
Partic in Dialog Corporation; OCLC Online Computer Library Center, Inc; Utoc

TAPPAN

P TAPPAN LIBRARY,* 93 Main St, 10983. SAN 312-5548. Tel: 914-359-3877. FAX: 914-359-3884. *Ch Servs*, Katherine Mazzella; *Ref*, Sara Nugent; *Dir*, Valerie Mammana; *Coll Develop*, Ellen Poppe
Founded 1956. Pop 6,867
Jan 1999-Dec 1999 Income $491,994, City $391,649, Locally Generated Income $55,345, Other $45,000. Mats Exp $105,669, Books $87,419, Per/Ser (Incl. Access Fees) $4,550, AV Equip $2,700, Electronic Ref Mat (Incl. Access Fees) $11,000. Sal $244,320
Library Holdings: Bk Vols 48,140
Subject Interests: Local history, Poetry
Special Collections: Major John Andre Coll
Publications: Newsletter
Mem of Ramapo Catskill Library System
Friends of the Library Group

TARRYTOWN

S AMERICAN BOOKSELLERS ASSOCIATION, Information Center,* 828 S Broadway, 10591-5112. SAN 322-6999. Tel: 914-591-2665. FAX: 914-591-2720. E-Mail: info@bookweb.org.
Founded 1989
Library Holdings: Bk Vols 5,200; Per Subs 100
Subject Interests: Book publ, Book selling
Restriction: By appointment only

S BAYER CORPORATION, Information Resources & Services,* 511 Benedict Ave, 10591. SAN 312-5602. Tel: 914-524-2339. FAX: 914-524-3075.
Founded 1962
Library Holdings: Bk Vols 15,000; Per Subs 350
Subject Interests: Bus, Medicine, Mgt, Sci, Technology
Restriction: Staff use only
Partic in Dialog Corporation

S CIBA SPECIALTY CHEMICAL, Corporate Library, 540 White Plains Rd, 10591. SAN 310-8074. Tel: 914-785-2478. FAX: 914-785-4674. *Librn*, Paul M McIlvaine; E-Mail: paul.mcilvaine@cibasc.com; Staff 3 (MLS 1, Non-MLS 2)
Founded 1956
Library Holdings: Bk Vols 10,600; Per Subs 600
Subject Interests: Bus admin, Organic chemistry, Plastics, Polymers
Restriction: Staff use only
Open Mon-Fri 8-4:30

S HISTORIC HUDSON VALLEY LIBRARY,* 150 White Plains Rd, 10591. SAN 312-5599. Tel: 914-631-8200, Ext 630. FAX: 914-631-0089. *Curator*, Jill Taylor
Founded 1951
Library Holdings: Bk Vols 25,000; Per Subs 90
Subject Interests: 17th, 18th, 19th Century Hudson River Valley hist, Architecture, Decorative arts
Special Collections: Washington Irving Editions
Partic in New York Metrop Ref & Res Libr Agency

S HISTORICAL SOCIETY SERVING SLEEPY HOLLOW & TARRYTOWN, Society Library,* One Grove St, 10591. SAN 312-5564. Tel: 914-631-8374. *Dir*, Sara Mascia
Founded 1889
Library Holdings: Bk Titles 3,500
Subject Interests: Am, Am Revolutionary War, Genealogy, Local, Local history, Regional newspapers, State
Special Collections: Children's Books of Earlier Times & Related History Books for Children; Civil War Memorabilia; Civil War Papers of Capt Charles H Rockwell; Indians (Leslie V Case Coll), artifacts; John Paulding, Isaac Van Wart & David Williams Coll, artifacts, docs; Life Along the Hudson River Valley, art, bks, per, photogs; Local Families & Their History, bks, genealogies, micro, records, VF; Local Newspapers, micro; Local Photographs Coll, 1800s- Present; Local Schools & Churches, art, bks; Local Writers, bks, mss; Major Andre: His Capture & His Captors, bks, pictures; Maps (Tarrytown, North Tarrytown, Pocantico Hills, Westchester County & New York State 1700 - Present); Old Dutch Church History & Burying Ground; Revolutionary War Memorabilia; Ward B Burnett Post GAR Coll, records; World War I & World War II Coll
Publications: postcards of local historic sites & events; The Capture of Major John Andre, September 23, 1780, an excerpt from Westchester County During the American Revolution by Otto Hufeland; The Chronicle (published twice a year)
Open Tues, Wed, Thurs & Sat 2-4

S KRAFT FOODS, Technology Information Group,* 555 S Broadway, 10591. SAN 354-3935. Tel: 914-335-2500. FAX: 914-335-6573.
Library Holdings: Bk Vols 5,000; Per Subs 300
Subject Interests: Food sci, Gen bus, Marketing, Marketing res, Technology
Special Collections: Technical Research Reports

C MARYMOUNT COLLEGE, Gloria Gaines Memorial Library, 100 Marymount Ave, 10591-3796. SAN 312-5572. Tel: 914-332-8385. Interlibrary Loan Service Tel: 914-332-8387. Reference Tel: 914-332-8388. FAX: 914-332-7109. E-Mail: library@mmc.marymt.edu. Web Site: www.marymt.edu/~library/. *Dir Libr Serv*, David Oettinger; Tel: 914-332-8251, E-Mail: oetting@mmc.marymt.edu; *Per*, St Edward McLaughlin, Sr; Tel: 914-332-8311, E-Mail: mclaughl@mmc.marymt.edu; *Res*, Cheryl Cohen; E-Mail: cohenc@mmc.marymt.edu; *Res*, Jo Ellen Morrison; E-Mail: morrison@mmc.marymt.edu; *Res*, Mary Tooher; E-Mail: tooher@mmc.marymt.edu; *Cat*, Dympna Haber, Sr; Tel: 914-332-7472, E-Mail: haber@mmc.marymt.edu; *Res*, Gabrila Cipollone; E-Mail: cippolon@mmc.marymt.edu; *Circ*, Marie Gorman; *Res*, Mrs Dana Kozelek; E-Mail: kozelek@mmc.marymt.edu; *Archivist*, Sandra Carpenter; Tel: 914-332-8320, E-Mail: carpsan@mmc.marymt.edu; *Media Spec Ad*, Julie Suvajac; Tel: 914-332-8238; *ILL*, Victoria Paterno; E-Mail: paterno@mmc.marymt.edu; *ILL*, MaryElizabeth Rathgeb, Sr; E-Mail: rathgeb@mmc.marymt.edu; *Circ*, Eileen Reid; E-Mail: reid@mmc.marymt.edu; *AV*, Julie Suvajac; Tel: 914-332-8238, E-Mail: suvajac@mmc.marymt.edu; Staff 11 (MLS 5, Non-MLS 6)
Founded 1920. Enrl 938; Fac 58; Highest Degree: Doctorate
Library Holdings: Bk Vols 100,000; Bk Titles 80,000; Per Subs 349
Special Collections: Catholic News, 1888-1965 (micro); Mussolini Papers (micro); Thomas More; Washington Irving; Women
Automation Activity & Vendor Info: (Cataloging) PALS; (OPAC) PALS
Database Vendor: Ebsco - EbscoHost, IAC - SearchBank, Lexis-Nexis, OCLC - First Search, ProQuest, Silverplatter Information Inc., Wilson - Wilson Web
Publications: Acquisitions List; Faculty & Students Information Sheets; Periodical List
Restriction: Restricted loan policy
Function: For research purposes
Mem of NY Metrop Ref & Res Libr Agency, Inc
Partic in New York Metrop Ref & Res Libr Agency; WALDO
Also serve as the graduate library for Fordham University-at-Tarrytown
Friends of the Library Group

P WARNER LIBRARY, 121 N Broadway, 10591. SAN 312-5610. Tel: 914-631-7734. FAX: 914-631-2324. Web Site: www.wls.lib.ny.us/libs/tarrytown/warner.htm. *Dir*, Kristin Weltzheimer; E-Mail: kweltzhe@lib.ny.us; Staff 14 (MLS 6, Non-MLS 8)
Founded 1929. Pop 18,891; Circ 104,412
Jul 2000-Jun 2001 Income $930,400, City $863,400, Locally Generated Income $13,000, Other $54,000. Mats Exp $90,000, Books $60,000, Per/Ser (Incl. Access Fees) $10,000, Micro $10,000, AV Equip $10,000. Sal $500,600 (Prof $237,663)
Library Holdings: Bk Vols 89,241; Bk Titles 78,458; Per Subs 194
Subject Interests: Local authors, Local history
Special Collections: Large print books; Washington Irving Coll, large print
Database Vendor: Dialog, Ebsco - EbscoHost, epixtech, inc., GaleNet, IAC - Info Trac
Publications: Warner Library News
Mem of Westchester Library System
Friends of the Library Group

S WITCO CORP, Library & Technical Information Service,* 771 Old Saw Mill River Rd, 10591-6799. SAN 354-2912. Tel: 914-784-4800. FAX: 914-784-4935. *Mgr*, Joan Schechtman; Staff 6 (MLS 3, Non-MLS 3)
Founded 1971
Library Holdings: Bk Vols 40,000; Per Subs 350
Subject Interests: Chemistry, Cryogenics, Engineering, Physics
Special Collections: Chemical Patents Coll, micro
Publications: Newsletter
Restriction: Staff use only
Partic in DARC/Questel; Dialog Corporation; Dow Jones News Retrieval; Infoline; Mead Data Cent; OCLC Online Computer Library Center, Inc; SDC Info Servs; STN

THERESA

P THERESA FREE LIBRARY,* 301 Main St & Pine, 13691. SAN 312-5629. Tel: 315-628-5972. FAX: 315-628-5972. *Librn*, Christine Rajner
Pop 1,853; Circ 12,132
Library Holdings: Bk Vols 7,000; Per Subs 165
Mem of North Country Library System
Friends of the Library Group

THOUSAND ISLAND PARK

P THOUSAND ISLAND PARK LIBRARY,* Saint Lawrence Ave, PO Box 1115, 13692. SAN 312-5637. Tel: 315-482-9435. *Librn*, Mabel Heath
Circ 6,247
Library Holdings: Bk Vols 6,750
Mem of North Country Library System

TICONDEROGA

P BLACK WATCH MEMORIAL LIBRARY,* 195 Montcalm St, 12883. SAN 312-5645. Tel: 518-585-7380. FAX: 518-585-3209. *Librn*, Maureen Johns
Founded 1906. Pop 5,486; Circ 19,421
Library Holdings: Bk Titles 14,110; Per Subs 17
Mem of Clinton-Essex-Franklin Library System
Friends of the Library Group

S FORT TICONDEROGA MUSEUM, Thompson-Pell Research Center, PO Box 390, 12883. SAN 312-5653. Tel: 518-585-2821. FAX: 518-585-2210. E-Mail: mail@fort-ticonderoga.org. Web Site: www.fort-ticonderoga.org. *Dir*, Nicholas Westbrook; E-Mail: nick@for-ticonderoga.org; *Curator*, Christopher D Fox
Founded 1908
Jan 1999-Dec 1999 Income $2,200,000. Mats Exp $31,500, Books $2,000, Per/Ser (Incl. Access Fees) $1,000, Presv $1,000, Micro $500, Manuscripts & Archives $27,000
Library Holdings: Bk Vols 13,000; Per Subs 20; Spec Interest Per Sub 20
Subject Interests: Colonial, Mil hist 1609-1780, Revolutionary wars in Champlain, Upper Hudson valleys
Special Collections: Manuscripts & maps, subject areas
Publications: Bulletin of the Fort Ticonderoga Museum, vol 1 (1927 - present)
Restriction: Non-circulating to the public
Partic in North Country Reference & Research Resources Council
Special research library of Fort Ticonderoga Museum

S TICONDEROGA HISTORICAL SOCIETY LIBRARY, Hancock House, Moses Circle, 12883. SAN 325-9668. Tel: 518-585-7868. Web Site: www.capital.net/~ths2/index/htm.. *Pres*, Carla G Staudt; *Asst Dir*, Stephen Blanchard
Founded 1898
Library Holdings: Bk Vols 10,000; Bk Titles 8,000
Special Collections: Account Books; Diaries; Local History Books; Manuscripts; Newspapers; Photos
Publications: Patches & Patterns Extended
Restriction: Non-circulating to the public

TIVOLI

P TIVOLI FREE LIBRARY,* 86 Broadway, PO Box 400, 12583. SAN 312-5661. Tel: 914-757-3771. Interlibrary Loan Service Tel: 914-471-6060. *Librn*, Bonnig Corrado; *Asst Librn*, Margaret S Lemon
Founded 1919. Circ 3,536
Library Holdings: Bk Vols 7,500
Mem of Mid-Hudson Library System
Open Tues & Thurs 2-5 & 7-8:30, Sat 2-5

TOMKINS COVE

P TOMKINS COVE PUBLIC LIBRARY,* 419 Liberty Dr N, 10986. SAN 312-567X. Tel: 914-786-3060. FAX: 914-947-5572. *Dir*, Robert S Devino; Staff 7 (MLS 1, Non-MLS 6)
Founded 1896. Pop 1,800; Circ 12,000
Library Holdings: Bk Vols 22,000; Per Subs 49
Special Collections: Birds & Conservation (Margaret Tomkins Memorial Coll)
Publications: Newsletter (quarterly)
Mem of Ramapo Catskill Library System

TONAWANDA

S PRAXAIR, INC LIBRARY, PO Box 44, 14151-0044. SAN 312-570X. Tel: 716-879-2031. FAX: 716-879-3101. *Librn*, Yvonne Curry; E-Mail: ycurry@praxair.com
Founded 1938
Library Holdings: Bk Vols 7,000; Per Subs 250
Subject Interests: Chemistry, Indust gases, Mech eng
Restriction: Staff use only, Use of others with permission of librarian
Partic in Western New York Library Resources Council

P TONAWANDA CITY PUBLIC LIBRARY, 333 Main St, 14150. SAN 312-5696. Tel: 716-693-5043. FAX: 716-693-0825. *Dir*, Mary Catherine McKee; E-Mail: mckeem@buffalolib.org; *Asst Librn*, Carol L Veach; Staff 2 (MLS 2)
Pop 17,284; Circ 149,278
Jan 1999-Dec 1999 Income $277,177. Mats Exp $42,797, Books $37,497, Per/Ser (Incl. Access Fees) $5,300. Sal $203,358 (Prof $106,918)
Library Holdings: Bk Vols 33,000; Per Subs 100
Mem of Buffalo & Erie County Public Library System
Friends of the Library Group

TROY

J HUDSON VALLEY COMMUNITY COLLEGE, Dwight Marvin Learning Resources Center,* 80 Vandenburgh Ave, 12180. SAN 312-5742. Tel: 518-629-7336. Interlibrary Loan Service Tel: 518-629-7387. FAX: 518-629-7509. Web Site: www.hvcc.edu. *Coll Develop, Dir*, Brenda Twiggs; *Archivist, Rare Bks*, Sue Grayson; *Tech Servs*, Michael Thayer; *ILL, Ref*, Christine Root; *Media Spec*, Lindsey Watson; *Per*, Susan Blandy; Staff 10 (MLS 10)
Founded 1953. Enrl 8,808; Fac 310
Library Holdings: Bk Vols 148,246; Bk Titles 110,585; Per Subs 682
Subject Interests: Automotive tech, Business, Child develop, Dental, Eng tech, Liberal arts, Medicine, Mortuary science, Sci-tech
Special Collections: History (Microbook Library Journal of American Civilization Coll), micro; History of Western Civ (Microbook); Video Encyclopedia of the 20th Century
Publications: Dwight Marvin LRC Guide; Faculty LRC Handbook; From the Library (acquisitions); Kaleidoscope; Policies & Procedures Manual; Previews (from the Media Center); Student Guide; Worksheets & Bibliographic
Partic in OCLC Online Computer Library Center, Inc
Special Services for the Deaf - Captioned film depository
Special Services for the Blind - Brailling & large print projects

GL NEW YORK STATE SUPREME COURT LIBRARY, Court House Second St Annex, 86 Second St, 12180-4098. SAN 312-5769. Tel: 518-270-3717. FAX: 518-274-0590. *Head Librn*, Karlye Ann Pillai; E-Mail: kpillai@atdial.net; Staff 3 (MLS 1, Non-MLS 2)
Founded 1909
Apr 1999-Mar 2000 Income State $318,909
Library Holdings: Bk Vols 41,735; Bk Titles 1,140
Subject Interests: Federal, Law, NY state
Automation Activity & Vendor Info: (Acquisitions) epixtech, inc.; (Cataloging) epixtech, inc.; (Circulation) epixtech, inc.; (OPAC) epixtech, inc.; (Serials) epixtech, inc.
Restriction: Open to public for reference only

S NORTON COMPANY COATED ABRASIVE DIVISION, Technical Library,* PO Box 808, 12181-0808. SAN 312-6439. Tel: 518-266-2741. FAX: 518-266-2299.
Library Holdings: Bk Vols 2,000; Bk Titles 1,800; Per Subs 65
Subject Interests: Abrasives, Adhesive, Chemistry, Eng-tech, Mgt
Special Collections: Company Research Reports
Restriction: Private library
Partic in Cap District Libr Coun for Ref & Res Resources; Dialog Corporation; Dow Jones News Retrieval; OCLC Online Computer Library Center, Inc; STN

S RECORD NEWSPAPER LIBRARY,* 501 Broadway, 12181. SAN 372-5669. Tel: 518-270-1280, Ext 1535. FAX: 518-270-1202.
Subject Interests: Local history
Special Collections: Clipping files dating back to the early '70s
Restriction: Not open to public

S RENSSELAER COUNTY HISTORICAL SOCIETY LIBRARY,* 59 Second St, 12180. SAN 312-5785. Tel: 518-272-7232. FAX: 518-273-1264. Web Site: www.rchs.online.org. *Dir*, Donna J Hassler; *Curator*, Stacy P Draper
Founded 1927
Library Holdings: Bk Titles 3,000
Subject Interests: Archives, Manuscripts, Photog, Rensselaer County hist
Special Collections: Cluett, Peabody & Co, Archives; Hart Family, papers
Publications: Rensselaer County History Research at the RCHS Research Library (brochure)
This research library is part of the ongoing activities of the Rensselaer County Historical Society. The Society also maintains a historic house museum, changing exhibition & programming space

C RENSSELAER LIBRARIES, Folsom Library, 110 Eighth St, 12180-3590. SAN 354-2971. Tel: 518-276-8300. Interlibrary Loan Service Tel: 518-276-8330. Reference Tel: 518-276-8320. FAX: 518-276-2044. E-Mail: lib.support@rpi.edu. Web Site: www.rpi.edu/dept/library/html/libinfo.html. *Dir*, Loretta Caren Ebert; *Tech Servs*, D Ellen Bonner; *Tech Servs*, Tanis Kreiger; *Publ Servs*, Irving E Stephens; *Coll Develop*, John Dojka; *Ref*, MaryAnne Waltz; Staff 23 (MLS 18, Non-MLS 5)
Founded 1824. Enrl 6,200; Fac 342; Highest Degree: Doctorate
Jul 1999-Jun 2000 Income (Main Library and Branch Library) $3,248,577, Locally Generated Income $352,969, Parent Institution $2,895,608. Mats Exp $1,572,389, Books $300,672, Per/Ser (Incl. Access Fees) $704,195, Presv $25,535, Other Print Mats $32,298, Electronic Ref Mat (Incl. Access Fees) $509,689. Sal $1,140,948 (Prof $696,882)
Library Holdings: Bk Vols 494,823; Per Subs 2,522
Subject Interests: Architecture, Biotechnology, Engineering, Info tech
Special Collections: Architecture; History of Science & Technology; Local History; Rare Bks; Reports; Research Reports
Automation Activity & Vendor Info: (Acquisitions) Innovative Interfaces Inc.; (Cataloging) Innovative Interfaces Inc.; (Circulation) Innovative Interfaces Inc.; (OPAC) Innovative Interfaces Inc.; (Serials) Innovative

Interfaces Inc.
Partic in Cap District Libr Coun for Ref & Res Resources; CNI; Educause; SPARC
Friends of the Library Group
Departmental Libraries:
ARCHITECTURE, Greene Bldg, 12180. SAN 354-3005. Tel: 518-266-6465. *Librn*, Frances Scott

S RYAN-BIGGS ASSOCIATES PC LIBRARY,* 291 River St, 12180. SAN 329-4226. Tel: 518-272-6266. FAX: 518-272-4467. *Librn*, Barbara Meagher
Library Holdings: Bk Titles 1,400; Per Subs 30

M SAMARITAN HOSPITAL, Medical Library,* 2215 Burdett Ave, 12180. SAN 312-5807. Tel: 518-271-3200. FAX: 518-271-3434. *Librn*, Annie Jean Smith
Founded 1950
Library Holdings: Bk Vols 621; Per Subs 66
Subject Interests: Gynecology, Internal medicine, Obstetrics, Pediatrics, Surgery
Special Collections: Health Sciences (Spafford)
Publications: The Book Bag

M SETON HEALTH SYSTEMS, Health Sciences Library,* 1300 Massachusetts Ave, 12180. SAN 312-5793. Tel: 518-268-5000. *Librn*, Debra Wellspeak
Founded 1955
Library Holdings: Bk Titles 2,310; Per Subs 75
Subject Interests: Medicine, Nursing
Partic in Capital District Library Council for Reference & Research Resources

C THE SAGE COLLEGES, James Wheelock Clark Library, 45 Ferry St, 12180. SAN 354-303X. Tel: 518-244-2249. Interlibrary Loan Service Tel: 518-244-2320. Reference Tel: 518-244-2432. FAX: 518-244-2400. E-Mail: libref@sage.edu. Web Site: www.sage.edu. *Dir*, Kingsley W Greene; Tel: 518-244-2346, E-Mail: greenk@sage.edu; *Assoc Dir*, Lynne King; Tel: 518-292-1721, Fax: 518-292-1904, E-Mail: kingl@sage.edu; *Archivist*, Aggie Stillman; Tel: 518-244-4522, E-Mail: stilla@sage.edu; *Tech Servs*, Terrance Wasielewski; Tel: 518-224-2435, E-Mail: wasiet@sage.edu; *Cat*, Carolyn Brigham; *Head Ref*, Debra Kirsch; E-Mail: kirscd@sage.edu; *Publ Servs*, Sharon Phillips; Tel: 518-244-3106, E-Mail: phills2@sage.edu; *Syst Coordr*, Christopher White; Tel: 518-244-4521, E-Mail: whitec2@sage.edu; Staff 16 (MLS 6, Non-MLS 10)
Founded 1916. Enrl 819; Fac 161; Highest Degree: Master
May 1999-Apr 2000 Income $948,256, State $9,522, Parent Institution $933,836, Other $4,898. Mats Exp $340,328, Books $50,485, Per/Ser (Incl. Access Fees) $147,573, Presv $8,775, AV Equip $7,311, Electronic Ref Mat (Incl. Access Fees) $29,099. Sal $593,508 (Prof $332,586)
Library Holdings: Bk Vols 174,297; Bk Titles 138,617; Per Subs 820
Subject Interests: Allied health, Women's studies
Special Collections: 20th Century Poetry (Carol Ann Donahue Memorial Coll)
Automation Activity & Vendor Info: (Acquisitions) SIRSI; (Cataloging) SIRSI; (Circulation) SIRSI; (Course Reserve) SIRSI; (OPAC) SIRSI; (Serials) SIRSI
Database Vendor: Ebsco - EbscoHost, GaleNet, Lexis-Nexis, OCLC - First Search, ProQuest, Silverplatter Information Inc.
Publications: Newsletter; Serials & Full-Text Lists; Serials List
Partic in Cap District Libr Coun for Ref & Res Resources; OCLC Online Computer Library Center, Inc; WALDO

P TROY PUBLIC LIBRARY,* 100 Second St, 12180-4005. SAN 354-3064. Tel: 518-274-7071. FAX: 518-271-9154. E-Mail: troyref@uhls.lib.ny.us. Web Site: www.uhls.org/troy. *Exec Dir*, Paul Hicok; E-Mail: hicokp@uhls.lib.ny.us
Founded 1835. Pop 53,000; Circ 172,000
Jan 1999-Dec 1999 Income (Main Library and Branch Library) $578,500, State $18,000, City $320,000, County $66,500, Locally Generated Income $171,000. Mats Exp $594,532, Books $52,700, Presv $1,000, AV Equip $2,000, Other Print Mats $6,700, Other Print Mats $2,000, Electronic Ref Mat (Incl. Access Fees) $5,000. Sal $359,000
Library Holdings: Bk Vols 131,000; Bk Titles 89,240; Per Subs 412
Subject Interests: Bus, Genealogy, Local history
Database Vendor: DRA, Ebsco - EbscoHost
Publications: Annual Report; Friends Newsletter
Mem of Upper Hudson Library System
Friends of the Library Group
Branches: 2
LANSINGBURGH, Fourth Ave & 114th St, 12182. SAN 354-3129. Tel: 518-235-5310. FAX: 518-235-5310. Web Site: www.global2000.net/troypl.
Library Holdings: Bk Vols 11,983
Friends of the Library Group
SYCAWAY, Hoosick & Lee Sts, 12180. SAN 354-3153. Tel: 518-274-1822. Web Site: www.global2000.net/troypl.
Library Holdings: Bk Vols 5,000
Friends of the Library Group

TRUMANSBURG

P ULYSSES PHILOMATHIC LIBRARY, 61 E Main St, PO Box 705, 14886-0705. SAN 312-5815. Tel: 607-387-5623. FAX: 607-387-3823. *Dir*, Judith Barkee; E-Mail: jbarkee@lakenet.org
Founded 1935. Circ 29,086
Jan 1999-Dec 1999 Income $80,293. Mats Exp $73,684, Books $9,268
Library Holdings: Bk Titles 12,177; Per Subs 39
Mem of Finger Lakes Library System
Friends of the Library Group

TUCKAHOE

P TUCKAHOE PUBLIC LIBRARY,* 71 Columbus Ave, 10707. SAN 312-5823. Tel: 914-961-2121. FAX: 914-961-3832. *Dir*, Debra Coppola; *Ad Servs*, Swadesh Pachnanda; *YA Servs*, Mary Ellen Golden; Staff 17 (MLS 6, Non-MLS 11)
Founded 1912. Pop 6,075; Circ 68,075
Jun 1999-May 2000 Mats Exp $33,805, Books $28,659, Per/Ser (Incl. Access Fees) $3,414, AV Equip $1,497, Electronic Ref Mat (Incl. Access Fees) $235. Sal $236,043 (Prof $152,959)
Library Holdings: Bk Vols 44,000; Per Subs 100
Special Collections: Tuckahoe History (files, newsps on microfilm 1918-1931, pamphlets, photogs)
Database Vendor: epixtech, inc.
Publications: Monthly calendar of events; newsletter
Mem of Westchester Library System
Open Mon & Wed 10:30-8:30, Tues, Thurs & Fri 10:30-5:30
Friends of the Library Group

TULLY

P TULLY FREE LIBRARY,* 12 State St, PO Box 250, 13159-0250. SAN 312-5858. Tel: 315-696-8606. FAX: 315-696-8120. *Dir*, Kelly Hell; Tel: 701-774-4227, E-Mail: khell@mail.wsc.nodak.edu
Circ 35,316
Library Holdings: Bk Vols 13,000; Per Subs 24
Special Collections: Civil War
Mem of Onondaga County Public Library
Friends of the Library Group

TUPPER LAKE

P GOFF-NELSON MEMORIAL LIBRARY, Tupper Lake Public Library, 41 Lake St, 12986. SAN 354-3188. Tel: 518-359-9421. FAX: 518-359-9421. E-Mail: gnelson@northnet.net. *Librn*, Chalice Dechene
Founded 1932. Pop 6,712; Circ 76,888
Library Holdings: Bk Vols 33,573; Bk Titles 33,007; Per Subs 153
Mem of Clinton-Essex-Franklin Library System
Open Mon-Fri 10-5:30 & Mon-Thurs 7-9

TURIN

P B E STRONG MEMORIAL LIBRARY,* W Main St, PO Box 27, 13473. SAN 312-5866. Tel: 315-348-6433. FAX: 315-348-6433. *Librn*, Sharon Stewart
Founded 1947. Circ 7,699
Jan 1998-Dec 1999 Income $19,354. Mats Exp $2,512. Sal $4,267
Library Holdings: Bk Vols 2,200; Per Subs 50
Mem of North Country Library System
Open Mon 4-6, Wed 4-9, Thurs 7-9; First Sat of the month 10-11: Children's Storyhour

TUXEDO

S INTERNATIONAL PAPER, Corporate Research Center-Technical Information Center, 1422 Long Meadow Rd, 10987. SAN 312-5874. Tel: 914-577-7262. FAX: 914-577-7307. *Mgr*, Bernadette Marasco; E-Mail: bernadette.marasco@ipaper.com; Staff 4 (MLS 2, Non-MLS 2)
Founded 1969
Library Holdings: Bk Vols 12,000; Per Subs 300
Subject Interests: Biology, Cellulose, Co-hist, Forest product, Forestry, Mat sci, Packaging, Papermaking, Pulp
Automation Activity & Vendor Info: (Cataloging) Bestseller; (Circulation) Bestseller; (OPAC) Bestseller
Partic in Dialog Corporation; EPIC; OCLC Online Computer Library Center, Inc; Southeastern New York Library Resources Council; STN

TUXEDO PARK

P TUXEDO PARK LIBRARY, PO Box 776, 10987-0776. SAN 312-5882. Tel: 914-351-2207. FAX: 914-351-2213. E-Mail: tuxpl@rcls.org. Web Site: www.rcls.org/tuxpl. *Dir*, Carmela Chase; *Asst Dir*, Florence Brady; *Ch Servs*, Barbara Spielmann; *Ref*, Jennifer Knoerzer; Staff 3 (MLS 3)
Founded 1901. Pop 3,023; Circ 72,200

1999-2000 Income $312,950, Locally Generated Income $286,100, Other $26,850. Mats Exp $46,500, Books $21,500, Per/Ser (Incl. Access Fees) $6,000, Presv $2,000, AV Equip $500, Manuscripts & Archives $2,000, Electronic Ref Mat (Incl. Access Fees) $11,000. Sal $201,831 (Prof $141,500)
Library Holdings: Bk Titles 23,100; Per Subs 145
Special Collections: Tuxedo Park Library Local History Coll, oral hist, photos, doc, & slides
Publications: Newsletter (quarterly)
Mem of Ramapo Catskill Library System
Open Mon, Tues & Thurs 9-5:30, Wed 1-9, Fri 9-1, Sat 10-4 & Sun 11-3 (Sept - June)
Friends of the Library Group

UNADILLA

P UNADILLA PUBLIC LIBRARY,* 70 Main St, PO Box 632, 13849-0632. SAN 312-5904. Tel: 607-369-3131. FAX: 607-369-4500. *Librn*, Nancy Marcello
Pop 1,489; Circ 6,116
Library Holdings: Bk Vols 12,000; Per Subs 18
Mem of Four County Library System
Friends of the Library Group

UNION SPRINGS

P SPRINGPORT FREE LIBRARY,* PO Box 501, 13160. SAN 312-5912. Tel: 315-889-7766. FAX: 315-889-7766. *Librn*, Carla Piperso-Jones
Pop 2,210; Circ 16,221
1997-1998 Income $26,975. Mats Exp $17,349, Books $4,262. Sal $6,811
Library Holdings: Bk Titles 9,000; Per Subs 16
Mem of Finger Lakes Library System
Open Mon 2-6, Tues & Thurs 2-8 & Sat 10-2

UNIONDALE

P NASSAU LIBRARY SYSTEM, 900 Jerusalem Ave, 11553-3039. SAN 354-3242. Tel: 516-292-8920. FAX: 516-565-0950. E-Mail: nls@nassaulibrary.org. Web Site: www.nassaulibrary.org. *Dir*, Jacquelyn Thresher; *Asst Dir*, Mary Beth Beidl; *Ch Servs*, Crystal Faris; *Media Spec*, Delia Gottlieb; *Doc, Online Servs, Ref*, Frances Stricoff; *Online Servs*, Brenda Giovanniello; *Cat*, Michelle Zwierski; *Outreach Serv*, Dorothy Puryear; Staff 10 (MLS 10)
Founded 1959. Pop 1,287,348
Jan 2000-Dec 2000 Income $3,980,110, State $3,640,693, Federal $115,903, County $90,000. Sal $1,228,014 (Prof $582,000)
Database Vendor: IAC - SearchBank
Publications: Illuminations (Newsletter)
Member Libraries: Baldwin Public Library; Bayville Free Library; Bellmore Memorial Library; Bethpage Public Library; Bryant Library; East Meadow Public Library; East Rockaway Public Library; East Williston Public Library; Elmont Public Library; Farmingdale Public Library; Floral Park Public Library; Franklin Square Public Library; Freeport Memorial Library; Garden City Public Library; George Mercer Jr School Of Theology; Glen Cove Public Library; Great Neck Library; Hempstead Public Library; Henry Waldinger Memorial Library; Hewlett-Woodmere Public Library; Hicksville Public Library; Hillside Public Library; Island Park Public Library; Island Trees Public Library; Jericho Public Library; Lakeview Public Library; Levittown Public Library; Locust Valley Library; Long Beach Public Library; Lynbrook Public Library; Malverne Public Library; Manhasset Public Library; Massapequa Public Library; Merrick Library; Mineola Public Library; New Hyde Park Public Library; North Bellmore Public Library; North Merrick Public Library; Oceanside Library; Oyster Bay-East Norwich Public Library; Peninsula Public Library; Plainedge Public Library; Plainview-Old Bethpage Public Library; Port Washington Public Library; Roosevelt Public Library; Sea Cliff Village Library; Seaford Public Library; Shelter Rock Public Library; Syosset Public Library; Uniondale Public Library; Wantagh Public Library; West Hempstead Public Library; Westbury Memorial Public Library; Williston Park Public Library
Special Services for the Deaf - Captioned film depository
Branches: 1

P SUBREGIONAL LIBRARY FOR THE BLIND & PHYSICALLY HANDICAPPED, 900 Jerusalem Ave, 11553. SAN 354-3277. Tel: 516-292-8920, Ext 222. *In Charge*, Connie Wermelinger; *In Charge*, Valerie Watkins; Staff 1 (MLS 1)
Founded 1967
Partic in Nat Libr Serv READS Prog

L RIVKIN, RADLER & KREMER, LLP, Law Library, EAB Plaza, 11556. SAN 372-2368. Tel: 516-357-3453, 516-357-3455. FAX: 516-357-3333. *Librn*, Kathy Greco
Library Holdings: Bk Vols 10,000; Per Subs 50

P UNIONDALE PUBLIC LIBRARY,* 400 Uniondale Ave, 11553-1995. SAN 312-5920. Tel: 516-489-2220. FAX: 516-489-4005. E-Mail: upl@lilrc.org. Web Site: www.nassaulibrary.org/uniondale. *Dir*, Susan K Kern; *Ad Servs, Asst Dir*, Sayeeda Banglawala; *Ch Servs, YA Servs*, Deirdre Escoffier; *Ch Servs, YA Servs*, Lorraine Bianco; *Tech Servs*, E M Doran
Founded 1954. Pop 24,654; Circ 160,000
Jan 1998-Dec 1998 Income $1,568,363. Mats Exp $223,700, Books $168,000, Per/Ser (Incl. Access Fees) $31,500, Presv $100, AV Equip $2,500, Other Print Mats $1,000. Sal $862,000 (Prof $409,000)
Library Holdings: Bk Vols 119,000
Publications: Uniondale Public Library Newsletter
Mem of Nassau Library System
Friends of the Library Group

UPPER JAY

P WELLS MEMORIAL LIBRARY,* Rte 9 N, Box 57, 12987-0057. SAN 312-5939. Tel: 518-946-2644. FAX: 518-946-2644. *Librn*, Peggy Swortout
Pop 2,000; Circ 3,385
Library Holdings: Bk Vols 10,200; Per Subs 15
Special Collections: Adirondack-NY Coll
Mem of Clinton-Essex-Franklin Library System

UPPER NYACK

R TEMPLE BETH TORAH LIBRARY, Rte 9W, 330 N Highland Ave, 10960. SAN 312-5947. Tel: 845-358-2248. FAX: 845-358-3450. Web Site: www.templebethtorah.org. *Actg Librn*, Seth Schlanger
Library Holdings: Bk Vols 1,250; Bk Titles 1,200; Per Subs 14

UPTON

BROOKHAVEN NATIONAL LABORATORY
S INFORMATION SERVICES DIVISION, Bldg 477A, 11973-5000. SAN 312-5955. Tel: 516-344-3483, 516-344-3489. Interlibrary Loan Service Tel: 516-282-3138. FAX: 516-344-2090. Web Site: www.bnl.gov/bnl.html. *Mgr*, Mary E White; Fax: 631-344-5951, E-Mail: mwhite@bnl.gov; *Mgr*, Bruce Style; Tel: 631-344-7832, Fax: 631-344-5951, E-Mail: style@bnl.gov; *Ref*, Judy Liu; Tel: 631-344-7860, E-Mail: jliu@bnl.gov; *Ser*, Madeline Windsor; Tel: 631-344-5069, E-Mail: windsor@bnl.gov; *Syst Coordr*, Betsy Schwartz; Tel: 631-344-2758, E-Mail: bjs@bnl.gov; Staff 12 (MLS 3, Non-MLS 9)
Founded 1947
Oct 1999-Sep 2000 Mats Exp $1,120,000, Books $20,000, Per/Ser (Incl. Access Fees) $1,100,000. Sal $700,000
Library Holdings: Bk Vols 95,000; Bk Titles 70,000; Per Subs 800
Subject Interests: Biology, Chemistry, Energy, Engineering, Medicine, Nuclear science, Physics
Publications: Newsletter (monthly)
Restriction: By appointment only
Partic in Dialog Corporation; Long Island Library Resources Council; OCLC Online Computer Library Center, Inc

UTICA

M FAXTON HOSPITAL, Medical Library,* 1676 Sunset Ave, 13502. SAN 328-5308. Tel: 315-738-6253. FAX: 315-732-3275. *Dir Libr Serv*, Halyna Liszczynskyj
Library Holdings: Bk Vols 546; Per Subs 140
Subject Interests: Cancer, Medicine, Nursing
Special Collections: Orthopedics, Rehabilitation, Cancer
Publications: Internet Newsletter; Medical Library Newsletter
Partic in BHSL; Central New York Library Resources Council; Docline; OCLC Online Computer Library Center, Inc

M FAXTON SAINT LUKE'S HEALTH CARE, Saint Luke's Campus, PO Box 479, 13503-0479. SAN 373-6148. Tel: 315-798-6059. FAX: 315-798-6947. E-Mail: hailstod@clrc.org. *Dir Libr Serv*, Deborah Hailston
Library Holdings: Bk Titles 850; Per Subs 128
Subject Interests: Pediatrics
Mem of Cent NY Libr Resources Coun

S HERKIMER-ONEIDA COUNTIES COMPREHENSIVE PLANNING PROGRAM LIBRARY,* 800 Park Ave, 13501. SAN 325-9706. Tel: 315-798-5710. FAX: 315-798-5852. *Dir*, Michael Gapin
Library Holdings: Bk Vols 505
Open Mon-Fri 8:30-4

M MASONIC MEDICAL RESEARCH LABORATORY LIBRARY, Max L Kamiel Library, 2150 Bleecker St, 13501-1787. SAN 312-598X. Tel: 315-735-2217, Ext 35. FAX: 315-724-0963. E-Mail: lib@mmrl.edu. *Head Librn*, Barbara Grimes; Staff 1 (MLS 1)
Founded 1959
Library Holdings: Bk Vols 13,287; Per Subs 60
Subject Interests: Biochemistry, Cardiovascular physiology, Immunology, Molecular biology, Pharmacology, Physiology
Special Collections: Early Medical References & Folklore (Van Gordon Coll)

Restriction: Open to others by appointment
Function: ILL available, Some telephone reference
Partic in Central New York Library Resources Council; EFTS; New York State Interlibrary Loan Network

P MID-YORK LIBRARY SYSTEM,* 1600 Lincoln Ave, 13502. SAN 312-5998. Tel: 315-735-8328. FAX: 315-735-0943. Web Site: www.midyork.org. *Dir*, Malcolm K Hill; E-Mail: hill@midyork.lib.ny.us; *Asst Dir*, Marylou Caskey; *Automation Syst Coordr*, Diane Berry; *Ref*, Beverly Choltco-Devlin; *ILL*, Jill Grundfest; Staff 6 (MLS 6)
Founded 1960. Pop 385,811
Jan 1998-Dec 1999 Income $2,158,157. Mats Exp $197,218. Sal $795,273 (Prof $271,042)
Library Holdings: Bk Vols 120,000
Automation Activity & Vendor Info: (Acquisitions) DRA; (Circulation) DRA
Publications: Book Buying Lists; Get Ready Sheet; MYLS Reporter; Union List of Periodicals
Member Libraries: Barneveld Free Library Association; Bridgewater Free Library; Camden Public Library; Canastota Public Library; Cazenovia Public Library Society, Inc; Clayville Library Association; CW Clark Memorial Library; Deruyter Free Library; Didymus Thomas Library; Dolgeville-Manheim Public Library; Dunham Public Library; Earlville Free Library; Erwin Library & Institute; Frank J Basloe Library Of Herkimer New York; Frankfort Free Library; Hamilton Public Library; Holland Patent Free Library; Ilion Free Public Library; Jervis Public Library Association; Jordanville Public Library; Kirby Free Library Of Salisbury; Kirkland Town Library; Little Falls Public Library; Middleville Free Library; Mohawk Valley Community College Library; Morrisville Library; New Hartford Public Library; New Woodstock Free Library; Newport Free Library; Old Forge Library; Oneida Library; Oriskany Public Library; Poland Public Library; Prospect Free Library; Sherrill-Kenwood Free Library; Sullivan Free Library; Utica Public Library; Vernon Public Library; Waterville Public Library; Weller Public Library; West Winfield Library; Western Town Library; Woodgate Free Library
Partic in Central New York Library Resources Council; OCLC Online Computer Library Center, Inc

J MOHAWK VALLEY COMMUNITY COLLEGE LIBRARY,* 1101 Sherman Dr, 13501-5394. SAN 312-6005. Tel: 315-792-5408. FAX: 315-792-5666. E-Mail: rfpster@mvcc.edu. Web Site: www.mvcc.edu/library. *Actg Dir*, Ron Foster; *Media Spec*, Mike Sprague; *Cat*, Krista Hartman; *ILL*, Sherry Day; *Acq*, Kathleen Salsbury; Staff 13 (MLS 13)
Founded 1946. Enrl 5,000
Sep 1997-Aug 1998 Income $1,047,663. Mats Exp $224,553, Books $55,000, Per/Ser (Incl. Access Fees) $150,600, Micro $18,953. Sal $713,449 (Prof $362,852)
Library Holdings: Bk Vols 90,000; Bk Titles 53,364; Per Subs 725
Special Collections: Career Center
Automation Activity & Vendor Info: (Circulation) DRA
Publications: Newsletter
Mem of Mid-York Library System
Partic in Central New York Library Resources Council; OCLC Online Computer Library Center, Inc
Utica Campus open Mon-Thurs 8-10, Fri 8-4, Sat 12-5 & Sun 1-6; Rome Campus open Mon-Thurs 8:30-8:30, Fri 8:30-4:30
Friends of the Library Group

M MOHAWK VALLEY PSYCHIATRIC CENTER, George M Lein Information Center, 1400 Noyes St at York, 13502-3852. SAN 354-3420. Tel: 315-738-4027, 315-797-6800, Ext 5102. FAX: 315-738-4407. *Librn*, Kay Sangani
Founded 1843
Library Holdings: Bk Titles 2,850; Per Subs 15
Subject Interests: Hist med, Medicine, Nursing, Psychiatry
Partic in Central New York Library Resources Council; Greater NE Regional Med Libr Program

S MUNSON-WILLIAMS-PROCTOR ARTS INSTITUTE LIBRARY, 310 Genesee St, 13502. SAN 354-3307. Tel: 315-797-0000, Ext 2123. FAX: 315-797-5608. Web Site: www.mwpi.edu. *Dir*, Cynthia Barth; E-Mail: cbarth@mwpi.edu; *Asst Librn*, Michael Schuyler; Staff 2 (MLS 1, Non-MLS 1)
Founded 1960
Library Holdings: Bk Vols 23,000; Per Subs 80
Special Collections: Autograph Coll; Contemporary Artists Coll; Rare Book Coll
Partic in Central New York Library Resources Council
Branches:
MEMBERS GALLERY, 310 Genesee St, 13502. Tel: 315-797-0000, Ext 2125.
Library Holdings: Bk Vols 400
Special Collections: Original Art Works for loan & rental

GL NEW YORK SUPREME COURT, Law Library - Oneida County, Oneida County Court House, 200 Elizabeth St, 13501. SAN 312-6013. Tel: 315-798-5703. FAX: 315-797-0531. *Senior Librn*, Robert Weiner; E-Mail: rjweiner@courts.state.ny.us; Staff 4 (MLS 1, Non-MLS 3)
Library Holdings: Bk Titles 50,000; Per Subs 300
Subject Interests: Am legal mats, NY legal mats
Special Collections: Legal Treatises for Practitioners, 18th & 19th Centuries
Partic in OCLC Online Computer Library Center, Inc; Westlaw

S THE OBSERVER-DISPATCH LIBRARY,* 221 Oriskany Plaza, 13501. SAN 312-6048. Tel: 315-792-5184. FAX: 315-792-5033. *Librn*, Debbie Dufresne
Founded 1922
Library Holdings: Bk Vols 172

S ONEIDA COUNTY HISTORICAL SOCIETY LIBRARY,* 1608 Genesee St, 13502. SAN 325-9684. Tel: 315-735-3642. FAX: 315-732-0806. E-Mail: ochs@borg.com. *Dir*, Kevin Markem
Library Holdings: Bk Vols 1,000

M SAINT ELIZABETH MEDICAL CENTER, College of Nursing Library, 2215 Genesee St, 13501. SAN 324-539X. Tel: 315-798-8209. *Librn*, Susan M Lonergan; Staff 2 (MLS 1, Non-MLS 1)
Enrl 125; Fac 12; Highest Degree: Associate
Jul 1999-Jun 2000 Income $30,500, Parent Institution $30,000, Other $500. Mats Exp $4,604, Books $500, Per/Ser (Incl. Access Fees) $3,609, Electronic Ref Mat (Incl. Access Fees) $495. Sal $25,000 (Prof $20,000)
Library Holdings: Bk Vols 5,156; Per Subs 48
Subject Interests: Nursing
Partic in Central New York Library Resources Council

C STATE UNIVERSITY OF NEW YORK INSTITUTE OF TECHNOLOGY LIBRARY,* Rte 12 N & Horatio St, 13502. (Mail add: PO Box 3051, 13504-3051), Tel: 315-792-7245. FAX: 315-792-7517. Web Site: www.sunyit.edu/library. *Dir*, Daniel Schabert; Tel: 315-792-7308, E-Mail: schabert@sunyit.edu; *Bibliog Instr, Ref*, Jacquelyn Coughlan; Tel: 315-792-7251, E-Mail: jackie@sunyit.edu; *Automation Syst Coordr*, Tom Tran; Tel: 315-792-7285, E-Mail: trant@sunyit.edu; *Tech Servs*, Nancy Kaiser; Tel: 315-792-7307, E-Mail: snak@sunyit.edu; Staff 12 (MLS 6, Non-MLS 6)
Founded 1969. Enrl 2,450; Fac 200; Highest Degree: Master
Jul 1998-Jun 1999 Mats Exp $411,299, Books $54,668, Per/Ser (Incl. Access Fees) $240,252, Micro $30,059, Electronic Ref Mat (Incl. Access Fees) $33,785. Sal $313,000
Library Holdings: Bk Vols 184,324; Bk Titles 165,829; Per Subs 970
Subject Interests: Business, Computer science, Health, Technologies, Telecommunications
Automation Activity & Vendor Info: (Acquisitions) SIRSI; (Cataloging) SIRSI; (Circulation) SIRSI; (Course Reserve) SIRSI; (OPAC) SIRSI; (Serials) SIRSI

C UTICA COLLEGE OF SYRACUSE UNIVERSITY, Frank E Gannett Memorial Library, 1600 Burrstone Rd, 13502-9973. SAN 312-603X. Tel: 315-792-3041. Interlibrary Loan Service Tel: 315-792-3262. FAX: 315-792-3361. Web Site: www.ucsu.edu. *Dir*, David Harralson; *Ref*, Elizabeth Patengil; *Cat, Ser*, Larissa John; *ILL*, Patricia Burchard; *Ref Serv*, Beverly Marcoline; Staff 4 (MLS 4)
Founded 1946. Enrl 1,887; Fac 111; Highest Degree: Bachelor
Library Holdings: Bk Vols 180,000; Per Subs 1,300
Special Collections: Fiction-Scene in Upstate New York Since 1929; Walter Edmonds; Welsh Language Imprints of New York State
Partic in Central New York Library Resources Council; NY State Libr; OCLC Online Computer Library Center, Inc

P UTICA PUBLIC LIBRARY, 303 Genesee St, 13501. SAN 354-348X. Tel: 315-735-2279. FAX: 315-734-1034. Web Site: www.uticapubliclibrary.org. *Dir*, Darby O'Brien; E-Mail: obrien@midyork.lib.ny.us; *Asst Dir*, Robert Quist; *Ch Servs*, Marjorie Cobane; *Ch Servs*, Roma Matott; *Ch Servs*, Cary Meltzer; *Ref*, Barbara Brookes; *Ref*, Joan Anne Caron; *Ref*, Susan Halloran; *Ref*, Robert Lalli; *Circ*, Margaret Hughes; Staff 24 (MLS 8, Non-MLS 16)
Founded 1893. Pop 68,637; Circ 221,765
Apr 2000-Mar 2001 Income $898,938, State $49,277, City $200,000, County $550,000, Other $88,000. Mats Exp $100,000, Books $46,500, Per/Ser (Incl. Access Fees) $39,500. Sal $530,087 (Prof $227,221)
Library Holdings: Bk Vols 144,613; Per Subs 3,614
Subject Interests: Genealogy
Special Collections: Local History & Genealogy
Database Vendor: Ebsco - EbscoHost, OCLC - First Search
Mem of Cent NY Libr Resources Coun; Mid-York Library System
Partic in Central New York Library Resources Council
Open Mon, Tues & Wed 8:30-8, Thurs & Fri 8:30-5:30, Sat 8:30-5; Closed Sat, June through Labor day weekend
Friends of the Library Group

VALATIE

P VALATIE FREE LIBRARY,* 3203 Church St, PO Box 336, 12184. SAN 312-6056. Tel: 518-758-9321. FAX: 518-758-6497. *Librn*, Jean Pallas
Circ 2,800
Library Holdings: Bk Vols 6,108
Mem of Mid-Hudson Library System
Open Mon & Tues noon-4, Thurs & Fri 9-noon

VALHALLA

M AMERICAN HEALTH FOUNDATION, Florence Wu Wang Library, One Dana Rd, 10595-1599. SAN 324-6213. Tel: 914-789-7171. FAX: 914-592-6317. Web Site: ahf.org. *Librn*, Joanne Braley; E-Mail: jebraley@aol.com; Staff 2 (MLS 1, Non-MLS 1)
Founded 1973
Subject Interests: Cancer, Epidemiology, Health promotion, Nutrition, Tobacco
Special Collections: Tobacco
Restriction: Staff use only
Partic in Medical Library Center Of New York; Nat Libr of Med

CM NEW YORK MEDICAL COLLEGE, Medical Sciences Library, Basic Science Bldg, 10595. SAN 312-6064. Tel: 914-594-4200. Reference Tel: 914-594-4210. FAX: 914-594-3171. E-Mail: msl_nymc@nymc.edu. Web Site: library.nymc.edu. *Assoc Dean, Dir*, Diana Cunningham; Tel: 914-594-4208, Fax: 914-594-4191; *Circ*, Suzanne Reichert; *Media Spec*, Michael Cotter; *ILL*, Wanda Bess Chaparro; *Publ Servs*, Janet A Ohles; *Ser*, Phyllis Niles; *Tech Servs*, Cheryl Silver; Staff 27 (MLS 11, Non-MLS 16)
Founded 1976. Enrl 1,535; Highest Degree: Doctorate
Jul 2000-Jun 2001 Income Parent Institution $2,000,000
Library Holdings: Bk Vols 180,154; Bk Titles 26,722; Per Subs 1,200
Subject Interests: Biomed sci, Health policy, Homeopathy, Medicine
Special Collections: History of Medicine & Homeopathy (Historical Coll); History of Orthopedics (Alfred Haas Coll); Rare Books (J Alexander van Heuven Coll)
Automation Activity & Vendor Info: (Cataloging) epixtech, inc.; (Circulation) epixtech, inc.; (Course Reserve) epixtech, inc.; (Media Booking) epixtech, inc.; (OPAC) epixtech, inc.; (Serials) epixtech, inc.
Database Vendor: Dialog, Ebsco - EbscoHost, epixtech, inc., IAC - Info Trac, Lexis-Nexis, OCLC - First Search, Silverplatter Information Inc.
Publications: FYI (newsletter)
Restriction: Not open to public
Function: Archival collection, Document delivery services, Literary searches, Research library
Partic in Dialog Corporation; Medical Library Center Of New York; National Network Of Libraries Of Medicine
Friends of the Library Group

S PEPSICO, Scientific Informative Center,* 100 Stevens Ave, 10595. SAN 312-6072. Tel: 914-742-4500. FAX: 914-749-3304.; Staff 4 (MLS 3, Non-MLS 1)
Founded 1950
Library Holdings: Bk Titles 3,500; Per Subs 450
Subject Interests: Beverages, Chemistry, Engineering, Food sci, Nutrition, Technology
Publications: Research Information Services News
Restriction: Staff use only
Partic in Dialog Corporation

S TOWERS PERRIN, Corporate Information Center, 100 Summit Lake Dr, 10595. SAN 312-0945. Tel: 914-745-4500. FAX: 914-745-4555. *Info Specialist*, Marianne Benjamin; *Info Specialist*, Claire Silverman; *Info Specialist*, Susan Weill; Staff 10 (MLS 4, Non-MLS 6)
Founded 1927
Library Holdings: Bk Titles 4,000; Per Subs 500
Subject Interests: Employee benefits, Gen mgt, Pension funds, Salaries
Automation Activity & Vendor Info: (Acquisitions) EOS; (Serials) EOS
Database Vendor: Dialog, Lexis-Nexis, ProQuest

J WESTCHESTER COMMUNITY COLLEGE, Harold L Drimmer Library & Learning Resource Center,* 75 Grasslands Rd, 10595. SAN 312-6080. Tel: 914-785-6960. FAX: 914-785-6511. E-Mail: reference@sunywcc.edu. Web Site: www.sunywcc.edu/library/homepage.htm. *Chairperson*, Lynne M Karen; Tel: 914-785-6511, E-Mail: lynne.karen@sunywcc.edu; *ILL*, Una Shih; Tel: 917-785-6573, E-Mail: una.shih@sunywcc.edu; *Per*, Sandy Schepis; Tel: 914-785-6629, E-Mail: sandy.schepis@sunywcc.edu; *Acq*, Dorothy Freeman; Tel: 914-785-6964, E-Mail: dorothy.freeman@sunywcc.edu; *Cat*, Catherine Ray; Tel: 914-785-6578, E-Mail: catherine.ray.sunywcc.edu; *Ref*, Mary Loomba; Tel: 914-785-6407, E-Mail: mary.loomba@sunywcc.edu; *Bibliog Instr*, Gloria Meisel; Tel: 914-785-6968, E-Mail: gloria.meisel@sunywcc.edu; *AV*, Dale Leifeste; *Syst Coordr*, Carol Jensen; Tel: 914-785-6672, E-Mail: carol.jensen@sunywcc.edu; *Automation Syst Coordr*, Carol Jensen; Tel: 914-785-6672, Fax: 914-785-6513, E-Mail: carol.jensen@sunywcc.edu; *Online Servs*, Dale Leifeste; Tel: 914-785-6961, Fax: 914-785-6531, E-Mail: dale.leifeste@sunywcc.edu; *Publ Servs*, Veronica Kenausis; Tel: 914-785-6177, E-Mail: veronica.kenausis@sunywcc.edu; Staff 43 (MLS 16, Non-MLS 27)
Founded 1946. Enrl 10,568; Fac 162
Sep 1998-Aug 1999 Mats Exp $360,276, Books $158,286, Per/Ser (Incl. Access Fees) $54,834, Electronic Ref Mat (Incl. Access Fees) $15,500. Sal $1,149,991 (Prof $834,242)
Library Holdings: Bk Vols 115,500; Bk Titles 101,310; Per Subs 411
Special Collections: College & Career Coll; Legal Collection New York State
Automation Activity & Vendor Info: (Circulation) PALS
Database Vendor: Dialog, GaleNet, IAC - Info Trac, Lexis-Nexis, OCLC - First Search, ProQuest, Silverplatter Information Inc.
Publications: Documentation Style Sheet; Medium, Periodicals List; Research Recommendations
Partic in New York Metrop Ref & Res Libr Agency; State University Of New York-NYLINK; WALDO

M WESTCHESTER MEDICAL CENTER, Health Sciences Library,* Eastview Hall, 10595. SAN 312-6099. Tel: 914-493-7033. FAX: 914-493-7607. E-Mail: sikorskic@wcmc.com. *Librn*, Charlene Sikorski; Staff 2 (MLS 1, Non-MLS 1)
Founded 1925
Library Holdings: Bk Titles 1,800; Per Subs 190
Subject Interests: Dentistry, Medicine, Nursing
Publications: Bookmark
Partic in BHSL; Hilow; MLA; New York Metrop Ref & Res Libr Agency

VALLEY COTTAGE

S TOLSTOY FOUNDATION, INC, Alexandra Tolstoy Memorial Library, 104 Lake Rd, 10989. SAN 371-1072. Tel: 845-268-6722. FAX: 845-268-6937. E-Mail: tfhq@aol.com. Web Site: www.tolstoyfoundation.org. *Librn*, George Doroshin
Library Holdings: Bk Vols 45,000
Open Mon 10-3

P VALLEY COTTAGE FREE LIBRARY, 110 Rte 303, 10989. SAN 312-6102. Tel: 845-268-7700. Web Site: www.vcl.org. *Dir*, Ellen Simpson; *Ad Servs*, Christy Clanchette; *Ch Servs*, Patricia Parker; *Tech Servs*, Liene Chaudhuri; Staff 32 (MLS 9, Non-MLS 23)
Founded 1959. Pop 23,805; Circ 150,000
Jan 1999-Dec 1999 Income $1,043,900, County $3,000, Locally Generated Income $1,040,900. Mats Exp $175,000, Books $150,000, Electronic Ref Mat (Incl. Access Fees) $35,000. Sal $560,000
Library Holdings: Bk Vols 70,000
Subject Interests: Art, Local history
Special Collections: Local History, photog
Automation Activity & Vendor Info: (Acquisitions) epixtech, inc.; (Cataloging) epixtech, inc.; (Circulation) epixtech, inc.; (ILL) epixtech, inc.; (OPAC) epixtech, inc.
Publications: Focus (newsletter)
Mem of Ramapo Catskill Library System
Friends of the Library Group

VALLEY FALLS

P VALLEY FALLS FREE LIBRARY, 42 State St, 12185. SAN 312-6110. Tel: 518-753-4230. *Librn*, Bobbi Crowther
Founded 1907. Pop 554; Circ 7,094
Library Holdings: Bk Vols 7,000; Per Subs 13
Mem of Upper Hudson Library System

VALLEY STREAM

M FRANKLIN HOSPITAL MEDICAL CENTER, Medical Library,* 900 Franklin Ave, 11580-2190. SAN 312-6129. Tel: 516-256-6000, Ext 6147. FAX: 516-256-6503. *In Charge*, Sydne Sannito
Founded 1965
Library Holdings: Bk Vols 1,100; Per Subs 50

P HENRY WALDINGER MEMORIAL LIBRARY, 60 Verona Pl, 11582. SAN 312-6137. Tel: 516-825-6422. FAX: 516-825-6551. Web Site: www.nassaulibrary.org/valleyst/. *Dir*, Marshall Botwinick; *Asst Dir*, Mamie Eng; *Ch Servs*, Aviva Kane; Staff 5 (MLS 4, Non-MLS 1)
Founded 1932. Pop 33,946; Circ 195,500
Jun 2000-May 2001 Income $944,213, State $17,500, Locally Generated Income $25,600, Other $901,113. Mats Exp $147,500, Books $114,436, Per/Ser (Incl. Access Fees) $20,264, AV Equip $7,500, Electronic Ref Mat (Incl. Access Fees) $5,300. Sal $616,329
Library Holdings: Bk Vols 117,700; Per Subs 228
Subject Interests: Photog, Valley Stream hist
Automation Activity & Vendor Info: (Circulation) DRA; (OPAC) DRA
Database Vendor: DRA
Mem of Nassau Library System
Partic in Long Island Library Resources Council

VAN HORNESVILLE

S VAN HORNESVILLE COMMUNITY CORP LIBRARY,* PO Box 16, 13475. SAN 376-1983. Tel: 315-858-0030. *Pres*, E Robert Mason
Library Holdings: Bk Vols 1,000

VERNON

P VERNON PUBLIC LIBRARY,* 4441 Peterboro St, 13476. SAN 312-6145. Tel: 315-829-2463. *Librn*, Patricia Dixon
Pop 1,300; Circ 32,841
Library Holdings: Bk Vols 8,500; Per Subs 16
Mem of Mid-York Library System
Friends of the Library Group

VESTAL

P FOUR COUNTY LIBRARY SYSTEM,* 304 Clubhouse Rd, 13850. SAN 310-866X. Tel: 607-723-8236. FAX: 607-723-1722. E-Mail: 4cty_david@4cty.org. Web Site: lib.4cty.org. *Publ Servs, YA Servs*, Starr Latronica; *Tech Servs*, Rosalind Conner; *Ref*, Anne Carroll; Staff 9 (MLS 9)
Founded 1960. Pop 371,670; Circ 33,969
Jan 1997-Dec 1998 Income $1,967,444, State $1,571,030, City $600, Federal $49,683, County $74,740, Other $271,391. Mats Exp $158,802, Books $141,597, Per/Ser (Incl. Access Fees) $2,304. Sal $826,349 (Prof $329,460)
Library Holdings: Bk Titles 189,732
Automation Activity & Vendor Info: (Serials) DRA
Publications: Calendar; Directory of Member Libraries; Newsletter; Printed Annual Report
Member Libraries: Afton Free Library; Andes Public Library; Bainbridge Free Library; Bovina Library Association; Broome County Public Library; Cannon Free Library; Cherry Valley Memorial Library; Deposit Free Library; Edmeston Free Library & Museum; Fairview Public Library; Fenton Free Library; Franklin Free Library; George F Johnson Memorial Library; Gilbertsville Free Library; Guernsey Memorial Library; Harris Memorial Library; Huntington Memorial Library; Kinney Memorial Library; Lisle Free Library; Louise Adelia Read Memorial Library; Mary Wilcox Memorial Library; Milford Free Library; Moore Memorial Library; New Berlin Library; Nineveh Public Library of Colesville Township; Oxford Memorial Library; Richfield Springs Public Library; Roxbury Library; Sherburne Public Library; Sidney Memorial Public Library; Skene Memorial Library; Smyrna Public Library; South New Berlin Free Library; Stamford Village Library; Unadilla Public Library; Vestal Public Library; Village Library Of Cooperstown; Village Library of Morris; William B Ogden Free Library; Worcester Free Library; Your Home Public Library
Partic in New York State Interlibrary Loan Network
Reading Center

R TEMPLE ISRAEL LIBRARY, 4737 Deerfield Pl, 13850-3762. SAN 324-0290. Tel: 607-723-7461. *Librn*, Leonard F Cohen; *Publ Servs*, Jacob Hurwitz; Staff 5 (MLS 1, Non-MLS 4)
Founded 1968
Library Holdings: Bk Vols 2,600; Bk Titles 2,000
Subject Interests: Dead Sea scrolls, Holocaust, Jewish-Am hist, Judaica
Friends of the Library Group

P VESTAL PUBLIC LIBRARY, 320 Vestal Pkwy E, 13850-1682. SAN 312-6153. Tel: 607-754-4243. FAX: 607-754-7936. E-Mail: ve_ref@4cty.org. Web Site: lib.4cty.org/vestal-r.html. *Dir*, James Holley; *Ch Servs*, Kathy Kretzmer; *Ad Servs*, Scott Clark; *ILL*, Carol Boyce; Staff 4 (MLS 4)
Founded 1970. Pop 26,733; Circ 318,125
2000-2001 Income $813,974, State $10,220, County $125,000, Locally Generated Income $447,703, Other $231,051. Mats Exp $132,263, Books $100,000, Per/Ser (Incl. Access Fees) $11,000, Micro $4,500, Other Print Mats $15,763, Electronic Ref Mat (Incl. Access Fees) $1,000
Library Holdings: Bk Vols 116,559; Bk Titles 90,000; Per Subs 200
Subject Interests: Local, New York State hist
Special Collections: David Ross Locke Book Coll
Automation Activity & Vendor Info: (Circulation) DRA
Publications: Friends Newsletter
Mem of Four County Library System
Friends of the Library Group

VICTOR

P VICTOR FREE LIBRARY,* 15 W Main, 14564. SAN 312-6161. Tel: 716-924-2637. FAX: 716-924-1893. *Dir*, Patricia Evans; *Ch Servs*, Lynne Madden
Founded 1939. Pop 14,801; Circ 116,342
Library Holdings: Bk Vols 35,000; Per Subs 102
Mem of Ont Coop Libr Syst; Pioneer Library System
Friends of the Library Group

VOORHEESVILLE

P VOORHEESVILLE PUBLIC LIBRARY, 51 School Rd, 12186. SAN 312-617X. Tel: 518-765-2791. FAX: 518-765-3007. E-Mail: voorefq@uhls.lib.ny.us. Web Site: www.voorheesvillelibrary.org. *Dir*, Gail Alter Sacco; *Circ*, Corinna Parker; *Ad Servs*, Suzanne Fisher; *YA Servs*, Joyce Laiosa; *Ref*, Suzanne Fisher; Staff 14 (MLS 6, Non-MLS 8)
Founded 1915. Pop 7,400; Circ 113,703
Jan 2000-Dec 2000 Income $599,100, State $8,500, Locally Generated Income $547,100, Other $43,500. Mats Exp $71,300, Books $50,500, Per/Ser (Incl. Access Fees) $10,800, Electronic Ref Mat (Incl. Access Fees) $10,000. Sal $362,700 (Prof $192,000)
Library Holdings: Bk Titles 36,500; Per Subs 1,754
Subject Interests: Local history
Automation Activity & Vendor Info: (Cataloging) DRA; (Circulation) DRA; (ILL) DRA
Database Vendor: DRA, Ebsco - EbscoHost
Publications: Bookworm (bi-monthly)
Mem of Upper Hudson Library System
Friends of the Library Group

WADDINGTON

P HEPBURN LIBRARY OF WADDINGTON, 30 Main St, 13694. (Mail add: PO Box 205, 13694), SAN 312-6188. Tel: 315-388-4454. FAX: 315-388-4454. E-Mail: wadington@northnet.org. *Dir Libr Serv*, Regina Hawkins Davis; *Librn*, Martha Sinkeldam; Staff 1 (Non-MLS 1)
Founded 1919
Library Holdings: Bk Vols 7,500; Per Subs 30
Mem of North Country Library System
Friends of the Library Group

WADHAMS

P WADHAMS FREE LIBRARY,* Rte 22, 12993. SAN 312-6196. Tel: 518-962-8717. E-Mail: wadh2@westelcom.com. *Librn*, Elizabeth Rapalee
Library Holdings: Bk Vols 5,000; Per Subs 12
Mem of Clinton-Essex-Franklin Library System

WALDEN

P JOSEPHINE-LOUISE PUBLIC LIBRARY,* 5 Scofield St, 12586. SAN 312-620X. Tel: 914-778-7621. FAX: 914-778-1946. *Dir*, Leslie Myers
Founded 1904. Pop 5,277; Circ 35,261
Library Holdings: Bk Vols 26,428; Bk Titles 20,000; Per Subs 35
Mem of Ramapo Catskill Library System
Open Mon, Tues & Thurs 12-8, Wed & Fri 10-6 & Sat 10-2
Friends of the Library Group

WALLKILL

S SHAWANGUNK CORRECTIONAL FACILITY LIBRARY,* Prison Rd, PO Box 750, 12589-0750. SAN 327-2559. Tel: 914-895-2081, Ext 4600. *Librn*, Linda Stopard; Staff 1 (MLS 1)
1998-1999 Income $16,800. Mats Exp $16,800, Books $12,000, Per/Ser (Incl. Access Fees) $4,800
Library Holdings: Bk Titles 12,000
Subject Interests: Fiction
Mem of Mid-Hudson Library System
Partic in Southeastern New York Library Resources Council

S WALLKILL CORRECTIONAL FACILITY LIBRARY,* Quick Rd, PO Box G, 12589-0286. SAN 325-8645. Tel: 914-895-2021, Ext 4811. FAX: 914-895-2021, Ext 4811. *Librn*, Richard Garey

P WALLKILL PUBLIC LIBRARY,* PO Drawer C, 12589. SAN 312-6218. Tel: 914-895-3707. FAX: 914-895-8659. *Librn*, Mary Lou Van Aken; *Asst Librn*, Linda Going
Founded 1906. Circ 18,460
Library Holdings: Bk Vols 13,200; Per Subs 162
Special Collections: Regional History Coll, rare bks, pamphlets
Publications: Newsletter (quarterly)
Mem of Ramapo Catskill Library System

WALTON

M DELAWARE VALLEY HOSPITAL,* One Titus Pl, 13856. SAN 325-0873. Tel: 607-865-4101 Ext 2040. *Dir*, Carol Vamvaketis
Library Holdings: Bk Vols 308; Per Subs 36
Subject Interests: Medicine

P WILLIAM B OGDEN FREE LIBRARY,* 42 Gardiner Pl, 13856. SAN 312-6226. Tel: 607-865-5929. FAX: 607-865-6821. E-Mail: wa_ill@4cty.org.; Staff 1 (MLS 1)
Founded 1809. Pop 3,329; Circ 35,553
Library Holdings: Bk Vols 18,691; Bk Titles 18,061; Per Subs 87
Special Collections: Local History (Loose Coll)
Automation Activity & Vendor Info: (Acquisitions) DRA
Mem of Four County Library System
Open Tues-Fri 2-5:30
Friends of the Library Group

WALWORTH

P WALWORTH-SEELY PUBLIC LIBRARY, 3600 Lorraine Dr, 14568. SAN 312-6234. Tel: 315-986-1511. FAX: 315-986-5917. Web Site: www.pls-net.org/walworth/walhome.htm. *Dir*, Mary C Zingerelle; E-Mail: maryz@pls-net.org; Staff 10 (MLS 1, Non-MLS 9)
Founded 1960. Pop 6,945; Circ 67,170
Jan 1999-Dec 1999 Income $204,139. Mats Exp $42,239. Sal $93,936 (Prof $30,140)
Library Holdings: Bk Titles 23,758; Per Subs 50
Mem of Pioneer Library System

WANTAGH

P WANTAGH PUBLIC LIBRARY, 3285 Park Ave, 11793. SAN 312-6250. Tel: 516-221-1200. FAX: 516-826-9357. E-Mail: wantaghplc@yahoo.com. Web Site: www.nassaulibrary.org/wantagh. *Dir*, Marilyn Kappenberg; *Librn*, Donna Rigali; Staff 34 (MLS 7, Non-MLS 27)
Founded 1962. Pop 18,610; Circ 160,000
Library Holdings: Bk Vols 124,678; Bk Titles 104,302; Per Subs 388
Subject Interests: Local history, Photog
Automation Activity & Vendor Info: (Circulation) DRA; (OPAC) DRA
Publications: News & Notes (monthly) (Newsletter)
Mem of Nassau Library System

WAPPINGERS FALLS

P GRINNELL LIBRARY ASSOCIATION,* 26 E Main St, 12590. SAN 312-6277. Tel: 914-297-3428. FAX: 914-297-1506. *Dir*, Margaret Keefe; E-Mail: mkeefe@sebridge.org; Staff 1 (MLS 1)
Founded 1867. Pop 26,008; Circ 123,025
Jan 1998-Dec 1998 Income $208,768, State $7,578, Locally Generated Income $201,190. Mats Exp $34,086, Books $22,384, Per/Ser (Incl. Access Fees) $4,352, Micro $350, Electronic Ref Mat (Incl. Access Fees) $7,000. Sal $107,428 (Prof $35,000)
Library Holdings: Bk Vols 40,635; Bk Titles 49,034; Per Subs 3,626; High Interest/Low Vocabulary Bk Vols 100
Special Collections: Civil War (Ferris Coll), bks, pamphlets
Automation Activity & Vendor Info: (Cataloging) GEAC; (Circulation) GEAC; (OPAC) GEAC
Database Vendor: ProQuest
Mem of Mid-Hudson Library System

WARRENSBURG

P RICHARDS LIBRARY,* 36-38 Elm St, 12885. SAN 312-6293. Tel: 518-623-3011. *Librn*, Sarah M Farrar
Circ 14,951
Library Holdings: Bk Vols 14,430
Special Collections: Local history
Mem of Southern Adirondack Library System

WARSAW

P WARSAW PUBLIC LIBRARY,* 130 N Main St, 14569. SAN 312-6307. Tel: 716-786-5650. FAX: 716-786-8706. *Dir*, Clare Keating; E-Mail: ckeating@pls-net.org
Founded 1870. Pop 5,074; Circ 75,753
Library Holdings: Bk Vols 35,000; Per Subs 35
Special Collections: Film Depot; Job Info Center; Large Print Coll
Mem of Pioneer Library System
Friends of the Library Group

WARWICK

S MID-ORANGE CORRECTIONAL FACILITY LIBRARY,* 900 Kings Hwy, 10990-0900. SAN 327-1781. Tel: 914-986-2291, Ext 4500. *Actg Librn*, Lopinto
Library Holdings: Bk Vols 7,300; Per Subs 84

P ALBERT WISNER PUBLIC LIBRARY,* 2 Colonial Ave, 10990-1191. SAN 312-6323. Tel: 914-986-1047. FAX: 914-987-1228. E-Mail: wisner@warwick.net. Web Site: www.cyberave.com/~wisner. *Dir*, Margery Kirby Cyr; *Ref*, David Hultgren; Staff 5 (MLS 5)
Founded 1974. Pop 18,241; Circ 150,000
Jul 1999-Jun 2000 Income $486,114. Mats Exp $72,243, Books $58,000, Per/Ser (Incl. Access Fees) $7,750, AV Equip $6,393, Other Print Mats $100. Sal $276,753 (Prof $133,386)
Library Holdings: Bk Titles 42,000; Per Subs 101
Subject Interests: Antiques, Art, Bus, Local history
Special Collections: Job Information Center
Automation Activity & Vendor Info: (Cataloging) epixtech, inc.
Mem of Ramapo Catskill Library System
Friends of the Library Group

WASHINGTONVILLE

P MOFFAT LIBRARY,* 6 W Main St, 10992. SAN 312-6331. Tel: 914-496-5483. FAX: 914-496-6854. *Dir*, Julie Baxter; Staff 6 (MLS 1, Non-MLS 5)
Founded 1887. Pop 16,000; Circ 70,000
Library Holdings: Bk Vols 15,600; Bk Titles 13,200; Per Subs 90
Mem of Ramapo Catskill Library System

WATERFORD

S GE SILICONES, Library & Information Center, 260 Hudson River Rd, 12188-1926. SAN 312-634X. Tel: 518-233-2264. FAX: 518-233-3866. *Librn*, Marianne Pouliott; E-Mail: marianne.pouliott@gepex.ge.com
Partic in CDLC

P WATERFORD PUBLIC LIBRARY, 117 Third St, 12188. SAN 312-6358. Tel: 518-237-0891. FAX: 518-237-2568. E-Mail: wat_sulli@sals.edu. Web Site: www,waterford.sals.edu. *Dir*, Sean Sullivan; *Ch Servs, YA Servs*, Karen DeAngelo
Founded 1895. Pop 6,800; Circ 60,000
Jan 2000-Dec 2000 Income $166,000, State $2,500, City $2,500, County $1,000, Locally Generated Income $140,000, Other $20,000. Mats Exp $38,000, Books $30,000, Per/Ser (Incl. Access Fees) $3,500, AV Equip $2,500, Electronic Ref Mat (Incl. Access Fees) $2,000. Sal $100,000 (Prof $61,000)
Library Holdings: Bk Vols 27,500; Per Subs 97
Automation Activity & Vendor Info: (Circulation) DRA; (ILL) DRA
Database Vendor: CARL, Dialog, Ebsco - EbscoHost, GaleNet
Mem of Southern Adirondack Library System

WATERLOO

P WATERLOO LIBRARY & HISTORICAL SOCIETY,* 31 E Williams St, 13165. SAN 312-6366. Tel: 315-539-3313. FAX: 315-539-7798. *Dir*, Sandra Snyder; E-Mail: ssnyder@lakenet.org
Founded 1876. Pop 5,116; Circ 31,998
Library Holdings: Bk Titles 26,449; Per Subs 607
Subject Interests: Genealogy, Local history
Mem of Finger Lakes Library System

WATERTOWN

P EAST HOUNSFIELD FREE LIBRARY,* 18184 NYS Rte 3, Arsnl St Rd, 13601. SAN 312-6374. Tel: 315-788-0637. *Librn*, Mary Farrington
Circ 3,879
Library Holdings: Bk Vols 3,892
Mem of North Country Library System

P ROSWELL P FLOWER MEMORIAL LIBRARY, 229 Washington St, 13601-3388. SAN 312-6382. Tel: 315-788-2352. FAX: 315-788-2584. *Dir, Librn*, Kenneth Hodosy Jr
Founded 1904. Pop 372,000
Library Holdings: Bk Vols 181,000; Per Subs 375
Subject Interests: Genealogy, Local history, Military history, State
Mem of North Country Library System
Special Services for the Deaf - Books on deafness & sign language; High interest/low vocabulary books; Special interest periodicals
Open Mon, Tues & Thurs 9:15-9, Wed 9:15-5:30, Fri & Sat 9:15-5
Friends of the Library Group

M GENESIS HEALTHCARE LIBRARY,* 218 Stone St, 13601. SAN 320-2208. Tel: 315-782-7400, Ext 2152. FAX: 315-788-1447. E-Mail: +vna+@northnet.org. Web Site: www.northnet.org/genesislib. *Librn*, Jeffrey M Garvey; *Circ*, Ellen Darabaner; *Circ*, Mark Uebler; Staff 5 (MLS 3, Non-MLS 2)
Founded 1972
1998-1999 Income $172,000. Mats Exp $13,000. Sal $150,000
Library Holdings: Bk Vols 2,100; Bk Titles 2,050; Per Subs 150
Subject Interests: Medicine, Mental health, Mgt, Nursing
Publications: Quarterly newsletter
Partic in New York State Interlibrary Loan Network; North Country Reference & Research Resources Council; NY & NJ Regional Med Libr

S JEFFERSON COUNTY HISTORICAL SOCIETY LIBRARY,* 228 Washington St, 13601. SAN 325-9765. Tel: 315-782-3491. FAX: 315-782-2913. *Dir*, Fred Rollins; *Archivist, Curator*, Elise D Chan
Special Collections: City Directories Coll (1830-1985); Nineteenth Century Maps of Jefferson County; Water Turbines & Water Turbine Catalogues
Publications: Exhibition catalogues; JCHS Bulletin
Open Tues-Fri 10-5 (May-Nov), Sat 10-5, research days are Tues & Fri

G NEW YORK STATE DEPARTMENT OF CORRECTIONAL SERVICES, Watertown Correctional Facility Library, 23147 Swan Rd, 13601-9340. SAN 322-8185. Tel: 315-782-7490, Ext 4600. *Dir*, Adrian Lavoie; Staff 2 (MLS 1, Non-MLS 1)
Library Holdings: Bk Vols 7,000; Bk Titles 6,500; Per Subs 108
Subject Interests: Black hist

Special Collections: Spanish Language & Culture
Mem of North Country Library System
Open 7:45am-9:15pm, whenever inmates are able to move around the prison. Open about 70 hrs per week, six days a week; Interlibrary loans are encouraged and work through the North Country Library System

GL NEW YORK STATE SUPREME COURT, Law Library at Watertown, Court House, 195 Arsenal St, 13601. SAN 312-6404. Tel: 315-785-3064. FAX: 315-785-3330. *Librn*, Patrica B Donaldson; E-Mail: pdonalds@courts.state.ny.us
Founded 1944
Apr 2000-Mar 2001 Income State $205,000. Mats Exp $122,300, Books $101,000, Per/Ser (Incl. Access Fees) $300, Micro $1,000, Electronic Ref Mat (Incl. Access Fees) $20,000. Sal $60,000
Library Holdings: Bk Vols 30,000; Bk Titles 700; Per Subs 34

P NORTH COUNTRY LIBRARY SYSTEM,* 22072 CR 190, PO Box 99, 13601-0099. SAN 312-6412. Tel: 315-782-5540. Interlibrary Loan Service Tel: 315-782-5895. FAX: 315-782-6883. E-Mail: ncls@northnet.org. Web Site: www.nc3r.org/ncls. *Dir*, Leonard J Meinhold; E-Mail: meinhold@northnet.org; *Info Tech*, Stephen Bolton; E-Mail: bolton@northnet.org; *Outreach Serv*, Susan J Charley; E-Mail: charley@northnet.org; *Pub Relations*, Deborah Lee; E-Mail: lee@northnet.org; *YA Servs*, Regan DeFranza; E-Mail: defranza@northnet.org; *Outreach Serv*, Mary Bidwell; E-Mail: bidwell@northnet.org; *Info Tech*, Yvonne Reff; E-Mail: reff@northnet.org
Founded 1947. Pop 371,484
Jan 1998-Dec 1998 Income $2,013,689, State $1,868,458, Federal $28,426, Other $85,305. Mats Exp $1,943,881, Books $217,298, Per/Ser (Incl. Access Fees) $3,383, AV Equip $7,974. Sal $878,358 (Prof $356,895)
Library Holdings: Bk Vols 223,371; Per Subs 44
Special Collections: Uncataloged Paperbacks for Outreach Mail Order Service
Automation Activity & Vendor Info: (Cataloging) DRA
Database Vendor: DRA
Publications: NCLS Youth Services News & Notes; Network: A Report for Our Special Patrons from North Country Library System Outreach Services; North Country Library News
Member Libraries: Adams Center Free Library; Adams Free Library; Annie Porter Ainsworth Memorial Library; B E Strong Memorial Library; Beaver Falls Library; Belleville Public Library; Black River Free Library; Bodman Memorial Library; Bremer Pond Memorial Library; Brownville-Glen Park Library; Byron G Merrill Library; Cape Vincent Community Library; Central Square Library; Clifton Community Library; Colton Hepburn Library; Constableville Village Library; Croghan Free Library; Crosby Public Library; Depauville Free Library; Dexter Free Library; East Hounsfield Free Library; Ellisburg Free Library; Evans Mills Public Library; Gilbert Public Library; Hammond Free Library; Harrisville Free Library; Hawn Memorial Library; Hay Memorial Library; Hepburn Library Of Edwards; Hepburn Library Of Hermon; Hepburn Library Of Madrid; Hepburn Library Of Norfolk; Hepburn Library Of Waddington; Heuvelton Free Library; Lowville Free Library; Lyme Free Library; Lyons Falls Free Library; Macsherry Library; Mannsville Free Library; Massena Public Library; Mexico Public Library; New York State Department Of Correctional Services; Norwood Library; Ogdensburg Correctional Facility General Library; Ogdensburg Public Library; Orford Free Library; Orleans Public Library; Orwell Library; Oswego City Library; Phoenix Public Library; Port Leyden Community Library; Potsdam Public Library; Pulaski Public Library; Reading Room Association Of Gouverneur; Richville Free Library; Rodman Public Library; Roswell P Flower Memorial Library; Shelburne Public Library; Theresa Free Library; Thousand Island Park Library; William H Bush Memorial Library
Partic in New York State Interlibrary Loan Network; North Country Reference & Research Resources Council; OCLC Online Computer Library Center, Inc
Special Services for the Deaf - TDD
Open Mon-Fri 8-4:30

M SAMARITAN MEDICAL CENTER, Health Sciences Library,* 830 Washington St, 13601. SAN 373-6962. Tel: 315-785-4191. FAX: 315-785-4292, 785-4190. *Librn*, Ellen Darabaner; *Asst Librn*, Marianne Berry; *Tech Servs*, Lori Thompson
Library Holdings: Bk Titles 1,000; Per Subs 150

J STATE UNIVERSITY OF NEW YORK - JEFFERSON COMMUNITY COLLEGE, Melvil Dewey Library, 1220 Coffeen St, 13601-1897. SAN 312-6390. Tel: 315-786-2225. FAX: 315-788-0716. Web Site: sunyjefferson.edu/library. *Dir*, Shirley Ellsworth; Tel: 315-786-2402, E-Mail: shirley_ellsworth@ccmgate.sunyjefferson.edu; *Media Spec*, Jacquelyn Young; Tel: 315-786-2413; *Bibliog Instr*, Inger Curth; Tel: 315-786-2314; *Ref*, Teresa Blacklaw; Tel: 315-786-2224; Staff 4 (MLS 4)
Founded 1963. Enrl 2,300; Fac 70; Highest Degree: Associate
Sep 1999-Aug 2000 Income $453,471, State $6,814, County $446,657. Mats Exp $137,235, Books $53,248, Per/Ser (Incl. Access Fees) $27,329, Presv $749, Micro $6,320, AV Equip $22,089, Electronic Ref Mat (Incl. Access Fees) $27,500. Sal $271,305 (Prof $182,150)
Library Holdings: Bk Vols 55,747; Bk Titles 54,000; Per Subs 322
Subject Interests: Jefferson County local hist
Automation Activity & Vendor Info: (Cataloging) MultiLIS; (Circulation) MultiLIS; (OPAC) MultiLIS; (Serials) MultiLIS
Database Vendor: Dialog, GaleNet, IAC - Info Trac, Lexis-Nexis, OCLC - First Search, ProQuest, Silverplatter Information Inc.
Publications: Annual Report; MDL Book Beat
Partic in North Country Reference & Research Resources Council; OCLC Online Computer Library Center, Inc

UNITED STATES ARMY
A POST LIBRARY, 2190 Nash Blvd, Fort Drum, 13602-5284. SAN 354-3579. Tel: 315-772-6005. FAX: 315-772-4912. *Tech Servs*, Allen Goudie; *Ref*, Wendy Newell
Founded 1941
Library Holdings: Bk Titles 56,207; Per Subs 100
Subject Interests: Job hunting, Mil, New York State, Self defense, YA
Publications: Ulrichs Periodical Directory
Partic in Fedlink; North Country Reference & Research Resources Council

S WATERTOWN DAILY TIMES LIBRARY,* 260 Washington St, 13601. SAN 322-9106. Tel: 315-782-1000, Ext 345. FAX: 315-782-1040. *Librn*, Lisa Carr-Bourcy; Staff 1 (MLS 1)
Subject Interests: Northern NY hist
Special Collections: Other Northern New York Newspapers - on microfilm

WATERVILLE

P WATERVILLE PUBLIC LIBRARY,* 220 Main St, 13480. SAN 312-6420. Tel: 315-841-4651. FAX: 315-841-4258. *Dir*, Wendy Sexton
Circ 27,244
Library Holdings: Bk Vols 13,000; Bk Titles 12,000
Special Collections: Waterville Times (local newspaper) 1855-1990, microfilm
Mem of Mid-York Library System
Friends of the Library Group
Branches: 1
DEANSBORO BRANCH, Marshall Community Ctr, Deansboro, 13328. SAN 329-5680. Tel: 315-841-4888. *Dir*, Bonnie Lewis
Friends of the Library Group

WATERVLIET

P WATERVLIET PUBLIC LIBRARY, 1501 Broadway, 12189. SAN 312-6455. Tel: 518-274-4471. FAX: 518-271-0667. *Dir, Librn*, Barbara Schoen; E-Mail: schoenb@uhls.lib.ny.us; Staff 2 (MLS 1, Non-MLS 1)
Founded 1953. Pop 11,061; Circ 12,536
Jan 1999-Dec 1999 Income $51,152, State $4,229, City $26,001, Locally Generated Income $20,922. Mats Exp $10,562, Books $5,934, Per/Ser (Incl. Access Fees) $484, Electronic Ref Mat (Incl. Access Fees) $4,144. Sal $23,033 (Prof $17,000)
Library Holdings: Bk Vols 13,575; Per Subs 29
Special Collections: City Directories (1855 to present)
Automation Activity & Vendor Info: (Circulation) DRA
Mem of Upper Hudson Library System

WATKINS GLEN

P WATKINS GLEN CENTRAL SCHOOL DISTRICT FREE PUBLIC LIBRARY, 610 S Decatur St, 14891. SAN 312-6463. Tel: 607-535-2346. FAX: 607-535-7338. E-Mail: wgl_harriet@stls.org. *Dir*, Harriet Eisman; Staff 5 (MLS 1, Non-MLS 4)
Founded 1870. Pop 8,302; Circ 48,635
Jul 2000-Jun 2001 Income $123,757, State $2,400, City $2,000, Locally Generated Income $35,500, Other $83,857. Mats Exp $27,000, Books $21,000, Per/Ser (Incl. Access Fees) $3,000. Sal $57,800 (Prof $19,736)
Library Holdings: Bk Vols 22,000; Per Subs 45
Special Collections: Career Coll
Automation Activity & Vendor Info: (Acquisitions) DRA; (Cataloging) DRA; (Circulation) DRA; (Media Booking) DRA; (OPAC) DRA
Publications: Friends of Watkins Library Newsletter
Mem of Southern Tier Library System
Friends of the Library Group

WAVERLY

P WAVERLY FREE LIBRARY, Elizabeth Sq, 18 Elizabeth St, 14892. SAN 312-6471. Tel: 607-565-9341. FAX: 607-565-3960. *Dir*, Beverly Ruth Dann; E-Mail: bdann@lakenet.org; Staff 6 (MLS 1, Non-MLS 5)
Founded 1929. Pop 4,787; Circ 35,753
Jan 1999-Dec 1999 Income $81,148, State $1,500, City $5,500, County $1,552, Locally Generated Income $55,246, Other $17,350. Mats Exp $14,803, Books $13,535, Per/Ser (Incl. Access Fees) $1,268. Sal $35,400 (Prof $16,750)
Library Holdings: Bk Vols 44,309; Bk Titles 42,353; Per Subs 35
Special Collections: Civil War Coll; Job Employment Center; Tioga County Law Library
Automation Activity & Vendor Info: (Circulation) Brodart

Database Vendor: GaleNet, IAC - SearchBank, OCLC - First Search
Function: ILL available
Mem of Finger Lakes Library System
Special Services for the Blind - Bks on cassette

WAYLAND

P WAYLAND FREE LIBRARY, Gunlocke Memorial Library, 101 W Naples St, 14572. SAN 312-648X. Tel: 716-728-5380. FAX: 716-728-5002. Web Site: www.gunlockelibrary.org. *Dir, Librn*, Marian Crawford; E-Mail: wyl_marian@stls.org
Founded 1913. Pop 5,000; Circ 33,917
Jul 1999-Jun 2000 Mats Exp $14,400, Books $7,500, Per/Ser (Incl. Access Fees) $2,000, Presv $500, Micro $400, AV Equip $1,000, Other Print Mats $500, Electronic Ref Mat (Incl. Access Fees) $2,500. Sal $49,000 (Prof $15,000)
Library Holdings: Bk Vols 20,604; Per Subs 63; High Interest/Low Vocabulary Bk Vols 80; Spec Interest Per Sub 13; Bks on Deafness & Sign Lang 40
Subject Interests: Local history
Special Collections: Railroad Coll
Mem of Southern Tier Library System
Special Services for the Deaf - TTY machine

WEBSTER

P WEBSTER PUBLIC LIBRARY,* One Van Ingen Dr, 14580. SAN 312-6501. Tel: 716-872-7078. FAX: 716-872-7073. Web Site: www.ggw.org/websterlibrary/. *Dir*, Marvin W Andrews; E-Mail: mandrews@mcls.rochester.lib.ny.us; *Assoc Dir*, Lisa Wemett; Tel: 716-872-7079; *Ad Servs*, Diane Kozlowski; Tel: 716-872-7079; *Ch Servs*, Mildred Rivers; Tel: 716-872-7077; *Electronic Resources*, Kimberly Bolan; Staff 22 (MLS 5, Non-MLS 17)
Founded 1929. Pop 31,639; Circ 388,829
Jan 1998-Dec 1998 Income $817,491, State $10,414, City $727,262, Locally Generated Income $79,815. Mats Exp $100,350, Books $90,099, Per/Ser (Incl. Access Fees) $10,251. Sal $503,287 (Prof $197,932)
Library Holdings: Bk Vols 266,239; Bk Titles 84,333; Per Subs 395
Database Vendor: CARL, Dialog, IAC - Info Trac
Mem of Monroe County Library System
Friends of the Library Group

S XEROX CORP, Technical Information Center,* Bldg 105-66C, 800 Phillips Rd, 14580. SAN 312-651X. Tel: 716-422-1391. Interlibrary Loan Service Tel: 716-422-1475. FAX: 716-422-8297. *Mgr*, Laura Tucker; Staff 19 (MLS 13, Non-MLS 6)
Founded 1958
Library Holdings: Bk Vols 35,000; Bk Titles 32,000; Per Subs 1,800
Subject Interests: Bus, Chemistry, Communications, Data processing, Electronics, Electrophotography, Engineering, Imaging syst, Mgt, Photog, Physics, Reprography
Special Collections: Corporate Technical Archives
Publications: Current Awareness Bulletin; Electronic Bulletin Board; Internal Reports Accession List; Technical Information Center Guide Book
Partic in BRS; Dialog Corporation; Dow Jones News Retrieval; Nat Libr of Med; OCLC Online Computer Library Center, Inc; SDC Info Servs

WEEDSPORT

S WEEDSPORT FREE LIBRARY,* 2795 E Brutus St, PO Box 1165, 13166. SAN 325-9781. Tel: 315-834-6222. FAX: 315-834-6222. E-Mail: weedlib@relex.com. Web Site: www.flls.org/weedsport. *Dir*, Anne Mlod; *Asst Dir*, Cheryl Austin
Library Holdings: Bk Vols 10,000; Per Subs 15
Subject Interests: Genealogy, Local government
Special Collections: Local History; References, clips, docs, maps; School Texts & Photographs
Mem of Finger Lakes Library System
Open Mon & Fri 2-6, Tues & Thurs 10-9, Wed & Sat 10-2
Friends of the Library Group

WELLSVILLE

P DAVID A HOWE PUBLIC LIBRARY,* 155 N Main St, 14895. SAN 312-6544. Tel: 716-593-3410. FAX: 716-593-4176. *Dir*, Mary S Jacobs; *Ch Servs*, Lois Bulger; Staff 1 (MLS 1)
Founded 1894. Pop 5,815; Circ 146,958
Jan 1999-Dec 1999 Income $310,000, Locally Generated Income $50,000, Other $260,000. Mats Exp $62,000, Books $48,000, Per/Ser (Incl. Access Fees) $3,500, Presv $500. Sal $169,000
Library Holdings: Bk Vols 87,000; Per Subs 91
Subject Interests: Literature
Special Collections: Bird's Egg Coll (Charles Munson Coll); Children's Reference Books; Currier & Ives Coll; Indian Artifacts (Avery Mosher Coll); Lincoln Pictures (Coyle Coll)
Automation Activity & Vendor Info: (Circulation) DRA; (OPAC) DRA
Mem of Southern Tier Library System
Friends of the Library Group

WEST BABYLON

P WEST BABYLON PUBLIC LIBRARY,* 211 Rte 109, 11704. SAN 324-4873. Tel: 516-669-5445. FAX: 516-669-6539. *Dir*, Anne Marie Dolan; *Ref, Tech Servs*, Claire Morga; *Ch Servs*, Mary Schmidt; *Ad Servs*, Millie Scott; Staff 27 (MLS 6, Non-MLS 21)
Founded 1982
Library Holdings: Bk Vols 64,500
Publications: Newsletter (monthly)
Mem of Suffolk Cooperative Library System
Special Services for the Deaf - TTY machine; Videos & decoder

WEST BRENTWOOD

PILGRIM PSYCHIATRIC CENTER
M PILGRIM READING ROOM & PATIENTS LIBRARY, Bldg 102, 998 Crooked Hill Rd, 11717-1087. SAN 354-3609. Tel: 516-761-3813. FAX: 516-761-3103. *Coordr*, Jeanne Murphy; Staff 3 (MLS 1, Non-MLS 2)
Founded 1933
Library Holdings: Bk Vols 8,000; Per Subs 22
Subject Interests: Gen interest

M PILGRIM PSYCHIATRIC CENTER, Medical Library, Bldg 82,* 998 Crooked Hill Rd, 11717-1087. SAN 311-3914. Tel: 516-761-3500. FAX: 516-761-2004. *Coll Develop*, Irving Tredwell Jr
Founded 1958
May 1996-Apr 1997 Mats Exp $7,000, Books $3,105, Per/Ser (Incl. Access Fees) $3,895
Library Holdings: Bk Titles 1,800; Per Subs 70
Subject Interests: Behav sci, Medicine, Nursing, Philosophy, Psychiatry, Psychology, Soc sci
Special Collections: History of Psychiatry
Partic in Long Island Library Resources Council; Medical & Scientific Libraries of Long Island

WEST CHAZY

P DODGE LIBRARY,* PO Box 353, 12992. SAN 312-6560. Tel: 518-493-6131. *Dir*, Jane Ryan
Circ 9,097
Library Holdings: Bk Vols 6,025; Per Subs 15
Special Collections: Local History Coll; New England, New York, Pennsylvania & New Jersey Genealogy (Nell B Sullivan Memorial Coll)
Mem of Clinton-Essex-Franklin Library System

WEST HAVERSTRAW

M HELEN HAYES HOSPITAL, Medical Library, Rte 9W, 10993. SAN 312-6579. Tel: 845-786-4185. Interlibrary Loan Service Tel: 845-786-4188. FAX: 845-786-4978. *Dir*, Kathleen Fiola; E-Mail: fiolak@helenhayeshosp.org; Staff 2 (MLS 1, Non-MLS 1)
Founded 1960
Library Holdings: Bk Vols 2,000; Per Subs 180
Subject Interests: Arthritis, Biomedical engineering, Hearing, Neurology, Occupational therapy, Orthopedics, Physical therapy, Rehabilitation med, Speech
Publications: Library newsletter (irregular)
Partic in Health Info Librs of Westchester; Middle Atlantic Regional Med Libr Prog; Southeastern New York Library Resources Council

WEST HEMPSTEAD

P WEST HEMPSTEAD PUBLIC LIBRARY,* 252 Chestnut St, 11552. SAN 312-6587. Tel: 516-481-6591. FAX: 516-481-2608. E-Mail: whempst@dorsai.org. Web Site: members.aol/pegabytes/whpl/. *Dir*, Regina Mascia; *Tech Servs*, Margaret Reilly; *Ref*, Austin Dridge; *Ch Servs*, Andrea Greco; *AV*, Joan Thorn; *YA Servs*, Jocklyn Carter; *Coll Develop*, Barbara Dreher; Staff 40 (MLS 14, Non-MLS 26)
Founded 1965. Pop 18,189; Circ 176,747
Jul 1999-Jun 2000 Income $1,149,631. Mats Exp $251,900, Books $111,000, Per/Ser (Incl. Access Fees) $35,000, Micro $4,000. Sal $628,821
Library Holdings: Bk Vols 84,720; Per Subs 212
Special Collections: Computer Books; Large Type Books
Automation Activity & Vendor Info: (Circulation) DRA
Database Vendor: DRA, Ebsco - EbscoHost, IAC - Info Trac, IAC - SearchBank, OCLC - First Search, ProQuest
Publications: Quarterly Newsletter
Mem of Nassau Library System
Partic in Long Island Library Resources Council; New York State

Interlibrary Loan Network
Special Services for the Blind - Large print bks
Special Services for Slow Learners - High interest/low vocabulary bk vols 25
Friends of the Library Group

WEST HURLEY

P WEST HURLEY PUBLIC LIBRARY,* 42 Clover St, 12491. SAN 312-6595. Tel: 914-679-6405. FAX: 914-679-2144. E-Mail: whpl@ulster.net. Web Site: ulster.net/~whpl. *Dir*, Halyna Barannik; Staff 1 (MLS 1)
Circ 45,000
Jan 1998-Dec 1999 Income $92,417, Provincial $54,399, County $4,946, Other $3,600. Mats Exp $19,315, Books $12,000, Per/Ser (Incl. Access Fees) $2,350, Presv $300. Sal $44,355
Library Holdings: Bk Vols 19,000; Bk Titles 18,500; Per Subs 25
Subject Interests: Local history
Mem of Mid-Hudson Library System
Open Mon & Wed 2-8, Tues & Fri 10-6, Sat 10-4

WEST ISLIP

M GOOD SAMARITAN HOSPITAL, Medical Library,* 1000 Montauk Hwy, 11795. SAN 312-6609. Tel: 631-376-3380. FAX: 631-376-4166. *Librn*, Maryann Emsig; E-Mail: memsig@gshsli.org; Staff 1 (MLS 1)
Founded 1961
Library Holdings: Bk Titles 600; Per Subs 80
Special Collections: Medical Coll, texts & journals
Publications: Newsletter (monthly)
Restriction: Staff use only
Function: Reference only
Partic in BHSL

P WEST ISLIP PUBLIC LIBRARY,* 3 Higbie Lane, 11795-3999. SAN 312-6617. Tel: 516-661-7080. FAX: 516-661-7137. E-Mail: wisplib@suffolk.lib.ny.us. Web Site: www.lilrc.org/~wispagen. *Dir*, Andrew Hamm; *Tech Servs*, Soo Oh; *Ad Servs*, N Brosnan; *Coll Develop*, Grace O'Connor; *Circ*, C Van Helden; *Ch Servs*, A McGrory; Staff 12 (MLS 12)
Founded 1957 Sal $1,301,584 (Prof $564,095)
Library Holdings: Bk Vols 164,732; Bk Titles 162,631; Per Subs 420
Special Collections: Career Center (Grace O'Connor)
Database Vendor: IAC - Info Trac, IAC - SearchBank, Innovative Interfaces INN - View, OCLC - First Search
Publications: Quarterly Newsletter
Mem of Suffolk Cooperative Library System

WEST NYACK

S CHAMPION INTERNATIONAL, Technical Information Center,* W Nyack Rd, 10994. SAN 312-6625. Tel: 914-578-7102. FAX: 914-578-7175. Web Site: www.championinternational.com. *Librn*, Ronnie Cohen
Founded 1962
Library Holdings: Bk Titles 5,000; Per Subs 200
Subject Interests: Papermaking, Pulping, Wood chemicals
Partic in Southeastern New York Library Resources Council

P WEST NYACK FREE LIBRARY,* 65 Strawtown Rd, 10994. SAN 312-6633. Tel: 914-358-6081. FAX: 914-358-4071. E-Mail: westnyacklib@rcknet.com. Web Site: www.rcknet.com/westnyack.lib/. *Dir*, Rita T Fogelman; *ILL*, Lynn Krashes; *Ch Servs*, Lois Beranbom; *Ch Servs*, Myrna Sigal; *Ref*, Susan Jacobs; *Ad Servs*, Vicki Ernst; *Coll Develop*, Eva Gruenebaum; Staff 3 (MLS 3)
Founded 1959. Pop 9,978; Circ 90,000
Library Holdings: Bk Vols 37,000; Per Subs 135
Publications: Newsletter
Mem of Ramapo Catskill Library System
Partic in Am Libr Asn; NY Libr Asn
Friends of the Library Group

WEST POINT

UNITED STATES ARMY
AM MEDDAC LIBRARY, USMA, Bldg 900, 10996-1197. SAN 354-3676. Tel: 914-938-4883. FAX: 914-938-7504. *Librn*, Joan M Stehn; E-Mail: joan_stehn@smtplink.westpoint.amedd.army.mil
Oct 1997-Sep 1998 Income $35,000. Mats Exp $6,000. Sal $37,000
Library Holdings: Bk Titles 5,250; Per Subs 150
Subject Interests: Sports med
Mem of Health Info Librs of Westchester
Partic in Southeastern New York Library Resources Council

A WEST POINT - POST LIBRARY, Bldg 622, USMA, 10996-1981. SAN 354-3668. Tel: 914-938-2974. FAX: 914-938-3019. *Librn*, Suzanne Moskala
Oct 1996-Sep 1997 Income $113,000, Other $3,000. Mats Exp $10,500, Books $7,000, Per/Ser (Incl. Access Fees) $2,500, Micro $1,000. Sal $95,000 (Prof $39,000)
Library Holdings: Bk Vols 35,000; Bk Titles 28,000; Per Subs 65
Subject Interests: Military history
Partic in OCLC Online Computer Library Center, Inc

C UNITED STATES MILITARY ACADEMY LIBRARY, Bldg 757, 10996-1799. SAN 312-6641. Tel: 845-938-3833. Interlibrary Loan Service Tel: 845-938-8326. FAX: 845-938-3752. E-Mail: 8lib@westpoint-emh2.a5rmy.mil. *Actg Dir*, Joseph Barth; Fax: 845-938-4000, E-Mail: uj7064@usma.edu; *ILL*, Celeste Evans; *AV*, Judith Sibley; Tel: 845-938-8295, E-Mail: uj4428@usma.edu; *Ref*, Daniel L Pritchard; Tel: 845-938-8330, E-Mail: ud9906@usma.edu; *Cat, Syst Coordr*, Rona N Steindler; Tel: 845-938-3185, Fax: 845-938-3456, E-Mail: ur7809@usma.edu; *Spec Coll*, Alan Aimone; Tel: 845-938-2954, Fax: 845-938-6444, E-Mail: ua3925@usma.edu; *Spec Coll*, Susan Lintelmann; Tel: 845-938-7052, Fax: 845-938-6444, E-Mail: us7689@usma.edu; *Ser*, Rosemary Robischon; Tel: 845-938-2843, Fax: 845-938-3456, E-Mail: ur6146@usma.edu; *Archivist*, Suzanne Christoff; Tel: 845-938-3259, Fax: 845-938-6444, E-Mail: us9792@usma.edu. Subject Specialists: *Government publications*, Paul T Nergelovic; *Humanities*, Dawn L Crumpler; *Mathematics*, Nicholas S Battipaglia; Staff 45 (MLS 20, Non-MLS 25)
Founded 1802. Enrl 4,500; Fac 550; Highest Degree: Bachelor
Oct 1999-Sep 2000 Income $2,560,000, Federal $2,500,000, Other $60,000. Mats Exp $530,161, Books $187,800, Per/Ser (Incl. Access Fees) $342,361. Sal $1,680,586 (Prof $934,143)
Library Holdings: Bk Vols 457,340; Bk Titles 377,174; Per Subs 900
Special Collections: Cadet Textbooks; Chess Collection; Hudson Highlands History; Military Arts & Sciences; Omar N Bradley Papers; Orientalia; Papers & Writings of Academy Graduates; US Army History; West Pointiana
Database Vendor: Innovative Interfaces INN - View
Publications: Archives & Manuscript Inventory Lists; Friends of the West Point Library Newsletter (semi-annual); Library Handbook; New Accessions; Subject Bibliographies
Partic in Fedlink; OCLC Online Computer Library Center, Inc; Southeastern New York Library Resources Council
Friends of the Library Group

WEST SAYVILLE

S LONG ISLAND MARITIME MUSEUM LIBRARY,* 86 West Ave, PO Box 184, 11796. SAN 312-665X. Tel: 516-447-8679, 516-854-4974. FAX: 516-854-4979. *Chair*, Robert Linekin; *Librn*, Barbara Forde
Founded 1966
Library Holdings: Bk Titles 1,500
Subject Interests: America's Cup races, Boatbuilding, Groundings, Lifesaving, Local captains, Local history, Local participants, Local shipwrecks, Racing, Shellfishing, Ship models, Vessels, Wildfowling, Yachting
Special Collections: Photograph Coll, copy prints, glass plates, original & copy negatives, original historic prints, slides
Restriction: By appointment only

WEST SENECA

J HOUGHTON COLLEGE-BUFFALO EXTENSION CAMPUS, Ada M Kidder Memorial Library, 910 Union Rd, 14224. SAN 312-6668. Tel: 716-674-6363, 716-674-8766. FAX: 716-674-0250. Web Site: www.campus.houghton.edu/library/index.htm, www.houghton.edu. *Dir*, George E Bennett; *Librn*, Linda Deeks
Founded 1969. Enrl 130; Fac 8
Library Holdings: Bk Vols 30,000
Subject Interests: Relig studies
Partic in State University Of New York-NYLINK; Western New York Library Resources Council

P WEST SENECA PUBLIC LIBRARY,* 1300 Union Rd, 14224. SAN 312-6676. Tel: 716-674-2928. FAX: 716-674-9206. *Dir*, Mary Moore; Staff 3 (MLS 3)
Founded 1935. Circ 332,994
Library Holdings: Bk Vols 62,587; Per Subs 316
Mem of Buffalo & Erie County Public Library System
Friends of the Library Group

G WESTERN NEW YORK CHILDREN'S PSYCHIATRIC CENTER, Medical Library, 1010 East & West Rd, 14224. SAN 327-5361. Tel: 716-674-9730, Ext 4480. FAX: 716-675-6455. *Dir*, Jed Cohen; *Mgr*, Ken Brallier
Library Holdings: Bk Vols 70
Restriction: Staff use only

GM WESTERN NEW YORK-DDSO, Medical Library,* Western New York DDSO, Bldg 16, 1200 East & West Rd, 14224. SAN 354-3692. Tel: 716-674-6300, Ext 2440. FAX: 716-765-6830.
Founded 1965
Library Holdings: Bk Vols 1,300; Per Subs 56
Subject Interests: Behav sci, Medicine, Mental retardation, Soc sci

Special Collections: Books for Parents; Mental Retardation Coll
Publications: Library News in Quarterly Senecan
Restriction: By appointment only
Partic in Western New York Library Resources Council

WEST SHOKAN

P OLIVE FREE LIBRARY ASSOCIATION,* Rte 28A, 12494. SAN 312-6684. Tel: 914-657-2482. FAX: 914-657-2664. E-Mail: olive@ulster.net. *Dir*, Rosalie Burgher; *Asst Dir*, Ruth Anne Muller
Pop 4,000
Library Holdings: Bk Vols 28,000; Per Subs 52
Mem of Mid-Hudson Library System
Open Mon & Wed 10-8, Tues & Thurs 10-5 & Sat 10-4

WEST WINFIELD

P WEST WINFIELD LIBRARY,* Bisby Hall, PO Box 140, 13491. SAN 312-6692. Tel: 315-822-6394. FAX: 315-822-6394. E-Mail: ww_circ@midyork.lib.ny.us. *Dir*, Susan C Anderson
Pop 871; Circ 25,196
Library Holdings: Bk Vols 22,000; Per Subs 16
Mem of Mid-York Library System
Friends of the Library Group

WESTBURY

S SULZER METCO, INC, Engineering Library,* 1101 Prospect Ave, 11590. SAN 312-6714. Tel: 516-338-2584. FAX: 516-338-2558. *In Charge*, Henry Budke
Founded 1964
Library Holdings: Bk Vols 650; Per Subs 150
Subject Interests: Ceramics, Chemistry, Electrical, Electronics, Mechanical, Metallurgical eng
Special Collections: Ceramic Engineering (Ceramic Abstracts Coll), per; Research (US Government Research & Development Reports), per; Standards (American Society for Testing & Materials & United States Government Research & Development Reports), per
Restriction: Staff use only
Partic in Long Island Library Resources Council

P WESTBURY MEMORIAL PUBLIC LIBRARY,* 445 Jefferson St, 11590. SAN 354-3870. Tel: 516-333-0176. FAX: 516-333-1752. E-Mail: westbury@lilrc.org. Web Site: www.nassaulibrary.org/westbury/index.html. *Dir*, Barbara E M Krampitz; Staff 32 (MLS 8, Non-MLS 24)
Founded 1924. Pop 20,596
Jul 1999-Jun 2000 Income (Main Library and Branch Library) $1,628,000. Mats Exp $156,500, Books $91,000, Per/Ser (Incl. Access Fees) $35,500. Sal $1,023,000
Library Holdings: Bk Vols 98,085; Per Subs 1,563
Special Collections: Art Coll, paintings, drawings, sculptures; Old English & American Children's Books
Automation Activity & Vendor Info: (Circulation) DRA; (OPAC) DRA
Publications: Bi-Monthly Program Schedules; Newsletters
Mem of Nassau Library System
Branches: 1
CHILDREN'S LIBRARY - ROBERT BACON MEMORIAL, 374 School St, 11590. SAN 354-3900. Tel: 516-333-0176. Web Site: www.nassaulibrary.org/westbury/index.html. *Librn*, Ann T Maria
Library Holdings: Bk Vols 15,300

WESTERLO

P WESTERLO PUBLIC LIBRARY,* Rte 143 & County Rte 1, 12193. SAN 376-3072. Tel: 518-797-3415. FAX: 518-797-3415. *Dir*, Elaine Albrecht
Jan 1997-Dec 1998 Income $30,000. Mats Exp $3,000. Sal $18,000
Library Holdings: Bk Titles 8,580; Per Subs 30
Mem of Upper Hudson Library System

WESTERNVILLE

P WESTERN TOWN LIBRARY,* 9172 Main St, PO Box 252, 13486-0252. SAN 312-6730. Tel: 315-827-4118. *Dir*, Julie Acton
Founded 1923. Pop 1,954; Circ 12,018
Library Holdings: Bk Titles 9,505; Per Subs 15
Mem of Mid-York Library System
Friends of the Library Group

WESTFIELD

S CHAUTAUQUA COUNTY HISTORICAL SOCIETY LIBRARY, PO Box 7, 14787. SAN 312-6749. Tel: 716-326-2977. *Dir*, Nancy Brown; *Pres*, Roderick Nixon
Founded 1950
Library Holdings: Bk Titles 2,000
Subject Interests: Chautauqua County Hist, Genealogy
Special Collections: Correspondence (Albion Tourgee Coll), micro; Diaries (E T Foote Papers)
Publications: History of Chautauqua County, 1938-1978
Restriction: Open to public for reference only

P PATTERSON LIBRARY, 40 S Portage St, 14787. SAN 312-6757. Tel: 716-326-2154. FAX: 716-326-2554. E-Mail: wlibrar2@cecomet.net. Web Site: www.cecomm.com/wlibrary/libfirst.htm. *Dir*, Deborah R Williams; *Ref*, Janice Hogenboom; Staff 2 (MLS 2)
Founded 1896. Pop 5,194; Circ 69,694
Library Holdings: Bk Titles 33,679; Per Subs 123
Subject Interests: Antiques, Collectibles, Cooking, Gardening, Local history
Special Collections: Genealogy & Local History (Crandall Coll); Mounted Birds; Photographs (Mateer Coll & Sherman Coll); Shell Coll; World War I Posters
Automation Activity & Vendor Info: (Cataloging) Sagebrush Corporation; (Circulation) Sagebrush Corporation; (OPAC) Sagebrush Corporation
Publications: Patterson Library; Westfield's Magnificent Legacy by M Poshka
Mem of Chautauqua-Cattaraugus Library System
Remodeled children's room with computer center
Friends of the Library Group

WESTHAMPTON BEACH

P WESTHAMPTON FREE LIBRARY,* 7 Library Ave, 11978-2697. SAN 312-6773. Tel: 516-288-3335. FAX: 516-288-5715. E-Mail: whamlib@suffolk.lib.ny.us. Web Site: www.suffolk.lib.ny.us/libraries/wham/. *Dir*, Mary Peck; *Ch Servs*, Leslie Milrod; *Ref*, Maureen Nicolazzi; *Coll Develop*, Shirley VanDeroef; Staff 4 (MLS 4)
Founded 1897. Pop 10,000; Circ 120,000
1997-1998 Income $550,000, State $1,500, Locally Generated Income $18,500, Other $70,000. Mats Exp $57,602, Books $40,000, Per/Ser (Incl. Access Fees) $7,000, Other Print Mats $1,000. Sal $400,000 (Prof $110,000)
Library Holdings: Bk Vols 50,000; Per Subs 300
Special Collections: Long Island Coll; Westhampton Beach Historical Archives & Records
Publications: Monthly calendar; Newsletter (monthly)
Mem of Suffolk Cooperative Library System
Friends of the Library Group

WESTPORT

P WESTPORT LIBRARY ASSOCIATION,* Washington St, 12993. SAN 312-6781. Tel: 518-962-8219. *Librn*, Marilyn Trienens
Founded 1887. Circ 7,980
Library Holdings: Bk Vols 16,000; Bk Titles 15,000
Mem of Clinton-Essex-Franklin Library System
Open Tues 10-7, Thurs 10-6 & Sat 9-1

WHITE PLAINS

S GANNETT SUBURBAN NEWSPAPERS, Editorial Library,* One Gannett Dr, 10604. SAN 325-139X. Tel: 914-694-5086, 914-694-9300. FAX: 914-694-5018. *Librn*, Frances Henry Riley; Staff 13 (MLS 4, Non-MLS 9)
Founded 1972
Library Holdings: Bk Vols 90; Per Subs 75
Subject Interests: Journalism
Restriction: Staff use only

S IBM-CHEM SYSTEMS, Information Center, 44 S Broadway, 10601-4425. SAN 311-6794. Tel: 914-288-3000, 914-288-5649. FAX: 914-288-5599. E-Mail: chem08@us.ibm.com. *Head of Libr, Info Specialist*, Denise Komonchak; E-Mail: komonch@us.ibm.com; *Asst Librn*, Nancy Newman; Tel: 914-288-5566; Staff 2 (Non-MLS 2)
Founded 1966
Library Holdings: Bk Titles 2,000; Per Subs 175
Subject Interests: Energy, Environment, Petrochem, Plastics, Refining, Specialty chem, Strategic studies

S INSTITUTE FOR SOCIOECONOMIC STUDIES LIBRARY,* 20 New King St, 10604. SAN 328-5707. Tel: 914-428-7400, Ext 217. FAX: 914-684-1809. E-Mail: info@socioeconomic.org. Web Site: www.socioecomonic.org. *Archivist*, Allan T Ostergren
Library Holdings: Bk Vols 5,075
Open Mon-Fri 8:30-5

L LIBRARY OF THE LEGAL AID SOCIETY OF WESTCHESTER COUNTY,* One N Broadway, Ste 910, 10601-2352. SAN 312-6838. Tel: 914-682-3400. FAX: 914-682-4112. *Librn*, M Pease; *Coll Develop*, Kay W Shames; *Coll Develop*, S Pittari
Founded 1936
Library Holdings: Bk Vols 6,100; Per Subs 10
Subject Interests: Criminology, Matrimonial legal mat

S MARCH OF DIMES BIRTH DEFECTS FOUNDATION, Resource Center, 1275 Mamaroneck Ave, 10605. SAN 320-4588. Tel: 914-428-7100. FAX: 914-997-4763. E-Mail: resourcecenter@modimes.org. Web Site: www.modimes.org/rc/help.htm.
Founded 1971
Library Holdings: Bk Titles 1,600; Per Subs 60
Subject Interests: Birth defects, Genetics, Health, Maternal, Obstetrics, Pediatrics, Pregnancy
Special Collections: Birth Defects Original Article Series
Partic in Basic Health Sciences Library Network; Hartford Consortium For Higher Education
Special Services for the Deaf - TTY machine

MERCY COLLEGE
See Dobbs Ferry

S NATIONAL ECONOMIC RESEARCH ASSOCIATES, INC LIBRARY, 50 Main St, 14th flr, 10606. SAN 311-922X. Tel: 914-448-4000, 914-448-4112. FAX: 914-448-4040. *Dir Libr Serv*, Jean-Ellen Trapani; *Librn*, James Berkise; Staff 4 (MLS 3, Non-MLS 1)
Founded 1961
Library Holdings: Bk Titles 7,000; Per Subs 350
Subject Interests: Antitrust, Bus, Economics, Environ econs, Finance, Utilities
Automation Activity & Vendor Info: (Cataloging) Inmagic, Inc.; (Serials) Inmagic, Inc.
Partic in Dialog Corporation; Dow Jones Interactive; Investext; SDC; Westlaw

M NEW YORK PRESBYTERIAN HOSPITAL-WEILL CORNELL, Westchester Division Medical Library, 21 Bloomingdale Rd, 10605. SAN 312-6870. Tel: 914-997-5897. FAX: 914-997-5861. *Librn*, Marcia A Miller; Staff 2 (MLS 1, Non-MLS 1)
Founded 1823
Library Holdings: Bk Vols 9,000; Per Subs 125
Subject Interests: Clinical psychol, Psychiat nursing, Psychiatry
Partic in Medical Library Center Of New York

GL NYS SUPREME COURT LIBRARY,* Ninth Judicial District, 9th flr, 111 Dr Martin Luther King Blvd, 10601. SAN 354-3994. Tel: 914-285-3904.; Staff 2 (MLS 2)
Founded 1908
Library Holdings: Bk Vols 300,000; Per Subs 45
Special Collections: Records on Appeal (Four Appellate Divisions & Court of Appeals)
Restriction: Open to public for reference only
Open Mon-Fri 9-5

PACE UNIVERSITY
CL SCHOOL OF LAW LIBRARY, 78 N Broadway, 10603-3796. SAN 312-6897. Tel: 914-422-4273. Interlibrary Loan Service Tel: 914-422-4137. Circulation Tel: 914-422-4120. Reference Tel: 914-422-4208. FAX: 914-422-4139. Web Site: www.law.pace.edu/lawlib/lawlib2.html. *Dir*, Marie S Newman; E-Mail: mnewman@law.pace.edu; *Acq, Coll Develop, Tech Servs*, Alice Pidgeon; E-Mail: apidgeon@law.pace.edu; *Cat*, Mary Keating; E-Mail: mkeating@law.pace.edu; *Cat*, Jindi Zhang; E-Mail: jzhang@law.pace.edu; *ILL, Res*, Margaret M Moreland; E-Mail: mmorelland@law.pace.edu; *Online Servs*, David Williams; E-Mail: dwilliams@law.pace.edu; *Head Ref*, John McNeill; E-Mail: jmcneill@law.pace.edu; *Ref Serv*, Cynthia Pittson; E-Mail: cpittson@law.pace.edu; Staff 9 (MLS 9)
Founded 1976. Enrl 752; Fac 40; Highest Degree: Doctorate
Sep 1999-Jun 2000 Income $2,151,665, Locally Generated Income $43,051, Parent Institution $2,108,614. Mats Exp $1,014,400, Books $96,057, Per/Ser (Incl. Access Fees) $539,160, Presv $17,768, Micro $107,607, Electronic Ref Mat (Incl. Access Fees) $48,769. Sal $687,644 (Prof $448,924)
Library Holdings: Bk Vols 343,610; Bk Titles 123,897; Per Subs 3,836
Subject Interests: Energy, Environmental law, Health law, International law
Automation Activity & Vendor Info: (Acquisitions) Innovative Interfaces Inc.; (Cataloging) Innovative Interfaces Inc.; (Circulation) Innovative Interfaces Inc.; (Course Reserve) Innovative Interfaces Inc.; (OPAC) Innovative Interfaces Inc.; (Serials) Innovative Interfaces Inc.
Publications: The Library Letter (newsletter)
Partic in New York Metrop Ref & Res Libr Agency; OCLC Online Computer Library Center, Inc
Friends of the Library Group

M SAINT AGNES HOSPITAL, Medical Library,* 305 North St, 10605. SAN 323-7737. Tel: 914-681-4500. FAX: 914-681-4948. *Librn*, Ed Temkin
1998-1999 Income $22,000. Mats Exp $9,800, Books $2,000, Per/Ser (Incl. Access Fees) $7,200, Other Print Mats $600. Sal $11,670
Library Holdings: Bk Vols 551; Per Subs 37

TEXACO INC
S BUSINESS INFORMATION CENTER, 2000 Westchester Ave, 10650-0001. SAN 324-4857. Tel: 914-253-6382. FAX: 004-253-6157. E-Mail: bizinfo@texaco.com. *Adminr*, Holly Furman; *Tech Servs*, Yvonne Howe; *Per*, Irene Hildinger; *Ref*, Loretta Wallace; *Ref*, Josephine Ndinyah; *Ref*, Fei Xiao; *Acq*, Debra Stefanicki
Founded 1981
Library Holdings: Bk Vols 15,850; Bk Titles 13,600; Per Subs 840
Subject Interests: Area studies, Bus, Finance, Gen ref sources, Gen sci-tech, Petroleum trade
Automation Activity & Vendor Info: (Acquisitions) EOS; (Cataloging) TechLIB; (Circulation) TechLIB; (OPAC) TechLIB; (Serials) EOS
Publications: Miscellaneous Subject Bibliographies (irregular); Serials List (semi-annual); The Source (monthly newsletter)
Restriction: By appointment only
Partic in CDA Investment Technologies Inc; CQ Washington Alert; Dialog Corporation; Dow Jones News Retrieval; Duns Direct Access; Info Globe; Metropolitan New York Library Council; OCLC Online Computer Library Center, Inc; OGJ Data; Petroscan; Reuters; RLIN; Wilsonline

S LAW-TAX LIBRARY, 2000 Westchester Ave, 10650. SAN 312-6900. Tel: 914-253-4383, 914-253-6040. FAX: 914-253-6127.
Library Holdings: Bk Vols 21,000; Per Subs 40
Subject Interests: Legal, Tax
Friends of the Library Group

G WESTCHESTER COUNTY DEPARTMENT OF PLANNING LIBRARY,* 148 Martine Ave, Rm 432, 10601. SAN 324-4156. Tel: 914-285-4400, 914-285-4418. FAX: 914-285-3780. *Librn*, Karen Duffy
Library Holdings: Bk Titles 5,000

M WHITE PLAINS HOSPITAL, Medical Library,* Davis Ave at E Post Rd, 10601. SAN 312-6919. Tel: 914-681-1231. FAX: 914-681-2905.
Library Holdings: Bk Vols 800; Per Subs 170
Subject Interests: Medicine, Nursing, Surgery
Publications: Library News (quarterly)
Restriction: Open to public for reference only
Partic in Health Info Librs of Westchester; Nat Libr of Med

P WHITE PLAINS PUBLIC LIBRARY,* 100 Martine Ave, 10601-2599. SAN 312-6927. Tel: 914-422-1400. FAX: 914-422-1462. E-Mail: cybrary@wppl1.lhrlc.org. Web Site: www.wppl.lib.ny.us. *Dir*, Sandra Miranda; *Ad Servs, Ref, Tech Servs*, Nancy T Young; *Ch Servs*, Rosemary Rasmussen; *YA Servs*, Patricia Thorsen; *Coll Develop*, Nancy Young; Staff 18 (MLS 18)
Founded 1899. Pop 49,718; Circ 600,947
1997-1998 Income $4,527,997. Mats Exp Per/Ser (Incl. Access Fees) $35,000. Sal $2,069,233
Library Holdings: Bk Vols 280,000; Per Subs 12,000
Subject Interests: Local history
Special Collections: Children's Literature Research Coll; Folklore/Fairy Tale Coll; New York State Public Service Commission Hearing Reports; Percy Grainger Music Coll; United States Nuclear Regulatory Commission on Indian Point Power Plant Hearings
Publications: Annual Report
Mem of Westchester Library System
Special Services for the Deaf - TTY machine
Friends of the Library Group

WHITESBORO

P DUNHAM PUBLIC LIBRARY, 76 Main St, 13492. SAN 312-6943. Tel: 315-736-9734. FAX: 315-736-3265. E-Mail: wh_ref@midyork.lib.ny.us. Web Site: www.midyork.org/whitesboro/. *Dir*, Janine C Krecidlo; E-Mail: krecidlo@midyork.lib.ny.us; *YA Servs*, Sandra Scofield; *Ref*, Cheryl Pula; Staff 18 (MLS 4, Non-MLS 14)
Founded 1926. Pop 24,784; Circ 152,084
Jan 1999-Dec 1999 Income $618,760, State $10,183, County $52,965, Locally Generated Income $499,084, Other $56,528. Mats Exp $90,231, Books $49,775, Per/Ser (Incl. Access Fees) $8,542, Micro $971, AV Equip $10,629, Other Print Mats $283, Electronic Ref Mat (Incl. Access Fees) $20,031. Sal $296,382 (Prof $143,520)
Library Holdings: Bk Vols 69,015; Per Subs 113
Special Collections: Helen Dunham Coll
Automation Activity & Vendor Info: (Acquisitions) DRA; (Cataloging) DRA; (Circulation) DRA; (Course Reserve) DRA; (ILL) DRA; (Media Booking) DRA; (OPAC) DRA; (Serials) DRA
Database Vendor: DRA
Mem of Mid-York Library System
Friends of the Library Group

WHITNEY POINT

P MARY WILCOX MEMORIAL LIBRARY,* 2630 Main St, 13862. SAN 312-696X. Tel: 607-692-3159. *Dir*, Mary Lou Katchuk; *Asst Librn*, Juanita Aleba
Founded 1959. Pop 1,008; Circ 25,555
Library Holdings: Bk Vols 15,430; Per Subs 23
Mem of Four County Library System
Open Mon-Fri 11-5, Tues & Fri evenings 7-9 & Sat 11-3
Friends of the Library Group

WILLIAMSON

P WILLIAMSON FREE PUBLIC LIBRARY,* 4170 E Main St, PO Box 30, 14589-0030. SAN 312-6978. Tel: 315-589-2048. FAX: 315-589-5077. E-Mail: williamson@pls-net.org. *Dir*, Lorraine M Miller
Founded 1913. Pop 6,540; Circ 190,471
1997-1998 Income $325,133, State $3,671, City $259,947, Locally Generated Income $15,454, Other $1,150. Mats Exp $52,440, Books $37,650, Per/Ser (Incl. Access Fees) $4,638, Presv $35. Sal $164,935
Library Holdings: Bk Vols 27,216; Per Subs 308
Mem of Pioneer Library System
Friends of the Library Group

WILLIAMSVILLE

J ERIE COMMUNITY COLLEGE-NORTH, RR Dry Memorial Library, 6205 Main St, 14221-7095. SAN 310-9712. Tel: 716-851-1273. FAX: 716-851-1277. Web Site: www.sunyerie.edu. *Acq*, Lynnette Mende; Tel: 716-851-1271, E-Mail: mende@ecc.edu; *Cat*, Kathleen McGriff Powers; *Ref*, Susan Basile; *Per*, Katherine Hill. Subject Specialists: *Health sciences*, Lynnette Mende; *Literature*, Lynnette Mende; *Religion*, Lynnette Mende; Staff 13 (MLS 6, Non-MLS 7)
Founded 1946. Enrl 8,900; Fac 278; Highest Degree: Associate
Sep 1999-Aug 2000 Income $634,848. Mats Exp $115,330, Books $44,625, Per/Ser (Incl. Access Fees) $41,808, Presv $346, Micro $14,874, AV Equip $8,400, Electronic Ref Mat (Incl. Access Fees) $5,277. Sal $498,709
Library Holdings: Bk Vols 71,061; Bk Titles 60,742; Per Subs 430; Bks on Deafness & Sign Lang 50
Subject Interests: Allied health, Technology
Special Collections: College Archives
Automation Activity & Vendor Info: (Cataloging) DRA
Database Vendor: CARL, GaleNet, Lexis-Nexis, OCLC - First Search
Publications: Faculty Handbook; Library Guidebook; Library Handbook; Workbook in Library Skills
Function: ILL limited
Partic in Western New York Library Resources Council
Special Services for the Deaf - Books on deafness & sign language

WILLISTON PARK

P WILLISTON PARK PUBLIC LIBRARY,* 494 Willis Ave, 11596. SAN 312-6986. Tel: 516-742-1820. FAX: 516-294-5004. *Dir*, Marilyn S Rosenbaum
Circ 78,161
Library Holdings: Bk Vols 35,000; Per Subs 86
Mem of Nassau Library System
Open Mon 10:30-8:30, Tues, Thurs & Fri 10:30-5:30, Wed 1:30-8:30, Sat 10-3
Friends of the Library Group

WILLSBORO

P PAINE MEMORIAL FREE LIBRARY, One School St, 12996. SAN 312-6994. Tel: 518-963-4478. FAX: 518-963-7778. E-Mail: janlib@willex.com. *Librn*, Cheryl Blanchard; *Asst Librn*, Janet Tucker
Pop 1,800; Circ 46,051
Library Holdings: Bk Vols 20,398; Per Subs 40
Mem of Clinton-Essex-Franklin Library System
Friends of the Library Group

WILMINGTON

P E M COOPER MEMORIAL LIBRARY,* Rte 86, Box 29, 12997. SAN 376-6896. Tel: 518-946-7701. E-Mail: library#1@whiteface.net. *Dir*, Meg Stone
Library Holdings: Bk Vols 40; Bk Titles 7,000
Mem of Clinton-Essex-Franklin Library System
Open Wed & Thurs 12:30-5:30, Fri & Sat 9-4, closed Sun-Tues
Friends of the Library Group

WILSON

P WILSON FREE LIBRARY,* 265 Young St, PO Box 579, 14172. SAN 312-7001. Tel: 716-751-6070. FAX: 716-751-6526. *Dir*, Connie Moss
Circ 25,754
Library Holdings: Bk Vols 15,500
Mem of Nioga Library System
Friends of the Library Group

WILTON

S MOUNT MCGREGOR CORRECTIONAL FACILITY LIBRARY, 1000 Mount McGregor Rd, 12831. SAN 321-0669. Tel: 518-587-3960, Ext 5866. *Librn*, Diane Duell Kiefer
Library Holdings: Bk Vols 7,600; Per Subs 63
Subject Interests: Law
Mem of Southern Adirondack Library System
Branches:
MOUNT MCGREGOR CAMP LIBRARY, 1000 Mount McGregor Rd, PO Box 2071, 12831. Tel: 518-587-3960, Ext 4600. FAX: 518-587-3960, Ext 2099.
Library Holdings: Bk Vols 2,300; Per Subs 38

WINDHAM

P WINDHAM PUBLIC LIBRARY,* Church & Main Sts, PO Box 158, 12496. SAN 312-701X. Tel: 518-734-4405. FAX: 518-734-4405. E-Mail: windham@mhonline.net. *Librn*, Donna Pidgeon; *Asst Librn*, Candace Begley; *Asst Librn*, Joan Sheridan; Staff 3 (Non-MLS 3)
Founded 1922. Pop 1,682; Circ 30,671
Library Holdings: Bk Vols 10,850; Bk Titles 10,420; Per Subs 37
Database Vendor: GaleNet, ProQuest
Publications: TOPS Booklist
Mem of Mid-Hudson Library System
Special Services for the Blind - Bks on cassette

WOLCOTT

P WOLCOTT CIVIC FREE LIBRARY,* 5890 New Hartford St, 14590. SAN 312-7028. Tel: 315-594-2265. FAX: 315-594-2681. *Librn*, Dottie Patt
Pop 1,496; Circ 222,584
Library Holdings: Bk Vols 16,300; Per Subs 32
Mem of Pioneer Library System

WOODBOURNE

S WOODBOURNE CORRECTIONAL FACILITY LIBRARY,* Pouch 1, 12788. SAN 327-1706. Tel: 914-434-7730. FAX: 914-434-7730, Ext 2099. *Librn*, Michael Ellis
Library Holdings: Bk Titles 5,000; Per Subs 23
Partic in Ramapo Catskill Libr Syst

WOODGATE

P WOODGATE FREE LIBRARY,* Woodgate Dr, PO Box 52, 13494. SAN 312-7060. Tel: 315-392-4814. FAX: 315-392-4814. *Librn*, Eleanor D Moon
Circ 4,485
1999-2000 Income $17,300, State $1,200, County $1,000, Locally Generated Income $4,000. Mats Exp $1,450, Books $1,000, Electronic Ref Mat (Incl. Access Fees) $450. Sal $3,200
Library Holdings: Bk Vols 3,100
Subject Interests: Adirondack Mountain hist
Mem of Mid-York Library System
Open Mon 6-9, Wed 3:30-6, Sat 10-4
Friends of the Library Group

WOODSTOCK

S WOODSTOCK ARTISTS ASSOCIATION, WAA Archives,* 28 Tinker St, 12498. SAN 370-3762. Tel: 914-679-2940. FAX: 914-679-2940. *Dir*, Lisa Williams; *Archivist*, Linda Freaney
Library Holdings: Bk Vols 1,250
Publications: Woodstock Art Heritage
Open Mon-Thurs 12-5

P WOODSTOCK LIBRARY,* 5 Library Lane, 12498-1299. SAN 312-7079. Tel: 914-679-2213. FAX: 914-679-7149. E-Mail: woodstck@sebridge.org. Web Site: www.woodstock.org/library. *Dir*, Diana B Stern; *Asst Dir*, Judith Fischetti; Staff 7 (MLS 2, Non-MLS 5)
Founded 1913. Pop 6,823; Circ 90,000
Library Holdings: Bk Vols 60,000
Subject Interests: Architecture, Art, Belles lettres, History, Music
Automation Activity & Vendor Info: (Circulation) GEAC
Mem of Mid-Hudson Library System

WORCESTER

P WORCESTER FREE LIBRARY,* 140 Main St, PO Box 461, 12197. SAN 312-7087. Tel: 607-397-7309. *Librn*, Pat Smith
Founded 1909. Pop 1,993
Library Holdings: Bk Vols 4,020; Per Subs 25
Mem of Four County Library System

WYANDANCH

P WYANDANCH PUBLIC LIBRARY,* 14 S 20th St, 11798. SAN 312-7095. Tel: 516-643-4848. FAX: 516-643-0703. *Dir*, Wendell Cherry; *Ch Servs*, Sandra Long
Founded 1974. Pop 8,200

1998-1999 Income $429,519, Locally Generated Income $10,000. Mats Exp $60,500, Books $40,000, Per/Ser (Incl. Access Fees) $4,000. Sal $190,482
Library Holdings: Bk Vols 33,000; Bk Titles 25,000; Per Subs 84
Mem of Suffolk Cooperative Library System
Friends of the Library Group

WYNANTSKILL

P NORTH GREENBUSH PUBLIC LIBRARY,* Main Ave, PO Box 249, 12198. SAN 321-0995. Tel: 518-283-0303. FAX: 518-283-0303. *Dir*, Daryl McCarthy; Staff 1 (MLS 1)
Founded 1965. Pop 10,304; Circ 63,500
Library Holdings: Bk Vols 39,000; Bk Titles 36,000; Per Subs 50
Mem of Upper Hudson Library System
Friends of the Library Group

WYOMING

S MIDDLEBURY HISTORICAL SOCIETY, Middlebury Academy Museum,* 22 S Academy St, PO Box 198, 14591-0198. SAN 325-9889. Tel: 716-495-6582. *Pres*, Robert Kelley
1998-1999 Income $5,000, Locally Generated Income $1,500, Other $3,500. Mats Exp $205, Books $60, Per/Ser (Incl. Access Fees) $40, Presv $85, Manuscripts & Archives $20
Library Holdings: Bk Vols 30
Subject Interests: Local history
Publications: History of the Town of Middlebury; Middlebury's Poet Norman Stothers; Wyoming-The Town Where I Grew Up

P WYOMING FREE CIRCULATING LIBRARY,* 15 S Academy St, 14591. SAN 312-7117. Tel: 716-495-6840. *Dir*, Jan Hochman
Circ 6,581
Library Holdings: Bk Titles 7,000; Per Subs 20
Mem of Pioneer Library System
Friends of the Library Group

YONKERS

S CONSUMERS UNION OF THE UNITED STATES, INC, Information Center,* 101 Truman Ave, 10703-1057. SAN 311-5291. Tel: 914-378-2261. FAX: 914-378-2913. *Mgr*, Kevin Manion; E-Mail: manike@consumer.org; *Assoc Dir*, Elena Falcone; Staff 11 (MLS 7, Non-MLS 4)
Founded 1936
Library Holdings: Bk Titles 5,000; Per Subs 1,000
Subject Interests: Consumer products testing, Consumer protection
Special Collections: History of the consumer movement

M SAINT JOHN'S RIVERSIDE HOSPITAL, Cochran Library, 967 N Broadway, 10701. SAN 327-2133. Tel: 914-964-4281. FAX: 914-964-4971. Web Site: www.riversidehealth.org. *Dir*, Laura Koepfler; E-Mail: lkoepfler@riversidehealth.org; Staff 3 (MLS 1, Non-MLS 2)
Library Holdings: Bk Vols 3,300; Per Subs 106
Subject Interests: Medicine, Nursing
Database Vendor: OVID Technologies
Function: Research library
Partic in BHSL; Health Infor Libr of West Chester Metro

R SAINT JOHN'S EPISCOPAL CHURCH, Winterbottom Library, Getty Sq, One Hudson St, 10701. SAN 312-7168. Tel: 914-963-3033, 914-969-1499. FAX: 914-963-4990. *Dir*, S Burtner Ulrich
Library Holdings: Bk Vols 2,050; Per Subs 14

M SAINT JOSEPH'S MEDICAL CENTER, Medical Library, 127 S Broadway, 10701. SAN 312-7176. Tel: 914-378-7539. FAX: 914-378-1071. E-Mail: stjoelib1@metgate.metro.org. *Librn*, Doris Carril; E-Mail: doris.carril@saintjosephs.org
Library Holdings: Bk Vols 600; Per Subs 110
Partic in BHSL; Hilow; Metro NY Libr Coun

R SAINT JOSEPH'S SEMINARY, Corrigan Memorial Library, 201 Seminary Ave, 10704. SAN 312-7184. Tel: 914-968-6200, Ext 8255. FAX: 914-376-2019, 914-968-7912. *Dir*, Sister Regina Melican; Tel: 914-968-6200, Ext 8256, E-Mail: rmelican@corriganlibrary.org; *ILL, Librn*, Barbara Carey; Tel: 914-968-6200, Ext 8262, E-Mail: bcarey@corriganlibrary.org; *Coll Develop*, Sr Kathleen McCann; Tel: 914-968-6200, Ext 8263, E-Mail: kmccann@corriganlibrary.org; Staff 4 (MLS 3, Non-MLS 1)
Founded 1896. Enrl 54; Fac 32; Highest Degree: Master
Sep 1998-Aug 1999 Mats Exp $65,394, Books $35,149, Per/Ser (Incl. Access Fees) $24,363, Micro $3,329, Electronic Ref Mat (Incl. Access Fees) $2,553. Sal $150,039 (Prof $92,367)
Library Holdings: Bk Vols 75,559; Bk Titles 75,555; Per Subs 288; Bks on Deafness & Sign Lang 20
Subject Interests: Canon law, Liturgy, Relig studies, Scriptures, Theology
Database Vendor: Ebsco - EbscoHost, OCLC - First Search
Partic in OCLC Online Computer Library Center, Inc

R SAINT VLADIMIR'S ORTHODOX THEOLOGICAL SEMINARY LIBRARY, Father Georges Florovsky Library, 575 Scarsdale Rd, 10707. SAN 312-7192. Tel: 914-961-8313, 914-961-9175. FAX: 914-961-0270. *Librn*, Eleana Silk; E-Mail: esilk@aol.com; *Asst Librn*, Karen Jermyn
Founded 1938. Enrl 84; Fac 9
2000-2001 Income $223,000. Mats Exp $85,251, Books $50,000, Per/Ser (Incl. Access Fees) $20,000, Presv $15,000, Micro $251
Library Holdings: Bk Vols 113,000; Per Subs 345
Subject Interests: Liturgical music, Rec
Special Collections: Byzantine History & Art; Russian History & Culture (incl 19th Century Russian theological periodicals); Theology, History & Culture of the Orthodox Church
Publications: Books Received
Partic in State University Of New York-NYLINK

S YONKERS GENERAL HOSPITAL, Medical Library,* 2 Park Ave, 10703. SAN 325-982X. Tel: 914-7580, 914-964-7300, Ext 7576. FAX: 914-964-7947. *Dir*, Michael Danber
Library Holdings: Bk Vols 200; Per Subs 20
Partic in Nat Libr of Med

S YONKERS HISTORICAL SOCIETY LIBRARY,* City Hall, Rm 415A, 40 S Broadway, 10701. SAN 371-4381. Tel: 914-965-0401. FAX: 914-965-0401. Web Site: www.yonkershistory.org. *Pres*, Patricia Mangold; *Dir*, Marianne Winstanley
Library Holdings: Bk Titles 225; Per Subs 75
Special Collections: City Directory Coll (1890-1930); Photograph Coll
Publications: Yonkers History (quarterly)
Restriction: By appointment only

P YONKERS PUBLIC LIBRARY,* 7 Main St, 10701. SAN 354-4230. Tel: 914-337-1500. FAX: 914-963-2301. Web Site: lib.ny.us/libs/yonkers/ypl_home.htm. *Dir*, Stephen E Force; *Coll Develop, ILL*, Leslie Dickinson; *Acq, Cat, Tech Servs*, Mary York. Subject Specialists: *Business and management*, Nedra Biegel; *Fine arts*, Leslie Dickinson; *Technology*, Nedra Biegel
Founded 1893. Pop 188,082; Circ 806,798
Library Holdings: Bk Vols 282,935; Bk Titles 232,146; Per Subs 652
Subject Interests: Agriculture, Architecture, Art, Bus, History, Indust, Mgt, Music, Sci-tech
Special Collections: Jewish Interest (Kogan Coll); Theatre & Dramatic Arts (John G Jutkowitz Memorial Coll)
Automation Activity & Vendor Info: (Cataloging) TLC
Publications: A Guide to Subjects & Concepts in Picture Book Format
Mem of Westchester Library System
Friends of the Library Group
Branches: 3
CRESTWOOD, 16 Thompson St, 10707. SAN 354-432X. Tel: 914-779-3774. *Librn*, Judith Schavrien
Library Holdings: Bk Vols 20,000
Friends of the Library Group
GETTY SQUARE, 7 Main St, 10701. SAN 375-8656. Tel: 914-337-1500. FAX: 914-963-2301. *Librn*, Lois Herzberg
Library Holdings: Bk Vols 121,000
Friends of the Library Group
GRINTON I WILL BRANCH, 1500 Central Park Ave, 10710. SAN 354-4389. Tel: 914-337-1500. FAX: 914-337-9114. *Librn*, Judith Schavrien
Library Holdings: Bk Vols 140,000
Subject Interests: Dramatic arts, Fine arts, Music
Friends of the Library Group

YORKTOWN HEIGHTS

S BOCES - PUTNAM-NORTHERN WESTCHESTER, Boces Professional Library,* 200 Boces Dr, 10598. SAN 371-0181. Tel: 914-248-2392. FAX: 914-248-2419. Web Site: www.pnwboces.org/library.htm. *Dir, Librn*, John Monahan; E-Mail: monahan@computer.net; *Admin Assoc*, Linda Donovan
Library Holdings: Bk Vols 13,804; Bk Titles 8,765; Per Subs 159
Open 8:30-5

S IBM CORP, Thomas J Watson Research Center Library, Rte 134, PO Box 218, 10598. SAN 312-7206. Tel: 914-945-1415. FAX: 914-945-4144. E-Mail: watlib@us.ibm.com. *Mgr*, Lisa Sampogna; Tel: 914-945-2822, E-Mail: sampogna@us.ibm.com; Staff 10 (MLS 6, Non-MLS 4)
Library Holdings: Bk Vols 45,000; Per Subs 1,000
Subject Interests: Business, Chemistry, Computer science, Engineering, Info tech, Mathematics, Physical science
Partic in State University Of New York-NYLINK

MERCY COLLEGE
See Dobbs Ferry

YOUNGSTOWN

S OLD FORT NIAGARA ASSOCIATION LIBRARY, PO Box 169, 14174-0169. SAN 325-9803. Tel: 716-745-7611. Reference Tel: 716-745-9667. FAX: 716-745-9141. E-Mail: ofn@oldfortniagara.org. Web Site:

www.oldfortniagara.org. *Curator*, Jerome P Brubaker; E-Mail: brubakerjp@aol.com
Founded 1929
Library Holdings: Bk Vols 2,500
Special Collections: Map Coll; Msp Items (1780-present), micro, archival material
Publications: Fortress Niagara, Journal of the Old Fort Niagara Association (Newsletter)
Restriction: Non-circulating
Historic Site Library

P YOUNGSTOWN FREE LIBRARY,* 240 Lockport St, 14174. SAN 312-7222. Tel: 716-745-3555. FAX: 716-745-7122. E-Mail: jgilg@nioga.org. *Dir, Librn*, Jan Gilgore
Founded 1949. Circ 37,523
Library Holdings: Bk Vols 21,000; Per Subs 54
Mem of Nioga Library System
Friends of the Library Group

NORTH CAROLINA

Date of Statistics: Fiscal 1999-2000
Population (est.): 7,650,699
Population Served by Public Libraries: 7,650,699
Total Volumes in Public Libraries: 15,278,564
Volumes Per Capita: 2.04
Total Public Library Circulation: 42,539,154
Circulation Per Capita: 4.63
Total Public Library Income (including Grants-in-Aid): $145,091,320
Source of Income Local: 80% public funds; 12% state aid; 1% federal; 7% other
Expenditures Per Capita: $18.02
Number of County or Multi-County (Regional) Libraries: 51 county, 15 regional, 10 municipal
Counties Served: 100
Number of Bookmobiles in State: 45
Grants-in-Aid to Public Libraries:
Federal (LSTA and LSCA): $1,605,516
State Aid: $14,934,554
Formula for State Aid: One half of appropriation in block grants; one half per capita income equalization grants.

ABERDEEN

P PAGE MEMORIAL LIBRARY, 100 N Poplar St, 28315. SAN 376-2874. Tel: 910-944-1200. FAX: 910-944-1200. *Dir*, Mark McGrath
Library Holdings: Bk Vols 3,320; Bk Titles 3,000
Mem of Sandhill Regional Library System

AHOSKIE

P AHOSKIE PUBLIC LIBRARY,* 210 E Church St, 27910. SAN 354-4419. Tel: 252-332-5500. FAX: 252-332-6435. *Librn*, Harriett Oliver; *Librn*, Annette Perry; *Librn*, Peggy Pomplin
Library Holdings: Bk Vols 16,000
Mem of Albemarle Regional Library
Statistics included with regional library. See Winton entry

J ROANOKE-CHOWAN COMMUNITY COLLEGE, Learning Resources Center, 109 Community College Rd, 27910. SAN 312-7249. Tel: 252-862-1200. Interlibrary Loan Service Tel: 252-862-1223. FAX: 252-862-1358. Web Site: www.cclinc.nccs.cc.nc.us. *Dir*, Margaret S Lefler; Tel: 252-862-1262, E-Mail: leflerp@roanoke.cc.nc.us; Staff 3 (MLS 2, Non-MLS 1)
Founded 1967. Enrl 1,000; Fac 28; Highest Degree: Associate
Jul 1999-Jun 2000 Income $195,246. Mats Exp $51,639, Books $22,142, Per/Ser (Incl. Access Fees) $12,679, Micro $2,210, AV Equip $8,000, Electronic Ref Mat (Incl. Access Fees) $6,608. Sal $111,306 (Prof $78,435)
Library Holdings: Bk Titles 31,544; Per Subs 172
Special Collections: Audiovisual Prof Learning Lab
Automation Activity & Vendor Info: (Acquisitions) SIRSI; (Cataloging) SIRSI; (Circulation) SIRSI; (Course Reserve) SIRSI; (ILL) SIRSI; (Media Booking) SIRSI; (OPAC) SIRSI; (OPAC) SIRSI; (Serials) SIRSI
Partic in CCLINC; NC State ILL Network

ALBEMARLE

J STANLY COMMUNITY COLLEGE, Learning Resources Center, Snyder Bldg, 28001. (Mail add: 141 College Dr, LRC, 28001), SAN 354-4621. Tel: 704-991-0259. FAX: 704-991-0112. Web Site: www.stanly.cc.nc.us. *Dean*, Dr Mary Avery; Tel: 704-982-0121, E-Mail: averymc@stanly.cc.nc.us; *Dir Libr Serv*, Elizabeth W Estes; Tel: 704-991-0337, E-Mail: estesew@stanly.cc.nc.us; *Librn*, Michael Hicks; Tel: 704-991-0261, E-Mail: hicksm@stanly.cc.nc.us; Staff 3 (MLS 2, Non-MLS 1)
Founded 1972
Jul 1999-Jun 2000 Income $66,331. Mats Exp $51,705, Books $31,331, Per/Ser (Incl. Access Fees) $14,903, Electronic Ref Mat (Incl. Access Fees) $5,471
Library Holdings: Bk Vols 22,000; Bk Titles 2,000; Per Subs 225
Subject Interests: Computer lang, Nursing, Respiratory therapy
Automation Activity & Vendor Info: (Cataloging) SIRSI; (Circulation) SIRSI
Database Vendor: Ebsco - EbscoHost, GaleNet, IAC - SearchBank, OCLC - First Search, Silverplatter Information Inc., Wilson - Wilson Web

P STANLY COUNTY PUBLIC LIBRARY, 133 E Main St, 28001. SAN 354-4478. Tel: 704-986-3755. FAX: 704-983-6713. Web Site: www.stanlylib.org. *Dir*, Penny Welling; E-Mail: pwelling@ncsl.dcr.state.nc.us; *Exten Serv*, Melanie Holles; *Ref*, Brenda Harris; *Ch Servs*, Daphne Hayer; *Electronic Resources*, Steve Grochowsky; Staff 27 (MLS 5, Non-MLS 22)
Founded 1927. Pop 56,000; Circ 211,624
1999-2000 Mats Exp $115,000, Books $105,000, Per/Ser (Incl. Access Fees) $10,000. Sal $539,000
Library Holdings: Bk Vols 118,745; Bk Titles 71,313; Per Subs 165
Subject Interests: Local history
Automation Activity & Vendor Info: (Cataloging) Gaylord; (Circulation) Gaylord; (OPAC) Gaylord
Friends of the Library Group
Branches: 4
BADIN BRANCH, PO Box 752, Badin, 28009. SAN 354-4508. Tel: 704-422-3218. *In Charge*, Jenny Allen; Staff 2 (Non-MLS 2)
LOCUST BRANCH, PO Box 400, Locust, 28097. SAN 375-2909. Tel: 704-888-0103. *In Charge*, Karen Hartsell; Staff 3 (Non-MLS 3)
NORWOOD BRANCH, PO Box 1217, Norwood, 28128. SAN 354-4532. Tel: 704-474-3625. *In Charge*, Julie Russell
OAKBORO BRANCH, 412 S Main St, Oakboro, 28129. SAN 354-4567. Tel: 704-485-4310. *In Charge*, Kay Hunter
Friends of the Library Group

ANDREWS

P ANDREWS PUBLIC LIBRARY,* 871 Main St, PO Box 700, 28901. SAN 312-7257. Tel: 828-321-5956. FAX: 828-321-3256. *Librn*, Jane B Payne; Staff 3 (MLS 1, Non-MLS 2)
Founded 1915. Circ 25,962
Library Holdings: Bk Vols 15,000
Mem of Nantahala Regional Library
Friends of the Library Group

ASHEBORO

J RANDOLPH COMMUNITY COLLEGE, Learning Resources Center, 629 Industrial Park Ave, 27204-1009. (Mail add: PO Box 1009, 27204-1009), SAN 312-7273. Tel: 336-633-0204. FAX: 336-629-4695. Web Site: biblio.randolph.cc.nc.us. *Dir Libr Serv*, Deborah Scott Luck; Tel: 336-633-0272, E-Mail: dsluck@randolph.cc.nc.us; *Ref*, Carol Hall; E-Mail: cshall@randolph.cc.nc.us; *AV*, Celia Hurley; *Info Tech*, Mario Ramos; Tel: 336-633-0204, E-Mail: msramos@randolph.cc.nc.us; *Media Spec*, Daniel Thornburg; Tel: 336-633-0231, E-Mail: djthornburg@randolph.cc.nc.us; Staff 7 (MLS 3, Non-MLS 4)
Founded 1963
Jul 1997-Jun 1998 Income $207,000. Mats Exp $81,000. Sal $105,900 (Prof $58,300)
Library Holdings: Bk Vols 34,000; Bk Titles 32,000; Per Subs 287
Subject Interests: Architecture, Art, Interior design, Nursing, Photog, Pottery, Tech educ, Vocational
Special Collections: Bienenstock Furniture Library (High Point, North

Carolina) microfiche collection
Automation Activity & Vendor Info: (Cataloging) SIRSI; (Circulation) SIRSI; (Course Reserve) SIRSI; (ILL) SIRSI; (Media Booking) SIRSI; (OPAC) SIRSI; (Serials) SIRSI
Database Vendor: Ebsco - EbscoHost, GaleNet, OCLC - First Search, ProQuest
Partic in CCLINC
Departmental Libraries:
ARCHDALE CAMPUS, 110 Park Dr, Archdale, 27263-8504. Tel: 336-861-4241.

P RANDOLPH PUBLIC LIBRARY,* 201 Worth St, 27203. SAN 354-4745. Interlibrary Loan Service Tel: 336-318-6800. FAX: 336-318-6823. *Dir*, Richard T Wells; E-Mail: rwells@ncsk.dcr.state.nc.us
Founded 1940. Pop 106,928; Circ 427,695
Library Holdings: Bk Vols 170,000; Per Subs 905
Special Collections: Local History (Core Coll), microfilm; Music (Interlibrary Loan Coll), bks & rec
Publications: Frandolphin Children's Newsletter; Randolph County Public Library News
Special Services for the Deaf - Books on deafness & sign language; Captioned film depository; High interest/low vocabulary books; Special interest periodicals
Friends of the Library Group
Branches: 7
ARCHDALE BRANCH, 10433 S Main St, Archdale, 27263. SAN 354-477X. Tel: 336-431-3811. FAX: 336-431-4619. *Librn*, Naomi Galbreath
ASHEBORO BRANCH, 201 Worth St, 27203. SAN 354-480X. Tel: 336-318-6800. FAX: 336-318-6823. *Librn*, Richard Wells; E-Mail: rwells@ncsk.dcr.state.nc.us
Library Holdings: Bk Vols 170,000
Subject Interests: Local history, NC hist
Friends of the Library Group
JOHN W CLARK PUBLIC, PO Box 278, Franklinville, 27248. SAN 354-4834. Tel: 336-824-4020. *Librn*, Martha Cain
Friends of the Library Group
LIBERTY BRANCH, S Fayetteville St, PO Box 1006, Liberty, 27298. SAN 354-4869. Tel: 336-622-4605. FAX: 336-622-4605. *Librn*, Susan Prim
Friends of the Library Group
RAMSEUR BRANCH, 1512 Main St, PO Box 546, Ramseur, 27316. SAN 354-4893. Tel: 336-824-2232. FAX: 336-824-2232. E-Mail: libraryramseurpublic@hotmail.com. *Librn*, Sandra Livingston
Friends of the Library Group
RANDLEMAN BRANCH, 122 Commerce Sq, Randleman, 27317. SAN 354-4923. Tel: 336-498-3141. FAX: 336-498-1139. *Librn*, Louise Hudson
Library Holdings: Bk Vols 75,000
Subject Interests: Art, Pottery
SEAGROVE BRANCH, Grange Hall, 354 Old Plank Rd, Seagrove, 27341. (Mail add: PO Box 258, Seagrove, 27341), SAN 354-4958. Tel: 336-873-7521. *Librn*, Glenda Lilly
Library Holdings: Bk Vols 6,000
Subject Interests: Pottery
Friends of the Library Group

ASHEVILLE

S ASHEVILLE CITIZEN-TIMES LIBRARY,* 14 O'Henry Ave, PO Box 2090, 28802. SAN 374-972X. Tel: 828-252-5610. FAX: 828-251-0585. *Librn*, Holly McKenzie
Library Holdings: Bk Titles 300; Per Subs 15
Open Mon-Fri 2-5pm

P ASHEVILLE-BUNCOMBE LIBRARY SYSTEM, 67 Haywood St, 28801. SAN 354-5040. Tel: 828-255-5203. FAX: 828-255-5213. Web Site: www.buncombecounty.org. *Dir*, Edward J Sheary; E-Mail: esheary@ablsys.abls.lib.nc.us; *Asst Dir*, Georgianna J Francis; *Br Coordr*, Robert Neufeld; *Ch Servs*, Julie Duke; *Ref*, Laura Gaskin; *Spec Coll*, Ann Wright; *Tech Servs*, Mary Bunner; Staff 78 (MLS 13, Non-MLS 65)
Founded 1879. Pop 192,000; Circ 1,380,966
Jun 1999-May 2000 Income (Main Library and Branch Library) $3,459,610, State $247,293, County $2,995,978, Locally Generated Income $216,339. Mats Exp $711,009. Sal $2,193,131
Library Holdings: Bk Vols 444,378; Per Subs 820
Subject Interests: North Carolina
Special Collections: Thomas Wolfe Coll
Automation Activity & Vendor Info: (Acquisitions) DRA; (Cataloging) DRA; (Circulation) DRA; (OPAC) DRA
Database Vendor: DRA
Publications: Happenings (monthly newsletter)
Friends of the Library Group
Branches: 10
BLACK MOUNTAIN BRANCH, 105 Dougherty St, Black Mountain, 28711. SAN 354-5067. Tel: 828-669-2652. *Librn*, Ann Butler
Library Holdings: Bk Vols 32,009
Friends of the Library Group
EAST ASHEVILLE, 902 Tunnel Rd, 28805. SAN 354-5075. Tel: 828-298-1889. *Librn*, Hilary Boram
Library Holdings: Bk Vols 24,969
ENKA-CANDLER BRANCH, 1404 Sandhill Rd, PO Box 1559, Enka, 28728. SAN 377-5941. Tel: 828-667-8153. *Librn*, Leisa Stamey
Friends of the Library Group
FAIRVIEW BRANCH, One Taylor Rd, Fairview, 28730. Tel: 828-628-5837. *Branch Mgr*, Elizabeth Parker
Library Holdings: Bk Vols 18,000
Friends of the Library Group
NORTH ASHEVILLE, 37 E Larchmont Dr, 28804. SAN 354-5105. Tel: 828-251-4991. *Librn*, Julie Niwinski
Library Holdings: Bk Vols 23,181
Friends of the Library Group
SOUTH ASHEVILLE, 749 Fairview Rd, 28803. SAN 354-513X. Tel: 828-274-1007. *Librn*, Cheryl Middelton
Library Holdings: Bk Vols 18,033
Friends of the Library Group
SOUTH BUNCOMBE, PO Box 912, Skyland, 28776. SAN 354-5121. Tel: 828-684-1827. *Librn*, Tim Daniels
Library Holdings: Bk Vols 24,859
Friends of the Library Group
SWANNANOA BRANCH, 101 W Charleston Ave, Swannanoa, 28778. SAN 354-5148. Tel: 828-686-5516. FAX: 828-686-5516. *Librn*, Marie Kaplan
Library Holdings: Bk Vols 12,232
Friends of the Library Group
WEAVERVILLE BRANCH, PO Box 633, Weaverville, 28787. SAN 354-5156. Tel: 828-645-3592. *Librn*, Jill Totman
Library Holdings: Bk Vols 24,124
Friends of the Library Group
WEST ASHEVILLE, 942 Haywood Rd, 28806. SAN 354-5164. Tel: 828-251-4990. *Librn*, Margaret Weaver
Library Holdings: Bk Vols 28,644
Bookmobiles: 1

J ASHEVILLE-BUNCOMBE TECHNICAL COMMUNITY COLLEGE, Learning Resource Center, 340 Victoria Rd, 28801. SAN 312-7281. Tel: 828-254-1921, Ext 300. FAX: 828-251-6074. *Dir*, Shirley McLaughlin; *Ref Serv*, Jacki Case; Staff 4 (MLS 4)
Founded 1959. Enrl 4,500; Fac 160; Highest Degree: Associate
Library Holdings: Bk Vols 40,000; Bk Titles 38,000; Per Subs 210
Subject Interests: Allied health, Eng tech, Law enforcement, Vocational-technical
Automation Activity & Vendor Info: (Acquisitions) epixtech, inc.; (Cataloging) epixtech, inc.; (Circulation) epixtech, inc.; (Course Reserve) epixtech, inc.; (OPAC) epixtech, inc.
Database Vendor: epixtech, inc.
Publications: Faculty Guide to Library & Audiovisual Services
Partic in Mountain College Libr Network; NC Dept of Commun Cols
Closed on weekends

GM DEPARTMENT OF VETERANS AFFAIRS MEDICAL CENTER LIBRARY,* 1100 Tunnel Rd, 28805. SAN 312-732X. Tel: 828-299-2525. FAX: 828-299-2500. Web Site: www.main.nc.us/va-ashville. *Librn*, Peggy Patterson
Library Holdings: Bk Titles 5,000; Per Subs 300
Subject Interests: Cardiovascular, Gen med, Thoracic surgery
Partic in Vets Admin Libr Network

M MOUNTAIN AREA HEALTH EDUCATION CENTER LIBRARY, Health Sciences Library, 501 Biltmore Ave, 28801-4686. SAN 354-4982. Tel: 828-257-4444. Interlibrary Loan Service Tel: 828-257-4446. FAX: 828-257-4712. E-Mail: info@mtn.ncahec.org. Web Site: www.mtn.ncahec.org/library. *Dir*, Joan Colburn; Tel: 828-257-4438, Fax: 828-258-2099, E-Mail: joan@mtn.ncahec.org; *Librn*, Brenda Benik; Tel: 828-257-4451, E-Mail: brendab@mtn.ncahec.org; *Librn*, Julia Covington; Tel: 828-257-4447, E-Mail: juliac@mtn.ncahec.org; *Librn*, Sue Stigleman; Tel: 828-257-4452, E-Mail: sues@mtn.ncahec.org; *Librn*, Linda Turner; Tel: 828-257-4441, E-Mail: lindat@mtn.ncahec.org; *ILL*, Lynne Hook; E-Mail: lhook@mtn@ncahec.org; Staff 7 (MLS 5, Non-MLS 2)
Founded 1972
Library Holdings: Bk Vols 6,000; Per Subs 400
Subject Interests: Allied health, Cultural diversity, Dentistry, Family practice, Health sci, Medicine, Nursing, Obstetrics and gynecology, Pharm, Public health
Database Vendor: CARL, Dialog, Ebsco - EbscoHost, OCLC - First Search, OVID Technologies
Restriction: Members only, Open to public for reference only
Function: Document delivery services, Literary searches, Mail loans to members, Professional lending library, Reference services available
Partic in NC Area Health Education Centers

G NATIONAL OCEANIC & ATMOSPHERIC ADMINISTRATION, National Climatic Data Center Library, 151 Patton Ave, Rm 400, 28801-5001. SAN 312-729X. Tel: 828-271-4677. FAX: 828-271-4328. *Librn*, Linda D Preston; E-Mail: linda.preston@noaa.gov; Staff 1 (MLS 1)
Founded 1961
Library Holdings: Bk Vols 14,000; Per Subs 400
Subject Interests: Climatology, Meteorology, Oceanography

Automation Activity & Vendor Info: (OPAC) SIRSI
Database Vendor: OCLC - First Search
Restriction: Staff use only
Partic in Dialog Corporation; Fedlink; OCLC Online Computer Library Center, Inc

S SOUTHERN HIGHLAND CRAFT GUILD, Folk Art Center Library,* PO Box 9545, 28815. SAN 325-7657. Tel: 828-298-7928. FAX: 704-298-7962. *Librn*, Caroline Manheimer
Jan 1998-Dec 1999 Income $5,000. Mats Exp $5,000, Books $2,000, Per/Ser (Incl. Access Fees) $1,500
Library Holdings: Bk Vols 5,526
Special Collections: Archives: History of Southern Highlands, Appalachian Heritage; Francis Goodrich Coll, Hand Sketched Weaving Patterns Accomplished by Appalachian Women Circa Late 1890

UNITED STATES AIR FORCE
S AIR FORCE WEATHER TECHNICAL LIBRARY FL4414, AFCCC/DOR, 151 Patton Ave Rm 120, 28801-5002. SAN 340-7500. Tel: 828-271-4270, 828-271-4277. FAX: 828-271-4334. Web Site: www.afccc.af.mil/html/afwtl/afwtl.html. *Librn*, Kathryn E Marshall; E-Mail: marshalk@afccc.af.mil; *Cat*, Susan A Tarbell; *ILL*, Karen Kelly; *Ref*, Gary S Swanson; Staff 11 (MLS 5, Non-MLS 6)
Founded 1975
Oct 1997-Sep 1998 Income $659,000. Mats Exp $44,535, Books $5,850, Per/Ser (Incl. Access Fees) $38,500, Micro $185. Sal $535,920 (Prof $317,416)
Library Holdings: Bk Titles 19,500; Per Subs 208
Subject Interests: Geophysics, Meteorology
Special Collections: Meteorology (Climatic Data Summaries), DTIC, TFRN's & AWS Historic Coll, tech rpts
Partic in Fedlink

C UNIVERSITY OF NORTH CAROLINA AT ASHEVILLE, D Hiden Ramsey Library, One University Heights, 28804-8504. SAN 312-7311. Tel: 828-251-6336. Circulation Tel: 828-251-6336. Reference Tel: 828-251-6111. TDD: 828-251-6301. FAX: 828-232-5147. Web Site: www.bullpup.lib.unca.edu/library/. *Dir*, James Robert Kuhlman; Tel: 828-251-6545, Fax: 828-232-5247, E-Mail: kuhlman@unca.edu; *ILL*, Nancy Hayes; Tel: 828-251-6436, E-Mail: nhayes@unca.edu; *Ref*, Anita White-Carter; Tel: 828-251-6434, E-Mail: whitecarter@unca.edu; *Cat*, Mark Stoffan; Tel: 828-251-6647, E-Mail: mstoffan@bulldog.unca.edu; *Circ*, Leith M Tate; Tel: 828-251-6639, E-Mail: ltate@unca.edu; *Spec Coll*, Helen Wykle; Tel: 828-251-6621, E-Mail: hwykle@unca.edu; *Automation Syst Coordr*, Robert Bland; Tel: 828-251-6543, E-Mail: bland@unca.edu; *Publ Servs*, Ellie Marsh; Tel: 828-251-6636, E-Mail: emarsh@unca.edu; *Coordr*, Lynne Olin; Tel: 828-251-6729, E-Mail: olin@unca.edu; *AV*, Rudy Moorrees; Tel: 828-251-6995, E-Mail: rudy@unca.edu; *Asst Prof*, Bryan Sinclair; Tel: 828-232-5094, E-Mail: sinclair@bulldog.unca.edu; Staff 28 (Non-MLS 28)
Founded 1928. Enrl 3,277; Fac 156; Highest Degree: Master
Jul 1998-Jun 1999 Income $1,866,613. Mats Exp $694,911, Books $258,818, Per/Ser (Incl. Access Fees) $285,512, Presv $9,644, Micro $47,403, Manuscripts & Archives $57, Electronic Ref Mat (Incl. Access Fees) $93,477. Sal $621,412 (Prof $285,862)
Library Holdings: Bk Vols 364,587; Bk Titles 243,945; Per Subs 2,096
Subject Interests: Liberal arts
Special Collections: Harrison Coll of Early American History; Manuscript & Photograph Coll, documents the history of Western North Carolina; Peckham Coll of WWI Narratives; University Archives
Automation Activity & Vendor Info: (Acquisitions) Innovative Interfaces Inc.; (Cataloging) Innovative Interfaces Inc.; (Circulation) Innovative Interfaces Inc.; (Course Reserve) Innovative Interfaces Inc.; (OPAC) Innovative Interfaces Inc.; (Serials) Innovative Interfaces Inc.
Database Vendor: CARL, Dialog, Ebsco - EbscoHost, IAC - Info Trac, Lexis-Nexis, OCLC - First Search, OVID Technologies, ProQuest, Silverplatter Information Inc.
Publications: An Introduction to Library Research
Partic in Solinet; Western North Carolina Library Network
Provides library support for Asheville Graduate Center
Friends of the Library Group

AULANDER

P SALLIE HARRELL JENKINS PUBLIC LIBRARY,* 302 Broad St, PO Box 189, 27805. SAN 312-7338. Tel: 252-345-4461. FAX: 252-345-4461. *Librn*, Dorothy Troutfield
Mem of Albemarle Regional Library
Statistics included with regional library. See Winton entry

AURORA

P HAZEL W GUILFORD MEMORIAL LIBRARY,* 524 Main St, PO Box 489, 27806. SAN 312-7346. Tel: 252-322-5046. FAX: 252-322-7109. *Librn*, John Carawan
Founded 1959. Pop 750; Circ 12,075
Library Holdings: Bk Vols 3,000; Per Subs 11
Partic in Beaufort, Hyde, Martin Regional Libr Syst
Open Tues & Thurs 9-5, Wed & Sat 9-12
Friends of the Library Group

AYDEN

P QUINERLY OLSCHNER PUBLIC LIBRARY,* 202 W Second St, PO Box 40, 28513. SAN 312-7354. Tel: 252-746-7026. FAX: 252-746-7041. E-Mail: qolib@greenvillenc.com. *Dir, Librn*, Pat Nichols
Pop 4,500; Circ 16,800
Library Holdings: Bk Vols 18,000; Per Subs 15

BAILEY

S COUNTRY DOCTOR MUSEUM LIBRARY,* 6642 Peele Rd. (Mail add: PO Box 34, 27807), SAN 322-6921. Tel: 252-235-4165. *Exec Dir*, Carolyn B Bissette
Library Holdings: Bk Titles 1,200
Open Tues-Sat 10-4, Sun 2-5

BAKERSVILLE

P MITCHELL COUNTY PUBLIC LIBRARY,* 18 N Mitchell Ave, PO Box 26, 28705. SAN 312-7370. Tel: 828-688-2511. Web Site: www.amy.lib.nc.us. *Librn*, Linda B Gouge; E-Mail: lgouge@ncsl.dcr.state.nc.us; *Asst Librn*, Cynthia Burleson
Pop 14,391
1998-1999 Income $89,555, County $40,287, Locally Generated Income $11,446, Other $37,822. Mats Exp $20,000, Books $10,000. Sal $35,979
Library Holdings: Bk Vols 35,000; Per Subs 39
Special Collections: North Carolina Mineral & Geology Coll
Mem of Avery-Mitchell-Yancey Regional Library System
Library Services for the aging, homebound & physically handicapped; Programs for children & young adults; Summer reading program; Bookmobile Service

BANNER ELK

C LEES-MCRAE COLLEGE, James H Carson Library, 150 Buena Vist, PO Box 67, 28604. SAN 312-7389. Tel: 828-898-8727. FAX: 828-898-8710. Web Site: www.lmc.edu/library/default.html. *Dir*, Richard Jackson; *Assoc Librn*, Patti Bowers; E-Mail: bowersp@bobcat.lmc.edu; *Asst Librn*, Charlotte Presswood; Staff 6 (MLS 2, Non-MLS 4)
Founded 1900
May 2000-Jun 2001 Income $254,867. Mats Exp $93,415, Books $51,750, Per/Ser (Incl. Access Fees) $28,600, Presv $4,700, Electronic Ref Mat (Incl. Access Fees) $8,365. Sal $138,627
Library Holdings: Bk Vols 96,628; Per Subs 343
Special Collections: Southern Appalachian Region (A B Stirling Coll)
Database Vendor: DRA
Publications: Puddingstone Press
Partic in Mountain College Libr Network

BARCO

P CURRITUCK COUNTY PUBLIC LIBRARY,* 4261 Caratoke Hwy, 27917. SAN 312-7966. Tel: 252-453-8345. FAX: 252-453-8717. Web Site: earlibrary.org. *Librn*, Jane Marshall; *Ch Servs*, Patsy Howard; Staff 5 (MLS 1, Non-MLS 4)
Founded 1948. Pop 16,000; Circ 50,000
Library Holdings: Bk Titles 29,000; Per Subs 40
Subject Interests: Genealogy
Special Collections: Family Genealogy Coll
Mem of East Albemarle Regional Library

BATH

P BATH COMMUNITY LIBRARY,* 100 Carteret St, PO Box 160, 27808. SAN 312-7397. Tel: 252-923-6371. FAX: 252-923-0497. *Librn*, Winifred Webster
Library Holdings: Bk Vols 653; Per Subs 12
Open Mon 2-5:30, Wed & Fri 10-5:30
Friends of the Library Group

BAYBORO

P PAMLICO COUNTY LIBRARY,* 603 Main St, 28515. SAN 312-7400. Tel: 252-745-3515. FAX: 252-745-3847. *Librn*, Jane McCann; *Librn*, Barbara Collier; Staff 4 (MLS 2, Non-MLS 2)
Founded 1964
Jul 1998-Jun 1999 Income $99,700
Library Holdings: Bk Vols 21,000; Per Subs 112

Database Vendor: epixtech, inc.
Mem of Craven-Pamlico-Carteret Regional Library
Open Mon-Thurs 8-8, Fri 8-6 & Sat 8-12 (winter), Mon, Wed & Fri 8-6, Tues & Thurs 8-8 & Sat 8-12 (summer); also serves as library for county high school

BEAUFORT

P CARTERET COUNTY PUBLIC LIBRARY, 210 Turner St, 28516. SAN 312-7419. Tel: 252-728-2050. FAX: 252-728-1857. Web Site: www4.coastalnet.com/community_orgs/cclibrary. *Chief Librn*, Susan W Simpson
Founded 1939. Pop 57,050; Circ 149,840
Library Holdings: Bk Vols 37,201; Per Subs 59
Special Collections: Genealogy, County History
Mem of Craven-Pamlico-Carteret Regional Library
Friends of the Library Group
Branches: 2
BOGUE BANKS, 320 Salter Path, Pine Knoll Shores, 28512. SAN 321-9569. Tel: 252-247-4660. FAX: 252-247-2802. *Librn*, Susan W Simpson
Circ 7,325
Library Holdings: Bk Vols 10,000; Per Subs 14
Friends of the Library Group
EMERALD ISLE BRANCH, 100 Leisure Lane, Emerald Isle, 28594. SAN 377-7987. Tel: 252-354-9219. FAX: 252-354-9266. Web Site: www4.coastalnet.com/community_orgs/cclibrary. *Librn*, Susan W Simpson
Library Holdings: Bk Titles 7,000
Friends of the Library Group
Bookmobiles: 1

C DUKE UNIVERSITY-NICHOLAS SCHOOL OF THE ENVIRONMENT, Pearse Memorial Library, Duke University Marine Laboratory, 135 Duke Marine Lab Rd, 28516-9721. SAN 321-0480. Tel: 252-504-7510. FAX: 252-504-7622. Web Site: www.env.duke.edu/marinelab/marlib.html. *Librn*, David Talbert; E-Mail: talbert@duke.edu
Founded 1938. Highest Degree: Bachelor
Library Holdings: Bk Titles 23,000; Per Subs 60
Automation Activity & Vendor Info: (OPAC) DRA
Publications: Serial publications list

BELMONT

C BELMONT ABBEY COLLEGE, Abbot Vincent Taylor Library, 100 Belmont-Mt Holly Rd, 28012. SAN 312-7443. Tel: 704-825-6740. Interlibrary Loan Service Tel: 704-825-6741. FAX: 704-825-6743. E-Mail: library@crusader.bac.edu. Web Site: www.bac.edu. *Dir*, Donald Beagle; *Circ*, Margrete Anderson; *Per*, Margaret Vickers; *Acq*, Vickie Jenkins; *Cat*, Julie Fisher; *Cat, Tech Servs*, Susan Mayes; *Ref*, Mary Coleman; Staff 3 (MLS 3)
Founded 1876. Enrl 939; Fac 40
Library Holdings: Bk Vols 115,000; Bk Titles 86,186; Per Subs 633
Subject Interests: History, Relig studies
Special Collections: Autographed Books; Benedictine Coll; Napoleonic Coll; North & South Carolina Coll, old & rare bks; Valuable Books from Fifteenth, Sixteenth, Seventeenth & Eighteenth Centuries, brought by monks from Europe
Publications: Friends Newsletter; Library Handbook; Operational Manual of the Library; Periodicals Holdings List
Friends of the Library Group

BESSEMER CITY

S FMC LITHIUM DIVISION, Ellestad Research Library, Hwy 161, PO Box 795, 28016. SAN 312-7486. Tel: 704-868-0897. FAX: 704-868-5496. *Info Specialist*, Rebecca Schwindeman
Founded 1960
Library Holdings: Bk Vols 2,500; Per Subs 40
Subject Interests: Chemistry
Restriction: Company library, Lending to staff only, Not open to public
Open Mon-Fri 8-5:15

BEULAVILLE

P PHILLIP LEFF MEMORIAL LIBRARY,* 807 E Broad St, 28518. SAN 376-2920. Tel: 910-298-4677. FAX: 910-298-5069. *In Charge*, Terri Lockerman
Library Holdings: Bk Vols 30,000; Bk Titles 20,000; Per Subs 10
Friends of the Library Group

BLACK MOUNTAIN

R EPISCOPAL DIOCESE OF WESTERN NORTH CAROLINA, Resource Center,* Vance Ave, PO Box 369, 28711. SAN 328-1213. Tel: 828-669-2921. FAX: 828-669-2756.; Staff 1 (MLS 1)
Founded 1974
Library Holdings: Bk Vols 4,000; Per Subs 30
Special Collections: Archives of Diocese & 62 Parishes

BOILING SPRINGS

C GARDNER-WEBB UNIVERSITY, Dover Memorial Library, West Branch Ave, PO Box 836, 28017. SAN 312-7508. Tel: 704-406-4290. FAX: 704-406-4623. Web Site: www.library.gardner-webb.edu. *Dir*, Valerie M Parry; Tel: 704-406-4293, E-Mail: vparry@gardner-webb.edu; *ILL*, Karen Bowen; Tel: 704-406-3883, E-Mail: kbowen@gardner-webb.edu; *Publ Servs*, Mary Parsons; E-Mail: mparsons@gardner-webb.edu; *Publ Servs*, Mary Thompson; Tel: 704-406-4294, E-Mail: mthompson@gardner-webb.edu; *AV*, Margaret Christopher; Tel: 704-406-4291, E-Mail: mchristopher@gardner-webb.edu; *Govt Doc*, Carolyn Hunt; Tel: 704-406-4290, E-Mail: chunt@gardner-webb.edu; *Cat*, Frank Newton; Tel: 704-406-4297, E-Mail: fnewton@gardner-webb.edu; *Admin Assoc*, Denise McGill; E-Mail: dmcgill@gardner-webb.edu; Staff 15 (MLS 4, Non-MLS 11)
Founded 1928. Enrl 3,200; Highest Degree: Master
Jul 1999-Jun 2000 Income Parent Institution $644,430. Mats Exp $186,890, Books $70,767, Per/Ser (Incl. Access Fees) $72,319, Micro $35,291. Sal $308,808 (Prof $159,311)
Library Holdings: Bk Vols 217,000; Bk Titles 208,000; Per Subs 4,200
Subject Interests: Religion
Special Collections: Thomas Dixon Coll; Washburn Baptist Curriculum Laboratory Coll
Automation Activity & Vendor Info: (Acquisitions) Innovative Interfaces Inc.; (Cataloging) Innovative Interfaces Inc.; (Circulation) Innovative Interfaces Inc.; (OPAC) Innovative Interfaces Inc.; (Serials) Innovative Interfaces Inc.
Database Vendor: CARL, Ebsco - EbscoHost, OCLC - First Search, ProQuest, Silverplatter Information Inc.
Partic in Metrolina Libr Asn; Mountain College Libr Network

BOONE

C APPALACHIAN STATE UNIVERSITY, Carol Grotnes Belk Library, Appalachian State University, 325 College St, 28608. SAN 354-5199. Tel: 828-262-2186. FAX: 828-262-3001. Web Site: www.library.appstate.edu. *Dir*, Mary Reichel; Tel: 828-262-2188, E-Mail: reichelml@appstate.edu; *Assoc Dir*, Larry Boyer; *Circ, ILL*, Catherine Wilkinson; Tel: 828-262-2774, E-Mail: wilkinsncl@appstate.edu; *Cat*, Amy Weiss; Tel: 828-262-2087, E-Mail: weissak@appstate.edu; *Publ Servs*, Ann Viles; Tel: 828-262-2769, E-Mail: vilesea@appstate.edu; *Automation Syst Coordr*, Lynne Lysiak; Tel: 828-262-2794, E-Mail: lysiakld@appstate.edu; *Coll Develop*, John Abbott; Tel: 828-262-2821, E-Mail: abbottjp@appstate.edu; *Ser*, Eleanor Cook; Tel: 828-262-2786, E-Mail: cookei@appstate.edu; *Govt Doc*, Virginia Branch; Tel: 828-262-4966, E-Mail: branchvc@appstate.edu; *Spec Coll*, Pat Farthing; Tel: 828-262-2778, E-Mail: farthingsp@appstate.edu; *Spec Coll*, Fred Hay; Tel: 828-262-2887, E-Mail: hayfj@appstate.edu; *Music*, Gary Boye; Staff 70 (MLS 28, Non-MLS 42)
Founded 1903. Enrl 11,996; Highest Degree: Doctorate
Jul 1999-Jun 2000 Income (Main and Other College/University Libraries) $5,845,700. Mats Exp $2,341,150, Books $725,700, Per/Ser (Incl. Access Fees) $948,200, Presv $43,150, Micro $150,700, Other Print Mats $7,800, Electronic Ref Mat (Incl. Access Fees) $465,600. Sal $2,190,750 (Prof $1,238,500)
Library Holdings: Bk Vols 780,111; Bk Titles 527,007; Per Subs 9,687
Subject Interests: Education
Special Collections: Appalachian Mountains Regional Materials
Automation Activity & Vendor Info: (Acquisitions) Innovative Interfaces Inc.; (Cataloging) Innovative Interfaces Inc.; (Circulation) Innovative Interfaces Inc.; (Course Reserve) Innovative Interfaces Inc.; (ILL) Innovative Interfaces Inc.; (Media Booking) Innovative Interfaces Inc.; (OPAC) Innovative Interfaces Inc.; (Serials) Innovative Interfaces Inc.
Database Vendor: Dialog, Ebsco - EbscoHost, GaleNet, IAC - SearchBank, Lexis-Nexis, OCLC - First Search, ProQuest, Silverplatter Information Inc., Wilson - Wilson Web
Publications: Appalnotes (newsletter)
Partic in Western North Carolina Library Network
Friends of the Library Group
Departmental Libraries:
WILLIAM LEONARD EURY APPALACHIAN COLLECTION Tel: 828-262-4041. FAX: 828-262-2553. *Librn*, Fred Hay
Friends of the Library Group
MUSIC Tel: 828-262-2388. FAX: 828-265-8642. *Librn*, Karl Van Ausdal

M NORTHWEST AREA HEALTH EDUCATION CENTER LIBRARY AT BOONE, Watauga Medical Ctr, 336 Deerfield Rd, 28607-5008. (Mail add: PO Box 2600, 28607-2600), SAN 325-7711. Tel: 828-262-4300. FAX: 828-265-5904. E-Mail: annmc@med.unc.edu. Web Site: www.wfubmc.edu/ahec/library.html. *Coordr, Librn*, Ann McGregor; Staff 3 (MLS 1, Non-MLS 2)
Library Holdings: Bk Vols 900; Bk Titles 900; Per Subs 90
Subject Interests: Allied health, Medicine, Nursing
Partic in Boone Libr Network

P WATAUGA COUNTY PUBLIC LIBRARY, 140 Queen St, 28607. SAN 320-8338. Tel: 828-264-8784. FAX: 828-264-1794. Web Site: www.arlibrary.org. *Librn*, Rhea Hebert; *Ch Servs*, Lisa Neal; E-Mail: lisaneal55@yahoo.com; *Ref Serv Ad*, Evelyn Johnson; E-Mail: ejohnson@ncsl.dcr.state.nc.us; *Mgr Libr Serv*, Betty H Sammis; E-Mail: bsammis@ncsl.dcr.state.nc.us; *Tech Servs*, Rebecca Moore; Staff 21 (MLS 3, Non-MLS 18)
Founded 1932. Pop 42,000; Circ 259,609
2000-2001 Income $466,110, State $90,000, City $15,300, County $315,000, Locally Generated Income $45,810. Mats Exp $43,500, Books $39,500, AV Equip $4,000. Sal $260,060 (Prof $92,168)
Library Holdings: Bk Vols 62,800; Per Subs 100
Subject Interests: NC
Friends of the Library Group
Branches: 1
WESTERN WATAUGA, 1085 Old US Hwy 421, Sugar Grove, 28679. SAN 376-8120. Tel: 704-297-5515. FAX: 704-0297-5515. Web Site: www.main.nc.us/wcpl/.
Friends of the Library Group

BOONVILLE

P BOONVILLE COMMUNITY PUBLIC LIBRARY,* 110 Carolina Ave N, 27011. (Mail add: PO Box 731, 27011-0731), Tel: 336-367-4450. FAX: 336-367-4450. *Dir*, Michael Sawyer; Tel: 336-835-4894, Fax: 336-526-2270, E-Mail: msawyer@ncsl.dcr.state.nc.us; *Librn*, Barbara Ireland; *Asst Librn*, Angie Walker; Staff 2 (Non-MLS 2)
Founded 1999. Pop 3,372
Library Holdings: Bk Vols 3,000; Per Subs 20
Mem of Northwestern Regional Library
Friends of the Library Group

BREVARD

C BREVARD COLLEGE, James Addison Jones Library, 400 N Broad St, 28712-3306. SAN 312-7516. Tel: 828-884-8268. Interlibrary Loan Service Tel: 828-883-8292, Ext 2223. FAX: 828-884-5424. E-Mail: library@brevard.edu. Web Site: www.brevard.edu/library. *Dir*, Michael M McCabe; *ILL*, Brenda Spillman; *Ref*, Peggy Higgins; *Tech Servs*, Constance B Engle; Staff 3 (MLS 3)
Founded 1934. Enrl 700; Fac 61; Highest Degree: Bachelor
Jun 2000-May 2001 Income Parent Institution $302,399. Mats Exp $109,186, Books $51,421, Per/Ser (Incl. Access Fees) $22,000, Presv $3,000, Micro $8,600, AV Equip $500, Manuscripts & Archives $500, Electronic Ref Mat (Incl. Access Fees) $17,153. Sal $136,986
Library Holdings: Bk Vols 51,175; Per Subs 300
Subject Interests: Art, Ecol, Environmental studies, Methodist hist, Music, Outdoor wilderness educ, Southern lit
Automation Activity & Vendor Info: (Cataloging) DRA; (Circulation) DRA; (Course Reserve) DRA; (OPAC) DRA
Database Vendor: Ebsco - EbscoHost, GaleNet, OCLC - First Search, ProQuest, Silverplatter Information Inc., Wilson - Wilson Web
Partic in Mountain College Libr Network; NC Asn of Independence Cols & Univs; OCLC Online Computer Library Center, Inc; SE Libr Network

SR FIRST BAPTIST CHURCH, Media Center,* 122 Gaston St, 28712. SAN 329-9813. Tel: 828-883-8251. *Chair*, Mrs James Harron
Library Holdings: Bk Vols 3,860

P TRANSYLVANIA COUNTY LIBRARY,* 105 S Broad St, 28712. SAN 312-7524. Tel: 828-884-3151. FAX: 828-877-4230. Web Site: www.transylvania.lib.nc.us. *Dir*, Anna L Yount; *Asst Dir*, Lisa Sheffield; *Mgr*, Saronda Lowe; *Circ*, Barbara Newman; *Circ*, Priscilla Chamlee; *Tech Servs*, Lodema Crowell; *Ch Servs*, Suzy Greene; *ILL, YA Servs*, Marcy Thompson; *Bkmobile Coordr*, Karen Plumley; Staff 12 (MLS 4, Non-MLS 8)
Founded 1912. Pop 27,558; Circ 216,358
Jul 1997-Jun 1998 Income $535,279, State $92,988, Federal $8,818, County $433,473. Mats Exp $109,113, Books $74,905, Per/Ser (Incl. Access Fees) $9,800, Micro $6,270. Sal $334,663
Library Holdings: Bk Vols 71,387; Per Subs 254
Subject Interests: NC
Publications: Library Herald (monthly newsletter of Friends of the Library)
Partic in NC Info Network
Friends of the Library Group
Bookmobiles: 1

BRYSON CITY

P FONTANA REGIONAL LIBRARY,* 33 Fryemont Rd, 28713. SAN 312-7540. Tel: 828-488-2382. FAX: 828-488-2638. Web Site: www.main.nc.us/libraries/fontana. *Dir*, Gail O Findlay; E-Mail: gfindlay@ncsl.dcr.state.nc.us; *Coll Develop*, Jeanette Newsom; Staff 7 (MLS 7)
Founded 1944. Pop 65,000; Circ 408,200
Jul 1997-Jun 1998 Income $1,345,694, State $345,835, City $34,000, Federal $65,873, County $724,475, Locally Generated Income $74,800, Other $100,680. Mats Exp $182,025, Books $155,060, Per/Ser (Incl. Access Fees) $15,329, Micro $533. Sal $615,605 (Prof $229,370)
Library Holdings: Bk Vols 176,978

P MARIANNA BLACK LIBRARY,* 33 Fryemont Rd, 28713. SAN 312-7532. Tel: 828-488-3030. FAX: 828-488-9857. Web Site: main.nc.us/libraries/fontana. *Dir*, Beverly Means; E-Mail: bmeans@ncsl.dcr.state.nc.us
Founded 1929. Pop 12,000
1997-1998 Income $194,180, City $6,000, County $130,500, Locally Generated Income $8,710, Parent Institution $35,890, Other $13,080. Mats Exp $33,858, Books $27,943, Per/Ser (Incl. Access Fees) $2,247. Sal $92,726 (Prof $35,890)
Library Holdings: Bk Titles 44,000
Subject Interests: Genealogy
Friends of the Library Group

BUIES CREEK

C CAMPBELL UNIVERSITY, Carrie Rich Memorial Library, 191 Main St, PO Box 98, 27506-0098. SAN 312-7559. Tel: 910-893-1460. Interlibrary Loan Service Tel: 910-893-1466. Circulation Tel: 910-893-1462. Reference Tel: 910-893-1467. FAX: 910-893-1470. Web Site: camel.campbell.edu/~kwok. *Dir*, Dr Ronnie Faulkner; E-Mail: faulkner@camel.campbell.edu; *Tech Servs*, Borree Kwok; E-Mail: kwok@camel.campbell.edu; *Ref*, Berry Marie; *Ref*, Sharon Lucas; *Ser*, Rosalie Ferrell; *Circ*, Donald Strother; *ILL, Ref*, Jennifer Carpenter; E-Mail: jcarp@camel.campbel.edu; *Business*, Daniel Maynard; *Materials Manager*, Sharron Bortz; Staff 17 (MLS 7, Non-MLS 10)
Founded 1887. Enrl 3,400; Fac 150; Highest Degree: Doctorate
Jun 1999-May 2000 Income (Main and Other College/University Libraries) $1,227,500. Mats Exp $508,000, Books $181,100, Per/Ser (Incl. Access Fees) $214,300, Presv $2,000, Micro $66,300, AV Equip $2,800, Other Print Mats $1,000, Manuscripts & Archives $500, Electronic Ref Mat (Incl. Access Fees) $40,000. Sal $455,290 (Prof $225,845)
Library Holdings: Bk Vols 196,556; Bk Titles 147,000; Per Subs 782
Subject Interests: Pharmacy, Religion
Special Collections: American History (Library of American Civilization/Sabin); Trust & Estate Coll
Publications: History of Carrie Rich Memorial; Newsline (Friends Newsletter)
Partic in Mid-Carolina Academic Library Network; NC Librs for Virtual Educ; OCLC Online Computer Library Center, Inc; SE Libr Network
Friends of the Library Group
Departmental Libraries:
SCHOOL OF LAW LIBRARY, Wiggins Hall, PO Box 458, 27506-0458. SAN 321-7124. Tel: 910-893-1790. Interlibrary Loan Service Tel: 910-893-1796. Reference Tel: 910-893-1796. FAX: 910-893-1829. Web Site: webster.campbell.edu/culawlib.htm. *Librn*, Karen C Sorvari; E-Mail: sorvari@webster.campbell.edu; *Assoc Librn*, Olivia Weeks; E-Mail: weeks@webster.campbell.edu; *Cat*, Sophia Gregory; E-Mail: gregory@webster.campbell.edu; *Tech Servs*, Teresa Teague; E-Mail: teague@webster.campbell.edu; *Computer Services*, Joseph Tuttle; E-Mail: tuttle@webster.campbell.edu; Staff 9 (MLS 5, Non-MLS 4)
Founded 1976. Enrl 304; Fac 21; Highest Degree: Doctorate
Jun 1999-May 2000 Income $1,060,128, Locally Generated Income $14,682, Parent Institution $1,045,446. Mats Exp $639,048, Books $15,915, Per/Ser (Incl. Access Fees) $514,654, Presv $10,190, Electronic Ref Mat (Incl. Access Fees) $37,257. Sal $356,150 (Prof $231,372)
Library Holdings: Bk Vols 174,160; Bk Titles 16,550; Per Subs 2,559
Restriction: Open to public for reference only
Partic in Dialog Corporation; OCLC Online Computer Library Center, Inc; Westlaw

BURGAW

P PENDER COUNTY PUBLIC LIBRARY, (PCPL), 103 S Cowan St, 28425. (Mail add: PO Box 879, 28425), SAN 312-7567. Tel: 910-259-1234. FAX: 910-259-1247. Web Site: www.tlc.library.net/pender. *Dir*, Michael Taylor; E-Mail: mtaylor@ncsl.dcr.state.nc.us; *Asst Dir*, Floyd Harris; *Br Coordr*, Marsha Dees; *Circ*, Misty Horrell; *Outreach Serv*, Jamie Parris; *Ref*, Amy English; *Tech Servs*, Jamie Moore; Staff 14 (MLS 1, Non-MLS 13)
Founded 1942. Pop 40,000; Circ 185,120
Jul 1999-Jun 2000 Income $545,107. Mats Exp $497,749, Books $90,000. Sal $281,311
Library Holdings: Bk Vols 97,418; Per Subs 187
Special Collections: American Indian (Arnold Coll)
Automation Activity & Vendor Info: (Cataloging) TLC; (Circulation) TLC
Database Vendor: OCLC - First Search
Friends of the Library Group

BURLINGTON

M ALAMANCE REGIONAL MEDICAL CENTER, Medical Library,* 1240 Huffman Mill Rd, 27216. SAN 371-2850. Tel: 336-538-7574. FAX: 336-538-7571. *Librn*, Marian Blecker; E-Mail: blecmari@armc.com
1997-1998 Income $48,000. Mats Exp $30,000
Library Holdings: Bk Vols 500; Per Subs 75

S BURLINGTON TIMES-NEWS LIBRARY,* 707 S Main, 27215. SAN 375-2305. Tel: 336-227-0131. FAX: 336-229-2463.
Library Holdings: Bk Titles 100

P CENTRAL NORTH CAROLINA REGIONAL LIBRARY,* 342 S Spring St, 27215. SAN 354-5288. Tel: 336-229-3588. FAX: 336-229-3592. E-Mail: mbb@interpath.com. Web Site: ils.unc.edu/nclibs/centralnc/home.htm. *Dir*, Margaret B Blanchard; *Librn*, James Thorsen; *Tech Servs*, Martha Sink; *Ch Servs*, Julia Walker; *ILL*, Martha Way; *Ref*, Judy Clayton; *Ref*, Lisa Kobrin; Staff 9 (MLS 9)
Founded 1962. Pop 144,412
Jul 1998-Jun 1999 Mats Exp $1,783,636, Books $250,000, Per/Ser (Incl. Access Fees) $22,000. Sal $907,529
Library Holdings: Bk Vols 292,204; Per Subs 564
Subject Interests: Local history
Member Libraries: Goldston Public Library; Graham Public Library; May Memorial Library
Branches: 1
NORTH PARK, North Park Community Ctr, 849 Sharpe Rd, 27215. SAN 354-5377. Tel: 910-226-7185. *Librn*, Katrine Moore

P MAY MEMORIAL LIBRARY, 342 S Spring St, 27215. SAN 354-5342. Tel: 336-229-3588. FAX: 336-229-3592. E-Mail: mbb@interpath.com. Web Site: ils.unc.edu/nclibs/centralnc/home.htm. *Chief Librn*, James Thorsen; *Ref*, Judy Clayton; *Ref*, Lisa Kobrin; *Ch Servs*, Julia Walker; *Tech Servs*, Martha Sink
Founded 1938. Pop 145,000; Circ 260,000
Library Holdings: Bk Titles 75,583
Subject Interests: Genealogy, Local history
Mem of Central North Carolina Regional Library
Friends of the Library Group

S VIKON CHEMICAL COMPANY INC LIBRARY,* PO Box 1520, 27216-1520. SAN 375-2186. Tel: 336-226-6331. FAX: 336-222-9568. *Pres*, Kris Arnold
Library Holdings: Bk Titles 1,000

BURNSVILLE

P AVERY-MITCHELL-YANCEY REGIONAL LIBRARY SYSTEM, 237 Old Hwy 19E, PO Drawer 310, 28714. SAN 313-0037. Tel: 828-682-4476. Interlibrary Loan Service Tel: 828-682-6277. FAX: 828-682-6277. *Dir Libr Serv*, Theresa Coletta; E-Mail: tcoletta@ncsl.dcr.state.nc.us; *Mgr*, Rella B Dale; E-Mail: rdale@ncsl.dcr.state.nc.us; *Librn*, James C Byrd; *Librn for Blind*, Jane M Crowder; *Ch Servs*, Nancy Daniel; *Bkmobile Coordr*, Carolyn Burleson; *ILL*, Barbara Byrd; *ILL*, Betty McMurray; *Tech Servs*, Barbara B Whittemore; E-Mail: bwhittem@ncsl.dcr.state.nc.us; Staff 8 (MLS 2, Non-MLS 6)
Founded 1961. Pop 42,979; Circ 256,933
Jul 1999-Jun 2000 Income $786,118, State $367,443, City $50,565, Federal $12,248, County $172,666, Locally Generated Income $31,570, Other $151,626. Mats Exp $176,444, Books $159,761, Micro $5,098, AV Equip $11,585. Sal $390,195
Library Holdings: Bk Vols 181,857; Per Subs 207
Subject Interests: Local history
Special Collections: Census Records on microfilm; Genealogy Holdings; North Carolina Mineral & Geology; Precious Stones Book Coll; Video Collections for all levels
Restriction: Restricted borrowing privileges
Member Libraries: Avery County Morrison Public Library; Mitchell County Public Library; Spruce Pine Public Library; Yancey County Public Library
Partic in OCLC Online Computer Library Center, Inc; SE Libr Network
Special Services for the Blind - Bks on cassette; Large print bks
Library Services for aging, homebound & handicapped; Programs for Children & Young Adults; Summer Reading Program; Bookmobile Service
Friends of the Library Group
Bookmobiles: 1

P YANCEY COUNTY PUBLIC LIBRARY,* 18 Town Sq, 28714. SAN 312-7575. Tel: 828-682-2600. FAX: 828-682-6277. *Librn*, Melanie Stallings; E-Mail: mstallings@ncsl.dcr.state.nc.us; *Asst Librn*, Frankie Murphy
Pop 14,955
1998-1999 Income $167,135. Mats Exp Books $4,000. Sal $51,243
Library Holdings: Bk Vols 40,000
Subject Interests: Genealogy, Local history, NC
Mem of Avery-Mitchell-Yancey Regional Library System
Library services for the aging, homebound & handicapped; Bookmobile Service; Programs for children & young adults; Inter-Library Loan Service (OCLC); Summer Reading Program; Public Access Internet

BUTNER

M JOHN UMSTEAD HOSPITAL, Learning Resource Center, 1003 12th St, 27509. SAN 371-179X. Tel: 919-575-7259. FAX: 919-575-6322. *Dir*, Lisa Dendy; E-Mail: lisa.dendy@ncmail.net
Library Holdings: Bk Vols 2,000; Per Subs 48

CAMP LEJEUNE

A UNITED STATES MARINE CORPS, Harriotte B Smith Library, Bldg 1220, 1401 West Rd, 28547-2539. SAN 354-5466. Tel: 910-451-5724. FAX: 910-451-1871. E-Mail: lejblib@internet.net. *Librn*, Martha Spencer; *Cat*, Darrel Hoerle; *Ref*, Linda Hopkins; Staff 23 (MLS 4, Non-MLS 19)
Founded 1942
Oct 1998-Sep 1999 Mats Exp $109,627, Books $63,460, Per/Ser (Incl. Access Fees) $46,167. Sal $620,000 (Prof $160,000)
Library Holdings: Bk Titles 140,700; Per Subs 308
Subject Interests: Military history
Bookmobiles: 2

UNITED STATES NAVY
AM MEDICAL LIBRARY, Naval Hospital, PO Box 10100, 28547. SAN 354-5490. Tel: 910-450-4076. FAX: 910-450-4077.
Founded 1942
Library Holdings: Bk Vols 1,000; Per Subs 100
Subject Interests: Medicine, Sci

CARTHAGE

P MOORE COUNTY PUBLIC,* 101 Saunders St, 28327. (Mail add: PO Box 400, 28327), SAN 312-7591. Tel: 910-947-5335. *Dir*, Mark McGrath
Pop 60,000
Library Holdings: Bk Vols 73,000; Per Subs 101
Subject Interests: Genealogy, Local history
Mem of Sandhill Regional Library System

CARY

S LORD CORP, Research Center Library,* 110 Lord Dr, 27511-7900. SAN 328-2465. Tel: 919-469-2500. FAX: 919-469-5915. Web Site: www.internal.lord.com/library/home.html. *Librn*, Pamela Lacy; E-Mail: pamela_lacey@lord.com; Staff 2 (MLS 1, Non-MLS 1)
Library Holdings: Bk Titles 2,800; Per Subs 200
Subject Interests: Chemistry, Engineering, Polymer chemistry
Special Collections: Audio-visuals, Rpts
Partic in SE Libr Network

CHAPEL HILL

S CAROLINA LIBRARY SERVICES, INC LIBRARY,* 303 N Columbia St, 27516-2119. SAN 324-5039. Tel: 919-929-4870. FAX: 919-933-1253. E-Mail: carolib@intrex.net. Web Site: www.intrex.net/carolib. *Librn, Online Servs*, Kate Millard; *Doc*, Rick Oxendine; Staff 8 (MLS 3, Non-MLS 5)
Founded 1977
Library Holdings: Bk Titles 3,000; Per Subs 10
Subject Interests: Biotechnology, Medicine

S CAROLINA POPULATION CENTER LIBRARY, University of North Carolina at Chapel Hill, 123 W Franklin St, 27516-2524. SAN 312-7621. Tel: 919-962-3081. FAX: 919-962-7217. E-Mail: cpclib@unc.edu. Web Site: www.cpc.unc.edu/services/infoserv/library.html. *Assoc Dir, Info Res*, Judy Dye; Tel: 919-968-8188, E-Mail: judy_dye@unc.edu; *Tech Servs*, Cheryl Ward; Tel: 919-962-3006, E-Mail: cheryl_ward@unc.edu; *Ref*, Laurie Leadbetter; E-Mail: laurie_leadbetter@unc.edu; *Ref*, MaryJane Hill; Staff 3 (MLS 3)
Founded 1967. Highest Degree: Doctorate
Library Holdings: Bk Titles 9,300; Per Subs 375
Subject Interests: Adolescent sexuality, Demography, Developing countries, Family planning, Human sexual behavior, Pop, Pregnancy
Special Collections: Area Files, rpts, papers; Reprint File, rpts & papers
Automation Activity & Vendor Info: (OPAC) DRA
Database Vendor: CARL, DRA, Ebsco - EbscoHost, Lexis-Nexis, OCLC - First Search, OVID Technologies, Silverplatter Information Inc.
Publications: In-house documentation for the Internet & other automated services
Function: Research library
Partic in Dialog Corporation; Medline; SDC Info Servs

P CHAPEL HILL PUBLIC LIBRARY,* 100 Library Dr, 27514. SAN 312-763X. Tel: 919-968-2777. FAX: 919-968-2838. *Dir*, Kathleen L Thompson; *Ref*, Jane L Dyer; *Ref*, Susan H McClure; *Ch Servs*, Karen Michaels; *Tech Servs*, M J Goodrum; *Publ Servs*, Mark S Bayles; *Acq*, Stacy Hagerty; Staff 7 (MLS 7)
Founded 1958. Pop 37,000; Circ 427,609

Library Holdings: Bk Vols 110,000; Bk Titles 90,000; Per Subs 150
Automation Activity & Vendor Info: (Cataloging) Innovative Interfaces Inc.; (Circulation) Innovative Interfaces Inc.
Friends of the Library Group

SR CHAPEL OF THE CROSS EPISCOPAL LIBRARY, 304 E Franklin St, 27514. SAN 375-054X. Tel: 919-929-2193. FAX: 919-933-9187. *Librn*, K T Vaughan
Library Holdings: Bk Vols 3,000
Restriction: Non-circulating to the public
Open Mon-Fri 9-5

M OFFICE OF THE MEDICAL EXAMINER, Forensic Library,* 27599-7580. SAN 312-7648. Tel: 919-966-2253. FAX: 919-962-6263.
Library Holdings: Bk Vols 1,000
Subject Interests: Forensic medicine

M SOUTHEAST INSTITUTE FOR GROUP & FAMILY THERAPY LIBRARY,* 103 Edwards Ridge Rd, 27514. SAN 375-0701. Tel: 919-929-1171. FAX: 919-929-1174. *Pres*, Vann Joines
Library Holdings: Bk Vols 500

C UNIVERSITY OF NORTH CAROLINA AT CHAPEL HILL, Walter Royal Davis Library, CB 3900, 27514-8890. SAN 354-5520. Tel: 919-962-1301 (Admin). Interlibrary Loan Service Tel: 919-962-0077. Circulation Tel: 919-962-1053. Reference Tel: 919-962-1151. TDD: 919-962-5108. FAX: 919-843-8936 (Admin), 919-962-0484 (Pub Servs). Interlibrary Loan Service FAX: 919-962-4451. Web Site: www.lib.unc.edu. *Dir*, Joe A Hewitt; E-Mail: joe_hewitt@unc.edu; *Access Serv*, Patrick J Mullin; E-Mail: mullin@email.unc.edu; *Bibliog Instr*, Paula Hinton; Tel: 919-962-1151, Fax: 919-962-4451, E-Mail: hinton@refstaff.lib.unc.edu; *Bibliog Instr*, Gary Momenee; Tel: 919-962-1355, Fax: 919-962-2697, E-Mail: momenee@email.unc.edu; *Circ*, Mitchell Whichard; Tel: 919-962-1053, Fax: 919-962-0484, E-Mail: mlwhicha@email.unc.edu; *Electronic Resources*, Donna Cornick; Tel: 919-962-1151, Fax: 919-962-4451, E-Mail: cornick@refstaff.lib.unc.edu; *ILL*, Michelle Neal; Fax: 919-962-4451, E-Mail: michelle_neal@unc.edu; *Publ Servs*, Diane Strauss; E-Mail: dstrauss@email.unc.edu; *Rare Bks*, Charles McNamara; Tel: 919-962-1143, Fax: 919-962-4452, E-Mail: cbmcnama@email.unc.edu; *Head Ref*, Carol Tobin; Tel: 919-962-1356, Fax: 919-962-4451, E-Mail: cmtobin@email.unc.edu; *Syst Coordr*, Will Owen; Tel: 919-962-1288, E-Mail: owen@email.unc.edu; *Bibliogr*, Teresa Chapa; Tel: 919-962-1095, Fax: 919-962-4450, E-Mail: tchapa@email.unc.edu; *Cat*, Sylvia Buckner; Fax: 919-962-4450, E-Mail: sbuckner@email.unc.edu. Subject Specialists: *English (language)*, Patricia Dominguez; *Manuscripts*, Lynn Holdzkom; *Manuscripts*, Tim Pyatt; *Maps*, Celia Pratt; *North Carolina*, Robert G Anthony, Jr; *Slavic history and literature*, Nadia Zilper; *Social sciences and issues*, Luke Swindler; Staff 328 (MLS 134, Non-MLS 194)
Founded 1789. Enrl 26,554; Fac 2,601; Highest Degree: Doctorate
Jul 1999-Jun 2000 Income (Main and Other College/University Libraries) $27,352,032. Mats Exp $9,605,761, Books $2,724,369, Per/Ser (Incl. Access Fees) $5,017,364. Sal $12,034,476 (Prof $6,383,792)
Library Holdings: Bk Vols 5,132,649; Per Subs 44,576
Special Collections: North Carolina History (North Caroliniana), Southern Historical Coll; Rare Book Coll
Database Vendor: DRA
Publications: Library Notes; Windows (FOL Newsletter)
Partic in Asn of Research Libraries; Center For Research Libraries; OCLC Online Computer Library Center, Inc; SE Libr Network
Friends of the Library Group
Departmental Libraries:

ACQUISITIONS, CB No 3902, 27514-8890. SAN 354-5539. Tel: 919-962-1120. FAX: 919-962-4450. *Acq*, Janet Flowers; E-Mail: janet_flowers@unc.edu

BRAUER (MATH-PHYSICS), 365 Phillips Hall, CB No 3250, 27599. SAN 354-5733. Tel: 919-962-2323. FAX: 919-962-2568. *Librn*, Zahra Kamarei; E-Mail: zkamarei@email.unc.edu
Library Holdings: Bk Vols 87,680
Partic in BRS; Dialog Corporation; SDC Search Serv

CHAPIN (CITY & REGIONAL PLANNING), New East, CB No 3140, 27599. SAN 354-5792. Tel: 919-962-3983. FAX: 919-962-5206. *Librn*, Linda Drake; E-Mail: ldrake.dcrp@mhs.unc.edu
Library Holdings: Bk Vols 14,148

COUCH BIOLOGY (BOTANY SECTION), 301 A Coker Hall, CB No 3280, 27599. SAN 354-561X. Tel: 919-962-3783. FAX: 919-962-1625. *Librn*, William Burk; E-Mail: wrburk@uncvm1.oit.unc.edu
Library Holdings: Bk Vols 37,298

COUCH BIOLOGY (ZOOLOGY SECTION), 213 Wilson Hall, CB No 3280, 27599. SAN 354-5822. Tel: 919-962-2264. FAX: 919-962-1625. *Librn*, David Romito; E-Mail: dromito@email.unc.edu
Library Holdings: Bk Vols 33,045

GEOLOGICAL SCIENCES, 120 Mitchell Hall, CB No 3315, 27599. SAN 354-5679. Tel: 919-962-2386. E-Mail: uncmls@unc.oit.unc.edu. *Librn*, Miriam Kennard; E-Mail: miriam_kennard@unc.edu
Library Holdings: Bk Vols 45,190

CM HEALTH SCIENCES, Campus Box 7585, 27599-7585. SAN 354-5857. Tel: 919-966-2111. Interlibrary Loan Service Tel: 919-966-4998. FAX: 919-966-1029. Web Site: www.hsl.unc.edu. *Dir*, Carol G Jenkins; E-Mail: cjenkins@med.unc.edu; Staff 24 (MLS 24)
Founded 1952. Highest Degree: Doctorate
Jul 1999-Jun 2000 Income $5,260,776. Mats Exp $1,859,790, Books $161,799, Per/Ser (Incl. Access Fees) $1,421,641. Sal $2,192,625 (Prof $1,265,920)
Library Holdings: Bk Vols 316,125; Per Subs 3,723
Subject Interests: Allied health, AV, Curriculum software, Dentistry, Medicine, Nursing, Pharmacy, Public health, Rare books
Automation Activity & Vendor Info: (Cataloging) DRA; (Circulation) DRA
Publications: Annual report; brochures; Friends Newsletter; News & Views Newsletter
Partic in National Network Of Libraries Of Medicine - South Central Region; OCLC Online Computer Library Center, Inc; SE Libr Network; Triangle Research Libraries Network
Friends of the Library Group

HIGHWAY SAFETY RESEARCH CENTER, 730 Airport Rd, CB No 3430, 27599. SAN 312-7656. Tel: 919-962-8701. FAX: 919-962-8710. Web Site: www.unc.edu/depts/hsrc/. *Librn*, Mary Ellen Tucker; Staff 3 (MLS 1, Non-MLS 2)
Founded 1970
Library Holdings: Bk Vols 81,136
Subject Interests: Alcohol, Bicycle, Cycle fac design, Driver behav, Driver educ, Evaluation of hwy safety progs, Licensing, Motorcycle safety, Pedestrian, Pedestrian safety, Restraint systs, Seatbelt, Traffic records, Traffic safety
Publications: Bibliography of Research Publications, 1963-1997; Catalog of Audiovisual Holdings, 1996
Restriction: Open to public for reference only
Partic in OCLC Online Computer Library Center, Inc; OCLC Transportation Access Group

ROBERT B HOUSE UNDERGRADUATE, CB No 3942, 27514-8890. SAN 354-5555. Tel: 919-962-1355. FAX: 919-962-2697. Web Site: www.lib.unc.edu/house/index.html. *Librn*, David Taylor; E-Mail: taylodc@email.unc.edu
Library Holdings: Bk Vols 81,136
Partic in TRLN

INFORMATION & LIBRARY SCIENCE, 114 Manning Hall, CB No 3360, 27599. SAN 354-5709. Tel: 919-962-8361. FAX: 919-962-8071. E-Mail: library@ils.unc.edu. Web Site: ils.unc.edu/ils/library.; Staff 2 (MLS 1, Non-MLS 1)
Founded 1931
Library Holdings: Bk Vols 85,790
Subject Interests: Children's literature, Library and information science
Automation Activity & Vendor Info: (Circulation) DRA; (OPAC) DRA

INSTITUTE OF GOVERNMENT, Knapp Bldg, CB No 3330, 27599-3330. SAN 354-5687. Tel: 919-966-4172. FAX: 919-966-4762. E-Mail: library@iogmail.iog.unc.edu. Web Site: www.ncinfo.iog.unc.edu/library/. *Librn*, Alex Hess, III; E-Mail: hess@iogmail.iog.unc.edu
Library Holdings: Bk Vols 15,760

JOSEPH CURTIS SLOANE ART LIBRARY, 102 Hanes Art Ctr, CB No 3405, 27599. SAN 354-558X. Tel: 919-962-2397. FAX: 919-962-0722. Web Site: www.lib.unc.edu/art/index.html/. *Librn*, Patricia Thompson; E-Mail: patt@unc.edu
Library Holdings: Bk Vols 92,886

KENAN (CHEMISTRY), 269 Venable, CB No 3290, 27599. SAN 354-5644. Tel: 919-962-1188. FAX: 919-962-2388. E-Mail: uchlib@unc.oit.unc.edu. *Librn*, Jimmy Dickerson; E-Mail: tjd@email.unc.edu
Library Holdings: Bk Vols 54,655
Special Collections: F P Venable Rare Book Coll
Partic in Dialog Corporation

L LAW LIBRARY, UNC Law School, CB No 3385, 100 Ridge Rd, 27599. SAN 354-5695. Tel: 919-962-1321. FAX: 919-962-1193. Web Site: www.library.law.unc.edu. *Dir*, Laura N Gasaway; E-Mail: unclng@email.unc.edu; *Tech Servs*, Carol A Nicholson; *Publ Servs*, Anne Klinefelter
Jul 1999-Jun 2000 Income $2,233,161. Mats Exp $1,053,511, Books $97,420, Per/Ser (Incl. Access Fees) $885,402. Sal $852,326 (Prof $532,726)
Library Holdings: Bk Vols 303,895; Per Subs 6,342
Subject Interests: Law
Database Vendor: Dialog, DRA, IAC - SearchBank, Lexis-Nexis, OCLC - First Search
Publications: LLUNCCH Times (monthly newsletter) (Newsletter)
Partic in Consortium Of South Eastern Law Libraries; OCLC Online Computer Library Center, Inc; TRLN

MUSIC, 106 Hill Hall CB No 3320, 27599. SAN 354-5768. Tel: 919-966-1113. FAX: 919-962-3376. Web Site: www.lib.unc.edu/music.
Library Holdings: Bk Vols 120,654

SERIALS ACQUISITIONS, CB No 3938, 27514-8890. SAN 377-6980. Tel: 919-962-1067. FAX: 919-962-4450. *In Charge*, Cyndie Cowan; E-Mail: cowanc@email.unc.edu

CHARLOTTE

J CENTRAL PIEDMONT COMMUNITY COLLEGE LIBRARY,* 1201 Elizabeth Ave, PO Box 35009, 28235. SAN 312-7680. Tel: 704-330-6041. Interlibrary Loan Service Tel: 704-330-6884. FAX: 704-330-6887. Web Site: www.cpcc.cc.nc.us/library/home.htm. *Dir*, Susan Melson; *ILL*, Calvin Craig; *Ref*, Margie Orell; *Cat*, Carol Lillard; *Acq*, Martha Taylor
Founded 1963
Jul 1997-Jun 1998 Income $1,192,012. Mats Exp $343,811, Books $95,178, Per/Ser (Incl. Access Fees) $128,613, Presv $2,648, AV Equip $90,000. Sal $738,832 (Prof $574,358)
Library Holdings: Bk Vols 99,109; Per Subs 4,350
Publications: Periodicals holdings; search guides

M CHARLOTTE AHEC, Information Resource Center, 1000 Blythe Blvd, 28203. SAN 312-7818. Tel: 704-355-3129. FAX: 704-355-3116. E-Mail: irc@cltahec.org. Web Site: www.cltahec.org. *Dir*, Leonora Kaufman; *Ref*, Larry Keesee
Founded 1909
Library Holdings: Bk Titles 6,000; Per Subs 520
Subject Interests: Allied health, Clinical medicine, Nursing
Publications: Annual Report
Partic in Dialog Corporation; Nat Libr of Med

P CHARLOTTE MECKLENBURG SCHOOLS, Curriculum Research Center Library,* 428 W Boulevard, 28203. SAN 325-7770. Tel: 704-343-5366. FAX: 704-343-5408. *Librn*, Barbara Waymer; *Tech Servs*, Barbara Epps; *Tech Servs*, Dondra Kinard
Jul 1997-Jun 1998 Income $31,300, County $27,615, Parent Institution $3,685. Mats Exp $32,000, Books $10,300, Per/Ser (Incl. Access Fees) $12,500, Micro $7,000. Sal $94,000 (Prof $46,000)
Library Holdings: Bk Vols 15,300; Bk Titles 1,400; Per Subs 250
Subject Interests: Education
Special Collections: Curriculum Library (KRAUS); ERIC
Professional library for school system

S CHARLOTTE MUSEUM OF HISTORY, Hezekiah Alexander Homesite - Lassiter Research Library, 3500 Shamrock Dr, 28215. SAN 325-7592. Tel: 704-568-1774. FAX: 704-566-1817. *Dir*, William Massey
Library Holdings: Bk Vols 3,500; Bk Titles 3,000; Per Subs 10
Special Collections: Alexander Geneology (Hez Alexander)

S CHARLOTTE OBSERVER LIBRARY, 600 S Tryon, PO Box 30308, 28230-0308. SAN 312-7788. Tel: 704-358-5212. FAX: 704-358-5203. *Mgr*, Marion Paynter; E-Mail: mpaynter@charlotte.observer.com; *Librn*, Sara Klemmer. Subject Specialists: *Photos*, Ann Bryant
Founded 1956
Library Holdings: Bk Vols 2,000
Partic in Dialog Corporation

R CHRIST EPISCOPAL CHURCH LIBRARY,* 1412 Providence Rd, PO Box 6124, 28207. SAN 312-7710. Tel: 704-333-0378. FAX: 704-333-8420. *Librn*, Elizabeth Preston
1999-2000 Income $1,250
Library Holdings: Bk Vols 2,425

S CLARIANT CORP, Corporate Information Center, 4331 Chesapeake Dr, 28216. SAN 312-7796. Tel: 704-395-6750. FAX: 704-395-6777. *Librn*, Jaqueline N Kirkman; Staff 1 (MLS 1)
Founded 1964
Library Holdings: Bk Vols 3,000; Per Subs 65
Subject Interests: Dye chem, Organic chemistry, Surfactants
Partic in Dialog Corporation; Nat Libr of Med, STN

DUKE ENERGY CORP

S DAVID NABOW LIBRARY, 526 S Church St, MC EC06H, PO Box 1006, 28201-1006. SAN 354-5946. Tel: 704-382-4095. FAX: 704-382-7826. *Librn*, Audrey W Caldwell; Tel: 704-382-5147, E-Mail: awcaldwe@duke-energy.com; Staff 2 (MLS 1, Non-MLS 1)
Founded 1967
Library Holdings: Bk Titles 50,000; Per Subs 200
Subject Interests: Automation, Bus, Civil, Electrical, Environ, Humanities, Mechanical, Mgt, Nuclear engineering, Soc sci, Technology
Special Collections: Standards (ANSI, NEMA, IEEE, EPRI, INPO)
Database Vendor: epixtech, inc.

L LEGAL DEPARTMENT LAW LIBRARY, PO Box 1244, 28201-1244. SAN 354-5970. Tel: 704-382-8138. FAX: 704-382-8137. *In Charge*, Larry Valenti; E-Mail: isvalent@duke-energy.com
Founded 1940
Library Holdings: Bk Titles 10,000
Subject Interests: Environment, Legal, North Caroliniana, Regulatory mat
Special Collections: Administrative codes; General Statutes; Government Documents

R FIRST PRESBYTERIAN CHURCH LIBRARY, 200 W Trade St, 28202-1696. SAN 312-7737. Tel: 704-332-5123. FAX: 704-334-4135. *Librn*, Susan Higgins
Library Holdings: Bk Vols 2,800
Special Collections: Church Histories (Mecklenburg City Coll)

S H CARL ROWLAND MEMORIAL LIBRARY,* 100 N Tyron St, Ste 3500, 28202-4012. SAN 312-7877. Tel: 704-376-0291. *Librn*, Debbie Brinkley
Founded 1970
Library Holdings: Bk Titles 847
Subject Interests: Healthcare planning
Branches:
DUKE ENDOWMENT LIBRARY, 100 N Tyron St, Ste 3500, 28202-4012. Tel: 704-376-0291. *Librn*, Marilyn MacKenzie

C JOHNSON C SMITH UNIVERSITY, James B Duke Memorial Library, 100 Beatties Ford Rd, 28216. SAN 312-7753. Tel: 704-371-6730. Interlibrary Loan Service Tel: 704-371-6732. Circulation Tel: 704-371-6731. Reference Tel: 704-371-6732. FAX: 704-378-3524. Web Site: www.jcsu.edu. *Dean*, Inja Hong; E-Mail: ihong@jcsu.edu; *Ref*, Jenna Duncan; *Electronic Resources, Ser*, Retha Hall; *Coll Develop, Syst Coordr*, Faye Priestly; *Circ*, Helen Holbert; E-Mail: hholbert@jcsu.edu; *Cat*, Barbara Carr; *Acq*, Gloria Russell; *Media Spec*, William Goodson; *Archivist*, David Cook; *Archivist*, Monika Rhue; *Ser*, Erin White; Staff 14 (MLS 7, Non-MLS 7)
Founded 1867. Pop 2,000; Fac 100; Highest Degree: Bachelor
Library Holdings: Bk Vols 114,146; Bk Titles 83,599; Per Subs 328
Special Collections: Black Life & Literature (Schomburg Coll), microfilm; Earl A Johnson Coll (Black Studies & Judaica & Art); Economics Governmental History (Calvin Hoover Coll); History & Governmental Biography (Neimeyer Coll)
Database Vendor: Innovative Interfaces INN - View
Partic in Innopac; NC Ctr for Independent Higher Educ; NC LIVE

L KENNEDY, COVINGTON, LOBDELL & HICKMAN, Law Library,* Nations Bank Corporate Ctr, 28202-4006. SAN 372-2104. Tel: 704-331-7482. FAX: 704-331-7598. *Librn*, Joyce Pritchard Furst
Library Holdings: Bk Vols 14,000; Per Subs 100

GM MECKLENBURG COUNTY HEALTH DEPARTMENT LIBRARY,* 249 Billingsley Rd, 28211. SAN 312-780X. Tel: 704-336-3354. FAX: 704-336-4714. Web Site: www.charweb.org/health/healthdept/hd.html.
Founded 1959. Pop 480,000
Library Holdings: Bk Vols 800; Per Subs 12

L MECKLENBURG COUNTY LAW & GOVERNMENT LIBRARY,* 700 E Trade St, 28202-3076. SAN 312-7699. Tel: 704-336-7359. FAX: 704-336-7935. *Librn*, Joyce Reimann
Founded 1991
1997-1998 Income $187,000. Mats Exp $151,000. Sal $75,000
Library Holdings: Bk Vols 30,000; Per Subs 28
Subject Interests: Legal
Partic in Westlaw

M MERCY SCHOOL OF NURSING LIBRARY, 1921 Vail Ave, 28207. SAN 312-7826. Tel: 704-379-5845. *Librn*, Roseanne Gilbert; Staff 2 (MLS 1, Non-MLS 1)
Founded 1906. Enrl 125; Fac 14; Highest Degree: Bachelor
Library Holdings: Bk Vols 4,327; Bk Titles 3,739; Per Subs 49
Subject Interests: Medicine, Nursing
Restriction: Open to student, faculty & staff

S MINT MUSEUM LIBRARY,* 2730 Randolph Rd, 28207. SAN 326-4599. Tel: 704-337-2000, 704-337-2023. FAX: 704-337-2101. Web Site: ww.mintmuseum.org. *Librn*, Sara H Wolf
Library Holdings: Bk Vols 9,000; Per Subs 122
Subject Interests: Fine arts
Special Collections: Decorative Arts (emphasis on ceramics)

L MOORE & VAN ALLEN PLLC, Law Library, Bank of America Corporate Ctr, 100 N Tryon, 47th Flr, 28202. SAN 372-235X. Tel: 704-331-1000. FAX: 704-331-1159. *Librn*, Melanie Snow; E-Mail: melaniesnow@mvalaw.com
Library Holdings: Bk Vols 10,500; Per Subs 61

§C PFEIFFER UNIVERSITY LIBRARY, 4701 Park Rd, 28209. SAN 375-4324. Tel: 704-521-9116. FAX: 704-521-8617. Web Site: ibrary.pfeiffer.edu. *Dir Info Resources & Res*, Beth Zeiss; E-Mail: bzeiss@pfeiffer.edu; Staff 2 (MLS 1, Non-MLS 1)
Highest Degree: Master
Jul 1999-Jun 2000 Income $69,000. Mats Exp $29,000, Books $25,000, Per/Ser (Incl. Access Fees) $4,000. Sal $40,000
Library Holdings: Bk Vols 6,563; Bk Titles 5,701; Per Subs 30
Subject Interests: Accounting, Bus admin, Christian educ, Criminal justice, Health administration, Info scis, Liberal arts, Organizational mgt
Automation Activity & Vendor Info: (Acquisitions) Endeavor; (Cataloging) Endeavor; (Circulation) Endeavor; (Course Reserve) Endeavor; (OPAC) Endeavor; (Serials) Endeavor
Database Vendor: Ebsco - EbscoHost, IAC - Info Trac, OCLC - First Search, ProQuest

S PREMIER INC, Corporate Resource Center,* 2320 Cascade Point Blvd No 106, 28208. (Mail add: PO Box 668800, 28266), SAN 324-7708. Tel: 704-357-0022. FAX: 704-357-6611. *Mgr*, T Joan Crouze; E-Mail: joan_crouze@premierinc.com; *Res*, Joyce White

Founded 1980
Library Holdings: Bk Vols 6,800; Bk Titles 6,500; Per Subs 400
Subject Interests: Health, Hospitals, Managed care mgt, Physician mgmt safety, Technology
Publications: Newsletter

M PRESBYTERIAN HOSPITAL, Learning Resource Center, 200 Hawthorne Lane, PO Box 33549, 28233-3549. SAN 312-7869. Tel: 704-384-4258. FAX: 704-384-5058. E-Mail: lrc@novanthealth.org. *Librn*, Mary Wallace Berry; *Media Spec*, William Barfield
Library Holdings: Bk Vols 6,500; Per Subs 315
Subject Interests: Medicine, Nursing
Automation Activity & Vendor Info: (Cataloging) EOS; (Circulation) EOS; (OPAC) EOS; (Serials) EOS
Database Vendor: OCLC - First Search, OVID Technologies

P PUBLIC LIBRARY OF CHARLOTTE & MECKLENBURG COUNTY, (PLCMC), 310 N Tryon St, 28202-2176. SAN 354-6039. Tel: 704-336-2801. FAX: 704-336-2677. Interlibrary Loan Service FAX: 704-336-2002. Web Site: www.plcmc.lib.nc.us. *Exec Dir*, Robert E Cannon; *Dep Dir*, Judith K Sutton; *Publ Servs*, Carol Myers; *Ref*, Susan Land; *AV*, Sam Shapiro; *Doc*, Mimi Curlee; *Coll Develop*, Cindy Miles; *Coll Develop*, Alice Peery; *ILL*, David Waters; *YA Servs*, Tony Tallent; *Automation Syst Coordr*, Orion Weber; *Ser*, Roger Mills; *Web Coordr*, Helene Blowers; *Ch Servs*, Melanie Huggins; Staff 447 (MLS 113, Non-MLS 334)
Founded 1903. Pop 661,091; Circ 6,305,590
Jul 1999-Jun 2000 Income (Main Library and Branch Library) $23,760,512. Mats Exp $23,504,564. Sal $14,478,241
Library Holdings: Bk Vols 1,708,078; Bk Titles 443,000; Per Subs 2,906
Subject Interests: Business, Children's literature, History, Popular culture, Textiles
Special Collections: Business Management Coll; Census; Genealogy Coll; Local History Coll; Mecklenburg Research Room
Automation Activity & Vendor Info: (Acquisitions) epixtech, inc.; (Cataloging) epixtech, inc.; (Circulation) epixtech, inc.; (ILL) epixtech, inc.; (OPAC) epixtech, inc.; (Serials) epixtech, inc.
Publications: African-American Album, Vol II (CD-ROM); American Folktales, Vol 1 (CD-ROM); An African-American Album; Annual Report; Books on Tape Catalog; Directory of Clubs, Organizations; Hornet's Nest; Large Print Books-A Finding List; Novello, Ten Years of Great American Writing (anthology); Novello: Ten Years of Great American Writing (Anthology); Plum Thickets & Field Daisies; Program Notes (monthly); The Imaginative Spirit; Trapping Time Between the Branches (poetry book); Video Collection Listing
Partic in OCLC Online Computer Library Center, Inc; SE Libr Network
Motto: Libraries of Tomorrow, Today
Friends of the Library Group
Branches: 30
BEATTIES FORD ROAD LIBRARY & LEARNING RESOURCE CENTER, 2412 Beatties Ford Rd, 28216. SAN 377-5968. Tel: 704-336-2882. Web Site: www.plcmc.lib.nc.us/branch/bfr./bfr.htm. *Mgr*, Myriette Ekechukwu; Staff 15 (MLS 3, Non-MLS 12)
Founded 1957
Library Holdings: Bk Vols 54,017
Special Collections: African-American Resource Coll
BELMONT CENTER, 700 Parkwood Ave, 28205. SAN 354-6098. Tel: 704-374-2470. Web Site: www.plcmc.lib.nc.us/branch/Belmont/bc.html. *Mgr*, Kutricia Spann; Staff 2 (MLS 1, Non-MLS 1)
Founded 1975
Library Holdings: Bk Vols 20,539
CARMEL, 6624 Walsh Blvd, 28226. SAN 325-4291. Tel: 704-542-0401. Web Site: www.plcmc.lib.nc.us/branch/carmel/carmel.htm. *Mgr*, Charles Williams; Staff 8 (MLS 1, Non-MLS 7)
Founded 1985
Library Holdings: Bk Vols 61,841
CHILDREN'S, 310 N Tryon St, 1st flr, 28202. Tel: 704-336-2409. *Mgr*, Beth Hutchinson
Library Holdings: Bk Vols 28,704
Subject Interests: Children's literature
Special Collections: Children's Book Illustrators Coll
CIRCULATION SERVICES, 310 N Tryon St, 28202. Tel: 704-336-2572. *Mgr*, Everett Blackmon
CITY VIEW, 1516 Alleghany St, 28216. SAN 354-6519. Tel: 704-374-2721. Web Site: www.plcmc.lib.nc.us/branch/cityv/cityv.htm. *Mgr*, Monet Wallace; Staff 6 (MLS 1, Non-MLS 5)
Founded 1993
Library Holdings: Bk Vols 46,844
Special Collections: Homework Assistance Coll
CORNELIUS BRANCH, 21105 Cataweb Ave, Cornelius, 28031. SAN 354-6128. Tel: 704-655-9409. *Mgr*, Teresa Bishop
Library Holdings: Bk Vols 24,380
Currently under construction
COULWOOD, 8410 Belhaven Blvd, 28216. SAN 354-6365. Tel: 704-394-7820. Web Site: www.plcmc.lib.nc.us/branch/coulwood/cw.htm. *Mgr*, Deanna Spake; Staff 5 (MLS 1, Non-MLS 4)
Founded 1983
Library Holdings: Bk Vols 36,907
DANIELS PERIODICALS, 310 N Tryon St, 28202. Tel: 704-336-2798. FAX: 704-336-2002.
Library Holdings: Bk Vols 47,000
DAVIDSON BRANCH, 119 Main St, Davidson, 28036. SAN 354-6152. Tel: 704-892-8557. Web Site: www.plcmc.lib.nc.us/branch/dvdsn/dvdsn.htm. *Mgr*, Nancy Dishman; Staff 5 (MLS 1, Non-MLS 4)
Founded 1995
Library Holdings: Bk Vols 33,124
HICKORY GROVE, 7209 E W T Harris Blvd, 28227. SAN 328-6940. Tel: 704-563-9418. Web Site: www.plcmc.lib.nc.us/branch/hg/hg.jpg. *Mgr*, Vanessa Ramseur; Staff 7 (MLS 1, Non-MLS 6)
Founded 1986
Library Holdings: Bk Vols 61,967
INDEPENDENCE REGIONAL, 6015 Conference Dr, 28212. SAN 354-6241. Tel: 704-568-3151. Web Site: www.plcmc.lib.nc.us/branch/irl/irl.htm. *Mgr*, Lydia S Williams; Staff 26 (MLS 7, Non-MLS 19)
Founded 1996
Library Holdings: Bk Vols 102,754
L LAW & GOVERNMENT, 700 E Trade St, 28202. SAN 377-5984. Web Site: www.plcmc.lib.nc.us/branch/law/law.htm. *Mgr*, Joyce Reimann; Staff 2 (MLS 1, Non-MLS 1)
Founded 1991
Library Holdings: Bk Vols 58,475
LIBRARY BY MAIL, 310 N Tryon St, 28202. Tel: 704-336-6208. *In Charge*, Cindy Miles
MATTHEWS BRANCH, 124 W John St, Matthews, 28105. SAN 354-6276. Tel: 704-847-6691. Web Site: www.plcmc.lib.nc.us/branch/matthews/matthws/htm. *Mgr*, Debbie McWreath; Staff 5 (MLS 1, Non-MLS 4)
Founded 1985
Library Holdings: Bk Vols 43,422
MINT HILL BRANCH, 6840 Matthews-Mint Hill Rd, Mint Hill, 28227. SAN 354-6306. Tel: 704-545-3932. Web Site: www.plmc.lib.nc.us/branch/minth/mh.htm. *Mgr*, Neily Conrad; Staff 17 (MLS 6, Non-MLS 11)
Founded 1999
Library Holdings: Bk Vols 56,453
MORRISON REGIONAL LIBRARY, 7015 Morrison Blvd, 28211. SAN 354-642X. Tel: 704-336-2109. Web Site: www.plcmc.lib.nc.us/branch/morrison/morr.htm. *Mgr*, Patrice Ebert; Staff 28 (MLS 7, Non-MLS 21)
Founded 1991
Library Holdings: Bk Vols 148,162
Subject Interests: Bus
MYERS PARK, 1361 Queens Rd, 28207. SAN 354-6454. Tel: 704-336-2011. FAX: 704-336-5287. E-Mail: myerspk@plcmc.lib.nc.us. Web Site: www.plcmc.lib.nc.us. *Mgr*, Judith Abner; E-Mail: jea@plcmc.lib.nc.us; Staff 7 (MLS 1, Non-MLS 6)
Founded 1956
Library Holdings: Bk Vols 48,710
NORTH COUNTY REGIONAL, 16500 Holly Crest Lane, Huntersville, 28078. SAN 377-600X. Tel: 704-895-4020. Web Site: www.plcmc.lib.nc.us/branch/nco/nco.htm. *Mgr*, John Zika; Staff 31 (MLS 8, Non-MLS 23)
Founded 1997
Library Holdings: Bk Vols 107,774
NORTH PARK, 101 Eastway Dr, 28212. SAN 354-6489. Tel: 704-336-2469. Web Site: www.plcmc.lib.nc.us/branch/npark/np.htm. *Mgr*, Dorothy Coggins; Staff 5 (MLS 1, Non-MLS 4)
Founded 1992
Library Holdings: Bk Vols 40,884
PLAZA MIDWOOD, 2001 Commonwealth Ave, 28205. SAN 354-6187. Web Site: www.plcmc.lib.nc.us/branch/plazam/pm1.jpg. *Mgr*, Susan Lands; Staff 6 (MLS 1, Non-MLS 5)
Founded 1995
Library Holdings: Bk Vols 49,441
ROBINSON-SPANGLER CAROLINA ROOM, 310 N Tryon St, 3rd flr, 28202. Tel: 704-336-2980. *Mgr*, Chris Bates
Library Holdings: Bk Vols 54,530
Subject Interests: Family hist, Local history
Special Collections: Carolina Photograph Coll; D A Tompkins Papers; Family History Center; Harry Golden Papers; Local Government Information Coll; Martha Evans Papers; Music Archives Coll; Newspapers, microfilm; North Carolina Author Coll; Theatre Charlotte Coll
SCALEYBARK, 101 Scaleybark Rd, 28209. SAN 325-4275. Tel: 704-529-0632. Web Site: www.plcmc.lib.nc.us/branch/sclyb/sb.htm.; Staff 6 (MLS 1, Non-MLS 5)
Founded 1985
Library Holdings: Bk Vols 53,031
SOUTH COUNTY REGIONAL, 5801 Rea Rd, 28277. SAN 377-6026. Tel: 704-341-5872. Web Site: www.plcmc.lib.nc.us/branch/sco/south.htm. *Mgr*, Lois Kilkka; Staff 54 (MLS 15, Non-MLS 39)
Founded 1998
Library Holdings: Bk Vols 129,125
Subject Interests: Bus, Children's
Currently under construction
STEELE CREEK, 9124-F S Tryon St, 28273. SAN 373-7187. Tel: 704-588-4345. Web Site: www.plcmc.lib.nc.us/branch/stlcrk/stlcrk.htm. *Mgr*,

Eleanor Tomlinson; Staff 6 (MLS 1, Non-MLS 5)
Founded 1994
Library Holdings: Bk Vols 42,341
UNIVERSITY CITY REGIONAL, 301 East W T Harris Blvd, 28262. SAN 372-008X. Tel: 704-595-9828. Web Site: www.plcmc.lib.nc.us/branch/uc/uc.jpg. *Mgr*, Elaine Novak; Staff 35 (MLS 10, Non-MLS 25)
Founded 1999
Library Holdings: Bk Vols 96,475
VAN EVERY BUSINESS, SCIENCE & TECHNOLOGY, 310 N Tyron St, 2nd flr, 28202. Tel: 704-336-2798. *Mgr*, Susan Land
Library Holdings: Bk Vols 272,190; Per Subs 234
Subject Interests: Careers, Int bus, Jobs, Small bus
Special Collections: Career/Jobs Center; International Business Coll
VIRTUAL LIBRARY, 310 N Tryon St, 2nd flr, 28202. Tel: 704-336-2801.
WEIL POPULAR LIBRARY, 310 N Tryon St, 1st flr, 28202. Tel: 704-336-2798. *Mgr*, Sam Shapiro
Library Holdings: Bk Vols 37,500; Per Subs 1,200
WEST BOULEVARD, 2157 West Blvd, 28208. SAN 322-5003. Tel: 704-373-1050. Web Site: www.plcmc.lib.nc.us/branch/wb/wb.jpg. *Mgr*, Janice Blakeney; Staff 14 (MLS 4, Non-MLS 10)
Founded 1996
Library Holdings: Bk Vols 44,602

C QUEENS COLLEGE, Everett Library, 1900 Selwyn Ave, 28274-0001. SAN 354-6543. Tel: 704-337-2401. Reference Tel: 704-337-2466. FAX: 704-337-2517. Web Site: www.queens.edu/library. *Actg Dir*, Dr Carol Walker Jordan; *Ref Serv*, Lawrence D Turner; *Cat, Info Res*, Colleen Turnage; *Publ Servs*, Sally Schulte; *Publ Servs*, Quandrico Rutledge; *Acq*, Paula Brown; *Ser*, Jean Moats; *Archivist*, Jean Reed. Subject Specialists: *Budgeting*, Paula Brown; Staff 9 (MLS 4, Non-MLS 5)
Founded 1857. Enrl 1,610; Fac 120; Highest Degree: Master
Jul 2000-Jun 2001 Income Parent Institution $493,343. Mats Exp $142,959, Books $47,994, Per/Ser (Incl. Access Fees) $48,785, Micro $23,680, Electronic Ref Mat (Incl. Access Fees) $22,500. Sal $252,987 (Prof $130,553)
Library Holdings: Bk Vols 130,863; Bk Titles 94,579; Per Subs 632
Subject Interests: 18th Century Charlotte, Queen's College hist
Special Collections: Asia Coll; North Carolina Coll
Automation Activity & Vendor Info: (Acquisitions) SIRSI; (Cataloging) SIRSI; (Circulation) SIRSI; (Course Reserve) SIRSI; (ILL) SIRSI; (Media Booking) SIRSI; (OPAC) SIRSI; (Serials) SIRSI
Publications: Friends of the Library Newsletter (3 per yr); Rena Herald Newsletter
Partic in Charlotte Area Educ Consortium; SE Libr Network
Friends of the Library Group

L SMITH, HELMS, MULLISS & MOORE, Law Library,* 201 N Tryon St, PO Box 31247, 28202. SAN 323-6633. Tel: 704-343-2000. FAX: 704-334-8467. *Librn*, Susan Kaydos; Staff 3 (MLS 2, Non-MLS 1)
Library Holdings: Bk Titles 2,500; Per Subs 270
Restriction: Staff use only

R SPEIZMAN JEWISH LIBRARY AT SHALOM PARK, 5007 Providence Rd, 28226. SAN 312-7893. Tel: 704-944-6763. FAX: 704-944-6766. E-Mail: speizman_library@shalomcharlotte.org. *Librn*, Amalia Warshenbrot
Library Holdings: Bk Titles 5,000
Special Collections: Judaica Coll

S US BUREAU OF THE CENSUS, Information Services Program-Charlotte Regional Office Library, 901 Center Park Dr Ste 106, 28217-2935. SAN 325-7576. Tel: 704-344-6144. TDD: 704-344-6548. FAX: 704-344-6549. Web Site: www.census.gov/ftp/pub/rocha/www/. *In Charge*, Ken Wright; E-Mail: w.kenneth.wright@ccmail.census.gov
Library Holdings: Bk Vols 5,000

C UNIVERSITY OF NORTH CAROLINA AT CHARLOTTE, J Murrey Atkins Library, 9201 University City Blvd, 28223-0001. SAN 312-7907. Tel: 704-687-3601. Interlibrary Loan Service Tel: 704-687-2416. FAX: 704-687-3050. Web Site: www.libweb.uncc.edu/library/. *Librn*, Cynthia I Gozzi; E-Mail: cigozzi@email.uncc.edu; *Spec Coll*, Robin Brabham; *Syst Coordr*, Dan Murphy; *Media Spec*, Beverly Mitzel; *Coll Develop*, Amanda Harmon; Staff 31 (MLS 31)
Founded 1946. Enrl 14,015; Fac 905; Highest Degree: Doctorate
Library Holdings: Bk Vols 694,897; Bk Titles 498,390; Per Subs 4,996
Subject Interests: Bus, Mgt
Special Collections: 17th & 18th Century English Drama; Contemporary, Social & Political History of Charlotte & Mecklenburg County; NC state & county document
Publications: Atlis
Partic in OCLC Online Computer Library Center, Inc

CHEROKEE

S MUSEUM OF THE CHEROKEE INDIAN, Archives Library,* 589 Tsali Blvd, PO Box 1599, 28719. SAN 325-7630. Tel: 828-497-3481. FAX: 828-497-4985. Web Site: www.cherokeemuseum.org. *Archivist*, James Taylor
Library Holdings: Bk Vols 1,500

P QUALLA BOUNDARY PUBLIC LIBRARY,* Acquoni Rd, Cherokee Indian Reservation, PO Box 1839, 28719. SAN 354-6632. Tel: 828-497-9023. FAX: 828-497-9184. *Dir*, Marina Catt
Founded 1970. Pop 8,000; Circ 15,000
Library Holdings: Bk Titles 21,000; Per Subs 55
Special Collections: Native Americans (Indian Coll)

CHERRY POINT

UNITED STATES MARINE CORPS
A AIR STATION LIBRARY, Bldg 298 E Street, PSC Box 8009, 28533-0009. SAN 354-6691. Tel: 252-466-3552. FAX: 252-466-6418. Web Site: library.usmc-mccs.org. *Dir*, Suzanne L Shell; Tel: 252-466-3532, E-Mail: shells@usmc-mccs.org; *Cat*, Patti S Hall; Tel: 252-466-3584, Fax: 252-466-2476, E-Mail: hallp@usmc-mccs.org; *Ref*, Kathleen L O'Connor; Fax: 252-466-2476, E-Mail: oconnork@usmc-mccs.org; Staff 10 (MLS 3, Non-MLS 7)
Founded 1942
Library Holdings: Bk Vols 58,788; Bk Titles 50,682; Per Subs 119
Subject Interests: Mgt, Mil hist (US), Mil sci
Special Collections: Library of American Civilization, ultrafiche; New York Times 1851-present, micro
Automation Activity & Vendor Info: (Cataloging) SIRSI; (Circulation) SIRSI; (OPAC) SIRSI
Database Vendor: Ebsco - EbscoHost, ProQuest, Wilson - Wilson Web

CLINTON

J SAMPSON COMMUNITY COLLEGE LIBRARY, PO Box 318, 28329-0318. SAN 312-794X. Tel: 910-592-8081. FAX: 910-592-8048. Web Site: www.sampson.cc.nc.us. *Dir*, Robert O Hudson; E-Mail: bhudson@sampson.cc.nc.us; *AV*, Mark Rushing; Staff 2 (MLS 1, Non-MLS 1)
Founded 1966. Enrl 1,330; Fac 44
Library Holdings: Bk Titles 32,000; Per Subs 250
Publications: AV Handbook; LRC Handbook; Manual of Policies & Procedures

P SAMPSON-CLINTON PUBLIC LIBRARY, J C Holliday Memorial, 217 Graham St, 28328. SAN 354-6721. Tel: 910-592-4153. FAX: 910-590-3504. Web Site: www.sampson.cc.nc.us/publiclibrary/. *Dir*, Robin Hollingsworth; E-Mail: rhollingsworth@ncsl.dcr.state.nc.us; *Bkmobile Coordr*, Stephanie Johnson; *Bkmobile Coordr*, Carletta McCullen; *Ch Servs*, Gail Buckrham; E-Mail: gbuckrha@ncsl.dcr.state.nc.us; *ILL*, Elizabeth McCullen; E-Mail: emcculle@ncsl.dcr.state.nc.us; *Tech Servs*, Anita Boney; Staff 17 (MLS 2, Non-MLS 15)
Founded 1935. Pop 54,155; Circ 196,954
Jul 1999-Jun 2000 Income (Main Library and Branch Library) $610,629, State $134,983, City $1,000, County $449,247, Locally Generated Income $25,399. Mats Exp $105,429, Books $85,990, Per/Ser (Incl. Access Fees) $13,999. Sal $316,373 (Prof $36,324)
Library Holdings: Bk Vols 104,000; Per Subs 159
Subject Interests: Local history
Special Collections: North Carolina & Local History Coll, bks & microflm
Automation Activity & Vendor Info: (Circulation) Gaylord; (OPAC) Gaylord
Function: ILL available
Friends of the Library Group
Branches: 3
BRYAN MEMORIAL, PO Box 264, Newton Grove, 28366. SAN 354-673X. Tel: 910-594-1260. Web Site: www.sampson.cc.nc.us/publiclibrary. *Librn*, Lark Thornton
Friends of the Library Group
MIRIAM B LAMB MEMORIAL, PO Box 314, Garland, 28441. SAN 354-6780. Tel: 910-529-2441. Web Site: www.sampson.cc.nc.us/publiclibrary. *Librn*, Connie Guyton
Friends of the Library Group
ROSEBORO BRANCH, Roseboro St, PO Box 2066, Roseboro, 28382. SAN 354-6810. Tel: 910-525-5436. Web Site: www.sampson.cc.nc.us/publiclibrary. *Librn*, Deborah Dudley
Friends of the Library Group
Bookmobiles: 1

CLYDE

J HAYWOOD COMMUNITY COLLEGE, Learning Resource Center,* 185 Freedlander Dr, 28721. SAN 312-7958. Tel: 828-627-4550. FAX: 828-627-4553. Web Site: www.haywood.cc.nc.us. *Coordr*, Joyce Cooper; Tel: 828-628-4551, E-Mail: jcooper@haywood.cc.nc.us; *Librn*, Arlene Davis; E-Mail: adavis@haywood.cc.nc.us; *Librn*, Polly Anna Sloan; E-Mail: psloan@haywood.cc.nc.us; Staff 3 (MLS 2, Non-MLS 1)
Founded 1967. Enrl 1,286; Fac 59
Jul 1999-Jun 2000 Mats Exp $84,725, Books $44,367, Per/Ser (Incl. Access Fees) $7,964, Micro $14,273, AV Equip $12,146, Electronic Ref Mat (Incl. Access Fees) $2,717. Sal $123,187
Library Holdings: Bk Vols 27,171; Bk Titles 25,925; Per Subs 183
Subject Interests: Auto trades, Bldg construction, Bus admin, Computer

programming, Cosmetology, Criminal justice, Electrical installation, Electronics eng tech, Fish, Forest mgt, Machinist, Manufacturing eng tech, Med off asst, Nursing educ, Production crafts, Saw mill trades, Secretarial sci, Welding, Wildlife mgt
Special Collections: Folkmoot
Database Vendor: Ebsco - EbscoHost, epixtech, inc., OCLC - First Search, ProQuest
Function: Professional lending library
Partic in CCLINK; NC Librs for Virtual Educ; North Carolina Community College System; OCLC Online Computer Library Center, Inc

COLUMBIA

P TYRRELL COUNTY PUBLIC LIBRARY,* PO Box 540, 27925. SAN 312-7974. Tel: 252-796-3771. FAX: 252-796-1167. *Librn*, Douglas Hoffman; Staff 1 (MLS 1)
Pop 3,856; Circ 33,703
Library Holdings: Bk Vols 6,000
Subject Interests: Local history
Mem of Pettigrew Regional Library

COLUMBUS

P POLK COUNTY PUBLIC LIBRARY,* 204 Walker St, 28722. SAN 312-7982. Tel: 828-894-8721. FAX: 828-894-2761. Web Site: www.publib.polknc.org. *Dir*, Mark Pumphrey; E-Mail: pumphrey@uncecs.edu; *Bkmobile Coordr*, Rita Owens; *Tech Servs*, Sarah Bollinger; *Publ Servs*, Sharon Spurlin; Staff 6 (MLS 1, Non-MLS 5)
Founded 1960. Circ 92,604
Library Holdings: Bk Vols 39,596; Per Subs 90
Subject Interests: Genealogy, Literacy, Local history
Publications: Polk County Library Newsletter
Friends of the Library Group

CONCORD

C BARBER SCOTIA COLLEGE, Sage Memorial Library, 145 Cabarrus Ave W, 28025. SAN 312-7990. Tel: 704-789-2953. FAX: 704-789-2955. E-Mail: mhicksbarbersco@vnet.net. *Dir*, Minora Hicks; *Ref*, Darryle Albert; *Media Spec*, Haywood A Keaton; *Coordr*, Christy Woodberry; Staff 4 (MLS 2, Non-MLS 2)
Founded 1867. Enrl 750; Fac 60; Highest Degree: Bachelor
Library Holdings: Bk Vols 40,000; Per Subs 285
Subject Interests: Afro-Am
Publications: The Sageline (newsletter)

P CHARLES A CANNON MEMORIAL LIBRARY,* 27 Union St N, 28025-4793. SAN 312-8016. Tel: 704-788-3167. FAX: 704-784-3822. *Dir*, Thomas W Dillard Jr; *ILL*, *Ref*, Laurence O Hull; *Ch Servs*, Leslie Cook; *Acq*, Janet S Barbee; *Cat*, JoAnn H Gresham; *Circ*, Sandra L Sweet; Staff 5 (MLS 5)
Founded 1911. Pop 104,785
Jul 1996-Jun 1997 Income $1,467,301, State $144,561, City $357,963, County $812,363, Locally Generated Income $152,414. Mats Exp $273,022, Books $232,069, Per/Ser (Incl. Access Fees) $28,500, Presv $800, Micro $3,500. Sal $1,004,585 (Prof $257,297)
Library Holdings: Bk Vols 205,650; Per Subs 499
Special Collections: Concord & Cabarrus County History Coll; Holt Coll, original art
Automation Activity & Vendor Info: (Circulation) epixtech, inc.
Publications: Conspectus (newsletter)
Friends of the Library Group
Branches: 2
KANNAPOLIS BRANCH, 850 Mountain St, Kannapolis, 28081. SAN 325-3813. Tel: 704-938-9121. FAX: 704-938-3512. *Librn*, Beth Young
Friends of the Library Group
MT PLEASANT BRANCH, 8556 Cook St, Mount Pleasant, 28124. SAN 377-6050. Tel: 704-436-2202. FAX: 704-436-8205. *Librn*, Kate Anderson
Library Holdings: Bk Titles 9,000; Per Subs 40
Friends of the Library Group
Bookmobiles: 1

M NORTHEAST MEDICAL CENTER LIBRARY, 920 Church St N, 28025. SAN 312-8008. Tel: 704-783-1726. FAX: 704-783-1776. *Librn*, Steve Owen; *Asst Librn*, Pat Linker; Staff 2 (MLS 1, Non-MLS 1)
Founded 1979
Library Holdings: Bk Vols 6,300; Per Subs 150
Subject Interests: Allied health, Medicine, Nursing
Special Collections: Health Care & Medical Subjects, V-tapes
Partic in Medline

CONOVER

S HARTSHORN FAMILY ASSOCIATION LIBRARY, 1204 Fourth St Dr SE, 28613-1847. SAN 371-5140. Tel: 704-464-4981. FAX: 828-466-0025. Web Site: www.homepages.rootsweb.com/~hartshrn. *Librn*, Lana C Hartshorn
Founded 1985
Library Holdings: Bk Titles 292; Per Subs 20
Special Collections: Genealogy (Hartshorn Coll), bks & doc copies
Publications: Hartshorn Hotline

COVE CITY

P COVE CITY PUBLIC LIBRARY, 101 S Main St, PO Box 399, 28523. SAN 320-4995. Tel: 252-638-6363. FAX: 252-638-6363. *Librn*, Nancy Chase; *Asst Librn*, Barbara Avery
Founded 1979. Pop 600; Circ 8,020
Library Holdings: Bk Titles 5,000; Per Subs 13
Mem of Craven-Pamlico-Carteret Regional Library
Open Mon & Thurs 2-8, Tues, Wed & Fri 2-6
Friends of the Library Group

CULLOWHEE

C WESTERN CAROLINA UNIVERSITY, (NMW), Hunter Library, 28723-4012. SAN 312-8024. Tel: 828-227-7307. Interlibrary Loan Service Tel: 828-227-7274. Circulation Tel: 828-227-7485. Reference Tel: 828-227-7465. FAX: 828-227-7015. Web Site: www.wcu.edu/library. *Dir*, Bill Stahl; E-Mail: stahl@wcu.edu; *Admin Assoc*, Clarissa Fisher; Tel: 828-227-7417, E-Mail: cfisher@wcu.edu; *Archivist*, George Frizzell; Tel: 828-227-7474, E-Mail: gfrizzell@wcu.edu; *Cat*, Timothy Carstens; Tel: 828-227-7188, E-Mail: carstens@wcu.edu; *Circ*, David Duvall; E-Mail: duvall@wcu.edu; *Coll Develop*, Pongacz J Sennyey; Tel: 828-227-7357, E-Mail: psennyey@wcu.edu; *Govt Doc*, Nancy Kolenbrander; Tel: 828-227-7252, E-Mail: kolenbrander@wcu.edu; *Publ Servs*, Lorna Dorr; E-Mail: dorr@wcu.edu; *Publ Servs*, Dana Edge; Tel: 828-227-7284, E-Mail: edge@wcu.edu; *Publ Servs*, Stephen Findlay; E-Mail: sfindlay@wcu.edu; *Publ Servs*, Becky Kornegay; Tel: 828-227-7284, E-Mail: kornegay@wcu.edu; *Publ Servs*, Anita Oser; Tel: 828-227-7316, E-Mail: aoser@wcu.edu; *Publ Servs*, Elizabeth Vihnanek; Tel: 828-227-7044, E-Mail: vihnanek@wcu.edu; *Reader Servs*, Nan Watkins; E-Mail: nwatkins@wcu.edu; *Publ Servs*, Betsy Whitley; Tel: 828-227-7284, E-Mail: whitley@wcu.edu; *Ser*, Nancy Newsome; Tel: 828-227-3489, E-Mail: newsome@wcu.edu; *Syst Coordr*, Gillian Ellern; Tel: 828-227-7109, E-Mail: jellern@wcu.edu; Staff 45 (MLS 16, Non-MLS 29)
Founded 1922. Enrl 6,360; Fac 300; Highest Degree: Doctorate
Jul 1999-Jun 2000 Income $3,526,553. Mats Exp $1,776,072, Books $697,692, Per/Ser (Incl. Access Fees) $696,913, Presv $20,374, Micro $234,499, AV Equip $51,954, Other Print Mats $10,455, Manuscripts & Archives $907, Electronic Ref Mat (Incl. Access Fees) $63,278. Sal $1,298,008 (Prof $654,429)
Library Holdings: Bk Vols 493,044; Bk Titles 380,205; Per Subs 3,145
Subject Interests: Acad support, Appalachia, Cherokee Indians, Maps
Special Collections: Spider Coll
Automation Activity & Vendor Info: (Cataloging) Innovative Interfaces Inc.; (Circulation) Innovative Interfaces Inc.; (Course Reserve) Innovative Interfaces Inc.; (ILL) Innovative Interfaces Inc.; (OPAC) Innovative Interfaces Inc.; (Serials) Innovative Interfaces Inc.
Database Vendor: CARL, Dialog, Ebsco - EbscoHost, Lexis-Nexis, OCLC - First Search, ProQuest, Silverplatter Information Inc.
Function: For research purposes
Partic in SE Libr Network; WNCLN
Friends of the Library Group

CURRIE

S US NATIONAL PARK SERVICE MOORES CREEK BATTLEFIELD LIBRARY, 40 Patriots Hall Dr, 28435. SAN 370-310X. Tel: 910-283-5591. FAX: 910-283-5351. *Librn*, Linda Brown; *Asst Librn*, Anne Childress
Library Holdings: Bk Vols 700

DALLAS

J GASTON COLLEGE, Morris Library & Media Center,* 201 Hwy 321 S, 28034. SAN 312-8040. Tel: 704-922-6359. Interlibrary Loan Service Tel: 704-922-6357. FAX: 704-922-6363. Web Site: www.gaston.cc.nc.us. *Dir*, Angela Lea Sox; Tel: 704-922-6355, E-Mail: alsox@gaston.cc.nc.us; *Circ*, Dr Pearlie Brown; Tel: 704-922-6358; *Circ*, Annette Mintz; *Res*, Brian Richard Williams; Tel: 704-922-6357, E-Mail: williams.brian@gaston.cc.nc.us; Staff 9 (MLS 5, Non-MLS 4)
Founded 1964. Enrl 4,000; Fac 106; Highest Degree: Associate
Library Holdings: Bk Vols 51,000; Per Subs 250
Subject Interests: Local history
Special Collections: Civil War Coll
Automation Activity & Vendor Info: (Circulation) epixtech, inc.; (Serials) epixtech, inc.
Database Vendor: Ebsco - EbscoHost, epixtech, inc., OCLC - First Search, ProQuest
Publications: Faculty Guide; Library & Media Center Handbook; Operations Manual of the Library & Media Center
Partic in CCLINC

DANBURY

P DANBURY PUBLIC LIBRARY,* PO Box 218, 27016. SAN 312-8059. Tel: 336-593-2419. FAX: 336-593-3232. E-Mail: danburylibrary@ncsl.dcr.state.nc.us. *Librn*, Nora Lawson
Founded 1945
Mem of Northwestern Regional Library
Friends of the Library Group

DAVIDSON

C DAVIDSON COLLEGE, E H Little Library, 202 D Rd, PO Box 1837, 28036-1837. SAN 312-8067. Tel: 704-892-1837. FAX: 704-892-2625. Web Site: www.davidson.edu. *Dir*, Dr Leland M Park; E-Mail: lepark@little.davidson.edu; *Mgr*, Denise Sherrill; *Head Tech Servs*, Kim Sanderson; *Tech Servs*, Susan Kerr; *Publ Servs*, Sharon H Byrd; *Bibliog Instr, Coll Develop*, Gina Overcash; *Acq, Ser*, Kelly Sink Wood; *Govt Doc*, Frank Molinek; *Archivist*, Dr Jan Blodgett; *Music*, Stephen Mantz; *Syst Coordr*, Derek Rodriguez; *Circ, ILL*, Jean Coates; Staff 12 (MLS 11, Non-MLS 1)
Founded 1837. Enrl 1,652; Fac 155; Highest Degree: Bachelor
Jul 1999-Jun 2000 Mats Exp $1,150,061, Books $409,715, Per/Ser (Incl. Access Fees) $571,142, Presv $30,040, Micro $144,002, Electronic Ref Mat (Incl. Access Fees) $169,204. Sal $804,509 (Prof $517,148)
Library Holdings: Bk Vols 569,981; Bk Titles 414,396; Per Subs 2,141
Special Collections: Bruce Rogers Coll; Davidsoniana Coll; Mecklenburg Declaration of Independence Coll; Peter S Ney Coll; Robert Burns Coll; W P Cumming Map Coll; Woodrow Wilson Coll
Automation Activity & Vendor Info: (Acquisitions) DRA; (Cataloging) DRA; (Circulation) DRA; (Course Reserve) DRA; (ILL) DRA; (OPAC) DRA; (Serials) DRA
Database Vendor: DRA
Partic in SE Libr Network

DOBSON

P DOBSON COMMUNITY LIBRARY,* 305 S Main St, PO Box 1264, 27017-1264. SAN 312-8091. Tel: 336-386-8208. FAX: 336-386-4086. *Librn*, Linda G Hamlin; *Asst Librn*, Cindy Brannak
Library Holdings: Bk Titles 20,000; Per Subs 26
Mem of Northwestern Regional Library
Holdings are included in Northwestern Regional Library entry, Elkin

J SURRY COMMUNITY COLLEGE, Learning Resources Center, 630 S Main St, 27017. (Mail add: PO Box 304, 27017), Tel: 336-386-8121, Ext 252. Interlibrary Loan Service Tel: 336-386-8121, Ext 317. Circulation Tel: 336-386-8121, Ext 259. Reference Tel: 336-386-8121, Ext 260. FAX: 336-386-8121, Ext 332. E-Mail: eref@surry.cc.nc.us. Web Site: www.surry.cc.nc.us/lrc/lrc.htm. *Dean*, Sheila A Core; Tel: 336-386-8121, Ext 252, E-Mail: cores@surry.cc.nc.us; *AV*, Josh Nixon; Tel: 336-386-8121, Ext 229, E-Mail: nixonj@surry.cc.nc.us; *Circ*, Debbi Eldridge; Tel: 336-386-8121 Ext 259, E-Mail: eldridged@surry.cc.nc.us; *Publ Servs*, Lisa Brown; Tel: 336-386-8121, Ext 350, E-Mail: brownl@surry.cc.nc.us; *Ref*, Catha Stroupe; Tel: 336-386-8121, Ext 317, E-Mail: stroupec@surry.cc.nc.us; *Tech Servs*, Doris S Pratt; Tel: 336-386-8121, Ext 215, E-Mail: prattd@surry.cc.nc.us; Staff 9 (MLS 4, Non-MLS 5)
Founded 1965. Enrl 3,100; Fac 94; Highest Degree: Associate
Jul 1999-Jun 2000 Income $417,907. Mats Exp $115,487, Books $50,530, Per/Ser (Incl. Access Fees) $36,441, Presv $452, Micro $18,420, AV Equip $1,870, Electronic Ref Mat (Incl. Access Fees) $7,774. Sal $270,397 (Prof $103,457)
Library Holdings: Bk Vols 47,526; Bk Titles 41,449; Per Subs 350
Subject Interests: Local history
Special Collections: Local History & Genealogy, Surratt Room
Database Vendor: Ebsco - EbscoHost, OCLC - First Search, ProQuest, Silverplatter Information Inc.
Partic in NC-Live; Solinet

DUBLIN

J BLADEN COMMUNITY COLLEGE LIBRARY,* PO Box 266, 28332. SAN 312-8105. Tel: 910-862-2164, Ext 270. FAX: 910-862-3484. Web Site: www.bladen.cc.nc.us. *Librn*, Judith M Jones; E-Mail: jjones@bladen.cc.nc.us; Staff 5 (MLS 2, Non-MLS 3)
Founded 1967. Pop 31,000; Enrl 750; Fac 26
Jul 1997-Jun 1998 Income $178,654. Mats Exp $28,784, Books $8,334, Per/Ser (Incl. Access Fees) $10,556, Micro $3,987, AV Equip $5,907. Sal $119,378 (Prof $61,766)
Library Holdings: Bk Titles 20,000; Per Subs 130

DURHAM

S BECTON DICKINSON, Research Information Center,* 21 Davis Dr, PO Box 12016, 27709-2016. SAN 312-9683. Tel: 919-549-8641, Ext 150. FAX: 919-549-7572. E-Mail: bates@bdrc.bd.com. *Head of Libr*, Barbara Post
Founded 1973
Library Holdings: Bk Titles 2,500; Per Subs 320
Subject Interests: Applied physics, Biomedical engineering, Immunology, Mat sci, Microbiology, Organic chemistry, Polymer chemistry
Partic in BRS; Dialog Corporation; Nat Libr of Med

S BLUE CROSS & BLUE SHIELD OF NORTH CAROLINA, Information Center,* 5901 Chapel Hill Rd, PO Box 2291, 27702. SAN 312-8121. Tel: 919-765-4176. FAX: 919-765-7105. *Librn, Mgr*, Elizabeth J Turner; E-Mail: elizabeth_turner@scp14.bcbsnc.com
Founded 1970
Library Holdings: Bk Titles 2,000; Per Subs 200
Subject Interests: Health econ, Health ins
Publications: Current Information Tracking Service (cumulative monthly index); For Your Information (monthly bulletin)

GM DEPARTMENT OF VETERANS AFFAIRS, Library Service (142D), 508 Fulton St, 27705. SAN 312-8172. Tel: 919-286-6929. FAX: 919-286-6859. *In Charge*, Jeff Kager; *ILL*, Pat Hawthorne; *Circ, Online Servs*, Steven Perlman; Staff 3 (MLS 2, Non-MLS 1)
Founded 1952
1999-2000 Mats Exp $240,000. Sal $170,000 (Prof $120,000)
Library Holdings: Bk Vols 3,200; Bk Titles 3,000; Per Subs 363
Subject Interests: Patient educ
Partic in Veterans Affairs Library Network

C DUKE UNIVERSITY, William R Perkins Library, 27708-0190. SAN 354-6845. Tel: 919-660-5800. Interlibrary Loan Service Tel: 919-660-5890. Circulation Tel: 919-660-5870. Reference Tel: 919-660-5880. FAX: 919-660-5923. Web Site: www.lib.duke.edu. *Librn*, David Ferriero; E-Mail: dsf1@duke.edu; *Coll Develop*, Virginia Gilbert; *Coll Develop*, Deborah Jakubs; *ILL*, Rebecca Gomez; *Cat*, Rosalyn Raeford; Tel: 919-660-5892; *Doc Delivery*, Robbin Ernest; *Circ*, Ashley Jackson; *Doc*, Ann Miller; Tel: 919-660-5851; *Media Spec*, Jane Agee; *Acq, Ser*, Geraldine Van Goethem; Tel: 919-660-5894; *Spec Coll*, Robert Byrd; *Info Specialist*, Jim Coble; *Ref*, Margaret Brill; Staff 88 (MLS 88)
Founded 1838. Enrl 11,564; Fac 2,073; Highest Degree: Doctorate
Jul 1998-Jun 1999 Mats Exp $6,496,485, Books $2,724,368, Per/Ser (Incl. Access Fees) $3,751,745. Sal $7,424,485 (Prof $3,867,006)
Library Holdings: Bk Vols 4,178,700; Per Subs 29,600
Subject Interests: Humanities, Social sciences
Special Collections: Advertising; American Almanacs; American Literary Historiography; Antebellum; Architecture; Bath, England; British pamphlets (18th century); Broadsides; Byron; city directories; Coleridge; Confederate & post-bellum music; Confederate imprints; Duke University authors; Emblem books; Emerson; English drama (19th century); German Baroque Lit; Greek, Latin, & Mediaeval manuscripts; Latin American history; Latin American languages & Lit; Manuscripts (exp, Southern states); Manx Coll; Methodist Church; New Testament Textual materials; newpapers (Germany, Great Britain & the Southern states); Philippines; Utopias; Wesleyana; Whitman
Publications: Duke University Libraries
Mem of Asn of Research Libraries
Partic in OCLC Online Computer Library Center, Inc; SE Libr Network; Triangle Research Libraries Network
Friends of the Library Group
Departmental Libraries:

CR DIVINITY SCHOOL LIBRARY, Gray Bldg, Two Chapel Dr, 27708. (Mail add: Duke University, PO Box 90972, 27708-0972), SAN 354-6969. Tel: 919-660-3452. Circulation Tel: 919-660-3450. Reference Tel: 919-660-3453. FAX: 919-681-7594. Web Site: www.lib.duke.edu/divinity/. *Librn*, Roger Loyd; E-Mail: roger.loyd@duke.edu; *Assoc Librn*, Roberta Schaafsma; E-Mail: roberta.schaafsma@duke.edu; *Electronic Resources*, Andrew Keck; Tel: 919-660-3549, E-Mail: andy.keck@duke.edu; Staff 5 (MLS 3, Non-MLS 2)
Jul 1999-Jun 2000 Mats Exp $303,540. Sal $299,212
Library Holdings: Bk Vols 334,160
Subject Interests: Biblical studies, Christian theology, Methodism

FUQUA SCHOOL OF BUSINESS LIBRARY, One Towerview Rd, 27708. Tel: 919-660-7870. FAX: 919-660-7950. E-Mail: fuqua_library@mail.duke.edu. Web Site: www.lib.duke.edu/fsb/index.htm. *Librn*, Margaret Trauner; Tel: 919-660-7869, E-Mail: trauner@mail.duke.edu; *Ref*, Jane Day; Tel: 919-660-7874, E-Mail: jnday@mail.duke.edu; *Cat*, Carlton Brown; Tel: 919-660-7871, E-Mail: cbrown@mail.duke.edu; *Access Serv*, David Solar; Tel: 919-660-7873, E-Mail: dsolar@mail.duke.edu; *Ref*, Paula Robinson; Tel: 919-660-7942, E-Mail: robinson@mail.duke.edu; Staff 5 (MLS 5)
Founded 1983. Enrl 720; Fac 85; Highest Degree: Doctorate
Jul 1999-Jun 2000 Income $902,789. Mats Exp $587,923, Books $62,056, Per/Ser (Incl. Access Fees) $211,617, Presv $899, Micro $20,921, Electronic Ref Mat (Incl. Access Fees) $256,696. Sal $314,866 (Prof $214,158)
Library Holdings: Bk Vols 24,606; Per Subs 1,348
Automation Activity & Vendor Info: (Acquisitions) Innovative Interfaces Inc.; (Cataloging) DRA; (Circulation) DRA; (OPAC) DRA; (Serials) Innovative Interfaces Inc.
Database Vendor: OCLC - First Search
Partic in OCLC Online Computer Library Center, Inc

CL LAW SCHOOL LIBRARY, Box 90361, 27708-0361. SAN 354-7051. Tel: 919-613-7171. Interlibrary Loan Service Tel: 919-613-7122. Reference Tel: 919-613-7121. FAX: 919-613-7237. Web Site: www.law.duke.edu/lib/library/html. *Assoc Dean*, Richard Danner; *Assoc Dir*, Mark Bernstein; *Tech Servs*, Hope Breeze; *Circ*, Janeen Denson; *Ref*, Katherine Topulos; *Ref*, Melanie Dunshee; *Acq*, Gretchen Wolf; *Publ Servs*, Janet Sinder; *Cat*, Doris Hinson; *Ref*, Michael Hannon; Staff 10 (MLS 10)
Founded 1868. Enrl 717; Fac 34; Highest Degree: Doctorate
Jul 1999-Jun 2000 Income $2,497,540. Mats Exp $1,169,131, Books $151,687, Per/Ser (Incl. Access Fees) $863,153, Presv $23,049, Micro $63,896, Electronic Ref Mat (Incl. Access Fees) $67,346. Sal $1,029,349 (Prof $630,400)
Library Holdings: Bk Vols 550,054; Bk Titles 197,861; Per Subs 6,658
Publications: Bibliographies; DULL News; Research Guides Series
Partic in SE Libr Network

MARINE LAB LIBRARY, Beaufort Campus, Beaufort, 28516. SAN 377-0702. Tel: 252-504-7510. FAX: 252-504-7622. *Librn*, Daivd Talbert
Library Holdings: Bk Vols 25,607
Subject Interests: Biochemistry, Botany, Coastal resource mgt, Marine biology, Marine biotech, Oceanography

CM MEDICAL CENTER, Seeley G Mudd Bldg, Box 3702, 27710-3702. SAN 354-7116. Tel: 919-660-1150. FAX: 919-681-7599. E-Mail: tlib.001@mc.duke.edu. Web Site: www.mc.duke.edu/mclibrary/. *Actg Dir*, Patricia Thibodeau; E-Mail: thibo001@mc.duke.edu; *Circ*, Virginia Carden; Tel: 919-660-1184, Fax: 919-684-5906, E-Mail: carde009@mc.duke.edu; *Cat*, Jane Trumbull; Tel: 919-660-1120, Fax: 919-684-5906, E-Mail: trumb001@mc.duke.edu; *Ser*, Judy Woodburn; Tel: 919-660-1140, Fax: 919-684-5906, E-Mail: woodb001@mc.duke.edu; *Curator*, Suzanne Porter; Tel: 919-660-1143, E-Mail: port004@mc.duke.edu; *Business*, Vanessa Sellars; Tel: 919-660-1149, E-Mail: sella004@mc.duke.edu; *Publ Servs*, Eric Albright; Tel: 919-660-1130, Fax: 919-684-5906, E-Mail: albri008@mc.duke.edu; *Publ Servs*, Julie Garrison; Tel: 919-660-1157, E-Mail: garri008.mc.duke.edu; *Coll Develop*, Mary Ann Brown; Tel: 919-660-1122, Fax: 919-684-5906, E-Mail: brown050@mc.duke.edu; *Doc*, Beverly Murphy; Staff 46 (MLS 16, Non-MLS 30)
Founded 1930. Circ 26,296
Jul 1998-Jun 1999 Income $504,902, Federal $6,000, Locally Generated Income $498,902. Mats Exp $1,991,104, Books $264,565, Per/Ser (Incl. Access Fees) $1,726,539. Sal $11,598,696 (Prof $843,894)
Library Holdings: Bk Vols 295,000; Per Subs 2,432
Special Collections: Andreas Vesalius; Anesthesia; Benjamin Rush; Benjamin Waterhouse; Early Printed Medical Books; Human Sexuality; Manuscripts; Military Medicine; Obstetrics; Pediatrics; Vivisection; Yellow Fever
Automation Activity & Vendor Info: (Circulation) DRA
Publications: Medical Center Library News (Newsletter); Newsletter; Trent Coll Report
Partic in SE Libr Network
Historical Images in Medicine database produced in-house

WILLIAM R PERKINS CHEMISTRY LIBRARY, 102 Paul M Gross Chemical Labs, Box 90355, 27708-0355. Tel: 919-660-1578. FAX: 919-681-8666. E-Mail: chemlib@chem.duke.edu. *Librn*, Anne Langley
Library Holdings: Bk Vols 62,483
Subject Interests: Chemistry

WILLIAM R PERKINS VESIC ENGINEERING LIBRARY Tel: 919-660-5368. FAX: 919-681-7595. *Librn*, Linda Martinez; *Librn*, Mary Ann Southern
Library Holdings: Bk Vols 126,912
Subject Interests: Computer science, Engineering

WILIAM R PERKINS BIOLOGICAL & ENVIRONMENTAL SCIENCES LIBRARY, 101 Biological Science Library, 27706. SAN 354-690X. Tel: 919-660-5971. FAX: 919-681-7606. *Librn*, Carol Fineman
Library Holdings: Bk Vols 191,290
Subject Interests: Botany, Environ, Forestry, Zoology

WILLIAM R PERKINS LILLY LIBRARY, 27708-0190. Tel: 919-660-5990. FAX: 919-660-5999. *Librn*, Cousineau Laura; *Ref*, Tracy Hull; *Ref*, Kelley Lawton; *Media Spec*, Jane Agee; *Bibliogr*, Lee Sorensen
Library Holdings: Bk Vols 275,268
Subject Interests: Art history, Drama, Philosophy, Visual arts

WILLIAM R PERKINS MUSIC LIBRARY, PO Box 90661, 27708-0661. SAN 354-7175. Tel: 919-660-5952. FAX: 919-684-6556. Web Site: www.lib.duke.edu/music/. *Librn*, John Druesedow; *Librn*, Yale Fineman
Library Holdings: Bk Vols 96,818
Subject Interests: Music
Special Collections: African-American Music (William Grant Still Coll); Venetian Music (Berdes Papers); Viennese Music (Weinmann Coll)

P DURHAM COUNTY LIBRARY, 300 N Roxboro St, PO Box 3809, 27702. SAN 354-7205. Tel: 919-560-0100. TDD: 919-560-0299. FAX: 919-560-0106. Web Site: ils.unc.edu/nclibs/durham/dclhome.htm. *Dir*, Dale Gaddis; Fax: 919-560-0137, E-Mail: dgaddis@co.durham.nc.us; *Asst Dir*, John McConagha; *Automation Syst Coordr*, Kathleen Moeller-Peiffer; *Outreach Serv*, Nancy Blood; *Ch Servs*, Sandra Roberson; *Exten Serv*, Priscilla Lewis; *Circ*, Myrtle Darden; *Cat*, Jean Amelang; *Tech Servs*, Rheda Epstein; *Ad Servs*, JoAnne Abel; *Coll Develop*, Roberta Tilden; *Ref*, Anne Berkley; Staff 106 (MLS 36, Non-MLS 70)
Founded 1897. Circ 1,460,754
Jul 1999-Jun 2000 Income (Main Library and Branch Library) $5,626,559, State $272,081, Federal $29,473, County $5,075,638, Locally Generated Income $249,367. Mats Exp $822,875. Sal $2,956,896
Library Holdings: Bk Vols 478,041; Per Subs 1,342
Subject Interests: Adult education, Early childhood, Vocational education
Special Collections: African-American History & Literature Coll, bks, per, newsp clippings, Durham Biography & History Coll, including Durham County Library History; Durham Historical Photographs (Archival); North Carolina History & Literature, bks, clippings, microfilm, per, newsp, rec, v-tapes, flm, slides
Automation Activity & Vendor Info: (Cataloging) epixtech, inc.; (Circulation) epixtech, inc.; (OPAC) epixtech, inc.
Database Vendor: OCLC - First Search
Publications: Directory of Durham Community Resources; Seasons Readings; The Best of Friends (Friends Newsletter)
Partic in OCLC Online Computer Library Center, Inc; SE Libr Network
Special Services for the Deaf - TTY machine
Friends of the Library Group
Branches: 7

BRAGTOWN, 3200 Dearborn Dr, 27704. SAN 354-723X. Tel: 919-560-0210. *In Charge*, Alma Burson
Friends of the Library Group

MCDOUGALD TERRACE, 1101 Lawson St, 27703. SAN 354-7299. Tel: 919-560-0240. *Librn*, Almena Walker

NORTH DURHAM, Riverview Shopping Ctr, 5120 N Roxboro Rd, 27704. SAN 354-7302. Tel: 919-560-0250. FAX: 919-560-0255. *Librn*, Nancy Scott

PARKWOOD, Parkwood Shopping Ctr, 5116 Revere Rd, 27713. SAN 354-7329. Tel: 919-560-0260. FAX: 919-560-0264. *Librn*, John Blake

SALVATION ARMY BOYS CLUB, 810 N Alston Ave, 27701. SAN 354-7353. Tel: 919-560-0280. *Librn*, Almena Walker

SOUTHWEST, 3605 Shannon Rd, 27707. SAN 354-7264. Tel: 919-560-0290. FAX: 919-560-0296. *Librn*, Lynne Barnette

STANFORD L WARREN BRANCH, 1201 Fayetteville St, 27707. SAN 354-7388. Tel: 919-560-0270. FAX: 919-560-0271. *Librn*, Brenda Watson
Special Collections: African-American Cultural History Coll
Friends of the Library Group
Bookmobiles: 1

DURHAM REGIONAL HOSPITAL

M MEDICAL LIBRARY, 3643 N Roxboro St, 27704-2763. SAN 312-813X. Tel: 919-470-6251. FAX: 919-470-6297. *Dir Libr Serv*, Anita Hasty-Speed; E-Mail: speedah@drh.duhs.duke.edu; Staff 1 (MLS 1)
Founded 1976
Jul 1996-Jun 1997 Income $197,000. Mats Exp $95,120, Books $17,214, Per/Ser (Incl. Access Fees) $60,144, AV Equip $2,000. Sal $73,549 (Prof $46,114)
Library Holdings: Bk Titles 5,000; Per Subs 250
Subject Interests: Allied health, Clinical medicine, Nursing, Pre-clinical scis
Partic in OCLC Online Computer Library Center, Inc; Resources For Health Information Consortium

J DURHAM TECHNICAL COMMUNITY COLLEGE,* 1637 Lawson St, PO Box 11307, 27703. SAN 312-8148. Tel: 919-686-3369. FAX: 919-686-3471. Web Site: www.dtce.cc.nc.us. *Asst Dean*, Bonnie V Stone; *Coll Develop, Dir Libr Serv*, Irene H Laube; E-Mail: laubei@gwmail.dtce.ec.nc.us; *Ref*, Jeanne Lauber; *Publ Servs, Ref*, Wendy Ramseur; *Media Spec*, Richard J Godfrey; Staff 4 (MLS 4)
Founded 1961. Enrl 4,859
1997-1998 Income $304,491, State $294,491, Federal $10,000. Mats Exp $125,803. Sal $124,161
Library Holdings: Bk Vols 43,819; Bk Titles 42,633; Per Subs 372
Subject Interests: Bus, Education, Law, Liberal arts, Medicine, Mgt, Sci-tech
Publications: Library Handbook; News from the Library; Periodical Holdings
Partic in OCLC Online Computer Library Center, Inc
Departmental Libraries:

NORTHERN DURHAM CENTER, 2401 Snow Hill Rd, 27712. SAN 377-0524. Tel: 919-686-3509. FAX: 919-686-3519. *Librn*, Stantosh Shonek

S FAMILY HEALTH INTERNATIONAL LIBRARY, 2224 E NC Hwy 54, 27713. (Mail add: PO Box 13950, 27709), SAN 322-8762. Tel: 919-544-7040. FAX: 919-544-7261. *Librn*, Ann Duffell; *Librn*, William Barrows; E-Mail: bbarrows@fhi.org; Staff 5 (MLS 4, Non-MLS 1)
Founded 1971
Library Holdings: Bk Titles 7,000; Per Subs 575
Subject Interests: AIDS prevention, Demography, Family planning, Maternal-child health
Publications: Library handbook; Serials holdings (annual); suggested journal & newsletter list for population & family planning libraries

S FOREST HISTORY SOCIETY LIBRARY,* 701 Vickers Ave, 27701-3162. SAN 301-5807. Tel: 919-682-9319. FAX: 919-682-2349. Web Site: www.lib.duke.edu/forest/library.html. *Archivist, Librn*, Cheryl Oakes; E-Mail: coakes@acpub.duke.edu
Founded 1946

1997-1998 Income $100,000, Locally Generated Income $2,000, Parent Institution $58,000. Mats Exp $3,500. Sal $65,000 (Prof $59,000)
Library Holdings: Bk Vols 7,000; Per Subs 259
Subject Interests: Conservation, Forestry
Special Collections: 250 Interviews - Tapes & Transcripts; American Forest Council Archives; American Forestry Association Archives; National Forest Products Association Archives; Society of American Foresters Archives

S LIGGETT GROUP INC, Research Center Information Services,* 710 W Main St, 27702. (Mail add: PO Box 1572, 27702-1572), SAN 325-7754. Tel: 919-683-8985. FAX: 919-683-8966. *In Charge*, Liz Mathias
Founded 1950
Library Holdings: Bk Titles 1,130; Per Subs 41
Subject Interests: Chemistry, Medicine, Tobacco

C NORTH CAROLINA CENTRAL UNIVERSITY, James E Shepard Memorial Library, 1801 Fayetteville St, 27707. SAN 354-7590. Tel: 919-560-6475. FAX: 919-530-7612. Web Site: www.nccu.edu/library/shepard.html. *Dir*, George C Grant; Tel: 919-560-5233, E-Mail: ggrant@wpo.nccu.edu; *Acq, Cat*, Gouri Dutta; Tel: 919-560-6430, E-Mail: goudutta@wpo.nccu.edu; *Circ*, Vickie Spencer; Tel: 919-530-7305, E-Mail: vspencer@wpo.ncu.edu; *Ref Serv*, Debora Hazel; Tel: 919-560-6473, Fax: 919-560-6187, E-Mail: dhazel@wpo.nccu.edu; *Publ Servs*, Yash Garg; Tel: 919-560-6383, E-Mail: ygarg@wpo.nccu.edu; *Publ Servs*, Shirley Lawrence; Tel: 919-530-7312, E-Mail: slawrence@wpo.nccu.edu; *Per*, Veola Williams; Tel: 919-560-6481, E-Mail: vwilliams@wpo.nccu.edu; *Music*, Gene W Leonardi; Tel: 919-530-7217, E-Mail: gleonard@wpo.nccu.edu; *Govt Doc*, Sandra Neal; Tel: 919-530-7306, E-Mail: sneal@wpo.nccu.edu; Staff 34 (MLS 18, Non-MLS 16)
Founded 1923. Enrl 5,482; Fac 284; Highest Degree: Master
Jul 2000-Jun 2001 Income (Main and Other College/University Libraries) State $2,139,957. Mats Exp $873,665, Books $170,850, Per/Ser (Incl. Access Fees) $440,000, Presv $20,000, Micro $135,000, Electronic Ref Mat (Incl. Access Fees) $107,815. Sal $1,006,000 (Prof $717,000)
Library Holdings: Bk Vols 497,150; Bk Titles 427,043; Per Subs 2,002
Subject Interests: Local history
Special Collections: Minorities (Martin Coll)
Automation Activity & Vendor Info: (Cataloging) DRA; (Circulation) DRA
Database Vendor: DRA, Ebsco - EbscoHost, IAC - Info Trac, OCLC - First Search, ProQuest, Silverplatter Information Inc.
Publications: Annual Reports; SNN: Shepard News Network
Partic in Solinet; Triangle Research Libraries Network
Friends of the Library Group
Departmental Libraries:
MUSIC Tel: 919-530-6220. *Librn*, Gene W Leonardi
Library Holdings: Bk Vols 12,000

CL SCHOOL OF LAW LIBRARY, 1512 S Alston Ave, 27707. SAN 354-768X. Tel: 919-560-6244. Circulation Tel: 919-560-5189. Reference Tel: 919-560-5188. FAX: 919-560-5321. Web Site: www.nccu.edu/lawlib.html. *Dir*, Deborah Mayo Jefferies; Tel: 919-560-6113, Fax: 919-530-7926, E-Mail: djeff@wpo.nccu.edu; *Asst Libr Dir*, Walter High; Tel: 919-560-5241, E-Mail: wmhigh@wpo.nccu.edu; *Asst Libr Dir*, Cynthia Ruffin; Tel: 919-560-5188, E-Mail: cruffin@wpo.nccu.edu; *Acq*, Hazel Lumpkin; Tel: 919-530-7926, E-Mail: hlumpkin@wpo.nccu.edu; *Cat*, Loretta Mershon; Tel: 919-530-7177, E-Mail: imershon@wpo.nccu.edu; *Ref*, Melanie Creech; Tel: 919-530-7183, E-Mail: mcreech@wpo.nccu.edu; Staff 18 (MLS 6, Non-MLS 12)
Founded 1939. Enrl 362; Highest Degree: Doctorate
Jul 1999-Jun 2000 Income State $1,362,256. Mats Exp $582,737, Books $92,073, Per/Ser (Incl. Access Fees) $446,941, Presv $9,141, Electronic Ref Mat (Incl. Access Fees) $34,582
Library Holdings: Bk Vols 128,904; Bk Titles 57,188; Per Subs 3,974
Subject Interests: Civil rights, NC law, Tax
Special Collections: Civil Rights (McKissick Coll)
Automation Activity & Vendor Info: (Cataloging) DRA; (Circulation) DRA
Database Vendor: Dialog, DRA, IAC - Info Trac, Lexis-Nexis, OCLC - First Search
Function: Reference services available
Partic in Consortium Of South Eastern Law Libraries; OCLC Online Computer Library Center, Inc; Triangle Research Libraries Network; Westlaw

SCHOOL OF LIBRARY & INFORMATION SCIENCES, 1801 Fayetteville St, 27707. Tel: 919-530-7323. FAX: 919-560-6402. Web Site: www.slis.nccu.edu/slislib/. *Librn*, Virginia Purefoy Jones; E-Mail: vpj@nccu.edu; Staff 2 (MLS 1, Non-MLS 1)
Founded 1939. Highest Degree: Master
Library Holdings: Bk Vols 36,561; Bk Titles 27,958; Per Subs 443
Subject Interests: Ch lit, Info sci, Libr sci
Special Collections: Black Librarian's Coll; William Tucker Coll
Automation Activity & Vendor Info: (Cataloging) DRA; (Circulation) DRA; (Course Reserve) DRA; (OPAC) DRA
Partic in Dialog Corporation; OCLC Online Computer Library Center, Inc; SE Libr Network; Triangle Research Libraries Network

S NORTH CAROLINA MUSEUM OF LIFE & SCIENCE LIBRARY, 433 Murray Ave, PO Box 15190, 27704-0190. SAN 328-1833. Tel: 919-220-5429. FAX: 919-220-5575. *Mgr*, Nancy A Dragotta-Lawson; E-Mail: nancyd@ncmls.org
Founded 1980
Library Holdings: Bk Titles 3,550; Per Subs 11

S ORGANIZATION FOR TROPICAL STUDIES INC LIBRARY, 410 Swift Ave, 27705. SAN 377-5259. Tel: 919-684-5774. FAX: 919-684-5661. E-Mail: nao@acpub.duke.edu. Web Site: www.ots.duke.edu. *Pres*, Dr Gary S Hartshorn; E-Mail: nao@duke.edu; *Coll Develop*, Ana Beatriz Azofeifa
1998-1999 Mats Exp $2,000
Library Holdings: Bk Vols 1,000
Subject Interests: Natural resources

S REICHHOLD, INC, Information Resources Center, 2400 Ellis Rd, 27703. (Mail add: PO Box 13582, 27709-3582), SAN 374-7050. Tel: 919-990-8054. FAX: 919-990-7859. *Dir*, Barbara Best-Nichols; E-Mail: barbara.best-nichols@reichhold.com; *Admin Assoc*, Carol Ann Clark
Library Holdings: Bk Titles 3,700; Per Subs 350
Restriction: By appointment only

M RHINE RESEARCH CENTER, Institute for Parapsychology, 402 N Buchanan Blvd, 27701. SAN 322-8851. Tel: 919-688-8241. FAX: 919-683-4338. E-Mail: info@rhine.org.
Founded 1930. Fac 4,500
Library Holdings: Per Subs 70
Subject Interests: Parapsychol, Psychol res, Related areas
Special Collections: J B Rhine & Louisa Rhine Archival Coll, unpublished mss, theses & dissertations

SR TEMPLE BAPTIST CHURCH, Media Library,* 807 W Chapel Hill St, 27701-3112. SAN 371-6708. Tel: 919-688-7397.
Founded 1950
Library Holdings: Bk Titles 5,000
Special Collections: Church History; Pastor Thesis
Publications: Newsletter (bi-monthly)

SR WATTS STREET BAPTIST CHURCH LIBRARY,* 800 Watts St, 27701. SAN 328-4433. Tel: 919-688-1366. FAX: 919-688-7255.
Library Holdings: Bk Titles 1,000

EAST BEND

P EAST BEND PUBLIC LIBRARY,* PO Box 69, 27018. SAN 376-2882. Tel: 336-699-3890. FAX: 336-699-2359. *Librn*, Erin Haynes
Library Holdings: Bk Vols 15,000; Bk Titles 15,000; Per Subs 18
Mem of Northwestern Regional Library
Friends of the Library Group

EDEN

P ROCKINGHAM COUNTY PUBLIC LIBRARY,* 527 Boone Rd, 27288. SAN 354-7744. Tel: 336-627-1106. FAX: 336-623-1258. Web Site: www.rcpl.org. *Dir*, Sue Williams; *Ch Servs*, Jacky Miller; *Tech Servs*, Barbara Bolden; *Asst Dir, Coll Develop*, Lynne Swaine; *Ref*, Amy Frazer; Staff 23 (MLS 23)
Founded 1934. Pop 86,152; Circ 508,519
Library Holdings: Bk Vols 306,563; Per Subs 740
Subject Interests: Afro-American, Business, Genealogy, Large print, Literacy, NC
Publications: Genealogy Bibliography; Literacy Newsletter; Rockingham County Public Library Patron Brochure; Suggested Reading List for Home Extension Groups (ann)
Partic in NC Info Network
Special services to the homebound & handicapped. Drop-in-Library to Day Care Centers
Friends of the Library Group
Branches: 6
EDEN BRANCH, 598 S Pierce, 27288. SAN 354-7779. Tel: 336-623-3168. FAX: 336-623-1171. Web Site: www.rcpl.org. *Librn*, Lynne Swaine
Friends of the Library Group
MADISON BRANCH, 140 E Murphy St, Madison, 27025. SAN 354-7809. Tel: 336-548-6553. FAX: 336-548-2010. *Librn*, Sarah Pell
Subject Interests: Genealogy, Local history
Friends of the Library Group
MAYODAN BRANCH, 101 N Tenth Ave, Mayodan, 27027. SAN 354-7833. Tel: 336-548-6951. FAX: 336-548-2015. *Librn*, Sarah Pell
Friends of the Library Group
REIDSVILLE BRANCH, 204 W Morehead St, Reidsville, 27320. SAN 354-7868. Tel: 336-349-8476. FAX: 336-342-4824. Web Site: www.rcpl.org. *Librn*, Amy Newnam
Subject Interests: Afro-American
Friends of the Library Group
STONEVILLE BRANCH, 201 E Main St, PO Box 26, Stoneville, 27048. SAN 354-7892. Tel: 336-573-9040. FAX: 336-573-2774. *Librn*, Sarah Pell

Friends of the Library Group
THE LEARNING PLACE (LITERACY), 116 N Scales St, Reidsville, 27320. SAN 370-9051. Tel: 336-349-6733. FAX: 336-349-7441. Web Site: www.rcpl.org. *Librn*, Joyce Burgart
Bookmobiles: 1

EDENTON

P SHEPARD-PRUDEN MEMORIAL LIBRARY,* 106 W Water St, 27932. SAN 312-8199. Tel: 252-482-4112. FAX: 252-482-5451. *Librn*, Rosalie V Boyd; Staff 4 (MLS 1, Non-MLS 3)
Founded 1921. Pop 14,368; Circ 48,748
Subject Interests: Local history
Mem of Pettigrew Regional Library
Friends of the Library Group

ELIZABETH CITY

J COLLEGE OF THE ALBEMARLE, Learning Resources Center, Hwy 17 N, PO Box 2327, 27909. SAN 354-7922. Tel: 252-335-0821, Ext 2270. FAX: 252-335-0649. Web Site: www.albemarle.cc.nc.us/acadaff/lrc/welcome.htm. *Dir*, Robert Schenck; E-Mail: rschenck@albermarle.cc
Founded 1961
Library Holdings: Bk Vols 34,399; Bk Titles 27,709; Per Subs 232
Subject Interests: North Caroliniana
Partic in NC Info Network; OCLC Online Computer Library Center, Inc

P EAST ALBEMARLE REGIONAL LIBRARY, 205 E Main St, 27909-0303. SAN 312-8202. Tel: 252-335-2511. FAX: 252-335-2386. Web Site: earlibrary.org. *Dir*, Elizabeth S Hamilton; E-Mail: ehamilton@ncsl.dcr.state.nc.us; *Librn*, Rebecca Callison; *Librn*, Jonathan Wark; *Tech Servs*, Jill Kramer; Staff 31 (MLS 4, Non-MLS 27)
Founded 1964. Pop 89,212; Circ 370,150
Jul 1999-Jun 2000 Income $1,552,979, State $411,085, City $8,420, Federal $11,435, County $936,532, Other $185,507. Mats Exp $239,755. Sal $899,659
Library Holdings: Bk Vols 161,282; Per Subs 273
Subject Interests: North Carolina
Automation Activity & Vendor Info: (Cataloging) TLC; (Circulation) TLC; (OPAC) TLC
Database Vendor: Ebsco - EbscoHost, OCLC - First Search, ProQuest
Member Libraries: Currituck County Public Library; Dare County Library; Pasquotank-Camden Library
Friends of the Library Group
Bookmobiles: 1

C ELIZABETH CITY STATE UNIVERSITY, GR Little Library, Parkview Dr, 27909. SAN 312-8210. Tel: 252-335-3586. Circulation Tel: 252-335-3427. Reference Tel: 252-335-3433. FAX: 252-335-3446. Web Site: www.ecsu.edu. *Actg Dir*, Rebecca A Ware; Tel: 252-335-3585, E-Mail: raware@mail.ecsu.edu; *Tech Servs*, Kathy Turner; *Acq*, Helen Jones; *Ref*, Patricia Hines; *Circ*, Juanita Midgette; *Ser*, Dennis Brown; Staff 7 (MLS 7)
Founded 1901. Enrl 2,300; Fac 120; Highest Degree: Bachelor
Library Holdings: Bk Vols 181,738; Per Subs 1,845
Automation Activity & Vendor Info: (Acquisitions) epixtech, inc.; (Cataloging) epixtech, inc.; (Circulation) epixtech, inc.; (OPAC) epixtech, inc.
Database Vendor: epixtech, inc.
Partic in Eastern Carolina Libr Network; NC State Libr Info Network; OCLC Online Computer Library Center, Inc; SE Libr Network

P PASQUOTANK-CAMDEN LIBRARY,* 205 E Main St, 27909. SAN 312-8229. Tel: 252-335-2473. FAX: 252-335-2386. Web Site: www.earlibrary.org. *Librn*, Rebecca Callison; *Circ*, Janet Gallop; *Circ*, Lori Midyette; *Circ*, Peggy Brabble; *Circ*, Myra Vagts; *Bkmobile Coordr*, Danny Rogerson; *Bkmobile Coordr*, Anne Histed; *Ref*, Earline Cole
Founded 1930. Pop 36,732; Circ 131,140
Library Holdings: Bk Vols 60,000; Per Subs 88
Subject Interests: NC hist
Mem of East Albemarle Regional Library

CR ROANOKE BIBLE COLLEGE, Watson-Griffith Library, 715 N Poindexter, 27902. SAN 312-8237. Tel: 252-334-2057. FAX: 252-334-2071. *Dir*, Patricia S Griffin; E-Mail: psg@roanokebible.edu; *Acq*, Alice K Andrews; Tel: 252-334-2027, E-Mail: aka@roanokebible.edu; Staff 4 (MLS 1, Non-MLS 3)
Founded 1948. Enrl 180; Fac 14; Highest Degree: Bachelor
Jul 1999-Jun 2000 Income $101,031. Mats Exp $17,474, Books $8,965, Per/Ser (Incl. Access Fees) $1,884, AV Equip $3,292, Electronic Ref Mat (Incl. Access Fees) $3,333. Sal $75,644 (Prof $23,408)
Library Holdings: Bk Vols 27,839; Bk Titles 24,612; Per Subs 194
Subject Interests: Christian educ, Deaf studies, Prof-life, Religion
Special Collections: Creationism Coll; Deaf Coll; Discipliana Coll
Automation Activity & Vendor Info: (Cataloging) Sagebrush Corporation; (Circulation) Sagebrush Corporation; (OPAC) Sagebrush Corporation
Function: ILL available
Partic in Christian Libr Network; Solinet

ELIZABETHTOWN

P BLADEN COUNTY PUBLIC LIBRARY,* Cypress & Queen St, PO Box 1419, 28337-1419. SAN 354-7981. Tel: 910-862-6990. FAX: 910-862-8777. *Dir*, Sherwin Rice; Staff 10 (MLS 1, Non-MLS 9)
Founded 1939. Pop 30,448; Circ 200,591
Library Holdings: Bk Vols 45,817
Subject Interests: Bladen County genealogy, NC genealogy
Special Collections: North Carolina Genealogy
Branches: 2
BRIDGER MEMORIAL, PO Box 1259, Bladenboro, 28320. SAN 354-8015. Tel: 910-863-4586. *Librn*, Faye Sykes
Library Holdings: Bk Titles 4,000
CLARKTON PUBLIC, PO Box 665, Clarkton, 28433. SAN 354-804X. Tel: 910-647-3661. *Librn*, Patricia Swanson
Library Holdings: Bk Vols 5,000
Bookmobiles: 3. Homebound van, Children's Services van

ELKIN

P ELKIN PUBLIC LIBRARY,* 111 N Front St, 28621. SAN 312-8245. Tel: 336-835-5586. FAX: 336-835-5008. *Librn*, Joan Sanders
Library Holdings: Bk Titles 25,000
Special Collections: Hendren Nature Coll; Lillard History Coll
Mem of Northwest Regional Library; Northwestern Regional Library
Friends of the Library Group

P NORTHWESTERN REGIONAL LIBRARY, 111 N Front St, 28621. SAN 312-8253. Tel: 336-835-4894. FAX: 336-526-2270. *Dir*, Michael Sawyer; *Coordr*, John Hedrick; *Coordr*, Joan Sherif; *Business*, Jewel Carpenter; *Tech Coordr*, Bill Boyd; *Ch Servs*, Tammy Williams; Staff 64 (MLS 5, Non-MLS 59)
Founded 1959. Pop 156,000; Circ 603,738
Jul 1999-Jun 2000 Income $2,156,654, State $492,872, City $265,061, Federal $23,295, County $1,129,851, Other $245,575. Mats Exp $289,309, Books $268,548, Per/Ser (Incl. Access Fees) $20,761. Sal $986,796 (Prof $153,581)
Library Holdings: Bk Vols 291,216; Per Subs 375
Subject Interests: Local history
Automation Activity & Vendor Info: (Circulation) SIRSI; (OPAC) SIRSI
Member Libraries: Alleghany County Public Library; Boonville Community Public Library; Charles H Stone Memorial Library; Danbury Public Library; Dobson Community Library; East Bend Public Library; Elkin Public Library; Jonesville-Arlington Public Library; King Public Library; Lowgap Public Library; Mount Airy Public Library; Walnut Cove Public Library; Yadkin County Public Library
Friends of the Library Group
Bookmobiles: 1

ELLERBE

P KEMP MEMORIAL LIBRARY,* 279 N Second St, 28338. SAN 320-5002. Tel: 910-652-6130. FAX: 910-652-6130. *Dir*, Anne Thrower
Founded 1978. Pop 1,500; Circ 7,983
Library Holdings: Bk Vols 6,254; Per Subs 13
Subject Interests: Artifacts, Local history
Mem of Richmond County Public Libr Syst; Sandhill Regional Library System
Friends of the Library Group

ELON COLLEGE

CR ELON COLLEGE, Carol Grotnes Belk Library, 2550 Campus Box, 27244-0187. SAN 354-8074. Tel: 336-278-6572. FAX: 336-278-6637. Web Site: www.elon.edu/library. *Dir*, Kate Hickey; E-Mail: hickey@elon.edu; *Business, Ref Serv*, Betty L Garrison; *Tech Servs*, Connie Keller; *Publ Servs, Ref*, Teresa LePors; *AV, Cat*, Terri Kirchen; *Cat*, Shannon Tennant; *Bibliog Instr*, Randall Bowman; *Doc, Ser*, Laura West; *Circ*, Margaret Jobe; *Ref*, Carole Svensson
Founded 1889. Enrl 3,800; Fac 182; Highest Degree: Master
Jun 1998-May 1999 Income (Main and Other College/University Libraries) Parent Institution $1,360,226. Mats Exp $404,500, Books $140,800, Per/Ser (Incl. Access Fees) $168,500, Presv $12,600, AV Equip $57,500, Electronic Ref Mat (Incl. Access Fees) $25,100. Sal $653,900 (Prof $396,200)
Library Holdings: Bk Vols 214,727; Bk Titles 146,120; Per Subs 9,500
Subject Interests: Bus admin, Education, History, Literature, Music, N Caroliniana, Physical educ, Religion, Virginiana
Special Collections: Church History Coll (United Church of Christ-Southern Conference Archives), bks, mss, memorabilia; Civil War (McClendon Coll); Elon College Archives; Faculty Publications; North Carolina Authors (Johnson Coll), autographed first editions
Automation Activity & Vendor Info: (Cataloging) DRA; (Circulation) DRA; (Course Reserve) DRA; (ILL) DRA; (OPAC) DRA; (Serials) DRA
Database Vendor: Ebsco - EbscoHost, OCLC - First Search, ProQuest, Silverplatter Information Inc.

Publications: brochures; Friends of the Libr Newsletter
Partic in NC-PALS; OCLC Online Computer Library Center, Inc; SE Libr Network
Friends of the Library Group
Departmental Libraries:
LAROSE RESOURCES CENTER, Mooney Bldg, 27244. SAN 354-8104. Tel: 910-584-2343. FAX: 910-538-6799. Web Site: www.elon.edu. 1997-1998 Income $286,000. Mats Exp $19,800, AV Equip $18,800. Sal $228,709 (Prof $71,915)
Subject Interests: AV

ENFIELD

P LILLY PIKE SULLIVAN MUNICIPAL LIBRARY, (LPSML), 103 Railroad St, 27823. SAN 312-8261. Tel: 252-445-5203. FAX: 919-445-4321. E-Mail: enfieldlib@coastalnet.com. *Librn*, Linda L Bunch
Founded 1938. Pop 3,000; Circ 40,570
Jul 2000-Jun 2001 Income $71,691. Mats Exp $12,870, Books $12,000, Per/Ser (Incl. Access Fees) $870. Sal $43,345 (Prof $24,049)
Library Holdings: Bk Vols 24,560; Per Subs 15
Special Collections: Commonwealth Microfilms 1908-; NC History Coll, AV

FAIRMONT

R FIRST BAPTIST CHURCH, Stinceon Ivey Memorial Library, 416 S Main, PO Box 663, 28340. SAN 312-8296. Tel: 910-628-0626. FAX: 910-628-0627. *Librn*, Alice Johnson
Founded 1956
Library Holdings: Bk Vols 5,000

P HECTOR MCLEON PUBLIC LIBRARY, 106 S Main St, PO Box 458, 28340. SAN 312-8288. Tel: 910-628-9331. *Librn*, Carolyn Bullard
Library Holdings: Bk Vols 1,500; Bk Titles 4,000
Partic in Beaufort, Hyde, Martin Regional Libr Syst
Open Fri only 2-5:30
Friends of the Library Group

FAISON

P EMILY HILL LIBRARY,* 109 Park Circle Dr, PO Box 129, 28341. SAN 376-2912. Tel: 910-267-0601. FAX: 910-267-0601. *Asst Librn*, Georgia High-Smith
Library Holdings: Bk Vols 1,500; Bk Titles 1,200
Friends of the Library Group

FAITH

P FAITH PUBLIC LIBRARY, 100 N Main St, PO Box 37, 28041-0064. SAN 312-830X. Tel: 704-279-7500. FAX: 704-279-0408. *Librn*, Karen Fink
Pop 625
Library Holdings: Bk Titles 3,100
Subject Interests: Adult fiction, Children's fiction, Local history

FARMVILLE

P FARMVILLE PUBLIC LIBRARY,* 115 W Church St, 27828. SAN 312-8318. Tel: 252-753-3355. FAX: 252-753-2855. *Asst Librn, Ch Servs*, Carol P Lundegard
Founded 1932. Pop 5,090; Circ 16,500
Library Holdings: Bk Vols 35,000; Per Subs 127

FAYETTEVILLE

M CAPE FEAR VALLEY HEALTH SYSTEM, Library Services, 1638 Owen Dr, PO Box 2000, 28302-2000. (Mail add: PO Box 2000, 28302-2000), SAN 321-4559. Tel: 910-609-6601. FAX: 910-609-7710. *Dir*, Patricia Hammond; E-Mail: pahammond@capefearvalley.com; Staff 2 (MLS 1, Non-MLS 1)
Library Holdings: Bk Titles 3,000; Per Subs 200
Subject Interests: Allied health, Medicine, Nursing
Partic in Nat Libr of Med

P CUMBERLAND COUNTY PUBLIC LIBRARY & INFORMATION CENTER, 300 Maiden Lane, 28301-5000. SAN 354-8139. Tel: 910-483-1580, Ext 102. FAX: 910-486-5372. Web Site: www.cumberland.lib.nc.us. *Dir*, Jerry A Thrasher; E-Mail: thrasher@cumberland.lib.nc.us; *Dep Dir*, Jody Risacher; *ILL*, Lyndia McLean; *Tech Servs*, David Aspinall; *Publ Servs*, Gail Terwilliger; *Circ*, Donna Lampkins; *Govt Doc*, Judith Stoddard; Staff 185 (MLS 45, Non-MLS 140)
Founded 1932. Pop 292,744; Circ 2,207,607
Jul 1999-Jun 2000 Income $8,009,801, State $719,154, County $7,018,905, Other $271,742. Mats Exp $1,024,998, Books $1,000,884, Micro $24,114. Sal $4,711,080
Library Holdings: Bk Vols 650,211
Subject Interests: Commun agencies, Foreign lang mat, Law, Local history, Orgn
Special Collections: Foreign Language Center, bks, newsp, per, compact disc, tapes, video
Automation Activity & Vendor Info: (Circulation) GEAC
Publications: Due Process: A Guide to Information at the Cumberland County Law Library; The Answer Book (community information & referral)
Special Services for the Deaf - Staff with knowledge of sign language; TTY machine
Friends of the Library Group
Branches: 7
BORDEAUX, 3711 Village Dr, 28304. SAN 354-8198. Tel: 910-424-4008. FAX: 910-423-1456. *Branch Mgr*, Robin Deffendall
Library Holdings: Bk Vols 48,830
CLIFFDALE, 6882 Cliffdale Rd, 28314. SAN 371-1374. Tel: 910-864-2600. FAX: 910-487-9090. *Regional Manager*, Eileen Yoshimoto; *Librn*, James Simonson
Library Holdings: Bk Vols 70,267

L CUMBERLAND COUNTY LAW LIBRARY, Courthouse, 117 Dick St, 28302. SAN 354-8163. Tel: 910-323-5618. FAX: 910-485-5291. Jul 1999-Jun 2000 Income $91,226. Mats Exp $38,000. Sal $33,934
Library Holdings: Bk Vols 11,331
Publications: Due Process (bibliography)
EAST REGIONAL, 4809 Clinton Rd, 28301-8992. SAN 378-150X. Tel: 910-485-2955. FAX: 910-485-5492. *Regional Manager*, Pamela Kource
Library Holdings: Bk Vols 51,356
HOPE MILLS BRANCH, 3411 Golfview Rd, Hope Mills, 28348. SAN 354-8317. Tel: 910-425-8455. FAX: 910-423-0997. *Branch Mgr*, Chris Benshoff; *Librn*, Lisa Olsen
Library Holdings: Bk Vols 43,643
Friends of the Library Group
NORTH REGIONAL, 855 McArthur Rd, 28311-1961. SAN 378-1488. Tel: 910-822-1998. FAX: 910-480-0030. *Regional Manager*, Mary Campbell
Library Holdings: Bk Vols 74,745
SPRING LAKE BRANCH, 101 Laketree Blvd, Spring Lake, 28390. SAN 354-8341. Tel: 910-497-3650. FAX: 910-497-0523. *Branch Mgr*, Cindee Campbell
Library Holdings: Bk Vols 26,820
Bookmobiles: 1

C DAVIS MEMORIAL LIBRARY, (Formerly Methodist College), 5400 Ramsey St, 28311. SAN 312-8350. Tel: 910-630-7645. Reference Tel: 910-630-7123. FAX: 910-630-7119. Web Site: www.methodist.edu/library/davis.htm. *Dir Libr Serv*, Susan Pulsipher; Tel: 910-630-7122, E-Mail: sue@methodist.edu; *Asst Libr Dir*, Cynthia Johnson; Tel: 910-630-7126, E-Mail: cjohnson@methodist.edu; *Spec Coll*, Arleen Fields; Tel: 910-630-7587, E-Mail: afields@methodist.edu; *Instr*, Kathryn S Zybeck; Tel: 910-630-7548, E-Mail: kathryns@methodist.edu; Staff 18 (MLS 4, Non-MLS 14)
Founded 1960. Enrl 1,800; Highest Degree: Bachelor
Jul 1999-Jun 2000 Income $467,484. Mats Exp $69,839, Books $66,727, Presv $3,112
Library Holdings: Bk Vols 86,440; Per Subs 728
Subject Interests: NC
Special Collections: Lafayette Coll; Teaching Materials Collection
Automation Activity & Vendor Info: (Acquisitions) Endeavor; (Cataloging) Endeavor; (Circulation) Endeavor; (Media Booking) Endeavor; (OPAC) Endeavor; (Serials) Endeavor
Database Vendor: Ebsco - EbscoHost, OCLC - First Search, Silverplatter Information Inc., Wilson - Wilson Web
Publications: Journal Holdings List
Partic in Cape Fear Health Sciences Information Consortium; Mid-Carolina Academic Library Network
Friends of the Library Group

GM DEPARTMENT OF VETERANS AFFAIRS, Medical Center Library Service,* 2300 Ramsey St, 28301. SAN 312-8369. Tel: 910-822-7072. FAX: 910-822-7907.; Staff 2 (MLS 1, Non-MLS 1)
Founded 1939
Library Holdings: Bk Vols 3,808; Per Subs 400
Subject Interests: Allied health, Medicine, Nursing
Publications: Newsletter
Partic in Cape Fear Health Sciences Information Consortium; Veterans Affairs Library Network

S FAYETTEVILLE PUBLISHING CO, Newspaper Library,* PO Box 849, 28302. SAN 325-7819. Tel: 910-486-3584. FAX: 910-486-3545. Web Site: www.fayettevillenc.com. *Dir*, Daisy Maxwell; E-Mail: dmaxwell@fayettevillenc.com; *Res*, Elina John; *Res*, Jessica Evans; *Res*, Sharon Masters
1998-1999 Income $2,000. Mats Exp $22,000, Books $15,000, Per/Ser (Incl. Access Fees) $5,000, Other Print Mats $2,000. Sal $70,000 (Prof $40,000)
Library Holdings: Bk Vols 3,500; Per Subs 79
Subject Interests: Local history
Special Collections: Fayetteville Observer-Times (newspaper)
Restriction: Staff use only

C FAYETTEVILLE STATE UNIVERSITY, Charles W Chesnutt Library, Newbold Sta, 1200 Murchinson Rd, 28301-4298. SAN 312-8334. Tel: 910-672-1233, Ext 1111. FAX: 910-672-1746. Web Site: www.usncfsu.edu/w5/

lib/libhome.htm. *Dir*, Bobby Wynn; *Publ Servs*, Eloise Cave; E-Mail: eloise@lib1.uncfsu.edu; *Tech Servs*, Daniel Pthol; *Assoc Dir, Coll Develop*, Teresa McManus; *Per*, Evelyn Council; *Circ*, Marian Smith; Staff 11 (MLS 11)
Founded 1937. Enrl 2,666; Fac 139; Highest Degree: Master
Library Holdings: Bk Vols 250,000; Bk Titles 125,000; Per Subs 2,100
Subject Interests: African Am, Ethnic studies
Special Collections: US Govt Doc, Archives
Publications: acquisitions list; Ches-Notes
Partic in SOQUIJ
Friends of the Library Group

J FAYETTEVILLE TECHNICAL COMMUNITY COLLEGE, Paul H Thompson Library, 2201 Hull Rd, 28303-4761. (Mail add: PO Box 35236, 28303-0236), SAN 312-8342. Tel: 910-678-8400. Interlibrary Loan Service Tel: 910-678-8247. FAX: 910-678-8401. Web Site: library.faytech.cc.nc.us. *Dir*, Susan Rose; E-Mail: roses@ftccmail.cc.nc.us; *Librn*, Jeff Campbell; *ILL, Librn*, Barbara Marson; *Media Spec*, Deborah Foster; Staff 3 (MLS 3)
Founded 1961. Enrl 7,965; Highest Degree: Associate
Jul 1999-Jun 2000 Income $1,159,823. Mats Exp $452,809, Books $122,534, Per/Ser (Incl. Access Fees) $88,857, AV Equip $24,651, Electronic Ref Mat (Incl. Access Fees) $20,254. Sal $707,014
Library Holdings: Bk Vols 60,000; Per Subs 370
Subject Interests: Bus, Funeral service, Health occupation, Law, Mgt
Partic in Westlaw

M SOUTHERN REGIONAL AREA HEALTH EDUCATION CENTER, (SRAHEC IAC), Information Access Center, 1601 Owen Dr, 28304. SAN 312-8326. Tel: 910-678-7273. Interlibrary Loan Service Tel: 910-678-7204. Reference Tel: 910-678-7276. FAX: 910-323-4007. E-Mail: reference@sr-ahec.org. Web Site: www.SouthernRegionalAHEC.org. *Actg Dir, Info Res*, Rebecca Johnston; Tel: 910-678-7270, E-Mail: rebecca.johnston@sr-ahec.org; *Info Res*, Michael Williams; Tel: 910-678-7222, E-Mail: mike.williams@sr-ahec.org; *Info Res*, Russet Hambrick; Tel: 910-678-7249, E-Mail: russet.hambrick@sr-ahec.org; Staff 8 (MLS 3, Non-MLS 5)
Founded 1977
Jul 2000-Jun 2001 Income $460,921, State $434,421, Locally Generated Income $26,500. Mats Exp $62,000, Books $6,500, Per/Ser (Incl. Access Fees) $44,000, Electronic Ref Mat (Incl. Access Fees) $11,500. Sal $260,065 (Prof $145,463)
Library Holdings: Bk Vols 6,000; Per Subs 249
Subject Interests: Allied health, Medicine, Mental health, Nursing
Automation Activity & Vendor Info: (Cataloging) EOS; (Circulation) EOS; (OPAC) EOS
Database Vendor: OCLC - First Search
Partic in Cape Fear Health Sciences Information Consortium; NC Area Health Education Centers; Regional Med Libr; S Cent Health Info Network of NC

FLAT ROCK

J BLUE RIDGE COMMUNITY COLLEGE LIBRARY,* College Dr, 28731. SAN 312-8377. Tel: 828-692-3572, Ext 272. FAX: 828-692-2059. *Librn*, Susan D Williams; E-Mail: susanw@blueridge.cc.nc.us
Founded 1969
1997-1998 Income $136,841. Mats Exp $47,655, Books $23,835, Per/Ser (Incl. Access Fees) $13,746, Presv $116. Sal $80,104
Library Holdings: Bk Vols 29,000
Automation Activity & Vendor Info: (Cataloging) epixtech, inc.; (Circulation) epixtech, inc.
Partic in NC Dept of Commun Cols
Open Mon-Thurs 8am-9pm & Fri 8-4:30

FOREST CITY

S AMERICAN HARP SOCIETY REPOSITORY,* 255 Weatherstone Dr, 28043. SAN 374-9061. Tel: 828-245-7052. FAX: 828-245-7052.

P MOONEYHAM PUBLIC LIBRARY, 240 E Main St, 28043. SAN 355-1288. Tel: 828-248-5224. FAX: 828-248-5224. E-Mail: mcostner@rfei.net. *Librn*, Mary S Costner
Library Holdings: Bk Vols 15,600

FORT BRAGG

UNITED STATES ARMY

A JOHN L THROCKMORTON LIBRARY, Bldg 1-3346, Randolph St, 28307-5000. SAN 354-8406. Tel: 910-396-3526. Interlibrary Loan Service Tel: 910-396-5407. FAX: 910-396-8872. *Chief Librn*, Gloritha Mercer; E-Mail: mercerg@bragg.army.mil; *Coll Develop, Ref*, Nancy Kutulas; *Tech Servs*, Fred Fuller; *ILL*, Careen Smith; Staff 11 (MLS 3, Non-MLS 8)
Founded 1941
Oct 1997-Sep 1998 Income $328,000. Mats Exp $70,000
Library Holdings: Bk Vols 98,921; Per Subs 220
Subject Interests: Current affairs, History, International relations, Mil sci
Publications: Bibliographies
Partic in Fedlink; OCLC Online Computer Library Center, Inc

S MARQUAT MEMORIAL LIBRARY, Bldg D-3915, Rm C-287, 28310. (Mail add: c/o Marquat Memorial Library, USAJFKSWCS, Attn: AOJK-HS-LB, 28310), SAN 354-8430. Tel: 910-396-3958, 910-396-5370. FAX: 910-432-7788. *Chief Librn*, Jane Crabill; E-Mail: crabillj@soc.mil; *Ref*, George Kinard; E-Mail: kinardg@soc.mil; *Acq, Cat*, Roberta Straight; Tel: 910-432-6503, E-Mail: straighr@soc.mil; *ILL*, Eva Murphy; Tel: 910-432-9222, E-Mail: murphye@soc.mil; *Circ*, Robert Boozer. Subject Specialists: *Civil serv*, George Kinard; *Psychology*, George Kinard; *Regional studies*, George Kinard; Staff 5 (MLS 2, Non-MLS 3)
Founded 1952
Oct 1999-Sep 2000 Income $72,800. Mats Exp $43,000, Books $9,000, Per/Ser (Incl. Access Fees) $34,000
Library Holdings: Bk Vols 29,000; Per Subs 200
Subject Interests: Geopolitics, International relations, Lang, Mil assistance, Political science, Spec forces, Spec operations, Terrorism, Unconventional warfare
Automation Activity & Vendor Info: (Cataloging) TLC; (Circulation) TLC; (Course Reserve) TLC; (ILL) TLC; (OPAC) TLC
Publications: (Accession list); Bibliographics (2/yr); Library Guide; Periodicals Holdings List
Restriction: Circulation to military employees only
Partic in Fedlink; OCLC Online Computer Library Center, Inc

AM WOMACK ARMY MEDICAL CENTER MEDICAL LIBRARY, 28310. Tel: 910-907-8275. FAX: 910-907-7449. *Librn*, Joan Hathaway; *ILL*, Brenda Lowery; *ILL*, Veronica Goss
Library Holdings: Bk Vols 3,622; Per Subs 170
Restriction: Not open to public
Function: ILL available, Photocopies available
Partic in Fedlink

FRANKLIN

P MACON COUNTY PUBLIC LIBRARY,* 108 Wayah St, 28734. SAN 312-8385. Tel: 828-524-3600, 828-524-3700. FAX: 828-524-9550. E-Mail: kwallace@ncsl.dcr.state.nc.us. Web Site: main.nc.us/libraries/fontana. *Librn*, Karen Wallace
Founded 1890
Jul 1997-Jun 1998 Income $420,809, State $1,000, City $15,000, County $281,642, Locally Generated Income $20,757, Parent Institution $35,890, Other $66,520. Mats Exp $44,811, Books $37,371, Per/Ser (Incl. Access Fees) $4,677, Micro $553. Sal $175,057 (Prof $62,077)
Library Holdings: Bk Vols 51,302
Friends of the Library Group
Branches: 1
HUDSON LIBRARY, 554 Main St, Highlands, 28741. SAN 312-8830. Tel: 828-526-3031. FAX: 828-526-5278. Web Site: main.nc.us/libraries/fontana. *Librn*, Mary Lou Worley; E-Mail: mworley@ncls.dcr.state.nc.us; Staff 4 (MLS 1, Non-MLS 3)
Founded 1884
Jul 1997-Jun 1998 Income $79,049, County $75,000, Locally Generated Income $4,048. Mats Exp $16,200, Books $14,000, Per/Ser (Incl. Access Fees) $2,200. Sal $49,152 (Prof $26,187)
Library Holdings: Bk Vols 22,367

FRANKLINTON

S NOVO NORDISK BIOCHEM NA, INC, Information Services,* 77 Perry Chapel Church Rd, Box 576, 27525-0576. SAN 326-6427. Tel: 919-494-3135. FAX: 919-494-3461. E-Mail: kwg@novo.dk. *Librn*, Robert Larson
Library Holdings: Bk Titles 3,300; Per Subs 300
Subject Interests: Biochemistry
Partic in BRS; Dialog Corporation; Infoline

GASTONIA

R FLINT-GROVES BAPTIST CHURCH LIBRARY,* 2017 E Ozark, 28054. SAN 312-8393. Tel: 704-865-4068.
Library Holdings: Bk Vols 17,525
Friends of the Library Group

P GASTON COUNTY PUBLIC LIBRARY,* 1555 E Garrison Blvd, 28054. SAN 312-8407. Tel: 704-868-2167. Interlibrary Loan Service Tel: 704-868-2168. FAX: 704-853-0609. Web Site: www.glrl.lib.nc.us. *Dir*, Cindy Moose; Fax: 704-853-6012, E-Mail: cmoose@ncsl.dcr.state.nc.us; *Asst Librn*, Laurel R Hicks; *Circ*, Barbara Daniels; Tel: 704-868-2164; *AV*, Martha H Wilson; Tel: 704-868-2166; *Cat*, Dorsey C Funderburk; Tel: 704-868-2169, Fax: 704-853-6012; *Ref*, Deidre Stevens; *Coll Develop*, Jane Kaylor; Tel: 704-868-2169, Fax: 704-853-6012; *Ch Servs*, Julie Shatterly; Tel: 704-868-2165; *Automation Syst Coordr*, Bonita King; Tel: 704-868-2169; *Ref*, Anne E Gometz; Staff 60 (MLS 11, Non-MLS 49)
Founded 1905. Pop 176,949; Circ 916,578
Jul 1998-Jun 1999 Income (Main Library and Branch Library) County $2,509,748. Mats Exp $406,000, Books $354,000, Per/Ser (Incl. Access Fees) $62,000, AV Equip $27,500, Electronic Ref Mat (Incl. Access Fees) $126,668. Sal $1,549,648
Library Holdings: Bk Vols 450,508; Per Subs 659

Subject Interests: Genealogy, Local history
Special Collections: Art (D E McConnell Coll); Art (Louis Orr Etchings); Local History & Genealogy
Automation Activity & Vendor Info: (Cataloging) Gaylord; (Circulation) Gaylord; (OPAC) Gaylord
Function: ILL available
Mem of Gaston-Lincoln Regional Library
Friends of the Library Group
Branches: 9
BELMONT BRANCH, 111 Central Ave, Belmont, 28012. SAN 312-7451. Tel: 704-825-5426. FAX: 704-825-4323.
BESSEMER CITY BRANCH, 207 N 12th St, Bessemer City, 28016. SAN 312-7478. Tel: 704-629-3321. FAX: 704-629-9804.
CHERRYVILLE BRANCH, 605 E Main St, Cherryville, 28021. SAN 312-7923. Tel: 704-435-6767. FAX: 704-435-8744.
DALLAS BRANCH, 105 S Holland St, Dallas, 28034. SAN 312-8032. Tel: 704-922-3621. FAX: 704-922-7744.
ERWIN CENTER, 913 Pryor St, 28052. SAN 372-5189. Tel: 704-868-8046. FAX: 704-868-8046.
LOWELL BRANCH, 203 McAdenville Rd, Lowell, 28098. SAN 312-908X. Tel: 704-824-1266. FAX: 704-824-5887.
MOUNT HOLLY BRANCH, 245 W Catawba Ave, Mount Holly, 28120. SAN 312-925X. Tel: 704-827-3581. FAX: 704-827-8573.
STANLEY BRANCH, 205 N Peterson St, Stanley, 28164. SAN 320-9083. Tel: 704-263-4166. FAX: 704-263-1201.
UNION ROAD, 5800 Union Road, 28056. Tel: 704-852-9631. FAX: 704-852-4073. *In Charge*, DeAnn Redwing
Library Holdings: Bk Vols 12,000

P GASTON-LINCOLN REGIONAL LIBRARY,* 1555 E Garrison Blvd, 28054. SAN 312-8415. Tel: 704-868-2164. Interlibrary Loan Service Tel: 704-868-2168. FAX: 704-853-0609. Web Site: www.glrl.lib.nc.us. *Dir*, Lucinda W Moose; E-Mail: cmoose@ncsl.dcr.state.nc.us; *Asst Dir*, Laurel Hicks; *ILL*, DeAnn Redwing; *ILL*, James Anderson
Founded 1964. Pop 231,273; Circ 1,197,151
Jul 1997-Jun 1998 Income $3,299,602, State $439,670, County $2,859,932. Mats Exp $1,218,437. Sal $1,770,980
Library Holdings: Bk Vols 541,627; Per Subs 1,017
Subject Interests: Genealogy, Local history
Member Libraries: Gaston County Public Library; Lincoln County Public Library
Friends of the Library Group

S SCHIELE MUSEUM OF NATURAL HISTORY LIBRARY, 1500 E Garrison Blvd, 28054-5199. SAN 328-0691. Tel: 704-866-6900. FAX: 704-866-6041. *Coll Develop*, Timothy Gamble
Library Holdings: Bk Vols 7,600; Bk Titles 7,000; Per Subs 20
Subject Interests: Archaeology, Astronomy, Mus studies, Natural history
Restriction: Open to others by appointment, Staff use only
Function: Research library
Partic in Library of Congress

GATESVILLE

P GATES COUNTY LIBRARY, 115 Court St, PO Box 27, 27938. SAN 312-8423. Tel: 252-357-0110. FAX: 252-357-1285. *Librn*, Patricia B Familar; Staff 2 (MLS 1, Non-MLS 1)
Pop 9,100
Library Holdings: Bk Vols 27,000; Per Subs 40
Mem of Albemarle Regional Library
Statistics included with regional library. See Winton entry

GOLDSBORO

S CHERRY HOSPITAL, Learning Resource Center Library, 201 Stevens Mill Rd, 27533. SAN 325-7827. Tel: 919-731-3447. FAX: 919-731-3429. Web Site: www.esn.net/win/cherry.htm. *Librn*, Marie M Edwards; E-Mail: medwards@dhr.state.nc.us
Library Holdings: Bk Vols 3,000; Per Subs 62
Partic in Wayne Info Network

J WAYNE COMMUNITY COLLEGE LIBRARY,* 3000 Wayne Memorial Dr, PO Box 8002, 27533-8002. SAN 312-8431. Tel: 919-735-5151, Ext 264. FAX: 919-736-3204. Web Site: www.wayne.cc.nc.us/library/wcclib.htm. *Dir Libr Serv*, Dr Shirley T Jones; Tel: 919-735-5152, E-Mail: sj@wcc.wayne.cc.nc.us; *Librn*, Susan Parris; Tel: 919-735-5152, E-Mail: sparris@wcc.wayne.cc.nc.us; *Coll Develop*, Dot Elledge; Tel: 919-735-5152, E-Mail: dee@wcc.wayne.cc.nc.us
Founded 1965. Enrl 2,600; Fac 115; Highest Degree: Associate
Library Holdings: Bk Vols 42,700; Bk Titles 40,500; Per Subs 401
Subject Interests: Genealogy
Automation Activity & Vendor Info: (Acquisitions) epixtech, inc.; (Cataloging) epixtech, inc.; (Circulation) epixtech, inc.; (OPAC) epixtech, inc.
Partic in Wayne Info Network

P WAYNE COUNTY PUBLIC LIBRARY, INC,* 1001 E Ash St, 27530. SAN 354-849X. Tel: 919-735-1824. FAX: 919-731-2889. *Dir*, Jane Rustin; *Ch Servs*, Donna Phillips; Staff 27 (MLS 4, Non-MLS 23)
Founded 1907. Pop 140,000
Library Holdings: Bk Vols 100,000; Per Subs 190
Subject Interests: Genealogy, Large print, Local history
Publications: Calendar; Friend Reminders; Friends Newsletter
Friends of the Library Group
Branches: 6
FREMONT PUBLIC, 202 N Goldsboro St, PO Box 488, Fremont, 27830. SAN 354-8554. Tel: 919-242-5442. *Mgr*, Cathy Bannister
L LAW, County Court House, 27530. SAN 370-9035. Tel: 919-731-1457. *Mgr*, Marshell Becton
PIKEVILLE PUBLIC, 107 W Main St, Pikeville, 27863. SAN 354-8589. Tel: 919-242-6446. Web Site: www.wcpl.org. *Mgr*, Cathy Bannister
Friends of the Library Group
ROSEWOOD, Rosewood High School Media Ctr, 900 Rosewood Rd, 27530. SAN 370-9043. Tel: 919-705-6045. FAX: 919-731-1309. Web Site: www.wcpl.org. *Mgr*, Belle Frazer
Friends of the Library Group
SEVEN SPRINGS PUBLIC, W Spring St, Seven Springs, 28578. SAN 354-8619. Tel: 919-569-2631. Web Site: www.wcpl.org. *Mgr*, June Joyner
STEELE MEMORIAL, 111 N Chestnut St, Mount Olive, 28365. SAN 354-8643. Tel: 919-658-2580. FAX: 919-658-2580. Web Site: www.wcpl.org. *Mgr*, Louise Bearfoot
Library Holdings: Bk Vols 8,000
Friends of the Library Group
Bookmobiles: 1

GOLDSTON

P GOLDSTON PUBLIC LIBRARY,* 355 Goldston-Glendon Rd, PO Box 40, 27252-0040. SAN 354-530X. Tel: 919-898-4522. FAX: 919-898-4522. Web Site: www.ils.unc.edu/nclibs/centralnc/home.htm. *Librn*, Karen Sheaffer; E-Mail: ksheaffe@ncsl.dcr.state.nc.us
1997-1998 Mats Exp Books $5,000
Library Holdings: Bk Titles 7,600; Per Subs 12
Mem of Central North Carolina Regional Library
Friends of the Library Group

GRAHAM

J ALAMANCE COMMUNITY COLLEGE, Learning Resources Center, 1247 Jimmie Kerr Rd, PO Box 8000, 27253-8000. SAN 312-8733. Tel: 336-506-4116. FAX: 336-578-5561. E-Mail: lrc@netpath.net. Web Site: www.alamance.cc.nc.us. *Dir*, Dr Laura Gorham; Tel: 336-506-4186, E-Mail: gorhamls@alamance.cc.nc.us
Founded 1960. Enrl 3,500
Library Holdings: Bk Vols 22,000; Per Subs 168
Subject Interests: Applied arts, Bus, Econ, Education, Eng tech, Human servs, Mechanical occupations, Sci-tech

S ALAMANCE COUNTY HISTORIC PROPERTIES COMMISSION, Historic Restoration Resources Library,* 124 W Elm St, 27253. SAN 325-7886. Tel: 336-228-1312. FAX: 336-570-6788. E-Mail: alamtlam@intertath.com. *Asst Dir*, Tom King
Subject Interests: Genealogy, Historic preservation

P GRAHAM PUBLIC LIBRARY,* 211 S Main St, PO Box 1097, 27253. SAN 354-5296. Tel: 336-570-6730. FAX: 336-570-6732. *Mgr*, Karen Favreau; *Librn*, Carolyn Allen
Library Holdings: Bk Titles 29,000
Mem of Central North Carolina Regional Library
Friends of the Library Group

GRANTSBORO

J PAMLICO COMMUNITY COLLEGE, Division of Learning Resources, 5049 Hwy 306 S, PO Box 185, 28529-0185. SAN 312-8474. Tel: 252-249-1851, Ext 3033. Interlibrary Loan Service Tel: 252-249-1851, Ext 3034. Circulation Tel: 252-249-1851, Ext 3034. Reference Tel: 252-249-1851, Ext 3034. FAX: 252-249-2377. Web Site: www.pamlico.cc.nc.us. *Dean of Libr*, Myra Blue; E-Mail: mblue@pamlico.cc.nc.us; Staff 4 (MLS 1, Non-MLS 3)
Founded 1963. Enrl 237; Fac 16; Highest Degree: Associate
Library Holdings: Bk Titles 20,000; Per Subs 142
Subject Interests: Black hist, Bus, Econ, Ethnic studies, Health, Local history, Mgt, Sci-tech
Automation Activity & Vendor Info: (Cataloging) SIRSI; (Circulation) SIRSI; (Course Reserve) SIRSI; (ILL) SIRSI; (Media Booking) SIRSI; (OPAC) SIRSI; (Serials) SIRSI
Database Vendor: Ebsco - EbscoHost, GaleNet, OCLC - First Search, ProQuest, Silverplatter Information Inc.
Mem of NC Dept of Community Cols
Partic in CCLINC; OCLC Online Computer Library Center, Inc
Friends of the Library Group
Bookmobiles: 1

GREENSBORO

C BENNETT COLLEGE, Thomas F Holgate Library, 900 E Washington St, Campus Box M, 27401-3239. SAN 312-8482. Tel: 336-370-8639. FAX: 336-230-1459. Web Site: www.bennett.edu/library. *Dir*, Dr Dorothy Burnett; Staff 5 (MLS 3, Non-MLS 2)
Founded 1939. Enrl 581; Fac 60
Library Holdings: Bk Vols 98,000; Bk Titles 94,790; Per Subs 365
Subject Interests: Black women
Special Collections: (Bennett College Archives), bks, clippings, photog; Art (Carnegie Art Coll), bks, repro; Bennett College History; Black Studies, Women (Afro-American Women's Coll), bks, clippings, photog; Individual Biography, Black (Norris Wright Cuney; Palmer Coll; Papers), clippings, correspondence
Partic in OCLC Online Computer Library Center, Inc

S CENTER FOR CREATIVE LEADERSHIP LIBRARY,* One Leadership Pl, PO Box 26300, 27438-6300. SAN 321-0553. Tel: 336-288-7210. FAX: 336-286-4087. *Dir, Librn*, Frank Freeman; E-Mail: freeman@leaders.ccl.org; *Ref*, Peggy Cartner; Staff 4 (MLS 4)
Founded 1969
Library Holdings: Bk Titles 5,800; Per Subs 200
Publications: bibliographies; information guides; Leadership Education: A Sourcebook of Courses & Programs; Leadership Resources: A Guide to Training & Development Tools
Partic in Dialog Corporation; Dow Jones News Retrieval; OCLC Online Computer Library Center, Inc

S CONE MILLS CORP LIBRARY,* 3101 N Elm St, 27408. SAN 312-8512. Tel: 336-379-6220. FAX: 336-379-6240.
Library Holdings: Bk Vols 4,053; Per Subs 90
Subject Interests: Bus, Chemistry, Marketing, Mgt, Textile tech

R CURRIE LIBRARY, 617 N Elm St, 27401. SAN 312-8547. Tel: 336-373-0445. FAX: 336-275-9398. *Librn*, Nancy Fuller; Staff 1 (MLS 1)
Founded 1925
Jan 2000-Dec 2000 Mats Exp $5,350, Books $3,000, Per/Ser (Incl. Access Fees) $350, AV Equip $2,000
Library Holdings: Bk Vols 18,000; Bk Titles 18,000; Per Subs 21
Subject Interests: Music
Open Mon-Fri 9:30-3:30, Sun 9:30-12:30

R FIRST BAPTIST CHURCH LIBRARY, PO Box 5443, 27435. SAN 312-8539. Tel: 336-274-3286. FAX: 336-274-3288. *Librn*, Elizabeth Qualls; Staff 1 (MLS 1)
Founded 1947
Library Holdings: Bk Vols 16,000; Per Subs 39
Subject Interests: Children's literature, Religion

C GREENSBORO COLLEGE, James Addison Jones Library, 815 W Market St, 27401. SAN 312-8555. Tel: 336-272-7102, Ext 241. FAX: 336-230-9854. *Dir*, Pamela McKirdy; Tel: 336-272-7102, Ext 240, E-Mail: mckirdyp@gborocollege.edu; *Chair*, Tony Wyatt; Tel: 336-272-7102, Ext 394, E-Mail: wyattt@gborocollege.edu; *Assoc Dir, Cat*, Elizabeth Bernhardt; Tel: 336-272-7102, Ext 315, E-Mail: bernhardtb@gborocollege.edu; *Spec Coll*, Patricia Humburg; Tel: 336-272-7102, Ext 377, E-Mail: humburgp@gborocollege.edu; *Circ*, Stephen Ford; Tel: 336-272-7102, Ext 328, E-Mail: fords@gborocollege.edu; *ILL, Ref*, Jennie Hunt; Tel: 336-272-7102, Ext 378, E-Mail: huntj@gborocollege.edu; Staff 6 (MLS 3, Non-MLS 3)
Founded 1838. Enrl 991; Fac 50; Highest Degree: Bachelor
Jul 1998-Jul 1999 Income $344,904, State $9,622, Parent Institution $335,282. Mats Exp $139,694, Books $29,015, Per/Ser (Incl. Access Fees) $28,118, Presv $1,881, AV Equip $3,036, Manuscripts & Archives $1,881, Electronic Ref Mat (Incl. Access Fees) $17,490. Sal $205,210 (Prof $117,000)
Library Holdings: Bk Vols 103,549; Bk Titles 69,472; Per Subs 302; High Interest/Low Vocabulary Bk Vols 11; Bks on Deafness & Sign Lang 9
Subject Interests: Music, Religious studies, Special education
Database Vendor: DRA, Ebsco - EbscoHost, Lexis-Nexis, OCLC - First Search, ProQuest, Silverplatter Information Inc., Wilson - Wilson Web
Publications: Friends of the Greensboro College Newsletter; Guide to the James Addison Jones Library
Partic in Solinet
Friends of the Library Group

S GREENSBORO HISTORICAL MUSEUM ARCHIVES LIBRARY,* 130 Summit Ave, 27401-3004. SAN 326-4521. Tel: 336-373-2043, 336-373-2976. FAX: 336-373-2204. *Dir*, William Moore; *Archivist*, Stephen Catlett
Founded 1924
Library Holdings: Bk Titles 2,500; Per Subs 10
Special Collections: Dolley Madison Coll, bks, letters, docs; O Henry Coll, bks, newsp clippings
Restriction: Staff use only

S GREENSBORO MASONIC MUSEUM LIBRARY,* 426 W Market St, PO Box 466, 27402. SAN 325-786X. Tel: 336-273-8502. FAX: 336-275-3579. *Curator*, Robert A Pinnix
Restriction: Not open to public

P GREENSBORO PUBLIC LIBRARY, 219 N Church St, 27401. SAN 354-8678. Tel: 336-373-2471. Interlibrary Loan Service Tel: 336-373-2159. Circulation Tel: 336-373-2159. Reference Tel: 336-373-2471, Ext 2. FAX: 336-333-6781. Reference FAX: 336-335-5416. Web Site: www.greensborolibrary.org. *Dir*, Sandra M Neerman; Tel: 336-373-2699, E-Mail: sandy.neerman@ci.greensboro.nc.us; *Asst Dir*, Brigette Blanton; *Acq, Coll Develop, Tech Servs*, Katherine S Shropshire; Tel: 336-373-2719, E-Mail: kathyt.shropshire@ci.greensboro.nc.us; *Asst Dir*, Steve L Sumerford; Tel: 336-297-5002, E-Mail: steve.sumerford@ci.greensboro.nc.us; *Ch Servs*, Jim B Young; Tel: 336-373-4103, Fax: 336-335-5415, E-Mail: jim.young@ci.greensboro.nc.us; *Commun Relations*, Steven L Sumerford; Tel: 336-297-5002, E-Mail: steve.sumerford@ci.greensboro.nc.us; *Ref*, Shearin Antonowicz; Tel: 336-373-2466, E-Mail: sherrie.antonowicz@ci.greensboro.nc.us; *Ref Serv*, Helen M Snow; Tel: 336-373-2706, E-Mail: helen.snow@ci.greensboro.nc.us; *Business*, Mary Alice Watkins; Tel: 336-373-4559, E-Mail: mary.watkins@ci.greensboro.nc.us; Staff 32 (MLS 32)
Founded 1902. Pop 294,964; Circ 1,358,996
Jul 1998-Jun 1999 Income $7,864,741, State $311,284, City $7,147,475, Federal $83,413, County $322,300, Other $83,682. Mats Exp $771,531. Sal $3,475,733
Library Holdings: Bk Vols 541,534; Per Subs 919
Subject Interests: Bus, Genealogy, Local history, Mgt
Automation Activity & Vendor Info: (Acquisitions) epixtech, inc.; (Cataloging) epixtech, inc.; (Circulation) epixtech, inc.; (Serials) epixtech, inc.
Publications: Clubs & Organizations Directory; Globa Greensboro Directory
Special Services for the Deaf - Books on deafness & sign language; Captioned film depository; High interest/low vocabulary books; Special interest periodicals; Staff with knowledge of sign language; TTY machine
Friends of the Library Group
Branches: 8
BENCHMARK SQUARE, 405 Rocky Knoll Rd, 27406. SAN 329-5931. Tel: 336-373-5870. FAX: 336-332-6450.
Library Holdings: Bk Vols 32,302
Friends of the Library Group
BENJAMIN, 1530 Benjamin Pkwy, 27408. SAN 354-8708. Tel: 336-545-5340. FAX: 336-545-5954.
Library Holdings: Bk Vols 54,693
Friends of the Library Group
GLENWOOD COMMUNITY, 1901 W Florida St, 27403. SAN 375-5517. Tel: 336-297-5000. FAX: 336-297-5005. *Librn*, Steven Sumerford; Tel: 336-297-5002, E-Mail: steve.sumerford@ci.greensboro.nc.us
Library Holdings: Bk Vols 32,800
Friends of the Library Group
GUILFORD COLLEGE, 619 Dolley Madison Rd, 27410. SAN 354-8767. Tel: 336-373-2923. FAX: 336-851-5047.
Library Holdings: Bk Vols 42,039
Friends of the Library Group
MCGIRT-HORTON, 2509 Phillips Ave, 27405. SAN 354-8732. Tel: 336-373-5810. FAX: 336-332-6458. *Librn*, Velma J Shoffner; E-Mail: velma.shoffner@ci.greensboro.nc.us
Library Holdings: Bk Vols 29,247
Friends of the Library Group
NORTHEAST, 2223 N Church St, 27405. SAN 370-9310. Tel: 336-373-5878. FAX: 336-412-5962. *Librn*, Velma Shoffner; Tel: 336-373-5810, Fax: 336-332-6458, E-Mail: velma.shoffner@ci.greensboro.nc.us
Library Holdings: Bk Vols 27,997
Friends of the Library Group
SOUTHWEST, 4707 High Point Rd, 27407. SAN 354-8821. Tel: 336-373-2925. *Librn*, Karen Favreau; Tel: 336-373-2926, Fax: 336-855-6635, E-Mail: karen.favreau@ci.greensboro.nc.us
Library Holdings: Bk Vols 41,771
Friends of the Library Group
VANCE H CHAVIS LIBRARY, 900 S Benbow Rd, 27406. SAN 354-8791. Tel: 336-373-5838. FAX: 336-333-6781. *Librn*, Lou Sua; Tel: 336-373-5841, Fax: 336-412-5960, E-Mail: lou.sua@ci.greensboro.nc.us
Library Holdings: Bk Vols 32,158
Friends of the Library Group
Bookmobiles: 1. Service to Daycares, Homebounders & Nursing Homes

C GUILFORD COLLEGE, Hege Library, 5800 W Friendly Ave, 27410-4175. SAN 312-8563. Tel: 336-316-2450. Reference Tel: 336-316-2265. FAX: 336-316-2950. Web Site: www.guilford.edu/original/libraryart/. *Dir*, Mary Ellen Chijioke; Tel: 336-316-2129, E-Mail: mchijiok@guilford.edu; *Online Servs, Ref*, Evelyn Blount; Tel: 336-316-2312, E-Mail: eblount@guilford.edu; *Ref Serv*, Diana Engel; Tel: 336-316-2380, E-Mail: dengel@guilford.edu; *Per*, Kate Hood; Tel: 336-316-2362, E-Mail: khood@guilford.edu; *Acq*, Carol Cothern; Tel: 336-316-2252, E-Mail: ccothern@guilford.edu; *Cat*, Ruth Scales; Tel: 336-316-2368, E-Mail: rscales@guilford.edu; *Cat*, Malone Stinson; Tel: 336-316-2368, E-Mail: mstinson@guilford.edu; *AV*, Stan Gilliam; Tel: 336-316-2345, E-Mail: sgilliam@guilford.edu; *AV*, Nabil Ahmed; Tel: 336-316-2261, E-Mail: nahmed@guilford.edu; *Circ*, Charlotte Divitci; Tel: 336-316-2251, E-Mail: cdivitci@guilford.edu; *Spec Coll*, Gwendolyn Erickson; Tel: 336-316-2264, E-Mail: gerickson@guilford.edu; *Spec Coll*, Carole Treadway; Tel: 336-316-2264, E-Mail: ctreadway@guilford.edu; Staff 7 (MLS 6, Non-MLS 1)
Founded 1837. Enrl 1,400; Fac 96; Highest Degree: Bachelor

Jun 1999-May 2000 Income $624,560, Parent Institution $614,997, Other $9,563. Mats Exp $624,561, Books $99,084, Per/Ser (Incl. Access Fees) $87,164, Presv $2,190, Micro $3,680, Electronic Ref Mat (Incl. Access Fees) $12,314. Sal $314,295 (Prof $189,397)
Library Holdings: Bk Vols 243,000; Per Subs 900
Subject Interests: Genealogy, History, North Caroliniana, Sci fi
Special Collections: Religious Society of Friends (Quaker)
Database Vendor: DRA
Publications: Bibliographies
Partic in NC-PALS; SE Libr Network
Friends of the Library Group

S LORILLARD TOBACCO CO LIBRARY, 420 N English St, PO Box 21688, 27420-1688. SAN 312-8571. Tel: 336-335-6896. FAX: 336-335-6640. *Mgr*, Larry Skladanowski; Staff 6 (MLS 4, Non-MLS 2)
Founded 1959
Library Holdings: Bk Titles 4,500; Per Subs 200
Subject Interests: Manufacturing, Related subjects, Tobacco chem, Tobacco products
Automation Activity & Vendor Info: (OPAC) Inmagic, Inc.
Database Vendor: Dialog, OCLC - First Search

S MORFLEX CHEMICAL LIBRARY,* 2110 High Point Rd, 27403. SAN 312-8601. Tel: 336-292-1781. FAX: 336-854-4058. *Dir*, Ralph May; *Tech Servs*, Sam Kennedy
Library Holdings: Bk Vols 780; Per Subs 16
Subject Interests: Chemistry

M MOSES CONE HEALTH SYSTEM, (Formerly Moses H Cone Memorial Hospital), Medical Library, 1200 N Elm St, 27401. SAN 312-8520. Tel: 336-832-7484. FAX: 336-832-7328. Web Site: www.gahec.org/library. *Librn*, Leslie Mackler; Staff 6 (MLS 3, Non-MLS 3)
Founded 1952
Library Holdings: Bk Titles 3,870; Per Subs 200
Subject Interests: Biomed, Life sci, Medicine
Special Collections: Consumer Health; Local History of Medicine
Publications: Newsletter-Offline
Partic in Dialog Corporation; Nat Libr of Med; SE Libr Network

S NEWS-RECORD LIBRARY, 200 E Market St, PO Box 20848, 27420. SAN 312-858X. Tel: 336-373-7169. FAX: 336-373-4437. Web Site: www.news-record.com, www.thedepot.com. *Librn*, Diane Lamb; E-Mail: dlamb@news-record.com; *Archivist*, David Bulgin; Tel: 336-373-5215, E-Mail: dbulgin@news-record.com; *Archivist*, Marcus Green; Tel: 336-373-7044, E-Mail: mgreen@news-record.com
Founded 1969
Library Holdings: Bk Vols 1,075; Bk Titles 1,000; Per Subs 50
Restriction: Private library

C NORTH CAROLINA AGRICULTURAL & TECHNICAL STATE UNIVERSITY, F D Bluford Library, 1601 E Market St, 27411-0002. SAN 312-8598. Tel: 336-334-7782. Circulation Tel: 336-334-7783. Reference Tel: 336-334-7159. Toll Free Tel: 888-246-1271. FAX: 336-334-7783. E-Mail: refemail@ncat.edu. Web Site: www.library.ncat.edu. *Dir Libr Serv*, Waltrene M Canada; Fax: 336-334-7281, E-Mail: canadaw@ncat.edu; *Assoc Dir*, Doris F Mitchell; Tel: 336-334-7158, Fax: 336-334-7281, E-Mail: mitcheld@ncat.edu; *Tech Servs*, Euthena Newman; Tel: 336-334-7668, E-Mail: newman@ncat.edu; *Publ Servs*, Jean Williams; *Cat*, Arneice Bowen; Tel: 336-334-7669, E-Mail: abowen@ncat.edu; *Govt Doc*, Inez Lyons; Tel: 336-334-7753, E-Mail: lyonsi@ncat.edu; *Ser*, Rebecca Floyd; Tel: 336-334-7668, E-Mail: floydr@ncat.edu; *ILL*, Gloria Pitts; E-Mail: gloriap@ncat.edu; *Coll Develop*, Peggy Markham; Tel: 336-334-7158, Fax: 336-334-7281, E-Mail: markham@ncat.edu; *Reader Servs*, Donald Bradsher; E-Mail: bradsher@ncat.edu; *Acq*, Ednita Bullock; Tel: 336-334-7668; Staff 51 (MLS 18, Non-MLS 33)
Founded 1892. Enrl 6,856; Fac 464; Highest Degree: Doctorate
Jul 1999-Jun 2000 Income $3,761,823, State $3,493,776, Federal $268,047. Mats Exp $1,797,499, Books $270,087, Per/Ser (Incl. Access Fees) $952,991, Presv $36,165, Micro $36,982, AV Equip $22,963, Electronic Ref Mat (Incl. Access Fees) $439,407. Sal $1,495,704 (Prof $640,321)
Library Holdings: Bk Vols 457,326; Per Subs 3,988
Subject Interests: Agriculture, Bus, Education, Engineering, Nursing, Technology
Special Collections: Afro-American Coll; Chemistry Library; University Archives
Automation Activity & Vendor Info: (Acquisitions) Innovative Interfaces Inc.; (Cataloging) Innovative Interfaces Inc.; (Circulation) Innovative Interfaces Inc.; (Course Reserve) Innovative Interfaces Inc.; (ILL) Innovative Interfaces Inc.; (Media Booking) Innovative Interfaces Inc.; (OPAC) Innovative Interfaces Inc.; (Serials) Innovative Interfaces Inc.
Database Vendor: CARL, Ebsco - EbscoHost, GaleNet, Lexis-Nexis, OCLC - First Search, ProQuest, Silverplatter Information Inc., Wilson - Wilson Web
Publications: Bluford Notes & Quotes (Newsletter)
Partic in NC LIVE; OCLC Online Computer Library Center, Inc; SE Libr Network

L SMITH, HELMS, MULLISS & MOORE, Law Library, 300 N Greene St, PO Box 21927, 27420. SAN 325-7908. Tel: 336-378-5272. FAX: 336-378-5400. *Mgr Libr Serv*, Anne Washburn; E-Mail: anne_washburn@shmm.com; *Asst Librn*, Carolyn Santanella; Staff 2 (MLS 1, Non-MLS 1)
Library Holdings: Bk Vols 20,000; Per Subs 140

S SYNGENTA CROP PROTECTION, (Formerly Novartis Crop Protection Library), 410 Swing Rd, 27409. SAN 312-8504. Tel: 336-632-2815. FAX: 336-299-8318. *Dir*, Jeff Stabnau; E-Mail: jeff.stabnau@syngenta.com; *Info Specialist*, Jennifer Wilson; Staff 3 (MLS 3)
Founded 1973
Library Holdings: Bk Vols 16,500; Bk Titles 12,000; Per Subs 200
Subject Interests: Agriculture, Bus, Dyestuffs, Mgt, Organic, Specialty chem
Publications: Newsletter
Restriction: Staff use only

C THE UNIVERSITY OF NORTH CAROLINA AT GREENSBORO, Walter Clinton Jackson Library, 1000 Spring Garden St, 27412-0001. (Mail add: PO Box 26175, 27402-6175), SAN 312-8628. Tel: 336-334-5880. Interlibrary Loan Service Tel: 336-334-5849. FAX: 336-334-5399. Interlibrary Loan Service FAX: 336-334-5097. Web Site: www.uncg.edu/lib. *Assoc Dir*, Dana M Sally; *Librn*, Doris J Hulbert; E-Mail: doris_hubert@uncg.edu; *Bibliog Instr*, Nancy C Fogarty; *Cat*, Betty Morrow; *Electronic Resources*, Tim Bucknall; *ILL*, Beth Bernhardt; *Ref*, Kathryn M Crowe; *Spec Coll*, William Finley; *Syst Coordr*, April Wreath; Staff 84 (MLS 29, Non-MLS 55)
Founded 1892. Enrl 12,700; Fac 767; Highest Degree: Doctorate
Library Holdings: Bk Vols 988,232; Bk Titles 674,422; Per Subs 6,500
Special Collections: American Trade Bindings; Cello Music & Literature, flms, scores; Children's Books (Lois Lenski Coll), bks, mss; Creative Writers Coll, bks, mss, photos; Early Dance Books; Early Juvenile Literature; Emily Dickinson Coll; George Herbert Coll, bks, mss; Guilford County Civil Rights Oral History, mss, tapes; Joseph Bryan Coll, mss; North Carolina Children's Authors, bks, mss; North Carolina Composers, mss; Papermaking; Physical Education Coll, bks, mss; Private Presses & Book Arts; Randall Jarrell Coll, tapes, bks, mss; Rare Books; Robbie Emily Dunn Coll of American Detective Fiction; Rupert Brooke Coll; T E Lawrence Coll; University Archives; Way & Williams Coll, artwork, bks, mss; Women Veterans Coll, artifacts, mss, textiles; Women's Studies (Woman's Coll), bks, mss, pamphlets
Automation Activity & Vendor Info: (Circulation) DRA
Database Vendor: CARL, Dialog, DRA, IAC - Info Trac, Lexis-Nexis, OCLC - First Search, Silverplatter Information Inc.
Publications: Library Columns
Partic in Dialog Corporation; Medline; OCLC Online Computer Library Center, Inc; Research Libraries Group, Inc; SE Libr Network
Special Services for the Deaf - Books on deafness & sign language
Friends of the Library Group

M WESLEY LONG COMMUNITY HOSPITAL, Hospital Library,* 501 N Elam Ave, 27403. SAN 325-3120. Tel: 336-832-1299. FAX: 336-832-0370. Web Site: www.med.unc.edu/gahec/celibdiv.htm. *Librn*, Margaret H Furr; E-Mail: mfurr@wlch.hbocvan.com
Founded 1978
Library Holdings: Bk Titles 500; Per Subs 61
Subject Interests: Health care, Medicine, Nursing
Part of Moses Cone Health System Library

SR WESTMINISTER PRESBYTERIAN CHURCH LIBRARY,* 3906 W Friendly Ave, 27410. SAN 375-1996. Tel: 336-299-3785. FAX: 336-299-5837. *Librn*, Mary G Harrill
Library Holdings: Bk Titles 250

GREENVILLE

S CATALYTICA PHARMACEUTICALS INC, Information Services, US 264 & US 13/NC 11, 27835-1887. (Mail add: PO Box 1887, 27835-1887), SAN 325-1411. Tel: 919-707-2146. FAX: 919-707-7252. *Head, Info Serv*, Lynda Stine Werdal; E-Mail: lwerdal@catalytica-pharm.com; Staff 1 (MLS 1)
Founded 1978
Library Holdings: Bk Vols 2,000; Bk Titles 15,000; Per Subs 150
Subject Interests: Analytical chemistry, Pharmaceutical
Special Collections: Career Assistance Wellness and Health
Automation Activity & Vendor Info: (Acquisitions) Sagebrush Corporation; (Serials) Sagebrush Corporation
Database Vendor: OCLC - First Search
Partic in BRS; Dialog Corporation; SDC Info Servs; SE Libr Network

EAST CAROLINA UNIVERSITY
A J FLETCHER MUSIC CENTRE, AJ Fletcher Music Center, Rm A110, 27858-4353. SAN 354-8899. Tel: 252-328-6250. FAX: 252-328-1243. Web Site: www.lib.ecu.edu/musiclib/music.html. *Librn*, David Hursh; Tel: 252-328-1241, E-Mail: hurshd@mail.ecu.edu; Staff 5 (MLS 2, Non-MLS 3)
Founded 1974. Enrl 18,000; Highest Degree: Doctorate
Library Holdings: Bk Vols 44,596; Bk Titles 32,975; Per Subs 166; Spec Interest Per Sub 166
Subject Interests: Music
Database Vendor: epixtech, inc., OCLC - First Search, ProQuest, Wilson

- Wilson Web
Friends of the Library Group
JOYNER LIBRARY Tel: 252-328-6514. FAX: 252-328-4834. Web Site: www.lib.ecu.edu. *Dir*, Carroll Varner; E-Mail: varnerc@mail.ecu.edu; *Assoc Dir*, Gail Munde; *ILL*, Patricia Guyette; *Ref*, Ali Abdulla; *Archivist*, Suellyn Lathrop; *Cat*, Margaret Foote; *Coll Develop*, Kathy D'Angelo; Staff 33 (MLS 33)
Founded 1907. Enrl 16,482; Fac 1,217; Highest Degree: Doctorate
Jul 1997-Jun 1998 Income $6,245,081. Mats Exp $2,060,347, Books $648,314, Per/Ser (Incl. Access Fees) $1,330,493, Presv $69,395. Sal $3,323,165 (Prof $1,088,120)
Library Holdings: Bk Vols 1,051,784; Bk Titles 742,834; Per Subs 6,014
Special Collections: Local History (North Carolina Coll); Regional History (East Carolina Manuscript Coll), print, micro, A-tapes
Partic in North Carolina Library & Information Network; SE Libr Network
Friends of the Library Group

CM WILLIAM E LAUPUS HEALTH SCIENCES LIBRARY, Brody Medical Sciences Bldg, 600 Moye Blvd, 27858-4354. SAN 354-8880. Tel: 252-816-2212. Circulation Tel: 252-816-2219. Reference Tel: 252-816-2230. Toll Free Tel: 877-816-3064. TDD: 252-816-3551. FAX: 252-816-2672. Web Site: www.hsl.ecu.edu. *Dir*, Dorothy A Spencer; *Assoc Dir*, Rick Peterson; Tel: 252-816-3633, E-Mail: petersona@mail.ecu.edu; *Asst Dir*, Patricia Greenstein; Tel: 252-816-2243, E-Mail: greensteinp@mail.brody.ecu.edu; *Head Tech Servs*, Donna McDonald; Tel: 252-816-2228, E-Mail: mcdonaldd@mail.ecu.edu. Subject Specialists: *Resources mgt*, Patricia Greenstein; Staff 17 (MLS 15, Non-MLS 2)
Founded 1969. Highest Degree: Doctorate
Jul 1999-Jun 2000 Income $2,936,640. Mats Exp $1,224,072, Books $181,254, Per/Ser (Incl. Access Fees) $933,633, Presv $13,360, Micro $2,282, AV Equip $9,037, Electronic Ref Mat (Incl. Access Fees) $84,506. Sal $1,555,605 (Prof $630,522)
Library Holdings: Bk Vols 184,151; Per Subs 1,573
Subject Interests: Allied health, Criminal justice, Medicine, Nursing, Soc work
Special Collections: History of Medicine Special Coll
Database Vendor: Ebsco - EbscoHost, IAC - Info Trac, IAC - SearchBank, OCLC - First Search, OVID Technologies, ProQuest, Silverplatter Information Inc.
Partic in Solinet
Special Services for the Deaf - TDD

S GREENVILLE MUSEUM OF ART,* 802 S Evans St, 27834. SAN 312-8644. Tel: 252-758-1946. *Dir*, Barbour Strickland
Library Holdings: Bk Vols 300
Publications: Exhibition catalogs
Restriction: Members only

J PITT COMMUNITY COLLEGE, Learning Resources Center,* Hwy 11 S, PO Drawer 7007, 27835. SAN 312-8652. Tel: 252-321-4357. Interlibrary Loan Service Tel: 252-321-4366. TDD: 252-321-4360. FAX: 252-321-4404. E-Mail: pittlrc@pcc.pitt.cc.nc.us. Web Site: www.pitt.cc.nc.us/lrc/lrc.htm. *Dean*, Lisa C Driver; E-Mail: ldriver@pcc.pitt.cc.nc.us; *Dir*, Linda C Leighty; Tel: 252-321-4352, E-Mail: lleighty@pcc.pitt.cc.nc.us; *Dir Libr Serv*, Linda M Teel; Tel: 252-321-4359, Fax: 252-321-4449, E-Mail: lmteel@pcc.pitt.cc.nc.us; *Acq*, Rita B Williams; E-Mail: rwilliam@pcc.pitt.cc.nc.us; *Tech Servs*, Mary K Godley; Tel: 252-321-4349, Fax: 252-321-4449, E-Mail: mgodley@pcc.pitt.cc.nc.us; *AV*, Teresa W Thompson; Tel: 252-321-4352, E-Mail: tthompson@pcc.pitt.cc.nc.us; *Circ*, Lottie N Joyner; Tel: 252-321-4350, E-Mail: ljoyner@pcc.pitt.cc.nc.us; *Coordr*, Alan R Bailey; Tel: 252-321-4358, E-Mail: abailey@pcc.pitt.cc.nc.us; *ILL*, Hazel J Walker; Fax: 252-321-4449, E-Mail: hwalker@pcc.pitt.cc.nc.us; *Media Spec Ad*, John L Griffin; Tel: 252-321-4345, E-Mail: jgriffin@pcc.pitt.cc.nc.us; *Ser*, Ann N Whitehurst; Tel: 252-321-4362, Fax: 252-321-4449, E-Mail: awhitehu@pcc.pitt.cc.nc.us; Staff 20 (MLS 6, Non-MLS 14)
Founded 1964. Enrl 5,000; Fac 240; Highest Degree: Associate
Jul 1998-Jun 1999 Income State $800,000. Mats Exp $181,378, Books $59,116, Per/Ser (Incl. Access Fees) $42,433, Presv $1,288, Micro $8,156, AV Equip $19,025, Electronic Ref Mat (Incl. Access Fees) $35,212. Sal $454,490 (Prof $285,753)
Library Holdings: Bk Vols 43,823; Bk Titles 33,952; Per Subs 575
Database Vendor: Ebsco - EbscoHost, epixtech, inc., GaleNet, IAC - SearchBank, OCLC - First Search, OVID Technologies, ProQuest, Silverplatter Information Inc.
Partic in CCLINC; Community Col Librs NC

P SHEPPARD MEMORIAL LIBRARY, 530 Evans St, 27858-2398. SAN 312-8660. Tel: 252-329-4580. Circulation Tel: 252-329-4579. Reference Tel: 252-329-4376. FAX: 252-329-4587. Web Site: sheppardlibrary.org. *Dir*, Willie E Nelms; E-Mail: wnelms@ncls.dcr.state.nc.us; *Mgr*, Lynn Branch; Tel: 252-329-4586, E-Mail: lbranch@ci.greenville.nc.us; *Ad Servs*, Tammy Fulcher; E-Mail: tfulcher@ncsl.dcr.state.nc.us; *Ch Servs*, Phyllis Conner; Tel: 252-329-4581, E-Mail: pconner@ncsl.dcr.state.nc.us; *Br Coordr*, Valereia Hoffman; Tel: 252-825-0782, 756-1786; *Br Coordr*, Maryjane Carbo; Tel: 252-329-4582, E-Mail: mcarbo@ncsl.dcr.state.nc.us; *Br Coordr*, Mildred Elliott; Tel: 252-329-4583, Fax: 252-329-4126, E-Mail: melliott@ncsl.dcr.state.nc.us; *Tech Servs*, Meredith Foltz; Tel: 252-329-4588; *Circ*, Charlene Thomas; *Ser*, Kim Averette; *Ch Servs*, Ann Sullivan; Tel: 252-329-4581, E-Mail: asullivan@ncsl.dcr.state.nc.us; *Reader Servs*, Peggy Pollock; Staff 5 (MLS 3, Non-MLS 2)
Founded 1929. Pop 124,395; Circ 420,582
Jul 1999-Jun 2000 Income (Main Library and Branch Library) $1,391,409, State $195,230, City $760,481, County $347,364, Locally Generated Income $84,334, Other $4,000. Mats Exp $194,443, Books $144,394, Per/Ser (Incl. Access Fees) $18,997, Micro $824, AV Equip $30,228. Sal $941,289
Library Holdings: Bk Titles 223,545; Per Subs 399
Automation Activity & Vendor Info: (Cataloging) TLC; (Circulation) TLC
Database Vendor: Ebsco - EbscoHost
Publications: Bookmark (library newsletter)
Function: ILL available
Friends of the Library Group
Branches: 4
C D LANGSTON -R E BOYD LIBRARY, Railroad & Main St, PO Box 395, Winterville, 28590. SAN 373-5389. Tel: 252-756-1786. FAX: 252-756-1786. Web Site: www2.coastalnet.com/~cn4185/index.html. *Librn*, Valeria Hoffman
Friends of the Library Group
EAST BRANCH, 2000 Cedar Lane, 27858. SAN 374-6798. Tel: 252-329-4582. FAX: 252-329-4127. Web Site: www2.coastalnet.com/~cn4185/index.html. *Librn*, Maryjane Carbo
Friends of the Library Group
GEORGE WASHINGTON CARVER LIBRARY, 618 W 14th Ave, 27834. SAN 374-678X. Tel: 252-329-4583. FAX: 252-329-4126. Web Site: www2.coastalnet.com/~cn4185/index.html. *Librn*, Mildred Elliott
Friends of the Library Group
THE MARGARET LITTLE BLOUNT LIBRARY, 201 Ives St, PO Box 1170, Bethel, 27812. SAN 373-5370. Tel: 252-825-0782. FAX: 252-825-0782. Web Site: www2.coastalnet.com/~cn4185/index.html. *Librn*, Valeria Hoffman
Friends of the Library Group
Bookmobiles: 1

GRIFTON

P GRIFTON PUBLIC LIBRARY,* 108 W Queen, PO Box 579, 28530. SAN 312-8679. Tel: 252-524-0345. *Coll Develop, Librn*, Judy Jester
Pop 4,500; Circ 6,602
Jul 1998-Jun 1999 Income $28,000, City $25,000, County $3,000. Mats Exp $3,500. Sal $13,600
Library Holdings: Bk Vols 15,000
Open Mon 12-8 & Tues-Fri 11-6

HALIFAX

P HALIFAX COUNTY LIBRARY, 33 Granville St, PO Box 97, 27839. SAN 312-8687. Tel: 252-583-3631. FAX: 252-583-8661. Web Site: www.halifax.nc.com. *Librn*, Virginia Orvedahl; E-Mail: vorvedah@ncsi.dcr.state.nc.us; Staff 13 (MLS 2, Non-MLS 11)
Founded 1941. Pop 55,432
Library Holdings: Bk Vols 64,000; Per Subs 175
Special Collections: Audio books; Genealogy; Large print books; Local history; Videocassettes
Automation Activity & Vendor Info: (Cataloging) Follett; (Circulation) Follett
Publications: Monthly newsletter
Friends of the Library Group
Branches: 3
SCOTLAND NECK MEMORIAL, 1600 Main St, PO Box 126, Scotland Neck, 27874. SAN 371-3679. Tel: 919-826-5578. FAX: 919-826-5037. *Librn*, Martha Leach
1994-1995 Income $60,000
Library Holdings: Bk Vols 13,000; Per Subs 25
Subject Interests: Genealogy, Ref
Friends of the Library Group
W C BILLY JONES JR MEMORIAL, PO Box 455, Littleton, 27850. SAN 328-6983. Tel: 252-586-3608. FAX: 252-586-3495. *Librn*, Sheila Milan
Friends of the Library Group
WELDON MEMORIAL, 6 W First St, Weldon, 27890. SAN 328-6967. Tel: 252-536-3837. FAX: 252-536-2477. *Librn*, Kim Fluke
Bookmobiles: 1

HAMLET

P HAMLET PUBLIC LIBRARY,* 302 Main St, 28345. SAN 312-8695. Tel: 910-582-3477. FAX: 910-582-3478. *Librn*, Anne Thrower
Founded 1922. Pop 6,800; Circ 39,517
Jul 1997-Jun 1998 Income $128,650. Mats Exp $11,350. Sal $68,470
Library Holdings: Bk Vols 24,000; Per Subs 47
Subject Interests: Fiction, Local history
Mem of Richmond County Public Libr Syst; Sandhill Regional Library System
Friends of the Library Group

J RICHMOND COMMUNITY COLLEGE LIBRARY,* Hwy 74, PO Box 1189, 28345. SAN 312-8709. Tel: 910-582-7000, 910-582-7043. FAX: 910-582-7045. Web Site: www.richmond.cc.nc.us. *Dean*, Emily U Hartzell; E-Mail: ehartzell@richmond.cc.nc.us
Founded 1964
Library Holdings: Bk Vols 30,000; Per Subs 200
Subject Interests: Col transfer, Technology, Vocational
Special Collections: Automobiliana Coll; North Carolina; Railroadiana Coll

HARKERS ISLAND

S US NATIONAL PARK SERVICE CAPE LOOKOUT NATIONAL SEASHORE LIBRARY, 131 Charles St, 28531. SAN 370-3118. Tel: 252-728-2250. FAX: 252-728-2160. Web Site: www.nps.calo/. *In Charge*, Karren Brown
Library Holdings: Bk Vols 700
Restriction: Open to public for reference only

HAVELOCK

P HAVELOCK-CRAVEN COUNTY LIBRARY, 300 Miller Blvd, 28532. SAN 312-8725. Tel: 252-447-7509. FAX: 252-447-7422. *Librn*, Margie Garrison; E-Mail: mgarrison@ncsl.dcr.nc.us; *Librn*, Peggy Pratt
Circ 10,725
Library Holdings: Bk Vols 7,000
Mem of Craven-Pamlico-Carteret Regional Library

HAYESVILLE

P MOSS MEMORIAL LIBRARY,* 26 Anderson St, PO Box 900, 28904. SAN 312-8741. Tel: 828-389-8401. FAX: 828-389-3734. Web Site: www.grove.net/~nrl. *Librn*, Mary Fonda; E-Mail: mfonda@ncsi.dcr.state.nc.us
Founded 1942
Library Holdings: Bk Vols 30,000; Per Subs 100
Mem of Nantahala Regional Library
Friends of the Library Group

HENDERSON

P H LESLIE PERRY MEMORIAL LIBRARY, 134 Rose Ave, 27536. SAN 354-8910. Tel: 252-438-3316. FAX: 252-438-3744. *Dir*, Jeanne Fox; E-Mail: jfox@ncsl.dcr.state.nc.us; *Ref*, Dorothea Critz; *Ch Servs*, Claire Basney; Staff 15 (MLS 3, Non-MLS 12)
Founded 1924. Pop 41,000; Circ 142,066
Jul 1999-Jun 2000 Income $632,657, State $114,381, City $238,638, Federal $15,000, County $238,638, Other $26,000. Mats Exp $133,259. Sal $341,382
Library Holdings: Bk Vols 81,711
Subject Interests: Local history
Automation Activity & Vendor Info: (Cataloging) epixtech, inc.; (Circulation) epixtech, inc.; (OPAC) epixtech, inc.
Publications: Friends Newsletter; Literacy Newsletter
Partic in SE Libr Network
Friends of the Library Group

J VANCE-GRANVILLE COMMUNITY COLLEGE, Learning Resources Center, PO Box 917, 27536. SAN 312-875X. Tel: 252-492-2061. FAX: 252-430-0460. E-Mail: oakley@admin.vgcc.cc.nc.us. Web Site: www.vgcc.cc.nc.us. *Dir*, Sondra Oakley; *Librn*, R Frank Sinclair; Staff 5 (MLS 2, Non-MLS 3)
Founded 1970
Jul 1998-Jun 1999 Income (Main and Other College/University Libraries) $366,230. Mats Exp $126,536, Books $82,100, Per/Ser (Incl. Access Fees) $22,452, Micro $1,095, AV Equip $9,644, Electronic Ref Mat (Incl. Access Fees) $11,245. Sal $147,773 (Prof $66,156)
Library Holdings: Bk Vols 45,308; Bk Titles 39,869; Per Subs 480
Subject Interests: Current novels, Easy bks, Internet bks, Young adults
Publications: LRC Brochure; Student Handbook
Partic in CCLINC; OCLC Online Computer Library Center, Inc
Departmental Libraries:
FRANKLIN CAMPUS, 8100 NC 56 Hwy, PO Box 777, Louisburg, 27549. Tel: 919-496-1567. FAX: 919-496-6604.
SOUTH CAMPUS, PO Box 39, Creedmoor, 27522. Tel: 919-528-4737. FAX: 919-528-1201.
WARREN CAMPUS, PO Box 207, Warrenton, 27589. Tel: 252-257-1900. FAX: 252-257-3612.

HENDERSONVILLE

SR FRUITLAND BAPTIST BIBLE INSTITUTE LIBRARY,* 1455 Gillaim Rd, 28792. SAN 312-8768. Tel: 828-685-8886. FAX: 828-685-8888. *Librn*, Nancy Martin; Staff 2 (MLS 1, Non-MLS 1)
Founded 1949
Library Holdings: Bk Vols 25,995; Per Subs 100

P HENDERSON COUNTY PUBLIC LIBRARY,* 301 N Washington St, 28739. SAN 354-897X. Tel: 828-697-4725. FAX: 828-692-8449. *Dir*, William E Snyder; *Ad Servs*, Nancy Snowden; *Ch Servs*, Loretta Potts; *AV*, Kathryn Conlon; *ILL*, Chris Kursten; *Tech Servs*, Sharon Arnette; Staff 7 (MLS 7)
Founded 1914. Circ 560,627
Library Holdings: Bk Vols 200,000; Per Subs 520
Automation Activity & Vendor Info: (Acquisitions) epixtech, inc.; (Cataloging) epixtech, inc.; (Circulation) epixtech, inc.
Friends of the Library Group
Branches: 4
EDNEYVILLE BRANCH, PO Box 526, 28727. SAN 377-8312. Tel: 828-685-0110. FAX: 828-685-0110. *Librn*, Theresa Weaver
Friends of the Library Group
ETOWAH BRANCH, 245 Brickyard Rd, PO Box 1748, Etowah, 28729. SAN 354-8988. Tel: 828-891-6577. FAX: 828-891-6577. *Librn*, Kay Orr
Library Holdings: Bk Vols 18,302
Friends of the Library Group
FLETCHER BRANCH, PO Box 999, Fletcher, 28732. SAN 354-9003. Tel: 828-687-1218. FAX: 828-684-9446. *Librn*, Cherry Waldrop
Library Holdings: Bk Vols 8,500
Friends of the Library Group
GREEN RIVER, PO Box 158, Tuxedo, 28784. SAN 377-8339. Tel: 828-697-4969. FAX: 828-697-4969. *Librn*, Cynthia Camp

HERTFORD

P PERQUIMANS COUNTY LIBRARY,* 110 W Academy St, 27944. SAN 312-8776. Tel: 252-426-5319. FAX: 252-426-1556. *Librn*, Jeri Oltman; E-Mail: joltman@ncsl.dcr.state.nc.us
Pop 11,000; Circ 45,467
Library Holdings: Bk Vols 26,500; Per Subs 54
Subject Interests: Genealogy, Local history
Mem of Pettigrew Regional Library
Friends of the Library Group

HICKORY

J CATAWBA VALLEY COMMUNITY COLLEGE, Learning Resource Center, 2550 Hwy 70 SE, 28602-9699. SAN 312-8784. Tel: 828-327-7000, Ext 4229. FAX: 828-324-5130. Web Site: www.cvcc.us. *Dir*, James M Payne; E-Mail: jpayne@cvcc.cc.nc.us; Staff 1 (MLS 1)
Founded 1960. Enrl 2,049; Fac 180
Library Holdings: Bk Titles 45,000; Per Subs 250
Subject Interests: Decoration, Furniture
Publications: AV handbook; student handbook

S HICKORY MUSEUM OF ART, INC, Fine Arts Library,* 243 Third Ave NE, PO Box 2572, 28603-2572. SAN 325-3147. Tel: 828-327-8576. FAX: 828-327-7281. E-Mail: hma@w3link.com. *Librn*, Virginia Sain
Founded 1981
Library Holdings: Bk Titles 1,484
Subject Interests: Art history, Studio art

P HICKORY PUBLIC LIBRARY, 375 Third St NE, 28601-5126. SAN 354-9038. Tel: 828-304-0500. Circulation Tel: 828-305-0500, Ext 243. Reference Tel: 828-304-0500, Ext 231. FAX: 828-304-0023. Web Site: www.ci.hickory.nc.us/library. *Dir*, Cora C Miller; Tel: 828-305-0500, Ext 224, E-Mail: cmiller@ci.hickory.nc.us; *Dep Dir*, Hannah Owen; Tel: 828-305-0500, Ext 246, E-Mail: howen@ci.hickory.nc.us; *Ad Servs*, Beth Bradshaw; Tel: 828-305-0500, Ext 225, E-Mail: bbradshaw@ci.hickory.nc.us; Staff 36 (MLS 7, Non-MLS 29)
Founded 1922. Pop 36,000; Circ 320,249
Jul 1999-Jun 2000 Income (Main Library and Branch Library) $1,809,753, State $264,709, City $1,274,228, Federal $1,000, County $168,155, Other $101,661. Mats Exp $439,438. Sal $772,438 (Prof $27,716)
Library Holdings: Bk Vols 115,323; Per Subs 344
Subject Interests: Genealogy, Learning disabilities, Local history
Special Collections: Baseball; Career Enhancement
Automation Activity & Vendor Info: (Cataloging) epixtech, inc.; (Circulation) epixtech, inc.; (Course Reserve) epixtech, inc.; (OPAC) epixtech, inc.
Database Vendor: Ebsco - EbscoHost, epixtech, inc., OCLC - First Search, Silverplatter Information Inc.
Publications: Newsletter (quarterly)
Open Mon-Thurs 9-9, Fri & Sat 9-6, Sun 2-6
Friends of the Library Group
Branches: 1

P RIDGEVIEW, 706 First St SW, 28602. SAN 354-9062. Tel: 828-345-6037. FAX: 828-267-0485. *Branch Mgr*, Julie Burns; Tel: 828-345-1931, E-Mail jburns@ci.hickory.nc.us; *Librn*, Andrea Williamson; Staff 4 (MLS 1, Non-MLS 3)
Circ 3,689
Library Holdings: Bk Vols 7,500
Subject Interests: African-Am
Automation Activity & Vendor Info: (Circulation) epixtech, inc.; (OPAC) epixtech, inc.

Database Vendor: epixtech, inc., OCLC - First Search, Silverplatter Information Inc.
Publications: Newsletter (monthly)
Open Mon-Thurs 9-9, Fri & Sat 9-6
Friends of the Library Group

C LENOIR-RHYNE COLLEGE, Carl A Rudisill Library, 7th Ave & 8th NE, 28603. SAN 312-8806. Tel: 828-328-7235. FAX: 828-328-7338. E-Mail: library@lrc.edu. Web Site: www.lrc.edu/library/library3.htm. *Dir*, A Curtis Paul; *Asst Dir*, Greg Callahan; *Circ*, C Schweikert; *Acq, ILL, Ref*, Burl McCuiston; *Media Spec*, Kevin Karrs; Staff 4 (MLS 4)
Founded 1891. Enrl 1,620; Fac 86; Highest Degree: Master
Jun 1998-May 1999 Income $561,436. Mats Exp $139,283, Books $51,411, Per/Ser (Incl. Access Fees) $72,551, Presv $2,400, Micro $9,621, AV Equip $3,300. Sal $355,664 (Prof $150,586)
Library Holdings: Bk Vols 144,781; Per Subs 3,797; Spec Interest Per Sub 10; Bks on Deafness & Sign Lang 4,327
Special Collections: Martin Luther Works Coll (Wiemar Edition); Quetzalcoatl Collection
Partic in Mountain College Libr Network; NC Asn of Independence Cols & Univs; OCLC Online Computer Library Center, Inc; SE Libr Network
Special Services for the Deaf - Books on deafness & sign language; Captioned film depository; High interest/low vocabulary books; Special interest periodicals; Staff with knowledge of sign language

S SIECOR CORPORATION, Corporate Library, Information Research Center - LI,* 489 Siecor Park, 28603-0489. SAN 325-7940. Tel: 828-327-5418.
Library Holdings: Bk Titles 800; Per Subs 125

S WAKE FOREST UNIVERSITY SCHOOL OF MEDICINE, Northwest Area Health Education Center Library at Hickory, Catawba Memorial Hospital, 810 Fairgrove Church Rd, 28602. SAN 325-7738. Tel: 828-326-3662. FAX: 828-326-3484. Web Site: northwestahec.wfubmc.edu/lindex. *Coordr*, Stephen Johnson; Tel: 828-326-3659, E-Mail: stjohnso@wfubmc.edu; *Ref*, Janice Moore; *AV*, Barbara Sigmon; Staff 5 (MLS 2, Non-MLS 3)
2000-2001 Mats Exp $30,000. Sal $125,000 (Prof $80,000)
Library Holdings: Bk Vols 2,300; Bk Titles 2,200; Per Subs 180
Subject Interests: Allied health, Medicine, Nursing
Partic in Northwest Ahec Library Information Network
Friends of the Library Group

HIGH POINT

S BERNICE BIENENSTOCK FURNITURE LIBRARY, 1009 N Main, 27262. SAN 325-7967. Tel: 336-883-4011. FAX: 336-883-6759. Web Site: www.furniturelibrary.com. *Curator*, Carl Vuncannon
Library Holdings: Bk Vols 7,000; Per Subs 10

P HIGH POINT PUBLIC LIBRARY, 901 N Main St, 27261-2530. (Mail add: PO Box 2530, 27261), SAN 354-9097. Tel: 336-883-3631. Circulation Tel: 336-883-3661. Reference Tel: 336-883-3641. TDD: 336-883-3675. FAX: 336-883-3636. Web Site: www.hipopl.org. *Dir*, Kem B Ellis; Tel: 336-883-3694, E-Mail: kem.ellis@ci.high-point.nc.us; *Mgr*, Nan Parrish; Tel: 336-883-3644, E-Mail: nan.parrish@ci.high-point.nc.us; *AV*, Catherine Moore; Tel: 336-883-3639, E-Mail: catherine.moore@ci.high-point.nc.us; *Bkmobile Coordr*, Kim Coleman; Tel: 336-883-3674, E-Mail: kim.coleman@ci.high-point.nc.us; *Business*, June Evans; Tel: 336-883-3671, E-Mail: june.evans@ci.high-point.nc.us; *Head, Cat*, Linda Davis; Tel: 336-883-3645, E-Mail: linda.davis@ci.high-point.nc.us; *Ch Servs*, Julie Dornberger; Tel: 336-883-3667, E-Mail: julie.dornberger@ci.high-point.nc.us; *Exten Serv*, Nancy Metzner; Tel: 336-883-3650, E-Mail: nancy.metzner@ci.high-point.nc.us; *ILL*, John Hedstrom; Tel: 336-883-3635, E-Mail: john.hedstrom@ci.high-point.nc.us; *Per*, Susan McClain; Tel: 336-883-3633, E-Mail: susan.mcclain@ci.high-point.nc.us; *Head Ref*, Tamara Ruebel; Tel: 336-883-3643, E-Mail: tamara.ruebel@ci.high-point.nc.us; *Ref*, Margaret Brannon; E-Mail: margaret.brannon@ci.high-point.nc.us; *Ref*, Carol King; Tel: 336-883-8541, E-Mail: carol.king@ci.high-point.nc.us; *Ref*, Jody Lohman; Tel: 336-883-3655, E-Mail: jody.lohman@ci.high-point.nc.us; *Ref*, Christina Roberts; E-Mail: christina.roberts@ci.high-point.nc.us; *Ref*, Lucy Tyndall; E-Mail: lucy.tyndall@ci.high-point.nc.us; *Ref Servs Ch*, Jim Zola; Tel: 336-883-3668, E-Mail: jim.zola@ci.high-point.nc.us; *Spec Coll*, Jackie Hedstrom; Tel: 336-883-8542, E-Mail: jackie.hedstrom@ci.high-point.nc.us; *Syst Coordr*, Jamie Saferight; Tel: 336-883-3693, E-Mail: jamie.saferight@ci.high-point.nc.us; *Web Coordr*, Ann Palmer; Tel: 336-883-8512, E-Mail: ann.palmer@ci.high-point.nc.us; Staff 68 (MLS 20, Non-MLS 48)
Founded 1926. Pop 80,789; Circ 634,531
Jul 1999-Jun 2000 Income $2,772,275, State $151,261, City $2,474,514, County $145,000, Other $1,500. Mats Exp $510,782. Sal $1,580,055
Library Holdings: Bk Vols 269,508; Per Subs 848
Subject Interests: Design, Furniture, Genealogy, Local history, North Carolina
Special Collections: Afro-American History; Family Literacy
Automation Activity & Vendor Info: (Acquisitions) epixtech, inc.; (Cataloging) epixtech, inc.; (Circulation) epixtech, inc.; (OPAC) epixtech, inc.; (Serials) epixtech, inc.
Database Vendor: Ebsco - EbscoHost, OCLC - First Search
Publications: Among Friends; Business Research; Library Daycare Connections; Library Whispers; Media Matters; North Carolina Collection Newsletter; Teacher Times
Special Services for the Deaf - TDD
Special Services for the Blind - Magnifiers
Friends of the Library Group

C HIGH POINT UNIVERSITY, Smith Library,* University Sta, Montlieu Ave, 27262-1949. SAN 312-8814. Tel: 336-841-9102. FAX: 336-841-5123. Web Site: www.highpoint.edu. *Coll Develop, Dir Libr Serv*, Judith K Hitchcock; E-Mail: judy@hplib.highpoint.edu; *Tech Servs*, Michael Ingram; *Publ Servs*, David L Bryden; *Ser*, Carol King; *Media Spec*, Elizabeth Bidrine; Staff 5 (MLS 5)
Founded 1924. Enrl 2,500; Fac 90; Highest Degree: Master
Library Holdings: Bk Vols 145,000; Per Subs 1,400
Subject Interests: Bus, Liberal arts
Special Collections: Home Furnishings Marketing Coll; Methodist Archives; North Carolina Coll
Partic in OCLC Online Computer Library Center, Inc

C JOHN WESLEY COLLEGE LIBRARY, 2314 N Centennial St, 27265. SAN 312-8822. Tel: 336-889-2262. FAX: 336-889-2261. Web Site: www.johnwesley.edu. *Dir*, April Lindsey; E-Mail: alindsey@johnwesley.edu
Founded 1936. Highest Degree: Bachelor
Library Holdings: Bk Vols 41,000; Per Subs 145
Subject Interests: Ch educ, Gen educ, Music, Relig studies
Special Collections: John Wesley

HILLSBOROUGH

P HYCONEECHEE REGIONAL LIBRARY,* 300 W Tryon St, PO Box 8181, 27278. SAN 313-0649. Tel: 919-732-8181, Ext 2525. FAX: 919-644-3003. *Dir*, Brenda W Stephens; *Ch Servs*, Ginger Holler; *Librn*, Kathleen Gemske
Founded 1948. Pop 102,676; Circ 362,536
Library Holdings: Bk Vols 115,000; Per Subs 800
Subject Interests: Antiques, Crafts, Genealogy, Geography, Large print, Local history
Automation Activity & Vendor Info: (Cataloging) Brodart
Member Libraries: Gunn Memorial Public Library; Orange County Public Library; Person County Public Library
Friends of the Library Group
Branches: 1
CARRBORO BRANCH, McDougle Middle School, 900 Old Fayetteville Rd, Chapel Hill, 27516. SAN 377-7901. Tel: 919-969-3006. FAX: 919-969-3008. *Head of Libr, Librn*, James Lehrer; E-Mail: jlehrer@ncsl.der.state.nc.us; Staff 6 (MLS 2, Non-MLS 4)
Library Holdings: Bk Vols 20,000; Bk Titles 16,000; Per Subs 60

P ORANGE COUNTY PUBLIC LIBRARY,* 300 W Tryon St, 27278. SAN 312-8849. Tel: 919-644-3011. FAX: 919-644-3003. Web Site: www.co.orange.nc.us/library. *Dir*, Brenda W Stephens; Tel: 919-245-2528, E-Mail: bstephens@co.organge.nc.us; *Ref Serv*, Kimberly Ann Sholar; Tel: 919-245-2525, E-Mail: ksholar@co.orange.nc.us; Staff 14 (MLS 7, Non-MLS 7)
Founded 1912. Pop 109,288; Circ 141,184
Library Holdings: Bk Vols 50,000; Per Subs 203
Subject Interests: Genealogy, Local history
Mem of Hyconeechee Regional Library
Friends of the Library Group

HUDSON

J CALDWELL COMMUNITY COLLEGE & TECHNICAL INSTITUTE, Broyhill Center for Learning Resources,* 2855 Hickory Blvd, 28638. SAN 312-9020. Tel: 828-726-2309. FAX: 828-726-2603. *Dir*, Marischa B Cooke; E-Mail: mcooke@caldwell.cc.nc.us; Staff 7 (MLS 1, Non-MLS 6)
Founded 1966
Library Holdings: Bk Vols 53,000; Per Subs 398
Publications: Audio-visual and book acquisitions lists; Audio-visual catalog

JACKSON

P NORTHAMPTON MEMORIAL LIBRARY,* Courier 10-02-07, PO Box 427, 27845. SAN 312-8857. Tel: 252-534-3571. FAX: 252-534-1017. *Librn*, Barbara Davis
Library Holdings: Bk Titles 30,100; Per Subs 32
Mem of Albemarle Regional Library
Statistics included with regional library. See Winton entry

JACKSONVILLE

J COASTAL CAROLINA COMMUNITY COLLEGE, Learning Resources Center, 444 Western Blvd, 28546-6877. SAN 312-8865. Tel: 910-455-1221, 910-938-6237. FAX: 910-455-7027. E-Mail: muirl@coastal.cc.nc.us. Web Site: www.coastal.cc.nc.us. *Dir*, Linda Muir; *Tech Servs*, Marilyn Gresham; *Publ Servs*, Nancy Hewett; *Tech Servs*, Sue Collins; Staff 7 (MLS 4, Non-MLS 3)

Founded 1965. Enrl 3,500; Fac 125
JulJun
Library Holdings: Bk Titles 42,500; Per Subs 300
Partic in CCLINC

P ONSLOW COUNTY PUBLIC LIBRARY, (OCPL), 58 Doris Ave E, 28540. SAN 354-9186. Tel: 910-455-7350. FAX: 910-455-1661. Web Site: www.co.onslow.nc.us/library. *Dir*, Maureen Fiorello; E-Mail: mfiorell@ncsl.dcr.state.nc.us; *Asst Dir*, Merilyn Givens Thomasson; Tel: 910-455-7354, E-Mail: mthomass@ncsl.dcr.state.nc.us; Staff 41 (MLS 4, Non-MLS 37)
Founded 1936. Pop 147,352; Circ 354,533
Jul 1999-Jun 2000 Income (Main Library and Branch Library) $1,458,069. Mats Exp $177,751, Books $146,156, Per/Ser (Incl. Access Fees) $16,410, AV Equip $15,185. Sal $1,109,710 (Prof $163,030)
Library Holdings: Bk Vols 134,216; Per Subs 245
Subject Interests: Genealogy, Local history
Special Collections: Oral History Coll Relating to Building Camp Lejeune Marine Base
Automation Activity & Vendor Info: (Cataloging) Gaylord; (Circulation) Gaylord; (OPAC) Gaylord
Publications: Civic Club Roster (Comt info); Human Resources Manual
Partic in NC-Live; NCIN; OCLC Online Computer Library Center, Inc
Friends of the Library Group
Branches: 4

L LAW LIBRARY, 109 Old Bridge St, 28540. SAN 329-5656. Tel: 910-455-4458, Ext 307. FAX: 910-455-8428. *In Charge*, David Dalimonte; Staff 1 (Non-MLS 1)
Jul 1999-Jun 2000 Income $57,879. Mats Exp Books $25,992. Sal $30,195
Library Holdings: Bk Vols 5,597

RICHLANDS BRANCH, 301 S Wilmington St, PO Box 86, Richlands, 28574. SAN 354-9216. Tel: 910-324-5321. FAX: 910-324-4682. *Branch Mgr*, Hildridge Owens; Staff 3 (Non-MLS 3)
Library Holdings: Bk Vols 20,994
Friends of the Library Group

SNEADS FERRY BRANCH, 242 Sneads Ferry Rd, Sneads Ferry, 28460. SAN 354-9232. Tel: 910-327-6471. FAX: 910-327-6471. *Branch Mgr*, Mary Rotchford-Nolan; Staff 3 (Non-MLS 3)
Library Holdings: Bk Vols 24,248
Friends of the Library Group

SWANSBORO BRANCH, 1460 W Corbett Ave, Swansboro, 28584. SAN 354-9240. Tel: 910-326-4888. FAX: 910-326-4888. *Branch Mgr*, Michelle King; Staff 4 (Non-MLS 4)
Library Holdings: Bk Vols 23,287
Friends of the Library Group

UNITED STATES MARINE CORPS

A MCAS STATION LIBRARY, New River, 28545-5001. SAN 354-9275. Tel: 910-450-6715. FAX: 910-450-6037. *Librn*, Ian R Smith
Founded 1956
Library Holdings: Bk Titles 21,000; Per Subs 74
Subject Interests: Alcohol-abuse control, Automobile maintenance repair, Drug, Human relations, Juv picture bks, Microcomputer, Mil preparedness, Sports, Vietnam conflict, World War II

JAMESTOWN

J GUILFORD TECHNICAL COMMUNITY COLLEGE, Mertys W Bell Library, 601 High Point Rd, 27282. (Mail add: PO Box 309, 27282-0309), SAN 354-9305. Tel: 336-334-4822, Ext 2292. FAX: 336-841-4350. Web Site: webster.gtcc.cc.nc.us/lr/library. *Dean*, A Beverly Gass; Tel: 336-334-4822, Ext 2434, E-Mail: gassb@gtcc.cc.nc.us; *Dir*, Linda Saunders; Tel: 336-334-4822, Ext 2232, E-Mail: sanderl@gtcc.cc.nc.us; *Coll Develop, Tech Servs*, Donald Forbes; Tel: 336-334-4822, Ext 2502, E-Mail: forbesd@gtcc.cc.nc.us; *Ref*, Belinda S Daniels-Richardson; Tel: 336-334-4822, Ext 2636, E-Mail: danielsb@gtcc.cc.nc.us; *Circ*, Betty Lipford; E-Mail: lipfordb@gtcc.cc.nc.us; Staff 15 (MLS 7, Non-MLS 8)
Founded 1963. Enrl 12,000; Fac 200; Highest Degree: Associate
Jul 1998-Jun 1999 Income $766,681, State $710,785, Locally Generated Income $6,409, Parent Institution $212, Other $49,275. Mats Exp $187,178, Books $105,730, Per/Ser (Incl. Access Fees) $15,870, Presv $313, Micro $7,411, Electronic Ref Mat (Incl. Access Fees) $57,854. Sal $369,129 (Prof $225,131)
Library Holdings: Bk Vols 79,926; Bk Titles 70,000; Per Subs 325
Subject Interests: Architecture, Automotive tech, Commercial art, Commun col, Dent sci, Engineering, Nursing, Paralegal, Surgical tech
Publications: Faculty guide; Periodicals list; Student-How-To-Bookmarks
Partic in NC Dept of Commun Cols
Friends of the Library Group

P JAMESTOWN PUBLIC LIBRARY, 200 W Main St, PO Box 1437, 27282. SAN 370-6648. Tel: 336-454-4815. *Mgr*, Cathy Durbin; E-Mail: durbincathy@hotmail.com; Staff 2 (Non-MLS 2)
Founded 1987. Pop 10,000; Circ 18,387
Jul 1999-Jun 2000 Income (Main and Other College/University Libraries) $54,844, City $50,000, County $5,500, Other $14,000. Mats Exp $15,000, Books $12,600, Per/Ser (Incl. Access Fees) $1,005. Sal $42,000
Library Holdings: Bk Vols 16,077; Bk Titles 16,000; Per Subs 50; High Interest/Low Vocabulary Bk Vols 423
Subject Interests: Civil War, Local history
Friends of the Library Group

JONESVILLE

P JONESVILLE-ARLINGTON PUBLIC LIBRARY, 150 W Main St, 28642. SAN 312-8873. Tel: 336-835-7604. FAX: 336-526-5226. *Head Librn*, Cynthia Freeman Allred; E-Mail: cfa1222@hotmail.com; *Asst Librn*, Ira Steven Macy; E-Mail: libcomdat@aol.com; *Circ*, Mendy Webb McMillian; Staff 3 (Non-MLS 3)
Founded 1962. Pop 3,500; Circ 50,000
Jul 2000-Jun 2001 Income $97,013, City $5,600, County $85,954, Locally Generated Income $4,409, Other $1,050. Mats Exp $14,262, Books $12,412, Per/Ser (Incl. Access Fees) $650, AV Equip $1,200. Sal $50,102
Library Holdings: Bk Vols 17,289; Bk Titles 15,737; Per Subs 16
Automation Activity & Vendor Info: (Circulation) TLC
Function: ILL available
Mem of Northwestern Regional Library
Friends of the Library Group

KENANSVILLE

P DUPLIN COUNTY LIBRARY, Dorothy Wightman Library, 107 Bowden Dr, PO Box 930, 28349-0930. SAN 312-889X. Tel: 910-296-2117. FAX: 910-296-2172. *Dir*, Linda Hadden
Founded 1920. Pop 39,995
Library Holdings: Bk Vols 54,000; Bk Titles 28,000; Per Subs 120
Subject Interests: Local, NC hist
Friends of the Library Group

J JAMES SPRUNT COMMUNITY COLLEGE LIBRARY, PO Box 398, 28349-0398. SAN 312-8903. Tel: 910-296-2474, 910-296-2476. FAX: 910-296-1636. Web Site: www.sprunt.com/library.html. *Librn*, Cindy Yelverton; E-Mail: cyelverton@scc.cc.nc.us; Staff 3 (MLS 1, Non-MLS 2)
Founded 1966. Enrl 970
Library Holdings: Bk Titles 21,050; Per Subs 218

KERNERSVILLE

S NORTH AMERICAN YOUTH SPORT INSTITUTE, NAYSI News, Information & Resource Center, 4985 Oak Garden Dr, 27284. (Mail add: PO Box 957, 27285), SAN 326-3479. Tel: 336-784-4926. FAX: 336-784-5546. Web Site: www.naysi.com. *Dir*, Dr Jack Hutslar; Tel: 336-784-4926, E-Mail: jack@naysi.com
Founded 1979
Library Holdings: Bk Titles 1,000
Subject Interests: Education, Fitness, Health, Recreation
Publications: Beyond Xs & Os (English & Spanish); KIDbits (demographics, annual); Munchkin Tennis; NAYSI News FYI; Player Evaluation Forms; Sport Scene (NAYSI on-line course)
Restriction: By appointment only

KING

P KING PUBLIC LIBRARY,* PO Box 629, 27021. SAN 312-8911. Tel: 336-983-3868. FAX: 336-983-0769. *Librn*, Julie Raynor
Jul 1998-Jun 1999 Income $162,838, City $20,000, County $82,279, Locally Generated Income $3,700. Mats Exp $17,063, Books $15,000, Per/Ser (Incl. Access Fees) $1,500. Sal $104,816
Library Holdings: Bk Vols 25,000; Per Subs 30
Mem of Northwest Regional Library System; Northwestern Regional Library

KINGS MOUNTAIN

P MAUNEY MEMORIAL LIBRARY, 100 S Piedmont Ave, 28086. SAN 312-892X. Tel: 704-739-2371. FAX: 704-734-4499. *Dir*, Rose Turner
Founded 1936. Pop 12,000; Circ 39,817
Library Holdings: Bk Vols 45,000; Per Subs 17
Subject Interests: Local family hist, NC
Automation Activity & Vendor Info: (Cataloging) SIRSI
Partic in CLEVE-NET; NCIN

KINSTON

S E I DUPONT COMPANY, DRL Library, PO Box 800, 28502-0800. SAN 312-8938. Tel: 252-522-6111. FAX: 252-522-6597. *Info Specialist*, Luella Graham Wills; Tel: 252-522-6349, E-Mail: luella.G.wills@usa.dupont.com
Founded 1954
Library Holdings: Bk Vols 5,000; Per Subs 170
Subject Interests: Organic, Polymer chemistry, Textiles

P KINSTON-LENOIR COUNTY PUBLIC LIBRARY, 510 N Queen St, 28501. SAN 312-8946. Tel: 919-527-7066. Circulation Tel: 252-527-7066, Ext 120. Reference Tel: 252-527-7066, Ext 134. FAX: 919-527-9235. E-Mail: neuselibrary@hotmail.com. Web Site: www.neuselibrary.org. *Dir*, Agnes Ho; Tel: 252-527-7066, Ext 131, Fax: 252-527-8220, E-Mail: aho@ncsl.dcr.state.nc.us; *Ch Servs*, Amy Jones; *Ch Servs*, Cherie Stegman; Tel: 252-527-7066, Ext 133; *Coll Develop, Tech Servs*, Senatra Murrell; Tel: 252-527-7066, Ext 126, E-Mail: nrltsdept@hotmail.com; *Circ*, Shannon Riggs; Tel: 252-527-7066, Ext 120, E-Mail: smr0317@hotmail.com; *Coll Develop, Tech Servs*, Theresa Hardy; *Ref*, Deborah Brody; *Ref*, Beth Boone; Tel: 252-527-7066, Ext 134, E-Mail: bab100boone@hotmail.com; *Business*, Stacey Humphrey; Tel: 252-527-7066, Ext 132, E-Mail: stacey_humphrey@yahoo.com
Founded 1962
Mem of Neuse Regional Library
Holdings are included in Neuse Regional Library entry
Friends of the Library Group

C LENOIR COMMUNITY COLLEGE, Learning Resources Center, 231 Hwy 58 South, PO Box 188, 28502-0188. SAN 312-8954. Tel: 252-527-6223, Ext 507. FAX: 252-527-0192. E-Mail: lrcinfo@email.lenoir.cc.nc.us. Web Site: www.lenoir.cc.nc.us. *Dir, Tech Servs*, Stephen N Hawkins; Tel: 252-527-6223, Ext 504; Staff 8 (MLS 3, Non-MLS 5)
Founded 1964. Fac 184
Library Holdings: Bk Vols 60,000; Bk Titles 50,000; Per Subs 399
Subject Interests: Distance learning classroom, Writing across the curric
Special Collections: Genealogy Coll; Local eastern North Carolina; Local History
Publications: Annual Report; Book Mark Schedules; Local History Brochure; LRC Handbook; Operations Report; Periodical Holdings Brochure
Partic in Highlands Regional Library Cooperative; NC Info Hwy; NC Info Network
One wing of the library is devoted to a museum, local history & a Genealogy collection

P NEUSE REGIONAL LIBRARY, 510 N Queen St, 28501. SAN 312-8962. Tel: 252-527-7066. Circulation Tel: 252-527-7066, Ext 120. Reference Tel: 252-527-7066, Ext 134. FAX: 252-527-9235. E-Mail: neuselibrary@hotmail.com. Web Site: www.neuselibrary.org. *Dir*, Agnes W Ho; Fax: 252-527-8220, E-Mail: aho@ncsl.dcr.state.nc.us; *Librn*, Marvette Spruill; Tel: 252-747-3437, Fax: 252-747-7489, E-Mail: greenelibrary@hotmail.com; *Tech Servs*, Theresa Hardy; E-Mail: thardy@ncsl.dcr.state.nc.us; *Tech Servs*, Senatra Murrell; Tel: 252-527-7066, Ext 126, E-Mail: nrltsdept@hotmail.com; *Ch Servs*, Tracie Below; Tel: 252-527-7066, Ext 133, E-Mail: tpod16@prodigy.net; *Ch Servs*, Tanya Cahoon; *Res*, Darrin Arvin; *Business*, Stacey Humphrey; Tel: 252-527-7066, Ext 132, E-Mail: stacey_humhrey@yahoo.com; *Circ*, Shannon Riggs; Tel: 252-527-7066, Ext 120, Fax: 252-527-7066, E-Mail: smr0317@hotmail.com; *Ref Serv Ad*, Beth Boone; Tel: 252-527-7066, Ext 134, E-Mail: bab100boon3@hotmail.com; Staff 46 (MLS 10, Non-MLS 36)
Founded 1962. Pop 89,000; Circ 560,000
Jul 2000-Jun 2001 Income (Main Library and Branch Library) $1,973,372, State $376,763, City $217,500, County $825,579, Other $553,530. Mats Exp $571,148, Books $189,298, Per/Ser (Incl. Access Fees) $30,000, Presv $2,300, AV Equip $20,000, Other Print Mats $35,350, Electronic Ref Mat (Incl. Access Fees) $32,000. Sal $972,446 (Prof $433,523)
Library Holdings: Bk Vols 232,994; Bk Titles 126,748; Per Subs 600; High Interest/Low Vocabulary Bk Vols 20,000
Special Collections: Eastern North Carolina Genealogy (Sybil Huatt Coll); Henry Pearson Art Coll; Modern Fiction on Cassette; North Carolina - Specialized in Eastern North Carolina; North Carolina Original Art Coll; Piranesi Art Print Coll
Automation Activity & Vendor Info: (Acquisitions) TLC; (Cataloging) TLC; (Circulation) TLC; (OPAC) TLC; (Serials) TLC
Database Vendor: Ebsco - EbscoHost, OCLC - First Search
Publications: A Trip to the Library (coloring bk); African American Bibliography; Calendar of Events (monthly); CD-ROM Training Manual; Personnel Policies Manual; School Video Annotated Catalog; Security Guard Manual; Statistical Report (quarterly)
Member Libraries: Comfort Public Library; Greene County Public Library; Kinston-Lenoir County Public Library; La Grange Public Library; Maysville Public Library; Pink Hill Public Library; Pollocksville Public Library; Trenton Public Library
Friends of the Library Group

KNIGHTDALE

S NATIONAL HUNTERS ASSOCIATION INC LIBRARY,* 590 Wendell Blvd, 27545-0820. (Mail add: PO Box 820, 27545), SAN 375-1651. Tel: 919-365-7157. FAX: 919-366-2142. Web Site: www.nationalhunters.com. *Pres*, D V Smith; Tel: 919-365-7157
Library Holdings: Bk Titles 1,000; Per Subs 100

LA GRANGE

P LA GRANGE PUBLIC LIBRARY,* 119 E Washington St, 28551. SAN 312-8989. Tel: 252-566-3722. FAX: 252-566-3722. *In Charge*, Margaret Frantz
Mem of Neuse Regional Library
Holdings are included in Neuse Regional Library entry
Friends of the Library Group

LAURINBURG

S INDIAN MUSEUM OF THE CAROLINAS LIBRARY,* 607 Turnpike Rd, 28352. SAN 374-5309. Tel: 910-276-5880. *Dir*, Margaret Houston
Library Holdings: Bk Titles 300
Restriction: Non-circulating to the public

C SAINT ANDREWS PRESBYTERIAN COLLEGE, DeTamble Library, 1700 Dogwood Mile, 28352. SAN 312-9012. Tel: 910-277-5049. Interlibrary Loan Service Tel: 910-277-5023. FAX: 910-277-5050. E-Mail: mhm@andrews.sapc.edu. Web Site: www.sapc.edu/awklib. *Dir*, Rita Durst Johnson; *Cat*, Schelley Childress; Staff 3 (MLS 2, Non-MLS 1)
Founded 1896. Enrl 700; Highest Degree: Bachelor
Library Holdings: Bk Titles 109,000; Per Subs 358
Special Collections: Scottish Coll; Silent Night Coll; Special & Rare Books Coll; Thistle & Shamrock Scottish Music Coll on tape
Partic in OCLC Online Computer Library Center, Inc; SE Libr Network

P SCOTLAND COUNTY MEMORIAL LIBRARY, (SCML), 312 W Church St, 28352-3720. (Mail add: PO Box 369, 28353-0369), SAN 354-933X. Tel: 910-276-0563. FAX: 910-276-4032. *Coll Develop, Dir*, Robert Busko; E-Mail: rbusko@ncsl.dcr.state.nc.us; *Ref*, Julie Harris; *Tech Servs*, Angie Chavis; *Bkmobile Coordr*, Joyce Rogers; *Ad Servs*, Margaret Uncapher; *Ch Servs*, Mildred Davis; *Outreach Serv*, Leora Davis
Founded 1941. Pop 35,006; Circ 119,001
Jul 1999-Jun 2000 Income $396,100, State $113,000, Federal $37,000, County $237,500, Locally Generated Income $8,600. Mats Exp $77,700, Books $60,000, Per/Ser (Incl. Access Fees) $9,500, Presv $1,200, Micro $1,000, AV Equip $1,000, Manuscripts & Archives $1,500, Electronic Ref Mat (Incl. Access Fees) $1,000. Sal $229,708 (Prof $40,800)
Library Holdings: Bk Vols 55,000; Per Subs 125
Special Collections: Heritage Room (North Carolina Coll)
Automation Activity & Vendor Info: (Acquisitions) TLC; (Cataloging) TLC; (Circulation) TLC; (Course Reserve) TLC; (OPAC) TLC
Publications: Annual report; brochures
Friends of the Library Group
Branches: 1
WAGRAM BRANCH, PO Box 118, Wagram, 28396. SAN 354-9399. Tel: 910-369-2966. *Librn*, Joy Davis
Founded 1976
Library Holdings: Bk Vols 6,000; Bk Titles 5,500
Automation Activity & Vendor Info: (Circulation) TLC; (OPAC) TLC
Database Vendor: Ebsco - EbscoHost
Friends of the Library Group
Bookmobiles: 1

LENOIR

P CALDWELL COUNTY PUBLIC LIBRARY, 120 Hospital Ave, 28645-4454. SAN 312-9039. Tel: 828-757-1270. FAX: 828-757-1413. Web Site: www.ils.unc.edu/nclibs/caldwell/home.htm. *Dir*, Jimmy D McKee; E-Mail: jmckee@co.caldwell.nc.us; *Librn*, Karen B Doll; *Ch Servs*, Peggy Carter; *Ref*, Diana Justice; Staff 19 (MLS 5, Non-MLS 14)
Founded 1930. Pop 70,245; Circ 285,015
Jul 1999-Jun 2000 Income (Main Library and Branch Library) $1,003,188, State $158,674, Federal $5,221, County $839,293. Mats Exp $127,552, Books $117,552, Per/Ser (Incl. Access Fees) $8,000, Micro $2,000. Sal $633,560
Library Holdings: Bk Titles 131,092; Per Subs 289
Subject Interests: Caldwell county hist
Automation Activity & Vendor Info: (Cataloging) TLC; (Circulation) SIRSI; (OPAC) SIRSI
Friends of the Library Group
Branches: 2
GRANITE FALLS PUBLIC, 30 Falls Ave, Granite Falls, 28630. SAN 312-8466. Tel: 828-396-7703. *Mgr*, Maxine Parsons
Automation Activity & Vendor Info: (Circulation) SIRSI; (OPAC) SIRSI
Friends of the Library Group
HUDSON PUBLIC, 530 Central St, Hudson, 28638-1230. SAN 324-5802. Tel: 828-728-4207. *Mgr*, Caroline Steiljes
Automation Activity & Vendor Info: (Circulation) SIRSI; (OPAC) SIRSI
Friends of the Library Group

LEXINGTON

J DAVIDSON COUNTY COMMUNITY COLLEGE, Grady E Love Learning Resources Center, Intersection of Business I-85 & Old Greensboro Rd, PO Box 1287, 27293-1287. SAN 312-9047. Tel: 336-249-8186, Ext 270, 336-475-7181. FAX: 336-248-8531. Web Site: www.davidson.cc.nc.us/~lrc. *Dir*, Martha E Davis; *Circ, ILL*, Brenda Farmer; *Per, Ref*, Linda Burke; E-Mail: lburke@davidson.cc.nc.us; Staff 3 (MLS 3)
Founded 1963. Enrl 1,862; Fac 66
Library Holdings: Bk Vols 55,475; Bk Titles 53,811; Per Subs 340
Subject Interests: Am lit, Architecture, Arts, Automotive, Criticism, Furniture, Law, Local history
Special Collections: Furniture Design & Decoration
Publications: Cooleemee Plantation and Its People (monograph); Country College on the Yadkin: A Historical Narrative (monograph); Index to Centennial History of Davidson County; Index to Dutch Settlement on Abbotts Creek; Index to Saints & Sinners; Index to Wheels of Faith & Courage: History of Thomasville NC; Records of the Evangelical Lutheran Congregation at Sandy Creek; Topical Index to Homespun Magazine

P DAVIDSON COUNTY PUBLIC LIBRARY SYSTEM, 602 S Main St, 27292. SAN 312-9055. Tel: 336-242-2040. FAX: 336-248-4122. E-Mail: ncs027/@interpath.com. Web Site: www.co.davidson.nc.us/library. *Dir*, Nancy F Bates; *Assoc Librn*, Gloria McBride; *Assoc Librn*, Barbara Seuberling; *Tech Servs*, Ronald F Ritter; Staff 42 (MLS 6, Non-MLS 36)
Founded 1928. Pop 142,512; Circ 594,473
Jul 1999-Jun 2000 Income $2,291,593, State $204,914, Federal $31,403, County $1,985,538, Locally Generated Income $69,738. Mats Exp $291,867, Books $249,474, Per/Ser (Incl. Access Fees) $18,944, Micro $783, AV Equip $21,159. Sal $1,085,247 (Prof $336,313)
Library Holdings: Bk Titles 122,458; Per Subs 138; Bks on Deafness & Sign Lang 26
Special Collections: Literature (Richard Walser Coll); Local History, Genealogy (North Carolina Coll), bk & microfilm
Automation Activity & Vendor Info: (Circulation) epixtech, inc.
Friends of the Library Group
Branches: 3
DENTON PUBLIC, 310 W Salisbury St, Denton, 27239-6944. (Mail add: PO Box 578, Denton, 27239-0578), SAN 312-8075. Tel: 336-869-2215. FAX: 336-869-5006. *Librn*, Debra Swaim
Founded 1946
Library Holdings: Bk Vols 23,355; Per Subs 47; Bks on Deafness & Sign Lang 12
NORTH DAVIDSON PUBLIC, 559 Critcher Dr, PO Box 1749, Welcome, 27374-1749. (Mail add: PO Box 1749, Welcome, 27374), SAN 313-0304. Tel: 336-242-2050. FAX: 336-731-3719. *Librn*, Alexandra Pinkston
Library Holdings: Bk Vols 29,023; Per Subs 49; Bks on Deafness & Sign Lang 29
Friends of the Library Group
THOMASVILLE PUBLIC, 14 Randolph St, Thomasville, 27360-4638. (Mail add: PO Box 519, Thomasville, 27361-0519), SAN 313-0142. Tel: 336-474-2690. FAX: 336-472-4690. *Asst Dir, Librn*, Ruth Ann Copley; *Librn*, Crystal Baird
Founded 1928
Library Holdings: Bk Vols 72,940; Per Subs 114; Bks on Deafness & Sign Lang 61
Special Collections: Gerald R Johnson Coll
Friends of the Library Group
Bookmobiles: 1

LILLINGTON

P HARNETT COUNTY PUBLIC LIBRARY, 601 N Main St, 27546-6107. (Mail add: PO Box 1149, 27546-1149), SAN 354-9429. Tel: 910-893-3446. FAX: 910-893-3001. Web Site: www.harnett.org/library/default.html. *Dir*, Melanie Collins; E-Mail: mcollins@ncsl.dcr.state.nc.us; *Ch Servs*, Laurel Jones; *Tech Servs*, Cathey Clifton; Staff 6 (MLS 3, Non-MLS 3)
Founded 1941. Pop 83,590; Circ 272,004
Jul 1999-Jun 2000 Income $544,309, State $166,977, Federal $45,498, County $308,548, Locally Generated Income $23,286. Mats Exp $82,447. Sal $315,162
Library Holdings: Bk Vols 158,074; Per Subs 467
Subject Interests: Cooking, Local history
Special Collections: Alcoholism Coll; Photo Coll
Automation Activity & Vendor Info: (Acquisitions) GEAC; (Cataloging) GEAC; (Circulation) GEAC; (OPAC) GEAC; (Serials) GEAC
Publications: Book Bag (quarterly newsletter)
Partic in NC Info Network; NC LIVE
Friends of the Library Group
Branches: 5
ANDERSON CREEK PUBLIC LIBRARY, 914 Anderson Creek School Rd, Bunnlevel, 28323. Tel: 910-814-4012. *Librn*, Georgette Dempster; E-Mail: gdempster@harnett.org
Open Tues, Wed & Thurs 4-9, Sat 10-2, Summers Mon-Sat 10-2
ANGIER PUBLIC LIBRARY, 28 N Raleigh St, Angier, 27501-6680. (Mail add: PO Box 1870, Angier, 27501-1870), SAN 354-9453. Tel: 919-639-4413. FAX: 919-639-4413. *Librn*, Terri Brooks; E-Mail: tbrooks@harnett.org
Library Holdings: Bk Vols 6,100
Automation Activity & Vendor Info: (Acquisitions) IME; (Cataloging) GEAC; (Circulation) GEAC; (Course Reserve) GEAC; (ILL) GEAC; (Media Booking) GEAC; (OPAC) GEAC; (Serials) GEAC
Friends of the Library Group
COATS BRANCH, 243 S McKinley St, Coats, 27521. SAN 354-9488. Tel: 910-897-5183. FAX: 910-897-2662. *Librn*, Terri Stephenson
Library Holdings: Bk Vols 5,033
Automation Activity & Vendor Info: (Acquisitions) GEAC; (Cataloging) GEAC; (Circulation) GEAC; (Course Reserve) GEAC; (ILL) GEAC; (Media Booking) GEAC; (OPAC) GEAC; (Serials) GEAC
DUNN PUBLIC LIBRARY, 110 E Divine St, Dunn, 28334. SAN 312-8113. Tel: 910-892-2899. FAX: 910-892-8385. *Dir*, Deborah Melvin; E-Mail: dmelvin@harnett.org
Pop 8,962; Circ 46,636
Library Holdings: Bk Vols 12,000; Per Subs 30
Open Mon-Thurs 9-6, Fri 9-5
Friends of the Library Group
ERWIN PUBLIC LIBRARY, 110 West F St, Erwin, 28339. SAN 354-9518. Tel: 910-897-5780. FAX: 910-897-4474. *Librn*, Gigi Hughes; E-Mail: ghughes@harnett.org
Library Holdings: Bk Vols 8,400; Per Subs 15
Automation Activity & Vendor Info: (Acquisitions) GEAC; (Cataloging) GEAC; (Circulation) GEAC; (Course Reserve) GEAC; (ILL) GEAC; (Media Booking) GEAC; (OPAC) GEAC; (Serials) GEAC
Bookmobiles: 1

LINCOLNTON

P LINCOLN COUNTY PUBLIC LIBRARY, 306 W Main, 28092. SAN 312-9063. Tel: 704-735-8044. FAX: 704-732-9042. Web Site: www.glrl.lib.nc.us. *Librn*, Lesley Brown Levine; E-Mail: llevine@ncsl.dcr.state.nc.us; Staff 12 (MLS 1, Non-MLS 11)
Founded 1925. Pop 56,415; Circ 251,386
Jul 1999-Jun 2000 Income (Main Library and Branch Library) County $500,388. Mats Exp $84,535, Books $72,144, Per/Ser (Incl. Access Fees) $11,990, Presv $401. Sal $241,939 (Prof $41,885)
Library Holdings: Bk Vols 89,668; Per Subs 208
Special Collections: Lincoln County Historical & Genealogical Coll
Automation Activity & Vendor Info: (Circulation) Gaylord
Mem of Gaston-Lincoln Regional Library
Branches: 1
EAST LINCOLN, 1251 Hwy 16 N, Denver, 28037. SAN 329-5885. Tel: 704-483-3589. FAX: 704-483-3589. Web Site: www.glrl.lib.nc.us. *In Charge*, Mary Brown; Staff 2 (Non-MLS 2)
Library Holdings: Bk Vols 16,055
Automation Activity & Vendor Info: (Circulation) Gaylord
Friends of the Library Group
Bookmobiles: 1

LOUISBURG

P FRANKLIN COUNTY LIBRARY, 906 N Main St, 27549-2199. SAN 354-9542. Tel: 919-496-2111. FAX: 919-496-1339. *Dir*, Hilda Fish; E-Mail: hfish@ncsl.dcr.state.nc.us; *Ref*, Holt Kornegay; Staff 5 (MLS 3, Non-MLS 2)
Founded 1937. Pop 44,000; Circ 142,066
Jul 1999-Jun 2000 Income $552,779. Mats Exp $77,012, Books $70,000, Per/Ser (Incl. Access Fees) $7,012. Sal $352,128
Library Holdings: Bk Vols 81,861; Per Subs 183
Subject Interests: NC
Publications: Board Room
Friends of the Library Group
Branches: 3
BUNN BRANCH, 610 Main St, PO Box 213, Bunn, 27508. SAN 375-3336. Tel: 919-496-6764. FAX: 919-497-5821. *Mgr*, Ruth Hatcher
FRANKLINTON PUBLIC, 9 W Mason St, Franklinton, 27525. SAN 354-9577. Tel: 919-494-2736. FAX: 919-494-2466. *Mgr*, Marguerite Satterwhite
YOUNGSVILLE PUBLIC, 218 USIA S, PO Box 1197, Youngsville, 27596. SAN 354-9607. Tel: 919-556-1612. FAX: 919-556-9633. *Mgr*, Erika Phipps
Friends of the Library Group
Bookmobiles: 1

J LOUISBURG COLLEGE, C W Robbins Library, 502 N Main St, 27549-7704. SAN 312-9071. Tel: 919-496-2521, Ext 279. FAX: 919-496-5444. Web Site: www.louisburg.edu. *Librn*, Judith B Parrish; E-Mail: judithparrish@yahoo.com; *Cat, Circ, Ref*, Curtis Edgerton; *Cat, ILL, Ref*, Pat Hinton; Staff 3 (MLS 3)
Founded 1890. Enrl 728; Fac 40
Library Holdings: Bk Titles 51,000; Per Subs 140
Subject Interests: NC, Relig in Am
Special Collections: Louisburg College & Town Archives, mixed

LOWGAP

P LOWGAP PUBLIC LIBRARY,* RFD 1, PO Box 10, 27024. SAN 376-6837. Tel: 336-352-3000. FAX: 336-652-3000. *Librn*, Linda Hice
Library Holdings: Bk Vols 6,000
Mem of Northwest Regional Library System; Northwestern Regional Library

LUMBERTON

J ROBESON COMMUNITY COLLEGE LIBRARY,* Hwy 301, PO Box 1420, 28359. SAN 312-9098. Tel: 910-738-7101, Ext 231. FAX: 910-618-5685. E-Mail: robeson@cc.nc.us. Web Site: www.robeson.cc.nc.us. *Dir*, Marilyn Locklear-Hunt; *AV*, Robin White; Staff 3 (MLS 3)
Founded 1965. Enrl 1,200; Fac 60
Library Holdings: Bk Titles 38,338; Per Subs 152
Subject Interests: Vocational tech
Partic in Cape Fear Health Sciences Information Consortium

P ROBESON COUNTY PUBLIC LIBRARY, (RCPL), 101 N Chestnut St, 28358. (Mail add: PO Box 988, 28359), SAN 354-9631. Tel: 910-738-4859. FAX: 910-739-8321. *Dir*, Robert F Fisher; E-Mail: rfisher@ncsl.dcr.state.nc.us; *Cat, Tech Servs*, Sheryl Jacobs; *Circ*, Mildred Curry; *ILL*, Lisa Matthews; *Coll Develop, Ref*, Barbara Allchin; Staff 20 (MLS 2, Non-MLS 18)
Founded 1967. Pop 105,179; Circ 169,650
Jul 1999-Jun 2000 Income (Main Library and Branch Library) $924,239, State $224,962, City $216,100, Federal $9,846, County $228,800, Other $244,531. Mats Exp $96,893, Books $82,038, Per/Ser (Incl. Access Fees) $10,855, Micro $4,000. Sal $436,872
Library Holdings: Bk Vols 134,717; Bk Titles 93,160; Per Subs 133
Subject Interests: Indian materials
Special Collections: Local History (McLean Coll) & Genealogy (Biggs Coll, Hodgin Coll, Rhodes Coll)
Automation Activity & Vendor Info: (Cataloging) Gaylord; (Circulation) Gaylord; (OPAC) Gaylord
Friends of the Library Group
Branches: 5
ANNIE HUBBARD MCEACHERN LIBRARY, 223 W Broad St, Saint Pauls, 28384. SAN 312-9888. Tel: 910-865-4002. *Librn*, Tara Harris; Staff 2 (Non-MLS 2)
Pop 2,130; Circ 5,304
Library Holdings: Bk Vols 20,000; Per Subs 25
GILBERT PATTERSON MEMORIAL, PO Box 56, Maxton, 28364. SAN 354-9666. Tel: 910-844-3884. FAX: 910-844-3884. *In Charge*, Pat Middleton; Staff 1 (Non-MLS 1)
Library Holdings: Bk Vols 6,500
Friends of the Library Group
HECTOR MACLEAN PUBLIC, S Main St, Fairmont, 28340. SAN 354-9682. Tel: 910-628-9331. FAX: 910-628-9331. *In Charge*, Carolyn Bullard; Staff 1 (Non-MLS 1)
PEMBROKE PUBLIC, PO Box 295, Pembroke, 28372. SAN 373-1839. Tel: 910-521-1554. FAX: 910-521-1554. *In Charge*, Mattie Locklear; Staff 2 (Non-MLS 2)
ROWLAND LIBRARY, PO Box 10, Rowland, 28383. SAN 328-6770. Tel: 910-422-8282. FAX: 910-422-8282. *In Charge*, Lisa Matthews; Staff 1 (Non-MLS 1)
Bookmobiles: 1

M SOUTHEASTERN REGIONAL MEDICAL CENTER, J Irvin Biggs Information Resource Center,* 300 W 27th St, PO Box 1408, 28358-1408. SAN 312-9101. Tel: 910-671-5046. FAX: 910-671-5337. Web Site: www.business.carolina.net/srmc. *Dir*, Kathy McGinniss; E-Mail: mcginn01@srmc.org
Founded 1953
Library Holdings: Bk Vols 1,345; Per Subs 92
Subject Interests: Medicine, Nursing, Surgery
Partic in Cape Fear Health Sciences Information Consortium; SC Health Info Network

MANTEO

S CAPE HATTERAS NATIONAL SEASHORE, Technical Library, 1401 National Park Dr, 27954-9708. SAN 312-911X. Tel: 252-473-2111. FAX: 252-473-2595. E-Mail: caha_resource_management@nps.gov. Web Site: nps.gov/caha. *In Charge*, Doug Stover; Tel: 252-473-2111, Ext 153, E-Mail: doug.stover@nps.gov
Founded 1955
Library Holdings: Bk Titles 4,142; Per Subs 10
Subject Interests: History, Natural hist of NC Outer Banks
Special Collections: US Lifesaving Service (Records & Annual Reports); Weather Bureau (19th Century Hatteras Station Logs)

P DARE COUNTY LIBRARY,* PO Box 1000, 27954. SAN 354-9690. Tel: 919-473-2372. FAX: 919-473-6034. Web Site: www.earlibrary.org. *Mgr*, Kathy Huddleston; *Ch Servs*, Julia McPherson; Staff 2 (MLS 2)
Founded 1935. Pop 27,000; Circ 174,000
Jul 1998-Jun 1999 Income $553,900, State $94,900, County $419,000, Locally Generated Income $40,000. Mats Exp Books $37,311. Sal $321,690 (Prof $31,000)
Library Holdings: Bk Titles 85,000; Per Subs 180
Special Collections: North Carolina & Dare County Maps
Mem of East Albemarle Regional Library
Friends of the Library Group
Branches: 2
HATTERAS BRANCH, PO Box 309, Hatteras, 27943. SAN 354-9720. Tel: 919-986-2385. FAX: 919-986-2952. Web Site: www.earlibrary.org. *In Charge*, D'andra Compher
Friends of the Library Group
KILL DEVIL HILLS BRANCH, 400 Mustian St, Kill Devil Hills, 27948. SAN 370-5994. Tel: 252-441-4331. FAX: 252-441-0608. Web Site: www.earlibrary.net. *In Charge*, Harriet Amarino
Friends of the Library Group
Bookmobiles: 1

G NORTH CAROLINA AQUARIUM LIBRARY, 374 Airport Rd, 27954. (Mail add: PO Box 967, 27954), SAN 325-7983. Tel: 252-473-3494. FAX: 252-473-1980. Web Site: www.ncaquariums.com. *Curator*, Terri Hathaway; Staff 1 (Non-MLS 1)
Founded 2000
2000-2001 Mats Exp $3,600, Books $3,000, Per/Ser (Incl. Access Fees) $300, Other Print Mats $300
Library Holdings: Bk Titles 700; Per Subs 15
Subject Interests: Marine biology
Restriction: Open to public for reference only

G NORTH CAROLINA DEPARTMENT OF CULTURAL RESOURCES, Division of Archives & History - Outer Banks History Center,* PO Box 250, 27954. SAN 373-1138. Tel: 252-473-2655. FAX: 252-473-1483. *Curator*, Wynne Dough
Library Holdings: Bk Vols 30,000; Per Subs 125
Friends of the Library Group
Branches:

S MARITIME MUSEUM LIBRARY, 315 Front St, Beaufort, 28516. SAN 374-9894. Tel: 252-728-7317. FAX: 252-728-2108. E-Mail: maritime@ncsl.dcr.state.nc.us. Web Site: www.ah.dcr.state.nc.us/sections/maritime/default.htm. *Dir*, Dr George Shannon; Staff 23 (Non-MLS 23)
Library Holdings: Bk Titles 4,000; Per Subs 40
Open Mon-Fri 9-5, Sat 10-5, Sun 1-5

MARION

FIRST BAPTIST CHURCH, Witherspoon Memorial Library, 99 N Main St, 28752. SAN 312-9128. Tel: 828-652-6030. FAX: 828-659-9111. *Actg Librn*, Sue Long
Founded 1950
Library Holdings: Bk Vols 5,200
Subject Interests: Religion

P MCDOWELL COUNTY PUBLIC LIBRARY, 90 W Court St, 28752. SAN 354-9755. Tel: 828-652-3858. FAX: 828-652-2098. Web Site: www.main.nc.us/libraries/mcdowell. *Dir*, Connie D Curtis; E-Mail: ccurtis@ncsl.dcr.state. nc.us; *Asst Dir*, Elizabeth House; E-Mail: ehouse@ncsl.dcr.state. nc.us; Staff 13 (MLS 2, Non-MLS 11)
Founded 1960. Pop 18,126; Circ 40,113
Library Holdings: Bk Vols 109,546; Bk Titles 52,000; Per Subs 252
Subject Interests: Genealogy, Local history
Automation Activity & Vendor Info: (Cataloging) Gaylord; (Circulation) Gaylord
Database Vendor: OCLC - First Search
Friends of the Library Group
Branches: 1
, 105 Mitchell St, Old Fort, 28762. (Mail add: PO Box 1119, Old Fort, 28762), SAN 354-978X. Tel: 828-668-7111. Web Site: www.main.nc.us/libraries/mcdowell. *Branch Mgr*, Dee Daughtridge; E-Mail: ldaughtridge@hotmail.com; Staff 2 (Non-MLS 2)
Founded 1960
Automation Activity & Vendor Info: (Circulation) Gaylord
Database Vendor: OCLC - First Search
Friends of the Library Group
Bookmobiles: 1

J MCDOWELL TECHNICAL COMMUNITY COLLEGE LIBRARY, 54 Universal Dr, 28752. SAN 312-9136. Tel: 828-652-6021, Ext 605. FAX: 828-652-1014. Web Site: www.mcdowelltech.cc.nc.us/newlib.html. *Dir*, Sharon Smith; E-Mail: sharons@mail.mcdowell.cc.nc.us; Staff 2 (MLS 1, Non-MLS 1)
Founded 1968. Enrl 1,078; Highest Degree: Associate
Jul 1999-Jun 2000 Income $156,736. Mats Exp $49,740, Books $30,358, Per/Ser (Incl. Access Fees) $9,246, Presv $502, Micro $3,684, AV Equip $1,114, Electronic Ref Mat (Incl. Access Fees) $4,836. Sal $89,938 (Prof $73,531)
Library Holdings: Bk Vols 25,618; Per Subs 209
Automation Activity & Vendor Info: (Cataloging) SIRSI; (Circulation) SIRSI; (Course Reserve) SIRSI; (OPAC) SIRSI
Database Vendor: Ebsco - EbscoHost, IAC - Info Trac, OCLC - First

Search, ProQuest
Publications: Handbook
Partic in Mountain College Libr Network; NC Dept of Commun Cols; NC Info Network; NCLC; OCLC Online Computer Library Center, Inc

MARS HILL

C RENFRO LIBRARY, Harris Media Center, 124 Cascade St, PO Box 220, 28754. SAN 312-9144. Tel: 828-689-1244, 828-689-1518. Interlibrary Loan Service Tel: 828-689-1492. Reference Tel: 828-689-1468. FAX: 828-689-1474. E-Mail: bkinyon@mhc.edu. Web Site: www.mhc.edu/library. *Dir Libr Serv*, Bill Kinyon; Tel: 828-689-1391; *ILL*, Roberta Williams; E-Mail: bwilliams@mhc.edu; *Res*, Bev Robertson; Tel: 828-689-1561, E-Mail: brobertson@mhc.edu; *Coll Develop*, Donna Seymour; Tel: 828-689-1443, E-Mail: dseymour@mhc.edu; *Circ, Publ Servs*, Ben Kearns; Tel: 828-689-1302, E-Mail: bkearns@mhc.edu; *Cat*, Theresa Fu; Tel: 868-689-1488, E-Mail: tfu@mhc.edu; Staff 10 (MLS 6, Non-MLS 4)
Founded 1856. Pop 1,200; Enrl 1,151; Fac 111; Highest Degree: Bachelor
Jun 1999-May 2000 Income Parent Institution $388,065. Mats Exp $101,190, Books $9,736, Per/Ser (Incl. Access Fees) $48,380, Presv $2,000, Micro $13,118, AV Equip $3,000, Other Print Mats $1,860, Manuscripts & Archives $1,000, Electronic Ref Mat (Incl. Access Fees) $22,096. Sal $254,414
Library Holdings: Bk Vols 86,000; Per Subs 545
Subject Interests: Education, Music
Special Collections: Folk Music (Bascom Lamar Lunsford Southern Appalachia Music); Southern Appalachia (Southern Appalachia Photo Archives)
Automation Activity & Vendor Info: (Cataloging) DRA; (Circulation) DRA; (OPAC) DRA
Database Vendor: Ebsco - EbscoHost, GaleNet, OCLC - First Search, ProQuest, Silverplatter Information Inc., Wilson - Wilson Web
Partic in Appalachian Libr Info Coop; Mountain College Libr Network; Solinet

MARSHALL

P MADISON COUNTY PUBLIC LIBRARY,* 90 S Main St, PO Box 236, 28753-0236. SAN 354-981X. Tel: 828-649-3741. FAX: 828-649-3504. *Coll Develop, Dir*, Jean Krause
Founded 1955. Pop 17,243; Circ 88,491
Jul 1997-Jun 1998 Income $190,000. Mats Exp $20,000, Books $10,000, Per/Ser (Incl. Access Fees) $1,000. Sal $101,000 (Prof $29,040)
Library Holdings: Bk Vols 90,000; Per Subs 43
Friends of the Library Group
Branches: 2
HOT SPRINGS BRANCH, PO Box 175, Hot Springs, 28743-0175. SAN 354-9879. Tel: 828-622-3584. *Librn*, Hazel Moore
Friends of the Library Group
MARS HILL BRANCH, Dogwood St, Mars Hill, 28754. SAN 354-9909. Tel: 828-689-5183. *Librn*, Ann Parks
Friends of the Library Group

MAYSVILLE

P MAYSVILLE PUBLIC LIBRARY,* 601 Seventh St, 28555. SAN 320-5924. Tel: 910-743-3796. FAX: 910-743-3796. *Librn*, Kay Toler
Pop 900
Library Holdings: Bk Titles 1,000; Per Subs 24
Mem of Neuse Regional Library
Holdings are included in Neuse Regional Library entry

MEBANE

P MEBANE PUBLIC LIBRARY,* 106 E Washington St, 27302. SAN 354-5318. Tel: 919-563-6431. FAX: 919-563-5098. Web Site: ils.unc.edu/nclibs/centralnc/home.htm. *Dir*, Margaret B Blanchard; *Librn*, Jacqueline Abercombie; E-Mail: jabercro@ncsl.dcr.state.nc.us
1998-1999 Mats Exp Books $20,000
Library Holdings: Bk Titles 25,000; Per Subs 21
Friends of the Library Group

MISENHEIMER

C PFEIFFER UNIVERSITY, G A Pfeiffer Library, 48380 US Hwy 52 N, 28109. (Mail add: PO Box 930, 28109-0930), SAN 312-9160. Tel: 704-463-1360, Ext 2600. Reference Tel: 704-463-1360, Ext 2604. FAX: 704-463-1363. Web Site: library.pfeiffer.edu. *Coll Develop*, Norman B Wilson; Tel: 704-463-1360, Ext 2603, E-Mail: nwilson@pfeiffer.edu; *Spec Coll*, Jonathan Hutchinson; Tel: 704-463-1360, Ext 2634; *Cat*, Jennifer Cease; Tel: 704-463-1360, Ext 2601, E-Mail: jcease@pfeiffer.edu; *Publ Servs*, Lara B Little; E-Mail: little@pfeiffer.edu. Subject Specialists: *Periodicals*, Lara B Little; Staff 4 (MLS 4)
Founded 1917. Enrl 1,496; Fac 58; Highest Degree: Master
Jul 1999-Jun 2000 Income $276,682. Mats Exp $120,277, Books $44,837, Per/Ser (Incl. Access Fees) $45,069, Presv $1,789, Micro $7,039, Electronic Ref Mat (Incl. Access Fees) $21,543. Sal $143,461
Library Holdings: Bk Vols 115,219; Bk Titles 102,068; Per Subs 396
Subject Interests: Am, Education, English literature, Music, Relig studies
Special Collections: Pfeiffer University Archival Materials
Database Vendor: Ebsco - EbscoHost, OCLC - First Search, ProQuest, Silverplatter Information Inc., Wilson - Wilson Web
Partic in Solinet
Friends of the Library Group

MOCKSVILLE

P DAVIE COUNTY PUBLIC LIBRARY,* 371 N Main St, 27028-2115. SAN 354-9933. Tel: 336-751-2023. FAX: 336-751-1370. *Dir*, Ruth A Hoyle; E-Mail: rhoyle@ncsl.dcr.state.nc.us; *YA Servs*, Annie Gardner; *Ch Servs*, Loretta Campbell; Staff 3 (MLS 3)
Founded 1943. Pop 31,198; Circ 103,162
Jul 1997-Jun 1998 Income $454,347, State $91,644, City $25,000, Federal $6,160, County $263,797, Locally Generated Income $14,305, Other $53,441. Mats Exp $80,137. Sal $230,195
Library Holdings: Bk Vols 60,000; Per Subs 208
Subject Interests: Local history
Publications: History of Davie County; The Historic Architecture of Davie County
Mem of Hq Davie County Pub Libr Syst
Friends of the Library Group

MONROE

P UNION COUNTY PUBLIC LIBRARY, 316 E Windsor St, 28112. SAN 354-9992. Tel: 704-283-8184. TDD: 704-225-8554. FAX: 704-282-0657. Web Site: www.union.lib.nc.us. *Dir*, David Eden; E-Mail: deden@ncsl.dcr.state.nc.us; *Asst Dir*, Dana Eure; E-Mail: deure@ncsl.dcr.state.nc.us; *Tech Servs*, Beth Worley; *Admin Assoc*, Kim Daugherty; E-Mail: kdaugherty@ncsl.dcr.state.nc.us
Founded 1930. Pop 115,344; Circ 490,867
Library Holdings: Bk Vols 172,855; Per Subs 356
Subject Interests: Local genealogy, NC
Publications: Local Geneology; NC
Special Services for the Deaf - Books on deafness & sign language; Captioned film depository; High interest/low vocabulary books; Special interest periodicals
Friends of the Library Group
Branches: 3
P INDIAN TRAIL BRANCH, 109 Navajo St, Indian Trail, 28079. SAN 355-0028. Tel: 704-821-7475. FAX: 704-821-4279. Web Site: www.union.lib.nc.us. *Branch Mgr*, Susan Worcester; *Admin Assoc*, Kim Daugherty; Tel: 704-283-8184, Fax: 704-282-0657, E-Mail: kdaugherty@ncsl.dcr.state.nc.us
Library Holdings: Bk Titles 10,767
Friends of the Library Group
P MARSHVILLE BRANCH, 118 E Union St, Marshville, 28103. SAN 355-0052. Tel: 704-624-2828. FAX: 704-624-2055. Web Site: www.union.lib.nc.us. *Branch Mgr*, Judy Ward; *Admin Assoc*, Kim Daugherty; Tel: 704-283-8184, Fax: 704-282-0657, E-Mail: kdaugherty@ncsl.dcr.state.nc.us
Library Holdings: Bk Titles 13,774
Friends of the Library Group
P WAXHAW BRANCH, 509 S Providence St, Waxhaw, 28173. SAN 355-0087. Tel: 704-843-3131. FAX: 704-843-5538. Web Site: www.union.lib.nc.us. *Branch Mgr*, Gloria Rodden; *Admin Assoc*, Kim Daugherty; Tel: 704-283-8184, Fax: 704-282-0657, E-Mail: kdaugherty@ncsl.dcr.state.nc.us
Library Holdings: Bk Titles 25,990
Friends of the Library Group
Bookmobiles: 1. Also have 1 REAP Exten Van

MONTREAT

C MONTREAT COLLEGE, L Nelson Bell Library, PO Box 1297, 28757. SAN 312-9187. Tel: 828-669-8011, Ext 3504. FAX: 828-669-1552. Web Site: www.montreat.edu. *Dir*, Elizabeth Pearson; E-Mail: epearson@montreat.edu; *Assoc Dir*, Judith Bugniazet; E-Mail: jbugniazet@montreat.edu; *Per*, Lynn Holman; E-Mail: lholman@montreat.edu; Staff 5 (MLS 3, Non-MLS 2)
Founded 1898. Enrl 1,171; Fac 35; Highest Degree: Master
Jul 1998-Jun 1999 Income $243,646. Mats Exp $67,534, Books $26,888, Per/Ser (Incl. Access Fees) $28,849, Presv $1,375, Micro $1,856, AV Equip $6,621, Other Print Mats $1,945. Sal $128,335 (Prof $79,850)
Library Holdings: Bk Vols 68,722; Bk Titles 65,229; Per Subs 245
Subject Interests: Business, Education, Environmental studies, History, Music, Theology
Special Collections: Crosby Adams Music Coll, bks, clippings, music
Automation Activity & Vendor Info: (OPAC) DRA

Publications: Friends Newsletter
Partic in Appalachian Col Asn; Mountain College Libr Network; OCLC Online Computer Library Center, Inc; SE Libr Network
Friends of the Library Group

R PRESBYTERIAN HISTORICAL SOCIETY, Presbyterian Church (USA) Library Services, 318 Georgia Terr, PO Box 849, 28757. SAN 312-9179. Tel: 828-669-7061. FAX: 828-669-5369. Web Site: www.history.pcusa.org. *Dep Dir*, Michelle A Francis; Staff 8 (MLS 4, Non-MLS 4)
Founded 1927
Library Holdings: Bk Titles 40,000; Per Subs 160
Subject Interests: Presbyterian churches of the Southern US
Publications: Presbyterian Heritage
Partic in OCLC Online Computer Library Center, Inc

MOORESVILLE

P MOORESVILLE PUBLIC LIBRARY,* 304 S Main St, 28115. SAN 312-9195. Tel: 704-664-2927. FAX: 704-663-5774. *Librn*, Karen P Khan; E-Mail: kkhan@ncslider.state.nc.us; *Asst Librn*, Kathy S Whitehead
Founded 1894. Pop 25,000; Circ 109,000
Library Holdings: Bk Vols 63,000; Per Subs 110

MOREHEAD CITY

J CARTERET COMMUNITY COLLEGE LIBRARY, 201 College Circle, 28557. SAN 312-9209. Tel: 252-222-6213. Circulation Tel: 252-222-6213. Reference Tel: 252-222-6247. FAX: 252-222-6219. Web Site: www.carteret.cc.nc.us/liblrc.html. *Dir*, Jean Baardsen; Tel: 252-222-6216, E-Mail: jmb@carteret.cc.nc.us; *Acq*, Tara Guthrie; Tel: 252-222-6214, E-Mail: tsg@carteret.cc.nc.us; *ILL*, Annette Davis; Tel: 252-222-6194, E-Mail: jad@carteret.cc.nc.us; Staff 6 (MLS 2, Non-MLS 4)
Enrl 1,500
Library Holdings: Bk Vols 18,022; Bk Titles 15,453; Per Subs 139
Special Collections: Consumer Health Coll; Legal Coll
Database Vendor: Ebsco - EbscoHost, epixtech, inc., OCLC - First Search, ProQuest, Silverplatter Information Inc., Wilson - Wilson Web
Publications: Staff, Faculty & Student Handbooks (Library handbook)
Partic in Dialog Corporation; NC Info Network; OCLC Online Computer Library Center, Inc

MORGANTON

S BROUGHTON HOSPITAL, Patients' Library,* 1000 S Sterling St, 28655. SAN 312-9217. Tel: 828-433-2164, 828-433-2435. FAX: 828-433-2574. *Librn*, Beth Cooke
Library Holdings: Bk Vols 3,753; Per Subs 38
Subject Interests: Patient educ, Self improvement
Publications: Anouncements of new materials
Branches:
ENOLA LEARNING CENTER, 1000 S Sterling St, 28655. SAN 372-4956. Tel: 828-433-2302. FAX: 828-433-2459.
JOHN S MCKEE MEMORIAL LIBRARY, 1000 S Sterling St, 28655. SAN 372-4948. Tel: 828-433-2303. FAX: 828-433-2097. *Librn*, Mary Bush
Library Holdings: Bk Vols 1,100; Per Subs 35

P BURKE COUNTY PUBLIC LIBRARY,* 204 S King St, 28655-3535. SAN 312-9225. Tel: 828-437-5638. FAX: 828-433-1914. E-Mail: library@bcpls.org. *Dir*, Steve Farlow; *Ref*, Wendy Evans; *Ref*, Valerie L Poust; *Tech Servs*, Jim Wilson; Staff 5 (MLS 5)
Founded 1923. Pop 78,434; Circ 257,256
Jul 1997-Jun 1998 Income $852,962. Mats Exp $79,417. Sal $362,674
Library Holdings: Bk Vols 130,779; Per Subs 180
Subject Interests: Art, Environmental studies
Special Collections: North Carolina History, bks, micro & VF
Publications: Brochure on services
Special Services for the Deaf - Books on deafness & sign language; Captioned film depository; High interest/low vocabulary books; Staff with knowledge of sign language; TTY machine
Adult Beginning to Read Books & Computer with teaching software packages
Friends of the Library Group
Branches: 2
C B HILDEBRAND PUBLIC, 201 S Center St, Hildebrand, 28637. SAN 378-1798. Tel: 828-397-3600. FAX: 828-397-3600. *Librn*, Rhea Hebeet
Friends of the Library Group
VALDESE, 213 St Germain Ave SE, 28690-2846. SAN 321-9283. Tel: 828-874-2421. FAX: 828-874-1211. *Librn*, Rhea Hebeet
Friends of the Library Group
Bookmobiles: 1

S NORTH CAROLINA DEPARTMENT OF CORRECTION, Western Youth Institution Library, Western Blvd, PO Box 1439, 28680-1439. SAN 372-5464. Tel: 828-438-6037, Ext 270. FAX: 828-438-6076. *Librn*, Phillip M Heavner; Staff 1 (MLS 1)
Founded 1971
Library Holdings: Bk Vols 13,000; Per Subs 161
Special Collections: NC DOC Educational Services Video Coll
Automation Activity & Vendor Info: (Cataloging) Follett; (Circulation) Follett
Special Services for the Deaf - Books on deafness & sign language; High interest/low vocabulary books

SR PRESBYTERY OF WESTERN NORTH CAROLINA, Resource Center,* 114 Silver Creek Rd, 28655. SAN 375-202X. Tel: 828-438-4217. Toll Free Tel: 800-435-7404. FAX: 828-437-8655. *Coordr*, Pamela Daniel
Library Holdings: Bk Vols 2,300

C WESTERN PIEDMONT COMMUNITY COLLEGE, Phifer Learning Resources Center, 1001 Burkemont Ave, 28655-4511. SAN 312-9233. Tel: 828-438-6195. Interlibrary Loan Service Tel: 828-438-6182. Circulation Tel: 828-438-6193. FAX: 828-438-6184. E-Mail: library@wp.cc.nc.us. Web Site: www.wp.cc.nc.us/library/libhome.htm. *Dean of Libr*, Winston R Lear; Tel: 828-438-6152, E-Mail: wlear@gw.wp.cc.nc.us; *Coll Develop*, Susan C Keller; Tel: 828-438-6182, E-Mail: skeller@gw.wp.cc.nc.us; *Publ Servs*, Steven G Weaver; E-Mail: sweaver@gw.wp.cc.nc.us; *Circ*, Ruth Ann Brisson; E-Mail: rbrisson@gw.wp.cc.nc.us; *Per*, Star Baughman; Tel: 828-438-6150, E-Mail: sbaughman@gw.wp.cc.nc.us; Staff 5 (MLS 3, Non-MLS 2)
Founded 1966. Enrl 2,314; Fac 75
Jul 1999-Jun 2000 Income $407,641, State $403,670, Locally Generated Income $3,921, Other $50. Mats Exp $131,934, Books $33,917, Per/Ser (Incl. Access Fees) $30,099, Presv $400, AV Equip $55,211, Electronic Ref Mat (Incl. Access Fees) $12,307. Sal $132,587 (Prof $79,744)
Library Holdings: Bk Vols 32,567; Bk Titles 30,427; Per Subs 402; Bks on Deafness & Sign Lang 47
Special Collections: Grace DiSanto Poetry Coll; Mark Twain (Ervin Coll); Senator Sam J Ervin, Jr Coll; Small Business Center Coll
Automation Activity & Vendor Info: (Circulation) EOS
Database Vendor: Ebsco - EbscoHost, OCLC - First Search, Wilson - Wilson Web
Publications: Periodical Holdings (Library handbook)
Function: ILL available
Partic in North Carolina Community College System; Northwest Ahec Library Information Network; OCLC Online Computer Library Center, Inc; Unifour Consortium Of Health Care & Educational Institutions
Friends of the Library Group

MOUNT AIRY

P MOUNT AIRY PUBLIC LIBRARY, 145 Rockford St, 27030-4759. SAN 312-9241. Tel: 336-789-5108. FAX: 336-786-5838. *Librn*, Pat Gwyn; Staff 7 (Non-MLS 7)
Founded 1930
Library Holdings: Bk Vols 57,000; Per Subs 45
Mem of Northwest Regional Library System; Northwestern Regional Library
Friends of the Library Group

MOUNT OLIVE

J MOUNT OLIVE COLLEGE, Moye Library, 634 Henderson St, 28365-1699. SAN 312-9268. Tel: 919-658-7168. FAX: 919-658-8934. Web Site: www.mountolive.edu. *Asst Dir, Tech Servs*, Pamela Wood; *Doc, Ser*, Annie Albertson; *Circ*, Gwin Cox; *Ref*, Susan Ryberg
Founded 1955. Enrl 1,700
Jul 1998-Jun 1999 Income Parent Institution $192,500. Mats Exp $66,411, Books $18,500, Per/Ser (Incl. Access Fees) $27,521, Presv $750, Micro $4,500, Electronic Ref Mat (Incl. Access Fees) $9,000. Sal $112,378 (Prof $95,544)
Library Holdings: Bk Titles 65,500; Per Subs 3,755
Special Collections: Free Will Baptist History, bks, flm, micro, mss, pamphlets, clippings
Database Vendor: OCLC - First Search
Partic in OCLC Online Computer Library Center, Inc

MURFREESBORO

C CHOWAN COLLEGE, Whitaker Library, 200 Jones Dr, 27855. SAN 312-9276. Tel: 252-398-6212. FAX: 252-398-1301. Web Site: www.library.chowan.edu. *Dir Libr Serv*, Julie Blake; Tel: 252-398-6439, E-Mail: blakej@chowan.edu; *Archivist*, Cindy Johnson; *Acq*, Al Swain; Tel: 252-398-6203, E-Mail: swaina@chowan.edu; *Cat*, Linda Hassell; Tel: 252-398-6293, E-Mail: hassel@chowan.edu; *Circ*, Georgia Williams; E-Mail: wllig@chowan.edu; *Per*, Patricia Cunnington; Tel: 252-398-6241, E-Mail: cunnip@chowan.edu; Staff 3 (MLS 3)
Founded 1848. Enrl 711; Fac 79; Highest Degree: Bachelor
Jun 1998-May 1999 Income Parent Institution $651,644. Mats Exp $403,563, Books $225,750, Per/Ser (Incl. Access Fees) $144,916, Electronic Ref Mat (Incl. Access Fees) $32,897. Sal $139,465 (Prof $79,962)
Library Holdings: Bk Vols 109,813; Per Subs 920
Special Collections: Baptist Coll
Automation Activity & Vendor Info: (Acquisitions) Innovative Interfaces Inc.; (Cataloging) Innovative Interfaces Inc.; (Circulation) Innovative

Interfaces Inc.; (Course Reserve) Innovative Interfaces Inc.; (ILL) Innovative Interfaces Inc.; (OPAC) Innovative Interfaces Inc.; (Serials) Innovative Interfaces Inc.
Database Vendor: Ebsco - EbscoHost, IAC - SearchBank, Lexis-Nexis, OCLC - First Search, ProQuest, Silverplatter Information Inc.
Partic in Mid-Carolina Academic Library Network; NC LIVE
Friends of the Library Group

P ELIZABETH SEWELL PARKER MEMORIAL LIBRARY, 213 E Main, PO Drawer 186, 27855. SAN 354-4443. Tel: 252-398-4494. FAX: 252-398-5724. *Librn*, Beverly Warrick; E-Mail: warrick213_@hotmail.com
Library Holdings: Bk Vols 10,000; Per Subs 25
Mem of Albemarle Regional Library
Statistics included with regional library. See Winton entry

MURPHY

P MURPHY PUBLIC LIBRARY, 9 Blumenthal St, 28906. SAN 312-9284. Tel: 828-837-2417. FAX: 828-837-6416. Web Site: www.grove.net/~nrl/mpl.htm. *Dir*, Becky Stiles; E-Mail: bstiles@ncsl.dcr.state.nc.us; Staff 4 (MLS 1, Non-MLS 3)
Founded 1919. Circ 74,958
Library Holdings: Bk Vols 20,000; Per Subs 92
Subject Interests: Genealogy
Special Collections: Genealogy
Mem of Nantahala Regional Library
Friends of the Library Group

P NANTAHALA REGIONAL LIBRARY, 11 Blumenthal St, 28906. SAN 312-9292. Tel: 828-837-2025. FAX: 828-837-6416. Web Site: www.grove.net/~nrl. *Dir*, Marcia Joyner Clontz; Fax: 828-837-6406, E-Mail: mclontz@ncsl.dcr.state.nc.us; *Ref*, Stephanie Short; *Ch Servs*, Pamela Ashbrook; Staff 20 (MLS 6, Non-MLS 14)
Founded 1942. Pop 38,482; Circ 227,818
Jul 1998-Jun 1999 Income $967,386, State $366,988, City $181,287, Federal $135,000, County $242,401, Other $41,710. Mats Exp $101,106, Books $82,567, Per/Ser (Incl. Access Fees) $6,725, Electronic Ref Mat (Incl. Access Fees) $11,814. Sal $559,549
Library Holdings: Bk Vols 118,203; Per Subs 289
Special Collections: Cherokee Indians (Our Heritage Indian Coll)
Database Vendor: Ebsco - EbscoHost, OCLC - First Search, ProQuest
Function: Photocopies available
Member Libraries: Andrews Public Library; Graham County Public Library; Moss Memorial Library; Murphy Public Library
Partic in NC Online Libr Network; NC-Live; OCLC Online Computer Library Center, Inc
Friends of the Library Group

J TRI-COUNTY COMMUNITY COLLEGE, Library-Media Center,* 4600 Hwy 64 E, 28906. SAN 312-9306. Tel: 828-837-6810. FAX: 828-837-3266. Web Site: www.tccc.cc.nc.us. *Dir*, Linda Kressal; Staff 2 (MLS 2)
Founded 1964. Enrl 613; Fac 34
Library Holdings: Bk Vols 28,000; Bk Titles 20,815; Per Subs 269

NEW BERN

J CRAVEN COMMUNITY COLLEGE, R C Godwin Memorial Library, 800 College Ct, 28562. SAN 312-9314. Tel: 252-638-7272. Interlibrary Loan Service Tel: 252-638-7276. Circulation Tel: 252-638-7281. FAX: 252-672-7516. *Dean of Libr*, Vance Harper Jones; *Dir, Tech Serv*, Catherine Campbell; Tel: 252-638-7276, E-Mail: campbell@admin.craven.cc.nc.us; *Librn*, Nancy Nye; *AV, Coordr*, John Hartge; Staff 3 (MLS 3)
Founded 1966. Enrl 2,500; Fac 100; Highest Degree: Associate
Jul 1998-Jun 1999 Mats Exp $73,998, Books $61,085, Per/Ser (Incl. Access Fees) $12,809, Presv $104. Sal $152,986 (Prof $121,101)
Library Holdings: Bk Vols 26,026; Bk Titles 21,783; Per Subs 324
Subject Interests: NC
Automation Activity & Vendor Info: (Acquisitions) SIRSI; (Cataloging) SIRSI; (Circulation) SIRSI
Publications: New Titles (quarterly)
Partic in CCLINC

P CRAVEN-PAMLICO-CARTERET REGIONAL LIBRARY,* 400 Johnson St, 28560. SAN 312-9322. Tel: 252-638-7800. FAX: 252-638-7817. *Dir*, Jackie Beach; E-Mail: jbeach@hcsl.dcr.state.nc.us; *Librn*, Linda Muir; *Ch Servs*, Ann Johnston; *Ref*, Melissa Barnes; Staff 4 (MLS 4)
Founded 1962. Pop 145,541; Circ 516,084
Library Holdings: Bk Vols 163,805; Per Subs 350
Special Collections: Genealogy East North Carolina; North Carolina Coll
Member Libraries: Carteret County Public Library; Cove City Public Library; Havelock-Craven County Library; Newport Public Library; Pamlico County Library; Vanceboro Public Library
Friends of the Library Group
Bookmobiles: 2

S EXCEPTIONAL HUMAN EXPERIENCE NETWORK, INC LIBRARY,* 414 Rockledge Rd, 28562. SAN 324-1688. Tel: 252-636-8734. FAX: 252-636-8371. Web Site: www.ehe.org. *Coll Develop, Dir*, Rhea A White; E-Mail: ehenwhite@coastalnet.com; *Tech Servs*, L Jean Spagnolo; Staff 1 (MLS 1)
Founded 1981
Library Holdings: Bk Titles 7,000; Per Subs 127
Subject Interests: Am Indian, Consciousness studies, Mysticism, Parapsychology, Philosophy, Psychical res, Psychology, Religion
Special Collections: C G Jung, bks, journals; Parapsychology, bks, journals
Publications: EHE News (newsletter); Evidential Bibliography on Parapsychology; Exceptional Human Experience (journal); Kirlian Photography Bibliography; On Being Psychic: A Bibliography; Parapsychology Dissertations and Theses (7th ed); Parapsychology for Parents; Parapsychology: A Reading & Buying Guide to the Best Books in Print; Psychic Experiences: A Bibliography)
Restriction: Staff use only, Use of others with permission of librarian
Open Mon-Fri 9am-5pm

P NEW BERN-CRAVEN COUNTY PUBLIC LIBRARY, 400 Johnson St, 28560. SAN 312-9330. Tel: 252-638-7800. FAX: 252-638-7817. *Librn*, Donna E Rhein; Staff 8 (MLS 4, Non-MLS 4)
Founded 1912. Pop 71,261; Circ 230,380
Library Holdings: Bk Vols 92,113; Per Subs 200
Special Collections: North Carolina Coll
Headquarters for Craven-Pamlico-Carteret Regional Libr
Friends of the Library Group

G TRYON PALACE RESEARCH LIBRARY,* 610 Pollock St, PO Box 1007, 28563. SAN 325-8009. Tel: 252-514-4900. FAX: 252-514-4876. *Librn*, J Dean Knight
Library Holdings: Bk Vols 2,650

NEWLAND

P AVERY COUNTY MORRISON PUBLIC LIBRARY,* Avery County, PO Box 250, 28657. SAN 312-9349. Tel: 828-733-9393. FAX: 828-682-6277. *Librn*, Phyllis Burroughs; E-Mail: pburroughs@ncsl.dcr.state.nc.us; *Asst Librn*, Debbie Mclean
Pop 14,422
1998-1999 Income $113,126, County $54,355, Locally Generated Income $12,725, Other $40,473. Mats Exp $25,000, Books $10,000. Sal $50,897
Library Holdings: Bk Vols 55,000
Subject Interests: Genealogy, Local history, NC
Special Collections: Robert Morrison Reference Coll
Mem of Avery-Mitchell-Yancey Regional Library System
Library Services for aging, homebound & physically handicapped; Programs for children & young adults; Summer reading program; Bookmobile Service

NEWPORT

P NEWPORT PUBLIC LIBRARY,* 210 Howard Blvd, 28570. SAN 312-9357. Tel: 252-223-5108. FAX: 252-223-6116. *Librn*, Carolyn Simmons
Circ 10,621
Library Holdings: Bk Vols 15,000; Per Subs 21
Mem of Craven-Pamlico-Carteret Regional Library
Friends of the Library Group

NEWTON

S CATAWBA COUNTY HISTORICAL MUSEUM LIBRARY, 15 N College Ave, PO Box 73, 28658. SAN 312-9365. Tel: 828-465-0383. FAX: 828-465-8477. *Dir*, Sidney Halma
Founded 1954
Library Holdings: Bk Vols 3,500; Bk Titles 3,006
Subject Interests: Family hist, Local, Regional hist
Special Collections: 19th Century Law (Shipp Coll) 1750-1885; Civil War (Long Island Coll), family papers; Clapp family letters; Col Cilley papers; Decorative Arts (Mrs Eaton Coll), 1920-1930 magazines
Friends of the Library Group

P CATAWBA COUNTY LIBRARY,* 115 West C St, 28658. SAN 355-0117. Tel: 828-464-2421. FAX: 828-465-8293. Web Site: www.co.catawba.nc.us. *Dir*, Karen Foss; *YA Servs*, Linda Bridges; *Cat*, Peggy Stinson; *Ref*, Andy Fynt; *Coll Develop, Coordr*, Jane Caldwell; Staff 5 (MLS 5)
Founded 1936. Pop 105,000; Circ 315,000
Library Holdings: Bk Vols 112,285; Per Subs 375
Publications: Better Business Views; Little Bits (youth services)
Branches: 5
CATAWBA COUNTY LAW LIBRARY, Justice Ctr, Hwy 321, 28658. SAN 355-0125. Tel: 828-464-2421. FAX: 828-465-8293. *Ref*, Andy Fynt
Library Holdings: Bk Vols 6,100
MAIDEN BRANCH, 11 S A Ave, Maiden, 28650. SAN 355-0133. Tel: 828-428-2712. FAX: 828-428-3845. *Librn*, Betty Jean Spinson

Library Holdings: Bk Titles 4,000
SAINT STEPHENS, 3225 Springs Rd, Hickory, 28601-9700. SAN 329-6490. Tel: 828-256-3030. FAX: 828-256-6029. *Librn*, Lynn Reed
SHERRILLS FORD BRANCH, 8456 Sherrills Ford Rd, Sherrills Ford, 28673. SAN 355-0141. Tel: 828-478-2729. FAX: 828-478-5837. *Librn*, Sandy Cooke
Library Holdings: Bk Titles 3,000
SOUTHWEST, West Over Plaza, 2944 Hwy 127 S, Hickory, 28602. SAN 376-9283. Tel: 828-294-2343. FAX: 828-294-2477.
Bookmobiles: 1

NORTH WILKESBORO

P APPALACHIAN REGIONAL LIBRARY, 215 Tenth St, 28659. SAN 375-5932. Tel: 336-838-2818. FAX: 336-667-2638. Web Site: www.arlibrary.org. *Dir*, Mary Montgomery Sizemore; E-Mail: msizemore@ncsl.dcr.state.nc.us; *Business*, Judy Blevins; Tel: 336-246-2041, Fax: 336-246-7503, E-Mail: jblevins@ncsl.dcr.state.nc.us; Staff 60 (MLS 11, Non-MLS 49)
Founded 1962. Pop 125,000; Circ 678,436
Jul 1999-Jun 2000 Income $1,552,418, State $412,787, City $15,000, Federal $40,874, County $916,000, Locally Generated Income $167,757. Mats Exp $197,279, Books $169,532, Per/Ser (Incl. Access Fees) $14,614, AV Equip $13,133. Sal $800,534
Library Holdings: Bk Vols 191,192; Per Subs 406
Subject Interests: Genealogy, Local history
Special Collections: Local histories of Ashe, Watauga & Wilkes Counties
Automation Activity & Vendor Info: (Cataloging) SIRSI
Database Vendor: Ebsco - EbscoHost, IAC - Info Trac, OCLC - First Search, ProQuest
Function: ILL available
Friends of the Library Group

P WILKES COUNTY PUBLIC LIBRARY, 215 Tenth St, 28659. SAN 312-9381. Tel: 336-838-2818. FAX: 336-667-2638. E-Mail: webmaster@arlibrary.org. Web Site: www.arlibrary.org. *Mgr*, Louise S Gerhard; E-Mail: lgerhard@ncsl.dcr.state.nc.us; *Ad Servs*, James R Ruszczyk; E-Mail: jruszczyk@ncsl.dcr.state.nc.us; *Tech Servs*, Janet R Kilby; *Ch Servs*, Christy D Blevins; Staff 26 (MLS 7, Non-MLS 19)
Founded 1909. Pop 63,760; Circ 271,780
Library Holdings: Bk Vols 70,233; Per Subs 108
Subject Interests: Genealogy, Local history
Automation Activity & Vendor Info: (Circulation) SIRSI
Regional information & referral for public services & functions for three counties
Friends of the Library Group
Branches: 2
RONDA BRANCH, 123 Chatham St, Ronda, 28670. (Mail add: PO Box 370, Ronda, 28670), SAN 377-0389. Tel: 336-835-2377. Web Site: www.arlibrary.org. *Branch Mgr*, Karen Mullins; Staff 1 (Non-MLS 1)
TRAPHILL BRANCH, 11964 Austin-Traphill Rd, Traphill, 28685. (Mail add: PO Box 113, Traphill, 28685), Tel: 336-957-2534. FAX: 336-957-2534. Web Site: www.arlibrary.org. *Branch Mgr*, Ola K Norman; Staff 1 (Non-MLS 1)
Friends of the Library Group
Bookmobiles: 2

OXFORD

P GRANVILLE COUNTY LIBRARY SYSTEM, Richard H Thornton Library, 210 Main St, 27565-3321. (Mail add: PO Box 339, 27565-0339), SAN 355-0176. Tel: 919-693-1121. Web Site: www.granville.lib.nc.us. *Dir*, Louise Dorton; Fax: 919-693-2244, E-Mail: ldorton@ncsl.dcr.state.nc.us; *Ch Servs*, Margaret Duckworth; *Tech Servs*, Amie Barto; Staff 19 (MLS 2, Non-MLS 17)
Founded 1935. Pop 44,500
Jul 1998-Jun 1999 Income (Main Library and Branch Library) $622,226, State $130,394, Federal $69,881, County $400,956, Locally Generated Income $20,995. Mats Exp $159,548, Books $88,365, Per/Ser (Incl. Access Fees) $5,627, Electronic Ref Mat (Incl. Access Fees) $65,556. Sal $327,389 (Prof $92,500)
Library Holdings: Bk Vols 59,301; Bk Titles 41,415; Per Subs 220
Special Collections: Granville County History; North Carolina History & Genealogy Coll
Database Vendor: Ebsco - EbscoHost
Friends of the Library Group
Branches: 3
BEREA BRANCH, Hwy 158, Berea, 27565. SAN 329-6326. Tel: 919-693-1231. *Librn*, Margaret Adcock
SOUTH, VGCC - South Campus, Hwy 56, Creedmoor, 27522-0039. (Mail add: PO Box 39, Creedmoor, 27522-0039), Tel: 919-528-1752. FAX: 919-528-1752. Web Site: www.granvillecounty.org/library.htm. *Librn*, Michelle Canada
STOVALL BRANCH, Hwy 15, Stovall, 27582. SAN 355-0265. Tel: 919-693-5722. *Librn*, Kathy DeShetler

PEMBROKE

C UNIVERSITY OF NORTH CAROLINA AT PEMBROKE, Sampson-Livermore Library, Faculty Row, PO Box 1510, 28372-1510. SAN 312-9438. Tel: 910-521-6516. FAX: 910-521-6547. Web Site: www.uncp.edu/library. *Dir*, Elinor Foster; *Asst Dir, Coordr*, Jean Sexton; *Ser*, Shirley Learn; *Instrul Serv*, Cindy Saylor; *Doc, Spec Coll*, Lillian Brewington; *Access Serv, Electronic Resources*, Robert Canida; *Acq, Coll Develop*, Susan Whitt; *Ref*, W Reed Austin; *Cat*, David W Young; Staff 23 (MLS 9, Non-MLS 14)
Founded 1887. Enrl 3,448; Fac 192; Highest Degree: Master
Jul 1999-Jun 2000 Income State $1,281,781. Mats Exp $501,496, Books $182,779, Per/Ser (Incl. Access Fees) $261,660, Presv $8,399, Electronic Ref Mat (Incl. Access Fees) $48,658. Sal $593,442 (Prof $315,352)
Library Holdings: Bk Vols 296,087; Bk Titles 242,246; Per Subs 1,471
Subject Interests: Am Indians
Special Collections: Lumbee Indian History
Automation Activity & Vendor Info: (Acquisitions) Innovative Interfaces Inc.; (Cataloging) Innovative Interfaces Inc.; (Circulation) Innovative Interfaces Inc.; (Course Reserve) Innovative Interfaces Inc.; (ILL) Innovative Interfaces Inc.; (OPAC) Innovative Interfaces Inc.; (Serials) Innovative Interfaces Inc.
Database Vendor: Innovative Interfaces INN - View
Publications: Informational Handouts (including fact sheet & bibliographies); Library Lines (newsletter)
Partic in Cape Fear Health Sciences Information Consortium; OCLC Online Computer Library Center, Inc; SE Libr Network
Friends of the Library Group

PILOT MOUNTAIN

P CHARLES H STONE MEMORIAL LIBRARY,* 319 W Main St, PO Box 10, 27041. SAN 312-9446. Tel: 336-368-2370. FAX: 336-368-9587. E-Mail: pilotmtlibrarian@yahoo.com. *Librn*, Melinda A Stamper
Pop 6,000
Library Holdings: Per Subs 20
Mem of Northwestern Regional Library
Partic in NW Regional Libr Syst

PINEBLUFF

P PINEBLUFF PUBLIC LIBRARY,* 305 E Baltimore Ave, PO Box 758, 28373. SAN 312-9454. Tel: 910-281-3004. FAX: 910-281-3004. E-Mail: pinebluffibrary@intepath.com. Web Site: www.204.211.56.212.com. *Mgr*, Melissa Smith
Pop 850; Circ 3,388
Library Holdings: Bk Vols 6,000; Per Subs 10
Open Tues-Fri 2-6, Sat 10-2

PINEHURST

J BOYD LIBRARY SANDHILLS COMMUNITY COLLEGE,* 3395 Airport Rd, 28374. SAN 312-7605. Tel: 910-695-3819. FAX: 910-695-3947. Web Site: www.sandhills.cc.nc.us.
Founded 1965. Enrl 2,400; Fac 123
Library Holdings: Bk Titles 78,000; Per Subs 358

P GIVEN MEMORIAL LIBRARY & TUFTS ARCHIVES, 150 Cherokee Rd, PO Box 159, 28370. SAN 312-9462. Tel: 910-295-6022. FAX: 910-295-9053. *Dir*, Alana Fisher; *Curator*, Khristine Januzik
Founded 1963. Pop 8,785; Circ 59,897
Jul 1999-Jun 2000 Income $200,327. Mats Exp $33,542, Books $14,750, Per/Ser (Incl. Access Fees) $4,686, Micro $330, Manuscripts & Archives $12,930, Electronic Ref Mat (Incl. Access Fees) $846. Sal $141,059
Library Holdings: Bk Vols 24,000; Per Subs 110
Subject Interests: Golf
Special Collections: Local History Coll, 1896-date (Tufts Archives Wing), correspondence, docs, negatives, micro, photogs; Original Donald Ross golf course plans
Automation Activity & Vendor Info: (Cataloging) CASPR; (Circulation) CASPR; (OPAC) CASPR; (Serials) CASPR
Publications: What's New (brochure monthly)
Friends of the Library Group

PINK HILL

P PINK HILL PUBLIC LIBRARY,* 114 W Broadway, 28572. SAN 312-9470. Tel: 252-568-3631. FAX: 252-568-3631. *Librn*, Sabra Waller
Mem of Neuse Regional Library
Holdings are included in Neuse Regional Library entry
Friends of the Library Group

PISGAH FOREST

S ECUSTA, Technical Library,* PO Box 200, 28768-0200. SAN 312-9489. Tel: 828-877-2211, 828-877-2310. FAX: 828-877-2385.
Founded 1939
Library Holdings: Bk Vols 9,946; Per Subs 65
Subject Interests: Air pollution, Cellulose, Chemistry, Paper manufacture, Polymer chemistry, Pulp, Water
Restriction: Staff use only
Division of P H Glatfelter Co

PITTSBORO

P PITTSBORO MEMORIAL LIBRARY,* 158 West St, PO Box 580, 27312. SAN 354-5326. Tel: 919-542-3524. FAX: 919-542-2290. Web Site: ils.unc.edu/nclibs/centralnc/home.htm. *Mgr*, Mary Beall; E-Mail: mbeall@ncsl.dcr.state.nc.us
1998-1999 Mats Exp Books $30,000
Library Holdings: Bk Vols 45,000; Per Subs 57
Friends of the Library Group

PLYMOUTH

P PETTIGREW REGIONAL LIBRARY, 201 E Third St, PO Box 906, 27962-0906. SAN 355-029X. Tel: 252-793-2875. FAX: 252-793-2818. *Dir*, Martha S Smith; E-Mail: msmith@ncsl.dcr.state.nc.us; Staff 24 (MLS 4, Non-MLS 20)
Founded 1955. Pop 42,986; Circ 174,467
Jul 1999-Jun 2000 Income $864,964, State $378,571, Federal $266, County $375,500, Other $110,627. Mats Exp $92,214, Books $69,788, Per/Ser (Incl. Access Fees) $10,792, AV Equip $6,393, Manuscripts & Archives $5,241. Sal $457,485 (Prof $161,952)
Library Holdings: Bk Vols 115,455; Per Subs 223
Subject Interests: Local history
Automation Activity & Vendor Info: (Cataloging) TLC; (Circulation) TLC; (OPAC) TLC
Member Libraries: Perquimans County Library; Shepard-Pruden Memorial Library; Tyrrell County Public Library; Washington County Library
Homebound service

P WASHINGTON COUNTY LIBRARY, 201 E Third St, PO Box 786, 27962. SAN 320-4081. Tel: 252-793-2113. FAX: 252-793-2818.; Staff 3 (Non-MLS 3)
Founded 1918. Pop 13,443; Circ 38,199
Library Holdings: Bk Titles 36,960; Per Subs 67
Subject Interests: Local history
Mem of Pettigrew Regional Library
Friends of the Library Group

POLKTON

J SOUTH PIEDMONT COMMUNITY COLLEGE LRC, (Formerly Anson Community College Library), Highway 74 East, 28135. (Mail add: PO Box 126, 28135), SAN 354-4710. Tel: 704-272-7635. Toll Free Tel: 800-766-0319. FAX: 704-272-8904. Web Site: www.ansoncounty.org/spcc/lrc.html. *Dir*, Julia Grace May; E-Mail: jmay@spcc.cc.nc.us; *Ref Serv Ad*, Christopher Meister; Fax: 704-272-0319; *Branch Mgr*, Lynn Gambon; Tel: 704-292-1200, Fax: 704-292-4178. Subject Specialists: *Mus*, Christopher Meister; Staff 7 (MLS 4, Non-MLS 3)
Founded 1967. Enrl 1,893; Highest Degree: Associate
Jul 1999-Jun 2000 Income State $279,724. Mats Exp $53,617, Books $33,869, Per/Ser (Incl. Access Fees) $12,284, Electronic Ref Mat (Incl. Access Fees) $7,464. Sal $117,250 (Prof $90,628)
Library Holdings: Bk Vols 18,200; Bk Titles 18,614; Per Subs 225
Subject Interests: Bus, Early childhood, Law, Literature, Mgt, Nursing, Religion, Sci-tech, Sociology
Special Collections: Civil War (Linn D Garibaldi Coll), bks, docs & pictures; Linn D Garibaldi Collection-Historical and Personal Memorabilia, docs, pictures, books; Survey Maps (Frank Clarke Coll)
Database Vendor: CARL, Ebsco - EbscoHost, IAC - Info Trac, OCLC - First Search, OVID Technologies, ProQuest, Silverplatter Information Inc.
Partic in CCLINC; NC Dept of Commun Cols

POLLOCKSVILLE

P POLLOCKSVILLE PUBLIC LIBRARY,* 415 Greenhill St, PO Box 6, 28573. SAN 320-5932. Tel: 252-224-5011. FAX: 252-224-5011. Web Site: www.newsregional.org. *Librn*, Rhonda Tillman
Library Holdings: Bk Vols 3,800; Per Subs 12
Special Collections: North Carolina Coll
Mem of Neuse Regional Library
Holdings are included in Neuse Regional Library entry

POPE AFB

UNITED STATES AIR FORCE
A POPE AIR FORCE BASE LIBRARY FL4488, 43 SVS/SVMG, 396 Sonic St Bldg 373, 28308-5225. SAN 355-0354. Tel: 910-394-1892. Interlibrary Loan Service Tel: 910-394-2195. FAX: 910-394-1171. Web Site: www.pope.af.mil. *Dir*, Robin Demark; E-Mail: robin.demark@pope.af.mil
Staff 6 (MLS 2, Non-MLS 4)
Oct 1997-Sep 1998 Income $150,000
Library Holdings: Bk Vols 110,000; Per Subs 74
Subject Interests: Aeronautics, Military history, Prof mil educ
Partic in Fedlink
Officers wives club
Friends of the Library Group

RAEFORD

P HOKE COUNTY PUBLIC LIBRARY,* 334 N Main St, 28376. SAN 312-9500. Tel: 910-875-2502. FAX: 910-875-2207.
Founded 1934. Pop 24,939; Circ 14,565
Library Holdings: Bk Titles 38,000
Mem of Sandhill Regional Library System

RALEIGH

S ALCATEL USA, Information Center, 2912 Wake Forest Rd, 27609. SAN 313-4865. Tel: 919-850-6414. FAX: 919-850-5131. *Librn*, Joan Viscounty; E-Mail: joan.viscounty@usa.alcatel.com
Founded 1971
Library Holdings: Bk Titles 2,200; Per Subs 129
Subject Interests: Computers, Electrical engineering, Mgt, Programming, Telephony
Publications: What's New
Partic in Dialog Corporation

S BFE-ARCHITECTS PLLC, 811 W Hargett St, 27603. SAN 370-3991. Tel: 919-839-6380. FAX: 919-833-6898.

S CAROLINA POWER & LIGHT CO, Research Services,* 410 S Wilmington St, PO Box 1551, 27601. SAN 324-6450. Tel: 919-546-6790. Interlibrary Loan Service Tel: 919-546-6749. FAX: 919-546-5365. *Librn*, C Mohrmann; *Librn*, J Reagan; *Librn*, P Harris; Staff 3 (MLS 2, Non-MLS 1)
Founded 1971
Library Holdings: Bk Titles 500; Per Subs 100
Special Collections: EPRI Reports; Industrial Standards
Publications: BiblioBulletin (acquisitions list)
Partic in NC Info Network

M DOROTHEA DIX HOSPITAL, Walter A Sikes Learning Resource Center, 820 S Boylan Ave, 27603-2176. SAN 312-9527. Tel: 919-733-5111. FAX: 919-733-9781. *Media Spec*, Ella M Williams
Founded 1957
Library Holdings: Bk Vols 10,800
Subject Interests: Internal medicine, Med educ, Pastoral counseling, Psychiat nursing, Psychiatry, Psychology, Soc work
Publications: Annotated New Acquisitions List (bimonthly)
Restriction: Open to public for reference only
Partic in Dialog Corporation; Docline; Medline

S EASTERN TECHNICAL ASSOCIATES LIBRARY,* PO Box 58495, 27658. SAN 375-1147. Tel: 919-878-3188. FAX: 919-872-5199. *Librn*, Sherrie Sigworth

L HUNTON & WILLIAMS, Law Library, One Hannover Sq, Ste 1400, Fayetteville St Mall, 27601. SAN 372-2538. Tel: 919-899-3057. FAX: 919-833-6352. Web Site: www.hunton.com. *Librn*, Jeanine Cali; Staff 2 (Non-MLS 2)
Founded 1980
Library Holdings: Bk Vols 10,000; Per Subs 700
Database Vendor: Lexis-Nexis
Function: Research library

L MAUPIN TAYLOR & ELLIS, PA, Law Library, 3200 Beechleaf Ct, Ste 500, 27604. SAN 372-2341. Tel: 919-981-4038. FAX: 919-981-4300. *Librn*, Catherine V Lambe; E-Mail: clambe@maupintaylor.com; Staff 2 (MLS 1, Non-MLS 1)
Library Holdings: Bk Vols 10,000; Per Subs 100
Subject Interests: Legal mat
Automation Activity & Vendor Info: (Cataloging) Inmagic, Inc.; (OPAC) Inmagic, Inc.; (Serials) Inmagic, Inc.
Database Vendor: Lexis-Nexis
Restriction: Staff use only

C MEREDITH COLLEGE, Carlyle Campbell Library, 3800 Hillsborough St, 27607-5298. SAN 312-9543. Tel: 919-760-8531. Interlibrary Loan Service Tel: 919-760-8446. FAX: 919-760-2830. *Dean of Libr*, Janet Freeman; E-Mail: freeman@carlyle.meredith.edu; Staff 5 (MLS 5)
Founded 1899. Enrl 2,257; Fac 115; Highest Degree: Master

Jul 1998-Jun 1999 Income (Main and Other College/University Libraries) $929,376. Mats Exp $303,676, Books $102,971, Per/Ser (Incl. Access Fees) $91,301, Presv $9,984, Micro $25,975, AV Equip $11,374, Manuscripts & Archives $481, Electronic Ref Mat (Incl. Access Fees) $61,590. Sal $530,338 (Prof $290,507)
Library Holdings: Bk Vols 136,914; Bk Titles 116,574; Per Subs 2,680
Subject Interests: Architecture, Art, British lit, Music, Women's studies
Special Collections: American History (Library of American Civilization Core Coll), micro; Anthropology (Human Relations Resource Files); micro
Database Vendor: DRA
Publications: Friends of Library (newsletter)
Partic in Mid-Carolina Academic Library Network; Solinet
Friends of the Library Group
Departmental Libraries:
MUSIC Tel: 919-760-8396. FAX: 919-760-2830. *Librn*, Carol Smith
Friends of the Library Group

S THE NEWS & OBSERVER PUBLISHING COMPANY, News Research Department Library, 215 S McDowell St, 27602. SAN 371-2664. Tel: 919-829-4580. Toll Free Tel: 800-365-6115. FAX: 919-829-8916. E-Mail: research@nando.com. Web Site: www.news-observer.com/nerd. *Dir*, Teresa G Leonard; Tel: 919-829-4866, E-Mail: tleonard@nando.com; Staff 16 (MLS 5, Non-MLS 11)
Founded 1964
Library Holdings: Bk Titles 4,000; Per Subs 50
Subject Interests: Journalism
Special Collections: Public Records Databases
Database Vendor: Dialog, Lexis-Nexis, ProQuest
Restriction: Staff use only
Function: Newspaper reference library

G NORTH CAROLINA DEPARTMENT OF ENVIRONMENT & NATURAL RESOURCES LIBRARY, 512 N Salisbury St, Rm 719, 27604-1170. (Mail add: 1610 Mail Service Ctr, 27604), SAN 321-7876. Tel: 919-715-4160. FAX: 919-733-2622. Web Site: www.enr.state.nc.us/enr/ee/library. *Librn*, Melanie Buckingham
Founded 1987
1998-1999 Income $87,000. Mats Exp $11,000, Books $4,000, Per/Ser (Incl. Access Fees) $7,000
Library Holdings: Bk Titles 20,000; Per Subs 50
Subject Interests: Health, Natural resources
Partic in NC Info Network; Resources For Health Information Consortium; SE Libr Network

G NORTH CAROLINA DEPARTMENT OF LABOR, Charles H Livengood Jr Memorial Library, 111 Hillsborough St, 27603. (Mail add: 4 W Edenton St, 27601-1092), SAN 322-7782. Tel: 919-807-2848, 919-807-2850. FAX: 919-807-2849. Web Site: www.dol.state.nc.us/bol/lib2.htm. *Dir*, Mary Jane Slipsky; E-Mail: mjslipsky@mail.dol.state.nc.us; Staff 2 (MLS 1, Non-MLS 1)
Founded 1973
Library Holdings: Bk Vols 7,000; Per Subs 50
Subject Interests: Labor law, Occupational law, Occupational safety
Special Collections: Labor Law (Charles H Livengood, Jr Coll), bks, arbitrations
Partic in Resources For Health Information Consortium
Friends of the Library Group

G NORTH CAROLINA LEGISLATIVE LIBRARY, (Formerly North Carolina General Assembly), Legislative Off Bldg, 300 N Salisbury St, 27603-5925. SAN 321-0863. Tel: 919-733-9390. FAX: 919-715-5460. Web Site: www.ncleg.net. *Librn*, Cathy L Martin; E-Mail: cathym@ncleg.net; *Res*, Jane Basnight; E-Mail: janeb@ncleg.net; *Res*, Karen Hunter; E-Mail: karenhu@ncleg.net; *Tech Servs*, Brian Peck; E-Mail: brianp@ncleg.net; Staff 5 (MLS 4, Non-MLS 1)
Founded 1967
Library Holdings: Bk Titles 18,000
Special Collections: Legislation (Standing & Study Committee Notebooks)
Partic in NC Info Network; SE Libr Network

S NORTH CAROLINA MUSEUM OF ART, Art Reference Library, 2110 Blue Ridge Rd, 27607-6494. (Mail add: 4630 Mail Service Center, 27699-4630), SAN 312-956X. Tel: 919-839-6262, Ext 2137. FAX: 919-733-8034. Web Site: www.ncartmuseum.org. *Librn*, Natalia J Lonchyna; Tel: 919-839-6262, Ext 2136, E-Mail: nlonchyna@ncmamail.dcr.state.nc.us; Staff 2 (MLS 1, Non-MLS 1)
Founded 1956
Library Holdings: Bk Vols 33,500; Bk Titles 35,000; Per Subs 90
Subject Interests: Decorative arts, Fine arts
Restriction: Not a lending library
Function: Reference only

P NORTH CAROLINA REGIONAL LIBRARY FOR THE BLIND & PHYSICALLY HANDICAPPED,* 1811 Capital Blvd, 27635-0001. SAN 312-9578. Tel: 919-733-4376. TDD: 919-733-1462. FAX: 919-733-6910. E-Mail: nclbph@ncsl.dcr.state.nc.us. *Librn*, Francine Martin; Staff 3 (MLS 3)
Founded 1959. Pop 9,000; Circ 348,825
Library Holdings: Bk Vols 21,080; Bk Titles 12,404
Special Collections: North Carolina, braille & cassette
Publications: Newsletter, braille, large type & tape (4 issues annually)
Special Services for the Deaf - TDD
Friends of the Library Group

G NORTH CAROLINA STATE DEPARTMENT OF PUBLIC INSTRUCTION, Education Information Center, Educ Bldg, Rm 540, 301 N Wilmington St, 27601-2825. SAN 312-9586. Tel: 919-715-1536. FAX: 919-715-4823. *Coordr*, Harriette Sparlin; E-Mail: hsparlin@dpi.state.nc.us
Founded 1960
Library Holdings: Bk Vols 520; Per Subs 200
Subject Interests: Education
Special Collections: North Carolina Archives on Education in NC

S NORTH CAROLINA STATE MUSEUM OF NATURAL SCIENCES, H H Brimley Memorial Library, 11 W Jones St, 27601-1029. SAN 312-9594. Tel: 919-733-7450, Ext 208. FAX: 919-733-1573. *Chief Librn*, Janet G Edgerton; E-Mail: janet.edgerton@ncmail.net; *Asst Librn*, Margaret Cotrufo; Staff 2 (MLS 1, Non-MLS 1)
Founded 1941
Jul 1998-Jun 1999 Mats Exp $9,000, Books $19,000, Per/Ser (Incl. Access Fees) $700, AV Equip $400, Electronic Ref Mat (Incl. Access Fees) $400. Sal $28,000
Library Holdings: Bk Vols 7,500; Bk Titles 6,000; Per Subs 50
Subject Interests: Ecology, Environmental studies, Natural history, Natural scis, Paleontology, Sci educ, Systematics, Vertebrate zool
Automation Activity & Vendor Info: (ILL) Athena
Function: Research library
Partic in Solinet

C NORTH CAROLINA STATE UNIVERSITY LIBRARIES, (NCSU), Campus Box 7111, 27695-7111. SAN 355-0443. Tel: 919-515-2595, 919-515-2843. FAX: 919-515-3628. Web Site: www.lib.ncsu.edu. *Dir*, Susan K Nutter; *Assoc Dir*, Kathleen Brown; E-Mail: kathy_brown@ncsu.edu; *Res*, Karen Ciccone; Tel: 919-515-5757, E-Mail: karen_ciccone@ncsu.edu; *Coll Develop*, Terry Wittig; Tel: 919-515-7110, E-Mail: terry_wittig@ncsu.edu; *Acq*, Nancy Gibbs; Tel: 919-515-7021, E-Mail: nancy_gibbs@ncsu.edu; *Spec Coll*, Bernard McTigue; Tel: 919-515-8119, E-Mail: bernard_mctigue@ncsu.edu; *Info Tech*, John Isenhour; E-Mail: john_isenhour@ncsu.edu; *Access Serv*, Susan Barnard; Tel: 919-515-3594, E-Mail: susan_barnard@ncsu.edu; *Publ Servs*, Carolyn Argentati; E-Mail: carolyn_argentati@ncsu.edu; *Cat*, Charles Pennell; Tel: 919-515-2743, E-Mail: charles_pennell@ncsu.edu
Founded 1887. Enrl 27,659; Fac 1,570; Highest Degree: Doctorate
Library Holdings: Bk Vols 2,829,312; Per Subs 26,438
Subject Interests: Agriculture, Architecture, Biol sci, Computer science, Design, Engineering, Humanities, Mathematics, Mgt, Natural resources, Physical science, Soc sci, Statistics, Textiles, Veterinary medicine
Special Collections: Architecture & Design Coll; Entomology (Tippman & Metcalf Coll); Industrial Standards; NTIS Research Reports, micro; Textiles Coll; United States Patent Coll
Automation Activity & Vendor Info: (OPAC) DRA
Publications: Focus; NCSU Libraries Newsletter; The Libraries of NC State Univ Bulletin (in-house distribution only)
Partic in Asn of Research Libraries; Association Of Southeastern Research Libraries (ASERL); Cooperative Raleigh Cols; Solinet; TRLN
Friends of the Library Group
Departmental Libraries:
BURLINGTON TEXTILES LIBRARY, 4411 College of Textiles, Campus Box 8301, 27695-8301. SAN 355-0508. Tel: 919-515-3043. FAX: 919-515-3926. E-Mail: tx-lib@tx.ncsu.edu. Web Site: www.lib.ncsu.edu. *Head of Libr*, Susan Weiner. Subject Specialists: *Engineering*, Honora Nerz; *Engineering*, Tamika Barnes; *Textiles*, Honora Nerz; Staff 3 (MLS 3)
Subject Interests: Polymers, Textiles
Special Collections: Harriss Fabrics & Speizman Hosiery
HARRYE B LYONS DESIGN LIBRARY, NCV Brooks Hall, Campus Box 7701, 27695-7701. SAN 355-0532. Tel: 919-515-2207. FAX: 919-515-7330. Web Site: www.lib.ncsu.edu.; Staff 4 (MLS 1, Non-MLS 3)
Subject Interests: Architecture, Art, Graphic, Landscape architecture, Town planning photog, Visual design
Special Collections: Slide Coll, pamphlet file, product file
Friends of the Library Group
LEARNING RESOURCES LIBRARY, Campus Box 7801, 27695-7801. SAN 366-0524. Tel: 919-515-3191. FAX: 919-515-7634. Web Site: www.lib.ncsu.edu. *Librn*, Margaret Ann Link; E-Mail: margaret_link@ncsu.edu; *Asst Librn*, Chrys Cranford
Library Holdings: Bk Vols 10,506
Subject Interests: Middle sch, Psychology, Secondary educ
Special Collections: North Carolina state adopted textbooks; Standardized Test Library
Publications: Information brochure, newsletter
Friends of the Library Group
NATURAL RESOURCES LIBRARY, 1102 Jordan Hall, Campus Box 7114, 27695-7114. SAN 355-0478. Tel: 919-515-2306. FAX: 919-515-7802. Web Site: www.lib.ncsu.edu. *Actg Librn*, Andrea Gabriel; Tel: 919-515-3513, E-Mail: andrea_gabriel@ncsu.edu; Staff 3 (MLS 1, Non-MLS 2)
Enrl 1,000; Fac 175

Library Holdings: Bk Vols 21,242
Subject Interests: Atmospheric scis, Earth scis, Forestry, GIS, Marine sciences, Paper scis, Parks, Recreation, Tourism mgt, Wood
Publications: Newsletter (monthly)
Partic in TRLN
Friends of the Library Group

CM VETERINARY MEDICAL LIBRARY, 4700 Hillsborough St, Campus Box 8401, 27606. SAN 355-0516. Tel: 919-513-6218. FAX: 919-513-6400. Web Site: www.lib.ncsu.edu. *Head of Libr*, Laura M Osegueda; E-Mail: laura_osegueda@ncsu.edu; Staff 5 (MLS 1, Non-MLS 4)
Library Holdings: Bk Vols 16,946; Per Subs 26,111
Subject Interests: Biochemistry, Biology, Medicine, Veterinary medicine
Publications: Bimonthly acquisitions list
Partic in Solinet; TRLN

GL NORTH CAROLINA SUPREME COURT LIBRARY, 2 E Morgan St, PO Box 28006, 27611-8006. SAN 312-9608. Tel: 919-733-3425. Web Site: www.aoc.state.nc.us/public/html/sc_library.htm. *Coll Develop, Librn*, Thomas Davis; E-Mail: tpd@sc.state.nc.us; *Asst Librn, Tech Servs*, Jennifer McLean; Staff 5 (MLS 3, Non-MLS 2)
Founded 1812
Jul 1999-Jun 2000 Income State $460,000. Mats Exp $460,000, Books $416,000, Per/Ser (Incl. Access Fees) $24,000, Micro $4,000, Electronic Ref Mat (Incl. Access Fees) $16,000
Library Holdings: Bk Vols 129,938; Per Subs 668
Subject Interests: Anglo-Am law
Automation Activity & Vendor Info: (Cataloging) SIRSI; (OPAC) SIRSI; (Serials) SIRSI
Restriction: Non-circulating to the public
Partic in SE Libr Network

L PARKER, POE, ADAMS & BERNSTEIN, Law Library,* 150 Fayettville Street Mall, Ste 1400, 27602-0389. SAN 372-2546. Tel: 919-828-0564. FAX: 919-834-4564. E-Mail: lww@ppab.com. *Librn*, Lisa W Williams
Library Holdings: Bk Vols 11,500; Per Subs 39

J PEACE COLLEGE, Lucy Cooper Finch Library, 15 E Peace St, 27604. SAN 312-9616. Tel: 919-508-2236. Interlibrary Loan Service Tel: 919-508-2377. Circulation Tel: 919-508-2377. FAX: 919-508-2335. Web Site: web.peace.edu/pages/lcflibry.html. *Coll Develop, Dir*, Paul F King; Tel: 919-508-2378, E-Mail: pking@peace.edu; Staff 4 (MLS 4)
Founded 1872. Enrl 560; Fac 35; Highest Degree: Bachelor
Jul 1999-Jun 2000 Income Parent Institution $216,000. Mats Exp $100,000, Books $53,600, Per/Ser (Incl. Access Fees) $27,000, Presv $1,600, Micro $6,000, AV Equip $3,500, Manuscripts & Archives $300, Electronic Ref Mat (Incl. Access Fees) $6,000. Sal $116,000
Library Holdings: Bk Vols 52,000; Bk Titles 40,000; Per Subs 3,900
Subject Interests: Liberal arts
Partic in Cooperative Raleigh Cols; Mid-Carolina Academic Library Network

L POYNER & SPRUILL, Law Library,* 3600 Glenwood Ave, PO Box 10096, 27605. SAN 372-2090. Tel: 919-783-6400. FAX: 919-783-1075. E-Mail: aollam@poynerspruill.com. Web Site: www.poynerspruill.com. *Librn*, Lou Lamm
Library Holdings: Bk Vols 20,000; Per Subs 100

M REX HEALTHCARE LIBRARY, 4420 Lake Boone Trail, 27607. SAN 312-9624. Tel: 919-784-3032. FAX: 919-784-1670. E-Mail: library.administrator@rexhealth.com. Web Site: www.rexhealth.com/main/library.html. *Librn*, Cynthia Williams; Staff 1 (MLS 1)
Library Holdings: Bk Vols 1,500; Per Subs 200
Subject Interests: Health care admin, Medicine, Nursing
Partic in Retit

C SAINT AUGUSTINE'S COLLEGE, The Prezell R Robinson Library, 1315 Oakwood Ave, 27610-2298. SAN 312-9632. Tel: 919-516-4000. FAX: 919-828-9841. Web Site: www.st.aug.edu. *Dir*, Linda Simmons-Henry; E-Mail: lshenry@es-st-aug.edu
Enrl 1,459
Library Holdings: Bk Vols 78,000; Per Subs 400
Subject Interests: Behav sci, Econ, Ethnic studies, Music, Soc sci
Special Collections: Curriculum Materials
Publications: Library newsletter
Friends of the Library Group

J SAINT MARY'S SCHOOL, Sarah Graham Kenan Library, 900 Hillsborough St, 27603-1689. SAN 312-9640. Tel: 919-424-4040. FAX: 919-424-4134. Web Site: www.saint-marys.edu. *Actg Dir, ILL*, Gloria Graham; Staff 1 (MLS 1)
Founded 1842. Enrl 240; Fac 35
Library Holdings: Bk Vols 45,322; Bk Titles 40,000; Per Subs 50
Subject Interests: Am writers, Art, Biog, English, History, Shakespeare, Women's studies
Partic in Cooperative Raleigh Cols; Mid-Carolina Academic Library Network

C SHAW UNIVERSITY, James E Cheek Learning Resources Center,* 118 E South St, 27601. SAN 312-9659. Tel: 919-546-8455. Interlibrary Loan Service Tel: 919-546-8348. FAX: 919-831-1161. E-Mail: library@shawu.edu. Web Site: www.shawuniversity.edu. *Dir*, Sheila Bourne; E-Mail: sbourne@shawu.edu; *Librn*, William Lewis; Tel: 919-546-8409, E-Mail: blewis@shawu.edu; *Librn*, Clifford Small; E-Mail: csmall@shawu.edu; *Cat*, Robena Bradley; Tel: 919-546-8406, E-Mail: rbradley@shawu.edu; *Circ*, Chaille Ahumada; Tel: 919-546-8407, E-Mail: cahumada@shawu.edu; *Coordr*, Rena Blyther Daniels; Tel: 919-546-8409, E-Mail: rblyther@shawu.edu. Subject Specialists: *Curriculum mat*, Rena Blyther Daniels; *Reference*, William Lewis; Staff 7 (MLS 5, Non-MLS 2)
Founded 1865
Library Holdings: Bk Vols 140,000; Bk Titles 132,000; Per Subs 687
Subject Interests: Oral hist
Special Collections: Art History Coll, Religion & Philosophy (Gilmour Coll); Black Coll; John W Fleming Afro-American Coll; North American Indian Coll; Schomburg Coll; Shaw University (Archives Coll); The John W Fleming African American Coll; The Schomberg Coll; Shaw University Archives Coll
Automation Activity & Vendor Info: (Cataloging) DRA; (Circulation) DRA; (OPAC) DRA
Database Vendor: DRA, Ebsco - EbscoHost, IAC - SearchBank, OCLC - First Search, ProQuest, Silverplatter Information Inc., Wilson - Wilson Web
Publications: Library manual; student assistant handbook; University Archives
Function: Professional lending library
Partic in Cooperative Raleigh Cols; Mid-Carolina Academic Library Network; NC Ctr for Independent Higher Educ

L SMITH, ANDERSON, BLOUNT, DORSETT, MITCHELL & JERNIGAN LIBRARY,* 2500 First Union Capitol Ctr. (Mail add: PO Box 2611, 27602-2611), Tel: 919-821-6658. FAX: 919-821-6800. *Dir Libr Serv*, Constance M Matzen; E-Mail: cmatzen@smithlaw.com
Library Holdings: Bk Vols 8,000
Subject Interests: Law

P STATE LIBRARY OF NORTH CAROLINA, 109 E Jones St, 27601-2807. (Mail add: 4640 Mail Service Ctr, 27699-4640), SAN 355-0389. Tel: 919-733-2570. FAX: 919-733-8748. Web Site: www.statelibrary.dcr.state.nc.us/. *State Librn*, Sandra M Cooper; *Asst Librn*, Robert E Burgin; E-Mail: rburgin@library.dcr.state.nc.us; *Librn for Blind*, Francine Martin; *Coll Develop*, Joyce Throckmorton; Staff 96 (MLS 33, Non-MLS 63)
Founded 1812. Pop 7,650,699
Jul 1999-Jun 2000 Income (Main Library and Branch Library) $25,624,464, State $21,008,940, Federal $4,427,241, Locally Generated Income $188,283. Mats Exp $300,851, Books $118,790, Per/Ser (Incl. Access Fees) $94,254, Micro $64,903, Electronic Ref Mat (Incl. Access Fees) $22,904. Sal $2,676,862 (Prof $1,151,657)
Library Holdings: Bk Vols 165,184; Bk Titles 133,998; Per Subs 1,237
Subject Interests: Demographics, North Caroliniana, Statistics
Automation Activity & Vendor Info: (Serials) epixtech, inc.
Database Vendor: Dialog, epixtech, inc., Lexis-Nexis
Publications: Checklist of Offiicial North Carolina State Publications
Partic in Dialog Corporation; OCLC Online Computer Library Center, Inc; SE Libr Network
Branches: 1
LIBRARY FOR THE BLIND & PHYSICALLY HANDICAPPED
See Separate Entry under North Carolina Regional Library for the Blind & Physically Handicapped

P WAKE COUNTY PUBLIC LIBRARY SYSTEM,* 4020 Carya Dr, 27610-2900. SAN 355-0567. Tel: 919-250-1200, 919-856-6868. FAX: 919-250-1209. Web Site: www.co.wake.nc.us/library. *Dir*, Thomas L Moore; *Syst Coordr*, Lanny Parker; *Cat*, Antoinette Foster; Staff 159 (MLS 41, Non-MLS 118)
Founded 1898. Pop 565,053; Circ 4,529,895
Jul 1997-Jun 1998 Income $9,757,029. Mats Exp $1,993,392. Sal $5,587,822
Library Holdings: Bk Vols 1,480,766; Bk Titles 200,000; Per Subs 1,700
Special Collections: African American (Mollie Houston Lee Coll), bks, clippings, fiche; North Carolina History Coll
Automation Activity & Vendor Info: (Acquisitions) epixtech, inc.; (Cataloging) Brodart; (Circulation) epixtech, inc.
Friends of the Library Group
Branches: 17
ATHENS DRIVE COMMUNITY, 1420 Athens Dr, 27606. SAN 355-0605. Tel: 919-233-4000, 919-233-4083. FAX: 919-233-4082. *Librn*, Betty Williams
Library Holdings: Bk Vols 50,000
Open Mon-Thurs 8-9, Fri 8-8:30 & Sun 1-5
Friends of the Library Group
CAMERON VILLAGE REGIONAL, 1930 Clark Ave, 27605. SAN 355-0621. Tel: 919-856-6710. FAX: 919-856-6722. Web Site: www.co.wake.nc.us/library. *Librn*, Dale Cousins; E-Mail: gcousins@co.wake.nc.us; Staff 21 (MLS 10, Non-MLS 11)
Founded 1974. Pop 156,000; Circ 750,000
1999-2000 Mats Exp Books $292,000
Library Holdings: Bk Vols 169,263; Bk Titles 80,000; Per Subs 400; Bks

on Deafness & Sign Lang 12
Special Collections: North Carolina
Open Mon-Fri 9-9, Sat 10-5 & Sun 1-5
Friends of the Library Group
CARY BRANCH, 310 S Academy St, Cary, 27511. SAN 355-0656. Tel: 919-460-3350. Web Site: ww.co.nc.us/library. *Librn, Mgr*, Janet Lockhart; Tel: 919-460-3357, E-Mail: jlockhart@co.wake.nc.us; Staff 9 (MLS 1, Non-MLS 8)
Pop 92,000; Circ 618,639
Library Holdings: Bk Vols 111,181; Bk Titles 68,565; Per Subs 114
Open Mon-Thurs 9-9, Fri & Sat 9-5 & Sun 1-5
Friends of the Library Group
EAST REGIONAL, 946 Stepel Square Ct, Knightdale, 27545. SAN 355-0869. Tel: 919-217-5300. FAX: 919-217-5327. Web Site: www.co.wake.nc.us/library.
Library Holdings: Bk Vols 90,000
Open Mon & Wed 2-8, Tues & Thurs 10-6, Fri 2-6 & Sat 10-2
Friends of the Library Group
ELECTRONIC INFORMATION CENTER, Wake County Off Bldg, 334 Fayetteville St Mall, 27602. SAN 376-9259. Tel: 919-856-6690. FAX: 919-856-6206. *Librn*, Traus Horton
EVA PERRY REGIONAL, 2100 Shepherd's Vineyard Dr, Apex, 27502. SAN 355-0591. Tel: 919-387-2100. FAX: 919-387-4320. Web Site: www.co.wake.nc.us/library. *Librn*, Terri M Luke; E-Mail: tluke@co.wake.nc.us; Staff 20 (MLS 9, Non-MLS 11)
Founded 1996
1999-2000 Mats Exp $308,000
Library Holdings: Bk Vols 190,000
Automation Activity & Vendor Info: (Acquisitions) epixtech, inc.; (Cataloging) epixtech, inc.; (Circulation) epixtech, inc.
Friends of the Library Group
FUQUAY-VARINA BRANCH, 133 S Fuquay Ave, Fuquay-Varina, 27526. SAN 355-0710. Tel: 919-557-2788. FAX: 919-557-2792. *Librn*, Cindy McConnell
Library Holdings: Bk Vols 38,393
Open Mon & Wed 2-8, Tues & Thurs 10-6, Fri 2-6 & Sat 10-2
Friends of the Library Group
GREEN ROAD, 4101 Green Rd, 27604. SAN 376-9267. Tel: 919-790-3200. FAX: 919-790-3250. Web Site: www.co.wake.nc.us/library. *Librn*, Betty Hill
Library Holdings: Bk Vols 75,000
Friends of the Library Group
NORTH REGIONAL, 200 Horizon Dr, 27615. SAN 355-0893. Tel: 919-870-4000. FAX: 919-870-4007. Web Site: www.co.wake.nc.us/library. *Librn*, Michael Wasilick
Library Holdings: Bk Vols 211,295
Open Mon-Fri 9-9, Sat 9-5 & Sun 1-5
Friends of the Library Group
OLIVIA RANEY LOCAL HISTORY, 4016 Carya Dr, 27610. SAN 376-9275. Tel: 919-250-1196. FAX: 919-212-0476. *Librn*, Sue Zolkowski
RICHARD B HARRISON BRANCH, 1313 New Bern Ave, 27610. SAN 355-0834. Tel: 919-856-5720. FAX: 919-856-6943. Web Site: www.co.wake.nc.us/library. *Librn*, Wanda Cox-Bailey
Library Holdings: Bk Vols 42,653
Special Collections: Black Literature (Mollie H Lee Coll)
Open Mon-Thurs 9-9, Fri & Sat 9-6
Friends of the Library Group
SOUTH RALEIGH, 1601-14 Crosslink Rd, 27610. SAN 355-0958. Tel: 919-856-6598. FAX: 919-856-6762. Web Site: www.co.wake.nc.us/library. *Librn*, Barbara Kenon
Library Holdings: Bk Vols 20,000
Open Mon-Thurs 10-8, Fri & Sat 10-6
Friends of the Library Group
SOUTHEAST REGIONAL, 908 Seventh Ave, Garner, 27529. SAN 329-6415. Tel: 919-662-2250. FAX: 919-662-2270. Web Site: www.co.wake.nc.us/library. *Librn*, E Gail Harrell
Library Holdings: Bk Vols 149,205
Open Mon-Fri 9-9, Sat 9-5 & Sun 1-5
Friends of the Library Group
WAKE FOREST BRANCH, 400 E Holding Ave, Wake Forest, 27587. SAN 355-0982. Tel: 919-554-8498. FAX: 919-554-8499. E-Mail: aburlingame@co.wake.nc.us. Web Site: www.co.wake.nc.us/library. *Librn*, Ann Burlingame; Tel: 919-554-3308, E-Mail: aburlingame@co.wake.nc.us; Staff 5 (MLS 2, Non-MLS 3)
Founded 1961. Pop 7,000; Circ 20,000
Library Holdings: Bk Vols 32,095; Per Subs 60
Automation Activity & Vendor Info: (Circulation) epixtech, inc.
Database Vendor: OCLC - First Search
Open Mon-Thurs 10-8, Fri 10-6, Sat 10-2
Friends of the Library Group
WENDELL BRANCH, 207 S Hollybrook Rd, Wendell, 27591. SAN 355-1016. Tel: 919-365-2600. FAX: 919-365-2602. *Librn*, Liz Bartlett
Founded 1950. Pop 4,500; Circ 98,000
Library Holdings: Bk Vols 31,000
Automation Activity & Vendor Info: (Acquisitions) epixtech, inc.; (Cataloging) epixtech, inc.; (Circulation) epixtech, inc.
Open Mon-Thurs 10-8, Fri 10-6 & Sat 10-2
WEST POPULAR LENDING, 5800 Duraleigh Rd, 27612. SAN 372-4123. Tel: 919-881-1344. FAX: 919-881-1317. *Librn*, Linda Cooper
Library Holdings: Bk Vols 60,000
Open Mon-Thurs 9-9, Fri & Sat 9-6
Friends of the Library Group
ZEBULON BRANCH, 1000 Dogwood Dr, Zebulon, 27597. SAN 355-1040. Tel: 919-404-3610. FAX: 919-404-3619. *Librn*, Jean Ells; E-Mail: jells@co.wake.nc.us; Staff 4 (MLS 1, Non-MLS 3)
Library Holdings: Bk Vols 29,821
Open Mon & Thurs 10-8, Tues, Wed & Fri 10-6 & Sat 10-2
Friends of the Library Group

J WAKE TECHNICAL COMMUNITY COLLEGE LIBRARY, 9101 Fayetteville Rd, 27603-5696. SAN 312-9667. Tel: 919-662-3309. Reference Tel: 919-662-3308. FAX: 919-662-3575. Web Site: www.wake.tec.nc.us/library/index.html. *Dir Libr Serv*, Robert Michael James; Tel: 919-662-3607, E-Mail: mjames@gwmail.wake.tec.nc.us; *Admin Assoc*, Becky Sayers; E-Mail: risayers@gwmial.wake.tec.nc.us; *Ref*, Peggy Quinn; E-Mail: pgquinn@gwmail.wake.tec.nc.us; *Br Coordr*, Gloria Sutton; Tel: 919-212-3837, Fax: 919-250-4329, E-Mail: gwsutton@gwmail.wake.tec.nc.us; *Tech Servs*, Jim Gray; E-Mail: jegray@gwmail.wake.tec.nc.us; *Asst Librn, AV*, Linda Gibbons; E-Mail: lbgibbon@gwmail.wake.tec.nc.us; *Asst Librn, Circ*, Lorraine Krichko; E-Mail: lpkrichk@gwmail.wake.tec.nc.us; *Ref*, Burnette Green; Tel: 919-212-3836, Fax: 919-250-4329, E-Mail: blgreen@gwmail.wake.tec.nc.us; *ILL*, Pat Sexton; E-Mail: phsexton@gwmail.wake.tec.nc.us; *Acq*, Krisan Gregson; E-Mail: kcgregso@gwmail.wake.tc.nc.us; *Acq*, Cheryl Rodger; Tel: 919-212-3836, Fax: 919-250-4329, E-Mail: carodger@gwmail.wake.tec.nc.us. Subject Specialists: *Health sci libr*, Gloria Sutton; *Health sci libr*, Burnette Green; Staff 10 (MLS 3, Non-MLS 7)
Founded 1962. Pop 5,931; Circ 31,399; Enrl 5,668; Highest Degree: Associate
Jul 1999-Jun 2000 Income $896,339, State $810,328, Federal $939, County $85,072. Mats Exp $432,935, Books $175,430, Per/Ser (Incl. Access Fees) $53,887, AV Equip $24,912. Sal $231,557 (Prof $230,908)
Library Holdings: Bk Vols 70,617; Per Subs 540
Subject Interests: Arts, Business, Computer info systs, Eng-tech, Health sciences, Sciences, Vocational tech
Automation Activity & Vendor Info: (Cataloging) SIRSI; (Circulation) SIRSI; (ILL) SIRSI; (OPAC) SIRSI
Publications: Library Handbook
Function: ILL available
Partic in Community Col Librs NC

M WAKEMED - NORTH CAROLINA AREA HEALTH EDUCATION CENTERS PROGRAM, Medical Library, 3024 New Bern Ave Ste G01, 27610. SAN 320-5843. Tel: 919-350-8529. FAX: 919-350-8836. E-Mail: medlibrary@wakemed.org. Web Site: www.wakeahec.org. *Dir Info Resources & Res*, Susan Speer; Tel: 919-350-8528, E-Mail: sspeer@wakemed.org; Staff 10 (MLS 5, Non-MLS 5)
Founded 1965
Library Holdings: Bk Titles 5,105; Per Subs 246
Subject Interests: Health admin, Medicine, Nursing, Pharmacology
Automation Activity & Vendor Info: (Cataloging) epixtech, inc.; (Circulation) epixtech, inc.; (OPAC) epixtech, inc.; (Serials) epixtech, inc.
Database Vendor: Ebsco - EbscoHost, epixtech, inc., OCLC - First Search, OVID Technologies
Publications: The Gauzette
Partic in Nat Libr of Med; NC Area Health Education Centers; Resources For Health Information Consortium

L YOUNG, MOORE, HENDERSON, PA LIBRARY, 3201 Glenwood Ave, PO Box 31627, 27622. SAN 323-6862. Tel: 919-782-6860. FAX: 919-782-6753. E-Mail: cs@ymh.com. *Librn*, Carolyn Scott
Library Holdings: Bk Vols 7,000; Per Subs 15
Subject Interests: Law
Restriction: Staff use only

RED SPRINGS

P MCMILLAN MEMORIAL LIBRARY, 205 E Second Ave, 28377. SAN 312-9675. Tel: 910-843-4205. *Librn*, Jane B Thrower
Founded 1964. Pop 5,000; Circ 12,000
Library Holdings: Bk Titles 13,000; Per Subs 24

REIDSVILLE

M ANNIE PENN HOSPITAL, Medical Library,* 618 S Main St, 27323. SAN 371-4608. Tel: 336-634-1010, Ext 694. FAX: 336-342-2799. *Librn*, Fred Moss; Staff 1 (MLS 1)
Jan 1999-Dec 1999 Income Parent Institution $16,730. Mats Exp $8,100, Books $1,200, Per/Ser (Incl. Access Fees) $6,900. Sal $7,110
Library Holdings: Bk Vols 700; Per Subs 25
Function: ILL available, Reference services available
Affiliated with Greensboro Area Health Educ Center

RESEARCH TRIANGLE PARK

S AMERICAN ASSOCIATION OF TEXTILE CHEMISTS & COLORISTS LIBRARY, PO Box 12215, 27709. SAN 329-8353. Tel: 919-549-8141. FAX: 919-549-8933. *Dir*, Jerry G Tew; E-Mail: tewj@aatcc.org
Library Holdings: Bk Vols 2,500; Per Subs 15

S CIII CENTERS FOR HEALTH RESEARCH, (Formerly CIII Centers for Health Research), Goldberg Library & Resource Center, 6 Davis Dr, PO Box 12137, 27709-2137. SAN 325-4577. Tel: 919-558-1215. FAX: 919-558-1300. *Librn*, Erin Knight; E-Mail: knight@ciit.org
Founded 1974
Library Holdings: Bk Titles 8,000; Per Subs 215
Subject Interests: Toxicology

G ENVIRONMENTAL PROTECTION AGENCY LIBRARY, MD 35 86 Alexander Dr, 27711. SAN 354-7507. Tel: 919-541-2777. FAX: 919-541-1405. E-Mail: library-rtp@cpa.gov. Web Site: www.epa.gov/library-rtp. *Librn*, Deborah K Balsamo; Staff 8 (MLS 3, Non-MLS 5)
Library Holdings: Bk Vols 14,000; Per Subs 345
Subject Interests: Air chem, Air pollution, Engineering, Health effects of pollution
Special Collections: APTIC File
Publications: Check It Out (newsletter)
Partic in Fedlink; OCLC Online Computer Library Center, Inc

S IBM RTP LIBRARY, Dept LFOA, Bldg 062, 3039 Cornwall Rd, 27709. SAN 312-9713. Tel: 919-543-1299. FAX: 919-543-1701. *Librn*, Dorothy Huey
Founded 1965
Library Holdings: Bk Vols 12,000; Per Subs 450
Subject Interests: Communications, Data proc equipment

S INSTRUMENTATION, SYSTEMS & AUTOMATION SOCIETY, (Formerly Instrument Society of America Library), Albert F Sperry Library, 67 Alexander Dr, PO Box 12277, 27709. SAN 315-0763. Tel: 919-549-8411, 919-990-9257. FAX: 919-549-8288. Web Site: www.isa.org. *Exec Dir*, James Pearson; *Librn*, Linda Wolffe; Fax: 919-549-8411, E-Mail: lwolffe@isa.org
Founded 1950
Library Holdings: Bk Vols 2,060
Subject Interests: Computer, Control tech, Electronic engineering, Instrumentation
Special Collections: ISA Archives; Measurement & Process Control Theory & Application; Process Control Engineering, journals & references
Publications: Intech (monthly); ISA Transactions; reference books on Process Control Engineering

S INTERNATIONAL LEAD ZINC RESEARCH ORGANIZATION LIBRARY,* PO Box 12036, 27709-2036. SAN 370-1387. Tel: 919-361-4647, Ext 3032. FAX: 919-361-1957. Web Site: www.ilzro.com.
Library Holdings: Bk Vols 1,500

S MCNC LIBRARY, 3021 Cornwallis Rd, PO Box 12889, 27709-2889. SAN 326-2839. Tel: 919-248-1985. FAX: 919-248-1455. Web Site: www.mcnc.org. *Mgr*, Bonnie Crotty Nelson; E-Mail: bonnie@mcnc.org; Staff 3 (MLS 1, Non-MLS 2)
Jul 1998-Jun 1999 Income $90,000. Mats Exp $9,300, Books $300, Per/Ser (Incl. Access Fees) $9,000
Library Holdings: Bk Titles 3,000; Per Subs 200
Partic in OCLC Online Computer Library Center, Inc; SE Libr Network
Branches:
J L REYNOLDS LIBRARY, 3021 Cornwallis Rd, PO Box 12889, 27709-2889. Tel: 919-248-1985. FAX: 919-248-1455.
Library Holdings: Bk Titles 1,500; Per Subs 200
NCSC TECHNICAL LIBRARY Tel: 919-248-1113. FAX: 919-248-1458.
Library Holdings: Bk Titles 500; Per Subs 50

S NATIONAL COUNCIL FOR AIR & STREAM IMPROVEMENT, INC LIBRARY, (NCASI), Bldg 4401 Ste 205, 79 TW Alexander Dr, 27709. (Mail add: PO Box 13318, 22709-3318), SAN 329-9449. Tel: 919-558-1981. FAX: 919-558-1998. Web Site: www.ncasi.org. *Librn*, Alicia Farris; Staff 1 (MLS 1)
Founded 1996
Library Holdings: Bk Vols 25,000

S NATIONAL HUMANITIES CENTER LIBRARY, PO Box 12256, 27709-2256. SAN 320-9334. Tel: 919-549-0661, Ext 119. FAX: 919-549-8396. E-Mail: nhc@ga.unc.edu. Web Site: www.nhc.rtp.nc.us:8080. *Dir*, Walter Alan Tuttle; *Assoc Librn, ILL*, Eliza S Robertson; *Circ*, Jean Houston; Staff 3 (MLS 2, Non-MLS 1)
Founded 1978
Library Holdings: Bk Vols 2,500; Bk Titles 2,200
Special Collections: Robert F & Margaret S Goheen Coll of Fellows' Works
Database Vendor: Dialog, OCLC - First Search
Publications: Library guide for users
Partic in OCLC Online Computer Library Center, Inc; SE Libr Network

G NATIONAL INSTITUTE OF ENVIRONMENTAL HEALTH SCIENCES LIBRARY, PO Box 12233, Mail Drop AO-01, 27709. SAN 312-973X. Tel: 919-541-3426. FAX: 919-541-0669. Web Site: library.niehs.nih.gov/home.htm. *Dir*, W Davenport Robertson; E-Mail: robert11@niehs.nih.gov; *Ref*, Larry Wright; *Head Tech Servs*, Ellen Leadem; Staff 9 (MLS 5, Non-MLS 4)
Founded 1967
Library Holdings: Bk Vols 28,000; Bk Titles 20,000; Per Subs 500
Subject Interests: Biophysics, Carcinogenesis, Environ res, Mutagenesis, Pharmacology, Toxicology
Automation Activity & Vendor Info: (Acquisitions) epixtech, inc.; (Cataloging) epixtech, inc.; (Circulation) epixtech, inc.; (Serials) epixtech, inc.
Database Vendor: epixtech, inc.
Publications: NIEHS Bibliography; NIEHS Newsletter
Function: Research library
Partic in Dialog Corporation; Fedlink; Mead Data Cent; Nat Libr of Med; OCLC Online Computer Library Center, Inc; STN
Also part of the National Institutes of Health & serves the National Toxicology Program

G NATIONAL OCEANIC & ATMOSPHERIC ADMINISTRATION, Atmospheric Sciences Modeling Division Library, National Environmental Research Ctr, 27711. SAN 312-9748. Tel: 919-541-4536. E-Mail: asmd-areal@epamail.epa.gov, epv@hpcc.epa.gov. Web Site: www.epa.gov/asmdnerl/library/library.htm. *Librn*, Evelyn Poole-Kober
Library Holdings: Bk Vols 3,200; Per Subs 100
Subject Interests: Climatic data material

S NORTH CAROLINA BIOTECHNOLOGY CENTER LIBRARY,* 15 Alexander Dr, PO Box 13547, 27709-3547. SAN 329-1111. Tel: 919-541-9366. FAX: 919-990-9521. E-Mail: xlibrary@ncbiotech.org. Web Site: ncbiotech.org. *Librn*, Nancy G Kozlowski
Jul 1997-Jun 1998 Mats Exp $26,900, Books $2,500, Per/Ser (Incl. Access Fees) $24,400
Library Holdings: Bk Titles 2,000; Per Subs 400
Special Collections: Companies Annual Reports; Japanese Biotechnology
Partic in NC Info Network; OCLC Online Computer Library Center, Inc; SE Libr Network

S RESEARCH TRIANGLE INSTITUTE, (IS), Information Services, 3040 Cornwallis Rd, PO Box 12194, 27709-2194. SAN 312-9756. Tel: 919-541-6364. FAX: 919-541-1221. Web Site: www.rti.org. *Librn*, Mark E Howell; E-Mail: meh@rti.org; *Info Specialist*, Mariel Christian; Tel: 919-541-8370; *Info Res, Web Coordr*, Lisa J Bachelder; Tel: 919-541-6304, E-Mail: ljb@rti.org; Staff 6 (MLS 3, Non-MLS 3)
Founded 1960
Library Holdings: Per Subs 1,125
Subject Interests: Chemistry, Education, Energy, Engineering, Environmental engineering, Environmental studies, International studies, Medicine, Social sciences

A UNITED STATES ARMY RESEARCH OFFICE, Technical Library,* 4300 S Miami Blvd, 27709. (Mail add: PO Box 12211, 27709), SAN 328-8102. Tel: 919-549-4227. FAX: 919-549-4310. Web Site: www.aro.ncren.net. *Librn*, Brenda Mann; E-Mail: bmann@aro-emh1.army.mil
Library Holdings: Bk Titles 500; Per Subs 241

ROANOKE RAPIDS

P ROANOKE RAPIDS PUBLIC LIBRARY,* 319 Roanoke Ave, 27870. SAN 312-9764. Tel: 252-533-2890. FAX: 252-533-2892. *Dir*, William B Wartman
Founded 1934. Pop 16,900
Library Holdings: Bk Titles 30,000; Per Subs 100
Special Collections: Census Records, micro
Partic in NC Info Network; SE Libr Network
Friends of the Library Group

ROBBINSVILLE

P GRAHAM COUNTY PUBLIC LIBRARY, 80 Knight St, 28771. (Mail add: PO Box 517, 28771), SAN 312-9772. Tel: 828-479-8796. FAX: 828-479-3156. *Branch Mgr*, Gary James Pressley; E-Mail: gpressle@ncsl.dcr.state.nc.us; Staff 3 (Non-MLS 3)
Founded 1984. Pop 7,500; Circ 27,000
Library Holdings: Bk Vols 16,000; Bk Titles 15,000; Per Subs 70
Mem of Nantahala Regional Library
Partic in Highlands Regional Library Cooperative
Friends of the Library Group

ROBERSONVILLE

P ROBERSONVILLE PUBLIC LIBRARY,* Main St, PO Box 1060, 27871. SAN 312-9780. Tel: 252-795-3591. FAX: 252-795-3359. *Librn*, Margaret Partin
Pop 72,087; Circ 206,259

Library Holdings: Bk Vols 6,000; Per Subs 20
Mem of B H M Regional Libr
Open Mon-Fri 9:30-5:30 & Sat 9:30-1
Friends of the Library Group

ROCKINGHAM

P THOMAS H LEATH MEMORIAL LIBRARY,* 412 E Franklin St, 28379. SAN 312-9799. Tel: 910-895-6337. FAX: 910-997-2516. *Librn*, Anne Thrower
Founded 1947. Pop 45,594; Circ 74,710
Library Holdings: Bk Vols 60,000; Per Subs 93
Subject Interests: Genealogy, Local history
Mem of Richmond County Public Libr Syst; Sandhill Regional Library System
Friends of the Library Group

P SANDHILL REGIONAL LIBRARY SYSTEM, 412 E Franklin St, 28379-4995. SAN 312-9802. Tel: 910-997-3388. FAX: 910-997-2516. *Dir*, Carol G Walters; E-Mail: cwalters@ncsl.dcr.state.nc.us; *Mgr*, Julia Bennett; *Mgr*, Sheila Evans; *Mgr*, Charles Lee; *Mgr*, Mark McGrath; *Mgr*, Anne Thrower; *Dir, Tech Serv*, Bonita Collins; Staff 5 (MLS 5)
Founded 1962. Pop 182,000; Circ 359,361
Jul 1999-Jun 2000 Income $2,236,335, State $596,126, City $247,820, Federal $19,758, County $995,916, Other $376,716. Mats Exp $841,841. Sal $1,290,895 (Prof $324,000)
Library Holdings: Bk Vols 343,196; Bk Titles 329,559; Per Subs 599
Special Collections: Local & State Genealogy Coll
Automation Activity & Vendor Info: (Cataloging) TLC; (Circulation) TLC; (OPAC) TLC
Publications: Statistical & Financial Reports
Member Libraries: Hamlet Public Library; Hampton B Allen Library; Hoke County Public Library; Kemp Memorial Library; Montgomery County Public Library; Moore County Public; Page Memorial Library; Thomas H Leath Memorial Library
Special Services for the Deaf - Staff with knowledge of sign language
Friends of the Library Group
Bookmobiles: 2

ROCKY MOUNT

P THOMAS HACKNEY BRASWELL MEMORIAL LIBRARY, 344 Falls Rd, 27804-4805. SAN 355-1075. Tel: 252-442-1937, 252-442-1951. FAX: 252-442-7366. Web Site: www.braswelllib.org. *Dir*, Martha K Turney; E-Mail: mturney@braswelllib.org; *Ref*, Alice Thomas Hildreth; *Ch Servs*, Patricia Glanzer; E-Mail: pglazener@braswelllib.org; *Circ*, Jane Blackburn; E-Mail: jblackburn@braswelllib.org; *Tech Servs*, Alice Niece; E-Mail: aniece@braswelllib.org; *Tech Coordr*, Phillip Whitford; E-Mail: pwhitford@braswelllib.org; Staff 25 (MLS 5, Non-MLS 20)
Founded 1922. Pop 106,000; Circ 402,000
Jul 1999-Jun 2000 Income $1,751,258, State $268,758, City $552,000, Federal $3,000, County $648,000, Locally Generated Income $279,500. Mats Exp $228,800, Books $162,000, Per/Ser (Incl. Access Fees) $23,000, Presv $4,000, Micro $14,800, AV Equip $17,000, Electronic Ref Mat (Incl. Access Fees) $8,000. Sal $685,000 (Prof $200,000)
Library Holdings: Bk Vols 114,000; Per Subs 247
Subject Interests: African-Am, Civil War, Genealogy, Large print
Special Collections: Parent-Teacher
Automation Activity & Vendor Info: (Acquisitions) TLC; (Cataloging) TLC; (Circulation) TLC; (OPAC) TLC; (Serials) TLC
Publications: Braswell Bookworm (bimonthly newsletter); brochures
Friends of the Library Group
Bookmobiles: 1

J NASH COMMUNITY COLLEGE LIBRARY, Old Carriage Rd, 27804-9441. (Mail add: PO Box 7488, 27804-0788), SAN 312-9837. Tel: 252-443-4011, Ext 244. FAX: 252-443-0828. Web Site: www.nash.cc.nc.us. *Librn*, Lynette Finch; E-Mail: lfinch@nash.cc.nc.us; Staff 2 (MLS 1, Non-MLS 1)
Founded 1968. Enrl 2,000; Fac 100; Highest Degree: Associate
Library Holdings: Bk Vols 40,000; Per Subs 130
Subject Interests: Bus, Mgt, North Carolina, Sci-tech

C NORTH CAROLINA WESLEYAN COLLEGE, Pearsall Library, 3400 N Wesleyan Blvd, 27804. SAN 312-9845. Tel: 252-985-5350. Interlibrary Loan Service Tel: 252-985-5232. Reference Tel: 252-985-5350. FAX: 252-985-5235. E-Mail: reference@ncwc.edu. Web Site: www.annex.ncwc.edu/library. *Dir*, Katherine R Winslow; Tel: 252-985-5134, E-Mail: kwinslow@ncwc.edu; *Cat*, Grace Wallace; Tel: 252-985-5234, E-Mail: gwallace@ncwc.edu; *ILL*, Dianne Taylor; Tel: 252-985-5232, E-Mail: dtaylor@ncwc.edu; *Acq, Purchasing*, Edna Farmer; *Ref*, Michael Alewine; Tel: 252-985-5233, E-Mail: malewine@ncwc.edu; Staff 5 (MLS 2, Non-MLS 3)
Founded 1960. Enrl 1,230; Fac 54; Highest Degree: Bachelor
Jun 1999-May 2000 Income $266,450. Mats Exp $141,690, Books $43,229, Per/Ser (Incl. Access Fees) $63,942, Presv $2,500, Micro $11,982, Electronic Ref Mat (Incl. Access Fees) $20,037. Sal $119,968
Library Holdings: Bk Vols 85,600; Bk Titles 65,300; Per Subs 430
Special Collections: Black Mountain College Coll, bks & art prints; Music Coll; United Methodist Church & North Caroliniana (Hardee-Rives Coll), rare bks, fine eds
Automation Activity & Vendor Info: (Acquisitions) Endeavor; (Cataloging) Endeavor; (Circulation) Endeavor; (OPAC) Endeavor; (Serials) Endeavor
Database Vendor: Ebsco - EbscoHost, GaleNet, OCLC - First Search, ProQuest, Silverplatter Information Inc.
Partic in Mid-Carolina Academic Library Network; NC LIVE
Friends of the Library Group

ROSE HILL

S DUPLIN COUNTY HISTORICAL SOCIETY, Leora H McEachern Library of Local History,* PO Box 130, 28458. SAN 375-1244. Tel: 910-289-2654. FAX: 910-289-3479. E-Mail: history@duplinnet.com. Web Site: www.duplinnet.com. *Librn*, William Dallas Herring
Library Holdings: Bk Vols 6,500; Per Subs 250
Special Collections: Leslie H Brown Jr Coll, 3600 index cards
Restriction: Restricted access

P ROSE HILL COMMUNITY MEMORIAL LIBRARY,* 116 E Church St, PO Box 940, 28458. SAN 320-8311. Tel: 910-289-2490. FAX: 910-289-2490. *Librn*, Zayne Rivenbark
Pop 1,500; Circ 11,000
Library Holdings: Bk Vols 7,150
Friends of the Library Group

ROWLAND

P ROWLAND PUBLIC LIBRARY,* PO Box 10, 28383. SAN 312-9853. Tel: 910-422-3996. *Mgr*, Lisa Matthews
Pop 1,460; Circ 2,173
Library Holdings: Bk Vols 7,000

ROXBORO

P PERSON COUNTY PUBLIC LIBRARY, 319 S Main St, 27573. SAN 312-9861. Tel: 336-597-7881. Reference Tel: 336-597-7884. FAX: 336-597-5081. Web Site: www2.person-net/person/library/index.htm. *Dir*, Meredith P Goins; Tel: 336-597-7883, E-Mail: mgoins@personcount.net; *Asst Dir*, Linda Howerton; Tel: 336-597-7885, E-Mail: lhowerton@personcounty.net; *Ref*, Mark Wilson; *Ch Servs*, Wanda Davis; Tel: 336-597-7889, E-Mail: wdavis@personcounty.net; *Bkmobile Coordr*, Vickie Clayton; Tel: 336-597-7887, E-Mail: vclayton@personcounty.net; *Tech Servs*, Carole Walker; Tel: 336-597-7888, E-Mail: cwalker@personcounty.net; *Admin Assoc*, Vicki Soloman; Tel: 336-597-7886, E-Mail: vsoloman@personcounty.net; Staff 8 (MLS 2, Non-MLS 6)
Founded 1936. Pop 33,242; Circ 120,000
1998-1999 Income $475,223, State $143,035, Federal $1,500, County $310,155, Locally Generated Income $20,533. Mats Exp $90,300, Books $70,000, Per/Ser (Incl. Access Fees) $7,000, Micro $1,000, AV Equip $5,000, Other Print Mats $1,600, Electronic Ref Mat (Incl. Access Fees) $5,700. Sal $313,385 (Prof $53,000)
Library Holdings: Bk Vols 40,000; Per Subs 164; Bks on Deafness & Sign Lang 28
Special Collections: Large Print Books; Local History; North Carolina Room (geneology, local hist)
Automation Activity & Vendor Info: (Acquisitions) Gaylord; (Cataloging) Gaylord; (Circulation) Gaylord; (OPAC) Gaylord; (Serials) Gaylord
Function: ILL available
Mem of Hyconeechee Regional Library
Friends of the Library Group

P PIEDMONT COMMUNITY COLLEGE, Learning Resources Center,* 1715 College Dr, PO Box 1197, 27573. SAN 376-5822. Tel: 336-599-1181. FAX: 336-598-9283. Web Site: www.piedmont.cc.nc.us. *Dean of Libr*, Gretchen M Bell; E-Mail: bellg@piedmont.cc.nc.us
Library Holdings: Bk Vols 25,000; Per Subs 250

RUTHERFORDTON

P NORRIS PUBLIC LIBRARY,* 132 N Main, 28139. SAN 355-1318. Tel: 828-287-4981. FAX: 828-287-0660. *Librn*, Patricia A Hardin; *Asst Librn*, Cindy Bowlin; *Asst Librn*, Diane Bailey
Library Holdings: Bk Vols 24,000
Subject Interests: Local history
Friends of the Library Group

SALEMBURG

G NORTH CAROLINA JUSTICE ACADEMY, Learning Resource Center, 204 Faculty Ave, 28385. SAN 321-0154. Tel: 910-525-4151, Ext 269. FAX: 910-525-4491. Web Site: www.jus.state.nc.us/justice/ncja/library.htm. *Librn*, Donald K Stacy; E-Mail: dstacy@mail.jus.state.nc.us; *ILL*, Jan Chauncey; *AV, Media Spec*, JoAnn L Melvin; Staff 4 (MLS 1, Non-MLS 3)
Founded 1975

Library Holdings: Bk Titles 20,000; Per Subs 150
Subject Interests: Law, Law enforcement
Special Collections: Law Enforcement Policy & Procedures Manuals
Publications: Acquisitions List (monthly); AV catalog (irregular)

SALISBURY

C CATAWBA COLLEGE, Corriher-Linn-Black Library, 2300 W Innes St, 28144-2488. SAN 312-9896. Tel: 704-637-4448. FAX: 704-637-4304. Web Site: www.catawba.edu (click on "Library"). *Dir*, Dr Plummer Alston Jones, Jr; E-Mail: pajones@catawba.edu; *Tech Servs*, Evelina Tseng; E-Mail: emtseng@catawba.edu; *Acq, Syst Coordr*, Rodney Lippard; E-Mail: rlippard@catawba.edu; *Publ Servs*, Jacquelyn Sims; E-Mail: jsims@catawba.edu; *Instrul Serv*, Martha W Cunningham; E-Mail: mwcunnin@catawba.edu; Staff 11 (MLS 5, Non-MLS 6)
Founded 1851. Enrl 1,400; Fac 75; Highest Degree: Master
Jun 1999-May 2000 Income Parent Institution $472,635. Mats Exp $109,971, Books $12,737, Presv $3,559. Sal $303,400 (Prof $288,431)
Library Holdings: Bk Vols 154,014; Bk Titles 112,447; Per Subs 604
Subject Interests: Environ sci, NC poetry, Teacher educ, Theatre arts
Special Collections: Catawba College Archives; Poetry Council of North Carolina Coll; United Church of Christ History (Southern Chapter of the Historical Society of the Evangelical & Reformed Church), bks & mss
Automation Activity & Vendor Info: (Acquisitions) Endeavor; (Cataloging) Endeavor; (Circulation) Endeavor; (Course Reserve) Endeavor; (OPAC) Endeavor; (Serials) Endeavor
Partic in Am Libr Asn; Asn Col & Res Librs; Charlotte Area Educ Consortium; Metrolina Libr Asn; NC Libr Asn; SE Libr Network
Friends of the Library Group

GM DEPARTMENT OF VETERANS AFFAIRS, Medical Center Library, 1601 Brenner Ave, 28144. SAN 312-9926. Tel: 704-638-9000, Ext 3403. FAX: 704-638-3483. *Chief Librn, Coll Develop*, Mary Cullop; E-Mail: mary.cullop@med.va.gov; Staff 2 (MLS 1, Non-MLS 1)
Founded 1953
Library Holdings: Bk Vols 3,230; Per Subs 282
Subject Interests: Geriatrics, Medicine, Nursing, Psychiatry, Psychology, Surgery
Special Collections: Business/Careers
Restriction: Staff use only

C LIVINGSTONE COLLEGE, Carnegie Library, 701 W Monroe St, 28144. SAN 355-1377. Tel: 704-797-1029. Reference Tel: 704-797-1030. FAX: 704-797-1798. Web Site: www.livingstonelibrary.org. *Actg Dir*, Chris Matz; E-Mail: cmatz@livingstone.edu; *Syst Coordr*, Matyas Becvarov; E-Mail: mbecvarov@livingstone.edu; Staff 7 (MLS 5, Non-MLS 2)
Founded 1879. Enrl 950; Fac 55; Highest Degree: Bachelor
Oct 1999-Sep 2000 Income (Main Library Only) $145,000, Federal $95,000, Parent Institution $50,000. Mats Exp $46,000, Books $30,000, Per/Ser (Incl. Access Fees) $6,000, Electronic Ref Mat (Incl. Access Fees) $10,000. Sal $185,000 (Prof $156,000)
Library Holdings: Bk Vols 75,000; Spec Interest Per Sub 15
Subject Interests: African-American hist
Special Collections: African-American Coll
Automation Activity & Vendor Info: (Cataloging) Endeavor; (Circulation) Endeavor; (OPAC) Endeavor
Database Vendor: Ebsco - EbscoHost, OCLC - First Search
Function: ILL available
Partic in Charlotte Area Educ Consortium; Metrolina Libr Asn
Departmental Libraries:
CR HOOD THEOLOGICAL SEMINARY LIBRARY, 800 W Thomas St, 28144. SAN 355-1407. Tel: 704-797-1110. FAX: 704-797-1897. *Dir, Publ Servs*, Cynthia D Keever; E-Mail: ckeever@livingstone.edu; *Tech Servs*, Scott Girard; Tel: 704-797-1109, E-Mail: sgirard@livingston.edu; Staff 3 (MLS 2, Non-MLS 1)
Founded 1885. Enrl 85; Highest Degree: Master
Jul 1998-Jun 1999 Income $88,604. Mats Exp $17,028, Books $14,918, Per/Ser (Incl. Access Fees) $2,110. Sal $75,204 (Prof $51,000)
Library Holdings: Bk Vols 22,000; Bk Titles 17,000; Per Subs 131
Subject Interests: Philosophy, Theology
Special Collections: The AME Zion Coll
Partic in American Theological Library Association
The library serves the seminary of the AME Zion Church

SR NORTH CAROLINA SYNOD OF THE ELCA, Heilig Resource Ctr,* 1988 Lutheran Synod Dr, 28144. SAN 327-6422. Tel: 704-633-4861. FAX: 704-638-0508. E-Mail: ncsenatesynod@ecunet.org. *Archivist*, George Rhyne; *Archivist*, Karl Park
Library Holdings: Bk Vols 800

M NORTHWEST AHEC LIBRARY, Rowan Regional Medical Center, 612 Mocksville Ave, 28144. SAN 312-990X. Tel: 704-210-5069. FAX: 704-636-5050. Web Site: northwestahec.wfubmc.edu. *Mgr*, Nancy Stine; E-Mail: nstine@wfubmc.edu; Staff 5 (MLS 2, Non-MLS 3)
Founded 1976
Library Holdings: Bk Vols 1,093; Bk Titles 1,034; Per Subs 110
Subject Interests: Medicine, Nursing
Publications: Newsmemo
Friends of the Library Group

P ROWAN PUBLIC LIBRARY, 201 W Fisher St, 28145-4039. (Mail add: PO Box 4039, 28145-4039), SAN 355-1431. Tel: 704-638-3005. Circulation Tel: 704-638-3025. Reference Tel: 704-638-3010. TDD: 704-638-3018. FAX: 704-638-3002. E-Mail: info@co.rowan.nc.us. Web Site: www.rowanpubliclibrary.org. *Dir*, Phillip K Barton; E-Mail: bartonp@co.rowan.nc.us; *Mgr*, Jeffrey Hall; Tel: 704-638-3027, E-Mail: hallj@co.rowan.nc.us; *Adminr*, Melody Moxley; E-Mail: moxleym@co.rowan.nc.us; *Ch Servs*, Marian M Lytle; Tel: 704-638-3030, E-Mail: lytlem@co.rowan.nc.us; *Publ Servs*, Lucinda C Epperson; E-Mail: eppersonl@co.rowan.nc.us; *Tech Servs*, Suzanne White; Tel: 704-638-3009, Fax: 740-638-3013, E-Mail: whites@co.rowan.nc.us. Subject Specialists: *Genealogy*, Melissa Oleen; *Local history*, Melissa Oleen; Staff 47 (MLS 10, Non-MLS 37)
Founded 1911. Circ 554,989
Jul 1999-Jun 2000 Income $2,166,664, State $224,780, Federal $14,975, County $1,798,508, Locally Generated Income $128,589, Other $128,401. Mats Exp $360,307. Sal $1,507,146
Library Holdings: Bk Vols 185,855; Per Subs 483
Subject Interests: Genealogy, Local history
Database Vendor: OCLC - First Search
Publications: News Etc Newsletter (Monthly)
Headquarters for Rowan Pub Libr Syst
Friends of the Library Group
Branches: 2
EAST, 110 Broad St, PO Box 550, 28138. SAN 312-9810. Tel: 704-279-5014. FAX: 704-279-7832. E-Mail: east_admin@co.rowan.nc.us. Web Site: www.rowanpubliclibrary.org. *Librn*, Lucinda Epperson
Friends of the Library Group
SOUTH, 102 N Central Ave, Landis, 28088. SAN 355-1466. Tel: 704-857-3579. FAX: 704-855-2449. E-Mail: south_admin@co.rowan.nc.us. Web Site: www.rowanpubliclibrary.org. *Librn*, Lucinda Epperson
Friends of the Library Group
Bookmobiles: 1

J ROWAN-CABARRUS COMMUNITY COLLEGE, Learning Resource Center-North Campus, 1333 Jake Alexander Blvd, PO Box 1595, 28145-1595. SAN 377-788X. Tel: 704-637-0760, Ext 253. FAX: 704-637-6642. *Dean*, Sheila Bailey; Staff 3 (MLS 3)
Founded 1964. Enrl 2,700; Fac 80
Library Holdings: Bk Titles 40,000; Per Subs 425
Subject Interests: Archives, Bus, Early childhood, Liberal arts, Medicine, Small bus, Technology
Automation Activity & Vendor Info: (Cataloging) epixtech, inc.; (Circulation) epixtech, inc.
Database Vendor: epixtech, inc.
Partic in OCLC Online Computer Library Center, Inc
Departmental Libraries:
SOUTH CAMPUS, 1531 Trinity Church Rd, Concord, 28072-7601. Tel: 704-788-3197, Ext 530-532. FAX: 704-788-2169. *Librn*, Nancy Williams

SANFORD

J CENTRAL CAROLINA COMMUNITY COLLEGE, Library Learning Resources, 1105 Kelly Dr, 27330. SAN 312-9934. Tel: 919-718-7244. FAX: 919-718-7378. Web Site: www.ccarolina.cc.nc.us/lrc/index.html. *Dean of Libr*, Linda Stone; Tel: 919-718-7208, E-Mail: lstone@gw.ccarolina.cc.nc.us; *Librn*, Felicity Callis; Tel: 919-718-7245, E-Mail: fcallis@gw.ccarolina.cc.nc.us; *Instrul Serv, Ref Serv*, Janice Pope; Tel: 919-718-7245, E-Mail: jpope@gw.ccarolina.cc.nc.us; *Publ Servs*, Lynn Henderson; E-Mail: lhenderson@gw.ccarolina.cc.nc.us; *Media Spec*, Renee Watson; Tel: 919-718-7435, E-Mail: rwatson@gw.ccarolina.cc.nc.us; *Tech Servs*, Alpha Levesque; Tel: 919-718-7207, E-Mail: alevesque@gw.ccarolina.cc.nc.us; Staff 6 (MLS 6)
Founded 1962. Enrl 4,000
Jul 2000-Jun 2001 Mats Exp $79,048, Books $64,048, Per/Ser (Incl. Access Fees) $15,000
Library Holdings: Bk Vols 53,668; Per Subs 257
Subject Interests: Automotive mechanics, Bus admin, Early childhood, Electro optics, Electronics, Indust maintenance tech, Internet, Laser, Law, Law enforcement, Libr sci, Med assisting, Microcomputers, Motorcycles, Networks, Nursing, Radio, TV broadcasting, Veterinary medicine
Automation Activity & Vendor Info: (Acquisitions) SIRSI; (Cataloging) SIRSI; (Circulation) SIRSI; (Course Reserve) SIRSI; (ILL) SIRSI; (Media Booking) SIRSI; (OPAC) SIRSI; (Serials) SIRSI
Partic in CCLINC
Budget & collection information includes Harnett & Chatham Campus Libraries
Departmental Libraries:
CHATHAM, 764 West St, Pittsboro, 27312. SAN 378-1275. Tel: 919-542-6495. FAX: 919-542-6798. *Librn*, Leigh Moser; E-Mail: lmoser@gw.ccarolina.cc.nc.us; *Tech Servs*, Lisa Knight; E-Mail: lknight@gw.ccarolina.cc.nc.us; *Tech Servs*, Pam Mantia; E-Mail: pmantia@

gw.ccarolina.cc.nc.us
HARNETT, 1075 E Cornelius Harnett Blvd, Lillington, 27546. SAN 378-1259. Tel: 910-893-9101. FAX: 910-893-3224. *Librn*, Carolyn Buchanan; E-Mail: cbuchanan@gw.ccarolina.cc.nc.us; *Librn*, Paula Fish; E-Mail: pfish@gw.ccarolina.cc.nc.us; *Tech Servs*, Barbara Wood; E-Mail: bwood@gw.ccarolina.cc.nc.us

P LEE COUNTY LIBRARY,* 107 Hawkins Ave, 27330-4399. SAN 355-1490. Tel: 919-774-6045. FAX: 919-775-1832. *Dir*, Michael J Matochik; E-Mail: mmatochi@ncsl.dcr.state.nc.us; *Ch Servs, YA Servs*, Doris Powell; *Circ, ILL*, Michael Williams
Founded 1933. Pop 42,800; Circ 218,488
1997-1998 Income $532,665. Mats Exp $105,086, Books $89,811, Per/Ser (Incl. Access Fees) $7,880, Micro $2,595. Sal $280,657
Library Holdings: Bk Vols 113,303; Per Subs 200
Special Collections: Central North Carolina Historic Newspapers (microfilm)
Automation Activity & Vendor Info: (Cataloging) epixtech, inc.; (Circulation) epixtech, inc.
Partic in NC Info Network
Friends of the Library Group
Branches: 2
BROADWAY BRANCH, 206 S Main St, Broadway, 27505. SAN 355-1520. Tel: 919-258-6513. *Librn*, Patricia Gravely
Friends of the Library Group
JONESBORO, 309 W Main St, 27330. SAN 355-1555. Tel: 919-776-3141. *Librn*, Patricia Gravely
Friends of the Library Group

SEYMOUR JOHNSON AFB

UNITED STATES AIR FORCE
A SEYMOUR JOHNSON AIR FORCE BASE LIBRARY FL4809, 4 SVS/SVMG, 1755 Wright Ave Bldg 3622, 27531-2461. SAN 355-158X. Tel: 919-736-5707. FAX: 919-705-2927. *Librn*, Teresa Mullins; Staff 5 (MLS 1, Non-MLS 4)
Founded 1956
1997-1998 Income $298,000, Federal $296,000, Other $2,000. Mats Exp $296,000
Library Holdings: Bk Vols 41,000; Per Subs 209
Subject Interests: Aeronautics, Biog, Education, Humanities, Mgt, Mil sci, Political science, Sci-tech
Partic in Dialog Corporation; Fedlink; OCLC Online Computer Library Center, Inc; Wayne Info Network

SHELBY

J CLEVELAND COMMUNITY COLLEGE, Learning Resources Center,* 137 S Post Rd, 28152. SAN 312-9950. Tel: 704-484-4000. Interlibrary Loan Service Tel: 704-484-4086. FAX: 704-484-4036. Web Site: www.cleveland.cc.nc.us/staff/mckibbin/default.htm. *Dir Libr Serv*, Barbara McKibbin
Founded 1965
Jul 1997-Jun 1998 Mats Exp $145,854, Books $36,855, Per/Ser (Incl. Access Fees) $75,000, Micro $2,944, AV Equip $25,855. Sal $19,721
Library Holdings: Bk Vols 27,594; Bk Titles 22,951; Per Subs 312
Subject Interests: Genealogy

P CLEVELAND COUNTY LIBRARY SYSTEM,* 104 Howie Dr, PO Box 1120, 28151-1120. SAN 312-9942. Tel: 704-487-9069. FAX: 704-487-4856. Web Site: www.shelby.net/cpo. *Dir*, Carol H Wilson; *Asst Dir*, JoAnne Owens; *Tech Servs*, Kathy Alexander
Founded 1909. Pop 86,158; Circ 330,000
Jul 1996-Jun 1997 Income $743,000. Mats Exp $62,000. Sal $382,000
Library Holdings: Bk Vols 95,000; Per Subs 126
Subject Interests: Genealogy, Local history
Publications: Libri Amicus (friends newsletter)
Site of host computer for multitype library electronic network
Friends of the Library Group
Branches: 1
SPANGLER LIBRARY, 112 Piedmont Dr, Lawndale, 28090. SAN 370-0127. Tel: 704-538-7005. *Librn*, Deborah Page
Friends of the Library Group
Bookmobiles: 1

SILER CITY

P WREN MEMORIAL LIBRARY,* 502 N Second Ave, 27344. SAN 354-5334. Tel: 919-742-2016. FAX: 919-742-5546. Web Site: www.ils.unc.edu/nclibs/centralnc/home.htm.
1997-1998 Mats Exp Books $15,335
Library Holdings: Bk Titles 28,000; Per Subs 63
Friends of the Library Group

SMITHFIELD

J JOHNSTON COMMUNITY COLLEGE LIBRARY, 245 College Rd, 27577. (Mail add: PO Box 2350, 27577), SAN 312-9977. Tel: 919-209-2101. FAX: 919-209-2186. Web Site: www.johnston.cc.nc.us. *Dir*, Linda Ramsey; E-Mail: ramseylinda@novell.johnston.cc.nc.us; *Librn*, Nancy Bailey; *Librn*, D Warrick; *Librn*, Kathryn Yensen; Staff 4 (MLS 3, Non-MLS 1)
Founded 1969
Jul 1999-Jun 2000 Mats Exp $251,869, Books $85,940, Per/Ser (Incl. Access Fees) $39,000, AV Equip $9,500, Electronic Ref Mat (Incl. Access Fees) $20,000. Sal $146,297
Library Holdings: Bk Vols 31,135; Bk Titles 27,199; Per Subs 350
Automation Activity & Vendor Info: (Cataloging) SIRSI; (Circulation) SIRSI
Database Vendor: Ebsco - EbscoHost, OVID Technologies, ProQuest, Silverplatter Information Inc., Wilson - Wilson Web
Friends of the Library Group

P PUBLIC LIBRARY OF JOHNSTON COUNTY & SMITHFIELD, Johnston County & Smithfield Public, 305 Market St, 27577-3919. SAN 355-1644. Tel: 919-934-8146. FAX: 919-934-8084. *Dir*, Joyce Mitchell; *Publ Servs*, Ruby Smith; *Cat*, Diane Gruber; *AV*, Christopher Aker; *Tech Servs*, Joy Vaughn; *Bkmobile Coordr*, Vickie Duren; *Ref*, Donna Tart; *Ch Servs*, Elaine Forman; *Circ*, Margo George; *Tech Servs*, Joanne Tart; *Ch Servs*, Wigmore Nancy; Staff 3 (MLS 3)
Founded 1966. Pop 106,000; Circ 196,294
Jul 1999-Jun 2000 Income (Main Library Only) $913,562, State $174,821, City $136,000, Federal $10,000, County $334,126, Other $258,615. Mats Exp $123,586, Books $106,086, Per/Ser (Incl. Access Fees) $15,000, Presv $2,500. Sal $342,284 (Prof $111,857)
Library Holdings: Bk Vols 82,876; Per Subs 119
Subject Interests: Genealogy, Local history
Automation Activity & Vendor Info: (Cataloging) Gaylord; (Circulation) Gaylord; (OPAC) Gaylord
Database Vendor: OCLC - First Search
Partic in NC LIVE
Friends of the Library Group
Branches: 6
ATKINSON MEMORIAL, 5438 North C, Hwy 39, Selma, 27576. SAN 355-1679. *Librn*, Patricia Franco; Staff 1 (Non-MLS 1)
Circ 56
Jul 1999-Jun 2000 Income Locally Generated Income $5,326. Sal $900
Library Holdings: Bk Vols 977
HOCUTT-ELLINGTON MEMORIAL, 100 S Church, Clayton, 27520. SAN 355-1709. Tel: 919-553-5542. FAX: 919-553-1529. *Librn*, Betty Coats; Staff 1 (Non-MLS 1)
Circ 69,330
Jul 1999-Jun 2000 Income City $168,252. Mats Exp Books $33,415. Sal $100,315
Library Holdings: Bk Vols 39,410
Automation Activity & Vendor Info: (Circulation) Gaylord; (OPAC) Gaylord
Partic in NC LIVE
Friends of the Library Group
JAMES BRYAN CREEK, Four Oaks, 27524. SAN 355-1768. Tel: 919-963-6013. *Librn*, Jean Adams
Circ 4,493
Jul 1999-Jun 2000 Income $4,705, City $877, Other $3,828. Mats Exp Books $2,062. Sal $376
Library Holdings: Bk Vols 8,494
Automation Activity & Vendor Info: (Circulation) Gaylord; (OPAC) Gaylord
Partic in NC LIVE
KENLY PUBLIC, 205 Edgerton St, Kenly, 27524. SAN 355-1792. Tel: 919-284-4217. *Librn*, Dianne M Bailey; Staff 1 (Non-MLS 1)
Circ 10,300
Jul 1999-Jun 2000 Income City $37,857. Mats Exp Books $5,437. Sal $22,154
Library Holdings: Bk Vols 12,771
Automation Activity & Vendor Info: (Circulation) Gaylord; (OPAC) Gaylord
Partic in NC LIVE
MARY DUNCAN PUBLIC, 100 W Main St, Benson, 27504. SAN 355-1733. Tel: 919-894-3724. *Librn*, Linda Haynes; Staff 1 (Non-MLS 1)
Circ 18,776
1999-2000 Income City $70,485. Mats Exp Books $17,912. Sal $43,800
Library Holdings: Bk Vols 14,279
Automation Activity & Vendor Info: (Circulation) Gaylord; (OPAC) Gaylord
Partic in NC-Live
Friends of the Library Group
SELMA PUBLIC LIBRARY, 301 N Pollock, Selma, 27576. SAN 355-1857. Tel: 919-965-8613. FAX: 919-965-8517. E-Mail: selma.library@mail.co.johnston.nc.us. *Librn*, Sue Wood; Staff 1 (MLS 1)
Circ 21,847
Jul 1999-Jun 2000 Income $106,713, City $92,316, Other $14,397. Mats

Exp $31,000, Books $30,000, Electronic Ref Mat (Incl. Access Fees) $1,000. Sal $48,488 (Prof $27,000)
Library Holdings: Bk Vols 19,096
Automation Activity & Vendor Info: (Circulation) Gaylord; (OPAC) Gaylord
Partic in NC LIVE
Bookmobiles: 1

SNOW HILL

P GREENE COUNTY PUBLIC LIBRARY, 229 Kingold Blvd, 28580. SAN 312-9985. Tel: 252-747-3437. FAX: 252-747-7489. E-Mail: greenelibrary@hotmail.com. *Librn*, Marvette Spruill
Automation Activity & Vendor Info: (Acquisitions) TLC; (Cataloging) TLC; (Circulation) TLC; (OPAC) TLC; (Serials) TLC
Mem of Neuse Regional Library
Holdings are included in Neuse Regional Library entry

SOUTHERN PINES

P SOUTHERN PINES PUBLIC LIBRARY,* 170 W Connecticut Ave, 28387. SAN 312-9993. Tel: 910-692-8235. FAX: 910-695-1037. Web Site: www.sppl.library.net. *Dir*, D Lynn Thompson; E-Mail: lthompso@ncsl.dcr.state.nc.us; *Asst Dir*, Lynn Bowness
Founded 1922. Pop 10,168; Circ 111,708
Jul 1998-Jun 1999 Income $512,779, State $8,285, City $471,620, Locally Generated Income $32,874. Mats Exp $107,262. Sal $333,226
Library Holdings: Bk Vols 52,329; Per Subs 139
Special Collections: Large Print; North Carolina
Publications: Bookends
Friends of the Library Group

SOUTHPORT

P BRUNSWICK COUNTY LIBRARY,* 109 W Moore St, 28461. SAN 355-1881. Tel: 910-457-6237. FAX: 910-457-6977. *Dir*, Maurice T Tate; *ILL*, Nancy Price; *Ch Servs*, Irma Bryant
Founded 1912. Pop 50,000; Circ 200,000
Library Holdings: Bk Vols 62,000
Subject Interests: Genealogy, Local history, Maritime studies
Friends of the Library Group
Branches: 3
G V BARBEE SR BRANCH, 818 Yaupon Dr, Yaupon Beach, 28465. SAN 375-2925. Tel: 910-278-4283. FAX: 910-278-4049. *Mgr*, Susan Phillips
Library Holdings: Bk Vols 10,000
Friends of the Library Group
LELAND BRANCH, 487 Village Rd, Leland, 28451. SAN 355-1911. Tel: 910-371-9442. FAX: 910-371-1856. *Mgr*, Lisa Milligan
Library Holdings: Bk Vols 10,000
Friends of the Library Group
ROURK, 5068 Main St, Shallotte, 28459. SAN 355-1946. Tel: 910-754-6578. FAX: 910-754-6874. *Mgr*, Felecia Hardy
Library Holdings: Bk Vols 10,000
Friends of the Library Group

SPARTA

P ALLEGHANY COUNTY PUBLIC LIBRARY, 122 N Main St, 28675-8608. (Mail add: PO Box 656, 28675-0656), SAN 313-0002. Tel: 336-372-5573. FAX: 336-372-4912. *Librn*, Debra Brewer; E-Mail: debdbre@hotmail.com
Library Holdings: Bk Vols 32,000; Per Subs 25
Subject Interests: Genealogy, Local history
Mem of Northwestern Regional Library
Holdings are included in Northwestern Regional Library entry, Elkin
Friends of the Library Group

SPENCER

P SPENCER PUBLIC LIBRARY,* 300 Fourth St, PO Box 152, 28159. SAN 313-0010. Tel: 704-636-9072. *Librn*, Debbie Bingham
Founded 1943. Pop 3,075; Circ 13,497
Library Holdings: Bk Vols 10,041; Per Subs 36

SPINDALE

J ISOTHERMAL COMMUNITY COLLEGE LIBRARY, 286 ICC Loop Rd, 28160-0804. SAN 313-0029. Tel: 828-286-3636. Circulation Tel: 828-286-4636. FAX: 828-286-8208. Web Site: www.isothermal.cc.nc.us. *Dir Info Resources & Res*, Susan Vaughan; Tel: 828-286-3636, Ext 216, E-Mail: svaughan@isothermal.cc.nc.us; *Asst Librn*, Becky Cleland; E-Mail: rcleland@isothermal.cc.nc.us; *ILL*, Michael Greene; E-Mail: mgreene@isothermal.cc.nc.us; *Circ*, Shirley Holland; E-Mail: sholland@isothermal.cc.nc.us; *Tech Servs*, Kenneth Odom; Staff 6 (MLS 2, Non-MLS 4)
Founded 1965. Enrl 1,925; Highest Degree: Associate
Jul 1999-Jun 2000 Mats Exp $66,002, Books $45,273, Per/Ser (Incl. Access Fees) $10,000, Electronic Ref Mat (Incl. Access Fees) $10,729. Sal $159,279 (Prof $73,596)
Library Holdings: Bk Vols 39,202; Bk Titles 36,752; Per Subs 238
Subject Interests: Local history
Special Collections: Old Tryon Historical Coll
Automation Activity & Vendor Info: (Cataloging) TLC; (Circulation) TLC; (Course Reserve) TLC; (OPAC) TLC
Database Vendor: CARL, Ebsco - EbscoHost, GaleNet, OCLC - First Search, ProQuest, Silverplatter Information Inc., Wilson - Wilson Web
Publications: Library Handbook; Media Catalog; Periodicals Directory
Mem of NC Dept of Community Cols
Special Services for the Blind - Kurzweil Reader

P RUTHERFORD COUNTY LIBRARY,* 255 Callahan Koon Rd, 28160. SAN 355-1229. Tel: 828-287-6115. FAX: 828-287-6119. E-Mail: mms@blueridge.net. Web Site: www.rclicc.library.net. *Dir*, Martha Schatz; E-Mail: mschatz@ncsl.dcr.state.nc.us; Staff 1 (MLS 1)
Founded 1939. Pop 57,000
1998-1999 Income $330,502, State $133,376, County $197,126. Mats Exp $83,500, Books $63,100, Per/Ser (Incl. Access Fees) $11,900. Sal $162,692 (Prof $39,271)
Library Holdings: Bk Vols 97,333; Per Subs 40
Subject Interests: Genealogy, Rutherford county hist
Special Collections: North Carolina History & Genealogy Coll
Publications: Booklist; Horn Book; Library Journal
Branches: 2
HAYNES PUBLIC, 141 N Main St Ste 110, 28076. SAN 355-1253. Tel: 828-657-5278, 828-657-9110. FAX: 828-657-9110. E-Mail: ncs1322@interpass.com. Web Site: www.rclicc.library.net. *Librn*, Deb Womack
Friends of the Library Group
MOUNTAINS, 150 Bills Creek Rd, Lake Lure, 28746. SAN 377-0249. Tel: 828-625-0456. FAX: 828-625-0453. E-Mail: ncs1290@interpass.com. Web Site: www.rclicc.library.net. *Dir*, Melanie Greenway
Friends of the Library Group

P SPINDALE PUBLIC LIBRARY,* 101 Tanner St, 28160. SAN 355-1342. Tel: 828-286-3879. FAX: 828-286-8338. E-Mail: spinlib@blueridge.net. *Librn*, Vickie Briscoe
Library Holdings: Bk Vols 20,000

SPRING HOPE

S INTERNATIONAL WILD WATERFOWL ASSOCIATION, Lee Ridge Aviaries Reference Library, PO Box 1251, 27882. SAN 372-6444. Tel: 252-478-5610. FAX: 252-478-7286.
Founded 1975
1998-1999 Income $1,000. Mats Exp $1,000, Books $900, Per/Ser (Incl. Access Fees) $100
Library Holdings: Bk Titles 650
Subject Interests: Arctic, Natural history
Special Collections: Natural History, bks, videos & slides

SPRUCE PINE

J MAYLAND COMMUNITY COLLEGE, Learning Resources Center, 200 Mayland Tech Dr, PO Box 547, 28777-0547. SAN 373-8698. Tel: 828-765-7351, Ext 243. FAX: 828-765-0728. Web Site: www.mayland.cc.nc.us. *Cat, Per, Tech Servs*, Jon Wilmesherr; *ILL, Online Servs*, Mamie Carpenter; Staff 5 (MLS 2, Non-MLS 3)
Founded 1972
Library Holdings: Bk Titles 20,000; Per Subs 125
Subject Interests: Appalachian studies, Genealogy, North Carolina, Nursing
Automation Activity & Vendor Info: (Cataloging) SIRSI; (Circulation) SIRSI
Partic in Community Col Librs NC

P SPRUCE PINE PUBLIC LIBRARY,* 142 Walnut Ave, 28777. SAN 313-0045. Tel: 828-765-4673. Web Site: www.amy.lib.nc.us. *Librn*, Cathy Silver; E-Mail: csilver@ncsl.dcr.state.nc.us; *Asst Librn*, Rosemarie Byrd
Pop 2,333
1998-1999 Income $82,437, City $47,462, County $8,000, Locally Generated Income $11,718, Other $15,257. Mats Exp $10,000, Books $5,000. Sal $43,791
Library Holdings: Bk Vols 45,000
Subject Interests: Genealogy, Local history, NC
Mem of Avery-Mitchell-Yancey Regional Library System
Library Services for the aging, blind & physical handicapped; Programs for children & young adults; Summer reading program; Bookmobile Service
Friends of the Library Group

STATESVILLE

P IREDELL COUNTY PUBLIC LIBRARY, 135 E Water St, PO Box 1810, 28687-1810. SAN 313-0061. Tel: 704-878-3090. Circulation Tel: 704-878-3145. Reference Tel: 704-878-3095. FAX: 704-878-5449. Web Site:

www.co.iredell.nc.us/library/icpl.html. *Dir*, Steve L Messick; Tel: 704-878-3092, E-Mail: smessick@co.iredell.nc.us; *Tech Coordr*, Theresa E Lynch; Tel: 704-878-3148, E-Mail: tlynch@co.iredell.nc.us; *Ad Servs*, Margie Wessels; Tel: 704-878-3098, E-Mail: mwessels@co.iredell.nc.us; *Ref*, Mardi J Durham; Tel: 704-878-3109, E-Mail: mdurham@co.iredell.nc.us; *Ch Servs*, Reitha Z Morrison; Tel: 704-878-3097, E-Mail: rmorrison@co.iredell.nc.us; *Circ*, Andy Flynt; Tel: 704-878-3146, E-Mail: aflynt@co.iredell.nc.us; *Info Tech*, Myra Patterson; Tel: 704-878-3148, E-Mail: mpatterson@co.iredell.nc.us; *Exten Serv*, Janet Hall; Tel: 704-878-3099, E-Mail: jhall@co.iredell.nc.us; *Acq*, Zelma Flowers; Tel: 704-878-5448, E-Mail: zflowers@co.iredell.nc.us; *Tech Servs*, Kimberly Crawford; Tel: 704-878-3147, E-Mail: kcrawford@co.iredell.nc.us; Staff 31 (MLS 7, Non-MLS 24)
Founded 1967. Pop 117,804; Circ 479,688
Jul 1999-Jun 2000 Income $1,289,178, State $154,896, Federal $3,397, County $1,130,885. Mats Exp $271,764, Books $195,500, Per/Ser (Incl. Access Fees) $5,610, Micro $8,976. Sal $622,317
Library Holdings: Bk Vols 163,275; Per Subs 285; High Interest/Low Vocabulary Bk Vols 82; Bks on Deafness & Sign Lang 86
Subject Interests: Genealogy, Local history
Automation Activity & Vendor Info: (Cataloging) epixtech, inc.
Database Vendor: Ebsco - EbscoHost, epixtech, inc., GaleNet, OCLC - First Search, ProQuest, Wilson - Wilson Web
Partic in Ebsco Masterfile; ProQuest
Special Services for the Deaf - TDD
Friends of the Library Group

J MITCHELL COMMUNITY COLLEGE, Mildred & J P Huskins Library, 500 W Broad St, 28677. SAN 313-007X. Tel: 704-878-3271. FAX: 704-878-3206. Web Site: www.mitchell.cc.nc.us. *Dir*, Rex E Klett; E-Mail: rklett@mitchell.cc.nc.us; *Librn*, Vicki Caldwell; E-Mail: vcaldwell@mitchell.cc.nc.us; *Acq*, Joan Jordan; E-Mail: jjordan@mitchell.cc.nc.us; *Circ*, Carolyn Morrison; E-Mail: cmorrison@mitchell.cc.nc.us
Founded 1852
1998-1999 Mats Exp $71,375, Books $42,896, Per/Ser (Incl. Access Fees) $28,141, Presv $338. Sal $162,189 (Prof $80,768)
Library Holdings: Bk Vols 39,226; Bk Titles 38,749; Per Subs 201
Subject Interests: Criminal justice, Literature, Nursing, Sci tech, Soc sci
Automation Activity & Vendor Info: (Cataloging) Endeavor; (Circulation) Endeavor; (OPAC) Endeavor; (Serials) Endeavor
Function: ILL available, Photocopies available
Partic in Charlotte Area Educ Consortium

SWANNANOA

C PEW LEARNING CENTER & ELLISON LIBRARY, (Formerly Warren Wilson College), Ellison Library, 701 Warren Wilson Rd, 28778. (Mail add: Campus Box 6358, PO Box 9000, 28815-9000), Circulation Tel: 828-771-3058. Reference Tel: 828-771-3035. FAX: 828-771-7085. Web Site: www.warren-wilson.edu/~library/. *Dir*, Bill M Hubbard; Tel: 828-771-3061, E-Mail: bhubbard@warren-wilson.edu; *Acq*, Joy Pastucha; Tel: 828-771-3063, E-Mail: jpastuch@warren-wilson.edu; *Cat*, Yoke Mei Mah; Tel: 828-771-3054, E-Mail: mmah@warren-wilson.edu; *Electronic Resources*, David O Bradshaw; Tel: 828-771-3059, E-Mail: dobrshaw@warren-wilson.edu; *Archivist*, Dr Linda Miles Coppens; Tel: 828-771-3055, E-Mail: lcoppens@warren-wilson.edu; *ILL*, Mary O Brown; Tel: 828-771-3062, E-Mail: mbrown@warren-wilson.edu; *Per*, Judy Tizzard; Tel: 828-771-3060, E-Mail: jtizzard@warren-wilson.edu; *Circ*, Linda Oakleaf; Tel: 828-771-3064, E-Mail: loakleaf@warren-wilson.edu; Staff 7 (MLS 5, Non-MLS 2)
Founded 1894. Enrl 786; Fac 64; Highest Degree: Master
Library Holdings: Bk Vols 90,400; Bk Titles 83,100; Per Subs 4,301; Per Subs 480
Subject Interests: Architecture, Art, Art history, Education, Environmental studies, Int area studies, Local history, Music, Peace studies
Special Collections: Archives; Arthur S Link Library of American History; James McClure Clarke papers
Automation Activity & Vendor Info: (Cataloging) DRA; (Circulation) DRA; (OPAC) DRA
Database Vendor: Ebsco - EbscoHost, GaleNet, OCLC - First Search, ProQuest, Silverplatter Information Inc.
Publications: Library Lines (Accession list)
Partic in Mountain College Libr Network; OCLC Online Computer Library Center, Inc; Solinet
Friends of the Library Group

SYLVA

P JACKSON COUNTY PUBLIC LIBRARY,* 755 W Main St, 28779. SAN 313-010X. Tel: 828-586-2016. FAX: 828-586-3423. Web Site: main.nc.us/libraries/fontana. *Librn*, Jeanette Newsom; E-Mail: jnewsom@ncsl.dcr.state.nc.us
Jul 1997-Jun 1998 Income $240,831, City $13,000, County $168,677, Locally Generated Income $14,925, Parent Institution $35,890, Other $8,339. Mats Exp $44,065, Books $37,608, Per/Ser (Incl. Access Fees) $3,814. Sal $130,338 (Prof $35,890)
Library Holdings: Bk Vols 39,198
Friends of the Library Group
Branches: 1
ALBERT CARLTON CASHIERS COMMUNITY LIBRARY, 249 Frank Allen Rd, PO Box 2127, Cashiers, 28717. SAN 375-5037. Tel: 828-743-0215. FAX: 828-743-1819. Web Site: main.nc.us/libraries/fontana. *Librn*, Diane Stumm; Staff 3 (MLS 1, Non-MLS 2)
Founded 1994. Pop 1,099
Jul 1997-Jun 1998 Income $85,434. Mats Exp $21,635. Sal $42,824
Library Holdings: Bk Vols 18,000
Friends of the Library Group

J SOUTHWESTERN COMMUNITY COLLEGE, Learning Resources Center,* 447 College Dr, 28779. SAN 313-0118. Tel: 828-586-4091, Ext 268. FAX: 828-586-3129. Web Site: www.southwest.cc.nc.us. *Dir*, Nelda M Reid; E-Mail: nelda@southwest.cc.nc.us
Founded 1964
Library Holdings: Bk Vols 28,000; Per Subs 250
Subject Interests: NC
Mem of NC Dept of Community Cols

TARBORO

J EDGECOMBE COMMUNITY COLLEGE, Learning Resources Center,* 2009 W Wilson St, 27886. SAN 312-9829. Tel: 252-823-5166. FAX: 252-823-6817. Web Site: www.edgecombe.cc.nc.us. *Dir*, Daniel Swartant; *Librn*, Sherrill Henry; *Tech Servs*, Dorothy Burress; Staff 8 (MLS 4, Non-MLS 4)
Founded 1968. Enrl 2,500; Fac 134
Jul 1998-Jun 1999 Mats Exp $114,364, Books $76,402, Micro $12,363, AV Equip $15,000, Electronic Ref Mat (Incl. Access Fees) $10,599. Sal $212,894 (Prof $92,962)
Library Holdings: Bk Vols 35,407; Bk Titles 30,532; Per Subs 214
Subject Interests: Accounting, Admin off tech, Auto mechanics, Autobody, Bus, Computer prog, Cosmetology, Elec, Health info tech, Imaging tech, Indust electrical-electronics tech, Indust maintenance tech, Law enforcement, Manufacturing eng tech, Mechanical drafting tech, Mgt, Nursing, Radiology, Respiratory care, Soc work, Surgical tech, Teacher associates
Special Collections: North Carolina County Records & History, bks, micro
Partic in OCLC Online Computer Library Center, Inc
Departmental Libraries:
ROCKY MOUNT CAMPUS, 225 Tarboro St, Rocky Mount, 27801. SAN 373-6210. Tel: 919-446-0436. FAX: 919-985-2212. *Librn*, Judy Brown; *Librn*, Sherrill Webb

P EDGECOMBE COUNTY MEMORIAL LIBRARY, (ECML), 909 Main St, 27886. SAN 313-0126. Tel: 252-823-1141. FAX: 252-823-7699. *Dir*, Kim Huskins Webb; E-Mail: kwebb@edgecombelibrary.org; *Asst Dir, Ref*, Dana Stone; *Ref*, Traci Thompson; *Outreach Serv*, Kathy Motley; *Ch Servs*, Brenda Pippen. Subject Specialists: *Local history*, Traci Thompson; Staff 14 (MLS 3, Non-MLS 11)
Founded 1920. Pop 56,000; Circ 126,468
Jul 1998-Jun 1999 Income $615,766, State $160,333, City $127,001, County $310,932, Other $17,500. Mats Exp $92,814, Books $83,000, Per/Ser (Incl. Access Fees) $8,964, Micro $600, Other Print Mats $250. Sal $314,064
Library Holdings: Bk Vols 111,382; Per Subs 150
Special Collections: NC History Coll
Automation Activity & Vendor Info: (Cataloging) TLC; (Circulation) epixtech, inc.; (OPAC) epixtech, inc.
Publications: Newsletter
Partic in NC State Libr Info Network; OCLC Online Computer Library Center, Inc
Friends of the Library Group
Branches: 1
PINETOPS BRANCH, PO Box 688, Pinetops, 27864. SAN 377-0338. Tel: 252-827-4621. FAX: 252-827-4621. *Librn*, Susan Webb
Library Holdings: Bk Vols 7,200

TAYLORSVILLE

P ALEXANDER COUNTY LIBRARY,* 115 First Ave SW, 28681. SAN 313-0134. Tel: 828-632-4058. FAX: 828-632-1094. *Dir*, Doris Stephens; E-Mail: dstephen@ncsl.dcr.state.nc.us
Founded 1967. Pop 28,544; Circ 93,842
Library Holdings: Bk Vols 59,530; Per Subs 154
Special Collections: Local History Room
Friends of the Library Group

TRENTON

P COMFORT PUBLIC LIBRARY,* 9801 Hwy 41 W, 28585. SAN 320-5959. Tel: 252-324-5061. *Librn*, Brenda Quinn
Pop 360
Library Holdings: Bk Vols 9,000
Mem of Neuse Regional Library
Holdings are included in Neuse Regional Library entry

P TRENTON PUBLIC LIBRARY,* PO Box 610, 28585-0610. SAN 320-5940. Tel: 252-448-4261. FAX: 252-448-4261. *Librn*, Janice Smith
Pop 1,048

Library Holdings: Bk Vols 5,000; Per Subs 17
Mem of Neuse Regional Library
Holdings are included in Neuse Regional Libr entry in Kinston
Friends of the Library Group

TROY

J MONTGOMERY COMMUNITY COLLEGE LIBRARY,* PO Box 787, 27371. SAN 313-0150. Tel: 910-576-6222. FAX: 910-576-2176. Web Site: www.montgomery.cc.nc.us. *Librn*, Diane Williams; E-Mail: williamss@mcc.montgomery.cc.nc.us
Founded 1967
Library Holdings: Bk Vols 15,000; Per Subs 340
Subject Interests: Applied tech sci, Bus, Criminology, Mgt, Police sci, Pottery, Sci-tech
Mem of NC Dept of Community Cols
Partic in NC State Ref Libr

P MONTGOMERY COUNTY PUBLIC LIBRARY,* 215 W Main, 27371. SAN 355-2004. Tel: 910-572-1311. FAX: 910-576-5565. Web Site: www.204.211.56.212. *Dir*, Julia M Bennett; E-Mail: jbennett@ncsldcr.state.nc.us
Pop 23,600; Circ 225,000
Jul 1996-Jun 1997 Income $211,295. Mats Exp $26,640. Sal $144,052
Library Holdings: Bk Vols 50,000; Per Subs 200
Subject Interests: Local history
Mem of Sandhill Regional Library System
Friends of the Library Group
Branches: 4
BISCOE BRANCH, 307 S Main St, Biscoe, 27209. SAN 355-2039. Tel: 910-428-2551. FAX: 910-428-2551. Web Site: www.204.211.56.212. *Librn*, Charles Gibbs
Friends of the Library Group
CANDOR BRANCH, Currie Rd, Candor, 27229. SAN 355-2063. Tel: 910-974-4033. FAX: 910-974-4033. Web Site: www.204.211.56.212. *Librn*, Diana Steed
Friends of the Library Group
MOUNT GILEAD BRANCH, 110 W Allenton Rd, Mount Gilead, 27306. SAN 355-2098. Tel: 910-439-6651. FAX: 910-439-6651. *Librn*, Linda Burkhead
STAR BRANCH, Municipal Bldg, 222 S Main St, Star, 27356. SAN 355-2128. Tel: 910-428-2338. FAX: 910-428-2338. *Librn*, Francis Poole

TRYON

P LANIER LIBRARY ASSOCIATION, INC, 72 Chestnut St, 28782. SAN 313-0169. Tel: 828-859-9535. *Adminr*, Vonda Krahn
Founded 1890. Circ 19,545
Library Holdings: Bk Titles 27,000; Per Subs 63
Subject Interests: Large print, NC
Special Collections: Sidney Lanier Coll; Tryon Area Authors
Publications: New Book List (monthly); Newsletter (quarterly)
Restriction: Members only
A subscription library, 817 members

VANCEBORO

P VANCEBORO PUBLIC LIBRARY, 7931 Main St, PO Box 38, 28586. SAN 313-0177. Tel: 252-244-0571. FAX: 252-244-0571. *Librn*, Marlene Copeland
Circ 12,546
Library Holdings: Bk Vols 12,222; Per Subs 10
Mem of Craven-Pamlico-Carteret Regional Library

WADESBORO

P HAMPTON B ALLEN LIBRARY,* 120 S Greene St, 28170. SAN 313-0185. Tel: 704-694-5177. FAX: 704-694-5178. *Dir*, Charles Lee; E-Mail: clee@ncsl.der.state.nc.us
Founded 1923. Pop 23,474; Circ 41,231
Jul 1997-Jun 1998 Income $269,815, County $100. Mats Exp $22,540, Books $11,438, Per/Ser (Incl. Access Fees) $2,600. Sal $96,162
Library Holdings: Bk Vols 48,361; Per Subs 80
Subject Interests: Genealogy, Local history
Mem of Sandhill Regional Library System
Partic in OCLC Online Computer Library Center, Inc

WAKE FOREST

R SOUTHEASTERN BAPTIST THEOLOGICAL SEMINARY LIBRARY, 114 N Wingate St, 27587. SAN 313-0193. Tel: 919-863-8250. Interlibrary Loan Service Tel: 919-863-8323. Circulation Tel: 919-863-8251. Reference Tel: 919-863-8258. FAX: 919-863-8150. E-Mail: library@sebts.edu. Web Site: www.library.sebts.edu. *Dir*, Shawn C Madden; E-Mail: smadden@sebts.edu; *Cat*, Richard Alford; Tel: 919-863-8255, E-Mail: ralford@sebts.edu; *Cat*, Joan McGorman; Tel: 919-863-8321, E-Mail: jmcgorman@sebts.edu; *Info Tech*, Ken Witcher; Tel: 919-863-8254, E-Mail: kwitcher@sebts.edu; *Acq*, Danny Williams; Tel: 919-863-8257, E-Mail: dwilliams@sebts.edu; *Bibliog Instr, Ref*, Terese Jerose; E-Mail: tjerose@sebts.edu; *Circ*, Judy A Durham; E-Mail: jdurham@sebts.edu; *Archivist*, Jim Lutzweiler; Tel: 919-863-8249, E-Mail: jlutzweiler@sebts.edu. Subject Specialists: *Baptist hist*, Jim Lutzweiler; *Hebrew*, Shawn C Madden; *Music*, Joan McGorman; Staff 9 (MLS 4, Non-MLS 5)
Founded 1951. Enrl 1,500; Fac 53; Highest Degree: Doctorate
1998-1999 Income $500,000. Mats Exp $167,200, Books $104,400, Per/Ser (Incl. Access Fees) $48,800, Presv $10,000, Micro $4,000. Sal $325,000
Library Holdings: Bk Vols 141,978; Bk Titles 117,825; Per Subs 834
Subject Interests: Baptist hist, Biblical studies, Christianity, Doctrine, Philosophy, Relig studies, Theology
Special Collections: Baptists (Baptist Documents Coll); Education Curriculum Lab; Lifeway Curriculum
Automation Activity & Vendor Info: (Acquisitions) epixtech, inc.; (Cataloging) epixtech, inc.; (Circulation) epixtech, inc.; (Course Reserve) epixtech, inc.; (OPAC) epixtech, inc.; (Serials) epixtech, inc.
Database Vendor: OCLC - First Search
Partic in American Theological Library Association; OCLC Online Computer Library Center, Inc; SE Libr Network

WALLACE

P THELMA DINGUS BRYANT LIBRARY,* 409 W Main St, PO Box 995, 28466. SAN 313-0207. Tel: 910-285-3796. FAX: 910-285-8224. E-Mail: tdblib@duplin.net. *Librn*, Robin Likens
Founded 1969. Circ 21,684
Jul 1997-Jun 1998 Income $85,152. Mats Exp $8,900, Per/Ser (Incl. Access Fees) $1,700. Sal $54,511 (Prof $23,500)
Library Holdings: Bk Vols 21,393
Friends of the Library Group

WALNUT COVE

P WALNUT COVE PUBLIC LIBRARY,* PO Box 706, 27052. SAN 313-0215. Tel: 336-591-7496. FAX: 336-591-8494. E-Mail: ncs1391@interpath.com. *Librn*, Betty Smith
Founded 1970. Pop 3,500
Mem of Northwest Regional Library System; Northwestern Regional Library
Friends of the Library Group

WARRENTON

P WARREN COUNTY MEMORIAL LIBRARY,* 117 S Main St, 27589. SAN 313-0223. Tel: 252-257-4990. FAX: 252-257-4089. E-Mail: library@gloryroad.net. *Dir*, Shelley Fearn
Founded 1937
Library Holdings: Bk Vols 21,000

WARSAW

P WARSAW PUBLIC LIBRARY,* 117 W College St, 28398. SAN 376-2904. Tel: 910-293-4664. FAX: 910-293-4664. *In Charge*, Georgia Highsmith
Library Holdings: Bk Vols 10,500; Bk Titles 10,000; Per Subs 12
Friends of the Library Group

WASHINGTON

J BEAUFORT COUNTY COMMUNITY COLLEGE LIBRARY, US 5337 Hwy 264 E, PO Box 1069, 27889. (Mail add: PO Box 1069, 27889), SAN 313-024X. Tel: 252-946-6194. FAX: 252-946-9575. Web Site: www.beaufort.cc.nc.us. *Head of Libr*, Betty Ferrell; *Instrul Serv*, Penny Sermons; E-Mail: pennys@em.beaufort.cc.nc.us; Staff 5 (MLS 2, Non-MLS 3)
Founded 1968
Library Holdings: Bk Vols 30,000; Per Subs 222
Automation Activity & Vendor Info: (Cataloging) epixtech, inc.; (Circulation) epixtech, inc.; (OPAC) SIRSI
Database Vendor: IAC - SearchBank, Innovative Interfaces INN - View, OCLC - First Search, ProQuest
Function: Reference services available

P BEAUFORT, HYDE & MARTIN COUNTY REGIONAL LIBRARY, Old Court House, 158 N Market St, 27889. SAN 313-0258. Tel: 252-946-6401. FAX: 252-946-0352. *Dir*, Barbara Walker; *Librn*, Debra Cayton; Staff 19 (MLS 3, Non-MLS 16)
Founded 1941. Pop 76,024; Circ 185,445
Jul 2000-Jun 2001 Income (Main Library and Branch Library) $847,381, State $350,966, City $92,998, Federal $111,364, County $207,390, Locally Generated Income $25,910, Other $58,753. Mats Exp $91,681, Books $85,181, Per/Ser (Incl. Access Fees) $6,500. Sal $407,502

Library Holdings: Bk Vols 105,441; Per Subs 275
Automation Activity & Vendor Info: (Cataloging) TLC; (Circulation) TLC; (OPAC) TLC
Friends of the Library Group
Branches: 7
BATH COMMUNITY, PO Box 160, Bath, 27808. SAN 377-6352. Tel: 252-923-6371. FAX: 252-923-0497. *Branch Mgr*, Winnifred Webster
Open Mon, Wed & Fri 9:30-5:30
BELHAVEN PUBLIC, 333 E Main St, PO Box 130, Belhaven, 27810-0130. SAN 312-7435. Tel: 252-943-2993. FAX: 252-943-2606. *Branch Mgr*, Joan Cahoon
Library Holdings: Bk Vols 6,000; Per Subs 31
Open Mon, Tues & Thurs 9:30-5:30, Wed 9:30-8, Fri 9:30-5 & Sat 10-1
Friends of the Library Group
HAZEL W GUILFORD MEMORIAL, 524 Main St, PO Box 489, Aurora, 27806. SAN 377-6417. Tel: 252-322-5046. FAX: 252-322-7109. *Actg Librn*, Jean Ives
Open Tues & Thurs 9-5, Wed & Sat 9-12
Friends of the Library Group
MARTIN MEMORIAL, 200 N Smithwick, Williamston, 27892. SAN 377-6433. Tel: 252-792-7476. FAX: 252-792-8964. *Head Librn*, Ann Phelps; Staff 7 (MLS 1, Non-MLS 6)
Library Holdings: Bk Vols 25,000; Per Subs 70
Open Mon-Tues & Fri-Sat 9:30-5:30, Wed & Thurs 9:30-8, Sun 2-5
Friends of the Library Group
MATTAMUSKEET, 20418 US 264, Swan Quarter, 27885. Tel: 252-926-0310. FAX: 252-926-0311. *Branch Mgr*, Shelly Spencer
OCRACOKE BRANCH, PO Box 130, Ocracoke, 27960. SAN 376-2890. Tel: 252-928-4436. FAX: 252-928-4436. *Librn*, Maryann Zbel
Open Tues & Thurs 2-6, Wed & Sat 10-1
Friends of the Library Group
ROBERSONVILLE PUBLIC, Main St, PO Box 1060, Robersonville, 27871. SAN 377-6468. Tel: 252-795-3591. FAX: 252-795-3359. *Branch Mgr*, Madge Partin
Open Mon-Fri 9:30-5:30, Sat 9:30-1
Friends of the Library Group
Bookmobiles: 2

P GEORGE H & LAURA E BROWN LIBRARY,* 122 Van Norden St, 27889. SAN 313-0266. Tel: 252-946-4300. FAX: 252-975-2015. *Dir*, Julie Hicks; E-Mail: jhicks@ncsl.ocr.state.nc.us; Staff 2 (MLS 2)
Founded 1911. Pop 15,000; Circ 72,000
Library Holdings: Bk Vols 52,000; Bk Titles 50,000; Per Subs 88
Subject Interests: Career Information Center, Carolina hist, Civil War, Genealogy
Special Collections: Bellamy Papers; Bible Translations Coll; C F Warren Coll; Cemetery Records; County Newspapers Found & Filmed by North Carolina State Archives, dated prior to 1900; Current Local Newspaper, microfilm; Dunstan Papers; E J Warren Coll; Ernest Harding Civil War Coll; Fowle Papers; Gould Marsh Ledger, 1805-11; Havens Ledgers; John Respess Papers, copy; Jonathan Havens Coll; Josiah Fowle Ledger, 1808-47, copy; Local Daughters of the American Revolution Records, copies; Wiswall Papers
Partic in NC Info Network; OCLC Online Computer Library Center, Inc
Friends of the Library Group

WAYNESVILLE

P HAYWOOD COUNTY PUBLIC LIBRARY,* 678 S Haywood St, 28786-4398. SAN 355-2152. Tel: 828-452-5169. FAX: 828-452-6746. Web Site: www.haywoodnc/org/government/haywoodlibrary.html. *Dir*, Jennifer Seavy Pratt; E-Mail: jpratt@ncsl.dcr.state.nc.us; *Ad Servs*, Toni Taylor; *Publ Servs*, Kathy Keyser; *Tech Servs*, Kim Garmon; *Ch Servs*, Laura Presnell; *Br Coordr*, Nan Williamson; Staff 25 (MLS 5, Non-MLS 20)
Founded 1891. Pop 52,000; Circ 465,000
Jul 1997-Jun 1998 Income $958,995, State $120,656, City $2,507, County $790,227, Locally Generated Income $45,605. Mats Exp $198,681, Books $142,993, Per/Ser (Incl. Access Fees) $16,305, Presv $438. Sal $576,014 (Prof $162,294)
Library Holdings: Bk Vols 133,145; Per Subs 518
Subject Interests: NC genealogy
Database Vendor: Dialog, epixtech, inc., GaleNet, OCLC - First Search, ProQuest, Wilson - Wilson Web
Publications: Paperclips: Haywood County Public Library & Friends Newsletter
Function: ILL available
Friends of the Library Group
Branches: 1
CANTON BRANCH, 11 Pennsylvania Ave, Canton, 28716. SAN 355-2187. Tel: 828-648-2924. FAX: 828-648-0377. Web Site: www.haywoodnc.org/government/haywoodlibrary. *Librn*, Nan Williamson
Friends of the Library Group
Bookmobiles: 1. Also have 2 Mini-Libraries

WELDON

J HALIFAX COMMUNITY COLLEGE LIBRARY,* PO Drawer 809, 27890. SAN 313-0312. Tel: 252-536-7237. FAX: 252-536-0474. Web Site: www.hcc.cc.nc.us. *Librn*, Carolyn E Mercer; E-Mail: mercerc@halifax.hcc.cc.nc.us
Founded 1968. Enrl 1,557; Fac 47
Jul 1997-Jun 1998 Income $182,487. Mats Exp $72,241. Sal $90,823
Library Holdings: Bk Vols 34,477; Bk Titles 27,676; Per Subs 167
Subject Interests: Architecture, Art, Bus, Econ, Government, History, Literature, Mgt, Nursing, Sci-tech
Special Collections: News Bank Library 1979-present
Career Lab, Learning Assistance Center, Small Business Center

WENTWORTH

J ROCKINGHAM COMMUNITY COLLEGE, Gerald B James Library,* PO Box 38, 27375-0038. SAN 313-0339. Tel: 336-342-4261. FAX: 336-342-1203. Web Site: www,rcc.cc.nc.us/lrc/index2.htm. *Dir*, John Wood; *Coll Develop, Librn*, Kimberly Shireman; *Librn*, Mary Gomez; *Media Spec*, Robert Smith; *Circ*, Carolyn Roberts; Staff 3 (MLS 3)
Founded 1966. Enrl 1,785; Fac 72
Jul 1997-Jun 1998 Income $375,000
Library Holdings: Bk Vols 40,919; Bk Titles 34,781; Per Subs 305
Subject Interests: N Caroliniana, Rockingham county
Partic in NC Dept of Commun Cols

WEST JEFFERSON

P ASHE COUNTY PUBLIC LIBRARY,* 148 Library Dr, 28694. SAN 320-5010. Tel: 336-246-2041. FAX: 336-246-7503. *Mgr*, Jo Green; *Ch Servs*, Lisa Calhoun; *Ad Servs*, Joanne Kemp; Staff 5 (MLS 1, Non-MLS 4)
Founded 1932. Pop 23,109; Circ 138,325
Library Holdings: Bk Vols 53,541; Per Subs 72
Subject Interests: Genealogy
Friends of the Library Group

WHITEVILLE

P COLUMBUS COUNTY PUBLIC LIBRARY, 407 N Powell Blvd, 28472. SAN 355-2217. Tel: 910-642-3116. Reference Tel: 910-641-3976. FAX: 910-642-3839. *Dir*, Jamie S Hansen; Tel: 910-641-3977, E-Mail: jhansen@ncsl.dcr.state.nc.us; *ILL*, Alice Soles; *Ch Servs*, Ann Fowler; *Tech Servs*, Faye King; *Circ*, Lizzett Dixon; Staff 16 (MLS 1, Non-MLS 15)
Founded 1921. Pop 50,198; Circ 257,350
Library Holdings: Bk Titles 111,631; Per Subs 318
Subject Interests: Genealogy, Local history
Special Collections: Genealogy & Local History; Local newspapers on microfilm; North Caroliniana
Automation Activity & Vendor Info: (Circulation) Gaylord
Publications: Columbus County, North Carolina: Recollections & Records
Branches: 5
CHADBOURN COMMUNITY, 301 N Wilson St, Chadbourn, 28431. SAN 377-8479. Tel: 910-654-3322. *Librn*, Dianne Milliken
Friends of the Library Group
EAST COLUMBUS LIBRARY, 100 Hwy 87, Riegelwood, 28456. SAN 355-2233. Tel: 910-655-4157. FAX: 910-655-9414. *Branch Mgr*, Robin Creech; Staff 2 (Non-MLS 2)
Library Holdings: Bk Titles 8,880
Automation Activity & Vendor Info: (Circulation) Gaylord
Friends of the Library Group
FAIR BLUFF COMMUNITY, 315 Railroad St, PO Box 428, Fair Bluff, 28439. SAN 355-2241. Tel: 910-649-7098. FAX: 910-649-7733. *Branch Mgr*, Carolyn Waddell; Staff 2 (Non-MLS 2)
Library Holdings: Bk Titles 10,010
Automation Activity & Vendor Info: (Circulation) Gaylord
Friends of the Library Group
RUBE MCCRAY MEMORIAL, 301 Flemington Dr, Lake Waccamaw, 28450. SAN 375-2933. Tel: 910-646-4616. FAX: 910-646-4747. *Branch Mgr*, Portia Starks-Maynor; *Librn*, Donna Askew; Staff 2 (Non-MLS 2)
Automation Activity & Vendor Info: (Circulation) Gaylord
Friends of the Library Group
TABOR CITY PUBLIC, 101 E Fifth St, Tabor City, 28439. SAN 355-2276. Tel: 910-653-3774. FAX: 910-653-3774. *Branch Mgr*, Sonya Gore; Staff 2 (Non-MLS 2)
Library Holdings: Bk Titles 11,738
Automation Activity & Vendor Info: (Circulation) Gaylord
Friends of the Library Group
Bookmobiles: 1

J SOUTHEASTERN COMMUNITY COLLEGE LIBRARY,* PO Box 151, 28472-0151. SAN 313-0347. Tel: 910-642-7141, Ext 218. FAX: 910-642-4513. Web Site: www.southeastern.cc.nc.us. *Librn*, Marian Williams; Staff 8 (MLS 3, Non-MLS 5)
Founded 1965. Enrl 1,600; Fac 80
Library Holdings: Bk Vols 59,264; Per Subs 216

Special Collections: North Carolina Colonial Records 1662-1789; North Carolina Genealogy & History Coll; Official Records of the Union & Confederate Armies; Southeastern North Carolina Records, micro; War of the Rebellion
Publications: Audio Visual Catalog; Library Handbook
Partic in North Carolina Community College System; OCLC Online Computer Library Center, Inc; SE Libr Network

WILKESBORO

J WILKES COMMUNITY COLLEGE, Learning Resources Library, 1328 Collegiate Dr, 28697-0120. (Mail add: PO Box 120, 28697-0120), SAN 313-0363. Tel: 336-838-6115. FAX: 336-838-6277. *Dir Libr Serv*, Fay Byrd; Tel: 336-838-6289, E-Mail: byrdf@wilkes.cc.nc.us; *Librn*, Janet B Atwood; E-Mail: atwoodj@wilkes.cc.nc.us; *Librn*, Audrey J Chapel; Tel: 336-838-6117, E-Mail: chapela@wilkes.cc.nc.us; *Tech Servs*, Vickie L Cothren-Millsaps; Tel: 336-838-6513, E-Mail: cothrenv@wilkes.cc.nc.us; *Tech Servs*, Rebecca P Queen; Tel: 336-838-6514, E-Mail: queenr@wilkes.cc.nc.us; Staff 5 (MLS 3, Non-MLS 2)
Founded 1966
Jul 1999-Jun 2000 Income $350,055. Mats Exp $83,440, Books $44,563, Per/Ser (Incl. Access Fees) $8,314, Electronic Ref Mat (Incl. Access Fees) $30,563. Sal $186,432 (Prof $146,725)
Library Holdings: Bk Titles 51,628; Per Subs 120
Special Collections: James Larkin Pearson Coll; Wilkes County Coll, bks & tapes
Database Vendor: Ebsco - EbscoHost, IAC - Info Trac, OCLC - First Search, ProQuest
Partic in North Carolina Library & Information Network

WILLIAMSTON

J MARTIN COMMUNITY COLLEGE LIBRARY,* 1161 Kehukee Park Rd, 27892-9988. SAN 313-038X. Tel: 252-792-1521. FAX: 252-792-4425. Web Site: www.martin.cc.nc.us. *Dir*, Peggy Cherry; Tel: 440-775-8280, E-Mail: pcherry@martin.cc.nc.us
Founded 1968
Library Holdings: Bk Vols 34,500; Per Subs 228
Subject Interests: Bus, Equine tech, Indust lab tech, Mgt, Physical therapy, Sci-tech
Special Collections: Martin County History Coll
Partic in NC Dept of Commun Cols; OCLC Online Computer Library Center, Inc

P MARTIN MEMORIAL LIBRARY, (MML), 200 N Smithwick St, 27892. SAN 313-0398. Tel: 252-792-7476. FAX: 252-792-8964. *Dir*, Barbara Walker; *Librn*, Ann Phelps; E-Mail: aphelps@ncsl.dcr.state.nc.us; Staff 1 (MLS 1)
Pop 6,159; Circ 29,910
Library Holdings: Bk Vols 30,000; Per Subs 25
Partic in Beaufort, Hyde, Martin Regional Libr Syst
Open Mon & Tues 9:30-5:30, Wed & Thurs 9:30-8, Fri & Sat 9:30-5:30, Sun 2-5
Friends of the Library Group

WILMINGTON

J CAPE FEAR COMMUNITY COLLEGE, Learning Resource Center, 415 N Second St, 28401-3993. (Mail add: 411 N Front St, 28401-3993), SAN 313-0401. Tel: 910-251-5130. Interlibrary Loan Service Tel: 910-251-5134. Reference Tel: 910-251-5134. FAX: 910-251-5105. Web Site: cfcc.net. *Coll Develop, Dir*, Carolyn C Oakley; E-Mail: coakley@capefear.cc.nc.us; *Ref*, Billie Mann; *Ref*, Jane Atkisson; *Ref*, Debbra Michaels; *Tech Servs*, Deanna Lewis; Staff 6 (MLS 4, Non-MLS 2)
Founded 1964. Enrl 5,800; Fac 200; Highest Degree: Associate
Jul 1999-Jun 2000 Income $665,126. Mats Exp $381,400, Books $138,000, Per/Ser (Incl. Access Fees) $44,000, Presv $7,800, Micro $8,000, AV Equip $170,000, Electronic Ref Mat (Incl. Access Fees) $13,600. Sal $371,041 (Prof $182,665)
Library Holdings: Bk Vols 34,600; Bk Titles 32,468; Per Subs 687
Subject Interests: Boat building, Fishing, Local history, Marine tech, NC, NC hist
Automation Activity & Vendor Info: (Acquisitions) epixtech, inc.; (Cataloging) epixtech, inc.; (Circulation) epixtech, inc.; (Course Reserve) epixtech, inc.; (ILL) epixtech, inc.; (Media Booking) epixtech, inc.; (OPAC) epixtech, inc.; (Serials) epixtech, inc.
Publications: A Guide to the LRC; A Walking Tour of the LRC

M COASTAL AREA HEALTH EDUCATION CENTER, (Formerly Robert M Fales Health Sciences Library), Robert M Fales Health Sciences Library, 2131 S 17th St, 28402-9025. (Mail add: PO Box 9025, 28402-9025), SAN 324-6418. Tel: 910-343-2180. FAX: 910-762-7600. Web Site: www.hsl.unc.edu/ahec/aheclib/coastal.htm. *Dir*, Donna Flake; E-Mail: donna.flake@coastalahec.org; *Ref*, Cyndy Oliver; E-Mail: cyndy.oliver.coastalahec.org; *Outreach Serv*, Angela Jones; E-Mail: angela.jones@coastalahec.org; *Tech Servs*, Sharon Welsh; E-Mail: sharon.welsh@coastalahec.org. Subject Specialists: *Education*, Cyndy Oliver; Staff 7 (MLS 4, Non-MLS 3)
1999-2000 Income $454,390. Mats Exp $111,425, Books $30,000, Per/Ser (Incl. Access Fees) $70,000. Sal $241,000
Library Holdings: Bk Titles 4,000; Per Subs 370
Subject Interests: Gynecology, Health admin, Internal medicine, Obstetrics, Pastoral care, Spanish language, Surg
Automation Activity & Vendor Info: (Cataloging) epixtech, inc.; (Circulation) epixtech, inc.; (OPAC) epixtech, inc.; (Serials) epixtech, inc.
Partic in Nat Libr of Med; National Network of Libraries of Medicine - Greater Midwest Region

P NEW HANOVER COUNTY PUBLIC LIBRARY, 201 Chestnut St, 28401. SAN 355-2306. Tel: 910-341-4389, 910-341-4390. Circulation Tel: 910-341-4391. FAX: 910-341-4357. Web Site: www.co.new-hanover.nc.us/lib/libmain.htm. *Dir*, David M Paynter; Tel: 910-772-7859, E-Mail: dpaynter@co.new-hanover.nc.us; *Assoc Dir*, Harry Tuchmayer; Tel: 910-772-7857, E-Mail: htuchmayer@co.new-hanover.nc.us; *Ch Servs*, Margaret Miles; Tel: 910-341-4392, E-Mail: mmiles@co.new-hanover.nc.us; *Ref*, Robert Cox; Tel: 910-341-4390, Fax: 910-341-4388, E-Mail: rcox@co.new-hanover.nc.us; *Tech Servs*, Caroline Eisenstein; Tel: 910-341-4036, E-Mail: ceisenstein@co.new-hanover.nc.us; *Publ Servs*, Dorothy Hodder; Tel: 910-772-7858, E-Mail: dhodder@co.new-hanover.nc.us; *Circ*, Jery Drye; Tel: 910-341-4391, Fax: 910-341-4388, E-Mail: jdrye@co.new-hanover.nc.us; *Spec Coll*, Beverly Tetterton; Tel: 910-341-4394, E-Mail: btetterton@co.new-hanover.nc.us; *AV*, Marie Spencer; Tel: 910-341-4390, Fax: 910-341-4388, E-Mail: mspencer@co.new-hanover.nc.us; Staff 31 (MLS 15, Non-MLS 16)
Founded 1906. Circ 1,207,744
Jul 2000-Jun 2001 Income (Main Library and Branch Library) $2,705,602. Sal $1,781,802
Library Holdings: Bk Vols 33,270; Bk Titles 219,755; Per Subs 400
Special Collections: Civil War Materials; Fales Collection; New Hanover County & City of Wilmington, North Carolina; North Carolina History; Old New Hanover Genealogical Society Publications
Partic in NC Info Network
Friends of the Library Group
Branches: 3
CAROLINA BEACH BRANCH, 300 Cape Fear Blvd, Carolina Beach, 28428. SAN 355-2314. Tel: 910-458-5016. FAX: 910-458-9422. *Librn*, Kip Register
MYRTLE GROVE, 5155 S College Rd, 28409. SAN 372-8323. Tel: 910-452-6414. FAX: 910-452-6417. *Librn*, Rebecca Taylor
PLAZA EAST, 1942 Eastwood Blvd, 28403. SAN 355-2330. Tel: 910-256-2173. FAX: 910-256-1238. *Librn*, Phyllis Smith; E-Mail: psmith@co.new-hanover.nc.us
Library Holdings: Bk Vols 9,828

S ST JOHN'S MUSEUM OF ART LIBRARY, 114 Orange St, 28401. SAN 313-041X. Tel: 910-763-0281. FAX: 910-341-7981. E-Mail: info@stjohnsmuseum.com. *Dir*, C Reynolds Brown
Founded 1962
Library Holdings: Bk Titles 250
Publications: Newsletter
Restriction: Members only
Open Tues-Sat 10-5, Sun 12-4

S TRI-MERIDIAN INC, MEDSEARCH Division Library, PO Box 7664, 28406. SAN 375-5002. Tel: 910-793-6456. FAX: 910-793-8280. *Dir*, Debbra D Michaels; E-Mail: michaels2@worldnet.att.net; Staff 2 (MLS 1, Non-MLS 1)
Jan 2000-Dec 2000 Income $195,000, Locally Generated Income $45,000, Parent Institution $150,000. Mats Exp $14,000. Sal $45,000 (Prof $32,000)
Subject Interests: Medicine, Pharmacology
Restriction: By appointment only
Partic in National Network Of Libraries Of Medicine - South Central Region

C UNIVERSITY OF NORTH CAROLINA AT WILMINGTON, William Madison Randall Library, 601 S College Rd, 28403-3297. SAN 313-0428. Tel: 910-962-3000. Interlibrary Loan Service Tel: 910-962-3273. Circulation Tel: 910-962-3272. Reference Tel: 910-962-3760. TDD: 910-962-3687. FAX: 910-962-3078. Web Site: www.library.uncwil.edu. *Librn*, Sherman Hayes; E-Mail: hayess@uncwil.edu; *ILL*, Madeleine Bombeld; E-Mail: bombeldm@uncwil.edu; *Circ*, Joyce Johnson; *Tech Servs*, Arlene Hanerfeld; *Doc*, Eileen Brown; *Spec Coll*, Andrew Dutka; *Syst Coordr*, Daniel Pfohl; *Head Ref*, Jerry Parnell; Staff 17 (MLS 17)
Founded 1947. Enrl 10,000; Fac 557; Highest Degree: Master
Jul 1999-Jun 2000 Income $3,573,740. Mats Exp $3,210,709, Books $1,822,817, Per/Ser (Incl. Access Fees) $1,255,452, Presv $132,440. Sal $1,406,234 (Prof $449,452)
Library Holdings: Bk Vols 480,391; Per Subs 4,304
Subject Interests: Education, History, Marine biology
Special Collections: Audiovisuals
Automation Activity & Vendor Info: (Acquisitions) Innovative Interfaces Inc.; (Cataloging) Innovative Interfaces Inc.; (Circulation) Innovative Interfaces Inc.; (Course Reserve) Innovative Interfaces Inc.; (ILL) Innovative Interfaces Inc.; (Media Booking) Innovative Interfaces Inc.; (OPAC) Innovative Interfaces Inc.
Partic in SE Libr Network

S WILMINGTON STAR-NEWS LIBRARY,* 1003 S 17th St, PO Box 840, 28402. SAN 329-708X. Tel: 910-343-2309. FAX: 910-343-2227. Web Site: starnews.wilmington.net. *Librn*, Mary MacCallum; E-Mail: mary-maccallum@wilmingtonstar.com; *Asst Librn*, Cheryl Whitaker; Staff 2 (MLS 1, Non-MLS 1)

WILSON

C BARTON COLLEGE, (NQZ), Hackney Library, PO Box 5000, 27893-7000. SAN 313-0444. Tel: 252-399-6500. FAX: 252-399-6571. E-Mail: reference@barton.edu. Web Site: library.barton.edu. *Dir*, Shirley Gregory; Tel: 252-399-6501, E-Mail: sgregory@barton.edu; *Ref*, Shonra McManus; Tel: 252-399-6502, E-Mail: smcmanus@barton.edu; *ILL*, Erika Seamanson; *Cat*, K Thompson; *Per*, N Williams; *Archivist*, E Holloway; *Acq*, Norma Williams; *Govt Doc*, Richard Fulling; Tel: 252-399-6504, E-Mail: rfulling@barton.edu; *Circ*, Angela Davis; Tel: 252-399-6502, E-Mail: circ@barton.edu; Staff 5 (MLS 4, Non-MLS 1)
Founded 1902. Fac 105; Highest Degree: Bachelor
Jul 1999-Jun 2000 Income Parent Institution $341,512. Mats Exp $99,886, Books $47,694, Per/Ser (Incl. Access Fees) $47,976, Presv $4,216. Sal $205,700 (Prof $157,453)
Library Holdings: Bk Vols 154,490; Bk Titles 6,450; Per Subs 388
Subject Interests: Deaf educ
Special Collections: Discipliana Coll
Automation Activity & Vendor Info: (Acquisitions) Innovative Interfaces Inc.; (Cataloging) Innovative Interfaces Inc.; (Circulation) Innovative Interfaces Inc.; (Serials) Innovative Interfaces Inc.
Restriction: Restricted loan policy
Partic in Mid-Carolina Academic Library Network; OCLC Online Computer Library Center, Inc; SE Libr Network
Friends of the Library Group

P WILSON COUNTY PUBLIC LIBRARY,* 249 W Nash St, PO Box 400, Courier 01-52-12, 27894-0400. SAN 355-2365. Tel: 252-237-5355. FAX: 252-243-4311. Web Site: www.wilson-co.com. *Dir*, Dr Patrick Valentine; E-Mail: pvalentine@wilson-co.com; *Ref*, Peter Bileckyj; *Commun Servs*, Liz Winters; Staff 5 (MLS 5)
Founded 1937. Pop 66,061; Circ 315,986
Jul 1997-Jun 1998 Income $1,202,250, State $141,100, County $1,025,950, Locally Generated Income $35,200. Mats Exp $162,621, Books $132,616, Per/Ser (Incl. Access Fees) $15,984, Micro $5,175. Sal $791,609
Library Holdings: Bk Vols 145,180; Per Subs 250
Subject Interests: Drama
Special Collections: Genealogy Coll; North Carolina, bks & microfilm
Publications: WCPL Newsletter; Wilson County Public Library: A History
Special Services for the Deaf - Books on deafness & sign language; High interest/low vocabulary books; Staff with knowledge of sign language
Friends of the Library Group
Branches: 5
BLACK CREEK LIBRARY, 103 Central Ave, Black Creek, 27813. SAN 370-9450. Tel; 252-237-3715. FAX: 252-237-3715. *Librn*, Betty MacLean; Staff 1 (Non-MLS 1)
Library Holdings: Bk Vols 7,600; Per Subs 14
Database Vendor: epixtech, inc.
EAST, 506 Ward Blvd SE, 27893. SAN 355-239X. Tel: 252-237-2627. *Librn*, Brenda Edmondson
Library Holdings: Bk Vols 9,169
ELM CITY BRANCH, PO Box 717, Elm City, 27822. SAN 355-242X. Tel: 919-236-4269. *Librn*, Susie Webb
Library Holdings: Bk Vols 9,193
LUCAMA BRANCH, 103 E Spring St, Lucama, 27851. SAN 355-2489. Tel: 352-239-0046. *Librn*, Brenda Barnes
Library Holdings: Bk Vols 10,060
STANTONSBURG BRANCH, 114 Main St, Stantonsburg, 27883. SAN 355-2519. Tel: 252-238-3758. *Librn*, Tim Thompson
Library Holdings: Bk Vols 7,143
Bookmobiles: 1

M WILSON MEMORIAL HOSPITAL LIBRARY, 1705 S Tarboro St, 27893-3428. SAN 320-409X. Tel: 252-399-8253. Interlibrary Loan Service Tel: 252-399-8181. FAX: 252-399-8119. E-Mail: rce@med.unc.edu. *Coordr*, Rosa Edwards; Staff 2 (MLS 1, Non-MLS 1)
Founded 1964
Library Holdings: Bk Titles 1,766; Per Subs 75
Special Collections: Leadership Coll; Wellness/Consumer Health Coll
Automation Activity & Vendor Info: (Cataloging) Athena
Publications: Bibliography of Resources; Library Links

J WILSON TECHNICAL COMMUNITY COLLEGE, Learning Resource Center,* 902 Herring Ave, PO Box 4305, 27893-4305. SAN 313-0452. Tel: 252-291-1195, Ext 235. FAX: 252-243-7148. Web Site: www.wilsontech.cc.nc.us. *Ref*, Gerry O'Neill; E-Mail: goneil@email.wilsontech.cc.nc.us; *AV*, Leon Crumpler; Staff 4 (MLS 2, Non-MLS 2)
Founded 1958. Enrl 1,285; Fac 65
Library Holdings: Bk Vols 33,000; Per Subs 330
Subject Interests: Sci-tech
Special Services for the Deaf - Books on deafness & sign language; High interest/low vocabulary books

WINDSOR

P LAWRENCE MEMORIAL PUBLIC LIBRARY,* 204 E Dundee St, 27983. SAN 313-0460. Tel: 252-794-2244. FAX: 252-794-1536. *Librn*, Nancy B Hughes
Statistics included with regional library. See Winton entry

WINGATE

R WINGATE BAPTIST CHURCH LIBRARY, 109 E Elm St, 28174. SAN 313-0479. Tel: 704-233-4256. FAX: 704-233-4257.
Library Holdings: Bk Vols 1,200
Subject Interests: Biog, Children's bks, Fiction

C WINGATE UNIVERSITY, Ethel K Smith Library, PO Box 219, 28174-0219. SAN 313-0487. Tel: 704-233-8089. Interlibrary Loan Service Tel: 704-233-8093. FAX: 704-233-8254. Web Site: www.wingate.edu. *Dean of Libr*, C T Harris; E-Mail: ctharris@wingate.edu; *Acq*, Yvonne Staton; Tel: 704-233-8089, Ext 8098; *ILL*, Susan Sganga; *Cat*, Marilyn Brown; *Ref*, Richard Pipes; *Ref*, Jimm Wetherbee; Staff 5 (MLS 5)
Founded 1896. Enrl 1,300; Fac 98; Highest Degree: Master
Library Holdings: Bk Vols 115,000; Bk Titles 110,000; Per Subs 650
Subject Interests: Bus, Education, Human servs, Mgt, Music, Relig studies
Special Collections: Charles A Cannon Family Papers; Wingate College History
Automation Activity & Vendor Info: (Acquisitions) Endeavor; (Circulation) Endeavor
Publications: Libr Handbook; PLL (Per in Libr Listing)
Partic in BRS; Dialog Corporation; OCLC Online Computer Library Center, Inc; SE Libr Network
Friends of the Library Group

WINSTON-SALEM

R FIRST BAPTIST CHURCH, John Davis Memorial Library, 700 N Highland Ave, 27101. SAN 313-0495. Tel: 336-722-5605. FAX: 336-722-6266. *Librn*, Selena Nichols
Founded 1958
Library Holdings: Bk Vols 1,250
Subject Interests: Architecture, Art, History, Recreation

P FORSYTH COUNTY PUBLIC LIBRARY,* 660 W Fifth St, 27101. SAN 355-2543. Tel: 336-727-2556. FAX: 336-727-2549. *Materials Manager*, Carla Beasley; *Dir*, Sylvia Sprinkle-Hamlin; *Ch Servs*, Laura Weigand; *Automation Syst Coordr, Tech Servs*, Thelma Bellamy; *Doc, Per*, George Taylor; Staff 43 (MLS 43)
Founded 1903. Pop 267,693; Circ 2,210,000
Library Holdings: Bk Vols 415,148; Per Subs 1,866
Subject Interests: Bible libr, BIP, Encyclopedia, Oxford English dictionary, Per
Special Collections: Frank Jones Photographic Print Coll; H Kapp Ogborn Philatelic Coll; North Caroliniana, bks, genealogy, micro, per
Publications: Children's Calendar; Monthly Calendar; Monthly Report
Partic in BRS; Dialog Corporation; OCLC Online Computer Library Center, Inc; Solinet
Special Services for the Deaf - Captioned film depository; Staff with knowledge of sign language; TTY machine
Friends of the Library Group
Branches: 10
CARVER SCHOOL BRANCH, 4915 Lansing Dr W, Carver School, 27105. SAN 378-1917. Tel: 336-661-4917. FAX: 336-661-4919. *Librn*, Lois Legget; E-Mail: l_leget@forsyth.lib.nc.us
Friends of the Library Group
CLEMMONS BRANCH, 3554 Clemmons Rd, Old Hwy 158, Clemmons, 27012. SAN 355-2578. Tel: 336-712-4450. FAX: 336-712-4452. *Librn*, Cindy Jones; E-Mail: c_jones@forsyth.lib.nc.us
Library Holdings: Bk Vols 20,000
Friends of the Library Group
EAST WINSTON HERITAGE CENTER, 1110 E Seventh St, 27101. SAN 355-2608. Tel: 336-727-2202. FAX: 336-727-8498. *Librn*, Tim Jackson, Jr; E-Mail: t_jackson@forsythlib.nc.us
Library Holdings: Bk Vols 28,000
Friends of the Library Group
KERNERSVILLE BRANCH, 130 E Mountain St, Kernersville, 27284. SAN 355-2632. Tel: 336-993-8141. FAX: 336-993-5216. *Librn*, Lisa Elmore; E-Mail: l_elmore@forsyth.lib.nc.us
Library Holdings: Bk Vols 27,000
Friends of the Library Group
LEWISVILLE BRANCH, Lewisville Plaza Shopping Ctr, Shallowford Rd, Lewisville, 27023. SAN 355-2667. Tel: 336-945-3786. FAX: 336-945-9745. *Librn*, Merrikay Brown; E-Mail: m_brown@forsyth.lib.nc.us

Library Holdings: Bk Vols 8,000
Friends of the Library Group
REYNOLDA MANOR, 2839 Fairlawn Dr, 27106. SAN 355-2691. Tel: 336-727-2948. FAX: 336-748-3318. *Librn*, Darla Johnson; E-Mail: d_johnson@forsyth.lib.nc.us
Library Holdings: Bk Vols 28,000
Friends of the Library Group
RURAL HALL BRANCH, 7125 Broad St, Rural Hall, 27045. SAN 355-2721. Tel: 336-969-9545. FAX: 336-969-9401. *Librn*, Tammy Baggett; E-Mail: baggett@forsyth.lib.nc.us
Library Holdings: Bk Vols 20,000
Friends of the Library Group
SOUTHSIDE, 3185 Buchanan St, 27127. SAN 355-2756. Tel: 336-771-4722. FAX: 336-771-4724. *Librn*, Elizabeth Skinner; E-Mail: e_skinner@forsyth.lib.nc.us
Library Holdings: Bk Vols 21,500
Friends of the Library Group
THRUWAY, Lower Mall, Thruway Shopping Ctr, 27103. SAN 355-2780. Tel: 336-727-2337. FAX: 336-727-8497. *Librn*, Karen Robertson; E-Mail: k_robertson@forsyth.lib.nc.us
Library Holdings: Bk Vols 24,800
Friends of the Library Group
WALKERTOWN BRANCH, 2969 Main St, Walkertown, 27051. SAN 374-4167. Tel: 336-595-6863. FAX: 336-595-9080. *Mgr*, William Durham; E-Mail: w_durham@forsyth.lib.nc.us; Staff 3 (MLS 2, Non-MLS 1)
Pop 20,000; Circ 60,000
Library Holdings: Bk Vols 13,000; Bk Titles 12,000; Per Subs 80
Special Services for the Deaf - Books on deafness & sign language; Captioned film depository; Staff with knowledge of sign language
Friends of the Library Group
Bookmobiles: 2

M FORSYTH MEDICAL CENTER, John C Whitaker Library, 3333 Silas Creek Pkwy, 27103-3090. SAN 355-2810. Tel: 336-718-5995. *Librn*, Margaret L Cobb; Staff 2 (MLS 1, Non-MLS 1)
Founded 1964
Library Holdings: Bk Vols 4,000; Bk Titles 900; Per Subs 130
Subject Interests: Allied health, Clinical medicine, Nursing
Automation Activity & Vendor Info: (Cataloging) EOS; (OPAC) EOS
Database Vendor: OVID Technologies
Publications: In-house newsletter (quarterly)

J FORSYTH TECHNICAL COMMUNITY COLLEGE LIBRARY,* 2100 Silas Creek Pkwy, 27103. SAN 355-287X. Tel: 336-723-0371, Ext 7216. FAX: 336-761-2465. Web Site: www.forsyth.tec.nc.us. *Dean*, J Randel Candelaria; E-Mail: rcandelarie@forsyth.cc.nc.us; *Publ Servs*, Tom Gordon; *Tech Servs*, Ted Labusky; *AV*, John Briggs
Founded 1964
Library Holdings: Bk Vols 34,000; Per Subs 300
Departmental Libraries:

S HISTORIC BETHABARA PARK LIBRARY,* 2147 Bethabara Rd, 27106. SAN 323-5157. Tel: 336-924-8191. FAX: 336-924-0535. *Dir*, J Rodney Meyer
Library Holdings: Bk Vols 911
Subject Interests: Early Moravian hist (1753-1803), Local history, State hist

S MORAVIAN MUSIC FOUNDATION, Peter Memorial Library, 20 Cascade Ave, 27127. SAN 313-0517. Tel: 336-725-0651. FAX: 336-725-4514. Web Site: www.moravianmusic.org. *Dir*, Dr Nola R Knouse
Founded 1961
Library Holdings: Bk Titles 6,000; Per Subs 10
Subject Interests: 18th Century music, 19th Century music, Am music, Hymnology, Moravian music
Special Collections: Music (Lowens Coll of Musical Americana & Manuscripts of Early American Music), bk, mss
Publications: Catalogs of Music Coll; Journal (quarterly); Publications
Restriction: Open to public for reference only

C NORTH CAROLINA SCHOOL OF THE ARTS, Semans Library, 1533 S Main St, 27127. SAN 313-0541. Tel: 336-770-3270. Circulation Tel: 336-770-3270. Reference Tel: 336-770-1479. FAX: 336-770-3271. Web Site: www.ncarts.edu/. *Coll Develop, Dir*, Vicki Montle; E-Mail: montlv@ncarts.edu; *Cat*, Christia Thomason; E-Mail: thomasonc@ncarts.edu; *Online Servs, Tech Servs*, Gayl Pearman; E-Mail: pearmg@ncarts.edu; *Bibliog Instr, Ref*, Susan Keely; E-Mail: keelys@ncarts.edu; *Cat*, Sylvia Koontz; E-Mail: koontzs@ncarts.edu; *Archivist*, Patrice Slattery; E-Mail: slatteryp@ncarts.edu; *Coll Develop, Music*, Leslie Kamtman; E-Mail: kamtml@ncarts.edu; Staff 18 (MLS 8, Non-MLS 10)
Founded 1965. Enrl 1,038; Fac 152; Highest Degree: Master
Jul 1999-Jun 2000 Income $809,000, State $800,000, Other $9,000. Mats Exp $211,500, Books $75,200, Per/Ser (Incl. Access Fees) $35,600, Presv $13,500, Micro $9,400, AV Equip $24,700, Other Print Mats $45,000, Electronic Ref Mat (Incl. Access Fees) $8,100. Sal $450,000 (Prof $250,000)
Library Holdings: Bk Vols 110,000; Per Subs 490
Subject Interests: Art, Dance, Drama, Film, Music
Special Collections: School Archives; Music Scores; Sound Recordings; Moving Image Materials
Automation Activity & Vendor Info: (Acquisitions) Innovative Interfaces Inc.; (Cataloging) Innovative Interfaces Inc.; (Circulation) Innovative Interfaces Inc.; (Course Reserve) Innovative Interfaces Inc.; (OPAC) Innovative Interfaces Inc.
Function: ILL available, Reference services available
Partic in NC LIVE; OCLC Online Computer Library Center, Inc; SE Libr Network
AV materials do not circulate via ILL

S OLD SALEM, INC, Museum of Early Southern Decorative Arts, 924 S Main St, 27101. SAN 325-8084. Tel: 336-721-7372. FAX: 336-721-7367. E-Mail: library@oldsalem.org. *Librn*, Katie Schlee; Staff 1 (MLS 1)
Library Holdings: Bk Vols 13,400
Restriction: By appointment only

CR PIEDMONT BAPTIST COLLEGE, George M Manuel Memorial Library, 716 Franklin St, 27101. SAN 313-055X. Tel: 336-725-8344. FAX: 336-725-5522. Web Site: www.pbc.edu. *Librn*, William P Thompson; *Asst Librn*, Cathie Chatmon; *Ser*, Roger Barnes; *Tech Servs*, Bernice Dougherty; Staff 2 (MLS 2)
Founded 1947. Enrl 300; Fac 23; Highest Degree: Master
Library Holdings: Bk Vols 47,572; Bk Titles 38,998; Per Subs 241
Subject Interests: Education, History, Music, Relig studies

R J REYNOLDS TOBACCO CO
S BUSINESS INFORMATION CENTER, 401 N Main St, 27102. (Mail add: PO Box 2959, 27102), SAN 355-3086. Tel: 336-741-7416. FAX: 336-741-7546. E-Mail: scisma@rjrt.com. *Mgr*, Anita Scism
Founded 1960
Special Collections: History of Tobacco Products, 1900 to date with Emphasis on Reynolds

C SALEM COLLEGE, Dale H Gramley Library, PO Box 10548, 27108-0548. SAN 313-0576. Tel: 336-721-2649. Interlibrary Loan Service Tel: 336-917-5420. FAX: 336-917-5339. Web Site: www.salem.edu. *Dir*, Rose Simon; E-Mail: simon@salem.edu; *Bibliog Instr, ILL, Ref*, Susan Taylor; *Cat, Tech Servs*, Peter Austin; *Circ*, Donna Milton
Founded 1772. Enrl 1,019; Fac 60; Highest Degree: Master
Library Holdings: Bk Vols 126,000; Per Subs 5,500
Subject Interests: Literature, Women's hist
Special Collections: Moravian Church Coll; Salem Academy & College Coll
Publications: Gramley Gram
Partic in NC-PALS; SE Libr Network
Friends of the Library Group

SR THE MORAVIAN CHURCH IN AMERICA, SOUTHERN PROVINCE, Archives & Research Library, 4 E Bank St, 27101-5307. SAN 326-341X. Tel: 336-722-1742. FAX: 336-724-7201. *Archivist*, C Daniel Crews; Staff 2 (MLS 2)
Founded 1760
Library Holdings: Bk Vols 3,000; Bk Titles 2,500
Publications: Annotations (printed newsletter); Moravian Archives News (news/sheet)
Restriction: Non-circulating to the public
Friends of the Library Group

S WACHOVIA BANK OF NORTH CAROLINA LIBRARY,* Wachovia Ctr, 100 N Main St, 27101. SAN 313-0584. Tel: 336-770-5000. FAX: 336-732-2145. *Librn*, Catherine Cannon
Library Holdings: Bk Vols 875; Per Subs 38

C WAKE FOREST UNIVERSITY, Z Smith Reynolds Library, Reynolda Sta, PO Box 7777, 27109-7777. SAN 355-3116. Tel: 336-758-5476. Interlibrary Loan Service Tel: 336-758-5475. Circulation Tel: 336-758-4931. Reference Tel: 336-758-5475. FAX: 336-758-3694, 336-758-8831. Web Site: www.wfu.edu/library. *Dir*, Rhoda K Channing; E-Mail: channing@wfu.edu; *Assoc Dir*, Deborah N Lambert; Tel: 336-758-4146, Fax: 336-758-3694, E-Mail: lamberdn@wfu.edu; *Circ*, Isabel Zuber; Tel: 336-758-6140, Fax: 336-758-5605, E-Mail: zuberie@wfu.edu; *Head Tech Servs*, Wanda Brown; Tel: 336-758-5094, Fax: 336-758-4652, E-Mail: brown@wfu.edu; *Rare Bks*, Sharon Snow; Tel: 336-758-5755, E-Mail: snowse@wfu.edu; *ILL*, Cristina Yu; Tel: 336-758-5675, Fax: 336-758-8831, E-Mail: yu@wfu.edu; *Govt Doc*, Mary C Horton; Tel: 336-758-5829, E-Mail: hortonm@wfu.edu; *Head Ref*, Elen Knott; Tel: 336-758-5473, E-Mail: knottmr@wfu.edu; *Coll Develop*, Jill Carraway; Tel: 336-758-5095, E-Mail: jill@wfu.edu; *Info Tech*, Susan Smith; Tel: 336-758-5828, E-Mail: smithss@wfu.edu; *Archivist*, John Woodard; Tel: 336-758-5089, E-Mail: woodarjr@wfu.edu; Staff 54 (MLS 21, Non-MLS 33)
Founded 1879. Enrl 4,285; Fac 414; Highest Degree: Doctorate
Jul 1999-Jun 2000 Income (Main Library Only) $5,712,131. Mats Exp $3,702,519, Books $670,886, Per/Ser (Incl. Access Fees) $1,472,051, Presv $56,484, Other Print Mats $5,579, Electronic Ref Mat (Incl. Access Fees) $366,149. Sal $2,069,612 (Prof $981,080)
Library Holdings: Bk Vols 1,309,014; Bk Titles 822,291; Per Subs 7,457
Special Collections: Anglo-Irish Literature; Dolman Press Archives; Gertrude Stein Coll; Giuseppe De Santis Film Archives; Harold Hayes Manuscripts; History Books & Printing; Holocaust Coll; Joseph E Smith

Music Coll; Mark Twain Coll; North Carolina Baptist History; Ronald Watkins Library & Personal Papers; Selected English & American Authors of the 20th Century; W J Cash Manuscripts; Wayne Dates Manuscripts
Database Vendor: Dialog, Ebsco - EbscoHost, GaleNet, IAC - Info Trac, Lexis-Nexis, OCLC - First Search, OVID Technologies, ProQuest, Silverplatter Information Inc., Wilson - Wilson Web
Publications: Library Gazette (in house) (Newsletter)
Partic in Association Of Southeastern Research Libraries (ASERL); Solinet
Departmental Libraries:

M COY C CARPENTER SCHOOL OF MEDICINE LIBRARY, Wake Forest University/School of Medicine, Medical Center Blvd, 27157-1069. SAN 355-3205. Tel: 336-716-4691. Circulation Tel: 336-716-4414. Reference Tel: 336-713-7100. FAX: 336-716-2186. Web Site: www.wfubmc.edu/library. *Dir*, Parks Welch; E-Mail: pwelch@wfubmc.edu; *Coll Develop*, Bonnie Poston; *Publ Servs*, David Stewart; *Tech Servs*, Molly Barnett; *Outreach Serv*, Marilyn Summers; Staff 34 (MLS 10, Non-MLS 24)
Founded 1941. Enrl 470; Highest Degree: Doctorate
Jul 1999-Jun 2000 Income $2,896,361, Locally Generated Income $237,251, Parent Institution $2,659,110. Mats Exp $2,896,361, Books $78,508, Per/Ser (Incl. Access Fees) $1,109,011, Presv $31,099. (Prof $1,013,468)
Library Holdings: Bk Vols 144,911; Per Subs 1,727
Subject Interests: Life sci, Medicine
Special Collections: Arts in Medicine; History of Medicine & Neurology (Rare Book Coll); Samuel Johnson Coll
Database Vendor: Dialog, Ebsco - EbscoHost, OCLC - First Search, OVID Technologies
Partic in OCLC Online Computer Library Center, Inc

L PROFESSIONAL CENTER LIBRARY, Worrell Professional Ctr. (Mail add: PO Box 7206, 27109-7206), SAN 355-3140. Tel: 336-758-5438. Reference Tel: 336-758-4520. FAX: 336-758-6077. Web Site: www.law.wfu.edu/library. *Dir*, Marian F Parker; *Tech Servs*, Mary Louise Corbett; *Publ Servs*, Maureen Eggert; Tel: 336-758-5072; *Cat, Ser*, Alan Keely; Staff 7 (MLS 7)
Founded 1894. Enrl 1,149; Fac 72; Highest Degree: Doctorate
Jul 1999-Jun 2000 Mats Exp $2,103,975, Books $33,227, Per/Ser (Incl. Access Fees) $937,148, Micro $95,520
Library Holdings: Bk Vols 196,561; Bk Titles 66,384
Subject Interests: Law, Mgt
Publications: Professional Center Library Times (newsletter); Users Guide
Partic in OCLC Online Computer Library Center, Inc

S WINSTON-SALEM JOURNAL LIBRARY, 418 N Marshall St, 27101. (Mail add: PO Box 3159, 27102-3159), SAN 313-0568. Tel: 336-727-7275. Interlibrary Loan Service Tel: 336-727-7276. FAX: 336-727-4071. E-Mail: library@w-s-journal.com. Web Site: www.journalnow.com. *Mgr*, Ginny Hauswald; E-Mail: vhauswald@w-s-journal.com
Founded 1947
Library Holdings: Bk Titles 1,500; Per Subs 96
Special Collections: Digital Image & Photo Negative Archives

C WINSTON-SALEM STATE UNIVERSITY, C G O'Kelly Library, 601 Martin Luther King Dr, Box CB 19543, 27110. SAN 313-0592. Tel: 336-750-2440. FAX: 336-750-2459. Web Site: www.wssu.edu/library.htm. *Dir*, Mae L Rodney; E-Mail: rodneyml@wssumits.wssu.edu; *Publ Servs*, Lizzie Alston-Reeder; *Ref*, Vicki S Miller; *Automation Syst Coordr, Ref*, Deanna Thomas; *Tech Servs*, Sandra Harris; *Archivist*, Carter Cue; *Cat*, Charles Tomlinson
Founded 1920
Jul 1998-Jun 1999 Income $1,309,337. Mats Exp $269,055, Books $117,591, Per/Ser (Incl. Access Fees) $115,531, Presv $1,000, Manuscripts & Archives $1,500. Sal $755,765 (Prof $177,137)
Library Holdings: Bk Vols 197,000; Per Subs 1,697
Special Collections: Black Studies (Curriculum Materials Center)
Publications: WSSU Friends of the Library (newsletter)
Partic in OCLC Online Computer Library Center, Inc
Friends of the Library Group

L WOMBLE, CARLYLE, SANDRIDGE & RICE, Law Library,* PO Drawer 84, 27102. SAN 372-2333. Tel: 336-721-3794. FAX: 336-721-3660. *Librn*, Don Adamick; E-Mail: dadamick@wcsr.com
Library Holdings: Bk Vols 20,000; Per Subs 85

WINTON

P ALBEMARLE REGIONAL LIBRARY, (ARL), 303 W Tryon St, PO Box 68, 27986-0068. SAN 313-0606. Tel: 252-358-7832. FAX: 252-358-7868. Web Site: www.albemarle-regional.lib.nc.us. *Dir*, Gary D Hoyle; E-Mail: ghoyle@ncsl.dcr.state.nc.us; Staff 22 (MLS 1, Non-MLS 21)
Founded 1948. Pop 73,735; Circ 144,756
Jul 1999-Jun 2000 Income $1,139,605, State $427,630, City $106,310, Federal $150,000, County $274,179, Locally Generated Income $159,404, Other $22,082. Mats Exp $307,182, Books $98,244, Per/Ser (Incl. Access Fees) $7,680, AV Equip $192,443, Electronic Ref Mat (Incl. Access Fees) $8,815. Sal $422,654 (Prof $54,324)
Library Holdings: Bk Vols 208,712; Bk Titles 32,194; Per Subs 532; High Interest/Low Vocabulary Bk Vols 49; Bks on Deafness & Sign Lang 24
Subject Interests: Genealogy, Local history
Automation Activity & Vendor Info: (Circulation) Gaylord; (OPAC) Gaylord
Database Vendor: OCLC - First Search
Member Libraries: Ahoskie Public Library; Elizabeth Sewell Parker Memorial Library; Gates County Library; Hertford County Library; Lawrence Memorial Library; Northampton Memorial Library; Sallie Harrell Jenkins Public Library
Partic in NC State Libr Info Network; OCLC Online Computer Library Center, Inc
Special Services for the Blind - Bks on tape

P HERTFORD COUNTY LIBRARY,* PO Box 68, 27986-0068. SAN 313-0614. Tel: 252-358-7855. FAX: 252-358-0368. *Librn*, Natalie Welker
Subject Interests: Genealogy, Local history
Mem of Albemarle Regional Library
Statistics included with regional library. See Winton entry

WRIGHTSVILLE BEACH

S LA QUE CENTER FOR CORROSION TECHNOLOGY INC LIBRARY,* PO Box 656, 28480. SAN 374-9347. Tel: 910-256-2271. FAX: 910-256-9816. E-Mail: info@laque.com.
Library Holdings: Bk Vols 5,000; Per Subs 1,000
Special Collections: Conference Proceedings

YADKINVILLE

P YADKIN COUNTY PUBLIC LIBRARY, PO Box 607, 27055. SAN 313-0622. Tel: 336-679-8792. FAX: 336-679-4625. *Librn*, Malinda S Sells; *Asst Librn*, Nancy W Williams
Founded 1942. Pop 32,000; Circ 58,000
Library Holdings: Bk Vols 58,000; Bk Titles 57,000; Per Subs 45
Special Collections: Local History
Mem of Northwest Regional Library System; Northwestern Regional Library

YANCEYVILLE

P GUNN MEMORIAL PUBLIC LIBRARY, 161 Main St E, 27379. SAN 313-0630. Tel: 336-694-6241. FAX: 336-694-9846. *Chief Librn*, Kathleen Gemske Upchurch; Staff 8 (MLS 1, Non-MLS 7)
Founded 1937. Circ 60,000
Library Holdings: Bk Vols 37,000
Subject Interests: Genealogy, Local history
Special Collections: Collectibles; Large Print Books
Mem of Hyconeechee Regional Library
Friends of the Library Group

NORTH DAKOTA

Date of Statistics: 1999
Population, 1998 Census: 638,800
Population Served by Public Libraries: 565,677
Unserved: 73,123
Total Volumes in Public Libraries: 2,126,285
Volumes Per Capita: 3.18
Total Public Library Circulation: 3,932,535
Circulation Per Capita: 6.95
Total Public Library Income (including Grants-in-Aid): $7,796,026
Source of Income: Mainly public funds
Expenditure Per Capita: $13.78
Number of County or Multi-county Libraries: 22 Counties Served: 30; Counties Unserved: 22
Number of Bookmobiles in State: 13
Grants-in-Aid for Public Libraries:
State Aid: $532,914

BEACH

P GOLDEN VALLEY COUNTY LIBRARY,* 54 Central Ave, PO Box 579, 58621. SAN 313-0665. Tel: 701-872-4627. *Librn*, Joanne Tescher
Founded 1910
Library Holdings: Bk Titles 14,000; Per Subs 35
Open Tues & Fri 1-5, Wed 10-12 & 1-5, Thurs 6-8 & Sat 11-2

BELCOURT

P TURTLE MOUNTAIN COMMUNITY COLLEGE LIBRARY,* PO Box 340, 58316-0340. SAN 313-0673. Tel: 701-477-7804. FAX: 701-477-7805. Web Site: www.turtle-mountain.cc.nd.us/Student-Affairs/lib/wksp.htm. *Librn*, Thomas David Eggers; E-Mail: eggerst@hotmail.com; Staff 2 (MLS 1, Non-MLS 1)
Founded 1977. Pop 10,000; Enrl 450
Library Holdings: Bk Vols 20,000; Per Subs 135
Subject Interests: Native Am
Special Collections: Indian Coll, bks
Database Vendor: Ebsco - EbscoHost, IAC - Info Trac

BISMARCK

P BISMARCK PUBLIC LIBRARY, 515 N Fifth St, 58503-4081. SAN 313-0789. Tel: 701-222-6410. Interlibrary Loan Service Tel: 701-222-6406. TDD: 701-221-6848. FAX: 701-221-6854. Web Site: www.infolynx.org. *Dir*, Thomas T Jones; Tel: 701-222-6403, E-Mail: t.jones@mail.infolynx.org; *Assoc Dir*, Mary Jane Schmaltz; Tel: 701-222-6404, E-Mail: mj.schmaltz@mail.infolynx.org; *Librn*, Kathy Waldera; Tel: 701-222-6416, E-Mail: w.waldera@mail.infolynx.org; *Bkmobile Coordr*, Donna Maston; Tel: 701-222-6414, E-Mail: d.maston@mail.infolynx.org; *Tech Servs*, Jennifer B Jones; Tel: 701-222-6407, E-Mail: j.jones@mail.infolynx.org; *Circ*, Betsy Porter; E-Mail: b.porter@mail.infolynx.org; *ILL*, Greta Knutson; E-Mail: g.knutson@mail.infolynx.org. Subject Specialists: *Reference*, Kathy Waldera; *Reference*, Mary Jane Schmaltz; Staff 11 (MLS 5, Non-MLS 6)
Founded 1917. Pop 66,000; Circ 599,000
Jan 2001-Dec 2001 Income $1,277,695, State $46,000, City $1,130,695, County $101,000. Mats Exp $229,400, Books $170,000, Per/Ser (Incl. Access Fees) $28,000, Presv $500, Micro $4,500, AV Equip $12,400, Electronic Ref Mat (Incl. Access Fees) $14,000. Sal $711,145
Library Holdings: Bk Titles 173,410; Per Subs 605
Subject Interests: Northern Mo River Hist
Automation Activity & Vendor Info: (Cataloging) epixtech, inc.; (Circulation) epixtech, inc.; (OPAC) epixtech, inc.
Database Vendor: GaleNet
Partic in Cent Dakota Coop Librs; MINITEX Library Information Network; OCLC Online Computer Library Center, Inc
Special Services for the Deaf - TDD
Friends of the Library Group
Bookmobiles: 1

J BISMARCK STATE COLLEGE LIBRARY, 1500 Edwards Ave, 58501-1299. (Mail add: PO Box 5587, 58506-5587), SAN 313-069X. Tel: 701-224-5450. Interlibrary Loan Service Tel: 701-224-5503. FAX: 701-224-5551. Web Site: www.bsc.nodak.edu. *Dir Libr Serv*, Marcella Schmaltz; Tel: 701-224-5451, E-Mail: schmaltz@gwmail.nodak.edu; *Cat*, Marlene Anderson; Tel: 701-224-5578, E-Mail: marander@gwmail.nodak.edu; *Circ*, Laura Kalvoda; Tel: 701-224-5483, E-Mail: lakalvoda@gwmail.nodak.edu; *Selection of Gen Ref Mat*, Traci Juhala; Tel: 701-224-5738, E-Mail: tjuhala@gwmail.nodak.edu; *Ser*, Carolyn Twingley; Tel: 701-224-5503, E-Mail: twingley@gwmail.nodak.edu; Staff 5 (MLS 3, Non-MLS 2)
Founded 1955. Enrl 2,700; Fac 102; Highest Degree: Associate
Jul 1999-Jun 2000 Mats Exp $106,024, Books $35,606, Per/Ser (Incl. Access Fees) $18,883, Presv $9,469, Micro $6,674, Other Print Mats $8,987, Electronic Ref Mat (Incl. Access Fees) $26,405. (Prof $149,012)
Library Holdings: Bk Vols 66,984; Bk Titles 53,898; Per Subs 415
Subject Interests: NDak hist
Partic in Online Dakota Info Network

S BISMARCK TRIBUNE LIBRARY,* 707 E Front Ave. (Mail add: PO Box 1498, 58502), SAN 329-0859. Tel: 701-223-2500. Web Site: www.ndmline.com. *Librn*, Barbara Herzberg-Bender
Founded 1930

R FIRST PRESBYTERIAN CHURCH LIBRARY,* 214 E Thayer, 58501. SAN 313-0703. Tel: 701-223-6091. FAX: 701-255-7344. *In Charge*, Kathy Henricksen
Library Holdings: Bk Vols 680

G NORTH DAKOTA DEPARTMENT OF HEALTH, Division of Emergency Health Services, 600 E Boulevard Ave, 58505-0200. SAN 324-5462. Tel: 701-328-2368. FAX: 701-328-1412. *In Charge*, Lynette Pitzer
Subject Interests: Adolescent develop, Cancer, Drug abuse, Nutrition, Preventive health, Preventive wellness, Women's health
Publications: Health Films Catalog

P NORTH DAKOTA STATE LIBRARY, 604 East Blvd Ave, Dept 250, 58505-0800. SAN 313-0746. Tel: 701-328-2492. Toll Free Tel: 800-472-2104. FAX: 701-328-2040. Web Site: www.ndsl.lib.state.nd.us. *Actg Librn*, Joe Linnertz; *Asst Librn*, Cynthia Larson; *Asst Librn*, Doris Ott; *Circ*, Betty Day; *ILL*, Kristine Shrauger; *Ref*, Stella Cone; Staff 29 (MLS 10, Non-MLS 19)
Founded 1907. Pop 638,800; Circ 55,000
Jul 1998-Jun 1999 Income $2,129,878, State $1,463,346, Federal $616,532, Locally Generated Income $50,000. Mats Exp $209,000, Books $50,000, Per/Ser (Incl. Access Fees) $59,000, Electronic Ref Mat (Incl. Access Fees) $100,000. Sal $842,124 (Prof $505,274)
Library Holdings: Bk Titles 197,953; Per Subs 137
Special Collections: North Dakota Coll (last copy in state); State Documents, bks & micro
Database Vendor: OCLC - First Search
Publications: Discovery; Library Statistics; ND Flickertale Newsletter
Partic in Minn Interlibr Telecommunication Exchange
Special Services for the Blind - Radio reading service; Talking Books

GL NORTH DAKOTA SUPREME COURT, Law Library, Judicial Wing, 2nd Flr, 600 E Boulevard Ave, Dept 182, 58505-0540. SAN 313-0762. Tel: 701-328-2227, 701-328-2229, 701-328-4496, 701-328-4594. FAX: 701-328-3609. *Librn*, Ted Smith
Founded 1889
Library Holdings: Bk Vols 60,000; Per Subs 50
Special Collections: North Dakota Legal Materials
Automation Activity & Vendor Info: (ILL) PALS; (OPAC) PALS
Partic in Mintex Libr Info Network; Westlaw

M Q&R MEDCENTER ONE, Health Sciences Library, 622 Avenue A East, 58501. SAN 313-0770. Tel: 701-323-5390. FAX: 701-323-6967. Web Site: www.medcenterone.com. *Dir*, Leeila Bina; E-Mail: lbina@mohs.org; *Librn*, Betty Lahn; Tel: 701-323-5391, E-Mail: blahn@mohs.org; *ILL, Librn*, Janet Schell; Tel: 701-323-5392; Staff 3 (MLS 2, Non-MLS 1)
Founded 1927. Enrl 80; Fac 13
Library Holdings: Bk Vols 24,345; Bk Titles 6,849; Per Subs 334
Subject Interests: Clinical medicine, Nursing
Database Vendor: GaleNet, IAC - Info Trac, ProQuest
Restriction: Circulation limited, In-house use for visitors, Private library
Function: Archival collection, Document delivery services, For research purposes, ILL available, Photocopies available, Reference services available, Some telephone reference
Partic in Midwest Health Sci Libr Network; Minn Interlibr Telecommunication Exchange; Nat Libr of Med

S STATE HISTORICAL SOCIETY OF NORTH DAKOTA, (SA&HRL), State Archives & Historical Research Library, Heritage Ctr, Capitol Grounds, 612 E Boulevard Ave, 58505. SAN 313-072X. Tel: 701-328-2668. FAX: 701-328-2650. Web Site: www.state.nd.us/hist. *Chief Librn*, Dolores Vyzralek; Tel: 701-328-3571, E-Mail: dvyzrale@state.nd.us; *Archivist*, Gerald Newborg; Tel: 701-328-2090, E-Mail: jnewborg@state.nd.us; *Archivist*, Lotte Bailey; Tel: 701-328-3570, E-Mail: lbailey@state.nd.us; *Archivist*, Todd Strand; Tel: 701-328-3563, E-Mail: thstrand@state.nd.us; *Cat*, Loren Jechort; Tel: 701-328-2644, E-Mail: ljechort@state.nd.us; Staff 13 (MLS 10, Non-MLS 3)
Founded 1895
Library Holdings: Bk Vols 102,104; Per Subs 594
Subject Interests: Archaeology, Hist of Northern Great Plains, NDak hist, Preservation
Database Vendor: OCLC - First Search
Publications: North Dakota History
Mem of Minitex Libr Info Network
Partic in Minn Interlibr Telecommunication Exchange; OCLC Online Computer Library Center, Inc

C UNIVERSITY OF MARY, Welder Library, 7500 University Dr, 58504-9652. SAN 313-0711. Tel: 701-255-7500, Ext 402. FAX: 701-255-7690. Web Site: www.infolynx.org. *Dir*, Cheryl M Bailey; *AV, Ref*, Roann Masterson
Founded 1959. Enrl 2,350; Highest Degree: Master
Library Holdings: Per Subs 525
Subject Interests: Bus, Education, Mgt, Nursing, Social work, Theology
Partic in Minn Interlibr Telecommunication Exchange; OCLC Online Computer Library Center, Inc

BOTTINEAU

P BOTTINEAU COUNTY PUBLIC LIBRARY, 314 W Fifth St, 58318-9600. SAN 375-4537. Tel: 701-228-2967. FAX: 701-228-2967. *Dir*, Pat Frykman; E-Mail: pfrykman@sendit.nodak.edu; *Bkmobile Coordr*, Penny Bernstein; Staff 3 (MLS 1, Non-MLS 2)
Founded 1922
Library Holdings: Per Subs 30
Automation Activity & Vendor Info: (Circulation) Sagebrush Corporation; (Serials) Sagebrush Corporation
Partic in Online Dakota Info Network
Bookmobiles: 1

J MINOT STATE UNIVERSITY-BOTTINEAU BRANCH, Fossum Foundation Library, 105 Simrall Blvd, 58318. SAN 313-0797. Tel: 701-228-5454. FAX: 701-228-5438. Web Site: www.misu-b.nodak.edu. *Librn*, Janice M Wysocki
Founded 1907. Enrl 392; Fac 26; Highest Degree: Associate
Jul 1999-Jun 2000 Income State $109,000. Mats Exp $37,223, Books $13,438, Per/Ser (Incl. Access Fees) $9,018, AV Equip $3,958, Electronic Ref Mat (Incl. Access Fees) $10,809. Sal $42,558 (Prof $29,000)
Library Holdings: Bk Vols 28,000; Bk Titles 25,255; Per Subs 220
Subject Interests: Forestry, Horticulture, Natural science, Parks, Recreation
Special Collections: M Truman Fossum Papers
Partic in Minn Interlibr Telecommunication Exchange; NDak Network for Knowledge

CARRINGTON

P CARRINGTON CITY LIBRARY,* 55 Ninth Ave S, 58421-1198. SAN 313-0819. Tel: 701-652-3921. *Librn*, Blanche Stangeland
Founded 1916. Circ 7,695
Library Holdings: Bk Vols 10,000; Per Subs 36
Partic in NDak Network for Knowledge
Friends of the Library Group

CASSELTON

P CASSELTON PUBLIC LIBRARY,* PO Box 1090, 58012-1090. SAN 313-0827. Tel: 701-347-4861. *Librn*, Bernice Mattson; *Asst Librn*, Harriet Gruel
Pop 1,650; Circ 22,680
Library Holdings: Bk Vols 22,000

CAVALIER

P CAVALIER PUBLIC LIBRARY,* 106A W Second Ave S, 58220. SAN 313-0835. Tel: 701-265-4746. FAX: 701-265-4786. E-Mail: cavlibry@polarcomm.com. *Librn*, Jan Morrison
Circ 13,170
Library Holdings: Bk Vols 8,000; Per Subs 35
Special Collections: Icelandic

COOPERSTOWN

P GRIGGS COUNTY LIBRARY, 902 Burrell Ave, 58425. (Mail add: PO Box 546, 58425), Tel: 701-797-2214. E-Mail: gcplibrary@mlgc.com. *Head Librn*, Bonnie Krenz; *Bkmobile Coordr*, Cindy Flatt
Founded 1944. Pop 3,303; Circ 34,887
Library Holdings: Bk Titles 26,883; Per Subs 52
Special Collections: Historical Coll
Automation Activity & Vendor Info: (Cataloging) Sagebrush Corporation; (Circulation) Sagebrush Corporation
Bookmobiles: 1

CROSBY

P DIVIDE COUNTY PUBLIC LIBRARY,* 204 First St NE, 58730. SAN 313-0851. Tel: 701-965-6305. E-Mail: dclib@crosby.ndak.net. *Dir*, Dorene Wenstad
Founded 1912. Pop 4,000
1998-1999 Income $38,154, State $8,706, County $28,207, Other $1,241. Mats Exp $38,753, Books $5,319. Sal $29,765
Library Holdings: Bk Vols 38,000; Per Subs 44
Subject Interests: Local history, State hist
Publications: Library newsletter (3 times a year)
Partic in NDak Network for Knowledge

DEVILS LAKE

P CARNEGIE PUBLIC LIBRARY, (DLP), Devils Lake Public Library, 623 Fourth Ave, 58301-2421. SAN 313-086X. Tel: 701-662-2220. Web Site: www.devilslakend.com. *Dir*, Jim Chattin; E-Mail: chattin@sendit.nodak.edu; Staff 1 (Non-MLS 1)
Founded 1908. Pop 11,900
Jan 1999-Dec 1999 Income $127,388, State $8,143, City $48,821, County $20,709, Locally Generated Income $12,303, Other $37,412. Mats Exp $10,963, Books $8,728, Per/Ser (Incl. Access Fees) $2,235. Sal $49,721 (Prof $18,926)
Library Holdings: Bk Vols 28,654; Per Subs 70
Subject Interests: History, Needlework, Recipes
Special Collections: Local History Coll; North Dakota Coll
Automation Activity & Vendor Info: (Cataloging) Sagebrush Corporation; (Circulation) Sagebrush Corporation

C LAKE REGION STATE COLLEGE, (LRS), Paul Hoghaug Library, 1801 N College Dr, 58301. SAN 313-0878. Tel: 701-662-1533. FAX: 701-662-1570. *Librn*, S L Evensen; E-Mail: evensens@lrsc.nodak.edu; Staff 2 (MLS 1, Non-MLS 1)
Founded 1966. Enrl 800
Library Holdings: Bk Vols 32,000; Per Subs 360
Subject Interests: Law, Paralegal
Special Collections: Irish History & Culture

S SCHOOL FOR THE DEAF LIBRARY, 1401 College Dr, 58301. SAN 313-0886. Tel: 701-662-9033. FAX: 701-662-9009. *Librn*, Celeste Ertelt; E-Mail: certelt@sendit.nodak.edu
Library Holdings: Bk Vols 10,000; Per Subs 50
Open Mon-Fri 8-5

DICKINSON

P DICKINSON PUBLIC LIBRARY,* 139 Third St W, 58601. SAN 313-0894. Tel: 701-225-8100. FAX: 701-227-3005. *Dir*, Cheryl Tollefson; *Tech Servs*, Mary Lovell; *Coll Develop*, Renee Paasch
Founded 1908. Pop 28,000; Circ 130,000
Library Holdings: Bk Titles 55,000; Per Subs 150
Special Collections: Dickinson Press, 1883-present
Publications: Library Skills for Adult Education
Partic in Minn Interlibr Telecommunication Exchange; NDak Network for Knowledge; OCLC Online Computer Library Center, Inc; Online Dakota Info Network
Friends of the Library Group

C DICKINSON STATE UNIVERSITY, Stoxen Library, 291 Campus Dr, 58601. SAN 313-0908. Tel: 701-483-2135. FAX: 701-483-2006. Web Site: www.dickinsonstate.com/library.asp. *Dir*, Bernnett Reinke; E-Mail: bernnett_reinke@dsu.nodak.edu; *Acq, Coll Develop, Govt Doc*, Jim Martz; E-Mail: jim_martz@dsu.nodak.edu; *Automation Syst Coordr, Cat, ILL*, Lillian Crook; E-Mail: lillian_crook@dsu.nodak.edu; *Circ, Ref*, Eileen Kopren; E-Mail: eileen_kopren@dsu.nodak.edu; Staff 4 (MLS 4)
Founded 1918. Enrl 2,012; Fac 76; Highest Degree: Bachelor
Jul 2000-Jun 2001 Income State $438,697. Mats Exp $166,010, Books $60,000, Per/Ser (Incl. Access Fees) $73,810, Micro $4,200, AV Equip $16,000, Electronic Ref Mat (Incl. Access Fees) $12,000. Sal $230,969 (Prof $180,969)
Library Holdings: Bk Vols 94,000; Bk Titles 80,000; Per Subs 630
Subject Interests: Bus, Education
Special Collections: Teddy Roosevelt Coll
Automation Activity & Vendor Info: (Acquisitions) PALS; (Cataloging) PALS; (Circulation) PALS; (ILL) PALS; (OPAC) PALS; (Serials) PALS
Partic in MINITEX Library Information Network; OCLC Online Computer Library Center, Inc; ODIN

M SAINT JOSEPH HOSPITAL MEDICAL LIBRARY, 30 W Seventh St, 58601. SAN 326-1018. Tel: 701-264-4000, Ext 4515. FAX: 701-264-4801. *In Charge*, Sheryl Binstock
Library Holdings: Bk Titles 1,500; Per Subs 75

EDGELEY

P SOUTH CENTRAL AREA LIBRARY, 530 Main St, PO Box 218, 58433. SAN 355-323X. Tel: 701-493-2769. FAX: 701-493-2959. E-Mail: eplscal@daktel.com. *Dir*, Lynda Dunn
Founded 1958. Pop 10,075; Circ 88,000
Library Holdings: Bk Titles 30,000; Per Subs 25
Special Collections: North Dakota Coll
Branches: 1
EDGELEY PUBLIC Tel: 701-493-2769. FAX: 701-493-2959. E-Mail: epscal@daktel.com. *Librn*, Linda Dunn
Library Holdings: Bk Titles 8,000
Bookmobiles: 1

ELLENDALE

P ELLENDALE PUBLIC LIBRARY,* PO Box 520, 58436. SAN 313-0916. Tel: 701-349-3852. *Librn*, Lonnie Wagner
Circ 16,383
1997-1998 Income $10,350, State $950, City $6,200, Locally Generated Income $200, Other $3,000. Mats Exp $4,000, Books $3,400, Per/Ser (Incl. Access Fees) $600
Library Holdings: Bk Vols 17,000
Open Mon 6:30-8:30, Tues & Wed 1-5, Thurs 1-8:30, Sat 9-12
Friends of the Library Group

CR TRINITY BIBLE COLLEGE, Fred J Graham Library, 50 Sixth Ave S, 58436-7150. SAN 313-0924. Tel: 701-349-5407. E-Mail: tbclibrary@hotmail.com. *Librn*, Phyllis C Kuno; *Asst Librn*, Kathleen Pelletier; Tel: 701-349-5430; Staff 2 (Non-MLS 2)
Founded 1948. Enrl 350; Fac 33; Highest Degree: Bachelor
Library Holdings: Bk Vols 70,000; Bk Titles 55,000; Per Subs 295
Subject Interests: Biblical studies, Evangelism, Missions, Relig studies, Soc sci
Special Collections: College & Denomination Archives; Graham Coll (NDak Hist)
Automation Activity & Vendor Info: (Circulation) PALS
Partic in MINITEX Library Information Network; ODIN

ENDERLIN

P ENDERLIN MUNICIPAL LIBRARY,* 303 Railway, 58027. SAN 313-0932. Tel: 701-437-2953. FAX: 701-437-2104. *Librn*, Susan Dopp
Founded 1911. Pop 1,550; Circ 5,895
Library Holdings: Bk Vols 12,000
Subject Interests: Education, History, Relig studies
Open Tues-Thurs 12-5:30, Fri 12-7 & Sat 12-4
Friends of the Library Group

FARGO

S DAKOTA HEARTLAND HEALTH SYSTEM LIBRARY, 1720 S University Dr, PO Box 6014, 58108-6014. SAN 313-0940. Tel: 701-280-4187. FAX: 701-280-4640. E-Mail: dhhslib@corpcomm.net. *Librn*, Jennie illerhagen
Founded 1979
Library Holdings: Bk Titles 2,000; Per Subs 290
Database Vendor: Silverplatter Information Inc.
Partic in Regional Med Libr - Region 3; Valley Medical Network

GM DEPARTMENT OF VETERANS AFFAIRS, Medical Library, 2101 N Elm St, 58102. SAN 313-1041. Tel: 701-239-3755. FAX: 701-239-3775. *Librn*, Diane Nordeng; E-Mail: nordeng.d@fargo.va.gov; *Coll Develop*, Joyce Nicholas
Founded 1930
Library Holdings: Bk Titles 3,515; Per Subs 245
Subject Interests: Clinical medicine
Partic in Tri-College University Libraries Consortium; Valley Medical Network; Valnet

P FARGO PUBLIC LIBRARY, 102 N Third St, 58102. SAN 313-0959. Tel: 701-241-1491. FAX: 701-241-8581. E-Mail: askreference@ci.fargo.nd.us. Web Site: www.fargolibrary.org. *Publ Servs*, Beth E Postema; Tel: 701-241-8198, E-Mail: bepostema@ci.fargo.nd.us; *Tech Servs*, Elizabeth Mason; *Ref*, J Stephen Hubbard; *Ch Servs*, Maxine Hilburn; Tel: 701-241-1496, E-Mail: mihilburn@ci.fargo.nd.us; *Circ*, Lori West; *Acq*, Mary Haedt; *Bkmobile Coordr*, Nancy Giere; Tel: 701-241-1498; *Cat*, Jackie Lang; Staff 36 (MLS 4, Non-MLS 32)
Founded 1900. Pop 85,000
Jan 2000-Dec 2000 Income $1,337,064, State $47,000, City $1,235,064, Locally Generated Income $55,000. Mats Exp $250,000. Sal $751,550
Library Holdings: Bk Titles 135,000; Per Subs 310
Database Vendor: GaleNet, OCLC - First Search
Partic in OCLC Online Computer Library Center, Inc; Online Dakota Info Network
Reciprocal borrowing with Lake Agassiz Regional Libr (MN), West Fargo PL (ND)
Friends of the Library Group

S MASONIC GRAND LODGE LIBRARY,* 201 14th Ave N, 58102. SAN 313-0975. Tel: 701-235-8321. FAX: 701-235-8323. *Coll Develop, Dir*, Allen Ohrt; *Mgr*, Sandra Lee
Founded 1889
Library Holdings: Bk Vols 2,800
Subject Interests: Masonic heritage, Philos lit, Ref
Publications: North Dakota Mason (newspaper)
Masonic Museum incorporated within library

M MERITCARE HEALTH SYSTEM LIBRARY, 720 Fourth St N, PO Box MC, 58122-0212. SAN 355-3442. Tel: 701-234-5571. FAX: 701-234-5927. *Dir*, Eileen Chamberlain; E-Mail: chamberlain@meritcare.com
Founded 1955
Library Holdings: Bk Titles 3,407; Per Subs 300
Subject Interests: Allied health, Medicine, Nursing
Partic in Valley Medical Network

J NORTH DAKOTA LEARNING RESOURCE CENTER, 1510 12th Ave N, PO Box 5036-University Sta, 58105-5036. SAN 371-9243. Tel: 701-231-6036. FAX: 701-231-6052. Web Site: www.dis.dpi.state.nd.us/lrc/lrcmain.html. *Coordr*, Jolene Richardson; E-Mail: jrichard@sendit.nodak.edu; *Asst Librn*, Donna Sell; Staff 1 (MLS 1)
Founded 1990
Library Holdings: Bk Titles 3,700
Special Collections: Character Education; Special Learner; State Dept of Pub Instr Gifted Educ
Publications: Learning Resource Center Newsletter
Open Mon-Fri 8-5

C NORTH DAKOTA STATE UNIVERSITY LIBRARY,* 1301 12th Ave N, 58108. (Mail add: PO Box 5599, 58105-5599), SAN 355-3329. Tel: 701-231-8886. Interlibrary Loan Service Tel: 701-231-8885. FAX: 701-231-7138. Web Site: www.lib.ndsu.nodak.edu. *Dir*, Richard Bovard; *Assoc Dir*, Thomas A Bremer; *Tech Coordr*, Mark England; *Humanities and Soc Sci*, Frances Fisher; *Circ*, Janet Miller; *Bibliogr*, Michael M Miller; *Govt Doc*, Kathryn Thomas; *ILL*, Deborah Sayler; *Archivist*, John Bye; *Ref*, Charlene Myhre. Subject Specialists: *Agriculture*, Katherine Richardson; *Physical science*, Lura Joseph; *Social sciences and issues*, Kathy Enger; Staff 27 (MLS 17, Non-MLS 10)
Founded 1890. Enrl 9,500; Fac 462; Highest Degree: Doctorate
Jul 1997-Jun 1998 Mats Exp $1,057,470, Books $173,036, Per/Ser (Incl. Access Fees) $849,142, Micro $35,292. Sal $1,169,942
Library Holdings: Bk Titles 500,000; Per Subs 3,855
Subject Interests: Agriculture, Engineering
Special Collections: Bonanza Farming; Fred Hultstrand History in Pictures Coll; Germans from Russia Heritage Coll; N Dak Historical Manuscript, Photograph & Book Coll; North Dakota Biography Index; North Dakota Pioneer Reminiscences; Senator Milton R Young Photograph Coll; University Archives

Automation Activity & Vendor Info: (Circulation) PALS
Publications: Library Instruction Book; North Dakota Institute for Regional Studies Guide to Manuscripts & Archives; Researching the Germans from Russia; Visual Images from the Northern Praires
Partic in MINITEX Library Information Network; NDak Network for Knowledge; OCLC Online Computer Library Center, Inc; Tri-College University Libraries Consortium
Departmental Libraries:
ARCHITECTURE Tel: 701-231-8616. FAX: 701-231-7138. *In Charge*, Irene Askelson
Subject Interests: Architecture, Landscape architecture
CHEMISTRY Tel: 701-231-8293. FAX: 701-231-7138. *In Charge*, Lura Joseph
Subject Interests: Chemistry, Coatings, Polymers
PHARMACY-NURSING Tel: 701-231-7748. FAX: 701-231-7138. *In Charge*, Charlene Myhre
Subject Interests: Nursing, Pharm

S PLAINS ART MUSEUM, Goldberg Reference Library, 704 First Ave N, 58102. (Mail add: PO Box 2338, 58108-2338), SAN 323-5017. Tel: 701-232-3821. FAX: 701-293-1082. E-Mail: museum@plainsart.org. Web Site: www.plainsart.org. *Dir*, Claudia M Pratt; Tel: 701-232-3821, Ext 126, E-Mail: cpratt@plainsart.org. Subject Specialists: *Education*, Claudia M Pratt
Library Holdings: Bk Vols 1,000; Per Subs 20
Subject Interests: Art, Art educ, Regional artists
Special Collections: Exhibition Catalogs; Museum Administration
Function: Reference only
Open Mon 10-5, Tues & Thurs 10-8, Wed, Fri & Sat 10-6, Sun 12-6
Friends of the Library Group

SR PRESENTATION CENTER LIBRARY,* 1101 32nd Ave S, 58103-6092. SAN 313-1009. Tel: 701-237-4857. *Librn*, Sister Marie Philip
Library Holdings: Bk Vols 5,067
Subject Interests: Religious

TEMPLE BETH EL, Max & Anne Goldberg Library, 809 11th Ave S, 58103. SAN 313-1033. Tel: 701-232-0441. FAX: 701-297-9114. *Librn*, Maxine Hilburn
Founded 1951
Library Holdings: Bk Vols 2,050; Bk Titles 1,510
Subject Interests: Judaica

G US COURTS BRANCH LIBRARY, 655 First Ave N, Ste 310, 58102. SAN 371-6538. Tel: 701-297-7280. FAX: 701-297-7285. *Librn*, Suzanne Morrison; E-Mail: suzanne_morrison@ca8.uscourts.gov
Founded 1986
Library Holdings: Bk Titles 12,500; Per Subs 150
Subject Interests: Law

FORMAN

P FORMAN PUBLIC LIBRARY, (FPL), PO Box 382, 58032-0382. SAN 372-5359. Tel: 701-724-3673. *Librn*, Margaret Scheller; Tel: 701-724-3214
Pop 1,000
Jan 1999-Dec 1999 Income $5,142, Federal $200, County $3,200, Locally Generated Income $1,742. Mats Exp $1,899, Books $1,100, Per/Ser (Incl. Access Fees) $320, Other Print Mats $479
Library Holdings: Bk Titles 4,000; Per Subs 12
Open Mon 9:30-11:30, Wed 3-5 & Sat 9:30-11:30

FORT YATES

J SITTING BULL COLLEGE LIBRARY,* 1341 92nd St, 58538. SAN 313-1068. Tel: 701-854-3861. FAX: 701-854-3403. *Librn*, Mary Bianco; E-Mail: maryb@sbci.edu
Founded 1972. Fac 35
Library Holdings: Bk Titles 20,000; Per Subs 127
Special Collections: College Archives; Sioux Indians Coll; Standing Rock Sioux Tribal Archives

GRAFTON

P CARNEGIE REGIONAL LIBRARY,* 49 W Seventh St, 58237. SAN 355-3531. Tel: 701-352-2754. FAX: 701-352-2757. *Dir*, Gary Littlefield; *Ch Servs*, Barbara Bracken; Staff 8 (MLS 1, Non-MLS 7)
Founded 1972. Pop 22,648
Library Holdings: Bk Titles 75,000; Per Subs 58
Subject Interests: NDak hist
Publications: Newsletter
Partic in Minn Interlibr Telecommunication Exchange
Bookmobiles: 3

GRAND FORKS

M ALTRU MEDICAL LIBRARY, Medical Park, 1200 S Columbia Rd, 58206-6002. (Mail add: PO Box 6002, 58206-6002), SAN 313-1092. Tel: 701-780-5187. FAX: 701-780-5772. *Librn*, Ann Pederson; E-Mail: apederso@medpark.grand-forks.nd.us; *ILL*, Nancy Nice; Staff 3 (MLS 1, Non-MLS 2)
Founded 1958
Library Holdings: Bk Vols 2,000; Per Subs 266
Subject Interests: Consumer health, Employee wellness, Health sci
Special Collections: Hospital Archival Coll
Automation Activity & Vendor Info: (Cataloging) PALS; (ILL) PALS; (OPAC) PALS
Database Vendor: OCLC - First Search, OVID Technologies, ProQuest
Partic in MINITEX Library Information Network; Valley Medical Network

P GRAND FORKS PUBLIC CITY-COUNTY LIBRARY, 2110 Library Circle, 58206-6324. SAN 313-1084. Tel: 701-772-8116. FAX: 701-772-1379. Web Site: www.grandforksgov.com/library. *Dir*, Dennis N Page; *ILL*, C Driscoll; *Ad Servs, Ref*, Antoinelle Vonaseck; *Ad Servs, Ref*, David Haney; *Ch Servs*, Rita Midstokke; *Circ*, Kay Berg; Staff 5 (MLS 5)
Founded 1900. Pop 70,683; Circ 688,525
Jan 1999-Dec 1999 Income $946,473, State $80,000, City $705,434, County $111,039, Locally Generated Income $50,000. Mats Exp $194,200, Books $130,000, Per/Ser (Incl. Access Fees) $22,000, Micro $8,000, AV Equip $1,200, Other Print Mats $8,000, Electronic Ref Mat (Incl. Access Fees) $25,000. Sal $525,922 (Prof $392,000)
Library Holdings: Bk Vols 288,847; Bk Titles 265,389; Per Subs 300
Subject Interests: Agriculture
Special Collections: Local History (Grand Forks Coll), bks & pictures
Publications: Mail order catalog; Newsletter
Partic in MINITEX Library Information Network; OCLC Online Computer Library Center, Inc
Friends of the Library Group

UNIVERSITY OF NORTH DAKOTA

C CHESTER FRITZ LIBRARY, PO Box 9000, 58202-9000. SAN 355-3655. Tel: 701-777-2617. Interlibrary Loan Service Tel: 701-777-4631. Circulation Tel: 701-777-4644. Reference Tel: 701-777-4629. TDD: 701-777-4644. FAX: 701-777-3319. E-Mail: cflib@sage.und.nodak.edu. Web Site: www.und.nodak.edu/dept/library/. *Dir*, Wilbur Stolt; Tel: 701-777-2189, E-Mail: wilbur_stolt@mail.und.nodak.edu; *Asst Libr Dir*, Patricia O Berntsen; Tel: 701-777-4630, E-Mail: patricia_berntsen@mail.und.nodak.edu; *Acq*, Stan Johnson; *Head Tech Servs*, Shelby Harken; Tel: 701-777-4634, E-Mail: shelby_harken@mail.und.nodak.edu; *Spec Coll & Archives*, Sandra Slater; Tel: 701-777-4627, E-Mail: sandy_slater@mail.und.nodak.edu; *Govt Doc, Per*, Nancy Mulhern; *Head Ref*, Betty Gard; Tel: 701-777-4632, E-Mail: betty_gard@mail.und.nodak.edu; *Syst Coordr*, Randy Pederson; Tel: 701-777-4643, E-Mail: randy_pederson@mail.und.nodak.edu; *Access Serv*, Paulette Dvorak; Tel: 701-777-4645, E-Mail: paulette_dvorak@mail.und.nodak.edu; Staff 39 (MLS 16, Non-MLS 23)
Founded 1883. Enrl 11,031; Fac 650; Highest Degree: Doctorate
Jul 2000-Jun 2001 Income $2,563,621, State $2,396,321, Locally Generated Income $79,627, Other $88,673. Mats Exp $1,109,086, Books $139,030, Per/Ser (Incl. Access Fees) $970,056. Sal $1,191,259
Library Holdings: Bk Vols 1,258,130; Bk Titles 695,244; Per Subs 5,113
Subject Interests: Education, Western hist
Special Collections: Great Plains (Fred G Aandahl Coll); North Dakota Ethnic Heritage/Family History; North Dakota History (Orin G Libby Coll), mss; Norwegian Local History
Automation Activity & Vendor Info: (Acquisitions) PALS; (Cataloging) PALS; (Circulation) PALS; (ILL) PALS; (OPAC) PALS; (Serials) PALS
Database Vendor: Dialog, IAC - Info Trac, OCLC - First Search, ProQuest, Silverplatter Information Inc.
Publications: CFL Newsletter; Guides to Collections; Lux et Lex
Partic in MINITEX Library Information Network; OCLC Online Computer Library Center, Inc; Online Dakota Info Network
Special Services for the Deaf - TDD

S ENERGY & ENVIRONMENTAL RESEARCH CENTER, PO Box 9000, 58202. SAN 313-1114. Interlibrary Loan Service Tel: 701-777-4631. FAX: 701-777-3319. *Branch Mgr*, DeLoris Smith; Tel: 701-777-5132, Fax: 707-777-5181, E-Mail: dlsmith@undeerc.org; Staff 1 (Non-MLS 1)
Library Holdings: Bk Vols 5,342; Per Subs 92
Special Collections: Bound Volumes of Journals (350)

C GORDON ERICKSON MUSIC LIBRARY, PO Box 7125, 58202. SAN 371-3261. Tel: 701-777-2817. FAX: 701-777-3319. Web Site: www.und.nodak.edu/dept/fac/muslib.html. *Branch Mgr*, Felecia Clifton; E-Mail: felecia_clifton@mail.und.nodak.edu; Staff 1 (Non-MLS 1)
Founded 1983. Pop 7,479; Circ 12,000
Jul 2000-Jun 2001 Mats Exp $19,500. Sal $10,000
Library Holdings: Bk Vols 18,593; Bk Titles 9,559
Subject Interests: Music
Automation Activity & Vendor Info: (Cataloging) PALS; (Circulation) PALS

S GEOLOGY, PO Box 9000, 58202. SAN 371-327X. Tel: 701-777-3221. Interlibrary Loan Service Tel: 701-777-4631. FAX: 701-777-3319. *Branch Mgr*, Kathy Spencer; Tel: 701-777-2408, Fax: 701-777-4409, E-Mail:

kathy_spencer@mail.und.nodak.edu; Staff 1 (Non-MLS 1)
Library Holdings: Bk Vols 15,256; Per Subs 248
Subject Interests: Maps, Photos
Friends of the Library Group

CM HARLEY E FRENCH LIBRARY OF THE HEALTH SCIENCES, 501 N Columbia Dr, 58203. (Mail add: PO Box 9002, 58202-9002), Tel: 701-777-3993. Interlibrary Loan Service Tel: 701-777-2606. Reference Tel: 701-777-3994. FAX: 701-777-4790. E-Mail: hflref@medicine.nodak.edu. Web Site: www.med.und.nodak.edu/depts/library/. *Dir*, Lila Pedersen; E-Mail: lpederse@medicine.nodak.edu; *Asst Dir, Coll Develop*, Judith L Rieke; Tel: 701-777-4129, E-Mail: jrieke@medicine.nodak.edu; *Cat*, Michael Safratowich; Tel: 701-777-2602, E-Mail: msafrat@medicine.nodak.edu; *Ref*, Barbara Knight; Tel: 701-777-2166, E-Mail: bknight@medicine.nodak.edu; *ILL*, Allison Ranisate; E-Mail: ranisate@medicine.nodak.edu; *Automation Syst Coordr*, Theresa Norton; Tel: 701-777-2946, E-Mail: tnorton@medicine.nodak.edu; Staff 13 (MLS 7, Non-MLS 6)
Founded 1950. Highest Degree: Doctorate
Jul 1999-Jun 2000 Income $1,020,690, Federal $25,000, Locally Generated Income $51,690, Parent Institution $944,000. Mats Exp $423,072, Books $40,600, Per/Ser (Incl. Access Fees) $323,400, Presv $15,821, Other Print Mats $21,213, Electronic Ref Mat (Incl. Access Fees) $22,038. Sal $477,300
Library Holdings: Bk Vols 41,000; Bk Titles 32,436; Per Subs 818
Subject Interests: Consumer health, Medicine, Nursing, Physical therapy
Special Collections: History of Medicine (Dr French Coll); History of Pathology (Dr Barger Coll)
Automation Activity & Vendor Info: (Acquisitions) PALS; (Cataloging) PALS; (Circulation) PALS; (Course Reserve) PALS; (ILL) PALS; (Media Booking) PALS; (OPAC) PALS; (Serials) PALS
Database Vendor: IAC - Info Trac, OCLC - First Search, ProQuest, Silverplatter Information Inc.
Publications: French Connections; newsletter
Function: ILL available
Partic in MINITEX Library Information Network; Nat Network of Libraries of Med - Region 3; OCLC Online Computer Library Center, Inc

CL THORMODSGARD LAW LIBRARY, PO Box 9004, 58202. SAN 355-371X. Tel: 701-777-2204. Interlibrary Loan Service Tel: 701-777-3538. FAX: 701-777-2217. Web Site: www.law.und.nodak.edu. *Dir*, Gary D Gott; E-Mail: gary.gott@thor.law.und.nodak.edu; *Asst Dir, Publ Servs*, Rhonda Schwartz; *Ser*, Ginny Millette; *Ser*, Karen Pupino; *Circ*, Joyce Spivey; Staff 5 (MLS 5)
Founded 1899. Enrl 270; Highest Degree: Doctorate
Jul 1997-Jun 1998 Mats Exp $438,000. Sal $267,000
Library Holdings: Bk Titles 32,609; Per Subs 2,736
Partic in Dialog Corporation; OCLC Online Computer Library Center, Inc; RLIN; Westlaw

GRAND FORKS AFB

UNITED STATES AIR FORCE

A GRAND FORKS AIR FORCE BASE LIBRARY FL4659, 319 SVS/SVRL, 511 Holzapple St Bldg 201, 58205-6309. SAN 355-3744. Tel: 701-747-3046. FAX: 701-747-4584. *Librn*, Kristen Rall; E-Mail: kristen.rall@granforks.af.mil
Oct 1997-Sep 1998 Income $138,000. Mats Exp $67,464, Books $45,000, Per/Ser (Incl. Access Fees) $20,000, AV Equip $464
Library Holdings: Bk Vols 45,000; Bk Titles 25,000; Per Subs 204
Special Collections: Air University; Air War College; Quality Improvement
Partic in Fedlink; OCLC Online Computer Library Center, Inc; Online Dakota Info Network; SENDIT

HANKINSON

P HANKINSON PUBLIC LIBRARY, City Hall, PO Box 244, 58041-0244. SAN 313-1130. Tel: 701-242-7929. E-Mail: hpl@rrt.net. *Librn*, Andrea Stein
Founded 1905. Pop 1,159; Circ 9,516
Library Holdings: Bk Vols 7,807; Per Subs 11

HARVEY

P HARVEY PUBLIC LIBRARY, 119 E Tenth St, 58341. SAN 313-1149. Tel: 701-324-2156. FAX: 701-324-2156. *Librn*, Marlene Ripplinger; *Asst Librn*, Stephina Gisi
Founded 1952. Pop 2,700; Circ 44,000
Library Holdings: Bk Titles 22,000; Per Subs 100
Subject Interests: Large print
Special Collections: Regional Coll, bks
Automation Activity & Vendor Info: (Cataloging) Sagebrush Corporation; (Circulation) Sagebrush Corporation

HEBRON

P HEBRON PUBLIC LIBRARY,* 606 Lincoln Ave, PO Box R, 58638. SAN 375-5967. Tel: 701-878-4110. *Adminr*, Georgiann Wehri; Tel: 701-878-4012, E-Mail: wehri@sendit.nodak.edu; *Asst Librn, Cat*, Adeline Tibor; Tel: 701-878-4000
Founded 1938. Pop 1,000; Circ 2,456
Jan 1999-Dec 2000 Income $5,384, State $593, City $4,644, Other $147. Mats Exp $3,524, Books $600, Per/Ser (Incl. Access Fees) $50, AV Equip $150. Sal $1,464
Library Holdings: Bk Titles 9,450
Partic in Online Dakota Info Network

HETTINGER

P ADAMS COUNTY LIBRARY,* 103 N Sixth St, 58639-7015. (Mail add: PO Box 448, 58639-0448), SAN 355-3868. Tel: 701-567-2741. FAX: 701-567-2910. Web Site: www.ctctel.com. *Dir*, La Dean S Moen; E-Mail: moen@sendit.nodak.edu; *Ch Servs*, Berniece Marion; Staff 4 (Non-MLS 4)
Founded 1961. Pop 2,750; Circ 7,890
Jan 2000-Dec 2000 Income (Main Library and Branch Library) $66,870, State $5,870, County $46,000, Other $15,000. Mats Exp $10,000, Books $3,200, Per/Ser (Incl. Access Fees) $600, AV Equip $1,300, Electronic Ref Mat (Incl. Access Fees) $4,400. Sal $24,000
Library Holdings: Bk Vols 21,789; Per Subs 21
Subject Interests: Norwegian hist
Automation Activity & Vendor Info: (Cataloging) Sagebrush Corporation; (Circulation) Sagebrush Corporation
Function: ILL available
Partic in Dakota West Cooperating Libraries
Friends of the Library Group
Branches: 1
REEDER BRANCH, PO Box 96, Reeder, 58649. SAN 355-3892. Tel: 701-853-2485. *Librn*, Ilene Kowis
Friends of the Library Group

HOPE

P HOPE CITY LIBRARY,* PO Box 115, 58046. SAN 313-1157. Tel: 701-945-2796. *Librn*, Spies Marton
Founded 1910
Library Holdings: Bk Titles 15,000
Open Fri 1-4:30
Friends of the Library Group

S STEELE COUNTY HISTORICAL SOCIETY ARCHIVES LIBRARY,* PO Box 144, 58046. SAN 327-2400. Tel: 701-945-2394. E-Mail: cultural@icts.com. *Dir*, Russell Ford-Dunker
Library Holdings: Bk Vols 500
Subject Interests: Local history
Special Collections: Newspapers; Photo Coll; Township Records

JAMESTOWN

P ALFRED DICKEY PUBLIC LIBRARY,* 105 SE Third St, 58401. SAN 313-1165. Tel: 701-252-2990. FAX: 701-252-6030. *Dir*, Daphne Drewello
Pop 16,000; Circ 120,000
Library Holdings: Bk Vols 46,159; Per Subs 104
Special Collections: Louis L'Amour Memorial Coll
Partic in MINITEX Library Information Network

C JAMESTOWN COLLEGE, (NDJ), Raugust Library, 6070 College Lane, 58405-0001. SAN 313-1173. Tel: 701-252-3467. Interlibrary Loan Service Tel: 701-252-3467, Ext 2441. Circulation Tel: 701-252-3467, Ext 2530. Reference Tel: 701-252-3467, Ext 2511. FAX: 701-253-4446. Web Site: www.jc.edu/Raugust. *Librn*, Phyllis Ann K Bratton; Tel: 701-252-3467, Ext 2433, E-Mail: pbratton@jc.edu; *Acq*, Carla Godfrey; Tel: 701-252-3467, Ext 2432; *Cat*, Beth Sorenson; Tel: 701-252-3467, Ext 2431, E-Mail: sorenson@jc.edu; *Circ*, Fischer Brenda; Tel: 701-252-3467, Ext 2530, E-Mail: bfischer@jc.edu; *ILL*, Sue Delzer; Tel: 701-252-3467, Ext 2441, E-Mail: sdelzer@jc.edu; *Ref*, TyRee Jenks; Tel: 701-252-3467, Ext 2511, E-Mail: tjenks@jc.edu; Staff 6 (MLS 2, Non-MLS 4)
Enrl 1,170; Fac 65; Highest Degree: Bachelor
Jul 2000-Jun 2001 Income $228,343. Mats Exp $160,345, Books $33,500, Per/Ser (Incl. Access Fees) $38,500, AV Equip $4,500, Other Print Mats $14,000, Electronic Ref Mat (Incl. Access Fees) $25,275. Sal $108,490 (Prof $72,100)
Library Holdings: Bk Vols 121,875; Per Subs 480; Bks on Deafness & Sign Lang 69
Subject Interests: NDak hist, Regional poets
Special Collections: Children's materials; Western Americana Coll
Automation Activity & Vendor Info: (Acquisitions) PALS; (Cataloging) PALS; (Circulation) PALS; (Course Reserve) PALS; (ILL) PALS
Database Vendor: Dialog, GaleNet
Partic in Minn Interlibr Telecommunication Exchange

S NORTH DAKOTA FARMERS UNION, Resource Library,* 1415 12th Ave SE, PO Box 2136, 58402-2136. SAN 313-1181. Tel: 701-252-2340. FAX: 701-252-6584. *Dir*, Sheri Kapp
Founded 1927
Library Holdings: Bk Titles 3,250; Per Subs 35
Subject Interests: Agriculture, Rural life
Special Collections: Cooperative & Farm organization historical materials

M NORTH DAKOTA STATE HOSPITAL, Health Science Library,* 1624 23rd St SE, PO Box 476, 58402-0476. SAN 355-3922. Tel: 701-253-3679. FAX: 701-253-3204. E-Mail: pahlde@state.nd.us. *Mgr*, Denise Pahl; Staff 2 (MLS 1, Non-MLS 1)
Founded 1958
Library Holdings: Bk Vols 5,000; Bk Titles 4,500; Per Subs 106
Subject Interests: Activity therapy, Adolescence, Alcoholism, Ch, Counseling, Families of alcoholics, Forensic psychiat, Geriatrics, Psychiatric nursing, Psychiatric treatment, Psychology, Psychopharmacology, Psychotherapy, Soc work, Vocational rehabilitation
Special Collections: North Dakota State Hospital Biennial Reports, 1890 to date; North Dakota State Hospital Newsletter (employee newsletter)
Partic in Midwest Health Sci Libr Network; Valley Medical Network
Open Mon-Fri 8-12 & 1-5
Branches:
PATIENTS Tel: 701-253-3678. *Mgr*, Gene Haugen
Jul 1997-Jun 1998 Income $6,400. Mats Exp $6,400
Library Holdings: Bk Vols 3,500
Subject Interests: Art, Biog, Consumer awareness, Health, Large print, Native Am, Patient educ, Self-help, Substance abuse, Westerns
Special Collections: Audio Cassettes; LP Records; ND Newspapers; Patient Education Video Coll
Open Mon-Fri 8-12 & 1-5

P STUTSMAN COUNTY LIBRARY,* 910 Fifth St SE, 58401. SAN 313-119X. Tel: 701-252-1531. FAX: 701-251-1603. *Librn*, Agnes Jensen; E-Mail: agjensen@sendit.nodak.edu
Founded 1954. Pop 6,670; Circ 45,600
Jan 1998-Dec 1998 Income $110,933, State $17,314, Federal $1,170, County $79,065, Other $13,384. Mats Exp Books $13,662. Sal $65,432 (Prof $30,275)
Library Holdings: Bk Vols 38,549; Bk Titles 30,000; Per Subs 33; High Interest/Low Vocabulary Bk Vols 20
Subject Interests: Large print bks

G UNITED STATES GEOLOGICAL SURVEY, Northern Prairie Wildlife Research Center Library, 8711 37th St SE, 58401-9736. SAN 313-1203. Tel: 701-253-5566. FAX: 701-253-5553. Web Site: library.npwrc.cr.usgs.gov. *Librn*, Keith Van Cleave; Staff 1 (MLS 1)
Founded 1965
Library Holdings: Bk Titles 6,000; Per Subs 125
Subject Interests: Ecology, Global climate change, Mgt of waterfowl, Plant ecology, Predation, Wetland ecology
Special Collections: Waterfowl Management (Unpublished Papers of Merrill C Hammond)
Partic in Fedlink; MINITEX Library Information Network; OCLC Online Computer Library Center, Inc

KILLDEER

P KILLDEER PUBLIC LIBRARY,* PO Box 579, 58640. SAN 355-4015. Tel: 701-764-5877. FAX: 701-764-5648. *Librn*, Fayleen Fischer
Pop 815; Circ 3,804
Library Holdings: Bk Titles 16,600; Per Subs 45

LA MOURE

P LA MOURE SCHOOL & PUBLIC LIBRARY,* PO Box 656, 58458. SAN 313-1211. Tel: 701-883-5396. FAX: 701-883-5144. *Librn*, Delvin Pfaff; *Librn*, Karen Sandness
Circ 17,671
Library Holdings: Bk Vols 23,000
Open Mon-Fri 8-5
Friends of the Library Group

LANGDON

P CAVALIER COUNTY LIBRARY,* 600 Fifth Ave, 58249. SAN 371-5973. Tel: 701-256-5353. FAX: 701-256-2735. *Librn*, Diane Ellingson; *Asst Librn*, Clarice Ring; Staff 4 (MLS 3, Non-MLS 1)
Founded 1986. Pop 6,000; Circ 25,500
Friends of the Library Group

LARIMORE

P EDNA RALSTON PUBLIC LIBRARY, PO Box 459, 58251. SAN 313-122X. Tel: 701-343-2650. *Dir*, Ethel J Eastgate
Library Holdings: Bk Vols 10,000

LIDGERWOOD

P LIDGERWOOD CITY LIBRARY,* 15 Wiley Ave N, PO Box 280, 58053. SAN 313-1238. Tel: 701-538-4135. *Librn*, Orva Krause
Pop 996; Circ 10,795
Library Holdings: Bk Vols 17,021; Per Subs 29
Friends of the Library Group

LINTON

P LINTON PUBLIC LIBRARY, Harry L Petrie Public Library, 101 First St NE, PO Box 416, 58552. SAN 313-1246. Tel: 701-254-4737. *Dir*, Suzanne Jangula
Founded 1937. Pop 7,000; Circ 8,000
Library Holdings: Bk Vols 11,000; Per Subs 17
Special Collections: Local Newspaper Bound Copies 1905-present; North Dakota Coll
Open Mon & Wed-Fri 3-5

LISBON

P LISBON PUBLIC LIBRARY,* 409 Forest St, 58054-0569. SAN 313-1254. Tel: 701-683-5174. *Dir*, Dana Steele
Circ 16,000
Library Holdings: Bk Vols 16,000
Open Tues 3-6, Wed 10-1 & 3-6, Thurs 3-8 & Fri-Sat 10-1

MANDAN

P MANDAN PUBLIC LIBRARY, 108 First St NW, 58554. SAN 313-1262. Tel: 701-667-3255, 701-667-3256. FAX: 701-667-3263. Web Site: www.infolynx.org. *Dir*, J Thom Hendricks; E-Mail: t.hendricks@mail.infolynx.org
Founded 1904. Pop 15,200; Circ 64,931
Library Holdings: Bk Titles 34,623; Per Subs 146
Subject Interests: Local history, Railroads
Special Collections: Indians of North America; Large Print Books; Railroads; Talking Books for the Blind
Automation Activity & Vendor Info: (Circulation) epixtech, inc.

P MORTON COUNTY LIBRARY,* 300 First St NW, 58554. SAN 313-1270. Tel: 701-667-3327. FAX: 701-667-3296. *Librn*, Sheila Huber; *Bkmobile Coordr*, Kimberly Willman
Founded 1960. Circ 51,751
Library Holdings: Bk Vols 25,059
Subject Interests: Morton County hist
Mem of NDak Libr Asn

MAYVILLE

C BYRNES-QUANBECK LIBRARY AT MAYVILLE STATE UNIVERSITY, 330 Third St NE, 58257. SAN 313-1319. Tel: 701-786-4815. Toll Free Tel: 800-437-4104, Ext 34814. FAX: 701-786-4846. Web Site: www.masu.nodak.edu/library/. *Dir*, Sarah Batesel; Tel: 701-786-4814, E-Mail: sarah_batesel@mail.masu.nodak.edu; *Asst Libr Dir*, Doreen Rosevold; Tel: 701-786-4816, E-Mail: doreen_rosevold@mail.masu.nodak.edu; *Asst Librn*, Shannon Hofer; Tel: 701-786-4635, E-Mail: shannon_hofer@mail.masu.nodak.edu; *Acq, ILL*, Mary Chilvers; *Ser*, Marjorie Fugleberg; Tel: 701-786-4817, E-Mail: marjorie_fugleberg@mail.masu.nodak.edu. Subject Specialists: *Bus admin*, Shannon Hofer; *Education*, Doreen Rosevold; *Mathematics*, Marjorie Fugleberg; *Reading*, Doreen Rosevold; Staff 5 (MLS 1, Non-MLS 4)
Founded 1889. Enrl 644; Fac 43; Highest Degree: Bachelor
Jul 1999-Jun 2000 Income $271,232, State $270,232, Other $1,000. Mats Exp $97,976, Books $30,504, Per/Ser (Incl. Access Fees) $34,020, Presv $384, Micro $9,376, AV Equip $3,000, Electronic Ref Mat (Incl. Access Fees) $20,692. Sal $159,232 (Prof $88,873)
Library Holdings: Bk Vols 91,476; Bk Titles 71,595; Per Subs 558
Special Collections: North Dakota Coll
Automation Activity & Vendor Info: (Cataloging) PALS; (Circulation) PALS; (Course Reserve) PALS; (ILL) PALS; (OPAC) PALS; (Serials) PALS
Database Vendor: GaleNet, IAC - Info Trac, OCLC - First Search, ProQuest
Partic in Minn Interlibr Telecommunication Exchange; OCLC Online Computer Library Center, Inc; Online Dakota Info Network
Open Mon-Thurs 8-10, Fri 8-5, Sat 11-2 & Sun 6-10

P MAYVILLE PUBLIC LIBRARY, 52 Center Ave N, 58257. SAN 313-1300. Tel: 701-786-3388. *Librn*, Margaret K Rice
Circ 13,000
Jan 1998-Dec 1999 Income $25,000, State $1,390, City $21,631, Other $1,890. Mats Exp $6,400, Books $6,000, Per/Ser (Incl. Access Fees) $400. Sal $16,557 (Prof $15,225)
Library Holdings: Bk Vols 15,000
Friends of the Library Group

MEDORA

G THEODORE ROOSEVELT NATIONAL PARK LIBRARY,* PO Box 7, 58645. SAN 323-6846. Tel: 701-623-4466. FAX: 701-623-4840. Web Site: www.nps.gov/thro (park).
1998-1999 Income $117,000. Mats Exp $2,200, Books $500, Per/Ser (Incl. Access Fees) $1,500, Presv $200. Sal $115,000 (Prof $70,000)
Library Holdings: Bk Titles 2,700; Per Subs 30
Subject Interests: Western Americana
Special Collections: Theodore Roosevelt Coll
Friends of the Library Group

MINOT

S MINOT DAILY NEWS LIBRARY, 301 Fourth St SE, PO Box 1150, 58702. SAN 313-1327. Tel: 701-857-1950. FAX: 701-857-1961.
Founded 1952
Library Holdings: Bk Vols 510
Special Collections: Newspapers, 1894 to present; North Dakota Current Events

P MINOT PUBLIC LIBRARY,* 516 Second Ave SW, 58701-3792. SAN 313-1335. Tel: 701-852-1045. TDD: 701-852-2723, Online Cat 701-852-1118. FAX: 701-852-2595. Web Site: www.minotlibrary.org. *Dir*, Jerry Kaup; E-Mail: jkaup@minotpl.ndak.net; *Ref*, Marilyn Holbach; *Ch Servs*, Paulette Nelson; Tel: 701-838-0606, E-Mail: pnelson@minotpl.ndak.net; *Cat*, Linda Ellingson; *Info Specialist*, Darla Schaeffer; *Circ, ILL*, Jeanne Narum; Staff 8 (MLS 5, Non-MLS 3)
Founded 1908. Pop 35,850; Circ 310,774
Dec 1998-Dec 1999 Income $703,367, State $51,900, City $599,167, Federal $4,000, Locally Generated Income $48,300. Mats Exp $132,355, Books $93,279, Per/Ser (Incl. Access Fees) $13,126, Presv $2,000, Micro $1,600. Sal $355,590 (Prof $181,016)
Library Holdings: Bk Vols 120,571; Per Subs 300
Subject Interests: Bus, Genealogy, Literacy, NDak
Special Collections: Literacy; North Dakota
Automation Activity & Vendor Info: (Circulation) Sagebrush Corporation
Publications: Directory of Clubs & Organizations; Directory of Human Service Agencies; Peddler newsletter
Partic in MINITEX Library Information Network
Special Services for the Deaf - Captioned media; TDD; Videos & decoder
Friends of the Library Group

C MINOT STATE UNIVERSITY, Gordon B Olson Library, 500 University Ave W, 58707. SAN 313-1343. Tel: 701-858-3200. FAX: 701-858-3581. Web Site: www.misu.nodak/library/index1.htm. *Dir*, Larry Greenwood; *Circ*, Jane LaPlante; *Coll Develop, Tech Servs*, Susan Podrygula; *Bibliog Instr, Ref*, George C Clark; *Bibliog Instr, Ref*, Marilyn Hedberg; *Per*, Janet Essency; *Cat*, David Iversen; *Electronic Resources*, Patty Hunt; Staff 12 (MLS 8, Non-MLS 4)
Founded 1913. Enrl 3,000; Fac 127; Highest Degree: Master
Library Holdings: Bk Vols 369,481; Per Subs 1,023
Subject Interests: American West, Education, Geology
Special Collections: Dakota Territory and North Dakota History; Indians of the North Central States
Publications: Library Information for Faculty

TRINITY HEALTH
M ANGUS L CAMERON MEDICAL LIBRARY, 20 Burdick Expressway W, 58702. SAN 355-4074. Tel: 701-857-5143. FAX: 701-857-5638. *Dir*, Karen Anderson; E-Mail: karenan1@plain.nodak.edu; Staff 1 (MLS 1)
Founded 1928
Library Holdings: Bk Titles 3,000; Per Subs 120
Subject Interests: Clinical medicine
Partic in Greater Midwest Regional Medical Libr Network
Affiliated with University of North Dakota School of Medicine

P WARD COUNTY PUBLIC LIBRARY,* 405 Third Ave SE, 58701-4020. SAN 355-4139. Tel: 701-852-5388. Toll Free Tel: 800-932-8932. FAX: 701-837-4960. *Dir*, Jan Hearn; *Bkmobile Coordr*, Mary Bintz; Staff 3 (MLS 1, Non-MLS 2)
Founded 1960. Pop 21,000; Circ 132,000
Library Holdings: Bk Vols 47,000
Partic in NDak Network for Knowledge
Open Mon-Fri 8-4:30
Branches: 1
KENMARE BRANCH, 5 NE Third, PO Box 104, Kenmare, 58746. SAN 355-4163. Tel: 701-385-4090. FAX: 701-385-4090. *Librn*, Pauline Nielsen
Bookmobiles: 1

MINOT AFB

UNITED STATES AIR FORCE
A MINOT AIR FORCE BASE LIBRARY FL4528, 5 SVS/SVMG, 210 Missile Ave Unit 1 Bldg 156, 58705-5026. SAN 355-4198. Tel: 701-723-3344. FAX: 701-727-9850. *Dir*, Marilyn Dailey; Staff 7 (MLS 2, Non-MLS 5)
Founded 1961
Oct 1996-Sep 1997 Income $239,500. Mats Exp $30,079, Books $9,800, Per/Ser (Incl. Access Fees) $19,000
Library Holdings: Bk Vols 39,757; Per Subs 100
Subject Interests: Aviation, Military history, Space studies
Special Collections: Air War College Coll; Defense Logistics Studies Information Exchange (DLSIE); Defense Technical Information Center (DTIC); McNaughton Rental Coll; Video Coll

MOHALL

P MOHALL PUBLIC LIBRARY,* Main St, PO Box 159, 58761. SAN 313-1378. Tel: 701-756-7242. *Librn*, Rita Erickson
Pop 1,400; Circ 8,250
Library Holdings: Bk Vols 9,800

MOTT

P MOTT PUBLIC LIBRARY,* PO Box 477, 58646. SAN 313-1386. Tel: 701-824-2163. *Librn*, Regina Vasey
Founded 1912. Pop 1,019; Circ 5,513
Library Holdings: Bk Titles 12,065

NEW ROCKFORD

P NEW ROCKFORD PUBLIC LIBRARY,* 811 First Ave N, 58356. SAN 313-1408. Tel: 701-947-5540. *Librn*, Theresa Deckert
Pop 2,000; Circ 4,241
Library Holdings: Bk Vols 11,500
Open Mon & Tues 2-5, Wed & Fri 2-5 & Thurs 3-8
Friends of the Library Group

NEW TOWN

J FORT BERTHOLD LIBRARY, 220 Eighth Ave N, 58763. (Mail add: PO Box 788, 58763), SAN 371-7275. Tel: 701-627-4738. FAX: 701-627-3609. *Dir*, Quinice Baker; E-Mail: qbaker@fbcc@bia.edu; *Tech Servs*, Michael Stevens; *Asst Librn*, Amy Matthews; Staff 4 (MLS 1, Non-MLS 3)
Founded 1985. Enrl 185; Fac 7
Library Holdings: Bk Titles 12,000; Per Subs 180
Special Collections: Indians of North America
Friends of the Library Group

OAKES

P OAKES PUBLIC LIBRARY,* 804 Main Ave, 58474. SAN 313-1432. Tel: 701-742-2466, 701-742-3234. FAX: 701-742-2812. *Librn*, Jeanne Pahl; *Librn*, Grace Oline
Founded 1927. Pop 2,500; Circ 20,000
Library Holdings: Bk Vols 23,000; Per Subs 35

PARK RIVER

P PARK RIVER PUBLIC LIBRARY, PO Box 240, 58270-0240. SAN 313-1440. Tel: 701-284-6116. *Librn*, Kathy Myrvik; Staff 1 (Non-MLS 1)
Founded 1900. Pop 2,000; Circ 4,800
Library Holdings: Bk Titles 16,500; Per Subs 45
Automation Activity & Vendor Info: (Cataloging) Sagebrush Corporation; (Circulation) Sagebrush Corporation
Open Mon 6:30-8:30, Tues 12-4, Wed 3:30-5:30, Thurs 6:30-8:30, Sat 10-2
Friends of the Library Group

PARSHALL

P PARSHALL PUBLIC LIBRARY,* 114 Fourth Ave NE, Box 345, 58770. SAN 313-1459. Tel: 701-862-3775. *Dir*, Deloise Frank
Founded 1954. Pop 1,250; Circ 9,000
Library Holdings: Bk Vols 7,500; Bk Titles 6,663
Open Tues & Sat 2-5

PEMBINA

P PEMBINA CITY LIBRARY,* PO Box 541, 58271. SAN 313-1467.
Pop 700; Circ 5,400
Library Holdings: Bk Vols 5,500
Subject Interests: Local, State hist
Open Tues & Thurs 4-8

RICHARDTON

SR ASSUMPTION ABBEY LIBRARY, 418 Third Ave W, PO Box A, 58652-0901. SAN 313-1475. Tel: 701-974-3315. FAX: 701-974-3317. *Librn*, Brother Aaron Jensen
Founded 1899
Jul 1999-Jun 2000 Income Parent Institution $23,459. Mats Exp $13,398,

Books $8,001, Per/Ser (Incl. Access Fees) $4,973, Presv $425. Sal $7,500
Library Holdings: Bk Vols 91,048; Per Subs 85
Subject Interests: Am Indians, Church history, Germans from Russia, Monastic hist, NDak hist
Restriction: By appointment only, Circulation limited, In-house use for visitors, Private library
Function: ILL limited, Research library
Partic in NDak Network for Knowledge

RIVERDALE

P MCLEAN-MERCER REGIONAL LIBRARY, PO Box 505, 58565-0505. SAN 355-4228. Tel: 701-654-7652. *Dir*, Roberta Steckler
Founded 1959. Pop 26,316; Circ 106,622
Library Holdings: Bk Vols 40,000; Per Subs 11
Branches: 8
BEULAH BRANCH, 22 N Central Ave, PO Box 239, Beulah, 58523. SAN 355-4252. Tel: 701-873-2884. *Librn*, Colleen Wiest
GARRISON BRANCH, 15 S Main, PO Box 67, Garrison, 58540. SAN 355-4287. Tel: 701-463-7336. *Librn*, Michele Gehring
HAZEN BRANCH, Main St, PO Box 471, Hazen, 58545. SAN 355-4317. Tel: 701-748-2977. *Librn*, Val Albrecht
MAX BRANCH, PO Box 102, Max, 58759. SAN 322-6212. Tel: 701-679-2263. *Librn*, Cindy Thompson
STANTON, PO Box 130, 58571. SAN 370-9078. Tel: 701-745-3235. *Librn*, Nancy Miller
TURTLE LAKE BRANCH, City Hall, PO Box 540, Turtle Lake, 58575. SAN 355-4341. Tel: 701-448-9170. *Librn*, Marge Sondrol
Library Holdings: Bk Vols 970
UNDERWOOD BRANCH, PO Box 304, Underwood, 58576. SAN 370-9086. Tel: 701-442-5481. *Librn*, Linda Hermanson
WASHBURN BRANCH, PO Box 637, Washburn, 58577. SAN 355-4376. Tel: 701-462-8180. *Librn*, Julie Petersen
Bookmobiles: 1. Librn, EllaMae Lockrem

ROLLA

P ROLLA PUBLIC LIBRARY,* 14 SE First St, 58367. SAN 313-1491. Tel: 701-477-3849. FAX: 701-477-3834. *Librn*, Peggy Johnson; *Librn*, Connie Hileman
Library Holdings: Bk Vols 12,219

RUGBY

P HEART OF AMERICA LIBRARY, 201 W Third St, 58368-1793. SAN 313-1505. Tel: 701-776-6223. *Dir*, Amy Bryn; *Asst Librn*, Dianne Tuff
Founded 1911. Pop 5,052; Circ 40,683
Jan 1999-Dec 1999 Income $82,051, State $5,925, City $23,846, County $38,707, Other $13,573. Mats Exp $15,969, Books $13,969, Per/Ser (Incl. Access Fees) $2,000. Sal $47,030
Library Holdings: Bk Vols 26,678; Per Subs 111
Subject Interests: Large print, NDak
Partic in NDak Network for Knowledge
Open Mon-Wed & Fri-Sat 10-5:30 & Thurs 10-9

SOUTH BOWMAN

P CLARA LINCOLN PHELAN MEMORIAL LIBRARY, Bowman Public Library, 104 Main St, 58623-4013. (Mail add: PO Box 179, 58623-0179), SAN 313-0800. Tel: 701-523-3797. *Librn*, Shirley Jensen; E-Mail: sjensen@sendit.ndak.edu
Founded 1913. Circ 2,945
Library Holdings: Bk Vols 11,000
Open Mon 2-5 & 7-9, Tues-Sat 2-5

STANLEY

P LINSON MEMORIAL LIBRARY,* 206 S Main St, 58784. (Mail add: Po Box 249, 58784-0249), SAN 313-1513. Tel: 701-628-2223. *Librn*, Patricia Jensen
Pop 1,800
Library Holdings: Bk Vols 6,100

STEELE

P KIDDER COUNTY LIBRARY,* PO Box 227, 58482. SAN 313-1521. Tel: 701-475-2855. *Librn*, Paulette Fischer
Founded 1964. Pop 3,833; Circ 25,800
Library Holdings: Bk Vols 16,800; Per Subs 15

VALLEY CITY

C VALLEY CITY STATE UNIVERSITY, (NDV), Allen Memorial Library, 101 College St SW, 58072-4098. SAN 313-1572. Tel: 701-845-7277. FAX: 701-845-7437. E-Mail: library_vcsu@mail.vcsu.nodak.edu. Web Site: libraryvcsu.edu/. *Acq, Coll Develop, Dir*, Darryl B Podoll; Tel: 701-845-7275, E-Mail: darryl_podoll@mail.vcsu.nodak.edu; *Bibliog Instr, Ref*, Margaret Wieland; Tel: 701-845-7278, E-Mail: margaret_wieland@mail.vcsu.nodak.edu; *Info Tech*, Donna V James; Tel: 701-875-7275, E-Mail: donna_james@mail.vcsu.nodak.edu; *ILL*, Mary Wolfgram; *Per*, Carole King Jefferson; Tel: 701-845-7285, E-Mail: carole_jefferson@mail.vcsu.nodak.edu; Staff 4 (MLS 3, Non-MLS 1)
Founded 1890. Enrl 1,077; Fac 59; Highest Degree: Bachelor
Jul 1998-Jun 1999 Income $327,887, Locally Generated Income $12,528. Mats Exp $103,407, Books $52,862, Per/Ser (Incl. Access Fees) $35,545, Electronic Ref Mat (Incl. Access Fees) $15,000. Sal $234,735 (Prof $138,760)
Library Holdings: Bk Vols 91,855; Per Subs 569
Subject Interests: Education
Special Collections: North Dakota Coll; Valley City State University Hist Coll; Woiwode Coll
Automation Activity & Vendor Info: (Acquisitions) PALS; (Cataloging) PALS; (Circulation) PALS; (ILL) PALS; (OPAC) PALS; (Serials) PALS
Partic in Minn Interlibr Telecommunication Exchange; NDak Network for Knowledge; OCLC Online Computer Library Center, Inc; Online Dakota Info Network
Friends of the Library Group

P VALLEY CITY-BARNES COUNTY PUBLIC LIBRARY, 410 N Central Ave, 58072. SAN 313-1564. Tel: 701-845-3821. FAX: 701-845-4884. E-Mail: vcbcpl@ispchannel.com. *Dir*, Mary E Fischer; E-Mail: mafische@fm-net.com; *Ch Servs*, Mary Ann Anderson; Staff 4 (MLS 4)
Founded 1903. Pop 12,545
Jan 1999-Dec 1999 Income $157,000. Mats Exp $10,900, Books $8,600, Per/Ser (Incl. Access Fees) $1,000, AV Equip $1,300. Sal $70,865
Library Holdings: Bk Vols 62,000
Subject Interests: Adult, Children
Special Collections: Large Print Coll, verticle file; North Dakota Coll
Partic in NDak Network for Knowledge
Special Services for the Blind - Bks on tape
Friends of the Library Group

VELVA

P VELVA SCHOOL & PUBLIC LIBRARY, 101 W Fourth St, 58790. SAN 313-1580. Tel: 701-338-2022. FAX: 701-338-2023. E-Mail: swedlund@sendit.nodak.edu. *Librn*, Iris Swedlund; Staff 2 (Non-MLS 2)
Founded 1913. Pop 1,300; Circ 26,779; Enrl 590; Fac 40; Highest Degree: Bachelor
Library Holdings: Bk Vols 25,000; Per Subs 180

WAHPETON

P LEACH PUBLIC LIBRARY,* 417 Second Ave N, 58075. SAN 313-1599. Tel: 701-642-5732. FAX: 701-642-5732. *Dir*, Bonnie R MacIver; E-Mail: bmaciver@rrt.net
Founded 1924. Pop 9,000; Circ 36,892
Jan 1998-Dec 1999 Income $79,768, State $8,900, City $60,021, Locally Generated Income $6,400, Other $4,397. Mats Exp $14,500, Books $10,000, Per/Ser (Incl. Access Fees) $3,500, AV Equip $1,000. Sal $43,044 (Prof $19,582)
Library Holdings: Bk Vols 38,400; Per Subs 72
Special Collections: Local Paper back to 1890, microfilm
Partic in NDak Network for Knowledge
Friends of the Library Group

J NORTH DAKOTA STATE COLLEGE OF SCIENCE, Mildred Johnson Library, 800 N Sixth St, 58076-0002. SAN 313-1602. Tel: 701-671-2298. Interlibrary Loan Service Tel: 701-671-2422. Circulation Tel: 701-671-2618. Reference Tel: 701-671-2360. FAX: 701-671-2674. Web Site: www.ndscs.nodak.edu. *Dir*, Jerald K Stewart; Tel: 701-671-2724, E-Mail: jerald_stewart@ndscs.nodak.edu; *Circ*, Dan Koper; E-Mail: dan_koper@ndscs.nodak.edu; *Media Spec*, Steven Krohn; *Tech Servs*, Mary Kroshus; Tel: 701-671-2129, E-Mail: mary_kroshus@ndscs.nodak.edu; *Ref*, Karen Chobot; Tel: 701-671-2385, E-Mail: karen_chobot@ndscs.nodak.edu; Staff 8 (MLS 4, Non-MLS 4)
Founded 1903. Enrl 2,450; Fac 135; Highest Degree: Associate
Library Holdings: Bk Titles 75,000; Per Subs 985
Subject Interests: Automotive, Behav sci, Bus, Electronics, Foods mgt, Health sciences, Mgt, Sci-tech, Soc sci
Partic in Minn Interlibr Telecommunication Exchange; NDak Network for Knowledge; OCLC Online Computer Library Center, Inc; ODIN
National Library for the ATEA (American Technical Education Association)

WALHALLA

P WALHALLA PUBLIC LIBRARY,* 1012 Central Ave, PO Box 587, 58282. SAN 313-1610. Tel: 701-549-3794. FAX: 701-549-3794. *Librn*, Diana Yeado
Circ 5,798
Library Holdings: Bk Vols 8,200; Bk Titles 7,100; Per Subs 8
Open Mon 2-5 & 7-9, Wed & Fri 2-5, Sun 2-4

WATFORD CITY

P MCKENZIE COUNTY PUBLIC LIBRARY, PO Box 990, 112 Second Ave NE, 58854-0990. SAN 313-1629. Tel: 701-842-3785. FAX: 701-842-3730. E-Mail: library@4eyes.net. *Dir*, Judy Murie; *Asst Dir*, Judith Omlid; *Asst Librn*, Diane DeFoe; *Asst Librn*, Sandra Transtrom
Founded 1958. Pop 6,400; Circ 35,000
Jan 1998-Dec 1999 Income $97,092, State $14,172, County $82,920. Mats Exp Books $11,000. Sal $41,925
Library Holdings: Bk Vols 23,360; Per Subs 40
Publications: Booklist; Library Journal; School Library Journal

WEST FARGO

P WEST FARGO PUBLIC LIBRARY, 401 Seventh St E, 58078. SAN 313-1637. Tel: 701-282-0415. *Dir*, Miriam Arves
Founded 1971. Pop 15,000
1998-1999 Income $158,450. Mats Exp $29,000, Books $25,000, Per/Ser (Incl. Access Fees) $4,000. Sal $85,000
Library Holdings: Bk Vols 60,000; Per Subs 150
Special Collections: United States (State & Local History)
Open Mon-Thurs 10-8, Fri 10-5 & Sat 10-4

WILLISTON

M BETHANY MEDICAL CENTER, Medical Library,* 1410 University Ave, 58801. SAN 313-1653. Tel: 913-281-8770. FAX: 913-281-7839. *Librn*, Sarah Kirby; Staff 2 (MLS 1, Non-MLS 1)
Founded 1968
Library Holdings: Bk Vols 3,000; Bk Titles 2,000; Per Subs 250
Subject Interests: Health sciences, Medicine, Nursing
Restriction: Open to public for reference only
Partic in Health Sciences Library Network of Kansas City, Inc
Open Mon-Fri 8:30-5

C UNIVERSITY OF NORTH DAKOTA, Williston State College Library, 1410 University Ave, PO Box 1326, 58801. (Mail add: PO Box 1326, 58802), Tel: 701-774-4226. FAX: 701-774-4547. *Dir Libr Serv*, Kelly Hell; *Librn*, Paula Mitchell; *Librn*, Suzanne Childers; E-Mail: schilders@mail.wsc.nodak.edu; Staff 2 (MLS 1, Non-MLS 1)
Founded 1966
Jul 1998-Jun 1999 Mats Exp $62,587, Books $30,332, Per/Ser (Incl. Access Fees) $14,550, Micro $832, AV Equip $4,865, Electronic Ref Mat (Incl. Access Fees) $7,984. Sal $47,270 (Prof $27,554)
Library Holdings: Bk Vols 20,176; Bk Titles 19,300; Per Subs 228
Partic in Online Dakota Info Network
Open Mon-Thurs 8-8, Fri 8-5, Sun 2-6; summer hours vary

P WILLISTON COMMUNITY LIBRARY, 1302 Davidson Dr, 58801. SAN 313-1645. Tel: 701-774-8805. FAX: 701-572-1186. *Librn*, Cynthia Schaff; Staff 3 (Non-MLS 3)
Founded 1983. Pop 23,000; Circ 250,000
Jan 1999-Dec 1999 Income $229,000, State $20,000, City $137,000, County $72,000. Mats Exp $84,000, Books $56,000, Per/Ser (Incl. Access Fees) $9,000, AV Equip $11,000, Electronic Ref Mat (Incl. Access Fees) $8,000. Sal $142,000
Library Holdings: Bk Vols 61,000; Per Subs 163
Special Collections: American Indian Coll; North Dakota
Automation Activity & Vendor Info: (Circulation) Sagebrush Corporation; (OPAC) Sagebrush Corporation
Database Vendor: Ebsco - EbscoHost, GaleNet, OCLC - First Search
Friends of the Library Group
Branches: 1
TIOGA COMMUNITY LIBRARY, 321 N Benson St, PO Box 221, Tioga, 58852. SAN 313-153X. Tel: 701-664-3627. *Librn*, Dorothy Placek
Jan 1999-Dec 1999 Income Locally Generated Income $6,750. Mats Exp $5,300, Books $3,500, Per/Ser (Incl. Access Fees) $400, AV Equip $400, Other Print Mats $1,000. Sal $11,200
Library Holdings: Bk Titles 8,000; Per Subs 19
Automation Activity & Vendor Info: (Circulation) Sagebrush Corporation; (OPAC) Sagebrush Corporation
Friends of the Library Group
Bookmobiles: 1

OHIO

Date of Statistics: Fiscal 1999
Population, 1996: 11,256,654
Total Volumes in Public Libraries: 45,748,259
Volumes Per Capita: 3.99
Total Public Library Circulation: 139,665,051
Circulation Per Capita: 12.46
Total Public Library Income (including State Aid): $574,223,190
Source of Income: Library & Local Government Support Fund
Expenditure Per Capita: $50.046
Number of County or Multi-county (Regional) Libraries: 7 Chartered Regional Library Systems; countywide service in all 88 counties
Number of Bookmobiles in State: 62
Grants-in-Aid to Public Libraries:
Federal:
Title I: $190,849
Title II: $765,808
LSTA: $3,918,210
Total: $4,874,867
State Aid: $3,184,385
Formula & amount for apportionment for State Aid: Library must meet certain performance standards; amount received determined by formula based on local tax collection & distribution.

ADA

P ADA PUBLIC DISTRICT LIBRARY,* 320 N Main St, 45810-1199. SAN 313-1688. Tel: 419-634-5246. FAX: 419-634-9747. *Librn*, Patricia Kusner
Founded 1916. Pop 6,000; Circ 41,447
Library Holdings: Bk Vols 19,614; Per Subs 60
Special Collections: City, County & State History
Partic in Norweld

C OHIO NORTHERN UNIVERSITY, Heterick Memorial Library, 45810. SAN 355-4406. Tel: 419-772-2181. FAX: 419-772-1927. Web Site: www.nwn.onu.edu/indra/index.html. *Dir, Ref*, Paul Logsdon; Tel: 419-772-2182, E-Mail: p_logsdon@onu.edu; *Acq, Syst Coordr*, Indra Canagaratna; Tel: 419-772-2183, E-Mail: i-canagaratna@onu.edu; *Cat*, Sharon Herr; Tel: 419-772-2193, E-Mail: s-herr@onu.edu; *Circ, Doc*, Lee Bowman; Tel: 419-772-2473, E-Mail: l-bowman@onu.edu; *ILL, Ser*, Charles Steele; Tel: 419-772-2188, E-Mail: c-steele@onu.edu; Staff 5 (MLS 5)
Founded 1915. Enrl 3,134; Fac 225; Highest Degree: Doctorate
Jun 1999-May 2000 Income $1,312,221. Mats Exp $681,945, Books $331,725, Per/Ser (Incl. Access Fees) $342,970, Micro $6,500, AV Equip $750. Sal $402,800
Library Holdings: Bk Vols 250,000; Per Subs 4,240
Special Collections: Ohio Northern University Authors
Automation Activity & Vendor Info: (Acquisitions) Innovative Interfaces Inc.; (Cataloging) Innovative Interfaces Inc.; (Circulation) Innovative Interfaces Inc.; (Course Reserve) Innovative Interfaces Inc.; (OPAC) Innovative Interfaces Inc.
Publications: Bookmarks; Library Handbook; Subject Bibliographies
Partic in OCLC Online Computer Library Center, Inc; Ohio Library & Information Network; OHIONET
Departmental Libraries:
CL JAY P TAGGART LAW LIBRARY, Taggart Law Library, Ohio Nothern University, 45810. Tel: 419-772-2250. Circulation Tel: 419-772-2239. FAX: 419-772-1875. E-Mail: librarians@eugene.onu.edu. Web Site: www.law.onu.edu/library/. *Dir*, Greg Laughlin; E-Mail: g-laughlin@postoffice.onu.edu; Staff 10 (MLS 4, Non-MLS 6)
Founded 1885. Enrl 285; Fac 3; Highest Degree: Doctorate
Library Holdings: Bk Vols 205,150; Bk Titles 51,150; Per Subs 800
Automation Activity & Vendor Info: (Acquisitions) Innovative Interfaces Inc.
Database Vendor: IAC - SearchBank, Lexis-Nexis, OCLC - First Search, Wilson - Wilson Web
Publications: Acquisitions List (monthly)
Function: Research library
Partic in Ohio Library & Information Network

AKRON

S AKRON ART MUSEUM, Martha Stecher Reed Art Reference Library,* 70 E Market St, 44308. SAN 313-1696. Tel: 330-376-9185. FAX: 330-376-1180. *Librn*, Jody Perkins
Library Holdings: Bk Titles 11,000; Per Subs 40
Subject Interests: Am Impressionism, Contemporary painting, Photog, Sculpture
Special Collections: Edwin C Shaw Archives
Open Tues-Fri 11-5

S AKRON BEACON JOURNAL, Editorial Reference Library, 44 E Exchange St, 44328. SAN 313-170X. Tel: 330-996-3898. FAX: 330-376-3235. Web Site: www.ohio.com. *Librn*, Catherine M Tierney; E-Mail: ctierney@thebeaconjournal.com; *Assoc Librn*, Norma Hill; Staff 6 (MLS 2, Non-MLS 4)
Founded 1936
Library Holdings: Bk Vols 2,500; Bk Titles 2,000
Subject Interests: Airships, Kent State University incident (May 4, 1970), Rubber indust
Partic in Dialog Corporation; Mediastream

G AKRON DEPARTMENT OF PLANNING & URBAN DEVELOPMENT LIBRARY, 403 Municipal Bldg, 166 S High St, 44308. SAN 328-5871. Tel: 330-375-2084. FAX: 330-375-2387. E-Mail: planlib@ci.akron.oh.us. *Librn*, Claudia A Burdge; *Asst Librn*, Mary Denise Robb
Library Holdings: Bk Vols 2,000; Per Subs 200

M AKRON GENERAL MEDICAL CENTER, J D Smith Memorial Library, 400 Wabash Ave, 44307. SAN 313-1726. Tel: 330-384-6242. FAX: 330-384-1834. Web Site: www.akrongeneral.org. *Dir Libr Serv*, Christine J Williams; E-Mail: cwilliams@agmc.org; *Librn*, Judy Knight
Library Holdings: Bk Titles 3,000; Per Subs 300
Open Mon, Wed & Fri 8-4:30, Tues & Thurs 8-8, Sat 12-4

L AKRON LAW LIBRARY ASSOCIATION,* 209 S High St, 4th flr, 44308-1675. SAN 313-1734. Tel: 330-643-2804. FAX: 330-535-0077. E-Mail: allarkc@en.com. Web Site: www.summitoh.net/lawlibrary. *Librn*, Rosemarie Chrisant; Staff 6 (MLS 3, Non-MLS 3)
Founded 1888
Jan 1997-Dec 1998 Income $504,116. Mats Exp $383,127, Books $375,018, Presv $2,735. Sal $127,689
Library Holdings: Bk Vols 79,999; Per Subs 233
Subject Interests: Law

P AKRON-SUMMIT COUNTY PUBLIC LIBRARY, 55 S Main St, 44326-0001. SAN 355-4465. Tel: 330-643-9000. TDD: 330-643-9005. FAX: 330-643-9033. E-Mail: ascpl@acorn.net. Web Site: www.ascpl.lib.oh.us. *Head of Libr*, Rick Ewing; Tel: 330-643-9081, Fax: 330-643-9167, E-Mail: rewing@ascpl.lib.oh.us; *Dir*, Steven Hawk; Tel: 330-643-9100, Fax: 330-643-9160, E-Mail: shawk@ascpl.lib.oh.us; *Asst Dir*, David Jennings; Tel: 330-643-9102, Fax: 330-643-9160, E-Mail: djenning@ascpl.lib.oh.us; *Br Coordr*, Judith Campbell; Tel: 330-643-9082, Fax: 330-643-9167, E-Mail: jcampbell@ascpl.lib.oh.us; *Circ*, Bruce Spohn; Tel: 330-643-9034, Fax: 330-643-9033, E-Mail: bspohn@ascpl.lib.oh.us; *AV*, Maria McLane; Tel: 330-643-9019, Fax: 330-643-9021, E-Mail: mmclane@ascpl.lib.oh.us; *Business*, Scott Morgan; Tel: 330-643-9120, Fax: 330-643-9130, E-Mail: smorgan@ascpl.lib.oh.us; *Tech Servs*, Diane Winans; Tel: 330-643-9103, Fax: 330-643-9167, E-Mail: dwinans@ascpl.lib.oh.us. Subject Specialists: *Business and management*, Dana Beezley-Kwasnicka; *Fine arts*, Bob Ethington;

Government, Dana Beezley-Kwasnicka; *History*, Cheryl Engel; *Literature*, Cheryl Engel; *Marketing*, Carla Davis; *Philosophy*, Nancy Mohler; *Recreation*, Bob Ethington; *Religious education*, Nancy Mohler; *Science/ technology*, Joyce McKnight; Staff 396 (MLS 123, Non-MLS 273)
Founded 1874. Pop 384,632; Circ 3,794,190
Jan 1999-Dec 1999 Income (Main Library and Branch Library) $20,921,033, State $14,582,961, County $4,880,080, Other $1,457,992. Mats Exp $19,002,519, Books $1,856,104, Per/Ser (Incl. Access Fees) $217,770, Presv $11,375, Micro $35,150, AV Equip $4,149, Electronic Ref Mat (Incl. Access Fees) $419,035. Sal $8,653,846
Library Holdings: Bk Vols 1,374,237; Bk Titles 488,000; Per Subs 1,374
Subject Interests: Local history, Patents-trademarks, Science fair projects
Special Collections: Lighter-than-Air; US patent & trademark
Automation Activity & Vendor Info: (Cataloging) epixtech, inc.; (Circulation) epixtech, inc.; (OPAC) epixtech, inc.
Database Vendor: Dialog, epixtech, inc., GaleNet
Publications: Science Fair Project Index
Function: Reference services available
Partic in Cleveland Area Metropolitan Library System; OCLC Online Computer Library Center, Inc
Special Services for the Deaf - High interest/low vocabulary books; TTY machine
Special Services for the Blind - Kurzweil Reading Machine
Friends of the Library Group
Branches: 17
AYRES, 1765 W Market St, 44313. SAN 355-449X. Tel: 330-836-1081. FAX: 330-836-1574. Web Site: www.ascpl.lib.oh.us. *Branch Mgr*, Gladys Rossi
Library Holdings: Bk Vols 54,079
Friends of the Library Group
CHAMBERLAIN, 760 E Archwood Ave, 44306. SAN 355-452X. Tel: 330-724-2126. FAX: 330-724-4391. Web Site: www.ascpl.lib.oh.us. *Branch Mgr*, Barbara Halfen
Library Holdings: Bk Vols 32,072
Friends of the Library Group
ELLET, 2470 E Market St, 44312. SAN 355-4619. Tel: 330-784-2019. FAX: 330-784-6692. Web Site: www.ascpl.lib.oh.us. *Branch Mgr*, Anita Marky
Library Holdings: Bk Vols 49,614
Friends of the Library Group
GOODYEAR, 60 Goodyear Blvd, 44305. SAN 355-4589. Tel: 330-784-7522. FAX: 330-784-6599. Web Site: www.ascpl.lib.oh.us. *Branch Mgr*, Deborah Catrone
Library Holdings: Bk Vols 41,330
Friends of the Library Group
GREEN, 4046 Massillon Rd, Uniontown, 44685. SAN 355-4643. Tel: 330-896-9074. FAX: 330-896-9412. Web Site: www.ascpl.lib.oh.us. *Branch Mgr*, Mary Miller
Library Holdings: Bk Vols 49,817
Friends of the Library Group
KENMORE, 2200 14th St SW, 44314. SAN 355-4678. Tel: 330-745-6126. FAX: 330-745-9947. Web Site: www.ascpl.lib.oh.us. *Branch Mgr*, Kathy Forsthoffer
Library Holdings: Bk Vols 43,160
Friends of the Library Group
MAPLE VALLEY, 1187 Copley Rd, 44320. SAN 355-4767. Tel: 330-864-5721. FAX: 330-864-8971. Web Site: www.ascpl.lib.oh.us. *Branch Mgr*, Andria Hawkins
Library Holdings: Bk Vols 43,046
Friends of the Library Group
MCDOWELL, 3101 Smith Rd, 44313. SAN 355-4708. Tel: 330-666-4888. FAX: 330-666-8741. Web Site: www.ascpl.lib.oh.us. *Branch Mgr*, Jill Stroud
Library Holdings: Bk Vols 48,723
Friends of the Library Group
MOGADORE BRANCH, 144 S Cleveland Ave, Mogadore, 44260. SAN 355-4791. Tel: 330-628-9228. FAX: 330-628-3256. Web Site: www.ascpl.lib.oh.us. *Branch Mgr*, Janet Hsu
Library Holdings: Bk Vols 49,783
Friends of the Library Group
NORDONIA HILLS, 9458 Olde Eight Rd, Northfield, 44607. SAN 355-4856. Tel: 330-467-8595. FAX: 330-467-4332. Web Site: www.ascpl.lib.oh.us. *Branch Mgr*, Janet Stavole
Library Holdings: Bk Vols 50,594
Friends of the Library Group
NORTH, 183 E Cuyahoga Falls Ave, 44310. SAN 355-4821. Tel: 330-535-9423. FAX: 330-535-0169. Web Site: www.ascpl.lib.oh.us. *Branch Mgr*, Lisa Weiser
Library Holdings: Bk Vols 37,572
Friends of the Library Group
NORTON BRANCH, 3930 S Cleveland-Massillon Rd, Norton, 44203. SAN 355-4880. Tel: 330-825-7800. FAX: 330-825-5155. Web Site: www.ascpl.lib.oh.us. *Branch Mgr*, Cindy Howe
Library Holdings: Bk Vols 56,358
Friends of the Library Group
PORTAGE LAKES, 4261 Manchester Rd, 44319. SAN 370-3509. Tel: 330-644-7050. FAX: 330-644-0977. Web Site: www.ascpl.lib.oh.us. *Branch Mgr*, Susan Rice
Library Holdings: Bk Vols 45,657
Friends of the Library Group
RICHFIELD BRANCH, 4400 W Streetsboro Rd, PO Box 287, Richfield, 44286. SAN 355-4910. Tel: 330-659-4343. FAX: 330-659-6205. Web Site: www.ascpl.lib.oh.us. *Branch Mgr*, Elizabeth Reed
Library Holdings: Bk Vols 39,279
Friends of the Library Group
TALLMADGE BRANCH, 137 East Ave, Tallmadge, 44278. SAN 355-4945. Tel: 330-633-4345. FAX: 330-633-6324. Web Site: www.ascpl.lib.oh.us. *Branch Mgr*, Karen Wiper
Library Holdings: Bk Vols 36,001
Friends of the Library Group
WEST HILL, 807 W Market St, 44303. SAN 355-497X. Tel: 330-376-2927. FAX: 330-376-9025. Web Site: www.ascpl.lib.oh.us. *Branch Mgr*, Barbara White
Library Holdings: Bk Vols 40,494
Friends of the Library Group
WOOSTER, 600 Wooster Ave, 44307. SAN 355-5003. Tel: 330-434-8726. FAX: 330-434-3750. Web Site: www.ascpl.lib.oh.us. *Branch Mgr*, Pam Jennings
Library Holdings: Bk Vols 39,653
Friends of the Library Group
Bookmobiles: 2. Also have 1 van

S BUSINESS INFORMATION CENTER, (Formerly FirstEnergy Corporation), Corporate Library, 76 S Main St, G02, 44308-1890. SAN 321-3951. Tel: 330-384-4934. FAX: 330-255-1720. E-Mail: malumphs@firstenergycorp.com. *Asst Librn*, Patricia Haller; *Asst Librn*, Joseph A Hecht; Tel: 330-384-4658, E-Mail: jahecht@firstenergycorp.com; *Asst Librn*, Susan R Lloyd; E-Mail: lloyds@firstenergycorp.com; Staff 3 (MLS 2, Non-MLS 1)
Founded 1981
Library Holdings: Bk Titles 10,000; Per Subs 60
Subject Interests: Electric power, Energy
Special Collections: Electric Power (Electric Power Research Institute Report Coll); Industry Standards
Database Vendor: Dialog, Lexis-Nexis
Publications: Library Update (Newsletter, irregular)
Restriction: Employees & their associates, Use of others with permission of librarian
Function: ILL available
Partic in Cleveland Area Metropolitan Library System

M CHILDREN'S HOSPITAL MEDICAL CENTER, Mary A Hower Medical Library, One Perkins Sq, 44308-1062. SAN 329-8566. Tel: 330-543-8250. *Mgr*, Julie Thom
Subject Interests: Pediatrics

R CHRIST UNITED METHODIST CHURCH LIBRARY, 380 Mineola Ave, 44320-1935. SAN 328-1574. Tel: 330-836-5563. FAX: 330-836-7209. *Librn*, Lee Griffiths; Staff 8 (MLS 1, Non-MLS 7)
Library Holdings: Bk Vols 1,950; Bk Titles 2,250
Subject Interests: Fiction, Religion
Special Collections: Children's books
Open Mon-Fri 8-12 & 1-4
Friends of the Library Group

FIRESTONE TIRE & RUBBER CO
S CENTRAL RESEARCH LIBRARY, 1200 Firestone Pkwy, 44317. SAN 355-5062. Tel: 330-379-7630. FAX: 330-379-7530. *Librn*, D Koo
Founded 1945
Library Holdings: Bk Vols 15,000; Bk Titles 6,000; Per Subs 100
Partic in Dialog Corporation; STN

S FLEXSYS AMERICA LP, Information Center, 260 Springside Dr, 44333. SAN 313-1793. Tel: 330-666-4111, Ext 201. FAX: 330-668-8345. *In Charge*, Julie Schillinger; E-Mail: julie.j.schillinger@flexsys.com
Founded 1929
Library Holdings: Bk Vols 1,600; Bk Titles 950; Per Subs 140
Subject Interests: Plastics chem, Polymer sci, Rubber, Technology
Restriction: Staff use only

R HIGH STREET CHRISTIAN CHURCH, H A Valentine Memorial Library, 131 S High St, 44308-1497. SAN 313-1785. Tel: 330-434-1039. FAX: 330-434-7271. *Librn*, Evelyn R Ling
Founded 1965
Library Holdings: Bk Vols 9,000
Subject Interests: Religion
Special Collections: Church Archives
Publications: Book Nook (monthly)

S INTERNATIONAL SOAP BOX DERBY LIBRARY,* Derby Downs, PO Box 7225, 44306-7225. SAN 329-8183. Tel: 330-733-8723. FAX: 330-733-1370. Web Site: www.aasbd.org. *Exec Dir*, Tony DeLuca
Library Holdings: Bk Titles 50
Special Collections: History of Soap Box Derby; Soap Box Derby Racing

S LOCKHEED MARTIN TACTICAL DEFENSE SYSTEMS,* 1210 Massillon Rd, 44315-0001. SAN 313-1769. Tel: 330-796-2557. FAX: 330-796-9693. *Coll Develop, Librn*, Louise Lariccia; E-Mail: lu.lariccia@

lmco.com
Founded 1940
1998-1999 Income $48,000
Library Holdings: Bk Titles 8,000; Per Subs 350
Subject Interests: Aerospace science, Astronautics, Computers, Electronics, Engineering, Guidance, Mat sci, Mathematics, Simulators, Weapons systs
Special Collections: Lighter Than Air Aircraft (LTA Coll)
Publications: Newsletter (bi-monthly)
Partic in Aviation/Aerospace Online; Dialog Corporation; DTIC; Nasa Libraries Information System - Nasa Galaxie; OCLC Online Computer Library Center, Inc

S NORTHEAST OHIO FOUR COUNTY REGIONAL PLANNING & DEVELOPMENT ORGANIZATION,* 969 Copley Rd, 44320. SAN 328-5340. Tel: 330-836-5731. FAX: 330-836-7703. E-Mail: nefco@worldnet.att.net. *Exec Dir*, Joseph Hadley
Library Holdings: Bk Titles 3,500

S OMNOVA TECHNOLOGY CENTER, Technical Information Center, 2990 Gilchrist Rd, 44305. SAN 313-1742. Tel: 330-794-6382. FAX: 330-794-6375. *Dir*, William Hollis; E-Mail: william.hollis@omnova.com
Founded 1946
Library Holdings: Bk Vols 9,000; Per Subs 50
Subject Interests: Adhesives, Plastics, Polymer chemistry, Rubber, Sci-tech
Database Vendor: Dialog
Partic in Dialog Corporation

S RUBBER DIVISION AMERICAN CHEMICAL SOCIETY, John H Gifford Library & Information Center, The University of Akron, 44325-3907. SAN 325-3376. Tel: 330-972-7197. FAX: 330-972-5574. Web Site: www.rubber.org/library/library.htm. *Librn*, Joan C Long; E-Mail: jclong@uakron.edu
Founded 1946
Subject Interests: Rubber chemistry, Rubber indust, Rubber sci
Special Collections: Rubber Division ACS publications & papers

M SUMMA HEALTH SYSTEM, Medical Library,* 55 N Arch, Ste G-3, 44304. SAN 313-1718. Tel: 330-375-3260. FAX: 330-375-3978. *Mgr*, Linda Bunyan; Tel: 330-375-3081, E-Mail: bunyanl@summa-health.org; *Ref*, Linda Maser; Staff 5 (MLS 3, Non-MLS 2)
Founded 1930
Library Holdings: Bk Titles 4,500; Per Subs 300
Subject Interests: Ethics
Automation Activity & Vendor Info: (Cataloging) EOS; (Circulation) EOS

C UNIVERSITY OF AKRON LIBRARIES, 44325-1701. SAN 355-5127. Tel: 330-972-7497. FAX: 330-972-6383, 972-5106. Web Site: www.uakron.edu/library. *Dean of Libr*, Delmus Williams; *Assoc Dean*, Roger W Durbin; *Asst Dean*, Phyllis G O'Connor; *Ref*, Jeffrey Franks; *Acq*, Julia A Gammon; *Cat*, Mary Konkel; *AV*, Thomas Bennett; *Archivist*, John V Miller, Jr; *Archivist*, John A Popplestone; *Science*, Sherri Edwards; Staff 44 (MLS 44)
Founded 1872. Highest Degree: Doctorate
1998-1999 Income $5,997,456. Mats Exp $2,339,404, Books $681,027, Per/Ser (Incl. Access Fees) $1,578,377, Presv $80,000. Sal $2,737,299 (Prof $1,556,534)
Library Holdings: Bk Vols 1,122,187; Per Subs 9,622
Subject Interests: Bio med eng, Hist of psyehol, Polymer, Polymer chemistry, Rubber indust
Special Collections: B-26 Archives; Brozek Coll; Herman Muehlstein Rare Book Coll; Paul Belcher Coll; Propaganda Coll, flm; Sylvia Smith Archives; The Archives of the History of American Psychology & the American History Research Center; The University of Akron Archives
Partic in BRS; Center For Research Libraries; OCLC Online Computer Library Center, Inc; Ohio Library & Information Network; OHIONET
Friends of the Library Group

ALEXANDRIA

P ALEXANDRIA PUBLIC LIBRARY, 10 Maple Dr, PO Box 67, 43001. SAN 313-1815. Tel: 740-924-3561. FAX: 740-924-3007. Web Site: ww.alexandria.lib.oh.us. *Dir*, Dorothy Hannahs; E-Mail: dhannahs@hpls.org
Founded 1935. Pop 5,000; Circ 66,146
Library Holdings: Bk Vols 40,000; Per Subs 75
Subject Interests: Local history
Automation Activity & Vendor Info: (Cataloging) epixtech, inc.; (Circulation) epixtech, inc.

ALGER

P ALGER PUBLIC LIBRARY,* 100 W Wagner St, PO Box 18, 45812. SAN 313-1823. Tel: 419-757-7755. E-Mail: hereweka@oplin.lib.oh.us. *Dir*, Kathy Herfurth
Circ 5,950
Library Holdings: Bk Vols 22,000; Per Subs 36
Partic in Norweld

ALLIANCE

S MCDERMOTT TECHNOLOGY, INC LIBRARY, 1562 Beeson St, 44601. SAN 313-1831. Tel: 330-829-7531. FAX: 330-829-7777. E-Mail: library@mcdermott.com. *Mgr*, Jim Carter; Tel: 330-829-7530; *Info Res*, Amy M Saus; Staff 2 (MLS 1, Non-MLS 1)
Founded 1947
Library Holdings: Bk Vols 20,000; Bk Titles 18,000; Per Subs 170
Subject Interests: Chemical engineering, Heat transfer, Mat, Metallurgy, Steam generation
Database Vendor: Dialog, IAC - SearchBank, Lexis-Nexis, OCLC - First Search
Publications: Bulletin Board on WAN (wide area network)
Restriction: Private library
Function: Research library

C MOUNT UNION COLLEGE LIBRARY,* 44601-3993. SAN 313-184X. Tel: 330-823-3844. FAX: 330-823-3963. Web Site: www.muc.edu. *Coll Develop, Dir*, Robert Garland; *ILL*, Susan Ray; *Tech Servs*, Linda Scott; *Ser*, Joanne Houmard; *Govt Doc*, Cheryl Paine. Subject Specialists: *Music*, Suzanne Moushey; Staff 5 (MLS 5)
Founded 1846. Enrl 2,100; Fac 110
Jul 1997-Jun 1998 Income $854,086. Mats Exp $373,755, Books $112,383, Per/Ser (Incl. Access Fees) $138,245, Presv $11,480, Micro $16,040. Sal $330,851 (Prof $182,100)
Library Holdings: Bk Titles 219,520; Per Subs 921
Subject Interests: Elem, Secondary educ, Sports med
Special Collections: Graphic Arts (Shilts Rare Books); Greek & Latin Classics (Charles Sutherin)
Partic in Dialog Corporation; East Central College; Mideastern Ohio Libr Orgn; OCLC Online Computer Library Center, Inc; OHIONET

P RODMAN PUBLIC LIBRARY,* 215 E Broadway St, 44601-2694. SAN 313-1858. Tel: 330-821-2665. FAX: 330-821-5053. E-Mail: hclem@roc.rodman.lib.oh.us. Web Site: www.rodman.lib.oh.us/rpl. *Dir*, Harriet M Clem; *Ad Servs*, Judith Hookway; *Ch Servs*, Patricia Stone; *Tech Servs*, Christine Kirven; *ILL, Ref*, Steven Mahr; *Syst Coordr*, Karen Perone; Staff 10 (MLS 7, Non-MLS 3)
Founded 1900. Pop 37,960
1997-1998 Income $1,770,410, State $1,635,853, Locally Generated Income $134,557. Mats Exp $261,965, Books $200,147, Per/Ser (Incl. Access Fees) $36,603, Presv $745. Sal $705,106 (Prof $272,118)
Library Holdings: Bk Vols 148,190; Bk Titles 108,056; Per Subs 392
Special Collections: Original Drawings by Brinton Turkle
Automation Activity & Vendor Info: (Acquisitions) Innovative Interfaces Inc.
Publications: Bibliographies; Genealogies
Partic in Ohio Pub Libr Info Network
Friends of the Library Group
Branches: 1
BRANCH IN THE MALL, 2500 W State St, 44601. SAN 374-4485. Tel: 330-821-1313. *Librn*, Roselyn Stephens
Library Holdings: Bk Vols 14,785
Friends of the Library Group
Bookmobiles: 1

AMHERST

P AMHERST PUBLIC LIBRARY,* 221 Spring St, 44001. SAN 313-1866. Tel: 216-988-4230. FAX: 216-988-4115. E-Mail: dworkiju@oplin.lib.oh.us. *Dir*, Judith Dworkin; *Ad Servs, Coll Develop*, Janet Turner; *Ch Servs*, Paula Shadle; Staff 12 (MLS 2, Non-MLS 10)
Founded 1906. Pop 22,583; Circ 309,197
Jan 1998-Dec 1998 Income $954,117, State $609,663, Locally Generated Income $291,094, Other $53,360. Mats Exp $91,313, Books $66,866, Per/Ser (Incl. Access Fees) $19,768, Electronic Ref Mat (Incl. Access Fees) $4,679. Sal $325,711
Library Holdings: Bk Vols 55,000
Automation Activity & Vendor Info: (Cataloging) Gaylord; (Circulation) Gaylord; (Course Reserve) Gaylord; (OPAC) Gaylord

ANDOVER

P ANDOVER PUBLIC LIBRARY,* 142 W Main St, PO Box 1210, 44003-1210. SAN 313-1882. Tel: 440-293-6792. FAX: 440-293-5720. E-Mail: andover@oplin.lib.oh.us. *Dir*, Mary Jo Orahood
Circ 104,669
Library Holdings: Bk Vols 30,000; Per Subs 87
Partic in Nola Regional Library System
Friends of the Library Group

APPLE CREEK

M APPLE CREEK DEVELOPMENTAL CENTER, Professional Library Resource Center,* 2532 S Apple Creek Rd, 44606. SAN 328-8129. Tel: 330-698-2411. FAX: 330-698-8461. *In Charge*, Frank Columbo
Library Holdings: Bk Titles 1,300

ARCANUM

P ARCANUM PUBLIC LIBRARY,* 101 North St, 45304-1126. SAN 313-1890. Tel: 937-692-8484. FAX: 937-692-8916. E-Mail: arclib@wesnet.com. Web Site: www.arclib.countystart.com. *Dir*, Marilyn Walden; *Assoc Dir*, Margaret Schenck
Founded 1911. Pop 9,000; Circ 53,756
Library Holdings: Bk Vols 47,593; Per Subs 193
Special Collections: Media: videos (1708), audios (742)
Partic in Miami Valley Librs
Friends of the Library Group

ARCHBOLD

P ARCHBOLD COMMUNITY LIBRARY,* 205 Stryker St, 43502-1191. SAN 313-1904. Tel: 419-446-2783. FAX: 419-446-2142. Web Site: www.library.norweld.lib.oh.us/archbold. *Dir*, Joyce Klingelsmith; E-Mail: klingejo@oplin.lib.oh.us; *Ch Servs*, Brenda Sensenig
Founded 1917. Pop 6,500; Circ 131,984
Library Holdings: Bk Vols 27,000; Per Subs 110
Subject Interests: Local history
Mem of NW Libr District

J NORTHWEST STATE COMMUNITY COLLEGE LIBRARY, 22-600 State Rte 34, 43502-9542. SAN 313-1912. Tel: 419-267-5511, Ext 235. FAX: 419-267-5657. Web Site: nwlink.nscc.cc.oh.us/. *Acq*, Minerva Rivas; *Cat*, Cathi Baer; *Syst Coordr*, Suzanna Green-Schroeder; Staff 3 (Non-MLS 3)
Founded 1969. Enrl 1,255; Fac 137
Jul 2000-Jun 2001 Income $389,943
Library Holdings: Bk Vols 20,270; Bk Titles 17,355; Per Subs 375
Subject Interests: Bus, Computer science, Early childhood educ, Engineering, Info, Nursing
Special Collections: Toy Library
Automation Activity & Vendor Info: (Acquisitions) Innovative Interfaces Inc.; (Cataloging) Innovative Interfaces Inc.; (Circulation) Innovative Interfaces Inc.; (Course Reserve) Innovative Interfaces Inc.; (ILL) Innovative Interfaces Inc.; (Media Booking) Innovative Interfaces Inc.; (OPAC) Innovative Interfaces Inc.; (Serials) Innovative Interfaces Inc.
Partic in OCLC Online Computer Library Center, Inc; Ohio Library & Information Network; OHIONET

ASHLAND

P ASHLAND SCHOOL DISTRICT PUBLIC LIBRARY, 224 Claremont Ave, 44805. SAN 313-1920. Tel: 419-289-8188. Circulation Tel: 419-289-8188, Ext 12. Reference Tel: 419-289-8188, Ext 15. FAX: 419-281-8552. E-Mail: flowerli@oplin.lib.oh.us. Web Site: www.ashland.lib.oh.us. *Dir*, Pamela A Carothers; E-Mail: carothpa@oplin.lib.oh.us; *Bkmobile Coordr*, Janet Hollingsworth; *Ref*, Bill Snyder; *Ref*, Elizabeth Glasgow; *Ch Servs*, Toni Whitney; *Syst Coordr*, Linda A Flowers; *Head Tech Servs*, Sharon Plank; *Head, Circ*, Dreama Knight; *Ref Serv Ad*, Deborah Madigan; Staff 37 (MLS 4, Non-MLS 33)
Founded 1923. Pop 52,000; Circ 461,456
Jan 1999-Dec 1999 Income $1,346,059. Mats Exp $360,854, Books $257,568, Per/Ser (Incl. Access Fees) $24,686, Micro $19,282, AV Equip $36,736, Other Print Mats $2,550, Electronic Ref Mat (Incl. Access Fees) $20,032. Sal $611,732 (Prof $166,827)
Library Holdings: Per Subs 195
Subject Interests: Genealogy, Local history
Automation Activity & Vendor Info: (Cataloging) Inlex
Database Vendor: DRA, Ebsco - EbscoHost, IAC - Info Trac
Partic in Northeastern Ohio Libr Asn
Friends of the Library Group
Bookmobiles: 1

R ASHLAND THEOLOGICAL SEMINARY, Roger E Darling Memorial Library, 910 Center St, 44805. SAN 313-1939. Tel: 419-289-5168. FAX: 419-289-5969. *Dir*, Bradley E Weidenhamer; *Res*, Dr Russell Morton
Founded 1930. Enrl 562; Fac 24
Library Holdings: Bk Vols 80,205; Bk Titles 68,152; Per Subs 435
Special Collections: artifacts; Mary, Queen of Scots (Ronk Coll); Religious Debates (Darling Debate)
Partic in Ohio Library & Information Network

C ASHLAND UNIVERSITY LIBRARY, 401 College Ave, 44805-3796. SAN 355-5186. Tel: 419-289-5400. Interlibrary Loan Service Tel: 419-289-5402. FAX: 419-289-5422. E-Mail: library@ashland.edu. Web Site: www.ashland.edu/library. *Dir*, William B Weiss; Tel: 419-289-5401, E-Mail: bweiss@ashland.edu; *Librn, Publ Servs*, Kathern Venditti; E-Mail: kvenditt@ashland.edu; *Librn*, Bradley Weidenhamer; E-Mail: bweiden@ashland.edu; *Ref*, Jeffrey Pinkham; *Acq*, Joan Hignett; E-Mail: jhignett@ashland.edu; *Media Spec*, David Straits; *Cat, Tech Servs*, Sue Ellen Ronk; E-Mail: sronk@ashland.edu; *Automation Syst Coordr*, Jan Marotta; E-Mail: jmarotta@ashland.edu; *Publ Servs*, Judith Albert; E-Mail: jalbert@ashland.edu. Subject Specialists: *Bus*, Jeffrey Pinkham; *Legal*, Jeffrey Pinkham; Staff 13 (MLS 7, Non-MLS 6)
Founded 1878. Enrl 5,995; Fac 198; Highest Degree: Doctorate
Jul 2000-Jun 2001 Income $954,031. Mats Exp $300,000, Books $115,000, Per/Ser (Incl. Access Fees) $110,000, Presv $10,000, Micro $17,500, AV Equip $3,000, Manuscripts & Archives $1,500, Electronic Ref Mat (Incl. Access Fees) $42,000. Sal $343,602 (Prof $282,651)
Library Holdings: Bk Vols 275,557; Bk Titles 235,000; Per Subs 900
Subject Interests: Art, Bus, Chemistry, Criminal justice, Econ, Education, Geology, Health educ, Human servs-home econ, Mathematics, Music, Philosophy, Physical educ, Physics, Radio-TV, Religion, Social work, Speech comm, Theatre, Toxicology
Special Collections: 19th Century English Literature (Andrews Special Books Coll), 1st editions; 19th Century Historical Children's Literature (Lulu Wood Coll), 1st editions; American Studies (Libr of American Civilization), microbk; Bibles
Automation Activity & Vendor Info: (Cataloging) Innovative Interfaces Inc.; (Circulation) Innovative Interfaces Inc.; (OPAC) Innovative Interfaces Inc.
Database Vendor: GaleNet, Lexis-Nexis, OCLC - First Search, ProQuest, Silverplatter Information Inc.
Publications: Friends of Library (newsletter)
Partic in OCLC Online Computer Library Center, Inc; Ohio Library & Information Network; OHIONET
Friends of the Library Group

ASHLEY

P WORNSTAFF MEMORIAL PUBLIC LIBRARY,* 302 E High St, 43003-9703. SAN 313-1947. Tel: 740-747-2085. FAX: 740-747-2085. *Coll Develop, Librn*, Elizabeth Barker; E-Mail: barkerel@oplin.lib.oh.us; *Ch Servs*, Vicky Collins
Circ 55,052
Library Holdings: Bk Vols 26,337
Subject Interests: Local history, Mysteries, Old westerns
Publications: Newsletter (monthly); weekly column in Morrow Co Independent

ASHTABULA

P ASHTABULA COUNTY DISTRICT LIBRARY, 335 W 44th St, 44004-6897. SAN 355-5305. Tel: 440-997-9341. TDD: 440-992-8066. FAX: 440-992-7714. E-Mail: ashref@oplin.lib.oh.us. Web Site: www.ashtabula.lib.oh.us. *Dir*, William J Tokarczyk; Tel: 440-997-9341, Ext 224, Fax: 440-998-1198, E-Mail: tokarcwi@oplin.lib.oh.us; *Asst Dir*, Donna M Wall; Tel: 440-997-9341, Ext 222, Fax: 440-998-1198, E-Mail: walldo@oplin.lib.oh.us; *Head Ref*, Douglas Anderson; *Tech Servs*, Alan Smith; *Ch Servs*, Barbara Tack; Staff 41 (MLS 7, Non-MLS 34)
Founded 1813. Pop 62,000
Jan 2000-Dec 2000 Income (Main Library and Branch Library) $1,701,112, State $1,599,565, Other $101,547. Mats Exp $259,050, Books $204,498, Per/Ser (Incl. Access Fees) $12,896, Presv $550, AV Equip $9,874, Other Print Mats $15,290, Electronic Ref Mat (Incl. Access Fees) $15,942. Sal $715,722
Library Holdings: Bk Vols 80,000; Per Subs 192
Special Collections: Ohio Room Local History Coll
Automation Activity & Vendor Info: (Cataloging) epixtech, inc.; (Circulation) epixtech, inc.; (OPAC) epixtech, inc.
Database Vendor: Ebsco - EbscoHost, GaleNet, IAC - SearchBank, OCLC - First Search
Publications: Kid 'n Kaboodle; The Library Scoop
Function: Professional lending library
Partic in Coun of Ashtabula County Librs; Nola Regional Library System
Special Services for the Deaf - TDD
Friends of the Library Group
Branches: 1
GENEVA PUBLIC, 860 Sherman St, Geneva, 44041. (Mail add: 335 W 44th St, 44004-6897), SAN 355-533X. Tel: 440-466-4521. TDD: 440-466-9268. FAX: 440-466-0162. E-Mail: genref@oplin.lib.oh.us. Web Site: www.ashtabula.lib.oh.us/geneva.htm. *Dir*, Bill Tokarczyk; E-Mail: tokarcwi@oplin.lib.oh.us; *Asst Dir*, Donna M Wall; Tel: 440-997-9341, Ext 222, Fax: 440-998-1198, E-Mail: walldo@oplin.lib.oh.us; *Br Coordr*, Mary Stokes; E-Mail: stokesma@oplin.lib.oh.us
Founded 1832. Pop 15,028
Library Holdings: Bk Titles 27,000
Special Collections: Archie Bell Materials; Ashtabula County Geneological Society; Leander Lyon Coll; Platt R Spencer Materials
Automation Activity & Vendor Info: (Cataloging) epixtech, inc.; (Circulation) epixtech, inc.; (OPAC) epixtech, inc.
Database Vendor: Ebsco - EbscoHost, GaleNet, IAC - SearchBank, OCLC - First Search

Function: Professional lending library
Partic in Coun of Ashtabula County Librs; Nola Regional Library System
Friends of the Library Group
Bookmobiles: 1

P HARBOR-TOPKY MEMORIAL LIBRARY, 1633 Walnut Blvd, 44004. SAN 313-1963. Tel: 440-964-9645. FAX: 440-964-6701. Web Site: www.harbortopky.lib.oh.us. *Dir*, Virginia Sharp March; E-Mail: marchvi@oplin.lib.oh.us; *Head Ref*, Shawna Gambol; E-Mail: gambolsh@oplin.lib.oh.us; Staff 14 (MLS 2, Non-MLS 12)
Founded 1924. Pop 9,600; Circ 83,301
Jan 1999-Dec 1999 Income $514,645, State $404,530, Other $110,115. Mats Exp Books $58,048. Sal $213,653
Library Holdings: Bk Vols 31,433; Per Subs 90
Automation Activity & Vendor Info: (Cataloging) epixtech, inc.; (Circulation) epixtech, inc.; (ILL) epixtech, inc.
Database Vendor: epixtech, inc., OCLC - First Search
Partic in Coun of Ashtabula County Librs; Northeastern Ohio Libr Asn
Friends of the Library Group

C KENT STATE UNIVERSITY, Ashtabula Campus Library,* 3431 W 13th St, 44004-2298. SAN 313-1955. Tel: 440-964-4239. FAX: 440-964-4271. Web Site: www.ashtabula.kent.edu/library. *Dir*, Kim Cook; Staff 3 (MLS 1, Non-MLS 2)
Founded 1961. Enrl 706; Fac 32
1997-1998 Mats Exp $124,827. Sal $98,119
Library Holdings: Bk Vols 55,102; Per Subs 218
Partic in Nola Regional Library System
Friends of the Library Group

ATHENS

L ATHENS COUNTY LAW LIBRARY,* Court House, 4th flr, 45701. SAN 327-8964. Tel: 740-593-8893. *Librn*, Edward Kruse
Library Holdings: Bk Vols 10,000; Per Subs 10

C OHIO UNIVERSITY, Vernon R Alden Library,* Park Pl, 45701-2978. SAN 355-5429. Tel: 740-593-2705. FAX: 740-593-0138. E-Mail: slibraryl@ohiou.edu. Web Site: www.library.ohiou.edu. *Dean of Libr*, Julia Zimmerman; *Assoc Dean*, Gary Hunt; *Coll Develop*, Kent Mulliner; *Circ*, Anita Grant; *Doc*, Judy Daso; *Automation Syst Coordr*, Elizabeth Hoffmann-Pinther; *Archivist, Spec Coll*, George Bain. Subject Specialists: *Dance*, Holly Oderle; *Fine arts*, Anne Braxton; *Music*, Holly Oderle; *Southeast Asia*, Lian The-Mulliner; Staff 55 (MLS 55)
Founded 1804. Enrl 27,382; Fac 971; Highest Degree: Doctorate
Jul 1998-Jun 1999 Mats Exp $3,679,152, Books $1,226,388, Per/Ser (Incl. Access Fees) $2,373,737. Sal $4,934,210 (Prof $2,430,283)
Library Holdings: Bk Vols 2,232,905; Per Subs 19,351
Special Collections: Botswana, Guatemala, Swaziland & Malaysia; Cornelius Ryan World War II Papers; Edmund Blunden Coll of Romantic & Georgian Literature; Morgan History of Chemistry; Southeast Asia
Automation Activity & Vendor Info: (Circulation) Innovative Interfaces Inc.
Publications: Gatherings; Guide to Local Government Records at the Ohio University Library; Informer
Partic in Dialog Corporation; OCLC Online Computer Library Center, Inc; Westlaw
Friends of the Library Group
Departmental Libraries:
ARCHIVES & SPECIAL COLLECTIONS Tel: 740-593-2710. FAX: 740-593-0138. *Dir*, George Bain; *Spec Coll*, Sheppard Black; Staff 4 (MLS 4)
Library Holdings: Bk Vols 49,000
Subject Interests: Georgian lit, Hist of chem, Local history, Romantic, World War II
ART Tel: 740-593-2663. FAX: 740-593-0138. *Librn*, Anne Braxton
Library Holdings: Bk Vols 63,000; Bk Titles 42,000
Subject Interests: Architecture, Art, Film, Photog
MUSIC DANCE Tel: 740-593-4256. FAX: 740-593-2959. *Librn*, Holly Oberle
Library Holdings: Bk Vols 37,000
CM HEALTH SCIENCES LIBRARY Tel: 740-593-2680. Interlibrary Loan Service Tel: 740-593-2691. FAX: 740-593-4693. *Dir*, Anne Goss; E-Mail: goss@ouvaxa.cats.ohiou.edu; *Ref*, Laura Windsor; Staff 4 (MLS 3, Non-MLS 1)
Founded 1977
Library Holdings: Bk Titles 40,667; Per Subs 1,233
Subject Interests: Audiology, Biomed, Exercise, Health educ, Medicine, Nursing, Nutrition, Physical therapy, Physiol
Publications: Shelf Life
Partic in Biomedical Telefacsimile Network of Ohio
SOUTHEAST ASIA COLLECTION Tel: 740-593-2657. FAX: 740-593-0138.
Library Holdings: Bk Vols 112,000
Subject Interests: Southeast Asia
Special Collections: Botswana, Quatemalan & Swaziland; Malay World, especially Malaysia, Singapore, Brunei, Indonesia; Overseas Chinese
Publications: Malaysia/Singapore/Brunei/Asian Bibliography (quarterly)

SOUTHEAST PSYCHIATRIC HOSPITAL
M PATIENTS' LIBRARY, 100 Hospital Dr, 45701. SAN 355-5399. Tel: 740-594-5000. FAX: 740-594-3006.; Staff 1 (MLS 1)
Library Holdings: Bk Vols 2,000; Per Subs 24
M STAFF LIBRARY, 100 Hospital Dr, 45701. SAN 355-5364. Tel: 740-594-5000. FAX: 740-594-3006. E-Mail: gekoskys@mhmail.mh.state.oh.us.; Staff 1 (MLS 1)
Founded 1966
Jul 2000-Jun 2001 Income Parent Institution $5,681. Mats Exp $5,600, Books $900, Per/Ser (Incl. Access Fees) $4,700. (Prof $20,000)
Library Holdings: Bk Titles 2,700; Per Subs 26
Subject Interests: Alcohol, Drugs, Medicine, Mental illness, Nursing, Psychiat nursing, Psychology, Soc work

ATTICA

P SENECA EAST PUBLIC LIBRARY, 14 N Main St, 44807-9487. (Mail add: PO Box 572, 44807-0572), SAN 313-1971. Tel: 419-426-3825. FAX: 419-426-3701. *Dir*, Vicki Eckenrod; E-Mail: eckenrvi@oplin.lib.oh.us; *Ch Servs*, Barbara Bayer; Staff 3 (MLS 1, Non-MLS 2)
Founded 1936. Pop 5,811
Jan 1999-Dec 2000 Income $167,451, State $159,214, Locally Generated Income $8,237. Mats Exp $145,696, Books $19,461, Per/Ser (Incl. Access Fees) $3,553. Sal $64,912 (Prof $21,250)
Library Holdings: Bk Titles 20,483; Per Subs 123
Automation Activity & Vendor Info: (Acquisitions) epixtech, inc.; (Cataloging) epixtech, inc.; (Circulation) epixtech, inc.; (Course Reserve) epixtech, inc.; (ILL) epixtech, inc.; (Media Booking) epixtech, inc.; (OPAC) epixtech, inc.; (Serials) epixtech, inc.
Partic in Norweld
Friends of the Library Group

AVON LAKE

P AVON LAKE PUBLIC LIBRARY, (ALPL), 32649 Electric Blvd, 44012-1669. SAN 313-198X. Tel: 440-933-8128. FAX: 440-933-5659, 933-6406. E-Mail: avonlake@oplin.lib.oh.us. Web Site: www.kellnet.com/allib/alpl.htm. *Asst Dir*, Marcia Waugaman; *Ch Servs*, Donna Bizga; *Tech Servs*, Sharron Smith
Founded 1930
Library Holdings: Bk Vols 90,700; Per Subs 244
Subject Interests: Art, Cookbooks, Gardening, Multi-cultural kits, Pre-school concept kits, Sci kits
Special Collections: Hands-on Learning Center
Automation Activity & Vendor Info: (Circulation) Gaylord
Partic in Cleveland Area Metropolitan Library System

BARBERTON

M BARBERTON CITIZENS HOSPITAL, Morris Medical Library, 155 Fifth St NE, 44203. SAN 313-2013. Tel: 330-848-7865. FAX: 330-848-7822. *Librn*, Charlotte Sievert; E-Mail: csievert@barbhosp.com; Staff 2 (MLS 1, Non-MLS 1)
Founded 1955
Library Holdings: Bk Titles 2,378; Per Subs 123
Subject Interests: Clinical medicine, Nursing
Automation Activity & Vendor Info: (Cataloging) Innovative Interfaces Inc.; (Circulation) Innovative Interfaces Inc.; (OPAC) Innovative Interfaces Inc.; (Serials) Innovative Interfaces Inc.
Restriction: Not open to public
Partic in GMR; Neoucom Council Of Associated Hospital Librarians; Ohio Library & Information Network
Open Mon-Thur 8-4 & Fri 8-1

P BARBERTON PUBLIC LIBRARY, 602 W Park Ave, 44203-2458. SAN 313-2021. Tel: 330-745-1194. FAX: 330-745-8261. *Dir*, Barbara Kirbawy; E-Mail: kirbawba@oplin.lib.oh.us; *Asst Dir, Cat*, Kathy Jones; *Librn*, Roni Greenberg; *Ch Servs*, Barbara Gercken; *Tech Servs*, Susanne Nirschl Cogar; *Ref*, Mary Kay Ball; *Ref*, Donald Boozer; *Ref*, Dia Thomas. Subject Specialists: *Local history*, Elizabeth Swartz; Staff 30 (MLS 9, Non-MLS 21)
Founded 1903. Pop 27,623; Circ 346,705
Jan 1999-Dec 1999 Income $1,256,461, State $1,092,494. Mats Exp $168,901, Books $104,742, Per/Ser (Incl. Access Fees) $23,370, AV Equip $20,572, Electronic Ref Mat (Incl. Access Fees) $20,217. Sal $534,135
Library Holdings: Bk Vols 104,264; Per Subs 372
Special Collections: Barberton History (William A Johnston Coll)
Automation Activity & Vendor Info: (Acquisitions) epixtech, inc.; (Cataloging) epixtech, inc.; (Circulation) epixtech, inc.; (OPAC) epixtech, inc.; (Serials) epixtech, inc.
Publications: Keylines (quarterly newsletter)
Friends of the Library Group

BARNESVILLE

P BARNESVILLE HUTTON MEMORIAL LIBRARY,* 308 E Main St, 43713-1410. SAN 313-2048. Tel: 740-425-1651. FAX: 740-425-3504. *Librn*, Jeff Scaggs; Staff 2 (MLS 2)
Founded 1924. Pop 12,000; Circ 200,075
Library Holdings: Bk Titles 53,500; Per Subs 143
Subject Interests: Ohio hist, Relig studies

BATAVIA

GL CLERMONT COUNTY LAW LIBRARY ASSOCIATION,* 270 Main St, 45103. SAN 327-716X. Tel: 513-732-7109. FAX: 513-732-0974. E-Mail: cclaw@cclla.org. *Librn*, Carol A Suhre
Library Holdings: Bk Vols 14,200; Per Subs 88
Partic in Am Asn of Law Librs; OHIONET; Westlaw

P CLERMONT COUNTY PUBLIC LIBRARY, 326 Broadway St, 45103. SAN 355-5542. Tel: 513-732-2736. FAX: 513-732-3177. Web Site: www.clermont.lib.oh.us. *Publ Servs*, Leslie Massey; E-Mail: masseyle@oplin.lib.ch.us; *Coll Develop*, Nancy Ehas; E-Mail: ehasna@oplin.lib.oh.us; Staff 159 (MLS 23, Non-MLS 136)
Founded 1955. Pop 178,749; Circ 936,719
Jan 1998-Dec 1999 Income (Main Library and Branch Library) $5,541,532, State $4,183,445, County $1,093,968, Locally Generated Income $264,119. Mats Exp $745,650, Books $597,000, Per/Ser (Incl. Access Fees) $56,000, Micro $9,150. Sal $2,445,867 (Prof $789,900)
Library Holdings: Bk Vols 377,223; Bk Titles 133,688; Per Subs 412
Subject Interests: Local history
Partic in Greater Cincinnati Library Consortium; Ohio Pub Libr Info Network
Branches: 10
AMELIA BRANCH, 58 Maple St, Amelia, 45102. SAN 329-594X. Tel: 513-752-5580. FAX: 513-752-5266. *Branch Mgr*, Sue Riggs; E-Mail: riggssu@oplin.lib.oh.us
BETHEL BRANCH, 111 W Plane St, Bethel, 45106-1302. SAN 355-5577. Tel: 513-734-2619. FAX: 513-734-1321. *Branch Mgr*, Valerie Folker; E-Mail: folkerva@oplin.lib.oh.us
FELICITY BRANCH, 209 Prather Rd, Felicity, 45120. SAN 374-4299. Tel: 513-876-4134. FAX: 513-876-3619. Web Site: www.clermont.lib.oh.us. *Branch Mgr*, Diana Schellenberger; E-Mail: schellda@oplin.lib.oh.us
Database Vendor: Innovative Interfaces INN - View
Partic in Greater Cincinnati Library Consortium
GOSHEN BRANCH, 6678 State Rte 132, Goshen, 45122. SAN 323-777X. Tel: 513-722-1221. FAX: 513-722-2158. *Branch Mgr*, Patty Greco; E-Mail: grecopa@oplin.lib.oh.us
MILFORD-MIAMI TOWNSHIP BRANCH, 1099 State Rte 131, Milford, 45150-2700. SAN 355-5607. Tel: 513-248-0700. FAX: 513-248-4579. *Branch Mgr*, Joann Tudor; E-Mail: tudorjo@oplin.lib.oh.us
NEW RICHMOND BRANCH, 212 Market St, New Richmond, 45157-1322. SAN 355-5615. Tel: 513-553-0570. FAX: 513-553-0574. Web Site: www.clermont.lib.oh.us. *Branch Mgr*, Alison Morgan; E-Mail: morganal@oplin.lib.oh.us
Partic in Greater Cincinnati Library Consortium
Friends of the Library Group
OWENSVILLE BRANCH, 2548 US Rte 50, PO Box 875, Owensville, 45160. SAN 377-7197. Tel: 513-732-6084. FAX: 513-732-9168. *Branch Mgr*, Elizabeth Fiene; E-Mail: fieneel@oplin.lib.oh.us
UNION TOWNSHIP, 4462 Mt Carmel-Tobasco Rd, Cincinnati, 45244-2224. SAN 355-5631. Tel: 513-528-1744. FAX: 513-528-0539. Web Site: www.clermont.lib.oh.us. *Branch Mgr*, Anita Haller; E-Mail: halleran@oplin.lib.oh.us
WILLIAMSBURG BRANCH, 594 Main St, Williamsburg, 45176. SAN 329-5966. Tel: 513-724-1070. FAX: 513-724-5549. *Branch Mgr*, Kathleen A Siry; E-Mail: siryka@oplin.lib.oh.us
DORIS WOOD BRANCH, 180 S Third St, 45103-2806. SAN 355-5550. Tel: 513-732-2128. FAX: 513-732-2498. *Librn*, Leslie Jacobs; E-Mail: jacobsle@oplin.lib.oh.us

C UNIVERSITY OF CINCINNATI, Clermont College Library, 4200 Clermont College Dr, 45103-1785. SAN 355-9149. Tel: 513-732-5206. FAX: 513-732-5237. Web Site: library.clc.uc.edu. *Dir*, Dr Fred Marcotte; E-Mail: fred.marcotte@uc.edu; *Tech Servs*, Ann Miller; *Circ*, Michael Howser; Staff 3 (MLS 1, Non-MLS 2)
Founded 1972. Enrl 1,240; Fac 97
Library Holdings: Bk Vols 25,000; Per Subs 172
Special Collections: Audio Visual Materials; Careers; SIRS
Partic in Greater Cincinnati Library Consortium; Ohio Library & Information Network

BEACHWOOD

M CLEVELAND COLLEGE OF JEWISH STUDIES, Aaron Garber Library,* 26500 Shaker Blvd, 44122. SAN 327-6856. Tel: 216-464-4050. FAX: 216-464-5827. E-Mail: ea308@po.cwru.edu, eb608@po.cwru.edu. *Librn*, Jean Loeb Lettofsky; *Asst Librn*, Ruth Dobres; *Asst Librn*, Susan Lipton
Library Holdings: Bk Vols 29,000; Per Subs 100
Friends of the Library Group

R CONGREGATION SHAAREY TIKVAH, Rabbi Enoch H Kronheim Memorial Library, 26811 Fairmount Blvd, 44122. SAN 313-6094. Tel: 216-765-8300. FAX: 216-765-0149. *Librn*, Karen Tucker
Founded 1961
Library Holdings: Bk Titles 3,000; Per Subs 16
Subject Interests: Holocaust, Judaica, Juvenile Jewish lit
Friends of the Library Group

R LEE & DOLORES HARTZMARK LIBRARY, 26000 Shaker Blvd, 44122. SAN 313-3842. Tel: 216-831-3233. FAX: 216-831-4216.
Founded 1896
Library Holdings: Bk Titles 10,000; Per Subs 75
Subject Interests: Judaica
Special Collections: Abba Hillel Silver Archives
Publications: The Loom & the Cloth
Friends of the Library Group

SR SUBURBAN TEMPLE, Gries Library,* 22401 Chargrin Blvd, 44122-5345. SAN 328-3291. Tel: 216-991-0700. FAX: 216-991-0705. *Librn*, Claudia Z Fechter
1998-1999 Mats Exp $1,500, Books $1,000, Per/Ser (Incl. Access Fees) $200, Other Print Mats $300
Library Holdings: Bk Vols 6,500; Bk Titles 6,000; Per Subs 15

BEDFORD

S BEDFORD HISTORICAL SOCIETY LIBRARY,* 30 S Park Ave, PO Box 46282, 44146. SAN 328-5057. Tel: 440-232-0796. *Dir*, Richard J Squire; *Librn*, V Spaulding
Library Holdings: Bk Titles 7,650
Special Collections: 1876 Centennial Coll; Civil War Coll; Lincolniana Coll; Local Archives Coll; Photograph Coll; Railroads Coll
Open Mon & Wed 7:30-10, Thurs 10-4, 2nd Sun of month 2-5

BELLAIRE

P BELLAIRE PUBLIC LIBRARY, 330 32nd St, 43906. SAN 313-2099. Tel: 614-676-9421. FAX: 614-676-7940. E-Mail: bellaire@oplin.lib.oh.us. *Dir*, John T Kniesner; *Ref*, Patricia Armstrong; Staff 11 (MLS 2, Non-MLS 9)
Founded 1927. Pop 18,000
Library Holdings: Bk Vols 56,476; Per Subs 130
Partic in Ohio Pub Libr Info Network; Southeastern Ohio Libr Orgn

BELLEFONTAINE

P LOGAN COUNTY DISTRICT LIBRARY,* 220 N Main St, 43311-2288. SAN 355-5666. Tel: 937-599-4189. FAX: 937-599-5503. Web Site: www.loganco.lib.oh.us. *Dir*, Judith A Goodrich; E-Mail: goodrich@opln.lib.oh.us; *Ch Servs*, Nancy Kuta
Founded 1901. Pop 42,310
Library Holdings: Bk Vols 110,530; Bk Titles 78,165; Per Subs 250
Mem of NW Libr District
Branches: 6
DEGRAFF BRANCH, 118 S Main, DeGraff, 43318. SAN 355-5690. Tel: 937-585-5010. Web Site: www.loganco.lib.oh.us. *Librn*, Shirley Sanford
Library Holdings: Bk Vols 2,900
EAST LIBERTY BRANCH, 3235 N Main, East Liberty, 43319. SAN 355-5720. Tel: 937-666-3444. Web Site: www.loganco.lib.oh.us. *Librn*, Rhonda Grove
Library Holdings: Bk Vols 1,550
LAKEVIEW BRANCH, 130 N Main, Lakeview, 43331. SAN 355-5755. Tel: 937-842-4144. Web Site: www.loganco.lib.oh.us. *Librn*, Kathy Ashbaugh
Library Holdings: Bk Vols 3,100
RUSHSYLVANIA BRANCH, 113 N Sandusky, Rushsylvania, 43347. SAN 355-578X. Web Site: www.loganco.lib.oh.us. *Librn*, Dorothy Strawser
WEST LIBERTY BRANCH, 117 N Detroit, West Liberty, 43357. SAN 355-581X. Tel: 937-465-3656. Web Site: www.loganco.lib.oh.us. *Librn*, Nancy Spragen
Library Holdings: Bk Vols 4,850
WEST MANSFIELD BRANCH, 127 N Main, West Mansfield, 43358. SAN 355-5844. Tel: 937-355-0033. Web Site: www.loganco.lib.oh.us. *Librn*, Sharon Beck

BELLEVUE

P BELLEVUE PUBLIC LIBRARY,* 224 E Main St, 44811-1409. SAN 313-2102. Tel: 419-483-4769. FAX: 419-483-0158. Web Site: www.bellevue.lib.oh.us. *Dir*, Molly Carver; Staff 16 (MLS 4, Non-MLS 12)
Founded 1904. Pop 8,170; Circ 185,000
Jan 1998-Dec 1998 Income $825,879, State $626,899, Locally Generated Income $146,755, Other $52,225. Mats Exp $767,539, Books $122,429, Per/Ser (Incl. Access Fees) $11,835. Sal $420,326
Library Holdings: Bk Vols 77,350
Subject Interests: Local history
Database Vendor: DRA
Mem of Cleveland Area Metrop Libr Syst
Partic in Clevnet
Friends of the Library Group

BEREA

C BALDWIN-WALLACE COLLEGE, Ritter Library, 55 E Bagley Rd, 44017. SAN 355-5879. Tel: 440-826-2455. Reference Tel: 440-826-2204. FAX: 440-826-8558. Web Site: www.bw.edu/~wwwlib. *Dir*, Dr Patrick J Scanlan; *Publ Servs*, Richard Densmore; Staff 4 (MLS 4)
Founded 1845. Enrl 3,000; Fac 166; Highest Degree: Master
Jul 1998-Jun 1999 Income $850,000. Mats Exp $270,000, Books $120,000. Sal $468,000
Library Holdings: Bk Vols 200,000; Bk Titles 160,000; Per Subs 980
Subject Interests: Education, History, Music
Special Collections: Folksongs (Harry E Ridenour Coll); Paul & Josephine Mayer Rare Book Coll; Religion (Methodist Historical Coll) bks, artifacts
Database Vendor: Innovative Interfaces INN - View
Partic in Cleveland Area Metropolitan Library System; Libr Coun of Greater Cleveland; OCLC Online Computer Library Center, Inc; Ohio Library & Information Network; OHIONET
Friends of the Library Group
Departmental Libraries:
CHEMISTRY READING ROOM, Wilker Hall, 320 Front St, 44017. (Mail add: Department of Chemistry, 275 Eastland Rd, 44017), SAN 355-5909. Tel: 440-826-2312.
Library Holdings: Bk Vols 875; Per Subs 30
CURRICULUM & MATERIALS CENTER, Wheeler Hall, 300 Front St, 44017. SAN 355-5933. Tel: 440-826-2166, 440-826-2174. *Coordr*, Marilyn A Evans
Founded 1974
Library Holdings: Bk Vols 5,000; Bk Titles 10,000
JONES MUSIC LIBRARY, 275 Eastland Rd, 44017-2088. SAN 355-5968. Tel: 440-826-2375. FAX: 440-826-6520. *Librn*, Susan L Hambley; E-Mail: shambley@bw.edu; *Asst Librn*, Donald R D R D Reams; Staff 3 (Non-MLS 3)
Founded 1976. Enrl 200; Fac 50
Library Holdings: Bk Titles 956
Subject Interests: Music, Music therapy
Special Collections: Delbert M Beswick Memorial Theory Curriculum Library; Mildred Kerschner Music Education Curriculum Center
RIEMENSCHNEIDER BACH INSTITUTE, Merner-Pfeiffer Hall, 49 Seminary St, 44017-2088. (Mail add: 275 Eastland Rd, 44017-2088), Tel: 440-826-2207. FAX: 440-826-3239. Web Site: www.bw.edu/~bachinst. *Dir*, Dr Melvin P Unger; E-Mail: munger@bw.edu; *Music*, Sandra Eichenberg; Tel: 440-826-2044, E-Mail: seichenb@bw.edu; Staff 4 (Non-MLS 4)
Founded 1969
Library Holdings: Bk Vols 10,554; Per Subs 28
Subject Interests: 17th Century music, 18th Century music, Albert Riemenschneider, J S Bach, Publications, Unpublished papers of Hans T David
Special Collections: Emmy Martin Coll including many 1st editions & presentation copies; Hans David's Coll mainly from the Baroque Era; J S Bach & His Contemporaries, bks, mss; Riemenschneider's Bach Coll; Tom Villella's Recording & Book Coll
Publications: BACH (the journal of the Riemenschneider Bach Institute)
Restriction: Not a lending library
Function: Archival collection
Partic in Ohio Library & Information Network; Opal

BETTSVILLE

P BETTSVILLE PUBLIC LIBRARY, 233 State St, PO Box 385, 44815. SAN 313-2110. Tel: 419-986-5198. FAX: 419-986-6012. *Librn*, Sandy Hartsel; E-Mail: hartsesa@oplin.lib.oh.us; *Librn*, Rose Lynn Steel; *Asst Librn*, Mary Lou Golden; Staff 6 (Non-MLS 6)
Founded 1940. Pop 1,500; Circ 17,424
Jan 2000-Dec 2000 Income $132,892. Mats Exp $133,830
Library Holdings: Bk Vols 20,328; Per Subs 71
Partic in Northwest Library District

BEXLEY

P BEXLEY PUBLIC LIBRARY,* 2411 E Main St, 43209. SAN 313-4032. Tel: 614-231-9709. Web Site: www.bexlib.org. *Dir*, Robert M Stafford; *Ch Servs*, Brenda Stenberg; *Ref*, Marilyn Battin; *AV*, Sharon Short; *Circ*, Jonina Chadwick; Staff 17 (MLS 10, Non-MLS 7)
Founded 1924. Circ 769,707
Jan 1998-Dec 1999 Income $2,114,684, State $1,843,283, Locally Generated Income $165,513. Mats Exp $439,125, Books $229,276, Per/Ser (Incl. Access Fees) $78,250, Other Print Mats $130. Sal $1,149,190
Library Holdings: Bk Vols 203,389; Per Subs 474
Partic in OCLC Online Computer Library Center, Inc
Friends of the Library Group

BLANCHESTER

P BLANCHESTER PUBLIC LIBRARY, 110 N Broadway, 45107-1250. SAN 313-2129. Tel: 937-783-3585. FAX: 937-783-2910. Web Site: blaachester.lib.oh.us. *Dir*, Marsha L Erickson; E-Mail: ericksma@oplin.lib.oh.us; Staff 21 (MLS 1, Non-MLS 20)
Founded 1935. Pop 9,000; Circ 84,692
Jan 2000-Dec 2000 Income $582,774, State $499,774, Locally Generated Income $83,000. Mats Exp $118,501, Books $106,857, Per/Ser (Incl. Access Fees) $5,864, AV Equip $1,972, Electronic Ref Mat (Incl. Access Fees) $5,780. Sal $235,894 (Prof $53,000)
Library Holdings: Bk Vols 48,291; Per Subs 164
Automation Activity & Vendor Info: (Cataloging) epixtech, inc.; (Circulation) epixtech, inc.; (OPAC) epixtech, inc.
Database Vendor: GaleNet
Partic in Southwestern Ohio Rural Librs; SW Ohio Regional Libr Syst
Friends of the Library Group

BLOOMVILLE

P BLISS MEMORIAL PUBLIC LIBRARY, 20 S Marion St, 44818. (Mail add: PO Box 39, 44818), SAN 313-2137. Tel: 419-983-4675. FAX: 419-983-4675. Web Site: library.norweld.lib.oh.us/bliss. *Dir*, Karen S Miller; E-Mail: millerka@oplin.lib.oh.us; *Dep Dir*, Dorothy Seitz; *Circ*, Phyllis Hoy; *Cat*, Karon Felter; Staff 5 (MLS 1, Non-MLS 4)
Founded 1935. Pop 2,000; Circ 28,799
Jan 1999-Dec 1999 Income State $145,679. Mats Exp $156,679, Books $32,235, Per/Ser (Incl. Access Fees) $4,436, Electronic Ref Mat (Incl. Access Fees) $16,057. Sal $63,209 (Prof $27,253)
Library Holdings: Bk Vols 28,592; Bk Titles 33,285; Per Subs 148; Bks on Deafness & Sign Lang 15
Subject Interests: Seneca County hist
Special Collections: Bloomville Gazette on Microfilm, 1928
Database Vendor: epixtech, inc.
Mem of NW Libr District; NW Ohio Libr District
Partic in Norweld
Friends of the Library Group

BLUFFTON

CR BLUFFTON COLLEGE, Musselman Library, 280 W College Ave, Ste 4, 45817-1704. SAN 313-2153. Tel: 419-358-3271. Reference Tel: 419-358-3450. FAX: 419-358-3384. Web Site: www.bluffton.edu/library/. *Actg Dir, Head Tech Servs*, Kathleen Aufderhaar; Tel: 419-358-3396, 358-3414, E-Mail: aufderhaark@bluffton.edu; *ILL*, Carrie Phillips; Tel: 419-358-3275, E-Mail: phillipsc@bluffton.edu; *Ref*, Paul Weaver; Tel: 419-358-3448, E-Mail: weaverp@bluffton.edu; *Spec Coll*, Ann Hilty; Tel: 419-358-3365, E-Mail: hiltya@bluffton.edu; Staff 7 (MLS 4, Non-MLS 3)
Founded 1899. Enrl 1,000; Fac 70; Highest Degree: Master
Jul 1999-Jun 2000 Income Parent Institution $416,265. Mats Exp $120,000, Books $55,000, Presv $2,000, Micro $8,000, Electronic Ref Mat (Incl. Access Fees) $25,000. Sal $193,670
Library Holdings: Bk Vols 156,334; Bk Titles 94,451; Per Subs 700
Special Collections: Mennonite Historical Libr
Automation Activity & Vendor Info: (Acquisitions) Innovative Interfaces Inc.; (Cataloging) Innovative Interfaces Inc.; (Circulation) Innovative Interfaces Inc.; (Course Reserve) Innovative Interfaces Inc.; (OPAC) Innovative Interfaces Inc.; (Serials) Innovative Interfaces Inc.
Function: Business archives
Partic in Ohio Pvt Acad Librs; OHIONET

P BLUFFTON-RICHLAND PUBLIC LIBRARY, 145 S Main St, 45817. SAN 313-2161. Tel: 419-358-5016. FAX: 419-358-9653. Web Site: www.library.norweld.lib.oh.us/bluffton/. *Dir*, Sheryl D Schirmer; E-Mail: schirmsh@oplin.lib.oh.us; *Pub Relations*, Carolyn B Boisvert; E-Mail: boisveca@oplin.lib.oh.us; *Ch Servs*, Terry Lambert; E-Mail: lamberte@oplin.lib.oh.us; *Head, Circ*, Martha Lee; E-Mail: leem1@oplin.lib.oh.us; *Tech Servs*, Gail Neff; E-Mail: neffga@oplin.lib.oh.us; *Outreach Serv*, Lisa Wenger; E-Mail: wengerli@oplin.lib.oh.us; Staff 12 (MLS 2, Non-MLS 10)
Founded 1935. Pop 6,500; Circ 86,600
Jan 2000-Dec 2000 Income $347,000, State $265,000, Locally Generated Income $60,000, Other $2,500. Mats Exp $75,000, Books $30,000, Per/Ser

(Incl. Access Fees) $11,000, Micro $1,000, AV Equip $15,000, Electronic Ref Mat (Incl. Access Fees) $18,000. Sal $170,500 (Prof $37,000)
Library Holdings: Bk Titles 28,153; Per Subs 111; High Interest/Low Vocabulary Bk Vols 159; Bks on Deafness & Sign Lang 15
Automation Activity & Vendor Info: (Cataloging) SIRSI; (Circulation) SIRSI; (OPAC) SIRSI
Database Vendor: Ebsco - EbscoHost, GaleNet, IAC - Info Trac, OCLC - First Search, ProQuest
Function: ILL available
Partic in Norweld
Friends of the Library Group

BOWERSTON

P BOWERSTON PUBLIC LIBRARY, 200 Main St, PO Box 205, 44695-0205. SAN 313-217X. Tel: 740-269-8531. FAX: 740-269-8503. *Dir*, Dawn Spencer; E-Mail: spenceda@oplin.lib.oh.us
Founded 1935. Circ 87,005
Jan 1999-Dec 1999 Income $311,602. Mats Exp $287,177, Books $32,041, Per/Ser (Incl. Access Fees) $3,256, AV Equip $3,742. Sal $100,755 (Prof $26,439)
Library Holdings: Bk Titles 38,861; Per Subs 100
Subject Interests: Local history, Ohio, Pottery
Automation Activity & Vendor Info: (Acquisitions) epixtech, inc.; (Cataloging) epixtech, inc.; (Circulation) epixtech, inc.; (Course Reserve) epixtech, inc.; (ILL) epixtech, inc.; (Media Booking) epixtech, inc.; (OPAC) epixtech, inc.; (Serials) epixtech, inc.
Database Vendor: epixtech, inc.
Partic in Mideastern Ohio Libr Orgn

BOWLING GREEN

C BOWLING GREEN STATE UNIVERSITY, Libraries & Learning Resources, 43403. SAN 355-6026. Tel: 419-372-2856. FAX: 419-372-7996. Interlibrary Loan Service FAX: 419-372-6877. Web Site: www.bgsu.edu/colleges/library/. *Actg Dean*, Chris Miko; E-Mail: cmiko@bgnet.bgsu.edu; *Librn*, Mary Wrighten; *Circ*, Mary Beth Zachary; *Tech Servs*, Cliff Glaviano; *Ref*, Kelly Broughton; *Acq*, Gail Richmond; *Govt Doc*, Coleen Parmer; *ILL*, Kausalya Padmaraj; *Coll Develop*, Linda Brown; *Ad Servs*, Colleen Boff; *Online Servs*, Stefanie Hunker; *Bibliog Instr*, Catherine Cardwell; *Ser*, Jeanne Langendorfer; *Info Specialist*, Elizabeth Wood; Staff 110 (MLS 25, Non-MLS 85)
Founded 1913. Enrl 18,000; Fac 696; Highest Degree: Doctorate
Library Holdings: Bk Vols 2,285,856
Subject Interests: Chemistry, Education, History, Psychology
Special Collections: Popular Culture Coll, bk, journal; Popular Recordings (Music Library)
Automation Activity & Vendor Info: (Cataloging) Innovative Interfaces Inc.; (Circulation) Innovative Interfaces Inc.; (Course Reserve) Innovative Interfaces Inc.; (ILL) Innovative Interfaces Inc.; (OPAC) Innovative Interfaces Inc.; (Serials) Innovative Interfaces Inc.
Publications: BGSU Libraries, The Archival Chronicle, Northwest Quarterly (ed)
Partic in Dialog Corporation; NW Ohio Consortium; OCLC; OHIONET
Friends of the Library Group
Departmental Libraries:
CENTER FOR ARCHIVAL COLLECTIONS Tel: 419-372-2411. FAX: 419-372-0155. *Dir*, Paul D Yon; *Asst Dir*, Ann Bowers; *Archivist*, Stephen M Charter
Founded 1968
Library Holdings: Bk Vols 23,584; Per Subs 156
Subject Interests: Genealogy, Hist preservation, Labor hist, State hist, Univ archives
Special Collections: Delbert Latta Papers; Lud Ashley Papers; Rare Books (Ray Bradbury); Sam Pollock Labor Coll
Partic in Ohio Network Of American History Research Centers
CURRICULUM RESOURCE CENTER Tel: 419-372-2956. *Librn*, Sara Bushong
Library Holdings: Bk Vols 53,838
Subject Interests: Juv lit
HISTORICAL COLLECTIONS OF THE GREAT LAKES Tel: 419-372-2411. FAX: 419-372-0155. *Archivist*, Robert Graham
Library Holdings: Bk Vols 7,798
Special Collections: Great Lakes Maritime History
INSTRUCTIONAL MEDIA SERVICES Tel: 419-372-2881. FAX: 419-372-8584. *Dir*, Dr Kevin Work
MUSIC LIBRARY & SOUND RECORDINGS ARCHIVES Tel: 419-372-2307. *Librn*, Bonna Boettcher; *Archivist*, William Schurk
Library Holdings: Bk Vols 33,701; Per Subs 274
Subject Interests: Classical music, Popular music
FRANK OGG SCIENCE & HEALTH LIBRARY Tel: 419-372-2591. FAX: 419-372-6817. *Librn*, Robin Sinn
Subject Interests: Chemistry, Health, Life sci, Phys, Technology
POPULAR CULTURE LIBRARY Tel: 419-372-2450. FAX: 419-372-7996.
Library Holdings: Bk Vols 130,000; Per Subs 122
Subject Interests: Comic arts, Comic bks, Leisure, Movies, Popular fiction, Radio, Recreation, Romances, Science fiction
Special Collections: Allen & John Saunders Coll; E T Ned Guymon Detective Fiction Coll; H James Horovitz Science Fiction Coll; Papers of noted fiction authors such as Ruth Rendell, Joanna Russ, Dorothy Daniels & Marcia Muller and archives of the Romance Writers of America

P WOOD COUNTY DISTRICT PUBLIC LIBRARY,* 251 N Main St, 43402-2477. SAN 355-6085. Tel: 419-352-5104. FAX: 419-354-0405. Web Site: www.wcnet.org/wcdpl. *Dir*, Elaine Paulette; E-Mail: epaulet@wcnet.org
Founded 1875. Pop 61,000; Circ 325,325
Library Holdings: Bk Vols 127,662; Per Subs 283
Subject Interests: Local history
Partic in Northwest Library District
Friends of the Library Group
Branches: 2
BRADNER BRANCH, 130 N Main St, Bradner, 43406. SAN 355-6115. Tel: 419-288-2442. FAX: 419-288-2442. *Librn*, Alice DeCristoforo; E-Mail: decrisal@oplin.lib.oh.us
Library Holdings: Bk Vols 3,000
WALBRIDGE BRANCH, 108 N Main, Walbridge, 43465. SAN 355-614X. Tel: 419-666-9900. FAX: 419-666-8217. *Librn*, Alice DeCristoforo
Library Holdings: Bk Vols 12,300
Friends of the Library Group
Bookmobiles: 1

GL WOOD COUNTY LAW LIBRARY,* 168 S Main St, 43402. SAN 313-2188. Tel: 419-353-3921. FAX: 419-352-9269. *Librn*, Judith Gill; E-Mail: jgill@wcnet.org
1997-1998 Income $150,000
Library Holdings: Bk Vols 24,000; Per Subs 40
Partic in Westlaw

BRADFORD

P BRADFORD PUBLIC LIBRARY, 138 E Main St, 45308-1108. SAN 313-2196. Tel: 937-448-2612. FAX: 937-448-2612. *Dir*, Wanda Costello
Founded 1935. Pop 2,500; Circ 51,282
Library Holdings: Bk Vols 28,972; Per Subs 132
Special Collections: Old Newspaper on Microfilm
Automation Activity & Vendor Info: (Cataloging) DRA; (Circulation) DRA
Partic in Miami Valley Librs

BRECKSVILLE

S B F GOODRICH CO, Charles Cross Goodrich Knowledge Center, 9921 Brecksville, 44141-3289. SAN 313-220X. Tel: 216-447-5154. FAX: 216-447-6247. *Librn*, Linda Lamoun Hash; Staff 6 (MLS 5, Non-MLS 1)
Founded 1914
Library Holdings: Bk Titles 8,600; Per Subs 450
Subject Interests: Aerospace, Plastics, Polymer tech, Rubber
Publications: Newsletter
Partic in Dialog Corporation

BRISTOLVILLE

P BRISTOL PUBLIC LIBRARY, 1855 Greenville Rd, PO Box 220, 44402. SAN 313-2218. Tel: 330-889-3651. FAX: 330-889-9794. E-Mail: bristol@oplin.lib.oh.us. Web Site: www.bristol.lib.oh.us. *Dir*, Jill Warren; *Asst Librn*, Mona Saltzmann; Staff 1 (MLS 1)
Founded 1912. Pop 3,026; Circ 174,564
Jan 1999-Dec 1999 Income $551,483, State $522,883, Locally Generated Income $20,973, Other $7,627. Mats Exp $81,886, Books $73,358, Per/Ser (Incl. Access Fees) $8,528. Sal $191,078
Library Holdings: Bk Titles 44,715; Per Subs 200
Automation Activity & Vendor Info: (Cataloging) TLC; (Circulation) Follett; (OPAC) Follett
Function: ILL available, Photocopies available, Reference services available, Some telephone reference
Partic in Nola Regional Library System
Friends of the Library Group

BRYAN

M NATIONAL REYE'S SYNDROME FOUNDATION, INC LIBRARY, 426 N Lewis St, 43506-1485. (Mail add: PO Box 829, 43506-0829), SAN 372-7394. Tel: 419-636-2679. Toll Free Tel: 800-233-7393. FAX: 419-636-9897. E-Mail: nrsf@reyessyndrome.org. Web Site: www.reyessyndrome.org. *Pres*, John E Freudenberger
Founded 1974
Special Collections: Reye's Syndrome

GL WILLIAMS COUNTY LAW LIBRARY ASSOCIATION,* Court House, 3rd flr, 43506. SAN 313-2226. Tel: 419-636-4600. FAX: 419-636-9886. *Librn*, John Shaffer
Library Holdings: Bk Vols 10,000

P WILLIAMS COUNTY PUBLIC LIBRARY, 107 E High St, 43506-1702. SAN 355-6174. Tel: 419-636-6734. FAX: 419-636-3970. Web Site: www.williamsco.lib.oh.us. *Dir*, Jeffrey A Yahraus; E-Mail: yahrauje@oplin.lib.oh.us; *Asst Dir*, Susan Irwin; *Ch Servs*, Vickie Zippay; *Circ*, Lila Scrabeck; *Tech Servs*, Cindy Riter; *Ref*, Nancy Bryce. Subject Specialists: *Local history*, Jane Martin; Staff 4 (MLS 4)
Founded 1882. Pop 37,588; Circ 450,000
Library Holdings: Bk Vols 120,000; Bk Titles 101,900; Per Subs 608
Subject Interests: Genealogy, Local history, Ohio
Publications: Newsletter (quarterly)
Partic in Norweld
Open Mon-Thurs 9-8, Fri & Sat 9-5
Friends of the Library Group
Branches: 5
EDGERTON BRANCH, 319 N Michigan Ave, Edgerton, 43517. SAN 355-6204. Tel: 419-298-3230. FAX: 419-298-3230. Web Site: www.williamsco.lib.oh.us. *Mgr*, Anne Fleischer
Library Holdings: Bk Vols 12,000
Open Mon & Wed 9-8, Tues, Thurs & Fri 9-5, Sat 9-1
Friends of the Library Group
EDON BRANCH, 104 E Indiana St, Edon, 43518. SAN 355-6239. Tel: 419-272-2839. FAX: 419-272-2839. Web Site: www.williamsco.lib.oh.us. *Mgr*, Sue Seaman
Library Holdings: Bk Vols 10,000
Open Mon & Wed 10-8, Tues, Thurs & Fri 10-5, Sat 9-1
Friends of the Library Group
PIONEER BRANCH, 106 Baubice St, Pioneer, 43554. SAN 355-6263. Tel: 419-737-2833. FAX: 419-737-2833. Web Site: www.williamsco.lib.oh.us. *Mgr*, Rose King
Library Holdings: Bk Vols 10,000
Open Mon & Wed 10-8, Tues, Thurs & Fri 10-5, Sat 9-1
Friends of the Library Group
STRYKER BRANCH, 304 S Defiance St, Stryker, 43557. SAN 355-6298. Tel: 419-682-5081. FAX: 419-682-5081. Web Site: www.williamsco.lib.oh.us. *Mgr*, Sally Davis
Library Holdings: Bk Vols 12,000
Open Mon, Wed & Thurs 10-8, Tues & Fri 10-5, Sat 9-1
Friends of the Library Group
WEST UNITY BRANCH, 109 S High St, West Unity, 43570. SAN 355-6328. Tel: 419-924-5237. FAX: 419-924-5237. Web Site: www.williamsco.lib.oh.us. *Mgr*, Jan Hodson
Library Holdings: Bk Vols 12,000
Open Mon, Wed & Thurs 10-8, Tues & Fri 10-5, Sat 9-1
Friends of the Library Group

BUCYRUS

P BUCYRUS PUBLIC LIBRARY, (BPL), 200 E Mansfield St, 44820-2381. SAN 313-2234. Tel: 419-562-7327. FAX: 419-562-7437. *Dir*, James Wilkins; E-Mail: wilkinji@oplin.lib.oh.us; Staff 10 (MLS 10)
Founded 1906. Pop 26,000; Circ 114,144
Jan 1999-Dec 1999 Income $697,548, State $639,285, Locally Generated Income $58,263. Mats Exp $100,434. Sal $266,466
Library Holdings: Bk Vols 46,000; Per Subs 125
Subject Interests: Genealogy, Local history
Automation Activity & Vendor Info: (Cataloging) epixtech, inc.; (Circulation) epixtech, inc.
Friends of the Library Group

BURTON

P BURTON PUBLIC LIBRARY, 14588 W Park, PO Box 427, 44021. SAN 313-2242. Tel: 440-834-4466. FAX: 440-834-0128. E-Mail: burton@oplin.lib.oh.us. Web Site: www.burton.lib.oh.us. *Dir*, Carol C Varga; E-Mail: vargaca@oplin.lib.oh.us; *Circ*, Kathleen Young; *Head Tech Servs*, Holly M Lynn; E-Mail: lynnho@oplin.lib.oh.us; *Head Ref*, Patricia Hauser; *Ch Servs*, Camilla K Horvath; E-Mail: horvatca@oplin.lib.oh.us; *YA Servs*, Marianne Ross; Staff 4 (MLS 3, Non-MLS 1)
Founded 1910. Pop 8,746; Circ 183,866
Jan 1999-Dec 1999 Income $624,460, State $465,851, Locally Generated Income $30,548, Other $128,061. Mats Exp $64,732, Books $52,872, Per/Ser (Incl. Access Fees) $1,924, AV Equip $9,936. Sal $386,613
Library Holdings: Bk Vols 71,775; Per Subs 187
Special Collections: Amish Coll; Books on Tape; Local History; Puppets
Automation Activity & Vendor Info: (Acquisitions) epixtech, inc.; (Cataloging) epixtech, inc.; (Circulation) epixtech, inc.; (OPAC) epixtech, inc.
Database Vendor: Ebsco - EbscoHost, epixtech, inc., OCLC - First Search
Publications: Friends Newsletter
Function: ILL available
Mem of NOLA Regional Libr Syst
Partic in OCLC Online Computer Library Center, Inc
Friends of the Library Group

S GEAUGA COUNTY HISTORICAL SOCIETY, Shanower Library, 14653 E Park St, PO Box 153, 44021-0153. SAN 325-4739. Tel: 440-834-1492. FAX: 440-834-4012. E-Mail: shanowerlibrary@geaugalink.com. Web Site: www.geaugahistory@geaugalink.com.
Founded 1941
Library Holdings: Bk Titles 2,000
Subject Interests: Genealogy, Local history
Special Collections: Geauga County, Ohio History, corresp, mss, photogs; Hitchcock Family Papers
Publications: Geauga County Historical Quarterly (members' newsletter)
Restriction: By appointment only
Function: Research library

C KENT STATE UNIVERSITY, Geauga Campus Library,* 14111 Claridon-Troy Rd, 44021-9535. SAN 324-4407. Tel: 440-834-4187. FAX: 440-834-0919. *Dir*, Mary Hricko; E-Mail: mhricko@geauga.kent.edu
Founded 1976. Enrl 290
Library Holdings: Bk Vols 18,000

CADIZ

P PUSKARICH PUBLIC LIBRARY, 200 E Market St, 43907-1185. SAN 313-2250. Tel: 740-942-2623. FAX: 740-942-8047. Web Site: winslo.state.oh.us/ppl. *Dir*, Sandi Thompson; E-Mail: thompss2@oplin.lib.oh.us; Staff 3 (MLS 1, Non-MLS 2)
Founded 1880. Pop 12,693; Circ 126,168
1998-1999 Income $540,000. Mats Exp $95,000, Books $75,000, Per/Ser (Incl. Access Fees) $10,000, AV Equip $10,000. Sal $250,000
Library Holdings: Bk Vols 50,591; Bk Titles 50,537; Per Subs 185
Subject Interests: Coal, Genealogy, Local history
Automation Activity & Vendor Info: (Acquisitions) epixtech, inc.; (Cataloging) epixtech, inc.; (Circulation) epixtech, inc.; (Course Reserve) epixtech, inc.; (ILL) epixtech, inc.; (OPAC) epixtech, inc.
Partic in Southeastern Ohio Libr Orgn
Friends of the Library Group

CALDWELL

P CALDWELL PUBLIC LIBRARY, 517 Spruce St, PO Box 230, 43724. SAN 313-2269. Tel: 740-732-4506. FAX: 740-732-4795. Web Site: caldwell.lib.oh.us. *Dir*, Marilyn S Blaney; E-Mail: blaneyma@oplin.lib.oh.us; Staff 10 (Non-MLS 10)
Founded 1930. Pop 14,810; Circ 93,038
Jan 1999-Dec 1999 Income $470,970, State $451,958, Locally Generated Income $18,017, Other $995. Mats Exp $95,996, Books $65,241, Per/Ser (Incl. Access Fees) $5,048, AV Equip $11,936, Electronic Ref Mat (Incl. Access Fees) $13,771. Sal $141,761 (Prof $37,519)
Library Holdings: Bk Vols 37,651; Per Subs 155
Subject Interests: Genealogy
Automation Activity & Vendor Info: (Circulation) epixtech, inc.; (OPAC) epixtech, inc.
Partic in Southeastern Ohio Libr Orgn
Friends of the Library Group

CAMBRIDGE

P GUERNSEY COUNTY DISTRICT PUBLIC LIBRARY,* 800 Steubenville Ave, 43725-2385. SAN 355-6352. Tel: 740-432-5946. FAX: 740-432-7142. *Dir*, Carla Hutchens; *Asst Dir*, Rich Goodwin; Staff 25 (MLS 2, Non-MLS 23)
Founded 1832. Pop 39,024; Circ 325,384
Library Holdings: Bk Vols 126,931; Per Subs 287
Special Collections: Local History & Genealogy (Finley Coll Room)
Partic in Southeastern Ohio Libr Orgn
Friends of the Library Group
Branches: 1
BYESVILLE BRANCH, 100 Glass Ave, Byesville, 43723. SAN 355-6387. Tel: 740-685-2236. FAX: 740-685-6105. *Dir*, Carla Hutchens; *Branch Mgr*, Linda Kostelnik
Friends of the Library Group
Bookmobiles: 1

L GUERNSEY COUNTY LAW LIBRARY,* Guernsey County Court House, 43725. SAN 325-4747. Tel: 740-432-9258. *Librn*, Richard A Baker; *Asst Librn*, Margot A Ringer
Library Holdings: Bk Vols 15,000
Subject Interests: Fed law, Ohio law
Restriction: Restricted public use

CANAL FULTON

P CANAL FULTON PUBLIC LIBRARY,* 154 E Market St NE, 44614-1196. SAN 313-2285. Tel: 330-854-4148. FAX: 330-854-9520. E-Mail: canful@oplin.lib.oh.us. Web Site: www.cand.lib.oh.us. *Dir*, Jean Kindry; *Ref*, Christopher Cumo; *Ch Servs*, Sharon Burnley; *Tech Servs*, Barbara Williams; *Ref*, Katrina Thomas

Founded 1937. Pop 12,023; Circ 175,353
1997-1998 Income $498,807, State $474,337, Locally Generated Income $6,046, Other $18,424. Mats Exp $87,043, Books $76,256, Per/Ser (Incl. Access Fees) $10,403, AV Equip $384. Sal $205,551 (Prof $50,000)
Library Holdings: Bk Vols 48,893; Per Subs 211
Partic in ME Ohio Libr Orgn

CANTON

M AULTMAN HOSPITAL, Health Sciences Library,* 2600 Sixth St SW, 44710-1797. SAN 313-2293. Tel: 330-452-9911, Ext 5000. FAX: 330-588-2604. *Librn*, Krystal Slivka; Staff 4 (MLS 1, Non-MLS 3)
Library Holdings: Bk Titles 4,276; Per Subs 257
Subject Interests: Medicine, Nursing

S CANTON MUSEUM OF ART, Purdy Memorial Library, 1001 Market Ave N, 44702. SAN 313-2307. Tel: 330-453-7666. FAX: 330-453-1034. E-Mail: laura@cantonart.org. Web Site: www.cantonart.org.
Founded 1941
Library Holdings: Per Subs 20
Subject Interests: Art, Music
Special Collections: Victorian Art (John Hemming Fry Coll), bks, portfolios

C KENT STATE UNIVERSITY, Stark Campus Library, 6000 Frank Ave NW, 44720. SAN 313-2331. Tel: 330-499-9600, Ext 53330. FAX: 330-494-6212. E-Mail: refdesk@stark.kent.edu. Web Site: www.stark.kent.edu/library. *Dir*, Rob Kairis; Tel: 330-499-9600, Ext 53326, E-Mail: rkairis@stark.kent.edu; *Ref*, Maureen Kilcullen; Tel: 330-499-9600, Ext 53322, E-Mail: mkilcullen@stark.kent.edu; *Ser*, Roger Davis; Tel: 330-499-9600, Ext 53328, E-Mail: rdavis@stark.kent.edu; *Coll Develop*, Judith Kooistra; Tel: 330-499-9600, Ext 53320, E-Mail: jkooistra@stark.kent.edu; *Cat*, Mary Birtalan; Tel: 330-499-9600, Ext 53323, E-Mail: mbirtalan@stark.kent.edu; *Acq*, Jeanne Hawley; Tel: 330-499-9600, Ext 53321, E-Mail: jhawley@stark.kent.edu; *Circ*, Mary Lou Hester; Tel: 330-499-9600, Ext 53324; Staff 7 (MLS 3, Non-MLS 4)
Founded 1967. Enrl 3,100; Fac 150; Highest Degree: Master
Jul 1999-Jun 2000 Mats Exp $143,251, Books $67,940, Per/Ser (Incl. Access Fees) $42,662, Presv $4,565, Electronic Ref Mat (Incl. Access Fees) $28,084. Sal $318,037 (Prof $200,444)
Library Holdings: Bk Vols 67,494; Bk Titles 41,492; Per Subs 261
Automation Activity & Vendor Info: (Cataloging) Innovative Interfaces Inc.; (Circulation) Innovative Interfaces Inc.; (Course Reserve) Innovative Interfaces Inc.; (OPAC) Innovative Interfaces Inc.; (Serials) Innovative Interfaces Inc.
Database Vendor: Innovative Interfaces INN - View, Lexis-Nexis, OCLC - First Search, Wilson - Wilson Web
Function: Research library
Partic in Molo Regional Library System; OCLC Online Computer Library Center, Inc; Ohio Library & Information Network

C MALONE COLLEGE, Everett L Cattell Library, 515 25th St NW, 44709-3897. SAN 313-234X. Tel: 330-471-8317. FAX: 330-454-6977. Web Site: www.malone.edu/academics/library/welcome.cfm. *Coll Develop, Dir*, Stanford Terhune; E-Mail: terhune@malone.edu; *Cat*, Bea Whitehead; Tel: 830-471-8315, E-Mail: white@malone.edu; *ILL, Ref*, Jan Anderson; Tel: 830-471-8312, E-Mail: anderson@malone.edu; *Acq*, Jackie Hisrich; Tel: 330-471-8333, E-Mail: hisrich@malone.edu; *Circ*, Becky Fort; Tel: 330-471-8313, E-Mail: fort@malone.edu; *Circ*, Deanna Dallas; Tel: 330-471-8319, E-Mail: ddallas@malone.edu; *Govt Doc, Ref*, Charlene Willey; Tel: 330-471-8324, E-Mail: willey@malone.edu; *Per*, Barbara Moginot; Tel: 330-471-8334, E-Mail: moginot@malone.edu; *Cat, Ref*, Heidi Beke-Harrigan; Tel: 330-471-8314, E-Mail: hbharrigan@malone.edu; *Cat, Govt Doc*, Kristine Owens; Tel: 330-471-8315, E-Mail: kowens@malone.edu; *Circ*, Amy Ferrebee; Tel: 330-471-8319; Staff 11 (MLS 5, Non-MLS 6)
Founded 1892. Enrl 2,004; Fac 148; Highest Degree: Master
Jul 1999-Jun 2000 Income Parent Institution $732,957. Mats Exp $367,225, Books $58,614, Per/Ser (Incl. Access Fees) $162,208, Presv $14,669, Micro $46,581, Electronic Ref Mat (Incl. Access Fees) $77,590. Sal $275,804 (Prof $173,594)
Library Holdings: Bk Vols 153,475; Bk Titles 113,500; Per Subs 1,292
Subject Interests: Society of Friends
Special Collections: Evangelical Friends Church-Eastern Region Archives; Friends Library (Quakers); US Federal Government documents Selective Depository
Automation Activity & Vendor Info: (Acquisitions) Innovative Interfaces Inc.; (Cataloging) Innovative Interfaces Inc.; (Circulation) Innovative Interfaces Inc.; (Course Reserve) Innovative Interfaces Inc.; (ILL) Innovative Interfaces Inc.; (OPAC) Innovative Interfaces Inc.; (Serials) Innovative Interfaces Inc.
Database Vendor: GaleNet, ProQuest, Silverplatter Information Inc.
Partic in Dialog Corporation; Molo Regional Library System; OCLC Online Computer Library Center, Inc; Ohio Library & Information Network; Ohio Pvt Acad Librs; OHIONET

S MCKINLEY MUSEUM OF HISTORY, SCIENCE & INDUSTRY, Ramsayer Research Library, 800 McKinley Monument Dr NW, 44708. SAN 327-683X. Tel: 330-455-7043. FAX: 330-455-1137. *Librn*, Wilbur Weber; Staff 10 (MLS 2, Non-MLS 8)
1999-2000 Mats Exp $650, Books $200, Per/Ser (Incl. Access Fees) $50, Presv $400. Sal $6,050
Library Holdings: Bk Titles 9,200
Subject Interests: City hist, State hist
Function: Research library
Friends of the Library Group

M MERCY MEDICAL CENTER, Medical Library,* 1320 Mercy Dr NW, 44708. SAN 355-6689. Tel: 330-489-1462. FAX: 330-489-1127. E-Mail: mrd@neoucom.edu. *Dir*, Marlene Derrick; Staff 2 (MLS 1, Non-MLS 1)
Founded 1960
Library Holdings: Bk Titles 1,300; Per Subs 184
Subject Interests: Allied health, Health admin, Medicine
Publications: Core Reference Collection; Journals Listing
Partic in Neoucom Council Of Associated Hospital Librarians

S OHIO POWER CO LIBRARY,* PO Box 24400, 44701-4400. SAN 313-2358. Tel: 330-438-7235. FAX: 330-438-7360.
Founded 1956
Library Holdings: Bk Vols 200
Subject Interests: Electrical engineering, Environmental studies, Law
Special Collections: Utility information & reports

S PRO FOOTBALL HALL OF FAME, Library Research Center,* 2121 George Halas Dr NW, 44708. SAN 313-2366. Tel: 330-456-8207. FAX: 330-456-9080. Web Site: www.profootballhof.com. *Res*, Saleem Choudhry
Founded 1963
Library Holdings: Bk Vols 2,100; Per Subs 15
Special Collections: Bert Bell Scrapbooks; Game Programs & Media Guides of all Teams; Individual & Team Files (1895 to present), VF; Spalding Football Guides (1892-1940)
Restriction: By appointment only

S REPOSITORY LIBRARY,* 500 Market Ave S, 44702. SAN 313-2315. Tel: 330-580-8300, Ext 8488. FAX: 330-454-5745. Web Site: www.cartonrep.com. *Librn*, Annie O Jones; E-Mail: ajones@rep-printing.com
Library Holdings: Bk Vols 483
Special Collections: William McKinley (McKinleyana Coll), photos, newsp clippings
Restriction: Staff use only

P STARK COUNTY DISTRICT LIBRARY, 715 Market Ave N, 44702-1080. SAN 355-6441. Tel: 330-452-0665. Interlibrary Loan Service Tel: 330-453-7951. FAX: 330-452-0403. E-Mail: scdl@oplin.lib.oh.us. Web Site: www.stark.lib.oh.us. *Dir*, Nancy B Johnston; *Assoc Dir*, Marjorie Baker; *Coordr, Pub Relations*, Marshall Thyra; E-Mail: marsahth@oplin.lib.oh.us; *Ch Servs*, Carol Carmack; *Coll Develop*, Penny Marshall; *Coll Develop*, Edlyn Theiss; *Tech Coordr*, Donovan Ackley; Fax: 330-452-0503; Staff 206 (MLS 25, Non-MLS 181)
Founded 1884. Pop 367,585; Circ 3,083,462
Jan 1998-Dec 1998 Mats Exp $7,434,203. Sal $4,918,229
Library Holdings: Bk Vols 1,038,312
Special Collections: Family History (Genealogy), bks, microfilm; Local Author Coll; Minority Literature (Black History)
Automation Activity & Vendor Info: (Circulation) epixtech, inc.
Database Vendor: Dialog, epixtech, inc., GaleNet, IAC - Info Trac, OCLC - First Search
Partic in Mid eastern Ohio Libr Orgn; OCLC Online Computer Library Center, Inc
Special Services for the Deaf - Books on deafness & sign language; High interest/low vocabulary books; TTY machine
Special Services - Books for the Handicapped/Disabled
Branches: 9
COMMUNITY CENTER, 1400 Sherrick Rd SE, 44707. SAN 326-7431. Tel: 330-453-8042. *Librn*, Linda Bennett
Library Holdings: Bk Vols 14,580
Special Collections: Black Hist Coll
DEHOFF MEMORIAL, 216 Hartford Ave SE, 44707. SAN 355-6476. Tel: 330-452-9014. *Librn*, Carole L Angerman
Library Holdings: Bk Vols 27,930
Special Collections: Black History Coll
EAST CANTON BRANCH, 224 N Wood St, East Canton, 44730. SAN 355-6506. Tel: 330-488-1501. *Librn*, Ruth Stephens
Library Holdings: Bk Vols 22,400
HARTVILLE BRANCH, 411 E Maple St, Hartville, 44632. SAN 355-6530. Tel: 330-877-9975. *Librn*, James Chivers
Library Holdings: Bk Vols 33,041
JACKSON TOWNSHIP, 7487 Fulton Rd NW, Massillon, 44646. SAN 373-5583. Tel: 330-833-1010. FAX: 330-833-3491. *Librn*, Mary Ann Renner
Library Holdings: Bk Vols 24,722
NORTH BRANCH, 189 25th St NW, 44709. SAN 355-6565. Tel: 330-456-4356. FAX: 330-580-1806. E-Mail: scdlnrth@oplin.lib.oh.us. Web Site: www.stark.oplin.lib.oh.us/north.html. *Branch Mgr*, Pat Johnson; E-Mail: johnsopa@oplin.lib.oh.us; Staff 16 (MLS 3, Non-MLS 13)
Founded 1960
Library Holdings: Bk Vols 92,350
Automation Activity & Vendor Info: (Circulation) epixtech, inc.;

(OPAC) epixtech, inc.
Database Vendor: Ebsco - EbscoHost, GaleNet, IAC - Info Trac, OCLC - First Search
Partic in OPLIN
Friends of the Library Group
PERRY HEIGHTS, 4001 13th St SW, Massillon, 44646. SAN 355-659X. Tel: 330-477-8482. *Branch Mgr*, Shirley Rembert
Library Holdings: Bk Vols 35,550
SANDY VALLEY, 9754 Cleveland Ave SE, Magnolia, 44643. SAN 355-662X. Tel: 330-866-3366. *Branch Mgr*, Karen Comstock
Library Holdings: Bk Vols 24,631
MADGE YOUTZ BRANCH, 2113 14th St NE, 44705. SAN 355-6654. Tel: 330-452-2618. *Librn*, Hilary Powell
Library Holdings: Bk Vols 24,131
Bookmobiles: 4

L STARK COUNTY LAW LIBRARY ASSOCIATION, 110 Central Plaza S, Ste 401, 44702. SAN 328-5812. Tel: 330-451-7380. FAX: 330-451-7381. E-Mail: info@starklawlibrary.org. Web Site: www.starklawlibrary.org. *Dir*, Niki Domenick; Staff 3 (MLS 3)
Founded 1890
Jan 1999-Dec 1999 Income (Main Library and Branch Library) $688,215, City $333,859, County $338,497, Other $15,857. Mats Exp $542,058, Books $7,964, Per/Ser (Incl. Access Fees) $464,647, Presv $679, Micro $4,101, Electronic Ref Mat (Incl. Access Fees) $64,667. Sal $152,976 (Prof $73,820)
Library Holdings: Bk Vols 53,430; Bk Titles 5,520; Per Subs 225
Subject Interests: Ohio law
Automation Activity & Vendor Info: (Cataloging) SIRSI; (Circulation) SIRSI; (OPAC) SIRSI; (Serials) SIRSI
Publications: Legally Speaking (Newsletter)
Restriction: Members only, Private library
Branches:
MASSILLON BRANCH, Two James Duncan Plaza, Massillon, 44646. (Mail add: 110 Central Plaza S, Ste 401, 44702), SAN 329-3807. Tel: 330-451-7380. FAX: 330-451-7381. E-Mail: info@starklawlibrary.org. Web Site: www.starklawlibrary.org.
Library Holdings: Bk Vols 500

S TIMKEN CO, Research Library-Res-06, 1835 Dueber Ave SW, 44706-0930. SAN 313-2382. Tel: 330-471-2049. FAX: 330-471-2282. E-Mail: cromip@timken.com.; Staff 2 (MLS 1, Non-MLS 1)
Founded 1966
Library Holdings: Bk Titles 30,000; Per Subs 280
Subject Interests: Eng res, Ferrous metallurgical res
Partic in Data Star; Dialog Corporation; OHIONET; SDC Info Servs

CARDINGTON

P CARDINGTON-LINCOLN PUBLIC LIBRARY,* 128 E Main St, 43315. SAN 313-2404. Tel: 419-864-8181. FAX: 419-864-8181. E-Mail: cardline@oplin.lib.oh.us. *Librn*, Shirley Robinson; *Asst Librn*, Patricia Coleman
Circ 10,349
Library Holdings: Bk Vols 30,000; Per Subs 100
Partic in Cent Ohio Interlibr Network; NCLC

CAREY

P DORCAS CAREY PUBLIC LIBRARY,* 236 E Findlay St, 43316-1250. SAN 313-2412. Tel: 419-396-7921. FAX: 419-396-3046. *Dir*, Linda Gatchell; E-Mail: gatcheli@oplin.lib.oh.us
Founded 1905. Pop 5,800; Circ 84,328
Library Holdings: Bk Vols 30,000; Per Subs 102
Partic in Norweld

CARROLLTON

P CARROLL COUNTY DISTRICT LIBRARY,* 70 Second St NE, 44615. SAN 355-6743. Tel: 330-627-2613. FAX: 330-627-2523. Web Site: www.carroll.lib.oh.us. *Actg Librn*, Helen Skinner
Founded 1935. Pop 26,521; Circ 201,769
1997-1998 Income (Main Library and Branch Library) $680,989, State $610,429, Locally Generated Income $70,560. Mats Exp $575,490, Books $121,628. Sal $310,422
Library Holdings: Bk Vols 50,409; Per Subs 234
Subject Interests: Local history, Sports
Special Collections: Large Print Coll, bks
Automation Activity & Vendor Info: (OPAC) epixtech, inc.
Database Vendor: epixtech, inc.
Branches: 1
MALVERN BRANCH, 108 E Porter St, PO Box 487, Malvern, 44644. SAN 355-6778. Tel: 330-330-863-0419. FAX: 216-863-0419. *Dir*, Ellen Finnicum
Bookmobiles: 1

CEDARVILLE

CR CEDARVILLE COLLEGE CENTENNIAL LIBRARY, 251 N Main St, 45314. (Mail add: PO Box 601, 45314-0601), SAN 313-2420. Tel: 937-766-7840. Reference Tel: 937-766-7850. FAX: 937-766-2337. E-Mail: library@cedarville.edu. Web Site: www.cedarville.edu/dept/ls/index.htm. *Dir Libr Serv*, Lynn Alan Brock; Tel: 937-766-7846; *Assoc Dir*, Jan M Bosma; *Bibliog Instr*, Ruth Martin; *Ref*, Lynne Funtik; *Media Spec*, Carl Brandon; *Automation Syst Coordr*, Judy Boddy; *Coll Develop*, Julie Deardorff; *Bibliog Instr*, Tonya Fawcett; Staff 23 (MLS 7, Non-MLS 16)
Founded 1895. Enrl 2,855; Fac 163; Highest Degree: Master
Jul 1999-Jun 2000 Income $1,243,742, Locally Generated Income $53,569, Parent Institution $1,190,173. Mats Exp $1,226,738, Books $151,074, Per/Ser (Incl. Access Fees) $92,963, Presv $8,235, Micro $4,517, AV Equip $49,314, Other Print Mats $892, Electronic Ref Mat (Incl. Access Fees) $62,324. Sal $659,131 (Prof $319,981)
Library Holdings: Bk Vols 139,026; Bk Titles 104,575; Per Subs 941
Subject Interests: Baptist hist, Theol studies
Special Collections: English Bible Coll; Limited Edition Book Club Coll; Michael Dewine Congressional Papers
Automation Activity & Vendor Info: (Acquisitions) Innovative Interfaces Inc.; (Cataloging) Innovative Interfaces Inc.; (Circulation) Innovative Interfaces Inc.; (OPAC) Innovative Interfaces Inc.; (Serials) Innovative Interfaces Inc.
Database Vendor: Innovative Interfaces INN - View, Lexis-Nexis, ProQuest, Silverplatter Information Inc.
Function: Reference services available
Partic in OCLC Online Computer Library Center, Inc; Ohio Library & Information Network; OHIONET; Southwestern Ohio Council For Higher Education

CELINA

P MERCER COUNTY DISTRICT LIBRARY,* 303 N Main St, 45822. SAN 355-6808. Tel: 419-586-4442. FAX: 419-586-3222. *Dir*, Austin R Schneider; *Ch Servs*, Karen Hart; *Circ*, L Muether; E-Mail: muetheel@oplin.lib.oh.us; *Asst Dir*, Vicki Debolt; *AV*, Jean Shaw
Founded 1899. Pop 39,000; Circ 240,000
1998-1999 Income $639,000. Mats Exp $70,000, Books $60,000, Per/Ser (Incl. Access Fees) $10,000. Sal $300,000
Library Holdings: Bk Vols 87,000; Per Subs 125
Subject Interests: Children's literature
Partic in Miami Valley Librs
Branches: 3
MENDON BRANCH, 105 W Market St, PO Box 302, Mendon, 45862. SAN 355-6832. Tel: 419-795-6472. FAX: 419-795-6472. *Librn*, Carol Mullins
Library Holdings: Bk Vols 5,000
Friends of the Library Group
SAINT HENRY & GRANVILLE TOWNSHIP BRANCH, 200 E Main St, Saint Henry, 45883. SAN 355-6867. Tel: 419-678-3128. FAX: 419-678-3128. *Librn*, Patricia Kunk
Library Holdings: Bk Vols 4,000
Friends of the Library Group
ZAHN-MARON TOWNSHIP BRANCH, 5 Franklin St, PO Box 219, Chickasaw, 45826. SAN 355-6824. Tel: 419-925-4966. FAX: 419-925-4996. *Librn*, Janet Schmackers
Friends of the Library Group

L MERCER COUNTY LAW LIBRARY ASSOCIATION, (MCLLA), Court House, Rm 206, N Main St, 45822. SAN 329-8841. Tel: 419-586-2122, 419-586-5669. FAX: 419-586-4000. *Librn*, Carolyn Leffler
Library Holdings: Bk Vols 50,000; Bk Titles 10,000

J WRIGHT STATE UNIVERSITY, Lake Campus Library,* 7600 State Rte 703 E, 45822-2921. SAN 313-2439. Tel: 419-586-0360. FAX: 419-586-0358. *Dir*, Alex Pittman; E-Mail: alexpittman@wright.edu
Founded 1962. Enrl 543; Fac 35
1997-1998 Mats Exp $98,829. Sal $35,129
Library Holdings: Bk Vols 23,000; Bk Titles 22,000; Per Subs 290
Subject Interests: Bibliog instruction, Mat on hist of the Am frontier, Modern lang
Special Collections: Material on History of the American Frontier
Partic in Ohio Library & Information Network

CENTERBURG

P CENTERBURG PUBLIC LIBRARY, 49 E Main St, PO Box 609, 43011-0609. SAN 313-2447. Tel: 740-625-6538. FAX: 740-625-7311. *Dir*, Mishelle Durbin
Founded 1924. Pop 5,500; Circ 83,186
Jan 1998-Dec 1998 Income $260,332, State $249,665, Other $10,667. Mats Exp $29,925, Books $26,705, Per/Ser (Incl. Access Fees) $3,220. Sal $81,598
Library Holdings: Bk Vols 33,000; Per Subs 106
Automation Activity & Vendor Info: (Cataloging) Sagebrush Corporation; (Circulation) Sagebrush Corporation

CENTERVILLE

P WASHINGTON-CENTERVILLE PUBLIC LIBRARY, 111 W Spring Valley Rd, 45458. SAN 355-6891. Tel: 937-433-8091. FAX: 937-433-1366. E-Mail: cvref@oplin.lib.oh.us. Web Site: www.wcpl.lib.oh.us. *Dir*, Cynthia A Klinck; Staff 14 (MLS 9, Non-MLS 5)
Founded 1930. Pop 50,213; Circ 1,529,557
Jan 1999-Dec 1999 Income $4,658,204, State $2,692,170, County $1,429,530, Locally Generated Income $120,364, Other $416,140. Mats Exp $695,487, Books $429,150, Per/Ser (Incl. Access Fees) $37,154. Sal $1,779,437
Library Holdings: Bk Vols 341,259; Per Subs 399
Automation Activity & Vendor Info: (Acquisitions) epixtech, inc.; (Cataloging) epixtech, inc.; (Circulation) epixtech, inc.; (OPAC) epixtech, inc.
Partic in Miami Valley Librs
Branches: 1
WOODBOURNE, 6060 Far Hills Ave, 45459-1924. SAN 374-681X. Tel: 937-435-3700. FAX: 937-435-6812. E-Mail: wbref@oplin.lib.oh.us. Web Site: www.wcpl.oh.us.

CHARDON

P GEAUGA COUNTY PUBLIC LIBRARY, 12701 Ravenwood Dr, 44024-1336. SAN 355-6956. Tel: 440-286-6811. FAX: 440-286-7419. Web Site: www.geauga.lib.oh.us. *Dir*, Deborah F O'Connor; Tel: 440-286-6811, Ext 101, E-Mail: oconnode@oplin.lib.oh.us; *Asst Dir*, Ellen Leavitt; E-Mail: leavitel@oplin.lib.oh.us; *Tech Servs*, John Springer; *Bkmobile Coordr*, Jane Attina; Staff 168 (MLS 17, Non-MLS 151)
Founded 1963. Pop 84,000; Circ 1,626,222
Jan 1999-Dec 1999 Income (Main Library and Branch Library) $5,302,715, State $3,395,971, County $1,401,068, Other $505,676. Mats Exp $976,612, Books $596,447, Per/Ser (Incl. Access Fees) $59,208, AV Equip $170,782, Other Print Mats $44,570, Electronic Ref Mat (Incl. Access Fees) $105,605. Sal $2,560,337
Library Holdings: Bk Titles 425,880; Per Subs 1,437
Subject Interests: Local genealogy
Special Collections: Geol Survey of Ohio; Geology-Ohio, bks, pamphlets
Automation Activity & Vendor Info: (Acquisitions) epixtech, inc.; (Cataloging) epixtech, inc.; (Circulation) epixtech, inc.; (OPAC) epixtech, inc.; (Serials) epixtech, inc.
Database Vendor: GaleNet
Partic in Cleveland Area Metropolitan Library System; Nola Regional Library System; OCLC Online Computer Library Center, Inc; OHIONET
Friends of the Library Group
Branches: 6
BAINBRIDGE, 17222 Snyder Rd, Chagrin Falls, 44023. SAN 355-6980. Tel: 440-543-5611. FAX: 440-543-4734. *Mgr*, Donna Fried
Friends of the Library Group
CHARDON LIBRARY, 110 E Park St, 44024. SAN 328-7025. Tel: 440-285-7601. FAX: 440-285-3808. *Librn*, Mary Fran Bennett
Friends of the Library Group
GEAUGA WEST, 13455 Chillicothe Rd, Chesterland, 44026. SAN 355-7014. Tel: 440-729-4250. FAX: 440-729-7517. *Librn*, Linda Yanko
Friends of the Library Group
MIDDLEFIELD LIBRARY, 15982 E High St, Middlefield, 44062. SAN 355-7049. Tel: 440-632-1961. FAX: 440-632-1407. *Librn*, Barbara Luther
Friends of the Library Group
NEWBURY PUBLIC LIBRARY STATION, 14775 Auburn Rd, Newbury, 44065. SAN 376-9151. Tel: 440-564-7552. FAX: 440-564-7117. *Librn*, Karen Chakford
Friends of the Library Group
THOMPSON LIBRARY STATION, 16700 Thompson Rd, Thompson, 44086. SAN 328-7041. Tel: 440-298-3831. FAX: 440-298-3921. *Librn*, Robin Kuhlman
Friends of the Library Group
Bookmobiles: 1

L LAW LIBRARY ASSOCIATION OF GEAUGA COUNTY,* 100 Short Court St, 44024. SAN 327-6813. Tel: 440-285-2222, Ext 2450. FAX: 440-285-3603. *Librn*, Susan Proboski
1997-1998 Income $200,000. Sal $25,000
Library Holdings: Bk Vols 20,000; Per Subs 250
Partic in Westlaw

CHESTERLAND

S ORGANIZATION DEVELOPMENT INSTITUTE LIBRARY,* 11234 Walnut Ridge Rd, 44026. SAN 374-8480. Tel: 440-461-4333. Web Site: www.members.aol.com/odinst. *Pres*, Dr Donald W Cole
Library Holdings: Bk Titles 100

CHESTERVILLE

P SELOVER PUBLIC LIBRARY,* PO Box 25, 43317-0025. SAN 313-2455. Tel: 419-768-3431. FAX: 419-768-2249. *Dir*, Gail Gress; *Librn*, Candie Crisci; *Librn*, Nancy Witzel; *Librn*, Connie Henthorn; *Librn*, Kristy Kanagy; *Librn*, Louella Chapman; *Librn*, Nancy Alspaugh; *Librn*, Marilyn Zeigler; *Asst Librn*, Stephanie Rhodes
Founded 1926. Pop 8,000; Circ 47,896
Library Holdings: Bk Titles 17,000; Per Subs 150
Subject Interests: Local history
Special Collections: National Geographic Coll

CHILLICOTHE

P CHILLICOTHE & ROSS COUNTY PUBLIC LIBRARY, 140-146 S Paint St, Box 185, 45601-0185. SAN 355-7073. Tel: 740-702-4145. TDD: 740-702-4100. FAX: 740-702-4156. E-Mail: chillcot@oplin.lib.oh.us. Web Site: www.chillicothe.lib.oh.us. *Dir*, Jennifer Thompson; E-Mail: thompsje@oplin.lib.oh.us; *Asst Dir*, Linda Higgins; *Branch Mgr*, Adrienne Clemons; *Ch Servs*, Lea Yoakem; *Pub Relations*, Karen Conley; *Circ*, Sue Uhrig; *Ad Servs*, Janine Shilling; *Tech Coordr*, Bruce Landis; *Cat*, Ya Lan Wu; Staff 11 (MLS 3, Non-MLS 8)
Founded 1859. Pop 73,941; Circ 465,895
Jan 1999-Dec 1999 Income $2,715,993, State $2,618,968, Locally Generated Income $89,877. Mats Exp $336,509. Sal $1,326,679
Library Holdings: Bk Vols 178,682; Per Subs 435
Subject Interests: Genealogy
Special Collections: Burton E Stevenson Coll; Ross County Census Records, 1820 through 1900, micro
Automation Activity & Vendor Info: (Acquisitions) epixtech, inc.; (Cataloging) epixtech, inc.; (Circulation) epixtech, inc.; (OPAC) epixtech, inc.; (Serials) epixtech, inc.
Special Services for the Deaf - Staff with knowledge of sign language; TDD
Special Services for the Blind - Talking Books
Friends of the Library Group
Branches: 6
HOWARD S YOUNG BRANCH, 167 W Springfield St, Frankfort, 45628. SAN 355-7103. Tel: 740-702-4175. FAX: 740-702-4176.
Library Holdings: Bk Vols 7,310
KINGSTON BRANCH, 19 Main St, Kingston, 45644. SAN 355-7138. Tel: 740-702-4180. FAX: 740-702-4181.
Library Holdings: Bk Vols 7,348; Per Subs 20
NORTHSIDE, 550 Buckeye St, 45601. SAN 377-0206. Tel: 740-702-4100. FAX: 740-702-4118. *Librn*, Linda Higgins
Library Holdings: Bk Vols 52,945
PAXTON TOWNSHIP, 204 N Quarry St, Bainbridge, 45612. SAN 355-7162. Tel: 740-702-4185. FAX: 740-702-4186.
Library Holdings: Bk Vols 9,709
RICHMOND DALE COMMUNITY BRANCH, PO Box 129, Richmond Dale, 45673-0129. SAN 355-7197. Tel: 740-702-4190. FAX: 740-702-4191.
Library Holdings: Bk Vols 9,033
SOUTH SALEM BRANCH, Buckskin Elementary School, South Salem, 45681. SAN 355-7227. Tel: 937-981-2400.
Library Holdings: Bk Vols 8,180

S CHILLICOTHE CORRECTIONAL INSTITUTION LIBRARY,* State Rte 104, PO Box 5500, 45601. SAN 325-0156. Tel: 740-773-2616. FAX: 740-773-8296. *Mgr*, Eugene Rigney; Staff 2 (MLS 1, Non-MLS 1)
1997-1998 Mats Exp $90,000. Sal $25,000
Library Holdings: Bk Vols 13,000; Bk Titles 7,814; Per Subs 100
Branches:
LAW LIBRARY
Library Holdings: Bk Titles 2,192

GM DEPARTMENT OF VETERANS AFFAIRS, Library Service,* 17273 State Rte 104, 45601. SAN 313-248X. Tel: 740-773-1141, Ext 7623. E-Mail: mlibrary@bright.net. *Librn*, Sylivia Holbrook; Staff 4 (MLS 2, Non-MLS 2)
Library Holdings: Bk Vols 6,506; Per Subs 373
Subject Interests: Nursing, Psychiatry
Partic in OHIONET; Vets Admin Libr Network

S MEAD CORP, Technical Information Center,* 232 Eighth St, PO Box 1700, 45601. SAN 313-2463. Tel: 740-772-3812. FAX: 740-772-3595. E-Mail: stm1@research.mead.com. *Mgr*, Sheldon T Miller
Founded 1930
Library Holdings: Bk Vols 5,000; Per Subs 180
Subject Interests: Board, Paper, Pulp manufacture
Special Collections: Dard Hunter Handmade Books
Publications: Central Research Library Bulletin
Partic in OHIONET

C OHIO UNIVERSITY CHILLICOTHE CAMPUS, Quinn Library, 571 W Fifth St, PO Box 629, 45601-0629. SAN 313-2471. Tel: 740-774-7201. FAX: 740-774-7268. Web Site: 132.235.130.224. *Dir*, Stanley Planton; E-Mail: planton@ohio.edu; *Asst Librn*, Lorraine Wochna; E-Mail: wochna@ohiou.edu; Staff 4 (MLS 2, Non-MLS 2)
Founded 1974. Enrl 1,600

Jul 1999-Jun 2000 Income $330,767. Mats Exp $104,281, Books $32,091, Per/Ser (Incl. Access Fees) $50,520, Presv $1,000, Micro $10,817, AV Equip $100, Electronic Ref Mat (Incl. Access Fees) $8,943. Sal $112,939 (Prof $62,108)
Library Holdings: Bk Vols 50,355; Bk Titles 44,925; Per Subs 400; Bks on Deafness & Sign Lang 77
Special Collections: Dard Hunter Coll; Ohio Historical Coll
Automation Activity & Vendor Info: (Acquisitions) Innovative Interfaces Inc.; (Cataloging) Innovative Interfaces Inc.; (Circulation) Innovative Interfaces Inc.; (Course Reserve) Innovative Interfaces Inc.; (ILL) Innovative Interfaces Inc.; (Media Booking) Innovative Interfaces Inc.; (OPAC) Innovative Interfaces Inc.; (Serials) Innovative Interfaces Inc.
Database Vendor: GaleNet, Lexis-Nexis, OCLC - First Search
Publications: QuinnEssentials newsletter
Partic in Ohio Library & Information Network; OHIONET

S US NATIONAL PARK SERVICE, Hopewell Culture National Historical Park Library, 16062 State Rte 104, 45601. SAN 370-3096. Tel: 740-774-1125. FAX: 740-774-1140. Web Site: www.nps.gov/hocu. *In Charge*, Bonnie Murray
Library Holdings: Bk Vols 2,000
Subject Interests: Archaeology
Special Collections: Hopewell Archeological Conference Papers

CINCINNATI

R ADATH ISRAEL SYNAGOGUE, Leshner Library, 3201 E Galbraith Rd, 45236. SAN 313-2498. Tel: 513-793-1800. FAX: 513-792-5085. E-Mail: rapp@tso.cin.ix.net. *Librn*, Andrea Rapp
Founded 1927
Library Holdings: Bk Vols 5,000
Subject Interests: Culture, Hebrew lit, Jewish hist, Jewish lit, Russian lang, Yiddish
Special Collections: Dr Seuss; Parent-Teacher Jewish Stories in Hebrew; Reisenfeld-Talmud; Sesame Easy Classics
Publications: Associated Jewish Libraries Newsletter; Haddash Magazine; Jewish Book World; Jewish Science Interpreter; Judaica Book News (Milton Sound); Melton Journal; Reform Judaism-Amer Israelite Moment Israel Scene; The Book Peddler
Serves religious schools (379 students & 20 classes) five days a week, pre-school through high school students in a congregation of 1000 families
Friends of the Library Group

S ANDREW JERGENS CO, Research Library,* 2535 Spring Grove Ave, 45214. SAN 313-2757. Tel: 513-421-1400, 513-455-5362. FAX: 513-455-5363.
Library Holdings: Bk Vols 1,500; Per Subs 95
Subject Interests: Chemistry, Cosmetics, Personal products

S ARCHDIOCESE OF CINCINNATI ARCHIVES, 6616 Beechmont Ave, 45230. SAN 371-2869. Tel: 513-231-0810. FAX: 513-231-3254. *Archivist*, Don H Buske
Library Holdings: Bk Vols 500

S ASSOCIATION FOR FACILITIES ENGINEERING, Information Resources Department,* 8180 Corporate Park Dr, No 305, 45242-3309. SAN 375-7218. Tel: 888-222-0155. FAX: 513-489-2473. E-Mail: afe@goodnews.net. Web Site: www.afe.org.
Library Holdings: Bk Titles 50

R ATHENAEUM OF OHIO, Eugene H Maly Memorial Library, 6616 Beechmont Ave, 45230. SAN 321-1177. Tel: 513-231-2223, Ext 136. FAX: 513-231-3254. Web Site: www.mtsm.org/library.htm. *Dir*, Sister Deborah Harmeling; Tel: 513-231-2223, Ext 135, E-Mail: dharmeli@mtsm.org; *Publ Servs*, Elizabeth Hamilton; E-Mail: ehamilo@mtsm.org; *Per*, Donna Vanderbosch; Tel: 513-231-2223, Ext 134, E-Mail: dvander@mtsm.org; Staff 5 (MLS 2, Non-MLS 3)
Founded 1829. Enrl 225; Fac 26; Highest Degree: Master
Jul 1999-Jun 2000 Income $221,581. Mats Exp $93,122, Books $45,706, Per/Ser (Incl. Access Fees) $24,105, Presv $4,132, Electronic Ref Mat (Incl. Access Fees) $7,747. Sal $105,554 (Prof $61,258)
Library Holdings: Bk Vols 99,318; Per Subs 414
Subject Interests: Biblical studies, Canon law, Church history, Moral, Pastoral counseling, Roman Catholic theology
Special Collections: American Catholic Church History (Archbishop Purcell Special Coll); Rare books & mss.; Roman Catholic liturgy; Unusual Bibles (Rare Book Coll)
Automation Activity & Vendor Info: (Acquisitions) Innovative Interfaces Inc.; (Cataloging) Innovative Interfaces Inc.; (Circulation) Innovative Interfaces Inc.; (Course Reserve) Innovative Interfaces Inc.; (OPAC) Innovative Interfaces Inc.; (Serials) Innovative Interfaces Inc.
Database Vendor: Innovative Interfaces INN - View
Partic in Greater Cincinnati Library Consortium; Ohio Library & Information Network; Ohio Pvt Acad Librs

M CHILDREN'S HOSPITAL, Edward L Pratt Library, 3333 Burnet Ave, 45229-3039. SAN 313-2528. Tel: 513-636-4320. FAX: 513-559-9669. E-Mail: hillb1@chmcc.org. Web Site: www.chmcc.org/pratt.html. *Mgr*, Barbarie Hill; Staff 4 (MLS 2, Non-MLS 2)
Founded 1931
Library Holdings: Bk Titles 4,500; Per Subs 350
Subject Interests: Developmental biol, Genetics, Pediatrics, Teratology
Publications: CHMC Library News; Studies of the Children's Hospital Research Foundation
Partic in Dialog Corporation; Nat Libr of Med; OCLC Online Computer Library Center, Inc

S CHIQUITA BRANDS INTERNATIONAL, INC, Law Library,* 250 E Fifth St, 45202. SAN 374-5783. Tel: 513-784-8063. FAX: 513-784-6691. *Librn*, Terri Suter; Staff 1 (MLS 1)
Founded 1990
Library Holdings: Bk Titles 1,600
Partic in Westlaw

M CHRIST HOSPITAL, Medical Library,* 2139 Auburn Ave, 45219. SAN 313-2536. Tel: 513-369-2737. FAX: 513-629-4353. *Mgr*, Regina Hartman; E-Mail: hartmanr@healthall.com; Staff 3 (MLS 1, Non-MLS 2)
Founded 1933
Library Holdings: Bk Titles 5,000; Per Subs 350
Subject Interests: Internal medicine, Surgery, Virology
Restriction: Private library
Partic in BRS; Medline; Ohio-Kentucky Coop Libraries

S CINCINNATI ART MUSEUM LIBRARY, 953 Eden Park Dr, 45202-1557. SAN 313-2544. Tel: 513-639-2978. FAX: 513-721-0129. Web Site: www.cincinnatiartmuseum.com. *Librn*, Mona L Chapin; E-Mail: mchapin@cincyart.org; Staff 3 (MLS 2, Non-MLS 1)
Founded 1881
Library Holdings: Bk Vols 63,000; Per Subs 150
Subject Interests: Am, Am Indian art, British painting, Islamic art, Old master prints, Photog, Rookwood pottery
Special Collections: Art in Cincinnati; Cincinnati Art Museum Coll; Cincinnati Artists Coll
Function: Reference only
Partic in OCLC Online Computer Library Center, Inc

CR CINCINNATI BIBLE COLLEGE & SEMINARY, George Mark Elliott Library, 2700 Glenway Ave, 45204-3200. SAN 313-2552. Tel: 513-244-8180. Interlibrary Loan Service Tel: 513-244-8435. Circulation Tel: 513-244-8680. Reference Tel: 513-244-8435. FAX: 513-244-8140. Web Site: www.cincybible.edu. *Coll Develop, Dir*, James H Lloyd; Tel: 513-244-8138, Fax: 513-244-8434, E-Mail: jim.lloyd@cincybible.edu; *Circ, ILL*, Scott Lloyd; Fax: 513-244-8434, E-Mail: scott.lloyd@cincybible.edu; *Tech Servs*, Jean Weber; Tel: 513-244-8139, Fax: 513-244-8434, E-Mail: jean.weber@cincybible.edu. Subject Specialists: *New Testament*, Scott Lloyd; *Theology*, James H Lloyd; *Theology*, Scott Lloyd; Staff 6 (MLS 2, Non-MLS 4)
Founded 1924. Enrl 1,198; Fac 38; Highest Degree: Master
Jul 1999-Jun 2000 Mats Exp $38,090. Sal $202,576
Library Holdings: Bk Vols 105,000; Bk Titles 79,000; Per Subs 625
Subject Interests: Biblical studies, Theology
Special Collections: Restoration Movement
Automation Activity & Vendor Info: (Cataloging) Innovative Interfaces Inc.; (Circulation) Innovative Interfaces Inc.; (Course Reserve) Innovative Interfaces Inc.; (ILL) Innovative Interfaces Inc.; (OPAC) Innovative Interfaces Inc.
Partic in Greater Cincinnati Library Consortium; Ohio Library & Information Network; OHIONET

M CINCINNATI CENTER FOR DEVELOPMENTAL DISORDERS, Jack H. Rubinstein Library, Sabin Education Bldg, 3333 Burnet Ave, 45229-3039. SAN 355-8789. Tel: 513-636-4626. FAX: 513-636-7361. Web Site: www.chmcc.org. *Actg Dir*, Barbara Johnson; E-Mail: johnbo@chmcc.org; *Cat*, Alison Kissling; *Res*, Jean Meier; Staff 3 (MLS 2, Non-MLS 1)
Founded 1957
Library Holdings: Bk Vols 12,000; Bk Titles 10,000; Per Subs 120
Subject Interests: Develop disabilities, Develop disorders, Genetics, Handicapping conditions, Learning disabilities, Mental retardation, Pediatrics, Rehabilitation
Special Collections: Parents' Library, bks, pamphlets & videos; Toy Library for Children with Special Needs
Publications: Bibliographies
Partic in Cincinnati Area Health Sci Libr Asn; Regional Med Libr - Region 3

S CINCINNATI COLLEGE OF MORTUARY SCIENCE LIBRARY,* 645 W North Bend Rd, 45224-1428. SAN 327-6791. Tel: 513-761-2020. FAX: 513-761-3333. Web Site: www.ccms.edu. *Pres*, Dan L Flory
Library Holdings: Bk Vols 6,000
Subject Interests: Mortuary science
Restriction: Students only

S CINCINNATI ENQUIRER LIBRARY,* 312 Elm St, 45202. SAN 313-2579. Tel: 513-768-8464. FAX: 513-768-8340. *Librn*, Ray Zwick; *Asst Librn*, Frank Harmon; *Asst Librn*, Sally Besten
Founded 1919
Library Holdings: Bk Vols 500; Per Subs 100

S CINCINNATI HISTORICAL SOCIETY LIBRARY, Museum Center-Cincinnati Union Terminal, 1301 Western Ave, 45203. SAN 313-2587. Tel: 513-287-7000. Interlibrary Loan Service Tel: 513-287-7094. Reference Tel: 513-287-7030. Toll Free Tel: 800-733-2077. FAX: 513-287-7095. E-Mail: library@cincymuseum.org. Web Site: www.cincymuseum.org. *Dir*, Ruby Rogers; Tel: 513-287-7080, E-Mail: rrogers@cincymuseum.org; *Curator*, Barbara J Dawson; Tel: 513-287-7098, E-Mail: bdawson@cincymuseum.org; *AV*, Cynthia Keller; Tel: 513-287-7073, E-Mail: ckeller@cincymuseum.org; *Spec Coll*, Scott L Gampfer; Tel: 513-287-7084, E-Mail: sgampfer@cincymuseum.org; *Rare Bks*, Laura L Chace; Tel: 513-287-7089, E-Mail: lchace@cincymuseum.org; *Reader Servs*, Anne B Shepherd; Tel: 513-287-7069; *Ref*, Linda Bailey; E-Mail: lbailey@cincymuseum.org; *Tech Servs*, Anne Wittekind Kling; Tel: 513-287-7070, E-Mail: akling@cincymuseum.org. Subject Specialists: *History*, Scott L Gampfer; *Prints*, Barbara J Dawson; Staff 8 (MLS 3, Non-MLS 5)
Founded 1831
Library Holdings: Bk Vols 90,000; Per Subs 300
Subject Interests: Metrop Cincinnati, Miami purchase, Ohio, Old Northwest territory
Special Collections: Cornelius J Hauck Coll; James Albert Green Coll; Peter G Thomson Ohio Coll; William Henry Harrison Coll
Restriction: Open to public for reference only
Function: Research library
Partic in Greater Cincinnati Library Consortium; OCLC Online Computer Library Center, Inc; OHIONET

S CINCINNATI INSTITUTE OF FINE ARTS, Taft Museum of Art Library, 316 Pike St, 45202-4293. SAN 313-2897. Tel: 513-241-0343. FAX: 513-241-2266. E-Mail: taftmuse@fuse.net. Web Site: www.taftmuseum.org. *Curator, Dep Dir*, David T Johnson; Tel: 513-241-0343, Ext 13, E-Mail: djohnson@taftmuseum.org
Founded 1932
Sep 1999-Aug 2000 Income Parent Institution $3,500. Mats Exp $3,500, Books $3,000, Per/Ser (Incl. Access Fees) $500
Library Holdings: Bk Vols 2,000
Subject Interests: Art, Decorative arts of 16th to 19th centuries
Special Collections: Taft Art Coll Archives
Publications: Taft Museum: Collections and Its History (4 vols)
Restriction: By appointment only

L CINCINNATI LAW LIBRARY ASSOCIATION,* 601 Hamilton County Court House, 1000 Main St, 45202. SAN 313-2595. Tel: 513-946-5300. FAX: 513-946-5252. *Librn*, Billie J Grey; *Asst Librn*, Julie Koeline; *Asst Librn*, Melissa Scheirey
Founded 1834
Library Holdings: Bk Vols 184,000; Per Subs 400
Subject Interests: Anglo-Am law, Digest, Loose-leaf servs, Reporters treatises, Statutes
Special Collections: CD-ROM network, ultrafiche; Rare Legal Treatises; United States Session Laws
Automation Activity & Vendor Info: (Cataloging) epixtech, inc.; (Circulation) epixtech, inc.; (OPAC) epixtech, inc.; (Serials) epixtech, inc.
Partic in OCLC Online Computer Library Center, Inc

S CINCINNATI MUSEUM CENTER, Science Library, 1301 Western Ave, 45203. SAN 313-2633. Tel: 513-621-3890. FAX: 513-345-8501. *Librn*, Philip Yannarella
Library Holdings: Bk Vols 7,500; Per Subs 80
Subject Interests: Natural history

S CINCINNATI POST LIBRARY,* 125 E Court St, 45202. SAN 371-2109. Tel: 513-352-2785. FAX: 513-621-3962. *Librn*, Bob Hahn
Library Holdings: Bk Vols 400; Bk Titles 400; Per Subs 12

S CINCINNATI PRESERVATION ASSOCIATION, Library & Information Center,* 342 W Fourth St, 45202. SAN 327-6775. Tel: 513-721-4506. FAX: 513-721-6832. E-Mail: cpa@queencity.com. Web Site: www.queencity.com/cpa. *Exec Dir*, Beth Sullebarger; Staff 2 (Non-MLS 2)
Library Holdings: Bk Titles 1,000; Per Subs 10

S CINCINNATI PSYCHOANALYTIC INSTITUTE, Frederic T Kapp Memorial Library, 3001 Highland Ave, 45219. SAN 328-1558. Tel: 513-961-8886. FAX: 513-961-0308. E-Mail: kappcpi@compuserve.com. *Librn*, Mary Sanker
Founded 1981
Library Holdings: Bk Titles 3,900; Per Subs 56
Subject Interests: Psychoanalysis, Psychotherapy
Restriction: Members only
Friends of the Library Group

P CINCINNATI REGIONAL LIBRARY FOR THE BLIND & PHYSICALLY HANDICAPPED,* Library Sq, 800 Vine St, 45202-2071. SAN 313-282X. Tel: 513-369-6999. Toll Free Tel: 800-582-0335. FAX: 513-369-3111. *Librn*, Donna Foust
Publications: Service Bulletin; Special Edition
Special Services for the Deaf - Captioned media
Arkenstone Open Book System

C CINCINNATI STATE TECHNICAL & COMMUNITY COLLEGE LIBRARY,* 3520 Central Pkwy, 45223-2612. SAN 375-2771. Tel: 513-569-1606. FAX: 513-559-0040. Web Site: www.cinstate.cc.oh.us/library. *Dir*, Kathryn C O'Gorman; E-Mail: ogormank@cinstate.cc.oh.us; *Tech Servs*, Susanne Phelps; *Coll Develop*, Debbie Bogenschutz
Jul 1997-Jun 1998 Income $805,043. Mats Exp $163,499, Books $42,435, Per/Ser (Incl. Access Fees) $63,812, Micro $16,955. Sal $427,138 (Prof $196,789)
Library Holdings: Bk Vols 26,431; Per Subs 339
Partic in Greater Cincinnati Library Consortium; OCLC Online Computer Library Center, Inc; Ohio Library & Information Network

M CITIZENS FOR A TOBACCO FREE SOCIETY LIBRARY,* PO Box 36236, 45236. SAN 375-7994. Tel: 513-677-6666. E-Mail: no2tobacco@aol.com. *Exec Dir*, Ahron Leichtman
Library Holdings: Bk Titles 300

S COGNIS, INC, (Formerly Henkel Corp), Emery Group Research Library, 4900 Este Ave, 45232-1491. SAN 313-2692. Tel: 513-482-2157. FAX: 513-482-2007. *Librn*, Jui-Chin Peng
Founded 1928
Library Holdings: Bk Vols 7,500; Per Subs 150
Subject Interests: Biological, Chemical engineering, Derivatives, Fatty acids, Organic chemistry, Ozone, Polymers, Synthetic lubricants

CR COLLEGE OF MOUNT SAINT JOSEPH, Archbishop Alter Library, 5701 Delhi Rd, 45233-1671. SAN 313-6299. Tel: 513-244-4216. Reference Tel: 513-244-4307. FAX: 513-244-4355. E-Mail: library@mail.msj.edu. Web Site: www.msj.edu/library. *Dir Libr Serv*, Paul Owen Jenkins; Tel: 513-244-4351, E-Mail: paul_jenkins@mail.msj.edu; *Head Ref*, Susan Falgner; Tel: 513-244-4352, E-Mail: susan_falgner@mail.msj.edu; *Cat*, Deborah DeGeorge; Tel: 513-244-4798, E-Mail: deborah_degeorge@mail.msj.edu; *Tech Coordr*, Jim Layden; Tel: 513-244-4762, E-Mail: jim_layden@mail.msj.edu; *Tech Servs*, Julie Flanders; Tel: 513-244-4798, E-Mail: julie_flanders@mail.msj.edu; *Electronic Resources*, Cynthia Gregory; Tel: 513-244-4762, E-Mail: cynthia_gregory@mail.msj.edu; Staff 11 (MLS 5, Non-MLS 6)
Founded 1920. Enrl 1,600; Fac 114; Highest Degree: Master
Jul 1999-Jun 2000 Mats Exp $241,922, Books $63,572, Per/Ser (Incl. Access Fees) $58,506, Presv $3,807, Micro $19,431. Sal $238,684 (Prof $165,394)
Library Holdings: Bk Vols 97,034; Bk Titles 58,363; Per Subs 600
Automation Activity & Vendor Info: (Acquisitions) Innovative Interfaces Inc.; (Cataloging) Innovative Interfaces Inc.; (Circulation) Innovative Interfaces Inc.; (OPAC) Innovative Interfaces Inc.; (Serials) Innovative Interfaces Inc.
Database Vendor: CARL, Ebsco - EbscoHost, IAC - SearchBank, Innovative Interfaces INN - View, Lexis-Nexis, OCLC - First Search, ProQuest
Partic in Ohio Library & Information Network

GM DEPARTMENT OF VETERANS AFFAIRS, Medical Center Library-142D,* 3200 Vine St, 45220-2213. SAN 313-296X. Tel: 513-475-6315. FAX: 513-475-6454. *Chief Librn*, Sandra Mason; *Ref*, Catherine Constance; Staff 2 (MLS 2)
Library Holdings: Bk Vols 483
Partic in BRS; Medline

L DINSMORE & SHOHL LIBRARY,* 255 E Fifth St, 1900 Chemed Ctr, 45202-3172. SAN 313-2668. Tel: 513-977-8338. FAX: 513-977-8141. *Librn*, Tammy Bottomley; E-Mail: tbottoml@dinslaw.com; *Res*, Maria Wetzel; Tel: 513-977-8146, E-Mail: mwetzel@dinslaw.com; *Res*, Heather P Wright; Tel: 513-977-5433, E-Mail: hwright@dinslaw.com; Staff 4 (MLS 2, Non-MLS 2)
Library Holdings: Bk Vols 24,000
Database Vendor: OCLC - First Search
Restriction: Private library

S FLUOR DANIEL FERNALD INC, Technical Information Center,* 7400 Willey Rd, PO Box 538704, 45253-8704. SAN 313-2811. Tel: 513-648-3000, Ext 7494. FAX: 513-648-3947.
Founded 1952
Library Holdings: Bk Titles 5,000; Per Subs 200
Subject Interests: Chemistry, Environ restoration, Metallurgy of uranium, Waste mgt
Special Collections: Government Publications
Publications: Library Accessions; Newsletter (monthly)
Restriction: Staff use only
Partic in Dialog Corporation; OCLC Online Computer Library Center, Inc

L FROST BROWN TODD LLP, (Formerly Frost Brown Jacobs LLP), Law Library, 2200 PNC Ctr, 201 E Fifth St, 45202. SAN 372-2147. Tel: 513-651-6800. FAX: 513-651-6981. Web Site: www.frostbrowntodd.com. *Librn*, Jeanne Dietrick; *Librn*, Tracie Tiegs; Staff 2 (MLS 2)
Library Holdings: Bk Vols 27,000; Per Subs 225
Partic in OHIONET

S GENERAL ELECTRIC AIRCRAFT ENGINE, AEG Technical Information Center,* One Neumann Way, Mail Drop N32, 45215-6301. SAN 313-2714. Tel: 513-243-4582. FAX: 513-243-7426. *Librn*, John Tebo; *Ref*, David

Hensley; Staff 1 (MLS 1)
Founded 1950
Library Holdings: Bk Vols 36,000; Per Subs 130
Subject Interests: Aerospace mat, Air breathing propulsion systs, Computations, Metallurgy, Physics, Related technology
Publications: Technical Information Preview Series (TIPS)
Partic in OCLC Online Computer Library Center, Inc

R GOD'S BIBLE SCHOOL & COLLEGE LIBRARY, 1810 Young St, 45210. SAN 313-2722. Tel: 513-721-7944, Ext 263. FAX: 513-721-3971. *Dir*, Chris Lambeth
Founded 1901. Enrl 401; Fac 30; Highest Degree: Bachelor
Library Holdings: Bk Titles 33,000; Per Subs 255
Subject Interests: Religion

M GOOD SAMARITAN HOSPITAL LIBRARY, 375 Dixmyth Ave, 45220-2489. SAN 313-2730. Tel: 513-872-2433. FAX: 513-872-4984. *Librn*, Rosalie V Zajac; E-Mail: rose_zajac@trihealth.com; Staff 5 (MLS 1, Non-MLS 4)
Founded 1915
Library Holdings: Bk Vols 9,500; Bk Titles 9,000
Subject Interests: Bio-med, Nursing, Obstetrics, Perinatology, Surgery
Special Collections: History of Nursing
Automation Activity & Vendor Info: (Cataloging) EOS; (Circulation) EOS; (OPAC) EOS; (Serials) EOS
Publications: Library News

L GRAYDON, HEAD & RITCHEY, Law Library, 1900 Fifth Third Ctr, PO Box 6464, 45201-6464. SAN 372-2074. Tel: 513-621-6464. FAX: 513-651-3836. Web Site: www.graydon.com. *Librn*, Katherine Michniuk Steen; E-Mail: ksteen@graydon.com
Library Holdings: Bk Vols 17,000; Per Subs 35

CR HEBREW UNION COLLEGE-JEWISH INSTITUTE OF RELIGION, Klau Library, Klau Library, HUC-JIR, 3101 Clifton Ave, 45220-2488. SAN 355-7316. Tel: 513-221-1875. Circulation Tel: 513-221-7444, Ext 287. Reference Tel: 513-221-7444, Ext 285. FAX: 513-221-0519. E-Mail: klau@cn.huc.edu. Web Site: www.huc.edu. *Dir*, David J Gilner; *Head Tech Servs*, Ellen S Kovacic; *Publ Servs*, Arnona Rudavsky; *Admin Assoc*, Melissa Ann Simmons; Tel: 513-221-1875, Ext 276, Fax: 513-221-0519, E-Mail: msimmons@cn.huc.edu; *Librn*, Laura S Wolfson; Staff 9 (MLS 8, Non-MLS 1)
Founded 1875. Enrl 160; Fac 55; Highest Degree: Doctorate
Library Holdings: Bk Vols 425,000; Per Subs 2,340
Subject Interests: Ancient and Near Eastern studies, Hebraic, Incunabula, Judaica, Rabbinics
Special Collections: 16th Century Hebrew Printing Coll; Assyriology Coll; Broadside Coll; Hebrew Manuscripts Coll; Inquisition Coll; Jewish Americana to 1850; Jewish Music Coll; Josephus Coll; Printed Bible Coll; Spinoza Coll; Yiddish Theater Coll
Automation Activity & Vendor Info: (Cataloging) VTLS; (Circulation) VTLS; (Course Reserve) VTLS; (OPAC) VTLS; (Serials) VTLS
Publications: Bibliographica Judaica (monograph ser)
Partic in Greater Cincinnati Library Consortium; Research Libraries Group, Inc

S HILL TOP RESEARCH INC LIBRARY,* PO Box 429501, 45242. SAN 323-4428. Tel: 513-831-3114. FAX: 513-831-1217. *Librn*, Shirley Lowe; *Asst Librn*, Linda Worsham
Library Holdings: Per Subs 105

SR HOME MISSIONERS OF AMERICA, Glenmary Novitiate Library, PO Box 465618, 45246-5618. SAN 328-5723. Tel: 513-874-8900. FAX: 513-874-1690. *Librn*, Fr Michael Kerin
Library Holdings: Bk Vols 900

R ISAAC M WISE TEMPLE LIBRARY, (Formerly Isaac M Wise Temple), 8329 Ridge Rd, 45236. SAN 313-3001. Tel: 513-793-2556. FAX: 513-793-3322. *Librn*, Jenny Schaffzin; E-Mail: jSchaffzin@wisetemple.org. Subject Specialists: *Israel*, Jenny Schaffzin; *Jewish holocaust*, Jenny Schaffzin; *Judaica*, Jenny Schaffzin; Staff 1 (MLS 1)
Founded 1931
Library Holdings: Bk Vols 20,000; Bk Titles 15,000; Per Subs 35
Subject Interests: Holocaust, Judaica

JEWISH HOSPITAL
M HEALTH SCIENCES LIBRARY, 4777 E Galbraith Rd, 45236. SAN 355-7340. Tel: 513-686-5173. FAX: 513-686-5418. *Librn*, Lisa McCormick; *Coordr*, Eva Colligan; Staff 3 (MLS 1, Non-MLS 2)
Founded 1959
Library Holdings: Bk Vols 3,000; Bk Titles 2,500; Per Subs 180
Subject Interests: Internal medicine, Nursing, Surgery
Special Collections: Leisurely Medical Reading Coll; Medical History Coll
Restriction: Staff use only
Partic in Greater Midwest Regional Medical Libr Network

S KZF INC LIBRARY, 655 Eden Park Dr, 45202. SAN 324-0606. Tel: 513-621-6211. FAX: 513-621-6530. *Mgr*, Dennis Hamilton
Founded 1974
Library Holdings: Bk Titles 4,000; Per Subs 120
Subject Interests: Architecture, Engineering, Interior design, Planning
Restriction: By appointment only
Partic in Dialog Corporation

S LLOYD LIBRARY & MUSEUM, 917 Plum St, 45202. SAN 313-2781. Tel: 513-721-3707. FAX: 513-721-6575. Web Site: www.libraries.uc.edu/lloyd. *Exec Dir*, Dennis B Worthen; E-Mail: dennis.worthen@uc.edu; Staff 6 (MLS 3, Non-MLS 3)
Founded 1885
Library Holdings: Bk Titles 200,000; Per Subs 350
Subject Interests: Botany, Horticulture, Pharmacy
Special Collections: Botany with an emphasis on Morphology & Taxonomy; eclectic medicine; Linnean Literature Original Editions; Materia Medica), bks, journals; Mycology, bks & mss; Natural History; Pharmacognosy, History of Pharmacy; Pharmacy (Pharmacopeias & related subjects; Plant Chemistry & Floras
Publications: Journal of Natural Products; Lloydiana: A Publication of the Friends of the Lloyd Library (quarterly)
Partic in OCLC Online Computer Library Center, Inc; Ohio Library & Information Network; OHIONET
Friends of the Library Group

M MERCY FRANCISCAN HOSPITAL MOUNT AIRY LIBRARY, 2446 Kipling Ave, 45239. SAN 328-8331. Tel: 513-853-5806. *Librn*, Carol Mayor
Founded 1978
Library Holdings: Bk Titles 500; Per Subs 120
Special Collections: Medicine & Nursing Coll, bks & journals
Partic in Docline

M MERCY FRANCISCAN HOSPITAL WESTERN HILLS LIBRARY, 3131 Queen City Ave, 45238. SAN 328-3976. Tel: 513-389-5118. *Librn*, Carol Mayor
Library Holdings: Bk Titles 1,000

SR MONTGOMERY PRESBYTERIAN CHURCH LIBRARY,* 9994 Zig Zag Rd, 45242. SAN 328-414X. Tel: 513-891-8670.
Circ 600
1999-2000 Income $500. Mats Exp $500, Books $400, Per/Ser (Incl. Access Fees) $100
Library Holdings: Bk Vols 2,250
Subject Interests: Religion
Special Collections: Audiovisual Materials; Children's bks

S MORTON INTERNATIONAL, Information Resource Center,* 2000 West St, 45215. SAN 313-2609. Tel: 513-733-2171. FAX: 513-733-2115.
Founded 1965
Library Holdings: Bk Vols 1,000; Per Subs 80
Subject Interests: Asphalt additives, Chemical engineering, Chemistry, Lubricant, Plastic

S NATIONAL ASSOCIATION FOR CREATIVE CHILDREN & ADULTS LIBRARY, 8080 Springvalley Dr, 45236. SAN 374-4957. Tel: 513-631-1777. *Librn*, Dr Ann Fabe Isaacs; Staff 1 (MLS 1)
Library Holdings: Bk Vols 5,000; Per Subs 40

S NATIONAL STEREOSCOPIC ASSOCIATION, Oliver Wendell Holmes Stereoscopic Research,* 3665 Erie Ave, 45208. SAN 326-1905. Tel: 513-871-1026, 513-871-1657. FAX: 513-321-5398. Web Site: www.stereoview.org. *Librn*, Wolfgang Sell
Founded 1974
Library Holdings: Bk Titles 400; Per Subs 50
Special Collections: Stereoviews (Helen D Moseley Coll)

R NORTHMINSTER PRESBYTERIAN CHURCH LIBRARY, 703 Compton Rd, 45231. SAN 328-2910. Tel: 513-931-0243. FAX: 513-931-0260. E-Mail: nmpc@one.net. Web Site: www.one.net/~nmpc. *Ad Servs*, Joan P Reul; *Ch Servs*, Marilyn Spreen
Library Holdings: Bk Titles 3,000

S PLANNED PARENTHOOD OF SOUTHWEST OHIO & NORTHERN KENTUCKY, Resource Center,* Education Training & Video Production Dept, 2314 Auburn Ave, 45219-2882. SAN 375-3492. Tel: 513-721-8932, Ext 254. FAX: 513-287-6491. E-Mail: ppsonk@fuse.net.; Staff 1 (MLS 1)
Library Holdings: Bk Titles 1,600; Per Subs 20
Subject Interests: Family planning, Reproductive rights, Sex educ, Women's health

P PUBLIC LIBRARY OF CINCINNATI & HAMILTON COUNTY, Cincinnati & Hamilton County Public, 800 Vine St, 45202-2071. SAN 355-7588. Tel: 513-369-6900. Interlibrary Loan Service Tel: 513-369-3121. FAX: 513-369-6993. Interlibrary Loan Service FAX: 513-369-3123. E-Mail: comments@plch.lib.oh.us. Interlibrary Loan Service E-Mail: doclib@plch.lib.oh.us. Web Site: plch.lib.oh.us. *Dir, Librn*, Kimber L Fender; Tel: 513-369-6970; *Mgr Libr Serv*, Gregory Edwards; *Publ Servs*, Keith Kuhn; *Head Tech Servs*, Catherine Sheanshang; *Pub Relations*, Amy Banister;

Head, Info Serv, Anne Herbert; *Ad Servs*, Sally Kramer; *Web Coordr*, Sandra Bolek; *Ch Servs*, Rebecca Shea; Staff 889 (MLS 234, Non-MLS 655)
Founded 1853. Pop 840,443; Circ 13,149,907
Jan 1999-Dec 1999 Income (Main Library and Branch Library) $53,288,331, State $50,385,935, Federal $82,940, Locally Generated Income $1,458,014, Other $1,361,442. Mats Exp $6,651,788, Books $3,955,506, Per/Ser (Incl. Access Fees) $1,719,439, Presv $307,491, Electronic Ref Mat (Incl. Access Fees) $669,052. Sal $23,165,953
Library Holdings: Bk Vols 4,769,131; Bk Titles 1,192,294; Per Subs 6,676
Subject Interests: Art, Genealogy, Local history, Music, Religion, Theology
Automation Activity & Vendor Info: (Serials) Innovative Interfaces Inc.
Publications: Large Print Catalog; Links; Ohioana Author List & Program; Seven Hills Review; Treasures III; Unabridged Fiction Books on Cassette
Partic in Greater Cincinnati Library Consortium; OCLC Online Computer Library Center, Inc
Special Services for the Deaf - TDD
Special Services for the Blind - Large print bks
Open Mon-Fri 9-9, Sat 9-6, Sun 1-5
Friends of the Library Group
Branches: 56
ANDERSON, 7450 State Rd, 45230. SAN 355-7685. Tel: 513-369-6030. FAX: 513-369-4444. *Branch Mgr*, Patricia Peterson
Library Holdings: Bk Vols 86,494
Open Mon-Fri 10-9, Sat 10-5:30, Sun Noon-4
Friends of the Library Group
ART & MUSIC Tel: 513-369-6955. FAX: 513-369-3123. *Mgr*, Anna Horton
Library Holdings: Bk Vols 201,184
Subject Interests: Antiques, Architecture, Art, Bronzes, Costume hist, Dance, Decorative arts, Film, Graphics, Music, Painting, Photog, Porcelain, Pottery, Sculpture, Theater
Special Collections: Doane Coll; Langstroth Lithograph Coll; Orpheus & Apollo Clubs Choral Coll; Plaut Coll; Roedter Coll; Russel Alger Frager Coll; Sackett Coll, ref mat; Straus Mayer Coll; Striker Coll; Theater, Dance & Music Programs; Trager Memorial Coll; Tragger Coll; Twentieth Century Artists Books; Valerio Coll
AVONDALE, 3566 Reading Rd, 45229. SAN 355-7677. Tel: 513-369-4440. FAX: 513-369-4539. *Branch Mgr*, Thelma Morris
Library Holdings: Bk Vols 20,502
Open Mon, Tues & Thurs 12-8, Wed, Fri & Sat 10-5:30
Friends of the Library Group
BLUE ASH BRANCH, 4911 Cooper Rd, Blue Ash, 45242. SAN 355-8630. Tel: 513-369-6051. FAX: 513-369-4464. *Branch Mgr*, Robert Burdick
Library Holdings: Bk Vols 83,120
Open Mon-Fri 10-9, Sat 10-5:30
Friends of the Library Group
BOND HILL, 1703 Dale Rd, 45237. SAN 355-7707. Tel: 513-369-4445. FAX: 513-369-4532. *Branch Mgr*, Eileen Horvath
Library Holdings: Bk Vols 17,648
Open Mon, Tues & Thurs 12-8, Wed 12-5:30, Fri & Sat 10-5:30
Friends of the Library Group
CHEVIOT, 3711 Robb Ave, 45211. SAN 355-7766. Tel: 513-369-6015. FAX: 513-369-6048. *Branch Mgr*, Kenneth Horne
Library Holdings: Bk Vols 41,508
Open Mon, Tues & Thurs 12-9, Wed 9-9, Fri & Sat 9-5:30
Friends of the Library Group
CHILDREN'S LEARNING CENTER Tel: 513-369-6922. FAX: 513-369-3123. *Mgr*, Sonia Church
Library Holdings: Bk Vols 144,685
Special Collections: DeMarke Coll; Goldsmith Coll; Guisatao Coll; Straus-Englander Coll
CIRCULATION SERVICES Tel: 513-369-6914. FAX: 513-369-3123. *Mgr*, Donald Baker
CLEVES BRANCH, 8 N Miami Ave, Cleves, 45002. SAN 355-8223. Tel: 513-369-6050. FAX: 513-369-4487. *Branch Mgr*, Linda Gromen
Library Holdings: Bk Vols 26,693
Open Mon-Wed 12-8, Thurs 12-5, Fri & Sat 9-5
Friends of the Library Group
CLIFTON, 351 Ludlow Ave, 45220. SAN 355-7790. Tel: 513-369-4447. FAX: 513-369-4448. *Branch Mgr*, Jenny Gomien
Library Holdings: Bk Vols 20,549
Open Mon, Tues & Thrus 12-9, Wed 12-5:30, Fri & Sat 9-5:30
Friends of the Library Group
COLLEGE HILL, 1400 W North Bend Rd, 45224. SAN 355-8339. Tel: 513-369-6036. FAX: 513-369-6043. *Branch Mgr*, Joseph Hamrick
Library Holdings: Bk Vols 46,641
Open Mon, Tues & Thurs 12-9, Wed 9-9, Fri & Sat 9-5:30
Friends of the Library Group
CORRYVILLE, 2802 Vine St, 45219. SAN 355-8304. Tel: 513-369-6034. *Mgr*, Marya Hunt-Kenny
Library Holdings: Bk Vols 39,598
Open Mon-Thurs 10-8, Fri & Sat 10-6
Friends of the Library Group
COVEDALE, 4980 Glenway Ave, 45238. SAN 355-8428. Tel: 513-369-4460. FAX: 513-369-4461. *Branch Mgr*, Eileen Mallory
Library Holdings: Bk Vols 51,474
Open Mon-Thurs 10-9, Fri & Sat 10-5:30
Friends of the Library Group
DEER PARK, 3970 E Galbraith Rd, 45236. SAN 355-7855. Tel: 513-369-4450. FAX: 513-369-4451. *Branch Mgr*, Kathryn Holm
Library Holdings: Bk Vols 36,924
Open Mon, Tues & Thurs 12-9, Wed 9-9, Fri & Sat 9-5:30
Friends of the Library Group
DELHI TOWNSHIP, 5095 Foley Rd, 45238. SAN 355-788X. Tel: 513-369-6019. FAX: 513-369-4453. *Branch Mgr*, Susan Hamrick
Library Holdings: Bk Vols 64,813
Open Mon-Thurs 10-9, Fri & Sat 10-5:30
Friends of the Library Group
EDUCATION & RELIGION Tel: 513-369-6940. FAX: 513-369-3123. *Mgr*, Susan Hettinger
Library Holdings: Bk Vols 245,386
Subject Interests: Education, Libr sci, Occult, Philosophy, Psychology, Recreation, Religion, Social welfare, Sociology, Sports
Special Collections: Foundation Center Regional Coll; Grants Resource Center; Kane/Merton Coll; Keller Coll; Sackett Coll; Theological & Religious Library Coll; Trager Memorial Coll
ELMWOOD PLACE, 6120 Vine St, 45216. SAN 355-791X. Tel: 513-369-4452. FAX: 513-369-4534. *Branch Mgr*, Deborah Carrico
Library Holdings: Bk Vols 21,517
Open Mon-Tues 12-7, Wed-Thurs 12-5:30, Fri-Sat 10-5:30
Friends of the Library Group
FICTION & YOUNG ADULTS Tel: 513-369-6918. FAX: 513-369-3123. *Mgr*, Vicki Newell
Library Holdings: Bk Vols 206,683
Special Collections: Marsh Coll, novels; Meister Coll, classic fiction bks
FILMS & RECORDINGS Tel: 513-369-6924. FAX: 513-369-3123. *Mgr*, Robert Hudzik
Special Collections: Adler Coll, rec; American International Music Fund Tapes; Dr Martin Luther King Jr Coll; Forshay Coll; Frederick Yeiser Coll; Futterman Coll, rec; Oscar Treadwell Coll
FOREST PARK, 655 Waycross Rd, Forest Park, 45240. SAN 355-8452. Tel: 513-369-4478. FAX: 513-369-4480. *Branch Mgr*, Harriet Robins
Library Holdings: Bk Vols 52,887
Open Mon, Tues & Thurs 12-9, Wed 9-9, Fri & Sat 9-5:30
Friends of the Library Group
GOVERNMENT & BUSINESS Tel: 513-369-6932. FAX: 513-369-3123. *Mgr*, Carl Marquette
Library Holdings: Bk Vols 230,099
Subject Interests: Bus, Computer use in bus, Employment, Finance, Government, International relations, Investments, Mil sci, Politics, Real estate
Special Collections: Dr Martin Luther King Jr Coll; Lenke Coll; Sackett Coll; Schild-SCORE; Seasongood Coll
GREEN TOWNSHIP, 6525 Bridgetown Rd, 45248. SAN 370-0968. Tel: 513-369-6095. FAX: 513-369-4482. *Branch Mgr*, Nancy Conant
Library Holdings: Bk Vols 90,051
Open Mon-Fri 10-9, Sat 10-5:30, Sun 12-4
Friends of the Library Group
GREENHILLS, 7 Endicott St, 45218. SAN 355-7979. Tel: 513-369-4441. FAX: 513-369-4535. *Branch Mgr*, Kathleen Ficker
Library Holdings: Bk Vols 20,339
Open Mon-Wed 1-9, Thurs 1-5:30, Fri & Sat 9-5:30
Friends of the Library Group
GROESBECK, 2994 W Galbraith Rd, 45239. SAN 355-8002. Tel: 513-369-4454. FAX: 513-369-4455. *Branch Mgr*, Peggy Stuhlreyer
Library Holdings: Bk Vols 51,264
Open Mon-Thurs 10-9, Fri & Sat 10-5:30
Friends of the Library Group
HARRISON BRANCH, 300 George St, Harrison, 45030. SAN 355-8037. Tel: 513-369-4442. FAX: 513-369-4443. *Branch Mgr*, Margaret Reider
Library Holdings: Bk Vols 29,361
Open Mon, Tues & Thurs 12-9, Wed 9-9, Fri & Sat 9-5:30
Friends of the Library Group
HISTORY & GENEALOGY Tel: 513-369-6905. FAX: 513-369-3123. *Mgr*, Patricia Vanskaik
Library Holdings: Bk Vols 252,369
Subject Interests: Current events, Genealogy, Local, Military history, Nat hist, State
Special Collections: Glueck Coll; J Richard Abell Coll; Lewis Coll; Mudge Coll; Sackett Coll; Trager Memorial Coll; US Census Records, 1790-1920
HYDE PARK, 2747 Erie Ave, 45208. SAN 355-8061. Tel: 513-369-4456. FAX: 513-369-4458. *Branch Mgr*, Margaret Osburn
Library Holdings: Bk Vols 48,844
Open Mon, Tues & Thurs 12-9, Wed 9-9, Fri & Sat 9-5:30
Friends of the Library Group
INSTITUTIONS, BOOKS-BY-MAIL, 800 Vine St, 45202-2071. SAN 355-7596. Tel: 513-369-6963. FAX: 513-369-3123. *Mgr*, Elizabeth Zuelke
Library Holdings: Bk Vols 239,062
Special Collections: Dwyer Coll; Fouch Coll; Kistner Coll, large print bks
Publications: Triennial Report of the Inland Rivers Library
Friends of the Library Group
LIBRARY FOR THE BLIND & PHYSICALLY HANDICAPPED
See Separate Entry under Cincinnati Regional Library for the Blind &

Physically Handicapped
LITERATURE & LANGUAGES Tel: 513-369-6991. FAX: 513-369-3123. *Mgr*, Donna Hornberger
Library Holdings: Bk Vols 246,587
Subject Interests: Communication, Journalism, Linguistics, Sign lang
Special Collections: Glueck Coll; Graydon Coll; Lewis Coll; Mudge Coll; Sackett Coll; Valerio Coll
LOVELAND, 649 Loveland-Madeira Rd, Loveland, 45140. SAN 355-8126. Tel: 513-369-4476. FAX: 513-369-4477. *Branch Mgr*, Rosemary Ogg
Library Holdings: Bk Vols 48,567
Open Mon, Tues & Thurs 12-9, Wed 9-9, Fri & Sat 9-5:30
Friends of the Library Group
MADEIRA BRANCH, 7200 Miami Ave, Madeira, 45243. SAN 355-8150. Tel: 513-369-6028. FAX: 513-369-4501. *Branch Mgr*, Vicki McClure
Library Holdings: Bk Vols 84,999
Open Mon-Fri 10-9, Sat 10-5:30, Sun 12-4
Friends of the Library Group
MADISONVILLE, 4830 Whetsel Ave, 45227. SAN 355-8185. Tel: 513-369-6029. FAX: 513-369-4537. *Branch Mgr*, Donna Barkley; Staff 4 (MLS 1, Non-MLS 3)
Library Holdings: Bk Vols 23,351
Open Mon, Tues & Thurs 12-8, Wed & Fri 12-5:30, Sat 9-5:30
Friends of the Library Group
MAGAZINES & NEWSPAPERS Tel: 513-369-6973. FAX: 513-369-3123. *Mgr*, Myron Neal
Library Holdings: Bk Vols 1,919
MARIEMONT, 3810 Pocahontas Ave, Mariemont, 45227. SAN 355-8215. Tel: 513-369-4467. FAX: 513-369-4468. *Branch Mgr*, Rebecca Kennedy
Library Holdings: Bk Vols 41,735
Open Mon, Tues & Thurs 12-9, Wed 9-9, Fri & Sat 9-5:30
Friends of the Library Group
MONFORT HEIGHTS, 3825 West Fork Rd, 45247. SAN 355-872X. Tel: 513-369-4472. FAX: 513-369-4473. *Branch Mgr*, Chris Holt
Library Holdings: Bk Vols 49,798
Open Mon, Tues & Thurs 12-9, Wed 9-9, Fri & Sat 9-5:30
Friends of the Library Group
MOUNT HEALTHY, 7608 Hamilton Ave, 45231. SAN 355-824X. Tel: 513-369-4469. FAX: 513-369-4470. *Branch Mgr*, Kathleen Due
Library Holdings: Bk Vols 47,900
Open Mon, Tues & Thurs 12-9, Wed 9-9, Fri & Sat 9-5:30
Friends of the Library Group
MOUNT WASHINGTON, 2049 Beechmont Ave, 45230. SAN 355-8274. Tel: 513-369-6033. FAX: 513-369-6044. *Branch Mgr*, Florence Thompson
Library Holdings: Bk Vols 41,081
Open Mon, Tues & Thurs 12-9, Wed 9-9, Fri & Sat 9-5:30
Friends of the Library Group
NORTH CENTRAL, 11109 Hamilton Ave, 45231. SAN 370-0976. Tel: 513-369-6068. FAX: 513-369-4459. *Branch Mgr*, Dale Snair
Library Holdings: Bk Vols 90,633
Open Mon-Fri 10-9, Sat 10-5:30, Sun 12-4
Friends of the Library Group
NORTHSIDE, 4219 Hamilton Ave, 45223. SAN 355-7820. Tel: 513-369-4449. FAX: 513-369-4533. Web Site: www.plch.lib.oh.us/branch/CU/index.html. *Branch Mgr*, Kathy Taylor
Library Holdings: Bk Vols 21,770
Open Mon-Wed 12-8, Thurs-Sat 10-5:30
Friends of the Library Group
NORWOOD, 4325 Montgomery Rd, 45212. SAN 355-8363. Tel: 513-369-6037. FAX: 513-369-6039. *Branch Mgr*, Lisa Hamrick
Library Holdings: Bk Vols 34,107
Open Mon, Tues & Thurs 12-9, Wed 9-9, Fri & Sat 9-5:30
Friends of the Library Group
OAKLEY, 4033 Gilmore Ave, 45209. SAN 355-8398. Tel: 513-369-6038. FAX: 513-369-6055. *Branch Mgr*, Jeanne Rettig
Library Holdings: Bk Vols 39,972
Open Mon, Tues & Thurs 12-9, Wed 9-9, Fri & Sat 9-5:30
Friends of the Library Group
PLEASANT RIDGE, 6233 Montgomery Rd, 45213. SAN 355-8487. Tel: 513-369-4488. FAX: 513-369-4489. *Branch Mgr*, David Dukart
Library Holdings: Bk Vols 27,308
Open Mon, Tues & Thurs 12-9, Wed 9-9, Fri & Sat 9-5:30
Friends of the Library Group
PRICE HILL, 3215 Warsaw Ave, 45205. SAN 355-8517. Tel: 513-369-4490. FAX: 513-369-4538. *Branch Mgr*, Katie Greifenkamp
Library Holdings: Bk Vols 22,710
Open Mon, Tues & Thurs 12-8, Wed, Fri & Sat 10-5:30
Friends of the Library Group
PUBLIC DOCUMENTS & PATENTS Tel: 513-369-6971. FAX: 513-369-3123. *Mgr*, John Graham
Library Holdings: Bk Vols 281,330
Special Collections: US Patent Coll, 1790-present
RARE BOOKS & SPECIAL COLLECTIONS Tel: 513-369-6957. FAX: 513-369-3123. E-Mail: rarebookhead@plch.lib.oh.us. *Mgr*, Sylvia Metzinger
Founded 1956
Library Holdings: Bk Vols 45,486
Special Collections: A Edward Newton Coll; Bible Coll; Charles Dickens Coll; Christopher Morley Coll; Cincinnati Coll; Cruikshank Coll; Discovery & Exploration of America Coll; Edgar Rice Burroughs Coll; English Language Dictionary Coll; Ernest Hemingway Coll; Fleischmann Coll; Frank & Dick Merriwell Coll; Hatfield Coll; Huenefeld Coll; Inland River Library; John Steinbeck Coll; Kahn Dictionary Coll; Lafeadio Hearn Coll; Lanstroth Lithograph Coll; Lazarus Coll; Loeb Coll; Mark Twain Coll; Nora May Nolan Irish Coll; Postcard Coll; Rockwell Kent Coll; Sir Winston Churchill Coll; W Somerset Maugham Coll; Walpole Coll; Willa Cather Coll; William Faulkner Coll; William Makepeace Thackeray Coll
Publications: Book of Treasures; Catalog of the Inland Rivers Library & Supplement
Friends of the Library Group
READING BRANCH, 9001 Reading Rd, Reading, 45215. SAN 355-8665. Tel: 513-369-4465. FAX: 513-369-4466. *Branch Mgr*, Mary Piepmeier
Library Holdings: Bk Vols 30,643
Open Mon, Tues & Thurs 12-9, Wed, Fri & Sat 9-5:30
Friends of the Library Group
ROSELAWN, Valley Ctr, 7617 Reading Rd, 45237. SAN 355-8541. Tel: 513-369-6045. FAX: 513-369-6046. *Branch Mgr*, Debbie Kiner
Library Holdings: Bk Vols 37,931
Open Mon, Tues & Thurs 12-9, Wed 9-9, Fri & Sat 9-5:30
Friends of the Library Group
SAINT BERNARD, 4803 Tower Ave, 45217. SAN 355-8576. Tel: 513-369-4462. FAX: 513-369-4463. *Branch Mgr*, Bianne Bobbitt
Library Holdings: Bk Vols 20,587
Open Mon, Tues & Thurs 12-8, Wed & Fri 12-5:30, Sat 9-5:30
Friends of the Library Group
SCIENCE & TECHNOLOGY Tel: 513-369-6936. FAX: 513-369-3123. *Mgr*, Mary Beth Brestel
Library Holdings: Bk Vols 243,887
Subject Interests: Applied sci, Chemistry, Consumer info, Cookery, Engineering, Horticulture, Natural history, Ornithology, Pure
Special Collections: ANSI Standards; ASTM Standards
SHARONVILLE, 10980 Thornview Dr, 45241. SAN 355-8606. Tel: 513-369-6049. FAX: 513-369-4504. *Branch Mgr*, Susan Reid
Library Holdings: Bk Vols 71,644
Open Mon-Fri 10-9, Sat 10-5:30, Sun 12-4
Friends of the Library Group
SYMMES TOWNSHIP, 11850 E Enyart Rd, Loveland, 45140. SAN 370-0984. Tel: 513-369-6001. FAX: 513-369-4481. *Branch Mgr*, Michael Suedkamp
Library Holdings: Bk Vols 69,755
Open Mon-Fri 10-9, Sat 10-5:30, Sun 12-4
Friends of the Library Group
WALNUT HILLS, 2533 Kemper Lane, 45206. SAN 355-869X. Tel: 513-369-6053. FAX: 513-369-4492. *Branch Mgr*, Barbara Furr
Library Holdings: Bk Vols 23,548
Open Mon-Wed 12-8, Thurs, Fri & Sat 10-5:30
Friends of the Library Group
WEST END, 805 Ezzard Charles Dr, 45203. SAN 355-8096. Tel: 513-369-6026. FAX: 513-369-4536. *Branch Mgr*, Paula Ivory
Library Holdings: Bk Vols 23,558
Open Mon-Wed 12-7, Thurs-Sat 10-5:30
Friends of the Library Group
WESTWOOD, 3345 Epworth Ave, 45211. SAN 355-8754. Tel: 513-369-4474. FAX: 513-369-4475. *Branch Mgr*, Joyce Baer
Library Holdings: Bk Vols 39,877
Open Mon, Tues & Thurs 12-9, Wed 9-9, Fri & Sat 9-5:30
Friends of the Library Group
WYOMING BRANCH, 500 Springfield Pike, Wyoming, 45215. SAN 355-7731. Tel: 513-369-6014. FAX: 513-369-6052. *Branch Mgr*, Christopher Holt
Library Holdings: Bk Vols 37,587
Open Mon, Tues & Thurs 12-9, Wed 9-9, Fri & Sat 9-5:30
Friends of the Library Group

S RAPHAEL KATZEN ASSOCIATES INTERNATIONAL INC LIBRARY,* 2300 Wall St, Ste K, 45212. SAN 375-6475. Tel: 513-351-7500. FAX: 513-351-0810. *Pres*, Philip W Madson
Library Holdings: Per Subs 30
Subject Interests: Chemical engineering, Mechanical engineering

R ROCKDALE TEMPLE, Sidney G Rose Library, 8501 Ridge Rd, 45236. SAN 313-2846. Tel: 513-891-9900. FAX: 513-891-0515. *Librn*, Ellen Dunsker; Staff 1 (Non-MLS 1)
Jul 1999-Jun 2000 Income $13,408, Parent Institution $5,310, Other $8,098. Mats Exp $3,753, Books $3,474, Per/Ser (Incl. Access Fees) $279. Sal $2,000
Library Holdings: Bk Vols 9,000; Per Subs 12
Subject Interests: Judaica

S RYDER-ATE MANAGEMENT & SERVICE COMPANY, INC, Resource Center Library,* 705 Central Ave, Ste 500, 45202. SAN 326-6079. Tel: 925-373-5534. FAX: 513-381-0149. *Librn*, Eleanor Horton
Founded 1974
Library Holdings: Bk Vols 5,344; Bk Titles 5,281; Per Subs 60
Publications: Directory of Transportation Libraries in North America
Partic in Greater Cincinnati Library Consortium; OHIONET

C SISTERS OF NOTRE DAME DE NAMUR, Ohio Province Archives,* Provincial House, 701 E Columbia Ave, 45215-3999. SAN 375-0833. Tel: 513-821-7448. FAX: 513-821-7476. *Archivist*, Sister Louanna Orth; E-Mail: louorth@aol.com
Library Holdings: Bk Vols 5,000

J SOUTHERN OHIO COLLEGE LIBRARY,* 1011 Glendale-Milford Rd, 45215. SAN 321-7094. Tel: 513-771-2424. FAX: 513-771-3413. *Librn*, Kathy Taylor
Founded 1978
Library Holdings: Bk Vols 8,000; Bk Titles 7,100; Per Subs 90
Departmental Libraries:
NORTHEAST CAMPUS, 2791 Mogadore Rd, Akron, 44312. SAN 321-7272. Tel: 330-733-8766. FAX: 330-733-5853. E-Mail: soc@raex.com. *Librn*, Jane Myers
Founded 1980. Enrl 283; Fac 24
Library Holdings: Bk Vols 4,428; Bk Titles 4,085
Subject Interests: Accounting, Bus, Computers, Liberal arts, Medicine, Real estate, Secretarial, Word proc
Automation Activity & Vendor Info: (Cataloging) Sagebrush Corporation; (Circulation) Sagebrush Corporation

L TAFT, STETTINIUS & HOLLISTER LIBRARY, 1800 Firstar Tower, 425 Walnut St, 45202-3957. SAN 313-2900. Tel: 513-381-2838. FAX: 513-381-0205. *Librn*, Barbara J Davis; E-Mail: davisb@taftlaw.com; *Asst Librn*, Patrick Points; E-Mail: points@taftlaw.com; Staff 3 (MLS 2, Non-MLS 1)
Library Holdings: Bk Vols 30,000

L THOMPSON, HINE & FLORY LLP, Law Library, 312 Walnut St, 14th flr, 45202. SAN 372-2112. Tel: 513-352-6528. FAX: 513-241-4771. *Librn*, Barbara W Silbersack; E-Mail: bsilbersack@thf.com; Staff 3 (MLS 2, Non-MLS 1)
Library Holdings: Bk Vols 10,000; Per Subs 100
Automation Activity & Vendor Info: (OPAC) epixtech, inc.; (Serials) epixtech, inc.
Restriction: Not open to public

SR UNITED METHODIST CHURCH, Armstrong Chapel Church Library, 5125 Drake Rd, 45243. SAN 374-9908. Tel: 513-561-4220. FAX: 513-561-3062.
Library Holdings: Bk Vols 3,000

G UNITED STATES DEPARTMENT OF HEALTH & HUMAN SERVICES, National Institute for Occupational Safety & Health Library, 4676 Columbia Pkwy, 45226. SAN 313-2943. Tel: 513-533-8321. FAX: 513-533-8382. *Librn*, Lawrence Foster; Staff 2 (MLS 2)
1998-1999 Income $225,000
Library Holdings: Bk Vols 10,000; Per Subs 175
Subject Interests: Health res, Occupational safety
Partic in Fedlink; OCLC Online Computer Library Center, Inc

C UNIVERSITY OF CINCINNATI, Raymond Walters College Library, 9555 Plainfield Rd, 45236-0086. SAN 355-9173. Tel: 513-745-5710. FAX: 513-745-5767. Web Site: www.rwc.uc.edu/library. *Dir*, Stephena Harmony; *Instrul Serv*, Lisa Barnett; *Coll Develop, Instrul Serv*, Debra Oswald; *Ref*, John Burk; *Media Spec*, H Michael Sanders; Staff 4 (MLS 4)
Founded 1967. Enrl 2,000; Fac 95
Library Holdings: Bk Vols 50,000; Per Subs 450
Subject Interests: Women's studies
Partic in Dialog Corporation; Dow Jones News Retrieval; Greater Cincinnati Library Consortium; OCLC Online Computer Library Center, Inc

C UNIVERSITY OF CINCINNATI, University Libraries, PO Box 210033, 45221-0033. SAN 355-8843. Tel: 513-556-1515. FAX: 513-556-0325. Web Site: www.libraries.uc.edu. *Asst Dean, Media Spec*, Marcia Deddens; *Info Specialist*, Cheryl Albrecht; Tel: 513-556-1784; *Access Serv*, Jacquelene Riley; Tel: 513-556-2484; Staff 48 (MLS 48)
Founded 1819. Enrl 35,825; Fac 1,111; Highest Degree: Doctorate
Jul 1998-Jun 1999 Mats Exp $17,437,734. Sal $7,979,932 (Prof $3,512,290)
Library Holdings: Per Subs 14,531
Special Collections: 18th Century British anonymus poetical pamphlets (Dobell Coll); 19th & 20th Century astronomy journals, monographs & records (Cincinnati Observatory Coll); 19th & 20th Century German-Americana (Fick Coll); 20th Century English language poetry (Elliston Poetry Coll); American Labor History (McNamara Coll); Classical Studies, including art, language, literature, history, civilization, philosophy, religion, archaeology, Greek & Latin paleography (Burnam Classical Library Coll); D H Lawrence manuscripts & Dorothy Brett correspondence (D H Lawrence Coll); Dissertations, progam schriften & pamphlets in Classical Studies, Urban Studies Coll; History of Chemistry (Oesper Coll); Modern Greek Studies (Modern Greek Coll)
Publications: Gathering
Mem of Asn of Research Libraries
Partic in Center For Research Libraries; Greater Cincinnati Library Consortium; Ohio Library & Information Network; OHIONET
Special Services for the Deaf - TDD
Special Services for the Blind - Braille printer & software; HP Scan Jet with photofinish software; Kurzweil Reading Machine; Large screen microcomputer monitor with software; Optelek 20/20 video magnification system; Reader services
Friends of the Library Group
Departmental Libraries:
ARCHIVES & RARE BOOKS, 808 Blegen Library, PO Box 210113, 45221-0113. SAN 323-5734. Tel: 513-556-1959. FAX: 513-556-2113. Web Site: www.uc.libraries.edu. *Head of Libr*, Alice Cornell
CHEMISTRY-BIOLOGY, A-3, 503 Rieveschl, PO Box 210151, 45221-0151. SAN 355-8878. Tel: 513-556-1498. FAX: 513-556-1103. Web Site: www.libraries.uc.edu. *Head of Libr*, John Tebo
Friends of the Library Group
CLASSICS, 320 Blegen Library, PO Box 210191, 45221-0191. SAN 355-8908. Tel: 513-556-1315. FAX: 513-556-6244. Web Site: www.uc.libraries.edu. *Head of Libr*, Jean Wellington
COLLEGE-CONSERVATORY OF MUSIC, 417 Blegen Library, PO Box 210152, 45221-0152. SAN 355-8932. Tel: 513-556-1970. FAX: 513-556-3777. Web Site: www.libraries.uc.edu. *Head of Libr*, Robert Johnson
CURRICULUM RESOURCES CENTER, 600 Blegen Library, PO Box 210219, 45221-0219. SAN 329-0166. Tel: 513-556-1430. FAX: 513-556-2113. Web Site: www.libraries.uc.edu. *Head of Libr*, Gary Lare
DESIGN, ARCHITECTURE ART & PLANNING, Aronoff Ctr for Design & Art, PO Box 210016, 45221-0016. SAN 355-8967. Tel: 513-556-1335. FAX: 513-556-3006. Web Site: www.libraries.uc.edu. *Librn*, Jane Carlin
ENGINEERING, 880 Baldwin Hall, PO Box 210018, 45221-0018. SAN 355-8991. Tel: 513-556-1550. FAX: 513-556-2654. Web Site: www.libraries.uc.edu. *Head of Libr*, Dorothy Byers
WALTER C LANGSAM LIBRARY Tel: 513-556-1515. FAX: 513-556-0325. Interlibrary Loan Service FAX: 513-556-2161. Web Site: www.libraries.uc.edu. *Head Librn*, David Kohl
MATHEMATICS, 840 Old Chem, PO Box 210025, 45221-0025. SAN 355-9084. Tel: 513-556-1330. FAX: 513-556-3417. Web Site: www.libraries.uc.edu. *Head of Libr*, Dorothy Byers
OMI-COLLEGE OF APPLIED SCIENCE LIBRARY, 2220 Victory Pkwy, 45206-2839. SAN 323-5750. Tel: 513-556-6594. FAX: 513-556-4217. Web Site: www.libraries.uc.edu. *Head of Libr*, Rosemary Young
GEOLOGY PHYSICS, 225 Braunstein, PO Box 210153, 45221-0153. SAN 355-9025. Tel: 513-556-1324. FAX: 513-556-1930. Web Site: www.libraries.uc.edu. *Head Librn*, Richard Spohn

CL UNIVERSITY OF CINCINNATI, Robert S Marx Law Library, Clifton & Calhoun Sts, PO Box 21042, 45221-0142. SAN 355-905X. Tel: 513-556-0159, 513-556-0163. FAX: 513-556-6265. Web Site: www.law.uc.edu. *Librn*, Virginia Thomas; E-Mail: virginia.thomas@law.uc.edu; *Asst Librn, Cat*, Swarn Varma; *Tech Servs*, John Hopkins; *Media Spec*, Mark Dinkelacker; *Info Specialist*, Cynthia Aninao; *Govt Doc*, Charles Parsons; *Ser*, Patricia Turpening; *Publ Servs*, James Hart; Staff 6 (MLS 6)
Founded 1874. Enrl 392; Fac 27; Highest Degree: Doctorate
Library Holdings: Bk Vols 258,335; Bk Titles 46,628
Subject Interests: Foreign law, Govt docs, Human rights, International law, Law
Special Collections: Church & State Coll; Cincinnati Legal History & Reports of Various Courts; Early Ohio Legal Coll, history reports; Human Rights; Land Planning (Robert N Cook Coll); Rare Book Coll
Publications: Underground Librarian
Partic in Dialog Corporation; ELLS; OCLC Online Computer Library Center, Inc

CM UNIVERSITY OF CINCINNATI MEDICAL CENTER, Health Sciences Library,* 231 Bethesda Ave, PO Box 670574, 45267-0574. SAN 355-9238. Tel: 513-558-5627. FAX: 513-558-2682. Web Site: www.mcl.uc.edu. *Dir*, Roger Guard; E-Mail: roger.guard@uc.edu; *Assoc Dir*, Leslie Schick; *Assoc Dir*, Stephen Marine; *Assoc Dir*, Ralph Brueggemann; *Dir*, Billie Broaddus; *Cat*, Sharon Bressert; *Syst Coordr*, Birsen Kaya; *Dir*, Doris Haag; Staff 38 (MLS 19, Non-MLS 19)
Founded 1974
Library Holdings: Bk Vols 259,657; Bk Titles 107,282; Per Subs 3,598
Subject Interests: Basic med sci, Clinical med sci, Health care delivery, Health sci, History of medicine, Non-print instrul mat in med, Nursing, Patient educ, Pharm
Publications: University of Cincinnati Serials Holdings List
Partic in Dialog Corporation; OCLC Online Computer Library Center, Inc
The Medical Center Libraries consist of the following: Health Sciences Library, Cincinnati Medical Heritage Center & College of Nursing & Health Library
Departmental Libraries:
CINCINNATI MEDICAL HERITAGE CENTER Tel: 513-558-5120. FAX: 513-558-0472. *Librn*, Billie Broaddus
Special Collections: 63 Archives (including Robert A Kehoe & Albert S Sabin Archives); History of Laser Medicine; History of Medicine in West (Daniel Drake, Reuben Dimond Mussey & David A Tucker Colls), bks & mss; Local & State Medical Archives, photogs & portraits
COLLEGE OF NURSING & HEALTH LIBRARY Tel: 513-558-8378. FAX: 513-558-9102. *Dir*, Doris Haag
Special Collections: Phoebe M Kandel Historical Coll

GL US COURT OF APPEALS FOR THE SIXTH CIRCUIT LIBRARY, 317 Potter Stewart US Courthouse, 45202. SAN 313-2927. Tel: 513-564-7321. FAX: 513-564-7329. *Syst Coordr*, Joseph Orth; *Archivist*, Rita Wallace; Tel: 513-564-7304; Staff 30 (MLS 17, Non-MLS 13)
Founded 1895
Library Holdings: Bk Vols 210,000; Bk Titles 2,500
Special Collections: Primarily Anglo-American Legal Coll
Automation Activity & Vendor Info: (Acquisitions) SIRSI; (Cataloging) SIRSI; (Serials) SIRSI
Publications: Sixth Circuit History; Sixth Circuit Libraries Newsletter
Restriction: Not open to public
Partic in Fedlink; OCLC Online Computer Library Center, Inc; Westlaw
Satellite libraries located in Louisville, Kentucky; Detroit & Grand Rapids, Michigan; Cleveland, Columbus & Toledo, Ohio; Chattanooga, Nashville & Memphis, Tennessee

S WESTERN-SOUTHERN LIFE INSURANCE LIBRARY,* 400 Broadway, 45202. SAN 313-2978. Tel: 513-629-1035. *Librn*, Karen Toerner
Founded 1952
Library Holdings: Bk Vols 3,171; Per Subs 31
Subject Interests: Bus, Ins, Recreational

R WESTMINSTER PRESBYTERIAN CHURCH, John H Holmes Library, 4991 Cleves-Warsaw Pike, 45238. SAN 313-2986. Tel: 513-921-1623. FAX: 513-921-4900. *Librn*, Carolyn Brinkerhoff
Founded 1960
1998-1999 Income $100. Mats Exp $100, Books $75, Per/Ser (Incl. Access Fees) $15
Library Holdings: Bk Vols 5,500; Per Subs 10
Subject Interests: Bible study, Devotional, Religious education
Special Collections: Old Bibles

R WESTWOOD FIRST PRESBYTERIAN CHURCH LIBRARY, 3011 Harrison Ave, 45211. SAN 313-2994. Tel: 513-661-6846. FAX: 513-389-3681. *Librn*, Marian B McNair; Staff 8 (MLS 3, Non-MLS 5)
Founded 1957
Jan 2000-Dec 2000 Income $1,600, Locally Generated Income $100, Parent Institution $1,200, Other $300. Mats Exp $1,200, Books $1,000, Per/Ser (Incl. Access Fees) $150, Manuscripts & Archives $50
Library Holdings: Bk Vols 4,200; Bk Titles 4,000; Per Subs 16
Subject Interests: Bible ref, Relig bks
Special Collections: Anchor Bible Series; Books & Materials on Cincinnati; General (Henderson Coll); Large Print Coll, bks & pers; New Interpreter's Bible Series; Presbyterian Church College Catalogue Coll
Automation Activity & Vendor Info: (Cataloging) Follett; (Circulation) Follett
Publications: Adult education class bibliographies; church curriculum materials lists; holiday bibliographies; newsletter (annual)
Special Services for the Blind - Large print bks

CR XAVIER UNIVERSITY, McDonald Memorial Library, 3800 Victory Pkwy, 45207-5211. SAN 313-301X. Tel: 513-745-3884. Circulation Tel: 513-745-3881. Reference Tel: 513-745-4808. FAX: 513-745-1932. Web Site: www.xu.edu/library/. *Dir Libr Serv*, JoAnne L Young; E-Mail: jyoung@xu.edu; *ILL*, Elaine M Cheng; *AV*, Robert Cotter; *Archivist*, Tim McCabe; Tel: 513-745-3884, Ext 4821, E-Mail: mccabe@xu.edu; *Cat*, Michelle Early; Tel: 513-745-3884, Ext 4817, E-Mail: early@xu.edu; *Bibliog Instr*, Victoria Young; Tel: 513-745-3884, Ext 4804, E-Mail: young@xu.edu; *Ser*, Margaret Groeschen; Tel: 513-745-3884, Ext 4805, E-Mail: groeschen@xu.edu; *Coll Develop*, Marty Ferrell; Tel: 513-745-3884, Ext 4806, E-Mail: ferrell@xu.edu; *Publ Servs*, Marcia Poggione; Tel: 513-745-3884, Ext 3971, E-Mail: poggione@xu.edu; *Electronic Resources*, John Stemmer; Tel: 513-745-3884, Ext 4822, E-Mail: stemmer@xu.edu; Staff 24 (MLS 11, Non-MLS 13)
Founded 1831. Enrl 6,504; Fac 322
1999-2000 Mats Exp $801,151, Books $287,424, Per/Ser (Incl. Access Fees) $221,825, Presv $15,789, Micro $25,941, AV Equip $47,535, Other Print Mats $13,295, Manuscripts & Archives $3,000, Electronic Ref Mat (Incl. Access Fees) $186,342. Sal $862,146 (Prof $458,523)
Library Holdings: Bk Vols 221,773; Bk Titles 148,610; Per Subs 1,586; High Interest/Low Vocabulary Bk Vols 828; Bks on Deafness & Sign Lang 112
Subject Interests: Gen, Philosophy, Theology
Special Collections: Bibles, Incunabula & Jesuitica; Catholic Boy's Fiction (Francis Finn, SJ, Coll)
Automation Activity & Vendor Info: (Acquisitions) Innovative Interfaces Inc.; (Cataloging) Innovative Interfaces Inc.; (Circulation) Innovative Interfaces Inc.; (ILL) Innovative Interfaces Inc.; (OPAC) Innovative Interfaces Inc.; (Serials) Innovative Interfaces Inc.
Database Vendor: CARL, Dialog, DRA, Ebsco - EbscoHost, GaleNet, IAC - Info Trac, IAC - SearchBank, Lexis-Nexis, OCLC - First Search, OVID Technologies, ProQuest, Silverplatter Information Inc., Wilson - Wilson Web
Publications: Update (Newsletter); X Libris Newsletter
Partic in Greater Cincinnati Library Consortium; OCLC Online Computer Library Center, Inc; Ohio Library & Information Network; OHIONET
Library holdings, income & expenditures include the campus library
Friends of the Library Group
Departmental Libraries:
INSTRUCTIONAL MEDIA SERVICES, 3800 Victory Pkwy, 45207-3171. SAN 370-7067. Tel: 513-745-3603. FAX: 513-745-1932. Web Site: www.xu.edu/library/. *AV*, Robert M Cotter; Tel: 513-745-3183, E-Mail: cotter@xu.edu
LODGE LEARNING LABORATORY, CURRICULUM RESOURCE CENTER, 3800 Victory Pkwy, 45207-7321. SAN 322-5593. Tel: 513-745-4830. Circulation Tel: 513-745-3319. Reference Tel: 513-745-3319. FAX: 513-745-1932. Web Site: www.xu.edu/library/. *Publ Servs*, Betty Porter; E-Mail: porter@xu.edu; *Media Spec*, Brian Kidd; Tel: 513-745-2998, E-Mail: kidd@xu.edu; Staff 2 (MLS 1, Non-MLS 1)
Founded 1970
Friends of the Library Group

S YOUNG MEN'S MERCANTILE LIBRARY ASSOCIATION, 414 Walnut St, 45202. SAN 313-3028. Tel: 513-621-0717. FAX: 513-621-2023. *Dir*, Albert Pyle; *Asst Librn*, Mark Pierce; *Asst Librn*, Mary Gruber
Founded 1835
Library Holdings: Bk Titles 150,000; Per Subs 80

S ZOOLOGICAL SOCIETY OF CINCINNATI LIBRARY, 3400 Vine St, 45220. (Mail add: PO Box 198073, 45219-8073), SAN 327-6759. Tel: 513-559-7760. FAX: 513-559-7776, 517-475-6101. Web Site: www.cincyzoo.org. *Coordr*, Jan Dietrich
1998-1999 Income $2,250, Locally Generated Income $50, Parent Institution $2,200. Mats Exp $2,000, Books $1,800, Per/Ser (Incl. Access Fees) $200
Library Holdings: Bk Titles 3,100; Per Subs 15
Subject Interests: Ecology, Horticulture, Zoology
Publications: newsletters; pamphlets
Restriction: Open to public for reference only
Function: Reference only

CIRCLEVILLE

CR CIRCLEVILLE BIBLE COLLEGE, Melvin & Laura Maxwell Library, PO Box 458, 43113. SAN 313-3036. Tel: 740-477-7736. FAX: 740-477-7855. *Dir*, Gary Metzenbacher; E-Mail: gmetzenbacher@biblecollege.edu; *Asst Librn*, Joanne Wolford
Founded 1947. Enrl 150
Library Holdings: Bk Vols 35,000; Per Subs 111
Subject Interests: Bible, Missions, Theology
Special Collections: Stout Bible Coll
Publications: New Books List

S DU PONT DE NEMOURS & CO, INC, Information Center Library, Rte 23 S, Box 89, 43113. SAN 313-3044. Tel: 740-474-0111, 740-474-0573. FAX: 740-474-0244. *In Charge*, Sharon Arledge
Founded 1958
Library Holdings: Bk Vols 3,150; Per Subs 100
Subject Interests: Polymer chemistry, Polymer physics

P PICKAWAY COUNTY DISTRICT PUBLIC LIBRARY, 165 E Main St, 43113-1725. SAN 313-3052. Tel: 740-477-1644. FAX: 740-474-2855. E-Mail: pickaway@clc.lib.oh.us. Web Site: www.clc.lib.oh.us. *Dir*, Jim Guenther; *Br Coordr*, Karen Wheeler; *Ch Servs*, Susan Smith; *ILL, Ref*, Marilyn Murrell; *Circ*, Mary Bees; *Coll Develop*, Angela Johnson; Staff 17 (MLS 8, Non-MLS 9)
Founded 1834. Pop 50,325
Library Holdings: Per Subs 168
Partic in Cent Libr Consortium; OCLC Online Computer Library Center, Inc; OHIONET
Friends of the Library Group
Branches: 1
FLOYD E YOUNKIN BRANCH, 51 Long St, Ashville, 43103. Tel: 740-983-8856. FAX: 740-983-4287. *Branch Mgr*, Shelah Smith; Tel: 740-983-8856 Ext 22
Open Mon-Thurs 9:30-8:30, Sat 9:30-5, Sun 1pm-5pm
Friends of the Library Group

GL PICKAWAY COUNTY LAW LIBRARY ASSOCIATION,* Courthouse, PO Box 727, 43113. SAN 313-3060. Tel: 740-474-6026. FAX: 740-477-6334. *In Charge*, William Ammer
1997-1998 Income $177,437, City $59,963, County $91,742. Mats Exp $128,390, Books $97,724. Sal $13,033

CLEVELAND

R ANSHE CHESED FAIRMOUNT TEMPLE, Arthur J Lelyveld Center for Jewish Learning, 23737 Fairmount Blvd, 44122. SAN 313-3443. Tel: 216-464-1330, Ext 123. FAX: 216-464-3628. Web Site: www.fairmounttemple.org. *Librn*, Julie Moss; E-Mail: jmoss@fairmounttemple.org; *Asst Librn*, Ronna Fox; *Asst Librn*, Rae Herman; Staff 3 (MLS 1, Non-MLS 2)
Library Holdings: Bk Titles 15,000; Per Subs 60
Subject Interests: Architecture, Bible, Festivals, History, Holidays, Holocaust, Jewish art, Jewish fiction, Jewish philos, Judaica, Theology
Special Collections: Celia Smith Rogovin Children's Library

L ARTER & HADDEN, Law Library, 1100 Huntington Bldg, 925 Euclid Ave, 44115-1475. SAN 313-3125. Tel: 216-696-1100. Reference Tel: 216-696-2418. FAX: 216-696-2645. *Dir*, Rob Myers; E-Mail: rmyers@arterhadden.com; *Librn*, Andy Zimmerman; E-Mail: azimmerm@arterhadden.com; Staff 3 (MLS 2, Non-MLS 1)
Library Holdings: Bk Vols 20,000
Restriction: Staff use only

L BAKER & HOSTETLER LLP LIBRARY, 3200 National City Ctr, 1900 E Ninth St, 44114-3485. SAN 313-3133. Tel: 216-861-7101. FAX: 216-696-0740. *Dir*, Alvin M Podboy; E-Mail: apodboy@baker-hostetler.com; *Librn*, Susan Miljinovic; Staff 2 (MLS 2)
Founded 1916. Circ 39,795
Library Holdings: Bk Vols 53,400
Automation Activity & Vendor Info: (Acquisitions) epixtech, inc.; (Cataloging) epixtech, inc.; (Circulation) epixtech, inc.; (Course Reserve) epixtech, inc.; (ILL) epixtech, inc.; (Media Booking) epixtech, inc.; (OPAC) epixtech, inc.; (Serials) epixtech, inc.
Restriction: Staff use only
Partic in Westlaw

S BRUSH WELLMAN, INC, Technical Library,* 17876 St Clair Ave, 44110. SAN 313-315X. Tel: 216-383-4004, 216-486-4200, Ext 383. FAX: 216-481-5480. *Librn*, Sophia Patterson
Founded 1961
Library Holdings: Bk Vols 4,000
Subject Interests: Beryllium, Beryllium copper, Ceramics, Metallurgy
Partic in Dialog Corporation; SDC Info Servs

L CALFEE, HALTER & GRISWOLD, Law Library,* 1400 McDonald Investment Ctr, 800 Superior Ave, 44114. SAN 372-2287. Tel: 216-622-8208. FAX: 216-241-0816. *Librn*, Susan Panasik; E-Mail: spanasik@calfee.com
Library Holdings: Bk Vols 18,000; Per Subs 100

C CASE WESTERN RESERVE UNIVERSITY, Kelvin Smith Library, 11055 Euclid Ave, 44106-7151. (Mail add: 10900 Euclid Ave, 44106-7151), SAN 355-9416. Tel: 216-368-2992. Interlibrary Loan Service Tel: 216-368-3517. Circulation Tel: 216-368-3506. Reference Tel: 216-368-6596. FAX: 216-368-6950. Web Site: www.cwru.edu/UL/homepage.html. *Dir*, Joanne Eustis; E-Mail: jde@po.cwru.edu; *Assoc Dir*, E Gail Reese; Tel: 216-368-5291, E-Mail: egr@po.cwru.edu; *Dep Dir*, Timothy D Robson; Tel: 216-368-6508, E-Mail: tdr@po.cwru.edu; *Acq*, Arlene Moore Sievers; Tel: 216-368-3328, Fax: 216-368-3669, E-Mail: axs23@po.cwru.edu; *Head, Cat*, Christopher Thornton; Tel: 216-368-6229, Fax: 216-368-3669, E-Mail: cpt3@po.cwru.edu; *Coll Develop*, William Claspy; Tel: 216-368-3595, E-Mail: wpc@ppo.cwru.edu; *Coll Develop*, Martin Coyne; Tel: 216-368-6599, Fax: 216-368-3669, E-Mail: mxc6@po.cwru.edu; *Coll Develop*, Elsie Finley; Tel: 216-368-3510, Fax: 216-368-3669, E-Mail: exf2@po.cwru.edu; *Coll Develop*, Ross Poli; Tel: 216-368-6502, E-Mail: rxp4@po.cwru.edu; *Coll Develop*, Dan Stabe; Tel: 216-368-6513, Fax: 216-368-3669, E-Mail: dms9@po.cwru.edu; *Electronic Resources*, Earnestine Adeyemon; Tel: 216-368-4248, E-Mail: exa2@po.cwru.edu; *Govt Doc*, Karen Thornton; Tel: 216-368-6512, Fax: 216-368-3669, E-Mail: kat4@po.cwru.edu; *Music*, Stephen Toombs; Tel: 216-368-2403, E-Mail: sht@po.cwru.edu; *Head Ref*, Catherine Wells; Tel: 216-368-5201, Fax: 216-368-3669, E-Mail: caw7@po.cwru.edu; *Spec Coll*, Norma Sue Hanson; Tel: 216-368-2993, E-Mail: nsh2@po.cwru.edu; *Tech Coordr*, SuHui Ho; Tel: 216-368-0321, Fax: 216-368-3669, E-Mail: shh2@po.cwru.edu. Subject Specialists: *Astronomy*, William Claspy; *Economics*, Catherine Wells; *Economics*, Martin Coyne; *Engineering*, Earnestine Adeyemon; *Engineering*, William Claspy; *Philosophy*, Dan Stabe; *Religion*, Dan Stabe; *Science/technology*, Earnestine Adeyemon; *Science/technology*, William Claspy; *Sociology*, Elsie Finley; *Statistics*, Ross Poli; Staff 60 (MLS 27, Non-MLS 33)
Enrl 9,614; Fac 2,030; Highest Degree: Doctorate
Jul 1999-Jun 2000 Mats Exp $2,715,025, Books $495,645, Per/Ser (Incl. Access Fees) $2,090,395, Presv $52,713, Other Print Mats $76,272. Sal $2,206,534 (Prof $1,236,806)
Library Holdings: Bk Vols 1,322,951
Special Collections: Bookplates (Lemperly & Sherwin Coll); British & American Autographs & Letters; Chemistry Periodicals (Morley Coll); French Revolution & Napoleonic Period (Bourne Coll); German Literature & Philology (Sherer Coll); Henry Adams Library; History of Printing (Eastman Coll); History of Science & Technology; Letters of Junius (Doty Coll); Medieval History (Severance Coll); Natural History (Kirtland Coll); Public Housing & Urban Development (Bohn Coll); Science Fiction; Thoreau (Bailey Coll); Victorian Illustrated Literature (Haskell Coll)
Automation Activity & Vendor Info: (Acquisitions) Innovative Interfaces Inc.; (Cataloging) Innovative Interfaces Inc.; (Circulation) Innovative Interfaces Inc.; (Serials) Innovative Interfaces Inc.
Partic in OCLC Online Computer Library Center, Inc; Ohio Library & Information Network; OHIONET
Departmental Libraries:
ASTRONOMY, 10900 Euclid Ave, 44106. SAN 355-9440. Tel: 216-368-6701. E-Mail: wpc@po.cwru.edu. Web Site: www.cwru.edu/UL/Subjects/ASTR/astr.html. *Librn*, William Claspy; Staff 1 (MLS 1)
Subject Interests: Astronomy, Astrophysics
DIGITAL MEDIA SERVICES, Kelvin Smith Library, 11055 Euclid, 44106. SAN 375-2887. Tel: 216-368-5888. FAX: 216-368-8720. *Actg Dir*, Ronald S Ryan
200 Databases
LILLIAN F & MILFORD J HARRIS LIBRARY, Mandel School of Applied Social Sciences, 11235 Bellflower Rd, 44106-7164. (Mail add: 10900 Euclid Ave, 44106-7164), SAN 355-9564. Tel: 216-368-2302. FAX: 216-368-2106. E-Mail: xx242@po.cwru.edu. Web Site: www.msass.cwru.edu/library/. *Dir*, Arthur Biagianti; Tel: 216-368-2283, E-Mail: asb2@po.cwru.edu; *Asst Dir*, Dorothy Jacobson; *Admin Dir*, Gina Midlik; Tel: 216-368-5292, Fax: 216-368-6950, E-Mail: gmm2@po.cwru.edu; *Circ, ILL*, Lena Ford; E-Mail: lmf4@po.cwru.edu; *Publ Servs*, Mary Lee Jensen; Tel: 216-368-1355, E-Mail: mxj32@po.cwru.edu; *Tech Servs*, June Hund; Tel: 216-368-0722, E-Mail: jxh18@po.cwru.edu; Staff 5 (MLS 3, Non-MLS 2)
Founded 1916. Enrl 600; Fac 30; Highest Degree: Doctorate
Jul 1999-Jun 2000 Mats Exp $70,542, Books $13,492, Per/Ser (Incl. Access Fees) $49,688, Presv $5,021, Electronic Ref Mat (Incl. Access Fees) $2,341. Sal $238,270 (Prof $106,374)
Library Holdings: Bk Vols 40,421; Per Subs 267
Subject Interests: Soc work
Automation Activity & Vendor Info: (Cataloging) Innovative Interfaces Inc.; (Circulation) Innovative Interfaces Inc.; (OPAC) Innovative Interfaces Inc.; (Serials) Innovative Interfaces Inc.
Publications: Update
Partic in Cleveland Area Metropolitan Library System; OCLC Online Computer Library Center, Inc; Ohio Library & Information Network
KULAS MUSIC LIBRARY, 11118 Bellflower Rd, 44106-7106. SAN 355-953X. Tel: 216-368-2403. E-Mail: sht@pocwru.edu. *Librn*, Stephen Toombs

CL SCHOOL OF LAW LIBRARY, 11075 East Blvd, 44106. SAN 355-9599. Tel: 216-368-2792. Interlibrary Loan Service Tel: 216-368-2842. Reference Tel: 216-368-5206. FAX: 216-368-1002. Web Site: lawwww.cwru.edu/library/. *Dir*, Kathleen M Carrick; Tel: 216-368-6357, E-Mail: kxc4@po.cwru.edu; *Admin Assoc*, Gina Midlik; Tel: 216-368-5292, Fax: 216-368-6950, E-Mail: gmm2@po.cwru.edu; *Access Serv*, Lisa Peters; Tel: 216-368-2793, E-Mail: lkp@po.cwru.edu; *AV, Ref*, Cheryl Cheatham; Tel: 216-368-1611, E-Mail: csc4@po.cwru.edu; *Head, Cat*, Deborah Dennison; Tel: 216-368-6040, E-Mail: dsd2@po.cwru.edu; *Electronic Resources*, Megan Allen; Tel: 216-368-5223, E-Mail: mja5@po.cwru.edu; *Info Tech*, Keith Bartou; Tel: 216-368-3275, E-Mail: kjb15@po.cwru.edu; *Publ Servs*, D R Jones; Tel: 216-368-2794, E-Mail: drj5@po.cwru.edu; *Head Ref*, Andy Dorchak; Tel: 216-368-2842, E-Mail: axd10@po.cwru.edu; *Ref Serv, Tech Coordr*, Judy Kaul; Tel: 216-368-8570, E-Mail: jak4@po.cwru.edu; *Head, Ser Acq*, Kathleen Kobyljanec; Tel: 216-368-8656, E-Mail: ksk8@po.cwru.edu; *Tech Servs*, Mary Hudson; Tel: 216-368-5220, E-Mail: mph@po.cwru.edu; Staff 21 (MLS 9, Non-MLS 12)
Founded 1893. Enrl 747; Fac 46; Highest Degree: Doctorate
Jul 1999-Jun 2000 Income $2,400,895. Mats Exp $888,201, Books $56,557, Per/Ser (Incl. Access Fees) $787,834, Presv $14,553, Micro $25,251, AV Equip $4,006. Sal $1,338,055 (Prof $707,948)
Library Holdings: Bk Vols 287,707; Bk Titles 86,037; Per Subs 7,799
Subject Interests: Comparative law, Computers, Foreign, Int, Law, Medicine
Special Collections: Anglo-American Common Law; Audiovisual Coll; Government Documents Coll; Legal Clinic; Microforms Coll; Rare Book Coll
Automation Activity & Vendor Info: (Acquisitions) Innovative Interfaces Inc.; (Cataloging) Innovative Interfaces Inc.; (Circulation) Innovative Interfaces Inc.; (OPAC) Innovative Interfaces Inc.; (Serials) Innovative Interfaces Inc.
Publications: Acquisitions list; computer lab manual (2nd ed); guide to periodicals; research guides and pathfinder series (basic legal research, topical legal research, foreign-international law, special)
Partic in Dialog Corporation; Lexis, OCLC Online Computer Libr Ctr, Inc; Ohio Library & Information Network; Quicklaw Inc; Westlaw; Worldcat

CM CASE WESTERN RESERVE UNIVERSITY & CLEVELAND MEDICAL LIBRARY ASSOCIATION, Cleveland Health Sciences Library, 2119 Abington Rd, 44106. SAN 355-9351. Tel: 216-368-3436. Interlibrary Loan Service Tel: 216-368-3641. FAX: 216-368-6421, 368-3008. E-Mail: lsl3@po.cwru. Web Site: www.cwru.edu/cwru/chsl/homepage.html. *Dir*, Virginia Saha; E-Mail: vmg2@p.cwru; *Asst Dir*, Karen Burt; Tel: 216-368-4542; *ILL*, Susan Hill; *Ser*, Kathleen Meneely; *Curator*, James Edmonson; Staff 15 (MLS 15)
Founded 1965
Library Holdings: Bk Vols 390,000
Subject Interests: Biology, Dentistry, Medicine, Nursing, Nutrition
Special Collections: Cole Coll of Venereals; Coll; Darwin; Freud Coll; History of Medicine Dittrick Museum of Medical History, all media, archival mat; Marshall Herbal Coll
Automation Activity & Vendor Info: (Acquisitions) Innovative Interfaces Inc.

Publications: Cleveland Medical Library Association (newsletter)
Partic in Cleveland Area Metropolitan Library System; NE Ohio Major Acad & Res Librs; OCLC Online Computer Library Center, Inc; Ohio Library & Information Network
Departmental Libraries:
ALLEN MEMORIAL LIBRARY, 11000 Euclid Ave, 44106. SAN 355-9386. Tel: 216-368-3642. *In Charge*, Dzwinka Holian
HISTORICAL DIVISION LIBRARY, RARE BOOKS & ARCHIVES Tel: 216-368-3648. FAX: 216-368-6421.

S CATHOLIC UNIVERSE BULLETIN PUBLISHING CO, INC LIBRARY, Chancery Bldg, 1027 Superior Ave, 44114-2556. SAN 313-3168. Tel: 216-696-6525. FAX: 216-696-6519. *In Charge*, Joseph Polito; E-Mail: jpolito@catholicuniversebulletin.org
Founded 1924

S CLEVELAND BOTANICAL GARDEN, Eleanor Squire Library, 11030 East Blvd, 44106. SAN 313-3486. Tel: 216-721-1600. FAX: 216-721-2056. *Dir*, Mary Ellen Armentront; E-Mail: marmentront@cbgarden.org; *Cat*, Christopher Thornton; *Info Specialist*, Laurie Hinkle; Staff 3 (MLS 2, Non-MLS 1)
Founded 1930
2000-2001 Mats Exp $8,000, Books $5,000, Other Print Mats $3,000
Library Holdings: Bk Vols 14,000; Bk Titles 16,000; Per Subs 175
Subject Interests: Garden hist, Gardening, Horticulture, Landscape design
Special Collections: Botany (Warren H Corning Coll); Flowering Plant Index of Illustration & Information
Restriction: Circulation limited
Partic in Council On Botanical Horticultural Libraries; LVIS; OCLC Online Computer Library Center, Inc

M CLEVELAND CLINIC ALUMNI LIBRARY, 9500 Euclid Ave NA30, 44195-5243. SAN 313-3184. Tel: 216-444-5697. FAX: 216-444-0271. E-Mail: library@ccf.org. *Mgr*, Gretchen Hallerberg; Staff 15 (MLS 8, Non-MLS 7)
Library Holdings: Per Subs 850
Subject Interests: Clinical medicine, Med res
Partic in Cleveland Area Metropolitan Library System; Med Libr Asn of NE Ohio

M CLEVELAND HEARING & SPEECH CENTER LIBRARY,* 11206 Euclid Ave, 44106. SAN 327-666X. Tel: 216-231-8787. FAX: 216-231-7141. *Exec Dir*, Dr Bernard P Henri
Library Holdings: Bk Titles 500; Per Subs 20

S CLEVELAND INSTITUTE OF ART, Jessica Gund Memorial Library, 11141 East Blvd, 44106. SAN 313-3214. Tel: 216-421-7440. FAX: 216-421-7439. *Dir Libr Serv*, Cristine C Rom; E-Mail: crom@gate.cia.edu; *Online Servs, Tech Servs*, Hyosoo Lee; Tel: 216-421-7443, E-Mail: hlee@gate.cia.edu; *Ref*, Laura M Ponikvar; Tel: 216-421-7442, E-Mail: lponikvar@gate.cia.edu; Staff 6 (MLS 3, Non-MLS 3)
Founded 1882. Enrl 507; Highest Degree: Bachelor
Jun 1999-May 2000 Income Parent Institution $267,930. Mats Exp $85,938, Books $26,000, Per/Ser (Incl. Access Fees) $12,800, Presv $5,400, Micro $685, AV Equip $1,200, Electronic Ref Mat (Incl. Access Fees) $4,000. Sal $165,921 (Prof $98,358)
Library Holdings: Bk Vols 38,575; Bk Titles 35,411; Per Subs 261
Subject Interests: Artists bks, Contemporary int art, Craft, Design, Modern art
Special Collections: International Contemporary Art; Modern Art; Twentieth Century American Arts & Crafts
Publications: Acquisitions list; library handbook
Partic in Cleveland Area Metropolitan Library System; OCLC Online Computer Library Center, Inc

S CLEVELAND INSTITUTE OF MUSIC LIBRARY, 11021 East Blvd, 44106-1776. SAN 313-3222. Tel: 216-795-3114. FAX: 216-791-3063. E-Mail: jst4@po.cwru.edu. Web Site: www.cim.edu. *Dir*, Jean Toombs; *Acq*, Janet Winzenburger; *Ref*, Paul Cary; Staff 5 (MLS 3, Non-MLS 2)
Founded 1922. Enrl 362; Fac 145; Highest Degree: Doctorate
Jul 1999-Jun 2000 Income $213,377. Mats Exp $39,019, Books $4,045, Per/Ser (Incl. Access Fees) $18,000, Presv $2,300, AV Equip $4,970, Other Print Mats $9,704. Sal $143,979
Library Holdings: Bk Vols 48,128; Per Subs 115
Subject Interests: Music
Special Collections: Audio Visual
Restriction: Private library
Partic in Cleveland Area Metropolitan Library System; OCLC Online Computer Library Center, Inc; OHIONET

L CLEVELAND LAW LIBRARY ASSOCIATION, 404 Cuyahoga County Court House, One Lakeside Ave, 44113-1023. SAN 313-3230. Tel: 216-861-5070. FAX: 216-861-1606. Web Site: www.clelaw.lib.oh.us. *Dir*, Jan Ryan Novak; E-Mail: jnovak@clelaw.lib.oh.us; Staff 11 (MLS 5, Non-MLS 6)
Founded 1869
Jan 2000-Dec 2000 Income Locally Generated Income $1,110,387. Mats Exp $787,269, Books $5,937, Per/Ser (Incl. Access Fees) $639,685, Presv $5,869, Micro $5,160, AV Equip $2,604, Other Print Mats $5,614, Electronic Ref Mat (Incl. Access Fees) $122,400. Sal $349,000
Library Holdings: Bk Vols 185,000; Per Subs 676
Subject Interests: Law
Special Collections: Ohio Records & Briefs
Automation Activity & Vendor Info: (Acquisitions) DRA; (Cataloging) DRA; (Circulation) DRA; (OPAC) DRA; (Serials) DRA
Publications: Research Guide Series
Restriction: Members only
Partic in Clevnet; OCLC Online Computer Library Center, Inc

S CLEVELAND METROPARKS ZOO LIBRARY, 3900 Wildlife Way, 44109. SAN 327-7631. Tel: 216-635-3333. FAX: 216-661-3312. *Librn*, Holly Gamble; E-Mail: holly@clevelandmetroparks.com. Subject Specialists: *Biology*, Holly Gamble; *Conservation*, Holly Gamble; *Edu*, Holly Gamble; *Zoology*, Holly Gamble; Staff 1 (MLS 1)
Founded 1992. Pop 230
Jan 2000-Dec 2000 Income $10,000. Mats Exp $10,000, Books $5,000, Per/Ser (Incl. Access Fees) $5,000
Library Holdings: Bk Vols 5,500; Per Subs 95
Subject Interests: Education, Zoology
Automation Activity & Vendor Info: (Cataloging) Sagebrush Corporation
Database Vendor: Ebsco - EbscoHost
Function: Research library
By appointment for general public, or Wed & Sat 9-noon

S CLEVELAND MUSEUM OF ART, Ingalls Library, 11150 East Blvd, 44106. SAN 313-3257. Tel: 216-421-7340. FAX: 216-421-0921. E-Mail: abid@cma-oh.org. *Head Librn*, Ann B Abid; E-Mail: abid@cma-oh.org; *AV*, Sara Jane Pearman; E-Mail: pearman@cma-oh.org; *Bibliogr*, Yunah Sung; E-Mail: sung@cma-oh.org; *Head, Cat*, Lori Thorrat; E-Mail: thorrat@cma-oh.org; *Coll Develop*, Elizabeth A Lantz; E-Mail: lantz@cma-oh.org; *Publ Servs*, Louis V Adrean; E-Mail: adrean@cma-oh.org; *Ser*, Maria C Downey; E-Mail: downey@cma-oh.org; *Syst Coordr*, James Viskochil; E-Mail: viskochi@cma-oh.org. Subject Specialists: *Asia*, Yunah Sung; Staff 21 (MLS 12, Non-MLS 9)
Founded 1916
Jan 1999-Dec 1999 Income $1,319,892
Library Holdings: Bk Vols 260,000; Per Subs 1,400
Subject Interests: Architecture, Art, Decorative arts, Oriental art
Special Collections: American Committee on South Asian Art Coll; Arndt-Brunn Greek & Roman Portraits Coll; Asian Art Photographic Distribution, photog; Bartsch Coll; Biblioteca Berenson Archive, photog; Christie's Coll, micro; Cicognara Fiche; Courtauld Institute of Art: The Witt Library, The Conway Library; Decimal Index to Art of the Low Countries (DIAL), photog; Foto Marburg; National Palace Museum; Victoria & Albert Museum
Automation Activity & Vendor Info: (Acquisitions) epixtech, inc.; (Cataloging) epixtech, inc.; (Circulation) epixtech, inc.; (OPAC) epixtech, inc.; (Serials) epixtech, inc.
Partic in Cleveland Area Metropolitan Library System; RLIN

S CLEVELAND MUSEUM OF NATURAL HISTORY, Harold T Clark Library,* University Circle, One Wade Oval Dr, 44106-1767. SAN 313-3265. Tel: 216-231-4600, Ext 222. FAX: 216-231-5919. E-Mail: library@cmnh.org. *Librn*, Joy Kiser
Founded 1922
1999-2000 Mats Exp $50,000, Per/Ser (Incl. Access Fees) $29,000
Library Holdings: Bk Vols 60,000
Subject Interests: Anthropology, Archaeology, Astronomy, Botany, Ecology, Geology, Mineralogy, Natural history, Paleontology, Zoology
Special Collections: Rare Book Coll (500 vol)
Restriction: Open to public for reference only

M CLEVELAND PSYCHOANALYTIC INSTITUTE LIBRARY,* 11328 Euclid Ave, 44106-3997. SAN 324-6922. Tel: 216-229-2111. FAX: 216-229-7321. *Librn*, Amy Crognale-Gemmill; *Librn*, Maureen Kendel; Staff 2 (MLS 1, Non-MLS 1)
Founded 1962
Library Holdings: Bk Titles 1,695; Per Subs 11
Subject Interests: Child analysis, Psychoanalysis
Special Collections: Sigmund Freud (Complete Psychological Works)

P CLEVELAND PUBLIC LIBRARY, Library for the Blind & Physically Handicapped, 17121 Lake Shore Blvd, 44110-4006. SAN 313-3303. Tel: 216-623-2911. Toll Free Tel: 800-362-1262. FAX: 216-623-7036. *Librn*, Barbara Mates; E-Mail: barbara.mates@cpl.org; Staff 13 (MLS 1, Non-MLS 12)
Founded 1931. Circ 627,712
Library Holdings: Bk Vols 300,000
Special Collections: Ohio Coll, braille & cassettes; Vertical File on Visual & Physical Disabilities
Automation Activity & Vendor Info: (Cataloging) DRA; (Circulation) DRA
Publications: bibliog; Catalogs of locally produced cassettes & braille; juvenile patrons newsletter (quarterly); Ohioana; patrons newsletter (quarterly)
Special Services for the Blind - Adapted computers & special software with speech output to assist learning disabled, mentally retarded & uneducated;

Multimedia reference service (large print, Braille using CD-ROM technology); OCR scanner to read & translate printed materials not available on special media & translate them to special media (braille, large print, voice)

P CLEVELAND PUBLIC LIBRARY, 325 Superior Ave, 44114-1271. SAN 355-9688. Tel: 216-623-2800. Interlibrary Loan Service Tel: 216-623-2868. TDD: 216-623-2916. FAX: 216-623-2972. E-Mail: info@library.cpl.org. Web Site: www./cpl.org. *Dir*, Andrew A Venable, Jr; Tel: 216-623-2827, Fax: 216-623-7015, E-Mail: a.a.venable@cpl.org; *Dep Dir*, Sari Feldman; Tel: 216-623-2832, E-Mail: sari.feldman@cpl.org; *Tech Servs*, Donald Tipka; Tel: 216-623-2817, Fax: 216-623-2977, E-Mail: donald.tipka@cpl.org; *Head of Libr*, Joan Clark; Tel: 216-623-2878, E-Mail: joan.clark@cpl.org; *Automation Syst Coordr*, Robert Carterette; Tel: 216-623-2854, E-Mail: bob.carterette@cpl.org; *Coll Develop*, Cynthia Orr; Tel: 216-623-2822, E-Mail: cynthia.orr@cpl.org; *Acq*, M Lynne Johngrass; Tel: 216-623-2949, Fax: 216-623-6980, E-Mail: lynne.johngrass@cpl.org; *Cat*, Margaret Shen; Tel: 216-623-2885, Fax: 216-623-6980, E-Mail: margaret.shen@cpl.org; *Spec Coll*, Stephen Zeitz; Tel: 216-623-2847, Fax: 216-623-2976, E-Mail: stephen.zeitz@cpl.org. Subject Specialists: *Fine arts*, Stephen Zeitz; Staff 582 (MLS 130, Non-MLS 452)
Founded 1869. Pop 505,616; Circ 5,052,723
Jan 1999-Dec 1999 Income (Main Library and Branch Library) $51,450,597, State $30,121,999, Locally Generated Income $21,328,598. Mats Exp $9,070,350, Books $3,556,236, Per/Ser (Incl. Access Fees) $1,142,879, Presv $583,601, Micro $581,782, Other Print Mats $874,342, Electronic Ref Mat (Incl. Access Fees) $1,169,139. Sal $21,789,863 (Prof $8,285,192)
Library Holdings: Bk Vols 3,890,959; Bk Titles 1,778,525; Per Subs 6,490
Special Collections: Chess; Cleveland Picture Coll; Folklore & Orientalia (John G White Coll); Orgn of Am States; Photograph Coll; United States Patent Coll
Automation Activity & Vendor Info: (Acquisitions) DRA; (Cataloging) DRA; (Circulation) DRA; (Course Reserve) DRA; (Media Booking) DRA; (OPAC) DRA; (Serials) DRA
Database Vendor: DRA
Publications: Cleveland News Index
Partic in Cleveland Area Metropolitan Library System; Clevnet; OCLC Online Computer Library Center, Inc; OHIONET
Special Services for the Deaf - High interest/low vocabulary books
Regional Library for Blind & Physically Handicapped
Friends of the Library Group
Branches: 46
ADDISON, 6901 Superior, 44103. SAN 370-9345. Tel: 216-623-6906. FAX: 216-623-6909. Web Site: www.cpl.org. *Librn*, Ann Hoehn; E-Mail: ann.hoehn@cpl.org; Staff 5 (MLS 1, Non-MLS 4)
Circ 127,722
Library Holdings: Bk Vols 31,498
AUDIO-VIDEO DEPT Tel: 216-623-2942. FAX: 216-902-4941. E-Mail: av5@library.cpl.org. *Librn*, Arnold McClain; E-Mail: arnold.mcclain@cpl.org; Staff 8 (MLS 2, Non-MLS 6)
Circ 404,791
BROADWAY, 5417 Broadway, 44127. SAN 356-0252. Tel: 216-623-6913. FAX: 216-623-7185. *Librn*, Gail Hanks; E-Mail: gail.hanks@cpl.org; Staff 2 (MLS 1, Non-MLS 1)
Circ 16,302
Library Holdings: Bk Vols 8,583
BROOKLYN, 3706 Pearl Rd, 44109. SAN 356-0287. Tel: 216-623-6920. FAX: 216-623-6970. Web Site: www.cpl.org. *Librn*, Cynthia Coccaro; E-Mail: cynthia.coccaro@cpl.org; Staff 4 (MLS 1, Non-MLS 3)
Circ 84,933
Library Holdings: Bk Vols 31,219
BUSINESS, ECONOMICS & LABOR Tel: 216-623-2927. FAX: 216-623-7008. E-Mail: bus1@library.cpl.org. Web Site: www.cpl.org. *In Charge*, Julius Bremer; E-Mail: julius.bremer@cpl.org; Staff 11 (MLS 6, Non-MLS 5)
Circ 36,108
CARNEGIE WEST, 1900 Fulton Rd, 44113. SAN 356-0317. Tel: 216-623-6927. FAX: 216-623-6929. Web Site: www.cpl.org. *Librn*, Mary Zunt; E-Mail: cal.zunt@cpl.org; Staff 6 (MLS 1, Non-MLS 5)
Circ 104,570
Library Holdings: Bk Vols 30,173
CHILDREN'S LITERATURE Tel: 216-623-2834. FAX: 216-902-4940. E-Mail: chlit1@library.cpl.org. Web Site: www.cpl.org. *Librn*, Caroline Barnett; E-Mail: caroline.barnett@cpl.org; Staff 4 (MLS 2, Non-MLS 2)
Circ 61,950
CLEVELAND RESEARCH CENTER Tel: 216-623-2999. FAX: 216-623-6987. E-Mail: crc2@library.cpl.org. Web Site: www.cpl.org. *In Charge*, Robert Hurnan; E-Mail: robert.hurnan@cpl.org; Staff 2 (MLS 1, Non-MLS 1)
Subject Interests: Business, Competitive intelligence, Econ data, Marketing
Partic in Dialog Corporation; Dow Jones News Retrieval
COLLINWOOD, 856 E 152nd St, 44110. SAN 356-0376. Tel: 216-623-6934. FAX: 216-623-6936. E-Mail: collinwood.branch@cpl.org. Web Site: www.cpl.org. *Librn*, Susannah Hamm; E-Mail: susannah.hamm@cpl.org; Staff 5 (MLS 1, Non-MLS 4)
Circ 101,665
Library Holdings: Bk Vols 31,395
EAST 131ST STREET, 3830 E 131st St, 44120. SAN 356-0430. Tel: 216-623-6941. FAX: 216-623-6978. Web Site: www.cpl.org. *Librn*, Magnolia Peters; E-Mail: magnolia.peters@cpl.org; Staff 4 (MLS 1, Non-MLS 3)
Circ 63,710
Library Holdings: Bk Vols 25,553
EASTMAN, 11602 Lorain Ave, 44111. SAN 356-049X. Tel: 216-623-6955. FAX: 216-623-6957. Web Site: www.cpl.org. *Librn*, Willelma Aldana; E-Mail: willelma.aldana@cpl.org; Staff 8 (MLS 2, Non-MLS 6)
Circ 182,377
Library Holdings: Bk Vols 47,852
FINE ARTS & SPECIAL COLLECTIONS - FINE ARTS UNIT Tel: 216-623-2848. FAX: 216-623-2976. E-Mail: fine@library.cpl.org, fine3@library.cpl.org. Web Site: www.cpl.org. *Librn*, Stephen Zeitz; E-Mail: stephen.zietz@cpl.org; Staff 6 (MLS 3, Non-MLS 3)
Circ 120,418
FINE ARTS & SPECIAL COLLECTIONS-SPECIAL COLLECTIONS UNIT Tel: 216-623-2818. FAX: 216-623-2976. E-Mail: white@cpl.org. Web Site: www.cpl.org. *In Charge*, Stephen Zeitz; E-Mail: stephen.zietz@cpl.org; Staff 4 (MLS 3, Non-MLS 1)
Library Holdings: Bk Vols 133,736
FLEET, 7224 Broadway Ave, 44105. SAN 356-052X. Tel: 216-623-6962. FAX: 216-623-6964. Web Site: www.cpl.org. *Librn*, Gayle Tetreault; E-Mail: gayle.tetreault@cpl.org; Staff 7 (MLS 2, Non-MLS 5)
Pop 160,063
Library Holdings: Bk Vols 47,132
FOREIGN LITERATURE Tel: 216-623-2895. FAX: 216-902-4940. E-Mail: foreignlit@cpl.org. Web Site: www.cpl.org. *In Charge*, A Issac Pulver; Tel: 216-623-2896, E-Mail: issac.pulver@cpl.org; Staff 7 (MLS 4, Non-MLS 3)
Circ 9,635
Library Holdings: Bk Vols 288,000
Subject Interests: Foreign Language, Foreign lit
Automation Activity & Vendor Info: (Acquisitions) DRA; (Cataloging) DRA; (Circulation) DRA; (OPAC) DRA; (Serials) DRA
FULTON, 3545 Fulton Rd, 44109. SAN 356-0538. Tel: 216-623-6969. FAX: 216-623-6972. Web Site: www.cpl.org. *Librn*, Kristin Gill; E-Mail: kristin.gill@cpl.org; Staff 6 (MLS 2, Non-MLS 4)
Circ 150,660
Library Holdings: Bk Vols 40,033
GARDEN VALLEY, 7100 Kinsman Rd, 44104. SAN 356-0554. Tel: 216-623-6976. FAX: 216-623-7186. Web Site: www.cpl.org. *Mgr*, Gail Hanks; E-Mail: gail.hanks@cpl.org; Staff 2 (MLS 1, Non-MLS 1)
Circ 6,903
Library Holdings: Bk Vols 9,918
GENERAL REFERENCE, 44114-1271. Tel: 216-623-2856. TDD: 216-623-2916. FAX: 216-623-2972. E-Mail: gen2@library.cpl.org. Web Site: www.cpl.org. *In Charge*, Jelena Fried; E-Mail: nina.fried@cpl.org; Staff 17 (MLS 6, Non-MLS 11)
Library Holdings: Bk Vols 8,545
GLENVILLE, 11900 St Clair Ave, 44108. SAN 356-0589. Tel: 216-623-6983. FAX: 216-623-6985. Web Site: www.cpl.org. *Librn*, Carolyn Williams; E-Mail: carolyn.williams@cpl.org; Staff 4 (MLS 1, Non-MLS 3)
Circ 69,926
Library Holdings: Bk Vols 32,082
GOVERNMENT DOCUMENTS Tel: 216-623-2870. FAX: 214-623-7030. E-Mail: doci@library.cpl.org. Web Site: www.cpl.org. *In Charge*, Robin Gray; E-Mail: robin.gray@cpl.org; Staff 5 (MLS 2, Non-MLS 3)
Library Holdings: Bk Vols 197,259
HARVARD-LEE, 16918 Harvard Ave, 44128. SAN 356-0619. Tel: 216-623-6990. FAX: 216-623-6992. Web Site: www.cpl.org. *Librn*, Shirley Hollingsworth; E-Mail: shirley.hollingsworth@cpl.org; Staff 5 (MLS 1, Non-MLS 4)
Circ 102,579
Library Holdings: Bk Vols 32,013
HISTORY & GEOGRAPHY, 325 Superior Ave, 44114-1271. Tel: 216-623-2864. FAX: 216-902-4978. E-Mail: hist1@library.cpl.org. Web Site: www.cpl.org. *In Charge*, Jo Ann Petrello; E-Mail: joann.petrello@cpl.org; Staff 14 (MLS 5, Non-MLS 9)
Circ 52,213
Library Holdings: Bk Vols 182,642
HOUGH, 1566 Crawford Rd, 44106. SAN 325-3368. Tel: 216-623-6997. FAX: 216-623-6999. Web Site: www.cpl.org. *Librn*, William Bradford; E-Mail: william.bradford@cpl.org; Staff 5 (MLS 1, Non-MLS 4)
Pop 65,182
Library Holdings: Bk Vols 26,664
Database Vendor: IAC - Info Trac
Friends of the Library Group
JEFFERSON, 850 Jefferson Ave, 44113. SAN 356-0643. Tel: 216-623-7004. FAX: 216-623-7007. Web Site: www.cpl.org. *Librn*, Thomas Edwards; E-Mail: thomas.edwards@cpl.org; Staff 4 (MLS 1, Non-MLS 3)
Circ 78,518
Library Holdings: Bk Vols 27,525
LANGSTON HUGHES BRANCH, 10200 Superior Ave, 44106. SAN 377-8029. Tel: 216-623-6975. FAX: 216-623-6974. Web Site: www.cpl.org. *Librn*, Melda English; E-Mail: melda.english@cpl.org; Staff 5 (MLS 1, Non-MLS 4)

Circ 93,175
Library Holdings: Bk Vols 33,014
LIBRARY FOR THE BLIND & PHYSICALLY HANDICAPPED
See Separate Entry
LITERATURE, 325 Superior Ave, 44114-1271. Tel: 216-623-2881. FAX: 216-623-7050. E-Mail: lit2@library.cpl.org. Web Site: www.cpl.org. *In Charge*, Evelyn Ward; E-Mail: evelyn.ward@cpl.org; Staff 6 (MLS 4, Non-MLS 2)
Circ 104,739
LORAIN, 8216 Lorain Ave, 44102. SAN 356-0708. Tel: 216-623-7011. FAX: 216-623-7014. Web Site: www.cpl.org. *Librn*, Richard Homzy; E-Mail: richard.homzy@cpl.org; Staff 4 (MLS 2, Non-MLS 2)
Circ 94,257
Library Holdings: Bk Vols 30,070
MAP COLLECTION, 325 Superior Ave, 44114-1271. Tel: 216-623-2880. FAX: 216-902-4978. E-Mail: map2@library.cpl.org. Web Site: www.cpl.org. *In Charge*, Maureen Farrell; E-Mail: maureen.farrell@cpl.org; Staff 3 (MLS 1, Non-MLS 2)
Library Holdings: Bk Vols 4,686
Restriction: Not a lending library
MARTIN LUTHER KING JR BRANCH, 1962 Stokes Blvd, 44106. SAN 356-0678. Tel: 216-623-7018. FAX: 216-623-7020. Web Site: www.cpl.org. *Librn*, Joyce Bowers; E-Mail: joyce.bowers@cpl.org; Staff 6 (MLS 2, Non-MLS 4)
Circ 93,175
Library Holdings: Bk Vols 39,872
MEMORIAL-NOTTINGHAM, 17109 Lake Shore Blvd, 44110. SAN 356-0732. Tel: 216-623-7039. FAX: 216-623-7042. Web Site: www.cpl.org. *Librn*, Francis Collins; E-Mail: francis.collins@cpl.org; Staff 7 (MLS 2, Non-MLS 5)
Circ 195,209
Library Holdings: Bk Vols 46,920
MOUNT PLEASANT, 14000 Kinsman Rd, 44120. SAN 356-0791. Tel: 216-623-7032. FAX: 216-623-7035. Web Site: www.cpl.org. *Librn*, Rekiat Olayiwola; E-Mail: rekiat.olayiwola@cpl.org; Staff 4 (MLS 1, Non-MLS 3)
Circ 57,342
Library Holdings: Bk Vols 25,946
PERIODICAL CENTER, 325 Superior Ave, 44114-1271. Tel: 216-623-2904. FAX: 216-623-2966. *Librn*, Jelena Fried
Library Holdings: Per Subs 149
POPULAR LIBRARY, 325 Superior Ave 1st flr E, 44114-1271. Tel: 216-623-2842. FAX: 216-902-4942. E-Mail: pop1@library.cpl.org. Web Site: www.cpl.org. *In Charge*, Richard Fox; E-Mail: richard.fox@cpl.org; Staff 4 (MLS 2, Non-MLS 2)
Circ 204,681
Library Holdings: Bk Vols 23,433
PUBLIC ADMINISTRATION, City Hall, 601 Lakeside Ave NE Rm 100, 44114. SAN 356-0104. Tel: 216-623-2919. FAX: 216-623-6948. E-Mail: pal1@cpl.org. Web Site: www.cpl.org. *Librn*, Karen Martines; E-Mail: karen.martines@cpl.org; Staff 4 (MLS 2, Non-MLS 2)
Library Holdings: Bk Vols 14,000
Administers City of Cleveland Law Library
RICE, 2820 E 116th St, 44120. SAN 356-0856. Tel: 216-623-7046. FAX: 216-623-7049. Web Site: www.cpl.org. *Librn*, Mirna Parker; E-Mail: mirna.parker@cpl.org; Staff 5 (MLS 1, Non-MLS 4)
Circ 108,059
Library Holdings: Bk Vols 31,236
ROCKPORT, 4421 W 140th St, 44135. SAN 356-0880. Tel: 216-623-7053. FAX: 216-623-7055. Web Site: www.cpl.org. *Librn*, Ricki Neubecker; E-Mail: ricki.neubecker@cpl.org; Staff 7 (MLS 1, Non-MLS 6)
Circ 206,399
Library Holdings: Bk Vols 48,151
SCIENCE & TECHNOLOGY, 325 Superior Ave NE, 44114-1271. Tel: 216-623-2932. FAX: 216-623-7029. E-Mail: sci2@library.cpl.org. Web Site: www.cpl.org. *In Charge*, Jean Piety; E-Mail: jean.piety@cpl.org; Staff 14 (MLS 5, Non-MLS 9)
Circ 127,116
Library Holdings: Bk Vols 192,411
SOCIAL SCIENCES, 525 Superior Ave, 44114-1271. Tel: 216-623-2860. FAX: 216-623-7064. E-Mail: soc.sci@cpl.org. Web Site: www.cpl.org. *In Charge*, Mary Ellen Kollar; E-Mail: maryellen.kollar@cpl.org; Staff 10 (MLS 5, Non-MLS 5)
Circ 116,097
Library Holdings: Bk Vols 145,778
Subject Interests: Baseball
SOUTH, 3096 Scranton Rd, 44113. SAN 356-0910. Tel: 216-623-7060. FAX: 216-623-7063. Web Site: www.cpl.org. *Librn*, Laura Diesing; E-Mail: laura.diesing@cpl.org; Staff 4 (MLS 1, Non-MLS 3)
Circ 79,648
Library Holdings: Bk Vols 31,793
SOUTH BROOKLYN, 4303 Pearl Rd, 44109. SAN 356-0945. Tel: 216-623-7067. FAX: 216-623-7069. Web Site: www.cpl.org. *Librn*, Lydia Pryszlak; E-Mail: lydia.pryszlak@cpl.org; Staff 7 (MLS 3, Non-MLS 4)
Circ 218,905
Library Holdings: Bk Vols 48,151
STERLING, 2200 E 30th St, 44115. SAN 356-097X. Tel: 216-623-7074. FAX: 216-623-7072. Web Site: www.cpl.org. *Librn*, Janet Hutch; E-Mail: janet.hutch@cpl.org; Staff 3 (MLS 1, Non-MLS 2)
Circ 71,647
UNION, 3463 E 93rd St, 44104. SAN 356-1062. Tel: 216-623-7088. FAX: 216-623-7082. Web Site: www.cpl.org. *Librn*, Sheba Marcus-Bey; E-Mail: sheba.marcus-bey@cpl.org; Staff 5 (MLS 1, Non-MLS 4)
Circ 54,140
Library Holdings: Bk Vols 25,258
WALZ, 7910 Detroit Ave, 44102. SAN 356-1097. Tel: 216-623-7095. FAX: 216-623-7099. Web Site: www.cpl.org. *Librn*, Ivan Miletic; E-Mail: ivan.miletic@cpl.org; Staff 6 (MLS 1, Non-MLS 5)
Circ 137,655
Library Holdings: Bk Vols 41,493
WEST PARK, 3805 W 157th St, 44111. SAN 356-1127. Tel: 216-623-7102. FAX: 216-623-7104. Web Site: www.cpl.org. *Librn*, Susan Martin; E-Mail: susan.martin@cpl.org; Staff 8 (MLS 3, Non-MLS 5)
Circ 238,394
Library Holdings: Bk Vols 48,563
WOODLAND, 5806 Woodland Ave, 44104. SAN 356-1186. Tel: 216-623-7109. FAX: 216-623-7113. Web Site: www.cpl.org. *Librn*, Darlene Ronney; E-Mail: darlene.ronney@cpl.org; Staff 4 (MLS 1, Non-MLS 3)
Circ 67,555
Library Holdings: Bk Vols 23,631

S CLEVELAND PUBLIC SCHOOLS, Max S Hayes Vocational School Library, 4600 Detroit Ave, 44102. SAN 326-1034. Tel: 216-634-8683. FAX: 216-634-2175. *Librn*, Tony Acosta
Founded 1921. Enrl 400; Fac 40
Library Holdings: Bk Vols 9,000; Bk Titles 6,500; Per Subs 36

CLEVELAND STATE UNIVERSITY
CL CLEVELAND-MARSHALL LAW LIBRARY, Cleveland-Marshall College of Law, 1801 Euclid Ave, 44115-2403. SAN 356-1240. Tel: 216-687-2250. Reference Tel: 216-687-6877. FAX: 216-687-5098. Web Site: www.gov.tdoc.law.usohio.edu/lawlib.html. *Assoc Dean, Dir*, Michael Slinger; *Asst Dir*, Felice Lowell; *Asst Dir*, Ellen Quinn; *Head Ref*, Marie Rehmar; *Ref*, Denise Carpenter; *Circ*, Leslie Pardo; *Ser*, Nancy M Hanacek; *Cat*, Yueseng Shen; *Govt Doc*, Schyuler Cook. Subject Specialists: *Pub servs tech*, Ellen Quinn; *Servs*, Marie Rehmar; *Tech info*, Felice Lowell; Staff 21 (MLS 8, Non-MLS 13)
Founded 1897. Enrl 752; Fac 43; Highest Degree: Doctorate
Library Holdings: Bk Vols 221,614; Bk Titles 59,418; Per Subs 3,817
Special Collections: Briefs & Records of Ohio Supreme Court, microform; Briefs & Records of US Supreme Court, microform; CIS Index & US Legislative Hist microfiche
Automation Activity & Vendor Info: (Acquisitions) Innovative Interfaces Inc.
Publications: User's Guide to the Law Library, Law Library Newsletter, Current Contents Service for Law Library Periodicals
Partic in Dialog Corporation; OCLC Online Computer Library Center, Inc; Westlaw
C UNIVERSITY LIBRARY, Rhodes Tower, 1860 E 22nd St, 44114-4435. SAN 356-1216. Tel: 216-687-2475. FAX: 216-687-9380. Web Site: www.ulib.csuohio.edu/. *Dir*, Glenda Thornton; E-Mail: g.thornton@csuohio.edu; *Assoc Dir*, George Lupone; E-Mail: g.lupone@csuohio.edu; *Head Ref*, Pamela Eyerdam; Tel: 216-687-2370, E-Mail: p.eyerdam@csuohio.edu; *Ref*, Gail Marredeth; Tel: 216-687-2291, E-Mail: g.marredeth@csuohio.edu; *Ref*, William Meloy; *Ref*, Marianne Nolan; Tel: 216-687-2376, Fax: 216-687-2376, E-Mail: m.nolan@csuohio.edu; *Ref*, Alice Smith; *Ref*, Pamela Tidwell; Tel: 216-523-7373, E-Mail: p.tidwell@csuohio.edu; *Doc*, Robert J Cieslick; Tel: 216-687-2256, Fax: 216-687-2383, E-Mail: r.cieslik@csuohio.edu; *Res*, Janet Mongan; Tel: 216-687-6961, Fax: 216-687-6961, E-Mail: jmongan@csuohio.edu; *Cat*, Michael Boock; Tel: 216-687-2362, Fax: 216-687-9328, E-Mail: m.boock@csuohio.edu. Subject Specialists: *Art*, Pamela Eyerdam; *Business and management*, Pamela Tidwell; *English (language)*, Lesley Jorbin; *Health sciences*, Gail Marredeth; *History*, Marianne Nolan; *Music*, Lesley Jorbin; *Science/technology*, Billie J Reinhart; *Social sciences and issues*, Pamela Tidwell; *Technology*, Billie J Reinhart; Staff 22 (MLS 17, Non-MLS 5)
Founded 1928. Enrl 10,684; Fac 497; Highest Degree: Doctorate
Jul 1997-Jun 1998 Income $4,555,038. Mats Exp $1,675,050, Books $325,331, Per/Ser (Incl. Access Fees) $1,349,719. Sal $1,842,227
Library Holdings: Bk Vols 932,464; Bk Titles 470,435; Per Subs 5,125
Special Collections: Black History (Walker Coll); Cleveland Press Coll; Cleveland Union Terminal Coll; French-American/Great Lakes Industrial History Coll; Hazel Hutchison Collister Contemporary Poetry Coll; Marquis de Lafayette Microfilm Collection; Watson Bridge Coll (Bridge Engineering)
Database Vendor: Innovative Interfaces INN - View
Partic in Cleveland Area Metropolitan Library System; OCLC Online Computer Library Center, Inc; Ohio Library & Information Network; OHIONET
Friends of the Library Group

S CONSOLIDATED NATURAL GAS INC, Knowledge Center,* 7165 E Pleasant Valley Rd, 44131-2537. SAN 370-7792. Tel: 216-736-6077. FAX: 216-736-5375. *Mgr*, Carol Brown; E-Mail: carol_a._brown@copp.cng.com; *ILL*, Sakina M Jaffer
Founded 1973
Library Holdings: Bk Vols 7,000; Bk Titles 5,500; Per Subs 200
Automation Activity & Vendor Info: (Acquisitions) Sydney; (Cataloging) Sydney; (Circulation) Sydney; (Serials) Sydney
Publications: Acquisitions list
Partic in American Gas Association-Library Services; Cleveland Area Metropolitan Library System; OCLC Online Computer Library Center, Inc

CUYAHOGA COMMUNITY COLLEGE

J EASTERN CAMPUS LIBRARY, 4250 Richmond Rd, Highland Hill Village, 44122-6195. SAN 320-9202. Tel: 216-987-2085, 216-987-2086, 216-987-2088, 216-987-2091. FAX: 216-987-2054. *Dir*, Terry Hancox; *Librn*, Patricia Gabriel; E-Mail: pat.gabriel@tri-c.cc.oh.us; *Librn*, Shahrokh Afshar; Staff 10 (MLS 3, Non-MLS 7)
Founded 1971. Enrl 2,764; Fac 130
Library Holdings: Bk Vols 47,011; Per Subs 410
Partic in Cleveland Area Metropolitan Library System; OCLC Online Computer Library Center, Inc

J METROPOLITAN CAMPUS LIBRARY, 2900 Community College Ave, 44115. SAN 356-1275. Tel: 216-987-4294. FAX: 216-987-4404. *Dir*, Lawrence Cole; E-Mail: lawrencecole@tri.c.cc.oh.us; *Librn*, John Horton; *Librn*, Margaret Barron; *Librn*, Nancy Conner; Staff 13 (MLS 4, Non-MLS 9)
Founded 1968. Enrl 3,666; Fac 205
Library Holdings: Bk Vols 58,775; Bk Titles 51,159; Per Subs 484

J TECHNICAL PROCESSING, 11000 Pleasant Valley Rd, Parma, 44130. SAN 322-5747. Tel: 216-987-5202. FAX: 216-987-5050. E-Mail: tpdacquisitions@tri-c.cc.oh.us. *Head Tech Servs*, Laverne Caldwell Jenkins; Tel: 216-987-5338, E-Mail: laverne.jenkins@tri-c.cc.oh.us; Staff 8 (MLS 1, Non-MLS 7)
Database Vendor: Innovative Interfaces INN - View
Partic in Cleveland Area Metropolitan Library System; OCLC Online Computer Library Center, Inc; OHIONET

J WESTERN CAMPUS LIBRARY, 11000 Pleasant Valley Rd, Parma, 44130. SAN 320-9210. Tel: 216-987-5410. FAX: 216-987-5050. Web Site: www.tri-c.cc.oh.us/libwebpage/index.htm. *Dir*, William Beuther; *Coll Develop, Librn*, Carol Toth; *Librn*, Raymond Jansen; *Librn*, Shirlee Muse; Staff 13 (MLS 4, Non-MLS 9)
Founded 1966. Enrl 5,049
Library Holdings: Bk Vols 64,088; Bk Titles 56,691; Per Subs 481
Partic in Cleveland Area Metropolitan Library System; OCLC Online Computer Library Center, Inc; Ohio Library & Information Network

G CUYAHOGA COUNTY ARCHIVES LIBRARY,* The Robert Russell Rhodes House, 2905 Franklin Blvd NW, 44113. SAN 313-3362. Tel: 216-443-7250. FAX: 216-443-3636. E-Mail: countyarchives@nls.net. *Mgr*, Judith G Cetina PhD
Founded 1975
Library Holdings: Bk Titles 2,150
Subject Interests: Cleveland, Cuyahoga County, Genealogy

S CUYAHOGA COUNTY PLANNING COMMISSION LIBRARY,* 323 Lakeside Ave W Ste 400, 44113-1009. SAN 327-7658. Tel: 216-443-3700. FAX: 216-443-3737. E-Mail: cpc@planning.co.cuyahoga.oh.us. Web Site: www.planning.co.cuyahoga.oh.us. *In Charge*, Phyllis Gordon
Library Holdings: Bk Vols 200; Per Subs 20

C DAVID N MYERS COLLEGE, Library Resource Center,* 112 Prospect Ave SE, 44115-1096. SAN 313-3397. Tel: 216-696-9000, Ext 653. FAX: 216-696-6430. E-Mail: rbrhel@dnmyers.edu. *Dir*, Richard Brhel; *Asst Librn*, Eartha Elridge; *Tech Servs*, Richard Brhel
Founded 1968. Highest Degree: Bachelor
Library Holdings: Bk Vols 16,522; Per Subs 143
Subject Interests: Bus, Corp hist, Econ, Law, Mgt, Pub admin
Special Collections: Spencerian Archives of History of Business & Business Education
Partic in Cleveland Area Metropolitan Library System

M DEACONESS HOSPITAL, Medical Library,* 4229 Pearl Rd, 44109-4218. SAN 373-7829. Tel: 216-459-6300, Ext 2172. FAX: 216-459-6831. *Librn*, Lucille Parsell
Library Holdings: Bk Vols 735; Bk Titles 644; Per Subs 89
Special Collections: Medical & Nursing Colls, bks, journals & v-tapes
Partic in Dialog Corporation; Nat Libr of Med

GM DEPARTMENT OF VETERANS AFFAIRS, Medical Center Library, 10701 East Blvd, 44106. SAN 313-3893. Tel: 216-791-3800, Ext 4291. FAX: 216-231-3242. *Chief Librn*, Janet Monk-Gillette; *AV*, Raisa Cherniv; Staff 10 (MLS 5, Non-MLS 5)
Library Holdings: Per Subs 639
Subject Interests: Medicine, Nursing, Psychiatry, Social work, Surgery
Partic in BRS; Dialog Corporation; Medline; Regional Med Libr - Region 3; Vets Admin Libr Network

S DUNHAM TAVERN MUSEUM LIBRARY,* 6709 Euclid Ave, 44103-3913. SAN 321-0871. Tel: 216-431-1060.
Founded 1954
Library Holdings: Bk Titles 750
Subject Interests: Antiques, Cleveland hist, Ohio
Open Wed & Sun 1-4

S ERNST & YOUNG, Center for Business Knowledge Library,* 1660 W Second St, 44113. SAN 313-3427. Tel: 216-861-5000. FAX: 216-622-0199. *Librn*, Naomi Clifford; E-Mail: naomi.clifford@ey.com; Staff 4 (MLS 3, Non-MLS 1)
Founded 1960
Library Holdings: Bk Vols 500; Bk Titles 400; Per Subs 415
Subject Interests: Accounting, Auditing, Mgt
Special Collections: Ernst & Young Archive
Partic in OHIONET

FAIRVIEW HEALTH SYSTEM

M MEDICAL LIBRARY, 18101 Lorain Ave, 44111. SAN 356-2115. Tel: 216-476-7117. FAX: 216-476-7803. *Librn*, Irene Szentkiralyi
Library Holdings: Bk Vols 3,000
Partic in Cleveland Network

S FEDERAL RESERVE BANK OF CLEVELAND, Research Library,* PO Box 5620, 44101. SAN 313-3451. Tel: 216-579-2961. FAX: 216-579-3172. *Librn*, Lee D Faulhaber; *Assoc Librn*, Lucia Green; *Assoc Librn*, Lynn Sniderman; *Assoc Librn*, Diane Mogren; Staff 5 (MLS 2, Non-MLS 3)
Founded 1918
Library Holdings: Bk Vols 22,000; Bk Titles 20,000; Per Subs 600
Subject Interests: Banking, Econ, Finance, Reserve syst
Publications: Acquisitions list; Bibliography of Bank Publications
Partic in OCLC Online Computer Library Center, Inc; OHIONET

G FEDERAL TRADE COMMISSION, Cleveland Regional Office,* 1111 Superior Ave, Ste 200, 44114. SAN 313-346X. Tel: 216-263-3455. FAX: 216-263-3426. *Actg Dir*, Laurel Price
Library Holdings: Bk Vols 2,500; Per Subs 15

S FOUNDATION CENTER-CLEVELAND, Kent H Smith Library, 1422 Euclid Ave, Rm 811, 44115-2001. SAN 313-3478. Tel: 216-861-1934. FAX: 216-861-1936. Web Site: www.fdncenter.org. *Dir*, Cynthia Glunt Bailie; *Outreach Serv, Ref*, Achala Wali; Staff 4 (MLS 1, Non-MLS 3)
Founded 1977
Library Holdings: Bk Vols 1,000; Spec Interest Per Sub 36
Subject Interests: Fundraising, Grantsmanship, Philanthropy
Special Collections: Foundations (Annual Reports & Tax Returns), micro & mss
Database Vendor: Ebsco - EbscoHost
Publications: Library Brochure, Worksheets For Grantseekers
Restriction: Open to public for reference only
Partic in Cleveland Area Metropolitan Library System; Dialog Corporation
Friends of the Library Group

S GLOBAL ISSUES RESOURCE CENTER LIBRARY, E I, Cuyahoga Community College, 4250 Richmond Rd, 44122. SAN 323-4274. Tel: 216-987-2224. FAX: 216-987-2133. E-Mail: info@global-issues.org. Web Site: www.global-issues.org. *Dir*, Joanne Lewis; *Librn*, Justine Smith; Tel: 216-987-2049, E-Mail: justine.smith@tri-c.cc.ch.us; Staff 3 (MLS 3)
Library Holdings: Bk Titles 2,000; Per Subs 60
Special Collections: Conflict Resolution; Curricula; Energy; Environment; Global Education
Publications: Audio-Visual Catalog; bibliographies on energy issues, enviromental concerns and global education; Games & Simulations Catalog; Resources to Teach About Conflict Resolution
Partic in Cleveland Area Metropolitan Library System
Friends of the Library Group

M GREATER CLEVELAND HOSPITAL ASSOCIATION LIBRARY,* Playhouse Sq, 1226 Huron Rd, 44115. SAN 327-6732. Tel: 216-696-6900. FAX: 216-696-1837. *Librn*, Sandy Anderson
Library Holdings: Per Subs 41

L HAHN, LOESER & PARKS, Law Library, 3300 BP America Bldg, 200 Public Sq, 44114-2301. SAN 372-2139. Tel: 216-621-0150. FAX: 216-241-2824. *Librn*, Susan B Hersch
Library Holdings: Bk Vols 7,000; Per Subs 40

L HOUSING ADVOCATES, INC, Law & Consumer Affairs Library,* 3655 Prospect Ave E, 44115. SAN 320-4138. Tel: 216-391-5444. FAX: 216-391-5404. *Dir*, Ed Kramer; E-Mail: kramere@aol.com
Founded 1979
1998-1999 Income $6,000. Mats Exp $6,000, Books $5,200, Per/Ser (Incl. Access Fees) $800
Library Holdings: Bk Titles 5,080; Per Subs 75
Special Collections: Housing Law Coll
Restriction: Staff use only

M HURON HOSPITAL, (Formerly Meridia Huron Hospital), Professional Library, 13951 Terrace Rd, 44112. SAN 313-3559. Tel: 216-761-7036. FAX: 216-761-7053. *Librn*, Keith Stincic; E-Mail: kstincic@meridia.org; Staff 1 (MLS 1)
Founded 1935
Library Holdings: Bk Titles 2,500; Per Subs 125
Subject Interests: Medicine, Nursing, Surgery
Partic in Greater Midwest Health Sci Libr Network; Med Libr Asn of NE Ohio

L JONES, DAY, REAVIS & POGUE LIBRARY,* 901 Lakeside Ave, 44114. SAN 313-3575. Tel: 216-586-3939. FAX: 216-579-0212. *Librn*, JoAnn Fisher; *Asst Librn*, Catherine Bransky; *Online Servs*, Suzanne Young
Library Holdings: Bk Vols 40,000; Per Subs 230
Subject Interests: Corp law, Taxation
Restriction: Staff use only

M KAISER PERMANENTE, Medical Center Library,* 12301 Snow Rd, 44130. SAN 322-8932. Tel: 216-362-2086. FAX: 216-362-2294. *Librn*, Bonnie Rosen; E-Mail: bonnie.rosen@kp.org
Founded 1976
Library Holdings: Per Subs 156
Partic in MLANO; Regional Med Libr

S LIGGETT-STASHOWER AVERTISING INC LIBRARY,* 1228 Euclid Ave, 44115. SAN 313-3583. Tel: 216-348-8500. FAX: 216-736-8113. Web Site: www.liggett.com. *Librn*, Theressa Burrage; E-Mail: tburrage@liggett.com
Library Holdings: Bk Vols 490; Per Subs 10

L MCDONALD, HOPKINS, BURKE & HABER, Law Library, 2100 Bank One Ctr, 600 Superior, 44114. SAN 372-2279. Tel: 216-348-5400. FAX: 216-348-5474. *Librn*, Ellen Smith
Library Holdings: Bk Vols 10,000; Per Subs 100

S MCGEAN-ROHCO, INC, Plant & Laboratory Library, 2910 Harvard Ave, 44105. SAN 313-3591. Tel: 216-441-4900. FAX: 216-441-1377. *Librn*, Colleen Carrocia
Founded 1935
Library Holdings: Bk Titles 1,800; Per Subs 65
Subject Interests: Analytical chemistry, Chrome, Computer programming, Electro-deposition of metals, Inorganic chemicals, Lubricants, Metal cleaners, Metal finishing, Plating on plastics
Special Collections: Comprehensive Inorganic Chem (Pergamon Coll), bks; Kirk-Othmer Chemistry Encylopedia; Kolthoff Treatise on Analytical Chemistry
Partic in Dialog Corporation

S MELDRUM & FEWSMITH INC, Business Information Center,* 1350 Euclid Ave, 44115. SAN 313-3613. Tel: 216-241-2141. FAX: 216-479-2438. E-Mail: elevin@meldrum.com.
Founded 1944
Library Holdings: Bk Vols 1,000; Per Subs 450
Subject Interests: Advertising, Mktg
Special Collections: Advertising Subject Files; Annual Reports
Publications: Library Update (monthly)
Partic in Dialog Corporation; Dow Jones News Retrieval

M METROHEALTH MEDICAL CENTER, Harold H Brittingham Memorial Library, 2500 MetroHealth Dr, 44101-1998. SAN 313-3249. Tel: 216-778-5623. FAX: 216-778-8242. E-Mail: library@metrohealth.org. Web Site: www.metrohealth.org. *Chief Librn*, Christine A Dziedzina; E-Mail: cdziedzina@metrohealth.org; *Librn*, Grove Steve; Staff 6 (MLS 2, Non-MLS 4)
Founded 1937
Library Holdings: Bk Vols 9,000; Per Subs 473
Subject Interests: Medicine, Nursing
Special Collections: Arthritis & Rheumatism (Stecher Coll); Highland View Hospital Library Coll
Automation Activity & Vendor Info: (Cataloging) Sydney
Partic in National Network Of Libraries Of Medicine - South Central Region
Friends of the Library Group

G NASA, John H Glenn Research Center at Lewis Field, 21000 Brookpark Rd, 44135. SAN 313-3664. Tel: 216-433-5762. FAX: 216-433-5777. E-Mail: library@lerc.nasa.gov. Web Site: itwebx.grc.nasa.gov/techlibpages/pubhome.html. *Acq*, Melanie Long; Tel: 216-433-5761; *Cat*, Marshall Catherine; *ILL*, Bev Louderback; *Coll Develop*, Susan Oberc; Staff 10 (MLS 4, Non-MLS 6)
Founded 1941
Library Holdings: Bk Vols 77,000; Per Subs 300
Subject Interests: Aeronautics, Engineering, Power, Propulsion, Space communications mat, Space science, Structures
Partic in Dialog Corporation; Nasa Libraries Information System - Nasa Galaxie; Nasa Libraries Information System - Nasa Galaxie; OCLC Online Computer Library Center, Inc; OHIONET

S NATIONAL CITY BANK OF CLEVELAND, Investment Division Library,* 1900 E Ninth St, Loc 2220, PO Box 5756, 44101-9957. SAN 313-3672. Tel: 216-575-2546. FAX: 216-575-3122. *Librn*, Laura O Cannon; Staff 2 (MLS 1, Non-MLS 1)
Founded 1930
Library Holdings: Bk Vols 1,045; Per Subs 72
Subject Interests: Finance, Securities analysis

G NORTHEAST OHIO AREAWIDE COORDINATING AGENCY LIBRARY, 1299 Superior Ave, 44114-3204. SAN 321-7892. Tel: 216-241-2414, Ext 240. FAX: 216-621-3024. Web Site: www.noaca.org/pages/about/irc. *Info Specialist, Librn*, Kenneth P Goldberg; E-Mail: kgoldberg@mpo.noaca.org
Founded 1965
Library Holdings: Per Subs 178
Subject Interests: Air pollution, Air quality, Archit preservation, Environ planning, Health planning, Housing, Labor studies, Land use, Legislation, Regional planning, Transportation planning, Water quality
Special Collections: Greater Cleveland Metropolitan Region US Census Material; Habitat (newspaper), Cleveland Edition (newspaper), Cleveland CBD Planning Documents; Northeast Ohio Government & History; Transportation Research Board Series
Publications: Annual publications related to newly cataloged materials & recent NOACA-produced reports; Grantsmanship services
Restriction: Open to public for reference only
Partic in Cleveland Area Metropolitan Library System; NE Ohio Govt DOC Interest Group; Ohio GODORT Affiliate
Librarian actively engaged in research projects. Staff manages federal Intergovernmental Review process, as agency is Metropolitan Planning Organization (MPO) & designated Clearinghouse for review of federal grant applications for five-county region

CM OHIO COLLEGE OF PODIATRIC MEDICINE LIBRARY,* 10515 Carnegie Ave, 44106. SAN 313-3710. Tel: 216-231-3300, Ext 247. FAX: 216-231-6537. *Librn*, Judy Mehl Cowell
Highest Degree: Doctorate
Library Holdings: Bk Vols 16,500; Per Subs 260
Subject Interests: Podiatric med
Partic in Medline

S PENTON RESEARCH SERVICES,* 1100 Superior Ave, 44114-2543. SAN 372-7408. Tel: 216-696-7000. FAX: 216-696-8130. *Mgr*, Michael Keating; E-Mail: mkeating@penton.com; Staff 2 (MLS 1, Non-MLS 1)
Founded 1960
Library Holdings: Bk Vols 3,400; Per Subs 100
Special Collections: Advertising; Business Markets; Marketing, articles, bks, rpts
Publications: How Business & Government Buy; How Business & Government Buyers Get Information; Industry Inquiry Trends; Introduction to the Government Market: Local, State, Federal; Know the Buyer Better; Market Profiles; Penton Research Overview Reports

S PLAIN DEALER PUBLISHING CO LIBRARY,* 1801 Superior Ave, 44114-2198. SAN 313-3745. Tel: 216-999-4195. FAX: 216-999-6363. E-Mail: library@plaind.com. *Dir*, Patti A Graziano; Staff 10 (MLS 3, Non-MLS 7)
Founded 1908
Library Holdings: Bk Vols 3,970; Per Subs 60
Subject Interests: Cleveland, Clippings from 1920 to present, Ohio hist, Photog from 1858 to present

S PLANNED PARENTHOOD OF GREATER CLEVELAND, INC LIBRARY, 3135 Euclid Ave, Ste 101, 44115. SAN 313-3753. Tel: 216-881-7742. FAX: 216-881-1834. *Exec Dir*, Betsey C Kaufman; E-Mail: betsy-kaufman@ppfa.org
Library Holdings: Bk Vols 1,000
Restriction: By appointment only
Function: For research purposes

S ROMANIAN ETHNIC ARTS MUSEUM LIBRARY, 3256 Warren Rd, 44111. SAN 321-0561. Tel: 216-941-5550. FAX: 216-941-3068. *Dir*, George Dobrea; E-Mail: dobreaart@aol.com; Staff 1 (MLS 1)
Founded 1928
Library Holdings: Bk Titles 5,500
Subject Interests: Culture, Romanian art

M THE BENJAMIN ROSE INSTITUTE LIBRARY,* 12200 Fairhill Rd, 44120. SAN 372-5987. Tel: 216-231-7230. FAX: 216-231-7323. *Librn*, Karen McNally Bensing
Founded 1971
Library Holdings: Bk Titles 3,500; Per Subs 100
Publications: Current Awareness Service (monthly)
Partic in Dialog Corporation

S ST ANDREW'S ABBEY, Slovak Institute Library, 10510 Buckeye Rd, 44104. SAN 328-3674. Tel: 216-721-5300. FAX: 216-791-8268. *Dir*, Andrew Pier
Library Holdings: Bk Vols 10,000

M SAINT MICHAEL HOSPITAL, Medical Library,* 5163 Broadway, 44127. SAN 326-3355. Tel: 216-429-8245. FAX: 216-429-8405. *Coordr*, Barbara Kahl
Library Holdings: Bk Vols 2,200; Per Subs 200
Partic in NLM

M SAINT VINCENT CHARITY HOSPITAL, Medical Library,* 2351 E 22nd St, 44115-3197. SAN 313-3818. Tel: 216-861-6200, Ext 2133. FAX: 216-363-3337. *Librn*, Joanne Billiar
Library Holdings: Bk Vols 2,200; Per Subs 150
Subject Interests: Medicine, Nursing, Psychiatry, Surgery
Restriction: Open to public for reference only

S SHERWIN-WILLIAMS AUTOMOTIVE FINISHES CORP LIBRARY, 4440 Warrensville Center Rd, 44128. SAN 375-9644. Tel: 216-332-8330. FAX: 216-332-8464. *Librn*, Beth Rimz
Library Holdings: Bk Titles 6,000; Per Subs 50
Automation Activity & Vendor Info: (Cataloging) EOS; (OPAC) EOS
Restriction: Staff use only
Mem of Chicago Libr Syst

S SHERWIN-WILLIAMS CO, Information Center,* 13 Midland Bldg, 101 Prospect Ave NW, 44115. SAN 375-2410. Tel: 216-566-2993. FAX: 216-566-2174.
Library Holdings: Bk Vols 300; Per Subs 200

R TEMPLE EMANUEL LIBRARY, 2200 S Green Rd, 44121. SAN 313-3834. Tel: 216-381-6600. FAX: 216-381-5509. E-Mail: emanuel18@aol.com.
Library Holdings: Bk Vols 13,000; Per Subs 25
Special Collections: Zaas Judaica Film Library
Friends of the Library Group

L THOMPSON, HINE & FLORY, Law Library,* 3900 Key Ctr, 127 Public Sq, 44114-1216. SAN 372-2295. Tel: 216-566-5651. FAX: 216-566-5800. *Librn*, Kyle Passmore
Library Holdings: Bk Vols 30,000; Per Subs 150

TRW, INC
L LAW LIBRARY, 1900 Richmond Rd, 44124. SAN 321-9399. Tel: 216-291-7213. FAX: 216-291-7070.; Staff 2 (MLS 1, Non-MLS 1)
Founded 1974
Library Holdings: Bk Titles 24,000; Per Subs 100
Subject Interests: Int property, International law
Restriction: Staff use only

S UCAR CARBON COMPANY, INC, Technical Information Services, PO Box 6116, 44101. SAN 313-668X. Tel: 216-676-2223. *Mgr*, Linda Riffle; Staff 3 (MLS 2, Non-MLS 1)
Founded 1945
Library Holdings: Bk Vols 20,000; Bk Titles 16,000; Per Subs 300
Subject Interests: Carbon, Graphite tech, High performance non-metallic mat
Partic in Dialog Corporation; Sci & Tech Info Network

S UKRAINIAN MUSEUM-ARCHIVES INC,* 1202 Kenilworth Ave, 44113. SAN 323-5270. Tel: 216-781-4329. E-Mail: staff@umacleveland.org. Web Site: www.umacleveland.org. *Dir*, Andrew Fedynsky
Library Holdings: Bk Vols 20,000; Per Subs 40
Special Collections: Taras Shevchenko, Ukrainian Revolution, Ukrainian Religion Periodical Coll outside of Ukraine, 1900-present

S UNITED STATES BOOK EXCHANGE LIBRARY,* 2969 W 25th St, 44113-5393. SAN 370-6370. Tel: 216-241-6960. FAX: 216-241-6966. E-Mail: usbe@usbe.com. *Acq, Pres*, John T Zubal; *Librn*, Thomas A Zubal; *Circ*, Jean Marie Zubal; *ILL, Per*, Marilyn Zubal; *Coll Develop*, Robert Farkas; Staff 9 (MLS 3, Non-MLS 6)
Founded 1948
Library Holdings: Bk Titles 20,000
Publications: USBE: For Members Only
Partic in OCLC Online Computer Library Center, Inc

M UNIVERSITY HOSPITALS OF CLEVELAND, Core Library Services,* 11100 Euclid Ave, 44106. SAN 371-859X. Tel: 216-844-1208. FAX: 216-844-1207. E-Mail: corelib@ohionet.org. *Dir*, Marcia Alcorn; Staff 6 (MLS 5, Non-MLS 1)
Library Holdings: Bk Titles 5,000; Per Subs 750
Restriction: Staff use only
Partic in Cleveland Area Metropolitan Library System; MLANO; OHIONET

S URS CORP, Resource Center, 800 W St Clair Ave, 44113. SAN 328-1477. Tel: 216-622-2400. FAX: 216-622-2428. Web Site: www.urscorp.com. *Asst Librn*, Shirley Peavy; Staff 2 (MLS 1, Non-MLS 1)
Library Holdings: Bk Vols 200; Per Subs 10
Subject Interests: Architecture, Engineering, Interior design, Planning
Restriction: Staff use only
Partic in OCLC Online Computer Library Center, Inc; OHIONET

L WALTER & HAVERFIELD, Law Library, 1300 Terminal Tower, 44113. SAN 325-5387. Tel: 216-781-1212. FAX: 216-575-0911. Web Site: www.walterhav.com. *Librn*, Leon Stevens; E-Mail: lstevens@walterhav.com; Staff 2 (MLS 1, Non-MLS 1)
Founded 1932
Library Holdings: Bk Vols 10,000; Per Subs 100
Subject Interests: Labor, Tax

S WESTERN RESERVE HISTORICAL SOCIETY LIBRARY,* 10825 East Blvd, 44106-1777. SAN 313-3915. Tel: 216-721-5722. FAX: 216-721-5702. E-Mail: reference@wrhs.org. Web Site: www.wrhs.org. *Dir*, Kermit J Pike; Staff 13 (MLS 6, Non-MLS 7)
Founded 1867
Library Holdings: Bk Titles 238,000
Subject Interests: Abolitionism, Am genealogy, Am Revolution, Black, Civil War, Cleveland hist incl urban, Ethnic, Shakers, Slavery
Special Collections: Charles Candee Baldwin Coll, maps, atlases; David Z Norton Napoleon Coll; Wallace Hugh Cathcart Coll of Shaker Literature, mss; William Pendleton Palmer Civil War Coll
Publications: Library News (quarterly)
Partic in OCLC Online Computer Library Center, Inc
Friends of the Library Group

L WESTON, HURD, FALLON, PAISLEY & HOWLEY, LLP, Law Library, 2500 Terminal Tower, 44113-2241. SAN 371-9057. Tel: 216-241-6602, Ext 3203. FAX: 216-621-8369. *In Charge*, Sandra Suchan
Library Holdings: Bk Titles 15,000
Special Collections: Insurance Law; Products Liability Law
Publications: Monthly Newsletter & Acquisitions Report
Restriction: Staff use only

SR WIDER CHURCH MINISTRIES LIBRARY, (Formerly United Church Board For World Ministries Library), 700 Prospect Ave, 44115. SAN 327-0416. Tel: 216-736-3200. FAX: 216-736-3203. *Librn*, Virginia Stowe
Library Holdings: Bk Vols 3,500; Per Subs 50

S JOHN T ZUBAL INC, RESEARCH LIBRARY, 2969 W 25th St, 44113-5393. SAN 373-5958. Tel: 216-241-7640. FAX: 215-241-7640. E-Mail: jzubal@zubal.com. Web Site: www.jzubal.com. *Dir*, Robert Farkas; *Coll Develop*, John T Zubal
Founded 1964
Library Holdings: Bk Titles 1,953; Per Subs 16
Special Collections: Dust Wrappers, pre-1905; Publishers Samples & Dummies

CLEVELAND HEIGHTS

S AMC RAMBLER CLUB INC LIBRARY, 2645 Ashton Rd, 44118. SAN 325-5417. Tel: 216-371-0226. FAX: 216-371-5946. *Librn*, Elaine V Wrenick; *Librn*, Frank E Wrenick; Staff 2 (MLS 1, Non-MLS 1)
Library Holdings: Bk Titles 1,000
Special Collections: American Motors Corporation (1958-1969), AMC vehicles

P CLEVELAND HEIGHTS-UNIVERSITY HEIGHTS PUBLIC LIBRARY, 2345 Lee Rd, 44118-3493. SAN 356-2387. Tel: 216-932-3600. TDD: 216-321-0739. FAX: 216-932-0932. Web Site: www.chuhpl.lib.oh.us. *Dir*, Stephen D Wood; E-Mail: swood@chuhpl.lib.oh.us; *Dep Dir*, Susan I Matisoff; E-Mail: smatisof@chuhpl.lib.oh.us; *Ch Servs*, Amy Switzer; E-Mail: aswitzer@chuhpl.lib.oh.us; *YA Servs*, Victoria Vannucci; Fax: 216-371-9148; *Tech Servs*, Mary Murphy; E-Mail: mmurphy@chuhpl.lib.oh.us; Staff 173 (MLS 33, Non-MLS 140)
Founded 1916. Pop 66,700; Circ 1,490,404
Jan 2000-Dec 2000 Income (Main Library and Branch Library) $6,234,839, State $3,175,318, Locally Generated Income $231,500, Other $2,828,021. Mats Exp $1,284,244, Books $894,270, Per/Ser (Incl. Access Fees) $72,000, Micro $23,100, Other Print Mats $133,408, Electronic Ref Mat (Incl. Access Fees) $150,780. Sal $3,241,079
Library Holdings: Bk Vols 342,697; Per Subs 1,542; High Interest/Low Vocabulary Bk Vols 500; Bks on Deafness & Sign Lang 1,000
Subject Interests: Deafness
Special Collections: Parenting Coll
Automation Activity & Vendor Info: (Cataloging) DRA; (Circulation) DRA; (OPAC) DRA
Database Vendor: DRA, Ebsco - EbscoHost, GaleNet, IAC - Info Trac, IAC - SearchBank, OCLC - First Search
Publications: Check Us Out; CH-UH Organizations; CH-UH Quick Information; Potamus Press
Partic in CLEVE-NET; Cleveland Area Metropolitan Library System
Special Services for the Deaf - High interest/low vocabulary books
Service to homebound, nursing homes, senior residences; service for early childhood center; public computer center
Friends of the Library Group
Branches: 3
COVENTRY VILLAGE, 1925 Coventry Rd, 44118-2001. SAN 356-2417. Tel: 216-321-3400. FAX: 216-321-0739. Web Site: www.chuhpl.lib.oh.us. *Librn*, Vicki Victoria; E-Mail: vvictori@chuhpl.lib.oh.us
Library Holdings: Bk Vols 31,705
Friends of the Library Group
NOBLE NEIGHBORHOOD, 2800 Noble Rd, 44121-2208. SAN 356-2441. Tel: 216-291-5665. FAX: 216-291-1798. Web Site: www.chuhpl.lib.oh.us.

Librn, Jo Ann Vicarel; E-Mail: jvicarel@chuhpl.lib.oh.us
Library Holdings: Bk Vols 39,728
Friends of the Library Group
UNIVERSITY HEIGHTS, 13866 Cedar Rd, University Heights, 44118-3201. SAN 356-2476. Tel: 216-321-4700. FAX: 216-321-3049. Web Site: www.chuhpl.lib.oh.us. *Librn*, Maureen Weisblatt; E-Mail: mweisbla@chuhpl.lib.oh.us
Library Holdings: Bk Vols 40,713
Friends of the Library Group

R PARK SYNAGOGUE, Kravitz Memorial Library, 3300 Mayfield Rd, 44118-1899. SAN 313-3729. Tel: 216-371-2244, Ext 141. FAX: 216-321-0639. Web Site: www.parksyn.org. *Librn*, Sarajane Dolinsky; E-Mail: sarajane@parksyn.org
Founded 1923
Library Holdings: Bk Vols 20,000; Per Subs 35
Subject Interests: Holocaust, Israel
Special Collections: Judaica (adult, juvenile, Hebrew, Yiddish & English fiction)
Friends of the Library Group
Branches:
ZEHMAN LIBRARY, 27575 Shaker Blvd, Pepper Pike, 44124. SAN 370-7083. Tel: 216-831-5365. FAX: 216-321-0639. Web Site: www.parksyn.org.
Subject Interests: Judaica, Juv
Friends of the Library Group

CLYDE

P CLYDE PUBLIC LIBRARY,* 222 W Buckeye St, 43410. SAN 313-394X. Tel: 419-547-7174. FAX: 419-547-0480. Web Site: www.library.norweld.lib.oh.us/clyde/index.htm. *Dir*, Victoria Balemian; *Ch Servs*, Deborah Meyer; Staff 3 (MLS 3)
Founded 1903. Pop 5,800; Circ 73,064
1997-1998 Income $629,773, State $272,857, Locally Generated Income $28,746, Other $328,170. Mats Exp $43,258, Books $28,138, Per/Ser (Incl. Access Fees) $5,511, Micro $167, AV Equip $6,614. Sal $157,119 (Prof $80,308)
Library Holdings: Bk Titles 24,712; Per Subs 141
Special Collections: Clyde Coll; James McPherson Coll; Ohio Coll; Roger Young Coll; Sherwood Anderson Coll
Partic in Clevnet; Northwest Library District
Friends of the Library Group

COLDWATER

P COLDWATER PUBLIC LIBRARY, 305 W Main St, 45828-1604. SAN 313-3958. Tel: 419-678-2431. FAX: 419-678-8516. Web Site: www.welcome.to/coldwater. *Dir*, Carol Forsthoefel; E-Mail: forsthca@oplin.lib.oh.us; Staff 2 (Non-MLS 2)
Founded 1936. Pop 5,000; Circ 100,675
Jan 1999-Dec 1999 Income $310,272, State $291,286, Locally Generated Income $18,986. Mats Exp $51,415, Books $43,277, Per/Ser (Incl. Access Fees) $2,673, Micro $86, AV Equip $5,379. Sal $120,715 (Prof $39,573)
Library Holdings: Bk Titles 48,300; Per Subs 98; Bks on Deafness & Sign Lang 25
Special Collections: Census, microfilm; Local Newspaper, microfilm
Automation Activity & Vendor Info: (Circulation) epixtech, inc.; (OPAC) epixtech, inc.
Database Vendor: epixtech, inc.
Mem of NW Libr District

COLUMBIANA

P COLUMBIANA PUBLIC LIBRARY, 332 N Middle St, 44408. SAN 313-3966. Tel: 330-482-5509. FAX: 330-482-9669. Web Site: www.columbiana.lib.oh.us. *Dir*, Carol Cobbs; E-Mail: cobbsca@oplin.lib.oh.us; *Ad Servs*, Carol Meissner; *Ch Servs*, Carrie Radman; *YA Servs*, Amy Geary; Staff 15 (MLS 3, Non-MLS 12)
Founded 1934. Pop 12,000; Circ 175,374
Jan 1999-Dec 1999 Income $621,567, State $485,551, Locally Generated Income $25,495, Other $110,521. Mats Exp $88,805, Books $66,270, Per/Ser (Incl. Access Fees) $4,927. Sal $200,410
Library Holdings: Bk Vols 40,268; Per Subs 192
Automation Activity & Vendor Info: (Cataloging) Gaylord; (Circulation) Gaylord; (OPAC) Gaylord
Friends of the Library Group

COLUMBUS

S ABB AUTOMATION INC, Engineering Library, 650 Ackerman Rd, 43202. SAN 313-4199. Tel: 614-261-5530. FAX: 614-261-2172. *Librn*, Mina Strayer
Library Holdings: Bk Vols 5,000; Per Subs 30
Subject Interests: Electronics, Optics, Paper indust, Proc control, Pulp, Software engineering
Publications: EX Libris

M ABBOTT LABORATORIES, Ross Products Division Library,* 625 Cleveland Ave, 43215. SAN 313-3974. Tel: 614-624-3800. FAX: 614-624-3868.; Staff 5 (MLS 2, Non-MLS 3)
Founded 1953
Library Holdings: Bk Titles 4,000; Per Subs 500
Subject Interests: Bus, Chemistry, Food tech, Medicine, Nutrition, Pediatrics
Publications: Internal newsletter; journal holdings list
Partic in Dialog Corporation; Dow Jones News Retrieval; Nat Libr of Med; OCLC Online Computer Library Center, Inc; OHIONET; STN

R AGUDAS ACHIM CONGREGATION, Stein Memorial Library, 2767 E Broad St, 43209. SAN 313-4008. Tel: 614-237-2747. FAX: 614-237-3576.
Founded 1961
Library Holdings: Bk Vols 3,238
Restriction: Not open to public

AMERICAN ELECTRIC POWER SERVICE CORP
L LAW LIBRARY, One Riverside Plaza, 43215. SAN 323-4932. Tel: 614-223-1690. FAX: 614-223-1687. E-Mail: slwedde@aep.com. *Librn*, Stephanie Weddle
Library Holdings: Bk Vols 1,600; Per Subs 50
Subject Interests: Pub utility law
Restriction: Private library
S LIBRARY & REFERENCE SERVICES, One Riverside Plaza, 43215. SAN 311-5771. Tel: 614-223-1827. FAX: 614-223-1828.; Staff 2 (MLS 2)
Founded 1950
Library Holdings: Bk Vols 40,000; Per Subs 1,000
Subject Interests: Bulk transmission, Civil, Distribution construction, Electric utility indust, Electrical, Energy statistics, Environ, Fuel supply, Legal mat, Mechanical engineering, Mgt, Nuclear power
Special Collections: Sporn Coll (Historical Company File)
Publications: Library bulletin
Partic in Columbus Area Library & Information Council Of Ohio (CALICO); OCLC Online Computer Library Center, Inc; OHIONET

L ARTER & HADDEN, Law Library,* 10 W Broad St 21st flr, 43215. SAN 372-2058. Tel: 614-221-3155. FAX: 614-221-0479. Web Site: www.arterhadden.com. *Librn*, Sarah Lynch
Library Holdings: Bk Vols 15,000; Per Subs 45

L BAKER & HOSTETLER LIBRARY, 65 E State St, Ste 2100, 43215-4260. SAN 329-0603. Tel: 614-228-1541, Ext 2608. FAX: 614-462-2616. *Librn*, Judith P Rodgers; E-Mail: jrodgers@baker-hostetler.com; Staff 2 (MLS 1, Non-MLS 1)
Library Holdings: Bk Vols 15,000; Per Subs 95
Subject Interests: Legal mat
Automation Activity & Vendor Info: (OPAC) epixtech, inc.
Database Vendor: Lexis-Nexis
Restriction: Staff use only
Partic in OHIONET; Westlaw

S BATTELLE MEMORIAL INSTITUTE, (TIC), Technical Information Center, 505 King Ave, 43201. SAN 356-2506. Tel: 614-424-6302. Interlibrary Loan Service Tel: 614-424-6304. Circulation Tel: 614-424-6301. FAX: 614-424-7186. E-Mail: tic@battelle.org. *Mgr*, Kemberly Lang; Tel: 614-424-3020; *Cat*, Sulo Ravi; Tel: 614-424-6303; *ILL*, Bobbie Powell; Tel: 614-424-6304; *Online Servs*, David Blum; Tel: 614-424-5138; *Per*, Darlene Fields; Tel: 614-424-6305; Staff 7 (MLS 3, Non-MLS 4)
Founded 1930
Oct 1999-Sep 2000 Mats Exp $510,200, Books $20,000, Per/Ser (Incl. Access Fees) $450,000, Micro $200, Electronic Ref Mat (Incl. Access Fees) $40,000. Sal $370,000 (Prof $259,696)
Library Holdings: Bk Titles 51,000; Per Subs 500
Subject Interests: Chemistry, Mathematics, Metallurgy, Physics, Sci-tech
Database Vendor: Dialog, epixtech, inc., Wilson - Wilson Web
Publications: The TechLine (newsletter)
Restriction: Company library, Open to public with supervision only
Function: Document delivery services, ILL available, Reference services available, Research fees apply
Partic in OCLC Online Computer Library Center, Inc; OHIONET

C BYRD POLAR RESEARCH CENTER, Goldthwait Polar Library, Ohio State University, 1090 Carmack Rd, 43210-1002. SAN 313-4202. Tel: 614-292-6715. FAX: 614-292-4697. *Librn*, Lynn B Lay; E-Mail: lay.1@osu.edu; Staff 2 (MLS 1, Non-MLS 1)
1999-1999 Income $8,000, Parent Institution $6,000, Other $2,000. Mats Exp $7,750, Books $2,500, Per/Ser (Incl. Access Fees) $4,000, Electronic Ref Mat (Incl. Access Fees) $1,250. Sal $44,431 (Prof $37,431)
Library Holdings: Bk Vols 12,000; Bk Titles 8,000; Per Subs 215
Subject Interests: Climatology, Geology, Geomorphology, Glaciology,

Global change, Meteorology, Polar regions
Special Collections: Reprint Coll
Publications: Library Accessions
Function: Research library

C CAPITAL UNIVERSITY, Blackmore Library, 2199 E Main St, 43209. SAN 356-2565. Tel: 614-236-6614. FAX: 614-236-6490. E-Mail: amaag@capital.edu. Web Site: www.capital.edu. *Dir*, Albert F Maag; *Acq, Doc, Per*, Mary Ann Morris; *ILL, Ref*, Anne Fields; *Cat*, Anita S Kao; *Rare Bks*, Stephen Long; Staff 7 (MLS 7)
Founded 1876. Enrl 2,500; Fac 146; Highest Degree: Doctorate
Library Holdings: Bk Vols 195,000; Per Subs 870
Subject Interests: Art, Bus, Education, Mgt, Music, Relig studies
Special Collections: Archives (University Archives); Juvenile Literature (Lois Lenski Coll), bk & mss
Publications: on demand bibliographies; Periodicals List
Partic in Columbus Area Library & Information Council Of Ohio (CALICO); OHIONET
Departmental Libraries:
CL LAW SCHOOL LIBRARY, 303 E Broad St, 43215. SAN 356-259X. Tel: 614-236-6464. FAX: 614-236-6957. Web Site: www.law.capital.edu. *Coll Develop, Dir*, Donald A Hughes, Jr; E-Mail: dhughes@law.capital.edu; *Tech Servs*, Phyllis Post; *Ref*, Susanna Marlowe; *Per*, Grace Mekaru; *Publ Servs*, Jacqueline Orlando; *Ref*, Jane Underwood; Staff 6 (MLS 6)
Founded 1903. Enrl 800; Fac 34; Highest Degree: Doctorate
Library Holdings: Bk Vols 239,000; Per Subs 2,000
Partic in OCLC Online Computer Library Center, Inc; Ohio Library & Information Network; Westlaw

S CENTER ON EDUCATION & TRAINING FOR EMPLOYMENT, Ohio State University, 1900 Kenny Rd, 43210. SAN 327-7674. Tel: 614-292-6991. FAX: 614-292-1260. Web Site: www.cete.org, www.ericacve.org, www.ohtpcs.org. *Librn*, Steve Chambers; E-Mail: chambers.2@osu.edu
Library Holdings: Bk Vols 68,000; Per Subs 171
Subject Interests: Vocational education

S CENTRAL OHIO TRANSIT AUTHORITY LIBRARY,* 1600 McKinley Ave, 43222. SAN 323-4045. Tel: 614-275-5845. FAX: 614-275-5892. *In Charge*, Allen Asbury
Library Holdings: Bk Vols 1,200; Per Subs 50

COLUMBIA GAS OF OHIO SYSTEM
L DISTRIBUTION COMPANIES LAW LIBRARY, 200 Civic Center Dr, PO Box 117, 43216. SAN 356-262X. Tel: 614-460-4665, 614-460-6000. FAX: 614-460-6986. *In Charge*, Stephen Seiple
Library Holdings: Bk Vols 1,700; Bk Titles 1,500; Per Subs 28
Restriction: Staff use only

C COLUMBUS COLLEGE OF ART & DESIGN, Packard Library, 107 N Ninth St, 43215-3875. SAN 313-4091. Tel: 614-224-9101. FAX: 614-222-4040. *Librn*, Chilin Yu; *Librn*, Gail Storer
Founded 1931. Highest Degree: Bachelor
Library Holdings: Bk Vols 41,396; Per Subs 254
Subject Interests: Art and architecture

S COLUMBUS DISPATCH LIBRARY,* 34 S Third St, 43216. SAN 313-4105. Tel: 614-461-5039. FAX: 614-461-5107. *Librn*, James Hunter; E-Mail: jhunter@dispatch.com
Library Holdings: Bk Titles 1,000; Per Subs 10

L COLUMBUS LAW LIBRARY ASSOCIATION,* 369 S High St, 10th flr, 43215-4518. SAN 313-4113. Tel: 614-221-4181. FAX: 614-221-2115. *Librn*, Keith Blough; E-Mail: kblough@ohionet.org
Founded 1887
Library Holdings: Bk Vols 78,000; Bk Titles 8,800; Per Subs 1,100
Subject Interests: Ohio law
Partic in OCLC Online Computer Library Center, Inc

P COLUMBUS METROPOLITAN LIBRARY, (CML), 96 S Grant Ave, 43215-4781. SAN 356-3790. Tel: 614-645-2800. Reference Tel: 614-645-2275. FAX: 614-645-2050. Web Site: www.cml.lib.oh.us. *Dir*, Larry D Black; E-Mail: lblack@cml.lib.oh.us; *Commun Relations*, Larry Allen; Tel: 614-645-2930, Fax: 614-645-2041, E-Mail: lallen@cml.lib.oh.us; *Asst Dir*, Rubye Kyles; E-Mail: rkyles@sml.lib.oh.us; *AV*, Susan Gerber; *Tech Servs*, Joanne Gilmore; E-Mail: jgilmore@cml.lib.oh.us; *Cat*, Marihelen Hatcher; *Cat*, Connie Sheridan; *Ref*, Mary Kelly; *Exten Serv*, Susan Studebaker; E-Mail: sstudebaker@cml.lib.oh.us; *Bkmobile Coordr*, Bernie Garrison; *Ch Servs*, Kathy Shahbodaghi; *ILL*, Julianne Phillips. Subject Specialists: *Business and management*, Larry Sheeley; *Fine arts*, Sue Fisher; *History*, John Newman; *Humanities*, Sue Fisher; *Technology*, Larry Sheeley; *Travel*, John Newman; Staff 512 (MLS 147, Non-MLS 365)
Founded 1872. Pop 762,235; Circ 11,811,189
Jan 2000-Dec 2000 Income (Main Library and Branch Library) $45,959,273, State $23,351,069, Federal $76,799, Locally Generated Income $19,406,405, Other $3,125,000. Mats Exp $6,731,704, Books $3,658,945, Per/Ser (Incl. Access Fees) $1,267,951, Presv $37,476, AV Equip $1,049,659, Other Print Mats $3,822. Sal $18,135,422 (Prof $8,649,207)
Library Holdings: Bk Vols 730,269; Per Subs 2,195
Special Collections: Black Heritage Coll; Local History (Columbus & Ohio), bks, micro, VF
Publications: Foreward; MetroScene; Novel Events; Unabridged
Partic in Discovery Place Librs; OCLC Online Computer Library Center, Inc
Special Services for the Deaf - Books on deafness & sign language; High interest/low vocabulary books; Special interest periodicals; Staff with knowledge of sign language; TDD; TTY machine
Friends of the Library Group
Branches: 23
DRIVING PARK BRANCH, 1566 E Livingston Ave, 43205. SAN 356-3944. Tel: 614-645-2370. FAX: 614-645-2379. Web Site: www.cml.lib.oh.us. *Librn*, Karen Richardson-Rogers; E-Mail: krichardson@cml.lib.oh.us
Library Holdings: Bk Vols 22,225
Friends of the Library Group
DUBLIN BRANCH, 75 N High St, Dublin, 43017. SAN 356-3979. Tel: 614-645-2170. Reference Tel: 614-645-2173. FAX: 614-645-2179. Web Site: www.cml.lib.oh.us. *Librn*, Sally Edwards; E-Mail: sedwards@cml.lib.oh.us
Library Holdings: Bk Vols 146,438
Friends of the Library Group
FRANKLINTON BRANCH, 1061 W Town St, 43222. SAN 356-4002. Tel: 614-645-2410. FAX: 614-645-2419. Web Site: www.cml.lib.oh.us. *Librn*, Brenda Dutton; E-Mail: bdutton@cml.lib.oh.us
Library Holdings: Bk Vols 32,169
Friends of the Library Group
GAHANNA BRANCH, 310 Granville St, Gahanna, 43230. SAN 356-4037. Tel: 614-645-2270. Reference Tel: 614-645-2273. FAX: 614-645-2279. Web Site: www.cml.lib.oh.us. *Librn*, Marilyn Clay Veracka; E-Mail: mveracka@cml.lib.oh.us; Staff 40 (MLS 6, Non-MLS 34)
Founded 1969. Circ 800,000
Library Holdings: Bk Vols 115,848
Function: Research library
Friends of the Library Group
HILLIARD BRANCH, 4772 Cemetery Rd, Hilliard, 43026. SAN 356-4061. Tel: 614-645-2140. Reference Tel: 614-645-2143. FAX: 614-645-2149. Web Site: www.cml.lib.oh.us. *Librn*, Grace Kendall; E-Mail: gkendall@cml.lib.oh.us
Library Holdings: Bk Vols 148,973
Friends of the Library Group
HILLTOP BRANCH, 511 S Hague Ave, 43204. SAN 356-4126. Tel: 614-645-2430. Reference Tel: 614-645-2433. FAX: 614-645-2439. Web Site: www.cml.lib.oh.us. *Librn*, Henry Taylor; E-Mail: htaylor@cml.lib.oh.us
Library Holdings: Bk Vols 131,588
Friends of the Library Group
KARL ROAD BRANCH, 5590 Karl Rd, 43229. SAN 356-424X. Tel: 614-645-2250. Reference Tel: 614-645-2253. FAX: 614-645-2259. Web Site: www.cml.lib.oh.us. *Librn*, Lee Buckner; E-Mail: lbuckner@cml.lib.oh.us
Library Holdings: Bk Vols 182,273
Friends of the Library Group
LINDEN BRANCH, 2432 Cleveland Ave, 43211. SAN 356-4185. Tel: 614-645-2230. Reference Tel: 614-645-2238. FAX: 614-645-2239. Web Site: www.cml.lib.oh.us. *Librn*, Cheryl Chlysta; E-Mail: cchlysta@cml.lib.oh.us
Library Holdings: Bk Vols 25,328
Friends of the Library Group
LIVINGSTON BRANCH, 3434 E Livingston Ave, 43227. SAN 356-4215. Tel: 614-645-2330. Reference Tel: 614-645-2332. FAX: 614-645-2339. Web Site: www.cml.lib.oh.us. *Librn*, Shirley Freeman; E-Mail: sfreeman@cml.lib.oh.us
Library Holdings: Bk Vols 85,804
Friends of the Library Group
MAIN LIBRARY, 96 S Grant Ave, 43215. SAN 356-3820. Tel: 614-645-2610. Reference Tel: 614-645-2275. TDD: 614-645-2934. FAX: 614-645-2051. Web Site: www.cml.lib.oh.us. *Dir*, Deb McWilliam; E-Mail: dmcwilliam@cml.lib.oh.us; *Librn*, Sue Fisher; *Librn*, Joe Fowler; *Librn*, John Newman; *Librn*, Larry Sheeley; *AV*, Susan Gerber; *Ref*, Mary Kelly; *Ch Servs*, Kathy Shahbodaghi; *ILL*, Julianne Phillips; Staff 512 (MLS 147, Non-MLS 365)
Founded 1873. Pop 750,000
Jan 2000-Dec 2000 Income (Main Library and Branch Library) $46,431,380, State $23,351,069, Locally Generated Income $19,406,405, Other $3,125,000
Library Holdings: Bk Vols 730,269
Special Collections: Black Heritage Coll; Local History (Columbus & Ohio), bks, micro, VF
Special Services for the Deaf - Books on deafness & sign language; High interest/low vocabulary books; Special interest periodicals; Staff with knowledge of sign language; TDD; TTY machine
Friends of the Library Group
MARTIN LUTHER KING BRANCH, 1600 E Long St, 43206. SAN 356-4150. Tel: 614-645-2210. Reference Tel: 614-645-2218. FAX: 614-645-2219. Web Site: www.cml.lib.oh.us. *Librn*, Gay Banks; E-Mail: gbanks@cml.lib.oh.us
Library Holdings: Bk Vols 24,713
Friends of the Library Group
NEW ALBANY BRANCH, 7600 Fodor Rd, New Albany, 43054. SAN 378-0333. Tel: 614-645-2280. Reference Tel: 614-645-2282. FAX: 614-645-2289. Web Site: www.cml.lib.oh.us. *Librn*, Katherine Scott; E-Mail:

kscott@cml.lib.oh.us
Library Holdings: Bk Vols 7,419
Friends of the Library Group
NORTHERN LIGHTS BRANCH, 4093 Cleveland Ave, 43224. SAN 356-4274. Tel: 614-645-2240, 614-645-2242. FAX: 614-645-2249. Web Site: www.cml.lib.oh.us. *Librn*, Kristin Shelley; E-Mail: kshelley@cml.lib.oh.us
Library Holdings: Bk Vols 65,340
Friends of the Library Group
NORTHSIDE BRANCH, 1423 N High St, 43201. SAN 356-4304. Tel: 614-645-2110. Reference Tel: 614-645-2118. FAX: 614-645-2119. Web Site: www.cml.lib.oh.us. *Librn*, Greg Denby; E-Mail: gdenby@cml.lib.oh.us
Library Holdings: Bk Vols 40,875
Friends of the Library Group
NORTHWEST, 2280 Hard Rd, 43235. SAN 378-035X. Tel: 614-645-2650. Reference Tel: 614-645-2656. FAX: 614-645-2642. Web Site: www.cml.lib.oh.us. *Librn*, Bonnie Beth Mitchell; E-Mail: bmitchell@cml.lib.oh.us
Library Holdings: Bk Vols 44,182
Northwest Library is a joint project between Columbus Metropolitan Library & the Worthington Public Library
OUTREACH DIVISION, 96 S Grant St, 43215. SAN 356-4312. Tel: 614-645-2530. FAX: 614-645-2539. Web Site: www.cml.lib.oh.us. *Librn*, Bernie Garrison; E-Mail: bgarrison@cml.lib.oh.us
Library Holdings: Bk Vols 29,045
Friends of the Library Group
PARSONS BRANCH, 845 Parsons Ave, 43206. SAN 356-4339. Tel: 614-645-2310. Reference Tel: 614-645-2318. FAX: 614-645-2319. Web Site: www.cml.lib.oh.us. *Librn*, Kathy Doss; E-Mail: kdoss@cml.lib.oh.us
Library Holdings: Bk Vols 32,650
Friends of the Library Group
REYNOLDSBURG BRANCH, 1402 Brice Rd, Reynoldsburg, 43068. SAN 356-4363. Tel: 614-645-2340. Reference Tel: 614-645-2343. FAX: 614-645-2349. Web Site: www.cml.lib.oh.us. *Librn*, Cecilia McAdams; E-Mail: cmcadams@cml.lib.oh.us
Library Holdings: Bk Vols 186,427
Friends of the Library Group
SHEPARD BRANCH, 790 N Nelson Rd, 43219. SAN 356-4398. Tel: 614-645-2220. FAX: 614-645-2229. Web Site: www.cml.lib.oh.us. *Librn*, Sheryl Owens; E-Mail: sowens@cml.lib.oh.us
Library Holdings: Bk Vols 25,450
Friends of the Library Group
SOUTH HIGH BRANCH, 3540 S High St, 43207. SAN 356-4428. Tel: 614-645-2360. Reference Tel: 614-645-2362. FAX: 614-645-2369. Web Site: www.cml.lib.oh.us. *Librn*, Rebecca Callender; E-Mail: bcallender@cml.lib.oh.us
Library Holdings: Bk Vols 73,301
Friends of the Library Group
SOUTHEAST, 3980 S Hamilton Rd, 43125. SAN 370-9418. Tel: 614-645-2350. FAX: 614-645-2359. Web Site: www.cml.lib.oh.us. *Librn*, Nancy Sullivan
Library Holdings: Bk Vols 74,774
Friends of the Library Group
WHETSTONE BRANCH, 3909 N High St, 43214. SAN 326-7938. Tel: 614-645-2150. Reference Tel: 614-645-2152. FAX: 614-645-2159. Web Site: www.cml.lib.oh.us. *Librn*, Pamela Ley; E-Mail: pley@cml.lib.oh.us
Library Holdings: Bk Vols 151,321
Friends of the Library Group
WHITEHALL BRANCH, 4371 E Broad St, 43213. SAN 356-4452. Tel: 614-645-2320. Reference Tel: 614-645-2322. FAX: 614-645-2329. Web Site: www.cml.lib.oh.us. *Librn*, Deborah Replogle; E-Mail: dreplogle@cml.lib.oh.us
Library Holdings: Bk Vols 51,908
Friends of the Library Group
Bookmobiles: 2

S COLUMBUS MUSEUM OF ART, Resource Center, 480 E Broad St, 43215. SAN 327-4179. Tel: 614-629-0360. FAX: 614-221-8946. Web Site: www.columbusart.mus.oh.us. *Librn*, Carol Genshaft; Staff 3 (MLS 1, Non-MLS 2)
Founded 1931
Library Holdings: Bk Titles 5,000; Per Subs 12
Subject Interests: 19th Century art, 20th Century art, Photography
Special Collections: Pre-Colombian, American Coverlets
Restriction: Non-circulating to the public
Function: For research purposes
Partic in OCLC Online Computer Library Center, Inc

J COLUMBUS STATE COMMUNITY COLLEGE, Educational Resources Center, 550 E Spring St, 43215. SAN 313-4121. Tel: 614-287-2465. Reference Tel: 614-287-2460. Toll Free Tel: 800-621-6407. FAX: 614-287-2457. Web Site: www.cscc.edu. *Dir*, Claire Fohl; Tel: 614-287-2466, E-Mail: cfohl@cscc.edu; *Coordr*, Martin Barry; Tel: 614-287-2463, E-Mail: mbarry@cscc.edu; *Online Servs, Ref*, Kim Leggett; *Publ Servs*, Deborah Foster; *Media Spec*, Nick Cenci. Subject Specialists: *AV*, Martin Barry; Staff 20 (MLS 8, Non-MLS 12)
Founded 1965. Enrl 17,000
Jul 1998-Jun 1999 Income $1,178,324. Mats Exp $364,860, Books $166,283, Per/Ser (Incl. Access Fees) $69,734. Sal $583,819
Library Holdings: Bk Vols 35,000; Bk Titles 29,000; Per Subs 508
Subject Interests: Allied health tech, Bus, Eng tech, Nursing, Pub servs tech
Database Vendor: Dialog
Publications: Handbook
Function: Reference services available
Partic in Ohio Library & Information Network; OHIONET

J DEVRY INSTITUTE OF TECHNOLOGY LIBRARY,* 1350 Alum Creek Dr, 43209. SAN 313-430X. Tel: 614-253-7291. FAX: 614-252-4108. Web Site: www.devrycols.learning/lrc01.htm. *Dir*, Bruce Weaver; Staff 1 (MLS 1)
Founded 1970. Enrl 3,000; Fac 80; Highest Degree: Bachelor
Library Holdings: Bk Vols 21,000; Bk Titles 18,000; Per Subs 50
Subject Interests: Accounting, Bus, Computer science, Electronics, Manufacturing
Special Collections: SAM's Photofact Series (electronic schematics for consumer products & computers)
Partic in OCLC Online Computer Library Center, Inc

M DOCTORS HOSPITAL OHIOHEALTH, William S Konold Memorial Library, 1087 Dennison Ave, 43201. SAN 356-2743. Tel: 614-297-4107. Circulation Tel: 614-297-4113. FAX: 614-299-2475. *Dir Libr Serv*, Holly L Lopeman; E-Mail: hlopeman@doctorshospital.org; *Cat*, Sheila Knapik; *Circ*, Julie Spaulding; Staff 3 (MLS 1, Non-MLS 2)
Founded 1973
Jul 1999-Jun 2000 Mats Exp $80,000, Books $40,000, Per/Ser (Incl. Access Fees) $40,000. (Prof $35,000)
Library Holdings: Bk Vols 3,993; Bk Titles 2,842; Per Subs 211
Subject Interests: Medicine
Special Collections: History of Medicine; History of Osteopathy
Database Vendor: OVID Technologies
Restriction: Lending to staff only, Non-circulating to the public
Function: For research purposes
Partic in CORE; Tri State Col Libr Coop

C FRANKLIN UNIVERSITY LIBRARY,* 303 S Grant Ave, 43215. (Mail add: 201 S Grant Ave, 43215), Tel: 614-341-6252. FAX: 614-461-0957. E-Mail: library@franklin.edu. Web Site: www.franklin.edu. *Dir*, Fred Helser; E-Mail: helserf@franklin.edu
Founded 1966. Enrl 4,500; Fac 170; Highest Degree: Master
Aug 1999-Jul 2000 Income $586,622. Mats Exp $252,818, Books $75,000, Per/Ser (Incl. Access Fees) $61,000, Presv $8,818, Micro $45,000, Other Print Mats $63,000. Sal $188,902
Library Holdings: Bk Titles 85,065; Per Subs 1,020
Subject Interests: Bus
Partic in Columbus Area Library & Information Council Of Ohio (CALICO); OHIONET

S FTI - SEA, INC LIBRARY, 7349 Worthington-Galena Rd, 43085. SAN 373-1111. Tel: 614-888-4160. FAX: 614-885-8014. E-Mail: msens@seaohio.com. Web Site: www.seaohio.com.
Library Holdings: Bk Vols 12,000; Per Subs 25
Subject Interests: Industrial safety, Standardization
Special Collections: Stapp Car Crash Conference Proceedings: 1963-2000
Partic in Dialog Corporation

S GLENCOE PUBLISHING COMPANY LIBRARY,* 8787 O'Rion Pl, 42240-4027. SAN 313-4210. Toll Free Tel: 800-848-1567. FAX: 614-430-4379. *Librn*, Darlene Yeager; E-Mail: darlene_yeager@mcgraw-hill.com
Subject Interests: Education
Special Collections: Textbooks
Restriction: Not open to public

P GRANDVIEW HEIGHTS PUBLIC LIBRARY, 1685 W First Ave, 43212-3399. SAN 313-4172. Tel: 614-486-2951. FAX: 614-481-7020. Web Site: www.ghpl.org. *Dir*, Carol Cowles Pelz; *Ch Servs*, Jennifer Nolte; *Acq*, Lisen Kowalsky; *Coll Develop, Ref*, Wendy Greenwood; *Circ*, Angela Baldree; *Cat*, Judy Shiddenhelm; *ILL*, Ruth Sloan; *Tech Coordr*, Don Yarman; Staff 11 (MLS 11)
Founded 1924. Pop 8,000; Circ 685,706
Jan 1999-Dec 1999 Income $3,079,079. Mats Exp $2,482,291. Sal $1,457,092
Library Holdings: Bk Vols 152,685; Per Subs 466
Subject Interests: Architecture, Art, Behav sci, Bus info, Computer, Cookery, Crafts, Large print bks, Relig studies, Soc sci
Automation Activity & Vendor Info: (Acquisitions) epixtech, inc.; (Cataloging) epixtech, inc.; (Circulation) epixtech, inc.; (ILL) epixtech, inc.; (OPAC) epixtech, inc.; (Serials) epixtech, inc.
Database Vendor: epixtech, inc., GaleNet, ProQuest
Partic in Central Ohio Hospital Library Consortium; OHIONET
Friends of the Library Group

M GRANT MEDICAL CENTER, Medical Library, 300 E Town St, 3rd Flr, 43215. (Mail add: 111 S Grant Ave, 43215), SAN 313-4180. Tel: 614-566-9468. Interlibrary Loan Service Tel: 614-566-9467. FAX: 614-566-8451. *Mgr Libr Serv*, Stacy Gall; E-Mail: sgall@ohiohealth.com; *Asst Librn*, Jean Thami; E-Mail: jthami@ohiohealth.com; Staff 2 (MLS 1, Non-MLS 1)

Founded 1960
Library Holdings: Bk Vols 10,000; Per Subs 230
Subject Interests: Allied health, Medicine, Nursing
Database Vendor: Ebsco - EbscoHost, OVID Technologies

L KEGLER, BROWN, HILL & RITTER, Law Library, 65 E State St, Ste 1800, 43215. SAN 372-1949. Tel: 614-462-5400. FAX: 614-464-2634. E-Mail: info@kbhr.com. Web Site: www.kbhr.com. *Librn*, Keith S Knopf; Tel: 614-462-5400, Ext 311, E-Mail: kknopf@kbhr.com; *Asst Librn*, Jessica Roberts; Tel: 614-462-5400, Ext 321, E-Mail: jroberts@kbhr.com; Staff 2 (MLS 1, Non-MLS 1)
Oct 1999-Sep 2000 Mats Exp $511,000, Books $244,000, Electronic Ref Mat (Incl. Access Fees) $267,000. Sal $64,000 (Prof $46,000)
Library Holdings: Bk Vols 18,000; Per Subs 25
Automation Activity & Vendor Info: (Serials) TLC
Database Vendor: Dialog, Lexis-Nexis

S MINNIE COBEY MEMORIAL LIBRARY,* 1354 E Broad St, 43205. SAN 313-4083. Tel: 614-253-8523. FAX: 614-253-6323. *Librn*, Sally Brown
Founded 1950
Library Holdings: Bk Vols 6,500; Bk Titles 4,500; Per Subs 30
Subject Interests: Bible, Judaism, Prayer bks, Relig studies, Talmud
Special Collections: Talmud (Babylonian Talmud Coll)

M MOUNT CARMEL, Library Services, 793 W State St, 43222-1560. SAN 313-4229. Tel: 614-234-5214. FAX: 614-234-1257. *Dir*, Pamela M Elwell; Tel: 614-234-1109, E-Mail: pelwell@mchs.com; Staff 10 (MLS 2, Non-MLS 8)
Founded 1964
Library Holdings: Bk Vols 15,000; Per Subs 500
Subject Interests: Allied health, Medicine, Nursing
Automation Activity & Vendor Info: (Cataloging) Innovative Interfaces Inc.; (OPAC) Innovative Interfaces Inc.
Partic in GMR; NNLM/SCR, OCLC Online Computer Libr Ctr, Inc; OHIONET; Opal

S NATIONWIDE LIBRARY, One Nationwide Plaza 1-01-05, 43215. SAN 313-4237. Tel: 614-249-6414. FAX: 614-249-2218. *Chief Librn*, John W Holtzclaw; E-Mail: holtzcj@nationwide.com; *Librn*, Vicki Blackford; *Librn*, Karen Hoyt; *Librn*, David Schneider; Staff 8 (MLS 4, Non-MLS 4)
Founded 1935
Library Holdings: Bk Vols 16,000; Per Subs 250
Subject Interests: Bus, Ins, Mgt
Special Collections: Corporate Archives
Automation Activity & Vendor Info: (Acquisitions) epixtech, inc.; (Cataloging) epixtech, inc.; (Circulation) epixtech, inc.; (OPAC) epixtech, inc.; (Serials) epixtech, inc.
Database Vendor: OCLC - First Search
Partic in OHIONET

S NUCON INTERNATIONAL INC LIBRARY,* 7000 Huntley Rd, 43229. SAN 374-8774. Tel: 614-846-5710. FAX: 614-431-0858.
Library Holdings: Bk Titles 2,000
Restriction: Staff use only

G OFFICE OF THE CONSUMERS COUNSEL,* 77 S High St, 15th flr, 43066-0550. SAN 325-1772. Tel: 614-466-9601. FAX: 614-466-9475. *Librn*, Vicki Gray; Staff 1 (MLS 1)
Library Holdings: Bk Vols 3,000; Bk Titles 2,500; Per Subs 70
Subject Interests: Acid rain, Pub utilities, Utility law, Utility regulation
Special Collections: Acid rain; newsclip (1981 to present)

GL OHIO ATTORNEY GENERAL, Law Library,* 30 E Broad St, 15th flr, 43215. SAN 313-4245. Tel: 614-466-2465, 614-466-4534. FAX: 614-752-9867. *Dir Libr Serv*, Susan M Cloutier; E-Mail: scloutier@ag.state.oh.us; *Asst Librn*, Kelli A Johnson; Staff 2 (MLS 1, Non-MLS 1)
Founded 1846
Library Holdings: Bk Vols 22,070; Per Subs 25
Subject Interests: Cases, Law statutes
Partic in OCLC Online Computer Library Center, Inc

S OHIO BUREAU OF WORKER'S COMPENSATION, Division of Safety & Hygiene Library,* 30 W Spring St, 3rd flr, 43215-2256. SAN 356-2891. Tel: 614-466-7388. FAX: 614-644-9634. E-Mail: library@bwc.state.oh.us. Web Site: www.ohiobwc.com. *Adminr*, Rosemary M Larkins; *Librn*, Karen Jensen; *Librn*, Ruth Pagorek; *Librn*, Melissa Hatfield
Founded 1974
Library Holdings: Bk Vols 5,000; Per Subs 260
Subject Interests: Accident prevention, Indust hygiene, Indust toxicology, Noise control, Occupational med, Occupational rehab, Occupational safety, Workers comp

G OHIO DEPARTMENT OF DEVELOPMENT, Research Library,* 77 S High St, 27th flr, 43215-6108. SAN 327-3741. Tel: 614-466-2116. Toll Free Tel: 800-282-1085. FAX: 614-466-9697. Web Site: cododcohio.gov. *Librn*, Hessie Jones
Partic in State of Ohio Libr Syst

G OHIO DEPARTMENT OF PUBLIC SAFETY, Film & Research Library, PO Box 182081, 43218-2081. SAN 313-4342. Tel: 614-466-4775. FAX: 614-752-8410. *Librn*, Louise Clifford
Founded 1955
Library Holdings: Bk Vols 1,300; Per Subs 10
Publications: Film catalog

G OHIO DEPARTMENT OF TAXATION, Tax Analysis Division Library,* 30 E Broad St, PO Box 530, 43266-0030. SAN 327-3725. Tel: 614-466-3960. FAX: 614-752-0700. *Librn*, Carol Wentzel
Library Holdings: Bk Vols 600; Per Subs 10

G OHIO DEPARTMENT OF TRANSPORTATION LIBRARY, 1980 W Broad St, 43223. SAN 325-0024. Tel: 614-466-7680. FAX: 614-728-6694. Web Site: www.slonet.state.oh.us. *Librn*, Janet Bix; E-Mail: jbix@dot.state.oh.us; Staff 4 (MLS 1, Non-MLS 3)
Jul 2000-Jun 2001 Income $175,000. Mats Exp $22,750, Books $12,000, Per/Ser (Incl. Access Fees) $8,250, Electronic Ref Mat (Incl. Access Fees) $2,500. Sal $130,000
Library Holdings: Bk Titles 25,000; Per Subs 150
Subject Interests: Primarily rds, Transport
Automation Activity & Vendor Info: (Cataloging) Innovative Interfaces Inc.; (Circulation) Innovative Interfaces Inc.; (OPAC) Innovative Interfaces Inc.; (Serials) Innovative Interfaces Inc.
Publications: New Acquisitions (quarterly)
Partic in Dialog Corporation; Ohio Library & Information Network

C OHIO DOMINICAN COLLEGE, Spangler Library, 1216 Sunbury Rd, 43219. SAN 356-2808. Tel: 614-251-4752. FAX: 614-252-2650. E-Mail: library@odc.edu. Web Site: www.odc.edu/lis/library/library.htm. *Dir*, Michelle Sarff; Tel: 614-251-4757, E-Mail: sarffm@odc.edu; *Librn*, Mary Ellen George; Tel: 614-251-4755, E-Mail: georgem@odc.edu; *Librn*, Jim Layden; Tel: 614-251-4758, E-Mail: laydenj@odc.edu; *Librn*, Terese Lord; *Librn*, Abigail Noland; Tel: 614-251-4637, E-Mail: nolanda@odc.edu; *Circ*, Susan Dillon; Tel: 614-251-4676, E-Mail: dillons@odc.edu; *Circ*, Leeann Gallaway; Tel: 614-251-4676, E-Mail: gallawal@odc.edu; *Circ*, Patricia Morrow; Tel: 614-251-4676, E-Mail: morrowp@odc.edu; *Acq*, Laura Evans; Tel: 614-251-4750, E-Mail: evansl@odc.edu; *Ser*, Ken Schloema; Tel: 614-251-4758, E-Mail: schloemk@odc.edu; Staff 9 (MLS 5, Non-MLS 4)
Founded 1924. Enrl 2,000; Fac 115; Highest Degree: Bachelor
Jul 1998-Jun 1999 Income Locally Generated Income $292,833. Mats Exp $191,000, Books $46,000, Per/Ser (Incl. Access Fees) $50,800, Presv $2,000, Micro $12,000, AV Equip $40,000, Electronic Ref Mat (Incl. Access Fees) $40,200. (Prof $166,000)
Library Holdings: Bk Vols 140,000; Bk Titles 98,000; Per Subs 550
Subject Interests: Education, Humanities, Philosophy, Theology
Special Collections: Anne O'Hara McCormick Coll; Mary Tetter Zimmerman Coll
Automation Activity & Vendor Info: (Cataloging) Innovative Interfaces Inc.; (Circulation) Innovative Interfaces Inc.; (Course Reserve) Innovative Interfaces Inc.; (OPAC) Innovative Interfaces Inc.; (Serials) Innovative Interfaces Inc.
Database Vendor: Dialog, Innovative Interfaces INN - View, Lexis-Nexis, OCLC - First Search, ProQuest, Wilson - Wilson Web
Function: ILL available
Partic in Columbus Area Library & Information Council Of Ohio (CALICO); OCLC Online Computer Library Center, Inc; Ohio Library & Information Network; OHIONET

G OHIO ENVIRONMENTAL PROTECTION AGENCY LIBRARY, 122 S Front St, PO Box 1049, 43215-1049. SAN 325-5522. Tel: 614-728-1804. FAX: 614-728-9500. Web Site: www.epa.ohio.gov/other/rcoutsid.html. *Librn*, Ruth Ann Evans; Staff 4 (MLS 2, Non-MLS 2)
Founded 1976
Library Holdings: Bk Vols 8,500; Bk Titles 8,000; Per Subs 100
Subject Interests: Environmental law, Pollution control tech
Special Collections: Ohio River Basin Water Quality, Ohio Solid Waste Management Reports
Automation Activity & Vendor Info: (Cataloging) Inmagic, Inc.; (Circulation) Inmagic, Inc.
Database Vendor: OCLC - First Search
Partic in OCLC Online Computer Library Center, Inc

M OHIO HEALTH - RIVERSIDE METHODIST HOSPITAL, (RHC), (Formerly OhioHealth - Riverside Methodist Hospital), D J Vincent Medical Library, 3535 Olentangy River Rd, 43214-3998. SAN 313-4407. Tel: 614-566-5230. FAX: 614-566-6949. E-Mail: medlib@ohiohealth.com. *Dir, Online Servs*, Jo Yeoh; E-Mail: yeohj@ohiohealth.com; *Coll Develop*, Jo Clark; Staff 7 (MLS 3, Non-MLS 4)
Founded 1960
Library Holdings: Bk Titles 24,000; Per Subs 420; Bks on Deafness & Sign Lang 12
Subject Interests: Hospital administration, Medicine, Mgt, Microcomputers, Nursing, Patient educ
Special Collections: Health Education Coll
Automation Activity & Vendor Info: (Acquisitions) EOS; (Cataloging) EOS; (Circulation) EOS; (OPAC) EOS; (Serials) EOS
Partic in Columbus Area Library & Information Council Of Ohio

(CALICO); Dialog Corporation; OCLC Online Computer Library Center, Inc; OHIONET
Health Education collection open to the public

S OHIO HISTORICAL SOCIETY, Archives-Library Division, 1982 Velma Ave, 43211-2497. SAN 313-4296. Tel: 614-297-2510. FAX: 614-297-2546. Web Site: www.ohiohistory.org. *In Charge*, George Parkinson; E-Mail: gparkinson@ohiohistory.org; *Res*, Louise Jones; *Archivist*, Charles Arp; *Automation Syst Coordr*, Emily Hicks
Founded 1885
Jul 1998-Jun 1999 Income $2,172,636. Sal $1,673,232
Library Holdings: Bk Vols 141,903; Per Subs 180
Subject Interests: Archaeology, Genealogy, Natural history, Ohio hist
Special Collections: State Archives of Ohio
Automation Activity & Vendor Info: (Cataloging) epixtech, inc.; (OPAC) epixtech, inc.
Restriction: Non-circulating to the public
Partic in OCLC Online Computer Library Center, Inc; Ohio Network Of American History Research Centers; OHIONET
Open Tues-Sat 9-5

G OHIO LEGISLATIVE SERVICE COMMISSION LIBRARY, 77 S High St, 9th flr, 43266-0342. SAN 313-4326. Tel: 614-466-2241, 614-466-5312. FAX: 614-644-1721. *Librn*, Debbie Tavenner; Staff 3 (MLS 2, Non-MLS 1)
Founded 1953
Library Holdings: Bk Titles 15,000; Per Subs 250
Subject Interests: Legislative mat, Ohio legal mat
Special Collections: Bulletins of the Ohio General Assembly; Journals of the Ohio House & Senate; Laws of Ohio
Automation Activity & Vendor Info: (Cataloging) Inmagic, Inc.
Restriction: Open to department staff only, Open to others by appointment, Restricted access
Partic in OHIONET

S OHIO SCHOOL FOR THE DEAF LIBRARY, 500 Morse Rd, 43214. SAN 373-1073. Tel: 614-728-1414. TDD: 614-728-1415. FAX: 614-728-4060. *Librn*, Ada G Kent; E-Mail: kent@osd.ode.state.oh.us; Staff 2 (MLS 1, Non-MLS 1)
Enrl 130; Fac 45
Library Holdings: Bk Vols 10,000; Per Subs 54
Special Collections: Deafness Coll, bks, videos, CDs; Ohio Chronicle 1868-1999

OHIO STATE UNIVERSITY

C ARCHIVES, 2700 Kenny Rd, 43210. SAN 326-6869. Tel: 614-292-2409. FAX: 614-688-4150. Web Site: www.lib.ohio-state.edu/arvweb. *Archivist*, Tamar Galed; *Archivist*, Raimund E Goerler; Tel: 614-688-8447, E-Mail: goerler.1@osu.edu; *Archivist*, Laura Kissel; *Ref*, Bertha Ihnat; Staff 7 (MLS 4, Non-MLS 3)
Founded 1965. Enrl 58,000; Fac 2,800
Special Collections: Papers of Admiral Richard E. Byrd; Papers of Sir Hubert Wilkins; Records of Dr. Frederick A. Cook Society; Senator John Glenn; Senator John Glenn Archives
Function: Archival collection
Partic in OCLC Online Computer Library Center, Inc

C BIOLOGICAL SCIENCES & PHARMACY, 102 Riffe Bldg, 496 W 12th Ave, 43210-1291. SAN 356-3049. Tel: 614-292-1744. Web Site: www.lib.ohio-state.edu/osu_profile/bosweb. *Head Librn*, Bruce A Leach; Tel: 614-292-1744, E-Mail: leach.5@osu.edu. Subject Specialists: *Biological sci*, Bruce A Leach; *Pharmacy*, Nancy Kupferberg; Staff 6 (MLS 2, Non-MLS 4)
Founded 1994
Library Holdings: Bk Vols 120,000; Per Subs 1,300
Subject Interests: Biochemistry, Biophysics, Biotech, Botany, Chemistry, Entomology, Genetics, Med chem, Microbiology, Pharmaceutics, Pharmacognosy, Pharmacology, Zoology
Partic in OCLC Online Computer Library Center, Inc
See Main Library for ILL

C BLACK STUDIES, 1858 Neil Ave Mall, Rm 226, 43210. SAN 356-3073. Tel: 614-688-8676. FAX: 614-292-7859. Web Site: www.lib.ohio-state.edu/osu_profile/bsweb. *Librn*, Lisa Pillow; Staff 2 (MLS 1, Non-MLS 1)
Founded 1971
1999-2000 Mats Exp $60,246, Books $35,000, Per/Ser (Incl. Access Fees) $15,246, Micro $10,000. Sal $61,000 (Prof $43,000)
Library Holdings: Bk Vols 22,240; Per Subs 200; High Interest/Low Vocabulary Bk Vols 100
Subject Interests: Africa, Afro-American studies
Partic in Ohio Library & Information Network
Friends of the Library Group

C BUSINESS LIBRARY, Raymond E Mason Hall, 250 W Woodruff Ave, 43210-1395. SAN 356-3138. Tel: 614-292-2136. FAX: 614-292-5559. Web Site: www.lib.ohio-state.edu/busweb. *Librn*, Charles Popovich; E-Mail: popovich.1@osu.edu; *Ref*, Meri Meredith; E-Mail: meredith.18@osu.edu
Library Holdings: Bk Vols 106,000; Per Subs 2,033
Subject Interests: Accounting, Economics, Human resources, Management, Marketing
Publications: New Books List
Partic in CIC; OCLC Online Computer Library Center, Inc

C CARTOON RESEARCH, Wexner Ctr, Rm 023L, 27 W 17th Ave, 43210-1393. SAN 326-6656. Tel: 614-292-0538. FAX: 614-292-9101. Web Site: www.lib.ohio-state.edu/cgaweb. *Curator*, Lucy Shelton Caswell; Staff 1 (MLS 1)
Founded 1977
Library Holdings: Bk Vols 15,000; Per Subs 660
Subject Interests: Film posters, Mag illustration, Photog, Print genres of cartoon art, Stills
Friends of the Library Group

C EDGAR DALE EDUCATIONAL MEDIA & INSTRUCTIONAL MATERIALS LABORATORY, Ramseyer Hall Rm 260, 29 W Woodruff Ave, 43210-1177. SAN 325-6030. Tel: 614-292-1177. FAX: 614-292-7900. *Assoc Dean*, Evelyn Freeman; Tel: 614-292-7231, Fax: 614-688-3942, E-Mail: freeman.5@osu.edu
Library Holdings: Bk Vols 26,762
Subject Interests: Curriculum related materials for K - 12
Special Collections: Historical Children's Literature Coll
Partic in OCLC Online Computer Library Center, Inc; OHIONET

C EDUCATION, HUMAN ECOLOGY, PSYCHOLOGY & SOCIAL WORK, 110 Sullivant Hall, 1813 N High St, 43210. SAN 356-3162. Tel: 614-292-2075. FAX: 614-292-8012. E-Mail: ehslib@osu.edu. Web Site: www.lib.ohio-state.edu/osu_profile/ehsweb/. *Head of Libr*, Laura Garvrelis Blomquist; Tel: 614-292-8602; *Ref*, Martin Jamison; *Bibliogr, Syst Coordr*, Leta Hendricks; *Bibliogr, Ref*, Marian Shemberg; *Bibliogr, Ref*, Cynthia Preston; *Bibliogr, Ref*, Gerald Greenberg; Staff 7 (MLS 7)
Founded 1998
Jul 1998-Jun 1999 Mats Exp $391,569, Per/Ser (Incl. Access Fees) $250,931, Other Print Mats $140,638. Sal $626,894
Library Holdings: Bk Vols 225,000; Per Subs 2,000
Subject Interests: Education, Health, Human nutrition, Physical educ, Psychology, Social work, Sport mgt, Textiles
Special Collections: Eric documents on microfiche; Kling Targeted Reading Coll (microfiche); William S Gray Research Coll on Reading (microfiche)
Database Vendor: Innovative Interfaces INN - View
Partic in CIC; Ohio Library & Information Network
Special services for the Blind include two large monitor computer workstations for visually impaired patrons & a digital scanner & Openbook (a text reading program)

C ENGLISH, THEATRE & COMMUNICATION READING ROOM, 224 Main Library, 1858 Neil Ave Mall, 43210-1286. SAN 356-3227. Tel: 614-292-2786. FAX: 614-292-7859. *Librn*, James Bracken
Library Holdings: Bk Vols 21,000; Per Subs 650
Subject Interests: Am lit, Communication, Engineering, Speech, Telecommunication
Publications: Current Content Service

C FINE ARTS, 035L Wexner Center for the Visual Arts, 27 W 17th Ave Mall, 43210. SAN 356-3251. Tel: 614-292-6184. FAX: 614-292-4573. Web Site: www.lib.ohio-state.edu/osu_profile/finweb/. *Librn*, Susan Wyngaard; Staff 3 (MLS 1, Non-MLS 2)
Library Holdings: Bk Vols 125,000; Per Subs 400
Subject Interests: Art, Art educ, Design, Hist of art, Photog
Publications: New acquisitions list (quarterly)
Partic in OCLC Online Computer Library Center, Inc; Ohio Library & Information Network

C GEOLOGY, 180 Orton Hall, 155 S Oval Mall, 43210. SAN 356-3316. Tel: 614-292-2428. Web Site: www.lib.ohio-state.edu/lib_osuinfo/geo.html. *Librn*, Regina A Brown
Library Holdings: Bk Vols 64,763; Per Subs 651
Subject Interests: Geology, Mineralogy, Polar studies
Partic in OCLC Online Computer Library Center, Inc

C GRANT MORROW III MD LIBRARY AT CHILDREN'S HOSPITAL, Children's Institute for Pediatric Education, 700 Children's Dr, Rm ED-244, 43205. SAN 356-3707. Tel: 614-722-3200. FAX: 614-722-3205. Web Site: www.childrenscolumbus.org/pro/library/shtml. *Librn, Mgr*, Linda DeMuro; E-Mail: demuro.1@osu.edu; Staff 4 (MLS 2, Non-MLS 2)
Founded 1953
Jan 2000-Dec 2000 Income $143,000. Mats Exp $79,800, Books $12,000, Per/Ser (Incl. Access Fees) $67,800. Sal $146,869
Library Holdings: Bk Vols 19,500; Bk Titles 7,500; Per Subs 260
Subject Interests: Pediatrics
Special Collections: Consumer Health in Pediatrics
Mem of Asn of Research Libraries
Partic in OSU Librs
Open Mon-Thurs 8:30am-7pm, Fri 8:30-5

C HILANDAR RESEARCH, 227 Main Library Mall, 43210-1286. SAN 326-9353. Tel: 614-292-0634. FAX: 614-292-7859. Web Site: www.cohums.ohio-state.edu/cmrs/scmss. *Curator*, Dr Predrag Matejic
Library Holdings: Bk Vols 2,500
Subject Interests: Medieval Slavic studies
Special Collections: Hilander Monastery (Mt Athos, Greece), mss, microfilm
Partic in LCS

C JEROME LAWRENCE & ROBERT E LEE THEATRE RESEARCH INSTITUTE LIBRARY, 1430 Lincoln Tower, 1800 Cannon Dr, 43210-1230. SAN 327-8913. Tel: 614-292-6614. FAX: 614-292-8417. E-Mail: theatreinst@osu.edu. Web Site: www.lib.ohio-state.edu/triweb. *Curator*,

Nena Couch; E-Mail: couch.1@osu.edu; *Spec Coll*, Valdan Pennington. Subject Specialists: *18th Century culture*, Nena Couch; *Dance*, Nena Couch; *Libr*, Nena Couch; *Performing arts*, Nena Couch; Staff 3 (MLS 1, Non-MLS 2)
Founded 1951. Enrl 140; Fac 18; Highest Degree: Doctorate
1999-2000 Income $30,000. Mats Exp Manuscripts & Archives $15,000
Library Holdings: Bk Vols 5,000
Subject Interests: Costume design, Regional theatre, Scene, Theatre, Theatrical dance
Special Collections: American Playwrights Theatre, American Theatre Critics Association, Armbruster Scenic Studio, As the World Turns, Dalcroze Society of America, Dramatists Play Service, Harmount Company, Hartman Theatre, International Al Jolson Society, Playwrights, Print, Washington Theatre, Windsor Indoor Chautauqua Colls; Artists, Japanese Theatre, Music & Opera, Dance Company, Production, Theatre Company, Print & Document Files; Contemporary American Theatre Company, Cupola, Ensemble Theatre of Cincinnati, Horse Cave Theatre, Los Angeles Theatre Center, John H McDowell Film, Players Theatre, Twyla Tharp Archives; Doris Cole Abrahams, Boris Anisfield, William Barclay, Isabel Bigley Barnett, Robert Breen, Lucien Bonheur, Sam Coit, Alexandra Exter, Tom Eyen, Samuel French, Ella Gerber, Paulette Goddard/Burgess Meredith, Mordecai Gorelik, Otis L Guernsey, George Hall, Jed Harris, Eileen Heckart, Holly Hill, Donald Horton, Norris Houghton, Ray Lee Jackson, Toni-Leslie James, Robert Edmond Jones, Gerald Kahan, Nancy Kelly, Madge Kenda, William F Kilmer Vaudeville, Sidney Kingsley, Jerome Lawrence & Robert E Lee, Simon Lissim, Katherine Locke, Sam Locke, Lancton Lucier Vaudeville, Elizabeth Maupin, Don Nigro, Ethel Outland, Oysher Family, John Patrick, Helene Pons, Robert Post, E B Radcliffe, Peter Ranking, Louis Robin, Sanford Roth, Tom Skelton, Randy Skinner, Robert Slusser Dance Photographs, Irwin Spector, Paul Stiga, Tony Straiges, Sophie Vielle, Robert A Wachsman, Clifton Webb, Sylvia Westerman, Earl Wilson, Luke Yankee Colls
Publications: Theatre Studies

CM JOHN A PRIOR HEALTH SCIENCES LIBRARY, 376 W Tenth Ave, 43210-1240. SAN 356-3677. Tel: 614-292-9810. FAX: 614-292-1920. Web Site: bones.med.ohio-state.edu. *Dir*, Susan Kroll; *Asst Dir*, Pamela Bradigan; *Curator, Tech Servs*, Barbara Van Brimmer; *Automation Syst Coordr*, Eric Schnell; *Coll Develop*, Lynda Hartel; Staff 10 (MLS 10)
Founded 1849. Enrl 3,462; Fac 791
Jul 1997-Jun 1998 Income $2,741,997. Mats Exp $225,337. Sal $1,149,197 (Prof $394,570)
Library Holdings: Bk Vols 224,971; Per Subs 2,214
Subject Interests: Allied med professions, Cancer, Dentistry, Medicine, Nursing, Optometry
Publications: Health Science Library Service Bulletin (monthly); Health Sciences Library List of Serials
Mem of Asn of Research Libraries
Partic in Medline; Regional Med Libr - Region 3

C JOURNALISM, Journalism Bldg, 242 W 18th Ave, 43210-1107. SAN 356-3405. Tel: 614-292-8747. Web Site: www.lib.ohio-state.edu/osu_profile/jouweb. *Librn*, Eleanor Block
Library Holdings: Bk Vols 30,112; Per Subs 350
Subject Interests: Broadcasting, Cinema, Journalism, Mass media
Partic in OCLC Online Computer Library Center, Inc

C MUSIC & DANCE, Sullivant Hall, 1813 N High St, 43210-1307. SAN 356-3499. Tel: 614-292-2319. FAX: 614-292-8012. Web Site: www.lib.ohio-state.edu/osu_profile/music_lib/. *Head of Libr*, Thomas Heck; *Ref*, Alan Green
Library Holdings: Bk Vols 140,000; Per Subs 615
Subject Interests: Dance, History, Music educ, Performance, Therapy
Special Collections: American Popular Songs; Dance, V-tapes; Medieval Chant, microfilm; Nordeo Music Archive; Renaissance Music, microfilm
Publications: Newsletter
Partic in Center For Research Libraries; OCLC Online Computer Library Center, Inc; OHIONET

C SCIENCE & ENGINEERING, 175 W 18th Ave, 43210. SAN 373-5923. Tel: 614-292-0211. Interlibrary Loan Service Tel: 614-292-6211. Reference Tel: 614-292-3022. FAX: 614-292-3062. Interlibrary Loan Service FAX: 614-292-3061. Web Site: www.lib.ohio-state.edu/osu_profile/phyweb. *Head Librn*, Mary Scott; Tel: 614-292-3046, E-Mail: scott.36@osu.edu. Subject Specialists: *Architecture*, Jane McMaster; *Chemistry*, Angela Gooden; *Engineering*, Mary J Arnold; *Mathematics*, Mary Scott; *Physics*, Jane Duffy; Staff 5 (MLS 5)
Library Holdings: Bk Vols 370,283; Per Subs 2,600
Subject Interests: Architecture, Astronomy, Chemistry, Computer, Eng genetic sci, Info servs, Landscape architecture, Mathematics, Physics, Statistics
Partic in OCLC Online Computer Library Center, Inc

C UNIVERSITY LIBRARIES, 1858 Neil Ave Mall, 43210-1286. SAN 356-2921. Tel: 614-292-6151. FAX: 614-292-7859. Interlibrary Loan Service FAX: 614-292-3061. E-Mail: library@osu.edu. Web Site: www.lib.ohio-state.edu. *Dir*, William J Studer; *Tech Servs*, Carol Diedrichs; *Publ Servs*, Patricia McCandless; *Circ*, Anthony Maniaci; *ILL*, Jennifer Kuehn; *Rare Bks, Spec Coll*, Geoffrey Smith; *Automation Syst Coordr*, Susan J Logan; *Archivist*, Raimund E Goerler; Staff 101 (MLS 101)
Founded 1873. Enrl 48,352; Fac 2,635; Highest Degree: Doctorate
Jul 1997-Jun 1998 Income $22,474,700. Mats Exp $9,430,738, Books $2,754,310, Per/Ser (Incl. Access Fees) $6,412,600, Presv $263,828. Sal $10,907,924 (Prof $4,683,881)
Library Holdings: Per Subs 36,020
Special Collections: 19th Century Paperback Coll; Admiral Richard E Byrd, papers; American Association of Editorial Cartoonist Archives; American Fiction 18th Century through Contemporary (William Charvat Coll); American Playwrights' Theatre records; American Sheet Music (ABC & Fanny Arms Colls); Arion Press; Armbruster Scenic Design; Australiana; Author Collections, including: Nelson Algren, W H Auden, Samuel Beckett, Robert Breen, William S Burroughs, Frederick Busch, Milton Caniff, Raymond Carver, Miguel de Cervantes, Hart Crane, Emily Dickinson, Will Eisner, T S Eliot, John Gardner, Nathaniel Hawthorne, Ernest Hemingway, Chester Hines, Eileen Heckart, T J Holmes, Jerome Lawrence & Robert E Lee, Richard Lewis, Jack London, Ralph D Mershon, Anais Nin, Jessica Mitford, James Purdy, Jesse Stuart, Twyla Tharp, Dylan Thomas, James Thurber, F L Utley, William T Vollman, Edith Wharton, Jon Whitcom; Book Plate Literature; Conjunctions Literary Journal Archive; Daguerrotypes & Ambrotypes (Floyd & Marion Rinhart Coll); Dance Notation; Emanuel Rudolph Children's Science Coll; English Drama; European Econ Community; Film Posters & Stills (Philip Sills Coll); Film Scripts; Little Magazines; Mather bibliography (T J Holmes Papers); Medieval Slavic Mss; Northprint Press German; Ohio News Photographers Association Archives; Oriole Press; Peter D Franklin Cookbook Coll; Reformation History; Renaissance to 18th Century; Science Fiction Paperbacks & Magazines; Secondary School Curricula (W W Charters Papers); Stanley J Kahrl 17th Century Drama Coll; UFO Coll
Automation Activity & Vendor Info: (Acquisitions) Innovative Interfaces Inc.; (Cataloging) Innovative Interfaces Inc.; (Circulation) Innovative Interfaces Inc.; (Serials) Innovative Interfaces Inc.
Mem of Asn of Research Libraries
Partic in Comt on Institutional Coop; OCLC Online Computer Library Center, Inc; Ohio Library & Information Network
Special Services for the Deaf - Captioned media
Friends of the Library Group

CM VETERINARY MEDICINE, 229 Sisson Hall, 1900 Coffey Rd, 43210. SAN 356-3618. Tel: 614-292-6107. Web Site: www.lib.ohio-state.edu/osu_profile/vetweb/index.html. *Librn*, Norma J Bruce
Library Holdings: Bk Vols 40,000; Per Subs 630
Partic in OCLC Online Computer Library Center, Inc

C WOMEN'S STUDIES, 228 Main Library, 1858 Neil Ave Mall, 43210. SAN 356-3642. Tel: 614-292-3035. FAX: 614-292-7859. Web Site: www.lib.ohio-state.edu/osu_profile/wmnweb/. *Librn*, Linda Krikos; E-Mail: krikos.1@osu.edu
Library Holdings: Bk Vols 17,922; Per Subs 112
Publications: African American Women Writers; Asian American Women; Bibliographies of Sources in OSU Libraries: African American Women; Chicana, Hispanic & Latina Women; Feminist Scholarship; Lesbian Literature; Lesbians; Media Participation of Women; Media Portrayal of Women; Native American Women; Women in Development; Women in Mid-Life; Women's Cross-Cultural Studies

M OHIO STATE UNIVERSITY HOSPITALS EAST, (Formerly Park Medical Center), Philip B Hardymon Medical Library, 1492 E Broad St, 43205. SAN 324-5888. Tel: 614-257-3248. FAX: 614-257-3248. *Coll Develop, In Charge*, Sarah Murphy; E-Mail: murphy-9@medctr.osu.edu
Founded 1956
Library Holdings: Bk Titles 4,000
Subject Interests: Medicine
Partic in Greater Midwest Regional Medical Libr Network
Open Mon-Fri 9-3

S OHIOANA LIBRARY, 274 E First Ave, 43201. SAN 313-413X. Tel: 614-466-3831. FAX: 614-728-6974. E-Mail: ohioana@winslo.state.oh.us. Web Site: www.oplin.lib.oh.us/ohioana/. *Dir*, Linda Hengst; *Coll Develop, Librn*, Barbara Meister; Staff 5 (Non-MLS 5)
Founded 1929
Jul 1999-Jun 2000 Income $317,400, State $263,750, Locally Generated Income $46,400, Other $7,250. Mats Exp $3,500, Books $1,500, Per/Ser (Incl. Access Fees) $500, Presv $1,500. Sal $150,000 (Prof $112,000)
Library Holdings: Bk Titles 41,000
Subject Interests: Bks by Ohioans or about Ohio, First editions, Music by Ohio composers, Rare books, Scrapbooks of biog info
Special Collections: Books written by Ohioans or about Ohio & Ohioans; Dawn Powell Coll; George Randolph Chester Coll; James Thurber Coll; Louis Bromfield Coll; Martha Finley Coll; Mildred Wirt Benson Coll; R L Stine Coll; Rollo W Brown Coll; Sherwood Anderson Coll; W D Howells Coll; Women's History in Ohio; Zane Gray Coll
Publications: Educational Resource List; Ohioana Quarterly; Ohioana-Ohio Literary Map
Restriction: In-house use for visitors, Not a lending library
Partic in OCLC Online Computer Library Center, Inc; OHIONET
Ohioana Awards for Books; Citations for Contributions to the Arts & Humanities; $1000 Poetry Award; $1000 Wood Award in Children's Literature; Career Award; $1000 Walter Rumsey Marvin Grant; Lucille Loy Kuck Ohioana Awards

S OTTAWA RESEARCH CORP, Irene Holm Memorial Library, 1465 Osborn Dr, 43221. SAN 313-4377. Tel: 614-433-1049. Web Site: www.geocities.com/hotsprings/3922. *Librn*, Bobbi Wilson. Subject Specialists: *History*, Bobbi Wilson; Staff 3 (MLS 2, Non-MLS 1)
Founded 1976
Library Holdings: Bks on Deafness & Sign Lang 100
Special Collections: Edwardian Music, A-tapes(Historical materials pertaining to the Louis Franke family, in machine-readable formats); ; Historic Radio Broadcasts (A E Lindner Memorial Coll), A-tapes; Louis Franke family historical materials, in machine-readable formats
Publications: Franke-ly Speaking (Newsletter)
Function: Archival collection
Special Services for the Deaf - Staff with knowledge of sign language
Internet only - collection is exclusively machine-readable

SR PONTIFICAL COLLEGE JOSEPHINUM, A T Wehrle Memorial Library, 7625 N High St, 43235-1498. SAN 313-8178. Tel: 614-885-5585. Reference Tel: 614-985-2295. FAX: 614-885-2307. E-Mail: libreqs@pcj.edu. Web Site: www.tcgc.capital.edu. *Dir*, Peter G Veracka; *Asst Librn*, Beverly S Lane; Staff 2 (MLS 2)
Founded 1888. Enrl 115; Fac 26; Highest Degree: Master
Jul 1999-Jun 2000 Income $353,380. Mats Exp $115,719, Books $69,273, Per/Ser (Incl. Access Fees) $35,242, Presv $4,932, Micro $121, Electronic Ref Mat (Incl. Access Fees) $6,151. Sal $189,752 (Prof $97,987)
Library Holdings: Bk Vols 132,290; Bk Titles 97,042; Per Subs 522
Subject Interests: Philosophy, Relig studies
Automation Activity & Vendor Info: (Acquisitions) Endeavor; (Cataloging) Endeavor; (Circulation) Endeavor; (Course Reserve) Endeavor; (ILL) Endeavor; (Media Booking) Endeavor; (OPAC) Endeavor; (Serials) Endeavor
Partic in OCLC Online Computer Library Center, Inc; OHIONET; Theol Consortium of Greater Columbus

L PORTER, WRIGHT MORRIS & ARTHUR, LLP, Law Library, 41 S High St, 43215-6194. SAN 326-1727. Tel: 614-227-2090. Reference Tel: 614-227-1927. FAX: 614-227-2100. Web Site: www.porterwright.com. *Librn*, Susan M Schaefgen; E-Mail: sschaefgen@porterwright.com; *Asst Librn*, Ann Mathewson; Tel: 614-227-1927, E-Mail: amathewson@portwrwright.com; *Cat, Web Coordr*, Melanie K Putnam; Tel: 614-227-1973, E-Mail: mputnam@porterwright.com; *Ref*, Kim Smith; Tel: 614-227-1948, E-Mail: kcsmith@porterwright.com; Staff 3 (MLS 2, Non-MLS 1)
Library Holdings: Bk Vols 28,000; Bk Titles 3,000
Partic in OHIONET

S PUBLIC UTILITIES COMMISSION OF OHIO LIBRARY,* 180 E Broad St, 12th flr, 43215. SAN 313-4385. Tel: 614-466-8054. FAX: 614-728-8373. *Librn*, Gail Blackmore
Founded 1974
Library Holdings: Bk Vols 16,000; Per Subs 220
Subject Interests: Accounting, Econ, Energy, Engineering, Govt doc, History, Law, Pub utilities, Transportation
Special Collections: Staff Reports, Public Utilities Commission Annual Reports 1867 to present
Publications: A Portion of the Laws of Ohio Applying to Railroads; Gas Pipeline Safety Codes; Public Utilities Commission of Ohio Code of Rules & Regulations; PUCO Recent Acquisitions Pamphlet form
Partic in State of Ohio Libr, Ohio State University, Westlaw, Lexis, Legislate

L SQUIRE, SANDERS & DEMPSEY, Law Library,* 1300 Huntington Ctr, 41 S High St, Ste 1300, 43215. SAN 323-8539. Tel: 614-365-2700. FAX: 614-365-2499. *Librn*, Patricia Cristian; Staff 3 (MLS 2, Non-MLS 1)
Library Holdings: Bk Vols 13,000; Bk Titles 1,200; Per Subs 50

P STATE LIBRARY OF OHIO,* 65 S Front St, Rm 510, 43215-4163. SAN 356-4487. Tel: 614-644-7061. Interlibrary Loan Service Tel: 614-644-6956. FAX: 614-466-3584. E-Mail: sloadm@mailslonet.ohio.gov, sloinfo@mail.slonet.ohio.gov. *State Librn*, Michael Lucas; Tel: 614-644-6843, E-Mail: mlucas@winslo.state.oh.us; *Dep Dir*, Peter Bates; *Publ Servs*, James Buchman; Tel: 614-644-6954, Fax: 614-644-7004, E-Mail: jbuchman@slom.state.oh.us; *Cat*, Jeffrey Heard; Tel: 614-644-6944, Fax: 614-728-2789, E-Mail: jheard@winslo.state.oh.us; Staff 120 (MLS 52, Non-MLS 68)
Founded 1817. Pop 11,021,419
Library Holdings: Bk Vols 2,872,981; Per Subs 449
Subject Interests: Admin, Behav sci, Econ, Education, Genealogy, Mgt, Soc sci
Special Collections: Rare Books
Automation Activity & Vendor Info: (Circulation) Innovative Interfaces Inc.
Publications: Allocating Library Funds; Annual Report; County by County in Ohio Genealogy; Directory of Ohio Libraries; Library News of Ohio; Marketing & Libraries Do Mix Handbook; National Guidelines for Bookmobile Service; Standards for Public Library Service in Ohio; Statistics Categorized by Income; Statistics of Ohio Libraries
Partic in OHIONET
Special Services for the Deaf - Staff with knowledge of sign language
Special Services for the Blind - Talking book center
Branches: 2
SOUTHEASTERN OHIO LIBRARY CENTER, 40780 State Rd 821, Caldwell, 43724. SAN 356-4606. Tel: 740-783-5705. Toll Free FAX: 800-446-4804. *Dir*, Christine L Tucker; Tel: 740-783-4385, E-Mail: ctucker@sloma.state.oh.us; *Info Tech*, Ben Rule; Staff 19 (MLS 3, Non-MLS 16)
Library Holdings: Bk Vols 198,172; Bk Titles 200,000
Database Vendor: epixtech, inc.
Function: Some telephone reference
SOUTHWESTERN REGIONAL LIBRARY, 4646 Park Rd, Fayetteville, 45118. SAN 356-4517. Tel: 513-875-3757. FAX: 513-875-3758. *Librn*, John Hiestand
Library Holdings: Bk Vols 95,890
Bookmobiles: 8

GL SUPREME COURT OF OHIO, Law Library,* 30 E Broad St, 43266-0419. SAN 313-4431. Tel: 614-466-2044. FAX: 614-466-1559. E-Mail: fup@sconet.ohio.gov. Web Site: www.sconet.ohio.gov/lawlibrary. *Coll Develop, Librn*, Paul S Fu; Staff 19 (MLS 9, Non-MLS 10)
Founded 1860
Library Holdings: Bk Vols 407,000; Per Subs 1,740
Special Collections: Ohio & US Legal Treatises, Cases & Statutes
Publications: Monthly Acquisition List; The Supreme Court of Ohio Law Library Handbook
Partic in OCLC Online Computer Library Center, Inc; OHIONET; Westlaw

R TEMPLE ISRAEL, Meta Marx Lazarus Memorial Library, 5419 E Broad St, 43213. SAN 313-444X. Tel: 614-866-0010. FAX: 614-866-9046. *Librn*, Gloria Wells
Founded 1932
Library Holdings: Bk Titles 5,000
Subject Interests: Judaica

S THE AMERICAN SOCIETY FOR NONDESTRUCTIVE TESTING, Samuel A Wenk Memorial Library, 1711 Arlingate Lane, PO Box 28518, 43228-0518. SAN 372-7963. Tel: 614-274-6003. Toll Free Tel: 800-222-2768. FAX: 614-274-6899. E-Mail: webmaster@asnt.org. Web Site: www.asnt.org. *Librn*, Brian Geary
Founded 1991
Library Holdings: Bk Titles 2,000; Per Subs 100

CL THE OHIO STATE UNIVERSITY, Moritz Law Library, 55 W 12th Ave, 43210-1391. SAN 313-4350. Tel: 614-292-6691. Circulation Tel: 614-292-3987. Reference Tel: 614-292-9463. FAX: 614-292-3202. Web Site: www.osu.edu/units/law/moritz2.htm. *Dir*, Bruce S Johnson; E-Mail: johnson.726@osu.edu; *Assoc Dir*, Carole L Hinchcliff; Tel: 614-292-0903, E-Mail: hinchcliff.1@osu.edu; *Circ*, Christopher Bloodworth; Tel: 614-292-9417, E-Mail: bloodworth.2@osu.edu; *Acq*, Kimberly Clarke; Tel: 614-292-3193, E-Mail: clarke.66@osu.edu; *Cat*, Helen Chirakos; Tel: 614-292-9438, E-Mail: chirakos.4@osu.edu; *Cat*, Mary Rider; Tel: 614-292-9466, E-Mail: rider.1@osu.edu; *Publ Servs*, Stephanie Davidson; *Web Coordr*, David Genzen; Tel: 614-292-9476, E-Mail: genzen.2@osu.edu; *Publ Servs*, Susanna Marlowe; Tel: 614-688-0052, E-Mail: marlowe.13@osu.edu; Staff 19 (MLS 9, Non-MLS 10)
Founded 1891. Enrl 672; Fac 35; Highest Degree: Doctorate
Jul 1999-Jun 2000 Mats Exp $1,375,370. Sal $827,668
Library Holdings: Bk Vols 691,723; Bk Titles 163,400; Per Subs 8,374
Subject Interests: Dispute resolution
Special Collections: Ohio Legal Materials
Database Vendor: IAC - Info Trac, Innovative Interfaces INN - View, Lexis-Nexis, OCLC - First Search
Function: ILL available
Partic in OCLC Online Computer Library Center, Inc; Ohio Library & Information Network; OHIONET

R TRINITY LUTHERAN SEMINARY, Hamma Library, 2199 E Main St, 43209-2334. SAN 313-4466. Tel: 614-235-4136. FAX: 614-238-0263. E-Mail: tlslibrary@trinity.capital.edu. Web Site: www.tcgc.capital.edu, www.trinity.capital.edu/hammalibrary/. *Senior Librn*, Ray A Olson; E-Mail: rolson@trinity.capital.edu; *Assoc Librn*, Linda L Fry; E-Mail: lfry@trinity.capital.edu; Staff 6 (MLS 4, Non-MLS 2)
Founded 1830. Enrl 213; Fac 20; Highest Degree: Master
Jul 1999-Jun 2000 Income $383,823. Mats Exp $95,211, Books $71,983, Per/Ser (Incl. Access Fees) $21,444, Presv $1,784. Sal $268,411 (Prof $170,497)
Library Holdings: Bk Vols 128,943; Per Subs 660
Subject Interests: Theology
Special Collections: New Testament Studies (Lenski Memorial Coll)
Automation Activity & Vendor Info: (Acquisitions) Endeavor; (Cataloging) Endeavor; (Circulation) Endeavor; (Course Reserve) Endeavor; (OPAC) Endeavor; (Serials) Endeavor
Database Vendor: ProQuest
Partic in OCLC Online Computer Library Center, Inc; OHIONET; Theological Consortium of Greater Columbus

TWIN VALLEY PSYCHIATRIC SYSTEM

M FORENSIC PATIENTS' LIBRARY, 2200 W Broad St, 43223. SAN 320-3565. Tel: 614-752-0333. FAX: 614-752-0385.
Library Holdings: Bk Vols 5,500; Per Subs 21
Subject Interests: Medicine, Psychiatry

M MARLIN R WEDEMEYER STAFF LIBRARY, 2200 W Broad St, 43223. SAN 313-4067. Tel: 614-752-0333. FAX: 614-752-0385.
Jul 1996-Jun 1997 Income $6,500. Mats Exp $6,000, Books $1,200, Per/Ser (Incl. Access Fees) $3,800, Other Print Mats $1,000. Sal $30,000
Library Holdings: Bk Titles 3,366; Per Subs 80
Subject Interests: Medicine, Psychiatry

S TWIN VALLEY PSYCHIATRIC SYSTEM, 2200 W Broad SE, 43223. SAN 323-4258. Tel: 614-752-0333, Ext 5461. FAX: 614-752-0385. *Media Spec*, Herbert Doherty
Subject Interests: Child develop, Mental health, Soc issues

SR WESTGATE FRIENDS MEETING LIBRARY,* 3750 Sullivant Ave, 43228. SAN 313-4482. Tel: 614-274-5131. FAX: 614-274-5920.
Founded 1969
Library Holdings: Bk Titles 3,200; Per Subs 55
Special Collections: Financial Doc of Fourth Street Meeting of Friends; Quaker History & Doctrine

CONNEAUT

P CONNEAUT PUBLIC LIBRARY,* 304 Buffalo St, 44030-2658. SAN 356-4630. Tel: 440-593-1608. TDD: 440-593-1608. FAX: 440-593-4470. E-Mail: conneaut@oplin.lib.oh.us. *Dir*, Deborah Zingaro; *Assoc Dir*, Elizabeth Seibert
Founded 1908. Pop 17,000
Library Holdings: Bk Vols 40,400; Bk Titles 37,050; Per Subs 165
Subject Interests: Local history, Local newsp, Music, Self help
Special Collections: Large Print; Local History, newspapers 1835-1982, micro; Media: audios (2100); New Grove Directory of Music & Musicians; Old Radio Shows Coll, cassettes; Young Adult
Publications: Annual report; Brochure of Services
Mem of NOLA Regional Libr Syst
Special Services for the Deaf - TDD
Friends of the Library Group

COSHOCTON

P COSHOCTON PUBLIC LIBRARY, 655 Main St, 43812-1697. SAN 323-679X. Tel: 740-622-0956. FAX: 740-622-4331. E-Mail: coshoctonpl@oplin.lib.oh.us. Web Site: www.coshocton.lib.oh.us. *Dir*, Ann Miller; E-Mail: milleran@oplin.lib.oh.us; *Asst Dir*, Mike Ontko; E-Mail: ontkomi@oplin.lib.oh.us; *Branch Mgr*, Margaret Lowe; E-Mail: lowema@oplin.lib.oh.us; *Bkmobile Coordr*, Ronald Martin; E-Mail: martinro@oplin.lib.oh.us; *ILL*, Elaine Jensen; E-Mail: jensenel@oplin.lib.oh.us; *Ch Servs*, Diane Jones; E-Mail: jonesdi@oplin.lib.oh.us; *Ref Serv Ad*, Barbara Custer; E-Mail: custerba@oplin.lib.oh.us; Staff 33 (MLS 3, Non-MLS 30)
Founded 1904. Pop 35,427; Circ 405,167
Jan 1999-Dec 1999 Income (Main Library and Branch Library) $1,456,907, State $1,367,178, Locally Generated Income $89,729. Mats Exp $173,533, Books $140,398, Per/Ser (Incl. Access Fees) $21,851, Presv $2,214, Electronic Ref Mat (Incl. Access Fees) $9,070. Sal $563,489
Library Holdings: Bk Vols 119,157; Per Subs 291
Subject Interests: Advertising, Genealogy, Local history
Automation Activity & Vendor Info: (Acquisitions) epixtech, inc.; (Cataloging) epixtech, inc.; (Circulation) epixtech, inc.; (OPAC) epixtech, inc.
Database Vendor: epixtech, inc.
Publications: Library Connections (Newsletter)
Mem of Mideastern Ohio Libr Orgn
Partic in Mideastern Ohio Libr Orgn
Special Services for the Deaf - Books on deafness & sign language; High interest/low vocabulary books
Special Services for the Blind - Talking Books
Special Services - Graphic arts; Homebound Service
Friends of the Library Group
Branches: 1
WEST LAFAYETTE BRANCH, 601 E Main St, West Lafayette, 43845. SAN 323-6811. Tel: 740-545-6672. FAX: 740-545-6418. Web Site: www.coshocton.lib.oh.us. *Dir*, Ann Miller; Tel: 740-622-0956, Fax: 740-622-4331, E-Mail: milleran@oplin.lib.oh.us; *Mgr*, Nellie Guilliams; *Branch Mgr*, Margaret Lowe; E-Mail: lowema@oplin.lib.oh.us; Staff 2 (Non-MLS 2)
Circ 25,010
Library Holdings: Bk Vols 7,000
Automation Activity & Vendor Info: (Circulation) epixtech, inc.; (OPAC) epixtech, inc.
Database Vendor: epixtech, inc
Friends of the Library Group
Bookmobiles: 1

S GENERAL ELECTRIC CO, Laminated Products Engineering Library,* 1350 S Second St, 43812. SAN 313-4490. Tel: 740-622-5310. FAX: 740-623-5240.
Founded 1966
Library Holdings: Bk Vols 2,000; Per Subs 23

COVINGTON

P J R CLARKE PUBLIC LIBRARY, 102 E Spring St, 45318. SAN 313-4512. Tel: 937-473-2226. FAX: 937-473-8118. *Dir*, Vicki Longendelpher; *Dir*, Marjorie F Mutzner; E-Mail: mutznema@oplin.lib.oh.us; Staff 1 (Non-MLS 1)
Founded 1917. Pop 3,000; Circ 118,683
1999-2000 Income $284,873, State $266,550, Other $18,323. Mats Exp $50,776, Books $43,635, Per/Ser (Incl. Access Fees) $5,907, Electronic Ref Mat (Incl. Access Fees) $1,234. Sal $113,340
Library Holdings: Bk Vols 49,384; Per Subs 161
Subject Interests: Civil War, History, Large print
Special Collections: J R Clarke Coll
Automation Activity & Vendor Info: (Cataloging) Sagebrush Corporation; (Circulation) Sagebrush Corporation
Publications: Newsletter (monthly)
Partic in Miami Valley Librs
Friends of the Library Group

CRESTLINE

P CRESTLINE PUBLIC LIBRARY, 324 N Thoman St, 44827-1410. SAN 313-4520. Tel: 419-683-3909. FAX: 419-683-3022. *Librn*, Cheryl Swihart; *Ch Servs*, Nancy Smith; *Circ*, Linda McClurg; Staff 6 (MLS 6)
Founded 1925. Pop 8,400; Circ 110,148
Library Holdings: Bk Vols 56,021; Per Subs 177
Subject Interests: Railroad printed mat
Special Collections: Books on Cassette; County Census Records; County Court Records; County Death Records, micro; Filmed Periodicals; Historical Picture Coll; Large Print Books; Ohio Local Newspaper, 113 years, micro; Read-Alongs; Videos
Special Services for the Deaf - Captioned film depository; High interest/low vocabulary books
Special Services for the Blind - Bks on tape; Large print bks

CUYAHOGA FALLS

S ALMOND TEA GALLERY LIBRARY,* 2250 Front St, 44221. SAN 313-4539. Tel: 330-929-1575. FAX: 330-929-2285. *Dir*, Jack Richards
Library Holdings: Bk Vols 2,000; Per Subs 20
Subject Interests: Art

M CUYAHOGA FALLS GENERAL HOSPITAL, Medical Library,* 1900 23rd St, 44223. SAN 325-0628. Tel: 330-971-7200. FAX: 330-971-7227.
1997-1998 Mats Exp $9,800, Books $6,500, Per/Ser (Incl. Access Fees) $3,300
Subject Interests: Teaching

R PILGRIM UNITED CHURCH OF CHRIST MEMORIAL LIBRARY, 130 Broad Blvd, 44221. SAN 313-4555. Tel: 330-869-8633, 330-928-4847.
Library Holdings: Bk Vols 800

P TAYLOR MEMORIAL PUBLIC LIBRARY,* 2015 Third St, 44221-3294. SAN 313-4563. Tel: 330-928-2117. FAX: 330-928-2535. E-Mail: harrispq@oplin.lib.oh.us. Web Site: www.taylor.lib.oh.us. *Dir*, Patricia Harris; *Commun Relations*, Linda Bayman; *Cat*, Dietra Cummings; *Ref*, David Allen; *Ch Servs*, Karen Sonderman; *Circ*, Donna Dixon; *Automation Syst Coordr*, Judith Parker; Staff 23 (MLS 7, Non-MLS 16)
Founded 1911. Pop 48,000; Circ 733,912
Jan 1998-Dec 1999 Income $1,905,963, State $1,757,682, Locally Generated Income $148,281. Mats Exp $236,073, Books $189,027, Per/Ser (Incl. Access Fees) $14,179. Sal $877,776
Library Holdings: Bk Vols 154,087; Per Subs 455
Subject Interests: Local history
Publications: Newsletter (monthly)
Partic in Lantastic
Open Mon-Thurs 10-9, Fri 10-6, Sat 10-5 & Sun 1-5
Friends of the Library Group

DAYTON

S AULLWOOD AUDUBON CENTER & FARM, 1000 Aullwood Rd, 45414. SAN 327-3784. Tel: 937-890-7360. FAX: 937-890-2382. *Dir*, Charity Krueger
Library Holdings: Bk Titles 3,000; Per Subs 15

M CHILDREN'S MEDICAL CENTER, Medical Library, One Children's Plaza, 45404-1815. SAN 313-4571. Tel: 937-641-3307. Interlibrary Loan Service Tel: 937-641-5072. FAX: 937-463-5409. *Librn*, Luz Sinha; E-Mail: lsinka@

cmc-dayton.org; Staff 1 (MLS 1)
Founded 1967
Library Holdings: Bk Vols 2,000; Per Subs 269

P DAYTON & MONTGOMERY COUNTY PUBLIC LIBRARY, 215 E Third St, 45402-2103. SAN 356-4754. Tel: 937-227-9500. Circulation Tel: 637-227-9540. Reference Tel: 937-227-9531. FAX: 937-227-9539. Web Site: www.dayton.lib.oh.us. *Dir*, Tim Kambitsch; *Head, Circ*, Mark Mabelitini; *Asst Dir*, David Slivken; *Ch Servs, YA Servs*, Letitia Wilson; *AV*, Theodore J Nunn, Jr; *Tech Servs*, Bonnie Doepker; *Exten Serv*, Miriam Morris; *Commun Relations*, Mark Willis; *Syst Coordr*, Rich Simmerman; *Per*, Kevin Smith; Staff 644 (MLS 75, Non-MLS 569)
Founded 1847. Pop 573,809; Circ 5,933,456
Jan 2000-Dec 2000 Income $21,699,893, State $18,899,813, County $1,651,894, Locally Generated Income $70,449, Other $1,077,737. Mats Exp $3,367,414, Books $2,265,755, Per/Ser (Incl. Access Fees) $290,253, Presv $20,197, Micro $762,875, Electronic Ref Mat (Incl. Access Fees) $28,334. Sal $10,034,506 (Prof $3,411,157)
Library Holdings: Bk Vols 1,705,556; Per Subs 1,125
Special Collections: Local History (Dayton Room)
Publications: Spotlight on Your Library
Partic in OHIONET; OPLIN
Special Services for the Deaf - High interest/low vocabulary books; TTY machine
Friends of the Library Group
Branches: 19
BELMONT, 1041 Watervliet Ave, 45420. SAN 356-4789. Tel: 937-227-9501. *Mgr*, Michael Grear
Library Holdings: Bk Vols 36,853
Friends of the Library Group
BROOKVILLE BRANCH, 425 Rona Parkway Dr, Brookville, 45309. SAN 356-4819. Tel: 937-833-2553. FAX: 937-833-4510. Web Site: www.dayton.lib.oh.us/brookville. *Mgr*, Elaine Lindstrom; Staff 14 (MLS 2, Non-MLS 12)
Founded 1917
Library Holdings: Bk Vols 44,417; Per Subs 90
Database Vendor: DRA, GaleNet, OCLC - First Search
Friends of the Library Group
BURKHARDT AVENUE, 4680 Burkhardt Ave, 45431. SAN 356-4843. Tel: 937-227-9503. *Mgr*, Sammie Allen
Library Holdings: Bk Vols 41,866
Friends of the Library Group
DAYTON MALL MINI, 2700 Miamisburg-Centerville Rd, 45459. SAN 373-5842. Tel: 937-227-9523. *Mgr*, Patricia Crawford
Library Holdings: Bk Vols 13,657
Friends of the Library Group
DAYTON VIEW, 1515 Salem Ave, 45406. SAN 356-4878. Tel: 937-227-9504. *Mgr*, Sharon Taste
Library Holdings: Bk Vols 31,861
Friends of the Library Group
EAST, 2008 Wyoming St, 45410. SAN 356-4932. Tel: 937-227-9505. *Mgr*, Pat Fetterhoff
Library Holdings: Bk Vols 32,726
ELECTRA C DOREN BRANCH, 701 Troy St, 45404. SAN 356-4908. Tel: 937-227-9506. FAX: 937-224-4473. *Mgr*, James A McQuinn; E-Mail: ec_jamie@dayton.lib.oh.us
Founded 1927
Library Holdings: Bk Vols 27,243
Friends of the Library Group
FORT MCKINLEY, 3735 Salem Ave, 45406. SAN 356-4967. Tel: 937-227-9507. *Mgr*, Beverly Moody
Library Holdings: Bk Vols 33,957
Friends of the Library Group
HUBER HEIGHTS, 6160 Chambersburg Rd, 45424. SAN 356-4991. Tel: 937-227-9508. FAX: 937-233-2231. *Mgr*, Treva Pickenpaugh
Pop 41,000; Circ 692,856
Library Holdings: Bk Vols 120,716
Friends of the Library Group
KETTERING-MORAINE, 3496 Far Hills Ave, Kettering, 45429. SAN 356-5025. Tel: 937-227-9509. *Mgr*, Thomas R Weitzel
Library Holdings: Bk Vols 84,619
Friends of the Library Group
MADDEN HILLS, 2542 Germantown St, 45408. SAN 356-505X. Tel: 937-227-9510.
Library Holdings: Bk Vols 48,165
Friends of the Library Group
MIAMISBURG BRANCH, 35 S Fifth St, Miamisburg, 45342. SAN 356-5084. Tel: 937-866-1071. *Mgr*, Jean Gaffney
Library Holdings: Bk Vols 69,904
Friends of the Library Group
NEW LEBANON BRANCH, 715 W Main St, New Lebanon, 45345. SAN 356-5114. Tel: 513-687-2311. *Mgr*, Sandra Bailey
Library Holdings: Bk Vols 34,513
Friends of the Library Group
NORTHMONT, 333 W National Rd, Englewood, 45322. SAN 356-5149. Tel: 937-836-1610. *Mgr*, Ann Ramsey
Library Holdings: Bk Vols 90,547
Friends of the Library Group
NORTHTOWN-SHILOH, 35 Bennington Dr, 45405. SAN 356-5173. Tel: 937-227-9514. *Mgr*, M J Brown
Library Holdings: Bk Vols 60,257
Friends of the Library Group
TROTWOOD BRANCH, 651 E Main St, Trotwood, 45426. SAN 356-5203. Tel: 937-837-1252. *Mgr*, Cynthia Butcher
Library Holdings: Bk Vols 57,518
Friends of the Library Group
VANDALIA BRANCH, 500 S Dixie Dr, Vandalia, 45377. SAN 356-5238. Tel: 937-898-6541. *Mgr*, Doris Pettit
Library Holdings: Bk Vols 58,466
Friends of the Library Group
WEST CARROLLTON BRANCH, 300 E Central Ave, West Carrollton, 45449. SAN 356-5262. Tel: 937-859-4011. *Mgr*, Lewis E Goodman
Library Holdings: Bk Vols 75,971
Friends of the Library Group
WESTWOOD, 3207 Hoover Ave, 45407. SAN 356-5297. Tel: 937-227-9518. *Mgr*, Noland Lester
Library Holdings: Bk Vols 30,734
Friends of the Library Group
Bookmobiles: 1

S DAYTON ART INSTITUTE LIBRARY,* 456 Belmonte Park N, 45405-4700. SAN 313-458X. Tel: 937-223-5277. FAX: 937-223-3140. Web Site: www.daytonartinstitute.org. *Librn*, Norma J Petkus; E-Mail: npetkus@daytonartinstitute.org; Staff 2 (MLS 1, Non-MLS 1)
Founded 1922
Library Holdings: Bk Titles 30,000; Per Subs 103
Subject Interests: Architecture, Art
Special Collections: Architecture (Lott-Schaeffer Memorial Architecture Library); Institutional Archives
Function: Reference only
Partic in Ohio-Kentucky Coop Libraries

L DAYTON LAW LIBRARY,* 41 N Perry St, PO Box 972, 45422. SAN 372-1981. Tel: 937-225-4496. FAX: 937-225-5056. *Librn*, Joanne Beal
Library Holdings: Bk Vols 141,260; Per Subs 4,214

S DAYTON NEWSPAPERS, INC, Reference Library,* 45 S Ludlow St, 45402. SAN 313-4601. Tel: 937-225-2430. FAX: 937-225-2277. Web Site: www.library.dni.com/.
Library Holdings: Bk Vols 2,000; Per Subs 12
Special Collections: Dayton Newspaper Coll, micro, photog

S ENGINEERS CLUB OF DAYTON LIBRARY,* 110 E Monument Ave, 45402. SAN 313-4636. Tel: 937-228-2148. FAX: 937-228-4794. E-Mail: eclub@donet.com.
Founded 1918
Subject Interests: Engineering
Partic in Miami Valley Librs

M GOOD SAMARITAN HOSPITAL, Shank Memorial Library, 2222 Philadelphia Dr, 45406-1891. SAN 313-4644. Tel: 937-278-6251, Ext 2143. FAX: 937-276-7634. *Dir*, Kristine Benishek; E-Mail: kbenishe@shp-dayton.org; *ILL*, Diana Kaylor
Founded 1965
Jan 1999-Dec 1999 Mats Exp $153,000, Books $22,000, Per/Ser (Incl. Access Fees) $89,700
Library Holdings: Bk Titles 6,200; Per Subs 400
Subject Interests: Medical, Psychiatry

M GRANDVIEW HOSPITAL, Medical Library, 405 Grand Ave, 45404. SAN 324-6280. Tel: 937-226-3379. FAX: 937-226-3609. *Librn*, Candy Winteregg; *Asst Librn*, Jonelle Venard; *ILL*, Jonelle Venard; Staff 3 (Non-MLS 3)
Library Holdings: Bk Titles 7,000; Per Subs 415
Subject Interests: Anesthesiology, Cardiology, Internal medicine, Neurology, Oncology, Ophthalmology, Orthopedics, Pediatrics, Radiology, Surgery, Urology
Mem of Miami Valley Libr Syst
Partic in BRS
Friends of the Library Group

S KETTERING FOUNDATION LIBRARY,* 200 Commons Rd, 45459. SAN 374-9320. Tel: 937-439-9822. FAX: 937-439-9804. Web Site: www.kettering.org.
Library Holdings: Bk Vols 1,800; Per Subs 100

M MIAMI VALLEY HOSPITAL, Craig Memorial Library, One Wyoming St, 45409. SAN 313-4687. Tel: 937-208-2612. FAX: 937-208-2569. *Librn*, Sally A Sexton; E-Mail: sasexton@mvh.org; *Asst Librn*, Shirley S Kinder; Staff 3 (MLS 2, Non-MLS 1)
Founded 1926
Library Holdings: Bk Vols 42,000; Bk Titles 10,000; Per Subs 600
Subject Interests: Hospital administration, Medicine, Nursing, Nutrition
Automation Activity & Vendor Info: (Acquisitions) Innovative Interfaces Inc.; (Cataloging) Innovative Interfaces Inc.; (Circulation) Innovative

Interfaces Inc.; (Course Reserve) Innovative Interfaces Inc.; (ILL) Innovative Interfaces Inc.; (Media Booking) Innovative Interfaces Inc.; (OPAC) Innovative Interfaces Inc.; (Serials) Innovative Interfaces Inc.

G MIAMI VALLEY REGIONAL PLANNING COMMISSION LIBRARY, 40 W Fourth St, Ste 400, 45402. SAN 327-3768. Tel: 937-223-6323. FAX: 937-223-9750. *Librn*, Helen Schooler
Library Holdings: Bk Vols 7,000; Per Subs 50

J MIAMI-JACOBS COLLEGE, Information Resource Center, 400 E Second St, PO Box 1433, 45401. SAN 313-4679. Tel: 937-461-5174. FAX: 937-461-3384. E-Mail: christine.dosland@miamijacobs.edu. Web Site: www.miamijacobs.edu.; Staff 1 (MLS 1)
Founded 1920. Enrl 612; Fac 32
Subject Interests: Info tech, Med assisting
Special Collections: Miami - Jacobs Archives; Miami Commercial & Jacobs Business Historical Information

S PRICE BROTHERS COMPANY LIBRARY,* 367 W Second St, PO Box 825, 45401. SAN 329-9872. Tel: 937-226-8700. FAX: 937-226-8711. E-Mail: marketing@pipesite.com. Web Site: www.pipesite.com. *Librn*, Marilen Simonson
Library Holdings: Bk Vols 5,000; Per Subs 140

S RONALD T DODGE CO, Memorial Library, 55 Westpark Rd, 45459-4812. (Mail add: PO Box 41630, 45441-0630), SAN 372-5723. Tel: 937-439-4497. FAX: 937-439-1704. E-Mail: rtdodge@rtdodge.com. Web Site: www.rtdodge.com.
Founded 1979
Library Holdings: Bk Titles 987; Per Subs 110
Special Collections: Controlled Release, bks, per; Microencapsulation, bks, per; Specialized Coll US patents
Restriction: Company library

J SINCLAIR COMMUNITY COLLEGE, Learning Resources Center, 444 W Third St, 45402-1456. SAN 313-475X. Tel: 937-512-2855. FAX: 937-512-4564. Web Site: www.library.sinclair.edu. *Dir*, H Virginia Peters; *Per, Ref*, Julie E Preisser; *Acq, Coll Develop, Ref*, Marlene Bundy; *Bibliog Instr, Online Servs, Ref*, Winnie Tseng; *ILL, Online Servs, Ref*, Sonya Kirkwood; *Ref*, Emmett Lombard; Staff 10 (MLS 10)
Founded 1887. Enrl 21,348; Fac 597
Jul 1999-Jun 2000 Mats Exp $332,172, Books $184,205, Per/Ser (Incl. Access Fees) $91,296, Presv $254, Micro $3,917, AV Equip $52,500. Sal $1,002,885
Library Holdings: Bk Vols 145,858; Bk Titles 137,585; Per Subs 573
Subject Interests: Allied health technologies, Computer science, Early childhood educ, Multicultural studies, Ohio law, Prof develop, Quality in higher educ
Automation Activity & Vendor Info: (Acquisitions) Innovative Interfaces Inc.; (Circulation) Innovative Interfaces Inc.
Partic in Ohio Library & Information Network; OHIONET; Southwestern Ohio Council For Higher Education
Special Services for the Deaf - Books on deafness & sign language

R TEMPLE ISRAEL LIBRARY, One Riverbend, 45405. SAN 313-4792. Tel: 937-496-0050. FAX: 937-496-0060.
Library Holdings: Bk Titles 5,000
Subject Interests: Judaica

L THOMPSON, HINE & FLORY, Law Library,* 2000 Courthouse Plaza NE, PO Box 8801, 45401-8801. SAN 328-3690. Tel: 937-331-6023. FAX: 937-443-6635. *Librn*, Janie Hack; E-Mail: jhack@thf.com
Library Holdings: Bk Vols 35,000; Per Subs 216

GM US VETERANS AFFAIRS MEDICAL CENTER, 4100 W Third St, 45428. SAN 356-5475. Tel: 937-268-6511, Ext 2381. FAX: 937-262-2181. *Chief Librn*, Niki Conca; Staff 7 (MLS 4, Non-MLS 3)
Founded 1871
Library Holdings: Bk Titles 5,000; Per Subs 300
Subject Interests: Chronic disease, Dentistry, Extended care facilities, Geriatrics, Rehabilitation
Publications: Monthly Newsletter; Quarterly Acquisitions List
Restriction: Staff use only
Partic in Docline; Miami Valley Librs; Vets Admin Libr Network
Branches:
PATIENTS LIBRARY: PATIENT EDUCATION RESOURCE CENTER
Subject Interests: Military hist
Special Collections: VA Archives

R UNITED THEOLOGICAL SEMINARY LIBRARY, 1810 Harvard Blvd, 45406. SAN 313-4806. Tel: 937-278-5817, Ext 119. FAX: 937-275-5701. Web Site: library.united.edu. *Dir*, Sara Blair; *ILL, Per*, Brillie Scott; *Acq*, Lesia Harvey; *Cat*, Janet McDermott; Staff 3 (MLS 3)
Founded 1871
Library Holdings: Bk Vols 180,000; Per Subs 500
Special Collections: Edmund S Lorenz Hymnal Coll; Evangelical Church; Evangelical United Brethren Church; J Allan Ranck Coll of Friendship Press; United Brethren in Christ Church; United Methodist Church; Waldensian-Methodist Coll
Partic in OCLC Online Computer Library Center, Inc; OHIONET

C UNIVERSITY OF DAYTON LIBRARIES, Roesch Library, 300 College Park Dr, 45469-1360. SAN 356-5416. Tel: 937-229-4221. FAX: 937-229-4590. *Dean of Libr, Dir*, Edward D Garten; Tel: 937-229-4265, E-Mail: garten@udayton.edu; *Bibliog Instr*, Susan Tsui; *Archivist, Spec Coll*, Kerrie Moore; *Govt Doc*, Heidi Good; Staff 21 (MLS 21)
Founded 1850. Enrl 9,850; Fac 505; Highest Degree: Doctorate
Library Holdings: Bk Vols 1,129,980; Bk Titles 856,000; Per Subs 5,025
Subject Interests: Am lit, Biology, Bus, Education, Engineering, English, Philosophy, Theology
Special Collections: Congressman Charles W Whalen, Jr Coll, public papers; Local Govt; Science Fiction Writers of America Coll
Publications: Roesch Library Update
Partic in Ohio Library & Information Network; OHIONET
Departmental Libraries:
CR MARIAN LIBRARY, 300 College Park Rd, 45469-1390. SAN 313-4814. Tel: 937-229-4214. FAX: 937-229-4258. *Dir*, Thomas A Thompson; E-Mail: thompson@notes.lib.udayton.edu
Library Holdings: Bk Vols 98,000; Per Subs 269
GL ZIMMERMAN LAW LIBRARY, 300 College Park, 45469-2780. SAN 356-5440. Tel: 937-229-2314. FAX: 937-229-2555. Web Site: www.udayton.edu/~lawlib. *Dir*, Thomas L Hanley; Tel: 937-229-2444, E-Mail: hanley@udayton.edu; *Acq, Ser*, Theodora Artz; *Automation Syst Coordr, Cat*, Benjamin Hu; *Publ Servs, Ref*, Kenneth Kozlowski; *Circ*, Joan Pallant; Staff 5 (MLS 5)
Founded 1974. Enrl 491; Fac 24; Highest Degree: Doctorate
Jul 1998-Jun 1999 Income $1,408,744. Mats Exp $690,150, Books $48,150, Per/Ser (Incl. Access Fees) $642,000. Sal $412,365 (Prof $261,206)
Library Holdings: Bk Vols 270,003; Per Subs 4,461
Automation Activity & Vendor Info: (Acquisitions) Innovative Interfaces Inc.; (Cataloging) Innovative Interfaces Inc.; (Circulation) Innovative Interfaces Inc.; (Serials) Innovative Interfaces Inc.
Publications: Aquisitions Update; Z News (newsletter)
Partic in Ohio Library & Information Network; Southwestern Ohio Council For Higher Education

C WRIGHT STATE UNIVERSITY, Libraries, 3640 Colonel Glenn Hwy, 45435-0001. SAN 356-553X. Tel: 937-775-4125. Interlibrary Loan Service Tel: 937-775-2289. FAX: 937-775-4109. Web Site: www.libraries.wright.edu. *Dir Libr Serv*, Chris Watson; Tel: 937-775-2608, E-Mail: chris.watson@wright.edu; *Dir*, Victoria Montavon; *Assoc Dir*, Sheila Shellabarger; *Assoc Dir*, Patricia Walker; *Archivist, Spec Coll*, Dawn Dewey; *Automation Syst Coordr*, Kathi Herick; *Head Tech Servs*, Karen Wilhoit; *Coll Develop*, Jan Maxwell; Staff 36 (MLS 36)
Founded 1967. Enrl 12,178; Fac 647; Highest Degree: Doctorate
Library Holdings: Bk Vols 755,794; Bk Titles 495,699; Per Subs 5,564
Subject Interests: Biochemistry, Cardiology, Medicine, Microbiology, Nursing, Physiology
Special Collections: Aerospace Medical Association Archives; Aerospace Medicine & Human Factors Engineering (Ross A McFarland Coll); Andrews S Iddings Papers; Children's Literature especially book illustrated by Arthur Rackham; Cincinnati, Dayton Ballet Company, Overholser Civil War Diary, Glenn Curtiss Photographs, Springfield Urban League Records, Clayton Bruckner Papers, Extensive early local records from Auglaize, Champaign, Clark, Darke, Greene, Mercer counties; Dayton Urban League Papers; Early Aviation Coll; Glenn Thompson Papers; Governor James M Cox Papers; History of Medicine; Howard Hashbrook Collection in Aviation Crash Research; HTE Hertzburg Coll in Anthropometry; Large Photograph Coll on Miami Valley Area & Early Aviation; Local & Regional Hisotry Coll - includes Miami Valley Genealogical Society Library; Miami, Montgomery, Logan, Preble & Shelby Counties; O S Kelly Company Papers, The Miami Conservancy District Papers; Paul Laurence Dunbar Coll; The Miami Conservatory District Papers; Unpublished Manuscripts Coll: Wright Brothers Papers, Governor James M Cox Papers, Dayton Urban League Papers; William Rhornton Coll in Space & Life Sciences; Wright Brothers Papers
Automation Activity & Vendor Info: (Acquisitions) Innovative Interfaces Inc.; (Cataloging) Innovative Interfaces Inc.; (Circulation) Innovative Interfaces Inc.; (Course Reserve) Innovative Interfaces Inc.; (Media Booking) Innovative Interfaces Inc.; (OPAC) Innovative Interfaces Inc.; (Serials) Innovative Interfaces Inc.
Publications: Access; Diaries: 1857-1917 by Bishop Milton Wright; Guide to Local Government Records & newspapers at WSU; Guide to Manuscripts
Partic in OCLC Online Computer Library Center, Inc; Ohio Library & Information Network; OHIONET
Friends of the Library Group

DEFIANCE

C DEFIANCE COLLEGE, Pilgrim Library, 201 College Pl, 43512-1667. SAN 313-4849. Tel: 419-783-2481. FAX: 419-783-2594. *Dir*, Edward S Warner; *Tech Servs*, Barbara Sedlock; Tel: 419-783-2487; *Ref*, Mary Bishop; *Circ*, Sharon Rumbaugh

Enrl 774; Fac 57; Highest Degree: Master
Library Holdings: Bk Vols 87,125; Per Subs 379
Special Collections: Afro-American Coll; American History (Indian Wars of Northwest Ohio, 1785-1815), bk & micro
Partic in NOLC; OHIONET

L DEFIANCE COUNTY LAW LIBRARY,* 510 Court St, 43512. SAN 372-2031. Tel: 419-782-1186. FAX: 419-782-2437. *Librn*, Rose J Brown
Library Holdings: Bk Vols 20,000; Per Subs 1,000

P DEFIANCE PUBLIC LIBRARY,* 320 Fort St, 43512-2186. SAN 356-5653. Tel: 419-782-1456. FAX: 419-782-6235. *Dir*, Marilyn Hite; E-Mail: hitema@oplin.lib.oh.us; Staff 3 (MLS 3)
Founded 1895. Pop 39,825; Circ 234,998
Library Holdings: Per Subs 280
Subject Interests: Local history
Special Collections: Ohioana; Slocum
Publications: Holding The Fort
Partic in Northwest Library District; Norweld
Multi-type Interlibrary Cooperative Resource Organization
Friends of the Library Group
Branches: 2
JOHNSON MEMORIAL, 116 W High St, Hicksville, 43526. SAN 356-5688. Tel: 419-542-6200. FAX: 419-542-6200. *Librn*, Mary Lou Durre
SHERWOOD BRANCH, 202 Harrison St, Sherwood, 43556. SAN 374-7190. Tel: 419-899-4343. FAX: 419-899-4343. *Librn*, Carol Hull

DELAWARE

P DELAWARE COUNTY DISTRICT LIBRARY, 84 E Winter St, 43015. SAN 313-4857. Tel: 740-362-3861. FAX: 740-369-0196. Web Site: rddelew@oplin.lib.oh.us. *Dir*, Patricia K Ebbatson; E-Mail: ebbaststr@oplinlib.oh.us; *Asst Dir*, Mary Jane Santos; *Ch Servs*, Linnea Davis; *ILL*, Shaun Powell; *Outreach Serv*, Charlotte Bay; *Tech Servs*, Thomas Brook; Staff 8 (MLS 6, Non-MLS 2)
Founded 1903. Pop 81,171
Jan 1999-Dec 1999 Income (Main Library and Branch Library) $2,063,938, State $1,961,166, Locally Generated Income $102,772. Mats Exp $267,452, Books $189,455, Per/Ser (Incl. Access Fees) $23,329. Sal $602,817 (Prof $193,698)
Library Holdings: Bk Titles 144,632; Per Subs 298
Subject Interests: Local history
Automation Activity & Vendor Info: (Circulation) Innovative Interfaces Inc.
Database Vendor: OCLC - First Search
Partic in Columbus Area Library & Information Council Of Ohio (CALICO)
Branches: 2
OSTRANDER, N Fourth St, 43015. SAN 372-5618. Tel: 614-666-1410. FAX: 614-666-1437. *Librn*, Harla Lawson
POWELL BRANCH, 460 S Liberty Rd, Powell, 43065. SAN 373-2908. Tel: 614-888-9160. FAX: 614-888-7358. *Librn*, Robbie Curry

GL DELAWARE COUNTY LAW LIBRARY,* Courthouse, 91 N Sandusky St, 43015. SAN 327-3806. Tel: 740-368-1775. FAX: 740-368-1776. *Res*, Lynn Seguin
Library Holdings: Bk Vols 6,000; Per Subs 45

CR METHODIST THEOLOGICAL SCHOOL IN OHIO LIBRARY, 3081 Columbus Pike, PO Box 8004, 43015-8004. SAN 313-4873. Tel: 740-363-1146. FAX: 740-362-3456. *Librn*, Paul Schrodt; *Cat, Ref*, Kevin Smith; Staff 2 (MLS 2)
Founded 1960. Enrl 191; Fac 22; Highest Degree: Master
Library Holdings: Per Subs 371
Subject Interests: Biblical studies, Church history, Theology
Special Collections: Denominational Coll of the United Methodist Church & its Predecessor Bodies, bks & micro; Philip Gatch Manuscripts
Automation Activity & Vendor Info: (Acquisitions) Endeavor; (Cataloging) Endeavor; (Circulation) Endeavor; (Course Reserve) Endeavor; (OPAC) Endeavor; (Serials) Endeavor
Partic in OCLC Online Computer Library Center, Inc; OHIONET; Theological Consortium of Greater Columbus

C OHIO WESLEYAN UNIVERSITY, L A Beeghly Library, 43 Rowland, 43015-4431. SAN 313-4881. Tel: 740-368-3225. Interlibrary Loan Service Tel: 740-368-3234. Circulation Tel: 740-368-3225. Reference Tel: 740-368-3242. FAX: 740-368-3222. E-Mail: refdesk@cc.owu.edu. Web Site: library.owu.edu/. *Dir*, Theresa Byrd; E-Mail: tsbyrd@cc.owu.edu; *Assoc Dir*, Tom Green; Tel: 740-368-3236, E-Mail: togreen@cc.owu.edu; *Assoc Dir*, Xudong Jin; Tel: 740-368-3258, E-Mail: xdjin@cc.owu.edu; *Ref*, Paul Burnam; Tel: 740-368-3240, E-Mail: bdburnam@cc.owu.edu; *Instrul Serv*, Danielle Clarke; Tel: 740-368-3237, E-Mail: dmclarke@cc.owu.edu; *Govt Doc*, Joy He; Tel: 740-368-3238, E-Mail: yyhe@cc.owu.edu; Staff 7 (MLS 6, Non-MLS 1)
Founded 1842. Enrl 1,905; Fac 138; Highest Degree: Bachelor
Jul 1999-Jun 2000 Income $1,593,088. Mats Exp $560,213, Books $241,573, Per/Ser (Incl. Access Fees) $300,169, Presv $11,417, AV Equip $7,054, Electronic Ref Mat (Incl. Access Fees) $88,225. Sal $509,455 (Prof $245,053)
Library Holdings: Bk Vols 248,381; Per Subs 1,064
Special Collections: Browning (Gunsaulus Coll); James Joyce (Staples Coll); Religion, (Methodist Historical Coll); Schubert (20th Century Imprints Coll); Walt Whitman, (Bayley Coll)
Database Vendor: Innovative Interfaces INN - View
Publications: At the Library (Newsletter)
Partic in Five Colleges of Ohio; OCLC Online Computer Library Center, Inc; Ohio Library & Information Network; OHIONET
Friends of the Library Group

DELPHOS

P DELPHOS PUBLIC LIBRARY,* 309 W Second St, 45833-1695. SAN 313-489X. Tel: 419-695-4015. FAX: 419-695-4025. *Dir*, Nancy Mericle; E-Mail: mericlna@oplin.lib.oh.us; *Ch Servs*, Denise Crossman; Staff 2 (MLS 2)
Founded 1901. Pop 15,000; Circ 230,145
1997-1998 Income $423,671, City $46,691, County $346,913, Other $30,067. Mats Exp $357,994, Books $61,500, Per/Ser (Incl. Access Fees) $11,900. Sal $258,110
Library Holdings: Bk Titles 71,643; Per Subs 328
Subject Interests: Local history
Special Collections: Delphos Newspapers, 1872-1946
Partic in Northwest Library District

DELTA

P DELTA PUBLIC LIBRARY,* 402 Main St, 43515-1304. SAN 313-4903. Tel: 419-822-3110. FAX: 419-822-5310. *Dir*, Patricia Grover; *Asst Dir*, Marj Bowerman
Founded 1911. Pop 7,000; Circ 79,840
Library Holdings: Bk Vols 53,000; Per Subs 215
Partic in NW Ohio Libr District
Friends of the Library Group

DESHLER

P PATRICK HENRY SCHOOL DISTRICT PUBLIC LIBRARY, 208 NE Ave, 43516. SAN 356-5718. Tel: 419-278-3616. FAX: 419-278-3616. *Dir*, Esther Nagel; E-Mail: nageles@oplin.lib.oh.us
Founded 1924. Pop 5,000
Jan 1998-Dec 1999 Income (Main Library and Branch Library) $253,302, State $229,532, County $16,200, Locally Generated Income $7,570. Mats Exp $37,247, Books $31,734, Per/Ser (Incl. Access Fees) $5,513. Sal $109,884 (Prof $23,100)
Library Holdings: Bk Vols 22,027; Per Subs 150
Special Collections: Genealogy, bks, flm; Ohio & Local History, bks, fs, slides
Branches: 2
HAMLER BRANCH, 240 S First St, Hamler, 43524. SAN 356-5742. Tel: 419-274-3821. FAX: 419-274-3821. *Librn*, Malinowski Ramona
Library Holdings: Bk Vols 13,760
MALINTA BRANCH, 204 N Henry St, Malinta, 43535. SAN 356-5777. Tel: 419-256-7223. *Librn*, Audrey Gilliland
Library Holdings: Bk Vols 18,147

DOVER

P DOVER PUBLIC LIBRARY,* 525 N Walnut St, 44622. SAN 313-4911. Tel: 330-343-6123. FAX: 330-343-2087. *Dir*, Daniel R Cooley
Founded 1923. Pop 20,000; Circ 226,778
Jan 1998-Dec 1998 Income $756,106, State $684,917, Locally Generated Income $71,189. Mats Exp $159,443, Books $135,000, Per/Ser (Incl. Access Fees) $11,943, AV Equip $12,500. Sal $302,761 (Prof $70,185)
Library Holdings: Bk Vols 78,500; Bk Titles 76,000; Per Subs 320
Automation Activity & Vendor Info: (Cataloging) Gaylord; (Circulation) Gaylord
Partic in Mideastern Ohio Libr Orgn

DUBLIN

S ASHLAND INC, Library & Information Services, 5200 Blazer Pkwy, 43017. SAN 371-0173. Tel: 614-790-3281. FAX: 614-790-4269. E-Mail: asolis@ashland.com. Web Site: www.ashchem.com. *Mgr*, Priscilla Ratliff; *Librn*, Joyce Klayman; Staff 6 (MLS 2, Non-MLS 4)
Founded 1970
Library Holdings: Bk Vols 12,000; Bk Titles 10,000; Per Subs 325
Subject Interests: Bus mgt, Chemical industry, Chemistry
Special Collections: US Chemical Patents & Microfilm (1960 to present)
Publications: LIS Bulletin (irregular)
Restriction: Company library
Partic in OHIONET
Library & Information Services offered for sale to the public. Contracts may be negotiated

S OCLC INFORMATION CENTER, 6565 Frantz Rd, 43017. (Mail add: PO Box 7777, 43017), SAN 320-9253. Tel: 614-764-4340. Circulation Tel: 614-764-4338. Toll Free Tel: 800-848-5878, Ext 4340. FAX: 614-793-8707. E-Mail: information_center@oclc.org. *Mgr*, Lawrence Olszewski; Tel: 614-764-6293, Fax: 614-718-7336, E-Mail: olszewsl@oclc.org; *Info Specialist*, Leslie Dillon; Tel: 614-764-6133, E-Mail: dillonl@oclc.org; *Info Tech*, Martha Klein; Tel: 614-764-6015, E-Mail: kleinm@oclc.org; *Ser*, Terry Butterworth; Tel: 614-764-4300, E-Mail: butterwt@oclc.org; Staff 6 (MLS 4, Non-MLS 2)
Founded 1977
Library Holdings: Bk Vols 21,608; Bk Titles 19,527; Per Subs 500
Subject Interests: Computer science, Engineering, Info sci, Libr sci, Marketing, Mgt, Telecommunications systs
Special Collections: Library Network Newsletters; State Library & State Library Association Newsletters
Automation Activity & Vendor Info: (Acquisitions) TechLIB; (Circulation) TechLIB; (Serials) TechLIB
Database Vendor: Dialog, Lexis-Nexis, OCLC - First Search, OVID Technologies, Silverplatter Information Inc.
Publications: OCC InfoLine (Newsletter)
Restriction: Open to others by appointment
Function: Archival collection
Friends of the Library Group

DUNKIRK

P HARDIN NORTHERN PUBLIC LIBRARY,* 250 N Maine St, 45836-1064. SAN 313-4938. Tel: 419-759-3558. FAX: 419-759-3558. *Librn*, Rebecca Motter; E-Mail: motterre@oplin.lib.oh.us
Library Holdings: Bk Vols 10,000; Per Subs 60
Mem of NW Libr District

EAST CLEVELAND

P EAST CLEVELAND PUBLIC LIBRARY,* 14101 Euclid Ave, 44112-3891. SAN 356-5807. Tel: 216-541-4128. FAX: 216-541-1790. E-Mail: ecpl@lib.oh.us. *Dir*, Gregory L Reese; *Asst Dir*, Ernestine Hawkins; Staff 33 (MLS 7, Non-MLS 26)
Founded 1916. Pop 37,000; Circ 211,743
Library Holdings: Bk Vols 206,164; Per Subs 194
Subject Interests: Behav sci, Black lit, Bus, Mgt, Soc sci
Special Collections: Black Heritage Coll; Holograph Letters of the Presidents from George Washington to James E Carter; Illustrated Children's Book (W H Quinby Coll)
Publications: Annual Report; Black Heritage Bibliography
Partic in Cleveland Area Metropolitan Library System
Friends of the Library Group
Branches: 2
CALEDONIA BRANCH, 960 Caledonia Ave, Cleveland Heights, 44112. SAN 356-5831. Tel: 216-268-6280. FAX: 216-268-6294. *Librn*, Anita Ferguson
Library Holdings: Bk Vols 25,032
Friends of the Library Group
NORTH BRANCH, 1425 Hayden Ave, 44112. SAN 356-5866. Tel: 216-268-6283. FAX: 216-268-6297. *Librn*, Mildred Hart
Library Holdings: Bk Vols 17,464
Friends of the Library Group

EAST LIVERPOOL

P CARNEGIE PUBLIC LIBRARY, 219 E Fourth St, 43920-3143. SAN 313-4946. Tel: 330-385-2048. FAX: 330-385-7600. E-Mail: eastliv@plin.lib.oh.us. Web Site: www.carnegie.lib.oh.us. *Dir*, Theodore R Allison; *Ch Servs*, Kim Blevins; *Ref*, Andrew Fearn; *Cat*, Tom Marlatt; *Circ*, Pete Allison; *AV*, Karen Zendhar; *Tech Coordr*, Terry Brown
Founded 1900. Pop 50,000; Circ 200,000
Jan 2000-Dec 2000 Income $971,734, State $923,234, Locally Generated Income $48,500. Mats Exp $329,000, Books $234,000, Per/Ser (Incl. Access Fees) $15,000, AV Equip $80,000. Sal $425,000 (Prof $150,000)
Library Holdings: Bk Vols 89,996; Bk Titles 90,960; Per Subs 140
Subject Interests: Local history, Pottery-ceramics col
Automation Activity & Vendor Info: (Cataloging) TLC; (Circulation) TLC; (OPAC) TLC
Partic in Northeastern Ohio Libr Asn
Friends of the Library Group

C KENT STATE UNIVERSITY, East Liverpool Campus Library,* 400 E Fourth St, 43920-5769. SAN 313-4954. Tel: 330-385-3805. FAX: 330-385-3757. *Dir*, Susan Weaver; E-Mail: sweaver@kenteliv.kent.edu
Founded 1968. Enrl 598; Fac 52
Library Holdings: Bk Vols 31,320; Per Subs 131
Partic in Nola Regional Library System

EAST PALESTINE

P EAST PALESTINE MEMORIAL PUBLIC LIBRARY, 309 N Market St, 44413. SAN 313-4962. Tel: 330-426-3778. FAX: 330-426-4950. Web Site: www.east-palestine.lib.oh.us. *Coll Develop, Librn*, Lisa Rohrbaugh
Founded 1920. Pop 7,500; Circ 91,360
Jan 1999-Dec 1999 Income $394,462, State $371,024, Locally Generated Income $16,371, Other $7,067. Mats Exp $78,396, Books $55,116, Per/Ser (Incl. Access Fees) $4,524, Presv $287, AV Equip $13,166, Other Print Mats $368, Electronic Ref Mat (Incl. Access Fees) $4,935. Sal $145,515 (Prof $96,795)
Library Holdings: Bk Vols 38,171; Bk Titles 33,505; Per Subs 111; High Interest/Low Vocabulary Bk Vols 15; Bks on Deafness & Sign Lang 28
Subject Interests: Local history
Special Collections: Ohio Canals
Automation Activity & Vendor Info: (Cataloging) Sagebrush Corporation; (Circulation) Sagebrush Corporation
Partic in Nola Regional Library System
Friends of the Library Group

EASTLAKE

C GOULD ELECTRONICS INC, Technical Information Center, 34929 Curtis Blvd, 44095. SAN 322-788X. Tel: 440-953-5000, Ext 5117. FAX: 440-953-5152. *Info Specialist*, Martha C Walunis; E-Mail: mwalunis@gouldelectronics.com
Founded 1981
Library Holdings: Bk Titles 5,000; Per Subs 150
Subject Interests: Electrochem, Electronic materials, Finishing, Plating
Restriction: Staff use only
Partic in Dialog Corporation; Dow Jones News Retrieval; OCLC Online Computer Library Center, Inc

EATON

P PREBLE COUNTY DISTRICT LIBRARY, 450 S Barron St, 45320-2402. SAN 356-5890. Tel: 937-456-4250. TDD: 937-456-4809. FAX: 937-456-6092. E-Mail: library@infinet.com. Web Site: www.pcdl.lib.oh.us. *Dir*, Susan H Kendall; E-Mail: skendall@infinet.com; *Cat*, Carol A Reckers; *Res*, Guy W Humphrey; Tel: 937-456-4331, Fax: 937-456-4774; *Ch Servs*, Dana Kesling; Tel: 937-456-4331, Fax: 937-456-4774; Staff 39 (MLS 3, Non-MLS 36)
Founded 1959. Pop 41,000
Jan 2000-Dec 2000 Income (Main Library and Branch Library) $1,359,187, State $1,319,587, Locally Generated Income $39,600. Mats Exp $317,500, Books $177,000, Per/Ser (Incl. Access Fees) $12,000, Micro $15,000, Electronic Ref Mat (Incl. Access Fees) $30,000. Sal $561,672
Library Holdings: Bk Vols 166,854; Bk Titles 140,000; Per Subs 980
Subject Interests: Genealogy, Local history
Automation Activity & Vendor Info: (Cataloging) MultiLIS; (Circulation) MultiLIS
Database Vendor: Ebsco - EbscoHost
Partic in Miami Valley Librs; Ohio Pub Libr Info Network; OHIONET
Special Services for the Deaf - TDD
Special Services for the Blind - Reading edge system
Branches: 8
BROOKE-GOULD MEMORIAL, 301 N Barron St, 45320-1705. SAN 356-5955. Tel: 937-456-4331. FAX: 937-456-4774. Web Site: www.pcdl.lib.oh.us. *Librn*, Phyllis Bennett
Friends of the Library Group
CAMDEN, 104 S Main St, 45311. SAN 356-5920. Tel: 937-452-3142. FAX: 937-452-7365. Web Site: www.pcdl.lib.oh.us. *Librn*, Norma Wilson
Special Collections: Eleanor I Jones Archives
Friends of the Library Group
ELDORADO, PO Box 244, 45321. SAN 356-598X. Tel: 513-273-4933. FAX: 937-273-5673. Web Site: www.pcdl.lib.oh.us. *Librn*, Teresa Deaton
LIBRARY ADMINISTRATION & RESOURCE CENTER Tel: 937-456-4250. FAX: 937-456-6092. Web Site: www.pcdl.lib.oh.us. *Dir*, Susan Kendall
Subject Interests: Local history
Special Collections: Preble County Historical Society & Preble County Genealogical Society Genealogy
NEW PARIS, 115 N Washington St, 45347. SAN 356-6013. Tel: 937-437-7242. FAX: 937-437-0772. Web Site: www.pcdl.lib.oh.us. *Librn*, Barbara Dungan
WEST ALEXANDRIA, 16 N Main St, 45381. SAN 356-6048. Tel: 937-839-4915. FAX: 937-839-4209. Web Site: www.pcdl.lib.oh.us. *Librn*, Louann Perry
Special Collections: West Alexandria Archives
Friends of the Library Group
WEST ELKTON, PO Box 100, West Elkton, 45070. SAN 328-7068. Tel: 937-787-4873. FAX: 937-787-3153. Web Site: www.pcdl.lib.oh.us. *Librn*, Brenda Phillabaum

Friends of the Library Group
WEST MANCHESTER BRANCH, PO Box 138, West Manchester, 45382. SAN 371-3032. Tel: 513-678-8503. FAX: 513-678-4030. Web Site: www.pcdl.lib.oh.us. *Librn*, Gloria Hyatt

ELMORE

P HARRIS-ELMORE PUBLIC LIBRARY, 328 Toledo St, PO Box 45, 43416. SAN 356-6072. Tel: 419-862-2482. FAX: 419-862-2123. Web Site: www.library.norweld.lib.oh.us/harris-elmore. *Dir*, Georgiana Huizenga; E-Mail: huizeng@oplin.lib.oh.us; *Dir*, Georgiana Ruth Huizenga; *Assoc Dir*, Kimberly Ann Jimison; E-Mail: jimisoki@oplin.lib.oh.us; *Ch Servs*, Peggie Avers; E-Mail: averspe@oplin.lib.oh.us. Subject Specialists: *Local history*, Grace Luebke; Staff 17 (Non-MLS 17)
Founded 1947. Pop 15,000; Circ 95,000
Library Holdings: Bk Vols 40,000; Per Subs 75
Automation Activity & Vendor Info: (Cataloging) epixtech, inc.; (Circulation) epixtech, inc.
Database Vendor: CARL, Ebsco - EbscoHost, epixtech, inc.
Function: Photocopies available
Mem of NW Libr District
Branches: 1
GENOA BRANCH, 602 West St, Genoa, 43430. SAN 356-6102. Tel: 419-855-3380. FAX: 419-855-7012. *Librn*, Amy Laity
Library Holdings: Bk Vols 35,000; Per Subs 60
Friends of the Library Group

ELYRIA

P ELYRIA PUBLIC LIBRARY, 320 Washington Ave, 44035-5199. SAN 313-4997. Tel: 440-323-5747. TDD: 440-323-1322. FAX: 440-323-5788. E-Mail: epl@elyria.lib.oh.us. Web Site: www.elyria.lib.oh.us. *Asst Dir*, Janet Stoffer; E-Mail: asstdir@elyria.lib.oh.us; *Reader Servs*, Ruth Felix; E-Mail: readerav@elyria.lib.oh.us; *Ch Servs*, Margaret Savoy; E-Mail: mchilda@elyria.lib.oh.us; *ILL, Ref*, Rose Burton; E-Mail: mrefa@elyria.lib.oh.us; *Tech Servs*, Kathy Webb; E-Mail: tsd@elyria.lib.oh.us; *Outreach Serv*, Lisa Kean; E-Mail: famlit@elyria.lib.oh.us; *AV*, Celeste Brlas; E-Mail: av@elyria.lib.oh.us
Founded 1870. Pop 70,000; Circ 770,308
Jan 1999-Dec 1999 Income $2,759,398, State $2,550,830, Other $208,568. Mats Exp $100,000. Sal $1,340,994
Library Holdings: Bk Vols 352,182; Per Subs 715
Special Collections: Ely Papers, local history
Automation Activity & Vendor Info: (OPAC) DRA
Publications: A Friendly Word - Friends of the Library newsletter
Partic in CLEVE-NET; Cleveland Area Metropolitan Library System
Adult Literacy Project: Read; Family Literacy Program
Friends of the Library Group
Bookmobiles: 1

M EMH REGIONAL HEALTHCARE SYSTEM, (EMHRHS), Dr Joseph M Strong Memorial Library, 630 E River St, 44035. SAN 313-4989. Tel: 440-329-7500, Ext 7588. FAX: 440-329-7405. *Mgr*, Jennifer Jung Gallant; Tel: 440-329-7855, E-Mail: jennifer.gallant@emhrhs.com. Subject Specialists: *Allied health*, Jennifer Jung Gallant; *Medicine*, Jennifer Jung Gallant; *Nursing*, Jennifer Jung Gallant; Staff 2 (MLS 1, Non-MLS 1)
Founded 1927
Library Holdings: Bk Vols 3,900; Per Subs 200
Subject Interests: Food, Hospital administration, Natural science, Nutrition, Public health
Database Vendor: Ebsco - EbscoHost
Partic in Cleveland Area Metropolitan Library System

C LORAIN COUNTY COMMUNITY COLLEGE LIBRARY, 1005 Abbe Rd N, 44035-1691. SAN 313-5004. Tel: 440-366-4126. Circulation Tel: 440-366-6024. Reference Tel: 440-366-7288. Toll Free Tel: 800-995-5222, Ext 4126. FAX: 440-366-7336. Web Site: www.lorainccc.edu. *Dir*, Keith E Washburn; Tel: 440-366-4795, Fax: 440-366-4127, E-Mail: kwashbur@lorainccc.edu; *Head Tech Servs*, Mary Jill Brophy; Tel: 440-366-7285, E-Mail: jbrophy@lorainccc.edu; *Ref*, Doris Patrick; *Head Ref*, Christine Sheetz; E-Mail: csheetz@lorainccc.edu; *Publ Servs*, Susan Paul; Tel: 440-366-7422, E-Mail: spaul@lorainccc.edu. Subject Specialists: *Allied health*, Susan Paul; *Sciences*, Christine Sheetz; *Social sciences*, Mary Jill Brophy; Staff 31 (MLS 7, Non-MLS 24)
Founded 1964. Enrl 8,000; Fac 263; Highest Degree: Associate
Jul 2000-Jun 2001 Income $1,427,984. Mats Exp $213,745, Books $103,020, Per/Ser (Incl. Access Fees) $88,205, Presv $1,100, Micro $21,420. Sal $749,422 (Prof $247,478)
Library Holdings: Bk Vols 110,000; Bk Titles 93,000; Per Subs 700
Automation Activity & Vendor Info: (Acquisitions) Innovative Interfaces Inc.; (Cataloging) Innovative Interfaces Inc.; (Circulation) Innovative Interfaces Inc.; (ILL) Innovative Interfaces Inc.; (OPAC) Innovative Interfaces Inc.
Database Vendor: Ebsco - EbscoHost, Innovative Interfaces INN - View, Lexis-Nexis, OCLC - First Search
Partic in Ohio Library & Information Network; OHIONET

S LORAIN COUNTY HISTORICAL SOCIETY, Gerald Hicks Memorial Library, 509 Washington Ave, 44035. SAN 327-3822. Tel: 440-322-3341. FAX: 440-322-2817. *Exec Dir*, William Bird; *Librn*, Karis Lyon; Staff 4 (Non-MLS 4)
Library Holdings: Bk Vols 3,500

GL LORAIN COUNTY LAW LIBRARY, 226 Middle Ave, 44035. SAN 313-5012. Tel: 440-329-5567. FAX: 440-322-1724. *Librn*, Mary Kovacs; Staff 3 (MLS 1, Non-MLS 2)
Library Holdings: Bk Titles 25,000; Per Subs 25
Subject Interests: Law
Restriction: Members only

S LORAIN COUNTY PRINTING & PUBLISHING CO, Chronicle-Telegram Library, 225 East Ave, 44035. SAN 313-4970. Tel: 440-329-7000. FAX: 329-7154, 440-329-7282. *Librn*, Kathy Boris
Founded 1955
Special Collections: Elyria & Lorain County, hist clippings & pictures

EUCLID

P EUCLID PUBLIC LIBRARY, 631 E 222nd St, 44123-2091. SAN 356-6137. Tel: 216-261-5300. FAX: 216-261-0628. Web Site: www.euclid.lib.oh.us. *Dir*, Donna L Perdzock; Tel: 216-261-5300, Ext 111, E-Mail: dperdzock@euclid.lib.oh.us; *Dep Dir*, Jeffrey French; Tel: 216-261-5300, Ext 116, E-Mail: jfrench@euclid.lib.oh.us; *Ad Servs*, Paul Gallmeier; Tel: 216-261-5300, Ext 134, Fax: 216-261-9559, E-Mail: pgallmeier@euclid.lib.oh.us; *Ch Servs*, Linda Spear; Tel: 216-261-5300, Ext 143, Fax: 216-261-9559, E-Mail: lspear@euclid.lib.oh.us; *Tech Servs*, Dale Greenbaum; Tel: 216-261-5300, Ext 120, E-Mail: dgreenbaum@euclid.lib.oh.us; *Circ*, Cheryl Burley; Tel: 216-261-5300, Ext 153, E-Mail: cburley@euclid.lib.oh.us; *Automation Syst Coordr*, Matthew Augustine; Tel: 216-261-5300, Ext 126, E-Mail: maugustine@euclid.lib.oh.us; Staff 90 (MLS 15, Non-MLS 75)
Founded 1935. Pop 54,875
Jan 2000-Dec 2000 Income $3,965,824, State $2,346,734, Locally Generated Income $1,320,548, Other $298,542. Mats Exp $824,772, Books $600,642, Per/Ser (Incl. Access Fees) $41,522, Presv $1,300, Micro $17,200, Electronic Ref Mat (Incl. Access Fees) $104,108. Sal $1,995,999 (Prof $1,070,500)
Library Holdings: Bk Vols 219,519; Per Subs 558
Automation Activity & Vendor Info: (Acquisitions) DRA; (Cataloging) DRA; (Circulation) DRA; (OPAC) DRA
Database Vendor: GaleNet, IAC - Info Trac, OCLC - First Search
Publications: Library Lines
Function: ILL available
Partic in Cleveland Area Metropolitan Library System; Clevnet
Friends of the Library Group

FAIRPORT HARBOR

S ELTECH SYSTEMS CORP LIBRARY,* 625 East St, 44077. SAN 375-1392. Tel: 440-357-4000, 440-357-4002. FAX: 440-357-4077. *In Charge*, Debbie Fultz; E-Mail: daf@eltechsystems.com
Library Holdings: Bk Vols 15,000; Per Subs 45
Restriction: Not open to public

P FAIRPORT HARBOR PUBLIC LIBRARY, 335 Vine St, 44077-5799. SAN 313-5020. Tel: 440-354-8191. FAX: 440-354-6059. *Dir*, Carol Murdoch-Miller; E-Mail: carol.murdoch-miller@fairport.lib.oh.us
Founded 1922. Pop 2,978; Circ 93,802
Library Holdings: Bk Vols 43,524; Bk Titles 36,199; Per Subs 120
Subject Interests: Applied sci, Finnish lit, Hungarian
Partic in CLEVE-NET; Nola Regional Library System
Also has branch facilities at one local school
Friends of the Library Group

FAYETTE

P NORMAL MEMORIAL LIBRARY, 301 N Eagle St, PO Box 100, 43521. SAN 313-5039. Tel: 419-237-2115. FAX: 419-237-2002. *Dir*, Verna Williams; E-Mail: williave@oplin.lib.oh.us; *ILL*, Sally Canfield
Founded 1929. Pop 2,500; Circ 31,608
Library Holdings: Bk Vols 21,000; Per Subs 92

FINDLAY

S COURIER LIBRARY,* 701 W Sandusky St, PO Box 609, 45839-0609. SAN 371-4616. Tel: 419-422-5151. FAX: 419-422-2937. Web Site: www.thecourier.com. *Librn*, Paula Alessi
Library Holdings: Per Subs 14

P FINDLAY-HANCOCK COUNTY PUBLIC LIBRARY, 206 Broadway, 45840-3382. SAN 356-6226. Tel: 419-422-1712. FAX: 419-422-0638. Web Site: www.findlay.lib.oh.us. *Dir*, Sybil Galer; *Circ*, Jill Hendricks; *AV, Media Spec*, Carol Dunn; *Ad Servs*, Lindell Clemens; Staff 10 (MLS 10)
Founded 1888. Pop 65,900; Circ 1,000,000

Jan 1999-Dec 1999 Income $2,700,255, State $2,518,680, Locally Generated Income $156,798, Other $24,777. Mats Exp $403,166, Books $262,018, Per/Ser (Incl. Access Fees) $23,952, Presv $1,821, AV Equip $106,826, Electronic Ref Mat (Incl. Access Fees) $8,549. Sal $1,167,570
Library Holdings: Bk Vols 176,405; Per Subs 299
Subject Interests: Genealogy, Local history
Automation Activity & Vendor Info: (Cataloging) epixtech, inc.; (Circulation) epixtech, inc.
Publications: Bookend (Newsletter)
Partic in OCLC Online Computer Library Center, Inc
Friends of the Library Group
Branches: 1
ARLINGTON BRANCH, 232 N Main, Arlington, 45814. SAN 356-6250. Tel: 419-365-5755. Web Site: www.findlay.lib.oh.us. *Librn*, Jeff Winkle
Bookmobiles: 1

L HANCOCK COUNTY LAW LIBRARY ASSOCIATION,* 300 S Main St, 4th flr, 45840. SAN 313-5055. Tel: 419-424-7077. FAX: 419-425-4136. *Librn*, Deborah L Ward
Library Holdings: Bk Vols 24,500

L MARATHON OIL CO, Law Library, 539 S Main St, Rm 854-M, 45840-3295. SAN 313-5063. Tel: 419-421-3392. FAX: 419-421-3578. Web Site: mweb.fdy.mol.com/. *Librn*, Kim Haley; E-Mail: kkhaley@marathonoil.com; Staff 2 (MLS 1, Non-MLS 1)
Founded 1930
1999-2000 Mats Exp $197,000, Books $177,000, Per/Ser (Incl. Access Fees) $20,000. Sal $34,000
Library Holdings: Bk Vols 12,000
Subject Interests: Energy law

C THE UNIVERSITY OF FINDLAY, Shafer Library, 1000 N Main St, 45840-3695. SAN 313-5047. Tel: 419-424-4627. FAX: 419-424-4822. *Dir*, Robert W Schirmer; E-Mail: schirmer@lucy.findley.edu; *Ref*, Naomi Adams; *Per*, Nancy Bickford; *Doc*, Geri Finn; *Publ Servs*, Chab Guthrie; *Tech Servs*, Mairi Meredith; *Circ*, Caroline Moore; *Acq*, Jenny Richards; Staff 10 (MLS 5, Non-MLS 5)
Founded 1882. Enrl 2,157; Fac 176; Highest Degree: Master
Library Holdings: Bk Vols 136,000; Bk Titles 82,000; Per Subs 1,080
Subject Interests: Bus, Education, Environ mgt, Equestrian studies, Fantasy, History, Juv lit, Mgt, Sci fict
Special Collections: Coll of Mid-Nineteenth Century Americana; College Historical Materials, print & nonprint; Congressional Papers (Jackson E Betts Coll & Tennyson Guyer Coll); History of Churches of God in North America, bks & archives; Wilfred W Black
Partic in OCLC Online Computer Library Center, Inc; OHIONET

SR TRINITY EPISCOPAL CHURCH, Ashton Library, 128 W Hardin St, 45840. SAN 328-4883. Tel: 419-422-3214, 419-422-3219.
Library Holdings: Bk Titles 650
Subject Interests: Christianity
Open 8:30-12:30

R WINEBRENNER THEOLOGICAL SEMINARY LIBRARY, 701 E Melrose Ave, PO Box 478, 45839. SAN 313-5071. Tel: 419-422-4824, Ext 161. Toll Free Tel: 800-992-4987. FAX: 419-422-3999. E-Mail: wts@winebrenner.edu. Web Site: www.winebrenner.edu. *Dir*, Gene Crutsinger; *Dir Libr Serv*, Kimball Winters; Tel: 419-422-4824, Ext 163, E-Mail: wintersk@mail.findlay.edu; *Cat*, Linda Ewing; *Cat*, Pauletta Henley; E-Mail: henleyp@mail.findlay.edu; *Acq*, Nancy Walter; Tel: 419-422-4824, Ext 159, E-Mail: waltern@mail.findlay.edu; *Circ*, Ellen Mohr; E-Mail: mohre@mail.findlay.edu. Subject Specialists: *Biblical studies*, Kimball Winters; *Theology*, Kimball Winters; Staff 4 (MLS 1, Non-MLS 3)
Founded 1942. Enrl 131
Jul 1999-Jun 2000 Mats Exp $27,331, Books $19,516, Per/Ser (Incl. Access Fees) $7,396, Presv $419. Sal $49,567
Library Holdings: Bk Vols 45,407; Per Subs 133
Automation Activity & Vendor Info: (Acquisitions) Innovative Interfaces Inc.; (Circulation) Innovative Interfaces Inc.
Partic in Ohio Library & Information Network; Opal

FOREST

P FOREST-JACKSON PUBLIC LIBRARY, 102 W Lima St, 45843-1128. SAN 313-508X. Tel: 419-273-2400. FAX: 419-273-2400. *Dir*, Karen Moore; E-Mail: mooreka@oplin.lib.oh.us; Staff 6 (Non-MLS 6)
Founded 1936. Pop 5,700; Circ 17,741
Jan 1999-Dec 1999 Income $87,000, State $85,000, Locally Generated Income $2,000. Mats Exp $12,500, Books $11,000, Per/Ser (Incl. Access Fees) $1,500. Sal $38,000
Library Holdings: Bk Vols 12,244
Automation Activity & Vendor Info: (Cataloging) epixtech, inc.; (Circulation) epixtech, inc.; (OPAC) epixtech, inc.
Database Vendor: Ebsco - EbscoHost, epixtech, inc.
Friends of the Library Group

FORT RECOVERY

P FORT RECOVERY PUBLIC LIBRARY, 113 N Wayne St, 45846. (Mail add: PO Box 309, 45846-0309), SAN 313-5098. Tel: 419-375-2869. FAX: 419-375-2525. *Librn*, Mary Lou Kramer; Staff 5 (Non-MLS 5)
Founded 1928. Circ 108,313
Library Holdings: Bk Vols 47,939
Partic in Western Ohio Regional Libr Develop Syst

FOSTORIA

P KAUBISCH MEMORIAL PUBLIC LIBRARY,* 205 Perry St, 44830-2265. SAN 313-5101. Tel: 419-435-2813. FAX: 419-435-5350. E-Mail: kaubisch@oplin.lib.oh.us. Web Site: www.library.norweld.lib.oh.us/kaubisch. *Dir*, Doris Ann Norris; *Assoc Dir*, Dee Conine; *Assoc Dir*, Kristi Smith; *Ch Servs*, Roxanne Rinehart; Staff 8 (MLS 1, Non-MLS 7)
Founded 1892. Pop 25,000
Library Holdings: Bk Titles 65,000; Per Subs 400
Partic in Ky-Ohio-Mich Regional Med Libr

FRANKLIN

P FRANKLIN PUBLIC LIBRARY, 400 Anderson St, 45005-2494. SAN 313-511X. Tel: 513-746-2896. FAX: 513-746-2847. Web Site: www.franklin.lib.oh.us. *Librn*, Mary S Novak; E-Mail: novakma@oplin.lib.oh.us; *Asst Dir*, Sally Pearson; Staff 16 (MLS 4, Non-MLS 12)
Founded 1923. Pop 42,000; Circ 335,743
Jan 1999-Dec 1999 Income $1,413,821, State $1,306,607, Other $107,214. Mats Exp $227,887, Books $164,744, Per/Ser (Incl. Access Fees) $18,041, AV Equip $27,344, Other Print Mats $5,526, Electronic Ref Mat (Incl. Access Fees) $12,232. Sal $464,252
Library Holdings: Bk Vols 107,032; Per Subs 342
Automation Activity & Vendor Info: (Cataloging) epixtech, inc.; (Circulation) epixtech, inc.
Partic in Miami Valley Librs
Friends of the Library Group
Branches: 1
SPRINGBORO PUBLIC, 125 Park Lane, Springboro, 45066. SAN 370-5765. Tel: 513-748-3200. FAX: 513-748-4831. *Mgr*, Phyllis Lowery; E-Mail: loweryph@oplin.lib.oh.us
Founded 1990
Friends of the Library Group

FREMONT

P BIRCHARD PUBLIC LIBRARY OF SANDUSKY COUNTY, (BPL), 423 Croghan St, 43420. SAN 356-6315. Tel: 419-334-7101. FAX: 419-334-4788. Web Site: www.birchard.lib.oh.us. *Dir*, Mary Anne Culbertson; E-Mail: mculbertson@birchard.lib.oh.us; *Access Serv*, Jessica Bushore; *Ad Servs*, Karen Vardyan; *Ch Servs*, Melinda Baty; *Tech Coordr*, Kelly Cox; *Tech Coordr*, Nathan Hellmers
Founded 1873. Pop 47,700; Circ 440,186
Jan 1999-Dec 1999 Income (Main Library and Branch Library) $1,850,147. Mats Exp $1,351,016
Library Holdings: Bk Vols 144,197; Bk Titles 103,768; Per Subs 335
Subject Interests: Local history, Pres Rutherford B Hayes
Partic in Northwest Library District
Friends of the Library Group
Branches: 3
GIBSONBURG BRANCH, 100 N Webster St, Gibsonburg, 43431. SAN 356-634X. Tel: 419-637-2173. *Dir*, Mary Anne Culbertson; Tel: 419-334-7101, Fax: 419-334-4788, E-Mail: mculbertson@birchard.lib.oh.us
Circ 39,792
GREEN SPRINGS MEMORIAL, 217 N Broadway, Green Springs, 44836. SAN 356-6374. Tel: 419-639-2014. *Dir*, Mary Anne Culbertson; Tel: 419-334-7101, Fax: 419-334-4788, E-Mail: mculbertson@birchard.lib.oh.us
Circ 11,403
WOODVILLE BRANCH, 101 E Main, Woodville, 43469. SAN 356-6404. Tel: 419-849-2744. *Dir*, Mary Anne Culbertson; Tel: 419-334-7101, Fax: 419-334-4788, E-Mail: mculbertson@birchard.lib.oh.us; *Librn*, Janet Andrews
Circ 32,051
Bookmobiles: 1

S RUTHERFORD B HAYES PRESIDENTIAL CENTER LIBRARY, Spiegel Grove, 43420-2796. SAN 313-5128. Tel: 419-332-2081. FAX: 419-332-4952. E-Mail: hayeslib@rbhayes.org. Web Site: www.rbhayes.org. *Librn*, Rebecca B Hill; Tel: 419-332-2081, Ext 31, E-Mail: bhill@rbhayes.org; *Librn*, Barbara A Paff; Tel: 419-332-2081, Ext 30, E-Mail: bpaff@rbhayes.org; *Res*, Thomas J Culbertson; Tel: 419-332-2081, Ext 23, E-Mail: tculbertson@rbhayes.org; *Res*, Gilbert Gonzalez; Tel: 419-332-2081, Ext 22, E-Mail: ggonzalez@rbhayes.org; *Archivist*, Nan Card; Tel: 419-332-2081, Ext 39, E-Mail: ncard@rbhayes.org; Staff 5 (MLS 3, Non-MLS 2)
Founded 1911
Library Holdings: Bk Vols 75,000; Per Subs 221
Subject Interests: Am hist, Croquet, Econ hist (1865-1917), Genealogy,

Gilded Age US (1865-1917), Local history, Ohio, Reconstruction in the South, US political soc
Special Collections: Abraham Lincoln; History of the United States, 19th-20th Century (Rutherford B Hayes Personal Library); Manuscript Colls (Rutherford B Hayes & His Family, William & Mary B Claflin, William M Evarts, William Dean Howells, David Ross Locke, Benson J Lossing & Thomas Nast); Nineteenth Century Cookbooks; Sandusky River Valley & the Great Lakes
Automation Activity & Vendor Info: (OPAC) Innovative Interfaces Inc.
Publications: The Statesman (quarterly newsletter)
Restriction: Non-circulating to the public
Function: ILL limited
Partic in OHIONET

M MEMORIAL HOSPITAL, Medical Library,* 715 S Taft Ave, 43420. SAN 370-6060. Tel: 419-334-6628. FAX: 419-332-7332. *Librn*, Sarah Hunt; Staff 1 (Non-MLS 1)
Library Holdings: Bk Titles 1,500; Per Subs 131
Special Services for the Deaf - Books on deafness & sign language; Staff with knowledge of sign language

GL SANDUSKY COUNTY LAW LIBRARY, Court House, 100 N Park Ave, 43420. SAN 327-3849. Tel: 419-334-6165. FAX: 419-334-6156. *Librn*, Sharon Hintze

J TERRA COMMUNITY COLLEGE, Learning Resource Center,* 2830 Napoleon Rd, 43420-9670. SAN 313-5136. Tel: 419-334-8400, Ext 318. FAX: 419-334-3667.; Staff 5 (MLS 1, Non-MLS 4)
Founded 1971. Enrl 1,581
Library Holdings: Bk Vols 26,255; Bk Titles 19,171; Per Subs 350
Automation Activity & Vendor Info: (OPAC) Innovative Interfaces Inc.
Publications: Catalogues
Partic in Ohio Library & Information Network

GALION

P GALION PUBLIC LIBRARY ASSOCIATION, 123 N Market St, 44833. SAN 313-5144. Tel: 419-468-3203. FAX: 419-468-7298. Web Site: www.galion.lib.oh.us. *Dir*, Lynn Dominick; *Ch Servs*, Mary L Court; Staff 16 (MLS 1, Non-MLS 15)
Founded 1901. Pop 13,000; Circ 220,078
Jan 1999-Dec 1999 Income $726,209, State $633,692, Other $92,517. Mats Exp $550,331, Books $84,216, Per/Ser (Incl. Access Fees) $6,023, Presv $385, AV Equip $17,832, Other Print Mats $420. Sal $48,300 (Prof $266,989)
Library Holdings: Bk Vols 96,584; Bk Titles 87,276; Per Subs 150
Automation Activity & Vendor Info: (Cataloging) Gaylord; (Circulation) Gaylord; (OPAC) Gaylord
Friends of the Library Group

GALLIPOLIS

P GALLIA COUNTY DISTRICT LIBRARY, Dr Samuel L Bossard Memorial Library, 7 Spruce St, 45631. SAN 313-5152. Tel: 740-446-7323. FAX: 740-446-1701. E-Mail: bossard@oplin.lib.oh.us. Web Site: www.bossard.lib.oh.us. *Dir*, Betty Lambert Clarkson; E-Mail: clarksbe@oplin.lib.oh.us; *Ref*, Rebecca Carroll; *Ch Servs*, Marion Cochran; E-Mail: cocranm@oplin.lib.oh.us; *Tech Coordr*, Renee Geary. Subject Specialists: *Genealogy*, Rebecca Carroll; Staff 41 (MLS 1, Non-MLS 40)
Founded 1899. Pop 32,000; Circ 360,000
Jan 2000-Dec 2000 Income $1,331,737, State $1,169,139, County $162,598. Mats Exp $302,590, Books $218,537, AV Equip $84,053. Sal $532,374 (Prof $122,650)
Library Holdings: Bk Vols 118,000; Bk Titles 96,000; Per Subs 250
Subject Interests: Genealogy, Local history
Special Collections: Genealogy Coll; O O McIntyre Coll
Automation Activity & Vendor Info: (Cataloging) epixtech, inc.; (Circulation) epixtech, inc.; (OPAC) epixtech, inc.
Database Vendor: Ebsco - EbscoHost, epixtech, inc., GaleNet
Function: Photocopies available
Friends of the Library Group

M HOLZER MEDICAL CENTER, Medical Library, 100 Jackson Pike, 45631. SAN 326-2863. Tel: 740-446-5057. FAX: 740-446-5068. *In Charge*, Beverly Jackson; E-Mail: tellison@holzer.org; Staff 1 (Non-MLS 1)
Library Holdings: Bk Titles 750; Per Subs 25
Partic in Ohio Regional Libr Network

GAMBIER

C KENYON COLLEGE, Olin-Chalmers Memorial Library, 43022-9623. SAN 313-5187. Tel: 740-427-5186. Interlibrary Loan Service Tel: 740-427-5692. FAX: 740-427-5272. Web Site: www.kenyon.edu. *Tech Servs*, Donna Wilson; E-Mail: wilson@kenyon.edu; *Info Res*, Frank Wojcik; *Govt Doc*, Andrea Peakovic; *ILL*, Cindy Wallace; *AV*, Susan Kempton; *Circ*, Joan Pomajevich; *Acq*, Karen Greaver. Subject Specialists: *Fine arts*, Carmen King; Staff 20 (MLS 6, Non-MLS 14)
Founded 1824. Enrl 1,548; Fac 132; Highest Degree: Bachelor
Library Holdings: Bk Vols 360,502; Per Subs 1,222
Subject Interests: Liberal arts, Scis
Special Collections: Charles Pettit McIlvaine Letters; Kenyon College Archives; Kenyon Review Archievs; Philander Chase Letters; Riker Coll of William Butler Yeats Publications; Typography Coll
Partic in OCLC Online Computer Library Center, Inc; Ohio Library & Information Network; OHIONET

GARRETTSVILLE

P PORTAGE COUNTY DISTRICT LIBRARY, 10482 South St, 44231. SAN 356-6854. Tel: 330-527-5082. TDD: 330-677-4278. FAX: 330-527-4370. Web Site: www.portagecounty.lib.oh.us. *Dir*, Lawrence Corbus; *Librn*, Kathleen Kozup
Founded 1935. Pop 85,000
2000-2001 Income (Main Library and Branch Library) $2,700,000. Mats Exp $426,089, Books $396,000, Presv $89, Other Print Mats $30,000. Sal $500,000 (Prof $140,000)
Library Holdings: Bk Vols 262,550; Per Subs 541
Subject Interests: Large print
Partic in Nola Regional Library System
Friends of the Library Group
Branches: 6
AURORA MEMORIAL, 115 E Pioneer Trail, Aurora, 44202-9349. SAN 356-6889. Tel: 330-562-6502. FAX: 330-562-2084. *Librn*, Kathy Bullard
Library Holdings: Bk Vols 76,000
Friends of the Library Group
BRIMFIELD BRANCH, 4064 State Rte 43, Kent, 44240. Tel: 330-677-5826. FAX: 330-677-5872. *Librn*, Norma McDonough
Library Holdings: Bk Vols 8,381
GARRETTSVILLE BRANCH, 10482 South St, 44231. Tel: 330-527-4378, 330-527-5082. FAX: 330-527-4370. *Librn*, Kathleen Kozup
Library Holdings: Bk Vols 65,000
RANDOLPH BRANCH, 1639 State Rte 44, PO Box 368, Randolph, 44265. SAN 356-6927. Tel: 330-325-7003. FAX: 330-325-7740. *Librn*, Norma McDonough
Library Holdings: Bk Vols 22,699
Friends of the Library Group
STREETSBORO, 8990 Kirby Lane, Streetsboro, 44241-1723. SAN 356-6943. Tel: 216-626-4458. FAX: 216-626-1739. *Librn*, Cecilia Swanson
Library Holdings: Bk Vols 42,179
Friends of the Library Group
WINDHAM BRANCH, 9647 E Center St, Windham, 44288. SAN 356-6978. Tel: 330-326-3145. FAX: 330-326-2490. *Librn*, Kathleen Baum
Library Holdings: Bk Vols 22,985
Friends of the Library Group
Bookmobiles: 2

GERMANTOWN

P GERMANTOWN PUBLIC LIBRARY, 51 N Plum St, 45327. SAN 313-5209. Tel: 937-855-4001. FAX: 937-855-6098. *Librn*, Robert C Ammerman; *Ch Servs, Librn*, Susan Bantz
Founded 1888. Pop 11,500; Circ 197,469
Jan 1998-Dec 1998 Income $951,514, County $922,636, Locally Generated Income $28,878. Mats Exp $116,587, Books $82,725, Per/Ser (Incl. Access Fees) $25,618, Presv $616, Other Print Mats $84, Electronic Ref Mat (Incl. Access Fees) $7,544. Sal $392,172
Library Holdings: Bk Titles 91,081; Per Subs 96
Special Collections: Local History (Germantown Historical Coll), bks, pamphlets
Automation Activity & Vendor Info: (Cataloging) epixtech, inc.; (OPAC) epixtech, inc.
Database Vendor: epixtech, inc.
Partic in Miami Valley Librs

GIRARD

P GIRARD FREE PUBLIC LIBRARY,* 105 E Prospect St, 44420-1899. SAN 313-5217. Tel: 330-545-2508. FAX: 330-545-8213. Web Site: www.http.girlib.us. *Dir*, Diane Fritz; E-Mail: fritzdi@oplin.lib.oh.us; *ILL*, Heather Walker; *Ch Servs*, Diane Fritz; *Acq*, Colleen Keller; *Cat*, Mary Barnes; *Circ*, Madeleine Kerr
Founded 1919. Pop 35,000; Circ 153,105
Library Holdings: Bk Vols 75,536; Per Subs 184
Subject Interests: Music nostalgia, World War II
Partic in Northeastern Ohio Libr Asn
Friends of the Library Group

GNADENHUTTEN

P GNADENHUTTEN PUBLIC LIBRARY,* 160 N Walnut St, PO Box 216, 44629-0216. SAN 313-5225. Tel: 740-254-9224. FAX: 740-254-9841. Web Site: www.gnaden.lib.oh.us. *Librn*, Marilyn Stocker; E-Mail: stockema@

oplin.lib.oh.us; Staff 5 (Non-MLS 5)
Founded 1936
Library Holdings: Bk Titles 22,197; Per Subs 60
Subject Interests: Early Ohio hist, Indians, Moravian missions
Automation Activity & Vendor Info: (Cataloging) Sagebrush Corporation; (Circulation) Sagebrush Corporation; (OPAC) Sagebrush Corporation

GRAFTON

P GRAFTON - MIDVIEW PUBLIC LIBRARY,* 983 Main St, 44044-1492. SAN 313-5233. Tel: 440-926-3317. TDD: 440-926-3317. FAX: 440-926-3000. E-Mail: aa1419@freenet.lorain.oberlin.edu. Web Site: www.gmpl.lib.oh.us. *Dir*, Mary Crenore; E-Mail: crehorma@oplin.lib.oh.us; *Asst Librn*, Kristine Anderson; *Ref*, Hilda Howell; *Ad Servs*, Dennis I Prichard; Staff 17 (MLS 2, Non-MLS 15)
Founded 1944. Pop 18,000; Circ 200,000
Library Holdings: Bk Vols 59,000; Per Subs 150
Subject Interests: Auto repair, Cookery
Special Collections: Automotive Repair Manuals Coll; Local History Coll
Automation Activity & Vendor Info: (Cataloging) TLC; (Circulation) TLC; (OPAC) TLC
Database Vendor: Dialog
Function: Reference services available
Mem of Cleveland Area Metrop Libr Syst
Friends of the Library Group

GRANVILLE

C DENISON UNIVERSITY LIBRARIES,* 43023-0612. SAN 313-5241. Tel: 740-587-6225. Interlibrary Loan Service Tel: 740-587-6431. FAX: 740-587-6285. Web Site: www.denison.edu/library/. *Dir, Govt Doc, Ref*, Mary Webb Prophet; *ILL*, Ann Watson; *Archivist*, Cara Gillenbach; *Bibliog Instr*, Susan Scott; *Coll Develop*, Earl Griffith; Staff 8 (MLS 8)
Founded 1831. Enrl 2,010; Fac 161; Highest Degree: Bachelor
Jul 1998-Jun 1999 Income $1,869,998. Mats Exp $637,073, Books $319,609, Per/Ser (Incl. Access Fees) $244,843, Presv $17,624, Micro $14,997, AV Equip $40,000. Sal $646,417 (Prof $321,765)
Library Holdings: Bk Vols 347,624; Per Subs 1,214
Special Collections: Geology (G K Gilbert)
Partic in Five Colleges of Ohio; OCLC Online Computer Library Center, Inc; OHIONET

P GRANVILLE PUBLIC LIBRARY,* 217 E Broadway, 43023-1398. SAN 313-525X. Tel: 740-587-0196. FAX: 740-587-0197. *Dir*, Nadine Robson; E-Mail: ncrobson@npls.org; *YA Servs*, Barbara Lukco; *Ch Servs*, Lesley Torello; *Ref*, Kay Bork; *Circ*, Rosemary Collard
Founded 1912. Circ 135,495
Library Holdings: Bk Titles 62,795; Per Subs 187
Partic in Columbus Area Library & Information Council Of Ohio (CALICO)
Friends of the Library Group

S OWENS-CORNING SCIENCE & TECHNOLOGY CENTER, Knowledge Research Center,* 2790 Columbus Rd, 43023. SAN 329-2436. Tel: 740-321-5000. FAX: 740-321-7255. *In Charge*, Robert Lonergan
Founded 1985
Library Holdings: Bk Vols 4,050; Bk Titles 4,000; Per Subs 144
Subject Interests: Chemistry, Engineering
Partic in Can-Ole; Dialog Corporation; Info-globe

S WENS CORNING CORP, Knowledge Resource Services,* 2790 Columbus Rd, Rte 16, 43023-1200. SAN 313-5268. Tel: 740-321-7265. FAX: 740-321-7255.
Library Holdings: Bk Vols 20,000; Per Subs 175
Publications: Newsletter
Partic in BRS; Dialog Corporation; OCLC Online Computer Library Center, Inc; SDC Info Servs; Vutext

GRATIS

P MARION LAWRANCE MEMORIAL LIBRARY,* 15 E Franklin St, 45330-0855. (Mail add: PO Box 855, 45330-0855), Tel: 937-787-3502. FAX: 937-787-3502. *Librn*, Penny Johnston
Circ 5,101
Jan 1998-Dec 1998 Income $78,552, State $67,220, Other $11,332. Mats Exp $13,058, Books $8,060, Per/Ser (Incl. Access Fees) $1,582, AV Equip $3,416. Sal $15,762
Library Holdings: Bk Vols 13,000; Per Subs 55
Partic in Miami Valley Librs
Friends of the Library Group

GREENFIELD

SR CHRISTIAN UNION BIBLE COLLEGE LIBRARY,* 1090 N Washington St, PO Box 27, 45123. SAN 327-6384. Tel: 937-981-2897. FAX: 937-981-2897. E-Mail: cubc@bright.net. *Dean of Libr*, Robert Uhrig; E-Mail: ruhrig@juno.com
Library Holdings: Bk Vols 7,601; Per Subs 10
Subject Interests: Philosophy, Psychology

GREENVILLE

GL GREENVILLE LAW LIBRARY, 124 W Fifth St, 45331. SAN 327-3865. Tel: 937-547-9741. FAX: 937-548-5730. E-Mail: darkelawlilbrary@wesnet.com. Web Site: www.npo.countystart.com/~lawlibrary. *Librn*, Eileen Litchfield; Staff 1 (Non-MLS 1)
Library Holdings: Bk Vols 12,500
Restriction: Non-circulating to the public
Open for public access Tues & Thurs 9-11am & Wed 11-1pm or by appointment

P GREENVILLE PUBLIC LIBRARY, 520 Sycamore St, 45331-1438. SAN 313-5284. Tel: 937-548-3915. FAX: 937-548-3837. E-Mail: greenvll@oplin.lib.oh.us. *Dir*, John L Vehre Jr; E-Mail: jlvehre@bright.net
Founded 1883. Pop 25,000; Circ 264,000
Jan 1999-Dec 1999 Income $778,000, State $725,000, Parent Institution $53,000. Mats Exp $208,000, Books $175,000, Per/Ser (Incl. Access Fees) $15,000, Presv $3,000, AV Equip $10,000, Electronic Ref Mat (Incl. Access Fees) $5,000. Sal $330,000 (Prof $45,500)
Library Holdings: Bk Vols 100,000; Per Subs 211
Special Collections: Annie Oakley Coll; Genealogy of Parke County Coll; Saint Clair Coll; Sheet Music Coll; Signed Limited Editions
Mem of Miami Valley Libr Syst
Special Services for the Blind - Magnifiers; Production of talking books
Friends of the Library Group
Bookmobiles: 1

GROVE CITY

P SOUTHWEST PUBLIC LIBRARIES, Grove City Library, SPL Admin, 3359 Park St, 43123. SAN 356-6439. Tel: 614-875-6716. FAX: 614-875-2219. Web Site: www.spl.lib.oh.us. *Dir*, Frances Black; E-Mail: fblack@cml.lib.oh.us; *Asst Dir*, Janice Niepert; E-Mail: jniepert@cml.lib.oh.us; *Asst Dir*, Judith Thornton; E-Mail: jthornton@cml.lib.oh.us; *Mgr*, Mark Shaw; E-Mail: mshaw@swpl.org; *Tech Servs*, Patrick Crossen; E-Mail: pcrossen@cml.lib.oh.us; *Outreach Serv*, Tonia Hall; E-Mail: thall@cml.lib.oh.us; Staff 15 (MLS 11, Non-MLS 4)
Founded 1891. Pop 110,000
Jan 2000-Dec 2000 Income (Main Library and Branch Library) $5,258,653. Mats Exp $729,450. Sal $2,572,741
Library Holdings: Bk Vols 248,043; Per Subs 372
Special Collections: Local History Coll
Publications: Extra! Extra! (newsletter distributed to the public); Happenings (newsletter distributed to public); The Update (house org)
Partic in Discovery Place Librs; OCLC Online Computer Library Center, Inc; OHIONET; OPLIN
Friends of the Library Group
Branches: 1
WESTLAND AREA, 4740 W Broad St, Columbus, 43228. SAN 356-6498. Tel: 614-878-1301. FAX: 614-878-3454. Web Site: www.spl.lib.oh.us. *Asst Dir*, Janice Niepert
Friends of the Library Group

HAMILTON

L BUTLER COUNTY LAW LIBRARY ASSOCIATION, 10 Journal Square, Ste 200, 45011. SAN 313-5292. Tel: 513-887-3456. FAX: 513-887-3696. *Dir*, Anita K Shew; E-Mail: shew@butlercountyohio.org; Staff 4 (MLS 1, Non-MLS 3)
Founded 1889
Library Holdings: Bk Vols 40,000; Per Subs 180
Automation Activity & Vendor Info: (Cataloging) EOS; (Circulation) EOS; (OPAC) EOS; (Serials) EOS
Publications: Bibliographies; Newsletter (monthly); User's Guide
Partic in OHIONET

M FORT HAMILTON-HUGHES MEMORIAL HOSPITAL CENTER, Sohn Memorial Library, 630 Eaton Ave, 45013. SAN 313-5306. Tel: 513-867-2248. FAX: 513-867-2414.
Library Holdings: Bk Vols 1,109; Per Subs 28
Restriction: Staff use only
Partic in Cincinnati Area Health Sci Libr Asn

P LANE PUBLIC LIBRARY,* 300 N Third St, 45011-1629. SAN 356-6587. Tel: 513-894-0113, 513-894-7156. FAX: 513-894-2718. Web Site: www.lanepl.lib.oh.us/cis/lpl/. *Dir*, Mary Pat Essman; *Librn*, Carol Bowling; *Cat, Online Servs, Tech Servs*, Sarah Alleman; *Pub Relations*, Eugenia Beecher; *Bkmobile Coordr*, Marcella Martin; *Syst Coordr*, Robert Krupphoffer
Founded 1866. Pop 165,466
Jan 1998-Dec 1998 Income $4,959,818, State $4,768,376, Locally Generated Income $191,442. Mats Exp $929,597, Books $728,325, Micro $14,560. Sal $1,629,763 (Prof $886,885)

Library Holdings: Bk Vols 471,711; Per Subs 364
Special Collections: Theater & Drama (CC Fracker Memorial & Kathleen Stuckey Memorial Coll)
Automation Activity & Vendor Info: (Circulation) epixtech, inc.
Mem of Greater Cincinnati Libr Consortium
Partic in OCLC Online Computer Library Center, Inc
Friends of the Library Group
Branches: 4
FAIRFIELD BRANCH, 701 Wessel Dr, Fairfield, 45014. SAN 356-6641. Tel: 513-858-3238. FAX: 513-858-3298. *Librn*, Stephanie Spurlock
Friends of the Library Group
LINDENWALD, 2121 Pleasant Ave, 45015. SAN 356-6676. Tel: 513-893-4691. FAX: 513-893-0111. *Librn*, Stephanie Spurlock
Friends of the Library Group
OXFORD BRANCH, 15 S College Ave, Oxford, 45056. SAN 356-6706. Tel: 513-523-7531. FAX: 513-523-6661. *Librn*, Glenda Rhodes
Special Collections: Smith Library of Regional History Coll
Friends of the Library Group
SMITH LIBRARY OF REGIONAL HISTORY, 15 S College Ave, Oxford, 45056-1791. SAN 329-8027. Tel: 513-523-3035. FAX: 513-523-6661. *Head of Libr*, Valerie Edwards Elliott; E-Mail: elliotva@oplin.lib.oh.us; Staff 3 (MLS 2, Non-MLS 1)
Founded 1981
Library Holdings: Bk Vols 3,176; Bk Titles 3,075; Per Subs 70
Special Collections: Area Newspapers; Church records, birth, death, marriage records, wills, deeds for Butler County; City Archives, mss, photogs, maps; Local Cemetery Records
Publications: Local history books
Restriction: Non-circulating
Partic in Greater Cincinnati Library Consortium
Open Mon-Fri 10-12 & 1-5, Thurs 6pm-9pm, Sat 10-1
Friends of the Library Group
Bookmobiles: 1

M MERCY HOSPITAL, Health Science Library,* 100 Riverfront Plaza, 45011-0418. SAN 313-5314. Tel: 513-867-6458. FAX: 513-867-1613. *Librn*, Diane Stone
Founded 1970
Library Holdings: Bk Vols 2,000; Per Subs 230
Special Collections: Health Coll
Partic in Medline

C MIAMI UNIVERSITY-HAMILTON CAMPUS, Rentschler Library, Schwarm Bldg 1601 Peck Blvd, 45011. SAN 313-5322. Tel: 513-785-3000. FAX: 513-785-3231. Web Site: www.lib.muchio.edu. *Dir*, Rebecca L Zartner; *Librn*, Paula Whitaker; Staff 2 (MLS 2)
Founded 1968. Fac 38; Highest Degree: Bachelor
Library Holdings: Bk Vols 71,275; Per Subs 356
Partic in OCLC Online Computer Library Center, Inc; OHIONET

HARRISON

S AMERICAN WATCHMAKERS INSTITUTE LIBRARY,* 701 Enterprise Dr, 45030. SAN 324-573X. Tel: 513-367-9800. FAX: 513-367-1414. *Librn*, Nancy L Danner
Founded 1960
Library Holdings: Bk Vols 1,400; Per Subs 90
Subject Interests: Clock historical, Hist of time, Jewelry, Repair, Watch
Publications: AWI Library Index; Horological Times

HILLSBORO

P HIGHLAND COUNTY DISTRICT LIBRARY, (HCDL), 10 Willettsville Pike, 45133. SAN 356-6730. Tel: 937-393-3114. FAX: 937-393-2985. E-Mail: mail@highlandco.org. Web Site: www.highlandco.org. *Dir*, Judith B Lindley; Staff 24 (MLS 4, Non-MLS 20)
Founded 1898. Pop 40,364; Circ 394,564
Jan 1999-Dec 1999 Income (Main Library and Branch Library) $1,951,727. Mats Exp $243,937. Sal $567,499
Library Holdings: Bk Vols 129,055; Per Subs 368
Subject Interests: Audio bks, Bus, Genealogy, Investment, Large print, Local history
Automation Activity & Vendor Info: (Acquisitions) epixtech, inc.
Function: ILL available
Special Services for the Blind - Large print bks
Branches: 3
GREENFIELD BRANCH, 300 E Jefferson St, Greenfield, 45123. SAN 356-6765. Tel: 937-981-3772. FAX: 937-981-3772. *Mgr*, Margaret Magee
LEESBURG BRANCH, 240 E Main, Leesburg, 45135. SAN 356-679X. Tel: 937-780-7295. FAX: 937-780-7295. *Mgr*, Carol Gustin
Pop 4,000
LYNCHBURG BRANCH, PO Box 529, Lynchburg, 45142. SAN 356-682X. Tel: 937-364-2511. FAX: 937-364-2511. *Mgr*, Gloria Dragoo

GL HIGHLAND COUNTY LAW LIBRARY,* Courthouse High & Main St, 45133. SAN 327-3903. Tel: 937-393-4863. FAX: 937-393-6878. E-Mail: db9575@dragonbbs.com. *Librn*, Michelle Vanzant-Salyer; Staff 1 (Non-MLS 1)
Library Holdings: Bk Titles 8,000; Per Subs 25
Subject Interests: Civil law, Criminal law, Domestic law
Restriction: Open to public with supervision only
Partic in Ohio Asn of Regional Law Libr

J SOUTHERN STATE COMMUNITY COLLEGE, Learning Resources Center, 100 Hobart Dr, 45133-9487. SAN 325-3260. Tel: 937-393-3431, Ext 2681. FAX: 937-393-9370. Web Site: www.lrc.southern.cc.oh.us. *Librn*, Louis Mays; Tel: 937-393-3431, Fax: 937-393-1890, E-Mail: lmays@soucc.southern.cc.oh.us; *Tech Servs*, Mary Ayres; Tel: 937-695-0307; *Tech Servs*, Barbara Edwards-Aldrich; Tel: 937-382-6645; *Tech Coordr*, Dennis Griffith; Tel: 937-393-3431, Fax: 937-393-1890; Staff 4 (MLS 1, Non-MLS 3)
Founded 1975. Enrl 1,720; Fac 47; Highest Degree: Associate
Jul 1998-Jun 1999 Income $307,800. Mats Exp $103,600, Books $31,000, Per/Ser (Incl. Access Fees) $27,800, Micro $2,500, AV Equip $29,100, Other Print Mats $1,200, Electronic Ref Mat (Incl. Access Fees) $12,000. Sal $138,700 (Prof $65,500)
Library Holdings: Bk Vols 42,100; Bk Titles 34,124; Per Subs 2,349
Subject Interests: Children's literature, Education, Genealogy, Medicine, Nursing, Teaching
Special Collections: Southern Ohio Genealogical Society Coll
Automation Activity & Vendor Info: (Acquisitions) Innovative Interfaces Inc.; (Cataloging) Innovative Interfaces Inc.; (Circulation) Innovative Interfaces Inc.; (Course Reserve) Innovative Interfaces Inc.; (OPAC) Innovative Interfaces Inc.; (Serials) Innovative Interfaces Inc.
Partic in Greater Cincinnati Library Consortium; Ohio Library & Information Network; OHIONET

HIRAM

C HIRAM COLLEGE LIBRARY, 11694 Hayden St, 44234-0067. SAN 313-5330. Tel: 330-569-5354, 330-569-5489. Interlibrary Loan Service Tel: 330-569-5359. FAX: 330-569-5491. Web Site: library.hiram.edu. *Dir*, David Everett; Tel: 330-569-5353, E-Mail: everettd@hiram.edu; *Doc*, Jeffery Wanser; Tel: 330-569-5358, E-Mail: wanserjc@hiram.edu; *Bibliog Instr, Ref*, Lisa Johnson; Tel: 330-569-5363, E-Mail: johnsonlh@hiram.edu; *Archivist, Spec Coll*, Joanne Sawyer; Tel: 330-569-5361, E-Mail: sawyerjm@hiram.edu; *ILL*, Jane Dye; E-Mail: dyejl@hiram.edu; *Media Spec*, Robert Warner; Tel: 330-569-5453, E-Mail: warnerrs@hiram.edu; Staff 6 (MLS 4, Non-MLS 2)
Founded 1850. Enrl 1,199; Fac 78; Highest Degree: Bachelor
Jul 1999-Jun 2000 Income Parent Institution $723,115. Mats Exp $307,068, Books $112,495, Per/Ser (Incl. Access Fees) $167,992, Presv $3,235, AV Equip $4,017, Electronic Ref Mat (Incl. Access Fees) $19,329. Sal $338,237 (Prof $198,510)
Library Holdings: Bk Vols 185,153; Per Subs 891
Subject Interests: Biology, Humanities
Special Collections: Education (Burke Aaron Hinsdale Coll, Textbooks 1773 to present & E B Wakefield Coll), corresp, mss; History (James A Garfield Coll & Henry Family Papers), corresp, mss; Literature (Nicholas Vachel Lindsay Coll & Juvenile Literature Coll 1828 to present), bks, corresp, mss, per
Automation Activity & Vendor Info: (Acquisitions) Innovative Interfaces Inc.; (Cataloging) Innovative Interfaces Inc.; (Circulation) Innovative Interfaces Inc.; (Course Reserve) Innovative Interfaces Inc.; (OPAC) Innovative Interfaces Inc.; (Serials) Innovative Interfaces Inc.
Publications: The Flyleaf
Restriction: Circulation limited, Non-circulating to the public
Function: Archival collection, ILL available, Photocopies available, Reference services available, Some telephone reference
Partic in Cleveland Area Metropolitan Library System; Ohio Library & Information Network; OHIONET
Friends of the Library Group

HOLGATE

P HOLGATE COMMUNITY LIBRARY,* 204 Railway Ave, 43527. SAN 313-5349. Tel: 419-264-7965. *Librn*, Lynn Swary
Founded 1921. Pop 3,000; Circ 31,273
Library Holdings: Bk Titles 21,948; Per Subs 170
Partic in Northwest Library District

HOMER

P HOMER PUBLIC LIBRARY, 385 South St NW, PO Box 49, 43027. SAN 313-5357. Tel: 740-892-2020. FAX: 740-892-2036. E-Mail: homer@oplin.lib.oh.us. Web Site: www.homer.lib.oh.us. *Dir*, Chet Geiger; E-Mail: geigerch@oplin.lib.oh.us; Staff 3 (Non-MLS 3)
Founded 1895. Circ 30,000
Library Holdings: Bk Vols 31,000; Bk Titles 30,000; Per Subs 115
Subject Interests: Agriculture
Automation Activity & Vendor Info: (Circulation) Sagebrush Corporation; (OPAC) Sagebrush Corporation
Database Vendor: Ebsco - EbscoHost

HOWARD

S LEOPOLD STOKOWSKI SOCIETY OF AMERICA ARCHIVE,* 70 Greenfield Ct, 43028. SAN 374-9266. Tel: 740-392-5772. FAX: 740-392-5772. Web Site: classical.net. *Pres*, Robert M Stumpf; E-Mail: stumpf@ecr.net

HUBBARD

P HUBBARD PUBLIC LIBRARY, 436 W Liberty St, 44425-1793. SAN 313-5365. Tel: 330-534-3512. FAX: 330-534-7836. Web Site: www.hubbard.lib.oh.us. *Dir*, Ruth Mizik; E-Mail: mizikru@oplin.lib.oh.us; *Asst Dir, Ref*, Lorraine Atwood; *Ch Servs*, Mary Anne Russo; *Tech Servs*, Gerraldine Leach; Staff 5 (MLS 5)
Founded 1937. Pop 16,520; Circ 221,341
Jan 1999-Dec 1999 Income $923,508. Mats Exp $149,956, Books $96,078, Per/Ser (Incl. Access Fees) $23,900, Presv $500, Micro $1,350, Other Print Mats $100. Sal $382,381 (Prof $238,293)
Library Holdings: Bk Vols 72,731; Bk Titles 59,206; Per Subs 176
Automation Activity & Vendor Info: (Cataloging) Follett; (Circulation) Follett; (OPAC) Follett
Database Vendor: Ebsco - EbscoHost
Publications: Library Link (Newsletter)
Mem of NOLA Regional Libr Syst
Partic in Ohio Pub Libr Info Network
Friends of the Library Group

HUDSON

P HUDSON LIBRARY & HISTORICAL SOCIETY, 22 Aurora St, 44236-2947. SAN 313-5373. Tel: 330-653-6658. FAX: 330-650-4693. Web Site: www.hudsonlibrary.org. *Dir*, E Leslie Polott; E-Mail: leslie@hudsonlib.oh.us; *Acq*, Susan Callaghan; *Head Tech Servs*, Gail Dowell; *Ch Servs*, Halle Bagnalo; *Ch Servs*, Nancy Burr; *Ch Servs*, Lisa Mertel; *Ch Servs, YA Servs*, Marjie Origlio; *Ch Servs*, Jane Spencer; *Publ Servs*, Ron Antonucci; *Ref*, Chris Donohoo; *Ref*, Monica Knooihuizen; *Ref*, Marjie Smith; *Circ*, Susan Malarik; *Ref, YA Servs*, Elaine Portalupi; *Archivist*, Jim Caccamo; Staff 12 (MLS 10, Non-MLS 2)
Founded 1910. Pop 25,000; Circ 385,854
Jan 1999-Dec 1999 Income $1,245,676, State $850,042, City $340,208, Locally Generated Income $55,426. Mats Exp $226,000, Books $200,000, Per/Ser (Incl. Access Fees) $16,000, Manuscripts & Archives $10,000. Sal $549,585
Library Holdings: Bk Vols 130,953; Per Subs 460
Subject Interests: Genealogy
Special Collections: John Brown, Abolitionist Leader (Clarence S Gee), bks, holographs, pictures, clippings
Automation Activity & Vendor Info: (Acquisitions) DRA; (Cataloging) DRA; (Circulation) DRA
Publications: Books to Bytes (quarterly newsletter)
Partic in Cleveland Area Metropolitan Library System; Clevnet
Friends of the Library Group

HURON

J BOWLING GREEN STATE UNIVERSITY, (BGF), Firelands College Library, 901 Rye Beach Rd, 44839-9791. SAN 313-5381. Tel: 419-433-5560, Ext 20652. Toll Free Tel: 800-322-4787 (Limited to area codes 419, 216, 440). FAX: 419-433-9696. E-Mail: firelib@bgnet.bgsu.edu. Web Site: www.firelands.bgsu.edu/library/index.htm. *Librn*, William W Currie; E-Mail: wcurrie@bgnet.bgsu.edu; *Asst Librn*, Pat Antonelli; E-Mail: antonel@bgnet.bgsu.edu; Staff 4 (MLS 2, Non-MLS 2)
Founded 1968. Enrl 858; Fac 42; Highest Degree: Bachelor
Jul 1999-Jun 2000 Income State $251,226. Mats Exp $47,250, Books $22,789, Per/Ser (Incl. Access Fees) $13,455, Micro $4,045, AV Equip $6,928, Other Print Mats $33. Sal $151,190 (Prof $77,710)
Library Holdings: Bk Vols 29,029; Bk Titles 25,035; Per Subs 239
Subject Interests: Firelands of the Conn Western Reserve
Automation Activity & Vendor Info: (Circulation) Innovative Interfaces Inc.; (Course Reserve) Innovative Interfaces Inc.; (OPAC) Innovative Interfaces Inc.; (Serials) Innovative Interfaces Inc.
Database Vendor: Lexis-Nexis, OCLC - First Search
Function: Archival collection, Photocopies available, Reference services available
Partic in OHIONET

P HURON PUBLIC LIBRARY,* 333 Williams St, 44839. SAN 313-539X. Tel: 419-433-5009. FAX: 419-433-7228. E-Mail: hintonan@oplin.lib.oh.us. Web Site: library.norweld.lib.oh.us/huron/. *Dir*, Anne E Hinton; *Ch Servs*, Mary Ann Bevington; Staff 16 (MLS 1, Non-MLS 15)
Founded 1933. Pop 9,229; Circ 134,645
Jan 1998-Dec 1998 Income $743,756, State $373,542, County $169,194, Other $201,020. Mats Exp $113,810, Books $102,061, Per/Ser (Incl. Access Fees) $7,188, AV Equip $4,561. Sal $212,496 (Prof $41,000)
Library Holdings: Bk Vols 52,508
Subject Interests: Art prints
Automation Activity & Vendor Info: (Cataloging) Gaylord; (Circulation) Gaylord; (OPAC) Gaylord
Partic in Northwest Library District
Friends of the Library Group

INDEPENDENCE

S FERRO CORPORATION, Tech Center Library, 7500 E Pleasant Valley Rd, 44131-5592. SAN 313-5411. Tel: 216-750-6607, 216-750-6925. FAX: 216-750-6953. E-Mail: library@ferro.com.; Staff 2 (MLS 2)
Library Holdings: Bk Titles 18,000; Per Subs 225
Subject Interests: Ceramics, Coatings, Glass, Plastics, Polymer sci, Porcelain enamels, Refractories, Specialty chem
Automation Activity & Vendor Info: (Cataloging) EOS; (Circulation) EOS; (OPAC) EOS; (Serials) EOS
Publications: Current Awareness Bulletins
Restriction: Not open to public
Partic in OHIONET

IRONTON

P BRIGGS LAWRENCE COUNTY PUBLIC LIBRARY, 321 S Fourth St, 45638. SAN 313-5446. Tel: 740-532-1124. FAX: 740-532-4948. E-Mail: cirblc@oplin.lib.oh.us. Web Site: www.lawrence.lib.oh.us. *Exec Dir*, Joseph Jenkins; E-Mail: dirblc@oplin.lib.oh.us; *Asst Dir*, Diana C Hunt; Tel: 740-867-3390, Fax: 740-867-4881, E-Mail: Cheblc@plin.lib.oh.us; *Asst Dir*, Jimmie Epling; E-Mail: autblc@oplin.lib.oh.us; *Asst Dir*, Larry Stanley; *Ref*, Julie Harris; *Ch Servs*, Cheryl Blankenship; E-Mail: chiblc@oplin.lib.oh.us; Staff 49 (MLS 4, Non-MLS 45)
Founded 1881. Pop 61,834; Circ 402,481
Jan 1999-Dec 1999 Income $2,411,384, State $2,295,882, Locally Generated Income $40,851, Other $74,651. Mats Exp $309,163, Books $230,367, Per/Ser (Incl. Access Fees) $25,084. Sal $814,196
Library Holdings: Bk Vols 141,133; Bk Titles 128,604; Per Subs 293
Subject Interests: Genealogy, Local history
Automation Activity & Vendor Info: (Cataloging) TLC; (Circulation) TLC
Publications: Book Mark (Newsletter)
Mem of Ohio Valley Area Librs
Special Services for the Blind - Lending of low vision aids; Talking bks & player equipment
Friends of the Library Group
Bookmobiles: 1

L LAWRENCE COUNTY BAR & LAW LIBRARY ASSOCIATION,* Laurence County Courthouse, Fourth Floor Annex, 45638-1586. SAN 313-5454. Tel: 740-533-0582. FAX: 740-533-1084. *Librn*, Randall L Lambert; *Asst Librn*, Sharon K Bradshaw
Founded 1911
Library Holdings: Bk Titles 25,000

C OHIO UNIVERSITY, Southern Campus Library, 1804 Liberty Ave, 45638-2296. SAN 313-5462. Tel: 740-533-4622. FAX: 740-533-4631. Web Site: www.southern.ohio.edu. *Dir*, Mary J Stout; Tel: 740-533-4649, E-Mail: stout@ohio.edu; Staff 5 (MLS 1, Non-MLS 4)
Founded 1956. Enrl 1,651; Highest Degree: Master
Jul 1998-Jun 1999 Income $278,357. Mats Exp $278,357. Sal $203,179
Library Holdings: Bk Vols 23,000; Per Subs 300
Database Vendor: Innovative Interfaces INN - View, Lexis-Nexis, OCLC - First Search, ProQuest
Partic in Bitnet; OCLC Online Computer Library Center, Inc; ONET
Special Services for the Blind - Magnifiers

JACKSON

P JACKSON CITY LIBRARY,* 21 Broadway St, 45640-1695. SAN 313-5470. Tel: 740-286-4111. FAX: 740-286-3438. *Dir*, Margaret Cochran; *Ch Servs*, Laura Thorne; Staff 1 (MLS 1)
Founded 1901. Pop 27,181; Circ 73,210
Library Holdings: Bk Vols 43,609; Per Subs 135
Subject Interests: Appalachian children's books, Genealogy, Jackson County hist
Special Collections: Appalachian Children's Books; Jackson County History & Genealogy

L JACKSON COUNTY LAW LIBRARY,* PO Box 882, 45640. SAN 327-3687. Tel: 740-286-2486.

JEFFERSON

L ASHTABULA COUNTY LAW LIBRARY ASSOCIATION,* County Courthouse, 44047. SAN 372-1957. Tel: 440-576-3690. FAX: 440-576-5106. *Librn*, Vickie Lee Brown
Library Holdings: Bk Vols 40,000; Per Subs 10

S DEZIGN HOUSE LIBRARY,* 4090 Lenox-New Lyme Rd, PO Box 188, 44047. SAN 313-3370. Tel: 440-294-2778. *Dir*, Ramon J Elias
Founded 1953
Library Holdings: Bk Titles 9,500
Special Collections: (Pitonak Coll); Design Coll (American, European & Japanese); History of Hawkesworth Family from 1608 (Hawkesworth Coll); Real Estate Documents of Pitonak Family; Socio-Geographical Influences of Two Families, mss; Theatre & Archaeology Coll, bks, docs

P HENDERSON MEMORIAL PUBLIC LIBRARY, 54 E Jefferson St, 44047-1198. SAN 313-5489. Tel: 440-576-3761. FAX: 440-576-8402. Web Site: www.henderson.lib.oh.us. *Dir*, Janet Moy; E-Mail: moyja@oplin.lib.oh.us; Staff 5 (MLS 3, Non-MLS 2)
Founded 1883. Pop 10,000; Circ 130,000
Jan 1999-Dec 1999 Income $430,811, City $25,249, Federal $308,037, Locally Generated Income $46,833, Other $50,692. Mats Exp $74,853, Books $57,616, Per/Ser (Incl. Access Fees) $8,238, Presv $1,218, AV Equip $7,781. Sal $167,737 (Prof $60,526)
Library Holdings: Bk Vols 50,000; Per Subs 150
Subject Interests: Career, History, Jobs, Large print, Quilts
Special Collections: Local History (Jefferson Gazette Coll), microfilm, archives
Automation Activity & Vendor Info: (Circulation) epixtech, inc.; (OPAC) epixtech, inc.
Database Vendor: Ebsco - EbscoHost
Partic in Coun of Ashtabula County Librs; Nola Regional Library System
Friends of the Library Group

JOHNSTOWN

S PUDDING HOUSE WRITERS INNVOATION CENTER, Bosveld Library on Applied Poetry, Pudding House, 60 N Main St, 43031. SAN 326-3541. Tel: 740-967-6060. E-Mail: pudding@johnstown.net. Web Site: www.puddinghouse.com. *Dir*, Jennifer Bosveld; Staff 1 (MLS 1)
Founded 1978
Library Holdings: Bk Titles 4,000
Subject Interests: Creative writing, Health educ, Poetry, Social justice, Writing
Special Collections: Ohio Poetry Therapy Center, Association for Applied Poetry, Pudding House Publications
Publications: Pudding Magazine: The International Journal of Applied Poetry
Restriction: By appointment only, Private library
Function: Research library

KENT

P KENT FREE LIBRARY, 312 W Main, 44240-2493. SAN 313-5497. Tel: 330-673-3384, 330-673-4414. TDD: 330-677-4278. FAX: 330-673-4893. Web Site: www.kentfreelibrary.org. *Dir*, Carmen Z Celigoj; *Asst Dir*, Van Victoria; *Asst Dir*, James Freeman; *Ch Servs*, H Noreen Bobersky; *Ch Servs*, Margy Warnicke; Staff 27 (MLS 7, Non-MLS 20)
Founded 1892. Pop 26,164
Jan 1999-Dec 1999 Income $1,701,491. Mats Exp $1,300,948, Books $343,170, Per/Ser (Incl. Access Fees) $20,990. Sal $511,452
Library Holdings: Bk Titles 164,221; Per Subs 364
Database Vendor: DRA
Partic in Nola Regional Library System

C KENT STATE UNIVERSITY LIBRARIES & MEDIA SERVICES, PO Box 5190, 44242-0001. SAN 356-7001. Tel: 330-672-2962. Interlibrary Loan Service Tel: 330-672-2670. FAX: 330-672-4811. Interlibrary Loan Service FAX: 330-672-2265. Web Site: www.library.kent.edu/. *Dean of Libr*, Mark Weber; *Archivist, Spec Coll*, Nancy Birk; *Bibliog Instr, Ref*, Barbara Schloman; *Cat*, Margaret Mauer; *Coll Develop*, Jeff Gatten; *Govt Doc*, Rosemary Harrick; *Syst Coordr*, Tom Klingler; Staff 52 (MLS 28, Non-MLS 24)
Founded 1913. Enrl 21,653; Fac 621; Highest Degree: Doctorate
Jul 1999-Jun 2000 Mats Exp $2,767,411, Books $527,774, Per/Ser (Incl. Access Fees) $2,105,576, Presv $83,719, Other Print Mats $16,926. Sal $4,097,884 (Prof $2,590,675)
Library Holdings: Bk Vols 2,127,096; Per Subs 10,899
Special Collections: 19th & 20th Century American Literature; Borowitz True Crime Coll; Contemporary American Poetry - especially James Broughton, Robert Duncan, Robert Frost, W C Williams; History of Books & Printing; Local Historical Archives; May 4 Coll; Open Theater; Queen Marie of Rumania; University Archives
Automation Activity & Vendor Info: (Acquisitions) Innovative Interfaces Inc.; (Cataloging) Innovative Interfaces Inc.; (Circulation) Innovative Interfaces Inc.; (Course Reserve) Innovative Interfaces Inc.; (ILL) Innovative Interfaces Inc.; (OPAC) Innovative Interfaces Inc.; (Serials) Innovative Interfaces Inc.
Publications: Matrix (1987-1991); The Serif (1963-1974)
Partic in Center For Research Libraries; Dialog Corporation; OCLC Online Computer Library Center, Inc; Ohio Library & Information Network
Friends of the Library Group
Departmental Libraries:
ARCHITECTURE, 309 Taylor Hall, PO Box 5190, 44242-0001. SAN 328-7572. Tel: 330-672-2876. *Librn*, Tom Gates
Library Holdings: Bk Vols 7,500
AUDIO VISUAL SERVICES, 330 Library, PO Box 5190, 44242-0001. SAN 356-7036. Tel: 330-672-3456. FAX: 330-672-3463. *Dir*, John Kerstetter
Founded 1947
Publications: Educational Video & Film Rental Catalog
CHEMISTRY & PHYSICS, 312 Williams Hall, PO Box 5190, 44242-0001. SAN 356-7044. Tel: 330-672-2532. *Head Librn*, Raghini Suresh
Library Holdings: Bk Vols 45,000; Per Subs 450
Subject Interests: Biochemistry, Chemistry, Liquid crystal, Physics
FASHION, 131 Rockwell Hall, 44242-0001. SAN 377-6344. Tel: 330-672-9500. *Librn*, Tom Gates
MAP, 406 McGilvery Hall, PO Box 5190, 44242-0001. SAN 356-701X. Tel: 330-672-2017.
Library Holdings: Bk Vols 2,035
Subject Interests: Climate, Geography, Geology, Soils, Topography, Urban geog
Special Collections: California AAA Map Coll (Depository); Sanborn Insurance Map & Atlas Coll
Map Library holdings, Geodex AGS-(Milwaukee)
MATHEMATICS, 313 Mathematics & Computer Science Bldg, PO Box 5190, 44242-0001. SAN 356-7028. Tel: 330-672-2430. FAX: 330-672-7824.
Library Holdings: Bk Vols 12,600
MUSIC, PO Box 5190, 44242-0001. SAN 356-7052. Tel: 330-672-2004. *Librn*, Mary DuMont
Library Holdings: Per Subs 150
Special Collections: Choralist Coll

S NATIONAL ASSOCIATION FOR CORE CURRICULUM, INC, 1640 Franklin Ave, Ste 104, 44240-4324. SAN 370-6575. Tel: 330-677-5008. FAX: 330-677-5008. *In Charge*, Dr Gordon F Vars; E-Mail: gvarsnacc@aol.com
Founded 1953
Library Holdings: Bk Titles 400
Special Collections: Curriculum Guides
Publications: The Core Teacher (quarterly newsletter)

KENTON

P MARY LOU JOHNSON HARDIN COUNTY DISTRICT LIBRARY, 325 E Columbus St, 43326-1546. SAN 313-5500. Tel: 419-673-2278. FAX: 419-674-4321. Web Site: www.library.norweld.lib.oh.us/kenton. *Dir*, Sue Wright-Petty; E-Mail: spettysu@oplin.lib.oh.us; *Asst Dir*, Sharon Newman; *Cat*, Jeri Newman; *Ch Servs*, Alexa Burke; *Circ*, Sandy Thompson; Staff 2 (MLS 2)
Founded 1853. Pop 34,000
Library Holdings: Bk Vols 72,098; Per Subs 180
Subject Interests: Genealogy
Special Collections: Circulating Hand Puppets
Partic in Northwest Library District; Norweld

KETTERING

CR KETTERING COLLEGE OF MEDICAL ARTS, Learning Resources Center, 3737 Southern Blvd, 45429-1299. SAN 356-7060. Tel: 937-297-8053. FAX: 937-296-7861. Web Site: www.kcma.edu/library. *Dir*, Ellen Rohmiller; E-Mail: ellen.rohmiller@kmcnetwork.org; *ILL*, Renate Hannaford; E-Mail: renate.hannaford@kmcnetwork.org; Staff 3 (MLS 2, Non-MLS 1)
Founded 1967. Enrl 473; Fac 40; Highest Degree: Bachelor
Jan 1999-Dec 1999 Income $250,000. Mats Exp $57,500, Books $20,000, Per/Ser (Incl. Access Fees) $27,000, Presv $1,000, Micro $9,500. Sal $116,402 (Prof $64,646)
Library Holdings: Bk Vols 26,401; Bk Titles 24,065; Per Subs 253
Subject Interests: Allied health, Nursing, Seventh-Day Adventists
Automation Activity & Vendor Info: (Cataloging) Innovative Interfaces Inc.; (Circulation) Innovative Interfaces Inc.; (OPAC) Innovative Interfaces Inc.; (Serials) Innovative Interfaces Inc.
Database Vendor: Ebsco - EbscoHost, GaleNet, IAC - Info Trac, ProQuest
Partic in Ohio Library & Information Network; OHIONET; Southwestern Ohio Council For Higher Education
Departmental Libraries:
MEDICAL LIBRARY, 3535 Southern Blvd, 45429. SAN 356-7095. Tel: 937-296-7815. FAX: 937-296-4273. Web Site: www.ketthealth.com/medlib. *Mgr*, Jane Buch; E-Mail: jane_buch@ketthealth.com; *ILL*, Cindy Lauricella; E-Mail: cindy.lauricella@ketthealth.com; *Circ*, Donna Lawrence; E-Mail: donna.lawrence@ketthealth.com; Staff 3 (MLS 2, Non-MLS 1)
Library Holdings: Bk Vols 4,000; Bk Titles 3,400; Per Subs 300
Restriction: Not open to public
Partic in Ohio Library & Information Network
Friends of the Library Group

KINGSVILLE

P KINGSVILLE PUBLIC LIBRARY,* 6006 Academy St, 44048-0057. SAN 313-5535. Tel: 440-224-0239. FAX: 440-224-0029. Web Site: www.kingsville.lib.oh.us. *Dir*, Mary L Novak; E-Mail: novakml@mail.oplin.lib.oh.us
Founded 1886. Circ 114,214
Library Holdings: Bk Vols 37,858; Per Subs 222
Subject Interests: Circulating per, Crafts, Current best sellers, Hobbies
Special Collections: Local Estate Memoriabilia; Local History
Mem of NOLA Regional Libr Syst
Partic in Coun of Ashtabula County Librs; Ohio Libr Coun
Special Services for the Deaf - TDD
Handicapped accessible; large-print books & audio books collection; homebound readers' delivery service; monthly collections to Ashtabula County Nursing Home; special collection service to Happy Hearts & Ashcraft Industries (MR & DD); Preschool story hours; class visitations & cooperation with elementary school; community meeting room; special programs as scheduled, "Teddy-Bear Time" Lap-Sit Program for Babies/Toddlers
Friends of the Library Group

KINSMAN

P KINSMAN FREE PUBLIC LIBRARY,* 6420 Church St, PO Box 166, 44428-9702. SAN 313-5543. Tel: 330-876-2461. FAX: 330-876-3335. E-Mail: kinsman@oplin.lib.oh.us. Web Site: www.kinsman.library.org. *Dir, Librn*, Cheryl Bugnone
Founded 1885. Pop 8,057; Circ 85,143
Library Holdings: Bk Vols 62,328; Bk Titles 44,537; Per Subs 190
Special Collections: Clarence Darrow Coll; Dr Ernest L Scott Coll

KIRTLAND

S HERB SOCIETY OF AMERICA LIBRARY, 9019 Kirtland Chardon Rd, 44094. SAN 329-4978. Tel: 440-256-0514. FAX: 440-256-0541. E-Mail: library@herbsociety.org. Web Site: www.herbsociety.org/library/. *Librn*, Michele Meyers; Staff 1 (MLS 1)
Library Holdings: Bk Vols 2,600; Per Subs 33
Subject Interests: Folklore, Herbs, Horticulture
Special Collections: Rare Herbals
Partic in Council On Botanical Horticultural Libraries
Special Services for the Blind - Braille

S HOLDEN ARBORETUM, Warren H Corning Library, 9500 Sperry Rd, 44094. SAN 313-6116. Tel: 440-256-1110. FAX: 440-256-5836. E-Mail: holdlib@holdenarb.org. Web Site: www.holdenarb.org. *Librn*, Nadia Aufderheide; *Rare Bks*, Stanley Johnston; Staff 2 (MLS 2)
Founded 1963
Library Holdings: Bk Vols 9,000; Bk Titles 8,000; Per Subs 60
Subject Interests: Botany, Environmental studies, Horticulture, Natural history, Natural science
Special Collections: Warren H Corning Horticulture Classics, 1200 vols
Automation Activity & Vendor Info: (Cataloging) EOS; (Circulation) EOS; (OPAC) EOS; (Serials) EOS
Database Vendor: OCLC - First Search
Publications: Arbor Day Resources (list of materials available for use at the Corning Library); Native Woody Plant Resources (list of materials for use at the Corning Library)
Partic in Cleveland Area Metropolitan Library System; Council On Botanical Horticultural Libraries

P KIRTLAND PUBLIC LIBRARY, (KPL), 9267 Chillicothe Rd, 44094. SAN 313-5551. Tel: 440-256-7323. FAX: 440-256-1372. E-Mail: reference@kirtland.lib.oh.us. Web Site: www.kirtland.lib.oh.us. *Dir*, Jane R Carle; E-Mail: jane.carle@kirtland.lib.oh.us; *Asst Librn*, Cecelia Vlchek; *Ref Serv Ad*, Marcia Koluder; E-Mail: marcia.koluder@kirtland.lib.oh.us; Staff 16 (MLS 2, Non-MLS 14)
Founded 1936. Pop 7,500; Circ 243,231
Jan 1999-Dec 1999 Income $589,415, State $518,017, Other $71,397. Mats Exp $78,058, Books $39,759, Per/Ser (Incl. Access Fees) $6,404, AV Equip $10,587, Electronic Ref Mat (Incl. Access Fees) $21,308. Sal $272,364
Library Holdings: Bk Titles 68,917; Per Subs 190
Special Collections: Local History
Automation Activity & Vendor Info: (Circulation) DRA
Database Vendor: DRA
Mem of NOLA Regional Libr Syst
Partic in Clevnet; Northern Ohio Libr Asn
Friends of the Library Group

J LAKELAND COMMUNITY COLLEGE LIBRARY,* 7700 Clocktower Dr, 44094. SAN 313-6132. Tel: 440-953-7069. FAX: 440-953-9710. Web Site: www.lakeland.cc.oh.edu. *Librn*, Jonathan A Birnbaum; *Ref*, John Lincoln; *Cat, Tech Servs*, Laura Alldridge; Staff 10 (MLS 3, Non-MLS 7)
Founded 1967. Enrl 4,300
Library Holdings: Bk Vols 63,000; Bk Titles 45,960; Per Subs 1,784
Partic in Cleveland Area Metropolitan Library System; Ohio Library & Information Network

LAKEWOOD

S LAKEWOOD HISTORICAL SOCIETY LIBRARY,* 14710 Lake Ave, 44107. SAN 329-9546. Tel: 216-221-7343. E-Mail: lkwdhist@bge.net. *Curator*, Mazie Adams
Library Holdings: Bk Vols 200
Subject Interests: Lakewood, Rockport Township
Publications: Lakewood: The First Hundred Years
Restriction: By appointment only

M LAKEWOOD HOSPITAL, Medical Library, 14519 Detroit Ave, 44107. SAN 327-3709. Tel: 216-521-4200, Ext 7846. FAX: 216-529-7094. *In Charge*, Susan Favorite; Staff 2 (MLS 1, Non-MLS 1)
Library Holdings: Bk Vols 13,879; Per Subs 154
Publications: Acquisitions; Library Guides
Partic in Greater Midwest Libr Asn

P LAKEWOOD PUBLIC LIBRARY, 15425 Detroit Ave, 44107-3890. SAN 356-7125. Tel: 216-226-8275. FAX: 216-521-4327. *Dir*, Kenneth Warren; *Dep Dir*, Kim Senft-Paras; *Circ, ILL*, Jan Mettler; Staff 6 (MLS 6)
Founded 1916. Pop 60,000
Library Holdings: Bk Titles 347,967; Per Subs 600
Mem of Cleveland Area Metrop Libr Syst
Partic in OCLC Online Computer Library Center, Inc; OHIONET
Friends of the Library Group
Branches: 1
MADISON, 13229 Madison Ave, 44107. SAN 356-715X. Tel: 216-228-7428. *Librn*, Judy Grzybowski
Library Holdings: Bk Vols 23,268; Bk Titles 18,200

LANCASTER

P FAIRFIELD COUNTY DISTRICT LIBRARY, 219 N Broad St, 43130-3098. SAN 356-7184. Tel: 740-653-2745, 740-653-2798. FAX: 740-653-4199. Web Site: www.clc.lib.oh.us/fcd, www.fairfield.lib.oh.us. *Dir*, Adrienne Isacke; E-Mail: isackead@oplin.lib.oh.us; *Ref*, Melanie Bucey; *Ad Servs, Coordr*, Jim Maxwell; Staff 62 (MLS 10, Non-MLS 52)
Founded 1878. Pop 119,000; Circ 918,412
Library Holdings: Bk Vols 271,232; Per Subs 483
Special Collections: History of Fairfield County & Lancaster
Publications: Dateline
Partic in CLC; Columbus Area Library & Information Council Of Ohio (CALICO); OCLC Online Computer Library Center, Inc
Friends of the Library Group
Branches: 4
BALTIMORE BRANCH, 205 E Market St, Baltimore, 43105. SAN 356-7214. Tel: 740-862-8505. FAX: 740-862-8505. *Librn*, Mary Lou McDaniel
Library Holdings: Bk Vols 15,404
BREMEN-RUSHCREEK BRANCH, 132 N Mulberry St, Bremen, 43107. SAN 356-7249. Tel: 740-569-7246. FAX: 740-569-7246. *Librn*, Judy Sowers
Library Holdings: Bk Vols 13,537
JOHNS MEMORIAL BRANCH, 116 E High St, PO Box 279, Amanda, 43102. SAN 329-2258. Tel: 740-969-2785. FAX: 740-969-2785. *Branch Mgr*, Deborah S Fields; Staff 4 (Non-MLS 4)
Founded 1987. Pop 800
Library Holdings: Bk Vols 11,083; Bk Titles 15,900; Per Subs 35
Automation Activity & Vendor Info: (Circulation) epixtech, inc.; (OPAC) epixtech, inc.
Database Vendor: Dialog, epixtech, inc., OCLC - First Search, ProQuest
Partic in Cent Libr Consortium
Friends of the Library Group
WEST BRANCH, 503 Lenwood Dr, 43130. SAN 356-7273. Tel: 740-653-2512. *Librn*, Joyce Smith
Library Holdings: Bk Vols 20,374
Bookmobiles: 1. Librn, Brenda Johnson

C OHIO UNIVERSITY-LANCASTER LIBRARY, 1570 Granville Pike, 43130-1097. SAN 313-5608. Tel: 740-654-6711, Ext 236. FAX: 740-687-9497. Web Site: www.library.ohiou.edu/libinfo/regional/lancaster.htm. *Dir*, Susan Collins; E-Mail: susan.phillips.1@ohiou.edu; *Circ*, Tami Walker; E-Mail: walkers1@ohio.edu; *Coll Develop, Ref*, Julia Robinson; E-Mail: julia.robinson.1@ohio.edu; *Cat*, Leah Lucas; E-Mail: ll421797@ohio.edu; Staff 5 (MLS 2, Non-MLS 3)
Founded 1956. Enrl 1,147; Fac 50
Jul 1999-Jun 2000 Income $456,626. Mats Exp $169,320, Books $76,399, Per/Ser (Incl. Access Fees) $34,153, Presv $713, Micro $20,640, AV Equip $32,960, Electronic Ref Mat (Incl. Access Fees) $4,455. Sal $184,638 (Prof $81,253)
Library Holdings: Bk Vols 87,274; Bk Titles 86,400; Per Subs 305
Special Collections: Charles Goslin Coll; Herbert M Turner Pioneer Coll

Database Vendor: Innovative Interfaces INN - View
Partic in OCLC Online Computer Library Center, Inc; Ohio Library & Information Network; OHIONET
Friends of the Library Group

EBANON

LEBANON CORRECTIONAL INSTITUTION LIBRARY,* 3791 SR 63, PO Box 56, 45036. SAN 313-5624. Tel: 513-932-1211, Ext 3728. FAX: 513-932-5803. *Librn*, Billy Bailey; Staff 1 (MLS 1)
Founded 1961
Jul 1997-Jun 1998 Income $62,500, Parent Institution $50,000. Mats Exp $26,000, Books $20,000, Per/Ser (Incl. Access Fees) $5,000, Micro $1,000. Sal $62,000 (Prof $33,000)
Library Holdings: Bk Vols 12,000
Subject Interests: Law

LEBANON PUBLIC LIBRARY, 101 S Broadway, 45036. SAN 313-5632. Tel: 513-932-2665. FAX: 513-932-7323. *Dir*, Raymond J Nienaber; *Ch Servs*, Julie Young; *Ad Servs*, Mary Ann Mulford; *Circ*, Paula Bradley
Founded 1902. Pop 33,000; Circ 261,866
Library Holdings: Bk Vols 101,312; Per Subs 200

WARREN COUNTY HISTORICAL SOCIETY, Museum & Library,* 105 S Broadway, 45036. SAN 327-7283. Tel: 513-932-1817. FAX: 513-932-1817. E-Mail: 76151.2067@compuserve.com, wchs@compuserve.com. *Dir*, Mary Payne
Library Holdings: Bk Titles 10,000; Per Subs 20
Special Collections: Genealogical & History of Warren County & Southwest Ohio in General; Marcus Mote Coll; Russel Wright Coll; Shaker Coll

GL WARREN COUNTY LAW LIBRARY ASSOCIATION,* 500 Justice Dr, 45036. SAN 313-5640. Tel: 513-932-4040, Ext 1381. FAX: 513-695-2947. *Librn*, Jill Montgomery
Library Holdings: Bk Vols 16,000

EETONIA

P LEETONIA COMMUNITY PUBLIC LIBRARY,* 24 Walnut St, 44431-1151. SAN 313-5659. Tel: 330-427-6635. FAX: 330-427-2378. Web Site: www.leetonia.lib.oh.us. *Dir*, Carol G Davis
Founded 1935. Pop 5,000; Circ 65,000
Jan 1997-Dec 1998 Income $204,678. Mats Exp $27,520. Sal $87,000
Library Holdings: Bk Vols 27,764; Per Subs 70
Partic in Nola Regional Library System

LEWISBURG

P BROWN MEMORIAL LIBRARY, 101 S Commerce St, 45338. (Mail add: PO Box 640, 45338), SAN 313-5667. Tel: 937-962-2377. FAX: 937-962-1010. E-Mail: brnmem@oplin.lib.oh.us. *Dir*, Dee Earl; Staff 1 (MLS 1)
Founded 1935. Pop 2,000; Circ 48,000
Jan 1999-Dec 1999 Income $95,000, State $80,000, Locally Generated Income $15,000. Mats Exp $16,000, Books $14,000, Per/Ser (Incl. Access Fees) $2,000. Sal $68,000 (Prof $35,000)
Library Holdings: Bk Titles 27,000; Per Subs 24
Automation Activity & Vendor Info: (Circulation) Sagebrush Corporation; (OPAC) Sagebrush Corporation
Database Vendor: Ebsco - EbscoHost
Partic in Miami Valley Librs

LIBERTY CENTER

P LIBERTY CENTER PUBLIC LIBRARY, 124 East St, PO Box 66, 43532. SAN 313-5675. Tel: 419-533-5721. FAX: 419-533-4849. E-Mail: sleema@oplin.lib.oh.us. Web Site: library.norweld.lib.oh.us/liberty center/index.htm. *Dir*, Mary Beth Slee; E-Mail: sleema@oplin.lib.oh.us; *Ref*, Emily Denes; *Ch Servs*, Arita Mae Silveus; E-Mail: silveuar@oplin.lib.oh.us; Staff 5 (Non-MLS 5)
Founded 1929. Pop 5,400; Circ 19,864
Jan 1999-Dec 1999 Income $491,836, State $171,069, Federal (MEX) $10,705, Locally Generated Income $310,062. Mats Exp $453,519, Books $13,347, Per/Ser (Incl. Access Fees) $2,916. Sal $65,112
Library Holdings: Bk Vols 12,650; Bk Titles 12,600; Per Subs 120
Database Vendor: Ebsco - EbscoHost, IAC - Info Trac, OCLC - First Search
Partic in Northwest Library District
Friends of the Library Group

LIMA

G ALLEN CORRECTIONAL INSTITUTION LIBRARY,* 2338 N West St, PO Box 4501, 45802. SAN 323-8237. Tel: 419-224-8000, Ext 3006. FAX: 419-998-5618. *Librn*, Elizabeth Osborne; Staff 1 (MLS 1)
Founded 1987
Jul 1997-Jun 1998 Mats Exp $24,834, Books $5,845, Per/Ser (Incl. Access Fees) $5,177, Other Print Mats $8,051. Sal $29,000
Library Holdings: Bk Titles 14,168; Per Subs 61
Special Collections: Law Library
Mem of NW Libr District
Special Services for the Deaf - Books on deafness & sign language; High interest/low vocabulary books; Special interest periodicals

S ALLEN COUNTY HISTORICAL SOCIETY, Elizabeth M MacDonell Memorial Library, 620 W Market St, 45801-4604. SAN 313-5683. Tel: 419-222-9426. FAX: 419-222-0649. E-Mail: acmuseum@worcnet.gen.oh.us. Web Site: www.worknet.gen.oh.us/~acmuseum. *Dir*, Pat Smith; *Curator*, Anna B Selfridge
Founded 1908
Library Holdings: Bk Titles 9,400; Per Subs 43
Special Collections: History of Ohio, Local History & Genealogy, bks, micro, clippings, photo, archives, mss; Labor, Railroad & Interurban History (John H Keller Railroad & Lima Locomotive Works Coll)
Publications: Allen County Historical Society Newsletter; The Allen County Reporter

L ALLEN COUNTY LAW LIBRARY, Court of Appeals, Rm 102, 204 N Main St, 45801-4456. (Mail add: 3233 Spencerville Rd, 45805), SAN 313-5691. Tel: 419-223-1426. *Librn*, Bonnie Everett; Tel: 419-999-4272, Fax: 419-999-9938; Staff 2 (Non-MLS 2)
Library Holdings: Bk Vols 24,000; Per Subs 18
Restriction: Not open to public, Private library
Function: Research library

S LIMA CORRECTIONAL INSTITUTION LIBRARY, 2350 N West St, 45801. (Mail add: PO Box 4571, 45802), Tel: 419-225-8060, Ext 2264. FAX: 419-221-1686. *Librn*, Virginia LaPoint; *Asst Librn*, Elizabeth Johnson; Staff 2 (MLS 1, Non-MLS 1)
Library Holdings: Bk Vols 7,800; Bk Titles 7,059; Per Subs 115
Subject Interests: Afro-American, Spanish

M LIMA MEMORIAL HOSPITAL, Health Sciences Library,* 1001 Bellefontaine Ave, 45804. SAN 313-5705. Tel: 419-228-3335, Ext 2211. FAX: 419-226-5061. *Librn*, Betsy A Creeley
Founded 1973
Library Holdings: Bk Vols 1,307; Bk Titles 1,056; Per Subs 60
Subject Interests: Medicine, Nursing, Pharmacology

P LIMA PUBLIC LIBRARY, 650 W Market St, 45801. SAN 356-7303. Tel: 419-228-5113. FAX: 419-228-0955. E-Mail: lima@oplin.lib.oh.us. Web Site: www.limalibrary.com. *Dir*, Scott L Shafer; E-Mail: shafers@limalibrary.com; *Br Coordr*, Candace Newland; E-Mail: newlandc@limalibrary.com; *AV*, Barbara Baker; E-Mail: bakerb@limalibrary.com; *Circ*, Barbara Sprandel; E-Mail: sprandelb@limalibrary.com; *Selection of Gen Ref Mat*, Shelia Collins; *Tech Coordr*, Gary Fraser; E-Mail: fraserg@limalibrary.com; Staff 86 (MLS 11, Non-MLS 75)
Founded 1884. Pop 108,734; Circ 775,017
Jan 2000-Dec 2000 Income (Main Library and Branch Library) $3,941,717, State $3,757,717, Locally Generated Income $184,000. Mats Exp $650,000, Books $585,000, Per/Ser (Incl. Access Fees) $65,000. Sal $1,847,129 (Prof $691,842)
Library Holdings: Bk Vols 287,704; Bk Titles 217,198; Per Subs 501
Subject Interests: Bibliographies
Special Collections: Art-architecture; Dorfmann Coll of Judaic Materials; Jewish Culture
Database Vendor: Ebsco - EbscoHost, IAC - SearchBank, OCLC - First Search
Partic in OCLC Online Computer Library Center, Inc; OHIONET
Special Services for the Blind - Talking book center
Friends of the Library Group
Branches: 5
CAIRO BRANCH, 519 Wall St, PO Box 216, Cairo, 45820. SAN 356-7338. Tel: 419-641-7744. FAX: 419-641-7744. *Librn*, Kim Sciranka; E-Mail: scirankak@limalibrary.com
Library Holdings: Bk Vols 4,100
ELIDA BRANCH, 200 W Main St, Elida, 45807. SAN 356-7362. Tel: 419-339-6097. FAX: 419-339-6097. *Librn*, Sue Wildermuth; E-Mail: wildermuths@limalibrary.com
Library Holdings: Bk Vols 3,400
HARROD BRANCH, PO Box 104, Harrod, 45850. SAN 356-7397. Tel: 419-648-3571. FAX: 419-648-3571. *Librn*, Nancy Gierhart; E-Mail: gierhartn@limalibrary.com
Library Holdings: Bk Vols 3,800
LAFAYETTE BRANCH, 225 E Sugar St, Lafayette, 45854. SAN 356-7427. Tel: 419-649-6482. FAX: 419-649-6482. *Librn*, Marcille Coates; E-Mail: coatesm@limalibrary.com
Library Holdings: Bk Vols 4,700
SPENCERVILLE BRANCH, 114 S Broadway, Spencerville, 45887. SAN 356-7451. Tel: 419-647-4307. FAX: 419-647-4307. *Librn*, Vija Hahn; E-Mail: hahnv@limalibrary.com
Library Holdings: Bk Vols 6,500
Friends of the Library Group
Bookmobiles: 1

S OAKWOOD CORRECTIONAL FACILITY LIBRARY, 3200 N West St, 45801-2048. SAN 313-5713. Tel: 419-225-8052, Ext 2263. FAX: 419-225-8000. *Coll Develop, Head Librn*, Ronald A Hawkins; *Asst Librn*, Mary Bice; Staff 2 (MLS 1, Non-MLS 1)
Jul 2000-Jun 2001 Mats Exp $9,100, Books $4,000, Per/Ser (Incl. Access Fees) $1,100, Other Print Mats $4,000. Sal $59,400 (Prof $44,100)
Library Holdings: Bk Vols 12,000; Per Subs 29
Subject Interests: Behav modification, Forensic psychiat
Publications: Newsletter (quarterly)

C OHIO STATE UNIVERSITY & LIMA TECHNICAL COLLEGE, Lima Campus Library, 4240 Campus Dr, 45804. SAN 313-5721. Tel: 419-995-8210. FAX: 419-995-8394. *Librn*, Dr Mohamed Zehery; E-Mail: zehery.1@osu.edu; *Ref*, Tina Schneider; *Circ*, Kathy Stedke
Founded 1966. Enrl 3,715; Fac 199; Highest Degree: Master
Library Holdings: Bk Vols 80,000; Per Subs 650
Publications: Library handbook for faculty; Serials list; Student assistants handbook; User instruction sheets
Library serves both Ohio State University & Lima Technical College

M SAINT RITA'S MEDICAL CENTER LIBRARY, 730 W Market St, 45801-4667. SAN 313-573X. Tel: 419-226-9332. FAX: 419-226-9818. *Librn*, Sharon Bilopavlovich
Founded 1948
Library Holdings: Bk Vols 1,041; Bk Titles 450; Per Subs 64
Subject Interests: Medicine
Partic in Health Sci Librs of NW Ohio; Medline; Regional Med Libr - Region 3

LISBON

L COLUMBIANA COUNTY LAW LIBRARY, Court House, 105 S Market St, 44432. SAN 327-7267. *Librn*, Jan Morley; Tel: 330-420-3662, Fax: 330-424-7902, E-Mail: jmorley@epohi.com
Library Holdings: Bk Vols 15,000
Subject Interests: Law

P LEPPER LIBRARY,* 303 E Lincoln Way, 44432-1419. SAN 313-5748. Tel: 330-424-3117. FAX: 330-424-7343. E-Mail: lepper@oplin.lib.oh.us. Web Site: www.lepper.lib.oh.us. *Librn*, Nancy J Simpson; *Tech Servs*, Diane Moore; *Bkmobile Coordr*, Toby Kupko; Staff 3 (MLS 3)
Founded 1897. Pop 58,000; Circ 179,448
1997-1998 Income $475,000
Library Holdings: Bk Vols 66,699; Bk Titles 45,102; Per Subs 184
Subject Interests: Local history
Partic in Nola Regional Library System

LITHOPOLIS

P THE WAGNALLS MEMORIAL LIBRARY, 150 E Columbus St, PO Box 217, 43136-0217. SAN 313-5756. Tel: 614-837-4765. FAX: 614-837-0781. *Dir*, Darren McDonough; E-Mail: dmcd@wagnalls.org; Staff 8 (MLS 4, Non-MLS 4)
Founded 1925. Pop 6,500; Circ 140,000
Sep 1999-Aug 2000 Income $500,000. Mats Exp $91,500, Books $65,000, Per/Ser (Incl. Access Fees) $10,000, Presv $500, AV Equip $15,000, Manuscripts & Archives $1,000. Sal $440,000
Library Holdings: Bk Vols 90,000; Per Subs 300
Special Collections: Letters (O Henry to Mabel Wagnalls Jones Coll); Paintings (John Ward Dunsmore Coll); Poetry Hand Written & Framed (Edwin Markham Coll)
Automation Activity & Vendor Info: (Circulation) epixtech, inc.; (OPAC) epixtech, inc.
Partic in Cent Libr Consortium
Friends of the Library Group

LOGAN

P LOGAN-HOCKING COUNTY DISTRICT LIBRARY, 230 E Main St, 43138. SAN 313-5764. Tel: 740-385-2348. FAX: 740-385-9093. *Dir Libr Serv*, Andrew D Herold; E-Mail: heroldan@oplin.lib.oh.us; *Cat*, Audrey Eschbacher; *Cat*, Nancy Johnson; Staff 12 (MLS 1, Non-MLS 11)
Founded 1948. Pop 29,000; Circ 287,575
Jan 1999-Dec 1999 Income $1,039,000. Mats Exp $224,672, Books $164,920, Per/Ser (Incl. Access Fees) $11,229, AV Equip $38,255, Electronic Ref Mat (Incl. Access Fees) $10,268. Sal $207,191 (Prof $35,000)
Library Holdings: Bk Titles 115,590; Per Subs 265
Special Collections: Ohio History & Literature
Automation Activity & Vendor Info: (Circulation) Follett
Branches: 2
HOCKING COUNTY LAW, Courthouse, One E Main St, 43138-1257. SAN 326-4718. Tel: 740-385-4968. *Librn*, John Wallace
Founded 1925
1997-1998 Income $40,000
Library Holdings: Bk Vols 1,500; Per Subs 75
LOGAN-HOCKING COUNTY PUBLIC, 230 E Main St, 43138-1257. SAN 378-1070. Tel: 740-385-2348. FAX: 740-385-9093. *Dir*, Andrew Herald

LONDON

P LONDON PUBLIC LIBRARY, 20 E First St, 43140. SAN 313-5772. Tel: 740-852-9543. FAX: 740-852-3691. E-Mail: london@oplin.lib.oh.us. Web Site: www.london.lib.oh.us. *Dir*, Anne Shepherd; *Asst Dir*, Gary Branson; Staff 14 (MLS 2, Non-MLS 12)
Founded 1905. Pop 11,500; Circ 110,000
Library Holdings: Bk Vols 38,000; Bk Titles 36,158; Per Subs 106; High Interest/Low Vocabulary Bk Vols 25; Bks on Deafness & Sign Lang 15
Automation Activity & Vendor Info: (Cataloging) Gaylord; (Circulation) Gaylord
Database Vendor: CARL, Ebsco - EbscoHost, Wilson - Wilson Web
Partic in Miami Valley Librs
Friends of the Library Group

GL MADISON COUNTY LAW LIBRARY, One N Main, Rm 205, 43140-1068. SAN 313-5780. Tel: 740-852-9515. FAX: 740-852-7144. *Librn*, Janet C Kronk; E-Mail: jkronk@ix.netcom.com
Founded 1903
Library Holdings: Bk Titles 20,000
Subject Interests: Fed, Ohio law, Statutes, Texts, Treatises
Partic in Westlaw

S STATE OF OHIO DEPARTMENT OF CORRECTIONS, London Correctional Institute Library, 1587 State Rte 56 SW, Box 69, 43140-0069. SAN 313-5799. Tel: 740-852-2454. FAX: 740-852-1591. *Librn*, Gilbert Arthur Hurwood; E-Mail: ghurwood@aol.com; Staff 9 (MLS 1, Non-MLS 8)
Founded 1970
Jul 1999-Jun 2000 Mats Exp $11,500, Per/Ser (Incl. Access Fees) $7,500, Micro $1,000, Electronic Ref Mat (Incl. Access Fees) $3,000. (Prof $40,000
Library Holdings: Bk Vols 17,000; Bk Titles 16,000; Per Subs 45; High Interest/Low Vocabulary Bk Vols 900; Spec Interest Per Sub 20
Subject Interests: Westerns
Automation Activity & Vendor Info: (Acquisitions) EOS; (Circulation) EOS

LORAIN

M COMMUNITY HEALTH PARTNERS, Professional Library Health Info Services,* 3700 Kolbe Rd, 44053. SAN 324-5500. Tel: 440-960-3327. FAX: 440-960-4632. *Dir*, Steven Grove; E-Mail: steve_grove@hmis.org
Founded 1979
Library Holdings: Bk Titles 2,000; Per Subs 130
Subject Interests: Disabilities, Hospice, Medicine, Obstetrics, Psychiatry, Substance abuse
Special Collections: Consumer Coll; Historical
Publications: Library newsletter
Mem of Cleveland Area Metrop Libr Syst
Partic in Dialog Corporation; Med Libr Asn of NE Ohio

§P LORAIN PUBLIC LIBRARY SYSTEM, (LPLS), 351 Sixth St, 44052. SAN 356-7486. Tel: 440-244-1192. Circulation Tel: 440-244-1192, Ext 248. Reference Tel: 440-244-1192, Ext 253. Toll Free Tel: 800-322-READ, 800-322-READ, 800-538-7172 (TDD only). TDD: 800-538-7172. FAX: 440-244-4888. Web Site: www.lorain.lib.oh.us. *Dir*, Kenneth L Cromer; Tel: 440-244-1192, Ext 227, E-Mail: ken.cromer@lorain.lib.oh.us; *Asst Dir*, Joanne N Eldridge; Tel: 440-244-1192, Ext 225, E-Mail: joanne.eldridge@lorain.lib.oh.us; *Mgr Libr, Outreach Serv*, Kevin Breen; Tel: 440-244-1192, Ext 245, E-Mail: kevin.breen@lorain.lib.oh.us; *Ad Servs, Mgr Libr*, Linda Chopra; Tel: 440-244-1192, Ext 275, E-Mail: linda.chopra@lorain.lib.oh.us; *AV, Circ, Mgr Libr*, Elizabeth Fahnert; Tel: 440-244-1192, Ext 257, E-Mail: elizabeth.fahnert@lorain.lib.oh.us; *Librn*, Susan Ballard; E-Mail: susan.ballard@lorain.lib.oh.us; *Librn*, Cheri Campbell; E-Mail: cheri.campbell@lorain.lib.oh.us; *Librn*, Sheila Ives; E-Mail: sheila.ives@lorain.lib.oh.us; *Librn*, Joseph Jeffries; *Librn*, S Alan Schweitzer; *Ch Servs*, Debra Jackson; Tel: 440-244-1192, Ext 240, E-Mail: debra.jackson@lorain.lib.oh.us; *Publ Servs*, Valerie Smith; Tel: 440-244-1192, Ext 254, E-Mail: valerie.smith@lorain.lib.oh.us; *AV, Circ*, Mary Conser; *Tech Servs*, Doris Garber; Tel: 440-244-1192, Ext 234, E-Mail: doris.garber@lorain.lib.oh.us; *Tech Coordr*, Robert Wenz; Tel: 440-244-1192, Ext 233, E-Mail: robert.wenz@lorain.lib.oh.us; *Publ Servs*, Terri Frederick; Staff 82 (MLS 14, Non-MLS 68)
Founded 1901. Pop 120,598; Circ 1,217,674
Jan 1999-Dec 1999 Income (Main Library and Branch Library) $6,935,778, State $4,566,771, Locally Generated Income $1,862,552, Other $506,455. Mats Exp $1,015,284, Books $708,166, Per/Ser (Incl. Access Fees) $90,533, AV Equip $216,585. Sal $2,669,624
Library Holdings: Bk Vols 476,645; Bk Titles 254,897; Per Subs 1,444
Subject Interests: Ethnic studies, Genealogy, History, Large print, Spanish (language)
Special Collections: Census Coll; Ohio History; Philosophy & Religion (Hageman Memorial Coll)

Automation Activity & Vendor Info: (Acquisitions) DRA; (Cataloging) DRA; (Circulation) DRA; (OPAC) DRA
Database Vendor: DRA, IAC - Info Trac, OCLC - First Search
Publications: Dimensions (Newsletter)
Partic in Cleveland Area Metropolitan Library System; Clevnet; OHIONET
Special Services for the Deaf - Captioned film depository; TDD
Special Services for the Blind - Reading edge system
Friends of the Library Group
Branches: 5
AVON BRANCH, 37485 Harvest Dr, Avon, 44011. SAN 356-7516. Tel: 440-934-4743. FAX: 440-934-4165. Web Site: www.lorain.lib.oh.us. *Branch Mgr*, Charlotte Picha; E-Mail: charlotte.picha@lorain.lib.oh.us; Staff 12 (MLS 1, Non-MLS 11)
Founded 1956. Pop 11,701; Circ 116,975
Library Holdings: Bk Vols 38,603; Per Subs 142
Automation Activity & Vendor Info: (Acquisitions) DRA; (Cataloging) DRA; (Circulation) DRA; (OPAC) DRA
Database Vendor: DRA, IAC - Info Trac, OCLC - First Search
Partic in CLEVE-NET; Cleveland Area Metropolitan Library System; OHIONET
Friends of the Library Group
COLUMBIA BRANCH, 13824 W River Rd N, Columbia Station, 44028. SAN 356-7540. Tel: 440-236-8751. FAX: 440-236-8956. Web Site: www.lorain.lib.oh.us. *Librn*, Sandra Mitchell; E-Mail: sandra.mitchell@lorain.lib.oh.us; Staff 7 (MLS 1, Non-MLS 6)
Founded 1935. Pop 7,390; Circ 54,972
Library Holdings: Bk Vols 25,292; Per Subs 86
Automation Activity & Vendor Info: (Acquisitions) DRA; (Cataloging) DRA; (Circulation) DRA; (OPAC) DRA
Database Vendor: DRA, IAC - Info Trac, OCLC - First Search
Partic in Cleveland Area Metropolitan Library System; Clevnet; OHIONET
Friends of the Library Group
NORTH RIDGEVILLE BRANCH, 6401 Jaycox Rd, North Ridgeville, 44039. SAN 356-7575. Tel: 440-327-8326. FAX: 440-327-4443. Web Site: www.lorain.lib.oh.us. *Librn*, Karen Sigsworth; E-Mail: karen.sigsworth@lorain.lib.oh.us; Staff 11 (MLS 1, Non-MLS 10)
Founded 1958. Pop 23,939; Circ 158,587
Library Holdings: Bk Vols 45,789; Per Subs 203
Automation Activity & Vendor Info: (Acquisitions) DRA; (Cataloging) DRA; (Circulation) DRA; (OPAC) DRA
Database Vendor: DRA, IAC - Info Trac, OCLC - First Search
Partic in Cleveland Area Metropolitan Library System; Clevnet; OHIONET
Friends of the Library Group
SHEFFIELD LAKE-DOMONKAS BRANCH, 4125 E Lake Rd, Sheffield Lake, 44054. SAN 356-7605. Tel: 440-949-7410. FAX: 440-949-7741. Web Site: www.lorain.lib.oh.us. *Librn*, Patricia Marsh; E-Mail: patty.marsh@lorain.lib.oh.us; Staff 9 (MLS 1, Non-MLS 8)
Founded 1964. Pop 9,725; Circ 154,521
Library Holdings: Bk Vols 48,284; Per Subs 170
Automation Activity & Vendor Info: (Acquisitions) DRA; (Cataloging) DRA; (Circulation) DRA; (OPAC) DRA
Database Vendor: DRA, IAC - Info Trac, OCLC - First Search
Partic in Cleveland Area Metropolitan Library System; Clevnet; OHIONET
Friends of the Library Group
SOUTH LORAIN, 2121 Homewood Dr, 44055. SAN 356-763X. Tel: 440-277-5672. FAX: 440-277-5727. Web Site: www.lorain.lib.oh.us. *Librn*, Norma Preston; E-Mail: norma.preston@lorain.lib.oh.us; Staff 12 (MLS 1, Non-MLS 11)
Founded 1907. Pop 15,227; Circ 85,799
Library Holdings: Bk Vols 36,362; Per Subs 105
Automation Activity & Vendor Info: (Acquisitions) DRA; (Cataloging) DRA; (Circulation) DRA; (OPAC) DRA
Database Vendor: DRA, IAC - Info Trac, OCLC - First Search
Partic in Cleveland Area Metropolitan Library System; OHIONET
Friends of the Library Group
Bookmobiles: 1

LOUDONVILLE

P LOUDONVILLE PUBLIC LIBRARY,* 122 E Main St, 44842-1267. SAN 313-5829. Tel: 419-994-5531. FAX: 419-994-4321. Web Site: www.loudonville.lib.oh.us. *Dir*, Gayle A Patton; E-Mail: pattonga@oplin.lib.oh.us; *Ch Servs*, Laura Lee Wilson; Staff 2 (MLS 2)
Founded 1905. Pop 10,000; Circ 127,808
Library Holdings: Bk Titles 50,000; Per Subs 195
Friends of the Library Group

LOUISVILLE

P LOUISVILLE PUBLIC LIBRARY, 700 Lincoln Ave, 44641-1474. SAN 313-5837. Tel: 330-875-1696. FAX: 330-875-3530. Web Site: www.louisville.lib.oh.us. *Dir*, Betsy E Ketchum; E-Mail: ketchube@oplin.lib.oh.us; *Asst Dir, Ref*, Barbara Digianantonio; *Ch Servs*, Cathy Brown; *Circ*, Karen Conner; *Tech Servs*, Jodi Maher; *AV*, Kathie Courtney; Staff 4 (MLS 4)
Founded 1935. Pop 13,000
Library Holdings: Bk Vols 120,000; Per Subs 225
Subject Interests: Constitution, Local history
Database Vendor: epixtech, inc.
Partic in Mideastern Ohio Libr Orgn
Friends of the Library Group

LUCASVILLE

S SOUTHERN OHIO CORRECTIONAL FACILITY LIBRARY,* PO Box 45699, 45699-0001. SAN 356-7664. Tel: 740-259-5544, Ext 3592. *Librn*, Joyce Brady; Staff 2 (MLS 1, Non-MLS 1)
Founded 1972
Library Holdings: Bk Vols 13,602; Per Subs 50
Branches:
GL LAW LIBRARY Tel: 614-259-5544, Ext 3592.; Staff 1 (Non-MLS 1)
Founded 1973
Library Holdings: Bk Titles 3,157

MADISON

P MADISON PUBLIC LIBRARY, 6111 Middle Ridge Rd, 44057-2818. SAN 313-587X. Tel: 440-428-2189. FAX: 440-428-7402. E-Mail: info@madison.lib.oh.us. Web Site: www.madison.lib.oh.us. *Dir*, Nancy Currie; E-Mail: nancy.currie@madison.lib.oh.us
Founded 1915. Pop 23,000; Circ 300,000
Jan 1999-Dec 1999 Income $1,063,501. Mats Exp $209,970. Sal $368,500
Library Holdings: Bk Vols 107,000; Per Subs 240
Subject Interests: Genealogy, Local history
Automation Activity & Vendor Info: (Acquisitions) DRA; (Cataloging) DRA; (Circulation) DRA; (OPAC) DRA
Partic in Nola Regional Library System
Special Services for the Deaf - High interest/low vocabulary books
Special Services for the Blind - Talking Books
Home delivery & service to senior center & nursing homes
Friends of the Library Group

MANCHESTER

P ADAMS COUNTY PUBLIC LIBRARIES,* 401 Pike St, 45144. SAN 356-7729. Tel: 937-549-3359. FAX: 937-549-4219. Web Site: ballinbr@oplin.lib.oh.us. *Librn*, Brenda Ballinger; *Asst Librn*, Rosemary Boden
Circ 48,704
Library Holdings: Bk Vols 30,000; Per Subs 42
Partic in South Western Ohio Rural Librs; Western Ohio Regional Libr Develop Syst
Friends of the Library Group
Branches: 2
PEEBLES BRANCH, 157 High St, Peebles, 45660. SAN 356-7753. Tel: 937-587-2085. FAX: 937-587-5043. *Librn*, Eugenia Gordley
Library Holdings: Bk Vols 43,000
Friends of the Library Group
WEST UNION PUBLIC, 212 Sparks Ave, West Union, 45693. SAN 376-9631. Tel: 937-544-2591. FAX: 973-544-2092. *Librn*, Shirley Pell
Friends of the Library Group

MANSFIELD

R FIRST CONGREGATIONAL CHURCH, Bradford Memorial Library, 640 Millsboro Rd, 44903. SAN 313-5888. Tel: 419-756-3046. FAX: 419-756-5834. *Actg Dir*, Deana Vail
Library Holdings: Bk Vols 2,500

R FIRST PRESBYTERIAN CHURCH LIBRARY, 399 S Trimble Rd, 44906. SAN 313-5896. Tel: 419-756-7066. FAX: 419-756-2349. *Librn*, Lisbeth Clever
Founded 1960
Library Holdings: Bk Titles 3,500
Special Collections: Old Bibles Coll

S KINGWOOD CENTER LIBRARY,* 900 Park Ave W, 44906-2999. SAN 313-590X. Tel: 419-522-0211, Ext 14. FAX: 419-522-0211, Ext 14. *Dir*, Chuck Gleaves; *Librn*, William W Collins
Founded 1953
Library Holdings: Bk Titles 8,500; Per Subs 100
Subject Interests: Horticulture
Friends of the Library Group

S MANSFIELD CORRECTIONAL INSTITUTION LIBRARY, 1150 N Main St, PO Box 788, 44901. SAN 313-5942. Tel: 419-525-4455, Ext 3050. FAX: 419-524-8023. *Adminr*, Rick Cantzler; *Librn*, John Babajide; *Asst Librn*, Cheryl Fry; *Asst Librn*, Charity Conn; Tel: 419-525-4455, Ext 4804; Staff 1 (Non-MLS 1)

Library Holdings: Bk Vols 28,000; Per Subs 25
Subject Interests: Criminal law
Automation Activity & Vendor Info: (Acquisitions) EOS; (Cataloging) EOS; (Circulation) EOS
Partic in State Libr of Ohio

S MANSFIELD FINE ARTS GUILD, INC, Mansfield Art Center Library,* 700 Marion Ave, 44903. SAN 313-5926. Tel: 419-756-1700. FAX: 419-756-0860. *Dir*, H Daniel Butts III
Pop 680
Library Holdings: Bk Vols 200; Per Subs 150

P MANSFIELD-RICHLAND COUNTY PUBLIC LIBRARY,* 43 W Third St, 44902-1295. SAN 356-7788. Tel: 419-521-3100. TDD: 419-521-3113. FAX: 419-525-3129. Web Site: www.mrcpl.lib.on.us. *Dir*, Joseph C Palmer; Tel: 419-521-3124; *Ad Servs, AV*, Diane Daniels; Fax: 419-525-4750; *Automation Syst Coordr*, Peter Moore; Fax: 419-525-4750; *Cat*, Marian Benjamin; *Ch Servs*, Susan Roberts; *Coll Develop*, Melinda Garrett; Fax: 419-525-4750
Founded 1887. Pop 131,217; Circ 1,655,647
Jan 1998-Dec 1998 Income (Main Library Only) $5,779,094, State $4,120,648, County $1,353,552, Locally Generated Income $304,894. Mats Exp $773,838, Books $675,878, Per/Ser (Incl. Access Fees) $97,960. Sal $1,960,055 (Prof $1,172,833)
Library Holdings: Bk Vols 355,071; Per Subs 500
Subject Interests: Adult literacy, Found, Genealogy, Grants, Local history
Special Collections: Personal Library of Senator John Sherman
Automation Activity & Vendor Info: (Acquisitions) epixtech, inc.; (Circulation) epixtech, inc.; (OPAC) epixtech, inc.
Publications: News From the Mansfield/Richland County Public Library (newsletter)
Friends of the Library Group
Branches: 7

P BELLVILLE BRANCH, 97 Bell St, Bellville, 44813. (Mail add: PO Box 365, Bellville, 44813), SAN 356-7818. Tel: 419-886-3811. *Mgr*, Carolyn J Applegate; E-Mail: Carolyn_Applegate@freenet.richland.oh.us
Founded 1920. Pop 1,568; Circ 127,959
Library Holdings: Bk Vols 13,370
Database Vendor: Dialog, GaleNet, ProQuest, Wilson - Wilson Web
Function: ILL available
Friends of the Library Group

BUTLER BRANCH, 21 Elm St, Butler, 44822. SAN 356-7842. Tel: 419-883-2220. *Librn*, Waunita Wharton
Library Holdings: Bk Vols 11,997
Friends of the Library Group

LEXINGTON BRANCH, 25 Lutz Ave, Lexington, 44904. SAN 356-7877. Tel: 419-884-2500. FAX: 419-884-3695. *Librn*, Sally Mersing
Library Holdings: Bk Vols 22,964
Friends of the Library Group

LUCAS BRANCH, 34 W Main St, Lucas, 44843. SAN 370-9213. Tel: 419-892-2576. *Librn*, Vikki Eckert
Library Holdings: Bk Vols 10,615
Friends of the Library Group

MADISON BRANCH, 1395 Grace St, 44903. SAN 376-1541. Tel: 419-589-7050. FAX: 419-589-7108. *Librn*, Marilyn Knapp
Library Holdings: Bk Vols 20,801
Friends of the Library Group

ONTARIO BRANCH, 3777 Park Ave W, Ontario, 44903. SAN 328-9842. Tel: 419-529-4912. *Librn*, Patricia Brewster
Library Holdings: Bk Vols 13,721
Friends of the Library Group

PLYMOUTH BRANCH, 29 W Broadway, Plymouth, 44865. SAN 356-7907. Tel: 419-687-5655. *Librn*, Mary Amick
Library Holdings: Bk Vols 12,194
Friends of the Library Group

M MEDCENTRAL HEALTH SYSTEM, Medical Library, 335 Glessner Ave, 44903-2265. SAN 371-6767. Tel: 419-526-8515. FAX: 419-526-8124. *Librn*, Marilyn J Roe; E-Mail: roe.28@pop.service.ohio-state.edu; Staff 1 (MLS 1)
Library Holdings: Bk Vols 1,000; Bk Titles 975; Per Subs 68
Subject Interests: Nursing
Partic in Docline; OCLC Online Computer Library Center, Inc

S OHIO GENEALOGICAL SOCIETY LIBRARY, 713 S Main St, 44907-1644. SAN 313-5934. Tel: 419-756-7294. FAX: 419-756-8681. E-Mail: ogs@ogs.org. Web Site: www.ogs.org/. *Dir*, Robert LaPrad; E-Mail: rlaprad@ogs.org; *Mgr*, Thomas Stephen Neel; *Librn*, Emily Brandel; E-Mail: ebrandel@ogs.org; Staff 2 (MLS 1, Non-MLS 1)
Founded 1959
Jan 1999-Dec 1999 Income $274,371. Mats Exp $25,500, Books $4,000, Presv $10,000, AV Equip $1,000, Other Print Mats $10,500. Sal $66,080
Library Holdings: Bk Vols 20,000; Bk Titles 19,000; Per Subs 150
Subject Interests: Genealogy, History
Special Collections: (pre-1820 settler lineage society); County & State Source Material, mss; First Families of Ohio; Ohio Bible Records File; Society of Civil War Families of Ohio
Publications: Ohio Civil War Genealogy Journal; Ohio Records & Pioneer Families; The Newsletter; The Report

C OHIO STATE UNIVERSITY-MANSFIELD CAMPUS, Louis Bromfield Library, 1660 University Dr, 44906-1599. SAN 313-5950. Tel: 419-755-4324. FAX: 419-755-4327. Web Site: www.mansfield.ohio-state.edu/lib. *Dir*, Elizabeth Burns; E-Mail: burns.152@osu.edu; *AV*, Woody Strohl; Tel: 419-755-4326, E-Mail: strohl.3@osu.edu; *Circ*, Joanne Miller; Tel: 419-755-4350, E-Mail: miller.1188@osu.edu; *Publ Servs*, Brian Hickam; Tel: 419-755-4322, E-Mail: hickam.4@osu.edu; *ILL*, Dixie Barton; Tel: 419-755-4323, E-Mail: barton.3@osu.edu. Subject Specialists: *Humanities*, Brian Hickam; *Reference*, Brian Hickam; Staff 7 (MLS 2, Non-MLS 5)
Founded 1966. Enrl 1,578; Fac 90; Highest Degree: Master
1999-2000 Income $370,000
Library Holdings: Bk Titles 48,000; Per Subs 500
Subject Interests: Education
Special Collections: Louis Bromfield Papers
Partic in Ohio Library & Information Network
Also serves the North Central Technical College

S RICHLAND CORRECTIONAL INSTITUTION LIBRARY, 1001 Olivesburg Rd, 44905-1228. (Mail add: PO Box 8107, 44901-8107), SAN 378-3685. Tel: 419-526-2100, Ext 3215. FAX: 419-521-2814. *Librn*, Rebecca Williams; E-Mail: drc_williamral@odnvms; Staff 2 (MLS 1, Non-MLS 1)
Founded 1998
Jul 1998-Jun 1999 Income $25,000, Locally Generated Income $17,000, Parent Institution $8,000. Mats Exp $25,000, Books $15,000, Per/Ser (Incl. Access Fees) $5,000, Presv $5,000. (Prof $43,000)
Library Holdings: Bk Vols 8,000; Bk Titles 7,000; Per Subs 30
Subject Interests: Law

L RICHLAND COUNTY LAW LIBRARY, 50 Park Ave E, 44902. SAN 313-5969. Tel: 419-774-5595. *Librn*, Traycee Conner; E-Mail: tconner@ridgenet.net
Library Holdings: Bk Vols 19,000; Per Subs 15

MARIETTA

C MARIETTA COLLEGE, Dawes Memorial Library, 45750-4027. SAN 313-5977. Tel: 740-376-4757. Interlibrary Loan Service Tel: 740-376-4544. FAX: 740-376-4843. E-Mail: library@marietta.edu. Web Site: www.marietta.edu/~library. *Librn*, Sandra B Neyman; Tel: 740-376-4758, E-Mail: neymans@marietta.edu; *Automation Syst Coordr*, Angela Burdiss; Tel: 740-376-4537, E-Mail: burdissa@marietta.edu; *Ref*, Kathyanne W Dobda; Tel: 740-376-4541, E-Mail: dobdak@marietta.edu; *Ref*, J Peter Thayer; Tel: 740-376-4361, E-Mail: thayerp@marietta.edu; Staff 4 (MLS 4)
Founded 1835. Enrl 1,099; Fac 85; Highest Degree: Master
Jul 1998-Jun 1999 Income $682,033. Mats Exp $250,479, Books $57,521, Per/Ser (Incl. Access Fees) $167,231, Presv $5,536, Micro $13,387, AV Equip $5,776, Manuscripts & Archives $1,028. Sal $325,847
Library Holdings: Bk Vols 249,800; Per Subs 560
Special Collections: 16th-19th Century Rare Book Coll; Americana (Rodney M Stimson Coll); Northwest Territory & Early Ohio (General Rufus Putnam Papers Coll & Ohio Company of Associates Coll), doc, mss; Notable Personnages (Charles G Slack Coll), autographs & doc; Ohio History & Scientific Coll (Samuel P Hildreth Coll), bks & mss
Database Vendor: Innovative Interfaces INN - View
Partic in East Central College; OHIONET

M MARIETTA MEMORIAL HOSPITAL, Medical Library,* 401 Matthew St, 45750-1699. SAN 373-8329. Tel: 740-374-1455. FAX: 740-374-4959. *Librn*, Angela Hammat; Staff 1 (MLS 1)
Library Holdings: Bk Vols 1,101; Bk Titles 963; Per Subs 70
Subject Interests: Hospital administration, Medicine, Nursing
Restriction: Staff use only
Partic in National Network Of Libraries Of Medicine - South Central Region

S OHIO HISTORICAL SOCIETY, Campus Martius Museum Library, 601 Second St, 45750-2122. SAN 313-5985. Tel: 740-373-3750. FAX: 740-373-3680. E-Mail: cmmoriv@marietta.edu. Web Site: www.ohiohistory.org/places/campus. *Mgr*, John B Briley; *Coordr*, Kim McGrew
Founded 1885
Library Holdings: Bk Titles 500
Subject Interests: Area genealogy prior to 1830, Early Northwest Territory, Ohio, River mat, Washington County
Function: For research purposes

S WASHINGTON COUNTY LAW LIBRARY,* 205 Putnam St, 45750-3017. SAN 370-3223. Tel: 740-373-6623, Ext 214. FAX: 740-373-2085. *Librn*, Juanita Hennigar
Jan 1999-Dec 1999 Income $151,400. Mats Exp $146,402
Library Holdings: Bk Vols 15,050; Per Subs 10
Special Collections: Ohio Law Cases 1800's Through Current
Restriction: Open to public for reference only

P WASHINGTON COUNTY PUBLIC LIBRARY, 615 Fifth St, 45750. SAN 356-7966. Tel: 740-373-1057. Circulation Tel: 740-373-1057, Ext 201. Reference Tel: 740-373-1057, Ext 204. TDD: 740-374-0022. FAX: 740-376-2171. Web Site: www.wcplib.lib.oh.us. *Dir*, Jill Goeller; Tel: 740-373-1057,

Ext 215, E-Mail: jill@wcplib.lib.oh.us; *Ch Servs*, Beata Gustin; Tel: 740-373-1057, Ext 218, E-Mail: beata@wcplib.lib.oh.us; *Head, Circ*, Carol Kulich; E-Mail: carol@wcplib.lib.oh.us; *Coll Develop*, Barbara Wainwright; Tel: 740-373-1057, Ext 210, E-Mail: barb@wcplib.lib.oh.us; *Spec Coll & Archives*, Ernest Thode; Tel: 740-373-1057, Ext 231, E-Mail: ernie@wcplib.lib.oh.us; *Outreach Serv*, Abbie Smith; Tel: 740-373-1057, Ext 226, E-Mail: abbie@wcplib.lib.oh.us; *Head Tech Servs*, Melanie Smith; Tel: 740-373-1057, Ext 211, E-Mail: melanie@wcplib.lib.oh.us; *Head Ref*, Lee Campbell; E-Mail: lee@wcplib.lib.oh.us; *Admin Assoc*, Roger O Young; Tel: 740-373-1057, Ext 224, E-Mail: roger@wcplib.lib.oh.us. Subject Specialists: *Genealogy*, Ernest Thode; *Local history*, Ernest Thode; Staff 68 (MLS 2, Non-MLS 66)
Founded 1901. Pop 64,454; Circ 498,281
Library Holdings: Bk Vols 134,429
Special Collections: Local History & Genealogy Coll
Automation Activity & Vendor Info: (Acquisitions) epixtech, inc.; (Cataloging) epixtech, inc.; (Circulation) epixtech, inc.
Partic in OPLIN; Southeastern Ohio Libr Orgn
Friends of the Library Group
Branches: 4

P BARLOWE BRANCH, 100 White Oak Professional Ctr, PO Box 175, Barlowe, 45712. SAN 378-1216. Tel: 740-678-0103. FAX: 740-678-0046. Web Site: www.wcplib.lib.oh.us. *Branch Mgr*, Anna Henry; E-Mail: anna@wcplib.lib.oh.us; Staff 9 (Non-MLS 9)
Founded 1998. Circ 75,253
Automation Activity & Vendor Info: (Circulation) epixtech, inc.
Partic in OPLIN; Southeastern Ohio Libr Orgn
Friends of the Library Group

BELPRE BRANCH, 2012 Washington Blvd, Belpre, 45714. SAN 356-7990. Tel: 740-423-8381. FAX: 740-423-8305. Web Site: www.wcplib.lib.oh.us. *Branch Mgr*, Carol Clark; E-Mail: carolc@wcplib.lib.oh.us
Circ 111,478
Partic in OPLIN; Southeastern Ohio Libr Orgn

LYMAN POMEROY BEVERLY BRANCH, PO Box 728, Beverly, 45715. SAN 356-8024. Tel: 740-984-4060. FAX: 740-984-2083. Web Site: www.nicl.state.lib.oh.us/wcclient.html. *Librn*, Patricia Graham
Library Holdings: Bk Vols 23,000; Per Subs 90

NEW MATAMORAS BRANCH, 100 Merchant St, PO Box 279, New Matamoras, 45767. SAN 356-8059. Tel: 740-865-3386. FAX: 740-865-2054. Web Site: www.wcplib.lib.oh.us. *Branch Mgr*, Carol Gay; E-Mail: anna@wcplib.lib.oh.us; Staff 4 (Non-MLS 4)
Founded 1936. Circ 29,471
Library Holdings: Bk Vols 12,000; Per Subs 50
Automation Activity & Vendor Info: (Circulation) epixtech, inc.; (OPAC) epixtech, inc.
Bookmobiles: 1

WASHINGTON STATE COMMUNITY COLLEGE, Learning Resource Center, 710 Colegate Dr, 45750. SAN 322-6948. Tel: 740-374-8716. Circulation Tel: 740-374-8716, Ext 401. Reference Tel: 740-374-8716, Ext. 405. FAX: 740-373-7496. Web Site: www.washcc.wscc.edu. *Dir Libr Serv*, Georgene Timko Johnson; Tel: 740-374-8716, Ext 405, E-Mail: gjohnson@wscc.edu; *Librn*, Joseph K Testerman; Staff 7 (MLS 1, Non-MLS 6)
Founded 1990. Enrl 1,350; Fac 48; Highest Degree: Associate
Jul 1999-Jun 2000 Income Parent Institution $287,300. Mats Exp $106,000, Books $18,500, Per/Ser (Incl. Access Fees) $16,000, Presv $2,000, Micro $9,000, AV Equip $2,500, Electronic Ref Mat (Incl. Access Fees) $58,000. Sal $177,972
Library Holdings: Bk Vols 19,200; Bk Titles 18,500; Per Subs 213
Subject Interests: Allied health, Computer tech, Nursing
Automation Activity & Vendor Info: (Cataloging) Innovative Interfaces Inc.; (Circulation) Innovative Interfaces Inc.
Database Vendor: Innovative Interfaces INN - View, Lexis-Nexis, ProQuest
Function: Research library
Partic in Ohio Library & Information Network; OHIONET

MARION

S MARION CORRECTIONAL INSTITUTION LIBRARY, (MCI), 940 Marion-Williamsport Rd, PO Box 57, 43301-0057. SAN 313-6000. Tel: 740-382-5781, Ext 3345. FAX: 740-382-0595. *Librn*, Thomas King; Staff 2 (MLS 1, Non-MLS 1)
Founded 1957
Jul 1998-Jun 1999 Income $60,000. Mats Exp $52,000, Books $35,000, Per/Ser (Incl. Access Fees) $15,000, Micro $2,000
Library Holdings: Bk Titles 15,000; Per Subs 100
Special Collections: Law Library Coll
Automation Activity & Vendor Info: (Cataloging) Sagebrush Corporation; (Circulation) Sagebrush Corporation; (OPAC) Sagebrush Corporation
Restriction: Internal circulation only
Function: ILL available, Reference services available
Partic in State Libr of Ohio

GL MARION COUNTY LAW LIBRARY,* Court House, 100 N Main, 43302. SAN 313-6019. Tel: 740-383-3509. FAX: 740-387-1587. E-Mail: lawlib@on-ramp.net. *In Charge*, Heather Ebert
Library Holdings: Bk Vols 17,000; Per Subs 18

M MARION GENERAL HOSPITAL, Medical Library, 1000 McKinnly Park Dr, 43302. SAN 325-4976. Tel: 740-383-8668. FAX: 740-382-2978. *Librn*, Pam Snyder; E-Mail: snyderp@ohiohealth.com
Feb 1998-Jan 1999 Income $23,000. Mats Exp $11,250, Books $3,000, Per/Ser (Incl. Access Fees) $8,000, AV Equip $250
Library Holdings: Bk Titles 350; Per Subs 167
Subject Interests: Medicine, Nursing
Partic in Central Ohio Hospital Library Consortium

P MARION PUBLIC LIBRARY, 445 E Church St, 43302-4290. SAN 356-8083. Tel: 740-387-0992. FAX: 740-387-9768. *Dir*, Frederick Allison; E-Mail: director@marion.lib.oh.us; *Ref*, Edith Wirth; *Ch Servs*, Suzanne Cline; *Online Servs*, Linda Carlson Condry; *Cat*, Amy L Deuble; Staff 12 (MLS 8, Non-MLS 4)
Founded 1886. Pop 68,051; Circ 417,675
Jan 1999-Dec 2000 Income (Main Library and Branch Library) $5,625,946, State $2,417,098. Mats Exp $2,425,892, Books $327,238, Per/Ser (Incl. Access Fees) $33,507, Presv $165, Micro $1,170, AV Equip $91,362, Electronic Ref Mat (Incl. Access Fees) $8,405. Sal $1,094,475 (Prof $424,001)
Library Holdings: Bk Vols 228,606; Per Subs 370
Special Collections: Marion Local History
Partic in Norweld; OHIONET
Friends of the Library Group
Branches: 4

CALEDONIA BRANCH, E Marion St, Caledonia, 43314. SAN 356-8113. Tel: 419-845-3666. FAX: 419-845-3666. *Librn*, Mildred Vaughn
Library Holdings: Bk Vols 7,815
Friends of the Library Group

GREEN CAMP COMMUNITY READING CENTER, 101 Columbus St, Green Camp, 43322. SAN 370-9302. Tel: 740-528-2412. FAX: 740-528-2412. *Librn*, Marilyn McBeth
Library Holdings: Bk Vols 1,798
Friends of the Library Group

HENKLE-HOLLIDAY MEMORIAL, 86 S High, La Rue, 43332. SAN 356-8148. Tel: 740-499-3066. FAX: 740-499-3066. *Librn*, Beverly Anderson
Library Holdings: Bk Vols 7,613
Friends of the Library Group

PROSPECT BRANCH, 116 N Main, Prospect, 43342. SAN 356-8172. Tel: 740-494-2684. FAX: 740-494-2684. *Librn*, Kim Ames
Library Holdings: Bk Vols 9,290

C OHIO STATE UNIVERSITY, Marion Campus Library, 1469 Mount Vernon Ave, 43302. SAN 313-6027. Tel: 740-389-6786. FAX: 614-292-2103. *Librn*, Betsy Blankenship; E-Mail: blankenship.5@osu.edu; Staff 2 (MLS 1, Non-MLS 1)
Founded 1957. Enrl 4,000; Fac 130
Jul 1998-Jun 1999 Mats Exp $85,000, Books $40,000, Per/Ser (Incl. Access Fees) $45,000. Sal $110,000 (Prof $33,000)
Library Holdings: Bk Vols 41,000; Per Subs 300
Subject Interests: Education, Psychology
Special Collections: Warren G Harding - Norman Thomas Research Coll
Automation Activity & Vendor Info: (Acquisitions) Innovative Interfaces Inc.; (Cataloging) Innovative Interfaces Inc.; (Circulation) Innovative Interfaces Inc.; (Course Reserve) Innovative Interfaces Inc.; (ILL) Innovative Interfaces Inc.; (Media Booking) Innovative Interfaces Inc.; (OPAC) Innovative Interfaces Inc.
Database Vendor: Innovative Interfaces INN - View
Partic in Ohio Library & Information Network

MARTINS FERRY

P MARTINS FERRY PUBLIC LIBRARY, 20 James Wright Pl, PO Box 130, 43935-0130. SAN 356-8202. Tel: 740-633-0314. FAX: 740-633-0935. Web Site: www.mfpl.org. *Dir*, Yvonne O Myers; E-Mail: myersyv@oplin.lib.oh.us; *Assoc Dir*, Evelyn McLaughlin; E-Mail: mclaugev@oplin.lib.oh.us; *Ref*, Mary Maker; *Ch Servs*, Charmyn Doty; E-Mail: dotych@oplin.lib.oh.us; *Circ Media*, Sherry Anderson; *Br Coordr*, William Cleary; E-Mail: clearybi@oplin.lib.oh.us; *Bkmobile Coordr*, Robert Kovack; *Circ*, Melissa Herr; Staff 33 (MLS 4, Non-MLS 29)
Founded 1927. Pop 37,000; Circ 209,614
Jan 1999-Dec 1999 Income (Main Library and Branch Library) $1,188,617, State $1,153,620, Locally Generated Income $34,997. Mats Exp $273,538, Books $190,301, Per/Ser (Incl. Access Fees) $34,763, Presv $1,209, Micro $16,891, AV Equip $8,309, Electronic Ref Mat (Incl. Access Fees) $22,065. Sal $473,771
Library Holdings: Bk Vols 188,902; Bk Titles 141,675; Per Subs 306
Special Collections: James Wright Poetry Coll
Automation Activity & Vendor Info: (Cataloging) epixtech, inc.; (Circulation) epixtech, inc.; (OPAC) epixtech, inc.
Database Vendor: Ebsco - EbscoHost, epixtech, inc., IAC - Info Trac, ProQuest, Wilson - Wilson Web
Partic in Solo
Friends of the Library Group
Branches: 6

BETHESDA BRANCH, PO Box 277, Bethesda, 43719. SAN 356-8237. Tel: 740-484-4532. FAX: 740-484-4532. *Librn*, Karen Davis

Library Holdings: Bk Vols 5,149
Friends of the Library Group
BRIDGEPORT BRANCH, 661 Main St, Bridgeport, 43912. SAN 356-8261. Tel: 740-635-2563. FAX: 740-635-6974. *Librn*, Mary Helms; E-Mail: helmsma@oplin.lib.oh.us
Library Holdings: Bk Vols 9,000
Friends of the Library Group
NEFFS BRANCH, PO Box 405, Neffs, 43940. SAN 356-8326. Tel: 740-676-0504. FAX: 740-676-0504. *Librn*, Shirley Kanzigg
Library Holdings: Bk Vols 4,724
Friends of the Library Group
POWHATAN POINT BRANCH, 158 First St, Powhatan Point, 43942. SAN 356-8350. Tel: 740-795-4624. FAX: 740-795-4624. *Librn*, Nancy Tomlinson
Library Holdings: Bk Vols 2,959
Friends of the Library Group
VICTORIA READ FLUSHING BRANCH, High St, PO Box 214, Flushing, 43977. SAN 356-8296. Tel: 740-968-3891. FAX: 740-968-3891. *Librn*, William Elliott
Library Holdings: Bk Vols 8,542
Friends of the Library Group
SHADYSIDE BRANCH, 4300 Central Ave, Shadyside, 43947. SAN 356-8385. Tel: 740-676-0506. FAX: 740-676-0123. *Librn*, Carol Hranko; E-Mail: hrankoca@oplin.lib.oh.us
Library Holdings: Bk Vols 21,838
Friends of the Library Group
Bookmobiles: 1

MARYFIELD HEIGHTS

M MERIDIA HILLCREST HOSPITAL, Medical Library,* 6780 Maryfield Rd, 44124. Tel: 216-449-4500, Ext 3250. *Librn*, Nancy Lynam - Davis
Library Holdings: Bk Titles 1,500; Per Subs 130

MARYSVILLE

P MARYSVILLE PUBLIC LIBRARY,* 231 S Plum St, 43040-1596. SAN 356-8415. Tel: 937-642-1876. FAX: 937-642-3457. *Dir*, Patricia Amis; *Asst Librn*, Annella Kay Glassburn; *Ad Servs*, Evelyn McCormick; *Ch Servs*, Ellen Gee
Founded 1910. Pop 36,520; Circ 196,393
1997-1998 Income $470,400. Mats Exp $63,000, Books $41,000, Per/Ser (Incl. Access Fees) $11,000. Sal $208,700 (Prof $92,700)
Library Holdings: Bk Vols 64,176; Per Subs 75
Subject Interests: Genealogy
Friends of the Library Group
Branches: 1
RAYMOND PUBLIC, 21698 Main St, Raymond, 43067. SAN 356-844X. Tel: 937-246-4795. *Librn*, Mary Eirich
Library Holdings: Bk Vols 33,933
Friends of the Library Group

S OHIO REFORMATORY FOR WOMEN, 1479 Collins Ave, 43040-1581. SAN 313-6035. Tel: 937-642-1065, Ext 3507. FAX: 937-642-7679. *Librn*, Frederick Gaieck; Staff 1 (MLS 1)
Founded 1959
Jul 1998-Jun 1999 Income $16,000. Mats Exp $13,000, Books $8,000, Per/Ser (Incl. Access Fees) $4,000, Micro $1,000. Sal $42,000
Library Holdings: Bk Vols 7,000; Per Subs 50
Subject Interests: Bks on cassettes, Large print

S THE SCOTT'S CO, Library & Information Services, Dwight Scott Research Ctr, 1411 Scotts Lawn Rd, 43041. SAN 313-6043. Tel: 937-644-0011, 937-644-7506. FAX: 937-644-7075. *Librn*, Matt Hodges; E-Mail: matt.hodges@scottsco.com
Founded 1955
Library Holdings: Bk Vols 500; Per Subs 100
Subject Interests: Fertilizers, Marketing, Organics, Pesticides, Turf mgt

MASON

P MASON PUBLIC LIBRARY,* 200 Reading Rd, 45040-1694. SAN 313-6051. Tel: 513-398-2711. FAX: 513-398-9342. E-Mail: masonpl@oplin.lib.oh.us. Web Site: www.masonpl/lib.oh.us. *Dir*, Sarah B Brown
Founded 1978. Pop 35,000; Circ 280,000
Library Holdings: Bk Titles 95,000; Per Subs 260
Special Collections: Mason History Coll
Publications: News & Views; Pulse Journal
Partic in MVLS
Friends of the Library Group

MASSILLON

M DOCTORS HOSPITAL, Medical Library, 400 Austin Ave NW, 44646. SAN 329-9147. Tel: 330-837-7371. FAX: 330-837-7379. *Librn*, Clare Leibfarth; Staff 2 (MLS 1, Non-MLS 1)
Library Holdings: Bk Vols 1,800; Bk Titles 300; Per Subs 165
Subject Interests: Osteopathy

MASSILLON PSYCHIATRIC CENTER
M PATIENT LIBRARY, PO Box 540, 44648. SAN 321-9542. Tel: 330-833-3135, Ext 1363. FAX: 330-833-7774. *Librn*, William Roberts
Library Holdings: Bk Titles 2,500; Per Subs 20
M STAFF LIBRARY, PO Box 540, 44648. SAN 313-606X. Tel: 330-833-3135, Ext 1367. FAX: 330-833-7774. *Librn*, Mary Blunt
Library Holdings: Bk Titles 1,600; Per Subs 34
Subject Interests: Psychiatric nursing, Psychiatry, Psychology

P MASSILLON PUBLIC LIBRARY, 208 Lincoln Way E, 44646-8488. SAN 356-8474. Tel: 330-832-9831. FAX: 330-830-2182. Web Site: www.massillon.lib.oh.us. *Dir*, Camille J Leslie; Staff 51 (MLS 5, Non-MLS 46)
Founded 1897. Pop 34,949; Circ 546,416
Jan 1999-Dec 1999 Income (Main Library and Branch Library) $2,050,667, State $1,638,940, Locally Generated Income $122,105, Other $289,622. Mats Exp $194,579, Books $169,080, Per/Ser (Incl. Access Fees) $6,319, Micro $1,916, Electronic Ref Mat (Incl. Access Fees) $12,264. Sal $775,137 (Prof $132,115)
Library Holdings: Bk Vols 164,660; Per Subs 184
Subject Interests: Cooking, Gardening
Special Collections: Early Ohio & Quaker History (Rotch-Wales Coll), mss; Lillian Gish Coll, letters, bks, films, videos, clippings
Automation Activity & Vendor Info: (Acquisitions) epixtech, inc.; (Circulation) epixtech, inc.; (OPAC) epixtech, inc.
Publications: Annual report; Check It Out! (Newsletter)
Function: Reference services available
Partic in Molo Regional Library System; OHIONET
Friends of the Library Group
Branches: 3
BARRY ASKREN MEMORIAL BRANCH, 148 N Main St, Navarre, 44662. SAN 356-8539. Tel: 330-879-2113. FAX: 330-879-5574. *Mgr*, Mildred Brainerd
Library Holdings: Bk Vols 14,332
Friends of the Library Group
BREWSTER BRANCH, 245 W Fifth St, Brewster, 44613. SAN 356-8504. Tel: 330-767-9939. FAX: 330-767-0192. *Mgr*, Mary Lou Klein
Library Holdings: Bk Vols 12,645
Friends of the Library Group
WEST SIDE BRANCH, 628 Tremont Ave SW, 44647. SAN 356-8563. Tel: 330-833-4271. FAX: 330-830-3033. *Mgr*, Jamie Inks
Library Holdings: Bk Vols 18,034
Friends of the Library Group

MATERIALS PARK

S ASM INTERNATIONAL LIBRARY, Materials Park, 44073. SAN 313-6167. Tel: 440-338-5151, 440-338-5155. FAX: 440-338-8091. E-Mail: asmlibr@po.asm-intl.org. Web Site: www.asm-intl.org. *Dir*, Eleanor Baldwin; Tel: 440-338-5476
Founded 1959
Library Holdings: Bk Vols 15,000
Subject Interests: Mat tech, Metals
Special Collections: Metallurgy Coll; William Hunt Eisenman Rare Book Coll
Function: Document delivery services, ILL available, Reference services available
Partic in Dialog Corporation; SDC Info Servs

MAUMEE

R SAINT PAUL'S EPISCOPAL CHURCH LIBRARY, 310 Elizabeth St, 43537. SAN 313-6078. Tel: 419-893-3381. FAX: 419-893-3383. *Librn*, Phyllis Gallo
Founded 1958. Pop 400
Jan 2000-Dec 2000 Income $1,000. Mats Exp Books $850
Library Holdings: Bk Vols 1,800
Subject Interests: Anglicana, Church, Religion
Special Collections: Anglicana

MAYFIELD VILLAGE

S PREFORMED LINE PRODUCTS CO, Research & Engineering Library,* 660 Beta Dr, 44143. SAN 313-377X. Tel: 440-461-5200, Ext 9149. FAX: 440-473-9103. Web Site: www.preformed.com. *Librn*, Edwina T Barron; Tel: 440-473-9149, E-Mail: ebarron@preformed.com
Founded 1956
Library Holdings: Bk Titles 5,010; Per Subs 125
Subject Interests: Cable fitting, Communication, Fiber optics, Overhead electrical transmission distribution, Telephone hardware, Termination, Transmission lines, Underground distribution
Special Collections: Electric Lines (International Conference on Large Electric Systems, American Institute of Electric; Engineers, Institute of

Electrical & Electronics Engineers); Experimental Stress Analysis); Strains & Stresses (Society for
Publications: Company Library Bulletin
Restriction: By appointment only

IC ARTHUR

HERBERT WESCOAT MEMORIAL LIBRARY, 120 N Market St, 45651-1218. SAN 313-5845. Tel: 740-596-5691. FAX: 740-596-2477. E-Mail: hwmlib@oplin.lib.oh.us. Web Site: www.vintorcountypublic.lib.oh.us. *Librn*, Katrina Conway; *Asst Dir*, Melissa Steel
Founded 1934
Library Holdings: Bk Vols 46,664; Per Subs 171
Subject Interests: Vinton County hist

IC COMB

MC COMB PUBLIC LIBRARY, 113 S Todd St, 45858. SAN 313-5853. Tel: 419-293-2425. FAX: 419-293-2748. Web Site: library.norweld.lib.oh.us/mccomb/. *Librn*, Debra Grose; E-Mail: grosede@oplin.lib.oh.us; *Asst Librn*, Jane Schaffner
Founded 1935. Circ 74,489
Jan 1999-Dec 1999 Income $339,258, State $314,610, Locally Generated Income $13,160, Other $11,488. Mats Exp $331,293, Books $30,231, Per/Ser (Incl. Access Fees) $4,686. Sal $155,035
Library Holdings: Bk Vols 53,101; Per Subs 117
Subject Interests: Local history
Special Collections: Art Coll, prints; Civil War (Andrews Raiders), displays
Automation Activity & Vendor Info: (Cataloging) Gaylord; (Circulation) Gaylord; (OPAC) Gaylord
Publications: Newsletter (monthly)
Partic in Northwest Library District

IC CONNELSVILLE

KATE LOVE SIMPSON MORGAN COUNTY LIBRARY, 358 E Main St, 43756. SAN 313-5861. Tel: 740-962-2533. FAX: 740-962-3316. *Dir*, Melissa Wagner; Staff 8 (MLS 1, Non-MLS 7)
Founded 1920. Pop 14,602; Circ 120,636
Jan 1999-Dec 1999 Income (Main Library and Branch Library) $441,328, State $407,299, Locally Generated Income $34,029. Mats Exp $88,877, Books $70,674, Per/Ser (Incl. Access Fees) $3,397, AV Equip $12,875, Other Print Mats $1,931. Sal $148,588
Library Holdings: Bk Vols 55,011; Per Subs 118
Special Collections: Genealogy; Local History
Automation Activity & Vendor Info: (Cataloging) epixtech, inc.; (Circulation) epixtech, inc.; (ILL) epixtech, inc.; (OPAC) epixtech, inc.
Partic in Southeastern Ohio Libr Orgn
Branches: 1
CHESTERHILL BRANCH, 7520 Marion St, Chesterhill, 43728. *Branch Mgr*, Janice Wogan; Staff 1 (Non-MLS 1)
Founded 1936
Library Holdings: Bk Vols 5,500
Bookmobiles: 1

MORGAN COUNTY BAR ASSOCIATION LIBRARY,* Court House, 19 E Main St, 43756. SAN 327-7224. Tel: 740-962-4752. FAX: 740-962-4522. *Librn*, David L White II
Library Holdings: Bk Vols 1,000

ICDERMOTT

P PORTSMOUTH PUBLIC LIBRARY, Northwest, 13056 State Rte 73, Rm 12, 45652. Tel: 740-372-8314. FAX: 740-372-4315. *Mgr*, Erin Montgomery; Staff 4 (Non-MLS 4)

IECHANICSBURG

MECHANICSBURG PUBLIC LIBRARY,* 60 S Main St, 43044. SAN 313-6108. Tel: 937-834-2004. FAX: 937-834-3396. *Dir*, Sunny Krugh
Library Holdings: Bk Vols 34,000; Per Subs 140
Friends of the Library Group

IEDINA

MEDINA COUNTY DISTRICT LIBRARY, 210 S Broadway St, 44256. SAN 356-8598. Tel: 330-725-0588. FAX: 330-725-2053. Web Site: www.medina.lib.oh.us. *Branch Mgr*, Christine Gramm; *Outreach Serv*, Barbara Gillespie
Founded 1905. Pop 130,500; Circ 1,773,519
Jan 1999-Dec 1999 Income (Main Library Only) $6,122,716, State $3,710,660, Federal $14,060, County $2,131,219, Other $266,777. Mats Exp $1,055,486, Books $667,493, Per/Ser (Incl. Access Fees) $104,472, AV Equip $212,779, Other Print Mats $5,744, Electronic Ref Mat (Incl. Access Fees) $65,000. Sal $2,461,388 (Prof $1,181,466)
Library Holdings: Bk Vols 492,556; Bk Titles 133,631; Per Subs 395
Subject Interests: Genealogy, Local history
Automation Activity & Vendor Info: (Circulation) DRA
Publications: Library Live
Partic in Cleveland Area Metropolitan Library System; OHIONET; OPLIN
Friends of the Library Group
Branches: 5
BRUNSWICK COMMUNITY, 3649 Center Rd, Brunswick, 44212-0430. SAN 356-8628. Tel: 330-273-4150. FAX: 330-225-0310. *Librn*, Michael Harris
Friends of the Library Group
HINCKLEY COMMUNITY, 1634 Center Rd, Hinckley, 44233-0415. SAN 356-8652. Tel: 216-278-4271. FAX: 216-278-9835. *Librn*, Diane Dermody
Library Holdings: Bk Vols 15,454
Friends of the Library Group
LODI COMMUNITY, 226 Wooster St, Lodi, 44254-1311. SAN 356-8687. Tel: 330-948-1885. FAX: 330-948-2410. *Librn*, Betsy Gilder
Library Holdings: Bk Vols 25,534
Friends of the Library Group
OUTREACH SERVICES, 210 S Broadway, 44256-2699. SAN 374-3535. Tel: 330-722-2490. FAX: 330-722-2490. *Librn*, Barbara Gillespie
Library Holdings: Bk Vols 21,096
SEVILLE COMMUNITY, PO Box 206, Seville, 44273-0206. SAN 356-8717. Tel: 330-769-2852. FAX: 330-769-1774. *Librn*, Lynn Wiandt
Library Holdings: Bk Vols 22,121
Friends of the Library Group
Bookmobiles: 1

L MEDINA COUNTY LAW LIBRARY ASSOCIATION, 93 Public Sq, 44256. SAN 320-2232. Tel: 330-725-9744. FAX: 330-725-9608. E-Mail: medlaw@bright.net. *Asst Librn*, Sally A Davis; E-Mail: saldavis@ohio.net; Staff 2 (Non-MLS 2)
Founded 1899
Library Holdings: Bk Vols 19,500
Restriction: Not open to public

S TECHNOLOGY TRANSFER SOCIETY LIBRARY,* 698 E Washington St, 44256. SAN 373-3661. Tel: 330-721-4635. FAX: 330-721-9139. E-Mail: 102234.166@compuserve.com. *Exec Dir*, Bruce Becker; *Librn*, Judy Janes; Tel: 312-644-0828, Fax: 312-644-8557, E-Mail: 102234.166@compiserve.com
1997-1998 Mats Exp $22,000, Books $6,000, Per/Ser (Incl. Access Fees) $16,000
Library Holdings: Bk Vols 200

MENTOR

S LAKE COUNTY HISTORICAL SOCIETY, (LCHS), P K Smith Research Library, 8610 King Memorial Rd, 44060-8207. SAN 313-6124. Tel: 440-255-8979. FAX: 440-255-8980. Web Site: www.lakehistory.org. *Curator, Librn*, Karon Tomlinson
Founded 1936
Library Holdings: Bk Vols 2,501; Bk Titles 3,592; Per Subs 15
Subject Interests: Antiques, Garfield family, Genealogy, Local history
Publications: Here is Lake County, Ohio (1964); Lake County Heritage (1990); Lake County Historical Society Quarterly

P MENTOR PUBLIC LIBRARY, 8215 Mentor Ave, 44060-5786. SAN 356-8741. Tel: 440-255-8811. FAX: 440-255-0520. E-Mail: tsb@oh.verio.com. Web Site: www.mentorpl.org. *Exec Dir*, Dale Warren Craig; Fax: 440-255-6894, E-Mail: dc@oh.verio.com; Staff 67 (MLS 7, Non-MLS 60)
Founded 1819. Pop 62,861; Circ 781,559
Jan 1999-Dec 1999 Income $2,936,985, State $1,944,669, Locally Generated Income $893,322, Other $98,994. Mats Exp $489,078, Books $361,493, Per/Ser (Incl. Access Fees) $39,855, Presv $2,898, Other Print Mats $5,480, Electronic Ref Mat (Incl. Access Fees) $23,500. Sal $1,222,559 (Prof $607,056)
Library Holdings: Bk Vols 228,918; Per Subs 256
Automation Activity & Vendor Info: (Acquisitions) epixtech, inc.; (Cataloging) epixtech, inc.; (OPAC) epixtech, inc.
Database Vendor: epixtech, inc.
Partic in Cleveland Area Metropolitan Library System; Nola Regional Library System
Friends of the Library Group
Branches: 2
HEADLANDS, 4669 Corduroy Rd, 44060. SAN 356-8776. Tel: 440-257-2000. Web Site: www.mentor.lib.oh.us. *Mgr*, Connie Hoback
MENTOR-ON-THE-LAKE, 5642 Andrews Rd, 44060. SAN 356-8806. Tel: 440-257-2512. FAX: 440-257-6886. Web Site: www.mentor.lib.oh.us. *Mgr*, Janice Kilker

METAMORA

P EVERGREEN COMMUNITY LIBRARY, (ECL), 253 Maple St, PO Box E, 43540. SAN 313-6175. Tel: 419-644-2771. Toll Free Tel: 800-308-8603. FAX: 419-644-5778. Web Site: www.library.norweld.lib.oh.us/evergreen/. *Dir*, Joan Pershing; E-Mail: pershijo@oplin.lib.oh.us

Founded 1927. Pop 7,000; Circ 74,039
Jan 1999-Dec 1999 Income $306,468. Mats Exp $338,635, Books $26,495, Per/Ser (Incl. Access Fees) $2,663, AV Equip $4,318. Sal $95,007
Library Holdings: Bk Vols 34,980; Per Subs 86
Automation Activity & Vendor Info: (Cataloging) Gaylord; (Circulation) Gaylord; (OPAC) Gaylord
Partic in Norweld

MIAMISBURG

S CYCOLOR LIBRARY,* 3385 Newmark Dr, 45342. SAN 329-2428. Tel: 937-428-1900. FAX: 937-428-1915. *In Charge*, Laurie Bryant; E-Mail: lbryant@cycolor.com; Staff 2 (MLS 1, Non-MLS 1)
Founded 1985
Library Holdings: Bk Titles 500; Per Subs 78

MIDDLEBURG HEIGHTS

R MIDDLEBURG HEIGHTS COMMUNITY CHURCH LIBRARY, United Church of Christ,* 7165 Big Creek Pkwy, 44130. SAN 313-6205. Tel: 440-842-7743. FAX: 440-842-7745. *Librn*, Pat Kerslake
Library Holdings: Bk Vols 1,068
Subject Interests: Children, Family, Religion

MIDDLETOWN

C MIAMI UNIVERSITY-MIDDLETOWN, Gardner-Harvey Library, 4200 E University Blvd, 45042. SAN 313-6221. Tel: 513—727-3222. FAX: 513-727-3434. Web Site: www.lib.muohio.edu. *Dir*, Joseph Phillips; Tel: 513-727-3232, E-Mail: phillijw@muohio.edu; *Asst Dir*, Nani Ball; Tel: 513-727-3293, E-Mail: ballkb@muohio.edu; *ILL*, Gayle Shidler; Tel: 513-727-3459, E-Mail: shidlego@muohio.edu; *Ser*, Belinda Martindell; Tel: 513-727-3221, E-Mail: martinbb@muohio.edu; *Tech Servs*, Diane Miller; Tel: 513-727-3291, E-Mail: millerd1@muohio.edu; *Ref*, Joanne Howard; Tel: 513-727-3225, E-Mail: howardev@muohio.edu. Subject Specialists: *Architecture*, Gayle Shidler; *Art*, Gayle Shidler; *Govt docs*, Nani Ball; Staff 6 (MLS 3, Non-MLS 3)
Founded 1966. Enrl 1,432; Fac 59
Jul 1998-Jun 1999 Income $439,616. Mats Exp $183,800, Books $125,800, Per/Ser (Incl. Access Fees) $51,000, Micro $4,000, AV Equip $500, Electronic Ref Mat (Incl. Access Fees) $3,000
Library Holdings: Bk Titles 71,000; Per Subs 528
Special Collections: Instructional Materials (IMC Coll), bk & AV; Teaching Effectiveness Coll
Database Vendor: GaleNet, OCLC - First Search, ProQuest
Publications: Library Handbook for faculty & staff; Periodicals Holdings List (including public library system holdings); Selected List of New Government Documents; Welcome to Gardner-Harvey Library (Orientation brochure)
Function: ILL available
Partic in Ohio Library & Information Network; OHIONET

S MIDDLETOWN FINE ARTS CENTER, 130 N Verity Pkwy, PO Box 441, 45042. SAN 313-623X. Tel: 513-424-2417. Toll Free Tel: 888-844-4246. FAX: 513-424-1682. E-Mail: mfac@siscom.net. Web Site: www.middletownfinearts.com.
Library Holdings: Bk Vols 500
Special Collections: Middletown Arts & Artists (Leah Verity Hook Coll)
Restriction: Members only
Volunteer service; non-profit organization

P MIDDLETOWN PUBLIC LIBRARY, 125 S Broad St, 45044. SAN 356-889X. Tel: 513-424-1251. FAX: 513-424-6585. *Dir*, Douglas J Bean; Tel: 513-424-0659, E-Mail: dbean@mail.mpl.lib.oh.us; *Asst Dir*, Judi Girton; Tel: 513-424-4918, E-Mail: jgirton@mail.mpl.lib.oh.us; *Ch Servs*, Judy Gehm; *Commun Relations*, Katherine A Stengel; Tel: 513-424-0659, E-Mail: kstengel@mail.mpl.lib.oh.us; *Ref*, Dirdre Root
Founded 1911. Pop 137,000; Circ 1,700,000
Library Holdings: Bk Vols 148,024; Per Subs 550
Subject Interests: Genealogy, Large type print, Ohioana, Talking books
Database Vendor: epixtech, inc.
Special Services for the Blind - Talking Books
Friends of the Library Group
Branches: 2
TRENTON LIBRARY, 21 E State St, Trenton, 45067. SAN 356-892X. Tel: 513-988-9050. FAX: 513-988-5059. *Asst Dir*, Judi Girton; Tel: 513-424-4918, Fax: 513-424-6585, E-Mail: jgirton@mail.mpl.lib.oh.us; *Librn*, R Diane Current; E-Mail: dcurrent@mail.mpl.lib.oh.us
Founded 1974
Library Holdings: Bk Vols 14,009; Per Subs 79
Friends of the Library Group
WEST CHESTER, 7900 Cox Rd, West Chester, 45069. SAN 356-8954. Tel: 513-777-3131. FAX: 513-777-8452. *Librn*, Steve Mayhugh; Tel: 513-777-3717, E-Mail: smayhugh@mail.mpl.lib.oh.us
Library Holdings: Bk Vols 117,530; Per Subs 275
Friends of the Library Group

M MIDDLETOWN REGIONAL HOSPITAL, Ada Leonard Memorial Library, 105 McKnight Dr, 45044-8787. SAN 313-6248. Tel: 937-420-5160. FAX: 937-420-5731. *Dir*, Judy Rudokas
Founded 1957
Library Holdings: Bk Titles 50; Per Subs 50
Subject Interests: Hist of nursing
Special Collections: Old Medical Text Coll
Restriction: Staff use only
Partic in Medline; Regional Med Libr - Region 3

MILAN

P MILAN-BERLIN TOWNSHIP PUBLIC LIBRARY, 19 E Church St, PO Box 1550, 44846. SAN 356-8989. Tel: 419-499-4117. FAX: 419-499-4697, 419-499-4699. *Asst Librn*, Josephine Yates
Founded 1877. Pop 10,000; Circ 63,507
Jan 1999-Dec 1999 Income $554,013, Locally Generated Income $6,073. Mats Exp $163,000, Manuscripts & Archives $250. Sal $198,000
Library Holdings: Bk Vols 86,000; Per Subs 204
Subject Interests: Genealogy, Local history
Special Collections: Barbour Coll; Birth & Death Records; Census Index; Family Genealogies; Immigration Records; Local (newspaper); Local Histor (Edison Coll); Passenger Lists
Partic in Northwest Library District
Open Mon-Fri 9:30-8:30, Sat 10-2, summer hours: Mon & Tues 9:30-7, Fri 9:30-5, Wed 9:30-7 & Sat 10-2
Branches: 1
BERLIN TOWNSHIP PUBLIC, 4 E Main St, PO Box 139, Berlin Heights, 44814. SAN 356-9012. Tel: 419-588-2250. *In Charge*, Joanne Chaffee

MILLERSBURG

P HOLMES COUNTY DISTRICT PUBLIC LIBRARY,* 3102 Glen Dr, PO Box 111, 44654. SAN 356-9047. Tel: 330-674-5972. FAX: 330-674-1938. E-Mail: raddenar@oplin.lib.oh.us. Web Site: www.holmes.lib.oh.us. *Dir*, Arlene Redden; *Exten Serv*, Claudia Zimmerman; *YA Servs*, Tammie Beers; Staff 30 (MLS 3, Non-MLS 27)
Founded 1928. Pop 40,000; Circ 380,000
Jan 1999-Dec 1999 Income (Main Library and Branch Library) $1,100,000, State $1,100,000. Mats Exp $248,000, Books $232,000, Per/Ser (Incl. Access Fees) $12,000, Other Print Mats $4,000. Sal $570,000 (Prof $141,000)
Library Holdings: Bk Vols 93,000; Bk Titles 63,500; Per Subs 128
Special Collections: Amish & Mennonite Genealogies Coll
Automation Activity & Vendor Info: (Circulation) epixtech, inc.
Publications: History of Holmes County
Partic in Mideastern Ohio Libr Orgn
Branches: 4
BERLIN BRANCH, Berlin, 44610. SAN 356-9071. Tel: 216-893-3038. *Librn*, Iris Biggs
Circ 18,000
KILLBUCK BRANCH, Killbuck, 44637. SAN 356-9136. Tel: 216-276-0882. *Librn*, Sharon Hoxworth
Circ 8,000
WALNUT CREEK BRANCH, Walnut Creek, 44687. SAN 356-9195. Tel: 216-893-3464. *Librn*, Karen Maust
Circ 18,000
WINESBURG BRANCH, Winesburg, 44690. SAN 356-9225. Tel: 216-359-5913. *Librn*, Cathy Compan
Circ 20,000
Bookmobiles: 1

L HOLMES COUNTY LAW LIBRARY,* Court House, Rm 305, E Jackson St, 44654. SAN 327-3911. Tel: 330-674-5086. *Librn*, Eleanor Teisher

MINERVA

P MINERVA PUBLIC LIBRARY, 677 Lynnwood Dr, 44657-1200. SAN 313-6256. Tel: 330-868-4101. FAX: 330-868-4267. *Dir*, Judith Z Phillips; E-Mail: phillipsju@opln.lib.oh.us; Staff 11 (MLS 3, Non-MLS 8)
Founded 1910. Pop 15,000; Circ 159,000
1998-1999 Income $645,000, State $583,000, Locally Generated Income $42,000, Other $20,000. Mats Exp $103,000, Books $74,000, Per/Ser (Incl. Access Fees) $13,000, Micro $13,000
Library Holdings: Bk Vols 62,000; Bk Titles 61,000; Per Subs 200
Subject Interests: Circus, Clowns, Local genealogy
Special Collections: Gypsies Coll
Publications: MPL Newsletter (monthly)
Partic in Mideastern Ohio Libr Orgn
Friends of the Library Group

MONROEVILLE

P MONROEVILLE PUBLIC LIBRARY,* 34 Monroe St, 44847-0276. SAN 313-6264. Tel: 419-465-2035. FAX: 419-465-2035. *Dir*, Janet Santana; *Librn*, Diane Henderson

Pop 2,000; Circ 17,140
Library Holdings: Bk Vols 18,655; Per Subs 32
Partic in Northwest Library District
Friends of the Library Group

MONTPELIER

P MONTPELIER PUBLIC LIBRARY, (MPL), 216 E Main St, 43543-1199. SAN 356-925X. Tel: 419-485-3287. FAX: 419-485-5671. Web Site: www.library.norweld.lib.oh.us/montpelier/. *Dir*, Philip R Scott; E-Mail: scottph@oplin.lib.oh.us; Staff 5 (MLS 1, Non-MLS 4)
Pop 36,369; Circ 67,433
Jan 2000-Dec 2000 Mats Exp $84,694, Books $61,884, Per/Ser (Incl. Access Fees) $10,528, Presv $500, AV Equip $11,782. Sal $124,200
Library Holdings: Bk Vols 31,488; Per Subs 175
Subject Interests: Coop learning, Sci fairs
Partic in Northwest Library District

S SOCIETY FOR THE STUDY OF MALE PSYCHOLOGY & PHYSIOLOGY LIBRARY, (SSMPP), 321 Iuka, 43543. SAN 326-3061. Tel: 419-485-3602. *Librn*, Dr Jerry Bergman; Staff 1 (MLS 1)
Founded 1974
Library Holdings: Bk Titles 12,400; Per Subs 62
Special Collections: Male Psychology & Physiology Coll

MORROW

P SALEM TOWNSHIP PUBLIC LIBRARY, 535 W Pike St, 45152. SAN 313-6272. Tel: 513-899-2588. FAX: 513-899-9420. *Dir*, Jerri A Short; E-Mail: shortje@oplin.lib.oh.us
Founded 1884. Pop 19,920; Circ 168,292
Jan 1999-Dec 1999 Income $728,145, State $713,219. Mats Exp $127,535, Books $70,872, Per/Ser (Incl. Access Fees) $16,243, AV Equip $24,177, Electronic Ref Mat (Incl. Access Fees) $16,243. Sal $262,159
Library Holdings: Bk Vols 69,588; Bk Titles 74,525; Per Subs 366
Automation Activity & Vendor Info: (Circulation) Sagebrush Corporation; (OPAC) Sagebrush Corporation
Database Vendor: Ebsco - EbscoHost, IAC - Info Trac
Function: ILL available
Partic in Miami Valley Librs

MOUNT GILEAD

P MOUNT GILEAD PUBLIC LIBRARY,* 35 E High St, 43338-1429. SAN 313-6280. Tel: 419-947-5866. FAX: 419-947-9252. *Dir*, Kay Todd
Founded 1908
Jan 1998-Dec 1998 Income $304,066. Mats Exp $26,564, Books $23,140, Per/Ser (Incl. Access Fees) $3,424. Sal $85,990
Library Holdings: Bk Vols 27,098; Per Subs 89
Friends of the Library Group

MOUNT ORAB

P BROWN COUNTY PUBLIC LIBRARY, 14878 US Rte 68, PO Box 527, 45154. Tel: 937-444-0181. FAX: 937-444-6502. E-Mail: brncty@oplin.lib.oh.us. *Exec Dir*, Lynn Book; Staff 23 (MLS 3, Non-MLS 20)
Founded 1920. Pop 32,000; Circ 156,585
Jan 1999-Dec 1999 Income $900,000. Mats Exp $147,000, Books $95,000, Per/Ser (Incl. Access Fees) $12,000, AV Equip $35,000, Electronic Ref Mat (Incl. Access Fees) $305. Sal $335,000 (Prof $102,000)
Library Holdings: Bk Vols 65,000; Per Subs 600
Automation Activity & Vendor Info: (Cataloging) epixtech, inc.; (Circulation) epixtech, inc.; (ILL) epixtech, inc.; (OPAC) epixtech, inc.
Friends of the Library Group
Branches: 4
FAYETTEVILLE-PERRY BRANCH, 406 East St, Fayetteville, 45118. Tel: 513-875-2665. FAX: 513-875-2738.
Library Holdings: Bk Vols 4,000
Friends of the Library Group
MARY P SHELTON BUILDING BRANCH, 200 W Grant Ave, Georgetown, 45121. Tel: 937-378-3197. FAX: 937-378-4296. *Mgr*, Fredricka Jenkins
MT ORAB BRANCH, 613 S High St, Mt Orab, 45154. Tel: 937-444-1414. FAX: 937-444-2191. *Mgr*, Susan Bellas
Library Holdings: Bk Vols 12,000
Friends of the Library Group
SARDINIA BRANCH, 13309 Purdy Rd, Sardinia, 45171. Tel: 937-446-1565. FAX: 937-445-1506. *Mgr*, Wanda McLain
Library Holdings: Bk Vols 4,000
Friends of the Library Group
Bookmobiles: 1

MOUNT STERLING

P MOUNT STERLING PUBLIC LIBRARY, 60 W Columbus St, 43143. SAN 313-6302. Tel: 740-869-2430. FAX: 740-869-3617. Web Site: www.mspl.msohio.net. *Dir*, Heidi Fletcher; *Pres*, Dennis Morris; Staff 14 (Non-MLS 14)
Founded 1911. Pop 1,750; Circ 14,534
Library Holdings: Bk Vols 21,000; Per Subs 56; Bks on Deafness & Sign Lang 20
Automation Activity & Vendor Info: (Acquisitions) epixtech, inc.; (Cataloging) epixtech, inc.; (Circulation) epixtech, inc.; (Course Reserve) epixtech, inc.; (OPAC) epixtech, inc.
Database Vendor: epixtech, inc.

MOUNT VERNON

M KNOX COMMUNITY HOSPITAL, Medical Library,* 1330 Coshocton Rd, 43050. SAN 327-5612. Tel: 740-393-9000. FAX: 740-399-3155. *Librn*, Sharon Collaros
Library Holdings: Bk Vols 1,215; Per Subs 15

C MOUNT VERNON NAZARENE COLLEGE, (MVNC), Thorne Library - Learning Resource Center, 800 Martinsburg Rd, 43050-9500. SAN 313-6310. Tel: 740-397-6862. Interlibrary Loan Service Tel: 740-397-6862, Ext 4243. Circulation Tel: 740-397-6862, Ext 4240. Reference Tel: 740-397-6862, Ext 4248. FAX: 740-397-8847. Web Site: www.mvnc.edu.149.143.2.3/. *Dir*, Edythe Feazel; *Tech Servs*, Phillip Estes; *Ref*, Sylvia Locher; *Media Spec*, Dave Arnold; Staff 4 (MLS 3, Non-MLS 1)
Founded 1968. Enrl 1,976; Fac 168; Highest Degree: Master
Jul 1999-Jun 2000 Mats Exp $232,078. Sal $315,515
Library Holdings: Bk Vols 93,743; Per Subs 560
Special Collections: Church of the Nazarene, Doctrine, History & Missions
Database Vendor: Ebsco - EbscoHost, Innovative Interfaces INN - View, OCLC - First Search
Partic in Ohio Library & Information Network; OHIONET

P PUBLIC LIBRARY OF MOUNT VERNON & KNOX COUNTY, Mount Vernon & Knox County Public, 201 N Mulberry St, 43050-2413. SAN 356-9314. Tel: 740-392-2665. FAX: 740-397-3866. E-Mail: library@knox.net. Web Site: www.knox.net. *Dir*, John K Chidester; E-Mail: jchidest@knox.net; *Asst Dir*, Mary H McGavick; *Circ*, Violet S Yarman; *YA Servs*, Trina Shrimplin; *Tech Servs*, Sharon Radermacher; Staff 16 (MLS 3, Non-MLS 13)
Founded 1888. Pop 51,890; Circ 532,985
Library Holdings: Bk Vols 166,395; Per Subs 651
Friends of the Library Group
Branches: 3
DANVILLE PUBLIC, 512 S Market St, PO Box 511, Danville, 43014. SAN 356-9349. Tel: 740-599-2665. FAX: 740-599-2665. *Librn*, Helen Austin; Staff 1 (Non-MLS 1)
Library Holdings: Bk Vols 21,000
FREDERICKTOWN COMMUNITY, One Burgett Dr, Fredericktown, 43019. SAN 356-9373. Tel: 740-694-2665. FAX: 740-694-3106. *Librn*, Barbara Blackford; Staff 1 (Non-MLS 1)
Library Holdings: Bk Vols 42,500
GAMBIER PUBLIC, 115 Meadowlane St, Gambier, 43002. SAN 370-0194. Tel: 740-427-2665. FAX: 740-427-2665. Web Site: www.knox.net. *Librn*, Diane Ridgway; Staff 1 (Non-MLS 1)
Library Holdings: Bk Vols 15,480
Bookmobiles: 1

MOUNT VICTORY

P RIDGEMONT PUBLIC LIBRARY,* 124 E Taylor St, 43340. SAN 356-9403. Tel: 937-354-4445. FAX: 937-354-4445. *Librn*, Nancy J Terrill; *Cat*, Vondale McNeal; *Ch Servs*, Beccy Ramsey
Circ 22,396
1998-1999 Income $90,000. Mats Exp $16,000, Books $15,000, Per/Ser (Incl. Access Fees) $1,000. Sal $36,000
Library Holdings: Bk Vols 17,000; Per Subs 19
Branches: 1
RIDGEWAY BRANCH, 109 Main St, PO Box 2, Ridgeway, 43345. SAN 356-9438. Tel: 937-363-3066. FAX: 937-363-3066. *Librn*, Molly Gallo

NAPOLEON

L HENRY COUNTY LAW LIBRARY,* 609 N Perry St, 43545. SAN 327-6570. Tel: 419-599-1936. FAX: 419-592-4451. *Librn*, John Donovan

P NAPOLEON PUBLIC LIBRARY, 310 W Clinton St, 43545. SAN 356-9462. Tel: 419-592-2531. FAX: 419-599-1472. E-Mail: morlocps@oplin.lib.oh.us. *Dir*, Pamela Jo Lieser; *Ch Servs*, Mary Hogan; Staff 2 (MLS 2)
Founded 1906. Pop 28,000; Circ 152,384
Jan 1999-Dec 1999 Income (Main Library and Branch Library) $810,710, State $545,413, Locally Generated Income $14,033, Other $251,264. Mats Exp $113,115, Books $99,873, Per/Ser (Incl. Access Fees) $13,242. Sal

$341,339 (Prof $70,846)
Library Holdings: Bk Vols 128,788; Bk Titles 102,533; Per Subs 284
Special Collections: County Papers from 1850's, microfilm
Automation Activity & Vendor Info: (Cataloging) Gaylord; (Circulation) Gaylord; (OPAC) Gaylord
Partic in Northwest Library District
Branches: 2
FLORIDA PUBLIC, Hill St, 43545-9215. SAN 356-9470. Tel: 419-762-5876. *Librn*, Pamela Jo Lieser
Library Holdings: Bk Vols 11,799
MCCLURE COMMUNITY, Haley St, McClure, 43534-0035. SAN 356-9497. Tel: 419-748-8922. *Librn*, Pamela Jo Lieser
Library Holdings: Bk Vols 16,363

NELSONVILLE

J HOCKING COLLEGE LIBRARY, 3301 Hocking Pkwy, 45764. SAN 313-6337. Tel: 740-753-3591, Ext 2181. Reference Tel: 740-735-3214. FAX: 740-753-3034. Web Site: www.hocking.edu/lrc/lrc.htm. *Dir*, Carrie Susan Ator-James; E-Mail: james_c@hocking.edu; Staff 4 (MLS 2, Non-MLS 2)
Founded 1968. Enrl 4,005
Jun 1999-Jul 2000 Income $208,760. Mats Exp $28,723, Books $11,782, Per/Ser (Incl. Access Fees) $13,544, Presv $275, Micro $3,122. Sal $142,387 (Prof $97,481)
Library Holdings: Bk Vols 17,526; Bk Titles 15,227; Per Subs 255
Subject Interests: Culinary arts, Forestry, Natural resources, Nursing, Police sci
Database Vendor: Ebsco - EbscoHost, Innovative Interfaces INN - View, Lexis-Nexis, ProQuest
Partic in Ohio Library & Information Network

S HOCKING CORRECTIONAL FACILITY LIBRARY,* 16759 Snake Hollow Rd, PO Box 59, 45764-0059. SAN 322-8134. Tel: 740-753-1917, Ext 213. FAX: 740-753-4277. *Librn*, Crys Cooper; Staff 1 (MLS 1)
Founded 1983
Library Holdings: Bk Titles 16,000; Per Subs 84
Special Collections: Ohio Criminal Law
Mem of Oval Valley Area Librs
Special Services for the Deaf - High interest/low vocabulary books
Special Services for the Blind - Bks on tape; Large print bks

P NELSONVILLE PUBLIC LIBRARY, 95 W Washington, 45764. SAN 356-9527. Tel: 740-753-2118. FAX: 740-753-3543. E-Mail: nelpl@athenscounty.lib.oh.us. Web Site: www.athenscounty.lib.oh.us. *Dir*, Stephen Hedges; *Asst Dir*, Lauren Miller; *ILL*, Victoria Bumpass; *Ch Servs*, Linda Cochran; Staff 11 (MLS 8, Non-MLS 3)
Founded 1936. Pop 61,000; Circ 506,000
Jan 1999-Dec 1999 Income (Main Library and Branch Library) $2,280,000, State $2,166,000, Other $114,000. Mats Exp $427,000, Books $325,000, Per/Ser (Incl. Access Fees) $13,000, AV Equip $80,000, Electronic Ref Mat (Incl. Access Fees) $9,000. Sal $917,000 (Prof $230,000)
Library Holdings: Bk Vols 60,000; Per Subs 150
Open Mon-Thurs 9-8, Tues, Fri 9-6, Sat 9-5
Branches: 6
ATHENS BRANCH, 30 Home St, Athens, 45701. SAN 356-9551. Tel: 740-592-4272. FAX: 740-594-4204. *Librn*, Lauren Miller
Library Holdings: Bk Vols 84,000
Open Mon-Thurs 9-9, Fri 9-6 & Sat 9-5
Friends of the Library Group
CHAUNCEY BRANCH, 29 Converse St, Chauncey, 45719. SAN 356-9586. Tel: 740-797-2512. FAX: 740-797-2512. *Librn*, Lois Simpson
Library Holdings: Bk Vols 7,000
Open Mon-Fri 11-6, Sat 9-5
COOLVILLE PUBLIC, 26401 Main St, PO Box 109, Coolville, 45723-0109. SAN 376-8503. Tel: 740-667-3354. FAX: 740-667-3354. *Librn*, Marilyn Zwayer
Library Holdings: Bk Vols 11,000
Open Mon-Fri 11-6, Sat 9-5
GLOUSTER BRANCH, 20 Toledo St, Glouster, 45732. SAN 356-9616. Tel: 740-767-3670. FAX: 740-767-3670. *Librn*, Karen Guffy
Library Holdings: Bk Vols 21,000
Open Mon-Thurs 9-7, Fri-Sat 9-5
THE PLAINS BRANCH, 14 S Plains Rd, The Plains, 45780. SAN 375-6009. Tel: 740-797-4579. FAX: 740-797-4579. *Librn*, Cheryl Blevins
Library Holdings: Bk Vols 35,000
Open Mon-Thurs 9-7, Fri & Sat 9-5
WELLS PUBLIC, 5200 Washington Rd, Albany, 45710. SAN 376-8511. Tel: 740-698-3059. FAX: 740-698-3059. *Librn*, Mary Young
Library Holdings: Bk Vols 14,000
Open Mon-Thurs 9-7, Fri & Sat 9-5
Bookmobiles: 1

NEW CARLISLE

P NEW CARLISLE PUBLIC LIBRARY, 111 E Lake Ave, 45344-1418. SAN 313-6345. Tel: 937-845-3601. FAX: 937-845-0908. E-Mail: newcar@oplin.lib.oh.us. Web Site: www.new-carlisle.lib.oh.us. *Dir*, Robin Weinstein; E-Mail: weinstro@oplin.lib.oh.us
Founded 1904. Pop 20,000; Circ 50,133
Jan 2000-Dec 2000 Income State $445,000. Mats Exp $80,915, Books $75,000, Per/Ser (Incl. Access Fees) $2,715, Micro $3,200. Sal $258,500 (Prof $66,500)
Library Holdings: Bk Titles 30,000; Per Subs 119
Automation Activity & Vendor Info: (Circulation) epixtech, inc.
Open Mon-Thurs 10-8, Fri 10-5 & Sat 10-5
Friends of the Library Group

NEW CONCORD

C MUSKINGUM COLLEGE LIBRARY, 163 Stormont St, 43762-1199. SAN 313-6353. Tel: 740-826-8152. FAX: 740-826-8404. Web Site: www.muskingum.edu/~library/index.htm. *Dir*, Sheila Ellenberger; Tel: 740-826-8260, E-Mail: sheilaj@muskingum.edu; *Media Spec*, Sallie Wetzel; Tel: 740-826-8261, E-Mail: swetzel@muskingum.edu; *Acq*, Connie Thomas; *Circ*, Zelda Patterson; *Ref*, Janalyn Moss; Tel: 740-826-8157, E-Mail: jmoss@muskingum.edu; *Ref*, Jennifer Pruchnic; Tel: 740-826-8015, E-Mail: pruchnic@muskingum.edu; *Cat*, Brian Kern; Tel: 740-826-8015, E-Mail: bkern@muskingum.edu; Staff 6 (MLS 5, Non-MLS 1)
Founded 1837. Enrl 1,135; Fac 85; Highest Degree: Master
Jul 2000-Jun 2001 Income $402,500. Mats Exp $184,000, Books $68,000, Per/Ser (Incl. Access Fees) $78,000, Presv $3,000, Micro $15,000, AV Equip $20,000. Sal $278,000 (Prof $143,000)
Library Holdings: Bk Vols 233,000; Per Subs 840
Special Collections: Archives Coll
Partic in East Central College; OCLC Online Computer Library Center, Inc; Ohio Library & Information Network; Ohio Pvt Acad Librs; OHIONET

NEW LEXINGTON

P PERRY COUNTY DISTRICT LIBRARY, 117 S Jackson St, 43764-1330. SAN 356-9640. Tel: 740-342-4194. FAX: 740-342-4204. E-Mail: pnl@seolib.state.lib.oh.us. Web Site: www.pcdl.org. *Dir*, Michael R Wantz; E-Mail: wantzmi@oplin.lib.oh.us; *Asst Dir*, Babette Coleen Wofter; E-Mail: wofterba@oplin.lib.oh.us; Staff 36 (MLS 4, Non-MLS 32)
Founded 1935. Pop 31,557; Circ 400,880
Library Holdings: Bk Vols 84,000; Bk Titles 47,500; Per Subs 198
Subject Interests: Genealogy, Local history
Mem of SE Ohio Libr Orgn
Friends of the Library Group
Branches: 6
CORNING BRANCH, Adams St, PO Box 395, Corning, 43730. SAN 356-9675. Tel: 740-347-4763. FAX: 740-347-4763. *Librn*, Roberta Fisher
CROOKSVILLE BRANCH, 116 E Main, Crooksville, 43731. SAN 356-9705. Tel: 740-982-4821. FAX: 740-982-4821. *Librn*, Marsha Stalling
JUNCTION CITY BRANCH, Main St, PO Box 157, Junction City, 43748. SAN 356-973X. Tel: 740-987-7646. FAX: 740-987-7646. *Librn*, Evelyn Wolfe
Friends of the Library Group
SHAWNEE BRANCH, Main St, PO Box 13, Shawnee, 43782. SAN 356-9764. Tel: 740-394-1182. FAX: 740-394-1182. *Librn*, Sue Peart
SOMERSET BRANCH, 100 A Public Sq, PO Box 277, Somerset, 43783. SAN 356-9799. Tel: 740-743-1161. FAX: 740-743-1161. *Librn*, Carol Williams
Friends of the Library Group
THORNVILLE BRANCH, One S Main St, PO Box 292, Thornville, 43076. SAN 356-9829. Tel: 740-246-5133. FAX: 740-246-5133. *Librn*, Erma McComb

NEW LONDON

P NEW LONDON PUBLIC LIBRARY, 67 S Main St, 44851-1137. SAN 313-6361. Tel: 419-929-3981. FAX: 419-929-0007. E-Mail: nwlondon@oplin.lib.oh.us. Web Site: www.newlondonohio.com. *Dir*, Steven N Musgrave; Staff 2 (MLS 1, Non-MLS 1)
Pop 2,564; Circ 61,000
Jan 1999-Dec 1999 Income $281,000. Mats Exp $48,500. Sal $122,570
Library Holdings: Bk Vols 39,753; Per Subs 110
Subject Interests: Genealogy, Local history
Friends of the Library Group

NEW MADISON

P NEW MADISON PUBLIC LIBRARY, 142 S Main St, PO Box 32, 45346-0032. SAN 313-637X. Tel: 937-996-1741. FAX: 937-996-1473. E-Mail: newmad@oplin.lib.oh.us. Web Site: www.new-madison.lib.oh.us. *Dir*, Kay Holcomb; Staff 7 (MLS 1, Non-MLS 6)
Founded 1935. Pop 6,000; Circ 99,327
Jan 1999-Dec 1999 Income $333,523. Mats Exp $54,565. Sal $152,633
Library Holdings: Bk Vols 44,830; Per Subs 260
Subject Interests: Local history

Automation Activity & Vendor Info: (Cataloging) epixtech, inc.; (Circulation) epixtech, inc.; (OPAC) epixtech, inc.
Partic in Miami Valley Librs
Friends of the Library Group

NEW PHILADELPHIA

KENT STATE UNIVERSITY, Tuscarawas Campus Library,* University Dr NE, 44663. SAN 313-6388. Tel: 330-339-3391, Ext 47456. FAX: 330-339-7888. *Librn*, Michael Kobulnicky; E-Mail: mkobul@tusc.kent.edu
Founded 1968. Enrl 817
1997-1998 Income $60,000. Mats Exp $60,000, Books $30,000
Library Holdings: Bk Vols 56,000; Bk Titles 45,000; Per Subs 350
Subject Interests: Local history, Nursing
Special Collections: Moravian Coll; Ohio Authors Coll; Olmstead Local History Coll

TUSCARAWAS COUNTY LAW LIBRARY ASSOCIATION,* 101 E High Ave, 44663-2599. SAN 313-640X. Tel: 330-364-3703. FAX: 330-343-5509. E-Mail: tusclawl@tusco.net. *Librn*, Kathy Moreland
Jan 1998-Dec 1999 Income $176,701, City $58,028, County $104,934. Mats Exp $175,166, Books $141,926. Sal $34,500 (Prof $30,000)
Library Holdings: Bk Vols 17,000
Partic in Westlaw

TUSCARAWAS COUNTY PUBLIC LIBRARY, 121 Fair Ave NW, 44663-2600. SAN 356-9853. Tel: 330-364-4474. FAX: 330-364-8217. E-Mail: tuscwref@oplin.lib.oh.us. Web Site: www.tusc.lib.oh.us. *Dir*, Susan B Hagloch; E-Mail: haglocsu@oplin.lib.oh.us; *Asst Dir*, Debra Ann Tristano; E-Mail: tristade@oplin.lib.oh.us; *Exten Serv*, Damaris Ann Eisinger; E-Mail: eisingda@oplin.lib.oh.us; *Ch Servs*, Michelle Ramsell; E-Mail: ramselmi@oplin.lib.oh.us; *Cat*, Lois Sevim Tsardoulias; E-Mail: tsardose@oplin.lib.oh.us; *Tech Servs*, James Richard Simpson; *Circ*, Stephanie Ann Baird; E-Mail: bairdst@oplin.lib.oh.us; *Tech Servs*, Jamie Simmons; Staff 62 (MLS 8, Non-MLS 54)
Founded 1905. Pop 51,418; Circ 570,841
Jan 1999-Dec 1999 Income (Main Library and Branch Library) $1,800,655, State $1,657,893, County $183,764, Locally Generated Income $76,074. Mats Exp $222,580, Books $930,339, Per/Ser (Incl. Access Fees) $24,265, Micro $789, Electronic Ref Mat (Incl. Access Fees) $14,000. Sal $930,339 (Prof $347,875)
Library Holdings: Bk Vols 148,677; Bk Titles 104,074; Per Subs 564
Automation Activity & Vendor Info: (Acquisitions) epixtech, inc.; (Cataloging) epixtech, inc.; (Circulation) epixtech, inc.; (Circulation) epixtech, inc.; (OPAC) epixtech, inc.
Database Vendor: Ebsco - EbscoHost, epixtech, inc., OCLC - First Search
Function: ILL available
Partic in Mideastern Ohio Libr Orgn
Special Services for the Deaf - Staff with knowledge of sign language; TDD
Special Services for the Blind - Bks on tape; Large print bks
Friends of the Library Group
Branches: 4
BOLIVAR BRANCH, PO Box 588, Bolivar, 44612. SAN 356-9888. Tel: 330-874-2720. *Librn*, Marsha Fortune
Library Holdings: Bk Titles 10,000
EMMA HUBER MEMORIAL LIBRARY, 356 Fifth St SW, Strasburg, 44680. SAN 356-9918. Tel: 330-878-5711. *Librn*, Brenda West
Library Holdings: Bk Titles 7,000
Friends of the Library Group
SUGARCREEK BRANCH, PO Box 309, Sugarcreek, 44681. SAN 356-9942. Tel: 330-852-2813. *Librn*, Linda Ladrach
Library Holdings: Bk Titles 9,000
TUSCARAWAS BRANCH, PO Box 337, Tuscarawas, 44682. SAN 356-9977. Tel: 330-922-2748. *Librn*, Leona Hinds
Library Holdings: Bk Titles 8,500
Bookmobiles: 1

NEW STRAITSVILLE

NEW STRAITSVILLE PUBLIC LIBRARY,* Railroad St, PO Box 8, 43766. SAN 313-6418. Tel: 740-394-2717. *Librn*, Kathy Gill; *Asst Librn*, Judy Burgess
Founded 1916. Circ 29,019
Library Holdings: Bk Vols 43,342
Partic in Southeastern Ohio Libr Orgn

NEWARK

DAWES ARBORETUM LIBRARY,* 7770 Jacksontown Rd SE, 43056-9380. SAN 325-2760. Tel: 740-323-2355. FAX: 740-323-4058. Web Site: www.dawesarb.org. *Librn*, Linda Milligan; *Publ Servs*, Luke Messinger
Founded 1970
Library Holdings: Bk Titles 6,500; Per Subs 40
Subject Interests: Horticulture, Natural history

S HEISEY COLLECTORS OF AMERICA, INC, 169 W Church St, 43055-0027. SAN 324-4555. Tel: 740-345-2932. FAX: 740-345-9638. E-Mail: heisey@infinet.com. Web Site: www.heiseymuseum.org. *Archivist*, Don Valdes; Staff 8 (MLS 2, Non-MLS 6)
Founded 1974
Library Holdings: Bk Titles 550; Per Subs 50
Subject Interests: A H Heisey and Co, Am glass
Special Collections: Heisey Company Correspondence & Information
Publications: Heisey News (monthly)
Friends of the Library Group

L LICKING COUNTY LAW LIBRARY ASSOCIATION,* 65 E Main St, 43055. SAN 371-439X. Tel: 740-349-6561. *Librn*, James W Pyle; *Adminr*, Jane Koehler
Library Holdings: Bk Vols 10,000; Per Subs 91

M LICKING MEMORIAL HOSPITAL, Medical Library,* 1320 W Main St, 43055-3699. SAN 327-3520. Tel: 740-348-4130. FAX: 740-348-4127. *Librn*, Lindsay Fretag; *Asst Librn*, Kathy Bradley
Library Holdings: Bk Vols 360; Per Subs 24

P NEWARK PUBLIC LIBRARY, 101 W Main St, 43055-5054. SAN 357-0002. Tel: 740-349-5500. FAX: 740-349-5535. *Dir*, Wilma J Bacigalupo; *Asst Dir*, Parmelee A Wheeler; *Tech Servs*, Robert Gale; *Ch Servs*, Sadie E Smith; *Outreach Serv*, Elizabeth Moore; *Ref*, Jeff Eling; Staff 24 (MLS 8, Non-MLS 16)
Founded 1908. Pop 127,000; Circ 743,186
Library Holdings: Bk Vols 273,385; Bk Titles 80,270; Per Subs 350
Subject Interests: Local history
Partic in Calico; Solo
Friends of the Library Group
Branches: 4
HEBRON BRANCH, 116 E Main St, Hebron, 43025. SAN 357-0037. Tel: 740-928-3923. FAX: 740-928-3923. *In Charge*, Pat Walters
HERVEY MEMORIAL, 15 N Main, PO Box 512, Utica, 43080-0512. SAN 357-0126. Tel: 740-892-2400. *Branch Mgr*, Dorothy Layton
JOHNSTOWN BRANCH, One S Main St, Johnstown, 43031. SAN 357-0061. Tel: 614-967-2982. *Br Coordr*, Shirley Beam; Tel: 740-967-2982
EMERSON R MILLER BRANCH, 990 W Main St, 43055. SAN 357-0096. Tel: 740-344-2155. FAX: 740-344-2155. *In Charge*, Kenton Daniels
Bookmobiles: 1. Supvr, Peggy Baker. Tel 614-344-2155

C THE OHIO STATE UNIVERSITY AT NEWARK & CENTRAL OHIO TECHNICAL COLLEGE, Newark Campus Library, 1179 University Dr, 43055-1797. SAN 313-6442. Tel: 740-366-9307. Reference Tel: 740-366-9308. FAX: 740-366-9264. Web Site: www.cotc.tec.oh.us. *Head of Libr*, John D Crissinger; Tel: 740-366-9306, E-Mail: crissinger.5@osu.edu; *Circ*, Shawn Brookbank; E-Mail: brookbank.14@osu.edu; *Circ*, Tauni Graham; E-Mail: graham.151@osu.edu; *Bibliog Instr*, Will McElhaney; Tel: 740-366-9308, E-Mail: mcelhaney.8@osu.edu; Staff 4 (MLS 2, Non-MLS 2)
Founded 1957. Enrl 2,831; Fac 102; Highest Degree: Master
Jul 1999-Jun 2000 Income Parent Institution $268,725. Mats Exp $120,975, Books $47,730, Per/Ser (Incl. Access Fees) $58,550, Presv $1,944, Micro $793, Other Print Mats $6,000, Electronic Ref Mat (Incl. Access Fees) $5,958. Sal $113,319 (Prof $76,279)
Library Holdings: Bk Vols 43,450; Bk Titles 40,000; Per Subs 430
Partic in Ohio Library & Information Network

NEWCOMERSTOWN

P NEWCOMERSTOWN PUBLIC LIBRARY,* 123 N Bridge St, 43832-1093. SAN 313-6450. Tel: 740-498-7706, 740-498-8228. FAX: 740-498-8221. Web Site: www.nctpl.lib.oh.us/. *Coll Develop, Librn*, Linda K Hren; E-Mail: hrenli@oplin.lib.oh.us; *Asst Dir*, Edith Freetage; *Ch Servs*, Helen Booth
Pop 12,000; Circ 127,525
Jan 1998-Dec 1998 Income $245,309, State $184,276, Locally Generated Income $5,605, Other $2,259. Mats Exp $67,891, Books $49,961, Per/Ser (Incl. Access Fees) $9,426. Sal $97,897
Library Holdings: Bk Vols 35,000; Per Subs 150
Mem of Mideastern Ohio Libr Orgn
Friends of the Library Group

NEWTON FALLS

P NEWTON FALLS PUBLIC LIBRARY,* 204 S Canal St, 44444-1694. SAN 313-6469. Tel: 330-872-1282. FAX: 330-872-9153. E-Mail: newtonpl@oplin.lib.oh.us, wynkoolo@oplin.lib.oh.us. Web Site: www.newtonfalls.org. *Dir*, Lois Wynkoop; *Asst Dir*, Jack Mullen
Founded 1930. Pop 10,000; Circ 114,069
Jan 1998-Dec 1998 Income $786,982, State $645,206, Locally Generated Income $115,324, Other $26,452. Mats Exp $115,744, Books $78,066, Per/Ser (Incl. Access Fees) $6,335, Presv $174, AV Equip $26,120, Electronic Ref Mat (Incl. Access Fees) $5,049. Sal $332,080 (Prof $202,110)
Library Holdings: Bk Vols 29,520; Per Subs 121
Subject Interests: Local history
Partic in Nola Regional Library System
Friends of the Library Group

NILES

P MCKINLEY MEMORIAL LIBRARY, 40 N Main St, 44446-5082. SAN 313-6477. Tel: 330-652-1704. FAX: 330-652-5788. E-Mail: mckinley@oplin.lib.oh.us. Web Site: www.mckinley.lib.oh.us. *Dir*, Patrick E Finan; E-Mail: finanpa@oplin.lib.oh.us; Staff 18 (MLS 7, Non-MLS 11)
Founded 1908
Library Holdings: Bk Vols 68,000; Bk Titles 66,000; Per Subs 130
Special Collections: President William McKinley, bk, micro & mus artifacts
Automation Activity & Vendor Info: (Cataloging) TLC; (Circulation) TLC; (OPAC) TLC
Database Vendor: GaleNet, IAC - SearchBank
Partic in Cleveland Area Metropolitan Library System; Nola Regional Library System
Friends of the Library Group

S RMI TITANIUM CO, Technical Center, 1000 Warren Ave, 44446. SAN 313-6485. Tel: 330-544-7643. *Chief Librn*, Carol Muszik
Library Holdings: Bk Vols 200
Subject Interests: Titanium

NORTH BALTIMORE

P NORTH BALTIMORE PUBLIC LIBRARY, 230 N Main St, 45872-1125. SAN 313-6493. Tel: 419-257-3621. FAX: 419-257-3859. *Dir*, Lesley McKinstry; E-Mail: mckinsle@oplin.lib.oh.us; *Asst Dir*, Connie Phillips; E-Mail: phillico@oplin.lib.oh.us; *Ch Servs*, Cheryl Heilman; E-Mail: heilman@oplin.lib.oh.us; Staff 2 (MLS 2)
Founded 1918. Pop 7,500; Circ 125,000
Library Holdings: Bk Vols 48,000; Bk Titles 46,404; Per Subs 185
Special Collections: Movies, TV & Stage
Partic in Northwest Library District
Friends of the Library Group

NORTH CANTON

P NORTH CANTON PUBLIC LIBRARY, 185 N Main St, 44720-2595. SAN 357-0150. Tel: 330-499-4712. FAX: 330-499-7356. E-Mail: ncanton@mail.oplin.lib.oh.us. Web Site: www.ncpl.lib.oh.us. *Dir*, Karen Sonderman; E-Mail: sonderka@oplin.lib.oh.us; *Ref*, Maria Meymarian; *Circ*, Geraldine Chufar; Staff 57 (MLS 7, Non-MLS 50)
Founded 1929. Pop 36,500; Circ 715,152
Jan 1999-Dec 1999 Income (Main Library and Branch Library) $1,373,414, State $1,183,497, Locally Generated Income $189,917. Sal $707,900
Library Holdings: Bk Vols 97,410; Bk Titles 93,000; Per Subs 348
Subject Interests: Art
Automation Activity & Vendor Info: (Cataloging) Gaylord; (Circulation) Gaylord; (OPAC) Gaylord
Database Vendor: Ebsco - EbscoHost, GaleNet
Function: ILL available
Mem of Mideastern Ohio Libr Orgn
Friends of the Library Group
Branches: 1
GREENTOWN BRANCH, 3300 Myers St NW, Greentown, 44630. SAN 357-0185. Tel: 330-499-3971. *Librn*, Jean Shelly
Library Holdings: Bk Vols 11,000; Bk Titles 8,000
Friends of the Library Group

C WALSH UNIVERSITY LIBRARY, 2020 Easton St NW, 44720-3396. SAN 313-2390. Tel: 330-490-7185. FAX: 330-490-7270. *Dir*, Daniel Suvak; E-Mail: suvak@alex.walsh.edu; *Assoc Librn*, Joanne Vennetti; Staff 3 (MLS 3)
Founded 1960. Enrl 1,200; Fac 70; Highest Degree: Master
Library Holdings: Bk Vols 130,000; Per Subs 700
Automation Activity & Vendor Info: (Circulation) TLC; (OPAC) TLC
Database Vendor: Dialog, GaleNet, IAC - Info Trac, IAC - SearchBank, OCLC - First Search, ProQuest
Publications: Periodical List
Partic in Molo Regional Library System; OCLC Online Computer Library Center, Inc; OHIONET

SR ZION UNITED CHURCH OF CHRIST LIBRARY, 415 S Main St, 44720. SAN 328-1426. Tel: 330-499-8191. FAX: 330-499-8194. *Librn*, Margaret Deibel; Staff 1 (MLS 1)
Library Holdings: Bk Vols 2,100; Bk Titles 2,000
Special Collections: Adult & Children's bks; Religious & Selected Secular bks

NORWALK

R FIRST PRESBYTERIAN CHURCH LIBRARY, 21 Firelands Blvd, 44857. SAN 313-6531. Tel: 419-668-1923. FAX: 419-663-5115. *Librn*, Jane Kerkhoff
Founded 1948
Library Holdings: Bk Titles 3,900; Per Subs 10
Subject Interests: Biog, Childrens educ, Family life, Fiction, Health, Personal problems, Relig-related
Special Collections: Archival Coll, Weekly Bulletin & Monthly Newsletter (1950- 1992 complete, 1921-49 incomplete)
Publications: Bulletins (weekly); Newsletter (monthly)

GL HURON COUNTY LAW LIBRARY ASSOCIATION,* Court House, 3rd flr, 2 E Main St, 44857. SAN 313-654X. Tel: 419-668-5127. FAX: 419-663-5026. E-Mail: hclawlib@accnorwalk.com. *Librn*, Erin Gail Bartle
Library Holdings: Bk Vols 13,000

P NORWALK PUBLIC LIBRARY,* 46 W Main St, 44857. SAN 313-6558. Tel: 419-668-6063. FAX: 419-663-2190. E-Mail: norwalk@oplin.lib.oh.us. Web Site: www.library.norwalk.lib.oh.us/norwalk. *Dir*, Martin L Haffey; Staff 2 (MLS 2)
Founded 1861. Pop 54,000; Circ 181,277
Library Holdings: Bk Titles 68,000; Per Subs 220
Special Collections: Huron County History & Genealogy; Local Newspapers, micro
Partic in Northwest Library District
Friends of the Library Group

OAK HARBOR

P OAK HARBOR PUBLIC LIBRARY, 147 W Main St, 43449-1344. SAN 313-6566. Tel: 419-898-7001. FAX: 419-898-0747. E-Mail: hoesmapa@oplin.lib.oh.us, oakharpl@oplin.lib.oh.us. Web Site: library.norweld.lib.oh.us/oak-harbor/. *Dir*, Pam Hoesman; Staff 10 (MLS 1, Non-MLS 9)
Founded 1908. Pop 8,837; Circ 78,527
Jan 1999-Dec 1999 Income $369,948, State $309,404, Other $60,544. Mats Exp $43,250, Books $36,000, Per/Ser (Incl. Access Fees) $7,250. Sal $109,672
Library Holdings: Bk Vols 26,000; Per Subs 139
Automation Activity & Vendor Info: (Cataloging) epixtech, inc.; (Circulation) epixtech, inc.; (ILL) epixtech, inc.; (OPAC) epixtech, inc.
Partic in Northwest Library District; SEO Automation Network
Friends of the Library Group

OAKWOOD

P WRIGHT MEMORIAL PUBLIC LIBRARY, 1776 Far Hills Ave, 45419-2598. SAN 313-4830. Tel: 937-294-7171. FAX: 937-294-8578. Web Site: www.wright.lib.oh.us. *Dir*, Antoinette Walder; E-Mail: walderan@oplin.lib.oh.us; *Circ*, Dianne Tankersley; *AV*, Meredith Hayes; *Ref*, Ann Snively; *Tech Servs*, Anne Frantz; *Ch Servs*, Emily Mummey; Staff 11 (MLS 8, Non-MLS 3)
Founded 1913. Pop 8,900; Circ 691,000
Jan 2000-Dec 2000 Income $1,828,634, State $1,535,208, Locally Generated Income $293,426. Mats Exp $369,200, Books $241,700, Per/Ser (Incl. Access Fees) $13,000, Micro $11,000, AV Equip $83,500, Electronic Ref Mat (Incl. Access Fees) $20,000. Sal $871,000 (Prof $400,000)
Library Holdings: Bk Vols 168,000; Bk Titles 135,000; Per Subs 520
Subject Interests: Literary criticism, Local history
Automation Activity & Vendor Info: (Cataloging) epixtech, inc.; (Circulation) epixtech, inc.; (OPAC) epixtech, inc.
Database Vendor: Dialog, IAC - SearchBank, OCLC - First Search, Wilson - Wilson Web
Publications: Bibliographies; Bookmarks
Partic in Miami Valley Librs; OCLC Online Computer Library Center, Inc

OBERLIN

C OBERLIN COLLEGE LIBRARY, 148 W College St, 44074. SAN 357-0215. Tel: 440-775-8285, Ext 229. FAX: 440-775-8739. E-Mail: reference.desk@oberlin.edu. Web Site: www.oberlin.edu/library/. *Dir*, Ray English; *Assoc Dir*, Alan Boyd; *Instrul Serv, Ref Serv*, Cynthia Comer; *Govt Doc, Ser*, Tom Hinders; *Circ, ILL*, Allison Gould; *Coll Develop*, Eric Carpenter; Staff 18 (MLS 17, Non-MLS 1)
Founded 1833. Enrl 2,913; Fac 249; Highest Degree: Master
Jul 1999-Jun 2000 Income $4,439,524. Mats Exp $1,760,036, Books $781,078, Per/Ser (Incl. Access Fees) $853,060, Presv $90,075, Micro $18,233. Sal $2,195,313 (Prof $876,249)
Library Holdings: Bk Vols 1,225,942; Per Subs 10,527
Special Collections: American dime novels; Anti-Slavery; Edwin Arlington Robinson; History of the Book; Oberliniana; Spanish Drama
Publications: Library of Congress Rule Interpretations for AACR2; Library Perspectives (external newsletter)
Partic in OHIONET
Friends of the Library Group
Departmental Libraries:
CLARENCE WARD ART LIBRARY, Allen Art Bldg, 91 N Main St, 44074-1193. SAN 357-024X. Tel: 440-775-8635. FAX: 440-775-8969. *Librn*, Barbara Prior; *Circ*, Paula Baymiller
Library Holdings: Bk Vols 74,813
MARY M VIAL MUSIC LIBRARY, Oberlin Conservatory of Music, 77 College St, 44074. SAN 357-0274. Tel: 440-775-8280. FAX: 440-775-8203. Web Site: www.oberlin.edu/library/conlib/. *Librn*, Deborah

Campana; E-Mail: deborah.campana@oberlin.edu; *Publ Servs*, Kathleen Abromeit; *Tech Servs*, David Knapp
Library Holdings: Bk Vols 188,905
Database Vendor: Innovative Interfaces INN - View
Partic in Ohio Library & Information Network
Friends of the Library Group
SCIENCE, Kettering Science Bldg, 130 W Lorain St, 44074-1083. SAN 357-0304. Tel: 440-775-8310. FAX: 440-775-8739. Web Site: www.oberlin.edu/library/sciencelib/. *Librn*, Alison Ricker; E-Mail: alison.ricker@oberlin.edu; Staff 2 (MLS 1, Non-MLS 1)
Founded 1965
Library Holdings: Bk Vols 84,407
Database Vendor: Dialog, Lexis-Nexis, OCLC - First Search, ProQuest, Silverplatter Information Inc.
Function: ILL limited

P OBERLIN PUBLIC LIBRARY, 65 S Main St, 44074-1626. SAN 313-6604. Tel: 440-775-4790. FAX: 440-774-2880. Web Site: www.oberlinpl.lib.oh.us. *Dir*, Charles Cook; E-Mail: cookc1@oplm.lib.oh.us; *Ref*, Eva Greenberg; *Ch Servs*, Helen Stutzenberger; Staff 3 (MLS 3)
Founded 1947. Pop 11,000
Jan 1999-Dec 1999 Income $917,163, State $535,840, Locally Generated Income $381,323. Mats Exp $155,195. Sal $460,707
Library Holdings: Bk Vols 120,000; Bk Titles 93,000; Per Subs 232
Subject Interests: Children's literature, Folklore, Ohio
Automation Activity & Vendor Info: (Acquisitions) Gaylord; (Cataloging) Gaylord; (Circulation) Gaylord
Friends of the Library Group

ORIENT

S PICKAWAY CORRECTIONAL INSTITUTION LIBRARY, PO Box 209, 43146-0209. SAN 371-6031. Tel: 614-877-4362. FAX: 614-877-0735. *Librn*, Eva Ballanger; Staff 1 (MLS 1)
Jul 2000-Jun 2001 Income Parent Institution $35,000. Mats Exp $35,000, Books $23,000, Per/Ser (Incl. Access Fees) $7,000, Micro $1,000, AV Equip $3,000, Electronic Ref Mat (Incl. Access Fees) $1,000. (Prof $47,000)
Library Holdings: Bk Titles 20,000; Per Subs 86
Automation Activity & Vendor Info: (Cataloging) EOS; (Circulation) EOS; (OPAC) EOS

ORRVILLE

P ORRVILLE PUBLIC LIBRARY, 230 N Main St, 44667. SAN 313-6620. Tel: 330-683-1065. TDD: 330-683-1065. FAX: 330-683-1984. Web Site: www.orrville.lib.oh.us. *Dir*, Cindy Lombardo; E-Mail: cindy.lombardo@orrville.lib.oh.us; *Asst Dir*, Margaret Sander; E-Mail: margaret.sander@orrville.lib.oh.us; *Ch Servs*, Deborah Bukovitz; E-Mail: deb.bukovitz@orrville.lib.oh.us; *Ref*, Maureen Lerch; E-Mail: maureen.lerch@orrville.lib.oh.us; Staff 5 (MLS 3, Non-MLS 2)
Founded 1925. Pop 14,792; Circ 273,906
Jan 2000-Dec 2000 Income $926,136, State $664,859, County $139,223, Locally Generated Income $122,054. Mats Exp $151,055, Books $88,506, Per/Ser (Incl. Access Fees) $7,398, AV Equip $18,794, Other Print Mats $4,424, Electronic Ref Mat (Incl. Access Fees) $31,933. Sal $392,702 (Prof $184,683)
Library Holdings: Bk Vols 73,143; Per Subs 200
Subject Interests: Railroads
Automation Activity & Vendor Info: (Acquisitions) DRA; (Cataloging) DRA; (Circulation) DRA
Partic in Cleveland Area Metropolitan Library System; Clevnet Automation Consortia
Friends of the Library Group

WAYNE COLLEGE LIBRARY,* University of Akron-Wayne College, 1901 Smucker Rd, 44667-9758. SAN 313-6639. Tel: 330-684-8950. FAX: 330-683-1381. *Dir*, Elys Kettling; E-Mail: elys@uakron.edu; Staff 4 (MLS 2, Non-MLS 2)
Founded 1972. Enrl 980
Jul 1997-Jun 1998 Income $243,427. Mats Exp $64,254, Books $35,190, Per/Ser (Incl. Access Fees) $25,043. Sal $120,994 (Prof $79,323)
Library Holdings: Bk Vols 20,000; Per Subs 440
Partic in Ohio Library & Information Network
Friends of the Library Group

ORWELL

P GRAND VALLEY PUBLIC LIBRARY,* One N School St, 44076-9537. SAN 313-6647. Tel: 440-437-6545. FAX: 440-437-1017. *Dir*, Nancy Evans
Founded 1903. Pop 2,500; Circ 70,841
1997-1998 Income $120,000
Library Holdings: Bk Vols 30,000; Per Subs 64
Partic in Northern Ohio Libr Asn

OTTAWA

P PUTNAM COUNTY DISTRICT LIBRARY,* 525 N Thomas St, PO Box 308, 45875-0308. SAN 357-0339. Tel: 419-523-3747. FAX: 419-523-6477. *Dir*, Ernie Kallay; *Ref*, Heidi Myers; *YA Servs*, Traci Welch-Moritz; *ILL*, Linda Hermiller
Founded 1924. Circ 350,000
Library Holdings: Bk Vols 19,000; Per Subs 185
Publications: Death, Administration, Marriage & Miscellaneous Notices from the Kalida; Index to the 1934 Centennial History Putnam County; List of letters at the Post office at Kalida Putnam County, from the Kalida Venture 1845-1854; Newspaper Notices from Kalida, Ohio Putnam County 1855-1860; Newspaper Notices from the Kalida Sentinel Putnam County, Ohio 1861-1866; The Putnam County, Ohio, Infirmary Journal 1869-1883
Partic in Northwest Library District
Friends of the Library Group
Branches: 7
COLUMBUS GROVE BRANCH, 317 N Main, Columbus Grove, 45830. SAN 357-0363. Tel: 419-659-2355. *Librn*, Judy Schroeder
Friends of the Library Group
CONTINENTAL BRANCH, City Bldg, Continental, 45831. SAN 357-0371. Tel: 419-596-3727. *Librn*, Theresa Jones
FORT JENNINGS BRANCH, Memorial Hall, PO Box 218, Fort Jennings, 45844. SAN 328-7807. Tel: 419-286-2351. *Librn*, Carol Meyer
KALIDA BRANCH, PO Box 183, Kalida, 45853. SAN 357-038X. Tel: 419-532-3636. *Librn*, Ruth Hermiller
LEIPSIC BRANCH, 305 W Main St, Leipsic, 45856. SAN 357-0398. Tel: 419-943-2604. *Librn*, Janet Steingass
Library Holdings: Bk Vols 8,400; Per Subs 30
Friends of the Library Group
OTTOVILLE BRANCH, Wayne St, PO Box 517, Ottoville, 45876. SAN 357-0428. Tel: 419-453-2111. *Librn*, Jann Eickholt
Founded 1962. Circ 28,000
Library Holdings: Bk Titles 10,000; Per Subs 22
Friends of the Library Group
PANDORA - RILEY BRANCH, PO Box 478, Pandora, 45877. SAN 328-8544. Tel: 419-384-3232. *Librn*, Bev Ricker
Friends of the Library Group
Bookmobiles: 1

OXFORD

C MIAMI UNIVERSITY, King Library, 45056. SAN 357-0452. Tel: 513-529-2800. Interlibrary Loan Service Tel: 513-529-6147. FAX: 513-529-3110. Interlibrary Loan Service FAX: 513-529-1682. Web Site: www.lib.muohio.edu. *Dean of Libr, Librn*, Judith A Sessions; *Assoc Dean*, Richard Pettitt; Tel: 513-529-1647, Fax: 513-529-1719; *Access Serv*, Scott Van Dam; Tel: 513-529-6148; *Doc*, Jean Sears; Tel: 513-529-3340, Fax: 513-529-1719; *Info Res*, Belinda Barr; Tel: 513-529-7096; *Rare Bks, Spec Coll*, C Martin Miller; Tel: 513-529-3324; *Syst Coordr*, Stan Brown; Tel: 513-529-2351; *Tech Servs*, Elizabeth Brice; Tel: 513-529-4140, Fax: 513-529-1719. Subject Specialists: *Science/technology*, Susan Hocker; Staff 38 (MLS 34, Non-MLS 4)
Founded 1824. Enrl 15,737; Fac 860; Highest Degree: Doctorate
Jul 1998-Jun 1999 Income (Main and Other College/University Libraries) $8,689,419, State $8,329,419, Federal $10,000, Other $350,000. Mats Exp $3,825,000, Books $1,000,000, Per/Ser (Incl. Access Fees) $2,350,000, Presv $200,000, Micro $200,000, Electronic Ref Mat (Incl. Access Fees) $75,000. Sal $3,700,000 (Prof $1,800,000)
Library Holdings: Bk Vols 2,190,506; Per Subs 10,314
Special Collections: 19th Century Medical Botany; Botanical Medicine; Ibsen, Strindberg, Shaftesbury, Cather, Orwell, Howells, Farrell, Bogan, O'Neill, Whitman, Shakespeare's first four folios.; King Coll of Early Juvenile Books & Periodicals (1536-Present); Literary Society Libraries; McGuffey & other 19th Century Textbooks; Ohio River Valley History, incl mss; Papers of Jefferson Davis (his cabinet members & officers); Pre-Revolutionary Russian Military History; Railroad Coll; Scripps Foundation; Shaker Coll; Transportation History; World Vegetation maps
Automation Activity & Vendor Info: (Acquisitions) Innovative Interfaces Inc.; (Circulation) Innovative Interfaces Inc.; (ILL) Innovative Interfaces Inc.; (OPAC) Innovative Interfaces Inc.; (Serials) Innovative Interfaces Inc.
Database Vendor: OCLC - First Search
Publications: Keepsakes; Words'Worth (Friends' Newsletter)
Partic in Greater Cincinnati Library Consortium; OCLC Online Computer Library Center, Inc; Ohio Library & Information Network; OHIONET
Friends of the Library Group
Departmental Libraries:
AMOS MUSIC LIBRARY, King Library, 45056. SAN 357-0517. Tel: 513-529-2299. *Librn*, Barry Zaslow; Staff 3 (MLS 1, Non-MLS 2)
Subject Interests: Music
BRILL SCIENCE LIBRARY, King Library, 45056. SAN 357-0541. Tel: 513-529-7201. FAX: 513-529-1736. Web Site: www.lib.muohio.edu/libinfo/depts/brill. *Head Librn*, Susan Hocker; Tel: 513-529-7206, E-Mail: shocker@lib.muohio.edu; Staff 5 (MLS 5)
Founded 1978. Enrl 16,000; Fac 1,000; Highest Degree: Doctorate
Special Collections: Kuchler Vegetation Maps
Automation Activity & Vendor Info: (Acquisitions) Innovative Interfaces

Inc.; (Cataloging) Innovative Interfaces Inc.; (Circulation) Innovative Interfaces Inc.; (Course Reserve) Innovative Interfaces Inc.; (OPAC) Innovative Interfaces Inc.; (Serials) Innovative Interfaces Inc.
Partic in Ohio Library & Information Network
WERTZ ART-ARCHITECTURE LIBRARY, King Library, 45056. SAN 357-0487. Tel: 513-529-1904. Web Site: www.lib.muohio.edu/libinfo/depts/artarch/. *Actg Librn*, Shannon Van-Kirk; Tel: 513-529-6650, Fax: 513-529-4159; Staff 1 (MLS 1)
Subject Interests: Architecture, Art

PAINESVILLE

C LAKE ERIE COLLEGE, James F Lincoln Library,* 391 W Washington St, 44077. SAN 313-6663. Tel: 440-639-7867. FAX: 440-639-7865. Web Site: www.lec.edu/library/index.htm. *Dir*, Christopher Bennett; Tel: 440-639-7865, E-Mail: bennett@lakeerie.edu; *Librn*, Maria Bagshaw; Tel: 440-639-4743, E-Mail: mbagshaw@lec.edu; *Cat*, Lori Greuber; Tel: 440-639-4742; Staff 3 (MLS 2, Non-MLS 1)
Founded 1856. Enrl 700; Fac 45; Highest Degree: Master
Library Holdings: Bk Vols 90,000; Per Subs 1,720
Subject Interests: Equestrian studies
Special Collections: Thomas Harvey Coll
Automation Activity & Vendor Info: (Cataloging) TLC; (Circulation) TLC; (Course Reserve) TLC; (OPAC) TLC
Database Vendor: IAC - SearchBank, Lexis-Nexis
Partic in Cleveland Area Metropolitan Library System; OHIONET

M LAKE HOSPITAL SYSTEM, INC, Health Science Libraries,* 10 E Washington, 44077. SAN 324-5349. Tel: 440-354-2400, Ext 2019 (East), 440-953-9600, Ext 3123 (West). E-Mail: eastlibrary@lhs.net. *Librn*, Holly Kimborowicz
Library Holdings: Bk Titles 2,314; Per Subs 220
Subject Interests: Allied health, Consumer health, Hospital administration, Medicine, Nursing
Publications: Newsletter
Partic in Dialog Corporation; Nat Libr of Med

P MORLEY LIBRARY, 184 Phelps St, 44077-3926. SAN 357-0665. Tel: 440-352-3383. FAX: 440-352-2653. Web Site: www.morleylibrary.org. *Dir*, Mary-Frances Burns; Fax: 440-352-2652, E-Mail: burnsmf@oplin.lib.oh.us; *ILL, Ref Serv Ad*, Laura Bunnell; Fax: 440-352-9097, E-Mail: bunnella@oplin.lib.oh.us; *YA Servs*, Krista Zivkovich; Fax: 440-352-9097, E-Mail: zivkovkr@oplin.lib.oh.us; *Tech Servs*, Patricia Parsons; Fax: 440-352-1069, E-Mail: parsonpa@oplin.lib.oh.us; *Head Ref*, Sara Eklund Payne; Tel: 440-352-3383, Ext 20, Fax: 440-352-9097, E-Mail: paynesa@oplin.lib.oh.us; *Ch Servs*, Deborah Anderson; E-Mail: andersda@oplin.lib.oh.us; *Ch Servs*, Anthony Petruzzi; Fax: 440-352-2653, E-Mail: petruzan@oplin.lib.oh.us; *Ref Serv Ad*, Carl Engel; E-Mail: engelca@oplin.lib.oh.us; *Ref Serv Ad*, Charley Voelker; Fax: 440-352-3383, E-Mail: voelkech@oplin.lib.oh.us; *Ref Serv Ad*, Krista Zivkovich; E-Mail: zivkovka@oplin.lib.oh.us; *Ref Serv Ad*, Sally Malone; E-Mail: mplgen@oplin.lib.oh.us. Subject Specialists: *Audio visual mats*, Charley Voelker; *Genealogy*, Sally Malone; *Local history*, Carl Engel; *Young adults*, Krista Zivkovich; Staff 46 (MLS 8, Non-MLS 38)
Founded 1877. Pop 42,757; Circ 676,275
Jan 1999-Dec 1999 Income $2,596,334, State $1,679,256, Locally Generated Income $779,941, Other $137,437. Mats Exp $560,716, Books $421,044, Per/Ser (Incl. Access Fees) $53,449, AV Equip $81,171, Other Print Mats $48,649, Electronic Ref Mat (Incl. Access Fees) $42,451. Sal $882,057 (Prof $355,034)
Library Holdings: Bk Vols 104,628; Per Subs 263
Subject Interests: Genealogy, Local history
Special Collections: Obituary Files, 1822 to Present
Automation Activity & Vendor Info: (OPAC) TLC
Database Vendor: Ebsco - EbscoHost, GaleNet, IAC - Info Trac
Function: Reference services available
Partic in Nola Regional Library System
Friends of the Library Group
Bookmobiles: 1

S RICERCA LLC, Information Services, 7528 Auburn Rd, PO Box 1000, 44077-1000. SAN 327-3504. Tel: 440-357-3462. FAX: 440-357-3484. E-Mail: infoserv@ricerca.com. *Head Ref*, Susan E Branchick; E-Mail: branchick_s@ricerca.com. Subject Specialists: *Chemistry*, Susan E Branchick; Staff 1 (Non-MLS 1)
Library Holdings: Bk Vols 4,500; Bk Titles 3,500; Per Subs 100
Subject Interests: Biology, Chemistry, Pharmaceuticals
Special Collections: Chemical Abstracts; FDA, EPA Regulations; US Patents (chemical)
Publications: Infocus Update (bimonthly)

PARMA

P CUYAHOGA COUNTY PUBLIC LIBRARY,* 2111 Snow Rd, 44134-2792. SAN 356-1305. Tel: 216-398-1800. Interlibrary Loan Service Tel: 216-398-1802. FAX: 216-398-1748. Web Site: www.cuyahogalibrary.org. *Exec Dir*, John Lonsak; *Tech Servs*, Louise Sevold; *ILL*, Beth French; *Cat*, Georgianne Wiersch; *AV*, Kenneth Katona; *Ch Servs*, Barbara Barstow; *Pub Relations*, Madeline Brookshire; Staff 523 (MLS 148, Non-MLS 375)
Founded 1922. Pop 608,000; Circ 10,041,302
Jan 1997-Dec 1998 Income $44,012,934, State $22,370,552, County $17,285,171. Mats Exp $4,621,165, Books $3,282,979, Per/Ser (Incl. Access Fees) $420,307. Sal $23,737,827
Library Holdings: Bk Vols 3,085,123; Bk Titles 425,000; Per Subs 1,856
Automation Activity & Vendor Info: (Acquisitions) DRA; (Cataloging) DRA; (Circulation) DRA; (Serials) DRA
Partic in OCLC Online Computer Library Center, Inc; OHIONET
Special Services for the Deaf - TTY machine
Friends of the Library Group
Branches: 28
BAY VILLAGE BRANCH, 502 Cahoon Rd, Bay Village, 44140-2194. SAN 356-133X. Tel: 440-871-6392. FAX: 440-871-5320. Web Site: www.cuyahogalibrary.org. *Branch Mgr*, Anita McNeal
Library Holdings: Bk Vols 64,487
Friends of the Library Group
BEACHWOOD BRANCH, 25501 Shaker Blvd, Beachwood, 44122-2398. SAN 356-1356. Tel: 216-831-6868. FAX: 216-831-0412.
Library Holdings: Bk Vols 61,682
Special Services for the Deaf - TTY machine
Friends of the Library Group
BEREA BRANCH, 7 Berea Commons, Berea, 44017-2524. SAN 356-1399. Tel: 440-234-5475. FAX: 440-234-2932. *Librn*, Lucinda Bereznay
Library Holdings: Bk Vols 62,925
Friends of the Library Group
BRECKSVILLE BRANCH, 9089 Brecksville Rd, Brecksville, 44141-2313. SAN 356-1429. Tel: 440-526-1102. FAX: 440-526-8793. *Librn*, Kathryn C Wilmer
Library Holdings: Bk Vols 43,911
Friends of the Library Group
BROOK PARK BRANCH, 6155 Engle Rd, Brook Park, 44142-2198. SAN 356-1453. Tel: 216-267-5250. FAX: 216-267-3776. Web Site: www.cuyahogalibrary.org. *Branch Mgr*, Jeanne DeLaney
Library Holdings: Bk Vols 70,966
Special Services for the Deaf - TTY machine
Friends of the Library Group
BROOKLYN BRANCH, 4480 Ridge Rd, Brooklyn, 44144-3353. SAN 356-1488. Tel: 216-398-4600. FAX: 216-398-1545. Web Site: www.cuyahogalibrary.org. *Branch Mgr*, Marie Link
Library Holdings: Bk Vols 37,151
Friends of the Library Group
CHAGRIN FALLS BRANCH, 100 E Orange St, Chagrin Falls, 44022-2799. SAN 356-1518. Tel: 440-247-3556. FAX: 440-247-0179. *Librn*, Karen Bossard
Library Holdings: Bk Vols 53,322
Friends of the Library Group
FAIRVIEW PARK REGIONAL, 21255 Lorain Rd, Fairview Park, 44126-2120. SAN 356-1542. Tel: 440-333-4700, 440-333-4898. FAX: 440-333-0697. *Librn*, John Bellamy
Library Holdings: Bk Vols 166,128
Subject Interests: Biog, Genealogy, History, Travel
Special Services for the Deaf - TTY machine
Friends of the Library Group
GARFIELD HEIGHTS BRANCH, 5409 Turney Rd, Garfield Heights, 44125-3299. SAN 356-1577. Tel: 216-475-8178. FAX: 216-475-1015. *Librn*, Kathy Heinrich
Library Holdings: Bk Vols 57,464
Friends of the Library Group
GATES MILLS MINI LIBRARY, 7580 Old Mill Rd, PO Box 249, Gates Mills, 44040-0249. SAN 356-1607. Tel: 440-423-4808. FAX: 440-423-1363. *Librn*, James McPeak
Library Holdings: Bk Vols 7,587
INDEPENDENCE BRANCH, 6361 Selig Dr, Independence, 44131-4926. SAN 356-1631. Tel: 216-447-0160. FAX: 216-447-1371. *Librn*, Judith Cramer
Library Holdings: Bk Vols 29,818
Friends of the Library Group
MAPLE HEIGHTS REGIONAL, 5225 Library Lane, Maple Heights, 44137-1291. SAN 356-1690. Tel: 216-475-5000. FAX: 216-587-7281. *Adminr*, Penelope Jeffrey; E-Mail: pjeffrey@cuyahoga.lib.oh.us; *YA Servs*, Mary Arnold; *Ch Servs*, Cynthia Alexa. Subject Specialists: *Business and management*, Sue McKimm; *Law*, Melissa Barr; *Social sciences and issues*, William Shea
Library Holdings: Bk Vols 208,386
Subject Interests: Bus, Law, Philosophy, Religion, Sociology
Partic in Cleveland Area Metropolitan Library System
Special Services for the Deaf - TDD
Friends of the Library Group
MAYFIELD REGIONAL, 6080 Wilson Mills Rd, Mayfield Village, 44143-2179. SAN 356-1720. Tel: 440-473-0350. FAX: 440-473-0774. *Adminr*, James J McPeak. Subject Specialists: *Art*, Kenneth Neal; *Literature*, Charla Coatoam; *Music*, Eric Van der Schalie
Library Holdings: Bk Vols 194,340
Subject Interests: Fine arts, Foreign Language, Literature

Friends of the Library Group
MIDDLEBURG HEIGHTS BRANCH, 15600 E Bagley Rd, Middleburg Heights, 44130-4897. SAN 356-1755. Tel: 440-234-3600. FAX: 440-234-0849. *Branch Mgr*, Rebecca Wills
Library Holdings: Bk Vols 66,237
Friends of the Library Group
NORTH OLMSTED BRANCH, 27425 Butternut Ridge Rd, North Olmsted, 44070-3186. SAN 356-178X. Tel: 440-777-6211. FAX: 440-777-4312. *Librn*, Donna Meyers
Library Holdings: Bk Vols 57,600
Friends of the Library Group
NORTH ROYALTON BRANCH, 14600 State Rd, North Royalton, 44133-5192. SAN 356-181X. Tel: 440-237-3800. FAX: 440-237-6149. *Librn*, Caroline Vicchiarelli
Library Holdings: Bk Vols 67,313
Friends of the Library Group
OLMSTED FALLS BRANCH, 7850 Main St, Olmsted Falls, 44138-2034. SAN 356-1844. Tel: 440-235-1150. FAX: 440-235-0954. *Librn*, Mark McKinstry
Library Holdings: Bk Vols 28,519
Friends of the Library Group
ORANGE, 31300 Chagrin Blvd, Pepper Pike, 44124-5975. SAN 356-1879. Tel: 216-831-4282. FAX: 216-831-0714. *Librn*, Marian Maldonado-Pagan
Library Holdings: Bk Vols 49,983
Friends of the Library Group
PARMA HEIGHTS BRANCH, 6206 Pearl Rd, Parma Heights, 44130-3086. SAN 356-1909. Tel: 440-884-2313. FAX: 440-884-2713.
Library Holdings: Bk Vols 51,674
Friends of the Library Group
PARMA REGIONAL, 7335 Ridge Rd, 44129-6602. SAN 356-1933. Tel: 440-885-5362. FAX: 440-885-2105. Web Site: www.cuyahogalibrary.org. *Adminr*, Dorothy Lettus. Subject Specialists: *Fiction*, Melanie Deutsch; *Science/technology*, Karin Weinhold; *Technology*, Karin Weinhold
Library Holdings: Bk Vols 170,873
Subject Interests: Fiction, Health, Sci, Technology
Friends of the Library Group
PARMA-RIDGE, 5850 Ridge Rd, 44129-3199. SAN 328-9753. Tel: 440-888-4300. FAX: 440-884-2097. *Librn*, Barbara Stiber
Library Holdings: Bk Vols 21,135
Friends of the Library Group
PARMA-SNOW, 2121 Snow Rd, 44134-2789. SAN 356-1968. Tel: 216-661-4240. FAX: 216-661-1019. Web Site: www.cuyahogalibrary.org. *Branch Mgr*, Jeanne Dzurenko
Library Holdings: Bk Vols 57,707
Friends of the Library Group
RICHMOND MINI LIBRARY, 691 Richmond Rd, Richmond Heights, 44143-2908. SAN 329-6075. Tel: 440-449-2666. Web Site: www.cuyahogalibrary.org. *Adminr*, James J McPeak
SOLON BRANCH, 34125 Portz Pkwy, Solon, 44139-4197. SAN 356-1992. Tel: 440-248-8777. FAX: 440-248-5369. *Librn*, Janet Everett
Library Holdings: Bk Vols 49,448
Friends of the Library Group
SOUTH EUCLID-LYNDHURST BRANCH, 4645 Mayfield Rd, South Euclid, 44121-4087. SAN 356-2026. Tel: 216-382-4880. FAX: 216-382-4584. *Librn*, Rosemary Kneale
Library Holdings: Bk Vols 53,920
Special Services for the Deaf - TTY machine
Friends of the Library Group
SOUTHEAST, 70 Columbus Rd, Bedford, 44146-2836. SAN 356-1364. Tel: 440-439-4997. FAX: 440-439-5846. Web Site: www.cuyahogalibrary.org. *Branch Mgr*, Vicki Adams-Cook
Library Holdings: Bk Vols 46,649
Friends of the Library Group
STRONGSVILLE BRANCH, 13213 Pearl Rd, Strongsville, 44136-3495. SAN 356-2050. Tel: 440-238-5530. FAX: 440-572-8685.
Library Holdings: Bk Vols 78,393
Friends of the Library Group
WARRENSVILLE HEIGHTS BRANCH, 22035 Clarkwood Pkwy, Warrensville Heights, 44128-4885. SAN 356-2085. Tel: 216-464-5280. FAX: 216-464-6475. *Librn*, Lena Nance
Library Holdings: Bk Vols 47,872
Friends of the Library Group

PATASKALA

PATASKALA PUBLIC LIBRARY,* 101 S Vine St, 43062. SAN 313-6698. Tel: 740-927-9986. FAX: 740-964-6204. *Dir*, Matthew J Nojonen; *Ch Servs*, Cathy Lantz; *Circ*, Scott Kammeyer; *Tech Servs, YA Servs*, Donna Willits; Staff 2 (MLS 2)
Founded 1937. Pop 4,551; Circ 113,005
Library Holdings: Bk Vols 69,500; Per Subs 60
Special Collections: Accords Coll
Friends of the Library Group

PAULDING

P PAULDING COUNTY CARNEGIE LIBRARY, 205 S Main St, 45879-1492. SAN 313-6701. Tel: 419-399-2032. FAX: 419-399-2114. Web Site: www.library.norweld.lib.oh.us/paulding. *Dir*, Susan Hill; E-Mail: hillsa@oplin.lib.oh.us; *Asst Dir*, Diana Coy
Founded 1898. Circ 55,723
Library Holdings: Bk Vols 80,000; Per Subs 120
Subject Interests: Genealogy
Special Collections: Paulding County Press (1859 to 1959), micro
Publications: Rural Library Service Newsletter
Partic in Northwest Library District; Norweld
Special Services for the Deaf - High interest/low vocabulary books; Special interest periodicals
Friends of the Library Group
Branches: 3
ANTWERP BRANCH, 205 N Madison, Antwerp, 45813. Tel: 419-258-2855. FAX: 419-258-2855. *Branch Mgr*, Laura Woodcox
Friends of the Library Group
OAKWOOD BRANCH, 230 N First St, Oakwood, 45873. Tel: 419-594-3337. FAX: 419-594-3337. *Branch Mgr*, Sue Thomas
Friends of the Library Group
PAYNE BRANCH, 101 N Main St, Payne, 45880. Tel: 419-263-3333. FAX: 419-263-3333. *Branch Mgr*, Ann Shuherk
Friends of the Library Group

PEMBERVILLE

P PEMBERVILLE PUBLIC LIBRARY, 375 E Front St, PO Box 809, 43450-0809. SAN 357-072X. Tel: 419-287-4012. FAX: 419-287-4620. E-Mail: pemlib@wcnet.org. Web Site: library.pembervillelibrary.org. *Dir*, Jane Kohlenberg; *Br Coordr*, Laura King; *Circ*, Janice Nollenberger; *Ch Servs*, Laurel Rakas; Staff 5 (MLS 2, Non-MLS 3)
Founded 1937. Pop 9,000; Circ 98,000
Jan 1999-Dec 1999 Income (Main Library and Branch Library) $436,729, State $15,088, Locally Generated Income $21,949. Mats Exp $79,916, Books $53,653, Per/Ser (Incl. Access Fees) $7,637, AV Equip $4,630, Electronic Ref Mat (Incl. Access Fees) $13,996. Sal $228,494 (Prof $82,000)
Library Holdings: Bk Titles 50,621; Per Subs 160; High Interest/Low Vocabulary Bk Vols 50
Subject Interests: Local history
Function: Document delivery services, ILL available, Photocopies available, Reference services available, Some telephone reference
Partic in Northwestern Libr District
Friends of the Library Group
Branches: 2
LUCKEY BRANCH, 228 Main St, Luckey, 43443. SAN 377-8274. Tel: 419-833-6040. FAX: 419-833-6040. Web Site: library.norweld.lib.oh.us/pemberville. *Head of Libr*, Carol Gambrell
Friends of the Library Group
STONY RIDGE BRANCH, 5805 Fremont Pike, Stony Ridge, 43463. SAN 357-0754. Tel: 419-837-5948. FAX: 419-837-5948. Web Site: library.norweld.lib.oh.us/pemberville. *Br Coordr*, Laura King
Library Holdings: Bk Vols 23,000
Friends of the Library Group

PENINSULA

P PENINSULA LIBRARY & HISTORICAL SOCIETY,* 6105 Riverview Rd, PO Box 236, 44264. SAN 313-671X. Tel: 330-657-2291. FAX: 330-657-2311. E-Mail: library@peninsula.lib.oh.us. *Librn*, Kim Lyon
Founded 1943. Pop 553,371
Library Holdings: Bk Vols 38,500; Per Subs 130
Subject Interests: Biography, Fine arts
Special Collections: Local History Coll
Publications: Bi-monthly Newsletter
Friends of the Library Group

PEPPER PIKE

R TEMPLE ON THE HEIGHTS, Jack Jacobson Memorial Library, 27501 Fairmount Blvd, 44124. SAN 313-3931. Tel: 216-831-6555. FAX: 216-831-4599. *Librn*, Ralph R Simon; Staff 2 (MLS 1, Non-MLS 1)
Founded 1928
Library Holdings: Bk Vols 9,000

C URSULINE COLLEGE, Ralph M Besse Library, 2550 Lander Rd, 44124-4398. SAN 313-3885. Tel: 440-449-4202. FAX: 440-449-3180. Web Site: www.ursuline.edu/library/index.htm. *Dir*, Betsey Belkin; E-Mail: bbelkin@ursuline.edu; *Cat, Media Spec*, Alice Crosetto; E-Mail: acrosetto@ursuline.edu; *Ser*, Myra Fortlage; *Acq*, Vivian Harris; E-Mail: vharris@ursuline.edu; *Ref*, Carol Shisler; E-Mail: cshisler@ursuline.edu; Staff 17 (MLS 8, Non-MLS 9)
Founded 1871. Enrl 1,300; Fac 92; Highest Degree: Master
Jul 2000-Jun 2001 Income $670,807. Mats Exp $263,125, Books $67,000,

Per/Ser (Incl. Access Fees) $55,000, Presv $6,400. Sal $407,682
Library Holdings: Bk Vols 128,431; Bk Titles 91,526; Per Subs 534
Subject Interests: Art therapy, Education, Health sci, Nursing
Special Collections: Besse Rivers Coll; Global Studies; Picture Archives Coll
Automation Activity & Vendor Info: (Acquisitions) Innovative Interfaces Inc.; (Cataloging) Innovative Interfaces Inc.; (Circulation) Innovative Interfaces Inc.; (OPAC) Innovative Interfaces Inc.; (Serials) Innovative Interfaces Inc.
Publications: Acquisitions List
Partic in Cleveland Area Metropolitan Library System; Ohio Library & Information Network; OHIONET
Friends of the Library Group

PERRY

S CLEVELAND ELECTRIC ILLUMINATING COMPANY, Perry Power Plant Information & Resource Center,* TEC 219 Bldg, 10 Center Rd, 44081. SAN 326-6729. Tel: 440-259-3737, Ext 5864. Toll Free Tel: 800-589-3101. FAX: 440-280-8027.
Founded 1984
Library Holdings: Bk Titles 12,090; Per Subs 50

P PERRY PUBLIC LIBRARY, 3753 Main St, 44081-9501. SAN 313-6728. Tel: 440-259-3300. FAX: 440-259-3977. Web Site: www.perrypubliclibrary.org. *Dir*, Elizabeth Brunson; E-Mail: peradm@library.cpl.org; *Ref*, Ann Freed; *Ch Servs*, Kara Cervelli; Staff 7 (MLS 4, Non-MLS 3)
Founded 1929. Pop 6,780; Circ 131,000
Jan 1999-Dec 1999 Income $885,486, State $416,971, Locally Generated Income $333,689, Other $134,826. Mats Exp $89,870, Books $58,769, Per/Ser (Incl. Access Fees) $6,552, AV Equip $20,070, Electronic Ref Mat (Incl. Access Fees) $4,479. Sal $325,345 (Prof $224,515)
Library Holdings: Bk Titles 66,350; Per Subs 225
Database Vendor: DRA
Partic in Cleveland Area Metropolitan Library System; Clevnet; Northeastern Ohio Libr Asn
Friends of the Library Group

PERRYSBURG

C NORTHWEST OHIO REGIONAL BOOK DEPOSITORY,* 12764 Levis Pkwy, 43551. SAN 376-9135. Tel: 419-874-4891. FAX: 419-874-4385. *Mgr*, Michael McHugh; Staff 1 (MLS 1)
Library Holdings: Bk Vols 1,100,000
Cooperative Library Facility of Bowling Green State University, University of Toledo & the Medical College of Ohio

J OWENS COMMUNITY COLLEGE LIBRARY, 30335 Oregon Rd, 43551. (Mail add: PO Box 10000, 43699-1947), Tel: 419-661-7221. Circulation Tel: 419-661-7015. Reference Tel: 419-661-7017. FAX: 419-661-7021. E-Mail: libhelp@owens.cc.oh.us. Web Site: www.owens.cc.oh.us/Library. *Dean of Libr*, Thomas R Sink; E-Mail: tsink@owens.cc.oh.us; *Dir*, Nancy J Emrick; E-Mail: nemrick@owens.cc.oh.us; *Acq*, Deborah Lewis; *Cat*, Laurel King; *Ser*, Patricia Breno; *AV*, Mark Karamol; E-Mail: mkaramol@owens.cc.oh.us; *Circ*, Jennifer Blum; *Coll Develop*, Sharon Stein; Staff 14 (MLS 6, Non-MLS 8)
Founded 1966. Enrl 17,000; Fac 800; Highest Degree: Associate
Jul 2000-Jun 2001 Income Parent Institution $1,184,576. Mats Exp $352,880, Books $128,220, Per/Ser (Incl. Access Fees) $80,164, AV Equip $64,286, Electronic Ref Mat (Incl. Access Fees) $80,210. Sal $750,464 (Prof $310,000)
Library Holdings: Bk Vols 49,800; Bk Titles 38,600; Per Subs 530
Database Vendor: Innovative Interfaces INN - View
Partic in OCLC Online Computer Library Center, Inc; Ohio Library & Information Network; OHIONET
Special Services for the Blind - Adapted computers & special software with speech output to assist learning disabled, mentally retarded & uneducated

P WAY PUBLIC LIBRARY,* 101 E Indiana Ave, 43551. SAN 313-6744. Tel: 419-874-3135. FAX: 419-874-6129. Web Site: www.library.norweld.lib.oh.us/perrysburg/. *Dir*, Nancy Kelley; E-Mail: kelleynn@oplin.lib.oh.us; *Ch Servs*, Peggy Pile; *Media Spec, Ref*, David Maurer; *ILL, Librn*, Deborah DiGennaro; *Librn*, Richard Baranowski. Subject Specialists: *Local history*, Lynne Michalak
Founded 1881. Pop 25,000
Jan 1999-Dec 1999 Income $1,089,048, State $955,554, Other $133,494. Mats Exp $211,000, Books $123,323, Per/Ser (Incl. Access Fees) $10,500, Presv $53, Other Print Mats $5,500. Sal $535,000 (Prof $234,500)
Library Holdings: Bk Vols 95,969; Per Subs 277
Special Collections: Perrysburg Local History
Partic in Northwest Library District; Norweld
Friends of the Library Group

PICKERINGTON

P PICKERINGTON PUBLIC LIBRARY,* 201 Opportunity Way, 43147-2221. SAN 313-6752. Tel: 614-837-4104. FAX: 614-837-8425. *Librn*, Bonnie F Boggs; *Ref*, Karen Stover; *Ch Servs*, Suellen Goldsberry; *Tech Servs*, Carol Plympton
Circ 144,706
Library Holdings: Bk Vols 40,119; Per Subs 225
Publications: Monthly newsletter
Friends of the Library Group

PIKETON

S UNITED STATES ENRICHMENT CORP, (Formerly Lockheed Martin Utility Services, Inc), X710 Technical Resource Center, 3930 US Rte 23S MS-2206 X710, PO Box 628, 45661-0628. SAN 313-6760. Tel: 740-897-5797. FAX: 740-897-3595. *Librn*, James David Cox; Tel: 740-897-8577, Fax: 740-897-2507, E-Mail: coxjd@ports.usec.com; Staff 1 (MLS 1)
Founded 1953
Library Holdings: Bk Vols 31,000; Bk Titles 40,000; Per Subs 300
Subject Interests: Analytical chemistry, Atomic, Engineering, Industrial safety, Inorganic chemistry, Mathematical, Science
Database Vendor: OCLC - First Search
Function: For research purposes

PIQUA

J EDISON STATE COMMUNITY COLLEGE LIBRARY,* 1973 Edison Dr, 45356. SAN 313-6779. Tel: 937-778-8600. FAX: 937-778-1920. E-Mail: library@edison.cc.oh.us. Web Site: elink.edison.cc.oh.us. *Dean*, Marybeth Aust-Keefer; Tel: 937-778-8600, Ext 289, E-Mail: austkeefer@edison.cc.oh.us; *Assoc Dir*, Rebecca Parrish Telford; Tel: 937-778-8600, Ext 290, E-Mail: telford@edison.cc.oh.us; Staff 5 (MLS 2, Non-MLS 3)
Founded 1974
Jul 1998-Jun 1999 Income $356,993. Mats Exp $49,908, Books $10,162, Per/Ser (Incl. Access Fees) $16,619, Micro $1,650, AV Equip $1,667, Other Print Mats $19,810. Sal $170,197 (Prof $147,114)
Library Holdings: Bk Vols 33,527; Per Subs 499; Bks on Deafness & Sign Lang 75
Subject Interests: History, Nursing
Automation Activity & Vendor Info: (Cataloging) Innovative Interfaces Inc.; (Circulation) Innovative Interfaces Inc.; (Course Reserve) Innovative Interfaces Inc.; (Media Booking) Innovative Interfaces Inc.; (OPAC) Innovative Interfaces Inc.; (Serials) Innovative Interfaces Inc.
Database Vendor: Lexis-Nexis, OCLC - First Search, ProQuest, Wilson - Wilson Web
Partic in Ohio Library & Information Network; Ohio-Kentucky Coop Libraries; Southwestern Ohio Council For Higher Education

P FLESH PUBLIC LIBRARY,* 124 W Greene St, 45356-2399. SAN 313-6787. Tel: 937-773-6753. FAX: 937-773-5981. *Dir*, James C Oda; E-Mail: odaja@oplin.lib.oh.us; *Ref*, Patricia Smith; *Ch Servs*, Nancy Spillane; *Tech Servs*, Tess Graves; *Circ*, Cheryl Hepner; Staff 3 (MLS 3)
Founded 1890. Pop 25,000; Circ 260,926
Library Holdings: Bk Vols 109,000; Per Subs 172
Subject Interests: Local history
Partic in Miami Valley Librs

PLAIN CITY

P PLAIN CITY PUBLIC LIBRARY,* 305 W Main St, 43064-1148. SAN 313-6795. Tel: 614-873-4912. FAX: 614-873-8364. Web Site: www.plain.lib.oh.us. *Dir*, Sue Wilson; E-Mail: swilson@plain.lib.oh.us
Circ 137,153
Library Holdings: Bk Vols 50,598; Per Subs 114
Subject Interests: Genealogy, Local history
Partic in Central Ohio Hospital Library Consortium

POMEROY

P MEIGS COUNTY DISTRICT PUBLIC LIBRARY,* 216 W Main, 45769-1032. SAN 357-0789. Tel: 740-992-5813. FAX: 740-992-6140. Web Site: www.meigs.lib.oh.us. *Dir*, Kristi Eblin; E-Mail: eblinkr@oplin.lib.oh.us; *Publ Servs*, Olita Heighton; *Ch Servs*, Emily Bass; Staff 4 (Non-MLS 4)
Founded 1881. Pop 23,641; Circ 140,062
Library Holdings: Bk Vols 94,000; Per Subs 100
Special Services for the Deaf - High interest/low vocabulary books
Branches: 3
EASTERN, 38850 State Rte 7, Reedsville, 45572. SAN 378-1232. Tel: 740-985-3747. FAX: 740-985-3746.
Friends of the Library Group
MIDDLEPORT BRANCH, 178 S Third St, Middleport, 45760. SAN 357-0819. Tel: 740-992-5713. FAX: 740-992-4207.

Friends of the Library Group
RACINE BRANCH, 608 Tyree Blvd, PO Box 735, Racine, 45771. SAN 377-8290. Tel: 740-949-8200. FAX: 740-949-8300. *Librn*, Wendi Maxson
Friends of the Library Group

ORT CLINTON

L OTTAWA COUNTY LAW LIBRARY ASSOCIATION,* 315 Madison St, 43452. SAN 313-6809. Tel: 419-734-6763. *Librn*, Gary Kohli
Library Holdings: Bk Vols 542; Per Subs 15

IDA RUPP PUBLIC LIBRARY, 310 Madison St, 43452. SAN 313-6817. Tel: 419-732-3212. E-Mail: idarupp@oplin.lib.oh.us. Web Site: www.idarupp.lib.oh.us. *Dir*, James Crawford; Tel: 419-732-3221, Fax: 419-285-4004, E-Mail: crawfoja@oplin.lib.oh.us; *Ch Servs*, Marilyn Panovec; E-Mail: panovema@oplin.lib.oh.us; *Ad Servs*, Nieca Nowels; E-Mail: nowelsni@oplin.lib.oh.us; Staff 28 (MLS 3, Non-MLS 25)
Founded 1913. Pop 20,000; Circ 220,361
Library Holdings: Bk Titles 85,771; Per Subs 254
Special Collections: Bataan Memorial Coll; Genealogy & Local History Coll; Ohioana and Rare Book Collection
Automation Activity & Vendor Info: (Cataloging) epixtech, inc.; (Circulation) epixtech, inc.
Publications: Off the Shelf (quarterly newsletter)
Partic in State of Ohio Libr Syst
Friends of the Library Group
Branches: 1
ERIE ISLANDS, 548 Catawba, PO Box 147, Put-In-Bay, 43456. SAN 328-0101. Tel: 419-285-4004.; Staff 3 (Non-MLS 3)
Library Holdings: Bk Titles 6,195
Friends of the Library Group

ORTSMOUTH

PORTSMOUTH BAR & LAW LIBRARY,* Scioto County Court House, 3rd flr, 70 Sixth & Court St, 45662. SAN 313-6825. Tel: 740-355-8259, 740-574-2521. *Librn*, Kevin Bloom
Library Holdings: Bk Vols 25,100
Restriction: Not open to public

PORTSMOUTH PUBLIC LIBRARY, 1220 Gallia St, 45662-4185. SAN 357-0843. Tel: 740-354-5688. TDD: 740-354-6039. FAX: 740-353-1249. Web Site: www.portsmouth.lib.oh.us. *Dir*, Beverly L Cain; Tel: 740-353-5990, E-Mail: cainbe@oplin.lib.oh.us; *Asst Dir*, Paige Williams; Tel: 740-354-5263, E-Mail: weghorpa@oplin.lib.oh.us; Staff 70 (MLS 3, Non-MLS 67)
Founded 1878. Pop 80,327; Circ 638,214
Jan 1999-Dec 1999 Income (Main Library and Branch Library) State $3,295,150. Mats Exp $411,673, Books $290,319, Per/Ser (Incl. Access Fees) $52,166. Sal $1,074,864 (Prof $122,000)
Library Holdings: Bk Vols 213,680; Bk Titles 102,787; Per Subs 390
Subject Interests: Local history
Special Collections: Northwest Territories Coll
Automation Activity & Vendor Info: (OPAC) TLC
Database Vendor: Ebsco - EbscoHost, ProQuest
Function: ILL available
Branches: 4
VERN RIFFE BRANCH, 3850 Rhodes Ave, New Boston, 45662. SAN 357-0878. Tel: 740-456-4412. FAX: 740-456-4047. Web Site: www.ppl.lib.oh.us. *Mgr*, Angela Fannin; Staff 4 (Non-MLS 4)
SOUTH WEBSTER BRANCH, 496 Webster St, South Webster, 45682. SAN 326-8462. Tel: 740-778-2122. FAX: 740-778-3436. Web Site: www.ppl.lib.oh.us. *Mgr*, Timothy Gamp; Staff 4 (Non-MLS 4)
W GORDON RYAN BRANCH, PO Box 744, Lucasville, 45648. SAN 370-9027. Tel: 740-259-6119. FAX: 740-259-3168. Web Site: www.ppl.lib.oh.us. *Mgr*, Everett Reeves; Staff 4 (Non-MLS 4)
WHEELERSBURG BRANCH, 666 Center St, Wheelersburg, 45694. SAN 357-0894. Tel: 740-574-6116. FAX: 740-574-6588. Web Site: www.ppl.lib.oh.us. *Mgr*, Carolyn Blackburn; Staff 4 (Non-MLS 4)
Bookmobiles: 1

RIVER VALLEY HEALTH SYSTEM
M PATIENTS & STAFF LIBRARY, 2201 25th St, 45662. SAN 357-0932. Tel: 614-354-2804. FAX: 614-353-3019. *In Charge*, Barbara Pratt
Founded 1967
Library Holdings: Bk Vols 250; Per Subs 10
Partic in State Libr of Ohio

C SHAWNEE STATE UNIVERSITY, Clark Memorial Library, 940 Second St, 45662-4303. SAN 357-0967. Tel: 740-355-2267. Circulation Tel: 740-355-2519. Reference Tel: 740-355-2321. FAX: 740-355-2432. Web Site: www.shawnee.edu/library. *Dir*, Tess D Midkiff; E-Mail: tmidkiff@shawnee.edu; *Assoc Dir, Publ Servs, Ref*, Connie Salyers Stoner; E-Mail: csalyers@shawnee.edu; *AV*, Pete Duncan; E-Mail: pduncan@shawnee.edu; *Tech Servs*, David Rodgers; Tel: 740-355-2410, E-Mail: drodgers@shawnee.edu; *Syst Coordr*, Barb Anderson; E-Mail: banderson@shawnee.edu; *Circ*, Ann Marie Short; E-Mail: ashort@shawnee.edu; Staff 8 (MLS 6, Non-MLS 2)
Founded 1967. Enrl 2,892
Jul 1999-Jun 2000 Income $1,063,104. Mats Exp $230,465, Books $94,556, Per/Ser (Incl. Access Fees) $71,605, Presv $2,077, Micro $35,143, AV Equip $4,434, Electronic Ref Mat (Incl. Access Fees) $22,650. Sal $551,831 (Prof $258,799)
Library Holdings: Bk Vols 152,961; Per Subs 917
Special Collections: Albert Parry Coll; Bob Wilson Coll; Jessie Stuart Coll; Louis A Brennan Coll; Southern Ohio Valley Writers; Vernal G Riffe Memorabilia
Automation Activity & Vendor Info: (Acquisitions) Innovative Interfaces Inc.; (Cataloging) Innovative Interfaces Inc.; (Circulation) Innovative Interfaces Inc.; (Course Reserve) Innovative Interfaces Inc.; (OPAC) Innovative Interfaces Inc.; (Serials) Innovative Interfaces Inc.
Partic in Ohio Library & Information Network

PROSPECT

SR SAINT PAUL'S LUTHERAN CHURCH LIBRARY, 200 E Water St, 43342. SAN 371-8743. Tel: 740-494-2885. *Librn*, Lois H Ward; Tel: 740-494-2117, E-Mail: lhward@acc-net.com; Staff 1 (MLS 1)
Founded 1988
Jan 2000-Dec 2000 Income $1,700, Parent Institution $1,000, Other $700. Mats Exp $1,550, Books $1,300, Presv $100, AV Equip $150
Library Holdings: Bk Vols 2,007; Bk Titles 1,861
Subject Interests: Religion

PUT-IN-BAY

C OHIO STATE UNIVERSITY, Franz Theodore Stone Laboratory,* PO Box 119, 43456-0119. SAN 327-3563. Tel: 419-285-2341. FAX: 419-285-4754. *Head of Libr*, Bruce Leach
Library Holdings: Bk Vols 6,500; Per Subs 40

RAVENNA

S PORTAGE COUNTY HISTORICAL SOCIETY & LIBRARY, 6549 N Chestnut St, 44266. SAN 326-4106. Tel: 330-296-3523. *Pres*, John Carson; *Librn*, Barb Petroski; *Res*, Betty O'Neil; Staff 9 (Non-MLS 9)
Founded 1951
Library Holdings: Bk Vols 1,000
Subject Interests: Genealogy, History, Local history
Special Collections: Frederick J Loudin Coll
Publications: Newsletter (quarterly)
Restriction: Not a lending library, Open to public with supervision only
Function: Archival collection, Photocopies available, Research library
Open Tues, Thurs & Sun 2-4; group tours by appointment

L PORTAGE COUNTY LAW LIBRARY, 241 S Chestnut St, 44266. SAN 372-2023. Tel: 330-297-3661. *Librn*, Mary Alice Law
Library Holdings: Bk Vols 15,000; Per Subs 20

P REED MEMORIAL LIBRARY, Ravenna Public Library, 167 E Main St, 44266-3197. SAN 313-6833. Tel: 330-296-2827. TDD: 330-677-4278. FAX: 330-296-3780. E-Mail: refreed@oplin.lib.oh.us. Web Site: www.reed.lib.oh.us. *Dir*, Phyllis Cettomai; E-Mail: cettomph@oplin.lib.oh.us; *Assoc Dir*, Cynthia Wenger; *Ch Servs*, Esther Cross; *Circ*, Bonnie Policano; Staff 22 (MLS 6, Non-MLS 16)
Founded 1915. Pop 21,030; Circ 206,950
Library Holdings: Bk Vols 93,000; Bk Titles 87,000; Per Subs 220
Subject Interests: Local history
Automation Activity & Vendor Info: (Cataloging) Inlex; (Circulation) Inlex; (OPAC) Inlex
Database Vendor: Ebsco - EbscoHost, IAC - Info Trac, ProQuest
Publications: Newsletter
Function: Reference services available
Mem of NOLA Regional Libr Syst; OPLIN/CNCP; Portage Libr Consortium
Special Services for the Deaf - TDD
Special Services for the Blind - Talking Books
Friends of the Library Group

RICHWOOD

P RICHWOOD NORTH UNION PUBLIC LIBRARY,* 4 E Ottawa St, 43344-1296. SAN 313-6841. Tel: 740-943-3054. FAX: 740-943-9211. *Librn*, Judith Lawler
Founded 1882. Pop 2,200; Circ 44,000
Library Holdings: Bk Vols 69,010; Bk Titles 66,000; Per Subs 149

RIO GRANDE

C UNIVERSITY OF RIO GRANDE, Jeanette Albiez Davis Library, 218 N College Ave, 45674-3131. SAN 313-685X. Tel: 740-245-5353, 740-245-7322. FAX: 740-245-7096. Web Site: rio.edu/library/index.htm. *Dir*, J David Mauer; *Bibliog Instr, Ref*, Timothy M Snow; Staff 3 (MLS 3)

Founded 1876. Enrl 1,760
Library Holdings: Bk Vols 78,000; Per Subs 800
Publications: Instructional Material; Pathfinders; Student Newspaper Column
Partic in OHIONET

RIPLEY

P UNION TOWNSHIP PUBLIC LIBRARY, 27 Main St, 45167-1231. SAN 313-6868. Tel: 937-392-4871. FAX: 937-392-1631. *Dir*, Allison J Gibson; E-Mail: gibsonal@oplin.lib.oh.us; *Circ*, Carol Cooper; *Ch Servs*, Patricia Fithen
Founded 1915. Pop 34,966; Circ 140,879
Library Holdings: Bk Vols 40,500; Per Subs 195
Special Collections: Local History, Ripley, Ohio
Friends of the Library Group
Branches: 2
ABERDEEN PUBLIC, 1330 US 52 W, Aberdeen, 45101. Tel: 937-795-2534. FAX: 937-795-2534.
Library Holdings: Bk Vols 3,000
RUSSELLVILLE PUBLIC, 280 W Main, Russellville, 47168. Tel: 937-377-2700. FAX: 937-377-1302.
Library Holdings: Bk Vols 4,500

ROCK CREEK

P ROCK CREEK PUBLIC LIBRARY, Frederick A Swan Memorial Bldg, 2988 High St, PO Box 297, 44084-9703. SAN 313-6876. Tel: 440-563-3340. FAX: 440-563-9566. Web Site: www.rockcreek.lib.oh.us. *Dir*, Carol A O'Donnell; E-Mail: odonneca@hotmail.com; Staff 5 (Non-MLS 5)
Founded 1937. Pop 3,000; Circ 70,000
Jan 2000-Dec 2000 Income $180,000, State $174,000, Locally Generated Income $6,000. Mats Exp $170,000, Books $27,000, Per/Ser (Incl. Access Fees) $2,800, Electronic Ref Mat (Incl. Access Fees) $1,000. Sal $7,800
Library Holdings: Bk Titles 22,000; Per Subs 90; Bks on Deafness & Sign Lang 52
Special Collections: Ruth E Smik Art Coll
Automation Activity & Vendor Info: (Cataloging) epixtech, inc.
Database Vendor: Dialog, OCLC - First Search
Function: Some telephone reference
Mem of NOLA Regional Libr Syst
Partic in Coun of Ashtabula County Librs
Friends of the Library Group

ROCKFORD

P ROCKFORD CARNEGIE LIBRARY,* 162 S Main St, PO Box 330, 45882. SAN 313-6884. Tel: 419-363-2630. FAX: 419-363-3723. Web Site: library.norweld.lib.oh.us/rockford. *Dir*, Rozann Maurer
Founded 1902. Circ 32,000
Library Holdings: Bk Vols 23,500; Per Subs 112
Partic in Norweld
Friends of the Library Group

ROCKY RIVER

P ROCKY RIVER PUBLIC LIBRARY, 1600 Hampton Rd, 44116-2699. SAN 313-6892. Tel: 440-333-7610. FAX: 440-333-4184. Web Site: www.rrpl.org. *Dir*, John S Weedon; *Dep Dir*, Patricia Belcastro; *Ad Servs*, Evelyn Janoch; *Ch Servs*, Frances Homa; *Tech Servs*, Ann Richey; *YA Servs*, Stacey Hayman; *Tech Coordr*, Phil Shirley; *Circ*, Camille Nice; Staff 12 (MLS 12)
Founded 1928. Pop 20,410; Circ 687,403
Jan 1999-Dec 1999 Income $2,527,514, State $998,048, Locally Generated Income $1,390,349, Other $139,117. Mats Exp $367,039, Books $200,142, Per/Ser (Incl. Access Fees) $44,023, Electronic Ref Mat (Incl. Access Fees) $43,519. Sal $1,406,380
Library Holdings: Bk Vols 112,611; Per Subs 345
Subject Interests: Rocky River city hist
Special Collections: Cowan Pottery Museum
Database Vendor: epixtech, inc.
Publications: Between the Covers; Cowan Pottery Journal; Ex Libris
Partic in Cleveland Area Metropolitan Library System
Friends of the Library Group

ROOTSTOWN

CM NORTHEASTERN OHIO UNIVERSITIES COLLEGE OF MEDICINE, Oliver Ocasek Regional Medical Information Center, PO Box 95, 4209 SR 44, 44272-0095. SAN 313-6914. Tel: 330-325-2511. FAX: 330-325-0522. E-Mail: lse@neoucom.edu. Web Site: www.neoucom.edu. *Dir*, Larry S Ellis; *Asst Dir*, Christina Pope; *ILL*, Lisa Barker; *Tech Servs*, Onadell Bly; *Tech Servs*, Lisa Plymale; Staff 10 (MLS 10)
Founded 1975. Enrl 421; Fac 72; Highest Degree: Doctorate
Library Holdings: Bk Vols 92,664; Per Subs 1,097
Subject Interests: Life sci, Medicine
Special Collections: Archival Coll; Audiovisual Coll; Medical Implements; Nineteenth Century Medical Books
Publications: Medical Periodicals in Northeastern Ohio; NEOU Communique (newsletter)
Mem of NOLA Regional Libr Syst
Partic in BRS; Dialog Corporation; Greater Midwest Regional Medical Libr Network; Nat Libr of Med; NE Ohio Major Acad & Res Librs; OCLC Online Computer Library Center, Inc

ROSSFORD

P ROSSFORD PUBLIC LIBRARY, 720 Dixie Hwy, 43460-1289. SAN 313-6922. Tel: 419-666-0924. FAX: 419-666-1989. E-Mail: frenchmi@oplin.lib.oh.us. *Dir*, Marsha Wagner; E-Mail: wagnerma@oplin.lib.oh.us; *Ref*, Anne Bushell; *Cat, Ref*, Mary Mura; *Ch Servs*, Amy Luker; *Ch Servs*, Sandra Sheehy; Staff 15 (MLS 4, Non-MLS 11)
Founded 1936. Pop 14,500; Circ 174,080
Library Holdings: Bk Vols 91,896; Bk Titles 50,000; Per Subs 108
Partic in Northwest Library District
Friends of the Library Group

SABINA

P SABINA PUBLIC LIBRARY,* 11 E Elm St, 45169-1330. SAN 313-6930. Tel: 937-584-2319. FAX: 937-584-2751. *Dir*, Bonnie Starcher
Circ 32,809
Library Holdings: Bk Vols 22,000; Per Subs 90
Partic in Southwestern Ohio Rural Librs

SAINT CLAIRSVILLE

L BELMONT COUNTY LAW LIBRARY,* Court House, 101 W Main St, 43950. SAN 313-6949. Tel: 740-695-2121, Ext 248. FAX: 740-695-4968. *Librn*, Katie Smith
Library Holdings: Bk Vols 25,000

J BELMONT TECHNICAL COLLEGE LIBRARY,* 120 Fox-Shannon Pl, 43950-9735. SAN 313-6957. Tel: 740-695-9500, Ext 1058. FAX: 740-695-2247. *Dir*, Cathy Bennett; E-Mail: cbennett@belmont.cc.oh.us
Founded 1971
Library Holdings: Bk Vols 6,422; Bk Titles 6,330
Subject Interests: Allied health, Nursing
Partic in OCLC Online Computer Library Center, Inc; OHIONET

C OHIO UNIVERSITY, Eastern Campus Library, 45425 National Rd, 43950-9724. SAN 313-6965. Tel: 740-695-1720, Ext 205. FAX: 740-695-7075. Web Site: www.eastern.ohiou.edu/services/library.htm. *Dir*, Patricia Murphy; E-Mail: murphy@ohio.edu; *Circ*, Brad Cecil; Staff 4 (MLS 1, Non-MLS 3)
Founded 1957. Enrl 1,009
Library Holdings: Bk Vols 57,500; Per Subs 673
Subject Interests: Bus, Education, Nursing
Special Collections: Contemporary American Poetry
Partic in OCLC Online Computer Library Center, Inc; OHIONET

P SAINT CLAIRSVILLE PUBLIC LIBRARY,* 108 W Main St, 43950-1225. SAN 313-6973. Tel: 740-695-2062. FAX: 740-695-6420. Web Site: www.winslo.state.oh.us/stclibrary/. *Librn*, Sheila D Perkins
Founded 1941. Circ 148,090
Library Holdings: Bk Vols 53,927; Per Subs 114
Partic in SE Ohio Regional Librs
Friends of the Library Group

SAINT MARTIN

J CHATFIELD COLLEGE LIBRARY, 20918 State Rte 251, 45118. SAN 313-6981. Tel: 513-875-3344. FAX: 513-875-3912. *Librn*, Dolores Berish
Founded 1860. Enrl 350
Library Holdings: Bk Titles 18,500; Per Subs 35
Subject Interests: Appalachian studies, Children's literature, Fiber arts, Local history
Partic in SW Ohio Regional Libr Syst

SAINT MARYS

P COMMUNITY PUBLIC LIBRARY, 140 S Chestnut, 45885-2316. SAN 313-699X. Tel: 419-394-7471. TDD: 419-394-7471. FAX: 419-394-7291. Web Site: library.norweld.lib.oh.us/stmarys/. *Dir*, Susan H Pittman; E-Mail: pittmasu@oplin.lib.oh.us
Founded 1922. Pop 12,000; Circ 88,380
Jan 1999-Dec 1999 Income $574,188, State $525,330, Other $48,858. Sal $246,259
Library Holdings: Bk Vols 60,914; Per Subs 180
Subject Interests: Local history
Special Collections: Jim Tully Coll

Automation Activity & Vendor Info: (Cataloging) epixtech, inc.; (Circulation) epixtech, inc.; (OPAC) epixtech, inc.
Partic in Norweld; SE Ohio Regional Librs
Friends of the Library Group

AINT PARIS

SAINT PARIS PUBLIC LIBRARY,* 127 E Main St, PO Box 740, 43072. SAN 313-7007. Tel: 937-663-4349. FAX: 937-663-0297. *Actg Dir, Automation Syst Coordr, Librn*, Beverly A Guenther; E-Mail: guenthbe@oplin.lib.oh.us; Staff 11 (Non-MLS 11)
Founded 1936. Pop 10,000; Circ 48,000
Library Holdings: Bk Vols 35,309; Bk Titles 31,404; Per Subs 105; Bks on Deafness & Sign Lang 31
Subject Interests: Genealogy
Special Collections: AB Graham
Friends of the Library Group

ALEM

R ALLEGHENY WESLEYAN COLLEGE LIBRARY,* 2161 Woodsdale Rd, 44460. SAN 313-7015. Tel: 330-337-6403. FAX: 330-337-6255. *Librn*, Crystal Muir; E-Mail: crystalmuir@yahoo.com; *Librn*, Arnold Fitzgerald
Founded 1973. Enrl 51; Fac 8; Highest Degree: Bachelor
1997-1998 Income $15,713
Library Holdings: Bk Vols 11,500; Per Subs 100

KENT STATE UNIVERSITY, Salem Campus Library,* 2491 State Rte 45-S, 44460-9412. SAN 313-704X. Tel: 330-332-0361. FAX: 330-332-5086. *Dir*, Lilith R Kunkel; E-Mail: kunkel@salem.kent.edu
Founded 1962. Fac 50
Library Holdings: Bk Vols 19,160; Per Subs 151
Partic in Northeastern Ohio Libr Asn

SALEM PUBLIC LIBRARY, 821 E State St, 44460-2298. SAN 313-7058. Tel: 330-332-0042. FAX: 330-332-4488. E-Mail: library@salemohio.com. Web Site: www.salemohio.com/library. *Dir*, George W S Hays; Tel: 330-332-2458, E-Mail: haysgws@oplin.lib.oh.us; *Tech Servs*, JoEllen Johnston; E-Mail: johnstjo@oplin.lib.oh.us; *AV*, June Drotleff; E-Mail: drotlefju@oplin.lib.oh.us; *Ch Servs*, Jacqueline M Hilditch; E-Mail: hilditja@oplin.lib.oh.us; *Ref Serv Ad*, Ann D Grimes; E-Mail: grimesan@oplin.lib.oh.us; *Outreach Serv*, Cheryl Kelly; E-Mail: kellych@oplin.lib.oh.us; *Syst Coordr*, M Jane Massa; E-Mail: massaja@oplin.lib.oh.us; Staff 24 (MLS 6, Non-MLS 18)
Founded 1895. Pop 17,215; Circ 360,000
Jan 2000-Dec 2000 Income $1,031,318, State $9,687,673, Other $62,645. Mats Exp $1,007,145, Books $130,362, Per/Ser (Incl. Access Fees) $19,871, AV Equip $22,300, Electronic Ref Mat (Incl. Access Fees) $5,550. Sal $435,000 (Prof $207,804)
Library Holdings: Bk Vols 79,037; Per Subs 199
Special Collections: Anti-Slavery; Columbiana County & Salem History; Quaker History & Biography
Automation Activity & Vendor Info: (Cataloging) Gaylord; (Circulation) Gaylord; (OPAC) Gaylord
Database Vendor: Ebsco - EbscoHost

SANDUSKY

SAINT STEPHEN UNITED CHURCH OF CHRIST, Centennial Library, 905 E Perkins Ave, 44870. SAN 328-1353. Tel: 419-626-1612. FAX: 419-626-1617. *Librn*, Edith Balduff; *Asst Librn*, Karen Miller; Staff 1 (MLS 1)
Founded 1982
Library Holdings: Bk Titles 3,400

GL SANDUSKY BAY LAW LIBRARY ASSOCIATION, INC,* 323 Columbus Ave, 44870. SAN 313-7066. Tel: 419-626-4823. FAX: 419-626-4826. *Librn*, Laurie Repp
Library Holdings: Bk Vols 14,450

SANDUSKY LIBRARY,* 114 W Adams St, 44870. SAN 357-1025. Tel: 419-625-3834. FAX: 419-625-4574. Web Site: www.sandusky.lib.oh.us. *Dir*, Julie Brooks; *Asst Dir*, Terri Estel; *Ref*, Kip Currier; Staff 40 (MLS 5, Non-MLS 35)
Founded 1895. Pop 52,000
Jan 1999-Dec 1999 Income $2,402,000, State $1,800,000, Locally Generated Income $512,000, Other $90,000. Mats Exp $450,000, Books $350,000, Per/Ser (Incl. Access Fees) $25,000, Electronic Ref Mat (Incl. Access Fees) $8,000. Sal $1,366,000 (Prof $300,000)
Library Holdings: Bk Vols 175,056; Per Subs 365
Special Collections: Johnson's Island; Local History Archives
Automation Activity & Vendor Info: (Cataloging) DRA; (Circulation) DRA; (OPAC) DRA
Publications: A View of Sandusky; From the Widow's Walk, Vol I & II
Partic in CLEVE-NET; Cleveland Area Metropolitan Library System; OPLIN

SHAKER HEIGHTS

P SHAKER HEIGHTS PUBLIC LIBRARY, 16500 Van Aken Blvd, 44120-5318. SAN 357-1084. Tel: 216-991-2030. FAX: 216-991-5951. Web Site: www.shpl.lib.oh.us. *Dir*, Edrice G Ivory; E-Mail: shadm@library.cpl.org; *Ad Servs*, Donna Fox; *Ch Servs*, Jean Hanson; *Tech Servs*, Judy Hardy; *Circ*, Anne Cowan; *Media Spec*, Kristen Drake; *Ser*, Jennifer Streater. Subject Specialists: *Fiction*, Mella Davies; Staff 34 (MLS 23, Non-MLS 11)
Founded 1936. Pop 35,281; Circ 818,489
Jan 1999-Dec 1999 Income $5,156,452, State $1,739,927, City $2,613,093, Locally Generated Income $337,283. Mats Exp $694,525, Books $496,455, Per/Ser (Incl. Access Fees) $94,570. Sal $1,959,971 (Prof $1,092,773)
Library Holdings: Bk Vols 261,497
Subject Interests: Black history, Fiction, Local history
Automation Activity & Vendor Info: (Circulation) DRA
Publications: Shaker Magazine
Mem of Cleveland Area Metrop Libr Syst
Friends of the Library Group
Branches: 1
BERTRAM WOODS, 20600 Fayette Rd, 44122-2979. SAN 357-1114. Tel: 216-991-2421. FAX: 216-991-3124. *Mgr*, Sara Schiller; *Ch Servs*, Susan Scheps; *Circ*, Pam Mastrobuono
Library Holdings: Bk Vols 71,334
Friends of the Library Group

SHELBY

P MARVIN MEMORIAL LIBRARY, 29 W Whitney Ave, 44875-1252. SAN 313-7112. Tel: 419-347-5576. FAX: 419-347-7285. Web Site: www.shelbymm.lib.oh.us. *Dir*, Ann Bavin; E-Mail: bavinan@oplin.lib.oh.us; *Ch Servs*, Christine Kalb; E-Mail: kalbch@oplin.lib.oh.us; *Ch Servs*, Linda Morrison; E-Mail: morrisli@oplin.lib.oh.us; *Ref, Tech Servs*, Heather Klock; E-Mail: klockhe@oplin.lib.oh.us; Staff 5 (MLS 2, Non-MLS 3)
Founded 1897. Pop 15,000; Circ 118,104
Jan 2000-Dec 2000 Income $634,673, State $536,931, Other $97,742. Mats Exp $123,000, Books $115,000, Per/Ser (Incl. Access Fees) $8,000. Sal $227,000 (Prof $130,000)
Library Holdings: Bk Vols 58,275; Per Subs 198
Automation Activity & Vendor Info: (Cataloging) Gaylord; (Circulation) Gaylord; (OPAC) Gaylord
Friends of the Library Group

SIDNEY

P AMOS MEMORIAL PUBLIC LIBRARY, 230 E North St, 45365-2733. SAN 357-1149. Tel: 937-492-8354. Interlibrary Loan Service Tel: 937-492-6851. FAX: 937-492-9229. *Dir*, Scott Parsons; *Asst Dir*, Rebecca Bertsch; E-Mail: bertscre@oplin.lib.oh.us; *AV*, Mike Grone; *Tech Servs*, Memory Wilson; *Ch Servs*, Bonnie Banks; *Ref*, Mark Kister; Staff 50 (MLS 6, Non-MLS 44)
Founded 1869. Pop 44,000; Circ 401,442
Library Holdings: Bk Vols 102,028; Per Subs 311
Special Collections: Bessie Schiff Coll; Lois Lenski Coll
Automation Activity & Vendor Info: (Cataloging) epixtech, inc.; (Circulation) epixtech, inc.; (OPAC) epixtech, inc.
Partic in Miami Valley Librs; OCLC Online Computer Library Center, Inc; OHIONET
Branches: 5
ANNA BRANCH, 304 N Second St, Anna, 45302. SAN 357-1173. Tel: 937-394-2761. FAX: 937-394-2761. *Br Coordr*, Sheila Strunk
Library Holdings: Bk Vols 10,885
Friends of the Library Group
BOTKINS BRANCH, 109 E Lynn St, Botkins, 45306. SAN 357-1203. Tel: 937-693-6671. FAX: 937-693-6671. *Br Coordr*, Jane Vehorn
Library Holdings: Bk Vols 14,527
Friends of the Library Group
FORT LORAMIE BRANCH, PO Box 342, Fort Loramie, 45845-0342. SAN 357-1238. Tel: 513-295-3155. FAX: 513-295-3155. *Br Coordr*, Karen Anthony
Library Holdings: Bk Vols 12,381
Friends of the Library Group
JACKSON CENTER MEMORIAL, 205 S Linden St, Jackson Center, 45334. SAN 357-1262. Tel: 937-596-5300. FAX: 937-596-5300. *Br Coordr*, Carolyn Olivieri
Library Holdings: Bk Vols 12,662
Friends of the Library Group
RUSSIA BRANCH, 200 Raider St, PO Box 445, Russia, 45363. SAN 372-5219. Tel: 937-526-4300. FAX: 937-526-4300. *Br Coordr*, Carla Briggs
Library Holdings: Bk Vols 7,151
Friends of the Library Group

S AMOS PRESS, INC LIBRARY, 911 Vandemark Rd, PO Box 4129, 45365-4129. SAN 323-6048. Tel: 937-498-2111, Ext 276. FAX: 937-498-0888. *Librn*, Krista Hesselbein; E-Mail: khesselbein@amospress.com
Founded 1960
Library Holdings: Bk Titles 30,000; Per Subs 800

Subject Interests: Numismatics, Philately
Automation Activity & Vendor Info: (Cataloging) Sagebrush Corporation; (Circulation) Sagebrush Corporation

SOLON

S ERICO INC, Information Resources Center,* 34600 Solon Rd, 44139. SAN 375-1201. Tel: 440-248-0100. FAX: 440-248-0723. *Dir*, San Kar
Library Holdings: Bk Titles 6,000; Per Subs 105

SOUTH EUCLID

C NOTRE DAME COLLEGE, Clara Fritzsche Library, 4545 College Rd, 44121. SAN 313-3699. Tel: 216-381-1680, Ext 267. FAX: 216-381-3227. Web Site: www.ndc.edu. *Dir*, Karen Zoller; E-Mail: kzoller@ndc.edu; *Media Spec*, Patricia Peyton; *Cat, Circ*, Sharon Douglass; *Circ*, David Schiopota; Staff 3 (MLS 2, Non-MLS 1)
Founded 1922. Enrl 476; Fac 86; Highest Degree: Master
Jul 1999-Jun 2000 Mats Exp $31,587, Books $8,116, Per/Ser (Incl. Access Fees) $21,275, Presv $658, Micro $1,017, AV Equip $521. Sal $86,715 (Prof $57,428)
Library Holdings: Bk Vols 89,534; Bk Titles 60,430; Per Subs 271
Subject Interests: Education, Literature, Theology
Special Collections: Eastern Church Resource Center; Law Library for Paralegal Program; Le Cercle des Conferences Francaises French Coll; Tolerance Resource Center (Holocaust, diversity & antibias resources)
Automation Activity & Vendor Info: (Cataloging) Innovative Interfaces Inc.; (Circulation) Innovative Interfaces Inc.; (OPAC) Innovative Interfaces Inc.
Mem of Cleveland Area Metrop Libr Syst
Partic in Ohio Library & Information Network

SPRINGFIELD

S CLARK COUNTY HISTORICAL SOCIETY LIBRARY, 105 N Thompson Ave, 45504. (Mail add: PO Box 2157, 45501), SAN 320-2240. Tel: 937-324-0657. FAX: 937-324-1992. *Dir*, Floyd Barmann; *Coll Develop, Curator*, Virginia Weygandt
Founded 1897
Library Holdings: Bk Vols 3,000; Bk Titles 1,000
Subject Interests: Early Clark County newspapers, Genealogy
Special Collections: Periodicals (Crowell-Collier Publishing Company Coll), mags
Open Tues-Fri 10-4

P CLARK COUNTY PUBLIC LIBRARY, 201 S Fountain Ave, PO Box 1080, 45501-1080. SAN 357-1297. Tel: 937-323-9751. Circulation Tel: 937-328-6901. Reference Tel: 937-328-6903. FAX: 937-328-6908. Web Site: www.ccpl.lib.oh.us. *Dir*, Robert E Saunter; E-Mail: rsaunter@ccpl.lib.oh.us
Founded 1872. Pop 147,500; Circ 995,716
Library Holdings: Bk Vols 420,015; Per Subs 511; High Interest/Low Vocabulary Bk Vols 200; Bks on Deafness & Sign Lang 75
Special Collections: Children's Literature (Lois Lenski Coll), bks, mss
Automation Activity & Vendor Info: (Acquisitions) Gaylord; (Cataloging) Gaylord; (Circulation) Gaylord; (OPAC) Gaylord
Partic in Miami Valley Librs
Special Services for the Deaf - High interest/low vocabulary books; Special interest periodicals
Operate Literacy Center
Friends of the Library Group
Branches: 5
HOUSTON, 5 W Jamestown St, South Charleston, 45368. SAN 357-1327. Tel: 937-462-8047. Web Site: www.ccpl.lib.oh.us. *Librn*, Tammy Harshbarger
Circ 45,999
Library Holdings: Bk Vols 18,000
INDIAN MOUND, 45 Indian Dr, Enon, 45323. SAN 357-1351. Tel: 937-864-2502. Web Site: www.ccpl.lib.oh.us. *Librn*, Armo Mazor
Circ 40,102
Library Holdings: Bk Vols 16,500
PARK, 1119 Bechtle Ave, 45504. SAN 357-1386. Tel: 937-322-2498. Web Site: www.ccpl.lib.oh.us. *Librn*, Elizabeth Hull
Circ 120,175
Library Holdings: Bk Vols 26,000
SOUTHERN VILLAGE, 1123 Sunset Ave, 45505. SAN 357-1416. Tel: 937-322-2226. Web Site: www.ccpl.lib.oh.us. *Librn*, Kristin Lemaster
Circ 67,639
Library Holdings: Bk Vols 31,000
WARDER LITERACY CENTER, 137 E High St, 45502. SAN 370-1018. Tel: 937-323-8617. *Dir*, Marsha Randall
Bookmobiles: 2

J CLARK STATE COMMUNITY COLLEGE LIBRARY,* 570 E Leffel Lane, PO Box 570, 45501. SAN 313-7163. Tel: 937-328-6022. FAX: 937-328-6133. Web Site: lib2.clark.cc.oh.us/library/library.html. *Chief Librn, Online Servs, Ref*, Nancy Schwerner; *Media Spec*, James Hebner; Staff 2 (MLS 2)
Founded 1966. Enrl 2,500; Fac 61
Library Holdings: Bk Vols 35,000; Per Subs 375
Partic in Ohio Library & Information Network

M COMMUNITY HOSPITAL, Health Sciences Library,* 2615 E High St, 45505. SAN 313-7171. Tel: 937-328-9468. FAX: 937-328-9006. *Librn*, Julie Ann McDaniel; Staff 1 (MLS 1)
Jul 1998-Jun 1999 Income $53,922. Mats Exp $24,800, Books $7,000, Per/Ser (Incl. Access Fees) $14,300, Electronic Ref Mat (Incl. Access Fees) $3,500. Sal $24,700
Library Holdings: Bk Vols 3,100; Bk Titles 1,000; Per Subs 90
Subject Interests: Nursing
Partic in Medline; Ohio-Kentucky Coop Libraries

M MERCY MEDICAL CENTER, Health Sciences Library, 1343 N Fountain Blvd, 45501. SAN 313-718X. Tel: 937-390-5000, Ext 2293. FAX: 937-390-5197. *Librn*, Julie McDaniel
Founded 1952
Library Holdings: Bk Titles 500; Per Subs 120
Subject Interests: Pediatrics
Partic in Docline

R SAINT JOHN'S EVANGELICAL LUTHERAN CHURCH LIBRARY, 27 N Wittenberg, 45502-1196. SAN 313-7198. Tel: 937-323-7508. FAX: 937-325-7925. *In Charge*, Bev Rutan
Founded 1961
Library Holdings: Bk Vols 2,100
Subject Interests: Art, Biog, Educ of ch, Education, Political science, Relig studies

S SPRINGFIELD MUSEUM OF ART LIBRARY,* 107 Cliff Park Rd, 45501. SAN 313-7201. Tel: 937-325-4673. FAX: 937-325-4674. E-Mail: smoa@main-net.com. Web Site: www.spfld-museum-of-art.org. *Dir*, Mark Chepp; *Librn*, Mary M Miller
Founded 1970
Library Holdings: Bk Titles 2,500; Per Subs 15
Special Collections: Photography (Alex Bahnsen Coll)

S SPRINGFIELD NEWS-SUN LIBRARY,* 202 N Limestone, 45503. SAN 375-0973. Tel: 937-328-0348. FAX: 937-328-0328. Web Site: www.//springfield.newsfund.com. *Librn*, Anita Beaver
Library Holdings: Bk Vols 200; Per Subs 25

C WITTENBERG UNIVERSITY, Thomas Library, 801 Woodlawn Ave, 45504. (Mail add: PO Box 7207, 45501-7207), SAN 357-1440. Tel: 937-327-7018. Interlibrary Loan Service Tel: 937-327-7532. Circulation Tel: 937-327-7513. Reference Tel: 937-327-7511. FAX: 937-327-6139. E-Mail: refdesk@wittenburg.edu. Web Site: www.wittenberg.edu/lib. *Dir*, Kathleen M Schulz; Tel: 937-327-7016, E-Mail: kschulz@wittenburg.edu; *Tech Coordr*, Suzanne A Smailes; Tel: 937-327-7020, E-Mail: ssmailes@wittenberg.edu; *Head, Circ*, Sandra Grube; Tel: 937-327-7512, E-Mail: sgrube@wittenberg.edu; *Head Tech Servs*, Norman R Pearson; Tel: 937-327-7529, E-Mail: npearson@wittenberg.edu; *Ref*, Regina P Entorf; Tel: 937-327-7533, E-Mail: rentorf@wittenburg.edu; *Ref*, Kenneth R Irwin; Tel: 937-327-7594, E-Mail: kirwin@wittenberg.edu; *Ref*, Alisa Mizikar; Tel: 937-327-7515, E-Mail: amizikar@wittenberg.edu; *Media Spec*, Lyndon McCurdy; Tel: 937-327-7325, E-Mail: lmcurdy@wittenberg.edu; Staff 16 (MLS 6, Non-MLS 10)
Founded 1845. Enrl 1,941; Fac 158; Highest Degree: Bachelor
Jul 1999-Jun 2000 Income (Main Library and Branch Library) $1,542,199. Mats Exp $501,201, Books $186,672, Per/Ser (Incl. Access Fees) $216,639, Presv $6,448, Micro $7,446, AV Equip $19,555, Electronic Ref Mat (Incl. Access Fees) $64,441. Sal $639,082 (Prof $303,023)
Library Holdings: Bk Vols 381,533; Bk Titles 259,678; Per Subs 1,175
Subject Interests: E Asian studies, Music
Special Collections: Dos Passos Entomological Library; Hymn Book Coll; Japan (Matsumoto Coll); Martin Luther Reformation
Database Vendor: CARL, Dialog, Lexis-Nexis, OCLC - First Search, ProQuest, Wilson - Wilson Web
Partic in OCLC Online Computer Library Center, Inc; Ohio Library & Information Network; OHIONET
Departmental Libraries:
SCIENCE Tel: 513-327-6124.

STEUBENVILLE

S BARIUM & CHEMICALS, INC, Research Library,* County Rd 44, PO Box 218, 43952. SAN 375-7269. Tel: 740-282-9776. FAX: 740-282-9161. *Librn*, Eleanor R Naylor
Library Holdings: Bk Titles 1,000

C FRANCISCAN UNIVERSITY OF STEUBENVILLE, John Paul II Library, 1235 University Blvd, 43952-1799. SAN 313-7236. Tel: 740-283-6208. FAX: 740-284-7239. Web Site: gabriel.franuniv.edu/jp2/. *Actg Dir*, William Jakub; E-Mail: bjakub@franuniv.edu; *Ref*, Kathleen Donohue; *Tech Servs*, Jack Wu; Staff 11 (MLS 4, Non-MLS 7)
Founded 1946. Enrl 2,000; Highest Degree: Master

Jul 1998-Jun 1999 Income $309,430. Mats Exp $309,000, Books $47,906, Per/Ser (Incl. Access Fees) $134,988, Presv $3,013, Micro $250, AV Equip $600. Sal $260,082 (Prof $144,000)
Library Holdings: Bk Vols 194,297; Per Subs 728
Subject Interests: Cath Orthodoxy, Counseling, Education, Franciscans, Liberal arts, Mulloy, Phenomenology, Psychology, Theology
Automation Activity & Vendor Info: (Cataloging) Innovative Interfaces Inc.
Partic in OCLC Online Computer Library Center, Inc; Ohio Library & Information Network; Ohio Pvt Acad Librs; OHIONET

JEFFERSON COMMUNITY COLLEGE LIBRARY, 4000 Sunset Blvd, 43952. SAN 313-7252. Tel: 740-264-5591, Ext 153. FAX: 740-264-1338. Web Site: www.jeffersoncc.org. *Dir*, Lois Rekowski; Tel: 740-264-5591, Ext 154; Staff 3 (MLS 1, Non-MLS 2)
Founded 1969. Enrl 1,000; Fac 40; Highest Degree: Associate
Jul 1999-Jun 2000 Income Parent Institution $176,777. Mats Exp $35,884, Books $14,080, Per/Ser (Incl. Access Fees) $20,000, Electronic Ref Mat (Incl. Access Fees) $1,804. Sal $76,009 (Prof $40,700)
Library Holdings: Bk Vols 14,777; Bk Titles 13,424; Per Subs 80
Subject Interests: Bus, Mgt, Para-medical, Sci-tech
Automation Activity & Vendor Info: (Cataloging) Innovative Interfaces Inc.; (Circulation) Innovative Interfaces Inc.; (Course Reserve) Innovative Interfaces Inc.; (ILL) Innovative Interfaces Inc.; (Media Booking) Innovative Interfaces Inc.; (OPAC) Innovative Interfaces Inc.; (Serials) Innovative Interfaces Inc.
Partic in Ohio Library & Information Network

GL JEFFERSON COUNTY LAW LIBRARY ASSOCIATION,* 301 Market St, 43952. SAN 313-7244. Tel: 740-283-8553. FAX: 740-283-8629. *Librn*, Jan Morley
Library Holdings: Bk Vols 20,000; Per Subs 30

PUBLIC LIBRARY OF STEUBENVILLE & JEFFERSON COUNTY, Steubenville & Jefferson County Public, 407 S Fourth St, 43952. SAN 357-153X. Tel: 740-282-9782. FAX: 740-282-2919. E-Mail: steubnul@oplin.lib.oh.us. Web Site: www.steubenville.lib.oh.us. *Dir*, Alan C Hall; *Asst Dir*, William Martino; *Ch Servs*, Linda Stuller; *Ref*, Donna Skeid; *Media Spec*, Cathy Hunt; *Cat*, Sandy Diederich; *Publ Servs*, Jennifer Faccinto; Staff 79 (MLS 3, Non-MLS 76)
Founded 1899. Pop 76,100; Circ 657,000
Jan 2001-Dec 2001 Income (Main Library and Branch Library) $3,415,000, State $3,295,000, Locally Generated Income $120,000. Mats Exp $495,000, Books $400,000, Per/Ser (Incl. Access Fees) $35,000, Presv $10,000, AV Equip $20,000, Electronic Ref Mat (Incl. Access Fees) $30,000. Sal $1,600,000 (Prof $160,000)
Library Holdings: Bk Vols 184,357; Bk Titles 101,293; Per Subs 218
Subject Interests: Local genealogy, Local history
Automation Activity & Vendor Info: (Acquisitions) epixtech, inc.; (Cataloging) epixtech, inc.; (Circulation) epixtech, inc.; (ILL) epixtech, inc.; (OPAC) epixtech, inc.; (Serials) epixtech, inc.
Publications: PLSJ Library News
Partic in Solo
Branches: 6
ADENA BRANCH, 167 Hanna Ave, PO Box 486, Adena, 43901. SAN 357-1548. Tel: 740-546-3782. *Librn*, Mary Hirt
BRILLIANT BRANCH, 103 Steuben St, Brilliant, 43913. SAN 357-1564. Tel: 740-598-4028. FAX: 740-598-4456. *Librn*, Audrey Owens
DILLONVALE-MT PLEASANT BRANCH, 192 Cole St, Dillonvale, 43917. SAN 357-1599. Tel: 740-769-2090. FAX: 740-769-2771. *Librn*, Sandy Scott
SCHIAPPA BRANCH, 4141 Mall Dr, 43952. SAN 328-7920. Tel: 740-264-6166. FAX: 740-264-7379. *Librn*, Linda Stuller. Subject Specialists: *Local history*, Sandy Day
Subject Interests: Genealogy, Local history, Ohio
TILTONSVILLE BRANCH, 702 Walden Ave, Tiltonsville, 43963. SAN 357-1688. Tel: 740-859-5163. *Librn*, Beverly Kelly
TORONTO BRANCH, 607 Daniels St, Toronto, 43964. SAN 357-1718. Tel: 740-537-1262. FAX: 740-537-5447. *Librn*, Beth VanWeelden
Bookmobiles: 1

M TRINITY HEALTH SYSTEMS, Health Sciences Library, 380 Summit Ave, 43952. SAN 320-9008. Tel: 740-283-7400. FAX: 740-283-7461. *Librn*, Joan Lloyd; E-Mail: jlloyd@weir.net; Staff 1 (MLS 1)
Library Holdings: Bk Vols 2,015; Per Subs 75
Subject Interests: Allied health, Medicine, Nursing
Special Collections: Rare Book Coll
Publications: Library Line (quarterly newsletter)

STOW

S SAINT-GOBAIN NORPRO, (Formerly Norton Chemical Process Products Corp), Chamberlain Technical Library, 3840 Fishcreek Rd, 44224. (Mail add: PO Box 350, 44309), SAN 313-7260. Tel: 330-677-3601. FAX: 330-677-3608. *Librn*, Catherine Whipple; E-Mail: cwhipple@sg-norpro.com; Staff 1 (MLS 1)
Founded 1958
Library Holdings: Bk Vols 4,000; Per Subs 150
Subject Interests: Ceramics, Chemical engineering, Chm, Patents
Restriction: Not open to public
Partic in Cleveland Area Metropolitan Library System

P STOW MUNROE FALLS PUBLIC LIBRARY,* 3512 Darrow Rd, 44224. SAN 313-7279. Tel: 330-688-3295. FAX: 330-688-3176. *Dir*, John Patane; *Syst Coordr*, David Lodwick; *Circ*, Barbara Richards; *Ad Servs*, Doug Dotterer
Founded 1924. Pop 37,000; Circ 617,000
Jan 1997-Dec 1998 Income $5,234,000. Mats Exp $162,465, Books $130,415, Per/Ser (Incl. Access Fees) $13,500. Sal $792,000 (Prof $528,000)
Library Holdings: Bk Titles 107,506; Per Subs 120
Subject Interests: Local hist archives
Partic in Cleveland Area Metropolitan Library System; OCLC Online Computer Library Center, Inc
Friends of the Library Group

STRONGSVILLE

S GARDENVIEW HORTICULTURAL PARK LIBRARY, 16711 Pearl Rd, 44136-6048. SAN 321-0146. Tel: 440-238-6653. FAX: 440-238-6653. E-Mail: grhp@raex.com. Web Site: www.geocities.com/heartland/cottage/9303. *Dir*, Henry A Ross
Founded 1949
Library Holdings: Bk Titles 5,000
Subject Interests: Animals, Birds, Crafts, Gardening, Self-sufficiency, Travel
Restriction: Open to public for reference only

S ICI PAINTS, Strongsville Research Center, Technical Info Services, 16651 Sprague Rd, 44136. SAN 313-7287. Tel: 440-826-5260. FAX: 440-826-5431. *Librn*, Pat Starrett; Staff 1 (MLS 1)
Founded 1968
Library Holdings: Bk Vols 5,500; Per Subs 125
Subject Interests: Coating, Paint, Polymer sci, Resin tech
Restriction: Not open to public
Function: Research library
Partic in OCLC Online Computer Library Center, Inc; OHIONET

SUNBURY

S COMMUNITY LIBRARY, 44 Burrer Dr, 43074. SAN 313-7295. Tel: 740-965-3901. FAX: 740-965-1258. Web Site: community.lib.oh.us. *Dir*, Polly Horn; E-Mail: pollyho@oplin.lib.oh.us; Staff 16 (MLS 1, Non-MLS 15)
Founded 1944
Jan 1999-Dec 1999 Income $653,575, State $605,300, Other $48,275. Mats Exp $604,236, Books $72,479, Per/Ser (Incl. Access Fees) $8,241, Micro $531, AV Equip $6,387. Sal $290,040 (Prof $26,389)
Library Holdings: Bk Titles 89,700; Per Subs 275
Subject Interests: Genealogy, Local history
Partic in Calico
Friends of the Library Group

SWANTON

P SWANTON LOCAL SCHOOL DISTRICT PUBLIC LIBRARY, 305 Chestnut St, 43558. SAN 313-7309. Tel: 419-826-2760. FAX: 419-826-1020. E-Mail: swantonpl@email.com. Web Site: www.swanton.lib.oh.us. *Dir*, S Gayle Hazelbaker; E-Mail: hazelbsg@oplin.lib.oh.us; *Asst Dir*, Linda S Slaninka; Staff 10 (MLS 1, Non-MLS 9)
Founded 1936. Pop 14,700
Library Holdings: Bk Titles 60,000; Per Subs 155
Function: ILL available
Partic in Northwest Library District

SYCAMORE

P MOHAWK COMMUNITY LIBRARY,* 200 S Sycamore Ave, PO Box 9, 44882-0009. SAN 313-7317. Tel: 419-927-2407. *Asst Dir*, Barbara Dayton
Library Holdings: Bk Vols 22,000; Per Subs 50
Mem of NW Libr District

SYLVANIA

R FIRST UNITED METHODIST CHURCH LIBRARY, 7000 Erie St, 43560-1920. SAN 328-5855. Tel: 419-882-2205. FAX: 419-882-2205. *Librn*, Anne Basile; E-Mail: anne.basile@sylvania.sev.org
Library Holdings: Bk Vols 1,000; Per Subs 10

C LOURDES COLLEGE, Duns Scotus Library, 6832 Convent Blvd, 43560. SAN 313-7325. Tel: 419-885-3211. FAX: 419-824-3511. E-Mail: srutkows@lourdes.edu. Web Site: www.lourdes.edu. *Dir*, Sister M Thomas More; Staff 5 (MLS 2, Non-MLS 3)
Founded 1916. Enrl 1,002; Fac 68

Library Holdings: Bk Titles 68,000; Per Subs 420
Subject Interests: Art, Gerontology, Occupational therapy, Rare books, Religious studies
Special Collections: Franciscan Order

R TEMPLE - CONGREGATION SHOMER EMUNIM LIBRARY, 6453 Sylvania Ave, 43560-3999. SAN 313-7341. Tel: 419-885-3341. FAX: 419-882-2778. *Dir*, Jon Robert Shepard; Staff 2 (MLS 1, Non-MLS 1)
Founded 1875
Jul 2000-Jun 2001 Income $1,500. Mats Exp $1,500, Books $1,000, Per/Ser (Incl. Access Fees) $500. Sal $1,125
Library Holdings: Bk Titles 14,310; Per Subs 23
Subject Interests: Judaica, Related mat
Special Collections: Art (Gertner Memorial Book Shelf)

TALLMADGE

S TALLMADGE HISTORICAL SOCIETY LIBRARY, PO Box 25, 44278. SAN 327-4551. Tel: 330-630-9760, 330-633-2510. *Archivist*, Tobi Battista
Library Holdings: Bk Titles 300
Special Collections: Four handwritten Civil War diaries of Charles H Sackett (1861, 1862, 1864 & 1869); The Bronson Papers Coll (10 large handwritten volumes of local history & family geneaology of Tallmadge from approx 1820 to his death in 1886
Friends of the Library Group

TIFFIN

C HEIDELBERG COLLEGE, Beeghly Library, 10 Greenfield St, 44883-2420. SAN 313-735X. Tel: 419-448-2104. FAX: 419-448-2578. Web Site: www.heidelberg.edu/depts/library. *Cat, Dir*, Edward Krakora; *Acq*, Susan Krieger; *ILL, Ref*, Nancy Rubenstein; *Media Spec*, R Douglas Ramsey; Staff 9 (MLS 3, Non-MLS 6)
Founded 1850. Enrl 1,548; Fac 91; Highest Degree: Master
Jul 1998-Jun 1999 Income Parent Institution $555,514. Mats Exp $168,500, Books $60,000, Per/Ser (Incl. Access Fees) $82,000, Presv $5,500, Micro $7,500, AV Equip $13,500. Sal $290,610 (Prof $126,226)
Library Holdings: Bk Vols 151,036; Bk Titles 118,843; Per Subs 656
Subject Interests: Relig studies
Special Collections: Ballet & Dance (Pohlable Coll); English & American Correspondence (Besse Coll)
Automation Activity & Vendor Info: (Acquisitions) Innovative Interfaces Inc.; (Cataloging) Innovative Interfaces Inc.; (Circulation) Innovative Interfaces Inc.; (Course Reserve) Innovative Interfaces Inc.; (ILL) Innovative Interfaces Inc.; (Media Booking) Innovative Interfaces Inc.; (OPAC) Innovative Interfaces Inc.; (Serials) Innovative Interfaces Inc.
Partic in East Central College; OCLC Online Computer Library Center, Inc; OHIONET

L SENECA COUNTY LAW LIBRARY,* Courthouse 4th flr, 103 S Washington, 44883-2352. SAN 372-2015. Tel: 419-447-2636. E-Mail: sencolaw@bright.net. *Librn*, Jane Allison
1997-1998 Income $65,000
Library Holdings: Bk Vols 17,000; Per Subs 20

C TIFFIN UNIVERSITY, Pfeiffer Library, 139 Miami St, 44883-2162. SAN 313-7376. Tel: 419-448-3435. FAX: 419-443-5013. *Dir*, Frances A Fleet; E-Mail: ffleet@tiffin.edu; Staff 2 (MLS 2)
Founded 1956. Enrl 1,500; Highest Degree: Master
1999-2000 Income $200,000. Mats Exp $51,000, Books $45,000, Micro $6,000. Sal $57,500
Library Holdings: Bk Titles 28,200; Per Subs 255
Subject Interests: Accounting, Bus, Econ, Law, Mgt, Secretarial sci
Partic in Northwest Library District

P TIFFIN-SENECA PUBLIC LIBRARY, 77 Jefferson St, 44883-2399. SAN 313-7368. Tel: 419-447-3751. FAX: 419-447-3045. Web Site: www.tiffinsen.lib.oh.us. *Dir*, Patricia Hillmer; E-Mail: hillmepa@oplin.lib.oh.us; *Dep Dir*, Karen Culp; *AV*, Julie Haferd; *Ch Servs*, Willa Jean Harner; *Circ*, Cathy Brandt; *Commun Relations*, Judith Reed; *Tech Coordr*, Christopher Brose; *Automation Syst Coordr*, Jo Anne Schiefer; *Bkmobile Coordr*, Janet Kimmet; Staff 40 (MLS 7, Non-MLS 33)
Founded 1880. Pop 40,000; Circ 332,494
Jan 1999-Dec 1999 Income $1,334,333, State $1,176,180, Parent Institution $156,123, Other $2,030. Mats Exp $283,181, Books $127,112, Per/Ser (Incl. Access Fees) $26,366, AV Equip $38,197, Other Print Mats $17,742, Electronic Ref Mat (Incl. Access Fees) $73,764. Sal $558,976 (Prof $310,000)
Library Holdings: Bk Vols 98,528; Bk Titles 101,124; Per Subs 360; High Interest/Low Vocabulary Bk Vols 600; Bks on Deafness & Sign Lang 30
Subject Interests: History, Seneca County genealogy
Special Collections: Sign Language Coll
Publications: Dimensions (monthly) (Newsletter)
Partic in Northwest Library District; Norweld
Special Services for the Deaf - Captioned film depository
Special Services for the Blind - Talking book center
Building is handicapped accessible; 3 meeting rooms
Friends of the Library Group
Bookmobiles: 1

TIPP CITY

P TIPP CITY PUBLIC LIBRARY,* 11 E Main St, 45371. SAN 313-7384. Tel: 937-667-3826. FAX: 937-667-7968. *Dir*, Patricia A Liening
Founded 1922. Pop 6,600; Circ 225,000
1998-1999 Income $500,000, State $450,000, Locally Generated Income $12,000. Mats Exp $53,635, Books $45,000, Per/Ser (Incl. Access Fees) $3,500, Presv $135. Sal $189,000
Library Holdings: Bk Vols 85,000; Per Subs 154
Automation Activity & Vendor Info: (Circulation) Sagebrush Corporation
Publications: Administrator's Digest; American Libraries; Library Journal; Public Libraries; Publisher Weekly; Unabashed Librarian
Partic in Miami Valley Librs
Friends of the Library Group

TOLEDO

SR ASHLAND AVENUE BAPTIST CHURCH LIBRARY,* 2001 Ashland Ave, 43620. SAN 371-9995. Tel: 419-243-3171, 419-841-5609. FAX: 419-243-3173.; Staff 1 (Non-MLS 1)
Library Holdings: Per Subs 5

J DAVIS COLLEGE, Resource Center,* 4747 Monroe St, 43623. SAN 313-7414. Tel: 419-473-2700. FAX: 419-473-2472. *Dir*, Peggy Peterson-Seniuk; E-Mail: seniuk@daviscollege.com; Staff 1 (MLS 1)
Jul 1997-Jun 1998 Mats Exp $6,146, Books $1,206, Per/Ser (Incl. Access Fees) $3,240. Sal $20,381 (Prof $15,025)
Library Holdings: Bk Vols 3,500; Per Subs 80
Subject Interests: Bus, Mgt

R EPWORTH UNITED METHODIST CHURCH LIBRARY, 3077 Valleyview Dr, 43615-2299. SAN 313-7430. Tel: 419-531-4236. FAX: 419-531-7487. *Librn*, Dana Jamqochian; Staff 5 (MLS 1, Non-MLS 4)
Founded 1960
Library Holdings: Bk Titles 2,530

L FULLER & HENRY LAW LIBRARY, One Seagate, 17th flr, PO Box 2088 43603. SAN 324-170X. Tel: 419-247-2891. *Librn*, Gail McCain; Staff 1 (MLS 1)
Founded 1892
Subject Interests: Law
Restriction: Staff use only

LIBBEY OWENS FORD CO
S PILKINGTON NORTH AMERICA CORPORATE LIBRARY, 811 Madison Ave, 43624. SAN 357-1777. Tel: 419-247-4368. FAX: 419-247-4466. *Mgr Libr*, Jennifer Anne Flint; E-Mail: jennifer.flint@us.pilkington.com; *Librn*, Nancy Scharding. Subject Specialists: *Glass*, Jennifer Anne Flint; Staff 1 (Non-MLS 1)
Founded 1946
Jun 2000-May 2001 Mats Exp $125,000, Books $30,000, Per/Ser (Incl. Access Fees) $70,000, Electronic Ref Mat (Incl. Access Fees) $25,000. (Prof $54,000)
Subject Interests: Automotive, Glass, Safety
Automation Activity & Vendor Info: (Cataloging) Sagebrush Corporation; (Circulation) Sagebrush Corporation
Database Vendor: Dialog
Function: For research purposes

L MARSHALL & MELHORN, Law Library,* 4 SeaGate, 8th flr, 43604. SAN 313-7473. Tel: 419-249-7100. FAX: 419-249-7151.
Founded 1895
Library Holdings: Bk Vols 14,230; Per Subs 26
Subject Interests: Civil, Corporate practice, General, Intellectual property, Labor law, Litigation, Probate, State, Tax
Partic in Dialog Corporation; Westlaw

CM MEDICAL COLLEGE OF OHIO, Raymon H Mulford Library, 3045 Arlington Ave, 43614. SAN 357-1807. Tel: 419-393-4223. Circulation Tel: 419-393-4225. Reference Tel: 419-383-4218. FAX: 419-383-6146. Web Site: www.mco.edu/lib/libmain.html. *Dir*, David W Boilard; E-Mail: dboilard@mco.edu; *Asst Dir*, Jeffrey Jablonski; *Asst Dir*, Barbara McNamee; *Head, Info Serv*, Marlene Porter; *Head Tech Servs*, Sheryl R Stevens; E-Mail: sstevens@mco.edu; *Outreach Serv*, Jonathan Hartmann; *Distance Educ*, Jolene Miller; *Head, Circ*, David Remaklus; *Automation Syst Coordr*, P Scott Lapinski; *Ref*, Janice Flahiff; Staff 22 (MLS 8, Non-MLS 14)
Founded 1967. Enrl 1,298; Fac 335; Highest Degree: Doctorate
Jul 1999-Jun 2000 Income $1,799,139, State $1,660,412, Federal $115,062, Locally Generated Income $23,665. Mats Exp $654,793, Books $64,250, Per/Ser (Incl. Access Fees) $548,925, Presv $11,719, AV Equip $1,025, Electronic Ref Mat (Incl. Access Fees) $28,874. Sal $955,512
Library Holdings: Bk Vols 145,199; Bk Titles 36,566; Per Subs 1,707
Subject Interests: Allied health, Medicine, Nursing

Automation Activity & Vendor Info: (Acquisitions) Innovative Interfaces Inc.; (Cataloging) Innovative Interfaces Inc.; (Circulation) Innovative Interfaces Inc.; (Course Reserve) Innovative Interfaces Inc.; (OPAC) Innovative Interfaces Inc.; (Serials) Innovative Interfaces Inc.
Function: ILL available
Partic in Nat Network of Libraries of Med - Region 3; Ohio Library & Information Network

MERCY COLLEGE OF NORTHWEST OHIO, Health Sciences Library, 2221 Madison Ave, 43624-1120. SAN 320-4146. Tel: 419-251-1700. FAX: 419-251-1730. E-Mail: burnslib@ohionet.org. *Dir*, Katherine Maluchnik; Staff 5 (MLS 2, Non-MLS 3)
Founded 1973. Enrl 200
Library Holdings: Bk Titles 3,000; Per Subs 170
Subject Interests: Allied health, Endocrinology, Hospital administration, Medicine, Metabolism, Nursing
Partic in Docline; Medline; OHIONET
Affiliated as Resource Library for Mercy College of Northwest Ohio

I NORTHCOAST BEHAVIORAL HEALTHCARE SYSTEM LIBRARY NBHS-TOLEDO , Toledo Campus Library, 930 S Detroit Ave, 43614-2701. SAN 313-7589. Tel: 419-381-1881, Ext 4662. TDD: 419-381-0815. FAX: 419-389-1967. *Coordr*, Jane Weber; Tel: 419-381-1881; Staff 1 (Non-MLS 1)
Founded 1937
Library Holdings: Bk Vols 5,000; Bk Titles 100
Subject Interests: Biographies, Fiction, Psychiatry, Psychology

PILGRIM CHURCH OF UNITED CHURCH OF CHRIST MEMORIAL LIBRARY, 1375 Sylvania, 43612. SAN 313-749X. Tel: 419-478-6012. *In Charge*, Lois Thompson; Staff 4 (MLS 1, Non-MLS 3)
Founded 1979
Library Holdings: Bk Vols 3,500

M RIVERSIDE HOSPITAL, Sarah & Julius Steinberg Memorial Library, 1600 N Superior St, 43604. SAN 327-3946. Tel: 419-729-6198. FAX: 419-729-6712. E-Mail: kmbooks@primenet.com. *Chief Librn*, Carolyn Jones
Library Holdings: Bk Titles 900; Per Subs 45
Subject Interests: Nursing, Orthopedics, Podiatry
Partic in Medline; OHIONET

R SAINT MICHAEL'S IN THE HILLS EPISCOPAL CHURCH, Parish Library, 4718 Brittany Rd, 43615-2314. SAN 328-137X. Tel: 419-531-1616. FAX: 419-531-9332. *Librn*, Linda Deubner
Library Holdings: Bk Titles 1,895; Per Subs 13
Subject Interests: Religious education
Special Collections: Summa Theologicae (St Thomas Aquinas), 60 vol
Special Services for the Deaf - Special interest periodicals

M SAINT VINCENT MERCY MEDICAL CENTER, Health Science Library,* 2213 Cherry St, 43608-2691. SAN 313-7503. Tel: 419-251-2659. FAX: 419-251-4967. *Dir*, Carrie Lepow; Staff 4 (MLS 1, Non-MLS 3)
Founded 1970
Jan 1997-Dec 1998 Income $147,560. Mats Exp $104,000, Books $15,000, Per/Ser (Incl. Access Fees) $89,000
Library Holdings: Bk Titles 5,000; Per Subs 600
Subject Interests: Clinical medicine, Hospital administration, Nursing
Partic in Nat Libr of Med; OCLC Online Computer Library Center, Inc

R TEMPLE B'NAI ISRAEL, Michael Lichtenstein Memorial Library, 2727 Kenwood Blvd, 43606. SAN 313-7538. Tel: 419-531-1677. FAX: 419-531-0555. *Librn*, Saretta Burke; E-Mail: sburke@buckeye-express.com; Staff 1 (MLS 1) Sal $2,500
Library Holdings: Bk Titles 4,000; Per Subs 30
Subject Interests: Judaica

S TOLEDO BLADE-LIBRARY, 541 N Superior St, 43660. SAN 313-7546. Tel: 419-724-6188. *Librn*, Mary F Mackzum
Founded 1926
Special Collections: Electronic Library; Newspaper Clippings

M TOLEDO HOSPITAL, Medical Library,* 2142 N Cove Blvd, 43606. SAN 313-7562. Tel: 419-471-3641. Interlibrary Loan Service Tel: 419-471-3640. FAX: 419-479-6953. *Dir*, Suzanne Gale; Staff 1 (MLS 1)
Library Holdings: Bk Titles 3,600; Per Subs 460
Subject Interests: Medicine, Nursing

L TOLEDO LAW ASSOCIATION LIBRARY,* Lucas County Family Court Center, 905 Jackson St, 43624-1546. SAN 313-7570. Tel: 419-213-4747. FAX: 419-213-4287. E-Mail: tla@norden1.com, toldeolaw@accesstoledo.com. *Librn, Online Servs*, Joseph Fugere; Staff 4 (MLS 1, Non-MLS 3)
Founded 1870
Library Holdings: Bk Vols 67,174; Per Subs 300
Partic in Westlaw

S TOLEDO MUSEUM OF ART, Art Reference Library,* 2445 Monroe St, PO Box 1013, 43697. SAN 313-7597. Tel: 419-255-8000, Ext 280. FAX: 419-255-5638. *Librn*, Anne O Morris; Staff 5 (MLS 3, Non-MLS 2)
Founded 1901
1997-1998 Income $153,555, Locally Generated Income $1,938, Other $31,225. Mats Exp $36,874, Books $18,754, Per/Ser (Incl. Access Fees) $10,833, Presv $892, Other Print Mats $6,395. Sal $126,794 (Prof $90,125)
Library Holdings: Bk Vols 57,000; Per Subs 316
Subject Interests: Hist of art, Music
Friends of the Library Group

S TOLEDO ZOOLOGICAL SOCIETY, Zoo Library, 2700 Broadway, 43609. (Mail add: PO Box 4010, 43609), SAN 328-0039. Tel: 419-385-5721, Ext 2043. Interlibrary Loan Service Tel: 419-385-5721, Ext 2043. FAX: 419-389-8670. *Librn*, Linda Trabbic; E-Mail: lynda@toledozoo.org
Founded 1937
Library Holdings: Bk Titles 2,000; Per Subs 112
Subject Interests: Conservation, Ecology, Zoology

P TOLEDO-LUCAS COUNTY PUBLIC LIBRARY, 325 Michigan St, 43624-1628. SAN 357-2013. Tel: 419-259-5207. Circulation Tel: 419-259-5201. FAX: 419-255-1334. Web Site: www.library.toledo.oh.us, www.toledolibrary.org. *Dep Dir*, Margaret Danziger; *Ad Servs, Coordr*, Nancy Foth; *Ch Servs*, Marilyn Clark; *Tech Servs*, Pat Lora; *Circ, ILL*, Jeannine Wilbarger; *Bkmobile Coordr*, David Harris. Subject Specialists: *Audio visual mats*, John Selzer; *Business and management*, Joanne Kosanke; *Business tech*, Karen Wiggins; *Humanities*, John Selzer; *Local history*, James Marshall; *Popular*, Tony Schaefer; *Social sciences and issues*, Susan Coburn; *Young adults*, Tony Schaefer; Staff 154 (MLS 105, Non-MLS 49)
Founded 1970. Pop 462,361; Circ 6,570,426
1999-1999 Income $26,819,022. Mats Exp $4,328,740. Sal $11,463,001
Library Holdings: Bk Vols 2,253,118; Per Subs 5,473
Subject Interests: Careers, Commun info, Genealogy, Glass technology, Govt proc, Grantsmanship
Automation Activity & Vendor Info: (Acquisitions) DRA; (Cataloging) DRA; (Circulation) DRA; (Course Reserve) DRA; (ILL) DRA; (Media Booking) DRA; (OPAC) DRA; (Serials) DRA
Publications: Library Line
Partic in OHIONET
Friends of the Library Group
Branches: 18
BIRMINGHAM, 203 Paine Ave, 43605. SAN 357-2048. Tel: 419-259-5210. FAX: 419-691-8242. *Mgr*, Catherine Bartel
Library Holdings: Bk Vols 26,219
Friends of the Library Group
HEATHERDOWNS, 3265 Glanzman, 43614. SAN 357-2072. Tel: 419-259-5270. FAX: 419-382-3231. *Mgr*, Kathleen Lundberg
Library Holdings: Bk Vols 134,437
Friends of the Library Group
HOLLAND BRANCH, 1032 S McCord Rd, Holland, 43528. SAN 326-8268. Tel: 419-259-5240. FAX: 419-865-6706. *Mgr*, Colleen Lehmann
Library Holdings: Bk Vols 107,939
Friends of the Library Group
KENT, 3101 Collingwood Blvd, 43610. SAN 357-2102. Tel: 419-259-5340. FAX: 419-243-6536. *Mgr*, Odessa Rowan
Library Holdings: Bk Vols 59,700
Friends of the Library Group
LAGRANGE CENTRAL, 3015 Lagrange St, 43608. SAN 357-2137. Tel: 419-259-5280. FAX: 419-242-3052. *Mgr*, Catherine Bartel
Library Holdings: Bk Vols 35,866
Friends of the Library Group
LOCKE, 806 Main St, 43605. SAN 357-2161. Tel: 419-259-5310. FAX: 419-691-3237. *Mgr*, Nicole Baumhower
Library Holdings: Bk Vols 56,118
Friends of the Library Group
MAUMEE BRANCH, 501 River Rd, Maumee, 43537. SAN 357-2196. Tel: 419-259-5360. FAX: 419-893-7953. Web Site: www.library.toledo.oh.us. *Mgr*, Joseph Ludwig; E-Mail: ludwig@tlc.lib.oh.us; Staff 15 (MLS 4, Non-MLS 11)
Founded 1918. Pop 15,000
Library Holdings: Bk Vols 94,616
Automation Activity & Vendor Info: (Acquisitions) DRA; (Cataloging) DRA; (Circulation) DRA; (Serials) DRA
Friends of the Library Group
MOTT, 1085 Dorr St, 43607. SAN 357-2226. Tel: 419-259-5230. FAX: 419-255-4237. *Mgr*, Judith Jones
Library Holdings: Bk Vols 56,138
Friends of the Library Group
OREGON BRANCH, 3340 Dustin Rd, Oregon, 43616. SAN 357-2250. Tel: 419-259-5250. FAX: 419-691-3341.
Library Holdings: Bk Vols 101,071
Friends of the Library Group
POINT PLACE, 2727 117th St, 43611. SAN 357-2285. Tel: 419-259-5390. FAX: 419-729-5363. *Mgr*, Janet Snider
Library Holdings: Bk Vols 69,346
Friends of the Library Group
REYNOLDS CORNERS, 4833 Dorr St, 43615. SAN 357-2315. Tel: 419-259-5320. FAX: 419-531-4076. *Mgr*, Marilee McSweeny
Library Holdings: Bk Vols 123,108

Friends of the Library Group
SANGER, 3030 W Central Ave, 43606. SAN 357-234X. Tel: 419-259-5370. FAX: 419-536-9573. *Mgr*, Margaret Delaney
Library Holdings: Bk Vols 129,055
Friends of the Library Group
SOUTH, 1638 Broadway, 43609. SAN 357-2374. Tel: 419-259-5380. FAX: 419-243-4217. *Mgr*, Catherine Bartel
Library Holdings: Bk Vols 36,977
Friends of the Library Group
SYLVANIA BRANCH, 6749 Monroe St, Sylvania, 43560. SAN 357-2439. Tel: 419-882-2089. FAX: 419-882-8993. *Mgr*, John Cleveland
Library Holdings: Bk Vols 136,619
Friends of the Library Group
TOLEDO HEIGHTS, 423 Shasta Dr, 43609. SAN 357-2463. Tel: 419-259-5220. FAX: 419-385-9297. *Mgr*, Mary Chwialkowski
Library Holdings: Bk Vols 50,200
Friends of the Library Group
WASHINGTON, 5560 Harvest Lane, 43623. SAN 357-2498. Tel: 419-259-5330. FAX: 419-472-4991. *Mgr*, Barbara Lough
Library Holdings: Bk Vols 118,801
Friends of the Library Group
WATERVILLE BRANCH, 800 Michigan Ave, Waterville, 43566. SAN 357-2528. Tel: 419-878-3055. FAX: 419-878-4688. *Mgr*, Campbell Brady
Library Holdings: Bk Vols 74,731
Friends of the Library Group
WEST TOLEDO, 1320 Sylvania Ave, 43612. SAN 357-2552. Tel: 419-259-5290. FAX: 419-476-0892. Web Site: www.library.toledo.oh.us. *Mgr*, Alan Borer; E-Mail: borer@tlc.lib.oh.us; Staff 16 (MLS 4, Non-MLS 12)
Library Holdings: Bk Vols 97,267
Friends of the Library Group
Bookmobiles: 2

L UNITED STATES COURTS, Law Library,* 418 US Courthouse, 1716 Spielbusch Ave, 43624. SAN 372-2007. Tel: 419-259-7539. FAX: 419-259-3738. *Librn*, Marianne C Mussett
Library Holdings: Bk Vols 18,000; Per Subs 30
Partic in OCLC Online Computer Library Center, Inc

C UNIVERSITY OF TOLEDO, William S Carlson Library, 2801 W Bancroft St, 43606-3399. SAN 357-2587. Tel: 419-530-4488. Interlibrary Loan Service Tel: 419-530-2808. FAX: 419-530-2726. Web Site: www.cl.utoledo.edu. *Dean of Libr*, Laurene Zaporozhetz; *Archivist*, Barbara Floyd; *ILL*, Joanne Hartough; *Doc*, Suhasini Kumar; Staff 27 (MLS 27)
Founded 1917. Enrl 17,322; Fac 735; Highest Degree: Doctorate
Jul 1998-Jun 1999 Income (Main and Other College/University Libraries) $5,415,819, Federal $3,719. Mats Exp $1,174,093, Books $569,227, Per/Ser (Incl. Access Fees) $588,820. Sal $3,051,340 (Prof $1,419,557)
Library Holdings: Bk Vols 731,308; Per Subs 4,527
Subject Interests: Bus, Education, Engineering, Great Lakes area, Humanities, International relations, Pharm, Psychology, Sci, Technology
Special Collections: Afro-American Literature Since the Harlem Renaissance; American Women's Social History, 1840-1920; Broadside Press Coll; Davis Besse Nuclear Power Documents; Department of Energy; Etheridge Knight Coll; Eudora Welty; Ezra Pound; Foy D Kohler Coll; Gift Books & Annuals; Glass Manufacturing; Henry David Thoreau Coll; Imagist Poets; Jean Gould Coll; Leigh Hunt; Richard Gosser Coll; Scott & Helen Nearing; Southern Authors; Stock Market; T S Eliot; University of Toledo Archives Coll; William Dean Howells; William Faulkner & others
Publications: Collections
Partic in Ohio Library & Information Network; OHIONET; STN
Special Apple & PC microcomputers are available to handicapped students in Multi-media Lab
Friends of the Library Group
Departmental Libraries:
CL LAW LIBRARY, 2801 W Bancroft Ave, 43606-3399. SAN 357-2617. Tel: 419-530-2733. FAX: 419-530-2821. Web Site: www.utoledo.edu/law/library.htm. *Dir*, Bruce Kennedy; *Assoc Librn*, Barbara West; *Cat*, Diane S Bitter-Gay; *Acq*, Claudia Dansby; *Publ Servs*, Chris Niedringhaus
Library Holdings: Bk Vols 198,393; Bk Titles 45,082; Per Subs 3,251
Special Collections: International Law Coll
Partic in OCLC Online Computer Library Center, Inc; OHIONET
LEARNING RESOURCE CENTER, Scott Park Campus, 43606. SAN 357-2641. Tel: 419-530-3175, 419-530-3188. FAX: 419-530-3194. E-Mail: msuter@atoledo.edu. Web Site: www.cl.utoledo.edu. *Dir*, Marcia Suter; *Librn*, Munawwar Khan

TROY

S ANALOG & DIGITAL PERIPHERALS, INC LIBRARY, PO Box 499, 45373. SAN 328-2120. Tel: 937-339-2241. Toll Free Tel: 800-758-1041. FAX: 937-339-0070. E-Mail: info@adpi.com. Web Site: www.aopi.com. *Pres*, Lyle Ellicott; Staff 20 (MLS 15, Non-MLS 5)
Library Holdings: Bk Vols 250; Bk Titles 50; Per Subs 500
Restriction: Staff use only

S HOBART INSTITUTE OF WELDING TECHNOLOGY, John H Blankenbuehler Memorial Library, 400 Trade Sq E, 45373-2400. SAN 313-7600. Tel: 937-332-5603. Toll Free Tel: 800-332-9448, Ext 5603. FAX: 937-332-5057. E-Mail: hiwt@welding.org. Web Site: www.welding.org. *Librn*, Martha A Baker; Staff 1 (Non-MLS 1)
Founded 1964. Fac 15; Highest Degree: Certificate
Library Holdings: Bk Vols 5,000; Bk Titles 5,000; Per Subs 100
Subject Interests: Chemistry, Metallurgy, Plasma tech, Quality assurance program evaluation, Radiography, Thermal spraying, Welding
Partic in Dialog Corporation; Questal Orbit

L MIAMI COUNTY LAW LIBRARY, 201 W Main St, 45373. SAN 313-7619. Tel: 937-332-6861. *Librn*, Carolyn Bolin
Library Holdings: Bk Vols 19,000; Per Subs 28

P TROY-MIAMI COUNTY PUBLIC LIBRARY,* 419 W Main St, 45373. SAN 357-2706. Tel: 937-339-0502. FAX: 937-335-4880. E-Mail: tmc-user@dayton.lib.oh.us. *Dir*, James A Miley; *Media Spec*, Cindy Kelly; *Tech Servs*, Sue Lepore; *Rare Bks*, Juda Moyer; *Br Coordr*, Jeannine Borton; *Exten Servs*, Dianne Niece; *Ad Servs, Coordr*, Deborah Matthews; *Ch Servs*, Susan Harbaugh
Founded 1896. Pop 39,163; Circ 579,494
1997-1998 Income $1,307,772. Mats Exp $244,499. Sal $558,690
Library Holdings: Bk Titles 190,000; Per Subs 275
Subject Interests: Architecture, Art, History
Mem of Miami Valley Libr Syst
Special Services for the Deaf - Books on deafness & sign language
Friends of the Library Group
Branches: 1
OAKES-BEITMAN MEMORIAL, 12 N Main St, Pleasant Hill, 45359-0811. SAN 357-2730. Tel: 937-676-2731. *Librn*, Jeannine Borton
Library Holdings: Bk Vols 15,000; Bk Titles 13,000
Friends of the Library Group
Bookmobiles: 1

TWINSBURG

P TWINSBURG PUBLIC LIBRARY,* 10050 Ravenna Rd, 44087-1796. SAN 313-7627. Tel: 330-425-4268. FAX: 330-425-3622. Web Site: www.twinsburg.lib.oh.us. *Dir*, Karen D Tschudy; Tel: 330-425-4268, Ext 21, E-Mail: ktschudy@twinsburg.lib.oh.us; *Assoc Dir*, David B Brown; Tel: 330-425-4268, Ext 34, E-Mail: dbrown@twinsburg.lib.oh.us; *Ad Servs*, Lori Holmes; Tel: 330-425-4268, Ext 12, E-Mail: lholmes@twinsburg.lib.oh.us; *Ref Servs YA*, Laura Leonard; Tel: 330-425-4268, E-Mail: lleonard@twinsburg.lib.oh.us; Staff 36 (MLS 7, Non-MLS 29)
Founded 1910. Pop 18,558; Circ 496,113
Jan 1998-Dec 1998 Income $1,564,547, State $915,332, City $559,444, Locally Generated Income $58,636, Other $31,135. Mats Exp $1,246,379, Books $196,924, Per/Ser (Incl. Access Fees) $15,676, Presv $236, AV Equip $44,914. Sal $524,925 (Prof $171,582)
Library Holdings: Bk Vols 107,303; Per Subs 375
Subject Interests: Twinsburg hist
Automation Activity & Vendor Info: (Cataloging) DRA; (Circulation) DRA; (OPAC) DRA; (Serials) DRA
Database Vendor: DRA, Ebsco - EbscoHost, GaleNet, IAC - Info Trac, OCLC - First Search, ProQuest, Wilson - Wilson Web
Publications: Newsletter (quarterly)
Function: ILL available
Partic in Cleveland Area Metropolitan Library System; Clevnet; OPLIN
Friends of the Library Group

UHRICHSVILLE

P CLAYMONT SCHOOL DISTRICT PUBLIC LIBRARY, 215 E Third St, 44683. SAN 357-2765. Tel: 740-922-3626. FAX: 740-922-3500. Web Site: www.claymont.lib.oh.us. *Dir*, Thomas A Adamich; E-Mail: adamicth@oplin.lib.oh.us; *Branch Mgr*, Lois Brown; Staff 2 (MLS 1, Non-MLS 1)
Founded 1934. Pop 12,000; Circ 131,122
Jan 1999-Dec 1999 Income (Main Library and Branch Library) $434,824, State $417,036, Locally Generated Income $17,788. Mats Exp $35,642, Books $20,277, Per/Ser (Incl. Access Fees) $4,017, AV Equip $11,100, Manuscripts & Archives $248. Sal $199,868 (Prof $73,740)
Library Holdings: Bk Vols 53,420; Bk Titles 53,420; Per Subs 104
Special Collections: Clay History
Automation Activity & Vendor Info: (Cataloging) Follett; (Circulation) Follett
Branches: 1
DENNISON BRANCH, 15 N Fourth St, Dennison, 44621. SAN 357-279X. Tel: 740-922-5851. *Asst Librn*, Debra McCune; Staff 1 (Non-MLS 1)
Library Holdings: Bk Vols 23,938; Per Subs 45

UNIVERSITY HEIGHTS

C JOHN CARROLL UNIVERSITY, (JCU), Grasselli Library & Breen Learning Center, 20700 N Park Blvd, 44118. SAN 313-7635. Tel: 216-397-4233. Interlibrary Loan Service Tel: 216-397-4232. Reference Tel: 216-397-4234. FAX: 216-397-4256. Web Site: library.jcu.edu. *Dir*, Dr Gorman L Duffett; Tel: 216-397-4231, E-Mail: gduffett@jcu.edu; *ILL*, Caron Viglianco; E-Mail: cviglianco@jcu.edu; *Assoc Dir*, Marcella Milota; Tel: 216-397-4259; *Acq*, Ruth Reider; Tel: 216-397-4712; *Doc*, Ruth Connell; Tel: 216-397-1635; *Ref*, Ruth Fenske; Tel: 216-397-4523; *Coll Develop*, Charles Wood; Tel: 216-397-3044; Staff 13 (MLS 10, Non-MLS 3)
Founded 1886. Enrl 4,384; Fac 467; Highest Degree: Master
Jun 1999-May 2000 Income $2,985,702. Mats Exp $1,056,262, Books $428,738, Per/Ser (Incl. Access Fees) $411,531, Presv $30,000, Micro $47,945, AV Equip $30,975, Electronic Ref Mat (Incl. Access Fees) $107,073. Sal $1,385,560 (Prof $562,481)
Library Holdings: Bk Vols 627,175; Per Subs 2,198
Subject Interests: Bus, Education, Mgt, Religion, Theology
Special Collections: Far East (Daniel A Hill Far Eastern); G K Chesterton (John R Bayer Chesterton Coll), bks, micro
Automation Activity & Vendor Info: (Acquisitions) Innovative Interfaces Inc.; (Cataloging) Innovative Interfaces Inc.; (Circulation) Innovative Interfaces Inc.; (ILL) Innovative Interfaces Inc.; (OPAC) Innovative Interfaces Inc.; (Serials) Innovative Interfaces Inc.
Publications: Library Notes (newsletter)
Partic in Cleveland Area Metropolitan Library System; Ohio Library & Information Network
Friends of the Library Group

UPPER ARLINGTON

P UPPER ARLINGTON PUBLIC LIBRARY, 2800 Tremont Rd, 43221. SAN 357-282X. Tel: 614-486-9621. Reference Tel: 614-486-3342. FAX: 614-486-4530. Web Site: www.ualibrary.org. *Dir*, Ann R Moore; E-Mail: moorea@oplin.lib.oh.us; *Ad Servs*, Robert Gilroy; *Ref*, Heather Phalen; *AV, Media Spec*, Stephen Harvey; *Br Coordr*, Evelyn Kennedy; *Ch Servs*, Lavonne Roscoe; Staff 136 (MLS 16, Non-MLS 120)
Founded 1967. Pop 995,565; Circ 1,367,225
Jan 1999-Dec 1999 Income (Main Library and Branch Library) $4,481,486, State $3,260,804, City $1,002,490, Locally Generated Income $163,000, Other $218,192. Mats Exp $4,411,311, Books $381,309, Per/Ser (Incl. Access Fees) $67,314, AV Equip $137,036. Sal $2,005,097
Library Holdings: Bk Vols 376,114; Bk Titles 246,740; Per Subs 529
Special Collections: Upper Arlington Hist, Authors & Composers Coll
Automation Activity & Vendor Info: (Circulation) VTLS
Database Vendor: GaleNet, OCLC - First Search, Wilson - Wilson Web
Partic in OCLC Online Computer Library Center, Inc; OHIONET
Friends of the Library Group
Branches: 2
LANE ROAD, 1945 Lane Rd, 43220. SAN 357-2854. Tel: 614-459-0273. FAX: 614-459-3437. Web Site: www.uapl.lib.oh.us. *Librn*, Evelyn Kennedy; E-Mail: kennedy1@uapl.lib.oh.us; *Ch Servs*, Laura Griffin
Library Holdings: Bk Vols 100,147; Per Subs 151
Friends of the Library Group
MILLER PARK, 1901 Arlington Ave, 43212. SAN 357-2889. Tel: 614-488-5710. FAX: 614-487-2032. Web Site: www.oplin.lib.oh.us. *Mgr*, Diane Bare
Library Holdings: Bk Vols 28,201; Per Subs 58
Friends of the Library Group

UPPER SANDUSKY

P UPPER SANDUSKY COMMUNITY LIBRARY, 301 N Sandusky Ave, 43351-1139. SAN 313-7643. Tel: 419-294-1345. FAX: 419-294-4499. *Dir*, Katherine M Hull; Staff 8 (MLS 1, Non-MLS 7)
Founded 1912. Pop 22,254; Circ 86,998
Jan 1999-Dec 1999 Income $462,414, State $359,454, Other $102,960. Mats Exp $51,616, Books $34,525, Per/Ser (Incl. Access Fees) $4,866, Presv $981, AV Equip $6,584, Electronic Ref Mat (Incl. Access Fees) $4,660. Sal $155,987 (Prof $35,000)
Library Holdings: Bk Vols 34,049; Per Subs 149
Subject Interests: Genealogy, Local history
Automation Activity & Vendor Info: (Cataloging) epixtech, inc.; (Circulation) epixtech, inc.; (OPAC) epixtech, inc.
Partic in Norweld
Friends of the Library Group

URBANA

L CHAMPAIGN COUNTY LAW LIBRARY,* County Court House, 200 N Main, 43078. SAN 323-4061. Tel: 937-653-2745.
Library Holdings: Bk Vols 9,000; Per Subs 163

P CHAMPAIGN COUNTY LIBRARY, 1060 Scioto St, 43078-2097. SAN 313-7651. Tel: 937-653-3811. FAX: 937-653-5679. Web Site: www.champaign.lib.oh.us. *Librn*, Zara Liskowiak; Staff 3 (MLS 1, Non-MLS 2)
Founded 1890. Pop 33,649; Circ 183,056
Library Holdings: Bk Vols 63,674; Bk Titles 57,486; Per Subs 210
Partic in Dayton-Montgomery County Pub Libr; Miami Valley Librs
Friends of the Library Group

C URBANA UNIVERSITY, Swedenborg Memorial Library, 579 College Way, 43078-2091. SAN 313-766X. Tel: 937-484-1335. Interlibrary Loan Service Tel: 937-484-1336. FAX: 937-653-8551. Web Site: www.urbana.edu. *Coll Develop, Dir, Online Servs*, Stephen Hupp; E-Mail: shupp@urbana.edu; *Circ*, Jennifer Midgley; *Tech Servs*, Jeanne Gamble; Staff 5 (MLS 1, Non-MLS 4)
Founded 1850. Enrl 825; Fac 51; Highest Degree: Master
2000-2001 Income $133,900. Mats Exp $96,000, Books $21,000, Per/Ser (Incl. Access Fees) $10,000, AV Equip $10,000, Electronic Ref Mat (Incl. Access Fees) $55,000
Library Holdings: Bk Vols 70,676; Bk Titles 53,861; Per Subs 459
Subject Interests: Emanuel Swedenborg
Special Collections: Children's Lit (19th Century); Emanuel Swedenborg Coll
Automation Activity & Vendor Info: (Acquisitions) Innovative Interfaces Inc.; (Cataloging) Innovative Interfaces Inc.; (Circulation) Innovative Interfaces Inc.; (Course Reserve) Innovative Interfaces Inc.; (ILL) Innovative Interfaces Inc.; (Media Booking) Innovative Interfaces Inc.; (OPAC) Innovative Interfaces Inc.; (Serials) Innovative Interfaces Inc.
Database Vendor: Innovative Interfaces INN - View
Partic in OCLC Online Computer Library Center, Inc; OHIONET; Opal

VAN WERT

P THE BRUMBACK LIBRARY,* 215 W Main St, 45891-1695. SAN 313-7678. Tel: 419-238-2168. FAX: 419-238-3180. E-Mail: brumback@im3.com. Web Site: www.brumbacklib.com. *Dir*, John J Carr; *Asst Dir*, Kelly Rist; *Ch Servs*, Sandra Kalb; Staff 20 (MLS 3, Non-MLS 17)
Founded 1901. Pop 32,000; Circ 404,620
Jan 1999-Dec 1999 Income $941,000. Mats Exp $265,000, Presv $2,000, Micro $500. Sal $320,000
Library Holdings: Bk Vols 132,000; Per Subs 198
Subject Interests: CD ROM mat, Children's bks, Genealogy, Large print, Local history, Popular works
Special Collections: Local History Coll Rare Books; Van Wert Newspapers, 1855 to present on microfilm
Automation Activity & Vendor Info: (Acquisitions) epixtech, inc.; (Cataloging) epixtech, inc.; (Circulation) epixtech, inc.; (OPAC) epixtech, inc.; (Serials) epixtech, inc.
Publications: Chapter & Verse Book Review; Chapter Notes (newsletter); The Preschool Primer
Partic in Norweld
First county library in the United States
Branches: 5
CONVOY BRANCH, PO Box 607, Convoy, 45832-0607. SAN 377-8886. Tel: 419-749-4000. *Librn*, Sarah Cearns
Library Holdings: Bk Vols 14,500
MIDDLE POINT BRANCH, 102 Railroad St, PO Box 295, Middle Point, 45863. SAN 377-8908. Tel: 419-968-2553. E-Mail: mpbranch@bright.net. *Librn*, Julie Johns
Library Holdings: Bk Vols 6,000
OHIO CITY BRANCH, 305 S Shane St, Ohio City, 45874. SAN 377-8924. Tel: 419-965-2918. *Librn*, Beth Keuneke
Library Holdings: Bk Vols 12,600
WILLSHIRE BRANCH, 311 S State St, Willshire, 45898. SAN 377-8940. Tel: 419-495-4138. *Librn*, Ellen Kohn
WREN BRANCH, 103 State Rte 49, Wren, 45899. SAN 377-8967. Tel: 419-495-4174. *Librn*, Marvine Weaver
Library Holdings: Bk Vols 9,300

GL VAN WERT COUNTY LAW LIBRARY ASSOCIATION,* Court House, 121 Main St, 3rd Flr, 45891. SAN 313-7686. Tel: 419-238-6935. *Librn*, Dennis Kimmet
Library Holdings: Bk Vols 17,900
Publications: First Reporter Series in Ultra Fiche; Second Federal Reporter & Supplement

VERMILION

S GREAT LAKES HISTORICAL SOCIETY, Clarence S Metcalf Research Library, 480 Main St, PO Box 435, 44089-0435. SAN 313-7694. Tel: 440-967-3467. Toll Free Tel: 800-893-1485. FAX: 440-967-1519. Web Site: www.inlandseas.org. *Chair*, William D Carle III; *Exec Dir*, Christopher Gilchrist; *Bibliog Instr*, Gordon Wendt
Founded 1944
Library Holdings: Bk Titles 2,400
Subject Interests: Commercial fishing, Great Lakes hist, Maritime, Original ship's logs, Photogs, Rec, Yachting
Special Collections: American Bureau of Shipping 1915-1958; Great Lakes Journal (Inland Seas Coll); Great Lakes Ships Coll, 12,000 photogs; Lloyd's Inland Register 1873-1907; Lloyd's Register 1926-1970; Marine Review

1883-1931; Maritime Directories (Beeson's Annual 1891-1920 & Green's 1911-1960); Merchant Vessels of the US 1872-1950
Publications: Chadburn (quarterly newsletter); Inland Seas (quarterly journal)
Restriction: Members only

P RITTER PUBLIC LIBRARY, 5680 Liberty Ave, 44089-1196. SAN 313-7708. Tel: 440-967-3798. FAX: 440-967-5482. Web Site: www.ritter.lib.oh.us. *Dir*, Janet L Ford; *Ch Servs*, Margaret A Townsend; E-Mail: margaret.townsend@ritter.lib.oh.us; *Ref*, Kathleen L Jozwiak; E-Mail: kathleen.jozwiak@ritter.lib.oh.us; Staff 22 (MLS 3, Non-MLS 19)
Founded 1912. Pop 11,100; Circ 270,432
Jan 1999-Dec 1999 Income $1,030,040, State $593,905, Locally Generated Income $268,080, Other $168,055. Mats Exp $198,494, Books $133,806, Per/Ser (Incl. Access Fees) $12,244, Presv $285, AV Equip $18,111, Other Print Mats $4,967, Electronic Ref Mat (Incl. Access Fees) $29,081. Sal $389,800 (Prof $88,423)
Library Holdings: Bk Vols 62,444; Per Subs 289
Database Vendor: DRA, Ebsco - EbscoHost, OCLC - First Search
Partic in Cleveland Area Metropolitan Library System; Ohio Libr Coun
Friends of the Library Group

VERSAILLES

P WORCH MEMORIAL PUBLIC LIBRARY,* 161 E Main St, 45380-1519. SAN 313-7724. Tel: 937-526-3416. FAX: 937-526-3416. *Dir, Media Spec*, Gail Benesh
Founded 1937. Pop 6,000; Circ 115,000
Library Holdings: Bk Vols 30,000; Per Subs 156
Subject Interests: Area genealogy, Family, Local genealogy
Friends of the Library Group

WADSWORTH

P ELLA M EVERHARD PUBLIC LIBRARY,* 132 Broad St, 44281-1897. SAN 313-7759. Tel: 330-334-5761. TDD: 330-335-1298. FAX: 330-334-6605. E-Mail: wdsadm@library.cpl.org. Web Site: www.wadsworth.lib.oh.us. *Dir*, C Allen Nichols; Tel: 330-335-1299, E-Mail: c.allen.nichols@wadsworth.lib.oh.us; *Coordr*, Jacqueline Lecky; *Circ*, Carolyn Hahn; *Publ Servs*, Janet Welch; *Tech Coordr*, Jim Haprian; *Ad Servs*, Tom Dillie; *YA Servs*, Abby Hindulak; *ILL*, Bobbie Richards; *Cat*, Barb Black; Staff 51 (MLS 6, Non-MLS 45)
Founded 1922
Library Holdings: Bk Vols 146,153; Per Subs 300
Subject Interests: Artwork, Lab kits, Local history
Publications: Ellagram (Newsletter)
Partic in Cleveland Area Metropolitan Library System; Clevnet
Special Services for the Deaf - TDD; TTY machine
Special Services for the Blind - Low vision aids & talking readers

M WADSWORTH-RITTMAN COMMUNITY HOSPITAL LIBRARY, 195 Wadsworth Rd, 44281. SAN 373-689X. Tel: 330-334-1504, Ext 2823. FAX: 330-336-0107. *Librn*, Barbara Black; Staff 1 (MLS 1)
Library Holdings: Bk Titles 200; Per Subs 27
Subject Interests: Medicine, Nursing

WAPAKONETA

GL AUGLAIZE COUNTY LAW LIBRARY,* County Courthouse, 201 Willipie St, Ste 207, 34895. SAN 313-7767. Tel: 419-738-3124. FAX: 419-738-4713. *Librn*, Bridget Weller
Founded 1898
Library Holdings: Bk Vols 22,000

P AUGLAIZE COUNTY PUBLIC DISTRICT LIBRARY, 203 S Perry St, 45895-1999. SAN 357-2919. Tel: 419-738-2921. FAX: 419-738-5168. Web Site: library.norweld.lib.oh.us/auglaizeco/. *Dir*, M Jo Derryberry; *Asst Dir*, Diana T Pham-Schneider; *Ch Servs*, Kelly Morris; Staff 22 (MLS 1, Non-MLS 21)
Founded 1925. Pop 47,103; Circ 320,139
Jan 1999-Dec 1999 Income (Main Library and Branch Library) $1,232,388, State $1,121,930, Locally Generated Income $110,458. Mats Exp $253,995, Books $178,641, Per/Ser (Incl. Access Fees) $22,782, Other Print Mats $52,572. Sal $512,200
Library Holdings: Bk Vols 149,537; Per Subs 400
Subject Interests: Dudley Nichols, Genealogy, Local, Neil Armstrong, Ohio hist
Automation Activity & Vendor Info: (Cataloging) Gaylord; (Circulation) Gaylord; (OPAC) Gaylord
Branches: 5
CRIDERSVILLE PUBLIC, 223 W Main St, Cridersville, 45806. SAN 357-2927. Tel: 419-645-5447. FAX: 419-645-6019. Web Site: www.library.norweld.lib.oh.us/auglaizeco/. *Librn*, Billie Connor
Open Winter: Mon & Wed 1-6, Tues 10-12 & 4-8, Thurs 4-8, Sat 10-2; Summer: Mon & Wed 1-6, Tues & Thurs 10-12 & 4-8, Sat 9-1
Friends of the Library Group
EDWARD R & MINNIE D WHITE MEMORIAL, 108 E Wapakoneta St, Waynesfield, 45896. SAN 357-3001. Tel: 419-568-5851. FAX: 419-568-2368. Web Site: library.norweld.lib.oh.us/auglaizeco/. *Librn*, Dee Sanders
Partic in Norweld
Open Winter & Summer: Mon 1-6, Tues 10-6, Wed & Thurs 1-7, Sat 10-2
FRANCIS J STALLO MEMORIAL, 196 E Fourth St, Minster, 45865. SAN 357-2978. Tel: 419-628-2925. FAX: 419-628-4556. Web Site: library.norweld.lib.oh.us/auglaizeco/. *Librn*, Becky Prenger
Open Winter & Summer: Mon & Tues 10-7:30, Wed 4-8, Fri 10-2, Sat 9am-12pm
Friends of the Library Group
NEW BREMEN PUBLIC, 45 W Washington St, New Bremen, 45869. SAN 357-2935. Tel: 419-629-2158. FAX: 419-629-1351. Web Site: www.library.norweld.lib.oh.us/auglaizeco/. *Head Librn*, Sue Maxson
Open Winter & Summer: Mon 12-7:30, Tues 10-7:30, Wed 12:30-7:30, Thurs & Fri 10-5, Sat 10am-12pm
Friends of the Library Group
NEW KNOXVILLE COMMUNITY, 304 S Main St, PO Box 370, New Knoxville, 45871. SAN 357-2943. Tel: 419-753-2724. FAX: 419-753-2594. Web Site: www.library.norweld.lib.oh.us/auglaizeco/. *Librn*, Ann Leffel
Open Winter & Summer: Mon & Thurs 1-8, Tues 10-5, Wed 1-5, Fri & Sat 10am-12pm
Bookmobiles: 1

WARREN

S AJAX MAGNETHERMIC CORP, Research & Development Library, 1745 Overland Ave NE, 44483. (Mail add: PO Box 991, 44482), SAN 313-7775. Tel: 330-372-8781. FAX: 330-372-8634. *Res*, Rosemary Cleary; E-Mail: rcleary@ajaxmag.com
Founded 1942
Jan 1999-Dec 1999 Income $6,500. Mats Exp $6,102, Books $343, Per/Ser (Incl. Access Fees) $4,635, Other Print Mats $1,124. Sal $30,000
Library Holdings: Bk Titles 3,500; Per Subs 60
Subject Interests: Electromagnetic fields, Heating equip, Indust melting
Special Collections: Dr E F Northrup, Founder & Inventor; Induction Melting & Heating (Literature Coll & Patent Coll), VF; of High Frequency Induction Furnace, papers, bks, patents, scrapbooks & VF
Publications: Digest of Literature (weekly) for internal use
Restriction: Company library

S TRIBUNE CHRONICLE LIBRARY,* 240 Franklin St, PO Box 1431, 44482-1431. SAN 371-8468. Tel: 330-841-1734. FAX: 330-841-1717. Web Site: www.tribune-chronicle.com. *Librn*, Denise Reed
Founded 1982
Library Holdings: Bk Vols 533; Bk Titles 391
Special Collections: Tribune 1891-present, microfilm

L TRUMBULL COUNTY LAW LIBRARY, 120 High St NW, 44481. SAN 372-199X. Tel: 330-675-2525. FAX: 330-675-2527. Web Site: www.trumbullaw.org. *Dir*, George Baker; E-Mail: gbaker9916@aol.com; *Asst Dir*, Karin L McKinney; Staff 3 (MLS 1, Non-MLS 2)
Library Holdings: Bk Vols 32,000; Per Subs 56

M TRUMBULL MEMORIAL HOSPITAL, Wean Medical Library, 1350 E Market St, 44482. SAN 313-7805. Tel: 330-841-9379. FAX: 330-393-6474. *Librn*, Carol Kamens
Founded 1967
1998-1999 Mats Exp $60,874, Books $11,352, Per/Ser (Incl. Access Fees) $44,952, Presv $4,570. Sal $35,306
Library Holdings: Bk Titles 1,767; Per Subs 190
Subject Interests: Gynecology, Obstetrics, Pediatrics, Surgery
Publications: Wean Library News (quarterly newsletter)
Partic in Ohio Library & Information Network

P WARREN-TRUMBULL COUNTY PUBLIC LIBRARY, (W-TCPL), 444 Mahoning Ave NW, 44483. SAN 313-7813. Tel: 330-399-8807. FAX: 330-395-3988. Web Site: www.wtcpl.lib.oh.us. *Dir*, Robert D Briell; *Asst Dir*, Mona Stevenson; *Ch Servs*, Ellen Finan; *Circ*, Susan Biggs; *Cat, Tech Servs*, Pat Latham; *Ref*, Micky Burnsworth; *ILL*, Vera Mallory; *Br Coordr*, Pam Daubenspeck; *Bkmobile Coordr*, Steve Svecz; *Pub Relations*, Jan Vaughn; Staff 35 (MLS 17, Non-MLS 18)
Founded 1890. Pop 160,721; Circ 948,683
Jan 1999-Dec 1999 Income (Main Library and Branch Library) $4,915,176, State $3,874,785, Locally Generated Income $780,000, Other $260,391. Mats Exp $887,900. Sal $2,122,949
Library Holdings: Bk Vols 328,495; Per Subs 602
Subject Interests: Local history, Ohio
Automation Activity & Vendor Info: (Cataloging) Inlex; (Circulation) Inlex; (OPAC) Inlex
Publications: By the Book
Partic in Nola Regional Library System; OHIONET
Friends of the Library Group
Branches: 5
BROOKFIELD BRANCH, 7032 Grove St, Brookfield, 44403. SAN 324-251X. Tel: 330-448-8134. Web Site: www.wtcpl.lib.oh.us. *Branch Mgr*,

Nancy Gaut; *Librn*, Linda Bailey
Library Holdings: Bk Vols 15,000
Friends of the Library Group
HOWLAND BRANCH, 9095 E Market St, 44484. SAN 370-9000. Tel: 330-856-2011. Web Site: www.wtcpl.lib.oh.us. *Librn*, Carol Mullen; Staff 2 (MLS 2)
Friends of the Library Group
LIBERTY, 3551 Belmont Ave, Youngstown, 44505. SAN 377-9971. Tel: 330-759-2589. Web Site: www.wtcpl.lib.oh.us. *Librn*, Carol Corrado; Staff 2 (MLS 1, Non-MLS 1)
Library Holdings: Bk Vols 10,000
LORDSTOWN BRANCH, 1471 Salt Springs Rd SW, Lordstown, 44481. SAN 325-3384. Tel: 330-824-2094. Web Site: www.wtcpl.lib.oh.us. *Librn*, Vera Riffle; Staff 1 (Non-MLS 1)
Library Holdings: Bk Vols 4,500
VIETS MEMORIAL, 212 N High St, Cortland, 44410. SAN 324-2528. Tel: 330-638-6335. Web Site: www.wtcpl.lib.oh.us. *Librn*, Mavis Riley
Library Holdings: Bk Vols 17,000
Bookmobiles: 1

WARRENSVILLE HEIGHTS

M SOUTH POINTE HOSPITAL LIBRARY, 4110 Warrensville Center Rd, 44122. SAN 325-1918. Tel: 216-491-7454. FAX: 216-491-7560. *In Charge*, Suzanne R Arnold; E-Mail: sarnold@meridia.org; Staff 2 (MLS 1, Non-MLS 1)
Founded 1978
Library Holdings: Bk Vols 4,791; Per Subs 400
Subject Interests: Osteopathic med
Automation Activity & Vendor Info: (Circulation) Follett
Database Vendor: OVID Technologies
Partic in Cleveland Area Metropolitan Library System; MLANO

WASHINGTON COURT HOUSE

P CARNEGIE PUBLIC LIBRARY,* 127 S North St, 43160. SAN 313-7848. Tel: 740-335-2540. FAX: 740-335-8409. Web Site: www.washington-ch.lib.oh.us. *Dir*, Susan Jewell-McDaniel; *Ad Servs*, Christopher Siscoe; *Ch Servs*, Deborah Roby; *Tech Servs*, Maria Wilburn
Founded 1891. Pop 28,500; Circ 190,000
Jan 1999-Dec 1999 Income $937,100, State $890,000, Locally Generated Income $47,100. Mats Exp $129,000, Books $120,000, Per/Ser (Incl. Access Fees) $6,000, Presv $3,000. Sal $387,500 (Prof $141,000)
Library Holdings: Bk Vols 56,900; Per Subs 98
Special Collections: Genealogy, bks, flm
Partic in Miami Valley Librs
Branches: 1

GL FAYETTE COUNTY LAW LIBRARY,* 110 E Court House, 43160-1355. SAN 313-783X. Tel: 740-335-3608. FAX: 740-333-3530. *Asst Librn*, Rollo Marchant
Library Holdings: Bk Vols 14,000
Subject Interests: Bankruptcy, Fed reports, Tax
Special Collections: Ohio Laws

WAUSEON

L FULTON COUNTY ASSOCIATION, Law Library,* Court House, 210 S Fulton, 43567. SAN 327-7208. Tel: 419-337-9260. FAX: 419-337-9293. *Librn*, Sue Behnfeldt

P WAUSEON PUBLIC LIBRARY,* 117 E Elm St, 43567. SAN 313-7856. Tel: 419-335-6626. FAX: 419-335-0642. Web Site: library.norweld.lib.oh.us/wauseon/. *Dir*, Francita Gasche; E-Mail: gaschefr@oplin.lib.oh.us; *Asst Dir*, Marcela De Leon; Staff 5 (MLS 2, Non-MLS 3)
Founded 1875. Pop 10,638; Circ 100,000
Library Holdings: Bk Titles 40,840; Per Subs 165
Subject Interests: Spanish
Publications: Annual Report
Partic in Norweld; NW Ohio Libr District; Ohio Pub Libr Info Network
Friends of the Library Group

WAVERLY

P GARNET A WILSON PUBLIC LIBRARY OF PIKE COUNTY, 207 N Market St, 45690-1176. SAN 313-7864. Tel: 740-947-4921. FAX: 740-947-2918. Web Site: www.pike.lib.oh.us. *Dir*, Thomas S Adkins; E-Mail: dirgaw@oplin.lib.oh.us; *Exten Serv*, Paula J Hays; E-Mail: gawextsc@oplin.lib.oh.us; *Automation Syst Coordr*, Daniel R Moore; E-Mail: gawasc@oplin.lib.oh.us; *Publ Servs*, Loreen M Colegrove; E-Mail: gawpcord@oplin.lib.oh.us; *Tech Servs*, Jennifer K Roberts; E-Mail: gawtcord@oplin.lib.oh.us; Staff 33 (MLS 2, Non-MLS 31)
Founded 1939. Pop 24,249; Circ 206,840
Jan 2000-Dec 2000 Income (Main Library and Branch Library) $981,074, State $961,074, Locally Generated Income $20,000
Library Holdings: Bk Vols 60,000; Per Subs 201
Special Collections: Pike County Local History/Genealogy Room
Database Vendor: Ebsco - EbscoHost, IAC - Info Trac, OVID Technologies, Wilson - Wilson Web
Special Services for the Blind - Talking Books
Branches: 2
EASTERN BRANCH, 310 Third St, Beaver, 45613. Tel: 740-226-4408. FAX: 740-226-4419. E-Mail: gawextsc@oplin.lib.oh.us. Web Site: www.pike.lib.oh.us. *Dir*, Thomas S Adkins; Staff 4 (MLS 1, Non-MLS 3)
Founded 2000
PIKETON BRANCH, 200 E Second St, PO Box 762, Piketon, 45661-0762. SAN 376-7914. Tel: 740-289-3064. FAX: 740-289-4204. E-Mail: gawextsc@oplin.lib.oh.us. Web Site: www.pike.lib.oh.us. *Exten Serv*, Paula Hays; Staff 4 (MLS 1, Non-MLS 3)
Founded 1997

WAYNE

P WAYNE PUBLIC LIBRARY,* 137 E Main St, 43466. SAN 357-3036. Tel: 419-288-2708. Interlibrary Loan Service Tel: 419-288-2708. FAX: 419-288-3766. Web Site: library.norweld.lib.oh.us/wayne. *Dir*, Teresa Barnhart; E-Mail: barnhate@oplin.lib.oh.us
Founded 1945. Pop 8,800; Circ 85,881
Library Holdings: Bk Vols 56,338
Partic in Northwest Library District
Friends of the Library Group
Branches: 2
BLOOMDALE BRANCH, 115 S Main St, Bloomdale, 44817. SAN 357-3060. Tel: 419-454-3021. FAX: 419-454-5095. Web Site: library.norweld.lib.oh.us/wayne. *Librn*, Sheila McNally
Library Holdings: Bk Vols 11,000
Friends of the Library Group
CYGNET BRANCH, 306 Front St, Cygnet, 43413. SAN 357-3079. Tel: 419-655-3495. FAX: 419-655-2509. Web Site: library.norweld.lib.oh.us/wayne. *Librn*, Cheryl MacDonald
Friends of the Library Group

WAYNESVILLE

P MARY L COOK PUBLIC LIBRARY,* 381 Old Stage Rd, 45068. SAN 313-7872. Tel: 513-897-4826. FAX: 513-897-9215. Web Site: mlcook.lib.oh.us. *Dir*, Linda Swartzel; E-Mail: swartzli@oplin.lib.oh.us; *YA Servs*, Joanne Coker; *Tech Servs*, Jan McCann
Founded 1917. Pop 10,685; Circ 170,114
Library Holdings: Bk Vols 65,000
Subject Interests: Genealogy
Special Collections: Early Quaker Theology; Media: videos (4982), audios (1687); Ohio & Local History
Publications: Newsletter (quarterly)
Partic in Miami Valley Librs
Friends of the Library Group

WELLINGTON

P HERRICK MEMORIAL LIBRARY,* 101 Willard Memorial Sq, 44090-1342. SAN 313-7880. Tel: 440-647-2120. FAX: 440-647-2103. E-Mail: hmladmin@oplin.lib.oh.us. Web Site: www.wellington.lib.oh.us. *Dir*, Patricia J Lindley; E-Mail: lindlepa@oplin.lib.oh.us; *Ch Servs*, Patricia A Strubbe; E-Mail: strubbpa@oplin.lib.oh.us; *Ref*, Lynne Welch; E-Mail: welchly@oplin.lib.oh.us
Founded 1873. Pop 8,300; Circ 101,454
Jan 1998-Dec 1998 Income $450,000, State $404,000, Locally Generated Income $46,000. Mats Exp $369,000
Library Holdings: Bk Vols 45,610; Bk Titles 36,500; Per Subs 160
Special Collections: Wellington Historic Photos (900 Images)
Automation Activity & Vendor Info: (Cataloging) Gaylord; (Circulation) Gaylord; (OPAC) Gaylord
Partic in Cleveland Area Metropolitan Library System
Friends of the Library Group

WELLSTON

P OHIO VALLEY AREA LIBRARIES, 252 W 13th St, 45692. SAN 322-2756. Tel: 740-384-2103. Toll Free Tel: 800-759-1537. FAX: 740-384-2106. E-Mail: oval@oplin.lib.oh.us, ovalrls@oplin.lib.oh.us. Web Site: www.oval.lib.oh.us. *Dir*, Eric S Anderson; Tel: 740-384-2103, Ext 6, E-Mail: anderser@oplin.lib.oh.us; *Purchasing*, Regina Ghearing; *Coordr*, Tricia Ramey; *Tech Coordr*, Karen Hamilton; E-Mail: hamiltka@oplin.lib.oh.us. Subject Specialists: *Automation*, Eric S Anderson; *Management*, Eric S Anderson; Staff 10 (MLS 2, Non-MLS 8)
Founded 1973
Automation Activity & Vendor Info: (Circulation) Follett
Function: consulting services, interlibrary loan, reference services

P SYLVESTER MEMORIAL WELLSTON PUBLIC LIBRARY,* 135 E Second St, 45692. SAN 313-7899. Tel: 740-384-6660. FAX: 740-384-5001. *Dir*, Jackie Shaw; Staff 11 (MLS 1, Non-MLS 10)

Pop 10,000
Library Holdings: Bk Vols 32,295; Bk Titles 38,000
Mem of Ohio Valley Area Librs

WELLSVILLE

P WELLSVILLE CARNEGIE PUBLIC LIBRARY, 115 Ninth St, 43968-1431. SAN 313-7902. Tel: 330-532-1526. FAX: 330-532-3127. Web Site: www.wellsville.lib.oh.us. *Dir*, Cheryl Foote; E-Mail: footech@oplin.lib.oh.us; *Ch Servs, Coordr*, Toni Lloyd; Staff 1 (MLS 1)
Founded 1908. Pop 14,299; Circ 46,000
Jan 1999-Dec 1999 Income $529,980, State $433,349, Locally Generated Income $18,315, Other $78,316. Mats Exp $47,627, Books $44,752, Per/Ser (Incl. Access Fees) $2,875. Sal $110,495 (Prof $60,192)
Library Holdings: Bk Vols 34,000; Per Subs 70
Special Collections: Early History of Columbiana County
Automation Activity & Vendor Info: (Cataloging) Gaylord; (Circulation) Gaylord; (OPAC) Gaylord
Mem of NOLA Regional Libr Syst
Special Services for the Blind - Talking Books

WEST JEFFERSON

P HURT-BATTELLE MEMORIAL LIBRARY OF WEST JEFFERSON,* 270 Lily Chapel Rd, 43162-1202. SAN 313-7910. Tel: 614-879-8448. FAX: 614-879-8668. *Dir*, Sharon Shrum; E-Mail: shrumsh@oplin.lib.oh.us; *Asst Dir*, Rosemary Darlington
Founded 1914. Pop 5,600; Circ 66,905
1997-1998 Income $245,018, State $236,796, Locally Generated Income $8,222. Mats Exp $44,700, Books $37,668, Per/Ser (Incl. Access Fees) $2,803
Library Holdings: Bk Titles 44,768; Per Subs 85
Subject Interests: Computers, Crafts, Medicine, Sci, Sports, Theatre
Friends of the Library Group

WEST MILTON

P MILTON-UNION PUBLIC LIBRARY, 560 S Main St, 45383. SAN 313-7929. Tel: 937-698-5515. FAX: 937-698-3774. *Dir*, Francesca L Hary; E-Mail: haryf@oplin.lib.oh.us; *Ch Servs*, Sharon Callicoat; *Ref Serv Ad*, Carol Coate; *YA Servs*, Rachelle Ramsey; Staff 10 (MLS 1, Non-MLS 9)
Founded 1937. Pop 10,000; Circ 152,300
Jan 2001-Dec 2001 Income $469,700, State $469,000, Locally Generated Income $700. Mats Exp $76,000, Books $65,000, Per/Ser (Incl. Access Fees) $7,000, AV Equip $4,000. Sal $168,900 (Prof $194,000)
Library Holdings: Bk Vols 49,000; Per Subs 158; Bks on Deafness & Sign Lang 18
Subject Interests: Local history
Automation Activity & Vendor Info: (Circulation) epixtech, inc.; (OPAC) epixtech, inc.
Partic in Miami Valley Librs
Friends of the Library Group

WEST UNION

GL ADAMS COUNTY LAW LIBRARY, Courthouse, Rm 222, 110 W Main St, 45693. SAN 328-8242. Tel: 937-544-3331. FAX: 937-544-5107. *Librn*, Kenneth L Armstrong, Jr
Library Holdings: Bk Vols 5,567; Per Subs 14

WESTERVILLE

S HONDROS COLLEGE RESOURCE CENTER,* 4140 Executive Pkwy, 43081-3855. SAN 374-7832. Tel: 614-841-3825. FAX: 614-841-3848. E-Mail: libraryhc@aol.com. *Librn*, Sharon Thomas
Library Holdings: Bk Titles 4,000; Per Subs 10
Subject Interests: Real estate

G NATIONAL GROUND WATER INFORMATION CENTER,* 601 Dempsey Rd, 43081. SAN 327-392X. Tel: 614-898-7791. Toll Free Tel: 800-551-7379. FAX: 614-898-7786. *Dir*, Sandy Masters; *Cat*, Julian Larson
Library Holdings: Bk Vols 24,000
Publications: Ground Water Network User's Guide; NGWIC News
Partic in OCLC Online Computer Library Center, Inc
NGWIC operates the Ground Water Network which provides access to a number of data bases including the Ground Water On-line

C OTTERBEIN COLLEGE, Courtright Memorial Library, 138 W Main St, 43081. (Mail add: One Otterbein College, 43081), SAN 313-7937. Tel: 614-823-1215. Reference Tel: 614-823-1984. FAX: 614-823-1921. E-Mail: library@otterbein.edu. Web Site: www.otterbein.edu/learning/library.htm. *Dir*, Lois F Szudy; Tel: 614-823-1414, E-Mail: LSzudy@otterbein.edu; *Head Ref*, Patricia Rothermich; Tel: 614-823-1366, E-Mail: PRothermich@otterbein.edu; *Automation Syst Coordr*, Jane Wu; Tel: 614-823-1027, E-Mail: JWu@otterbein.edu; *ILL*, Allen Reichert; Tel: 614-823-1164, E-Mail: PReichert@otterbein.edu; *Archivist*, Stephen Grinch; Tel: 614-823-1761, E-Mail: SGrinch@otterbein.edu; *Per*, LaVerne Austin; Tel: 614-823-1264, E-Mail: LAustin@otterbein.edu; *Acq*, Paul Heath; Tel: 614-823-1938, E-Mail: PHeath@otterbein.edu; *Govt Doc*, Sandra Hume; *Circ*, Jessica Mize *Circ*, Amy Pickenpaugh; Tel: 614-823-1799, E-Mail: APickenpaugh@otterbein.edu; *Circ*, Rebecca Raeske; Tel: 614-823-3072, E-Mail: ERaeske@otterbein.edu; *Circ*, William Stoddard; Tel: 614-823-1985, E-Mail: WStoddard@otterbein.edu; *Coll Develop*, Doris Ebbert; Tel: 614-823-1314, E-Mail: DEbbert@otterbein.edu; *Cat*, Matt Polcyn; Tel: 614-823-1026, E-Mail: PPolcyn@otterbein.edu; *Cat*, Elizabeth Salt; Tel: 614-823-1939, E-Mail: ESalt@otterbein.edu; Staff 13 (MLS 7, Non-MLS 6)
Founded 1847. Enrl 2,383; Fac 160; Highest Degree: Master
Jul 1999-Jun 2000 Income $734,873. Mats Exp $742,830, Books $36,494, Per/Ser (Incl. Access Fees) $146,046, Presv $10,837, Micro $9,151, Other Print Mats $1,092, Electronic Ref Mat (Incl. Access Fees) $24,631. Sal $461,954 (Prof $273,331)
Library Holdings: Bk Vols 242,847; Per Subs 1,059
Special Collections: Americana (J Burr & Jessie M Hughes Memorial); Classics (Marshall B & Mary M Fanning Fund); Ethnics & Political Science (Lewis E Myers Memorial); Humanities (NEH Fund); Science (Elvin & Ruth Warrick Fund)
Automation Activity & Vendor Info: (Acquisitions) Innovative Interfaces Inc.; (Cataloging) Innovative Interfaces Inc.; (Circulation) Innovative Interfaces Inc.; (Course Reserve) Innovative Interfaces Inc.; (ILL) Innovative Interfaces Inc.; (OPAC) Innovative Interfaces Inc.; (Serials) Innovative Interfaces Inc.
Database Vendor: Innovative Interfaces INN - View, Lexis-Nexis, OCLC - First Search, ProQuest, Wilson - Wilson Web
Partic in Calico; OCLC Online Computer Library Center, Inc; Ohio Library & Information Network; Ohio Pvt Acad Librs; OHIONET
Friends of the Library Group

S THE AMERICAN CERAMIC SOCIETY, James I Mueller Memorial Library-Ceramic Information, 735 Ceramic Pl, 43081. SAN 313-4016. Tel: 614-794-5810. FAX: 614-794-5812. E-Mail: cic@acers.org. Web Site: www.acers.org. *Chief Librn*, Terry Fogle; E-Mail: tfogle@acers.org; *Mgr*, Greg Geiger; E-Mail: ggeiger@acers.org
Founded 1954
Library Holdings: Bk Titles 10,500; Per Subs 900
Subject Interests: Brick, Cement, Ceramic hist, Clay, Electronic ceramics, Glass, Indust, Porcelain, Pottery, Refractories, Tech ceramics
Special Collections: Ross Coffin Purdy Coll
Database Vendor: Ebsco - EbscoHost, GaleNet, IAC - SearchBank
Function: Research library
Document delivery service & literature search service

P WESTERVILLE PUBLIC LIBRARY,* 126 S State St, 43081-2095. SAN 313-7945. Tel: 614-882-7277. FAX: 614-882-4160. *Dir*, Don W Barlow; *Mgr, Publ Servs*, Tom Szudy; *Tech Servs*, Esther Turoci; *Ad Servs, Ref*, Laura Moorman; *Ch Servs, YA Servs*, Nancy Smith; *Circ*, Judy Allison; *Publ Servs*, Linda Wilkins; *AV*, Tanya Jamison
Founded 1930. Pop 85,093; Circ 934,468
Library Holdings: Bk Vols 238,946; Per Subs 343
Subject Interests: Local history
Special Collections: Temperance Coll
Publications: Between the Pages (newsletter)
Partic in OCLC Online Computer Library Center, Inc; OHIONET
Special Services for the Deaf - Books on deafness & sign language; Captioned film depository; Special interest periodicals; Videos & decoder
Friends of the Library Group
Branches: 1
ANTI SALOON LEAGUE MUSEUM & LOCAL HISTORY RESOURCE CENTER, 126 S State St, 43081. SAN 371-3466. Tel: 614-882-7277, Ext 160. FAX: 614-882-4160. *Librn*, Beth Weinhardt
Library Holdings: Bk Vols 7,219

WESTLAKE

S EVEREADY BATTERY COMPANY, INC, Technical Information Center,* 25225 Detroit Rd, PO Box 450777, 44145. SAN 313-3877. Tel: 440-835-7634. FAX: 440-835-8479.; Staff 8 (MLS 4, Non-MLS 4)
Founded 1956
Library Holdings: Bk Titles 12,000; Per Subs 350
Subject Interests: Electrochemical energy sources
Publications: Lit Review (weekly)
Partic in Dialog Corporation; Dow Jones News Retrieval; Orbit; STN

S OMG, INC LIBRARY,* 811 Sharon Dr, 44145. SAN 313-3648. Tel: 440-899-2950. FAX: 440-808-7114. *In Charge*, Laura Sydro
Library Holdings: Bk Vols 300; Per Subs 60

M SAINT JOHN & WEST SHORE HOSPITAL, Media Center,* 29000 Center Ridge Rd, 44145. SAN 313-2064. Tel: 440-835-8000. FAX: 216-414-6251. *Dir*, Marge Auping
Library Holdings: Bk Titles 1,900; Per Subs 101
Special Collections: Osteopathic
Partic in Nat Libr of Med

P WESTLAKE PORTER PUBLIC LIBRARY, 24350 Center Ridge Rd, 44145-4212. SAN 313-7953. Tel: 440-871-2600. FAX: 440-871-6969. Web Site: www.westlakelibrary.org. *Dir*, Paula Miller; *Asst Dir*, Jacqueline Duffy; *Tech Servs*, Ginny Hendron; *Ref*, Deb Ludwig; *Publ Servs*, Nancy Sherwin; *YA Servs*, Mary Worthington
Founded 1884. Pop 33,000; Circ 853,411
Library Holdings: Bk Vols 114,004; Bk Titles 113,874; Per Subs 379
Subject Interests: Bus, Genealogy, Local history
Automation Activity & Vendor Info: (Circulation) Inlex
Partic in Cleveland Area Metropolitan Library System; OCLC Online Computer Library Center, Inc; OHIONET
Friends of the Library Group

WESTON

P WESTON PUBLIC LIBRARY, 13153 Main St, PO Box 345, 43569. SAN 313-7961. Tel: 419-669-3415. FAX: 419-669-3216. Web Site: library.norweld.oh.us/weston/. *Dir*, Shelen A DeWitt; E-Mail: dewittsh@oplin.lib.oh.us
Founded 1942. Pop 24,000; Circ 88,989
Library Holdings: Bk Vols 64,000; Per Subs 180
Subject Interests: Local history
Publications: Weston Advocate-Monthly
Partic in Northwest Library District
Friends of the Library Group
Branches: 1
GRAND RAPIDS BRANCH, 17620 Bridge St, Grand Rapids, 43522. SAN 320-0981. Tel: 419-832-5231. FAX: 419-832-8061. Web Site: library.norweld.lib.oh.us/weston/. *Mgr*, Darla Froman; E-Mail: dfroman@acnet.org
Friends of the Library Group

WICKLIFFE

S LUBRIZOL CORP CHEMICAL LIBRARY, Information Center,* 29400 Lakeland Blvd, 44092. SAN 313-7988. Tel: 440-943-4200, Ext 2509. FAX: 440-943-5337.; Staff 4 (MLS 2, Non-MLS 2)
Founded 1946
Library Holdings: Bk Titles 10,200; Per Subs 210
Subject Interests: Analytical chemistry, Chemical engineering, Organic chemistry, Petroleum chem, Polymer chemistry
Publications: Lubrizol Periodical Abstracts
Restriction: Staff use only

R SAINT MARY SEMINARY, Bruening-Marotta Library, 28700 Euclid Ave, 44092-2585. SAN 313-380X. Tel: 440-943-7665. FAX: 440-585-3528. *Librn*, Alan K Rome; Staff 1 (MLS 1)
Founded 1848. Enrl 90; Fac 15
Library Holdings: Bk Vols 69,232; Per Subs 326
Subject Interests: Canon law, Church history, Ecumenism, Liturgy, Pastoral care, Religious educ, Scripture, Spirituality, Theology
Special Collections: Theology (Horstmann Coll)
Mem of Cleveland Area Metrop Libr Syst

R TELSHE YESHIVA, Rabbi A N Schwartz Library, 28400 Euclid Ave, 44092. SAN 370-4203. Tel: 440-943-5300. FAX: 440-943-5303.
Library Holdings: Bk Titles 20,000; Per Subs 10

P WICKLIFFE PUBLIC LIBRARY,* 1713 Lincoln Rd, 44092. SAN 313-8003. Tel: 440-944-6010. FAX: 440-944-7264. Web Site: www.wickliffe.lib.oh.us. *Dir*, Nancy Fisher; E-Mail: fisherna@oplin.lib.oh.us; *Publ Servs*, Linda Sperry; *Ch Servs*, Jeanne Schimmelmann
Founded 1934. Pop 16,850
1997-1998 Income $1,098,697. Mats Exp $204,000, Books $126,000, Per/Ser (Incl. Access Fees) $37,000, Micro $33,500, AV Equip $6,500, Other Print Mats $1,000. Sal $492,094 (Prof $262,000)
Library Holdings: Bk Vols 102,467; Per Subs 272
Subject Interests: Auto repair, Cookbooks, Local history
Publications: Adult New Reader: Expressions (quarterly); Great Finds (quarterly newsletter)
Partic in Cleveland Area Metropolitan Library System
Special Services for the Deaf - Books on deafness & sign language
Friends of the Library Group

WILBERFORCE

C CENTRAL STATE UNIVERSITY, Hallie Q Brown Memorial Library, PO Box 1006, 45384. SAN 313-8011. Tel: 937-376-6106. FAX: 937-376-6132. *Dir*, Johnny W Jackson; *Per, Ref*, Lugene Bailey; *AV*, Beverly White; *Cat*, Wonki Nam; *Circ*, Janet L English; *Circ*, O'Keshia Wilson; *Archivist*, Shiela Darrow; Staff 10 (MLS 5, Non-MLS 5)
Founded 1948. Enrl 2,482; Fac 120
Library Holdings: Bk Vols 106,097; Bk Titles 105,133; Per Subs 800
Special Collections: Afro-American Coll
Publications: Index to Periodical Articles by & about Blacks
Partic in Dayton-Miami Valley Consortium; OCLC Online Computer Library Center, Inc
Friends of the Library Group

R PAYNE THEOLOGICAL SEMINARY, Reverdy C Ransom Memorial Library, 1230 Wilberforce-Clifton Rd, PO Box 474, 45384-0474. SAN 313-802X. Tel: 937-376-2946. FAX: 937-376-3330. *Dir*, J Dale Balsbaugh
Founded 1890
Library Holdings: Bk Vols 32,000; Per Subs 67
Subject Interests: Biblical studies, Church history, Doctrinal theol, Ethnic studies, Ethnics, Judaica, Philosophy
Special Collections: African American Coll

C WILBERFORCE UNIVERSITY, Rembert Stokes Learning Resources Center Library, 1055 N Bickett Rd, 45384-1003. SAN 313-8038. Tel: 937-708-5628. FAX: 937-376-5787. Web Site: www.wilberforce.edu. *Dir*, Jean Mulhern; Tel: 937-708-5629; *Assoc Librn*, Jacqueline Brown; *Tech Servs*, Lynn Ayers; Staff 2 (MLS 2)
Founded 1856. Enrl 755; Fac 51; Highest Degree: Bachelor
Library Holdings: Bk Titles 64,000; Per Subs 350
Special Collections: Afro-American History (Arnett-Coppin & Payne), scrapbks, newsp clippings, handbills & some correspondence; History of African Methodist Episcopal Church
Partic in OCLC Online Computer Library Center, Inc

WILLARD

P WILLARD MEMORIAL LIBRARY, 6 W Emerald St, 44890-1498. SAN 357-3095. Tel: 419-933-8564. TDD: 800-750-0750. FAX: 419-933-4783. E-Mail: willard@oplinilib.oh.us. Web Site: library.norweld.lib.oh.us/willard. *Dir*, Cinda S Bretz Wallace; *Ch Servs*, Suellen Jacobs; *Tech Servs*, Margrate White; Staff 3 (MLS 1, Non-MLS 2)
Founded 1921. Pop 50,000; Circ 178,800
Jan 1999-Dec 1999 Income (Main Library and Branch Library) $822,166, State $777,358, City $3,600, Locally Generated Income $41,208. Mats Exp $799,597, Books $127,552, Per/Ser (Incl. Access Fees) $11,563. Sal $362,034
Library Holdings: Bk Vols 74,035; Per Subs 262
Special Collections: Coll), bks, micro, photog; Local History (Huron County; Ohio History, bks, pamphlets, letters; Railroad History, photog, bks
Automation Activity & Vendor Info: (Cataloging) Gaylord; (Circulation) Gaylord; (OPAC) Gaylord
Mem of NW Libr District
Branches: 3
GREENWICH PUBLIC LIBRARY, 4 New St, Greenwich, 44837. SAN 357-3125. Tel: 419-752-7331. TDD: 800-750-0750. FAX: 419-752-7331. *Librn*, Nellie Reynolds; Staff 1 (Non-MLS 1)
Friends of the Library Group
NORTH FAIRFIELD PUBLIC LIBRARY, 5 E Main St, PO Box 175, North Fairfield, 44855. SAN 357-315X. Tel: 419-744-2285. TDD: 800-750-0750. FAX: 419-744-2285. *Librn*, Donna Abbott; Staff 1 (Non-MLS 1)
Friends of the Library Group
WAKEMAN COMMUNITY LIBRARY, 33 Pleasant St, PO Box 278, Wakeman, 44889. SAN 357-3184. Tel: 440-839-2976. FAX: 440-839-2560. *Librn*, Jeanette Burke; Staff 1 (Non-MLS 1)
Friends of the Library Group

WILLOUGHBY

S THE MORGAN LIBRARY OF OHIO IMPRINTS, 4425 Glenbrook Rd, 44094-8219. SAN 378-1526. Tel: 440-951-7316. FAX: 440-951-9423. E-Mail: ohioimprints@stratos.net. *Dir*, Richard P Morgan
Founded 1989
Library Holdings: Bk Vols 2,450; Bk Titles 2,150
Special Collections: Ohio Imprints before 1850; Reference Coll to Support History of the Book Research

S SCHOOL OF FINE ARTS LIBRARY, 38660 Mentor Ave, 44094. SAN 313-8046. Tel: 440-951-7500. FAX: 440-975-4592.
Founded 1972
Library Holdings: Bk Vols 3,650; Bk Titles 3,600; Per Subs 20
Subject Interests: Ballet, Dance, Drama, Fine arts, Music

WILLOWICK

P WILLOUGHBY-EASTLAKE PUBLIC LIBRARY, 263 E 305th St, 44095. SAN 357-3214. Tel: 440-943-2203. Interlibrary Loan Service Tel: 440-944-5722. FAX: 440-943-2383. Web Site: www.wepl.lib.oh.us. *Dir*, Holly Carroll; E-Mail: hcarroll@wepl.lib.oh.us; *Dep Dir*, Diana Rogers; E-Mail: drogers@wepl.lib.oh.us; *Automation Syst Coordr*, Carole Brachna; Tel: 440-944-6900, E-Mail: cbrachna@wepl.lib.oh.us; *Automation Syst Coordr*, Carole Byrnes; Staff 54 (MLS 12, Non-MLS 42)
Founded 1827. Pop 67,004; Circ 672,534
Jan 1999-Dec 1999 Income (Main Library and Branch Library) $2,608,821, State $2,160,227, County $348,394, Locally Generated Income $100,200.

Mats Exp $492,315, Books $312,785, Per/Ser (Incl. Access Fees) $28,935, Micro $3,071, AV Equip $71,829, Other Print Mats $37,095, Electronic Ref Mat (Incl. Access Fees) $38,600. Sal $1,078,661
Library Holdings: Bk Vols 215,921; Bk Titles 131,097; Per Subs 744; High Interest/Low Vocabulary Bk Vols 237
Subject Interests: Architecture, Art
Special Collections: Willoughby Historical Society & News/Herald, micro
Automation Activity & Vendor Info: (Acquisitions) DRA; (Cataloging) DRA; (Circulation) DRA; (OPAC) DRA; (Serials) DRA
Partic in Cleveland Area Metropolitan Library System; Cleveland Integrated Automated Libr Regional Network
Friends of the Library Group
Branches: 3
EASTLAKE LIBRARY, 36706 Lake Shore Blvd, Eastlake, 44095. SAN 357-3249. Tel: 440-942-7880. FAX: 440-942-4095. Web Site: www.wepl.lib.oh.us. *Mgr*, Virginia Billson; E-Mail: gbillson@wepl.lib.oh.us
Circ 204,254
Library Holdings: Bk Vols 70,395; High Interest/Low Vocabulary Bk Vols 56
Database Vendor: DRA
Friends of the Library Group
WILLOUGHBY LIBRARY, 30 Public Sq, Willoughby, 44094. SAN 357-3273. Tel: 440-942-3200. FAX: 440-942-4312. Web Site: www.wepl.lib.oh.us. *Librn*, Nancy Schrott; E-Mail: nschrott@wepl.lib.oh.us
Circ 240,243
Library Holdings: Bk Vols 73,986; High Interest/Low Vocabulary Bk Vols 113
Special Collections: Microfilm Coll; News-Herald Coll; Willoughby Historical Society Coll
Database Vendor: DRA
Friends of the Library Group
WILLOWICK LIBRARY, 263 E 305th St, 44095. SAN 357-3303. Tel: 440-943-4151. FAX: 440-944-6901. Web Site: www.wepl.lib.oh.us. *Branch Mgr*, Gary Esmonde; E-Mail: gesmonde@wepl.lib.oh.us
Circ 227,848
Library Holdings: Bk Vols 72,994; High Interest/Low Vocabulary Bk Vols 68
Database Vendor: DRA
Friends of the Library Group

WILMINGTON

GL CLINTON COUNTY LAW LIBRARY,* 46 S South St, 45177. SAN 313-8062. Tel: 937-382-2428. FAX: 937-382-7632. E-Mail: cclibr1@erinet.com. *Librn*, Judy A Gano
Founded 1905
Library Holdings: Bk Vols 25,000

C WILMINGTON COLLEGE, Sheppard Arthur Watson Library, 251 Ludovic St, 45177-2499. SAN 313-8070. Tel: 937-382-6661, Ext 345. FAX: 937-382-7077. *Dir*, David Gansz; Tel: 937-382-6661 Ext 346; *Spec Coll*, Ina Kelley; *Circ, ILL*, Mary Lou Mann; *AV*, Melissa Hendrix; *Ref*, Patti Kinsinger; *Govt Doc, Per*, Amy Moffat; Staff 8 (MLS 4, Non-MLS 4)
Founded 1870. Fac 76; Highest Degree: Bachelor
Library Holdings: Bk Vols 103,706; Bk Titles 76,364; Per Subs 408
Special Collections: Peace Resources Center-Hiroshima & Nagasaki Memorial Coll, bks; Quakers-Quakerism Coll, bks, mss & per
Partic in Greater Cincinnati Library Consortium; OHIONET

P WILMINGTON PUBLIC LIBRARY OF CLINTON COUNTY,* 268 N South St, 45177-1696. SAN 313-8089. Tel: 937-382-2417. FAX: 937-382-1692. Web Site: www.wilminlib.oplin.lib.oh.us. *Coll Develop, Dir*, Judith Meyers; E-Mail: meyersju@oplin.lib.oh.us
Founded 1899. Pop 36,000; Circ 121,105
Library Holdings: Bk Vols 75,000; Per Subs 123
Subject Interests: Genealogy, Ohio
Special Collections: Ohio Coll; Wilmington News-Journal (newsp)
Publications: Library Line
Friends of the Library Group

WOODSFIELD

P MONROE COUNTY DISTRICT LIBRARY,* 96 Home Ave, 43793. SAN 313-8100. Tel: 740-472-1954. FAX: 740-472-1110. *Librn*, Shirley Matz
Founded 1939. Pop 17,200; Circ 145,000
Library Holdings: Bk Vols 48,000; Per Subs 129
Partic in Southeastern Ohio Libr Orgn

WOOSTER

C THE COLLEGE OF WOOSTER LIBRARIES, (WOO), 1140 Beall Ave, 44691-2364. SAN 313-8119. Tel: 330-263-2442. Interlibrary Loan Service Tel: 330-263-2136. FAX: 330-263-2253. Web Site: www.wooster.edu/library/. *Dir*, Dr Damon D Hickey; Tel: 330-263-2483, E-Mail: dhickey@acs.wooster.edu; *Admin Assoc*, Mimi Lewellen; Tel: 330-263-2152, E-Mail: mlewellen@wooster.edu; *Media Spec*, Patti McVay-Gorrell; *Media Spec*, Tony Bordac; *Acq*, Prue Holtman; *Cat*, Barbara Bettison; Tel: 330-263-2192 E-Mail: bbettison@wooster.edu; *Cat*, Margaret Hasenmyer; *Coll Develop, Tech Servs*, Margo Warner Curl; *Archivist, Spec Coll*, Denise Monbarren; *Spec Coll & Archives*, Elaine Snyder; Tel: 330-263-2155, E-Mail: esnyder@wooster.edu; *Govt Doc*, Barbara Bell; *Govt Doc*, Jennifer McMullen; Tel: 330-2632-2119, E-Mail: jmcmullen@wooster.edu; *Govt Doc*, Margaret Powell; *Circ*, Kathy Connor; *ILL*, Carolyn Rahnema; *Electronic Resources*, Julie Gustafson; Tel: 330-263-2315, E-Mail: jgustafson@wooster.edu; *Science*, Donna Jacobs; Tel: 330-263-2280, E-Mail: dkjacobs@wooster.edu; *Science*, Wesley Tree; Tel: 330-263-2275, E-Mail: wtree@wooster.edu; *Ser*, Day Logan; Tel: 330-263-2130, E-Mail: dlogan@wooster.edu; *Purchasing, Rare Bks*, Sue Dunlap; Tel: 330-263-2107, E-Mail: sdunlap@wooster.edu; Staff 6 (MLS 6)
Founded 1866. Enrl 1,809; Fac 140; Highest Degree: Bachelor
Jul 1999-Jun 2000 Mats Exp $2,140,777, Books $233,175, Per/Ser (Incl. Access Fees) $366,918, Presv $16,125. Sal $645,454 (Prof $299,159)
Library Holdings: Bk Vols 592,773
Special Collections: 17th Century British Studies (Wallace Notestein Coll); American Politics (Paul O Peters Coll); Drama & Theatre (Gregg D Wolfe Memorial Library of the Theatre)
Automation Activity & Vendor Info: (Acquisitions) Innovative Interfaces Inc.; (Cataloging) Innovative Interfaces Inc.; (Circulation) Innovative Interfaces Inc.; (Course Reserve) Innovative Interfaces Inc.; (ILL) Innovative Interfaces Inc.; (Media Booking) Innovative Interfaces Inc.; (OPAC) Innovative Interfaces Inc.; (Serials) Innovative Interfaces Inc.
Partic in Five Colleges of Ohio; OCLC Online Computer Library Center, Inc; Ohio Library & Information Network; OHIONET
Friends of the Library Group

S NORMAN LATHROP ENTERPRISES LIBRARY, 2342 Star Dr, 44691-9019. (Mail add: PO Box 198, 44691-0198), SAN 323-4401. Tel: 330-262-5587. FAX: 330-262-5587. E-Mail: lathropnle@sssnet.com. *Mgr*, Norman Lathrop; Staff 2 (MLS 1, Non-MLS 1)
Library Holdings: Bk Titles 1,000; Per Subs 100
Subject Interests: Computerized indexing, How-to-do-it info, Magazine indexing, Newspapers
Publications: Index to How to do it information (annual), index; Lathrop Report on Newspaper Indexes
Restriction: Private library
Function: Archival collection

S OHIO AGRICULTURAL RESEARCH & DEVELOPMENT CENTER LIBRARY, 1680 Madison Ave, 44691-4096. SAN 313-8135. Tel: 330-263-3773. Interlibrary Loan Service Tel: 330-263-3690. Circulation Tel: 330-202-3580. FAX: 330-263-3689. E-Mail: library_oardc@osu.edu. Web Site: www.oardc.ohio-state.edu/www/depts/libhp.html. *Head Librn*, Constance Britton; E-Mail: britton.4@osu.edu; Staff 3 (MLS 1, Non-MLS 2)
Founded 1892
Jul 1999-Jun 2000 Income $234,553. Mats Exp $178,095, Books $7,557, Per/Ser (Incl. Access Fees) $170,538. Sal $114,035
Library Holdings: Bk Vols 64,000; Per Subs 275
Subject Interests: Sci related to agr
Automation Activity & Vendor Info: (Acquisitions) Innovative Interfaces Inc.; (Cataloging) Innovative Interfaces Inc.; (Circulation) Innovative Interfaces Inc.; (OPAC) Innovative Interfaces Inc.
Database Vendor: Dialog
Partic in OCLC Online Computer Library Center, Inc; Ohio Library & Information Network; OHIONET
Friends of the Library Group

C OHIO STATE UNIVERSITY, Agricultural Technical Institute Library,* 1328 Dover Rd, 44691-4099. SAN 313-8143. Tel: 330-264-3911, Ext 1224. FAX: 330-262-7634. Web Site: www.lib.ohio-state.edu. *Chief Librn*, Ella G Copeland; *Per*, Judy Taylor; *Acq*, Thai Hoang; *Circ, ILL*, Connie Voss; Staff 4 (MLS 1, Non-MLS 3)
Founded 1972. Enrl 965; Fac 44
Library Holdings: Bk Vols 18,670; Per Subs 615
Subject Interests: Agriculture, Am hist, Construction, Engineering, Floral design, Gardening, Horticulture, Sci-tech, Sociology
Special Collections: Beekeeping Journals; Ohio County Soil Surveys; OhioLink
Partic in OHIONET
Friends of the Library Group

GL WAYNE COUNTY LAW LIBRARY ASSOCIATION,* Wayne County Courthouse, 107 W Liberty St, 44691. SAN 313-816X. Tel: 330-262-5561. FAX: 330-262-5561. *Librn*, Michael Senger
Founded 1903
Library Holdings: Bk Vols 25,000

P WAYNE COUNTY PUBLIC LIBRARY,* 304 N Market St, 44691-3593. SAN 357-3338. Tel: 330-262-0916. E-Mail: phs@wayne.lib.oh.us. Web Site: www.wayne.lib.oh.us. *Dir*, Pamela Hickson-Stevenson; Fax: 330-262-2905; *Asst Dir*, Alice R Finley; *ILL*, David Waltz; *Ch Servs*, Kay Bowen; *Tech Servs*, Jean McConnell; *Bkmobile Coordr*, Jennifer Schatzer; *AV*, Ron Fross; *Circ*, Sherry Hatter-Miller; *Exten Serv*, Glenna Morris; *YA Servs*, Linda

Davis; Staff 63 (MLS 13, Non-MLS 50)
Founded 1897. Pop 101,461; Circ 1,078,240
Library Holdings: Bk Vols 335,146; Per Subs 525
Subject Interests: Genealogy
Special Collections: City Law
Automation Activity & Vendor Info: (Circulation) DRA
Partic in Cleveland Area Metropolitan Library System
Friends of the Library Group
Branches: 5
CRESTON BRANCH, Main at Erie, PO Box 396, Creston, 44217. SAN 357-3397. Tel: 330-435-4204. FAX: 330-435-6279. Web Site: www.wayne.lib.oh.us. *Librn*, Jackie Allen; E-Mail: jallen@wayne.lib.oh.us; *Asst Librn*, Kathy Horman
Library Holdings: Bk Vols 31,500
Friends of the Library Group
DALTON BRANCH, 127 S Church St, PO Box 597, Dalton, 44618. SAN 323-8342. Tel: 330-828-8486. FAX: 330-828-0255. E-Mail: getit@wayne.lib.oh.us. Web Site: www.wayne.lib.oh.us. *Librn*, Rita Lowe
Library Holdings: Bk Vols 19,683
DEAN & DONALD BONNET MEMORIAL, 189 W McConkey, Shreve, 44676. SAN 357-3362. Tel: 330-567-2219. FAX: 330-567-2791. E-Mail: getit@wayne.lib.oh.us. Web Site: www.wayne.lib.oh.us. *Librn*, Marilyn Arwood
Library Holdings: Bk Vols 25,867; Per Subs 64
PAULLIN, 20 S Portage, Doylestown, 44230. SAN 357-3427. Tel: 330-658-4677. FAX: 330-658-4668. Web Site: www.wayne.lib.oh.us. *Librn*, Lora Goman; E-Mail: lora.goman@wayne.lib.oh.us
Library Holdings: Bk Vols 25,500; Per Subs 65
Friends of the Library Group
RITTMAN BRANCH, 49 W Ohio St, Rittman, 44270. SAN 357-3451. Tel: 330-925-2761. FAX: 330-925-6217. Web Site: www.wayne.lib.oh.us. *Librn*, Barbara Silchuk
Library Holdings: Bk Vols 24,998; Per Subs 65
Bookmobiles: 1

WORTHINGTON

S WORTHINGTON HISTORICAL SOCIETY LIBRARY,* 50 W New England Ave, 43085-3536. SAN 327-5639. Tel: 614-885-1247. FAX: 614-885-1040.
Subject Interests: Interior design, Local history

P WORTHINGTON PUBLIC LIBRARY, Old Worthington Library, 820 High St, 43085-3182. SAN 313-8186. Tel: 614-645-2620. TDD: 614-645-2639. FAX: 614-645-2642. Web Site: www.worthington.lib.oh.us. *Dir*, Meribah Mansfield; E-Mail: meribah@worthington.lib.oh.us; *Tech Servs*, Linda Roberts; *Commun Relations*, Lisa Fuller; *Tech Coordr*, Chuck Gibson; *Mgr*, Ann Badger; Tel: 614-645-2626, Fax: 614-645-2629; Staff 133 (MLS 31, Non-MLS 102)
Founded 1925. Pop 55,000; Circ 1,557,116
Library Holdings: Bk Vols 1,727,834; Per Subs 392
Subject Interests: Local authors
Special Collections: Worthington History Coll
Database Vendor: OCLC - First Search
Publications: Off the Shelf
Partic in Discovery Place Librs
Special Services for the Deaf - TDD
Friends of the Library Group
Branches: 1
NORTHWEST LIBRARY, 2280 Hard Rd, Columbus, 43235. Tel: 614-645-2656. Circulation Tel: 614-645-2650. FAX: 614-645-2659. Web Site: www.worthington.lib.oh.us. *Mgr*, Bonnie Beth Mitchell

WRIGHT-PATTERSON AFB

UNITED STATES AIR FORCE
A ACADEMIC LIBRARY FL3319, AFIT/LD, 2950 P St Bldg 642, 45433-7765. SAN 357-3664. Reference Tel: 937-255-3005. FAX: 937-656-7746. *Dir*, James Helling; E-Mail: james.helling@afit.af.mil; *Chief Librn, Reader Servs*, Barry Boettcher; *Librn, Tech Servs*, Gwendolyn Canada; Staff 18 (MLS 9, Non-MLS 9)
Founded 1946. Fac 300; Highest Degree: Doctorate
Library Holdings: Bk Vols 130,000; Per Subs 1,500
Subject Interests: Astronautics, Bus, Computers, Engineering, Mathematics, Mgt, Mil logistics, Sci-tech
Special Collections: Rand Research Coll
Partic in Defense Technical Information Center; Dialog Corporation; OCLC Online Computer Library Center, Inc; Southwestern Ohio Council For Higher Education
G AIR FORCE RESEARCH LAB, WRIGHT RESEARCH SITE TECHNICAL LIBRARY, Det 1 AFRL/WST, Bldg 642, 2950 P St, 45433-7765. SAN 357-3605. Tel: 937-255-5511. Interlibrary Loan Service Tel: 937-255-8404. Circulation Tel: 937-255-6565, Ext 3005. Reference Tel: 937-255-5511, Ext 4238. FAX: 937-656-7746. Web Site: www.wrs.afrl.af.mil/library. *Dir*, Carolyn Ray; *Coordr*, Tom Rohmiller; *Publ Servs*, Patrick Colucci; *Tech Servs*, Peri I Switzer; Tel: 937-255-5511, Ext 4242; *Online Servs*, Dan Sell; *Ref*, Bill Benson; Tel: 937-255-5511, Ext 4267; *Ref*, Patrick Colucci; *Ref*, Lynn Heinzeroth; Staff 11 (MLS 5, Non-MLS 6)
Founded 1919
Oct 1999-Sep 2000 Income Federal $1,186,500
Library Holdings: Bk Vols 102,262; Per Subs 329
Subject Interests: Aeronautical res, Aerospace med, Avionics, Co-applications to aeronaut, Computer science, Engineering, Flight dynamics, Mat, Physical sci, Propulsion
Special Collections: Lahm-Chandler Coll of Aeronautica
Database Vendor: Dialog, epixtech, inc., Lexis-Nexis, OCLC - First Search
Publications: Bibliographies; Guide; New Books List
Function: ILL available
A NATIONAL AIR INTELLIGENCE CENTER INFORMATION CENTER, NAIC/DXOA, 4180 Watson Way, 45433-5648. SAN 357-363X. Tel: 937-257-2452. FAX: 937-257-0122. *Acq, Ref*, Janet Burke; Tel: 937-257-3531, E-Mail: jgb93@naic.upafb.af.mil; *Circ, ILL*, Pam McCarthy; Tel: 937-257-2452, E-Mail: pam289@naic.wpafb.af.mil; *Cat*, Rob Wix; Tel: 937-257-3531, E-Mail: rjw24Wnaic.upafb.af.mil; Staff 15 (MLS 3, Non-MLS 12)
Library Holdings: Bk Titles 15,500; Per Subs 800
Automation Activity & Vendor Info: (Acquisitions) SIRSI; (Cataloging) SIRSI; (Circulation) SIRSI; (Course Reserve) SIRSI; (ILL) SIRSI; (OPAC) SIRSI
Restriction: Private library
A RESEARCH DIVISON MUA, 2601 E St, 45433-7609. SAN 370-2421. Tel: 937-255-3286, Ext 737, 937-255-4644. FAX: 937-255-9204. *Chief Librn, Res*, Wesley Henry; E-Mail: whenry@afmsmtp.wpafb.af.mil
A WRIGHT-PATTERSON AIR FORCE BASE LIBRARY FL2300, 88 SPTG/SVMG, Bldg 1044, 5651 Fir St, Ste 3, 45433-5428. SAN 357-3575. Tel: 937-257-4815. FAX: 937-656-1776. *Chief Librn*, Mary Rinas; E-Mail: mary.rinas@wpafb.af.mil
Founded 1942
Library Holdings: Bk Titles 58,000; Per Subs 500
Subject Interests: Military history
Special Collections: Total Quality Management Coll
AM WRIGHT-PATTERSON MEDICAL CENTER LIBRARY, 74 MDSS/SSGSSF, Bldg 830, 4881 Sugar Maple Dr, 45433-5529. SAN 357-3540. Tel: 937-257-4506. FAX: 937-257-0741. *Dir*, Mary A Auer; E-Mail: auerm@medcenoa.wpafb.af.mil; *Ref*, Melissa Knox; *Coll Develop*, Jackie Hough
Founded 1942
Library Holdings: Per Subs 758
Subject Interests: Aerospace med, Cardiology, Clinical medicine, Dentistry, Psychology, Toxicology, Veterinary medicine
Publications: New Book List (quarterly)
Partic in Knight-Ridder Info, Inc; Miami Valley Librs; OCLC Online Computer Library Center, Inc
Affiliated with Medical & Nursing School, Wright State Univ & Nursing Dept, Sinclair Community College, Dayton, Ohio; serves as Regional Library for Military Medical Treatment Facilities for 11-state region

G UNITED STATES DEPARTMENT OF DEFENSE, Defense Institute of Security Assistance Management Library,* Bldg 125, 2335 Seventh St, Rm 2317, 45433-7803. SAN 357-3516. Tel: 937-255-5567, 937-255-9211. FAX: 937-255-3441. Web Site: www.disam.osd.mil. *Dir*, Patricia White; E-Mail: pwhite@disam.wpafb.af.mil; *Circ*, Janet Conover; *Acq, Ref*, Helen Brinkley
Founded 1977. Enrl 2,000; Fac 25
Library Holdings: Bk Vols 10,400; Per Subs 221
Subject Interests: Political science
Special Collections: Human Rights; Regional Studies; Security Assistance
Partic in Fedlink; OCLC Online Computer Library Center, Inc; Ohio-Kentucky Coop Libraries

XENIA

GL GREENE COUNTY LAW LIBRARY,* Court House, Rm 309, 45385. SAN 313-8194. Tel: 937-376-5115. FAX: 937-376-5116. *Librn*, Nancy Hedges
Library Holdings: Bk Vols 24,000; Per Subs 50

P GREENE COUNTY PUBLIC LIBRARY, 76 E Market St, PO Box 520, 45385-0520. SAN 357-3729. Tel: 937-376-2996. FAX: 937-372-4673. Web Site: www.gcpl.lib.oh.us. *Dir*, Martha Gardin; Tel: 937-376-2996, Ext 201, E-Mail: mgardin@mailserv.gcpl.lib.oh.us; *Asst Dir*, Lawrence Clark Ostrowski; Tel: 937-376-2996, Ext 204, E-Mail: lostrowski@mailserv.gcpl.lib.oh.us; *Ref*, Marianne Newman; Tel: 937-376-2996, Ext 311; *Coll Develop*, R J Richards; Tel: 937-376-2996, Ext 230; *Ch Servs*, Kay Webster; Tel: 937-376-2996, Ext 231
Founded 1878. Pop 136,731; Circ 1,968,750
Jan 2000-Dec 2000 Income (Main Library and Branch Library) $6,395,274, State $5,262,072, County $762,394, Locally Generated Income $370,808. Mats Exp $1,166,819. Sal $3,232,121
Library Holdings: Bk Vols 450,000; Bk Titles 295,000; Per Subs 635
Subject Interests: Local history
Database Vendor: DRA, Ebsco - EbscoHost, IAC - Info Trac, OCLC - First

Search
Partic in Miami Valley Librs; OCLC Online Computer Library Center, Inc; OPLIN
Friends of the Library Group
Branches: 7
BEAVERCREEK COMMUNITY, 3618 Dayton-Xenia Rd, Beavercreek, 45432-2884. SAN 357-3753. Tel: 937-426-4442. FAX: 937-426-0481. *Branch Mgr*, Toni White
Library Holdings: Bk Vols 113,765
Friends of the Library Group
BELLBROOK-WINTERS COMMUNITY, 57 W Franklin St, Bellbrook, 45305-1904. SAN 357-3788. Tel: 937-848-2751. FAX: 937-848-3074. *Branch Mgr*, Judy Brucken
Library Holdings: Bk Vols 42,461
Friends of the Library Group
CEDARVILLE COMMUNITY, 74 N Main St, PO Box 26, Cedarville, 45314-0026. SAN 357-3818. Tel: 937-766-4511. FAX: 937-766-2847. *Branch Mgr*, Roxanne Spencer; *Librn*, Pat McLaughlin
Library Holdings: Bk Vols 25,288
Friends of the Library Group
FAIRBORN COMMUNITY, One E Main St, Fairborn, 45324-4798. SAN 357-3842. Tel: 937-878-9383. FAX: 937-878-0374. *Branch Mgr*, Charny Branda
Library Holdings: Bk Vols 92,585
Friends of the Library Group
JAMESTOWN COMMUNITY, 86B Seaman Dr, Jamestown, 45335. SAN 357-3877. Tel: 937-675-4411. FAX: 937-675-6605. *Branch Mgr*, Peggy Tidd
Library Holdings: Bk Vols 32,951
XENIA COMMUNITY, 76 E Market St, 45385-0520. Tel: 937-376-2996. FAX: 937-376-5523. *Branch Mgr*, Patricia Siemer
Library Holdings: Bk Vols 130,919
Friends of the Library Group
YELLOW SPRINGS COMMUNITY, 415 Xenia Ave, Yellow Springs, 45387-1837. SAN 357-3931. Tel: 937-767-7661. FAX: 937-767-2044. *Branch Mgr*, Connie Collett
Library Holdings: Bk Vols 49,131
Friends of the Library Group

YELLOW SPRINGS

C ANTIOCH COLLEGE, (OKL), Olive Kettering Memorial Library, 925 Livermore St, 45387-1694. SAN 313-8216. Tel: 937-769-1238. Interlibrary Loan Service Tel: 937-769-1236. Circulation Tel: 937-769-1235. Reference Tel: 937-769-1235. FAX: 937-769-1239. Web Site: www.antioch-college.edu/okl. *Dir*, Joseph J Cali; E-Mail: jcali@antioch-college.edu; *Ref*, Jan Miller; E-Mail: jmiller@antioch-college.edu; *Ser*, Janet Hulm; Tel: 937-767-6384, E-Mail: jhulm@antioch-college.edu; *Spec Coll*, Nina Myatt; Tel: 937-769-1237, E-Mail: nmyatt@antioch-college.edu; *Spec Coll*, Scott Sanders; Tel: 937-769-1237, E-Mail: ssanders@antioch-college.edu; Staff 8 (MLS 3, Non-MLS 5)
Founded 1852. Enrl 681; Fac 68; Highest Degree: Bachelor
Jul 1999-Jun 2000 Income $634,041. Mats Exp $167,445, Books $44,402, Per/Ser (Incl. Access Fees) $92,618, Presv $12,653, Micro $4,674, Electronic Ref Mat (Incl. Access Fees) $8,995. Sal $277,724 (Prof $138,579)
Library Holdings: Bk Vols 289,135; Bk Titles 189,862; Per Subs 997
Special Collections: Antioch hist; Arthur Morgan Coll, doc, files; Horace Mann (Robert Straker Coll), bks, doc
Automation Activity & Vendor Info: (Acquisitions) Innovative Interfaces Inc.; (Cataloging) Innovative Interfaces Inc.; (Circulation) Innovative Interfaces Inc.; (Course Reserve) Innovative Interfaces Inc.; (ILL) Innovative Interfaces Inc.; (Media Booking) Innovative Interfaces Inc.; (OPAC) Innovative Interfaces Inc.; (Serials) Innovative Interfaces Inc.
Partic in OCLC Online Computer Library Center, Inc; OHIONET; Opal

S COMMUNITY SERVICE, INC LIBRARY, 114 E Whiteman St, PO Box 243, 45387. SAN 313-8224. Tel: 937-767-2161. FAX: 937-767-2826. E-Mail: communityservice@usa.net. *Dir*, Marianne MacQueen
Founded 1940
Library Holdings: Bk Titles 1,500; Per Subs 300
Subject Interests: Am Indians, Commun, Homesteading, Int commun, Land trusts, People's movement, Reform, Soc change, Urban commun bldg
Publications: Community Service (quarterly newsletter)

S GLEN HELEN ASSOCIATION LIBRARY,* Glen Helen Bldg, 405 Corry St, 45387. SAN 370-8845. Tel: 937-767-7375, 937-767-7648. FAX: 937-767-6659. *Librn*, Mrs George Asakawa
Library Holdings: Bk Titles 600; Per Subs 30

YOUNGSTOWN

S BUTLER INSTITUTE OF AMERICAN ART, Hopper Research Library, 524 Wick Ave, 44502. SAN 313-8259. Tel: 330-743-1711. FAX: 330-743-9567. E-Mail: butler@cisnet.com. Web Site: www.butlerart.com. *Curator*, Melissa Wolfe; *Archivist, Res*, Samantha Kimpel; Staff 2 (Non-MLS 2)
Founded 1986
Library Holdings: Bk Vols 5,000; Per Subs 21
Subject Interests: Am art, Artists
Special Collections: American Colonial to Contemporary Art, oils, watercolors, drawings, original prints; Sculpture & Ceramics
Restriction: By appointment only, Members only, Non-circulating to the public

L MAHONING LAW LIBRARY ASSOCIATION, (MLLA),* Courthouse 4th Flr, 120 Market St, 44503-1752. SAN 313-8267. Tel: 330-740-2295. FAX: 330-744-1406. *Librn*, Robert R Hawkins; Staff 6 (MLS 1, Non-MLS 5)
Founded 1904
Library Holdings: Bk Vols 30,000; Per Subs 140
Subject Interests: Mahoning County legal mat, Ohio, Pa law, Selected city ordinances
Special Collections: Ohio Legal Journals
Partic in Am Asn of Law Librs
Serves courts, attorneys & governing bodies

P REUBEN MCMILLAN FREE LIBRARY ASSOCIATION, Public Library of Youngstown & Mahoning County, 305 Wick Ave, 44503-1079. SAN 357-3966. Tel: 330-744-8636. FAX: 330-744-3355. Web Site: www.libraryvisit.org, www.ymc.lib.oh.us. *Dir*, Carlton A Sears; E-Mail: csears@ymc.lib.oh.us; *Commun Relations, Mgr*, Janet S Loew; *Asst Dir*, Mary Pullin; *Automation Syst Coordr*, Diane Gross; *Tech Servs*, Gary Simon; *Ad Servs, Mgr*, Deborah McCullough; *Ch Servs, Mgr*, Josephine Nolfi; Staff 186 (MLS 69, Non-MLS 117)
Founded 1880. Pop 255,165; Circ 1,744,660
Jan 1999-Dec 1999 Income $11,523,720, State $10,052,369, Locally Generated Income $1,218,334, Other $253,017. Mats Exp $1,245,230, Books $940,983, Per/Ser (Incl. Access Fees) $107,316, Presv $7,145, AV Equip $129,175. Sal $4,201,000 (Prof $2,376,413)
Library Holdings: Bk Vols 892,786; Per Subs 1,402
Subject Interests: Genealogy, Sci-tech
Automation Activity & Vendor Info: (Cataloging) Inlex; (Circulation) Inlex; (OPAC) Inlex
Database Vendor: DRA, Ebsco - EbscoHost, GaleNet, IAC - Info Trac, OCLC - First Search
Publications: Bookends; It's Happening This Month
Partic in OCLC Online Computer Library Center, Inc; OHIONET
Friends of the Library Group
Branches: 18
AUSTINTOWN, 5650 Mahoning Ave, 44515. SAN 357-3990. Tel: 330-792-6982. FAX: 330-792-2275. *Branch Mgr*, Ann Martini
Library Holdings: Bk Vols 57,572
BOARDMAN, 7680 Glenwood Ave, 44512. SAN 357-4024. Tel: 330-758-1414. FAX: 330-758-7918. *Branch Mgr*, Joan Kovacich
Library Holdings: Bk Vols 99,465
Friends of the Library Group
BROWNLEE WOODS, 4010 Sheridan Rd, 44514. SAN 357-4059. Tel: 330-782-2512. *Branch Mgr*, Mary Frum
Library Holdings: Bk Vols 37,049
Friends of the Library Group
CAMPBELL BRANCH, 374 Sanderson Ave, Campbell, 44405. SAN 357-4083. Tel: 330-755-4227. *Branch Mgr*, Mary Frum
Library Holdings: Bk Vols 25,347
Friends of the Library Group
CANFIELD BRANCH, 43 W Main St, Canfield, 44406. SAN 357-4113. Tel: 330-533-5631. FAX: 330-533-9127. *Branch Mgr*, Patricia Yurchekfrodl
Library Holdings: Bk Vols 42,866
Friends of the Library Group
EAST, 6 N Jackson St, 44506. SAN 357-4148. Tel: 330-744-2790. *Branch Mgr*, Pamela Witte
Library Holdings: Bk Vols 18,778
Friends of the Library Group
GREENFORD BRANCH, 7441 W South Range Rd, Greenford, 44422. SAN 369-7835. Tel: 330-533-7025. *Branch Mgr*, Patricia Yurchekfrodl
Library Holdings: Bk Vols 11,675
Friends of the Library Group
LAKE MILTON-CRAIG BEACH, 1320 Grandview Ave, Lake Milton, 44429. SAN 371-3334. Tel: 330-654-4454. *Branch Mgr*, Ann Martini
Library Holdings: Bk Vols 10,616
Friends of the Library Group
LOWELLVILLE BRANCH, 151 Second St, Lowellville, 44436. SAN 357-4202. Tel: 330-536-6216. *Branch Mgr*, Gayle Ridge
Library Holdings: Bk Vols 12,540
Friends of the Library Group
NEW MIDDLETOWN BRANCH, 10719 Main St, New Middletown, 44442. SAN 369-7851. Tel: 330-542-2715. *Branch Mgr*, Gayle Ridge
Library Holdings: Bk Vols 10,456
Friends of the Library Group
NORTH, 1344 Fifth Ave, 44504. SAN 357-4261. Tel: 330-747-3719. FAX: 330-747-3722. *Branch Mgr*, Pamela Witte
Library Holdings: Bk Vols 60,661
NORTH JACKSON BRANCH, 10775 Mahoning Ave Ext, North Jackson, 44451. SAN 369-786X. Tel: 330-538-2455. *Branch Mgr*, Ann Martini
Library Holdings: Bk Vols 9,761

Friends of the Library Group
NORTH LIMA BRANCH, 11822 South Ave Ext, North Lima, 44452. SAN 357-4296. Tel: 330-549-2255. *Branch Mgr*, Patricia Yurchekfrodl
Library Holdings: Bk Vols 20,162
Friends of the Library Group
POLAND BRANCH, 311 S Main St, Poland, 44514. SAN 357-4326. Tel: 330-757-1852. FAX: 330-757-1570. *Branch Mgr*, Gayle Ridge
Library Holdings: Bk Vols 39,039
Friends of the Library Group
SEBRING BRANCH, 195 W Ohio Ave, Sebring, 44672. SAN 357-4385. Tel: 330-938-6119. *Branch Mgr*, Patricia Yurchekfrodl
Library Holdings: Bk Vols 26,466
Friends of the Library Group
SOS-WEST, 2815 Mahoning Ave, 44509. SAN 357-4350. Tel: 330-799-7171. *Branch Mgr*, Mona Pocatko
Library Holdings: Bk Vols 56,018
Friends of the Library Group
SOUTH, 1771 Market St, 44507. SAN 357-4415. Tel: 330-747-6424. *Branch Mgr*, Pamela Witte
Library Holdings: Bk Vols 40,919
Friends of the Library Group
STRUTHERS, 95 Poland Ave, 44471. SAN 357-444X. Tel: 330-755-3322. *Branch Mgr*, Mary Frum
Library Holdings: Bk Vols 51,095
Friends of the Library Group

M SAINT ELIZABETH HOSPITAL HEALTH CENTER, Medical Library,* 1044 Belmont Ave, 44501-1790. SAN 357-4504. Tel: 330-480-3039. FAX: 330-480-2957. *Librn*, Barbara Rosenthal; E-Mail: rosenthal@neoucom.edu
Founded 1911
Library Holdings: Bk Titles 3,325; Per Subs 239
Subject Interests: Medicine, Surgery

C YOUNGSTOWN STATE UNIVERSITY LIBRARY, William F Maag Library, One University Plaza, 44555. SAN 313-8291. Tel: 330-742-3675. Interlibrary Loan Service Tel: 330-742-3702. Circulation Tel: 330-742-3678. Reference Tel: 330-742-3686. FAX: 330-742-3734. E-Mail: library@cc.ysu.edu. Web Site: www.maag.ysu.edu. *Exec Dir*, Thomas C Atwood; E-Mail: tcatwood@cc.ysu.edu; *Asst Librn, Cat*, Sara Greenleaf; *Cat*, Jeffrey Trimle; Tel: 330-742-2483, E-Mail: jtrimle@cc.ysu.edu; *Publ Servs*, Debra N Beronja; Tel: 330-742-2739, E-Mail: dberonja@cc.ysu.edu; *Head Ref*, Jean A Romeo; Tel: 330-742-1720, E-Mail: jaromeo@cc.ysu.edu; *Branch Mgr*, Paul H Rorbaugh; Tel: 330-742-5348, E-Mail: phrohrba@cc.ysu.edu; *Syst Coordr*, Christine Rigda; Tel: 330-742-2922, E-Mail: crigda@cc.ysu.edu; *Ser*, Angela K Mudrak; Tel: 330-742-1722, E-Mail: akmudrak@cc.ysu.edu; *Govt Doc*, Jan W Schnall; Tel: 330-742-3126, E-Mail: jwschnal@cc.ysu.edu; *Acq*, Susan D Jacobson; Tel: 330-742-3679, E-Mail: sdjacobs@cc.ysu.edu; *Per*, Robert D Ault; Tel: 330-742-3500, E-Mail: rdault@cc.ysu.edu; *Ref*, Ericablue L Bartik; Tel: 330-742-3788, E-Mail: ebartik@cc.ysu.edu; *Ref*, Allison B Brungard; Tel: 330-742-3680, E-Mail: abrungard@cc.ysu.edu; *Ref*, George F Heller, Jr; Tel: 330-742-3680, E-Mail: gfheller@cc.ysu.edu; *Ref*, Robert D Tupaj; Tel: 330-742-3680, E-Mail: rtupaj@cc.ysu.edu; *Tech Coordr*, Martina L Nicholas; Tel: 330-742-2941, E-Mail: mlnichol@cc.ysu.edu; *Archivist*, Sterling V Fleischer; Tel: 330-742-4662, E-Mail: svfleisc@cc.ysu.edu. Subject Specialists: *Business*, Allison B Brungard; *Education*, Paul H Rorbaugh; *Music*, Ericablue L Bartik; Staff 38 (MLS 17, Non-MLS 21)
Founded 1931. Enrl 12,801; Highest Degree: Doctorate
Jul 1999-Jun 2000 Income $3,632,389. Mats Exp $1,537,001, Books $559,331, Per/Ser (Incl. Access Fees) $785,849, Presv $64,821, Micro $50,000, AV Equip $15,000, Other Print Mats $35,000, Manuscripts & Archives $11,000, Electronic Ref Mat (Incl. Access Fees) $16,000. Sal $1,788,860 (Prof $589,155)
Library Holdings: Bk Vols 742,287; Bk Titles 610,640; Per Subs 3,318
Subject Interests: Behavior sci, Business, Education, Management, Science/technology, Social sciences
Special Collections: Early Americana
Automation Activity & Vendor Info: (Cataloging) Innovative Interfaces Inc.; (Circulation) Innovative Interfaces Inc.; (Course Reserve) Innovative Interfaces Inc.; (ILL) Innovative Interfaces Inc.; (OPAC) Innovative Interfaces Inc.; (Serials) Innovative Interfaces Inc.
Database Vendor: IAC - Info Trac, Lexis-Nexis, OCLC - First Search, OVID Technologies, Silverplatter Information Inc.
Publications: Newsletter
Function: ILL available
Partic in Nola Regional Library System; OCLC Online Computer Library Center, Inc; Ohio Library & Information Network; OHIONET
Friends of the Library Group

ZANESFIELD

S DR EARL S SLOAN LIBRARY,* 2817 Sandusky St, PO Box 116, 43360-0116. SAN 374-5759. Tel: 937-592-8343. FAX: 937-592-6474. E-Mail: earlsln@oplin.lib.oh.us. *Librn*, Polly Bargar; *Asst Librn*, Jean Brugler; Staff 3 (MLS 1, Non-MLS 2)
Founded 1914
Library Holdings: Bk Vols 8,277; Bk Titles 9,100; Per Subs 36

ZANESVILLE

M GENESIS HEALTHCARE SYSTEM, (Formerly Bethesda Hospital), Medical Library, 2951 Maple Ave, 43701-1465. SAN 313-8305. Tel: 740-454-4624. FAX: 740-454-4799. *In Charge*, Sharon Duffy
Founded 1958
Library Holdings: Bk Vols 800; Per Subs 78
Restriction: Not open to public

S MUSKINGUM COUNTY GENEALOGICAL SOCIETY LIBRARY,* 220 N Fifth St, 43702-3066. SAN 313-8321. Tel: 740-453-0391. FAX: 740-455-6357. Web Site: www.muskingum.org. *Pres*, Betty W Acker; *Dir*, Tom Blair; Staff 1 (MLS 1)
Founded 1975
Library Holdings: Bk Vols 1,000; Per Subs 12
Special Collections: Early Muskingum Co Newspapers, micro; Genealogical Society Newsletters; History (Professor Kline Coll), rpts; International Genealogical Index from Salt Lake City, Utah; Marriage & Cemetary Records; Muskingum County History & Genealogy; Norris Schneider Coll, mss; Passenger & Immigration Lists Indexes, Naturalizations, Local Probate Court Records on microfilm, Maps, Atlases, Ancestor Chart File; United States Wars
Publications: books on county marriages, cemeteries, county courthouse dockets; The Muskingum (monthly newsletter)
Friends of the Library Group

GL MUSKINGUM COUNTY LAW LIBRARY,* Court House, 401 Main St, 43701. SAN 313-833X. Tel: 740-455-7154. FAX: 740-455-7177. *Librn*, Donna Herron
Library Holdings: Bk Vols 13,000

P MUSKINGUM COUNTY LIBRARY SYSTEM,* 220 N Fifth St, 43701-3587. SAN 357-4563. Tel: 740-453-0391. FAX: 740-455-6357. *Dir*, Sandi Plymire; *Ad Servs, YA Servs*, Jeff Eling; *Ch Servs*, Cheryl Fields; *Mgr*, Carla Roberts; *Mgr, Tech Servs*, Judy Stanbery; *Commun Relations*, Blair Tom; Staff 61 (MLS 11, Non-MLS 50)
Founded 1903. Pop 88,000; Circ 696,308
Jan 1998-Dec 1998 Income $2,250,881, State $2,151,594, Locally Generated Income $99,287. Mats Exp $406,474, Books $317,153, Per/Ser (Incl. Access Fees) $18,826. Sal $984,000
Library Holdings: Bk Vols 218,260; Per Subs 242
Special Collections: Business & Industry; History (Ohio Coll); Zanesville & Muskingum County History
Publications: Newsletter
Partic in OHIONET; Southeastern Ohio Libr Orgn
Friends of the Library Group
Branches: 5
DRESDEN BRANCH, 816 Main St, Dresden, 43821. SAN 357-4598. Tel: 740-754-1003.
Circ 58,123
Library Holdings: Bk Vols 26,254
Friends of the Library Group
DUNCAN FALLS-PHILO BRANCH, PO Box 472, Duncan Falls, 43734-0472. SAN 373-8515. Tel: 740-674-7100.
Circ 46,551
Library Holdings: Bk Vols 21,749
Friends of the Library Group
NEW CONCORD BRANCH, 77 W Main St, New Concord, 43762. SAN 357-4652. Tel: 740-826-4184.
Circ 56,458
Library Holdings: Bk Vols 29,733
Friends of the Library Group
ROSEVILLE BRANCH, 41 N Main, Roseville, 43777. SAN 357-4687. Tel: 740-697-0237.
Circ 28,097
Library Holdings: Bk Vols 21,938
Friends of the Library Group
SOUTH BRANCH, 2530 Maysville Pike, South Zanesville, 43701. SAN 357-4717. Tel: 740-454-1511.
Circ 36,251
Library Holdings: Bk Vols 21,340
Friends of the Library Group

C OHIO UNIVERSITY-ZANESVILLE, Muskingum Area Technical College, Zanesville Campus Library, 1425 Newark Rd, 43701. SAN 313-8348. Tel: 740-588-1404. Interlibrary Loan Service Tel: 740-588-1406. FAX: 740-453-0706. Web Site: cscwww.cats.ohiou.edu/library/zanesville/html or www.library.ohiou.edu/libinfo/regional/zanesvill.htm. *Dir*, Shana Fair; Staff 6 (MLS 2, Non-MLS 4)
Enrl 2,622
Library Holdings: Bk Titles 61,000; Per Subs 350
Subject Interests: Local history
Special Collections: Muskingum County History (Zanesville Heritage Coll)
Publications: Zanesville Campus Library Newsletter
Partic in OCLC Online Computer Library Center, Inc; OHIONET

S ZANESVILLE ART CENTER LIBRARY,* 620 Military Rd, 43701. SAN 313-8356. Tel: 614-452-0741. FAX: 452-0797. *Dir*, Philip LaDouceur; *Librn*, Debbie Lowe
Founded 1936
Library Holdings: Bk Titles 7,500
Subject Interests: Arts, Crafts
Restriction: Open to public for reference only

OKLAHOMA

Date of Statistics: Fiscal 1998
Population, 1998 Est.: 3,295,315
Population Served by Public Libraries: 2,725,313
Total Volumes in Public Libraries: 5,862,467
Volumes Per Capita: 1.78
Total Public Library Circulation: 16,072,699
Circulation Per Capita Served: 5.89
Total Public Library Operating Expenditures: $43,731,834
Expenditures Per Capita: $13.27
Expenditures Per Capita Served: $16.05
Number of County or Systems Libraries: 6 multi-county; 2 city-county; 6 county
Counties Served: 29 served by library systems; 6 served by County libraries; 42 counties partially served by 105 city libraries
Number of Bookmobiles in State: 5
Grants-in-Aid to Libraries:
Federal (Library Services & Construction Act): $923,000
State Aid: $1,651,482

ADA

P ADA PUBLIC LIBRARY,* 124 S Rennie, 74820. SAN 313-8364. Tel: 580-436-8121. Interlibrary Loan Service Tel: 580-436-8123. FAX: 580-436-0534. *Dir*, Jennifer Greenstreet; *Tech Servs*, Debbie Whelchel; *Ch Servs*, Janet Lee; *Circ*, Betty Blansett; *ILL*, Carol Norton
Founded 1939. Pop 15,820; Circ 140,000
Jul 1998-Jun 1999 Income $286,000. Mats Exp $49,000. Sal $193,000
Library Holdings: Bk Vols 60,000; Bk Titles 55,000; Per Subs 282
Subject Interests: Large print, Music, Okla hist
Friends of the Library Group

C EAST CENTRAL UNIVERSITY, Linscheid Library,* 74820-6899. SAN 357-4741. Tel: 580-332-8000. FAX: 580-436-3242. *Dir*, Charles E Perry; *Librn*, Patrick Baumann; *Circ, Ref*, Mary Evans; *Acq, Coll Develop, Ser*, Dana Belcher; *Bibliog Instr*, Lori Mardis; *Cat*, Farooq Ali; Staff 15 (MLS 7, Non-MLS 8)
Founded 1909. Enrl 4,394; Fac 180
Jul 1997-Jun 1998 Income $957,740. Mats Exp $205,065. Sal $613,182 (Prof $230,610)
Library Holdings: Bk Vols 214,648; Per Subs 800
Partic in Amigos Library Services, Inc; Okla Telecommunications Interlibr Syst

G ENVIRONMENTAL PROTECTION AGENCY - R S KERR ENVIRONMENTAL RESEARCH CENTER, Subsurface Protection & Remediation Division Library, 919 Kerr Research Dr, 74820. (Mail add: PO Box 1198, 74821), Tel: 580-436-8505. Interlibrary Loan Service Tel: 580-436-8502. FAX: 580-436-8503. Web Site: www.epa.gov/earth100/records/a00159.html, www.epa.gov/natilibra/ols.htm. *Dir*, Tanya Steed Wiggins; E-Mail: wiggins.tanya@epa.gov; *ILL*, Cindy Sue Cooper; Tel: 580-436-8502, E-Mail: cooper.cindy@epa.gov; *Circ*, Aphion Moore; Tel: 580-436-8639, E-Mail: moore.apion@epa.gov; *Ser*, Kay Cooper; Tel: 580-436-8651, E-Mail: cooper.kay@epa.gov; Staff 4 (MLS 1, Non-MLS 3)
Founded 1966
Library Holdings: Bk Vols 9,901; Bk Titles 8,986; Per Subs 110
Subject Interests: Analytical chemistry, Ecology, Environ sci, Hydrology, Microbiology, Soil sci
Database Vendor: CARL, IAC - SearchBank, OCLC - First Search
Publications: Acquisitions, monthly (internal distribution only); Publication List, Library User's guide; Serials Holdings List
Function: ILL available
Partic in Amigos Library Services, Inc; EPA; OCLC Online Computer Library Center, Inc; Okla Libr Technology Network
Subsurface Remediation Information Center - 580-436-8651

ALLEN

P ALLEN PUBLIC LIBRARY,* 207 S Commerce St, PO Box 343, 74825. SAN 377-2020. Tel: 580-857-2933. FAX: 580-857-2933. *Librn*, Paula Nelson
Library Holdings: Bk Titles 3,000; Per Subs 12

ALTUS

P ALTUS PUBLIC LIBRARY,* 421 N Hudson, 73521. SAN 313-8380. Tel: 580-477-2890. FAX: 580-477-3626. Web Site: www.spls.lib.ok.us. *Librn*, Donna Smith; *Automation Syst Coordr*, Janet Howard
Founded 1936. Pop 23,000
Library Holdings: Bk Vols 60,000; Per Subs 75
Mem of Southern Prairie Library System
Friends of the Library Group

M OKLAHOMA HISTORICAL SOCIETY - MUSEUM OF THE WESTERN PRAIRIE, Bernice Ford-Price Memorial Reference Library, 1100 Memorial Dr, 73521. (Mail add: PO Box 574, 73522), SAN 327-9227. Tel: 580-482-1044. FAX: 580-482-0128. E-Mail: muswestpr@ok-history.mus.ok.us. *In Charge*, Burna Cole; *Curator*, Bart McClenny; Staff 2 (Non-MLS 2)
Founded 1973
Library Holdings: Bk Vols 2,200
Subject Interests: Native Americans, Okla hist, Oklahoma, Photographs, Rare books
Special Collections: Archival Coll; Family History Coll, docs, photos
Restriction: By appointment only, Non-circulating to the public
Function: For research purposes
Friends of the Library Group

P SOUTHERN PRAIRIE LIBRARY SYSTEM,* 421 N Hudson, PO Drawer U, 73521. SAN 313-8399. Tel: 580-477-2890. FAX: 580-477-3626. *Dir*, Katherine Hale; *Librn*, Donna Smith; Staff 6 (MLS 2, Non-MLS 4)
Founded 1973. Pop 32,324; Circ 120,036
Library Holdings: Bk Vols 68,791; Per Subs 145
Subject Interests: Alternate sources of energy, Black heritage, Genealogy, Hispanic-American heritage, Spanish language
Special Collections: English-As-A-Second Language; Literacy
Member Libraries: Altus Public Library; Hollis Public Library
Partic in OCLC Online Computer Library Center, Inc; Okla Telecommunications Interlibr Syst
Friends of the Library Group

J WESTERN OKLAHOMA STATE COLLEGE, Learning Resources Center, 2801 N Main St, 73521. SAN 313-8402. Tel: 580-477-7770. FAX: 580-477-7777. Web Site: www.western.cc.ok.us. *Coll Develop, Dir*, Julie Brooks; Tel: 580-477-7776, E-Mail: jabrooks@western.cc.ok.us; Staff 1 (MLS 1)
Founded 1926. Enrl 1,950; Fac 97
Jul 1999-Jun 2000 Income $269,133. Mats Exp $74,343, Books $25,788, Per/Ser (Incl. Access Fees) $18,389, Micro $7,096, AV Equip $23,070, Electronic Ref Mat (Incl. Access Fees) $417. Sal $119,095 (Prof $55,515)
Library Holdings: Bk Vols 32,524; Bk Titles 30,000
Automation Activity & Vendor Info: (Cataloging) epixtech, inc.; (Circulation) epixtech, inc.; (OPAC) epixtech, inc.
Database Vendor: OCLC - First Search
Partic in Amigos Library Services, Inc

ALTUS AFB

UNITED STATES AIR FORCE

A ALTUS AIR FORCE BASE LIBRARY FL4419, 97 SVS/SVMG, 303 J Ave Bldg 301, 73525-5134. Tel: 580-481-6302. FAX: 580-482-0469. *Librn*, Sharon McKenna
Founded 1953
Oct 1998-Sep 1999 Income $285,340. Mats Exp $43,866, Books $14,858, Per/Ser (Incl. Access Fees) $8,257, Micro $14,575. Sal $222,100
Library Holdings: Bk Vols 21,758; Per Subs 185
Subject Interests: Aeronautics, Political science
Automation Activity & Vendor Info: (Circulation) CLSI LIBS
Partic in Dialog Corporation; OCLC Online Computer Library Center, Inc

ALVA

C NORTHWESTERN OKLAHOMA STATE UNIVERSITY, J W Martin Library, 709 Oklahoma Blvd, 73717. SAN 357-4830. Tel: 580-327-8574. FAX: 580-327-8501. *Dir*, Ray D Lau; Tel: 580-327-8570; Staff 5 (MLS 5)
Founded 1897. Enrl 1,700; Fac 75; Highest Degree: Master
Library Holdings: Bk Vols 159,000; Per Subs 1,405
Subject Interests: Agriculture, Behav sci, Education, Libr sci, Okla hist, Soc sci
Special Collections: Indian Artifacts; William J Mellor Coll, bks, paintings, sculpture, stereoptican slides, cylinder records & player

ANADARKO

P ANADARKO COMMUNITY LIBRARY,* 215 W Broadway, 73005. SAN 313-8429. Tel: 405-247-7351. FAX: 405-247-2024. E-Mail: library@tanet.net. *Librn*, Christina Owen; *Asst Librn*, Gina Wooster
Founded 1901. Pop 8,200; Circ 45,638
Jul 1998-Jun 1999 Income $120,420, State $3,000. Mats Exp $20,000, Books $16,500, Per/Ser (Incl. Access Fees) $3,500. Sal $83,370
Library Holdings: Bk Vols 34,743; Per Subs 72
Special Collections: Native American History; Oklahoma History
Friends of the Library Group

ANTLERS

P ANTLERS PUBLIC LIBRARY, 202 S High St, 74523. SAN 313-8437. Tel: 580-298-5649. FAX: 580-298-3567. *Librn*, Melanie Burgess
Founded 1959. Pop 2,989; Circ 9,600
2000-2001 Income $56,000, City $28,000, Locally Generated Income $28,000
Library Holdings: Bk Vols 15,557

ARDMORE

§C ARDMORE HIGHER EDUCATION CENTER LIBRARY, 611 Veterans Blvd, 73401. SAN 375-426X. Tel: 580-223-1441. FAX: 405-521-6141. Web Site: www.ahec.osrhe.edu. *Dir*, Cindy D Pollard; E-Mail: cpollard@ahec.osrhe.edu; Staff 3 (MLS 2, Non-MLS 1)
Jul 2000-Jun 2001 Mats Exp $57,000
Library Holdings: Bk Vols 13,000; Per Subs 100
Automation Activity & Vendor Info: (Cataloging) DRA; (Circulation) DRA; (OPAC) DRA
Database Vendor: OCLC - First Search

P ARDMORE PUBLIC LIBRARY, 320 E Street NW, 73401. SAN 313-8445. Tel: 580-223-8290. FAX: 580-223-2033. Web Site: www.ardmorepublic.lib.ok.us. *Ad Servs, Commun Servs, Dir*, Carolyn J Franks; *ILL*, Angela Armstrong; *Ch Servs*, Lorena L Smith; *Acq, Tech Servs*, Shirley Strawn; *Ref*, Daniel Gibbs; *Automation Syst Coordr*, Mary Ann Phillips
Founded 1906. Pop 23,689; Circ 148,067
Jul 1999-Jun 2000 Income $652,326, State $11,974, City $488,882. Mats Exp $68,660, Books $58,501, Per/Ser (Incl. Access Fees) $7,604, Electronic Ref Mat (Incl. Access Fees) $2,555. Sal $386,830
Library Holdings: Bk Vols 60,000; Per Subs 254
Special Collections: Eliza Cruce Hall Doll Museum Coll, dolls, bks & slides; McGalliard Local History Coll, photogs, publications, clippings; Tomlinson Geological Coll, bks, journals & maps
Automation Activity & Vendor Info: (Cataloging) epixtech, inc.; (Circulation) epixtech, inc.; (OPAC) epixtech, inc.
Publications: Eliza Cruce Hall Doll Museum Catalogue
Partic in Okla Telecommunications Interlibr Syst
Friends of the Library Group

P CHICKASAW REGIONAL LIBRARY SYSTEM,* 601 Railway Express, 73401. SAN 357-4954. Tel: 580-223-3164. FAX: 580-223-3280. E-Mail: crlsdir@oltn.odl.state.ok.us. *Dir*, Lynn McIntosh; *Br Coordr*, Diana McMahan; *Bkmobile Coordr*, Katherine Cross; *Business*, Vicki Mills; *Ch Servs*, Jana Howard; *ILL*, Louise Rankin; *Media Spec*, Leila Milberg; *Ref*, Sharlotte Riggle; *Syst Coordr*, Alaine Smith; *Tech Servs*, David Moran
Founded 1960. Pop 92,800; Circ 319,501
Library Holdings: Bk Vols 126,035; Per Subs 342
Subject Interests: Art, Civilized tribes, OK hist, Texoma
Automation Activity & Vendor Info: (Cataloging) epixtech, inc.; (Circulation) epixtech, inc.
Publications: Five County Gazette
Partic in Amigos Library Services, Inc
Branches: 7
ATOKA COUNTY LIBRARY, 215 East A St, Atoka, 74525. SAN 357-4989. Tel: 580-889-3555. FAX: 580-889-1905. E-Mail: crlsato@oltn.odl.state.ok.us. *Branch Mgr*, Alice Withrow
Friends of the Library Group
DAVIS PUBLIC, 209 E Benton, Davis, 73030. SAN 357-5047. Tel: 580-369-2468. FAX: 580-369-3290. E-Mail: crlsdav@oltn.odl.state.ok.us. *Branch Mgr*, Earlene Piercy
Friends of the Library Group
HEALDTON COMMUNITY, 18 S Fourth, Healdton, 73438. SAN 357-5071. Tel: 580-229-0590. FAX: 580-229-0055. E-Mail: crlshcl@oltn.odl.state.ok.us. *Branch Mgr*, Carol Stewart
Friends of the Library Group
JOHNSTON COUNTY, 502 W Main, Tishomingo, 73460. SAN 357-5160. Tel: 580-371-3006. FAX: 580-371-0042. E-Mail: crlstis@oltn.odl.state.ok.us. *Branch Mgr*, Renee Yocum
LOVE COUNTY, 500 S Hwy 77, Marietta, 73448. SAN 357-5101. Tel: 580-276-3783. FAX: 580-276-1483. E-Mail: crlsmar@oltn.odl.state.ok.us. *Branch Mgr*, Jerri Buckmaster
Friends of the Library Group
MARY E PARKER MEMORIAL LIBRARY, 500 W Broadway, Sulphur, 73086. SAN 357-5136. Tel: 580-622-5807. FAX: 580-622-6395. E-Mail: crlssul@oltn.odl.state.ok.us. *Branch Mgr*, Mary McLemore
WILSON PUBLIC, 114 E Main, Wilson, 73463. SAN 357-5195. Tel: 580-668-2486. FAX: 580-668-3056. *Branch Mgr*, Betty Manley
Friends of the Library Group
Bookmobiles: 2

S SAMUEL ROBERTS NOBLE FOUNDATION, INC., (SRN), Noble Foundation Library, 2510 Sam Noble Pkwy, 73402. SAN 313-8453. Tel: 580-221-7330. Circulation Tel: 580-221-7332. FAX: 580-221-7483. Web Site: www.noble.org. *Head Librn*, Patrick W Brennen; Tel: 580-221-7338, E-Mail: pbrennen@noble.org; *Asst Librn*, Nancy Sprehe; Tel: 580-221-7334, E-Mail: nksprehe@noble.org; *Acq*, Shirley Folsom; Tel: 580-221-7389, E-Mail: spfolsom@noble.org; *ILL*, Ernest Lane; E-Mail: elane@noble.org; Staff 5 (MLS 2, Non-MLS 3)
Founded 1951
2000-2001 Income Parent Institution $683,100. Mats Exp $455,550, Books $54,250, Per/Ser (Incl. Access Fees) $247,800, Presv $1,500, Electronic Ref Mat (Incl. Access Fees) $152,000. Sal $209,300
Library Holdings: Bk Vols 29,300; Per Subs 530
Subject Interests: Agriculture, Chemistry, Forage, Plant biol
Special Collections: Plant Specimen Identity Coll & Archives
Automation Activity & Vendor Info: (Acquisitions) Endeavor; (Cataloging) Endeavor; (Circulation) Endeavor; (Course Reserve) Endeavor; (ILL) Endeavor; (Media Booking) Endeavor; (OPAC) Endeavor; (Serials) Endeavor
Database Vendor: Dialog, OCLC - First Search, OVID Technologies, Silverplatter Information Inc.
Publications: Library Guide; Monthly Accessions List
Restriction: In-house use for visitors
Partic in Amigos Library Services, Inc

ARKOMA

P ARKOMA COMMUNITY LIBRARY,* 1000 Main St, PO Box 446, 74901. SAN 376-5946. Tel: 918-875-3971. FAX: 918-875-3013. *Dir*, Carol Burgess
Library Holdings: Bk Titles 11,000; Per Subs 18
Mem of Southeastern Public Library System Of Oklahoma
Friends of the Library Group

BARNSDALL

P BARNSDALL PUBLIC,* 410 S Fifth, PO Box 706, 74002. SAN 313-8461. Tel: 918-847-2118. FAX: 918-847-2118. *Librn*, Elsie Aldridge
Founded 1931. Pop 1,400; Circ 8,065
1997-1998 Income $5,645, State $5,000
Library Holdings: Bk Titles 12,204
Subject Interests: History, Music

BARTLESVILLE

P BARTLESVILLE PUBLIC LIBRARY,* 600 S Johnstone, 74003. SAN 313-847X. Tel: 918-337-5353. Interlibrary Loan Service Tel: 918-336-4636. TDD: 918-337-5359. FAX: 918-337-5338. Web Site: www.bartlesville.lib.ok.us/. *Dir*, Jan Sanders; Tel: 918-337-5363, E-Mail: jsanders@bartlesville.lib.ok.us; *YA Servs*, Beth DeGeer; Tel: 918-337-5335, E-Mail: bdeg@bartlesville.lib.ok.us; *Ref*, Katherine Hanson; *Ref*, Kathleen Mulligan; Tel: 918-337-5334; *Cat*, Elsie Green; Tel: 918-337-5342, E-Mail: egreen@bartlesville.lib.ok.us; *Publ Servs*, Joan Singleton; Tel: 918-337-5332,

E-Mail: jsinglet@bartlesville.lib.ok.us; Staff 17 (MLS 6, Non-MLS 11)
Founded 1913. Pop 34,256; Circ 441,534
Jul 1998-Jun 1999 Income $881,516, State $17,477, City $779,300, Other $84,605. Mats Exp $140,480, Books $126,328, Per/Ser (Incl. Access Fees) $11,413, Micro $2,289, Electronic Ref Mat (Incl. Access Fees) $450. Sal $411,281 (Prof $216,590)
Library Holdings: Bk Vols 94,118; Bk Titles 79,047; Per Subs 240
Subject Interests: Am Indian, Okla tribes
Special Collections: Genealogy Coll; Local Historical Museum; Local History Coll; Oklahoma History Coll
Automation Activity & Vendor Info: (Acquisitions) epixtech, inc.; (Cataloging) epixtech, inc.; (Circulation) epixtech, inc.
Publications: The Bartlesville Bookmark (newsletter)
Friends of the Library Group

C BARTLESVILLE WESLEYAN COLLEGE LIBRARY,* 2201 Silver Lake Rd, 74006-6299. SAN 313-8488. Tel: 918-335-6285. FAX: 918-335-6220. E-Mail: libraryadulted@hotmail.com. Web Site: www.bwc.edu. *Dir*, Wendell Thompson; *Asst Librn*, Amelia Thompson
Founded 1958. Enrl 608; Fac 48; Highest Degree: Bachelor
Jul 1998-Jun 1999 Income $217,000. Mats Exp $63,020, Books $19,772, Per/Ser (Incl. Access Fees) $27,560, Micro $840. Sal $168,800 (Prof $100,000)
Library Holdings: Bk Vols 158,600; Per Subs 2,312
Partic in Libr Works; Library Network

S THE FRANK PHILLIPS FOUNDATION, INC, Woolaroc Museum Library, Rte 3 Box 2100, 74003. SAN 370-4149. Tel: 918-336-0307. FAX: 918-336-0084. E-Mail: woolaroc1@aol.com. Web Site: www.woolaroc.org. *Curator*, Linda Stone; Tel: 918-336-0307, Ext 32
Library Holdings: Bk Vols 3,000
Subject Interests: Americana, History, Zoology

PHILLIPS PETROLEUM CO
S CORPORATE LIBRARY, 122 PLB, 74004. SAN 357-5314. Tel: 918-661-3433. FAX: 918-662-2171. *Dir*, Annabeth Robin; E-Mail: arob@ppco.com; *Librn*, Connie Battiste; E-Mail: clbatti@ppco.com; Staff 4 (MLS 2, Non-MLS 2)
Founded 1947
Library Holdings: Bk Vols 40,000; Per Subs 240
Subject Interests: Chemistry, Geosci, Petroleum sci, Physics, Plastics, Polymer sci, Technology
Automation Activity & Vendor Info: (Circulation) VTLS; (OPAC) VTLS; (Serials) VTLS
Database Vendor: IAC - SearchBank, OCLC - First Search
Publications: L&IRC E-News
Restriction: Not open to public
Partic in Amigos Library Services, Inc; OCLC Online Computer Library Center, Inc

BEAVER

P BEAVER COUNTY PIONEER LIBRARY,* Second & Douglas St, PO Box 579, 73932. SAN 313-850X. Tel: 580-625-3076. FAX: 580-625-3076. E-Mail: mail@beaver.lib.ok.us. *Librn*, Annette Harness
Circ 8,899
Library Holdings: Bk Vols 13,060; Per Subs 10
Friends of the Library Group

BETHANY

C SOUTHERN NAZARENE UNIVERSITY, R T Williams Learning Resources Center, 4115 N College, 73008. SAN 313-8518. Tel: 405-491-6350. FAX: 405-491-6355. Web Site: ruth.snu.edu/. *Circ, Dir*, Jan Reinbold; *Bibliog Instr, Ref*, Joshua Achipa; *Coordr, Tech Servs*, Joy Pauley; *Govt Doc, Per*, Peggy Clark; *Ref*, Ellen Apple; *Ref*, Sybill Connolly; *Ref*, Janice Cramer; *Ref*, Nancy Jurney
Founded 1920. Enrl 1,950; Fac 75; Highest Degree: Master
1998-1999 Mats Exp $80,000, Books $40,000, Per/Ser (Incl. Access Fees) $40,000
Library Holdings: Bk Vols 95,020; Bk Titles 74,905; Per Subs 1,000
Subject Interests: Bus, Education, Nursing, Religion
Special Collections: Hymnological Coll; Ross Hayslip Bible Coll; Signatures (John E Moore Letter Coll)
Partic in Amigos Library Services, Inc; Metronet; OCLC Online Computer Library Center, Inc

J SOUTHWESTERN COLLEGE OF CHRISTIAN MINISTRIES LIBRARY,* 7210 NW 39th Expressway, PO Box 340, 73008. SAN 313-9654. Tel: 405-789-7661, Ext 3451. FAX: 405-495-0078. *Librn*, Patsy Rutherford
Founded 1946. Enrl 140; Highest Degree: Master
Library Holdings: Bk Vols 40,600; Per Subs 130
Subject Interests: Relig-church growth
Special Collections: Pentecostal Resource Center

BLACKWELL

P BLACKWELL PUBLIC LIBRARY, 123 W Padon, 74631-2805. SAN 313-8534. Tel: 580-363-1809. FAX: 580-363-7214. E-Mail: blklib@kskc.net. *Dir*, Karen Kincheloe; Staff 1 (Non-MLS 1)
Founded 1903. Pop 7,500; Circ 117,807
Library Holdings: Bk Vols 36,250; Bk Titles 34,000; Per Subs 79
Subject Interests: Genealogy
Friends of the Library Group

BOISE CITY

P SOUTAR MEMORIAL LIBRARY,* 102 S Ellis, PO Box 1088, 73933. SAN 313-8542. Tel: 580-544-2715. *Librn*, Nina Hinderliter; E-Mail: nhinderliter@yahoo.com
Founded 1959. Pop 3,648; Circ 11,376
Library Holdings: Bk Vols 20,000; Per Subs 3
Friends of the Library Group

BOLEY

S JOHN H LILLEY CORRECTIONAL CENTER, Leisure Library,* PO Box 308, 74829. SAN 371-7070. Tel: 918-667-3381, Ext 240. *Tech Servs*, Credell Phillips
Library Holdings: Bk Vols 10,500; Bk Titles 10,000; Per Subs 50

BRISTOW

P BRISTOW PUBLIC LIBRARY, Montfort & Allie B Jones Memorial Library, 111 W Seventh Ave, 7401-2401. SAN 313-8550. Tel: 918-367-6562. FAX: 918-367-1156. *Librn*, Connie Green; E-Mail: csgreen@bristow.lib.ok.us; *Asst Librn*, Jessie Allen; *Asst Librn*, Neoma Hutchings
Pop 4,062; Circ 68,000
Jul 1998-Jun 1999 Income City $89,000
Library Holdings: Bk Titles 30,000; Per Subs 65
Subject Interests: Oklahoma
Special Collections: Henson Room - Olympic memorabila/olympic medals/wrestling bks, art, etc
Automation Activity & Vendor Info: (Circulation) Follett

BROKEN BOW

P BROKEN BOW PUBLIC LIBRARY,* 404 Broadway, 74728. SAN 313-8569. Tel: 580-584-2815. *Librn*, Doris Stevenson; *Asst Librn*, Debbie Short; *Asst Librn*, Lisa Lewis
Founded 1920
Library Holdings: Bk Titles 25,000
Mem of Southeastern Public Library System Of Oklahoma
Friends of the Library Group

CARNEGIE

P CARNEGIE PUBLIC LIBRARY,* Carnegie Memorial Bldg, PO Box 9, 73015-1017. SAN 313-8577. Tel: 580-654-1980. FAX: 580-654-1551. E-Mail: camnilibr@carnegienet.net. *Librn*, Lillian Cotten
Founded 1953. Pop 2,016; Circ 4,890
Library Holdings: Bk Vols 12,011
Subject Interests: Genealogy, History, Relig studies
Partic in Okla Telecommunications Interlibr Syst

CHANDLER

P CHANDLER PUBLIC LIBRARY,* 1021 Manvell Ave, 74834. SAN 329-7101. Tel: 405-258-3204. FAX: 405-258-3205. *Librn*, Carmen Harkins; Staff 2 (MLS 1, Non-MLS 1)
Founded 1987. Pop 3,500; Circ 3,680
Library Holdings: Bk Titles 10,030

CHECOTAH

P THE JIM LUCAS CHECOTAH PUBLIC LIBRARY,* 626 W Gentry, 74426-2218. SAN 313-8593. Tel: 918-473-6715. FAX: 918-473-6603. E-Mail: checotahpl@eodlf.lib.ok.us. *Librn*, Kathy Smith
Founded 1971
Library Holdings: Bk Vols 10,000
Subject Interests: Genealogy, Literacy, Local history
Mem of Eastern Oklahoma District Library System
Statistics included in library system
Friends of the Library Group

CHELSEA

P CHELSEA PUBLIC LIBRARY,* 618 Pine, 74016-0064. SAN 313-8607. Tel: 918-789-3364. FAX: 918-789-3364. *Librn*, Debi Van Auken
Pop 2,500
Library Holdings: Bk Vols 4,200; Per Subs 10

CHEROKEE

P CHEROKEE-CITY-COUNTY PUBLIC LIBRARY, 602 S Grand Ave, 73728. SAN 313-8615. Tel: 580-596-2366. FAX: 580-596-2968. E-Mail: cherlb_2000@yahoo.com. *Librn*, Milton Ream; Staff 1 (MLS 1)
Founded 1907. Pop 7,000
Library Holdings: Bk Vols 15,000; Per Subs 14
Subject Interests: Agriculture, Bus, Genealogy, Mgt, Relig studies
Automation Activity & Vendor Info: (Cataloging) Sagebrush Corporation; (Circulation) Sagebrush Corporation

CHEYENNE

P MINNIE R SLIEF MEMORIAL LIBRARY,* 100 Donald Cearlock St, 73628-0370. (Mail add: PO Box 370, 73628-0370), SAN 376-5962. Tel: 580-497-3777. FAX: 580-497-3777. E-Mail: wplssc@itl.net. *Librn*, Marcella Cearlock
Library Holdings: Bk Vols 9,000; Per Subs 15
Mem of Western Plains Library System

CHICKASHA

P CHICKASHA PUBLIC LIBRARY,* 527 Iowa Ave, 73018. SAN 313-8623. Tel: 405-222-6075. FAX: 405-222-6072. E-Mail: chickasha@oltn.odl.state.ok.us, chicklib@chickasha.lib.ok.us. *Dir*, Catharine Cook; Tel: 405-222-6077, E-Mail: cathcook@chickasha.lib.ok.us; *Librn*, Jimmie L Welch; *Ch Servs*, Recilla Harms; Tel: 405-222-6076; *Tech Servs*, Joetta Jeanette Cotton; Tel: 405-222-6078, E-Mail: jcotton@chickasha.lib.ok.us; Staff 7 (MLS 2, Non-MLS 5)
Pop 15,800; Circ 115,855
Jul 1998-Jun 1999 Income $185,207, State $8,278, City $176,929. Mats Exp $30,377, Books $24,036, Per/Ser (Incl. Access Fees) $4,492, Micro $1,109, AV Equip $691, Other Print Mats $49. Sal $126,135 (Prof $50,151)
Library Holdings: Bk Vols 64,191; Bk Titles 60,462; Per Subs 165
Automation Activity & Vendor Info: (Circulation) Sagebrush Corporation
Friends of the Library Group

C UNIVERSITY OF SCIENCE & ARTS OF OKLAHOMA, Nash Library, 1901 S 17 St, PO Box 1909, 73018. SAN 313-8631. Tel: 405-574-1343. FAX: 405-522-3178. Web Site: www.usao.edu/library. *Dir, Ref*, Mark Vargas; E-Mail: facvargasm@usao.edu; *Cat, Tech Servs*, Colleen Montgomery; *ILL*, Mitzi Cook; E-Mail: faccookmk@usao.edu; Staff 2 (MLS 2)
Founded 1909. Fac 54; Highest Degree: Bachelor
Jul 1998-Jun 1999 Income $407,176. Mats Exp $103,432, Books $63,000, Per/Ser (Incl. Access Fees) $46,000, Presv $2,000. Sal $216,429 (Prof $90,900)
Library Holdings: Bk Vols 80,000; Bk Titles 75,000; Per Subs 200; Bks on Deafness & Sign Lang 300
Automation Activity & Vendor Info: (Acquisitions) Gaylord; (Cataloging) Gaylord; (Circulation) Gaylord; (OPAC) Gaylord; (Serials) Gaylord
Database Vendor: OCLC - First Search, Silverplatter Information Inc.
Partic in OCLC Online Computer Library Center, Inc
Special Services for the Deaf - Books on deafness & sign language; Special interest periodicals

CLAREMORE

S J M DAVIS ARMS & HISTORICAL MUSEUM, Research Library,* 333 N Lynn Riggs Blvd, PO Box 966, 74018. SAN 327-6309. Tel: 918-341-5707. FAX: 918-341-5771.
Library Holdings: Bk Titles 2,000

P WILL ROGERS LIBRARY, 1515 N Florence Ave, 74017. SAN 313-8658. Tel: 918-341-1564. FAX: 918-342-0362. *Librn*, Margaret Guffey; *Asst Librn*, Elaine Wienhold; Staff 6 (Non-MLS 6)
Founded 1936. Pop 60,000
Jul 2000-Jun 2001 Income $435,882. Mats Exp Books $78,000. Sal $184,200
Library Holdings: Bk Titles 75,000; Per Subs 92
Subject Interests: Okla hist, Okla newsp from before statehood to present day
Special Collections: Indians; 5 civilized tribes, microfilm; Will Rogers
Automation Activity & Vendor Info: (Acquisitions) TLC; (Cataloging) TLC; (Circulation) TLC; (Course Reserve) TLC; (ILL) TLC; (Media Booking) TLC; (OPAC) TLC; (Serials) TLC
Literacy Council office in library
Friends of the Library Group

S WILL ROGERS MEMORIAL LIBRARY,* 1720 W Will Rogers Blvd, 74018. SAN 320-2259. Tel: 918-341-0719. Toll Free Tel: 800-324-9455. FAX: 918-343-8119. Web Site: www.willrogers.org. *Dir*, Michelle LeFebvre *Librn*, Patricia Lowe; *Curator*, Gregory Malak; Staff 3 (MLS 3)
Founded 1938
Library Holdings: Bk Vols 2,402
Subject Interests: Aviation, Cherokee Indians, Civil War, Flm, Genealogy, Local history, Okla hist, Politics, Vaudeville, Will Rogers
Publications: Will Rogers, genealogy (bibliographies)

J ROGERS STATE UNIVERSITY, Thunderbird Library, 1701 W Will Rogers Blvd, 74017-3252. SAN 313-864X. Tel: 918-343-7716. FAX: 918-343-7897. *Dir*, Alan Lawless; *Acq*, Laura Bottoms; *Publ Servs*, Janice Ferris; *AV*, R L Williams; Staff 4 (MLS 4)
1998-1999 Income $665,000. Mats Exp $119,000. Sal $240,000
Library Holdings: Bk Titles 45,000; Per Subs 443
Partic in Dialog Corporation; OCLC Online Computer Library Center, Inc

CLINTON

P CLINTON PUBLIC LIBRARY,* 721 Frisco, 73601-3320. SAN 376-5938. Tel: 580-323-2165. FAX: 580-323-2165. *Librn*, Nancy Sheppard; Staff 3 (Non-MLS 3)
Library Holdings: Bk Vols 75,000; Per Subs 50; Bks on Deafness & Sign Lang 50
Mem of Western Plains Library System
Friends of the Library Group

P WESTERN PLAINS LIBRARY SYSTEM, 605 Avant, PO Box 1027, 73601-3996. SAN 313-8666. Tel: 580-323-0974. Interlibrary Loan Service Tel: 580-323-0991. FAX: 580-323-0991. E-Mail: wplssc@itlnet.net. *Dir*, Dee Ann Ray; *Ref*, Jane Janzen
Founded 1966. Pop 48,000; Circ 201,000
1998-1999 Income State $63,000
Library Holdings: Per Subs 246
Member Libraries: Clinton Public Library; Cordell Public Library; Hazel Cross Library; Minnie R Slief Memorial Library; Seiling Public Library; Sentinel Public Library
Friends of the Library Group

COALGATE

P COALGATE PUBLIC LIBRARY,* 115 W Ohio, PO Box 49, 74538. SAN 376-6446. Tel: 580-927-3103. FAX: 580-927-3846. *Librn*, Margie Jump
Library Holdings: Bk Vols 12,500; Bk Titles 12,000; Per Subs 13
Mem of Southeastern Public Library System Of Oklahoma

CORDELL

P CORDELL PUBLIC LIBRARY,* 208 S College, PO Box 340, 73632-0340. SAN 376-5954. Tel: 580-832-3530. FAX: 580-832-3530. *Librn*, Carol Corbett
Library Holdings: Bk Titles 50,000; Per Subs 12
Mem of Western Plains Library System
Friends of the Library Group

COYLE

SR ST FRANCIS LIBRARY,* PO Box 400, 73027-0400. SAN 326-7016. Tel: 405-466-3774. FAX: 405-466-3722. *Librn*, Diane Lamecker
Founded 1982
Library Holdings: Bk Vols 21,000; Bk Titles 18,000
Subject Interests: Religion
Special Collections: C G Jung Writings Coll, bks, journals; Francis of Assisi (St Francis Coll)
Publications: Newsletter for St Francis of the Woods (quarterly)

CUSHING

P CUSHING PUBLIC LIBRARY,* 215 N Steele, PO Box 551, 74023-3319. SAN 313-8674. Tel: 918-225-4188. FAX: 918-225-6201. *Dir*, Ruth Ann Johnson
Founded 1939. Pop 7,500; Circ 56,760
Jul 1997-Jun 1998 Income $172,600. Mats Exp $18,000. Sal $65,800
Library Holdings: Bk Vols 65,000; Per Subs 82
Subject Interests: Law
Special Collections: Genealogy (Cushing Family), bks, flm, micro; Law (Payne County Law Books); Local History

DEWEY

P HERBERT F TYLER MEMORIAL LIBRARY,* 821 N Shawnee, 74029. SAN 313-8682. Tel: 918-534-2106. FAX: 918-534-2106. E-Mail: tylerli@ionet.net. *Librn*, Cheryl J Schiermeier
Founded 1958. Pop 4,000; Circ 16,012
Library Holdings: Bk Vols 15,000
Friends of the Library Group

DRUMRIGHT

P DRUMRIGHT PUBLIC LIBRARY, 104 E Broadway, 74030. SAN 313-8690. Tel: 918-352-2228. FAX: 918-352-9261. *Librn*, Brenda L Grisham; E-Mail: blgrisham@drumright.lib.ok.us; *Librn*, Frances E Miller
Circ 4,152
Library Holdings: Bk Vols 30,000

DUNCAN

P DUNCAN PUBLIC LIBRARY,* 815 Ash, 73533. SAN 313-8704. Tel: 580-255-0636. FAX: 580-255-6136. E-Mail: duncanpl@texhoma.net. *Dir*, Wendy Allen; *ILL*, Brenda Strong; *Ch Servs*, Darbie LaFontain; *Cat*, Jacqui Wilmoth; Staff 8 (MLS 1, Non-MLS 7)
Founded 1921. Pop 30,000; Circ 153,900
1998-1999 Income $277,042, State $11,425, City $265,381, Other $236. Mats Exp $40,445, Books $32,562, Per/Ser (Incl. Access Fees) $4,597, Micro $2,039. Sal $171,550
Library Holdings: Bk Vols 59,479; Bk Titles 58,700; Per Subs 125
Subject Interests: Genealogy, Okla hist
Partic in Okla Telecommunications Interlibr Syst
Friends of the Library Group

S HALLIBURTON ENERGY SERVICES, Research Center Library, 2600 S Second St, PO Box 1431, 73536-0400. SAN 313-8712. Tel: 580-251-3516. FAX: 580-251-3008.; Staff 1 (MLS 1)
Library Holdings: Bk Titles 13,100; Per Subs 150
Subject Interests: Chemical engineering, Oil well servs, Petroleum
Special Collections: Lab Notebooks, micro
Restriction: Staff use only
Function: Research library
Partic in Sci & Tech Info Network

DURANT

P ROBERT L WILLIAMS PUBLIC LIBRARY, (RLWPL), 323 W Beech, 74701. SAN 313-8739. Tel: 580-924-3486. FAX: 580-924-8843. E-Mail: dlibrary@redriverok.com. *Librn*, Alice Moore; *Asst Librn*, Troy Tucker; *Circ*, Brandy Pate; *Cat*, Donald Maupin
Founded 1925. Pop 12,000; Circ 20,000
Library Holdings: Bk Titles 50,397; Per Subs 25
Automation Activity & Vendor Info: (Cataloging) Follett; (Circulation) Follett; (OPAC) Follett
Database Vendor: IAC - Info Trac, OCLC - First Search
Function: ILL available
Friends of the Library Group

C SOUTHEASTERN OKLAHOMA STATE UNIVERSITY, Henry G Bennett Memorial Library, Sixth Street University Blvd, 74701-0609. SAN 313-8720. Tel: 580-745-2702. Interlibrary Loan Service Tel: 580-745-2931. Circulation Tel: 580-745-2168. Reference Tel: 580-745-2935. FAX: 580-745-7463. Web Site: www.sosu.edu/lib. *Dir*, Dottie Davis; E-Mail: ddavis@sosu.edu; *Tech Servs*, Susan Webb; Tel: 580-745-2934, E-Mail: swebb@sosu.edu; *Automation Syst Coordr, Ref*, Dennis Miles; Tel: 580-745-2396, E-Mail: dmiles@sosu.edu; *Ref, Ser*, Wanda Donica; Tel: 580-745-2933, E-Mail: wdonica@sosu.edu; *ILL, Ref Serv*, Sandra Thomas; E-Mail: sthomas@sosu.edu; Staff 6 (MLS 6)
Founded 1913. Enrl 3,800; Highest Degree: Master
Jul 1999-Jun 2000 Income $727,390. Mats Exp $214,277, Books $91,513, Per/Ser (Incl. Access Fees) $81,181, Electronic Ref Mat (Incl. Access Fees) $22,883. Sal $358,132 (Prof $195,800)
Library Holdings: Bk Vols 184,833; Bk Titles 103,183; Per Subs 1,241
Subject Interests: American Indian, Education, History, Literature, Native Americans, Okla hist
Special Collections: Curriculum Materials
Database Vendor: DRA, Ebsco - EbscoHost, OCLC - First Search
Partic in Amigos Library Services, Inc; OCLC Online Computer Library Center, Inc

EDMOND

CR OKLAHOMA CHRISTIAN UNIVERSITY, Tom & Ada Beam Library, 2501 E Memorial Rd, 73013. (Mail add: PO Box 11000, 73136-1100), SAN 313-945X. Tel: 405-425-5312. FAX: 405-425-5313. Web Site: www.oc.edu/academics/library/. *Dir*, Tamie Lyn Willis; Tel: 405-425-5320, E-Mail: tamie.willis@oc.edu; *Head Ref*, Geneva Hoover; Tel: 405-425-5315, E-Mail: geneva.hoover@oc.edu; *Ref*, Lee Anne Paris; Tel: 405-425-5317, E-Mail: leeanne.paris@oc.edu; *Head Tech Servs*, Sandra Lockwood; Tel: 405-425-5314, E-Mail: sandra.lockwood@oc.edu; *Acq*, April Ford; Tel: 405-425-5319, E-Mail: april.ford@oc.edu; *ILL*, Connie Maple; Tel: 405-425-5324, E-Mail: connie.maple@oc.edu; Staff 6 (MLS 3, Non-MLS 3)
Founded 1950. Enrl 1,504; Fac 92; Highest Degree: Master
Library Holdings: Bk Vols 93,000; Bk Titles 86,250; Per Subs 1,210
Subject Interests: Bible, Bus educ, Engr
Special Collections: Oklahoma Symphony Orchestra Master Tapes 1950-1984; Rare Books & Clipping File Daily Oklahoman (1907-1981)
Automation Activity & Vendor Info: (Acquisitions) SIRSI; (Cataloging) SIRSI; (Circulation) SIRSI; (Course Reserve) SIRSI; (OPAC) SIRSI; (Serials) SIRSI
Database Vendor: IAC - SearchBank, OCLC - First Search, Wilson - Wilson Web
Partic in Amigos Library Services, Inc; Christian Col Libr

C UNIVERSITY OF CENTRAL OKLAHOMA LIBRARY, 100 N University, 73034-5210. SAN 313-8747. Tel: 405-974-3361. Circulation Tel: 405-974-3361. Reference Tel: 405-974-2878. FAX: 405-974-3806, 405-974-3874. E-Mail: library@ucok.edu. Web Site: library.ucok.edu. *Dean of Libr*, Dr John Lolley; *Dir Libr Serv*, Carolyn Mahin; Tel: 405-974-2595, E-Mail: cmahin@ucok.edu; *Archivist*, Nicole Willard; Tel: 405-974-2885, E-Mail: nwillard@ucok.edu; *Head Tech Servs*, Ron Curtis; Tel: 405-974-2866, E-Mail: rcurtis@ucok.edu; *Head, Cat*, Sue McGee; Tel: 405-974-2872, E-Mail: smcgee@ucok.edu; *Dir, Publ Servs*, Carol Barry; *Acq, Ser*, John Purdy; *Head Ref*, Jane Taylor; Tel: 405-974-2946, E-Mail: jtaylor@ucok.edu; Staff 17 (MLS 16, Non-MLS 1)
Founded 1890. Enrl 14,247; Fac 479; Highest Degree: Master
Jul 1999-Jun 2000 Income $2,659,471, State $2,620,741, Federal $38,730. Mats Exp $681,354, Books $110,074, Per/Ser (Incl. Access Fees) $569,180, Manuscripts & Archives $2,100. Sal $1,507,468 (Prof $621,634)
Library Holdings: Bk Vols 311,373; Bk Titles 218,565; Per Subs 2,360
Subject Interests: Bus, Education, Liberal arts, Mathematics, Sci
Special Collections: Oklahoma Coll
Automation Activity & Vendor Info: (Acquisitions) NOTIS; (Cataloging) NOTIS; (Serials) NOTIS
Database Vendor: Dialog, Ebsco - EbscoHost, epixtech, inc., IAC - SearchBank, OCLC - First Search, ProQuest, Silverplatter Information Inc., Wilson - Wilson Web
Partic in Amigos Library Services, Inc; Dialog Corporation
Friends of the Library Group

EL RENO

S BUREAU OF PRISONS, Federal Correctional Institution Library,* PO Box 1000, 73036. SAN 313-8755. Tel: 405-262-4875. FAX: 405-262-6266. *Librn*, Wayne Huffman
Founded 1960
Library Holdings: Bk Vols 12,000; Bk Titles 10,000; Per Subs 14

S CANADIAN COUNTY HISTORICAL MUSEUM LIBRARY,* 300 S Grand, 73036. SAN 327-571X. Tel: 405-262-5121. *Curator*, Pat Reuter
Library Holdings: Bk Vols 300
Subject Interests: Local history
Special Collections: Indian artifacts, Rock Island Railroad Effects, domestic, church & farming implements
Early 19th century rural schoolhouse & first Red Cross canteen at a railroad station in US.

P EL RENO CARNEGIE LIBRARY, (ERCL), 215 E Wade, 73036-2753. SAN 313-8763. Tel: 405-262-2409. FAX: 405-422-2136. E-Mail: ercl215@netscape.net. *Librn*, Dianne Costin
Pop 15,000; Circ 101,659
Library Holdings: Bk Vols 54,643; Per Subs 149
Special Collections: Edna May Armold Archives
Friends of the Library Group

J REDLANDS COMMUNITY COLLEGE, Learning Resources Center,* 1300 S Country Club Rd, 73036. SAN 313-8771. Tel: 405-262-2552, Ext 1255. FAX: 405-422-1200. *Dir*, Karen D Olive
Founded 1965. Fac 44
1997-1998 Income $120,398. Mats Exp $46,398, Books $22,500. Sal $74,000
Library Holdings: Bk Vols 18,676; Per Subs 224
Partic in Okla Telecommunications Interlibr Syst

ELK CITY

P ELK CITY CARNEGIE LIBRARY,* 221 W Broadway, 73644. SAN 313-878X. Tel: 580-225-0136. FAX: 580-225-1051. *Ad Servs*, Pat Sprowls; *Ch Servs*, Sharon Fisk
Founded 1912. Pop 10,000; Circ 76,000
Library Holdings: Bk Vols 44,000; Per Subs 50
Special Collections: Southwest Literature
Friends of the Library Group

ENID

P PUBLIC LIBRARY OF ENID & GARFIELD COUNTY, 120 W Maine, 73701. (Mail add: PO Box 8002, 73702-8002), Tel: 580-234-6313. Toll Free Tel: 888-261-4904. FAX: 580-233-2948. Web Site: www.enid.org/library.htm. *Dir*, Glenda B Lamb; Tel: 580-234-6313, Ext 109; *Ch Servs*, Kathy Logan; *Tech Servs*, Mary Shaklee; Tel: 580-234-6313, Ext 111; *YA Servs*, Carla Hickey; *Info Tech*, Mike Murray; *Ref*, Mary Arthur; *Ref Serv*, Wilita Larrison; Staff 23 (MLS 4, Non-MLS 19)
Founded 1899. Pop 57,300; Circ 216,764
Jul 1998-Jun 1999 Income $693,167, State $29,688, City $642,599, County $20,880. Mats Exp $87,444, Books $73,500, Per/Ser (Incl. Access Fees) $12,050, Electronic Ref Mat (Incl. Access Fees) $1,894. Sal $433,558 (Prof $35,238)
Library Holdings: Bk Vols 95,295; Bk Titles 85,765; Per Subs 233
Special Collections: Marquis James (Oklahoma Books & Authors)
Database Vendor: OCLC - First Search
Partic in Amigos Library Services, Inc
Houses Literacy Council office & tutoring program
Friends of the Library Group

M SAINT MARY'S REGIONAL MEDICAL CENTER, Medical Library, 305 S Fifth, PO Box 232, 73701. SAN 320-4154. Tel: 580-249-3092. FAX: 580-249-3091. *Librn*, Janet L Puckett; E-Mail: jpucket1@uhsinc.com
Founded 1964
Library Holdings: Bk Vols 4,517; Bk Titles 2,300; Per Subs 200
Subject Interests: Health sci

EUFAULA

P EUFAULA MEMORIAL LIBRARY,* 301 S First St, 74432-3201. SAN 313-8801. Tel: 918-689-2291. FAX: 918-689-4124. *Librn*, Shirley Thomas
Founded 1971
Library Holdings: Bk Titles 20,000; Per Subs 30
Subject Interests: Audio, Video
Mem of Eastern Oklahoma District Library System
Statistics included in library system
Friends of the Library Group

FAIRFAX

P FAIRFAX PUBLIC LIBRARY,* 158 E Elm, 74637. SAN 313-881X. Tel: 918-642-5535. FAX: 918-642-3350. *Librn*, Carol Irons
Founded 1922. Pop 1,749; Circ 8,995
Library Holdings: Bk Vols 17,117
Special Collections: Area History
Partic in Okla Telecommunications Interlibr Syst
Friends of the Library Group

FAIRVIEW

P FAIRVIEW CITY LIBRARY, 115 S Sixth Ave, 73737-2141. (Mail add: PO Box 419, 73737-0419), SAN 313-8828. Tel: 580-227-2190. FAX: 580-227-2190. E-Mail: bookladies@auroraok.org. Web Site: www.fairviewok.org. *Dir*, Ernestine Titus; Staff 4 (Non-MLS 4)
Pop 3,730; Circ 15,907
Jul 1999-Jun 2000 Income City $60,301
Library Holdings: Bk Vols 25,000; Bk Titles 20,400; Per Subs 38
Special Collections: Oklahoma Heritage
Friends of the Library Group

FORT GIBSON

P Q B BOYDSTUN LIBRARY,* 200 W Hickory, PO Box 700, 74434. SAN 313-8836. Tel: 918-478-3587. *Mgr*, Gayle Ledford
Founded 1978
Library Holdings: Bk Vols 6,000; Per Subs 25
Subject Interests: Mysteries, Western
Mem of Eastern Oklahoma District Library System
Statistics included in library system

FORT SILL

UNITED STATES ARMY

A MORRIS SWETT TECHNICAL LIBRARY, Snow Hall, Bldg 730, 73503-0312. SAN 357-5438. Tel: 580-442-4525. FAX: 580-442-5102. *Librn*, Sheila Duckworth; E-Mail: duckwors@usafas.army.mil; *Tech Servs*, Richard Copus; Staff 2 (MLS 1, Non-MLS 1)
Founded 1911
Oct 1997-Sep 1998 Income $24,000. Mats Exp $24,000
Library Holdings: Per Subs 70
Subject Interests: Ammunition, Ballistics, Field artillery, Mil sci, Military history, Missiles, Ordnance, Weapon systs, Weapons
Special Collections: In-House Indexes; Janes Series; Military Periodical Analytical Index File, VF; Rare Books Coll; Special Bibliographies; Subject Headings to the Library Collection; U Military Science Classification System; Unit Histories-Field Artillery, bk, microfilm, fiche
Partic in Defense Technical Information Center; Fedlink; OCLC Online Computer Library Center, Inc

A NYE LIBRARY, Bldg 1640, 73503-5100. SAN 357-5462. Tel: 580-442-5111. FAX: 580-442-7347. *Head of Libr*, Andrea Freeman; E-Mail: freeman1@dolmex1.sill.army.mill; *Ref, Tech Servs*, Cebrun Mayse
Founded 1953
Oct 1997-Sep 1998 Mats Exp $34,000
Library Holdings: Bk Vols 87,000; Bk Titles 67,500; Per Subs 230
Subject Interests: Adult education, Consumer educ, Family life, Home, Mil sci
Special Collections: Books for College Libraries, microfiche; College Catalogs, microfiche; Webster University Deposit Coll
Publications: Newsletter (monthly)
Partic in Fedlink; OCLC Online Computer Library Center, Inc

FORT SUPPLY

M WESTERN STATE PSYCHIATRIC CENTER, Clients Library, PO Box 1, 73841. SAN 328-8269. Tel: 580-766-2311, Ext 148. FAX: 580-766-2017. *Tech Servs*, Karen Connell
Library Holdings: Bk Titles 2,000; Per Subs 15
Subject Interests: Fiction, Nonfiction, Psychology

FREDERICK

P FREDERICK PUBLIC LIBRARY, 200 E Grand, PO Box 969, 73542. SAN 313-8844. Tel: 580-335-3601. FAX: 580-335-3601. E-Mail: fredlibrary@onenet.net. *Dir*, Dena Northcutt; *Asst Librn*, Mary Frances Copeland; Staff 2 (MLS 1, Non-MLS 1)
Founded 1915. Circ 16,384
Library Holdings: Bk Vols 15,000; Per Subs 36
Friends of the Library Group

GATE

S GATEWAY TO THE PANHANDLE MUSEUM LIBRARY, Main St, PO Box 27, 73844. SAN 321-5776. Tel: 580-934-2004. *Librn*, Ernestine Maphet; Staff 6 (MLS 1, Non-MLS 5)
Founded 1975
Library Holdings: Bk Vols 8,000
Subject Interests: Local history

GEARY

P GEARY PUBLIC LIBRARY,* 127 N Broadway, 73040-0216. SAN 313-8852. Tel: 405-884-2372. FAX: 405-884-2372. E-Mail: grylib@pldi.net. *Librn*, Joyce Shawver; *Asst Librn*, Donna Taylor
Founded 1933. Pop 1,500; Circ 7,673
Library Holdings: Bk Titles 10,000; Per Subs 10
Open Wed-Fri 9-12 & 1-6

GOODWELL

C PANHANDLE STATE UNIVERSITY, Marvin E McKee Library, PO Box 370, 73939-0370. SAN 313-8860. Tel: 580-349-2611, Ext 345. Toll Free Tel: 1-800-664-6778. FAX: 580-349-2302. E-Mail: mckeelib@opsu.edu. Web Site: www.opsu.edu/library/lib1.htm. *Dir*, C Evlyn Schmidt; E-Mail: ceschmidt@opsu.edu; *Circ Ch*, Elaina Stewart; Tel: 580-349-2611, Ext 348, E-Mail: estewart@opsu.edu; *Cat*, Sonya Smith; Tel: 580-349-2611, Ext 347, E-Mail: ssmith@opsu.edu; *Tech Servs*, Michele Seikel; Tel: 580-349-2611, Ext 347, E-Mail: mseikel@opsu.edu; *Acq*, Maggie Cline; E-Mail: mags@opsu.edu; Staff 5 (MLS 3, Non-MLS 2)
Founded 1909. Enrl 1,200; Fac 70; Highest Degree: Bachelor
Jul 1999-Jun 2000 Income Parent Institution $431,000. Mats Exp $80,000, Books $28,000, Per/Ser (Incl. Access Fees) $38,000, Micro $9,000, Electronic Ref Mat (Incl. Access Fees) $5,000. Sal $137,000 (Prof $120,000)
Library Holdings: Bk Vols 116,000; Bk Titles 90,000; Per Subs 320; High Interest/Low Vocabulary Bk Vols 100; Bks on Deafness & Sign Lang 20
Subject Interests: Children's, Curric
Special Collections: Textbook Review Center
Automation Activity & Vendor Info: (Acquisitions) Endeavor; (Cataloging) Endeavor; (Circulation) Endeavor; (OPAC) Endeavor; (Serials) Endeavor
Database Vendor: IAC - Info Trac, OCLC - First Search
Partic in Amigos Library Services, Inc
Special Services for the Blind - ZoomText software to enlarge computer screen

GRANDFIELD

GRANDFIELD PUBLIC LIBRARY,* 101 W Second St, 73546. (Mail add: PO Box 725, 73546), SAN 313-8879. Tel: 580-479-5598. FAX: 580-479-5665. *Librn*, Sharron Challis; *Asst Librn*, Nancy Whitson
Founded 1944. Pop 1,450
Library Holdings: Bk Vols 10,092; Bk Titles 9,006; Per Subs 10
Open Tues-Wed 2-6, Thurs-Fri 8-1, Sat 9-1
Friends of the Library Group

GRANITE

S OKLAHOMA STATE REFORMATORY LIBRARY,* PO Box 514, 73547. SAN 313-8887. Tel: 580-535-2186. FAX: 580-535-4803. *Librn*, John Slater
Library Holdings: Bk Vols 926; Per Subs 59

GROVE

P GROVE PUBLIC LIBRARY,* 206 S Elk St, 74344-8602. SAN 313-8895. Tel: 918-786-2945. FAX: 918-786-5233. *Mgr*, Marcia Austin
Founded 1963. Pop 20,000
Library Holdings: Bk Vols 26,000; Per Subs 38
Subject Interests: Genealogy
Mem of Eastern Oklahoma District Library System

GUTHRIE

P GUTHRIE PUBLIC LIBRARY, 201 N Division, 73044-3201. SAN 313-8909. Tel: 405-282-0050. FAX: 405-282-2804. Web Site: www.guthrie.lib.ok.us. *Dir*, Richard Cheek; E-Mail: rocheek@guthrie.lib.ok.us; *Asst Librn*, Carolyn Engle; Staff 2 (MLS 2)
Founded 1899. Pop 12,500; Circ 78,000
Jul 1998-Jun 1999 Income $128,000, State $5,000, City $120,000, Locally Generated Income $3,000. Mats Exp $21,500, Books $16,500, Per/Ser (Incl. Access Fees) $5,000. Sal $68,800
Library Holdings: Bk Titles 32,000; Per Subs 120
Automation Activity & Vendor Info: (Cataloging) Follett; (Circulation) Follett; (OPAC) Follett
Friends of the Library Group

GUYMON

P GUYMON PUBLIC LIBRARY,* 206 NW Fifth St, 73942. SAN 313-8917. Tel: 580-338-7330. FAX: 580-338-2659. *Librn*, Rachel Sides; E-Mail: rsides@guymon.lib.ok.us
Pop 8,000; Circ 59,406
Library Holdings: Bk Vols 30,000; Per Subs 45
Friends of the Library Group

HARTSHORNE

P HARTSHORNE PUBLIC LIBRARY, 720 Penn Ave, 74547. SAN 376-592X. Tel: 918-297-2113. FAX: 918-297-7004. *Asst Librn*, Catherine Tucker
Library Holdings: Bk Vols 5,000; Per Subs 20
Mem of Southeastern Public Library System Of Oklahoma

HASKELL

P RIEGER MEMORIAL LIBRARY,* 116 N Broadway, PO Box 429, 74436. SAN 313-8925. Tel: 918-482-3614. FAX: 918-482-3266. *Mgr*, Helen C Kirk
Founded 1971
Library Holdings: Bk Vols 13,000; Per Subs 35
Mem of Eastern Oklahoma District Library System
Statistics included in library system

HEAVENER

P HEAVENER PUBLIC LIBRARY, 203 E Ave C, PO Box 246, 74937-0246. SAN 313-8933. Tel: 918-653-2870. FAX: 918-653-4805. *Librn*, Jana Manifold; E-Mail: manifold@sepl.lib.ok.us; *Asst Librn*, Jane Naylor
Pop 2,566; Circ 27,917
Library Holdings: Bk Vols 20,035; Per Subs 25
Mem of Southeastern Public Library System Of Oklahoma
Friends of the Library Group

HENNESSEY

P HENNESSEY PUBLIC LIBRARY,* 525 S Main, 73742. SAN 313-8941. Tel: 405-853-2073. Web Site: www.hennessey.lib.ok.us. *Dir*, Mary L Haney; *Asst Librn*, Guyla Foster; *Ch Servs*, Nettie Racer; *Ch Servs*, Kay Campbell; Staff 1 (Non-MLS 1)
Founded 1939. Pop 1,800; Circ 12,191
Jul 1998-Jun 1999 Income $57,988, City $40,630, County $5,244, Locally Generated Income $5,115, Other $5,499. Mats Exp $4,609, Books $3,473, Per/Ser (Incl. Access Fees) $577, Micro $559. Sal $25,462
Library Holdings: Bk Vols 24,000; Per Subs 34; Bks on Deafness & Sign Lang 10
Special Collections: AFI 100 Best Films; Hennessey Clipper from 1890; Hennessey Heritage Coll; National Geographic, complete, leather bound; Ortman Film Memorial
Database Vendor: IAC - Info Trac, OCLC - First Search
Function: ILL available
Friends of the Library Group

HENRYETTA

P HENRYETTA PUBLIC LIBRARY,* 518 W Main, 74437. SAN 313-895X. Tel: 918-652-7377. FAX: 918-652-2796. E-Mail: hplib@ocevnet.org. Web Site: www.ocevnet.org/henlib/index.htm. *Librn*, Ruby Wesson; *Asst Librn*, Beth Whisman
Founded 1910. Pop 6,500; Circ 36,150
Library Holdings: Bk Vols 25,000; Bk Titles 20,000; Per Subs 100
Partic in Okla Libr Technology Network
Friends of the Library Group

HOBART

P HOBART PUBLIC LIBRARY,* 200 S Main St, 73651. SAN 313-8968. Tel: 580-726-2535. FAX: 580-726-2535. *Librn*, Jerry Menz
Circ 39,609
Library Holdings: Bk Vols 24,000; Per Subs 32
Special Collections: Kate F Phelps Genealogical Coll
Friends of the Library Group

HODGEN

S OUACHITA CORRECTIONAL CENTER, Leisure Library,* HC 63 Box 5390, 74939. SAN 371-7704. Tel: 918-653-7831, Ext 372. FAX: 918-653-7813. *In Charge*, Janice K Brower
Jul 1998-Jun 1999 Income $3,527, State $3,000, Federal $527. Mats Exp $2,695, Books $787, Per/Ser (Incl. Access Fees) $1,908. Sal $20,277
Library Holdings: Bk Titles 6,014; Per Subs 61

HOLDENVILLE

P GRACE M PICKENS PUBLIC LIBRARY, 209 E Ninth St, 74848. SAN 313-8976. Tel: 405-379-3245. FAX: 405-379-5725. *Librn*, Fran Cook; E-Mail: fcook@aol.com; *Asst Librn*, Kim McNaughton; E-Mail: kmcnaughton866@aol.com
Pop 5,181; Circ 26,912
Library Holdings: Bk Vols 24,000; Per Subs 15
Friends of the Library Group

HOLLIS

P HOLLIS PUBLIC LIBRARY,* 201 W Broadway & Second St, PO Box 73, 73550. SAN 313-8984. Tel: 580-688-2744. FAX: 580-688-2744. *Mgr*, Donna Norton; *Asst Librn*, Rochelle Rippetoe
Founded 1973. Pop 3,500; Circ 9,991
1997-1998 Income $60,000
Library Holdings: Bk Vols 14,200; Per Subs 25
Mem of Southern Prairie Library System

HOMINY

S DICK CONNER CORRECTIONAL CENTER LIBRARY,* PO Box 220, 74035. SAN 324-0126. Tel: 918-885-2192. *Librn*, Peggy Dunlop
Founded 1979
Jul 1997-Jun 1998 Income $3,000
Library Holdings: Bk Titles 7,000; Per Subs 50
Partic in Okla Telecommunications Interlibr Syst

P HOMINY PUBLIC LIBRARY, 121 W Main, 74035. SAN 313-8992. Tel: 918-885-4486. FAX: 918-885-2837. E-Mail: hominy@ionet.net. *Dir*, Kathryn Ramsay; Staff 3 (MLS 1, Non-MLS 2)
Founded 1925. Pop 2,274; Circ 12,500
Library Holdings: Bk Vols 10,000
Automation Activity & Vendor Info: (Cataloging) Brodart; (Circulation) Brodart
Database Vendor: Innovative Interfaces INN - View, OVID Technologies

HOOKER

P OLIVE WARNER MEMORIAL LIBRARY,* 111 S Broadway, 73945-0576. (Mail add: PO Box 576, 73945-0576), SAN 313-900X. Tel: 580-652-2835. FAX: 580-652-2488. E-Mail: hookerpl@ptsi.net. Web Site: www.hookerok.com. *Dir*, Janie Jacobs
Founded 1916. Pop 1,551
Jul 1997-Jun 1998 Income $15,200. Mats Exp Books $2,700. Sal $8,400

Library Holdings: Bk Vols 20,500
Special Collections: Hooker Advance Microfilm, 1907-present
Publications: Hooker History Vols I, II & III
Partic in Tri-State Libr Consortium
Friends of the Library Group

HUGO

P CHOCTAW COUNTY LIBRARY,* 208 E Jefferson, 74743. SAN 313-9018. Tel: 580-326-5591. FAX: 580-326-7388. Web Site: www.sepl.lib.ok.us. *Librn*, Sharon Swift; *Asst Librn*, Shelia Baldwin; *Asst Librn*, Karen Hart
Pop 15,203
Library Holdings: Bk Vols 16,500
Mem of Southeastern Public Library System Of Oklahoma
Partic in OCLC Online Computer Library Center, Inc
Friends of the Library Group

IDABEL

P IDABEL PUBLIC LIBRARY, 2 SE Avenue D, PO Box 778, 74745-0778. SAN 313-9026. Tel: 580-286-6406. FAX: 580-286-3708. E-Mail: www.idabel@sepl.lib.ok.us. Web Site: idabel.lib.ok.us. *Librn*, Linda Potts; E-Mail: potts@sepl.lib.ok.us; *Asst Librn*, Sue McBrayer; E-Mail: mcbrayer@sepl.lib.ok.us
Pop 5,946
Library Holdings: Bk Vols 40,000; Per Subs 40
Automation Activity & Vendor Info: (Acquisitions) SIRSI; (Cataloging) SIRSI; (Circulation) SIRSI; (Course Reserve) SIRSI; (ILL) SIRSI; (Media Booking) SIRSI
Mem of Southeastern Public Library System Of Oklahoma
Friends of the Library Group

JAY

P DELAWARE COUNTY LIBRARY,* 429 S Ninth St, PO Box 387, 74346. SAN 313-9034. Tel: 918-253-8521. FAX: 918-253-8726. *Librn*, Deanna Smith
Founded 1970. Pop 1,594
Library Holdings: Bk Vols 19,088; Per Subs 38
Mem of Eastern Oklahoma District Library System
Statistics included in library system
Friends of the Library Group

KAW CITY

P KAW CITY PUBLIC LIBRARY,* 900 Morgan Sq E, PO Box 26, 74641-0026. SAN 321-9917. Tel: 580-269-2525. FAX: 580-269-2957. *Dir*, Jerry Palmer
Founded 1902. Pop 370
1997-1998 Income $1,000
Library Holdings: Bk Vols 3,300
Subject Interests: Indian

KINGFISHER

P KINGFISHER MEMORIAL LIBRARY,* 505 W Will Rogers St, 73750. SAN 313-9042. Tel: 405-375-3384. FAX: 405-375-3306. E-Mail: memlib@aol.com. *Librn*, Jeanne Dial; *Circ*, Shari Cruz; *Ch Servs*, Emelia Turner; *Spec Coll*, Gary Williams; *Ref*, Rena Tollison
Pop 16,100; Circ 42,000
Library Holdings: Bk Vols 35,000; Per Subs 115
Special Collections: Civil War Coll; Kingfisher Coll; Okla Coll
Publications: Library Journal; Wilson
Friends of the Library Group

LANGSTON

C LANGSTON UNIVERSITY, G Lamar Harrison Library,* PO Box 1600, 73050-1600. SAN 313-9050. Tel: 405-466-3293. FAX: 405-466-3459. E-Mail: library@lunet.edu. *Dir*, Njambi Kamoche; *Tech Servs*, Cecila Essenmacher; *Curator*, Bettye Black; *Coordr, Ref*, Darcy Rankin; *Coordr, Online Servs*, Clarence Harkins
Founded 1949. Enrl 2,172; Fac 69; Highest Degree: Master
Library Holdings: Per Subs 1,507
Subject Interests: Allied health, Muticultural, Urban
Special Collections: Black Studies (M B Tolson Black Heritage Center), multi-media
Publications: The G Lamar Harrison Library Handbook

LAWTON

C CAMERON UNIVERSITY LIBRARY, 2800 W Gore Blvd, 73505-6377. SAN 313-9069. Tel: 580-581-2403. Circulation Tel: 580-581-2956. Reference Tel: 580-581-2958. FAX: 580-581-2386. E-Mail: library@cameron.edu. Web Site: www.cameron.edu/admin/library. *Dir*, Dr Sherry Young; Tel: 580-581-2408, E-Mail: sherryy@cameron.edu; *Asst Dir*, Barbara L Pickthorn; Tel: 580-581-2958, E-Mail: barbarap@cameron.edu; *Ser*, Victoria K Swinney; Tel: 580-581-2960, E-Mail: vswinney@cameron.com; *ILL*, Cathy Blackman; Tel: 580-581-2382, E-Mail: cathyb@cameron.edu; *Info Tech*, Robert Baca; Tel: 580-581-2958, E-Mail: robertb@cameron.edu; Staff 16 (MLS 7, Non-MLS 9)
Founded 1908. Enrl 5,098; Fac 191; Highest Degree: Master
Jul 1999-Jun 2000 Income $1,188,237, State $1,140,107, Federal $24,700, Locally Generated Income $23,430. Mats Exp $506,961, Books $124,448, Per/Ser (Incl. Access Fees) $275,067, Presv $5,503, Micro $100,335, Other Print Mats $1,608. Sal $482,256 (Prof $271,724)
Library Holdings: Bk Vols 180,625; Bk Titles 174,920; Per Subs 1,879
Subject Interests: Agriculture, Behav sci, Bus, Education, Media, Mgt, Soc sci
Special Collections: SCAN
Automation Activity & Vendor Info: (Cataloging) VTLS; (Circulation) VTLS; (OPAC) VTLS; (Serials) VTLS
Database Vendor: IAC - Info Trac, IAC - SearchBank, OCLC - First Search, ProQuest
Partic in Dialog Corporation; First Search; OCLC Online Computer Library Center, Inc; Search Bank

P LAWTON PUBLIC LIBRARY,* 110 SW Fourth St, 73501-4034. SAN 357-5497. Tel: 580-581-3450. FAX: 580-248-0243. *Dir*, Marion F Donaldson; *Librn*, Paul Follett; *Ref*, Ann Brown; *Ref*, David Snider; *Ch Servs*, Jim Maroon; *Tech Servs*, Denise Flusche
Founded 1904. Pop 108,144; Circ 259,215
1997-1998 Income $671,114. Mats Exp $75,303
Library Holdings: Bk Vols 120,513; Per Subs 327
Special Collections: Oklahoma (Voices of Oklahoma); Southwest Oklahoma Genealogical Research Coll
Partic in Amigos Library Services, Inc; Okla Telecommunications Interlibr Syst
Friends of the Library Group
Branches: 1
BRANCH LIBRARY, 1304 NW Kingswood, 73505-4076. SAN 357-5527. Tel: 580-581-3457.
Library Holdings: Bk Vols 4,200
Bookmobiles: 1

S MUSEUM OF THE GREAT PLAINS, Research Center,* 601 NW Ferris Ave, 73507. SAN 313-9077. Tel: 405-581-3460. FAX: 405-581-3458. E-Mail: mgp@sirinet.net. Web Site: www.museumgreatplains.org. *Curator, Spec Coll*, Deborah Baroff
Founded 1960
Library Holdings: Bk Titles 30,000
Subject Interests: Agriculture, Anthropology, Archaeology, Ecology, Hist of trans-Mississippi West, Settlement on southern Plains, SW
Special Collections: Business of Early Lawton (Harry Buckingham Coll), archives; Extensive Hist of Transportation Coll with wagon & carriage manufacturers' catalogs & trade magazines (1869-1926); Manuscript Coll; Plains Indians Photograph Coll; Politics & Law of Early Lawton (Charles Black Coll & L M Gensman Coll) archives; Settlement of Southwestern Oklahoma, agr & hardware cat; Show Business 1900-1940 (Mildred Chrisman Coll), archives; State Politics in 1960s (Fred Harris Coll), archives; Wedel Collection, anthropological library
Publications: Great Plains Journal; MGP Record (Newsletter)
Restriction: Non-circulating to the public

LEONARD

S OKLAHOMA GEOLOGICAL SURVEY OBSERVATORY LIBRARY,* PO Box 8, 74043-0008. SAN 374-888X. Tel: 918-366-4152. FAX: 918-366-4156. Web Site: www.okgeosurvey1.gov.
Library Holdings: Bk Titles 400

MADILL

P MADILL CITY PUBLIC LIBRARY,* 205 E Overton St, 73446. SAN 313-9107. Tel: 580-795-2749. FAX: 580-795-2749. *Librn*, Susan Hale
Founded 1915. Pop 10,000; Circ 8,866
Library Holdings: Bk Vols 11,026
Friends of the Library Group

MANGUM

P MARGARET CARTER PUBLIC LIBRARY,* 203 W Lincoln, 73554. SAN 313-9115. Tel: 580-782-3185. FAX: 580-782-5308. E-Mail: manglib@intplsrv.net. *Librn*, Donna Norton; *Asst Librn*, Hettie Day
Circ 12,568
Library Holdings: Bk Titles 26,413; Per Subs 30
Friends of the Library Group

MARLOW

P MARLOW PUBLIC LIBRARY, 407 W Seminole, 73055. SAN 313-9123. Tel: 580-658-5354. FAX: 580-658-9110. E-Mail: marlowlc@starcomm.net. *Librn*, Lois Bannister; *Asst Librn*, Joyce Skelton; Staff 2 (Non-MLS 2)
Founded 1938. Pop 5,000; Circ 26,400
Jul 2000-Jun 2001 Income City $47,000. Mats Exp Books $6,000. Sal $34,000
Library Holdings: Bk Vols 12,000
Automation Activity & Vendor Info: (Circulation) Sagebrush Corporation
Friends of the Library Group

MAYSVILLE

P ELLIOTT LASATER MAYSVILLE PUBLIC LIBRARY,* 508 Williams St, PO Box 878, 73057. SAN 313-9719. Tel: 405-867-4748. FAX: 405-867-4748. *Librn*, Samantha Robb
Founded 1963. Pop 1,500
Library Holdings: Bk Vols 31,500; Bk Titles 31,000

MC ALESTER

P MCALESTER PUBLIC LIBRARY, 401 N Second St, 74501. SAN 313-9093. Tel: 918-426-0930. Toll Free Tel: 800-562-9520. FAX: 918-423-5731. E-Mail: mlibrary@icok.net, mplib@mcalester.lib.ok.us. Web Site: www.icok.net/~mlibrary. *Asst Librn*, Larry Miller; *Asst Librn*, Darlene Rising; *Ch Servs*, Anita Ross; *Ch Servs*, Betty Weeks; *Ref*, Christopher Elliott; *Circ*, Glenda Traux
Pop 40,524; Circ 122,805
Library Holdings: Bk Vols 75,000; Per Subs 115
Subject Interests: Okla hist
Special Collections: Local Coll (newspapers back to 1890's)
Publications: Book List; Library Journal; Publisher's Weekly; School Library Journal
Friends of the Library Group

S OKLAHOMA DEPARTMENT OF CORRECTIONS & THE OKLAHOMA DEPARTMENT OF LIBRARIES, State Penitentiary Library,* PO Box 97, 74501. SAN 357-5551. Tel: 918-423-4700. FAX: 918-423-3862. *Librn*, Lee Mann
Founded 1975
Library Holdings: Bk Vols 12,000; Per Subs 30
Subject Interests: All types of general non-fiction, Career guidance, Fiction, Law ref bks, Prisoners, Prisons, Vocational
Partic in Okla Teletype Info Serv
Branches:
L LAW LIBRARY STATE PENITENTIARY, PO Box 97, 74501. SAN 357-5586. Tel: 918-423-4700, Ext 130. *Librn*, Lee Mann
Library Holdings: Bk Titles 2,600; Per Subs 12
Subject Interests: About prisons, Bks by prisoners
Partic in Okla Teletype Info Serv

P SOUTHEASTERN PUBLIC LIBRARY SYSTEM OF OKLAHOMA, (SEPLSO), 401 N Second St, 74501. SAN 313-9085. Tel: 918-426-0456. FAX: 918-426-0543. *Exec Dir*, Wayne Hanway; E-Mail: whanway@sepl.lib.ok.us; *Tech Servs*, June Doyle; E-Mail: doyle@sepl.lib.ok.us; *ILL*, Ann McAfee; Staff 65 (MLS 2, Non-MLS 63)
Founded 1967. Pop 159,639; Circ 732,328
Jul 1999-Jun 2000 Income $2,444,896, State $151,955, Federal $26,000, County $2,151,949, Locally Generated Income $114,992. Mats Exp $315,101, Books $249,617, Per/Ser (Incl. Access Fees) $26,111, Micro $1,618, AV Equip $35,040, Electronic Ref Mat (Incl. Access Fees) $2,715. Sal $940,246
Library Holdings: Bk Vols 270,123; Bk Titles 241,394; Per Subs 554
Special Collections: All County Newspapers on Microfilm
Automation Activity & Vendor Info: (Acquisitions) SIRSI; (Cataloging) SIRSI; (Circulation) SIRSI; (OPAC) SIRSI; (Serials) SIRSI
Publications: Newsletter (bi-monthly)
Member Libraries: Arkoma Community Library; Broken Bow Public Library; Buckley Public Library; Choctaw County Library; Coalgate Public Library; Hartshorne Public Library; Heavener Public Library; Idabel Public Library; Spiro Public Library; Stigler Public Library; Talihina Public Library; Wister Public Library
Friends of the Library Group

MCALESTER

A UNITED STATES ARMY, John L Byrd, Jr Technical Library for Explosives Safety, Bldg 35, One C Tree Rd, 74501. SAN 375-0671. Tel: 918-420-8707. FAX: 918-420-8705. E-Mail: techlib@dac-emh2.army.mil. Web Site: www.dac.army.mil. *Librn*, Christine L Holiday; Tel: 918-420-8722, E-Mail: holiday@dac-emh2.army.mil; *Cat*, Blossom Hampton; Tel: 918-420-8707, E-Mail: hampton@dac-emh2.army.mil; Staff 4 (MLS 2, Non-MLS 2)
Founded 1989
Library Holdings: Bk Vols 268; Per Subs 35
Special Collections: Accident Reports; Archives Search Reports; Site Plans & Maps; World War II Ordinance Minutes
Automation Activity & Vendor Info: (OPAC) SIRSI
Database Vendor: OCLC - First Search
Partic in Fedlink

MEDFORD

P MEDFORD PUBLIC LIBRARY,* 123 S Main St, 73759. SAN 313-9131. Tel: 580-395-2801. FAX: 580-395-2342. *Dir*, Tomi Jill Rogers; *Librn*, Nancy Wilson; *Librn*, Sandra Harlen; *Librn*, Betty Lebeba
Founded 1933. Pop 5,000; Circ 11,883
Library Holdings: Bk Vols 11,000; Bk Titles 9,000; Per Subs 40

MIAMI

R FIRST BAPTIST CHURCH, Library-Media Center, First & A St SW, PO Box 1030, 74355. SAN 313-914X. Tel: 918-542-1691. FAX: 918-542-1753. *Dir*, Ruth Ann Farris; Staff 7 (MLS 1, Non-MLS 6)
Library Holdings: Bk Titles 5,400
Subject Interests: Christian life, Growth, Missions

P MIAMI PUBLIC LIBRARY, 200 N Main, 74354. SAN 313-9158. Tel: 918-541-2292. FAX: 918-542-9363. Web Site: www.miami.lib.ok.us. *Dir*, Joyce M Wallen; E-Mail: jwallen@miami.lib.ok.us; *Ad Servs*, Marsha Von Moss; *Ch Servs*, Connie Bradley; Staff 9 (MLS 1, Non-MLS 8)
Founded 1920. Pop 13,142; Circ 180,080
Jul 1999-Jun 2000 Income $303,169, State $6,518, City $260,588, Federal $759, Locally Generated Income $20,906, Other $14,398. Mats Exp $46,966, Books $35,711, Per/Ser (Incl. Access Fees) $5,160, Micro $560, AV Equip $5,535. Sal $199,797 (Prof $35,755)
Library Holdings: Bk Vols 47,782; Per Subs 146
Subject Interests: Genealogy, Indian hist, Oklahoma
Automation Activity & Vendor Info: (Circulation) Follett
Partic in Okla Telecommunications Interlibr Syst
Special Services for the Blind - Homebound delivery; Reading machine; Talking Books
Friends of the Library Group

J NORTHEASTERN OKLAHOMA A&M COLLEGE, Learning Resources Center,* 200 I NE, 74354. SAN 313-9166. Tel: 918-540-6250. FAX: 918-542-7065. Web Site: www.neoam.cc.ok.us. *Dir*, Charles T Bain; *Tech Servs*, Mary L Largent; *ILL, Ref*, William Pfannenstiel; Staff 10 (MLS 3, Non-MLS 7)
Founded 1925. Enrl 2,286; Fac 123
Jul 1997-Jun 1998 Income $575,000. Mats Exp $174,549, Books $66,485, Per/Ser (Incl. Access Fees) $43,485, AV Equip $64,579. Sal $220,285 (Prof $114,443)
Library Holdings: Bk Titles 76,000; Per Subs 476
Partic in Okla Telecommunications Interlibr Syst

MIDWEST CITY

J ROSE STATE COLLEGE, Learning Resources Center, 6420 SE 15th St, 73110. SAN 313-9174. Tel: 405-733-7323. Interlibrary Loan Service Tel: 405-736-0261. FAX: 405-736-0260. Web Site: www.rose.cc.ok.us/lrc.htm. *Dir*, James F Beavers; E-Mail: jfbeavers@ms.rose.cc.ok.us; *Head Librn*, Sharon Saulmon; E-Mail: ssaulmon@ms.rose.cc.ok.us; *ILL*, Alan Neitzel; E-Mail: aneitzel@ms.rose.cc.ok.us; *Acq*, Mary Kirk; E-Mail: mkirk@ms.rose.cc.ok.us; *Tech Servs*, Carolyn Hust; E-Mail: chust@ms.rose.cc.ok.us; *Ref*, Jeanie Cavett; E-Mail: jcavett@ms.rose.cc.ok.us; *Access Serv*, Melissa Huffman; E-Mail: mhuffman@ms.rose.cc.ok.us; Staff 10 (MLS 8, Non-MLS 2)
Founded 1970. Enrl 7,500; Fac 335; Highest Degree: Associate
Library Holdings: Bk Vols 90,375; Per Subs 425
Automation Activity & Vendor Info: (Circulation) VTLS
Database Vendor: Ebsco - EbscoHost, OCLC - First Search, Wilson - Wilson Web
Partic in OCLC Online Computer Library Center, Inc

MOORE

C HILLSDALE FREE WILL BAPTIST COLLEGE LIBRARY,* PO Box 7208, 73153-1208. SAN 313-9182. Tel: 405-912-9025. FAX: 405-912-9050. *Dir*, Nancy Draper; E-Mail: ndraper@hc.edu
Founded 1968. Enrl 180; Fac 30; Highest Degree: Bachelor
Jul 1997-Jun 1998 Income $66,000. Mats Exp $25,314, Books $11,449, Per/Ser (Incl. Access Fees) $6,039, Presv $25, Micro $876, AV Equip $216. Sal $37,723 (Prof $27,000)
Library Holdings: Bk Titles 19,000; Per Subs 350
Special Collections: Free Will Baptist Historical Coll

MOUNTAIN VIEW

P ADDIE DAVIS MEMORIAL LIBRARY,* 301 N Fourth St, PO Box 567, 73062-0356. SAN 372-6614. Tel: 580-347-2397. FAX: 580-347-2397. *Librn*, Gerri Roseberry
Founded 1983. Pop 1,086; Circ 4,360
Library Holdings: Bk Vols 6,472; Bk Titles 6,368; Per Subs 29

MULDROW

P MULDROW PUBLIC LIBRARY,* 711 W Shanntel Smith Blvd, 74948-0449. SAN 313-9190. Tel: 918-427-6703. FAX: 918-427-7315. *Dir*, Bethia Owens
Founded 1979
Library Holdings: Bk Vols 10,000; Per Subs 15
Subject Interests: Local history
Publications: Willison Library Bulletin
Mem of Eastern Oklahoma District Library System
Statistics included in library system
Friends of the Library Group

MUSKOGEE

J BACONE COLLEGE LIBRARY,* 2299 Old Bacone Rd, 74403. SAN 313-9204. Tel: 918-683-4581, Ext 263. FAX: 918-687-5913. *Dir, Librn*, Frances Donelson; Staff 2 (MLS 1, Non-MLS 1)
Founded 1880. Enrl 375; Fac 40
Library Holdings: Bk Vols 30,991; Per Subs 125
Subject Interests: Behav sci, Local history, Native Am studies, Nursing, Para-med, Soc sci

P EASTERN OKLAHOMA DISTRICT LIBRARY SYSTEM, 814 W Okmulgee, 74401-6839. SAN 313-9212. Tel: 918-683-2846. FAX: 918-683-0436. Web Site: www.eodls.lib.ok.us. *Exec Dir*, Marilyn L Hinshaw; Tel: 918-683-2846, Ext 234, E-Mail: mhinshaw@eok.lib.ok.us; *Asst Dir*, Mary J S Moroney; Tel: 918-683-2846, Ext 239, E-Mail: mmoroney@eodls.lib.ok.us; Staff 72 (MLS 7, Non-MLS 65)
Founded 1973. Pop 199,225; Circ 836,620
Jul 1999-Jun 2000 Income $3,286,534, State $196,712, Federal $17,794, County $2,590,081, Other $474,274. Mats Exp $577,870, Books $442,441, Per/Ser (Incl. Access Fees) $59,304, Micro $17,440, AV Equip $49,720, Electronic Ref Mat (Incl. Access Fees) $8,965. Sal $1,445,747 (Prof $64,000)
Library Holdings: Bk Vols 372,915; Bk Titles 175,204; Per Subs 772
Subject Interests: Early hist Indian Territory, Genealogy
Special Collections: Local History (Essa Gladney Coll), Tahlequah Branch; Native Americans & Early Oklahoma History (Grant Foreman Coll), Muskogee Branch
Automation Activity & Vendor Info: (Acquisitions) epixtech, inc.; (Cataloging) epixtech, inc.; (Circulation) epixtech, inc.; (ILL) epixtech, inc.; (OPAC) epixtech, inc.
Database Vendor: epixtech, inc., IAC - Info Trac, IAC - SearchBank, OCLC - First Search
Function: ILL available
Member Libraries: Delaware County Library; Eufaula Memorial Library; Grove Public Library; John F Henderson Public Library; Latimer County Public Library; Muldrow Public Library; Muskogee Public Library; Q B Boydstun Library; Rieger Memorial Library; Stanley Tubbs Memorial Library; Stilwell Public Library; Tahlequah Public Library; The Jim Lucas Checotah Public Library; Warner Public Library
Partic in OCLC Online Computer Library Center, Inc
Friends of the Library Group

S FIVE CIVILIZED TRIBES MUSEUM LIBRARY, (5CTM), Agency Hill on Honor Heights Dr, 74401. SAN 313-9220. Tel: 918-683-1701. FAX: 918-683-3070. Web Site: www.fivetribes.com. *Exec Dir*, Clara Reeke
Founded 1966
Library Holdings: Bk Vols 3,700
Special Collections: Indian Art (Largest Traditional Coll)
Restriction: By appointment only

L MUSKOGEE LAW LIBRARY ASSOCIATION,* Muskogee County Court House, 74401. SAN 313-9239. Tel: 918-682-7873. *In Charge*, Adaina Riley
Library Holdings: Bk Vols 10,000

P MUSKOGEE PUBLIC LIBRARY,* 801 W Okmulgee, 74401. SAN 313-9247. Tel: 918-682-6657. FAX: 918-682-9466. *Ref*, Karen Thomas; *Ref*, Wally Waites; *Circ*, Alice Moschak; Staff 3 (MLS 3)
Founded 1909. Pop 199,225; Circ 148,417
Library Holdings: Bk Vols 247,015; Per Subs 625
Special Collections: Local Hist (Grant Foreman Room)
Mem of Eastern Oklahoma District Library System
Friends of the Library Group

GM VA MEDICAL CENTER, (VAMC), Department of Veterans Affairs Library Service (142D), 1011 Honor Heights Dr, 74401. SAN 313-9263. Tel: 918-680-3754. FAX: 918-680-3752. E-Mail: jeanine.barrett@med.va.gov.; Staff 1 (MLS 1)
Founded 1946
Library Holdings: Bk Vols 6,847
Subject Interests: Allied health fields, Medicine, Nursing
Publications: Journal Holdings
Partic in Veterans Affairs Library Network
Branches:
M PATIENT EDUCATION & GENERAL LIBRARY Tel: 918-680-3752. FAX: 918-680-3752. E-Mail: jeanine.barrett@med.va.gov.
Library Holdings: Bk Vols 3,400
Special Collections: Persian Gulf War; Vietnam Veterans

NEWKIRK

P NEWKIRK PUBLIC LIBRARY,* W Seventh St, 74647-0204. SAN 313-9271. Tel: 580-362-1028. FAX: 580-362-3934. E-Mail: newkirk@ponacity.net. *Librn*, Sandra S Cline
Founded 1910. Pop 2,600; Circ 21,169
Library Holdings: Bk Vols 17,945; Bk Titles 18,000; Per Subs 33

NORMAN

M GRIFFIN MEMORIAL HOSPITAL, Professional Medical Research Library, 900 E Main St, 73071. (Mail add: PO Box 151, 73070-0150), SAN 313-928X. Tel: 405-321-4880. FAX: 405-573-6684. *Actg Librn, Admin Assoc*, Charlotte Jean Lewis; Tel: 405-321-4880, Ext 2141, E-Mail: jlewis@odmhsas. Subject Specialists: *Psychiatry*, Charlotte Jean Lewis; Staff 1 (Non-MLS 1)
Library Holdings: Bk Vols 6,000; Per Subs 50
Subject Interests: Psychiatry
Special Collections: Old Psychiatry Book Archive
Database Vendor: OCLC - First Search, Silverplatter Information Inc.
Restriction: Medical staff only
Function: Archival collection, For research purposes, ILL to other special libraries, Reference only, Research library, Some telephone reference
Friends of the Library Group

G NATIONAL OCEANIC & ATMOSPHERIC ADMINISTRATION, National Severe Storms Laboratory Library, 1313 Halley Circle, 73069. SAN 313-9298. Tel: 405-366-0421. FAX: 405-366-0472. *Librn*, Mary Meacham; E-Mail: mary.meacham@nssl.noaa.gov
Founded 1973
Oct 1999-Sep 2000 Income Federal $25,170. Mats Exp $24,922, Books $1,345, Per/Ser (Incl. Access Fees) $19,423, Presv $1,140, Other Print Mats $14, Electronic Ref Mat (Incl. Access Fees) $3,000. Sal $29,990
Library Holdings: Bk Vols 755; Bk Titles 750; Per Subs 35
Subject Interests: Atmospheric physics, Meteorology, Radar storm detection, Severe storms dynamics, Storm hazards to aircraft, Tornado studies
Database Vendor: Ebsco - EbscoHost

M NORMAN REGIONAL HOSPITAL, Health Sciences Library, 901 N Porter, PO Box 1308, 73070. SAN 313-9301. Tel: 405-307-1425. FAX: 405-307-1428. *Librn*, Michelynn McKnight; E-Mail: mmcknight@aardvark.ucs.ou.edu; Staff 3 (MLS 2, Non-MLS 1)
Founded 1973
Library Holdings: Bk Titles 2,000; Per Subs 150
Subject Interests: Allied health care prof, Medicine, Nursing
Database Vendor: OVID Technologies
Restriction: Staff use only

G OKLAHOMA DEPARTMENT OF WILDLIFE CONSERVATION, Fishery Research Laboratory Library, 500 E Constellation, 73072. SAN 325-0857. Tel: 405-325-7248, 405-325-7288. FAX: 405-325-7631. *Librn*, Sherylann Densow; Staff 1 (Non-MLS 1)
Founded 1949
Library Holdings: Bk Vols 300; Per Subs 20
Subject Interests: Freshwater fishery bio
Publications: Bulletin of the Oklahoma Fishery Research Laboratory

P PIONEER LIBRARY SYSTEM, 225 N Webster Ave, 73069-7133. SAN 357-5616. Tel: 405-701-2600. FAX: 405-701-2649. E-Mail: mary@pls.lib.ok.us. Web Site: www.pioneer.lib.ok.us. *Dir*, Mary Sherman; E-Mail: mary@pls.lib.ok.us; *Asst Dir*, Debra Engel; E-Mail: debra@pls.lib.ok.us; *Assoc Dir*, Andy Peters; E-Mail: andy@pls.lib.ok.us; *Business, Mgr*, Gwen Witherspoon; Tel: 405-701-2644, E-Mail: gwen@pls.lib.ok.us; *Coll Develop, Tech Servs*, Theresa Dickson; E-Mail: theresa@pls.lib.ok.us
Founded 1957. Pop 245,600; Circ 1,283,632
Jul 1999-Jun 2000 Income (Main Library and Branch Library) $4,465,672, State $165,312, County $4,097,326, Other $203,034. Mats Exp Books $699,972. Sal $2,885,629 (Prof $1,571,262)
Library Holdings: Bk Vols 315,519; Bk Titles 119,643
Special Collections: Oklahoma Coll
Automation Activity & Vendor Info: (Acquisitions) Brodart; (Circulation) epixtech, inc.

Publications: Opening Our Doors Manual; Pioneer Library System Annual Report; Pioneer Spirit (monthly system newsletter)
Partic in Amigos Library Services, Inc
Friends of the Library Group
Branches: 9
BLANCHARD PUBLIC, PO Box 614, Blanchard, 73010. SAN 357-5640. Tel: 405-485-2275. FAX: 405-485-9452. Web Site: www.pioneer.lib.ok.us. *Mgr*, Jane Kimbrough; E-Mail: janie@pls.lib.ok.us
Library Holdings: Bk Vols 11,561
Friends of the Library Group
MCLOUD PUBLIC LIBRARY, 113 N Main, McLoud, 74851. SAN 370-9019. Tel: 405-964-2960. FAX: 405-964-5389. Web Site: www.pioneer.lib.ok.us. *Business, Mgr*, Angie Woolbright; Tel: 405-701-2644, Fax: 405-701-2649, E-Mail: gwen@pls.lib.ok.us; *Branch Mgr*, Cindy Stevens; E-Mail: cindy@pls.lib.ok.us
Library Holdings: Bk Vols 5,275
Friends of the Library Group
MOORE PUBLIC, 225 S Howard, Moore, 73160. SAN 357-5675. Tel: 405-793-5100. FAX: 405-793-8755. Web Site: www.pioneer.lib.ok.us. *Mgr*, Elizabeth Romero
Library Holdings: Bk Vols 57,846
Friends of the Library Group
NEWCASTLE PUBLIC, 900 N Carr St, PO Box 780, Newcastle, 73065. SAN 357-5691. Tel: 405-387-5076. FAX: 405-387-5204. Web Site: www.pioneer.lib.ok.us. *Mgr*, Kathie Thomas; E-Mail: kathie@pls.lib.ok.us
Library Holdings: Bk Vols 12,648
Friends of the Library Group
NOBLE PUBLIC, 204 N Fifth St, Noble, 73068. SAN 328-7238. Tel: 405-872-5713. FAX: 405-872-8329. Web Site: www.pioneer.lib.ok.us. *Branch Mgr*, Caroline Dulworth; E-Mail: caroline@pls.lib.ok.us
Library Holdings: Bk Vols 22,172
Friends of the Library Group
NORMAN PUBLIC, 225 N Webster, 73069. SAN 357-5705. Tel: 405-701-2600. FAX: 405-701-2608. Web Site: www.pioneer.lib.ok.us. *Mgr*, Susan Gregory; E-Mail: susang@pls.lib.ok.us
Library Holdings: Bk Vols 112,126
Friends of the Library Group
PURCELL PUBLIC, 919 N Ninth, Purcell, 73080. SAN 357-573X. Tel: 405-527-5546. FAX: 405-527-7140. Web Site: www.pioneer.lib.ok.us. *Mgr*, Lisa Wells; E-Mail: lisa@pls.lib.ok.us
Library Holdings: Bk Vols 25,388
Friends of the Library Group
SHAWNEE PUBLIC, 101 N Philadelphia, Shawnee, 74801. SAN 357-5764. Tel: 405-275-6353. FAX: 405-273-0590. Web Site: www.pioneer.lib.ok.us. *Mgr*, Yvonne Hinchee; E-Mail: yvonne@pls.lib.ok.us
Library Holdings: Bk Vols 49,856
Friends of the Library Group
TECUMSEH PUBLIC, 114 N Broadway, Tecumseh, 74873. SAN 357-5799. Tel: 405-598-5955. FAX: 405-598-5416. Web Site: www.pioneer.lib.ok.us. *Mgr*, Jan Anthony; E-Mail: janthony@pls.lib.ok.us
Library Holdings: Bk Vols 15,141
Friends of the Library Group

C UNIVERSITY OF OKLAHOMA, University Libraries, 401 W Brooks, 73019. SAN 357-5829. Tel: 405-325-2611. Interlibrary Loan Service Tel: 405-325-6422. FAX: 405-325-7550. Web Site: www-lib.uoknor.edu. *Dean of Libr*, Sul H Lee; *Actg Dir, Publ Servs*, Don Dewitt; *Acq*, Starla Doescher; Tel: 405-325-2141; *Bibliog Instr*, Beverly Joyce; Tel: 405-325-4231; *Cat*, Katherine Wong; Tel: 405-325-4081; *Ref*, Kay Womack; Tel: 405-325-4231; *Dir, Tech Serv*, Pat Weaver-Meyers. Subject Specialists: *Business history*, Daniel Wren; *History of science*, Marilyn Ogilvie; Staff 36 (MLS 29, Non-MLS 7)
Founded 1895. Enrl 21,052; Highest Degree: Doctorate
Jul 1999-Jun 2000 Income (Main Library and Branch Library) $9,526,938. Mats Exp $5,564,324. Sal $3,162,045
Library Holdings: Bk Vols 3,702,754; Per Subs 11,316
Automation Activity & Vendor Info: (Circulation) SIRSI
Publications: Library Newsletter
Mem of Asn of Research Libraries
Partic in Amigos Library Services, Inc; OCLC Online Computer Library Center, Inc; Okla Telecommunications Interlibr Syst; Research Libraries Group, Inc
Departmental Libraries:
ARCHITECTURE, Gould Hall Lower Level, 73019. SAN 357-5853. Tel: 405-325-5521. FAX: 405-325-2943. *Tech Servs*, Tracy Chapman
Library Holdings: Bk Vols 20,248
BASS BUSINESS HISTORY COLLECTION, Rm 507 NW, 73019. SAN 357-5845. Tel: 405-325-3941. *Curator*, Daniel Wren
Library Holdings: Bk Vols 22,515
Subject Interests: Biographies, Bus, Economic history, Entrepreneurship, Labor hist, Numismatics, Transportation
CHEMISTRY-MATHEMATICS, Physical Sci 207, 73019. SAN 357-5918. Tel: 405-325-5628. FAX: 405-325-7650. *Librn*, Cecelia Brown
Library Holdings: Bk Vols 64,367
ENGINEERING, Felgar Hall 222, 73019. SAN 357-5977. Tel: 405-325-2941. FAX: 405-325-0345. *Librn*, Jimmie Lee
Library Holdings: Bk Vols 71,886
FINE ARTS, Catlett Music Ctr, 73019. SAN 357-5888. Tel: 405-325-6759. FAX: 405-325-4243. *Librn*, Susan Booker
Library Holdings: Bk Vols 76,413
Subject Interests: Art, Arts management, Dance, Music
Special Collections: Bixler files (clippings on theater, film, and dance)
GEOLOGY, Energy Ctr R220, 73019. SAN 357-6000. Tel: 405-325-6451. FAX: 405-325-6451. *Librn*, Claren Kidd
Library Holdings: Bk Vols 99,457
HISTORY OF SCIENCE COLLECTION, Rm 521 NW, 73019. SAN 357-5837. Tel: 405-325-2741. *Curator*, Marilyn Ogilvie
Library Holdings: Bk Vols 87,852
Subject Interests: Biological sci, Mathematical, Physical
Special Collections: Early Science, per; Histories of Sciences; Histories of Scientific Institutions; History of Science Journals; Science Biographies, Encyclopedias & Dictionaries; Textbooks & Popular Science Works
CL LAW LIBRARY, 300 Timberdell Rd, 73019. SAN 357-606X. Tel: 405-325-4311. FAX: 405-325-6282. Web Site: www.law.ou.edu. *Dir*, Alma N Singleton; *Tech Servs*, Marilyn Nicely; Staff 10 (MLS 10)
Founded 1909. Enrl 670; Fac 34; Highest Degree: Doctorate
Jul 1999-Jun 2000 Income $1,328,878. Mats Exp $760,286. Sal $445,335
Library Holdings: Bk Vols 192,082; Per Subs 4,517
Special Collections: Native Peoples Law
Publications: User's Guide
Partic in OCLC Online Computer Library Center, Inc; Westlaw
PHYSICS & ASTRONOMY, Nielson Hall 219, 73019. SAN 357-6078. Tel: 405-325-3962. FAX: 405-325-2887. *Tech Servs*, Kathryn Caldwell
Library Holdings: Bk Vols 36,442
WESTERN HISTORY COLLECTION, Monnet Hall 452, 73019. SAN 357-5861. Tel: 405-325-3641. FAX: 405-325-2943. *Curator*, Donald DeWitt
Library Holdings: Bk Vols 68,723
Special Collections: Alan W Farley Coll (history of Kansas and surrounding states, North American Indians, cattle trade, mining); collections of Indian Nation papers; congressional papers (48 congressmen); Doris Duke Coll (oral history of Oklahoma Indian tribes); Edward Everett Dale Coll (Western Americana); Fred P Schonwald Coll (North American Indians and Indian art); Helen Gahagan Douglas Coll (political speeches); Henry B Bass Coll (Abraham Lincoln and the Civil War); Indian Music Tapes Coll; Indian-Pioneer Papers (interviews with early day Indian, Black and White residents of Indian Territory and Oklahoma)

NOWATA

P NOWATA CITY-COUNTY LIBRARY,* 224 S Pine, PO Box 738, 74048. SAN 324-0002. Tel: 918-273-3363. FAX: 918-273-1818. *Librn*, Marilyn Biggerstaff; Staff 2 (MLS 2)
Founded 1966. Pop 9,992; Circ 16,484
1997-1998 Income $41,736. Mats Exp $9,920. Sal $27,000
Library Holdings: Bk Titles 23,080; Per Subs 40

OKEENE

P OKEENE PUBLIC LIBRARY,* 215 N Main, PO Box 706, 73763. SAN 313-9328. Tel: 580-822-3306. FAX: 580-822-3306. *Dir*, Alice Dotter; *Librn*, Rosemary Dixon; *Asst Librn*, Shelia Fisher
Founded 1934. Pop 1,500; Circ 2,000
Library Holdings: Bk Vols 4,000
Open Mon-Fri 2-5:30

OKLAHOMA CITY

L ANDREWS, DAVIS, LEGG, BIXLER, MILSTEN & PRICE, Law Library,* 500 W Main Ste 500, 73102. SAN 372-2228. Tel: 405-272-9241. FAX: 405-235-8786. *Librn*, Jan S Davis
Library Holdings: Bk Vols 12,000; Per Subs 50

M COLUMBIA PRESBYTERIAN HOSPITAL, Medical Library,* 700 NE 13th St, 73104. SAN 313-9603. Tel: 405-271-4266. FAX: 405-271-6897. *Dir*, Mary Lou Tremblay
Founded 1919
Library Holdings: Bk Vols 7,356; Bk Titles 3,700; Per Subs 140

M DEACONESS HOSPITAL, Library Resource Center,* 5501 N Portland, 73112-2097. SAN 313-9360. Tel: 405-946-5581, Ext 3308. *Librn*, Jean Burrows
Founded 1972
Library Holdings: Bk Titles 1,100; Per Subs 124
Subject Interests: Auxiliary health servs, Hospital administration, Medicine, Nursing
Partic in Docline; Medline

GM DEPARTMENT OF VETERANS AFFAIRS, Medical Center Library,* 921 NE 13th St 142D, 73104. SAN 313-9662. Tel: 405-270-0501, Ext 3688. FAX: 405-270-5145. *In Charge*, Sara Hill
Founded 1946
Library Holdings: Bk Vols 1,975; Per Subs 380

Subject Interests: Biomed
Special Collections: Patient Health Education
Publications: Library Notes
Partic in Vets Admin Libr Network
Open Mon-Fri 8-4:30

R EMANUEL SYNAGOGUE, William Davis Memorial Library, 900 NW 47th, 73118. SAN 313-9387. Tel: 405-528-2113. FAX: 405-528-2121. Web Site: www.ionet.net~emanuel/. *In Charge*, Nora Hood
Library Holdings: Bk Vols 2,500; Per Subs 10
Subject Interests: Hebrew, Judaica
Partic in Metronet

FEDERAL AVIATION ADMINISTRATION
S CIVIL AEROMEDICAL INSTITUTE LIBRARY, 6500 S MacArthur, AAM-400a, Rm 269, PO Box 25082, 73125. SAN 357-6213. Tel: 405-954-4398. FAX: 405-954-1010. Web Site: www.cami.jccbi.gov. *Librn*, Katherine Wade; E-Mail: kathy_wade@mmacmail.jccbi.gov
Library Holdings: Bk Vols 5,000; Per Subs 222
Subject Interests: Aviation med, Aviation psychol
Partic in Fedlink

S MIKE MONRONEY AERONAUTICAL CENTER LIBRARY, Academy Bldg, 6500 S MacArthur Blvd, 73169. (Mail add: AMI-100A, PO Box 25082, 73125), SAN 357-6183. Tel: 405-954-2665. FAX: 405-954-4742. Web Site: mmaclib.jccbi.gov. *Librn*, Virginia C Hughes; E-Mail: virginia_c_hughes@mmacmail.jccbi.gov; Staff 2 (MLS 1, Non-MLS 1)
Founded 1962
Library Holdings: Bk Vols 15,000; Per Subs 65
Subject Interests: Aviation, Education, Electronics, Management
Special Collections: Aviation, bks, microfiche; FAA Research Reports; NASA Research Reports, microfiche
Automation Activity & Vendor Info: (OPAC) EOS
Database Vendor: Dialog, OCLC - First Search
Publications: Brochure
Restriction: Open to public for reference only
Function: ILL available, Reference services available
Partic in Fedlink; OCLC Online Computer Library Center, Inc

M INTEGRIS BAPTIST MEDICAL CENTER, Wann Langston Memorial Library, 3300 Northwest Expressway, 73112. SAN 313-9352. Tel: 405-949-3766. FAX: 405-949-3883. *Librn*, Cheryl Suttles; E-Mail: suttcm@integris_health.com; *Asst Librn*, Dan Chandler; Staff 3 (MLS 2, Non-MLS 1)
Founded 1968
Library Holdings: Bk Vols 3,700; Bk Titles 3,100; Per Subs 400
Subject Interests: Bus, Geriatrics, Hospital administration, Medicine, Mgt, Nursing, Transplantation
Database Vendor: OVID Technologies
Partic in Metronet; National Network Of Libraries Of Medicine - South Central Region

M INTEGRIS SOUTHWEST MEDICAL CENTER, Scott Hendren Medical Library, 4401 S Western, 73109-3607. SAN 371-5507. Tel: 405-636-7087. FAX: 405-636-7660. *Head Librn*, Cheryl Suttles; *Asst Librn*, Sandy Palmer; Tel: 405-636-7437
Founded 1966
Library Holdings: Bk Titles 1,200; Per Subs 125
Subject Interests: Clinical medicine
Partic in Metronet

KERR-MCGEE CHEMICAL CORP
S TECHNICAL CENTER LIBRARY, 3301 NW 150th St, 73134. SAN 357-6272. Tel: 405-775-5620. FAX: 405-775-5632. *Mgr*, Virginia Phillips; E-Mail: vphillips@kmg.com; *Librn*, Vicki Vann; E-Mail: vvann@kmg.com
Founded 1964
Library Holdings: Bk Vols 12,500; Per Subs 110
Subject Interests: Chemical technology, Chemistry
Special Collections: Patent-Chemicals Coll, flm, microcard & paper; Rare Earth Coll, articles & rpt

S MACFEE & TAFT LAW OFFICES, Law Library, 2 Leadership Sq, 10th flr, 73102. SAN 326-5900. Tel: 405-235-9621. FAX: 405-235-0439. *Librn*, Patsy Trotter; E-Mail: patsy.trotter@mcafeetaft.com; Staff 1 (MLS 1)
Founded 1952
Library Holdings: Bk Vols 14,000; Per Subs 50
Subject Interests: Aviation, Banking, Bankruptcy, Corporate securities, Employee benefits, Environment, Intellectual property, Litigation, Real estate, Tax
Restriction: Staff use only
Partic in Westlaw

M MERCY HEALTH CENTER, Medical Library,* 4300 W Memorial Rd, 73120. SAN 329-8922. Tel: 405-752-3390. FAX: 405-752-3670. *Librn*, May Cordry; E-Mail: mcordry@okla.smhs.com
Jun 1998-Jul 1999 Mats Exp $49,000, Books $5,000, Per/Ser (Incl. Access Fees) $38,000, Electronic Ref Mat (Incl. Access Fees) $6,000. Sal $38,110
Library Holdings: Bk Vols 3,000; Per Subs 200
Subject Interests: Gynecology, Neurology, Oncology, Pain mgt
Publications: Mercy Medical News
Partic in Docline; First Search; Nat Libr of Med; OCLC Online Computer Library Center, Inc

P METROPOLITAN LIBRARY SYSTEM IN OKLAHOMA COUNTY, (MLS), 131 Dean A McGee Ave, 73102-6499. SAN 357-6302. Tel: 405-231-8635. FAX: 405-231-8638. Web Site: www.mls.lib.ok.us. *Exec Dir*, Norman Maas; *Dep Dir*, Donna Morris; *Info Tech*, Jim Welch; *Cat*, Pauline Rodriguez
Founded 1965. Pop 599,611; Circ 4,168,130
Jul 1998-Jun 1999 Income (Main Library and Branch Library) $15,480,071, State $333,109, County $14,086,219, Other $1,060,743. Mats Exp $2,071,942, Books $1,491,387, Per/Ser (Incl. Access Fees) $110,676, Micro $41,407, AV Equip $350,306, Other Print Mats $113,185, Electronic Ref Mat (Incl. Access Fees) $78,166. Sal $5,959,148
Library Holdings: Bk Vols 785,590; Bk Titles 151,468
Special Collections: Local Black History (Black Chronicles Coll), letters, clippings & memorabilia; Local History (Oklahoma Coll), bks & pictures
Publications: Ad Libs (bi-monthly system newsletter)
Partic in Amigos Library Services, Inc; BRS; Dialog Corporation; Metronet; Okla Telecommunications Interlibr Syst
Friends of the Library Group
Branches: 19
BELLE ISLE, 5501 N Villa, 73112-7164. SAN 357-6361. Tel: 405-843-9601. FAX: 405-843-4560. Web Site: www.mls.lib.ok.us. *Mgr*, Priscilla Doss
Friends of the Library Group
BETHANY BRANCH, 3510 N Mueller, Bethany, 73008-3952. SAN 357-6396. Tel: 405-789-8363. FAX: 405-789-5318. Web Site: www.mls.lib.ok.us. *Mgr*, Barbara Beasley
Friends of the Library Group
CAPITOL HILL, 334 SW 26, 73109-6711. SAN 357-6426. Tel: 405-634-6308. FAX: 405-631-0701. Web Site: www.mls.lib.ok.us. *Mgr*, Phil Tolber
Friends of the Library Group
CHOCTAW BRANCH, 14385 NE 23rd, Choctaw, 73020-9999. SAN 357-6663. Tel: 405-390-8418. FAX: 405-390-3536. Web Site: www.mls.lib.ok.us. *Mgr*, Rosemary Czarski
Friends of the Library Group
DEL CITY BRANCH, 4509 SE 15 St, Del City, 73115-3098. SAN 357-6450. Tel: 405-672-1377. FAX: 405-670-9668. Web Site: www.mls.lib.ok.us. *Mgr*, Katrina Prince
Friends of the Library Group
DOWNTOWN, 131 Dean A McGee Ave, 73102-6499. SAN 357-6337. Tel: 405-231-8650. FAX: 405-232-5493. Web Site: www.mls.lib.ok.us. *Mgr*, Debra Spindle
Friends of the Library Group
DREXEL EXTENSION, NW 16th & Drexel, 73107-9999. SAN 374-7379. Tel: 405-943-9149. FAX: 405-943-2534. Web Site: www.mls.lib.ok.us. *In Charge*, Ruth Butler
Friends of the Library Group
EDMOND BRANCH, 10 South Blvd, Edmond, 73034-3798. SAN 357-6515. Tel: 405-341-9282. FAX: 405-341-4848. Web Site: www.mls.lib.ok.us. *Mgr*, Karen Bays
Friends of the Library Group
RALPH ELLISON BRANCH, 2000 NE 23, 73111-3402. SAN 357-6485. Tel: 405-424-1437. FAX: 405-424-1443. Web Site: www.mls.lib.ok.us. *Mgr*, Denyvetta Davis
Friends of the Library Group
HARRAH EXTENSION, 1930 N Church Ave, Harrah, 73045-9085. SAN 327-9960. Tel: 405-454-2001. FAX: 405-454-0322. Web Site: www.mls.lib.ok.us.
Friends of the Library Group
JONES EXTENSION, 210 W Main, Jones, 73049-9999. SAN 374-7387. Tel: 405-399-5471. FAX: 405-399-3679. Web Site: www.mls.lib.ok.us. *In Charge*, Louisa Smith
Friends of the Library Group
LUTHER EXTENSION, 115 S Main, Luther, 73054-9999. SAN 374-7395. Tel: 405-277-9967. FAX: 405-277-9238. Web Site: www.mls.lib.ok.us. *In Charge*, Angela Paeltz
Friends of the Library Group
MIDWEST CITY BRANCH, 8143 E Reno, Midwest City, 73110-3999. SAN 357-654X. Tel: 405-732-4828. FAX: 405-733-4699. Web Site: www.mls.lib.ok.us. *Mgr*, Randy Wayland
Friends of the Library Group
NICOMA PARK EXTENSION, NE 23 & Nichols Rd, Nicoma Park, 73066-0250. SAN 357-6698. Tel: 405-769-9452. FAX: 405-769-4020. Web Site: www.mls.lib.ok.us. *In Charge*, Mary Mahan
Friends of the Library Group
SOUTHERN OAKS, 6900 S Walker, 73139-7299. SAN 357-6574. Tel: 405-631-4468. FAX: 405-634-9809. Web Site: www.mls.lib.ok.us. *Mgr*, Kay Bauman
Friends of the Library Group
SPENCER EXTENSION, 8310 1/2 NE 36th, 73084. SAN 374-7409. Tel: 405-771-4031. FAX: 405-771-5927. Web Site: www.mls.lib.ok.us. *In Charge*, Joyce Helms

Friends of the Library Group
VILLAGE, 10307 N Pennsylvania Ave, 73159. SAN 357-6604. Tel: 405-755-0710. FAX: 405-751-4881. Web Site: www.mls.lib.ok.us. *Mgr*, Lisa Weissenbuehler
Friends of the Library Group
WARR ACRES, 5901 NW 63, 73132-2401. SAN 357-6639. Tel: 405-721-2616. FAX: 405-721-1008. Web Site: www.mls.lib.ok.us. *Mgr*, Mary Patton
Friends of the Library Group
WRIGHT EXTENSION, 2101 Exchange Ave, 73108-2625. SAN 357-6728. Tel: 405-235-5035. FAX: 405-235-8938. Web Site: www.mls.lib.ok.us. *In Charge*, L Marie Nichols
Friends of the Library Group

CR MID-AMERICA BIBLE COLLEGE, Charles Ewing Brown Library, 3500 SW 119th St, 73170-9797. SAN 316-4438. Tel: 405-691-3800. FAX: 405-692-3172. E-Mail: ceblib@mabc.edu. Web Site: www.mabc.edu/library/. *Dir*, Linda Bollenbacher; E-Mail: lindab@mabc.edu; *Cat*, Elissa Laird; Tel: 405-691-3800, Ext 168; *Circ*, Anna L Schick; Tel: 405-691-3800, Ext 101; Staff 5 (MLS 2, Non-MLS 3)
Founded 1953. Enrl 650; Fac 20; Highest Degree: Bachelor
Library Holdings: Bk Titles 48,000; Per Subs 250; Spec Interest Per Sub 20
Subject Interests: Behav sci, Biblical studies, Bus (non-profit), Christian, Church ministries, English, Sacred music, Teacher educ
Special Collections: Archives of Church of God (Charles Ewing Brown Coll); Wesleyan Holiness Theology (Kenneth E Jones Coll)
Database Vendor: IAC - Info Trac, OCLC - First Search, Silverplatter Information Inc.
Partic in Metropolitan Libraries Network Of Central Oklahoma Inc; Onenet

S NATIONAL COWBOY & WESTERN HERITAGE MUSEUM, Donald C & Elizabeth M Dickinson Research Center, 1700 NE 63rd St, 73111. SAN 327-5655. Tel: 405-478-2250, Ext 273. Reference Tel: 405-478-2250, Ext 276. FAX: 405-478-6421. E-Mail: researchcenter@cowboyhalloffame.org. Web Site: www.cowboyhalloffame.org. *Dir*, Charles E Rand; E-Mail: cerand@cowboyhalloffame.org; *Asst Dir*, Jerri Stone; Staff 2 (MLS 1, Non-MLS 1)
Founded 1997
Library Holdings: Bk Titles 20,000; Per Subs 50
Subject Interests: Cowboys, Fine arts, Moving image arts, Native Americans, Ranching, Rodeos, Western art, Western hist
Special Collections: Photographic archives, over 110,000 images - primarily Rodeo
Database Vendor: epixtech, inc.

S NINETY-NINES INCORPORATED LIBRARY,* Will Rogers Airport, 7100 Terminal Dr, Box 965, 73159-0965. SAN 371-2303. Tel: 405-685-7969. FAX: 405-685-7985. E-Mail: lhq99s@cs.com. Web Site: www.ninety-nines.org. *Exec Dir*, Lu Hollander
Library Holdings: Bk Vols 850

S OKLAHOMA CITY ART MUSEUM LIBRARY, 3113 Pershing Blvd, 73107. SAN 373-109X. Tel: 405-946-4477. FAX: 405-946-7671. Web Site: www.okcartmuseum.com. *Dir*, Carolyn Hill
Library Holdings: Bk Vols 6,000

J OKLAHOMA CITY COMMUNITY COLLEGE LIBRARY, 7777 S May Ave, 73159. SAN 313-9646. Tel: 405-682-7564. FAX: 405-682-7585. Web Site: library.okc.cc.ok.us. *Dir*, Barbara King; *Tech Servs*, John Rosenhamer; *Publ Servs*, Jay Ramanjulu; *Coll Develop, Ref*, Rachel Butler; *Circ*, Helen Webbink; Staff 6 (MLS 6)
Founded 1972. Enrl 12,000; Fac 130
Library Holdings: Bk Vols 60,000; Per Subs 500
Subject Interests: Humanities, Nursing, Soc sci
Automation Activity & Vendor Info: (Cataloging) SIRSI; (OPAC) SIRSI; (Serials) SIRSI
Database Vendor: OCLC - First Search
Partic in Amigos Library Services, Inc; Dialog Corporation

OKLAHOMA CITY UNIVERSITY
C DULANEY-BROWNE LIBRARY, 2501 N Blackwelder, 73106. SAN 357-6752. Tel: 405-521-5065. FAX: 405-521-5291. *Dir*, Danelle Hall; E-Mail: dhall@frodo.okcu.edu; *Ref*, Edwin Wiles; *ILL*, Joyce Peterson; *Access Serv, ILL*, Retha Robertson; *Acq*, Carolyn Knight; *Ser*, John Heisch; *Circ*, Leslie Savage; *Doc*, Chariyar Nillpraphan; Staff 6 (MLS 6)
Founded 1904. Enrl 3,148; Fac 175; Highest Degree: Master
Jul 1999-Jun 2000 Income $830,115. Mats Exp $265,000, Books $125,000, Per/Ser (Incl. Access Fees) $140,000. Sal $574,663
Library Holdings: Bk Vols 208,604; Bk Titles 119,187; Per Subs 1,464
Special Collections: Alexander the Third & Chinese Communism, micro; Methodist History; Oklahoma History (George H Shirk History Center Coll); Russian Revolution Coll, micro
Partic in OCLC Online Computer Library Center, Inc
Friends of the Library Group
CL LAW LIBRARY, 2501 N Blackwelder, 73106. SAN 357-6787. Tel: 405-521-5271. FAX: 405-521-5172. Web Site: www.okcu.edu/~law/home.htm. *Librn*, Judith Morgan; E-Mail: jmorgan@okcu.edu; *Assoc Dir*, Patricia Monk; E-Mail: pmonk@okcu.edu; *Tech Servs*, Nancy A Cowden; E-Mail: ncowden@okcu.edu; Staff 8 (MLS 8)
Founded 1922. Enrl 522
Jul 1998-Jun 1999 Income $1,533,526. Mats Exp $846,828, Books $102,243, Per/Ser (Incl. Access Fees) $536,837, Micro $15,000. Sal $558,201 (Prof $316,727)
Library Holdings: Bk Vols 271,739; Bk Titles 67,749
Database Vendor: OCLC - First Search
Partic in Amigos Library Services, Inc; Mid-Am Law Sch Libr Consortium; OCLC Online Computer Library Center, Inc; Westlaw

S OKLAHOMA CITY ZOO, Zoological Library, 2101 NE 50th, 73111. SAN 321-1894. Tel: 405-424-3344, Ext 288, 405-425-0277. FAX: 405-425-0207, 405-425-0243. *Librn*, Amy Dee Smith
Founded 1970
2000-2001 Mats Exp $7,000, Books $5,000, Per/Ser (Incl. Access Fees) $2,000
Library Holdings: Bk Titles 4,000; Per Subs 45
Automation Activity & Vendor Info: (Circulation) Follett

S OKLAHOMA CORPORATION COMMISSION LAW LIBRARY,* Jim Thorpe Bldg, 2101 N Lincoln Blvd, Ste 400, PO Box 52000-2000, 73152-2000. SAN 313-9476. Tel: 405-521-2255. FAX: 405-521-4150. *In Charge*, Kent Talbot
Library Holdings: Bk Vols 8,000

GL OKLAHOMA COUNTY LAW LIBRARY, 321 Park Ave, Rm 247, 73102-3695. SAN 313-9484. Tel: 405-713-1353. FAX: 405-713-1852. *Acq, Dir, Ref*, Venita L Hoover; E-Mail: venhoo@oklahomacounty.org; Staff 1 (MLS 1)
Library Holdings: Bk Vols 33,000; Per Subs 25

G OKLAHOMA DEPARTMENT OF HUMAN SERVICES, Resource Center, 114 NE 31st St, 73105. SAN 313-9506. Tel: 405-962-1717. FAX: 405-524-9633. *Librn*, Mary Gail Foster; E-Mail: Mary.Foster@okdhs.org; Staff 1 (MLS 1)
Founded 1966
Library Holdings: Bk Vols 8,943; Bk Titles 6,946; Per Subs 140; Spec Interest Per Sub 100
Special Collections: History of Oklahoma Department of Human Services (Welfare Department); Social Work Materials
Publications: Departmental publications & flyers
Restriction: Staff use only
Function: Referrals accepted

P OKLAHOMA DEPARTMENT OF LIBRARIES, 200 NE 18th St, 73105. SAN 313-9514. Tel: 405-521-2502. Circulation Tel: 405-522-3641. Reference Tel: 405-522-3505. Toll Free Tel: 800-522-8116. FAX: 405-525-7804. Web Site: www.odl.state.ok.us. *Dir*, Susan McVey; E-Mail: smcvey@oltn.odl.state.ok.us; *Mgr Libr Serv*, Susan Gilley; E-Mail: sgilley@oltn.odl.state.ok.us; *Librn*, Kitty Pittman; E-Mail: kpittman@oltn.odl.state.ok.us; *Syst Coordr*, Mike Adams; E-Mail: madams@oltn.odl.state.ok.us; *Doc*, Steve Beleu; E-Mail: sbeleu@oltn.odl.state.ok.us; *Tech Servs*, Freda Chen; E-Mail: fehen@oltn.odl.state.ok.us; *ILL, Publ Servs*, Mary Hardin; E-Mail: mhardin@oltn.odl.state.ok.us; *Ref*, Marilyn Jacobs; E-Mail: mjacobs@oltn.odl.state.ok.us; *Archivist*, Tom Kremm; E-Mail: tkremm@oltn.odl.state.ok.us; *Ch Servs*, Donna Norvell; E-Mail: dnorvell@oltn.odl.state.ok.us; *Govt Doc*, Vicki Sullivan; E-Mail: vsullivan@oltn.odl.state.ok.us; *Pub Relations*, Bill Young; E-Mail: byoung@oltn.odl.state.ok.us. Subject Specialists: *Law*, Susan Gilley; *Legis ref*, Susan Gilley; *Technology*, Mike Adams; Staff 110 (MLS 26, Non-MLS 84)
Founded 1890
Library Holdings: Bk Vols 326,909; Per Subs 2,227
Subject Interests: Law
Special Collections: Oklahoma Coll
Automation Activity & Vendor Info: (Acquisitions) Endeavor; (Cataloging) Endeavor; (Circulation) Endeavor; (ILL) Endeavor; (Serials) Endeavor
Database Vendor: Dialog, Ebsco - EbscoHost, GaleNet, IAC - Info Trac, IAC - SearchBank, Lexis-Nexis, OCLC - First Search, Silverplatter Information Inc.
Publications: Annual Directory of Oklahoma Libraries; Annual Report of Oklahoma Libraries; Governors of Oklahoma; Oklahoma Almanac; Oklahoma Government Publications; Oklahoma State Agencies, Boards, Commissions, Courts, Institutions, Legislature & Officers; Who's Who in the Oklahoma Legislature
Function: Archival collection
Partic in OCLC Online Computer Library Center, Inc

OKLAHOMA HISTORICAL SOCIETY
S ARCHIVES & MANUSCRIPTS DIVISION, Historical Bldg, 2100 N Lincoln Blvd, 73105-4997. SAN 357-6825. Tel: 405-522-5206, 405-522-5209. Reference Tel: 405-522-5209. FAX: 405-521-2492. E-Mail: mrarchives@ok-history.mus.ok.us. Web Site: www.ok-history.mus.ok.us. *Archivist, Dir*, William D Welge; *Archivist*, Chester Cowen; Tel: 405-225-5208; *Tech Servs*, Phyllis Adams. Subject Specialists: *Indian*, William D Welge; *Photos*, Chester Cowen
Founded 1893
Jul 1999-Jun 2000 Income $400,000, State $110,000, Locally Generated

Income $172,000. Mats Exp $5,100, Books $2,500, Per/Ser (Incl. Access Fees) $600, AV Equip $2,000. Sal $404,600 (Prof $210,680)
Library Holdings: Bk Vols 8,000
Subject Interests: 65 Indian tribes of Okla, Hist of Okla, SW
Special Collections: Alice Robertson Papers; Barde Coll; David L Payne Papers; Emmett Starr's Manuscripts; Frederic B Severs Papers; Grant Foreman Papers; Indian-Pioneer History; Oklahoma Photograph Coll; Robert L Williams Papers; Whipple Coll, bks, mss, photogs

S DIVISION OF LIBRARY RESOURCES, Wiley Post Historical Bldg, 2100 N Lincoln Blvd, 73105-4997. SAN 357-6817. Tel: 405-521-2491, 405-522-5221, 405-522-5225. FAX: 405-521-2492. E-Mail: libohs@ok_history.mus.ok.us. Web Site: www.ok-history.mus.ok.us. *Dir*, Edward Connie Shoemaker; *Publ Servs*, Fred S Standley; Staff 9 (MLS 2, Non-MLS 7)
Founded 1893
Library Holdings: Bk Vols 66,000; Per Subs 218
Subject Interests: Genealogy, Native Am studies
Special Collections: Early Oklahoma College Yearbooks; Sandborn Fire Insurance maps for Oklahoma
Database Vendor: OCLC - First Search
Publications: Family Histories: A Bibliography of the Collections in the Oklahoma Historical Society (1992); Five Civilized Tribes: A Bibliography (1991); Library Resources Division Brochure; Oklahoma Cemeteries: A Bibliography (1993); Oklahoma History: A Bibliography (1991)
Restriction: Not a lending library
Function: Reference only, Research library
Partic in Amigos Library Services, Inc; OCLC Online Computer Library Center, Inc
Open Mon 9-8, Tues-Sat 9-5

S NEWSPAPER LIBRARY, 2100 N Lincoln, 73105. SAN 357-6841. Tel: 405-522-5210. FAX: 405-521-2492.
Founded 1957
Subject Interests: Okla newsp from before statehood to present day
Income for Newspaper Library is included in the listing for the Archives & Manuscripts Division

P OKLAHOMA LIBRARY FOR THE BLIND & PHYSICALLY HANDICAPPED,* 300 NE 18th St, 73105. SAN 313-9549. Tel: 405-521-3514. Toll Free Tel: 800-523-0288. TDD: 405-521-4672. FAX: 405-521-4582. E-Mail: olbph@oltn.odl.state.ok.us. Web Site: www.state.ok.us/~library. *Dir*, Geraldine Adams; *Librn*, Julia Alderson; *Librn*, Linda Boyd; *Librn, Online Servs*, David Slemmons; *Librn*, Mary Huffman
Founded 1933
Special Collections: Oklahoma History & Oklahoma Authors
Publications: Bright Future (quarterly in large print)
Special Services for the Deaf - TDD
Friends of the Library Group

S OKLAHOMA WATER RESOURCES BOARD LIBRARY, 3800 N Classen Blvd, 73118. SAN 313-959X. Tel: 405-530-8800. FAX: 530-8900.
Library Holdings: Bk Vols 5,500; Per Subs 25
Subject Interests: Dam safety, Floodplain mgt, Geology, Groundwater, Surface water, Water resources, Water resources planning

S OMNIPLEX SCIENCE MUSEUM, Education Library,* 2100 NE 52nd St, 73111. SAN 375-3069. Tel: 405-602-6664. FAX: 405-602-3768. *Exec Dir*, Chuck Schillings
Library Holdings: Bk Titles 300

J OSU-OKC LIBRARY,* 900 N Portland, 73107-6187. SAN 313-9581. Tel: 405-945-3251. FAX: 405-945-3289. Web Site: www.osuokc.edu/library.html, www.osuokc.edu/library/home.htm. *Asst Dir*, Elaine Warner; Staff 3 (MLS 3)
Founded 1961. Enrl 4,000; Fac 58
Library Holdings: Bk Vols 14,000; Per Subs 245
Subject Interests: Fire, Horticulture, Nursing, Police
Automation Activity & Vendor Info: (Circulation) Follett
Publications: Periodical list
Partic in Dialog Corporation; OCLC Online Computer Library Center, Inc
Friends of the Library Group

L PHILLIPS, MCFALL, MCCAFFREY, MCVAY & MURRAH PC, Law Library, One Leadership Sq 12th flr, 211 N Robinson, 73102. SAN 372-2120. Tel: 405-235-4100. FAX: 405-235-4133. *Librn*, Kathy Schmidt
Library Holdings: Bk Vols 3,000; Per Subs 15

M SAINT ANTHONY HOSPITAL, O'Donoghue Medical Library, 1000 N Lee St, PO Box 205, 73102. SAN 313-9611. Tel: 405-272-6285. FAX: 405-272-7075. *Librn*, Sharon Jorski
Founded 1950
Library Holdings: Bk Vols 8,000; Per Subs 178
Subject Interests: Cardiology, Dentistry, Health care, Neurology, Nursing, Orthopedics, Psychiatry
Partic in S Cent Regional Med Libr Program

SR SAINT LUKE'S UNITED METHODIST CHURCH LIBRARY, 222 NW 15th St, 73103. SAN 313-9638. Tel: 405-232-1371. FAX: 405-239-7095.
Founded 1962
Library Holdings: Bk Vols 6,000; Bk Titles 4,100
Subject Interests: Religion

G US COURTS LIBRARY, 2305 US Courthouse, 200 NW Fourth, 73102. SAN 374-6038. Tel: 405-231-4967. FAX: 405-231-5921. *Librn*, Jerry E Stephens; E-Mail: jerry_stephens@ca10.uscourts.gov; *Tech Servs*, Sheila Camp; Staff 2 (MLS 1, Non-MLS 1)
Founded 1990
Library Holdings: Bk Vols 20,000; Bk Titles 1,020; Per Subs 300
Subject Interests: Law
Restriction: Open to public for reference only

CM UNIVERSITY OF OKLAHOMA HEALTH SCIENCES CENTER, Robert M Bird Health Sciences Library, 1000 Stanton L Young Blvd, 73190-3046. (Mail add: PO Box 26901, 73190-3046), SAN 357-6876. Tel: 405-271-2285 Reference Tel: 405-271-2285, Ext 48752. FAX: 405-271-2285. Web Site: library.ouhsc.edu. *Dir*, Clinton M Thompson; Fax: 405-271-6186, E-Mail: marty-thompson@ouhsc.edu; *Automation Syst Coordr*, Joy Summers-Ables; Tel: 405-271-2285, Ext 48755, Fax: 405-271-6186, E-Mail: joy-summers-ables@ouhsc.edu; *Bibliogr*, Shari Clifton; Tel: 406-271-2285, Ext 48752, Fax: 405-271-3297, E-Mail: shari-clifton@ouhsc.edu; *Cat*, Jack Wagner; Tel: 405-271-2285, Ext 48758, Fax: 405-271-3297, E-Mail: jack-wagner@ouhsc.edu; *Circ*, Jennifer Goodson; Tel: 405-271-2285, Ext 48755, Fax: 405-271-6186, E-Mail: jennifer-goodson@ouhsc.edu; *Ser*, Judy Wilkerson; Tel: 405-271-2285, Ext 48756, Fax: 405-271-3297, E-Mail: judy-wilkerson@ouhsc.edu; Staff 35 (MLS 8, Non-MLS 27)
Founded 1928. Enrl 3,000; Fac 876; Highest Degree: Doctorate
Jul 1999-Jun 2000 Income State $2,400,000. Mats Exp $1,008,000, Books $46,000, Per/Ser (Incl. Access Fees) $875,000, Electronic Ref Mat (Incl. Access Fees) $87,000. Sal $843,193 (Prof $440,808)
Library Holdings: Bk Vols 280,463; Bk Titles 112,000; Per Subs 2,071
Subject Interests: Allied health, Dentistry, Health, Medicine, Nursing, Pharmacy, Public health
Special Collections: American Indian Health Coll; Medical History Coll; Rare Books
Automation Activity & Vendor Info: (Acquisitions) SIRSI; (Cataloging) SIRSI; (Circulation) SIRSI; (Course Reserve) SIRSI; (OPAC) SIRSI; (Serials) SIRSI
Database Vendor: Dialog, GaleNet, IAC - Info Trac, OCLC - First Search, OVID Technologies
Function: ILL available
Partic in National Network of Libraries of Medicine - Greater Midwest Region; OCLC Online Computer Library Center, Inc; Okla Telecommunications Interlibr Syst; S Cent Regional Med Libr Program
Friends of the Library Group

S WESTERNERS INTERNATIONAL LIBRARY,* 1700 NE 63rd St, 73111. SAN 328-1310. Tel: 405-478-8408, 405-721-2250. Toll Free Tel: 800-541-4650. *Curator*, Donald Reeves
Library Holdings: Bk Vols 500; Per Subs 10

R WESTMINSTER PRESBYTERIAN CHURCH LIBRARY, 4400 N Shartel, 73118-6499. SAN 313-9689. Tel: 405-524-2204. FAX: 405-524-4740. E-Mail: wstchrch@aol.com. Web Site: www.westminster-okc.org. *Librn*, June White
Founded 1946
Library Holdings: Bk Vols 1,350
Subject Interests: Theology

OKMULGEE

S CREEK INDIAN MEMORIAL ASSOCIATION, Creek Council House Museum,* Town Sq, 106 W Sixth St, 74447. SAN 320-8699. Tel: 918-756-2324. FAX: 918-756-3671. *Dir*, Debbie Martin
Founded 1930
Library Holdings: Bk Titles 500

J OKLAHOMA STATE UNIVERSITY, Okmulgee Library, 1801 E Fourth, 74447-0088. SAN 313-9697. Tel: 918-293-4678. FAX: 918-293-4628. Web Site: www.osu-okmulgee.edu/lib.htm. *Librn*, Rebecca Kirkbride; E-Mail: bkirk@osu-okmulgee.edu; Staff 1 (MLS 1)
Founded 1947. Enrl 1,843; Fac 118
Library Holdings: Bk Vols 10,925; Per Subs 499
Subject Interests: Vocational-technical
Partic in Amigos Library Services, Inc

P OKMULGEE PUBLIC LIBRARY,* 218 S Okmulgee Ave, 74447. SAN 313-9700. Tel: 918-756-1448. FAX: 918-758-1148. E-Mail: okmulib@ocevnet.org. *Dir*, Robert Finch; *Asst Dir*, Betty A Himes; *Ch Servs*, Kelly Beam; Staff 2 (MLS 2)
Founded 1907. Pop 15,000; Circ 125,600
Jul 1998-Jun 1999 Income $323,700, State $7,000, City $316,700. Mats Exp $42,000, Books $35,000, Per/Ser (Incl. Access Fees) $6,500, Micro $200. Sal $131,000
Library Holdings: Bk Vols 63,000; Per Subs 150
Subject Interests: Creek Indians, Okla hist
Automation Activity & Vendor Info: (Cataloging) epixtech, inc.; (Circulation) epixtech, inc.
Publications: Index to Okmulge Daily Times Obituaries 1970-
Friends of the Library Group

AWHUSKA

PAWHUSKA PUBLIC LIBRARY,* 301 E Sixth St, 74056. SAN 313-9735. Tel: 918-287-3989. FAX: 918-287-3989. *Dir*, Edna C Conley
Founded 1924. Pop 3,800; Circ 61,243
Library Holdings: Bk Vols 28,834
Special Collections: audio cassettes & videos; Genealogy Coll; Newspapers, microfilm; Osage Indian Coll; United States Census, microfilm
Publications: Library Brochure

AWNEE

PAWNEE PUBLIC LIBRARY,* 413 Illinois St, 74058. SAN 313-9743. Tel: 918-762-2138. *Librn*, Kathy Barnes
Founded 1936. Pop 2,443; Circ 5,671
Library Holdings: Bk Titles 6,000
Special Collections: Talking Books for the Blind & Handicapped
Friends of the Library Group

ERKINS

THOMAS WILHITE MEMORIAL LIBRARY, 129 S Main St, PO Box 519, 74059. SAN 313-9751. Tel: 405-547-5185. Toll Free Tel: 888-525-4654. FAX: 405-547-5185. E-Mail: perkinspubliclibrary@provalue.net. *Librn*, Barbara Ahring; *Asst Librn*, Carlletta Brown; Staff 2 (MLS 2)
Founded 1954. Pop 4,000; Circ 15,122
1998-1999 Income City $8,000. Mats Exp $29,753, Books $2,932, AV Equip $40, Other Print Mats $4,079. Sal $19,500
Library Holdings: Bk Vols 12,000; Bk Titles 11,000
Subject Interests: Christian fiction, Frontier, Oklahoma, Pioneer life
Special Collections: Frontier Coll; Oklahoma Coll; Will Rogers Coll, bks
Automation Activity & Vendor Info: (Cataloging) Follett; (Circulation) Follett
Special Services for the Deaf - High interest/low vocabulary books
Friends of the Library Group

ERRY

PERRY CARNEGIE LIBRARY, 302 N Seventh St, 73077. SAN 313-976X. Tel: 580-336-4721. FAX: 580-336-5497. *Librn*, Karen Bigbee; *Ch Servs*, Trudie O'Connor; Staff 1 (MLS 1)
Founded 1909. Pop 5,000; Circ 30,000
Jul 1999-Jun 2000 Income $158,850, State $4,600, City $132,500, Locally Generated Income $21,750. Mats Exp $112,300, Books $12,600, Per/Ser (Incl. Access Fees) $1,150. Sal $79,250
Library Holdings: Bk Vols 24,000; Per Subs 40
Automation Activity & Vendor Info: (Cataloging) Sagebrush Corporation; (Circulation) Sagebrush Corporation

PONCA CITY

CONOCO INCORPORATED, TECHNOLOGY, Technical Information Center,* 1000 S Pine St, PO Box 1267, 74602-1267. SAN 313-9778. Tel: 580-767-2334. Interlibrary Loan Service Tel: 580-767-2587. FAX: 580-767-4014. *Chief Librn*, Debra McConaghy
Founded 1950
Library Holdings: Bk Titles 10,000; Per Subs 200
Subject Interests: Chemistry, Coal, Engineering, Mineralogy, Petroleum
Restriction: By appointment only
Partic in Dialog Corporation; Nat Libr of Med; SDC Search Serv

S CULTURAL CENTER MUSEUM LIBRARY,* 1000 E Grand, 74601. SAN 320-4162. Tel: 580-767-0427. FAX: 580-767-0344.
Founded 1967
Library Holdings: Bk Titles 200; Per Subs 15
Subject Interests: American cowboy, American Indian, Anthropology, Archaeology, Crafts, Indian arts, Museology
Special Collections: 101 Ranch Coll, photog; Osage Fingerweaving Coll, slides, bks; Ponca Indian Music, phono rec, audio tapes

P PONCA CITY LIBRARY,* 515 E Grand, 74601. SAN 313-9786. Tel: 580-767-0345. FAX: 580-767-0377. *Dir*, Holly La Bossiere; *Ad Servs*, Julie Rutter; *Ch Servs*, Julianne Johnson; Staff 3 (MLS 3)
Founded 1904. Pop 30,000; Circ 221,896
Jul 1997-Jun 1998 Income $631,000
Library Holdings: Bk Vols 75,000; Per Subs 264
Subject Interests: Genealogy
Special Collections: Oriental & 20th Century Western Paintings (Matzene Art Coll)
Automation Activity & Vendor Info: (Acquisitions) SIRSI
Partic in Amigos Library Services, Inc; OCLC Online Computer Library Center, Inc; OLTN
Friends of the Library Group

POND CREEK

P POND CREEK CITY LIBRARY,* 105 S Second, 73766. (Mail add: PO Box 6, 73766), SAN 323-4711. Tel: 580-532-6319. *Librn*, Ruby Williams
Founded 1934. Pop 1,050
Library Holdings: Bk Vols 10,000; Bk Titles 9,750; Per Subs 17
Special Services for the Deaf - Books on deafness & sign language; High interest/low vocabulary books

POTEAU

P BUCKLEY PUBLIC LIBRARY, 408 Dewey Ave, 74953. SAN 313-9794. Tel: 918-647-3833, 918-647-4444. FAX: 918-647-8910. Web Site: www.buckley.lib.ok.us. *Librn*, Elizabeth Neff
Pop 8,500; Circ 120,244
Library Holdings: Bk Vols 30,000; Per Subs 60
Subject Interests: Genealogy, Literacy
Mem of Southeastern Public Library System Of Oklahoma
Friends of the Library Group

J CARL ALBERT STATE COLLEGE, Joe E White Library, 1507 S McKenna, 74953. SAN 313-9808. Tel: 918-647-1310. FAX: 918-647-1314. E-Mail: kaneurohr@casc.cc.ok.us. Web Site: www.casc.library.net. *Dir*, Karen Neurohr; Staff 1 (MLS 1)
Founded 1934. Enrl 1,254; Fac 69
Jul 2000-Jun 2001 Income $244,118. Mats Exp $96,680. Sal $116,288
Library Holdings: Bk Vols 25,037; Per Subs 97
Automation Activity & Vendor Info: (Cataloging) SIRSI; (Circulation) SIRSI; (Course Reserve) SIRSI; (OPAC) SIRSI
Database Vendor: IAC - Info Trac, OCLC - First Search, Silverplatter Information Inc.
Partic in Amigos Library Services, Inc; OCLC Online Computer Library Center, Inc

PRAGUE

P PRAGUE PUBLIC LIBRARY,* 1115 Jim Thorpe Blvd, 74864. SAN 313-9824. Tel: 405-567-4013. FAX: 405-567-4013. E-Mail: praguepl@chickasaw.com. *Librn*, Norma Kelly; *Asst Librn*, Lorraine Stone
Circ 16,675
Library Holdings: Bk Vols 14,982

PRYOR

P PRYOR PUBLIC LIBRARY, 505 E Graham, 74361. SAN 313-9832. Tel: 918-825-0777. FAX: 918-825-0856. E-Mail: pcl-@pryor.k12.ok.us. *Librn*, David Johansson; *Ad Servs*, Donna St John; *Ad Servs*, Sandra Hixson; *Ad Servs*, Joan Cobler; *Ch Servs*, Betty Vevers
Founded 1939. Pop 32,000; Circ 103,063
Library Holdings: Bk Titles 30,000; Per Subs 124
Subject Interests: History
Special Collections: Autographs of United States Presidents (Harrison Coll), letters; Civil War; Genealogy
Friends of the Library Group

RINGLING

P GLEASON MEMORIAL LIBRARY,* 101 E Main St, PO Box 585, 73456. SAN 377-5666. Tel: 580-662-2925. FAX: 580-662-2925. *Librn*, Diane McCornack
Library Holdings: Bk Titles 6,000
Friends of the Library Group

RUSH SPRINGS

P GLOVER SPENCER MEMORIAL LIBRARY,* Sixth & Blakely, PO Box 576, 73082. SAN 313-9840. Tel: 580-476-2108. FAX: 580-476-2108. *Librn*, Almata Lindsey
Pop 1,500; Circ 7,440
Library Holdings: Bk Vols 8,000; Per Subs 6
Friends of the Library Group

SALLISAW

P STANLEY TUBBS MEMORIAL LIBRARY,* 101 E Cherokee, 74955. SAN 313-9859. Tel: 918-775-4481. FAX: 918-775-4129. E-Mail: sallisawlib@inet.net. *Librn*, *Mgr*, Ollie J Grosclaude; Staff 5 (Non-MLS 5)
Founded 1967. Pop 8,000
Jul 1999-Jun 2000 Income $159,220, State $17,841, City $15,000, County $117,190, Locally Generated Income $9,189
Library Holdings: Bk Vols 34,000
Automation Activity & Vendor Info: (Acquisitions) epixtech, inc.; (Cataloging) epixtech, inc.; (Circulation) epixtech, inc.
Mem of Eastern Oklahoma District Library System

SAPULPA

P SAPULPA PUBLIC LIBRARY,* 27 W Dewey, 74066. SAN 313-9875. Tel: 918-224-5624. FAX: 918-224-3546. *Dir*, Mary A Sage; *Asst Dir*, Edith Bullock; *Circ*, Bessie Krajicek; *Ch Servs*, Anita Sutrick; *Doc*, Loy Sunday; *Assoc Librn*, Karen Skaggs; Staff 1 (MLS 1)
Founded 1917. Pop 18,000
Jul 1997-Jun 1998 Income $192,807. Mats Exp $181,676
Library Holdings: Bk Vols 52,226; Bk Titles 52,000; Per Subs 59
Special Collections: Indians of North America Coll; Oklahoma Coll; Sylvia Welch Genealogical Library Coll, bks & micro
Friends of the Library Group

SAYRE

P SAYRE PUBLIC LIBRARY,* 113 E Poplar, 73662. SAN 329-8043. Tel: 580-928-2641. Toll Free Tel: 888-363-9678. FAX: 580-928-1189. E-Mail: sayrepl1@sayre.lib.ok.us. Web Site: www.sayre.lib.ok.us. *Dir*, Stacy L Akins
Founded 1921. Pop 2,881; Circ 7,500
Jul 1998-Jun 1999 Income $36,222, State $7,220, City $20,502, Federal $7,502, Other $1,000. Mats Exp $20,700, Books $3,091, Per/Ser (Incl. Access Fees) $205, Micro $66, AV Equip $7,885, Electronic Ref Mat (Incl. Access Fees) $9,653. Sal $14,402
Library Holdings: Bk Vols 7,239; Bk Titles 7,500
Special Collections: Genealogical Research (1900-present); Local Newspapers for Sayre Journal & Sayre Record, 1901-Present, microfilm; Sayre Record, microfilm
Automation Activity & Vendor Info: (Cataloging) Follett; (Circulation) Follett; (OPAC) Follett
Database Vendor: IAC - Info Trac, IAC - SearchBank, OCLC - First Search
Function: ILL available
Friends of the Library Group

J SOUTHWESTERN OKLAHOMA STATE UNIVERSITY AT SAYRE LIBRARY, 409 E Mississippi, 73662. Tel: 580-928-5533. FAX: 580-928-5533. Web Site: www.swosu.edu. *Librn*, Janice Hodge; Staff 2 (Non-MLS 2)
Founded 1971. Enrl 462; Fac 18; Highest Degree: Associate
Jul 2000-Jun 2001 Income $18,000
Library Holdings: Bk Titles 6,500; Per Subs 50
Special Collections: Medical Reserve
Database Vendor: DRA

SEILING

P SEILING PUBLIC LIBRARY,* PO Box 70, 73663-0070. SAN 376-5997. Tel: 580-922-4259. FAX: 580-922-4259. *Librn*, Beverly Autrey
Library Holdings: Bk Vols 13,400; Bk Titles 13,000; Per Subs 14
Mem of Western Plains Library System

SEMINOLE

P SEMINOLE PUBLIC LIBRARY, 424 N Main, 74868. SAN 313-9905. Tel: 405-382-4221. FAX: 405-382-0050. E-Mail: seminolepl@onenet.net. Web Site: www.ci.seminole.ok.us/splibrary/library.html. *Librn*, Gwyneth Ayres
Founded 1929. Pop 17,071; Circ 45,516
Jul 1999-Jun 2000 Income $132,085, State $836, City $107,000, Locally Generated Income $3,500. Mats Exp $19,599, Books $17,000, Per/Ser (Incl. Access Fees) $2,500, Micro $99. Sal $66,000 (Prof $27,500)
Library Holdings: Bk Vols 31,500; Per Subs 69
Subject Interests: Native Am - Seminole Tribe
Special Collections: Large Print Coll
Automation Activity & Vendor Info: (Cataloging) Follett; (Circulation) Follett
Database Vendor: OCLC - First Search
Function: ILL available, Photocopies available, Reference services available
Partic in Okla Telecommunications Interlibr Syst
Friends of the Library Group

J SEMINOLE STATE COLLEGE, David L Boren Library, Junction Hwy 9 & David L Boren Blvd, PO Box 351, 74818-0351. SAN 313-9891. Tel: 405-382-9950, Ext 243. FAX: 405-382-9511. *Librn*, Jonna Bunyan; *Asst Librn*, Gerald Hickman
Founded 1970. Enrl 1,439; Fac 41
Library Holdings: Bk Titles 31,000; Per Subs 301
Special Collections: Library of American Civilization (American History Coll), ultrafiche

SENTINEL

P SENTINEL PUBLIC LIBRARY,* 312 E Main, 73664-0178. (Mail add: PO Box 178, 73664-0178), SAN 376-5989. Tel: 580-393-2244. FAX: 580-393-2244. E-Mail: wplssc@itlnet.net. *Dir*, Carol Rice
Library Holdings: Bk Titles 3,000; Per Subs 14
Mem of Western Plains Library System

SHATTUCK

P SHATTUCK PUBLIC LIBRARY,* 101 S Main St, General Delivery, 73858. SAN 320-5037. Tel: 580-938-5104. FAX: 580-938-5104. *Librn*, Jud Abbott; *Asst Librn*, Neoma Matthews
Library Holdings: Bk Vols 13,500; Bk Titles 11,231; Per Subs 36
Subject Interests: Ellis county hist, Gardening, Laws
Special Collections: County; History (Northwest Oklahoman Coll), newsps
Partic in Okla Telecommunications Interlibr Syst

SHAWNEE

J JAMES KELLY LIBRARY AT SAINT GREGORY'S UNIVERSITY, 190 W MacArthur Dr, 74801-2499. SAN 313-9921. Tel: 405-878-5408. FAX: 405-878-5198. *Dir*, Patrick McCool; *Assoc Librn*, Benet Exton; *Tech Servs*, Elizabeth Schipul; *Ref Serv*, Sylvia Cobb; *Ref Serv*, Anita Semtner
Founded 1915
1997-1998 Income $105,000. Mats Exp $22,000. Sal $65,000 (Prof $47,000
Library Holdings: Bk Vols 65,000; Per Subs 140

CR OKLAHOMA BAPTIST UNIVERSITY, Mabee Learning Center, 500 W University, OBU Box 61310, 74801-2590. SAN 313-9913. Tel: 405-878-2249. FAX: 405-878-2270. Web Site: www.okbu.edu/library/. *Dean of Libr, Online Servs*, Jon Sparks; Tel: 405-878-2249, E-Mail: jon_sparks@mail.okbu.edu; *ILL, Ref*, Pattisue Thoman; Tel: 405-878-2269, E-Mail: pattisue_thoman@mail.okbu.edu; *Circ Media, Media Spec*, Clifford Lehman Tel: 405-878-2248, E-Mail: cliff_lehman@mail.okbu.edu; *Cat, Ref*, Diane Shank; Tel: 405-878-2257, E-Mail: diane_shank@mail.okbu.edu; *Govt Doc, Ref, Ser*, Junie Janzen; Tel: 405-878-2255, E-Mail: junie_janzen@mail.okbu.edu; *Archivist*, Tom Terry; Tel: 405-878-2254, E-Mail: tom_terry@mail.okbu.edu; *Spec Coll & Archives*, Denise Jett; Tel: 405-878-2252, E-Mail: denise_jett@mail.okbu.edu; *Music, Spec Coll*, Cindy Hicks; Tel: 405-878-2253, E-Mail: cindy_hicks@mail.okbu.edu; *Bibliog Instr, Publ Servs, Ref*, Jason Dupree; Tel: 405-878-2259, E-Mail: jason_dupree@mail.okbu.edu; *Acq*, Nora Inman; Tel: 405-878-2268, E-Mail: nora_inman@mail.okbu.edu; *Circ*, Mary Price; Tel: 405-878-2264, E-Mail: mary_price@mail.okbu.edu; *Govt Doc, Ser*, Vernell Ward; Tel: 405-878-2255, E-Mail: vernell_ward@mail.okbu.edu; Staff 13 (MLS 6, Non-MLS 7)
Founded 1911. Enrl 2,100; Fac 105; Highest Degree: Master
1999-2000 Income $657,000, Parent Institution $652,000, Other $5,000. Mats Exp $432,455, Books $92,500, Per/Ser (Incl. Access Fees) $65,000, Presv $4,000, Micro $4,500, AV Equip $7,500, Manuscripts & Archives $5,000, Electronic Ref Mat (Incl. Access Fees) $45,000. Sal $278,000 (Prof $194,000)
Library Holdings: Bk Vols 250,000; Per Subs 650
Subject Interests: Archives, Religion
Special Collections: Baptist Resource Center; Hershel Hobbs Coll
Automation Activity & Vendor Info: (Acquisitions) SIRSI; (Cataloging) SIRSI; (Circulation) SIRSI; (OPAC) SIRSI
Database Vendor: Ebsco - EbscoHost, GaleNet, IAC - Info Trac, OCLC - First Search, Silverplatter Information Inc., Wilson - Wilson Web
Partic in American Theological Library Association; Amigos Library Services, Inc; Dialog Corporation; Metronet; OCLC Online Computer Library Center, Inc

SPIRO

P SPIRO PUBLIC LIBRARY,* 208 S Main, 74959. SAN 313-993X. Tel: 918 962-3461. FAX: 918-962-3461. Web Site: www.members.clnk.com/spirolib. *Exec Dir*, Wayne Hanaway; *Librn*, Glenda Stokes; E-Mail: stokes@scpl.lib.ok.us; *Asst Librn*, Beverly Carr
Pop 2,057; Circ 6,485
Library Holdings: Bk Vols 10,000; Per Subs 30
Mem of Southeastern Public Library System Of Oklahoma
Friends of the Library Group

STIGLER

P STIGLER PUBLIC LIBRARY,* 402 NE Sixth St, 74462. SAN 313-9948. Tel: 918-967-4801. FAX: 918-967-4801. *Librn*, Lola L Hill; *Asst Librn*, Judy Eakle
Pop 2,347
1997-1998 Mats Exp $17,360, Books $15,920, Per/Ser (Incl. Access Fees) $1,440. Sal $41,071
Library Holdings: Bk Titles 24,600; Per Subs 42
Mem of Southeastern Public Library System Of Oklahoma

STILLWATER

S NATIONAL CLEARINGHOUSE OF REHABILITATION TRAINING MATERIALS, Reference Collection,* Oklahoma State University, 5202 N Richmond Hill Dr, 74078-4080. SAN 329-8329. Tel: 405-624-7650. Toll Free Tel: 800-223-5219. TDD: 405-624-3156. FAX: 405-624-0695. E-Mail: u3714aa@vms.ucc.okstate.edu. Web Site: www.nchrtm.okstate.edu. *Dir*, David Brooks; E-Mail: brooksdj@okstate.edu; *Info Specialist*, Sharrie Walters; *Tech Coordr*, Jo Kahn

Founded 1961
Library Holdings: Bk Vols 5,000
Subject Interests: Audio, Monographs, Video, Vocational rehabilitation, Vocational training
Special Collections: Oral Interpretation Training Videos
Publications: NCRTM News

NATIONAL WRESTLING HALL OF FAME LIBRARY & MUSEUM, 405 W Hall of Fame Ave, 74075. SAN 313-9972. Tel: 405-377-5243. FAX: 405-377-5244. E-Mail: info@wrestlinghalloffame.org. *Dir*, Tony Linville; *Pres*, Myron Roderick; Staff 3 (MLS 3)
Founded 1976
Library Holdings: Bk Vols 170; Bk Titles 112
Subject Interests: Wrestling

G OKLAHOMA DEPARTMENT OF CAREER & TECHNOLOGY EDUCATION, (Formerly Oklahoma Department Of Vocational-Technical Education), Resource Center, 1500 W Seventh Ave, 74074-4364. SAN 313-9956. Tel: 405-377-2000, Ext 161. FAX: 405-743-5142, 743-6809. Web Site: www.okcareertech.org/resrc/default.htm. *Mgr*, Denise Christy; E-Mail: dchri@careertech.org
Founded 1970
Library Holdings: Bk Vols 20,000; Bk Titles 14,000
Subject Interests: Vocational education

C OKLAHOMA STATE UNIVERSITY LIBRARIES, 74078-1071. SAN 357-6965. Tel: 405-744-9729. Interlibrary Loan Service Tel: 405-744-9727. Toll Free Tel: 877-744-9161. FAX: 405-744-5183. Web Site: www.library.okstate.edu. *Dean of Libr*, Edward R Johnson; *Asst Dean*, Sheila Grant Johnson; *Asst Dean*, Norman L Nelson; Tel: 405-744-6322, Fax: 405-744-7579, E-Mail: nln6783@okstate.edu; *Access Serv*, Carolyn Warmann; *Head, Acq*, Guyla Houston; *Head, Cat*, Co-Ming Chan; *Doc*, John B Phillips; *Spec Coll*, Jennifer M Paustenbaugh. Subject Specialists: *Engineering*, Vicki Phillips; *Humanities*, Richard Paustenbaugh; *Science/technology*, Vicki Phillips; *Social sciences and issues*, Richard Paustenbaugh; Staff 50 (MLS 46, Non-MLS 4)
Founded 1894. Enrl 21,612; Fac 899; Highest Degree: Doctorate
Jul 1999-Jun 2000 Income (Main Library and Branch Library) $8,333,651. Mats Exp $3,874,360, Books $879,001, Per/Ser (Incl. Access Fees) $2,249,041, Presv $88,133. Sal $3,340,063 (Prof $2,057,018)
Library Holdings: Bk Vols 2,090,643; Per Subs 18,014
Subject Interests: Agriculture, Biochemistry, Botany, Bus, Chemistry, Econ, Education, Engineering, Geology, Hist of the Am West, Mathematics, Physics
Special Collections: Architecture, bks & per; Curriculum Guides & Text Books (Curriculum Materials Library); Oklahoma Governors (Papers of Gov Henry S Johnston & Gov Henry Bellmon, Senate Papers of Henry Bellmon); OSU History & Publications, bks, mss; Papers of Angie Debo; Soil Conservation, Water Resources & Agriculture (Oklahoma), bks, mss; State & US Regional, US Patent, USGS, NASA & DMA; Veterinary Medicine, bks & per; Women's Archives, per & mss
Database Vendor: OCLC - First Search
Publications: Perspectives (External Newsletter)
Partic in Amigos Library Services, Inc; Asn of Research Libraries; Big Twelve Plus Libr Consortium; Okla Libr Technology Network; Okla Res & Commun Librs Consortium
Friends of the Library Group
Departmental Libraries:
ARCHITECTURE, 201-A Architecture Bldg, 74078-1071. SAN 357-699X. Tel: 405-744-6047. FAX: 405-744-5183.; Staff 1 (MLS 1)
CURRICULUM MATERIALS, 001 Willard, 74078-1071. SAN 373-8841. Tel: 405-744-6310. FAX: 405-744-1726. *Librn*, Shonda Brisco; Staff 1 (MLS 1)
DOCUMENTS DEPARTMENT, Edmon Low Library, 5th flr, 74078-1071. SAN 374-4205. Tel: 405-744-6546. FAX: 405-744-5183. *Head of Libr*, John B Phillips; Staff 5 (MLS 5)
HUMANITIES & SOCIAL SCIENCES DIVISION, Edmon Low Library, 3rd flr, 74078-1071. SAN 327-9014. Tel: 405-744-6545. FAX: 405-744-5183. *Head of Libr*, Richard Paustenbaugh; Staff 9 (MLS 9)
PATENT & TRADEMARK, 206 Wes Watkins Ctr for Int Trade Development, 74078-1071. SAN 373-885X. Tel: 405-744-7086. FAX: 405-744-7083. *Librn*, Julia Crawford; Staff 2 (MLS 2)
SCIENCE & ENGINEERING DIVISION, Edmon Low Library, 1st flr, 74078-1071. SAN 327-8999. Tel: 405-744-6309. FAX: 405-744-5183. *Head of Libr*, Vicki W Phillips; Staff 4 (MLS 4)
CM VETERINARY MEDICINE, 102 Veterinary Medicine Bldg, 74078-1071. SAN 357-7023. Tel: 405-744-6655. FAX: 405-744-5609.

P STILLWATER PUBLIC LIBRARY, 1107 S Duck, 74074. SAN 313-9964. Tel: 405-372-3633. Reference Tel: 405-372-3633, Ext 106. TDD: 405-747-8007. FAX: 405-624-0552. Web Site: www.stillwater.lib.ok.us. *Dir*, John F Augelli; Tel: 405-372-3633, Ext 101, E-Mail: libdirector@stillwater.org; *Head Ref*, Jolene Armstrong; Tel: 405-372-3633, Ext 102, E-Mail: adultservices@stillwater.org; *Head Tech Servs*, Lynda Reynolds; Tel: 405-372-3633, Ext 117, Fax: 405-747-8009, E-Mail: techserv@stillwater.org; *ILL*, Jeanna Shore; Tel: 405-372-3633, Ext 119, E-Mail: libraryloan@stillwater.org; Staff 29 (MLS 3, Non-MLS 26)
Founded 1923. Pop 40,000
Jul 2000-Jun 2001 Income $1,010,170, State $25,210, City $954,386, Locally Generated Income $30,574. Mats Exp $128,936, Books $108,825, Per/Ser (Incl. Access Fees) $20,111
Library Holdings: Bk Vols 102,064; Per Subs 269
Special Collections: Genealogy; Stillwater Coll
Automation Activity & Vendor Info: (Cataloging) SIRSI; (Circulation) SIRSI; (OPAC) SIRSI
Database Vendor: Ebsco - EbscoHost, GaleNet, IAC - Info Trac
Partic in Amigos Library Services, Inc
Special Services for the Deaf - TDD
Friends of the Library Group

STILWELL

P STILWELL PUBLIC LIBRARY,* 5 N Sixth St, 74960. SAN 313-9980. Tel: 918-696-7512. FAX: 918-696-4007. *Librn, Mgr*, Patricia A Gordon; E-Mail: pgordon@eodls.lib.ok.us; *Asst Librn*, Lori Johnson; *Asst Librn*, Mary Wheeler
Founded 1972
1997-1998 Income $96,000. Mats Exp $15,000
Library Holdings: Bk Vols 12,000; Per Subs 25
Mem of Eastern Oklahoma District Library System

STROUD

P SAC & FOX NATIONAL PUBLIC LIBRARY,* Rte 2, Box 246, 74079. SAN 374-6690. Tel: 918-968-3526. FAX: 918-968-4837. *Asst Librn*, Juanita Goodreau; Staff 2 (MLS 1, Non-MLS 1)
Founded 1987. Pop 34,000
1997-1998 Mats Exp $2,605. Sal $40,500 (Prof $23,000)
Special Collections: Sac & Fox History & Culture (Sac & Fox Archives), multi-media; Sac & Fox Nation; Sac & Fox Oral History Coll, audio-rec, photos & transcriptions
Publications: books; brochures; index; Sac & Fox News

P STROUD PUBLIC LIBRARY,* 301 W Seventh St, PO Box 599, 74079-0599. SAN 313-9999. Tel: 918-968-2567. FAX: 918-968-4700. *Librn*, Marsha Morgan
Founded 1936. Pop 3,000; Circ 15,000
Library Holdings: Bk Vols 10,000
Friends of the Library Group

SULPHUR

S NATIONAL PARK SERVICE, Travertine Nature Center Library, Chickasaw Nat Recreation Area, PO Box 201, 73086-0201. SAN 314-0008. Tel: 580-622-3165. *In Charge*, Ron Parker
Founded 1969
Library Holdings: Bk Vols 1,200; Per Subs 24
Subject Interests: Biology, Botany, Ecology, Geology, Native Am

S OKLAHOMA SCHOOL FOR THE DEAF LIBRARY,* 1100 E Oklahoma, 73086. SAN 314-0016. Tel: 580-622-3186. FAX: 580-622-4950. E-Mail: osdlib@brightok.net. *Librn*, Sue Galloway
Circ 4,000
Library Holdings: Bk Vols 5,797; Per Subs 53
Special Collections: Books & Periodicals about Deafness

TAFT

S JESS DUNN CORRECTIONAL CENTER LIBRARY,* PO Box 316, 74463-0312. SAN 324-4334. Tel: 918-682-7841, Ext 221. FAX: 918-682-4372. *Librn*, Larry Stogner; Staff 9 (MLS 1, Non-MLS 8)
Library Holdings: Bk Vols 8,596; Per Subs 60
Publications: Library Gazette (monthly)

S OKLAHOMA DEPARTMENT OF CORRECTIONS, Dr Eddie W Warrior Correctional Center Library,* 400 N Oak St, PO Box 315, 74463-0315. SAN 371-5329. Tel: 918-683-8365. FAX: 918-682-4782.; Staff 1 (MLS 1)
Founded 1989
Library Holdings: Bk Titles 3,138; Per Subs 26
Special Services for the Deaf - High interest/low vocabulary books; Special interest periodicals

TAHLEQUAH

S CHEROKEE NATIONAL HISTORICAL SOCIETY, INC LIBRARY,* Cherokee Nat Mus, TSA-LA-GI, PO Box 515, 74465. SAN 314-0024. Tel: 918-456-6007. FAX: 918-456-6165. Web Site: www.powersource.com./powersource/heritage. *Dir*, Mary Ellen Meredith; *Bibliog Instr, Online Servs*, Tom Mooney
Founded 1969
Library Holdings: Bk Titles 3,200; Per Subs 15
Subject Interests: Cherokee hist
Special Collections: C C Victory Coll, Vice Chief 1949-71; Cherokee Executive Committee Papers 1948-71; Cherokee Nation & Subsidiaries

Papers 1969-74; Earl Boyd Pierce Papers 1928-1983; J B Milam Coll; John J Gillespie Coll, rec & micro; Ross Family Papers Coll; W W Keeler Papers, Principal Chief 1949-75
Restriction: Non-circulating to the public

C NORTHEASTERN STATE UNIVERSITY, (JVL), John Vaughan Library-Learning Resource Center, 711 N Grand Ave, 74464-2300. SAN 314-0032. Tel: 918-456-5511, Ext 3200. FAX: 918-458-2197. Web Site: www.nsuok.edu/jvl/index.html. *Dean of Libr*, Bela Foltin, Jr; E-Mail: foltin@cherokee.nsuok.edu; *Coll Develop*, Jeanette McQuitty; E-Mail: mcquitty@cherokee.nsuok.edu; *Dir, Tech Serv*, Linda West; E-Mail: west@cherokee.nsuok.edu; *Archivist*, Victoria Sheffler; E-Mail: sheffler@cherokee.nsuok.edu; *ILL*, Renee Ridge; E-Mail: ridge@cherokee.nsuok.edu; *Spec Coll*, Delores Sumner; E-Mail: Sumner@cherokee.nsuok.edu; Staff 30 (MLS 14, Non-MLS 16)
Founded 1909. Enrl 8,462; Fac 340; Highest Degree: Doctorate
Library Holdings: Bk Vols 402,611; Bk Titles 291,526; Per Subs 5,106
Special Collections: Native American History Coll
Automation Activity & Vendor Info: (Cataloging) VTLS; (Circulation) VTLS; (ILL) VTLS; (OPAC) VTLS; (Serials) VTLS
Partic in Amigos Library Services, Inc; Dialog Corporation; First Search; Grateful Med; IAC Searchbank; Marcive; OCLC Online Computer Library Center, Inc; Okla Libr Technology Network; ProQuest; WebDocs; Westlaw

P TAHLEQUAH PUBLIC LIBRARY,* 120 S College Ave, 74464. SAN 376-6438. Tel: 918-456-2581. FAX: 918-458-0590. *Librn*, Georgie Drees
Library Holdings: Bk Vols 32,000; Bk Titles 30,000; Per Subs 12
Mem of Eastern Oklahoma District Library System
Friends of the Library Group

TALIHINA

P TALIHINA PUBLIC LIBRARY,* Hwy 271 N, Rte 1, Box 1124, 74571. SAN 314-0059. Tel: 918-567-2002. FAX: 918-567-2921. *Librn*, Mary R Fitzgerald; *Asst Librn*, Irene Fletcher
Library Holdings: Bk Vols 19,000; Per Subs 22
Subject Interests: Large print
Publications: Publishers Weekly
Mem of Southeastern Public Library System Of Oklahoma

TEXHOMA

P TEXHOMA PUBLIC LIBRARY,* PO Box 647, 73949. SAN 314-0067. Tel: 580-423-7150. *Librn*, Carol Coble
Founded 1926. Pop 1,200; Circ 4,708
Library Holdings: Bk Vols 15,000

THOMAS

P HAZEL CROSS LIBRARY,* Hwy 33 E, PO Box 410, 73669-0410. SAN 376-6004. Tel: 580-661-3532. FAX: 580-661-3532. *Librn*, Carol Conkin
Library Holdings: Bk Vols 5,100; Bk Titles 5,000; Per Subs 10
Mem of Western Plains Library System

TINKER AFB

UNITED STATES AIR FORCE
AM MEDICAL LIBRARY, 72 MDSS/SGSOL, Bldg 5801, 5700 Arnold St, 73145-8102. SAN 324-7287. Tel: 405-736-2626. FAX: 405-734-4163. *Librn*, Lennie Foster; E-Mail: foster.lennie@72medgrp.tinker.af.mil
Oct 1998-Sep 1999 Mats Exp $32,000, Books $15,000, Per/Ser (Incl. Access Fees) $10,000. Sal $32,000
Library Holdings: Bk Vols 1,600; Bk Titles 1,480; Per Subs 65
Partic in Greater Oklahoma Area Health Sciences Library Consortium

A TINKER AIR FORCE BASE LIBRARY FL2030, 72 SPTG/SVMG, Bldg 1045D Rapcon Rd, 73145-8101. SAN 357-7058. Tel: 405-734-2626. *Librn*, Joy Coleman; *Asst Librn*, Bruce Daver; E-Mail: daver.bruce@tinker.af.mil
Founded 1943
Oct 1997-Sep 1998 Income $121,885. Mats Exp $13,989. Sal $104,641
Library Holdings: Bk Vols 28,861; Per Subs 303
Subject Interests: Aeronautical eng, Mgt, Recreational
Special Collections: Total Quality Management
Partic in Fed Libr & Info Network; OCLC Online Computer Library Center, Inc

TISHOMINGO

J MURRAY STATE COLLEGE, Library - Learning Resource Center, One Murray Campus St LS 101, 73460. SAN 314-0075. Tel: 580-371-2371. FAX: 580-371-9844. *Dir*, Jim Kennedy; E-Mail: jkennedy@msc.cc.ok.us; Staff 3 (MLS 1, Non-MLS 2)
Founded 1930. Enrl 985; Fac 43; Highest Degree: Associate
Jul 1999-Jun 2000 Mats Exp $42,800, Books $14,000, Per/Ser (Incl. Access Fees) $6,400, Presv $21,400, Electronic Ref Mat (Incl. Access Fees) $1,000. Sal $86,039 (Prof $43,655)
Library Holdings: Bk Vols 26,477; Bk Titles 21,995; Per Subs 220
Special Collections: Oklahoma History; Physical Fitness
Database Vendor: Ebsco - EbscoHost, GaleNet, IAC - Info Trac, OCLC - First Search
Publications: Library Handbook; Student Worker's Handbook
Partic in Amigos Library Services, Inc; OCLC Online Computer Library Center, Inc

TONKAWA

J NORTHERN OKLAHOMA COLLEGE, Vineyard Library, 1220 E Grand, PO Box 310, 74653. SAN 314-0083. Tel: 580-628-6250. FAX: 580-628-6209. Web Site: www.north-ok.edu/Information/LIBRARY.htm. *Dir*, Ben K Hainline; E-Mail: bhainlin@nocaxp.north-ok.edu; *Media Spec*, Doris Nesselrode; *Librn*, Amita Ward; Staff 6 (MLS 2, Non-MLS 4)
Founded 1901. Enrl 1,336; Fac 65
Library Holdings: Bk Titles 40,000; Per Subs 225
Subject Interests: Indian hist
Special Collections: Oklahoma Coll
Database Vendor: IAC - Info Trac, IAC - SearchBank, OCLC - First Search, ProQuest
Function: Research library

P TONKAWA PUBLIC LIBRARY,* 216 N Seventh, 74653. SAN 314-0091. Tel: 580-628-3366. FAX: 580-628-3688. *Librn*, Betsy Garino; E-Mail: bgarino@onenet.ne
Founded 1922. Pop 3,127; Circ 33,412
Library Holdings: Bk Titles 20,000; Per Subs 64
Special Collections: Oklahoma Coll
Friends of the Library Group

TULSA

S AMERICAN AIRLINES, INC, Engineering Library-MD107,* 3900 N Mingo Rd, 74116. SAN 329-5060. Tel: 918-292-2426, 918-292-3365. FAX: 918-292-3789. *In Charge*, Terry Arning
Library Holdings: Bk Titles 5,000

S AMERICAN ASSOCIATION OF PETROLEUM GEOLOGISTS, AAPG Foundation,* 1444 S Boulder, PO Box 979, 74101. SAN 321-1185. Tel: 918-560-2620, 918-584-2555, Ext 620. FAX: 918-560-2642. E-Mail: library@aapg.org. *Librn*, Karen Piqune
Founded 1976
Library Holdings: Bk Titles 3,500; Per Subs 85
Subject Interests: Geol with emphasis on petroleum exploration, Geology
Special Collections: Petroleum Geology (American Association of Petroleum Geologists Publications)
Restriction: Open to public for reference only

S BOEING-NORTH AMERICAN, INC, Technical Information Center, 3330 N Mingo Rd, PO Box 582808, 74158-2808. SAN 314-0245. Tel: 918-832-2573. FAX: 918-832-2611. *Res*, Wenona Hurd; E-Mail: wenona.a.hurd@boeing.com
Founded 1962
Library Holdings: Bk Vols 2,100; Per Subs 100

R FIRST UNITED METHODIST CHURCH LIBRARY,* 1115 S Boulder, 74119-2492. SAN 314-0121. Tel: 918-587-9481, Ext 219. FAX: 918-584-5228. *Librn*, Nancy Kinard; Staff 18 (MLS 1, Non-MLS 17)
Founded 1940
Library Holdings: Bk Titles 15,263; Per Subs 22
Subject Interests: Christian life, Education
Special Collections: Children's Library; Famous Christian Art Reproductions; Methodist Rare Book Coll
Friends of the Library Group

L GABLE & GOTWALS, INC, Law Library, 1100 Oneok Plaza, 100 W Fifth St, 74103-4217. SAN 372-2236. Tel: 918-595-4800. FAX: 918-595-4990. Web Site: gablelaw.com. *Adminr*, Shelley J Bradley; Tel: 918-595-4938, E-Mail: sbradley@gablelaw.com; *Librn*, Terry Fisher; Tel: 918-595-4955, E-Mail: tfisher@gablelaw.com; Staff 4 (MLS 2, Non-MLS 2)
Founded 1944
Library Holdings: Bk Vols 10,000; Per Subs 100

M HILLCREST MEDICAL CENTER LIBRARY, 1120 S Utica, 74104-4090. SAN 357-7201. Tel: 918-579-8357. Reference Tel: 918-579-8356. FAX: 918-579-8388. *ILL*, Janice E Hunt; E-Mail: jhunt@hillcrest.com; *Librn*, Peggy Miller Cook; E-Mail: pcook@hillcrest.com. Subject Specialists: *Medicine*, Peggy Miller Cook; *Nursing*, Peggy Miller Cook; Staff 2 (MLS 1, Non-MLS 1)
Founded 1976
Library Holdings: Bk Vols 2,280; Bk Titles 2,089; Per Subs 190
Subject Interests: Allied health, Medicine, Nursing
Special Collections: Hillcrest Patient/Family Health Information Center
Database Vendor: IAC - Info Trac, OCLC - First Search, OVID Technologies
Publications: List of Recent Acquisitions
Partic in Nat Network of Librs of Med, S Cent Res Libr Coun

OKLAHOMA STATE UNIVERSITY - (OSU) TULSA LIBRARY, 700 N Greenwood Ave, 74106-0700. SAN 326-8993. Tel: 918-594-8130. Interlibrary Loan Service Tel: 918-594-8138. Reference Tel: 918-594-8137. FAX: 918-594-8145. Web Site: tulsa.okstate.edu/library. *Dir*, Beth Freeman; E-Mail: freeman@lib.uct.edu; *Publ Servs*, Dona Davidson; *Tech Servs*, Robin Leech; *Ref Serv*, R D Bell; Staff 16 (MLS 5, Non-MLS 11)
Founded 1986. Enrl 4,265; Highest Degree: Doctorate
Jul 1999-Jun 2000 Income State $982,025. Mats Exp $367,160. Sal $429,985 (Prof $211,597)
Library Holdings: Bk Vols 90,295; Bk Titles 75,417; Per Subs 1,283
Subject Interests: Bus, Computer science, Education, Engineering, Psychology, Telecommunications
Special Collections: Eric Coll (from 1980)
Database Vendor: Ebsco - EbscoHost
Partic in Amigos Library Services, Inc

CM OKLAHOMA STATE UNIVERSITY - COLLEGE OF OSTEOPATHIC MEDICINE, Medical Library, 1111 W 17th St, 74107-1898. SAN 314-0156. Tel: 918-561-8449. FAX: 918-561-8412. Web Site: osu.com.okstate.edu. *Dir*, Ursula Scott; *Asst Librn*, G David Money; Staff 3 (MLS 3)
Founded 1974. Enrl 349; Fac 51; Highest Degree: Doctorate
Library Holdings: Bk Vols 50,000; Bk Titles 20,000; Per Subs 665
Subject Interests: Biomed
Special Collections: Anatomical Models & Realia Coll; Case Histories for Massachusetts General Hospital; College Archives; National Library of Medicine Literature Searches Coll; Osteopathy Coll
Partic in SCAMeL

OKLAHOMA WELL LOG LIBRARY, INC,* 427 S Boston, Ste 1100, 74103. SAN 314-0180. Tel: 918-582-6188. FAX: 599-798-2198. *Librn*, Janice Weaver
Founded 1960
Library Holdings: Bk Vols 350

C ORAL ROBERTS UNIVERSITY, John D Messick Learning Resources Center, 7777 S Lewis, 74171-0001. SAN 314-0199. Tel: 918-495-6723. Interlibrary Loan Service Tel: 918-495-7377. FAX: 918-495-6893. Web Site: www.oru.edu/library. *Dean of Libr*, Dr William W Jernigan; E-Mail: wjernign@oru.edu; *Music*, Lana Allen; Tel: 918-495-7519, E-Mail: lallen@oru.edu; *Distance Educ, ILL*, Carolyn Baker; Tel: 918-495-7378, Fax: 918-495-7428, E-Mail: carbaker@oru.edu; *ILL*, Thelma Burden; Tel: 918-495-7377, Fax: 918-495-7428, E-Mail: thburden@oru.edu; *Bibliog Instr*, Myra Bloom; Tel: 918-495-7174, E-Mail: mbloom@oru.edu; *Circ*, Karolyn Braun; Tel: 918-495-6392, E-Mail: kbraun@oru.edu; *Circ*, Angela Jones; Tel: 918-495-6028, E-Mail: ajones@oru.edu; *Computer Services*, Marcia Bridgewater; Tel: 918-495-7189, E-Mail: mbridgewater@oru.edu; *Acq*, Sherri Bridgewater; Tel: 918-495-6896, E-Mail: sbridgewater@oru.edu; *Res*, Dr David Dorries; Tel: 918-495-6894, E-Mail: ddorries@oru.edu; *Media Spec*, Dr Linda Dunham; Tel: 918-495-7085, E-Mail: ldunham@oru.edu; *Cat*, Louise Hightower; Tel: 918-495-7168, E-Mail: lhightower@oru.edu; *Cat*, Dana Higeons; Tel: 918-495-6885, E-Mail: dhigeons@oru.edu; *Cat*, Sally Shelton; Tel: 918-495-6902, E-Mail: sshelton@oru.edu; *Admin Assoc*, Glenda Luelf; E-Mail: gluelf@oru.edu; *Reader Servs*, Peggy Pixley; Tel: 918-495-6732, E-Mail: pepixley@oru.edu; *Reader Servs*, Evelyn Rogers; Tel: 918-495-7463, E-Mail: erogers@oru.edu; *Electronic Resources*, Marion Prudlo; Tel: 918-495-6843, E-Mail: mprulo@oru.edu; *Acq*, Judith Rigsby; Tel: 918-495-6895, Fax: 918-495-6727, E-Mail: jurigsby@oru.edu; *Spec Coll*, Mark Roberts; Tel: 918-495-6898, Fax: 918-495-6662, E-Mail: mroberts@oru.edu; *Archivist*, Roger Rydin; Tel: 918-495-6750, Fax: 918-495-6751, E-Mail: rrydin@oru.edu; *Tech Servs*, Carol Sterner; Tel: 918-495-6880, E-Mail: csterner@oru.edu; *Tech Servs*, Janelle Sullivan; Tel: 918-495-6882, E-Mail: jsullivan@oru.edu; *Electronic Resources, Per*, Judy Stubbs; Tel: 918-495-6889, Fax: 918-495-6727, E-Mail: justubbs@oru.edu; *Per*, MaryAnn Walker; Tel: 918-495-6881, E-Mail: mwalker@oru.edu; Staff 25 (MLS 9, Non-MLS 16)
Founded 1963. Enrl 5,253; Fac 300; Highest Degree: Doctorate
Aug 1999-Jul 2000 Income (Main Library Only) $884,797. Mats Exp $262,625, Books $99,037, Per/Ser (Incl. Access Fees) $128,066, Presv $10,000, Micro $11,397, Electronic Ref Mat (Incl. Access Fees) $14,125. Sal $641,628 (Prof $384,163)
Library Holdings: Bk Vols 261,668; Bk Titles 212,750; Per Subs 6,207
Subject Interests: Biblical studies, Bus, Mgt
Special Collections: Elmar Camillo Dos Santos Coll; Holy Spirit Research Center; Jewish Theological Coll; Oral History Program; Oral Roberts Ministry Archives; William Sanford LaSor Coll
Automation Activity & Vendor Info: (Acquisitions) epixtech, inc.; (Cataloging) epixtech, inc.; (Circulation) epixtech, inc.; (Course Reserve) epixtech, inc.; (OPAC) epixtech, inc.; (Serials) epixtech, inc.
Database Vendor: epixtech, inc.
Function: ILL available
Partic in OCLC Online Computer Library Center, Inc
Open 7am-4pm, dress code & no food or drink
Departmental Libraries:
HOLY SPIRIT RESEARCH CENTER Tel: 918-495-6898. FAX: 918-495-6662. Web Site: www.oru.edu/university/library. *Librn*, Mark Roberts; Staff 1 (MLS 1)
Library Holdings: Bk Vols 16,500; Per Subs 484
Subject Interests: Charismatic, Pentecostal
Special Collections: Bishop Dan T Muse Coll; Edward Irving Coll

S PALOMINO HORSE BREEDERS OF AMERICA LIBRARY, 15253 E Skelly Dr, 74116-2637. SAN 326-4130. Tel: 918-438-1234. FAX: 918-438-1232. E-Mail: yellahrses@aol.com. Web Site: www.palominohba.com. *Librn*, Cindy Chilton
Founded 1941
Library Holdings: Bk Vols 300; Per Subs 175

S PHILBROOK MUSEUM OF ART, H A & Mary K Chapman Library, 2727 S Rockford Rd, 74114-4104. (Mail add: PO Box 52510, 74152-0510), SAN 314-0210. Tel: 918-748-5306. FAX: 918-743-4230. *Librn*, Thomas Elton Young; E-Mail: tyoung@philbrook.org; Staff 1 (MLS 1)
Founded 1940
Library Holdings: Bk Vols 15,000; Per Subs 135
Subject Interests: Fine arts, Visual arts
Special Collections: American Indian (Roberta Campbell Lawson Coll)
Automation Activity & Vendor Info: (Cataloging) Sagebrush Corporation; (Circulation) Sagebrush Corporation; (OPAC) Sagebrush Corporation
Database Vendor: IAC - Info Trac, OCLC - First Search
Partic in OCLC Online Computer Library Center, Inc
Open by appointment, Mon-Fri 10-12 & 1-5

R PHILLIPS THEOLOGICAL SEMINARY LIBRARY, 4242 S Sheridan Rd, 3rd flr, 74145. SAN 357-5403. Tel: 918-610-8303. FAX: 918-610-8404. E-Mail: library@mail.gorilla.net. Web Site: www.ptsem.org. *Dir*, Roberta Hamburger; *Acq, Per*, Beverly Nelson; E-Mail: bnelson@ptsadmin.com; *Coll Develop*, Steven Edscorn; Tel: 918-631-3905, Fax: 918-582-1806, E-Mail: steven-edscorn@utulsa.edu; *ILL*, Norma Lansberry; Tel: 580-237-7886, Fax: 580-237-7686; Staff 4 (MLS 2, Non-MLS 2)
Founded 1950. Enrl 180; Fac 13; Highest Degree: Doctorate
Jul 1999-Jun 2000 Income $174,818. Mats Exp $51,054, Books $32,730, Per/Ser (Incl. Access Fees) $18,324. Sal $105,012 (Prof $66,555)
Library Holdings: Bk Vols 102,116; Bk Titles 85,665; Per Subs 419
Subject Interests: Religion, Theology
Database Vendor: OCLC - First Search
Partic in Amigos Library Services, Inc; OCLC Online Computer Library Center, Inc

M SAINT FRANCIS HOSPITAL, Health Sciences Library, 6161 S Yale Ave, 74136. SAN 314-0253. Tel: 918-494-1210. FAX: 918-494-1893. *Librn*, Beth Treaster; E-Mail: bhtreaster@saintfrancis.com; Staff 2 (MLS 1, Non-MLS 1)
Founded 1962
Library Holdings: Bk Titles 1,000; Per Subs 195
Subject Interests: Hospitals, Medicine, Nursing, Pharm
Automation Activity & Vendor Info: (Circulation) Athena; (OPAC) Athena
Database Vendor: IAC - Info Trac, OCLC - First Search, OVID Technologies
Restriction: In-house use for visitors
Partic in Amigos Library Services, Inc

M SAINT JOHN MEDICAL CENTER, Health Sciences Library,* 1923 S Utica, 74104. SAN 314-0261. Tel: 918-744-2970. FAX: 918-744-3209. *Librn*, James M Donovan; E-Mail: jdonovan@sjmc.org
Founded 1946
Library Holdings: Bk Vols 12,000; Per Subs 135
Subject Interests: Behav sci, Bus, Catholic bio ethics, Education, Medicine, Mgt, Nursing, Soc sci

S THOMAS GILCREASE INSTITUTE OF AMERICAN HISTORY & ART LIBRARY, 1400 Gilcrease Museum Rd, 74127-2100. SAN 314-0148. Tel: 918-596-2700. FAX: 918-596-2770. *Curator*, Sarah Erwin
Founded 1942
Library Holdings: Bk Titles 40,000; Per Subs 15
Subject Interests: Native Am hist, Western hist
Special Collections: Manuscripts

P TULSA CITY-COUNTY LIBRARY, 400 Civic Ctr, 74103. SAN 357-735X. Tel: 918-596-7977. Interlibrary Loan Service Tel: 918-596-7963. TDD: 918-596-7965, 596-7922. FAX: 918-596-7964. Web Site: www.tulsalibrary.org. *Exec Dir*, Linda Saferite; Fax: 918-596-7990; *Acq*, Judy Brightwell; *Cat*, Charlotte Frazier; *Ch Servs*, Kelly Jennings; *Circ*, Pat Gross; *Coll Develop*, Laurie Sundborg; *Media Spec*, Wayne Hardy; *Online Servs*, Martha Gregory; *Reader Servs*, Ruth Wiens; *YA Servs*, Rosemary Moran. Subject Specialists: *Business and management*, Robert Sears; *Technology*, Robert Sears; Staff 224 (MLS 56, Non-MLS 168)
Founded 1961. Pop 525,100; Circ 3,290,015
Jul 1999-Jun 2000 Income (Main Library and Branch Library) $16,944,186, State $275,000, County $14,836,178, Locally Generated Income $1,086,007, Other $747,001. Mats Exp $2,593,631, Books $1,402,500, Per/Ser (Incl. Access Fees) $759,000, Presv $19,000. Sal $7,306,632
Library Holdings: Bk Vols 1,201,901; Per Subs 2,600
Subject Interests: Black hist, Bus, Indust, Mgt, Sci-tech
Special Collections: A J Levorsen Geology Coll, bks, maps; Land Office Survey Map Coll; Shakespeare Coll
Automation Activity & Vendor Info: (Acquisitions) Innovative Interfaces Inc.; (Circulation) Innovative Interfaces Inc.; (ILL) Innovative Interfaces

Inc.; (OPAC) Innovative Interfaces Inc.
Database Vendor: Ebsco - EbscoHost
Publications: Annual Report; INFO (bi-monthly); Open Book (quarterly)
Partic in Amigos Library Services, Inc; BRS; Dialog Corporation; IAC; Okla Libr Technology Network; SDC Search Serv
Special Services for the Deaf - High interest/low vocabulary books; TDD
Friends of the Library Group
Branches: 24
BIXBY BRANCH, 20 E Breckinridge, Bixby, 74008. SAN 357-7449. Tel: 918-366-3397. FAX: 918-366-3392. *Librn*, Carolyn Trammell; Staff 2 (MLS 1, Non-MLS 1)
Library Holdings: Bk Vols 26,830
BROKEN ARROW BRANCH, 300 W Broadway, Broken Arrow, 74012. SAN 357-7473. Tel: 918-251-5359. FAX: 918-258-0324. *Librn*, Ann Gaebe
Library Holdings: Bk Vols 43,201
BROOKSIDE, 4515 S Owasso, 74105. SAN 357-7503. Tel: 918-746-5012. FAX: 918-746-5014. *Librn*, Kathy Doss
Library Holdings: Bk Vols 33,191
CENTRAL LIBRARY, 400 Civic Ctr, 74103. SAN 357-7414. Tel: 918-596-7897. *Librn*, Charley Shannon
Library Holdings: Bk Vols 334,116
COLLINSVILLE BRANCH, 1223 Main, Collinsville, 74021. SAN 357-7538. Tel: 918-596-2840. FAX: 918-596-2841. *Librn*, Susan Babbitt; Staff 2 (MLS 1, Non-MLS 1)
Library Holdings: Bk Vols 20,008
GLENPOOL BRANCH, 730 E 141st St, Glenpool, 74033. SAN 326-7954. Tel: 918-746-5190. FAX: 918-746-5191. *Librn*, Cheryl Newman
Library Holdings: Bk Vols 22,982
NATHAN HALE BRANCH, 6038 E 23rd St, 74114. SAN 357-7627. Tel: 918-669-6060. FAX: 918-669-6062. *Librn*, Bobbi Crumb; Staff 4 (MLS 1, Non-MLS 3)
Library Holdings: Bk Vols 28,003
HARDESTY SOUTH REGIONAL, 6737 S 85th East Ave, 74133. SAN 357-7937. Tel: 918-250-7307. FAX: 918-250-7843. *Librn*, Lola Todd
Library Holdings: Bk Vols 96,300
JENKS BRANCH, 523 West B St, Jenks, 74037. SAN 357-7651. Tel: 918-746-5180. FAX: 918-746-5181. *Librn*, Mike Williams; Staff 2 (MLS 1, Non-MLS 1)
Library Holdings: Bk Vols 29,176
KENDALL-WHITTIER BRANCH, 21 S Lewis St, 74104. SAN 357-7562. Tel: 918-596-7303. FAX: 918-596-7304. *Librn*, Marilou Marlar
Library Holdings: Bk Vols 21,693
MARTIN EAST REGIONAL, 2601 S Garnett, 74129. SAN 357-7686. Tel: 918-669-6340. FAX: 918-669-6344. *Librn*, Christie Chilton; Staff 10 (MLS 2, Non-MLS 8)
Library Holdings: Bk Vols 75,712
MAXWELL PARK, 1313 N Canton, 74112. SAN 328-7947. Tel: 918-669-6055. FAX: 981-669-6057. *Librn*, Marilyn Neal; Staff 4 (MLS 1, Non-MLS 3)
Library Holdings: Bk Vols 27,249
NORTH REGIONAL LIBRARY, 1520 N Hartford, 74106. SAN 357-7740. Tel: 918-596-7280. FAX: 918-596-7283. *Librn*, Keith Jemison; Staff 6 (MLS 1, Non-MLS 5)
Library Holdings: Bk Vols 40,290
OUTREACH SERVICES Tel: 918-596-7922. FAX: 918-596-7283. *Librn*, Amy Stephens; Staff 7 (MLS 1, Non-MLS 6)
Founded 1970
Library Holdings: Bk Vols 9,939
Special Collections: Blindness & Other Handicaps Reference Material
OWASSO BRANCH, 105 W Broadway, Owasso, 74055. SAN 357-7775. Tel: 918-591-4566. FAX: 918-591-4568. *Librn*, Barbara Barnes; Staff 4 (MLS 1, Non-MLS 3)
Library Holdings: Bk Vols 30,056
PAGE MEMORIAL, 6 E Broadway, Sand Springs, 74063. SAN 357-7805. Tel: 918-591-4585. FAX: 918-591-4586. *Librn*, Mary Lou Divelbiss; Staff 2 (MLS 1, Non-MLS 1)
Library Holdings: Bk Vols 22,522
PEGGY V HELMERICH LIBRARY, 5131 E 91st, 74114. SAN 371-4942. Tel: 918-596-2466. FAX: 918-596-2468. *Librn*, Marilyn Prosser; Staff 7 (MLS 1, Non-MLS 6)
Library Holdings: Bk Vols 49,221
PRATT, 3219 S 113th West Ave, Sand Springs, 74063. SAN 357-783X. Tel: 918-591-4595. FAX: 918-591-4597. *Librn*, Harriett Briggeman; Staff 3 (MLS 1, Non-MLS 2)
Library Holdings: Bk Vols 34,691
SCHUSTERMAN-BENSON, 3333 E 32nd Pl, 74114. SAN 357-7597. Tel: 918-746-5024. FAX: 918-746-5026. *Librn*, Cyndi Appel; Staff 6 (MLS 1, Non-MLS 5)
Library Holdings: Bk Vols 42,313
SKIATOOK BRANCH, 316 E Rogers Blvd, Skiatook, 74070. SAN 357-7929. Tel: 918-596-2830. FAX: 918-596-2831. *Librn*, Leslie Jones
Library Holdings: Bk Vols 21,074
SOUTH BROKEN ARROW, 3600 S Chestnut, Broken Arrow, 74012. SAN 374-7093. Tel: 918-451-0002. *Librn*, Theresa Fowler; Staff 5 (MLS 1, Non-MLS 4)
Library Holdings: Bk Vols 33,459
SPERRY BRANCH, 15 E Main, Sperry, 74073. SAN 357-7953. Tel: 918-591-4690. *Librn*, Suzi Smith; Staff 2 (MLS 1, Non-MLS 1)
Library Holdings: Bk Vols 13,909
SUBURBAN ACRES, 4606 N Garrison, 74126. SAN 357-7988. Tel: 918-591-4004. FAX: 918-591-4005. *Librn*, Sherrie Wallace
Library Holdings: Bk Vols 16,822
WEST REGIONAL, 2224 W 51st, 74107. SAN 357-8003. Tel: 918-591-4366. FAX: 918-591-4368. *Librn*, Barry Hensley; Staff 5 (MLS 1, Non-MLS 4)
Library Holdings: Bk Vols 39,451
Bookmobiles: 1

J TULSA COMMUNITY COLLEGE, (MC-LRC), Metro Campus Learning Resources Center, 909 S Boston, 74119-2095. SAN 357-8046. Tel: 918-595-7172. FAX: 918-595-7179. Web Site: www.tulsa.cc.ok.us. *Dean of Libr*, Michael David Rusk; *Coordr*, Gary Minnerath; *Publ Servs*, Janet Riggs; *Cat*, Connie Hacker; *Cat*, Paula Thomas; *Acq*, Mary Kent; *ILL*, Louise Manes; *Ser*, Brenda Haley; *Media Spec*, Casey Ashe; Staff 50 (MLS 5, Non-MLS 45)
Founded 1970. Enrl 4,284; Highest Degree: Associate
Library Holdings: Bk Titles 50,000; Per Subs 900
Subject Interests: Computer science, Health sciences
Departmental Libraries:
NORTHEAST, 3727 E Apache, 74115. SAN 357-8070. Tel: 918-595-7555. FAX: 918-595-7504. *Coordr*, Pat McCall; *Ref*, Gisele McDaniel; *Ref*, Ron Root; *Circ*, Ruth Whitson; Staff 12 (MLS 2, Non-MLS 10)
Founded 1978. Enrl 1,056; Highest Degree: Associate
Library Holdings: Bk Vols 25,000; Bk Titles 22,500; Per Subs 250
Subject Interests: Electronics, Horticulture, Natural science, Psychology
Partic in Tulsa Area Libr Coop
SOUTHEAST, 10300 E 81st St, 74133. SAN 357-8089. Tel: 918-595-7703. FAX: 918-595-7706. *Coordr*, Pat McCall; *Ref*, Suzanne Haynes; *Ref*, Amy Norman; *Circ*, Mary Estrada; *Media Spec*, Mandy Harris; Staff 5 (MLS 3, Non-MLS 2)
Library Holdings: Bk Vols 28,000; Bk Titles 26,000; Per Subs 250
Automation Activity & Vendor Info: (Circulation) Endeavor
Partic in Tulsa Area Libr Coop
WEST, 7505 W 41st St, 74107. SAN 376-9542. Tel: 918-595-8011. FAX: 918-595-7970. *Coordr*, Jeff Siddons; *Librn*, Paula Eggert; *Circ*, Lucy Colley; Staff 4 (MLS 2, Non-MLS 2)
Founded 1995

GL TULSA COUNTY LAW LIBRARY,* 500 S Denver Ave, 74103. SAN 314-027X. Tel: 918-596-5404. FAX: 918-596-4509. E-Mail: info@tulsalawlib.com. Web Site: www.tulsalawlib.com. *Dir*, Colleen F Cable; *Librn*, Joyce M Pacenza; Staff 3 (MLS 2, Non-MLS 1)
Founded 1949
Library Holdings: Bk Vols 30,000; Bk Titles 471; Per Subs 16
Partic in Am Asn of Law Librs

M TULSA REGIONAL MEDICAL CENTER, L C Baxter Medical Library H230, 744 W Ninth, 74127. SAN 324-198X. Tel: 918-599-5297. FAX: 918-599-5829. *Librn*, Beth Gault; Staff 2 (MLS 1, Non-MLS 1)
Jul 1999-Jun 2000 Mats Exp $34,000, Per/Ser (Incl. Access Fees) $29,000, Micro $5,000
Library Holdings: Bk Titles 3,000
Subject Interests: Clinical medicine, Ophthalmology, Otolaryngology, Surgery
Publications: Library News (annual newsletter)
Restriction: Staff use only

S TULSA WORLD, Library Department, 315 S Boulder, 74103-3423. (Mail add: PO Box 1770, 74102-1770), SAN 314-0288. Tel: 918-581-8583. FAX: 918-581-8425. E-Mail: worldlib@ionet.net. Web Site: www.tulsaworld.com. *Librn*, Austin Farley
Founded 1941
Library Holdings: Bk Vols 1,000
Special Collections: The Tulsa Tribune; Tulsa World
Partic in Data Time

G TULSA ZOOLOGICAL PARK LIBRARY,* 5701 E 36th St N, 74115. SAN 326-1603. Tel: 918-669-6220. FAX: 918-669-6260. *Librn*, Carol Eames; Staff 1 (Non-MLS 1)

L UNITED STATES COURTS LIBRARY,* 333 W Fourth St, 74103. SAN 372-2163. Tel: 918-581-7498. FAX: 918-581-7403. *Librn*, Leslie B McGuire; E-Mail: mcguire@oknd.uscourts.gov
Library Holdings: Bk Vols 10,000; Bk Titles 200; Per Subs 40

CM UNIVERSITY OF OKLAHOMA, Health Sciences Tulsa Schusterman Center, 1502 E 41st St, 74135. SAN 321-9771. Tel: 918-838-4613. FAX: 918-838-3215. Web Site: www.tulsa.ouhsc.edu. *Asst Dir*, Elaine Johnston; *ILL*, Marilyn Hammon; Staff 8 (MLS 2, Non-MLS 6)
Founded 1976
Library Holdings: Bk Vols 7,500; Bk Titles 6,632; Per Subs 550

Subject Interests: Medicine
Partic in Amigos Library Services, Inc; National Network Of Libraries Of Medicine - South Central Region; OCLC Online Computer Library Center, Inc

UNIVERSITY OF TULSA LIBRARIES, McFarlin Library, 2933 E Sixth St, 74104-3123. SAN 357-8135. Tel: 918-631-2873. TDD: 918-631-2873. FAX: 918-631-3791. Web Site: www.lib.utulsa.edu. *Coll Develop, Dir*, Francine Fisk; Tel: 918-631-2352, Fax: 918-631-2150, E-Mail: francine-fisk@utulsa.edu; *Access Serv*, Tom Messner; Tel: 918-631-2829, E-Mail: tom-messner@utulsa.edu; *Acq*, Steve Nobles; Tel: 918-631-2869, E-Mail: steve-nobles@utulsa@edu; *Ref*, Ann Blakely; Tel: 918-631-3061, E-Mail: ann-blakely@utulsa.edu; *Cat*, James Hoffman; Tel: 918-631-3486, E-Mail: james-hoffman@utulsa.edu; Staff 37 (MLS 14, Non-MLS 23)
Founded 1894. Enrl 4,171; Highest Degree: Doctorate
Library Holdings: Bk Vols 680,172; Bk Titles 507,637; Per Subs 2,341
Subject Interests: Am, British, Earth science, Irish lit, Liberal arts, Modern hist, Modernist, Petroleum
Special Collections: American Indian law & history (Robertson-Shleppey-Milam Coll); Modernist Literature including libraries of Edmond Wilson & Cyril Connelly; papers of Jean Rhys, Anna Kavan, Stevie Smith, Rebecca West, Richard Ellmann, Richard Murphy, V S Naipaul, publisher Andre Deutsch, & others; strong holdings of James Joyce, Robert Graves, D H Lawrence & others
Automation Activity & Vendor Info: (Acquisitions) Innovative Interfaces Inc.; (Cataloging) Innovative Interfaces Inc.; (Circulation) Innovative Interfaces Inc.; (ILL) Innovative Interfaces Inc.; (OPAC) Innovative Interfaces Inc.; (Serials) Innovative Interfaces Inc.
Database Vendor: Innovative Interfaces INN - View
Publications: Annual Keepsakes; Exhibition Catalogues
Partic in Amigos Library Services, Inc; BCR; LVIS; OCLC Online Computer Library Center, Inc; Research Libraries Group, Inc
Departmental Libraries:

L COLLEGE OF LAW LIBRARY, 3120 E Fourth Pl, 74104-3189. SAN 357-8194. Tel: 918-631-2404. Interlibrary Loan Service Tel: 918-631-2460. FAX: 918-631-3556. Web Site: www.utulsa.edu/law/library. *Dir*, Richard E Ducey; *Assoc Dir*, Lou Lindsey; E-Mail: louise-lindsey@utulsa.edu; *Access Serv, ILL*, Carol Arnold; *Cat*, Katherine J Tooley; *Ref*, Kathy Kane; *Electronic Resources, Media Spec*, Toni Forrester; *Acq, Govt Doc*, Melanie Nelson; *Ser*, Ryan Christy; Staff 16 (MLS 8, Non-MLS 8)
Founded 1923. Enrl 559; Fac 56; Highest Degree: Doctorate
Library Holdings: Bk Vols 279,864; Bk Titles 41,471; Per Subs 3,964
Subject Interests: Energy, Environ, Native Am
Automation Activity & Vendor Info: (Acquisitions) Innovative Interfaces Inc.; (Cataloging) Innovative Interfaces Inc.; (Circulation) Innovative Interfaces Inc.; (Course Reserve) Innovative Interfaces Inc.; (ILL) Innovative Interfaces Inc.; (OPAC) Innovative Interfaces Inc.; (Serials) Innovative Interfaces Inc.
Publications: Faculty publications; Library Guide
Restriction: Members only
Partic in Amigos Library Services, Inc; Mid-Am Law Sch Libr Consortium; OCLC Online Computer Library Center, Inc

THE WILLIAMS COMPANIES, Law Library,* Legal Dept-Law Library 41-3, One Williams Center, 74172. SAN 372-218X. Tel: 918-573-2000, 918-573-4738. FAX: 918-573-3005. *Librn*, Janet Esch; E-Mail: jesch@lgl.twc.com
Library Holdings: Bk Vols 10,000; Per Subs 50
Subject Interests: Corporate law

VANCE AFB

UNITED STATES AIR FORCE

A VANCE AIR FORCE BASE LIBRARY, 71 FTW/NW-CL, 446 McAffrey Ave Bldg 314 Ste 24, 73705-5710. SAN 357-8259. Tel: 580-213-7368. FAX: 580-237-8106. *Librn*, Tom L Kirk; E-Mail: kirkt@vnc.gate1.vnc.aetc.af.mil
Founded 1941
Library Holdings: Bk Vols 15,000; Per Subs 128
Subject Interests: Aviation, Flying
Partic in Fed Librns Round Table

VINITA

M EASTERN STATE HOSPITAL, Medical Library,* PO Box 69, 74301-0069. SAN 324-6299. Tel: 918-256-7841, Ext 402. FAX: 918-256-4491. *Librn*, Mary Floyd
Library Holdings: Bk Titles 450; Per Subs 75
Special Collections: Historical Coll
Partic in S Cent Regional Med Libr Program
Special Services for the Deaf - Books on deafness & sign language; Videos & decoder

WAGONER

P WAGONER CARNEGIE LIBRARY, 102 S State St, 74467. SAN 314-0318. Tel: 918-485-2126. FAX: 918-485-0179. E-Mail: wagonerlibrary@wagoner.lib.ok.us. *Librn*, Jean Willey; *Asst Librn*, Phylis Hobbs
Pop 7,000; Circ 29,779
Jul 2000-Jun 2001 Income $15,000, State $3,000, City $12,000. Mats Exp $15,000, Books $12,000, Per/Ser (Incl. Access Fees) $600, Electronic Ref Mat (Incl. Access Fees) $2,400. Sal $60,000
Library Holdings: Bk Vols 19,000; Per Subs 21
Friends of the Library Group

WALTERS

P WALTERS PUBLIC LIBRARY, 202 N Broadway St, 73572-1226. SAN 314-0326. Tel: 580-875-2006. FAX: 580-875-2023. E-Mail: walterspublic@yahoo.com. *Librn*, Nancy Lee Adkison; *Assoc Librn*, Corella Fletcher; Staff 2 (Non-MLS 2)
Founded 1922. Pop 2,774; Circ 23,942
2000-2001 Income $21,211, State $1,500, City $19,000, Federal $721. Mats Exp $2,256, Books $2,000, Per/Ser (Incl. Access Fees) $256, Electronic Ref Mat (Incl. Access Fees) $250. Sal $17,851 (Prof $10,800)
Library Holdings: Bk Vols 9,940; Bk Titles 9,879; Per Subs 35
Subject Interests: Genealogy
Special Collections: Oklahoma Section
Automation Activity & Vendor Info: (Circulation) Sagebrush Corporation
Database Vendor: IAC - SearchBank, Innovative Interfaces INN - View
Function: ILL available

WARNER

J CONNORS STATE COLLEGE LIBRARY, Rte 1, Box 1000, 74469-9700. SAN 314-0334. Tel: 918-463-2931. FAX: 918-463-6314. *Dir*, Margaret Rigney; *Dir*, Izoro Daphane Kerley; E-Mail: idkerle@connors.cc.ok.us; Staff 5 (MLS 1, Non-MLS 4)
Founded 1950. Enrl 2,200; Highest Degree: Associate
Jul 1999-Jun 2000 Income $486,350. Mats Exp $107,065, Per/Ser (Incl. Access Fees) $25,000, Micro $14,000, AV Equip $8,065, Other Print Mats $40,000, Electronic Ref Mat (Incl. Access Fees) $20,000. Sal $392,003 (Prof $170,079)
Library Holdings: Bk Vols 33,400; Per Subs 300
Database Vendor: OCLC - First Search
Partic in Amigos Library Services, Inc; Onenet

P WARNER PUBLIC LIBRARY,* 207 Eighth St, PO Box 120, 74469. SAN 376-5970. Tel: 918-463-2363. FAX: 918-463-2711. *Librn*, Peggy Matthews
Library Holdings: Bk Vols 5,000; Per Subs 30
Mem of Eastern Oklahoma District Library System
Friends of the Library Group

WATONGA

P WATONGA PUBLIC LIBRARY,* 301 N Prouty, 73772. SAN 314-0342. Tel: 580-623-7748. FAX: 580-623-7747. E-Mail: bookwoman@pldi.net. *Chief Librn*, Terri Crawford; *Asst Librn*, Sharon Barnes; Staff 4 (MLS 2, Non-MLS 2)
Founded 1906. Pop 5,000; Circ 38,313
Library Holdings: Bk Vols 30,000; Bk Titles 28,000; Per Subs 75
Subject Interests: Local genealogy, Local history, Okla hist
Special Collections: Local History (Blaine County Coll), bks & interviews tapes
Publications: Books in Print; Publishers Weekly; Subject Guide to Books in Print
Partic in Okla Telecommunications Interlibr Syst
Participate in a statewide serials Information Exchange with other libraries via fax machine
Friends of the Library Group

WAURIKA

P WAURIKA LIBRARY,* 98th Meridian St, 73573. SAN 314-0350. Tel: 580-228-3274. FAX: 580-228-3274. *Librn*, Molly Hobbs
Circ 17,938
Library Holdings: Bk Vols 10,048

WAYNOKA

P WAYNOKA PUBLIC LIBRARY,* 113 E Cecil St, 73860. SAN 314-0369. Tel: 580-824-6181. FAX: 580-824-6181. *Librn*, Sue Whipple
Pop 1,370; Circ 5,404
Library Holdings: Bk Vols 12,000

WEATHERFORD

C SOUTHWESTERN OKLAHOMA STATE UNIVERSITY, Al Harris Library, 809 N Custer, 73096-3002. SAN 357-8283. Tel: 580-774-3730. Interlibrary Loan Service Tel: 580-774-7026. TDD: 580-774-7075. FAX: 580-774-3112. Web Site: www.swosu.edu/library/. *Actg Dir, Coll Develop*, Linda Pye; Tel: 580-774-7081, E-Mail: pyel@swosu.edu; *Doc, ILL, Ref*, Carolyn Armold Torrence; Tel: 580-774-3031, E-Mail: torrenc@swosu.edu; *Acq*, Jeannie Moss; Tel: 580-774-7021, E-Mail: mossj@swosu.edu; *Cat*, George Alsbach; Tel: 580-774-3089, E-Mail: alsbacg@swosu.edu; *Ser*, Audrey DeFrank; Tel: 580-774-3030, E-Mail: defrana@swosu.edu; *Publ Servs*, David Scott; Tel: 580-774-7089, E-Mail: scottd@swosu.edu; *Automation Syst Coordr*, Jonathan Woltz; Tel: 580-774-7074, E-Mail: woltzj@swosu.edu; Staff 7 (MLS 7)
Founded 1902. Enrl 4,355; Fac 256; Highest Degree: Master
Jul 1999-Jun 2000 Income $1,360,668. Mats Exp $669,345, Books $176,100, Per/Ser (Incl. Access Fees) $446,805, Presv $17,000, Micro $27,848, Electronic Ref Mat (Incl. Access Fees) $1,592. Sal $556,588 (Prof $285,394)
Library Holdings: Bk Vols 291,923; Bk Titles 182,600; Per Subs 1,394
Subject Interests: Education, Pharmacy
Special Collections: SWOSU University publications
Automation Activity & Vendor Info: (Acquisitions) DRA; (Cataloging) DRA; (Circulation) DRA; (Course Reserve) DRA; (ILL) DRA; (OPAC) DRA; (Serials) DRA
Partic in OCLC Online Computer Library Center, Inc

P WEATHERFORD PUBLIC LIBRARY, 219 E Frankin, 73096-5134. SAN 325-1330. Tel: 580-772-3591. FAX: 580-772-3591. E-Mail: wplswpl@itlnet.net. *Librn*, Kathy Megli; *Asst Librn*, Ella Olson
Library Holdings: Bk Vols 63,000; Per Subs 40
Friends of the Library Group

WESTVILLE

P JOHN F HENDERSON PUBLIC LIBRARY,* 116 N Williams, PO Box 580, 74965-0580. SAN 314-0377. Tel: 918-723-5002. FAX: 918-723-3400. *Librn*, Sue Ann Ghormley
Founded 1969. Pop 1,049
Library Holdings: Bk Vols 10,000; Per Subs 25
Mem of Eastern Oklahoma District Library System

WETUMKA

P WETUMKA PUBLIC LIBRARY,* 202 N Main, 74883. SAN 324-0347. Tel: 405-452-5825. FAX: 405-452-5825. *Librn*, Joan Hill
Pop 2,000
Library Holdings: Bk Titles 10,000

WEWOKA

S SEMINOLE NATION MUSEUM LIBRARY, 524 S Wewoka, PO Box 1532, 74884. SAN 375-6718. Tel: 405-257-5580. E-Mail: semuseum@chickasaw.com. *Curator*, Lewis Johnson; *Pres*, Jerry McNally
Founded 1974
Library Holdings: Bk Titles 2,500
Subject Interests: Black history, Cultural hist
Restriction: In-house use for visitors

P WEWOKA PUBLIC LIBRARY, 118 W Fifth, 74884. SAN 314-0385. Tel: 405-257-3225. FAX: 405-257-5049. *Librn*, Carolyn Trimble; *Asst Librn*, Barbara Crelia
Founded 1928
Library Holdings: Bk Vols 23,355

WILBURTON

C EASTERN OKLAHOMA STATE COLLEGE LIBRARY, Media Center, 1301 W Main St, 74578. SAN 314-0393. Tel: 918-465-2361, Ext 218. FAX: 918-465-0112. Web Site: www.eosc.cc.ok.us/library. *Dir Libr Serv*, Mary Edith Butler; Tel: 918-465-2361, Ext 352, E-Mail: mebutler@eosc.cc.ok.us; *Cat*, Kim Pendergraft; Tel: 918-465-2361, Ext 218, E-Mail: kdpendergraft@eosc.cc.ok.us. Subject Specialists: *History*, Mary Edith Butler; Staff 5 (MLS 2, Non-MLS 3)
Founded 1919. Enrl 1,800; Fac 52; Highest Degree: Associate
Jul 2000-Jun 2001 Income $74,100. Mats Exp $58,100, Books $30,000, Per/Ser (Incl. Access Fees) $8,800, AV Equip $6,300, Electronic Ref Mat (Incl Access Fees) $13,000
Library Holdings: Bk Vols 41,000; Per Subs 220; Spec Interest Per Sub 4 Bks on Deafness & Sign Lang 12
Special Collections: Native American Coll
Database Vendor: IAC - Info Trac, OCLC - First Search
Function: Photocopies available
Partic in Amigos Library Services, Inc; OCLC Online Computer Library Center, Inc

P LATIMER COUNTY PUBLIC LIBRARY,* 301 W Ada Ave, PO Box 126 74578. SAN 314-0407. Tel: 918-465-3751. FAX: 918-465-4287. *Librn*, Shirley Bambeck; *Asst Librn*, Latoyah Pendergraft
Pop 3,000
Library Holdings: Bk Vols 15,000; Per Subs 25
Mem of Eastern Oklahoma District Library System

WISTER

P WISTER PUBLIC LIBRARY, 101 Caston, 74966. (Mail add: PO Box 408, 74966), SAN 314-0415. Tel: 918-655-7654. FAX: 918-655-3267. *Head Librn*, Leslie H Langley; E-Mail: langley@sepl.lib.ok.us; *Librn*, Carole Brents; *Asst Librn*, Crystal Burden; *Ch Servs*, Kara Hammons; E-Mail: hammons@sepl.lib.ok.us; Staff 2 (Non-MLS 2)
Pop 1,200; Circ 13,000
Library Holdings: Bk Titles 8,600
Function: ILL available
Mem of Southeastern Public Library System Of Oklahoma

WOODWARD

P WOODWARD PUBLIC LIBRARY, 1500 Main St, 73801. SAN 314-0423. Tel: 580-254-8544, 580-254-8545 (Children's Room). FAX: 580-254-8546. E-Mail: wwbks@woodward.lib.ok.us. *Dir*, Kay Bell; E-Mail: kbell@woodwardlib.ok.us; *Ch Servs*, Connie Terry; *Ad Servs*, Paula Odell; Staff 6 (Non-MLS 6)
Founded 1899. Pop 12,340; Circ 75,448
Jul 1999-Jun 2000 Income $270,843, State $6,145, City $234,740, Locally Generated Income $29,958. Mats Exp $35,562, Books $24,754, Per/Ser (Incl. Access Fees) $5,185, Micro $231, AV Equip $2,057, Other Print Mats $1,985, Electronic Ref Mat (Incl. Access Fees) $1,350. Sal $195,918
Library Holdings: Bk Vols 37,485; Bk Titles 33,737; Per Subs 97; High Interest/Low Vocabulary Bk Vols 313; Bks on Deafness & Sign Lang 18
Subject Interests: Genealogy, Literacy
Special Collections: Genealogy; Oklahoma History Coll, bks, pamphlets
Automation Activity & Vendor Info: (Circulation) Follett; (OPAC) Follett
Database Vendor: Ebsco - EbscoHost
Special Services for the Blind - Bks on tape
Friends of the Library Group

YALE

P YALE PUBLIC LIBRARY, 213 N Main, 74085. SAN 314-0431. Tel: 918-387-2135. FAX: 918-387-2616. E-Mail: yale_lib@swbell.net. *Librn*, Janice Clark; *Asst Librn*, Linda Butcher; Staff 2 (Non-MLS 2)
Founded 1919. Pop 1,392; Circ 18,531
1999-2000 Income $57,587, State $1,500, City $45,807, Federal $1,258, Other $9,022. Mats Exp $15,479, Books $4,603, Per/Ser (Incl. Access Fees) $312, AV Equip $389, Other Print Mats $610, Electronic Ref Mat (Incl. Access Fees) $9,565. Sal $27,968
Library Holdings: Bk Vols 12,085; Per Subs 27
Subject Interests: Large print, Videos
Function: ILL available
Partic in OLTN
Friends of the Library Group

YUKON

P MABEL C FRY PUBLIC LIBRARY,* 1200 Lakeshore Dr, 73099. SAN 314-044X. Tel: 405-354-8232. FAX: 405-350-7928. Web Site: www.yukon.lib.ok.us. *Librn*, Sue Kilmer; E-Mail: skilmer@yukon.lib.ok.us; *Asst Librn*, Corby Poursaba
Founded 1905. Circ 48,300
Library Holdings: Bk Vols 33,000; Per Subs 80
Friends of the Library Group

Date of Statistics: 1999-2000
Population, 1999 (From Portland State University, Center for Population Research and Census): 3,300,800
Population Served by Public Libraries: 3,107,215
Unserved: 160,335
Total Volumes in Public Libraries: 9,059,515
Volumes Per Capita: 2.96
Total Public Library Circulation: 31,792,471
Circulation Per Capita: 10.27
Total Public Library Expenditure: $96,000,000
Expenditures Per Capita: $30.00
Number of County Libraries: 17
Counties Served: 36
Counties Unserved: 0
Number of Bookmobiles in State: 8
Grants-in-Aid to Public Libraries
State (2000-01): $704,311
Federal: (2000 Library Services & Technology Act): $1,775,030; Grants: $1,420,873
State Library's Share from Federal Sources: $354,157

ADAMS

P ADAMS PUBLIC LIBRARY,* 190 Main St, PO Box 20, 97810-0017. SAN 328-9079. Tel: 541-566-2298. FAX: 541-566-2298. *Librn*, Martha Mitchell
Library Holdings: Bk Vols 4,000

AGNESS

P AGNESS COMMUNITY LIBRARY, 03509 Cougar Lane, 97406. (Mail add: PO Box 33, 97406-0033), SAN 314-0458. Tel: 541-247-6323. FAX: 541-247-6323. E-Mail: agnesslb@harborside.com. *Coll Develop, Librn*, Deborah D Crouse; Staff 4 (Non-MLS 4)
Founded 1943. Pop 220; Circ 5,921
Jul 1999-Jun 2000 Income $16,000. Mats Exp $750, Books $450, Per/Ser (Incl. Access Fees) $50, Other Print Mats $250. Sal $10,000
Library Holdings: Bk Vols 12,000; Per Subs 11
Subject Interests: Local Native Am

ALBANY

S ALBANY GENERAL HOSPITAL, Stanley K Davis Library,* 1046 SW Sixth St, 97321. SAN 325-7835. Tel: 541-812-4446. FAX: 541-812-4482. *Librn*, Roger Davis; E-Mail: rdavis@firstcarehealth.org
Library Holdings: Bk Vols 700; Per Subs 200
Partic in OCLC Online Computer Library Center, Inc

P ALBANY PUBLIC LIBRARY, 1390 Waverly Dr SE, 97321-6945. SAN 357-8348. Tel: 541-917-7580. Interlibrary Loan Service Tel: 541-917-7582. Circulation Tel: 541-917-7581. Reference Tel: 541-917-7582. FAX: 541-917-7586. Web Site: www.ci.albany.or.us. *Dir*, Edward House, Jr; Tel: 541-917-7589, E-Mail: ehouse@ci.albany.or.us; *Admin Assoc*, Kathy Grosso; Tel: 541-917-7590, E-Mail: kgrosse@ci.albany.or.us; *Senior Librn*, Diane White; Tel: 541-917-7592, E-Mail: dwhite@ci.albany.or.us; *Ch Servs*, Scott Keeney; Tel: 541-917-7591, E-Mail: skeeney@ci.albany.or.us; *Tech Servs*, Laurel Langenwalter; Tel: 541-917-7580, Ext 4700, E-Mail: llangenwalter@ci.albany.or.us; *Ref Serv*, Ed Gallagher; Tel: 541-917-7580, Ext 4306, E-Mail: egallagher@ci.albany.or.us; *Ref Serv*, Mary Kontny; Tel: 541-917-7580, Ext 4702, E-Mail: mkontny@ci.albany.or.us; *YA Servs*, Doris Hicks; Tel: 541-917-7580, Ext 4319, E-Mail: dhicks@ci.albany.or.us; Staff 8 (MLS 7, Non-MLS 1)
Founded 1907. Pop 40,010; Circ 441,264
Jul 1999-Jun 2000 Income (Main Library and Branch Library) $1,105,785, State $10,179, City $1,054,052, Other $41,554. Mats Exp $187,943, Books $138,057, AV Equip $49,886. Sal $721,884
Library Holdings: Bk Vols 114,393; Per Subs 257
Special Collections: Oregon History
Automation Activity & Vendor Info: (Acquisitions) Inlex; (Cataloging) Inlex; (Circulation) Inlex; (OPAC) Inlex
Database Vendor: Ebsco - EbscoHost
Publications: Between the Covers (quarterly newsletter)
Partic in OCLC Online Computer Library Center, Inc
Friends of the Library Group

Branches: 1
DOWNTOWN CARNEGIE, 302 Ferry St SE, 97321-2216. SAN 357-8372. Tel: 541-917-7585. *Branch Mgr*, Marcia Timm; E-Mail: mtimm@ci.albany.or.us; Staff 1 (MLS 1)
Founded 1913
Library Holdings: Bk Vols 20,400
Subject Interests: Hist home renovation
Friends of the Library Group

J LINN-BENTON COMMUNITY COLLEGE LIBRARY, 6500 SW Pacific Blvd, 97321-3799. SAN 314-0466. Tel: 541-917-4638. FAX: 541-917-4659. Web Site: www.lbcc.cc.or.us/library/. *Dean of Libr*, Diane Watson; *Media Spec*, Paul Snyder; *Acq, Coll Develop, Tech Servs*, Jorry Rolfe; Tel: 541-917-4649, E-Mail: rolfej@gw.lbcc.cc.or.us; *Bibliog Instr, Ref*, Charles Weyant; Tel: 541-917-4641, 4645, E-Mail: weyantc@gw.lbcc.cc.or.us; *Bibliog Instr, Ref*, Judith Turner; Tel: 541-917-4646, 4645, E-Mail: turnerj@gw.lbcc.cc.or.us; Staff 3 (MLS 3)
Founded 1969. Enrl 6,042; Fac 200
Jul 2000-Jun 2001 Income $433,160. Mats Exp $80,840, Books $48,284, Per/Ser (Incl. Access Fees) $10,000, Micro $900, AV Equip $5,000, Electronic Ref Mat (Incl. Access Fees) $16,656. Sal $320,802 (Prof $162,000)
Library Holdings: Bk Vols 50,000; Bk Titles 45,000; Per Subs 175
Subject Interests: Linn-Benton County hist, Nursing, Vocational-tech mat
Automation Activity & Vendor Info: (Cataloging) DRA; (Circulation) DRA; (OPAC) DRA
Database Vendor: OCLC - First Search
Partic in OCLC Online Computer Library Center, Inc; Valley Link

G UNITED STATES DEPARTMENT OF ENERGY, (ARC), Albany Research Center Library, 1450 Queen Ave SW, 97321-2198. SAN 314-0490. Tel: 541-967-5864. FAX: 541-967-5936. Web Site: www.alrc.doe.gov/library/alrclib.html. *Info Specialist*, Cathy Wright; E-Mail: clark@alrc.doe.gov; Staff 1 (Non-MLS 1)
Founded 1943
Library Holdings: Bk Vols 13,000; Bk Titles 10,000; Per Subs 80
Subject Interests: Chemistry, Energy, Mat sci, Metallurgy, Mineralogy, Physics
Automation Activity & Vendor Info: (Cataloging) CASPR; (Circulation) CASPR; (ILL) CASPR; (Serials) CASPR
Restriction: Open to public upon request
Partic in Fedlink; OCLC Online Computer Library Center, Inc

AMITY

P AMITY PUBLIC LIBRARY,* 307 Trade St, PO Box 470, 97101-0470. SAN 376-3315. Tel: 503-835-8181. *Librn*, Eileen Lewis
Library Holdings: Bk Vols 7,000; Bk Titles 6,000
Partic in Chemeketa Cooperative Regional Library Service

ARLINGTON

P ARLINGTON PUBLIC LIBRARY,* PO Box 339, 97812-0339. SAN 357-8704. Tel: 541-454-2444. *Librn*, Kathy Covey
Pop 525; Circ 2,453
1997-1998 Income $4,500, City $2,500, County $2,000. Mats Exp $1,044, Books $800, Per/Ser (Incl. Access Fees) $44. Sal $3,300
Library Holdings: Bk Vols 6,310

ASHLAND

C SOUTHERN OREGON UNIVERSITY LIBRARY,* 1250 Siskiyou Blvd, 97520-5076. SAN 314-0504. Tel: 541-552-6441. Interlibrary Loan Service Tel: 541-552-6823. FAX: 541-552-6429. Web Site: www.sou.edu/library. *Dir*, Sue Burkholder; *Ref*, Connie Anderson; *Tech Servs*, Teresa Montgomery; *Cat*, Xudong Jin; *Circ, ILL*, Deborah Cook; *Doc*, Deborah Hollens; *Coll Develop*, Mary Jane Cedar Face
Founded 1926. Enrl 5,023; Fac 272; Highest Degree: Master
1998-1999 Income $1,535,048. Mats Exp $498,134, Books $169,501, Per/Ser (Incl. Access Fees) $193,336, Presv $15,956, Micro $27,891, AV Equip $10,609, Electronic Ref Mat (Incl. Access Fees) $80,841. Sal $883,472 (Prof $494,283)
Library Holdings: Bk Vols 327,337; Bk Titles 252,997; Per Subs 2,085
Subject Interests: Bus, Education, Local history, Shakespeare studies, Theater
Special Collections: Oregon State Documents; Shakespeare-Renaissance (Bailey)
Automation Activity & Vendor Info: (Acquisitions) Innovative Interfaces Inc.; (Cataloging) Innovative Interfaces Inc.; (Circulation) Innovative Interfaces Inc.; (Course Reserve) Innovative Interfaces Inc.; (OPAC) Innovative Interfaces Inc.; (Serials) Innovative Interfaces Inc.
Database Vendor: OCLC - First Search
Partic in OCLC Online Computer Library Center, Inc; Orbis
Friends of the Library Group

ASTORIA

P ASTORIA PUBLIC LIBRARY, 450 Tenth St, 97103. SAN 314-0512. Tel: 503-325-7323. FAX: 503-325-2997. *Head Librn*, Jane Tucker; E-Mail: jtucker@astoria.or.us; Staff 6 (MLS 2, Non-MLS 4)
Founded 1892. Pop 10,000
Library Holdings: Bk Vols 72,000
Automation Activity & Vendor Info: (Cataloging) epixtech, inc.; (Circulation) epixtech, inc.
Database Vendor: epixtech, inc.
Function: ILL limited
Friends of the Library Group

J CLATSOP COMMUNITY COLLEGE LIBRARY, 1680 Lexington, 97103. SAN 314-0520. Tel: 503-338-2462. FAX: 503-338-2387. Web Site: library.clatsop.cc.or.us. *Dir*, Claire Rivers; *Acq*, Maria Koehmstedt; *Cat*, Sara Campbell; Staff 3 (MLS 3)
Founded 1962. Enrl 1,450; Fac 40; Highest Degree: Associate
Library Holdings: Bk Vols 42,307; Bk Titles 38,969; Per Subs 670; High Interest/Low Vocabulary Bk Vols 100
Subject Interests: Local, Marine tech, Regional hist
Automation Activity & Vendor Info: (Acquisitions) Endeavor; (Cataloging) Endeavor; (Circulation) Endeavor; (Course Reserve) Endeavor; (OPAC) Endeavor; (Serials) Endeavor
Restriction: Restricted access
Partic in OCLC Online Computer Library Center, Inc

S COLUMBIA RIVER MARITIME MUSEUM LIBRARY,* 1792 Marine Dr, 97103. SAN 314-0539. Tel: 503-325-2323. FAX: 503-325-2331. *Curator*, Dave Pearson
Founded 1962
1997-1998 Mats Exp $300
Library Holdings: Bk Titles 5,085; Per Subs 194
Subject Interests: Folklore, Maritime history, Technology
Special Collections: Maritime Photo Archive; Vessel Plans Coll
Publications: Quarterdeck (quarterly newsletter)
Restriction: Non-circulating to the public

ATHENA

P ATHENA PUBLIC LIBRARY,* 418 E Main St, PO Box 450, 97813-0450. SAN 358-0474. Tel: 541-566-2470. FAX: 541-566-2470. *Librn*, Carrie Bremer
Library Holdings: Bk Titles 9,000; Per Subs 68
Open Mon & Thurs 12:30-5

BAKER CITY

P BAKER COUNTY PUBLIC LIBRARY, 2400 Resort St, 97814-2798. SAN 357-8437. Tel: 541-523-6419. FAX: 541-523-9088. *Dir*, Aletha G Bonebrake; E-Mail: alethab@oregontrail.net; *Bkmobile Coordr*, Doneita Clair; *ILL*, Carmen Wickam; Staff 9 (MLS 1, Non-MLS 8)
Founded 1906. Pop 16,750; Circ 131,820
Jul 2000-Jun 2001 Income $436,493, State $8,972, County $393,021, Locally Generated Income $9,000, Other $25,500. Mats Exp $67,000, Book $57,000, Per/Ser (Incl. Access Fees) $9,000, Presv $700. Sal $284,695 (Pro $49,642)
Library Holdings: Bk Vols 107,093; Per Subs 305
Special Collections: Baker County Coll; Oregon History Coll
Automation Activity & Vendor Info: (Cataloging) Innovative Interfaces Inc.; (Circulation) Innovative Interfaces Inc.; (OPAC) Innovative Interfaces Inc.
Database Vendor: Innovative Interfaces INN - View
Function: ILL available
Friends of the Library Group
Branches: 4
HAINES BRANCH, Haines, 97833. SAN 357-8461. *Librn*, Donna Kilgore
HALFWAY BRANCH, Halfway, 97834. SAN 357-8496. *Librn*, Linda Bergeron
HUNTINGTON BRANCH, Huntington, 97907. SAN 357-8526. *Librn*, Dixi Griffin
RICHLAND BRANCH, Richland, 97870. SAN 357-8550. *Librn*, Bonnaden Nicolescu
Bookmobiles: 1

BANDON

P BANDON PUBLIC LIBRARY,* City Hall, Hwy 101, PO Box 128, 97411-0128. SAN 314-0563. Tel: 541-347-3221. FAX: 541-347-9363. *Librn*, Judy Romans; *Asst Librn*, Susan Kling; Staff 2 (MLS 2)
Pop 6,871; Circ 74,607
Jul 1997-Jun 1998 Income $180,000, State $1,251, County $159,124, Locally Generated Income $1,579. Mats Exp $25,747, Books $21,531, Per/Ser (Incl. Access Fees) $2,481. Sal $78,716
Library Holdings: Bk Titles 26,000; Per Subs 92
Special Collections: Oral history on the Banvon Fire of 1936
Publications: Friends (quarterly newsletter)
Partic in Coos County Library Service District, Extended Service Office
Friends of the Library Group

BANKS

P BANKS PUBLIC LIBRARY, 111 Market St, 97106. SAN 314-0571. Tel: 503-324-1382. FAX: 503-324-1382. *Adminr*, Denise Holmes
Founded 1976
Mem of Washington County Cooperative Library Services
Open Tues-Thurs 11-7, Fri & Sat 11-5

BEAVERTON

P BEAVERTON CITY LIBRARY,* 12375 SW Fifth St, 97005-2883. SAN 314-058X. Tel: 503-644-2197. FAX: 503-526-2636. Web Site: www.wilinet.wccls.lib.or.us (OPAC County Coop). *YA Servs*, Valerie Talbert; *Circ*, Chuck Amsberry; *Ref*, Anna Kalinak; *Tech Servs*, John Switzer; Staff 12 (MLS 12)
Pop 110,000; Circ 1,258,252
Jul 1997-Jun 1998 Income $3,400,000, State $9,818, City $904,893, County $2,292,215, Locally Generated Income $80,000, Other $120,000. Mats Exp $483,829. Sal $2,191,427
Library Holdings: Bk Vols 302,859; Per Subs 1,230
Special Collections: United States Government Publications
Mem of Washington County Cooperative Library Services
Open Mon-Thurs 9:30-8:45, Fri & Sat 9:30-5:15 & Sun 12-5:15
Friends of the Library Group

S GEMSTONE SYSTEMS, INC, Corporate Information Center,* 20575 NW Von Neumann Dr, 97006. SAN 328-073X. Tel: 503-533-3000. FAX: 503-690-7205. Web Site: www.gemstone.com.
Founded 1982
Library Holdings: Bk Titles 1,900; Per Subs 160
Subject Interests: Computer science, Electrical engineering
Restriction: Staff use only
Partic in OCLC Online Computer Library Center, Inc

C OREGON GRADUATE INSTITUTE OF SCIENCE & TECHNOLOGY LIBRARY, 20000 NW Walker Rd, 97006-8921. SAN 314-0601. Tel: 503-748-1383. Interlibrary Loan Service Tel: 503-748-1061. Circulation Tel: 503-748-1383. Reference Tel: 503-748-7399. FAX: 503-748-1029. E-Mail: library@admin.ogi.edu. Web Site: www.ogi.edu/library. *Dir Libr Serv*, Carol S Resco; Tel: 503-748-1060, E-Mail: resco@admin.ogi.edu; *Ref*, Peng Zhang; Tel: 503-748-7311, E-Mail: pengz@admin.org.edu; *Tech Servs*, Julianne Williams; Tel: 503-748-1062, E-Mail: williams@admin.ogi.edu. Subject Specialists: *Computer science*, Julianne Williams; *Science/technology*, Carol S Resco; Staff 6 (MLS 3, Non-MLS 3)
Founded 1968. Enrl 350; Highest Degree: Doctorate
Jun 2000-Jul 2001 Income $580,000, Locally Generated Income $20,000, Parent Institution $560,000. Mats Exp $280,000, Books $60,000, Per/Ser

(Incl. Access Fees) $200,000, Electronic Ref Mat (Incl. Access Fees) $20,000. Sal $224,676 (Prof $120,000)
Library Holdings: Bk Vols 35,000; Bk Titles 18,000; Per Subs 370
Subject Interests: Biochemistry, Computer science, Electrical engineering, Environ scis
Automation Activity & Vendor Info: (Acquisitions) epixtech, inc.; (Cataloging) epixtech, inc.; (Circulation) epixtech, inc.; (Course Reserve) epixtech, inc.; (OPAC) epixtech, inc.; (Serials) epixtech, inc.
Database Vendor: Ebsco - EbscoHost, OCLC - First Search, OVID Technologies
Publications: Serials Catalog
Partic in Portland Area Libr Syst; Washington County Cooperative Library Services

M OREGON REGIONAL PRIMATE RESEARCH CENTER, McDonald Library, 505 NW 185th Ave, 97006. SAN 314-061X. Tel: 503-690-5311. FAX: 503-690-5243. *Assoc Librn*, Marlene Abrams; *Librn*, Cooky Abrams; E-Mail: abramsc@ohsu.edu. Subject Specialists: *Primatology*, Cooky Abrams; Staff 2 (MLS 1, Non-MLS 1)
Founded 1961
Library Holdings: Per Subs 180
Subject Interests: Biomedical lit, Primates
Special Collections: Primatology Coll
Partic in Washington County Libr Network

TEKTRONIX, INC LIBRARY, 14150 SW Karl Brawn Dr, MS 50-510, 97005. (Mail add: PO Box 500, MS 50-510, 97077-0001), Tel: 503-627-5385. Interlibrary Loan Service Tel: 503-627-5388. FAX: 503-627-4853. *Mgr*, Yan Y Soucie; E-Mail: yan.soucie@tektronix.com; Staff 2 (MLS 1, Non-MLS 1)
Founded 1959
Library Holdings: Bk Vols 27,500; Per Subs 225
Subject Interests: Computer science, Electronics, Optics
Database Vendor: Dialog

BEND

C CENTRAL OREGON COMMUNITY COLLEGE, Library-Media Services, Library/Media Services, 2600 NW College Way, 97701-5998. SAN 314-0636. Tel: 541-383-7560. Reference Tel: 541-383-7567. FAX: 541-383-7507. E-Mail: dbilyeu@cocc.edu. Web Site: www.cocc.edu/library2/default.htm. *Dir*, David Bilyeu; Tel: 541-383-7563, E-Mail: dbilyeu@cocc.edu; *Head Ref*, Tina Hovekamp; Tel: 541-383-7295, E-Mail: thovekamp@cocc.edu; *Assoc Prof*, Catherine Finney; Tel: 541-383-7559, E-Mail: cfinney@cocc.edu; *Tech Coordr*, Mark Dahl; Tel: 541-383-7783, E-Mail: mdahl@cocc.edu; Staff 20 (MLS 5, Non-MLS 15)
Founded 1950. Enrl 3,653; Highest Degree: Associate
Jul 1999-Jun 2000 Income $854,738, Federal $14,537, Locally Generated Income $1,259, Parent Institution $721,578, Other $117,364. Mats Exp $183,425, Books $111,196, Per/Ser (Incl. Access Fees) $30,318, Presv $2,356, Micro $10,314, AV Equip $11,584, Electronic Ref Mat (Incl. Access Fees) $29,241. Sal $499,882 (Prof $249,984)
Library Holdings: Bk Vols 66,452; Bk Titles 58,294; Per Subs 364; High Interest/Low Vocabulary Bk Vols 163; Bks on Deafness & Sign Lang 89
Subject Interests: Native Am
Automation Activity & Vendor Info: (Acquisitions) Innovative Interfaces Inc.; (Cataloging) Innovative Interfaces Inc.; (Circulation) Innovative Interfaces Inc.; (Course Reserve) Innovative Interfaces Inc.; (ILL) Innovative Interfaces Inc.; (Media Booking) Innovative Interfaces Inc.; (OPAC) Innovative Interfaces Inc.; (Serials) Innovative Interfaces Inc.
Database Vendor: Ebsco - EbscoHost, Lexis-Nexis, OCLC - First Search
Publications: College Library Skills (materials for 1 credit course)
Partic in Orbis

P DESCHUTES PUBLIC LIBRARY DISTRICT, 507 NW Wall St, 97701-2698. SAN 357-8585. Tel: 541-617-7040. FAX: 541-617-7044. *Dir*, Michael Gaston; E-Mail: michaelg@dpls.lib.or.us; Staff 8 (MLS 8)
Founded 1920. Pop 103,000; Circ 702,504
Jul 1998-Jun 1999 Income $3,856,530, Federal $17,886, County $3,838,644. Mats Exp $399,495, Books $315,412, Per/Ser (Incl. Access Fees) $21,280, AV Equip $27,268, Electronic Ref Mat (Incl. Access Fees) $35,535. Sal $2,645,651 (Prof $735,423)
Library Holdings: Bk Vols 257,651; Bk Titles 135,166; Per Subs 326
Partic in OCLC Online Computer Library Center, Inc
Open Tues-Thurs 10-8, Fri 10-6 & Sat 10-5
Friends of the Library Group
Branches: 5
BEND BRANCH, 601 NW Wall St, 97701. SAN 376-9402. Tel: 541-388-6679. Reference Tel: 541-617-7080. FAX: 541-617-7044. *Mgr*, Michael Gaston
Friends of the Library Group
LA PINE BRANCH, 16425 First St, La Pine, 97739. SAN 325-3236. Tel: 541-536-0515. FAX: 541-536-0752. *Regional Manager*, Carla Hopkins
Circ 48,652
Library Holdings: Per Subs 53
Friends of the Library Group
REDMOND BRANCH, 827 Deschutes Ave, Redmond, 97756. SAN 357-8615. Tel: 541-548-3141. FAX: 541-548-6358. *Branch Mgr*, Todd Durkelberg; Staff 5 (MLS 1, Non-MLS 4)
Founded 1917. Circ 114,839
Library Holdings: Per Subs 96
Friends of the Library Group
SISTERS BRANCH, 291 E Main Ave, Sisters, 97759. SAN 357-864X. Tel: 541-549-2921. FAX: 541-549-9620. *Branch Mgr*, Peg Bermel
Founded 1939. Circ 42,260
Library Holdings: Per Subs 47
Friends of the Library Group
SUNRIVER AREA BRANCH, 56855 Venture Lane, Sunriver, 97707. SAN 377-6700. Tel: 541-593-9285. FAX: 541-593-9286. *Regional Manager*, Carla Hopkins

BOARDMAN

P OREGON TRAIL LIBRARY DISTRICT,* PO Box 107, 97818-0107. SAN 321-5490. Tel: 541-481-2665. FAX: 541-481-2668. E-Mail: otlboar2@orednet.org. Web Site: www.orednet.org/. *Librn*, Gilbert T Chavez
Founded 1992. Pop 1,400; Circ 3,158
Library Holdings: Bk Titles 24,000
Partic in OCLC Online Computer Library Center, Inc; Ore State Libr Network
Friends of the Library Group

BROOKINGS

P CHETCO COMMUNITY PUBLIC LIBRARY,* 405 Alder St, 97415. SAN 314-0644. Tel: 541-469-7738. FAX: 541-469-6746. *Dir*, Susana Fernandez
Founded 1947. Pop 13,309; Circ 162,969
Jul 1998-Jun 1999 Income $416,593, State $1,996, County $371,296, Other $43,301. Mats Exp $81,339, Books $63,908, Per/Ser (Incl. Access Fees) $6,268, AV Equip $11,163. Sal $173,417
Library Holdings: Bk Vols 47,082; Bk Titles 45,037; Per Subs 126
Subject Interests: Large print, NW hist
Automation Activity & Vendor Info: (Cataloging) epixtech, inc.; (Circulation) epixtech, inc.
Partic in Ore Libr Asn; Southern Oregon Library Federation
Open Mon & Fri 10-6, Tues & Thurs 10-7, Wed 10-8 & Sat 10-5
Friends of the Library Group

BROWNSVILLE

P BROWNSVILLE COMMUNITY LIBRARY, 146 Spaulding, 97327. (Mail add: PO Box 68, 97327-0068), SAN 314-0652. Tel: 541-466-5454. FAX: 541-466-5118. *Dir*, Paul K Smith; Staff 1 (Non-MLS 1)
Founded 1911. Pop 1,400; Circ 17,000
Library Holdings: Bk Vols 18,500; Per Subs 15
Subject Interests: Genealogy, NW hist
Friends of the Library Group

BURNS

P HARNEY COUNTY LIBRARY,* 80 W D St, 97720-1299. SAN 314-0679. Tel: 541-573-6670. E-Mail: harneycl@oregontrail.net. *Librn*, Jolyn Wynn; *Asst Librn*, Gordon Andrews
Founded 1903. Pop 7,000; Circ 34,069
Library Holdings: Bk Vols 30,000; Per Subs 120

CANBY

P CANBY PUBLIC LIBRARY,* 292 N Holly St, 97013-3732. SAN 314-0687. Tel: 503-266-3394. FAX: 503-266-1709. Web Site: www.web.ster.com/~worldclass/library.html. *Dir*, Beth Saul
Pop 15,000; Circ 87,000
Library Holdings: Bk Vols 32,000
Subject Interests: Children's bks, Christianity, Computer, Herbs, Oregon
Special Collections: Emma Wakefield Coll (materials on herbs)
Automation Activity & Vendor Info: (Cataloging) epixtech, inc.; (Circulation) epixtech, inc.
Partic in Library Information Network Of Clackamas County
Open Mon & Thurs 12-8, Fri & Sat 10-5, Sun 1-5
Friends of the Library Group

CLACKAMAS

M KAISER PERMANENTE NORTHWEST REGIONAL, Health Sciences Library, 10180 SE Sunnyside Rd, 97015. SAN 321-5571. Tel: 503-571-4293. FAX: 503-571-4291. *Dir*, Ann H Haines; E-Mail: ann.h.haines@kp.org; Staff 3 (MLS 1, Non-MLS 2)
Founded 1975

Library Holdings: Bk Titles 700; Per Subs 275
Subject Interests: Medical, Nursing
Database Vendor: Dialog, IAC - Info Trac, OVID Technologies
Partic in Oregon Health Sciences Libraries Association

CLATSKANIE

P CLATSKANIE LIBRARY DISTRICT, 11 Lillich St, PO Box 577, 97016-0577. SAN 314-0695. Tel: 503-728-3732. E-Mail: clpublic@aone.com. Web Site: clatskanie.com. *Dir*, Elizabeth A Kruse; Staff 1 (Non-MLS 1)
Pop 6,700; Circ 25,000
Jul 2000-Jun 2001 Income $194,780, County $95,000, Locally Generated Income $49,119. Mats Exp $58,670, Books $16,000, Electronic Ref Mat (Incl. Access Fees) $1,250. Sal $56,000
Library Holdings: Bk Vols 20,000; Per Subs 46
Subject Interests: Columbia County hist
Open Mon-Wed 10-7, Thurs-Sat 10-5:30
Friends of the Library Group

CONDON

P GILLIAM COUNTY LIBRARY,* 310 S Main, PO Box 34, 97823-0034. SAN 357-8674. Tel: 541-384-6052. E-Mail: gcl@oregonvos.net. *Dir, Librn*, Wendi Griffith
Circ 5,905
Library Holdings: Bk Vols 6,600; Per Subs 33
Friends of the Library Group

COOS BAY

P COOS BAY PUBLIC LIBRARY, 525 Anderson St, 97420-1678. SAN 314-0717. Tel: 541-269-1101. FAX: 541-269-7567. E-Mail: library@coosnet.com. Web Site: www.coosnet.com/library. *Dir*, Carol Ventgen; *Asst Dir*, Ellen Thompson; *Acq*, Ann Couture; *Ch Servs*, Patricia Flitcroft; Staff 12 (MLS 4, Non-MLS 8)
Founded 1910. Pop 25,000; Circ 265,403
Jul 1999-Jun 2000 Income $712,161, State $5,374, Locally Generated Income $586,871, Other $119,916. Mats Exp $666,248, Books $76,347, Per/Ser (Incl. Access Fees) $8,782, Micro $849. Sal $363,812
Library Holdings: Bk Vols 99,807; Per Subs 259
Special Collections: Oregon History (Helene Stack Bower Oregon Coll)
Automation Activity & Vendor Info: (Cataloging) Innovative Interfaces Inc.; (Circulation) Innovative Interfaces Inc.; (OPAC) Innovative Interfaces Inc.
Database Vendor: Innovative Interfaces INN - View
Partic in Coos County Library Service District, Extended Service Office; Southern Oregon Library Federation
Friends of the Library Group

J SOUTHWESTERN OREGON COMMUNITY COLLEGE LIBRARY, (SWOCC), 1988 Newmark, 97420-2956. SAN 314-0725. Tel: 541-888-7431. Interlibrary Loan Service Tel: 541-888-7270. Circulation Tel: 541-888-7270. Reference Tel: 541-888-7448. FAX: 541-888-7605. Web Site: www.southwestern.cc.or.us. *Dir Libr Serv*, Mary Stricker; E-Mail: mstricke@southwestern.cc.or.us; *Librn, Tech Servs*, Pauline Smith; Tel: 541-888-7429, E-Mail: psmith@southwestern.cc.or.us; *Coll Develop, Librn*, Sharon Tashjian; Tel: 541-888-7448, E-Mail: stashjia@southwestern.cc.or.us; Staff 3 (MLS 3)
Founded 1962. Highest Degree: Associate
Jul 1999-Jun 2000 Income $317,602, Locally Generated Income $2,050, Parent Institution $303,552, Other $12,000. Mats Exp $63,769, Books $37,669, Per/Ser (Incl. Access Fees) $20,200, Electronic Ref Mat (Incl. Access Fees) $4,100. Sal $189,341 (Prof $106,025)
Library Holdings: Bk Vols 46,632; Bk Titles 35,742; Per Subs 271; Bks on Deafness & Sign Lang 40
Automation Activity & Vendor Info: (Cataloging) Innovative Interfaces Inc.; (Circulation) Innovative Interfaces Inc.; (Course Reserve) Innovative Interfaces Inc.; (OPAC) Innovative Interfaces Inc.
Database Vendor: Ebsco - EbscoHost, OCLC - First Search
Partic in Coastline; OCLC Online Computer Library Center, Inc; Southern Oregon Library Federation

COQUILLE

P COQUILLE PUBLIC LIBRARY, (COQ), 105 N Birch St, 97423-1299. SAN 314-0733. Tel: 541-396-2166. FAX: 541-396-2174. E-Mail: coqpl@ucinet.com. *Dir*, Terry Logan; *Cat*, Mary Graham; *Ch Servs*, Shelly Wilson; Staff 1 (Non-MLS 1)
Pop 6,500; Circ 85,586
1999-2000 Income $194,539, State $1,531. Mats Exp $37,006, Books $31,435, Per/Ser (Incl. Access Fees) $4,247, Micro $1,324. Sal $107,313
Library Holdings: Bk Titles 30,210; Per Subs 141
Database Vendor: Innovative Interfaces INN - View, OCLC - First Search
Publications: Children's newsletter
Partic in Coos County Library Service District, Extended Service Office

CORNELIUS

P CORNELIUS PUBLIC LIBRARY, 1355 N Barlow St, 97113-8912. (Mail add: PO Box 608, 97113-0607), SAN 314-075X. Tel: 503-357-4093. FAX: 503-357-7775. E-Mail: library@ci.cornelius.or.us. Web Site: www.ci.cornelius.or.us. *Dir*, Stephanie Lind; E-Mail: slind@ci.cornelius.or.us; Staff 5 (MLS 1, Non-MLS 4)
Founded 1913. Pop 8,342
Jul 1999-Jun 2000 Income $160,534, State $1,611, City $34,000, Federal $1,695, County $106,735, Other $16,493. Mats Exp $7,131, Books $2,847, Per/Ser (Incl. Access Fees) $1,997, Presv $911, AV Equip $1,376. Sal $92,435 (Prof $44,064)
Library Holdings: Bk Vols 21,726; Per Subs 60
Subject Interests: Large print, Spanish
Special Collections: Educational CD-ROMs
Automation Activity & Vendor Info: (Cataloging) Gaylord; (Circulation) Gaylord; (OPAC) Gaylord
Mem of Washington County Cooperative Library Services
Open Mon-Thurs 12-8, Fri & Sat 10-5
Friends of the Library Group

CORVALLIS

L BENTON COUNTY LAW LIBRARY, 559 NW Monroe Ave, 97330. (Mail add: PO Box 3020, 97339-3020), SAN 373-6652. Tel: 541-766-6673. FAX: 541-766-6014. *Librn*, Martha A Jenkins; E-Mail: martha.a.jenkins@co.benton.or.us. Subject Specialists: *Law*, Martha A Jenkins; Staff 1 (MLS 1
Jul 2000-Jun 2001 Mats Exp Books $21,500
Library Holdings: Bk Vols 5,797; Bk Titles 282
Restriction: Public use on premises
Function: Research library

S CH2M HILL, Engineering Information Center Library, 2300 NW Walnut Blvd, PO Box 428, 97330. SAN 321-5172. Tel: 541-752-4271, Ext 3115. FAX: 541-752-0276. *Librn*, Linda Risen
Founded 1946
Library Holdings: Bk Vols 12,110; Per Subs 250
Restriction: Staff use only

P CORVALLIS-BENTON COUNTY PUBLIC LIBRARY, 645 NW Monroe Ave, 97330. SAN 357-8739. Tel: 541-757-6928. Circulation Tel: 541-766-6926. Reference Tel: 541-766-6793. FAX: 541-757-6915. Web Site: www.ci.corvallis.or.us/library/. *Dir*, Carolyn Rawles-Heiser; *Tech Servs*, Meryl Miasek; Staff 46 (MLS 18, Non-MLS 28)
Founded 1899. Pop 76,700; Circ 1,422,140
Jul 1999-Jun 2000 Income (Main Library and Branch Library) $623,292, State $13,542, City $2,250,100, County $1,601,883, Other $234,725
Library Holdings: Bk Vols 266,393; Bk Titles 194,773; Per Subs 882
Database Vendor: DRA, Ebsco - EbscoHost, GaleNet, IAC - SearchBank, Lexis-Nexis, OCLC - First Search, Wilson - Wilson Web
Open Mon-Fri 9-9 , Sat 9-6 & Sun noon-6
Friends of the Library Group
Branches: 3
ALSEA BRANCH, PO Box 7, Alsea, 97324. SAN 357-8798. Tel: 541-487-5061. *Librn*, Mary Rounds
MONROE BRANCH, 658 Commercial, Monroe, 97456. SAN 314-1284. Tel: 541-847-5174. *Librn*, Dena Elliot
PHILOMATH BRANCH, 1213 Main, PO Box 789, Philomath, 97370-0569. SAN 325-3953. Tel: 541-929-3016. *Librn*, Margaret Wetmore
Bookmobiles: 2

M GOOD SAMARITAN HOSPITAL, Health Sciences Library, 3600 NW Samaritan Dr, 97339-3700. (Mail add: PO Box 1068, 97339-1068), SAN 371-8557. Tel: 541-757-5007. FAX: 541-757-5087. Web Site: www.goodsam.com. *Librn*, Anne Fraser
Founded 1976
1998-1999 Income $67,000. Mats Exp $30,000, Books $11,000, Per/Ser (Incl. Access Fees) $19,000. Sal $50,000
Library Holdings: Bk Titles 1,100; Per Subs 305
Subject Interests: Medicine

S HEWLETT-PACKARD, Research Center, 1000 NE Circle Blvd, MS 422A, 97330. SAN 324-1165. Tel: 541-715-0206. FAX: 541-715-4015. Web Site: www.lib.utc.edu. *Mgr*, Sharon Williams; *Mgr, Res*, Alice Kirby; *Res*, Nora Stoecker; *Automation Syst Coordr*, Ruth Von Dracek; *Circ, ILL*, Margie Gilliam; *Res*, Camille Wallin; *Acq*, Tracey Finnegan-Wiese; *Automation Syst Coordr*, Ruth Vondracek; *Res*, Kathleen Morley; E-Mail: kathleen_morley@hp.com; *Per*, Lisa Riggs; *Res*, Laurel Espell; Staff 7 (MLS 5, Non-MLS 2)
Library Holdings: Bk Vols 13,000; Bk Titles 12,500; Per Subs 460
Subject Interests: Applications software, Chemistry, Computer tech, Electronics, Engineering, Info mgt, Physics, Related tech
Automation Activity & Vendor Info: (Acquisitions) VTLS
Publications: Newsletter
Partic in Dialog Corporation; Dow Jones News Retrieval; OCLC Online Computer Library Center, Inc; Sci & Tech Info Network

NORTH AMERICAN TRUFFLING SOCIETY, INC LIBRARY,* 34197 NE Colorado Lake Dr, PO Box 296, 97339. SAN 371-6643. Tel: 541-752-2243. *Librn*, Pat Rawlinson
Founded 1978
Library Holdings: Bk Titles 15

NORTHWEST GEOPHYSICAL ASSOCIATES INC LIBRARY,* PO Box 1063, 97339. SAN 374-8545. Tel: 541-757-7231. FAX: 541-757-7331.
Library Holdings: Bk Titles 500

OREGON STATE UNIVERSITY, The Valley Library,* 121 the Valley Library, 97331-4501. SAN 314-0792. Tel: 541-737-3411. Interlibrary Loan Service Tel: 541-737-4488. FAX: 541-737-3453. Web Site: www.orst.edu/mc/libcom.htm. *Librn*, Karyle S Butcher; E-Mail: karyle.butcher@orst.edu; *Circ*, Lorraine Bouchers; *Ref*, Loretta Rielly; *Online Servs*, Jeanne Davidson; *Bibliog Instr*, Cheryl Middleton; *Acq*, Richard Brumley; *Automation Syst Coordr*, Richard Griffin; *Spec Coll*, Cliff Mead; *Cat*, Debra Hackleman; Staff 47 (MLS 47)
Founded 1887. Fac 2,368; Highest Degree: Master
Jul 1997-Jun 1998 Income $7,485,257, State $5,952,702, Locally Generated Income $107,800, Other $417,704. Mats Exp $3,263,578, Books $369,418, Per/Ser (Incl. Access Fees) $2,384,567, Presv $54,850, Micro $58,029, AV Equip $218,944. Sal $3,492,364 (Prof $1,499,435)
Library Holdings: Per Subs 50
Subject Interests: Agriculture, Environmental studies, Forestry, Natural science, Oceanography, Sci-tech
Special Collections: Ava Helen & Linus Pauling Coll; Northwest Coll
Publications: Library Messenger
Partic in Orbis; Ore State Syst of Higher Educ

US ENVIRONMENTAL PROTECTION AGENCY, NHEERL Western Ecology Division Library, 200 SW 35th St, 97333. SAN 314-0768. Tel: 541-754-4731. FAX: 541-754-4799. E-Mail: library@mail.cor.epa.gov. *Librn*, Mary C O'Brien; E-Mail: mco@mail.cor.epa.gov; *ILL*, Donovan M Reves; Tel: 541-754-4740, E-Mail: donovan@mail.cor.epa.gov; Staff 2 (MLS 1, Non-MLS 1)
Founded 1966
Library Holdings: Bk Vols 4,100; Bk Titles 4,000; Per Subs 120
Subject Interests: Air pollution effects on vegetation, Biodiversity, Genetic eng, Global climate, Wetlands
Automation Activity & Vendor Info: (Circulation) CASPR; (Serials) CASPR
Database Vendor: Dialog
Restriction: Open to public for reference only
Function: For research purposes
Partic in Fedlink

COTTAGE GROVE

W A WOODARD MEMORIAL LIBRARY, Cottage Grove Public Library,* 700 Gibbs Ave, 97424-1640. SAN 314-0806. Tel: 541-942-3828. FAX: 541-942-1267. *Librn*, Dan Kaye; Staff 5 (MLS 3, Non-MLS 2)
Founded 1912. Pop 7,010; Circ 84,116
Library Holdings: Bk Vols 21,681; Per Subs 67
Special Collections: Oregon Coll
Friends of the Library Group

DALLAS

DALLAS PUBLIC LIBRARY,* 950 Main St, 97338-2802. SAN 314-0822. Tel: 503-623-2633. FAX: 503-623-7357. Web Site: www.ccrls.org/dallas. *Dir*, Margaret Barnes; *Ch Servs*, Donna Zehner; *Info Tech*, Gary Coville; Staff 6 (MLS 2, Non-MLS 4)
Founded 1908. Pop 13,000; Circ 190,000
Jul 1997-Jun 1998 Income $324,580. Mats Exp $36,000, Books $30,000, Per/Ser (Incl. Access Fees) $6,000. Sal $239,733
Library Holdings: Bk Titles 66,000; Per Subs 103
Subject Interests: Ore hist
Partic in Chemeketa Cooperative Regional Library Service
Friends of the Library Group

DAYTON

P MARY GILKEY CITY LIBRARY, 416 Ferry St, PO Box 339, 97114-0339. SAN 329-7586. Tel: 503-864-2221. FAX: 503-864-2956. *Librn*, Debra Lien
Founded 1922. Pop 1,930
Library Holdings: Bk Vols 11,000; Per Subs 10
Friends of the Library Group

ECHO

P ECHO PUBLIC LIBRARY,* 20 S Bonanza, PO Box 9, 97826-0009. SAN 358-0539. Tel: 541-376-8411. FAX: 541-376-8218. *Dir*, Diane Berry; *Asst Librn*, Joyce Mackay
Library Holdings: Bk Vols 12,000

ELGIN

P ELGIN PUBLIC LIBRARY,* 260 N Tenth, PO Box 67, 97827-0067. SAN 314-0830. Tel: 541-437-2860. E-Mail: elginlib@eoni.com. *Librn*, Sandra Good; *Asst Librn*, Annette Howell
Founded 1911. Pop 2,600
Jul 1997-Jun 1998 Income $22,094, State $655, City $20,644, County $795. Mats Exp $5,142, Books $4,521, Per/Ser (Incl. Access Fees) $192. Sal $13,062
Library Holdings: Bk Vols 12,500
Special Collections: Northwest, bks

ENTERPRISE

P ENTERPRISE CITY LIBRARY,* 101 NE First St, 97828-1173. SAN 314-0849. Tel: 541-426-3906.
Founded 1911. Pop 1,980; Circ 14,929
Library Holdings: Bk Vols 10,000; Per Subs 50

P WALLOWA COUNTY LIBRARY, (WCL), 207 NW Logan, 97828-0186. SAN 314-0857. Tel: 541-426-3969. FAX: 541-426-3969. *Dir*, Claudia Jones; Staff 1 (Non-MLS 1)
Founded 1964. Pop 3,140; Circ 6,633
Jul 2000-Jun 2001 Income $67,289, State $6,645, Federal $3,470, County $47,024, Locally Generated Income $150, Other $10,000. Mats Exp $5,122, Books $4,782, Per/Ser (Incl. Access Fees) $115, Electronic Ref Mat (Incl. Access Fees) $225. Sal $36,420 (Prof $22,962)
Library Holdings: Bk Vols 15,380; Bk Titles 15,368
Subject Interests: Local history, Nez Perce Indians, Ore hist, Pac NW hist
Restriction: Not open to public, Public access by telephone only
Bookmobiles: 1

ESTACADA

P ESTACADA PUBLIC LIBRARY, 475 SE Main, PO Box 609, 97023-0609. SAN 314-0865. Tel: 503-630-8273. FAX: 503-630-8282. Web Site: www.estacada.lib.or.us. *Dir*, Beth McKinnon; E-Mail: bethm@hncc.lib.or.us; *Librn, Ref*, Katinka Bryk; E-Mail: katinka@hncc.lib.or.us; Staff 4 (MLS 2, Non-MLS 2)
Pop 16,000; Circ 217,449
Jul 1999-Jun 2000 Income $394,000. Mats Exp $111,000. Sal $128,400
Library Holdings: Bk Vols 27,760; Per Subs 200
Subject Interests: Estacada hist, NW authors, Pacific Northwest
Special Collections: Estacada History
Automation Activity & Vendor Info: (Cataloging) epixtech, inc.; (Circulation) epixtech, inc.
Mem of Libr Info Network of Clackamas County
Open Mon-Thurs 9-8, Fri 9-6, Sat 10-5 & Sun 12-5

EUGENE

CR EUGENE BIBLE COLLEGE, Flint Memorial Library, 2155 Bailey Hill Rd, 97405. SAN 314-0873. Tel: 541-485-1780. FAX: 541-343-5801. *Librn*, Priscilla Cameron; Staff 1 (MLS 1)
Founded 1926. Enrl 200; Highest Degree: Bachelor
Library Holdings: Bk Vols 34,500; Per Subs 249
Special Collections: Flint Memorial Coll

P EUGENE PUBLIC LIBRARY, 100 W 13th Ave, 97401. SAN 314-0881. Tel: 541-682-5450. Reference Tel: 541-682—5353. TDD: 541-682-3035. FAX: 541-682-8470. Web Site: www.ci.eugene.or.us/library/. *Dir Libr Serv*, Jackie Griffin; E-Mail: jackie.y.griffin@ci.eugene.or.us; *Branch Mgr*, Carolyn Forde; *Branch Mgr*, Michael McCarthy; *Head Tech Servs*, Patricia Dunham; *Publ Servs*, Rob Everett; E-Mail: rob.e.everett@ci.eugene.or.us; *YA Servs*, Claire Ribaud; Staff 44 (MLS 15, Non-MLS 29)
Founded 1895
Jul 1999-Jun 2000 Income $4,521,508, State $23,071, City $4,389,701, Federal $5,246, Other $103,490. Mats Exp $447,201, Books $345,286, Per/Ser (Incl. Access Fees) $31,522, AV Equip $57,500, Other Print Mats $6,096, Electronic Ref Mat (Incl. Access Fees) $6,797. Sal $3,199,227
Library Holdings: Bk Vols 258,506; Bk Titles 194,001; Per Subs 589
Automation Activity & Vendor Info: (Circulation) Gaylord
Special Services for the Deaf - Books on deafness & sign language; High interest/low vocabulary books
Special Services for the Blind - VisualTek closed circuit TV reading aid
Friends of the Library Group

S LANE COUNTY HISTORICAL MUSEUM ARCHIVES, 740 W 13th, 97402. SAN 314-092X. Tel: 541-682-4242. FAX: 541-682-7361. E-Mail: lchm@efn.org. *Dir*, Evearad Stelfox
Founded 1969
Library Holdings: Bk Titles 4,000
Subject Interests: Agriculture, Lane county hist, Logging, Manuscripts, Mining, Oregon Trail, Pioneer families, Transportation

Special Collections: Manuscripts Coll; Photography Museum Coll
Publications: Catalog of Manuscript Collections; Coburg Remembered; Looking Back at the Trail; Lost Wagon Train; Story of Eugene
Friends of the Library Group

GL LANE COUNTY LAW LIBRARY,* Court House, 125 E Eighth Ave, 97401. SAN 314-0911. Tel: 541-687-4337. FAX: 541-687-4315. *Librn*, R Burdett Mafit; Staff 2 (MLS 1, Non-MLS 1)
Founded 1948
Library Holdings: Bk Vols 19,200; Per Subs 12
Special Collections: Oregon Law
Publications: Bibliographic series; newsletter
Partic in Dialog Corporation; Westlaw

S OREGON RESEARCH INSTITUTE LIBRARY, 1715 Franklin Blvd, 97403-1983. SAN 325-8122. Tel: 541-484-2123. FAX: 541-484-1108. Web Site: www.ori.org. *Mgr*, Amy Greenwold; E-Mail: amy@ori.org; *Electronic Resources*, Elaine Shuman; E-Mail: elaines@ori.org; Staff 4 (MLS 2, Non-MLS 2)
2000-2001 Mats Exp $58,000, Books $8,000, Per/Ser (Incl. Access Fees) $40,000, Electronic Ref Mat (Incl. Access Fees) $10,000
Library Holdings: Bk Vols 5,000; Per Subs 160
Subject Interests: Adolescence, Behav sci, Personalities, Psychology, Smoking, Women's health
Automation Activity & Vendor Info: (Cataloging) Inmagic, Inc.; (Circulation) Inmagic, Inc.; (OPAC) Inmagic, Inc.; (Serials) TLC
Database Vendor: Dialog, Ebsco - EbscoHost, Silverplatter Information Inc.
Restriction: Staff use only
Partic in Docline; OCLC Online Computer Library Center, Inc

S REGISTER-GUARD LIBRARY, 3500 Chad Dr, 97408-7348. (Mail add: PO Box 10188, 97440-2188), SAN 314-089X. Tel: 541-485-1234. FAX: 541-683-7631. *Librn*, Suzanne Boyd; E-Mail: sboyd@guardnet.com; Staff 2 (MLS 1, Non-MLS 1)
Founded 1950
Subject Interests: Lane county

M SACRED HEART MEDICAL CENTER, Professional Library Services, 1255 Hilyard St, 97401. SAN 314-0946. Tel: 541-686-6837. FAX: 541-686-7391. E-Mail: libraryshmc@peacehealth.org. *Dir*, Kim Tyler; E-Mail: ktyler@peacehealth.org; Staff 6 (MLS 3, Non-MLS 3)
Founded 1971
Library Holdings: Bk Vols 3,027; Per Subs 450
Subject Interests: Computers in health care, Medicine, Mgt develop, Nursing
Special Collections: Archives (School of Nursing, 1942-70), print, tapes & transcription; Nurse Dolls in Uniform
Automation Activity & Vendor Info: (Acquisitions) EOS; (Cataloging) EOS; (Circulation) EOS; (OPAC) EOS
Database Vendor: Dialog, IAC - SearchBank, OCLC - First Search, OVID Technologies
Restriction: Circulates for staff only, Not open to public
Function: Document delivery services, ILL available, Photocopies available, Reference services available

CL SCHOOL OF LAW, UNIVERSITY OF OREGON, Ocean & Coastal Law Center Library, 1221 Univ of Oregon, 1515 Agate St, 97403-1221. SAN 326-5072. Tel: 541-346-1567. FAX: 541-346-1564. Web Site: www.law.uoregon.edu/library/library.html. *Librn*, Andrea Coffman; E-Mail: acoffman@law.uoregon.edu
Founded 1968. Enrl 477; Fac 49
Library Holdings: Bk Titles 5,900; Per Subs 168
Subject Interests: Maritime law
Publications: Periodicals Holdings List; Recent Acquisitions List; Recent Articles in Marine Legal Affairs
Partic in Int Asn of Aquatic & Marine Sci Libr & Info Centers

C UNIVERSITY OF OREGON LIBRARY SYSTEM, 1299 University of Oregon, 97403-1299. SAN 357-8976. Tel: 541-346-3056. FAX: 541-346-3485. Web Site: www.libweb.uoregon.edu. *Assoc Librn*, Deborah Carver; *Admin Assoc*, Andrew R Bonamici; *Tech Servs*, Mark R Watson; *Doc*, Thomas A Stave; *ILL*, Joanne Halgren; *Coll Develop*, Linda Long; *Ref*, Barbara Jenkins; *Acq*, Nancy Slight-Gibney; *Cat*, Carol Hixson; *Archivist*, Susan Storch; *Coll Develop*, Faye Chadwell; Staff 141 (MLS 50, Non-MLS 91)
Founded 1883. Enrl 17,169; Fac 1,701; Highest Degree: Doctorate
Library Holdings: Bk Vols 2,100,000; Per Subs 15,000
Subject Interests: Architecture, Art, Bus, Law, Mathematics, Music, Sci
Special Collections: American History (The American West), mss; American Missions & Missionaries, mss; Children's Literature, Book & Magazine Illustrations, mss, bk; Esperanto; Oriental Literature & Art; Politics (20th Century American Politics, particularly Conservatism), mss; Zeppelins
Mem of Asn of Research Libraries
Partic in Center For Research Libraries; OCLC Online Computer Library Center, Inc
Departmental Libraries:
ARCHITECTURE & ALLIED ARTS, 200 Lawrence Hall, 97403. SAN 357-900X. Tel: 541-346-3637. FAX: 541-346-2205. Web Site: www.libweb.uoregon.edu. *Curator*, Christine Sundt
Founded 1915
Library Holdings: Bk Vols 45,751

CL LAW, 270 Knight Law Ctr, 97403-1221. SAN 357-9093. Tel: 541-346-3088 FAX: 541-346-1669. Web Site: www.libweb.uoregon.edu. *Librn*, Dennis F Hyatt
Founded 1893
Library Holdings: Bk Vols 131,755; Per Subs 3,188

MAP, 165 Convon Hall, 97403-1251. SAN 357-9123. Tel: 541-346-4565. Web Site: www.libweb.uoregon.edu. *Librn*, Larry Laliberte
Founded 1970
Special Collections: Aerial Photographs; Maps of Pacific Northwest, US, Central America, West Africa, World

MATHEMATICS, 1222 University of Oregon, 97403-1222. SAN 357-9131. Tel: 541-346-3023. Web Site: www.libweb.uoregon.edu. *Ref*, Isabel Stirling
Founded 1980
Library Holdings: Bk Vols 24,974; Per Subs 350

SCIENCE, Lower Level Onyx Bridge, 97403-5201. SAN 357-9158. Tel: 541-346-3075. FAX: 541-346-3012. Web Site: www.libweb.uoregon.edu.
Founded 1968
Library Holdings: Bk Vols 156,609; Per Subs 2,794

FAIRVIEW

S NACCO MATERIALS HANDLING GROUP, INC, CBDC Technical Support Resource Center, 4000 NE Blue Lake Rd, 97024-8710. SAN 314-1594. Tel: 503-721-6234. FAX: 503-721-1364. *In Charge*, Melissa Hardenbergh; E-Mail: cpmharde@nmng.com
Founded 1961
1999-2000 Mats Exp $9,000, Books $7,000, Per/Ser (Incl. Access Fees) $2,000
Library Holdings: Bk Vols 20,000; Bk Titles 16,000; Per Subs 60
Subject Interests: Construction safety, Domestic societies, Eng design for mat handling equip, Foreign societies, Industrial safety
Restriction: By appointment only

FALLS CITY

P FALLS CITY PUBLIC LIBRARY,* PO Box 310, 97344-0310. SAN 320-5045. Tel: 503-787-3631.
Pop 855
Library Holdings: Bk Titles 4,000

FLORENCE

P SIUSLAW PUBLIC LIBRARY, 1460 Ninth St, PO Box A, 97439-0022. SAN 314-0954. Tel: 541-997-3132. FAX: 541-997-4007. *Dir*, Stephen C Skidmore; E-Mail: skidmore@siuslaw.lib.or.us; *Ch Servs*, Gayle Waiss; E-Mail: gwaiss@siuslaw.lib.or.us; *Tech Coordr*, LInda Weight; *Ref Serv Ad*, Kevin Mittge; E-Mail: mittge@siuslaw.lib.or.us; Staff 11 (MLS 4, Non-MLS 7)
Founded 1985. Pop 15,923; Circ 161,291
Jul 1999-Jun 2000 Income $511,043, State $2,916, Federal $7,429, Locally Generated Income $458,865, Other $41,833. Mats Exp $68,014, Books $44,957, Per/Ser (Incl. Access Fees) $10,101, AV Equip $10,222, Electronic Ref Mat (Incl. Access Fees) $2,734. Sal $209,759 (Prof $134,718)
Library Holdings: Bk Vols 67,257; Bk Titles 60,966; Per Subs 223
Special Collections: Newspapers published in Florence, 1891 to date, micro, Oregon Past & Present Coll; Reference Library of Frank Herbert
Database Vendor: Ebsco - EbscoHost
Publications: The Bookmark
Friends of the Library Group

FOREST GROVE

P FOREST GROVE CITY LIBRARY, 2114 Pacific Ave, 97116-2497. SAN 314-0962. Tel: 503-992-3247. FAX: 503-992-3201. Web Site: www.wilinet.wccls.lib.or.us. *Dir*, Colleen Winters; Tel: 503-992-3246, E-Mail: winters@wccls.lib.or.us; *Dir Libr Serv*, Robyn Cram; E-Mail: robync@wccls.lib.or.us; *Ref*, Kiera Koester; Tel: 503-992-3248, E-Mail: kierak@wccls.lib.or.us; *Ref Serv Ad*, Carolyn Gates; Tel: 503-992-3248, E-Mail: cgates@wccls.lib.or.us; *Ref Serv Ad*, Linda Minor; Tel: 503-992-3280, E-Mail: lindam@wccls.lib.or.us; *Ch Servs*, Ann Dondero; Tel: 503-992-3281, E-Mail: anndo@wccls.lib.or.us; Staff 10 (MLS 3, Non-MLS 7)
Founded 1909. Pop 22,130; Circ 199,817
Jul 1999-Jun 2000 Income $596,947, State $5,191, City $125,920, County $453,790, Other $12,046. Mats Exp $101,116. Sal $354,737
Library Holdings: Bk Vols 96,137; Per Subs 260
Special Collections: Large Print Coll; Spanish Language Coll
Automation Activity & Vendor Info: (Acquisitions) Gaylord; (Cataloging) Gaylord; (Circulation) Gaylord; (OPAC) Gaylord
Mem of Washington County Cooperative Library Services
Friends of the Library Group

PACIFIC UNIVERSITY, Harvey W Scott Memorial Library, 2043 College Way, 97116. SAN 357-9182. Tel: 503-359-2204. FAX: 503-359-2236. Web Site: www.pacificu.edu/library/index.html. *Dir*, Drew Harrington; *Electronic Resources, Ref Serv*, Lynda Larremore; *Science*, Nancy Henderson; *Spec Coll*, Alex Toth; E-Mail: tothalex@pacificu.edu; *Syst Coordr*, Sue Kopp. Subject Specialists: *Soc sci*, Alex Toth; Staff 5 (MLS 5)
Founded 1849. Enrl 2,000; Fac 180; Highest Degree: Doctorate
Library Holdings: Bk Vols 126,000; Bk Titles 102,000; Per Subs 1,200
Subject Interests: Clinical psych, Occupational therapy, Optometry, Physical therapy, Physicians assistance studies
Special Collections: Optometry
Automation Activity & Vendor Info: (Acquisitions) Innovative Interfaces Inc.; (Cataloging) Innovative Interfaces Inc.; (Circulation) Innovative Interfaces Inc.; (OPAC) Innovative Interfaces Inc.; (Serials) Innovative Interfaces Inc.
Partic in Northwest Association of Private Colleges & Universities Libraries; Orbis; PORTALS

LADSTONE

GLADSTONE PUBLIC LIBRARY,* 135 E Dartmouth St, 97027-2496. SAN 314-0970. Tel: 503-656-2411. FAX: 503-655-2438. *Dir*, Catherine Nicolas
Pop 17,859; Circ 178,150
Library Holdings: Bk Vols 53,231; Bk Titles 45,417; Per Subs 120
Partic in Library Information Network Of Clackamas County
Friends of the Library Group

OLD BEACH

CURRY PUBLIC LIBRARY DISTRICT,* 29775 Colvin St, PO Box 625, 97444-0625. SAN 314-0989. Tel: 541-247-7246. FAX: 541-247-4411. *Librn*, Dianne Zarder; *Ch Servs*, Sandra Mathers
Founded 1955. Pop 5,200; Circ 53,868
Library Holdings: Bk Vols 28,715; Per Subs 108
Friends of the Library Group

RANTS PASS

JOSEPHINE COUNTY HISTORICAL SOCIETY, Research Library, 512 SW Fifth St, 97526. SAN 326-1891. Tel: 541-479-7827. FAX: 541-472-8928. E-Mail: jchs@terragon.com. Web Site: www.webtrail.com/jchs/. *Exec Dir*, Rose Scott; Staff 1 (MLS 1)
Founded 1970
Library Holdings: Bk Vols 945
Subject Interests: Local history
Special Collections: Josephine County (Amos Voorhies Coll), photogs
Publications: The Oldtimer Newsletter, Books
Restriction: Not a lending library
Function: Research library
Partic in Southern Oregon Library Federation

JOSEPHINE COUNTY LAW LIBRARY, County Courthouse, 500 NW Sixth St, 97526. SAN 325-8343. Tel: 541-474-5488. FAX: 541-474-5485. *Branch Mgr*, John Raviolo
Library Holdings: Bk Vols 14,134

JOSEPHINE COUNTY LIBRARY SYSTEM, 200 NW C St, 97526-2094. SAN 357-9247. Tel: 541-474-5482. FAX: 541-474-5485. *Dir*, Sue Luce; *Ad Servs*, Teresa Fouste; *Ch Servs*, Linda Garrick; *Circ*, Cessa Vichi
Founded 1913. Pop 72,000; Circ 402,000
Jul 1999-Jun 2000 Income $1,599,417, State $15,391, County $1,484,007, Locally Generated Income $73,018. Mats Exp Books $195,000. Sal $919,253
Library Holdings: Bk Vols 176,941; Per Subs 277
Subject Interests: Ore hist
Publications: Ad Lib (library newsletter)
Friends of the Library Group
Branches: 3
ILLINOIS VALLEY, 209 W Palmer St, Cave Junction, 97523-0190. SAN 357-9271. Tel: 541-592-3581. *Branch Mgr*, Nakia Berglund
Circ 58,646
Library Holdings: Bk Vols 25,000
Friends of the Library Group
WILLIAMS BRANCH, Williams, 97544. SAN 357-9301. Tel: 541-846-7020. *Branch Mgr*, Premila Miles
Circ 10,476
Library Holdings: Bk Vols 7,000
Friends of the Library Group
WOLF CREEK BRANCH, Wolf Creek, 97497. SAN 357-9336. Tel: 541-866-2606. *Branch Mgr*, Dolores Holland
Circ 10,687
Library Holdings: Bk Vols 7,000
Friends of the Library Group

J ROGUE COMMUNITY COLLEGE LIBRARY,* 3345 Redwood Hwy, 97527. SAN 314-0997. Tel: 541-956-7500. FAX: 541-471-3588. Web Site: ch.rogue.or.us/departments/library.html. *Dir Libr Serv*, Lynda Kettler; E-Mail: lkettler@rogue.cc.or.us; Staff 4 (MLS 4)
Founded 1971. Enrl 1,400; Fac 100
Library Holdings: Bk Titles 33,600; Per Subs 390
Subject Interests: Allied health, Nursing, Small bus
Special Collections: Oregon Outdoors
Partic in OCLC Online Computer Library Center, Inc; Southern Oregon Library Federation
Friends of the Library Group

GRESHAM

J MOUNT HOOD COMMUNITY COLLEGE LIBRARY,* 26000 SE Stark St, 97030. SAN 314-1004. Tel: 503-491-7161. FAX: 503-491-7389. Web Site: www.mhcc.cc.or.us. *Dir*, Jacqueline McCrady; E-Mail: mccradyj@mhcc.cc.or.us; *Ref*, Elizabeth Anne West; *Ref*, Glenn Heiserman; *Publ Servs*, Diane Braithwaite; *Tech Servs*, Sharon Jackson; Staff 5 (MLS 3, Non-MLS 2)
Founded 1965. Pop 13,000; Circ 106,279
1998-1999 Income $658,332. Mats Exp $110,000, Books $27,500, Per/Ser (Incl. Access Fees) $34,375, AV Equip $7,095, Other Print Mats $41,030. Sal $349,296 (Prof $139,640)
Library Holdings: Bk Vols 57,691; Per Subs 483
Partic in OCLC Online Computer Library Center, Inc

HELIX

P HELIX PUBLIC LIBRARY, Columbia St, PO Box 324, 97835-0324. SAN 358-0504. Tel: 541-457-6132. FAX: 541-457-6131. E-Mail: mlm@oregontrail.net. *Dir*, Martha Mitchell; Staff 1 (Non-MLS 1)
Founded 1906
Jul 1998-Jun 1999 Income County $12,500. Mats Exp $2,200, Books $2,000, Per/Ser (Incl. Access Fees) $200. Sal $7,200
Library Holdings: Bk Vols 5,216; Bk Titles 5,216; Per Subs 69
Subject Interests: Local history
Mem of Umatilla County Spec Libr Dist
Friends of the Library Group

HEPPNER

P HEPPNER PUBLIC LIBRARY, N Main St, PO Box 325, 97836-0325. SAN 314-1012. Tel: 541-676-9964. FAX: 541-676-9964. E-Mail: otlhepp@oregonvos.net. *Dir*, Marsha Richmond; *Librn*, Dorthy Wilson
Founded 1898. Pop 1,400; Circ 13,913
Library Holdings: Bk Vols 11,600
Friends of the Library Group

HERMISTON

P HERMISTON PUBLIC LIBRARY, 235 E Gladys Ave, 97838-1827. SAN 358-0563. Tel: 541-567-2882. Web Site: www.hermiston.or.us/library. *Dir*, M Lou Williams; E-Mail: mwilliams@hermiston.or.us; *Ref*, Heidi Florenzen; Staff 8 (MLS 2, Non-MLS 6)
Founded 1918. Pop 18,000
Jul 1998-Jun 1999 Income $282,000. Mats Exp $19,400, Books $15,000, Per/Ser (Incl. Access Fees) $1,900, Presv $2,000, Micro $500. Sal $216,450 (Prof $78,000)
Library Holdings: Bk Vols 40,000; Bk Titles 38,000; Per Subs 80; High Interest/Low Vocabulary Bk Vols 400; Bks on Deafness & Sign Lang 10
Special Collections: National Geographic 1899-present
Automation Activity & Vendor Info: (Cataloging) epixtech, inc.; (Circulation) epixtech, inc.; (OPAC) epixtech, inc.
Publications: "Friendly Notes" for Friends of Library
Partic in Umatilla County Spec Libr District
Open Mon-Thurs 11-7, Fri & Sat 10-5
Friends of the Library Group

HILLSBORO

P HILLSBORO PUBLIC LIBRARIES, Shute Park, 775 SE Tenth, 97123-4798. SAN 314-1020. Tel: 503-615-6500. TDD: 503-648-9181. FAX: 503-615-6501. Web Site: www.ci.hillsboro.or.us/Library/Library_Main_Page.htm. *Dir*, Debra L Brodie; *Asst Dir*, Michael R Smith; *Ad Servs, Ref*, Linda Lybecker; *YA Servs*, Carol Reich; *Br Coordr*, Dorothy Swanson; Staff 58 (MLS 18, Non-MLS 40)
Founded 1914. Pop 116,950; Circ 1,232,923
Jul 1999-Jun 2000 Income (Main Library and Branch Library) $3,518,343, State $12,832, City $876,594, Federal $65,000, County $2,461,492, Locally Generated Income $102,425. Mats Exp $489,337, Books $440,043, Per/Ser (Incl. Access Fees) $37,899, Presv $7,010, Electronic Ref Mat (Incl. Access Fees) $4,385. Sal $1,666,571
Library Holdings: Bk Vols 203,569; Per Subs 983
Subject Interests: Japanese lang mat, Spanish lang mat

Automation Activity & Vendor Info: (Acquisitions) Gaylord; (Cataloging) Gaylord; (Circulation) Gaylord
Mem of Washington County Cooperative Library Services
Partic in Washington County Cooperative Library Services
Friends of the Library Group
Branches: 2
BOOKS BY RAIL STATION, 83 Saint Light Rail Sta, 97123. SAN 378-1887. *Asst Dir*, Michael R Smith
TANASBOURNE, 2453 NW 185th Ave, 97124. SAN 314-1837. Tel: 503-615-6500. FAX: 503-615-6601.
Friends of the Library Group

M KAISER-PERMANENTE, Health Resource Center,* 19400 NW Evergreen Pkwy, 97124. SAN 374-5899. Tel: 503-645-2762. FAX: 503-690-5029. *Librn*, Laura Dickinson; E-Mail: dickinsonla@kpnwoa.mts.kpnw.org; *Tech Servs*, Barbara Melser; Staff 2 (MLS 2)
Library Holdings: Bk Titles 1,000
Special Collections: Attention Deficit Disorder Materials

M TUALITY COMMUNITY HOSPITAL, Health Science Library, 335 SE Eighth Ave, PO Box 309, 97123. SAN 326-3401. Tel: 503-681-1121. FAX: 503-681-1729. *Librn*, Judith Hayes; Staff 1 (MLS 1)
Oct 1999-Sep 2000 Income $62,916, Parent Institution $51,516, Other $11,400. Mats Exp $36,616, Books $6,400, Per/Ser (Incl. Access Fees) $21,400, Electronic Ref Mat (Incl. Access Fees) $6,000. Sal $26,300 (Prof $12,375)
Library Holdings: Bk Vols 800; Bk Titles 750; Per Subs 140
Subject Interests: Clinical medicine, Hospital administration
Database Vendor: Ebsco - EbscoHost, OVID Technologies
Restriction: Open to others by appointment, Staff use only

P WASHINGTON COUNTY COOPERATIVE LIBRARY SERVICES, 111 NE Lincoln St, No 230-L MS58, 97124-3036. SAN 320-2305. Tel: 503-846-3222. TDD: 503-690-7755. FAX: 503-846-3220. Web Site: www.wilinet.wccls.lib.or.us. *Mgr*, Eva Calcagno; Tel: 503-846-3233, E-Mail: calcagno@wccls.lib.or.us; *Outreach Serv*, Sandra Portz; Tel: 503-617-6330, E-Mail: sandrap@wccls.lib.or.us; *Ch Servs*, Angela Reynolds; Tel: 503-466-1894, E-Mail: angelar@wccls.lib.or.us; *ILL, Ref*, Barbara O'Neill; E-Mail: barbarao@wccls.lib.or.us; *Automation Syst Coordr*, Barbara Kesel; Tel: 503-846-3238, E-Mail: barbarak@wccls.lib.or.us; Staff 22 (MLS 9, Non-MLS 13)
Founded 1976. Pop 404,750; Circ 4,500,000
Jul 1999-Jun 2000 Income (Main Library and Branch Library) $10,422,637, State $56,908, County $9,784,743, Other $580,986. Mats Exp $11,536,940. Sal $1,226,688
Library Holdings: Bk Vols 43,019; Per Subs 154
Subject Interests: Large print
Special Collections: Library Professional Coll
Automation Activity & Vendor Info: (Acquisitions) Gaylord; (Cataloging) Gaylord; (Circulation) Gaylord; (OPAC) Gaylord; (Serials) Gaylord
Publications: The Cooperative
Member Libraries: Banks Public Library; Beaverton City Library; Cedar Mill Community Library; Cornelius Public Library; Forest Grove City Library; Hillsboro Public Libraries; Sherwood Public Library; Tigard Public Library; Tualatin Public Library
Partic in OCLC; OCLC Online Computer Library Center, Inc
Special Services for the Deaf - TDD
Special Services for the Blind - Bks on tape
Consortium of Libraries & Countrywide Services
Branches: 1
WEST SLOPE COMMUNITY, 3678 SW 78th Ave, Portland, 97225. SAN 324-248X. Tel: 503-292-6416. FAX: 503-292-6932. Web Site: www.wilinet.wccls.lib.or.us. *Librn*, Veronica Eden; Staff 2 (MLS 2)
Founded 1950
Jul 1999-Jun 2000 Income Parent Institution $343,943. Mats Exp $39,023. Sal $203,689
Library Holdings: Bk Vols 32,307
Automation Activity & Vendor Info: (Acquisitions) Gaylord; (Cataloging) Gaylord; (Circulation) Gaylord; (OPAC) Gaylord
Friends of the Library Group

GL WASHINGTON COUNTY LAW LIBRARY,* 111 NE Lincoln St, 97124. SAN 314-1039. Tel: 503-648-8880. FAX: 503-640-3515. *Librn*, Ann Karlen
Founded 1926
Library Holdings: Bk Vols 17,000

HOOD RIVER

P HOOD RIVER COUNTY LIBRARY, 502 State St, 97031-2042. SAN 357-9360. Tel: 541-386-2535. FAX: 541-386-3835. E-Mail: hrclib@gorge.net. Web Site: community.gorge.net/libraries/hoodriver/services.htm. *Dir*, June M Knudson; *Librn*, Hillary Steighner; *Librn*, Kathy Thomas; *Ch Servs*, Jayne Guidinger; Staff 8 (MLS 3, Non-MLS 5)
Founded 1912. Pop 17,600; Circ 141,792
1998-1999 Income $348,560. Mats Exp $44,800, Books $39,500, Per/Ser (Incl. Access Fees) $5,300. Sal $177,899 (Prof $74,314)
Library Holdings: Bk Vols 83,000; Per Subs 207
Partic in Ore State Libr Network
Friends of the Library Group
Branches: 2
CASCADE LOCKS BRANCH, PO Box 158, Cascade Locks, 97014-0158. SAN 357-9395. Tel: 541-374-8484. *Librn*, Nancy Evers; *Asst Librn*, Nona Abbott
Circ 16,061
PARKDALE BRANCH, PO Box 220, 97041-0220. SAN 357-9425. Tel: 541-352-6502. *Librn*, Janette Dillon
Circ 13,437

INDEPENDENCE

P INDEPENDENCE PUBLIC LIBRARY,* 311 S Monmouth St, 97351-1998. SAN 314-1047. Tel: 503-838-1811. FAX: 503-838-4486. Web Site: www.ccrls.org/independence. *Librn*, Robin Puccetti; E-Mail: robin@ccrls.org; Staff 5 (MLS 1, Non-MLS 4)
Founded 1912. Pop 5,500; Circ 40,000
Jul 1997-Jun 1998 Income $106,298. Mats Exp $18,386. Sal $74,600
Library Holdings: Bk Vols 26,000; Per Subs 50
Special Collections: Local History Coll; Oregon History Coll; Spanish Language Coll
Partic in Chemeketa Cooperative Regional Library Service
Friends of the Library Group

JEFFERSON

P JEFFERSON PUBLIC LIBRARY, 128 N Main St, PO Box 1068, 97352-0626. SAN 376-3323. Tel: 541-327-3826. FAX: 541-451-4099. E-Mail: jeffpl@open.org. *Dir*, Laurie Linda Baker; E-Mail: jeffpl@open.org; Staff 2 (Non-MLS 2)
Founded 1938. Pop 2,380; Circ 14,660
Jul 1999-Jun 2000 Income $28,479, State $339, City $20,280, Locally Generated Income $3,390, Other $4,470. Mats Exp $3,522, Books $2,029, Per/Ser (Incl. Access Fees) $627, AV Equip $866. Sal $17,415
Library Holdings: Bk Vols 13,504; Bk Titles 13,031; Per Subs 25
Subject Interests: World War II
Database Vendor: Ebsco - EbscoHost, epixtech, inc.
Partic in Chemeketa Cooperative Regional Library Service
Open Tues-Thurs 11-6, Sat 10-4
Friends of the Library Group

JOHN DAY

P GRANT COUNTY LIBRARY,* 507 S Canyon Blvd, 97845-1050. SAN 314-1055. Tel: 541-575-1992. *Chief Librn*, Melody Jackson; *Asst Librn*, Vicky Waters
Pop 8,250; Circ 60,567
Library Holdings: Bk Vols 30,000
Open Mon-Thurs 2-5
Friends of the Library Group

JOSEPH

P JOSEPH CITY LIBRARY, 201 N Main, PO Box 15, 97846-0015. SAN 314-1063. Tel: 541-432-0141. E-Mail: josephpl@eoni.com. *Librn*, Genene Kingsford
Founded 1912. Pop 1,170; Circ 11,069
Library Holdings: Bk Vols 10,650; Per Subs 30
Special Collections: Wallowa County History
Open Mon-Fri 12-4
Friends of the Library Group

JUNCTION CITY

P JUNCTION CITY PUBLIC LIBRARY,* 726 Greenwood, PO Box 280, 97448-0280. SAN 314-1071. Tel: 541-998-8942. FAX: 541-998-6340. Web Site: www.continet.com/junctioncitylib. *Librn*, Lynn Frost; *Asst Librn*, Freda Darling
Founded 1924. Pop 4,000; Circ 35,712
1997-1998 Income $84,355, City $78,855, Locally Generated Income $5,500. Mats Exp $7,700, Books $7,000, Per/Ser (Incl. Access Fees) $500, Presv $200. Sal $53,527 (Prof $35,527)
Library Holdings: Bk Vols 20,000; Per Subs 41
Special Collections: Scandinavian Coll, bks, pamphlets
Publications: JCPL: A Plan for Service (planning committee report)
Open Mon & Tues 12-7, Wed & Thurs 12-6, Sat 10-3
Friends of the Library Group

LAMATH FALLS

KLAMATH COUNTY LIBRARY SERVICE DISTRICT, 126 S Third St, 97601-6394. SAN 357-9484. Tel: 541-882-8894. Reference Tel: 541-882-8897. Toll Free Tel: 800-230-3871. TDD: 541-885-7183. FAX: 541-882-6166. E-Mail: kcl@kfalls.net. Web Site: www.co.klamath.or.us:8080/library/klamathcountylibrary.html. *Dir*, Andy Swanson; Tel: 541-882-8896, E-Mail: aswanson@co.klamath.or.us; *Ad Servs*, Karen Kunz; Tel: 541-882-8896, E-Mail: kkunz_klamathcolib@altavista.com; *Ch Servs*, Margaret Harmon; Tel: 541-882-8896, E-Mail: mehkclchild@altavista.com; *Br Coordr*, Christy Davis; Tel: 541-882-8896, E-Mail: christdiva@hotmail.com; Staff 2 (MLS 2)
Founded 1913. Pop 70,085; Circ 206,373
Jun 1999-Jul 2000 Income (Main Library and Branch Library) $1,037,546, State $23,351, Federal $1,808, County $987,689, Locally Generated Income $24,698. Mats Exp $77,742, Books $50,630, Presv $9,588, Electronic Ref Mat (Incl. Access Fees) $17,524. Sal $426,896 (Prof $144,411)
Library Holdings: Bk Vols 148,215; Bk Titles 112,712; Per Subs 251
Subject Interests: Genealogy, Oregon
Automation Activity & Vendor Info: (Acquisitions) Gaylord; (Cataloging) Gaylord; (Circulation) Gaylord; (ILL) Gaylord; (OPAC) Gaylord
Database Vendor: Ebsco - EbscoHost, ProQuest
Special Services for the Deaf - TDD
Friends of the Library Group
Branches: 10
BLY BRANCH, PO Box 366, Bly, 97623. SAN 377-7677. Tel: 541-353-2299. FAX: 541-353-2299. E-Mail: blylib@yahoo.com. *Asst Librn*, Roseann Sciurba; Staff 1 (Non-MLS 1)
Circ 2,830
Library Holdings: Bk Titles 1,000; Per Subs 5
BONANZA BRANCH, Hwy 70 & Fourth St, PO Box 218, Bonanza, 97623. SAN 357-9549. Tel: 541-545-6944. FAX: 541-545-6944. E-Mail: bonanzalib@yahoo.com.; Staff 1 (Non-MLS 1)
Circ 8,073
Library Holdings: Bk Vols 4,704
Automation Activity & Vendor Info: (Circulation) Gaylord
CHEMULT BRANCH, Hwy 97 N, PO Box 155, Chemult, 97731. SAN 377-7693. Tel: 541-365-2412. FAX: 541-365-2412. E-Mail: chemultlib@yahoo.com.; Staff 1 (Non-MLS 1)
Circ 1,027
Library Holdings: Bk Titles 1,000
CHILOQUIN BRANCH, 216 & 218 S First St, PO Box 666, Chiloquin, 97624. SAN 357-9573. E-Mail: chiloquin@hotmail.com.; Staff 1 (Non-MLS 1)
Pop 5,968
Library Holdings: Bk Vols 3,423
Automation Activity & Vendor Info: (Circulation) Gaylord
Friends of the Library Group
GILCHRIST BRANCH, Gilchrist School, PO Box 668, Gilchrist, 97737. SAN 378-1461. Tel: 541-433-2167. FAX: 541-433-2167. E-Mail: gilchristbr@yahoo.com.; Staff 1 (Non-MLS 1)
Pop 283
Library Holdings: Bk Titles 200
KENO BRANCH, 15309 Hwy 66, Keno, 97601. E-Mail: kenolib@yahoo.com.
LOYD DELAP LAW LIBRARY, 126 S Third St, 97601-6388. SAN 357-9662. Tel: 541-883-5128. FAX: 541-885-3624. E-Mail: lawdelaw@cdsnet.net. *In Charge*, Gail Corey; E-Mail: gcorey@co.klamath.or.us; Staff 1 (Non-MLS 1)
Founded 1929
Jul 1999-Jun 2000 Income $103,924, County $2,491, Locally Generated Income $3,287, Other $98,146. Mats Exp $50,975, Books $7,328, Presv $421, Electronic Ref Mat (Incl. Access Fees) $9,668. Sal $6,251
Library Holdings: Bk Vols 5,000
MALIN BRANCH, 4 Front St, Malin, 97632. SAN 357-9697. Tel: 541-723-2772. FAX: 541-723-2772. E-Mail: malinlib@hotmail.com.; Staff 1 (Non-MLS 1)
Circ 3,999
Library Holdings: Bk Vols 5,762
MERRILL BRANCH, 365 W Front, Merrill, 97633. SAN 377-7715. Tel: 541-798-5393. FAX: 541-798-5393. E-Mail: merrilllib@hotmail.com.; Staff 1 (Non-MLS 1)
Circ 910
Library Holdings: Per Subs 2,500
SPRAGUE RIVER BRANCH, Sprague River Hwy, PO Box 29, Sprague River, 97639. SAN 377-7731. Tel: 541-882-8894. FAX: 541-882-6166. E-Mail: librsr@hotmail.com. *Mgr*, Mitchell Cobb; E-Mail: scobb@co.klamath.or.us; Staff 1 (Non-MLS 1)
Circ 910
Library Holdings: Bk Titles 500
Bookmobiles: 1

S KLAMATH COUNTY MUSEUM & BALDWIN HOTEL MUSEUM, Research Library, 1451 Main St, 97601. SAN 314-108X. Tel: 541-883-4208. Web Site: www.kchs.org. *Mgr*, Kimberly Bellavia
Founded 1960
JulJun
Library Holdings: Bk Titles 10,000
Subject Interests: History, Natural science, Pre-hist, Wildlife of area
Special Collections: Early; Early Photographs (Floyd), negatives-prints; Photo Glass Plates (Baldwin), negatives-prints; Photographs, Modoc Indian War & Logging & Lumbering (Ogle), negatives-prints, bks, doc & micro
Publications: Research Papers
Restriction: By appointment only
Function: Research library

C OREGON INSTITUTE OF TECHNOLOGY LIBRARY, 3201 Campus Dr, 97601-8801. SAN 314-1098. Tel: 541-885-1772. Circulation Tel: 541-885-1771. Reference Tel: 541-885-1773. FAX: 541-885-1777. E-Mail: reference@oit.edu. Web Site: www.oit.edu/library. *Dir*, Thomas W Leonhardt; Tel: 541-885-1770, E-Mail: leonhart@oit.edu; *Coll Develop*, Marita Kunkel; Tel: 541-885-1774, E-Mail: kunkelm@oit.edu; *Info Res*, Susanna Flodin; Tel: 541-885-1965, E-Mail: flodins@oit.edu; *Spec Coll*, Kacy Guill; Tel: 541-885-1686, E-Mail: guillk@oit.edu; Staff 12 (MLS 5, Non-MLS 7)
Founded 1950. Enrl 1,904; Fac 171
Jun 1999-Jul 2000 Income Parent Institution $1,092,461. Mats Exp $345,000, Books $130,000, Per/Ser (Incl. Access Fees) $140,000, Presv $15,000, Electronic Ref Mat (Incl. Access Fees) $60,000. Sal $338,396 (Prof $201,104)
Library Holdings: Bk Vols 142,180; Bk Titles 87,484; Per Subs 1,693
Subject Interests: Bus, Computer science, Eng tech, Hist of sci and tech, Medicine, Sci-tech
Special Collections: Shaw Historical Library Coll; Western History (Klamath Basin Coll)
Automation Activity & Vendor Info: (Acquisitions) Innovative Interfaces Inc.; (Cataloging) Innovative Interfaces Inc.; (Circulation) Innovative Interfaces Inc.; (OPAC) Innovative Interfaces Inc.; (Serials) Innovative Interfaces Inc.
Database Vendor: Ebsco - EbscoHost, OCLC - First Search, OVID Technologies, Silverplatter Information Inc.
Publications: Journal of the Shaw Historical Library (Local historical information)
Function: Reference only
Partic in OCLC Online Computer Library Center, Inc; Orbis

LA GRANDE

C EASTERN OREGON UNIVERSITY, Walter M Pierce Library, One University Blvd, 97850. SAN 314-1101. Tel: 541-962-3792. Circulation Tel: 541-962-3864. Reference Tel: 541-962-3780. FAX: 541-962-3335. Web Site: pierce.eou.edu. *Dir*, Patricia J Cutright; E-Mail: cutright@eou.edu; *Assoc Dir*, Shirley J Roberts; Tel: 541-962-3540, E-Mail: sroberts@eou.edu; *Librn*, Leah Starr; Tel: 541-962-3699, E-Mail: starrl@eou.edu; *Res*, Theresa Gillis; Tel: 541-962-3605, E-Mail: tgillis@eou.edu; *Publ Servs*, Ken Watson; Tel: 541-962-3546, E-Mail: kwatson@eou.edu; *Online Servs*, Debra Spidal; Tel: 541-962-3523, E-Mail: spidald@eou.edu. Subject Specialists: *Business*, Shirley J Roberts; *History*, Debra Spidal; *Outreach*, Leah Starr; *Sciences*, Ken Watson; *Sociology*, Patricia J Cutright; *Sociology*, Theresa Gillis; Staff 13 (MLS 5, Non-MLS 8)
Founded 1929. Enrl 2,039; Fac 125; Highest Degree: Master
Jul 1999-Jun 2000 Income $1,057,055, State $1,000,650, Other $56,405. Mats Exp $349,995, Books $46,215, Per/Ser (Incl. Access Fees) $236,432, Micro $13,000, Electronic Ref Mat (Incl. Access Fees) $28,859. Sal $417,904 (Prof $194,745)
Library Holdings: Bk Vols 140,848; Bk Titles 100,920; Per Subs 992
Subject Interests: Genealogy, Local history
Special Collections: Native American Literature; Oregon, bks & doc
Automation Activity & Vendor Info: (Acquisitions) Innovative Interfaces Inc.; (Cataloging) Innovative Interfaces Inc.; (Circulation) Innovative Interfaces Inc.; (Course Reserve) Innovative Interfaces Inc.; (OPAC) Innovative Interfaces Inc.; (Serials) Innovative Interfaces Inc.
Database Vendor: Ebsco - EbscoHost, OCLC - First Search, OVID Technologies, ProQuest, Silverplatter Information Inc., Wilson - Wilson Web
Publications: Newsletter
Mem of Pioneer Library System
Partic in Orbis
Friends of the Library Group

P LA GRANDE PUBLIC LIBRARY, 1006 Penn Ave, 97850-2496. SAN 314-111X. Tel: 541-962-1339. FAX: 541-962-1338. Web Site: www.orednet.org/llibrary. *Dir*, Jo E Cowling; E-Mail: jcowling@orednet.org
Founded 1912. Pop 24,000; Circ 123,068
Jul 1999-Jun 2000 Income $308,775. Mats Exp $48,000
Library Holdings: Bk Vols 49,571; Per Subs 121
Automation Activity & Vendor Info: (Circulation) Innovative Interfaces Inc.; (OPAC) Innovative Interfaces Inc.
Friends of the Library Group

LAKE OSWEGO

P LAKE OSWEGO PUBLIC LIBRARY, 706 Fourth St, 97034-2399. SAN 314-1128. Tel: 503-636-7628. FAX: 503-635-4171. Web Site: www.ci.oswego.or.us. *Dir*, Carole Dickerson; E-Mail: cdickerson@ci.oswego.or.us; *Ch Servs*, Jacqueline Rose

Founded 1930. Pop 47,000; Circ 944,263
Jul 1999-Jun 2000 Income $4,252,923, State $8,395, City $795,432, Federal $3,983, County $1,271,525, Locally Generated Income $2,066,957, Other $106,631. Mats Exp $360,291, Books $220,996, Per/Ser (Incl. Access Fees) $17,131, Presv $16,911, AV Equip $72,945, Other Print Mats $20,353, Electronic Ref Mat (Incl. Access Fees) $11,955. Sal $1,222,246
Library Holdings: Bk Vols 141,219; Bk Titles 113,600; Per Subs 418
Subject Interests: Genealogy
Special Collections: City; Northwest Coll, bks & files
Automation Activity & Vendor Info: (Acquisitions) epixtech, inc.; (Cataloging) epixtech, inc.; (Circulation) epixtech, inc.; (OPAC) epixtech, inc.; (Serials) epixtech, inc.
Database Vendor: OCLC - First Search
Mem of Coop Libr Network of Clackamas County
Partic in OCLC Online Computer Library Center, Inc
Friends of the Library Group

LAKESIDE

P LAKESIDE PUBLIC LIBRARY, 915 N Lake Ave, PO Box R, 97449. SAN 329-7608. Tel: 541-759-4432. FAX: 541-759-4752. E-Mail: lakstaff@presys.com. *Librn*, Deirdre S Krumper
Founded 1987. Pop 1,519
Jul 1998-Jun 1999 Income $42,025, State $386, County $41,639. Mats Exp $3,500, Books $3,100, Per/Ser (Incl. Access Fees) $400. Sal $34,200
Library Holdings: Bk Titles 21,680; Per Subs 30
Partic in Coos County Library Service District, Extended Service Office
Friends of the Library Group

LAKEVIEW

P LAKE DISTRICT LIBRARY,* 513 Center St, 97630-1582. SAN 357-9786. Tel: 541-947-6019. FAX: 541-947-6034. *Librn*, Cecilia K Elder; Staff 1 (MLS 1)
Founded 1948. Pop 7,500; Circ 67,757
Library Holdings: Bk Titles 36,530; Per Subs 56
Subject Interests: Agriculture, Americana
Special Collections: Oregon Coll
Partic in Southern Oregon Library Federation
Friends of the Library Group
Branches: 3
CHRISTMAS VALLEY, PO Box 87, 97641-2146. SAN 357-9794. Tel: 541-576-2146. *Librn*, Barbara Remy
Friends of the Library Group
PAISELY BRANCH, PO Box 99, Paisley, 97636-0099. SAN 357-9816. Tel: 541-943-3911. FAX: 541-943-3911. *Librn*, Jan Murphy
Library Holdings: Bk Titles 6,500
Friends of the Library Group
SILVER LAKE BRANCH, PO Box 87, Silver Lake, 97638-0087. SAN 357-9840. Tel: 541-576-2146. FAX: 541-576-2146. *Librn*, Laura Parks
Library Holdings: Bk Titles 3,046
Friends of the Library Group

LANGLOIS

P LANGLOIS PUBLIC LIBRARY,* 94322 E First St, PO Box 277, 97450-0277. SAN 314-1144. Tel: 541-348-2278. FAX: 541-348-2278. *Librn*, Tobe Porter
Circ 11,372
Library Holdings: Bk Vols 13,000; Per Subs 35
Open Tues 1-7, Wed 1-6, Thurs 10-6, Fri 1-6 & Sat 10-2

LEBANON

P LEBANON PUBLIC LIBRARY,* 626 Second St, 97355-3320. SAN 314-1152. Tel: 541-451-7461. FAX: 541-258-2080. E-Mail: lebanonpl@proaxis.com. *In Charge*, Susan Messersmith
Pop 12,610; Circ 85,633
Jul 1998-Jun 1999 Income $205,692, State $1,692. Mats Exp $22,353. Sal $155,713
Library Holdings: Bk Vols 33,000; Per Subs 51
Special Collections: Genealogy (End of the Trail Research Coll)
Friends of the Library Group

LINCOLN CITY

P DRIFTWOOD PUBLIC LIBRARY, 801 SW Hwy 101 Ste 201, 97367-2720. SAN 314-1160. Tel: 541-996-2277. FAX: 541-996-1262. E-Mail: driftwoodlib@harborside.com. Web Site: www.driftwoodlib.org. *Dir*, Susan J Jenkins; Tel: 541-996-1251, E-Mail: sjenkins@harborside.com; Staff 9 (MLS 3, Non-MLS 6)
Founded 1965. Pop 9,995
Jul 1998-Jun 1999 Income $481,858, State $855, City $369,000, County $109,000, Locally Generated Income $3,000. Mats Exp $91,580, Books $65,324, Per/Ser (Incl. Access Fees) $3,500, Presv $1,000, Micro $100, AV Equip $15,314, Electronic Ref Mat (Incl. Access Fees) $3,000. Sal $264,53 (Prof $106,000)
Library Holdings: Bk Titles 68,616; Per Subs 150; High Interest/Low Vocabulary Bk Vols 52
Subject Interests: Pacific Northwest
Automation Activity & Vendor Info: (Circulation) DRA; (OPAC) DRA
Database Vendor: DRA, OCLC - First Search
Publications: Driftwood Gazette
Partic in Coastal Resource Sharing Network
Special Services for the Blind - Closed circuit television
Friends of the Library Group

LYONS

P LYONS PUBLIC LIBRARY, 448 Cedar St, PO Box 100, 97358-0100. SAN 376-3293. Tel: 503-859-2366. E-Mail: lyonspl@open.org. *Librn*, Brenda Harris
Circ 16,500
Jul 1999-Jun 2000 Income $28,240, State $203, City $16,200, Federal $44, Locally Generated Income $8,280, Other $3,513. Mats Exp $1,427, Books $557, Per/Ser (Incl. Access Fees) $202, Presv $246, AV Equip $94, Other Print Mats $299, Electronic Ref Mat (Incl. Access Fees) $29. Sal $19,807
Library Holdings: Bk Vols 19,000; Per Subs 20; High Interest/Low Vocabulary Bk Vols 100; Bks on Deafness & Sign Lang 25
Automation Activity & Vendor Info: (Cataloging) epixtech, inc.; (Circulation) epixtech, inc.
Restriction: Residents only
Function: ILL available, Photocopies available, Reference services available
Mem of Cent Colorado Libr Syst
Partic in Chemeketa Cooperative Regional Library Service
Special Services for the Deaf - Staff with knowledge of sign language
Friends of the Library Group

MADRAS

P JEFFERSON COUNTY LIBRARY DISTRICT, 241 SE Seventh St, 97741-1611. SAN 314-1209. Tel: 541-475-3351. FAX: 541-475-7434. E-Mail: library@jcld.lib.or.us. Web Site: www.jcld.lib.or.us. *Dir*, Melanie Webber Lightbody; Tel: 541-475-4678, E-Mail: director@ispchannel.com; *Asst Dir*, DeRese Hall; E-Mail: dehall@ispchannel.com; *ILL*, Jackie May; E-Mail: jjmay@ispchannel.com; *Outreach Serv*, Deanna Fender; E-Mail: dfender@ispchannel.com; *Ch Servs*, Marrero Yirah; E-Mail: yam@ispchannel.com. Subject Specialists: *Spanish*, Marrero Yirah; *Youth*, Marrero Yirah; Staff 9 (MLS 2, Non-MLS 7)
Founded 1915. Pop 17,000; Circ 65,531
Jul 1999-Jun 2000 Income $158,718, City $2,500, Federal $8,921, County $100,000, Locally Generated Income $42,123. Mats Exp $24,929, Books $22,378, Per/Ser (Incl. Access Fees) $1,925
Library Holdings: Bk Titles 45,000; Per Subs 100
Subject Interests: Ore hist
Special Collections: Jefferson County History
Automation Activity & Vendor Info: (Cataloging) Follett; (Circulation) Follett
Database Vendor: Ebsco - EbscoHost
Function: ILL available
Friends of the Library Group

MANZANITA

L INFORMATION MASTERS LIBRARY,* PO Box 525, 97130. SAN 372-2171. Tel: 503-368-6990. FAX: 503-368-7118. E-Mail: 70140.350@compuserve.com. *Librn*, Signe E Larson
Library Holdings: Bk Vols 11,300; Per Subs 50
Subject Interests: Bus law, Business

MARYLHURST

C MARYLHURST UNIVERSITY, Shoen Library, 17600 Pacific Hwy (Hwy 43), PO Box 261, 97036-0261. SAN 314-1217. Tel: 503-699-6261. FAX: 503-636-1957. E-Mail: library@marylhurst.edu. Web Site: www.marylhurst.edu/student/shoenlibrary.html. *Librn*, Jan Marie Fortier; E-Mail: jfortier@maryhurst.edu; *Syst Coordr*, Nancy Hoover; *Publ Servs*, Kirk Howard; *Coll Develop, Electronic Resources*, Richard Severson; *Circ*, Paulette Switzer; *Per*, Paula Germond; *ILL*, Kristine Simpson; *Acq, Cat*, Patti Russell. Subject Specialists: *English literature*, Jan Marie Fortier; *Philosophy*, Richard Severson; Staff 4 (MLS 4)
Founded 1893. Enrl 900; Highest Degree: Master
Jul 2000-Jun 2001 Income $610,426. Mats Exp $177,195, Books $111,270, Per/Ser (Incl. Access Fees) $38,843, AV Equip $16,570, Electronic Ref Mat (Incl. Access Fees) $10,512. Sal $239,460 (Prof $127,435)
Library Holdings: Bk Vols 93,418; Bk Titles 74,857; Per Subs 564
Subject Interests: Art, Art therapy, Music, Religion
Special Collections: Sacred Music
Automation Activity & Vendor Info: (Cataloging) Innovative Interfaces Inc.; (Circulation) Innovative Interfaces Inc.; (Course Reserve) Innovative

Interfaces Inc.; (OPAC) Innovative Interfaces Inc.; (Serials) Innovative Interfaces Inc.
Database Vendor: Ebsco - EbscoHost, Lexis-Nexis, OCLC - First Search
Partic in NAPCU; Orbis; Portland Area Libr Syst
Friends of the Library Group

IC MINNVILLE

LINFIELD COLLEGE, Northup Library, 900 S Baker St, 97128. SAN 314-1187. Tel: 503-434-2517. FAX: 503-434-2566. Web Site: www.linfield.edu/library/northup.htm/. *Dir Libr Serv*, Susan Barnes Whyte; E-Mail: swhyte@linfield.edu; *Librn*, Jean Caspers; Tel: 503-434-2261, E-Mail: jcaspers@linfield.edu; *Librn*, Carol McCulley; Tel: 503-434-2595, E-Mail: cmccull@linfield.edu; *Librn*, Barbara Valentine; Tel: 503-434-2573, E-Mail: bvalen@linfield.edu; *Coll Develop, Tech Servs*, Mary Margaret Benson; E-Mail: mbenson@linfield.edu; *ILL*, Frances Rasmussen; Tel: 503-434-2534, E-Mail: frasmuss@linfield.edu; *Media Spec*, Susan DeHut. Subject Specialists: *Ref*, Barbara Valentine; *Systs*, Barbara Valentine; Staff 12 (MLS 8, Non-MLS 4)
Founded 1849. Pop 2,565; Circ 49,960; Enrl 2,565; Fac 122; Highest Degree: Bachelor
Jul 1999-Jun 2000 Income $1,352,565. Mats Exp $455,735, Books $210,093, Per/Ser (Incl. Access Fees) $239,721, Presv $5,921. Sal $571,485 (Prof $347,491)
Library Holdings: Bk Vols 145,589; Per Subs 1,173
Subject Interests: Canadiana, Costa Rica, Pac NW hist, Thomas Hobbes
Special Collections: Baptist Pioneer History Coll
Automation Activity & Vendor Info: (Acquisitions) Innovative Interfaces Inc.; (Cataloging) Innovative Interfaces Inc.; (Circulation) Innovative Interfaces Inc.; (Serials) Innovative Interfaces Inc.
Database Vendor: Ebsco - EbscoHost, GaleNet, IAC - Info Trac, Innovative Interfaces INN - View, Lexis-Nexis, OCLC - First Search, OVID Technologies, ProQuest, Silverplatter Information Inc.
Publications: Northup News (irregular) (Newsletter)
Partic in OCLC Online Computer Library Center, Inc; Orbis; PORTALS
Departmental Libraries:
PORTLAND CAMPUS, 2255 NW Northrup, Portland, 97210. SAN 370-4793. Tel: 503-413-7820. FAX: 503-413-8016. E-Mail: library@linfield.edu. Web Site: www.linfield.edu/library/northup.html. *Librn*, Patrice O'Donovan; E-Mail: odonovan@linfield.edu
Library Holdings: Bk Vols 10,180; Per Subs 148
Subject Interests: Nursing

ICMINNVILLE

MCMINNVILLE PUBLIC LIBRARY, 225 NW Adams St, 97128-5425. SAN 314-1195. Tel: 503-435-5555. TDD: 503-435-5555. FAX: 503-472-1429. Web Site: www.ci.mcminnville.or.us. *Dir*, Anne Van Sickle; Tel: 503-435-5550, E-Mail: vansica@ci.mcminnville.or.us; *Senior Librn*, Jill Poyer; Tel: 503-435-5555, Ext 2366, E-Mail: poyerj@ci.mcminnville.or.us; *Ch Servs*, Nola Olmsted; Tel: 503-435-5552; *Tech Servs*, Suzanne Beppu; Tel: 503-435-5555, Ext 2393; *Coordr*, Dee Goldman; Tel: 503-435-5551; *Circ*, Judith Folgate; Tel: 503-435-5555, Ext 2300; *Web Coordr*, Michelle Boisvenue-Fox; Tel: 503-435-5555, Ext 2301, E-Mail: boisvm@ci.mcminnville.or.us; Staff 8 (MLS 3, Non-MLS 5)
Founded 1912. Pop 38,000; Circ 278,000
Library Holdings: Bk Titles 82,500; Per Subs 168
Database Vendor: Ebsco - EbscoHost
Publications: Friends of the Library News
Function: ILL available, Outside services via phone, cable & mail, Photocopies available, Reference services available
Partic in Chemeketa Cooperative Regional Library Service
Friends of the Library Group

IEDFORD

BUREAU OF LAND MANAGEMENT LIBRARY,* 3040 Biddle Rd, 97504. SAN 314-1225. Tel: 541-770-2200. FAX: 541-770-2400. *Librn*, Jay Hart
Library Holdings: Bk Vols 100
Subject Interests: Endangered animals, Endangered plants, Environ concerns, Forestry, Personal relations, Rare animals, Rare plants, Road construction, Road maintenance, Silviculture, Water resources

JACKSON COUNTY LAW LIBRARY, Justice Bldg, 100 S Oakdale, 97501. SAN 325-8149. Tel: 541-776-7214. FAX: 541-774-6767. E-Mail: lawlib@jcls.org. *Librn*, Pam Pfeil
Library Holdings: Bk Vols 15,000; Per Subs 10

JACKSON COUNTY LIBRARY SERVICES, 413 W Main St, 97501-2730. SAN 357-9875. Tel: 541-774-8689. Interlibrary Loan Service Tel: 541-774-6421. Circulation Tel: 541-774-8690. FAX: 541-774-6749. Web Site: www.jcls.org. *Dir*, Ronnie Lee Budge; Tel: 541-744-8673, E-Mail: budgerl@jacksoncounty.org; *Mgr*, Judith Baalman; Tel: 541-774-6402, Fax: 541-774-6748, E-Mail: baalmaja@jacksoncounty.org; *Mgr*, Meghan O'Flaherty; *Regional Manager*, Margaret Jakubcin; *Regional Manager*, Ted Stark; *Regional Manager*, Bob Wilson; *Tech Servs*, Sylvia Lee; *Ch Servs*, Anne Billeter. Subject Specialists: *Business*, Judith Baalman; Staff 23 (MLS 23)
Founded 1908. Pop 174,550; Circ 1,236,475
Jul 1999-Jun 2000 Income $6,200,054. Mats Exp $583,428, Books $454,975, Per/Ser (Incl. Access Fees) $57,566, Presv $1,671, Electronic Ref Mat (Incl. Access Fees) $19,211. Sal $3,699,790
Library Holdings: Bk Vols 452,829; Per Subs 1,531
Special Collections: Music Coll; Oregon Coll
Automation Activity & Vendor Info: (Cataloging) Gaylord; (Circulation) Gaylord
Database Vendor: Ebsco - EbscoHost
Partic in Southern Oregon Library Federation
Open Mon-Thurs 9:30-8, Fri & Sat 9:30-5
Friends of the Library Group
Branches: 14
APPLEGATE BRANCH, 15095 Hwy 238, PO Box 308, Applegate, 97530-1501. SAN 358-0261. Tel: 541-846-7346. FAX: 541-846-7346. *Branch Mgr*, Gail Gartner
Friends of the Library Group
ASHLAND BRANCH, 410 Siskiyou Blvd, Ashland, 97520-2196. SAN 357-9905. Tel: 541-482-1151. Reference Tel: 541-482-1197. FAX: 541-482-3071. *Regional Manager*, Robert R Wilson
Special Collections: Shakespeare
Friends of the Library Group
BUTTE FALLS BRANCH, 626 Fir St, PO Box 138, Butte Falls, 97522-0138. SAN 357-993X. Tel: 541-865-3511. FAX: 541-865-3511. *Branch Mgr*, Laura Smith
Friends of the Library Group
CENTRAL POINT BRANCH, 226 E Pine St, Central Point, 97502-2252. SAN 357-9964. Tel: 541-644-3228. FAX: 541-644-3228. *Branch Mgr*, Jeanette M Cooper
Friends of the Library Group
EAGLE POINT BRANCH, 158 W Main St, PO Box 459, Eagle Point, 97524-0459. SAN 357-9999. Tel: 541-826-3313. Reference Tel: 541-826-2145. FAX: 541-826-2993. *Branch Mgr*, Jeannette Blankenship
Friends of the Library Group
GOLD HILL BRANCH, 420 Sixth Ave, PO Box 258, Gold Hill, 97525-0258. SAN 358-0024. Tel: 541-855-1994. FAX: 541-855-1994. *Branch Mgr*, Anne Boydston
Friends of the Library Group
JACKSONVILLE BRANCH, 170 S Oregon St, PO Box 490, Jacksonville, 97530-0490. SAN 358-0059. Tel: 541-899-1665. FAX: 541-899-1665. *Branch Mgr*, Janice Sanders
Friends of the Library Group
PHOENIX BRANCH, 120 W Second St, Phoenix, 97535. (Mail add: PO Box 277, Phoenix, 97535-0277), SAN 358-0083. Tel: 541-535-7090. FAX: 541-535-7090. *Branch Mgr*, Camille Korsmo
Friends of the Library Group
PROSPECT BRANCH, 300 Mill Creek Dr, PO Box 39, Prospect, 97536-0039. SAN 358-0113. Tel: 541-560-3668. FAX: 541-560-3668. *Branch Mgr*, Laura Smith
Friends of the Library Group
ROGUE RIVER BRANCH, 412 E Main St, PO Box 1075, Rogue River, 97537-1075. SAN 358-0148. Tel: 541-582-1714. Reference Tel: 541-582-0042. FAX: 541-582-4026. *Branch Mgr*, Mary Ann Ross
Friends of the Library Group
RUCH, 7388 Hwy 238, Jacksonville, 97530-9728. SAN 329-6628. Tel: 541-899-7438. FAX: 541-899-7438. *Branch Mgr*, Janis Mohr-Tipton
Friends of the Library Group
SHADY COVE BRANCH, 22477 Hwy 62, PO Box 706, Shady Cove, 97539-0706. SAN 358-0172. Tel: 541-878-2270. FAX: 541-878-2270. *Branch Mgr*, Karen Rickerd
Friends of the Library Group
TALENT BRANCH, 105 N I St, PO Box 597, Talent, 97540-0597. SAN 358-0202. Tel: 541-535-4163. FAX: 541-535-4163. *Branch Mgr*, Betty Smith
Friends of the Library Group
WHITE CITY BRANCH, 2399 Antelope Rd, White City, 97503-1718. SAN 358-0237. Tel: 541-826-1333. FAX: 541-826-1333. *Branch Mgr*, Tess G Kusel
Friends of the Library Group

S MEDFORD MAIL TRIBUNE LIBRARY,* 111 N Fir St, PO Box 1108, 97501. SAN 314-1233. Tel: 541-776-4411, Ext 3325. FAX: 541-776-4376. E-Mail: tellus@mailtribune.com. *Librn*, Pamela S Sieg
Founded 1975
Library Holdings: Bk Titles 1,000
Subject Interests: Southern Ore
Special Collections: Medford Mail Tribune & early predecessors (1892-1993), micro

S SOUTHERN OREGON HISTORICAL SOCIETY, Research Library, 106 N Central, 97501. SAN 320-510X. Tel: 541-773-6536. FAX: 541-776-7994. Web Site: www.sohs.org. *Archivist, Coordr*, Jacquelyn Sundstrand; Staff 4 (MLS 1, Non-MLS 3)
Founded 1946
Jul 2000-Jun 2001 Mats Exp $1,900, Books $700, Per/Ser (Incl. Access Fees) $1,200

Library Holdings: Bk Vols 5,500; Bk Titles 5,100; Per Subs 30
Subject Interests: Historic preservation, Museum techniques
Special Collections: Southern Oregon History, mss, photogs
Database Vendor: OCLC - First Search
Restriction: Non-circulating

MILTON-FREEWATER

P MILTON-FREEWATER PUBLIC LIBRARY, (MFPL), 815 S Main, 97862-1529. SAN 358-0598. Tel: 541-938-5531, Ext 132. FAX: 541-938-9310. E-Mail: mfplbob@hscis.net. *Dir*, Robert A Jones; *Ch Servs*, Leeann Rizzuti; *Circ*, Marilyn Clark; Staff 3 (MLS 1, Non-MLS 2)
Founded 1913. Pop 11,000; Circ 49,450
Jul 1999-Jun 2000 Income $119,679, State $5,108, Locally Generated Income $4,873, Other $109,698. Mats Exp $27,010, Books $17,587, Per/Ser (Incl. Access Fees) $3,911, AV Equip $5,012, Electronic Ref Mat (Incl. Access Fees) $500. Sal $68,843
Library Holdings: Bk Vols 33,267; Per Subs 89
Automation Activity & Vendor Info: (Cataloging) epixtech, inc.; (Circulation) epixtech, inc.
Publications: The Bookie (Newsletter)
Function: ILL available, Photocopies available
Mem of Umatilla County Spec Libr Dist
Friends of the Library Group

MILWAUKIE

P LEDDING LIBRARY OF MILWAUKIE, Milwaukie Public Library, 10660 SE 21st Ave, 97222-7586. SAN 314-1241. Tel: 503-786-7580. FAX: 503-659-9497. Web Site: milwaukie.lib.or.us. *Senior Librn*, Cynthia Sturgis; Tel: 503-786-7584, E-Mail: cynthias@lincc.lib.or.us; *Circ*, Nancy Wittig; *Cat*, Paula Mishaga; *Ref*, Josef Sandfort; Staff 6 (MLS 5, Non-MLS 1)
Founded 1934. Pop 34,000; Circ 384,890
Jul 1999-Jun 2000 Income $1,257,015, State $3,773, City $580,040, Federal $16,450, County $620,924, Locally Generated Income $35,828. Mats Exp $114,114, Books $89,184, Per/Ser (Incl. Access Fees) $7,878, AV Equip $17,052. Sal $580,483
Library Holdings: Bk Vols 90,073; Bk Titles 75,823; Per Subs 236
Subject Interests: Automotive repair, Northwest
Special Collections: Local Historical Coll
Automation Activity & Vendor Info: (Circulation) epixtech, inc.
Database Vendor: Ebsco - EbscoHost, OCLC - First Search
Function: ILL available
Mem of Libr Info Network of Clackamas County
Friends of the Library Group

MOLALLA

P MOLALLA PUBLIC LIBRARY,* 117 N Molalla Ave, PO Box 208, 97038-0208. SAN 314-125X. Tel: 503-829-2593. FAX: 503-829-3676. *Librn*, Randy Collver
Pop 14,500; Circ 115,000
Library Holdings: Bk Vols 26,000; Per Subs 100
Special Collections: Animal Husbandry Coll
Mem of Clackamas County Syst
Open Mon-Thurs 10-8, Fri 10-6, Sat 10-5
Friends of the Library Group

MONMOUTH

S JENSEN ARCTIC MUSEUM-WEST OREGON UNIVERSITY, Research Library, 590 W Church St, 97361. SAN 329-1952. Tel: 503-838-8468. FAX: 503-838-8289. *Curator*, Mariana Mace; E-Mail: macem@wou.edu
Founded 1985
Library Holdings: Bk Titles 1,200

P MONMOUTH PUBLIC LIBRARY, 168 S Ecols St, PO Box 10, 97361. SAN 314-1268. Tel: 503-838-1932. FAX: 503-838-3899. Web Site: www.ccrls.org/monmouth/. *Dir*, Ronald Baker; *Coll Develop, Ref*, Howard Feltmann; *YA Servs*, Diane Adams; *Circ*, Fran Kosko
Founded 1934. Pop 17,125; Circ 145,000
Library Holdings: Bk Vols 64,500; Per Subs 167
Subject Interests: Local history
Partic in Chemeketa Cooperative Regional Library Service
Friends of the Library Group
Branches: 1
MONMOUTH SENIOR CENTER, 180 S Warren, 97361. SAN 378-0821.

C WESTERN OREGON UNIVERSITY, Wayne & Lynn Hamersly Library, 345 N Monmouth Ave, 97361-1396. SAN 314-1276. Tel: 503-838-8418. Circulation Tel: 503-838-8902. Reference Tel: 503-838-8899. TDD: 503-838-8418. FAX: 503-838-8399. E-Mail: refdesk@wou.edu. Web Site: www.library.wou.edu. *Dir Libr Serv*, Dr Gary D Jensen; Tel: 503-838-8886, E-Mail: jenseng@wou.edu; *Bibliog Instr*, Janeanne Rockwell-Kincanon; Tel: 503-838-8888, E-Mail: kincanj@wou.edu; *Coll Develop*, Laura Groves; Tel: 503-838-8818, E-Mail: grovesl@wou.edu; *Head Ref*, M Anne Fox; Tel: 503-838-8892, E-Mail: foxa@wou.edu; *Syst Coordr*, Roy V Bennett; Tel: 503-838-8893, E-Mail: bennetr@wou.edu; *Head Tech Servs*, Shirley Linciculm; Tel: 503-838-8890, E-Mail: lincics@wou.edu. Subject Specialists: *Education*, Laura Groves; *History*, Shirley Linciculm; *Humanities*, Janeanne Rockwell-Kincanon; *Natural science*, M Anne Fox; *Social sciences*, Roy V Bennett; Staff 16 (MLS 8, Non-MLS 8)
Founded 1882. Enrl 4,150; Fac 340; Highest Degree: Master
Jul 1999-Jun 2000 Income State $1,377,488. Mats Exp $360,087. Sal $890,157 (Prof $332,595)
Library Holdings: Bk Titles 186,000; Per Subs 1,800
Special Collections: Archival materials & special collections relating to the history of the University
Automation Activity & Vendor Info: (Acquisitions) Innovative Interfaces Inc.; (Cataloging) Innovative Interfaces Inc.; (Circulation) Innovative Interfaces Inc.; (Course Reserve) Innovative Interfaces Inc.; (OPAC) Innovative Interfaces Inc.; (Serials) Innovative Interfaces Inc.
Database Vendor: Ebsco - EbscoHost, GaleNet, Lexis-Nexis, OCLC - First Search, Silverplatter Information Inc., Wilson - Wilson Web
Publications: Hamersly Library Guide (Library handbook)
Partic in OCLC Online Computer Library Center, Inc; Orbis

MOUNT ANGEL

P MOUNT ANGEL PUBLIC LIBRARY, 245 E Church, PO Box 870, 97362. SAN 314-1306. Tel: 503-845-6401. FAX: 503-845-6261. *Librn*, Sharon Flakser
Pop 3,010; Circ 42,060
Jul 1999-Jun 2000 Income $86,217. Mats Exp $85,406, Books $12,262, Per/Ser (Incl. Access Fees) $1,025. Sal $48,738
Library Holdings: Bk Vols 31,079; Per Subs 54
Friends of the Library Group

MYRTLE POINT

P DORA PUBLIC LIBRARY, 56125 Goldbrick Rd, 97458. SAN 376-7256. Tel: 541-572-6009. FAX: 541-572-6009. E-Mail: dorapl@gte.net. *Dir*, Betty H Vaughn; *Librn*, Krista Walsh; Staff 2 (Non-MLS 2)
Pop 350
Library Holdings: Bk Vols 9,000; Bk Titles 7,800; Per Subs 25
Database Vendor: Ebsco - EbscoHost, OCLC - First Search
Function: ILL available

S INTERNATIONAL MARITIME INC LIBRARY,* 14758 Sitkum Lane, 97458. SAN 373-1049. Tel: 541-572-2313. FAX: 541-572-4041. *Mgr*, Don Walsh; *Mgr*, Joan Walsh
Library Holdings: Bk Vols 6,000; Per Subs 12
Subject Interests: Oceanography
Special Collections: Undersea Technology

P MYRTLE POINT LIBRARY, Flora M Laird Memorial Library, 435 Fifth St, 97458-1113. SAN 314-1314. Tel: 541-572-2591. FAX: 541-572-5168. E-Mail: mplib@uscinet.com. *Librn*, Barbara Caffey
Founded 1925. Pop 4,308; Circ 46,996
Library Holdings: Bk Vols 28,000; Per Subs 95

NEWBERG

C GEORGE FOX UNIVERSITY, Murdock Learning Resource Center, 416 N Meridian St, 97132. SAN 314-1322. Tel: 503-554-2410. Reference Tel: 503-554-2419. FAX: 503-554-3599. Web Site: www.georgefox.edu/library. *Dir*, Merrill Johnson; *Tech Servs*, Charlie Kamilas; *Publ Servs*, Louise Newswanger; *Bibliog Instr, Ref*, Janis Tyhurst
Founded 1891. Highest Degree: Doctorate
Jul 1999-Jun 2000 Income $996,279. Mats Exp $345,841, Books $158,900, Per/Ser (Incl. Access Fees) $137,071, Presv $6,694, Micro $12,131, AV Equip $1,542, Electronic Ref Mat (Incl. Access Fees) $29,503. Sal $423,033 (Prof $195,639)
Library Holdings: Bk Vols 95,888; Per Subs 925
Special Collections: Herbert Hoover Coll, bks, pamphlets, per, photogs; Peace Coll, bks, periodicals; Society of Friends (Quaker Coll), bks, pamphlets, per, photogs
Automation Activity & Vendor Info: (Acquisitions) Innovative Interfaces Inc.; (Cataloging) Innovative Interfaces Inc.; (Circulation) Innovative Interfaces Inc.; (OPAC) Innovative Interfaces Inc.; (Serials) Innovative Interfaces Inc.
Partic in OCLC Online Computer Library Center, Inc; Orbis; PORTALS
Departmental Libraries:
PORTLAND CENTER, Hampton Plaza, 12753 SW 68th Ave, Portland, 97223. SAN 314-1934. Tel: 503-554-6130. Web Site: www.georgefox.edu/library. *Librn*, Chuck Church
Highest Degree: Doctorate
Jul 1999-Jun 2000 Income $250,503. Mats Exp $83,624, Books $33,514, Per/Ser (Incl. Access Fees) $24,831, Presv $7,064, Micro $13,293, AV Equip $3,733, Electronic Ref Mat (Incl. Access Fees) $1,189. Sal $121,439 (Prof $45,350)
Library Holdings: Bk Vols 51,314; Per Subs 334

Subject Interests: Counseling, Theology
Automation Activity & Vendor Info: (Acquisitions) Innovative Interfaces Inc.; (Cataloging) Innovative Interfaces Inc.; (Circulation) Innovative Interfaces Inc.; (OPAC) Innovative Interfaces Inc.; (Serials) Innovative Interfaces Inc.
Partic in OCLC Online Computer Library Center, Inc; Orbis; PORTALS

NEWBERG PUBLIC LIBRARY, 503 E Hancock St, 97132-2899. SAN 314-1330. Tel: 503-538-7323. FAX: 503-538-9720. E-Mail: newlibr@open.org. Web Site: www.open.org/newlibr. *Dir*, Leah Griffith; Tel: 503-537-1256, E-Mail: leahg@ccrls.org; Staff 11 (MLS 3, Non-MLS 8)
Founded 1907. Pop 20,000; Circ 188,810
Jul 1999-Jun 2000 Income $657,854, State $3,574, City $551,429, Federal $45,429, Locally Generated Income $4,200, Other $15,322. Mats Exp $71,752, Books $49,588, Per/Ser (Incl. Access Fees) $8,500, Micro $400, Other Print Mats $9,764, Electronic Ref Mat (Incl. Access Fees) $3,500. Sal $334,557 (Prof $132,000)
Library Holdings: Bk Vols 58,881; Bk Titles 52,717; Per Subs 220; High Interest/Low Vocabulary Bk Vols 100; Bks on Deafness & Sign Lang 10
Automation Activity & Vendor Info: (Cataloging) epixtech, inc.; (Circulation) epixtech, inc.; (OPAC) epixtech, inc.
Database Vendor: Ebsco - EbscoHost
Partic in Chemeketa Cooperative Regional Library Service
Friends of the Library Group

EWPORT

NEWPORT PUBLIC LIBRARY, 35 NW Nye St, 97365-3714. SAN 314-1349. Tel: 541-265-2153. FAX: 541-265-2793. Web Site: www.newportlibrary.org. *Dir*, Wyma Jane Rogers; *Asst Dir*, Kay Eldon; E-Mail: keldon@newportnet.com; *Outreach Serv*, Lynn Dennis; *Ch Servs*, Rebecca Cohen; *Tech Servs*, Dennis Moler; Staff 13 (MLS 7, Non-MLS 6)
Founded 1945. Pop 17,500; Circ 200,203
Jul 1998-Jun 1999 Income $708,625, State $1,820, City $559,712, County $143,093, Locally Generated Income $4,000. Mats Exp $87,300, Books $63,236, Per/Ser (Incl. Access Fees) $6,713, AV Equip $11,293, Electronic Ref Mat (Incl. Access Fees) $6,058. Sal $298,046
Library Holdings: Bk Vols 70,442; Per Subs 165
Special Collections: Oregon
Database Vendor: DRA, Ebsco - EbscoHost, OCLC - First Search
Open: Mon-Thurs 10-9, Fri & Sat 10-6, Sun 1-4

OREGON COAST COMMUNITY COLLEGE LIBRARY, 332 SW Coast Hwy, 97365-4928. SAN 374-5945. Tel: 541-574-7126. FAX: 541-265-3820. Web Site: www.occc.cc.or.us/library/. *Dir*, Charles Piquett; E-Mail: cpiquett@occc.cc.or.us
Founded 1993. Enrl 474; Fac 35; Highest Degree: Associate
Jul 2000-Jun 2001 Income $135,600. Mats Exp $30,400, Books $17,000, Per/Ser (Incl. Access Fees) $3,500, AV Equip $2,900, Electronic Ref Mat (Incl. Access Fees) $7,000
Library Holdings: Bk Vols 6,700; Bk Titles 6,500; Per Subs 105
Automation Activity & Vendor Info: (Cataloging) DRA; (Circulation) DRA; (OPAC) DRA
Database Vendor: OCLC - First Search
Partic in Coastal Resource Sharing Network; OCLC Online Computer Library Center, Inc

OREGON COAST HISTORY CENTER LIBRARY, (Formerly Lincoln County Historical Society Library), 545 SW Ninth St, 97365. SAN 370-548X. Tel: 541-265-7509. FAX: 541-265-3992. E-Mail: coasthistory@newportnet.com. *Dir*, Loretta Harrison; *Curator, Librn*, Steve Wyatt; Staff 2 (Non-MLS 2)
Founded 1961
Library Holdings: Bk Titles 600
Special Collections: Lincoln County History, bks, docs, photos; Siletz Tribal History, docs, maps, photos, artifacts

OREGON STATE UNIVERSITY, (Formerly Hatfield Marine Science Center Library), Marilyn Potts Guin Library, 2030 Marine Science Dr, 97365. SAN 321-5342. Tel: 541-867-0249. FAX: 541-867-0105. E-Mail: hmsc.library@orst.edu. Web Site: osulibrary.orst.edu/guin. *Head of Libr*, Janet G Webster; Tel: 541-867-0108, E-Mail: janet.webster@orst.edu; Staff 3 (MLS 1, Non-MLS 2)
Founded 1967
Jul 2000-Jun 2001 Income Other $265,000. Mats Exp $218,500, Books $8,500, Per/Ser (Incl. Access Fees) $110,000, Other Print Mats $100,000. Sal $148,000 (Prof $58,000)
Library Holdings: Bk Vols 30,000; Bk Titles 19,000; Per Subs 312
Subject Interests: Aquaculture, Marine fisheries, Marine mammals, Marine sci
Automation Activity & Vendor Info: (Acquisitions) Innovative Interfaces Inc.; (Cataloging) Innovative Interfaces Inc.; (Circulation) Innovative Interfaces Inc.; (Course Reserve) Innovative Interfaces Inc.; (ILL) Innovative Interfaces Inc.; (Media Booking) Innovative Interfaces Inc.; (OPAC) Innovative Interfaces Inc.; (Serials) Innovative Interfaces Inc.
Database Vendor: CARL, IAC - Info Trac, Lexis-Nexis, OCLC - First Search, OVID Technologies, ProQuest, Silverplatter Information Inc., Wilson - Wilson Web
Function: Research library
Partic in OCLC Online Computer Library Center, Inc; Orbis
Friends of the Library Group

NORTH BEND

G BUREAU OF LAND MANAGEMENT, District Office Library,* 1300 Airport Lane, 97459-2000. SAN 314-0709. Tel: 541-756-0100. FAX: 541-756-9303. *In Charge*, Pat Richardson
Library Holdings: Bk Vols 2,500; Per Subs 25

P NORTH BEND PUBLIC LIBRARY, 1800 Sherman Ave, 97459. SAN 314-1357. Tel: 541-756-0400. FAX: 541-756-1073. *Dir*, Gary Sharp; *Asst Dir*, Scott Gallagher-Starr; Staff 2 (MLS 2)
Founded 1914. Pop 18,000; Circ 228,803
Library Holdings: Bk Vols 100,000; Per Subs 220
Special Collections: City; Oregoniana (Oregon Coll), bks, clippings, pamphlets
Automation Activity & Vendor Info: (Circulation) Innovative Interfaces Inc.; (OPAC) Innovative Interfaces Inc.
Partic in Coos County Library Service District, Extended Service Office; OCLC Online Computer Library Center, Inc; Southern Oregon Library Federation
Friends of the Library Group

OAK GROVE

P CLACKAMAS COUNTY LIBRARY, Oak Lodge, 16201 SE McLoughlin Blvd, 97267-4653. SAN 314-139X. Tel: 503-655-8543. Reference Tel: 503-650-3058. FAX: 503-794-8006. *Dir*, Doris Grolbert; *Ref*, Mary Pauli; Staff 8 (MLS 6, Non-MLS 2)
Founded 1938. Pop 168,760; Circ 785,559
Jul 1999-Jun 2000 Income (Main Library and Branch Library) $1,754,343, State $14,306, Federal $14,803, County $1,678,302, Other $46,932
Library Holdings: Bk Vols 134,945; Bk Titles 93,608; Per Subs 497
Publications: Off the Shelf (newsletter)
Mem of Libr Info Network of Clackamas County
Friends of the Library Group
Branches: 1
CLACKAMAS CORNER, 11750 SE 82nd Ave, Ste D, Portland, 97266-1204. SAN 328-7106. Tel: 503-652-2640. FAX: 503-650-3105. *Librn*, Doris Grolbert
Bookmobiles: 1

OAKRIDGE

P OAKRIDGE PUBLIC LIBRARY, 48318 E First St, PO Box 385, 97463-0385. SAN 314-1365. Tel: 541-782-2258. FAX: 541-782-1081. E-Mail: olibrary@efn.org. *Librn*, Gloria Boyd
Founded 1950. Pop 3,734; Circ 16,800
Library Holdings: Per Subs 23
Open Mon, Wed & Fri 1-5, Tues 9-5 & Thurs 1-8

ONTARIO

P MALHEUR COUNTY LIBRARY, (MCL), 388 SW Second Ave, 97914. SAN 358-0350. Tel: 541-889-6371. FAX: 541-889-4279. E-Mail: malheurlibrary@yahoo.com. Web Site: www.malheur.or.us/library.html. *Dir*, Patricia Bradshaw; *ILL*, Betty Lee; Staff 6 (MLS 1, Non-MLS 5)
Founded 1906. Pop 27,800; Circ 168,980
Jul 1999-Jun 2000 Income $335,000, City $112,000, County $223,000. Mats Exp $28,500, Books $25,000, Per/Ser (Incl. Access Fees) $3,000, Micro $500. Sal $280,000 (Prof $41,000)
Library Holdings: Bk Titles 96,544; Per Subs 100
Subject Interests: Literacy
Special Collections: Oregon Coll
Automation Activity & Vendor Info: (Cataloging) epixtech, inc.; (Circulation) epixtech, inc.; (ILL) epixtech, inc.
Database Vendor: epixtech, inc.
Function: Internet access, Reference services available
Open Mon, Wed & Thurs 10-9, Tues & Fri 10-6, Sat 11-4
Friends of the Library Group
Bookmobiles: 1

J TREASURE VALLEY COMMUNITY COLLEGE LIBRARY,* 650 College Blvd, 97914. SAN 314-1373. Tel: 541-889-6493, Ext 248. FAX: 541-881-2724. Web Site: www.tvcc.cc.or.us/library/index.htm. *Dir Libr Serv*, Dale L Edwards; Tel: 541-889-6493, Ext 247, E-Mail: dale_edwards@mailman.tvcc.cc.or.us; *ILL*, Jean Ruud; Tel: 541-889-6493, Ext 336, E-Mail: jean_ruud@mailman.tvcc.cc.or.us; *Circ*, Kimberly Holling; E-Mail: kimberly_holling@mailman.tvcc.cc.or.us; Staff 6 (MLS 1, Non-MLS 5)
Founded 1963. Pop 55,000; Enrl 1,432; Fac 60
Library Holdings: Bk Vols 33,000; Bk Titles 29,500; Per Subs 165
Special Collections: Indian Artifact (Horace & Roa Arment)

Database Vendor: epixtech, inc., IAC - Info Trac
Publications: Daily Argus Observer Index, 1979-82
Function: ILL available
Partic in OCLC Online Computer Library Center, Inc

OREGON CITY

J CLACKAMAS COMMUNITY COLLEGE, Marshall N Dana Memorial Library, 19600 S Molalla Ave, 97045. SAN 314-1381. Tel: 503-657-6958, Ext 2417. FAX: 503-655-8925. E-Mail: reference@clackamas.cc.or.us. Web Site: www.cladcamas.cc.or.us/library/library.htm. *Dir*, Cynthia R Andrews; E-Mail: cyndia@clackamas.cc.or.us; *Librn*, Karen Halliday; *Librn*, Terry Mackey; *Librn*, Doris M Munson; Tel: 503-657-6958, Ext 2463, E-Mail: dorism@clackamas.cc.or.us; *Circ*, Katie Hovanic; Tel: 503-657-6958, Ext 2464, E-Mail: katieh@clackamas.cc.or.us; *ILL*, Tracey Mc Fadin; *Acq*, Bonnie M McCloud; Tel: 503-657-6958, Ext 2466, E-Mail: bonniem@ clackamas.cc.or.us; Staff 7 (MLS 3, Non-MLS 4)
Founded 1967. Enrl 4,987; Fac 150; Highest Degree: Associate
Library Holdings: Bk Vols 48,884; Per Subs 294
Special Collections: Oregon Coll
Database Vendor: Ebsco - EbscoHost, epixtech, inc., ProQuest
Function: Research library
Partic in Clackamas County Coop Libr Servs
Friends of the Library Group

L CLACKAMAS COUNTY OREGON, Alden E Miller Law Library, Courthouse, Rm 101, 807 Main St, 97045. SAN 323-4177. Tel: 503-655-8248. *Librn*, Ailsa Mackenzie Werner
Library Holdings: Bk Vols 25,000

P OREGON CITY PUBLIC LIBRARY,* 362 Warner Milne Rd, 97045. SAN 314-1403. Tel: 503-657-8269. FAX: 503-657-3702. Web Site: www.lincc.or.us. *Dir*, Roger A McClurg; *Cat*, Judy Storgaard; *Ad Servs*, Debbie Dodd; *Ch Servs*, Lynda Ackerson; *Ref*, Steven Rauch; Staff 15 (MLS 5, Non-MLS 10)
Founded 1904. Pop 42,000; Circ 450,000
Jul 1998-Jun 1999 Income $938,300, State $7,600, City $250,000, County $620,000, Locally Generated Income $60,700. Mats Exp $114,300, Books $80,000, Per/Ser (Incl. Access Fees) $7,300, AV Equip $20,000, Other Print Mats $7,000. Sal $561,000
Library Holdings: Bk Vols 90,000; Per Subs 220
Subject Interests: Genealogy, Local history, Oregon
Special Collections: Oregon History (The Oregon Coll), bk, micro
Automation Activity & Vendor Info: (Cataloging) epixtech, inc.; (Circulation) epixtech, inc.
Publications: Library Newsletter (quarterly)
Partic in Library Information Network Of Clackamas County
Friends of the Library Group

M WILLIAMETTE FALLS HOSPITAL, Medical Library,* 1500 Division St, 97045. SAN 375-0647. Tel: 503-650-6757. FAX: 503-650-6836. *Librn*, Katherine R Martin
Library Holdings: Bk Vols 500; Per Subs 86

PENDLETON

J BLUE MOUNTAIN COMMUNITY COLLEGE LIBRARY, 2411 NW Carden Ave, 97801. SAN 314-1411. Tel: 541-278-5916. Circulation Tel: 541-278-5915. Reference Tel: 541-278-5917. FAX: 541-276-6119. Web Site: bmcc.cc.or.us/bmcc_web/dept/library/libhome.htm. *Dir*, Darcy Dauble; E-Mail: ddauble@bmcc.cc.or.us; *Cat*, Marjorie Hoeft; Tel: 541-278-5913, E-Mail: mhoeft@bmcc.cc.or.us; Staff 9 (MLS 3, Non-MLS 6)
Founded 1963. Enrl 2,108; Fac 79
Jul 1999-Jun 2000 Income Parent Institution $467,442. Mats Exp $484,590, Books $440,000, Per/Ser (Incl. Access Fees) $27,134, Presv $700, Micro $450, AV Equip $6,650, Electronic Ref Mat (Incl. Access Fees) $9,656. Sal $256,016 (Prof $125,697)
Library Holdings: Bk Vols 37,991; Bk Titles 35,946; Per Subs 253
Subject Interests: World War II
Special Collections: Affiliate Data Center (census materials)
Automation Activity & Vendor Info: (Cataloging) epixtech, inc.; (Circulation) epixtech, inc.; (ILL) epixtech, inc.; (OPAC) epixtech, inc.
Database Vendor: Ebsco - EbscoHost, Silverplatter Information Inc.
Function: For research purposes
Mem of Umatilla County Spec Libr Dist

P PENDLETON PUBLIC LIBRARY, 502 SW Dorion, 97801-1698. SAN 358-0601. Tel: 541-966-0380. FAX: 541-966-0382. *Dir*, Tom Hilliard; Tel: 541-966-0385; *Publ Servs*, Mary Finney; Tel: 541-966-0386; Staff 6 (MLS 2, Non-MLS 4)
Founded 1987
Jul 1998-Jun 1999 Income $301,855, State $2,453, City $41,085, County $231,045, Locally Generated Income $27,272. Mats Exp $47,151, Books $32,715, Per/Ser (Incl. Access Fees) $3,489, AV Equip $5,212, Other Print Mats $4,339, Electronic Ref Mat (Incl. Access Fees) $1,396. Sal $209,893 (Prof $114,823)
Library Holdings: Bk Vols 56,724; Bk Titles 47,949; Per Subs 160; High Interest/Low Vocabulary Bk Vols 231
Special Collections: Northeast Oregon; Pacific Northwest; Rodeo & Western Literature
Automation Activity & Vendor Info: (Cataloging) epixtech, inc.; (Circulation) epixtech, inc.; (OPAC) epixtech, inc.
Mem of Umatilla County Spec Libr Dist
Friends of the Library Group

PILOT ROCK

P PILOT ROCK PUBLIC LIBRARY,* 144 N Alder Pl, PO Box 520, 97868-0520. SAN 358-0628. Tel: 541-443-3285. FAX: 541-443-2123. *Librn*, Susa Hilliard; E-Mail: shilliar@orednet.org
Library Holdings: Bk Titles 4,500
Partic in Umatilla County Spec Libr District
Open Mon & Wed 2-8, Tues 12-5, Thurs 10-5 & Fri 1-6

PORT ORFORD

P PORT ORFORD PUBLIC LIBRARY DISTRICT,* 555 W 20th, PO Box 130, 97465-0130. SAN 314-1446. Tel: 541-332-5622. FAX: 541-332-2140. *Librn*, Tobie Porter
Pop 1,070; Circ 27,205
Library Holdings: Bk Vols 18,000; Bk Titles 17,500; Per Subs 50
Open Mon 1-8, Tues & Sat 1-5, Wed & Fri 10-12 & 1-5 & Thurs 1-8
Friends of the Library Group

PORTLAND

S ART INSTITUTE OF PORTLAND LIBRARY, 2000 SW Fifth Ave, 97201 4972. SAN 314-1454. Tel: 503-228-6528. Toll Free Tel: 800-547-0937, 888 228-6528. FAX: 503-228-4227. Web Site: www.aii.edu. *Dir*, Nancy Thurston; E-Mail: thurston@aii.edu
Founded 1966. Enrl 659; Fac 70; Highest Degree: Bachelor
Library Holdings: Bk Vols 19,000; Per Subs 200
Subject Interests: Apparel design, Fashion hist, Furniture, Graphic design, Interior design
Automation Activity & Vendor Info: (Circulation) Athena
Database Vendor: ProQuest
Restriction: Open to employees & special libraries, Open to others by appointment, Open to students

L ATER, WYNNE, LLP, Law Library, 222 SW Columbia, Ste 1800, 97201. SAN 372-2201. Tel: 503-226-1191. FAX: 503-226-0079. Web Site: www.aterwynne.com. *Librn*, Doreen Smith; E-Mail: dss@aterwynne.com
Library Holdings: Bk Vols 20,000; Per Subs 50

G BONNEVILLE POWER ADMINISTRATION LIBRARY - CILL-1, (Formerly United States Department Of Energy), 905 NE 11th Ave, 97208. (Mail add: PO Box 3621, 97208), SAN 314-1853. Tel: 503-230-4171. Reference Tel: 503-230-4171. FAX: 503-230-5911. *Librn*, John Fenker; Tel: 503-230-4174; *Librn*, Linda L Kuriger; Tel: 503-230-4178, E-Mail: llkuriger@bpa.gov; Staff 9 (MLS 3, Non-MLS 6)
Founded 1939
Oct 1999-Sep 2000 Mats Exp $326,000, Books $20,000, Per/Ser (Incl. Access Fees) $100,000. Sal $400,000 (Prof $180,000)
Library Holdings: Bk Vols 50,000; Bk Titles 35,000; Per Subs 300
Subject Interests: Computer science, Electrical engineering, Energy conservation, Fish, Law, Utilities industry, Wildlife
Special Collections: BPA Collection
Database Vendor: Dialog, Ebsco - EbscoHost, epixtech, inc., ProQuest
Publications: book lists; brochure - Pathfinders
Function: Some telephone reference
Partic in Dialog Corporation; Dow Jones News Retrieval; OCLC Online Computer Library Center, Inc

L BULLIVANT, HOUSER & BAILEY, Law Library,* 300 Pioneer Tower, 888 SW Fifth Ave, 97204-2089. SAN 372-221X. Tel: 503-228-6351. FAX: 503-295-0915. *Librn*, Elizabeth Sanders; E-Mail: elizabeth.sanders@ bullivant.com
Library Holdings: Bk Vols 10,000; Per Subs 90

S CH2M HILL INC LIBRARY, 825 NE Multnomah, Ste 1300, 97232. SAN 324-0320. Tel: 503-235-5000. FAX: 503-736-2000. *Librn*, Barbara Stollberg
Library Holdings: Bk Titles 5,000; Per Subs 50
Subject Interests: Engineering, Environ sci

P CEDAR MILL COMMUNITY LIBRARY, 12505 NW Cornell Rd, 97229. SAN 314-1470. Tel: 503-644-0043, 503-646-3039. FAX: 503-644-3964. Web Site: www.cedarmill.org/library. *Dir*, Peter Leonard; E-Mail: leonard@ wccls.lib.or.us; *Tech Servs*, Rita Rivera; *Ad Servs*, Lynne Erlandson; *YA Servs*, Nancy Spaulding; *Circ*, Diana Palmer; Staff 31 (MLS 10, Non-MLS 21)
Founded 1975. Pop 50,300; Circ 731,000
Jul 2000-Jun 2001 Income $1,630,665, State $10,000, County $1,536,665, Locally Generated Income $84,000. Mats Exp $215,400, Books $195,900, Per/Ser (Incl. Access Fees) $10,000, Electronic Ref Mat (Incl. Access Fees)

$9,500. Sal $1,005,141
Library Holdings: Bk Vols 156,257; Bk Titles 121,398; Per Subs 333
Special Collections: Oregon & Pacific Northwest, bks, per; Parent-Teacher Res Coll
Automation Activity & Vendor Info: (Cataloging) Gaylord; (Circulation) Gaylord; (OPAC) Gaylord
Publications: Library News (monthly)
Mem of Washington County Cooperative Library Services

CONCORDIA UNIVERSITY LIBRARY, 2811 NE Holman St, 97211-6099. SAN 314-1497. Tel: 503-280-8507. FAX: 503-280-8518. *Dir*, Nolan R Bremer; E-Mail: nbremer@cu-portland.edu; *Publ Servs*, Karen E Hicks; E-Mail: khicks@cu-portland.edu; Staff 3 (MLS 2, Non-MLS 1)
Founded 1905. Enrl 938; Fac 60; Highest Degree: Master
Jul 1999-Jun 2000 Mats Exp $97,013, Books $62,877, Per/Ser (Incl. Access Fees) $22,038, Presv $452, Micro $10,646, Electronic Ref Mat (Incl. Access Fees) $1,000. Sal $98,849
Library Holdings: Bk Vols 52,337; Bk Titles 45,944; Per Subs 368
Subject Interests: Behav sci, Bus, Elementary educ, Health care admin, Soc sci, Theology
Special Collections: Religious History (Luther & Reformation Research Coll)
Automation Activity & Vendor Info: (Acquisitions) Endeavor; (Cataloging) Endeavor; (Circulation) Endeavor; (Course Reserve) Endeavor; (ILL) Endeavor; (Media Booking) Endeavor; (OPAC) Endeavor; (Serials) Endeavor
Database Vendor: Ebsco - EbscoHost, Lexis-Nexis, OCLC - First Search, ProQuest
Partic in OCLC Online Computer Library Center, Inc

S CONTEMPORARY CRAFTS ASSOCIATION LIBRARY, 3934 SW Corbett Ave, 97201. SAN 323-519X. Tel: 503-223-2654. FAX: 503-223-2659. E-Mail: ccg3934@aol.com. *Dir*, Darcy Edgar
Library Holdings: Bk Vols 750
Open Tues-Sat 10-5 & Sun 1-5

L DAVIS WRIGHT TREMAINE, Law Library,* 1300 SW Fifth Ave, Ste 2300, 97201. SAN 372-2198. Tel: 503-241-2300. FAX: 503-778-5299. *Librn*, Carol L Kreger; E-Mail: carolkreger@dwt.com
Library Holdings: Bk Vols 10,000; Per Subs 40

GM DEPARTMENT OF VETERANS AFFAIRS, Medical Center Library,* 3710 SW US Veterans Hospital Rd. (Mail add: PO Box 1034, 97207), SAN 314-1888. Tel: 503-220-8262, Ext 5955. FAX: 503-721-7816. Web Site: www.teleport.com/~brayson. *Chief Librn*, Mara R Wilhelm; E-Mail: wilhelm.mara@forum.va.gov; *Coll Develop, Librn*, Cathy M Jordan; E-Mail: jordan.cathy@forum.va.gov; *Librn*, Sandra Brayson; Staff 5 (MLS 3, Non-MLS 2)
Library Holdings: Bk Titles 12,652; Per Subs 779
Subject Interests: Geriatrics, Liver transplant, Medicine, Nursing, Patient health info, Psychology, PTSD
Publications: Acquisitions List (quarterly)
Partic in Dialog Corporation; Medline; National Network Of Libraries Of Medicine - South Central Region; OCLC; OCLC Online Computer Library Center, Inc; Oregon Health Sciences Libraries Association; Vets Admin Libr Network

C E W MCMILLAN LIBRARY AT CASCADE COLLEGE, 9101 E Burnside, 97216-1515. SAN 314-1489. Tel: 503-257-1360. FAX: 503-257-1222. E-Mail: library@cascade.edu. Web Site: www.cascade.edu/lib. *Librn*, Lindsey Hoffman; Tel: 503-257-1227, E-Mail: lhoffman@cascade.edu; *Librn*, Veronika Rudolph; Tel: 503-262-1446, E-Mail: vrudolph@cascade.edu; Staff 4 (MLS 2, Non-MLS 2)
Founded 1957. Enrl 300; Fac 19; Highest Degree: Bachelor
Library Holdings: Bk Vols 33,500; Bk Titles 33,000; Per Subs 245
Subject Interests: Bible, Bus, Education, Environmental studies
Automation Activity & Vendor Info: (OPAC) SIRSI
Database Vendor: IAC - Info Trac, OCLC - First Search
Partic in Metro Washington Libr Coun

M EASTMORELAND HOSPITAL, Health Sciences Library,* 2900 SE Steele, 97202. SAN 324-5489. Tel: 503-234-0411, Ext 519. FAX: 503-231-0476. *Librn*, Kathleen Martin
Library Holdings: Bk Vols 550; Bk Titles 500; Per Subs 55
Subject Interests: Medicine, Nursing, Osteopathic med
Restriction: Staff use only

S GENEALOGICAL FORUM OF OREGON, INC LIBRARY, 1505 SE Gideon St, 97202-2441. (Mail add: PO Box 42567, 97242-0567), SAN 321-5377. Tel: 503-963-1932.
Library Holdings: Bk Titles 14,000; Per Subs 235
Subject Interests: Genealogy
Special Collections: Index Civil War Veterans who lived in Oregon; Nellie Hiday Research Coll; Willis Corbit Research Coll
Publications: Bulletin, Genealogical Forum of Oregon (quarterly)
Open Mon, Wed & Sat 9:30-3, Tues & Thurs 9:30-8, Sun 12-5

S HISTORIC PRESERVATION LEAGUE OF OREGON,* 322 NW Fifth Ave, Ste 301, 97209. SAN 324-3826. Tel: 503-243-1923. FAX: 503-224-2311. *Pres*, Mike Byrnes
Library Holdings: Bk Vols 1,400
Subject Interests: Bldg restoration, Hist presv

S INTERCULTURAL COMMUNICATION INSTITUTE, (ICI), Research Library, 8835 SW Canyon Lane, Ste 238, 97225. SAN 323-5866. Tel: 503-297-4622. FAX: 503-297-4695. *Librn*, Sandra Garrison
Founded 1987. Fac 14
Library Holdings: Bk Titles 5,700; Per Subs 18; Bks on Deafness & Sign Lang 16
Special Collections: Dean Barnlund Bequeathment Coll

KAISER PERMANENTE MEDICAL CENTER

M CENTER FOR HEALTH RESEARCH LIBRARY, 3800 N Interstate Ave, 97227-1110. SAN 358-0776. Tel: 503-335-2442. FAX: 503-335-2428. Web Site: chrfo3.kpnw.org, www.kpnw.org/chr/chr/html.
Founded 1964
Jan 1998-Dec 1999 Income $75,000
Library Holdings: Bk Vols 7,385; Per Subs 244
Subject Interests: Health maintenance, Health serv res, Preventive med, Social med
Partic in Am Soc of Info Sci; Oregon Health Sciences Libraries Association; Pac NW Libr Asn

L LANE POWELL SPEARS LUBERSKY, Law Library, 601 SW Second Ave, No 2100, 97204. SAN 371-6023. Tel: 503-778-2100. FAX: 503-778-2200. Web Site: www.lanepowell.com. *Mgr*, Annetta C Lawson; E-Mail: lawsona@lanepowell.com; Staff 2 (MLS 2)
Library Holdings: Bk Vols 10,000; Per Subs 100
Automation Activity & Vendor Info: (Cataloging) Inmagic, Inc.; (Serials) Inmagic, Inc.
Restriction: Private library
Partic in Dialog Corporation; Lexis, OCLC Online Computer Libr Ctr, Inc; Westlaw

M LEGACY EMANUEL HOSPITAL & HEALTH CENTER LIBRARY,* 2801 N Gantenbein Ave, 97227. SAN 314-1519. Tel: 503-413-2558. FAX: 503-413-2544. *Mgr*, Carolyn Olson
Founded 1949
Library Holdings: Bk Vols 2,700; Bk Titles 2,200; Per Subs 300
Subject Interests: Emergency med, Med genetics, Pediatrics surgery, Trauma med
Partic in Nat Libr of Med
Open Mon-Fri 8-4:30

M LEGACY GOOD SAMARITAN HOSPITAL & MEDICAL CENTER, Health Sciences Library, 1015 NW 22nd Ave, 97210. SAN 314-1586. Tel: 503-413-7335. FAX: 503-413-8016. *Mgr*, Carolyn Olson; E-Mail: olsonc@ohsu.edu; *Publ Servs*, Phyllis McCulloch; Staff 3 (MLS 2, Non-MLS 1)
Library Holdings: Bk Vols 10,000; Per Subs 531
Subject Interests: Medicine, Nursing
Restriction: Staff use only

LEWIS & CLARK COLLEGE

C AUBREY R WATZEK LIBRARY, 0615 SW Palatine Hill Rd, 97219. SAN 358-0806. Tel: 503-768-7274. FAX: 503-768-7282. Web Site: library.lclark.edu/. *Dir*, Jim Kopp; E-Mail: kopp@lclark.edu; *Assoc Dir*, Elaine Heras; Staff 8 (MLS 8)
Founded 1867. Enrl 2,400; Fac 142; Highest Degree: Master
Jun 1999-May 2000 Income $1,750,053. Mats Exp $902,126, Books $270,000, Per/Ser (Incl. Access Fees) $510,000, Presv $9,361, AV Equip $765, Electronic Ref Mat (Incl. Access Fees) $112,000. Sal $680,000 (Prof $360,000)
Library Holdings: Bk Vols 260,000; Per Subs 1,820
Subject Interests: Gender studies, Pac NW hist
Special Collections: Lewis & Clark Expedition Coll
Automation Activity & Vendor Info: (Acquisitions) Innovative Interfaces Inc.; (Cataloging) Innovative Interfaces Inc.; (Circulation) Innovative Interfaces Inc.; (Course Reserve) Innovative Interfaces Inc.; (OPAC) Innovative Interfaces Inc.; (Serials) Innovative Interfaces Inc.
Partic in OCLC Online Computer Library Center, Inc; Orbis; PORTALS
Friends of the Library Group

CL PAUL L BOLEY LAW LIBRARY, Lewis & Clark Law School, Northwestern School of Law, 10015 SW Terwilliger Blvd, 97219. SAN 358-0830. Tel: 503-768-6776. Reference Tel: 503-768-6688. FAX: 503-768-6760. Web Site: lclark.edu/~lawlib. *Dir*, Peter S Nycum; *Assoc Dir*, Tami Gierloff; *Asst Dir, Tech Servs*, Kathy Faust; *Asst Dir, Reader Servs*, Lynn Williams; *Electronic Resources*, Rob Truman; *Head Ref*, Seneca Gray; Staff 7 (MLS 5, Non-MLS 2)
Founded 1884. Enrl 720; Fac 34; Highest Degree: Doctorate
Jun 1999-May 2000 Income $1,874,864. Mats Exp $1,029,866, Books $309,126, Per/Ser (Incl. Access Fees) $545,175, Presv $19,757, Micro $72,996, Electronic Ref Mat (Incl. Access Fees) $82,812. Sal $645,609 (Prof $436,601)
Library Holdings: Bk Vols 191,547; Bk Titles 45,293; Per Subs 4,956
Subject Interests: Am law, Antitrust, Environmental studies, Taxation

Special Collections: Milton S Pearl Environmental Law Library; Patent Law Coll; Samuel S Johnson Public Land Law Review Commission Coll
Automation Activity & Vendor Info: (Acquisitions) Innovative Interfaces Inc.; (Cataloging) Innovative Interfaces Inc.; (Circulation) Innovative Interfaces Inc.; (Course Reserve) Innovative Interfaces Inc.; (ILL) Innovative Interfaces Inc.; (Media Booking) Innovative Interfaces Inc.; (OPAC) Innovative Interfaces Inc.; (Serials) Innovative Interfaces Inc.
Database Vendor: Lexis-Nexis, OCLC - First Search
Publications: Handbook (annual); subject bibliographies
Function: ILL available, Reference services available
Partic in OCLC; OCLC Online Computer Library Center, Inc; OLIS; Westlaw

S MAZAMAS LIBRARY, 909 NW 19th Ave, 97209. SAN 325-8165. Tel: 503-227-2345, Ext 2. FAX: 503-227-0862. E-Mail: librarian@mazamas.org. Web Site: www.mazamas.org. *Librn*, Robert William Lockerby; Staff 1 (MLS 1)
Founded 1915
Library Holdings: Bk Vols 4,500; Per Subs 36
Subject Interests: Mountaineering
Restriction: Members only
Function: Photocopies available

S METRO WASHINGTON PARK ZOO LIBRARY,* 4001 SW Canyon Rd, 97221. SAN 325-8262. Tel: 503-226-1561, Ext 766. FAX: 503-226-0074. *Librn*, Jan Hixon; E-Mail: hixonj@metro.dst.or.us
1997-1998 Income $2,500
Library Holdings: Bk Titles 1,050
Subject Interests: Biology, Conservation, Natural history
Restriction: By appointment only

L MILLER NASH LLP LIBRARY, 111 SW Fifth Ave Ste 3500, 97204-3699. SAN 314-1624. Tel: 503-224-5858. FAX: 503-224-0155. *Librn*, Leslie Meserve; E-Mail: meserve@millernash.com; *Ref*, Shannon Marich; E-Mail: marich@millernash.com; Staff 5 (MLS 2, Non-MLS 3)
Library Holdings: Bk Vols 25,000; Bk Titles 8,000; Per Subs 400
Subject Interests: Law

CR MULTNOMAH BIBLE COLLEGE, John & Mary Mitchell Library, 8435 NE Glisan St, 97220-5898. SAN 314-1640. Tel: 503-251-5321. FAX: 503-254-1268. Web Site: www.multnomah.edu. *Dir*, Dr Philip M Johnson; *Asst Dir*, Sue Kelly; Staff 2 (MLS 2)
Founded 1936. Enrl 800; Fac 40; Highest Degree: Master
Library Holdings: Bk Vols 80,000; Bk Titles 60,000; Per Subs 400; Bks on Deafness & Sign Lang 11
Subject Interests: Biblical studies, Christian educ, Church history, Practical theol, Theology
Special Collections: Bible Coll
Automation Activity & Vendor Info: (Acquisitions) Endeavor; (Cataloging) Endeavor; (Circulation) Endeavor; (Course Reserve) Endeavor; (ILL) Endeavor; (Media Booking) Endeavor; (OPAC) Endeavor; (Serials) Endeavor
Database Vendor: Ebsco - EbscoHost
Partic in OCLC Online Computer Library Center, Inc

P MULTNOMAH COUNTY LIBRARY, 205 NE Russell, 97212. SAN 358-0865. Tel: 503-988-5402. Interlibrary Loan Service Tel: 503-988-5245. FAX: 503-988-5441. Web Site: www.multnomah.lib.or.us/lib/. *Dir*, Ginnie Cooper; E-Mail: ginniec@nethost.multnomah.lib.or.us; *Dir*, Cindy Gibbon; *Dep Dir, Publ Servs*, Ruth Metz; *Pub Relations*, Tanya Gross; *Commun Servs*, Janet Kinney; *YA Servs*, Ellen Fader; Staff 66 (MLS 66)
Founded 1864. Pop 646,850; Circ 10,686,253
Jul 1999-Jun 2000 Income $43,841,129, State $110,404, Federal $177,620, County $34,155,574, Other $9,397,531. Mats Exp $4,519,040, Books $2,446,169, Per/Ser (Incl. Access Fees) $695,668, Presv $20,000, AV Equip $991,405, Electronic Ref Mat (Incl. Access Fees) $365,798. Sal $14,929,612
Library Holdings: Bk Vols 1,511,389; Bk Titles 507,402; Per Subs 3,847
Special Collections: John Wilson Room; McCormack Coll, rec, bks; Oregon Coll; Roses (Thomas Newton Cook Rose Library & Jesse A Currey Memorial Rose Coll)
Automation Activity & Vendor Info: (Circulation) epixtech, inc.
Publications: LAP Newspaper Index (microfiche)
Partic in OCLC; OCLC Online Computer Library Center, Inc
Friends of the Library Group
Branches: 14
ALBINA, 3605 NE 15th Ave, 97212-2358. SAN 358-089X. Tel: 503-988-5362. FAX: 503-988-5482. *In Charge*, Carol Uhte
BELMONT, 1038 SE 39th Ave, 97214-4318. SAN 358-092X. Tel: 503-988-5382. FAX: 503-988-5481. *In Charge*, Steve Armitage
CAPITOL HILL, 10723 SW Capitol Hwy, 97219-6816. SAN 358-0954. Tel: 503-988-5385. FAX: 503-988-5479. *In Charge*, Patti Vincent
GREGORY HEIGHTS, 7921 NE Sandy Blvd, 97213-7150. SAN 358-0989. Tel: 503-988-5386. FAX: 503-988-5278. *In Charge*, Sharon Klemp
GRESHAM BRANCH, 385 NW Miller, Gresham, 97030-7291. SAN 358-1012. Tel: 503-988-5387. FAX: 503-988-5198. *Mgr*, Gretchen Goekjian; *Coordr*, Karen Hein
HILLSDALE, 1525 SW Sunset Blvd, 97201-2614. SAN 358-1349. Tel: 503-988-5388. FAX: 503-988-5197. *In Charge*, Virginia Tribe
HOLGATE, 7905 SE Holgate Blvd, 97206-3367. SAN 358-1047. Tel: 503-988-5389. FAX: 503-988-5194. *Mgr*, Steven Rauch
HOLLYWOOD, 3930 NE Hancock St, 97212-5391. SAN 358-1071. Tel: 503-988-5391. FAX: 503-988-5192. *Adminr*, Mary Goldie; *In Charge*, David Miles
MIDLAND, 805 SE 122nd Ave, 97233-1107. SAN 358-1160. Tel: 503-988-5392. FAX: 503-988-5189. *Branch Mgr*, Carolyn Schell
NORTH PORTLAND, 512 N Killingsworth St, 97217-2330. SAN 358-122 Tel: 503-988-5394. FAX: 503-988-5187. *Adminr*, Patricia Welch
Special Collections: Black Res Coll
ROCKWOOD, 17917 SE Stark St, 97233-4825. SAN 358-125X. Tel: 503-988-5396. FAX: 503-988-5178. *In Charge*, Rebecca Teasdale
SAINT JOHNS, 7510 N Charleston Ave, 97203-3709. SAN 358-1284. Tel: 503-988-5397. FAX: 503-988-5176. *Coordr, YA Servs*, Ellen Fader; *In Charge*, Nancy Arvesen
SELLWOOD-MORELAND, 7904 SE Milwaukie Ave, 97202-6703. SAN 358-1314. Tel: 503-988-5398. FAX: 503-988-5175. *In Charge*, Margot Moore-Wilson
WOODSTOCK, 6008 SE 49th Ave, 97206-6117. SAN 358-1373. Tel: 503-988-5399. FAX: 503-988-5173. *In Charge*, Kari Hauge
Friends of the Library Group
Bookmobiles: 2

L MULTNOMAH LAW LIBRARY,* County Courthouse, 4th flr, 97204-1183 SAN 314-1632. Tel: 503-248-3394. FAX: 503-248-3395. *Librn*, Jacquelyn Jurkins
Founded 1890
Library Holdings: Bk Vols 216,112
Partic in Westlaw

M NATIONAL COLLEGE OF NATUROPATHIC MEDICINE LIBRARY, 049 SW Porter, 97201. SAN 314-1659. Tel: 503-499-4343. FAX: 503-219-9709. E-Mail: librarian@ncnm.edu. *Coll Develop, Librn*, Letty Chen; *Librn*, Friedhelm Kirchfeld
Founded 1956. Enrl 322; Fac 45
Jul 1996-Jun 1997 Income $70,000. Mats Exp $40,400, Books $25,000, Per/Ser (Incl. Access Fees) $15,000, Presv $300. Sal $72,000
Library Holdings: Bk Titles 9,600; Per Subs 131
Subject Interests: Acupuncture, Botanical med, Homeopathy, Naturopathic med, Nutrition, Physical therapy
Special Collections: Homeopathic Journals; Naturopathic Journals
Database Vendor: Ebsco - EbscoHost

G NORTHWEST POWER PLANNING COUNCIL, Library & Public Reading Room, 851 SW Sixth Ave, Ste 1100, 97204. SAN 325-8203. Tel: 503-222-5161. Toll Free Tel: 800-452-5161. FAX: 503-820-2370. Web Site: www.nwppc.org.
Subject Interests: Energy
Open Mon-Fri 8am-5pm

S NORTHWEST REGIONAL EDUCATIONAL LABORATORY, Informatior Center Library, 101 SW Main St,Ste 500, 97204. SAN 314-1667. Tel: 503-275-9554. FAX: 503-275-0660. *Librn*, Linda Fitch; E-Mail: fitchl@nwrel.org; Staff 2 (Non-MLS 2)
Founded 1965
Library Holdings: Bk Titles 7,000; Per Subs 200
Subject Interests: Educ computer tech, Educ evaluation, Educ res, Educ test center, Educ work, Math teacher educ, Parent educ, Rural educ, Sci
Special Collections: ERIC Coll
Partic in Dialog Corporation

S OREGON COLLEGE OF ART & CRAFT LIBRARY, (OCAC), 8245 SW Barnes Rd, 97225. SAN 314-1683. Tel: 503-297-5544, Ext 119. FAX: 503-297-9651. *Coll Develop*, Lori Johnson; E-Mail: lorij@wccls.lib.or.us; Staff 1 (Non-MLS 1)
Highest Degree: Bachelor
Library Holdings: Bk Vols 7,800; Per Subs 100
Subject Interests: Craft hist, Crafts, Design
Partic in Washington County Cooperative Library Services

CM OREGON COLLEGE OF ORIENTAL MEDICINE LIBRARY, 10525 SE Cherry Blossom Dr, 97216. SAN 375-4952. Tel: 503-262-1646. FAX: 503-253-2701. E-Mail: ocomlib@teleport.com. Web Site: www.ocom.edu. *Librn*, Cheryl Silverblatt; Staff 1 (MLS 1)
Founded 1988. Enrl 160; Fac 15; Highest Degree: Master
1998-1999 Income $8,900. Mats Exp $7,700, Books $4,500, Per/Ser (Incl. Access Fees) $3,200
Library Holdings: Bk Titles 2,500; Per Subs 62
Subject Interests: Acupuncture
Automation Activity & Vendor Info: (Cataloging) Inmagic, Inc.; (OPAC) Inmagic, Inc.

G OREGON DEPARTMENT OF ENVIRONMENTAL QUALITY LIBRARY,* 811 SW Sixth Ave, 97204. SAN 323-5912. Tel: 503-229-6854. FAX: 503-229-5850. *Librn*, Olivia Jonason
Founded 1988
Library Holdings: Bk Vols 10,000; Per Subs 315
Partic in Dialog Corporation; OCLC Online Computer Library Center, Inc

S OREGON DEPARTMENT OF GEOLOGY & MINERAL INDUSTRIES LIBRARY, Ste 965, No 28, 800 NE Oregon St, 97232-2162. SAN 314-1691. Tel: 503-731-4100. FAX: 503-731-4066. *Librn*, Klaus K Neuendorf; E-Mail: klaus.neuendorf@state.or.us
Founded 1937
Library Holdings: Bk Vols 30,000; Bk Titles 10,000; Per Subs 20
Subject Interests: Geol of Oregon, Geosci
Special Collections: Theses & dissertations on Geology of Oregon; Unpublished Data & Reports on Geology of Oregon includes site-specific seismic studies

CM OREGON HEALTH SCIENCES UNIVERSITY LIBRARY, 3181 SW Sam Jackson Park Rd, PO Box 573, 97207-0573. SAN 358-1551. Tel: 503-494-3460. FAX: 503-494-3227. Web Site: www.ohsu.edu/library. *Librn*, James Morgan; Tel: 503-494-6057, E-Mail: morgan@ohsu.edu; *Head Ref*, Dolores Judkins; Tel: 503-494-3478, E-Mail: judkinsd@ohsu.edu; *Bibliog Instr*, Janet Crum; Tel: 503-494-0691, E-Mail: crumj@ohsu.edu; *Bibliog Instr, Head Tech Servs*, Carrie Willman; Tel: 503-494-5667, E-Mail: willman@ohsu.edu; *Access Serv*, Cindy Cunningham; Tel: 503-494-3481, E-Mail: cunningc@ohsu.edu; *Outreach Serv*, Steve Teich; E-Mail: teich@ohsu.edu; *Planning Services*, Diane Carroll; *Cat*, Dan L Kniesner; Tel: 503-494-3216, E-Mail: kniesner@ohsu.edu; Staff 11 (MLS 9, Non-MLS 2)
Founded 1919. Enrl 1,854; Fac 1,523; Highest Degree: Doctorate
Jul 1999-Jun 2000 Income (Main Library Only) $3,824,522, State $3,448,205, Federal $29,776, Locally Generated Income $292,252, Other $54,289. Mats Exp $1,087,530, Books $154,871, Per/Ser (Incl. Access Fees) $846,617, Presv $1,562, AV Equip $5,453, Electronic Ref Mat (Incl. Access Fees) $79,027. Sal $2,061,532 (Prof $708,923)
Library Holdings: Bk Vols 210,090; Bk Titles 66,082; Per Subs 1,168
Special Collections: History of Medicine Coll (Pacific Northwest & Rare Book)l; Manuscripts & Archives; Medical Museum (artifacts); OHSU Oral History Project; Oregon Memorial Library for Bereaved Parents; Photograph Coll
Automation Activity & Vendor Info: (Acquisitions) Innovative Interfaces Inc.; (Cataloging) Innovative Interfaces Inc.; (Circulation) Innovative Interfaces Inc.; (Course Reserve) Innovative Interfaces Inc.; (OPAC) Innovative Interfaces Inc.; (Serials) Innovative Interfaces Inc.
Database Vendor: OVID Technologies
Partic in National Network Of Libraries Of Medicine - Pacific Northwest Region; OCLC Online Computer Library Center, Inc; Orbis; Portland Area Libr Syst
Departmental Libraries:
CHILD DEVELOPMENT & REHABILITATION CENTER, 707 SW Gaines Rd, 97201-2998. SAN 372-8331. Tel: 503-494-2762. FAX: 503-494-0931. Web Site: www.ohsu.edu/library. *In Charge*, Betty Karleskint; E-Mail: karleski@ohsu.edu; Staff 1 (Non-MLS 1)
Founded 1989
Jul 1999-Jun 2000 Income $27,791. Mats Exp $8,043, Books $2,820, Per/Ser (Incl. Access Fees) $5,223. Sal $19,723
Library Holdings: Bk Vols 3,387; Bk Titles 3,133; Per Subs 26
Subject Interests: Child development, Developmental disabilities
Special Collections: Parents Coll
CM VAN HASSEL DENTAL LIBRARY, 611 SW Campus Dr, 97201-3097. SAN 358-1586. Tel: 503-494-8822. FAX: 503-494-7869. Web Site: www.ohsu.edu/library. *Branch Mgr*, Mary Letts Botcheos; E-Mail: botcheos@ohsu.edu
Founded 1897
Jul 1999-Jun 2000 Income $128,389. Mats Exp $39,997, Books $6,790, Per/Ser (Incl. Access Fees) $32,098, AV Equip $627, Electronic Ref Mat (Incl. Access Fees) $482. Sal $80,266
Library Holdings: Bk Vols 16,319; Bk Titles 5,744; Per Subs 99
Special Collections: History of Dentistry Coll

S OREGON HISTORICAL SOCIETY LIBRARY,* 1200 SW Park Ave, 97205. SAN 314-1675. Tel: 503-306-5240. FAX: 503-219-2040. E-Mail: orhist@ohs.org. Web Site: www.ohs.org. *Ref*, John Mead. Subject Specialists: *Maps*, Elizabeth Winroth; Staff 21 (MLS 12, Non-MLS 9)
Founded 1898
Library Holdings: Per Subs 420
Subject Interests: Hist Pacific NW
Partic in OCLC Online Computer Library Center, Inc

S THE OREGONIAN LIBRARY,* 1320 SW Broadway, 97201. SAN 314-1721. Tel: 503-221-5375. FAX: 503-294-4021. *Librn*, Sandra Macomber; E-Mail: sandymacomber@news.oregonian; Staff 9 (MLS 8, Non-MLS 1)
Founded 1925
Library Holdings: Bk Titles 5,500; Per Subs 35
Restriction: Staff use only
Partic in Vutext
Open Mon-Fri 7-8:30, Sat & Sun 7-6

L PERKINS COIE, Law Library,* 1211 SW Fifth Ave, Ste 1500, 97204. SAN 372-2260. Tel: 503-727-2051. FAX: 503-727-2222. Web Site: www.perkins.coie.com. *Librn*, Angela Hodge; E-Mail: hodga@perkinscoie.com
Library Holdings: Bk Vols 10,000; Per Subs 50

S PORT OF PORTLAND LIBRARY,* PO Box 3529, 97208-3529. SAN 314-1748. Tel: 503-731-7582. FAX: 503-731-7626. E-Mail: shannl@portptld.com. *Res*, Lynn Shannon
Founded 1964
Library Holdings: Bk Titles 5,000; Per Subs 468
Subject Interests: Aviation, Engineering, Indust develop, Marine facilities, Marketing, Operations
Special Collections: Port of Portland Studies, hist mat
Open Mon-Fri 8:30-4:30

S PORTLAND ART MUSEUM, Rex Arragon Library, 1219 SW Park Ave, 97205-2486. SAN 314-1756. Tel: 503-276-4215. E-Mail: library@pam.org. Web Site: www.pam.org. *Dir*, Debra Royer; Tel: 503-276-4526; Staff 4 (Non-MLS 4)
Founded 1892
Jul 1999-Jul 2000 Income $102,979. Mats Exp $19,000, Books $14,000, Per/Ser (Incl. Access Fees) $5,000. Sal $54,834
Library Holdings: Bk Titles 25,000; Per Subs 75
Subject Interests: Art history, Fine art
Special Collections: Arts of the Pacific Northwest Coast Indians; Auction Catalogs; Contemporary Art; English Silver; Japanese Prints; Northwest Artists File

J PORTLAND COMMUNITY COLLEGE, Instructional Technology & Learning Resources,* 12000 SW 49th Ave, 97219-7197. SAN 358-1403. Tel: 503-977-4497. FAX: 503-977-4977. Web Site: www.pcc.edu/lrc/index.htm. *Dir*, Leslie Riester; *Coll Develop, Tech Servs*, B Owen; *Ref*, M Rose; *Ref*, Pam Kessinger; *Ref*, S Njoku; *Ref*, S L Smith; *Ref*, A Cordle; *Ref*, F Lippert
Founded 1964
Jul 1997-Jun 1998 Income $1,969,420. Mats Exp $294,735, Books $149,129, Per/Ser (Incl. Access Fees) $85,697, AV Equip $59,909. Sal $1,530,898 (Prof $725,924)
Library Holdings: Bk Vols 160,000; Per Subs 2,038
Automation Activity & Vendor Info: (Acquisitions) epixtech, inc.; (Circulation) epixtech, inc.
Departmental Libraries:
CASCADE CENTER, 705 N Killingsworth, 97211. SAN 358-1438. Tel: 503-614-5322. FAX: 503-240-5318.
ROCK CREEK, 17705 NW Springville Rd, 97229. SAN 358-1462. Tel: 503-614-7413. FAX: 503-690-7329.
SYLVANIA, 12000 SW 49th St, 97219. SAN 358-1489. Tel: 503-977-4935. FAX: 503-452-4977.

S PORTLAND GENERAL ELECTRIC, Business Information Services, 121 SW Salmon St, 3WTC-0501, 97204-2991. SAN 314-1764. Tel: 503-464-8700. FAX: 503-464-8706. *Librn, Ref*, Bette Stewart; Staff 1 (MLS 1)
Founded 1914
Library Holdings: Bk Titles 8,000
Subject Interests: Bus, Electric utilities, Energy alternatives, Environmental aspects of power plants, Mgt, Nuclear engineering
Automation Activity & Vendor Info: (Acquisitions) Inmagic, Inc.; (Cataloging) Inmagic, Inc.; (Circulation) Inmagic, Inc.
Database Vendor: Lexis-Nexis
Partic in OCLC Online Computer Library Center, Inc

C PORTLAND STATE UNIVERSITY, Branford Price Millar Library, 951 SW Hall, 97207. (Mail add: PO Box 1151, 97207-1151), SAN 314-1772. Tel: 503-725-4617. FAX: 503-725-4524. Web Site: www.lib.pdx.edu. *Dir*, Tom Pfingsten; *Acq*, Mary Ellen Kenreich; *ILL*, Cyril Oberlander; *Cat*, Kit Dusky; *Cat*, Laurel Jizba; *Cat*, Kristen Kern; *Cat*, Oren Ogle; *Cat*, Jian Wang; *Exten Serv*, Evie Crowell; *Cat*, William Wilson; *Tech Servs*, Terry Rohe; *Doc*, Judy Andrews; *Syst Coordr*, Judy Anderson; *Bibliog Instr*, Sharon Elteto; *Business*, Daphne Allen; *Ser*, Wendy Stewart; *Science*, Michael Bowman; *Science*, Gretta Siegel. Subject Specialists: *Education*, Sarah Beasley; *Education*, Faye Powell; *Humanities*, Robert Westover; *Social sci*, Sarah Beasley; *Social sci*, Faye Powell; Staff 27 (MLS 27)
Founded 1946. Enrl 17,303; Fac 745; Highest Degree: Doctorate
Jul 1998-Jun 1999 Income $7,045,084. Mats Exp $2,855,990, Books $632,495, Per/Ser (Incl. Access Fees) $1,939,607, Micro $105,189, Electronic Ref Mat (Incl. Access Fees) $178,699. Sal $2,808,773 (Prof $1,561,595)
Library Holdings: Bk Vols 1,247,885; Bk Titles 837,382; Per Subs 24,541
Special Collections: Middle East Studies
Partic in Ore State Syst of Higher Educ
Friends of the Library Group

S PRICE WATERHOUSE LIBRARY,* 121 SW Morrison St, Ste 1800, 97204. SAN 328-008X. Tel: 503-224-9040, Ext 256. FAX: 503-223-9081. *Librn*, Lynn Trueblood
Library Holdings: Bk Vols 500
Subject Interests: Accounting, Auditing
Publications: New books List

M PROVIDENCE PORTLAND MEDICAL CENTER, Health Sciences Library, 4805 NE Glisan St, 97213. SAN 314-1780. Tel: 503-215-6075. FAX: 503-232-4298. *Mgr*, Peggy Baldwin; E-Mail: pegbaldwin@providence.org

Founded 1944
Library Holdings: Bk Vols 650; Per Subs 250
Partic in Nat Libr of Med
Open Mon-Fri 8:30-4

M PROVIDENCE SAINT VINCENT HOSPITAL & MEDICAL CENTER, Health Sciences Library,* 9205 SW Barnes Rd, 97225. SAN 314-1810. Tel: 503-216-2257. FAX: 503-297-2085. *Dir*, Ann M Von Segen
Library Holdings: Bk Vols 5,000; Bk Titles 4,000; Per Subs 570
Subject Interests: Hospital administration, Nursing
Restriction: Not open to public
Partic in Ore Health Info Network

C REED COLLEGE, Eric V Hauser Memorial Library, 3203 SE Woodstock Blvd, 97202-8199. SAN 314-1802. Tel: 503-777-7702. Interlibrary Loan Service Tel: 503-777-7750. Reference Tel: 503-777-7554. FAX: 503-777-7786. Web Site: www.library.reed.edu. *Dir*, Victoria L Hanawalt; *Acq*, Jack Levine; *Syst Coordr*, Jennie McKee; *Spec Coll*, Marilyn Kierstead; *Electronic Resources*, Heather Whipple; *Media Spec*, Elizabeth Woerner; *Cat*, Marcia Bianchi; *Doc*, Dena Hutto; *Science*, Victoria Mitchell; Staff 9 (MLS 9)
Founded 1912. Enrl 1,325; Fac 109; Highest Degree: Master
Jul 1999-Jun 2000 Income $2,629,119. Mats Exp $1,510,810, Books $637,690, Per/Ser (Incl. Access Fees) $601,490, Presv $48,574, AV Equip $4,486, Other Print Mats $39,682, Electronic Ref Mat (Incl. Access Fees) $178,888. Sal $686,473 (Prof $415,440)
Library Holdings: Bk Vols 466,707; Bk Titles 293,091; Per Subs 1,858
Automation Activity & Vendor Info: (Acquisitions) Innovative Interfaces Inc.; (Cataloging) Innovative Interfaces Inc.; (Circulation) Innovative Interfaces Inc.; (OPAC) Innovative Interfaces Inc.; (Serials) Innovative Interfaces Inc.
Partic in OCLC Online Computer Library Center, Inc; Orbis; Portland Area Libr Syst

L SCHWABE, WILLIAMSON & WYATT LIBRARY, Pacwest Center, 1211 SW Fifth Ave, Ste 1800, 97204-3795. SAN 373-6067. Tel: 503-796-2071. FAX: 503-796-2900. Web Site: www.schwabe.com. *Librn*, LaJean Humphries; *Res*, Angela Irwin; Staff 4 (MLS 2, Non-MLS 2)
Library Holdings: Bk Vols 20,000; Bk Titles 3,000; Per Subs 218
Restriction: Not open to public

S SJO CONSULTING ENGINEERS INC, Engineering Library,* 6650 SW Redwood Lane, Ste 360, 97224-7171. SAN 375-6653. Tel: 503-226-3921. FAX: 503-226-3926. E-Mail: mailroom@sjoeng.com. Web Site: www.sjoeng.com.
Library Holdings: Per Subs 40

S STANDARD INSURANCE CO, Home Office Library,* 1100 SW Sixth Ave, PO Box 711, 97207. SAN 314-1829. Tel: 503-321-7000. FAX: 503-321-6776. *Librn*, Terri Tregaskif
Library Holdings: Bk Vols 2,000; Per Subs 30
Open Mon-Fri 8-5

L STOEL RIVES LLP, Law Library, 900 SW Fifth Ave, 26th flr, 97204. SAN 314-1500. Tel: 503-294-9576. FAX: 503-220-2480. Web Site: www.stoel.com. *Mgr*, Diana Gleason; E-Mail: dlgleason@stoel.com; Staff 10 (MLS 3, Non-MLS 7)
Founded 1906
Library Holdings: Bk Vols 50,000
Partic in Dialog Corporation; Westlaw

L TONKON TORP LLP, Law Library, 1600 Pioneer Tower, 888 SW Fifth Ave, 97204-2099. SAN 372-2244. Tel: 503-221-1440. FAX: 503-274-8779. Web Site: www.tonkon.com. *Librn*, Richard LaSasso; E-Mail: rich@tonkon.com
Library Holdings: Bk Vols 10,000; Per Subs 50

G TRI-COUNTY METROPOLITAN TRANSPORTATION DISTRICT OF OREGON (TRI-MET) LIBRARY, 4012 SE 17th Ave, 97202. SAN 370-4092. Tel: 503-962-4814. FAX: 503-962-6469. E-Mail: webmaster@tri-met.org. Web Site: www.tri.met.org. *Mgr Libr Serv*, Dareth Lee Murray; E-Mail: murrayd@tri-met.org; *Info Specialist*, Mark Foster McGrath; E-Mail: mcgrathm@tri-met.org; Staff 2 (MLS 1, Non-MLS 1)
Founded 1985
Jun 1999-Jul 2000 Income $15,000, Parent Institution $15,000. Mats Exp $12,500, Books $3,500, Per/Ser (Incl. Access Fees) $5,000, Other Print Mats $2,000, Electronic Ref Mat (Incl. Access Fees) $2,000. Sal $97,000 (Prof $58,000)
Library Holdings: Bk Titles 10,000; Per Subs 80
Subject Interests: Planning, Prof develop, Transportation
Database Vendor: Ebsco - EbscoHost

UNITED STATES ARMY
A CORPS OF ENGINEERS, TECHNICAL LIBRARY, PORTLAND DISTRICT & NORTH PACIFIC DIVISION, 333 SW First Ave, PO Box 2946, 97208-2946. SAN 358-1527. Tel: 503-808-5140. FAX: 503-808-5142. E-Mail: library@nwp01.usace.army.mil. Web Site: lepac1.brodart.com/search/um/browse.html. *Librn*, Kelly Laslie
Founded 1938
Library Holdings: Bk Titles 14,000; Per Subs 195
Subject Interests: Civil engineering, Dredging, Water res planning
Special Collections: Portland District & N Pac Div Rpts
Partic in Dialog Corporation; OCLC Online Computer Library Center, Inc

GL UNITED STATES COURT OF APPEALS, Ninth Circuit Library, Pioneer Courthouse, 555 SW Yamhill, 97204-1494. SAN 321-3862. Tel: 503-326-2124. FAX: 503-326-7047. *Librn*, Scott McCurdy; *Asst Librn*, Diane Schauer; Staff 3 (MLS 3)
Library Holdings: Bk Vols 14,000; Bk Titles 850; Per Subs 50
Automation Activity & Vendor Info: (Cataloging) SIRSI; (OPAC) SIRSI

GL UNITED STATES DISTRICT COURT, Central Library,* 7A40 Mark O Hatfield US Courthouse, 1000 SW Third Ave, 97204. SAN 321-3870. Tel: 503-326-8140. FAX: 503-326-8144. *Librn*, Scott McCurdy; *Asst Librn*, Diane Schauer
Founded 1975
Library Holdings: Bk Vols 17,000; Bk Titles 1,000; Per Subs 150
Restriction: Staff use only

C UNIVERSITY OF PORTLAND, Wilson W Clark Memorial Library, 5000 N Willamette Blvd, PO Box 83017, 97283-0017. SAN 314-1861. Tel: 503-943-7111. FAX: 503-943-7491. E-Mail: library@up.edu. Web Site: lewis.up.edu/library. *Dir*, Rich Hines; *Head Ref*, Heidi Senior; *Head Tech Servs*, Susan E Hinken; *Access Serv*, Caroline Mann; *Cat*, Carolyn Piatz; Staff 8 (MLS 8)
Founded 1901. Enrl 2,480; Fac 134; Highest Degree: Master
Jun 1998-May 1999 Income Parent Institution $1,638,293. Mats Exp $645,800, Books $227,675, Per/Ser (Incl. Access Fees) $241,545, Micro $77,006, Electronic Ref Mat (Incl. Access Fees) $89,196. Sal $486,442 (Prof $303,465)
Library Holdings: Bk Vols 350,000; Bk Titles 190,000; Per Subs 1,400
Subject Interests: Catholic theol, Philosophy
Database Vendor: Innovative Interfaces INN - View
Partic in NAPCU; OCLC Online Computer Library Center, Inc; Orbis; PORTALS
Open Mon-Thurs 7:30-12, Fri 8-10, Sat 10-6 & Sun 12-midnight

M WALLA WALLA COLLEGE, PORTLAND CAMPUS, School of Nursing Library,* 10345 SE Market, 97216. SAN 314-1896. Tel: 503-251-6115, Ext 7306. FAX: 503-251-6249. *Asst Librn*, Shirley A Cody; E-Mail: codysh@wwc.edu
Enrl 80; Highest Degree: Bachelor
Library Holdings: Bk Vols 10,000; Per Subs 100

CR WARNER PACIFIC COLLEGE, Otto F Linn Library, 2219 SE 68th Ave, 97215-4099. SAN 314-190X. Tel: 503-517-1102. FAX: 503-517-1351. Web Site: opall.mtangel.edu. *Dir Libr Serv*, Alice J Kienberger; Tel: 503-517-1032, E-Mail: akienberger@warnerpacific.edu; *Ad Servs, Media Spec*, Derek Bradford; Tel: 503-517-1034, E-Mail: dbradford@warnerpacific.edu; *Tech Coordr*, Daniel Jones; Tel: 503-517-1037, E-Mail: catolog@warnerpacific.edu; *Publ Servs*, Karla Kesell; Tel: 503-517-1118, E-Mail: kkessell@warnerpacific.edu; *Tech Servs*, Elizabeth Liebman; Tel: 503-517-1035, E-Mail: eliebman@wanerpacific.edu; *Circ*, Amasa Henderson; Tel: 503-517-1371, E-Mail: ahenderson@warnerpacific.edu; Staff 5 (MLS 2, Non-MLS 3)
Founded 1937. Enrl 625; Highest Degree: Master
Jul 1998-Jun 1999 Income Parent Institution $353,582. Mats Exp $158,502, Books $81,212, Micro $35, AV Equip $6,382, Other Print Mats $46,357, Other Print Mats $4,385, Electronic Ref Mat (Incl. Access Fees) $20,131. Sal $173,077 (Prof $71,936)
Library Holdings: Bk Vols 55,000; Bk Titles 43,610; Per Subs 315
Special Collections: Church of God Archives
Automation Activity & Vendor Info: (Cataloging) Endeavor; (Circulation) Endeavor; (Course Reserve) Endeavor; (OPAC) Endeavor
Database Vendor: Ebsco - EbscoHost, OCLC - First Search, ProQuest, Silverplatter Information Inc.
Restriction: Open to faculty, students & qualified researchers
Function: ILL available
Partic in Ore Pvt Acad Libr Link

S WASHINGTON COUNTY HISTORICAL SOCIETY & MUSEUM LIBRARY, 17677 NW Springville Rd, 97229. SAN 329-2460. Tel: 503-645-5353. FAX: 503-645-5650. E-Mail: wchs@teleport.com. *Exec Dir*, Joan H Smith; *Curator*, Barbara Doyle; Staff 4 (Non-MLS 4)
Founded 1956
2000-2001 Mats Exp $100, Per/Ser (Incl. Access Fees) $50, Micro $50
Library Holdings: Bk Vols 600
Subject Interests: History, Presv
Publications: This Far-Off Sunset Land
Restriction: Non-circulating to the public, Not a lending library

R WESTERN SEMINARY, Cline-Tunnell Library, 5511 SE Hawthorne Blvd, 97215-3399. SAN 314-1926. Tel: 503-517-1840. Reference Tel: 503-517-1842. Toll Free Tel: 800-547-4546. FAX: 503-517-1801. Web Site: www.westernseminary.edu. *Head of Libr*, Dr Robert A Krupp; Tel: 503-517-1838, E-Mail: rkrupp@westernseminary.edu; *Tech Servs*, Karen J Arvin; Tel: 503-517-1841, E-Mail: kjarvin@westernseminary.edu; *Per*, Audrey K Arnst; Tel: 503-517-1842, E-Mail: akarnst@westernseminary.edu; *Circ*, Vivian J Woo; Tel: 503-517-1843, E-Mail: vjwoo@westernseminary.edu; Staff 6

(MLS 2, Non-MLS 4)
Founded 1927. Enrl 375; Fac 19; Highest Degree: Doctorate
Jul 1999-Jun 2000 Income Locally Generated Income $5,750. Mats Exp $31,025, Books $9,690, Per/Ser (Incl. Access Fees) $14,680, AV Equip $375, Electronic Ref Mat (Incl. Access Fees) $6,300. Sal $107,150
Library Holdings: Bk Vols 81,313; Bk Titles 71,625; Per Subs 737; Bks on Deafness & Sign Lang 14
Special Collections: Baptist History; Instructional Resource Center, bks, curric, kits, tapes, videos
Automation Activity & Vendor Info: (Acquisitions) Endeavor; (Cataloging) Endeavor; (Circulation) Endeavor; (ILL) Endeavor; (OPAC) Endeavor
Database Vendor: Ebsco - EbscoHost, ProQuest
Publications: Library Handbook
Function: ILL available
Partic in OCLC Online Computer Library Center, Inc; Ore Pvt Acad Libr Link
Special Services for the Deaf - Books on deafness & sign language

M WESTERN STATES CHIROPRACTIC COLLEGE, W A Budden Memorial Library, 2900 NE 132nd Ave, 97230-3099. SAN 314-1942. Tel: 503-251-5752. Interlibrary Loan Service Tel: 503-251-5753. FAX: 503-251-5759. Web Site: www.wschiro.edu. *Dir*, Pam Bjork; Tel: 503-251-5757, E-Mail: pbjork@wschiro.edu; *Asst Librn*, Valerie Lawrence; *AV*, James Etheridge; *Circ*, Lynn Attwood; Staff 5 (MLS 2, Non-MLS 3)
Founded 1904. Enrl 450; Fac 50; Highest Degree: Doctorate
Library Holdings: Bk Vols 13,500; Bk Titles 9,000; Per Subs 300
Subject Interests: Chiropractic, Neurology, Nutrition, Orthopedics
Database Vendor: OCLC - First Search, OVID Technologies
Publications: Index to Chiropractic Literature
Restriction: Open to public for reference only
Partic in Chiropractic Libr Consortium; OCLC Online Computer Library Center, Inc

WORLD FOREST INSTITUTE LIBRARY,* 4033 SW Canyon Rd, 97221. SAN 375-0639. Tel: 503-228-1367. FAX: 503-228-3624. Web Site: www.vpm.com/wfi.foreststore. *Dir*, Sara Woo

POWERS

HAZEL M LEWIS LIBRARY, 511 Third Ave, PO Box 559, 97466-0559. SAN 314-1969. Tel: 541-439-5311. FAX: 541-439-5311. E-Mail: powersl2@ucinet.com. *Dir*, Joanie Bedwell; *Asst Librn*, Melinda Stallard; Staff 2 (Non-MLS 2)
Founded 1935. Pop 665; Circ 13,000
1999-2000 Income $49,890, State $116, Federal $648, County $47,728, Locally Generated Income $1,398. Mats Exp $11,255, Books $7,452, Per/Ser (Incl. Access Fees) $711, Presv $681, AV Equip $1,893, Electronic Ref Mat (Incl. Access Fees) $518. Sal $21,340
Library Holdings: Bk Vols 17,318; Bk Titles 17,318; Per Subs 13
Subject Interests: History
Automation Activity & Vendor Info: (Circulation) Innovative Interfaces Inc.
Database Vendor: Ebsco - EbscoHost, Innovative Interfaces INN - View, OCLC - First Search
Function: ILL available

PRINEVILLE

P CROOK COUNTY LIBRARY, 175 NW Meadow Lakes Dr, 97754-1997. Tel: 541-447-7978. FAX: 541-447-1308. Web Site: www.crooklib.org. *Librn*, Richard L Chrisinger
Founded 1931. Pop 16,700; Circ 151,816
Jul 1998-Jun 1999 Income $290,296, State $5,978, County $250,007, Locally Generated Income $12,864, Other $34,311. Mats Exp $129,526, Books $28,885, Per/Ser (Incl. Access Fees) $6,363, Presv $2,278, AV Equip $92,000. Sal $218,336 (Prof $57,242)
Library Holdings: Bk Vols 28,834; Bk Titles 27,684; Per Subs 106
Automation Activity & Vendor Info: (Cataloging) Follett; (Circulation) Follett
Open Mon-Wed 9-8, Thurs & Fri 9-6, Sat 10-4
Friends of the Library Group

RAINIER

S PORTLAND GENERAL ELECTRIC, Trojan Technical Library, 71760 Columia River Hwy, 97048. SAN 371-7496. Tel: 503-556-7914. FAX: 503-556-7901.; Staff 1 (MLS 1)
Founded 1989
Library Holdings: Bk Titles 174; Per Subs 29
Automation Activity & Vendor Info: (Acquisitions) Sydney; (Cataloging) Sydney; (Circulation) Sydney; (Serials) Sydney
Restriction: Staff use only
Partic in Dialog Corporation

P RAINIER CITY LIBRARY,* 106 B St W, PO Box 100, 97048-0100. SAN 314-1993. Tel: 503-556-7301. FAX: 503-556-3200. E-Mail: rainier@columbia/center.org. *Librn*, Patricia Stanley
Pop 1,800; Circ 11,500
Jul 1997-Jun 1998 Income $51,000
Library Holdings: Bk Vols 12,000; Per Subs 30
Special Collections: Rainier History Coll

ROSEBURG

GM DEPARTMENT OF VETERANS AFFAIRS, Library Service (142D),* 913 NW Garden Valley Blvd, 97470. SAN 314-2043. Tel: 541-440-1000, Ext 4226. FAX: 541-440-1206.
Founded 1933
Library Holdings: Bk Titles 4,400; Per Subs 167
Special Collections: Health Science Coll; Patient Health Education Coll
Publications: Library Service Newsletter (quarterly)
Partic in BRS; Medline; Vets Admin Libr Network

L DOUGLAS COUNTY LAW LIBRARY, Justice Bldg, Rm 305, 97470. SAN 372-2252. Tel: 541-440-4341. FAX: 541-440-4334. E-Mail: dclawlib@rosenet.net. *Librn*, Diana L Hadley-White; Staff 1 (MLS 1)
Jul 1999-Jun 2000 Income $98,000. Mats Exp Books $58,500. Sal $36,600
Library Holdings: Bk Vols 11,000; Per Subs 10
Restriction: In-house use for visitors
Function: For research purposes

P DOUGLAS COUNTY LIBRARY SYSTEM, 1409 NE Diamond Lake Blvd, 97470. SAN 358-1616. Tel: 541-440-4305. Interlibrary Loan Service Tel: 541-440-4304. TDD: 541-957-4783. FAX: 541-957-7798. Web Site: www.co.douglas.or.us/library. *Dir*, Max Leek; Tel: 541-440-4311; *Br Coordr*, Terri Washburn; Tel: 541-440-4204, E-Mail: tlwasb@co.douglas.or.us; *Publ Servs*, Betty Abdmishani; Tel: 541-957-4635, E-Mail: bpabdmis@co.douglas.or.us; *Tech Servs*, Carol McGeehon; Tel: 541-440-6005, E-Mail: clmcgeeh@co.douglas.or.us; Staff 12 (MLS 10, Non-MLS 2)
Founded 1955. Pop 99,100; Circ 827,758
Jul 1999-Jun 2000 Income $2,148,614, State $18,972, Federal $11,813, County $2,048,900, Other $59,975. Mats Exp $2,064,653, Books $145,461, Per/Ser (Incl. Access Fees) $26,588, AV Equip $21,198, Electronic Ref Mat (Incl. Access Fees) $1,100. Sal $1,690,942
Library Holdings: Bk Vols 306,240; Bk Titles 214,322; Per Subs 1,097
Subject Interests: Community needs
Automation Activity & Vendor Info: (Acquisitions) DRA; (Cataloging) DRA; (Circulation) DRA; (ILL) DRA; (OPAC) DRA
Partic in Southern Oregon Library Federation
Special Services for the Deaf - TDD
Friends of the Library Group
Branches: 10
C GILES HUNT MEMORIAL LIBRARY, PO Box 429, Sutherlin, 97479. SAN 358-1764. Tel: 541-459-9161. FAX: 541-459-9161. Web Site: www.co.douglas.or.us/library. *Librn*, Marcella Rimbeck; E-Mail: vmrimbec@co.douglas.or.us
Library Holdings: Bk Vols 21,924; Per Subs 441
Database Vendor: DRA
Friends of the Library Group
CANYONVILLE BRANCH, PO Box 216, Canyonville, 97417. SAN 358-1640. Tel: 541-839-4727. FAX: 541-839-4727. Web Site: www.co.douglas.or.us/library. *Librn*, Charlotte Cooper; E-Mail: cecooper@co.douglas.or.us
Library Holdings: Bk Vols 15,358; Per Subs 240
Database Vendor: DRA
Friends of the Library Group
GLENDALE BRANCH, PO Box 680, Glendale, 97442. SAN 358-1705. Tel: 541-832-2360. FAX: 541-832-2360. Web Site: www.co.douglas.or.us/library. *Librn*, Linda Kitchens; E-Mail: lskitche@co.douglas.or.us
Library Holdings: Bk Vols 11,785; Per Subs 241
Database Vendor: DRA
Friends of the Library Group
MYRTLE CREEK BRANCH, PO Box 5006, Myrtle Creek, 97457. SAN 358-1799. Tel: 541-863-5945. FAX: 541-863-5945. Web Site: www.co.douglas.or.us/library. *Librn*, Joy Sanada; E-Mail: jesanada@co.douglas.or.us
Library Holdings: Bk Vols 21,778; Per Subs 457
Database Vendor: DRA
OAKLAND BRANCH, PO Box 87, Oakland, 97462. SAN 358-1829. Tel: 541-459-9784. FAX: 541-459-9784. Web Site: www.co.douglas.or.us/library. *Librn*, Ellinor Gordon; E-Mail: ergordon@co.douglas.or.us
Library Holdings: Bk Vols 11,190; Per Subs 214
Database Vendor: DRA
REEDSPORT BRANCH, 395 Winchester St, Reedsport, 97467. SAN 358-1853. Tel: 541-271-3500. FAX: 541-271-3500. Web Site: www.co.douglas.or.us/library. *Librn*, Juanita Steiner; E-Mail: jmsteine@co.douglas.or.us
Library Holdings: Bk Vols 19,146; Per Subs 573
Database Vendor: DRA
Friends of the Library Group
RIDDLE BRANCH, PO Box 33, Riddle, 97459. SAN 358-1888. Tel: 541-874-2070. FAX: 541-874-2070. Web Site: www.co.douglas.or.us/library. *Librn*, Darla Schofield; E-Mail: djschofi@co.douglas.or.us
Library Holdings: Bk Vols 16,103; Per Subs 270

Database Vendor: DRA
Friends of the Library Group
MILDRED WHIPPLE LIBRARY DRAIN BRANCH, PO Box 128, Drain, 97435. SAN 358-1675. Tel: 541-836-2648. FAX: 541-836-2304. Web Site: www.co.douglas.or.us/library. *Librn*, Beckie Smith
Library Holdings: Bk Vols 16,637; Per Subs 336
Database Vendor: DRA
Friends of the Library Group
WINSTON BRANCH, PO Box 640, Winston, 97495. SAN 358-1918. Tel: 541-679-5501. FAX: 541-679-0838. Web Site: www.co.douglas.or.us/library. *Librn*, Carolyn Lee
Library Holdings: Bk Vols 17,686; Per Subs 456
Database Vendor: DRA
YONCALLA BRANCH, PO Box 157, Yoncalla, 97499. SAN 358-1942. Tel: 541-849-2128. FAX: 541-849-2128. Web Site: www.co.douglas.or.us/library. *Librn*, Jill Denley
Library Holdings: Bk Vols 12,476; Per Subs 217
Database Vendor: DRA
Friends of the Library Group

S DOUGLAS COUNTY MUSEUM, Lavola Bakken Research Library, 123 Museum Dr, 97470. SAN 314-2019. Tel: 541-957-7007. FAX: 541-957-7017. E-Mail: museum@co.douglas.or.us.
Founded 1969
Library Holdings: Bk Vols 2,800
Subject Interests: Agriculture, Dougla develop, Douglas county hist, Logging mills, Marine hist, Mining, Natural history, Railroads, Saw mills, Umpqua Indians
Special Collections: Herbarium Coll of Douglas County; History of Douglas County Coll, ledgers, scrapbooks, county records, unpublished articles, letters, diaries, mss, census & cemetery records, genealogies

J UMPQUA COMMUNITY COLLEGE LIBRARY, 1140 College Rd, 97470. (Mail add: PO Box 967, 97470), SAN 314-2035. Tel: 541-440-4640. Toll Free Tel: 800-820-5161. TDD: 541-440-4626. FAX: 541-440-4637. Web Site: www.umpqua.cc.or.us/library/libhome.htm. *Dir Libr Serv*, David Hutchinson; Tel: 541-440-4638, E-Mail: hutchid@umpqua.cc.or.us; *Librn*, Jen Jones; Tel: 541-677-3244, E-Mail: jonesj@umpqua.cc.or.us; *Materials Manager*, Rochelle Fernandes; Tel: 541-677-3245, E-Mail: fernanr@umpqua.cc.or.us; Staff 8 (MLS 2, Non-MLS 6)
Founded 1964. Enrl 3,378; Fac 69; Highest Degree: Associate
Jul 1999-Jun 2000 Income Parent Institution $355,672. Mats Exp $50,207, Books $32,306, Per/Ser (Incl. Access Fees) $10,729, Presv $204, Electronic Ref Mat (Incl. Access Fees) $6,968. Sal $176,725 (Prof $86,396)
Library Holdings: Bk Vols 40,617; Per Subs 188
Special Collections: Fire Science; Grant
Automation Activity & Vendor Info: (Cataloging) DRA; (Circulation) DRA; (Course Reserve) DRA; (ILL) DRA; (OPAC) DRA
Database Vendor: DRA, Ebsco - EbscoHost, IAC - Info Trac, Lexis-Nexis, ProQuest
Publications: Oregon Regional Union List of Serials
Function: ILL available
Partic in Douglas County Libr Syst; OCLC Online Computer Library Center, Inc

SAINT BENEDICT

C MOUNT ANGEL ABBEY LIBRARY,* One Abbey Dr, 97373. SAN 314-2051. Tel: 503-845-3303, 503-845-3317. FAX: 503-845-3500. *Dir, Publ Servs*, Victoria Ertelt; E-Mail: victoria@mtangel.edu; *Tech Servs*, Bede Partridge; *Coll Develop, Tech Servs*, Joseph Sprug; *Acq*, Laurie Jiricek; Staff 10 (MLS 4, Non-MLS 6)
Founded 1882. Highest Degree: Master
Jul 1997-Jun 1998 Income $471,851. Mats Exp $109,500, Books $10,000, Per/Ser (Incl. Access Fees) $35,000, Presv $10,000, Micro $4,000, Manuscripts & Archives $500. Sal $341,854
Library Holdings: Bk Vols 300,000; Per Subs 1,000
Subject Interests: Humanities, Philosophy, Theology
Special Collections: Africa (William Redman Duggan Coll); Civil War; McKuen Philosophy Coll; Patristic & Latin Christian Studies
Publications: Mt Angel Library Newsletter
Partic in Dialog Corporation; OCLC Online Computer Library Center, Inc
Friends of the Library Group

SAINT HELENS

P SAINT HELENS PUBLIC LIBRARY,* 375 S 18th St, 97051-2022. SAN 314-206X. Tel: 503-397-4544. FAX: 503-366-3020. E-Mail: shpubliclibrary@columbia-center.org. *Librn*, Karen Macfarlane; Staff 3 (MLS 2, Non-MLS 1)
Jul 1999-Jun 2000 Income $219,722, City $219,722. Mats Exp $31,800, Books $27,250, Per/Ser (Incl. Access Fees) $4,550. Sal $171,061 (Prof $30,833)
Library Holdings: Bk Vols 41,000; Bk Titles 40,000; Per Subs 140
Special Collections: Northwest Coll
Friends of the Library Group

SALEM

J CHEMEKETA COMMUNITY COLLEGE, Learning Resource Center,* 4000 Lancaster Dr NE, PO Box 14007, 97309-7070. SAN 314-2094. Tel: 503-399-5043, Ext 5177. FAX: 503-399-5214. E-Mail: coch@chemek.cc.or.us. *Dir*, Linda Cochrane; *Automation Syst Coordr*, Janet Snowhill; *Ref*, Stephen Fadel; Staff 12 (MLS 3, Non-MLS 9)
Founded 1962
1998-1999 Income $491,977. Mats Exp $127,466, Books $82,800, Per/Ser (Incl. Access Fees) $44,666. Sal $346,239
Library Holdings: Bk Vols 57,588; Per Subs 721
Automation Activity & Vendor Info: (Circulation) epixtech, inc.
Partic in Chemeketa Cooperative Regional Library Service; OCLC Online Computer Library Center, Inc; Valley Link

R FIRST BAPTIST CHURCH, Curry Memorial Library, 395 Marion St NE, 97301. SAN 314-2116. Tel: 503-364-2285. FAX: 503-391-9272. *Librn*, Sco Dutkiewicz
Library Holdings: Bk Vols 6,000
Subject Interests: Biblical studies, Christian fiction, Christian living

L MARION COUNTY LAW LIBRARY,* County Courthouse, 100 High St NE, Rm 5110, 97301. SAN 372-2155. Tel: 503-588-5090. FAX: 503-373-4386. Web Site: www.oper.org/mlaw. *Librn*, Marcia Hoak; E-Mail: mhoak@open.org
Library Holdings: Bk Vols 10,000; Per Subs 50

G OREGON DEPARTMENT OF TRANSPORTATION LIBRARY, 355 Capitol St NE, Rm 22, 97301-3871. SAN 358-1977. Tel: 503-986-3280. FAX: 503-986-4025. Web Site: www.odot.state.or.us/ssbbsrvcpublic/rm/library.htm. *Info Res*, Garnet Elliott; E-Mail: garnet.k.elliott@odot.state.or.us Staff 1 (MLS 1)
Founded 1937
Library Holdings: Bk Vols 17,000; Bk Titles 10,000; Per Subs 90
Subject Interests: Aeronautics, Bus, Engineering, Environ, Mgt, Motor vehicles, Planning, Soils, Traffic safety, Transit, Transportation
Special Collections: Transportation Safety, 850 video tapes (vhs)
Automation Activity & Vendor Info: (Cataloging) EOS; (OPAC) EOS
Database Vendor: OCLC - First Search
Restriction: Open to public for reference only

G OREGON LEGISLATIVE LIBRARY, 347 State Capitol, 900 Court St, 97310. SAN 374-5635. Tel: 503-986-1668. FAX: 503-986-1005. Web Site: www.leg.state.or.us/comm/commsrvs/home.htm. *Res*, David Harrell; E-Mail: david.b.harrell@state.or.us; Staff 2 (Non-MLS 2)
Library Holdings: Per Subs 160

S OREGON SCHOOL FOR THE BLIND LIBRARY,* 700 Church St SE, 97301. SAN 314-2132. Tel: 503-378-8676. FAX: 503-373-7537. *Media Spec*, Margie C Jordan
Library Holdings: Bk Vols 2,250
Special Services for the Blind - Braille & recorded books; Talking book center

S OREGON SCHOOL FOR THE DEAF LIBRARY, 999 Locust St NE, 97303. SAN 314-2140. Tel: 503-378-3825, 503-378-6779. FAX: 503-373-7879. E-Mail: librarian@osd.k12.or.us. Web Site: www.osd.k12.or.us. *Librn, Media Spec*, Charleen Hoiland
Founded 1970
Library Holdings: Bk Vols 14,000; Per Subs 35

S OREGON STATE CORRECTIONAL INSTITUTION, Law Library,* 3405 Deer Park Dr SE, 97310. SAN 314-2159. Tel: 503-373-7523. FAX: 503-378 8919. *Librn*, Greg Hunter; Staff 1 (MLS 1)
Founded 1959. Circ 35,000
Library Holdings: Bk Titles 13,000

G OREGON STATE DEPARTMENT OF REVENUE LIBRARY, Revenue Bldg, 955 Center St NE, 97301. SAN 314-2183. Tel: 503-945-8383. FAX: 503-945-8738. *In Charge*, Craig Fischer
Founded 1958
Library Holdings: Bk Vols 3,500; Per Subs 20
Subject Interests: Tax laws
Special Collections: CCH State Tax Reports; Oregon Laws; Survey of Current Businesses
Publications: Oregon Personal Income Tax Statistics; Oregon Property Tax Statistics; Tax Research Publications
Restriction: Not a lending library, Open to department staff only
Open Mon-Fri 8:30am-4:30pm

OREGON STATE HOSPITAL
M PATIENTS' LIBRARY, 2600 Center St NE, 97310. SAN 358-2035. Tel: 503-945-2800, 503-945-2904.
Library Holdings: Bk Vols 5,500; Per Subs 20
Special Collections: Large Print Book Coll
M PROFESSIONAL STAFF LIBRARY, Bldg 29, 2600 Center St NE, 97310-1319. SAN 358-2000. Tel: 503-945-2880. FAX: 503-945-2867. *Librn*, Carol Snyder

Founded 1950
Library Holdings: Bk Titles 1,900; Per Subs 66
Subject Interests: Psychiatry
Restriction: Staff use only

OREGON STATE LIBRARY,* 250 Winter St NE, 97301-3950. SAN 358-206X. Tel: 503-378-4243. Interlibrary Loan Service Tel: 503-378-4498. FAX: 503-588-7119. Web Site: www.osl.state.or.us/oslhome.html. *State Librn*, James B Scheppke; Tel: 503-378-4367, Fax: 503-585-8059, E-Mail: jim.b.scheppke@state.or.us; Staff 16 (MLS 16)
Founded 1905. Pop 2,742,750; Circ 121,079
Library Holdings: Bk Vols 241,163; Bk Titles 221,776; Per Subs 588
Subject Interests: Agriculture, Forestry, Government
Special Collections: Family History (Genealogy Coll), bks, micro; Grants & Funding, Patent, US Census; Oregon History (Oregoniana Coll); State & Federal Government, bks, doc
Automation Activity & Vendor Info: (Circulation) DRA; (OPAC) DRA
Publications: Letter to Libraries Online
Partic in OCLC Online Computer Library Center, Inc
Special Services for the Blind - Braille; Talking Books
Open Mon-Fri: 10-5
Branches: 1

OREGON STATE LIBRARY TALKING BOOK & BRAILLE SERVICES, 250 Winter St NE, 97310-3950. SAN 314-2124. Tel: 503-378-3849. Toll Free Tel: 800-452-0292. FAX: 503-588-7119. Web Site: www.osl.state.or.us/tbabs/tbabs.html.; Staff 2 (MLS 2)
Founded 1932. Circ 352,974
1998-1999 Income $622,603, State $540,888, Other $81,715. Mats Exp Books $1,690. Sal $302,037 (Prof $63,000)
Subject Interests: Oregon
Special Collections: Descriptive Video Coll
Publications: Talking Book & Braille News (quarterly patron newsletter)

OREGON STATE PENITENTIARY LIBRARY,* 2605 State St, 97310. SAN 358-2124. Tel: 503-378-2081. FAX: 503-378-3897. *Librn*, Trent Axen
Founded 1953
Library Holdings: Bk Vols 13,000; Per Subs 15,000
Subject Interests: Agriculture, Architecture, Art, Horticulture, Philosophy
Special Collections: Indian History; Paintings by Inmate Artists; Recordings of Classical Radio Broadcasts
Restriction: Staff use only
Special Services for the Deaf - High interest/low vocabulary books; Special interest periodicals
Branches:
OREGON WOMEN'S CORRECTIONAL CENTER, 2809 State St, 97310. SAN 358-2272. Tel: 503-373-1911. FAX: 503-378-8335.
Library Holdings: Bk Vols 10,000

GL OREGON SUPREME COURT, Law Library,* Supreme Court Bldg, 1163 State St, 97310-0270. SAN 314-2205. Tel: 503-986-5640. FAX: 503-986-5623. *Dir*, Joe Stephens; E-Mail: jstephen@willamette.edu; *Librn*, Gary Morgan; E-Mail: gmorgan@willamette.edu; Staff 3 (MLS 2, Non-MLS 1)
Library Holdings: Bk Vols 170,000; Bk Titles 23,500; Per Subs 450
Restriction: Open to public for reference only

M SALEM HOSPITAL, Health Sciences Library,* 665 Winter SE, PO Box 14001, 97309-5014. SAN 321-5474. Tel: 503-561-5377. FAX: 503-561-4777. E-Mail: chips@teleport.com. *Dir*, Carol Jones; Staff 3 (MLS 1, Non-MLS 2)
Founded 1972
Library Holdings: Per Subs 150
Subject Interests: Medicine
Partic in OCLC Online Computer Library Center, Inc

P SALEM PUBLIC LIBRARY, 585 Liberty St SE, PO Box 14810, 97309-5020. SAN 358-2396. Tel: 503-588-6315. Interlibrary Loan Service Tel: 503-588-6078. Circulation Tel: 503-588-6090. Reference Tel: 503-588-6052. TDD: 503-588-6021. FAX: 503-588-6055. E-Mail: library@open.org. Web Site: www.open.org/library. *Dir*, Gail J Warner; Tel: 503-588-6084, Fax: 503-589-2011, E-Mail: gwarner@open.org; *Asst Dir, Automation Syst Coordr*, Bob Miller; Tel: 503-588-6064, Fax: 503-589-2011, E-Mail: rmiller@open.org; *Circ*, Cliff Smith; E-Mail: cdsmith@open.org; *YA Servs*, B J Quinlan; Tel: 503-588-6039, E-Mail: bjquinlan@open.org; *Cat, Tech Servs*, Kari Martinez; Tel: 503-588-6020, E-Mail: kmartinez@open.org; *Ad Servs, Coll Develop*, Janice Weide; Tel: 503-588-6449, E-Mail: jweide@open.org; Staff 11 (MLS 11)
Founded 1904. Pop 213,798; Circ 1,248,889
Jul 1999-Jun 2000 Income (Main Library and Branch Library) $3,060,869, State $24,855, City $2,316,383, Federal $39,306, Locally Generated Income $369,103, Other $308,238. Mats Exp $436,512, Books $338,578, Per/Ser (Incl. Access Fees) $39,919, Presv $6,497, AV Equip $23,305, Other Print Mats $5,967, Electronic Ref Mat (Incl. Access Fees) $22,246. Sal $2,264,450
Library Holdings: Bk Vols 334,901; Bk Titles 217,683; Per Subs 744
Special Collections: Original Art; Salem Historic Photos Coll
Automation Activity & Vendor Info: (Circulation) epixtech, inc.; (OPAC) epixtech, inc.
Database Vendor: Dialog, Ebsco - EbscoHost, OCLC - First Search
Publications: OPEN Community News; Salem Public Library (newsletter)
Function: ILL available, Photocopies available, Reference services available
Partic in Chemeketa Cooperative Regional Library Service
Friends of the Library Group
Branches: 1
WEST SALEM, 395 Glen Creek Rd NW, 97304. SAN 358-2426. Tel: 503-588-6301. FAX: 503-588-6397. Web Site: www.open.org.library/ws.html. *Librn*, Mary Beth Hustoles; E-Mail: cdsmith@open.org
Circ 141,649
Library Holdings: Bk Vols 3,000

C WESTERN BAPTIST COLLEGE LIBRARY, 5000 Deer Park Dr SE, 97301-9392. SAN 314-2221. Tel: 503-375-7016. FAX: 503-375-7196. E-Mail: fvotaw@wbc.edu. Web Site: www.wbc.edu. *Dir, ILL*, Floyd M Votaw; E-Mail: fvotaw@wbc.edu; *Assoc Dir*, J Richard Muntz; *Circ*, Denise Olson; *Ser*, Connie Edgar
Founded 1946. Enrl 692; Fac 45; Highest Degree: Bachelor
Jul 1999-Jun 2000 Income $229,351. Mats Exp $106,940, Books $31,374, Per/Ser (Incl. Access Fees) $14,501, Presv $1,900, Micro $1,408, Electronic Ref Mat (Incl. Access Fees) $13,533. Sal $122,411 (Prof $51,000)
Library Holdings: Bk Vols 80,712; Per Subs 575
Subject Interests: Bible, Missions, Theology
Special Collections: Prewitt-Allen Archaeology Museum
Database Vendor: Ebsco - EbscoHost, Lexis-Nexis
Partic in NAPCU
Open Mon-Thurs 7:30-10, Fri 7:30-5, Sat 10:30-5, Sun 2-5 & 8-10:30

C WILLAMETTE UNIVERSITY, Mark O Hatfield Library, 900 State St, 97301. SAN 358-2450. Tel: 503-370-6312. FAX: 503-370-6141. E-Mail: library@willamette.edu. Web Site: library.willamette.edu/home. *Librn*, Larry R Oberg; *Coll Develop, Publ Servs*, Joni Roberts; *Head Ref*, Ford Schmidt; *Syst Coordr*, Michael Spalti; *ILL*, Liz Butterfield; *Circ*, Maresa Kirk; Staff 9 (MLS 9)
Founded 1843. Enrl 2,166; Fac 252; Highest Degree: Master
Library Holdings: Bk Vols 298,407; Per Subs 1,424
Automation Activity & Vendor Info: (Acquisitions) Innovative Interfaces Inc.; (Serials) Innovative Interfaces Inc.
Publications: Friends of the Library Newsletter; Moveable Type
Partic in Northwest Association of Private Colleges & Universities Libraries; OCLC Online Computer Library Center, Inc
Friends of the Library Group
Departmental Libraries:
CL JW LONG LAW LIBRARY, 245 Winter St SE, 97301. SAN 358-2485. Tel: 503-370-6386. FAX: 503-375-5426. Web Site: www.willamette.edu/wucl/longlib/. *Dir*, Richard Breen; E-Mail: dbreen@willamette.edu; *Cat, Head Tech Servs*, Elysabeth Hall; *Ref*, Timothy Kelly
Founded 1842. Fac 24; Highest Degree: Doctorate
Library Holdings: Bk Vols 270,000; Per Subs 1,825
Partic in OCLC Online Computer Library Center, Inc; Westlaw

SANDY

P SANDY PUBLIC LIBRARY,* 38980 Proctor Blvd, PO Box 578, 97055-0578. SAN 314-223X. Tel: 503-668-5537. FAX: 503-668-3153. E-Mail: snew5@aol.com. *Dir*, Sue Newlands; *Asst Librn*, Beth Scarth; Staff 2 (MLS 1, Non-MLS 1)
Founded 1934. Pop 19,000; Circ 210,000
Jul 1998-Jun 1999 Income $350,000, County $330,000. Mats Exp $52,000, Books $40,000, Per/Ser (Incl. Access Fees) $4,000. Sal $142,800 (Prof $44,000)
Library Holdings: Bk Titles 37,000; Per Subs 181
Special Collections: Oregon Revised Statutes
Automation Activity & Vendor Info: (Cataloging) epixtech, inc.
Publications: Between the Covers (quarterly newsletter)
Partic in Library Information Network Of Clackamas County
Open Mon-Wed 10-8, Thurs & Fri 10-6, Sat 10-5, Sun 1-5
Friends of the Library Group

SCAPPOOSE

P SCAPPOOSE PUBLIC LIBRARY, 52469 SE 2nd St, 97056. (Mail add: PO Box 400, 97056), Tel: 503-543-7123. FAX: 503-543-7123. E-Mail: scappl@centurytel.net. Web Site: columbia/center.org/scappooselibrary. *Librn*, Luana Nelson; Staff 5 (Non-MLS 5)
Founded 1929. Pop 11,688
Jul 1999-Jun 2000 Income $197,280. Mats Exp $205,402. Sal $85,579
Library Holdings: Bk Vols 29,333; Per Subs 106
Subject Interests: Northwest
Database Vendor: epixtech, inc.
Friends of the Library Group

SCIO

P SCIO PUBLIC LIBRARY, c/o Town Hall, PO Box 37, 97374-0037. SAN 329-3262. Tel: 503-394-3342. FAX: 503-394-2340. E-Mail: slibrary@wvi.com. *Librn*, Janelle Unruh
Founded 1940. Pop 2,000
Library Holdings: Bks on Deafness & Sign Lang 10
Database Vendor: OCLC - First Search
Friends of the Library Group

SEASIDE

P SEASIDE PUBLIC LIBRARY, 60 N Roosevelt Dr, 97138. SAN 314-2256. Tel: 503-738-6742. FAX: 503-738-6742. E-Mail: thelibrary@theoregonshore.com. *Dir*, Rita Fackerell
Founded 1935. Pop 6,200; Circ 95,000
Jul 2000-Jun 2001 Income $271,000, City $270,000, Locally Generated Income $1,000. Mats Exp $28,600, Books $28,000, Presv $600. Sal $202,000
Library Holdings: Bk Vols 32,000; Per Subs 68
Friends of the Library Group

SHERIDAN

P SHERIDAN PUBLIC LIBRARY,* 142 NW Yamhill, PO Box 248, 97378-1843. SAN 314-2264. Tel: 503-843-3420. *Librn*, Toni Rose
Pop 2,260; Circ 12,852
Library Holdings: Bk Vols 16,000; Per Subs 42
Partic in Chemeketa Cooperative Regional Library Service
Open Mon 10-5, Tues-Thurs 2-8, Fri-Sat 10-4

SHERWOOD

P SHERWOOD PUBLIC LIBRARY, 955 N Sherwood Blvd, 97140. SAN 314-2272. Tel: 503-625-6688. FAX: 503-625-3208. E-Mail: roseberrya@sherwood.or.us. *Dir*, Ann Roseberry; Staff 3 (MLS 3)
Founded 1936. Pop 11,300; Circ 101,240
Jul 2000-Jun 2001 Income $470,090. Mats Exp $54,000, Books $40,000, Per/Ser (Incl. Access Fees) $4,000, Electronic Ref Mat (Incl. Access Fees) $10,000
Library Holdings: Bk Titles 22,000
Special Collections: Sherwood Newspaper 1911-present
Mem of Washington County Cooperative Library Services
Open Mon-Thurs 10-8, Fri & Sat 10-6, Sun 1-5
Friends of the Library Group

SILETZ

P SILETZ PUBLIC LIBRARY, 243 W Buford, PO Box 71, 97380-0071. SAN 376-7248. Tel: 541-444-2855. E-Mail: siletzpl@teleport.com. *Librn*, Lorraine Rich
Library Holdings: Bk Titles 13,600; Per Subs 15
Database Vendor: DRA
Mem of Lincoln County Libr Syst
Partic in Coastal Resource Sharing Network
Open Tues 4-6, Wed 10:30-6, Thurs 10:30-6 & 7-9, Fri 9:30-6 & Sat 9:30-3
Friends of the Library Group

SILVERTON

P SILVER FALLS LIBRARY DISTRICT, 410 S Water St, 97381-2198. SAN 314-2280. Tel: 503-873-5173. Reference Tel: 503-873-8796. FAX: 503-873-6227. E-Mail: silvfals@ccrls.org. Web Site: www.open.org/silverpl/. *Dir*, Connie J Bennett; Tel: 503-873-6513, E-Mail: connieb@ccrls.org; *Circ*, Kathleen Cemper; E-Mail: kathleen@ccrls.org; *Ch Servs*, Janay Mulligan; Tel: 503-873-7633, E-Mail: janaym@ccrls.org; *Ch Servs*, Janet Smith; *Per*, Arce Valentina; *Ref*, Robert Gimmi; Tel: 717-477-1475, E-Mail: rdg@ship.edu; *Ad Servs*, Spring Quick; Tel: 503-873-8796, E-Mail: squick@ccrls.org; Staff 15 (MLS 3, Non-MLS 12)
Founded 1911. Pop 15,642; Circ 156,003
Jul 1999-Jun 2000 Income $504,027, State $3,352, Federal $63,184, County $37,720, Locally Generated Income $23,667, Other $376,104. Mats Exp $61,525, Books $50,714, Per/Ser (Incl. Access Fees) $6,704, Micro $528, Electronic Ref Mat (Incl. Access Fees) $3,579. Sal $303,869
Library Holdings: Bk Vols 53,066; Bk Titles 50,869; Per Subs 166
Special Collections: Homer Davenport Coll (political cartoonist), art & historical materials; Oregon Garden Coll, historical materials
Automation Activity & Vendor Info: (Cataloging) epixtech, inc.; (Circulation) epixtech, inc.; (OPAC) epixtech, inc.
Database Vendor: Ebsco - EbscoHost, ProQuest
Partic in Chemeketa Cooperative Regional Library Service
Friends of the Library Group

SPRINGFIELD

P SPRINGFIELD PUBLIC LIBRARY, 225 Fifth St, 97477-4697. SAN 314-2299. Tel: 541-726-3766. FAX: 541-726-3747. *Dir*, Robert C Russell; *Ch Servs*, Judith Harold; *Tech Servs*, Debbie Steinman; *Cat*, Yolanda Bombardier; *Ref*, Jennifer G Peterson; *YA Servs*, Barbara Thompson; *Spec Coll*, Woody Dwinell; Staff 7 (MLS 5, Non-MLS 2)
Founded 1908. Pop 52,000; Circ 345,000
Library Holdings: Bk Vols 129,713; Bk Titles 114,510; Per Subs 188
Special Collections: Mystery & Detective Fiction Coll (1920 to present)
Partic in OCLC Online Computer Library Center, Inc
Friends of the Library Group

STANFIELD

P STANFIELD PUBLIC LIBRARY, 180 W Coe Ave, PO Box 489, 97875-0489. SAN 358-0652. Tel: 541-449-1254. FAX: 541-449-3264. *Librn*, Zola (Sandy) Seibel; E-Mail: sseibel@orednet.org; Staff 2 (Non-MLS 2)
Founded 1914. Pop 3,000
Jul 2000-Jun 2001 Income $28,375, State $375. Mats Exp $3,810, Books $3,000, Per/Ser (Incl. Access Fees) $250, Micro $560
Library Holdings: Bk Vols 6,450
Subject Interests: Local history
Mem of Umatilla County Spec Libr Dist
Partic in Dynix Consortium

STAYTON

S AMERICAN PRIVATE PRESS ASSOCIATION, Library of Amateur Journalism, PO Box 834, 97383-0741. SAN 328-0438. Tel: 503-769-6088. FAX: 503-767-6455. E-Mail: library@amateurjournalism.com. Web Site: www.amateurjournalism.com. *Librn*, Martin M Horvat; E-Mail: mike@amateurjournalism.com; *Asst Librn*, John Bullis; E-Mail: jbullis@sierranv.net; *Coll Develop*, Dale A Goble, Jr; E-Mail: otedit@wvi.com; Staff 3 (MLS 3)
Founded 1904
Library Holdings: Bk Vols 600; Bk Titles 1,200; Spec Interest Per Sub 200
Subject Interests: Science fiction
Special Collections: Amateur Journalism (Library of Amateur Journalism Coll), bks; Fossil Coll; Press Asn & Printer's Asn; Science Fiction Fanzines (Papers of GM Carr), letters & mss; Willametta Keffer Coll, bks & correspondence

P STAYTON PUBLIC LIBRARY, 515 N First Ave, 97383-1703. SAN 314-2302. Tel: 503-769-3313. FAX: 503-769-3218. *Librn*, Sharon Russell; E-Mail: sharonr@ccrls.org; *Ch Servs*, Karen Mills; *Tech Servs*, Nancy Grant; Staff 1 (Non-MLS 1)
Pop 10,000
Jul 2000-Jun 2001 Income $177,188, City $123,196, Locally Generated Income $17,152, Other $36,840. Mats Exp $24,340, Books $17,426, Per/Ser (Incl. Access Fees) $384, Presv $4,258, Micro $156. Sal $117,373 (Prof $42,612)
Library Holdings: Bk Vols 42,001; Bk Titles 41,300; Per Subs 31
Subject Interests: Pacific Northwest
Automation Activity & Vendor Info: (Acquisitions) epixtech, inc.; (Cataloging) epixtech, inc.; (Circulation) epixtech, inc.; (ILL) epixtech, inc.
Partic in Chemeketa Cooperative Regional Library Service
Friends of the Library Group

SWEET HOME

P SWEET HOME PUBLIC LIBRARY, (SHPL), 1101 13th Ave, 97386-2197. SAN 314-2310. Tel: 541-367-5007. FAX: 541-367-3754. E-Mail: sweethomepl@yahoo.com. *Dir*, Leona McCann; Staff 3 (Non-MLS 3)
Founded 1942. Pop 7,500; Circ 36,914
Jul 2000-Jun 2001 Income $147,643, State $1,487, City $137,828, Locally Generated Income $7,328, Other $1,000. Mats Exp $44,458, Books $26,458, Presv $4,500. Sal $76,451 (Prof $26,808)
Library Holdings: Bk Vols 47,000; Per Subs 87
Subject Interests: Cooking, Medical, Northwest
Friends of the Library Group

THE DALLES

J COLUMBIA GORGE COMMUNITY COLLEGE LIBRARY, 400 E Scenic Dr, 97058. SAN 375-3395. Tel: 541-298-3116. FAX: 541-298-3120. Web Site: www.cgcc.cc.or.us/library/startext.html. *Librn*, Rosemary Ross; E-Mail: rross@cgcc.cc.or.us; Staff 3 (MLS 1, Non-MLS 2)
Founded 1977. Enrl 810; Highest Degree: Associate
Library Holdings: Bk Titles 16,000; Per Subs 135
Database Vendor: Innovative Interfaces INN - View

P THE DALLES-WASCO COUNTY LIBRARY, 722 Court St, 97058-2270. SAN 357-8852. Tel: 541-296-2815. FAX: 541-296-4179. *Dir Libr Serv*, Sheila Dooley; E-Mail: sdooley@clicknc.com; Staff 7 (MLS 1, Non-MLS 6)
Founded 1909. Pop 20,845; Circ 84,433

Jul 1999-Jun 2000 Income $692,418, City $265,931, Federal $2,117, County $253,666, Other $170,704. Mats Exp $45,144, Books $42,343, Per/Ser (Incl. Access Fees) $2,737, Micro $64. Sal $165,375
Library Holdings: Bk Vols 57,673; Bk Titles 51,789; Per Subs 70
Subject Interests: Ore hist
Automation Activity & Vendor Info: (Acquisitions) epixtech, inc.; (Cataloging) epixtech, inc.; (Circulation) epixtech, inc.
Partic in Gorge LINK
Friends of the Library Group

M MID-COLUMBIA MEDICAL CENTER, Planetree Health Resource Center, 200 E Fourth St, 97058. SAN 377-628X. Tel: 541-296-8444. FAX: 541-296-6054. Web Site: www.mcmc.net/phrc.htm. *Dir*, Michele Spatz; E-Mail: micheles@mcmc.net; Staff 3 (MLS 1, Non-MLS 2)
Founded 1992
Library Holdings: Bk Titles 3,300; Per Subs 60
Automation Activity & Vendor Info: (Circulation) epixtech, inc.
Partic in Docline; Gorge LINK; Oregon Health Sciences Libraries Association

TIGARD

P TIGARD PUBLIC LIBRARY,* 13125 SW Hall Blvd, 97223-8144. SAN 314-2329. Tel: 503-684-6537. FAX: 503-684-7297. Web Site: www.ci.tigard.or.us/lib.tplmain.htm. *Librn*, Mara Sani; Staff 19 (MLS 5, Non-MLS 14)
Founded 1964. Pop 33,953
Jul 1997-Jun 1998 Income $1,514,472. Mats Exp $200,984. Sal $998,754
Library Holdings: Bk Vols 94,000; Per Subs 400
Subject Interests: NW, Writer's resources
Mem of Washington County Cooperative Library Services
Open Mon-Thurs 9:30-5, Fri & Sat 9:30-5, Sun 1-5
Friends of the Library Group

S TOC MANAGEMENT SERVICES, INC, TOC Library - Headquarters, 6825 SW Sandburg St, 97223-8009. SAN 370-5382. Tel: 503-620-1710, Ext 339. FAX: 503-620-3935. *Librn*, Margret Iadanza; E-Mail: maggie_iadanza@toc.org; Staff 2 (MLS 1, Non-MLS 1)
Library Holdings: Bk Vols 1,800; Bk Titles 1,300; Per Subs 150
Subject Interests: Employee benefits, Employment law, Labor law
Publications: Library Update

TILLAMOOK

P TILLAMOOK COUNTY LIBRARY,* 210 Ivy Ave, 97141. SAN 358-2515. Tel: 503-842-4792. FAX: 503-842-1120. *Dir*, Sara Charlton; E-Mail: sarachar@wcn.com; *Asst Dir*, Marilyn White; *Ch Servs*, Kathy Chadsey; *Exten Serv*, Leo Schreiner; Staff 15 (MLS 6, Non-MLS 9)
Founded 1947. Pop 24,000; Circ 302,620
Jul 1999-Jun 2000 Income (Main Library and Branch Library) $1,073,575, State $5,600, County $1,067,975. Mats Exp $90,000, Books $80,000, Per/Ser (Incl. Access Fees) $10,000. Sal $518,050
Library Holdings: Bk Vols 120,000; Per Subs 300
Special Collections: Local History (Oregon)
Automation Activity & Vendor Info: (Cataloging) DRA; (Circulation) DRA; (OPAC) DRA
Partic in OCLC Online Computer Library Center, Inc
Friends of the Library Group
Branches: 4
BAY CITY BRANCH, City Hall, Bay City, 97107. SAN 358-254X. Tel: 503-377-2288. *Librn*, Susan Parker
Friends of the Library Group
GARIBALDI BRANCH, Garibaldi, 97118. SAN 358-2574. *Librn*, Donna Erickson
MANZANITA BRANCH, Manzanita, 97130. SAN 358-2604. Tel: 503-368-6665. *Librn*, Charlotte Forster
Friends of the Library Group
PACIFIC CITY BRANCH, Pacific City, 97135. SAN 358-2639. Tel: 503-965-6163. *Librn*, Debbie Buck
Friends of the Library Group
Bookmobiles: 1

S TILLAMOOK COUNTY PIONEER MUSEUM, Research Library, 2106 Second St, 97141. SAN 375-510X. Tel: 503-842-4553. FAX: 503-842-4553. *Dir*, M Wayne Jensen, Jr; Staff 1 (MLS 1)
Jul 1999-Jun 2000 Mats Exp $1,000, Books $1,000
Library Holdings: Bk Titles 4,000
Restriction: Non-circulating to the public, Not a lending library, Open to public with supervision only
Function: ILL available, Some telephone reference

TOLEDO

P TOLEDO PUBLIC LIBRARY, 173 NW Seventh St, 97391. SAN 314-2337. Tel: 541-336-3132. FAX: 541-336-3428. E-Mail: toledolibrary@cityoftoledo.org. Web Site: www.cityoftoledo.org/city_staff_library.html. *Dir*, Peter Rayment; E-Mail: librarydirector@cityoftoledo.org; *Asst Dir*, Lisa A Miller; *Ch Servs*, Jill Presley; *Cat, Tech Servs*, Andrea Haller; Staff 7 (MLS 1, Non-MLS 6)
Founded 1916. Pop 6,034; Circ 67,675
Jul 1999-Jun 2000 Income $204,984, State $636, City $155,596, Locally Generated Income $48,092, Other $660. Sal $142,078
Library Holdings: Bk Vols 33,000
Subject Interests: Genealogy
Special Collections: Yaquina Genealogical Society Coll
Automation Activity & Vendor Info: (Circulation) DRA
Database Vendor: DRA
Partic in Coastal Resource Sharing Network

TUALATIN

P TUALATIN PUBLIC LIBRARY, 18880 SW Martinazzi Ave, 97062. SAN 314-2345. Tel: 503-692-2000. TDD: 503-692-0574. FAX: 503-692-5421. Web Site: www.ci.tualatin.or.us. *Mgr*, Julia Corkett; Fax: 503-691-6884, E-Mail: jcorkett@ci.tualatin.or.us; *Librn*, Nancy Hovan; *Coordr*, Beverly Phillips; E-Mail: bphillips@ci.tualatin.or.us; *Circ*, Linda Kelleher; E-Mail: lkelleher@ci.tualatin.or.us; *YA Servs*, Carol Sibray; E-Mail: csibray@ci.tualatin.or.us; *Ad Servs*, Juliann Ross; E-Mail: jross@ci.tualatin.or.us; *Tech Servs*, Andrea Keifer; E-Mail: akeifer@ci.tualatin.or.us. Subject Specialists: *Programming*, Beverly Phillips; Staff 21 (MLS 4, Non-MLS 17)
Founded 1977. Pop 21,000; Circ 190,000
Library Holdings: Bk Vols 90,000; Per Subs 175
Automation Activity & Vendor Info: (Cataloging) Gaylord; (Circulation) Gaylord; (OPAC) Gaylord
Database Vendor: Ebsco - EbscoHost, OCLC - First Search
Publications: Tualatin Library News
Mem of Washington County Cooperative Library Services
Open Sun 12:30-5:30, Mon-Thurs 9:30-8:30, Fri & Sat 9:30-5:30

UKIAH

P UKIAH SCHOOL-PUBLIC LIBRARY,* PO Box 218, 97880-0218. SAN 376-3285. Tel: 541-427-3431. FAX: 541-427-3432. *Librn*, Sherri Contreras; E-Mail: sherricontreras@hotmail.com
Library Holdings: Bk Vols 10,000; Per Subs 25
Partic in Umatilla County Spec Libr District

UMATILLA

P UMATILLA PUBLIC LIBRARY,* 911 Seventh St, PO Box 820, 97882. SAN 358-0687. Tel: 541-922-5704. FAX: 541-922-5708. *Librn*, Marie Baldo; E-Mail: mbaldo@orednet.org
1997-1998 Income $38,000
Library Holdings: Bk Titles 16,000; Per Subs 12
Open Mon, Wed & Fri 10-5, Tues & Thurs 9-2:30

UNION

P CARNEGIE PUBLIC LIBRARY, 182 N Main St, PO Box 928, 97883-0928. SAN 314-2353. Tel: 541-562-5811. FAX: 541-562-5196. E-Mail: uclib@eoni.com. *Dir*, M Louise Weeks; *Librn*, Lenora F Clark
Founded 1913. Pop 2,000; Circ 168,364
Library Holdings: Bk Vols 10,000; Per Subs 26
Subject Interests: Alternate energy resources
Function: ILL available
Open Mon, Tues, Thurs & Fri 10-5:30, Wed 6-8

VENETA

P FERN RIDGE LIBRARY DISTRICT,* 88026 Territorial Rd, PO Box 397, 97487-0397. SAN 314-2361. Tel: 541-935-7512. FAX: 541-935-8013. *Dir*, Rozella Van Meter; E-Mail: rvanmete@lane.k12.or.us
Founded 1966. Pop 9,850; Circ 80,000
Library Holdings: Bk Titles 27,000; Per Subs 70
Automation Activity & Vendor Info: (Cataloging) SIRSI; (Circulation) SIRSI
Publications: Newsletter (quarterly)
Friends of the Library Group

VERNONIA

P VERNONIA PUBLIC LIBRARY,* 701 Weed Ave, 97064-1102. SAN 314-237X. Tel: 503-429-1818. *Dir*, Nancy Burch
Founded 1925. Pop 1,750; Circ 9,633
Library Holdings: Bk Vols 9,700; Per Subs 25
Open Mon & Fri 1-5, Wed 9-5 & Sat 10-2
Friends of the Library Group

WALDPORT

P WALDPORT PUBLIC LIBRARY, PO Box 1357, 97394-1357. SAN 314-2388. Tel: 541-563-5880. FAX: 541-563-5810. E-Mail: wpl@casco.net. *Librn*, Jill Tierce; Staff 1 (Non-MLS 1)
Founded 1912. Pop 4,600; Circ 45,000
Jul 1999-Jun 2000 Income $63,350, State $350, City $13,000, County $45,000, Locally Generated Income $5,000. Mats Exp $11,000
Library Holdings: Bk Titles 18,000; Per Subs 32
Open Mon & Thurs 11-7, Tues, Wed & Fri 11-5 & Sat 11-4
Friends of the Library Group

WEST LINN

P WEST LINN PUBLIC LIBRARY,* 1595 Burns St, 97068-3231. SAN 314-240X. Tel: 503-656-7853. FAX: 503-656-2746. Web Site: www.westlinn.lib.or.us. *Dir, Librn*, Pamella Williams; E-Mail: pam@westlinn.lib.or.us; *Coll Develop*, Sandy Glover
1999-2000 Income $921,143, State $6,029, Provincial $533,280, City $353,471, Locally Generated Income $28,363. Mats Exp $157,550, Books $110,100, Per/Ser (Incl. Access Fees) $13,000, AV Equip $33,350, Electronic Ref Mat (Incl. Access Fees) $1,100
Library Holdings: Bk Vols 73,234; Bk Titles 54,489; Per Subs 261
Automation Activity & Vendor Info: (Circulation) Inlex
Publications: Newsletter
Mem of Clackamas County Syst
Friends of the Library Group

WESTON

P WESTON PUBLIC LIBRARY,* 108 E Main, PO Box 267, 97886-0267. SAN 358-0717. Tel: 541-566-2378. FAX: 541-566-2378. *Librn*, Kathleen Schmidtgall
Library Holdings: Bk Titles 11,265; Per Subs 60

WHITE CITY

GM DEPARTMENT OF VETERANS AFFAIRS, Hospital Library,* VA Domiciliary, 142-D, 8495 Crater Lake Hwy, 97503. SAN 314-2418. Tel: 541-826-2111, Ext 3690. FAX: 541-830-3503. *Librn*, Margaret Rose; *Chief Librn*, Sarah L Fitzpatrick
1997-1998 Income $65,451. Mats Exp $44,335, Books $15,963, Per/Ser (Incl. Access Fees) $23,126. Sal $73,598
Library Holdings: Bk Vols 13,707
Partic in Veterans Affairs Library Network

WILLAMINA

P WILLAMINA PUBLIC LIBRARY, 385 NE C St, PO Box 273, 97396-0273. SAN 376-3307. Tel: 503-876-6182. FAX: 503-876-1121. E-Mail: willapl@open.org. *Librn*, Melissa Hansen
Pop 2,000
Jul 1999-Jun 2000 Income $51,684, State $1,587, City $35,481, Locally Generated Income $3,819, Other $10,797. Mats Exp $7,372, Books $4,892, Per/Ser (Incl. Access Fees) $420, AV Equip $1,805, Other Print Mats $255. Sal $25,323
Library Holdings: Bk Vols 28,819; Per Subs 64
Automation Activity & Vendor Info: (Acquisitions) epixtech, inc.; (Cataloging) epixtech, inc.; (Circulation) epixtech, inc.
Mem of Chemeketa Coop Regional Libr Serv
Partic in Chemeketa Cooperative Regional Library Service
Friends of the Library Group

WILSONVILLE

P WILSONVILLE PUBLIC LIBRARY, 8200 SW Wilsonville Rd, 97070. SAN 329-9287. Tel: 503-682-2744. E-Mail: wvref@lincc.lib.or.us. Web Site www.wilsonville.lib.or.us. *Dir*, Stephen W Turner; *Ad Servs, Publ Servs*, Patrick L Duke; *Ch Servs*, Sheila Shapiro; Staff 12 (MLS 3, Non-MLS 9)
Founded 1982. Circ 262,122
Jul 1999-Jun 2000 Income $604,419, State $3,248, City $100,376, Federal $12,670, County $453,018, Locally Generated Income $35,107. Mats Exp $111,703, Books $71,585, Per/Ser (Incl. Access Fees) $1,615, Presv $3,395, Micro $3,255, AV Equip $31,163, Electronic Ref Mat (Incl. Access Fees) $690. Sal $352,723
Library Holdings: Bk Vols 55,000; Bk Titles 51,800; Per Subs 131
Subject Interests: Japan, Pacific Northwest
Special Collections: Japanese Language Children's Books
Automation Activity & Vendor Info: (Cataloging) epixtech, inc.; (Circulation) epixtech, inc.; (OPAC) epixtech, inc.
Partic in Library Information Network Of Clackamas County
Friends of the Library Group

S XEROX OFFICE PRINTING BUSINESS LIBRARY, (Formerly Xerox - Tektronix Library), 26600 Southwest Pkwy, PO Box 1000 MS 63-531, 97070. SAN 314-2434. Tel: 503-685-3986. FAX: 503-685-2296. *Librn*, Linda Appel; E-Mail: linda.appel@opbu.xerox.com; Staff 1 (MLS 1)
Founded 1978
Library Holdings: Bk Titles 3,800; Per Subs 150
Subject Interests: Bus mgt, Electronics, Programming
Partic in Clackamas County Coop Libr Servs; OCLC; Washington County Cooperative Library Services

WOODBURN

P WOODBURN PUBLIC LIBRARY, (WPL), 280 Garfield St, 97071-3698. SAN 314-2442. Tel: 503-982-5252, 503-982-5263 (admin office). Circulation Tel: 503-982-5262. Reference Tel: 503-982-5252. FAX: 503-982-2808. E-Mail: woodburn@ccrls.org. Web Site: www.ccrls.org/woodburn. *Dir*, Linda Sprauer; *Circ*, Nicolette Wonacott; *ILL, Ref*, Judy Brunkal; *Cat, Tech Servs*, Donna Melendez; *Ch Servs*, Mary Parra; Staff 8 (MLS 3, Non-MLS 5)
Founded 1914. Pop 19,526; Circ 158,719
Jul 2000-Jun 2001 Mats Exp $89,243
Library Holdings: Bk Vols 73,845; Per Subs 221; Bks on Deafness & Sign Lang 41
Subject Interests: Large print
Special Collections: Language (Russian & Spanish Coll)
Database Vendor: epixtech, inc.
Mem of Chemeketa Coop Regional Libr Serv
Open Sun 1-5 (Sept-May), Mon-Thurs 10-8, Fri & Sat 10-5
Friends of the Library Group

YACHATS

P YACHATS PUBLIC LIBRARY, PO Box 817, 97498-0234. SAN 314-2450. Tel: 541-547-3741. *Librn*, Pat Bierman
Pop 490; Circ 4,580
Library Holdings: Bk Vols 7,000

PENNSYLVANIA

Date of Statistics: 1997-98
Population, 1990: 11,888,910
Population Served by Public Libraries: 11,627,557
Unserved: 261,353
Total Volumes in Public Libraries: 27,479,885
Volumes Per Capita: 2.36 (population served)
Total Public Circulation: 55,940,985
Circulation Per Capita: 4.81 (population served)
Total Public Library Income: $209,944,387
Mean Income (excluding Philadelphia & Pittsburgh): $274,007
Source of Income:
Public Funds: $133,186,589
State Aid: $34,545,537
Federal: $2,481,118
Private Funds (including gifts): $39,731,143
Total Operating Expenditures: $208,771,850
Total Capital Expenditures: $23,012,521
Operating Expenditures Per Capita: $17.95 (population served)
Number of County or Multi-County (Regional) Libraries: 54
Counties Served: 67
Number of Bookmobiles in State: 32

Grants-in-Aid to Public Libraries:
Federal (Library Services & Technology Act), 1997-98
Public Libraries: $4,767,036
Other Libraries: $835,047
State Aid (1997-98):$29,407,000
Formula or Amount for Apportionment: Changed in 1980. Seven categories of aid: amended in 1985 to increase equalization aid.
Local Libraries: Basic aid of not less than 25 cents per capita; incentive aid of up to 50 cents per dollar of surplus local effort; an equal grant of about $2,238 per library unit; and equalization aid to libraries serving distressed communities.
County Libraries: An additional amount of aid which is based on a percent of the county government's appropriation and class of county.
District Library Centers: An additional amount of aid of not less than 25 cents per capita for the population of the district.
Regional Resource Center Aid: An additional amount of aid of not less than $100,000 per library (4 libraries). All categories of aid increase with the amount of the appropriation.
Special Use of Federal Funds: Collection development and cooperative collection development; education for paraprofessionals; effective use of technology, including electronic mail, network and satellite equipment; information provision to rural and urban areas; and connectivity and linking databases into networks.

ABINGTON

P ABINGTON FREE LIBRARY, 1030 Old York Rd, 19001-4594. SAN 358-2663. Tel: 215-885-5180. FAX: 215-885-9242. *Dir*, Nancy Byouk Hammeke; *Cat*, Barbara Wengert; *Ref*, Karen Byrne; *Ch Servs*, Carolyn DuBois; Staff 9 (MLS 9)
Founded 1971. Pop 59,001; Circ 503,196
Jan 1999-Dec 1999 Income (Main Library and Branch Library) $1,630,860, State $201,473, City $1,353,138, Federal $12,983, Locally Generated Income $63,266. Mats Exp $162,932, Books $142,048, Per/Ser (Incl. Access Fees) $10,396. Sal $893,809
Library Holdings: Bk Titles 134,097; Per Subs 285
Automation Activity & Vendor Info: (Cataloging) Gaylord; (Circulation) Gaylord
Partic in Montgomery County Libr & Info Network Consortium
Special Services for the Deaf - TTY machine
Open Mon-Fri 10-9, Sat 10-5 & Sun 2-5
Friends of the Library Group
Branches: 1
ROSLYN BRANCH, 2412 Avondale Rd, Roslyn, 19001-4292. SAN 358-2698. Tel: 215-886-9818. *Librn*, Cecelia Frankford
Library Holdings: Bk Vols 23,393; Per Subs 41
Automation Activity & Vendor Info: (Circulation) Gaylord
Partic in Montgomery County Libr & Info Network Consortium
Friends of the Library Group

M ABINGTON MEMORIAL HOSPITAL, Wilmer Memorial Medical Library, 1200 York Rd, 19001. SAN 314-2469. Tel: 215-481-2096. *Asst Librn*, Ellen Kerrigan; Staff 1 (MLS 1)
Founded 1914
Library Holdings: Bk Titles 4,000
Subject Interests: Dentistry, Gyn, Medicine, Nursing, OB, Surgery
Partic in Basic Health Sciences Library Network; Delaware Valley Information Consortium; NY Regional Med Libr
Branches:

R ABINGTON PRESBYTERIAN CHURCH LIBRARY, 1082 Old York Rd, 19001. SAN 314-2477. Tel: 215-887-4530. FAX: 215-887-5988. Web Site: www.libertynet.org/~apcusa.
Founded 1956
Library Holdings: Bk Vols 6,046
Subject Interests: Environmental studies, Local Presbyterian church hist, Mostly non-fiction

S HAROLD M LAMBERT STUDIOS, Stock Photo Library,* 1063 Easton Rd, 19001-4410. SAN 329-8515. Tel: 215-885-3355. FAX: 215-885-3364. *Asst Librn, VPres*, Harold Lambert, Jr

R OLD YORK ROAD TEMPLE BETH AM LIBRARY, 971 Old York Rd, 19001. SAN 314-2493. Tel: 215-886-8000. FAX: 215-886-8320. *In Charge*, Elise Waintrup; *In Charge*, Karen Schwartz; *In Charge*, Katie Gaines
Founded 1964
Library Holdings: Bk Titles 5,000
Subject Interests: Judaica, Relig studies

C PENNSYLVANIA STATE UNIVERSITY, Abington College Library (University Libraries),* 1600 Woodland Rd, 19001. SAN 314-2507. Tel: 215-881-7424. FAX: 215-881-7423. E-Mail: pxw21@psu.edu. *Librn*, Patricia Weaver; *Ref*, Binh Le; Staff 6 (MLS 2, Non-MLS 4)
Founded 1950. Enrl 2,493; Fac 90
Library Holdings: Bk Vols 58,227
Publications: New Books in the Library
Partic in OCLC Online Computer Library Center, Inc; RLIN

ALBION

P ALBION AREA PUBLIC LIBRARY,* 111 E Pearl St, 16401-1202. SAN 314-2523. Tel: 814-756-5400. FAX: 814-756-5400. E-Mail: albion@erie.net. *Librn*, Margaret Platz
Pop 1,575; Circ 30,858
Library Holdings: Bk Vols 13,000; Per Subs 24

ALCOA CENTER

S ALCOA TECHNICAL CENTER LIBRARY,* 100 Technical Dr, 15069-0001. SAN 314-2531. Tel: 724-337-2396. FAX: 724-337-2394. *Mgr*, Christine Hennrich; Tel: 724-337-2413, E-Mail: christine.hennrich@alcoa.com; *Librn*, Nickolas Kotow; *Librn*, Earl Mounts; E-Mail: earl.mounts@alcoa.com; Staff 6 (MLS 3, Non-MLS 3)
Founded 1919
Library Holdings: Bk Vols 22,000; Bk Titles 20,000; Per Subs 200
Subject Interests: Aluminum, Auto tech, Light metals, Mat sci, Packaging, Surface sci
Special Collections: Alcoa Laboratories History; Alcoa Publications; Technical Translations
Database Vendor: Dialog, GaleNet, OCLC - First Search
Publications: Intranet
Restriction: Employees & their associates, Use of others with permission of librarian
Partic in OCLC Online Computer Library Center, Inc; PALINET & Union Library Catalogue of Pennsylvania

ALEXANDRIA

P MEMORIAL PUBLIC LIBRARY OF THE BOROUGH OF ALEXANDRIA,* Main St, 16611. SAN 314-254X. Tel: 814-669-4313. *Librn*, Lynn S Rennell
Founded 1899. Pop 3,465; Circ 12,445
Library Holdings: Bk Vols 17,488; Per Subs 23
Open Mon & Thurs 10:30-5 & 6:30-8, Tues & Fri 9-5, Sat 10-12, closed Wed

ALIQUIPPA

P B F JONES MEMORIAL LIBRARY, Aliquippa District Library Center,* 663 Franklin Ave, 15001-3736. SAN 314-2566. Tel: 724-375-2900. FAX: 724-375-3274. E-Mail: bfjones@shrsys.hslc.org. Web Site: www.aliquippa.lib.pa.us. *Dir*, Mary Elizabeth Colombo; *Assoc Dir*, Lawrence Silverstein; *Coll Develop*, Nancy Leuzinger
Founded 1926. Pop 186,093; Circ 95,490
Library Holdings: Bk Vols 61,650; Per Subs 181
Special Collections: LPDR for Nuclear Reg Com for Beaver Valley I & II Power Stations; PA Airhelp Resource Center
Mem of Beaver County Federated Library System
Partic in Interlibrary Delivery Service of Pennsylvania; OCLC Online Computer Library Center, Inc; Pittsburg Regional Libr Ctr
Friends of the Library Group

ALLENTOWN

S ALLENTOWN ART MUSEUM, Reference Library,* Fifth & Court Sts, PO Box 388, 18105-0388. SAN 314-2574. Tel: 610-432-4333. FAX: 610-434-7409. *Librn*, Sofia Bakis
Founded 1959
Library Holdings: Bk Titles 10,000; Per Subs 78
Subject Interests: Art history

P ALLENTOWN PUBLIC LIBRARY, 1210 Hamilton St, 18102. SAN 358-2728. Tel: 610-820-2400. FAX: 610-820-0640. E-Mail: allentownpl@cliu.org. Web Site: www.allentownpl.org. *Dir*, Kathryn Stephanoff; *Acq*, Barbara Sefraneck; *Ad Servs, Commun Servs*, Kathy Kneiss; *Ch Servs*, Sharon Frankenfield; *ILL*, Diana Defanti; Staff 13 (MLS 13)
Founded 1912. Pop 118,000; Circ 1,000,000
Jul 1999-Jun 2000 Income (Main Library and Branch Library) $2,405,176. Mats Exp $404,251, Books $225,000, Per/Ser (Incl. Access Fees) $17,000, Micro $5,000, AV Equip $33,000, Electronic Ref Mat (Incl. Access Fees) $40,000. Sal $1,515,053
Library Holdings: Bk Vols 221,000; Per Subs 580
Subject Interests: Local history
Special Collections: City
Partic in OCLC Online Computer Library Center, Inc; PALINET & Union Library Catalogue of Pennsylvania
Open Mon-Thurs 9-9, Fri 9-6, Sat 9-5; Drive-in Serv: Mon-Thurs 7:30am-8pm, Fri 7:30-5, Sat 7:30-3
Friends of the Library Group
Branches: 1
SOUTH, 601 W Emmaus Ave, 18103. SAN 358-2787. Tel: 610-797-3832. Web Site: www.allentownpl.org. *Librn*, Linda Cassaday; Staff 1 (MLS 1)
Library Holdings: Bk Vols 32,000
Open Mon-Thurs 12-8:30, Fri 12-6, Sat 9-1
Friends of the Library Group

M ALLENTOWN STATE HOSPITAL, Heim Memorial Library, 1600 Hanover Ave, 18109-2498. SAN 314-2590. Tel: 610-740-3406. FAX: 610-740-3616.; Staff 1 (Non-MLS 1)
Founded 1959
Jan 2000-Dec 2000 Income State $56,000. Mats Exp $10,000, Books $3,000, Per/Ser (Incl. Access Fees) $6,000, Micro $300, AV Equip $700. Sal $46,000
Library Holdings: Bk Vols 423; Per Subs 45
Subject Interests: Psychiatry, Psychoanalysis, Psychology, Psychotherapy, Soc work
Restriction: Open to others by appointment
Function: For research purposes, ILL available, ILL to other special libraries, Photocopies available
Partic in Basic Health Sciences Library Network; Berks County Library Association; Cooperating Hospital Libraries Of The Lehigh Valley Area

C CEDAR CREST COLLEGE, Cressman Library, 100 College Dr, 18104-6196. SAN 314-2620. Tel: 610-437-4471, 610-606-4605, Ext 3535. FAX: 610-740-3769. Web Site: library.cedarcrest.edu. *Coll Develop, Dir*, Mary Beth Freeh; *ILL*, Dana Bart-Bell; *AV*, Karen Heckman; *Acq, Ser*, Holly Hoffman; *Cat*, Barbara Bollinger; *Ref*, Carolyn Nippert; *Ref*, Charlotte Fisler; Staff 3 (MLS 3)
Founded 1867. Enrl 1,035; Fac 68; Highest Degree: Bachelor
Library Holdings: Bk Vols 133,763; Per Subs 670
Subject Interests: Women studies
Special Collections: American Poetry, bks, journals; Social Work, bks, journals; Women in the United States, bks, journals
Automation Activity & Vendor Info: (Acquisitions) DRA; (Cataloging) DRA; (Circulation) DRA; (OPAC) DRA; (Serials) DRA
Database Vendor: DRA
Publications: Bibliographic Instruction Bibliographies; Library Services Information Leaflets
Partic in Dialog Corporation; Interlibrary Delivery Service of Pennsylvania; Lehigh Valley Association Of Independent Colleges, Inc; OCLC Online Computer Library Center, Inc; PALINET & Union Library Catalogue of Pennsylvania

SR DIOCESE OF ALLENTOWN, Office of Pro-Life Activities Library, 900 S Woodward St, 18103. SAN 321-4540. Tel: 610-289-8906. FAX: 610-289-7917. *Librn*, Suzanne Mello; Staff 1 (MLS 1)
Founded 1977
Library Holdings: Bk Vols 700; Per Subs 11

M GOOD SHEPHERD MEDICAL LIBRARY, 543 St John St, 18063. SAN 374-8626. Tel: 610-776-3294. FAX: 610-776-3368. *Coordr*, Kathryn L Crist; E-Mail: kcrist@gsrh.org; Staff 1 (MLS 1)
Library Holdings: Bk Vols 400; Per Subs 51
Restriction: Employees & their associates, Medical staff only
Partic in BHSL

S LEHIGH COUNTY HISTORICAL SOCIETY, Scott Andrew Trexler II Memorial Library, Old Court House, Fifth & Hamilton Sts, 18101. (Mail add: PO Box 1548, 18105-1548), SAN 314-2655. Tel: 610-435-1072. FAX: 610-435-9812. E-Mail: lchs@voicenet.com. Web Site: www.voicenet.com/~lchs. *Archivist, Librn*, Jan S Ballard; Staff 2 (MLS 1, Non-MLS 1)
Founded 1906
Library Holdings: Bk Titles 10,000; Per Subs 20
Subject Interests: Lehigh County
Special Collections: Allentown Imprints; City Directories; Early German Newspapers; Local Church Records; Manuscript Coll; Photograph Coll

GL LEHIGH COUNTY LAW LIBRARY, County Court House, 455 W Hamilton St, 18101-1614. SAN 314-2663. Tel: 610-782-3385. FAX: 610-820-3311. *In Charge*, Lorelei A Broskey; E-Mail: loreleibroskey@lehighcounty.org; Staff 4 (MLS 1, Non-MLS 3)
Founded 1869
Jan 2000-Dec 2000 Income County $374,742. Mats Exp $246,700, Books $200,700, Per/Ser (Incl. Access Fees) $4,000, Presv $2,000, Electronic Ref Mat (Incl. Access Fees) $40,000. Sal $121,746 (Prof $40,336)
Library Holdings: Bk Vols 20,611; Per Subs 35
Special Collections: Ordinances Coll; Pennsylvania Law, Local Municipal & Legislative History

M LEHIGH VALLEY HOSPITAL, Cedar Crest & I-78, PO Box 689, 18105-1556. SAN 371-5426. Tel: 610-402-8410. FAX: 610-402-8409. *Dir*, Barbara J Iobst
Founded 1974
Library Holdings: Bk Vols 2,800; Per Subs 350
Restriction: Open to public for reference only
Function: Photocopies available
Partic in Cooperating Hospital Libraries Of The Lehigh Valley Area
Branches:
LEHIGH VALLEY HOSPITAL, 17th & Chew, PO Box 7017, 18105-7017. SAN 314-2582. Tel: 610-402-2263. FAX: 610-402-2548. *Dir*, Barbara J Iobst
Founded 1940
Library Holdings: Bk Titles 2,000; Per Subs 110
Restriction: Open to public for reference only
Partic in Cooperating Hospital Libraries Of The Lehigh Valley Area

M MUHLENBERG MEDICAL LIBRARY, 2545 Schoenersville Rd, Bethlehem, 18017. SAN 327-0904. Tel: 484-884-2237. FAX: 484-884-0711. *Dir*, Barbara J Iobst
Library Holdings: Bk Vols 750; Per Subs 115
Partic in Cooperating Hospital Libraries Of The Lehigh Valley Area

G THE LEHIGH VALLEY PLANNING COMMISSION LIBRARY,* 961 Marcon Blvd, Ste 310, 18103-9397. SAN 326-9221. Tel: 610-264-4544. FAX: 610-264-2616. *Exec Dir*, Michael Kaiser
Library Holdings: Per Subs 10
Subject Interests: Census reports, Land use planning, Transportation planning
Publications: Lehigh Valley Planning Commission Newsletter (bi-monthly)

C MUHLENBERG COLLEGE, Harry C Trexler Library, 2400 Chew St, 18104-5586. SAN 314-2671. Tel: 484-664-3500. Reference Tel: 484-664-3600. FAX: 484-664-3511. Web Site: www.muhlenberg.edu/library. *Dir*, Thomas M Gaughan; Tel: 484-664-3551, E-Mail: gaughan@muhlenberg.edu; *Acq*, Elizabeth Fishman; Tel: 484-664-3570, E-Mail: efishman@muhlenberg.edu; *Head Tech Servs*, Linda L Bowers; Tel: 484-664-3575, E-Mail: bowers@muhlenberg.edu; *Ref*, Kelly Cannon; Tel: 484-664-3602, E-Mail: kcannon@muhlenberg.edu; *Humanities and Soc Sci*, Amy Abruzzi; Tel: 484-664-3552, E-Mail: aabruzi@muhlenberg.edu; *Head Ref*, Martha Stevenson; Tel: 484-664-3601, E-Mail: msteven@muhlenberg.edu; *ILL*, Doug Moore; *Circ*, Barbara C Howard; Tel: 484-664-3542, E-Mail: bhoward@muhlenberg.edu; *Ser*, Barbara B Eastland; Tel: 484-664-3561, E-Mail: eastland@muhlenberg.edu; *ILL*, Kristin Harakal; Tel: 484-664-3510, E-Mail: harakal@muhlenberg.edu; *Govt Doc*, Donna L Whary; Tel: 484-664-3564, E-Mail: dwhary@muhlenberg.edu; *Spec Coll*, Diane Koch; Tel: 484-664-3694, E-Mail: dkoch@muhlenberg.edu; *Tech Coordr*, Karl Henson; Tel: 484-664-3520, E-Mail: henson@muhlenberg.edu. Subject Specialists: *Humanities*, Kelly Cannon; *Sci*, Martha Stevenson; Staff 17 (MLS 7, Non-MLS 10)
Founded 1867
Jul 1999-Jun 2000 Income $1,285,285. Mats Exp $571,900, Books $120,550, Per/Ser (Incl. Access Fees) $158,400, Presv $8,500, Micro $9,000,

Other Print Mats $28,400, Electronic Ref Mat (Incl. Access Fees) $115,000. Sal $489,410 (Prof $288,627)
Library Holdings: Bk Vols 215,042; Bk Titles 161,225; Per Subs 838; Bks on Deafness & Sign Lang 70
Subject Interests: European history, German lit
Special Collections: Abram Samuels Sheet Music Coll; Muhlenberg Family, mss; Pennsylvania German coll; Rare Book coll; Raymond Brennan Map Coll
Automation Activity & Vendor Info: (Acquisitions) Innovative Interfaces Inc.; (Cataloging) Innovative Interfaces Inc.; (Circulation) Innovative Interfaces Inc.; (Course Reserve) Innovative Interfaces Inc.; (ILL) Innovative Interfaces Inc.; (Media Booking) Innovative Interfaces Inc.; (OPAC) Innovative Interfaces Inc.; (Serials) Innovative Interfaces Inc.
Database Vendor: Dialog, Ebsco - EbscoHost, Innovative Interfaces INN - View, Lexis-Nexis, OCLC - First Search, OVID Technologies, Silverplatter Information Inc., Wilson - Wilson Web
Function: ILL available
Partic in Lehigh Valley Association Of Independent Colleges, Inc; PALINET & Union Library Catalogue of Pennsylvania

PARKLAND COMMUNITY LIBRARY,* 4422 Walbert Ave, 18104-1619. SAN 314-5646. Tel: 610-398-1333. FAX: 610-398-3538. E-Mail: parklandpl@cliu.org. *Librn*, Marjorie Stevens; *Cat*, Margaret Tyrrell; *Ref*, Renee Stanche; Staff 19 (MLS 3, Non-MLS 16)
Founded 1973. Pop 37,845
Jul 1998-Jun 1999 Income $323,868, State $68,779, City $188,920, Federal $19,350, Locally Generated Income $46,819. Mats Exp $68,519, Books $45,550, Per/Ser (Incl. Access Fees) $3,059, AV Equip $8,451, Other Print Mats $6,382, Electronic Ref Mat (Incl. Access Fees) $3,064. Sal $164,001
Library Holdings: Bk Vols 60,934; Per Subs 158; High Interest/Low Vocabulary Bk Vols 20; Bks on Deafness & Sign Lang 40
Subject Interests: Jobs, Large-print fiction, Occupations
Special Collections: Local History containing most of the Publications of the Penna-German Society (formerly Penna-German Folklore Society), Birdsbiro, PA
Automation Activity & Vendor Info: (Cataloging) Sagebrush Corporation; (Circulation) Sagebrush Corporation; (OPAC) Sagebrush Corporation
Publications: Friends of the Library Information Paper (FLIP); Whisperings (PCL Newsletter for Young People)
Special Services for the Blind - Talking Books
Friends of the Library Group

S QUACKWATCH, INC LIBRARY, PO Box 1747, 18105. SAN 326-2502. Tel: 610-437-1795. E-Mail: library@quackwatch.com. Web Site: www.quackwatch.com. *Librn*, Stephen Barrett
Library Holdings: Bk Titles 3,500; Per Subs 130
Subject Interests: Alternative med, Chiropractic, Consumer health, Nutrition

S RAILWAY TO YESTERDAY LIBRARY, 12th & Cumberland Sts, PO Box 1601, 18105. SAN 370-6176. Tel: 610-797-3242. *Librn*, Douglas E Peters; *Asst Dir*, Peter T Patterson
Founded 1965
Subject Interests: Railroad, Transit
Special Collections: Lehigh Valley Transit Co, corporate rec, maps

M SACRED HEART HOSPITAL, Medical Library, 421 Chew St, 18102. SAN 314-268X. Tel: 610-776-4747. FAX: 610-606-4422. Web Site: www.shh.org. *Librn*, Diane M Horvath; E-Mail: dhorvath@fast.net
Founded 1949
Library Holdings: Bk Vols 6,668; Per Subs 128
Subject Interests: Dental, Diagnostic radiology, Family practice, Ophthalmology, Otolaryngology, X-ray
Partic in Nat Libr of Med

M ST LUKE'S HOSPITAL-ALLENTOWN CAMPUS, Learning Resource Center, 1736 Hamilton St, 18104. SAN 322-8266. Tel: 610-770-8300, 610-770-8355. FAX: 610-770-8736. *Librn*, Linda Schwartz; Staff 1 (Non-MLS 1)
Library Holdings: Bk Vols 2,000; Bk Titles 1,800; Per Subs 135
Database Vendor: OVID Technologies
Restriction: Open to others by appointment, Open to public for reference only
Function: Archival collection, ILL limited, Literary searches, Photocopies available
Partic in Basic Health Sciences Library Network; Cooperating Hospital Libraries Of The Lehigh Valley Area

S THE MORNING CALL, Newspaper Library, 101 N Sixth St, PO Box 1260, 18105. SAN 314-2612. Tel: 610-820-6500, 610-820-6523. FAX: 610-820-6672. Web Site: mcall.com/library/search.htm. *Dir Libr Serv*, Lois A Doncevic; E-Mail: doncevic@mcall.com; *Librn*, Dianne Knauss; *Librn*, Ruth Burns; *Librn*, Laurel Bruce; Staff 4 (MLS 4)
Founded 1932
Library Holdings: Bk Vols 3,000; Per Subs 30
Special Collections: Newspaper Microfilm-1870 to Present, photogs & micro
News articles available on Dialog, 1990 to present; Nexis, 1995 to present; Dow Jones & Bell & Howell, 1996 to present

ALTOONA

P ALTOONA AREA PUBLIC LIBRARY, 1600 Fifth Ave, 16602-3693. SAN 358-2817. Tel: 814-946-0417. Interlibrary Loan Service Tel: 814-946-0417, Ext 126. Circulation Tel: 814-946-0417, Ext 125. Reference Tel: 814-946-0417, Ext 131. FAX: 814-946-3230. E-Mail: altpublib@aasdcat.com. Web Site: www.altoonalibrary.org. *Dir*, Deborah Weakland; *Acq, Cat, Tech Servs*, Mary Ellen Crock; Tel: 814-946-0417, Ext 128, E-Mail: maryellen@altoonalibrary.org; *Ad Servs, Circ*, Patricia Foose; Tel: 814-946-0417, Ext 135, E-Mail: foose@altoonalibrary.org; *Ad Servs, Media Spec, Ref*, Sonia Keiper; Tel: 814-946-0417, Ext 147, E-Mail: skeiper@altoonalibrary.org; *Ch Servs*, Mary Lykens; Tel: 814-946-0417, Ext 123, E-Mail: mlykens@altoonalibrary.org; *ILL*, Patricia Shirley; *Syst Coordr*, Susan Chinault; Tel: 814-946-0417, Ext 132, E-Mail: suec@altoonalibrary.org; Staff 6 (MLS 6)
Founded 1927. Pop 65,100; Circ 338,000
Jul 1999-Jun 2000 Income $914,415, State $354,836, County $54,559, Locally Generated Income $397,020, Other $108,000. Mats Exp $116,467, Books $99,368, Per/Ser (Incl. Access Fees) $7,917, Micro $7,582, AV Equip $600, Electronic Ref Mat (Incl. Access Fees) $1,000. Sal $493,906 (Prof $177,464)
Library Holdings: Bk Vols 167,000; Bk Titles 155,000; Per Subs 254
Subject Interests: Adult literacy, Railroad hist
Special Collections: Local History (Pennsylvania Room); Railroad Photographs
Automation Activity & Vendor Info: (Cataloging) SIRSI; (Circulation) SIRSI; (OPAC) SIRSI
Database Vendor: OCLC - First Search
Mem of Blair County Library System
Partic in Interlibrary Delivery Service of Pennsylvania; OCLC Online Computer Library Center, Inc; PALINET & Union Library Catalogue of Pennsylvania
Adult Literacy Project - Volunteer reading tutors & full-time coordinator.
Workplace Project - Computer Aided Resume Writing & Career Guidance
Friends of the Library Group

M ALTOONA HOSPITAL, Glover Memorial Library, 620 Howard Ave, 16601-4899. SAN 314-2728. Tel: 814-946-2318. FAX: 814-946-2074. E-Mail: library@altoonahospital.org. Web Site: www.altoonahospital.org. *In Charge*, Tracie L Kahler; E-Mail: tkahler@altoonahospital.org; Staff 2 (MLS 1, Non-MLS 1)
Founded 1940
Library Holdings: Bk Vols 4,238; Bk Titles 4,020; Per Subs 300
Subject Interests: Allied health, Cancer, Medicine, Nursing
Special Collections: Altoona Hospital (Historical Coll), bks, doc, artifacts, photogs
Restriction: Circulates for staff only, Non-circulating to the public, Open to public for reference only, Public use on premises
Function: ILL limited, Reference services available
Partic in Nat Libr of Med
Friends of the Library Group

J ALTOONA SCHOOL OF COMMERCE LIBRARY,* 508 58th St, 16602. SAN 314-2736. Tel: 814-944-6134. FAX: 814-944-4684. *Dir*, J William Laughlin
Library Holdings: Bk Vols 700; Per Subs 14

P BLAIR COUNTY LIBRARY SYSTEM, 1600 Fifth Ave, 16602-3621. SAN 314-2744. Tel: 814-946-0417. FAX: 814-946-3230. E-Mail: blacolib@aasdcat.com. Web Site: www.altoonalibrary.org. *Syst Coordr*, Susan M Chinault
Pop 130,436
Jul 1999-Jun 2000 Income $1,597,037, State $605,136, City $468,168, Federal $23,292, County $133,000, Other $367,441. Mats Exp $324,053. Sal $1,110,085
Library Holdings: Bk Vols 438,220; Per Subs 725
Automation Activity & Vendor Info: (Circulation) SIRSI; (Circulation) Follett; (OPAC) SIRSI; (OPAC) Follett
Member Libraries: Altoona Area Public Library; Bellwood-Antis Public Library; Claysburg Area Public Library; Hollidaysburg Free Public Library; Martinsburg Community Library; Roaring Spring Community Library; Tyrone-Snyder Township Public Library; Williamsburg Public Library
The Blair County Library System is an administrative agency which coordinates certain county-wide library services and overseas the distribution of state and county funding

GM DEPARTMENT OF VETERANS AFFAIRS, Medical Center Library,* 2907 Pleasant Valley Blvd, 16602-4377. SAN 314-2760. Tel: 814-943-8164, Ext 7156. FAX: 814-940-7895.
Founded 1950
Library Holdings: Bk Vols 4,817
Subject Interests: Medicine, Patient educ
Special Collections: Medical Journal Coll, microfilm
Partic in Vets Admin Libr Network
Open Mon-Fri 8-4:30

C PENNSYLVANIA STATE UNIVERSITY, ALTOONA COLLEGE, Robert E Eiche Library (University Libraries), 3000 Ivy State Park, 16601-3760. SAN 314-2752. Tel: 814-949-5255. FAX: 814-949-5246. E-Mail: tlw@

psulias.psu.edu. *Librn*, Timothy Wherry; *Ref*, Mila Su; Staff 6 (MLS 3, Non-MLS 3)
Founded 1939. Enrl 3,485; Fac 105
Library Holdings: Bk Vols 57,000
Special Collections: Drama & The Dance (Cutler Coll); Drama on Records (Buzzard Coll); Lincoln Coll (Klevan Coll)
Partic in OCLC Online Computer Library Center, Inc; RLIN

AMBLER

S LTK ENGINEERING SERVICES LIBRARY, 100 W Butler Ave, 19002. Tel: 215-542-0700. FAX: 215-542-7676. *Librn*, Marie S Knup
Founded 1974
Library Holdings: Bk Titles 5,500; Per Subs 100
Publications: Accession List (monthly-for internal distrib only)

TEMPLE UNIVERSITY OF THE COMMONWEALTH SYSTEM OF HIGHER EDUCATION
For Ambler Campus Library, see Philadelphia , .

AMBRIDGE

P LAUGHLIN MEMORIAL LIBRARY, 99 11th St, 15003-2305. SAN 314-2795. Tel: 724-266-3857. FAX: 724-266-5670. *Coll Develop, Dir*, Alyce Grubbs; *Ch Servs*, Sandra Gaitanis; Staff 3 (MLS 3)
Founded 1929. Pop 13,298; Circ 89,780
Jan 2000-Dec 2000 Income $155,831, State $27,758, City $13,100, County $11,616, Locally Generated Income $43,781, Other $59,576. Mats Exp $18,948, Books $16,063, Per/Ser (Incl. Access Fees) $2,299, AV Equip $42, Other Print Mats $544. Sal $70,165 (Prof $57,088)
Library Holdings: Bk Vols 46,243; Bk Titles 36,238; Per Subs 92
Subject Interests: Econ, History, Music
Special Collections: Local History (Pennsylvania), bks, maps, slides; Music, rec, tapes, cassettes
Automation Activity & Vendor Info: (Course Reserve) Innovative Interfaces Inc.
Mem of Beaver County Federated Library System
Special Services for the Deaf - TTY machine

S PENNSYLVANIA HISTORICAL & MUSEUM COMMISSION, Old Economy Village Historical Site Museum,* 14th & Church Sts, 15003-2298. SAN 314-2809. Tel: 724-266-4500. FAX: 724-266-7506. *Actg Dir*, Mary Ann Landis
Founded 1805
Library Holdings: Bk Titles 5,000
Subject Interests: 19th Century indust, German lit, Music
Special Collections: Harmony Society (1805-1905), music, papers
Old Economy Village is a historic site (1824-1905) built as the third & last home of the Harmony Society (1785-1905). Seventeen original buildings are open to the public by the Pennsylvania Historical & Museum Commission & are furnished with 16,000 Harmonist-made or Harmonist acquired objects

R TRINITY EPISCOPAL SCHOOL FOR MINISTRY LIBRARY,* 311 11th St, 15003. SAN 371-6937. Tel: 724-266-3838. FAX: 724-266-4617. *Dir*, Dr Robert S Munday; *Asst Dir*, David Mills; *Acq*, Amy O Mason; *ILL*, Jan Bova; Staff 4 (MLS 2, Non-MLS 2)
Founded 1975. Enrl 90; Fac 12
Library Holdings: Bk Vols 63,000; Per Subs 413
Subject Interests: Biblical studies, Theology
Partic in American Theological Library Association; Pittsburgh Regional Libr Consortium

ANDALUSIA

R CHURCH OF THE REDEEMER, King Library, 1065 Bristol Pike, 19020. SAN 314-2817. Tel: 215-639-4387. *Librn*, Dr John S Keefer; Staff 1 (Non-MLS 1)
Founded 1882
2000-2001 Income Parent Institution $3,000. Sal $2,000 (Prof $2,000)
Library Holdings: Bk Titles 12,400
Subject Interests: Classical literature, History, Religion, Science
Special Collections: Key Coll
Restriction: Access at librarian's discretion

ANNVILLE

P ANNVILLE FREE LIBRARY,* 216 E Main St, 17003-1599. SAN 314-2825. Tel: 717-867-1802. FAX: 717-867-5754. Web Site: www.leblibrarysys.org. *Dir*, Dee Kneff
Founded 1941. Pop 12,000; Circ 77,000
Library Holdings: Bk Titles 34,662; Per Subs 98
Subject Interests: Architecture, Art
Function: ILL available
Mem of Lebanon County Library System
Open Mon-Thurs 10-8, Fri & Sat 10-5
Friends of the Library Group

C LEBANON VALLEY COLLEGE, Bishop Library, 17003-0501. SAN 314-2833. Tel: 717-867-6970. FAX: 717-867-6979. Web Site: www.lvc.edu/www/library/index.html. *Dir*, P Robert Paustian; E-Mail: paustian@lvc.edu *ILL, Ref*, Donna L Miller; Tel: 717-867-6972, E-Mail: miller@lvc.edu; *Tec Servs*, Julia L Harvey; Tel: 717-867-6971, E-Mail: harvey@lvc.edu; *Ref, Sy Coordr*, Stanley Furmanak; Tel: 717-867-6973, E-Mail: furmanak@lvc.edu; *Archivist*, Alice Diehl; Tel: 717-867-6982, E-Mail: diehl@lvc.edu; Staff 8 (MLS 4, Non-MLS 4)
Founded 1867. Enrl 2,068; Fac 80; Highest Degree: Master
Jul 1999-Jun 2000 Income $810,510. Mats Exp $407,160, Books $160,000, Per/Ser (Incl. Access Fees) $170,000, Presv $10,160, Micro $25,000, Electronic Ref Mat (Incl. Access Fees) $42,000. Sal $306,550 (Prof $187,400)
Library Holdings: Bk Vols 139,355; Per Subs 720
Subject Interests: Behav sci, Music, Soc sci
Special Collections: Early Iron Industry (C B Montgomery); Pennsylvania German (Hiram Herr Shenk)
Automation Activity & Vendor Info: (Acquisitions) SIRSI; (Cataloging) SIRSI; (Circulation) SIRSI; (OPAC) SIRSI; (Serials) SIRSI
Partic in Associated College Libraries of Central Pennsylvania; Dialog Corporation; OCLC Online Computer Library Center, Inc; PALINET & Union Library Catalogue of Pennsylvania

APOLLO

P APOLLO MEMORIAL LIBRARY,* 219 N Pennsylvania Ave, 15613-1397. SAN 314-2841. Tel: 724-478-4214. FAX: 724-478-1693. E-Mail: apollolibrary@hotmail.com. *Chief Librn*, Paula Mahar; Staff 1 (MLS 1)
Founded 1908. Pop 3,699; Circ 28,000
Library Holdings: Bk Vols 30,000; Per Subs 108
Subject Interests: Genealogy, Local history
Publications: Newsletter (quarterly)
Mem of New Castle County Public Library System
Open (Sept-May) Mon-Thurs 11:30-7, Fri 11:30-3:30, Sat 9-12, (June-Aug) Mon-Thurs 11:30-7, Fri 9-1

ARDMORE

P ARDMORE FREE LIBRARY, 108 Ardmore Ave, 19003-1399. SAN 314-2868. Tel: 610-642-5187. FAX: 610-649-2618. Web Site: ardmorelibrary@lower-merion.lib.pa.us. *Librn*, Peggy Newman; E-Mail: pnewman@lower_merion.libr.pa.us
Founded 1899. Pop 68,000; Circ 85,000
Library Holdings: Bk Titles 36,000; Per Subs 62
Subject Interests: Black studies
Automation Activity & Vendor Info: (Cataloging) Gaylord; (Circulation) Gaylord; (OPAC) Gaylord
Mem of Lower Merion Library System
Open Mon, Tues & Thurs 10-8, Wed 1-8, Fri 10-5 & Sat 10-5

R FIRST PRESBYTERIAN CHURCH, William Faulds Memorial Library, 5 W Montgomery Ave, 19003. SAN 314-2876. Tel: 610-642-6650. FAX: 610-645-0517. *Librn*, Connie Hoelscher; Staff 1 (MLS 1)
Founded 1962
Library Holdings: Bk Titles 3,000
Subject Interests: Behav sci, Relig studies, Soc sci
Separate children's library established for weekday pre-school - 2000 children's books collected from classrooms

P LOWER MERION LIBRARY SYSTEM,* 75 E Lancaster Ave, 19003-2388. SAN 314-3589. Tel: 610-645-6110. FAX: 610-649-8835. *Dir*, Maryam Phillips; E-Mail: mphillip@lowermenon.lib.pa.us; *Ch Servs, YA Servs*, Margery Hall; *Ref*, Patricia Rayfield; *Coll Develop*, Christine Stedde; Staff 14 (MLS 14)
Founded 1935. Pop 58,003; Circ 1,330,166
Library Holdings: Bk Vols 347,280; Bk Titles 177,122; Per Subs 350
Subject Interests: Architecture, Art, Horticulture, Local history, Music
Member Libraries: Ardmore Free Library; Bala-Cynwyd Library; Belmont Hills Public Library; Gladwyne Free Library; Ludington Public Library; Penn Wynne Library

ASHLAND

P ASHLAND PUBLIC LIBRARY, 1229 Center St, 17921-1207. SAN 314-2884. Tel: 570-875-3175. FAX: 570-875-2699. E-Mail: ash@iu29.schiu.k12.pa.us. *Librn*, Ann Helwig
Pop 20,212; Circ 18,006
Library Holdings: Bk Vols 36,000; Per Subs 50
Mem of Pottsville Free Public Library
Open Mon, Tues & Thurs 8:30-7, Wed 8:30-12, Fri 8:30-5

ASTON

P ASTON PUBLIC LIBRARY, 257 Concord Rd, 19014. SAN 320-8494. Tel: 610-494-5877. FAX: 610-494-1314. E-Mail: aston@delco.lib.pa.us. *Dir*, Agatha A Lyons; Staff 7 (MLS 1, Non-MLS 6)

Pop 15,080
Library Holdings: Bk Vols 25,000; Per Subs 60
Mem of Delaware County Library System
Friends of the Library Group

NEUMANN COLLEGE LIBRARY, One Neumann Dr, 19014-1297. SAN 325-2841. Tel: 610-558-5545. FAX: 610-459-1370. E-Mail: fergusof@neumann.edu. Web Site: www.neumann.edu. *Dir*, Frank Ferguson; *ILL*, Barbara Selletti; *Tech Servs*, Virginia Blair; *Reader Servs*, Jennifer Suder; *Acq*, Ann Gardner; *AV*, Nick Repino; Staff 6 (MLS 4, Non-MLS 2)
Founded 1965. Enrl 1,700; Fac 90; Highest Degree: Master
Library Holdings: Bk Vols 96,000; Per Subs 1,000
Subject Interests: Liberal arts, Nursing, Pastoral counseling
Special Collections: Betty Neuman Archives; Curriculum, Rare bks; Delaware County Tax Records; Franciscan Coll
Database Vendor: DRA, Ebsco - EbscoHost, Lexis-Nexis, OCLC - First Search, OVID Technologies
Partic in Consortium For Health Information & Library Services; OCLC Online Computer Library Center, Inc; PALINET & Union Library Catalogue of Pennsylvania; Southeastern Pa Consortium for Higher Educ; Tri-State College Library Cooperative (TCLC)

ATGLEN

P ATGLEN READING CENTER,* 413 Valley Ave, PO Box 190, 19310-0190. SAN 314-2906. Tel: 610-593-6848. FAX: 610-593-7231. *Dir*, Bridget Weaver
Pop 740; Circ 3,540
Library Holdings: Bk Vols 6,000; Per Subs 30
Mem of Chester County Library
Open Mon-Thurs 3-7, Fri 12-4 & Sat 10-12

ATHENS

P SPALDING MEMORIAL LIBRARY,* 724 S Main St, 18810-1010. SAN 314-2914. Tel: 717-888-7117. FAX: 717-882-9202. *Librn*, Janet Gigee; *Asst Librn*, Diane Sidey
Founded 1897. Pop 8,795; Circ 54,354
Library Holdings: Bk Vols 28,000; Per Subs 80
Subject Interests: County hist for genealogy, State hist for genealogy
Automation Activity & Vendor Info: (Cataloging) Sagebrush Corporation; (Circulation) Sagebrush Corporation
Friends of the Library Group

AVALON

P AVALON PUBLIC LIBRARY, 640 California Ave, 15202. SAN 314-2922. Tel: 412-761-2288. FAX: 412-761-7745. E-Mail: avalon@einetwork.net. *Librn*, Maria Baker; E-Mail: bakerm@einetwork.net
Founded 1940. Pop 5,784; Circ 7,700
Jan 1999-Dec 1999 Income $20,175, State $5,739, County $14,436. Mats Exp $6,800, Books $6,000, Per/Ser (Incl. Access Fees) $800
Library Holdings: Bk Vols 14,850; Per Subs 30
Automation Activity & Vendor Info: (Cataloging) DRA
Partic in Allegheny County Libr Asn

AVELLA

P AVELLA AREA PUBLIC LIBRARY, PO Box 547, 15312-0547. SAN 376-5725. Tel: 724-587-5688. FAX: 724-587-3432. E-Mail: aaplib@hky.com. *Dir*, Carolyn McGill. Subject Specialists: *Children's literature*, Carolyn McGill
Library Holdings: Bk Vols 9,000; Per Subs 12
Mem of Washington County Libr Syst
Open Mon, Tues & Thurs 2-8, Wed 9-8 & Sat 9-3

AVONDALE

S AMERICAN MUSHROOM INSTITUTE LIBRARY, 1284 Gap Newport Pike, 19311. SAN 375-9075. Tel: 610-268-7483. FAX: 612-268-8015. *Pres*, Laura Phelps; *Librn*, Sara Manning
Library Holdings: Bk Vols 300
Restriction: Members only

AVONMORE

P AVONMORE PUBLIC LIBRARY,* 619 Allegheny Ave, 15618. SAN 314-2930. Tel: 724-697-4828. *Librn*, Sallie Corridoni
Pop 3,248
Library Holdings: Bk Vols 5,210
Mem of Pittsburgh Libr District
Open Wed 10-1 & Thurs 5-7

BADEN

P BADEN MEMORIAL LIBRARY,* 385 State St, 15005-1946. SAN 314-2949. Tel: 724-869-3960. FAX: 724-869-8816. *Librn*, Janet Zajackowski
Founded 1941. Pop 5,299; Circ 27,317
Library Holdings: Bk Vols 25,000; Per Subs 48
Mem of Beaver County Federated Library System
Open Mon, Wed & Thurs 1-8, Tues 12-8 & Sat 10-4

BALA-CYNWYD

P BALA-CYNWYD LIBRARY,* Old Lancaster Rd & N Highland Ave, 19004-3095. SAN 314-2957. Tel: 610-664-1196. FAX: 610-664-5534. Web Site: www.lower-merion.lib.pa.us. *Librn*, Jean Knapp; *Circ*, Carol Cobaugh
Founded 1915. Pop 14,538; Circ 369,980
Library Holdings: Bk Vols 89,533; Per Subs 186
Subject Interests: Judaica, Music
Special Collections: Children's Historical Book Coll; Judaica Coll; Music Coll, bks, cassettes, scores, compact discs
Mem of Lower Merion Library System
Friends of the Library Group

P BELMONT HILLS PUBLIC LIBRARY,* 120 Mary Watersford Rd, 19004. SAN 314-2965. Tel: 610-664-8427. FAX: 610-664-8427. *Librn*, Pat Rayfield
Founded 1935. Circ 61,498
Library Holdings: Bk Vols 22,200
Automation Activity & Vendor Info: (Circulation) Inlex
Mem of Lower Merion Library System

S PHILADELPHIA ASSOCIATION FOR PSYCHOANALYSIS, Louis S Kaplan Memorial Library, 15 St Asaph's Rd, 19004. SAN 314-2973. Tel: 610-667-8719. FAX: 610-667-8719. *Librn*, Zoe Friedberg
Library Holdings: Bk Vols 3,500; Per Subs 12
Subject Interests: Psychoanalysis

BANGOR

P BANGOR PUBLIC LIBRARY, 39 S Main St, 18013-2690. SAN 314-2981. Tel: 610-588-4136. FAX: 610-588-1931. E-Mail: bngrpublib@fast.net. Web Site: www.bangorlibrary.org. *Dir*, Barbara Evinger; Staff 1 (Non-MLS 1)
Founded 1922. Circ 24,982
Jul 1999-Jun 2000 Income $131,731. Mats Exp $37,707. Sal $32,659
Library Holdings: Bk Vols 26,893; Per Subs 47
Subject Interests: Local history
Special Collections: Local Newspaper, flm
Automation Activity & Vendor Info: (Circulation) Follett
Publications: Footnotes (quarterly)
Open Mon & Wed 1-8, Tues & Thurs 10-8, Fri 1-5, Sat 12-3
Friends of the Library Group

BEAVER

P BEAVER AREA MEMORIAL LIBRARY, 100 College Ave, 15009-2794. SAN 314-3015. Tel: 724-775-1132. FAX: 724-775-6982. *Librn*, Diane Wakefield; *Asst Librn*, Mary Jane Ulmer; *Ch Servs*, Deborah Yovanovic
Founded 1948. Pop 18,833; Circ 150,874
Jan 1999-Dec 1999 Income $274,724, State $41,608, City $29,250, County $14,300, Locally Generated Income $36,646, Other $152,920. Mats Exp $37,879, Books $29,665, Per/Ser (Incl. Access Fees) $3,099, AV Equip $3,937, Electronic Ref Mat (Incl. Access Fees) $1,178. Sal $146,764
Library Holdings: Bk Vols 41,000; Per Subs 100
Automation Activity & Vendor Info: (Circulation) Innovative Interfaces Inc.
Mem of Beaver County Federated Library System
Friends of the Library Group

GL BEAVER COUNTY LAW LIBRARY, Court House, 810 Third St, 15009. SAN 314-3023. Tel: 724-728-3934, Ext 361. FAX: 724-728-4133. Web Site: www.co.beaver.pa.us/lawlibrary. *Head of Libr*, Bette Sue Dengel; E-Mail: bdengel@co.beaver.pa.us; Staff 2 (MLS 1, Non-MLS 1)
Founded 1972
Jan 2000-Dec 2000 Income (Main Library Only) $153,000, County $150,000, Locally Generated Income $3,000. Mats Exp $90,000, Books $84,500, Per/Ser (Incl. Access Fees) $1,500, Electronic Ref Mat (Incl. Access Fees) $4,000. Sal $37,000 (Prof $36,000)
Library Holdings: Bk Vols 26,600; Bk Titles 900; Per Subs 80
Subject Interests: Pa legal practice
Special Collections: Local court opinions & ordinances
Restriction: Circulation limited
Function: ILL by photocopy only

S BEAVER COUNTY TIMES LIBRARY, 400 Fair Ave, 15009. SAN 314-3031. Tel: 724-775-3201. FAX: 724-775-4180. Web Site: www.timesonline.com. *Librn*, Linda B DiSante; E-Mail: ldisante@

calkinsnewspapers.com; *Asst Librn*, Gladys Wallace
Special Collections: Beaver County Times on microfilm from 1900 to present; Clip files from 1955; News Tribune on microfilm from 1900 to 1975

M THE MEDICAL CENTER, BEAVER PA, Health Sciences Library, 1000 Dutch Ridge Rd, 15009. SAN 326-3827. Tel: 724-773-1941. FAX: 724-728-7429. *ILL*, Bonita Lombardo; Staff 2 (MLS 1, Non-MLS 1)
Library Holdings: Bk Titles 4,200; Per Subs 195
Subject Interests: Internal medicine, Nursing, Oncology
Partic in Basic Health Sciences Library Network

BEAVER FALLS

P CARNEGIE FREE LIBRARY, 1301 Seventh Ave, 15010-4219. SAN 314-304X. Tel: 724-846-4340. FAX: 724-846-0370. *Acq, Dir*, Linda Focer; *Head Tech Servs*, Sam Allen; E-Mail: sallen_45@yahoo.com; Staff 3 (MLS 2, Non-MLS 1)
Founded 1902. Pop 21,259; Circ 79,900
Jan 2000-Dec 2000 Income $240,000, State $62,000, City $2,000, County $15,000, Locally Generated Income $37,000, Parent Institution $75,000, Other $49,000. Mats Exp $32,000, Books $24,500, Per/Ser (Incl. Access Fees) $5,000. Sal $140,000 (Prof $35,000)
Library Holdings: Bk Vols 50,000; Per Subs 204
Subject Interests: Genealogy, Pennsylvania
Special Collections: Resource & Research Center for Local History
Automation Activity & Vendor Info: (Circulation) Innovative Interfaces Inc.; (OPAC) Innovative Interfaces Inc.
Database Vendor: Ebsco - EbscoHost, Innovative Interfaces INN - View
Mem of Beaver County Federated Library System

C GENEVA COLLEGE, McCartney Library, 3200 College Ave, 15010-3599. SAN 358-2930. Tel: 724-847-6563. Interlibrary Loan Service Tel: 724-847-6740. Circulation Tel: 724-847-6685. Reference Tel: 724-847-6764. FAX: 724-847-6687. Web Site: www.geneva.edu. *Dir*, Gerald D Moran; Tel: 724-847-6692, E-Mail: gmoran@geneva.edu; *Librn, Syst Coordr*, John Delivuk; *Acq, Per*, Kevin Danielson; Tel: 724-847-6691, E-Mail: kdaniels@geneva.edu; *Bibliog Instr, ILL, Ref*, John Allen Shearer, Jr; *Cat*, Marilyn VanDyke; *Circ*, Sharon Myers; *Media Spec*, David Rhoades; *Per*, R Triance; Staff 7 (MLS 5, Non-MLS 2)
Founded 1931. Enrl 2,100; Fac 131; Highest Degree: Master
Jun 1999-May 2000 Income (Main Library and Branch Library) $904,735, Locally Generated Income $12,000, Parent Institution $810,022, Other $82,713. Mats Exp $238,205, Books $94,537, Per/Ser (Incl. Access Fees) $143,668, Presv $14,686, Manuscripts & Archives $764. (Prof $266,024)
Library Holdings: Bk Vols 163,632; Bk Titles 160,123; Per Subs 915
Special Collections: Early American Imprints, microcard, microfiche; Library of American Civilization, microfiche; Personal Library & Papers of Dr Clarence Macartney (Macartney Coll); Reformed Presbyterian Church (Covenanter Coll); Shaw Shoemaker Coll, microfiche
Database Vendor: OCLC - First Search
Publications: McCartney Library Views; Miscellaneous Pathfinders; The Tower
Partic in OCLC Online Computer Library Center, Inc; PALINET & Union Library Catalogue of Pennsylvania
Friends of the Library Group
Departmental Libraries:
BROOKS EDUCATIONAL CURRICULUM CENTER *Librn*, Constance Braun
Subject Interests: Educ textbooks for primary teaching, Educ textbooks for secondary teaching
CAREER GUIDANCE CENTER *Dir*, Ann Bender
Subject Interests: Career counseling, Careers
CROSS SCIENCE CENTER
Subject Interests: Biology, Chemistry, Computers, Mathematics, Physics

BEAVERDALE

P BEAVERDALE COMMUNITY LIBRARY,* 506 Jefferson Ave, PO Box 81, 15921-9998. SAN 314-3058. Tel: 814-487-7742. FAX: 814-487-4886. E-Mail: beaverpl@aol.com. *Librn*, Bernadette Headrick
Founded 1965. Pop 4,000; Circ 8,860
1997-1998 Income $32,070, Other $7,482. Mats Exp $7,482. Sal $9,988
Library Holdings: Bk Titles 10,701; Per Subs 19
Subject Interests: History
Special Collections: Jay Krantzler Memorial Shelf
Mem of Cambria County Library System & District Center
Open Mon, Tues, Wed, Fri 9-12 & 4-7, Thurs 4-7, Sat 9-12

BEDFORD

P BEDFORD COUNTY LIBRARY, 240 S Wood St, 15522. SAN 314-3066. Tel: 814-623-5010. E-Mail: rock@bedford.k12.pa.us. Web Site: www.bedford.net/library. *Librn*, Leslie Rock; *Bkmobile Coordr*, Sue Falvey; E-Mail: library@bedford.k12.pa.us; *Ch Servs*, Rebecca Claar; E-Mail: bclarr@hotmail.com; Staff 6 (MLS 1, Non-MLS 5)
Founded 1944. Pop 47,728; Circ 102,422
Jan 2000-Dec 2000 Income $260,000, State $135,000, County $73,000, Other $52,000. Mats Exp $50,850, Books $43,000, Per/Ser (Incl. Access Fees) $2,850. Sal $139,000 (Prof $36,000)
Library Holdings: Bk Vols 35,000; Per Subs 65
Automation Activity & Vendor Info: (Cataloging) Follett
Friends of the Library Group
Bookmobiles: 1

S PIONEER HISTORICAL SOCIETY OF BEDFORD COUNTY INC, Pioneer Historical Library, 242 E John St, 15522-1750. SAN 374-4930. Tel: 814-623-2011. FAX: 814-623-2011. E-Mail: history@bedford.net. *Librn*, Kay Williams; Staff 2 (Non-MLS 2)

BELLE VERNON

P BELLE VERNON PUBLIC LIBRARY,* 505 Speer St, 15012-1540. SAN 314-3074. Tel: 724-929-6642. FAX: 724-929-4197. E-Mail: bvlibrary@dp.net. Web Site: www.dp.net/~bulibrary. *Librn*, Bonnie Egros
Founded 1937. Circ 9,514
Library Holdings: Bk Vols 20,500; Per Subs 20
Mem of Monessen District Libr Ctr
Open Mon, Tues & Thurs 12-7, Fri 10-4

BELLEFONTE

GL CENTRE COUNTY LAW LIBRARY,* Court House, 3rd flr, 16823. SAN 314-3082. Tel: 814-355-6754. FAX: 814-355-6707. *Dir*, Barbara Gallo; E-Mail: bggallo@centreco.centre.pa.us
Library Holdings: Bk Vols 20,000; Per Subs 15

P CENTRE COUNTY LIBRARY & HISTORICAL MUSEUM & CENTRAL PENNSYLVANIA DISTRICT LIBRARY CENTER,* 203 N Allegheny St, 16823-1691. SAN 358-3058. Tel: 814-355-1516. Interlibrary Loan Service FAX: 814-355-0334. *Ad Servs*, Charlene Brungord; *Ch Servs, YA Servs*, Charlene Brungard; *Media Spec*, Judy Spangler; Staff 5 (MLS 5)
Founded 1939. Circ 325,966
Library Holdings: Bk Vols 125,308; Bk Titles 88,000; Per Subs 157
Subject Interests: History
Special Collections: County Documents; Genealogy (Spangler Coll)
Publications: Bookworm Bugle (newsletter)
Partic in Interlibrary Delivery Service of Pennsylvania; OCLC Online Computer Library Center, Inc; Pittsburgh Regional Libr Consortium
Branches: 2
AARONSBURG BRANCH, PO Box 70, Aaronsburg, 16820. SAN 358-3082. Tel: 814-349-5328. FAX: 814-349-5288. *Librn*, Janet VanGilder
Library Holdings: Bk Vols 15,896; Bk Titles 14,900
HOLT MEMORIAL, 200 Shady Lane, Philipsburg, 16866. SAN 358-3112. Tel: 814-342-1987. FAX: 814-342-0530. *Librn*, Merry Jo Van Cleve
Library Holdings: Bk Vols 16,251; Bk Titles 14,500
Bookmobiles: 1

BELLEVUE

P ANDREW BAYNE MEMORIAL LIBRARY,* 34 N Balph Ave, 15202-3297. SAN 314-3104. Tel: 412-766-7447. FAX: 412-766-3620. *Librn*, Suzanne Clark
Founded 1927. Pop 9,800; Circ 27,559
Library Holdings: Bk Vols 24,764; Per Subs 30
Subject Interests: Bellevue genealogy, Bellevue hist
Partic in Pittsburgh Regional Libr Consortium
Open Mon & Wed 12-8, Tues & Thurs 12-6 & Fri & Sat 12-5

BELLWOOD

P BELLWOOD-ANTIS PUBLIC LIBRARY, 526 Main St, 16617-1910. SAN 314-3112. Tel: 814-742-8234. FAX: 814-742-8235. E-Mail: hab@tome.bapl.lib.pa.us. Web Site: www.tome.bapl.lib.pa.us. *Librn*, Hazel A Bilka
Founded 1965. Pop 8,152; Circ 41,371
1999-2000 Income $89,636, State $15,977, Federal $2,603. Mats Exp $31,221, Books $20,009, Per/Ser (Incl. Access Fees) $1,889, AV Equip $400. Sal $61,273
Library Holdings: Bk Vols 50,263; Per Subs 75
Mem of Altoona District Pub Libr Syst; Blair County Library System

BENTLEYVILLE

P BENTLEYVILLE PUBLIC LIBRARY,* 931 Main St, 15314-1119. SAN 314-3120. Tel: 724-239-5122. FAX: 724-239-5122. E-Mail: bentpub@nauticom.net. Web Site: www.nauticom.net/www/bentpub. *Dir Libr Serv*, Denise Renee Brna; Fax: 724-239-5196; Staff 3 (MLS 1, Non-MLS 2)
Founded 1941. Pop 9,843; Circ 38,000
Library Holdings: Bk Titles 22,000; Per Subs 18
Database Vendor: Ebsco - EbscoHost
Function: ILL available
Open Mon & Wed 1-8, Tues & Thurs 12-8, Fri 10-5, Sat 9-5

BERWICK

P BERWICK PUBLIC LIBRARY,* 205 Chestnut St, 18603. SAN 314-3139. Tel: 570-752-2241. FAX: 570-752-8893. E-Mail: berlibr@postoffice.ptd.net. Web Site: townhall.bafn.org/bplib/. *Dir Libr Serv*, Rick Miller; *Circ*, Alice Zaikoski; Staff 10 (MLS 1, Non-MLS 9)
Founded 1916. Pop 15,277
1997-1998 Income $100,000
Library Holdings: Bk Vols 30,000; Per Subs 85
Subject Interests: Pa hist
Special Collections: Landmark Audio Book Leasing; McNaughton Book Leasing, lg print
Mem of N Cent Libr Dist
Friends of the Library Group

BERWYN

P EASTTOWN LIBRARY & INFORMATION CENTER, 720 First Ave, 19312-1769. SAN 314-3147. Tel: 610-644-0138. FAX: 610-251-9739. Web Site: www.ccls.org/othlibs/etown.htm. *Dir*, Peggy Mahan; E-Mail: pmahan@ccls.org; *Asst Dir, Ref*, Ann Plambeck; *Ch Servs*, Anne Houle; Staff 26 (MLS 3, Non-MLS 23)
Founded 1905. Pop 10,000; Circ 146,190
Jan 1999-Dec 1999 Income $528,132, State $37,060, City $356,587, County $40,235, Locally Generated Income $94,250. Mats Exp $520,459, Books $74,051, Per/Ser (Incl. Access Fees) $6,903, AV Equip $15,221. Sal $333,671
Library Holdings: Bk Vols 47,176; Per Subs 150
Subject Interests: Chester county, Pa railroad
Automation Activity & Vendor Info: (Acquisitions) Innovative Interfaces Inc.; (Cataloging) Innovative Interfaces Inc.; (Circulation) Innovative Interfaces Inc.; (OPAC) Innovative Interfaces Inc.
Database Vendor: Ebsco - EbscoHost, Innovative Interfaces INN - View
Publications: Reach (Newsletter)
Mem of Chester County Library
Friends of the Library Group

BESSEMER

P FRANK D CAMPBELL MEMORIAL LIBRARY, 15 S Main St, 16112-2535. (Mail add: PO Box 666, 16112-0666), SAN 314-3155. Tel: 724-667-7939. FAX: 724-667-0898. E-Mail: read-books@hotmail.com. *Librn*, Jean Workman; Staff 1 (Non-MLS 1)
Founded 1920. Pop 8,000
1999-2000 Income $27,595, State $4,037, City $3,812, County $16,685, Locally Generated Income $3,061. Mats Exp $4,193, Books $3,846, Per/Ser (Incl. Access Fees) $167, Electronic Ref Mat (Incl. Access Fees) $180. Sal $4,030
Library Holdings: Bk Vols 10,635; Per Subs 25

BETHEL

P BETHEL-TULPEHOCKEN PUBLIC LIBRARY,* 8601 Lancaster Ave, 19507. SAN 314-3163. Tel: 717-933-4060. FAX: 717-933-4060. E-Mail: library@mbcomp.com. Web Site: www.mbcomp.com/library. *Dir*, Shirley D Behney; *Asst Librn*, Daphne Meyer
Founded 1963. Pop 6,519
Library Holdings: Bk Titles 13,000; Per Subs 60
Subject Interests: Behav sci, Education, Environmental studies, Local history, Soc sci
Automation Activity & Vendor Info: (Cataloging) epixtech, inc.; (Circulation) epixtech, inc.
Mem of Berks County Libr Syst

BETHEL PARK

P BETHEL PARK PUBLIC LIBRARY,* 5100 W Library Ave, 15102-2790. SAN 314-3171. Tel: 412-835-2207. FAX: 412-835-9360. Web Site: www.clpgh.org/ein/bethpark/. *YA Servs*, Margaret Butzler; *Tech Servs*, Mary Roellinger; *Ch Servs*, Diane Ornato; *Syst Coordr*, Fayth Groesch; Staff 4 (MLS 4)
Founded 1955. Pop 34,000; Circ 246,201
Library Holdings: Bk Vols 123,850; Bk Titles 117,959; Per Subs 210
Subject Interests: Adult care homes, Adult day care ctrs, Am railroad hist, Bus servs, Career, Employment, Investment servs, Local history, Pre-school-daycare, Teacher res ctr
Special Collections: Fed
Friends of the Library Group

R CHRIST UNITED METHODIST CHURCH LIBRARY, 44 Highland Rd, 15102. SAN 314-318X. Tel: 412-835-6621. FAX: 412-835-9130.
Founded 1960
Library Holdings: Bk Vols 3,600

BETHLEHEM

P BETHLEHEM AREA PUBLIC LIBRARY, 11 W Church St, 18018. SAN 358-3147. Tel: 610-867-3761. Circulation Tel: 610-867-3761, Ext 203. Reference Tel: 610-867-3761, Ext 209. FAX: 610-867-2767. Web Site: www.bapl.org. *Exec Dir*, Jack M Berk; E-Mail: jberk@bapl.org; *Automation Syst Coordr*, Karen Gartner; *Publ Servs*, Jane Gill; *Ch Servs*, Elizabeth Rosania; *AV*, Loris Baker; *Tech Servs*, Dan Solove; *ILL*, Justina Rossnagle; *Admin Dir*, Mary S Kupferschmid; Tel: 610-867-3761, Ext 212, E-Mail: mkupferschmid@bapl.org; *Selection of Gen Ref Mat*, Donna Horvath; Staff 58 (MLS 13, Non-MLS 45)
Founded 1901. Pop 108,114; Circ 675,054
Jan 1999-Dec 1999 Income (Main Library and Branch Library) $2,590,635, State $324,137, City $2,022,117, Other $244,381. Mats Exp $247,564. Sal $1,519,998
Library Holdings: Bk Vols 188,426; Bk Titles 140,866; Per Subs 400
Special Collections: Literacy; Local History; Spanish
Automation Activity & Vendor Info: (Cataloging) epixtech, inc.; (Circulation) epixtech, inc.; (OPAC) epixtech, inc.
Database Vendor: Ebsco - EbscoHost, epixtech, inc.
Partic in Access Pa; PALINET & Union Library Catalogue of Pennsylvania
Friends of the Library Group
Branches: 1
SOUTH SIDE, 400 Webster St, 18015. SAN 358-3171. Tel: 610-867-7852. FAX: 610-867-9821. Web Site: www.bapl.org. *Branch Mgr*, Brenda Grow; E-Mail: bgrow@bapl.org; Staff 4 (Non-MLS 4)
Special Collections: Literacy; Spanish
Database Vendor: Ebsco - EbscoHost, epixtech, inc.
Friends of the Library Group
Bookmobiles: 1

BETHLEHEM STEEL CORP

L BERNARD D BROEKER LAW LIBRARY, Martin Tower, Rm 2027, 1170 Eighth Ave, 18016-7699. SAN 358-3260. Tel: 610-694-5002. FAX: 610-694-1447. *Librn*, Ethel H Vary
Founded 1954
Library Holdings: Bk Vols 19,000; Per Subs 100
Partic in Am Asn of Law Librs

S RESEARCH LIBRARY - G61, Homer Research Laboratories, 18016-7699. SAN 358-3236. Interlibrary Loan Service Tel: 610-694-6443. FAX: 610-694-1739.
Founded 1970
Library Holdings: Bk Vols 3,000; Per Subs 250
Subject Interests: Beneficiation of ore, Mining of ore, Rolling of final steel products, Sound pollution, Water pollution
Publications: Acquisitions lists (quarterly)

S SCHWAB INFORMATION CENTER, 1170 Eighth Ave, Rm 100, 18016-7699. SAN 358-3201. Tel: 610-694-3325. FAX: 610-694-3290. *Dir*, Marie F Sterlein; E-Mail: sterlein@bethsteel.com
Founded 1949
Library Holdings: Bk Vols 15,100; Per Subs 200
Subject Interests: Allied eng fields, Bus, Econ, Mgt, Steel indust, Steelmaking eng fields
Automation Activity & Vendor Info: (Acquisitions) epixtech, inc.; (Cataloging) epixtech, inc.; (Circulation) epixtech, inc.
Database Vendor: Ebsco - EbscoHost, OCLC - First Search
Publications: Acquisitions List; Audio/Video List, Guide to Library Services, Periodicals List
Partic in Dialog Corporation; Dow Jones News Retrieval; OCLC Online Computer Library Center, Inc

S HISTORIC BETHLEHEM PARTNERSHIP LIBRARY,* 459 Old York Rd, 18018-5830. SAN 327-0947. Tel: 610-691-5300. FAX: 610-882-0460. E-Mail: histbeth4@aol.com. Web Site: www.historicbethlehem.org. *Mgr*, Jan Ballard
Library Holdings: Bk Vols 3,000

C LEHIGH UNIVERSITY INFORMATION RESOURCES, Fairchild-Martindale Library, 8A E Packer Ave, 18015-3170. SAN 358-3295. Tel: 610-758-3025. Interlibrary Loan Service Tel: 610-758-3055. Circulation Tel: 610-758-3030. Reference Tel: 610-758-4357. FAX: 610-758-6524. Web Site: www.lehigh.edu/ir. *Admin Dir*, Susan Cady; Tel: 610-758-4645, E-Mail: sac0@lehigh.edu; *Ref Serv*, Jennifer Heise; Tel: 610-758-3072, E-Mail: jahb@lehigh.edu; *Ref Serv*, Stacey Kimmel; Tel: 610-758-4768, E-Mail: sek2@lehigh.edu; *Business*, William Fincke; Tel: 610-758-3052, E-Mail: wjf0@lehigh.edu; *Circ, ILL*, Gail Kriebel; Tel: 610-758-3028, E-Mail: gpk0@lehigh.edu; *Acq*, Helen Mack; Tel: 610-758-3035, E-Mail: hpm0@lehigh.edu; *Cat*, Judith McNally; Tel: 610-758-3040, E-Mail: njm0@lehigh.edu; *Syst Coordr*, George Motter; Tel: 610-758-4998, E-Mail: gfm2@lehigh.edu; *Info Res*, Bruce Taggart; Tel: 610-758-3025, E-Mail: bmt2@lehigh.edu; *Tech Servs*, Sharon Wiles-Young; Tel: 610-758-3046, E-Mail: slw0@lehigh.edu; *Curator, Spec Coll*, Philip Metzger; Tel: 610-758-5185, E-Mail: pam5@lehigh.edu; *Doc*, Roseann Bowerman; Tel: 610-758-3053, E-Mail: rb04@lehigh.edu; *Instrul Serv*, Elia Schoomer; Tel: 610-758-3058, E-Mail: ens0@lehigh.edu; *Science*, Brian Simboli; Tel: 610-758-5003, E-Mail: brs4@lehigh.edu. Subject Specialists: *Education*, Jean Johnson; *Engineering*, Sharon Siegler; *Humanities*, Kathleen Morrow; *Soc sci*, Roseann Bowerman; Staff 26 (MLS 18, Non-MLS 8)

Founded 1865. Enrl 5,600; Fac 410; Highest Degree: Doctorate
Jul 1999-Jun 2000 Income (Main and Other College/University Libraries) Parent Institution $6,500,000. Mats Exp $3,184,423, Books $582,169, Per/Ser (Incl. Access Fees) $2,097,423, Presv $59,064, AV Equip $30,000, Manuscripts & Archives $13,215, Electronic Ref Mat (Incl. Access Fees) $402,552. Sal $2,260,000 (Prof $1,530,000)
Library Holdings: Bk Vols 1,200,000; Bk Titles 548,000; Per Subs 3,000
Special Collections: Bayer Galleria of Rare Books; Lehigh Coll
Automation Activity & Vendor Info: (Acquisitions) SIRSI; (Circulation) SIRSI; (Media Booking) SIRSI; (OPAC) SIRSI
Database Vendor: OCLC - First Search
Publications: IR Connection (newsletter); Special Collections Flyer
Partic in Interlibrary Delivery Service of Pennsylvania; Lehigh Valley Association Of Independent Colleges, Inc; OCLC Online Computer Library Center, Inc; Pa Academic Librs Connection Coun; PALINET & Union Library Catalogue of Pennsylvania
Combined organization includes computing & telecommunications
Friends of the Library Group
Departmental Libraries:
LINDERMAN LIBRARY, 30 Library Dr, 18015. SAN 358-3325. Tel: 610-758-4506 (Special Collections). Circulation Tel: 610-758-3030. Reference Tel: 610-758-3050. FAX: 610-758-5605.
Subject Interests: Humanities

S MINERALS TECHNOLOGIES, INC, 9 Highland Ave, 18017. SAN 314-4720. Tel: 610-861-3482. FAX: 610-861-3412. *Librn*, A Cynthia Weber; E-Mail: a.cynthia.weber@mineralstech.com; Staff 1 (MLS 1)
Founded 1965
Library Holdings: Bk Vols 3,000; Per Subs 133
Subject Interests: Calcium carbonate, Mineralogy, Refractories
Automation Activity & Vendor Info: (Cataloging) Sydney; (OPAC) Sydney; (Serials) Sydney

R MORAVIAN ARCHIVES, 41 W Locust St, 18018-2757. SAN 314-321X. Tel: 610-866-3255. FAX: 610-866-9210. *Archivist*, Vernon H Nelson; *Archivist*, Dr Albert H Frank; *Archivist*, Dr Lothar Madaheim; Staff 4 (MLS 3, Non-MLS 1)
Library Holdings: Bk Vols 20,000; Per Subs 12
Subject Interests: Moravian Church hist
Restriction: Non-circulating to the public

C MORAVIAN COLLEGE & MORAVIAN THEOLOGICAL SEMINARY, Reeves Library, 1200 Main St, 18018-6650. SAN 314-3228. Tel: 610-861-1541. Interlibrary Loan Service Tel: 610-861-1545. Circulation Tel: 610-861-1544. Reference Tel: 610-861-1543. FAX: 610-861-1577. E-Mail: mejtm02@moravian.edu. Web Site: www.moravian.edu/public/reeves/index.htm. *Coll Develop, Dir*, John Thomas Minor; Tel: 610-861-1540; *Cat, Tech Servs*, Rita Berk; Tel: 610-625-7876, E-Mail: merjb01@moravian.edu; *Per*, Melanie Fiske; Tel: 610-861-1546, E-Mail: memrf01@moravian.edu; *Publ Servs, Ref*, Bonnie Falla; Tel: 610-861-1676, E-Mail: mebjf01@moravian.edu; *Publ Servs, Ref*, Dorothy Glew; Tel: 610-861-1579, E-Mail: medfg01@moravian.edu; *Publ Servs, Ref, Syst Coordr*, Linda LaPointe; Tel: 610-761-1547, E-Mail: melml01@moravian.edu; Staff 6 (MLS 6)
Founded 1742. Enrl 1,310; Fac 92; Highest Degree: Master
Jul 1999-Jun 2000 Income $968,550. Mats Exp $398,100, Books $170,973, Per/Ser (Incl. Access Fees) $194,275, Electronic Ref Mat (Incl. Access Fees) $32,852. Sal $398,840
Library Holdings: Bk Vols 247,841; Per Subs 1,318
Subject Interests: Liberal arts, Seminary, Theology
Special Collections: History of the Moravian Church Coll; Moravian Theological Seminary Coll; Music dept contains the (Herman Adler Coll) of 4500 Baroque & predominantly German Classic & Romantic recordings
Automation Activity & Vendor Info: (Acquisitions) epixtech, inc.; (Cataloging) epixtech, inc.; (Circulation) epixtech, inc.; (Course Reserve) epixtech, inc.; (OPAC) epixtech, inc.; (Serials) epixtech, inc.
Database Vendor: OCLC - First Search
Publications: Reeves Library Guide (1998)
Partic in Lehigh Valley Association Of Independent Colleges, Inc; OCLC Online Computer Library Center, Inc; PALINET & Union Library Catalogue of Pennsylvania; Southeastern Pennsylvania Theological Library Association
Friends of the Library Group

S NATIONAL ASSOCIATION OF COLLEGES & EMPLOYERS, Information Center,* 62 Highland Ave, 18017. SAN 371-019X. Tel: 610-868-1421, Ext 47. Toll Free Tel: 800-544-5272. FAX: 610-868-0208. E-Mail: webmaster@jobweb.org. *Info Specialist*, Sara Jurasits
Library Holdings: Bk Vols 3,000; Per Subs 10
Subject Interests: Career

J NORTHAMPTON COMMUNITY COLLEGE LIBRARY, 3835 Green Pond Rd, 18020-7599. SAN 314-3236. Tel: 610-861-5300. Interlibrary Loan Service Tel: 610-861-5358. Circulation Tel: 610-861-5360. Reference Tel: 610-861-5359. FAX: 610-861-5373. Web Site: www.northampton.edu/office/library. *Dir*, Olga F Conneen; E-Mail: oconneen@northampton.edu; Staff 10 (MLS 5, Non-MLS 5)
Founded 1967. Enrl 3,814; Fac 97; Highest Degree: Associate
Jul 1999-Jun 2000 Mats Exp $206,250, Books $87,500, Per/Ser (Incl. Access Fees) $32,500, Presv $450, Micro $5,000, Other Print Mats $45,000, Electronic Ref Mat (Incl. Access Fees) $35,800
Library Holdings: Bk Vols 62,489; Bk Titles 51,103; Per Subs 376
Subject Interests: Dentistry, Dying, Nursing, Radiologic tech, Veterinary tech
Special Collections: Foundation-Grant Resources
Automation Activity & Vendor Info: (Acquisitions) SIRSI; (Cataloging) SIRSI; (Circulation) SIRSI; (OPAC) SIRSI
Database Vendor: OCLC - First Search
Publications: Faculty & Student Handbooks; Guide to Periodicals
Partic in OCLC Online Computer Library Center, Inc; PALINET & Union Library Catalogue of Pennsylvania; Pennsylvania Community College Library Consortium
Open Mon-Thurs 7:45-10, Fri 7:45-5, Sat 8:30-4:30, Sun 1-8

SAINT LUKE'S HOSPITAL
M W L ESTES JR MEMORIAL LIBRARY, 801 Ostrum St, 18015. SAN 358-335X. Tel: 610-954-3407. Interlibrary Loan Service Tel: 610-954-4652. Reference Tel: 610-954-4650. FAX: 610-954-4651. *Dir*, Maria C Collette; E-Mail: colletm@slhn.org; *Librn*, Diane Frantz; E-Mail: frantzd@slhn.org; Staff 4 (MLS 2, Non-MLS 2)
Founded 1947
Jul 1999-Jun 2000 Income $303,600. Mats Exp $126,736, Books $15,456, Per/Ser (Incl. Access Fees) $74,530, Presv $850, Micro $21,590, AV Equip $4,310, Electronic Ref Mat (Incl. Access Fees) $10,000. Sal $142,700 (Prof $88,200)
Library Holdings: Bk Vols 8,300; Bk Titles 8,000; Per Subs 325
Subject Interests: Allied health, Medicine, Nursing, Surgery
Special Collections: Nursing (Historical Coll)
Database Vendor: OVID Technologies
Partic in Basic Health Sciences Library Network; Cooperating Hospital Libraries Of The Lehigh Valley Area; Greater NE Regional Med Libr Program

R UNITED CHURCH OF CHRIST LIBRARY, 75 E Market St, 18018. SAN 314-3201. Tel: 610-865-6565. FAX: 610-865-9128.
Library Holdings: Bk Vols 2,500

S URBAN RESEARCH & DEVELOPMENT CORP LIBRARY,* 28 Bethlehem Plaza, 18018. SAN 314-3244. Tel: 610-865-0701. FAX: 610-868-7613. *Pres*, Martin C Gilchrist
Founded 1968
Library Holdings: Bk Titles 3,500; Per Subs 25
Subject Interests: Architecture, Art, Behav sci, Econ, Engineering, Geography, Graphic design, Landscape architecture, Regional planning, Soc sci, Urban planning
Restriction: Non-circulating to the public

BIRD-IN-HAND

S CARRIAGE MUSEUM OF AMERICA LIBRARY, (CMA), PO Box 417, 17505. SAN 372-7823. Tel: 717-656-7019. FAX: 717-656-6251. Web Site: www.carriagemuseumlibrary.org. *Librn*, Susan Green
Founded 1978
Jan 2000-Dec 2000 Income $60,000. Mats Exp $40,500, Books $300, Presv $40,000, Micro $200
Library Holdings: Bk Titles 1,000
Subject Interests: Horses
Special Collections: Ken Sowles Coll; Paul Downing Coll; Richard B Harrington Coll; Thomas Ryder Coll
Restriction: By appointment only
Friends of the Library Group

BIRDSBORO

P BIRDSBORO COMMUNITY LIBRARY,* 105 S Furnace St, 19508-2340. SAN 314-3252. Tel: 610-582-5666. FAX: 610-582-6826. E-Mail: birdpl@ptd.net. *Librn*, Susan Shipe
Pop 6,519
Jan 1997-Dec 1998 Income $57,500. Mats Exp $8,000. Sal $25,300 (Prof $15,800)
Library Holdings: Bk Vols 15,000; Per Subs 30
Partic in Berks County Public Libraries
Open Mon 10-1 & 6-8:30, Wed & Fri 10-1, Tues & Thurs 1-8:30, Sat 10-1:30

S CROMPTON & KNOWLES COLORS INC, Gibraltar Library,* 2529 Main St, 19508. (Mail add: PO Box 341, 19603-0341), SAN 310-1517. Tel: 610-582-8765. FAX: 610-404-4059. *In Charge*, Florence Sheehan
Founded 1973
Library Holdings: Bk Vols 1,500; Per Subs 30
Special Collections: Literature of Dyes & Dyeing; Organic Chemistry Coll
Mem of Berks County Libr Syst
Open Mon-Fri 8-5

LACK LICK

BURRELL TOWNSHIP LIBRARY,* Park Dr, PO Box 476, 15716. SAN 324-3702. Tel: 724-248-7122. FAX: 724-248-7122. *Librn*, Annette Bondra
Founded 1977. Pop 3,669
Library Holdings: Bk Titles 17,694; Per Subs 30
Open Mon-Fri 2-8 & Sat 10-3

LAIRSVILLE

BLAIRSVILLE PUBLIC LIBRARY,* 113 N Walnut St, 15717-1348. SAN 314-3260. Tel: 724-459-6077. FAX: 724-459-6097. E-Mail: blairspl@aol.com. *Librn*, Joni Melnick
Pop 3,595; Circ 75,000
Library Holdings: Bk Vols 26,000; Per Subs 52
Open Mon & Thurs 1:30-8, Tues & Fri 1:30-5, Wed 10-2 & Sat 1-4

EDUCATION AMERICA, VALE Technical Institute Library, 135 W Market St, 15717. SAN 314-3279. Tel: 724-459-9500. FAX: 412-459-6499. *Librn*, Louisa Fordyce; E-Mail: lfordyce@hotmail.com
Founded 1946. Enrl 250; Fac 22; Highest Degree: Associate
Nov 1998-Oct 1999 Income (Main Library Only) $10,000. Mats Exp $2,300, Books $500, Per/Ser (Incl. Access Fees) $1,000. Sal $20,000
Library Holdings: Bk Vols 1,500; Per Subs 36
Subject Interests: Automotive, Computer applications, Electronics

BLOOMSBURG

P BLOOMSBURG PUBLIC LIBRARY, 225 Market St, 17815-1726. SAN 314-3287. Tel: 570-784-0883. FAX: 570-784-8541. E-Mail: bloompl@sunlink.net. *Dir*, Hal Pratt; *Asst Librn*, Kathleen Taylor; *Ch Servs*, Karen Roszel; Staff 1 (MLS 1)
Founded 1903. Pop 18,408; Circ 120,000
Library Holdings: Bk Titles 30,000; Per Subs 100
Special Collections: Genealogy Coll
Open Mon-Thurs 9-8, Fri 9-5 & Sat 9-1
Friends of the Library Group

C BLOOMSBURG UNIVERSITY OF PENNSYLVANIA, Harvey A Andruss Library, 400 E Second St, 17815-1301. SAN 314-3295. Tel: 570-389-4224. Interlibrary Loan Service Tel: 570-389-4218. FAX: 570-389-3066. Interlibrary Loan Service FAX: 570-389-3895. Web Site: www.bloomu.edu/library. *Dir Libr Serv*, John B Pitcher; E-Mail: jpitcher@bloomu.edu; *Business*, Michael J Coffta; *Librn*, Janet Olsen; *Librn*, Anatole Scuan; *Librn*, Nancy S Weyant; *Spec Coll*, Robert A Dunkelberger; *Acq, Coll Develop*, Maria Silva Kuhn; *Cat*, Marilou Z Hinchcliff; *Cat*, Mary Van Atta; *Access Serv*, Stephen R Wiist; *Web Coordr*, William J Frost. Subject Specialists: *Archives*, Robert A Dunkelberger; *Govt docs*, Janet Olsen; *Humanities*, Nancy S Weyant; *Nursing*, Anatole Scuan; *Science*, Anatole Scuan; *Social sci*, Mary Van Atta; Staff 25 (MLS 11, Non-MLS 14)
Founded 1839. Enrl 6,860; Fac 395; Highest Degree: Master
Jul 1999-Jun 2000 Income $2,594,118. Mats Exp $1,166,135, Books $519,577, Per/Ser (Incl. Access Fees) $463,848, Presv $20,461, Micro $27,807, Electronic Ref Mat (Incl. Access Fees) $134,442. Sal $1,098,145 (Prof $697,538)
Library Holdings: Bk Vols 408,647; Bk Titles 380,949; Per Subs 1,709
Subject Interests: Children's literature
Special Collections: Art Exhibit Catalogs; Bloomsburg University Archives; Covered Bridges Newbery & Caldecott Awards (Elinor R Keefer Coll)
Automation Activity & Vendor Info: (Acquisitions) Endeavor; (Cataloging) Endeavor; (Circulation) Endeavor; (Course Reserve) Endeavor; (Media Booking) Endeavor; (OPAC) Endeavor; (Serials) Endeavor
Database Vendor: Dialog, Ebsco - EbscoHost, Lexis-Nexis, OCLC - First Search, ProQuest, Silverplatter Information Inc.
Mem of Keystone Libr Network
Partic in Interlibrary Delivery Service of Pennsylvania; OCLC Online Computer Library Center, Inc; PALCI; PALINET & Union Library Catalogue of Pennsylvania; Susquehanna Library Cooperative
Friends of the Library Group

S COLUMBIA COUNTY HISTORICAL & GENEALOGICAL SOCIETY LIBRARY, 225 Market St, PO Box 360, 17815-0360. SAN 314-3309. Tel: 570-784-1600. Web Site: rootsweb.com/~pacolumb/cchome.htm, www.colcohist-gensoc.org. *Exec Dir*, Bonnie L Farver
Founded 1914
Library Holdings: Bk Titles 1,700
Subject Interests: Columbia County, Genealogy, Local history, Material culture
Publications: historical leaflets; monographs; The Columbian
Restriction: Non-circulating to the public
Open: Tues & Fri 9-3, Thurs 9-7:30 & Sat 9-12:30

P COLUMBIA COUNTY TRAVELING LIBRARY, 15 Perry Ave, 17815. SAN 320-8125. Tel: 717-387-8782. *Librn*, Dorothy C Coady
Founded 1941
Library Holdings: Bk Vols 18,614
Friends of the Library Group
Bookmobiles: 1

BLOSSBURG

P BLOSSBURG MEMORIAL LIBRARY,* 307 Main St, 16912. SAN 314-3317. Tel: 570-638-2197. FAX: 570-638-2197. *Librn*, Sharon Thomas
Pop 10,321; Circ 23,034
Library Holdings: Bk Vols 20,727; Per Subs 57
Mem of James V Brown Library Of Williamsport & Lycoming County; Potter-Tioga Library System
Open Mon-Thurs 1-8, Fri 1-5

BLUE BELL

J MONTGOMERY COUNTY COMMUNITY COLLEGE, Learning Resources Center, 340 DeKalb Pike, PO Box 440, 19422-0796. SAN 314-3333. Tel: 215-641-6300. FAX: 215-619-7182. Web Site: www.mc3.edu/peopplac/lib/lrc2.htm#bot. *Dir, Tech Servs*, Diane Lovelace; *ILL*, Janet Perry; *AV*, Barbara Koeller; *Cat*, Shelby A Martin; *Ref*, Merry Rosenberger; *Electronic Resources, Publ Servs*, Amy Gunn; Staff 9 (MLS 9)
Founded 1966. Enrl 9,500; Fac 153
Library Holdings: Bk Vols 95,000; Per Subs 409
Special Collections: College Archives
Partic in OCLC Online Computer Library Center, Inc; PALINET & Union Library Catalogue of Pennsylvania; Pennsylvania Community College Library Consortium; Tri-State College Library Cooperative (TCLC)

R REFORM EPISCOPAL, (Formerly Philadelphia Theological Seminary), Fred C Kuehner Memorial Library, 826 Second Ave, 19422. SAN 314-9919. Tel: 610-292-9852. FAX: 610-292-9853. E-Mail: library@ptsofrec.edu. *In Charge*, Rollin J Blackburn
Founded 1886
Library Holdings: Bk Vols 23,000
Subject Interests: British church hist, Liturgy, Puritans, Reformed Episcopal church
Partic in Southeastern Pennsylvania Theological Library Association

UNISYS CORP

S CORPORATE INFORMATION CENTER, Union Meeting & Township Line Rds, PO Box 500 E3-112, 19422-0500. SAN 328-7211. Tel: 215-986-2324, 215-986-2459. FAX: 215-986-6733. *In Charge*, Diane Gagliardi
Founded 1952
Jan 1999-Dec 1999 Income $200,000
Library Holdings: Bk Vols 5,000; Per Subs 200
Subject Interests: Electronics, Marketing, Technology
Special Collections: Market Research; Photo Archives

L LAW LIBRARY, Unisys Way E8 108, PO Box 500, 19424. SAN 346-1734. Tel: 215-986-4789. FAX: 215-986-5721. *Librn*, Marsha Frederick-Fritz; E-Mail: marsha.frederick-fritz@unisys.com; Staff 2 (MLS 2)
Founded 1971
Library Holdings: Bk Vols 10,000; Bk Titles 1,700; Per Subs 50
Subject Interests: Patents, Securities

P WISSAHICKON VALLEY PUBLIC LIBRARY, 650 Skippack Pike, 19422. SAN 358-2906. Tel: 215-643-1320. Circulation Tel: 215-643-1320, Ext 10. Reference Tel: 215-643-1320, Ext 19. FAX: 215-643-6611. E-Mail: library@wvpl.org. Web Site: www.wvpl.org. *Dir*, David J Roberts; Tel: 215-643-1320, Ext 11, E-Mail: droberts@wvpl.org; *Asst Librn*, Gertrude Buri; Tel: 215-643-1320, Ext 12, E-Mail: tburi@wvpl.org; *Asst Librn, Ch Servs*, Kathleen Berry; Tel: 215-643-1320, Ext 14, E-Mail: kberry@wvpl.org; *Circ*, Marva Jones; Staff 7 (MLS 7)
Founded 1934. Pop 32,240; Circ 270,930
Jul 1999-Jun 2000 Income (Main Library and Branch Library) $910,419, State $129,542, City $654,210, Other $126,667. Mats Exp $173,794, Books $137,977, Per/Ser (Incl. Access Fees) $11,517. Sal $420,096
Library Holdings: Bk Vols 108,818; Per Subs 229
Automation Activity & Vendor Info: (Cataloging) TLC; (Circulation) epixtech, inc.; (OPAC) epixtech, inc.
Friends of the Library Group
Branches: 1
AMBLER BRANCH, 209 Race St, Ambler, 19002. SAN 358-2876. Tel: 215-646-1072. FAX: 215-654-0161. *Dir*, Lois McMullen; Staff 5 (MLS 5)
Founded 1923. Pop 32,240; Circ 61,655
Library Holdings: Bk Titles 35,000; Per Subs 287
Subject Interests: Architecture, Art, Education, Natural science, Sci-tech
Publications: Annual report

BOYERTOWN

P BOYERTOWN COMMUNITY LIBRARY, 29 E Philadelphia Ave, 19512-1125. SAN 376-5741. Tel: 610-369-0496. FAX: 610-369-0542. E-Mail: boyerpl@ptd.net, boyertowncl@berks.lib.pa.us. Web Site:

www.reading.lib.pa.us/boyertowncl/index.htm. *Dir*, Kathee Rhode; *Ch Servs*, Dayna DiMarco
Founded 1989
Library Holdings: Bk Vols 22,000; Per Subs 50
Automation Activity & Vendor Info: (Circulation) epixtech, inc.
Partic in Berks County Public Libraries
Friends of the Library Group

S CABOT PERFORMANCE MATERIALS LIBRARY,* County Line Rd, 19512. SAN 314-3368. Tel: 610-369-8414. FAX: 610-367-2068.
Library Holdings: Bk Vols 2,000; Per Subs 50
Subject Interests: Alloys, Chemistry, Metals
Partic in Dialog Corporation

BRACKENRIDGE

S ALLEGHENY LUDLUM CORP, Technical Center Library,* Alabama & Pacific Aves, 15014. SAN 314-3376. Tel: 724-226-5076. FAX: 724-226-6430. *Dir*, Teresa Stumpf; *Librn*, Sylvia C Rowe; E-Mail: srowe@alleghenyludlum.com
Founded 1952
Library Holdings: Bk Vols 3,500; Per Subs 200
Subject Interests: Metallurgy
Restriction: Not open to public

BRADDOCK

M UPMC, BRADDOCK, Health Sciences Library, 400 Holland Ave, 15104. SAN 314-3384. Tel: 412-636-5000, 412-636-5030. FAX: 412-636-5604.
1998-1999 Income $30,000. Mats Exp $19,110, Books $2,000, Per/Ser (Incl. Access Fees) $12,000, Micro $3,000. Sal $16,000
Library Holdings: Per Subs 100
Subject Interests: Clinical medicine, Nursing
Partic in Pittsburgh-East Hospital Libr Coop

BRADFORD

P BRADFORD AREA PUBLIC LIBRARY, 67 W Washington St, 16701-1234. SAN 314-3392. Tel: 814-362-6527. Web Site: www.bradfordlibrary.org. *ILL*, Cathy Doyle; Staff 13 (MLS 1, Non-MLS 12)
Founded 1900. Pop 22,384; Circ 63,048
Jan 2000-Dec 2000 Income $221,000, State $75,909, City $25,000. Mats Exp $33,000, Books $28,500, Per/Ser (Incl. Access Fees) $4,500. Sal $92,350 (Prof $24,780)
Library Holdings: Bk Vols 55,700; Bk Titles 54,500; Per Subs 100
Special Collections: Art & Literature (Dr T E Hanley Coll)
Automation Activity & Vendor Info: (Cataloging) Sagebrush Corporation; (Circulation) Sagebrush Corporation
Open Mon & Wed 10-8, Tues, Thurs & Fri 10-6, Sat 10-5
Friends of the Library Group

M BRADFORD HOSPITAL, Huff Memorial Library, 116 Interstate Pkwy, 16701. SAN 324-640X. Tel: 814-362-8253. FAX: 814-368-5722. *In Charge*, Anita J Herbert
Library Holdings: Bk Titles 750; Per Subs 37
Restriction: Staff use only

C UNIVERSITY OF PITTSBURGH AT BRADFORD, T Edward & Tullah Hanley Library, 300 Campus Dr, 16701. SAN 314-3406. Tel: 814-362-7610. FAX: 814-362-7688. Web Site: www.ubp.pitt.edu/libr/index.htm. *Dir*, Trisha A Morris; E-Mail: tmorrist@imap.pitt.edu; *Cat*, Maryellen Brooks; *Circ*, James Hutter; *Syst Coordr*, Nancy Cook; *Ser*, Sheri Christjohn; *Publ Servs*, Marietta Frank; *Acq of Monographs*, Gloria Saar; Staff 10 (MLS 3, Non-MLS 7)
Founded 1963. Highest Degree: Bachelor
Jul 1999-Jun 2000 Income $493,751. Mats Exp $120,907, Books $33,937, Per/Ser (Incl. Access Fees) $80,987, Micro $4,470, Other Print Mats $1,513. Sal $229,133 (Prof $131,603)
Library Holdings: Bk Vols 77,427; Per Subs 439
Subject Interests: Am studies (lit and hist), Behav sci, Bus admin, Criminal law and justice, Exercise, Liberal arts, Soc sci
Special Collections: Lowenthal Collection, Forres Stewart Photos; Montaigne, French Literature (Lowenthal Coll)
Automation Activity & Vendor Info: (Acquisitions) Endeavor; (Cataloging) Endeavor; (Circulation) Endeavor; (OPAC) Endeavor
Database Vendor: Dialog, Ebsco - EbscoHost, IAC - Info Trac, Lexis-Nexis, OCLC - First Search, OVID Technologies, ProQuest, Silverplatter Information Inc.
Publications: Facts & Figures-Among Friends
Partic in OCLC Online Computer Library Center, Inc; PALCI; Pittsburgh Regional Libr Consortium
Friends of the Library Group

BRIDGEVILLE

P BRIDGEVILLE PUBLIC LIBRARY, 441 Station St, 15017. SAN 314-341 Tel: 412-221-3737. FAX: 412-220-8124. *Pres*, Gloria Lutz; *Dir*, Elaine Downing; *Dir*, Elaine Downing; Staff 2 (MLS 2)
Founded 1962. Pop 6,072; Circ 30,101
Jan 1998-Dec 1998 Income $99,400. Mats Exp $92,800
Library Holdings: Bk Titles 20,400; Per Subs 69
Database Vendor: DRA
Partic in Allegheny County Libr Asn; Electronic Info Network
Friends of the Library Group

MAYVIEW STATE HOSPITAL

S PATIENTS LIBRARY, 1601 Mayview Rd, 15017-1599. SAN 358-3414. Tel: 412-257-6610. FAX: 412-257-6320. E-Mail: maymedlib@hslc.org. *Dir*, Elaine Gabauer
Founded 1976
Library Holdings: Bk Titles 2,500; Per Subs 18
Subject Interests: Mental health
Special Collections: Large Print Books

M PROFESSIONAL LIBRARY, 1601 Mayview Rd, 15017-1599. SAN 358-3449. Tel: 412-257-6496. FAX: 412-257-6320. E-Mail: maymedlib@yahoo.com. *Librn*, William A Suvak Jr
Founded 1968
Jul 1999-Jun 2000 Income $70,172. Mats Exp $18,807, Books $4,507, Per/Ser (Incl. Access Fees) $13,600, AV Equip $700. Sal $54,000
Library Holdings: Bk Titles 4,500; Per Subs 84
Subject Interests: Clinical psychol, Pharmacology, Psychiat nursing, Psychiatry, Psychoanalysis, Soc work
Special Collections: History of Mayview State Hospital
Publications: Newsletter; serial holdings
Partic in Basic Health Sciences Library Network

BRISTOL

P MARGARET R GRUNDY MEMORIAL LIBRARY,* 680 Radcliffe St, 19007-5199. SAN 314-3422. Tel: 215-788-7891. FAX: 215-788-4976. E-Mail: grundy@shrsys.hslc.org. Web Site: www.buckslib.org. *Dir*, Mary Jane Mannherz; *Ch Servs*, Shirley Hickey; *Ad Servs*, Cecilia C Flis; Staff 17 (MLS 5, Non-MLS 12)
Founded 1966. Pop 22,000; Circ 161,590
Library Holdings: Bk Titles 68,465; Per Subs 237
Subject Interests: Local history
Special Collections: Bucks County Census 1790-1910, microfilm; Bucks County Courier Time 1911-Present, microfilm
Automation Activity & Vendor Info: (Circulation) Inlex
Open Mon-Thurs 11-9, Fri 11-6, Sat 10-4:30, closed Sat in summer

J PENNCO TECHNICAL LIBRARY,* 3815 Otter St, 19007. SAN 314-3430. Tel: 215-824-3200. FAX: 215-785-1945. *Dir*, Eric Jacobs; *Librn*, Jen Abbott
Library Holdings: Bk Vols 3,000; Per Subs 20

BROCKWAY

P JEFFERSON COUNTY LIBRARY SYSTEM, 324 Main St, 15824. SAN 315-1441. Tel: 814-265-8245. FAX: 814-265-1125. *Dir*, Darlene Marshall; E-Mail: mengle@penn.com
Pop 46,000
1999-2000 Income County $34,000
Member Libraries: Redfield Public Library; Reynoldsville Public Library; Summerville Public Library; Sykesville Public Library

P MENGLE MEMORIAL LIBRARY, 324 Main, 15824-0324. SAN 314-3457. Tel: 814-265-8245. FAX: 814-265-1125. Web Site: users.penn.com/~mengle/. *Librn*, Darlene Marshall; *Cat*, Patricia Erickson; Staff 1 (MLS 1)
Founded 1965. Pop 6,986; Circ 40,000
1999-2000 Income $100,000, State $30,000, City $2,700, County $7,000, Locally Generated Income $10,000, Other $50,300. Mats Exp $21,000, Books $18,000, Per/Ser (Incl. Access Fees) $3,000. Sal $55,000 (Prof $25,000)
Library Holdings: Bk Titles 25,000; Per Subs 82
Special Collections: Japanese Literature (Yamamura Coll)
Mem of Oil Creek District Library Center
Partic in Jefferson County Library System
Friends of the Library Group

BRODHEADSVILLE

P WESTERN POCONO COMMUNITY LIBRARY,* Bond Lane, PO Box 318, 18322-0318. SAN 320-2313. Tel: 717-992-7934. FAX: 717-992-7915. Web Site: www.wpcl.lib.pa.us. *Pres*, Marian Mackes; *VPres*, Robert Reeder; *Dir*, Carol Kern
Founded 1974. Pop 27,053; Circ 137,500
Jan 1998-Dec 1998 Income $237,694, State $27,694, Other $210,000. Mats Exp $64,474, Books $30,403, Per/Ser (Incl. Access Fees) $2,915, Presv $587, Micro $11,496, AV Equip $446, Other Print Mats $966. Sal $119,901 (Prof $28,000)

Library Holdings: Bk Vols 35,800; Per Subs 102
Special Collections: Monroe County History
Automation Activity & Vendor Info: (Cataloging) Follett; (Circulation) Follett; (OPAC) Follett
Literacy Program - Laubach Literacy Program; Monroe County Literacy Council
Friends of the Library Group

BROOKVILLE

REBECCA M ARTHURS MEMORIAL LIBRARY,* 223 Valley St, 15825-0223. SAN 314-3465. Tel: 814-849-5512. FAX: 814-849-6211. *Librn*, Rosalee Pituch; Staff 2 (MLS 1, Non-MLS 1)
Founded 1958. Pop 12,357; Circ 60,736
Library Holdings: Bk Vols 28,000; Per Subs 52
Subject Interests: Local history
Mem of Oil Creek District Library Center

BROOMALL

R BETH EL NER TAMID LIBRARY, 715 Paxon Hollow Rd, 19008-9998. SAN 314-3473. Tel: 610-356-8700. FAX: 610-325-9248. *Librn*, Joyce Friedman
Founded 1959
Library Holdings: Bk Vols 2,150
Subject Interests: Judaica

SR CHURCH OF JESUS CHRIST OF LATTER-DAY SAINTS-PHILADELPHIA, PENNSYLVANIA, Stake Family History Center, 721 Paxon Hollow Rd, 19008. SAN 375-2402. Tel: 610-356-8507. FAX: 610-687-9499. Web Site: www.valleyforgefhc.com. *Dir*, Martine Green
Library Holdings: Bk Vols 1,000; Per Subs 10
Subject Interests: Genealogy
Open Tues 11-4 & 7-10, Wed & Thurs 9:30-2:30 & 7-10, Sat 9:30-2:30

S DELAWARE COUNTY HISTORICAL SOCIETY, 85 N Malin Rd, 19008-1928. SAN 314-402X. Tel: 610-359-1148. FAX: 610-359-4155. Web Site: www.delcohistory.org/dchs. *Admin Assoc*, Trudy Carroll
Founded 1895
Library Holdings: Bk Vols 6,500
Subject Interests: Genealogy, Hist of Delaware county, Maps
Special Collections: Chester Baker & Dr Anna Broomall Coll, scrapbooks
Publications: The Bulletin (newsletter)
Function: Research library

P MARPLE PUBLIC LIBRARY,* 2259 S Sproul Rd, 19008-2399. SAN 314-3481. Tel: 610-356-1510. FAX: 610-356-3589. E-Mail: marple@delco.lib.pa.us. *Dir*, Deborah Parsons; *Ch Servs*, Andrea Mandel; *Ref*, Rachel Reilly; Staff 5 (MLS 5)
Founded 1951. Pop 23,642
Jan 1998-Dec 1999 Income $533,715, State $40,583, City $336,000, County $17,500, Locally Generated Income $83,900. Mats Exp $74,100, Books $56,500, Per/Ser (Incl. Access Fees) $8,000. Sal $296,500
Library Holdings: Bk Vols 92,000; Bk Titles 90,000
Special Collections: Delaware County Literacy Council Coll; Delaware County Local History Coll
Mem of Delaware County Library System
Open Mon-Thurs 9:30-9, Fri 9:30-6, Sat 9:30-5 & Sun 1:30-5
Friends of the Library Group

R TEMPLE SHOLOM OF BROOMALL LIBRARY, 55 N Church Lane, 19008. SAN 314-349X. Tel: 610-356-5165. FAX: 610-356-6713. E-Mail: templesholom@juno.com. *Librn*, Barbara Clarke
Library Holdings: Bk Vols 2,500; Per Subs 50
Special Collections: Judaica Coll
Publications: Jerusalem Post; Jewish Exponent; Reform Judaism Inside

BROWNSVILLE

P BROWNSVILLE FREE PUBLIC LIBRARY, 100 Seneca St, 15417-1974. SAN 314-3511. Tel: 724-785-7272. FAX: 724-785-6087. E-Mail: brpublib@hhs.net. Web Site: www.basd.org/bvillepubl.html. *Librn*, Barry Richard Blaine; Staff 1 (MLS 1)
Founded 1927. Pop 15,590
Jan 1999-Dec 1999 Income $54,228. Mats Exp $59,752, Books $10,383, Per/Ser (Incl. Access Fees) $1,817. Sal $21,597
Library Holdings: Bk Vols 21,811; Per Subs 34
Mem of Fayette County Library System; Monessen District Libr Ctr
Friends of the Library Group

BRYN ATHYN

C BRYN ATHYN COLLEGE, Swedenborg Library, 2875 College Dr, PO Box 740, 19009-0740. SAN 314-352X. Tel: 215-938-2547. FAX: 215-938-2637. Web Site: www.newchurch.edu/college. *Dir*, Carroll C Odhner; E-Mail: ccodhner@newchurch.edu; Staff 8 (MLS 3, Non-MLS 5)
Founded 1877. Enrl 158; Fac 28; Highest Degree: Master
Jul 1999-Jun 2000 Income $289,083. Mats Exp $56,499, Books $15,565, Per/Ser (Incl. Access Fees) $29,814, Presv $800, Manuscripts & Archives $1,854. Sal $224,539 (Prof $69,175)
Library Holdings: Bk Vols 93,627; Per Subs 189
Subject Interests: Behav sci, Education, History, Natural science, Relig studies, Soc sci
Special Collections: Religion (Swedenborgiana); Scientific Books (Published in 16th, 17th & 18th Centuries)
Automation Activity & Vendor Info: (Cataloging) SIRSI; (Circulation) SIRSI; (OPAC) SIRSI; (Serials) SIRSI
Publications: BI-Lines
Partic in Health Sci Libr Info Consortium; OCLC Online Computer Library Center, Inc; PALINET & Union Library Catalogue of Pennsylvania; Tri-State College Library Cooperative (TCLC)
Friends of the Library Group

BRYN MAWR

C AMERICAN COLLEGE, Vane B Lucas Memorial Library, 270 S Bryn Mawr Ave, 19010-2916. SAN 314-3538. Tel: 610-526-1305, 610-526-1307. FAX: 610-526-1322. Web Site: www.amercoll.edu/pages/library/library.htm. *Librn*, Judith Hill; E-Mail: judithh@amercoll.edu; *Asst Librn*, Deborah A Jenkins; Staff 3 (MLS 2, Non-MLS 1)
Founded 1927. Enrl 30,000; Highest Degree: Master
Library Holdings: Bk Titles 10,000; Per Subs 6,000
Subject Interests: Financial servs, Insurance (finance), Taxation
Special Collections: Insurance (Solomon S Huebner Coll), bks, papers & flm; Insurance History Coll
Automation Activity & Vendor Info: (Acquisitions) EOS; (Cataloging) EOS; (Circulation) EOS; (OPAC) EOS; (Serials) EOS
Database Vendor: OCLC - First Search
Publications: Library Bulletin
Partic in OCLC Online Computer Library Center, Inc; PALINET & Union Library Catalogue of Pennsylvania; Tri State Col Libr Coop

C BRYN MAWR COLLEGE, Mariam Coffin Canaday Library, 101 N Merion Ave, 19010-2899. SAN 314-3546. Tel: 610-526-5276. Interlibrary Loan Service Tel: 610-526-5278. Reference Tel: 610-526-5279. FAX: 610-526-7480. Web Site: www.brynmawr.edu/library. *Dir*, Elliott Shore; Tel: 610-526-5270, E-Mail: eshore@brynmawr.edu; *Publ Servs*, Florence D Goff; Tel: 610-526-5275, E-Mail: fgoff@brynmawr.edu; *Ser*, Jeremy Blatchley; Tel: 610-526-5296, E-Mail: jblatchl@brynmawr.edu; *ILL*, Charles Burke; Tel: 610-526-5278, E-Mail: caburke@brynmawr.edu; *Tech Servs*, Scott Silverman; Tel: 610-526-5281, E-Mail: ssilverma@brynmawr.edu; *Cat*, Berry Chamness; Tel: 610-526-5295, E-Mail: bchamnes@brynmawr.edu; *Acq*, Jane McGarry; Tel: 610-526-5283, E-Mail: jmcgarry@brynmawr.edu; *Bibliogr*, John Dooley; Tel: 610-526-5273, E-Mail: jdooley@brynmawr.edu; *Archivist*, Lorett Treese; Tel: 610-526-5285, E-Mail: ltreese@brynmawr.edu; *Coll Develop*, Eric Pumroy; Tel: 610-526-5272, E-Mail: epumroy@brynmawr.edu; *Ref*, Mark Colvson; Tel: 610-526-7465, E-Mail: mcolvson@brynmawr.edu; Staff 39 (MLS 21, Non-MLS 18)
Founded 1885. Enrl 1,523; Fac 117; Highest Degree: Doctorate
Jun 1999-May 2000 Income (Main Library and Branch Library) $3,974,260. Mats Exp $3,974,260, Books $704,148, Per/Ser (Incl. Access Fees) $710,903, Presv $60,737, Other Print Mats $11,803, Electronic Ref Mat (Incl. Access Fees) $226,497. Sal $1,232,111 (Prof $880,793)
Library Holdings: Bk Vols 1,081,868; Per Subs 1,827
Special Collections: Books about Books; College Archives; English & Dutch History; Fine & Graphic Arts; History of & Writing by Women; History of Religion; History of Science; Natural History; Press Books; Theater & Performing Arts; Travel & Exploration; Twentieth Century Lithography; Urban History (New York, London, Paris)
Automation Activity & Vendor Info: (Acquisitions) Innovative Interfaces Inc.; (Cataloging) Innovative Interfaces Inc.; (Circulation) Innovative Interfaces Inc.; (Course Reserve) Innovative Interfaces Inc.; (ILL) Innovative Interfaces Inc.; (Media Booking) Innovative Interfaces Inc.; (OPAC) Innovative Interfaces Inc.; (Serials) Innovative Interfaces Inc.
Database Vendor: IAC - Info Trac, Lexis-Nexis, OCLC - First Search, ProQuest, Silverplatter Information Inc., Wilson - Wilson Web
Publications: Bryn Mawr Library Card Catalog; Campus Newsletter, catalog, cards, bks, pamplets; Campus Newsletter, catalog, cards, books, pamplets; Friends Newsletter; Keepsakes; Mirabile Dicta; Palladium
Partic in PALCI; PALINET & Union Library Catalogue of Pennsylvania; Philadelphia Area Consortium Of Special Collections Libraries; Tri-College University Libraries Consortium
Friends of the Library Group
Departmental Libraries:
LOIS & REGINALD COLLIER SCIENCE LIBRARY Tel: 610-526-5118. FAX: 610-526-7464. *Head of Libr*, Terri Freedman; Tel: 610-526-5116, E-Mail: tfreedma@brynmawr.edu
RHYS CARPENTER LIBRARY FOR ART, ARCHAEOLOGY & CITIES, 101 N Merion Ave, 19104-2899. Circulation Tel: 610-526-7912. FAX: 610-526-7911. Web Site: www.brynmawr.edu/library. *Librn*, Eileen Markson; Tel: 610-526-7910, E-Mail: emarkson@brynmawr.edu; *Ref*, Krista Ivy; Tel: 610-526-7918, E-Mail: kivy@brynmawr.edu

M BRYN MAWR HOSPITAL LIBRARY,* 130 S Bryn Mawr, 19010. SAN 314-3554. Tel: 610-526-3160. FAX: 610-525-5931. *Librn*, Alex Kulchar; *Cat*, Doris Mohn; Staff 4 (MLS 3, Non-MLS 1)
Founded 1893
Library Holdings: Bk Titles 7,500; Per Subs 250
Subject Interests: Allied health sci, Hist of nursing, History of medicine
Special Collections: Medical Antique Instrument Coll
Publications: Bryn Mawr Hospital Bulletin
Restriction: Open to public for reference only
Partic in Delaware Valley Information Consortium

R BRYN MAWR PRESBYTERIAN CHURCH, Converse Library, 625 Montgomery Ave, 19010-3599. SAN 314-3562. Tel: 610-525-2821. *Librn*, Kathleen Rais; Staff 3 (MLS 1, Non-MLS 2)
Library Holdings: Bk Vols 2,000
Subject Interests: Presbyterian Church, Soc issues, Spirituality, Theology
Special Collections: Children's Books; Rare Book Coll

J HARCUM COLLEGE LIBRARY, 750 Montgomery Ave, 19010-3476. SAN 314-3570. Tel: 610-526-6085. Interlibrary Loan Service Tel: 610-526-6066. FAX: 610-526-6086. *Dir*, Carol Puchalski; E-Mail: puchalski@harcum.edu; *Ref*, Kathleen Klocko; E-Mail: kklocko@harcum.edu; *Circ*, David Robinson; *Acq*, Peg Langberg; *Bibliogr*, Clara Salloom; *Tech Servs*, Luminita Vulcu; E-Mail: lvulcu@harcum.edu; Staff 4 (MLS 4)
Founded 1915. Enrl 700; Fac 40
Jul 1999-Jun 2000 Income $252,650. Mats Exp $89,141, Books $35,000, Per/Ser (Incl. Access Fees) $22,500, Micro $4,000, AV Equip $10,000, Other Print Mats $3,475, Electronic Ref Mat (Incl. Access Fees) $9,900. Sal $161,079 (Prof $112,800)
Library Holdings: Bk Vols 38,400; Per Subs 285
Subject Interests: Dental, English literature, Physical therapy, Veterinary tech, Womens' studies
Automation Activity & Vendor Info: (Acquisitions) SIRSI; (Cataloging) SIRSI; (Circulation) SIRSI; (Course Reserve) SIRSI; (ILL) SIRSI; (Media Booking) SIRSI; (OPAC) SIRSI; (Serials) SIRSI
Database Vendor: Ebsco - EbscoHost, OCLC - First Search
Restriction: Open to public for reference only
Function: ILL by photocopy only
Partic in Access-Pa Health Sci Libr Consortium; OCLC Online Computer Library Center, Inc; PALINET & Union Library Catalogue of Pennsylvania; Tri-State College Library Cooperative (TCLC)

P LUDINGTON PUBLIC LIBRARY, 5 S Bryn Mawr Ave, 19010-3471. SAN 314-3597. Tel: 610-525-1776. FAX: 610-525-1783. *Librn*, Margery Hall; *ILL*, Julie Magnus; Staff 6 (MLS 6)
Founded 1916. Pop 13,000; Circ 516,767
Library Holdings: Bk Vols 150,000; Per Subs 300
Subject Interests: Architecture, Art, Horticulture
Publications: Main Line; Union List of Periodicals & Newspapers
Mem of Lower Merion Library System; Montgomery County District Libr Syst
Friends of the Library Group

BURGETTSTOWN

P BURGETTSTOWN COMMUNITY LIBRARY,* 2 Kerr St, 15021-1127. SAN 314-3600. Tel: 724-947-9780. FAX: 724-947-5116. *Librn*, Arletta C Zelenko; Staff 1 (MLS 1)
Founded 1946. Pop 12,094
Library Holdings: Bk Vols 28,992; Per Subs 40
Open Mon-Thurs 1-8, Fri 10-5 & Sat (Oct-May) 1-5

BUTLER

S BURT, HILL, KOSAR & RITTELMANN ASSOCIATES LIBRARY,* 400 Morgan Ctr, 16001. SAN 373-1065. Tel: 724-285-4761. FAX: 724-285-6815. Web Site: www.burthill.com. *In Charge*, Mark Stuleny
Library Holdings: Bk Vols 1,000; Per Subs 20
Subject Interests: Architecture, Engineering, Interior design
Restriction: Company library

P BUTLER AREA PUBLIC LIBRARY,* 218 N McKean St, 16001-4971. SAN 314-3643. Tel: 724-287-1715. FAX: 724-285-5090. *Dir*, E Gibson; *Ad Servs, Cat*, Cindy Betres; *Ref*, Jean Grohman; *Ch Servs*, Susan Grossman; Staff 3 (MLS 3)
Founded 1894. Circ 150,296
Library Holdings: Bk Titles 100,472; Per Subs 143
Automation Activity & Vendor Info: (Circulation) CLSI LIBS
Publications: Annual Report; Children Chatter; Users Handbook
Mem of Butler County Libr Syst
Friends of the Library Group

J BUTLER COUNTY COMMUNITY COLLEGE, John A Beck Jr Library,* College Dr, Oak Hills, PO Box 1203, 16003-1203. SAN 314-3619. Tel: 724-287-8711, Ext 299. FAX: 724-285-6047. E-Mail: smj1652@bc3.cc.pa.us. *Asst Dean*, Stephen Joseph; *ILL, Media Spec, Ref*, Jane Gilliand; *Cat, Tech Servs*, Martin Miller; Staff 3 (MLS 3)
Founded 1966. Enrl 2,500; Fac 165
Library Holdings: Bk Vols 45,122; Bk Titles 41,218; Per Subs 255
Subject Interests: Allied health, Literature, Soc issues
Publications: Acquisitions List; bibliographies; library instruction on video; newsletter; periodicals list; student handbook
Partic in OCLC Online Computer Library Center, Inc

GL BUTLER COUNTY LAW LIBRARY,* Courthouse, 16001. SAN 314-3627. Interlibrary Loan Service Tel: 724-284-5206. FAX: 724-284-5210. *Librn*, Susan Megarry
Library Holdings: Bk Titles 20,000; Per Subs 60
Subject Interests: Law, Pennsylvania
Restriction: Open to public for reference only

M BUTLER MEMORIAL HOSPITAL, Armstrong Memorial Medical Library, 911 E Brady St, 16001. SAN 324-7570. Tel: 724-283-6666, 724-284-4240. FAX: 724-284-4532. *Librn*, Karen L Baughman; Staff 2 (MLS 1, Non-MLS 1)
Library Holdings: Bk Vols 700; Bk Titles 670; Per Subs 90
Partic in Greater NE Regional Med Libr Program
Open Mon 9-4:30, Wed 10-4:30, Fri 9-3:30

GM DEPARTMENT OF VETERANS AFFAIRS, Medical Center Library, 325 New Castle Rd, 16001. SAN 314-366X. Tel: 724-285-2250. FAX: 724-477-5073. *Librn*, Mary Ann Wagner
Founded 1946
Library Holdings: Bk Titles 1,200; Per Subs 131
Subject Interests: Geriatrics, Medicine, Nursing, Psychology, Soc work
Restriction: Staff use only
Partic in Vets Admin Libr Network

CALIFORNIA

P CALIFORNIA AREA PUBLIC LIBRARY, 100 Wood St, 15419. SAN 314-3678. Tel: 724-938-2907. FAX: 724-938-9119. E-Mail: callib@stargate.net. Web Site: calpublib.org. *Dir*, Debbie M Tustin; *Librn*, Wyona Coleman; *Asst Librn*, Irene Zopetti; *Circ*, Hildred Folmar; *Circ*, Dorothy Hambacher; Staff 4 (MLS 1, Non-MLS 3)
Founded 1934. Pop 10,700
Jan 2000-Dec 2000 Income $49,365, State $27,000, County $4,000, Locally Generated Income $4,000, Other $14,365. Mats Exp $10,150, Books $6,850, Per/Ser (Incl. Access Fees) $500, AV Equip $2,000, Other Print Mats $800. Sal $25,230 (Prof $15,000)
Library Holdings: Bk Vols 24,600; Per Subs 50
Subject Interests: Home based bus, Home computers, Small based bus
Special Collections: Local Hist; Pa Regimental Histories; Railroads
Publications: California Journal (Newsletter)
Function: ILL available
Mem of Washington County Libr Syst
The library is on the National Registry of Historic Places. The library has a Summer Bookmobile program sponsored by a yearly grant.
Friends of the Library Group

C CALIFORNIA UNIVERSITY OF PENNSYLVANIA, Louis L Manderino Library, 250 University Ave, 15419-1394. SAN 314-3686. Tel: 724-938-4096. Interlibrary Loan Service Tel: 724-938-4049. Circulation Tel: 724-938-4091. Reference Tel: 724-938-4094. FAX: 724-938-5901. Web Site: www.library.cup.edu. *Dean*, William L Beck; E-Mail: beck@cup.edu; *ILL*, Diane Turosik; E-Mail: turosik@cup.edu; *Tech Servs*, Karen Chan; Tel: 724-938-1650, E-Mail: chan@cup.edu; *Bibliog Instr*, Marsha L Nolf; Tel: 724-938-4048, E-Mail: nolf@cup.edu; *Acq*, Cora Russell; Tel: 724-938-4093, E-Mail: russell@cup.edu; *Online Servs, Ref Serv*, Betty Shaw; Tel: 724-398-4097, E-Mail: shaw_b@cup.edu; Staff 24 (MLS 10, Non-MLS 14)
Founded 1852. Pop 5,800; Enrl 5,200; Fac 280; Highest Degree: Master
Jul 1999-Jun 2000 Income State $2,214,786. Mats Exp $458,795, Books $150,003, Per/Ser (Incl. Access Fees) $172,350, Presv $23,384, Micro $27,466, AV Equip $8,000, Electronic Ref Mat (Incl. Access Fees) $77,592. Sal $1,539,986 (Prof $846,992)
Library Holdings: Bk Vols 384,813; Per Subs 7,640
Automation Activity & Vendor Info: (Acquisitions) Endeavor; (Cataloging) Endeavor; (Circulation) Endeavor; (Course Reserve) Endeavor; (Media Booking) Endeavor; (OPAC) Endeavor; (Serials) Endeavor
Mem of Keystone Libr Network
Partic in Interlibrary Delivery Service of Pennsylvania; PALINET & Union Library Catalogue of Pennsylvania; State System Of Higher Education Libraries Council

CAMBRIDGE SPRINGS

P CAMBRIDGE SPRINGS PUBLIC LIBRARY, 158 McClellan St, 16403-1018. SAN 314-3716. Tel: 814-398-2123. FAX: 814-398-2123. *Dir*, Connie Bullock
Founded 1928. Pop 6,805; Circ 25,388
Jan 1999-Dec 1999 Income $54,738. Sal $27,882
Library Holdings: Bk Titles 19,000; Per Subs 50
Mem of Erie-Crawford District Libr Ctr
Open Mon 2-9, Fri 2-5, Tues & Thurs 10-1 & 2-9, Sat 9-4

CAMP HILL

CLEVE J FREDRICKSEN LIBRARY, (Formerly West Shore Public Library), 30 N 31st St, 17011-2998. SAN 314-3732. Tel: 717-761-3900. FAX: 717-761-3093. E-Mail: westshore@ccpa.net. Web Site: www.ccpa.net/wshorepl/. *Dir*, Roberta Greene; *Asst Dir*, Joy Hamsher; *Cat, Tech Servs*, Erin Coldren; *Coll Develop*, Martha Skinner; Staff 5 (MLS 5)
Founded 1957. Pop 66,863; Circ 404,089
Jan 1999-Dec 1999 Income $628,858, State $131,574, County $317,233, Other $180,051. Mats Exp $62,063, Books $46,572, Per/Ser (Incl. Access Fees) $5,878, Micro $522, AV Equip $6,232, Electronic Ref Mat (Incl. Access Fees) $2,859. Sal $369,672
Library Holdings: Bk Vols 78,703
Automation Activity & Vendor Info: (Circulation) epixtech, inc.; (OPAC) epixtech, inc.
Mem of Cumberland County Library System
Friends of the Library Group
Branches: 1
EAST PENNSBORO, 98 S Enola Dr, Enola, 17025. SAN 376-5695. Tel: 717-732-4274. FAX: 717-732-4274. E-Mail: eastpennsboro@ccpa.net. Web Site: www.ccpa.net/eastpennbl/. *Dir*, Roberta Greene; *Asst Dir*, Joy Hamsher
Pop 26,305; Circ 54,933
Jan 1999-Dec 1999 Income $628,858, State $131,574, County $317,233, Other $180,051. Mats Exp Books $5,286. Sal $20,352
Library Holdings: Bk Vols 12,020
Automation Activity & Vendor Info: (Circulation) epixtech, inc.; (OPAC) epixtech, inc.
Open Mon-Thurs 10-8, Fri 10-5
Friends of the Library Group

M HOLY SPIRIT HOSPITAL, Medical Library,* 503 N 21st St, 17011. SAN 325-0164. Tel: 717-763-2664. FAX: 717-763-2136. *Librn*, Edie Asbury; E-Mail: easbury@hsh.org; Staff 2 (MLS 2)
Library Holdings: Bk Vols 2,500; Per Subs 250
Subject Interests: Consumer health, Medicine, Mental health
Publications: Medical Library Newsletter

CANONSBURG

P GREATER CANONSBURG PUBLIC LIBRARY, 68 E Pike St, 15317-1312. SAN 314-3740. Tel: 724-745-1308. FAX: 724-745-4958. E-Mail: ill@nb.net. Web Site: www.cbgpublib.org. *Head Librn*, Lyn Crouse; E-Mail: lcrouse@nb.net; Staff 8 (MLS 1, Non-MLS 7)
Founded 1879
Library Holdings: Bk Titles 35,000; Per Subs 64
Special Collections: Canonsburg Notes, micro; History of Western Pennsylvania (Johnson Memorial Coll)
Partic in Washington County Cooperative Library Services
Friends of the Library Group
Bookmobiles: 1

CANTON

P GREEN FREE LIBRARY,* 14 N Center St, 17724-1304. SAN 314-3767. Tel: 570-673-5744. FAX: 570-673-5005. E-Mail: greenfre@epix.net. *Librn*, Leslie A Larcom
Pop 6,449; Circ 16,460
Library Holdings: Bk Vols 15,150; Per Subs 25
Open Mon-Fri 2-5 & 7-9, Sat 9-12, Childrens Hours: Wed 9-12
Friends of the Library Group

CARBONDALE

P CARBONDALE PUBLIC LIBRARY,* 5 N Main St, 18407-2319. SAN 314-3775. Tel: 570-282-4281. FAX: 570-282-7031. E-Mail: car9@idt.net. *Librn*, Anne Muldoon
Pop 12,808; Circ 26,169
Library Holdings: Bk Vols 22,936; Per Subs 65
Mem of Lackawanna County Library System
Friends of the Library Group

CARLISLE

P BOSLER FREE LIBRARY,* 158 W High St, 17013-2988. SAN 314-3791. Tel: 717-243-4642. FAX: 717-243-8281. *Dir*, Linda K Rice; E-Mail: lrice@ccpa.net; *Asst Dir*, Ricky Prado; E-Mail: rprado@ccpa.net; *Ch Servs*, Melissa A Killinger; E-Mail: mkillinger@ccpa.net; *Tech Servs*, Felicity Hajjar; E-Mail: fhajjar@ccpa.net; *ILL, Ref*, Connie Weaver; E-Mail: cweaver@ccpa.net
Founded 1900. Pop 45,101; Circ 278,607
Jan 1998-Dec 1998 Income $450,824. Mats Exp $103,000, Books $50,000, Per/Ser (Incl. Access Fees) $8,000, AV Equip $8,000, Other Print Mats $36,000. Sal $201,999 (Prof $123,120)
Library Holdings: Bk Vols 62,000; Per Subs 150
Special Collections: Adult Basic Education Coll; High Interest-low Vocabulary bk vols 100; Local History Coll
Automation Activity & Vendor Info: (Circulation) epixtech, inc.
Mem of Cumberland County Library System
Friends of the Library Group

M CARLISLE HOSPITAL, Medical Library,* 246 Parker St, PO Box 310, 17013-0310. SAN 375-2593. Tel: 717-245-5184. FAX: 717-245-5234. *Librn*, Judith Welch; E-Mail: jwelch@chhs.org
Library Holdings: Bk Vols 800; Per Subs 125
Subject Interests: Medicine, Nursing

S CUMBERLAND COUNTY HISTORICAL SOCIETY, Hamilton Library, 21 N Pitt, PO Box 626, 17013. SAN 314-3805. Tel: 717-249-7610. FAX: 717-258-9332. E-Mail: info@historicalsociety.com. Web Site: www.historicalsociety.com. *Dir*, Linda Franklin Witmer; *Librn*, Christa Bassett
Founded 1874
Library Holdings: Per Subs 20
Subject Interests: Architect, Genealogy, Local history
Special Collections: A A Line, J N; Carlisle; Cartography (John V Miller, M D Coll), maps; Choate & Carlisle Indian School, photog; Cumberland County; Cumberland County Firms Business Records, bd; Genealogy, VF; Imprints; Index to Cumberland County Church & Cemetery Records; Judge James Hamilton, papers, bks & mss; Newspapers, 1749-present & Carlisle Indian School Publications, 1880-1917, bd & micro; Official Cumberland County, records, bks & mss; Papers of Robert Whitehill, Sylvester B Sadler, Jeremiah Zeamer & others, mss
Publications: bi-annual journals; hard cover books; Monographs
Restriction: Not a lending library
Function: Archival collection, For research purposes

L CUMBERLAND COUNTY LAW LIBRARY,* One Courthouse Sq, 17013-3387. SAN 327-098X. Tel: 717-240-6200. FAX: 717-240-6462.
Library Holdings: Per Subs 150

P CUMBERLAND COUNTY LIBRARY SYSTEM, 158 W High St, 17013-2988. SAN 314-3813. Tel: 717-240-6175. FAX: 717-240-7770. E-Mail: ccls@ccpa.net. Web Site: www.ccpa.net. *Dir*, Jonelle Prether Darr; *Outreach Serv*, Nan Cavenaugh; *Automation Syst Coordr*, Barbara Leach; *Tech Servs*, Gretchen Beach; Staff 3 (MLS 3)
Founded 1961. Pop 201,964
Jan 2000-Dec 2000 Income $2,196,448, State $734,106, Federal $13,942, County $1,436,085, Locally Generated Income $12,315. Mats Exp $7,900, Books $3,926, Per/Ser (Incl. Access Fees) $475, AV Equip $3,499. Sal $155,558
Automation Activity & Vendor Info: (Acquisitions) epixtech, inc.; (Cataloging) epixtech, inc.; (Circulation) epixtech, inc.; (OPAC) epixtech, inc.; (Serials) epixtech, inc.
Member Libraries: Amelia S Givin Free Library; Bosler Free Library; Cleve J Fredricksen Library; John Graham Public Library; Mechanicsburg Area Public Library; New Cumberland Public Library; Shippensburg Public Library
Partic in PALINET & Union Library Catalogue of Pennsylvania
Cumberland County Library System is the administrative headquarters of a federated library system

C DICKINSON COLLEGE, Waidner Spahr Library, 17013-2896. SAN 314-3821. Tel: 717-245-1396. Reference Tel: 717-245-1397. FAX: 717-245-1439. Web Site: www.library.dickinson.edu. *ILL*, Tina Maresco; *Govt Doc, Ref*, Sue Norman; *Online Servs, Ref*, Kirk Moll; *Cat, Tech Servs*, Yongyi Song; *Acq, Ser*, Kristin Senecal; *Ser*, Jim Gereneser; *AV*, Julie Bockensteat; *Ser*, John Stacha; *Coll Develop*, Kris Senecal; Staff 9 (MLS 9)
Founded 1784. Enrl 1,828; Fac 157; Highest Degree: Bachelor
Library Holdings: Bk Vols 452,632; Per Subs 1,759
Subject Interests: Am hist, East European hist, Int bus, Russian hist, Russian lit
Special Collections: Carl Sandburg Coll, bks, letters, mss; Eli Slifer Coll, letters; Isaac Norris Coll; Jacobs Asian Coll; James Buchanan Coll, letters, mss; John Drinkwater Coll, bks, letters, mss; John F Kennedy Coll, artifacts, bks, per; Joseph Priestly Coll, bks, mss; Marianne Moore Coll, bks, letters; Martin Native American Coll; Moncure Conway Coll, letters
Publications: John & Mary's Journal; Manuscript Collections of Dickinson College; Spahr Library Notes
Partic in Associated College Libraries of Central Pennsylvania; Central Pennsylvania Consortium; OCLC Online Computer Library Center, Inc; PALINET & Union Library Catalogue of Pennsylvania
Friends of the Library Group

CL PENNSYLVANIA STATE UNIVERSITY - DICKINSON SCHOOL OF LAW (UNIVERSITY LIBRARIES), Sheely-Lee Law Library, 150 S College St, 17013. SAN 314-383X. Tel: 717-240-5267. FAX: 717-240-5127. Web Site: www.dsl.edu/libhome.html. *Librn*, James R Fox; *Cat*, Debra Jones; *Cat*, Richard Paone; *Circ, ILL*, Mark Podvia; *Doc*, Cecily Giardina; *Ref*, Gail Partin
Founded 1834. Enrl 530; Fac 30
Library Holdings: Bk Vols 420,000; Bk Titles 85,000; Per Subs 1,400
Subject Interests: European commun law, Int human rights

Database Vendor: Innovative Interfaces INN - View
Partic in Interlibrary Delivery Service of Pennsylvania; Mid-Atlantic Law Library Cooperative; OCLC Online Computer Library Center, Inc

A UNITED STATES ARMY MILITARY HISTORY INSTITUTE LIBRARY,* 22 Ashburn Dr, 17013-5008. SAN 321-3684. Tel: 717-245-4139. FAX: 717-245-4370. Web Site: carlisle-www.army.mil/usamhi. *Asst Dir*, Nancy L Gilbert; *Tech Servs*, Norma J Umbrell; Staff 14 (MLS 5, Non-MLS 9)
Founded 1967
Oct 1998-Sep 1999 Mats Exp $130,900, Books $31,600, Per/Ser (Incl. Access Fees) $4,400, Presv $15,000, Micro $26,200, Other Print Mats $200, Manuscripts & Archives $51,200, Electronic Ref Mat (Incl. Access Fees) $2,300
Library Holdings: Bk Vols 296,135; Per Subs 245
Special Collections: Civil War (Military Order of the Loyal Legion of the United States - Massachusetts Commandery), bks, bd per
Database Vendor: epixtech, inc.
Partic in Fedlink

C UNITED STATES ARMY WAR COLLEGE LIBRARY, 122 Forbes Ave, 17013-5220. SAN 314-3848. Tel: 717-245-4300. Interlibrary Loan Service Tel: 717-245-4298. Circulation Tel: 717-245-4288. Reference Tel: 717-245-3660,, 717-245-4260, 717-245-4280. FAX: 717-245-3323. E-Mail: awcc-sl@carlisle.army.mil. Web Site: carlisle-www.army.mil/library/. *Dir*, Bohdan I Kohutiak; E-Mail: awcc-sl@carlisle.army.mil; *Coll Develop*, Kathryn Davis; Tel: 717-245-4704, E-Mail: librarys@carlisle.army.mil; *Ref, Res*, James Dorrian; Tel: 717-245-4259, E-Mail: libraryr@carlisle.army.mil; Staff 25 (MLS 9, Non-MLS 16)
Library Holdings: Bk Vols 182,421; Bk Titles 97,535; Per Subs 1,105
Subject Interests: Area studies, Foreign policy, International law, International relations, Leadership, Mil sci, Strategy
Database Vendor: epixtech, inc.
Publications: Bibliographies; Library Notes
Partic in Fedlink

CARMICHAELS

P FLENNIKEN PUBLIC LIBRARY, 102 E George St, 15320-1202. SAN 314-3856. Tel: 412-966-5263. FAX: 412-966-9511. E-Mail: fleniken@greenepa.net. Web Site: www.greenepa.net/~flenniken. *Chief Librn*, June Kim; *Ch Servs*, Tina Gresko; *Ref*, Joan Brandsetter; Staff 3 (MLS 1, Non-MLS 2)
Founded 1946. Pop 12,356
Jan 1999-Dec 1999 Income $71,067, State $30,238, County $31,741, Other $9,088. Mats Exp $19,000, Books $15,000, Per/Ser (Incl. Access Fees) $2,000, AV Equip $2,000. Sal $55,000
Library Holdings: Bk Vols 31,000; Per Subs 89
Subject Interests: Coal, Fictions, Local history, Women
Automation Activity & Vendor Info: (Cataloging) Athena; (Circulation) Athena; (OPAC) Athena
Mem of Green County Libr Syst
Special Services - Outreach Program; Childrens & Adults Program & Service, 5 locations (1 Reading Center, 5 Deposit Stations)
Friends of the Library Group

CARNEGIE

P ANDREW CARNEGIE FREE LIBRARY, 300 Beechwood Ave, 15106-2699. SAN 314-3864. Tel: 412-276-3456. FAX: 412-276-9472. E-Mail: andrcarn@alphaclp.clpgh.org. Web Site: www.clpgh.org/ein/andrcarn. *Dir*, Mary Malysko; *Librn*, Helene Dalcanton
Founded 1899. Pop 10,864; Circ 30,855
Library Holdings: Bk Vols 32,600; Per Subs 72
Special Collections: Civil War Memorabilia Coll; Local Newspapers, back to Jan 7, 1872
Open Tues-Thurs 12-8, Fri 12-5 & Sat 10-4
Friends of the Library Group

S THE O HOMMEL CO, Research Library, 235 Hope St, 15106. SAN 315-0720. Tel: 412-279-0700, Ext 212. FAX: 412-279-1213. *In Charge*, Ralph Hoover
Founded 1918
Library Holdings: Bk Titles 2,500
Subject Interests: Govt publications, Patents
Restriction: Staff use only

CARROLLTOWN

P CARROLLTOWN PUBLIC LIBRARY,* 140 E Carol St, PO Box 316, 15722-9998. SAN 314-3880. Tel: 814-344-6300. FAX: 814-344-6355. *Librn*, Deborah Gresco
Pop 5,318; Circ 10,068
Library Holdings: Bk Vols 8,100; Per Subs 15
Mem of Cambria County Library System & District Center

CASTLE SHANNON

P COMMUNITY LIBRARY OF CASTLE SHANNON, 3677 Myrtle Ave, 15234-2198. SAN 314-3899. Tel: 412-563-4552. FAX: 412-563-8228. Web Site: www.clpgh.org/ein/castshan/. *Dir*, Lorene Wood; E-Mail: woodl@clpgh.org; Staff 10 (MLS 3, Non-MLS 7)
Founded 1953. Circ 59,230
Jan 1998-Dec 1999 Income $254,900, State $16,200, City $161,400, County $77,300. Mats Exp $46,900, Books $34,400, Per/Ser (Incl. Access Fees) $6,000. Sal $136,600 (Prof $75,600)
Library Holdings: Bk Vols 40,000; Bk Titles 37,000
Friends of the Library Group

CATASAUQUA

P PUBLIC LIBRARY OF CATASAUQUA, Catasauqua Public,* Third & Bridge Sts, 18032-2510. SAN 314-3902. Tel: 610-264-4151. FAX: 610-264-4593. E-Mail: catasauquapl@liu.org. *Librn*, Martha L Birtcher; Staff 4 (MLS 1, Non-MLS 3)
Founded 1923. Pop 11,668; Circ 28,231
Library Holdings: Bk Vols 18,500; Per Subs 50
Subject Interests: Local history
Open Mon 12-5 & 6-8, Tues-Fri 2-5 & 6-8, Sat 10-1
Friends of the Library Group

CENTER VALLEY

C DESALES UNIVERSITY, (Formerly Allentown College), Trexler Library, 2755 Station Ave, 18034. SAN 314-3910. Tel: 610-282-1100, Ext 1266. FAX: 610-282-2342. E-Mail: cck0@ms1.allencol.edu. *Dir*, Debbie Malone; Tel: 610-282-1100, Ext 1253, E-Mail: dm03@desales.edu; *Publ Servs*, Loretta Ullney; E-Mail: lou0@email.allencol.edu; *Tech Servs*, Phyllis Vogel; E-Mail: pjv@email.allencol.edu; *Syst Coordr*, Kate Brewer; E-Mail: kjb0@email.allencol.edu; *Publ Servs*, Michele Mrazik; Staff 6 (MLS 5, Non-MLS 1)
Founded 1965. Enrl 1,800; Fac 92; Highest Degree: Master
Jul 1999-Jun 2000 Mats Exp $157,828, Books $72,789, Per/Ser (Incl. Access Fees) $44,868, Micro $3,000, AV Equip $3,476, Electronic Ref Mat (Incl. Access Fees) $33,695. Sal $220,000 (Prof $180,361)
Library Holdings: Bk Vols 132,256; Bk Titles 105,747; Per Subs 910
Subject Interests: History, Nursing, Roman Catholic religion
Special Collections: American Theatre (John Y Kohl Coll), bks & pamphlets; St Francis De Sales; St Thomas More
Automation Activity & Vendor Info: (Acquisitions) Innovative Interfaces Inc.; (Cataloging) Innovative Interfaces Inc.; (Circulation) Innovative Interfaces Inc.; (Media Booking) Innovative Interfaces Inc.; (OPAC) Innovative Interfaces Inc.; (Serials) Innovative Interfaces Inc.
Publications: New Titles; Newsletter
Partic in Lehigh Valley Association Of Independent Colleges, Inc; OCLC Online Computer Library Center, Inc; PALINET & Union Library Catalogue of Pennsylvania

CHADDS FORD

S BRANDYWINE CONSERVANCY, INC, Brandywine River Museum Library, US Rte 1, Box 141, 19317. SAN 314-3929. Tel: 610-388-2700. FAX: 610-388-1197. E-Mail: bmuse2@aol.com. *Librn*, Ruth Bassett; *Librn*, Gail Stanislow
Founded 1971
Library Holdings: Bk Vols 5,171; Bk Titles 3,622; Per Subs 22
Subject Interests: Am art, Andrew Wyeth, Howard Pyle, James Wyeth, Local artists, N C Wyeth
Special Collections: American Illustration; N C Wyeth Coll, prints, posters, proofs, calendars; Stanley Arthurs (Blanche Swayne Coll), scrapbks
Restriction: Open to public for reference only

CHAMBERSBURG

P COYLE FREE LIBRARY,* 102 N Main St, 17201-1676. SAN 314-3945. Tel: 717-263-1054. FAX: 717-263-2248. *Librn*, Patricia Reuse
Founded 1924. Pop 174,000; Circ 175,000
1997-1998 Income $287,763, State $29,168, City $79,500, County $42,934, Locally Generated Income $59,544. Mats Exp $50,000, Books $37,000, Per/Ser (Incl. Access Fees) $13,000. Sal $206,000
Library Holdings: Bk Titles 85,000; Per Subs 205
Special Collections: Genealogy Coll
Publications: American Revolution, a Bibliography
Mem of Conococheaque District Libr Ctr
Friends of the Library Group

GL FRANKLIN COUNTY LAW LIBRARY, Courthouse, 157 Lincoln Way E, 17201-0459. SAN 314-3953. Tel: 717-263-4809. FAX: 717-264-1992. E-Mail: fcll@innernet.net. *Librn*, Paula S Rabinowitz
Founded 1840
Library Holdings: Bk Titles 21,300; Per Subs 10

FRANKLIN COUNTY LIBRARY SYSTEM,* Coyle Libr Bldg, 102 N Main St, 17201-1676. SAN 314-3937. Tel: 717-263-1054. FAX: 717-263-2248. *Librn*, Patricia A Reuse; *ILL*, Glennis S Garnes; *Acq*, Mary Grace Jones; *Cat*, Alice Yankowsky; *Ref*, Paula Schechter
Founded 1968. Pop 142,759; Circ 356,015
Library Holdings: Bk Vols 154,500; Per Subs 160
Subject Interests: Genealogy, Local history
Member Libraries: Alexander Hamilton Memorial Free Library; Alexander Hamilton Memorial Free Library; Ragged Edge Library
Partic in OCLC Online Computer Library Center, Inc
Friends of the Library Group

KITTOCHTINNY HISTORICAL SOCIETY LIBRARY,* 175 E King St, 17201. SAN 374-9231. Tel: 717-264-1667. *Pres*, Lillian F Colletta
Library Holdings: Bk Vols 25,000

RAGGED EDGE LIBRARY, 35 Ragged Edge Rd, 17201. SAN 314-3961. Tel: 717-264-9663. FAX: 717-264-9663. E-Mail: realexlib@yahoo.com. *Coll Develop, Dir*, Louisa Cowles
Founded 1948. Pop 125,999; Circ 156,781
Library Holdings: Bk Vols 60,000
Subject Interests: Local history, Needlework
Automation Activity & Vendor Info: (Circulation) Follett; (OPAC) Follett
Mem of Franklin County Library System
Friends of the Library Group
Bookmobiles: 1

WILSON COLLEGE, John Stewart Memorial Library, 1015 Philadelphia Ave, 17201. SAN 314-397X. Tel: 717-264-4141, Ext 3344. FAX: 717-264-1578. *Librn*, Susan Matusak; *Ref*, Sara Kait; *ILL*, LaWanda Youngblood; Staff 2 (MLS 2)
Founded 1869. Enrl 318; Fac 29; Highest Degree: Bachelor
Library Holdings: Bk Vols 168,000; Bk Titles 140,000; Per Subs 364
Subject Interests: English hist, Relig studies, Women's studies
Partic in Associated College Libraries of Central Pennsylvania; Interlibrary Delivery Service of Pennsylvania; OCLC Online Computer Library Center, Inc; PALINET & Union Library Catalogue of Pennsylvania

HARLEROI

JOHN K TENER LIBRARY, 638 Fallowfield Ave, 15022-1996. SAN 314-3988. Tel: 724-483-8282. FAX: 724-483-3478. E-Mail: charlibrary@home.com. *Actg Dir*, Toni Gajan
Founded 1941. Pop 10,001; Circ 16,000
Library Holdings: Bk Vols 17,500; Per Subs 27
Mem of Monessen District Libr Ctr; Washington County Libr Syst
Friends of the Library Group

HELTENHAM

EAST CHELTENHAM FREE LIBRARY, 400 Myrtle Ave, 19012-2038. SAN 314-3996. Tel: 215-379-2077. FAX: 215-379-1275. E-Mail: eastcheltenham@mclinc.org. *Head Librn*, Michael W Rechel; E-Mail: mrechel@mclinc.org; *Tech Servs*, Dorothy L Sutton; Tel: 215-885-0457, Fax: 215-885-1239, E-Mail: dsutton@mclinc.org; Staff 3 (MLS 1, Non-MLS 2)
Founded 1957
Jan 1999-Dec 1999 Income $125,354. Mats Exp $29,206. Sal $71,061
Library Holdings: Bk Vols 26,822; Per Subs 72
Subject Interests: Handicrafts, Multicultural mat
Mem of Cheltenham Township Library System
Partic in Montgomery County Dist Libr Syst; Montgomery County Libr & Info Network Consortium
Open Mon 10-9, Tues 10-5, Wed 1-9, Thurs 1-6, Fri 1-5, Sat & Sun 1-4
Friends of the Library Group

CHESTER

M CROZER CHESTER MEDICAL CENTER, Community Division-Health Sciences Library,* 2600 W Ninth St, 19013-2098. SAN 370-6761. Tel: 610-494-0700, Ext 7418. FAX: 610-447-6162. *Librn*, Judith Ziegler; Staff 1 (MLS 1)
Library Holdings: Bk Vols 1,100; Bk Titles 1,000; Per Subs 125
Partic in Consortium For Health Information & Library Services

P J LEWIS CROZER LIBRARY, 620 Engle St, 19013-2199. SAN 314-4011. Tel: 610-494-3454. Interlibrary Loan Service Tel: 610-494-3459. FAX: 610-494-8954. E-Mail: crozerlib@hslc.org. *Dir*, James G Gear; Staff 7 (MLS 3, Non-MLS 4)
Founded 1894. Pop 41,856
Jan 2000-Dec 2000 Income $399,259, State $130,000, City $31,500, Locally Generated Income $237,759. Mats Exp $53,725, Books $45,000, Per/Ser (Incl. Access Fees) $4,500, AV Equip $4,225. Sal $201,000 (Prof $104,890)
Library Holdings: Bk Vols 47,250; Bk Titles 16,300; Per Subs 90
Subject Interests: Black hist, Chester city hist, Delaware County hist
Automation Activity & Vendor Info: (Circulation) TLC; (ILL) TLC
Mem of Delaware County Library System

C WIDENER UNIVERSITY, Wolfgram Memorial Library, One University Ave, 19013-5792. SAN 358-3503. Tel: 610-499-4087. Interlibrary Loan Service Tel: 610-499-4070. FAX: 610-499-4588. Web Site: www.widener.edu/libraries.html. *Dir*, Robert Danford; *Asst Dir*, Jane McCloskey; *Tech Servs*, Deborah Holl; *Ref*, Janet Alexander; *Ref*, Teresa Cartularo; *Ref*, Mike Powell; *Acq*, Deena Medzie; *Cat, Ser*, Rosalyn Goldstein; Staff 11 (MLS 11)
Founded 1821. Enrl 5,042; Fac 273; Highest Degree: Doctorate
Jul 1998-Jun 1999 Income $3,673,268. Mats Exp $887,736, Books $280,000, Per/Ser (Incl. Access Fees) $439,687, Presv $33,600, Electronic Ref Mat (Incl. Access Fees) $134,449. Sal $1,029,765 (Prof $558,285)
Library Holdings: Bk Vols 403,889; Bk Titles 157,631; Per Subs 2,256
Subject Interests: Bus, Clinical psychol, Education, Engineering, Hotel mgt, Mgt, Nursing, Physical therapy, Soc work
Special Collections: Lindsay Law; Wolfgram Coll (English & American Literature)
Database Vendor: Innovative Interfaces INN - View
Publications: AV Catalog; Faculty Handbook; Monthly List of Acquisitions, Periodical Holdings; User Guides; WolfGRAM (newsletter)
Partic in Consortium For Health Information & Library Services; Interlibrary Delivery Service of Pennsylvania; OCLC Online Computer Library Center, Inc; PALINET & Union Library Catalogue of Pennsylvania; Tri-State College Library Cooperative (TCLC)

CHESTER SPRINGS

P CHESTER SPRINGS LIBRARY,* 1685 A Art School Rd, 19425-1402. SAN 320-8508. Tel: 610-827-9212. FAX: 610-827-1148. E-Mail: csprings@chester-county.lib.pa.us. Web Site: www.ccls.org. *Librn*, Kate Woodward
Pop 1,420; Circ 3,679
Library Holdings: Bk Vols 15,000; Per Subs 30
Special Collections: Dance Coll
Mem of Chester County Library
Friends of the Library Group

CHEYNEY

C CHEYNEY UNIVERSITY, Leslie Pinckney Hill Library, Cheyney Rd, 19319-0200. SAN 314-4062. Tel: 610-399-2203. FAX: 610-399-2491. *Dir*, Lut R Nero; *Circ, Ref*, Alla R Reddy; *Acq, Cat*, Helen Boyd; *Doc, Media Spec*, Karen C Humbert; Staff 6 (MLS 6)
Founded 1853. Enrl 1,600; Fac 100; Highest Degree: Master
Library Holdings: Bk Vols 226,510; Bk Titles 195,281; Per Subs 1,100
Special Collections: Afro-American studies; Ethnic Coll; University Archives
Publications: Annual Report; Newsletter; Student & Faculty Handbooks
Partic in OCLC Online Computer Library Center, Inc; PALINET & Union Library Catalogue of Pennsylvania; State System Of Higher Education Libraries Council; Tri-State College Library Cooperative (TCLC)

CHRISTIANA

P MOORES MEMORIAL LIBRARY,* 326 N Bridge St, 17509-1202. SAN 314-4070. Tel: 610-593-6683. FAX: 610-593-7044. E-Mail: chrlib@epix.net. Web Site: www.epix.net/~chrlib. *Dir*, Claudia Roun; *Asst Librn*, Joanne Kennel
Founded 1881. Pop 3,757; Circ 17,000
Jan 1999-Dec 1999 Income $23,384, State $6,468, City $1,000, County $1,610, Locally Generated Income $9,393, Other $3,963. Mats Exp $6,700, Books $5,500, Per/Ser (Incl. Access Fees) $700, AV Equip $500. Sal $11,800
Library Holdings: Bk Titles 8,182; Per Subs 33
Subject Interests: Local history
Special Collections: Christiana Riot of 1851 - Prelude to Civil War
Mem of Library System of Lancaster County
Friends of the Library Group

CLAIRTON

P CLAIRTON PUBLIC LIBRARY, 616 Miller Ave, 15025-1497. SAN 358-3538. Tel: 412-233-7966. FAX: 412-233-2536. Web Site: www.einpgh.org/ein/clairton/. *Dir*, Alison Spence; *Ad Servs*, Emma J Anderson; Staff 1 (MLS 1)
Founded 1920. Pop 9,656; Circ 35,000
Jan 2000-Dec 2000 Income $114,800, State $35,800, City $33,000, County $36,000, Other $10,000. Mats Exp $4,000, Books $1,000, AV Equip $3,000. Sal $63,000 (Prof $21,000)
Library Holdings: Bk Vols 35,600; Per Subs 66
Automation Activity & Vendor Info: (Cataloging) DRA; (Circulation) DRA

CLARION

S CLARION COUNTY HISTORICAL SOCIETY MUSEUM-LIBRARY, 18 Grant St, 16214-1015. SAN 326-2871. Tel: 414-361-5517, 814-226-4450. FAX: 814-226-7160. E-Mail: cchs@csoline.net. Web Site: www.csonline.net/cchs. *Curator, Dir*, Lindsley A Dunn; Staff 1 (Non-MLS 1)
Founded 1955
Library Holdings: Bk Titles 2,000; Per Subs 20
Special Collections: family trees, American Indians; genealogy (bks & mss); Pennsylvania German Coll; Theo Wilson Coll; Western Pennsylvania History
Publications: Iron County Chronicle (newsletter)
Partic in OCLC via Clarion District Libr Asn

P CLARION COUNTY LIBRARY SYSTEM, Main St, PO Box 663, 16214. SAN 375-8737. Tel: 814-226-6340. FAX: 814-226-6750. E-Mail: clarflib@mail.clarion.edu.
Founded 1961. Pop 48,130
Jan 1998-Dec 1999 Income $121,480, State $80,430, County $29,000, Locally Generated Income $9,750, Other $2,300. Mats Exp $2,000. Sal $9,500
Library Holdings: Bk Vols 91,000
Member Libraries: Clarion Free Library; Eccles-Lesher Memorial Library; Foxburg Free Library; Knox Public Library; New Bethlehem Area Free Public Library

P CLARION FREE LIBRARY, 644 Main St, PO Box 663, 16214-6750. SAN 314-4119. Tel: 814-226-7172. FAX: 814-226-6750. *Ch Servs*, Jean Gethers-Smith; E-Mail: cflsmith@usachoice.net; *Dir*, Julie Schill; E-Mail: cflschill@usachoice.net; Staff 4 (MLS 1, Non-MLS 3)
Founded 1914. Pop 21,096; Circ 110,000
Jan 2000-Dec 2000 Income $137,850, State $35,362, City $39,899, County $5,189, Locally Generated Income $57,400. Mats Exp $161,000, Books $13,500, Per/Ser (Incl. Access Fees) $394, Presv $1,093, AV Equip $83, Electronic Ref Mat (Incl. Access Fees) $180. Sal $96,000 (Prof $40,000)
Library Holdings: Bk Vols 34,900; Bk Titles 34,477; Per Subs 85
Special Collections: Census 1790 to 1920, microfiche; Clarion News & Leader-Vindicator, newspapers on micro from 1868 to present
Automation Activity & Vendor Info: (Circulation) Follett; (OPAC) Follett
Mem of Clarion County Library System

C CLARION UNIVERSITY OF PENNSYLVANIA, Rena M Carlson Library, 840 Wood St, 16214. SAN 358-3597. Tel: 814-393-2343. Interlibrary Loan Service Tel: 814-227-2469. Circulation Tel: 814-393-2301. Reference Tel: 814-393-1841. FAX: 814-393-1842. Web Site: www.clarion.edu/library. *Dean of Libr*, Dr Howard McGinn; Fax: 814-393-1862, E-Mail: hmcginn@clarion.edu; *Reader Servs*, Constance Gamaluddin; Tel: 814-393-1841, E-Mail: gamaludd@clarion.edu; *Circ*, Lori Norris; Tel: 814-393-2301, E-Mail: norris@clarion.edu; *Tech Servs*, Janice Horn; Tel: 814-393-2417, E-Mail: horn@clarion.edu; *ILL*, Judy Bowser; Tel: 814-227-2468, Fax: 814-227-2549, E-Mail: bowser@clarion.edu; *Per*, Debra Decker; Tel: 814-393-2748, E-Mail: decker@clarion.edu; *Automation Syst Coordr*, William Trimble; Tel: 814-393-2017, Fax: 814-393-1862, E-Mail: wtrimble@clarion.edu; Staff 24 (MLS 10, Non-MLS 14)
Founded 1867. Enrl 6,028; Highest Degree: Master
Jul 1999-Jun 2000 Income (Main Library Only) $2,052,875. Mats Exp $495,740, Books $135,369, Per/Ser (Incl. Access Fees) $187,025, Presv $10,318, Micro $145,724, AV Equip $14,763. Sal $979,373 (Prof $485,337)
Library Holdings: Bk Vols 384,957; Bk Titles 249,535; Per Subs 532
Subject Interests: British Commonwealth
Automation Activity & Vendor Info: (OPAC) Endeavor
Database Vendor: Ebsco - EbscoHost, epixtech, inc., GaleNet, IAC - SearchBank, Lexis-Nexis, ProQuest, Silverplatter Information Inc.
Publications: The United Kingdom of Great Britain & Ireland: An Annotated Bibliography of Documentary Sources in Carlson Library
Function: ILL available, Photocopies available
Partic in NICOP; Northwest Interlibrary Cooperative Of Pennsylvania; OCLC Online Computer Library Center, Inc; PALCI; PALINET & Union Library Catalogue of Pennsylvania
Friends of the Library Group

L W W BARR LAW LIBRARY, Court House, 16214. SAN 375-2208. Tel: 814-226-9351. FAX: 814-226-1097.
Library Holdings: Bk Titles 500

CLARKS SUMMIT

P ABINGTON COMMUNITY LIBRARY, 1200 W Grove St, 18411-9501. SAN 314-4127. Tel: 570-587-3440. FAX: 570-587-3809. *Dir*, Mary Tuthill
Founded 1961. Pop 22,523; Circ 221,459
Library Holdings: Bk Vols 55,000; Per Subs 115
Special Collections: Audio-Visual Coll
Mem of Lackawanna County Library System
Friends of the Library Group

CR BAPTIST BIBLE COLLEGE OF PENNSYLVANIA, Murphy Memorial Library, 538 Venard Rd, PO Box 800, 18411. SAN 358-3627. Tel: 570-585-9280. Interlibrary Loan Service Tel: 570-585-9282. Circulation Tel: 570-585-9284. FAX: 570-586-1753. Web Site: www.bbc.edu/onlinelibrary. *Head Librn*, David C McClain; E-Mail: dmcclain@bbc.edu; Staff 1 (MLS 1)
Founded 1932. Highest Degree: Doctorate
Library Holdings: Bk Vols 80,781; Per Subs 492
Subject Interests: Biblical studies, Christian educ, Church history, Church ministries, Church music, Theology
Automation Activity & Vendor Info: (Cataloging) TLC; (Circulation) TL((OPAC) TLC
Departmental Libraries:
INSTRUCTIONAL MATERIALS CENTER, 538 Venard Rd, PO Box 800, 18411. Tel: 570-585-9220. Circulation Tel: 570-585-9221. FAX: 570-586-1753. Web Site: www.bbc.edu/onlinelibrary. *Dir*, Richard N Erickson; E-Mail: rerickson@bbc.edu; Staff 3 (MLS 1, Non-MLS 2)
Library Holdings: Bk Vols 12,347
Subject Interests: Christian educ, Youth ministries
Automation Activity & Vendor Info: (Cataloging) TLC; (Circulation) TLC; (OPAC) TLC

CLAYSBURG

P CLAYSBURG AREA PUBLIC LIBRARY, Bedford St, PO Box 189, 16625-0403. SAN 314-4135. Tel: 814-239-2782. FAX: 814-239-8647. E-Mail: cklibrary1@cove.net. *Asst Librn*, Jean Markle; *Ch Servs*, Louise Speck; *Tech Servs*, Viola Fersueson; *Tech Servs*, Pam Musselman; Staff 6 (MLS 1, Non-MLS 5)
Founded 1965. Pop 6,417; Circ 58,000 Sal $27,000
Library Holdings: Bk Vols 43,550; Per Subs 100
Mem of Blair County Library System
Friends of the Library Group

CLEARFIELD

L CLEARFIELD COUNTY LAW LIBRARY, Courthouse, 2nd flr, Ste 228, 230 E Market St, 16830. SAN 327-1102. Tel: 814-765-2641. FAX: 814-765 6089. *Dir*, Sandra Finn
Library Holdings: Bk Vols 10,000
Friends of the Library Group

P JOSEPH & ELIZABETH SHAW PUBLIC LIBRARY,* One S Front St, 16830-2386. SAN 314-4143. Tel: 814-765-3271. FAX: 814-765-6316. E-Mail: shaw2@penn.com.
Founded 1940. Pop 19,715
1997-1998 Income $180,000, State $2,000, City $3,000, County $21,000, Locally Generated Income $140,000, Other $9,000. Mats Exp $178,854, Books $12,000, Per/Ser (Incl. Access Fees) $2,500. Sal $72,048
Library Holdings: Bk Vols 46,507; Bk Titles 45,022; Per Subs 72
Subject Interests: Genealogy, Local history
Special Collections: Art (Thomas Murray Chase Coll)
Mem of Clearfield County Public Library Federation
Friends of the Library Group

COATESVILLE

M BRANDYWINE HOSPITAL & TRAUMA CENTER, Health Sciences Library,* 201 Reeseville Rd, 19320. SAN 322-7340. Tel: 610-383-8147. FAX: 610-383-8243. *Dir*, Rosemary Conway; Staff 2 (MLS 2)
Library Holdings: Bk Titles 3,000; Per Subs 250
Special Collections: Nursing Education & Research Coll
Restriction: By appointment only
Partic in Dialog Corporation; Nat Libr of Med

P COATESVILLE AREA PUBLIC LIBRARY, Dr Michael Margolies Library, 501 E Lincoln Hwy, 19320-3414. SAN 314-4151. Tel: 610-384-4115. FAX: 610-384-7551. E-Mail: coastaff@ccls.org. Web Site: www.ccls.org/othlibs/coats.htm. *Dir*, Mike Geary; E-Mail: mgeary@ccls.org; *ILL*, Charlene Coates; *Ref*, Susan Vreeland; E-Mail: svreeland@ccls.org; *Ch Servs*, Danielle Stokes; E-Mail: dstokes@mail.ccls.org; *Head Tech Servs*, Joanne Budzik; Staff 5 (MLS 2, Non-MLS 3)
Founded 1936. Pop 41,418; Circ 46,108
Jan 2000-Dec 2000 Income $283,000, State $97,400, County $55,895, Locally Generated Income $130,000. Mats Exp $40,250, Books $33,000, Per/Ser (Incl. Access Fees) $2,750, AV Equip $3,500. Sal $146,600 (Prof $53,160)
Library Holdings: Bk Vols 56,750; Per Subs 85; Bks on Deafness & Sign Lang 15
Subject Interests: Local history, Multicultural
Database Vendor: Innovative Interfaces INN - View
Publications: Annual Report
Mem of Chester County Library
Open Mon & Thurs 10-8, Tues, Wed & Fri 10-6, Sat 9-4

GM DEPARTMENT OF VETERANS AFFAIRS, Medical Center Library,* 1400 Black Horse Hill Rd, 19320-2097. SAN 314-4178. Tel: 610-384-7711, Ext 3902. FAX: 610-383-0245. E-Mail: vamc@hslc.org. *Chief Librn*, Andrew Henry; Staff 1 (MLS 1)
Founded 1931
Library Holdings: Bk Titles 12,039; Per Subs 350

Subject Interests: Longterm care, Neurology, Patient health educ, Psychiatry
Partic in BRS; Consortium For Health Information & Library Services; Docline; Nat Libr of Med; Vets Admin Libr Network

COCHRANTON

COCHRANTON AREA PUBLIC LIBRARY,* 107 W Pine St, 16314-0296. SAN 314-4186. Tel: 814-425-3996. FAX: 814-425-3996. *Librn*, Deanna Gray; *Asst Librn*, Amy Bruno
Founded 1969. Pop 5,390; Circ 12,411
Library Holdings: Bk Vols 8,400; Per Subs 25
Friends of the Library Group

COLLEGEVILLE

URSINUS COLLEGE, Myrin Library, 19426-1000. SAN 314-4194. Tel: 610-409-3607. FAX: 610-489-0634. *Acq, Dir*, Charles A Jamison; *Online Servs, Ref*, David Mill; *Online Servs, Ref*, Judith Fryer; *Tech Servs*, Doreen M Kopycinski; *ILL*, Joan Rhodes; *Circ*, Theresa Tuscano; *Media Spec*, Kimberly Sando
Founded 1870. Enrl 1,100; Fac 100; Highest Degree: Bachelor
Library Holdings: Bk Vols 190,000; Per Subs 900
Subject Interests: Behav sci, History, Natural science, Pa German, Recreation studies, Soc sci, Women's studies
Special Collections: Linda Grace Hoyer Updike Literary Papers; Pennsylvania German Studies Archives
Automation Activity & Vendor Info: (Circulation) DRA
Database Vendor: DRA
Publications: Myrin Library News
Partic in Interlibrary Delivery Service of Pennsylvania; PALINET & Union Library Catalogue of Pennsylvania; Tri-State College Library Cooperative (TCLC)

COLLINGDALE

COLLINGDALE PUBLIC LIBRARY,* 823 MacDade Blvd, 19023-1422. SAN 314-4208. Tel: 610-583-2214. FAX: 610-583-0172. E-Mail: collingdale@delco.lib.pa.us. *Dir*, Gerry Finley
Founded 1937. Pop 9,100; Circ 16,463
Jan 2000-Dec 2000 Mats Exp Books $5,100
Library Holdings: Bk Vols 14,300; Per Subs 15
Mem of Delaware County Library System

COLUMBIA

P COLUMBIA PUBLIC LIBRARY, 24 S Sixth St, 17512-1599. SAN 314-4224. Tel: 717-684-2255. FAX: 717-684-5920. Web Site: www.columbia.lib.pa.us. *Adminr*, Joanne M Stecz; E-Mail: stecz@lancaster.lib.pa.us
Pop 10,701; Circ 33,210
Jan 1999-Dec 1999 Income $66,600, State $10,700, City $2,000, Federal $2,200, County $5,550, Locally Generated Income $1,200, Other $33,130. Mats Exp $14,300, Books $8,400, Per/Ser (Incl. Access Fees) $1,200, Presv $200, AV Equip $1,500, Other Print Mats $2,600, Manuscripts & Archives $400. Sal $29,000 (Prof $17,000)
Library Holdings: Bk Vols 22,000; Per Subs 50
Subject Interests: Civil War, Local art, Local history
Special Collections: Lloyd Mifflin Works
Publications: Quarterly newsletter
Mem of Library System of Lancaster County

S NATIONAL WATCH & CLOCK MUSEUM, Library & Research Center, 514 Poplar St, 17512. SAN 321-0251. Tel: 717-684-8261. FAX: 717-684-0878. Web Site: www.nawcc.org. *Archivist, Dir*, Beth Bisbano; E-Mail: bbisbano@nawcc.org; *Librn*, Sharon Gordon; E-Mail: sharong@nawcc.org
Founded 1965
Library Holdings: Bk Vols 10,000; Bk Titles 5,000; Per Subs 50
Special Collections: Hamilton Watch Co Records & Publications.
Restriction: Open to public for reference only

CONCORDVILLE

P RACHEL KOHL COMMUNITY LIBRARY, 689 Smithbirdge Rd, 19331-0170. SAN 376-3129. Tel: 610-358-3445. FAX: 610-558-0693. *Dir*, Meg Hawkins
Library Holdings: Bk Vols 24,200; Bk Titles 24,000; Per Subs 58
Mem of Delaware County Library System
Partic in Am Pub Libr Asn; Pennsylvania Library Association
Open Mon & Fri 10-5, Tues, Wed & Thurs 10-8, Sat 10-5
Friends of the Library Group

CONNEAUT LAKE

P MARGARET SHONTZ MEMORIAL LIBRARY, Conneaut Lake Public Library, 145 Second St, 16316-5117. SAN 320-5053. Tel: 814-382-6666. FAX: 814-382-5875. *Librn*, Betty Ecklund
Founded 1971. Pop 8,600
Library Holdings: Bk Titles 12,000; Per Subs 26
Mem of Erie County Libr Syst

CONNEAUTVILLE

P STONE MEMORIAL LIBRARY, 1101 Main St, PO Box 281, 16406. SAN 314-4240. Tel: 814-587-2142. FAX: 814-587-2142. *Librn*, Doreen Nelson; *Asst Librn, Ch Servs*, Telce McCann
Founded 1903. Pop 2,086; Circ 19,681
1999-2000 Mats Exp $10,800, Books $10,000, Per/Ser (Incl. Access Fees) $800
Library Holdings: Bk Titles 19,000; Per Subs 41

CONNELLSVILLE

P CARNEGIE FREE LIBRARY,* 299 S Pittsburgh St, 15425-3580. SAN 314-4259. Tel: 724-628-1380. FAX: 724-628-5636. *Dir*, Julia Allen
Founded 1903. Pop 37,283; Circ 54,496
Library Holdings: Bk Vols 60,882; Per Subs 114
Special Collections: Local & Fayette County History (Pennsylvania Coll)
Publications: Newsletter
Friends of the Library Group

CONSHOHOCKEN

S PQ CORP, Technical Information Center, 280 Cedar Grove Rd, 19428-2240. SAN 314-6731. Tel: 610-651-4629. FAX: 610-832-2931. *Mgr*, Dolores A Whitehurst; E-Mail: dwhiteh@pqcorp.com; *Asst Librn*, Jerry Luciani; Tel: 610-651-4677, E-Mail: jlucian@pqcorp.com; Staff 2 (MLS 1, Non-MLS 1)
Founded 1925
Library Holdings: Bk Titles 3,000; Per Subs 140
Subject Interests: Ceramics, Chemistry, Potassium silicates, Sodium
Database Vendor: Dialog, IAC - Info Trac, OCLC - First Search, ProQuest
Publications: Bulletin
Function: Research library
Partic in OCLC Online Computer Library Center, Inc; PALINET & Union Library Catalogue of Pennsylvania

S QUAKER CHEMICAL CORP, Information Center, 19428-0873. SAN 314-4267. Tel: 610-832-4000. FAX: 610-832-4498. *In Charge, Online Servs*, J L Williams; E-Mail: jlwillia@quakerchem.com; Staff 1 (MLS 1)
Founded 1952
Library Holdings: Bk Vols 6,500; Per Subs 150
Subject Interests: Bus info, Chemistry, Eng for metals, Lubricants, Technology
Publications: New Books Bulletin; What's New in the Information Center
Restriction: Staff use only

COOPERSBURG

P SOUTHERN LEHIGH PUBLIC LIBRARY,* 6339 Beverly Hills Rd, 18036. SAN 314-4283. Tel: 610-965-2364. FAX: 610-965-7698. E-Mail: solehipl@cliu.org. Web Site: www.members.spree.com/siplslpl. *Dir, Librn*, Lynnette Saeger; *Asst Librn*, JoAnne Herring
Founded 1963. Pop 15,643; Circ 53,577
Jul 1999-Jun 2000 Income $177,777. Mats Exp $37,200. Sal $88,107
Library Holdings: Bk Vols 38,179; Per Subs 158
Open Mon-Thurs 10-9, Fri 10-5 & Sat 10-2
Friends of the Library Group

COOPERSTOWN

P COOPERSTOWN PUBLIC LIBRARY, Main St, PO Box 264, 16317-0264. SAN 371-5442. Tel: 814-374-4605. FAX: 814-374-4606. E-Mail: cpl@csonline.net. *Dir*, Jane Beach
Founded 1987. Pop 4,153
1999-2000 Income $30,000, City $11,100, Locally Generated Income $18,900. Mats Exp $9,410, Books $3,600, Per/Ser (Incl. Access Fees) $1,200, Electronic Ref Mat (Incl. Access Fees) $4,610. Sal $8,680 (Prof $6,000)
Library Holdings: Bk Titles 12,186; Per Subs 30; High Interest/Low Vocabulary Bk Vols 100
Automation Activity & Vendor Info: (Cataloging) Follett; (Circulation) Follett; (OPAC) Follett
Mem of Oil Creek District Library Center

COPLAY

P COPLAY PUBLIC LIBRARY,* 49 S Fifth, 18037-1398. SAN 314-4291. Tel: 610-262-7351. FAX: 610-262-4937. *Librn*, Anne Morris
Founded 1962. Pop 3,267; Circ 35,159
Library Holdings: Bk Vols 29,921; Per Subs 52

CORAOPOLIS

S MICHAEL BAKER JR, INC LIBRARY, 420 Rouser Rd, 15108. SAN 314-3007. Tel: 412-269-4679. FAX: 412-269-6097. *Librn*, Ruth J Williams; E-Mail: rjwilliams@mbakercorp.com
Founded 1972
Library Holdings: Bk Titles 9,000; Per Subs 100
Subject Interests: Bus, Civil engineering, Environ planning, Graphics, Mgt, Transportation, Urban planning
Special Collections: Civil Engineering (American Society of Civil Engineers Publications), journal; State & Federal Government Publications; Transportation Research Board Publications, journal; Urban Planning (Company Planning Reports)
Partic in Dialog Corporation

P CORAOPOLIS MEMORIAL LIBRARY, 601 School St, 15108-1196. SAN 314-4305. Tel: 412-264-3502. FAX: 412-269-8982. Web Site: www.einpgh.org/ein/coraopls/. *Librn*, Christine P Rice; E-Mail: ricec@einetwork.net; Staff 6 (MLS 1, Non-MLS 5)
Founded 1937. Pop 8,020; Circ 17,836
1999-2000 Income $111,024, State $12,508, County $25,000, Locally Generated Income $73,516. Mats Exp $23,424, Books $16,519, Per/Ser (Incl. Access Fees) $1,395. Sal $28,700 (Prof $12,500)
Library Holdings: Bk Vols 32,000; Per Subs 89
Subject Interests: Genealogy, Pennsylvania
Special Collections: Story Coll

CORRY

P CORRY PUBLIC LIBRARY, 117 W Washington St, 16407. SAN 314-4321. Tel: 814-664-4404, 814-664-7611. FAX: 814-663-0742. E-Mail: corrypubliclibrary@corry.iu5.org, cplib@tbscc.com. Web Site: www.corrylibrary.org. *Dir*, Frances Church; E-Mail: fchurch@corry.iu5.org; *Ch Servs*, Bonnie Aikens
Founded 1900. Pop 15,137
Jul 1999-Jun 2000 Income $245,950, State $46,728, County $31,631, Locally Generated Income $56,091, Other $111,500. Mats Exp $27,600, Books $24,000, Per/Ser (Incl. Access Fees) $3,600. Sal $114,833 (Prof $55,433)
Library Holdings: Bk Vols 47,697; Per Subs 95
Subject Interests: Genealogy, Pa hist
Database Vendor: Ebsco - EbscoHost
Function: ILL available
Partic in Share NW Consortium
Friends of the Library Group

COUDERSPORT

P COUDERSPORT PUBLIC LIBRARY,* 502 Park Ave, 16915-1672. SAN 314-433X. Tel: 814-274-9382. FAX: 814-274-9137. *Librn*, Darlene Peasley
Founded 1850. Pop 5,405; Circ 36,711
Jan 1999-Dec 1999 Income $78,970, State $11,380, City $22,000, County $6,740, Locally Generated Income $31,000, Other $7,850. Mats Exp $17,400, Books $15,000, Per/Ser (Incl. Access Fees) $2,000, Presv $300, Micro $100. Sal $40,842
Library Holdings: Bk Vols 20,000; Bk Titles 23,000; Per Subs 76
Automation Activity & Vendor Info: (Circulation) EOS
Mem of Potter-Tioga Library System; Williamsport District Libr Ctr

GL POTTER COUNTY LAW LIBRARY, Court House, 16915. SAN 374-8383. Tel: 814-274-9720. FAX: 814-274-8284.
Library Holdings: Bk Titles 50; Per Subs 15

P POTTER-TIOGA LIBRARY SYSTEM,* 502 Park Ave, 16915-1672. SAN 314-7290. Tel: 814-274-7422. FAX: 814-274-9137. *Librn*, Laurie Shear; E-Mail: lshear@adelphia.net
Founded 1975
Library Holdings: Bk Vols 6,220
Special Collections: Books on Tape & Music Cassettes; Large Print Books Coll
Restriction: Not open to public
Member Libraries: Blossburg Memorial Library; Coudersport Public Library; Genesee Area Library; Green Free Library; Mansfield Free Public Library; Oswayo Valley Memorial Library
Operates 17 deposit libraries with varied collections of more than 100 books changed quarterly. Coordinates efforts of literacy volunteers of Potter County

CRANBERRY TOWNSHIP

P CRANBERRY PUBLIC LIBRARY, 2525 Rochester Rd, 16066-6423. SAN 314-7339. Tel: 724-776-9100. FAX: 724-776-2490. E-Mail: cranpl@zbzoom.net. Web Site: www.bcfls.org/cranberry/. *Librn*, Carol B Troese; *Ch Servs*, Jeanne N Cooley; *Ad Servs*, Patricia DiFiore; Staff 4 (MLS 1, Non-MLS 3)
Founded 1974. Pop 18,200; Circ 168,248
Jan 2001-Dec 2001 Income $349,896, State $68,691, County $24,870, Locally Generated Income $256,335. Mats Exp $71,075, Books $55,000, Per/Ser (Incl. Access Fees) $5,100, AV Equip $7,475, Electronic Ref Mat (Incl. Access Fees) $3,500. Sal $109,000 (Prof $181,686)
Library Holdings: Bk Titles 63,827; Per Subs 143; High Interest/Low Vocabulary Bk Vols 200
Automation Activity & Vendor Info: (Cataloging) TLC; (Circulation) TLC
Mem of Butler County Libr Syst
Friends of the Library Group

CRESSON

P CRESSON PUBLIC LIBRARY,* 231 Laurel Ave, 16630-1118. SAN 314-4356. Tel: 814-886-2619. FAX: 814-886-2619. E-Mail: cressonpl@aol.com. *Librn*, Kelly Clark; *Asst Librn*, Mary Beth Eckenrode
Founded 1927. Pop 4,923; Circ 18,904
1997-1998 Income $21,000. Mats Exp $8,300. Sal $9,000
Library Holdings: Bk Vols 11,041; Per Subs 13
Open Mon-Fri 1-5 & 7-9

C MOUNT ALOYSIUS COLLEGE LIBRARY, 7373 Admiral Peary Hwy, 16630-1999. SAN 314-4364. Tel: 814-886-6445. FAX: 814-886-5767. *Dir*, Lisa Dallape Matson; E-Mail: lmatson@mtaloy.edu; *Archivist, Ref*, Eileen Bentsen; *Cat*, Robert Stere; *ILL, Ref*, Shamin Rajpar; *Ref*, David Dwulit; Staff 9 (MLS 5, Non-MLS 4)
Founded 1939. Enrl 2,181; Fac 60; Highest Degree: Bachelor
Library Holdings: Bk Vols 59,046; Per Subs 275
Special Collections: Law Library
Publications: Speaking of the Library (newsletter)
Partic in Laurel Highlands Health Sciences Library Consortium; OCLC Online Computer Library Center, Inc; PALINET & Union Library Catalogue of Pennsylvania

CURWENSVILLE

P CLEARFIELD COUNTY PUBLIC LIBRARY FEDERATION,* 601 Beech St, 16833. SAN 358-3716. Tel: 814-236-0589. FAX: 814-236-3620. *Dir*, Daniel Bogey
Founded 1940. Pop 74,288; Circ 125,000
Library Holdings: Bk Titles 137,996; Per Subs 125
Special Collections: Oral History of Curwensville
Member Libraries: Joseph & Elizabeth Shaw Public Library
Branches: 2
CURWENSVILLE BRANCH Tel: 814-236-0355. FAX: 814-236-3620. *Mgr*, Dorothy Augustine
Library Holdings: Bk Titles 28,000; Per Subs 60
Friends of the Library Group
OSCEOLA MILLS BRANCH, 600 Lingle St, Osceola Mills, 16666. SAN 358-3775. Tel: 814-339-7229. FAX: 814-339-7719.
Open Mon-Fri 10-5:30, Sat 9-1
Bookmobiles: 1. Coordr, Mark Cercennek

DALLAS

P BACK MOUNTAIN MEMORIAL LIBRARY, 96 Huntsville Rd, 18612. SAN 314-4372. Tel: 570-675-1182. FAX: 570-674-5863. E-Mail: backmtlb@epix.net. *Dir*, Martha Butler; *Ch Servs*, Marilyn Rudolph; *ILL*, Elaine Phoneix; *Business*, Margaret Susko; Staff 1 (MLS 1)
Founded 1945. Pop 34,000; Circ 93,000
2000-2001 Income $333,861, State $47,185, County $28,205, Locally Generated Income $237,371. Mats Exp $48,354, Books $41,439, Per/Ser (Incl. Access Fees) $5,026, AV Equip $1,889. Sal $126,576 (Prof $35,500)
Library Holdings: Bk Vols 62,200; Per Subs 152
Friends of the Library Group

C COLLEGE MISERICORDIA, Francesca McLaughlin Memorial Library, 301 Lake St, 18612-1098. SAN 314-4380. Tel: 570-674-6224. FAX: 570-674-6342. E-Mail: library@miseri.edu. Web Site: www.miseri.edu/academic/library/home.htm. *Dir*, Sr Mary Sharon Gallagher; *Circ, ILL*, Bonnie Oldham; *Acq, Coll Develop*, Charles Riedlinger; *Cat*, Jennifer Luksa; *Ref, Ser*, Joseph Luksic; *Archivist*, Dawn Pangrazzi; Staff 5 (MLS 5)
Founded 1924
Library Holdings: Bk Vols 73,628; Per Subs 597
Subject Interests: Education, Nursing, Occupational therapy
Special Collections: ANA & NLN Coll, publications currently in print
Partic in Northeastern Pennsylvania Library Network; PALINET & Union Library Catalogue of Pennsylvania

DALTON

DALTON COMMUNITY LIBRARY,* 113 E Main St, PO Box 86, 18414-0086. SAN 314-4399. Tel: 570-563-2014. FAX: 570-563-2512. E-Mail: dal39@idt.net. *Dir*, Shu Qiu; Staff 1 (MLS 1)
Founded 1948. Pop 2,382; Circ 31,000
Library Holdings: Bk Vols 19,000
Subject Interests: Lackawana County hist
Special Collections: Local History
Publications: Newsletter
Mem of Lackawanna County Library System

SAINT PIUS X SEMINARY LIBRARY, 1000 Seminary Rd, 18414. SAN 314-4402. Tel: 717-563-1131. FAX: 717-563-8520. *Dir*, David Bohr; *Librn*, Judi Comerford
Founded 1962
Library Holdings: Bk Titles 16,500; Per Subs 32
Subject Interests: Philosophy, Theology
Restriction: Private library

DANVILLE

THOMAS BEAVER FREE LIBRARY, 25 E Market St, PO Box 177, 17821. SAN 314-4410. Tel: 570-275-4180. FAX: 570-275-8480. E-Mail: tbfl2@ptd.net. *Dir*, Thomas E Jenkins; *Librn*, Judith B Andrews; *Cat*, Judith Gori; *Circ*, Beth Lynn; *ILL*, Jane Bradford; *Publ Servs*, Laura Christian; *Publ Servs*, Karen Litterer; *Publ Servs*, Cindy Sutherland. Subject Specialists: *Am Civil War*, Thomas E Jenkins; Staff 7 (MLS 1, Non-MLS 6)
Founded 1888. Pop 20,823; Circ 50,000
Jan 2000-Dec 2000 Income $180,001, State $55,191, County $4,500, Locally Generated Income $47,747, Other $72,563. Mats Exp $24,520, Books $18,020, Per/Ser (Incl. Access Fees) $5,000, Presv $500, AV Equip $1,000. Sal $70,000 (Prof $27,000)
Library Holdings: Bk Vols 33,150; Per Subs 122
Database Vendor: Ebsco - EbscoHost
Friends of the Library Group

M GEISINGER HEALTH SYSTEM, (Formerly Penn State - Geisinger Health System), Health Sciences Library, 100 N Academy Ave, 17822-2101. SAN 358-383X. Tel: 570-271-6463. FAX: 570-271-5738. *Dir*, Britain Roth; Tel: 570-271-8197, E-Mail: broth@geisinger.edu; *Asst Dir*, Susan Robishaw; Tel: 570-271-8198, E-Mail: srobishaw@geisinger.edu; *Librn*, Valerie Gross; Tel: 570-271-5638, E-Mail: vgross@geisinger.edu; *Librn*, Claire Huntington; Tel: 570-271-6288, E-Mail: chuntington@geisinger.edu; Staff 8 (MLS 4, Non-MLS 4)
Founded 1927
2000-2001 Mats Exp $384,968. Sal $250,680
Library Holdings: Bk Titles 6,666; Per Subs 1,126
Subject Interests: Allied health, Bus, History of medicine, Med specialities, Medicine, Mgt
Special Collections: Geisinger Archives
Publications: Audiovisual Listing; Guide to Use & Services - Medical Library; Library Bulletin; Periodical Holdings List
Partic in Dialog Corporation; Nat Libr of Med; OCLC Online Computer Library Center, Inc

GL MONTOUR COUNTY LAW LIBRARY,* Courthouse, 29 Mill St, 17821. SAN 374-9983. Tel: 717-275-1331. FAX: 717-271-3088. *Dir*, Althea M Wertman
1998-1999 Mats Exp $2,039. Sal $1,244
Library Holdings: Bk Titles 1,500

DARBY

P DARBY FREE LIBRARY,* 1001 Main St, 19023-0164. SAN 314-4429. Tel: 610-586-7310. FAX: 610-586-2781. E-Mail: darbylib@hscl.org. *Dir*, Susan Eshbach; *Coll Develop*, Terri Cianci
Founded 1743. Pop 11,500
1998-1999 Income $40,881, State $8,121, City $12,250, Locally Generated Income $6,079, Other $14,431. Mats Exp $5,732, Books $5,100, Per/Ser (Incl. Access Fees) $632. Sal $21,697
Library Holdings: Bk Vols 22,870
Subject Interests: Darby hist, Environ
Mem of Philadelphia District Libr Ctr
Open Mon-Fri 11-5 & Sat 10-12:30

M MERCY FITZGERALD HOSPITAL, Health Science Library, 1500 Lansdowne Ave, 19023-1295. SAN 314-4437. Tel: 610-237-4150. FAX: 610-237-4830. *Mgr Libr Serv*, Janet C Clinton; E-Mail: clinton@hslc.org; Staff 2 (MLS 1, Non-MLS 1)
Founded 1933
Library Holdings: Bk Vols 6,975; Bk Titles 1,259; Per Subs 292
Subject Interests: Medicine, Nursing, Surgery
Database Vendor: OCLC - First Search
Partic in Basic Health Sciences Library Network; Consortium For Health Information & Library Services; Health Science Library Information Consortium

DELMONT

P DELMONT PUBLIC LIBRARY, 77 Greensburg St, 15626. SAN 314-4445. Tel: 724-468-5329. *Librn*, Helen A Colclaser
Founded 1931. Pop 2,159; Circ 18,000
Library Holdings: Bk Titles 14,000; Per Subs 25
Automation Activity & Vendor Info: (Acquisitions) Athena; (Cataloging) Athena; (Circulation) Athena; (Course Reserve) Athena

DILLSBURG

P DILLSBURG AREA PUBLIC LIBRARY,* 17 S Baltimore St, 17019. SAN 314-4453. Tel: 717-432-5613. FAX: 717-432-7641. *Librn*, Jean Pelletiere; Staff 9 (MLS 1, Non-MLS 8)
Founded 1953. Pop 19,000; Circ 44,300
Library Holdings: Bk Vols 20,000; Per Subs 41
Mem of York County Library System
Open Mon-Thurs 10-8, Fri & Sat 10-5

DONORA

P DONORA PUBLIC LIBRARY, 510 Meldon Ave, 15033-1333. SAN 314-4461. Tel: 724-379-7940. FAX: 724-379-8809. E-Mail: donlibr@home.com. *Librn*, Barbara Ferguson
Founded 1930. Pop 11,739; Circ 16,603
Jan 2000-Dec 2000 Income $58,700, State $38,700, Locally Generated Income $20,000. Mats Exp $25,700, Books $23,000, Per/Ser (Incl. Access Fees) $700, Electronic Ref Mat (Incl. Access Fees) $2,000. Sal $40,000 (Prof $15,000)
Library Holdings: Bk Vols 22,000; Bk Titles 20,500; Per Subs 33; Bks on Deafness & Sign Lang 12
Open Mon-Thurs 10-7, Fri & Sat 9-4
Friends of the Library Group

DOUGLASSVILLE

S STV INC LIBRARY, 205 W Welsh Dr, 19518. SAN 315-1352. Tel: 610-385-8200, 610-385-8280. FAX: 610-385-8501. *Librn*, C Leh
Library Holdings: Bk Vols 2,443
Subject Interests: Architecture, Engineering
Publications: What's New in the Library
Restriction: Company library

DOWNINGTOWN

P DOWNINGTOWN LIBRARY CO,* 330 E Lancaster Ave, 19335-2946. SAN 314-447X. Tel: 610-269-2741. FAX: 610-269-3639. *Dir*, Karen Miller; Staff 1 (MLS 1)
Founded 1876. Pop 7,749; Circ 52,482
Library Holdings: Bk Titles 22,000; Per Subs 53
Subject Interests: Local history
Mem of Chester County Library
Friends of the Library Group

DOYLESTOWN

P BUCKS COUNTY FREE LIBRARY, 150 S Pine St, 18901-4932. SAN 358-3899. Tel: 215-348-0332. Interlibrary Loan Service Tel: 215-348-1866. FAX: 215-348-4760. Web Site: www.bucks.lib.org. *Exec Dir*, Marilyn D Moody; E-Mail: moodym@bucks.lib.org; *Ch Servs*, Mary Ann Crozier; *Ad Servs*, Jan O'Rourke; *Tech Servs*, Christina M Snyder; Staff 90 (MLS 36, Non-MLS 54)
Founded 1956. Pop 414,336; Circ 2,360,544
Jan 1999-Dec 1999 Income (Main Library and Branch Library) $6,467,566, State $1,415,390, County $4,238,400, Locally Generated Income $445,161, Other $368,615. Mats Exp $968,189, Books $669,768, Per/Ser (Incl. Access Fees) $164,314, AV Equip $106,416, Electronic Ref Mat (Incl. Access Fees) $27,691. Sal $4,127,722
Library Holdings: Bk Vols 772,761; Per Subs 1,124
Subject Interests: Celtic literacy, Foreign fiction, Large print
Special Collections: The Woods Handicapped & Gifted Coll
Automation Activity & Vendor Info: (Acquisitions) Innovative Interfaces Inc.; (Cataloging) DRA; (Circulation) DRA; (Course Reserve) DRA; (OPAC) DRA
Database Vendor: OCLC - First Search
Publications: Beeline (children's programs); Directory of Libraries in Bucks County; Large Print Book Catalog; List of magazines, newspapers, abstracts & indexes available in libraries in Bucks County, Pennsylvania; What's Happening (adult programs)
Member Libraries: Fallsington Library Co; Free Library of New Hope & Solebury; Free Library of Northampton Township; Southampton Free Library; Township Library Of Lower Southampton; Village Library Of Wrightstown; Warminster Township Free Library
Special Services for the Deaf - TTY machine
Friends of the Library Group

Branches: 7
BENSALEM BRANCH, 3700 Hulmeville Rd, Bensalem, 19020-4449. SAN 358-3929. Tel: 215-638-2030. FAX: 215-638-2192. Web Site: www.buckslib.org./bensalem. *Branch Mgr*, Jerome S Szpila; Staff 5 (MLS 2, Non-MLS 3)
Pop 56,788; Circ 230,866
Library Holdings: Bk Vols 106,934; Per Subs 161
Subject Interests: Large print
Friends of the Library Group
JAMES A MICHENER BRANCH, 229 California Rd, Quakertown, 18951-2482. SAN 358-4011. Tel: 215-536-3306. FAX: 215-536-8397. Web Site: www.buckslib.org/quakertown. *Ch Servs*, Aileen Johnson; *Branch Mgr*, Diane M Wood; Staff 3 (MLS 3)
Pop 40,249; Circ 192,912
Library Holdings: Bk Vols 73,444; Per Subs 115
Subject Interests: Large print
Friends of the Library Group
LEVITTOWN REGIONAL, 7311 New Falls Rd, Levittown, 19055-1006. SAN 358-3988. Tel: 215-949-2324. FAX: 215-949-0643. Web Site: www.buckslib.org/levittown. *Regional Manager*, Jean Stevens; Staff 9 (MLS 5, Non-MLS 4)
Pop 104,870; Circ 458,330
Library Holdings: Bk Vols 164,575; Per Subs 173
Friends of the Library Group
LIBRARY CENTER AT DOYLESTOWN, 150 S Pine St, 18901-4932. SAN 358-3953. Tel: 215-348-9082. FAX: 215-348-9489. Web Site: www.buckslib.org/doylestown. *Regional Manager*, Inita Rusis; Staff 14 (MLS 7, Non-MLS 7)
Pop 71,164; Circ 803,253
Library Holdings: Bk Vols 190,450; Per Subs 279
Subject Interests: Large print
Friends of the Library Group
PENNWOOD BRANCH, 301 S Pine St, Langhorne, 19047-2887. SAN 358-4046. Tel: 215-757-2510. FAX: 215-757-9579. Web Site: www.bucks.lib.org/langhorne. *Branch Mgr*, Richard F Strauss; Staff 5 (MLS 3, Non-MLS 2)
Pop 65,100; Circ 179,969
Library Holdings: Bk Vols 80,407; Per Subs 191
Special Collections: Handicapped & Gifted individual (The Wood Coll)
Special Services for the Deaf - TTY machine
Friends of the Library Group
SAMUEL PIERCE BRANCH, 491 Arthur Ave, Perkasie, 18944-1033. SAN 358-4070. Tel: 215-215-257-9718. FAX: 215-257-0759. Web Site: www.buckslib.org/perkasie. *Branch Mgr*, Diane Kraus; Staff 4 (MLS 2, Non-MLS 2)
Pop 42,845; Circ 204,321
Library Holdings: Bk Vols 66,723; Per Subs 106
Friends of the Library Group
YARDLEY-MAKEFIELD BRANCH, 1080 Edgewood Rd, Yardley, 19067-1648. SAN 358-4100. Tel: 215-493-9020. FAX: 215-493-0279. Web Site: www.buckslib.org/yardley. *Branch Mgr*, Janet Fricker; Staff 5 (MLS 2, Non-MLS 3)
Pop 33,320; Circ 290,893
Library Holdings: Bk Vols 90,228; Per Subs 106
Friends of the Library Group

S BUCKS COUNTY HISTORICAL SOCIETY, Spruance Library, 84 S Pine St, 18901-4999. SAN 314-4496. Tel: 215-345-0210, Ext 41. FAX: 215-230-0823. Web Site: www.libertynet.org:80/~bchs. *Dir*, Betsy Smith
Founded 1880
Library Holdings: Bk Vols 25,000
Special Collections: American Folk Art; Antiques; Bucks County History & Genealogy; Early American Technology
Open Tues 1-9, Wed-Sat 10-5

GL BUCKS COUNTY LAW LIBRARY,* 55 E Court St, Court House, 18901. SAN 314-450X. Tel: 215-348-6023. FAX: 215-348-6827. *Dir*, David D Hendley; Staff 3 (MLS 2, Non-MLS 1)
Library Holdings: Bk Vols 32,000; Per Subs 100
Special Collections: Fed Statutes, State Statutes (PA,NJ,NY,DE,FL,MD), National Reporter & system, Law Encyclopedias, Treaties, Dictionaries, Periodicals (law-related), Form Books, Court Rules, Digests, Case Law

G BUCKS COUNTY PLANNING COMMISSION, Staff Library, 1260 Almshouse Rd, Neshaminy Manor Ctr, 18901. SAN 314-4518. Tel: 215-345-3431. FAX: 215-345-3886. *Dir*, Lynn Bush; *Librn*, Cheryl Zabinski
Founded 1960
Library Holdings: Bk Vols 5,500; Per Subs 108
Subject Interests: Demographics, Environ res, Planning, Preservation, Transportation
Restriction: Open to public for reference only

C DELAWARE VALLEY COLLEGE OF SCIENCE & AGRICULTURE, Joseph Krauskopf Memorial Library, 700 E Butler Ave, 18901-2699. SAN 314-4534. Tel: 215-345-1500, Ext 2254, 215-489-2254. Interlibrary Loan Service Tel: 215-489-2385. Circulation Tel: 215-489-2953. Reference Tel: 215-489-2994. FAX: 215-230-2967. Web Site: www.devalcol.edu. *Dir*, Peter Kupersmith; E-Mail: kupersmith@devalcol.edu; *Cat, ILL*, Charles Columbo; *Per*, Joyce Kunkle; *Coll Develop*, June Bitzer; *Ref*, Janet Klaessig; Staff 9 (MLS 4, Non-MLS 5)
Highest Degree: Bachelor
Jul 2000-Jun 2001 Income $516,000. Mats Exp $275,000. Sal $264,000
Library Holdings: Bk Vols 55,000; Per Subs 736
Subject Interests: Animal sci, Plant sci
Special Collections: Joseph Krauskopf Coll
Automation Activity & Vendor Info: (OPAC) SIRSI
Partic in OCLC Online Computer Library Center, Inc; PALINET & Union Library Catalogue of Pennsylvania; Tri-State College Library Cooperative (TCLC)
Open Mon-Thurs 8am-11:45pm, Fri 8-5:30, Sat 9:30-5:30 & Sun 1-11
Friends of the Library Group

S EARLY AMERICAN INDUSTRIES ASSOCIATION LIBRARY,* 84 S Pine St, 18901-4930. SAN 377-5364. Tel: 215-345-0210, Ext 19. FAX: 215-230-0823. *Librn*, Betsy Smith
Library Holdings: Bk Titles 5,000

DRESHER

R TEMPLE SINAI LIBRARY, 1401 Limekiln Pike, 19025. SAN 315-0119. Tel: 215-643-6510, Ext 110. FAX: 215-643-9441.
Library Holdings: Bk Vols 7,500
Subject Interests: Judaica
Friends of the Library Group

DRUMS

S MTC, Keystone Jobs Corps Center Library, PO Box 37, 18222. SAN 314-4569. Tel: 570-788-1164. FAX: 570-788-1119. *Librn*, Dennis Graham
Founded 1967
Library Holdings: Bk Vols 7,000

DU BOIS

P DU BOIS PUBLIC LIBRARY, 31 S Brady St, 15801. SAN 314-4577. Tel: 814-371-5930. FAX: 814-371-2282. E-Mail: library@key-net.net. *Dir*, Leah Green; Staff 5 (MLS 1, Non-MLS 4)
Founded 1920. Pop 18,800; Circ 110,000
Jan 2000-Dec 2000 Income $153,625, State $47,000, City $43,000, Locally Generated Income $31,500, Other $32,125. Mats Exp $32,000, Books $28,000, Per/Ser (Incl. Access Fees) $4,000. Sal $91,365
Library Holdings: Bk Titles 46,000; Per Subs 120
Automation Activity & Vendor Info: (Cataloging) Brodart; (Circulation) Brodart; (OPAC) Brodart
Partic in Central Pennsylvania Consortium
Friends of the Library Group

C PENNSYLVANIA STATE UNIVERSITY, Dubois Commonwealth College Library (University Libraries),* College Pl, 15801. SAN 314-4585. Tel: 814-375-4756. FAX: 814-375-4784. E-Mail: lab28@psu.edu. *Librn*, Lisa Beinhoff; Staff 3 (MLS 1, Non-MLS 2)
Founded 1935. Enrl 920; Fac 50
Jul 1997-Jun 1998 Mats Exp $78,534
Library Holdings: Bk Vols 38,966; Per Subs 233
Special Collections: Wildlife Technology (Paul A Handwerk & David D Wanless Coll)
Partic in OCLC Online Computer Library Center, Inc; RLIN

DUNMORE

C PENNSYLVANIA STATE UNIVERSITY, Worthington Scranton Commonwealth College Library (University Libraries),* 120 Ridge View Dr, 18512-1699. SAN 314-4593. Tel: 717-963-2630. FAX: 717-963-2635. E-Mail: rxf@psulias.psu.edu. *Librn*, Richard Fitzsimmons; Staff 3 (MLS 1, Non-MLS 2)
Founded 1923. Enrl 1,325; Fac 44
Jul 1997-Jun 1998 Mats Exp $77,239
Library Holdings: Bk Vols 44,254; Per Subs 234
Partic in OCLC Online Computer Library Center, Inc; RLIN

DUSHORE

P SULLIVAN COUNTY LIBRARY,* 216 Center St, PO Box 309, 18614-0309. SAN 314-4615. Tel: 570-928-9352. FAX: 570-928-8820. *Dir*, Carol Roinick
Founded 1947. Pop 6,104; Circ 35,500
Library Holdings: Bk Vols 15,057; Per Subs 60
Subject Interests: Local history

AGLEVILLE

M EAGLEVILLE HOSPITAL, Henry S Louchheim Medical Library, 100 Eagleville Rd, 19408-0045. SAN 314-4623. Tel: 610-539-6000, Ext 112. FAX: 610-539-5123.
Founded 1971
Library Holdings: Bk Titles 3,500; Per Subs 116
Subject Interests: Alcoholism, Drug addiction, Psychology, Psycotherapy, Soc work
Special Collections: Black History & Culture; Change; Homosexuality; Management & Organizational; Therapeutic Community Life
Restriction: Non-circulating to the public
Partic in Consortium of Health Info; Delaware Valley Information Consortium

P LOWER PROVIDENCE TOWNSHIP,* 50 Parklane Dr, 19403-1171. SAN 375-3115. Tel: 610-666-6640. FAX: 610-666-5109. Web Site: www.mclinc.org. *Dir*, Lucyann M Ennis; Tel: 610-666-6641, E-Mail: lennis@mclinc.org; *Circ*, Barbara Auris; *Per*, Betty Thul; *ILL*, Anne Foy; *Ch Servs*, Ginger May; Staff 6 (MLS 2, Non-MLS 4)
Founded 1985. Pop 19,350; Circ 130,000
Jan 1999-Dec 1999 Income $500,000, State $60,000, City $180,000, Locally Generated Income $260,000. Mats Exp $32,000, Books $27,000, Per/Ser (Incl. Access Fees) $5,000. Sal $100,000 (Prof $41,000)
Library Holdings: Bk Vols 36,000; Per Subs 55
Automation Activity & Vendor Info: (Cataloging) Gaylord; (Circulation) Gaylord; (OPAC) Gaylord
Partic in Montgomery County Libr & Info Network Consortium
Special Services for the Deaf - Books on deafness & sign language
Friends of the Library Group

AST BERLIN

P EAST BERLIN COMMUNITY LIBRARY,* 105 Locust St, PO Box 1014, 17316-0514. SAN 321-6640. Tel: 717-259-9000. FAX: 717-259-7651. E-Mail: eblib@blazenet.net. Web Site: www.adamslibrary.org/eb. *Dir*, Pat Dixon
Pop 6,763; Circ 35,524
Jan 1998-Dec 1998 Income (Main Library Only) $85,000. Mats Exp $9,178. Sal $29,270
Library Holdings: Bk Vols 14,844; Per Subs 22
Automation Activity & Vendor Info: (Cataloging) Gaylord; (Circulation) Gaylord; (OPAC) Gaylord
Mem of Adams County Library System
Friends of the Library Group

EAST STROUDSBURG

C EAST STROUDSBURG UNIVERSITY, Kemp Library,* Smith & Normal Sts, 18301-2988. SAN 314-4666. Tel: 570-422-3465. Circulation Tel: 717-422-3126. TDD: 570-422-3126. FAX: 570-422-3151. E-Mail: library@po-box.esu.edu. Web Site: www.esu.edu/library/index.html. *Dir Libr Serv*, David G Schappert; Tel: 570-422-3152, E-Mail: dgs@po-box.esu.edu; *ILL, Ref*, Patricia J Jersey; Tel: 570-422-3154, E-Mail: pjersey@po-box.esu.edu; *Acq*, John B Lalley; Tel: 570-422-3544, E-Mail: jlaley@po-box.esu.edu; *Cat*, Angella Angelini; Tel: 570-422-3584, E-Mail: aangelini@po-box.esu.edu; *Cat*, Paul M Graham; Tel: 570-422-3797, E-Mail: pgraham@po-box.esu.edu; *Chairperson, Ref*, Mary Kay Lavalle; Tel: 570-422-3154, E-Mail: mlavelle@po-box.esu.edu; *Per*, Leslie A Berger; Tel: 570-422-3597, E-Mail: leslieab@po-box.esu.edu; *Doc*, Judith Feller; *Govt Doc*, Ramona Hylton; Tel: 570-422-3150, E-Mail: ramona.hylton@po-box.esu.edu; *Circ*, Michelle P Star; Tel: 570-422-3541, E-Mail: mstar@po-box.esu.edu; Staff 22 (MLS 10, Non-MLS 12)
Founded 1893. Enrl 5,300; Fac 250; Highest Degree: Master
Jul 1998-Jun 1999 Income Parent Institution $1,764,458. Mats Exp $470,131, Books $134,331, Per/Ser (Incl. Access Fees) $283,000, Micro $50,000, Electronic Ref Mat (Incl. Access Fees) $2,800. Sal $1,433,856 (Prof $608,549)
Library Holdings: Bk Vols 437,977; Per Subs 1,900
Subject Interests: Behav sci, Computer science, Econ, Education, Fine arts, History, Natural science, Soc sci
Automation Activity & Vendor Info: (Cataloging) Endeavor; (Circulation) Endeavor; (OPAC) Endeavor; (Serials) Endeavor
Database Vendor: CARL, Ebsco - EbscoHost, OCLC - First Search, Silverplatter Information Inc.
Mem of Keystone Libr Network
Partic in Northeastern Pennsylvania Library Network; PALCI; PALINET & Union Library Catalogue of Pennsylvania

M POCONO MEDICAL CENTER, Marshall R Metzgar Medical Library, 206 E Brown St, 18301. SAN 327-1048. Tel: 570-476-3515. FAX: 570-476-3472. *Librn*, Sharon Hrabina; E-Mail: shrabina@pmchealthsystem.org; Staff 1 (MLS 1)
Founded 1976
Library Holdings: Bk Vols 1,000; Per Subs 180
Partic in BHSL

EASTON

P EASTON AREA PUBLIC LIBRARY & DISTRICT CENTER, 515 Church St, 18042-3587. SAN 314-4682. Tel: 610-258-2917. FAX: 610-253-2231. E-Mail: eappublic@hslc.org. Web Site: www.eastonpl.org. *Librn*, Andrew Levas; *Automation Syst Coordr*, Scott Bohon; *Commun Relations*, Barbara Bauer; *Ref*, Diane Fisher; *Cat, Tech Servs*, Barbara Wiemann; *Coll Develop*, Jennifer Stocker; *Publ Servs*, Ellen Selmasska; Staff 6 (MLS 6)
Founded 1811
Library Holdings: Bk Vols 176,988; Per Subs 313
Subject Interests: Bus, History, Literary criticism, Mgt
Special Collections: Genealogy & Local History, Pennsylvania, Eastern Ohio & Western New Jersey (Henry F Marx Local History Room)
Publications: Exlibris (quarterly newsletter)
Partic in OCLC Online Computer Library Center, Inc
Friends of the Library Group
Branches: 2
PALMER TOWNSHIP, One Weller Pl, 18042. SAN 320-054X. Tel: 610-258-7492. *Librn*, Debbie Osmun
Friends of the Library Group
SOUTHSIDE, Berwick & Seitz Ave, 18042. SAN 321-9461. Tel: 610-258-3121. *Librn*, Caryn Kunz

M EASTON HOSPITAL, Frank J D'Agostino, MD Medical Library, 250 S 21st St, 18042-3892. SAN 326-3207. Tel: 610-250-4130. FAX: 610-250-4905. Web Site: www.eastonhospital.org/library.htm. *Dir Libr Serv*, Lucy Wrightington; Staff 2 (MLS 2)
Library Holdings: Bk Titles 2,500; Per Subs 180
Subject Interests: Medicine, Nursing, Pediatrics, Surgery

C LAFAYETTE COLLEGE, David Bishop Skillman Library, 18042. SAN 358-4194. Tel: 610-330-5151. Interlibrary Loan Service Tel: 610-330-5157. FAX: 610-252-0370. Web Site: www.library.lafayette.edu. *Dir*, Neil J McElroy; *Librn*, Mercedes Sharpless; Tel: 610-330-5398, E-Mail: sharplem@lafayette.edu; *Access Serv, ILL*, Daniel Evans; Tel: 610-330-5161, E-Mail: evansd@lafayette.edu; *Acq, Ser*, Vaswati Sinha; Tel: 610-330-5636, E-Mail: sinhav@lafayette.edu; *Cat*, Helen Dungan; Tel: 610-330-5160, E-Mail: dunganh@lafayette.edu; *Head, Info Serv*, Terese Heidonwolf; Tel: 610-330-5153, E-Mail: heidenwt@lafayette.edu; *Info Tech*, Patricia Facciponti; Tel: 610-330-5632, E-Mail: faccipop@lafayette.edu; *Info Tech*, John O'Keefe; Tel: 610-330-5609; *Ref*, Amy Abruzzi; Tel: 610-330-5631, E-Mail: abruzzia@lafayette.edu; *Ref*, Anne Barnhart-Park; Tel: 610-330-5152, E-Mail: barnhara@lafayette.edu; *Ref*, Reid Larson; Tel: 610-330-5154, E-Mail: larsonr@lafayette.edu; *Spec Coll*, Diane W Shaw; Tel: 610-330-5401, E-Mail: shawd@lafayette.edu; *Syst Coordr*, Robert Duncan; Tel: 610-330-5156, E-Mail: duncanr@lafayette.edu; Staff 13 (MLS 11, Non-MLS 2)
Founded 1826. Enrl 2,208; Fac 183; Highest Degree: Bachelor
Jul 1999-Jun 2000 Mats Exp $2,693,000, Books $407,000, Per/Ser (Incl. Access Fees) $635,000, Presv $21,000, Micro $25,000. Sal $918,000 (Prof $547,000)
Library Holdings: Bk Vols 506,000; Bk Titles 330,000; Per Subs 2,526
Special Collections: American Friends of Lafayette; Conahay, Tinsman & Fox Angling Coll; Howard Chandler Christy Coll; Jay Parini Coll; Marquis de LaFayette Coll; Robt & Helen Meyner Coll; Stephen Crane Coll; Wm E Simon Coll
Automation Activity & Vendor Info: (Acquisitions) Innovative Interfaces Inc.; (Cataloging) Innovative Interfaces Inc.; (Circulation) Innovative Interfaces Inc.; (Course Reserve) Innovative Interfaces Inc.; (ILL) Innovative Interfaces Inc.; (Media Booking) Innovative Interfaces Inc.; (OPAC) Innovative Interfaces Inc.; (Serials) Innovative Interfaces Inc.
Publications: Bytes & Books; Cur Non
Partic in Interlibrary Delivery Service of Pennsylvania; Lehigh Valley Association Of Independent Colleges, Inc; PALCI; PALINET & Union Library Catalogue of Pennsylvania
Friends of the Library Group
Departmental Libraries:
KIRBY LIBRARY OF GOVERNMENT & LAW, Kirby Hall, Lafayette College, 18042. SAN 358-4224. Tel: 610-250-5399. FAX: 610-250-5397. *Librn*, Mercedes Benitez-Sharpless; Tel: 610-330-5398
Library Holdings: Bk Vols 27,000; Per Subs 126
Subject Interests: Civil rights, International relations, Political science
Automation Activity & Vendor Info: (Acquisitions) Innovative Interfaces Inc.; (Cataloging) Innovative Interfaces Inc.; (Circulation) Innovative Interfaces Inc.; (Course Reserve) Innovative Interfaces Inc.; (ILL) Innovative Interfaces Inc.; (Media Booking) Innovative Interfaces Inc.; (OPAC) Innovative Interfaces Inc.; (Serials) Innovative Interfaces Inc.

P MARY MEUSER MEMORIAL LIBRARY, 1803 Northampton St, 18042-3183. SAN 314-4690. Tel: 610-258-3040. FAX: 610-258-8170. E-Mail: meuserlib@enter.net. Web Site: www.enternet/~meuserlib/. *Dir*, Daniel L Redington; *Ch Servs*, Christy Fot; Staff 3 (Non-MLS 3)
Founded 1962. Pop 13,500; Circ 49,000
Jan 1999-Dec 1999 Income $170,625, State $19,700, Locally Generated Income $19,865, Other $10,000. Mats Exp $20,700, Books $17,000, Per/Ser (Incl. Access Fees) $3,300, AV Equip $400. Sal $104,000 (Prof $72,300)
Library Holdings: Bk Vols 41,000; Per Subs 76
Subject Interests: Art, Poetry

Special Collections: Contemporary Poetry Coll
Publications: For Kids Only (children's newsletter); Rediscover Reading Newsletter
Friends of the Library Group

S NATIONAL CANAL MUSEUM & PENNSYLVANIA CANAL SOCIETY, National Canal Museum Library Archives, 30 Centre Sq, 18042-7743. SAN 314-4674. Tel: 610-250-6703. E-Mail: archive@canals.org. Web Site: www.canals.org. *Coll Develop, Publ Servs*, Tom Smith; *Exec Dir*, J Steven Humphrey
Founded 1970
Library Holdings: Bk Titles 5,000
Subject Interests: Am Canal hist, Anthracite iron, Bethlehem Steel, Related technologies
Special Collections: Bethlehem Steel Corp, bks, film, papers, photogs; Buehler Furniture Co Coll, drawings, photogs, rec; Charles Schwab Coll; John Fritz Coll, papers; Lehigh Coal & Navigation Company, corporate records, papers, photogs; Pennsylvania Pump Co Coll, photogs; Reading Anthracite Company, photogs; William Rau lantern slides
Publications: Annual Symposium Proceedings
Open Mon-Fri 8:30am-4:30pm, advance notice required
Friends of the Library Group

S NORTHAMPTON COUNTY HISTORICAL & GENEALOGICAL SOCIETY, Mary Illick Memorial Library, 107 S Fourth St, 18042. SAN 314-4712. Tel: 610-253-1222. FAX: 610-253-4701. *Librn*, Jane S Moyer
Founded 1906
Library Holdings: Bk Titles 7,000
Subject Interests: County hist of Pa, Hist rec, Northampton County
Special Collections: Deed Coll; Genealogical File Coll; Manuscript Coll; Merchants' Ledgers; Picture Coll
Publications: Newsletter; Northhampton Notes (semi-annual bulletin)
Restriction: Open to public for reference only
Partic in Deed Coll; Genealogical; Genealogical File Coll; Manuscript Coll; Merchants' Ledgers; Picture Coll
Open Mon-Fri 9-12 & 1-4

GL NORTHAMPTON COUNTY LAW LIBRARY, 669 Washington St, 18042-7468. SAN 314-4704. Tel: 610-559-3076. FAX: 610-559-3163. E-Mail: ncll@nccpa.org. Web Site: www.nccpa.org. *Librn*, Anita L DeBona
Founded 1860
Library Holdings: Bk Titles 23,399
Special Collections: Typical Coll for Pa County Law Libr

EBENSBURG

GL CAMBRIA COUNTY FREE LAW LIBRARY,* Court House, S Center St, 15931. SAN 314-4739. Tel: 814-472-5440, Ext 501. *Librn*, Jeanne Wolf
Founded 1920
Library Holdings: Bk Vols 35,000

S CAMBRIA COUNTY HISTORICAL SOCIETY LIBRARY,* 615 N Center, PO Box 278, 15931-1122. SAN 314-4747. Tel: 814-472-6674. *Curator*, Leslie Conrad
Founded 1925
Library Holdings: Bk Vols 3,100; Bk Titles 2,400
Subject Interests: Genealogy of families within Cambria County, Hist of Cambria county, Indust, Pa soc and relig life of citizens
Publications: Heritage (quarterly newsletter)

P EBENSBURG FREE PUBLIC LIBRARY,* 225 W Highland Ave, 15931-1507. SAN 314-4755. Tel: 814-472-7957. FAX: 814-472-2037. *Librn*, Marcia Springer; *Asst Librn*, Antoinette Huber
Founded 1923. Pop 4,818; Circ 20,751
Library Holdings: Bk Vols 16,000; Per Subs 12
Special Collections: Local History Coll
Mem of Cambria County Library System & District Center

EDINBORO

C EDINBORO UNIVERSITY OF PENNSYLVANIA, Baron-Forness Library, 16444. SAN 358-4259. Tel: 814-732-2779. Interlibrary Loan Service Tel: 814-732-2946. FAX: 814-732-2883. E-Mail: internet: library@edinboro.edu. Web Site: www.edinboro.edu/cwis/library/menu.html. *Dir*, Dr Donald Dilmore; E-Mail: ddilmore@vax.edinboro.edu; *Bibliog Instr, Publ Servs*, Jack Widner; *Online Servs*, Monty McAdoo; *AV, Tech Servs*, John Fleming; *Cat*, Ed Bercik; *Circ*, Judy Wilson; *Doc, Ref*, Raymond Dengel; *Archivist, Spec Coll*, David Obringer; *Acq*, Loralyn Whitney; Staff 26 (MLS 13, Non-MLS 13)
Founded 1857. Enrl 7,200; Fac 397; Highest Degree: Master
Jul 1999-Jun 2000 Income (Main Library and Branch Library) $2,289,271. Mats Exp $525,598, Books $147,444, Per/Ser (Incl. Access Fees) $262,038, Presv $20,252, Micro $23,614, Electronic Ref Mat (Incl. Access Fees) $72,250. Sal $1,205,726 (Prof $812,949)
Library Holdings: Bk Vols 460,889; Bk Titles 291,900; Per Subs 1,678
Subject Interests: Education
Special Collections: Art; Southeast Asia Coll
Automation Activity & Vendor Info: (Acquisitions) Endeavor; (Cataloging) Endeavor; (Circulation) Endeavor; (OPAC) Endeavor; (Serials) Endeavor
Database Vendor: Dialog, Ebsco - EbscoHost, Lexis-Nexis, OCLC - First Search, Silverplatter Information Inc.
Publications: Faculty Guide; PAC User Guide; Student Guide
Partic in OCLC Online Computer Library Center, Inc; PALCI; PALINET & Union Library Catalogue of Pennsylvania
Departmental Libraries:
MILLER LEARNING CENTER Tel: 814-732-2569. *Librn*, Elaine Bercik
Library Holdings: Bk Vols 13,242

ELDRED

S ENSANIAN PHYSICOCHEMICAL INSTITUTE, Institute Library, Barden Brook Rd, PO Box 98, 16731. SAN 358-4313. Tel: 814-225-3296. *Chief Librn*, Elisabeth Anahid Ensanian; Staff 3 (MLS 1, Non-MLS 2)
Founded 1963
Library Holdings: Bk Titles 3,300; Per Subs 125
Subject Interests: Artificial intelligence, Automation, Bioengineering, Biol diagnostic med, Conceptual foundations of quantum physics, Econ, Energy conversion, ESP, Evaluations of metals, Fingerprinting of odors, Manufacturing in zero gravity, Mat sci, Mathematics, Mats, Metallurgy, Non-destructive testing, Non-linear thermodynamics, Pattern recognition, Physical chem, Plant physiology, Processes controls, Quantum computers, Robots, Solid state, Theoretical physics, Total automated manufacturing in the metalworking industries, Water structure
Special Collections: Cosmology (Structure of the Universe), bks, rpt; Geotropism (Gravitation Biology), rpt; Gravitation (Information Center for Gravitation Chemistry), bks, rpt; Non-Destructive Testing of Materials, bks, rpt; Physiochemical Robotic Sensors; Quantum Physics; Robotics & Robot Sensors (Tactile); Stored Energy in Metals (Electrotopography Information Center), rpt
Restriction: Staff use only

ELIZABETHTOWN

C ELIZABETHTOWN COLLEGE, The High Library, One Alpha Dr, 17022-2227. SAN 314-4771. Tel: 717-361-1451. Circulation Tel: 717-361-1222. Reference Tel: 717-361-1461. FAX: 717-361-1167. Web Site: www.etown.edu/library. *Dir*, Dr Nelson P Bard; Tel: 717-361-1428, E-Mail: bardnp@etown.edu; *Asst Dir*, Sandra Hilsher; E-Mail: hilshesa@etown.edu; *Head Tech Servs*, Carol H Warfel; Tel: 717-361-1456, E-Mail: warfelch@etown.edu; *Ref*, Sylvia Tiffany Morra; Tel: 717-361-1452, E-Mail: morrast@etown.edu; Staff 11 (MLS 6, Non-MLS 5)
Founded 1899. Enrl 1,633; Fac 113; Highest Degree: Master
Jul 1999-Jun 2000 Income $461,100. Mats Exp $368,215, Books $180,610, Per/Ser (Incl. Access Fees) $158,205, Other Print Mats $3,700, Electronic Ref Mat (Incl. Access Fees) $29,400
Library Holdings: Bk Vols 230,906; Bk Titles 171,054; Per Subs 1,090
Special Collections: Brethren Heritage Coll
Automation Activity & Vendor Info: (Acquisitions) SIRSI; (Cataloging) SIRSI; (Circulation) SIRSI; (Course Reserve) SIRSI; (OPAC) SIRSI; (Serials) SIRSI
Database Vendor: Dialog, Ebsco - EbscoHost, Lexis-Nexis, OCLC - First Search
Partic in Associated College Libraries of Central Pennsylvania; Dialog Corporation; OCLC Online Computer Library Center, Inc; PALINET & Union Library Catalogue of Pennsylvania
Friends of the Library Group

P ELIZABETHTOWN PUBLIC LIBRARY, 399 N Hanover, 17022-1699. SAN 314-478X. Tel: 717-367-7467. FAX: 717-367-5019. E-Mail: subowser@ptd.net. *Librn*, Susan Bowser
Founded 1925. Pop 21,000; Circ 150,000
Library Holdings: Bk Vols 35,000; Bk Titles 32,000; Per Subs 80
Automation Activity & Vendor Info: (Cataloging) Gaylord; (Circulation) Gaylord; (OPAC) Gaylord
Database Vendor: Ebsco - EbscoHost, Lexis-Nexis
Mem of Library System of Lancaster County
Friends of the Library Group

ELKINS PARK

R BETH SHOLOM CONGREGATION, Joseph & Elizabeth Schwartz Library, 8231 Old York Rd, 19027. SAN 314-4798. Tel: 215-887-1342. FAX: 215-887-6605.
Founded 1959
Library Holdings: Bk Titles 7,500; Per Subs 10
Subject Interests: Jewish art
Special Collections: Jewish Music (Gedaliah Rabinowitz Library); Judaica

P ELKINS PARK FREE LIBRARY,* 563 E Church Rd, 19027-2499. SAN 314-481X. Tel: 215-635-5000. FAX: 215-635-5844. E-Mail: elkinspark@mclinc.org. Web Site: www.mclinc.org. *Librn*, Helen Alexander; *Tech Servs*, Dorothy L Sutton; Staff 11 (MLS 3, Non-MLS 8)
Founded 1958

Jan 1997-Dec 1998 Income $385,726, State $31,939, Locally Generated Income $109,181, Other $2,668. Mats Exp $82,468, Books $50,415, Per/Ser (Incl. Access Fees) $8,333, Micro $2,983. Sal $185,426
Library Holdings: Bk Vols 56,511; Per Subs 154
Subject Interests: Art, Large print bks, Multicultural mat
Mem of Cheltenham Township Library System; Montgomery County District Libr Syst; Montgomery County Libr & Info Network Consortium
Friends of the Library Group

KENESETH ISRAEL REFORM CONGREGATION, Meyers Library, 8339 Old York Rd, 19027. SAN 314-4836. Tel: 215-887-8704. FAX: 215-887-1070. *Coordr*, Norma Meshkov; *Librn*, Beth Langsdorf; Staff 3 (MLS 1, Non-MLS 2)
Jul 1998-Jun 1999 Income $2,000. Mats Exp $2,000, Books $1,600, Per/Ser (Incl. Access Fees) $100
Library Holdings: Bk Vols 14,000; Bk Titles 10,000; Per Subs 30
Subject Interests: Judaica

M PENNSYLVANIA COLLEGE OF OPTOMETRY LIBRARY,* 8360 Old York Rd, 19027. SAN 314-9625. Tel: 215-780-1400. FAX: 215-780-1263. Web Site: www.pco.edu. *Dir*, Keith Lammers; E-Mail: keith@pco.edu
Founded 1919. Enrl 585
Jul 1997-Jun 1998 Income $250,000. Mats Exp $83,600. Sal $112,960
Library Holdings: Bk Vols 20,000; Per Subs 210
Subject Interests: Blindness, Clinical medicine, Low vision, Ocular anatomy, Ocular pharmacology, Ophthalmology, Optometry, Rehabilitation optics, Vision res, Visually impaired
Special Collections: Antique Eyewear & Ophthalmic Instruments; Old Visual Science Books
Publications: Infovision (newsletter); Ocular Bibliographies
Partic in Association of Vision Science Librarians (AVSL); Basic Health Sciences Library Network; Delaware Valley Information Consortium; Docline; Health Sci Libr Info Consortium; Nat Libr of Med; Regional Med Libr Network
Open Mon-Fri 8am-11:45pm, Sat & Sun 10am-11:45pm

ELKLAND

ELKLAND AREA COMMUNITY LIBRARY,* 110 Parkway Dr, 16920-1311. SAN 314-4844. Tel: 814-258-7576. FAX: 814-258-7414. *Librn*, Rosemary Hackett
Pop 3,927; Circ 12,599
Library Holdings: Bk Vols 13,000; Per Subs 60
Special Collections: Elkland Journal Coll, bd copies & microfilm
Open Tues & Thurs 6-9PM, Wed 9-3, Fri 11-4, Sat 9-12

ELLWOOD CITY

ELLWOOD CITY AREA PUBLIC LIBRARY, 510 Crescent Ave, 16117-1944. SAN 314-4852. Tel: 724-758-6458. FAX: 724-758-0115. E-Mail: ecapl@usaor.net. Web Site: www.lawrencecountylibrary.org. *Head Librn*, Jean Ann Barsotti; E-Mail: ecapl@usaor.net; Staff 6 (MLS 1, Non-MLS 5)
Founded 1914. Pop 17,933; Circ 61,994
Jan 1999-Dec 1999 Income $192,398, State $28,260, City $27,500, County $56,617, Locally Generated Income $53,921, Other $26,100. Mats Exp $36,666, Books $30,751, Per/Ser (Incl. Access Fees) $2,313, Presv $300, AV Equip $2,069, Electronic Ref Mat (Incl. Access Fees) $1,233. Sal $85,638
Library Holdings: Bk Vols 40,283; Per Subs 75
Database Vendor: DRA
Friends of the Library Group

ELVERSON

US DEPARTMENT OF INTERIOR, NATIONAL PARK SERVICE, Hopewell Furnace National Historic Site Library, 2 Mark Bird Lane, 19520. Tel: 610-582-8773. FAX: 610-582-2768. E-Mail: hofu_superintendent@nps.gov. Web Site: www.nps.gov/hofu/index.html.
Library Holdings: Bk Vols 1,200; Per Subs 5
Subject Interests: History
Special Collections: Old & Rare Books on the History of Iron Making (30)
Restriction: By appointment only, Not open to public, Open to researchers by request

ELWYN

S ELWYN, INC, (PLE), Staff Library, 111 Elwyn Rd, 19063. SAN 326-4300. Tel: 610-891-2084. FAX: 610-891-2088. E-Mail: elwynlib@hslc.org. *Librn*, Joyce Lentz; Staff 1 (MLS 1)
Founded 1968
Jul 1999-Jun 2000 Income Parent Institution $78,996. Mats Exp $12,851, Books $3,258, Per/Ser (Incl. Access Fees) $9,214, AV Equip $110, Electronic Ref Mat (Incl. Access Fees) $269. Sal $45,757
Library Holdings: Bk Vols 2,800; Bk Titles 2,700; Per Subs 82; Bks on Deafness & Sign Lang 97
Subject Interests: Mental health, Mental retardation, Psychology, Social servs, Special education
Database Vendor: OCLC - First Search
Publications: Acquisitions List
Function: ILL available, Reference services available
Partic in Consortium For Health Information & Library Services
Special Services for the Deaf - Books on deafness & sign language; Videos & decoder

ELYSBURG

P RALPHO TOWNSHIP PUBLIC LIBRARY,* 32B Market St, PO Box 315, 17824-0315. SAN 314-4860. Tel: 570-672-9449. *Dir*, Patricia Bidding; *Asst Librn*, Jo Sheptock; *Asst Librn*, Pat Reed; Staff 1 (MLS 1)
Founded 1974. Pop 3,131; Circ 14,058
Library Holdings: Bk Vols 13,207; Bk Titles 15,437; Per Subs 35
Mem of Pottsville Free Public Library
Open Mon & Tues 2-8:30, Wed 10-8:30, Thurs 2-8:30, Fri 2-6:30 & Sat 10-1
Friends of the Library Group

EMMAUS

P EMMAUS PUBLIC LIBRARY,* 11 E Main St, 18049. SAN 314-4879. Tel: 610-965-9284. FAX: 610-965-6446. E-Mail: emmauspl@cliu.org. *Dir*, Frances A Larash; *ILL*, Marybeth Havanko; *Ref*, Dorothy Russell; Staff 11 (MLS 6, Non-MLS 5)
Founded 1966. Pop 38,344
Jan 1997-Dec 1998 Income $238,903, State $37,461, City $66,942, Locally Generated Income $24,000, Other $1,500. Mats Exp $59,225, Books $38,900, Per/Ser (Incl. Access Fees) $5,013, Presv $320. Sal $143,500
Library Holdings: Bk Vols 72,000; Per Subs 120
Special Collections: Art & Reference Books (Roeder Coll); Local History (Shelter House Coll)
Mem of Allentown Dist Libr Syst
Friends of the Library Group

S RODALE INC, Library & Information Services, 33 E Minor St, 18098. SAN 324-7805. Tel: 610-967-8729. Interlibrary Loan Service Tel: 610-967-8189. FAX: 610-967-7708. *Dir, Tech Servs*, Lynn Donches; E-Mail: lynn.donches@rodale.com; *Mgr*, Adrienne Kreger-May; Tel: 610-967-8285, Fax: 610-967-8691, E-Mail: Adrienne.May@Rodale.com; *Per*, Shirley Labert; *ILL*, Jennifer Keiser; Staff 8 (MLS 2, Non-MLS 6)
Founded 1976
Library Holdings: Bk Vols 42,000; Bk Titles 40,000; Per Subs 2,300
Subject Interests: Agriculture, Fitness, Gardening, Health, Nutrition, Sports
Database Vendor: Dialog, OCLC - First Search
Publications: Abstract bulletins; Periodical List
Restriction: By appointment only

EMPORIUM

GL CAMERON COUNTY LAW LIBRARY,* Court House, E Fifth St, 15834. SAN 328-0047. Tel: 814-486-3349. FAX: 814-486-0464. *Dir*, David J Reed
Founded 1890
Library Holdings: Bk Vols 3,000

P CAMERON COUNTY PUBLIC LIBRARY, One E Fourth St, 15834-0430. (Mail add: PO Box 430, 15834), SAN 358-4526. Tel: 814-486-8011. FAX: 814-486-3725. E-Mail: cameronp@penn.com. Web Site: www.penn.com/cameronlibrary/. *Dir*, Lois Ann Strycula; Staff 5 (MLS 1, Non-MLS 4)
Founded 1940. Pop 5,745; Circ 20,643
Jan 1999-Dec 1999 Income $149,974, State $50,216, County $64,056, Locally Generated Income $35,702. Mats Exp $23,819, Books $16,541, Per/Ser (Incl. Access Fees) $1,704, Presv $2,634, AV Equip $1,733, Electronic Ref Mat (Incl. Access Fees) $1,207. Sal $54,315 (Prof $23,378)
Library Holdings: Bk Vols 17,015; Per Subs 72
Subject Interests: Pa hist
Automation Activity & Vendor Info: (Cataloging) Follett; (Circulation) Follett; (OPAC) Follett
Database Vendor: Dialog, Ebsco - EbscoHost
Friends of the Library Group

EPHRATA

P EPHRATA PUBLIC LIBRARY, 550 S Reading Rd, 17522. SAN 314-4887. Tel: 717-738-9291. FAX: 717-721-3003. Web Site: www.ephratapubliclibrary.org. *Librn*, Jennifer T Raimo; E-Mail: jenraimo@ptd.net
Pop 28,168; Circ 325,000
Jan 2000-Dec 2000 Income $449,100. Mats Exp $59,000. Sal $249,000 (Prof $103,000)
Library Holdings: Bk Vols 55,000; Per Subs 50
Automation Activity & Vendor Info: (Cataloging) Gaylord; (Circulation) Gaylord; (OPAC) Gaylord
Mem of Library System of Lancaster County
Friends of the Library Group

S THE HISTORICAL SOCIETY OF THE COCALICO VALLEY LIBRARY, 249 W Main St, 17522. (Mail add: PO Box 193, 17522), SAN 326-5331. Tel: 717-733-1616. *Librn*, Cynthia Marquet; Staff 1 (MLS 1)
Founded 1957
Library Holdings: Bk Vols 1,880; Bk Titles 1,550
Special Collections: Ephrata Cloister imprints (Walter Moyer Coll), bks; historical photographs (9315)
Publications: Annual Journal
Restriction: Non-circulating to the public

ERDENHEIM

S ANTONELLI INSTITUTE OF ART & PHOTOGRAPHY LIBRARY, 300 Montgomery Ave, 19038. SAN 372-6967. Tel: 215-836-2222. FAX: 215-836-2794. *Librn*, Dr Thomas Treacy
Founded 1938. Enrl 150; Fac 22
Library Holdings: Bk Titles 1,300; Per Subs 68

ERIE

SR ANSHE HESED TEMPLE LIBRARY,* 930 Liberty St, 16502. SAN 328-6363. Tel: 814-454-2426. FAX: 814-454-2427. E-Mail: anshhsd@velocity.net. *Librn*, Barbara Shapiro
Library Holdings: Bk Vols 3,000
Special Collections: Congregational Archives

GM DEPARTMENT OF VETERANS AFFAIRS MEDICAL CENTER, Medical Library, 135 E 38th St, 16504-1559. SAN 314-5050. Tel: 814-860-2444. FAX: 814-860-2469. *In Charge*, Mary E Nourse; E-Mail: mary.nourse@med.va.gov; Staff 3 (MLS 1, Non-MLS 2)
Founded 1951
Library Holdings: Bk Titles 2,228; Per Subs 150
Subject Interests: Nursing, Primary health care
Partic in Docline; Erie Area Health Information Library Cooperative; NICOP; NLM

S ERIE COUNTY HISTORICAL SOCIETY & MUSEUMS, Erie History Ctr, 419 State St, 16501. SAN 324-7619. Tel: 814-454-1813. FAX: 814-452-1744. E-Mail: echs@velocity.net. *Coll Develop, Librn*, Annita Andrick; *Publ Servs*, Melinda Meyer; Staff 4 (MLS 2, Non-MLS 2)
Library Holdings: Bk Vols 5,000; Per Subs 46
Subject Interests: Historic preservation, Local history, Pa hist
Special Collections: Adam Grimler Papers; Agricultural Almanacs Coll; Almhagen/Deaner Coll; Andrews Land Co/Corp Coll; Ashby Printing Coll; Baldwin Building Exhibit Research Coll; Barnhard Family Coll; Barry Casselman Literary Coll; Battles Bank Coll; Bible Coll; Burke Electric Company Coll; C B Hall Photograph Coll; C Paxton Cody Architecture Coll; Central Presbyterian Church Records; Cervone Family Coll; Chacona Family Coll; City of Erie Coll; Cosmopolite Herald Photograph Coll; Crawford County Credit Exchange Coll; Crawford Family Coll; Curtze Family Coll; Daniel Dobbins Family Coll; DAR Genealogical Records of Waterford & Crawford County; David W Hutchinson Coll (on loan); Deeds Coll; Dickson Family Coll; Dickson Tavern Papers (on loan); Dobbins Family Bible; Dobbins Lane Photograph Coll; Dr Benjamin Ely Coll; Ebenizer Gunnison Papers; Edward J Allen Coll; Elizabeth Geer Coll; Ephemera Coll; Erie Academy Papers; Erie Area Bicentennial Celebration Coll; Erie Art Center Coll; Erie Art Museum Archives; Erie Brewing Co, Inc & Koehler Brewery Coll; Erie Business & Professional Women's Club Coll; Erie City Building Inspector's Office Plans & Drawings Coll; Erie City Passenger Railway Coll; Erie Civic Music Association Coll; Erie Club Coll; Erie Club Preservation Program Coll; Erie Conference on Community Development Archives & Reports; Erie County Almshouse Papers; Erie County Appearance Papers; Erie County Council Minute Books; Erie County Court Exhibits Photograph Coll; Erie County Deed Books Coll; Erie County Deputy Sheriff's Affidavits Coll; Erie County Government Study Commission Coll; Erie County Historical Society Archives; Erie County Mechanics Lein Waivers Coll (& Dockets); Erie County Mortgage Books Coll; Erie County Naturalization Record Coll (partial); Erie County Quarter Sessions Criminal Records; Erie County Tavern Licenses; Erie County: Gateway to the Great Lakes Coll; Erie Engineering Societies Council Minute Book; Erie Imprint Coll; Erie Morning Telegraph Coll; Erie Oil Company Coll & Papers; Erie Philharmonic Papers; Erie Redevelopment Authority Photograph Coll; Erie Resistor Newsletter Coll; Erie Resistor/Erie Technological Products Coll; Erie School District Budgets; Erie Social Hygiene Association Papers; Erie Story Archives; Erie Tageblatt Newspaper Coll; Erie Yacht Club Coll; Erie: Chronicle of a Great Lakes City Coll; Ervite Corp Coll; Faustine Family Coll; First Christian Church Coll; First National Bank of Erie Records; Flagship Niagara Commission Coll; Fort LeBoeuf Records; Francis Bassett Glassplate Negative Coll; Frontier Improvement Association Papers; General Electric Corp Coll; General Telephone Museum Coll; George Griswold Coll; Gest Coll; Gideon Ball Coll; Girard Universalist Church Coll; Grace Davies Coll; Grand Army of the Republic Post 67 Papers; Griswold Manufacturing Company Catalogues; Grubb-Reed Family Coll; H U Johnson Coll; Hammermill Paper Co, Inc Coll; Hamot Hospital Coll; Harriett Crouch Bury Coll; Harry Burleigh Coll; Hauser Family Coll; Hayes Manufacturing Company Papers; Hayes Papers; Held Family Coll; Helen Bard Coll; Helen Perry Benny Photograph Coll; Henry A Clark Coll; Hermine Bauschard Coll; Hotel Fischer Registers; Ida Kuck Coll; Irene Andrews Coll; Irving Literary Institute Coll; Iwanowski Funeral Home Records; Jack Hindson Photograph Coll; James B Landmesser Coll; Jarecki Glassplate Negative Coll; Jean Holtzhauser Photograph Coll; John Baker Photograph Coll; John Burton Arbuckle Coll) John Chaffee Coll; John Dickson Coll; Johnson, McGill & Willard Busines Records; Jordan Photograph Coll; Josiah Kellogg Coll; Judah Colt Coll; Judson Coll; Judson Papers; Justina Baron Coll; Kirschner Bros Contractor & Builders Business Papers; Kruse Coll; Laurin C Bort Sheet Music Coll; Litton Industries, Marine Division Coll; Litton Shipyard Papers; Mark Davi Coll; Mary Benedict Coll; Maurice E Kolpien Coll; Oliver Hazard Perry Ferguson Coll; Reed M Grunden Coll; Richard S Cheney Coll (also Notebooks); Robert Cross Photograph Coll; Robert J Krider Photograph Coll; Rudolph Conrader Coll; Samuel Diehl Coll; Susan Beates Coll; Thomas King Coll; Vee Lamb Coll; Virginia Ahern Davis Coll; W Edwin Coon Coll; William Forster Coll
Publications: Journal of Erie Studies
Partic in OCLC Online Computer Library Center, Inc; PALINET & Union Library Catalogue of Pennsylvania

GL ERIE COUNTY LAW LIBRARY,* Court House, Rm 217, 16501. SAN 314-4933. Tel: 814-451-6319. FAX: 814-451-6320. E-Mail: eccmcp@erie.net. *Dir*, Max C Peaster
Founded 1876
Library Holdings: Bk Vols 25,000; Per Subs 65
Partic in Westlaw

P ERIE COUNTY PUBLIC LIBRARY,* 160 E Front St, 16507. SAN 358-4585. Tel: 814-451-6900. TDD: 814-451-6931. FAX: 814-451-6907. E-Mai reference@erielibrary.ecls.lib.pa.us. Web Site: www.ecls.lib.pa.us. *Dir*, Greg W Lubelski; *Asst Dir*, Margaret Z Stewart; Tel: 814-451-6914, Fax: 814-451-6969, E-Mail: mstewart@erielibrary.ecls.lib.pa.us; *ILL*, Evelyn Wesman *Cat, Tech Servs*, Sarah Wright; *Tech Coordr*, Ann Randall-Dill; *Br Coordr*, K Loring Summer; Staff 74 (MLS 18, Non-MLS 56)
Founded 1895. Pop 247,474; Circ 1,655,352
Jan 1999-Dec 1999 Income (Main Library and Branch Library) $4,133,133, State $869,314, Federal $56,000, County $2,856,305, Locally Generated Income $199,759, Other $151,755. Mats Exp $538,413, Books $375,604, Per/Ser (Incl. Access Fees) $28,000, Presv $3,500, Micro $30,000, AV Equi $75,309. Sal $2,959,435 (Prof $1,095,405)
Library Holdings: Bk Vols 45,000; Per Subs 241
Special Collections: Genealogy (Western Pennsylvania)
Automation Activity & Vendor Info: (Cataloging) GEAC; (Circulation) GEAC; (OPAC) CLSI LIBS; (Serials) CLSI LIBS
Database Vendor: Ebsco - EbscoHost, OCLC - First Search
Partic in Access Pa Share NW; NICOP; OCLC Online Computer Library Center, Inc; PALINET & Union Library Catalogue of Pennsylvania
Special Services for the Deaf - Books on deafness & sign language
Special Services for the Blind - Braille; Internet workstation with adaptive software for use by people with visual limitations; Kurzweil Reader; Large print bks
Family Search - compact disc holdings of LDS
Friends of the Library Group
Branches: 6
EDINBORO BRANCH, 124 Meadville St, Edinboro, 16412-2508. SAN 358-4615. Tel: 814-451-7081. *Asst Dir*, Margaret Z Stewart; Tel: 814-451-6914, Fax: 814-451-6969, E-Mail: mstewart@erielibrary.ecls.lib.pa.us; *Mgr*, Belle Koncewicz
Library Holdings: Bk Vols 10,999
LAWRENCE PARK, 4212 Iroquois Ave, 16511-2198. SAN 358-4674. Tel: 814-451-7082. *Asst Dir*, Margaret Z Stewart; Tel: 814-451-6914, Fax: 814-451-6969, E-Mail: mstewart@erielibrary.ecls.lib.pa.us; *Mgr*, Carol Gettinger
Library Holdings: Bk Vols 36,516
LIBERTY, 3528 Liberty Plaza, 16508-2533. SAN 358-4704. Tel: 814-451-7083. *Asst Dir*, Margaret Z Stewart; Tel: 814-451-6914, Fax: 814-451-6969, E-Mail: mstewart@erielibrary.ecls.lib.pa.us; *Mgr*, Ann Joslin
Library Holdings: Bk Vols 26,283
MILLCREEK, 600 Millcreek Mall, 5800 Peach St, 16565-0601. SAN 358-4739. Tel: 814-451-7084. *Asst Dir*, Margaret Z Stewart; Tel: 814-451-6914, Fax: 814-451-6969, E-Mail: mstewart@erielibrary.ecls.lib.pa.us; *Mgr*, Belle Koncewicz
Library Holdings: Bk Vols 38,775
PRESQUE ISLE, 902 W Erie Plaza Blvd, Millcreek, 16505-4536. SAN 358-4763. Tel: 814-451-7085. *Asst Dir*, Margaret Z Stewart; Tel: 814-451-6914, Fax: 814-451-6969, E-Mail: mstewart@erielibrary.ecls.lib.pa.us; *Mgr*, Ann Joslin
Library Holdings: Bk Vols 35,713
SOUTHEAST, 1815 E 38th St, 16501-3599. SAN 358-4798. Tel: 814-451-7086. *Asst Dir*, Margaret Z Stewart; Tel: 814-451-6914, Fax: 814-451-6969, E-Mail: mstewart@erielibrary.ecls.lib.pa.us; *Mgr*, Carol Gettinger
Library Holdings: Bk Vols 17,899
Bookmobiles: 1

R FIRST PRESBYTERIAN CHURCH OF THE COVENANT, Brittain Library, 250 W Seventh St, 16501. SAN 314-4909. Tel: 814-456-4243. FAX 814-454-3350. *Librn*, Jean Tauber
Library Holdings: Bk Vols 7,000

GANNON UNIVERSITY, Nash Library, University Sq, PO Box 295, 16541. SAN 314-4968. Tel: 814-871-7557. Interlibrary Loan Service Tel: 814-871-7559. FAX: 814-871-5666. Web Site: www.gannon.edu. *Dir*, Marion F Gallivan; *Tech Servs*, Lori Grossholz; *Media Spec*, Ginny Caldwell; *ILL, Online Servs, Ref*, Deborah West; *Asst Dir, Circ*, Robert Dobiesz; *Archivist*, Robert Sparks; *Per*, Christine Troutman; *Coll Develop*, Lawrence Maxted; Staff 9 (MLS 9)
Founded 1925. Enrl 3,377; Fac 208; Highest Degree: Doctorate
Jul 1999-Jun 2000 Income $907,446, Federal $26,000. Mats Exp $295,304, Books $113,216, Per/Ser (Incl. Access Fees) $124,099, Presv $3,956, Micro $8,103, Electronic Ref Mat (Incl. Access Fees) $45,930. Sal $475,591 (Prof $281,466)
Library Holdings: Bk Vols 197,203; Per Subs 938
Special Collections: Early American Imprints, microcard; Human Relations Area Files, microfiche; Polish Hist & Polit Sci (K Symmons Coll), curriculum materials
Automation Activity & Vendor Info: (Acquisitions) epixtech, inc.; (Cataloging) epixtech, inc.; (Circulation) epixtech, inc.; (OPAC) epixtech, inc.; (Serials) epixtech, inc.
Database Vendor: epixtech, inc.
Partic in Erie Area Health Information Library Cooperative; Northwest Interlibrary Cooperative Of Pennsylvania; Pa Acad Libr Coop; PALINET & Union Library Catalogue of Pennsylvania

HAMOT MEDICAL CENTER, Library Services,* 201 State St, 16550. SAN 314-4984. Tel: 814-877-6000, Ext 2273. FAX: 814-877-6188. *Chief Librn, Dir*, Sandra Williams; *Ref*, Linda Gillette
Founded 1964
Library Holdings: Bk Titles 2,000; Per Subs 300
Subject Interests: Gen surgery, Hospital administration, Internal medicine, Orthopedics, Trauma med
Publications: Columns In-house Publications (brochure)

KEYSTONE UNIVERSITY RESEARCH CORP, Pennsylvania Department of Health Research & Information Clearing House, 652 W 17th St, 16502. SAN 376-1894. Tel: 814-459-0245. Toll Free Tel: 800-582-7746. TDD: 800-203-8405. FAX: 814-453-4714. E-Mail: padohric@kurc.org. Web Site: www.padohric.org. *Dir*, Dr Mark Iutocovich
Library Holdings: Bk Vols 5,000
Subject Interests: HIV-AIDS, Substance abuse

KEYSTONE UNIVERSITY RESEARCH CORP LIBRARY,* 652 W 17th St, 16502. SAN 372-848X. Tel: 814-453-4713. FAX: 814-453-4714. Web Site: www.kurc.org. *Dir*, Dr Mark Iutcovich; E-Mail: marki@kurc.org; *Pres*, Joyce Iutcovich
Library Holdings: Bk Vols 6,000; Per Subs 16
Subject Interests: Aging, Cancer, Child care, Sociology

LORD CORP, Corporate Library, 2000 W Grandview Blvd, PO Box 10040, 16514-0040. SAN 314-500X. Tel: 814-868-0924. FAX: 814-866-6323. *Librn*, Sharon Patterson; *Assoc Librn*, Carol Welch; *Archivist*, Elizabeth Critchfield
Founded 1943
Jan 1999-Dec 1999 Income $970,453. Mats Exp $547,000. Sal $157,000
Library Holdings: Bk Titles 14,000; Per Subs 500
Subject Interests: Adhesives, Chemistry, Coatings, Computers, Mechanical vibration, Polymeric mats, Rubber
Partic in Northwest Interlibrary Cooperative Of Pennsylvania; PALINET & Union Library Catalogue of Pennsylvania

MERCYHURST COLLEGE, HAMMERMILL LIBRARY, 501 E 38th St, 16546. SAN 314-5018. Tel: 814-824-2232, 814-824-2234. FAX: 814-824-2219. Web Site: hamlet.mercyhurst.edu. *Dean of Libr*, Michael McQuillen; E-Mail: mcquilln@mercyhurst.edu; *Syst Coordr*, Ken Brundage; E-Mail: kbrundag@mercyhurst.edu; *Archivist, Ref*, Earleen Glaser; *ILL*, Lynn Falk; *Ser*, Sharon Wieczorek; *Circ*, Joe Kloss
Founded 1926. Highest Degree: Master
Jul 2000-Jun 2001 Income $897,956. Mats Exp $290,000, Books $160,000, Per/Ser (Incl. Access Fees) $84,747, Presv $8,500, Micro $3,400, Electronic Ref Mat (Incl. Access Fees) $31,967. Sal $379,233
Library Holdings: Per Subs 877
Special Collections: Ethnic History Concentrating on Northwest Pennsylvania, bks, micro & doc; Northwest Pennsylvania History, bks, micro & doc; Pennsylvania, bks, micro & doc; Women's History
Partic in Interlibrary Delivery Service of Pennsylvania; Northwest Interlibrary Cooperative Of Pennsylvania; OCLC Online Computer Library Center, Inc; PALINET & Union Library Catalogue of Pennsylvania
Friends of the Library Group
Departmental Libraries:
D'ANGELO MUSIC, 501 E 38th St, 16546. Tel: 814-824-2234.
Library Holdings: Bk Vols 250
EIMER CURRICULUM, 501 E 38th St, 16546. Tel: 814-824-2469. *Librn*, Sr Phyllis Marie McDonald
Library Holdings: Bk Vols 5,200
MERCYHURST - NORTH EAST LIBRARY, 501 E 38th St, Eire, 16546. Tel: 814-725-6143. FAX: 814-725-6112.
Library Holdings: Bk Vols 6,700; Per Subs 38

C PENNSYLVANIA STATE UNIVERSITY AT ERIE, Behrend College Library (University Libraries), 5091 Station Rd, 16563-1502. SAN 314-5026. Tel: 814-898-6106. FAX: 814-898-6350. Web Site: www.pserie.psu.edu/library/bdindex.htm. *Dir*, Richard Hart; *Circ*, Patricia Gainer; *ILL*, Patti Mrozowski; *Ser*, Lisa Moyer; *Bibliog Instr*, Patience Simmonds; *Ref*, Jane Ingold; *Ref*, Anna Pilston; Staff 8 (MLS 5, Non-MLS 3)
Founded 1948. Enrl 3,800; Fac 175; Highest Degree: Master
1999-2000 Mats Exp $443,700, Books $131,000, Per/Ser (Incl. Access Fees) $209,000, Presv $13,700, Electronic Ref Mat (Incl. Access Fees) $90,000. Sal $270,300
Library Holdings: Bk Vols 102,562; Per Subs 1,019
Partic in OCLC Online Computer Library Center, Inc

M SAINT VINCENT HEALTH CENTER, Health Sciences Library,* 232 W 25th St, 16544. SAN 314-5042. Tel: 814-452-5736. FAX: 814-454-8741. *Librn*, Joni M Alex-Vatavuk; Staff 2 (MLS 1, Non-MLS 1)
Founded 1940. Enrl 86
Library Holdings: Bk Titles 3,596; Per Subs 378
Subject Interests: Dentistry, Hospital administration, Medicine, Nursing
Special Collections: History of Medicine
Partic in Dialog Corporation; Mideastern Regional Med Libr Serv
Special Services for the Blind - Talking book center
Open Mon-Fri 8-4:30

ESSINGTON

P TINICUM MEMORIAL PUBLIC LIBRARY, 620 Seneca St, 19029-1199. SAN 314-5085. Tel: 610-521-9344. FAX: 610-521-3463. E-Mail: tinicum@delco.lib.pa.us. *Librn*, Agnes Davis; *Asst Librn*, Esther Berry
Pop 4,906; Circ 31,379
Library Holdings: Bk Vols 18,203; Per Subs 30

EVANS CITY

P EVANS CITY PUBLIC LIBRARY, 232 E Main St, 16033-1218. SAN 314-5093. Tel: 724-538-8695. FAX: 724-538-5630. E-Mail: ecpl@zbzoom.net. *Librn*, Judith Pfeifer; *Asst Librn*, Pat Pflug
Founded 1932. Pop 4,836; Circ 10,000
Library Holdings: Bk Titles 17,000; Per Subs 30
Mem of Butler County Libr Syst

EVERETT

§C ALLEGANY COLLEGE OF MARYLAND LIBRARY, Bedford County Campus, 18 N River Lane, 15537. Tel: 814-652-9528. FAX: 814-652-9775.
Library Holdings: Bk Vols 56,359; Bk Titles 48,880; Per Subs 440
Automation Activity & Vendor Info: (Acquisitions) GEAC; (Cataloging) GEAC; (Circulation) GEAC; (Course Reserve) GEAC; (ILL) GEAC; (Media Booking) GEAC; (OPAC) GEAC; (Serials) GEAC

P EVERETT FREE LIBRARY, 137 E Main St, 15537-1259. SAN 314-5115. Tel: 814-652-5922. FAX: 814-652-5425. Web Site: www.everettarea.org/efl. *Librn*, Diana Megdad; E-Mail: dianaevt@bedford.net; Staff 1 (MLS 1)
Founded 1923. Pop 12,903; Circ 45,910
Jan 1999-Dec 1999 Income $102,580, State $19,932, County $32,090, Locally Generated Income $50,558. Mats Exp $15,005, Books $10,850, Per/Ser (Incl. Access Fees) $1,588, Other Print Mats $2,340, Electronic Ref Mat (Incl. Access Fees) $227. Sal $44,055 (Prof $27,648)
Library Holdings: Bk Titles 33,416; Per Subs 46; Bks on Deafness & Sign Lang 25
Subject Interests: Local census data
Special Collections: Bedford County History; Everett Bicentennial Records Coll; Genealogy; PA History
Automation Activity & Vendor Info: (Circulation) Follett; (OPAC) Follett
Publications: Directory of Pennsylvania Libraries; Library Journal
Mem of Bedford County Federated Libr Syst

EXTON

P CHESTER COUNTY LIBRARY, 450 Exton Sq Pkwy, 19341-2496. SAN 315-3312. Tel: 610-280-2600. FAX: 610-280-2694. Interlibrary Loan Service FAX: 610-280-2693. E-Mail: ccl@ccls.org. Web Site: www.ccls.org. *Dir*, Antoinette C Hoffacker; *Syst Coordr*, Cecy Keller; *Ch Servs*, Jeanne Clancy Watkins; *Tech Servs*, Robert Pardyjak; *Librn*, Joseph McIlhenney; *Circ*, Flora Jeanne Hoch; *AV*, Diane Silver; *Acq*, Sylvia Doyle; *ILL*, Carol Welch; *Coll Develop*, Harriet Jarosh; Staff 75 (MLS 19, Non-MLS 56)
Founded 1928. Pop 412,170
Jan 1999-Dec 1999 Income $4,424,341, State $878,531, Federal $75,642, County $2,679,720, Locally Generated Income $543,428. Mats Exp $477,424, Books $425,946, Per/Ser (Incl. Access Fees) $26,951, Micro $23,277, Other Print Mats $1,250. Sal $2,235,300
Library Holdings: Bk Vols 278,245; Per Subs 950
Special Collections: Adult Reading Large Type Coll; AGR (adult graded reading); Chester County Coll; Chester's Reading (large-type); Children's Reading Large Type Coll; Computer Software Coll; Literacy; Local

Newspaper Coll; State & Local Government Rare Books Coll; Work Place Job & Career Information Coll
Automation Activity & Vendor Info: (Acquisitions) Innovative Interfaces Inc.; (Cataloging) Innovative Interfaces Inc.; (Circulation) Innovative Interfaces Inc.; (ILL) Innovative Interfaces Inc.; (OPAC) Innovative Interfaces Inc.; (Serials) Innovative Interfaces Inc.
Publications: Chester County Library Business News; Chester County Library System (Newsletter)
Member Libraries: Atglen Reading Center; Avon Grove Library; Bayard Taylor Memorial Library; Chester Springs Library; Coatesville Area Public Library; Downingtown Library Co; Easttown Library & Information Center; Honey Brook Community Library; Malvern Public Library; Oxford Public Library; Paoli Library; Parkesburg Free Library; Phoenixville Public Library; Spring City Free Public Library; Tredyffrin Public Library; West Chester Public Library
Partic in Interlibrary Delivery Service of Pennsylvania; OCLC Online Computer Library Center, Inc; PALINET & Union Library Catalogue of Pennsylvania
Special Services - Computer Literacy Training; Literacy Program; Public Computer Center
Friends of the Library Group
Bookmobiles: 1

M PENNSYLVANIA STATE DEPARTMENT OF HEALTH, Herbert Fox Memorial Library, PO Box 500, 19341-0500. SAN 327-8689. Tel: 610-280-3464. FAX: 610-436-3346. *Librn*, M Jeffrey Shoemaker; *Asst Librn*, Andrea O'Leary; E-Mail: aoleary@health.state.pa.us
Library Holdings: Bk Vols 100; Per Subs 50
Subject Interests: Public health

FACTORYVILLE

P FACTORYVILLE PUBLIC LIBRARY,* 163 College Ave, PO Box 238, 18419-0238. SAN 314-5131. Tel: 570-945-3788. *Librn*, Lenore Walsh
Pop 1,500; Circ 4,715
Library Holdings: Bk Vols 4,600
Mem of Pocono District Libr Ctr
Open Tues, Wed & Fri 2-5 & Sat 10-12

FALLSINGTON

P FALLSINGTON LIBRARY CO,* 139 Yardley Ave, 19054-1119. SAN 314-514X. Tel: 215-295-4449. *Dir*, Karen Suscovich
Founded 1800. Pop 35,830
Library Holdings: Bk Vols 20,000; Per Subs 42
Special Collections: Bucks County; History Coll; Pennsylvania State History Coll; Society of Friends Coll
Mem of Bucks County Free Library

FARMINGTON

S NATIONAL PARK SERVICE, DEPARTMENT OF INTERIOR, Fort Necessity National Battlefield Library, One Washington Pkwy, 15437. SAN 323-8644. Tel: 724-329-5512. FAX: 724-329-8682. *In Charge*, Carney Rigg; Tel: 724-329-5819
Founded 1979
Library Holdings: Bk Vols 3,000

FARRELL

M SHENANGO VALLEY MEDICAL CENTER, Medical Library,* 2200 Memorial Dr, 16121. SAN 326-6443. Tel: 724-981-3500, Ext 7553. FAX: 724-981-7945. *Librn*, Melany Mealy
Library Holdings: Bk Titles 560; Per Subs 40

FEASTERVILLE

P TOWNSHIP LIBRARY OF LOWER SOUTHAMPTON, 1500 N Desire Ave, 19053-4493. SAN 314-5166. Tel: 215-355-1183. FAX: 215-364-5735. Web Site: www.buckslib.org. *Librn*, Sally Pollock; E-Mail: pollocks@buckslib.org; Staff 7 (MLS 1, Non-MLS 6)
Founded 1956. Pop 19,860
Jan 2000-Dec 2000 Income $356,193. Mats Exp $78,756, Books $59,111, Per/Ser (Incl. Access Fees) $6,290, AV Equip $8,000, Electronic Ref Mat (Incl. Access Fees) $5,355. Sal $165,011
Library Holdings: Bk Titles 45,000; Per Subs 98
Automation Activity & Vendor Info: (Circulation) DRA; (OPAC) DRA
Mem of Bucks County Free Library
Open Mon & Wed 10-9, Tues & Thurs 1-9, Sat 9-4
Friends of the Library Group

FLEETWOOD

P FLEETWOOD AREA PUBLIC LIBRARY, 110 W Arch St, PO Box 7, 19522-1301. SAN 376-5857. Tel: 610-944-0146. FAX: 610-944-9064. E-Mail: fleetwoodapl@berks.lib.pa.us. Web Site: www.berks.lib.pa.us/fleetwoodapl, www.fleetwoodlibrary.org. *Dir*, Lois A Bailey; Staff 4 (Non-MLS 4)
Founded 1990. Pop 10,314
Library Holdings: Bk Titles 10,000; Per Subs 12
Automation Activity & Vendor Info: (Cataloging) epixtech, inc.; (Circulation) epixtech, inc.
Database Vendor: Dialog
Mem of Berks County Libr Syst
Open Mon & Tues 3-8, Wed & Fri 9:30-12:30 & 1-5, Thurs 9:30-12:30 & 1-8, Sat 9:30-12

FOGELSVILLE

C PENNSYLVANIA STATE UNIVERSITY, LEHIGH VALLEY, Berks-Lehigh Valley College Library-Learning Resource Center,* 8380 Mohr Lan 18051-9999. SAN 314-5174. Tel: 610-285-5027. FAX: 610-285-5158. E-Mail: dbp@psulias.psu.edu. *Librn*, Dennis Phillips; Staff 4 (MLS 2, Non-MLS 2)
Founded 1912. Enrl 624; Fac 20
Jul 1997-Jun 1998 Mats Exp $58,788
Library Holdings: Bk Vols 34,453; Per Subs 172
Partic in OCLC Online Computer Library Center, Inc; RLIN

FOLCROFT

P BOROUGH OF FOLCROFT PUBLIC LIBRARY,* Delmar Dr & Ashland Ave, 19032-2002. SAN 314-5182. Tel: 610-586-1690. FAX: 610-586-2179. *Actg Librn*, Sueann Smith
Pop 8,231; Circ 11,346
Library Holdings: Bk Vols 12,415; Per Subs 20
Mem of Delaware County Library System

FOLSOM

P RIDLEY TOWNSHIP PUBLIC LIBRARY, MacDade Blvd & Morton Ave, 19033-2592. SAN 314-5190. Tel: 610-583-0593, 610-583-7525. FAX: 610-583-9505. E-Mail: ridleytownship@deico.lib.pa.us, ridleytwplib@hslc.org. *Dir*, Francis X Mullen; *Ad Servs*, Gail Kaplan; *Publ Servs*, Mary Tobin; *Re* Clara Salloom; Staff 15 (MLS 5, Non-MLS 10)
Founded 1957. Pop 33,725; Circ 159,014
Jan 2000-Dec 2000 Income $638,512, State $121,754, City $387,254, County $17,500, Locally Generated Income $49,400, Other $35,000. Mats Exp $117,950, Books $85,000, Per/Ser (Incl. Access Fees) $15,750, Presv $1,200, Micro $14,500, AV Equip $1,500. Sal $354,276 (Prof $152,445)
Library Holdings: Bk Vols 80,495; Per Subs 327; Spec Interest Per Sub 2
Special Collections: Irish literature; Law (Pennsylvania Annotated Code & US Code)
Automation Activity & Vendor Info: (Acquisitions) Innovative Interfaces Inc.; (Cataloging) Innovative Interfaces Inc.; (Circulation) Innovative Interfaces Inc.; (Course Reserve) Innovative Interfaces Inc.; (ILL) Innovativ Interfaces Inc.; (Media Booking) Innovative Interfaces Inc.; (OPAC) Innovative Interfaces Inc.; (Serials) Innovative Interfaces Inc.
Database Vendor: Innovative Interfaces INN - View
Publications: Annual report; business newsletter
Mem of Delaware County Library System
Special Services - Shut-in service; variety of story hours; adult senior citize programs; investment series & retirement planning

FORD CITY

P FORD CITY PUBLIC LIBRARY,* 1136 Fourth Ave, 16226-1202. SAN 314-5204. Tel: 724-763-3591. FAX: 724-763-2705. E-Mail: fcpl@nb.net. *Librn*, Elizabeth Switzer; Staff 1 (MLS 1)
Founded 1946. Pop 3,410; Circ 31,390
Jan 1998-Dec 1999 Income $47,741, State $7,425, Locally Generated Income $7,064, Other $499. Mats Exp $11,700, Books $10,200, Per/Ser (Incl. Access Fees) $1,500. Sal $21,046
Library Holdings: Bk Titles 30,626; Per Subs 59
Special Collections: Ancestry (Claypool Family in America, Jack Family & Schall/Shaull Family Collections), pamphlets; Apollo People; Armstrong County of Pennsylvania (J H Beers, 1914); Bethel Evangelical Lutheran Church Cemetery Listing 1979; Bethel Township 1878-1978 Centennial; Decendants of Jacob Nunamaker & Katherine (Zell) Nunamaker; Dulany-Furlong & Kindred Families; Easley-Rooker Family History (2nd draft); Elderton Plumcreek Area-Through the Years; Ford City Centennial 1887-1987; Ford City History (75th Anniversary Book of Ford City); History of Armstrong County (R W Smith, 1883); History of Manorville, pamphlets; History of Slate Lich Presbyterian Church, pamphlets; Lives & Letters Fron Kiester House; Michael A Sheely Family; The Anderson Family History; The Family of Samuel Wysalin America; The Ziebler Family & Related Families in Pennsylvania; Thomas Graham Benner Family

ORT WASHINGTON

HONEYWELL, INC, Process Controls Div, Information Center,* 1100 Virginia Dr, 19034. SAN 314-5220. Tel: 215-641-3000. FAX: 215-641-3291.
Founded 1935
Library Holdings: Bk Titles 2,800; Per Subs 100
Subject Interests: Bus, Computers, Control systs, Electronic engineering, Mechanical engineering, Mgt

MCNEIL CONSUMER HEALTHCARE, Information Center, 7050 Camp Hill Rd, 19034. SAN 321-4826. Tel: 215-273-7171. FAX: 215-273-4082. *Dir*, Helen J Hohman; Tel: 215-273-7603, E-Mail: hhohman@mccus.jnj.com; *Info Specialist*, Nancy B Rainey; Tel: 215-273-7170, E-Mail: nrainey@mccus.jnj.com; Staff 7 (MLS 5, Non-MLS 2)
Founded 1980
Library Holdings: Bk Vols 6,000; Bk Titles 4,000; Per Subs 400
Subject Interests: Chemistry, Marketing, Pharmaceuticals
Restriction: Not open to public
Partic in Dialog Corporation; Dow Jones News Retrieval

UPPER DUBLIN PUBLIC LIBRARY,* 805 Loch Alsh Ave, 19034. SAN 358-4135. Tel: 215-628-8744. FAX: 215-628-8763. Web Site: www.udp.mclinc.org. *Dir*, Mary Lou Troy; *Tech Servs*, Patricia Morrissette; Staff 5 (MLS 5)
Founded 1932. Pop 24,028; Circ 156,000
Library Holdings: Bk Vols 51,000; Per Subs 125
Subject Interests: Amer art, Antiques, Ethnic studies, Feminism
Partic in Montgomery County Libr & Info Network Consortium
Friends of the Library Group
Branches: 1
NORTH HILLS COMMUNITY, 212 Girard Ave, North Hills, 19038. SAN 358-416X. Tel: 215-884-4760. *Librn*, Gladys Poulson
Library Holdings: Bk Vols 6,000

'OXBURG

FOXBURG FREE LIBRARY, 31 Main St, PO Box 304, 16036-0304. SAN 314-5255. Tel: 724-659-3431. FAX: 724-659-3214. E-Mail: foxburgfl@csonline.net. *Librn*, Virginia Lytle; Staff 1 (Non-MLS 1)
Founded 1910. Pop 4,295; Circ 11,346
Library Holdings: Bk Vols 10,904; Per Subs 17
Automation Activity & Vendor Info: (Cataloging) Follett
Mem of Clarion County Library System; Oil Creek District Library Center

'RACKVILLE

FRACKVILLE FREE PUBLIC LIBRARY, 56 N Lehigh Ave, 17931-1424. SAN 314-5263. Tel: 570-874-3382. FAX: 570-874-3382. Web Site: www.north-schuylkill.k12.pa.us/publib/fracklib.shtml. *Dir*, Velma L Sippie; *Asst Librn*, Marge Rench
Founded 1939. Pop 9,663; Circ 27,747
Jan 1999-Dec 1999 Income $61,169, State $20,300, City $15,669, County $3,500, Locally Generated Income $19,000, Other $2,700. Mats Exp $8,000, Books $7,400, Per/Ser (Incl. Access Fees) $600. Sal $37,000 (Prof $8,000)
Library Holdings: Bk Titles 20,106; Per Subs 35
Subject Interests: Local history
Partic in OCLC Online Computer Library Center, Inc

'RANKLIN

FRANKLIN PUBLIC LIBRARY,* 421 12th St, 16323-0421. SAN 314-5271. Tel: 814-432-5062. FAX: 814-432-8998. E-Mail: franklinpl@galacticis.com. *Librn*, Deborah Oaks; *ILL*, Mary Ann Hartle; *Rare Bks, Ref*, Sylvia Coast
Founded 1894. Pop 27,285; Circ 90,922
Library Holdings: Bk Titles 50,463; Per Subs 105
Special Collections: Pennsylvania & Venango County History Coll
Mem of Clarion Dist Libr Asn; Oil Creek District Library Center
Friends of the Library Group

M NORTHWEST MEDICAL CENTER-FRANKLIN CAMPUS, Medical Library,* One Spruce St, 16323-2587. SAN 324-6930. Tel: 814-437-7000, Ext 5331. E-Mail: nwmc@mail.cosmosbbs.com. *Librn*, L P Gilliland; *Librn*, Ann L Lucas
Library Holdings: Bk Vols 900; Bk Titles 850; Per Subs 120
Subject Interests: Medicine, Nursing
Partic in Erie Area Health Information Library Cooperative; National Network Of Libraries Of Medicine - South Central Region; Northwest Interlibrary Cooperative Of Pennsylvania

GL VENANGO COUNTY LAW LIBRARY, Venango County Court House, Liberty St, PO Box 831, 16323. SAN 324-1173. Tel: 814-432-9500, Ext 243. FAX: 814-432-9615. *Librn*, Sandy Baker
Library Holdings: Bk Titles 22,000; Per Subs 60
Subject Interests: Law cases from 25 reporter systs

FRANKLIN CENTER

S THE FRANKLIN MINT, Information Research Center,* 19091. SAN 314-528X. Tel: 610-459-6868. FAX: 610-459-7526. E-Mail: fmirc@omni.voicenet.com. Web Site: www.thefranklinmint. *Mgr*, Jeannie Fitzpatrick; Staff 9 (MLS 9)
Founded 1969
Library Holdings: Bk Vols 25,000; Per Subs 360
Subject Interests: Architecture, Art, Collectibles, Description, History, Numismatics, Travel
Publications: On the Inside

FREDERICKTOWN

P FREDERICKTOWN AREA PUBLIC LIBRARY,* 38 Water St, PO Box 625, 15333-0625. SAN 376-575X. Tel: 724-377-0017. FAX: 724-377-0017. E-Mail: fredpl@hhs.net. *Dir*, Dawn M Bell
Library Holdings: Bk Titles 10,551; Per Subs 25
Mem of Washington County Libr Syst
Open Mon & Wed 1-8, Tues, Thurs & Fri 1-5, Sat 11-1
Friends of the Library Group

FREEDOM

P FREEDOM PUBLIC LIBRARY,* Borough Complex, 901 Third Ave, 15042-1738. SAN 314-5298. Tel: 724-775-7160. FAX: 724-728-5578. E-Mail: fpl@iu27.bviu.k12.us. *Librn*, Frances Ambrose
Founded 1939. Pop 1,897; Circ 6,038
1998-1999 Income $20,100, State $3,800, City $4,000, County $3,200, Locally Generated Income $2,000. Mats Exp $3,039, Books $2,500, Per/Ser (Incl. Access Fees) $250, Micro $289. Sal $7,893
Library Holdings: Bk Vols 11,397; Per Subs 25
Mem of Beaver County Federated Library System

FREEPORT

P FREEPORT AREA LIBRARY, 428 Market St, 16229-1122. SAN 314-5301. Tel: 724-295-3616. FAX: 724-295-3616. Web Site: www.users.sgi.net.prprtlib. *Librn*, Pamela S Eberle; *Asst Librn*, Sandy Powell
Pop 9,599; Circ 29,313
1998-1999 Income $29,989, City $600. Mats Exp $9,186, Books $8,529, Per/Ser (Incl. Access Fees) $657. Sal $14,199
Library Holdings: Bk Vols 26,864; Per Subs 15
Friends of the Library Group

GALETON

P GALETON PUBLIC LIBRARY, 3 W Main St, 16922-1001. SAN 314-531X. Tel: 814-435-2321. FAX: 814-435-2321. E-Mail: gpl@top.penn.com. Web Site: www.ncldistrict.org/galeton/. *Librn*, Jane G Churchill
Founded 1907. Pop 2,131; Circ 6,025
Library Holdings: Bk Vols 10,000; Bk Titles 9,539; Per Subs 21
Subject Interests: Local history
Open Mon & Fri 1-5 & 7-9, Tues & Wed 1-5, Thurs 11-5, Sat 10-5

GALLITZIN

P GALLITZIN PUBLIC LIBRARY,* 411 Convent St, Ste 30, 16641-1234. SAN 314-5328. Tel: 814-886-4041. FAX: 814-886-2125. E-Mail: glibrary@penn.com. *Dir*, Paulette Schmelzlen
Founded 1957. Pop 2,315; Circ 28,000 Sal $15,600
Library Holdings: Bk Vols 10,000; Per Subs 30
Mem of Cambria County Library System & District Center
Friends of the Library Group

GENESEE

P GENESEE AREA LIBRARY,* 301 Main St, PO Box 135, 16923. SAN 376-7272. Tel: 814-228-3328. E-Mail: gal@netsync.net. *Dir*, Angela Dunbar
Library Holdings: Bk Vols 7,000; Per Subs 30
Mem of Potter-Tioga Library System
Open Mon 1-5 & Wed 1-8

GETTYSBURG

S ADAMS COUNTY HISTORICAL SOCIETY LIBRARY, Lutheran Theological Seminary Campus, 111 Seminary Ridge, 17325. (Mail add: PO Box 4325, 17325-4325), SAN 314-5336. Tel: 717-334-4723. *Dir*, Charles H Glatfelter
Founded 1940
Library Holdings: Bk Titles 2,000; Per Subs 10
Subject Interests: Adams County hist
Publications: Adams County History; annual newsletter

L ADAMS COUNTY LAW LIBRARY,* Court House, 111-117 Baltimore St, 17325. SAN 327-1080. Tel: 717-334-6781, Ext 262. FAX: 717-334-2091. *Librn*, Cecelia Brown
Library Holdings: Bk Vols 25,000; Per Subs 25
Open Mon-Fri 8-4, 9-2:30 (Librn available)

P ADAMS COUNTY LIBRARY SYSTEM, Central Library,* 140 Baltimore St, 17325. SAN 358-4887. Tel: 717-334-5716. FAX: 717-334-7992. E-Mail: adamslib@czn.net. Web Site: www.wideopen.net/adamslib. *Dir*, Carl Heidenblad
Founded 1945. Pop 78,274; Circ 318,948
Jan 1997-Dec 1998 Income $1,152,107. Mats Exp $220,000. Sal $640,000
Library Holdings: Bk Vols 80,000; Per Subs 160
Special Collections: Art; Eisenhower Room Coll (Civil War & Local Hist)
Member Libraries: East Berlin Community Library; New Oxford Area Library
Open Mon-Thurs 9-8:30, Fri & Sat 9-5, Sun 1-5
Friends of the Library Group

C GETTYSBURG COLLEGE, Musselman Library, 300 N Washington St, Box 420, 17325-1493. SAN 314-5344. Tel: 717-337-7024. Reference Tel: 717-337-6600. FAX: 717-337-6666. E-Mail: gerhart@gettysburg.edu. Web Site: www.gettysburg.edu. *Head of Libr*, Robin Wagner; Tel: 717-337-6768, E-Mail: rowagner@gettysburg.edu; *Admin Assoc*, Jamee Conover; Tel: 717-337-6604, E-Mail: jconover@gettysburg.edu; *Coll Develop*, David T Hedrick; Tel: 770-337-7011, E-Mail: hedrick@gettysburg.edu; *Head Tech Servs*, Patricia Tully; Tel: 717-337-7002, E-Mail: ptully@gettysburg.edu; *Head Ref*, Janelle Wertzberger; Tel: 717-337-7010, E-Mail: jwertzbe@getysburg.edu; *Head, Acq*, Pamela Matthews; Tel: 717-337-7007, E-Mail: pmatthew@gettysburg.edu; *Syst Coordr*, Laura Bowen; Tel: 717-337-7020, E-Mail: lbowen@gettysburg.edu; *Head, Circ*, Cynthia Gibbon; Tel: 717-337-6951, E-Mail: cgibbon@gettysburg.edu; *Media Spec*, Nancy Johnson; Tel: 717-337-7022, E-Mail: njohnson@gettysburg.edu; *ILL*, Susan Roach; Tel: 717-337-6893, E-Mail: sroach@gettysburg.edu; *Archivist*, Karen Drickamer; Tel: 717-337-7015, E-Mail: kdrickam@gettysburg.edu; Staff 27 (MLS 10, Non-MLS 17)
Founded 1832. Enrl 2,384; Fac 150; Highest Degree: Bachelor
Library Holdings: Bk Vols 284,903; Bk Titles 246,448; Per Subs 2,032
Special Collections: Civil War Maps Coll
Automation Activity & Vendor Info: (Acquisitions) Innovative Interfaces Inc.; (Cataloging) Innovative Interfaces Inc.; (Circulation) Innovative Interfaces Inc.; (Course Reserve) Innovative Interfaces Inc.; (OPAC) Innovative Interfaces Inc.; (Serials) Innovative Interfaces Inc.
Database Vendor: CARL, Ebsco - EbscoHost, Innovative Interfaces INN - View, Lexis-Nexis, OCLC - First Search, ProQuest, Silverplatter Information Inc., Wilson - Wilson Web
Publications: A Guide to Musselman Library & Special Collections Brochure
Partic in Associated College Libraries of Central Pennsylvania; Central Pennsylvania Consortium; OCLC Online Computer Library Center, Inc; Pa Acad Libr Coop; PALINET & Union Library Catalogue of Pennsylvania; Research Libraries Group, Inc

S GETTYSBURG NATIONAL MILITARY PARK LIBRARY, 97 Taneytown Rd, 17325. SAN 314-5352. Tel: 717-334-1124, Ext 428. FAX: 717-334-1997. Web Site: www.nps.gov/gett. *In Charge*, D Scott Hartwig; E-Mail: scott_hartwig@nps.gov; *In Charge*, John S Heiser; E-Mail: john_heiser@nps.gov
Founded 1895
Library Holdings: Bk Vols 6,100; Bk Titles 3,600; Per Subs 12
Subject Interests: Battle of Gettysburg, Campaign, Cycloramas, Eisenhower at Gettysburg, Gettysburg National Cemetery, Lincoln's Gettysburg Address
Special Collections: Photography (William H Tipton Coll)
Restriction: By appointment only, Open to public for reference only
Function: Research library

R LUTHERAN THEOLOGICAL SEMINARY, AR Wentz Library, 66 Seminary Ridge, 17325. SAN 314-5360. Tel: 717-338-3014. FAX: 717-337-1611. *Librn*, Bonnie L VanDelinder; Tel: 717-338-3018, E-Mail: bvandelinder@ltsg.edu; *Cat*, Susann Posey; Tel: 717-338-3032, E-Mail: sposey@ltsg.edu; *Publ Servs*, Sara E Mummert; *Acq*, Luxie R Althoff; Tel: 717-334-6286, Ext 2102, E-Mail: lalthoff@ltsg.edu; Staff 6 (MLS 2, Non-MLS 4)
Founded 1826. Enrl 218; Highest Degree: Master
Jul 1998-Jun 1999 Income Parent Institution $331,474. Mats Exp $82,266, Books $51,348, Per/Ser (Incl. Access Fees) $29,313, AV Equip $1,605. (Prof $93,554)
Library Holdings: Bk Vols 169,000; Per Subs 616
Subject Interests: Biblical studies, Church history, Church-related subjects, Lutheran Church, Pastoral studies, Philosophy, Preaching, Stewardship, Theology, Worship
Special Collections: Lutheran Church History in America
Automation Activity & Vendor Info: (Cataloging) TLC; (Circulation) TLC; (OPAC) TLC; (Serials) TLC
Function: Outside services via phone, cable & mail
Partic in Southeastern Pennsylvania Theological Library Association; Washington Theological Consortium
Open Mon-Fri 8:30-5, Sat 9-12 & 1-4:30, Sun-Thurs 6-10

GIBSONIA

P NORTHERN TIER LIBRARY ASSOCIATION, Richland Center,* 4015 Dickey Rd, 15044-9713. SAN 314-5379. Tel: 412-449-2665. FAX: 412-443 6755. Web Site: www.einpgh.org/ein/richland/. *Dir*, Sharon L Dawe; E-Mail dawes@clpgh.org; *Librn*, Charles Quinn; E-Mail: quinnc@clpgh.org; *Br Coordr*, Amy O Mason; Tel: 724-625-5655; *Commun Relations*, Diane C Illis; E-Mail: illisd@clpgh.org; *Ch Servs*, Suzanna Wanat; *Ch Servs*, Joyce Anne VonVreckin; E-Mail: vonvreckinj@clpgh.org; Staff 16 (MLS 4, Non-MLS 12)
Founded 1954. Pop 16,145; Circ 142,465
Jan 1999-Dec 1999 Income $375,437, State $38,610, County $96,935, Locally Generated Income $222,235, Other $17,657. Mats Exp $48,630, Books $41,830, Per/Ser (Incl. Access Fees) $1,800, AV Equip $5,000. Sal $240,375 (Prof $103,800)
Library Holdings: Bk Vols 40,000; Per Subs 61
Automation Activity & Vendor Info: (Cataloging) DRA; (Circulation) DRA; (OPAC) DRA
Database Vendor: DRA, Ebsco - EbscoHost, GaleNet, IAC - Info Trac, IAC - SearchBank, ProQuest
Publications: The Libray Link (monthly)
Partic in Allegheny County Libr Asn; Electronic Info Network
Friends of the Library Group

GIRARD

P RICE AVENUE COMMUNITY PUBLIC LIBRARY, (Formerly Willcox Public Library), 8 E Main St, 16417-1733. SAN 314-5387. Tel: 814-774-4982. E-Mail: willcox@erie.net. *Dir*, Stacey M Lasher
Founded 1893. Pop 6,500; Circ 31,000
Library Holdings: Bk Vols 11,000; Per Subs 30

GLADWYNE

R BETH DAVID REFORM CONGREGATION, Jewel K Markowitz Library, 1130 Vaughans Lane, 19035-0287. SAN 314-8661. Tel: 610-896-7485. FAX 610-642-5406. E-Mail: office@bdavid.org. Web Site: www.bdavid.org.
Founded 1947
Library Holdings: Bk Vols 4,500
Subject Interests: Judaica
Special Collections: Judaica for Children

P GLADWYNE FREE LIBRARY, 362 Righters Mill Rd, 19035-1587. SAN 314-5395. Tel: 610-642-3957. FAX: 610-642-3985. Web Site: www.lower-merion.lib.pa.us. *Librn*, Carolyn G Conti; *Ch Servs*, Alicemarie Collins
Founded 1931. Pop 5,349; Circ 180,782
1998-1999 Income $268,910. Mats Exp $69,868, Books $48,482, Per/Ser (Incl. Access Fees) $6,474. Sal $135,329
Library Holdings: Bk Vols 46,897; Per Subs 114
Special Collections: Cookbooks; Pennsylvania History Coll
Mem of Lower Merion Library System
Friends of the Library Group

GLASSPORT

P SAMUEL A WEISS COMMUNITY LIBRARY, Fifth St at Monongahela Ave, 15045-1474. SAN 314-5425. Tel: 412-672-7400. FAX: 412-672-7090. *Librn*, Ann Dzurko
Founded 1943. Pop 7,000
Library Holdings: Bk Vols 12,000
Open Tues-Thurs 6:30-8

GLEN ROCK

P THE ARTHUR HUFNAGEL -GLEN ROCK PUBLIC LIBRARY, 32 Main St, PO Box 65, 17327-0065. SAN 314-5433. Tel: 717-235-1127. FAX: 717-235-0330. E-Mail: grlib2@blazenet.net. *Librn*, Kathy Custer; Staff 2 (Non-MLS 2)
Founded 1936. Pop 7,528
Library Holdings: Bk Vols 13,000; Per Subs 30
Subject Interests: Local history
Special Collections: Pamphlet Coll
Mem of York County Library System
Open Mon & Thurs 12-5 & 7-9, Tues 12-5 & 7-9, Wed 10-5 & 7-9, Fri 7-9, Sat 9-2

GLENOLDEN

P GLENOLDEN LIBRARY,* 211 S Llanwellyn Ave, 19036-2118. SAN 314-545X. Tel: 610-583-1010. FAX: 610-583-7610. E-Mail: glenoldenlib@hslc.org. *Dir*, Jacqueline Boggs; *Ch Servs*, Peggy Bauer
Founded 1894. Pop 7,633; Circ 17,116

Library Holdings: Bk Titles 15,200; Per Subs 50
Mem of Delaware County Library System
Open Mon, Tues & Thurs 1-4:30 & 6:30-8:30, Wed 10-4:30 & 6:30-8:30, Fri 12-5 & Sat 11-2

LENSHAW

GLENSHAW PUBLIC LIBRARY, 1504 Butler Plank Rd, 15116-2397. SAN 314-5468. Tel: 412-487-2121. *Dir*, Violet F Rowe
Founded 1895. Circ 7,334
1999-1999 Income Locally Generated Income $4,000. Sal $2,400
Library Holdings: Bk Vols 12,991; Per Subs 12

SHALER NORTH HILLS LIBRARY, 1822 Mount Royal Blvd, 15116. SAN 314-5476. Tel: 412-486-0211. FAX: 412-486-8286. E-Mail: shalerref@cinetwork.net. Web Site: www.clpgh.org/ein/shaler. *Dir*, Diane G Yates; *Ad Servs*, Sharon McRae; *Tech Servs*, Lesle Dunn; *Acq*, Betty Kakavis; *YA Servs*, Kara Falck; *Ch Servs*, Ann-Marie Balzer; *Ch Servs*, Nancy Fields; Staff 18 (MLS 8, Non-MLS 10)
Founded 1942. Pop 30,523; Circ 321,947
Jan 1999-Dec 1999 Income $764,133, State $88,036, City $343,000, County $263,117, Locally Generated Income $58,153, Other $11,827. Mats Exp $142,444, Books $109,984, Per/Ser (Incl. Access Fees) $9,180, AV Equip $10,901, Electronic Ref Mat (Incl. Access Fees) $12,379. Sal $405,509 (Prof $214,647)
Library Holdings: Bk Titles 103,043; Per Subs 216
Special Collections: Puppets
Automation Activity & Vendor Info: (Cataloging) DRA; (Circulation) DRA; (OPAC) DRA; (Serials) DRA
Database Vendor: DRA
Partic in Electronic Info Network
Special Services for the Blind - Assistive Technology Center for Persons who are blind or physically handicapped
Friends of the Library Group

LENSIDE

CHELTENHAM TOWNSHIP LIBRARY SYSTEM,* 215 S Keswick Ave, 19038-4420. SAN 314-5506. Tel: 215-885-0457. FAX: 215-885-1239. E-Mail: ctllibsys@mclinc.org. *Dir*, Carrie L Turner; E-Mail: cturner@mclinc.org; *Tech Servs*, Dorothy L Sutton; E-Mail: dsutton@mclinc.org; Staff 27 (MLS 8, Non-MLS 19)
Founded 1968. Pop 34,923; Circ 277,411
Library Holdings: Bk Vols 142,373; Per Subs 448
Subject Interests: Art, Black hist, Bus ref, Compact discs, Educ software, Handicrafts, History, Large print, Local history, Multicultural mat, Videos
Member Libraries: East Cheltenham Free Library; Elkins Park Free Library; Glenside Free Library; La Mott Free Library
Partic in Montgomery County Libr & Info Network Consortium
Friends of the Library Group

CHILD CUSTODY EVALUATION SERVICES, INC, Resource Center Library,* PO Box 202, 19038-0202. SAN 326-6184. Tel: 215-576-0177. FAX: 215-576-9411. *Librn*, Jean Bruno
Founded 1980
Library Holdings: Bk Titles 800; Per Subs 40

EUGENIA FULLER ATWOOD LIBRARY, (Formerly Beaver College), 450 S Easton Rd, 19038-3295. SAN 314-5484. Tel: 215-572-2975. Interlibrary Loan Service Tel: 215-572-2141. Reference Tel: 215-572-2138. FAX: 215-572-0240. Web Site: www.beaver.edu/library. *Dir*, Charles Myers; Tel: 215-572-2973, E-Mail: myersc@camelot.beaver.edu; *Head Tech Servs*, Ann Ranieri; Tel: 215-572-2136, E-Mail: ranieria@camelot.beaver.edu; *Reader Servs*, Suzanne Kinard; Tel: 215-572-4097, E-Mail: kinards@camelot.beaver.edu; Staff 9 (MLS 3, Non-MLS 6)
Founded 1963. Enrl 2,700; Fac 289; Highest Degree: Doctorate
Jul 2000-Jun 2001 Income Parent Institution $397,700. Mats Exp $354,700, Books $186,700, Per/Ser (Incl. Access Fees) $132,000, Electronic Ref Mat (Incl. Access Fees) $36,000
Library Holdings: Bk Vols 136,903; Bk Titles 95,274; Per Subs 798
Automation Activity & Vendor Info: (Acquisitions) SIRSI; (Cataloging) SIRSI; (Circulation) SIRSI; (Course Reserve) SIRSI; (OPAC) SIRSI; (Serials) SIRSI
Database Vendor: Lexis-Nexis, OCLC - First Search, ProQuest
Partic in Delaware Valley Information Consortium; Interlibrary Delivery Service of Pennsylvania; OCLC Online Computer Library Center, Inc; PALINET & Union Library Catalogue of Pennsylvania; Southeastern Pa Consortium for Higher Educ; Tri-State College Library Cooperative (TCLC)

GLENSIDE FREE LIBRARY, (GFLF), 215 S Keswick Ave, 19038-4420. SAN 314-5514. Tel: 215-885-0455. FAX: 215-885-1019. E-Mail: glenside@mclinc.org. Web Site: www.mclinc.org. *Librn*, Megan Johnson; E-Mail: mjohnson@mclinc.org; *Tech Servs*, Dorothy L Sutton; Staff 7 (MLS 2, Non-MLS 5)
Founded 1928
Library Holdings: Bk Vols 55,023; Per Subs 182
Subject Interests: Bus ref, History, Large print, Local history, Multicultural mat
Special Collections: Business
Automation Activity & Vendor Info: (OPAC) Gaylord
Mem of Cheltenham Township Library System
Partic in Montgomery County Libr & Info Network Consortium
Friends of the Library Group

R SAINT PETER'S EPISCOPAL CHURCH, Daniel Memorial Library, 654 N Easton Rd, 19038. SAN 314-5522. Tel: 215-887-1765. FAX: 215-887-1046. *Librn*, Kathryn Darby
Library Holdings: Bk Vols 1,000

R WESTMINSTER THEOLOGICAL SEMINARY, Montgomery Library, 2960 W Church Rd, 19038. (Mail add: PO Box 27009, 19118), SAN 315-0267. Tel: 215-887-5511. FAX: 215-887-5404. E-Mail: wtslib@shrsys.hslc.org. *Actg Dir, Archivist, Publ Servs*, Grace Mullen; Tel: 215-572-3822, E-Mail: gmullen@wts.edu; *Cat*, Melvin Hartwick; Staff 4 (Non-MLS 4)
Founded 1929. Enrl 600; Fac 20; Highest Degree: Doctorate
Jul 1999-Jun 2000 Mats Exp $113,000, Books $75,000, Per/Ser (Incl. Access Fees) $38,000
Library Holdings: Bk Vols 110,250; Per Subs 800
Subject Interests: Biblical studies, Reformation, Systematic theol
Special Collections: Bible Texts & Versions; Early Reformed Theology
Database Vendor: OCLC - First Search
Partic in OCLC Online Computer Library Center, Inc; PALINET & Union Library Catalogue of Pennsylvania; Southeastern Pennsylvania Theological Library Association

GRANTHAM

CR BRETHREN IN CHRIST CHURCH & MESSIAH COLLEGE ARCHIVES, One College Ave, 17027-9795. (Mail add: PO Box 3002, 17027-9999), SAN 374-9835. Tel: 717-691-6048. FAX: 717-691-6042. E-Mail: archives@messiah.edu. *Dir*, Dori I Steckbeck; E-Mail: dsteckbe@messiah.edu; Staff 1 (Non-MLS 1)
Founded 1952
Library Holdings: Bk Titles 500; Per Subs 20
Special Collections: Anabaptist, Pietist & Wesleyan Studies; Brethren in Christ Church Coll; Historical Library Coll

C MESSIAH COLLEGE, Murray Library, One College Ave, 17027-0800. SAN 358-4941. Tel: 717-691-6006. Interlibrary Loan Service Tel: 717-691-6006, Ext 7242. Circulation Tel: 717-691-6006, Ext 3860. Reference Tel: 717-691-6006, Ext 3910. FAX: 717-691-6042. Web Site: www.messiah.edu/library/home.htm. *Dir*, Jonathan D Lauer; Tel: 717-691-6006, Ext 3820, E-Mail: jlauer@messiah.edu; *Librn*, Michael Brown; Tel: 717-691-6006, Ext 3810, E-Mail: mbrown@messiah.edu; *Librn, Tech Servs*, Liz Kielley; Tel: 717-691-6006, Ext 3850, E-Mail: ekielley@messiah.edu; *ILL*, Dee Porterfield; E-Mail: dporterf@messiah.edu; *Instrul Serv, Librn*, Beth Mark; Tel: 717-691-6006, Ext 3590, E-Mail: bmark@messiah.edu; *Librn, Ref*, Laurie Merz; Tel: 717-691-6006, Ext 3880, E-Mail: lmerz@messiah.edu; *Automation Syst Coordr, Librn*, Michael Rice; Tel: 717-691-6006, Ext 7069, E-Mail: mrice@messiah.edu; *Circ*, Deb Roof; Tel: 717-691-6006, Ext 7293, E-Mail: droof@messiah.edu; *Archivist*, Dorcas Steckbeck; Tel: 717-691-6006, Ext 6048, E-Mail: dsteckbe@messiah.edu; *Per*, David Stevick; Tel: 717-691-6006, Ext 7018, E-Mail: dstevick@messiah.edu; Staff 16 (MLS 6, Non-MLS 10)
Founded 1909. Enrl 2,735; Fac 144; Highest Degree: Bachelor
Jul 1999-Jun 2000 Mats Exp $486,200, Books $200,692, Per/Ser (Incl. Access Fees) $181,447, Presv $12,600, Micro $10,799, Electronic Ref Mat (Incl. Access Fees) $80,662. Sal $633,880 (Prof $290,390)
Library Holdings: Bk Titles 353,500; Per Subs 1,260
Special Collections: Artists' Books; Brethren in Christ Archives, bks, mss & micro; Science & Religion (W Jim Neidhardt Coll)
Automation Activity & Vendor Info: (Acquisitions) epixtech, inc.; (Cataloging) epixtech, inc.; (Circulation) epixtech, inc.; (Course Reserve) epixtech, inc.; (OPAC) epixtech, inc.
Database Vendor: OCLC - First Search
Partic in Associated College Libraries of Central Pennsylvania; Interlibrary Delivery Service of Pennsylvania; OCLC Online Computer Library Center, Inc; PALINET & Union Library Catalogue of Pennsylvania
Friends of the Library Group

GREENCASTLE

P LILIAN S BESORE MEMORIAL LIBRARY,* 305 E Baltimore St, 17225-1004. SAN 314-5530. Tel: 717-597-7920. FAX: 717-597-5320. *Librn*, Victoria Y Williams
Founded 1963. Pop 12,124; Circ 73,920
Library Holdings: Bk Vols 40,000; Per Subs 110
Special Collections: Local History
Mem of Conococheaque District Libr Ctr
Friends of the Library Group

GREENSBURG

P GREENSBURG HEMPFIELD AREA LIBRARY,* 237 S Pennsylvania Ave, 15601-3086. SAN 314-5557. Tel: 724-837-5620. FAX: 724-836-0160. Web Site: www.ghal.org. *Dir*, Cesare J Muccari; *Ch Servs*, Mary Jane Mason
Founded 1936. Pop 79,000; Circ 150,000
Library Holdings: Bk Vols 73,000; Bk Titles 61,856; Per Subs 170
Subject Interests: Genealogy
Special Collections: Pennsylvania Room (Pa History & Geneology)
Mem of Westmoreland County Libr Syst

CR REEVES MEMORIAL LIBRARY, (Formerly Seton Hill College), One Seton Hill Dr, 15601. SAN 314-5565. Tel: 724-838-4291. FAX: 724-838-4203. E-Mail: reeves@setonhhill.edu. Web Site: www.setonhill.edu/~library. *Dir*, David H Stanley; Tel: 724-838-4270, E-Mail: stanley@setonhill.edu; *Tech Servs*, Rosalie Michael; Tel: 724-838-2438, E-Mail: michael@setonhill.edu; *Publ Servs*, Denise Sticha; E-Mail: sticha@setonhill.edu; *Per*, Joann Janosko; *Syst Coordr*, Anthony McMullen; Tel: 724-830-4616, E-Mail: mcmullen@setonhill.edu; *Per*, Judith Koveleskie; Tel: 724-838-7828, E-Mail: kovelesk@setonhill.edu; Staff 7 (MLS 5, Non-MLS 2)
Founded 1918. Enrl 1,342; Fac 81; Highest Degree: Master
Jul 2000-Jun 2001 Mats Exp $129,628, Books $61,000, Per/Ser (Incl. Access Fees) $60,000, Presv $8,628
Library Holdings: Bk Vols 119,000; Per Subs 495
Subject Interests: Entrepreneurship, Fine arts, Holocaust, Women's studies
Database Vendor: Ebsco - EbscoHost, Lexis-Nexis, OCLC - First Search
Partic in OCLC Online Computer Library Center, Inc; PALINET & Union Library Catalogue of Pennsylvania; Share Westmoreland Consortium; Westmoreland Acad Librs Consortium

C UNIVERSITY OF PITTSBURGH AT GREENSBURG, Millstein Library, 1150 Mount Pleasant Rd, 15601-5898. SAN 314-5573. Tel: 724-836-9687. FAX: 724-836-7043. Web Site: www.pitt.edu/~upg/library.html. *Dir*, Patricia Duck; *Asst Dir*, Clara Vana; *Publ Servs*, Evan Cornell; Staff 3 (MLS 3)
Founded 1963. Enrl 1,506; Fac 105; Highest Degree: Bachelor
Jul 1999-Jun 2000 Mats Exp $95,099, Books $33,136, Per/Ser (Incl. Access Fees) $16,825, Presv $1,017, Micro $24,518, Other Print Mats $12,372, Electronic Ref Mat (Incl. Access Fees) $2,132. Sal $194,629
Library Holdings: Bk Vols 74,581; Per Subs 415
Subject Interests: Bus, History, Info sci, Literature
Special Collections: UPG Archives
Publications: Acquisitions List
Partic in OCLC Online Computer Library Center, Inc; PALINET & Union Library Catalogue of Pennsylvania; Share Westmoreland Consortium; Westmoreland Acad Librs Consortium
Friends of the Library Group

S WESTMORELAND COUNTY HISTORICAL SOCIETY, Calvin E Pollins Memorial Library, 951 Old Salem Rd, 15601. SAN 326-3940. Tel: 724-836-1800. FAX: 724-836-2702. E-Mail: history@wchspa.com. Web Site: www.wchspa.com. *Librn*, Linda Umbaugh
Founded 1946. Enrl 1,000
Library Holdings: Bk Vols 4,200
Subject Interests: Genealogy, Local history, Regional history, State hist
Special Collections: Archival Coll (over 150,000 items); Local History Document Coll
Publications: Westmoreland County History Union List & Bibliography List
Restriction: Non-circulating to the public

L WESTMORELAND COUNTY LAW LIBRARY, 2 N Main St, Ste 202, 15601. SAN 314-5549. Tel: 724-830-3267. FAX: 724-830-3042. *Librn*, Betty Ward
Library Holdings: Bk Vols 22,000; Per Subs 35
Subject Interests: Legal mat
Partic in Share Westmoreland Consortium

M WESTMORELAND REGIONAL HOSPITAL LIBRARY,* 532 W Pittsburgh St, 15601-2282. SAN 358-500X. Tel: 724-832-4088. FAX: 724-832-4661. *Librn*, Janet C Petrak
Founded 1952
Library Holdings: Bk Titles 3,000; Per Subs 110
Special Collections: History of Nursing, hospital archives
Restriction: Staff use only

GREENVILLE

P GREENVILLE AREA PUBLIC LIBRARY,* 330 Main St, 16125-2619. SAN 314-5603. Tel: 724-588-5490. FAX: 724-588-5481. *Dir*, Sheila A Kretser; *Cat*, Devona Thompson; Staff 3 (MLS 2, Non-MLS 1)
Founded 1921. Pop 12,582; Circ 67,710
Library Holdings: Bk Vols 35,174; Per Subs 80
Mem of New Castle County Public Library System
Friends of the Library Group

C THIEL COLLEGE, Langenheim Memorial Library, 75 College Ave, 16125-2183. SAN 314-5611. Tel: 724-589-2119, 724-589-2205. FAX: 724-589-2122. *Dir*, Douglas J Cerroni; E-Mail: dcerroni@thiel.edu; *Ref, Ser*, Lida Mason; *Ref*, Dorothy Brunoel; *Cat, Ref*, Joyce Minor; *Doc, Ref*, Deborah E Ross; *Circ*, Bonnie Madura; Staff 7 (MLS 5, Non-MLS 2)
Founded 1866. Enrl 900; Fac 62; Highest Degree: Bachelor
Library Holdings: Bk Titles 137,000; Per Subs 800
Special Collections: Northwestern Pennsylvania Synod, Southwestern Pennsylvania Synod & West Virginia - Western Maryland Synod/Evangelica Lutheran Church in America Archives Coll
Partic in Dialog Corporation; OCLC Online Computer Library Center, Inc; Pittsburgh Regional Libr Consortium

GROVE CITY

C GROVE CITY COLLEGE, Henry Buhl Library, 300 Campus Dr, 16127-2198. SAN 314-562X. Tel: 724-458-2047. FAX: 724-458-2181. *Dir, Ref*, Diane Grundy; *Coll Develop, Dep Dir*, Barbra Munnell; E-Mail: bmmunnell@gcc.edu; *Acq*, Jill Forsythe; *Cat*, Wendy Riggi; *Ref*, Carol Singleton; Tel: 724-450-4038; *Bibliog Instr, Ref*, Mary Sodergren; *Syst Coordr*, Heather Pittock; *ILL*, Vera Molsky; *Ser*, Joyce M Kebert; Tel: 724-458-3821, E-Mail: jmkebert@gcc.edu; Staff 11 (MLS 5, Non-MLS 6)
Founded 1900. Enrl 2,250; Fac 120; Highest Degree: Master
Library Holdings: Bk Vols 145,000
Subject Interests: Am, Am lit, Behav sci, British, English, European history, Soc sci
Special Collections: Ludwig von Mises Papers, letters, pamphlets & mss; Mathematics (Locke Coll), bks & pamphlets
Automation Activity & Vendor Info: (Cataloging) TLC; (Circulation) TLC (OPAC) TLC
Database Vendor: Ebsco - EbscoHost, Lexis-Nexis, OCLC - First Search, ProQuest, Silverplatter Information Inc., Wilson - Wilson Web
Partic in PALINET & Union Library Catalogue of Pennsylvania

P GROVE CITY COMMUNITY LIBRARY,* 125 W Main St, 16127-1569. SAN 314-5638. Tel: 724-458-7320. FAX: 724-458-7332. E-Mail: grovecpl@pathway.net. Web Site: www.grovecitypalibrary.org. *Librn*, Linda Bennett; *Asst Librn*, Lori Campbell
Founded 1958. Pop 11,924; Circ 32,353
Library Holdings: Bk Vols 29,000; Per Subs 40
Friends of the Library Group

GWYNEDD VALLEY

J GWYNEDD-MERCY COLLEGE, Lourdes Library, Sumneytown Pike, 19437. SAN 314-5654. Tel: 215-646-7300, Ext 496. FAX: 215-641-5596. Web Site: www.gmc.edu. *Dir*, Kathy Mulroy; E-Mail: mulroy.k@gmc.edu; Staff 10 (MLS 5, Non-MLS 5)
Founded 1958. Enrl 1,128; Fac 60; Highest Degree: Master
Jul 1999-Jun 2000 Income $549,882, State $8,000, Federal $22,000, Locally Generated Income $8,000, Parent Institution $511,882. Mats Exp $186,574, Books $60,700, Per/Ser (Incl. Access Fees) $104,996, Micro $12,878, AV Equip $8,000. Sal $286,910
Library Holdings: Bk Vols 96,590; Per Subs 727
Subject Interests: Ireland
Automation Activity & Vendor Info: (Cataloging) DRA; (Circulation) DRA; (Course Reserve) DRA; (OPAC) DRA; (Serials) DRA
Database Vendor: Ebsco - EbscoHost, Silverplatter Information Inc., Wilson - Wilson Web
Partic in OCLC Online Computer Library Center, Inc; PALINET & Union Library Catalogue of Pennsylvania; Southeastern Pa Consortium for Higher Educ; Tri-State College Library Cooperative (TCLC)

HAMBURG

G HAMBURG CENTER, Staff Development Library,* Old Rte 22, 19526. SAN 326-2499. Tel: 610-562-6053. FAX: 610-562-6081. *Cat, Circ*, Linda Brown
Founded 1981
Library Holdings: Bk Titles 350; Per Subs 10
Subject Interests: Nursing, Public health
Special Services for the Deaf - Books on deafness & sign language
Open Mon-Fri 8-4:30

P HAMBURG PUBLIC LIBRARY,* 35 N Third St, 19526-1502. SAN 314-5670. Tel: 610-562-2843. FAX: 610-562-8136. E-Mail: hambrgpl@ptd.net. *Librn*, Daniel LaRue
Founded 1903. Pop 13,190; Circ 30,500
1998-1999 Income $96,000, State $16,500, City $18,200, County $17,000, Locally Generated Income $42,000. Mats Exp $15,800, Books $13,300, Per/Ser (Incl. Access Fees) $2,500. Sal $35,400 (Prof $23,400)
Library Holdings: Bk Vols 17,000; Per Subs 80
Special Collections: Hamburg Items 1902-Present, microfilm
Publications: American Libraries Booklist; Pennsylvania Library Association Bulletin
Mem of Berks County Libr Syst

AMLIN

SALEM PUBLIC LIBRARY,* Wimmers Sta, Rte 191, Box 98, 18427-9720. SAN 314-5689. Tel: 717-689-0903. *Librn*, Dianne Henry
Founded 1969. Pop 8,732
Library Holdings: Bk Vols 6,500
Special Collections: Civil War Coll; Lincoln Coll; Railroad Coll; Zane Grey Coll
Open Tues-Thurs 10-6; May-Nov, Sat 12-3
Friends of the Library Group

ANOVER

HANOVER PUBLIC LIBRARY, 2 Library Pl, 17331-2283. SAN 314-5697. Tel: 717-632-5183. FAX: 717-632-7565. E-Mail: hnlib@blazenet.net. Web Site: www.hellohanover.com/library.html. *Dir*, Priscilla Greco McFerren; *Ref*, Raymond Van de Castle; *Tech Servs*, Melody Dewberry; *ILL*, Linda Gladfelter; *ILL*, Jeanette Miller; *Circ*, Connie McInturff; *Ch Servs*, George Matthew; *Automation Syst Coordr*, Julie K Moul; Staff 17 (MLS 2, Non-MLS 15)
Founded 1911. Pop 39,655; Circ 252,520
Jan 1999-Dec 1999 Income $432,635, State $89,166, City $44,581, County $24,911, Locally Generated Income $59,699, Other $214,278. Mats Exp $76,302, Books $50,543, Per/Ser (Incl. Access Fees) $6,987, AV Equip $16,722, Electronic Ref Mat (Incl. Access Fees) $2,000. Sal $233,500
Library Holdings: Bk Vols 59,822; Bk Titles 56,871; Per Subs 150
Subject Interests: Genealogy, Local history, Pennsylvania
Database Vendor: Ebsco - EbscoHost, GaleNet, IAC - Info Trac
Publications: Weekly newspaper column
Mem of York County Library System
Partic in Spires
Special Services for the Deaf - TDD
Friends of the Library Group

ARLEYSVILLE

MENNONITE HISTORIANS OF EASTERN PENNSYLVANIA, Mennonite Historical Library & Archives, 565 Yoder Rd, PO Box 82, 19438. SAN 326-3444. Tel: 215-256-3020. FAX: 215-256-3023. E-Mail: info@mhep.org, mennhist@pond.com. Web Site: www.mhep.org. *Librn*, Joel D Alderfer; Staff 1 (Non-MLS 1)
Founded 1967
Library Holdings: Bk Titles 6,720; Per Subs 100
Subject Interests: Genealogy, Hist of Bucks, Local biog, Mennonite hist, Montgomery counties, Pa German studies, Peace studies, Theology
Special Collections: Franconia Mennonite Mission Board Coll, 1917-1971; J C Clemens Coll; Jacob B Mensch Coll; Jacob Fretz Coll; John E Lapp Coll; Local History (Robert C Bucher Coll); Mennonite Church; Mennonite Church History (Towamencin Mennonite Coll); Salford Mennonite Church Coll, 1718-1936
Publications: MHEP Newsletter
Restriction: Non-circulating to the public

ARRISBURG

AMP, INC, Technology Information Center, MS 140, PO Box 3608, 17105-3608. SAN 314-5700. Tel: 717-986-3576. FAX: 717-986-3468. *Mgr*, Robert Kuhn; E-Mail: rckuhn@amp.com; Staff 5 (MLS 2, Non-MLS 3)
Founded 1956
Library Holdings: Bk Vols 12,000; Per Subs 10,000
Subject Interests: Electrical, Electronics, Mechanical engineering, Plastics tech, Solid state physics
Publications: handbook; Monthly booklist; SDI bulletin
Restriction: Staff use only
Partic in Dialog Corporation; OCLC Online Computer Library Center, Inc

COMMONWEALTH COURT LIBRARY, 603 South Office Bldg, PO Box 11730, 17108. SAN 314-5719. Tel: 717-255-1615. FAX: 717-787-7427. Web Site: www.aopc.org/index.htm. *Librn*, Mary Rinesmith; E-Mail: mary.rinesmith@commonwealth.court.state.pa.us
Founded 1970
Library Holdings: Bk Vols 20,000; Bk Titles 2,000; Per Subs 12
Database Vendor: Lexis-Nexis
Restriction: Not open to public

L DAUPHIN COUNTY LAW LIBRARY, Dauphin County Courthouse, 101 Market St, 17101. SAN 314-5735. Tel: 717-255-2797. FAX: 717-255-2817. E-Mail: tmccall@dauphinc.org. Web Site: www.dauphine.org. *Chief Librn*, Tracey E McCall; E-Mail: tmccall@dauphinc.org; *Asst Librn*, Laura Hain; E-Mail: lhain@dauphinic.org; Staff 1 (Non-MLS 1)
Founded 1865
Jan 2001-Dec 2001 Income County $294,000. Mats Exp $163,000. Sal $94,880 (Prof $43,000)
Library Holdings: Bk Vols 42,000; Per Subs 28
Automation Activity & Vendor Info: (Cataloging) Gateway; (Circulation) Gateway
Publications: Law Library Update
Restriction: Circulation limited

P DAUPHIN COUNTY LIBRARY SYSTEM, 101 Walnut St, 17101. SAN 358-5034. Tel: 717-234-4961. Circulation Tel: 717-652-9380. Reference Tel: 717-652-9380. FAX: 717-234-7479. Web Site: www.dcls.org. *Exec Dir*, Richard Bowra; Tel: 717-234-4961, Ext 102, E-Mail: bowra@dcls.org; *Assoc Dir*, Mike Mabe; Tel: 717-234-4961, Ext 107, E-Mail: mabe@dcls.org; *Coordr*, James Hollinger; Tel: 717-234-4961, Ext 106, E-Mail: hollinger@dcls.org; *Commun Relations*, Karen Cullings; Tel: 717-234-4961, Ext 104, E-Mail: cullings@dcls.org; *Ch Servs*, Wendy Lukehart; Tel: 717-234-4961, Ext 199, E-Mail: lukehart@dcls.org; *Tech Coordr*, Keith Ostertag; Tel: 717-652-9380, Ext 112, Fax: 717-545-3584, E-Mail: ostertag@dcls.org; Staff 30 (MLS 16, Non-MLS 14)
Founded 1889. Pop 210,151; Circ 986,903
Jan 1998-Dec 1998 Income (Main Library and Branch Library) $4,021,916, State $828,308, City $143,193, Federal $156,754, County $2,513,025, Other $523,829. Mats Exp $483,943, Books $450,553, Electronic Ref Mat (Incl. Access Fees) $36,390. Sal $2,227,242
Library Holdings: Bk Vols 285,016; Per Subs 322
Subject Interests: Local history, Pennsylvania
Special Collections: Grants Info; Job/Career Ctr
Automation Activity & Vendor Info: (Circulation) epixtech, inc.
Database Vendor: Dialog, epixtech, inc., IAC - Info Trac
Publications: A Directory of Libraries of Central Pennsylvania; Film Catalog-Dauphin County Library Systems; Large Print Catalog; Newsletter; Newsletter, District Service; Serials Catalog; Stepping Into Books; Stitch-In-Time
Member Libraries: Amelia S Givin Free Library; Dauphin County Library System; Johnson Memorial Library; Middletown Public Library; Myerstown Community Library; New Cumberland Public Library
Headquarters for Harrisburg District Library Center
Friends of the Library Group
Branches: 9
EAST SHORE AREA, 4501 Ethel St, 17109. SAN 358-5093. Tel: 717-652-9380. FAX: 717-545-3584. *Dir*, Carolyn Poff; Tel: 717-652-9380, Ext 122, E-Mail: poff@dcls.org; *Librn*, Carol Giblin; *Coordr*, James Hollinger; Tel: 717-234-4961, Ext 106, Fax: 717-234-7479, E-Mail: hollinger@dcls.org
Library Holdings: Bk Vols 97,782
Mem of Dauphin County Library System
Friends of the Library Group
ELIZABETHVILLE BRANCH, 80 N Market St, Elizabethville, 17023. SAN 358-5123. Tel: 717-362-9825. FAX: 717-362-8119. *Librn*, Bonita Hoffman
Library Holdings: Bk Vols 29,655
Friends of the Library Group
HARRISBURG DOWNTOWN, 101 Walnut St, 17101. SAN 358-5069. Tel: 717-234-4976. FAX: 717-234-7479. *Librn*, Walter Zimmerman
Library Holdings: Bk Vols 41,755
Friends of the Library Group
HARRISBURG UPTOWN, Uptown Plaza, 17110. SAN 358-5158. Tel: 717-232-7286. FAX: 717-232-9707. *Librn*, Mary Ward
Library Holdings: Bk Vols 18,100
Friends of the Library Group
HUMMELSTOWN COMMUNITY, 205 S John St, Hummelstown, 17036. SAN 314-6278. Tel: 717-566-0949. FAX: 717-566-7178. *Librn*, Cecelia Fox
Library Holdings: Bk Vols 30,112
Friends of the Library Group
JOHNSON MEMORIAL, 799 E Center St, Millersburg, 17061. SAN 376-9291. Tel: 717-698-2658. FAX: 717-692-5003. *Librn*, Darlee Lebo
Library Holdings: Bk Vols 25,039
KLINE VILLAGE, Kline Plaza, 17104. SAN 358-5212. Tel: 717-234-3934. FAX: 717-234-7713. *Librn*, Stephanie Liva
Library Holdings: Bk Vols 16,745
Friends of the Library Group
NORTHERN DAUPHIN, 571 N Second St, Lykens, 17048. SAN 358-5247. Tel: 717-453-9315. FAX: 717-453-9524. *Librn*, Diane Klinger
Library Holdings: Bk Vols 17,203
Friends of the Library Group
WILLIAMSTOWN BRANCH, 200 S West St, Ste B, Williamstown, 17098. SAN 358-5271. Tel: 717-647-2179. FAX: 717-647-4964. *Librn*, Terri Kulp
Library Holdings: Bk Vols 8,986

GL DEPARTMENT OF AUDITOR GENERAL, Law Library,* Finance Bldg, Rm 223, 17120-0018. SAN 314-5816. Tel: 717-787-4546. FAX: 717-772-3691.
Library Holdings: Bk Vols 4,000

J HARRISBURG AREA COMMUNITY COLLEGE, McCormick Library, One HACC Dr, 17110-2999. SAN 314-5778. Tel: 717-780-2460. Interlibrary Loan Service Tel: 717-780-2623. FAX: 717-780-2462. Web Site: lib1.hacc.edu/. *Dean*, Charles R Pequese; E-Mail: crpegues@hacc.edu; *Coordr*, Suzanne Buser; *Cat, Tech Servs*, Cathryn Hintze; *Circ*, Mattie Woods; *Bibliog Instr*, James Davis; *Automation Syst Coordr*, Michael L Bowden; *Coll Develop*, Beverly Segina; Staff 10 (MLS 10)
Founded 1964. Enrl 8,500; Fac 193
Jul 1998-Jun 1999 Income $1,611,756. Mats Exp $243,299, Books

$115,474, Per/Ser (Incl. Access Fees) $71,994, Presv $5,000, Micro $18,069. Sal $966,994
Library Holdings: Bk Vols 132,000; Bk Titles 111,000; Per Subs 616
Subject Interests: Photog
Publications: Faculty guide to services; Guide to the use of McCormick Library; Library Instruction Workbook; Reference Guide Series; Viewpoints
Partic in Associated College Libraries of Central Pennsylvania; Interlibrary Delivery Service of Pennsylvania; OCLC Online Computer Library Center, Inc; PALINET & Union Library Catalogue of Pennsylvania

M HARRISBURG HOSPITAL, Library Services, 111 S Front St, 17101-2099. SAN 314-5786. Tel: 717-782-5510. FAX: 717-782-5512. *Mgr*, Cheryl A Capitani
Founded 1936
Library Holdings: Bk Titles 3,796; Per Subs 506
Subject Interests: Allied health fields, Clinical medicine, Consumer health info, Hospital mgt, Nursing
Special Collections: Archives of Harrisburg Hosp
Publications: Library Newsletter; Nursing Contents
Partic in BRS; Central Pennsylvania Health Science Library Association (CPHSLA); Greater NE Regional Med Libr Program; Nat Libr of Med; OCLC Online Computer Library Center, Inc; PALINET & Union Library Catalogue of Pennsylvania

HARRISBURG STATE HOSPITAL

S RESIDENT LIBRARY FOR PATIENTS, Cameron & McClay St, PO Box 61260, 17106-1260. SAN 324-6760. Tel: 717-772-7650. Circulation Tel: 717-772-7651. Reference Tel: 717-772-7615. FAX: 717-772-7653. E-Mail: hshlibrary@bigfoot.com. *Librn*, Martha Ruff; Staff 3 (MLS 1, Non-MLS 2)
Founded 1851
Jul 1999-May 2000 Mats Exp $3,350, Books $2,100, Per/Ser (Incl. Access Fees) $300, AV Equip $400, Other Print Mats $150, Electronic Ref Mat (Incl. Access Fees) $400. Sal $53,000 (Prof $24,000)
Library Holdings: Bk Titles 1,600; Per Subs 29; High Interest/Low Vocabulary Bk Vols 25
Special Collections: Consumer Health materials; Educational films & videos
Publications: In-house Newsletter (bi-monthly)
Function: ILL limited
Partic in State Libr Network
This library serves the cultural, educational and informational needs of our psychiatric patients.

M STAFF LIBRARY, Cameron & McClay Sts, PO Box 61260, 17106-1260. Tel: 717-772-7615. FAX: 717-772-7653. E-Mail: hshlibrary@bigfoot.com. *Chief Librn*, Martha Ruff; Tel: 717-772-7650; Staff 1 (MLS 1)
Jul 1999-Jun 2000 Mats Exp $5,335, Books $2,200, Per/Ser (Incl. Access Fees) $50, AV Equip $550, Other Print Mats $2,000, Electronic Ref Mat (Incl. Access Fees) $535. Sal $28,000 (Prof $25,000)
Library Holdings: Bk Titles 1,600; Per Subs 58
Subject Interests: Psychiatric rehabilitation, Psychiatry, Psychology
Function: ILL available
Partic in BHSL; Docline; NNLM/SCR, OCLC Online Computer Libr Ctr, Inc; UCMP

S HISTORICAL SOCIETY OF DAUPHIN COUNTY LIBRARY, 219 S Front St, 17104. SAN 326-4270. Tel: 717-233-3462. FAX: 717-233-6059. *Librn*, Warren W Wirebach; Staff 1 (Non-MLS 1)
Library Holdings: Bk Titles 500

M HOSPITAL & HEALTHSYSTEM ASSOCIATION OF PENNSYLVANIA LIBRARY,* 4750 Lindle Rd, PO Box 8600, 17111. SAN 321-057X. Tel: 717-564-9200. FAX: 717-561-5333. *Mgr*, Fran Cohen; E-Mail: fcohen@hap2000.org
Founded 1976
Library Holdings: Bk Vols 1,500; Per Subs 175
Subject Interests: Personnel management
Special Collections: Hospital trustees; Pennsylvania Hospital hist
Restriction: Staff use only
Partic in Greater NE Regional Med Libr Program

§L KLETT, ROONEY, LIEBER & SCHORING LIBRARY, Harrisburg, 240 N Third St, Ste 600, 17101.

L MCNEES, WALLACE & NURICK, Information Center, 100 Pine St, PO Box 1166, 17108-1166. SAN 326-9361. Tel: 717-232-8000. FAX: 717-237-5300. Web Site: www.mwn.com. *Librn*, Margaret J Ross; Tel: 717-237-5205, E-Mail: mross@mwn.com; Staff 1 (Non-MLS 1)
Library Holdings: Bk Vols 15,000; Per Subs 200
Database Vendor: Dialog, Lexis-Nexis, OCLC - First Search

S PATRIOT NEWS COMPANY LIBRARY,* 812 Market St, PO Box 2265, 17105. SAN 374-5910. Tel: 717-255-8402. FAX: 717-255-8456. E-Mail: pnlibrary@microserve.com. *Chief Librn*, Deanna Mills; *Asst Librn*, Barbara Roth
Founded 1980

P PAXTANG-SWATARA AREA COMMUNITY LIBRARY,* 3700 Rutherford St, 17111. SAN 314-5808. Tel: 717-564-0385.
Founded 1966
Library Holdings: Bk Titles 15,000
Mem of Harrisburg District Libr Ctr
Open 6pm-8pm; staffed by volunteers

G PENNSYLVANIA BOARD OF PROBATION & PAROLE LIBRARY,* 1101 S Front St, Ste 5600, 17104-2552. SAN 314-5824. Tel: 717-787-6151 FAX: 717-772-4185. *Dir*, Paul Strizzi; *Librn*, Brenda Fleming
Founded 1972
Library Holdings: Bk Titles 1,000
Subject Interests: Criminal justice, Criminology, Law, Parole, Probation, Psychology
Publications: County Adult Probation Standards; PBPP Annual Report; PBPP Monthly Statistical Report; Police Procedures in the Handling of Parolees; Policies & Procedures for Improvement Grants; Staff Developmer Division Training Quarterly Catalog
Open Mon-Fri 8:30-4:30

G PENNSYLVANIA DEPARTMENT OF CONSERVATION & NATURAL RESOURCES, Bureau of Topographic & Geologic Survey Library, PO Box 8453, 17105-8453. SAN 358-5336. Tel: 717-783-8077. FAX: 717-783-7267 *Librn*, Richard C Keen
Founded 1850
Library Holdings: Bk Titles 10,000; Per Subs 70
Subject Interests: Earth science, Geography, Geology
Special Collections: Aerial Photography, contact prints; Maps (United State Geologic Survey Seven & One Half Minute Maps)
Publications: In House Newsletter

PENNSYLVANIA DEPARTMENT OF ENVIRONMENTAL PROTECTION

G CENTRAL LIBRARY, Rachel Carson State Office Bldg, 400 Market S, 3r flr, 17101. (Mail add: PO Box 8458, 17105-8458), SAN 358-5301. Tel: 717-787-9647. FAX: 717-772-0288. *Librn*, Sandra Blust; E-Mail: blust.sandra@dep.state.pa.us; *Librn*, Dr Linda Rambler; E-Mail: rambler.linda@dep.state.pa.us; Staff 2 (MLS 2)
Founded 1971
Library Holdings: Bk Vols 9,500; Per Subs 400
Subject Interests: Botany, Environ scis, Forestry
Special Collections: Pennsylvania Sewage Facilities Plans; Pennsylvania State Coal Research Series
Database Vendor: Dialog, OCLC - First Search, Wilson - Wilson Web
Restriction: In-house use for visitors
Partic in OCLC Online Computer Library Center, Inc

GL LAW LIBRARY, OFFICE OF CHIEF COUNSEL, Rachel Carson St Office Bldg, 9th flr, 17105. SAN 358-5395. Tel: 717-783-8440. FAX: 717-787-9378. *Librn*, Brenda Houck; E-Mail: houck.brenda@a1.dep.state.pa.us
Library Holdings: Bk Vols 3,200; Per Subs 30
Subject Interests: Environ law of Pa
Restriction: Staff use only

PENNSYLVANIA DEPARTMENT OF TRANSPORTATION

G KNOWLEDGE CENTER, Commonwealth Keystone Bldg, 5th flr, 17120-0041. (Mail add: PO Box 3054, 17105-3054), Tel: 717-705-1546. FAX: 717-787-3466. Web Site: www.dot.state.pa.us. *Senior Librn*, Judy Gutsha E-Mail: gutshaj@penndot.state.pa.us; *Librn*, Cheryl Bodan; Tel: 717-787-6527, E-Mail: cbodan@penndot.state.pa.us; Staff 3 (MLS 2, Non-MLS 1)
Founded 1979
1999-2000 Mats Exp $131,000, Books $60,000, Per/Ser (Incl. Access Fees) $50,000, Electronic Ref Mat (Incl. Access Fees) $21,000. Sal $93,000 (Prof $80,000)
Library Holdings: Bk Titles 20,000; Per Subs 300
Subject Interests: Business, Engineering, Transportation
Special Collections: Transportation Research Board Series
Automation Activity & Vendor Info: (Circulation) EOS; (Serials) EOS
Database Vendor: Dialog
Restriction: Open to public for reference only

GL LAW LIBRARY, 555 Walnut St, 9th flr, 17101-1900. SAN 358-545X. Tel: 717-705-1358, 717-787-5473. FAX: 717-772-2741. *In Charge*, Brandi Hauck
Library Holdings: Bk Vols 6,000; Per Subs 20
Restriction: Staff use only

S PENNSYLVANIA HISTORICAL & MUSEUM COMMISSION, Reference Library,* State Museum of Pennsylvania, Third & N Sts, PO Box 1026, 17108-1026. SAN 314-5913. Tel: 717-783-9898. FAX: 717-783-4558. *Librn* Paula Heiman; E-Mail: pheiman@phmc.state.pa.us; *Librn*, Sally Biel; Staff 2 (MLS 2)
Founded 1947
Library Holdings: Bk Vols 22,000; Per Subs 180
Subject Interests: Archival, Mus tech, Pa hist
Restriction: By appointment only, Open to public for reference only
Partic in OCLC Online Computer Library Center, Inc; PALINET & Union Library Catalogue of Pennsylvania

PENNSYLVANIA JOINT STATE GOVERNMENT COMMISSION LIBRARY, Finance Bldg, Rm G-16, 17120. SAN 314-5921. Tel: 717-787-6803. FAX: 717-787-7020. *Librn*, Carolyn Pfeifer; E-Mail: cpfeifer@legis.state.pa.us
Library Holdings: Bk Titles 3,500; Per Subs 75
Subject Interests: Education, Finance, Government, Legislative ref mat from other states, Pa statutes
Automation Activity & Vendor Info: (OPAC) Endeavor; (Serials) Endeavor
Database Vendor: OCLC - First Search
Restriction: Non-circulating to the public

L PENNSYLVANIA LEGISLATIVE BUDGET & FINANCE COMMITTEE LIBRARY,* Finance Bldg, Rm 400, 17105-8737. SAN 314-5948. Tel: 717-783-1600. FAX: 717-787-5487. *Librn*, Chuck Saia
Special Collections: Pennsylvania Fiscal documents (Historical Coll), computer file

L PENNSYLVANIA LEGISLATIVE REFERENCE BUREAU LIBRARY, Main Capitol, Rm 641, 17120-0033. SAN 314-5956. Tel: 717-787-4816. FAX: 717-783-2396. E-Mail: lrblibrary@legis.state.pa.us. *Librn*, Susan K Zavacky; Staff 1 (Non-MLS 1)
Founded 1909
Library Holdings: Bk Vols 10,000; Per Subs 50
Subject Interests: Law, Pa legislature
Restriction: Not a lending library

L PENNSYLVANIA OFFICE OF ATTORNEY GENERAL, Law Library,* 1525 Strawberry Sq, 17120. SAN 314-5891. Tel: 717-787-3176. FAX: 717-772-4526. *Librn*, Ellen R Chack; Staff 3 (MLS 1, Non-MLS 2)
Founded 1873
Library Holdings: Bk Vols 26,500
Restriction: Staff use only
Partic in Mead Data Cent

PENNSYLVANIA PUBLIC UTILITY COMMISSION LIBRARY,* N Office Bldg, Rm 100, PO Box 3265, 17105-3265. SAN 324-6078. Tel: 717-787-4466. FAX: 717-787-4193. *Librn*, William M Smith
Founded 1977
Library Holdings: Bk Titles 8,400; Per Subs 74
Subject Interests: Econ, Energy, Engineering, Law, Pub utilities
Restriction: Not open to public

PENNSYLVANIA STATE DEPARTMENT OF PUBLIC WELFARE, Office of Children, Youth & Families Library,* PO Box 2675, 17105. SAN 377-5216. Tel: 717-787-6574. FAX: 717-772-4957. *Dir*, Dr Richard Fiene
Library Holdings: Bk Vols 3,000

L PENNSYLVANIA STATE SUPREME COURTS LIBRARY,* Main Capitol Bldg, Rm 434, PO Box 624, 17108. SAN 314-6006. Tel: 717-787-6199. FAX: 717-787-1549. *In Charge*, Joan Stehulak
Library Holdings: Bk Vols 500
Special Collections: Legal Documents Coll

PINNACLE HEALTH HOSPITALS, Community General Osteopathic Hospital Library, 4300 Londonderry Rd, PO Box 3000, 17105-3000. SAN 314-5727. Tel: 717-657-7247. FAX: 717-657-7248. *Librn*, Helen L Houpt; E-Mail: hhoupt@pinnaclehealth.org; Staff 1 (MLS 1)
Founded 1977
Library Holdings: Bk Vols 660; Per Subs 50
Subject Interests: Allied health, Hospital administration, Medicine, Nursing
Automation Activity & Vendor Info: (Acquisitions) Sydney; (Cataloging) Sydney; (Circulation) Sydney; (OPAC) Sydney; (Serials) Sydney
Restriction: Open to public for reference only
Partic in Central Pennsylvania Health Science Library Association (CPHSLA)

POLYCLINIC MEDICAL CENTER, Medical Staff Library,* 2601 N Third St, 17110. SAN 314-6014. Tel: 717-782-4292. FAX: 717-782-4293. *Librn*, Elizabeth Coldsmith; E-Mail: l.coldsmith@clinicalhealth.org
Founded 1925
Library Holdings: Bk Vols 2,000; Per Subs 199
Subject Interests: Allied health, Hosp admin, Hosp mgt, Medicine, Nursing
Special Collections: History of Medicine
Partic in Health Science Library Information Consortium; National Network Of Libraries Of Medicine - South Central Region

SENATE LIBRARY OF PENNSYLVANIA, Main Capitol Bldg, Rm 157, 17120-0030. SAN 314-5999. Tel: 717-787-6120. FAX: 717-783-5021. *Librn*, Evelyn F Andrews; E-Mail: eandrews@os.pasen.gov
Library Holdings: Bk Vols 7,500
Special Collections: Histories of Legislation for Senate & House of Representatives of Pennsylvania; Legislative Journals for Senate and House of Representatives of Pennsylvania; Transcripts of Hearings For Senate & House of Representatives of Pennsylvania

STATE LIBRARY OF PENNSYLVANIA, Department of Education, Office of Commonwealth Libraries,* Forum Bldg, Walnut St & Commonwealth Ave, 17120. (Mail add: PO Box 1601, 17105-1601), SAN 314-6022. Reference Tel: 717-787-4440. TDD: 717-772-2863. Interlibrary Loan Service FAX: 717-783-2070. E-Mail: reference@stlib.state.pa.us. Web Site: www.statelibrary.state.pa.us. *State Librn*, Gary D Wolfe; Tel: 717-787-2646, Fax: 717-772-3265, E-Mail: wolfe@stlib.state.pa.us; *Dir Libr Serv*, Alice L Lubrecht; Tel: 717-783-5968, Fax: 717-772-8268, E-Mail: ali@stlib.state.pa.us; *ILL*, Karen Carlson; Tel: 717-787-4130, Fax: 717-783-2070, E-Mail: kec@stlib.state.pa.us; *Publ Servs*, Susan G Payne; Tel: 717-783-5986, E-Mail: sgp@stlib.state.pa.us; *Tech Servs*, Mary Lou Sowden; Tel: 717-783-5964, E-Mail: mps@stlib.state.pa.us; Staff 88 (MLS 32, Non-MLS 56)
Founded 1745
Jul 1997-Jun 1998 Income $53,112,401, State $47,398,288, Federal $1,009,058, Locally Generated Income $30,270, Other $4,674,785. Mats Exp $951,299, Books $331,264, Per/Ser (Incl. Access Fees) $186,351, Presv $20,377, Micro $413,307. Sal $3,897,133
Library Holdings: Bk Vols 1,000,494; Per Subs 4,170
Subject Interests: Education, History, Law
Special Collections: Central PA Genealogy; Jansen - Shirk Bookplate Coll; Jansen Manuscript Letters Coll; PA Colonial Assembly Coll; PA Imprints, 1689-1850; PA Newspapers - Historic & Current
Automation Activity & Vendor Info: (Cataloging) Endeavor; (Circulation) Endeavor; (OPAC) Endeavor; (Serials) Endeavor
Database Vendor: Dialog, Ebsco - EbscoHost, OCLC - First Search, ProQuest
Publications: Checklist of Official PA Publications; Directory - PA Libraries; Directory of Libraries Serving the Government of PA; First 100 Years of PA Imprints; Guide to the State Library of PA; Handbook for District Library Consultants; Handbook for Public Library Trustees; Integrating Information Management Skills: A Process for Incorporating Media Skills into Content Areas: Pennyslvania Guidelines for School Library Media Programs; Pennsylvania Online: A Curriculum Guide for School Media Centers; Revised Classification Scheme for PA State Publications
Mem of Keystone Libr Network
Partic in Access Pa; Associated College Libraries of Central Pennsylvania; Interlibrary Delivery Service of Pennsylvania; PALINET & Union Library Catalogue of Pennsylvania
Special Services for the Deaf - TDD

S SUSQUEHANNA RIVER BASIN COMMISSION LIBRARY,* 1721 N Front St, 17102-2391. SAN 314-6030. Tel: 717-238-0425. FAX: 717-238-2436. E-Mail: srbc@srbc.net. *Librn*, JoAnn Painter
Library Holdings: Bk Vols 3,000; Per Subs 12
Subject Interests: Water resources

C THOMPSON INSTITUTE CENTER RESOURCE ROOM,* 5650 Derry St, 17111. SAN 314-6049. Tel: 717-564-4112. FAX: 717-564-3779. *Dir*, Thomas Bryant
Library Holdings: Bk Vols 1,500; Per Subs 30
Subject Interests: Bus, Data proc, Electronics, Medicine, Secretarial

HARRISON CITY

P PENN AREA LIBRARY,* PO Box 499, 15636. SAN 359-5897. Tel: 724-744-4414. FAX: 724-744-0226. *Librn*, Maryanne Fulmer
Pop 16,153; Circ 50,000
1997-1998 Income $98,100, State $18,500, County $1,500, Locally Generated Income $4,800, Other $8,300. Mats Exp $19,900, Books $12,000, Per/Ser (Incl. Access Fees) $2,000, Other Print Mats $5,000. Sal $42,000 (Prof $21,000)
Library Holdings: Bk Vols 13,000; Per Subs 66
Subject Interests: Civil War, Local history
Friends of the Library Group

HASTINGS

P HASTINGS PUBLIC LIBRARY,* 312 Beaver St, PO Box 515, 16646-0515. SAN 314-6065. Tel: 814-247-8231. FAX: 814-247-8871. E-Mail: hastings@forspeed.com. *Librn*, Frances Rhoa; *Asst Librn*, Patricia Sibert-Klein
Pop 2,846; Circ 13,510
Library Holdings: Bk Titles 14,481; Per Subs 35
Mem of Cambria County Library System & District Center

HATBORO

R HATBORO BAPTIST CHURCH LIBRARY, 32 N York Rd, 19040. SAN 314-6073. Tel: 215-675-8400. FAX: 215-675-4697. *Librn*, Carolyn Zimmerman
Founded 1950
1998-1999 Income $525, Other $500
Library Holdings: Bk Titles 4,940
Subject Interests: Christian living, Devotionals, Missions, Religion, Sermons

P UNION LIBRARY COMPANY OF HATBOROUGH, 243 S York Rd, 19040-3429. SAN 323-5475. Tel: 215-672-1420. FAX: 215-672-1546. E-Mail: ulchatboro@adelphia.net. *Librn*, Harriet Ehrsam; E-Mail: hatlib@adelphia.net; Staff 4 (MLS 1, Non-MLS 3)

Founded 1775. Pop 7,380; Circ 30,000
1999-2000 Mats Exp $85,000
Library Holdings: Bk Vols 21,000; Bk Titles 22,000; Per Subs 41
Special Collections: American Civil War; American Revolution; Colonial Subscription Library, circa 1770; Pennsylvania History
Automation Activity & Vendor Info: (Acquisitions) Follett; (Cataloging) Follett; (Circulation) Follett
Database Vendor: Ebsco - EbscoHost
Partic in Montgomery County Libr & Info Network Consortium
Friends of the Library Group

HATFIELD

R BIBLICAL THEOLOGICAL SEMINARY LIBRARY,* 200 N Main St, 19440-2499. SAN 314-609X. Tel: 215-368-5000, Ext 123. FAX: 215-368-7002. E-Mail: library@biblical.edu. Web Site: www.biblical.edu/library. *Coll Develop, Librn*, Joanna Hause; Staff 2 (MLS 1, Non-MLS 1)
Founded 1971. Fac 8; Highest Degree: Doctorate
Library Holdings: Per Subs 360
Subject Interests: Theology
Special Collections: Biblical Seminary Theses (New York Coll)
Publications: Serials Holdings List
Partic in Southeastern Pennsylvania Theological Library Association
Open Mon, Tues & Thurs 8am-10pm, Wed & Fri 8-5, Sat 12-5

HAVERFORD

C HAVERFORD COLLEGE, James P Magill Library, 370 Lancaster Ave, 19041-1392. SAN 358-5514. Tel: 610-896-1175. Interlibrary Loan Service Tel: 610-896-1171. Circulation Tel: 610-896-1175. Reference Tel: 610-896-1356. FAX: 610-896-1102. Web Site: www.haverford.edu/library. *Dir*, Robert Kieft; *Coll Develop, Reader Servs*, Donna Fournier; *Tech Servs*, Norm Medeiros; *Spec Coll*, Elisabeth Potts Brown; *Spec Coll*, Emma Lapsansky; *Spec Coll*, Diana Peterson; *ILL*, Trudi Swain; *Circ*, Dawn Heckert; *Automation Syst Coordr*, Linda Bills; *Ref*, James Gulick; *Ref*, Mary Lynn Morris; *Ref*, Margaret Schaus; *Science*, Julie Miran; *Music*, John Anderies; Staff 27 (MLS 13, Non-MLS 14)
Founded 1833. Circ 64,268; Enrl 1,135; Fac 109; Highest Degree: Bachelor
Jul 1999-Jun 2000 Income $2,388,383. Mats Exp $985,989, Books $297,000, Per/Ser (Incl. Access Fees) $650,000, Presv $16,000, Micro $22,989. Sal $917,744 (Prof $630,490)
Library Holdings: Bk Vols 532,588; Per Subs 2,368
Special Collections: Christopher Morley Coll; Cricket Coll; Elizabethan Studies (Philips Coll); Maxfield Parrish Coll; Mysticism (Jones Coll); Near Eastern Manuscripts (Harris Coll) Photography Coll; Quakerism: Friends Tracts of 17th Century (Jenks Coll), Yearly Meeting Minutes, mss, docs, maps, pic, journals, papers, rec, archives; Roberts Manuscripts Coll; Rufus Jones Writings (Tobias Coll)
Automation Activity & Vendor Info: (Acquisitions) Innovative Interfaces Inc.; (Cataloging) Innovative Interfaces Inc.; (Circulation) Innovative Interfaces Inc.; (Course Reserve) Innovative Interfaces Inc.; (ILL) Innovative Interfaces Inc.; (OPAC) Innovative Interfaces Inc.; (Serials) Innovative Interfaces Inc.
Publications: Collection Catalog; Evans Finding Aids on the Web; Guide to Quaker Coll; Library Newsletter; Medieval Feminist Index; Oberlin Group; Pa Acad Libr Connection Initiative; Reference Guide
Partic in OCLC Western Service Center; PALINET & Union Library Catalogue of Pennsylvania; Philadelphia Area Consortium Of Special Collections Libraries; Tri-College University Libraries Consortium
Friends of the Library Group
Departmental Libraries:
OBSERVATORY (ASTRONOMY) Tel: 610-896-1291. FAX: 610-896-1224. Web Site: www.haverford.edu/library/science/scilibs.html. *Librn*, Julie Miran
Subject Interests: Astronomy, Biology
SHARPLESS (BIOLOGY) Tel: 610-896-1488. FAX: 610-896-1102. Web Site: www.haverford.edu/library/science/scilibs.html. *Librn*, Julie Miran
STOKES (CHEMISTRY, MATH, PHYSICS) Tel: 610-896-1291. FAX: 610-896-1102. Web Site: www.haverford.edu/library/science/scilibs.html. *Librn*, Julie Miran
UNION (MUSIC) Tel: 610-896-1005. FAX: 610-896-1102. Web Site: www.haverford.edu/library/music/music.html. *Librn*, John Anderies

HAVERTOWN

P HAVERFORD TOWNSHIP FREE LIBRARY, 1601 Darby Rd, 19083-3798. SAN 314-6111. Tel: 610-446-3082. Interlibrary Loan Service Tel: 610-853-5875. Circulation Tel: 610-446-3082. Reference Tel: 610-853-5859. FAX: 610-853-3090. E-Mail: haverford@hslc.org. *Dir*, Virginia C Smith; *Ref*, Sue Vision; *Tech Servs*, Judy Turnbull; *Ch Servs*, Patricia Evans
Founded 1934. Pop 56,873; Circ 242,963
Jan 1999-Dec 1999 Income $902,130, State $97,463, Parent Institution $690,000, Other $114,667. Mats Exp $104,311, Books $70,787, Per/Ser (Incl. Access Fees) $4,636, Micro $11,825, AV Equip $7,638, Other Print Mats $7,873, Electronic Ref Mat (Incl. Access Fees) $1,552. Sal $434,130 (Prof $141,589)
Library Holdings: Bk Vols 111,971; Bk Titles 113,587; Per Subs 148
Mem of Delaware County Library System

HAWLEY

P THE HAWLEY LIBRARY,* 103 Main St, 18428-1325. SAN 314-6138. Tel: 570-226-4620. FAX: 570-226-8233. *Dir*, Maura Rottmund
Founded 1961. Circ 28,000
Library Holdings: Bk Vols 34,000; Per Subs 30
Special Collections: Large Print Books Coll; Memorial Art Coll (von Hake
Open Mon 1-4:30, Tues, Wed & Fri 10-4:30, Thurs 10-7:30, Sat 10-1

HAZLETON

P HAZLETON AREA PUBLIC LIBRARY,* 55 N Church St, 18201-5893. SAN 358-5603. Tel: 570-454-2961. FAX: 570-454-0630. *Dir*, Jim Reinmiller; *Br Coordr*, Alexis Neapolitan, Jr; *ILL, Ref*, Jane Dougherty; *Ch Servs*, Michele Kushmeder; *Tech Servs*, Melissa O'Connell-Cook; Staff 5 (MLS 2, Non-MLS 3)
Founded 1907. Pop 73,057; Circ 221,591
Library Holdings: Bk Vols 140,000; Per Subs 490
Special Collections: Classical & Operatic (Sidney Laub Coll), rec; Hazleton-Mining History (Local History Coll), photog, maps, bks; Pennsylvania History (Gladys Jones Markle Coll)
Publications: HAPL Happenings (quarterly newsletter)
Mem of Luzerne County Libr Syst
Branches: 4
FREELAND BRANCH, 515 Front St, Freeland, 18224. SAN 358-5662. Tel 570-636-2125. *Librn*, Colleen Tatar
MCADOO, SOUTHSIDE BRANCH, 15 Kelayres Rd, McAdoo, 18237. SAN 358-5697. Tel: 570-929-1120. *Librn*, Kathy Matweecha
NUREMBURG BRANCH, PO Box 36, Nuremburg, 18241-0036. SAN 358-5727. Tel: 570-384-4101. *Librn*, Alice Lisefski
VALLEY, PO Box Q, Conyngham, 18219-0516. SAN 358-5638. Tel: 570-788-1339. *Librn*, Pat Walser

M HAZLETON GENERAL HOSPITAL, Medical Library,* 700 E Broad St, 18201. SAN 328-0136. Tel: 570-501-4257. FAX: 570-501-4280. Web Site: www.ghha.org. *Librn*, Elaine M Curry; E-Mail: ecurry@ghha.org
Library Holdings: Bk Titles 1,545; Per Subs 266
Subject Interests: Allied health, Consumer health, Medicine, Nursing
Partic in Basic Health Sciences Library Network; Northeastern Pennsylvania Library Network

C PENNSYLVANIA STATE UNIVERSITY, Hazelton Library (University Libraries), Highacres, 18201-1291. SAN 314-6146. Tel: 570-450-3170. Reference Tel: 570-450-3562. FAX: 570-450-3128. E-Mail: rst@psulias.psu.edu. *Head Librn*, Joseph A Fennewald; E-Mail: jaf23@psulias.psu.edu; *Ref*, Richie G Shannon; Tel: 570-450-3562, E-Mail: sgri@psu.edu; Staff 6 (MLS 2, Non-MLS 4)
Founded 1934. Enrl 1,316; Fac 69
Jul 1997-Jun 1998 Mats Exp $73,655
Library Holdings: Bk Vols 77,995; Per Subs 1,018
Partic in OCLC Online Computer Library Center, Inc; RLIN

HEGINS

P TRI-VALLEY FREE PUBLIC LIBRARY,* 633 E Main St, PO Box 6, 17938-0006. SAN 320-8427. Tel: 717-682-8922. FAX: 717-682-8922. E-Mail: trvtl@epix.net. Web Site: www.schiu.kiz.pa.us/tripl. *Librn*, Lorraine Oldham
Founded 1978. Pop 3,600
1999-2000 Mats Exp $4,650, Books $3,850, Per/Ser (Incl. Access Fees) $400, AV Equip $400. Sal $23,500 (Prof $16,000)
Library Holdings: Bk Vols 18,000; Per Subs 20; Bks on Deafness & Sign Lang 12
Special Collections: Puppets
Mem of Schuylkill County Libr Syst
Open Mon, Wed & Fri 9-12 & 1-5, Tues & Thurs 1-5 & 6-8, Sat 8-3
Friends of the Library Group

HELLERTOWN

S GILMAN MUSEUM LIBRARY,* At the Cave, 726 Durham St, PO Box M 18055. SAN 328-8285. Tel: 610-838-8767. FAX: 610-838-2961. E-Mail: info@lostcave.com. Web Site: www.lostcave.com. *Dir*, B L Rozewicz

HERMINIE

P SEWICKLEY TOWNSHIP PUBLIC LIBRARY,* 215 Highland Ave, 15637-1311. SAN 314-6162. Tel: 724-446-9940. FAX: 724-446-9114. *Librn*, Arlene Merlino
Founded 1952. Pop 7,100
Library Holdings: Bk Vols 14,000; Per Subs 30
Friends of the Library Group

ERMITAGE

MERCER COUNTY REGIONAL PLANNING COMMISSION LIBRARY,* 2491 Highland Rd, 16148. SAN 329-8825. Tel: 724-981-2412. FAX: 724-981-7677. *Librn*, Dennis G Puko
Library Holdings: Bk Vols 350

ERSHEY

ANTIQUE AUTOMOBILE CLUB OF AMERICA, (AACA), Library & Research Center, 501 W Governor Rd, PO Box 417, 17033. SAN 325-0377. Tel: 717-534-2082. Toll Free Tel: 866-222-2572. FAX: 717-534-9101. E-Mail: libraryaaca@aol.com. Web Site: www.aaca.org. *Librn*, Kim M Miller; Staff 3 (MLS 2, Non-MLS 1)
Library Holdings: Bk Vols 3,000; Per Subs 220

HERSHEY FOODS CORP, Information Analysis Center,* 1025 Reese Ave, PO Box 805, 17033-0805. SAN 358-5751. Tel: 717-534-5106. FAX: 717-534-5069. *Mgr*, Ronald Dressler; *Info Specialist*, Colleen Shannon; *Info Specialist*, Jennifer Cessna; Staff 4 (MLS 2, Non-MLS 2)
Founded 1979
Library Holdings: Bk Vols 2,000; Per Subs 150
Subject Interests: Bus, Chocolate, Confectionery, Financial, Food analysis, Grocery indust, Manufacture, Mgt, Nutrition
Restriction: By appointment only
Partic in PALINET & Union Library Catalogue of Pennsylvania

HERSHEY PUBLIC LIBRARY, 701 Cocoa Ave, 17033. SAN 314-6170. Tel: 717-533-6555. FAX: 717-534-1666. Web Site: www.hersheylibrary.org. *Dir*, Catherine S Alloway; E-Mail: calloway@redrose.net; *Ch Servs*, Rita Hunt; *Ref Serv*, Donna Waldron; E-Mail: dwaldron@redrose.net; *Circ*, Linda Tully; *ILL*, Pam Langenbach; E-Mail: illhershey@yahoo.com; *Coll Develop, Tech Servs*, Barbara Nwoke; E-Mail: bnwoke@redrose.net
Founded 1913. Pop 19,000; Circ 360,000
Jan 1999-Dec 1999 Income $685,570, State $78,000, Federal $29,000, Locally Generated Income $20,000, Other $558,570. Mats Exp $90,600, Books $52,600, Per/Ser (Incl. Access Fees) $9,000, Electronic Ref Mat (Incl. Access Fees) $16,000. Sal $376,970
Library Holdings: Bk Vols 90,000; Per Subs 185
Special Collections: Chocolate, Pennsylvania Coll
Automation Activity & Vendor Info: (Circulation) Gaylord; (OPAC) Gaylord
Partic in Access Pa; OCLC Online Computer Library Center, Inc; PALINET & Union Library Catalogue of Pennsylvania
Friends of the Library Group

M PENNSYLVANIA STATE UNIVERSITY, COLLEGE OF MEDICINE, Milton S Hershey Medical Center, George T Harrell Library (University Libraries), 500 University Dr, 17033. SAN 314-6189. Tel: 717-531-8631. Interlibrary Loan Service Tel: 717-531-8633. Circulation Tel: 717-531-8626. Reference Tel: 717-531-8634. FAX: 717-531-8635. Web Site: www.hmc.psu.edu/library. *Ref*, M Sandra Wood; *Cat*, Virginia Lingle; *ILL, Ref Serv*, Esther Dell; Staff 5 (MLS 5)
Founded 1965. Enrl 662; Fac 662; Highest Degree: Doctorate
Jul 1999-Jun 2000 Income $1,187,131. Mats Exp $928,666, Books $45,811, Per/Ser (Incl. Access Fees) $882,855. Sal $585,000 (Prof $228,654)
Library Holdings: Bk Vols 25,489; Per Subs 1,379
Subject Interests: Bioengineering, Humanities, Medicine, Nursing
Automation Activity & Vendor Info: (Cataloging) DRA; (Circulation) DRA; (OPAC) DRA
Database Vendor: OVID Technologies
Publications: information.now
Restriction: Open to student, faculty & staff
Partic in Dialog Corporation; Docline; Greater NE Regional Med Libr Program; Health Sciences Libraries Consortium; Nat Libr of Med; OCLC Online Computer Library Center, Inc

OLLIDAYSBURG

L BLAIR COUNTY LAW LIBRARY, Blair County Courthouse, Ste 227, 423 Allegheny St, 16648. SAN 314-6197. Tel: 814-693-3090. *Librn*, Lucille H Wolf
Founded 1900
Library Holdings: Bk Vols 11,000; Per Subs 30
Open Mon-Fri 8:30-4:30

HOLLIDAYSBURG FREE PUBLIC LIBRARY, 405 Clark St, 16648-2101. SAN 314-6200. Tel: 814-695-5961. FAX: 814-695-6824. E-Mail: hfpl3@alt3.com. Web Site: www.hollidaysburgasd.k12.pa.us/hapl.html. *Dir*, Deborah Young; *Ad Servs*, Bette Baronner; *Ch Servs*, Barbara Bundy; Staff 1 (MLS 1)
Founded 1943. Pop 23,670; Circ 61,259
Library Holdings: Bk Vols 40,000; Per Subs 80
Subject Interests: Pennsylvania
Mem of Altoona District Pub Libr Syst; Blair County Library System
Open Mon-Thurs 10-8, Fri & Sat 10-5
Friends of the Library Group

HONESDALE

P BETHANY PUBLIC LIBRARY,* RD 3, Box 650, 18431. SAN 314-6227. Tel: 570-253-4349. E-Mail: betpulib@ptd.net. *Librn*, Elizabeth Here-Gelate
Founded 1936. Pop 1,180; Circ 4,000
Library Holdings: Bk Titles 6,200; Per Subs 20

P WAYNE COUNTY PUBLIC LIBRARY, 1406 N Main St, 18431-2006. SAN 314-6235. Tel: 570-253-1220. FAX: 570-253-1240. E-Mail: wcpublib@ptd.net. Web Site: www.plowc.org. *Dir*, Molly Rodgers
Pop 21,000; Circ 62,000
Jan 1999-Dec 1999 Income $260,200, State $56,200, County $96,000, Locally Generated Income $108,000. Mats Exp $46,000. Sal $92,450 (Prof $32,000)
Library Holdings: Bk Titles 24,600; Per Subs 85
Automation Activity & Vendor Info: (Circulation) Follett; (OPAC) Follett
Friends of the Library Group

HONEY BROOK

P HONEY BROOK COMMUNITY LIBRARY,* 91 Pequea Ave, PO Box 1082, 19344. SAN 314-6243. Tel: 610-273-3303. FAX: 610-273-9382. Web Site: www.ccls.org. *Dir*, Paula McGinness; E-Mail: pmcginness@ccls.org; Staff 4 (MLS 1, Non-MLS 3)
Founded 1963. Pop 1,164; Circ 20,377
Jan 1998-Dec 1998 Income (Main Library Only) $63,660, State $3,646, City $1,500, County $15,614, Locally Generated Income $40,400, Other $2,500. Mats Exp $5,110, Books $4,130, Per/Ser (Incl. Access Fees) $980. Sal $26,700 (Prof $19,100)
Library Holdings: Bk Vols 13,000; Per Subs 26
Mem of Chester County Library
Friends of the Library Group

HORSHAM

L PENN MUTUAL LIFE INSURANCE CO, Law Library,* 600 Dresher Rd, 19044. SAN 314-9595. Tel: 215-956-7752. FAX: 215-956-7750.; Staff 1 (Non-MLS 1)
Founded 1940
Restriction: Not open to public

HOUSTON

P CHARTIERS-HOUSTON COMMUNITY LIBRARY,* 730 W Grant St, 15342-1334. SAN 314-6251. Tel: 724-745-4300. FAX: 724-745-4233. E-Mail: chcl@sgi.net. *Dir*, Helen B Armstrong; Staff 9 (MLS 2, Non-MLS 7)
Founded 1965. Pop 9,136; Circ 56,658
Library Holdings: Bk Vols 45,717; Per Subs 97
Publications: On & Off the Shelf
Friends of the Library Group

HUGHESVILLE

P HUGHESVILLE AREA PUBLIC LIBRARY, 3 S Main St, 17737. SAN 314-626X. Tel: 570-584-3762. FAX: 570-584-2689. E-Mail: hapl@lycoming.org. Web Site: www.ncldistrict.org/hughesville. *Librn*, Penny J Blair; *Asst Librn*, Phyllis Stevens; Staff 4 (MLS 1, Non-MLS 3)
Pop 5,000; Circ 28,000
Library Holdings: Bk Vols 22,000; Per Subs 32
Database Vendor: Ebsco - EbscoHost
Mem of Lycoming County Libr Syst
Friends of the Library Group

HUNTINGDON

P HUNTINGDON COUNTY LIBRARY,* 330 Penn St, 16652-1487. SAN 358-5816. Tel: 814-643-0200. FAX: 814-643-0132. *Dir*, Cynthia M Lubert; Staff 1 (MLS 1)
Founded 1935. Pop 44,164; Circ 95,914
Library Holdings: Bk Vols 78,235; Per Subs 192
Special Collections: State & Local History (Pennsylvania Room)
Mem of Altoona Area Pub Libr Syst
Open Mon & Fri 9:30am-9pm & Tues, Wed, Thurs & Sat 9:30am-4:30pm
Friends of the Library Group
Branches: 2
LOWER HUNTINGTON COUNTY, Cromwell St, PO Box 70, Orbisonia, 17243-0070. SAN 358-5840. Tel: 814-447-3796. *Librn*, Christine Morgan
Library Holdings: Bk Vols 7,351
Friends of the Library Group
MOUNT UNION BRANCH, 11 W Market St Rear, Mount Union, 17066. SAN 358-5875. Tel: 814-542-4572. FAX: 814-542-4572. *Librn*, Christine

Morgan
Library Holdings: Bk Vols 12,291
Friends of the Library Group
Bookmobiles: 1

C JUNIATA COLLEGE, L A Beeghly Library, 1815 Moore St, 16652-2120. SAN 314-6286. Tel: 814-641-3450. FAX: 814-641-3435. E-Mail: lib@juniata.edu. *Dir*, John Mumford; *Circ, ILL*, Lynn Jones; *Instrul Serv*, Julie Woodling; *Ref*, Andrew Dudash; *Cat*, Patricia Lightner; *Acq*, Beth Yocum; *Per*, Donna Grove; Staff 7 (MLS 3, Non-MLS 4)
Founded 1876. Enrl 1,300; Fac 90; Highest Degree: Bachelor
Library Holdings: Bk Vols 142,000; Per Subs 1,000
Special Collections: Church of the Brethren (College Archives), bks, mss; Early Pennsylvania German Imprints (Abraham Harley Cassel Coll), bks & pamphlets; Pennsylvania Folklore (Henry W Shoemaker Coll); Snow Hill Coll
Automation Activity & Vendor Info: (Acquisitions) SIRSI; (Cataloging) SIRSI; (Circulation) SIRSI; (Course Reserve) SIRSI; (ILL) SIRSI; (Media Booking) SIRSI; (OPAC) SIRSI; (Serials) SIRSI
Partic in ACLCP: The Dialog Corp, PLC; OCLC Online Computer Library Center, Inc; PALINET & Union Library Catalogue of Pennsylvania
Friends of the Library Group

S SWIGART MUSEUM LIBRARY, Museum Pk, Rte 22 E, 16652. (Mail add: PO Box 214, 16652), SAN 327-6201. Tel: 814-643-0885. FAX: 814-643-2857. E-Mail: tours@swigartmuseum.com. *Exec Dir*, William E Swigart Jr
Library Holdings: Bk Titles 1,000
Restriction: By appointment only

HUNTINGDON VALLEY

P HUNTINGDON VALLEY LIBRARY, 625 Red Lion Rd, 19006-6297. SAN 314-6294. Tel: 215-947-5138. FAX: 215-938-5894. Web Site: www.huntingdonvalleylibrary.com. *Dir*, Dan W Golden; *Ref*, Tetjana Danyliw; *ILL*, Sandra Glass; *Ch Servs, YA Servs*, Nancy Hensler; *Ad Servs*, Patricia Harrington; Staff 9 (MLS 4, Non-MLS 5)
Founded 1953. Pop 11,768
1998-1999 Income $383,036, State $16,716, Locally Generated Income $32,520, Other $5,004. Mats Exp $49,000, Books $44,000, Per/Ser (Incl. Access Fees) $5,000. Sal $225,010 (Prof $101,000)
Library Holdings: Bk Vols 57,000; Per Subs 101
Automation Activity & Vendor Info: (Circulation) Gaylord; (OPAC) Gaylord
Publications: Huntingdon Valley Library Newsletter; Huntingdon Valley Library's Directory of Community Organizations
Partic in Montgomery County Libr & Info Network Consortium
Friends of the Library Group

HYNDMAN

P HYNDMAN LONDONBERRY PUBLIC LIBRARY, 161 Clarence St, 15545-0733. SAN 376-5733. Tel: 814-842-3782. FAX: 814-842-3737. E-Mail: hilolib@bedford.net. Web Site: www.bedford.net/hilolib. *Librn*, Mary Ellis; Staff 1 (MLS 1)
Founded 1991. Pop 2,902
Library Holdings: Bk Vols 11,000; Bk Titles 10,000; Per Subs 20
Function: ILL available
Mem of Bedford County Federated Libr Syst
Partic in Pennsylvania Library Association

IMMACULATA

C IMMACULATA COLLEGE, Gabriele Library, 1145 King Rd, 19345-0705. SAN 314-6308. Tel: 610-647-4400. Reference Tel: 610-647-4400, Ext 3829. FAX: 610-640-5828. Web Site: www.immaculata.edu/library. *Dir*, Patricia J Connell; Tel: 610-647-4400 Ext 3841, E-Mail: pconnell@immaculata.edu; *Head Ref*, Sister Marita David Kirsch; Tel: 610-647-4400, Ext 3826, E-Mail: mkirsch@immaculata.edu; *Ref*, Linda Roddi; Tel: 610-647-4400, Ext 3831, E-Mail: lrossi@immaculata.edu; *Tech Servs*, Marilyn Darrone; *Per*, Marie Schultz; Staff 17 (MLS 5, Non-MLS 12)
Founded 1920. Highest Degree: Doctorate
Jul 1999-Jun 2000 Mats Exp $188,803, Books $68,881, Per/Ser (Incl. Access Fees) $84,280, Presv $7,444, Micro $3,444, AV Equip $1,898, Manuscripts & Archives $506, Electronic Ref Mat (Incl. Access Fees) $22,350
Library Holdings: Bk Vols 129,699; Bk Titles 90,389; Per Subs 769
Special Collections: Dietetics; Spanish American & Chicano Literature Col
Automation Activity & Vendor Info: (Acquisitions) SIRSI; (Cataloging) SIRSI; (Circulation) SIRSI; (Course Reserve) SIRSI; (OPAC) SIRSI; (Serials) SIRSI
Database Vendor: Ebsco - EbscoHost, Lexis-Nexis, OCLC - First Search, Silverplatter Information Inc.
Publications: The Gabriele Herald (Newsletter)
Restriction: In-house use for visitors
Function: Research library
Partic in Consortium For Health Information & Library Services; OCLC Online Computer Library Center, Inc; PALINET & Union Library Catalogu of Pennsylvania; Tri-State College Library Cooperative (TCLC)

SR SISTERS, SERVANTS OF THE IMMACULATE HEART OF MARY, Archives, Villa Maria House of Studies, 1140 King Rd, PO Box 200, 1934 0200. SAN 375-6408. Tel: 610-647-2160. Reference Tel: 610-647-2160, Ex 522. FAX: 610-889-4874. *Archivist*, Sister M St Michel Mullany; E-Mail: sstmmullany@yahoo.com
Library Holdings: Bk Titles 1,000

INDIANA

S HISTORICAL & GENEALOGICAL SOCIETY OF INDIANA COUNTY LIBRARY, 200 S Sixth St, 15701-2999. SAN 326-9302. Tel: 724-463-960 FAX: 724-463-9899. E-Mail: clarkhs@microserve.net. Web Site: www.rootsweb.com/~paircgs/. *Librn*, Carol Bernie; *Librn*, Karen Wood
Library Holdings: Bk Vols 15,000; Per Subs 200
Subject Interests: Antiques, Local history
Special Collections: Cecil Smith Coll, bks mss; Frances Strong Helman Coll, bks, mss
Publications: Indiana County Heritage (twice a year); monthly newsletter; Quarterly
Restriction: Open to public for reference only

GL INDIANA COUNTY LAW LIBRARY, County Court House, 15701. SAN 314-6316. Tel: 724-465-3956. FAX: 724-465-3152. Toll Free FAX: 724-46 5152. *Librn*, Bonnie Brady King
Library Holdings: Bk Vols 15,000
Open Mon-Fri 9-4:30

P INDIANA FREE LIBRARY, INC,* 845 Philadelphia St, 15701-3908. SAN 320-8516. Tel: 724-465-8841. FAX: 724-465-9902. E-Mail: indpub@arin.k12.pa.us. Web Site: www.indianafreelibrary.org. *Dir*, Susan Miller; *Ch Servs*, Cheryl Barry; *Ch Servs*, Katy Christodouleas
Pop 32,118; Circ 139,684
Library Holdings: Bk Vols 63,391; Per Subs 123
Mem of Cambria County Library System & District Center
Open Mon-Thurs 10-9, Fri & Sat 10-5
Friends of the Library Group

M INDIANA HOSPITAL, Health Science Library, PO Box 788, 15701-0788. SAN 314-6332. Tel: 724-357-7055. FAX: 724-357-7216.
Library Holdings: Bk Vols 725; Per Subs 35
Partic in Laurel Highlands Health Sciences Library Consortium
Open Mon-Fri 7-7

C INDIANA UNIVERSITY OF PENNSYLVANIA, Stapleton Library, 431 S 11th St, 15705-1096. SAN 358-5905. Tel: 724-357-2330. Interlibrary Loan Service Tel: 724-357-3037. FAX: 724-357-4891. Web Site: www.lib.iup.edu *Dean of Libr*, Rena Fowler; *Acq*, Karen Brown; *Cat*, Daniel C Shively; *Doc* Theresa McDevitt; *Per*, Blaine E Knupp; *Media Spec*, Walter Laude; *Spec Coll*, Phillip Zorich; *Coll Develop*, Carol Connell; Staff 22 (MLS 22)
Founded 1875
Library Holdings: Bk Vols 806,000; Per Subs 4,268
Subject Interests: Education, Liberal arts
Special Collections: Charles Darwin Coll; Herman Melville Coll; James Abbott McNeill Whistler Coll; John Greenleaf Whittier Coll; Nathaniel Hawthorne Coll; Norman Mailer Coll; Regional Coal & Steel Labor & Industrial Archives
Publications: MONUMENTAE: A Union List of Music Monuments in Pennsylvania Chapter, Music Library Assn
Partic in Center For Research Libraries; Laurel Highlands Health Sciences Library Consortium; Pittsburgh Regional Libr Consortium
Friends of the Library Group
Departmental Libraries:
MUSIC, Cogswell Hall, 3rd flr, 422 S 11th St, 15705-1096. SAN 358-5921 Tel: 724-357-2892. *Librn*, Carl J Rahkonen
UNIVERSITY SCHOOL, Davis Hall, Rm 104, 570 S 11th St, 15705-1096. SAN 358-593X. Tel: 724-357-5697. *Librn*, Lynne Lucas
Library Holdings: Bk Vols 9,987; Bk Titles 9,771

IRWIN

P NORWIN PUBLIC LIBRARY ASSOCIATION INC,* 299 Third St, 15642-3553. SAN 358-5964. Tel: 724-863-4700. FAX: 724-863-6195. E-Mail: norwinpl@nb.net. Web Site: trfn.clpgh.org/norwinpl/main.shtml. *Dir*, Eleano M Silvis; Staff 3 (MLS 3)
Founded 1937. Pop 40,363; Circ 117,291
Library Holdings: Bk Vols 57,511; Per Subs 95
Special Collections: Standard-Observer (local newspaper)
Publications: Annual report
Friends of the Library Group

Branches: 1
NORWIN PUBLIC, 100 Billot Ave, North Huntingdon, 15642-2014. SAN 358-5999. Tel: 724-864-4066.
Library Holdings: Bk Vols 9,194
Friends of the Library Group

EANNETTE

JEANNETTE DISTRICT MEMORIAL HOSPITAL, Medical Library,* 600 Jefferson Ave, 15644. SAN 322-8738. Tel: 724-527-9154. FAX: 724-523-6548.
Founded 1983
Library Holdings: Bk Vols 230; Bk Titles 200; Per Subs 75
Restriction: Medical staff only
Partic in Docline; Nat Libr of Med; Regional Med Libr - Region 3; SE Pittsburgh Libr Consortium

JEANNETTE PUBLIC LIBRARY ASSOCIATION, S Sixth & Magee, 15644-3416. SAN 314-6359. Tel: 724-523-5702. FAX: 724-523-2357. E-Mail: jntlib@.nb.net. Web Site: www.nb.net/~jntlib/. *Librn*, Ellen O'Toole; Staff 9 (MLS 1, Non-MLS 8)
Founded 1932. Pop 13,745; Circ 41,985
Jan 1999-Dec 1999 Income $126,555, State $19,226, City $22,100, County $2,400, Locally Generated Income $66,604. Mats Exp $18,513, Books $11,840, Per/Ser (Incl. Access Fees) $3,523, Presv $200, Micro $150, AV Equip $2,500, Manuscripts & Archives $100, Electronic Ref Mat (Incl. Access Fees) $200. Sal $70,000 (Prof $24,000)
Library Holdings: Bk Vols 46,437; Bk Titles 45,251; Per Subs 92; High Interest/Low Vocabulary Bk Vols 25; Bks on Deafness & Sign Lang 10
Subject Interests: Glass industry, Local history
Automation Activity & Vendor Info: (Acquisitions) Athena; (Cataloging) Athena; (Circulation) Athena
Mem of Westmoreland County Libr Syst
Partic in Share Westmoreland Consortium
Friends of the Library Group

MONSOUR MEDICAL CENTER, Health Sciences Library,* 70 Lincoln Way E, 15644. SAN 314-6367. Tel: 724-527-1511. FAX: 724-527-4234.
Founded 1971
Library Holdings: Bk Vols 320; Per Subs 59
Subject Interests: Cardiology, Psychiatry
Restriction: Staff use only
Partic in Basic Health Sciences Library Network; National Network Of Libraries Of Medicine New England Region; Pittsburgh BHSL; Share Westmoreland Consortium

EFFERSON HILLS

JEFFERSON HILLS PUBLIC LIBRARY, 925 Old Clairton Rd, 15025-3158. SAN 314-4097. Tel: 412-655-7741. FAX: 412-655-4003. *Dir*, Jan Reschenthaler; *Tech Coordr*, Maureen Edinger; E-Mail: edingerm@einetwork.net; Staff 7 (MLS 1, Non-MLS 6)
Founded 1959. Pop 9,533
Library Holdings: Bk Vols 22,000; Per Subs 50
Mem of Carnegie Libr Syst of Pittsburgh
Partic in ELN
Friends of the Library Group

ENKINTOWN

GRA INC LIBRARY, 115 West Ave, Ste 201, 19046. SAN 314-6383. Tel: 215-884-7500. FAX: 215-884-1385. Web Site: www.gra-inc.com. *Librn, Online Servs*, Dorothy K Finn; E-Mail: dotf@gra-inc.com; Staff 1 (MLS 1)
Founded 1975
Library Holdings: Bk Titles 10,000; Per Subs 125
Subject Interests: Econ analysis, Regulatory analysis, Transportation
Special Collections: US Airline Annual Reports
Publications: New publications listing (monthly)
Restriction: Staff use only
Open Mon-Fri 9-5

GRACE PRESBYTERIAN CHURCH, Cecil Harding Jones Library, 444 Old York Rd, 19046. SAN 314-6391. Tel: 215-887-6117. FAX: 215-887-5724. *Librn*, Mary Parker
Founded 1952
Library Holdings: Bk Titles 2,800
Subject Interests: Children's bks, Christian educ, Current soc problems, Ecology, Meditation and pvt relig, Travel
Special Collections: Bibles; Religious Art
Open Mon-Fri 8:30-4

JENKINTOWN LIBRARY,* 460 Old York Rd, 19046-2829. SAN 314-6405. Tel: 215-884-0593. FAX: 215-884-2243. Web Site: www.jenkintown.com. *Coll Develop, Librn*, Rosalind Lubeck; *ILL*, Bonnie Miller; *Acq*, Edith Prout; Staff 10 (MLS 1, Non-MLS 9)
Founded 1803. Pop 5,000; Circ 52,000
Library Holdings: Bk Vols 47,000; Per Subs 70
Subject Interests: Local history, Pennsylvania
Open Mon-Thurs 10-9, Fri 10-5, Sat & Sun 1-4
Friends of the Library Group

J MANOR JUNIOR COLLEGE, Basileiad Library, 700 Fox Chase Rd, 19046-3399. SAN 314-6413. Tel: 215-885-2360, Ext 238. FAX: 215-576-6564. Web Site: www.library.manor.edu. *Asst Librn*, Maria Zin; *Dir*, Jerome Holst; *Spec Coll*, Anna Maksymovych; *Acq*, Sr Mary Carmela; Staff 3 (MLS 3)
Founded 1947. Enrl 670
Jul 1998-Jun 1999 Income $160,000. Mats Exp $48,342. Sal $91,188
Library Holdings: Bk Titles 45,000; Per Subs 213
Subject Interests: Literature, Ukrainian hist

JERSEY SHORE

P JERSEY SHORE PUBLIC LIBRARY, 110 Oliver St, 17740. SAN 314-6421. Tel: 570-398-9891. FAX: 570-398-9897. *Librn*, Barbara Weaver
Founded 1950
Library Holdings: Bk Vols 12,000
Mem of Williamsport District Libr Ctr
Friends of the Library Group

JIM THORPE

GL CARBON COUNTY LAW LIBRARY,* Carbon County Courthouse, PO Box 207, 18229-0207. SAN 314-643X. Tel: 717-325-3111. *Librn*, Mary Alice Herman
Library Holdings: Bk Titles 14,143; Per Subs 30

P DIMMICK MEMORIAL LIBRARY,* 54 Broadway, 18229-2022. SAN 314-6448. Tel: 570-325-2131. FAX: 570-325-9339. *Librn*, Jean A Zellers; *Asst Librn*, Gwen Gillespie
Founded 1889. Pop 11,530; Circ 22,882
Library Holdings: Bk Vols 22,787; Per Subs 72
Subject Interests: Census, Coal, Genealogy, Local history, Mining, Railroads
Special Collections: Firemen Materials for Area Firefighters
Mem of Allentown Dist Libr Syst
Friends of the Library Group

JOHNSONBURG

P JOHNSONBURG PUBLIC LIBRARY, 520 Market St, 15845-0240. SAN 314-6456. Tel: 814-965-4110. FAX: 814-965-3320. E-Mail: johnsbg@penn.com. *Dir*, Cathleen M VanAken
Founded 1939. Pop 3,350; Circ 20,892
Library Holdings: Bk Vols 18,000; Per Subs 51
Subject Interests: Genealogy, Local history, Pa hist
Automation Activity & Vendor Info: (Circulation) Follett; (OPAC) Follett

JOHNSTOWN

§J CAMBRIA COUNTY AREA COMMUNITY COLLEGE LIBRARY, 727 Goucher St, 15905. SAN 375-4413. Tel: 814-255-8219. FAX: 814-255-9589. E-Mail: library@mail.ccacc.cc.pa.us. Web Site: www.ccacc.cc.pa.us/library/libhome.htm. *Assoc Dean*, Barbara A Zaborowski; E-Mail: bzabor@mail.ccacc.cc.pa.us; *Asst Librn*, Mary Lou Patrick; E-Mail: mpatrick@mail.ccacc.cc.pa.us; *Asst Librn*, Matthew Kesseler; Tel: 814-472-2517, Fax: 814-472-2519, E-Mail: mkess@mail.ccacc.cc.pa.us; Staff 3 (MLS 3)
Founded 1994. Enrl 1,565; Highest Degree: Associate
Jul 2000-Jun 2001 Income $114,831. Mats Exp $82,406, Books $54,000, Per/Ser (Incl. Access Fees) $7,500, Electronic Ref Mat (Incl. Access Fees) $20,906. Sal $110,175 (Prof $87,000)
Library Holdings: Bk Vols 8,286; Bk Titles 7,673; Per Subs 135; Bks on Deafness & Sign Lang 345
Subject Interests: Deafness, Hearing impaired
Special Collections: Greater Johnstown Genealogy Coll
Automation Activity & Vendor Info: (Acquisitions) Athena; (Cataloging) Athena; (Circulation) Athena; (OPAC) Athena
Database Vendor: Ebsco - EbscoHost, GaleNet, Lexis-Nexis, OCLC - First Search, ProQuest, Wilson - Wilson Web
Partic in PALINET & Union Library Catalogue of Pennsylvania; Pennsylvania Community College Library Consortium

P CAMBRIA COUNTY LIBRARY SYSTEM & DISTRICT CENTER, David A Glosser Memorial Libr Bldg, 248 Main St, 15901. SAN 358-6022. Tel: 814-536-5131. Interlibrary Loan Service Tel: 814-536-5131, Ext 217. Circulation Tel: 814-536-5131, Ext 216. Reference Tel: 814-536-5131, Ext 210. FAX: 814-536-6905. E-Mail: campub@ns.cclib.lib.pa.us. Web Site: www.ns.cclib.lib.pa.us. *Dir*, Lyn Meek; *Acq, Tech Servs*, Linda Young; *Ref*, Nancy Blue; *Doc*, Louis Pocchiari; *AV*, Karen Betts; *ILL*, Hall Karen; *Ch Servs*, Georgia Tiffany; *Circ*, Dolores Berg; *Per*, Patricia Bowman; Staff 7 (MLS 7)
Founded 1870. Pop 118,973; Circ 165,213

Jan 1999-Dec 1999 Income $1,481,645, State $737,373, City $39,408, Federal $70,421, County $512,329, Locally Generated Income $122,114. Mats Exp $140,695, Books $77,891, Per/Ser (Incl. Access Fees) $18,092, Micro $1,292, AV Equip $19,460, Other Print Mats $16,442, Electronic Ref Mat (Incl. Access Fees) $7,518. Sal $522,309 (Prof $176,562)
Library Holdings: Bk Vols 143,048; Per Subs 173; High Interest/Low Vocabulary Bk Vols 830
Special Collections: Local History (Pennsylvania Room Coll)
Automation Activity & Vendor Info: (Cataloging) DRA; (Circulation) DRA; (OPAC) DRA
Member Libraries: Beaverdale Community Library; Carrolltown Public Library; Ebensburg Free Public Library; Gallitzin Public Library; Hastings Public Library; Highland Community Library; Indiana Free Library, Inc; Lilly-Washington Public Library; Meyersdale Public Library; Nanty Glo Public Library; Northern Cabria Public Library; Patton Public Library; Portage Public Library; South Fork Public Library; Spangler Public Library Inc
Partic in OCLC Online Computer Library Center, Inc; PALINET & Union Library Catalogue of Pennsylvania
Friends of the Library Group
Bookmobiles: 1

M CONEMAUGH HOSPITAL, Health Sciences Library,* 1086 Franklin St, 15905-4398. SAN 314-6472. Tel: 814-534-9111. FAX: 814-534-3244. *Dir*, Catherine Geiser; E-Mail: cgeiser@conemaugh.org; *AV*, Mark Kush
Library Holdings: Bk Titles 6,198; Per Subs 360
Special Collections: allied health; Hospital archives; medicine
Automation Activity & Vendor Info: (Circulation) Follett
Partic in Central Pennsylvania Health Science Library Association (CPHSLA); Medical Libr Asn

R FIRST LUTHERAN CHURCH, Walden M Holl Parish Library, 415 Vine St, 15901. SAN 314-6480. Tel: 814-536-7521. FAX: 814-536-0855. *Librn*, Carol S Massingill; Staff 2 (MLS 1, Non-MLS 1)
Founded 1954
Library Holdings: Bk Vols 5,750

P HIGHLAND COMMUNITY LIBRARY, 330 Schoolhouse Rd, 15904. SAN 314-6499. Tel: 814-266-5610. FAX: 814-262-0130. E-Mail: highcomlib@aol.com. *Dir*, Dorene C Miller; Staff 1 (MLS 1)
Founded 1962. Pop 15,481; Circ 67,862
Library Holdings: Bk Titles 30,000; Per Subs 75
Automation Activity & Vendor Info: (Cataloging) Athena
Mem of Cambria County Library System & District Center
Friends of the Library Group

C UNIVERSITY OF PITTSBURGH, Johnstown Campus Owen Library, 450 Schoolhouse Rd, 15904. SAN 314-6537. Tel: 814-269-7300. FAX: 814-269-7286. Web Site: www.library.pitt.edu/~libref/. *Actg Dir*, Deborah Rinderknecht; E-Mail: drinderk@pitt.edu; *Bibliog Instr*, Robert Russell; E-Mail: rrussell@@pitt.edu; *Coll Develop*, Patricia Balko; E-Mail: balko@pitt.edu; *Ref*, James Langan; E-Mail: jlangan@pitt.edu; Staff 11 (MLS 5, Non-MLS 6)
Founded 1927. Enrl 3,300; Highest Degree: Bachelor
Jul 1999-Jun 2000 Income (Main Library Only) $498,640. Mats Exp $184,478, Books $28,396, Per/Ser (Incl. Access Fees) $138,972, Presv $3,225, Micro $13,885. Sal $276,062 (Prof $174,616)
Library Holdings: Bk Vols 138,900
Automation Activity & Vendor Info: (Acquisitions) Endeavor; (Cataloging) Endeavor; (Circulation) Endeavor; (Course Reserve) Endeavor; (ILL) Endeavor; (Media Booking) Endeavor; (OPAC) Endeavor; (Serials) Endeavor
Partic in OCLC Online Computer Library Center, Inc; Pittcat

KANE

P FRIENDS MEMORIAL PUBLIC LIBRARY,* 230 Chase St, 16735. SAN 358-612X. Tel: 814-837-7010. E-Mail: friends@penn.com. Web Site: www.friends1.com. *Librn*, Susanne Zampogna
Circ 2,400
Jan 1998-Dec 1999 Income $31,000. Mats Exp $8,162. Sal $15,000
Library Holdings: Bk Vols 14,000; Per Subs 40
Friends of the Library Group

P KANE PUBLIC & SCHOOL LIBRARIES,* 300 Hemlock Ave, 16735-1802. SAN 358-6081. Tel: 814-837-9640, Ext 4. FAX: 814-837-6158. Web Site: www.kasd.k12.pa.us. *Librn*, Timothy Casey; Staff 2 (MLS 2)
Founded 1910. Circ 16,000
Jan 1998-Dec 1999 Income $17,000. Mats Exp $15,000. Sal $145,000
Library Holdings: Bk Titles 19,000; Per Subs 100
Special Collections: Newspaper Articles since 1897
Mem of Seneca District Libr Ctr
Branches: 1
CHILDREN'S BRANCH, Chestnut St, 16735. SAN 358-6111. Tel: 814-837-9641. FAX: 814-837-9270. *Librn*, Virginia Coppersmith
Circ 37,157
Library Holdings: Bk Titles 17,000

KEMPTON

S HAWK MOUNTAIN SANCTUARY LIBRARY, 1700 Hawk Mountain Rd 19529. SAN 375-3638. Tel: 610-756-6000, 610-756-6961. FAX: 610-756-4468. Web Site: www.hawkmountain.org. *Dir, Res*, Keith Bildstein; E-Mail: bildstein@hawkmountain.org
Founded 1934
Library Holdings: Bk Titles 2,100; Per Subs 55
Restriction: Not a lending library, Open to students
Function: Research library

KENNETT SQUARE

S AMERICAN ASSOCIATION OF BOTANICAL GARDENS & ARBORETA, Resource Center, 351 Longwood Rd, 19348. SAN 372-929X Tel: 610-925-2500. FAX: 610-925-2700. Web Site: www.aabga.org. *In Charge*, Karen Daubmann
Library Holdings: Bk Vols 300; Per Subs 26

S LONGWOOD GARDENS, INC LIBRARY, 409 Conservatory Rd, 19348-1805. (Mail add: PO Box 501, 19348-0501), SAN 314-6545. Tel: 610-388-1000, Ext 510. FAX: 610-388-2078. *Librn*, Enola Jane N Teeter; E-Mail: eteeter@longwoodgardens.org; *Acq*, Kathleen Tidona; Staff 2 (Non-MLS 2)
Founded 1960
Library Holdings: Bk Vols 20,000; Per Subs 425
Special Collections: Horticulture & Botany (Curtis' Botanical Magazine, Volume One, 1787 - present)
Automation Activity & Vendor Info: (Acquisitions) Sydney; (Cataloging) Sydney; (Circulation) Sydney; (Course Reserve) Sydney; (ILL) Sydney; (Serials) Sydney
Database Vendor: OCLC - First Search
Restriction: By appointment only, Lending to staff only, Open to public for reference only
Function: ILL available, Photocopies available
Partic in Council On Botanical Horticultural Libraries; PALINET & Union Library Catalogue of Pennsylvania

P BAYARD TAYLOR MEMORIAL LIBRARY,* 216 E State St, PO Box 730, 19348-3112. SAN 314-6553. Tel: 610-444-2702. Interlibrary Loan Service Tel: 610-444-2988. FAX: 610-444-1752. *Dir*, Joseph A Lordi; *ILL*, Ana M Feliciano; *Ref*, Donna Smith; *Tech Servs*, Michael R Cooney; *Ch Servs*, Rebecca Schultz
Founded 1895. Pop 24,253; Circ 133,000
Jan 1998-Dec 1999 Income $485,000. Mats Exp $80,000. Sal $272,000
Library Holdings: Bk Titles 55,000; Per Subs 150
Subject Interests: Antiques, Architecture, Art, Environmental studies, History, Horticulture
Special Collections: Antiques (Harlan R Cole Coll); Art & Architecture (Atlantis Coll); Literature (Bayard Taylor Coll); Local History (Chester County); Wildflowers (Botanica Coll)
Publications: Views a-Foot
Mem of Chester County Library

KING OF PRUSSIA

S LAWRENCE G SPIELVOGEL INC LIBRARY, 203 Hughes Rd, 19406-3785. SAN 375-0981. Tel: 610-687-5900. FAX: 610-687-5370. *Librn*, Lawrence G Spielvogel
Library Holdings: Bk Titles 5,000; Per Subs 200
Subject Interests: Energy
Special Collections: Energe in Buildings

G PENNSYLVANIA RESOURCES & INFORMATION CENTER FOR SPECIAL EDUCATION, Eastern Instructional Support Center,* 200 Anderson Rd, 19406. SAN 314-6561. Tel: 610-265-7321. FAX: 610-265-5737. *Dir*, James Duffey; *Librn*, Sunanda Banerjee; Staff 15 (MLS 15)
Founded 1968
Library Holdings: Bk Titles 15,000; Per Subs 800
Subject Interests: All aspects of special educ res, Mat, Methods
Publications: Prise Reporter; RRC Resources

P UPPER MERION TOWNSHIP LIBRARY, 175 W Valley Forge Rd, 19406-2399. SAN 314-6596. Tel: 610-265-1196. Circulation Tel: 610-265-4805. FAX: 610-265-3398. E-Mail: umerpublib@shrys.hslc.org. Web Site: www.umtownship.org. *Dir*, Karl Helicher; Tel: 610-205-8548, E-Mail: khelicher@mclinc.org; *Asst Dir, Ch Servs*, Joane McNamara; *Ref*, Jill Kozol; *Ref*, Denise Long; *ILL*, Maryanne Buddy; *Tech Servs*, Karen Zadroga; *Ch Servs*, Jeanne Kaufman; Staff 18 (MLS 6, Non-MLS 12)
Founded 1963. Pop 25,722; Circ 250,000
Jan 2001-Dec 2001 Income $187,100, State $84,000, City $1,169,920, Locally Generated Income $43,700. Mats Exp $187,100, Books $153,450, Per/Ser (Incl. Access Fees) $19,800, Micro $3,200, AV Equip $10,650. Sal $878,620 (Prof $36,520)
Library Holdings: Bk Vols 94,000; Per Subs 380

Publications: Township Lines (monthly newsletter); Township Lines (semi-annual newsletter)
Partic in Montgomery County Libr & Info Network Consortium
Friends of the Library Group

KINGSTON

HOYT LIBRARY,* 284 Wyoming Ave, 18704-3597. SAN 314-660X. Tel: 570-287-2013. FAX: 570-283-2081. *Librn*, Bill Frederick; *Cat*, Carrie Murray; *Ch Servs*, Mary Ann Hovan; *Acq*, Audrey Johnson; *Cat, Ch Servs*, Elaine Lacina; *ILL, Ref*, Diane Rebar
Founded 1928. Pop 57,017; Circ 115,480
Jan 1998-Dec 1999 Income $399,580. Mats Exp $53,150. Sal $236,000
Library Holdings: Bk Vols 93,000; Per Subs 215
Special Collections: Early Americana (William Brewster Coll), maps, bks; Holocaust (Reuben Levy Coll); Jewish History (Levison Coll)
Mem of Luzerne County Libr Syst
Partic in Northeastern Pennsylvania Library Network
Open Mon-Thurs 9-9, Fri 9-6 & Sat 9-5
Friends of the Library Group

WYOMING SEMINARY, Kirby Library, 201 N Sprague Ave, 18704-3593. SAN 314-6626. Tel: 570-283-6068. *Librn*, John A Mason, Jr
Founded 1976
Library Holdings: Bk Vols 21,000; Per Subs 110
Special Collections: Alinikoff Middle East History Coll; Leroy Bugbee Memorial History Coll; Robert E Shortz Chess Coll
Partic in Access Pa
Friends of the Library Group

KITTANNING

INDIANA UNIVERSITY OF PENNSYLVANIA, Armstrong County Campus Library,* 704 N McKean St, 16201-9998. SAN 314-6634. Tel: 724-545-3393. FAX: 724-545-3394. *Dean of Libr*, Rena Fowler; *Coll Develop*, Karen Brown; Staff 1 (MLS 1)
Founded 1962. Enrl 800; Fac 23
Library Holdings: Bk Vols 23,054; Bk Titles 20,000; Per Subs 163
Automation Activity & Vendor Info: (Acquisitions) Endeavor; (Cataloging) Endeavor; (Serials) Endeavor
Partic in PALINET & Union Library Catalogue of Pennsylvania
Open Mon-Fri 8-4:30 & 6-9

KITTANNING PUBLIC LIBRARY,* 280 N Jefferson, 16201. SAN 314-6642. Tel: 724-543-1383. FAX: 724-543-1383. E-Mail: library@penn.com. *Librn*, Nancy Reed; Staff 1 (MLS 1)
Founded 1923. Pop 5,432; Circ 63,750
Library Holdings: Bk Titles 30,000; Per Subs 75
Special Collections: County Histories Coll (Including Allegheny, Armstrong, Butler, Clarion, Clearfield, Indiana, Jefferson, Washington & Westmoreland); Family Histories Coll (Including Adams, Anderson, Barrackman, Bowser, Booth, Boyer, Claypool, Corbett, Hawk, Lookabaugh, McCullough, Marshall, Minteer, Oblinger, Ralston, Schall, Shellhamer & Wolfe); Kittanning & Armstrong County Notebooks Coll; Newspaper Coll (Armstrong Democrat 1828-1841 & Kittanning Gazette 1825-1833)
Mem of New Castle County Public Library System
Open Mon & Wed 12-8, Tues & Thurs 12-5, Fri 12-6 & Sat 12-4
Friends of the Library Group

KNOX

KNOX PUBLIC LIBRARY, 620 S Main St, PO Box 510, 16232-0510. SAN 314-6650. Tel: 814-797-1054. FAX: 814-797-1054. E-Mail: knoxplib@penn.com. Web Site: users.penn.com/~knoxplib/. *Dir*, Roxanne J Miller; Staff 3 (Non-MLS 3)
Founded 1935. Pop 7,622; Circ 32,000
Jan 2000-Dec 2000 Income $45,000, State $23,300, City $6,100, County $2,505, Locally Generated Income $13,100. Mats Exp $10,500, Books $4,500, Per/Ser (Incl. Access Fees) $1,200, Presv $300, AV Equip $300. Sal $35,463
Library Holdings: Bk Titles 18,000; Per Subs 35
Automation Activity & Vendor Info: (Cataloging) Follett; (Circulation) Follett; (OPAC) Follett
Database Vendor: Ebsco - EbscoHost
Mem of Clarion County Library System; Oil Creek District Library Center

KNOXVILLE

P KNOXVILLE PUBLIC LIBRARY, 112 E Main St, PO Box 277, 16928-0277. SAN 314-6669. Tel: 814-326-4448. FAX: 814-326-4448. E-Mail: knoxplib@mail.northerntiogasd.k12.pa.us. *Librn*, Viola Mortimer; *Asst Librn*, Elaine Van Sickle
Founded 1921. Pop 1,668; Circ 7,664
Jan 1999-Dec 1999 Income $30,193, State $6,727, County $1,783, Locally Generated Income $1,828, Other $19,855. Mats Exp $8,334, Books $4,916, Per/Ser (Incl. Access Fees) $514, AV Equip $398, Other Print Mats $2,366. Sal $7,656
Library Holdings: Bk Vols 13,914; Per Subs 36
Subject Interests: Genealogy, Loca, State hist
Mem of Williamsport District Libr Ctr
Open Mon 2:30-8:30, Wed 9-3:30 & 6-8:30, Fri 11-4 & Sat 8-3

KUTZTOWN

C KUTZTOWN UNIVERSITY, Rohrbach Library, 19530-0721. SAN 314-6685. Tel: 610-683-4745. Interlibrary Loan Service Tel: 610-683-4482. Circulation Tel: 610-683-4480. Reference Tel: 610-683-4165. FAX: 610-683-4483. Web Site: www.kutztown.edu/library/home.html. *Dean*, Margaret K Devlin; E-Mail: devlin@kutztown.edu; *Access Serv, Syst Coordr*, Susan Czerny; *Acq*, Stephanie Steely; E-Mail: steely@kutztown.edu; *Electronic Resources*, Anita Sprankle; *Ref*, Janet Bond; *Coll Develop*, Sandra Allen; *ILL, Per*, Bruce Gottschall; Staff 26 (MLS 13, Non-MLS 13)
Founded 1866. Enrl 7,900; Fac 341; Highest Degree: Master
Jul 1999-Jun 2000 Income Parent Institution $2,423,374. Mats Exp $851,965, Books $300,000, Per/Ser (Incl. Access Fees) $401,965, AV Equip $35,000, Other Print Mats $40,000, Electronic Ref Mat (Incl. Access Fees) $75,000. Sal $1,571,409 (Prof $1,070,837)
Library Holdings: Bk Vols 486,211; Per Subs 1,937; Bks on Deafness & Sign Lang 93
Subject Interests: Art, Education, History
Special Collections: Library Science, bks & per; Pennsylvania, bks, per & micro; Russian Culture, bks, per & micro
Automation Activity & Vendor Info: (Acquisitions) Endeavor; (Cataloging) Endeavor; (Circulation) Endeavor; (Media Booking) Endeavor; (OPAC) Endeavor; (Serials) Endeavor
Database Vendor: Dialog
Partic in Interlibrary Delivery Service of Pennsylvania; PALINET & Union Library Catalogue of Pennsylvania
Special Services for the Blind - Reading edge system

P LOUISA GONSER COMMUNITY LIBRARY,* 70 Bieber Alley, 19530-1113. SAN 314-6677. Tel: 610-683-5820. FAX: 610-683-8155. Web Site: www.angelfire.com/pa/louisagonsercl/. *Dir*, Patt McCloskey
Founded 1959. Pop 10,000
1998-1999 Mats Exp $8,000
Library Holdings: Bk Vols 15,000; Per Subs 52
Special Collections: Antique Book Coll
Friends of the Library Group

S PENNSYLVANIA GERMAN HERITAGE LIBRARY,* 15197 Kutztown Rd, 19530. (Mail add: PO Box 306, 19530-0304), Tel: 610-683-1589. *Dir*, Dr David L Valuska; Tel: 610-683-1330, Fax: 610-683-4638, E-Mail: valuska@kutztowne.edu
Founded 1978
1997-1998 Mats Exp $5,450, Books $5,000, Per/Ser (Incl. Access Fees) $100, Presv $200, Other Print Mats $150. Sal $5,500
Library Holdings: Bk Titles 1,500; Per Subs 10
Subject Interests: Folklore, Genealogy, Local history
Special Collections: Publications of the Pennsylvania German Society
Publications: Pennsilfaanisch Agitsch Barichta
Function: Research library

LA MOTT

P LA MOTT FREE LIBRARY, 7420 Sycamore Ave, 19027-1005. SAN 320-1732. Tel: 215-635-4419. FAX: 215-635-4419. E-Mail: lamott@mclinc.org. *Tech Servs*, Dorothy L Sutton; Tel: 215-885-0457, Fax: 215-885-1239, E-Mail: dsutton@mclinc.org; *Asst Librn*, Dorothy Jeffries; E-Mail: djeffries@mclinc.org; Staff 1 (Non-MLS 1)
Founded 1966
Jan 1999-Dec 1999 Income $25,296. Mats Exp $5,781. Sal $11,365
Library Holdings: Bk Vols 7,323; Per Subs 37
Mem of Cheltenham Township Library System
Partic in Montgomery County Dist Libr Syst; Montgomery County Libr & Info Network Consortium
Open Mon & Fri 3-5, Tues 3-5 & 6:30-8:30, Wed 2-5, Thurs 10:30-11:30, 3-5 & 6:30-8:30 & Sat 12-4
Friends of the Library Group

LA PLUME

J KEYSTONE COLLEGE, Miller Library, One College Green, 18440-0200. SAN 314-6707. Tel: 570-945-6965. FAX: 570-945-6962. E-Mail: libraryl@pheonix.telsprint.com. Web Site: www.keystone.edu/libindex.html. *Dir*, Mari Flynn; Staff 4 (MLS 4)
Founded 1934. Enrl 649; Fac 127
Library Holdings: Bk Vols 38,000; Per Subs 283
Special Collections: Local History (Christy Mathewson Coll)
Publications: Library guides
Partic in Northeastern Pennsylvania Library Network; OCLC Online Computer Library Center, Inc; PALINET & Union Library Catalogue of Pennsylvania

LACEYVILLE

P LACEYVILLE PUBLIC LIBRARY,* W Main St, PO Box 68, 18623-0068. SAN 314-6715. Tel: 570-869-1958. *Librn*, Betty Holdren
Circ 5,751
Library Holdings: Bk Vols 8,000; Per Subs 10
Friends of the Library Group

LAFAYETTE HILL

P WILLIAM JEANES MEMORIAL LIBRARY, 4051 Joshua Rd, 19444-1400. SAN 314-6723. Tel: 610-828-0441. FAX: 610-828-4049. *Dir*, Mary Torrey; Tel: 610-828-0573, E-Mail: mtorrey@mclinc.org; *Asst Dir*, Danielle Quinnette; E-Mail: DQuinnette@mclinc.org; *ILL*, June Behrman; *Ch Servs*, Beth Hargis; E-Mail: BHargis@mclinc.org; Staff 16 (MLS 2, Non-MLS 14)
Founded 1933. Pop 15,101; Circ 75,193
Jan 1999-Dec 1999 Income $324,903, State $37,293, City $226,610, Federal $13,596, Locally Generated Income $47,404. Mats Exp $48,643. Sal $150,720
Library Holdings: Bk Titles 49,000; Per Subs 210
Subject Interests: Art, Cookbooks, Quaker hist
Automation Activity & Vendor Info: (Cataloging) Gaylord; (Circulation) Gaylord
Database Vendor: Ebsco - EbscoHost
Friends of the Library Group

LAKE CITY

P LAKE CITY PUBLIC LIBRARY,* 12014 Sampson Ave, 16423. SAN 314-674X. Tel: 814-774-8286. E-Mail: lakecity@moose.erie.net. *Librn*, Janie Washok
Founded 1925. Pop 2,451; Circ 7,436
Library Holdings: Bk Vols 8,500; Per Subs 12
Mem of Erie-Crawford District Libr Ctr

LANCASTER

R ARCHIVES OF THE EVANGELICAL & REFORMED HISTORICAL SOCIETY, 555 W James St, 17603. SAN 314-6758. Tel: 717-290-8711. *Librn*, Diane Russell
Founded 1863
Library Holdings: Bk Titles 7,000
Special Collections: A R Bartholomew Coll on Missions; Church and; Colonial; Congregations (German Reformed) in Pennsylvania & Surrounding States, church recs; History (William J Hinke Manuscript Coll); Mercersburg Theology Coll; Missionary History (German Reformed Church Manuscript Coll), mss, off doc; US Church Records of the Reformed Church, the Evangelical & Reformed Church
Publications: Newsletter of the Evangelical & Reformed Historical Society

ARMSTRONG WORLD INDUSTRIES, INC
S INFORMATION CENTER LIBRARY, Information Center, PO Box 3511, 17604. SAN 358-6170. Tel: 717-396-5213. FAX: 717-396-5234.
Founded 1929
Jan 1998-Dec 1999 Income $400,000
Library Holdings: Bk Titles 11,000; Per Subs 700
Subject Interests: Accounting, Bldg mat, Bus, Chemistry, Decorating, Factory mgt, Heat, Home furnishings, Mgt, Physics, Polymer sci, Sound, Wood tech
Publications: Current Awareness Bulletin; Monthly Resource Readings
Partic in BRS; Dialog Corporation; Lockheed Info Syst Network; SDC Search Serv
Internal documents retrievable by computer-based system

S PRODUCT STYLING & DESIGN LIBRARY, 2500 Columbia Ave, PO Box 3511, 17604. SAN 358-6200. Tel: 717-396-5175, 717-396-5585. FAX: 717-396-5761. *Librn*, Susan I Wood
Library Holdings: Bk Vols 2,500; Per Subs 65
Subject Interests: Art, Color, Design

S JAMES BUCHANAN FOUNDATION FOR THE PRESERVATION OF WHEATLAND LIBRARY,* 1120 Marietta Ave, 17603. Tel: 717-392-8721. FAX: 717-295-8825. E-Mail: wheatland@wheatland.org. *Dir*, Kathy Bratton
Library Holdings: Bk Vols 175

SR FIRST BAPTIST CHURCH LIBRARY,* 612 N Duke St, 17602. SAN 326-3509. Tel: 717-392-8818. FAX: 717-392-2182. *Librn*, Linda Wilcox
Library Holdings: Bk Titles 1,050
Special Collections: Church Archives, membership lists & minutes

C FRANKLIN & MARSHALL COLLEGE, Shadek-Fackenthal Library, 450 College Ave, 17603-3318. (Mail add: PO Box 3003, 17603-3003), SAN 358-626X. Tel: 717-291-4223. Interlibrary Loan Service Tel: 717-291-4224. FAX: 717-291-4160. Web Site: www.fandm.edu/departments/library/library_home.html. *Dir*, Pamela Snelson; Tel: 717-291-3896, E-Mail: p_snelson@admin.fandm.edu; *Dep Dir*, Robert A Siever; Tel: 717-291-3840, E-Mail: r_siever@admin.fandm.edu; *Acq*, Martin Gordon; Tel: 717-291-3842, E-Mail: m_gordon@admin.fandm.edu; *Archivist*, Ann Upton; Tel: 717-291-4225, E-Mail: a_upton@admin.fandm.edu; *Cat*, Renate Sachse; Tel: 717-399-4435, E-Mail: r_sachse@admin.fandm.edu; *Coordr*, Linda M Danner; Tel: 717-291-4216, E-Mail: l_danner@admin.fandm.edu; *Publ Servs*, Andrew Gulati; Tel: 717-291-4261, E-Mail: a_gulati@admin.fandm.edu; *Publ Servs*, Thomas A Karel; Tel: 717-291-3845, E-Mail: t_karel@admin.fandm.edu; *Publ Servs*, Lisa Stillwell; Tel: 717-291-3844, E-Mail: l_stillwell@admin.fandm.edu; Staff 24 (MLS 9, Non-MLS 15)
Founded 1787. Enrl 1,915; Fac 161; Highest Degree: Bachelor
Jul 1999-Jun 2000 Income (Main Library and Branch Library) $2,400,000. Mats Exp $1,624,757, Books $499,125, Per/Ser (Incl. Access Fees) $1,033,000, Presv $48,200, Micro $32,445, AV Equip $11,987. Sal $747,82 (Prof $443,560)
Library Holdings: Bk Vols 437,789; Per Subs 1,671
Special Collections: German Language Books in America (German American Imprint Coll); Lincoln (W W Griest Coll), photog; Theatre Arts (Anne Figgat Coll); Theatre Memorabilia (Alexander Corbett Coll), photog
Automation Activity & Vendor Info: (Acquisitions) DRA; (Cataloging) DRA; (Circulation) DRA; (ILL) DRA; (Serials) DRA
Database Vendor: CARL, Dialog, DRA, Ebsco - EbscoHost, Lexis-Nexis, OCLC - First Search, ProQuest, Silverplatter Information Inc., Wilson - Wilson Web
Function: Archival collection, ILL limited, Mail loans to members, Photocopies available, Reference services available, Some telephone reference
Partic in Associated College Libraries of Central Pennsylvania; Interlibrary Delivery Service of Pennsylvania; OCLC Online Computer Library Center, Inc; PALCI; PALINET & Union Library Catalogue of Pennsylvania
Open Mon-Thurs 8am-midnight, Fri 8am-10pm, Sat 11am-10pm, Sun 11am 2am
Friends of the Library Group
Departmental Libraries:
MARTIN LIBRARY OF THE SCIENCES, PO Box 3003, 17604-3003. SAN 370-7075. Tel: 717-291-3843. FAX: 717-291-4088. *Librn*, Dale Riordan; E-Mail: d_riordan@admin.fandm.edu; *Coordr*, Linda M Danner; Tel: 717-291-4216, E-Mail: l_danner@admin.fandm.edu; Staff 3 (MLS 1, Non-MLS 2)
Founded 1991
Subject Interests: Astronomy, Biology, Chemistry, Computer science, Geology, Physics, Psychology
Database Vendor: DRA
Open Sun 11am-2am, Mon-Thurs, 8am-2am, Fri 8am-midnight, Sat 9am-midnight

P LANCASTER AREA LIBRARY, 125 N Duke St, 17602-2883. SAN 358-6324. Tel: 717-394-2651. FAX: 717-394-3083. Web Site: www.lancaster.lib.pa.us. *Exec Dir*, James B Stetina; Tel: 717-394-2651, Fax: 717-394-3083, E-Mail: jimstetina@lancaster.lib.pa.us; *Asst Dir*, Jo Anne Foss; *Ref Servs Ch*, Karen Payonk; *Ref*, Gerald Bruce; *Ref*, Philip Crnkovich; *Ref*, Bob Edinoff. Subject Specialists: *Business and managemen*, Philip Crnkovich
Founded 1759. Pop 202,000; Circ 894,394
Library Holdings: Bk Titles 299,033; Per Subs 535
Subject Interests: Health, Local history, Popular lit, Wellness
Mem of Libr Syst of Lancaster County; Library System of Lancaster County
Partic in OCLC Online Computer Library Center, Inc; PALINET & Union Library Catalogue of Pennsylvania
Friends of the Library Group
Branches: 3
LEOLA BRANCH, 46 Hillcrest Ave, Leola, 17540. SAN 358-6413. Tel: 717-656-7920. *Librn*, Doris Krammes
Friends of the Library Group
MANHEIM TOWNSHIP, 401 Granite Run Dr, 17601. SAN 373-8086. Tel: 717-560-6441. *Coordr*, Connie Jeff
Friends of the Library Group
MOUNTVILLE AREA BRANCH, 2 College Ave, Mountville, 17554. SAN 358-6472. Tel: 717-285-3231. *Librn*, Elaine Radcliffe
Friends of the Library Group

CR LANCASTER BIBLE COLLEGE LIBRARY,* 901 Eden Rd, 17601. SAN 314-6766. Tel: 717-560-8250. FAX: 717-560-8213. E-Mail: glincoln@lbc.edu. *Dir*, Gerald Lincoln; *Tech Servs*, Margaret Shickley; *Assoc Dir*, Fred Guyette; Tel: 864-379-8784, E-Mail: fguyette@erskine.edu; Staff 4 (MLS 4)
Founded 1933. Enrl 779; Fac 58; Highest Degree: Master
Jul 1998-Jun 1999 Income $222,841. Mats Exp $47,892, Books $29,197, Per/Ser (Incl. Access Fees) $10,557, Presv $3,551, Micro $2,623. Sal $146,243 (Prof $91,534)
Library Holdings: Bk Vols 139,543; Per Subs 502
Subject Interests: Bible, Christian educ, Missions, Music, Theology
Special Collections: LBC Coll; Lloyd M Perry Coll (Pastoral Theology)
Partic in OCLC Online Computer Library Center, Inc; PALINET & Union Library Catalogue of Pennsylvania

S LANCASTER COUNTY HISTORICAL SOCIETY LIBRARY,* 230 N President Ave, 17603-3125. SAN 314-6782. Tel: 717-392-4633. FAX: 717-293-2739. E-Mail: lchs@ptd.net. Web Site: www.lanclio.org. *Librn*, Mary Virginia Shelley
Founded 1886

Library Holdings: Bk Titles 15,000; Per Subs 25
Subject Interests: Genealogy, Lancaster County, Pa hist
Special Collections: 18th & 19th Century Law Library (Judge Jasper Yeates Law Library Coll); Lancaster History (Lancaster County Archives-Legal Records from 1729 through 1929), mss; Lancaster History (Manuscript
Publications: Journal of the Lancaster County Historical Society
Restriction: Non-circulating to the public

L LANCASTER COUNTY LAW LIBRARY, 50 N Duke St, PO Box 83480, 17608. SAN 314-6790. Tel: 717-299-8090. FAX: 717-295-2509. *Librn*, Eleanor Gerlott; Staff 2 (MLS 1, Non-MLS 1)
Founded 1867
Library Holdings: Bk Vols 25,589; Per Subs 25

I LANCASTER GENERAL HOSPITAL, Mueller Health Sciences Library, 555 N Duke St, 17604-2207. (Mail add: PO Box 3555, 17604-3555), SAN 314-6804. Tel: 717-290-5698. FAX: 717-290-4923. *Mgr Libr Serv*, Cindy King; E-Mail: ckking@lha.org
Founded 1967
Jul 2000-Jun 2001 Income Parent Institution $261,000. Mats Exp $118,000, Books $40,000, Per/Ser (Incl. Access Fees) $78,000. Sal $80,000 (Prof $40,000)
Library Holdings: Bk Titles 5,500; Per Subs 340
Subject Interests: Health sci
Automation Activity & Vendor Info: (OPAC) Sagebrush Corporation
Database Vendor: OVID Technologies
Partic in Basic Health Sciences Library Network; Central Pennsylvania Health Science Library Association (CPHSLA); EFTS

LANCASTER MENNONITE HISTORICAL SOCIETY LIBRARY, 2215 Mill Stream Rd, 17602-1499. SAN 314-6812. Tel: 717-393-9745. FAX: 717-393-8751. *Dir*, Carolyn C Wenger; *Librn*, Lloyd Zeager. Subject Specialists: *Genealogy*, David J Rempel Smucker; Staff 3 (MLS 1, Non-MLS 2)
Founded 1958
1999-2000 Mats Exp $8,090, Books $4,710, Per/Ser (Incl. Access Fees) $1,255, Presv $1,600, Micro $525. Sal $62,196 (Prof $51,155)
Library Holdings: Bk Titles 28,249; Per Subs 256
Subject Interests: Amish hist of southeastern Pa, European background to Reformation era, Mennonite, Southeastern Pa local hist and genealogy, Theology
Publications: Pennsylvania Mennonite Heritage; The Mirror (newsletter)
Restriction: Open to public for reference only
Friends of the Library Group

LANCASTER NEWSPAPERS, INC LIBRARY,* 8 W King St, 17603. (Mail add: PO Box 1328, 17608), SAN 314-6820. Tel: 717-291-8773. FAX: 717-399-6506. E-Mail: inp@inpnews.com. *Librn*, Susan Sweeney
Founded 1952
Library Holdings: Bk Titles 1,000
Special Collections: Biography Clippings on World, National, State & Local People; Remington Rand Lektrievers Subject & Biography Coll, VF

M LANCASTER REGIONAL MEDICAL CENTER, (Formerly Saint Joseph Hospital), William O Umiker Medical Library, 250 College Ave, PO Box 3509, 17604. SAN 314-6871. Tel: 717-291-8119. FAX: 717-291-8130. *Librn*, Barbara Miller; Staff 1 (MLS 1)
Founded 1940
Library Holdings: Bk Vols 4,000; Per Subs 175
Subject Interests: Allied health, Medicine, Nursing

R LANCASTER THEOLOGICAL SEMINARY, Philip Schaff Library, 555 W James St, 17603-9967. SAN 314-6839. Tel: 717-290-8707. FAX: 717-393-4254. Web Site: www.lts.org. *Dir*, Richard R Berg; E-Mail: rberg@lts.org; Staff 3 (MLS 2, Non-MLS 1)
Founded 1825. Enrl 250; Fac 13; Highest Degree: Doctorate
Jul 1999-Jun 2000 Income $105,900. Mats Exp $105,900, Books $42,000, Per/Ser (Incl. Access Fees) $36,000, AV Equip $600, Manuscripts & Archives $200, Electronic Ref Mat (Incl. Access Fees) $27,100. Sal $151,600 (Prof $101,000)
Library Holdings: Bk Vols 116,373; Bk Titles 101,703; Per Subs 388
Subject Interests: Biblical studies, Education, History, Theology
Special Collections: Albright Coll in Church history & liturgics
Automation Activity & Vendor Info: (Acquisitions) TLC; (Cataloging) TLC; (Circulation) TLC; (OPAC) TLC; (Serials) TLC
Database Vendor: OCLC - First Search
Partic in OCLC Online Computer Library Center, Inc; PALINET & Union Library Catalogue of Pennsylvania

S LANDIS VALLEY MUSEUM, Reference Library,* 2451 Kissel Hill Rd, 17601. SAN 314-6847. Tel: 717-569-0401. FAX: 717-560-2147. Web Site: www.landisvalleymuseum.org. *Dir*, Stephen S Miller
Founded 1925
Library Holdings: Bk Vols 12,000
Subject Interests: Arts, Crafts, Folklife, Folklore, History, Pa agr hist, Pa rural life and culture, Trade catalogs

§P LIBRARY SYSTEM OF LANCASTER COUNTY, 29 E King St, Ste 222, 17602-2852. Tel: 717-207-0500. FAX: 717-207-0504. *Exec Dir*, Mary Ellen Pellington; E-Mail: mpellington@lancasterlibraries.org; *Info Tech*, Bill Hudson; *Business, Coordr*, Rhonda Kleiman; *Commun Relations, Coordr*, Mary Ann Heltshe
Member Libraries: Columbia Public Library; Eastern Lancaster County Library; Elizabethtown Public Library; Ephrata Public Library; Lancaster Area Library; Lititz Public Library; Milanof-Schock Library; Moores Memorial Library; Strasburg-Heisler Library

S TECHNOMIC PUBLISHING CO INC, Business Library,* 851 New Holland Ave, PO Box 3535, 17604-9961. SAN 326-9264. Tel: 717-291-5609. FAX: 717-295-4538. E-Mail: marketing@techpub.com. Web Site: www.techpub.com.
Library Holdings: Bk Vols 2,570
Subject Interests: Applied sci, Directories, Technology

J THADDEUS STEVENS COLLEGE OF TECHNOLOGY, Kenneth W Schuler Learning Resources Center, 750 E King St, 17602-3198. SAN 370-7539. Tel: 717-299-7753. FAX: 717-396-7186. E-Mail: friedline@stevenstech.org. *Librn*, George Friedline; *ILL*, Brenda Smith; *Publ Servs*, John Riner; Staff 3 (MLS 3)
Founded 1976. Circ 17,000; Enrl 600; Fac 55; Highest Degree: Associate
Library Holdings: Bk Titles 27,000; Per Subs 600
Partic in OCLC Online Computer Library Center, Inc; PALINET & Union Library Catalogue of Pennsylvania

S THOMSON-CSF, Thomson Consumer Electronics Library, 1002 New Holland Ave, 17601. SAN 370-6079. Tel: 717-295-6608. FAX: 717-295-6092. *Librn*, Ethel M Swank; E-Mail: swanke@tce.com; Staff 1 (Non-MLS 1)
Founded 1989
1999-2000 Mats Exp $9,600, Books $7,000, Per/Ser (Incl. Access Fees) $2,600
Library Holdings: Bk Vols 2,010; Per Subs 21
Subject Interests: Chemistry, Electronics, Optics, Physics

LANGHORNE

CR PHILADELPHIA COLLEGE OF BIBLE, Masland Learning Resource Center, 200 Manor Ave, 19047. SAN 314-9684. Tel: 215-702-4370. Reference Tel: 215-702-4225. FAX: 215-702-4374. Web Site: www.pcb.edu/academic/lrc. *Dir*, Timothy K Hui; Tel: 215-702-4377, E-Mail: thui@pcb.edu; Staff 8 (MLS 3, Non-MLS 5)
Founded 1913. Enrl 1,700; Fac 48; Highest Degree: Master
Library Holdings: Bk Vols 145,000; Bk Titles 95,000; Per Subs 680
Subject Interests: Relig studies
Database Vendor: Ebsco - EbscoHost, Innovative Interfaces INN - View
Function: ILL available
Partic in OCLC Online Computer Library Center, Inc; Southeastern Pennsylvania Theological Library Association; Tri-State College Library Cooperative (TCLC)
Friends of the Library Group

LANSDALE

R CALVARY BAPTIST THEOLOGICAL SEMINARY LIBRARY, 1380 Valley Forge Rd, 19446. SAN 321-0243. Tel: 215-368-7538. FAX: 215-368-1003. Web Site: www.cbs.edu. *Dir*, Clint J Banz; Tel: 215-368-7538, Ext 137, E-Mail: cbanz@cbs.edu; *ILL*, JoAnne Lovik; Tel: 215-368-7538, Ext 138, E-Mail: jlovik@cbs.edu; *Cat*, Joanne Troth; E-Mail: jtroth@cbs.edu; *Ser*, Christine Bright; E-Mail: cbright@cbs.edu; Staff 2 (MLS 1, Non-MLS 1)
Founded 1975. Enrl 62; Fac 6; Highest Degree: Doctorate
Sep 1999-Aug 2000 Income $101,094, Parent Institution $82,492, Other $18,602. Mats Exp $101,094, Books $7,419, Per/Ser (Incl. Access Fees) $11,183, Presv $3,469, Micro $105, Electronic Ref Mat (Incl. Access Fees) $2,359. Sal $64,650 (Prof $39,736)
Library Holdings: Bk Vols 70,871; Per Subs 345
Subject Interests: Biblical studies, Theology
Automation Activity & Vendor Info: (Cataloging) TLC; (Circulation) TLC; (OPAC) TLC; (Serials) TLC
Database Vendor: OCLC - First Search
Restriction: In-house use for visitors
Function: ILL available
Partic in American Theological Library Association; Southeastern Pennsylvania Theological Library Association

P LANSDALE PUBLIC LIBRARY,* Susquehanna Ave & Vine St, 19446-3690. SAN 314-6898. Tel: 215-855-3228. FAX: 215-855-6440. *Dir*, Deborah Ahrens
Founded 1928. Pop 16,362; Circ 116,486
Library Holdings: Bk Vols 58,000; Per Subs 187
Subject Interests: Local history
Open Mon-Fri 10-9, Sat 10-3

S TRACOR LIBRARY,* 305 Richardson Rd, 19446. SAN 323-4959. Tel: 215-996-2328. FAX: 215-996-2088. *Librn*, Mary Ann Blauert
Library Holdings: Bk Vols 6,000; Per Subs 122

LANSDOWNE

R FIRST PRESBYTERIAN CHURCH, DRA Carson Memorial Library, Lansdowne & Greenwood Aves, PO Box 277, 19050. SAN 314-6901. Tel: 610-622-0800. FAX: 610-622-0881. Web Site: www.colleenmrsfish.aol.com. *Librn*, Paula Curran
Founded 1945
Library Holdings: Bk Vols 3,025
Special Collections: Lansdowne & Lansdowne Presbyterian Church, clippings, brochures, mss, photos & pictures

P LANSDOWNE PUBLIC LIBRARY, 55 S Lansdowne Ave, 19050-2804. SAN 314-691X. Tel: 610-623-0239. FAX: 610-623-6825. E-Mail: lansdowne@delco.lib.pa.us. Web Site: www.delco.lib.pa.us. *Dir*, Addie Ciannella; Staff 10 (MLS 2, Non-MLS 8)
Founded 1898. Pop 11,712; Circ 147,005
1999-2000 Income $243,576, State $42,359, Locally Generated Income $161,078. Mats Exp $63,585, Books $49,878, Per/Ser (Incl. Access Fees) $6,644, AV Equip $7,063. Sal $110,362 (Prof $32,800)
Library Holdings: Bk Vols 52,683; Per Subs 100
Mem of Delaware County Library System
Open Mon-Thurs 9-9, Fri 9-6, Sat 10-4, Sun 1-4
Friends of the Library Group

LAPORTE

GL SULLIVAN COUNTY LAW LIBRARY,* Court House, 18626. SAN 375-247X. Tel: 717-946-5201. FAX: 717-946-4421. *Dir*, Lynne Stabryla
Library Holdings: Bk Vols 500

LATROBE

P ADAMS MEMORIAL LIBRARY, 1112 Ligonier St, 15650-1994. SAN 314-6928. Tel: 724-539-1972. FAX: 724-537-0338. E-Mail: adamslib@westol.com. *Dir*, Tracy Trotter; *Asst Dir*, Nancy Okonak; *Ch Servs*, Karen Herc; *Ref*, Kathleen M Tobolewski; E-Mail: ktobi@westol.com; *Ch Servs*, Lisa Williams; Staff 20 (MLS 5, Non-MLS 15)
Founded 1927. Pop 51,000; Circ 300,000
Library Holdings: Bk Vols 100,000; Per Subs 130
Subject Interests: Bk tapes, Large print
Automation Activity & Vendor Info: (Cataloging) Athena; (Circulation) Athena; (OPAC) Athena
Database Vendor: Ebsco - EbscoHost
Partic in Monessen District Libr Ctr
Special Services for the Blind - Assistive Technology Center for Persons who are blind or physically handicapped

M LATROBE AREA HOSPITAL, Health Sciences Library,* 121 W Second Ave, 15650-1096. SAN 314-6944. Tel: 724-537-1275. FAX: 724-537-1890. *Librn*, Marilyn Daniels; Staff 2 (MLS 1, Non-MLS 1)
Founded 1963
Library Holdings: Bk Vols 2,500; Per Subs 150
Subject Interests: Allied health, Medicine, Nursing
Publications: Newsletter
Partic in Basic Health Sciences Library Network
Open Mon-Fri 7-6

CR SAINT VINCENT COLLEGE & SEMINARY LIBRARY,* 300 Fraser Purchase Rd, 15650-4558. SAN 314-6952. Tel: 724-539-9761. FAX: 724-537-4558. *Dir*, Chrysostom V Schlimm; *Asst Librn*, John C Benyo; *ILL*, Margaret B Friloux; *Cat, Online Servs*, John F Macey; *Publ Servs*, Denise Hegemann; *Cat*, Pamela Reed; Staff 5 (MLS 5)
Founded 1846. Enrl 1,086; Highest Degree: Master
Library Holdings: Bk Vols 354,086; Per Subs 839
Subject Interests: History, Relig studies
Special Collections: Benedictina; Ecclesiastical History; Incunabula; Medievalia; Patrology; Pennsylvaniana; Theology
Partic in OCLC Online Computer Library Center, Inc; Pittsburgh Regional Libr Consortium

LAURELDALE

P MUHLENBERG COMMUNITY LIBRARY, 3612 Kutztown Rd, 19605-1842. SAN 314-6960. Tel: 610-929-0589. FAX: 610-929-8165. E-Mail: muhlenbergcl@berks.lib.pa.us. *Dir*, Annette Pendleton
Founded 1960. Pop 22,020; Circ 39,124
Library Holdings: Bk Vols 22,776; Per Subs 60
Special Collections: Berks County, PA History Coll
Friends of the Library Group

LEBANON

M GOOD SAMARITAN HOSPITAL, Krohn Memorial Library,* Fourth & Walnut Sts, PO Box 1281, 17042-1281. SAN 371-8719. Tel: 717-270-7826. FAX: 717-270-7946. *Librn*, Deborah G Lovett; E-Mail: dlovett@gshleb.com; Staff 1 (MLS 1)
Jul 1996-Jun 1997 Income $65,000. Mats Exp $32,000, Books $10,000, Per Ser (Incl. Access Fees) $19,000, AV Equip $3,000. Sal $30,000
Library Holdings: Bk Titles 600; Per Subs 150
Partic in Basic Health Sciences Library Network

P LEBANON COMMUNITY LIBRARY, 125 N Seventh St, 17046-5000. SAN 320-4189. Tel: 717-273-7624. FAX: 717-273-2719. Web Site: www.leblibrarysys.org. *Dir*, Jayne Tremaine; E-Mail: tremaine@leblibrarysys.org; Staff 19 (MLS 2, Non-MLS 17)
Founded 1925. Pop 65,000; Circ 250,000
Library Holdings: Bk Vols 90,000; Bk Titles 80,000; Per Subs 150
Subject Interests: Local history
Automation Activity & Vendor Info: (Cataloging) Gaylord; (Circulation) Gaylord; (ILL) Gaylord; (OPAC) Gaylord
Publications: Footnotes
Mem of Lebanon County Library System
Friends of the Library Group

S LEBANON COUNTY HISTORICAL SOCIETY LIBRARY, 924 Cumberland St, 17042-5186. SAN 314-6979. Tel: 717-272-1473. FAX: 717-272-7474. Web Site: www.leba.net/~history2/.
Founded 1898
Library Holdings: Bk Vols 2,000; Bk Titles 1,750; Per Subs 17
Subject Interests: Genealogy, German immigrants in Pa, Lebanon County hist, Lebanon County newspapers, Pa hist
Special Collections: Coleman-Cornwall Papers, 1757-1940
Publications: Society publications

GL LEBANON COUNTY LAW LIBRARY, 400 S Eighth St, 17042. SAN 377-1202. Tel: 717-274-2801, Ext 2301. FAX: 717-273-7490. *Librn*, Luz Rosario
Jul 1998-Jun 1999 Mats Exp $43,000. Sal $23,000
Library Holdings: Bk Vols 14,000; Bk Titles 6,000

P LEBANON COUNTY LIBRARY SYSTEM, (LCLS), 125 N Seventh St, 17046. SAN 358-6561. Tel: 717-273-7624. FAX: 717-273-4849. Web Site: www.leblibrarysys.org. *Admin Dir*, Jayne Tremaine; E-Mail: tremaine@leblibrarysys.org; Staff 1 (MLS 1)
Founded 1969
Library Holdings: Bk Vols 40; Bk Titles 40
Special Collections: Rotating audio book
Member Libraries: Annville Free Library; Lebanon Community Library; Myerstown Community Library; Palmyra Public Library; Richland Community Library

G VA MEDICAL CENTER LIBRARY, (Formerly Department Of Veterans Affairs), 1700 S Lincoln Ave, 17042-7597. SAN 314-6987. Tel: 717-272-6621, Ext 4749. FAX: 717-228-6059. *Chief Librn*, David E Falger; *Librn*, Michelle A Clark; *Librn*, Barbara E Deaven; E-Mail: barbara.deaven@lebanon.va.gov; Staff 3 (MLS 1, Non-MLS 2)
Library Holdings: Bk Vols 7,100; Bk Titles 4,000; Per Subs 425
Subject Interests: Geriatric problems of the veteran patient, Psychiatry
Database Vendor: Dialog, OCLC - First Search, Silverplatter Information Inc.
Function: ILL limited
Partic in Central Pennsylvania Health Science Library Association (CPHSLA); Depart of Vet Affairs Libr Network

LEECHBURG

P LEECHBURG PUBLIC LIBRARY,* 215 First St, 15656-1375. SAN 314-6995. Tel: 724-845-1911. *Librn*, Phyllis Rossetti
Founded 1923
Library Holdings: Bk Vols 10,000; Per Subs 100
Open Mon-Fri 3:30-5, Mon-Thurs 6:30-8:30

LEESPORT

P SCHUYLKILL VALLEY COMMUNITY LIBRARY, 1310 Washington Rd, 19533-9708. SAN 370-6842. Tel: 610-926-1555. FAX: 610-926-3710. E-Mail: svcl@berks.lib.pa.us. Web Site: www.berks.lib.net/svcl. *Dir*, Barbara Brophy
Founded 1989. Pop 13,050; Circ 10,250
Library Holdings: Bk Vols 9,000; Per Subs 32
Database Vendor: Ebsco - EbscoHost
Mem of Berks County Libr Syst
Friends of the Library Group

LEHIGHTON

P LEHIGHTON AREA MEMORIAL LIBRARY, 124 North St, 18235-1589. SAN 314-7002. Tel: 610-377-2750. FAX: 610-377-5803. E-Mail: liblehtn@ptdprolog.net. Web Site: www.library.cpals.com. *Chief Librn*, Geraldine Duffy; *Asst Librn*, MaryAnn Balogach
Founded 1948. Pop 16,869; Circ 27,193
1999-2000 Income $92,500. Mats Exp $8,500. Sal $52,200
Library Holdings: Bk Vols 26,354; Per Subs 51

Mem of Allentown Dist Libr Syst
Open Mon, Wed & Fri 10-4:50, Tues & Thurs 1:30-7:50, Sat 9-2:50, ((10 weeks in summer 9-12:50)
Friends of the Library Group

EHMAN

PENNSYLVANIA STATE UNIVERSITY, WILKES-BARRE COMMONWEALTH COLLEGE, Nesbitt Library (University Libraries), PO Box PSU, 18627-0217. SAN 315-3460. Tel: 570-675-2171. FAX: 570-675-7436. E-Mail: wilkes-barre@psulias.psu.edu. Web Site: www.wb.psu.edu/seclevel/seclevellib.html. *Librn*, Mark Horan; *Publ Servs*, Bruce D Reid; Staff 5 (MLS 2, Non-MLS 3)
Founded 1916. Enrl 810; Fac 53; Highest Degree: Bachelor
Jul 1998-Jun 1999 Mats Exp $77,872
Library Holdings: Bk Vols 30,585; Per Subs 484
Partic in OCLC Online Computer Library Center, Inc; PALCI; PALINET & Union Library Catalogue of Pennsylvania; RLIN
Friends of the Library Group

EVITTOWN

BUCKS COUNTY COURIER TIMES LIBRARY,* 8400 Rte 13, 19057-5198. SAN 371-2036. Tel: 215-949-4000. FAX: 215-949-4177. *Librn*, Susan Y Ditterline
Library Holdings: Bk Vols 500; Per Subs 12

EWISBURG

BUCKNELL UNIVERSITY, Ellen Clarke Bertrand Library, 17837-2088. SAN 314-7010. Tel: 570-577-1557. FAX: 570-577-1237. Web Site: www.isr.bucknell.edu/. *Dir*, Ray Metz; E-Mail: metz@bucknell.edu; *Assoc Dir*, Gene Spencer; E-Mail: gspencer@bucknell.edu; *Assoc Dir*, Nancy Dagle; E-Mail: ndagle@bucknell.edu; *Spec Coll*, Doris Dysinger; E-Mail: dysinger@bucknell.edu; *Coll Develop*, Kathleen McQuiston; E-Mail: mcquisto@bucknell.edu. Subject Specialists: *Anthropology*, Nathan Rupp; *Art*, Isabella O'Neill; *Business and management*, Dot Thompson; *Economics*, Dot Thompson; *French (Language)*, Nancy Dagle; *History*, Kathleen McQuistion; *Humanities*, Isabella O'Neill; *Philosophy*, Judy Zebrowski; *Religion*, Judy Zebrowski; *Sociology*, Nathan Rupp; *Women's studies*, Pam Ross; Staff 18 (MLS 11, Non-MLS 7)
Founded 1846. Enrl 3,540; Fac 278; Highest Degree: Master
Jul 1998-Jun 1999 Income $2,500,751. Mats Exp $1,750,791, Books $582,303, Per/Ser (Incl. Access Fees) $842,986, Presv $32,054, Micro $23,091. Sal $1,295,854 (Prof $785,466)
Library Holdings: Bk Vols 668,532; Bk Titles 580,388; Per Subs 2,268
Subject Interests: Bus, Engineering, Liberal arts
Special Collections: Fine Presses; Irish Literature
Automation Activity & Vendor Info: (Acquisitions) DRA; (Cataloging) DRA; (Circulation) DRA; (Serials) DRA
Database Vendor: DRA
Publications: ISR@Bucknell (quarterly) (Newsletter)
Partic in Associated College Libraries of Central Pennsylvania; Coalition for Networked Info; OCLC Online Computer Library Center, Inc; Pa Academic Librs Connection Coun; PALINET & Union Library Catalogue of Pennsylvania; Susquehanna Library Cooperative
Friends of the Library Group
Departmental Libraries:
ACQUISITIONS Tel: 570-577-1473. FAX: 570-577-1237. *Acq*, Jennifer Perdue; E-Mail: perduej@bucknell.edu
CATALOGING Tel: 570-577-1662. FAX: 570-577-1237. *Librn*, Nathan Rupp
CIRCULATION Tel: 570-577-1882. FAX: 570-577-1237. *Circ*, Mary Jean Woland; E-Mail: woland@bucknell.edu
INTERLIBRARY LOAN Tel: 570-577-3229. FAX: 570-577-1237. *Acq*, Jennifer Perdue; E-Mail: perduej@bucknell.edu
REFERENCE Tel: 570-577-1461. FAX: 570-577-1237. *Assoc Dir*, Tara Fulton
SERIALS Tel: 570-577-3238. FAX: 570-577-1237. *Ser*, Linda Forster; E-Mail: lforster@bucknell.edu

P PUBLIC LIBRARY FOR UNION COUNTY, 205 Reitz Blvd, 17837-9211. SAN 314-7029. Tel: 570-523-1172. FAX: 570-524-7779. Web Site: www.publibuc.org. *Dir*, Kathleen Vellam; E-Mail: kvellam@jdweb.com; *Ch Servs*, Jane Reichenbach; E-Mail: jreichen@jdweb.com; Staff 4 (MLS 2, Non-MLS 2)
Founded 1910. Pop 37,000; Circ 216,000
Jan 1999-Dec 1999 Income $393,037, State $58,626, County $127,009. Mats Exp $89,582, Books $84,617, Per/Ser (Incl. Access Fees) $4,965. Sal $195,426 (Prof $39,900)
Library Holdings: Bk Vols 77,201; Per Subs 100
Subject Interests: Local history, Pa hist
Publications: Newsletter (quarterly)

S UNION COUNTY HISTORICAL SOCIETY LIBRARY, Second & St Louis Sts, 17837. SAN 327-618X. Tel: 570-524-8666. FAX: 570-524-8743. E-Mail: hstoricl@ptd.net. Web Site: www.rootsweb.com/~paunion/society.html. *Coll Develop*, Gary Slear
Founded 1963
Library Holdings: Bk Titles 500
Subject Interests: Genealogy
Special Collections: Business & Craftsmen Ledgers (slides & videos)
Publications: Union County Heritage
Open Mon-Fri 8:30-4:30

LEWISTOWN

M LEWISTOWN HOSPITAL MEDICAL LIBRARY,* 400 Highland Ave, 17044-9983. SAN 314-7037. Tel: 717-248-5411. FAX: 717-242-7245.
Founded 1974
Library Holdings: Bk Vols 1,500; Per Subs 55
Partic in Greater NE Regional Med Libr Program
Open Mon-Fri 8-4

S MIFFLIN COUNTY HISTORICAL SOCIETY LIBRARY & MUSEUM, One W Market St, 17044. SAN 326-9205. Tel: 717-242-1022. E-Mail: mchistory@acsworld.net. Web Site: www.mccoyhouse.com. *Librn*, Jean Suloff
Founded 1921
Subject Interests: Genealogy, Local history
Restriction: Open to public for reference only
Hours: Tues & Wed - 10-4, 1st & 3rd Sat 10-3 & by appointment

P MIFFLIN COUNTY LIBRARY, 123 N Wayne St, 17044-1794. SAN 358-6626. Tel: 717-242-2391. FAX: 717-242-2825. Web Site: mifflincolib@acsworld.net. *Dir*, Carol J Veitch; Fax: 717-242-2391; Staff 12 (MLS 2, Non-MLS 10)
Founded 1842. Pop 46,197; Circ 136,242
Jan 1999-Dec 1999 Income (Main Library and Branch Library) $400,122, State $98,879, Federal $13,984, County $204,101, Locally Generated Income $56,158, Other $27,000. Mats Exp $87,563, Books $59,984, Per/Ser (Incl. Access Fees) $4,752, Presv $4,074, AV Equip $2,800, Electronic Ref Mat (Incl. Access Fees) $15,953. Sal $190,103 (Prof $48,000)
Library Holdings: Bk Vols 58,604; Bk Titles 48,709; Per Subs 151; High Interest/Low Vocabulary Bk Vols 368
Automation Activity & Vendor Info: (Cataloging) TLC; (Circulation) TLC; (OPAC) TLC
Function: ILL available, Internet access, Photocopies available
Partic in Cent Pa District
Branches: 4
ALLENSVILLE BRANCH, Water St, Allensville, 17002. (Mail add: PO Box 176, Allensville, 17002-0176), Tel: 717-483-6968. E-Mail: allensville@acsworld.net. *Br Coordr*, Charlotte Fogg; Staff 1 (Non-MLS 1)
Founded 1978. Pop 1,637
Library Holdings: Bk Vols 8,036; Bk Titles 7,041; Per Subs 32; High Interest/Low Vocabulary Bk Vols 350
Automation Activity & Vendor Info: (Cataloging) TLC; (Circulation) TLC; (OPAC) TLC
Function: ILL available, Internet access
Partic in Cent Pa District
KISHACOQUILLAS, Walnut St, Belleville, 17004. (Mail add: PO Box 996, Belleville, 17004-0996), Tel: 717-935-2880. E-Mail: kish@acsworld.net. *Br Coordr*, Sharon Spickler; Staff 1 (Non-MLS 1)
Founded 1961. Pop 3,265
Library Holdings: Bk Vols 8,198; Bk Titles 7,589; Per Subs 32; High Interest/Low Vocabulary Bk Vols 312
Automation Activity & Vendor Info: (Cataloging) TLC; (Circulation) TLC; (OPAC) TLC
Function: ILL available, Internet access
Partic in Cent Pa District
MILROY BRANCH, 25 S Main St, Milroy, 17063. (Mail add: PO Box 760, Milroy, 17063-0760), SAN 358-6715. Tel: 717-667-2866. E-Mail: milroy@acsworld.net. *Br Coordr*, Kristy Kline; Staff 1 (Non-MLS 1)
Founded 1959. Pop 3,627
Library Holdings: Bk Vols 5,777; Bk Titles 5,373; Per Subs 25
Automation Activity & Vendor Info: (Cataloging) TLC; (Circulation) TLC; (OPAC) TLC
Function: ILL available, Internet access
Partic in Cent Pa District
ROTHROCK, 10 N Queen St, PO Box 331, McVeytown, 17051-0331. SAN 358-674X. Tel: 717-899-6851. E-Mail: rothrock@acsworld.net. *Br Coordr*, Elizabeth Vaughan; Staff 1 (Non-MLS 1)
Founded 1988. Pop 3,673
Library Holdings: Bk Vols 6,650; Bk Titles 6,100; Per Subs 30; High Interest/Low Vocabulary Bk Vols 347
Automation Activity & Vendor Info: (Cataloging) TLC; (Circulation) TLC; (OPAC) TLC
Function: ILL available, Internet access
Partic in Cent Pa District

LIBRARY

S CONSOL, INC, Research & Development Division, Technical Resource Center,* 4000 Brownsville Rd, 15129. SAN 314-7045. Tel: 412-854-6688. FAX: 412-854-6613.
Founded 1947
Library Holdings: Bk Vols 10,000; Per Subs 150
Subject Interests: Coal tech utilization, Fuel chem, Technology
Partic in Dialog Corporation; OCLC Online Computer Library Center, Inc

P SOUTH PARK TOWNSHIP LIBRARY,* 2575 Brownsville Rd, 15129-8527. SAN 314-7053. Tel: 412-833-5585. FAX: 412-833-7368. Web Site: www.einpgh.org/ein/southprk. *Dir*, Linda L Lee Yee; *AV, Ch Servs, Ref*, Mary Caryl Planiczki; Staff 3 (MLS 3)
Founded 1970. Pop 14,251; Circ 60,000
Jan 1997-Dec 1998 Income $246,015, State $18,000, County $72,000
Library Holdings: Bk Titles 36,000; Per Subs 105
Partic in Electronic Info Network
Friends of the Library Group

LIGONIER

S FORT LIGONIER ASSOCIATION, Henry Bouquet Room Library, 216 S Market St, 15658-1206. SAN 327-6457. Tel: 724-238-9701. FAX: 724-238-9732. E-Mail: ftlig@westol.com. *Dir*, Martin West
Library Holdings: Bk Vols 2,000

P LIGONIER VALLEY LIBRARY ASSOCIATION, INC,* 120 W Main St, 15658-1200. SAN 314-7061. Tel: 724-238-6451. FAX: 724-238-6989. E-Mail: lvlibrary@wpa.net. Web Site: www.wpa.net/lvlibrary. *Librn*, Janet Hudson; *Ch Servs*, Linda Norris; Staff 2 (MLS 2)
Founded 1946. Pop 16,644; Circ 100,666
Library Holdings: Bk Titles 53,000; Per Subs 120
Subject Interests: History
Special Collections: Large Print Coll; Ligonier Echo, micro; Newbery-Caldecott Coll; Pennsylvania History (Pennsylvania Room), bks & micro; Writer's Coll
Art Gallery; Drug & Alcohol Info Collections

LILLY

P LILLY-WASHINGTON PUBLIC LIBRARY,* 520 Church St, 15938-1118. SAN 314-707X. Tel: 814-886-7543. FAX: 814-886-7543. E-Mail: lilwashlib@aol.com. *Librn*, Scott Salzman; Tel: 864-294-3204
Founded 1963. Pop 1,162; Circ 14,529
Library Holdings: Bk Vols 6,523; Per Subs 21
Mem of Cambria County Library System & District Center
Open Mon-Wed 10:30-6, Thurs 1-6, Fri 2-5, Sat 11-2

LIMA

M FAIR ACRES, Medical Library,* 340 N Middletown Rd, PO Box 496, 19037. SAN 323-424X. Tel: 610-891-5717. FAX: 610-891-8087. *In Charge*, Lisa Maffei Hahn
Subject Interests: Medicine, Nursing
Open Mon-Fri 8:30-4:30

P MIDDLETOWN FREE LIBRARY,* 21 N Pennell Rd, PO Box 275, 19037-0275. SAN 314-7088. Tel: 610-566-7828. FAX: 610-892-0880. E-Mail: middletown@delco.lib.pa.us. *Librn*, Marjorie H Spencer
Founded 1956. Pop 14,130; Circ 115,418
Library Holdings: Bk Vols 39,000; Per Subs 97
Mem of Delaware County Library System
Open Mon 11-9
Friends of the Library Group

LINCOLN UNIVERSITY

C LINCOLN UNIVERSITY, Langston Hughes Memorial Library, 19352. SAN 314-7096. Tel: 610-932-8300, Ext 261. FAX: 610-932-1206. *Dir*, Emery Wimbish Jr; *Asst Dir*, Mahinder S Chopra; *Circ, Reader Servs*, Diane Ambruso; *Circ, Reader Servs*, Lurerlene Crook; *Ser*, R Neal Carlson; *Cat*, Albert Bryson
Founded 1898. Highest Degree: Master
Library Holdings: Bk Vols 175,481; Per Subs 652
Subject Interests: Liberal arts, Presbyterianism lit, Protestant theol, Sci
Special Collections: African Studies, bks, per; Afro-American Studies, micro, vf; bks, per, memorabilia; Langston Hughes (Personal Library); Therman O'Daniel Spec Coll
Publications: Accessions List; Catalog of the Special Negro & African Collection, 2 vols & supplement; Library Instruction Workbook
Partic in Interlibrary Delivery Service of Pennsylvania; OCLC Online Computer Library Center, Inc; PALINET & Union Library Catalogue of Pennsylvania; Tri State Col Libr Coop

LINESVILLE

P LINESVILLE PUBLIC LIBRARY,* 111 Penn, PO Box 97, 16424-0097. SAN 376-5709. Tel: 814-683-4354. FAX: 814-683-4354. *Librn*, Lana J Hartzell
Library Holdings: Bk Vols 18,500; Bk Titles 18,200; Per Subs 52
Mem of Crawford County Federated Library System
Open Mon 9-5, Tues & Thurs 4-8, Wed 9-1 & 4-8, Fri & Sat 9-1

LITITZ

P LITITZ PUBLIC LIBRARY, 651 Kissel Hill Rd, 17543. SAN 314-7118. Tel: 717-626-2255. FAX: 717-627-4191. *Dir*, Donna Ann Hammond; E-Mail: dhammond@ptd.net; Staff 1 (MLS 1)
Founded 1935. Pop 26,000; Circ 51,195
Library Holdings: Bk Vols 17,000; Per Subs 20
Mem of Library System of Lancaster County
Friends of the Library Group

LOCK HAVEN

C LOCK HAVEN UNIVERSITY, George B Stevenson Library, 401 Fairview Ave, 17745-2390. SAN 314-7134. Tel: 570-893-2309. Interlibrary Loan Service Tel: 570-893-2545. FAX: 570-893-2506. Web Site: www.lhup.edu/library/home.htm. *ILL*, Rick R Lilla; *Cat*, Shirley L Chang; *Spec Coll*, Elsa W Schwartz; *Per*, Brenda M Corman; Staff 8 (MLS 8)
Founded 1870. Enrl 3,395; Fac 215; Highest Degree: Master
Library Holdings: Bk Titles 360,000; Per Subs 1,230
Special Collections: Eden Phillpotts Coll, bks, micro
Publications: Library handbook; library newsletter
Partic in Interlibrary Delivery Service of Pennsylvania; OCLC Online Computer Library Center, Inc; PALINET & Union Library Catalogue of Pennsylvania; State System Of Higher Education Libraries Council; Susquehanna Library Cooperative

P ANNIE HALENBAKE ROSS LIBRARY, 232 W Main St, 17745-1298. SAN 358-6774. Tel: 717-748-3321. FAX: 717-748-1050. E-Mail: ross@oak.kcsd.k12.pa.us. Web Site: oak.kcsd.k12.pa.us/~ross/library. *Dir*, Diane Whitaker; *Asst Dir*, Rosalie A Long; *Publ Servs*, Denise Selmer-Larsen; *Ch Servs*, Nancy Antram; *Librn*, Joseph Bitner; *Ref*, Andrea Glossner; *Cat*, Tracey Dow; Staff 1 (MLS 1)
Founded 1910. Pop 37,182; Circ 37,182
Jan 1999-Dec 1999 Income (Main Library and Branch Library) $354,879, State $86,779, City $18,000, Federal $24,760, County $62,688, Other $162,652. Mats Exp $50,086, Books $33,549, Per/Ser (Incl. Access Fees) $4,563, Presv $5,902, Micro $635, Other Print Mats $5,437. Sal $183,569 (Prof $29,543)
Library Holdings: Bk Vols 121,584; Per Subs 118
Special Collections: Local genealogical materials; Pennsylvaniana (Pennsylvania Room), bks, census reports, local photo coll, micro
Automation Activity & Vendor Info: (Cataloging) EOS; (Circulation) EOS
Publications: Another Peek at the Past; Clinton County: A Journey Through Time; Final Peek at the Past; Flemington Mosaic; Indians of Clinton County; Journal of Travels, Adventures & Remarks of Jerry Church; Maynard's Historical Clinton County; Mountain Folks: Fragments of Central Pennsylvania Folklore; No Rain in Heaven; Old Town: A History of Early Lock Haven; Peek at the Past; Third Peek at the Past
Friends of the Library Group
Branches: 1
RENOVO AREA BRANCH, 317 Seventh St, Renovo, 17764. SAN 358-6804. Tel: 717-923-0390. *Librn*, Elizabeth Cowfer; Staff 1 (Non-MLS 1)
Founded 1968. Pop 5,000; Circ 5,000
Jan 1999-Dec 1999 Income $46,993, State $8,136, County $9,493, Parent Institution $29,364. Mats Exp Books $5,739. Sal $16,317
Library Holdings: Bk Vols 10,630; Per Subs 27
Bookmobiles: 1

LORETTO

CR SAINT FRANCIS COLLEGE, Pasquerilla Library, Franciscan Way, 15940. (Mail add: PO Box 600, 15940-0600), Tel: 814-472-3011. Circulation Tel: 814-472-3160. Reference Tel: 814-472-3161. FAX: 814-472-3154. E-Mail: refli@sfcpa.edu. Web Site: www.library.sfcpa.edu. *Dir Libr Serv*, Patricia Bartley Serotkin; E-Mail: pserotkin@sfcpa.edu; *Head, Info Serv*, Brian D Anater; Tel: 814-472-3315, Fax: 814-472-3180, E-Mail: banater@sfcpa.edu; *Head Tech Servs*, Sandra A Balough; Tel: 814-472-3153, Fax: 814-474-3093 E-Mail: sbalough@sfcpa.edu; Staff 19 (MLS 6, Non-MLS 13)
Founded 1847. Enrl 1,800; Fac 86; Highest Degree: Master
Jul 1999-Jun 2000 Income $788,312. Mats Exp $285,381, Books $69,861, Per/Ser (Incl. Access Fees) $112,868, Presv $10,364, Micro $32,048, Electronic Ref Mat (Incl. Access Fees) $60,240. Sal $375,435 (Prof $259,381)
Library Holdings: Bk Vols 21,663; Bk Titles 77,411; Per Subs 5,621
Subject Interests: Local history, Theology
Special Collections: Captain Paul Boyton Coll; Charles Schwab Coll; Franciscan Archives; Franciscana; Pope Pius XII Coll; Prince Gallitzin Coll;

Saint Francis College Archives
Automation Activity & Vendor Info: (Acquisitions) Innovative Interfaces Inc.; (Cataloging) Innovative Interfaces Inc.; (Circulation) Innovative Interfaces Inc.; (Course Reserve) Innovative Interfaces Inc.; (Media Booking) Innovative Interfaces Inc.; (OPAC) Innovative Interfaces Inc.; (Serials) Innovative Interfaces Inc.
Database Vendor: Ebsco - EbscoHost, GaleNet, OCLC - First Search, ProQuest, Silverplatter Information Inc., Wilson - Wilson Web
Publications: Tales From the Stacks (Newsletter); Users Guide
Partic in HSLC; PALINET & Union Library Catalogue of Pennsylvania

IAHANOY CITY

MAHANOY CITY PUBLIC LIBRARY,* 17-19 W Mahanoy Ave, 17948-2615. SAN 314-7231. Tel: 570-773-1610. *Dir*, Linda Ernst
Pop 10,749; Circ 14,162
Library Holdings: Bk Vols 30,000; Per Subs 28
Mem of Pottsville Free Public Library
Open Mon-Fri 9-7, Sat 10-2

IALVERN

AMERICAN INSTITUTE FOR CHARTERED PROPERTY CASUALTY UNDERWRITERS LIBRARY, 720 Providence Rd, 19355-0716. SAN 321-9968. Tel: 610-644-2100, Ext 7511. FAX: 610-725-0613. Web Site: www.aicpcu.org. *Dir*, Kim Holston; E-Mail: holston@cpcuiia.org; Staff 1 (MLS 1)
Founded 1977
Aug 1999-Jul 2000 Mats Exp $35,574, Books $17,304, Per/Ser (Incl. Access Fees) $8,570, Other Print Mats $7,000, Electronic Ref Mat (Incl. Access Fees) $2,700. Sal $53,200 (Prof $46,200)
Library Holdings: Bk Vols 9,500; Bk Titles 9,300; Per Subs 170
Subject Interests: Economics, Liability ins, Property ins, Risk mgt
Special Collections: Life Insurance (O D Dickerson Coll)
Automation Activity & Vendor Info: (Cataloging) TLC
Publications: CPCU-IIA Library Report (newsletter)
Function: ILL available, Research library

MALVERN PUBLIC LIBRARY, One E First Ave, 19355-2420. SAN 314-724X. Tel: 610-644-7259. FAX: 610-644-5204. Web Site: www.ccls.org/othlibs/malvern.htm. *Dir*, Rosalie Dietz; E-Mail: rdietz@ccls.org
Founded 1873. Circ 26,480
Jan 1999-Dec 1999 Income $286,250, State $49,372, City $93,600, County $24,838, Locally Generated Income $118,440. Mats Exp $37,117, Books $25,000, Per/Ser (Incl. Access Fees) $4,500, AV Equip $4,100. Sal $124,500 (Prof $27,000)
Library Holdings: Bk Vols 35,000; Per Subs 91
Mem of Chester County Library
Friends of the Library Group

C PENNSYLVANIA STATE UNIVERSITY, Great Valley Library (University Libraries), 30 E Swedesford Rd, 19355. SAN 315-1492. Tel: 610-648-3215. Interlibrary Loan Service Tel: 610-648-3236. FAX: 610-725-5223. Web Site: www.gv.psu.edu/library. *Head Librn*, Dr Dolores Fidishun; Tel: 610-648-3227, E-Mail: dxf19@psu.edu
Founded 1963. Enrl 1,700; Fac 35; Highest Degree: Master
Library Holdings: Bk Vols 25,000; Per Subs 380
Subject Interests: Computer science, Education, Engineering, Management, Mathematics
Special Collections: Curriculum; Psychological Tests; Thesis
Partic in OCLC Online Computer Library Center, Inc; RLIN; Tri State Col Libr Coop

S SANOFI-SYNTHFLABO PHARMACEUTICALS INC, (RIS), Sanofi-Synthflabo Research, 9 Great Valley Pkwy, 19355. SAN 374-4736. Tel: 610-889-8652. FAX: 610-889-8988. *Dir*, Don Miles; *ILL, Per, Tech Servs*, Karalee Sheaffer; *Acq, Cat, Circ*, Glenn Steinke; *Online Servs, Ref*, Ann Marie Weis; *Online Servs, Ref*, Mindy Paquette-Murphy; Staff 5 (MLS 4, Non-MLS 1)
Founded 1985
Library Holdings: Bk Vols 4,200; Bk Titles 3,600; Per Subs 325
Subject Interests: Chemistry, Clinical medicine

MANSFIELD

P MANSFIELD FREE PUBLIC LIBRARY,* 71 N Main St, 16933. SAN 314-7274. Tel: 570-662-3850. *Dir*, Mary Sirgey
Founded 1901. Pop 5,929; Circ 20,694
Library Holdings: Bk Vols 23,000; Per Subs 72
Special Collections: Books on tape; Large Print Coll; Pennsylvania & Tioga County; Records
Mem of Potter-Tioga Library System
Open Mon & Tues 1-8, Wed 10-8, Thurs 1-8, Sat 10-2
Friends of the Library Group

C MANSFIELD UNIVERSITY, North Hall Library, North Hall, 16933. SAN 314-7282. Tel: 717-662-4670. Reference Tel: 570-662-4671. FAX: 570-662-4993. Web Site: www.mnsfld.edu/depts/. *Dir*, Larry L Nesbit; Tel: 570-662-4672, E-Mail: lnesbit@mnsfld.edu; *Chairperson*, Priscilla Older; Tel: 570-662-4686, E-Mail: polder@mnsfld.edu; *Cat*, LesErick Achey; Tel: 570-662-4775, E-Mail: lachey@mnsfld.edu; *Acq*, Elizabeth Henry; Tel: 570-662-4673, E-Mail: ehenry@mnsfld.edu; *Bibliog Instr*, Monty McAdoo; *Ref*, Frances Garrison; Tel: 570-662-4688, E-Mail: fgarriso@mnsfld.edu; *Ref*, Sheila Kasperek; Tel: 570-662-4675, E-Mail: skaspere@mnsfld.edu; *Ref*, Larry Schankman; Tel: 570-662-4684, E-Mail: lschankm@mnsfld.edu; *Ref*, Matt Syrett; Tel: 570-662-4679, E-Mail: msyrett@mnsfld.edu; *Ref*, Sylvia Yamashita; Tel: 570-662-4681, E-Mail: skuhlyam@mnsfld.edu. Subject Specialists: *Health sciences*, Monty McAdoo; Staff 20 (MLS 8, Non-MLS 12)
Founded 1857. Enrl 3,200; Fac 207; Highest Degree: Master
Jul 1999-Jun 2000 Income Parent Institution $1,569,649. Mats Exp $334,581, Books $135,315, Per/Ser (Incl. Access Fees) $136,449, Presv $6,003, Micro $34,524, AV Equip $22,290. (Prof $972,877)
Library Holdings: Bk Vols 217,911
Subject Interests: Education, Music
Special Collections: Annual Report
Automation Activity & Vendor Info: (Acquisitions) Endeavor; (Cataloging) Endeavor; (Circulation) Endeavor; (ILL) Endeavor; (Serials) Endeavor
Database Vendor: Dialog, Ebsco - EbscoHost, IAC - Info Trac, Lexis-Nexis, OCLC - First Search, ProQuest, Silverplatter Information Inc., Wilson - Wilson Web
Partic in PALCI; PALINET & Union Library Catalogue of Pennsylvania; State System Of Higher Education Libraries Council; Susquehanna Library Cooperative

MAPLE GLEN

SR SUPPLEE MEMORIAL PRESBYTERIAN CHURCH LIBRARY,* 855 Welsh Rd, 19002. SAN 328-3410. Tel: 215-646-4123. FAX: 215-646-8895. *Librn*, Suzanne P Stahler
Library Holdings: Bk Titles 2,496
Special Collections: Antique Bibles

MARCUS HOOK

P MARY M CAMPBELL PUBLIC LIBRARY,* Tenth & Green Sts, 19061-4592. SAN 314-7304. Tel: 610-485-6519. *Librn*, Irene H Wallin; Staff 5 (MLS 1, Non-MLS 4)
Founded 1923. Pop 2,546; Circ 15,800
Jan 1998-Dec 1998 Income $67,700, State $9,619. Mats Exp $9,650, Books $7,000, Per/Ser (Incl. Access Fees) $2,000. Sal $53,800
Library Holdings: Bk Vols 22,400; Per Subs 57
Mem of Delaware County Library System
Friends of the Library Group

MARIANNA

P MARIANNA COMMUNITY PUBLIC LIBRARY, Jefferson & Broad St, 15345-0457. SAN 314-7320. Tel: 724-267-3888. FAX: 724-267-3888. E-Mail: mcl@cobweb.net. *Librn*, Eda Niverth
Founded 1969. Pop 2,486; Circ 8,331
Library Holdings: Bk Vols 9,000; Per Subs 22
Mem of Washington County Libr Syst

MARIENVILLE

P FOREST COUNTY LIBRARY, Marienville Area Public Library, 110 E Spruce St, Box 306, 16239-0306. SAN 358-6898. Tel: 814-927-8552. FAX: 814-927-8552. E-Mail: marien@penn.com. *Librn*, Marlene Furnish; *Asst Librn*, Kathy Henschel
Founded 1969. Pop 2,426; Circ 17,000
Library Holdings: Bk Vols 7,500; Per Subs 27
Open Mon & Thurs 10-5 & 7-8:30, Tues & Wed 9-5, Sat 9-4
Friends of the Library Group

MARS

P MARS AREA PUBLIC LIBRARY, 107 Grand Ave, PO Box 415, 16046. SAN 314-7347. Tel: 724-625-9048. FAX: 724-625-2871. E-Mail: mapl@zbzoom.net. *Librn*, Sally D Sturm
Founded 1947. Pop 5,954; Circ 44,000
Jan 2000-Dec 2000 Income $80,000, State $20,000, Provincial $25,000, County $10,000, Other $25,000. Mats Exp $8,200, Books $9,000, Per/Ser (Incl. Access Fees) $700, AV Equip $500. Sal $46,000 (Prof $27,300)
Library Holdings: Bk Vols 26,000; Per Subs 50
Subject Interests: Audio, Large print
Automation Activity & Vendor Info: (Cataloging) Brodart; (Circulation)

Brodart
Mem of Butler County Libr Syst
Special Services for the Blind - Audiotape library; Large print bks
Friends of the Library Group

MARTINSBURG

P MARTINSBURG COMMUNITY LIBRARY,* 201 S Walnut St, 16662-1129. SAN 314-7355. Tel: 814-793-3335. FAX: 814-793-9755. E-Mail: jp@mail.aasdcat.com. *Librn*, Joyce M Paden; *Asst Librn*, Joanne Stern
Founded 1948. Pop 2,000; Circ 34,000
Jul 1997-Jun 1998 Income $55,000. Mats Exp $17,000. Sal $30,000
Library Holdings: Bk Vols 25,000; Per Subs 78
Special Collections: Genealogy (George H Liebegott Coll)
Mem of Blair County Library System
Open Mon-Thurs 1-4:30 & 6:30-8:30, Fri 9:30-11:30 & 1-4:30, Sat 1-4:30
Friends of the Library Group

MARYSVILLE

P MARYSVILLE-RYE LIBRARY,* 198 Overcrest Rd, 17053-1157. SAN 314-7363. Tel: 717-957-2851. *Librn*, Susan Schmick
Founded 1964. Pop 6,000
Library Holdings: Bk Vols 13,000; Per Subs 29
Open Mon-Thurs 4-8, Wed 9-1 & 4-8, Fri 1-9, Sat 9-3, Sun 1-4

MASONTOWN

P GERMAN-MASONTOWN PUBLIC LIBRARY, 9 S Washington St, 15461-2025. SAN 314-7371. Tel: 724-583-7030. FAX: 724-583-0979. E-Mail: germanma@hhs.net.
Founded 1965. Pop 11,500; Circ 30,779
Library Holdings: Bk Vols 30,155; Per Subs 34
Subject Interests: Local history
Mem of Fayette County Library System
Partic in Washington District Ctr
Friends of the Library Group

MC CONNELLSBURG

P FULTON COUNTY LIBRARY, 227 N First St, 17233-1003. SAN 321-5105. Tel: 717-485-5327. FAX: 717-485-5646. E-Mail: flibrary@cvn.net. Web Site: www.users.desupernet.net/flibrary. *Dir*, Jamie Brambley; Staff 6 (MLS 1, Non-MLS 5)
Founded 1975. Pop 13,837
Jul 1999-Jun 2000 Income (Main Library and Branch Library) $166,833, State $48,985, City $650, Federal $6,522, County $5,000, Locally Generated Income $63,919, Other $41,757. Mats Exp $26,989, Books $20,263, Per/Ser (Incl. Access Fees) $1,471, AV Equip $3,081, Electronic Ref Mat (Incl. Access Fees) $220. Sal $64,629 (Prof $27,000)
Library Holdings: Bk Vols 28,338; Per Subs 62
Subject Interests: Civil War
Special Collections: Handicapped; Special Needs
Automation Activity & Vendor Info: (Cataloging) Follett; (Circulation) Follett; (OPAC) Follett
Friends of the Library Group
Branches: 1
HUSTONTOWN BRANCH, 313 Pitt St, Ste B, PO Box 426, Hustontown, 17229. SAN 329-3653. Tel: 717-987-3606. FAX: 717-987-3606. *Librn*, Beverly Rouzer
Library Holdings: Bk Vols 4,899; Per Subs 10
Automation Activity & Vendor Info: (Cataloging) Follett; (Circulation) Follett; (OPAC) Follett
Friends of the Library Group

MC DONALD

P HERITAGE PUBLIC LIBRARY,* 52 Forest St, PO Box 37, 15057-0037. SAN 314-7142. Tel: 724-926-8400. FAX: 724-926-4686. E-Mail: hpl@cobweb.net. Web Site: www.members.tripod.com/heritagepl/index.htm.
Pop 5,500; Circ 22,000
Library Holdings: Bk Vols 17,000; Per Subs 25

MC EWENSVILLE

P MONTGOMERY HOUSE, Warrior Run Area Public Library,* 20 Church St, PO Box 5, 17749-0005. SAN 314-7150. Tel: 570-538-1381. Interlibrary Loan Service Tel: 570-326-0536. E-Mail: mhwrapl@sunlink.net. *Dir*, Marian Keister
Founded 1967. Pop 9,157; Circ 11,381
Library Holdings: Bk Vols 29,000; Per Subs 83
Subject Interests: Local history
Special Collections: Pennsylvania Coll
Friends of the Library Group

MC KEES ROCKS

P F O R STO-ROX LIBRARY,* 500 Chartiers Ave, 15136. SAN 314-7177. Tel: 412-771-1222. FAX: 412-771-2340. Web Site: www.clpgh.org/ein/forstorx. *Dir*, Melissa McGaw; E-Mail: mcgawm@clpgh.org
Library Holdings: Bk Titles 6,346
A semi-autonomous arm of the Focus On Renewal Sto-Rox Neighborhood Corporation, an independent nonprofit organization
Friends of the Library Group

M OHIO VALLEY GENERAL HOSPITAL LIBRARY, Heckel Rd, 15136. SAN 314-7169. Tel: 412-777-6159. FAX: 412-777-6866. *Coordr*, Lynne Scanga
Founded 1905
Library Holdings: Bk Vols 2,000; Per Subs 100
Subject Interests: Consumer health info, Gen med, Nursing

MC KEESPORT

P CARNEGIE FREE LIBRARY OF MC KEESPORT,* 1507 Library Ave, 15132. SAN 314-7185. Tel: 412-672-0625. FAX: 412-672-7860. Web Site: www.clpgh.org/ein/mckeespx/. *Dir*, Jo Ellen Kenney; E-Mail: kenneyj@clpgh.org; *Asst Dir*, Dorothy Haas; *Ch Servs*, Chris Kritikos; *Cat*, Nancy Henderson; Staff 4 (MLS 2, Non-MLS 2)
Founded 1902. Pop 39,490; Circ 72,950
Library Holdings: Bk Vols 82,322; Per Subs 127
Subject Interests: Education, History, Literature
Special Collections: Local History (Western Pennsylvania), bks, pamphlets, pictures; Pennsylvania Archives
Mem of Pittsburgh Libr District
Friends of the Library Group

M MCKEESPORT HOSPITAL, Health Service Library, 1500 Fifth Ave, 15132. SAN 314-7193. Tel: 412-664-2363. FAX: 412-664-2581. *Librn*, Karen Zundel; E-Mail: zundelkm@msx..upmc.edu
Founded 1975
Library Holdings: Bk Vols 2,000; Per Subs 80
Subject Interests: Hospital administration, Medicine, Nursing
Open Mon-Fri 9am-3pm & Tues-Thurs 8am-4:30pm

MC MURRAY

P PETERS TOWNSHIP PUBLIC LIBRARY,* 616 E McMurray Rd, 15317-3495. SAN 314-7215. Tel: 724-941-9430. FAX: 724-941-9438. E-Mail: ptlib@ptlibrary.org. Web Site: www.ptlibrary.org. *Dir*, Pier M Lee; E-Mail: plee@ptlibrary.org; *Ad Servs*, Mary Anne Brown; *Ch Servs*, Joanne Robinson; Staff 20 (MLS 4, Non-MLS 16)
Founded 1957. Pop 14,467
Jan 1999-Dec 1999 Income (Main Library Only) $567,000. (Prof $372,672)
Library Holdings: Bk Vols 81,000; Bk Titles 78,000; Per Subs 100
Database Vendor: Ebsco - EbscoHost
Mem of Washington County Libr Syst
Friends of the Library Group

MCKEESPORT

C PENNSYLVANIA STATE UNIVERSITY, MCKEESPORT COMMONWEALTH COLLEGE, J Clarence Kelly Library (University Libraries), Penn State McKeesport, 4000 University Dr, 15132-7698. SAN 314-7207. Tel: 412-675-9110. Circulation Tel: 412-675-9199. Reference Tel: 412-675-9114. FAX: 412-675-9113. E-Mail: jxd37@psu.edu. Web Site: www.libraries.psu.edu/crsweb/mckeesport/. *Head of Libr*, Kay Ellen Harvey; Tel: 412-675-9109, E-Mail: keh4@psu.edu; Staff 6 (MLS 2, Non-MLS 4)
Founded 1948. Enrl 878; Fac 59; Highest Degree: Bachelor
Library Holdings: Bk Vols 40,000; Per Subs 381
Automation Activity & Vendor Info: (OPAC) SIRSI
Database Vendor: Ebsco - EbscoHost, Lexis-Nexis, OCLC - First Search, OVID Technologies, ProQuest, Silverplatter Information Inc., Wilson - Wilson Web
Partic in Access Pa; OCLC Online Computer Library Center, Inc; PALINET & Union Library Catalogue of Pennsylvania; RLIN

MEADVILLE

C ALLEGHENY COLLEGE, Lawrence Lee Pelletier Library, 555 N Main St, 16335. SAN 314-738X. Tel: 814-332-3768. Interlibrary Loan Service Tel: 814-332-3769. FAX: 814-337-5673. Web Site: allecat.alleg.edu. *Dir*, Cole Puvogel; *ILL, Online Servs*, Cynthia Burton; *Acq*, Nancy L Brenot; *Cat*, Barry J Gray; *Ref*, Donald A Vrabel; *Rare Bks*, Jane Westenfeld; *AV*, Helen O McCullough; *Syst Coordr*, Alan E Bartlett; *Circ*, Jennifer Corbin; Staff 8 (MLS 8)
Founded 1815. Enrl 1,898; Fac 131; Highest Degree: Bachelor
Jul 1999-Jun 2000 Income $1,302,242. Mats Exp $535,850, Books $220,000, Per/Ser (Incl. Access Fees) $253,000, Presv $9,000, Micro $9,000, Manuscripts & Archives $4,850. Sal $633,067 (Prof $348,398)
Library Holdings: Bk Vols 722,290; Per Subs 1,032

Special Collections: Archives of the Western Pennsylvania Conference of the United Methodist Church; Ida M Tarbell, letters, mss, bks; Lincoln, bks, pamphlets; Original Library, 1819-23 (Gifts of James Winthrop, Isaiah Thomas & William Bentley)
Automation Activity & Vendor Info: (Cataloging) Innovative Interfaces Inc.; (Circulation) Innovative Interfaces Inc.; (Course Reserve) Innovative Interfaces Inc.; (OPAC) Innovative Interfaces Inc.
Publications: @ the Library; Guide to the Archives of the Western Pennsylvania Conference of the United Methodist Church (1980)
Partic in Northwest Interlibrary Cooperative Of Pennsylvania; OCLC Online Computer Library Center, Inc; PALCI; PALINET & Union Library Catalogue of Pennsylvania

CRAWFORD COUNTY FEDERATED LIBRARY SYSTEM, 848 N Main St, 16335-2689. SAN 314-7398. Tel: 814-336-1773. FAX: 814-333-8173. Web Site: www.ccfls.org.
Founded 1978
1998-1999 Income $903,000, State $270,000, County $590,000, Locally Generated Income $43,000. Mats Exp $14,000
Library Holdings: Bk Vols 1,200
Special Collections: Rotating Books on Cassette Coll
Member Libraries: Benson Memorial Library; Linesville Public Library; Meadville Library Art & Historical Association; Mulberry Public Library; Saegertown Area Library; Springboro Public Library

CRAWFORD COUNTY HISTORICAL SOCIETY LIBRARY,* 848 N Main St, 16335-2689. SAN 314-7401. Tel: 814-336-1773. FAX: 814-333-8173. *Dir*, John Brice; Staff 2 (MLS 1, Non-MLS 1)
Founded 1879
Library Holdings: Bk Vols 2,600
Subject Interests: Crawford County hist, Genealogies
Special Collections: Huidekoper, Reynolds & Dick Families
Publications: Crawford County History (newsletter)
Open Mon 1-5

GL CRAWFORD COUNTY LAW LIBRARY,* Court House, Rm 212, 903 Diamond Sq, 16335. SAN 314-741X. Tel: 814-336-1151, Ext 480. FAX: 814-337-0457. *Librn*, Catherine A Consla; Tel: 814-333-7480
Library Holdings: Bk Vols 20,000
Open Mon-Fri 8:30-4:30

P MEADVILLE LIBRARY ART & HISTORICAL ASSOCIATION, Meadville Public, 848 N Main St, 16335-2689. SAN 314-7436. Tel: 814-336-1773. FAX: 814-333-8173. Web Site: www.ccfls.org. *Dir*, John J Brice, III; E-Mail: jbrice@ccfls.org; *Asst Dir, Ch Servs*, Mary Lee Minnis; *ILL*, Linda Eidell; *Online Servs, Ref*, Jane Blaguszewski; *Rare Bks*, Laura Polo; Staff 14 (MLS 6, Non-MLS 8)
Founded 1879. Pop 38,071; Circ 250,000
1998-1999 Income $600,000, State $120,000, County $320,000, Locally Generated Income $160,000. Mats Exp $104,000, Books $80,000, Per/Ser (Incl. Access Fees) $12,000, Other Print Mats $12,000. Sal $300,000 (Prof $150,000)
Library Holdings: Bk Vols 65,691; Bk Titles 62,343; Per Subs 216
Subject Interests: History
Special Collections: Crawford County Historical Coll, books & mss
Automation Activity & Vendor Info: (Cataloging) Sagebrush Corporation; (Circulation) Sagebrush Corporation; (OPAC) Sagebrush Corporation
Publications: Snippets from the Shelves (quarterly newsletter)
Mem of Crawford County Federated Library System; Erie-Crawford District Libr Ctr
Partic in Northwest Interlibrary Cooperative Of Pennsylvania; PALINET & Union Library Catalogue of Pennsylvania
Friends of the Library Group

M MEADVILLE MEDICAL CENTER, Winslow Medical Library, 751 Liberty St, 16335. SAN 314-7428. Tel: 814-333-5740. FAX: 814-333-5714. *Librn*, Barbara Ewing
Library Holdings: Bk Vols 1,500; Per Subs 90
Partic in Erie Area Health Information Library Cooperative; Nat Libr of Med; Northwest Interlibrary Cooperative Of Pennsylvania
Open Mon-Fri 9-4:30 (closed during lunch)

MECHANICSBURG

P MECHANICSBURG AREA PUBLIC LIBRARY, 16 N Walnut St, 17055-3362. SAN 314-7444. Tel: 717-766-0171. FAX: 717-766-0152. E-Mail: mechanicsburg@ccpa.net. Web Site: ww.ccpa.net/mapl. *Dir*, Sue Erdman; E-Mail: serdman@ccpa.net; Staff 14 (MLS 4, Non-MLS 10)
Founded 1961. Pop 38,203; Circ 400,000
Jan 2000-Dec 2000 Income $510,948, State $189,050, County $219,707, Locally Generated Income $94,691, Other $7,500. Mats Exp $75,700, Books $68,000, Per/Ser (Incl. Access Fees) $7,700. Sal $310,000 (Prof $115,000)
Library Holdings: Bk Vols 59,757; Per Subs 130
Special Collections: Irving College, Mechanicsburg, Pennsylvania
Automation Activity & Vendor Info: (Cataloging) epixtech, inc.; (Circulation) epixtech, inc.; (OPAC) epixtech, inc.
Mem of Cumberland County Library System
Open Mon-Thurs 10-9, Fri & Sat 10-5, Sat (July-Aug) 10-2, Sun (Sept-June) 1-5
Friends of the Library Group

MEDIA

S COLONIAL PENNSYLVANIA PLANTATION, Sol Feinstone Library, Ridley Creek State Park, 19063. SAN 314-4763. Tel: 610-566-1725.
Founded 1973
Library Holdings: Bk Vols 1,500
Subject Interests: History, Revolutionary periods, Social life and customs of the Am Colonial
Special Collections: Southeastern Pennsylvania History-Folklore, VF

J DELAWARE COUNTY COMMUNITY COLLEGE LIBRARY, 901 S Media Line Rd, 19063-1094. SAN 314-7452. Tel: 610-359-5149, 610-359-5326. FAX: 610-359-5272. Web Site: www.dccc.edu. *Actg Dir*, Pedro Navarro; Tel: 610-359-5145, E-Mail: pnavarro@iss.dccc.edu; *Mgr*, Thomas Parkinson; Tel: 610-359-4150; *Ref*, Ourania Kontopoulos; Tel: 610-359-5146; *Ref*, Carol Videon; Tel: 610-359-5146; *Ref*, Mary Ann Gillette; Tel: 610-359-5146; Staff 3 (MLS 3)
Founded 1967
Library Holdings: Bk Vols 70,900; Per Subs 525
Subject Interests: Bus, Law, Nursing, Police sci
Database Vendor: Dialog, Ebsco - EbscoHost, epixtech, inc., Wilson - Wilson Web
Partic in OCLC, Inc through Palinet; Tri State Col Libr Coop
Open Mon-Thurs 8-10, Fri & Sat 8-4

P DELAWARE COUNTY LIBRARY SYSTEM, 340 N Middletown Rd Bldg 19, 19063-5597. SAN 320-2267. Tel: 610-891-8622. FAX: 610-891-8641. E-Mail: headquarters@delco.lib.pa.us. Web Site: www.delco.lib.pa.us. *Dir*, David L Belanger; *Automation Syst Coordr*, Rene Kelly; *Ch Servs*, Margie Stern; *Coll Develop*, Janis T Stubbs; *Ref*, Helen Subbio; *Tech Servs*, Kristin Suda; *Librn*, Barbara Goodman; *YA Servs*, Stefanie Cordoro. Subject Specialists: *Law*, Barbara Goodman; Staff 23 (MLS 6, Non-MLS 17)
Founded 1978. Pop 547,651; Circ 2,124,862
Jan 1999-Dec 1999 Income $1,834,022, State $537,000, Federal $53,000, County $1,068,327, Locally Generated Income $175,695. Mats Exp $497,421, Books $273,034, Per/Ser (Incl. Access Fees) $4,003, AV Equip $60,602, Electronic Ref Mat (Incl. Access Fees) $159,782. Sal $516,196
Library Holdings: Bk Vols 1,985; Per Subs 107
Subject Interests: Libr sci
Automation Activity & Vendor Info: (Acquisitions) Innovative Interfaces Inc.; (Cataloging) Innovative Interfaces Inc.; (Circulation) Innovative Interfaces Inc.; (ILL) Innovative Interfaces Inc.; (Media Booking) Innovative Interfaces Inc.; (OPAC) Innovative Interfaces Inc.; (Serials) Inmagic, Inc.
Publications: The DCLS Dispatch (system staff newsletter)
Member Libraries: Aston Public Library; Borough Of Folcroft Public Library; Collingdale Public Library; Glenolden Library; Haverford Township Free Library; Helen Kate Furness Free Library; J Lewis Crozer Library; Judge Francis J Catania Law Library; Lansdowne Public Library; Marple Public Library; Mary M Campbell Public Library; Memorial Library Of Radnor Township; Middletown Free Library; Newtown Public Library; Norwood Public Library; Pennsylvania Institute Of Technology Library; Rachel Kohl Community Library; Ridley Park Public Library; Ridley Township Public Library; Springfield Township Library; Swarthmore Public Library; Upper Darby Township & Sellers Free Public Library; Yeadon Public Library
Partic in PALINET & Union Library Catalogue of Pennsylvania
Holdings & circulation figures for DCLS headquarters & 28 independent member libraries. Expenditures for headquarters only.

GL JUDGE FRANCIS J CATANIA LAW LIBRARY, (Formerly Delaware County Law Library), Court House, 201 W Front St, 19063. SAN 314-7460. Tel: 610-891-4462. FAX: 610-891-4480. E-Mail: lawlib@delco.lib.pa.us. Web Site: www.delco.lib.pa.us. *Dir*, Barbara Goodman; E-Mail: bgoodman@delco.lib.pa.us; Staff 2 (MLS 1, Non-MLS 1)
Founded 1902
Jan 2000-Dec 2000 Income County $225,000
Library Holdings: Bk Vols 28,000; Per Subs 25
Function: Research library
Mem of Delaware County Library System

P MEDIA-UPPER PROVIDENCE FREE LIBRARY,* Front & Jackson Sts, 19063. SAN 314-7487. Tel: 610-566-1918. FAX: 610-566-9056. E-Mail: media@delco.lib.pa.us. Web Site: www.geocities.com/~delawarecounty/library/. *Dir*, Janice Y Doan; Staff 2 (MLS 2)
Founded 1901. Pop 15,678
Library Holdings: Bk Titles 35,000; Per Subs 90
Open Mon 11-8, Tues-Thurs 11-5 & 7-9, Fri 11-6, Sat 11-4 & Sun 1-4

C PENNSYLVANIA INSTITUTE OF TECHNOLOGY LIBRARY, LRC, 800 Manchester Ave, 19063-4098. SAN 328-5839. Tel: 610-892-1531. Circulation Tel: 610-892-1534. Toll Free Tel: 800-422-0025. FAX: 610-892-1533. E-Mail: info@pit.edu. Web Site: www.pit.edu/lrc.html. *Dir*, Linda Lee

Rossi; E-Mail: lrossi@pit.edu; *Asst Librn*, Barbara Kurimchak; Tel: 610-892-1532, E-Mail: bkurimchak@pit.edu. Subject Specialists: *Science/technology*, Linda Lee Rossi; Staff 8 (MLS 1, Non-MLS 7)
Founded 1962. Enrl 400; Highest Degree: Associate
Jul 1999-Jun 2000 Income $100,760
Library Holdings: Bk Vols 15,217; Bk Titles 13,768; Per Subs 153
Subject Interests: Engineering, Technology
Special Collections: Hinderliter Architecture & Archaeology; Honeywell Tech; McNee Eng
Database Vendor: Ebsco - EbscoHost, IAC - Info Trac, OCLC - First Search
Restriction: Public use on premises
Function: ILL available
Mem of Delaware County Library System
Partic in OCLC Online Computer Library Center, Inc; PALINET & Union Library Catalogue of Pennsylvania; Tri-State College Library Cooperative (TCLC)

C PENNSYLVANIA STATE UNIVERSITY, Delaware County Commonwealth College Library (University Libraries), 25 Yearsley Mill Rd, 19063. SAN 314-7495. Tel: 610-892-1380. FAX: 610-892-1359. E-Mail: slw@psulias.psu.edu. *Librn*, Sara Lou Whildin; *Ref*, Susan Ware; Staff 4 (MLS 2, Non-MLS 2)
Founded 1967. Enrl 1,540; Fac 74
Library Holdings: Bk Vols 60,000; Per Subs 200
Partic in OCLC Online Computer Library Center, Inc; RLIN

MELROSE PARK

S AUERBACH CENTRAL AGENCY FOR JEWISH EDUCATION, Seidman Educational Resource Center, 7607 Old York Rd, 19027. SAN 359-0569. Tel: 215-635-8940. FAX: 215-635-8946. E-Mail: info@acaje.org. Web Site: www.acaje.org. *Dir*, Nancy M Messinger; E-Mail: nmessinger@acaje.org; *Cat*, Marcia Goldberg; *Admin Assoc*, Batsheva Kotler; Staff 3 (MLS 1, Non-MLS 2)
Sep 1999-Aug 2000 Mats Exp $5,200
Library Holdings: Bk Titles 15,000
Subject Interests: Education, Judaism
Special Collections: Holocaust Resources; Judaic Video Tapes; Kossman Children's Literature Lending Library
Publications: Highlights (tri-annual); topical bibliographs
Friends of the Library Group

C GRATZ COLLEGE, The Tuttleman Library, 7605 Old York Rd, 19027. SAN 359-0550. Tel: 215-635-7300, Ext 169. FAX: 215-635-7320. Web Site: www.gratzcollege.edu/. *Dir*, Rebecca Landau; *Head, Cat*, Marcia Goldberg; *Cat*, Randi Cohen; *ILL*, Robert Manstein; *Head Ref*, Hayim Sheynin
Founded 1895
Subject Interests: Bible, Hebrew lang, History, Holocaust, Israel studies, Jewish educ, Literature, Music, Rabbinics
Special Collections: Anti-Semitica Coll; Archives Coll; Hebraica & Judaica; Materials for Training Teachers of Hebrew Language & Culture
Publications: A Select List of Recent Acquisitions
Partic in OCLC Online Computer Library Center, Inc
Departmental Libraries:
HOLOCAUST ORAL HISTORY ARCHIVE Tel: 215-635-7300, Ext 130. FAX: 215-635-7320. *Dir*, Josey Fisher
Founded 1980
Special Collections: Holocaust Coll, a-tapes, memorial bks, photos, survivor registers, transcribed memorabilia, unpublished diaries, letters, memoirs
Partic in OCLC Online Computer Library Center, Inc
ABNER & MARY SCHREIBER JEWISH MUSIC LIBRARY Tel: 215-635-7300. FAX: 215-635-7320. *Music*, Randi Cohen
Founded 1950
Special Collections: Choral Jewish Music of the 16th-20th Centuries (Eric Mandell Coll); Folk, Liturgical, Secular, Popular, Manuscripts & Published Music; Music For Small Ensembles, Virtuoso Instruments & Symphonic Scores by Jewish Composers or on Jewish; Preserved From Nazi Holocaust-Liturgical & Secular, Vocal, Instrumental & Choral (Arno Nadel Estate); Themes (Joseph Kutler Instrumental Library of Jewish Music)
Partic in OCLC Online Computer Library Center, Inc

MERCER

P MERCER AREA LIBRARY,* 143 N Pitt St, 16137-1283. SAN 314-7517. Tel: 724-662-4233. FAX: 724-662-4233. E-Mail: mercerarealib@pathway.net. *Dir*, Connie Jewell
Founded 1916. Pop 10,472; Circ 59,022
1998-1999 Income $75,124, State $12,231. Mats Exp $9,356, Books $7,832, Per/Ser (Incl. Access Fees) $1,524, Electronic Ref Mat (Incl. Access Fees) $203. Sal $42,589
Library Holdings: Bk Vols 25,059; Per Subs 47
Special Collections: Video Collections
Partic in Tri County Libr Consortium
Friends of the Library Group

GL MERCER COUNTY LAW LIBRARY, 305 Courthouse, 16137-0305. SAN 327-0653. Tel: 724-662-3800, Ext 2302. FAX: 724-662-0620. Web Site: www.mcc.co.mercer.pa.us/library/default. *Dir Libr Serv*, Kim Deniker; E-Mail: kdeniker@mcc.co.mercer.pa.us
Jan 1999-Dec 1999 Mats Exp $114,000. Sal $21,523
Library Holdings: Bk Vols 17,500
Function: Research library
Partic in Westlaw

S STATE REGIONAL CORRECTIONAL FACILITY LIBRARY,* 801 Butl Pike, 16137. SAN 371-6155. Tel: 724-662-1837, Ext 156. FAX: 724-662-1940. *Librn*, Marjorie Lemon; Staff 1 (MLS 1)
Library Holdings: Bk Titles 12,000; Per Subs 80
Special Collections: Black History
Special Services for the Deaf - Books on deafness & sign language; High interest/low vocabulary books

MERION STATION

R AKIBA HEBREW ACADEMY, Joseph M First Library, 223 N Highland Ave, 19066-1798. SAN 314-7533. Tel: 610-667-4070, Ext 135. FAX: 610-667-9870. Web Site: www.akibahebrewacademy.com. *Head Librn*, Wendi Gabay; *Asst Librn*, Jane Schofer
Library Holdings: Bk Vols 14,000
Subject Interests: Judaica
Database Vendor: Ebsco - EbscoHost, IAC - Info Trac
Partic in Access Pa

R TEMPLE ADATH ISRAEL, Ruben Library, 250 N Highland Ave, 19066. SAN 314-755X. Tel: 610-664-5150. FAX: 610-664-0959. *Dir*, Shelly Milakofsky; *Librn*, Gladys Kates
Founded 1955
Library Holdings: Bk Titles 6,000; Per Subs 10
Subject Interests: Judaica
Restriction: Members only, Use of others with permission of librarian

MESHOPPEN

P FRANCES E KENNARD PUBLIC LIBRARY,* United Penn Bank Bldg, PO Box 39, 18630-0039. SAN 314-7568. Tel: 717-833-5060. E-Mail: beckabooboo99@hotmail.com. *Librn*, Cathy Marie Stone
Founded 1900. Pop 938; Circ 6,500
Library Holdings: Bk Titles 3,300; Per Subs 10
Mem of Pocono District Libr Ctr
Open Tues & Fri 7-9, Wed 3-5, Sat 10-12

MEYERSDALE

P MEYERSDALE PUBLIC LIBRARY, 210 Center St, PO Box 98, 15552-1322. SAN 314-7576. Tel: 814-634-0512. FAX: 814-634-0512. E-Mail: smalltwn@wpra.net. Web Site: www.sctc.net/mpl. *Dir*, Diane Saylor Daniels
Founded 1939. Pop 19,000; Circ 35,355
Jan 2000-Dec 2000 Income $100,000, State $21,000, County $9,000, Locally Generated Income $70,000
Library Holdings: Bk Titles 27,800; Per Subs 25; Bks on Deafness & Sign Lang 20
Subject Interests: Local history
Automation Activity & Vendor Info: (Cataloging) Athena
Mem of Cambria County Library System & District Center
Open Mon-Fri 10-8, Sat 10-12

MIDDLEBURG

S SNYDER COUNTY HISTORICAL SOCIETY, INC LIBRARY, 30 E Market St, PO Box 276, 17842. SAN 328-8188. Tel: 570-837-6191. FAX: 570-837-4282. *Librn*, LaRue Knepp; *Asst Librn*, Lorraine Meadows
Library Holdings: Bk Titles 3,200
Publications: Snyder Co Historical Society Bulletin

L SNYDER COUNTY LAW LIBRARY, Courthouse, PO Box 217, 17842. SAN 328-1167. FAX: 717-837-5481. *In Charge*, Charlotte Kratzer
Library Holdings: Bk Vols 7,500
Open Mon-Fri 8:30-4

MIDDLETOWN

S AMERGEN ENERGY, (Formerly GPU Nuclear), Three Mile Island Technical Library, Three Mile Island Nuclear Generating Station, PO Box 480, 17057. SAN 320-992X. Tel: 717-948-8105. FAX: 717-948-8824. *Librn*, Joan H Slavin; E-Mail: jslavin@amergenenergy.com; Staff 2 (MLS 1, Non-MLS 1)
Library Holdings: Bk Titles 2,500; Per Subs 225
Subject Interests: Nuclear power, Radiation

MIDDLETOWN PUBLIC LIBRARY, 20 N Catherine St, 17057-1498. SAN 314-7584. Tel: 717-944-6412. FAX: 717-930-0510. E-Mail: mdt@desupernet.com. Web Site: www.middletownpubliclib.org. *Dir*, Stacie M Lejcar; Staff 2 (MLS 2)
Founded 1928. Pop 9,254; Circ 73,600
Library Holdings: Bk Vols 28,000; Per Subs 75
Special Collections: Interviews from Early 1970s, indexed; Middletown Journal (local newspaper from 1886)
Mem of Dauphin County Library System
Friends of the Library Group

C PENNSYLVANIA STATE UNIVERSITY-HARRISBURG LIBRARY (UNIVERSITY LIBRARIES), 351 Olmsted Dr, 17057-4850. SAN 314-7592. Tel: 717-948-6070. Interlibrary Loan Service Tel: 717-948-6071. Interlibrary Loan Service FAX: 717-948-6381. E-Mail: jcd3@psu.edu. Web Site: www.hbg.psu.edu/library. *Dir*, Harold B Shill; *ILL*, Ruth Runion-Slear; *Tech Servs*, Carolee Roman; *Publ Servs*, Gregory Crawford; *Per*, Henry Koretzky; Staff 6 (MLS 6)
Founded 1966. Enrl 3,600; Fac 144; Highest Degree: Doctorate
Library Holdings: Bk Vols 207,920; Bk Titles 186,440; Per Subs 1,552
Subject Interests: Behav sci, Bus, Computer science, Education, Engineering, Humanities, Pub affairs
Special Collections: Energy Coll; Environment Coll; HRAF; Women's History
Publications: Heindel News
Partic in Associated College Libraries of Central Pennsylvania; OCLC Online Computer Library Center, Inc; PALINET & Union Library Catalogue of Pennsylvania

MIDLAND

P CARNEGIE FREE LIBRARY, 61 Ninth St, 15059-1503. SAN 314-7606. Tel: 724-643-8980. FAX: 724-643-8985. E-Mail: midlandpl@mail.com. Web Site: libcom.co.beaver.pa.us/search. *Librn*, Linda Slopek
Founded 1916. Pop 5,672; Circ 21,180
Library Holdings: Bk Vols 18,122; Per Subs 52
Special Collections: Deaf & Hearing Impaired (Special Resource Coll), print & non-print mat
Automation Activity & Vendor Info: (Cataloging) Innovative Interfaces Inc.; (Circulation) Innovative Interfaces Inc.; (ILL) Innovative Interfaces Inc.; (OPAC) Innovative Interfaces Inc.
Mem of Beaver County Federated Library System

MIFFLINBURG

P JANE I & ANNETTA M HERR MEMORIAL LIBRARY,* 500 Market St, 17844. SAN 314-7614. Tel: 570-966-0831. E-Mail: herrlibr@ptdprolog.net. *Librn*, Jeanne L Roberts
Founded 1945. Pop 7,600
Library Holdings: Bk Vols 15,500; Per Subs 48
Mem of Williamsport District Libr Ctr
Open Tues 11-5, Mon, Wed & Fri 7-9, Thurs 1-5 & 7-9, Sat 10-12
Friends of the Library Group

MIFFLINTOWN

P JUNIATA COUNTY LIBRARY, INC,* 498 Jefferson St, 17059-1424. SAN 358-7010. Tel: 717-436-6378. FAX: 717-436-9324. *Dir*, Thomas Hipple; Staff 1 (MLS 1)
Founded 1966. Pop 20,600
Library Holdings: Bk Vols 46,000; Bk Titles 44,000; Per Subs 98
Subject Interests: Local history
Publications: Literacy Newsletter
Mem of Cent Pa Libr District; Pittsburgh Libr District
Additional Services: Literacy, Historical Society, Meeting Rooms . Mail-A-Book Service; Bk vols 6000

MILFORD

L PIKE COUNTY LAW LIBRARY,* Courthouse, 412 Broad St, 18337. SAN 328-0829. Tel: 717-296-7231. FAX: 717-296-6054. *Coll Develop*, Matthew J Parker
Pop 29,000
Library Holdings: Bk Vols 2,400

P PIKE COUNTY PUBLIC LIBRARY,* 201 Broad St, 18337-1398. SAN 358-707X. Tel: 570-296-8211. FAX: 570-296-8987. E-Mail: pikpubli@pikeonline.net. Web Site: members.tridod.com/~pikepubliclibrary. *Dir*, Theodore R Laabs; *Asst Librn*, Jane Orben; *ILL*, Betty Fabian; *Mgr*, Virginia Harris
Founded 1902. Pop 27,966; Circ 104,000
Jan 1997-Dec 1998 Income $242,309, State $71,000, County $110,000, Other $31,309. Mats Exp $212,649, Books $37,000, Per/Ser (Incl. Access Fees) $3,800. Sal $118,000 (Prof $37,000)
Library Holdings: Bk Vols 43,500
Publications: Print & Email Newsletters
Friends of the Library Group
Branches: 2
DINGMAN-DELAWARE BRANCH, RD 1, Box 94F, Dingmans Ferry, 18328-0194. SAN 321-849X. Web Site: members.tridod.com/~pikepubliclibrary. *Mgr*, Jane Butler
GREELEY BRANCH, PO Box 45, Greeley, 18425. SAN 371-3776. Tel: 570-685-3100. FAX: 570-685-3100. Web Site: members.tridod.com/~pikepubliclibrary. *Librn*, Jodielynn Kuhn

MILLERSBURG

P JOHNSON MEMORIAL LIBRARY,* 799 E Center St, 17061. SAN 314-7622. Tel: 717-692-2658. FAX: 717-692-5003. *Dir*, Sandra Jane Graham
Founded 1931. Pop 10,092; Circ 28,067
1998-1999 Income $70,000, County $57,400, Parent Institution $6,000, Other $2,000. Mats Exp $17,600, Books $14,000. (Prof $51,900)
Library Holdings: Bk Vols 28,500
Mem of Dauphin County Library System

MILLERSVILLE

C MILLERSVILLE UNIVERSITY OF PENNSYLVANIA, Helen A Ganser Library, PO Box 1002, 17551-0302. SAN 314-7630. Tel: 717-872-3608. Interlibrary Loan Service Tel: 717-872-3853. FAX: 717-872-3854. Web Site: www.millersville.edu. *Dir*, David S Zubatsky; E-Mail: dzubatsk@marauder.millersv.edu; *Cat*, Elaine Pease; *Ref*, Leo Shelly; *Rare Bks, Spec Coll*, Dieter Ullrich; *Bibliog Instr, Online Servs*, Marjorie Warmkessel; *Coll Develop*, Irene Risser; Staff 13 (MLS 13)
Founded 1855. Fac 332; Highest Degree: Master
Library Holdings: Bk Vols 498,000; Per Subs 3,500
Subject Interests: Local, Pa hist
Special Collections: Archives of American Industrial Arts Association; Archives of Pennsylvania Sociological Association; Archives of the Pennsylvania State Modern Language Association; The Carl Van Vechten Memorial Coll of Afro American Arts & Letters, bks, photog; Wickersham Coll of 19th Century Textbooks
Partic in Associated College Libraries of Central Pennsylvania; Dialog Corporation; OCLC Online Computer Library Center, Inc; Pa Syst of Higher Educ Libr Coun
Friends of the Library Group

MILTON

S IHFP INC, Technical Library, 25 Marr St, PO Box 148, 17847. SAN 329-0506. Tel: 570-742-9614. FAX: 717-742-6600. *Admin Assoc*, Stacey Trate; Tel: 570-742-6627, E-Mail: trates@ihfp.com; Staff 50 (MLS 43, Non-MLS 7)
Founded 1984
Library Holdings: Bk Vols 603; Bk Titles 572; Per Subs 53
Subject Interests: Analytical chemistry
Restriction: Staff use only
Partic in Dialog Corporation

P MILTON PUBLIC LIBRARY, 23 S Front St, 17847. SAN 314-7649. Tel: 717-742-7111. E-Mail: milpulib@sunlink.net. *Dir*, Susan C Brandau
Founded 1923. Pop 6,749; Circ 24,097
Jan 1999-Dec 1999 Income $80,332, State $11,465, City $27,576, Locally Generated Income $7,000, Other $34,291. Mats Exp $19,223, Books $17,262, Per/Ser (Incl. Access Fees) $1,920, Micro $41. Sal $35,900
Library Holdings: Bk Vols 22,065; Per Subs 39
Subject Interests: Hist of Milton, Northumberland County
Special Collections: Milton Daily Standard Newspaper, 1816 to present, micro

MINERSVILLE

P MINERSVILLE PUBLIC LIBRARY, 220 S Fourth St, 17954. SAN 314-7657. Tel: 570-544-5196. E-Mail: min@iu29.schiu.k12.pa.us. Web Site: www.iu29.schiu.k12.pa.us/minpl. *Librn*, Rita M Geiger; *Circ*, Ruth Berner; Staff 1 (Non-MLS 1)
Founded 1934. Pop 4,877; Circ 16,497
Jan 1999-Dec 1999 Income $51,999, State $10,120, City $11,180, Federal $16,638, Locally Generated Income $12,935, Parent Institution $1,126. Mats Exp $8,548, Books $5,747, Per/Ser (Incl. Access Fees) $307. Sal $29,939
Library Holdings: Bk Vols 12,998; Bk Titles 11,073; Per Subs 20
Database Vendor: epixtech, inc.
Mem of Schuylkill County Libr Syst
Friends of the Library Group

MONACA

P BEAVER COUNTY FEDERATED LIBRARY SYSTEM,* 1260 N Brodhead Rd, 15061-2523. SAN 314-2558. Tel: 724-728-3737. FAX: 724-728-8024. *Dir*, Diane L Ambrose; *Ch Servs, Coordr*, Rose Celio
Pop 211,420; Circ 526,453
Library Holdings: Bk Vols 309,325; Per Subs 50
Special Collections: Large print coll; record album coll
Publications: quarterly newsletter; Resources for Program Planning (bi-annual)
Member Libraries: B F Jones Memorial Library; Baden Memorial Library; Beaver Area Memorial Library; Carnegie Free Library; Carnegie Free Library; Freedom Public Library; Laughlin Memorial Library; Monaca Public Library; New Brighton Public Library; Rochester Public Library
Partic in OCLC Online Computer Library Center, Inc; Pittsburgh Regional Libr Consortium

J COMMUNITY COLLEGE OF BEAVER COUNTY LIBRARY,* One Campus Dr, 15061. SAN 314-7665. Tel: 412-775-8561, Ext 115. FAX: 412-774-8995. *Dir*, J M Kistler; E-Mail: john.kistler@ccbc.cc.pa.us; *Ref*, Linda Ciani
Founded 1967. Enrl 2,000; Fac 69
1998-1999 Income $236,000. Mats Exp $62,000, Books $17,000, Per/Ser (Incl. Access Fees) $36,000, Manuscripts & Archives $9,000. Sal $127,000 (Prof $93,000)
Library Holdings: Bk Vols 52,857; Per Subs 342
Subject Interests: Aviation, Law enforcement, Nursing
Open Mon-Fri 7:30-8, Sat 9-1

P MONACA PUBLIC LIBRARY, 609 Pennsylvania Ave, 15061. SAN 314-7673. Tel: 724-775-9608. FAX: 724-775-1637. E-Mail: monacapl@hotmail.com. *Librn*, Pat Smith
Founded 1973. Pop 7,661; Circ 20,014
Library Holdings: Bk Vols 12,000; Per Subs 30
Mem of Beaver County Federated Library System

C PENNSYLVANIA STATE UNIVERSITY, Beaver Commonwealth College Library (University Libraries), 100 University Dr, 15061. SAN 314-7681. Tel: 412-773-3790. FAX: 412-773-3793. E-Mail: mmg@psulias.psu.edu. *Head Librn*, Martin Goldberg; Tel: 412-773-3791, E-Mail: mxg35@psu.edu; *Librn*, Heather Lyle; Staff 2 (MLS 2)
Founded 1965. Enrl 767; Fac 63; Highest Degree: Bachelor
Jul 1999-Jun 2000 Mats Exp $52,198, Books $17,875, Per/Ser (Incl. Access Fees) $34,323
Library Holdings: Bk Vols 45,000; Per Subs 125
Subject Interests: Steel indust
Special Collections: Afro-American Autobiographies
Partic in OCLC Online Computer Library Center, Inc; RLIN

MONESSEN

P FAYETTE COUNTY LIBRARY SYSTEM,* 326 Donner Ave, 15062-1182. SAN 371-7216. Tel: 724-684-4750. FAX: 724-684-7077.
Founded 1989. Pop 90,208
Member Libraries: Brownsville Free Public Library; German-Masontown Public Library

P MONESSEN PUBLIC LIBRARY & DISTRICT CENTER,* 326 Donner Ave, 15062-1182. SAN 314-7703. Tel: 724-684-4750. FAX: 724-684-7077. *Dir*, S Fred Natale; *Ch Servs*, Mary Matovich; *Doc, ILL, Tech Servs*, J Allen Feryok; *Circ*, Yvonne Morgan; *ILL*, Houlis Stephanie; *Doc, Tech Servs*, Frank Bristol; *Cat*, Dan Zyglowicz; *Coll Develop, Ref*, David Zilka; *ILL*, Karen Evangelist; Staff 7 (MLS 7)
Founded 1936. Pop 259,824
Library Holdings: Bk Vols 96,532; Bk Titles 95,000; Per Subs 275; High Interest/Low Vocabulary Bk Vols 1,500
Publications: M-news letter
Partic in OCLC Online Computer Library Center, Inc
Open Mon-Fri 9am-8pm, Sat 10am-5pm & Sun 1-4pm
Friends of the Library Group

MONONGAHELA

P MONONGAHELA AREA LIBRARY, 813 W Main St, 15063-2815. SAN 314-7711. Tel: 724-258-5409. FAX: 724-258-5440. E-Mail: monareal@usaor.net. Web Site: www.monarealibrary.org. *Dir*, Edward J Shanahan
Founded 1905. Pop 20,000; Circ 36,000
Jan 2000-Dec 2000 Income $105,000, State $36,000, City $20,000, County $6,000, Locally Generated Income $43,000. Mats Exp $23,000, Books $18,000, Per/Ser (Incl. Access Fees) $3,000, Other Print Mats $2,000. Sal $34,000 (Prof $16,200)
Library Holdings: Bk Titles 25,250; Per Subs 39
Subject Interests: Local history
Special Collections: Genealogical Coll; Monongahela Daily Newspapers, 1851-1982 (micro)
Database Vendor: Ebsco - EbscoHost
Mem of Washington County Libr Syst
Open Mon-Thurs 12-8, Fri 12-5 & Sat 10-5
Friends of the Library Group

MONROETON

P MONROETON PUBLIC LIBRARY, 110 College Avenue, 18832. (Mail add: PO Box 145, 18832), SAN 314-772X. Tel: 570-265-2871. FAX: 570-265-7995. E-Mail: mplib@epix.net. *Librn*, Alice R Clock; *Asst Librn*, Alberta Fice; Staff 3 (Non-MLS 3)
Founded 1939. Pop 633; Circ 3,000
Library Holdings: Bk Vols 4,153; Per Subs 15
Mem of Bradford County Library System Headquarters
Open Mon 10-2 & 4-7PM, Tues 10-2PM, Wed 4-7PM, Thurs 2-6PM & Sat 10-12PM
Friends of the Library Group

MONROEVILLE

J COMMUNITY COLLEGE OF ALLEGHENY COUNTY, Boyce Campus Library, 595 Beatty Rd, 15146. SAN 358-7134. Tel: 724-325-6712. FAX: 724-325-6696. *Ref*, Raymond Martin; Staff 8 (MLS 5, Non-MLS 3)
Founded 1966. Enrl 5,400; Fac 80
Library Holdings: Bk Vols 63,403; Per Subs 337
Subject Interests: Allied health, Food serv, Hospitality, Nursing, Paralegal
Special Collections: Paralegal Coll
Publications: Acquisitions Lists; Bibliographies; Library Handbook; Library Newspaper
Partic in OCLC Online Computer Library Center, Inc; Pittsburgh Regional Libr Consortium
Open Mon-Thurs 8-9, Fri 8-4, Sat 9-1
Departmental Libraries:
NORTH Tel: 412-366-7000. FAX: 412-369-3626. *Dir*, Clifford Baylis PhD; *Librn*, Barbara Thompson; *Librn*, Elliot Binns
Library Holdings: Bk Vols 21,827; Bk Titles 18,944; Per Subs 227
Open Mon-Thurs 8am-9pm, Fri 8-5 & Sat 8-2

M FORBES REGIONAL HOSPITAL, Medical Library, 2570 Haymaker Rd, 15146. SAN 314-7746. Tel: 412-858-2422. FAX: 412-858-2532. *Librn*, Amy Haugh; E-Mail: ahaugh@wpahs.org; Staff 1 (MLS 1)
Founded 1978
Library Holdings: Bk Titles 1,825; Per Subs 98
Subject Interests: Family practice, Gynecology, Obstetrics, Oncology, Pediatrics, Psychiatry
Publications: Forbes Libraries Booktales (irregular)
Partic in BRS; Nat Libr of Med; Pittsburgh-East Hospital Libr Coop

P MONROEVILLE PUBLIC LIBRARY, 4000 Gateway Campus Blvd, 15146-3381. SAN 314-7770. Tel: 412-372-0500. FAX: 412-372-1168. Web Site: www.clpgh.org/ein/monroevl. *Dir*, Kathy K Kennedy; Tel: 412-372-0500, Ext 11, E-Mail: kennedyk@clpgh.org; *Ad Servs*, C Diane Thomas; Tel: 412-372-0500, Ext 13, E-Mail: thomasd@clpgh.org; *Ch Servs*, Lou Anne Sokolowski; Tel: 412-372-0500, Ext 21, E-Mail: sokolowskil@clpgh.org; *Ref*, Agnes Chow; *Info Tech*, Janet Balas; Tel: 412-372-0500, Ext 23, E-Mail: balasj@clpgh.org; *Tech Servs*, Sally Michalski; E-Mail: michalskis@clpgh.org; Staff 17 (MLS 8, Non-MLS 9)
Founded 1960. Pop 33,256; Circ 179,549
Jan 1999-Dec 1999 Income $1,434,173, State $106,661, City $694,652, Federal $13,988, County $222,248, Locally Generated Income $280,922, Other $115,702. Mats Exp $105,075, Books $64,951, Per/Ser (Incl. Access Fees) $10,897, Presv $214, Micro $5,360, AV Equip $15,275, Electronic Ref Mat (Incl. Access Fees) $1,468. Sal $518,463 (Prof $308,682)
Library Holdings: Bk Vols 87,874; Per Subs 265
Subject Interests: Bus, Careers, Local history
Special Collections: New Reader Coll; Newbery & Caldecott Coll
Automation Activity & Vendor Info: (Acquisitions) DRA; (Cataloging) DRA; (Circulation) DRA; (OPAC) DRA
Database Vendor: DRA
Publications: Newsletter (quarterly)
Partic in Allegheny County Libr Asn
Friends of the Library Group

S USS DIVISION OF USX CORP, Knowledge Resource Center, 4000 Tech Center Dr, MS-88, 15146. SAN 314-7789. Tel: 412-825-2345. FAX: 412-825-2050. *Info Specialist*, Megan Dennis; E-Mail: mhdennis@uss.com
Founded 1928
Library Holdings: Bk Titles 30,000; Per Subs 200
Subject Interests: Bus, Ceramics, Chemical technology, Econ, Mat sci, Metallurgy, Physics, Statistics, Steelmaking
Special Collections: Historical Books on Steel
Publications: Newsletter
Partic in Dialog Corporation; Dow Jones Interactive; Dun & Bradstreet Info Servs

IONT ALTO

PENNSYLVANIA STATE UNIVERSITY, Mont Alto Commonwealth College Library (University Libraries),* Rte 233 N, 17237-9703. SAN 314-7797. Tel: 717-749-6040. FAX: 717-749-6059. E-Mail: jve@psulias.psu.edu. *Librn*, Johanna Ezell; Staff 4 (MLS 2, Non-MLS 2)
Founded 1963. Enrl 1,261; Fac 65
Jul 1996-Jun 1997 Mats Exp $78,395
Library Holdings: Bk Vols 32,097; Per Subs 296
Partic in OCLC Online Computer Library Center, Inc; RLIN

IONTGOMERY

MONTGOMERY AREA PUBLIC LIBRARY, One S Main St, 17752-1150. SAN 314-7800. Tel: 570-547-6212. FAX: 570-547-6212. *Librn*, Susan Thomas; Staff 1 (MLS 1)
Founded 1911. Pop 4,942; Circ 8,542
Library Holdings: Bk Vols 14,000; Per Subs 32
Open Mon-Wed & Fri 12-8

IONTOURSVILLE

DR W B KONKLE MEMORIAL LIBRARY,* 384 Broad St, 17754-2206. SAN 314-7819. Tel: 570-368-1840. *Librn*, Jean Reeder
Founded 1943. Pop 7,694
Library Holdings: Bk Titles 23,000; Per Subs 45
Special Collections: Pennsylvania Coll, bks & pamphlets
Mem of Lycoming County Libr Syst
Open Tues-Fri 1-8, Sat 10-1
Friends of the Library Group

MONTROSE

P SUSQUEHANNA COUNTY HISTORICAL SOCIETY & FREE LIBRARY ASSOCIATION,* 2 Monument Sq, 18801-1115. SAN 358-7169. Tel: 570-278-1881. FAX: 570-278-9336. E-Mail: suspublib@epix.net. Web Site: www.epix.net/~suspulib/. *Publ Servs, Ref*, Hilary Caws-Elwitt; *ILL*, Amy LaRue; Staff 1 (MLS 1)
Founded 1907. Pop 40,380; Circ 175,857
Jan 1998-Dec 1999 Income $425,029, State $83,487, Federal $3,150, County $128,797, Locally Generated Income $194,241, Other $12,649. Mats Exp $57,465, Books $43,858, Per/Ser (Incl. Access Fees) $6,559. Sal $219,885
Library Holdings: Bk Vols 65,800; Per Subs 250
Special Collections: Genealogy (Census Records), micro; Genealogy (New England Historical & Genealogical Register); Local newspapers, micro
Publications: Centennial History of Susquehanna County, Pennsylvania; cookbooks; County Atlas; History of Susquehanna County, Pennsylvania; Susquehanna County Historical Society & Free Library Association (1907-1982)
Friends of the Library Group
Branches: 3
FOREST CITY BRANCH, 531 Main St, Forest City, 18421-1421. SAN 358-7193. Tel: 570-785-5590. FAX: 570-785-5590. Web Site: www.epix.net/~suspulib/. *Librn*, Diana Junior
Library Holdings: Bk Vols 12,734
HALLSTEAD-GREAT BEND BRANCH, 201 Franklin St, PO Box 476, Hallstead, 18822-0476. SAN 314-5662. Tel: 570-879-2227. FAX: 570-879-0982. E-Mail: hallib@epix.net. *Dir*, Angie Wolfe
Founded 1917. Pop 6,000; Circ 10,500
Library Holdings: Bk Titles 7,200
Automation Activity & Vendor Info: (Circulation) DRA
Database Vendor: Ebsco - EbscoHost
Function: ILL available
Friends of the Library Group
SUSQUEHANNA BRANCH, 127 Main St, Susquehanna, 18847-1209. SAN 358-7223. Tel: 570-853-4106. FAX: 570-853-4106. Web Site: www.epix.net/~suspulib/. *Librn*, Catherine Grausgruber
Library Holdings: Bk Vols 10,565
Friends of the Library Group
Bookmobiles: 1

GL SUSQUEHANNA COUNTY LAW LIBRARY,* Court House, PO Box 218, 18801. SAN 372-9044. Tel: 717-278-4600. *Dir*, Mary Foster
Library Holdings: Bk Vols 12,000

MOON TOWNSHIP

C ROBERT MORRIS COLLEGE LIBRARY, 881 Narrows Run Rd, 15108-1189. SAN 358-3686. Tel: 412-262-8367. Circulation Tel: 412-262-8306. Reference Tel: 412-262-8272. FAX: 412-262-4049. E-Mail: library@robert-morris.edu. Web Site: library.robert-morris.edu. *Dir*, Fran Caplan; Tel: 412-262-8366, E-Mail: caplan@robert-morris.edu; *Acq*, Henrietta Angus; Tel: 412-262-8255, E-Mail: angus@robert-morris-edu; *Head Ref*, Chris Devine; Tel: 412-262-8358, E-Mail: devinec@robert-morris.edu; *ILL*, Don Luisi; Tel: 412-262-8359, E-Mail: luisi@robert-morris.edu; Staff 22 (MLS 10, Non-MLS 12)
Founded 1962. Enrl 3,614; Fac 191; Highest Degree: Doctorate
Jun 1999-May 2000 Income Parent Institution $1,343,166. Mats Exp $334,980, Books $198,904, Per/Ser (Incl. Access Fees) $95,222, Presv $6,981, Micro $31,157, AV Equip $2,716, Electronic Ref Mat (Incl. Access Fees) $51,556. Sal $761,572
Library Holdings: Bk Vols 131,559; Bk Titles 93,586; Per Subs 853
Subject Interests: Bus
Automation Activity & Vendor Info: (Acquisitions) Endeavor; (Cataloging) Endeavor; (Circulation) Endeavor; (Media Booking) Endeavor; (OPAC) Endeavor; (Serials) Endeavor
Database Vendor: Dialog, Ebsco - EbscoHost, Lexis-Nexis, OCLC - First Search, ProQuest
Publications: Discover Robert Morris College Libraries (newsletter); Library Tip Sheets; Pathfinders
Function: ILL available
Partic in OCLC Online Computer Library Center, Inc; PALCI; PALINET & Union Library Catalogue of Pennsylvania

MORGANTOWN

P VILLAGE LIBRARY OF MORGANTOWN, Walnut St, 19543-0997. SAN 314-7827. Tel: 610-286-1022. FAX: 610-286-1024. E-Mail: morgantownpl@berks.lib.pa.us. Web Site: www.reading.lib.pa.us/morganpl/. *Librn*, Kay Price; Tel: 610-326-7680, E-Mail: jsprice@dca.net
Founded 1965. Pop 8,000; Circ 52,018
Jan 1998-Dec 1999 Income $84,720, State $22,575, Federal $735, County $25,273, Locally Generated Income $12,950, Other $23,187. Mats Exp $16,301, Books $12,375, Per/Ser (Incl. Access Fees) $1,012, AV Equip $1,907. Sal $33,802
Library Holdings: Bk Titles 15,993; Per Subs 40
Mem of Berks County Libr Syst
Open Mon & Wed 10-8, Tues & Thurs 10-5, Sat 10-2
Friends of the Library Group

MORRISVILLE

P MORRISVILLE FREE LIBRARY ASSOCIATION,* 300 N Pennsylvania Ave, 19067-6621. SAN 314-7835. Tel: 215-295-4850. *Librn*, Diane Hughes
Founded 1904. Pop 9,845; Circ 34,408
Library Holdings: Bk Vols 25,000; Per Subs 55
Open Mon 2-9, Wed 2-8, Tues & Thurs 11-8, Fri & Sat 2-6, Sun 1-5
Friends of the Library Group

MOSCOW

P NORTH POCONO PUBLIC LIBRARY, 113 Van Brunt St, 18444-9254. SAN 376-5717. Tel: 570-842-4700. FAX: 570-842-1304. E-Mail: npoadmin@albright.org. *Dir*, Sheila Flaherty
Founded 1985. Pop 16,000 Sal $50,670 (Prof $19,000)
Library Holdings: Bk Vols 10,000; Per Subs 75
Mem of Lackawanna County Library System
Open Mon, Wed & Fri 9-5, Tues & Thurs 12-8 & Sat 9-4

MOUNT CARMEL

P MOUNT CARMEL PUBLIC LIBRARY, 30 S Oak St, 17851-2185. SAN 314-7843. Tel: 570-339-0703. E-Mail: mcpublib@ptd.net. *Librn*, Clara Hudson
Founded 1961. Pop 16,402; Circ 35,000
Library Holdings: Bk Vols 37,000; Per Subs 65
Subject Interests: Cookbooks, Handicrafts, World War II
Special Collections: Proceedings Northunderland County, Hist Soc, Local Hist Coll
Mem of Pottsville Free Public Library
Open Mon, Tues & Wed 9-7, Thurs 9-1, Fri-Sat 9-4

MOUNT HOLLY SPRINGS

P AMELIA S GIVIN FREE LIBRARY,* 114 N Baltimore Ave & 6th St, 17065-1201. SAN 314-7851. Tel: 717-486-3688. FAX: 717-486-7170. *Dir*, Cynthia Stratton Thomson; Staff 5 (MLS 1, Non-MLS 4)
Founded 1889. Pop 9,000; Circ 60,000
Library Holdings: Bk Vols 22,000; Per Subs 85
Mem of Cumberland County Library System; Dauphin County Library System

MOUNT JEWETT

P MOUNT JEWETT MEMORIAL LIBRARY, PO Box Y, 16740. SAN 314-786X. Tel: 814-778-5588. FAX: 814-778-5588. *Librn*, Marge Faull
Founded 1938. Pop 1,992; Circ 14,847
Library Holdings: Bk Vols 15,000; Per Subs 22
Open Mon-Thurs 10-12, 2-5 & 7-9, Fri 10-12 & 2-5

MOUNT JOY

P MILANOF-SCHOCK LIBRARY, (Formerly Mount Joy Library), 1184 Anderson Ferry Rd, 17552. SAN 314-7878. Tel: 717-653-1510. FAX: 717-653-6590. Web Site: www.mountjoy.lib.pa.us. *Dir*, Linda Bolton Kean; E-Mail: kean@lancaster.lib.pa.us; *Asst Dir*, Nancy L Behney; E-Mail: nbehney@lancaster.lib.pa.us; Staff 9 (Non-MLS 9)
Founded 1964. Pop 20,879; Circ 78,000
1998-1999 Income $43,126, State $13,440, County $3,150, Locally Generated Income $5,498, Other $4,434. Mats Exp $16,850, Books $14,000, Per/Ser (Incl. Access Fees) $800, Other Print Mats $250. Sal $23,173 (Prof $15,581)
Library Holdings: Bk Vols 11,500; Per Subs 50
Mem of Libr Syst of Lancaster County; Library System of Lancaster County
Friends of the Library Group

MOUNT PLEASANT

M FRICK HOSPITAL, Joseph F Bucci Health Sciences Library, 508 S Church St, 15666. SAN 329-0689. Tel: 724-547-1352. FAX: 724-547-1693. *Librn*, Rosemary C Panichella; E-Mail: rpanic@faywesthealth.org; Staff 2 (MLS 1, Non-MLS 1)
Founded 1980
Library Holdings: Bk Titles 784; Per Subs 124
Publications: The Next Chapter
Partic in National Network Of Libraries Of Medicine - South Central Region

P MOUNT PLEASANT FREE PUBLIC LIBRARY, 120 S Church St, 15666-1879. SAN 314-7886. Tel: 724-547-3850. *Librn*, Carole A Klocek
Founded 1936. Pop 5,895; Circ 19,935
Library Holdings: Bk Titles 19,440; Per Subs 63
Subject Interests: Civil War
Special Collections: Mother Goose Coll
Mem of Monessen District Libr Ctr
Open Mon-Fri 12-8, Sat 12-5

MOUNTAIN TOP

P MARIAN SUTHERLAND KIRBY LIBRARY, 35 Kirby Ave, 18707-1214. SAN 376-5687. Tel: 570-474-9313. FAX: 570-474-2587. E-Mail: kirbylib@ptd.net. *Dir*, Margaret Young; Staff 3 (MLS 1, Non-MLS 2)
Library Holdings: Bk Titles 23,000; Per Subs 45
Mem of Luzerne County Libr Syst
Partic in Pennsylvania Library Association
Friends of the Library Group

MOUNTAINHOME

P BARRETT FRIENDLY LIBRARY,* PO Box 604, 18342-0604. SAN 314-7894. Tel: 570-595-7171. FAX: 570-595-7879. E-Mail: brfpublib@hslc.org. *Librn*, Cindy DeLuca
Founded 1910. Pop 5,467; Circ 28,330
Library Holdings: Bk Titles 19,000; Per Subs 118
Mem of Easton District Libr Ctr
Open Mon-Thurs 12-5 & 6-9, Fri 12-4 & Sat 11:30-3
Friends of the Library Group

MUNCY

S MUNCY HISTORICAL SOCIETY & MUSEUM OF HISTORY, Historical Library,* 40 N Main St, PO Box 11, 17756-1341. SAN 372-9060. Tel: 717-546-5917. *Librn*, Linda Poulton
Library Holdings: Bk Vols 400
Restriction: By appointment only
Friends of the Library Group

P MUNCY PUBLIC LIBRARY, 108 S Main St, 17756-0119. SAN 314-7916. Tel: 570-546-5014. FAX: 570-546-5014. *Librn*, Laurie Bay
Pop 7,000; Circ 27,000
Library Holdings: Bk Vols 25,000
Special Collections: Pennsylvania History, micro
Mem of Lycoming County Libr Syst
Friends of the Library Group

MURRYSVILLE

S ENERGY & ENVIRONMENTAL MANAGEMENT, INC (E2M) LIBRARY, 4115 William Penn Hwy, Ste 201, PO Box 71, 15668. SAN 370-2332. Tel: 724-733-0022. FAX: 724-733-0018. E-Mail: 70611.1645@compuserve.com. *Pres*, Larry L Simmons
Library Holdings: Bk Vols 1,600

P MURRYSVILLE COMMUNITY LIBRARY, 4130 Sardis Rd, 15668-1120. SAN 314-7924. Tel: 724-327-1102. FAX: 724-327-7142. E-Mail: murrlib1@nb.net. Web Site: www.nb.net/~murrlib1. *Dir*, Margaret J Wilson; *Cat*, Susan Lyons; *Ch Servs*, Carol Siefken; *Ref*, Mindy Duch; Staff 4 (MLS 3, Non-MLS 1)
Founded 1922. Pop 25,946; Circ 122,170
Jan 1999-Dec 1999 Income $282,419. Mats Exp $56,705, Books $46,272, Per/Ser (Incl. Access Fees) $9,303, Electronic Ref Mat (Incl. Access Fees) $1,130. Sal $150,666
Library Holdings: Bk Vols 52,970; Per Subs 118
Subject Interests: Large print
Automation Activity & Vendor Info: (Cataloging) Follett; (Circulation) Follett; (OPAC) Follett
Mem of Westmoreland County Libr Syst
Partic in Share Westmoreland Consortium

MYERSTOWN

R EVANGELICAL SCHOOL OF THEOLOGY, Rostad Library, 121 S College St, 17067. SAN 314-7932. Tel: 717-866-5775. FAX: 717-866-4667. Web Site: www.rostad.library.net. *Librn*, Terry Heisey; E-Mail: theisey@evangelical.edu; Staff 1 (MLS 1)
Founded 1954. Enrl 160; Fac 7; Highest Degree: Master
Library Holdings: Bk Vols 70,000; Per Subs 550
Subject Interests: Biblical studies
Special Collections: Evangelical Association; Evangelical Congregational Church Archives; Pietism
Automation Activity & Vendor Info: (Cataloging) TLC; (Circulation) TLC (OPAC) TLC
Partic in Southeastern Pennsylvania Theological Library Association

P MYERSTOWN COMMUNITY LIBRARY,* 199 N College St, PO Box 246, 17067-0246. SAN 314-7940. Tel: 717-866-2800. FAX: 717-866-5898. E-Mail: llm@leblibrarysys.org. Web Site: www.leblibrarysys.org. *Dir*, Linda Manwiller; Staff 1 (MLS 1)
Founded 1936. Pop 12,765; Circ 59,990
Library Holdings: Bk Titles 22,000; Per Subs 60
Subject Interests: Local counties, Local genealogies, Pa archives, Pa German Folklore Society, Pa hist
Mem of Dauphin County Library System; Lebanon County Library System

NANTICOKE

J LUZERNE COUNTY COMMUNITY COLLEGE LIBRARY, 1333 S Prospect St, 18634. SAN 314-7959. Tel: 570-740-0415. Circulation Tel: 570-740-7415. Reference Tel: 570-740-0424. Toll Free Tel: 800-377-5222, Ext 415. FAX: 570-735-6130. Web Site: www.luzerne.edu/students/library. *Dir*, Mia W Bassham; Tel: 570-740-0420, E-Mail: mbassham@luzerne.edu; *Assoc Librn*, Susan Bevan; Tel: 570-740-0419, E-Mail: sbevan@luzerne.edu; *Ref*, Fred Walters; Tel: 570-740-0424, E-Mail: fwalters@luzerne.edu; Staff 4 (MLS 2, Non-MLS 2)
Founded 1966. Enrl 3,979; Fac 140
Jul 1999-Jun 2000 Income $593,237. Mats Exp $164,235, Books $49,950, Per/Ser (Incl. Access Fees) $50,000, Presv $3,285, Micro $16,000, AV Equip $24,000, Electronic Ref Mat (Incl. Access Fees) $21,000. Sal $417,317 (Prof $197,325)
Library Holdings: Bk Vols 59,649; Bk Titles 55,400; Per Subs 317
Subject Interests: Dental assisting, Hotel, Hygiene, Nursing, Restaurant mgt
Special Collections: Criminal Justice, bks, flm; Fire Science Technology, bks, flm
Automation Activity & Vendor Info: (Acquisitions) epixtech, inc.; (Cataloging) epixtech, inc.; (Circulation) epixtech, inc.; (OPAC) epixtech, inc.; (Serials) epixtech, inc.
Database Vendor: Ebsco - EbscoHost, GaleNet, IAC - Info Trac, Lexis-Nexis, ProQuest, Wilson - Wilson Web
Partic in Health Science Library Information Consortium; Northeastern Pennsylvania Library Network; OCLC Online Computer Library Center, Inc; PALINET & Union Library Catalogue of Pennsylvania; Pennsylvania Community College Library Consortium

P MILL MEMORIAL LIBRARY, 495 E Main St, 18634-1897. SAN 314-7967. Tel: 717-735-3030. FAX: 717-735-0340. E-Mail: mmlib@gna.liu18.k12.pa.us. Web Site: www.gnasd.com/millmemorial.htm. *Dir*, Claudia Koenig; *Ch Servs*, Ruth Kresge; Staff 1 (MLS 1)
Founded 1945. Pop 27,149; Circ 64,740
1999-2000 Income $158,344, State $34,628, City $6,281, County $19,821, Locally Generated Income $88,964. Mats Exp $20,962, Books $17,398, Per/Ser (Incl. Access Fees) $2,476. Sal $84,878
Library Holdings: Bk Vols 48,247; Per Subs 111
Mem of Luzerne County Libr Syst
Friends of the Library Group

NANTY GLO

P NANTY GLO PUBLIC LIBRARY,* 942 Roberts St, 15943-1302. SAN 314-7975. Tel: 814-749-0111. FAX: 814-749-0111. E-Mail: nglopl@surfshop.net. *Librn*, Ann Gongloff; *Asst Librn*, Janet Llewllyn
Founded 1962. Pop 10,000; Circ 41,806
Library Holdings: Bk Vols 24,000; Per Subs 42

Special Collections: Large Print Books; Library of America
Mem of Cambria County Library System & District Center
Open Mon, Tues, Thurs & Fri 1-7, Wed 10-7 & Sat 10-1

ARBERTH

NARBERTH COMMUNITY LIBRARY,* Windsor Ave, 19072-2296. SAN 314-7991. Tel: 610-664-2878. *Librn,* Christine Atwater Jackson
Founded 1921. Pop 4,900; Circ 45,617
Library Holdings: Bk Vols 42,521; Per Subs 40
Subject Interests: Children's literature
Mem of Montgomery County District Libr Syst
Open Mon-Thurs 10-5:30 & 7-9, Fri 10-12 & 1-5:30, Sat 10-12 & 1-4:30
Friends of the Library Group

IAZARETH

MEMORIAL LIBRARY OF NAZARETH & VICINITY, 295 E Center St, 18064-2298. SAN 314-8009. Tel: 610-759-4932. FAX: 610-759-9513. Web Site: www.nazarethlibrary.org. *Dir, Librn,* Lynn Snodgrass-Pilla; E-Mail: lynnsp@nazarethlibrary.org; *Ch Servs,* Catherine Stewart; Staff 20 (MLS 1, Non-MLS 19)
Founded 1949. Pop 19,121; Circ 110,000
Jan 2001-Dec 2001 Income $394,000. Mats Exp $47,000. Sal $290,000
Library Holdings: Bk Vols 42,000; Bk Titles 38,000; Per Subs 100
Subject Interests: Genealogy, History
Automation Activity & Vendor Info: (Cataloging) Sagebrush Corporation; (Circulation) Sagebrush Corporation; (OPAC) Sagebrush Corporation
Open Mon-Thurs 10-9, Sat 9-4
Friends of the Library Group

MORAVIAN HISTORICAL SOCIETY, Museum & Library, 214 E Center St, 18064. SAN 374-552X. Tel: 610-759-5070. FAX: 610-759-5070. *Exec Dir,* Susan M Dreydoppel; *Curator,* Mark Turdo
Founded 1857
1999-2000 Mats Exp $400, Books $300, Per/Ser (Incl. Access Fees) $100
Library Holdings: Bk Titles 5,000; Per Subs 10
Restriction: Not a lending library
Function: Research library

NEW ALBANY

NEW ALBANY COMMUNITY LIBRARY, 98 Front St, 18833. (Mail add: PO Box 54, 18833), SAN 314-8017. Tel: 570-363-2418. *Dir,* Doris Hugo; Tel: 570-363-2226
Founded 1963
Library Holdings: Bk Vols 5,000
Friends of the Library Group

NEW ALEXANDRIA

P NEW ALEXANDRIA PUBLIC LIBRARY,* W Main St, PO Box 405, 15670-0022. SAN 314-8025. Tel: 724-668-7747. *Librn,* Jacqueline Snyder
Founded 1921. Pop 700; Circ 691
Library Holdings: Bk Vols 3,756
Open Mon-Thurs 6-8, Tues & Thurs 12:30-2:30

NEW BETHLEHEM

P NEW BETHLEHEM AREA FREE PUBLIC LIBRARY, 246 Broad St, 16242-1098. SAN 314-8033. Tel: 814-275-2870. FAX: 814-275-2870. E-Mail: nbafpl@penn.com. Web Site: users.penn.com/~nbafpl/index.html. *Dir,* Lynne Elaine Tharan; Staff 5 (MLS 1, Non-MLS 4)
Founded 1955. Pop 8,801; Circ 28,600
Jan 2000-Dec 2000 Income $80,101, State $31,101, County $3,700, Locally Generated Income $45,300. Mats Exp $9,770, Books $8,200, Per/Ser (Incl. Access Fees) $1,100, AV Equip $350. Sal $44,273 (Prof $23,465)
Library Holdings: Bk Vols 16,000; Per Subs 65; Bks on Deafness & Sign Lang 45
Automation Activity & Vendor Info: (Circulation) Follett
Database Vendor: Ebsco - EbscoHost
Function: ILL available
Mem of Clarion County Library System; Clarion Dist Libr Asn; Oil Creek District Library Center
Friends of the Library Group

NEW BLOOMFIELD

L PERRY COUNTY LAW LIBRARY,* Court House, PO Box 668, 17068. SAN 372-9079. Tel: 717-582-2131, Ext 234. FAX: 717-582-2852.
Library Holdings: Bk Vols 2,000; Per Subs 100

NEW BRIGHTON

P NEW BRIGHTON PUBLIC LIBRARY,* 1021 Third Ave, 15066-3011. SAN 314-8041. Tel: 724-846-7991. FAX: 724-846-0717. *Librn,* Elizabeth L Mowry
Pop 8,300; Circ 27,359
Library Holdings: Bk Vols 28,000; Per Subs 29
Mem of Beaver County Federated Library System
Open Mon & Thurs 10-8, Tues & Wed 11-5, Sat 10-1
Friends of the Library Group

NEW CASTLE

S ERIE BUSINESS CENTER SOUTH LIBRARY,* 170 Cascade Galleria, 16101. SAN 372-9087. Tel: 724-658-9066. FAX: 724-658-3083. *Dir,* Irene G Marburger
Library Holdings: Bk Vols 1,624; Per Subs 100
Subject Interests: Accounting

SR FIRST CHRISTIAN CHURCH LIBRARY,* 23 W Washinton, 16101. SAN 320-2275. Tel: 724-652-6657. *Librn,* Eileen McEwen
Founded 1959
Library Holdings: Bk Titles 4,100; Per Subs 23
Subject Interests: Religion
Special Collections: Historical

SR HIGHLAND PRESBYTERIAN CHURCH, Elizabeth Milholland Library, 708 Highland Ave, 16101. SAN 329-8450. Tel: 724-654-7391. *Librn,* Anne M Graham
Library Holdings: Bk Titles 2,398
Subject Interests: Religion
Special Collections: Ministry of Encouragement - coping with death, divorce & other problems

M JAMESON MEMORIAL HOSPITAL, School of Nursing Library,* 1211 Wilmington Ave, 16105-2595. SAN 358-7258. Tel: 724-656-4050. FAX: 724-656-4179. E-Mail: clark@hslc.org. *Librn,* Leann Isaac
Founded 1898. Enrl 120
Library Holdings: Bk Vols 4,440; Bk Titles 3,000; Per Subs 120
Subject Interests: Medicine, Nursing, Sci-tech
Partic in Greater NE Regional Med Libr Program
Branches:
MEDICAL Tel: 724-656-4048. FAX: 724-656-4179. *Librn,* Leann Isaac

L LAWRENCE COUNTY LAW LIBRARY,* 430 Court St, 16101. SAN 328-0551. Tel: 724-656-2136. FAX: 724-658-4489. *Librn,* Amy N Ball
Library Holdings: Bk Vols 25,000; Per Subs 15

P NEW CASTLE PUBLIC LIBRARY, (NCPL), 207 E North St, 16101-3691. SAN 314-8068. Tel: 724-658-6659. FAX: 724-658-7209. *Dir,* Susan Walls; E-Mail: swalls@newcastle.lib.pa.us; *Ch Servs,* Anne Graham; *Ref,* Helen Gilpin; *Per, Ref,* Pat McCormick; *Tech Servs,* John Patterson; Staff 8 (MLS 6, Non-MLS 2)
Founded 1908. Pop 69,575; Circ 179,075
1998-1999 Income $850,000, State $309,000, City $75,000, County $280,000, Locally Generated Income $64,000. Mats Exp $107,000, Books $100,000, Per/Ser (Incl. Access Fees) $7,000. Sal $450,000
Library Holdings: Bk Vols 110,900; Bk Titles 98,000; Per Subs 135
Subject Interests: History
Special Collections: Architecture (Jane Jackson Coll), bks, microflm; Brotherhood (Joshua A Kaplan Coll); Gardening, Landscape (Wylie McCaslin Coll); Judaism (Council Corner Coll); Local History &; Pharmacy (Lawrence C Pharmaceutical Coll); Polish Culture (Polish Falcons Coll); Women's World (Federation Coll)
Automation Activity & Vendor Info: (Circulation) MultiLIS
Database Vendor: OCLC - First Search
Partic in Tri County Libr Consortium
Friends of the Library Group
Bookmobiles: 1

R NORTHMINSTER PRESBYTERIAN CHURCH LIBRARY, 2434 Wilmington Rd, 16105. SAN 314-8076. Tel: 412-658-9051. FAX: 412-658-9052. *Librn,* Susan Dexter
Founded 1957
Library Holdings: Bk Vols 4,400
Subject Interests: Christian educ, Religion

NEW CUMBERLAND

P NEW CUMBERLAND PUBLIC LIBRARY,* One Benjamin Plaza, 17070-1597. SAN 314-8084. Tel: 717-774-7820. FAX: 717-774-7824. *Dir,* Judith Dillen; *Cat,* Leatrice Calderelli; *Ch Servs,* Eilleen Franz; Staff 1 (MLS 1)
Founded 1941. Pop 7,665; Circ 192,707
1998-1999 Income $299,602. Mats Exp $38,588. Sal $161,475
Library Holdings: Bk Titles 55,000; Per Subs 120
Subject Interests: Local history

Automation Activity & Vendor Info: (Cataloging) epixtech, inc.
Mem of Cumberland County Library System; Dauphin County Library System
Friends of the Library Group

NEW FLORENCE

P NEW FLORENCE COMMUNITY LIBRARY,* 164 Ligonier St, PO Box 248, 15944-0428. SAN 314-8092. Tel: 724-235-2249. FAX: 724-235-2249. E-Mail: nfcl_lib@yahoo.com. Web Site: www.wiukiz.pa.us/ligonier/nflib.html. *Librn*, Shannon Metcalfe; *Asst Librn*, Margaret Betz
Pop 2,979; Circ 14,389
Library Holdings: Bk Vols 25,521; Per Subs 68
Mem of Pittsburgh Libr District

NEW FREEDOM

P NEW FREEDOM LIBRARY CENTER, 6 S Front St, 17349, (Mail add: PO Box 98, 17349-0098), SAN 314-8106. Tel: 717-235-4313. FAX: 717-235-4313. Web Site: www.yorklibraries.org/newfreedom. *Dir*, Chris Chilcote
Founded 1968. Pop 10,000; Circ 30,000
Library Holdings: Bk Vols 18,500; Per Subs 28
Mem of York County Library System
Open Mon-Wed 10-5, Thurs 10-1, Mon, Tues & Thurs evening 7-9, Sat 9-4
Friends of the Library Group

NEW HOLLAND

P EASTERN LANCASTER COUNTY LIBRARY,* 11 Chestnut Dr, 17557-1398. SAN 314-8114. Tel: 717-354-0525. FAX: 717-354-7787. *Dir*, Karen Hutchison; E-Mail: hkaren@ptd.net
Pop 15,500
Library Holdings: Bk Vols 25,000
Mem of Library System of Lancaster County
Friends of the Library Group

S NEW HOLLAND NORTH AMERICA INC, Engineering Library-MS 638,* 200 George Delp Rd, PO Box 1895, 17557-0903. SAN 370-8462. Tel: 717-355-1395. FAX: 717-355-1939.
Library Holdings: Per Subs 10
Restriction: Staff use only

NEW HOPE

P FREE LIBRARY OF NEW HOPE & SOLEBURY, 93 W Ferry St, 18938-1332. SAN 314-8122. Tel: 215-862-2330. FAX: 215-862-1071. *Mgr*, Mary Lou Chianese; *Librn*, Frances Greene
Founded 1894. Pop 8,800; Circ 32,000
Library Holdings: Bk Vols 17,500; Per Subs 40
Subject Interests: Architecture, Art
Special Collections: Art (Migliorini Coll: New Hope Reference Coll); Performing & Fine Arts Reference Coll
Mem of Bucks County Free Library

S THE FREEDONIA GAZETTE, Marx Brothers Library & Archives, 335 Fieldstone Dr, 18938-1012. SAN 326-1808. Tel: 215-862-9734. E-Mail: tfg@cheerful.com. *Dir, Ref*, Paul G Wesolowski
Founded 1982
Library Holdings: Bk Titles 140
Special Collections: Effect of Marx Brothers on popular culture (Gloria Teasdale Coll), toys, games, T-shirts, greeting cards, cups & statues
Publications: The Freedonia Gazette - The magazine devoted to the Marx Brothers

NEW KENSINGTON

C PENNSYLVANIA STATE UNIVERSITY, NEW KENSINGTON COMMONWEALTH COLLEGE, Elisabeth S Blissell Library (University Libraries), 3550 Seventh St Rd, Rte 780, 15068-1798. SAN 314-8149. Tel: 724-334-6071. FAX: 724-334-6113. E-Mail: jrg15@psu.edu. Web Site: www.nk.psu.edu/library/library.htm. *Librn*, Claire Hoffman; *Ref*, Jennifer R Gilley; Staff 2 (MLS 1, Non-MLS 1)
Founded 1958. Enrl 983; Fac 40
Library Holdings: Bk Vols 29,240; Per Subs 200
Partic in OCLC Online Computer Library Center, Inc; RLIN

P PEOPLES LIBRARY,* 880 Barnes St, 15068-6235. SAN 358-7371. Tel: 724-339-1021. FAX: 724-339-2027. Web Site: www.peopleslink.org. *Dir*, Rhonda Kepple Buttacavoli; E-Mail: rbuttaca@mailexcite.com; *Circ*, Denise Thompson; *Ch Servs*, Mary Wesolek; Staff 15 (MLS 1, Non-MLS 14)
Founded 1928. Pop 46,312; Circ 92,207
Jan 1999-Dec 1999 Income (Main Library and Branch Library) $285,000, State $57,000, City $106,000, County $5,000, Locally Generated Income $111,500, Other $117,000. Mats Exp $53,400, Books $42,300, Per/Ser (Incl. Access Fees) $3,500, AV Equip $4,500, Electronic Ref Mat (Incl. Access Fees) $3,100. Sal $143,000
Library Holdings: Bk Vols 58,992; Bk Titles 56,745; Per Subs 36; High Interest/Low Vocabulary Bk Vols 134
Subject Interests: Am hist, Careers, Cookbks, Large print, Local history, Westerns
Automation Activity & Vendor Info: (Circulation) Athena; (OPAC) Athena
Database Vendor: Ebsco - EbscoHost
Publications: Library Newsletter
Mem of Westmoreland County Libr Syst
Partic in Access Pa; Monessen District Libr Ctr; Share Westmoreland Consortium
Branches: 1
BURRELL, 3052 Wachter Ave, Lower Burrell, 15068-2594. SAN 358-7401. Tel: 412-339-1565. *Librn*, Denise Thompson
Library Holdings: Bk Vols 29,583

NEW MILFORD

P PRATT MEMORIAL LIBRARY, Main St, PO Box 407, 18834. SAN 314-8157. Tel: 570-465-3098. E-Mail: prattml@nep.net. *Librn*, Betty Mitchell
Pop 2,400; Circ 7,400
Library Holdings: Bk Vols 6,000; Per Subs 15
Mem of Pocono District Libr Ctr
Open Mon 2-5, Wed 2-7, Fri 6:30-8:30 & Sat 2-5

NEW OXFORD

P NEW OXFORD AREA LIBRARY,* 122 N Peter St, 17350-1229. SAN 324-5764. Tel: 717-624-2182. FAX: 717-624-1358. *Coordr*, Wilma Krepps
Founded 1983. Pop 3,000; Circ 12,000
Library Holdings: Bk Titles 12,500; Per Subs 13
Mem of Adams County Library System
Open Mon & Wed 2-8pm & Tues, Thurs & Sat 10am-2pm
Friends of the Library Group

NEW WILMINGTON

C WESTMINSTER COLLEGE, McGill Library, 16172-0001. SAN 358-7436. Tel: 724-946-7330. FAX: 724-946-6220. Web Site: www.westminster.edu/library. *Dir*, Molly P Spinney; E-Mail: mspinney@westminster.edu; *Ref*, Dorita F Bolger; Staff 4 (MLS 4)
Founded 1852. Enrl 1,350; Fac 100; Highest Degree: Master
Library Holdings: Bk Vols 240,000; Bk Titles 222,425; Per Subs 864
Special Collections: Autographed Books; Bibles in Foreign Languages; James Fenimore Cooper, early eds
Automation Activity & Vendor Info: (Cataloging) DRA; (Circulation) DRA
Database Vendor: DRA
Publications: Friends of the Library Newsletter
Partic in Dialog Corporation; OCLC Online Computer Library Center, Inc; Pittsburgh Regional Libr Consortium
Open Mon-Thurs 8am-11pm, Fri 8am-9pm, Sat 9-5 & Sun 1-11pm
Friends of the Library Group

NEWFOUNDLAND

P NEWFOUNDLAND AREA PUBLIC LIBRARY,* Main St, PO Box 214, 18445. SAN 314-8165. Tel: 570-676-4518. *Pres*, Jean Haushussler; *Dir*, Jean Pensyl
Pop 2,800; Circ 4,394
Library Holdings: Bk Vols 13,000; Per Subs 15

NEWPORT

P NEWPORT PUBLIC LIBRARY, 316 N Fourth St, 17074-1203. SAN 314-8173. Tel: 717-567-6860. FAX: 717-567-3373. E-Mail: nppublib@pa.net. Web Site: www.newportpubliclibrary.org. *Librn*, Marjorie McKensie; *Asst Librn*, Jeanne Heicher; Staff 2 (Non-MLS 2)
Founded 1914. Pop 10,400; Circ 40,619
Jan 1999-Dec 1999 Income $76,336, State $17,400, Locally Generated Income $54,536, Other $4,400. Mats Exp $11,300, Books $9,000, Per/Ser (Incl. Access Fees) $800, AV Equip $1,500. Sal $29,500
Library Holdings: Bk Vols 26,000; Per Subs 30
Automation Activity & Vendor Info: (Cataloging) Sagebrush Corporation; (Circulation) Sagebrush Corporation
Mem of Harrisburg District Libr Ctr
Open Mon & Wed 1-8, Tues & Thurs 10-5, Fri 1-5 & Sat 10-12
Friends of the Library Group

S PERRY HISTORIANS LIBRARY, PO Box 73, 17074-0073. SAN 371-8336. Tel: 717-582-4896. *Librn*, Jim Kapp
Founded 1976
Library Holdings: Bk Vols 5,000
Subject Interests: Genealogy, Local history
Publications: The Airy View; The Perry Review

NEWTOWN

J BUCKS COUNTY COMMUNITY COLLEGE LIBRARY,* 18940-0999. SAN 314-8181. Tel: 215-968-8009. FAX: 215-968-8005. Web Site: www.bucks.edu/library/library.html.; Staff 28 (MLS 7, Non-MLS 21)
Founded 1965. Enrl 5,290
Jul 1997-Jun 1998 Income $1,332,302. Mats Exp $161,382, Books $83,178, Per/Ser (Incl. Access Fees) $61,704, Presv $3,500, Micro $13,000. Sal $1,049,363 (Prof $400,472)
Library Holdings: Bk Vols 177,512; Per Subs 652
Subject Interests: County bus, Nat trade data base, US census
Special Collections: Bucks County History; College History
Partic in OCLC Online Computer Library Center, Inc; PALINET & Union Library Catalogue of Pennsylvania; Tri-State College Library Cooperative (TCLC)
Special Services for the Blind - VisualTek closed circuit TV reading aid
Friends of the Library Group

S LOCKHEED MARTIN, Communication & Power Center, 100 Campus Dr, STB, 1st flr, 18940. SAN 351-3122. Tel: 215-497-1100 497-4031. FAX: 215-497-2811. *Senior Librn*, Halina Kan; E-Mail: halina.s.kan@lmco.com
Founded 1959
Library Holdings: Bk Vols 242,235; Bk Titles 5,000; Per Subs 1,259
Subject Interests: Electronics, Space science
Special Collections: NASA Coll
Mem of NJ Regional Libr Coop
Partic in Aerospace Res Info Network; Dialog Corporation; Dow Jones News Retrieval

S NEWTOWN HISTORIC ASSOCIATION, INC, Research Facility Library, Court & Centre Ave, PO Box 303, 18940. SAN 326-4289. Tel: 215-968-4004. E-Mail: dcnhh@aol.com. Web Site: www.twp.newtown.pa.us/historic/nha.html. *Librn*, Mary Kester; Tel: 215-968-2317; Staff 11 (MLS 5, Non-MLS 6)
Founded 1983
Apr 1998-Mar 1999 Income $3,908. Mats Exp $3,908, Per/Ser (Incl. Access Fees) $50, Other Print Mats $100
Library Holdings: Bk Vols 950
Special Collections: Hicks Family (Edward Hicks Coll); New Century Club, records 1890-present; Newtown (Barnsley Coll), orig docs, clippings; Newtown Records of Local Insurance Company 1831-1989; People & Places in Early Newtown, pictures & postcards; Reliance Company, records
Publications: Newsletter
Function: Reference only
Open Tues 9am-2pm & Thurs 7-9pm
Friends of the Library Group

S NEWTOWN LIBRARY CO, 114 Centre Ave, 18940. SAN 314-8203. Tel: 215-968-7659. *Librn*, Dorothy S Fitzgerald; *Asst Librn*, Kathleen Shaw; Staff 2 (MLS 1, Non-MLS 1)
Founded 1760
Nov 1998-Oct 1999 Income Locally Generated Income $15,000. Mats Exp $4,184, Books $1,584, Per/Ser (Incl. Access Fees) $500, Manuscripts & Archives $2,000. Sal $400
Library Holdings: Bk Vols 40,000; Bk Titles 45,000; Per Subs 40
Special Collections: Civil War; Old Books for Children (19th Century); Pa & Local Area Coll; Revolutionary War Coll
Publications: Newtown Borough Council; Newtown Library Under Two Kings; Newtown's First Library Building
Open Mon & Fri 10-12, 3-5 & 7-9, Wed 9-11:30, 3-5 & 7-9, Sat 10-12

NEWTOWN SQUARE

S ARCO CHEMICAL CO, Business & Technical Information Center,* 3801 W Chester Pike, 19073. SAN 314-5441. Tel: 610-359-2909. FAX: 610-359-6025. E-Mail: cnssxd@arcochem.com.
Founded 1920
Library Holdings: Bk Vols 25,000; Per Subs 400
Subject Interests: Bus, Chemical industry, Chemistry, Engineering, Environ health, Petrochemicals, Polymer chemistry, Polymers, Sci
Publications: Library Bulletin
Partic in OCLC Online Computer Library Center, Inc; PALINET & Union Library Catalogue of Pennsylvania

P NEWTOWN PUBLIC LIBRARY,* 3544 W Chester Pike, 19073-4176. SAN 314-8211. Tel: 610-353-1022. FAX: 610-353-2611. E-Mail: newtown@delco.lib.pa.us. *Dir*, Jeri L Cain; *Asst Librn*, Helen VanValkenburg; *ILL*, Susan Knorr; Staff 3 (MLS 1, Non-MLS 2)
Founded 1974. Pop 11,940; Circ 56,000
Library Holdings: Bk Vols 41,121; Per Subs 86
Special Collections: Nedurian Law Shelf
Mem of Delaware County Library System
Friends of the Library Group

NEWVILLE

P JOHN GRAHAM PUBLIC LIBRARY,* 9 Parsonage St, 17241-1399. SAN 314-822X. Tel: 717-776-5900. FAX: 717-776-4408. E-Mail: grahampl@co.cumberland.pa.us. Web Site: www.ccpa.net. *Librn*, Sallyann M Smith; Staff 6 (Non-MLS 6)
Founded 1960. Pop 10,306; Circ 53,350
Jan 2000-Dec 2000 Income (Main Library Only) $98,000, State $14,000, County $52,000, Parent Institution $20,000, Other $12,000. Mats Exp $20,500, Books $18,000, Per/Ser (Incl. Access Fees) $500, AV Equip $2,000. Sal $48,000 (Prof $20,000)
Library Holdings: Bk Titles 20,904; Per Subs 78
Subject Interests: Genealogy, Pennsylvania, Religion
Automation Activity & Vendor Info: (Cataloging) epixtech, inc.; (Circulation) epixtech, inc.; (OPAC) epixtech, inc.
Database Vendor: Ebsco - EbscoHost, epixtech, inc.
Mem of Cumberland County Library System; Harrisburg District Libr Ctr
Friends of the Library Group

NORRISTOWN

S DAY & ZIMMERMANN INFORMATION SOLUTIONS,* 1010 Adams Ave, 19403. SAN 370-8640. Tel: 610-650-6250. FAX: 610-650-6234. *Librn*, Candace Jenner
Library Holdings: Bk Vols 500; Per Subs 75

GL LAW LIBRARY OF MONTGOMERY COUNTY, Court House, PO Box 311, 19404-0311. SAN 314-8254. Tel: 610-278-3806. FAX: 610-278-5998. *Librn*, Arthur S Zanan; Tel: 610-278-3805, E-Mail: azanan@mail.montcopa.org; *Asst Librn*, Bruce S Piscadlo; E-Mail: bpiscadl@mail.montcopa.org; *Tech Servs*, Doreen Kopycinski; E-Mail: dkopycin@mail.montcopa.org
Founded 1869
Jan 2000-Dec 2000 Income $524,000, County $460,000, Locally Generated Income $64,000. Mats Exp $436,000, Books $430,000, Presv $6,000. Sal $174,200 (Prof $130,000)
Library Holdings: Bk Vols 66,500; Per Subs 100
Partic in Westlaw

S MONTGOMERY COUNTY PLANNING COMMISSION LIBRARY,* PO Box 311, 19404-0311. SAN 314-8262. Tel: 610-278-3722. FAX: 610-278-3941. *Admin Assoc*, William T Morgan
Founded 1950
Library Holdings: Per Subs 30
Subject Interests: Environmental studies, Housing, Land use, Landscape architecture, Parks, Recreation, Transportation planning
Special Collections: 1980 Census of Population & Housing (Computer; 1990 Census; Printouts); Subdivision Files: Maps & Correspondence, micro & flm
Open Mon-Fri 8:30-4:15

P MONTGOMERY COUNTY-NORRISTOWN PUBLIC LIBRARY,* 1001 Powell St, 19401-3817. SAN 358-7495. Tel: 610-278-5100. Interlibrary Loan Service FAX: 610-278-5110. E-Mail: montpublib@shrsys.hslc.org. *Exec Dir*, Laurie Tynan; *Tech Servs*, Beth Slating; *Pub Relations*, Nancy Mack; *Coll Develop, Ref*, Loretta Righter; *Exten Serv*, Alan Reider; *Circ*, Asha Verma; *ILL*, Dorothy Griffith; *Media Spec*, Paul Bronson; Staff 18 (MLS 18)
Founded 1794. Pop 678,111
Library Holdings: Bk Vols 485,632; Per Subs 811
Subject Interests: Pa hist
Special Collections: Carolyn Wicker Field Coll (autographed children's books & correspondence from children's authors & illustrations); Old Fiction (before 1969-closed bookstacks); Pennsylvania (Steinbright Local History)
Partic in Interlibrary Delivery Service of Pennsylvania; OCLC Online Computer Library Center, Inc; Pa Area Libr Network
Special Services for the Deaf - Books on deafness & sign language; High interest/low vocabulary books; Special interest periodicals
Friends of the Library Group
Branches: 4
CONSHOHOCKEN FREE BRANCH, 301 Fayette St, Conshohocken, 19428. SAN 358-7525. Tel: 610-825-1656. *Librn*, Andrea Philo
Library Holdings: Bk Vols 21,500
Friends of the Library Group
PERKIOMEN VALLEY, Second & Church Sts, Schwenksville, 19473. SAN 376-8074. Tel: 610-287-8360. *Librn*, Dolores Drobile
Friends of the Library Group
ROYERSFORD PUBLIC, 200 S Fourth St, Royersford, 19468. SAN 375-4758. Tel: 610-948-7277. *Librn*, Marilyn Duffy
Library Holdings: Bk Vols 25,000
Friends of the Library Group
UPPER PERKIOMEN VALLEY, 350 Main St, Red Hill, 18076. SAN 358-755X. Tel: 215-679-2020. *Librn*, Carolyn Wiker
Library Holdings: Bk Vols 25,000
Friends of the Library Group
Bookmobiles: 2

M MONTGOMERY HOSPITAL, Medical Library, 1301 Powell St, 19404. SAN 324-4946. Tel: 610-270-2232. *Librn*, Margaret Almon; Staff 1 (MLS 1)
Founded 1978
Library Holdings: Bk Titles 2,200; Per Subs 108
Subject Interests: Family practice
Partic in BHSL; DEVIC

NORRISTOWN STATE HOSPITAL
S NOYES MEMORIAL LIBRARY, 1001 Sterigere St, 19401. SAN 358-7614. Tel: 610-313-5369. FAX: 610-313-5370. *Librn*, Elizabeth Sorg
Founded 1955. Pop 565
Jul 1997-Jun 1998 Income $57,853. Mats Exp $16,279. Sal $41,185
Library Holdings: Bk Vols 9,000; Per Subs 99

M PROFESSIONAL STAFF LIBRARY SYSTEM, Professional Staff Library, Bldg 11, 1001 Sterigere St, 19401. SAN 358-7584. Tel: 610-313-5369, 610-313-5637. FAX: 610-313-5370. E-Mail: nshstaff@hslc.org. *Dir*, Betsy Sorg
Founded 1975. Pop 1,200
Jul 1999-Jun 2000 Income Parent Institution $101,000. Mats Exp $21,938, Books $1,921, Per/Ser (Incl. Access Fees) $19,541, Electronic Ref Mat (Incl. Access Fees) $476
Library Holdings: Bk Vols 9,136; Per Subs 100
Subject Interests: Alcoholism, Drug abuse, Geriatrics-gerontology, Hort therapy, Music, Nutrition-diet therapy, Occupational therapies, Pastoral psych-counseling, Pharmacology-psychopharmacology, Psychiat nursing, Psychiat soc works, Psychiat-neurology, Psychotherapy-psychoanalysis, Recreational
Special Collections: 19th Century Psychiatric Journals & Annual Reports NSH-Archives
Partic in DEVIC; Nat Network of Librs of Med, S Cent Res Libr Coun; OCLC Online Computer Library Center, Inc

P RESEARCH & INFORMATION SERVICES FOR EDUCATION, RISE-MCIU Library, 1605-B W Main St, 19403-3290. SAN 326-9280. Tel: 610-630-7905. FAX: 610-630-7950. *Dir*, Richard R Brickley
Library Holdings: Per Subs 250

NORTH EAST

S LAKE SHORE RAILWAY HISTORICAL SOCIETY MUSEUM & LIBRARY,* 31 Wall St (at Robinson St), PO Box 571, 16428-0571. SAN 326-6206. Tel: 814-825-2724. E-Mail: lakeshorerwy@juno.com. *Dir*, Jim Caldwell
Jan 1998-Dec 1999 Income $75. Mats Exp $75, Per/Ser (Incl. Access Fees) $50, Presv $25
Library Holdings: Bk Titles 1,000; Per Subs 40
Special Collections: Locomotive Builder's Photogs (General Electric Co) film negs; Locomotive Builder's Photogs (Heisler Locomotive Works) glass plate, film negs
Restriction: By appointment only

P MCCORD MEMORIAL LIBRARY, 32 W Main St, 16428-1136. (Mail add: PO Box 427, 16428-0427), SAN 314-8319. Tel: 814-725-4057. FAX: 814-725-3142. E-Mail: mccord.lib@juno.com. Web Site: www.mccordlibrary.org. *Dir*, Sandra O'Niell; Staff 5 (MLS 1, Non-MLS 4)
Founded 1899. Pop 10,900; Circ 65,000
Jan 1999-Dec 1999 Income $122,511, State $15,293, City $35,281, County $31,000, Locally Generated Income $32,750, Other $8,187. Mats Exp $28,427, Books $26,816, Per/Ser (Incl. Access Fees) $1,611. Sal $81,000 (Prof $25,000)
Library Holdings: Bk Vols 32,000; Per Subs 70
Subject Interests: Agriculture, Local history
Automation Activity & Vendor Info: (Cataloging) TLC; (Circulation) TLC; (OPAC) TLC
Friends of the Library Group

NORTH VERSAILLES

P NORTH VERSAILLES PUBLIC LIBRARY,* 1401 Greensburg Ave, 15137. SAN 314-8270. Tel: 412-823-2222. FAX: 412-823-2012. Web Site: www.einpgh.org/ein/nversals/. *Dir*, Eleanor Lowden; Staff 1 (Non-MLS 1)
Founded 1974. Pop 12,302; Circ 23,450
1998-1999 Income $53,000, State $9,000, City $15,000, County $29,000. Mats Exp $13,000
Library Holdings: Bk Vols 18,000; Bk Titles 16,000; Per Subs 20
Mem of Carnegie Libr Syst of Pittsburgh
Friends of the Library Group

NORTH WALES

P NORTH WALES MEMORIAL FREE LIBRARY, 201 Summit St, 19454-3298. SAN 314-8297. Tel: 215-699-5410. *Librn*, Dorothy Rorer
Pop 4,400; Circ 41,000
Library Holdings: Bk Vols 40,000; Per Subs 20
Open Mon-Fri 1-5 & 7-9

NORTHAMPTON

P NORTHHAMPTON AREA PUBLIC LIBRARY, 1615 Laubach Ave, 18067-1597. SAN 358-7673. Tel: 610-262-7537. FAX: 610-262-4356. Web Site: www.northampton.k12.pa.us/pub.library.htm. *Librn*, Mary Beller; *Ch Servs*, Nancy Mumma; Staff 2 (MLS 2)
Founded 1965. Pop 36,241; Circ 99,727
Jul 1999-Jun 2000 Income $434,037, State $100,482, City $213,157, Locally Generated Income $56,097, Other $64,301. Mats Exp $67,500, Books $60,000, Per/Ser (Incl. Access Fees) $3,000, Presv $2,500, Electronic Ref Mat (Incl. Access Fees) $2,000. Sal $194,046 (Prof $40,000)
Library Holdings: Bk Vols 60,000; Bk Titles 54,320; Per Subs 110
Subject Interests: Local history
Automation Activity & Vendor Info: (Cataloging) TLC; (Circulation) TLC (Course Reserve) TLC
Database Vendor: Ebsco - EbscoHost

NORTHUMBERLAND

P PRIESTLEY FORSYTH MEMORIAL LIBRARY, 100 King St, 17857-1670. SAN 314-8327. Tel: 570-473-8201. FAX: 570-473-8807. E-Mail: pfml@ptd.net. Web Site: www.priestleyforsyth.org. *Librn*, Barbara Bish; Staff 5 (Non-MLS 5)
Founded 1926. Pop 7,400; Circ 42,000
Library Holdings: Bk Vols 25,000; Per Subs 100
Subject Interests: Local history
Special Collections: Joseph Priestley
Automation Activity & Vendor Info: (Circulation) ComPanion Corp
Mem of Williamsport District Libr Ctr

NORWOOD

P NORWOOD PUBLIC LIBRARY, 513 Welcome Ave, 19074-1425. SAN 314-8335. Tel: 610-534-0693. FAX: 610-532-8785. E-Mail: norwoodlib@delco.lib.pa.us. *Dir*, Jane Lloyd
Founded 1938. Pop 6,162; Circ 25,698
Library Holdings: Bk Vols 17,125; Per Subs 41
Mem of Delaware County Library System
Open Mon-Thurs 11-8:30 & Sat 9-4

OAKDALE

J PITTSBURGH TECHNICAL INSTITUTE, Student Resource Center, 1111 McKee Rd, 15071. SAN 315-0976. Tel: 412-809-5100. FAX: 412-809-5219. *Pres*, J R McCartan; *Dir*, Ruth Walter
Library Holdings: Bk Vols 1,900; Per Subs 99

P WESTERN ALLEGHENY COMMUNITY LIBRARY, 8042 Steubenville Pike, 15071-9375. SAN 370-730X. Tel: 724-695-8150. FAX: 724-695-2860. E-Mail: westallegheny@einwork.net. Web Site: www.clpgh.org/ein/wallegny/. *Dir*, Marianne A Sforza; E-Mail: sforzam@einwork.com; *Ch Servs*, Nancy Howell; E-Mail: howelln@einwork.net; *YA Servs*, Joan Trautman; Staff 9 (MLS 2, Non-MLS 7)
Founded 1990. Pop 16,000; Circ 59,368
Jan 1999-Dec 1999 Income $184,783, State $16,627, County $53,476, Locally Generated Income $114,680. Mats Exp $27,402, Books $23,980, Per/Ser (Incl. Access Fees) $2,817, AV Equip $500, Electronic Ref Mat (Incl. Access Fees) $105. Sal $94,304 (Prof $62,730)
Library Holdings: Bk Vols 22,396; Bk Titles 19,381; Per Subs 70
Automation Activity & Vendor Info: (Cataloging) DRA; (Circulation) DRA
Database Vendor: DRA, GaleNet, IAC - Info Trac, IAC - SearchBank, Innovative Interfaces INN - View
Partic in Allegheny County Libr Asn; Allegheny County Pub Librs Electronic Info Network; Electronic Info Network
Friends of the Library Group

OAKMONT

P OAKMONT CARNEGIE LIBRARY, 700 Allegheny River Blvd, 15139. SAN 314-8343. Tel: 412-828-9532. FAX: 412-828-5979. Web Site: www.einpgh.org/ein/oakmont. *Dir*, Janice H Beiber; E-Mail: beiberj@clp2.clpgh.org; Staff 6 (Non-MLS 6)
Founded 1901. Pop 6,961; Circ 71,961
Jan 1999-Nov 1999 Income $152,738, State $23,627, City $75,505, County $35,986, Locally Generated Income $17,620. Mats Exp $26,974, Books $21,160, Per/Ser (Incl. Access Fees) $3,427, AV Equip $2,189, Electronic Ref Mat (Incl. Access Fees) $198. Sal $74,975
Library Holdings: Bk Titles 24,755; Per Subs 90
Special Collections: Local Newspaper (Advance Leader 1917-1945), micro; local photography archive
Automation Activity & Vendor Info: (Cataloging) DRA; (Circulation) DRA; (OPAC) DRA
Database Vendor: Ebsco - EbscoHost, GaleNet, IAC - Info Trac
Friends of the Library Group

IL CITY

CLARION UNIVERSITY OF PENNSYLVANIA, Venango Campus Library, 1801 W First St, 16301. SAN 314-836X. Tel: 814-676-6591, Ext 1242. FAX: 814-676-6591. Web Site: www.clarion.edu/library/homepage.htm. *Coordr*, Rich Snow; E-Mail: snow@vaxa.clarion.edu; *Assoc Librn*, Nancy Clemente; Staff 2 (MLS 2)
Founded 1961. Enrl 653; Highest Degree: Master
Library Holdings: Per Subs 189
Subject Interests: Bus, Habilitative servs, Mgt, Nursing, Occupational therapy, Paralegal
Automation Activity & Vendor Info: (Acquisitions) Endeavor; (Cataloging) Endeavor; (Circulation) Endeavor; (Course Reserve) Endeavor; (ILL) Endeavor; (Media Booking) Endeavor; (Serials) Endeavor
Partic in Erie Area Health Information Library Cooperative; Interlibrary Delivery Service of Pennsylvania; PALINET & Union Library Catalogue of Pennsylvania

OIL CITY LIBRARY, 2 Central Ave, 16301-2795. SAN 314-8378. Tel: 814-678-3072. FAX: 814-676-8028. E-Mail: ocensle@csonline.net. Web Site: www.csonline.net/oclibrary. *Dir*, Kay E Ensle; Tel: 814-678-3071; *Ch Servs*, Sandee Lalley; *ILL*, Deborah Wilson; Staff 2 (MLS 2)
Founded 1904. Pop 16,001; Circ 163,535
Jan 1999-Dec 1999 Income (Main Library Only) $401,420, State $37,000, City $280,985, Locally Generated Income $83,435. Mats Exp $71,150, Books $61,000, Per/Ser (Incl. Access Fees) $9,100, Presv $1,000, AV Equip $50. Sal $179,020
Library Holdings: Bk Vols 93,997; Per Subs 250
Subject Interests: Hist of oil
Special Collections: Genealogy (Selden Coll)
Automation Activity & Vendor Info: (Cataloging) epixtech, inc.; (Circulation) epixtech, inc.; (OPAC) epixtech, inc.
Mem of Oil Creek District Library Center
Partic in Access Pa
Friends of the Library Group

OIL CREEK DISTRICT LIBRARY CENTER, 2 Central Ave, 16301. SAN 321-2416. Tel: 814-678-3054. FAX: 814-676-0359. E-Mail: oclibrary@csonline.net. *Adminr*, Kay E Ensle; Tel: 814-678-3071, Fax: 814-678-8028, E-Mail: ocensle@csonline.net; Staff 3 (MLS 2, Non-MLS 1)
Founded 1995. Pop 147,163
Jul 1999-Jun 2000 Income $105,465, State $102,352, Locally Generated Income $2,993, Other $120. Mats Exp Books $2,680. Sal $50,000 (Prof $25,971)
Special Collections: Professional Coll, V-tape, bks on tape
Member Libraries: Cooperstown Public Library; Eccles-Lesher Memorial Library; Foxburg Free Library; Franklin Public Library; Knox Public Library; Mengle Memorial Library; New Bethlehem Area Free Public Library; Oil City Library; Punxsutawney Memorial Library; Rebecca M Arthurs Memorial Library; Reynoldsville Public Library; Summerville Public Library; Sykesville Public Library
Partic in PALINET & Union Library Catalogue of Pennsylvania

ORWIGSBURG

P ORWIGSBURG AREA FREE PUBLIC LIBRARY,* 115 E Tammany St, 17961-1904. SAN 320-5061. Tel: 717-366-1638. *Librn*, Joyce Stripe; Staff 1 (Non-MLS 1)
Founded 1978. Pop 12,000; Circ 14,640
Library Holdings: Bk Vols 9,336; Per Subs 31
Mem of Pottsville Free Public Library

OXFORD

P OXFORD PUBLIC LIBRARY, 48 Second St, 19363. SAN 314-8394. Tel: 610-932-9625. FAX: 610-932-9251. *Dir*, Susan Waggoner
Founded 1784. Pop 13,000; Circ 49,000
1998-1999 Income $120,000. Mats Exp $24,700, Books $18,500, Per/Ser (Incl. Access Fees) $2,800. Sal $76,000 (Prof $28,000)
Library Holdings: Bk Vols 28,000; Per Subs 90
Special Collections: Local History (Holcombe Coll)
Mem of Chester County Library
Friends of the Library Group

PALMERTON

P PALMERTON LIBRARY ASSOCIATION, 402 Delaware Ave, 18071-1995. SAN 314-8416. Tel: 610-826-3424. FAX: 610-826-6248. E-Mail: amadeus@ptclprolog.net. Web Site: www.palmerton.k12.pa.us. *Librn*, Gerald D Geiger
Founded 1928. Pop 12,300; Circ 37,000
Jan 1999-Dec 1999 Income $152,000, State $18,000, City $8,000, County $1,000, Locally Generated Income $125,000. Mats Exp $20,100, Books $18,000, Per/Ser (Incl. Access Fees) $600, AV Equip $1,500. Sal $68,000 (Prof $18,500)
Library Holdings: Bk Vols 39,000; Per Subs 55
Subject Interests: Local history, Pa hist
Mem of Allentown Dist Libr Syst
Participates in literacy & Institute for Learning in Retirement programs; provides facilities for Lehigh Gap Historical Society; features art exhibits & live classical chamber music programs
Friends of the Library Group

PALMYRA

P PALMYRA PUBLIC LIBRARY, Borough Bldg, 325 S Railroad St, 17078-2449. SAN 314-8424. Tel: 717-838-1347. Web Site: www.leblibrarysys.org. *Ref*, Cynthia Beam; E-Mail: cbeam@leblibrarysys.org; Staff 10 (Non-MLS 10)
Founded 1954. Pop 18,600; Circ 100,000
Jan 1999-Dec 1999 Income $140,000. Mats Exp $13,700, Books $11,500, Per/Ser (Incl. Access Fees) $2,200. Sal $80,000
Library Holdings: Bk Vols 35,000; Per Subs 81
Mem of Harrisburg District Libr Ctr; Lebanon County Library System
Friends of the Library Group

PAOLI

M JEFFERSON HEALTH SYSTEM, PAOLI MEMORIAL HOSPITAL, (PMH), Robert M White Memorial Library, 255 Lancaster Ave, 19301. SAN 314-8467. Tel: 610-648-1570. FAX: 610-648-1551. E-Mail: pmhmedlib@hslc.org. *Dir*, Les Gundry; *Librn*, Lynn Osika; E-Mail: losika@sdln.net
Founded 1970
Library Holdings: Bk Titles 1,100; Per Subs 75
Subject Interests: Allied health, Medicine, Nursing
Publications: News Leaf (monthly)
Partic in BHSL; Consortium For Health Information & Library Services; Delaware Valley Information Consortium; Nat Libr of Med

P PAOLI LIBRARY, 18 Darby Rd, 19301-1416. SAN 314-8459. Tel: 610-296-7996. FAX: 610-296-9708. Web Site: www.ccls.org/othlibs/paoli.htm. *Branch Mgr*, Eleanor Erokine; E-Mail: eerokine@ccls.org; Staff 11 (MLS 1, Non-MLS 10)
Founded 1910. Pop 18,700; Circ 91,298
Jan 1999-Dec 1999 Income $248,200, State $25,929, City $140,832, County $17,046, Locally Generated Income $57,393, Other $7,000. Mats Exp $34,959, Books $24,360, Per/Ser (Incl. Access Fees) $5,534, AV Equip $5,065. Sal $131,548
Library Holdings: Bk Titles 27,876; Per Subs 90
Subject Interests: Local history
Automation Activity & Vendor Info: (Circulation) Innovative Interfaces Inc.; (OPAC) Innovative Interfaces Inc.
Mem of Chester County Library
Friends of the Library Group

PARKESBURG

P PARKESBURG FREE LIBRARY, 105 West St, 19365-1499. SAN 314-8475. Tel: 610-857-5165. FAX: 610-857-1193. Web Site: www.ccls.org. *Librn*, Celeste Reiffer; Staff 5 (MLS 4, Non-MLS 1)
Founded 1916. Pop 2,971; Circ 62,608
Library Holdings: Bk Vols 26,000; Per Subs 52
Special Collections: Local Historical Files
Mem of Chester County Library
Open Mon-Thurs 12-8, Fri 12-5, Sat 9-1

PATTON

P PATTON PUBLIC LIBRARY,* 404 Magee Ave, 16668-1210. SAN 314-8483. Tel: 814-674-8231. E-Mail: pappublib@aol.com, pappublib@soundcity.net. *Librn*, Monica Rohac
Founded 1962. Pop 2,441; Circ 12,322
Library Holdings: Bk Vols 10,000; Per Subs 21
Mem of Cambria County Library System & District Center
Open Mon-Tues 1-5 & 6-8:30 & Wed-Thurs 1-5 & 6-8

PECKVILLE

P INTERBORO UNITED DISTRICTS LIBRARY ASSOCIATION, (IBUD), Interboro Public Library, 802 Main St, 18452. SAN 328-0578. Tel: 717-489-1765. FAX: 717-383-9657. E-Mail: intadmin@albright.org. Web Site: www.albright.org, www.scranton.web.com/interboro. *Dir*, Mary Barna; Fax: 570-383-9652; Staff 7 (MLS 1, Non-MLS 6)
Founded 1985. Pop 33,000; Circ 71,313
Jan 1999-Dec 1999 Income $166,000. Mats Exp $165,000
Library Holdings: Bk Titles 21,000; Per Subs 45
Subject Interests: Lackawana County hist, Local history
Mem of Lackawanna County Library System
Open Mon, Fri & Sat 10-5, Tues-Thurs 10-8
Friends of the Library Group

M MID-VALLEY HOSPITAL, Physician's Library,* 1400 Main St, 18452. SAN 324-6221. Tel: 717-489-7546, Ext 5635. FAX: 717-383-5504.
Library Holdings: Bk Titles 860

PENN VALLEY

SR HAR ZION TEMPLE, Ida & Matthew Rudofker Library, 1500 Hagys Ford Rd, 19072. SAN 327-8662. Tel: 610-667-5000. FAX: 610-667-2032. *Asst Librn*, Anne Stein
Library Holdings: Bk Vols 9,000; Per Subs 23
Open Mon-Thurs 3:30-6 & Sun 9-1

PENNSBURG

P SCHWENKFELDER LIBRARY & HERITAGE CENTER, 105 Seminary St, 18073. SAN 314-8491. Tel: 215-679-3103. FAX: 215-679-8175. E-Mail: schwenkfeld@netcarrier.com. Web Site: www.schwenkfelder.com. *Exec Dir*, David W Luz; *Assoc Dir*, Peter C Erb; Staff 3 (Non-MLS 3)
Founded 1884
Apr 1999-Mar 2000 Mats Exp $193,000
Library Holdings: Bk Titles 25,000
Subject Interests: History
Special Collections: Montgomery County History, bks, mss; Reformation; Schwenkfelder History & Theology, bks, mss; Silesean History
Restriction: Open to public for reference only
Function: Archival collection, Research library
Friends of the Library Group

PERKASIE

SR TRINITY EVANGELICAL LUTHERAN CHURCH, Library & Media Center,* 19 S Fifth St, 18944. SAN 328-4530. Tel: 215-257-6801. FAX: 215-257-1025. E-Mail: snyderlib@erols.com. *Librn*, Charles Snyder
Jan 1998-Dec 1999 Income $700, Parent Institution $250, Other $450. Mats Exp $259
Library Holdings: Bk Titles 7,200
Special Collections: Children (gen & relig)
Publications: AV Catalog (periodically); Monthly Reviews-new material in church newsletter Trinity Chimes
Friends of the Library Group

PERKIOMENVILLE

S NATIONAL ASSOCIATION OF CHILDBEARING CENTERS LIBRARY,* 3123 Gottschall Rd, 18074-9604. SAN 326-7385. Tel: 215-234-8068. FAX: 215-234-8829. *Librn*, Kate Baur; Staff 2 (MLS 2)
Library Holdings: Bk Titles 1,000; Per Subs 25
Special Collections: Birth Centers; CBCN News Coll; NACC News Coll, doc bd & newsletters
Publications: Maternity Care in Ferment; NACC News; Policies & Procedures Manual; Public Information Flyer; Quality Assurance Manual; Workshop Manual

PERRYOPOLIS

P MARY FULLER FRAZIER MEMORIAL SCHOOL & COMMUNITY LIBRARY,* 403 W Constitution St, 15473-9310. SAN 314-8513. Tel: 724-736-8480. *In Charge*, Valerie Madorma; Staff 2 (MLS 2)
Founded 1960. Pop 2,500; Circ 18,000
Library Holdings: Bk Vols 20,000; Bk Titles 15,000; Per Subs 44
Subject Interests: Fayette County hist

PHILADELPHIA

S ACADEMY OF NATURAL SCIENCES OF PHILADELPHIA, Ewell Sale Stewart Library, 1900 Benjamin Franklin Pkwy, 19103-1195. SAN 314-8521. Tel: 215-299-1040. Interlibrary Loan Service Tel: 215-299-1063. Reference Tel: 215-299-1140. FAX: 215-299-1144. E-Mail: library@acnatsci.org. Web Site: www.acnatsci.org/library. *Dir*, C Danial Elliott; Tel: 215-299-1041, E-Mail: elliott@acnatsci.org; *Ref*, Eileen Mathias; Tel: 215-299-1140, E-Mail: mathias@acnatsci.org; *Archivist*, Carol M Spawn; Tel: 215-299-1093, E-Mail: spawn@acnatsci.org; *Cat*, Lorena Boylan; Tel: 215-299-1145, E-Mail: boylan@acnatsci.org
Founded 1812
Library Holdings: Bk Vols 200,000; Bk Titles 58,000; Per Subs 2,500
Subject Interests: Botany, Entomology, Environ res, Evolution, Expeditions, Exploration, History of science, Limnology, Malacology, Ornithology, Systematic biology, Zoology
Special Collections: Entomology (Library of the American Entomological Society); Manuscripts (Academy History and Archives); Photograph Coll; Portrait & Drawing Coll; Pre-Linnaean Coll
Automation Activity & Vendor Info: (Acquisitions) Innovative Interfaces Inc.; (Cataloging) Innovative Interfaces Inc.; (OPAC) Innovative Interfaces Inc.
Publications: Guide to microfilm publication of Academy minutes & correspondence; Guide to the Manuscripts Collections of ANSP; Library Catalog; Serial Titles; Wolf Room Rare Book Collection Checklist
Partic in OCLC Online Computer Library Center, Inc; PALINET & Union Library Catalogue of Pennsylvania; Philadelphia Area Consortium Of Special Collections Libraries
Friends of the Library Group

P AIDS INFORMATION NETWORK, AIDS Library, 1233 Locust St, 2nd Flr, 19107. SAN 370-7601. Tel: 215-985-4851. TDD: 215-985-0458. FAX: 215-985-4492. E-Mail: library@aidsllibrary.org. Web Site: www.aidslibrary.org. *Tech Servs*, Allie Fraser; *Publ Servs*, Jenny Pierce; Sta 2 (MLS 2)
Founded 1987. Pop 5,000,000; Circ 10,000
Library Holdings: Bk Vols 5,423; Bk Titles 2,710; Per Subs 131
Special Services for the Deaf - TDD

ALBERT EINSTEIN HEALTHCARE NETWORK

M KORMAN-MOSSREHAB LIBRARY, 5501 Old York Rd, 19141. SAN 37- 7980. Tel: 215-456-5995. FAX: 215-456-5994. E-Mail: library@aehn2.einstein.edu. *Dir Libr Serv*, Lillian Brazin; Tel: 215-456-5882, Fax 215-456-8267, E-Mail: brazinl@aehn2.einstein.edu; *Circ*, Lynette Hills; E-Mail: hillsl@aehn2.einstein.edu. Subject Specialists: *Rehabilitation of the handicapped*, Lynette Hills; *Rehabilitation of the handicapped*, Lillian Brazin; Staff 1 (MLS 1)
Founded 1952
Library Holdings: Bk Vols 2,000; Per Subs 14
Restriction: Open to others by appointment
Function: Research library
Partic in BHSL; DEVIC
Satellite library for Luria Memorial

M LURIA MEDICAL LIBRARY, 5501 Old York Rd, 19141. SAN 358-8068. Tel: 215-456-6345. Reference Tel: 215-456-6346. FAX: 215-456-8267. E-Mail: library@aehn2.einstein.edu. *Dir Libr Serv*, Lillian Brazin; Tel: 215-456-5882, E-Mail: brazinl@aehn2.einstein.edu; *Coordr*, Florence Rosenthal; E-Mail: rosenthf@aehn2.einstein.edu; *Automation Syst Coordr* Davis Kitchen; E-Mail: kitchend@aehn2.einstein.edu. Subject Specialists: *Medicine*, Florence Rosenthal; Staff 4 (MLS 2, Non-MLS 2)
Founded 1963
Library Holdings: Bk Vols 2,000; Bk Titles 1,700; Per Subs 260
Subject Interests: Med admin, Medicine, Nursing
Database Vendor: OVID Technologies
Restriction: Company staff only, Open to others by appointment
Function: Research library
Partic in Basic Health Sciences Library Network; DEVIC

S AMBRIC TESTING & ENGINEERING ASSOCIATES, INC LIBRARY,* 3502 Scotts Lane, 19129. SAN 370-4068. Tel: 215-438-1800. FAX: 215-438-7110. E-Mail: ambric@aol.com. *In Charge*, Dee McNicholas
Library Holdings: Bk Titles 550

S AMERICAN ACADEMY OF POLITICAL & SOCIAL SCIENCE LIBRARY, 3937 Chestnut St, 19104. SAN 372-9133. Tel: 215-386-4594. FAX: 215-386-4630. E-Mail: aapss@netaxs.com. *In Charge*, Alan W Hestor Tel: 215-386-4660
Founded 1889
Library Holdings: Bk Vols 3,500; Per Subs 40

L AMERICAN LAW INSTITUTE LIBRARY, 4025 Chestnut St, 19104. SAN 314-8556. Tel: 215-243-1654. FAX: 215-243-1636. Web Site: www.ali.org/alilibrary.htm. *Librn*, Harry Kyriakodis; Staff 1 (MLS 1)
Founded 1965
Library Holdings: Bk Vols 5,500; Per Subs 100
Subject Interests: Law
Special Collections: ALI publications on microfiche; ALI-ABA materials & periodicals.

S AMERICAN MEDICAL FOUNDATION FOR PEER REVIEW & EDUCATION LIBRARY, The Barclay, 237 S 18th St, Ste 11-D, 19103-6164. SAN 329-4323. Tel: 215-545-6363. FAX: 215-545-2163. E-Mail: info@amf_fame.org. *In Charge*, Jeanette Colacicco
Library Holdings: Bk Vols 400

S AMERICAN PHILOSOPHICAL SOCIETY LIBRARY,* 105 S Fifth St, 19106-3386. SAN 314-8564. Tel: 215-440-3400. FAX: 215-440-3423. E-Mail: 110253@vm.temple.edu. *Librn*, Dr Edward C Carter II; *Curator*, Roy E Goodman; *Cat*, Marian Christ; Staff 15 (MLS 11, Non-MLS 4)
Founded 1743
Library Holdings: Bk Titles 230,000; Per Subs 850
Subject Interests: Am hist to 1840, Clark expedition, Darwin, Electricity, European background, Evolution, Genetics, Hist of sci in Am, Lewis, Modern physics, Quantum, Thomas Paine
Special Collections: American Indian Linguistics (Franz Boas et al); Benjamin Franklin and his Circle; Medical Research (Simon Flexner et al); Stephen Girard Papers, flm
Publications: Annual Report of the Committee on Library
Partic in RLIN
Friends of the Library Group

AMERICAN SWEDISH HISTORICAL MUSEUM LIBRARY, 1900 Pattison Ave, 19145. SAN 314-8580. Tel: 215-389-1776. FAX: 215-389-7701. E-Mail: ashm@libertynet.org. Web Site: www.libertynet.org/ashm. *Exec Dir*, Richard Waldron
Founded 1926
Library Holdings: Bk Titles 5,000; Per Subs 30
Subject Interests: Genealogy, Original correspondence, Scandinavian hist, Swedish hist, Swedish-Am hist
Special Collections: Fredrika Bremer Coll; Jenny Lind Coll; John Ericsson Coll
Publications: Newsletter

ATHENAEUM OF PHILADELPHIA, 219 S Sixth St, East Washington Square, 19106-3794. SAN 314-8610. Tel: 215-925-2688. FAX: 215-925-3755. E-Mail: athena@philaathenaeum.org. Web Site: www.philaathenaeum.org. *Dir*, Roger W Moss; E-Mail: rwross@pobox.upenn.edu; *Asst Dir*, Eileen Magee; E-Mail: magee@philaathenaeum.org; *Circ*, Ellen Rose; E-Mail: erose@philaathenaeum.org; *Archivist*, Bruce Laverty; E-Mail: laverty@philaathenaeum.org; *Cat*, Alison Warner; E-Mail: warner@philaathenaeum.org; *Bibliogr*, Jill LeMin; E-Mail: lemin@libertynet.org; Staff 10 (MLS 6, Non-MLS 4)
Founded 1814
Jul 1999-Jun 2000 Income $1,116,243. Mats Exp $1,077,440
Library Holdings: Bk Vols 75,000
Special Collections: Architectural Drawings (180,000); Architecture & Design, 1814-1940; Historic Photographs (60,000)
Publications: Athenaeum Annotations (quarterly); Catalog of Architectural Drawings
Restriction: Non-circulating to the public
Partic in Philadelphia Area Consortium Of Special Collections Libraries; RLIN
Friends of the Library Group

R AUDIO-VISUAL RESOURCE LIBRARY, Gateson House, 3725 Chestnut St, 19104. SAN 329-2088. Tel: 215-387-6335. FAX: 215-387-5613. *Librn*, R S Snyder
Founded 1965
Library Holdings: Bk Titles 200

S BALCH INSTITUTE FOR ETHNIC STUDIES LIBRARY,* 18 S Seventh St, 19106-2314. SAN 314-8637. Tel: 215-925-8090. FAX: 215-925-4392. E-Mail: balchlib@balchinstitute.org. Web Site: www.libertynet.org/~balch. *Dir*, Maryann Coyle; *Admin Assoc*, Charmaine Willis; *Cat*, Sheila Walker; *Archivist*, Don Davis; *Coll Develop*, Karl Krueger; Staff 3 (MLS 3)
Founded 1971
Library Holdings: Bk Titles 60,000; Per Subs 300
Subject Interests: Ethnicity, N Am immigration hist
Special Collections: Ethnic Heritage Studies Clearing House Coll; Philadelphia Jewish Archives Center at the Balch Institute; Scotch Irish Foundation Coll; St Andrews Society of Philadelphia Coll; Welsh Society of Philadelphia Coll
Publications: Selected List of Newspapers and Manuscript Holdings
Partic in PALINET & Union Library Catalogue of Pennsylvania
Open Tues, Thurs, Sat 10-4

L BALLARD, SPAHR, ANDREWS & INGERSOLL, LLP LIBRARY, 1735 Market St, 51st flr, 19103-7599. SAN 314-8645. Tel: 215-864-8150. FAX: 215-864-8999. *Dir*, David Proctor; E-Mail: proctor@ballardspahr.com; *Automation Syst Coordr, Ref*, David Webster; E-Mail: webster@ballardspahr.com; *Web Coordr*, Eugenie Tyburski; E-Mail: tyburski@ballardspahr.com; Staff 5 (MLS 3, Non-MLS 2)
Library Holdings: Bk Vols 25,000; Per Subs 400
Subject Interests: Law
Partic in PALINET & Union Library Catalogue of Pennsylvania

L BEASLEY, CASEY & ERBSTEIN LIBRARY, 1125 Walnut St, 19107-4997. SAN 372-9095. Tel: 215-592-1000. FAX: 215-592-8360. E-Mail: lawyers@tortlaw.com. Web Site: www.tortlaw.com. *Librn*, Joel Tuckman
Subject Interests: Medicine

C BEREAN INSTITUTE LIBRARY,* 1901 W Girard Ave, 19130. SAN 326-436X. Tel: 215-763-4833. FAX: 215-236-6011. *Librn*, Anita Samuel; Staff 3 (MLS 2, Non-MLS 1)
Founded 1899. Enrl 300; Fac 16
Library Holdings: Bk Vols 5,000; Bk Titles 3,900; Per Subs 27
Special Collections: Ingraham Coll
Publications: List of Acquisitions

S BIO-RAD LABORATORIES, INC, Sadtler Research Laboratories Library, 3316 Spring Garden St, 19104-2596. SAN 314-9951. Tel: 215-382-7800, Ext 7323. FAX: 215-662-0585. *Librn*, Bernadette Steiner
Founded 1966
Library Holdings: Bk Titles 5,000
Subject Interests: Analytical chemistry, Instrumental chem analysis
Special Collections: Spectra for over 250,000 compounds

L BLANK, ROME, COMISKY & MCCAULEY LLP, Law Library, One Logan Square, 18th & Cherry Sts, 19103-2599. SAN 372-2309. Tel: 215-569-5500. FAX: 215-569-5555. Web Site: www.blankrome.com. *Dir*, Manuel Paredes; Tel: 215-569-5490, E-Mail: paredes@blankrome.com; Staff 6 (MLS 3, Non-MLS 3)
Library Holdings: Bk Vols 20,000; Bk Titles 2,500; Per Subs 400
Automation Activity & Vendor Info: (Cataloging) Sydney; (OPAC) Sydney; (Serials) Inmagic, Inc.
Partic in OCLC Online Computer Library Center, Inc
Open Mon-Fri 9-5
Friends of the Library Group

S BOEING PHILADELPHIA, Lydia Rankin Technical Library MS P32-01,* PO Box 16858, 19142-0858. SAN 314-8718. Tel: 610-591-2536. FAX: 610-591-9008. *Librn*, Joan Davis
Founded 1945
Library Holdings: Bk Vols 7,000; Per Subs 100
Subject Interests: Aeronautics, Bus, Helicopters, Mgt
Special Collections: Peterson Coll of Transportation Books

S CENTER FOR FORENSIC ECONOMIC STUDIES, Information Center, 1608 Walnut St, Ste 1200, 19103. SAN 372-9117. Tel: 215-546-5600. Toll Free Tel: 800-966-6099. FAX: 215-732-8158. *Librn*, Kathleen D Baggs; E-Mail: kdewane@comcat.com. Subject Specialists: *Business*, Kathleen D Baggs; *Economics*, Kathleen D Baggs; Staff 1 (MLS 1)
Founded 1987
Library Holdings: Bk Vols 500; Per Subs 140
Database Vendor: Dialog

C CENTER FOR JUDAIC STUDIES LIBRARY, 420 Walnut St, 19106. SAN 314-8939. Tel: 215-238-1290. FAX: 215-238-1540. Web Site: www.library.upenn.edu/cjs. *Curator*, Dr Arthur Kiron; Fax: 215-238-1290, E-Mail: kiron@pobox.upenn.edu; *ILL*, Judith Leifer; E-Mail: leifer@mail.cjs.upenn.edu; *Circ*, Lois Satalof; *Cat*, Tova Sperber; Staff 4 (MLS 1, Non-MLS 3)
Founded 1907
Library Holdings: Bk Vols 180,000
Subject Interests: Biblical studies, Judaica, Near Eastern studies
Special Collections: American-Jewish History, archives; Arabica (Prof Skoss Coll); Bible (Prof Max Margolis Coll); Geniza Fragments; Hebrew Manuscripts; History of Jewish & Oriental Studies; History of Philadelphia; Oriental Manuscripts & Papyri; Poland & Hungary Coll; Rare Printed Judaica; USSR Coll
Publications: The Jewish Quarterly Review
Partic in Dialog Corporation; OCLC Online Computer Library Center, Inc; PALINET & Union Library Catalogue of Pennsylvania; Philadelphia Area Consortium Of Special Collections Libraries; RLIN

C CHESTNUT HILL COLLEGE, Logue Library,* 9601 Germantown Ave, 19118-2695. SAN 314-8769. Tel: 215-248-7050, 215-248-7055. FAX: 215-248-7066. Web Site: www.chc.edu/library.html. *Per*, Celia Frankford; *Circ*, Marian Ehnow; *ILL*, C Consorto; Staff 4 (MLS 4)
Founded 1924. Highest Degree: Doctorate
Jul 1997-Jun 1998 Income $315,582. Mats Exp $84,307, Books $76,760, Presv $7,547. Sal $176,431
Library Holdings: Bk Vols 138,000; Per Subs 550
Subject Interests: Education, Liberal arts, Relig studies
Special Collections: Catholic Church Music (Montani Coll); Irish History & Literature
Automation Activity & Vendor Info: (Acquisitions) SIRSI; (Cataloging) SIRSI; (Circulation) SIRSI; (Serials) SIRSI
Partic in PALINET & Union Library Catalogue of Pennsylvania; Tri-State College Library Cooperative (TCLC)

M CHESTNUT HILL HOSPITAL, Medical Library,* 8835 Germantown Ave, 19118. SAN 314-8777. Tel: 215-248-8206. FAX: 215-248-8240. *Librn*, Susan H Couch; E-Mail: couch@chh.org
Founded 1930
Library Holdings: Bk Titles 1,000; Per Subs 120
Subject Interests: Consumer health, Gyn, Medicine, Nursing, OB, Pediatrics, Surgery
Special Collections: Rare Medical Books, Medical Humanities, Hospital Archives
Publications: Library Bulletin
Partic in Basic Health Sciences Library Network; Delaware Valley Information Consortium

M CHILDREN'S HOSPITAL OF PHILADELPHIA, Medical Library, 34th & Civic Center Blvd, 19104. SAN 314-8785. Tel: 215-590-2317. FAX: 215-590-1470. *Dir*, Swaran Chopra; E-Mail: chopra@email.chop.edu; *Asst Librn*, Natalie Gorvine
Founded 1956
Library Holdings: Bk Titles 4,245; Per Subs 178
Subject Interests: Medicine, Nursing, Pediatrics, Surgery
Publications: Newsletter
Restriction: Open to public for reference only

S CHINATOWN BUILDING & EDUCATION FOUNDATION, Chinese Cultural & Community Center,* 125 N Tenth St, 19107. SAN 370-9574. Tel: 215-923-6767. *In Charge*, Mrs T T Chang
Library Holdings: Bk Vols 2,000
Special Collections: Chinese Language, bks

S CIGNA CORP, Philadelphia Research Library, 1601 Chestnut St, TLP 5, 19192-2051. SAN 314-9315. Tel: 215-761-1000, 215-761-4120, 215-761-4152. FAX: 215-761-5588. *Librn*, Patricia Malahan; E-Mail: patricia.malahan@cigna.com
Founded 1945
Library Holdings: Bk Vols 5,000; Bk Titles 3,000
Subject Interests: Bus, Ins, Mgt
Special Collections: Occupational Safety & Health (Safety Science Coll), bk, per
Publications: Acquisitions List
Partic in Dialog Corporation; Dow Jones News Retrieval; SDC Info Servs

J COMMUNITY COLLEGE OF PHILADELPHIA LIBRARY,* 1700 Spring Garden St, 19130. SAN 314-9730. Tel: 215-751-8000, 215-751-8383. FAX: 215-751-8762. Web Site: library.ccp.cc.pa. *Exec Dir*, Joan Johnson; *Acq, ILL*, Jerry Fedorijczuk; *Ref*, Don Jones; *Ref*, Rena Hawes; *Automation Syst Coordr*, Elaine Spyker; *Circ*, Jae Fisher; *Cat*, Shu-erh Fu; *ILL*, Jalyn Warren; *Publ Servs*, Rosemary McAndrew; Staff 19 (MLS 9, Non-MLS 10)
Founded 1964. Enrl 14,684; Highest Degree: Associate
Jul 1998-Jun 1999 Mats Exp $184,178, Books $126,384, Per/Ser (Incl. Access Fees) $57,794. Sal $825,467 (Prof $473,496)
Library Holdings: Bk Vols 100,000; Per Subs 450
Automation Activity & Vendor Info: (Acquisitions) Innovative Interfaces Inc.; (Cataloging) Innovative Interfaces Inc.; (Circulation) Innovative Interfaces Inc.; (Media Booking) Innovative Interfaces Inc.; (OPAC) Innovative Interfaces Inc.; (Serials) Innovative Interfaces Inc.
Database Vendor: Ebsco - EbscoHost, Silverplatter Information Inc.
Partic in PALINET & Union Library Catalogue of Pennsylvania; Tri-State College Library Cooperative (TCLC)

L COMMUNITY LEGAL SERVICES INC LIBRARY,* 1424 Chestnut St, 19102. SAN 358-7827. Tel: 215-981-3771. FAX: 215-981-0434. *Dir Libr Serv*, Carl E Mitchell; E-Mail: cmitchell@clsphila.org; *Asst Librn*, Betty Tinsley; Staff 2 (MLS 1, Non-MLS 1)
Founded 1968
Library Holdings: Bk Titles 15,000; Per Subs 35
Subject Interests: Civil law, Poverty law
Restriction: Not open to public
Partic in Handsnet; Westlaw
Branches:
LAW CENTER NORTH CENTRAL, 3638 N Broad St, 19140. SAN 358-7886. Tel: 215-227-2400. FAX: 215-227-2435.

S CONGREGATION MIKVEH ISRAEL ARCHIVES,* Independence Mall E, 44 N Fourth St, 19106. SAN 329-8094. Tel: 215-922-5446. FAX: 215-922-1550. E-Mail: info@mikvehisrael.org. Web Site: www.mikvehisrael.org. *Chair*, Ruth Hoffman

R CONGREGATION RODEPH SHALOM, Philadelphia & Elkins Park Suburban Center Library, 615 N Broad St, 19123. SAN 358-8009. Tel: 215-627-6747 (Philadelphia Center), 215-635-2500 (Elkins Park Center). FAX: 215-627-1313. E-Mail: rshalom@libertynet.org. *Librn*, Lois Hirsch
Founded 1802
Library Holdings: Bk Vols 10,300; Per Subs 22
Subject Interests: History, Judaica-Jewish biog, Religion
Special Collections: (Roberta Lee Magaziner Memorial), bks, music; Children's Books; Family Life (Sadie Goldberg Memorial); Jewish Music
Restriction: Open to public for reference only

S CONSECO DIRECT LIFE INSURANCE COMPANY, Market Research Dept Library, 399 Market St, 5th flr, 19106. SAN 320-2283. Tel: 215-928-6657. FAX: 215-928-6035. *Librn*, Amy Stone; E-Mail: astone@consecodirect.com; Staff 1 (MLS 1)
Founded 1975
Library Holdings: Bk Titles 500; Per Subs 100
Subject Interests: Direct marketing, Health ins, Internet, Life ins, Older Americans
Automation Activity & Vendor Info: (Cataloging) EOS; (Serials) EOS
Publications: Newsletter (weekly)

L CONSOLIDATED RAIL CORPORATION, Law Library 16-B,* 2 Commerce Sq, 2001 Market St, 19101-1416. SAN 321-0588. Tel: 215-209-5044. FAX: 215-209-4817. *Librn*, Sandra Compo
Founded 1976
Library Holdings: Bk Vols 20,000; Bk Titles 5,000; Per Subs 50
Subject Interests: Interstate commerce, Legal, Railroad mats
Partic in Dialog Corporation; Westlaw

L COZEN & O'CONNOR, Law Library,* 1900 Market St, 3rd flr, 19103. SAN 372-1965. Tel: 215-665-2000. FAX: 215-864-8037. Web Site: www.cozen.com. *Librn*, Loretta F Osadorff; E-Mail: losadorff@cozen.com
Library Holdings: Bk Vols 8,000; Per Subs 125
Subject Interests: Law

S CURTIS INSTITUTE OF MUSIC LIBRARY,* 1726 Locust St, 19103. SAN 314-8831. Tel: 215-893-5252. FAX: 215-893-0194. Web Site: www.curtis.edu. *Dir*, Elizabeth Walker; *Asst Dir*, Kenton Meyer; *Cat*, Peter Eisenberg; Staff 3 (MLS 3)
Founded 1926. Enrl 167; Fac 87; Highest Degree: Master
Jun 1997-May 1998 Income $295,221. Mats Exp $65,852, Books $7,571, Per/Ser (Incl. Access Fees) $4,074, Presv $8,970, AV Equip $290, Other Print Mats $26,080, Manuscripts & Archives $12,968. Sal $200,226 (Prof $114,116)
Library Holdings: Bk Vols 13,024; Per Subs 72
Subject Interests: Music
Publications: Library Guide (student handbook)
Partic in PALINET & Union Library Catalogue of Pennsylvania

S CHARLOTTE CUSHMAN CLUB, Theatre Research Library,* 239 S Camac St, 19107. SAN 325-9595. Tel: 215-735-4676. FAX: 215-735-6676. *Exec Dir*, Judith Klein
Library Holdings: Bk Titles 4,000
Special Collections: Theatrical Memorabilia Coll

S DAY & ZIMMERMANN INTERNATIONAL, INC LIBRARY,* 1818 Market St, 21st flr, 19103. SAN 314-884X. Tel: 215-299-8222. FAX: 215-299-2236. *Librn*, Sandy Davis
Founded 1945
Library Holdings: Bk Vols 2,300; Per Subs 75
Subject Interests: Chemistry, Electrical, Mechanical engineering

L DECHERT LIBRARY, (Formerly Dechert, Price & Rhoads Library), 4000 Bell Atlantic Tower, 1717 Arch St, 19103-2793. SAN 314-8858. Tel: 215-994-4000. FAX: 215-994-2222. *Dir*, Susan G Alford; *Asst Librn*, Elizabeth Collins; Staff 7 (MLS 4, Non-MLS 3)
Library Holdings: Bk Vols 35,000; Per Subs 200
Subject Interests: Law

S DEFENSE INDUSTRIAL SUPPLY CENTER, Technical Data Management Branch (DISC-SD),* Product Services Technical & Quality Assurance, 700 Robbins Ave, 19111-5096. SAN 314-8866. Tel: 215-697-0418. *In Charge*, Mark Siegal
Founded 1961
Subject Interests: Eng data, Indust hardware

M DEFENSE PERSONNEL SUPPORT CENTER, Medical Information Center DPSC-MB, RMF 315,* 2800 S 20th St, Bldg 9-3-F, 19101-8419. SAN 314-8874. Tel: 215-737-2110. FAX: 215-737-2081, 215-737-8144. *Librn*, Pearl Adams
Founded 1961
Library Holdings: Bk Titles 3,200
Subject Interests: Biology, Chemistry, Engineering, Mathematics, Medicine Physics
Special Collections: fed, Military & Hot Specifications, Micro; Government Reports Announcements & Index, Industry Standards, Historical Mil Specs; Pharmacy; US Military, History of War; War Surgery/Medicine, Micro
Publications: 1 Newsletter In House
Partic in Defense Technical Information Center; Fedlink; Medline; OCLC Online Computer Library Center, Inc

GM DEPARTMENT OF VETERANS AFFAIRS, Library Services,* University & Woodland Aves, 19104. SAN 359-2472. Tel: 215-823-5860. FAX: 215-823-5108. *Chief Librn*, Mark Marchino; E-Mail: marchino@shrsys.hslc.org
Library Holdings: Bk Vols 9,889; Bk Titles 6,600; Per Subs 453
Subject Interests: Gen med
Publications: New Books (quarterly listing); Special Interest Bibliographies
Partic in Delaware Valley Information Consortium; Veterans Affairs Library Network; Vets Admin Libr Network

L DILWORTH, PAXSON LLP, Law Library, 1735 Market St Ste 3200, 19103-7595. SAN 372-1868. Tel: 215-575-7112. FAX: 215-575-7200. Web Site: www.dilworthlaw.com. *Librn*, Karen Callahan; E-Mail: callaghk@dilworthlaw.com; Staff 1 (MLS 1)
Library Holdings: Bk Vols 15,000; Per Subs 50
Partic in OCLC Online Computer Library Center, Inc

C DREXEL UNIVERSITY, W W Hagerty Library, 32nd & Chestnut Sts, 19104-2875. SAN 314-8912. Tel: 215-895-2750. Interlibrary Loan Service Tel: 215-895-2769. Circulation Tel: 215-895-2767. Reference Tel: 215-895-2755. FAX: 215-895-2070. Web Site: www.library.drexel.edu. *Dean*, Carol Montgomery; E-Mail: montgoch@drexel.edu; *Assoc Dean*, JoAnne Sparks; E-Mail: sparks@drexel.edu; *ILL*, Deidre Harper; Tel: 215-895-2769; *Tech Servs*, Mari Katherine Hodges; E-Mail: mkh22@drexel.edu; *Syst Coordr*, Kristen Costello; Tel: 215-895-1871, E-Mail: Kristen.Costello@drexel.edu; *Access Serv*, Ruth Johnson; E-Mail: johnson@drexel.edu; *Electronic Resources*, Kathryn Brady; Tel: 215-895-2771, E-Mail: klb28@drexel.edu; *Humanities and Soc Sci*, Jenifer Baldwin; *Science*, Margaret Dominy; Tel: 215-895-2754, E-Mail: dominymf@drexel.edu; *Business*, Ken Johnson; Tel: 215-895-6164, E-Mail: kjohnson@drexel.edu; *Ref*, Bruce Whitham. Subject Specialists: *Art*, Judy Donovan; *Design*, Judy Donovan; *Engineering*, Jay Bhatt; *Libr sci*, Kenneth Garson; Staff 23 (MLS 16, Non-MLS 7)
Founded 1891. Enrl 10,100; Fac 600; Highest Degree: Doctorate
Jul 1999-Jun 2000 Income $4,052,000, Parent Institution $3,782,000, Other $270,000. Mats Exp $1,312,600, Books $436,600, Per/Ser (Incl. Access Fees) $429,000, Micro $6,000, Electronic Ref Mat (Incl. Access Fees) $441,000
Library Holdings: Bk Vols 360,000; Bk Titles 100,000; Per Subs 6,000
Subject Interests: Art, Bus, Design, Info-sci, Libr sci, Sci, Technology

Special Collections: A J Drexel & Family; Charles Lukens Huston, Jr Ethics Coll; Drexel Archives; History of the Book
Automation Activity & Vendor Info: (Acquisitions) Innovative Interfaces Inc.; (Cataloging) Innovative Interfaces Inc.; (Circulation) Innovative Interfaces Inc.; (Course Reserve) Innovative Interfaces Inc.; (ILL) Innovative Interfaces Inc.; (Media Booking) Innovative Interfaces Inc.; (OPAC) Innovative Interfaces Inc.; (Serials) Innovative Interfaces Inc.
Database Vendor: OCLC - First Search
Restriction: Open to student, faculty & staff
Partic in PALCI; PALINET & Union Library Catalogue of Pennsylvania

DRINKER, BIDDLE & REATH, Law Library,* Philadelphia National Bank Bldg, 1345 Chestnut St, 19107. SAN 314-8920. Tel: 215-988-2951. FAX: 215-988-2757, 564-1329. *Dir*, Linda-Jean Schneider; E-Mail: schneilj@dbr.com
Library Holdings: Bk Vols 20,000
Partic in PALINET & Union Library Catalogue of Pennsylvania

DUANE, MORRIS & HECKSCHER LIBRARY,* One Liberty Pl, 19103-7396. SAN 314-8955. Tel: 215-979-1720. FAX: 215-979-1020. *Librn*, David W Falk; *Ref*, Greg Weyant; Staff 5 (MLS 2, Non-MLS 3)
Founded 1904
Library Holdings: Bk Vols 18,000
Subject Interests: Law
Partic in OCLC Online Computer Library Center, Inc

EDUCATIONAL MANAGEMENT CORPORATION, Art Institute of Philadelphia Library, 1622 Chestnut St, 19103. SAN 322-8347. Tel: 215-567-7080, Ext 6402. FAX: 215-405-6398. *Dir*, Ruth Schachter; Tel: 215-405-6378, E-Mail: schachtr@aii.edu; Staff 3 (MLS 1, Non-MLS 2)
Founded 1974. Enrl 2,700; Fac 200; Highest Degree: Bachelor
Library Holdings: Bk Vols 17,500; Bk Titles 14,000; Per Subs 187
Subject Interests: Animation, Applied arts, Fashion design, Graphic design, Industrial design, Video production
Automation Activity & Vendor Info: (Circulation) Sagebrush Corporation; (OPAC) Sagebrush Corporation
Database Vendor: OCLC - First Search, ProQuest
Restriction: Students only
Partic in PALINET & Union Library Catalogue of Pennsylvania; Tri-State College Library Cooperative (TCLC)

S EDWARD M DAVID LIBRARY,* Woodmere Art Museum, 9201 Germantown Ave, 19118. SAN 325-2191. Tel: 215-247-0476. FAX: 215-247-2387. *Dir*, Dr Michael Schantz; *Librn*, Edith Schwatz
Founded 1981
Library Holdings: Bk Titles 2,200
Subject Interests: Philadelphia artists
Special Collections: American 19th Century (Charles Knox Smith Coll), paintings; Philadelphia 20th Century (Woodmere Coll), paintings
Restriction: Not open to public

S EI DU PONT DE NEMOURS & CO, INC, Marshall Laboratory Library, 3401 Grays Ferry Ave, 19146. SAN 314-8947. Tel: 215-539-6263. Reference Tel: 215-539-6213. FAX: 215-539-6305. *Librn*, Virginia L Maier; *Info Specialist*, Kristin Rokosky
Founded 1951
Library Holdings: Per Subs 225
Subject Interests: Analytical, Coatings, Organics, Paint and coatings, Physical, Polymer chemistry
Restriction: Company library
Partic in Dialog Corporation; Orbit; STN

M EPISCOPAL HOSPITAL, Medical Library, Front St & Lehigh Ave, 19125. SAN 314-8998. Tel: 215-427-7487. FAX: 215-427-7490. *Dir*, Marita J Krivda; E-Mail: krivda@hslc.org; Staff 1 (MLS 1)
Founded 1962
2000-2001 Income $107,620. Mats Exp $65,000, Books $10,000, Per/Ser (Incl. Access Fees) $42,000, Presv $5,000, Electronic Ref Mat (Incl. Access Fees) $8,000. Sal $41,000
Library Holdings: Bk Titles 2,500; Per Subs 210
Subject Interests: Cardiology, Internal medicine, Nursing, Nursing educ, Surg
Special Collections: Hospital Archives Coll
Partic in BSHL; Delaware Valley Information Consortium; National Network Of Libraries Of Medicine - South Central Region
Open Mon-Fri 9-5

S ERNST & YOUNG LLP LIBRARY, 2001 Market St, Ste 4000, 19103-7096. SAN 375-4901. Tel: 215-448-5375. FAX: 215-448-5880. *Assoc Dir, Librn, Res*, Jeanne Bohlen; E-Mail: jeanne.bohlen@ey.com; Staff 1 (MLS 1)
Library Holdings: Per Subs 250
Subject Interests: Accounting, Auditing
Automation Activity & Vendor Info: (Acquisitions) Inmagic, Inc.; (Cataloging) Inmagic, Inc.; (Serials) Inmagic, Inc.
Restriction: Staff use only

S EXELON CORPORATION, (Formerly Peco Energy Co), Library Services, 2301 Market St, PO Box 8699, 19101. SAN 314-9757. Interlibrary Loan Service Tel: 215-841-4358. FAX: 215-841-4088. *Librn*, Christian C Braig; Staff 2 (MLS 2)
Founded 1909
Library Holdings: Per Subs 250
Subject Interests: Bus, Engineering, Pub utilities
Special Collections: Electric Power Research Institute, rpts
Automation Activity & Vendor Info: (Acquisitions) Inmagic, Inc.; (Cataloging) Inmagic, Inc.; (Circulation) Inmagic, Inc.; (ILL) Inmagic, Inc.; (OPAC) Inmagic, Inc.; (Serials) Inmagic, Inc.
Restriction: By appointment only

S FARM JOURNAL, Marketing Library,* Center Sq West, 1500 Market St, 28th flr, 19102-2181. SAN 314-9005. Tel: 215-557-8900. FAX: 215-568-3989. *Librn*, Kandace Hereog; E-Mail: kandyjo@aol.com; Staff 3 (MLS 1, Non-MLS 2)
Founded 1945
Library Holdings: Bk Vols 750; Bk Titles 250; Per Subs 75
Subject Interests: Advertising, Agriculture, Farm markets, Marketing, Media
Restriction: Open to public for reference only

S FEDERAL RESERVE BANK OF PHILADELPHIA, Research Library, 10 Independence Mall, 19106-1574. SAN 314-9021. Tel: 215-574-6540. FAX: 215-574-3847. Web Site: ww.phil.frb.org. *Mgr*, Christine Le; E-Mail: christine.le@phil.frb.org; *ILL, Publ Servs*, July Platt; *Tech Servs*, Carol Aldridge; Staff 7 (MLS 4, Non-MLS 3)
Founded 1922
1998-1999 Mats Exp $210,000, Micro $4,000. Sal $227,000
Library Holdings: Bk Titles 20,000; Per Subs 300
Subject Interests: Cent banking, Finance hist, Urban res econ
Automation Activity & Vendor Info: (Acquisitions) EOS
Publications: Fed in Print
Restriction: Open to public for reference only
Partic in Dialog Corporation; Dow Jones News Retrieval; OCLC Online Computer Library Center, Inc; PALINET & Union Library Catalogue of Pennsylvania

S FOREIGN POLICY RESEARCH INSTITUTE LIBRARY,* 1528 Walnut St Ste 610, 19102. SAN 314-9072. Tel: 215-732-3774, Ext 102. FAX: 215-732-4401. E-Mail: fpri@fpri.org. Web Site: www.fpri.org. *VPres*, Allen Luxenberg
Founded 1962
Library Holdings: Bk Titles 4,000; Per Subs 150
Subject Interests: Area studies, Int econ, International relations, Mil, Political science
Special Collections: Foreign Broadcast Information Service Reports
Open Mon-Fri 9-5

M FOX CHASE CANCER CENTER, Talbot Research Library, 7701 Burholme Ave, 19111. SAN 314-9323. Tel: 215-728-2710. FAX: 215-728-3655. *Dir, Librn*, Karen Albert; E-Mail: albert@hslc.org; *Librn*, Beth Lewis; *Librn*, Nina Galpern; Staff 7 (MLS 2, Non-MLS 5)
Founded 1926
Library Holdings: Bk Vols 5,000; Per Subs 420
Subject Interests: Biochemistry, Cancer, Cell biol, Clinical res, Crystallography, Genetics, X-rays
Special Collections: X-Ray Crystallography (A L Patterson Coll)
Restriction: Open to public for reference only
Partic in Health Science Library Information Consortium; National Network Of Libraries Of Medicine - South Central Region; PALINET & Union Library Catalogue of Pennsylvania

L FOX, ROTHSCHILD, O'BRIEN & FRANKEL, Law Library, 2000 Market St, 19103-3291. SAN 325-965X. Tel: 215-299-2108, 215-299-2140. FAX: 215-299-2150. E-Mail: library@frof.com. *Dir Libr Serv*, Catherine M Monte
Library Holdings: Bk Vols 20,000
Partic in Dialog Corporation

S FRANK C FARNHAM CO INC LIBRARY,* 1930 Chestnut St, Ste 1203, 19103-4512. SAN 325-9676. Tel: 215-567-1500. FAX: 215-567-0382. *Mgr*, Connie Devlin; *Pres*, Frank C Farnham
Library Holdings: Bk Titles 1,200

FRANKFORD HOSPITAL
M HEALTH SCIENCES LIBRARIES, Red Lion & Knights Rds, 19114. SAN 324-6302. Tel: 215-612-4135, 215-831-2182, 215-831-6776. FAX: 215-949-7821. *Dir Libr Serv*, Gary J Christopher; Tel: 215-949-5160, E-Mail: gchris@hslc.org; *Tech Servs*, Rosemary Jones; Staff 2 (MLS 1, Non-MLS 1)
Founded 1950. Fac 25
Jul 1999-Jun 2000 Income Parent Institution $193,000. Mats Exp $68,300, Books $4,900, Per/Ser (Incl. Access Fees) $44,000, Electronic Ref Mat (Incl. Access Fees) $19,400. Sal $81,000 (Prof $52,000)
Library Holdings: Bk Titles 2,420; Per Subs 315
Subject Interests: Allied health, Consumer health, Health care, Medical, Nursing
Database Vendor: Ebsco - EbscoHost, OVID Technologies
Restriction: Open to public upon request, Staff use only, Students only

Function: ILL to other special libraries
Partic in Basic Health Sciences Library Network; DEVIC
Three library branches, 2 hospital & 1 school of nursing

M SCHOOL OF NURSING LIBRARY, 4918 Penn St, 19124. SAN 324-7481. Tel: 215-831-6776. FAX: 215-831-6782. E-Mail: fraschlib@hslc.org. *Librn*, Deborah Kogan
Enrl 600; Fac 25
Jul 1998-Jun 1999 Income $25,000. Mats Exp $25,000, Books $9,100, Per/Ser (Incl. Access Fees) $12,900
Library Holdings: Bk Vols 4,259; Per Subs 125
Subject Interests: Nursing
Partic in Medline

S FRANKLIN INSTITUTE, Science Museum Library,* 222 N 20th St, 19103-1194. SAN 314-9080. Tel: 215-448-1227. FAX: 215-448-1364. *Librn*, Irene D Coffey; Staff 2 (MLS 1, Non-MLS 1)
Founded 1824
Library Holdings: Bk Vols 46,500
Subject Interests: Mathematics, Physical science, Sci educ
Special Collections: Underwater Man Coll; Ware Sugar Coll
Partic in OCLC Online Computer Library Center, Inc; PALINET & Union Library Catalogue of Pennsylvania
Open Mon-Fri 9:30-5 by appointment

P FREE LIBRARY OF PHILADELPHIA, Library for the Blind & Physically Handicapped, 919 Walnut St, 19107-5289. SAN 314-9102. Tel: 215-683-3213. Toll Free Tel: 800-222-1754. FAX: 215-683-3211. Web Site: www.library.phila.gov. *Dir*, Vickie Collins; *Tech Servs*, Richard Riddell; *Ch Servs*, Doreen Velnich; *Reader Servs*, Rene Snowten; Staff 5 (MLS 5)
Founded 1897. Circ 850,000
Library Holdings: Bk Titles 47,000
Special Collections: Blindness & Handicaps
Publications: 919 NEWS, reader newsletter (quarterly)
Special Services for the Blind - ABE/GED & braille classes for the visually impaired & print handicapped, recording studio; Braille translation & printing software & equipment; Information on aids & appliances; Magazine & book reproduction/duplication; Magnifiers; Optacon, Visualtek closed circuit TV reading aid; Reading room; Volunteer braiilling & taping
Open Mon-Fri 9-5
Friends of the Library Group

P FREE LIBRARY OF PHILADELPHIA, 1901 Vine St, 19103-1189. SAN 358-8181. Tel: 215-686-5322. Interlibrary Loan Service Tel: 215-686-5360. TDD: 215-963-0202. FAX: 215-563-3628. Web Site: www.library.phila.gov. *Dir, Pres*, Elliot L Shelkrot; *Assoc Dir*, Kathy Gosliner; *Dir, Publ Servs*, Helen M Miller; *Info Tech*, H E Broadbent III; *Acq*, Toni Hoagland; *Publ Servs*, Hedra L Peterman; *Info Tech*, Jack Newcombe; *Coll Develop*, Mary Fischer
Founded 1891. Circ 6,700,000
Jul 1997-Jun 1998 Income $63,767,334, State $6,601,900, City $43,929,515, Federal $370,271. Mats Exp $7,971,421
Automation Activity & Vendor Info: (Cataloging) DRA; (Circulation) DRA
Partic in OCLC Online Computer Library Center, Inc
Special Services for the Deaf - Books on deafness & sign language; Captioned film depository; High interest/low vocabulary books; Special interest periodicals; TDD
Headquarters for the Philadelphia District Library Center
Friends of the Library Group
Branches: 73
ANDORRA, 705 E Cathedral Rd, 19128-2106. SAN 358-8998. *Head of Libr*, Marianne Fulton
ART *Head Librn*, Debora H Litwack
Subject Interests: Architecture, Costume, Crafts, Decorative arts, Fine arts, Graphic arts, Photog
Special Collections: (American Institute of Architects, Philadelphia Chapter Coll); Illustrations (Joseph Pennell Coll); John Frederick Lewis Coll; of Fine Prints & Print Making; Old Philadelphia Survey: Restorations & Measured Drawings; Stained Glass (Lawrence Saint Coll & Henry Lee Willet Coll)
AUTOMOBILE REFERENCE COLLECTION *Curator*, Stuart MacDougall
Special Collections: Books & Photographs Tracing the Automobile from 1896 to date; Instruction, Parts & Shop Manuals; Sales Catalogs
BLANCHE A NIXON COBBS LIBRARY, 5800 Cobbs Creek Pkwy, 19143-3036. SAN 358-9110. *Head of Libr*, Patti McLaughlin
BUSHROD, 6304 Castor Ave, 19149-2731. SAN 358-9021. *Head of Libr*, Fred Rosenzweig
BUSINESS, SCIENCE & INDUSTRY *Head Librn*, Charles Smith
Subject Interests: Business, Computers, Consumer info, Philatelic lit, Science, Technology
Special Collections: Trade Periodical Literature
BUSTLETON AVENUE, 10199 Bustleton Ave, 19116-3718. SAN 358-9056. *Head of Libr*, Sharon Dennison
CECIL B MOORE AVE, 2320 W Cecil B Moore Ave, 19121-2927. SAN 358-9145. *Head of Libr*, Audrey Roll
CENTRAL CHILDREN'S DEPARTMENT *Head Librn*, Irene Wright; *Spec Coll*, Diane J McDowell
Special Collections: Bibliographies; Bibliographies for the Adult Researcher; Children's Books in 60 Different Languages; Collection of Original Children's Book Illustrations & Manuscripts; Folklore; Foreign Language; Historical Bibliography: Books about Children's Literature; Historical Coll of Children's Literature from 1837 to present; Kathrine McAlarney Coll of Illustrated Children's Books
CHARLES L DURHAM BRANCH, 3320 Haverford Ave, 19104-2021. SAN 358-9641. *Head of Libr*, Jennifer Suder
CHESTNUT HILL, 8711 Germantown Ave, 19118-2716. SAN 358-9080. FAX: 215-248-9877. *Head of Libr*, Margaret Brunton
DATABASE & NEWSPAPER CENTER *Head Librn*, Patricia Kelker
Extensive Philadelphia coverage kept indefinitely; other selected titles retained up to six months; Philadelphia area community & commercial newspapers & major national newspapers on microfilm; periodicals in microforms covering all subjects; city directories & telephone directories in microforms
EASTWICK, 2851 Island Ave, 19153-2314. SAN 359-0224. *Head of Libr*, Paula Hansen
EDUCATION, PHILOSOPHY & RELIGION *Head Librn*, Walt Stock
Subject Interests: Education, Libr, Librarianship, Philosophy, Psychology, Relig studies
Special Collections: (Moses Marx Coll); Bibles; Judaica-Hebraica; The Workplace - Job & Career Information Center
EDWIN A FLEISHER COLL OF ORCHESTRAL MUSIC *Curator*, Kile Smith
Special Collections: Archives of American Composers; Conductor's scores & complete instrumental parts for approximately 15,000 orchestral works & approximately 1500 reference scores available for loan on application; Reference files on over 1500 composers; Repository for discs & cassettes of works from the collection; Repository for tapes of American-International Music Fund's Recording Guarantee Project
FALLS OF SCHUYLKILL, 3501 Midvale Ave, 19129-1633. SAN 358-920X.
FISHTOWN COMMUNITY, 1217 E Montgomery Ave, 19125-3445. SAN 358-917X. *Head of Libr*, Barbara Maxwell
FOX CHASE, 501 Rhawn, 19111-2504. SAN 358-9234. *Head of Libr*, Julie Doty
FRANKFORD, 4634 Frankford Ave, 19124-5804. SAN 358-9269. FAX: 215-289-6914. *Head of Libr*, Pat Hoberg
FUMO FAMILY BRANCH, 2437 S Broad St, 19148-3508. SAN 358-9951. *Head of Libr*, Marilyn Barr
GENERAL INFORMATION *Head Librn*, Joe Perry
Special Collections: Telephone Directories
Information Center for all Collections of the Library
GEORGE INSTITUTE, 1461 N 52nd St, 19131-4435. SAN 358-9293. FAX 215-477-9293. *Head of Libr*, Frank Bonifante
GOVERNMENT PUBLICATIONS Tel: 215-686-5330. *Head Librn*, Bob Briggs
Special Collections: US Patent Coll; US Patents
GREATER OLNEY, 5501 N Fifth St, 19120-2805. SAN 358-9323. FAX: 215-548-2605. *Head of Libr*, Eileen Ert
HADDINGTON, 446 N 65th St, 19151-4003. SAN 358-9382. *Head of Libr*, Matt Beatty
HAVERFORD AVE, 5543 Haverford Ave, 19139-1432. SAN 358-9390. *Head of Libr*, Catherine Westervelt
HOLMESBURG, 7810 Frankford Ave, 19136-3013. SAN 358-9412. *Head of Libr*, Cathy Huntzberry
INTERLIBRARY LOAN Tel: 215-686-5360. FAX: 215-563-3628. *Head Librn*, Larry Richards
KATHARINE DREXEL BRANCH, 11099 Knights Rd, 19154-3516. SAN 358-9447. *Head of Libr*, Anne Ash
KENSINGTON, 104 W Dauphin St, 19133-3701. SAN 358-9471. *Head of Libr*, Chris Kottcamp
KINGSESSING, 1201 S 51st, 19143-4353. SAN 358-9501. *Head of Libr*, Kelly Anne McDermott
LAWNCREST, 6098 Rising Sun Ave, 19111-6009. SAN 358-9536. *Head of Libr*, Jane Gottfried
LEHIGH AVENUE, 601 W Lehigh Ave, 19133-2228. SAN 358-9560. FAX: 215-685-9795. *Head of Libr*, Lillian Marrero
LIBRARY FOR THE BLIND & PHYSICALLY HANDICAPPED
See Separate Entry
LITERATURE *Head Librn*, Michele Gendron
Subject Interests: Belles lettres, Folklore, Journalism, Language arts, Literature
Special Collections: Granger Coll; Ottemiller Coll
LOGAN, 1333 Wagner Ave, 19141-2916. SAN 358-9595. *Head of Libr*, Belita Thornton
LOVETT MEMORIAL, 6945 Germantown Ave, 19119-2189. SAN 358-9625. *Head of Libr*, Eileen Levinson
MAP COLLECTION *Curator*, Richard C Boardman
Subject Interests: Cartobibliography, Geography, Hist of cartography, Map librarianship
Special Collections: 19th and 20th century Philadelphia Fire Insurance Atlases, suburban atlases; 19th century Pennsylvania County Atlases; Decorative maps and maps of imaginary lands; Historical Philadelphia Map Collection; William G Kelzo Collection of Jansson-Visscher Maps of America
MCPHERSON SQUARE, 601 E Indiana Ave, 19134-3042. SAN 358-965X.

Head of Libr, Judi Moore
MUSIC *Head Librn*, K Paul Savedow
Subject Interests: Bibliog, Biog, Chamber, Collected works, Criticism, Dance, Essays, Instrumental music, Manuscripts
Special Collections: Collection of Musical Fund Society; Drinker Library of Choral Music; Harvey Husten & Huber Jazz Libraries, rec; Historical Record Coll; Sheet Music (incl Americana)
Primarily Reference collection, but does circulate large collection of musical scores
NICETOWN-TIOGA, 3720 N Broad St, 19140-3608. SAN 358-9684. *Head of Libr*, Roben Manker
NORTHEAST REGIONAL, 2228 Cottman Ave, 19149-1297. SAN 358-8904. Tel: 215-685-0500. FAX: 215-742-3225. *Head of Libr*, Viola Jones
Library Holdings: Bk Vols 170,000
NORTHWEST REGIONAL, 68 W Chelten Ave, 19144-2795. SAN 358-8939. Tel: 215-685-2150. FAX: 215-848-7790. *Head of Libr*, Beryl Evans
Library Holdings: Bk Vols 116,000
OAK LANE, 6614 N 12th St, 19126-3299. SAN 358-9714. *Head of Libr*, Jan Kalaminsky
OGONTZ, 6017 Ogontz Ave, 19141. SAN 376-8554. *Head of Libr*, Suzin Weber
OVERBROOK PARK, 7422 Haverford Ave, 19151-2995. SAN 358-9749. FAX: 215-685-0185. *Head of Libr*, Bruce Siebers
Library Holdings: Bk Vols 47,146
PASCHALVILLE, 6942 Woodland Ave, 19142-1823. SAN 358-9773. FAX: 215-685-2664. *Head of Libr*, Curtis Datko
PASSYUNK, 1935 Shunk St, 19145-4234. SAN 358-9803. FAX: 215-685-1652. *Head of Libr*, David Mariscotti
PHILADELPHIA CITY INSTITUTE, 1905 Locust St, 19103-5730. SAN 358-9838. FAX: 215-685-6622. *Head of Libr*, David Ninemire
PHILBRICK LENDING LIBRARY *Head Librn*, Jim Quinn
PRINT & PICTURE *Curator*, Joseph Benford
Special Collections: Centennial Exhibition of 1876 Photographs; Circulating Collection of Pictures on all subjects; Contemporary Graphic Arts; Greeting cards; Napoleonica (Carson Coll); Philadelphia; Portrait Prints (Lewis Coll)
QUEEN MEMORIAL, 1201 S 23rd St, 19146-4316. SAN 374-7328. *Head of Libr*, Ida Gowans
RAMONITA G DE RODRIGUEZ BRANCH, 600 W Girard Ave, 19123-1311. SAN 358-9897. FAX: 215-686-1769. *Head of Libr*, Denise Shaver
RARE BOOK *Head Librn*, William F Lang
Special Collections: (Margaret Leaf Coll); A B Frost (C Barton Brewster Coll); A E Newton (Swift Newton Coll) American Pamphlets (Charles J Biddle Coll); Agnes Repplier (Anne Von Moschzisker Coll); American Historical Autographs incl Jay Treaty Papers (Elkins Coll); American Sunday School Union Publications; Americana (William M Elkins Coll); Angling Prints (Evan Randolph Coll); Arthur Rackham (Grace Clark Haskell Coll); Beatrix Potter (Collamore, Cridland, Elkins & Stevens Coll); Bookplates (J Somers Smith Coll); Bret Harte (Edward F R Wood Coll); British Engravers (Lewis Coll); Calligraphy (9th-20th Centuries Coll); Children's Books Printed in America, 1682-1850 (ASW Rosenbach, Emerson Greenaway, Mrs William H Allen, Frederick R Gardner Coll); Christopher Morley Coll; Common Law (Hampton L Carson Coll); Cuneiform Tablets (John Frederick Lewis Coll); Dickens First Editions, Letters & Memoriabilia (Elkins Coll); Dickens Letters (Benoliel Coll); Early Bibles; Edgar Allan Poe (Richard Gimbel Coll); English & Irish Pamphlets; European Manuscripts (Lewis & Widener Coll); Four Folios of Shakespeare (Joseph E Widener Coll); Gift Books; Goldsmith First Editions & Papers (Elkins Coll); Horace (Moncure Biddle Coll); Horn Books (Elisabeth Ball Coll); Howard Pyle & His School (Thornton Oakley Coll); Incunabula (Copinger-Widener Coll); James Branch Cabell (D Jaques Benoliel Coll); John Gilpin (Brewster Coll); Kate Greenaway; Letters of the Presidents (Strouse Coll); Munro Leaf Coll; Oriental Manuscripts & Miniatures (Lewis Coll); Palmer Cox; Pennsylvania German Imprints, Manuscripts & Fraktur (Henry S Borneman & Others Coll); Philadelphia Views (Randolph Coll); Press Books; Robert Lawson (Frederick R Gardner Coll); Title Pages & Printer's Marks (John Ashhurst Coll); Wing, Short Title Catalogue Books
Partic in OCLC Online Computer Library Center, Inc
READER DEVELOPMENT *Head Librn*, Susan McDougall
REGIONAL FOUNDATION CENTER *In Charge*, Gloria Hibbett
Subject Interests: Fundraising, Info on area foundations, Nat foundations, Nonprofit organization management, Philanthropy
RICHMOND, 2987 Almond St, 19134-4955. SAN 358-9927. *Head of Libr*, Lucille Cychowski
ROXBOROUGH, 6245 Ridge Ave, 19128-2630. SAN 358-9986. FAX: 215-509-2982. *Head of Libr*, Joe Paradin
SOCIAL SCIENCE & HISTORY *Head Librn*, James DeWalt
Subject Interests: Anthropology, Archaeology, Behav sci, Bibliog, Biog, History, International relations, Political science, Soc sci, Sports, Travel
Special Collections: American Imprint Series, micro; American Indian (Wilberforce Eames Coll); Chess (Charles Willing Coll); Confederate Imprints (Simon Gratz Coll); Rowing (Lewis H Kenney Coll)
SOUTH PHILADELPHIA, 1700 S Broad St, 19145-2392. SAN 359-0011. FAX: 215-685-1868. *Head of Libr*, Mary Costigan
SOUTHWARK, 932 S Seventh St, 19147-2932. SAN 359-0046. *Head of Libr*, Joseph Levandoski
TACONY, 6742 Torresdale Ave, 19135-2416. SAN 359-0070. *Head of Libr*, Edna Lamb
THEATRE COLLECTION *In Charge*, Geraldine Duclow
Subject Interests: Circus, Minstrels, Motion pictures, Radio, Television, Theatre, Vaudeville
Special Collections: Lubin Film Co Archive
TORRESDALE, 3079 Holme Ave, 19136-1101. SAN 359-0100. *Head of Libr*, Dorothy Jaworski
WADSWORTH AVENUE, 1500 Wadsworth Ave, 19150-1699. SAN 359-0135. *Head of Libr*, Ann Reinhardt
WALNUT STREET WEST, 3927 Walnut St, 19104-3609. SAN 359-016X. FAX: 215-685-7679. *Head of Libr*, Tamar Sarnoff
WELSH ROAD, 9233 Roosevelt Blvd, 19114-2205. SAN 359-0194. FAX: 215-685-0496. *Head of Libr*, Jennifer Schatz
WEST OAK LANE, 2000 Washington Lane, 19138-1344. SAN 325-4097. *Head of Libr*, Marie Watson
WEST PHILADELPHIA REGIONAL, 125 S 52nd St, 19139-3408. SAN 358-8963. Tel: 215-685-7424. FAX: 215-685-7438. *Head of Libr*, Claudia Martinez
Library Holdings: Bk Vols 115,000
WHITMAN, 200 Snyder Ave, 19148-2620. SAN 359-0259. *Head of Libr*, Lynn Pearson
WIDENER, 2531 W Lehigh Ave, 19132-3296. SAN 359-0283. *Head of Libr*, Jeff Bullard
WYNNEFIELD, 5325 Overbrook Ave, 19131-1498. SAN 359-0313. FAX: 215-685-2094. *Head of Libr*, Allison Freyermuth
WYOMING, 231 E Wyoming Ave, 19120-4439. SAN 359-0348. *Head of Libr*, Doreen Velnich

P FRIENDS FREE LIBRARY OF GERMANTOWN, 5418 Germantown Ave, 19144. SAN 314-9129. Tel: 215-951-2355. FAX: 215-951-2697. *Dir*, Helen M Eigabroadt
Founded 1845. Pop 7,000; Circ 26,000
Library Holdings: Bk Vols 60,000; Per Subs 198
Subject Interests: Black studies, Natural science, Quaker hist
Special Collections: Irvin C Poley Theatre Coll 1900-1975

S GAY, LESBIAN, BISEXUAL & TRANSGENDERED LIBRARY, Archives of Philadelphia,* 1315 Spruce St, 19107. SAN 377-2500. Tel: 215-732-2220. FAX: 215-732-0770. E-Mail: wwcenter@yahoo.com. Web Site: www.waygay.org. *Librn*, Steve Campelone
Library Holdings: Bk Vols 8,000; Bk Titles 4,000; Per Subs 15

L GENERAL ACCIDENT INSURANCE LIBRARY,* 436 Walnut St, 19105. SAN 314-9153. Tel: 215-625-1059. FAX: 215-625-4350. *Librn*, Jeff Mingle; E-Mail: jmingle@genacc-us.com
Library Holdings: Bk Vols 1,500; Per Subs 25

S GERMAN SOCIETY OF PENNSYLVANIA, Joseph Horner Memorial Library, 611 Spring Garden St, 19123. SAN 314-917X. Tel: 215-627-4365, 215-627-9240. FAX: 215-627-5297. E-Mail: germanscty@aol.com. Web Site: www.libertynet.org/gsp. *Librn*, Bettina Hess; E-Mail: bhess@sas.upenn.edu; Staff 1 (MLS 1)
Founded 1817
Library Holdings: Bk Titles 100,000; Per Subs 10
Subject Interests: Fine arts, German current fiction, History, Literature, Politics
Special Collections: Americana-Germanica Coll; Archives of German-American Singing Societies; Early American Imprints; German-American Newspapers
Publications: News Bulletin

S GERMANTOWN HISTORICAL SOCIETY, Library & Archives, 5501 Germantown Ave, 19144-2291. SAN 314-9188. Tel: 215-844-0514. FAX: 215-844-2831. E-Mail: ghs@libertynet.org. Web Site: www.libertynet.org/ghs. *Exec Dir*, Mary Dabney; *Librn*, David Moore
Founded 1900
Library Holdings: Bk Vols 4,100
Subject Interests: Genealogy, History
Special Collections: African-American Genealogy Archives; German Emigrants; Germantown Industries & Architecture; Horticulture (Edwin C Jellett & Thomas Meehan Coll); Local History (Chestnut Hill, Germantown, Mt Airy, Wissahickon Valley & Environs); Local Photographs, 1849 to Present; Pre-Photographic Images; Victoriana (Ebenezer Maxwell Mansion Restoration Resource Coll); War of the Revolution
Publications: Germantown Crier (bi-annual devoted to local hist)
Restriction: Public use on premises
Function: Outside services via phone, cable & mail, Research fees apply

M GRADUATE HOSPITAL LIBRARY,* 1800 Lombard St, 19146. SAN 325-9692. Tel: 215-893-2401. FAX: 215-893-2431. *Librn*, Diane Farny
Library Holdings: Bk Vols 8,000; Bk Titles 2,000; Per Subs 325
Partic in Delaware Valley Information Consortium

S GRAND ARMY OF THE REPUBLIC MUSEUM & LIBRARY, 4278 Griscom St, 19124-3954. SAN 372-9176. Tel: 215-289-6484. E-Mail: garmuslib@aol.com. Web Site: www.suvcw.org/garmus.htm. *Pres*, Elmer Atkinson

Founded 1926
Library Holdings: Bk Vols 2,600; Per Subs 4
Subject Interests: Civil War
Restriction: Not a lending library
Function: Research library
Friends of the Library Group

J GREAT LAKES COLLEGES ASSOCIATION, Philadelphia Center,* 121 S Broad St, 7th flr, 19107. SAN 325-9714. Tel: 215-735-7300. FAX: 215-735-7373. *Dir*, Stevens E Brooks; *Coordr, Librn*, Eileen Baker
Library Holdings: Bk Vols 250

S H ARMSTRONG ROBERTS INC, Stock Picture Library,* 4203 Locust St, 19104. SAN 329-8590. Tel: 215-386-6300. FAX: 215-386-3521. *Pres*, H Armstrong Roberts, III
Subject Interests: Engravings, Hist images

L HARVEY, PENNINGTON, CABOT, GRIFFITH & RENNEISEN, LTD, Law Library, 11 Penn Center Plaza, 1835 Market St 29th flr, 19103. SAN 372-1930. Tel: 215-563-4470, Ext 236. FAX: 215-568-1044. Web Site: www.harvpenn.com. *Librn*, Charlotte Braunstein
Library Holdings: Bk Vols 10,000; Per Subs 20

S THE HAY GROUP, Corporate Library,* Wanamaker Bldg, 100 Penn Square E, 19107-3388. SAN 314-9242. Tel: 215-861-2434. FAX: 215-861-2102. E-Mail: hay_library@haygroup.com. *Librn*, Claire DiPardo
Library Holdings: Bk Vols 1,200; Bk Titles 1,000; Per Subs 120
Subject Interests: Human res
Restriction: Not open to public

S HISTORICAL SOCIETY OF PENNSYLVANIA LIBRARY, 1300 Locust St, 19107-5699. SAN 314-9250. Tel: 215-732-6200. FAX: 215-732-2680. E-Mail: hsppr@hsp.org. Web Site: www.hsp.org. *Dir Libr Serv*, Lee Arnold; *Ref Serv*, Daniel Rolph; *Res*, Laura Beardsley; *Archivist*, Bruce Scherer; *Cat*, Rong Wang. Subject Specialists: *Art*, Kristen Froehlich; *Artifacts*, Kristen Froehlich; *Graphics*, Bruce Scherer; *Servs*, Laura Beardsley; Staff 25 (MLS 4, Non-MLS 21)
Founded 1824
Jul 1999-Jun 2000 Income Locally Generated Income $1,584,852. Mats Exp $24,182. Sal $1,166,750 (Prof $593,198)
Library Holdings: Bk Vols 500,000; Per Subs 2,000
Subject Interests: Genealogical, History, Materials dealing with the Delaware Valley region, Original thirteen colonies
Special Collections: At Least One Newspaper for Every Day a Paper was Published in Philadelphia; Baker Collection of Washingtoniana; Black History, mss; Census Records, Tax Records, Church Records, Wills, all on micro; Economic History, mss; Eighteenth & Nineteenth Century Paintings; First & Second Manuscript Drafts of the Constitution of the United States; Frankliniana; Genealogies, Original Mss & Family, Church & Civil Records; Large Collection of Washington Documents, mss; Library Company of Philadelphia, mss; Martha Washington's Cookbook; Museum Objects including Pieces Owned by William Penn; Papers of Secretary of the Treasury Salmon P Chase & General George Meade, mss; President James Buchanan's Papers, mss; Printer's Proof of the Declaration of Independence with two sets of Its Signers; Prints & Drawings of Pennsylvania; Quakeriana; Revolution & Early Nation, mss; Simon Gratz Coll, autographs; The William Penn Family & Other Important Colonial Families of Pennsylvania, mss; Tower Collection of Colonial Laws
Publications: Guide to the Manuscript Collection of the Historical Society of Pennsylvania; Pennsylvania Correspondent; Pennsylvania Magazine of History & Biography; Philadelphia Convention & Visitors Bureau; Philadelphia Convention & Visitors Bureau Index to The Pennsylvania Magazine of History and Biography (vols. 76-123, 1952-1999); Serving History in a Changing World; The Historical Society of Pennsylvania in the Twentieth Century, by Sally F. Griffith
Partic in Independent Res Libr Asn; PALINET & Union Library Catalogue of Pennsylvania; Philadelphia Area Consortium Of Special Collections Libraries; Research Libraries Group, Inc

C HOLY FAMILY COLLEGE LIBRARY,* Grant & Frankford Aves, 19114. SAN 314-9269. Tel: 215-637-5828. FAX: 215-632-8067. E-Mail: holcollib@hslc.org. *Dir*, Lori Schwavenvauar; *Ref*, Charles Seeburger; *Ref*, Robert Ellermeyer; *Tech Servs*, Milda Wallace; *Tech Servs*, Patricia Wagner; *Circ*, Florence Dolan; *Acq, Per*, Florence Tilsner; *ILL*, Florence Hogan; *Archivist*, Gail Farr
Founded 1954. Enrl 2,000; Fac 129; Highest Degree: Master
Library Holdings: Bk Vols 114,828; Per Subs 719
Special Collections: Polish History & Culture Coll, bks, realia, per; Radium (Frank Hartman Coll), bks, per
Automation Activity & Vendor Info: (Circulation) DRA
Publications: New books (monthly)
Partic in Consortium For Health Information & Library Services; Interlibrary Delivery Service of Pennsylvania; OCLC Online Computer Library Center, Inc; PALINET & Union Library Catalogue of Pennsylvania; Tri-State College Library Cooperative (TCLC)

M HOSPITAL OF THE UNIVERSITY OF PENNSYLVANIA, Robert Dunning Dripps Library of Anesthesia,* 3400 Spruce St, 19104-4283. SAN 325-9730. Tel: 215-662-3793, 215-662-4000 (Hospital). FAX: 215-662-745
Library Holdings: Bk Vols 550; Per Subs 45

L HOYLE, MORRIS & KERR, Law Library,* 1650 Market St, Ste 4900, 19103. SAN 323-6250. Tel: 215-981-5852. FAX: 215-981-5959. *Librn*, Gwendolyn R Yohannan; Staff 2 (MLS 1, Non-MLS 1)
Founded 1985
Library Holdings: Bk Vols 10,000; Bk Titles 1,000; Per Subs 200
Subject Interests: Environmental law

M INDEPENDENCE BLUE CROSS CORPORATE RESEARCH CENTER,* 1901 Market St, 34th flr, 19103-1480. SAN 314-870X. Tel: 215-241-2400, 215-241-3300. FAX: 215-241-2040.
Founded 1965
Library Holdings: Bk Vols 3,700; Bk Titles 3,500; Per Subs 160
Subject Interests: Bus, Health care, Health ins, Managed care, Marketing, Mgt
Special Collections: History of Blue Cross
Automation Activity & Vendor Info: (Cataloging) Inmagic, Inc.; (Serials) Inmagic, Inc.
Publications: Corporate Newsletter
Restriction: Open to public for reference only

S INDEPENDENCE SEAPORT MUSEUM LIBRARY,* 211 S Columbus Blvd, 19106. SAN 314-9781. Tel: 215-925-5439. FAX: 215-925-6713. Web Site: www.libertynet.org/seaport. *Librn*, Michael Angelo
Founded 1974
Library Holdings: Bk Vols 15,000; Bk Titles 14,000
Subject Interests: Maritime heritage of the Delaware, Port of Philadelphia, Schuylkill rivers, South Jersey maritime history, Susquehanna rivers
Special Collections: Manuscript Coll; Map & Chart Coll; Maritime Related Personal Family & Business Papers; Philadelphia Shipbuilding, (NY Shipbuilding Corp, Cramp Shipbuilding Co), vessel registers; Photograph Coll; Rare Book Coll
Publications: John Lenthall, Naval Architect: A Guide to Plans and Drawings of American Naval and Merchant Vessels 1790-1874; Massachusetts Steam Navigation Company, Salem, Massachusetts Records (1816-1818) and the Newhall Family Business Papers (1809-1852): A Descriptive Guide) Shipbuilding at Cramp & Sons: A History and Guide to Collections of the William Cramp & Sons Ship and Engine Building Company (1830-1927) and the Cramp Shipbuilding Company (1941-46) of Philadelphia; The Barry-Hayes Papers: A Descriptive Guide
Partic in OCLC Online Computer Library Center, Inc

S INSTITUTE FOR SCIENTIFIC INFORMATION, Business Intelligence Center Library,* 3501 Market St, 19104. SAN 314-9331. Tel: 215-386-0100. FAX: 215-386-6362.
Founded 1961
Subject Interests: Biblometrics, History of science, Scientometrics
Partic in BRS; Dialog Corporation; SDC

S INTERNATIONAL ADVISORY GROUP INC LIBRARY,* 528 Rahwn, PO Box 5071, 19111. SAN 372-851X. Tel: 215-742-5107. FAX: 215-742-1068. E-Mail: iag@fastnet.com. *Mgr*, George Fassnacht
Library Holdings: Bk Vols 5,000; Per Subs 20
Patent library of 35,000 patents on firearms

L THEODORE F JENKINS MEMORIAL LAW LIBRARY,* 841 Chestnut St 12th flr, 19107. SAN 314-9366. Tel: 215-592-5697. FAX: 215-574-7920. *Dir*, Regina A Smith; *Coll Develop*, Constance Smith; *Assoc Dir*, Kathy Coon; *Publ Servs*, Ida Weingram; *Automation Syst Coordr*, Katrina Piechnik *ILL*, Jenny Hohenstein; *Ref*, Ann Liivak; *Ref*, Christine Herz; *ILL*, Kristen McKeaney; *Cat*, Marianne Muha; Staff 25 (MLS 11, Non-MLS 14)
Founded 1802
Library Holdings: Bk Vols 267,667; Bk Titles 35,464; Per Subs 400
Special Collections: Roman & Canon Law (John Marshall Gest Coll)
Publications: Membership Memo; Newsletter
Partic in Mid-Atlantic Law Library Cooperative; OCLC Online Computer Library Center, Inc; PALINET & Union Library Catalogue of Pennsylvania

L KLEHR, HARRISON, HARVEY, BRANZBURG & ELLERS LIBRARY, 260 S Broad St, 19102. SAN 376-1584. Tel: 215-568-6060. FAX: 215-568-6603. Web Site: www.klehr.com. *Librn*, Margaret S Fallon; Tel: 215-569-3091, E-Mail: mfallon@klehr.com; Staff 3 (MLS 1, Non-MLS 2)
Library Holdings: Bk Vols 10,000
Database Vendor: Lexis-Nexis

§L KLETT, ROONEY, LIEBER & SCHORLING LIBRARY, Philadelphia, 2 Logan Sq, 12th Flr, 19103.

C LA SALLE UNIVERSITY, Connelly Library, 1900 W Olney Ave, 19141-1199. SAN 314-9382. Tel: 215-951-1287. FAX: 215-951-1595. *Dir*, John S Baky; Tel: 215-951-1285, E-Mail: baky@lasalle.edu; *Cat*, John K McAskill; *ILL, Ref*, W Stephen Breedlove; *Online Servs*, Eithne Bearden; *Bibliog Instr*, Bernetta Robinson; *Coll Develop*, Georgina Murphy; Staff 30 (MLS 10, Non-MLS 20)
Founded 1863. Enrl 3,957; Highest Degree: Doctorate

Library Holdings: Bk Vols 338,000; Per Subs 1,650
Subject Interests: Holocaust, Vietnam War
Special Collections: Catholic Convert Coll; Charles Willson Peale Coll; Germantowniana Coll; Graham Green; Japanese Tea Ceremony; Katherine Ann Porter Coll; Lasalliana; Literature Coll; Vietnam War; Walker Percy Coll
Database Vendor: Dialog, Ebsco - EbscoHost, Innovative Interfaces INN - View, Lexis-Nexis, OCLC - First Search, ProQuest
Publications: Connelly Chronicle
Function: Research library
Partic in PALINET & Union Library Catalogue of Pennsylvania

LANKENAU HOSPITAL
MEDICAL LIBRARY, 100 Lancaster Ave, Wynnewood, 19096. SAN 359-0615. Tel: 610-645-2698. FAX: 610-645-3425. *Librn*, Les Gundry
Founded 1860
Library Holdings: Bk Vols 6,000; Per Subs 300
Subject Interests: Gen med, Surgery
Special Collections: Collected Papers of the Lankenau Research Center
Partic in Nat Libr of Med; Regional Med Libr Network

LAVIN, COLEMAN, O'NEIL, RICCI, FINARELLI & GRAY LIBRARY,* Penn Mutual Tower, 10th flr, 510 Walnut, 19106. SAN 323-7389. Tel: 215-627-0303, Ext 7814. FAX: 215-627-2551. *Librn*, Barry Wilner
Library Holdings: Bk Vols 4,500; Per Subs 24

AL PAUL LEFTON CO, INC, Research Library, Rohm & Haas Bldg, 100 Independence Mall W, 19106. SAN 314-9390. Tel: 215-923-9600. FAX: 215-351-4298. E-Mail: alefton@lefton.com. Web Site: www.lefton.com.
Library Holdings: Per Subs 1,000
Subject Interests: Advertising, Marketing

LIBRARY COMPANY OF PHILADELPHIA, 1314 Locust St, 19107-5698. SAN 314-9404. Tel: 215-546-3181, 215-546-8229 (Print Room). Interlibrary Loan Service Tel: 215-546-2465. FAX: 215-546-5167. E-Mail: refdept@librarycompany.org. Web Site: www.librarycompany.org. *Assoc Librn*, James Green; *Librn*, John C Van Horne; *Ref*, Phillip Lapsansky; Staff 25 (MLS 15, Non-MLS 10)
Founded 1731
Jan 1999-Dec 1999 Income $6,494,276, City $15,435, Locally Generated Income $1,808,562. Mats Exp $1,615,614, Books $95,328, Presv $9,338. Sal $618,276 (Prof $550,000)
Library Holdings: Bk Titles 450,000
Subject Interests: 18th Century med, 18th Century sci, 19th Century women's hist, Afro-Americana, Am archit, Am political hist, Background of Am civilization to 1880, Early 19th Century med, Early 19th Century sci, History, Iconography of Philadelphia to 1930
Special Collections: Afro-American Coll, early American natural history, agriculture, education & philanthropy; American Imprints to 1880; American Juddica to 1850; American Technology & Business to 1860; Bks from Libraries of William Byrd, Benjamin Franklin, James Logan, Benjamin Rush & other Early American Book Collectors; English & American Literature; German Americana to 1830; Philadelphiana, bks & prints; Prints & Photographs of Philadelphia to 1930
Publications: Annual Report; exhibition catalogues; newsletter (occasional)
Partic in Independent Res Libr Asn; Research Libraries Group, Inc; RLIN
Short-term research fellowships offered
Friends of the Library Group

M LIBRARY OF THE COLLEGE OF PHYSICIANS OF PHILADELPHIA, (Formerly College Of Physicians Of Philadelphia Library), 19 S 22nd St, 19103-3097. SAN 358-7762. Tel: 215-563-3737, Ext 232. FAX: 215-569-0356. E-Mail: cppinfo@collphyphil.org. Web Site: www.collphyphil.org. *Coordr, Tech Servs*, Joan McKenzie; Tel: 215-563-3737, Ext 256, E-Mail: mckenzie@collphyphil.org; *Curator*, Charles Greifenstein; Tel: 215-563-3737, Ext 275, E-Mail: greitenstein@collphyphil.org; *Admin Assoc*, Josefa Sereda; E-Mail: sereda@collphyphi.org; *Librn*, Edward Morman; E-Mail: emorman@collphyphil.org; *Cat*, Laura Guelle; Tel: 215-563-3737, Ext 253, E-Mail: lguelle@collphyphil.org; *Ref*, Christopher Stanwood; Tel: 215-563-3737, Ext 297, E-Mail: cstanwood@collphyphil.org; Staff 6 (MLS 4, Non-MLS 2)
Founded 1788
Jul 2000-Jun 2001 Mats Exp $33,000, Books $10,000, Per/Ser (Incl. Access Fees) $23,000
Library Holdings: Bk Vols 350,000; Bk Titles 170,000; Per Subs 130
Subject Interests: Dermatology, History of medicine, Medicine
Special Collections: Archives of the College of Physicians; Gerontology (Joseph T Freeman Coll); Helfand-Radbill Medical Bookplate Coll; Medical Autograph Coll; Medical Portraits Coll; Samuel Gross Library of Surgery; Samuel Lewis Curio Coll; Samuel X Radbill Pediatric Historical Library Coll; William Harvey
Automation Activity & Vendor Info: (Acquisitions) Endeavor; (Cataloging) Endeavor; (Circulation) Endeavor; (OPAC) Endeavor
Partic in Health Science Library Information Consortium; National Network Of Libraries Of Medicine - South Central Region; OCLC Online Computer Library Center, Inc; PALINET & Union Library Catalogue of Pennsylvania; Philadelphia Area Consortium Of Special Collections Libraries
Friends of the Library Group

S LIBRARY OF THE NATIONAL ADOPTION CENTER, 1500 Walnut St Ste 701, 19102. SAN 326-4904. Tel: 215-735-9988. FAX: 215-735-9410. E-Mail: nac@adopt.org. Web Site: www.adopt.org. *Dir*, Carolyn Johnson; *Asst Librn*, Peggy Pearson
Library Holdings: Bk Vols 1,500
Partic in Nat Adoption Exchange

S LOCKHEED MARTIN LIBRARY,* Bldg 10, PO Box 8048, 19101-8048. SAN 359-0372. Interlibrary Loan Service Tel: 610-354-2110. FAX: 610-354-5660. *In Charge*, Roni Danilowicz
Founded 1945
Library Holdings: Bk Vols 10,000; Per Subs 90
Subject Interests: Aerospace tech, Artificial intelligence, Computer tech, Telecommunications
Automation Activity & Vendor Info: (Cataloging) TechLIB; (Circulation) TechLIB
Partic in ARIN Network; Defense Technical Information Center; Dialog Corporation; Dow Jones News Retrieval; Nasa Libraries Information System - Nasa Galaxie

R LUTHERAN THEOLOGICAL SEMINARY, (KML), Krauth Memorial Library, 7301 Germantown Ave, 19119-1794. SAN 314-9412. Tel: 215-248-6329. FAX: 215-248-6327. E-Mail: lutthelib@ltsp.edu. *Coll Develop, Dir*, David J Wartluft; *Asst Librn, ILL*, Karl Krueger; Tel: 215-248-6330, E-Mail: kkrueger@ltsp.edu; *Archivist*, John Peterson; Tel: 215-248-6383; *Cat*, Lois Reibach; *ILL*, Ronald Townsend; *Acq*, Mae Green; Staff 3 (MLS 3)
Founded 1864. Enrl 360; Fac 17; Highest Degree: Doctorate
Jul 1998-Jun 1999 Mats Exp $68,482, Books $55,356, Per/Ser (Incl. Access Fees) $13,126. Sal $229,795 (Prof $139,900)
Library Holdings: Bk Titles 185,264; Per Subs 520
Subject Interests: Architecture, Evangelical Lutheran Church in America, Liturgy, Lutheran hist, Relig art, Religion, Urban studies, Women
Special Collections: Lutheran Archives, Region 7
Automation Activity & Vendor Info: (Cataloging) epixtech, inc.; (Circulation) epixtech, inc.; (OPAC) epixtech, inc.; (Serials) epixtech, inc.
Database Vendor: epixtech, inc.
Partic in OCLC Online Computer Library Center, Inc; PALINET & Union Library Catalogue of Pennsylvania; Southeastern Pennsylvania Theological Library Association

M MAGEE REHABILITATION HOSPITAL, Patient Learning Resource Center Library,* 6 Franklin Plaza, 19102. SAN 326-1611. Tel: 215-587-3423. FAX: 215-568-3533. *Librn*, Kim Heeney
Library Holdings: Bk Vols 550; Bk Titles 500; Per Subs 80

R MANNA BIBLE INSTITUTE LIBRARY, PO Box 21464, 19141. Tel: 215-424-4551. FAX: 215-843-9870. *Librn*, Idawease Griswold; Staff 1 (MLS 1)
Founded 1944. Enrl 41; Fac 6
Library Holdings: Bk Vols 13,000; Per Subs 65
Subject Interests: Christianity

S THE MASONIC LIBRARY & MUSEUM OF PENNSYLVANIA,* Masonic Temple, One N Broad St, 19107. SAN 314-9099. Tel: 215-988-1933. FAX: 215-988-1972. *Librn*, Glenys A Waldman; *Curator*, John C Minott; *Archivist*, Milton Kenin
Founded 1871
Library Holdings: Bk Vols 70,000
Subject Interests: Philosophy, Religion
Special Collections: General Works on Freemasonry; Masonic Biography & General History; Masonic Manuscript Coll
Publications: Grand Lodge Proceedings; The Pennsylvania Freemason
Friends of the Library Group

S MATESON CHEMICAL CORP LIBRARY,* 1025 E Montgomery Ave, 19125. SAN 329-8884. Tel: 215-423-3200. FAX: 215-423-1164. *In Charge*, Bonnie Mateson
Library Holdings: Bk Vols 500; Per Subs 10

M MCP HAHNEMANN UNIVERSITY, Hahnemann Library, 245 N 15th St MS 449, 19102-1192. SAN 314-9234. Tel: 215-762-7184. Interlibrary Loan Service Tel: 215-762-7630. Circulation Tel: 215-762-7631. FAX: 215-762-8180. Web Site: library.mcphu.edu. *Assoc Dir*, Carl Anderson; *Dir*, Lenore Hardy; *Assoc Dir, Publ Servs*, Judith Baker; *ILL*, Lynda Sadusky; *Tech Servs*, Leopoldo Montoyo; *Ref*, Gary Childs; Staff 8 (MLS 8)
Founded 1868. Enrl 1,792; Highest Degree: Doctorate
Library Holdings: Bk Vols 108,451; Bk Titles 40,716; Per Subs 831
Subject Interests: Behav sci, Health sci, Medical
Special Collections: Paracelsus Coll
Automation Activity & Vendor Info: (Acquisitions) Innovative Interfaces Inc.; (Cataloging) Innovative Interfaces Inc.; (Circulation) Innovative Interfaces Inc.; (Course Reserve) Innovative Interfaces Inc.; (OPAC) Innovative Interfaces Inc.; (Serials) Innovative Interfaces Inc.
Database Vendor: OVID Technologies
Partic in Health Science Library Information Consortium; PALINET & Union Library Catalogue of Pennsylvania
Friends of the Library Group

CM MCP HAHNEMANN UNIVERSITY, Florence A Moore Library of Medicine, 3300 Henry Ave, 19129. SAN 314-9420. Tel: 215-842-6910. FAX: 215-849-1380. Web Site: library.mcphu.edu. *Coordr*, Linda Katz; E-Mail: linda.katz@drexel.edu; *Ref*, Kevin Block; E-Mail: kblock@drexel.edu; *ILL*, Margaret Mozi; E-Mail: mm88@drexel.edu; Staff 7 (MLS 3, Non-MLS 4)
Founded 1850. Highest Degree: Doctorate
Library Holdings: Bk Vols 62,000; Per Subs 704
Subject Interests: Biol sci, Medicine
Special Collections: Women in Medicine
Automation Activity & Vendor Info: (Cataloging) Innovative Interfaces Inc.; (Circulation) Innovative Interfaces Inc.; (Serials) Innovative Interfaces Inc.
Database Vendor: OCLC - First Search
Publications: Library web site; Newsletter; reference handouts
Partic in Health Science Library Information Consortium; OCLC Online Computer Library Center, Inc; PALINET & Union Library Catalogue of Pennsylvania
Friends of the Library Group
Departmental Libraries:
EASTERN PENNSYLVANIA PSYCHIATRIC INSTITUTE LIBRARY, 3200 Henry Ave, 19129. SAN 314-8971. Tel: 215-842-4509. FAX: 215-849-0820. Web Site: library.mcphu.edu. *Coordr*, Linda Katz; E-Mail: linda.katz@drexel.edu; *ILL*, Randall Blackwell; E-Mail: blackwell@drexel.edu; Staff 3 (MLS 1, Non-MLS 2)
Founded 1956
Library Holdings: Bk Vols 31,151; Per Subs 233
Subject Interests: Neuroscience, Psychiatry
Automation Activity & Vendor Info: (Cataloging) Innovative Interfaces Inc.; (Circulation) Innovative Interfaces Inc.; (OPAC) Innovative Interfaces Inc.; (Serials) Innovative Interfaces Inc.
Database Vendor: OCLC - First Search
Publications: Newsletter; Reference handouts
Restriction: Open to public for reference only
Partic in Health Science Library Information Consortium; OCLC Online Computer Library Center, Inc; PALINET & Union Library Catalogue of Pennsylvania
Friends of the Library Group
QUEEN LANE LIBRARY, 2900 Queen Lane, 19129. SAN 372-8447. Tel: 215-991-8740. FAX: 215-843-0840. Web Site: library.mcphu.edu. *Coordr*, Martha Kirby; E-Mail: mk56@drexel.edu; *Asst Librn*, Adrienne Jenness; E-Mail: aj24@drexel.edu; Staff 4 (MLS 2, Non-MLS 2)
Library Holdings: Bk Vols 18,619; Per Subs 154
Subject Interests: Biochemistry, Immunology, Med educ, Microbiology, Physiology
Automation Activity & Vendor Info: (Cataloging) Innovative Interfaces Inc.; (Circulation) Innovative Interfaces Inc.; (OPAC) Innovative Interfaces Inc.; (Serials) Innovative Interfaces Inc.
Publications: Newsletter, reference handouts
Partic in Health Science Library Information Consortium; OCLC Online Computer Library Center, Inc; PALINET & Union Library Catalogue of Pennsylvania
Friends of the Library Group

SR MEDICAL MISSION SISTERS LIBRARY,* 8400 Pine Rd, 19111. SAN 314-9439. Tel: 215-742-6100. FAX: 215-342-3948. *Librn*, Sr Judy Garbaccio
Library Holdings: Bk Titles 16,000; Per Subs 50
Subject Interests: Relig studies
Restriction: Not open to public

M MERCY HOSPITAL OF PHILADELPHIA, Medical Library, 501 S 54th Ave, 19143. SAN 320-4596. Tel: 215-748-9415. FAX: 215-748-9341. E-Mail: misericordia@hslc.org.; Staff 1 (MLS 1)
Founded 1918
Library Holdings: Bk Vols 1,096; Per Subs 115
Subject Interests: Medicine
Partic in Basic Health Sciences Library Network; Consortium For Health Information & Library Services; Health Science Library Information Consortium

L MESIROV, GELMAN, JAFFE, CRAMER & JAMIESON LIBRARY,* 1735 Market St, 19103-7598. SAN 328-1108. Tel: 215-994-1128. FAX: 215-994-1111. *Librn*, Denise Mines; Staff 3 (MLS 1, Non-MLS 2)
Library Holdings: Bk Vols 10,000; Bk Titles 750; Per Subs 40
Subject Interests: Law

S MONELL CHEMICAL SENSES CENTER, Morley R Kare Library, 3500 Market St, 19104-3308. SAN 322-9181. Tel: 215-898-6666. FAX: 215-898-2084. *Librn*, Joseph Brand; *Asst Librn*, Douglas Bayley
Library Holdings: Bk Titles 500; Per Subs 10
Subject Interests: Chemical senses, Neurosciences, Nutrition
Restriction: By appointment only

L MONTGOMERY, MCCRACKEN, WALKER & RHOADS LIBRARY, 123 S Broad St, 19109. SAN 314-948X. Tel: 215-772-7611. FAX: 215-772-7620. *Librn*, Georgeanne H Brown; E-Mail: gbrown@mmwr.com
Library Holdings: Bk Vols 15,000
Subject Interests: Law

C MOORE COLLEGE OF ART & DESIGN LIBRARY, 20th & The Race, 19103-1179. SAN 314-9498. Tel: 215-568-4515, Ext 1203. FAX: 215-568-8017. *Acq, Actg Dir, Archivist*, Sophia Hewryk; *Curator*, Helen F McGinnis; *Circ*, Suzanne Kopko; *AV*, George Stewart; Staff 8 (MLS 3, Non-MLS 5)
Founded 1848
Library Holdings: Per Subs 273
Subject Interests: Art history, Professional, Studio arts, Women's studies in visual arts
Special Collections: Bookworks Coll, artists' books; Joseph Moore Jr Coll; Philadelphia School of Design for Women Archives
Partic in OCLC Online Computer Library Center, Inc; PALINET & Union Library Catalogue of Pennsylvania

L MORGAN, LEWIS & BOCKIUS LLP, Law Library, 1701 Market St, 13th flr, 19103. SAN 314-9501. Tel: 215-963-5633. FAX: 215-963-5299. Web Site: www.morganlewis.com. *Librn*, Jill Grosman; E-Mail: jgrosman@morganlewis.com; Staff 10 (MLS 3, Non-MLS 7)
Founded 1873
Library Holdings: Bk Titles 46,000; Per Subs 200
Subject Interests: Legal mat
Automation Activity & Vendor Info: (Acquisitions) Innovative Interfaces Inc.; (Cataloging) Innovative Interfaces Inc.; (Circulation) Innovative Interfaces Inc.; (OPAC) Innovative Interfaces Inc.; (Serials) Innovative Interfaces Inc.
Open Mon-Fri 8:30-5:30

G NATIONAL ARCHIVES, Mid Atlantic Region,* 900 Market St, 19107-4292. SAN 314-9528. Tel: 215-597-3000. FAX: 215-597-2303. E-Mail: archives@philarch.nara.gov. Web Site: www.nara.gov. *Dir*, Kellee L Blake; Tel: 215-597-0921, E-Mail: kellee.blake@philarch.nara.gov; Staff 8 (MLS 3, Non-MLS 5)
Founded 1968
Library Holdings: Bk Titles 350
Special Collections: Genealogy (United States Census Schedules, 1790-1920), micro; United States District Courts Records (Delaware, Maryland, Pennsylvania, Virginia, West Virginia)
Publications: Research Sources in the Archives Branch

G NATIONAL ARCHIVES & RECORDS ADMINISTRATION, Mid Atlantic Region (Center City Philadelphia),* 900 Market St, 19107-4292. Tel: 215-597-9770. FAX: 215-597-2303. E-Mail: archives@philarch.nara.gov. Web Site: www.nara.gov/regional/philacc.html. *Archivist*, Kellee Blake
Special Collections: Archival Records of Federal Agencies & Courts in Delaware, Maryland, Pennsylvania, Virginia & West Virginia; Indian Affairs Records, microfilm; Passenger Arrival & Naturalization Records, microfilm; Population Censuses for All States, 1790-1920, microfilm; Pre-Federal & Early Federal History, microfilm; Pre-World War I Military Service Records, microfilm; US Diplomacy Records, microfilm
Restriction: Reference only to non-staff
Open Mon-Fri 8-5 & 2nd Sat each month 8-4

S NATIONAL FEDERATION OF ABSTRACTING & INFORMATION SERVICES, 1518 Walnut St, Ste 307, 19102-3403. SAN 372-9109. Tel: 215-893-1561. FAX: 215-893-1564. E-Mail: nfais@nfais.org. Web Site: www.nfais.org. *Exec Dir*, Richard T Kaser; E-Mail: kaser@nfais.org; *Asst Dir*, Jill O'Neill; E-Mail: jilloneill@nfais.org
Library Holdings: Bk Vols 55; Per Subs 40

S NATIONAL PARK SERVICE, Independence National Historical Park Library, 120 S Third St. (Mail add: 313 Walnut St, 19106), SAN 314-9536. Tel: 215-597-8047. FAX: 215-597-3969. Web Site: www.nps.gov/inde. *Archivist*, Karen Stevens; Tel: 215-597-2069, E-Mail: karen_stevens@nps.gov; Staff 2 (MLS 1, Non-MLS 1)
Founded 1951
Oct 2000-Sep 2001 Income $110,000. Mats Exp $4,000
Library Holdings: Bk Vols 10,550; Per Subs 23
Subject Interests: 18th Century Philadelphia, Am decorative arts of the 18th century, Am Revolution, Constitution politics, History
Special Collections: Edwin Owen Lewis Papers, 1927-1974; History & Restoration of Independence Hall (Horace Wells Sellers Coll, 1730-1930); Isidor Ostroff Papers, 1941-1968; National Museum Board of Managers Records, 1873-1918 (collected by William H Staake, Ellen Waln Harrison & Mary B Chew); Philadelphia Bureau of City Property, Independence Hall Records, 1896-1950; The Independence Hall Association Records, 1906-1962; The Morris Family Papers associated with the Deshler-Morris House in Germantown
Restriction: By appointment only, Circulates for staff only, In-house use for visitors
Function: Archival collection, Reference services available

S NATIONAL RAILWAY HISTORICAL SOCIETY LIBRARY,* 100 N 17th St, PO Box 58547, 19102-8547. SAN 327-0572. Tel: 215-557-6606. FAX: 215-557-6740. Web Site: www.nrhs.com. *Chief Librn*, Lynn Burshtin; E-Mail: nrhs@compuserve.com
Library Holdings: Bk Vols 10,000
Function: Research library

M NEUMANN MEDICAL CENTER,* 1741 Frankfort Ave, 19125. SAN 314-9994. Tel: 215-291-2000. FAX: 215-291-2028. *Mgr*, Hank Schnider
Library Holdings: Bk Titles 2,000; Per Subs 1,255

NEW YEAR SHOOTERS & MUMMERS MUSEUM LIBRARY, 1100 S Second St, 19147. SAN 328-297X. Tel: 215-336-3050. FAX: 215-389-5630. E-Mail: mummersmus@aol.com. Web Site: www.mummers.com. *Dir*, Palma Lucas; *Curator*, Jack Cohen
Library Holdings: Per Subs 200
Subject Interests: Photographs, Videos
Friends of the Library Group

M NORTHEASTERN HOSPITAL SCHOOL OF NURSING LIBRARY, 2301 E Allegheny Ave, 19134. SAN 314-9579. Tel: 215-291-3168. FAX: 215-291-3159. *Librn*, Marita Krivda; E-Mail: krivda@hslc.org
Founded 1925. Enrl 120; Fac 12
Jul 1998-Jun 1999 Income $50,600. Mats Exp $7,100, Books $1,500, Per/Ser (Incl. Access Fees) $5,000, Micro $600. Sal $43,500 (Prof $32,000)
Library Holdings: Bk Vols 2,250; Bk Titles 2,200; Per Subs 75
Subject Interests: Nursing
Partic in Delaware Valley Information Consortium

OTHMER LIBRARY OF CHEMICAL HISTORY, (Formerly Chemical Heritage Foundation), 315 Chestnut St, 19106. SAN 326-6885. Tel: 215-925-2222. Circulation Tel: 215-925-2222, Ext 486. Reference Tel: 215-873-8271, Ext 487. FAX: 215-925-1954. Web Site: www.othmerlib.chemheritage.org. *Dir Libr Serv*, Elizabeth Swan; Tel: 215-925-2222, Ext 226, E-Mail: eswan@chemheritage.org; *Head Tech Servs*, Elsa B Atson; Tel: 215-925-2222, Ext 235, E-Mail: elsaa@chemheritage.org; *Archivist*, Susan G Hamson; Tel: 215-925-2222, Ext 306, E-Mail: susanh@chemheritage.org; Staff 7 (MLS 2, Non-MLS 5)
Founded 1988
Library Holdings: Bk Vols 72,000; Bk Titles 25,000; Per Subs 40
Subject Interests: Hist of chem
Special Collections: Archives; Archives; Pictorial Coll; Scientific Instruments; Scientific Instruments
Automation Activity & Vendor Info: (Cataloging) Innovative Interfaces Inc.; (Circulation) Innovative Interfaces Inc.; (ILL) Innovative Interfaces Inc.; (OPAC) Innovative Interfaces Inc.; (Serials) Innovative Interfaces Inc.
Database Vendor: Dialog, OCLC - First Search
Publications: Chemical Heritage
Restriction: Non-circulating to the public
Function: Research library
Partic in OCLC Online Computer Library Center, Inc
The Foundation is sponsored by the American Chemical Society, the American Institute of Chemical Engineers & other professional societies in the chemical sciences

OVERBROOK SCHOOL FOR THE BLIND LIBRARY, 6333 Malvern Ave, 19151-2597. SAN 329-9309. Tel: 215-877-0313, Ext 269. TDD: 215-877-0313. FAX: 215-877-2466. Web Site: www.obs.org. *Librn*, Julia Flinchbaugh; E-Mail: julia@obs.org; Staff 2 (MLS 1, Non-MLS 1)
Founded 1832. Enrl 197; Fac 25
Library Holdings: Bk Vols 12,000; Bk Titles 6,500; Per Subs 87
Special Collections: Blindness (Blindiana Coll)
Special Services for the Deaf - TDD

M PARKVIEW HOSPITAL MEDICAL LIBRARY, (Formerly Allegheny University Hospitals), 1331 E Wyoming Ave, 19124. SAN 324-6310. Tel: 215-537-7449. FAX: 215-537-7723. *Mgr*, Eileen Smith; E-Mail: eileensmith@hslc.org
Subject Interests: Nursing
Restriction: By appointment only, In-house use for visitors
Partic in Delaware Valley Information Consortium

C PEIRCE COLLEGE LIBRARY,* 1420 Pine St, 19102-4699. SAN 314-9846. Tel: 215-545-6400, Ext 269. FAX: 215-545-3689. E-Mail: prccollib@hslc.org. Web Site: www.pierce.edu. *Chief Librn*, Debra S Schrammel; *Ref*, Gary Shecter
Founded 1963
Library Holdings: Bk Vols 39,000; Per Subs 150
Subject Interests: Bus
Special Collections: Law Coll
Partic in Philadelphia Area Consortium Of Special Collections Libraries

S PENN COUNCIL FOR RELATIONSHIPS LIBRARY,* 4025 Chestnut St First Flr, 19104. SAN 327-0610. Tel: 215-382-6680. FAX: 215-386-1743. Web Site: www.pcfr.org.
Library Holdings: Bk Titles 2,500

S PENNSYLVANIA ACADEMY OF FINE ARTS LIBRARY,* 1301 Cherry St, 19107. SAN 314-9617. Tel: 215-972-7600, Ext 2030. FAX: 215-569-0153. E-Mail: pafine@hslc.org. *Librn*, Aurora Deshauteurs
Enrl 400; Fac 35
Library Holdings: Bk Titles 14,500; Per Subs 89
Subject Interests: Visual arts
Partic in PALINET & Union Library Catalogue of Pennsylvania

S PENNSYLVANIA ENVIRONMENTAL COUNCIL LIBRARY,* 117 South 17th St, Ste 2300, 19103-5022. SAN 372-9141. Tel: 215-563-0250. Toll Free Tel: 800-322-9214. FAX: 215-563-0528. Web Site: www.libertynet.org/pecphila.
Library Holdings: Bk Vols 400; Per Subs 200
Subject Interests: Transportation

S PENNSYLVANIA HORTICULTURAL SOCIETY, McLean Library, 100 N 20th St, 19103-1495. SAN 314-9641. Tel: 215-988-8772. FAX: 215-988-8783. Web Site: www.libertynet.org/phs/phslibrary.html. *Librn*, Janet Evans; E-Mail: jevans@pennhort.org
Founded 1827
Library Holdings: Bk Titles 14,000; Per Subs 200
Subject Interests: Botany, Early American horticulture, Horticultural therapy, Landscape design, Ornamental horticulture, Specifically Pennsylvania
Special Collections: 15th-20th Century Horticultural Material; Pennsylvania Horticulture, Herbals, Medical Botany, rare bks
Partic in OCLC Online Computer Library Center, Inc; PALINET & Union Library Catalogue of Pennsylvania; Philadelphia Area Consortium Of Special Collections Libraries

PENNSYLVANIA HOSPITAL

S HISTORIC LIBRARY, 800 Spruce St, 19107-6192. SAN 359-0763. Tel: 215-829-3998. FAX: 215-829-7155. Web Site: www.pahosp.com.
Founded 1762
Library Holdings: Bk Titles 13,000
Subject Interests: Anatomy, Botany, Med texts from 1700 to 1930, Natural history, Surgery
Special Collections: Benjamin Smith Barton; Lloyd Zachary; The Meigs Family; Thomas Story Kirkbride; William Byrd of Westover
Friends of the Library Group

M MEDICAL LIBRARY - THREE PINE, 800 Spruce St, 19107-6192. SAN 359-0798. Tel: 215-829-3370. Interlibrary Loan Service Tel: 215-829-5436. FAX: 215-829-7155. Web Site: www.pahosp.com. *Mgr*, Patricia Wilson; E-Mail: pawils@pahosp.com; Staff 2 (MLS 2)
Founded 1940
Library Holdings: Bk Titles 19,000
Subject Interests: Allied health, Hist of Pa hosp, Hist of psychiat, History of medicine, Medicine, Nursing, Psychiatry, Psychoanalysis
Friends of the Library Group

S PENNSYLVANIA SCHOOL FOR THE DEAF LIBRARY,* 100 W School House Lane, 19144. SAN 327-0599. Tel: 215-951-4700. FAX: 215-951-4708. *Librn*, Judy Nelson; *Asst Librn*, Fern Quillen
Library Holdings: Bk Vols 13,000; Per Subs 35
Branches:
EDUCATIONAL RESOURCE CENTER Tel: 215-951-4748. FAX: 215-951-4708. *Librn*, Allen Zollman
Houses PSD Professional Library. Specialize in deafness; 3000 items including monographs & periodicals. Open Mon-Fri 7:30-4

L PEPPER HAMILTON LLP, Law Library, 3000 Two Logan Sq, 18th & Arch Sts, 19103-2799. SAN 314-965X. Tel: 215-981-4100. FAX: 215-981-4750. *Dir Libr Serv*, Robyn L Beyer; E-Mail: beyerr@pepperlaw.com
Library Holdings: Bk Vols 35,000; Per Subs 500
Subject Interests: Bus, Law, Medicine, Mgt
Partic in Dialog Corporation; Westlaw

S PEW CHARITABLE TRUSTS LIBRARY,* One Commerce Sq, 2005 Market St, Ste 1700, 19103-7017. SAN 374-5430. Tel: 215-575-4814. *Librn*, C Suzanne Cole; Staff 2 (MLS 1, Non-MLS 1)
Founded 1989
Library Holdings: Bk Vols 1,000; Per Subs 180

G PHILADELPHIA CITY ARCHIVES, 3101 Market St, First flr, 19104. SAN 314-9668. Tel: 215-685-9400. FAX: 215-685-9409. *Archivist*, Ward J Childs; *Archivist*, Jefferson M Moak; *Archivist*, Lee Stanley
Founded 1952
Subject Interests: County govt rec, Philadelphia city
Special Collections: authorities of the City of Philadelphia; of the Centennial and Sesquicentennial Exhibitions & Philadelphia's 1976 Bicentennial Celebration; Recorder of Deeds and other offices of the County of Philadelphia; records; Records of the 28 political subdivisions of the County other than the City of Philadelphia that existed prior to the consolidation of the City and County; Records of the Guardians of the Poor (Inspectors of County Prisons, County Commissioners, Board of Health, County Courts); Records of the Mayor, Cabinet Officers, all departments, bureaus, boards, commissions and
Publications: City Archives Newsletter; Descriptive Inventory of the Archives of the City & County of Philadelphia; Subject Index to the Photograph Collection of the Philadelphia City Archives

CM PHILADELPHIA COLLEGE OF OSTEOPATHIC MEDICINE, O J Snyder Memorial Library, 4170 City Ave, 19131-1694. SAN 314-9692. Tel: 215-871-6470. FAX: 215-871-6478. E-Mail: hansav@pcom.edu. Web Site: www.pcom.edu/library. *Dir*, Etheldra Templeton; *Assoc Dir*, Gerri Stevenson; *Cat*, Kathryn Picardo; *ILL*, Julia Lewis; *Circ, Coordr, Publ Servs*, Kathleen Gallagher; *AV, Coordr*, Yvonne Scholfield; *Per*, Jane Alvardo

Founded 1899
Library Holdings: Bk Vols 34,244; Per Subs 672
Subject Interests: Medicine, Osteopathic med, Psychology
Special Collections: Archival History of Medicine; first editions in osteopathy; Osteopathic Periodicals
Publications: Archival Coll; Audio-Visual Coll; bibliographies; Library Handbook; Library Newsletter; Osteopathic Coll; Osteopathic Colleges & Hospital Libraries Survey Book; periodicals & pamphlets; Union List of Osteopathic Literature
Partic in Health Science Library Information Consortium; PALINET & Union Library Catalogue of Pennsylvania; Tri-State College Library Cooperative (TCLC)
Friends of the Library Group

GL PHILADELPHIA COMMON PLEAS & MUNICIPAL COURT LAW LIBRARY, Office of Court Administration,* Rm 600, City Hall, 19107. SAN 321-0596. Tel: 215-686-3799. FAX: 215-686-3737. *Librn*, James M Clark; *Assoc Librn*, Francis F Klock; Staff 2 (MLS 2)
Founded 1970
Library Holdings: Bk Vols 36,000; Bk Titles 1,000; Per Subs 125
Subject Interests: United States law (Penna)
Restriction: Open to public for reference only
Partic in OCLC Online Computer Library Center, Inc

S PHILADELPHIA CORPORATION FOR AGING LIBRARY, 642 N Broad St, 19130-3409. SAN 327-0696. Tel: 215-765-9000, Ext 5565. FAX: 215-765-9066. Web Site: www.pcaphl.org. *Librn*, Scott Spencer; E-Mail: sspencer@pcaphl.org; Staff 2 (MLS 1, Non-MLS 1)
Circ 500
Jul 1998-Jun 1999 Income $73,000. Mats Exp $15,000, Per/Ser (Incl. Access Fees) $11,000, Micro $200. Sal $59,000 (Prof $38,000)
Library Holdings: Bk Titles 3,462; Per Subs 100
Subject Interests: Geriatrics-gerontology
Automation Activity & Vendor Info: (Acquisitions) Inmagic, Inc.; (Cataloging) Inmagic, Inc.; (Circulation) Inmagic, Inc.; (ILL) Inmagic, Inc.; (OPAC) Inmagic, Inc.; (Serials) Inmagic, Inc.
Database Vendor: OVID Technologies
Restriction: By appointment only
Mem of Nat Network of Librs of Med

S PHILADELPHIA HISTORICAL COMMISSION LIBRARY,* 1515 Arch St, 13th flr, 19102. Tel: 215-683-4590. FAX: 215-683-4594. *In Charge*, Dr Richard Tyler
Library Holdings: Bk Vols 3,000; Bk Titles 2,500; Per Subs 10

S PHILADELPHIA JEWISH ARCHIVES CENTER, Balch Institute, 18 S Seventh St, 19106-1423. SAN 327-0556. Tel: 215-925-8090, Ext 229. FAX: 215-925-4413. E-Mail: pjarch@balchinstitute.org. Web Site: www.libertynet.org/pjac. *Exec Dir*, Nan Beth Wallace; Tel: 215-925-8090, Ext 228, E-Mail: pjacexec@balchinstitute.org; *Archivist*, Davis Donald
Founded 1972
Library Holdings: Bk Vols 2,000
Subject Interests: Cultural hist, Philadelphia city, Religious education
Restriction: In-house use for visitors
Function: Archival collection

S PHILADELPHIA MUSEUM OF ART LIBRARY, 26th St & Benjamin Franklin Pkwy, PO Box 7646, 19101-7646. SAN 314-979X. Tel: 215-684-7650. FAX: 215-236-0534. Web Site: www.philamuseum.org/html/library.html. *Librn*, Allen Townsend; E-Mail: aktownsend@philamuseum.org; *Cat*, Linda Martin-Schaff; *Ref*, Lilah Mittelstaedt; *Archivist*, Susan K Anderson; Staff 6 (MLS 3, Non-MLS 3)
Founded 1876
Library Holdings: Bk Titles 140,000; Per Subs 523
Special Collections: Johnson Coll; Kiensbusch Arms & Armor Coll
Partic in PALINET & Union Library Catalogue of Pennsylvania
Friends of the Library Group

S PHILADELPHIA NEWSPAPERS, INC, Inquirer & Daily News Library, 400 N Broad St, PO Box 8263, 19101. SAN 314-9749. Tel: 215-854-4669. FAX: 215-854-5697. E-Mail: research@phillynews.com. *Res*, Connie Pickett; Staff 14 (MLS 14)
Founded 1926
Library Holdings: Bk Vols 8,000; Per Subs 30
Special Collections: Newspaper Clippings; Photographs; Vertical Files
Partic in Dialog Corporation

S PHILADELPHIA ORCHESTRA LIBRARY, Academy of Music, Broad & Locust Sts, 19102-4297. SAN 321-060X. Tel: 215-893-1929, 215-893-1954, 215-893-1960. FAX: 215-875-7664. *Librn*, Clinton F Nieweg; E-Mail: cnieweg@philorch.org; *Librn*, Nancy M Bradburd; *Librn*, Robert M Grossman; Staff 6 (MLS 3, Non-MLS 3)
Founded 1900
Library Holdings: Bk Vols 8,000; Bk Titles 4,000
Subject Interests: Sheet music
Publications: Marcato (newsletter)

C PHILADELPHIA UNIVERSITY, Paul J Gutman Library, School House Lane & Henry Ave, 19144. SAN 314-9722. Tel: 215-951-2840. Interlibrary Loan Service Tel: 215-951-2580. Reference Tel: 215-951-2848. FAX: 215-951-2574. Web Site: www.philau.edu/library. *Dir*, Steven Bell; Tel: 215-951-2847, E-Mail: bells@philau.edu; *Coll Develop, ILL*, Stan Gorski; Tel: 215-951-2581, E-Mail: gorskis@philau.edu; *Automation Syst Coordr, Tech Servs*, Barbara Lowry; Tel: 215-951-2842, E-Mail: lowryb@philau.edu; *AV*, Angela Smedley; Tel: 215-951-2975, E-Mail: smedley@philau.edu; *ILL, Ref*, Sherri Litwiller; E-Mail: litwillers@philau.edu; *Ref*, Jordana Shane; Tel: 215-951-2629, E-Mail: shanej@philau.edu; Staff 4 (MLS 4)
Founded 1884. Enrl 2,100; Fac 99; Highest Degree: Master
2000-2001 Income $1,042,000. Mats Exp $300,000. Sal $452,000
Library Holdings: Bk Vols 87,500; Per Subs 1,575
Subject Interests: Apparel, Architecture, Bus, Design, Fashion, Hist of textile, Indust, Mgt, Textiles, Textiles manufacture
Special Collections: Textile History
Automation Activity & Vendor Info: (Acquisitions) epixtech, inc.; (Cataloging) epixtech, inc.; (Circulation) epixtech, inc.
Database Vendor: epixtech, inc.
Restriction: Authorized scholars by appointment, Open to student, faculty & staff
Partic in OCLC Online Computer Library Center, Inc; Tri-State College Library Cooperative (TCLC)

SR PHILADELPHIA YEARLY MEETING OF THE RELIGIOUS SOCIETY OF FRIENDS, (Formerly Society Of Friends), Henry J Cadbury Library, 1515 Cherry St, 19102. SAN 315-0046. Tel: 215-241-7220. FAX: 215-567-2096. E-Mail: library@pym.org. Web Site: www.pym.org/library. *Head Librn*, Rita Varley; Tel: 215-241-7219; *Asst Librn*, Esther Darlington
Founded 1961
Jul 2000-Jun 2001 Mats Exp $3,000. Sal $54,000
Library Holdings: Bk Titles 18,000
Subject Interests: African Amer, Civil rights, Community, Criminal justice, Environmental studies, Family life, Native Americans, Peace, Quaker hist, Quakers, Religious education, Spiritual life, Women's studies
Special Collections: Non Violent Alternatives; Peace Education Resources; Quakerism & Quaker History; Religion & Psychology (Dora Wilson Coll), bks & papers
Automation Activity & Vendor Info: (Cataloging) Follett; (Circulation) Follett
Publications: Teaching Peace & Supplement to Teaching Peace (bibliog)
Restriction: Members only

S PLANNED PARENTHOOD SOUTHEASTERN PENNSYLVANIA, Resource Center,* 1144 Locust St, 19107. SAN 327-053X. Tel: 215-351-5590. FAX: 215-351-5595. E-Mail: ppsepa@libertynet.org. Web Site: www.libertynet.org/ppsepa.
Library Holdings: Bk Vols 2,000; Per Subs 50
Publications: Sexuality Resources Update; Teachable Moments

S POLISHER RESEARCH INSTITUTE LIBRARY, Philadelphia Geriatric Center Library, c/o TCCC, 5301 Old York Rd, 19141-2996. SAN 322-7758. Tel: 215-456-2971. Circulation Tel: 215-456-2001. Reference Tel: 215-456-2987. FAX: 215-456-2017. Web Site: www.pgc.org/research/resources.html. *Librn*, Sheryl Panka-Bryman; E-Mail: sherylpanka-bryman@rcn.com; *Librn*, Joyce A Post; *ILL*, Mary McCaffrey; E-Mail: mmccaffrey@rcn.com. Subject Specialists: *Geriatrics and gerontology*, Sheryl Panka-Bryman; Staff 2 (MLS 1, Non-MLS 1)
Founded 1959
Jun 2000-May 2001 Income Parent Institution $118,000. Mats Exp $18,000, Books $5,500, Per/Ser (Incl. Access Fees) $11,000, Electronic Ref Mat (Incl. Access Fees) $1,500. Sal $63,000
Library Holdings: Bk Vols 11,000; Per Subs 60
Subject Interests: Death, Dying, Geriatrics, Gerontology, Long term care admin, Psychology, Sociology
Publications: Library & Acquisitions Newsletter (bimonthly)
Restriction: Open to public for reference only
Function: Research library
Partic in Basic Health Sciences Library Network; Delaware Valley Information Consortium; Nat Libr of Med

L POST & SCHELL, Law Library, 1800 JFK Blvd, 19th Flr, 19103. SAN 372-1825. Tel: 215-587-1460. FAX: 215-587-1444. Web Site: www.postschell.com. *Librn*, Kathryn Brewer; E-Mail: kbrewer@postschell.com
Library Holdings: Bk Vols 2,000
Partic in AALL; Greater Philadelphia Law Library Association

R PRESBYTERIAN CHURCH (USA), Department of History Library, 425 Lombard St, 19147-1516. SAN 315-0178. Tel: 215-627-1852. Reference Tel: 215-928-3892. FAX: 215-627-0509. E-Mail: reference@history.pcusa.org. Web Site: www.history.pcusa.org. *Dir*, Frederick J Heuser; *Mgr*, Richard Bater; Staff 19 (MLS 6, Non-MLS 13)
Founded 1852
Library Holdings: Bk Titles 180,000; Per Subs 150
Subject Interests: Am Presbyterian hist
Special Collections: Alaska (Sheldon Jackson Coll); American Indian Missionary Correspondence & Papers, mss & micro; American Sunday

School Union, mss; Archives of Presbyterian Church (USA) & Predecessor Denominations; Board of Foreign Missions, mss & micro; Missions; National Council of Churches Archives
Automation Activity & Vendor Info: (Cataloging) Inmagic, Inc.
Publications: American Presbyterians; Journal of Presbyterian History; Presbyterian Heritage Newsletter
Partic in OCLC Online Computer Library Center, Inc; PALINET & Union Library Catalogue of Pennsylvania
Open Mon-Fri 8:30-4:30

PRESBYTERIAN MEDICAL CENTER OF PHILADELPHIA, Health Sciences Library,* 51 N 39th St, 19104. SAN 314-9862. Tel: 215-662-9181. FAX: 215-662-8453. Web Site: www.libertynet.org/~presby. *Dir*, Miranda Scott; E-Mail: scottm@shrsys.hslc.org
Founded 1972
Library Holdings: Bk Vols 3,300; Bk Titles 2,700; Per Subs 300
Subject Interests: Allied health, Consumer health, Medicine, Nursing
Special Collections: Ophthalmology (De Schweinitz Coll); Ophthalmology (Harold G Scheie MD Coll), bks, flm, art

RAWLE & HENDERSON, Law Library, Widener Bldg, One S Penn Sq, 19107. SAN 314-9897. Tel: 215-575-4480. FAX: 215-563-2583. *Librn*, Christine Harvan; E-Mail: charvan@raule.com
Founded 1783
Library Holdings: Bk Vols 14,500
Subject Interests: Admiralty law, General law
Partic in Dialog Corporation; Westlaw

REED, SMITH, SHAW & MCCLAY, Law Library,* One Liberty Pl Ste 2500, 1650 Market St, 19103. SAN 372-1701. Tel: 215-851-1413. FAX: 215-851-1420. *Mgr*, Joe Maguire; E-Mail: jmaguire@rssm.com; *Acq*, Charlene Hinson; *Automation Syst Coordr*, Pin-sheng Hsiao; *ILL*, Pat Steele; *Ref*, Sarah Gootzait
Library Holdings: Bk Vols 8,000; Per Subs 100

RESEARCH FOR BETTER SCHOOLS, INC, Resource Center,* 444 N Third St, 19123. SAN 327-8816. Tel: 215-574-9300. FAX: 215-574-0133. *Coordr*, Peter Donahoe; E-Mail: donahoe@rbs.org
Library Holdings: Bk Vols 11,000; Per Subs 100
Special Collections: CSAP Archives; High Risk Students; Math/Science Education; Rural Education; School Restructuring
Restriction: By appointment only

ROBERT MORRIS ASSOCIATES LIBRARY,* 1650 Market St, Ste 2300, 19103. SAN 329-2800. Tel: 215-446-4111. FAX: 215-446-4039. E-Mail: hyou@rmanq.org, rmainfo@rmahq.org. Web Site: www.rmahq.org. *Librn*, Heng You; Tel: 215-446-4113; Staff 2 (MLS 1, Non-MLS 1)
Library Holdings: Bk Titles 2,000; Per Subs 150
Database Vendor: Dialog, Lexis-Nexis
Function: Research library
Partic in Dialog Corporation; Dow Jones News Retrieval; OCLC Online Computer Library Center, Inc

ROBERT W RYERSS LIBRARY & MUSEUM,* Burholme Park, 7370 Central Ave, 19111-3055. SAN 314-9943. Tel: 215-745-3061. *Librn*, Ermioni Rousseas
Founded 1910
Library Holdings: Bk Vols 20,000; Per Subs 35
Special Collections: Victoriana Coll
Open Fri, Sat & Sun 10-5

ROSENBACH MUSEUM & LIBRARY, 2010 DeLancey Pl, 19103. SAN 314-9935. Tel: 215-732-1600. FAX: 215-545-7529. E-Mail: info@rosenbach.org. Web Site: www.rosenbach.org. *Dir*, Derick Dreher; Tel: 215-732-1600, Ext 21, E-Mail: ddreher@rosenbach.org; *Librn*, Elizabeth E Fuller; Tel: 215-732-1600, Ext 15, E-Mail: eefuller@rosenbach.org; *Curator*, Judith M Guston; Tel: 215-732-1600, Ext 12, E-Mail: jmguston@rosenbach.org; Staff 20 (MLS 1, Non-MLS 19)
Founded 1954
Library Holdings: Bk Vols 30,000
Subject Interests: 20th Century Am lit, Am lit, Americana, Bk illustration, British lit, Hist of bks, Latin Americana, Printing
Special Collections: Marianne Moore coll bks, mss, furnishings, photogs, drawings; Maurice Sendak Coll, bks, mss, drawings; Rosenbach Company Archives, mss, bks; Rush-Williams-Biddle Family Papers, mss
Publications: Collection Guides; Exhibition Catalogs; Fine Press & Facsimile Editions of Rare Books & Mss; The Rosebach Newsletter
Restriction: By appointment only, Not a lending library
Function: Outside services via phone, cable & mail, Research library
Mem of Philadelphia District Libr Ctr
Partic in Research Libraries Group, Inc
Friends of the Library Group

M ROXBOROUGH MEMORIAL HOSPITAL, School of Nursing & Medical Staff Libraries, 5800 Ridge Ave, 19128. SAN 325-2868. Tel: 215-487-4345. FAX: 215-487-4591. *Librn*, John P English; Staff 1 (MLS 1)
Founded 1945
Library Holdings: Bk Titles 2,000; Per Subs 180

Subject Interests: Allied health, Medicine, Nursing
Restriction: Circulation limited
Mem of Nat Network of Librs of Med
Partic in Basic Health Sciences Library Network; Delaware Valley Information Consortium

M SAINT AGNES MEDICAL CENTER, Joseph M Gambescia Health Science Library, 1900 S Broad St, 19145. SAN 314-996X. Tel: 215-339-4448. FAX: 215-755-1295. Web Site: www.chi-east.org. *Librn*, Jata Ghosh; Tel: 215-339-4100; Staff 1 (MLS 1)
Founded 1939
Library Holdings: Bk Vols 3,000; Bk Titles 98; Per Subs 98
Subject Interests: Health sci
Partic in BHSL; DEVIC
Open Mon-Fri 8-5:30

M SAINT CHRISTOPHER'S HOSPITAL FOR CHILDREN, Margery H Nelson Medical Library, 3601 A St, 19134-1095. SAN 329-2940. Tel: 215-427-5374. FAX: 215-427-6872. *Librn*, Frances B Pinnel; E-Mail: frances.b.pinnel@tenethealth.com
Library Holdings: Bk Titles 4,400; Per Subs 204
Open Mon-Fri 9-5

M SAINT JOSEPH'S HOSPITAL, Medical Library, 16th St & Girard Ave, 19130-1615. SAN 314-9978. Tel: 215-787-9000, 215-787-9156. *Librn*, Sr Mary Carmelita
Library Holdings: Bk Vols 2,075; Per Subs 50

SAINT JOSEPH'S UNIVERSITY

S CAMPBELL LIBRARY, Academy of Food Marketing, 5600 City Ave, 19131-1395. SAN 359-100X. Tel: 610-660-1196. Interlibrary Loan Service Tel: 610-660-1907. Circulation Tel: 610-660-1195. FAX: 610-660-1604. Web Site: www.sju.edu/libraries/campbell. *Dir*, Patricia Weaver; E-Mail: pweaver@sju.edu; Staff 2 (MLS 1, Non-MLS 1)
Founded 1965
Library Holdings: Bk Titles 2,200; Per Subs 260
Subject Interests: Food mrketing
Special Collections: USDA Series Reports & Yearbooks
Automation Activity & Vendor Info: (Acquisitions) GEAC; (Cataloging) GEAC; (Circulation) GEAC; (OPAC) GEAC
Database Vendor: GaleNet, OCLC - First Search
Publications: Serials list (annual); subject bibliographies
Partic in OCLC Online Computer Library Center, Inc

C FRANCIS A DREXEL LIBRARY, 5600 City Ave, 19131-1395. SAN 359-0976. Tel: 610-660-1905. Interlibrary Loan Service Tel: 610-660-1907. Circulation Tel: 610-660-1900. Reference Tel: 610-660-1904. FAX: 610-660-1916. Web Site: www.sju.edu/libraries/drexel. *Dir Libr Serv*, Evelyn Minick; E-Mail: minick@sju.edu; *Assoc Dir, Publ Servs*, Ene Andrilli; Tel: 610-660-1913, E-Mail: eandrill@sju.edu; *Assoc Dir, ILL*, Tim LaBorie; Tel: 610-660-1914, E-Mail: tlaborie@sju.edu; *Assoc Dir*, Marjorie Rathbone; Tel: 610-660-1912, E-Mail: rathbone@sju.edu; *Business*, Cynthia Slater; Tel: 610-660-1139, E-Mail: cslater@sju.edu; *Cat, Tech Servs*, Erin Stalberg; Tel: 610-660-1915, E-Mail: stalberg@sju.edu; *Circ*, Dolores McCaughan; Tel: 610-660-1900, E-Mail: dmccaugh@sju.edu; *Govt Doc*, Christopher Dixon; Tel: 610-660-1139, E-Mail: cdixon@sju.edu; *ILL, Ser*, Rebecca Reilly; Tel: 610-660-1057, E-Mail: rreilly@sju.edu; *Web Coordr*, Linda Kubala; Tel: 610-660-1531, E-Mail: lkubala@sju.edu
Founded 1851. Enrl 7,000; Fac 392; Highest Degree: Doctorate
Library Holdings: Bk Vols 335,000; Bk Titles 215,000; Per Subs 1,850
Subject Interests: History, Philosophy, Theology
Special Collections: SJU publications Coll
Automation Activity & Vendor Info: (Acquisitions) GEAC; (Cataloging) GEAC; (Circulation) GEAC; (OPAC) GEAC
Database Vendor: OCLC - First Search
Publications: Library Lines
Partic in Interlibrary Delivery Service of Pennsylvania; OCLC Online Computer Library Center, Inc; Pa Tri-State Col Libr Coop; PALINET & Union Library Catalogue of Pennsylvania

SR SAINT MARK'S CHURCH, Isaiah V Williamson Library, 1625 Locust St, 19103. SAN 314-9986. Tel: 215-735-1416. FAX: 215-735-0572. *Librn*, James Young
Library Holdings: Bk Vols 1,800; Per Subs 17
Subject Interests: Anglo-Catholicism, Episcopal church, Spirituality

L SAUL, EWING, REMICK & SAUL, Law Library,* 3800 Centre Sq W, 19102. SAN 325-9757. Tel: 215-972-7873. FAX: 215-972-1945. *Dir*, Judith W Abriss; *Asst Librn*, Richard Weston
Library Holdings: Bk Vols 24,500
Open Mon-Fri 8-5

L SCHNADER, HARRISON, SEGAL & LEWIS LIBRARY, 1600 Market St, Ste 3600, 19103. SAN 315-0011. Tel: 215-751-2111. FAX: 215-751-2205. *Dir*, Bobbi Cross; Tel: 215-751-2399, E-Mail: bcross@schnader.com; *Asst Librn*, Linda Hauck; *Ref*, Annemarie Lorenzen; Staff 4 (MLS 4)
Library Holdings: Bk Vols 35,000; Per Subs 1,000
Subject Interests: Law

Database Vendor: Dialog, Ebsco - EbscoHost, Lexis-Nexis, OCLC - First Search
Partic in OCLC Online Computer Library Center, Inc; RLIN

S SCHOOL DISTRICT OF PHILADELPHIA, Pedagogical Library, 2120 Winter St, 19103. SAN 315-002X. Tel: 215-299-2543. FAX: 215-299-2540. E-Mail: beryrich@phila.k12.pa.us. Web Site: www.phila.k12.pa.us/ll/libraryservices/dept-lib.html. *Adminr*, Crystal H Patterson; Tel: 215-299-7379, E-Mail: cwalker@phila.k12.pa.us; *Librn*, Berry Richards; *Asst Librn*, Elaine Herrmann; *Circ*, Elaine Love; *Tech Coordr*, Katherine Wester; E-Mail: cwester@phila.k12.pa.us; Staff 4 (MLS 2, Non-MLS 2)
Founded 1883
Library Holdings: Bk Vols 56,000; Bk Titles 44,000; Per Subs 320
Subject Interests: Education
Special Collections: School District of Philadelphia Archives
Automation Activity & Vendor Info: (Cataloging) DRA
Database Vendor: DRA, Ebsco - EbscoHost, OCLC - First Search, Wilson - Wilson Web
Publications: Current Periodicals List
Restriction: Lending to staff only
Function: Professional lending library
Partic in Access Pa; OCLC Online Computer Library Center, Inc; PALINET & Union Library Catalogue of Pennsylvania

S SCHUYLKILL ENVIRONMENTAL RESOURCE & INFORMATION CENTER, 8480 Hagy's Mill Rd, 19128. SAN 327-0769. Tel: 215-482-7300, Ext 126. FAX: 215-482-8158.
Library Holdings: Bk Vols 10,300
Subject Interests: Natural history
Special Collections: Children's Books (Natural History & Science); Rare Books Coll (Natural History)
Publications: The Quill (quarterly newsletter)
Friends of the Library Group

S SETTLEMENT MUSIC SCHOOL, Blanche Wolf Kohn Library, 416 Queen St, PO Box 25120, 19147. SAN 359-1158. Tel: 215-336-0400. FAX: 215-551-0483. *Dir*, Eric Anderson; Tel: 215-336-0400, Ext 19, E-Mail: smsmlc@smsmusic.org; *Librn*, Jean Peoples; Staff 1 (Non-MLS 1)
Founded 1969. Enrl 3,100
Library Holdings: Bk Titles 800; Per Subs 12
Special Collections: Chamber Music (Mischa Schneider & J Gershon Cohen Coll), scores & parts; Flute Music (William Kincaid Coll), scores & parts
Branches:
GERMANTOWN, 6128 Germantown Ave, 19144. SAN 359-1182. Tel: 215-438-0200. *Dir*, Patricia Manley; E-Mail: smsgtn@smsmusic.org; *Librn*, Emily Grusky; Staff 1 (Non-MLS 1)
Subject Interests: Am studies, Int security studies, Latin America, Russia, The Caribbean, USSR
JENKINTOWN MUSIC SCHOOL, 515 Meetinghouse Rd, Jenkintown, 19046. SAN 328-8501. Tel: 215-885-6166. *Dir*, Marsha Hogan; E-Mail: smsjms@smsmusic.org; *Librn*, Jane Walker; Staff 1 (Non-MLS 1)
KARDON-NORTHEAST, 3745 Clarendon St, 19114. SAN 359-1212. Tel: 215-637-1500. *Dir*, Mark Huxsoll; E-Mail: smskne@smsmusic.org; *Librn*, Vasiliy Kifyak

SMITHKLINE BEECHAM PHARMACEUTICALS
S MARKETING LIBRARY, One Franklin Plaza, PO Box 7929 FP 1260, 19101-7929. SAN 359-1271. Tel: 215-751-5576. FAX: 215-751-5509. *Bibliog Instr, Librn, Online Servs*, Doris Shalley; Staff 1 (Non-MLS 1)
Founded 1946
Library Holdings: Bk Vols 2,000; Per Subs 200
Publications: Acquisitions Bulletin; Mark Alert (quarterly abstract serv)
S RESEARCH & DEVELOPMENT LIBRARY, UW2322, 709 Swedeland Rd, PO Box 1539, King of Prussia, 19406-0939. SAN 359-1247. Tel: 610-270-6400. FAX: 610-270-4127. *Mgr*, Arlene Smith; E-Mail: arlene_g_smith@sbphrd.com; Staff 12 (MLS 12)
Founded 1947
Library Holdings: Bk Titles 15,000; Per Subs 1,000
Subject Interests: Biochemistry, Chemistry, Medicine, Microbiology, Pharm, Pharmacology
Publications: List of Recent Acquisitions
Restriction: Not open to public
Partic in PALINET & Union Library Catalogue of Pennsylvania

S SOUTHEASTERN PENNSYLVANIA TRANSPORTATION AUTHORITY LIBRARY,* 1234 Market St, 9th flr, 19107. SAN 315-0054. Tel: 215-580-7387. FAX: 215-580-7163.
Founded 1966
Library Holdings: Bk Titles 6,000; Per Subs 60
Subject Interests: Commuter railroads, Pub transportation, Traffic eng, Urban studies
Special Collections: Urban Traffic & Transportation Board
Publications: Acquisitions list (monthly); News Highlights-Transit USA
Partic in Dialog Corporation; PALINET & Union Library Catalogue of Pennsylvania

SR SPIRITUAL FRONTIERS FELLOWSHIP INTERNATIONAL, Lending Library,* 3619 Baring St, PO Box 7868, 19101-7868. SAN 371-0939. Tel: 215-222-1991. *Exec Dir*, Elizabeth W Fenske
Library Holdings: Bk Vols 15,000
Subject Interests: Psychology, Religion
Publications: Lending Library Catalog

L STRADLEY, RONON, STEVENS & YOUNG LIBRARY,* 2600 One Commerce Sq, 19103-7098. SAN 315-0070. Tel: 215-564-8190. FAX: 215-564-8120.; Staff 3 (MLS 1, Non-MLS 2)
Founded 1972
Library Holdings: Bk Vols 12,000; Bk Titles 4,000; Per Subs 250
Subject Interests: Corporation, Litigation, Securities, Tax
Special Collections: PA Pamphlet laws since 1700
Publications: In-house letter
Partic in PALINET & Union Library Catalogue of Pennsylvania

R TEMPLE BETH ZION-BETH ISRAEL LIBRARY, 300 S 18th St, 19103. SAN 314-8688. Tel: 215-735-5148. FAX: 215-735-7838. *Librn*, Marc Levit
Founded 1970
Library Holdings: Bk Vols 2,270; Bk Titles 2,200
Subject Interests: Haggodahs, Israel, Jewish educ, Judaica

C TEMPLE UNIVERSITY, National Center for the Study of Corporal Punishment & Alternatives in the Schools Library, 253 Ritter Hall, 19122. SAN 372-9168. Tel: 215-204-6091, 215-579-4865. FAX: 215-204-6013. Web Site: www.temple.edu/psych/edu.ncspa.htm/. *Dir*, Irwin A Hyman
Founded 1976
Library Holdings: Bk Vols 1,000; Per Subs 10
Special Collections: Archives on Corporal Punishment, newsp clippings

M TEMPLE UNIVERSITY HEALTH SCIENCE CENTER, Gustavus C Bird Library Diagnostic Imaging, 3401 N Broad, 19140. SAN 329-0301. Tel: 215-707-4226. FAX: 215-707-1460. *Dir*, Nancy G Washburne; E-Mail: ngwash@astro.ocis.temple.edu
Founded 1963
Library Holdings: Bk Titles 1,700; Per Subs 45
Subject Interests: Nuclear medicine, Radiology
Partic in Health Science Library Information Consortium
Barcode accessable CD collections in Diagnostic Imaging & 2 CD readers

C TEMPLE UNIVERSITY LIBRARIES, Samuel Paley Library, Paley Library (017-00), 1210 W Berks St, 19122-6088. SAN 359-1301. Tel: 215-204-823 FAX: 215-204-5201. Web Site: www.library.temple.edu. *Librn*, Linda Cotilla; Tel: 215-283-1390, E-Mail: cotilla@temple.edu; *Head, Cat*, Laila E Zein; Tel: 215-204-3274, E-Mail: lzein@temple.edu; *Access Serv*, Penelope Myers; Tel: 215-204-0749, Fax: 215-204-0769, E-Mail: pmyers@astro.ocis.temple.edu; *Ref*, Martha Henderson; Tel: 215-204-4585, E-Mail: joneside@astro.ocis.temple.edu; *Spec Coll*, Thomas Whitehead; Tel: 215-204-4371, E-Mail: whitetm@temple.edu; *Adminr*, Ivy Bayard; Tel: 215-204-3184, E-Mail: ivy@blue.temple.edu; *Archivist*, Margaret Jerrido; Tel: 215-204-6639, E-Mail: mj@astro.ocis.temple.edu; *Coll Develop*, Frank Immler; Tel: 215-204-8244, E-Mail: fimmler@astro.ocis.temple.edu; *Science*, Gretchen Sneff; Tel: 215-204-4724, Fax: 215-204-7720, E-Mail: gsneff@unix.temple.edu; *Syst Coordr*, Byron Mayes; Tel: 215-204-5797, E-Mail: bcmayes@temple.edu. Subject Specialists: *Engineering*, Gretchen Sneff
Founded 1892. Enrl 28,126; Fac 1,045; Highest Degree: Doctorate
Jul 1999-Jun 2000 Mats Exp $5,829,959, Books $1,398,050, Per/Ser (Incl. Access Fees) $3,631,224, Presv $149,344. Sal $4,218,898 (Prof $3,187,759)
Library Holdings: Bk Vols 2,449,366; Per Subs 16,574
Special Collections: Philadelphia News Photographs from the Philadelphia Inquirer & Bulletin from Individuals & Organizations; Post-Civil War 1854 Philadelphia Urban Planning, Housing Social Welfare, Education & Labor records (Urban Archives); Richard Ellis Library, War Posters (Rare Book & Manuscript Coll); Russell H Conwell & Temple University archives, publications, sermons, lectures, faculty & alumni publications, oral history (Cornwellana-Templana Coll); Science Fiction & Fantasy; Small Press & Alternative Press Publications, 1960's-date (Contemporary Culture Coll); Symbolist Literature, 20th Century English Literature, Richard Aldington, Walter de la Mare, 17th Century English History & Religion, Bibles, Herbals & Horticulture, Business & Accounting History, Printing, Publishing & Graphic Arts
Database Vendor: Innovative Interfaces INN - View
Publications: Descriptive Guide to the University Archives; Manuscript Register Series; Monitor; Temple University Libraries Newsletter; Urban Archives Notes
Partic in Asn of Research Libraries; CNI; Coalition for Networked Info; Nerl; OCLC Online Computer Library Center, Inc; PALCI; PALINET & Union Library Catalogue of Pennsylvania; Research Libraries Group, Inc
Library holdings incl University Libraries, Law Library & Health Sciences Center Libraries
Departmental Libraries:
AMBLER, Meetinghouse Rd, Ambler, 19002. SAN 314-2779. Tel: 215-283-1383. Circulation Tel: 215-283-1393. Reference Tel: 215-283-1577. FAX: 215-283-1539. Web Site: www.library.temple.edu/ambler/ambler.htm. *Chief Librn*, Linda Cotilla; Tel: 215-283-1390, E-Mail: cotilla@astro.temple.edu; *Librn*, Jeanne Chen; Tel: 215-283-1389, E-Mail: jeanchen@astro.temple.edu; *Librn*, Sandra Thompson; Tel: 215-283-1387, E-Mail:

sandi@astro.temple.edu; Staff 8 (MLS 3, Non-MLS 5)
Highest Degree: Doctorate
Library Holdings: Bk Vols 90,000; Per Subs 446

BIOLOGY, 248 Biol Life Sciences Bldg (015-00), 19122. SAN 375-8664. Tel: 215-204-8878. FAX: 215-204-9318. Web Site: www.library.temple.edu/scilib/bio.htm. *In Charge*, Jason Ronallo; E-Mail: jronallo@temple.edu

BLOCKSON AFRO-AMERICAN COLLECTION, Sullivan Hall, 1st flr, 19122. SAN 376-2262. Tel: 215-204-6632. FAX: 215-204-5197. Web Site: www.library.temple.edu/blockson/. *Librn*, Aslaku Berhanu; E-Mail: aberhanu@temple.edu
Special Collections: Prints & Photographs; Slave Narrative Coll; Underground Railroad Coll

CHEMISTRY, Beury Hall, 1st flr (016-00), 19122. SAN 375-8672. Tel: 215-204-7120. FAX: 215-204-8924. Web Site: www.library.temple.edu/scilib/chem.htm.

ENGINEERING & ARCHITECHTURE LIBRARY, COLLEGE OF ENGINEERING, 1947 N 12th St, 19122. SAN 359-1395. Tel: 215-204-7828. FAX: 215-204-7720. Web Site: www.library.temple.edu/seilib/engr.htm. *Chief Librn*, Gretchen Sneff; Tel: 215-204-4724, E-Mail: gsneff@unix.temple.edu; Staff 1 (MLS 1)
Library Holdings: Bk Vols 26,000; Per Subs 306
Subject Interests: Architecture, Biomed, Civil, Electrical, Environ, Mechanical engineering

M HEALTH SCIENCE CENTER, 3440 N Broad, 19140. SAN 359-1425. Tel: 215-707-2402. FAX: 215-707-4135. Web Site: blue.temple.edu/~tums/departments/clinical/library/index.htm, www.temple.edu/hse_library. *Dir*, Mark-Allen Taylor; E-Mail: mat@temple.edu; *Assoc Dir*, Stephanie Ferretti; Tel: 215-707-8936, E-Mail: sferrett@temple.edu; *Assoc Dir*, Barbara Kuchan; Tel: 215-707-3738, E-Mail: bkuchan@temple.edu
Founded 1901. Enrl 2,282; Highest Degree: Doctorate
Jul 1999-Jun 2000 Income $1,956,678. Mats Exp $917,754, Books $49,955, Per/Ser (Incl. Access Fees) $844,847, Presv $22,952. Sal $873,880 (Prof $412,909)
Library Holdings: Bk Vols 129,925; Per Subs 1,619
Subject Interests: Allied health, Dentistry, Medicine, Nursing, Pharm
Partic in Health Sciences Libraries Consortium; Interlibrary Delivery Service of Pennsylvania; Medline; PALINET & Union Library Catalogue of Pennsylvania
Friends of the Library Group

L LAW LIBRARY, 1719 N Broad St, 19122. SAN 359-145X. Tel: 215-204-3669. FAX: 215-204-1785. Web Site: www.temple.edu/lawschool/lawlibrary.htm. *Dir*, John Necci; Tel: 215-204-4538, E-Mail: necci@vm.temple.edu; *Librn*, Scott Finet; *Cat*, Ethel Fiderer; *Cat*, Janice McDonnell; *Ref*, Steve Paulo; *Acq, Ser*, Paul Carino; Staff 10 (MLS 10)
Jul 1999-Jun 2000 Income $1,320,000. Mats Exp $685,549, Books $119,121, Per/Ser (Incl. Access Fees) $564,846, Presv $14,877. Sal $724,765 (Prof $533,110)
Library Holdings: Bk Vols 363,450; Per Subs 2,765
Special Collections: Historic Trials (Temple University Trials Coll)

MATHEMATICAL SCIENCES, Wachman Hall, 4th flr (038-16), 19122. SAN 375-8680. Tel: 215-204-8434. Web Site: www.library.temple.edu/scilib/math.htm. *In Charge*, Joyce Dennis; E-Mail: jade@temple.edu

PHYSICS, Barton-A Hall, 2nd flr (009-00), 19122. SAN 377-7499. Tel: 215-204-7649. Web Site: www.library.temple.edu/scilib/physics.htm. *In Charge*, Victoria Newton; E-Mail: vnewton@thunder.temple.edu

TYLER SCHOOL OF ART, 7725 Penrose Ave, Elkins Park, 19027. SAN 359-1514. Tel: 215-782-2849. FAX: 215-782-2799. Web Site: www.library.temple.edu/tyler/tyler.htm. *Chief Librn*, Linda Cotilla; Tel: 215-283-1390, E-Mail: cotilla@astro.temple.edu; *Librn*, Andrea Goldstein; Tel: 215-782-2850, E-Mail: andrea@astro.temple.edu; Staff 5 (MLS 3, Non-MLS 2)
Library Holdings: Bk Vols 34,000; Per Subs 118
Subject Interests: Art, Art industries, Trade

ZAHN LIBRARY, Ritter Annex 139 (004-00), 13th & Cecil B Moore Ave, 19122. SAN 359-1573. Tel: 215-204-8481. *In Charge*, Derik Badman; E-Mail: dbadman@temple.edu
Founded 1965
Library Holdings: Bk Vols 37,142; Per Subs 156
Subject Interests: Primary, Secondary educ, Social work

CM TEMPLE UNIVERSITY SCHOOL OF PODIATRIC MEDICINE, Charles E Krausz Library, Eighth St at Race, 19107. SAN 359-0674. Tel: 215-629-0300, Ext 6047. FAX: 215-629-1622. Web Site: www.pcpm.edu. *Dir*, Carol Vincent; Staff 2 (MLS 2)
Founded 1962. Enrl 445; Fac 114; Highest Degree: Doctorate
1998-1999 Mats Exp $100,000, Books $30,000, Per/Ser (Incl. Access Fees) $70,000. Sal $105,000 (Prof $45,000)
Library Holdings: Bk Titles 10,500; Per Subs 350
Subject Interests: Medicine, Orthopedics, Podiatry, Sports med
Special Collections: Anthony Sabatella Coll; Center for the History of Foot Care; Stewart E Reed Coll, bks, prints, per, monographs
Publications: Footnotes; Library newsletter
Partic in Health Science Library Information Consortium; Medline

S THE CIVIL WAR LIBRARY & MUSEUM, (CWLM), 1805 Pine St, 19103. SAN 314-9471. Tel: 215-735-8196. FAX: 215-735-3812. *Exec Dir*, John J Craft; Staff 1 (Non-MLS 1)
Founded 1888
Library Holdings: Bk Titles 16,000
Subject Interests: Abraham Lincoln, Civil War era
Special Collections: Edged Weapons; Firearms; Flags; Relics; Uniforms
Friends of the Library Group

THOMAS JEFFERSON UNIVERSITY

CM SCOTT MEMORIAL LIBRARY, 1020 Walnut St, 19107. SAN 359-1603. Tel: 215-503-8848. Interlibrary Loan Service Tel: 215-503-6773. FAX: 215-923-3203. *Dir*, Edward W Tawyea; *Tech Servs*, Paula Manzella; *Cat*, Elizabeth Mikita; *Ref*, Ann Koopman; *Archivist*, Beth Bensman; *Bibliog Instr, Ref*, Elizabeth Warner; *Bibliog Instr, Ref*, Gui Van Moorsel; Staff 14 (MLS 14)
Founded 1896. Enrl 2,028; Fac 611; Highest Degree: Doctorate
Library Holdings: Bk Vols 180,249; Bk Titles 74,904; Per Subs 2,331
Subject Interests: Medicine
Special Collections: Obstetrics & Gynecology (Bland)
Publications: Monthly Newsletter
Partic in BRS; Dialog Corporation; Georgetown LIS Health Sci Libr Consortium; Greater NE Regional Med Libr Serv; Medline; OCLC Online Computer Library Center, Inc; PALINET & Union Library Catalogue of Pennsylvania; SDC Info Servs
Friends of the Library Group

S UNION LEAGUE OF PHILADELPHIA LIBRARY, 140 S Broad St, 19102. SAN 315-0151. Tel: 215-587-5594. FAX: 215-587-5598. E-Mail: library@unionleague.org. Web Site: www.unionleague.org. *Librn*, Robyn Train
Founded 1862
Library Holdings: Bk Vols 26,000; Per Subs 61
Special Collections: American Civil War; Lincolniana; Philadelphia & Pennsylvania History Coll
Friends of the Library Group

UNITED STATES ARMY

A ARMY CORPS OF ENGINEERS, PHILADELPHIA DISTRICT LIBRARY, Wanamaker Bldg, 100 Penn Square E, 19107-3390. SAN 359-1662. Interlibrary Loan Service Tel: 215-656-6821. FAX: 215-656-6828. *Tech Servs*, Linda Carnevale Skale; E-Mail: linda.c.skale@nap02.usace.army.mil; Staff 1 (MLS 1)
Founded 1969
Library Holdings: Bk Vols 6,000; Bk Titles 4,000; Per Subs 60
Subject Interests: Engineering, Sciences
Special Collections: Congressional Documents: Rivers & Harbors, from 1933; Transactions of the ASCE, from 1941
Publications: Accessions list (monthly); bibliography series
Partic in Fedlink

GL UNITED STATES COURT OF APPEALS, Third Circuit Library,* 1609 US Courthouse, 601 Market St, 19106. SAN 315-0186. Tel: 215-597-2009. FAX: 215-597-6913. *Cat*, Cheryl A Berninger; *Tech Servs*, Susan E Appleby; *Ref*, Judith F Ambler; Staff 13 (MLS 7, Non-MLS 6)
Library Holdings: Bk Vols 100,000; Per Subs 150
Subject Interests: Judicial admin
Special Collections: Govt
Open Mon-Fri 8:30-4:30

S US DEPARTMENT OF LABOR, Region III Library, Curtis Bldg, Ste 740 W, 170 S Independence Mall W, 19106-3309. SAN 370-2766. Tel: 215-861-4900. FAX: 215-861-4904. *Librn*, Barbara Bray; Tel: 215-861-4912, E-Mail: bray_barbara@dol.gov; Staff 1 (MLS 1)
Library Holdings: Bk Vols 2,000; Per Subs 11
Subject Interests: Industrial hygiene, Occupational health, Occupational safety
Partic in Fed Libr & Info Network

G UNITED STATES ENVIRONMENTAL PROTECTION AGENCY REGION 3, (RCEI), Regional Center for Environmental Information, 1650 Arch St 3PM52, 19103. SAN 314-898X. Tel: 215-814-5254. FAX: 215-814-5253. E-Mail: library-reg3@epa.gov. Web Site: www.epa.gov/reg3rcei/. *Head Librn*, Ann Fletcher; Tel: 215-814-5362, E-Mail: fletcher.anne@epa.gov; *Librn*, Dawn Shellenberger; Tel: 215-814-5364, E-Mail: shellenberger.dawn@epa.gov; Staff 3 (MLS 2, Non-MLS 1)
Founded 1972
Library Holdings: Bk Vols 14,000; Bk Titles 9,500; Per Subs 200
Subject Interests: Biodiversity, Ecology, Environmental law, Hazardous waste, Pollution control, Toxicology, Wetland ecology
Database Vendor: Dialog, Lexis-Nexis, OCLC - First Search
Function: ILL available, Reference services available
Partic in Fedlink; OCLC Online Computer Library Center, Inc

UNITED STATES NAVY

A NAVAL SHIP SYSTEMS ENGINEERING STATION LIBRARY, Philadelphia Naval Surface Warfare Center-Carderock Div, Bldg 4, 19112-5083. SAN 359-1816. Tel: 215-897-7816. FAX: 215-897-7162.
Founded 1909
Library Holdings: Bk Vols 25,000; Per Subs 25

Subject Interests: Chemistry, Electrical, Marine eng, Mechanical, Metallurgy
Special Collections: Navy Technical Manuals
Restriction: Not open to public
Partic in Defense Technical Information Center; Dialog Corporation

C UNIVERSITY OF PENNSYLVANIA, Development Research & Analysis Library,* 538 Franklin Bldg, 3451 Walnut St, 19104-6285. SAN 371-7895. Tel: 215-898-6374. FAX: 215-898-6864. *Dir*, Joe Huges; Staff 11 (MLS 11)
Founded 1976
Library Holdings: Bk Titles 800; Per Subs 20
Restriction: Staff use only
Partic in Dialog Corporation; Dow Jones News Retrieval

C UNIVERSITY OF PENNSYLVANIA LIBRARIES, 3420 Walnut St, 19104-6206. SAN 359-1840. Tel: 215-898-7091. Interlibrary Loan Service Tel: 215-898-7558. FAX: 215-898-0559. Web Site: www.library.upenn.edu. *Dir*, Paul H Mosher; E-Mail: mosher@pobox.upenn.edu; *Assoc Dir, Tech Servs*, H Carton Rogers; Tel: 215-898-2814, E-Mail: rogers@pobox.upenn.edu; *ILL*, Robert Krall; Tel: 215-898-7559, E-Mail: krallrn@pobox.upenn.edu; *Circ*, Emily Batista; Tel: 215-898-0701, E-Mail: batista@pobox.upenn.edu; *Acq*, Gail Defendorf; Tel: 215-898-5932, E-Mail: gldefend@pobox.upenn.edu; *Acq*, Jean Shuttleworth; Tel: 215-898-7563, E-Mail: jeannes@pobox.upenn.edu; *Cat*, Louise Rees; Tel: 215-898-7548, E-Mail: rees@pobox.upenn.edu; *Cat*, Rachelle Nelson; Tel: 215-898-9048, E-Mail: nelsonrr@pobox.upenn.edu; *Syst Coordr*, Roy Heinz; E-Mail: heinzr@pobox.upenn.edu; *Ref*, Jane Bryan; Tel: 215-898-2817, E-Mail: bryanj@pobox.upenn.edu; *Ser*, Robert Persing; Tel: 215-898-2815, E-Mail: persing@pobox.upenn.edu; *Coll Develop*, Dennis Hyde; Tel: 215-898-6675, E-Mail: hyde@pobox.upenn.edu; Staff 285 (MLS 112, Non-MLS 173)
Founded 1750. Enrl 18,290; Fac 2,110; Highest Degree: Doctorate
Jul 1999-Jun 2000 Income (Main Library and Branch Library) $33,526,467. Mats Exp $10,305,052. Sal $15,862,471
Library Holdings: Bk Vols 4,914,244
Special Collections: 16th Century Imprints; 18th Century English Fiction (Singer-Mendenhall Coll); American Drama (Clothier, Speiser, Edwin Forrest Library & Manuscripts); Aristotle Texts & Commentaries; Benjamin Franklin Imprints (Curtis Coll); Bibles (Ross & Block Coll); Church History, Spanish Inquisition, Canon Law & Witchcraft (Henry Charles Lea Library); Cryptography (Mendelsohn Coll); Early Americana (Dechert Coll); Elzevier Imprints (Krumbhaar Coll); English Economic History (Colwell Coll, Carey Coll); Eugene Ormandy Archive; Franz Werfel (Alma Mahler Werfel Coll); French Plays of the 18th & 19th Century Coll; French Revolution Pamphlets (McClure Coll); History of Alchemy & Chemistry (Edgar Fahs Smith Library); Indic Manuscripts; Italian Renaissance Literature (Macaulay Coll); James Fenimore Cooper Coll; James T Farrell Coll; Jonathan Swift (Teerink Coll); Leibniz (Schrecker Coll); Lewis Mumford Coll; Marian Anderson Coll; Mark Twain Coll; Neo-Latin Literature (Neufforge Coll); Robert Montgomery Bird Coll; Shakespeariana, Tudor & Stuart Drama (Horace Howard Furness Library); Spanish Golden Age Literature (Rennert & Crawford Coll); Spanish-American texts, 17th-19th centuries (Keil Coll); Theodore Dreiser Coll; Van Wyck Brooks Coll; Waldo Frank Coll; Walt Whitman Coll; Washington Irving Coll
Publications: Penn Library Facts; Penn Library News; Penn Library Resource Guide
Mem of Asn of Research Libraries
Partic in OCLC Online Computer Library Center, Inc; PALINET & Union Library Catalogue of Pennsylvania; Research Libraries Group, Inc
Friends of the Library Group
Departmental Libraries:
ANNENBERG SCHOOL OF COMMUNICATION, 3620 Walnut-6220, 19104. SAN 359-1905. Tel: 215-898-7027. FAX: 215-898-2024. *Librn*, Sharon Black; Tel: 215-898-6106, E-Mail: sblack@asc.upenn.edu
Founded 1962
Library Holdings: Per Subs 251
Subject Interests: Attitude and opinion research, Communications, Hist and tech of communication, Interpersonal communications, Res in mass media, Theory
Special Collections: Faculty Publications; Film (16mm) catalogs; Financial Reports of the Communication Companies & Public TV Stations of the US; Sol Worth Archive; Television Script Archive
Publications: Reference Sources in Communications; Selected Acquisitions
BIDDLE LAW LIBRARY, 3460 Chesnut St, 19104-3406. SAN 359-193X. Tel: 215-898-7488. FAX: 215-898-6619. *Librn*, Elizabeth S Kelly; E-Mail: ekelly@law.upenn.edu
Subject Interests: Administrative regulations, Anglo-Am, Canon law, Decisions, Foreign, International law, Judicial rpts, Roman law
Special Collections: 16th Century English Year Books; Anglo-American & Foreign Law, bks, monographs, digests; Early American & English Law Books; Early American Legal Mss; Records & Briefs of Pennsylvania Supreme & Superior Courts, United States Court of Appeals for Third Circuit & United States Supreme Court, micro
Partic in Mid-Atlantic Law Library Cooperative
CM BIOMEDICAL LIBRARY, Johnson Pavilion, 36th & Hamilton Walk, 19104-6060. SAN 359-2111. Tel: 215-898-5817. FAX: 215-573-2075. *Librn*, Valerie Pena; Tel: 215-898-8020, Fax: 215-573-4143, E-Mail: penav@mail.med.upenn.edu
Library Holdings: Bk Vols 169,859
Subject Interests: Biology, Clinical medicine, Health care, Nursing
Partic in Health Sciences Libraries Consortium; RLG; RML
CHEMISTRY, 3301 Spruce St, 19104-6323. SAN 359-1964. Tel: 215-898-2177. FAX: 215-898-0741. *Librn*, Judith Currano; E-Mail: currano@pobox.upenn.edu
Library Holdings: Bk Vols 33,580
Subject Interests: Biochemistry, Inorganic, Organic, Physical chem
CM DENTAL, 4001 Spruce St, 19104-6041. SAN 359-1999. Tel: 215-898-896 FAX: 215-898-7985. *Librn*, Pat Heller; Tel: 215-898-8978, E-Mail: heller@pobox.upenn.edu
Library Holdings: Bk Vols 57,509
Subject Interests: Dentistry, Hist of dent, Oral biol
Special Collections: Dental Catalogs; Dental Patents; Foreign Dental Dissertations; Thomas W Evans Historical Documents
Publications: Acquisitions List of Books & Periodicals
Mem of Health Sci Librs Consortium
Partic in RML
ENGINEERING & APPLIED SCIENCE, 220 S 33rd St, 19104-6315. SAN 359-2235. Tel: 215-898-7266. FAX: 215-573-2010.
Library Holdings: Bk Vols 119,118
Subject Interests: Bio-med eng, Chemistry, Civil, Computers, Electrical engineering, Electronics, Incl optics, Mat sci, Mechanical, Metallurgical eng, Robotics, Systs, Tech aspects of transportation
Special Collections: Fluid Mechanics; Heat Transfer; NASA Reports; Robotics
FINE ARTS, Furness Bldg, 220 S 34th St, 19104-6308. SAN 359-2022. Te 215-898-8325. FAX: 215-573-2066. *Librn*, William Keller; E-Mail: wkeller@pobox.upenn.edu
Library Holdings: Bk Vols 126,926
Subject Interests: Appropriate tech, Architecture, City, Hist of art, Hist preservation, Landscape architecture, Regional planning, Urban design
Special Collections: Rare Architectural Books, 16th to 20th C
HIGH DENSITY STORAGE-VAN PELT LIBRARY, 3001 Market St, 19104-6316. SAN 359-2413. Tel: 215-573-5662. FAX: 215-898-0964. *In Charge*, Emily Batista; Tel: 215-898-0701, Fax: 215-898-0559, E-Mail: batista@pobox.upenn.edu
Founded 1900
Special Collections: Depository for all United States Geological Survey, National Ocean Survey Charts, Defense Mapping Agency & Canadian Geological Survey
JOHN PENMAN WOOD LIBRARY OF NATIONAL DEFENSE (ROTC), 3205 Lancaster Ave, 19104-6325. SAN 359-2383. Tel: 215-590-8808. FAX: 215-590-8618. Web Site: dolphin.upenn.edu/~arotc. *Librn*, Zbigniev Kania; E-Mail: kania@pobox.upenn.edu
Founded 1928
Library Holdings: Per Subs 42
Subject Interests: Leadership, Med servs, Mgt, Military history, Operations, Orgn, Strategy, Tactics, War games, Weaponry
LIPPINCOTT-WHARTON SCHOOL, 3420 Walnut St, 19104-6207. SAN 359-2057. Tel: 215-898-5924. FAX: 215-898-2261. *Librn*, Michael Halperin; E-Mail: halperin@wharton.upenn.edu
Subject Interests: Bus, Finance, Labor, Marketing, Mgt incl acctg, Real property, Taxation, Transportation
Special Collections: Corporation Annual Reports; Financial; Investment Sources; Lipman Criminology Coll; New York Stock Exchange & American Stock Exchange, microfiche
MATH-PHYSICS-ASTRONOMY LIBRARY, David Rittenhouse Lab, 33rd & Walnut Sts, 19104-6317. SAN 359-2081. Tel: 215-898-8173. FAX: 215-573-2009. *Librn*, Gwenn Lochster; E-Mail: gsl@pobox.upenn.edu
Subject Interests: Astronomy, Mathematics, Physics
MORRIS ARBORETUM LIBRARY, 9414 Meadowbrook Ave, 19118-2697 SAN 359-2359. Tel: 215-247-5777, Ext 115. FAX: 215-248-4439. *Librn*, Joan Markham
Founded 1933
Library Holdings: Bk Vols 6,000; Per Subs 60
Subject Interests: Botany, Conservation, Ecology, Garden design, History, Horticulture, Plant pathology, Urban forestry
Special Collections: Historical (Botanical Books from 19th Century)
MUSEUM, 3260 South St, 19104-6324. SAN 359-2170. Tel: 215-898-7840. FAX: 215-573-2008. *Librn*, John Weeks; E-Mail: weeksj@pobox.upenn.edu
Subject Interests: Anthropology, Archaeology, Ethnology
Special Collections: Aboriginal American Linguistics & Ethnology (Daniel Garrison Brinton Coll); Egyptology
POPULATION STUDIES CENTER-DEMOGRAPHY LIBRARY, 3718 Locust Walk, 19104-6298. SAN 359-1980. Tel: 215-898-5375. FAX: 215-898-2124. Web Site: lexis.pop.upenn.educ/library/demlib.html. *Librn*, Lisa A Newman; E-Mail: lnewman@pop.upenn.edu; Staff 2 (MLS 1, Non-MLS 1)
Founded 1970. Fac 30; Highest Degree: Doctorate
Library Holdings: Per Subs 110
Subject Interests: Demographic hist, Foreign population censuses, Int develop, Soc
Special Collections: African Censuses Coll; Durand Coll-Historical Demograph

Publications: Acquisitions List (monthly)
Partic in APLIC International Census Network
Library is separately funded & maintained collection for the Research Associates of the Population Studies Center, as well as for graduate students, faculty & staff of the Sociology & Economics departments. The Demography Library is not part of the University of Pennsylvania Libraries system

M VETERINARY SCHOOL, 3800 Spruce St, 19104-6008. SAN 359-226X. Tel: 215-898-8895. FAX: 215-573-2007. *Librn*, Lillian Bryant; E-Mail: bryant@pobox.upenn.edu
Special Collections: Fairman Rogers Coll on Equitation & Horsemanship

UNIVERSITY OF PENNSYLVANIA SCHOOL OF NURSING, Center for the Study of the History of Nursing, 420 Guardian Dr, 19104-6096. SAN 370-6826. Tel: 215-898-4502. FAX: 215-573-2168. E-Mail: nhistory@upenn.edu. Web Site: www.nursing.upenn.edu/history. *Curator*, Gail E Farr; *Admin Assoc*, Betsy Weiss; E-Mail: ehweiss@nursing.upenn.edu. Subject Specialists: *Nursing hist*, Gail E Farr; Staff 3 (MLS 2, Non-MLS 1)
Founded 1985
Library Holdings: Bk Titles 1,500
Special Collections: Health Care & Nursing History, bks, mss, photos
Publications: The Chronicle (bi-annual)
Offer 2 Summer Scholarships for the study of Nursing history

UNIVERSITY OF THE ARTS, (Formerly University of the Arts Libraries), University Library, 320 S Broad St, 19102. SAN 359-0828. Tel: 215-717-6280. FAX: 215-717-6287. Web Site: library.uarts.edu. *Dir*, Carol H Graney; Tel: 215-717-6281, E-Mail: graney@uarts.edu; *Music*, Mark Germer; Tel: 215-717-6293, E-Mail: germer@uarts.edu; *Publ Servs*, Sara J MacDonald; Tel: 215-717-6282, E-Mail: macdonald@uarts.edu; *Ref Serv*, Mary Louise Castaldi; Tel: 215-717-6283, E-Mail: castaldim@uarts.edu; *Tech Servs*, Scott Hanscom; Tel: 215-717-6285, E-Mail: hanscom@uarts.edu; Staff 6 (MLS 5, Non-MLS 1)
Founded 1876. Pop 2,400; Enrl 1,964; Fac 163; Highest Degree: Master
Jul 1999-Jun 2000 Income (Main Library and Branch Library) $550,680. Mats Exp $179,200, Books $96,000, Per/Ser (Incl. Access Fees) $52,000, Presv $12,500, AV Equip $6,700, Electronic Ref Mat (Incl. Access Fees) $12,000. Sal $366,858 (Prof $201,452)
Library Holdings: Bk Vols 134,967; Bk Titles 91,264; Per Subs 360
Subject Interests: Communication arts, Media, Performing arts, Textiles, Visual arts
Special Collections: Published works by or about PCA College-affiliated authors & illustrators (PCA)
Automation Activity & Vendor Info: (Acquisitions) Innovative Interfaces Inc.; (Cataloging) Innovative Interfaces Inc.; (Circulation) Innovative Interfaces Inc.; (Course Reserve) Innovative Interfaces Inc.; (OPAC) Innovative Interfaces Inc.; (Serials) Innovative Interfaces Inc.
Database Vendor: Dialog, Innovative Interfaces INN - View
Function: ILL available
Partic in PALINET & Union Library Catalogue of Pennsylvania
Departmental Libraries:
MUSIC, 320 S Broad St, 19102. SAN 328-7122. Tel: 215-875-2248.; Staff 1 (MLS 1)
SLIDE, 320 S Broad, 19102. SAN 359-0852. Tel: 215-875-1006.; Staff 1 (MLS 1)
Founded 1958

UNIVERSITY OF THE SCIENCES IN PHILADELPHIA, Joseph W England Library, 4200 Woodland Ave, 19104-4491. SAN 314-9714. Tel: 215-596-8960. Interlibrary Loan Service Tel: 596-8969. Circulation Tel: 215-596-8960. Reference Tel: 215-596-8967. FAX: 215-596-8760. Web Site: www.usip.edu/library. *Dir*, Mignon Adams; Tel: 215-596-8790, E-Mail: m.adams@usip.edu/library; *AV, Media Spec*, Jacqueline Smith; Tel: 215-596-8994, E-Mail: j.smith@usip.edu; *Bibliog Instr*, Leslie Bowman; Tel: 215-596-8964, E-Mail: l.bowman@usip.edu; *Circ, ILL*, Nicole Duncan-Kinard; Tel: 215-596-8961, E-Mail: n.duncan@usip.edu; *Electronic Resources*, Jeanette McVeigh; Tel: 215-895-1197, E-Mail: j.mcveig@usip.edu; *Outreach Serv*, Amy Christopher; Tel: 215-596-8730, E-Mail: a.christ@usip.edu; *Ref*, Robert Woodley; Tel: 215-596-8962, E-Mail: r.woodle@usip.edu; *Tech Servs*, Gina Kaiser; Tel: 215-596-8963, E-Mail: g.kaiser@usip.edu; Staff 20 (MLS 8, Non-MLS 12)
Founded 1822. Enrl 1,946; Fac 130; Highest Degree: Doctorate
Jul 1999-Jun 2000 Income $1,516,866. Mats Exp $478,385, Books $71,968, Per/Ser (Incl. Access Fees) $367,522, Presv $13,874, AV Equip $25,021. Sal $814,448 (Prof $349,308)
Library Holdings: Bk Vols 82,011; Per Subs 2,155
Subject Interests: Biology, Chemistry, Pharm, Pharmacognosy, Pharmacology, Physical therapy, Related health sci, Toxicology
Special Collections: College Archives; Rare Books
Automation Activity & Vendor Info: (Acquisitions) Endeavor; (Cataloging) Endeavor; (Circulation) Endeavor; (OPAC) Endeavor; (Serials) Endeavor
Partic in Dialog Corporation; Health Sciences Libraries Consortium; Nat Libr of Med; OCLC Online Computer Library Center, Inc; PALINET & Union Library Catalogue of Pennsylvania; Tri-State College Library Cooperative (TCLC)

M VICTOR PICCONE MEMORIAL LIBRARY, (Formerly Methodist Hospital Library), Hunter Bldg, 3rd flr, 2301 S Broad St, 19148. SAN 314-9447. Tel: 215-952-9408. FAX: 215-952-9966. E-Mail: methodist@hslc.org. *Dir Libr Serv*, Maura Sostack; Tel: 215-952-9417; Staff 2 (MLS 1, Non-MLS 1)
Founded 1959
1997-1998 Mats Exp $34,000, Books $5,000, Per/Ser (Incl. Access Fees) $21,000, Other Print Mats $5,000. Sal $42,000
Library Holdings: Bk Vols 3,200; Bk Titles 3,000; Per Subs 130
Subject Interests: Clin med, Nursing educ
Database Vendor: Ebsco - EbscoHost, OVID Technologies
Publications: Book list (quarterly); newsletter (quarterly)
Restriction: Staff use only
Function: ILL available
Partic in BHSL; Delaware Valley Information Consortium

S WAGNER FREE INSTITUTE OF SCIENCE LIBRARY,* 1700 W Montgomery Ave, 19121. SAN 315-0240. Tel: 215-763-6529. FAX: 215-763-1299. E-Mail: wgninst@hslc.org. *Librn*, Rita Dockery
Founded 1855
Library Holdings: Bk Vols 24,000
Special Collections: 19th Century US & State Geological Surveys; History of Science Coll; Natural Science Coll; Science Education Coll; William Wagner Coll
Partic in OCLC Online Computer Library Center, Inc

L WHITE & WILLIAMS, Law Library,* 1650 Market St, 18th flr, 19103-7395. SAN 329-0484. Tel: 215-864-7493. FAX: 215-864-7123. Web Site: www.whitewms.com. *Librn*, Carolyn Woods; E-Mail: woodsc@whitewms.com; *Asst Librn*, Evelyn Quillen; Staff 2 (MLS 1, Non-MLS 1)
Library Holdings: Bk Vols 15,092
Open Mon-Fri 7—5:30

S WILLET STAINED GLASS STUDIOS LIBRARY, 10 E Moreland Ave, 19118-3597. SAN 315-0275. Tel: 215-247-5721. Toll Free Tel: 877-709-4106. FAX: 215-247-2951. Web Site: www.willetglass.com. *Senior Librn*, Helene H Weis; *Librn*, Nora Fleming; E-Mail: nfleming@earthlink.net; *Librn*, Anne Dale Marshall; E-Mail: adalemarshall@earthlink.net. Subject Specialists: *Iconography of Philadelphia to 1930*, Helene H Weis; *Stained glass*, Helene H Weis
Founded 1890
Library Holdings: Bk Vols 1,000
Subject Interests: Bible commentaries, Christian symbolism, Church archit, Lives of saints, Stained glass
Special Collections: Willet Studio Archives

M WILLS EYE HOSPITAL, Arthur J Bedell Memorial Library, 900 Walnut St, 19107. SAN 315-0283. Tel: 215-928-3288. FAX: 215-928-7247. Web Site: www.willseye.org/willseyehospital.html. *Librn*, Judith Schaeffer-Young; E-Mail: young@hslc.org
Founded 1944
Library Holdings: Bk Titles 3,000; Per Subs 85
Subject Interests: Ophthalmology
Special Collections: History of Ophthalmology
Partic in Dialog Corporation; Health Sci Libr Info Consortium

S WISTAR INSTITUTE LIBRARY, 3601 Spruce St, Rm 215, 19104-4268. SAN 320-5851. Tel: 215-898-3826. Interlibrary Loan Service Tel: 215-898-3816. Reference Tel: 215-898-3816. FAX: 215-898-3856. Web Site: www.wistar.upenn.edu. *Archivist, Dir Libr Serv*, Nina P Long; E-Mail: nlong@wistar.upenn.edu; *Librn*, Leslie A Pope; E-Mail: pope@wistar.upenn.edu; Staff 2 (MLS 2)
Founded 1892
Library Holdings: Per Subs 125
Subject Interests: Biochemistry, Cell biol, Genetics, Immunology, Oncology, Virology
Special Collections: Archives; Historical Book Coll; Wistar Institute & Family Papers
Partic in National Network of Libraries of Medicine - Greater Midwest Region

L WOLF, BLOCK, SCHORR & SOLIS-COHEN LLP, Law Library, 1650 Arch St, 19103. SAN 372-1973. Tel: 215-977-2000. FAX: 215-977-2783. Web Site: www.wolfblock.com. *Mgr*, Mary Louise Hess
Library Holdings: Bk Vols 6,000; Per Subs 300
Subject Interests: Finance, Labor
Partic in OCLC Online Computer Library Center, Inc
Open Mon-Fri 9-5

S ZOOLOGICAL SOCIETY OF PHILADELPHIA LIBRARY,* 3400 W Girard Ave, 19104. SAN 314-9838. Tel: 215-243-1100. FAX: 215-243-0219.
Founded 1874
Library Holdings: Bk Vols 3,000; Per Subs 70
Subject Interests: Animal behavior, Biology, Birds, Botany, Conservation, Ecology, Herpetology, Horticulture, Ichthyology, Mammals, Natural history, Nutrition, Pathology, Veterinary medicine, Zool mgt, Zoology
Special Collections: Zool & aquarium newsletters, guide books, study books, videos, conference proceedings, pathology reports

PHILADEPHIA

R FAITH THEOLOGICAL SEMINARY LIBRARY,* 1001 W 70th Ave, 19126. SAN 314-4828. Tel: 215-927-3372. FAX: 215-927-6144.
Founded 1937
Library Holdings: Bk Vols 28,000; Per Subs 20

PHOENIXVILLE

R CONGREGATION B'NAI JACOB, Sisterhood B'nai Jacob Library, Starr & Manovon Sts, 19460. SAN 315-0305. Tel: 610-933-5550. FAX: 610-933-8197. Web Site: www.uscj.org/epenn/phoenixville. *Librn*, Dorothy Mandell; Tel: 610-933-7474
Founded 1965
Library Holdings: Bk Titles 1,200
Subject Interests: Judaica
Special Services for the Blind - Braille
Friends of the Library Group

R FIRST PRESBYTERIAN CHURCH LIBRARY, 145 Main St, 19460. SAN 315-0313. Tel: 610-933-8816. FAX: 610-933-8060. *Librn*, Lynn Schmitt
Library Holdings: Bk Vols 2,500
Publications: Christianity Today-Virtue-Concern

CR J ROBERT ASHCROFT MEMORIAL LIBRARY, 1401 Charlestown Rd, 19460. SAN 315-033X. Tel: 610-917-1473. FAX: 610-935-9353. E-Mail: library@vfcc.edu. *Tech Coordr*, Ernest Brummer; Staff 4 (MLS 1, Non-MLS 3)
Founded 1939. Enrl 609; Fac 23; Highest Degree: Bachelor
Library Holdings: Bk Vols 54,000; Bk Titles 49,527; Per Subs 223
Subject Interests: Bible, Religion
Database Vendor: OCLC - First Search

P PHOENIXVILLE PUBLIC LIBRARY,* 183 Second Ave, 19460-3420. SAN 315-0321. Tel: 610-933-3013. FAX: 610-933-4338. Web Site: www.pasd.com/ppl. *Exec Dir*, John Kelley; E-Mail: jkelley@chester-county.lib.pa.us; *Ch Servs*, Linda Wentzel
Founded 1896. Pop 26,500; Circ 138,000
Jul 1997-Jun 1998 Income $405,000. Mats Exp $59,000. Sal $200,000
Library Holdings: Bk Vols 51,000; Per Subs 120
Special Collections: Local History
Mem of Chester County Library
Open Mon-Thurs 9-9, Fri & Sat 9-5, Sun 1-5 (Oct-May)
Friends of the Library Group

PITTSBURGH

S AIR & WASTE MANAGEMENT ASSOCIATION LIBRARY,* One Gateway Ctr, 3rd flr, 15222. SAN 329-8957. Tel: 412-232-3444. FAX: 412-232-3450. E-Mail: info@awma.org. Web Site: www.awma.org. *In Charge*, Andy Knopes
Library Holdings: Bk Vols 800; Per Subs 15

L ALLEGHENY COUNTY COURT OF COMMON PLEAS LIBRARY,* 921 City County Bldg, 9th flr, 414 Grant St, 15219. SAN 325-979X. Tel: 412-350-5353. FAX: 412-350-5889. *Librn*, Joel Fishman
Library Holdings: Bk Titles 24,000; Per Subs 500
Subject Interests: Law

GM ALLEGHENY COUNTY HEALTH DEPARTMENT LIBRARY, 301 39th St, 15201. SAN 315-0348. Tel: 412-578-8028. FAX: 412-578-8144.; Staff 1 (MLS 1)
Founded 1973
Library Holdings: Bk Titles 13,230; Per Subs 133
Subject Interests: Air pollution, Environmental studies, Pub health med
Restriction: Staff use only

GL ALLEGHENY COUNTY LAW LIBRARY,* 921 City-County Bldg, 414 Grant St, 15219-2465. SAN 315-0356. Tel: 412-350-5353. FAX: 412-350-5889. *Librn*, Joel Fishman
Founded 1867
Library Holdings: Bk Vols 130,000
Special Collections: Alaskan Boundary Dispute 1893; Manuscripts of D T Watson; United States Supreme Court Records & Briefs, 1912 to present
Publications: Allegheny County Law Library Law, History & Genealogy Series
Partic in Pittsburgh Regional Libr Consortium

M ALLEGHENY GENERAL HOSPITAL, Health Sciences Library,* 320 E North Ave, 15212-4772. SAN 315-0364. Tel: 412-359-3040. FAX: 412-359-4420. *Dir*, Susan Hoehl; Staff 10 (MLS 6, Non-MLS 4)
Founded 1935
Library Holdings: Bk Titles 10,000; Per Subs 750
Subject Interests: Anesthesiology, Cancer res, Cardiology, Gynecology, Heart surgery, Internal medicine, Neurology, Obstetrics, Oncology, Oral surgery, Orthopedics, Pathology, Pediatrics, Rehabilitation, Renal med, Respiratory diseases, Sports med, Thoracic
Publications: What's New
Partic in Basic Health Sciences Library Network; Dialog Corporation; Greater NE Regional Med Libr Program; Inc; Nat Libr of Med
Open Mon-Fri 8-7, Sat & Sun 10-2

S ALUMINUM COMPANY OF AMERICA INC, Alcoa Corporate Center Libraries, 201 Isabella St, 15212. SAN 315-0372. Tel: 412-553-4482. FAX 412-553-4562. *Librn*, Barbara R Stewart; E-Mail: barbara.stewart@alcoa.com; Staff 1 (MLS 1)
Founded 1949
Library Holdings: Bk Vols 5,000
Subject Interests: Aluminum indust, Bus, Environment, Health, Law, Safe
Automation Activity & Vendor Info: (Cataloging) EOS; (Serials) EOS

P BALDWIN BOROUGH PUBLIC LIBRARY, 41 Macek Dr, 15227-3638. SAN 324-3982. Tel: 412-885-2255. FAX: 412-885-5255. Web Site: www.einpgh.org/ein/baldwin. *Dir*, Christine M McInosh; E-Mail: mcintoshc@einetwork.net; *Librn*, Judith I Smith; E-Mail: smith2@clpgh.or *Ref*, Nancy Musser; E-Mail: mussern@einetwork.net; *Ch Servs*, Joyce Chiapetta; E-Mail: chiapettaj@einetwork.net; Staff 9 (MLS 2, Non-MLS 7)
Founded 1965. Pop 21,923
Library Holdings: Bk Vols 31,000; Per Subs 77
Automation Activity & Vendor Info: (Cataloging) DRA; (Circulation) DRA; (OPAC) DRA
Database Vendor: Ebsco - EbscoHost, GaleNet, IAC - Info Trac, IAC - SearchBank
Friends of the Library Group

S BAYER CORP LIBRARY,* 100 Bayer Rd, 15205-9741. SAN 315-0895. Tel: 412-777-2782. FAX: 412-777-2758. *Librn*, Nancy A Alstadt
Founded 1954
Library Holdings: Bk Titles 8,000; Per Subs 100
Subject Interests: Coatings, Market res, Plastics, Sci-tech, Thermoplastics, Urethane tech
Special Collections: Chemical Economics Handbook; German Language (Varied; Language Courses), bk, flm, cassettes; Manufacturing (State Industrial Directories)
Partic in Dialog Corporation

P BRENTWOOD LIBRARY,* 3501 Brownsville Rd, 15227-3115. SAN 315-0437. Tel: 412-882-5694. FAX: 412-882-0266. Web Site: www.clpgh.org/ei brentwd/. *Librn*, Monica R Stoicovy
Founded 1948. Pop 13,732; Circ 44,203
Library Holdings: Bk Vols 45,000; Per Subs 75
Subject Interests: Health
Partic in Pittsburgh Regional Libr Consortium
Open Mon & Tues 10-8:30, Wed & Thurs 12:30-8:30, Sat 10-3 & Sun 12:30-4
Friends of the Library Group

S BROWN & ROOT CORPORATION, Technical Library,* Foster Plaza, No 7, 661 Anderson Dr, 5th flr, 15220-2745. SAN 315-095X. Tel: 412-921-7090. FAX: 412-921-4040. *Librn*, Janet Cox
Founded 1964
Subject Interests: Analytical chemistry, DOE, Environ health, Environ protection, EPA, Geol, Hazardous waste, Safety, Toxicology
Publications: Newsletter

R BYZANTINE CATHOLIC SEMINARY OF SAINTS CYRIL & METHODIUS LIBRARY, 3605 Perrysville Ave, 15214-2297. SAN 315-0445. Tel: 412-321-8383. FAX: 412-321-9936. E-Mail: bcsoff@sgi.net. *Librn*, Rose Schneider; *Rare Bks*, John Custer; E-Mail: jackus@aol.com; Staff 2 (MLS 1, Non-MLS 1)
Founded 1950. Enrl 20; Fac 12
Sep 1999-Aug 2000 Income $13,300, Locally Generated Income $1,300, Parent Institution $7,000, Other $5,000. Mats Exp $13,300, Books $9,000, Per/Ser (Incl. Access Fees) $2,000, Electronic Ref Mat (Incl. Access Fees) $2,300. Sal $24,500
Library Holdings: Bk Titles 25,000
Subject Interests: Byzantine studies, Eastern Christian theology, Ruthenian studies
Special Collections: Church Slavonic Language (Byzantine Catholic Liturgical Books Coll); History of the Byzantine Catholic Church in Carpatho-Ruthenia & in the United States; Ruthenian Cultural Coll; Ruthenian Historical Coll

P C C MELLOR MEMORIAL LIBRARY, Edgewood Library, One Pennwoo Ave Edgewood, 15218-1627. SAN 315-0844. Tel: 412-731-0909. Web Site: www.clpgh.org/ein/ccmellor. *Dir*, Sally Bogie; *Ch Servs*, Andrea McNeill
Founded 1918. Pop 5,200; Circ 36,000
Library Holdings: Bk Vols 36,000; Per Subs 63
Open Mon-Thurs 10-8, Fri 10-5 & Sat 10-3

C CARLOW COLLEGE, Grace Library, 3333 Fifth Ave, 15213. SAN 315-0453. Tel: 412-578-6139. FAX: 412-578-6242. Web Site: www.carlow.edu. *Dir Libr Serv*, Elaine J Misko; Tel: 412-578-6137, E-Mail: elainem@carlow.edu; *Head Tech Servs*, Karen Goldbach; Tel: 412-578-6145, E-Mail: kmgold@carlow.edu; *Publ Servs*, Theodore Bergfelt; E-Mail: tberg@carlow.edu; *Publ Servs*, Nola Coulson; Tel: 412-578-6144, E-Mail: nola@

carlow.edu; *Syst Coordr*, Linda VanKeuren; Tel: 412-578-6137, E-Mail: lindavk@carlow.edu; Staff 7 (MLS 5, Non-MLS 2)
Founded 1929. Enrl 1,313; Fac 106; Highest Degree: Master
Jul 1998-Jun 1999 Income $405,244. Mats Exp $128,488, Books $53,360, Per/Ser (Incl. Access Fees) $33,864, Presv $3,455, Micro $3,928, AV Equip $8,796, Other Print Mats $438, Electronic Ref Mat (Incl. Access Fees) $24,647. Sal $232,386 (Prof $192,000)
Library Holdings: Bk Vols 98,491; Bk Titles 79,667; Per Subs 397; Bks on Deafness & Sign Lang 113
Subject Interests: Am lit, Early childhood educ, English, Irish, Theology, Women's studies
Special Collections: Black Studies; Career Resources; Peace Studies
Automation Activity & Vendor Info: (Cataloging) DRA; (Circulation) DRA; (OPAC) DRA
Database Vendor: DRA
Publications: Student Handbook
Partic in OCLC Online Computer Library Center, Inc; PALINET & Union Library Catalogue of Pennsylvania

CARNEGIE LIBRARY OF PITTSBURGH, 4400 Forbes Ave, 15213-4080. SAN 359-2561. Tel: 412-622-3114. Circulation Tel: 412-622-3118. FAX: 412-621-1267. Web Site: www.clpgh.org. *Dir*, Herb Ellish; Tel: 412-622-1912, E-Mail: elishh@carnegielibrary.org; *Dep Dir*, Gladys Maharam; Tel: 412-622-3129, E-Mail: maharamg@carnegielibrary.org; *Asst Dir*, Sheila T Jackson; Tel: 412-622-3110, Fax: 412-687-8982, E-Mail: jacksons@carnegielibrary.org; *Commun Servs*, Jane Dayton; Tel: 412-622-6502, Fax: 412-622-5567, E-Mail: daytonj@carnegielibrary.org; *Asst Dir, Tech Servs*, Tina LaMark; Tel: 412-622-5758, Fax: 412-622-5527, E-Mail: lamarkt@carnegielibrary.org; *Librn for Blind*, Sue O Murdock; Tel: 412-622-2440, Fax: 412-687-2442, E-Mail: murdocks@carnegielibrary.org; *Bibliog Instr*, Peggy Dusch; Tel: 412-622-3190, Fax: 412-688-8964, E-Mail: duschp@carnegielibrary.org; *Coll Develop*, Patricia James; Tel: 412-688-8639, E-Mail: jamesp@carnegielibrary.org; *Ser*, Mark Sachan; Tel: 412-622-3156, Fax: 412-688-8694, E-Mail: sachonm@carnegielibrary.org; *Mgr, Spec Coll*, Greg Priore; Tel: 412-622-1932, E-Mail: prioreg@carnegielibrary.org; *YA Servs*, Georgene DeFillippo; Tel: 412-237-1878, Fax: 412-237-1899, E-Mail: defilippog@carnegielibrary.org; *Cat*, Mary McDonough; Tel: 412-622-6576, Fax: 412-688-8694, E-Mail: mcdonoughm@carnegielibrary.org; *Ch Servs*, L Dallas Di Leo; Tel: 412-622-3122, Fax: 412-578-2595, E-Mail: dileod@carnegielibrary.org; *Business*, Roye Werner; Tel: 412-281-7133, Fax: 412-471-1724, E-Mail: wernerr@carnegielibrary.org; *Access Serv, Mgr*, Jennifer Raynor; Tel: 412-578-2593, E-Mail: raynorj@carnegielibrary.org; *Pub Relations*, Gina Pferdehirt; Tel: 412-622-8872, E-Mail: pferdehirtg@carnegielibrary.org. Subject Specialists: *Art*, Kathryn P Logan; *Humanities*, Susan Lanna; *Music*, Kathryn P Logan; *Pennsylvania*, Marilyn Holt; *Science/technology*, James Bobick; *Social sciences and issues*, Marion Streiff; Staff 96 (MLS 96)
Founded 1895. Pop 1,336,449; Circ 2,659,648
Jan 2000-Dec 2000 Income $5,641,462, State $3,642,000, City $40,000, County $700,000, Other $1,259,462. Mats Exp Books $2,927,500. Sal $9,154,000
Library Holdings: Bk Vols 2,110,644; Per Subs 2,690
Subject Interests: Architecture, Art, Bus, Children lit, Genealogy, Humanities, Indust, Local history, Mgt, Music, Natural science, Sci-tech, Soc sci
Special Collections: 19th Century American & German Music Journals (Merz Music Library) Narratives (Imbrie Memorial); Architecture & Design (Bernd); Atomic Energy Commission Reports, micro; Cartoons (Cy Hungerford), originals on pasteboard; English translation of DIN Stds, Trade catalogs; Local History (Isaac Craig, Pittsburgh Newspapers, 1786-date, Pittsburgh Photographic Library) US Patents 1872-date & British Patents 1617-date, bk, micro; US Government Research Reports (PB Reports incl OTS Translations), micro; World War I Personal
Automation Activity & Vendor Info: (Circulation) DRA; (Course Reserve) DRA; (OPAC) DRA
Database Vendor: OCLC - First Search
Publications: A Purchase Guide for Branch & Public Libraries; Science & Technology; Science & Technology Desk Reference
Partic in Electronic Info Network; Oakland Libr Consortium; OCLC Online Computer Library Center, Inc; PALINET & Union Library Catalogue of Pennsylvania
Special Services for the Deaf - TDD
Friends of the Library Group
Branches: 18
ALLEGHENY REGIONAL, 5 Allegheny Sq, 15212-5326. SAN 359-2650. Tel: 412-237-1890. FAX: 412-321-3144. Web Site: www.clpgh.org/clp/al/. *In Charge*, Richard Kaplan; E-Mail: kaplanr@carnegielibrary.org
Library Holdings: Bk Vols 162,839
Friends of the Library Group
BEECHVIEW, 1910 Broadway Ave, 15216. SAN 359-2685. Tel: 412-563-2900. FAX: 412-563-7530. Web Site: www.clpgh.org/clp/bv/. *Mgr*, Sharon Verminski; E-Mail: verminskis@carnegielibrary.org
Library Holdings: Bk Vols 36,743
Friends of the Library Group
BROOKLINE, 708 Brookline Blvd, 15226. SAN 359-2715. Tel: 412-561-1003. FAX: 412-561-1131. Web Site: www.clpgh.org/clp/br/. *Mgr*, Margaret Solonika; E-Mail: solomikap@carnegielibrary.org
Library Holdings: Bk Vols 48,794
Friends of the Library Group
CARRICK, 1811 Brownsville Rd, 15210-3906. SAN 359-274X. Tel: 412-882-3897. FAX: 412-882-0131. Web Site: www.clpgh.org/clp/ck/. *In Charge*, Suzanna Wanat; E-Mail: wanats@carnegielibrary.org
Library Holdings: Bk Vols 20,805
Friends of the Library Group
COUNTY BOOKMOBILE CENTER, 50 Alexander St, 15220. SAN 359-3169. Tel: 412-921-2521. FAX: 412-921-4555. *In Charge*, Constance Galbraith; E-Mail: galbraithc@carnegielibrary.org
Library Holdings: Bk Vols 101,157
EAST LIBERTY, 5920 Ralph Munn Mall, 15206-3408. SAN 359-2804. Tel: 412-363-8232. FAX: 412-363-4457. Web Site: www.clpgh.org/clp/el. *In Charge*, Amanda Albright; E-Mail: albrighta@carnegielibrary.org
Library Holdings: Bk Vols 88,546
Houses Greater Pittsburgh Literary Council
Friends of the Library Group
HAZELWOOD, 4748 Monongahela St, 15207-1506. SAN 359-2839. Tel: 412-421-2517. FAX: 412-421-7282. Web Site: www.clpgh.org/clp/ha. *Mgr*, Mary Ann McHarg; E-Mail: mchargm@carnegielibrary.org
Library Holdings: Bk Vols 31,279
Friends of the Library Group
HILL DISTRICT, 419 Dinwiddie St, 15219-3396. SAN 359-3134. Tel: 412-281-3753. FAX: 412-281-6272. Web Site: www.clpgh.org/clp/hd. *Mgr*, Lydia Scott; E-Mail: scottl@carnegielibrary.org
Library Holdings: Bk Vols 29,665
Friends of the Library Group
HOMEWOOD, 7101 Hamilton Ave, 15208-1052. SAN 359-2863. Tel: 412-731-3080. FAX: 412-731-5518. Web Site: www.clpgh.org/clp/ho. *Mgr*, Joyce Broadus; E-Mail: broadusj@carnegielibrary.org
Library Holdings: Bk Vols 60,938
Subject Interests: Black culture
Friends of the Library Group
KNOXVILLE, 400 Brownsville Rd, 15210-2251. SAN 359-2898. Tel: 412-381-6543. FAX: 412-381-9833. Web Site: www.clpgh.org/clp/kn. *Mgr*, Jackie Schmitt-Marsteller; E-Mail: schmittmarsj@carnegielibrary.org
Library Holdings: Bk Vols 49,454
Friends of the Library Group
LAWRENCEVILLE, 279 Fisk St, 15201-2898. SAN 359-2928. Tel: 412-682-3668. FAX: 412-682-5943. Web Site: www.clpgh.org/clp/lv. *Mgr*, Mildred Glenn; E-Mail: glennm@carnegielibrary.org
Library Holdings: Bk Vols 36,428
Friends of the Library Group
S LIBRARY CENTER OF POINT PARK COLLEGE & CARNEGIE LIBRARY OF PITTSBURGH, 414 Wood St, 15222-1818. SAN 359-2626. Tel: 412-281-5945. FAX: 412-281-7149. Web Site: www.clpgh.org/clp.libctr. *Dir*, Pam Craychee; Tel: 412-281-7137, E-Mail: craycheep@carnegielibrary.org
Founded 1997
Library Holdings: Bk Vols 155,000; Per Subs 764
Subject Interests: Bus, Computer science, Finance, Marketing, Performing arts
Special Collections: Industrial & trade directories; Pittsburgh Company Index; Point Park College Academic Coll
Publications: bibliographies; Pathfinders; What's New
Special Services for the Blind - DECTalk/JAWS for synthetic voice output of computer screen contents
Combined public/academic library; partnership between urban public library & private college; opened May 1997
Friends of the Library Group
MOUNT WASHINGTON, 315 Grandview Ave, 15211-1549. SAN 359-2952. Tel: 412-381-3380. FAX: 412-381-9876. Web Site: www.clpgh.org/clp/mw. *Mgr*, Linda Gonzalez; E-Mail: gonzalezl@carnegielibrary.org
Library Holdings: Bk Vols 22,461
Friends of the Library Group
SHERADEN, 720 Sherwood Ave, 15204-1793. SAN 359-2987. Tel: 412-331-1135. FAX: 412-331-2755. Web Site: www.clpgh.org/clp/sh. *Mgr*, Holly McCullough; E-Mail: mcculloughh@carnegielibrary.org
Library Holdings: Bk Vols 28,432
Friends of the Library Group
SOUTH SIDE, 2205 E Carson St, 15203. SAN 359-3010. Tel: 412-431-0505. FAX: 412-431-7968. Web Site: www.clpgh.org/clp/ss. *In Charge*, Denise Graham; E-Mail: grahamd@carnegielibrary.org
Library Holdings: Bk Vols 14,727
Friends of the Library Group
SQUIRREL HILL, 5801 Forbes Ave, 15217-1601. SAN 359-3045. Tel: 412-422-9650. FAX: 412-422-5811. Web Site: www.clpgh.org/clp/sq. *In Charge*, Blanche McManus; E-Mail: mcmanusb@carnegielibrary.org
Library Holdings: Bk Vols 102,550
Special Collections: Jewish History & Culture (Olender Foundation)
Friends of the Library Group
WEST END, 47 Wabash Ave, 15220-5493. SAN 359-307X. Tel: 412-921-1717. FAX: 412-921-3494. Web Site: www.clpgh.org/clp/we. *Mgr*, Marlene Demarest; E-Mail: demarestm@carnegielibrary.org
Library Holdings: Bk Vols 19,825

Friends of the Library Group
WOODS RUN, 1201 Woods Run Ave, 15212-2335. SAN 359-310X. Tel: 412-761-3730. FAX: 412-761-3445. Web Site: www.clpgh.org/clp/wr/. *Actg Mgr*, Tom Barnes; E-Mail: barnest@carnegielibrary.org
Library Holdings: Bk Vols 38,449
Friends of the Library Group
Bookmobiles: 5

P CARNEGIE LIBRARY OF PITTSBURGH, Library for the Blind & Physically Handicapped,* Leonard C Staisey Bldg, 4724 Baum Blvd, 15213-1389. SAN 315-0461. Tel: 412-687-2440. Toll Free Tel: 800-242-0586. FAX: 412-687-2442. E-Mail: clbph@clpgh.org. Web Site: www.clpgh.org/clp/LBPH. *Head of Libr*, Sue Murdock; *Asst Librn*, Kathleen Kappel; *Online Servs*, Tracey Morsek; Staff 5 (MLS 5)
Circ 614,438
Jul 1999-Jun 2000 Income $1,196,272
Library Holdings: Bk Vols 15,104
Special Collections: Blindness & Handicap Reference Material
Publications: Three Rivers News (quarterly newsletter)
Partic in NLSNET
Special Services for the Blind - Descriptive videos; Large print bks

C CARNEGIE MELLON UNIVERSITY, University Libraries,* Hunt Library, 4909 Frew St, 15213-3890. SAN 359-3193. Tel: 412-268-2446. FAX: 412-268-2793. Interlibrary Loan Service FAX: 412-268-6944. Web Site: www.library.cmu.edu. *Librn*, Dr Gloriana St Clair; Tel: 412-268-2447, E-Mail: gstclair@andrew.cmu.edu; *Assoc Dir*, Barbara G Richards; *Assoc Librn*, Erika C Linke; *Asst Librn*, Denise Troll; *Spec Coll*, Mary Kay Johnsen; *Archivist*, Gabrielle Michalek; Staff 32 (MLS 32)
Founded 1920. Enrl 7,209; Fac 525; Highest Degree: Doctorate
1996-1997 Income $5,977,040. Mats Exp $2,002,459, Books $543,685, Per/Ser (Incl. Access Fees) $1,367,853, Presv $71,791, Micro $17,114. Sal $2,494,692 (Prof $1,141,692)
Library Holdings: Bk Vols 906,069; Per Subs 3,293
Special Collections: Architecture Archives; Bookbindings (including Edwards of Halifax); Early Scientific Works; Important Early Printers (Aldus, Plantin & Estienne Coll); Private Presses (Kimscott & Doves Coll; Senator John Heinz III Archives
Automation Activity & Vendor Info: (Cataloging) SIRSI
Publications: Bibliographic & instructional guides; CMU Libraries News: Resources; Mercury Technical Report
Partic in Center For Research Libraries; Interlibrary Delivery Service of Pennsylvania; Oakland Libr Consortium; OCLC Online Computer Library Center, Inc; Pa Academic Librs Connection Coun; PALINET & Union Library Catalogue of Pennsylvania
Departmental Libraries:
ENGINEERING & SCIENCE, Wean Hall, 15213. SAN 359-3223. Tel: 412-268-2426. FAX: 412-681-1998. *Head of Libr*, Lynn Berard; Tel: 412-268-2428, E-Mail: lberard@andrew.cmu.edu
Founded 1971
Subject Interests: Computer science, Energy, Engineering, Environ, Mathematics, Physics, Robotics
Special Collections: Energy & Environment; Robotics & Computer Science
MELLON INSTITUTE LIBRARY, 4400 Fifth Ave, 15213. SAN 359-3258. Tel: 412-268-3171. FAX: 412-268-6945. *Head of Libr*, Lynn Labun; Tel: 412-268-7384, E-Mail: labun@andrew.cmu.edu
Founded 1911
Subject Interests: Biological sci, Chemistry, Environ scis

S CARNEGIE MUSEUM OF NATURAL HISTORY LIBRARY, 4400 Forbes Ave, 15213-4080. SAN 315-047X. Tel: 412-622-3264, 412-622-8870. FAX: 412-622-8837. Web Site: www.clpgh.org/cmnh/library/. *Mgr*, Xianghua Sun; E-Mail: sunx@carnegiemuseums.org; *Librn*, Bernadette G Callery; E-Mail: calleryb@carnegiemuseums.org; Staff 4 (MLS 2, Non-MLS 2)
Founded 1898
Jan 1999-Dec 1999 Mats Exp $61,000, Books $8,000, Per/Ser (Incl. Access Fees) $52,000, Presv $1,000
Library Holdings: Bk Vols 132,000; Bk Titles 28,000; Per Subs 1,500
Subject Interests: Anthropology, Archaeology, Botany, Entomology, Geology, Herpetology, Invertebrates, Mammalogy, Mineralogy, Ornithology, Palaeontology
Special Collections: Botany (Otto E Jennings Coll, Western Pennsylvania Botanical Society Coll); Entomology (Hugh Kahl Coll, George A Ehrman Coll, B Preston Clark Coll; Geology & Paleontology (E R Eller Coll, John E Guilday Coll, Reprint Coll, O A Peterson Reprint Coll, J B Hatcher Reprint Coll); Herpetology (Albert C L G Gunther Reprint Coll); Invertebrates (Arnold E Ortmann Coll, George E Clapp Conchology Coll, Victor Sterki Coll); John Hamilton Coll); Mammalogy (Boone & Crockett Club Coll); Ornithology (W E Clye Todd Ornithological Reprint Coll, John P Robin Coll, Bernard Van Cleve Coll)
Automation Activity & Vendor Info: (Cataloging) DRA; (OPAC) DRA; (Serials) DRA
Restriction: By appointment only
Function: For research purposes
Partic in OCLC Online Computer Library Center, Inc; PALINET & Union Library Catalogue of Pennsylvania

M CENTER FOR EMERGENCY MEDICINE OF WESTERN PENNSYLVANIA LIBARARY,* 230 McKee Pl, Ste 500, 15213. SAN 37 2400. Tel: 412-578-3200. FAX: 412-578-3241. *Dir*, Paul Paris
Library Holdings: Bk Titles 360

C CHATHAM COLLEGE, Jennie King Mellon Library, Woodland Rd, 1523 SAN 315-0496. Tel: 412-365-1245. Reference Tel: 412-365-1670. FAX: 41 365-1528. Web Site: www.chatham.edu. *Dir*, Jill Ausel; Tel: 412-365-1244, E-Mail: jausel@chatham.edu; *Ref*, Irma Smith; Tel: 412-365-1247; *Ref*, Amanda Mottorn; Tel: 412-365-1619; *Head Tech Servs*, Lynne Patton; Tel: 412-365-1243; Staff 7 (MLS 4, Non-MLS 3)
Founded 1869. Pop 1,000; Enrl 1,000; Fac 50; Highest Degree: Master
1998-1999 Income $150,000. Mats Exp $114,800, Books $9,800, Per/Ser (Incl. Access Fees) $80,000, Micro $5,000, Other Print Mats $20,000
Library Holdings: Bk Vols 97,000; Bk Titles 94,000; Per Subs 600
Subject Interests: Women studies
Special Collections: African-American (Wray Coll); Mayan Art & Civilization (Snowdon Coll)
Automation Activity & Vendor Info: (Cataloging) Gaylord
Database Vendor: Dialog, Ebsco - EbscoHost, IAC - Info Trac, Lexis-Nexis, Silverplatter Information Inc.
Partic in OCLC Online Computer Library Center, Inc; OHIONET; PALINE & Union Library Catalogue of Pennsylvania

M CHILDREN'S HOSPITAL OF PITTSBURGH, Blaxter Memorial Library, 3705 Fifth Ave, 15213-2583. SAN 315-050X. Tel: 412-692-5288. FAX: 41 692-5287.
Library Holdings: Bk Vols 1,040; Bk Titles 1,000; Per Subs 200
Subject Interests: Pediatrics
Partic in BRS; Dialog Corporation; Medline

S CHILDREN'S INSTITUTE LIBRARY, 6301 Northumberland St, 15217. SAN 315-1115. Tel: 412-420-2247. FAX: 412-521-0570. E-Mail: nsp@the-institute.org. Web Site: www.amazingkids.org. *Dir*, Nancy J Sakino-Spears
Founded 1972
Library Holdings: Bk Vols 7,500; Per Subs 120
Subject Interests: Asthma, Burn injury, Cerebral palsy, Children's literatur Head injury, Learning disabilities, Pediatrics, Prader-Willi, Rehabilitation, Spina bifida, Unusual syndromes (staff libr)
Automation Activity & Vendor Info: (Acquisitions) EOS; (Cataloging) EOS; (Circulation) EOS; (OPAC) EOS; (Serials) EOS

L COHEN & GRIGSBY PC, Law Library, 11 Stanwix St, 15th Flr, 15222-3110. SAN 374-6224. Tel: 412-297-4870. FAX: 412-209-0672. Web Site: www.cohenlaw.com. *Librn*, Beth Smith; E-Mail: bsmith@cohenlaw.com; Staff 1 (MLS 1)
Library Holdings: Bk Titles 650; Per Subs 160
Subject Interests: Employment, Immigration
Automation Activity & Vendor Info: (Acquisitions) Inmagic, Inc.; (Cataloging) Inmagic, Inc.
Restriction: By appointment only
Partic in OCLC Online Computer Library Center, Inc

J COMMUNITY COLLEGE OF ALLEGHENY COUNTY, Allegheny Campus Library,* 808 Ridge Ave, 15212-6097. SAN 315-0526. Tel: 412-237-2585. FAX: 412-237-6563. Web Site: www.acd.ccac. *Librn*, Dennis Hennessey; *Online Servs, Ref*, Ray Edward Raab; Tel: 901-352-4084, E-Mail: raabr@bethel-college.edu; *Archivist*, Pat Moran; Staff 5 (MLS 5)
Founded 1966. Enrl 5,400; Fac 177
Library Holdings: Bk Titles 82,021; Per Subs 366
Partic in Knight-Ridder Info, Inc; OCLC Online Computer Library Center, Inc; PALINET & Union Library Catalogue of Pennsylvania

S CONFLICT RESOLUTION CENTER INTERNATIONAL LIBRARY, 204 37th St, 15201-1859. SAN 371-6120. Tel: 412-687-6210. FAX: 412-687-6232. Web Site: conflictres.org. *Pres*, Paul Wahrhaftig; E-Mail: paul@conflictres.org
Founded 1981
Library Holdings: Bk Titles 3,000
Subject Interests: Mediation
Publications: Conflict Resolution Notes

S CONSAD RESEARCH CORPORATION LIBRARY,* 121 N Highland Ave 15206. SAN 371-0211. Tel: 412-363-5500. FAX: 412-363-5509. *Librn*, Sheila Steger; E-Mail: ssteger@consad.com
Library Holdings: Bk Vols 1,700; Per Subs 160
Open Mon-Fri 9-5

S CONSOL, INC, Technical Library,* Consol Plaza, 1800 Washington Rd, 15241. SAN 375-7536. Tel: 412-831-4497. FAX: 412-831-4975. Web Site: www.consolenergy.com. *Librn*, Timothy Schivley; E-Mail: timshivley@consolenergy.com
1998-1999 Mats Exp $1,700, Books $700, Other Print Mats $300
Library Holdings: Per Subs 47

R CRAFTON UNITED PRESBYTERIAN CHURCH LIBRARY, 80 Bradford Ave, 15205. SAN 315-0550. Tel: 412-921-2293. *Librn*, Georgiann Maurer
Library Holdings: Bk Vols 400
Open Mon-Fri 8-3:30

CRUCIBLE MATERIALS CORPORATION, Research Center Library, 6003 Campbells Run Rd, 15205. SAN 315-0518. Tel: 412-923-2955, Ext 255. FAX: 412-788-4665. *Librn*, Patricia J Aducci; E-Mail: paducci@cruciblereseach.com
Founded 1954
Subject Interests: Ferrous metallurgy, Metallurgy, Particle metallurgy, Powder, Proc control, Product, Superalloys, Titanium alloys, Tool steels

R DIOCESE OF PITTSBURGH, Learning Media Center,* 2900 Noblestown Rd, 15205. SAN 315-0577. Tel: 412-928-5817. FAX: 412-928-5833. Web Site: www.diopitt.org. *Dir*, Jeff Hirst
Library Holdings: Bk Vols 3,500; Per Subs 81

DORMONT PUBLIC LIBRARY,* 2950 W Liberty Ave, 15216-2594. SAN 315-0585. Tel: 412-531-8754. FAX: 412-531-1601. Web Site: www.clpgh-org/ein/dormont/. *Dir*, Mardi Centinaro
Founded 1936. Pop 9,772; Circ 44,740
1997-1998 Income $157,983, State $13,500, County $50,358. Mats Exp $28,750, Books $20,700, Per/Ser (Incl. Access Fees) $1,200. Sal $83,240
Library Holdings: Bk Vols 46,975; Per Subs 70
Subject Interests: Accelerated readers, Automotive repair, Careers, Classics, Consumer guides, Large print, Literacy, Small bus

R DUQUESNE UNIVERSITY LIBRARY, Gumberg Library, 600 Forbes Ave, 15282. SAN 359-3282. Tel: 412-396-6130. Reference Tel: 412-396-6133. FAX: 412-396-5356. E-Mail: askref@duq.edu. Web Site: www.duq.edu/library. *Chief Librn, Dir*, Dr Paul J Pugliese; Tel: 412-396-6136, Fax: 412-396-1658, E-Mail: pugliese@duq.edu; *Coll Develop*, Melodie Thoms; Tel: 412-396-5231, Fax: 412-396-1658, E-Mail: thoms@duq.edu; *Info Res*, Diana Sasso; Tel: 412-396-5680, Fax: 412-396-1658, E-Mail: sasso@duq.edu; Staff 74 (MLS 13, Non-MLS 61)
Founded 1928. Enrl 9,552; Highest Degree: Doctorate
Jul 1999-Jun 2000 Income (Main Library Only) $2,937,668, Parent Institution $2,441,023, Other $496,645. Mats Exp $1,095,282, Books $186,041, Per/Ser (Incl. Access Fees) $588,362, Presv $23,292, Micro $29,665, Electronic Ref Mat (Incl. Access Fees) $267,922. Sal $1,185,033 (Prof $524,851)
Library Holdings: Bk Vols 535,259; Bk Titles 316,920; Per Subs 8,549; Bks on Deafness & Sign Lang 138
Subject Interests: Education, Music, Nursing, Philosophy, Psychology, Theology
Special Collections: Cardinal John Wright Coll; Judge Michael Musmanno Coll; Medieval Judaic-Christian Relations (Rabbi Herman Hailperin); Simon Silverman Phenomenology Coll
Automation Activity & Vendor Info: (Acquisitions) DRA; (Cataloging) DRA; (Circulation) DRA; (OPAC) DRA; (Serials) DRA
Database Vendor: Dialog, DRA, OCLC - First Search, ProQuest, Silverplatter Information Inc.
Publications: BiblioTECH (Newsletter)
Partic in PALCI
Special Services for the Blind - Kurzweil Reading Machine
Departmental Libraries:
L SCHOOL OF LAW LIBRARY, 600 Forbes Ave, 15282. SAN 359-3312. Tel: 412-396-5017. Circulation Tel: 412-396-5017. Reference Tel: 412-396-1697. FAX: 412-396-6294. Web Site: www.duq.edu/law/lawlib.htm. *Dir*, Frank Y Liu; Tel: 412-396-5018, E-Mail: liu@duq.edu; *Assoc Dir*, Dittakavi Rao; Tel: 412-396-5014, E-Mail: rao@duq.edu; *Cat*, Amy Lovell; Tel: 412-396-6292, E-Mail: lovell@duq.edu; *Publ Servs*, Tsegaye Beru; Tel: 412-396-4423, E-Mail: beru@duq.edu; *Tech Coordr*, Milan Komljenovic; Tel: 412-396-5533, E-Mail: komljeno@duq.edu; *Tech Servs*, Patricia Horvath; Tel: 412-396-5016, E-Mail: horvath@duq.edu; Staff 21 (MLS 6, Non-MLS 15)
Founded 1911
Jul 1999-Jun 2000 Mats Exp $693,092. Sal $511,776 (Prof $313,237)
Library Holdings: Bk Vols 247,427; Bk Titles 65,839; Per Subs 3,383
Database Vendor: IAC - Info Trac, Innovative Interfaces INN - View, Lexis-Nexis, OCLC - First Search
Publications: Duquesne Law Library Notes; Duquesne University Law Library Information Guide
Partic in OCLC Online Computer Library Center, Inc; Westlaw

R EAST LIBERTY PRESBYTERIAN CHURCH LIBRARY, 116 S Highland Ave, 15206. SAN 315-0615. Tel: 412-441-3800. FAX: 412-441-4422. *Librn*, Carol Kirkpatrick; E-Mail: carolk@coh.net
Library Holdings: Bk Vols 2,000; Per Subs 18

FORBES HEALTH SYSTEM LIBRARIES
M FORBES METROPOLITAN HOSPITAL LIBRARY, 225 Penn Ave, 15221. SAN 359-3371. Tel: 412-247-2422, 412-852-2422. *Librn*, Kathryn Fowler
Founded 1947
Library Holdings: Bk Vols 2,600; Per Subs 1,211
Subject Interests: Allied health, Medicine, Nursing
Publications: Booktales
Partic in Greater NE Regional Med Libr Program; Nat Libr of Med

GREEN TREE PUBLIC LIBRARY, (GTPL), 10 W Manilla Ave, 1st Fl, 15220. SAN 315-0666. Tel: 412-921-9292. TDD: 412-921-9004. FAX: 412-921-4004. Web Site: www.clpgh.org/ein/greentre. *Dir*, Carol Kieda; E-Mail: kiedac@dpgh.org; Staff 6 (MLS 1, Non-MLS 5)
Pop 4,905; Circ 55,000
Library Holdings: Bk Vols 28,000; Per Subs 85
Automation Activity & Vendor Info: (Acquisitions) DRA; (Cataloging) DRA; (Circulation) DRA; (Course Reserve) DRA; (ILL) DRA; (Media Booking) DRA; (OPAC) DRA; (Serials) DRA
Publications: Chapter Notes (newsletter)
Partic in Allegheny County Libr Asn
Friends of the Library Group

S H J HEINZ COMPANY, Corporate Information Center,* 1062 Progress St, PO Box 57, 15230. SAN 325-0032. Tel: 412-237-5948. FAX: 412-237-5725. *Librn*, Nancy Winstanley
Library Holdings: Bk Titles 6,000; Per Subs 250
Subject Interests: Food eng, Food indust, Food proc
Publications: Weekly Abstracts from Current Magazines
Restriction: Staff use only

M HEALTHSOUTH HARMARVILLE REHABILITATION HOSPITAL, Staff Library,* Guys Run Rd, PO Box 11460, 15238. SAN 325-9536. Tel: 412-828-1300, Ext 7821. FAX: 412-826-6722. *Librn*, Lynn Scanga
Library Holdings: Bk Vols 2,090; Bk Titles 2,016
Publications: acquisitions & holdings lists; Bibliographies; Current Awareness
Partic in BRS; Docline; Pittsburgh-East Hospital Libr Coop
Open Mon-Fri 8-4:30

S HIGHMARK BLUE CROSS BLUE SHIELD, Business Research Services, 120 Fifth Ave, Ste 1925, Information Research Services, 15222-3099. SAN 315-0429. Tel: 412-544-8027. FAX: 412-544-0898. *Dir*, Judith L Lesso; Tel: 412-544-8027, Fax: 412-544-8098, E-Mail: judy.lesso@highmark.com; *Librn*, William R Harrison; Staff 1 (MLS 1)
Founded 1940
Library Holdings: Bk Titles 4,000
Subject Interests: Employee benefits, Health care, Health ins
Automation Activity & Vendor Info: (Cataloging) Inmagic, Inc.
Database Vendor: Dialog, ProQuest
Restriction: Staff use only
Partic in BHSL; OCLC Online Computer Library Center, Inc; PALINET & Union Library Catalogue of Pennsylvania

S HISTORICAL SOCIETY OF WESTERN PENNSYLVANIA LIBRARY & ARCHIVES, 1212 Smallman St, 15222. SAN 315-0712. Tel: 412-454-6364. FAX: 412-454-6028. E-Mail: library@hswp.org. Web Site: www.pghhistory.org. *Librn*, Sharon Watson-Mauro; *Acq*, David Grinnell; *Cat*, C Arthur Louderback; *Archivist*, Stephen Doell; *Archivist*, Tom White; *Archivist*, Doug McGregor; Staff 7 (MLS 6, Non-MLS 1)
Founded 1879
Library Holdings: Bk Vols 32,000; Bk Titles 17,000; Per Subs 300
Subject Interests: Genealogy, Hist of Western Pa
Special Collections: African-American Archives; Business Coll; Italian Archives; Jewish Archives; Polish Archives; Slovak Archives; Women's Coll
Open Tues-Sat 10-5

S HUNT INSTITUTE FOR BOTANICAL DOCUMENTATION, Hunt Botanical Library, Carnegie Mellon Univ, 15213-3890. (Mail add: 5000 Forbes Ave, 15213-3890), SAN 315-0739. Tel: 412-268-7301. FAX: 412-268-5677. E-Mail: ct0u@andrew.cmu.edu. *Librn*, Charlotte A Tancin; *Asst Librn*, Candace Lisle; Tel: 412-268-2436, E-Mail: clisle@andrew.cmu.edu; Staff 2 (MLS 2)
Founded 1961
Library Holdings: Bk Vols 25,000; Per Subs 275
Subject Interests: Biogs of people in plant sci, Botanical bibliography, Botanical illustration, Hist of bot, History of science
Special Collections: Michel Adanson Coll (18th-century taxonomy), bks, mss; Strandell Coll of Linnaeana, bks, clippings
Partic in OCLC Online Computer Library Center, Inc; PALINET & Union Library Catalogue of Pennsylvania

S INDUSTRIAL HEALTH FOUNDATION, INC LIBRARY,* 34 Penn Circle W, 15206-3612. SAN 315-0755. Tel: 412-363-6600. FAX: 412-363-6605. E-Mail: ihsincorp@aol.com. Web Site: www.members.aol.com/ihfincorp. *Pres*, Marianne Kaschak; *Info Res*, Janice O'Polka
Founded 1969
Library Holdings: Bk Titles 1,800; Per Subs 30
Subject Interests: Hygiene, Indust, Occupational health, Toxicology
Special Collections: Industrial Health & Toxicology, abstracts
Publications: Bibliographies; Industrial Hygiene Digest (monthly abstract); symposia proceedings; technical bulletins
Partic in Greater NE Regional Med Libr Program

R JEWISH EDUCATION INSTITUTE, Sol Rosenbloom Library, 6424 Forward, 15217. SAN 372-9222. Tel: 412-521-1100. FAX: 412-521-4511. *Librn*, Maryann Wingenbach
Library Holdings: Bk Vols 3,000; Per Subs 11

L JONES, DAY, REAVIS & POGUE, Law Library, 500 Grant St, 15219. SAN 372-1884. Tel: 412-394-7226. FAX: 412-394-7959. *Librn*, Heather R Love; E-Mail: hrlove@jonesday.com
Library Holdings: Bk Vols 15,000; Per Subs 100
Partic in OCLC Online Computer Library Center, Inc

L KIRKPATRICK & LOCKHART LLP LIBRARY, Henry W Oliver Bldg, 535 Smithfield St, 15222. SAN 315-0798. Tel: 412-355-6718. Reference Tel: 412-355-6311. FAX: 412-355-6501. Web Site: www.kl.com. *Dir Libr Serv*, Gwen S Vargas; E-Mail: gvargas@kl.com
Founded 1956
Subject Interests: Corporations, Securities, Tax

L KLETT, ROONEY, LIEBER & SCHORLING LIBRARY, (Formerly Klett, Lieber, Rooney & Schorling Library), One Oxford Ctr, 41st flr, 15219-6498. SAN 372-8544. Tel: 412-392-2046. FAX: 412-392-2128. Web Site: www.klettrooney.com. *Dir*, Ann P Orsag; E-Mail: aporsao@klettrooney.com; Staff 2 (MLS 1, Non-MLS 1)
Library Holdings: Bk Vols 15,000; Per Subs 300
Subject Interests: Law
Special Collections: Commerce Clearing House Standard Federal Tax Reporter (all years); Pennsylvania Bar Institute Seminar Coursebooks
Branches:
HARRISBURG BRANCH
See Separate Entry in Harrisburg
PHILADELPHIA BRANCH
See Separate Entry in Philadelphia

S KTA-TATOR INC LIBRARY,* 115 Technology Dr, 15275-1085. SAN 372-9184. Tel: 412-788-1300. FAX: 412-788-1306.
Library Holdings: Bk Vols 320; Per Subs 13
Open Mon-Fri 8-5

S KVAERNER METALS LIBRARY,* 1200 Penn Ave, 15222-4204. SAN 371-4179. Tel: 412-918-3881, 412-918-4500. FAX: 412-918-5000. *Librn*, Marjorie Trunzo
Library Holdings: Bk Vols 4,000; Per Subs 30
Open Tues-Thurs 8:30-12

C LA ROCHE COLLEGE, John J Wright Library, 9000 Babcock Blvd, 15237. SAN 315-081X. Tel: 412-536-1058. FAX: 412-536-1062. E-Mail: puvogec1@laroche.edu. *Dir*, LaVerne P Collins; Tel: 412-536-1061, E-Mail: collinl1@laroche.edu; *Asst Dir*, Darlene Veghts; Tel: 412-536-1055, E-Mail: veghtsd1@laroche.edu; *Circ*, Sally Knapp; Tel: 412-536-1063
Founded 1963. Enrl 1,150; Fac 45; Highest Degree: Master
1999-2000 Mats Exp $155,200, Books $65,000, Per/Ser (Incl. Access Fees) $76,000, Presv $4,000, Micro $5,500, AV Equip $1,200, Electronic Ref Mat (Incl. Access Fees) $3,500
Library Holdings: Bk Vols 61,000; Bk Titles 70,000; Per Subs 604
Automation Activity & Vendor Info: (Acquisitions) Innovative Interfaces Inc.; (Cataloging) Innovative Interfaces Inc.; (Circulation) Innovative Interfaces Inc.; (Course Reserve) Innovative Interfaces Inc.; (ILL) Innovative Interfaces Inc.; (Media Booking) Innovative Interfaces Inc.; (OPAC) Innovative Interfaces Inc.; (Serials) Innovative Interfaces Inc.
Partic in OCLC Online Computer Library Center, Inc; PALINET & Union Library Catalogue of Pennsylvania

MERCY HOSPITAL OF PITTSBURGH
M BRADY LIBRARY OF THE HEALTH SCIENCES, 1400 Locust St, 15219. SAN 359-3614. Tel: 412-232-7520. FAX: 412-232-8422. E-Mail: library@mercy.pmhs.org. Web Site: www.mercylink.org. *Mgr*, Linda Hogan; *Archivist*, Kathleen Washy; *Circ, Doc Delivery*, Viola Pope; *Coll Develop*, Susan Walko; *Publ Servs*, Robert Neumeyer; *Web Coordr*, Ann Perbohner; Staff 6 (MLS 5, Non-MLS 1)
Founded 1922
Library Holdings: Bk Vols 2,000; Per Subs 320
Subject Interests: Gen surgery, Medicine
Automation Activity & Vendor Info: (Acquisitions) EOS; (Cataloging) EOS; (Circulation) EOS; (OPAC) EOS; (Serials) EOS
Database Vendor: Dialog
Restriction: Company library
Function: Archival collection, Document delivery services, ILL available, Literary searches, Reference services available
Partic in Pittsburgh BHSL; Pittsburgh-East Hospital Libr Coop

P MT LEBANON PUBLIC LIBRARY, 16 Castle Shannon Blvd, 15228-2252. SAN 315-0917. Tel: 412-531-1912. TDD: 412-531-5268. FAX: 412-531-1161. E-Mail: mtleb@clpgh.org. Web Site: www.clpgh.org/ein/mtleb/. *Dir*, Cynthia K Richey; E-Mail: richeyc@einetwork.net; *Ad Servs*, Kathy Ober; E-Mail: oberk@einetwork.net; *Ch Servs*, Judith Sutton; E-Mail: suttonj@einetwork.net; *Publ Servs*, John Walker; E-Mail: walkerj@einetwork.net; Staff 11 (MLS 11)
Founded 1932. Pop 33,362; Circ 414,956
Jan 1999-Dec 1999 Income (Main Library Only) $1,294,294, State $96,049, City $795,691, Federal $15,500, County $306,982, Locally Generated Income $80,072. Mats Exp $181,337, Books $144,396, Per/Ser (Incl. Access Fees) $14,107, Presv $1,500, Micro $3,598, AV Equip $17,557, Electronic Ref Mat (Incl. Access Fees) $179. Sal $682,033 (Prof $387,731)
Library Holdings: Bk Vols 135,245; Per Subs 282
Subject Interests: Small business, Study guides
Special Collections: Local History Coll; Pennsylvania Coll
Automation Activity & Vendor Info: (Cataloging) DRA; (Circulation) DRA; (ILL) DRA; (OPAC) DRA
Publications: Friends of Library Newsletter
Partic in Allegheny County Libr Asn; Electronic Info Network
Friends of the Library Group

S NATIONAL CENTER FOR JUVENILE JUSTICE, Technical Assistance Resource Center, 710 Fifth Ave, 15219. SAN 372-9214. Tel: 412-227-6950. FAX: 412-227-6955. E-Mail: ncjj@ncjj.org. *Librn*, Kevin Spangenberg; Sta 1 (MLS 1)
Founded 1974
Library Holdings: Bk Titles 16,000; Per Subs 50
Subject Interests: Juvenile delinquency
Function: Research library

S NATIONAL FLAG FOUNDATION, Flag Plaza Library,* Flag Plaza, 1275 Bedford Ave, 15219-3630. SAN 326-0410. Tel: 412-261-1776. FAX: 412-261-9132. E-Mail: nfflag@aol.com. Web Site: www.americanflags.org. *In Charge*, David L White; *Librn*, Anthony A Martin
Founded 1968
Library Holdings: Bk Vols 750
Special Collections: Amercana Coll, paintings
Publications: The New Constellation

S NATIONAL INSTITUTE FOR OCCUPATIONAL SAFETY & HEALTH, PRL Library, Cochrans Mill Rd, PO Box 18070, 15236. SAN 370-2758. Te 412-386-4431. FAX: 412-386-4592. E-Mail: kis2@cdc.gov. *Dir*, Kathleen Stabryla; *Librn*, Chia-ling Wu; Staff 3 (MLS 2, Non-MLS 1)
Library Holdings: Bk Vols 165,000; Per Subs 150
Automation Activity & Vendor Info: (OPAC) TechLIB

S NEVILLE CHEMICAL COMPANY, Research & Development Library, 2800 Neville Rd, 15225-1496. SAN 371-6899. Tel: 412-331-4200, Ext 429. FAX: 412-771-0226. *Librn*, John E Henderson; E-Mail: jhenderson@nevchem.com; Staff 2 (MLS 1, Non-MLS 1)
Library Holdings: Bk Vols 2,100; Bk Titles 1,800; Per Subs 200
Subject Interests: Chemistry
Automation Activity & Vendor Info: (OPAC) Follett
Function: Research library

P NORTHLAND PUBLIC LIBRARY, 300 Cumberland Rd, 15237-5455. SA 315-0941. Tel: 412-366-8100. Toll Free Tel: 888-292-2798. FAX: 412-366-2064. Web Site: www.clpgh.org/ein/northland. *Dir*, Sandra A Collins; Tel: 412-366-8100, Ext 109, E-Mail: collins3@einetwork.net; *Circ*, Kim Englert *Head Ref*, Jane Jubb; Tel: 412-366-8100, Ext 137, E-Mail: jubbj@einetwork.net; *Ch Servs*, Mary Morgan Smith; Tel: 412-366-8100, Ext 121, E-Mail: mms0916@aol.com; *Tech Servs*, Betty Berkey; E-Mail: berkeyb@clpgh.org; *Automation Syst Coordr*, Mary Jean Voigt; Tel: 412-366-8100, E 130, E-Mail: voigtm@clpgh.org; *Head, Circ*, Lynne Solomon; Tel: 412-366 8100, Ext 120; *ILL*, Lisa Pochan; Tel: 412-366-8100, Ext 138, E-Mail: pochanl@einetwork.net; *Coll Develop*, Karen Shah; Tel: 412-366-8100, Ext 137, E-Mail: shahk@einetwork.net; *Automation Syst Coordr*, Samuel Taylor Staff 91 (MLS 19, Non-MLS 72)
Founded 1968. Pop 78,690; Circ 698,077
Jan 1999-Dec 1999 Income $2,154,922, State $144,034, City $1,274,178, County $515,956, Locally Generated Income $200,754, Other $20,000. Mat Exp $197,312, Books $147,855, Per/Ser (Incl. Access Fees) $12,518, Other Print Mats $263, Electronic Ref Mat (Incl. Access Fees) $11,047. Sal $1,003,767 (Prof $511,669)
Library Holdings: Bk Vols 144,220; Bk Titles 126,125; Per Subs 320
Automation Activity & Vendor Info: (Cataloging) SIRSI; (Circulation) SIRSI; (OPAC) SIRSI
Database Vendor: Ebsco - EbscoHost, GaleNet, IAC - Info Trac
Publications: The Page (Newsletter)
Partic in Electronic Info Network; PALINET & Union Library Catalogue of Pennsylvania
Special Services for the Deaf - TTY machine
Special Services for the Blind - Volunteer taping & brailling
Friends of the Library Group

P PENN HILLS LIBRARY, 240 Aster St, 15235-2099. SAN 315-0968. Tel: 412-798-2187. FAX: 412-798-2186. E-Mail: phlibrary@clpgh.org. Web Site www.clpgh.org/ein/pennhills. *Dir*, Edward Mandell; E-Mail: mandelle@clpgh.org; *Librn*, Jean Kanouff; E-Mail: kanouffj@clpgh.org; *Librn*, Mary Ann Zeak; E-Mail: zeakm@clpgh.org; Staff 31 (MLS 3, Non-MLS 28)
Founded 1966. Pop 51,742; Circ 273,157
Library Holdings: Bk Titles 130,641; Per Subs 243
Special Collections: Penn Hills Historical Committee Coll
Automation Activity & Vendor Info: (Acquisitions) DRA; (Cataloging) DRA; (Circulation) DRA; (Course Reserve) DRA; (ILL) DRA; (Media Booking) DRA; (OPAC) DRA; (Serials) DRA
Publications: Friend of Penn Hills Library (newsletter)
Partic in Electronic Info Network
Friends of the Library Group

PEOPLES NATURAL GAS COMPANY, Law Library,* CNG Tower, 625 Liberty Ave, 15222-3197. SAN 327-8794. Tel: 412-497-6821, 412-497-6850. FAX: 412-497-6838. *Librn*, Barbara Mason
Library Holdings: Bk Vols 1,000
Restriction: Not open to public
Open Mon-Fri 8-4:45

PITTSBURGH BOARD OF EDUCATION, Professional Library,* 1501 Bedford Ave, 15219. SAN 325-9552. Tel: 412-338-8086. FAX: 412-338-8088. *Asst Librn*, Jill Sella
Library Holdings: Bk Vols 20,000; Per Subs 100

PITTSBURGH HISTORY & LANDMARKS FOUNDATION, James D Van Trump Library, One Station Sq, Ste 450, 15219. SAN 315-100X. Tel: 412-471-5808. FAX: 412-471-1633. Web Site: www.phlf.org. *Librn*, Albert Tannler
Founded 1964
1998-1999 Mats Exp Books $400
Library Holdings: Bk Vols 8,000; Per Subs 30
Subject Interests: Architecture, Art, Crafts, Gardening, Historic preservation, Landscaping, Pa hist, Pittsburgh hist, Transportation, Western Pa

PITTSBURGH INSTITUTE OF MORTUARY SCIENCE LIBRARY, 5808 Baum Blvd, 15206. SAN 315-1018. Tel: 412-362-8500. FAX: 412-362-1684. *Librn*, Roberta J Egelston
Library Holdings: Bk Vols 2,100; Per Subs 40
Subject Interests: Last Rights Indust
Automation Activity & Vendor Info: (Cataloging) Sagebrush Corporation; (Circulation) Sagebrush Corporation

PITTSBURGH POST GAZETTE, Information Center,* 34 Blvd of the Allies, 15222. SAN 327-0726. Tel: 412-263-1619. FAX: 412-391-8452. *Librn*, Angelika Kane
Library Holdings: Bk Titles 1,400; Per Subs 170
Subject Interests: Education, Religion, Sports, Transportation
Special Collections: Pittsburgh Newspapers, picture files (Pittsburgh Post-Gazette & Pittsburgh Press, folders of clippings dating back to 1930s)
Producer of Pittsburgh Post-Gazette Database (available on Dialog, Data/Times & Lexis/Nexis)

PITTSBURGH THEOLOGICAL SEMINARY, Clifford E Barbour Library, 616 N Highland Ave, 15206-2596. SAN 315-1042. Tel: 412-441-3304, Ext 2174. Interlibrary Loan Service Tel: 412-441-3304, Ext 2211. FAX: 412-362-2329. *Dir*, Steven Perry; *Mgr, Tech Servs*, Patricia G Beam; E-Mail: pat_beam@pts.edu; *Acq*, Mariam Sogoian; *Cat*, Sandra Howard; *Per*, Patricia Roncevich; *Publ Servs*, Anita Johnson; *Circ*, Ellen Little; Staff 4 (MLS 4)
Founded 1794. Enrl 228; Fac 20; Highest Degree: Doctorate
Library Holdings: Bk Titles 157,435; Per Subs 936
Subject Interests: Behav sci, History, Relig studies, Soc sci
Special Collections: Hymnology (Warrington Coll); Reformation Theology (John M Mason Coll)
Automation Activity & Vendor Info: (Acquisitions) DRA; (Circulation) DRA; (Serials) DRA
Database Vendor: DRA
Publications: Bibliographia Tripotamopolitana
Partic in OCLC Online Computer Library Center, Inc; PALINET & Union Library Catalogue of Pennsylvania

PITTSBURGH TOY LENDING LIBRARY,* 5410 Baum Blvd, 15232. SAN 372-5502. Tel: 412-682-4430. *Pres*, Daviea Davis
Library Holdings: Bk Titles 100
Special Collections: Parenting; Toys (imaginative & cognitive)
Publications: Newsletter
Special Services for the Deaf - Books on deafness & sign language

PITTSBURGH ZOO, Aqua Zoo Library, One Hill Rd, 15206. SAN 370-7113. Tel: 412-665-3640. FAX: 412-665-3661.
Founded 1983
Library Holdings: Bk Titles 14,000; Per Subs 15
Special Collections: Ciguatera (Inia geoffrensis) Poisoning, research papers; Gambierdiscus toxicus; Platanistidae Dolphins, research papers
Restriction: Staff use only

PLANNED PARENTHOOD OF WESTERN PENNSYLVANIA, (Formerly Planned Parenthood Of Western Pennsylvania), Mary Richards Culbertson Resource Center, 209 Ninth St, Ste 400, 15222-3509. (Mail add: 817 Franklin St, 15901-2825), Tel: 412-434-8964. Circulation Tel: 412-434-8964. Toll Free Tel: 800-230-7526. FAX: 412-434-8974. E-Mail: bgreen@ppwp.org. Web Site: www.ppwp.org.
Founded 1979
Library Holdings: Bk Titles 1,200; Per Subs 13
Subject Interests: Admin, Family planning, Family studies, Human sexuality, Marriage, Med ref, Pop, Professional educ, Relig perspectives, Sexuality, Women
Partic in Laurel Highlands Health Sciences Library Consortium

CM POWER MEMORIAL LIBRARY, Howard Anderson-Power Medical Library, 300 Halket St, 15213. SAN 359-4548. Tel: 412-641-4288. FAX: 412-641-4854. *Librn*, Bernadette Kaelin; E-Mail: bkaelin@mail.magee.edu
Founded 1965
Library Holdings: Bk Titles 1,450; Per Subs 140
Subject Interests: Medicine
Partic in Medline

PPG INDUSTRIES, INC

S GLASS TECHNOLOGY CENTER, Guys Run Rd, Harmar Township, 15238. (Mail add: PO Box 2844, 15230-2844), Tel: 412-820-4936. FAX: 412-820-8696. *Librn*, Martha Dunckhorst; E-Mail: dunckhorst@ppg.com
Founded 1975
Library Holdings: Bk Titles 18,000; Per Subs 200
Subject Interests: Fiber glass
Special Collections: Foreign & Domestic Patents on Fiber Glass Science & Technology; Internal Documents Coll; VSMF ASTM Standards
Publications: Current Contents; Journal List
Partic in BRS; Dialog Corporation; SDC Info Servs

S CHEMICALS TECHNICAL INFORMATION CENTER, 440 College Park Dr, Monroeville, 15146. SAN 370-7784. Tel: 724-325-5221. FAX: 724-325-5105. *Librn*, Denise Callihan; E-Mail: callihan@ppg.com; *Info Specialist*, Audrey Anderson; Staff 3 (MLS 1, Non-MLS 2)
Library Holdings: Bk Vols 14,000; Per Subs 220
Subject Interests: Organic chemistry
Publications: Technical Reports Abstract Bulletin

S GLASS TECHNOLOGY CENTER LIBRARY, PO Box 11472, 15238-0472. SAN 359-3738. Tel: 412-820-8566. FAX: 412-820-8625. *Librn*, Amy Watson
Founded 1912
Library Holdings: Bk Vols 20,000; Per Subs 130
Subject Interests: Chemistry, Engineering, Glass sci, Mat, Physics, Technology
Partic in Dialog Corporation; OCLC Online Computer Library Center, Inc

S TECHNICAL INFORMATION CENTER, 4325 Rosanna Dr, Allison Park, 15101. SAN 359-3762. Tel: 412-492-5262. FAX: 412-492-5509. *Librn*, William Birkmeyer; E-Mail: birkmeyer@ppg.com
Library Holdings: Bk Vols 10,000; Per Subs 425
Subject Interests: Coatings, Paints, Polymers, Resins

S PSP HUMAN RESOURCE DEVELOPMENT LIBRARY, Union Trust Bldg, 501 Grant St, 15219-4407. SAN 372-6290. Tel: 412-261-1333. FAX: 412-261-5014. Web Site: www.psp-hrd.com. *Librn*, Dina J Fulmer; E-Mail: dfulmer@psp-hrd.com
Founded 1946
Jan 1999-Dec 1999 Income $30,000. Mats Exp $5,500, Books $4,500, Per/Ser (Incl. Access Fees) $500, Manuscripts & Archives $500. Sal $17,000
Library Holdings: Bk Titles 500; Per Subs 30
Special Collections: Industrial-Organizational Psych, Work Motivation Management Development

L REED SMITH LLP, Law Library, 435 Sixth Ave, 15219. SAN 315-1093. Tel: 412-288-3377. Interlibrary Loan Service Tel: 412-288-3084. FAX: 412-288-3063. *Dir*, Ronda W Fisch; E-Mail: rfisch@reedsmith.com; Staff 8 (MLS 4, Non-MLS 4)
Founded 1970
Library Holdings: Bk Vols 35,000; Bk Titles 10,000; Per Subs 2,000
Subject Interests: Federal, Labor law, Pa law, Tax law
Automation Activity & Vendor Info: (Acquisitions) SIRSI; (Cataloging) SIRSI; (Circulation) SIRSI; (OPAC) SIRSI; (Serials) SIRSI
Database Vendor: Dialog, Lexis-Nexis, OCLC - First Search
Partic in OCLC Online Computer Library Center, Inc

R REFORMED PRESBYTERIAN THEOLOGICAL SEMINARY LIBRARY, 7418 Penn Ave, 15208-2594. SAN 315-1107. Tel: 412-731-8690. FAX: 412-731-4834. E-Mail: rpseminary@aol.com. Web Site: www.rpts.edu. *Dir*, Thomas Reid
Founded 1810. Enrl 96; Fac 10; Highest Degree: Master
Jan 1999-Dec 1999 Income $91,532. Mats Exp $32,222, Books $20,297, Per/Ser (Incl. Access Fees) $5,000, Presv $4,625, Micro $100, Other Print Mats $100, Electronic Ref Mat (Incl. Access Fees) $2,100. Sal $48,127
Library Holdings: Bk Vols 48,103; Per Subs 221
Subject Interests: Church history, Theology
Special Collections: 16th, 17th & 18th century rare theological works
Publications: Guide to Library Resources; Library handbook
Partic in American Theological Library Association; OCLC Online Computer Library Center, Inc

L ROSE, SCHMIDT, HASLEY & DISALLE PC, Law Library, 900 Oliver Bldg, 15222-2310. SAN 315-114X. Tel: 412-434-8600. FAX: 412-263-2829. *Admin Dir*, Joan M Mitsch; E-Mail: jmitsch@rsdhlaw.com
Library Holdings: Bk Vols 29,000
Partic in Westlaw

M SAINT FRANCIS MEDICAL CENTER, Health Sciences Library,* 400 45th St, 15201-1198. SAN 315-1158. Tel: 412-622-4110. FAX: 412-622-8061. E-Mail: ill@sfhs.edu. Web Site: www.sfhs.edu/library. *Dir Libr Serv*, David Brennan; Tel: 412-622-4109, Fax: 412-622-6310, E-Mail: brennan@sfhs.edu;

Staff 4 (MLS 2, Non-MLS 2) Sal $135,000 (Prof $62,000)
Library Holdings: Bk Vols 5,000
Subject Interests: Internal medicine, Nursing, Psychiatry, Rehabilitation
Database Vendor: Dialog, Ebsco - EbscoHost, Silverplatter Information Inc.
Publications: The Pager
Restriction: Not open to public
Function: ILL available
Partic in BHSL; Pittsburgh BHSL; Pittsburgh-East Hospital Libr Coop; UCMP

SR SAINT PAUL'S EPISCOPAL CHURCH LIBRARY, 1066 Washington Rd, 15228-2024. SAN 329-9724. Tel: 412-531-7153. FAX: 412-531-9820. *Librn*, Mary Wetherwax
Library Holdings: Bk Titles 4,000

S SOCIETY FOR PROTECTIVE COATINGS, SSPC Library, 40 24th St 6th Flr, 15222. SAN 377-8843. Tel: 412-281-2331. Toll Free Tel: 877-281-7772. FAX: 412-281-9992. Web Site: www.sspc.org. *Librn*, Marge Sroka; E-Mail: sroka@sspc.org
Founded 1998
Subject Interests: Coatings, Paints
Partic in Spec Libr Asn

S SOUTH HILLS HEALTH SYSTEM, Behan Health Science Library,* Coal Valley Rd, PO Box 18119, 15236. SAN 371-1625. Tel: 412-469-5786. FAX: 412-469-5468. *Librn*, Ann Ferrari
Library Holdings: Bk Vols 300; Per Subs 200
Open Mon-Fri 8-4:30

L THORP REED & ARMSTRONG, LLP LIBRARY, One Riverfront Ctr, 20 Stanwix St, 15222. SAN 372-9206. Tel: 412-394-2358. FAX: 412-394-2555. *Dir*, Donna M Kielar; E-Mail: dkielar@thorpreed.com; Staff 2 (MLS 2)
Library Holdings: Bk Vols 14,000; Per Subs 110
Subject Interests: Corporate law, Labor

C UNIVERSITY OF PITTSBURGH, University Libraries, 15260. SAN 359-3916. Tel: 412-648-7710. Interlibrary Loan Service Tel: 412-648-7891. FAX: 412-648-7887. Web Site: www.library.pitt.edu/. *Dir, Librn*, Rush Miller; E-Mail: rgmiller@pitt.edu; *Assoc Librn*, Pamela Vance; E-Mail: vance1@pitt.edu; *Tech Servs*, Fern Brody; E-Mail: feb@pitt.edu; Staff 108 (MLS 108)
Founded 1873. Enrl 25,867; Fac 1,486
Jul 1999-Jun 2000 Mats Exp $12,177,550. Sal $9,260,562
Library Holdings: Bk Vols 4,038,413; Per Subs 28,658
Subject Interests: Bolivia, Cuba, E Asian, E European, Latin America, Russia, W European
Special Collections: 18th & 20th Century historical records & mss including photographs, glass plates & negatives of organizations, societies, institutions, businesses, city & county governmental agencies in Southwestern Penn (Archives of Industrial Society); 19th & 20th Century American & English Theatre (Ford & Harriet Curtis Coll); 20th Century Children's Literature (Clifton Fadiman Coll); Archive of Popular Culture; Canadian; Flora & Norman Winkler Coll; Foundation Center Coll; Frank P Ramsey Papers; Hervey Allen Coll, mss, bks; Historical Children's Literature, dating to 18th century, incl Mr Rogers Neighborhood (Elizabeth Nesbitt Room), tv archives, videotapes, puppets, mss; Human Relations Area Files; Izaak Walton's Compleat Angler (Bernard S Horne Coll); John A Nietz Textboook Coll (Early America School Books); Mary Roberts Rinehart Coll, mss, bks; Music & Memorabilia of Stephen Collins Foster (Foster Memorial Library); Pavlowa-Heinrich Ballet Coll; Pennsylvania Industry, Institutions, Ethnic Organizations (Archives of Industrial Society), legis papers, hist rec; Ramon Gomez de la Serna Coll, bks, mss; Rudolf Carnap & Hans Reichenbach Coll, bks, mss; Walter & Martha Leuba Coll; Western Pennsylvania, Early History & Travel (Darlington Memorial Library); William Steinberg Coll
Automation Activity & Vendor Info: (Cataloging) Endeavor
Publications: Bibliographies; Guide to Libraries
Mem of Asn of Research Libraries
Partic in Center For Research Libraries; OCLC Online Computer Library Center, Inc; PALCI
Departmental Libraries:

CL AFRICAN-AMERICAN COLLECTION, Hillman Library, 1st Flr, 15260. SAN 359-3932. Tel: 412-648-7712. FAX: 412-648-7798. Web Site: pw1@pitt.edu. *Librn*, Pearl Woolridge
Library Holdings: Bk Vols 21,572; Per Subs 109

ALLEGHENY OBSERVATORY, Riverview Park, 15214. SAN 359-3940. Tel: 412-321-2400. FAX: 412-321-0606. *Librn*, Lance Lugar
Library Holdings: Bk Vols 4,088; Per Subs 11

BARCO LAW LIBRARY, Law Bldg, 3900 Forbes Ave, 4th flr, 15260. SAN 359-4513. Tel: 412-648-1330. Interlibrary Loan Service Tel: 412-648-1304. FAX: 412-648-1352. Web Site: www.law.pitt.edu/librhome.htm. *Dir*, George Pike; *Publ Servs*, Mark Silverman; *Tech Servs*, Cynthia Cicco; *Acq, Ser*, Suzanne Kaufman
Founded 1915
Library Holdings: Bk Vols 181,558; Per Subs 4,964
Publications: Research Guides; The Barconian; User's Guide
Partic in OCLC Online Computer Library Center, Inc; Westlaw

BEVIER ENGINEERING, 126 Benedum Hall, 15261. SAN 359-4122. Te 412-624-9620. FAX: 412-624-8103. *Librn*, Kate Thomes; E-Mail: kthomes@pitt.edu
Library Holdings: Bk Vols 64,854; Per Subs 969

BUHL LIBRARY OF SOCIAL WORK, Hillman Library, First Flr, 15260. SAN 359-3975. Tel: 412-648-7714. FAX: 412-648-7798. *Librn*, Arif Jan
Library Holdings: Bk Vols 13,281; Per Subs 151

BUSINESS LIBRARY, 138 Mervis Hall, 15260. SAN 359-436X. Tel: 412-648-1669. FAX: 412-648-1586. *Librn*, Susan Neuman
Library Holdings: Bk Vols 53,735; Per Subs 666

CHEMISTRY LIBRARY, 200 Eberly Hall, 15260. SAN 359-4009. Tel: 412-624-8294. FAX: 412-624-8296. *Librn*, Margarete Bower
Library Holdings: Bk Vols 34,182; Per Subs 208

COMPUTER SCIENCE LIBRARY, 200 Eberly Hall, 15260. SAN 359-4068. Tel: 412-624-8294. FAX: 412-624-8296. *Librn*, Margarete Bower
Library Holdings: Bk Vols 14,987; Per Subs 145

GRADUATE SCHOOL OF PUBLIC & INTERNATIONAL AFFAIRS ECONOMICS LIBRARY, 1G12 Posvar Hall, 15260. SAN 359-4033. Tel: 412-648-7575. FAX: 412-648-7569. *Librn*, Dennis R Smith
Library Holdings: Bk Vols 129,283; Per Subs 751

CM FALK LIBRARY OF THE HEALTH SCIENCES, 200 Scaife Hall, 15261 SAN 359-4335. Interlibrary Loan Service Tel: 412-648-2037. Circulation Tel: 412-648-8866. Reference Tel: 412-648-8824. FAX: 412-648-9020. E-Mail: medlibq+@pitt.edu. Web Site: www.hsls.pitt.edu. *Dir*, Patricia Mickelson; Staff 49 (MLS 18, Non-MLS 31)
Library Holdings: Bk Vols 429,581; Bk Titles 185,261; Per Subs 2,379
Subject Interests: Dentistry, Health, Medicine, Nursing, Pharm, Public health
Special Collections: History of Medicine
Publications: HSLS Update

FRICK FINE ARTS LIBRARY, 15260. SAN 359-4157. Tel: 412-648-241 FAX: 412-648-7568. Web Site: www.library.pitt.edu/libraries/frick/fine_arts.html. *Librn*, Ray Anne Lockard; E-Mail: frickart@pitt.edu. Subject Specialists: *Art history*, Ray Anne Lockard
Library Holdings: Bk Vols 81,895; Per Subs 334
Subject Interests: Archit hist, Art history

HILLMAN LIBRARY, 271 Hillman Library, 15260. SAN 359-419X. Tel: 412-648-7710. FAX: 412-648-7887. *Dir, Librn*, Rush Miller
Library Holdings: Bk Vols 1,279,960; Per Subs 10,135

INFORMATION SCIENCES LIBRARY, L I S Bldg, 3rd Flr, 15260. SAN 359-4394. Tel: 412-624-4710. FAX: 412-624-4062. Web Site: www.pitt.edu/~inscilib. *Librn*, E Tillapaugh Mahoney; Tel: 412-624-7404 E-Mail: etm@pitt.edu; Staff 6 (MLS 3, Non-MLS 3)
Special Collections: Elizabeth Nesbitt Room

LANGLEY LIBRARY, 217 Langley Hall, 15260. SAN 359-4181. Tel: 412-624-4490. FAX: 412-624-1809. *Librn*, Drynda Johnston
Library Holdings: Bk Vols 86,483; Per Subs 554

MATHEMATICS LIBRARY, 430 Thackeray Hall, 15260. SAN 359-4211. Tel: 412-624-8205. FAX: 412-624-4180. *Librn*, Kate Thomes
Library Holdings: Bk Vols 26,451; Per Subs 271

PHYSICS, GEOLOGY & PLANETARY SCIENCES, Old Engineering Ha Rm 208, 15260. SAN 359-4270. Tel: 412-624-8770. FAX: 412-624-3239 *Librn*, Lance Lugar
Library Holdings: Bk Vols 43,211; Per Subs 326

THEODORE M FINNEY MUSIC LIBRARY, B30 Music Bldg, 15260. SAN 359-4246. Tel: 412-624-4130. FAX: 412-624-4180. Web Site: www.library.pitt.edu/libraries/music/music.html. *Head of Libr*, James P Cassaro; Staff 4 (MLS 2, Non-MLS 2)
Founded 1966
Library Holdings: Bk Vols 50,849; Per Subs 182

CM WESTERN PSYCHIATRIC INSTITUTE & CLINIC LIBRARY, 3811 O'Hara St, 15213-2593. SAN 359-4572. Tel: 412-624-2378. FAX: 412-624-6042. Web Site: wpic.library.pitt.edu.; Staff 6 (MLS 3, Non-MLS 3)
Founded 1942
Library Holdings: Bk Titles 70,000; Per Subs 400
Subject Interests: Behav sci, Mental health, Psychiatry
Publications: Video Catalog

M UPMC PASSAVANT, Medical Library, 9100 Babcock Blvd, 15237-5842. SAN 315-0933. Tel: 412-367-6320. FAX: 412-367-6889. Web Site: www.upmc.edu/passavant/library. *Librn*, Margaret Trevanion; E-Mail: trevanionmu@ph.upmc.edu; Staff 2 (MLS 1, Non-MLS 1)
Founded 1971
Library Holdings: Per Subs 200
Subject Interests: Medicine, Nursing
Special Collections: Consumer Health Pamphlets
Database Vendor: OVID Technologies
Partic in Basic Health Sciences Library Network; Nat Libr of Med; Pittsburgh-East Hospital Libr Coop

UPMC SAINT MARGARET

M HEALTH SCIENCES LIBRARY, 815 Freeport Rd, 15215. SAN 359-3827 Tel: 412-784-4121, 412-784-4238. FAX: 412-784-4989. *Dir*, Amy Haugh E-Mail: haughaj@msx.upmc.edu; *Tech Servs*, Nancy Zachocki
Founded 1951
Library Holdings: Bk Vols 2,500; Per Subs 200

Subject Interests: Family med, Gerontology, Nursing educ, Occupational therapy, Orthopedics, Phys, Rheumatoid arthritis, Sports med
Special Collections: Historical Coll (Harry M Margolis MD)
Publications: Article in Physician Newsletter
Partic in Basic Health Sciences Library Network

UPMC SHADYSIDE, James Frazer Hillman Health Science Library, 5230 Centre Ave, 15232. SAN 315-1166. Tel: 412-623-2441. FAX: 412-683-8027. *Mgr Libr Serv*, Michele Klein-Fedyshin; Staff 2 (MLS 2)
Founded 1973
Library Holdings: Bk Titles 2,223; Per Subs 225
Subject Interests: Clinical medicine, Consumer health info, Nursing
Database Vendor: Dialog, Ebsco - EbscoHost, OVID Technologies

UPPER SAINT CLAIR TOWNSHIP LIBRARY, 1820 McLaughlin Run Rd, Upper Saint Clair, 15241-2397. SAN 315-1204. Tel: 412-835-5540. FAX: 412-835-6763. Web Site: www.twbusc.org/libmain/lib.html. *Dir*, Lois Hoop; E-Mail: hoopl@clpgh.org; *ILL*, Linda Messer; *Ad Servs, Ref*, Jean Forry; *Ch Servs*, Debra Conn; Staff 11 (MLS 11)
Founded 1957. Pop 19,700; Circ 224
Jan 2000-Dec 2000 Income $800,609
Library Holdings: Bk Vols 92,409; Per Subs 178
Database Vendor: epixtech, inc.
Partic in PALINET & Union Library Catalogue of Pennsylvania
Friends of the Library Group

VA PITTSBURGH HEALTH CARE SYSTEM
M MEDICAL LIBRARY, 7180 Highland Dr, 15206. SAN 359-4602. Tel: 412-365-5515. FAX: 412-365-4809.; Staff 2 (MLS 2)
Founded 1954
Library Holdings: Bk Vols 6,300; Per Subs 224
Subject Interests: Neurologic, Patient educ, Psychiatry
Partic in Pittsburgh Med Libr Asn; Regional Med Libr Prog; Vets Admin Libr Network

VIKING SYSTEMS LIBRARY,* 2070 William Pitt Way, 15238. SAN 314-7738. Tel: 412-826-3358. FAX: 412-826-3353. *In Charge*, Jack Saluja
Founded 1953
Library Holdings: Bk Vols 11,000; Per Subs 59

WESTERN PENNSYLVANIA HOSPITAL
MEDICAL LIBRARY, 4800 Friendship Ave, 15224. SAN 359-4661. Tel: 412-578-5257. FAX: 412-578-7317. *Librn*, Barbara L Brooks
Library Holdings: Bk Vols 11,000
Subject Interests: Medicine
Partic in National Network Of Libraries Of Medicine - South Central Region; Pittsburgh-East Hospital Libr Coop
SCHOOL OF NURSING LIBRARY, 4900 Friendship Ave, 15224. SAN 359-4696. Tel: 412-578-5556. FAX: 412-578-1837.
Library Holdings: Bk Titles 2,007; Per Subs 62
Subject Interests: Nursing
Partic in Pittsburgh-East Hospital Libr Coop

WESTMINSTER PRESBYTERIAN CHURCH LIBRARY, 2040 Washington Rd, 15241. SAN 315-1220. Tel: 412-835-6630. FAX: 412-835-5690. *Librn*, Tom Sanders
Library Holdings: Bk Vols 5,000
Friends of the Library Group

WHITEHALL PUBLIC LIBRARY,* 100 Borough Park Dr, 15236-2098. SAN 315-1239. Tel: 412-882-6622. FAX: 412-882-9556. Web Site: www.clpgh.org/ein/whitehal. *Librn*, Lee E Boyd; *Ch Servs*, Sharon Julian-Milas
Founded 1963
Library Holdings: Bk Vols 42,000; Per Subs 100
Subject Interests: Popular paperbacks, Travel info
Special Collections: Bks on tapes; Business Coll; College Career Information; Large Print Coll; Parenting Coll; Toddler Board & Cloth Books Coll
Friends of the Library Group

WILKINSBURG PUBLIC LIBRARY,* 605 Ross Ave, 15221-2195. SAN 315-1247. Tel: 412-244-2940. FAX: 412-243-6943. Web Site: www.clpgh.org/ein/wlksbrg/. *Dir*, Joel D Minnigh; E-Mail: minnighj@clpgh.org; *Librn*, Tom Shaw; Tel: 412-244-4378, E-Mail: shawt@clpgh.org; *Assoc Librn*, Linda Jennings; Tel: 412-244-2942, E-Mail: jenningsl@clpgh.org; Staff 3 (MLS 3)
Founded 1899. Pop 21,080; Circ 91,050
Jan 1999-Dec 1999 Income (Main Library Only) $940,000, State $495,000, City $270,000, Federal $25,000, County $150,000. Mats Exp $59,700, Books $50,000, Per/Ser (Incl. Access Fees) $6,200, AV Equip $1,500, Electronic Ref Mat (Incl. Access Fees) $2,000. Sal $152,000 (Prof $58,000)
Library Holdings: Bk Titles 82,000; Per Subs 195; High Interest/Low Vocabulary Bk Vols 150; Bks on Deafness & Sign Lang 17
Subject Interests: Biographies, Local history, Mysteries
Friends of the Library Group

PITTSTON

S JAMES PETTINGER MEMORIAL LIBRARY,* EDCNP, 1151 Oak St, 18640-3795. SAN 329-0824. Tel: 570-655-5581. FAX: 570-654-5137. *Librn*, Kathryn A Reedy; *Res*, Dan Hilger; Staff 20 (MLS 20)
Fac 31
Library Holdings: Bk Titles 3,000; Per Subs 50
Special Collections: Pennsylvania State Data Center Foundation Library
Publications: Annual Report; Newsletters, State of the Region, Overall Econ Deve Prog
Partic in Dialog Corporation

P PITTSTON MEMORIAL LIBRARY, City Hall, 34 Broad St, 18640-2563. SAN 315-1255. Tel: 717-654-9565. FAX: 717-654-6078. *Librn*, Mary Dotter
Founded 1971. Pop 9,389; Circ 15,000
Library Holdings: Bk Vols 7,500; Per Subs 40
Mem of Wilkes-Barre District Libr Ctr
Friends of the Library Group

PLEASANT HILLS

P PLEASANT HILLS PUBLIC LIBRARY,* 302 Old Clairton Rd, 15236-4399. SAN 315-1263. Tel: 412-655-2424. FAX: 412-655-2292. Web Site: www.clpgh.org/ein/pleasant/. *Librn*, Holly Ferkett
Founded 1945. Pop 8,884; Circ 74,000
Jan 1998-Dec 1999 Income $197,400, State $24,700, County $69,000, Locally Generated Income $13,700. Mats Exp $24,600, Books $21,000, Per/Ser (Incl. Access Fees) $2,000. Sal $103,917 (Prof $46,847)
Library Holdings: Bk Vols 42,000; Per Subs 105
Subject Interests: Literature
Friends of the Library Group

PLEASANT MOUNT

P PLEASANT MOUNT PUBLIC LIBRARY,* Main St, 18453-9801. SAN 320-8389. Tel: 570-448-2573. *Librn*, Maryann Saam
Founded 1975
Library Holdings: Bk Vols 5,000; Per Subs 12
Open Mon 4-6, Tues 1:30-3:30 & 6-8, Thurs & Sat 1:30-3:30

PLUMSTEADVILLE

S SCOTT SPECIALTY GASES, INC, Scott Technical Information Center Library, 6141 Easton Rd, PO Box 310, 18949. SAN 315-1271. Tel: 215-766-8861. Toll Free Tel: 800-217-2688. FAX: 215-766-2476. E-Mail: mhaurin@scottgas.com. Web Site: www.scottgas.com.
Founded 1960
Library Holdings: Bk Vols 800; Per Subs 50
Subject Interests: Environmental studies
Publications: Scott Specialty Gas (Reference guide)

PLYMOUTH

P PLYMOUTH PUBLIC LIBRARY, 107 W Main St, 18651-2919. SAN 315-128X. Tel: 570-779-4775. FAX: 570-779-5616. E-Mail: ppl@epix.com. Web Site: home.epix.net/~ppl/. *Coll Develop, Dir*, Lillian M Caffrey
Founded 1938. Pop 11,834; Circ 18,214
Jan 1999-Dec 1999 Income $100,409, State $24,473, City $5,769, County $12,370, Locally Generated Income $11,000, Other $46,797. Mats Exp $8,752, Books $7,018, Per/Ser (Incl. Access Fees) $1,366, Presv $368. Sal $69,768 (Prof $22,358)
Library Holdings: Bk Vols 34,986; Per Subs 65
Subject Interests: Children's bks, Cookbks, Local history
Mem of Luzerne County Libr Syst; Wilkes-Barre District Libr Ctr
Friends of the Library Group

PLYMOUTH MEETING

S ECRI LIBRARY, 5200 Butler Pike, 19462. SAN 315-1301. Tel: 610-825-6000, Ext 5309. FAX: 610-834-7366. *Chief Librn*, Evelyn Kuserk; E-Mail: ekuserk@ecri.org; *Cat*, Evelyn Udell; E-Mail: eudell@ecri.org; *ILL*, Angela Siciliano; *Electronic Resources*, Julie Esparza; E-Mail: jesparza@ecri.org; Staff 6 (MLS 3, Non-MLS 3)
Founded 1966
Library Holdings: Bk Titles 9,000; Per Subs 1,900
Subject Interests: Biomedical engineering, Med tech
Special Collections: Medical & Health Care Related Devices (Health Devices Evaluation Services), misc
Automation Activity & Vendor Info: (Acquisitions) Inmagic, Inc.; (Cataloging) Inmagic, Inc.; (Circulation) Inmagic, Inc.; (Serials) Inmagic, Inc.
Restriction: Open to others by appointment
Partic in Delaware Valley Information Consortium; Greater NE Regional Med Libr Program

POCONO PINES

P CLYMER LIBRARY, HC 89, Box 39B, 18350-9705. SAN 324-3974. Tel: 570-646-0826. FAX: 570-646-6181. E-Mail: clymer@clymerlibrary.org. Web Site: www.clymerlibrary.org. *Dir*, Wayne R Wheeler; E-Mail: wwheeler@clymerlibrary.org; Staff 4 (MLS 1, Non-MLS 3)
Founded 1902. Pop 8,000; Circ 60,000
Library Holdings: Bk Titles 30,000; Per Subs 50
Database Vendor: Ebsco - EbscoHost
Function: ILL available, Photocopies available, Some telephone reference
Open Mon, Wed, Fri & Sat 10-5, Tues & Thurs 10-8
Friends of the Library Group

POINT MARION

P POINT MARION PUBLIC LIBRARY,* Ontario St, 15474. SAN 370-7458. Tel: 724-725-9553. *Librn*, Nancy Shuluga
Founded 1928. Pop 7,675; Circ 2,067
Library Holdings: Bk Titles 5,000

PORT ALLEGANY

P SAMUEL W SMITH MEMORIAL PUBLIC LIBRARY, 22 Church St, 16743-1193. SAN 315-131X. Tel: 814-642-9210. FAX: 814-642-7555. E-Mail: swsmith@adelphia.net. Web Site: home.adelphia.net/~swsmith. *Dir*, Janna C Shaffer; Staff 5 (MLS 1, Non-MLS 4)
Founded 1930. Pop 9,417; Circ 40,359
Jan 2000-Dec 2000 Income $115,747, State $36,168, City $18,363, Locally Generated Income $59,470. Mats Exp $13,890, Books $12,390, Per/Ser (Incl. Access Fees) $1,500. Sal $45,752 (Prof $20,000)
Library Holdings: Bk Vols 21,367; Per Subs 40
Subject Interests: Glass
Automation Activity & Vendor Info: (Circulation) Follett
Database Vendor: Ebsco - EbscoHost
Friends of the Library Group
Bookmobiles: 1

PORT CARBON

P PORT CARBON PUBLIC LIBRARY, 111 Pike St, 17965-1814. SAN 315-1328. Tel: 570-622-6115. FAX: 570-622-7141. E-Mail: ptc@iv29.schio.k12.pa.us. *Dir*, Janet Eich; Staff 1 (Non-MLS 1)
Library Holdings: Bk Titles 24,000; Per Subs 30
Mem of Pottsville Free Public Library; Schuylkill County Libr Syst

PORTAGE

P PORTAGE PUBLIC LIBRARY,* 704 Main St, PO Box 205, 15946-1715. SAN 315-1336. Tel: 814-736-4340. FAX: 814-736-4413. *Librn*, Beverly Rank
Founded 1927. Pop 8,133; Circ 42,203
Library Holdings: Bk Vols 21,000; Per Subs 18
Mem of Cambria County Library System & District Center
Friends of the Library Group

POTTSTOWN

M POTTSTOWN MEMORIAL MEDICAL CENTER, Medical Library, 1600 E High St, 19464. SAN 372-9230. Tel: 610-327-7468. FAX: 610-327-7432. *Librn*, Cindy Yeager; E-Mail: cyeager@pmmctr.org
Library Holdings: Bk Vols 3,000
Subject Interests: Medicine, Nursing

P POTTSTOWN PUBLIC LIBRARY,* 500 High St, 19464-5656. SAN 315-1344. Tel: 610-970-6551. FAX: 610-970-6553. *Librn*, Kathleen Arnold-Yerger; *Ad Servs, ILL*, Scott Elmer; Staff 3 (MLS 3)
Founded 1921. Pop 37,710; Circ 170,595
Jan 1997-Dec 1998 Income $352,000, State $40,000, Federal $2,000, Other $120,972. Mats Exp $60,700, Books $44,000, Per/Ser (Incl. Access Fees) $7,200. Sal $183,988
Library Holdings: Bk Vols 66,000
Subject Interests: Large type, Pa hist
Special Collections: Limerick Nuclear Power Plant
Friends of the Library Group

POTTSVILLE

M GOOD SAMARITAN REGIONAL MEDICAL CENTER, Health Science Library, 700 E Norwegian St, 17901-2798. SAN 372-6215. Tel: 570-621-4466. FAX: 570-621-4073. *Librn*, Velma L Sippie; Staff 1 (MLS 1)
Jul 1998-Jun 1999 Income Parent Institution $25,500. Mats Exp $11,000, Books $2,500, Per/Ser (Incl. Access Fees) $8,500. Sal $14,500
Library Holdings: Bk Vols 1,225; Bk Titles 902; Per Subs 30
Automation Activity & Vendor Info: (Cataloging) Follett
Partic in Central Pennsylvania Health Science Library Association (CPHSLA); Nat Libr of Med

R OHEB ZEDECK SYNAGOGUE CENTER LIBRARY, 2300 Mahantongo St, 17901. SAN 315-1360. Tel: 570-622-5890. FAX: 570-622-4518. *In Charge*, Rabbi Michael Pont
Founded 1958
Library Holdings: Bk Vols 1,000
Subject Interests: Judaica

P POTTSVILLE FREE PUBLIC LIBRARY,* 215 W Market St, 17901-297 SAN 315-1379. Tel: 570-622-8105, 570-622-8880. FAX: 570-622-2157. E-Mail: potlib@pottsville.infi.net. Web Site: www.pottsville.com/library/. *Dir*, Nancy Smink; E-Mail: njs@lu29.schiu.k12.pa.us; *ILL*, Gina Bensinge E-Mail: potill@lu29.schiu.k1.pa.us; *Ch Servs*, Carol Orlick; E-Mail: potchild@lu29.schiu.k12.pa.us; *Ad Servs*, Denise Miller; E-Mail: potcirc@lu29.schiu.k12.pa.us; *Tech Servs*, Shelley Rogers; *Ref*, Becky White; E-Ma potref@lu29.schiu.k12.pa.us
Founded 1911. Pop 92,985; Circ 173,667
Jan 1998-Dec 1998 Income $701,409, State $312,152, City $52,000, Fede $98,000, County $50,000, Locally Generated Income $134,257, Other $55,000. Mats Exp $70,695, Books $51,000, Per/Ser (Incl. Access Fees) $14,400, Micro $3,400, Electronic Ref Mat (Incl. Access Fees) $1,895. Sa $289,762 (Prof $178,774)
Library Holdings: Bk Vols 146,096; Per Subs 239
Special Collections: Anthracite Coll; Lincoln Coll; Molly Maguires Coll
Automation Activity & Vendor Info: (Circulation) Brodart; (OPAC) Brodart
Database Vendor: OCLC - First Search
Member Libraries: Ashland Public Library; Mahanoy City Public Library Mount Carmel Public Library; Orwigsburg Area Free Public Library; Port Carbon Public Library; Ralpho Township Public Library; Schuylkill Haver Free Public Library; Schuylkill Haven Free Public Library; Shamokin-Coa Township Public Library, Inc; Shenandoah Area Free Public Library; Tamaqua Public Library; Tower-Porter Community Library; Tremont Area Free Public Library
Partic in PALINET & Union Library Catalogue of Pennsylvania
Headquarters for Schuylkill County Library System & District Library Center
Friends of the Library Group

M THE POTTSVILLE HOSPITAL & WARNE CLINIC, Medical Library,* 420 S Jackson St, 17901. SAN 326-5439. Tel: 717-621-5033. FAX: 717-622-8221. *Librn*, Diane Leinheiser
Library Holdings: Bk Titles 176; Per Subs 26
Subject Interests: Medicine
Publications: Newsletter (quarterly)

GL SCHUYLKILL COUNTY LAW LIBRARY,* 401 N Second St, 17901. SAN 315-1395. Tel: 570-628-1235. FAX: 570-628-1017. *Librn*, D Susan Kost
Founded 1888
Jan 1997-Dec 1998 Income $169,093. Mats Exp $125,250, Books $124,25 Per/Ser (Incl. Access Fees) $1,000. Sal $38,843 (Prof $24,287)
Library Holdings: Bk Vols 30,000; Per Subs 20

PROSPECT PARK

P PROSPECT PARK FREE LIBRARY, 720 Maryland Ave, 19076-1318. SA 315-1417. Tel: 610-532-4643. FAX: 610-532-5648. *Chief Librn*, Amy Strauss; Staff 2 (MLS 2)
Founded 1924. Pop 7,000; Circ 14,000
Library Holdings: Bk Titles 15,352; Per Subs 26
Open Mon-Thurs 10-8, Fri 10-6, Sat 8:30-3, Summer Mon-Thurs 10-8, Fri 10-6 & Sat 10-2

PUNXSUTAWNEY

C INDIANA UNIVERSITY OF PENNSYLVANIA, Punxsutawney Campus Library, 1010 Winslow St, 15767. SAN 315-1425. Tel: 814-938-4870. FAX 814-938-5900. Web Site: www.lib.iup.edu. *Librn*, Robert J Kirby; E-Mail: rkirby@grove.iup.edu; Staff 2 (MLS 1, Non-MLS 1)
Founded 1962. Enrl 250
Jul 1999-Jun 2000 Income $100,000, Federal $5,000, Parent Institution $95,000. Mats Exp $17,500, Per/Ser (Incl. Access Fees) $15,000, Micro $2,500. Sal $80,000 (Prof $63,000)
Library Holdings: Bk Titles 18,000; Per Subs 95
Automation Activity & Vendor Info: (Acquisitions) Endeavor; (Catalogin Endeavor; (Circulation) Endeavor; (OPAC) Endeavor; (Serials) Endeavor
Partic in OCLC Online Computer Library Center, Inc; PALINET & Union Library Catalogue of Pennsylvania

P PUNXSUTAWNEY MEMORIAL LIBRARY,* 301 E Mahoning St, 1576 0301. SAN 315-145X. Tel: 814-938-5020. FAX: 814-938-3180. E-Mail: punxlib@key-net.net. *Librn*, Roberta M Dinsmore

Founded 1916. Pop 16,541; Circ 72,000
Jan 1998-Dec 1999 Income $93,300. Mats Exp $8,500. Sal $54,400
Library Holdings: Bk Vols 37,000
Subject Interests: Cookery, Drama, Large print bks, Pennsylvania
Mem of Oil Creek District Library Center
Partic in Jefferson County Library System
Friends of the Library Group

UAKERTOWN

ST LUKES QUAKERTOWN COMMUNITY HOSPITAL, Health Sciences Library,* 1021 Park Ave, 18951-9003. SAN 329-2452. Tel: 215-538-4563. *Librn*, Kerry Dennigan; Staff 1 (MLS 1)
Library Holdings: Bk Titles 400; Per Subs 140

ADNOR

AMERICAN HOME PRODUCTS, Wyeth-Ayerst Research Radnor Library, 145 King of Prussia Rd, 19087. SAN 315-1468. Tel: 610-341-2491. FAX: 610-989-4581. E-Mail: nistaa@war.wyeth.com. *Assoc Dir*, Ann Nista; *Asst Librn*, Judith C Bryant; *Asst Librn*, Laura Lo; Staff 10 (MLS 6, Non-MLS 4)
Founded 1945
Library Holdings: Bk Titles 9,000; Per Subs 500
Subject Interests: Biochemistry, Chemistry, Endocrinology, Medicine, Microbiology
Partic in HSLC; PALINET & Union Library Catalogue of Pennsylvania

CABRINI COLLEGE LIBRARY, 610 King of Prussia Rd, 19087-3698. SAN 315-1476. Tel: 610-902-8538. FAX: 610-902-8539. E-Mail: library@cabrini.edu. Web Site: www.peter.cabrini.edu/library. *Dir*, Roberta C Jacquet; Tel: 610-902-8260, E-Mail: jacquet@cabrini.edu; *Publ Servs*, Linda Roccas; Tel: 610-902-8538, E-Mail: lroccas@cabrini.edu; *Tech Servs*, Alan Silverman; Tel: 610-902-8537, E-Mail: asilver@cabrini.edu; Staff 7 (MLS 4, Non-MLS 3)
Founded 1957. Enrl 1,376; Fac 60; Highest Degree: Master
Jul 1998-Jun 1999 Income (Main Library Only) $468,351. Mats Exp $152,204, Books $42,567, Per/Ser (Incl. Access Fees) $71,137, Presv $8,500, Micro $18,000, Electronic Ref Mat (Incl. Access Fees) $12,000. Sal $204,303 (Prof $128,640)
Library Holdings: Bk Vols 177,215; Per Subs 589
Subject Interests: Education
Special Collections: Cabriniana Coll; Franklin Delano Roosevelt Coll
Automation Activity & Vendor Info: (Cataloging) SIRSI; (Circulation) SIRSI; (OPAC) SIRSI; (Serials) SIRSI
Database Vendor: Lexis-Nexis, OCLC - First Search, ProQuest, Silverplatter Information Inc.
Partic in SEPCHE

WELLINGTON MANAGEMENT COMPANY, Research Library,* 2 Radnor Corporate Ctr, Ste 300, 19087. SAN 329-3300. Tel: 610-631-3500. FAX: 610-631-3569. *Librn*, Jeanne Wilmer; Staff 1 (MLS 1)
Library Holdings: Per Subs 100
Subject Interests: Coop finance, Indust
Open Mon-Fri 9-5

EADING

ALBRIGHT COLLEGE, F Wilbur Gingrich Library, 13th & Exeter Sts, 19604. (Mail add: PO Box 15234, 19612-5234), SAN 315-1514. Tel: 610-921-7517. Reference Tel: 610-921-7211. FAX: 610-921-7509. E-Mail: libraryref@alb.edu. Web Site: www.albright.edu/library/. *Dir*, Rosemary L Deegan; Tel: 610-921-7202, E-Mail: rosemaryd@alb.edu; *AV*, George E Missonis; Tel: 610-921-7201, E-Mail: georgm@alb.edu; *ILL*, Christine L Kantner; Tel: 610-921-7209, E-Mail: chrisk@alb.edu; *Cat*, Arlene Breiner; *Tech Servs*, Fianna D Holt; Tel: 610-921-7201, E-Mail: fiannah@alb.edu; *Ref*, Sandra L Stump; Tel: 610-921-7205, E-Mail: sandyst@alb.edu; *Distance Educ*, Ronald Saska; Tel: 610-921-7234, E-Mail: rons@alb.edu; Staff 14 (MLS 7, Non-MLS 7)
Founded 1856. Enrl 1,200
Jun 1999-May 2000 Income Parent Institution $1,006,000. Mats Exp $478,690, Books $166,510, Per/Ser (Incl. Access Fees) $144,130, Presv $14,560, Micro $37,960, AV Equip $63,730, Other Print Mats $2,920, Electronic Ref Mat (Incl. Access Fees) $48,880. Sal $351,500 (Prof $214,285)
Library Holdings: Bk Vols 211,600; Per Subs 930; Per Subs 930; Bks on Deafness & Sign Lang 60
Subject Interests: Behav sci, Holocaust, Natural science, Soc sci
Special Collections: Albrightiana; American Enterprise Institute for Public Research; Dick Coll of the Limited Editions Club; Norse-American Coll; Reading & Berks County (J Bennett Nolan Coll)
Automation Activity & Vendor Info: (Acquisitions) Bestseller; (Cataloging) Bestseller; (Circulation) Bestseller; (OPAC) Bestseller; (Serials) Bestseller
Database Vendor: CARL, Dialog, GaleNet, Lexis-Nexis, OCLC - First Search, ProQuest
Publications: Library Link (Newsletter); Library Workbook; Pathfinders; Serials List; User's Guide
Function: ILL available
Partic in Associated College Libraries of Central Pennsylvania; Berks County Library Association; Dialog Corporation; Interlibrary Delivery Service of Pennsylvania; LVIS; OCLC Online Computer Library Center, Inc; PALINET & Union Library Catalogue of Pennsylvania
Special Services for the Blind - Printed text enlargers
Friends of the Library Group

C ALVERNIA COLLEGE, Dr Frank A Franco Library, 400 Saint Bernardine St, 19607-1799. SAN 315-1522. Tel: 610-796-8223. Interlibrary Loan Service Tel: 610-796-8395. Circulation Tel: 610-796-8224. FAX: 610-796-8347. Web Site: www.alvernia.edu/library/. *Dean of Libr*, Eugene S Mitchell; Tel: 610-796-8351, E-Mail: mitcheu@alvernia.edu; *Instrul Serv*, Katrina H Miller; Tel: 610-796-8398, E-Mail: milleka@alvernia.edu; *Access Serv*, Jennifer Allen; Tel: 610-796-8395, E-Mail: allenjn@alvernia.edu; Staff 5 (MLS 4, Non-MLS 1)
Founded 1958. Highest Degree: Master
Jul 1999-Jun 2000 Income Parent Institution $240,000. Mats Exp $193,100, Books $86,500, Per/Ser (Incl. Access Fees) $65,100, Presv $4,000, Other Print Mats $5,300, Electronic Ref Mat (Incl. Access Fees) $32,200
Library Holdings: Bk Vols 98,500; Bk Titles 75,600; Per Subs 400
Subject Interests: Criminal justice, Education, Nursing, Occupational therapy, Physical therapy
Special Collections: Italian-American Cultural Center; Polish Coll
Automation Activity & Vendor Info: (Circulation) epixtech, inc.; (OPAC) epixtech, inc.
Database Vendor: Dialog, OCLC - First Search, ProQuest
Partic in Access Pa; Advan Libr Info Network; Associated College Libraries of Central Pennsylvania; OCLC Online Computer Library Center, Inc; PALINET & Union Library Catalogue of Pennsylvania

GL BERKS COUNTY LAW LIBRARY,* 633 Court St, 19601-3566. SAN 315-1549. Tel: 610-478-6370. FAX: 610-478-6375. E-Mail: lffisk@epix.net. *Librn*, Linda Fuerle Fisk
Founded 1859
Jan 1998-Dec 1999 Income $171,126. Mats Exp $96,790. Sal $64,981 (Prof $36,639)
Library Holdings: Bk Vols 31,000; Bk Titles 2,000; Per Subs 186
Subject Interests: Fed, state and county law

S CARPENTER TECHNOLOGY CORP, Research & Development Library,* Center Ave & Union St, PO Box 14662, 19612-4662. SAN 315-1557. Tel: 610-208-2583. FAX: 610-208-3256. *Librn*, Wendy M Schmehl; *Info Specialist*, Frances M Walters
Founded 1950
Library Holdings: Bk Titles 4,100; Per Subs 160
Subject Interests: Chemistry, Electronics, Metallurgy
Partic in Berks County Library Association

S EXIDE CORP, Technical Center Library,* 4440 Pottsville Pike, 19605. SAN 323-665X. Tel: 610-921-4470. FAX: 610-921-4463. E-Mail: cghqbc@aol.com, extechlib@hslc.org. *Librn*, Deborah G Hirneisen
Founded 1978
Library Holdings: Bk Vols 1,663; Bk Titles 1,485; Per Subs 15
Subject Interests: Inorganic chemistry
Mem of Berks County Libr Syst
Partic in Health Science Library Information Consortium

S HISTORICAL SOCIETY OF BERKS COUNTY, Museum & Library, 940 Centre Ave, 19601. SAN 315-1581. Tel: 610-375-4375. FAX: 610-375-4376. E-Mail: lorebee@epix.net. Web Site: www.berksweb.com/histsoc. *Archivist, Dir*, Marion Rosenbaum
Founded 1869
Library Holdings: Bk Titles 14,500; Per Subs 10
Special Collections: Becks County Family Histories; German & English Newspapers of Reading & Berks County 1797-1907, newsp bd; Iron History of Berks County; Original Manuscripts
Publications: The Historical Review of Berks County
Open Tues-Sat 9-4

R KESHER ZION SYNAGOGUE SISTERHOOD LIBRARY, 1245 Perkiomen Ave, 19602-1318. SAN 315-1603. Tel: 610-372-3818, 610-374-1763. FAX: 610-375-1352. *Librn*, Rachel Yaffee; *Ad Servs*, Karol Page
Library Holdings: Bk Vols 2,500
Subject Interests: Judaica

S PARSONS, Library & Information Services,* 2675 Morgantown Rd, 19603-1498. SAN 315-1565. Tel: 610-775-2600. FAX: 610-855-2001.
Library Holdings: Bk Titles 20,000; Per Subs 500
Subject Interests: Analysis, Civil, Electrical engineering, Environmental studies, Fuels tech, Mechanical, Nuclear safety, Quality assurance, Structural engineering
Special Collections: Corporate Reports; Public Utility Rate & Regulatory; Standards; Vendor Catalogs, hard copy & micro
Open Mon-Fri 8-4:30

C PENNSYLVANIA STATE UNIVERSITY, Berks, Berks-Lehigh Valley College Thun Library, Tulpehocken Rd, PO Box 7009, 19610-6009. SAN 315-1611. Tel: 610-396-6240. FAX: 610-396-6249. E-Mail: djm@psulias.psu.edu. Web Site: www.lias.psu.edu. *Librn*, Deena J Morganti; *Ref*, Nancy Dewald; Staff 3 (MLS 3)
Founded 1958. Enrl 2,100; Fac 80
Jul 1998-Jun 1999 Mats Exp $120,000
Library Holdings: Bk Vols 46,000; Per Subs 300
Partic in OCLC Online Computer Library Center, Inc; RLIN

J READING AREA COMMUNITY COLLEGE, The Yocum Library, PO Box 1706, 19603-1706. SAN 315-1638. Tel: 610-372-4721. FAX: 610-607-6254. *Dir Libr Serv*, Mary Ellen G Heckman; *Tech Servs*, Linda Lawrence
Founded 1971
Library Holdings: Bk Vols 30,000; Per Subs 425
Subject Interests: Nursing, Science fiction
Special Collections: Comic Books; Music Score Coll; Schuylkill Navigation Co Maps
Partic in OCLC Online Computer Library Center, Inc

S READING EAGLE CO, Eagle-Times Library, 345 Penn St, 19601. SAN 315-1646. Tel: 610-371-5077. FAX: 610-371-5098. *Librn*, Margaret Gannon
Subject Interests: Local, National, Regional, World news
All local regional news published in Eagle or Times on Basis database-available through Datatimes.

S READING MUSEUM LIBRARY,* 500 Museum Rd, 19611. SAN 327-0742. Tel: 610-371-5854. FAX: 610-371-5632. *Dir*, Robert P Metzer
Library Holdings: Bk Vols 1,000
Subject Interests: Art, Astronomy

P READING PUBLIC LIBRARY, 100 S Fifth St, 19602. SAN 359-4963. Tel: 610-655-6365. FAX: 610-478-9035. E-Mail: rplref@reading.lib.pa.us. Web Site: www.reading.lib.pa.us. *Dir*, Luren Dickinson; *Asst Dir*, Bryan Leithiser; *Asst Dir*, Frank Kasprowicz; *Ch Servs*, Lynn Miller; *Tech Servs*, Virginia Lash; *Ref*, Donna Geib; *ILL*, Pamela Hehr
Founded 1763. Pop 349,583
Jan 1999-Dec 1999 Income $1,852,893, State $345,137, City $813,790, Federal $5,260, County $258,364, Locally Generated Income $424,908. Mats Exp $251,219, Books $185,237, Per/Ser (Incl. Access Fees) $17,759, Micro $10,955, AV Equip $27,166, Electronic Ref Mat (Incl. Access Fees) $10,102. Sal $1,277,300 (Prof $544,019)
Library Holdings: Bk Vols 311,785; Bk Titles 134,164; Per Subs 542
Special Collections: John Updike Coll; Local Imprints, Berks Authors Coll; Pennsylvania German Coll
Automation Activity & Vendor Info: (Cataloging) epixtech, inc.; (Circulation) epixtech, inc.; (OPAC) epixtech, inc.
Database Vendor: Ebsco - EbscoHost, GaleNet
Mem of Berks County Libr Syst
Partic in OCLC Online Computer Library Center, Inc
Friends of the Library Group
Branches: 3
NORTHEAST, 11th & Pike, 19604-1509. SAN 359-4998. Tel: 610-655-6361. FAX: 610-655-6668. *In Charge*, Kathy Jastrzembski
Library Holdings: Bk Vols 28,336
Friends of the Library Group
NORTHWEST, Schuylkill Ave & Windsor St, 19601. SAN 359-5021. Tel: 610-655-6360. FAX: 610-655-6667. *Mgr*, Sue Belz
Library Holdings: Bk Vols 14,966
Friends of the Library Group
SOUTHEAST, 1426 Perkiomen Ave, 19602-2136. SAN 359-5056. Tel: 610-655-6362. FAX: 610-655-6669. *In Charge*, Nancy Starr
Library Holdings: Bk Vols 23,291
Friends of the Library Group
Bookmobiles: 1

S READING PUBLIC MUSEUM LIBRARY,* 500 Museum Rd, 19611-1425. SAN 315-1654. Tel: 610-371-5850. FAX: 610-371-5632. *Dir*, Robert P Metzger
Founded 1904
Library Holdings: Bk Titles 12,000; Per Subs 30
Subject Interests: Anthropology, Architecture, Art, Natural science
Restriction: Open to public for reference only

M SAINT JOSEPH MEDICAL CENTER, Health Sciences Library,* 12th & Walnut Sts, 19603. SAN 315-1662. Tel: 610-378-2393. FAX: 610-378-2390. *Dir*, Kathleen A Mazurak; Staff 3 (MLS 1, Non-MLS 2)
Founded 1973
Library Holdings: Bk Vols 3,500; Bk Titles 3,290; Per Subs 190
Subject Interests: Allied health sci, Behav sci, Hospital administration, Medicine, Nursing, Psychology, Soc sci
Publications: Library Ledger (monthly acquisition list)
Partic in BRS; Dialog Corporation; Nat Libr of Med; Regional Med Libr - Region 1
Open Mon-Fri 8-5

RED LION

P KALTREIDER-BENFER LIBRARY, 147 S Charles St, 17356. SAN 315-1689. Tel: 717-244-2032. FAX: 717-246-2394. E-Mail: kalib@blazenet.net. Web Site: www.kaltreiderbenfer.org. *Dir*, JoAnn B Miller; Staff 1 (MLS 1)
Founded 1963. Pop 21,226; Circ 114,607
Library Holdings: Bk Titles 34,000; Per Subs 45
Publications: Red Lion Community Directory
Mem of York County Library System
Friends of the Library Group

REYNOLDSVILLE

P REYNOLDSVILLE PUBLIC LIBRARY,* Municipal Bldg, 460 Main St, 15851-9999. SAN 315-1700. Tel: 814-653-9471. FAX: 814-653-9471. E-Mail: reylib@penn.com. *Dir*, Mary M Snyder; *Dir*, Sharon Bobal
Founded 1929. Pop 6,870; Circ 35,212
Library Holdings: Bk Vols 12,500; Per Subs 47
Mem of Jefferson County Library System; Oil Creek District Library Cent
Partic in Jefferson County Library System
Open Mon, Tues & Fri 2-5:30 & 7-9, Wed & Thurs 2-5:30, Sat 10-12 & 2-5:30

RICHBORO

P FREE LIBRARY OF NORTHAMPTON TOWNSHIP, 25 Upper Holland Rd, 18954-1514. SAN 315-1719. Tel: 215-357-3050. FAX: 215-357-0234. Web Site: www.buckslib.org/northampton. *Dir*, Virginia Volkman; *Asst Librn, Ch Servs*, Barbara Lewis; *Circ*, Heather Pine; Staff 7 (MLS 2, Non-MLS 5)
Founded 1970. Pop 35,406; Circ 247,580
Library Holdings: Bk Titles 83,000; Per Subs 109
Mem of Bucks County Free Library
Open Mon-Thurs 12-9, Fri 10-5 & Sat 10-4

RICHLAND

P RICHLAND COMMUNITY LIBRARY,* 111 E Main St, PO Box 89, 17087-0089. SAN 315-1727. Tel: 717-866-4939. FAX: 717-866-2661. E-Mail: rclibrary@redrose.net. *Librn*, Mary L Weigley
Founded 1886. Pop 3,958; Circ 34,467
Jan 1997-Dec 1998 Income $25,000. Mats Exp $5,500. Sal $12,050
Library Holdings: Bk Titles 15,000; Per Subs 20
Mem of Lebanon County Library System
Open Mon & Thurs 9-1 & 6-8, Tues & Wed 9-4, Fri 9-1 & Sat 9-12

RIDGWAY

P RIDGWAY PUBLIC LIBRARY,* 329 Center St, 15853. SAN 315-1735. Tel: 814-773-7573. FAX: 814-776-1093. E-Mail: ridgway@ncentral.com. *Dir*, Pamela C Freeburg; Staff 1 (MLS 1)
Founded 1922. Pop 9,280; Circ 35,286
Library Holdings: Bk Titles 15,000; Per Subs 70
Friends of the Library Group

RIDLEY PARK

P RIDLEY PARK PUBLIC LIBRARY,* 107 E Ward St, 19078-3097. SAN 315-1743. Tel: 610-583-7207. FAX: 610-583-2160. *Dir*, Margaret Rooney; *Ch Servs*, Joyce Elliot
Founded 1888. Pop 7,889; Circ 25,450
Library Holdings: Bk Vols 22,000; Per Subs 35
Mem of Delaware County Library System; Philadelphia District Libr Ctr
Open Mon, Tues, Thurs & Fri 12-9:30 & 7-8:30, Wed 10-4:30 & Sat 10-1
Friends of the Library Group

M TAYLOR HOSPITAL, Medical Library,* 175 E Chester Pike, 19078. SAN 372-6134. Tel: 610-595-6027. FAX: 610-595-6047.
Founded 1977
Library Holdings: Bk Titles 350; Per Subs 116

RIEGELSVILLE

P RIEGELSVILLE PUBLIC LIBRARY, 615 Easton Rd, PO Box 65, 18077-0065. SAN 320-8397. Tel: 610-749-2357. *Dir*, Sara Burns; E-Mail: burnss@buckslib.org
Pop 2,112; Circ 12,000
1999-2000 Income $28,345, State $7,655, City $7,500, Locally Generated Income $12,150, Other $1,040. Mats Exp $28,345, Books $6,500. Sal $16,050 (Prof $12,500)
Library Holdings: Bk Vols 12,000; Per Subs 31
Friends of the Library Group

IMERSBURG

ECCLES-LESHER MEMORIAL LIBRARY, 673 Main St, PO Box 359, 16248-0359. SAN 315-1751. Tel: 814-473-3800. FAX: 814-473-8200. E-Mail: ecclesh@alpha.clarion-net.com. Web Site: www.csonline.net/ecclesh/. *Librn*, Joanne Hosey; E-Mail: ecclesdir@csonline.net; *Ch Servs*, Nancy Shanafelt; E-Mail: nshanafelt@yahoo.com; *ILL*, Sherri Campbell; E-Mail: ecclesill@csonline.net; *Tech Servs*, Sharon Custer; Staff 4 (Non-MLS 4)
Founded 1968. Pop 5,975; Circ 51,878
Jan 1999-Dec 1999 Income $173,413, State $19,318, Federal $21,630, Locally Generated Income $6,948, Parent Institution $71,611, Other $14,216. Mats Exp $25,213, Books $13,341, Per/Ser (Incl. Access Fees) $2,108, Presv $1,994, Micro $340, AV Equip $2,096, Electronic Ref Mat (Incl. Access Fees) $5,007. Sal $72,857
Library Holdings: Bk Vols 25,127; Per Subs 52
Subject Interests: Crafts, Fishing, Hunting, Relig studies
Special Collections: Genealogy Histories of Local Families; Local Newspapers, microfilm
Automation Activity & Vendor Info: (OPAC) Follett
Publications: Monthly activities calendar
Mem of Clarion County Library System; Oil Creek District Library Center
Friends of the Library Group

INGTOWN

RINGTOWN AREA LIBRARY,* 132 W Main St, 17967-9538. SAN 320-8400. Tel: 570-889-5503. *Librn*, Lorraine Engle
Pop 1,535; Circ 3,750
Library Holdings: Bk Vols 11,000; Per Subs 6
Open Mon-Fri 9-5

)ARING SPRING

ROARING SPRING COMMUNITY LIBRARY,* 320 E Main St, 16673-1009. SAN 315-176X. Tel: 814-224-2994. FAX: 814-224-4472. E-Mail: rslibrary2@cove.net. *Librn*, Michelle McIntyre
Founded 1959. Pop 6,400; Circ 12,660
Library Holdings: Bk Titles 24,000; Per Subs 31
Mem of Blair County Library System
Open Summer: Mon & Wed 3-7, Tues, Thurs & Fri 10-3:30, Sat 10-2; Winter: Mon, Wed & Thurs 3-8, Tues 11-4:30, Fri 11-3, Sat 10-2
Friends of the Library Group

)BESONIA

READING ALLOYS INC LIBRARY,* Old William Penn Hwy, PO Box 53, 19551-0053. SAN 372-624X. Tel: 610-693-5822, Ext 218. FAX: 610-693-5542.
Founded 1962
Library Holdings: Bk Vols 2,274; Bk Titles 1,956; Per Subs 68
Subject Interests: Metallurgy

ROBESONIA COMMUNITY LIBRARY,* 75-A S Brooke St, 19551-1401. SAN 315-1778. Tel: 610-693-3264. FAX: 610-693-6864. E-Mail: roblib@talon. *Librn*, Toni Ujczo
Founded 1969. Pop 4,745; Circ 37,562
Jan 1998-Dec 1998 Income $52,307. Mats Exp $41,875
Library Holdings: Bk Vols 13,071; Per Subs 50
Mem of Berks County Libr Syst
Open Mon & Wed 9:30-5 & 6-8, Tues 3-5 & 6-8, Thurs 9:30-5, Fri 9-1, Sat 9-3
Friends of the Library Group

)CHESTER

ROCHESTER PUBLIC LIBRARY,* 252 Adams St, 15074-2137. SAN 315-1786. Tel: 724-774-7783. FAX: 724-774-6518. *Dir*, Heather Metheny
Founded 1922. Pop 4,739; Circ 9,084
Library Holdings: Bk Titles 27,000; Per Subs 15
Mem of Beaver County Federated Library System
Open Mon & Wed 12-7, Tues & Thurs 9-5 & Fri 12-5

)SEMONT

ROSEMONT COLLEGE, Gertrude Kistler Memorial Library, 1400 Montgomery Ave, 19010-1699. SAN 315-1794. Tel: 610-527-0200, Ext 2271. FAX: 610-525-2930. Web Site: trellis.rosemont.edu. *Dir*, Catherine Fennell; Tel: 610-527-0200, Ext 2973, E-Mail: fennell@rosemont.edu; *Ref*, Judith Cayer; E-Mail: jcayer@rosemont.edu; *Cat, Tech Servs*, April M Nelson; E-Mail: nelson@rosemont.edu; *ILL*, Anne Trotter; E-Mail: trotter@rosemont.edu; *Per, Ref*, Elizabeth Bartle; E-Mail: bbartle@rosemont.edu; *Acq*, Sara Sargent; E-Mail: ssargent@rosemont.edu; *Circ*, Kathleen Deeming; E-Mail: kdeeming@rosemont.edu; *Media Spec*, Linda Dadzaa; E-Mail: ldadzaa@rosemont.edu; Staff 13 (MLS 5, Non-MLS 8)
Founded 1921. Enrl 500; Fac 55; Highest Degree: Master
Library Holdings: Bk Vols 154,218; Bk Titles 125,785; Per Subs 736; Bks on Deafness & Sign Lang 47
Subject Interests: Gen liberal arts
Special Collections: Rosemont Coll; Women's Poetry Coll
Automation Activity & Vendor Info: (Acquisitions) SIRSI; (Cataloging) SIRSI; (Circulation) SIRSI; (Course Reserve) SIRSI; (Media Booking) SIRSI; (OPAC) SIRSI; (Serials) SIRSI
Partic in Interlibrary Delivery Service of Pennsylvania; OCLC Online Computer Library Center, Inc; PALINET & Union Library Catalogue of Pennsylvania; Southeastern Pa Consortium for Higher Educ; Tri-State College Library Cooperative (TCLC)
Special Services for the Deaf - Staff with knowledge of sign language; TTY machine
Friends of the Library Group

ROSTRAVER

P ROSTRAVER PUBLIC LIBRARY,* 800 Fellsburg Rd, 15012-9720. SAN 370-7466. Tel: 724-379-5511. FAX: 724-379-6090. E-Mail: rospblib@sgi.net. *Librn*, Fran Rendulic
Founded 1958. Pop 12,000; Circ 4,828
Library Holdings: Bk Titles 15,300; Per Subs 28
Subject Interests: Local history
Mem of Monessen District Libr Ctr
Open Mon-Thurs 10-7, Fri 10-4, Sat 10-2
Friends of the Library Group

ROYERSFORD

P ROYERSFORD FREE PUBLIC LIBRARY,* 200 S Fourth St, 19468. SAN 315-1816. Tel: 610-948-7277. *Librn*, Marilyn Duffy; Staff 1 (MLS 1)
Founded 1890. Pop 5,200; Circ 61,000
Library Holdings: Bk Titles 43,000; Per Subs 10
Special Collections: Civil War Coll
Mem of Montgomery County-Norristown Libr Syst
Open Mon, Wed & Fri 10-1, Mon-Thurs 6-8:30pm

SAEGERTOWN

P SAEGERTOWN AREA LIBRARY, 325 Broad St, PO Box 871, 16433-0871. SAN 376-642X. Tel: 814-763-5203. FAX: 814-763-5203. E-Mail: sal@ccfls.org. *Dir*, Judith L Miller
1999-2000 Income $35,000, State $16,000, County $13,000, Other $6,000. Mats Exp $8,000, Books $7,000, Per/Ser (Incl. Access Fees) $1,000. Sal $17,000
Library Holdings: Bk Vols 11,000; Bk Titles 10,000; Per Subs 22
Automation Activity & Vendor Info: (Cataloging) Sagebrush Corporation; (Circulation) Sagebrush Corporation; (OPAC) Sagebrush Corporation
Mem of Crawford County Federated Library System
Partic in Share NW Consortium
Friends of the Library Group

SAINT DAVIDS

C EASTERN COLLEGE, Warner Memorial Library, 1300 Eagle Rd, 19087. SAN 315-1824. Interlibrary Loan Service Tel: 610-341-5958. FAX: 610-341-1375. Web Site: www.eastern.edu/library/library.html. *Dir*, James L Sauer; Tel: 610-341-5957, E-Mail: jsauer@eastern.edu; *Reader Servs*, Jonathan Beasley; Tel: 610-341-5981, E-Mail: jbeasley@eastern.edu; *Tech Servs*, Phoebe Law; Tel: 610-225-5003, E-Mail: plaw@eastern.edu; *Ref*, Mark Puterbaugh; Tel: 610-341-1461, E-Mail: mputerba@eastern.edu; Staff 10 (MLS 6, Non-MLS 4)
Founded 1952. Enrl 2,500; Fac 110; Highest Degree: Master
Jul 1998-Jun 1999 Mats Exp $250,000, Books $125,000, Per/Ser (Incl. Access Fees) $60,000, Micro $15,000
Library Holdings: Bk Vols 155,000; Per Subs 1,000
Special Collections: Bruce Rogers Coll, Marcus Aurelius; Harry C Goebel Coll on Fine Printing, bks, bk plates & prints
Automation Activity & Vendor Info: (Cataloging) SIRSI; (Circulation) SIRSI; (OPAC) SIRSI
Database Vendor: Ebsco - EbscoHost, OCLC - First Search
Partic in Asn of Christian Librs; OCLC Online Computer Library Center, Inc; PALINET & Union Library Catalogue of Pennsylvania; Tri-State College Library Cooperative (TCLC)
Friends of the Library Group

S WYETH-AYERST LABORATORIES, Commercial Research Information Center,* 555 E Lancaster Ave, 19087. SAN 375-5657. Tel: 610-971-5555. FAX: 610-995-3371.
Founded 1995
Library Holdings: Bk Titles 2,500; Per Subs 300
Subject Interests: Finance
Special Collections: Company Annual Reports; Decision Resources Spectrum; SRI Business Intelligence Programs
Partic in Dialog Corporation; Dow Jones News Retrieval

SAINT MARYS

S KEYSTONE POWDERED METAL CO,* 1933 State St, 15857-1661. SAN 315-1832. Tel: 814-781-4416. FAX: 814-781-3893. *Librn*, Kathleen Meyer
Library Holdings: Bk Vols 4,500

S PURE CARBON CO LIBRARY,* 441 Hall Ave, 15857. SAN 315-1840. Tel: 814-781-1573. FAX: 814-781-9249. *Librn*, Chrissy Cheatle
Founded 1956
Library Holdings: Bk Vols 1,000
Subject Interests: Computer tech, Marketing, Sales, Sci-tech

P SAINT MARY'S PUBLIC LIBRARY, 127 Center St, 15857. SAN 315-1859. Tel: 814-834-6141. FAX: 814-834-9814. E-Mail: library@stmaryslibrary.org. Web Site: www.stmaryslibrary.org. *Tech Servs*, Jane Vavala; *Librn*, Jane Vavala; *Coll Develop*, Velma Gross; *Ch Servs*, Vicki Miller; *ILL*, Diana Smith; *Purchasing*, Justine McCafferty; Staff 7 (MLS 1, Non-MLS 6)
Founded 1921. Pop 15,225
Jan 1999-Jan 2000 Income $123,000, State $17,000, City $106,000. Mats Exp $30,755. Sal $84,950
Library Holdings: Bk Titles 33,643; Per Subs 85
Subject Interests: Elk County, St Mary's area hist
Friends of the Library Group

SALTSBURG

P SALTSBURG FREE LIBRARY,* 307 Point St, Ste 2, 15681-1118. SAN 315-1875. Tel: 724-639-9763. FAX: 724-639-9763. E-Mail: sflibry@kiski.net. Web Site: www.kiski.net/~sflibry. *Librn*, Brenda Mitsko
Jan 1997-Dec 1998 Income $18,950, State $4,000, City $1,200, Other $13,300. Mats Exp $8,665, Books $4,200, Per/Ser (Incl. Access Fees) $365, AV Equip $4,000. Sal $5,500 (Prof $4,500)
Library Holdings: Bk Vols 12,658; Per Subs 15
Friends of the Library Group

SAXONBURG

P SAXONBURG AREA LIBRARY,* 240 W Main St, PO Box 454, 16056-0454. SAN 320-5096. Tel: 724-352-4810. FAX: 724-352-1815. *Librn*, Steven Twentier; Staff 2 (MLS 2)
Founded 1978. Pop 12,600; Circ 32,028
Library Holdings: Bk Titles 19,400; Per Subs 42
Subject Interests: Cooking, Craft, Gardening
Special Collections: Butler County History
Mem of Butler County Libr Syst
Friends of the Library Group

SAXTON

P SAXTON COMMUNITY LIBRARY, 315 Front St, 16678-8612. (Mail add: PO Box 34, 16678-0034), SAN 315-1891. Tel: 814-635-3533. FAX: 814-635-3001. E-Mail: saxlib@nb.net. Web Site: www.nb.net/~saxlib. *Librn*, Judy Williams
Founded 1968. Pop 4,571; Circ 13,305
Jan 1999-Dec 1999 Income $36,495, State $2,094, City $525, County $18,070, Locally Generated Income $15,188, Other $618. Mats Exp $6,327, Books $5,818, Per/Ser (Incl. Access Fees) $199, AV Equip $310. Sal $14,909
Library Holdings: Bk Vols 13,274; Per Subs 15; High Interest/Low Vocabulary Bk Vols 14; Bks on Deafness & Sign Lang 11
Special Collections: Nuclear Regulatory Commission Local Public Document Room
Automation Activity & Vendor Info: (Cataloging) Follett; (Circulation) Follett
Mem of Bedford County Federated Libr Syst
Partic in Access Pa
Open Mon & Wed 10:30-8, Tues & Thurs 2:30-8 & Sat 9-4
Bookmobiles: 1

SAYRE

M WILLIAM C BECK HEALTH SCIENCE LIBRARY & RESOURCE CENTER,* Guthrie Sq, 18840. SAN 315-1905. Tel: 717-888-6666, Ext 4700. FAX: 717-882-4703.
Founded 1922
Library Holdings: Bk Vols 7,673; Bk Titles 4,200; Per Subs 500
Subject Interests: History, Med ethics, Medicine, Nursing
Special Collections: Mayock Coll
Partic in S Cent Res Libr Coun; Susquehanna Library Cooperative

P SAYRE PUBLIC LIBRARY, INC, 122 S Elmer Ave, 18840. SAN 315-1913. Tel: 717-888-2256. FAX: 717-888-3355. E-Mail: sapublb@cyber-quest.com. *Librn*, Maureen A Sweeney; Staff 1 (Non-MLS 1)
Founded 1939. Pop 7,473
Library Holdings: Bk Vols 23,400; Per Subs 45
Subject Interests: Local history
Automation Activity & Vendor Info: (Circulation) Sagebrush Corporation
Database Vendor: Ebsco - EbscoHost
Mem of Bradford County Library System Headquarters
Open Tues & Thurs 10-7:30, Wed, Fri & Sat 10-5

SCHAEFFERSTOWN

S HISTORIC SCHAEFFERSTOWN, INC, Thomas R Brendle Memorial Library & Museum, N Market St, PO Box 307, 17088. SAN 371-1579. Tel: 717-949-2444. *Curator*, Diane Wenger; *Admin Assoc*, Andrew Wyatt
Library Holdings: Bk Vols 340
Restriction: Access at librarian's discretion, Not a lending library
Function: Archival collection, Reference only

SCHNECKSVILLE

J LEHIGH CARBON COMMUNITY COLLEGE LIBRARY,* 4525 Education Park Dr, 18078-9372. SAN 315-1921. Tel: 610-799-1150. FAX: 610-779-1159. Web Site: www.ws200.lccc.edu. *Dir*, David Voros; Tel: 610-799-1196, E-Mail: dsv1@lccc.edu; *ILL*, Susan Mattern; *Ref*, Barbara Balas; *Ref*, Richard Schollenberger; *Cat*, Jane Yagerhofer; *Circ*, Barbara Hoffman; *Circ*, Darlene Coleman; Staff 5 (MLS 5)
Founded 1967. Enrl 4,384; Fac 80
Library Holdings: Bk Vols 51,000; Per Subs 462
Subject Interests: Allied health, Criminal justice
Special Collections: College Archives; New York Times, 1851-present, micro
Database Vendor: Ebsco - EbscoHost, IAC - Info Trac, Lexis-Nexis, OCLC - First Search, ProQuest, Silverplatter Information Inc.
Publications: Library Handbook; Library Skills Workbook
Partic in Health Science Library Information Consortium; Interlibrary Delivery Service of Pennsylvania; OCLC Online Computer Library Center, Inc; PALINET & Union Library Catalogue of Pennsylvania

SCHUYLKILL HAVEN

C PENNSYLVANIA STATE UNIVERSITY, SCHUYLKILL CAMPUS, CAPITAL COLLEGE, Ciletti Memorial Library (University Libraries), 240 University Dr, 17972-2210. SAN 315-193X. Tel: 717-385-6234. FAX: 717-385-6232. E-Mail: mw12@psu.edu. *Librn*, Michael W Loder; Staff 5 (MLS 2, Non-MLS 3)
Founded 1934. Enrl 1,124; Fac 45
Jul 1998-Jun 1999 Mats Exp $82,359
Library Holdings: Bk Vols 33,609; Per Subs 264
Special Collections: County Coll (Pennsylvania German & Dutch Material, Coal Industry); O'Hara Coll (materials by & on John O'Hara); Richter Coll (materials by & on Conrad Richter); Treasure Coll (Jones' family bks & recs)
Partic in OCLC Online Computer Library Center, Inc; RLIN

P SCHUYLKILL HAVEN FREE PUBLIC LIBRARY,* 104 Saint John St, 17972-1614. SAN 315-1948. Tel: 570-385-0542. FAX: 570-385-2523. E-Mail: sch@iu29.schiu.k12.pa.us. Web Site: www.haven.k12.pa.us/havenpl *Pres*, Hamilton Handling Jr; *Dir*, Carol M Morey
Founded 1934. Pop 7,688; Circ 26,016
Jan 1998-Dec 1998 Income (Main Library Only) $89,175, State $11,391, City $38,892, Locally Generated Income $38,892. Mats Exp $9,958, Books $7,680, Per/Ser (Incl. Access Fees) $1,091, AV Equip $215. Sal $57,726 (Prof $24,664)
Library Holdings: Bk Titles 25,685; Per Subs 35
Special Collections: Large Print Coll
Automation Activity & Vendor Info: (Cataloging) Sagebrush Corporation; (Circulation) Sagebrush Corporation
Mem of Pottsville Free Public Library; Pottsville Free Public Library

SCOTTDALE

P SCOTTDALE PUBLIC LIBRARY,* 235 Pittsburgh St, 15683-1796. SAN 315-1956. Tel: 412-887-6140. *Librn*, Patricia E Miller; E-Mail: bookworm@cvzoom.net; *Asst Librn*, Angie Pitzer
Founded 1910. Pop 5,833; Circ 26,294
Library Holdings: Bk Vols 22,166; Per Subs 45
Mem of Monessen District Libr Ctr
Open Mon-Wed & Fri 12-5:30, Thurs 2-7 & Sat 9:30-2:30
Friends of the Library Group

SCRANTON

COMMUNITY MEDICAL CENTER
M DOCTOR'S LIBRARY, 1800 Mulberry St, 18510. SAN 359-5110. Tel: 570-969-8197. FAX: 570-969-8902. *Head Librn*, MaryJo Devereaux; E-Mail: maryjo.devereaux@cmchealthsys.org; Staff 2 (MLS 1, Non-MLS 1) Sal $30,000 (Prof $9,000)

Library Holdings: Bk Vols 1,200; Per Subs 225
Database Vendor: OVID Technologies
Partic in Basic Health Sciences Library Network; Health Information Library Network of Northeastern Pennsylvania; Northeastern Pennsylvania Library Network

JOHNSON TECHNICAL INSTITUTE LIBRARY,* 3427 N Main Ave, 18508. SAN 315-1999. Tel: 717-342-6404. FAX: 717-348-2181. E-Mail: johteclib@hslc.org. *Dir*, Michele Srebro; Staff 2 (MLS 1, Non-MLS 1)
Founded 1969. Enrl 349; Fac 21
Library Holdings: Bk Vols 5,217; Bk Titles 4,410; Per Subs 115

LACKAWANNA BAR ASSOCIATION, Law Library,* Courthouse, 200 N Washington Ave, Ground Floor, 18503. SAN 315-2006. Tel: 570-963-6712. FAX: 570-344-2944. E-Mail: pap95@gateway.net. *Librn*, Marita E Paparelli
Founded 1879
Library Holdings: Bk Vols 20,000; Bk Titles 1,200
Subject Interests: Law

LACKAWANNA COUNTY LIBRARY SYSTEM, 520 Vine St, 18509-3298. SAN 324-8062. Tel: 570-348-3003. Interlibrary Loan Service Tel: 570-348-3018. FAX: 570-348-3028. E-Mail: sfelix@albright.org. Web Site: www.albright.org/lcls. *Adminr*, Sally T Felix; Staff 2 (MLS 1, Non-MLS 1)
Founded 1983. Pop 219,139
Jan 2000-Dec 2000 Income $4,144,000, State $1,266,000, County $2,575,000, Locally Generated Income $253,000, Other $50,000. Sal $91,500 (Prof $58,000)
Automation Activity & Vendor Info: (Acquisitions) SIRSI; (Cataloging) SIRSI; (Circulation) SIRSI; (OPAC) SIRSI; (Serials) SIRSI
Member Libraries: Abington Community Library; Carbondale Public Library; Dalton Community Library; Interboro United Districts Library Association; North Pocono Public Library; Scranton Public Library; Taylor Public Library
Bookmobiles: 1. Operated by Scranton Public Library, system headquarters; 39' Thomas Built from Matthews Specialty Vehicles, handicapped lift, 4000-5000 book capacity equipped with 4 computer & online with SIRSI system

LACKAWANNA HISTORICAL SOCIETY LIBRARY, 232 Monroe Ave, 18510. SAN 315-2014. Tel: 717-344-3841. FAX: 717-344-3815. *Exec Dir*, Mary Ann Moran
Founded 1886
Library Holdings: Bk Vols 2,500
Subject Interests: Antiques, Architecture, Coal mining, Ethnic hist, Family hist, Local history, Photog, Transportation
Special Collections: Lackawanna County & Pennsylvania History; Scranton History, mss, photog & newsp files bd
Publications: Lackawana Historical Society Journal (quarterly)

LACKAWANNA JUNIOR COLLEGE, Seeley Memorial Library, 501 Vine St, 18509. SAN 359-5145. Tel: 570-961-7831. FAX: 570-961-7858. *Librn*, Carol Mae Campion; *AV*, Elaine Pencek
Founded 1965
Library Holdings: Bk Vols 20,000; Per Subs 60

MARYWOOD UNIVERSITY, Learning Resources Center, 2300 Adams Ave, 18509-1598. SAN 315-2022. Tel: 570-348-6211. Interlibrary Loan Service Tel: 570-348-6205. FAX: 570-961-4769. E-Mail: library@ac.marywood.edu. Web Site: www.marywood.edu/www2/libweb. *Dir*, Cathy Schappert; *Coordr, Publ Servs*, William Calhoon; *ILL, Ref*, Annette Fisher; *Coordr, Ser*, Michelle Sitko; *Publ Servs*, Miao Hong; Staff 9 (MLS 9)
Founded 1915. Enrl 2,218; Fac 140; Highest Degree: Doctorate
Jul 1999-Jun 2000 Mats Exp $306,428, Books $120,257, Per/Ser (Incl. Access Fees) $114,531, Presv $7,547, AV Equip $24,174, Electronic Ref Mat (Incl. Access Fees) $39,919
Library Holdings: Bk Vols 215,117; Per Subs 984
Subject Interests: Art, Behav sci, Bus, Education, Music, Nutrition, Relig studies, Soc sci, Soc work
Automation Activity & Vendor Info: (Acquisitions) epixtech, inc.; (Cataloging) epixtech, inc.; (Circulation) epixtech, inc.; (Course Reserve) epixtech, inc.; (OPAC) epixtech, inc.; (Serials) epixtech, inc.
Partic in Northeastern Pennsylvania Library Network; PALCI

1 MERCY HOSPITAL, Medical Library,* 746 Jefferson Ave, 18501. SAN 359-517X. Tel: 570-348-7800. FAX: 570-340-4871. E-Mail: scrlibrary@mhs-nepa.com. *Dir Libr Serv*, Sister Elizabeth A Brandreth; Staff 2 (MLS 1, Non-MLS 1)
Founded 1958
Library Holdings: Bk Vols 1,974; Bk Titles 1,244; Per Subs 131
Partic in BHSL; Greater NE Regional Med Libr Program; Health Information Library Network of Northeastern Pennsylvania; Northeastern Pennsylvania Library Network

SCRANTON PUBLIC LIBRARY, Albright Memorial Library, Albright Memorial Bldg, 500 Vine St, 18509-3298. SAN 359-5269. Tel: 570-348-3000. FAX: 570-961-3041. E-Mail: spl@albright.org. Web Site: www.albright.org. *Dir*, Jack Finnerty; *Publ Servs*, Marie Crispino; *Ref*, Evelyn Gibbons; *Tech Coordr*, Scott Thomas; *Ch Servs*, Mary Yeager
Founded 1893
Library Holdings: Bk Vols 180,000; Per Subs 300
Subject Interests: Local history
Mem of Lackawanna County Library System
Friends of the Library Group
Branches: 3
GREEN RIDGE, Wyoming Ave & Green Ridge St, 18509. SAN 359-5293. Tel: 570-207-0764. *Librn*, Jean Marie Lynn
Library Holdings: Bk Vols 8,500
HYDE PARK BRANCH, 401 N Main Ave, Hyde Park, 18504. SAN 359-5323. Tel: 570-207-0765. *Librn*, Joanne Vancosky
Library Holdings: Bk Vols 9,991
PROVIDENCE, 2006 N Main Ave, 18508. SAN 359-5358. Tel: 570-207-0766. *Librn*, Elizabeth Finnerty
Library Holdings: Bk Vols 9,649
Bookmobiles: 1

S SCRANTON TIMES, Tribune Reference Library,* 149 Penn Ave, 18503. SAN 315-2030. Tel: 570-348-9140. FAX: 570-348-9135. *Asst Librn*, Jerry Moon
Founded 1920
Library Holdings: Bk Vols 3,200
Subject Interests: Anthracite mining, Coal, Government, Local history, Railroads

M MOSES TAYLOR HOSPITAL LIBRARY,* 700 Quincy Ave, 18510. SAN 326-1581. Tel: 717-340-2100, 717-340-2125. FAX: 717-963-8994. *Dir Libr Serv*, Jo Ann Babish; *Asst Librn*, Belinda Shaughnessy; Staff 2 (MLS 1, Non-MLS 1)
Founded 1977
Library Holdings: Bk Titles 1,300; Per Subs 250
Partic in Greater NE Regional Med Libr Program; Health Information Library Network of Northeastern Pennsylvania; Northeastern Pennsylvania Library Network

C UNIVERSITY OF SCRANTON, Harry & Jeanette Weinberg Memorial Library, Monroe & Linden, 18510-4634. SAN 315-2049. Tel: 570-941-4008. Interlibrary Loan Service Tel: 570-941-4003. Circulation Tel: 570-941-7524. Reference Tel: 570-941-4000. FAX: 570-941-7817. Web Site: www.scranton.edu. *Dir*, Charles E Kratz; E-Mail: kratzc1@scranton.edu; *Assoc Dir*, Bonnie Strohl; Tel: 570-941-4006, Fax: 570-941-4002, E-Mail: strohlb1@scranton.edu; *Cat*, Donna Ramos; Tel: 570-941-4004, E-Mail: ramosd1@scranton.edu; *Online Servs*, Kevin Norris; Fax: 570-941-4002, E-Mail: norrisk1@scranton.edu; *Ser*, Jane Wang; Tel: 570-941-7807, Fax: 570-941-4002, E-Mail: wangc1@scranton.edu; *Acq*, Narda Tafuri; Tel: 570-941-7811, Fax: 570-941-7809, E-Mail: tafurin1@scranton.edu; *Media Spec*, Karen Heckman; Tel: 570-941-6330, E-Mail: heckmank1@scranton.edu; *Circ*, Annette Kalwaytis; E-Mail: kalwaytisa1@scranton.edu; *Ref*, Betsey Moylan; Fax: 570-941-4002, E-Mail: moylanm1@scranton.edu; *Bibliog Instr*, Katie S Duke; Fax: 570-941-4002, E-Mail: dukek1@scranton.edu; *Spec Coll*, Michael Knies; Tel: 570-941-6341, E-Mail: kniesm2@scranton.edu; *ILL*, Magdalene Restuccia; Fax: 570-941-4002, E-Mail: restucciam1@scranton.edu; Staff 20 (MLS 14, Non-MLS 6)
Founded 1888. Enrl 4,773; Fac 393; Highest Degree: Master
Jun 1999-May 2000 Income Parent Institution $2,385,924. Mats Exp $889,772, Books $265,067, Per/Ser (Incl. Access Fees) $428,963, Presv $24,690, Micro $26,637, AV Equip $8,365, Electronic Ref Mat (Incl. Access Fees) $136,050. Sal $1,020,210 (Prof $569,986)
Library Holdings: Bk Vols 426,347; Bk Titles 7,553; Bks on Deafness & Sign Lang 140
Special Collections: Congressman Joseph McDade Coll; Early Printed Books & Manuscripts (William W Scranton Coll); Joseph Polakoff Coll, papers; University Archives Coll
Automation Activity & Vendor Info: (Acquisitions) DRA; (Cataloging) DRA; (Circulation) DRA; (Course Reserve) DRA; (OPAC) DRA; (Serials) DRA
Database Vendor: Dialog, DRA, IAC - Info Trac, Lexis-Nexis, OCLC - First Search, Silverplatter Information Inc.
Publications: A Modern Renaissance Library: 200 Selections from the Collection of Edward R Leahy; Faculty & Student Guides; Newsletters; Reference Bibliographies; Weinberg Memorial Library Information Update Newsletter; William Morris & the Kelmscott Press Exhibition Catalog
Partic in Interlibrary Delivery Service of Pennsylvania; Northeastern Pennsylvania Library Network; OCLC Online Computer Library Center, Inc; PALCI; PALINET & Union Library Catalogue of Pennsylvania; SPARC
Special Services for the Blind - ZoomText software to enlarge computer screen
Friends of the Library Group

SELINSGROVE

P SNYDER COUNTY LIBRARY,* One N High St, 17870. SAN 359-5382. Tel: 570-374-7163. FAX: 570-374-2120. *Dir*, Lynn Broschart; Staff 9 (MLS 2, Non-MLS 7)
Founded 1976. Pop 36,000; Circ 99,740
Jan 1999-Dec 1999 Income (Main Library and Branch Library) $238,200, State $57,000, County $60,000, Locally Generated Income $28,000, Other $93,200. Mats Exp (MEX) $76,000, Books (MEX) $47,000, Per/Ser (Incl.

Access Fees) (MEX) $6,000, Electronic Ref Mat (Incl. Access Fees) $23,000. Sal $142,000 (Prof $57,000)
Library Holdings: Bk Titles 63,240; Per Subs 162
Automation Activity & Vendor Info: (Acquisitions) EOS; (Cataloging) EOS; (Circulation) EOS; (OPAC) EOS
Mem of James V Brown Library Of Williamsport & Lycoming County
Branches: 3
BEAVERTOWN BRANCH, Beavertown, 17813. SAN 359-5412. Tel: 570-658-3437. *Librn*, Roxanne Weaver
Library Holdings: Bk Vols 4,000; Per Subs 13
MCCLURE COMMUNITY, Library Lane, McClure, 17841. SAN 359-5447. Tel: 570-658-7700. FAX: 570-658-7700. *Librn*, Joe Hall
Library Holdings: Bk Vols 6,000; Per Subs 27
MIDDLEBURG COMMUNITY, 13 N Main St, Middleburg, 17842. SAN 359-5471. Tel: 570-837-5931. FAX: 570-837-5931. *Librn*, Lucille Sprenkle
Library Holdings: Bk Vols 6,000; Per Subs 29

C SUSQUEHANNA UNIVERSITY, Blough-Weis Library, 514 University Ave, 17870-1050. SAN 315-2065. Tel: 570-372-4319. Interlibrary Loan Service Tel: 570-372-4326. Circulation Tel: 570-372-4022. Reference Tel: 570-372-4160. FAX: 570-372-4310. Web Site: www.susqu.edu/library. *Dir*, Kathleen Gunning; Tel: 570-372-4320, E-Mail: gunning@susqu.edu; *Assoc Dir, Librn*, Rebecca Wilson; Tel: 570-372-4321, E-Mail: wilsonb@susqu.edu; *ILL*, Sheila Fisher; Tel: 570-372-4326, E-Mail: fishers@susqu.edu; *Cat*, Patricia B Fishbein; Tel: 570-372-4323, E-Mail: fishbein@susqu.edu; *Ref Servs YA*, Kathleen Dalton; Tel: 570-372-4160, E-Mail: dalton@susqu.edu; *Acq*, James Smillie; Tel: 570-372-4322, E-Mail: smillie@susqu.edu. Subject Specialists: *Info servs*, Kathleen Dalton; *Systs*, James Smillie; Staff 14 (MLS 6, Non-MLS 8)
Founded 1858. Enrl 1,650; Fac 171; Highest Degree: Bachelor
Jul 1999-Jun 2000 Mats Exp $489,071, Books $171,324, Per/Ser (Incl. Access Fees) $272,533, Presv $3,710, Micro $20,000, AV Equip $12,123, Other Print Mats $6,065, Electronic Ref Mat (Incl. Access Fees) $3,316. Sal $458,174 (Prof $319,863)
Library Holdings: Bk Vols 265,655; Bk Titles 175,337; Per Subs 2,799
Subject Interests: Business, Environmental studies, Music, Theater
Special Collections: Jane Apple Shakespeare Coll; Music (Wilt Coll)
Automation Activity & Vendor Info: (Acquisitions) SIRSI; (Cataloging) SIRSI; (Course Reserve) SIRSI; (Course Reserve) SIRSI; (ILL) SIRSI; (Media Booking) SIRSI; (OPAC) SIRSI
Database Vendor: Ebsco - EbscoHost, IAC - Info Trac, IAC - SearchBank, Lexis-Nexis, OCLC - First Search, ProQuest, Wilson - Wilson Web
Publications: Guides to Library; Newsletter
Function: Research library
Partic in Associated College Libraries of Central Pennsylvania; PALINET & Union Library Catalogue of Pennsylvania; Susquehanna Library Cooperative
Open Mon-Thurs 8am-midnight, Fri 8-5, Sat 10-8 & Sun 1-midnight

SELLERSVILLE

M GRAND VIEW HOSPITAL, Edward F Burrow Memorial Library, 700 Lawn Ave, 18960. SAN 324-5519. Tel: 215-453-4632. FAX: 215-453-4133. *Tech Servs*, Annette McGough
Library Holdings: Bk Titles 500; Per Subs 70
Subject Interests: Medicine, Nursing, Surgery

SEWICKLEY

S GRAPHIC ARTS TECHNICAL FOUNDATION, E H Wadewitz Memorial Library, 200 Deer Run Rd, 15143-2600. SAN 315-0658. Tel: 412-741-6860, Ext 608. FAX: 412-741-2311. E-Mail: info@gatf.org. Web Site: www.gatf.org. *Librn*, Amy J Watson; Tel: 412-741-6860, Ext 216, E-Mail: awatson@gatf.org; *Info Specialist*, Deanna M Gentile; E-Mail: dgentile@gatf.org. Subject Specialists: *Printing*, Deanna M Gentile; Staff 2 (MLS 1, Non-MLS 1)
Founded 1924
Aug 1998-Jul 1999 Mats Exp $5,000
Library Holdings: Bk Titles 6,000; Per Subs 185
Subject Interests: Education, Graphic arts, Printing, Publishing
Special Collections: Augustine Coll; Billmeyer Coll; Preucil Coll; Stevens Coll
Database Vendor: Ebsco - EbscoHost, IAC - Info Trac, OCLC - First Search
Publications: GATFWorld (Newsletter)
Restriction: Non-circulating
Function: Research library

P SEWICKLEY PUBLIC LIBRARY,* 500 Thorn St, 15143-1333. SAN 315-2081. Tel: 412-741-6920. FAX: 412-741-6099. *Dir*, Carolyn Toth
Founded 1873. Pop 14,625; Circ 144,442
Library Holdings: Bk Vols 64,900; Per Subs 297
Subject Interests: Western Pa hist
Publications: Newsletter
Open Mon-Thurs 9:30-9, Fri & Sat 9:30-5 & Sun 1-5
Friends of the Library Group

SHAMOKIN

P SHAMOKIN-COAL TOWNSHIP PUBLIC LIBRARY, INC, 210 E Independence St, 17872-6888. SAN 315-209X. Tel: 570-648-3202. FAX: 570-648-3202. E-Mail: shamlib@ptd.net. Web Site: www.sctpubliclibrary.lib.pa.us. *Dir*, Mary Ellen Lowe; Staff 1 (MLS 1)
Founded 1941. Pop 21,449; Circ 60,000
Library Holdings: Bk Vols 46,188; Per Subs 94
Special Collections: History of Pennsylvania, Northcumberland County & Shamokin (Pennsylvania Coll)
Mem of Pottsville Free Public Library

SHARON

C PENNSYLVANIA STATE UNIVERSITY, Shenango Commonwealth College (University Libraries), 147 Shenango Ave, 16146. SAN 315-2111. Tel: 724-983-2876. FAX: 724-983-2881. E-Mail: r2a@psulias.psu.edu. *Libr* Rebecca Albitz; Staff 5 (MLS 2, Non-MLS 3)
Founded 1965. Enrl 1,005; Fac 35
Jul 1999-Jun 2000 Mats Exp $57,920
Library Holdings: Bk Vols 28,000; Per Subs 438
Partic in OCLC Online Computer Library Center, Inc; RLIN

M SHARON REGIONAL HEALTH SYSTEM, School of Nursing Library,* 740 E State St, 16146. SAN 329-5206. Tel: 724-983-3911, Ext 4432. FAX: 724-983-5524. E-Mail: srhssn@infonline.net. *Librn*, Beth Butcher
Jul 1996-Jun 1997 Income $9,000. Mats Exp $6,700, Books $1,000, Per/Se (Incl. Access Fees) $2,700, AV Equip $1,500
Library Holdings: Bk Titles 1,500
Subject Interests: History, Medicine, Nursing
Partic in Dialog Corporation; Docline; Netcom
Satellite Television, HSTN, VHA

P SHENANGO VALLEY LIBRARY,* 11 N Sharpsville Ave, 16146. SAN 315-2103. Tel: 724-981-4360. FAX: 724-981-5208. E-Mail: svclib@infonline.net. *Ad Servs, Dir*, K L Spak; *Ch Servs*, V J Zahniser; Staff 2 (MLS 2)
Founded 1923. Pop 32,813; Circ 80,000
Library Holdings: Bk Vols 53,556; Bk Titles 48,000; Per Subs 115
Subject Interests: Genealogy, Local history
Automation Activity & Vendor Info: (Cataloging) Brodart; (Circulation) Brodart
Publications: The Bookmark (quarterly newsletter)
Friends of the Library Group

SHARON HILL

P SHARON HILL PUBLIC LIBRARY,* 246 Sharon Ave, 19079-2098. SAN 315-2138. Tel: 610-586-3993. FAX: 610-586-8233. *Librn*, Patricia Collington-Boothroyd
Founded 1938. Pop 7,464; Circ 14,561
Library Holdings: Bk Vols 15,000; Per Subs 20

SHEFFIELD

P SHEFFIELD TOWNSHIP LIBRARY,* 20 Leather St, PO Box 607, 16347-0607. SAN 315-2146. Tel: 814-968-3439. FAX: 814-968-5761. E-Mail: sheff@penn.com. *Librn*, Janet L Gustafson
Pop 2,793; Circ 4,127
Library Holdings: Bk Vols 10,100; Per Subs 33
Mem of Seneca District Libr Ctr
Open Mon 6-8, Tues 1:30-5 & Wed-Sat 1-5

SHENANDOAH

P SHENANDOAH AREA FREE PUBLIC LIBRARY, 15 W Washington St, 17976-1708. SAN 315-2154. Tel: 570-462-9829. E-Mail: she@iu29.schiu.k12.pa.us. *Librn*, Theresa Kolonsky; Staff 1 (Non-MLS 1)
Founded 1975. Pop 6,221; Circ 15,566
Jan 1999-Dec 1999 Income $22,295, State $6,895, City $1,500, County $1,200, Locally Generated Income $10,200, Other $2,500. Mats Exp $5,002 Per/Ser (Incl. Access Fees) $913, AV Equip $150, AV Equip $3,939. Sal $14,700
Library Holdings: Bk Vols 8,601; Per Subs 10
Mem of Pottsville Free Public Library

SHINGLEHOUSE

P OSWAYO VALLEY MEMORIAL LIBRARY,* Academy St, PO Box 188, 16748. SAN 315-2162. Tel: 814-697-6691. *Librn*, Bonnie Chappell; *Asst Librn*, Fran Fox
Founded 1915. Pop 3,568; Circ 29,411
Library Holdings: Bk Vols 6,000; Per Subs 25
Mem of Potter-Tioga Library System

HIPPENSBURG

SHIPPENSBURG PUBLIC LIBRARY, 73 W King St, 17257-1299. SAN 315-2170. Tel: 717-532-4508. FAX: 717-532-2454. E-Mail: shippensburg@ccpa.net. *Librn*, M Kay Heller; Staff 15 (MLS 2, Non-MLS 13)
Founded 1933. Pop 24,796; Circ 122,399
Jan 2000-Dec 2000 Income $253,123. Mats Exp $44,900, Books $35,000, Per/Ser (Incl. Access Fees) $3,300, Presv $2,000, Micro $500, Other Print Mats $4,100. Sal $129,680
Library Holdings: Bk Vols 53,451; Per Subs 107
Automation Activity & Vendor Info: (Cataloging) epixtech, inc.; (Circulation) epixtech, inc.
Mem of Cumberland County Library System
Friends of the Library Group

SHIPPENSBURG UNIVERSITY, Ezra Lehman Memorial Library, 1871 Old Main Dr, 17257-2299. SAN 359-5560. Tel: 717-477-1463. Interlibrary Loan Service Tel: 717-477-1462. Circulation Tel: 717-477-1465. Reference Tel: 717-477-1474. FAX: 717-477-1389. E-Mail: libref@ship.edu. Web Site: www.ship.edu/~library. *Dean of Libr*, Madelyn Valunas; E-Mail: mfv@ship.edu; *ILL*, Diane Kalathas; E-Mail: dmkala@ship.edu; *Coll Develop*, Barbara Rotz; Tel: 717-477-1466, E-Mail: bdrotz@ship.edu; *Head Ref*, Berkley Laite; Tel: 717-477-1473, E-Mail: bhl@ship.edu; *Govt Doc*, Katherine Warkentin; Tel: 717-477-1634, E-Mail: kwarke@ship.edu; *Bibliog Instr*, Karen Ellis; Tel: 717-477-1516, E-Mail: kdd@ship.edu; *Media Spec*, Douglas Cook; Tel: 717-477-1470, E-Mail: dlcook@ship.edu; *Automation Syst Coordr, Per*, Robert Gimmi; Tel: 717-477-1475, E-Mail: rdg@ship.edu; *Coll Develop*, Judith Culbertson; *Spec Coll*, Signe Kelker; Tel: 717-477-1289, E-Mail: sjkelk@ship.edu; *Cat*, Linda Gatchel; Tel: 717-477-1325, E-Mail: lmgatc@ship.edu; *Circ*, Mary Mowery; Tel: 717-477-1461, E-Mail: mamowe@ship.edu; Staff 25 (MLS 9, Non-MLS 16)
Founded 1871. Enrl 7,034; Fac 360; Highest Degree: Master
Jul 1999-Jun 2000 Income $2,303,310. Mats Exp $600,000, Books $124,840, Per/Ser (Incl. Access Fees) $266,642, Presv $21,473, Electronic Ref Mat (Incl. Access Fees) $150,279. Sal $1,079,880 (Prof $569,449)
Library Holdings: Bk Vols 445,631; Per Subs 1,269
Subject Interests: Bus, Criminal justice, Education, History, Liberal arts, Mgt
Special Collections: Media/Curricular Center; University Archives
Automation Activity & Vendor Info: (Acquisitions) Endeavor; (Cataloging) Endeavor; (Circulation) Endeavor; (Course Reserve) Endeavor; (Media Booking) Endeavor; (OPAC) Endeavor; (Serials) Endeavor
Database Vendor: Dialog, Ebsco - EbscoHost, Lexis-Nexis, ProQuest, Silverplatter Information Inc., Wilson - Wilson Web
Partic in Associated College Libraries of Central Pennsylvania; OCLC Online Computer Library Center, Inc; Pa Academic Librs Connection Coun; Pa Syst of Higher Educ Libr Coun; PALINET & Union Library Catalogue of Pennsylvania

HREWSBURY

SHREWSBURY BOROUGH PUBLIC LIBRARY,* 44 Main St, 17361-1533. SAN 320-8532. Tel: 717-235-5806. *Librn*, Eleanor Kosko
Pop 6,252
Library Holdings: Bk Vols 10,000; Per Subs 30
Open Mon 9-11 & 7-9, Tues & Thurs 7-9, Wed 9-11 & 7-9 & Sat 9:30-12:30
Friends of the Library Group

INKING SPRING

SINKING SPRING PUBLIC LIBRARY,* 506 Penn Ave, 19608. SAN 315-2189. Tel: 610-678-4311. FAX: 610-670-4826. E-Mail: sinkpl@ptdprolog.net. *Dir*, Valerie Monroe-Myers; *Asst Librn*, Ester Leiby
Founded 1965. Pop 8,467; Circ 27,070
Library Holdings: Bk Titles 8,000; Per Subs 30
Mem of Berks County Libr Syst
Friends of the Library Group

LATINGTON

SLATINGTON LIBRARY,* 650 Main St, PO Box 147, 18080-1420. SAN 315-2197. Tel: 610-767-6461. FAX: 610-767-6461. *Librn*, Rosanne Pugh
Founded 1962. Pop 13,395; Circ 20,310
Library Holdings: Bk Vols 24,027
Mem of Allentown Dist Libr Syst

WILDLIFE INFORMATION CENTER LIBRARY, 624 Main St, 18080-1445. (Mail add: PO Box 198, 18080-0198), SAN 375-1864. Tel: 610-760-8889. FAX: 610-760-8889. E-Mail: wildlife@fast.net. Web Site: www.wildlifeinfo.org. *Pres*, Dan R Kunkle
1999-2000 Mats Exp $1,600, Books $1,200, Per/Ser (Incl. Access Fees) $400
Library Holdings: Bk Titles 1,900; Per Subs 150
Subject Interests: Conservation, Ecology, Ornithology

SLICKVILLE

P SALEM TOWNSHIP PUBLIC LIBRARY-CIVIC CENTER, PO Box 157, 15684-0157. SAN 315-2200. Tel: 724-468-4492. *Librn*, Mary Gabrielcik
Founded 1965. Pop 12,000
Library Holdings: Bk Vols 9,000; Per Subs 12
Automation Activity & Vendor Info: (Cataloging) Gaylord
Open Tues & Thurs 6-9 & Sat 10:30-2:30

SLIPPERY ROCK

C SLIPPERY ROCK UNIVERSITY OF PENNSYLVANIA, Bailey Library, 16057-9989. SAN 315-2219. Tel: 724-738-2058. FAX: 724-738-2661. Web Site: www.sru.edu. *Dir Libr Serv*, Dr Barbara D Farah; Tel: 724-738-2630, E-Mail: barbara.farah@sru.edu; *Syst Coordr, Tech Coordr*, Delphine Hamilton; *Coll Develop, Ref Serv*, Jessica Marshall; *Publ Servs*, Susan Ferrandiz; *Publ Servs*, Lynn R Hoffmann; *Publ Servs*, Jane Scott-Cleary; *Publ Servs*, Melba Tomeo; *Ser*, Nancy Hanks; *Govt Doc*, Jane Smith; Staff 20 (MLS 9, Non-MLS 11)
Founded 1970. Enrl 6,900; Fac 327; Highest Degree: Doctorate
Jul 2000-Jun 2001 Income $1,164,770, State $554,770, Parent Institution $610,000. Mats Exp $435,000, Per/Ser (Incl. Access Fees) $120,000, Presv $15,000, Micro $50,000, AV Equip $30,000, Other Print Mats $150,000, Electronic Ref Mat (Incl. Access Fees) $70,000. Sal $853,600
Library Holdings: Bk Vols 599,974; Per Subs 820
Special Collections: Italy, bks, flm, micro; Japan, bks, flm, micro; Physical Education, Recreation & Sports, bks, flm, micro
Database Vendor: Ebsco - EbscoHost, GaleNet, IAC - SearchBank, Lexis-Nexis, ProQuest, Silverplatter Information Inc., Wilson - Wilson Web
Publications: Japanese Collection; Japanese Collection Supplement
Partic in Access Pa; Interlibrary Delivery Service of Pennsylvania; OCLC Online Computer Library Center, Inc; Pa Acad Libr Coop; State System Of Higher Education Libraries Council
Open Mon-Thurs 8-11, Fri 8-5, Sat 9-5 & Sun 1-11
Friends of the Library Group

SMETHPORT

P HAMLIN MEMORIAL LIBRARY, 123 S Mechanic St, PO Box 422, 16749. SAN 315-2235. Tel: 814-887-9262. FAX: 814-887-9234. E-Mail: hamlin@penn.com. Web Site: www.home.penn.com/hamlin. *Dir*, Lorine Rounsville
Founded 1967. Pop 5,933; Circ 21,111
Jan 1999-Dec 1999 Income $70,337, State $5,602, City $3,611, Locally Generated Income $12,124, Other $49,000. Mats Exp $15,366, Books $6,208, Per/Ser (Incl. Access Fees) $1,036. Sal $16,691
Library Holdings: Bk Vols 20,135; Per Subs 42
Subject Interests: Automotive hist, Civil War
Friends of the Library Group

GL MCKEAN COUNTY LAW LIBRARY, PO Box 1507, 16749-0536. SAN 315-2227. Tel: 814-887-3325, 814-887-5571. *Librn*, Joanne Bly
Library Holdings: Bk Vols 12,000

SMITHTON

P SMITHTON PUBLIC LIBRARY,* Center & Second St, PO Box 382, 15479-0382. SAN 315-2243. Tel: 724-872-0701. *Librn*, Donna Kruper
Founded 1959. Pop 552; Circ 6,884
Library Holdings: Bk Vols 6,000; Per Subs 10
Mem of Monessen District Libr Ctr
Open Mon & Fri 5-8, Tues & Thurs 3-5

SOMERSET

M BEDFORD-SOMERSET MENTAL HEALTH, MENTAL RETARDATION CENTER LIBRARY,* 245 W Race St, 15501. SAN 320-7277. Tel: 814-443-4891. FAX: 814-443-4898. *In Charge*, Randy Hay
Library Holdings: Bk Vols 100

P MARY S BIESECKER PUBLIC LIBRARY, 230 S Rosina Ave, 15501. SAN 315-2251. Tel: 814-445-4011. FAX: 814-443-0725. E-Mail: maryslib@shol.com. *Dir*, Dawn J Davis; *Asst Libr Dir*, Denise A Sanner; *Ch Servs*, JoAnn Critchfield; Staff 4 (Non-MLS 4)
Founded 1914. Pop 6,454; Circ 38,000
Jan 2000-Dec 2000 Income $122,474, State $24,574, City $82,000, Locally Generated Income $15,900. Mats Exp Books $16,000
Library Holdings: Bk Vols 34,020; Bk Titles 26,861
Special Collections: Civil War; Geneaology; Local & Pennsylvania History; Somerset County Newspapers, microfilms

GL SOMERSET COUNTY LAW LIBRARY,* Court House, 111 E Union St, Ste 60, 15501. SAN 315-2278. Tel: 814-443-9770. FAX: 814-445-1455. *Librn*, Lori Polonchak
Library Holdings: Bk Vols 21,785; Per Subs 75

P SOMERSET COUNTY LIBRARY, 6022 Glades Pike, Ste 120, 15501-4300. SAN 315-2286. Tel: 814-445-5907. FAX: 814-443-0650. E-Mail: somcolib@wpia.net. Web Site: www.sctc.net/somcounlib/. *Dir*, Eve Kline
Founded 1947. Pop 71,764
Jan 2000-Dec 2000 Income $204,878, State $48,784, Federal $20,725, Locally Generated Income $135,369. Mats Exp $26,566, Books $25,421, Per/Ser (Incl. Access Fees) $1,145. Sal $99,937 (Prof $24,000)
Library Holdings: Bk Vols 61,002; Bk Titles 44,901; Per Subs 174
Subject Interests: Large print, Videos
Special Services for the Blind - Bks on cassette
Friends of the Library Group
Bookmobiles: 1

SOUDERTON

S UNION NATIONAL BANK & TRUST CO LIBRARY,* 14 N Main St, PO Box 197, 18964. SAN 315-2308. Tel: 215-721-2400. FAX: 215-721-2433. *Librn*, Susan Swope
Library Holdings: Bk Vols 318; Per Subs 27
Subject Interests: Bank marketing, Servs

P ZION MENNONITE CHURCH & PUBLIC LIBRARY,* 149 Cherry Lane, PO Box 495, 18964. SAN 320-7285. Tel: 215-723-3592. *Librn*, Mrs Gerald F Hartzel
Founded 1945
Library Holdings: Bk Vols 5,500; Per Subs 15
Subject Interests: Bibles, Mennonite hist
Publications: Christianity Today; Mennonite Weekly Review

SOUTH CANAAN

R PATRIARCH SAINT TIKHON LIBRARY, (T4K), (Formerly St Patriarch Tikhon Library), Saint Tikhon's Orthodox Theological Seminary, St Tikhon's Rd, PO Box 130, 18459-0130. SAN 315-2316. Tel: 570-937-4411. Interlibrary Loan Service Tel: 570-937-3209. FAX: 570-937-3100. Web Site: www.stots.edu/library.html. *Librn*, Sergei Arhipov; *Asst Librn*, Juvenaly Repass; Staff 4 (MLS 2, Non-MLS 2)
Founded 1938. Highest Degree: Master
Library Holdings: Bk Vols 36,000; Per Subs 120
Subject Interests: Orthodox Eastern church, Orthodox theol
Special Collections: Russian & Church Slavic Theological & Literature Coll
Partic in Southeastern Pennsylvania Theological Library Association

SOUTH FORK

P SOUTH FORK PUBLIC LIBRARY,* 320 Main St, 15956-9998. SAN 315-2324. Tel: 814-495-4812. FAX: 814-495-4812. *Librn*, Sheila Ferchalk
Pop 1,600; Circ 13,782
Library Holdings: Bk Vols 18,000; Per Subs 12
Mem of Cambria County Library System & District Center
Open Mon-Fri 1-6
Friends of the Library Group

SOUTH STERLING

S CINEMA ARTS, INC, Motion Picture Archives,* Art Bldg, Huckleberry Hill. (Mail add: PO Box 70, 18463-0070), SAN 323-7206. Tel: 570-676-4145. FAX: 570-676-9194. *Acq, Librn*, John E Allen; *Tech Servs*, Mike Kolvek; *VPres*, Beverly Allen; Staff 6 (MLS 3, Non-MLS 3)
Founded 1987
Subject Interests: Education, Transportation, Travel, World War I, World War II
Special Collections: Kinograms & Telenews, reels; Posters; silent film; Still Photographs
Specializing in preservation of old film & transfer to film or tape

SOUTHAMPTON

P SOUTHAMPTON FREE LIBRARY, 947 Street Rd, 18966. SAN 315-2332. Tel: 215-322-1415. FAX: 215-396-9375. Web Site: www.southamptonpa.com/library. *Coll Develop, Dir*, Susan Rork; *ILL*, Elaine Nieckoski; *Ch Servs, Coll Develop, YA Servs*, Lora Terifay; *Cat*, Norma Ewing; Staff 6 (MLS 3, Non-MLS 3)
Founded 1921. Pop 16,076; Circ 169,004
Jan 1999-Dec 1999 Income $381,109, State $50,406. Mats Exp $63,868, Books $52,194, Per/Ser (Incl. Access Fees) $4,413, AV Equip $7,261. Sal $215,601
Library Holdings: Bk Vols 68,780; Per Subs 132
Subject Interests: Large print
Automation Activity & Vendor Info: (Acquisitions) DRA
Mem of Bucks County Free Library
Friends of the Library Group

SPANGLER

P SPANGLER PUBLIC LIBRARY INC,* 1904 Bigler Ave, PO Box 548, 15775-9998. SAN 315-2340. Tel: 814-948-8222. FAX: 814-948-8222. E-Mail: spangler@forspeed.com. *Librn*, Kathleen Artley; *Asst Librn*, Dorothy Anderson
Founded 1952. Pop 2,399; Circ 14,336
Library Holdings: Bk Titles 10,500; Per Subs 19
Mem of Cambria County Library System & District Center

SPRING CITY

P SPRING CITY FREE PUBLIC LIBRARY, 245 Broad St, 19475-1702. SAN 315-2367. Tel: 610-948-4130. FAX: 610-948-9478. *Dir*, Anita Regester
Founded 1910. Pop 3,389; Circ 33,468
Library Holdings: Bk Vols 16,000; Per Subs 54
Automation Activity & Vendor Info: (Circulation) Innovative Interfaces Inc.
Database Vendor: Ebsco - EbscoHost
Function: ILL available, Photocopies available
Mem of Chester County Library
Open Mon & Tues 10-8, Wed 1-8, Thurs 1-6, Sat 10-5

SPRING GROVE

P GLATFELTER MEMORIAL LIBRARY,* 101 Glenview Rd, 17362. SAN 315-2383. Tel: 717-225-3220. FAX: 717-225-9808. E-Mail: gmlib@blazenet.net. Web Site: www.yorklibraries.org/glatselter. *Librn*, Kathy Silvin
Pop 10,588; Circ 37,610
Jan 1997-Nov 1998 Income $90,256, State $13,968, County $6,125. Mats Exp $11,444, Books $10,500, Per/Ser (Incl. Access Fees) $944. Sal $29,286
Library Holdings: Bk Vols 19,000; Per Subs 30
Mem of York County Library System
Hours: Mon 12-8, Wed & Thurs 1-8, Tues 9-8, Sat 9-2

SPRING HOUSE

S R W JOHNSON PHARMACEUTICAL RESEARCH INSTITUTE LIBRARY, Welsh & McKean Rd, 19477-0776. SAN 314-5239. Tel: 215-628-5623. FAX: 215-628-5984. *Mgr*, June Bente; E-Mail: jbente@prius.jnj.com; Staff 8 (MLS 3, Non-MLS 5)
Library Holdings: Per Subs 300
Subject Interests: Biology, Chemistry, Medicine

S ROHM & HAAS CO, Research Division, Knowledge Center, 727 Norristown Rd, 19477. SAN 359-5625. Tel: 215-641-7818. FAX: 215-641-7811. *Mgr*, Andrea Kirk; *Online Servs*, Joanne L Witiak; *Librn*, Deanna Caporicci. Subject Specialists: *Chemistry*, Deanna Caporicci; Staff 19 (MLS 8, Non-MLS 11)
Library Holdings: Bk Titles 3,500; Per Subs 300
Subject Interests: Chemistry, Coatings, Fibers, Leather, Paper, Plastics, Resins, Textiles, Toxicology
Restriction: By appointment only
Partic in Dialog Corporation; Nat Libr of Med; OCLC Online Computer Library Center, Inc
Branches:

S RESEARCH DIVISION, INFORMATION SERVICES DEPARTMENT, Rtes 13 & 413, Box 718, Bristol, 19007. SAN 325-531X. Tel: 215-785-8000, 215-785-8063. FAX: 215-785-8999. *Online Servs*, Susan E Jones; Staff 2 (MLS 2)
Library Holdings: Bk Vols 6,800; Bk Titles 6,400; Per Subs 840
Subject Interests: Chemical engineering, Chemistry
Restriction: Open to public for reference only
Partic in OCLC Online Computer Library Center, Inc; PALINET & Union Library Catalogue of Pennsylvania

S SPRINGHOUSE CORPORATION LIBRARY, 1111 Bethlehem Pike, 19477-1100. (Mail add: PO Box 908, 19477-0908), SAN 325-9927. Tel: 215-646-8700, Ext 1438. FAX: 215-653-0232. *Librn*, Catherine Heslin; Staff 1 (MLS 1)
Library Holdings: Bk Vols 3,000; Per Subs 50
Subject Interests: Nursing
Partic in Delaware Valley Information Consortium; Tri-State College Library Cooperative (TCLC)

SPRINGBORO

P SPRINGBORO PUBLIC LIBRARY,* 110 S Main St, PO Box 51, 16435-0116. SAN 315-2391. Tel: 814-587-3901. FAX: 814-587-3901. *Librn*, Faith Scott
Pop 2,800; Circ 10,000
Library Holdings: Bk Vols 10,000; Per Subs 15
Mem of Crawford County Federated Library System
Open Tues & Thurs 2-9 & Sat 10-4

RINGDALE

SPRINGDALE FREE PUBLIC LIBRARY,* 331 School St, 15144-1343. SAN 315-2405. Tel: 724-274-9729. FAX: 724-274-6125. *Librn*, Janet Tyree
Founded 1933
Library Holdings: Bk Titles 25,000; Per Subs 40
Open Mon-Fri 2-5 & 6-8

PRINGFIELD

COVENANT UNITED METHODIST CHURCH LIBRARY, 212 W Springfield Rd, 19064. SAN 315-2413. Tel: 610-544-1400. FAX: 610-544-2862.
Library Holdings: Bk Vols 1,850

SPRINGFIELD HOSPITAL, Medical Library,* 190 W Sproul Rd, 19064-2097. SAN 329-2908. Tel: 610-328-8700, 610-328-8749. FAX: 610-328-8712. *Librn*, Judith Ziegler
Library Holdings: Bk Titles 1,000; Per Subs 105
Subject Interests: Medicine, Nursing, Osteopathic med
Under auspices of Crozer-Chester Medical Center; Hours: Tues & Thurs 10-3

SPRINGFIELD TOWNSHIP LIBRARY,* 70 Powell Rd, 19064-2495. SAN 315-2421. Tel: 610-543-2113. FAX: 610-543-1356. E-Mail: springfld.lib@hslc.org. *Dir*, Audrey Blossic; *Ch Servs*, Margaret H Wyppich; *Coll Develop*, Doris Glazer
Founded 1937. Pop 24,160; Circ 143,079
Library Holdings: Bk Vols 82,489; Per Subs 207
Special Collections: Genealogy Coll; Local History Coll
Mem of Delaware County Library System
Friends of the Library Group

TATE COLLEGE

AMERICAN PHILATELIC RESEARCH LIBRARY,* 100 Oakwood Ave, PO Box 8000, 16803-8000. SAN 315-243X. Tel: 814-237-3803. FAX: 814-237-6128. Web Site: www.stamps.org. *Librn*, Virginia Horn; *Asst Librn*, Martha Micuda; Staff 6 (MLS 3, Non-MLS 3)
Founded 1968
Library Holdings: Bk Titles 17,000; Per Subs 404
Subject Interests: Philately, Postal hist, Postal law
Special Collections: AFDCS Archives; Ellis File; Piper File
Publications: Philatelic Literature Review
Open Mon-Fri 8-4:30

CENTRE COMMUNITY HOSPITAL, Esker W Cullen Library, 1800 E Park Ave, 16803. SAN 326-419X. Tel: 814-234-6191. FAX: 814-231-7031. *Librn*, Elinor Snow; E-Mail: esnow@cch1.org; Staff 1 (MLS 1)
Library Holdings: Bk Vols 1,500; Per Subs 100
Subject Interests: Medicine, Nursing
Publications: List of Journals; Orientation Info Sheet
Partic in BHSL; Central Pennsylvania Health Science Library Association (CPHSLA); Nat Libr of Med

ENVIRONMENTAL COALITION ON NUCLEAR POWER LIBRARY,* 433 Orlando Ave, 16803. SAN 372-9265. Tel: 814-237-3900. FAX: 814-237-3900. *Mgr*, Judith Johnsrud
Library Holdings: Bk Vols 1,500; Per Subs 10
Subject Interests: Energy, Nuclear power, Technology

PENNSYLVANIA FISH & BOAT COMMISSION, Benner Spring Fish Research Station Library, 1225 Shiloh Rd, 16801-8495. SAN 314-3090. Tel: 814-355-4837. FAX: 814-355-8264. *In Charge*, Sherry Lucas
Founded 1953
Library Holdings: Bk Vols 450; Per Subs 50
Special Collections: Fisheries & fisheries related texts, journals & reprints

PENNSYLVANIA STATE UNIVERSITY
APPLIED RESEARCH LABORATORY INFORMATION SERVICES, N Atherton St, 16801. (Mail add: PO Box 30, 16804-0030), Tel: 814-863-9939. FAX: 814-865-7044. E-Mail: pghl@psu.edu. Web Site: www.arl.psu.edu.; Staff 4 (MLS 1, Non-MLS 3)
Founded 1945
Library Holdings: Bk Vols 3,700; Bk Titles 4,300; Per Subs 300
Subject Interests: Applied math, Computers, Electronics, Engineering, Manufacturing eng, Oceanography, Physics
Special Collections: Children's Diversity Coll; Eric Walker Coll
Automation Activity & Vendor Info: (Acquisitions) Inmagic, Inc.; (Cataloging) Inmagic, Inc.; (Circulation) Inmagic, Inc.; (Course Reserve) Inmagic, Inc.; (Serials) Inmagic, Inc.
Publications: New Titles (monthly)
Restriction: Not open to public
Mem of Asn of Research Libraries
Partic in Dialog Corporation; RECON
Friends of the Library Group

S ENVIRONMENTAL RESOURCES RESEARCH INSTITUTE LIBRARY, Land & Water Research Bldg, University Park, 16802. SAN 321-9070. Tel: 814-863-0140. FAX: 814-865-3378. E-Mail: emb7@psu.edu. Web Site: www.research.psu.edu/erri/library.; Staff 1 (Non-MLS 1)
Founded 1963
Library Holdings: Bk Titles 1,500; Per Subs 70
Subject Interests: Acid precipitation, Biodiversity, Climate change, Control of air pollution, Environ health, Land reclamation econ, Remote sensing, Risk assessment, Sources effects of air pollution, Waste mgt, Water quality
Special Collections: State Water Research Institute Reports
Mem of Asn of Research Libraries

P SCHLOW MEMORIAL LIBRARY,* 100 E Beaver Ave, 16801-4986. SAN 315-2472. Tel: 814-237-6236. FAX: 814-238-8508. E-Mail: refdesk@schlowlibrary.org. Web Site: schlowlibrary.org. *Dir*, Elizabeth Allen; *Ch Servs*, Anita Ditz; *Tech Servs*, Ann Lindsay; *Acq*, Linda Lorich; *Ad Servs*, Patricia Griffith; Staff 22 (MLS 5, Non-MLS 17)
Founded 1957. Pop 70,164; Circ 439,904
Jan 1999-Dec 1999 Income $1,020,414, State $83,830, City $286,303, County $101,779, Locally Generated Income $79,434, Other $469,068. Mats Exp $151,411, Books $105,258, Per/Ser (Incl. Access Fees) $10,728, AV Equip $16,767, Other Print Mats $12,238, Electronic Ref Mat (Incl. Access Fees) $6,420. Sal $626,448
Library Holdings: Bk Vols 115,567; Per Subs 210
Automation Activity & Vendor Info: (Acquisitions) epixtech, inc.; (Cataloging) epixtech, inc.; (Circulation) epixtech, inc.; (OPAC) epixtech, inc.
Partic in Access Pa; Cent Pa District; Centre County Fed of Pub Librs; OCLC Online Computer Library Center, Inc; PALINET & Union Library Catalogue of Pennsylvania
Open Mon-Wed 9-9, Thurs 12-9, Fri 9-6, Sat 9-5 & Sun 1:30-5
Friends of the Library Group

STERLING

S BROWN BROTHERS PHOTOGRAPH COLLECTION,* 100 Boretree Rd, PO Box 50, 18463. SAN 372-9273. Tel: 717-689-9688. FAX: 717-689-7873. *Pres*, Raymond A Collins

STEWARTSTOWN

P MASON-DIXON PUBLIC LIBRARY, (MD LIB), 2 N Main St, PO Box 458, 17363. SAN 315-2499. Tel: 717-993-2404. FAX: 717-993-9201. Web Site: www.geocities.com/Heartland/8074/MD.html. *Dir*, Carol Stampler
Founded 1961. Pop 10,072
Library Holdings: Bk Vols 25,000; Per Subs 52
Special Collections: Farm Coll
Mem of York County Library System
Open Mon-Thurs 1-8, Fri 10-8 & Sat 10-5
Friends of the Library Group

STRASBURG

P STRASBURG-HEISLER LIBRARY,* 143 Precision Ave, 17579. SAN 376-6055. Tel: 717-687-8969. FAX: 717-687-9795. *Dir*, Sandra H Dinoff
Library Holdings: Bk Vols 18,000; Bk Titles 16,000; Per Subs 25
Mem of Library System of Lancaster County

S TRAIN COLLECTORS ASSOCIATION, Toy Train Reference Library,* 300 Paradise Lane, 17579-0248. (Mail add: PO Box 248, 17579-0248), SAN 326-2553. Tel: 717-687-8623. FAX: 717-687-0742. E-Mail: toytrain@traincollectors.org. Web Site: www.traincollectors.org. *Ref*, Jan Athey; Staff 1 (MLS 1)
Founded 1982
Library Holdings: Bk Titles 1,000; Per Subs 27
Publications: Train Collectors Quarterly (Parent Organization)
Restriction: Open to public for reference only
Friends of the Library Group

STROUDSBURG

P EASTERN MONROE PUBLIC LIBRARY, 1002 N Ninth St, 18360. SAN 315-2529. Tel: 570-421-0800. Toll Free Tel: 888-601-4192. FAX: 570-424-1546. E-Mail: mcpl@ptd.net. Web Site: www.monroepl.org. *Dir*, Debra Messling; *Head Tech Servs*, Hildegarde Brazzle; *Ch Servs*, Sherry Crawford; *Reader Servs*, Ann Kane; *Publ Servs*, James Adams; *Ad Servs*, Barbara Keiser; Staff 35 (MLS 5, Non-MLS 30)
Founded 1913. Pop 56,100; Circ 451,000
Jan 2000-Dec 2000 Income (Main Library and Branch Library) $1,014,132, State $192,888, County $821,244. Mats Exp $202,960, Books $151,182, Per/Ser (Incl. Access Fees) $15,009, Micro $4,268, AV Equip $19,851, Electronic Ref Mat (Incl. Access Fees) $12,650. Sal $514,644 (Prof $152,000)
Library Holdings: Bk Vols 110,000; Bk Titles 126,164; Per Subs 331
Subject Interests: Local history

Special Collections: Monroe County History Coll
Automation Activity & Vendor Info: (Cataloging) MultiLIS; (Circulation) MultiLIS; (OPAC) MultiLIS; (OPAC) DRA
Database Vendor: Ebsco - EbscoHost, GaleNet, OCLC - First Search
Publications: Title Tales (Newsletter)
Function: ILL available
Friends of the Library Group
Branches: 2
POCONO TOWNSHIP BRANCH, Municipal Bldg, Rte 611, Tannersville, 18372. SAN 320-8370. Tel: 717-629-5858. FAX: 717-620-1963. *In Charge*, Pat Lasecki
Founded 1987
SMITHFIELDS BRANCH, Foxmoor Village, Marshalls Creek, 18335. SAN 371-9308. Tel: 717-223-1881. FAX: 717-223-1886. *In Charge*, Evonne Rouzer
Founded 1991
Bookmobiles: 1

S MONROE COUNTY HISTORICAL ASSOCIATION LIBRARY, 900 Main St, 18360-2012. SAN 325-5344. Tel: 570-421-7703. FAX: 570-421-9199. E-Mail: mcha@ptdprolog.net. *Exec Dir*, Candace McGreery
Founded 1921
Library Holdings: Bk Vols 10,000; Bk Titles 5,000; Per Subs 17
Special Collections: Monroe County Hist & Genealogy, bks, docs, mss, photos
Publications: Fanlight
Function: Research library

L MONROE COUNTY LAW LIBRARY,* Court House, 18360. SAN 327-0866. Tel: 717-420-3642. *Librn*, Roy Kleinle
Library Holdings: Bk Vols 8,000
Open Mon-Fri 8:30-4:30

SUGAR GROVE

P SUGAR GROVE FREE LIBRARY, Harmon & School St, PO Box 313, 16350-0313. SAN 315-2537. Tel: 814-489-7872. Interlibrary Loan Service Tel: 814-723-4650. FAX: 814-489-7826. E-Mail: sgrove@penn.com. Web Site: www.penn.com/sugargrovelibrary. *Librn*, Sharon Gage; *Asst Librn*, Karen Enos; *Asst Librn*, Barbara J Stoddard; Staff 3 (MLS 1, Non-MLS 2)
Founded 1936. Pop 4,954
Library Holdings: Bk Vols 19,136; Per Subs 50
Subject Interests: Early oil industry, Gardening, Religion
Special Collections: Artist Coll, bks
Publications: Newsletter listing new acquisitions & news (monthly)
Partic in Warren County Libr Syst
Open Mon-Wed 2-8, Tues-Thurs 10-4, Fri 2-7, Sat 8-3
Friends of the Library Group

SUMMERVILLE

P SUMMERVILLE PUBLIC LIBRARY,* W Penn St, PO Box 301, 15864-0301. SAN 315-2545. Tel: 814-856-3169. FAX: 814-856-3169. *Librn*, C Barbara Reitz
Founded 1932. Pop 2,086; Circ 4,420
Library Holdings: Bk Vols 14,774; Bk Titles 14,642; Per Subs 42
Special Collections: Cookery; Crafts; Local hist
Mem of Jefferson County Library System; Oil Creek District Library Center
Partic in Jefferson County Library System
Open Mon-Fri 12:30-3:30 & 6-9

SUNBURY

P JOHN R KAUFFMAN JR PUBLIC LIBRARY,* 228 Arch St, 17801. SAN 315-2553. Tel: 570-286-2461. FAX: 570-286-4203. E-Mail: kaufpubl@ptd.net. Web Site: www.sunlink.net~kaufpubl. *Dir*, Gail E Broome
Founded 1937. Pop 16,717; Circ 66,564
1996-1997 Income $261,881, State $24,822, City $15,824, Federal $54,211. Mats Exp $23,279, Books $17,669, Per/Ser (Incl. Access Fees) $3,475. Sal $113,565
Library Holdings: Bk Vols 56,039; Per Subs 115
Subject Interests: Local history
Special Collections: Local History; Pennsylvania History Room
Publications: Sunbury Pa 1772-1972; Sunbury Photo Guide
Open Mon 1-9, Tues, Wed & Fri 10-6, Thurs 10-9 & Sat 9-5
Friends of the Library Group

GL NORTHUMBERLAND COUNTY LAW LIBRARY, Court House, 201 Market St, 17801-3471. SAN 315-2561. Tel: 570-988-4162. FAX: 570-988-4497. *Librn*, Catherine L Kroh
Founded 1886
Jan 1999-Dec 1999 Income $30,000. Mats Exp Books $43,610. Sal $18,651
Library Holdings: Bk Vols 10,550
Restriction: Open to public for reference only
Function: Research library

SWARTHMORE

S FRIENDS HISTORICAL LIBRARY OF SWARTHMORE COLLEGE, 50 College Ave, 19081-1399. SAN 315-2588. Tel: 610-328-8496. Interlibrary Loan Service Tel: 610-328-8498. FAX: 610-690-5728. E-Mail: friends@swarthmore.edu. Web Site: www.swarthmore.edu/library/friends. *Dir*, J William Frost; *Curator*, Christopher J Densmore; Tel: 610-328-8497, E-Mail: cdensmo1@swarthmore.edu; Staff 2 (Non-MLS 2)
Founded 1871
Library Holdings: Bk Vols 44,000; Per Subs 212
Subject Interests: Quaker hist
Special Collections: (Whittier Coll), bks, mss & pictures; Friends Meeting Records (Record Group 2), mss & archives; John G Whittier; Lucretia Mo mss; Swarthmore College Archives
Publications: Catalog of the Book & Serials Collections of the Friends Historical Library; Guide to the Manuscript Collections of Friends Historic Library of Swarthmore College; Guide to the Records of Philadelphia Year Meeting
Partic in OCLC, Inc through Palinet
Friends of the Library Group

C SWARTHMORE COLLEGE, McCabe Library, 500 College Ave, 19081-1399. SAN 359-5773. Tel: 610-328-8477. Interlibrary Loan Service Tel: 610-328-8491. FAX: 610-328-7329. *Librn*, Peggy Seiden; *ILL*, Sandy Vermeycnuk; *Access Serv*, Alison Masterpasqua; *Tech Servs*, Barb Weir; *Head Ref*, Anne Garrison; *Instrul Serv, Outreach Serv*, Pam Harris; *Ref Ser* Ed Fuller; *Computer Services*, Tammy Rabideau. Subject Specialists: *Soc sci*, Megan Adams; *Video*, Ed Fuller; Staff 18 (MLS 10, Non-MLS 8)
Founded 1864. Enrl 1,428; Fac 166; Highest Degree: Bachelor
2000-2001 Income (Main and Other College/University Libraries) $3,138,581
Library Holdings: Bk Vols 716,315; Per Subs 1,908
Special Collections: British Writings on Travel in America (British Americana Coll); History of Technology (Bathe Coll); Private Press (Charle B Shaw Coll); Recorded Literature (Potter Coll); Romantic Poetry (Wells Wordsworth & Thomson Coll); W H Auden Coll
Automation Activity & Vendor Info: (Acquisitions) Innovative Interfaces Inc.; (Cataloging) Innovative Interfaces Inc.; (Circulation) Innovative Interfaces Inc.; (Course Reserve) Innovative Interfaces Inc.; (ILL) Innovati Interfaces Inc.; (Media Booking) Innovative Interfaces Inc.; (OPAC) Innovative Interfaces Inc.; (Serials) Innovative Interfaces Inc.
Restriction: Open to student, faculty & staff
Partic in Interlibrary Delivery Service of Pennsylvania; Mideastern Regiona Med Libr Serv; OCLC Online Computer Library Center, Inc; PALCI; PALINET & Union Library Catalogue of Pennsylvania
Friends of the Library Group
Departmental Libraries:
CORNELL SCIENCE & ENGINEERING Tel: 610-328-8262. *Head of Libr* Meg E Spencer
Library Holdings: Bk Vols 62,100
DANIEL UNDERHILL MUSIC Tel: 610-328-8232. *Librn*, George K Hube Subject Specialists: *Performing arts*, George K Huber

P SWARTHMORE PUBLIC LIBRARY, Borough Hall, 121 Park Ave, 19081 1536. SAN 315-260X. Tel: 610-543-0436. FAX: 610-328-6699. E-Mail: swarthmore@delco.lib.pa.us. Web Site: www.delco.lib.pa.us. *Dir, Librn*, Ve Orthlieb; *Asst Librn*, Carol Mackin; E-Mail: swreference@delco.lib.pa.us; *Ch Servs*, Sharon Ford; E-Mail: swcsd@delco.lip.pa.us; *ILL*, Betty Barbara Smart; E-Mail: illsw@delco.lib.pa.us; Staff 1 (MLS 1)
Founded 1929. Pop 6,157; Circ 69,558
Jan 1999-Dec 1999 Income $156,425, State $11,275, City $69,750, Locally Generated Income $75,400. Mats Exp $36,202, Books $32,469, Per/Ser (Incl. Access Fees) $3,733. Sal $107,374 (Prof $34,125)
Library Holdings: Bk Vols 38,903; Per Subs 96
Automation Activity & Vendor Info: (Circulation) TLC
Database Vendor: Ebsco - EbscoHost, IAC - SearchBank
Function: ILL available
Mem of Delaware County Library System
Friends of the Library Group

SWISSVALE

P CARNEGIE FREE LIBRARY OF SWISSVALE, 1800 Monongahela Ave, 15218. SAN 315-2618. Tel: 412-731-2300. FAX: 412-731-6716. Web Site: www.einpgh.org/ein/swissval/. *Dir*, Bruce Egli; E-Mail: eglib@einetwork.net; Staff 5 (MLS 2, Non-MLS 3)
Founded 1916. Pop 13,140; Circ 25,847
Jul 1999-Jun 2000 Income $149,716. Mats Exp $18,822. Sal $52,837
Library Holdings: Bk Titles 16,345; Per Subs 100
Automation Activity & Vendor Info: (Cataloging) DRA; (Circulation) DRA; (ILL) DRA; (OPAC) DRA
Database Vendor: DRA, Ebsco - EbscoHost, GaleNet, IAC - Info Trac, IAC - SearchBank
Partic in Allegheny County Libr Asn
Friends of the Library Group

KESVILLE

SYKESVILLE PUBLIC LIBRARY,* 21 E Main St, 15865-0021. SAN 315-2626. Tel: 814-894-5243. FAX: 814-894-5243. *Librn*, Ruth Sackash
Founded 1968. Pop 1,976; Circ 4,255
Library Holdings: Bk Vols 9,000; Per Subs 25
Mem of Jefferson County Library System; Oil Creek District Library Center
Partic in Jefferson County Library System

AMAQUA

TAMAQUA PUBLIC LIBRARY, 30 S Railroad St, 18252. SAN 315-2642. Tel: 570-668-4660. FAX: 570-668-4660. E-Mail: tamaquapubliclibrary@hotmail.com. *Assoc Dir*, Georgia Depos
Founded 1934. Pop 17,297
Library Holdings: Bk Titles 39,000; Per Subs 52
Mem of Pottsville Free Public Library

ARENTUM

COMMUNITY LIBRARY OF ALLEGHENY VALLEY, 315 E Sixth Ave, 15084-1596. SAN 315-2650. Tel: 724-226-0770. FAX: 724-226-3526. *Dir*, Kathy Firestone
Founded 1923. Pop 30,116; Circ 44,573
Library Holdings: Bk Vols 55,000; Per Subs 77
Open Mon 12-8, Tues & Wed 10-6, Fri 10-4, Sat 10-2
Friends of the Library Group
Branches: 1
NATRONA HEIGHTS BRANCH, 1522 Broadview Blvd, Natrona Heights, 15065. SAN 378-1674. Tel: 724-226-3491. FAX: 724-226-3821. *Librn*, Kathy Firestone
Friends of the Library Group

VALLEY NEWS DISPATCH NEWSPAPER LIBRARY, 210 Fourth Ave, 15084. SAN 325-1969. Tel: 724-224-4321. FAX: 724-226-4677.
Founded 1978
Library Holdings: Per Subs 2
Special Collections: Valley News Dispatch (1904- present), clips, microfiche

AYLOR

TAYLOR PUBLIC LIBRARY,* 200 Union St, 18517-1774. SAN 315-2677. Tel: 570-562-3180. FAX: 570-562-3140. *Librn*, Jeanie Sluck
Founded 1954. Pop 7,200; Circ 10,249
Library Holdings: Bk Vols 29,000; Per Subs 20
Mem of Lackawanna County Library System
Open Mon & Wed 2-8, Tues & Thurs 9-11:30 & 2-8, Fri 11-5 & Sat 9:30-2:30
Friends of the Library Group
Bookmobiles: 1

ELFORD

INDIAN VALLEY PUBLIC LIBRARY, 100 E Church Ave, 18969. SAN 315-2685. Tel: 215-723-9109. FAX: 215-723-0583. Web Site: www.ivpl.org. *Dir*, Linda Beck; E-Mail: lbeck@ivpl.org; *Ad Servs*, Deborah Faulkner; E-Mail: dfaulkner@ivpl.org; *Ch Servs*, Jerri Cumielefski; *Tech Servs*, Mary Porter; E-Mail: mporter@ivpl.org; *AV*, Margy Watson; E-Mail: mwatson@ivpl.org; Staff 22 (MLS 6, Non-MLS 16)
Founded 1963. Pop 37,000; Circ 520,000
Jan 2000-Dec 2000 Income (Main Library Only) $962,726, State $157,516, City $684,810, Locally Generated Income $120,400. Mats Exp $182,411, Books $137,018, AV Equip $35,393, Manuscripts & Archives $10,000. Sal $547,632 (Prof $216,282)
Library Holdings: Bk Vols 103,000; Per Subs 130
Special Collections: Charles Price Genealogy Coll; Chinese Culture Coll; Local Newspaper 1881-date; Pennsylvania Archives
Automation Activity & Vendor Info: (Cataloging) epixtech, inc.; (Circulation) epixtech, inc.
Database Vendor: Ebsco - EbscoHost, epixtech, inc., IAC - Info Trac, OCLC - First Search, ProQuest
Mem of Montgomery County District Libr Syst
Friends of the Library Group

TIDIOUTE

P TIDIOUTE PUBLIC LIBRARY, 197 Main St, PO Box T, 16351-0225. SAN 315-2693. Tel: 814-484-3581. FAX: 814-484-3581. *Librn*, Sallie Urbanik
Founded 1921. Pop 939; Circ 10,815
Library Holdings: Bk Vols 27,000; Per Subs 45
Friends of the Library Group

TIONESTA

P SARAH STEWART BOVARD MEMORIAL LIBRARY,* 156 Elm St, PO Box 127, 16353-0127. SAN 315-2707. Tel: 814-755-4454. FAX: 814-755-4333. *Librn*, Judith A Ellis
Founded 1942. Pop 5,072; Circ 14,000
Library Holdings: Bk Titles 17,100; Per Subs 47
Special Collections: Artifacts (Forest County Logging & Boat Building Tools Coll); Forest County History & Geography, bks, pamphlets, photog, etc
Open Mon-Wed & Fri 9-4:30 & 6:30-8:30, Thurs 12-5 & 6:30-8:30 & Sat 9-12

TITUSVILLE

P BENSON MEMORIAL LIBRARY,* 213 N Franklin St, 16354-1788. SAN 315-2715. Tel: 814-827-2913. FAX: 814-827-9836. *Dir*, Gail K Myer; *Asst Dir*, Phyllis Skinner; *Ch Servs*, Carol G Scott
Founded 1904. Pop 16,355
Library Holdings: Bk Vols 45,000; Per Subs 200
Subject Interests: Early petroleum indust, Genealogy, Local history
Special Collections: Oil City Births & Marriages (1882-1909); Titusville Births & Deaths (1857-1917); Titusville Herald (1865-present), micro; US Census for Crawford Forest, Venango & Warren Counties (1850-1900), micro
Mem of Crawford County Federated Library System
Open Mon-Thurs 10-8, Fri & Sat 10-5
Friends of the Library Group

S PENNSYLVANIA HISTORICAL & MUSEUM COMMISSION, Drake Well Museum Library, RD 3, Box 7, 16354. SAN 315-2723. Tel: 814-827-2797. FAX: 814-827-4888. Web Site: www.drakewell.org. *Dir*, Barbara Zolli
Founded 1934
Library Holdings: Bk Titles 4,000; Per Subs 16
Subject Interests: Hist of region, Petroleum indust
Special Collections: (Brewer), doc; Early Petroleum Industry; Early Petroleum Industry (Townsend), doc; Nitroglycerine (Roberts), doc; Personal Papers (Fletcher), doc; Standard Oil Company (Ida M Tarbell), doc
Restriction: By appointment only, Not a lending library
Function: Research library

C UNIVERSITY OF PITTSBURGH AT TITUSVILLE, Haskell Memorial Library, 520 E Main, PO Box 287, 16354. SAN 315-2731. Tel: 814-827-4439. FAX: 814-827-4449. *Dir*, Allan R Hughes
Founded 1963
Library Holdings: Bk Vols 47,200; Per Subs 185
Partic in OCLC Online Computer Library Center, Inc
Open Mon-Thurs 8:30-10, Fri 8:30-5, Sat 10-2, Sun 2-10, Mon-Fri 8:30-5 (May-Aug)

TOBYHANNA

P POCONO MOUNTAIN PUBLIC LIBRARY, (PMPL), 5540 Memorial Blvd, 18466. SAN 372-7289. Tel: 570-894-8860. FAX: 570-894-8852. E-Mail: pmpl@ptd.net. Web Site: www.poconomountpl.org. *Dir*, Loren McCrory; Staff 7 (MLS 1, Non-MLS 6)
Founded 1975. Pop 12,070; Circ 127,494
Jan 1999-Dec 1999 Income $265,972. Sal $38,000
Library Holdings: Bk Vols 38,000; Per Subs 100
Automation Activity & Vendor Info: (Cataloging) Follett; (Circulation) Follett; (OPAC) Follett
Database Vendor: Ebsco - EbscoHost
Friends of the Library Group

UNITED STATES ARMY
A TOBYHANNA ARMY DEPOT POST LIBRARY Tel: 717-895-7316. FAX: 717-895-7419. *Librn*, Jeff Davis; E-Mail: jdavis@tobyhanna.army.mil
Founded 1959
Library Holdings: Bk Vols 16,500; Per Subs 29
Partic in Fedlink; OCLC Online Computer Library Center, Inc

TOPTON

P BRANDYWINE COMMUNITY LIBRARY, 60 Tower Dr, 19562-1301. SAN 323-9411. Tel: 610-682-7115. FAX: 610-682-7385. E-Mail: brandywinecl@berks.lib.pa.us. Web Site: www.berks.lib.pa.us/brandywinecl. *Dir*, Cheryl DuBois Knight; *Asst Librn*, Brita Hicks; Staff 2 (MLS 1, Non-MLS 1)
Founded 1989. Pop 11,271; Circ 51,700
Jan 2000-Dec 2000 Income $46,548, State $11,971, County $23,235, Locally Generated Income $3,400. Mats Exp $9,893, Books $7,221, Per/Ser (Incl. Access Fees) $697, AV Equip $1,000. Sal $29,347 (Prof $12,500)
Library Holdings: Bk Titles 13,787; Per Subs 45
Database Vendor: epixtech, inc.
Partic in Berks County Public Libraries
Friends of the Library Group

TOWANDA

S OSRAM SYLVANIA LIBRARY, Hawes St, 18848. SAN 315-274X. Tel: 570-268-5320. FAX: 570-268-5350. *In Charge*, Kathryn Wilcox
Founded 1956
Library Holdings: Bk Vols 10,500; Per Subs 351
Subject Interests: Ceramics, Chemistry, Metallurgy

P TOWANDA PUBLIC LIBRARY,* 104 Main St, 18848-1895. SAN 315-2758. Tel: 570-265-2470. FAX: 570-265-7212. *Chief Librn*, Jean B Vande Mark
Founded 1880. Pop 10,461; Circ 48,100
Library Holdings: Bk Vols 28,000; Per Subs 76
Special Collections: Civil Service Exams; Local History
Mem of Bradford County Library System Headquarters
Open Mon-Thurs 11-8, Fri 11-5, Sat 11-2
Friends of the Library Group

TOWER CITY

P TOWER-PORTER COMMUNITY LIBRARY, 230 E Grand Ave, 17980-1124. SAN 315-2766. Tel: 717-647-4900. *Librn*, Gary Bender
Pop 4,185
Jan 1999-Dec 1999 Income $11,500, State $4,500, Provincial $6,000, Parent Institution $1,000
Library Holdings: Bk Vols 8,197; Per Subs 12
Mem of Pottsville Free Public Library
Open Mon, Tues & Thurs 1-8, Wed 3-7, Fri 3-6 & Sat 9-4
Friends of the Library Group

TRAFFORD

P TRAFFORD COMMUNITY PUBLIC LIBRARY,* 433 Cavitt Ave, PO Box 173, 15085-1062. SAN 315-2774. Tel: 412-372-5115. FAX: 412-372-0993. *Librn*, Lois Baker
Pop 3,662; Circ 12,715
Library Holdings: Bk Vols 11,000; Per Subs 25
Open Mon-Thurs 10-3 & 6:30-8

TREMONT

P TREMONT AREA FREE PUBLIC LIBRARY,* 55 Clay St, 17981-1505. SAN 315-2782. Tel: 570-695-3325. *Librn*, Bonnie Wiscount
Pop 1,796; Circ 3,308
Library Holdings: Bk Vols 7,902; Per Subs 15
Mem of Pottsville Free Public Library
Open Mon 12-3 & 6-8, Tues, Thurs & Fri 12-5
Friends of the Library Group

TREVOSE

S HERCULES, INC, (Formerly Betz Dearborn, Inc), Betz Dearborn Technology Library, 4636 Somerton Rd, 19053-6783. SAN 315-2790. Tel: 215-953-2545. FAX: 215-953-2494. E-Mail: library.betzdearborn.trevose@betzdearborn.com. *Mgr*, Dianne E Rose; E-Mail: dianne.e.rose@betzdearborn.com; *Tech Servs*, Debby Kramer; *Tech Servs*, Carol Sweeney; Staff 4 (MLS 3, Non-MLS 1)
Founded 1925
Library Holdings: Bk Vols 5,500; Bk Titles 4,500; Per Subs 200
Subject Interests: Corrosion, Industrial wastes, Water pollution, Water treatment
Publications: Acquisitions List
Partic in Dialog Corporation; Nat Libr of Med; PALINET & Union Library Catalogue of Pennsylvania

TREXLERTOWN

AIR PRODUCTS & CHEMICALS, INC
S CORPORATE BUSINESS INFORMATION CENTER, 7201 Hamilton Blvd, Allentown, 18195. SAN 359-5951. Tel: 610-481-7442. Interlibrary Loan Service Tel: 610-481-6794. FAX: 610-481-8081.; Staff 1 (MLS 1)
Founded 1975
Library Holdings: Bk Titles 1,600; Per Subs 153
Subject Interests: Bus, Chem industry, Indust statistics, Int bus, Marketing, Mgt, Planning
Publications: What's New in the CBIC
Restriction: Staff use only
Partic in Data Star; Dialog Corporation; Dow Jones News Retrieval; Questal Orbit
S INFORMATION & LIBRARY SERVICES, 7201 Hamilton Blvd, Allentown, 18195-1501. SAN 359-5986. Tel: 610-481-7288. FAX: 481-6495, 610-481-6517. *Mgr Libr Serv*, Valerie Ryder; *ILL*, Diane Ward; *Ref*, Stacy Hortner; *Ref*, Mary Moulton; Staff 14 (MLS 8, Non-MLS 6)
Founded 1953
Library Holdings: Bk Vols 34,000; Per Subs 500
Subject Interests: Bus, Catalysts, Chemical industry, Chemistry, Cryogenics, Engineering, Gas tech, Indust statistics, Mgt, Polymerization Polymers
Special Collections: Family Safety & On-the-Job Safety Audio-Visual Coll
Database Vendor: epixtech, inc.
Partic in OCLC Online Computer Library Center, Inc; PALINET & Unic Library Catalogue of Pennsylvania

TROY

P BRADFORD COUNTY LIBRARY SYSTEM HEADQUARTERS,* RD 3, Box 320, 16947-9440. SAN 315-2812. Tel: 717-297-2436. FAX: 717-297-4197. *Librn*, Fanna Proper
Founded 1941. Pop 75,000; Circ 144,069
Library Holdings: Bk Vols 46,000
Special Collections: Local History
Member Libraries: Mather Memorial Library; Monroeton Public Library; Sayre Public Library, Inc; Towanda Public Library
Open Mon-Fri 8-8 & Sat 9-2
Friends of the Library Group

P ALLEN F PIERCE FREE LIBRARY,* 115 Center St, 16947-1125. SAN 315-2820. Tel: 717-297-2745. FAX: 717-297-2745. *Librn*, Susan Wolfe
Founded 1912. Pop 5,000; Circ 6,000
Library Holdings: Bk Vols 11,851; Per Subs 17

TUNKHANNOCK

P TUNKHANNOCK PUBLIC LIBRARY, 9 Marion St, 18657-1210. SAN 315-2839. Tel: 570-836-1677. FAX: 570-836-2148. E-Mail: tunpubli@epix.net. Web Site: www.tunkhannock.com/library. *Librn*, Susan Turrell
Founded 1890. Pop 28,076; Circ 100,000
Jan 1999-Dec 1999 Income $120,458, State $35,607, County $12,000, Locally Generated Income $68,538. Mats Exp $22,847, Books $20,587, Per Ser (Incl. Access Fees) $1,900, Electronic Ref Mat (Incl. Access Fees) $36(Sal $64,735
Library Holdings: Bk Vols 29,880; Per Subs 75
Friends of the Library Group

TYRONE

P TYRONE-SNYDER TOWNSHIP PUBLIC LIBRARY,* 1019 Logan Ave, 16686-1521. SAN 315-2847. Tel: 814-684-1133. FAX: 814-684-1878. E-Mail: info@tyronelibrary.org. Web Site: www.tyronelibrary.org. *Librn*, Marilyn H Nearhoof; *Asst Librn*, Judie Adams
Founded 1964. Circ 36,020
Library Holdings: Bk Vols 21,060; Per Subs 49
Special Collections: Local history
Mem of Blair County Library System

ULSTER

P MATHER MEMORIAL LIBRARY,* PO Box 230, 18850-0230. SAN 315-2855. Tel: 570-358-3595. FAX: 570-358-3595. *Librn*, Dawn Gillette
Founded 1921. Pop 2,462; Circ 13,576
Library Holdings: Bk Vols 12,500; Per Subs 56
Mem of Bradford County Library System Headquarters
Open Tues & Thurs 2-8 & Fri 6-8
Friends of the Library Group

ULYSSES

P ULYSSES LIBRARY ASSOCIATION,* 401 N Main St, PO Box 316, 16948-0316. SAN 315-2863. Tel: 814-848-7226. FAX: 814-848-7226. E-Mail: ulylib@penn.com. *Librn*, Sheri Graves
Founded 1916. Pop 1,200; Circ 11,547
1997-1998 Income $19,630, State $4,700, City $2,000, County $1,500, Locally Generated Income $11,430. Mats Exp $5,950, Books $5,500, Per/Ser (Incl. Access Fees) $450. Sal $7,738
Library Holdings: Bk Vols 13,451
Mem of Williamsport District Libr Ctr

UNION CITY

P UNION CITY PUBLIC LIBRARY,* S Main & Stranahan, 16438-1322. SAN 315-2871. Tel: 814-438-3209. FAX: 814-438-8031. Web Site: www.ucpl.org. *Dir*, Ruth Cogan
Founded 1908. Pop 6,491; Circ 7,111
Library Holdings: Bk Titles 24,678; Per Subs 46
Special Collections: Local Newspaper, micro
Automation Activity & Vendor Info: (Circulation) Sagebrush Corporation;

(OPAC) Sagebrush Corporation
Open Mon & Thurs 9-7:30, Tues & Fri 9-5:30 & Sat 9-4, Summer only Sat 9-1
Friends of the Library Group

NIONTOWN

L FAYETTE COUNTY LAW LIBRARY, Court House, 61 E Main St, 15401. SAN 315-288X. Tel: 724-430-1228. FAX: 724-430-4886. E-Mail: falawlib@hhs.net. *Librn*, Elida M Micklo; *Asst Librn*, Bonnie Petros
Founded 1927
Library Holdings: Bk Vols 25,000

PENNSYLVANIA STATE UNIVERSITY, Fayette Commonweath College Library (University Libraries),* Rte 119 N, Box 519, 15401. SAN 315-2898. Tel: 724-430-4155. FAX: 724-430-4152. E-Mail: jec@psulias.psu.edu.; Staff 2 (MLS 1, Non-MLS 1)
Founded 1965. Enrl 994; Fac 48
Jul 1997-Jun 1998 Mats Exp $64,115
Library Holdings: Bk Vols 49,620; Per Subs 431
Partic in OCLC Online Computer Library Center, Inc; RLIN

UNIONTOWN HOSPITAL
1 PROFESSIONAL LIBRARY, 500 W Berkeley St, 15401. SAN 327-084X. Tel: 724-430-5178. FAX: 724-430-3349. *Librn*, Barbara Palso; Staff 1 (MLS 1)
Library Holdings: Bk Vols 500; Per Subs 90
Partic in BHSL; National Network of Libraries of Medicine - Greater Midwest Region; Pittsburgh BHSL

UNIONTOWN PUBLIC LIBRARY,* 24 Jefferson St, 15401. SAN 315-2901. Interlibrary Loan Service Tel: 724-437-1165. FAX: 724-439-5689. *Librn*, Christy Fusco; Staff 2 (MLS 2)
Founded 1928. Pop 12,034; Circ 66,454
Jan 1997-Dec 1998 Income $126,000, State $23,000, City $103,000. Mats Exp $29,000, Books $25,000, Per/Ser (Incl. Access Fees) $4,000
Library Holdings: Bk Vols 92,000; Per Subs 100
Subject Interests: Local history
Mem of Monessen District Libr Ctr
Friends of the Library Group

JNIVERSITY PARK

C PENNSYLVANIA STATE UNIVERSITY, Pattee Library & Paterno Library, 510 Paterno Library, 16802-1812. (Mail add: 515 Paterno Library, 16802-1812), SAN 359-601X. Tel: 814-865-0401. FAX: 814-865-3665. E-Mail: s2w@psulias.psu.edu. Web Site: www.libraries.psu.edu. *Dean of Libr*, Nancy Eaton; *Assoc Dean*, Sally Kalin; *Assoc Dean*, John Sulzer; *Access Serv, Asst Dean, Tech Servs*, Rosann Bazirjian; *Asst Dean*, Bonnie MacEwan; *Automation Syst Coordr*, Eric Ferrin; *Access Serv*, Cordelia Swinton; *Acq*, Nancy Stanley; *Cat*, Rebecca Mugridge; *ILL*, Barbara Coopey; *ILL*, Joyce Harwell; *Archivist*, Leon Stout; *Info Tech*, Linda Friend; *Publ Servs*, Laura Probst; *Ser*, Robert Alan; *Electronic Resources*, Becky Albitz; *Pub Relations*, Catherine S Grigor; *Tech Coordr*, Michael Pelikan. Subject Specialists: *Preservation*, Sue Kellerman; Staff 129 (MLS 113, Non-MLS 16)
Founded 1857. Enrl 80,873; Fac 4,100; Highest Degree: Doctorate
Jul 1999-Jun 2000 Mats Exp $13,032,634, Books $3,642,975, Per/Ser (Incl. Access Fees) $6,952,192. Sal $16,515,052 (Prof $5,900,419)
Library Holdings: Bk Vols 4,391,055; Per Subs 38,593
Subject Interests: Agriculture, Architecture, Art, Behav sci, Commonwealth, Feminism, History, Latin Am lit, Natural science, Sci-tech, Soc sci
Special Collections: 18th Century England (Williamscote Library Coll); Ambit Magazine Archives; American & English Gift Books & Annuals; American Literature (Hay & Pattee Coll); Amy Bonner Coll; Ann Radcliffe Coll; Antiquarian Bookman's Weekly, archives; Arnold Bennett Coll; Art & Architectural History Coll; Arthur O Lewis, Jr Papers; Australiana (Moody & Sutherland Coll), bks & pictures; Barbara Hackman Franklin Papers; Be Glad Then America, opera recs & papers; Berkshire Knitting Mills Coll; Bibles (Plumb Coll); Black Literature Coll; Black Sparrow Press Archives; Boal Family Papers; C R Carpenter Papers; Century-Strand Corooration (Theatre Lighting Coll), archives; Children's Drawings (Dale Harris Papers & Coll); Christopher Logue Papers; Clara Tice Coll; Classic Latin Books (Goodman Coll); Conrad Richter Coll, mss; Dorothy Harris Sport Psychology Coll; Edward Lucie-Smith Papers; Eigth Air Force Archive; Emblem Books; English Literature, 1600-1800 Coll; Eric A Walker Papers; Erwin Mueller Papers; Eugene Wettstone Coll; Evan Pugh Coll & Papers; Fay S Lincoln Photography Coll; Forrest Remick Nuclear Engineering Coll; Francisco de Quevedo Coll; Francoise Sagan Coll, mss; Fred L Pattee Papers; Fred Waring Archives & Music Library; George M Rhodes Papers; George T Harrell Papers; George W Atherton Papers; German-American Literature (Allison-Shelley Coll), bks & mss; Glass Bottle Blowers Association Archives; Grace Metalious, mss; Grant Allen Coll, bks & mss; Graphic Communications International Union Archive; Hale-Mull Family Papers, microfilm; Harold Greenberg Papers; Harry Anslinger Papers; Henry M Shoemaker Coll; History of Photography (Heinz & Bridget Henisch Coll); I W Abel Papers; Jacques Brunius Coll; James A Beaver Papers; James Dugan Papers; James J Tietjen Papers; Jean Giraudoux Coll; Jeremy Reed Coll; Jessie Bernard Papers; John C Griffiths Papers; John O Almquist Papers; John O'Hara Coll; John W Oswald Papers; Joseph J Rubin Papers; Joseph Priestley Coll; Kenneth Burke Coll; Labor History, bks & papers; Lace & Embroidery; Leon Kneebone Mushroom Research Coll & Papers; Luis Alberto Sanchez Coll; Lumbering in Pennsylvania, glass slides; Luther Bernard Coll; M Nelson McGeary Papers; MacKintosh-Hemphill Company Archives; Maurice Goddard Papers; Meyer Bernstein Papers; Milton S Eisenhower Papers; National Art Education Association Archives; National Committee for Citizens in Education Archives; New Zealand Poetry Coll; Noran Kersta Television History Coll; Nunzio J Palladino Papers & Nuclear Engineering Coll; Otis Brubaker Papers; Paul West, mss; Pennsylvania (Beaver Coll); Pennsylvania AFL-CIO Archives; Pennsylvania Art Education Association Archives; Pennsylvania German Imprints (Ammon Stapleton Coll); Pennsylvania Imprints; Pennsylvania State University Archives; Peter Porter Coll; Ralph Dorn Hetzel Papers; Ramon del Valle-Inclan Coll; Renaissance (Bovard Coll); Richard Henry Stoddard & Elizabeth Drew Barstow Stoddard Coll, mss; Roxburghe Club Coll; Russell E Marker Papers; Russelton Miners Clinic Coll; Science Fiction Coll; Sebastian Martorana Papers; Struwwelpeter Coll; Surrealism, bks & papers, Bayard Taylor Coll; Theatre History (Cutler Coll); Theodore Roethke Coll; Theophrastus Coll; Three Mile Island Reactor Clean-up Videotapes; Tony Harrison Coll; United Mine Workers of America Archives; United Steelworkers of America Archives; United Wallpaper Craftsmen of North America Archives; Utopias & Fabulous Voyages Coll; Vance Packard Papers; Victorian Chromolithography Coll; Warren S Smith Papers; William C Darrah Cartes de Visite Coll; William Frear Papers; William G Waring Papers; William Scranton Papers; Yves Navarre Coll
Publications: Guide to the University Libraries; Library Bibliographical Series; Penn State Libraries Newsletter; Special Collections Newsletter
Partic in Comt on Institutional Coop; OCLC Online Computer Library Center, Inc; PALCI; PALINET & Union Library Catalogue of Pennsylvania; Research Libraries Group, Inc
Special Services for the Blind - Kurzweil Reading Machine
Departmental Libraries:
ARCHITECTURE, 207 Eng Unit C, 16802. SAN 359-6044. Tel: 814-865-3614. FAX: 814-865-5073. E-Mail: cja@psulias.psu.edu. Web Site: www.libraries.psu.edu/crsweb/arch/arch.htm. *In Charge*, Henry Pisciotta; Tel: 814-865-3665, E-Mail: henryp@psu.edu; Staff 4 (MLS 1, Non-MLS 3)
EARTH & MINERAL SCIENCES, 105 Deike Bldg, 16802. SAN 359-6079. Tel: 814-865-9517. FAX: 814-865-1379. E-Mail: ems@psulias.psu.edu. Web Site: www.libraries.psu.edu/emsl/. *Head Librn*, Linda Musser; Tel: 814-863-7073, E-Mail: lrm4@psu.edu; *Librn*, Kristi Wensen; Tel: 814-865-3694, E-Mail: klj5@psu.edu; Staff 5 (MLS 2, Non-MLS 3)
EBERLY FAMILY SPECIAL COLLECTIONS, 104 Paterno Library, 16802-1808. Tel: 814-865-1793, 814-865-7931. FAX: 814-863-5318. Web Site: www.libraries.psu.edu/crsweb/speccol/spcoll.htm. *Librn*, William Joyce; E-Mail: wlj2@psulias.psu.edu; *Cat*, Sue Hamburger; Tel: 814-865-2067, E-Mail: sxh@psulias.psu.edu; *Archivist*, Lee Stout; E-Mail: ljs@psulias.psu.edu; Staff 5 (MLS 5)
Founded 1890. Enrl 40,000; Highest Degree: Doctorate
Library Holdings: Bk Titles 100,000
Subject Interests: Archives, Manuscripts, Rare books
Special Collections: Historical Collections & Labor Archives(www.libraries.psu.edu/crsweb/speccol/labor.htm); ; Pennsylvania State University Archives(www.libraries.psu.edu/crsweb/speccol/univarch.htm); ; Rare Books & Manuscripts
Restriction: Non-circulating
EDUCATION & BEHAVIORAL SCIENCES, 501 Paterno Library, 16802-1812. SAN 371-8638. Tel: 814-865-2842. E-Mail: slh@psulias.psu.edu. Web Site: www.libraries.psu.edu/crsweb/ed/edhm2.htm. *Head Librn*, Steven Herb; E-Mail: slh@psulias.psu.edu; *Ref Serv*, Carol Wright; Tel: 814-865-0666, E-Mail: ciw@psulias.psu.edu. Subject Specialists: *Edu*, Justina Osa; Staff 8 (MLS 3, Non-MLS 5)
ENGINEERING, 325 Hammond Bldg, 16802. SAN 359-6109. Tel: 814-865-3451. E-Mail: twc@psulias.psu.edu. Web Site: www.libraries.psu.edu/crsweb/eng/enghp4.htm. *Head Librn*, Thomas Conkling; Tel: 814-865-3698, E-Mail: twc@psulias.psu.edu; *Librn*, Bonnie Osif; Tel: 814-865-3697, E-Mail: bao@psulias.psu.edu; Staff 6 (MLS 2, Non-MLS 4)
GEORGE & SHERRY MIDDLEMAS ARTS & HUMANITIES LIBRARY, 201 Pattee Library, 16802-1801. Tel: 814-865-6481. Web Site: www.libraries.psu.edu/crsweb/arts/welcome1.htm. *Head of Libr*, Amanda Maple; E-Mail: alm8@psulias.psu.edu; *Librn*, Roberta Astroff; E-Mail: ra4@psulias.psu.edu; *Librn*, Donald Mack; E-Mail: dcm11@psu.edu; *Librn*, Eric Novotny; *Librn*, Henry Pisciotta; E-Mail: henryp@psu.edu. Subject Specialists: *Art and architecture*, Henry Pisciotta; *History*, Eric Novotny; *Humanities*, Roberta Astroff; *Humanities*, Donald Mack; Staff 8 (MLS 5, Non-MLS 3)
LIFE SCIENCES, 408 Paterno Library, 16802-1811. Tel: 814-865-7056. Web Site: www.libraries.psu.edu/crsweb/lifesci/lifepage.htm. *Head Librn*, Amy Paster; Tel: 814-865-3708, E-Mail: alp@psulias.psu.edu; *Librn*, Kathy Fescemyer; Tel: 814-865-3703, E-Mail: kafia@psulias.psu.edu; *Librn*, Nancy Henry; Tel: 814-865-3713, E-Mail: nih@psulias.psu.edu; *Librn*, Janet Hughes; Tel: 814-865-3705, E-Mail: jah@psulias.psu.edu; *Librn*, Helen Smith; Tel: 814-865-3706, E-Mail: hfs@psulias.psu.edu. Subject Specialists: *Agri*, Helen Smith; *Biol sci*, Janet Hughes; *Health sci*,

Nancy Henry; Staff 5 (MLS 5)
MAPS, 001 Paterno Library, B-level, Curtin Rd, 16802-1807. Tel: 814-863-0094. E-Mail: maproom@psu.edu. Web Site: www.libraries.psu.edu/crsweb/docs/mapgeo.htm. *Librn*, Joanne Perry; Tel: 814-865-0139, E-Mail: jup4@psulias.psu.edu; Staff 3 (MLS 1, Non-MLS 2)
MATHEMATICS, 109 McAllister Bldg, 16802. SAN 359-6133. Tel: 814-865-6822. E-Mail: math@psulias.psu.edu. Web Site: www.libraries.psu.edu/crsweb/math/reena.htm. *Librn*, Robert S Seeds; Tel: 814-865-3714, E-Mail: rss@psulias.psu.edu; Staff 3 (MLS 1, Non-MLS 2)
PHYSICAL SCIENCES, 230 Davey Lab, 16802. SAN 359-6168. Tel: 814-865-7617. E-Mail: njb@psulias.psu.edu. Web Site: www.libraries.psu.edu/cvsweb/physci/. *Librn*, Nancy Butkovich; E-Mail: njb@psulias.psu.edu; Staff 3 (MLS 1, Non-MLS 2)
SAMUEL I & KATE SIDEWATER GATEWAY COMMONS, 104 Pattee Library, 16802-1800. Tel: 814-865-6368. E-Mail: gateway@psulias.psu.edu. Web Site: www.libraries.psu.edu/crswebs/gateway/. *Actg Librn*, Lesley Moyo; E-Mail: lmm@psulias.psu.edu; *Librn*, Ashley Robinson; E-Mail: axr23@psu.edu; Staff 3 (MLS 2, Non-MLS 1)
SOCIAL SCIENCES, 208 Paterno Library, 16802. Tel: 814-865-4861. FAX: 814-865-1403. Web Site: www.libraries.psu.edu/crsweb/docs/ssmain.htm. *Head Librn*, Debora Cheney; Tel: 814-863-1345, E-Mail: dcheney@psu.edu; *Librn*, Rebecca M Bichel; Tel: 814-865-8864, E-Mail: rbichel@psu.edu; *Librn*, Cindy Ingold; Tel: 814-865-0665, E-Mail: cingold@psu.edu; *Librn*, Helen M Sheehy; Tel: 814-863-1347, Fax: 814-865-1403, E-Mail: hms@psulias.psu.edu. Subject Specialists: *Afro-American studies*, Cindy Ingold; *Anthropology*, Rebecca M Bichel; *Crime*, Rebecca M Bichel; *Global issues*, Helen M Sheehy; *Government*, Debora Cheney; *International studies*, Helen M Sheehy; *Law*, Rebecca M Bichel; *Sociology*, Rebecca M Bichel; *US govt doc*, Debora Cheney; *Women's studies*, Cindy Ingold; Staff 5 (MLS 2, Non-MLS 3)
Library Holdings: Per Subs 1,200
WILLIAM & JOAN SCHREYER BUSINESS LIBRARY, 301 Paterno Library, 16802-1810. Tel: 814-865-6369. FAX: 814-865-5835. E-Mail: business_ref@psulias.psu.edu. Web Site: www.libraries.psu.edu/crsweb/business/. *Head Librn*, Gary W White; E-Mail: gww2@psulias.psu.edu; *Librn*, Kevin Harwell; E-Mail: krh@psulias.psu.edu; *Librn*, Diane Zable; E-Mail: dmz@psulias.psu.edu; Staff 7 (MLS 3, Non-MLS 4)

UPLAND

M CROZER-CHESTER MEDICAL CENTER LIBRARY, One Medical Center Blvd, 19013-3995. SAN 314-4003. Tel: 610-447-2600. FAX: 610-447-6162. *Dir*, Judith E Ziegler; E-Mail: ziegler@hslc.org; Staff 4 (MLS 2, Non-MLS 2)
Founded 1966
Library Holdings: Bk Titles 3,000; Per Subs 650
Subject Interests: Burns
Publications: Newsletter; serials list
Restriction: By appointment only
Partic in Consortium For Health Information & Library Services; Delaware Valley Information Consortium

UPPER DARBY

P UPPER DARBY TOWNSHIP & SELLERS FREE PUBLIC LIBRARY, Sellers Free Public,* 76 S State Rd, 19082. SAN 359-6192. Tel: 610-789-4440. FAX: 610-789-5319. E-Mail: upperdarby@delco.lib.pa.us. *Dir Libr Serv*, Carolyn Ringsdorf; *Ch Servs*, Pat Newman; *Tech Servs*, Elaine Irwin; *Ref*, Alicia Bozza; *Circ*, Maria Polymenakos; Staff 22 (MLS 8, Non-MLS 14)
Founded 1930. Pop 84,377; Circ 219,102
Jan 1998-Dec 1998 Income (Main Library and Branch Library) $937,655, State $125,335, City $732,260, Locally Generated Income $80,060. Mats Exp $139,997, Books $102,463, Per/Ser (Incl. Access Fees) $22,731, Micro $8,955, AV Equip $4,548, Electronic Ref Mat (Incl. Access Fees) $1,300. Sal $597,841
Library Holdings: Bk Vols 96,621; Per Subs 138
Subject Interests: Local history
Automation Activity & Vendor Info: (Circulation) TLC
Database Vendor: Ebsco - EbscoHost, GaleNet, IAC - SearchBank
Mem of Delaware County Library System
Friends of the Library Group
Branches: 2
MUNICIPAL, 100 Garrett Rd, 19082. SAN 359-6222. Tel: 610-734-7649. FAX: 610-734-5781. E-Mail: upperdarbymunicipal@delco.lib.pa.us. *Librn*, Charles McCardell, Jr
Library Holdings: Bk Titles 17,895
Friends of the Library Group
PRIMOS BRANCH, 10 Bunting Lane, Primos, 19018. SAN 359-6249. Tel: 610-622-8091. FAX: 610-626-9861. E-Mail: upperdarbyprimos@delco.lib.pa.us. *Librn*, Caroline Jushchyshyn
Library Holdings: Bk Titles 17,719
Friends of the Library Group

VALENCIA

S CENTER FOR THE HISTORY OF AMERICAN NEEDLEWORK LIBRARY,* 6459 Old Rte 8, PO Box 359, 16059-0359. SAN 370-5269. Tel: 724-586-5325. *Librn*, Sally Pollifren
Founded 1974
Library Holdings: Bk Titles 1,500; Per Subs 10
Special Collections: History of Needlework Techniques
Publications: Anthologies of Varied Techniques ie. Spider Crochet, Butterfl Patterns & Tatting; Chan newsletter (quarterly); Needlework - Knitting, patterns only; Needlework- Crochet, patterns only
Restriction: By appointment only
Research fee $8/hour - will copy non-copyright materials

VALLEY FORGE

AMERICAN BAPTIST CHURCHES-USA
R AMERICAN BAPTIST HISTORICAL SOCIETY-RESEARCH LIBRARY & ARCHIVES CENTER, PO Box 851, 19482-0851. SAN 376-2289. Tel: 610-768-2378. FAX: 610-768-2266. *Dir*, Debra Bingham-Van Broekhaven
Founded 1854
Library Holdings: Bk Vols 80,000
Special Collections: Am Baptist Church/USA Nat Boards & Baptist World Alliance; Mission Artifacts
Publications: American Baptist Quarterly
Restriction: By appointment only
R BOARD OF INTERNATIONAL MINISTRIES LIBRARY & CENTRAL FILES, PO Box 851, 19482-0851. SAN 359-6281. Tel: 610-768-2365. FAX: 610-768-2088. *Librn*, Ferron Okewole
Founded 1890
Library Holdings: Bk Vols 4,680; Per Subs 35
Subject Interests: Mission mat
Special Collections: Biographical Material on Adoniram Judson & His Wives
R EDITORIAL LIBRARY, BOARD OF EDUCATIONAL MINISTRIES, PO Box 851, 19482-0851. SAN 359-6257. Tel: 610-768-2374. FAX: 610-768-2266. *Librn*, Betty Layton
Founded 1923
1998-1999 Income $4,300
Library Holdings: Bk Vols 3,000; Bk Titles 2,500; Per Subs 15
Subject Interests: Baptists, Religion
Special Collections: Religion (Judson Press Coll)
Restriction: Open to public for reference only

S FREEDOMS FOUNDATION LIBRARY,* 1601 Valley Forge Rd, 19482. SAN 315-291X. Tel: 610-933-8825. FAX: 610-935-0522. *Chief Librn*, Hal Badger
Founded 1965
Library Holdings: Bk Vols 17,500; Per Subs 80
Subject Interests: 20th Century totalitarianism, Current events, Foreign policy, Modern econ, Political, Political systs, Pub policy
Special Collections: United States Radical Movements

S HOUGHTON INTERNATIONAL, Technical Center Library,* PO Box 930, 19482. SAN 314-8246. Tel: 610-666-4146. FAX: 610-666-7354. *Librn*, Margaret C Schweitzer
Founded 1921
Library Holdings: Bk Vols 6,300
Subject Interests: Analytical tech, Biology, Chemistry, Hydraulic oils, Lubricants, Metal-working proc, Microbiology
Publications: Houghton Line
Partic in Dialog Corporation

G UNITED STATES NATIONAL PARK SERVICE, Valley Forge National Historical Park - Horace Willcox Memorial Library,* PO Box 953, 19481-0953. SAN 375-2011. Tel: 610-296-2593. FAX: 610-296-4834. *In Charge*, Lee Boyle
Library Holdings: Bk Titles 65,000; Per Subs 25

S VALLEY FORGE HISTORICAL SOCIETY, Washington Memorial Library, Rte 23, PO Box 122, 19481. SAN 370-324X. Tel: 610-783-0535. FAX: 610-783-0957. E-Mail: vfhs@ix.netcom.com. Web Site: www.ushistory.org/valleyforge. *Dir*, Stacey A Swigart; E-Mail: staceyswigart@ix.netcom.com. Subject Specialists: *17th Century Am War hist*, Stacey A Swigart; Staff 1 (Non-MLS 1)
Founded 1918
Library Holdings: Bk Titles 3,500
Special Collections: 18th to 19th century library of Reverend Andrew Hunter, Chaplain in the Revolutionary War
Restriction: By appointment only
Function: Reference only

S WATER RESOURCES ASSOCIATION OF THE DELAWARE RIVER BASIN LIBRARY,* PO Box 867, 19482-0867. SAN 329-9325. Tel: 610-917-0090. FAX: 610-917-0091. E-Mail: wradrb@aol.com. *Exec Dir*, William

H Palmer
Special Collections: Delaware River Basin
Publications: Alerting Bulletins; Annual Report; Conference/Seminar Proceedings; Newsletters

ANDERGRIFT

VANDERGRIFT PUBLIC LIBRARY ASSOCIATION,* 128C Washington Ave, 15690-1214. SAN 315-2952. Tel: 724-568-2212. Web Site: www.home.kiski.net/~library/. *Chief Librn*, Joan Iagnemma; *Ch Servs*, Terry Tometsko
Founded 1901. Pop 5,904; Circ 23,963
Library Holdings: Bk Titles 18,000; Per Subs 40
Open Mon, Tues & Thurs 1-8, Wed 10-8, Fri 1-6 & Sat 9-1

ENANGO

CLARK MEMORIAL LIBRARY,* Cussewago St, PO Box 197, 16440. SAN 315-2960. Tel: 814-398-4074. *Librn*, Shirley Bausch
Pop 298; Circ 1,389
Library Holdings: Bk Vols 5,061; Per Subs 6
Partic in Crawford County Federated Libr Bd
Open Tues & Thurs 6-8 & Sat 2-4

ILLANOVA

DEVEREUX FOUNDATION, Behavioral Healthcare Library,* 444 Devereux Dr, PO Box 638, 19085. SAN 321-6349. Tel: 610-542-3056. Interlibrary Loan Service Tel: 610-542-3051. FAX: 610-542-3092. *Dir*, Joyce Matheson; E-Mail: matheson@hslc.org; *Asst Librn*, Rachel Roth
Founded 1957
Library Holdings: Bk Titles 2,100; Per Subs 135
Subject Interests: Psychiatry, Special education
Special Collections: Mental Health (ICTR Coll), A-tapes; Psychology (ICTR Psychodiagnostic Test Coll)
Partic in DEVIC; Dialog Corporation; Docline; National Network Of Libraries Of Medicine New England Region; OCLC Online Computer Library Center, Inc; PALINET & Union Library Catalogue of Pennsylvania

ENVIRONMENTAL RESEARCH ASSOCIATES INC LIBRARY,* PO Box 219, 19085. SAN 372-9354. Tel: 610-449-7400. *Librn*, Dr M H Levin
Library Holdings: Bk Vols 2,000; Per Subs 35

C VILLANOVA UNIVERSITY, Falvey Memorial Library, 19085. SAN 359-6346. Tel: 610-519-4500. Interlibrary Loan Service Tel: 610-519-4274. FAX: 610-519-4204. Web Site: www.library.villanova.edu/. *Dir*, James Mullins; Tel: 610-519-4290, Fax: 610-519-5018, E-Mail: james.mullins@villanova.edu; *Media Spec*, Michael Hoffberg; Tel: 610-519-4264, E-Mail: michael.hoffberg@villanova.edu; *Online Servs, Publ Servs, Ref*, Louise Green; Tel: 610-519-4283, E-Mail: Louise.Green@villanova.edu; *Tech Servs*, Taras Ortynsky; Tel: 610-519-4282, E-Mail: taras.ortynsky@villanova.edu; *Per*, Susan Markley; Tel: 610-519-6729, E-Mail: susan.markley@villanova.edu; *Coll Develop*, Dennis Lambert; Tel: 610-519-7966, E-Mail: dennis.lambert@villanova.edu; Staff 28 (MLS 19, Non-MLS 9)
Founded 1842. Highest Degree: Doctorate
Jun 1999-May 2000 Income $5,121,459. Mats Exp $2,722,415, Books $846,033, Per/Ser (Incl. Access Fees) $1,231,184, Presv $48,142, Micro $45,912, AV Equip $87,412, Manuscripts & Archives $15,227, Electronic Ref Mat (Incl. Access Fees) $448,505. Sal $2,142,330 (Prof $1,072,505)
Library Holdings: Bk Vols 624,000; Per Subs 3,070
Special Collections: Irish American History & Literature (Joseph McGarrity Coll); Saint Augustine Coll
Partic in OCLC Online Computer Library Center, Inc; PALINET & Union Library Catalogue of Pennsylvania
Departmental Libraries:
AUGUSTINIAN HISTORICAL INSTITUTE LIBRARY, 301 Old Falvey, 19085. SAN 315-2995. Tel: 610-519-7590. FAX: 610-519-5000. E-Mail: ahi@villanova.edu. *Dir*, Karl A Gersbach; Staff 1 (Non-MLS 1)
Founded 1972
Library Holdings: Bk Titles 4,700; Per Subs 47
Subject Interests: Biog, Hist of the Augustinian Order, Missiology, Philosophy, Theology
Publications: Collectanea Augustiniana V 1-5; Proceedings of the PMR Conference & the American Cassiciacum Series

CL LAW LIBRARY, School of Law, 19085. SAN 359-6370. Tel: 610-519-7020. FAX: 610-519-7033. E-Mail: lawstaff@law.villanova.edu. Web Site: www.law.villanova.edu/vis/lawlib/index.html. *Dir*, William James; *Asst Dir*, Steve Elkins; *Asst Dir*, Yolanda Jones; *Asst Dir*, Lyne Maxwell; *Asst Dir*, Nazareth Pantaloni; *Tech Servs*, Marla McDaniel; *Circ*, Maura Buri; *Ref*, Mary Cornelius; *Ref*, Karen Jordan; *Ref*, Etheldra Scoggin; *Ref*, Rita Young-Jones; Staff 23 (MLS 10, Non-MLS 13)
Founded 1953. Enrl 700; Fac 35; Highest Degree: Doctorate
Jun 1999-May 2000 Mats Exp $1,110,073, Books $45,036, Per/Ser (Incl. Access Fees) $804,425, Presv $43,463, Micro $34,150. Sal $879,326 (Prof $542,433)
Library Holdings: Bk Vols 293,376; Per Subs 3,322
Subject Interests: Tax law
Special Collections: Church & State Coll
Publications: New Aquisitions
Partic in OCLC Online Computer Library Center, Inc; Westlaw

WALLINGFORD

P HELEN KATE FURNESS FREE LIBRARY, 100 N Providence Rd, 19086. SAN 315-3002. Tel: 610-566-9331. FAX: 610-566-9337. E-Mail: furnesslibrary@delco.lib.pa.us. *Dir*, Sandra J Nailor; *Librn*, Jannette Vickers; *Librn*, Martha Trzepacz; *Ch Servs*, Lori L Friedgen-Veitch; *Tech Servs*, Mary Otto; Staff 6 (MLS 3, Non-MLS 3)
Founded 1902. Pop 13,768; Circ 82,015
Library Holdings: Bk Titles 45,000; Per Subs 81
Mem of Delaware County Library System

R OHEV SHALOM SYNAGOGUE, Ray Doblitz Memorial Library, Two Chester Rd, 19086. SAN 315-3010. Tel: 610-874-1465. FAX: 610-874-1466. *Chair*, Rose A Isaacson; *Librn*, Evelyn Schott; *Librn*, Ed Welsh
Founded 1955
Library Holdings: Bk Vols 5,500; Bk Titles 5,300; Per Subs 14
Subject Interests: Judaica

R PENDLE HILL LIBRARY, 338 Plush Mill Rd, 19086. SAN 372-9281. Tel: 610-566-4507. FAX: 610-566-3679. *Actg Librn*, Doug Gwyn
Library Holdings: Bk Vols 10,000; Per Subs 24

WARMINSTER

S ALFA-LAVAL SEPARATIONS, INC LIBRARY,* 955 Mearns Rd, 18974. SAN 315-3045. Tel: 215-443-4000. FAX: 215-443-4013. *Librn*, Linda Farnsworth
Founded 1942
Library Holdings: Bk Vols 1,250; Per Subs 17
Subject Interests: Engineering

R NESHAMINY-WARWICK PRESBYTERIAN CHURCH LIBRARY, 1401 Meetinghouse Rd, 18974. SAN 315-3037. Tel: 215-343-6060. *Librn*, Bernard E Deitrick
Founded 1959
Library Holdings: Bk Titles 7,200; Per Subs 10
Subject Interests: Christian educ, Inspirational lit, Relig studies
Special Collections: History of Presbyterians in local area
Publications: Church & Synagogue Libraries

P WARMINSTER TOWNSHIP FREE LIBRARY, 1076 Emma Lane, 18974. SAN 315-3053. Tel: 215-672-4362. FAX: 215-672-3604. Web Site: www.bucks.edu. *Dir*, Caroline C Gallis; E-Mail: gallisc@buckslib.org; *Ad Servs*, Carolyn C Larsen; E-Mail: larsenc@bucklib.org; *Tech Servs*, Brena Balczarek; Staff 3 (MLS 3)
Founded 1960. Pop 34,322; Circ 279,447
Jan 2000-Dec 2000 Income (Main Library Only) $562,225, State $100,200, City $352,025, Locally Generated Income $59,000. Mats Exp $96,000, Books $75,000, Per/Ser (Incl. Access Fees) $8,000, Micro $11,000, AV Equip $2,000. Sal $279,490 (Prof $145,000)
Library Holdings: Bk Titles 104,000; Per Subs 141
Subject Interests: Large print
Mem of Bucks County Free Library

WARREN

S WARREN COUNTY HISTORICAL SOCIETY, Library & Archives, 210 Fourth Ave, PO Box 427, 16365. SAN 327-0459. Tel: 814-723-1795. FAX: 814-723-1795. E-Mail: warrenhistory@allegany.com. Web Site: nathan.allegany.com/warrenhistory/. *Exec Dir*, Rhonda J Hoover
Library Holdings: Bk Vols 2,200
Subject Interests: Local history
Special Collections: Allegheny River Travel & History

M WARREN GENERAL HOSPITAL, Health Sciences Library,* 2 Crescent Park Dr, 16365. SAN 370-6931. Tel: 814-723-3300, Ext 1825. FAX: 814-723-2248.
Library Holdings: Bk Titles 800; Per Subs 100
Restriction: Staff use only
Partic in Nat Libr of Med

P WARREN LIBRARY ASSOCIATION, 205 Market St, 16365. SAN 315-3061. Tel: 814-723-4650. FAX: 814-723-4521. E-Mail: wla@warrenlibrary.org. Web Site: www.warrenlibrary.org. *Dir*, Patricia Hutchison; *Ad Servs, Coll Develop*, Suellen Snapp; *Cat*, Laura A Alberth; *Ch Servs*, Ellen Eberly; *ILL*, Barbara C Tubbs; *Ref*, Penelope Wolboldt; Staff 21 (MLS 5, Non-MLS 16)
Founded 1873. Pop 45,050; Circ 265,445
Jan 1999-Dec 1999 Income (Main Library Only) $923,942, State $232,850, Federal $53,807, County $250,000, Locally Generated Income $52,579, Other $211,224. Mats Exp $787,311, Books $49,541, Per/Ser (Incl. Access Fees) $7,156, Presv $5,950, Micro $4,508. Sal $426,446

Library Holdings: Bk Vols 164,998; Bk Titles 79,915; Per Subs 216
Special Collections: Local History; Local newspapers 1824-current; Petroleum History Coll, bks, maps, pamphlets; Sheet Music, Popular Show Tunes, 1834-1955 (Robertson Music Coll)
Automation Activity & Vendor Info: (Cataloging) SIRSI; (Circulation) SIRSI; (OPAC) SIRSI
Publications: The Fulcrum (Newsletter)
Headquarters for Seneca Libr District (incl 17 libraries)
Friends of the Library Group

WARREN STATE HOSPITAL
S LIBRARY SERVICES DEPARTMENT, 33 Main Dr, North Warren, 16365. SAN 359-6524. Tel: 814-726-4223. FAX: 814-726-4562. *Dir Libr Serv*, Karen Smialek; E-Mail: ksmialek@dpw.state.pa.us; *Librn*, Christina Bauschard. Subject Specialists: *Medical*, Karen Smialek; Staff 1 (MLS 1)
Library Holdings: Bk Vols 10,034; Per Subs 74
Subject Interests: Medicine, Nursing, Psychiatry, Psychology, Social servs
Special Collections: Self-help/patient recovery Coll
Automation Activity & Vendor Info: (Cataloging) Endeavor
Function: ILL available

M MEDICAL LIBRARY, 33 Main Dr, 16365-5099. SAN 359-6494. Tel: 814-723-5500, Ext 223. FAX: 814-726-4562. E-Mail: warmedlib@hslc.org. *Librn*, Christina Bauschard
Founded 1930
Library Holdings: Bk Titles 16,421; Per Subs 95
Subject Interests: Alcohol, Death, Drug abuse, Dying, Gerontology, Neurology, Occupational therapy, Psychiatric nursing, Psychiatry, Psychology, Sociology
Publications: Periodicals Union List
Partic in OCLC Online Computer Library Center, Inc

WARRENDALE

S SOCIETY OF AUTOMOTIVE ENGINEERS, INC LIBRARY, 400 Commonwealth Dr, 15096-0001. SAN 315-307X. Tel: 724-772-8503. FAX: 724-776-5760. Web Site: www.sae.org. *Librn*, Janet Jedlicka; E-Mail: janet@sae.org; Staff 2 (Non-MLS 2)
Founded 1905
Library Holdings: Bk Vols 3,000; Bk Titles 100,000
Subject Interests: Aerospace, Automotive, Bus, Fuels, ITS hist, Lubricants, Trucking
Special Collections: SAE Material, 1905-present, bks, mag, papers
Restriction: By appointment only
Function: Photocopies available, Research fees apply
Partic in SDC Search Serv

WARRINGTON

S POLYSCIENCES, INC LIBRARY,* 400 Valley Rd, 18976. SAN 370-1964. Tel: 215-343-6484. FAX: 215-343-0214. E-Mail: polysci@tigger.jvnc.net. *Librn*, Joy Myers
Library Holdings: Bk Vols 1,267; Per Subs 29

WASHINGTON

P CITIZENS LIBRARY, 55 S College St, 15301. SAN 315-3088. Tel: 724-222-2400. Interlibrary Loan Service Tel: 724-222-2400, Ext 225. TDD: 724-222-2400. FAX: 724-225-7303. E-Mail: citlib@citlib.org. Web Site: www.citlib.org. *Dir*, Susan E Priest; *Ref*, Carol Ann Steele; *YA Servs*, Marcia Read; *Ch Servs*, Rebecca Rankin; *Tech Servs*, Carol Levy; *AV, ILL*, Ella Hatfield; *Circ*, Patricia Thompson; Staff 8 (MLS 8)
Founded 1870. Pop 60,080; Circ 215,206
Library Holdings: Bk Vols 126,597; Per Subs 351
Special Collections: Genealogy & Local History (Iams Coll), mss
Database Vendor: Ebsco - EbscoHost
Partic in Asn for Libr Info; OCLC Online Computer Library Center, Inc
Special Services for the Deaf - Books on deafness & sign language; High interest/low vocabulary books; Special interest periodicals; TDD
Friends of the Library Group

C WASHINGTON & JEFFERSON COLLEGE LIBRARY, U Grant Miller Library, 141 E Wheeling St, 15301-4802. SAN 315-310X. Tel: 724-223-6070. FAX: 412-223-5272. Web Site: www.washjeff.edu/library/web~3.htm. *Acq, Cat, Tech Servs*, Rebecca H Keenan; Tel: 724-223-6069, E-Mail: rkeenan@washjeff.edu; *Bibliog Instr, ILL, Ref*, David W Kraeuter; Tel: 724-223-6072, E-Mail: dkraeuter@washjeff.edu; Staff 3 (MLS 3)
Founded 1781
Library Holdings: Bk Vols 140,000; Bk Titles 139,082
Subject Interests: Behav sci, History, Natural science, Sci-tech, Soc sci
Special Collections: College History; Washington County (Historical); Western Pennsylvania & Upper Ohio Valley, mss
Automation Activity & Vendor Info: (Acquisitions) DRA; (Cataloging) DRA; (Circulation) DRA; (Course Reserve) DRA; (OPAC) DRA; (Serials) DRA
Partic in Dialog Corporation; OCLC Online Computer Library Center, Inc; OHIONET; Pittsburgh Regional Libr Consortium

S WASHINGTON COUNTY HISTORICAL SOCIETY LIBRARY, 49 E Maiden St, 15301. SAN 327-0637. Tel: 724-225-6740. FAX: 724-225-8495 Web Site: www.wchspa.org. *Admin Dir*, James Ross
Founded 1900
Library Holdings: Bk Titles 1,847
Special Collections: Military History of Washington County
Special Services - Education coordinator available to develop in-school programs. Research Services - Researchers will research written genealogic & historical inquiries. Research kit is also available. Open Tues-Fri 11-4 & Sat-Sun 12-4

GL WASHINGTON COUNTY LAW LIBRARY, One S Main St Ste G004, 15301-6813. SAN 315-3118. Tel: 724-228-6747. FAX: 724-228-6890. *Librn* Dorothy Schwerha; E-Mail: schwerhd@wc.co.washington.pa.us; *Asst Librn*, Patricia Stavovy; Tel: 724-250-4026, E-Mail: stavovyp@wc.co.washington.pa.us; Staff 2 (MLS 1, Non-MLS 1)
Founded 1867
Jan 2000-Dec 2000 Mats Exp Books $89,000
Library Holdings: Bk Vols 23,000; Bk Titles 1,000; Per Subs 20
Restriction: Non-circulating to the public
Open Mon-Fri 9-4:30

§P WASHINGTON COUNTY LIBRARY SYSTEM, 55 S College St, 15301. Tel: 724-222-2400. FAX: 724-225-7303. *Dir*, Susan E Priest

M WASHINGTON HOSPITAL, Health Sciences Libraries, 155 Wilson Ave, 15301-3398. SAN 315-3126. Tel: 724-223-3144. FAX: 724-223-4096. *Dir*, Heidi L Marshall; E-Mail: marshall@hslc.org
Founded 1927. Enrl 220; Fac 30
Library Holdings: Bk Vols 5,000
Subject Interests: Medicine, Nursing, Surgery

WASHINGTON CROSSING

S DAVID LIBRARY OF THE AMERICAN REVOLUTION, 1201 River Rd, 18977. (Mail add: PO Box 748, 18977), SAN 315-3134. Tel: 215-493-6776. FAX: 215-493-9276. E-Mail: dlar@libertynet.org. Web Site: www.dlar.org. *Dir*, Dr David J Fowler; E-Mail: djfowler@libertynet.org; *Res*, Diana Hanle Loreman; *Res*, Rachel Onuf. Subject Specialists: *American history*, Diana Hanley Loreman; *American revolution*, Dr David J Fowler; *New Jersey*, Dr David J Fowler; Staff 6 (MLS 1, Non-MLS 5)
Founded 1958
Library Holdings: Bk Titles 7,500; Per Subs 25
Subject Interests: American history, American revolution
Special Collections: American History - circa 1750-1800 (18th & early 19th century), approximately 300 rare books, pamphlets; Sol Feinstone Coll, 18th century American mss
Publications: Guide to Sol Feinstone Collection of the David Library of the American Revolution
Restriction: Not a lending library
Function: Research library

S WASHINGTON CROSSING HISTORIC PARK LIBRARY,* PO Box 103, 18977. SAN 315-3142. Tel: 215-493-4076. FAX: 215-493-4820. *Dir*, Pat Patrucio
Founded 1961
Library Holdings: Bk Titles 300
Subject Interests: Am Revolution 1776, Gen George Washington, Regional hist of 1700's

WATERFORD

P WATERFORD PUBLIC LIBRARY, 24 S Park Row, PO Box 820, 16441-0820. SAN 315-3150. Tel: 814-796-4729. FAX: 814-796-4729. E-Mail: wplpa@velocity.net. *Librn*, Bethany Schaaf
Founded 1936. Pop 1,492; Circ 19,239
Jul 1999-Jun 2000 Income $23,389, State $5,460, City $9,369, County $4,200, Locally Generated Income $3,435, Other $925. Mats Exp $7,968, Books $6,533, Per/Ser (Incl. Access Fees) $853, Presv $463, Electronic Ref Mat (Incl. Access Fees) $119. Sal $10,307
Library Holdings: Bk Vols 12,574; Per Subs 40
Automation Activity & Vendor Info: (Circulation) Follett
Mem of Erie-Crawford District Libr Ctr

WAVERLY

P WAVERLY MEMORIAL LIBRARY,* Main St, PO Box 142, 18471. SAN 315-3169. Tel: 570-586-8191. FAX: 570-586-0185. *Dir*, Terri Bannon Brier
Pop 1,800; Circ 4,100
Library Holdings: Bk Vols 3,000
Subject Interests: Children's bks, Fiction
Open Mon-Fri 9-5, Sat 10-12

AYNE

MEMORIAL LIBRARY OF RADNOR TOWNSHIP,* 114 W Wayne Ave, 19087-4098. SAN 315-3185. Tel: 610-687-1124. FAX: 610-687-1454. E-Mail: radnor@delco.lib.pa.us. Web Site: www.delco.lib.pa.us. *Dir*, Barbara Casini; *Asst Dir*, Betilou Shieh; *Ref*, Joann Iantorno; *Ch Servs*, Dorothy Carlson; Staff 5 (MLS 5)
Founded 1892. Pop 29,000; Circ 255,000
1997-1998 Income $675,200, State $41,300, City $422,000, Locally Generated Income $211,900. Mats Exp $96,360, Books $73,600, Per/Ser (Incl. Access Fees) $11,000, Micro $4,660, AV Equip $4,500. Sal $343,000 (Prof $171,402)
Library Holdings: Bk Vols 115,294; Per Subs 225
Subject Interests: Architecture, Art, Bus, Drama, Foreign Language, History, Literature
Special Collections: Pennsylvania History; Reader Development Coll
Mem of Delaware County Library System
Friends of the Library Group

RADNOR HISTORICAL SOCIETY, Research Library & Museum,* 113 W Beech Tree Lane, 19087. SAN 370-6559. Tel: 610-688-2668. *Pres*, J Bennett Hill
Founded 1964
Library Holdings: Bk Titles 400
Publications: Radnor Historical Society Bulletin (annual)
Open Tues-Sat 2-5 & by appointment

TREDYFFRIN PUBLIC LIBRARY,* 582 Upper Gulph Rd, 19087-2096. SAN 315-2502. Tel: 610-644-9029, 610-688-7092. FAX: 610-688-2014. *Dir*, Marian Stevens; E-Mail: mstevens@ccls.org; *Asst Dir*, Mame Purce; *Ch Servs*, Maureen Lok; *Ref*, Jacqueline Roach; *ILL*, Maureen Thorne; *Circ*, Nancy Pickands
Founded 1965. Pop 29,550; Circ 423,500
Library Holdings: Bk Vols 105,824; Per Subs 285
Subject Interests: Local history
Automation Activity & Vendor Info: (Circulation) CLSI LIBS
Mem of Chester County Library
Partic in OCLC Online Computer Library Center, Inc
Friends of the Library Group
Branches: 1
PAOLI BRANCH, 18 Darby Rd, Paoli, 19301. SAN 321-8708. Tel: 610-296-7996. FAX: 610-296-9708. *Librn*, Eleanor Erskine; *Ch Servs*, Beverly Michaels
Circ 104,600
Library Holdings: Bk Vols 25,500
Friends of the Library Group

VALLEY FORGE MILITARY ACADEMY & COLLEGE LIBRARY, May H Baker Memorial Library, 1001 Eagle Rd, 19087. SAN 315-3193. Tel: 610-989-1364. FAX: 610-989-1365. Web Site: www.vfmac.edu. *In Charge*, Jata S Ghosh; Staff 6 (MLS 4, Non-MLS 2)
Founded 1928. Enrl 744; Fac 72; Highest Degree: Master
Jul 1998-Jun 1999 Income $255,768, County $358. Mats Exp $41,728, Books $19,973, Per/Ser (Incl. Access Fees) $6,308, AV Equip $5,619. Sal $160,510
Library Holdings: Bk Vols 76,100; Bk Titles 100,000; Per Subs 175
Special Collections: Military & Naval History Coll
Publications: Webs of the Week (weekly)

R WAYNE PRESBYTERIAN CHURCH LIBRARY, 125 E Lancaster Ave, 19087. SAN 315-3207. Tel: 610-688-8700. FAX: 610-688-8743. *Librn*, Betty Royal
Founded 1957
Library Holdings: Bk Vols 4,200; Per Subs 15
Special Collections: Religion Coll

WAYNESBORO

P ALEXANDER HAMILTON MEMORIAL FREE LIBRARY, Waynesboro Library, 45 E Main St, 17268-1691. SAN 315-3215. Tel: 717-762-3335. FAX: 717-762-5226. E-Mail: ahmfl@cvn.net. Web Site: www.users.desupernet.net/ahms/. *Dir*, Scott Valentine; *Asst Dir*, Carla M Crouse; *Media Spec Ch*, Barbara Seibert; Staff 2 (MLS 1, Non-MLS 1)
Founded 1921. Pop 23,789; Circ 150,000
Jan 2000-Dec 2000 Income $190,000, State $48,000, City $35,000, County $35,000, Other $72,000. Mats Exp $29,200, Books $25,000, Per/Ser (Incl. Access Fees) $4,200. Sal $124,175 (Prof $41,000)
Library Holdings: Bk Vols 55,000; Bk Titles 42,000; Per Subs 78
Subject Interests: Civil War, Genealogy, Pa hist
Mem of Franklin County Library System
Friends of the Library Group
Branches: 1

P BLUE RIDGE SUMMIT FREE LIBRARY, 13676 Monterey Lane, Blue Ridge Summit, 17214. (Mail add: PO Box 34, Blue Ridge Summit, 17214-0034), Tel: 717-794-2240. FAX: 717-794-5929. E-Mail: brsummit@yahoo.com. Web Site: members.tripod.com/~FCLS/BRS/BRindex.html. *Librn*, Nancy L Bert; *Asst Librn*, Deb Simpson; Staff 2 (MLS 2)
Founded 1922. Pop 9,000
Jan 2000-Dec 2000 Income $31,677, State $12,196, City $1,000, County $17,502, Locally Generated Income $9,669, Other $1,589. Mats Exp $8,500, Books $7,000, Per/Ser (Incl. Access Fees) $1,500. Sal $20,500 (Prof $17,160)
Library Holdings: Bk Vols 17,333; Per Subs 20
Automation Activity & Vendor Info: (Circulation) Follett
Mem of Franklin County Library System

WAYNESBURG

P EVA K BOWLBY PUBLIC LIBRARY, 311 N West St, 15370-1238. SAN 359-6559. Tel: 724-627-9776. FAX: 724-852-1900. E-Mail: bowlby@greenepa.net. *Admin Dir*, Barbara Ferguson; *Tech Servs*, Betsy Summers; *Ch Servs*, Kathy McClure; Tel: 724-727-9776, Ext 15; Staff 13 (MLS 1, Non-MLS 12)
Founded 1943. Pop 40,476; Circ 71,573
Jan 2000-Dec 2000 Income $312,000. Sal $170,000 (Prof $26,500)
Library Holdings: Bk Vols 55,000; Per Subs 100
Subject Interests: Agriculture
Special Collections: Local History (Rare Books Coll); W & W Railroad (Roach Coll), photog
Automation Activity & Vendor Info: (Acquisitions) Athena; (Circulation) Athena
Publications: Quarterly Newsletter
Mem of Green County Libr Syst
Partic in OCLC Online Computer Library Center, Inc
Friends of the Library Group

GL GREENE COUNTY LAW LIBRARY, Court House, 15370. SAN 315-3223. Tel: 412-852-5237. FAX: 412-627-4716. *Librn*, Audrey Szoyka
Library Holdings: Bk Vols 12,500

P GREENE COUNTY LIBRARY SYSTEM,* 311 N West St, 15370-1238. SAN 359-6613. Tel: 724-852-1878. FAX: 724-852-1900.; Staff 14 (MLS 3, Non-MLS 11)
Founded 1976. Pop 40,476; Circ 101,969
Jan 1997-Dec 1998 Income $348,670. Mats Exp AV Equip $5,136. Sal $148,000
Friends of the Library Group

C WAYNESBURG COLLEGE, Eberly Library, 15370. SAN 315-3231. Tel: 724-627-8191. FAX: 724-627-4188. Web Site: www.waynesburg.edu/. *Dir*, Suzanne Wylie; Tel: 724-852-3419, E-Mail: swylie@waynesburg.edu; *Librn*, Beth Boehn; Tel: 724-852-3278, E-Mail: bboehn@waynesburg.edu; *Assoc Librn*, Beth DiGiustino; *Syst Coordr*, Rea Redd; Tel: 724-852-3254, E-Mail: rredd@waynesburg.edu; Staff 6 (MLS 4, Non-MLS 2)
Founded 1849. Enrl 1,372; Fac 122; Highest Degree: Master
Jul 1999-Jun 2000 Mats Exp $128,570, Books $45,000, Per/Ser (Incl. Access Fees) $60,000, Micro $6,600, AV Equip $6,480, Manuscripts & Archives $10,490
Library Holdings: Bk Vols 97,880; Bk Titles 91,880; Per Subs 410
Subject Interests: Bus, Education, Nursing, Sports med
Special Collections: Western Pennsylvania History (Trans-Appalachian Coll)
Database Vendor: Innovative Interfaces INN - View
Publications: Library handbook
Partic in OCLC Online Computer Library Center, Inc; OHIONET; Pittsburgh Regional Libr Consortium
Friends of the Library Group

WELLSBORO

P GREEN FREE LIBRARY, 134 Main St, 16901-1412. SAN 315-324X. Tel: 570-724-4876. FAX: 570-724-7605. E-Mail: greenlib@epix.net. Web Site: epix.net/~greenlib/. *Dir*, Danice Jean Trindell; *Asst Librn*, Stephanie Farr; Staff 6 (MLS 2, Non-MLS 4)
Founded 1911. Pop 11,435; Circ 54,000
Jan 1999-Dec 1999 Income $201,000, State $8,900, Federal $9,300, County $7,000, Locally Generated Income $160,000. Mats Exp $38,000, Books $30,000, Per/Ser (Incl. Access Fees) $4,000, Micro $3,000, Electronic Ref Mat (Incl. Access Fees) $1,000. Sal $100,000 (Prof $27,000)
Library Holdings: Bk Vols 34,000; Per Subs 150
Subject Interests: Civil War, Genealogy, Local history
Automation Activity & Vendor Info: (Cataloging) EOS; (Circulation) EOS; (OPAC) EOS
Function: ILL available, ILL by photocopy only
Mem of Potter-Tioga Library System
Friends of the Library Group

M LAUREL HEALTH SYSTEM, Soldiers & Sailors Memorial Hospital Health Science Library, 32-36 Central Ave, 16901. SAN 322-8193. Tel: 570-723-0191. FAX: 570-724-7235. *Librn*, Charlean Patterson
Founded 1975
Library Holdings: Bk Vols 1,000; Bk Titles 850; Per Subs 120
Publications: Newsletter (in-house)
Partic in Susquehanna Library Cooperative

WERNERSVILLE

P WERNERSVILLE PUBLIC LIBRARY, 208 W Penn Ave, 19565-1412. SAN 315-3266. Tel: 610-678-8771. FAX: 610-678-8771. E-Mail: wernersvillepl@berks.lib.pa.us. *Dir*, Janet L Moore
Founded 1906. Pop 8,600; Circ 15,000
1998-1999 Income $70,620
Library Holdings: Bk Titles 9,000; Per Subs 21
Subject Interests: Civil War, Local history
Mem of Berks County Libr Syst
Open Mon-Wed 10-8, Thurs 12-8, Sat 9-4
Friends of the Library Group

WEST CHESTER

M CEPHALON, INC, Information Resources,* 145 Brandywine Pkwy, 19380-4245. SAN 375-3557. Tel: 610-344-0200, Ext 301. FAX: 610-344-0065. *Mgr*, Beverly Cantor
Founded 1992
Library Holdings: Bk Titles 200; Per Subs 75
Partic in Health Sciences Libraries Consortium

S CHEM SERVICE, INC LIBRARY,* 660 Tower Lane, PO Box 0599, 19381-0599. SAN 315-3282. Tel: 610-692-3026. FAX: 610-692-8729. *Librn*, John Conrad
Founded 1969
Library Holdings: Bk Vols 300
Subject Interests: Organic chemistry, Pesticides
Restriction: Private library

G CHESTER COUNTY ARCHIVES & RECORDS SERVICES LIBRARY, 601 Westtown Rd, Ste 080, 19382. (Mail add: PO Box 2747, 19380-0940), SAN 323-5181. Tel: 610-344-6760. FAX: 610-344-5616. *Dir*, Jeffrey Rollison
Subject Interests: Local history

S CHESTER COUNTY HISTORICAL SOCIETY LIBRARY,* 225 N High St, 19380. SAN 315-3304. Tel: 610-692-4800. FAX: 610-692-4357. *Dir*, Jeffery Rollison; *Librn*, Diane P Rofini; *Asst Librn*, Marion Strode; *Asst Librn*, Wesley Sollenberger; *Asst Librn*, William Meltzer; *Archivist*, Pamela Powell
Founded 1893
1997-1998 Income $17,000. Mats Exp $19,000, Books $500, Per/Ser (Incl. Access Fees) $1,200, Micro $300, Manuscripts & Archives $2,000. Sal $70,000
Library Holdings: Bk Vols 40,000; Per Subs 110
Subject Interests: Decorative arts, Genealogy, Hist of Chester county, Local family hist, Local history
Special Collections: Chester County Newspapers; paper dolls and paper toys; photographs; Postal History; William Penn (A C Myers Coll)
Restriction: Non-circulating to the public
Partic in OCLC Online Computer Library Center, Inc
Open Mon, Tues, Thurs, Fri & Sat 10-4, Wed 10-6

M CHESTER COUNTY HOSPITAL, Medical Staff Library, 701 E Marshall St, 19380. SAN 329-7063. Tel: 610-431-5204. FAX: 610-696-8411. *Librn*, Ginny Moll; E-Mail: gmoll@cchosp.com; *Librn*, Inger Wallin; Staff 2 (MLS 2)
Library Holdings: Bk Titles 186; Per Subs 75
Automation Activity & Vendor Info: (Cataloging) EOS; (Circulation) EOS
Partic in BHSL

L CHESTER COUNTY LAW LIBRARY,* 15 W Gay St, 19380-3049. SAN 315-3290. Tel: 610-344-6166. FAX: 610-344-6994. *Librn*, Jeannie Naftzger; *Asst Librn*, Pat Schaefer
Founded 1862
Library Holdings: Bk Vols 30,000; Per Subs 40
Restriction: Open to public for reference only
Partic in Westlaw

S EVALUATION ASSOCIATES INC LIBRARY,* 1350 Telegraph Rd, 19380. SAN 373-1103. Tel: 610-692-7686. FAX: 610-692-7687.
Library Holdings: Bk Vols 3,000; Per Subs 60

R GROVE UNITED METHODIST CHURCH LIBRARY, 490 W Boot Rd, 19380. SAN 315-3320. Tel: 610-696-2663. FAX: 610-696-5625. *Librn*, Marjorie Wille; E-Mail: bwille@worldnet.att.net
Founded 1774
Library Holdings: Bk Vols 1,000
Subject Interests: Bible, Christianity, Methodism

S JOHNSON MATTHEY INC, Technical Library, 1401 King Rd, 19380-1497. SAN 314-7258. Tel: 610-648-8178. FAX: 610-648-8105. *Librn*, Alice Seidel
Library Holdings: Bk Titles 4,000
Subject Interests: Catalysis, Environ, Platinum group metals
Special Collections: Platinum Metals Review
Open Mon-Fri 8-5

S SPI SUPPLIES DIVISION OF STRUCTURE PROBE, INC, Electron Microscopy Library,* 569 E Gay St, 19381-0656. (Mail add: PO Box 656 19381-0656), SAN 328-1604. Tel: 610-436-5400. FAX: 610-436-5755. E-Mail: spi2spi@2spi.com. Web Site: www.2spi.com. *In Charge*, Kim Murray
Library Holdings: Bk Vols 300
Subject Interests: Electron microscopy

SR SWEDENBORG FOUNDATION LIBRARY,* 506 N Church St, 19380. SAN 327-0319. Tel: 610-430-3222. FAX: 610-430-7982. E-Mail: info@swedenborg.com. *Coll Develop*, Elizabeth A Pitt
Founded 1874
Library Holdings: Bk Vols 1,500

P WEST CHESTER PUBLIC LIBRARY, 415 N Church St, 19380-2401. SA 315-3339. Tel: 610-696-1721. FAX: 610-429-1077. Web Site: www.ccls.or othlibs/west.htm. *Dir*, Victoria E Dow; E-Mail: vdow@ccls.org; Staff 15 (MLS 1, Non-MLS 14)
Founded 1872. Pop 56,000; Circ 105,000
Library Holdings: Bk Titles 39,077; Per Subs 120
Special Collections: National Geographic, bd per
Automation Activity & Vendor Info: (Circulation) Innovative Interfaces Inc.; (OPAC) Innovative Interfaces Inc.
Database Vendor: Innovative Interfaces INN - View
Mem of Chester County Library
Friends of the Library Group

C WEST CHESTER UNIVERSITY, Francis Harvey Green Library, High St Rosedale Ave, 19383. SAN 359-6672. Tel: 610-436-2747. FAX: 610-436-2251. Web Site: www.wcupa.edu/library.fhg. *Dir*, Frank Q Helms; Tel: 610 436-2643, E-Mail: fhelms@wcupa.edu; *Asst Dir*, Mary E Nehlig; Tel: 610-436-2263, E-Mail: mnehlig@wcupa.edu; *Cat*, Jean Burton; Tel: 610-436-2917, E-Mail: jburton@wcupa.edu; *Coll Develop*, Diana B Thomas; Tel: 610-436-3409, E-Mail: dthomas@wcupa.edu; *Cat*, Patricia DeSalvo; Tel: 610-436-2256, E-Mail: pdesalvo@wcupa.edu; *Rare Bks, Spec Coll*, R Gera Schoelkopf; Tel: 610-436-3456, E-Mail: rschoelkop@wcupa.edu; *Circ*, Dan McDonnell; Tel: 610-436-1098, E-Mail: dmcdonnell@wcupa.edu; *Acq, Ser*, Christina McCawley; Tel: 610-436-2187, 436-2656, E-Mail: cmccawley@wcupa.edu; *Doc*, Mary Anne Burns Duffy; Tel: 610-436-3206, E-Mail: mburnsduff@wcupa.edu; *ILL*, Mary Sweeney; Tel: 610-436-3454, E-Mail: msweeney@wcupa.edu; *Instrul Serv*, Patricia Lenkowski; Tel: 610-436-339 E-Mail: plenkowski@wcupa.edu; *Ref*, Richard Swain; Staff 33 (MLS 13, Non-MLS 20)
Founded 1871. Enrl 10,055; Fac 585; Highest Degree: Master
Jul 1998-Jun 1999 Income (Main Library and Branch Library) Parent Institution $3,397,767. Mats Exp $1,353,109, Books $199,058, Per/Ser (Inc Access Fees) $661,209, Presv $34,081, AV Equip $1,500, Manuscripts & Archives $500, Electronic Ref Mat (Incl. Access Fees) $100,816. Sal $1,471,341 (Prof $809,976)
Library Holdings: Bk Vols 538,381; Bk Titles 348,184; Per Subs 2,824
Subject Interests: Art, Bus, Education, Health, Humanities, Kinesiology, Music, Nursing
Special Collections: Anthony Wayne Letters (Rare Book), bks, letters; History of County (Chester County Coll, including Darlington Coll of Rare Scientific & Botanical; John Sanderson's Biographies of the Signers of the Declaration of Independence; Philips Coll of Autographed Books & Letters; Physical Education (Ehinger Coll), bks; Shakespeare Folios; Stanley Weintraub Coll, mss & related materials
Restriction: Circulation limited
Function: ILL available, Reference services available
Mem of Keystone Libr Network
Partic in OCLC Online Computer Library Center, Inc; Pa Academic Librs Connection Coun; PALINET & Union Library Catalogue of Pennsylvania; State System Of Higher Education Libraries Council; Tri-State College Library Cooperative (TCLC)
Friends of the Library Group
Departmental Libraries:
MUSIC Tel: 610-436-2379, 610-436-2430. FAX: 610-436-2251. *Librn*, Paul Emmons; E-Mail: pemmons@wcupa.edu
Friends of the Library Group

S ROY F WESTON INC, Corporate Information Center,* 1400 Weston Way, 19380. (Mail add: PO Box 2653, 19380), SAN 315-3347. Tel: 610-701-3405. FAX: 610-701-3158. *Dir, Online Servs*, Mary Walker; E-Mail: walkerm@wcmail.rfweston.com; Staff 3 (MLS 2, Non-MLS 1)
Founded 1965
Library Holdings: Bk Titles 3,000; Per Subs 150
Subject Interests: Air pollution, Energy, Environmental engineering, Environmental studies, Hazardous wastes, Health, Land use planning, Nuclear wastes, Solid waste, Toxicology, Water pollution
Publications: Newsletter
Restriction: Staff use only
Partic in Dialog Corporation; Nat Libr of Med; OCLC Online Computer Library Center, Inc

EST CONSHOHOCKEN

AMERICAN SOCIETY FOR TESTING & MATERIALS, Information Center,* 100 Barr Harbor Dr, 19428-2959. SAN 314-8572. Tel: 610-832-9500. FAX: 610-832-9555. E-Mail: infoctr@astm.org. Web Site: www.astm.org. *Mgr*, Tracy Bekett
Founded 1969
Library Holdings: Bk Vols 1,500; Per Subs 75
Subject Interests: Engineering, Physical sci

COOPERS CREEK CHEMICAL CORPORATION LIBRARY,* 884 River Rd, 19428. SAN 370-8632. Tel: 610-828-0375. *In Charge*, Glen Kornfeind
Library Holdings: Bk Vols 50

VEST ELIZABETH

HERCULES, INC, Research Library,* State Hwy 837, 15088-0567. SAN 314-4089. Tel: 412-384-2520. FAX: 412-384-9634. *In Charge*, Norman E Daughenbaugh
Founded 1940
Library Holdings: Bk Vols 1,500; Per Subs 15

VEST GROVE

AVON GROVE LIBRARY,* 11 Exchange Pl, 19390-1207. SAN 315-3355. Tel: 610-869-2004. FAX: 610-869-2957. *Dir*, Kim Ringler
Pop 8,310; Circ 36,000
Library Holdings: Bk Vols 12,000; Per Subs 12
Mem of Chester County Library
Open Mon & Fri 10-6, Tues-Thurs 10-8 & Sat 10-3
Friends of the Library Group

VEST LAWN

WEST LAWN-WYOMISSING HILLS LIBRARY, 101 Woodside Ave, 19609. SAN 315-3363. Tel: 610-678-4888. FAX: 610-678-9210. Web Site: www.berks.lib.pa.us/wlwhl. *Dir*, Paparella Bonnie; *Librn*, Dennis McAfee; Staff 4 (Non-MLS 4)
Founded 1937. Pop 10,000
Library Holdings: Bk Vols 9,000; Per Subs 25
Mem of Berks County Libr Syst
Partic in Access Pa
Friends of the Library Group

WEST MIFFLIN

COMMUNITY COLLEGE OF ALLEGHENY COUNTY, South Campus Library, ER Crawford,* 1750 Clairton Rd, 15122-3097. SAN 315-3371. Tel: 412-469-6295. FAX: 412-469-6370. Web Site: www.ccac.edu. *Dir*, Barbara Chandler; *Librn*, Irene Grimm; *Librn*, Ruth Collura; *Online Servs*, Linda Ohnahaus; Staff 2 (MLS 2)
Founded 1967
Library Holdings: Bk Vols 61,000; Per Subs 437
Subject Interests: Allied health, Nursing
Partic in PALINET & Union Library Catalogue of Pennsylvania; Pittsburgh Council On Higher Education (PCHE)

S R H I REFRACTORIES AMERICA, (Formerly Global Industrial Technologies, Inc), P C W M Library, 1001 Pittsburgh-McKeesport Blvd, 15122. SAN 315-338X. Tel: 412-469-6119. FAX: 412-469-3889. Web Site: www.hwr.com. *Librn*, Timothy Gaus; E-Mail: gaust@hwr.com; Staff 1 (MLS 1)
Founded 1959
Library Holdings: Bk Vols 2,500; Bk Titles 2,000; Per Subs 30
Subject Interests: Ceramics, Metallurgy cement, Refractories
Database Vendor: OCLC - First Search
Function: For research purposes

WEST NEWTON

P WEST NEWTON PUBLIC LIBRARY,* 124 N Water St, 15089. SAN 370-7474. Tel: 724-872-8555. *Dir*, Linda Bachrik
Founded 1939. Circ 5,260
Library Holdings: Bk Titles 11,500
Subject Interests: Civil War, Genealogy, Local history
Mem of Monessen District Libr Ctr
Friends of the Library Group

WEST PITTSTON

P WEST PITTSTON LIBRARY,* 200 Exeter Ave, 18643-2442. SAN 315-3398. Tel: 570-654-9847. FAX: 570-654-8037. E-Mail: wplib@microserve.net. *Librn*, Charlene Berti
Library Holdings: Bk Vols 18,800; Per Subs 30
Friends of the Library Group

WEST POINT

MERCK & CO, INC

S MARKETING INFORMATION CENTER, Bldg WP35150, 19486. SAN 359-6761. Tel: 215-652-6934. FAX: 215-652-5185. *Mgr*, Rhea Mihalisin
Founded 1963
Library Holdings: Bk Vols 2,275; Per Subs 209
Subject Interests: Advertising, Bus, Drugs, Econ, Health, Marketing, Mgt, Statistics

S PUBLISHED INFORMATION RESOURCES, Sumneytown Pike, 19486. SAN 359-6737. Tel: 215-652-6026. FAX: 215-652-0721. *Mgr*, Sarah C Williams; E-Mail: sarah_williams@merck.com; Staff 16 (MLS 4, Non-MLS 12)
Founded 1921
Library Holdings: Bk Titles 7,219; Per Subs 1,275
Subject Interests: Biochemistry, Immunology, Medicine, Microbiology, Organic chemistry, Pharmacology, Physiology, Veterinary medicine, Virology
Publications: Literature Resources Center Announcement (monthly); Literature Resources Center Meetings (quarterly)
Restriction: Not open to public
Partic in Dialog Corporation; Nat Libr of Med; PALINET & Union Library Catalogue of Pennsylvania

WESTFIELD

P WESTFIELD PUBLIC LIBRARY, 147 Maple St, 16950-1616. SAN 315-3401. Tel: 814-367-5411. FAX: 814-367-5411. E-Mail: wplib@penn.com. *Librn*, Olga Gray; *Asst Librn*, Rebecca Nagy
Pop 2,441; Circ 26,000
1999-2000 Income $22,000. Mats Exp $7,788, Books $6,420, Per/Ser (Incl. Access Fees) $268, Micro $400, AV Equip $400. Sal $9,000
Library Holdings: Bk Vols 11,000; Per Subs 23
Open Mon & Fri 1-7, Tues 10-5, Thurs & Sat 9-3
Friends of the Library Group

WHITEHALL

P WHITEHALL TOWNSHIP PUBLIC LIBRARY, 3700 Mechanicsville Rd, 18052-3399. SAN 315-341X. Tel: 610-432-4339. FAX: 610-432-9387. E-Mail: whitehallpl@cliu.org. Web Site: whitehall.lib.pa.us. *Dir*, Nancy J Adams; *Ref*, Christine Andrews; *AV*, Cheryl Hixson; *Syst Coordr*, Lauren Krupa; *Ch Servs*, Marcia Rabuck; *Circ*, Phyllis Mizgerd; Staff 9 (MLS 1, Non-MLS 8)
Founded 1964. Pop 26,046
Jul 2000-Jun 2001 Income $546,500, State $104,500, Locally Generated Income $442,000. Mats Exp $108,720, Books $54,000, Per/Ser (Incl. Access Fees) $12,000, Presv $7,900, Micro $14,000, AV Equip $14,000, Electronic Ref Mat (Incl. Access Fees) $6,800. Sal $317,300 (Prof $143,600)
Library Holdings: Bk Vols 96,886; Bk Titles 74,671; Per Subs 200
Subject Interests: Art, Auto repair, Bus, Fiction, Health, How-to, Local history, Mgt, Parenting, Plays, Recorded music, Songbooks
Special Collections: Braille Bible; Framed Art Prints; Juvenile Braille Picture Books
Automation Activity & Vendor Info: (Cataloging) TLC; (Circulation) TLC; (OPAC) TLC
Database Vendor: Ebsco - EbscoHost
Publications: Brochure for new members; Monthly Bibliography of New Acquisitions
Partic in CLC
Book-by-mail for homebound
Friends of the Library Group

WILCOX

P WILCOX PUBLIC LIBRARY, Marvin & Buchanan Sts, PO Box 58, 15870-0058. SAN 315-3428. Tel: 814-929-5639. FAX: 814-929-9934. E-Mail: wilcoxlib@ncentral.com. *Dir*, Lann M Yurchick
Founded 1963. Pop 1,850; Circ 3,404
Library Holdings: Bk Vols 4,730; Per Subs 10
Open Mon, Tues & Fri 6-8, Wed 2-4 & 6-8, Thurs 9-11 & 6-8

WILKES-BARRE

GM DEPARTMENT OF VETERANS AFFAIRS, Medical Center Library,* 1111 E End Blvd, 18711. SAN 315-3479. Tel: 717-824-3521, Ext 7422. FAX: 717-821-7264. *Librn*, Jay Suffren
Founded 1950
Library Holdings: Bk Vols 5,518; Per Subs 285

M GEISINGER WYOMING VALLEY MEDICAL CENTER LIBRARY, 1000 E Mountain Dr, 18711. SAN 372-7939. Tel: 570-826-7809. FAX: 570-826-7682. *Librn*, Judith Jones; E-Mail: jajones@geisinger.edu; Staff 1 (MLS 1)
Founded 1981
Jul 1999-Jun 2000 Income $80,000. Mats Exp $80,000. (Prof $17,500)
Library Holdings: Bk Vols 1,000; Per Subs 150

Database Vendor: OVID Technologies
Function: Document delivery services, ILL available, Literary searches, Photocopies available, Reference services available, Research library
Special Services for the Deaf - Books on deafness & sign language; TTY machine

L HOURIGAN, KLUGER & QUINN, Law Library, 700 Mellon Bank Ctr, 8 W Market St, 18701-1867. SAN 372-1833. Tel: 570-825-9401. FAX: 570-829-3460. E-Mail: hkq@epix.net. Web Site: www.hkqpc.com. *Librn*, Michael J Reilly
Library Holdings: Bk Vols 9,000; Per Subs 50
Open Mon-Fri 8-5

C KING'S COLLEGE, D Leonard Corgan Library, 14 W Jackson St, 18711-0850. SAN 315-3436. Tel: 570-208-5840. FAX: 570-208-6022. Web Site: www.kings.edu/~library/. *Dir*, Dr Terrence Mech; Tel: 570-208-5943, E-Mail: tfmech@kings.edu; *Circ*, Thomas Ruddy; *Coll Develop*, Judith Tierney; *Instrul Serv*, Marianne Sodoski; *ILL, Ref*, Janet DuMond; *Tech Servs*, Mary Jane Donnelly; Staff 5 (MLS 5)
Founded 1946. Enrl 1,936; Fac 126; Highest Degree: Master
Jul 1999-Jun 2000 Income $920,700. Mats Exp $464,065, Books $193,826, Per/Ser (Incl. Access Fees) $131,605, Presv $4,243, Micro $31,726. Sal $392,231
Library Holdings: Bk Vols 163,239; Per Subs 822
Special Collections: Folklore (George Korson Coll), tapes, mss, bks; Public & Private Papers of Honorable Daniel J Flood, MC
Automation Activity & Vendor Info: (Acquisitions) epixtech, inc.; (Cataloging) epixtech, inc.; (Circulation) epixtech, inc.; (OPAC) epixtech, inc.; (Serials) epixtech, inc.
Database Vendor: Dialog, Ebsco - EbscoHost, IAC - Info Trac, Silverplatter Information Inc., Wilson - Wilson Web
Publications: Daniel J Flood Collection Register; Edward Welles Catalog of Artists; George Korson Folklore Archive Register
Partic in Northeastern Pennsylvania Library Network; OCLC Online Computer Library Center, Inc; PALINET & Union Library Catalogue of Pennsylvania

M LUZERNE COUNTY MEDICAL SOCIETY LIBRARY,* 130 S Franklin St, 18701. SAN 315-3444. Tel: 717-823-0917. FAX: 717-823-5458. *Exec Dir*, Duane Kersteen; *Librn*, Donna Stahl
Founded 1892
Library Holdings: Bk Titles 100; Per Subs 110
Partic in Health Information Library Network of Northeastern Pennsylvania; Mid-Eastern Regional Med Libr Serv

M MERCY HOSPITAL, Medical Library,* 25 Church St, 18765. SAN 315-3452. Tel: 570-826-3699. FAX: 570-826-3233. *Dir*, Sr Elizabeth Brandreth; Staff 1 (MLS 1)
Founded 1974
Library Holdings: Bk Vols 1,500; Bk Titles 1,715; Per Subs 81
Subject Interests: Hospital administration, Medicine, Nursing
Partic in Health Information Library Network of Northeastern Pennsylvania

P OSTERHOUT FREE LIBRARY,* 71 S Franklin St, 18701-1287. SAN 359-6850. Tel: 570-823-0156. FAX: 570-823-5477. E-Mail: ostpublib@hslc.org. *Exec Dir*, Diane Suffren; *Tech Servs*, Gail Frew; *Circ*, Elaine Schall; *Ch Servs*, Elaine Rash; *ILL*, Donnal Fromel
Founded 1889. Pop 154,707; Circ 258,489
1998-1999 Income $1,329,891, State $406,848, City $100,097, County $72,483, Locally Generated Income $165,000, Other $562,965. Mats Exp $169,212, Books $140,996, Per/Ser (Incl. Access Fees) $16,771, Micro $1,823. Sal $713,385
Library Holdings: Bk Vols 200,000; Per Subs 300
Subject Interests: Local history
Publications: Osterhout Free Library Newsletter (quarterly)
Partic in Northeastern Pennsylvania Library Network; PALINET & Union Library Catalogue of Pennsylvania
Special Services for the Deaf - Books on deafness & sign language; High interest/low vocabulary books
Friends of the Library Group
Branches: 3
NORTH, 235 George Ave, 18705. SAN 359-6885. Tel: 570-822-4660. FAX: 570-822-4660. *Librn*, Joanne Austin
Library Holdings: Bk Vols 12,800
PLAINS TOWNSHIP, 126 N Main St, Plains, 18705. SAN 359-6915. Tel: 570-824-1862. FAX: 570-824-1862. *Librn*, Catherine Zahay
Library Holdings: Bk Vols 12,000
SOUTH, 2 Airy St, 18702. SAN 359-694X. Tel: 570-823-5544. *Librn*, Melissa Szafran
Library Holdings: Bk Vols 8,916

L ROSENN, JENKINS & GREENWALD LIBRARY,* 15 S Franklin St, 18711-0075. SAN 321-9011. Tel: 717-821-4709. FAX: 717-826-5640. *Librn*, Jill Burke
Library Holdings: Bk Vols 8,000; Bk Titles 680

C WILKES UNIVERSITY, Farley Library,* 187 S Franklin St, 18755-0998. SAN 359-6974. Tel: 717-408-4250. FAX: 717-408-4975. Web Site: www.wilkes.edu. *Dir*, Jon Lindgren; E-Mail: lindgrej@wilkes.edu; *Circ*, Jean Krohle; *Syst Coordr*, James Berg; *Acq*, Heidi Selecky; *Cat*, Lorna Darte; *Ref*, Janell Carter; *Bibliog Instr*, Sharon Ellenberger; *ILL, Online Servs*, Brian Sacolic; Staff 6 (MLS 6)
Founded 1933. Enrl 2,060; Fac 153; Highest Degree: Doctorate
Jun 1998-May 1999 Income $875,436. Mats Exp $391,871, Books $181,70 Per/Ser (Incl. Access Fees) $180,314, Presv $14,693, Micro $4,000, AV Equip $5,000. Sal $360,865 (Prof $204,230)
Library Holdings: Bk Vols 231,493; Bk Titles 171,803; Per Subs 983
Special Collections: Northeast Pennsylvania History; Poland, Culture & History (Polish Room)
Publications: Library News Brief; New Books List
Partic in Northeastern Pennsylvania Library Network; OCLC Online Computer Library Center, Inc; PALINET & Union Library Catalogue of Pennsylvania

L WILKES-BARRE LAW & LIBRARY ASSOCIATION,* Court House, Rm 23, 18711. SAN 315-3509. Tel: 717-822-6712. FAX: 717-822-8210. *Librn*, Joseph Burke III
Founded 1866
Library Holdings: Bk Vols 40,000; Per Subs 40

S WYOMING HISTORICAL & GEOLOGICAL SOCIETY, Bishop Memorial Library, 49 S Franklin St, 18701. SAN 315-3517. Tel: 717-823-6244. FAX: 717-823-9011. Web Site: www.whgs.org. *Archivist, Librn*, Jesse Teitelbaum
Founded 1858
Library Holdings: Bk Vols 7,000; Per Subs 15
Subject Interests: Anthracite mining, Hist of Wyoming Valley, Pennsylvania
Special Collections: Business Records of Coal Companies; Manuscripts of Personal & Family Papers of Prominent Wyoming Valley Individuals

M WYOMING VALLEY HEALTH CARE SYSTEM, Library Services, 575 N River St, 18764. SAN 315-3495. Tel: 570-552-1175. FAX: 570-552-1183. E-Mail: library@wvhcs.org. Web Site: www.wvhc.org. *Mgr*, Rosemarie Kazda Taylor; Staff 2 (MLS 2)
Founded 1935
Library Holdings: Bk Vols 4,000; Per Subs 444
Subject Interests: Health administration, Health sci, Medicine, Nursing
Publications: Infobits
Partic in Basic Health Sciences Library Network; Health Information Library Network of Northeastern Pennsylvania; Middle Atlantic Regional Med Libr Prog; National Network Of Libraries Of Medicine - South Central Region; Northeastern Pennsylvania Library Network

WILKINSBURG

S KNOW, INC, 807 Penn Ave, 15221. SAN 370-1468. Tel: 412-241-4844. FAX: 412-241-4855. Web Site: www.hometown.aol.com/knowinc/index.html *Pres*, Phyllis Wetherby
Library Holdings: Bk Vols 1,000
Subject Interests: Equal rights amendments, Feminist lit

WILLIAMSBURG

P WILLIAMSBURG PUBLIC LIBRARY,* 420 W Second St, 16693-1210. SAN 315-3525. Tel: 814-832-3367. FAX: 814-832-3845. E-Mail: willpublib@hslc.org. *Librn*, Lujene Shelley; Staff 1 (MLS 1)
Founded 1950. Pop 5,993; Circ 7,853
Jul 1997-Jun 1998 Income $36,235, State $9,736, Federal $1,412, County $8,048, Locally Generated Income $17,039. Mats Exp $8,691, Books $7,695, Per/Ser (Incl. Access Fees) $304. Sal $12,470
Library Holdings: Bk Vols 13,294; Per Subs 21
Subject Interests: Pa hist
Mem of Blair County Library System

WILLIAMSPORT

P JAMES V BROWN LIBRARY OF WILLIAMSPORT & LYCOMING COUNTY,* 19 E Fourth St, 17701-6390. SAN 359-7067. Tel: 570-326-0536. FAX: 570-323-6938. E-Mail: jvbrown@jvbrown.edu. Web Site: www.jvbrown..edu. *Dir*, Janice Trapp; *Ref*, Rhonda Fisher; *Publ Servs*, Maryann Baker; *Tech Servs*, Laura Spencer; *Ch Servs*, Jeff Swope; Staff 30 (MLS 8, Non-MLS 22)
Founded 1905. Pop 118,710; Circ 889,386
Jan 1998-Dec 1998 Income $1,674,084, State $753,208, Federal $120,520, County $564,800, Locally Generated Income $235,556. Mats Exp $339,009, Books $244,260, Per/Ser (Incl. Access Fees) $8,000, AV Equip $35,000, Electronic Ref Mat (Incl. Access Fees) $25,092. Sal $810,550 (Prof $259,321)
Library Holdings: Bk Vols 155,444
Special Collections: Pennsylvania Coll
Automation Activity & Vendor Info: (Cataloging) Gaylord; (Cataloging) Gaylord; (OPAC) Gaylord
Member Libraries: Blossburg Memorial Library; Snyder County Library
Partic in PALINET & Union Library Catalogue of Pennsylvania
Open Mon-Thurs 9-9, Fri 9-6, Sat 9-5 & Sun 1-5
Friends of the Library Group
Bookmobiles: 3

LYCOMING COLLEGE, John G Snowden Memorial Library, 700 College Pl, 17701-5192. SAN 315-355X. Tel: 570-321-4053. FAX: 570-321-4090. Web Site: www.lycoming.edu/dept/library. *Dir*, Bruce M Hurlbert; *Coll Develop*, Susan K Beidler; Tel: 570-321-4084, E-Mail: beidler@lycoming.edu; Staff 12 (MLS 5, Non-MLS 7)
Founded 1812. Enrl 1,362; Fac 92; Highest Degree: Bachelor
Library Holdings: Bk Vols 183,626; Per Subs 1,162
Subject Interests: Bus, Psychology, Relig studies, Sociology
Special Collections: Religion (Central Pennsylvania Conference of the United Methodist Church Archives)
Partic in Associated College Libraries of Central Pennsylvania; PALINET & Union Library Catalogue of Pennsylvania; Susquehanna Library Cooperative

L LYCOMING COUNTY LAW LIBRARY, Court House, 48 W Third St, Basement, 17701. SAN 315-3568. Tel: 570-327-2475. FAX: 570-327-2288. *Librn*, Nancy Borgess
Founded 1927
Library Holdings: Bk Titles 20,500; Per Subs 15

PENNSYLVANIA COLLEGE OF TECHNOLOGY LIBRARY, One College Ave, 17701. SAN 315-3576. Tel: 570-327-4523. Circulation Tel: 570-320-2400, Ext 7016. Reference Tel: 570-320-2400, Ext 2409. Toll Free Tel: 800-367-9222. FAX: 570-327-4503. Web Site: www.pct.edu/library. *Dir*, Mary L Sieminski; Tel: 570-320-2400, Ext 7211, E-Mail: msiemins@pct.edu; *Reader Servs*, Marilyn Bodnar; Tel: 570-320-2400, Ext 7459, E-Mail: mbodnar@pct.edu; *Automation Syst Coordr*, Robert C Johnston; *Ser*, Judy McConnell; Tel: 570-320-2400, Ext 7458, E-Mail: jmcconne@pct.edu; *Cat*, Alan Buck; Tel: 570-320-2400, Ext 7742, E-Mail: abuck@pct.edu; *Ref*, Lisette Ormsbee; Tel: 570-320-2400, Ext 7828, E-Mail: lormsbee@pct.edu; *Coll Develop*, Patricia Scott; Tel: 570-320-2400, Ext 7840, E-Mail: pscott@pct.edu; *Electronic Resources*, Cindy Whitmoyer; Tel: 570-320-2400, Ext 7464, E-Mail: cwhitmoy@pct.edu; Staff 20 (MLS 8, Non-MLS 12)
Founded 1965. Enrl 4,811; Fac 252; Highest Degree: Bachelor
Library Holdings: Bk Vols 86,484; Bk Titles 70,720; Per Subs 929
Subject Interests: Architecture, Art, Technology
Special Collections: Sloan Art Coll
Automation Activity & Vendor Info: (Acquisitions) SIRSI; (Cataloging) SIRSI; (Circulation) SIRSI; (Media Booking) SIRSI; (OPAC) SIRSI; (Serials) SIRSI
Database Vendor: GaleNet, Lexis-Nexis, OCLC - First Search, ProQuest
Partic in Access Pa; Interlibrary Delivery Service of Pennsylvania; OCLC Online Computer Library Center, Inc; PALINET & Union Library Catalogue of Pennsylvania; Pals; Susquehanna Library Cooperative

M WILLIAMSPORT HOSPITAL & MEDICAL CENTER, Susquehanna Health System Learning Resources Center, 777 Rural Ave, 17701-3198. SAN 315-3584. Tel: 570-321-2266. Web Site: www.shscares.org/lrc. *Dir*, Michael Heyd; E-Mail: mheyd@shscares.org; Staff 3 (MLS 1, Non-MLS 2)
Founded 1951
Jul 1999-Jun 2000 Income Parent Institution $204,700. Mats Exp $66,220, Books $2,750, Per/Ser (Incl. Access Fees) $45,970, AV Equip $2,000, Electronic Ref Mat (Incl. Access Fees) $15,500. Sal $48,900 (Prof $43,600)
Library Holdings: Bk Titles 4,600; Per Subs 240
Subject Interests: Allied health, Hosp mgt, Medicine, Nursing, Pastoral care
Database Vendor: IAC - Info Trac
Partic in Susquehanna Library Cooperative

WILLOW GROVE

M ABINGTON MEMORIAL HOSPITAL, School of Nursing Library,* 2500 Maryland Rd, 19090-1284. SAN 373-7349. Tel: 215-481-5591. FAX: 215-481-5550. *Dir*, Marion Chayes; Staff 2 (MLS 1, Non-MLS 1)
Founded 1914. Enrl 175
Library Holdings: Bk Vols 2,000; Bk Titles 1,800; Per Subs 75
Partic in Delaware Valley Information Consortium; Nat Libr of Med

P UPPER MORELAND FREE PUBLIC LIBRARY, 109 Park Ave, 19090-3277. SAN 315-3630. Tel: 215-659-0741. FAX: 215-830-1223. Web Site: www.mclinc.org. *Dir*, Lillian W Burnley; E-Mail: lburnley@mclinc.org; *Ch Servs*, James Moran; *Ad Servs*, Joan Greenberg; *Ref Serv Ad*, Rachel Davies; *Tech Servs*, Cheryl Adams; Staff 5 (MLS 4, Non-MLS 1)
Founded 1959. Pop 25,874; Circ 117,561
Jan 2001-Dec 2001 Income $562,000, State $90,000, City $431,000, Locally Generated Income $30,000. Mats Exp $67,600, Books $59,600, Per/Ser (Incl. Access Fees) $6,000, Electronic Ref Mat (Incl. Access Fees) $2,000. (Prof $316,500)
Library Holdings: Bk Vols 57,164; Bk Titles 50,000; Per Subs 120; Bks on Deafness & Sign Lang 15
Automation Activity & Vendor Info: (Cataloging) Gaylord; (Circulation) Gaylord; (OPAC) Gaylord; (Serials) Gaylord
Partic in Montgomery County Libr & Info Network Consortium
Special Services for the Blind - Large screen microcomputer monitor with software

R WILLOW GROVE BAPTIST CHURCH LIBRARY, 1872 Kimball Ave, 19090. SAN 318-9392. Tel: 215-659-4505. *Librn*, Jean Beyerle
Library Holdings: Bk Vols 1,100
Subject Interests: Psychology, Recreation

WINDBER

M WINDBER MEDICAL CENTER, Medical Library,* 600 Somerset Ave, 15963. SAN 315-3657. Tel: 814-467-6611. FAX: 814-266-8230. *Librn*, Heather W Brice
Library Holdings: Bk Vols 2,370; Per Subs 12
Publications: Current Awareness Listings
Partic in Greater NE Regional Med Libr Program; Laurel Highlands Health Sciences Library Consortium; Nat Libr of Med

P WINDBER PUBLIC LIBRARY, INC,* 1401 Graham Ave, 15963-1710. SAN 315-3665. Tel: 814-467-4950. FAX: 814-467-0960. E-Mail: windpublib@aol.com. *Dir, Librn*, Grace Buchkovich; *Ch Servs*, Linda Bokinsky
Founded 1918. Pop 11,194
Jan 1998-Dec 1998 Income $98,413, City $3,475, County $7,782, Locally Generated Income $79,829, Other $7,327. Mats Exp $9,684, Books $7,217, Per/Ser (Incl. Access Fees) $1,380, Electronic Ref Mat (Incl. Access Fees) $1,087. Sal $24,826
Library Holdings: Bk Vols 27,521; Per Subs 64
Friends of the Library Group

WORCESTER

S PETER WENTZ FARMSTEAD LIBRARY, 1100 Schultz Rd, 19490. (Mail add: PO Box 240, 19490), SAN 374-8820. Tel: 610-584-5104. FAX: 610-584-6860. *In Charge*, Dianne M Cram; Staff 6 (Non-MLS 6)
Founded 1976
Library Holdings: Bk Titles 500
Subject Interests: Decorative arts, Local history, Pennsylvania
Research only
Friends of the Library Group

WORTHINGTON

P WORTHINGTON-WEST FRANKLIN COMMUNITY LIBRARY, 214 E Main St, PO Box 85, 16262-0085. SAN 370-7326. Tel: 724-297-3762. FAX: 724-297-3762. E-Mail: wwflibrary@alltel.net. *Librn*, Dianne Hohn; Staff 1 (MLS 1)
Founded 1986. Pop 2,800
Library Holdings: Bk Titles 16,497; Per Subs 22
Automation Activity & Vendor Info: (Cataloging) Brodart
Database Vendor: Dialog
Friends of the Library Group

WRIGHTSTOWN

P VILLAGE LIBRARY OF WRIGHTSTOWN,* 727 Penns Park Rd, 18940-0812. SAN 315-3681. Tel: 215-598-3322. *Dir*, Alisa Marcus Feltzin
Founded 1958. Pop 2,266; Circ 18,136
Library Holdings: Bk Titles 15,000; Per Subs 72
Publications: Newsletter (biannual)
Mem of Bucks County Free Library

WYALUSING

P WYALUSING PUBLIC LIBRARY,* PO Box 98, 18853-0098. SAN 315-369X. Tel: 570-746-1711. FAX: 570-746-1711. E-Mail: wyalib@exit.net. *Librn*, Kristin Smith-Gary; *Asst Librn*, Kathy Brady; *Asst Librn*, Lora Ely
Pop 1,927; Circ 11,987
Library Holdings: Bk Vols 11,000; Per Subs 30
Subject Interests: Local history
Mem of Williamsport District Libr Ctr
Open Mon-Fri 10-8 & Sat 9-1

WYNCOTE

CR RECONSTRUCTIONIST RABBINICAL COLLEGE, Mordecai M Kaplan Library, 1299 Church Rd, 19095. SAN 314-9900. Tel: 215-576-0800, Ext 234. FAX: 215-576-6143. *Dir*, Eliezer M Wise; E-Mail: ewise@rrc.edu; *Assoc Dir*, Terry Constant; Tel: 215-576-0800, Ext 232; Staff 4 (MLS 2, Non-MLS 2)
Founded 1968. Enrl 70; Fac 20; Highest Degree: Master
Library Holdings: Bk Vols 45,800; Per Subs 125
Subject Interests: Hasidism, Israelana, Jewish hist, Jewish law, Middle East, Mysticism, Rabbinics
Special Collections: Judaica (Mordecai M Kaplan Coll); Mordecai M Kaplan Archives
Publications: Ha-Sefer (newsletter)
Function: Research library
Partic in Council Of Archives & Research Libraries In Jewish Studies; Southeastern Pennsylvania Theological Library Association

WYNDMOOR

P FREE LIBRARY OF SPRINGFIELD TOWNSHIP, 1600 Paper Mill Rd, 19038. SAN 372-7726. Tel: 215-836-5300. FAX: 215-836-2404. *Coll Develop, Librn*, M A Baroski; E-Mail: mbaroski@mclinc.org; *Asst Librn, Ref*, E Keller; *ILL*, Eileen Taddei; *Tech Servs*, Joy Utz; *Circ, Per*, Patricia Ennis; *Ch Servs*, Carol Bunting; Staff 3 (MLS 2, Non-MLS 1)
Founded 1965. Pop 19,612
Library Holdings: Bk Titles 59,000; Per Subs 110
Special Collections: Art (Malta Fund); Business; Outdoor Sports (Brodsky Fund); Performing Arts; Popular Medicine (Ramsey Coll)
Partic in Montgomery County Libr & Info Network Consortium
Friends of the Library Group

G UNITED STATES DEPARTMENT OF AGRICULTURE, Agricultural Research Service, Eastern Regional Research Center, Scientific Information Resources, 600 E Mermaid Lane, 19038-8598. SAN 315-0194. Tel: 215-233-6602, 215-233-6604, 215-233-6772. FAX: 215-233-6606. *In Charge*, Wendy H Kramer; E-Mail: wkramer@arserrc.gov; Staff 3 (MLS 1, Non-MLS 2)
Founded 1940
Library Holdings: Bk Vols 31,000; Per Subs 270
Subject Interests: Agriculture, Biochemistry, Biotech, Chemical engineering, Chemistry, Food eng, Food safety, Food tech, Leather res, Microbiology, Plant sci, Wool res
Publications: Journal list
Partic in Fedlink; Nat Libr of Med; OCLC Online Computer Library Center, Inc

WYNNEWOOD

R EASTERN BAPTIST THEOLOGICAL SEMINARY, Austen K DeBlois Library, 6 Lancaster Ave, 19096. SAN 314-8963. Tel: 610-645-9318. FAX: 610-645-5707. E-Mail: library@ebts.edu. Web Site: www.library.ebts.edu. *Dir*, Melody Mazuk; Tel: 610-645-9319, E-Mail: mazuk@ebts.edu; *Dir, Tech Serv*, Nancy R Adams; Tel: 610-645-9317, E-Mail: nadams@ebts.edu; *Cat*, Barrett Holmgren; Tel: 610-645-9317, E-Mail: bholmgren@ebts.edu; Staff 6 (MLS 2, Non-MLS 4)
Founded 1925
Library Holdings: Bk Vols 111,452; Per Subs 586
Special Collections: Barbour Black Studies; MacBride Coll; Soto-Fontanz Hispanic Studies
Automation Activity & Vendor Info: (OPAC) TLC

R MAIN LINE REFORM TEMPLE, Beth Elohim Library, 410 Montgomery Ave, 19096. SAN 315-3711. Tel: 610-649-7800. FAX: 610-642-6338. *Librn*, Erica Miller; Staff 2 (MLS 1, Non-MLS 1)
Founded 1961
Library Holdings: Bk Titles 8,000
Subject Interests: Judaica
Special Collections: Young Adult (Steven Berman Memorial Coll)

P PENN WYNNE LIBRARY, 130 Overbrook Pkwy, 19096-3211. SAN 314-9609. Tel: 610-642-7844. FAX: 610-642-2761. Web Site: www.lower-merion.lib.pa.us. *Librn*, Judy Soret
Circ 191,282
Library Holdings: Bk Vols 40,000
Special Collections: Judaica; Play reading; Puppets
Automation Activity & Vendor Info: (Circulation) Gaylord
Mem of Lower Merion Library System

R PHILADELPHIA ARCHDIOCESAN HISTORICAL RESEARCH CENTER, Archives & Historial Collections,* 100 E Wynnewood Rd, 19096-3001. SAN 359-0941. Tel: 610-667-2125. FAX: 610-667-2730. *Dir*, Joseph J Casino
Library Holdings: Per Subs 8,000
Subject Interests: Immigration
Special Collections: American Catholic Newspapers (19th Century) Religious American Coll; Catechism Coll; Popular Piety Coll
Restriction: Open to public for reference only

R SAINT CHARLES BORROMEO SEMINARY, (RSC), Ryan Memorial Library, 100 E Wynnewood Rd, 19096. SAN 359-0917. Tel: 610-785-6274. Reference Tel: 610-785-6277. FAX: 610-664-7913. Web Site: www.scs.edu/library. *Dir Libr Serv*, Cait Kokolus; E-Mail: ckokolus@adphila.org; *Head Tech Servs*, Christine Schwartz; Staff 6 (MLS 2, Non-MLS 4)
Founded 1832. Enrl 350
Jul 1999-Jun 2000 Income $357,910. Mats Exp $89,407, Books $52,263, Per/Ser (Incl. Access Fees) $28,577, Micro $3,292, Electronic Ref Mat (Incl. Access Fees) $5,275. Sal $215,210 (Prof $112,260)
Library Holdings: Bk Vols 130,567; Bk Titles 100,000; Per Subs 564
Subject Interests: Catholic theol, Philosophy, Scripture studies
Special Collections: Nineteenth Century Devotional Literature; Pre-Vatican II Liturgical Books; Rare Books
Database Vendor: Ebsco - EbscoHost
Publications: Aquisitions list
Partic in Auto-Graphics; PALINET & Union Library Catalogue of Pennsylvania; Philadelphia Area Consortium Of Special Collections Libraries; Southeastern Pennsylvania Theological Library Association; Tri-State College Library Cooperative (TCLC)

WYOMING

P WYOMING FREE LIBRARY,* 358 Wyoming Ave, 18644-1822. SAN 31[illegible] 372X. Tel: 570-693-1364. *Librn*, Mary Cowallsen
Library Holdings: Bk Vols 10,000; Per Subs 12
Open Mon-Fri 3-5, Sat 10-12 & 1-3, Mon, Wed & Thurs 7-9
Friends of the Library Group

WYOMISSING

P WYOMISSING PUBLIC LIBRARY, 9 Reading Blvd, 19610-2084. SAN 315-3738. Tel: 610-374-2385. FAX: 610-374-8424. E-Mail: wyopl@ptd.net Web Site: www.wyopublib.org. *Dir*, Joan S King
Founded 1913. Pop 7,332; Circ 66,000
Jan 2000-Dec 2000 Income $259,400. Mats Exp $34,650. Sal $158,150 (Prof $147,000)
Library Holdings: Bk Vols 25,332; Per Subs 80
Automation Activity & Vendor Info: (Cataloging) Sagebrush Corporation (Circulation) Sagebrush Corporation

YEADON

P YEADON PUBLIC LIBRARY, 809 Longacre Blvd, 19050-3398. SAN 315-3762. Tel: 610-623-4090. FAX: 610-394-9374. E-Mail: yeadon@delco.lib.pa.us.
Founded 1937. Pop 11,727; Circ 38,000
Library Holdings: Bk Vols 29,000; Per Subs 93
Special Collections: African-American Cultural Center; Brodie/Johnson African-American Cultural Center for Children; Fifty-Plus Center; Parenting Center
Publications: What's Happening (calendar of events)
Mem of Delaware County Library System
Friends of the Library Group

YORK

S BAKER REFRACTORIES LIBRARY,* 320 N Baker Rd, 17404. SAN 372-9303. Tel: 717-792-4615. FAX: 717-792-5103. *Librn*, Nancy Stough
Library Holdings: Bk Vols 200; Per Subs 52
Restriction: Staff use only

R FIRST CHURCH OF THE BRETHREN LIBRARY, 2710 Kingston Rd, 17402-3799. SAN 315-3797. Tel: 717-755-0307. *Librn*, Helen Lehman; *Coordr*, Leah Brant
Founded 1966
Library Holdings: Bk Titles 6,132
Subject Interests: Biog, Ch bks, Family studies, Fiction, Inspiration, Outreach, Recreation, Ref, Relig studies
Special Collections: Church of the Brethren Coll

P MARTIN MEMORIAL LIBRARY, 159 E Market St, 17401. SAN 315-3819. Tel: 717-846-5300. FAX: 717-848-2330. E-Mail: martinlib@blazenet.net. Web Site: www.yorklibraries.org. *Exec Dir*, William Schell; *Admin Dir*, Paula Gilbert; *ILL*, Ruth Schaeberle; *Coll Develop, Head Tech Servs*, Shawn Sipe; *Head Ref*, Dottie Fitton; *Electronic Resources*, Lora Lynn Stevens; Staff 28 (MLS 6, Non-MLS 22)
Founded 1935. Pop 110,000; Circ 500,000
Jan 2000-Dec 2000 Income $2,271,396, State $495,000, City $90,000, Locally Generated Income $1,686,396. Mats Exp $500,000. Sal $1,440,000
Library Holdings: Bk Vols 100,000; Per Subs 200
Automation Activity & Vendor Info: (Circulation) epixtech, inc.
Mem of York County Library System
Friends of the Library Group

M MEMORIAL HOSPITAL LIBRARY,* 325 S Belmont St, 17403-2609. (Mail add: PO Box 15118, 17405-7118), SAN 315-3827. Tel: 717-849-5305. FAX: 717-849-5489. *Librn*, Laurie Yourist
Library Holdings: Bk Vols 950; Per Subs 80
Subject Interests: Health admin, Medicine
Restriction: Medical staff only
Partic in Basic Health Sciences Library Network; Central Pennsylvania Health Science Library Association (CPHSLA); Greater NE Regional Med Libr Serv

C PENNSYLVANIA STATE UNIVERSITY, York Commonwealth College Library (University Libraries),* 1031 Edgecomb Ave, 17403. SAN 315-3835. Tel: 717-771-4023. FAX: 717-771-4022. E-Mail: sdv1@psu.edu. *Librn*, David Van de Streek; Staff 6 (MLS 2, Non-MLS 4)
Enrl 2,106; Fac 86
Jul 1997-Jun 1998 Mats Exp $97,666
Library Holdings: Bk Vols 40,263; Per Subs 298
Partic in OCLC Online Computer Library Center, Inc; RLIN

M PHILIP A HOOVER MD LIBRARY, (Formerly York Hospital), 1001 S George St, 17405. SAN 315-3878. Tel: 717-851-2495. Circulation Tel: 717-851-3323. FAX: 717-851-2487. E-Mail: library@wellspan.org. Web Site: www.yorkhealth.org/yh_services/meded/library.htm. *Dir Libr Serv*, Suzanne M Shultz; E-Mail: sshultz@wellspan.org; Staff 5 (MLS 2, Non-MLS 3)
Founded 1931
2000-2001 Mats Exp $149,300, Books $28,300, Per/Ser (Incl. Access Fees) $113,700, Electronic Ref Mat (Incl. Access Fees) $7,300
Library Holdings: Bk Vols 31,300; Bk Titles 6,300; Per Subs 508
Subject Interests: Clinical medicine, History of medicine, Nursing
Automation Activity & Vendor Info: (Cataloging) epixtech, inc.; (Circulation) epixtech, inc.; (OPAC) epixtech, inc.
Database Vendor: epixtech, inc., OCLC - First Search, OVID Technologies
Function: Research library
Partic in Basic Health Sciences Library Network; Central Pennsylvania Health Science Library Association (CPHSLA)
Open Mon-Fri 7:30-4:30

C YORK COLLEGE OF PENNSYLVANIA, Schmidt Library, 17405-7199. SAN 315-3843. Tel: 717-846-7788, Ext 1345. FAX: 717-849-1608. Web Site: www.ycp.edu/library. *Dir*, Susan Campbell; E-Mail: scampbel@ycp.edu; *Automation Syst Coordr, Tech Servs*, Vickie Kline; *Archivist*, Jean Mundis; *Coll Develop*, Greg Szczyrbak; *AV*, Patricia Bassinger; *ILL*, Sue Uhler; *Per*, Louise Pierce; *Online Servs*, Zehao Zhou; Staff 7 (MLS 7)
Founded 1787. Enrl 4,100; Fac 420; Highest Degree: Master
Library Holdings: Bk Vols 180,000; Per Subs 1,054
Subject Interests: Bus, Mgt, Nursing
Partic in Associated College Libraries of Central Pennsylvania; OCLC Online Computer Library Center, Inc; PALINET & Union Library Catalogue of Pennsylvania

S YORK COUNTY HERITAGE TRUST, (Formerly Historical Society Of York County Library-Archives), Historical Society of York County Library-Archives, 250 E Market St, 17403. SAN 315-3800. Tel: 717-848-1587. FAX: 717-812-1204. Web Site: www.yorkheritage.org. *Librn*, June Lloyd; *Asst Librn*, Lila Fourhman-Shaull; E-Mail: lshaull@yorkheritage.org
Founded 1895
Library Holdings: Bk Vols 25,000; Per Subs 50
Subject Interests: Decorative arts, Fine arts, Genealogy, Local history
Special Collections: Art (Lewis Miller Folk Drawing Coll), mss; Circus & Theater (James Shettel Circus & Theater in America Coll), photog, mss & broadsides; Folk; Genealogy of York & Adams County (York County Genealogical Coll), mss & bks; General Jacob Devers Coll; Governmental Archives (Archives of York City & York County, mss; History (York County Historical Coll), mss & bks; Local Newspers Coll, 1789 to present, micro; York Gazette & Daily, 1815-1970, micro
Restriction: Non-circulating to the public
Function: Reference only

GL YORK COUNTY LAW LIBRARY,* Court House, 17401-1583. SAN 315-3851. Tel: 717-854-0754. FAX: 717-843-7394. E-Mail: lawlibrary@york-county.org. *Librn*, Susan Hedge; *Asst Librn*, Jan Bryner
Jan 1998-Dec 1999 Income $179,000, County $173,000, Locally Generated Income $6,000. Mats Exp Books $130,000. Sal $30,000

P YORK COUNTY LIBRARY SYSTEM,* 118 Pleasant Acres Rd, 2nd flr, 17402-9004. SAN 315-386X. Tel: 717-840-7435. FAX: 717-751-0741. E-Mail: yclsadmn@blazenet.net. Web Site: www.martinlibrary.org. *Dir*, Patricia Calvani; *Automation Syst Coordr*, Barbara Summers
Pop 336,902; Circ 1,300,000
Jan 1997-Dec 1998 Income $1,500,000, State $480,000, County $750,000, Locally Generated Income $100,000, Other $45,000. Mats Exp $52,050, Books $38,000, Per/Ser (Incl. Access Fees) $1,550
Library Holdings: Bk Vols 333,251; Per Subs 661
Member Libraries: Dillsburg Area Public Library; Glatfelter Memorial Library; Hanover Public Library; Kaltreider-Benfer Library; Martin Memorial Library; Mason-Dixon Public Library; New Freedom Library Center; The Arthur Hufnagel -Glen Rock Public Library; York County Public Library
Branches: 5
COLLINSVILLE COMMUNITY, PO Box 18, Brogue, 17302. SAN 324-007X. Tel: 717-927-9014. FAX: 717-927-9664. *Librn*, Martha Miranda
Library Holdings: Bk Vols 8,625
Friends of the Library Group
DOVER AREA COMMUNITY, 3700-3 Davidsburg Rd, Dover, 17315. SAN 377-7154. Tel: 717-292-6814. FAX: 717-292-9774. *Librn*, Lucinda Jacoby
Library Holdings: Bk Vols 15,000
KREUTZ CREEK VALLEY, 66 Walnut Springs Rd, Hellam, 17406. SAN 377-7170. Tel: 717-252-4080. FAX: 717-255-0283. *Librn*, Claire Doerrman
Library Holdings: Bk Vols 10,377
REDLAND COMMUNITY, 48 Robin Hood Dr, Etters, 17319. SAN 324-0088. Tel: 717-938-5599. FAX: 717-938-5599. Web Site: www.martinlibrary.com. *Librn*, Patricia Long
Library Holdings: Bk Vols 17,046; Per Subs 58
Friends of the Library Group
VILLAGE, 35-C N Main St, Jacobus, 17407. SAN 324-3184. Tel: 717-428-1034. FAX: 717-428-3869. *Librn*, Suzy Hershey
Library Holdings: Bk Vols 13,014
Friends of the Library Group

YORK HAVEN

P NORTHEASTERN COMMUNITY LIBRARY,* 2 N Front St, 17370. SAN 315-3886. Tel: 717-266-4712. FAX: 717-266-4712. *Librn*, Roberta Hudson
Library Holdings: Bk Titles 10,009
Friends of the Library Group

YORK SPRINGS

S PACKARD TRUCK ORGANIZATION LIBRARY,* 1196 Mountain Rd, 17372. SAN 370-1832. Tel: 717-528-4920. *In Charge*, David B Lockard; E-Mail: dblockard@desupernet.net
Library Holdings: Per Subs 43
Special Collections: Packard trucks 1905-1923, brochures & clippings

YOUNGSVILLE

P YOUNGSVILLE PUBLIC LIBRARY,* 44 W Main St, 16371-1421. SAN 315-3894. Tel: 814-563-7670. FAX: 814-563-7670. *Librn*, Nancy Theuret; *Asst Librn*, Beckie Abraham
Founded 1931. Pop 2,158; Circ 10,671
Library Holdings: Bk Titles 8,500; Per Subs 34
Open Mon-Thurs 1-7:30, Fri 1-5 & Sat 10-4
Friends of the Library Group

YOUNGWOOD

J WESTMORELAND COUNTY COMMUNITY COLLEGE, Learning Resources Center,* 400 Armbrust Rd, 15697-1895. SAN 315-3908. Tel: 724-925-4100. Toll Free Tel: 800-262-2103. FAX: 724-925-1150. Web Site: www.westmoreland.cc.pa.us. *Dir*, Mary Stubbs; Tel: 724-925-4097, E-Mail: stubbsms@wccc.westmoreland.cc.pa.us; *Publ Servs, Ref*, Kathleen Keefe; Tel: 724-925-4101, E-Mail: keefeka@wcc.westmoreland.cc.pa.us; *Tech Servs*, Belinda Sedlak; Tel: 724-925-4096, E-Mail: sedlakbs@wccc.westmoreland.cc.pa.us; Staff 6 (MLS 4, Non-MLS 2)
Founded 1970. Enrl 6,400; Fac 82; Highest Degree: Associate
Library Holdings: Bk Vols 66,712; Bk Titles 62,014; Per Subs 500
Database Vendor: Ebsco - EbscoHost, epixtech, inc., Lexis-Nexis
Partic in Access Pa; OCLC Online Computer Library Center, Inc; PALINET & Union Library Catalogue of Pennsylvania; Share Westmoreland Consortium

P YOUNGWOOD AREA PUBLIC LIBRARY, 17 S Sixth St, 15697-1623. SAN 320-8540. Tel: 724-925-9350. FAX: 724-925-0124. E-Mail: yapl53@hotmail.com. Web Site: www.youngwood.org/library. *Librn*, Jean Antoline
Pop 3,749; Circ 11,272
Library Holdings: Bk Vols 11,940

ZELIENOPLE

P ZELIENOPLE PUBLIC LIBRARY, 227 S High St, 16063-1319. SAN 315-3916. Tel: 724-452-9330. FAX: 724-452-9318. E-Mail: zapl1@zbzoom.net. Web Site: www.zelienople.library-online.org. *Dir*, Janice Lawrence; *Ch Servs*, Kelli Rector; *Ad Servs*, Amy Kellner; Staff 3 (Non-MLS 3)
Founded 1919. Pop 11,500; Circ 95,000
Jan 2000-Dec 2000 Income $149,400, State $34,400, City $37,000, County $19,000, Locally Generated Income $59,000. Mats Exp $40,000, Books $32,000, Per/Ser (Incl. Access Fees) $4,000, AV Equip $4,000. Sal $94,000 (Prof $28,000)
Library Holdings: Bk Titles 62,000; Per Subs 100
Special Collections: Preschool AV Coll, puppets, videos, teaching devices
Automation Activity & Vendor Info: (Cataloging) TLC; (Circulation) TLC; (OPAC) TLC
Database Vendor: Ebsco - EbscoHost
Mem of Butler County Libr Syst

RHODE ISLAND

Date of Statistics: 1997
Population, 1996 Census: 1,034,547
Population Served by Public Libraries: 1,034,547
Total Volumes in Public Libraries: 4,098,667
Total Public Library Circulation: 6,462,068
Number of Regional Libraries: 0; Principal Public Library: 1
Number of Bookmobiles in State: 2
Grants-in-Aid to Public Libraries: 1996
  Services: $4,854,729 (state)
  Construction: $1,567,008

ASHAWAY

ASHAWAY FREE LIBRARY, 15 Knight St, 02804-1410. (Mail add: PO Box 70, 02804-0002), Tel: 401-377-2770. Interlibrary Loan Service Tel: 401-377-2770. FAX: 401-377-2770. *Head Librn*, Heather Field; *Asst Librn*, Catherine Danie; *Asst Librn*, Margaret Roever
Founded 1907. Pop 3,500; Circ 17,500
Library Holdings: Bk Vols 16,000
Subject Interests: Crafts, Fishing, Local history
Special Collections: Chariho Times, complete ed
Publications: Ashaway Notes (quarterly newsletter)
Partic in CLAN
Children's programs; outreach program; handicap access & restrooms

BARRINGTON

P BARRINGTON PUBLIC LIBRARY,* 281 County Rd, 02806. SAN 315-3940. Tel: 401-247-1920. FAX: 401-247-3763. *Dir*, Debbie Barchie; *Ref*, Ronald Reeves; *Tech Servs*, B Douglas Swiszcz; *Commun Servs*, Lauri Burke; *Ch Servs*, Mary Masse Harty; *YA Servs*, Peggie Chase; Staff 20 (MLS 6, Non-MLS 14)
Founded 1880. Circ 313,666
Jul 1997-Jun 1998 Income $747,048. Mats Exp Per/Ser (Incl. Access Fees) $6,868
Library Holdings: Bk Vols 119,000
Automation Activity & Vendor Info: (Circulation) epixtech, inc.
Publications: Calendar of Events (monthly)
Partic in Coop Librs Automated Network; Library of Rhode Island
Friends of the Library Group

R ZION BIBLE INSTITUTE LIBRARY, 27 Middle Hwy, 02806. SAN 320-7358. Tel: 401-246-0900, Ext 49. FAX: 401-246-0906. *Circ, Librn*, Ginger McDonald
Library Holdings: Bk Vols 37,000
Subject Interests: Rare books
Open Mon & Sat 9am-10pm, Tues-Fri 9-10:45 & 12:15-10, Sun 3-10

BLOCK ISLAND

P ISLAND FREE LIBRARY,* Dodge St, PO Box 520, 02807. SAN 315-3967. Tel: 401-466-3233. FAX: 401-466-3236. *Dir*, Lonni Todd; Staff 1 (MLS 1)
Founded 1875. Circ 10,307
Library Holdings: Bk Titles 23,000; Per Subs 152
Subject Interests: Natural history
Mem of S County Interrelated Libr Syst
Friends of the Library Group

BRISTOL

S BRISTOL HISTORICAL PRESERVATION SOCIETY LIBRARY, 48 Court St, PO Box 356, 02809. SAN 372-9311. Tel: 401-253-7223. *Librn*, Ray Battcher
Library Holdings: Bk Vols 1,000
Open Wed & Fri 1-5
Friends of the Library Group

C ROGER WILLIAMS UNIVERSITY LIBRARY, One Old Ferry Rd, 02809-2921. SAN 315-3975. Tel: 401-254-3031. Interlibrary Loan Service Tel: 401-254-3112. Circulation Tel: 401-254-3084. Reference Tel: 401-254-3375. Toll Free Tel: 800-458-7144. FAX: 401-254-0818. Web Site: www.rwu.edu/library. *Dean of Libr*, Peter V Deekle; Tel: 401-254-3063, E-Mail: pvd@alpha.rwu.edu; *Govt Doc, ILL, Ser*, John Fobert; E-Mail: jpf@alpha.rwu.edu; *Info Res*, Susan McMullen; E-Mail: stm@alpha.rwu.edu; *Archivist, Ref, Spec Coll*, Wendell B Pols; Tel: 401-254-3169, E-Mail: wbp@alpha.rwu.edu; *Circ*, Mary Lou Leocadio; Tel: 401-254-3316, E-Mail: mll@alpha.rwu.edu; *Acq, Coll Develop*, Christine Fagan; Tel: 401-254-3029, E-Mail: csf@alpha.rwu.edu; *Media Spec*, Veronica Maher; Tel: 401-254-3114, E-Mail: vtm@alpha.rwu.edu; *Tech Servs*, Mary Anne Golda; Tel: 401-254-3054, E-Mail: mag@alpha.edu; Staff 8 (MLS 8)
Founded 1948. Highest Degree: Bachelor
Jul 1999-Jun 2000 Income (Main Library and Branch Library) Parent Institution $1,541,248. Mats Exp $645,281, Books $173,500, Per/Ser (Incl. Access Fees) $225,000, Presv $9,000, Micro $19,500, AV Equip $16,000, Electronic Ref Mat (Incl. Access Fees) $55,900. Sal $899,299 (Prof $591,840)
Library Holdings: Bk Vols 170,000; Per Subs 1,225
Subject Interests: British hist, Bus, Marine biology, Poetry, Psychology, RI hist
Special Collections: Roger Williams Family Association Papers; United States Census Coll
Automation Activity & Vendor Info: (Acquisitions) Innovative Interfaces Inc.; (Cataloging) Innovative Interfaces Inc.; (Circulation) Innovative Interfaces Inc.; (Course Reserve) Innovative Interfaces Inc.; (ILL) Innovative Interfaces Inc.; (Media Booking) Innovative Interfaces Inc.; (OPAC) Innovative Interfaces Inc.; (Serials) Innovative Interfaces Inc.
Database Vendor: epixtech, inc., OCLC - First Search, ProQuest
Publications: Faculty Newsletter
Partic in Association of Rhode Island Health Sciences Libraries (ARIHSL); Consortium Of Rhode Island Academic & Research Libraries; Higher Educ Libr Info Network; Library of Rhode Island; Nelinet, Inc
Friends of the Library Group
Departmental Libraries:
ARCHITECTURE Tel: 401-254-3625. Web Site: www.rwu.edu/library. *Librn*, Elizabeth Peck Learned; Staff 1 (MLS 1)
  Library Holdings: Bk Vols 17,645; Per Subs 200
  Subject Interests: Architecture, Historic pres

P ROGERS FREE LIBRARY,* 525 Hope St, PO Box 538, 02809. SAN 315-3983. Tel: 401-253-6948. FAX: 401-253-5270. *Dir*, Joan C Prescott; E-Mail: joanpt@dsl.rhilinet.gov; Staff 15 (MLS 1, Non-MLS 14)

Founded 1878. Pop 22,000; Circ 75,000
Library Holdings: Bk Titles 51,000
Special Collections: Portuguese Language Coll
Partic in Cooperating Libraries Automated Network (CLAN)
Friends of the Library Group

CAROLINA

P CLARK MEMORIAL LIBRARY,* 7 Pinehurst Dr, PO Box 190, 02812-0190. SAN 315-4688. Tel: 401-364-6100. FAX: 401-364-7675. Web Site: seq.clan.lib.ri.us/cla/index.htm. *Dir*, Lynn Thompson; *Coll Develop*, Johanna Wolke
Pop 5,900
Jul 1997-Jun 1998 Income $107,176, State $13,090. Mats Exp $7,600, Books $6,500, Per/Ser (Incl. Access Fees) $1,000, Presv $100. Sal $45,661 (Prof $25,000)
Library Holdings: Bk Vols 25,000; Per Subs 57
Subject Interests: Local history, Rhode Island
Special Collections: Emily Hoxie Archives; Richmond Conservation Commission Coll; Richmond Historical Society Archives; Richmond Historical Society Costume Coll
Publications: Newsletter
Partic in Coop Librs Automated Network

CENTRAL FALLS

P CENTRAL FALLS FREE PUBLIC LIBRARY, Adams Library, 205 Central St, 02863. SAN 315-3991. Tel: 401-727-7440. FAX: 401-727-7442. *Dir*, Thomas Shannahan; *Ch Servs*, Maria Baxter; *Circ*, Donna Woodworth; *Tech Servs*, Judith Wilson Shanahan; Staff 1 (MLS 1)
Founded 1882. Pop 17,637; Circ 28,700
Library Holdings: Bk Vols 45,000; Per Subs 300
Special Collections: Civil War Coll; Local History Coll; Rhode Island Coll; Spanish Coll; Textile Special Coll
Automation Activity & Vendor Info: (Circulation) epixtech, inc.
Mem of Northern Interrelated Libr Syst

CHARLESTOWN

P CROSS' MILLS PUBLIC LIBRARY,* 4417 Old Post Rd, PO Box 1680, 02813-0909. SAN 315-4009. Tel: 401-364-6211. FAX: 401-364-0609. E-Mail: anncd@lori.state.ri.us. Web Site: www.charlestown.com. *Dir*, Ann Crawford; Staff 2 (Non-MLS 2)
Founded 1913. Pop 7,000; Circ 57,025
Jul 1997-Jun 1998 Income $190,911, State $15,675, City $139,972, Locally Generated Income $35,264. Mats Exp $7,713, Books $2,976, Per/Ser (Incl. Access Fees) $1,719, Presv $200. Sal $141,243
Library Holdings: Bk Titles 31,000; Per Subs 129
Subject Interests: Eclectic approach to self improvement, Indians of North America with local emphasis, Power resources incl alternate energy
Publications: Coop Librs Automated Network; OCLC Online Computer Libr Ctr, Inc
Partic in OCLC Online Computer Library Center, Inc
Open Mon 1-8, Tues & Thurs 9-1, Wed 9-6, Fri 1-6 & Sat 9-3

CHEPACHET

P GLOCESTER MANTON FREE PUBLIC LIBRARY,* 1137 Putnam Pike, 02814. SAN 377-2047. Tel: 401-568-6077. FAX: 401-567-0140. Web Site: www.204.17.98.72/gloweb.html. *Dir*, Gayle Wolstenholme
Library Holdings: Bk Titles 27,000; Per Subs 34

COVENTRY

P COVENTRY PUBLIC LIBRARY,* 1672 Flat River Rd, 02816. SAN 315-4017. Tel: 401-822-9100. Interlibrary Loan Service Tel: 401-822-9105. FAX: 401-822-9133. Web Site: www.seq.clan.lib.ri.us/cov/index.htm. *Dir*, Lynn H Blanchette; *Ch Servs*, Jeanne Bent; *Ch Servs*, Elizabeth J Farmer; *Tech Servs*, Brenda Fecteau; *Ref*, Sandra Dupree; Staff 20 (MLS 7, Non-MLS 13)
Founded 1972. Pop 32,000; Circ 176,000
Library Holdings: Bk Vols 100,000; Per Subs 90
Subject Interests: Adult literacy, Local history
Special Collections: Civil War Coll; High-Low Materials; Literacy Materials for Tutors & Students Including ESL
Publications: Newsletter
Mem of Western Interrelated Libr Syst
Partic in Cooperating Libraries Automated Network (CLAN)
Special Services - Outreach service to housebound & nursing homes; active literacy & English as a Second Language programs; library is a Rhode Island State Data Center affiliate & depository as well as an affiliate of Literacy Volunteers of America
Friends of the Library Group

CRANSTON

P CRANSTON PUBLIC LIBRARY, 140 Sockanosset Cross Rd, 02920-5539. SAN 359-7156. Tel: 401-943-9080. FAX: 401-946-5079. Web Site: seg.clan.lib.ri.us/cra/index.htm. *Dir*, David Macksam; Tel: 401-943-9080, E 103, E-Mail: davidmm@seq.clan.lib.ri.us; *Asst Dir*, John F Cory; *Ad Servs* Lynda L Ross; *Syst Coordr, Tech Servs*, Paul H Holliday Jr; *Ch Servs*, Michelle Vallee; *AV, YA Servs*, Linda C Archetto; Staff 66 (MLS 14, Non-MLS 52)
Founded 1966. Pop 77,000; Circ 724,853
Jul 1999-Jun 2000 Income (Main Library and Branch Library) $2,352,235, State $393,752, City $1,831,688, Locally Generated Income $126,795. Mat Exp $271,788, Books $200,000, Per/Ser (Incl. Access Fees) $24,753, AV Equip $36,335, Electronic Ref Mat (Incl. Access Fees) $10,700. Sal $1,730,273
Library Holdings: Bk Vols 217,575; Per Subs 493
Subject Interests: Boating, Boats, Careers, Child, Parent
Special Collections: Civil Service Test Books; Italian language books
Automation Activity & Vendor Info: (Circulation) epixtech, inc.
Database Vendor: Ebsco - EbscoHost, epixtech, inc.
Partic in Coop Librs Automated Network
Special Services for the Blind - Reading edge system
Friends of the Library Group
Branches: 5
ARLINGTON READING ROOM, 1064 Cranston St, 02920-7344. SAN 359-7180. Tel: 401-944-1662. *Librn*, Nancy Sousa
Library Holdings: Bk Vols 3,927
Partic in CLAN
AUBURN, 396 Pontiac Ave, 02910-3322. SAN 359-7210. Tel: 401-781-6116. FAX: 401-781-6132. *Librn*, Karen McGrath
Library Holdings: Bk Vols 20,154
Friends of the Library Group
KNIGHTSVILLE, 1847 Cranston St, 02920-4112. SAN 359-7245. Tel: 401 942-2504. *Librn*, Nancy Sousa
Library Holdings: Bk Vols 6,836
Friends of the Library Group
OAK LAWN, 230 Wilbur Ave, 02921-1046. SAN 359-727X. Tel: 401-942-1787. *Librn*, Joan Smith
Library Holdings: Bk Vols 14,426
Special Collections: Parent & Child Coll
Friends of the Library Group
WILLIAM H HALL FREE LIBRARY, 1825 Broad St, 02905-3599. SAN 322-5658. Tel: 401-781-2450. FAX: 401-781-2494. *Librn*, John Bucci
Library Holdings: Bk Vols 45,683
Subject Interests: Boating, Boats
Friends of the Library Group

ELEANOR SLATER HOSPITAL
M MEDICAL LIBRARY, Regan Bldg, PO Box 8269, 02920. SAN 315-4025. Tel: 401-464-3439. FAX: 401-464-3466. *Librn*, Grace Varghese
Library Holdings: Bk Vols 1,800; Per Subs 43
Mem of Asn of RI Health Sci Librs
M PATIENTS LIBRARY, Regan Bldg, PO Box 8269, 02920. SAN 329-6830. Tel: 401-464-3439. *Librn*, Grace Varghese
Library Holdings: Bk Vols 750; Per Subs 10

S TECHNIC INC LIBRARY,* One Spectacle St, 02910. SAN 328-4840. Tel: 401-781-6100. FAX: 401-781-2890. E-Mail: sales@technic.com. Web Site: www.technic.com. *Librn*, Al Weisberg
Library Holdings: Bk Vols 300; Per Subs 20
Open by appointment only 8-5

CUMBERLAND

P CUMBERLAND PUBLIC LIBRARY, Edward J Hayden Library, 1464 Diamond Hill Rd, 02864-5510. SAN 359-7369. Tel: 401-333-2552. Circulation Tel: 401-333-2552, Ext 4. Reference Tel: 401-333-2552, Ext 2. TDD: 401-333-9711. FAX: 401-334-0578. Web Site: www.clan.lib.ri.us/cum/index.htm. *Admin Dir*, Janet A Levesque; Tel: 401-333-2552, Ext 127, E-Mail: janetle@lori.state.ri.us; *Asst Dir*, Celeste M Dyer; Tel: 401-333-2552, Ext 128, E-Mail: celestdr@lori.state.ri.us; *Ch Servs*, Sharon R Brown; Tel: 401-333-2552, Ext 125, E-Mail: sharonbn@lori.state.ri.us; *Ref Serv Ad*, Cheryl A Maraj; Tel: 401-333-2552, Ext 201, E-Mail: cmaraj@hotmail.com; *Ad Servs*, Elizabeth Karageorge; Tel: 401-333-2552, Ext 121, E-Mail: elizabke@lori.state.ri.us; *YA Servs*, Jennifer J Hood; Tel: 401-333-2552, Ext 203, E-Mail: jennifhd@lori.state.ri.us; *Head Tech Servs*, Elaine Sumner; Tel: 401-333-2552, Ext 131; *Tech Servs*, Nancy Ross; Tel: 401-333-2552, Ext 31, E-Mail: nancyrs@lori.state.ri.us; *Per*, Carolyn Arnold; Tel: 401-333-2552, Ext 22; Staff 7 (MLS 7)
Founded 1946. Pop 29,038; Circ 218,861
Jul 1999-Jun 2000 Income $874,491, State $147,213, City $697,584, Locally Generated Income $28,661, Other $1,033. Mats Exp $158,029, Books $86,784, Per/Ser (Incl. Access Fees) $12,289, Presv $500, AV Equip $13,036, Other Print Mats $2,560, Electronic Ref Mat (Incl. Access Fees) $42,860. Sal $447,867 (Prof $257,328)
Library Holdings: Bk Vols 76,170; Per Subs 218; High Interest/Low Vocabulary Bk Vols 166; Bks on Deafness & Sign Lang 42

Subject Interests: City hist, Cookery, Local history, Rhode Island
Automation Activity & Vendor Info: (Cataloging) epixtech, inc.; (Circulation) epixtech, inc.; (OPAC) epixtech, inc.
Database Vendor: epixtech, inc., GaleNet, IAC - Info Trac, IAC - SearchBank, ProQuest
Publications: The Monastery Reader (Newsletter)
Partic in Coop Librs Automated Network
Special Services for the Deaf - TDD
Special Services for the Blind - Talking Books
Friends of the Library Group

:AST GREENWICH

EAST GREENWICH FREE LIBRARY,* 82 Peirce St, 02818. SAN 315-4033. Tel: 401-884-9510. FAX: 401-884-3790. *Dir*, Karen A Taylor; *Ch Servs*, Margaret Davis; Staff 9 (MLS 4, Non-MLS 5)
Founded 1869. Pop 12,000; Circ 72,852
Library Holdings: Bk Vols 55,368; Per Subs 110
Subject Interests: Genealogy, RI hist
Publications: Friends Newsletter
Mem of Western Interrelated Libr Syst
Partic in RI Libr Film Coop
Friends of the Library Group

NEW ENGLAND WIRELESS & STEAM MUSEUM INCORPORATED LIBRARY,* 1300 Frenchtown Rd, 02818. SAN 371-2559. Tel: 401-885-0545. FAX: 401-884-0683. E-Mail: newsm@ids.net. Web Site: www.users.ids.net/~newsm. *Dir*, Robert W Merriam; *Librn*, Nancy Merriam
Library Holdings: Bk Vols 20,000

:AST PROVIDENCE

EAST PROVIDENCE PUBLIC LIBRARY, 41 Grove Ave, 02914. SAN 359-7423. Tel: 401-434-2453. TDD: 401-435-5542. FAX: 401-434-3324. Web Site: www.clan.lib.ri.us/epl/index.htm. *Dir*, Roberta A E Cairns; *Asst Dir*, Eileen Socha; *Ref*, Diane Swindlehurst
Pop 50,000; Circ 317,986
Nov 2000-Oct 2001 Income State $50,845. Mats Exp $148,000, Books $110,000, Per/Ser (Incl. Access Fees) $13,000, Electronic Ref Mat (Incl. Access Fees) $5,000. Sal $986,273 (Prof $480,338)
Library Holdings: Bk Vols 186,500; Per Subs 312
Subject Interests: Literature, Portuguese, Psychology, Travel
Special Collections: East Bay Literacy
Publications: Newsletter
Partic in Cooperating Libraries Automated Network (CLAN)
Friends of the Library Group
Branches: 3
FULLER, 260 Dover Ave, 02914. SAN 359-7458. Tel: 401-434-1136. FAX: 401-434-3896.
RIVERSIDE, 100 Bullocks Point Ave, 02915. SAN 359-7482. Tel: 401-433-4877.
RUMFORD, 1392 Pawtucket Ave, 02916. SAN 359-7512. Tel: 401-434-8559.

ESMOND

P EAST SMITHFIELD PUBLIC LIBRARY, 50 Esmond St, 02917-3016. SAN 315-405X. Tel: 401-231-5150. FAX: 401-231-2940. E-Mail: esm@seq.clan.lib.ri.us. Web Site: www.204.17.98.73/esmlib/. *Dir*, Elodie E Blackmore. Subject Specialists: *Cookery*, Elodie E Blackmore; *Medicine*, Elodie E Blackmore; Staff 10 (MLS 1, Non-MLS 9)
Founded 1916. Pop 19,163; Circ 55,602
Jul 1999-Jun 2000 Income $269,700, State $57,635, Locally Generated Income $206,850, Other $74. Mats Exp $42,551, Books $36,574, AV Equip $3,635. Sal $154,235
Library Holdings: Bk Titles 51,855; Per Subs 562
Special Collections: Cookery; Medicine for the Layman
Database Vendor: IAC - SearchBank
Publications: Monthly Newsletter
Partic in Coop Librs Automated Network
Open Mon, Tues, Thurs & Fri 10-5 & 7-9, Wed 10-5, Sat 10-3
Friends of the Library Group

FOSTER

P FOSTER PUBLIC LIBRARY, 184 Howard Hill Rd, 02825. SAN 315-4068. Tel: 401-397-4801. FAX: 401-392-3101. Web Site: 204.17.98.73/foslib.; Staff 8 (MLS 1, Non-MLS 7)
Pop 4,200; Circ 40,130
1999-2000 Income $50,474. Mats Exp $13,369, Books $9,000, Per/Ser (Incl. Access Fees) $1,854. Sal $29,343 (Prof $16,000)
Library Holdings: Bk Vols 14,000; Per Subs 64
Publications: Newsletter (irregular)
Partic in Cooperating Libraries Automated Network (CLAN)
Open Tues-Thurs 1-9pm, Sat 10am-4pm & Sun 1-4pm

P TYLER FREE LIBRARY, 81A Moosup Valley Rd, 02825. SAN 315-4076. Tel: 401-397-7930. FAX: 401-397-7930. Web Site: 204.17.98.73/foslib.; Staff 5 (MLS 1, Non-MLS 4)
Founded 1900. Circ 17,375
1999-2000 Income $67,007. Mats Exp $12,400, Books $9,500, Per/Ser (Incl. Access Fees) $900, Other Print Mats $2,000. Sal $26,713
Library Holdings: Bk Vols 11,000; Per Subs 25
Partic in Cooperating Libraries Automated Network (CLAN)
Open Mon 1-8, Wed 10-8, Fri 1-5 & Sat 11-4

GREENVILLE

P GREENVILLE PUBLIC LIBRARY,* 573 Putnam Pike, 02828-2195. SAN 315-4084. Tel: 401-949-3630. FAX: 401-949-0530. E-Mail: gvref@aol.com. Web Site: www.ultranet.com/~greenvil/. *Dir*, Christopher LaRoux; *Asst Dir*, Carol Gallant; Staff 14 (MLS 6, Non-MLS 8)
Founded 1882. Pop 19,000; Circ 153,000
Library Holdings: Bk Vols 59,000; Per Subs 163
Subject Interests: Arts, Crafts
Special Collections: High/Low Young adult & Adult new reader materials
Publications: Libraries of Smithfield (monthly newsletter)
Partic in Cooperating Libraries Automated Network (CLAN)
Friends of the Library Group

HARMONY

P HARMONY LIBRARY, 195 Putnam Pike, Box 419, 02829. SAN 377-2063. Tel: 401-949-2850. FAX: 401-949-2868. Web Site: 204.17.98.73/harlib/. *Librn*, Joan Hackett
Library Holdings: Bk Titles 25,000; Per Subs 45
Partic in Coop Librs Automated Network; Library of Rhode Island

HARRISVILLE

P JESSE M SMITH MEMORIAL LIBRARY,* 144 Main St, PO Box 511, 02830-0511. SAN 315-4092. Tel: 401-568-8244. FAX: 401-568-8244. E-Mail: jmslibrary@yahoo.com. *Dir*, Sandra Mundy; *Ch Servs*, Cynthia L Szymanski; Staff 2 (MLS 2)
Pop 16,200; Circ 47,750
Library Holdings: Bk Vols 37,200; Per Subs 64
Subject Interests: Disabilities, Special education, Substance abuse
Special Collections: Animal Husbandry; Antiques & Collectibles; Early Americana
Partic in Library of Rhode Island

HOPE

P HOPE LIBRARY, 374 North Rd, PO Box 310, 02831. SAN 315-4106. Tel: 401-821-7910. FAX: 401-822-4068. *Dir*, Holly Wendy Albanese; E-Mail: halbanes@seq.clan.lib.ri.us
Founded 1875
Library Holdings: Bk Vols 19,500; Per Subs 50
Database Vendor: IAC - SearchBank
Publications: Newsletter
Mem of Maine State Library
Friends of the Library Group

HOPE VALLEY

P LANGWORTHY PUBLIC LIBRARY, 24 Spring St, 02832. (Mail add: PO Box 478, 02832), SAN 315-4114. Tel: 401-539-2851. FAX: 401-539-2851. Web Site: www.langworthy.org. *Dir*, David J Panciera; E-Mail: d_epanciera@yahoo.com; Staff 3 (MLS 1, Non-MLS 2)
Founded 1888. Pop 3,600; Circ 27,000
Jul 1999-Jun 2000 Income $95,000, State $20,000, City $45,000, Locally Generated Income $25,000, Other $5,000. Mats Exp $12,500, Books $10,000, Per/Ser (Incl. Access Fees) $1,750, Manuscripts & Archives $750. Sal $47,000
Library Holdings: Bk Vols 25,000; Per Subs 64
Subject Interests: Genealogy, Local history
Function: Archival collection
Mem of Coop Libr Automated Network
Open Mon 2-5 & 6-9, Tues & Thur 6-9, Wed 10-5 & 6-9, Fri & Sat 10-5

JAMESTOWN

P JAMESTOWN PHILOMENIAN LIBRARY, 26 North Rd, 02835. SAN 359-7547. Tel: 401-423-7280. FAX: 401-423-7281. Web Site: www.jamestownri.com/library. *Librn*, Judith H Bell; Staff 8 (MLS 3, Non-MLS 5)
Founded 1847. Pop 4,999; Circ 76,000
Mar 2000-Feb 2001 Income (Main Library Only) $237,603, State $43,000, City $194,603

Library Holdings: Bk Vols 41,000; Per Subs 60
Subject Interests: Movies, Sailing, Theatre, Wildflowers
Partic in Coop Librs Automated Network
Friends of the Library Group
Branches: 1
SIDNEY L WRIGHT MUSEUM, 26 North Rd, 02835. SAN 359-7571. Tel: 401-423-7280. *Librn*, Judith H Bell
Library Holdings: Bk Vols 100
Special Collections: Indian Artifacts(Collection currently belongs to the Narragansett Indian Tribe);
Friends of the Library Group

JOHNSTON

S FM GLOBAL LIBRARY, 1301 Atwood Ave, PO Box 7500, 02919. SAN 315-4122. Tel: 401-275-3000, Ext 1464. FAX: 401-275-3029. *Librn*, Janice Totilo; E-Mail: janice.totilo@fmglobal.com
Founded 1973
Library Holdings: Bk Titles 3,000
Subject Interests: Bus, Fire protection, Ins, Loss prevention, Mgt
Open Mon-Fri 8:30-4:15

P MARIAN J MOHR MEMORIAL LIBRARY, One Memorial Ave, 02919-3271. SAN 315-4130. Tel: 401-231-4980. FAX: 401-231-4984. *Dir*, Derryl R Johnson; E-Mail: derryljn@lori.state.ri.us; *Ref Serv, Tech Servs*, Jon Anderson; *Ch Servs*, Carolyn Tarpey; Staff 3 (MLS 3)
Founded 1961. Pop 26,500; Circ 81,500
Jul 1999-Jun 2000 Income $455,136, State $96,043, City $336,193, Other $22,900. Mats Exp $77,142, Books $51,947, Per/Ser (Incl. Access Fees) $4,875, Presv $3,019, Electronic Ref Mat (Incl. Access Fees) $12,191. Sal $245,315
Library Holdings: Bk Titles 74,467; Per Subs 137
Subject Interests: Italian Am, Italy
Special Collections: Local history
Automation Activity & Vendor Info: (Circulation) epixtech, inc.
Partic in Coop Librs Automated Network
Friends of the Library Group

KINGSTON

S METASCIENCE FOUNDATION LIBRARY, PO Box 32, 02881. SAN 324-3966. Tel: 401-294-2414. FAX: 401-294-2414. Web Site: www.netsense.net/tesla. *Librn*, Marc Seifer; *Asst Librn*, Lois Pazienza
Founded 1977
Library Holdings: Bk Titles 600; Per Subs 12
Subject Interests: Astrology, Gurdjieff, Lobsang Rampa, Palmistry, Parapsychol, Precognition, Psychics, Psychokinesis, Quantum physics of consciousness, Synchronicity, Tarot, Telepathy, Uri Geller, Wilhelm Reich
Special Collections: Graphology Coll, text books, translations, transparencies, articles; Nikola Tesla Coll, patents, biographies, articles, doc; parapsychology journals
Publications: Journal of Occult Studies; MetaScience Annual

S PETTAQUAMSCUTT HISTORICAL SOCIETY LIBRARY, 2636 Kingstown Rd, 02881. SAN 374-8464. Tel: 401-783-1328, 401-783-3969. *Dir*, Christopher Bickford; Staff 1 (Non-MLS 1)
Founded 1958
2000-2000 Mats Exp $300. Sal $15,000
Library Holdings: Bk Titles 400
Subject Interests: Genealogy, RI hist
Special Collections: Washington County

C UNIVERSITY OF RHODE ISLAND LIBRARY, 15 Lippitt Rd, 02881. SAN 359-7601. Tel: 401-874-2666. Circulation Tel: 401-874-2672. Reference Tel: 401-874-2653. TDD: 800-745-5555. FAX: 401-874-4608. E-Mail: library@uri.edu. Web Site: www.library.uri.edu/. *Dir*, Kirk G Artemis; E-Mail: akirk@uri.edu; *Dean*, Paul Gandel; E-Mail: gandel@uri.edu; *Govt Doc*, Deborah Mongeau; Tel: 401-874-4610, E-Mail: dmongeau@uri.edu; *Head, Cat*, Amar Lahiri; Tel: 401-874-2660, E-Mail: aklahair@uri.edu; *ILL, Online Servs, Ser*, Sylvia Krausse; Tel: 401-874-2640, E-Mail: skrausse@uri.edu; *Spec Coll*, David Maslyn; Tel: 401-874-2594, E-Mail: dcm@uri.edu; *Coll Develop*, Michael Vocino; Tel: 401-874-4605, E-Mail: vocino@uri.edu; *Media Spec*, Eileen Tierney; Tel: 401-874-4267, E-Mail: eileent@uri.edu; *Syst Coordr*, Laury Turkalo; Tel: 401-874-2820, E-Mail: laury@uri.edu; *Web Coordr*, Andree Rathemacher; Tel: 401-874-5096, E-Mail: andree@uri.edu; *Tech Servs*, William T O'Malley; Tel: 401-874-4799, E-Mail: rka101@uri.edu; *Head, Circ*, James Teliha; Tel: 406-874-4619, E-Mail: telihaj@uri.edu; *Publ Servs*, Robin Devin; Tel: 401-874-2640, E-Mail: rdevin@uri.edu; Staff 60 (MLS 15, Non-MLS 45)
Founded 1892. Enrl 15,765; Highest Degree: Doctorate
Jul 1999-Jun 2000 Income (Main and Other College/University Libraries) Parent Institution $5,298,142. Mats Exp $2,225,000, Books $325,000, Per/Ser (Incl. Access Fees) $1,900,000. Sal $2,843,534 (Prof $1,462,053)
Library Holdings: Bk Vols 1,255,678; Bk Titles 820,876; Per Subs 7,809
Subject Interests: Behav sci, Education, Engineering, Environmental studies, Humanities, Indust, Marine, Natural science, Sci-tech, Soc sci
Special Collections: Archives; Episcopal Diocese of RI Records; Fritz Eichenberg Collection; Manuscript Coll (Records of the Episcopal Diocese of Rhode Island; Oral Histories; Rare Books (Ezra Pound, Edna St Vincent Millay, Walt Whitman); Rare Books (Pound, St. Vincent Millay, Whitman); Rhode Island History & Literature; Rhode Island History & Literature; Rhode Island Oyster Bed Records 1844-1935; Rhode Island Oyster Bed Records 1844-1935); RI Political Papers; Senator Claiborne Pell Papers; Senator John Chafee papers; Senator Pell Papers
Automation Activity & Vendor Info: (Acquisitions) Innovative Interfaces Inc.; (Cataloging) Innovative Interfaces Inc.; (Circulation) Innovative Interfaces Inc.; (Circulation) Innovative Interfaces Inc.; (ILL) Innovative Interfaces Inc.; (Media Booking) Innovative Interfaces Inc.; (OPAC) Innovative Interfaces Inc.
Publications: Bibliographies; Library Letter; Library Link
Partic in Consortium Of Rhode Island Academic & Research Libraries; Helin; Nelinet, Inc; New Eng Res Librs
Departmental Libraries:
COLLEGE OF CONTINUING EDUCATION
See Separate Entry in Providence , Shepard Bldg, 80 Washington St, Providence, 02881. Tel: 401-277-3818. FAX: 401-351-8262.
PELL MARINE SCIENCE LIBRARY
See Separate Entry in Narragansett

LINCOLN

J COMMUNITY COLLEGE OF RHODE ISLAND, William F Flanagan Campus, 1762 Louisquisset Pike, 02865-4585. SAN 315-4157. Tel: 401-333-7058. FAX: 401-333-7115. *Dean of Libr*, Charles D'Arezzo; *Coll Develop*, Marla Wallace; *Circ*, Ruth E Souto; *AV*, Linda Richard; *Ref*, Rae Horodysky; *Ref*, Frank St Pierre
Founded 1972
Library Holdings: Bk Vols 43,648; Per Subs 400

P LINCOLN PUBLIC LIBRARY, 145 Old River Rd, 02865. SAN 315-4149. Tel: 401-333-2422. FAX: 401-333-4154. Web Site: www.lincolnlibrary.com. *Dir*, Becky A Boragine; E-Mail: beckybe@lori.state.ri.us; *Asst Libr Dir*, Diane Dexter; E-Mail: dianedr@lori.state.ri.us; *Ch Servs*, Lori McNaught; Staff 11 (MLS 4, Non-MLS 7)
Founded 1875. Pop 18,045; Circ 159,566
Jul 1999-Jun 2000 Income $665,747, State $107,184, City $558,563. Mats Exp $166,836, Books $113,116, Per/Ser (Incl. Access Fees) $6,965, Presv $3,528, AV Equip $14,974, Electronic Ref Mat (Incl. Access Fees) $28,253. Sal $356,298
Library Holdings: Bk Vols 62,613; Per Subs 178
Subject Interests: Local history
Special Collections: Descriptive videos for Blind/visually handicapped
Database Vendor: Ebsco - EbscoHost, ProQuest
Publications: Newsletter (quarterly)
Partic in Coop Librs Automated Network
Friends of the Library Group

LITTLE COMPTON

P BROWNELL LIBRARY, Little Compton Free Public Library, 44 Commons PO Box 146, 02837. SAN 315-4165. Tel: 401-635-8562. FAX: 401-635-8562. *Librn*, Beth Galembeske; E-Mail: bethga@lori.state.ri.us
Founded 1879. Circ 11,200
Library Holdings: Bk Vols 25,000; Per Subs 41
Mem of Island Interrelated Libr Syst
Open Mon 9-5, Tues-Thurs 1-5
Friends of the Library Group

MIDDLETOWN

P MIDDLETOWN PUBLIC LIBRARY, 700 W Main Rd, 02842-6391. SAN 315-4173. Tel: 401-846-1573. FAX: 401-846-3031. Web Site: www.204.17.98.73/midlib. *Dir*, Robert L Balliot; E-Mail: robertbt@lori.state.ri.us; *Assoc Dir*, Barbara Camadeco; *Ref Servs YA*, Heather Huggins; *Res*, Joanne Gorman; Staff 18 (MLS 5, Non-MLS 13)
Founded 1848. Pop 19,460
Jul 1999-Jun 2000 Income $580,000, State $99,000, City $446,000, Other $35,000. Mats Exp $112,000, Books $50,000, Per/Ser (Incl. Access Fees) $7,000, AV Equip $35,000, Electronic Ref Mat (Incl. Access Fees) $20,000. Sal $255,000
Library Holdings: Bk Vols 53,000; Per Subs 100
Special Collections: Rhode Island-Middletown History (Rhode Island Historical Coll)
Automation Activity & Vendor Info: (Circulation) epixtech, inc.; (ILL) epixtech, inc.
Database Vendor: Ebsco - EbscoHost, epixtech, inc., IAC - SearchBank, OCLC - First Search, ProQuest
Publications: Friends of the Library (newsletter)
Function: Reference services available
Mem of Coop Libr Automated Network
Partic in Coop Librs Automated Network
Friends of the Library Group

TEMPLE SHALOM, Judaica Library, 223 Valley Rd, 02842-4372. SAN 323-8687. Tel: 401-846-9002. *Librn*, Marc S Jagolinzer
Friends of the Library Group

ARRAGANSETT

NARRAGANSETT PUBLIC LIBRARY,* 35 Kingstown Rd, 02882. SAN 315-419X. Tel: 401-789-9507. FAX: 401-782-0677. Web Site: www.204.17.98.73/narlib/. *Dir*, Barbara Mirabelli; *Ref*, Joyce Brothers; *Circ*, Marilyn Sherman; Staff 2 (MLS 2)
Founded 1903. Pop 25,000; Circ 102,000
Library Holdings: Bk Vols 40,000; Per Subs 102
Subject Interests: Local history, Poetry, Travel
Partic in Coop Librs Automated Network
Open Mon 10-9, Tues-Fri 10-6 & Sat 10-5
Friends of the Library Group

NATIONAL SEA GRANT LIBRARY, Pell Library Bldg, URI-Bay Campus, 02882-1197. SAN 359-7695. Tel: 401-874-6114. FAX: 401-874-6160. E-Mail: nsgd@gso.uri.edu. Web Site: nsgl.gso.uri.edu. *Mgr*, Cynthia Murray; Tel: 401-874-6539; *ILL*, Joyce Winn; Staff 3 (MLS 1, Non-MLS 2)
Founded 1970
Library Holdings: Bk Titles 30,000; Per Subs 62
Subject Interests: Applied oceanog, Aquaculture, Coastal mgt, Ecosystem res, Fisheries, Law, Marine educ, Marine recreation, Marine transportation, Ocean engineering, Pollution, Soc
Publications: Sea Grant Abstracts (quarterly)
Depository contains technical reports, advisory reports, annual reports, conference proceedings, reference material & reprints

UNITED STATES ENVIRONMENTAL PROTECTION AGENCY, National Health and Environmental Effects Research Laboratory Library, 27 Tarzwell Dr, 02882-1198. SAN 315-4181. Tel: 401-782-3025. FAX: 401-782-3140. *Librn*, Martha Caterson-Beazley; E-Mail: beazley.martha@epa.gov
Founded 1967
Library Holdings: Bk Vols 3,200
Subject Interests: Biological oceanog, Effects of pollutants on marine life, Fisheries biol, Marine culture systs, Water-marine pollution

UNIVERSITY OF RHODE ISLAND, GRADUATE SCHOOL OF OCEANOGRAPHY, Pell Marine Science Library, Narragansett Bay Campus, 02882-1197. SAN 359-7660. Tel: 401-874-6161. FAX: 401-874-6101. E-Mail: pellib@gso.uri.edu. Web Site: www.gso.uri.edu/pell/pell.html. *Dir*, Eleanor Uhlinger; Staff 5 (MLS 1, Non-MLS 4)
Founded 1959. Enrl 103; Fac 33; Highest Degree: Doctorate
Jul 1999-Jun 2000 Mats Exp $163,581, Books $12,581, Per/Ser (Incl. Access Fees) $138,000, Electronic Ref Mat (Incl. Access Fees) $13,000. Sal $241,523
Library Holdings: Bk Vols 50,578; Per Subs 854
Subject Interests: Marine biology, Oceanography
Special Collections: Barge North Cape Oil Spill; Marine & Polar Expeditionary Reports; Narragansett Bay; Quonset Point/Davisville (RI) Port Development.
Automation Activity & Vendor Info: (Cataloging) Innovative Interfaces Inc.; (Circulation) Innovative Interfaces Inc.; (Course Reserve) Innovative Interfaces Inc.; (OPAC) Innovative Interfaces Inc.
Database Vendor: Ebsco - EbscoHost, OCLC - First Search
Mem of Rhode Island Interrelated Libr Syst
Partic in Asn Col & Res Librs; Consortium Of Rhode Island Academic & Research Libraries; HELIN NELGU; IAMSLIC; Library of Rhode Island; Nelinet, Inc; OCLC Online Computer Library Center, Inc

NEWPORT

S INTERNATIONAL TENNIS HALL OF FAME & TENNIS MUSEUM LIBRARY, Newport Casino, 194 Bellevue Ave, 02840-3515. SAN 315-4203. Tel: 401-849-3990. FAX: 401-849-8780. Web Site: www.tennisfame.org. *Archivist, Librn, Res*, Mark S Young, II; E-Mail: markyoung3@aol.com
Founded 1954
Library Holdings: Bk Vols 10,000
Subject Interests: Architects, Enshrinees, Gilded age, Newport Casino, Tennis, Tennis develop, Tennis hist, Tennis players
Publications: Hall of Fame News (quarterly)

S MUSEUM OF YACHTING, (MOY), Phil Weld Memorial Library, Fort Adams State Park, PO Box 129, 02840. SAN 323-8210. Tel: 401-847-1018. FAX: 401-847-8320. E-Mail: museum@moy.org. Web Site: www.moy.org. *Dir*, J Peter Marnane; Tel: 401-847-1035; *Archivist*, Phil Crowther, Jr; Tel: 401-847-1035
Founded 1980
Library Holdings: Bk Vols 2,500
Special Collections: America's Cup (Crowther Coll); Galleries; Hall of Fame for Singlehanded Sailors, America's Cup, Small Boats, Own 12-meter courageous
Publications: The Spinnaker (quarterly newsletter)
Restriction: Not a lending library
Function: Research library
Open May 15-Oct 31, seven days a week, open Nov 1-May 15 by appointment

GM NAVAL AMBULATORY CARE CENTER, NEWPORT (NACC, NEWPORT), Medical Library, One Riggs Rd Bldg 43, 02841-1002. SAN 325-4534. Tel: 401-841-4512. FAX: 401-841-4192. E-Mail: wmjacome@us.med.navy.mil.
Library Holdings: Bk Titles 1,169; Per Subs 225
Subject Interests: Medicine, Ophthalmology, Orthopedics
Publications: Bulletin of the Medical Library Association
Mem of Rhode Island Interrelated Libr Syst
Partic in Association of Rhode Island Health Sciences Libraries (ARIHSL); Basic Health Sciences Library Network; Consortium of Navy Librs
Open Mon-Fri 8-5

S NEWPORT HISTORICAL SOCIETY LIBRARY, 82 Touro St, 02840. SAN 315-4211. Tel: 401-846-0813. FAX: 401-846-1853. Web Site: www.newporthistorical.org. *Librn*, Bertram Lippincott, III; *Curator*, Ronald Potvin. Subject Specialists: *Genealogy*, Bertram Lippincott, III; *Manuscripts*, Ronald Potvin
Founded 1854
Library Holdings: Bk Titles 13,000
Subject Interests: 18th Century colonial merchants, Architecture, Church rec, Decorative arts, Genealogy, Newport hist, Newport Town Council
Special Collections: Merchant Account Books; Newport Imprints
Publications: Newport History (quarterly bulletin); Newport: An Historical Sketch
Restriction: In-house use for visitors, Non-circulating
Mem of Island Interrelated Libr Syst
Open Tues-Fri 9:30-4:30 & Sat 9:30-noon

M NEWPORT HOSPITAL, Ina Mosher Library Resource Center,* 11 Friendship St, 02840. SAN 315-422X. Tel: 401-846-6400, Ext 1311. FAX: 401-845-1073. *Librn*, Tosca N Carpenter
Founded 1958
Library Holdings: Bk Vols 5,602; Bk Titles 4,702; Per Subs 173
Subject Interests: Health sci
Partic in New Eng Regional Med Libr Serv
Open Mon-Thurs 8-8 & Fri 8-5

P NEWPORT PUBLIC LIBRARY,* 300 Spring St, 02840. SAN 315-4238. Tel: 401-847-8720. FAX: 401-847-8756, Ext 116. *Dir*, Regina Slezak; *Asst Librn, Ref*, Patricia LaRose; *Circ*, Edna Wells; *Ch Servs*, Kathy Ryan; *Bkmobile Coordr*, Mary Barrett; Staff 13 (MLS 4, Non-MLS 9)
Founded 1868. Pop 28,700; Circ 197,940
Library Holdings: Bk Vols 126,000; Per Subs 290
Subject Interests: Black hist, Cookery, Newport hist
Special Collections: Afro-American Coll; Chinese Room Coll; Cookbooks
Mem of Rhode Island Interrelated Libr Syst
Partic in CLAN
Friends of the Library Group

S REDWOOD LIBRARY & ATHENAEUM, 50 Bellevue Ave, 02840-3292. SAN 315-4246. Tel: 401-847-0292. FAX: 401-841-5680. E-Mail: redwood@edgenet.net. Web Site: www.redwood1747.org. *Dir*, Cheryl V Helms; *Coll Develop, Dir Libr Serv*, Lynda Bronaugh; *Tech Servs*, Wendy Kieron-Sanchez; *Head, Circ*, Nancy Hacket; *ILL*, Kathy Weber; *Spec Coll & Archives*, Maris Humphreys; *Syst Coordr*, Petriona Ross; *Web Coordr*, Jennifer Caswell; Staff 6 (MLS 5, Non-MLS 1)
Founded 1747
Jul 1999-Jun 2000 Income $714,823, State $3,200, Locally Generated Income $295,623, Other $416,000. Mats Exp $60,125, Books $45,195, Per/Ser (Incl. Access Fees) $12,600, Presv $2,330. Sal $512,388
Library Holdings: Bk Vols 162,000; Per Subs 221
Subject Interests: Arts, Gen, Humanities
Special Collections: Calvert, Greenvale & Perry Colls (important 19th century personal libraries); Cary Coll (early 18th, 19th century furniture, interior design & decoration); Fine & Decorative Arts - Fine Arts Coll (18th & 19th century paintings, sculpture & furniture); Gladys Moore Vanderbilt Szechenyi Memorial Coll (18th & early 19th century American portraits); Original Coll (mid 18th century), bks & mss; Pre-1800 imprints; Schumacher Coll (Newportiana)
Automation Activity & Vendor Info: (Circulation) Sagebrush Corporation; (OPAC) Sagebrush Corporation
Database Vendor: Ebsco - EbscoHost, OCLC - First Search
Publications: 1968: A Talk by the Honorable Marshall Brement; Annual reports; Booklist (quarterly); Charles Bird King Catalog; Furniture in Print; Henry James, Edith Wharton & Newport; Newsletter (quarterly); Pattern Books from the Redwood Library; Photographs of Lisette Prince; Recollection of Daniel Berkeley Updike; Redwood Papers: A Bicentennial Collection; The Viking Tower: A Finding Aid; Vetruvius Americanus Catalog
Restriction: Circulation limited
Partic in OCLC Online Computer Library Center, Inc

C SALVE REGINA UNIVERSITY, McKillop Library, 100 Ochre Point Ave, 02840-4192. SAN 315-4254. Tel: 401-341-2330. FAX: 401-341-2951. Web Site: www.library.salve.edu. *Dir*, Kathleen Boyd; *Cat*, Ann Kowalski; *Circ*, Joe Foley; *Coll Develop*, Joan Bartrman; *ILL*, Christine Bagley; *Ref*, John Lewis; Staff 15 (MLS 11, Non-MLS 4)
Founded 1947. Enrl 2,400; Fac 120; Highest Degree: Doctorate
Library Holdings: Bk Vols 120,000; Bk Titles 100,000; Per Subs 888
Special Collections: Jewish Holocaust (Dora & Elias Blumen Libr for the Study of Holocaust Literature); Whiteker Record Coll
Automation Activity & Vendor Info: (OPAC) Innovative Interfaces Inc.
Database Vendor: GaleNet, Lexis-Nexis, OCLC - First Search, OVID Technologies, ProQuest, Silverplatter Information Inc.
Function: Research library
Partic in Association of Rhode Island Health Sciences Libraries (ARIHSL); Consortium Of Rhode Island Academic & Research Libraries; Higher Educ Libr Info Network; Nelinet, Inc; OCLC Online Computer Library Center, Inc
Friends of the Library Group

C UNITED STATES NAVAL WAR COLLEGE LIBRARY, 686 Cushing Rd, 02841-1207. SAN 315-4262. Tel: 401-841-2641. Interlibrary Loan Service Tel: 401-841-6509. Circulation Tel: 401-841-4386. Reference Tel: 401-841-4551. FAX: 401-841-1140, 401-841-4804, 401-841-6491. E-Mail: libref@nwc.navy.mil. Web Site: www.nwc.navy.mil/library. *Dir*, Robert E Schnare; Tel: 401-841-2641, Fax: 401-841-6491, E-Mail: schnarer@nwc.navy.mil; *Tech Servs*, Lucille M Rosa; Tel: 401-841-6492, Fax: 401-841-6562, E-Mail: rosal@nwc.navy.mil; *Cat*, Gina Brown; Tel: 401-841-4307, Fax: 401-841-6562, E-Mail: browng@nwc.navy.mil; *Reader Servs*, Michael C Riggle; Tel: 401-841-2642, E-Mail: rigglem@nwc.navy.mil; *Ref*, Doris B Ottaviano; Tel: 401-841-6500, E-Mail: ottaviad@nwc.navy.mil; *ILL*, Alice Juda; Tel: 401-841-6503, E-Mail: judaa@nwc.navy.mil; *ILL*, Robin Lima; Tel: 401-841-6509, E-Mail: limar@nwc.navy.mil; *Archivist*, Evelyn M Cherpak; Tel: 401-841-2435, Fax: 401-841-7790, E-Mail: cherpake@nwc.navy.mil; *Coll Develop*, Loretta Silvia; Tel: 401-841-4345, Fax: 401-841-6562, E-Mail: silvial@nwc.navy.mil; Staff 14 (MLS 11, Non-MLS 3)
Founded 1884. Enrl 500; Fac 150; Highest Degree: Master
Oct 1999-Sep 2000 Income $404,728. Mats Exp $261,548, Books $53,950, Per/Ser (Incl. Access Fees) $90,927, Presv $13,872, Micro $45,792, Manuscripts & Archives $7,261, Electronic Ref Mat (Incl. Access Fees) $49,746. Sal $1,300,000
Library Holdings: Bk Vols 269,005; Bk Titles 158,342; Per Subs 747
Subject Interests: Area studies, History, International law, International relations, Mil art, Mil sci, Naval art, Naval sci, Political science
Special Collections: US Pre-1900 geography, manuscripts, personal papers & oral histories concerning the Navy & Narragansett Bay; US Pre-1900 naval & military history, art & science
Automation Activity & Vendor Info: (Acquisitions) epixtech, inc.; (Cataloging) epixtech, inc.; (Circulation) epixtech, inc.; (OPAC) epixtech, inc.; (Serials) epixtech, inc.
Publications: Accessions lists; bibliographies; Faculty Guide; Library Notes; library use handbooks; Research in the Library; Summary Record of Research & Publications
Restriction: Open to faculty, students & qualified researchers
Partic in Consortium Of Rhode Island Academic & Research Libraries; Fedlink; Nelinet, Inc; OCLC Online Computer Library Center, Inc

UNITED STATES NAVY
A ACADEMIC RESOURCES INFORMATION CENTER (ARIC), 440 Meyerkord Ave, 02841. SAN 359-7725. Tel: 401-841-4352, 401-841-6631. Web Site: www.aric.org. *Dir*, James F Aylward; Tel: 401-841-6631, Fax: 401-841-2805, E-Mail: jim.aylward@smtp.cnet.navy.mil; *Asst Librn*, Robert S Wessells; *Circ*, Paul Cotsoridis; Staff 3 (MLS 3)
Founded 1917
Library Holdings: Bk Vols 100,000; Per Subs 275
Subject Interests: Academic, Adult education, Education, Leadership-mgt
Special Collections: Military Documents, fiche; Naval Training Manuals
Automation Activity & Vendor Info: (Cataloging) Endeavor; (Circulation) Endeavor; (OPAC) Endeavor; (Serials) Endeavor
Database Vendor: IAC - Info Trac, IAC - SearchBank
Publications: Library Handbook; Special Interest Bibliographies
Restriction: Open to faculty, students & qualified researchers
Function: Literary searches
Partic in Defense Logistics Studies Info Exchange; Defense Technical Information Center
A NAVAL UNDERSEA WARFARE CENTER DIVISION, NEWPORT TECHNICAL LIBRARY, 5141, Bldg 103, 02841. SAN 320-2321. Tel: 401-832-3124. FAX: 401-832-3699. *Librn*, Carolyn Prescott; *Librn*, Mary N Barravecchia; *Librn*, Chuck Logan; *Librn*, George Scheck
Founded 1970
Library Holdings: Bk Vols 20,000; Per Subs 150
Subject Interests: Computers, Engineering, Mgt, Underwater acoustics, Underwater ordnance
Partic in BRS; Defense Technical Information Center; Dialog Corporation; SDC Info Servs
A OFFICER INDOCTRINATION SCHOOL LIBRARY, 3112 SE Menlo Dr, Apt 40, Vancouver, 98683-9274. SAN 359-7814. Tel: 401-841-4310. FAX: 401-841-3323. *Dir*, Michael Hann
Founded 1972
Library Holdings: Bk Vols 9,500; Per Subs 72
Subject Interests: Leadership, Naval, Ocean sci
Special Collections: Naval Manuals

NORTH KINGSTOWN

P DAVISVILLE FREE LIBRARY,* Davisville Rd, 02852. SAN 315-4270. Tel: 401-884-5524. FAX: 401-884-9615. *Librn*, Patricia DiBella
Founded 1916
Library Holdings: Bk Vols 12,000
Subject Interests: Genealogy, Local history
Mem of S County Interrelated Libr Syst

P NORTH KINGSTOWN FREE LIBRARY,* 100 Boone St, 02852-5176. SAN 315-4289. Tel: 401-294-3306. FAX: 401-294-1690. Web Site: clan.lib.ri.us/nki/index.htm. *Dir*, Donna Dufault; *Ad Servs, Asst Dir*, Susan Berman; *Asst Dir, Tech Servs*, Susan Aylward; *Asst Dir, YA Servs*, H Paul Lefebure; Staff 6 (MLS 6)
Founded 1898. Pop 23,786; Circ 288,072
Library Holdings: Bk Vols 104,699; Bk Titles 84,002; Per Subs 356
Subject Interests: Local interest
Publications: Among Friends (newsletter)
Partic in Coop Librs Automated Network; Library of Rhode Island
Friends of the Library Group

NORTH PROVIDENCE

P NORTH PROVIDENCE UNION FREE LIBRARY, Mayor Salvatore Mancini Union Free Public Library & Cultural Center,* 1810 Mineral Spring Ave, 02904. SAN 315-4297. Tel: 401-353-5600. *Librn*, Mary Ellen Hardiman; *Ref*, Joseph Uscio; *Circ*, Gina Marciano; *Ch Servs*, Donna O'Connor; Staff 7 (MLS 7)
Founded 1869. Pop 32,000; Circ 252,872
Library Holdings: Bk Vols 128,000; Per Subs 219
Subject Interests: Elderly concerns, Large print
Special Collections: Careers-Vocational Guidance, vocational mat; Computer Software (Rhode Island Coll)
Partic in Cooperating Libraries Automated Network (CLAN)
Friends of the Library Group

M SAINT JOSEPH HOSPITAL, Health Science Library,* 200 High Service Ave, 02904. SAN 359-8624. Tel: 401-456-3036. FAX: 401-456-3702. *Dir Libr Serv*, Mary F Zammerelli
Founded 1954
Library Holdings: Bk Vols 5,065; Per Subs 129
Subject Interests: Allied health, Medicine, Nursing, Surgery
Special Collections: Historical & Current Nursing Coll

NORTH SCITUATE

P NORTH SCITUATE PUBLIC LIBRARY,* 606 W Greenville Rd, 02857. SAN 315-4300. Tel: 401-647-5133. FAX: 401-647-5680. *Dir*, Leslie McDonough; *Ch Servs*, Brenda D'Aguano
Founded 1906. Pop 9,711; Circ 63,000
Library Holdings: Bk Vols 40,000; Per Subs 102
Subject Interests: Crafts, Local history, Mysteries
Publications: NSPL Newsletter (quarterly)
Partic in Coop Librs Automated Network

PASCOAG

P PASCOAG PUBLIC LIBRARY,* 57 Church St, 02859. SAN 315-4319. Tel: 401-568-6226. FAX: 401-567-9372. *Librn*, Raymond Tellier
Circ 7,646
Library Holdings: Bk Vols 30,000; Per Subs 10

M ELEANOR SLATER HOSPITAL, Zambarano Unit Patient's Library,* 2090 Wallam Lake Rd, 02859. SAN 377-1881. Tel: 401-568-2551. *Librn*, Ray Vadaboncoeur
Library Holdings: Bk Titles 2,500; Per Subs 10
Partic in Library of Rhode Island

PAWTUCKET

M MEMORIAL HOSPITAL, Health Sciences Library,* 111 Brewster St, 02860. SAN 315-4343. Tel: 401-729-2211. FAX: 401-729-3383. *Coordr*, Kimberly Lavoie; *Ref*, Carol-Ann Rausch; E-Mail: carolannrh@dsl.rhilinet.gov
Founded 1958
Library Holdings: Bk Titles 6,764; Per Subs 184
Subject Interests: Basic sci, Clinical medicine

S OLD SLATER MILL ASSOCIATION, Slater Mill Historic Site Library, 67 Roosevelt Ave, PO Box 696, 02862. SAN 315-4335. Tel: 401-725-8638. FAX: 401-722-3040. E-Mail: samslater@aol.com. Web Site: slatermill.org.

Exec Dir, Dr Gail F Mohanty; E-Mail: gail_mohanty@hotmail.com; *Curator*, Karin Conopask. Subject Specialists: *Textiles*, Karin Conopask; *Weaving*, Dr Gail F Mohanty; Staff 25 (Non-MLS 25)
Founded 1955
1998-1999 Income $4,000. Mats Exp $4,000, Books $2,000, Per/Ser (Incl. Access Fees) $2,000
Library Holdings: Bk Vols 550
Subject Interests: Hist of machine tools, Local indust hist, Local soc hist, Textile processes
Special Collections: Manuscript Coll; Photograph Coll
Publications: The Newsletter (quarterly)

PAWTUCKET PUBLIC LIBRARY, 13 Summer St, 02860. SAN 315-4351. Tel: 401-725-3714. FAX: 401-728-2170. Web Site: www.204.17.98.73/pawlib. *Dir*, Susan L Reed; *Asst Dir*, Christine Jeffers; *Ch Servs*, Gloria Prevost; *Tech Servs*, Paul Arsenault; *Ref*, Paul Martin; *YA Servs*, Matt Bennett; *Electronic Resources*, Colleen Wolf; Staff 10 (MLS 9, Non-MLS 1)
Founded 1852. Pop 72,644; Circ 184,000
Jul 2000-Jun 2001 Income $1,121,790. Mats Exp $1,215,379
Library Holdings: Bk Vols 160,000; Per Subs 262
Special Collections: Local and Rhode Island History; Polish Coll
Automation Activity & Vendor Info: (Circulation) epixtech, inc.
Database Vendor: Ebsco - EbscoHost
Publications: The Carousel
Partic in CLAN
Open Mon-Thurs 9-9, Fri & Sat 9-5
Friends of the Library Group
Bookmobiles: 1

EACE DALE

SOUTH KINGSTOWN PUBLIC LIBRARY, 1057 Kingstown Rd, 02879-2434. SAN 359-7873. Tel: 401-789-1555. Interlibrary Loan Service Tel: 401-783-4085. FAX: 401-782-6370. E-Mail: skp@lori.state.ri.us. Web Site: 204.17.98.73/SKiLIB/. *Dir*, Connie Lachowicz; E-Mail: connielz@dsl.rhilinet.gov; *Head Ref*, Rebecca Turnbaugh; E-Mail: beckyth@hotmail.com; *Ch Servs*, Lynda Gamble; E-Mail: lyndage@lori.state.ri.us; Staff 33 (MLS 7, Non-MLS 26)
Founded 1975. Pop 29,943; Circ 255,542
Jul 1999-Jun 2000 Income (Main Library and Branch Library) $766,170, State $115,128, City $519,387, Federal $1,353, Other $130,302. Mats Exp $76,881, Books $67,502, Per/Ser (Incl. Access Fees) $7,385, Micro $64, Electronic Ref Mat (Incl. Access Fees) $1,930. Sal $441,956 (Prof $295,611)
Library Holdings: Bk Vols 67,103; Per Subs 312
Subject Interests: Bus info, Consumer info, Home improvement
Special Collections: Adult New Reader Coll; Books on Tape Coll, compact discs; Child Development Coll, V-Tapes; Large Print; Rhode Island History
Automation Activity & Vendor Info: (Serials) epixtech, inc.
Database Vendor: Ebsco - EbscoHost, epixtech, inc., Wilson - Wilson Web
Mem of Rhode Island Interrelated Libr Syst
Partic in Coop Librs Automated Network
Special Services for the Blind - Large print & cassettes
Friends of the Library Group
Branches: 2
KINGSTON FREE BRANCH, 2605 Kingstown Rd, Kingston, 02881. SAN 359-7962. Tel: 401-783-8254. FAX: 401-783-8254. E-Mail: skpl@lori.state.ri.us. Web Site: 204.17.98.73/SKiLib/. *Branch Mgr*, Pamela Meade; E-Mail: pamelasd@lori.state.ri.us; *Ch Servs*, Judith Munson
Founded 1975
Library Holdings: Bk Vols 21,161
Automation Activity & Vendor Info: (ILL) epixtech, inc.
Database Vendor: Ebsco - EbscoHost, epixtech, inc., Wilson - Wilson Web
Partic in CLAN
Special Services for the Blind - Large print & cassettes
Friends of the Library Group
ROBERT BEVERLEY HALE LIBRARY, 2601 Commodore Perry Hwy, Wakefield, 02879. SAN 359-7938. Tel: 401-783-5386. FAX: 401-783-5385. E-Mail: skpl@lori.state.ri.us. Web Site: 204.17.98.73/SKiLib/. *Branch Mgr*, Mary Ann Hunt; E-Mail: maryaht@seq.clan.lib.ri.us
Library Holdings: Bk Vols 13,341
Automation Activity & Vendor Info: (ILL) epixtech, inc.
Database Vendor: Ebsco - EbscoHost, epixtech, inc., Wilson - Wilson Web
Partic in Coop Librs Automated Network
Special Services for the Blind - Large print & cassettes
Friends of the Library Group

ORTSMOUTH

PORTSMOUTH FREE PUBLIC LIBRARY,* 2658 E Main Rd, 02871. SAN 315-436X. Tel: 401-683-9457. FAX: 401-683-5013. *Dir*, Rosemary Finneran; *Ch Servs*, Margaret Chatfield; *Publ Servs*, Carolyn B Magnus; Staff 2 (MLS 2)
Founded 1898. Pop 16,615; Circ 80,330
Library Holdings: Bk Vols 36,574
Mem of Island Interrelated Libr Syst

S RAYTHEON CO, Research Library, 1847 W Main Rd, 02871-1087. SAN 315-4378. Tel: 401-842-4372. FAX: 401-842-5206. *Librn*, Mark Baldwin; Staff 2 (MLS 1, Non-MLS 1)
Founded 1960
Library Holdings: Bk Vols 14,000; Per Subs 150
Subject Interests: Antisubmarine warfare, Electronics, Oceanography, Sonar, Surface mount
Publications: Accession list; News & Views; TIC Bulletin
Partic in Defense Technical Information Center; Dialog Corporation; Dow Jones News Retrieval; OCLC Online Computer Library Center, Inc

PROVIDENCE

L ADLER POLLOCK & SHEEHAN PC LIBRARY, 2300 Bank Boston Plaza, 02903-2443. SAN 324-6043. Tel: 401-274-7200. FAX: 401-751-0604. Web Site: www.apslaw.com. *Info Res, Mgr*, Paul R Dumaine; E-Mail: pdumaine@apslaw.com; *Librn*, Eileen F Paolino; E-Mail: epaolino@apslaw.com; Staff 2 (MLS 2)
Library Holdings: Bk Vols 7,000; Bk Titles 2,500; Per Subs 300
Subject Interests: Law
Automation Activity & Vendor Info: (OPAC) Inmagic, Inc.
Partic in CourtLink; CT Advantage; Dun & Bradstreet Info Servs; Pacer; Westlaw

BROWN UNIVERSITY
C JOHN CARTER BROWN LIBRARY, George & Brown Sts, PO Box 1894, 02912. SAN 359-8055. Tel: 401-863-2725. FAX: 401-863-3477. E-Mail: jcbl_information@brown.edu. Web Site: www.jcbl.org. *Librn*, Norman Fiering; *Asst Librn, Curator*, Susan L Danforth; *Ref*, Richard Ring; *Curator*, Dennis Landis; *Cat*, Burton Von Edwards; *Cat*, Valeria Gauz; *Cat*, Michael Homerly; *Cat*, Susan Newbury; *Cat*, Eileen Smith; Staff 10 (MLS 10)
Founded 1846
1998-1999 Income $1,500,000
Library Holdings: Bk Vols 54,500; Per Subs 13
Special Collections: Colonial History of the Americas (North & South) 1492-1835, archives, bks, maps, mss & prints
Publications: Bibliographies; Exhibition Catalogs; Facsimiles; Newsletters; Pamphlets
Mem of Asn of Research Libraries
Partic in RLIN
Library provides fellowships to post doctoral students & professors for Colonial American History Research (20 per year)
Friends of the Library Group
UNIVERSITY LIBRARY, Box A, 02912. SAN 359-7997. Tel: 401-863-2167. Interlibrary Loan Service FAX: 401-863-1250, 401-863-2753. Web Site: www.brown.edu/facilities/university_library/. *Librn*, Merrily E Taylor; Tel: 401-863-2162; *Assoc Librn, Coll Develop, Publ Servs*, Florence K Doksansky; Tel: 401-863-2405; *Acq*, Patricia E Putney; Tel: 401-863-2954; *Cat*, Dominique Coulombe; Tel: 401-863-2950; *Circ*, Bonnie Buzzell; Tel: 401-863-2165; *Coll Develop*, William Monroe; Tel: 401-863-2406; *Doc*, Daniel O'Mahony; Tel: 401-863-2522; *ILL*, Bart Hollingsworth; Tel: 401-863-2554; *Ref*, Ronald K Fark; *Ser*, Steven E Thompson; Tel: 401-863-2515; *Spec Coll*, Rosemary Cullen; Tel: 401-863-3723; *Spec Coll*, Samuel A Streit; Tel: 401-863-2146; *Syst Coordr*, Howard Pasternack; Tel: 401-863-3346. Subject Specialists: *Preservation*, Eric Shoaf; Staff 163 (MLS 70, Non-MLS 93)
Founded 1767. Enrl 7,335; Fac 548; Highest Degree: Doctorate
Jul 1999-Jun 2000 Mats Exp $5,413,160, Books $1,404,490, Per/Ser (Incl. Access Fees) $3,577,262, Presv $262,815, Micro $55,753, Other Print Mats $112,840. Sal $6,258,169 (Prof $3,181,474)
Library Holdings: Bk Vols 3,020,867; Per Subs 14,050
Special Collections: Abraham Lincoln (McLellan Coll); Alcohol & Temperance (Kirk Coll); American Poetry, Plays & Sheet Music (Harris Coll); American Sermons 18th & 19th Centuries; Archives; Broadsides Coll; Children's Books (Aldrich Pillar Coll); Comic Books; Dante (Chambers Coll); East Asia; Edgar Allan Poe; Fireworks; G B Shaw (Albert Coll); Gay & Lesbian Literature (Katzoff); H G Wells; H P Lovecraft Machiavelli; Henry D Thoreau (Lownes Coll); History of Medicine (Rhode Island Medical Society Library); History of Science (Lownes Coll); Humor, 19th & 20th Century (Miller Coll); Imperialism (Schirmer Coll); Incunabula (Annmary Brown Memorial); John Buchan (Bloomingdale Coll); John Hay; Legend of the Wandering Jew (Louttit Coll); Lester Frank Ward; Magic (Smith Coll); Mexican History; Military History & Iconography (Brown Coll); Napoleon (Hoffman Coll); Napoleon Caricatures (Bullard Coll); Occult (Damon Coll); Pharmacopeia (Reitman Coll); Propaganda (Hall-Hoag Coll); Rhode Island History (Rider Coll); Silver (Gorham Archives); Small Press Archives; South America (Church Coll); St Martin's Press; UNESCO, World Orgn; US Diplomatic History (John Hay & Jonathan Russell); US Postage Stamps (Knight); US Special Delivery Stamps (Peltz); Walt Whitman; Whaling (Morse); William Blake (Damon Coll); World-wide Postage Stamps (Champlin)

Automation Activity & Vendor Info: (Acquisitions) Innovative Interfaces Inc.; (Circulation) Innovative Interfaces Inc.
Publications: BiblioFile; Books at Brown
Partic in Boston Library Consortium; Center For Research Libraries; Consortium Of Rhode Island Academic & Research Libraries; Greater NE Regional Med Libr Program; OCLC Online Computer Library Center, Inc; RLIN
Friends of the Library Group

M BUTLER HOSPITAL, Issac Ray Medical Library, 345 Blackstone Blvd, 02906. SAN 315-4394. Tel: 401-455-6248. FAX: 401-455-6293. *Librn*, Ruthann Gildea
Founded 1952
Library Holdings: Bk Titles 3,000; Per Subs 100
Subject Interests: Behav sci, Pschiat, Psychology, Soc sci
Special Collections: Archives on early psychiatry (pre-20th century)
Restriction: Staff use only

SR CATHEDRAL CHURCH OF SAINT JOHN, Nathan Bourne Crocker Library, 271 N Main St, 02903. SAN 371-8891. Tel: 401-331-4622. FAX: 401-331-9430. *Chairperson, Librn*, Patricia Bailey; E-Mail: deaconpat@aol.com; *Cat, Ref*, Wendell B Pols; *Res*, Steele Martin
Library Holdings: Bk Vols 3,200; Bk Titles 3,000
Subject Interests: Anglicanism, Church history, Theology
Special Collections: Diocese of Rhode Island-Parish Histories, bks, pamphlets
Friends of the Library Group

GM DEPARTMENT OF VETERANS AFFAIRS, Health Science Library, Library Service CIO-L, 830 Chalkstone Ave, 02908-4799. SAN 315-4629. Tel: 401-457-3001. FAX: 401-457-3097. *Chief Librn*, Nicola F Pallotti; E-Mail: nicky.pallotti@med.va.gov; *Asst Librn, ILL*, Cheryl R Banick; E-Mail: cheryl.banick@med.va.gov; Staff 3 (MLS 1, Non-MLS 2)
Founded 1945
Oct 1999-Sep 2000 Income $69,200. Mats Exp $68,428, Books $3,557, Per/Ser (Incl. Access Fees) $56,754, AV Equip $1,334, Electronic Ref Mat (Incl. Access Fees) $7,421. Sal $68,358 (Prof $19,460)
Library Holdings: Bk Vols 1,329; Per Subs 148
Database Vendor: OVID Technologies
Restriction: Open to public for reference only
Function: ILL available, Literary searches, Photocopies available, Reference services available, Some telephone reference
Partic in Association of Rhode Island Health Sciences Libraries (ARIHSL); BHSL; Library of Rhode Island; NLM; Veterans Affairs Library Network

SR DIOCESAN RESOURCE CENTER, Office of Religious Education Library,* 34 Fenner St, 02903. SAN 320-7382. Tel: 401-278-4646. FAX: 401-278-4645. *Librn*, Pauline Prew
Library Holdings: Bk Vols 2,000; Per Subs 30
Subject Interests: Religion
Open Mon-Fri 9-4:30

L EDWARDS & ANGELL, LLP LIBRARY, 2800 Financial Plaza, 02903. SAN 323-6382. Tel: 401-276-6521. FAX: 401-276-6611. *Dir Libr Serv*, Mary M Ames; E-Mail: mames@ealaw.com; *Asst Librn*, Sarah Ide; E-Mail: side@ealaw.com; Staff 2 (MLS 2)
Library Holdings: Bk Vols 25,000

S ENVIRONMENTAL SCIENCE SERVICES LIBRARY,* 272 W Exchange St, 02903. SAN 372-9346. Tel: 401-421-0398. FAX: 401-421-5731. *Pres*, Robert Bibbo
Library Holdings: Bk Vols 150; Per Subs 10
Open Mon-Fri 8:30-5:30

L HINCKLEY, ALLEN & SNYDER, Law Library, 1500 Fleet Ctr, 02903. SAN 327-1242. Tel: 401-274-2000, Ext 2692. FAX: 401-277-9600. Web Site: www.haslaw.com. *Res*, Dawn F Oliveri; E-Mail: doliveri@haslaw.com; Staff 5 (MLS 2, Non-MLS 3)
Library Holdings: Bk Vols 2,000
Restriction: Access at librarian's discretion
Function: Research library
Partic in Dialog Corporation; LOIS; Westlaw

C JOHNSON & WALES UNIVERSITY LIBRARY,* 111 Dorrance St, 02903. (Mail add: 8 Abbott Park Pl, 02903), SAN 315-4424. Tel: 401-598-1098. FAX: 401-598-1834. E-Mail: library@jwu.edu. Web Site: www.jwu.edu. *Dean of Libr*, Dr Helena Rodrigues
Founded 1914. Enrl 8,524
Library Holdings: Bk Vols 65,872; Per Subs 848
Subject Interests: Bus, Culinary arts, Data proc, Equine studies, Hospitality mgt, Mgt, Secretarial, Travel tourism
Special Collections: Fritzche Cookbook Coll (7000 vols of US & foreign cookbooks)
Mem of Providence Interrelated Libr Systs
Open Mon-Thurs 8am-midnight; Fri 8-6, Sat 9-6, Sun noon-midnight
Departmental Libraries:
HARBORSIDE LIBRARY, 265 Harborside Blvd, 02905. SAN 370-7679. Tel: 401-598-1894. *Dir*, Barbara Janson
Library Holdings: Bk Titles 10,000; Per Subs 100
Subject Interests: Culinary arts

MIRIAM HOSPITAL
M HEALTH SCIENCES LIBRARY, 164 Summit Ave, 02906. SAN 359-808. Tel: 401-793-2291. FAX: 401-274-9568. *Librn*, Mary Ann Slocomb; E-Mail: mslocomb@lifespan.org
Library Holdings: Bk Vols 1,450; Bk Titles 1,300; Per Subs 250
Subject Interests: Cardiology, Internal medicine, Surgery
Publications: Annual reports; Book list; Journal list; Library News; Orientation Brochure
Partic in Medline

S PATIENTS' LIBRARY, 164 Summit Ave, 02906. SAN 359-811X. Tel: 401-331-8500, Ext 32510. FAX: 401-331-8505.
Founded 1970
Library Holdings: Bk Titles 100; Per Subs 80
Subject Interests: Biog, Current per, Fiction, Foreign Language, Large-print bks, Prayer bks, Talking books
Friends of the Library Group

P OFFICE OF LIBRARY & INFORMATION SERVICES, OLIS, Library Programs, One Capitol Hill, 02908. SAN 359-8446. Tel: 401-222-2726. FAX: 401-222-4195. Web Site: www.lori.state.ri.us. *Ref*, Beth Perry; Tel: 401-222-5775, E-Mail: bethpy@gw.doa..state.ri.us; *Ch Servs*, Melody Allen; Tel: 401-222-5758, E-Mail: melodyan@gw.doa.state.ri.us; *Ref*, Frank P Iacono; Tel: 401-222-5816, E-Mail: frankio@gw.doa.state.ri.us; *Media Spec*, Joseph McGovern; Tel: 401-222-5771, E-Mail: joemn@gw.doa.state.ri.us; *Coordr*, Ann Piascik; Tel: 401-222-5776, E-Mail: piascik@gw.doa.state.ri.us; Staff 22 (MLS 12, Non-MLS 10)
Founded 1964
Library Holdings: Bk Vols 5,000
Subject Interests: Libr sci
Automation Activity & Vendor Info: (Circulation) epixtech, inc.; (Course Reserve) epixtech, inc.; (ILL) epixtech, inc.; (Media Booking) epixtech, inc.; (OPAC) epixtech, inc.; (Serials) epixtech, inc.
Database Vendor: OCLC - First Search
Publications: Newsletter
Partic in Nelinet, Inc
Administers Regional Library for the Blind & Physically Handicapped, State Institutional Library Services, Rhode Island Library Network; coordinates library services among all types of libraries
Branches: 1
TALKING BOOKS PLUS
See Separate Entry

S PRESEL MEMORIAL LIBRARY, The Providence Center,* 520 Hope St, 02906. SAN 329-7780. Tel: 401-276-4005. FAX: 401-276-4015. *Librn*, Lawrence S Fein; E-Mail: lfein@provetr.org
Founded 1985
1998-1999 Mats Exp Per/Ser (Incl. Access Fees) $1,500. Sal $11,000
Library Holdings: Bk Titles 750; Per Subs 40
Subject Interests: Psychiatry, Psychology
Publications: Book News

P PROVIDENCE ATHENAEUM, 251 Benefit St, 02903-2799. SAN 315-4432. Tel: 401-421-6970. FAX: 401-421-2860. Web Site: www.providenceathenaeum.org. *Dir*, Gary Mason; *Tech Servs*, Kate Wodehouse; *Mgr Libr Serv*, Catherine Poirier; *Ch Servs*, Lindsay Shaw; *Rare Bks*, Susan Newkirk; Staff 6 (MLS 3, Non-MLS 3)
Founded 1753
Jan 2000-Dec 2000 Income $657,930, Locally Generated Income $286,700, Parent Institution $343,230, Other $28,000. Mats Exp $638,000, Books $42,200, Per/Ser (Incl. Access Fees) $8,000, Presv $1,000, AV Equip $10,000, Electronic Ref Mat (Incl. Access Fees) $1,200. Sal $324,944 (Prof $196,277)
Library Holdings: Bk Titles 167,000; Per Subs 150
Subject Interests: 19th Century Am lit, 19th Century English lit, Art, Biog, Ch bks, Exploration, Fiction, History, Natural history, Travel
Special Collections: Audubon Elephant Folios; Holder Borden Bowen Coll; Rare Bk Library; Robert Burns Coll; Voyage & Travel
Automation Activity & Vendor Info: (Acquisitions) Innovative Interfaces Inc.; (Cataloging) Innovative Interfaces Inc.; (Circulation) Innovative Interfaces Inc.; (OPAC) Innovative Interfaces Inc.; (Serials) Innovative Interfaces Inc.
Database Vendor: Innovative Interfaces INN - View
Publications: "Owl" (quarterly newsletter); Annual Report; Summer Bulletin; The Natural History Collection of the Providence Athenaeum (selected annotated bibliography); Travel & Exploration: A Catalogue of the Providence Athenaeum Collection (collection catalog)
Mem of Providence Interrelated Libr Systs

C PROVIDENCE COLLEGE, Phillips Memorial Library, River Ave at Eaton St, 02918. SAN 315-4440. Tel: 401-865-2242. FAX: 401-865-2823. *Dir*, Harvey Varnet; *Publ Servs*, Janice Schuster; *ILL*, Francine Mancini; *Cat*, Martha Beshers; *Acq*, Norman Desmarais; *Ref*, Constance Cameron; *Ref*, Julia Tryon; Staff 8 (MLS 8)
Founded 1919. Enrl 5,955; Fac 262; Highest Degree: Doctorate
Library Holdings: Bk Vols 300,000; Per Subs 1,700
Special Collections: Aime J Forand Coll; Alice Lafond Altieri Coll;

Blackfriars' Guild Coll; Bonniwell Coll; Cornelius Moore Papers; Coutu Genealogy Coll; Dennis J Roberts Papers; Edward J Higgins Coll; Edward P Beard Coll; English & Colonial 18th Century Trade Statistics Coll, IBM cards; Irish Literature; J Howard McGrath Coll; J Lyons Moore Coll; John E Fogarty Papers; John J Fawcett Coll; John O Pastore Coll; Joseph A Doorley Jr Coll; Louis Francis Budenz Papers, pamphlets, per; National Association for the Advancement of Colored People Coll; Nazi Bund Coll; Quonset Point Coll; Reunification of Ireland Clippings; Rhode Island Constitutional Convention, 1964-1968; Rhode Island Court Records Coll, 1657-1905; Rhode Island Library Association Coll; Rhode Island United States Colored Artillery (Heavy) 11th Regiment Coll; Rhode Island Urban League Papers; Robert E Quinn Papers & Oral History Project; Social Justice, 1936-1942; The Confederation Period in Rhode Island Newspapers Coll; The Limited Constitutional Convention, 1973; Thomas Matthes McGlynn, OP Coll; Walsh Civil War Diary; William Henry Chamberlin Papers, micro
Partic in Consortium Of Rhode Island Academic & Research Libraries; Nelinet, Inc
Open Mon-Thurs 8-10:45 PM

PROVIDENCE JOURNAL CO, News Library, 75 Fountain St, 02902. SAN 315-4467. Tel: 401-277-7662. FAX: 401-277-7665. Web Site: www.projo.com/newsweb. *Librn*, Linda L Henderson; Staff 5 (MLS 1, Non-MLS 4)
Founded 1900
Library Holdings: Bk Titles 2,500; Per Subs 45
Subject Interests: Current events, Past events
Special Collections: Journal/Bulletin Almanac (1887-1998); Rhode Island & Rhode Islanders, clippings & pictures

PROVIDENCE PARKS DEPARTMENT, Roger Williams Park Museum of Natural History Library, Roger Williams Park, 02905. SAN 315-4645. Tel: 401-785-9457. Reference Tel: 401-785-9457, Ext 248. FAX: 401-461-5146. Web Site: osfn.org/museum. *Coll Develop, Curator*, Marilyn R Massaro; E-Mail: massarom@ride.ri.net
Founded 1896
Library Holdings: Bk Vols 10,000
Subject Interests: Astronomy, Botany, Ethnology, Geology, Landscape architecture, Natural history, Zoology
Special Collections: Roger Williams Park Museum & Park Archives
Publications: All Things Connected (collection/exhibit catalog); Park Museum Bulletins (1909-1929)
Restriction: Non-circulating to the public

PROVIDENCE PUBLIC LIBRARY,* 225 Washington St, 02903-3283. SAN 359-8144. Tel: 401-455-8000. TDD: 401-455-8089. FAX: 401-455-8080, 455-8065. Web Site: www.clan.lib.ri.us/pro/ppl.htm. *Dir*, Dale Thompson; *Tech Servs*, Peter Bennett; *Publ Servs*, Shirley Long; *Pub Relations*, Beth Sousa; *Spec Coll*, Philip Weimerskirch; *Spec Coll*, Elizabeth Fitzgerald; Staff 46 (MLS 46)
Founded 1875. Pop 1,003,464
Jul 1997-Jun 1998 Income $6,110,062, State $822,484, City $2,500,000, Federal $21,783, Locally Generated Income $441,330, Parent Institution $1,789,638, Other $130,561. Mats Exp $352,314, Books $253,614, Per/Ser (Incl. Access Fees) $68,000, Micro $10,200. Sal $3,901,358 (Prof $1,911,378)
Library Holdings: Bk Vols 1,215,202; Per Subs 922
Subject Interests: Art, Bus, Music, Rhode Island
Special Collections: Architecture (Nickerson Coll); Band Music (David W Reeves Coll); Black History & Culture (Edna Frazier Coll); Checkers (Edward B Hanes Coll); Checkers Coll; Children's Books (Wetmore Coll); Civil War & Slavery (Harris Coll); Irish Culture (Potter/Williams Coll); Italian Coll; Jewelry Coll; Magic (Percival Coll); Printing (Updike Coll); Providence Journal (online access); Regional Foundation Coll; Rhode Island Coll; Textile Coll; US Patents & Depository; Whaling (Nicholson Coll)
Automation Activity & Vendor Info: (Acquisitions) epixtech, inc.; (Circulation) epixtech, inc.
Publications: Annual Report; Newsletter (bi-monthly)
Partic in Consortium Of Rhode Island Academic & Research Libraries; Cooperating Libraries Automated Network (CLAN); Nelinet, Inc; RI Interrelated Libr Network
Special Services for the Deaf - TDD
Serves as Reference Resource Center for the State of RI
Friends of the Library Group
Branches: 9
FOX POINT, 90 Ives St, 02906. SAN 359-8179. Tel: 401-455-8112. *Librn*, Jacquelyn B Cooper
Library Holdings: Bk Vols 17,369
Subject Interests: Portuguese lang
Friends of the Library Group
KNIGHT MEMORIAL, 275 Elmwood Ave, 02907. SAN 359-8209. Tel: 401-455-8102. *Librn*, Kathleen Vernon
Library Holdings: Bk Vols 84,558
Subject Interests: Spanish lang
Special Collections: Arnold Tombstone Records; RI History
MOUNT PLEASANT, 315 Academy Ave, 02908. SAN 359-8233. Tel: 401-455-8105. *Librn*, Roberta Smith
Library Holdings: Bk Vols 34,260
Friends of the Library Group
OLNEYVILLE, One Olneyville Sq, 02909. SAN 370-9221. Tel: 401-455-8113. *Librn*, Roberta Smith
Library Holdings: Bk Vols 10,373
ROCHAMBEAU, 708 Hope St, 02906. SAN 359-8292. Tel: 401-455-8110. FAX: 401-455-8116. *Librn*, Jacquelyn B Cooper
Library Holdings: Bk Vols 44,989
Subject Interests: Russian lang
Friends of the Library Group
SMITH HILL, 31 Candace St, 02908. SAN 359-8322. Tel: 401-455-8104. *Librn*, Jacquelyn B Cooper
Library Holdings: Bk Vols 23,787
Friends of the Library Group
SOUTH PROVIDENCE, 441 Prairie Ave, 02905. SAN 359-8357. Tel: 401-445-8107. *Librn*, Kathleen Vernon
Library Holdings: Bk Vols 27,691
Special Collections: Edna Frazier Coll
Friends of the Library Group
WANSKUCK, 233 Veazie St, 02904. SAN 329-5850. Tel: 401-455-8108. *Librn*, Roberta Smith
Library Holdings: Bk Vols 7,568
Friends of the Library Group
WASHINGTON PARK, 1316 Broad St, 02905. SAN 359-8411. Tel: 401-455-8109. *Librn*, Kathleen Vernon
Library Holdings: Bk Vols 23,517

C RHODE ISLAND COLLEGE, James P Adams Library, 600 Mt Pleasant Ave, 02908. SAN 315-4475. Tel: 401-456-8126. FAX: 401-456-9646. *Dir*, Richard A Olsen
Founded 1854. Enrl 5,707; Fac 375; Highest Degree: Master
Library Holdings: Bk Vols 375,000; Per Subs 1,869
Subject Interests: Education, Soc work
Special Collections: Children's Literature (Amy Thompson Coll)
Mem of Rhode Island Interrelated Libr Syst
Partic in Consortium Of Rhode Island Academic & Research Libraries; New England Libr Info Network

GM RHODE ISLAND DEPARTMENT OF HEALTH LIBRARY,* 3 Capitol Hill, Rm 103, 02908. SAN 315-4564. Tel: 401-222-2068. TDD: 401-277-2506. FAX: 401-222-6548. *Librn*, Barry J Levin; E-Mail: barryln@dsl.rhilinet.gov; Staff 2 (MLS 1, Non-MLS 1)
Founded 1939
Library Holdings: Bk Vols 175; Bk Titles 3,000
Subject Interests: Health policy, Preventative med, Public health, Toxicology
Publications: Library newsletter
Special Services for the Deaf - TDD

G RHODE ISLAND DEPARTMENT OF TRANSPORTATION LIBRARY,* State Office Bldg, 2 Capitol Hill, 02903. SAN 371-1137. Tel: 401-222-4203. FAX: 401-222-2207. *Librn*, Brenda Myette
Library Holdings: Bk Vols 250
Subject Interests: Transportation

G RHODE ISLAND ECONOMIC DEVELOPMENT CORP, Research Division Library,* One W Exchange St, 02903. SAN 323-5173. Tel: 401-222-2601. FAX: 401-459-6430. Web Site: www.riedc.com. *Dir*, Jean Burritt Robertson; E-Mail: jroberts@riedc.com
Library Holdings: Bk Vols 500
Subject Interests: Census data, Census of manufacturers, Census of retail, Census of wholesale trade, Earnings, Employment, Monthly labor review, State law, Statistical

S RHODE ISLAND HISTORICAL SOCIETY LIBRARY, 121 Hope St, 02906. SAN 315-4491. Tel: 401-331-8575. FAX: 401-751-7930. Web Site: www.rihs.org. *Dir*, Allison Cywin; *Curator*, Richard Stattler; *Ref*, Meredith Paine Sorozan; *Tech Servs*, Laura Dixon; Staff 15 (MLS 4, Non-MLS 11)
Founded 1823
Library Holdings: Bk Vols 150,000; Per Subs 1,000; Spec Interest Per Sub 980
Subject Interests: Genealogy, Graphics, Hist of RI, Manuscripts, New Eng genealogy, Newspapers, Vital records
Database Vendor: OCLC - First Search
Publications: Rhode Island History
Restriction: Not a lending library
Function: Research library
Partic in Consortium Of Rhode Island Academic & Research Libraries; Library of Rhode Island; Nelinet, Inc

M RHODE ISLAND HOSPITAL, Peters Health Sciences Library, 593 Eddy St, 02902. SAN 359-8500. Tel: 401-444-4671, 401-444-8070, 401-444-8074. *Dir*, Irene M Lathrop
Founded 1932
Library Holdings: Bk Vols 25,000; Per Subs 650
Publications: Peters Library Newsletter
Partic in BRS; Dialog Corporation; Medline; OCLC Online Computer Library Center, Inc

R RHODE ISLAND JEWISH HISTORICAL ASSOCIATION LIBRARY, 130 Sessions St, 02906. SAN 315-4505. Tel: 401-331-1360. FAX: 401-272-6729. E-Mail: rjhist@aol.com. Web Site: www.dowtech.com/rijha/. *Librn*, Eleanor F Horvitz
Founded 1951. Circ 700
1998-1999 Income $25,000. Mats Exp $1,000, Books $333, Per/Ser (Incl. Access Fees) $100, Presv $397. Sal $7,000 (Prof $3,400)
Library Holdings: Bk Titles 821; Per Subs 12
Special Collections: Jewish History of Rhode Island
Publications: Newsletter & Annual book (published for membership in Association)
Restriction: Non-circulating to the public
Partic in Asn of Jewish Librs

G RHODE ISLAND PUBLIC EXPENDITURE COUNCIL LIBRARY,* 300 Richmond St, Ste 200, 02903-4214. SAN 372-9338. Tel: 401-521-6320. FAX: 401-751-1915. E-Mail: ripec@ripec.com. Web Site: www.ripec.com. *Exec Dir*, Gary S Sasse
Library Holdings: Bk Vols 100; Per Subs 16

S RHODE ISLAND SCHOOL FOR THE DEAF LIBRARY, One Corliss Park, 02908. SAN 315-4548. Tel: 401-222-7441. FAX: 401-222-6998. *In Charge*, Peter Blackwell; *Librn*, Mary Cummings
Library Holdings: Bk Vols 10,000
Special Services for the Deaf - Books on deafness & sign language; High interest/low vocabulary books; Staff with knowledge of sign language; TTY machine

C RHODE ISLAND SCHOOL OF DESIGN LIBRARY, 236 Benefit St, 02903. (Mail add: 2 College St, 02903), SAN 315-4556. Tel: 401-454-6365. FAX: 401-454-6226. Web Site: www.risd.edu/risd_library.cfm. *Dir Libr Serv*, Carol S Terry; Tel: 401-454-6278, E-Mail: cterry@risd.edu; *Tech Servs*, Robert Garzillo; Tel: 401-454-6276, E-Mail: rgarzill@risd.edu; *Reader Servs*, Laurie Whitehill Chong; Tel: 401-454-6227, E-Mail: lwhitehi@risd.edu; *ILL*, Gail Geisser; Tel: 401-454-6104, E-Mail: ggeisser@risd.edu; *AV*, Debra Kruse; Tel: 401-454-6229, E-Mail: dkruse@risd.edu; *Archivist*, Andrew Martinez; Tel: 401-454-6398, Fax: 401-454-6415, E-Mail: amartine@risd.edu. Subject Specialists: *Artists bks*, Laurie Whitehill Chong; *Visual*, Debra Kruse; Staff 19 (MLS 6, Non-MLS 13)
Founded 1878. Enrl 2,100; Fac 187; Highest Degree: Master
Jul 1999-Jun 2000 Income $1,151,614, Locally Generated Income $38,452, Parent Institution $1,113,162. Mats Exp $188,656, Books $115,823, Per/Ser (Incl. Access Fees) $27,704, Presv $12,512, Other Print Mats $16,467, Electronic Ref Mat (Incl. Access Fees) $16,150. Sal $916,184 (Prof $338,071)
Library Holdings: Bk Vols 95,161; Bk Titles 84,587; Per Subs 423
Subject Interests: Architecture, Art, Artists bks, Design, Picture bks
Special Collections: Landscape Architecture (Lowthorpe Coll)
Automation Activity & Vendor Info: (Acquisitions) Innovative Interfaces Inc.; (Cataloging) Innovative Interfaces Inc.; (Circulation) Innovative Interfaces Inc.; (OPAC) Innovative Interfaces Inc.; (Serials) Innovative Interfaces Inc.
Database Vendor: Ebsco - EbscoHost, Innovative Interfaces INN - View, OCLC - First Search, Wilson - Wilson Web
Partic in Consortium Of Rhode Island Academic & Research Libraries; Nelinet, Inc; OCLC Online Computer Library Center, Inc; Providence Athenaeum-RISD Libr Consortium

G RHODE ISLAND STATE ARCHIVES, 337 Westminster St, 02903. SAN 321-4192. Tel: 401-222-2353. FAX: 401-222-3199. E-Mail: reference@archives.state.ri.us. Web Site: www.state.ri.us/archives. *Archivist*, Gwenn Stearn; Staff 7 (MLS 6, Non-MLS 1)
Founded 1930
Library Holdings: Bk Vols 1,000
Subject Interests: Genealogy, History
Special Collections: Acts & Resolves; Census; Charters; Colony Records; Correspondence (Governors' Coll); Land Records
Publications: Compilation of Rules of State Agencies

S RHODE ISLAND STATE DEPARTMENT OF ELDERLY AFFAIRS LIBRARY,* 160 Pine St, 02903. SAN 327-1188. Tel: 401-222-2858. FAX: 401-222-3389. *Librn*, Will Speck
Library Holdings: Bk Titles 400

G RHODE ISLAND STATE ENERGY OFFICE,* One Capital Hill, 2nd flr, 02908. SAN 372-932X. Tel: 401-222-3370. FAX: 401-222-1260.
Library Holdings: Bk Vols 50; Per Subs 10
Subject Interests: Energy
Restriction: Staff use only

GL RHODE ISLAND STATE LAW LIBRARY, Frank Licht Judicial Complex, 250 Benefit St, 02903. SAN 315-4572. Tel: 401-222-3275. FAX: 401-222-3865. *Govt Doc*, Colleen McConaghy Hanna; E-Mail: channa@courts.state.ri.us; *Ref*, Marcia Lakomski; Tel: 401-458-5274; Staff 5 (MLS 5)
Founded 1827
Jul 1999-Jun 2000 Income $1,166,894. Mats Exp $752,000, Books $613,000, Micro $4,000, Electronic Ref Mat (Incl. Access Fees) $135,000. Sal $414,083 (Prof $337,283)
Library Holdings: Bk Vols 100,000; Per Subs 360
Subject Interests: Am law
Special Collections: Rhode Island Colonial Laws
Automation Activity & Vendor Info: (Acquisitions) EOS; (Cataloging) EOS; (Circulation) EOS; (OPAC) EOS; (Serials) EOS
Partic in New England Law Library Consortium, Inc; OCLC Online Computer Library Center, Inc
Special Services for the Blind - Closed circuit television; Kurzweil Reader
Branches:
GARRAHY JUDICIAL COMPLEX, One Dorrance Plaza, 02903. Tel: 401-458-5274. *Librn*, Marcia Oakes
Library Holdings: Bk Vols 5,000
KENT COUNTY LAW LIBRARY, Leighton Judicial Complex, 222 Quaker Lane, Warwick, 02886.
Library Holdings: Bk Vols 5,000
NEWPORT COUNTY LAW LIBRARY, Newport County Courthouse, 45 Washington Square, Newport, 02840.
Library Holdings: Bk Vols 5,000
WASHINGTON COUNTY LAW LIBRARY, McGrath Judicial Complex, 4800 Tower Hill Rd, South Kingstown, 02879.
Library Holdings: Bk Vols 5,000

GL RHODE ISLAND STATE LIBRARY,* State House, Rm 208, 02903. SAN 315-4580. Tel: 401-222-2473. FAX: 401-331-6430. Web Site: www.sec.state.ri.us/library/web.htm. *Ref, State Librn*, Thomas R Evans; *Doc*, Margaret Gordon; *Per*, Mary Daly; Staff 5 (MLS 3, Non-MLS 2)
Founded 1852
Library Holdings: Bk Titles 157,000; Per Subs 90
Subject Interests: Law, Legis ref, Legis res, Local history
Publications: Checklist of Rhode Island State Documents

P TALKING BOOKS PLUS, One Capitol Hill, 02908. SAN 315-453X. Tel: 401-222-5800. Toll Free Tel: 800-734-5141. FAX: 401-222-4195. E-Mail: tbplus@lori.state.ri.us. Web Site: www.lori.state.ri.us/tbp/. *Regional Librarian*, Andrew I Egan; Tel: 401-222-5767, E-Mail: andyen@gw.doa.state.ri.us; Staff 4 (MLS 2, Non-MLS 2)
Founded 1968
Publications: Newsletter (bi-monthly, DSLS); Newsletter (quarterly, Regional Library)
Mem of Rhode Island Interrelated Libr Syst
Partic in OCLC Online Computer Library Center, Inc

R TEMPLE BETH EL CONGREGATION SONS OF ISRAEL & DAVID, William G Braude Library, 70 Orchard Ave, 02906. SAN 315-4408. Tel: 401-331-6070. FAX: 401-331-8068. *Librn*, Reini Silverman; Fax: 401-521-6012, E-Mail: rsilverman@temple-beth-el.org
Founded 1892
2000-2001 Mats Exp $7,000, Books $6,000, Per/Ser (Incl. Access Fees) $1,000. Sal $24,000
Library Holdings: Bk Vols 25,000; Per Subs 73
Subject Interests: Bible studies, Childrens' bks, Hebraica, Holocaust, Judaica, Young adult bks
Special Collections: Latin American Jewish Studies
Automation Activity & Vendor Info: (Cataloging) Sagebrush Corporation; (Circulation) Sagebrush Corporation

R TEMPLE EMANUEL LIBRARY, 99 Taft Ave, 02906. SAN 315-4602. Tel: 401-331-1616. FAX: 401-421-9279. *Librn*, Mara Sokolsky
Library Holdings: Bk Titles 9,000; Per Subs 20
Subject Interests: Judaica
Friends of the Library Group

S THE TWINS FOUNDATION RESEARCH LIBRARY, PO Box 6043, 02940-6043. SAN 326-4327. Tel: 401-751-8946. FAX: 401-751-4642. E-Mail: twins@twinsfoundation.com. Web Site: www.twinsfoundation.com. *Coordr*, Kay Cassill
Founded 1983
Library Holdings: Bk Vols 1,072; Per Subs 9,500
Special Collections: Medical Data/Stats Coll; Twin Achievers Coll/National Twin Registry; Twins Multiples Coll
Publications: Cumulative Index; Research Update (occasional); The Twins Letter (quarterly quality newsletter)
Restriction: By appointment only
Friends of the Library Group

GL UNITED STATES COURT OF APPEALS FIRST CIRCUIT SATELLITE LIBRARY, One Exchange Terrace, Rm 503, 02903-1746. SAN 371-9065. Tel: 401-752-7240. FAX: 401-752-7245. *Librn*, Stephanie S Mutty; E-Mail: stephanie_mutty@ca1.uscourts.gov
Founded 1990
Library Holdings: Bk Vols 10,000; Per Subs 20
Special Collections: Legal
Publications: Tome Tidings
Restriction: Not open to public
Partic in Lexus; OCLC Online Computer Library Center, Inc; Westlaw

C UNIVERSITY OF RHODE ISLAND - PROVIDENCE CAMPUS, College of Continuing Education Library, 80 Washington St, 02903-1803. SAN 315-4610. Tel: 401-277-5130. FAX: 401-277-5148. Web Site: www.uri.edu/library. *Dir*, Joanna M Burkhardt; E-Mail: jburkhardt@uri.edu; Staff 4 (MLS

1, Non-MLS 3)
Founded 1964. Circ 18,580; Enrl 5,300; Highest Degree: Master
Jul 1998-Jun 1999 Income $164,000. Mats Exp $108,000, Books $26,000, Per/Ser (Incl. Access Fees) $63,000, Micro $8,000, Other Print Mats $11,000. Sal $158,000 (Prof $56,000)
Library Holdings: Bk Vols 23,000; Per Subs 325
Subject Interests: Adult education, Bus, English literature, Psychology
Automation Activity & Vendor Info: (Circulation) Innovative Interfaces Inc.; (Media Booking) Innovative Interfaces Inc.; (OPAC) Innovative Interfaces Inc.
Partic in BRS; Consortium Of Rhode Island Academic & Research Libraries; Higher Educ Libr Info Network; OCLC Online Computer Library Center, Inc

ROGER WILLIAMS HOSPITAL, Health Sciences Library, 825 Chalkstone Ave, 02908. SAN 315-4637. Tel: 401-456-2036. FAX: 401-751-9717. *Librn*, Kimberly R Lavoie; Fax: 401-456-2546, E-Mail: klavoie@ids.net; *Asst Librn*, Catherine Ryan; Staff 2 (MLS 2)
Library Holdings: Bk Vols 2,000; Per Subs 125
Database Vendor: Ebsco - EbscoHost, OVID Technologies
Partic in Association of Rhode Island Health Sciences Libraries (ARIHSL); BHSL

IVERSIDE

READE ADVANCED MATERIALS, PO Drawer 15039, 02915-0039. SAN 325-0733. Tel: 401-433-7000. FAX: 401-433-7001. E-Mail: librarian@reade.com. Web Site: www.reade.com. *Librn*, A B Reade
Founded 1976
Subject Interests: Advanced mat, Advertising, Ceramic compositions, Countertrade, Emerging tech, Export, High tech coatings, Import, Metal alloy, Powder metallurgy, Pub relations, Size reduc of metals, Size reduc of minerals
Special Collections: Advanced Ceramics; Atomization of Metals & Minerals; Ceramic & Metal Powders; CVD, EVD, PVD Coatings; Global Market Intelligence; Industrial Promotions; Markets for Advanced Metal; Metal Powders; Nanocrystals; Superconducting Compounds & Polymer/Matrix Composites
Friends of the Library Group

AUNDERSTOWN

WILLETT FREE LIBRARY,* 45 Ferry Rd, PO Box 178, 02874. SAN 315-467X. Tel: 401-294-2081. FAX: 401-294-2081. *Librn*, Margaret B Cocroft; E-Mail: margaret@lori.state.ri.us
Founded 1886. Circ 9,609
Library Holdings: Bk Vols 10,025
Mem of S County Interrelated Libr Syst

LATERSVILLE

NORTH SMITHFIELD PUBLIC LIBRARY,* Slater Bldg, 20 Main St, PO Box 950, 02876. SAN 315-4696. Tel: 401-767-2780. FAX: 401-767-2782. *Dir*, Carol H Brouwer
Founded 1928. Circ 68,142
Jul 1998-Jun 1999 Income $186,105, State $18,936, City $159,169, Locally Generated Income $8,000. Mats Exp $30,284, Books $24,589, Per/Ser (Incl. Access Fees) $3,502, Presv $2,193. Sal $119,529
Library Holdings: Bk Vols 34,648; Per Subs 115
Subject Interests: Child care, Parenting
Partic in Cooperating Libraries Automated Network (CLAN)
Friends of the Library Group

MITHFIELD

AUDUBON SOCIETY OF RHODE ISLAND, Hathaway Library of Conservation & Natural History, 12 Sanderson Rd, Rte 5, 02917. SAN 315-4386. Tel: 401-949-5454. FAX: 401-949-5788. Web Site: asri.org. *Dir*, Eugenia Marks; E-Mail: audubon_ri@ids.net; *Librn*, Sibi Rhodes; *Librn*, Marcia Sprague
Founded 1930
1999-2000 Income Parent Institution $1,500. Mats Exp $1,400, Books $900, Per/Ser (Incl. Access Fees) $400, Presv $100
Library Holdings: Bk Titles 2,500; Per Subs 200
Subject Interests: Conservation, Ecology, Nat hist
Special Collections: Bonapartes Ornithology; Elizabeth Dickens Diaries; J J Audubon's Viviperous Quadrupeds of North America; Natural Specimens Coll; Wilson's Ornithology

BRYANT COLLEGE, Edith M Hodgson Memorial Library, 1150 Douglas Pike, 02917-1284. SAN 315-470X. Tel: 401-232-6125. Interlibrary Loan Service Tel: 401-232-6296. FAX: 401-232-6126. E-Mail: library@bryant.edu. Web Site: www.bryant.edu/~library. *Dir*, Mary Moroney; E-Mail: mmoroney@bryant.edu; *Ref*, Colleen Anderson; Tel: 401-232-6299, E-Mail: canderso@bryant.edu; *Ref*, Paul Roske; E-Mail: proske@bryant.edu; *Media Spec*, Roger Acosta; Tel: 401-232-6128, E-Mail: racosta@bryant.edu; Staff 15 (MLS 6, Non-MLS 9)
Founded 1955. Enrl 4,400; Fac 130; Highest Degree: Master
Aug 1998-Jul 1999 Mats Exp $346,758, Books $85,111, Per/Ser (Incl. Access Fees) $261,647. Sal $455,489 (Prof $255,924)
Library Holdings: Bk Vols 140,000; Per Subs 3,000
Subject Interests: Finance, Financial servs, Small business, Taxation
Automation Activity & Vendor Info: (Acquisitions) Innovative Interfaces Inc.; (Cataloging) Innovative Interfaces Inc.; (Circulation) Innovative Interfaces Inc.; (Course Reserve) Innovative Interfaces Inc.; (ILL) Innovative Interfaces Inc.; (Media Booking) Innovative Interfaces Inc.; (OPAC) Innovative Interfaces Inc.; (Serials) Innovative Interfaces Inc.
Database Vendor: Dialog, Lexis-Nexis
Mem of Rhode Island Interrelated Libr Syst
Partic in Consortium Of Rhode Island Academic & Research Libraries; Nelinet, Inc; OCLC Online Computer Library Center, Inc

TIVERTON

P TIVERTON LIBRARY SERVICES, 238 Highland Rd, 02878. SAN 320-460X. Tel: 401-625-6796. FAX: 401-625-5499. E-Mail: amrtiv@hotmail.com. Web Site: www.clan.lib.ri.us/tiv/tiv-lib.htm. *Dir*, Lisa Walling; E-Mail: lisawg@seq.clan.lib.ri.us; *YA Servs*, Janice Griffin; E-Mail: jgriffin@seq.clan.lib.ri.us; *Ch Servs*, Janet Kosinski; *Head Ref*, Richard F Joslin; Staff 12 (MLS 4, Non-MLS 8)
Pop 14,000
Jul 1999-Jun 2000 Income $275,760. Sal $175,878
Library Holdings: Bk Vols 65,000; Per Subs 30
Subject Interests: Local history
Database Vendor: IAC - Info Trac, OVID Technologies
Mem of Coop Libr Automated Network
Open Mon-Thurs 9-8, Fri 9-5 & Sat 9-3
Friends of the Library Group
Branches: 1
UNION, 3832 Main Rd, 02878-1321. SAN 320-4634. Tel: 401-625-6799. Web Site: www.clan.lib.ri.us/tiv/tiv-lib.htm. *Dir*, Ann Richard
Circ 3,547
Library Holdings: Bk Vols 14,000
Open Tues 12:30-7:30, Thurs 12:30-5:30, Sat 9-12

WARREN

P GEORGE HAIL FREE LIBRARY, 530 Main St, 02885. SAN 315-4734. Tel: 401-245-7686. FAX: 401-245-7470. *Dir*, Anne Toll; E-Mail: sarahwd@lori.state.ri.us; *Ch Servs*, Peggy Gossage; Staff 7 (MLS 1, Non-MLS 6)
Founded 1888. Pop 11,500; Circ 41,000
Library Holdings: Bk Vols 28,000; Per Subs 60
Subject Interests: American Indian, Cookery
Special Collections: Charles W Greene Museum; Whaling Industry Coll
Partic in Coop Librs Automated Network
Friends of the Library Group

WARWICK

J COMMUNITY COLLEGE OF RHODE ISLAND, Learning Resources Center, 400 East Ave, 02886-1805. SAN 359-8659. Tel: 401-825-2216. FAX: 401-825-2421. Web Site: www.ccri.cc.ri.us/web/libr/lib.htm. *Dean of Libr*, Charles C D'Arezzo; E-Mail: cdarezzo@ccri.cc.ri.us; *Coll Develop, Ref*, Brenda Andrade; E-Mail: bandrade@ccri.cc.ri.us; *Tech Servs*, James R Frechette; E-Mail: jfrechette@ccri.cc.ri.us; *Ref*, Roger E Proulx; E-Mail: rproulx@ccri.cc.ri.us; *Per*, David Kaplan; E-Mail: dkaplan@ccri.cc.ri.us; *AV, Coordr*, Linda Richard; E-Mail: lrichard@ccri.cc.ri.us; *ILL*, Frank St Pierre; E-Mail: fstpierre@ccri.cc.ri.us; *Coll Develop*, Christine Peterson; E-Mail: cpeterson@ccri.cc.ri.us; Staff 8 (MLS 8)
Founded 1964. Enrl 5,210; Fac 297
Library Holdings: Bk Vols 54,000; Per Subs 710
Special Collections: Career & College Information CLSI; College Catalog Coll, micro
Partic in Consortium Of Rhode Island Academic & Research Libraries; Helin; Nelinet, Inc
Open Mon-Thurs 8-8, Fri 8-4 & Sat 10-2

S IN-SIGHT LIBRARY,* 43 Jefferson Blvd, 02888-9961. SAN 320-7420. Tel: 401-941-3322. FAX: 401-941-3356. *Librn*, Mary Manning; Staff 1 (MLS 1)
Library Holdings: Bk Vols 425; Per Subs 20
Subject Interests: Bks on tape, Blindness, Braille, Large print bks, Videos

M KENT COUNTY MEMORIAL HOSPITAL, Health Sciences Library,* 455 Toll Gate Rd, 02886. SAN 320-7447. Tel: 401-737-7000, Ext 1309. FAX: 401-736-1000. E-Mail: kcmhlibrary@ids.net. *Librn, Online Servs*, Jo-Anne Aspri
Founded 1970
Library Holdings: Bk Vols 1,100; Per Subs 200
Subject Interests: Medicine, Nursing
Partic in Association of Rhode Island Health Sciences Libraries (ARIHSL); Basic Health Sciences Library Network; Medline
Open Mon-Fri 8:30-4:30

S METROPOLITAN PROPERTY & CASUALTY INSURANCE, Law Department,* 700 Quaker Lane, 02887. SAN 315-4750. Tel: 401-827-3158. FAX: 401-827-2674.; Staff 1 (MLS 1)
Founded 1974
Library Holdings: Bk Vols 500; Per Subs 15
Subject Interests: Bus, Insurance, Law, Mgt
Publications: Library list
Partic in Westlaw

S NATIONAL FOUNDATION FOR GIFTED & CREATIVE CHILDREN LIBRARY, 395 Diamond Hill Rd, 02886. SAN 372-9370. Tel: 401-738-0937. Web Site: www.nfgcc.org. *Exec Dir*, Marie Friedel
Library Holdings: Bk Vols 1,000; Per Subs 12

C NEW ENGLAND INSTITUTE OF TECHNOLOGY, Learning Resources Center, 2500 Post Rd, 02886-2266. SAN 320-2291. Tel: 401-739-5000. Circulation Tel: 401-739-5000, Ext 3409. Reference Tel: 401-739-5000, Ext 3472. FAX: 401-738-4061. *Dir*, Sharon J Charette; Tel: 401-739-5000, Ext 3447, E-Mail: scharette@neit.edu; *Cat*, Cynthia A Pankiewicz; Tel: 401-739-5000, Ext 3474; *Acq*, Leslie E Tracey; Tel: 401-739-5000, Ext 3473; Staff 7 (MLS 4, Non-MLS 3)
Enrl 2,203; Fac 207; Highest Degree: Bachelor
Jul 1999-Jun 2000 Mats Exp $94,205, Books $59,470, Per/Ser (Incl. Access Fees) $13,326, Presv $967, Micro $2,170, AV Equip $972, Electronic Ref Mat (Incl. Access Fees) $17,300
Library Holdings: Bk Vols 33,473; Bk Titles 31,525; Per Subs 378; Bks on Deafness & Sign Lang 32
Subject Interests: Allied health, Computers, Electronics, Engr, Tech subjects
Automation Activity & Vendor Info: (Circulation) TLC; (OPAC) TLC
Database Vendor: Ebsco - EbscoHost, OCLC - First Search, ProQuest
Publications: Faculty Development Bibliography Series; Faculty Series; Library Skills Series; Subject Resource Series (Reference guide); Technology Outline Series; Writing Skills Series
Partic in Nelinet, Inc; OCLC Online Computer Library Center, Inc; RI Interrelated Libr Network

S PLAN INTERNATIONAL, United States of America Library, 155 Plan Way, 02886. SAN 372-9362. Tel: 401-738-5600. FAX: 401-738-5608. E-Mail: n-usno@plan.geis.com. *In Charge*, Donna Louise Brown; Tel: 401-738-5600, Ext 108
Library Holdings: Bk Vols 500; Per Subs 30
Publications: Annual report
Open Mon-Fri 8:30-5

P PONTIAC FREE LIBRARY ASSOCIATION,* 101 Greenwich Ave, 02886. SAN 315-4769. Tel: 401-737-3292. FAX: 401-737-3292. *Dir*, Jeanne Warren; E-Mail: jeannewn@lori.state.ri.us; *Asst Dir*, Jean Cole
Founded 1884. Pop 3,000; Circ 16,000
Library Holdings: Bk Titles 18,587; Per Subs 47
Mem of Western Regional Libr Syst
Friends of the Library Group

P WARWICK PUBLIC LIBRARY,* 600 Sandy Lane, 02886-3998. SAN 359-8683. Tel: 401-739-5440. TDD: 401-739-3689. FAX: 401-732-2055. Web Site: www.wpl.lib.ri.us. *Dir*, Douglas A Pearce; *Dep Dir*, Carol S Drought; *Ad Servs*, Susan Dunn; *Ch Servs*, Susan Lepore; *Tech Servs*, Sharon Fredette; *Circ*, Kathleen Berrigan; *Acq, Coll Develop*, Deborah Rock; Staff 12 (MLS 12)
Founded 1965. Pop 87,123; Circ 554,275
Jul 1998-Jun 1999 Income $1,444,000. Mats Exp $218,537. Sal $1,134,000
Library Holdings: Bk Vols 237,767; Per Subs 462
Automation Activity & Vendor Info: (Circulation) epixtech, inc.
Partic in Cooperating Libraries Automated Network (CLAN); RI Libr Film Coop
Special Services for the Deaf - TDD
Friends of the Library Group
Branches: 3
APPONAUG, 3267 Post Rd, 02886. SAN 359-8713. Tel: 401-739-6411. Web Site: www.wpl.lib.ri.us. *Br Coordr*, Margaret Cashion
Library Holdings: Bk Vols 14,000
Friends of the Library Group
CONIMICUT, 55 Beach Ave, 02889. SAN 359-8748. Tel: 401-737-6546. Web Site: www.wpl.lib.ri.us. *Br Coordr*, Irene M Ovalles
Library Holdings: Bk Vols 12,000
Friends of the Library Group
NORWOOD, 328 Pawtuxet Ave, 02888. SAN 359-8772. Tel: 401-941-7545. Web Site: www.wpl.lib.ri.us. *Br Coordr*, Teresa Carberry
Library Holdings: Bk Vols 12,000
Friends of the Library Group

WEST GREENWICH

P LOUTTIT LIBRARY,* 274 Victory Hwy, 02817. SAN 315-4785. Tel: 401-397-3434. Web Site: www.204.17.98.73/wgrweb.html. *Dir*, Elsie Oltedale; *Ref*, Patricia DiBella; *Ch Servs*, Laureen Young
Pop 3,492; Circ 30,456
Jul 1997-Jun 1998 Income $141,657, State $1,407, City $41,750, Other $98,500. Mats Exp $9,792, Books $8,010, Per/Ser (Incl. Access Fees) $542, Micro $790, AV Equip $450. Sal $21,494
Library Holdings: Bk Vols 10,000
Subject Interests: West Greenwich hist
Open Tues 10-8, Wed & Thurs 2-8, Fri & Sat 10-4
Friends of the Library Group

WEST WARWICK

P WEST WARWICK PUBLIC LIBRARY, Robert H Champlin Memorial Library, 1043 Main St, 02893. SAN 359-8802. Tel: 401-828-3750. FAX: 401-828-8493. Web Site: www.ultranet.com/~wwpublib. *Dir*, Frances Farrell-Bergeron; *Asst Dir*, Cynthia Desrochers; *Circ*, Andrea Plaziak; *Ch Servs*, Anne McLaughlin; *Ref*, Maureen Delovio
Founded 1967. Pop 29,268; Circ 139,238
Jul 1999-Jun 2000 Income $884,683, State $138,456, City $606,777, Other $139,450. Mats Exp $82,871, Books $47,178, Per/Ser (Incl. Access Fees) $9,190, Electronic Ref Mat (Incl. Access Fees) $14,175. Sal $484,270
Library Holdings: Bk Vols 79,877; Per Subs 140
Special Collections: Rhode Island; Science Fiction; West Warwick
Publications: Newsletter (monthly)
Partic in Cooperating Libraries Automated Network (CLAN)

WESTERLY

M WESTERLY HOSPITAL, Medical Library,* 25 Wells St, 02891. SAN 315-4807. Tel: 401-348-3260. FAX: 401-348-3774. *Librn*, Rae A Serio; E-Mail: rserio@edgenet.net
Library Holdings: Bk Vols 678; Per Subs 77
Subject Interests: Medicine, Surgery

P WESTERLY PUBLIC LIBRARY,* 44 Broad St, 02891. SAN 315-4815. Tel: 401-596-2877. FAX: 401-596-5600. Web Site: seq.clan.lib.ri.us/wes/index.htm. *Dir*, Kathryn T Taylor; *Circ*, Carla Chase; *Ch Servs, Coll Develop*, Helen Mochetti; *Coll Develop, Tech Servs*, Karen Light; *Ref*, Margaret Victoria; Staff 9 (MLS 9)
Founded 1894. Pop 27,000; Circ 252,515
Jul 1997-Jun 1998 Income $1,134,244, State $9,787, City $323,588, Locally Generated Income $161,340, Parent Institution $557,594. Mats Exp $97,588, Books $70,000, Per/Ser (Incl. Access Fees) $16,300, Micro $11,288
Library Holdings: Bk Vols 150,022; Per Subs 340
Subject Interests: Art, Genealogy, Granite indust, Local hist archives
Special Collections: Children's Literature (Margaret Wise Brown), mss; Granite Carving & Quarrying Gallery; Museum Coll, artifacts
Publications: First Westerly Coloring Book; Life's Little Pleasures
Mem of Coop Libr Automated Network
Partic in Cooperating Libraries Automated Network (CLAN)
Library operates 14 1/2 acre arboretum
Friends of the Library Group

WOONSOCKET

S AMERICAN-FRENCH GENEALOGICAL SOCIETY LIBRARY, 78 Earle St, 02895. (Mail add: PO Box 2113, 02861), Tel: 401-765-6141. FAX: 401-765-6141. E-Mail: afgs@afgs.org. Web Site: www.afgs.org. *Pres*, Roger Beaudry; E-Mail: rbeaudry@afgs.org
Founded 1978
Library Holdings: Bk Vols 8,000; Bk Titles 100; Per Subs 11
Special Collections: Drouin Coll of Canadian baptism, marriage & death records from the Province of Quebec
Restriction: Not a lending library
Function: Research library

S UNION SAINT-JEAN BAPTISTE, Bibliotheque Mallet,* 68 Cumberland St, PO Box F, 02895-9987. SAN 315-4823. Tel: 401-769-0520, Ext 143. FAX: 401-766-3014.
Founded 1908
Library Holdings: Bk Vols 5,119; Bk Titles 3,659; Per Subs 48
Subject Interests: Franco-Am civilization, Franco-Am hist, Genealogy

P WOONSOCKET HARRIS PUBLIC LIBRARY, 303 Clinton St, 02895. SAN 315-4831. Tel: 401-769-9044. FAX: 401-767-4140. E-Mail: whpl@ultranet.com. Web Site: www.ultranet.com/~whpl. *Dep Dir*, Leslie Page; E-Mail: lesliepe@lori.state.ri.us; *Ch Servs*, Christine Wallace; Staff 30 (MLS 7, Non-MLS 23)
Founded 1863. Pop 44,000
Jul 1999-Jun 2000 Income $830,650, State $102,421, City $651,906, Federal $11,102, Other $65,221. Mats Exp $78,812, Books $68,493, Per/Ser (Incl. Access Fees) $6,824, Presv $395, Micro $600, Electronic Ref Mat (Incl. Access Fees) $2,500. Sal $439,662 (Prof $210,000)
Library Holdings: Bk Vols 101,535; Per Subs 133
Subject Interests: Local history
Partic in Coop Librs Automated Network
Friends of the Library Group

SOUTH CAROLINA

Date of Statistics: 1999-2000
Population, 1990 Census: 3,486,703
Total Volumes in Public Libraries: 8,065,290
Volumes Per Capita: 2.31
Total Public Library Circulation: 17,475,637
Circulation Per Capita: 5.01
Total Public Library Income (including Grants-in-Aid): $71,910,878
Source of Income: Mainly public funds
Expenditures Per Capita: $20.41
Number of County or Multi-county (Regional) Libraries: 37 county libraries; 3 regional libraries, 1 municipal library
Counties Served: 46
Number of Bookmobiles in State: 38
Grants-in-Aid to Public Libraries (including federal & state grants but not construction funds): 7,238,737
Federal (Library Services & Technology Act): $551,230
State Aid: $6,610,377
Formula for Apportionment: County & regional libraries; maintenance of local effort & specified standards of service required

IKEN

AIKEN TECHNICAL COLLEGE, Learning Resources Center, Hwy 1 & 78, 29802. (Mail add: PO Drawer 696, 29802-0696), Tel: 803-593-9954, Ext 1312. FAX: 803-593-2169. E-Mail: rystrom@aik.tec.sc.us. Web Site: www.aik.tec.sc.us. *Dir*, Barbara Rystrom; Tel: 803-593-9954, Ext 1312, E-Mail: rystrom@aik.tec.sc.us; *Tech Servs*, Dorothy Hartley; Tel: 803-593-9954, Ext 1229, E-Mail: library@aik.tec.sc.us; *Circ*, Jennifer Pinckney; Tel: 803-593-9954, Ext 1755, E-Mail: pinckney@aik.tec.sc.us; Staff 4 (MLS 2, Non-MLS 2)
Founded 1973. Enrl 2,358; Highest Degree: Associate
Jul 1999-Jun 2000 Income $349,858, State $54,244. Mats Exp $59,380, Books $28,505, Per/Ser (Incl. Access Fees) $23,375, Micro $7,500, Other Print Mats $20,972. Sal $142,213
Library Holdings: Bk Vols 31,893; Bk Titles 26,255; Per Subs 221
Subject Interests: Engineering, Technology
Automation Activity & Vendor Info: (Cataloging) epixtech, inc.; (Circulation) epixtech, inc.; (OPAC) epixtech, inc.
Database Vendor: GaleNet, IAC - Info Trac
Partic in Solinet

AIKEN-BAMBERG-BARNWELL-EDGEFIELD REGIONAL LIBRARY SYSTEM, 314 Chesterfield St SW, 29801-7117. SAN 359-8861. Tel: 803-642-7575. FAX: 803-642-7597. *Dir*, Mary Jo Dawson; E-Mail: maryjod@abbe-lib.org; *Exten Serv, Librn*, Sara Thigpen; E-Mail: sarat@abbe-lib.org; *Ch Servs, Librn*, Jeannie Simmons; E-Mail: jeannies@abbe-lib.org; Staff 16 (MLS 11, Non-MLS 5)
Founded 1958. Pop 176,510
Jul 1999-Jun 2000 Income (Main Library and Branch Library) $1,761,300, State $345,597, City $24,000, Federal $1,000, County $1,202,318, Locally Generated Income $188,385. Mats Exp $271,527, Books $212,165, Per/Ser (Incl. Access Fees) $19,436, Micro $1,702, AV Equip $38,116, Electronic Ref Mat (Incl. Access Fees) $108. Sal $1,197,847
Library Holdings: Bk Vols 214,174; Per Subs 413
Special Collections: South Carolina Coll
Automation Activity & Vendor Info: (Acquisitions) EX Libris; (Cataloging) Gaylord; (Circulation) Gaylord; (OPAC) Gaylord
Friends of the Library Group
Branches: 14
AIKEN COUNTY, 314 Chesterfield St SW, 29801. SAN 359-8896. Tel: 803-642-2020. Circulation Tel: 803-642-2023. Reference Tel: 803-642-2022. FAX: 803-642-7570. *Chief Librn*, Lee Roderick; *Ref*, Elizabeth Caldwell; *Ref*, Sally Farris
Library Holdings: Bk Vols 55,000
Subject Interests: SC
Friends of the Library Group
BAMBERG COUNTY, Railroad Ave, PO Box 305, Bamberg, 29003-0305. SAN 359-8926. Tel: 803-245-3022. FAX: 803-245-2422. *Chief Librn*, Carol Ann Bunch
Library Holdings: Bk Vols 18,000
BARNWELL COUNTY, 617 Hagood St, Barnwell, 29812. SAN 359-8950. Tel: 803-259-3612. FAX: 803-259-7497. *Chief Librn*, Ellen B Jenkins; Staff 1 (Non-MLS 1)
Library Holdings: Bk Vols 14,000
Special Collections: South Carolina Genealogy
Friends of the Library Group
BLACKVILLE BRANCH, 19420 N Sol Blatt Ave, Blackville, 29817. SAN 359-8985. Tel: 803-284-2295. FAX: 803-284-2295. *Branch Mgr*, J Gordon
Friends of the Library Group
NANCY BONNETTE BRANCH LIBRARY, 204 Park St, PO Box 629, Wagener, 29164. SAN 359-9191. Tel: 803-564-5396. FAX: 803-564-5396. *Branch Mgr*, Dianne Keadle
DENMARK BRANCH, 204 S Maple St, Denmark, 29042-1649. (Mail add: PO Box 314, Denmark, 29042-0314), SAN 359-9019. Tel: 803-793-4511. FAX: 803-793-4511. *Branch Mgr*, Darlene McAlhany
EDGEFIELD COUNTY, 105 Courthouse Sq, Edgefield, 29824. SAN 359-9043. Tel: 803-637-4025. FAX: 803-637-4026. *Chief Librn*, Anuradha S Acharekar; E-Mail: anua@abbe-lib.org; Staff 3 (MLS 1, Non-MLS 2)
Library Holdings: Bk Vols 18,100
JACKSON BRANCH, 106 Main St, Jackson, 29831-2616. (Mail add: PO Box 599, Jackson, 29831-0599), SAN 377-0443. Tel: 803-471-3811. FAX: 803-471-3811. *Branch Mgr*, Caroline Sparks
Friends of the Library Group
JOHNSTON BRANCH, 505 Academy St, Johnston, 29832. SAN 359-9078. Tel: 803-275-5157. *Branch Mgr*, Jane Mims
Friends of the Library Group
MIDLAND VALLEY, 9 Hillside Rd, PO Box 1070, Langley, 29834-1070. SAN 377-046X. Tel: 803-593-5253. FAX: 803-593-5253. *Branch Mgr*, Susan Toole; E-Mail: susant@abbe-lib.orgl
NANCY CARSON LIBRARY, 135 Edgefield Rd, North Augusta, 29841-2423. SAN 359-9132. Tel: 803-279-5767. FAX: 803-202-3588. *Chief Librn*, Nancy Carver; E-Mail: nancyc@abbe-lib.org; *Ref*, Jennifer Jones; Staff 8 (MLS 3, Non-MLS 5)
Library Holdings: Bk Vols 35,000
Friends of the Library Group
NEW ELLENTON BRANCH, Main St, PO Box 86, New Ellenton, 29809-0086. SAN 359-9108. Tel: 803-652-7845. FAX: 803-652-7845. *Branch Mgr*, Julia Burton
TRENTON BRANCH, 201 Wise St, PO Box 66, Trenton, 29847-0066. SAN 359-9167. Tel: 803-275-4840. *Branch Mgr*, Becky Rhoden
WILLISTON BRANCH, 205 Springfield Rd, Williston, 29853-1239. (Mail add: PO Box 482, Williston, 29853-0482), SAN 359-9221. Tel: 803-266-3027. FAX: 803-266-3027. *Branch Mgr*, Jo Crider
Friends of the Library Group
Bookmobiles: 1. Clerk, Elizabeth H Harding & Geri Viator. Bk vols 3500

C UNIVERSITY OF SOUTH CAROLINA - AIKEN, Gregg-Graniteville Library, 471 University Pkwy, 29801. SAN 315-4866. Tel: 803-648-6851, Ext 3465. FAX: 803-641-3302. Web Site: library.usca.sc.edu. *Dir, Tech Servs*, Jane H Tuten; *Ref*, Amy Duerenberger; *Ref*, Thomas C Hobbs; *Doc*, Paul Lewis; Staff 14 (MLS 6, Non-MLS 8)
Founded 1961. Enrl 2,173; Fac 147; Highest Degree: Master
Jul 1998-Jun 1999 Income $985,000, State $737,206, Federal $84,000, Locally Generated Income $28,000, Other $100,000. Mats Exp $282,390, Books $59,400, Per/Ser (Incl. Access Fees) $129,379, Presv $7,885, Micro $14,206, Electronic Ref Mat (Incl. Access Fees) $8,859. Sal $456,710 (Prof

$260,617)
Library Holdings: Bk Vols 168,012; Per Subs 850
Special Collections: Department of Energy Public Documents Coll; Gregg-Graniteville Historical Files; May Coll of Southern History
Automation Activity & Vendor Info: (Acquisitions) NOTIS; (Cataloging) NOTIS; (Circulation) NOTIS; (OPAC) NOTIS; (Serials) NOTIS
Publications: Inter-Intra Library Loan Service Pamphlet; New Faculty Library Guide; Report of the Dean
Partic in OCLC Online Computer Library Center, Inc; SC Libr Network; South Carolina State Library

S WESTINGHOUSE SAVANNAH RIVER CO, Savannah River Site Technical Library, Bldg 773A, 29808. SAN 327-0815. Tel: 803-725-7752. FAX: 803-725-1169. *Librn*, Darra Combs; Tel: 803-208-0914, E-Mail: darra.combs@srs.gov; Staff 7 (MLS 3, Non-MLS 4)
Library Holdings: Bk Vols 30,500; Per Subs 300
Subject Interests: Nuclear, Safety, Technology, Training

ALLENDALE

P ALLENDALE-HAMPTON-JASPER REGIONAL LIBRARY, 158 McNair St, PO Box 768, 29810-0768. SAN 359-9256. Tel: 803-584-2371, 803-584-3513. FAX: 803-584-8134. *Dir*, Betty Anne Todd; E-Mail: bettyannetodd@yahoo.com
Founded 1905. Pop 43,363; Circ 84,574
Library Holdings: Bk Vols 61,279
Partic in State Libr Network
Branches: 5
ALLENDALE, 158 McNair St, PO Box 280, 29810. Tel: 803-584-2371. FAX: 803-584-8134. *Librn*, Barbara Reed
Library Holdings: Bk Vols 20,000
ESTILL BRANCH, 276 Third Ave, Estill, 29918-1128. SAN 359-9310. Tel: 803-625-4560. FAX: 803-625-3341. *Librn*, Chelsea Devore
Library Holdings: Bk Vols 2,000
HAMPTON, 12 Locust St, East Hampton, 29924. SAN 359-9345. Tel: 803-943-7528. FAX: 803-943-3261. *Librn*, Tammy Hadwin
Library Holdings: Bk Vols 16,279
HARDEEVILLE BRANCH, Main St, PO Box 837, Hardeeville, 29927-0837. SAN 359-937X. Tel: 803-784-3426. FAX: 803-784-5277. *Librn*, Lynda Cadell
Library Holdings: Bk Vols 5,000
Friends of the Library Group
PRATT MEMORIAL LIBRARY, 123-A E Wilson St, PO Drawer 1540, Ridgeland, 29936-1540. SAN 359-940X. Tel: 803-726-7744. FAX: 803-726-7813. *Librn*, Marsha Cleland
Library Holdings: Bk Vols 18,000
Bookmobiles: 1

J UNIVERSITY OF SOUTH CAROLINA, Salkehatchie Regional Campus Library,* PO Box 617, 29810. SAN 315-4874. Tel: 803-584-3446, Ext 152. FAX: 803-584-5038. Web Site: www.sc.edu/system.html.salkehatchie. *Librn*, Marvin Light; E-Mail: mjlight@vm.sc.edu; Staff 1 (MLS 1)
Founded 1965. Enrl 820
Jul 1997-Jun 1998 Mats Exp $70,235, Books $24,937, Per/Ser (Incl. Access Fees) $36,000, Presv $500, Micro $1,798, AV Equip $2,000, Other Print Mats $5,000. Sal $99,324
Library Holdings: Bk Vols 45,251; Bk Titles 37,948; Per Subs 481
Subject Interests: African Amer, Women's studies
Special Collections: South Carolina, Five County Area Coll (Allendale, Bamberg, Barnwell, Colleton & Hampton counties)
Publications: Newsletter
Mem of Asn of Research Libraries
Partic in SE Libr Network
Friends of the Library Group
Departmental Libraries:
WALTERBORO, PO Box 1337, Walterboro, 29488. SAN 378-1607. Tel: 843-549-6007. FAX: 843-549-4345.

ANDERSON

M ANDERSON AREA MEDICAL CENTER LIBRARY, 800 N Fant St, 29621. SAN 315-4890. Tel: 864-261-1253. FAX: 864-261-1552. *Librn*, Clara Elizabeth Addis; E-Mail: baddis@anmed.com; Staff 2 (MLS 1, Non-MLS 1)
Oct 1999-Sep 2000 Mats Exp $25,032, Books $5,032, Per/Ser (Incl. Access Fees) $20,000
Library Holdings: Bk Vols 1,250; Per Subs 115
Subject Interests: Medicine, Nursing, Surgery
Automation Activity & Vendor Info: (Cataloging) Sagebrush Corporation; (OPAC) Sagebrush Corporation
Restriction: Employees & their associates, Staff use only
Partic in Docline; Nat Libr of Med; South Carolina Ahec

C ANDERSON COLLEGE LIBRARY, Johnston Memorial Library, 316 Boulevard St, 29621. SAN 315-4882. Tel: 864-231-2050. FAX: 864-231-2191. E-Mail: aclibrary@anderson-college.edu. *Librn*, Kent Millwood; Tel: 864-231-2049, E-Mail: kmillwood@anderson-college.edu; *Librn*, Kay Maynard; E-Mail: kmaynard@anderson-college.edu; *Circ*, Brenda DuBose; E-Mail: bduboise@anderson-college.edu; *Tech Servs*, Cheryl deHoll; E-Ma cdeholl@anderson-college.edu; Staff 6 (MLS 3, Non-MLS 3)
Founded 1911. Enrl 1,000; Highest Degree: Bachelor
Library Holdings: Bk Vols 60,000
Automation Activity & Vendor Info: (Cataloging) TLC; (Circulation) TL (Course Reserve) TLC; (Media Booking) TLC; (OPAC) TLC
Partic in First Search; OCLC Online Computer Library Center, Inc

P ANDERSON COUNTY LIBRARY,* 202 E Greenville St, PO Box 4047, 29622-4047. SAN 359-9434. Tel: 864-260-4500, Ext 4503. FAX: 864-260-4510. *Dir*, Carl Stone; E-Mail: cstone@anderson.lib.sc.us; *Tech Servs*, Car Renfro; *Ad Servs*, Philip Cheney; *Ch Servs*, Janelle Ramsey; *Commun Relations*, Pat Pace; *Circ, Ref*, Mary Montanacci; Staff 7 (MLS 7)
Founded 1907. Pop 145,196
Library Holdings: Per Subs 996
Special Collections: Foundation Center Cooperating Coll; South Carolina Coll, bks, microflm & newsp
Publications: Bookmarks (newsletter)
Partic in Dialog Corporation; SCLN; SE Libr Network
Friends of the Library Group
Branches: 8
BELTON BRANCH, 100 Breazeale St, Belton, 29627. SAN 359-9469. Te 864-338-8330. FAX: 864-338-8330. *Librn*, Martha Kay
Friends of the Library Group
JENNIE ERWIN BRANCH, 318 Shirley Ave, Honea Path, 29654. SAN 359-9493. Tel: 864-369-7751. FAX: 864-369-7751. *Librn*, Cheryl Hughe
IVA BRANCH, 203 W Cruette St, Iva, 29655. SAN 359-9523. Tel: 864-348-6150. FAX: 864-348-6150. *Librn*, Becky Thompson
LANDER MEMORIAL REGIONAL, 925 Greenville Dr, Williamston, 29697. SAN 359-9558. Tel: 864-847-5238. FAX: 864-847-5238. *Librn*, Theresa Linebarger
PENDLETON BRANCH, Micasa Dr, Pendleton, 29670. SAN 359-9612. Tel: 864-646-3923. FAX: 864-646-3923. *Librn*, Hattie Fant
PIEDMONT BRANCH, 1407 Hwy 86, Piedmont, 29673. SAN 359-9647. Tel: 864-845-6534. FAX: 864-845-6534. *Librn*, Betty Davenport
POWDERSVILLE, 205 Siloam Rd, Rte 7, Easley, 29640. SAN 328-7599. Tel: 864-295-1190. FAX: 864-295-1190. *Librn*, Linda Hiott
WEST SIDE COMMUNITY CENTER, 1110 W Market St, 29624. SAN 378-1623. Tel: 864-260-4660. FAX: 864-260-4660. *Librn*, Elma Lee-Norris
Bookmobiles: 1

BEAUFORT

P BEAUFORT COUNTY LIBRARY, 311 Scott St, 29902-5591. SAN 359-9825. Tel: 843-525-4000. Interlibrary Loan Service Tel: 843-525-4062. FA 843-525-4055. Web Site: www.co.beaufort.sc.us/library/beaufort. *Dir*, Julie Zachowski; *Acq*, Kathy Mitchell; *Tech Servs*, Rosa Cummings; *Ch Servs*, Wendy Allen; *Ref*, Dennis Adams; *ILL*, Pat Porter. Subject Specialists: *Sou Carolina*, Grace Cordial; Staff 6 (MLS 6)
Founded 1963. Pop 101,892; Circ 279,114
Library Holdings: Bk Vols 158,000; Per Subs 353
Subject Interests: Local history
Database Vendor: DRA
Partic in Lowcounty Libr Fedn; South Carolina State Library
Friends of the Library Group
Branches: 4
BLUFFTON COMMUNITY, 48 Boundary St, Bluffton, 29910. (Mail add: PO Box 1569, Bluffton, 29910), Tel: 843-757-1519. FAX: 843-757-1505. Web Site: www.co.beaufort.sc.us.library/beaufort/bluffton.htm.; Staff 3 (MLS 1, Non-MLS 2)
Database Vendor: DRA
Friends of the Library Group
DALE, PO Box 809, Lobeco, 29940. SAN 375-5177. Tel: 843-846-3937. FAX: 843-846-3937. *Librn*, Scott Strawn
Database Vendor: DRA
HILTON HEAD ISLAND BRANCH, 11 Beach City Rd, Hilton Head Island, 29926. SAN 359-985X. Tel: 843-342-9200. FAX: 843-342-9220.; Staff 17 (MLS 5, Non-MLS 12)
Database Vendor: DRA
Friends of the Library Group
SAINT HELENA BRANCH, PO Box 308, Saint Helena Island, 29920. SA 375-5185. Tel: 843-838-8304. FAX: 843-838-8304.
Database Vendor: DRA

J TECHNICAL COLLEGE OF THE LOWCOUNTRY, Learning Resources Center,* 921 Ribaut Rd, PO Box 1288, 29902. SAN 320-233X. Tel: 843-525-8304. FAX: 843-525-8237. *Dir*, Richard Shaw; Staff 4 (MLS 2, Non-MLS 2)
Founded 1961
Library Holdings: Bk Vols 19,644; Per Subs 215
Subject Interests: Aquaculture, Black studies, Data processing, Nursing, Small bus
Publications: Check it out (newspaper column); LRC Information Brochur
Mem of State Libr of SC
Partic in OCLC Online Computer Library Center, Inc

UNITED STATES MARINE CORPS
AIR STATION LIBRARY, PO Box 55018, 29904. Tel: 843-228-7682. FAX: 843-228-7682. *Librn*, Shirley Holcomb; E-Mail: holcomb@clb.usmc.mil
Founded 1957
Library Holdings: Bk Titles 27,752; Per Subs 100
Subject Interests: Hist of aircraft, Maintenance of aircraft, Mil art, Mil sci
Special Collections: Children's Stories, Fairytales, Classics; General Fiction & Non-fiction Coll

UNITED STATES NAVY
M NAVAL HOSPITAL LIBRARY, One Pickney Blvd, 29902. Tel: 843-525-5551. FAX: 843-525-5399. E-Mail: bfh.10@med.navy.mail. *Librn*, Patricia Johnson
Library Holdings: Bk Vols 3,400; Per Subs 250
Subject Interests: Medicine, Patient educ
Partic in SC Health Info Network

UNIVERSITY OF SOUTH CAROLINA AT BEAUFORT LIBRARY,* 801 Carteret St, 29902. SAN 315-4912. Tel: 843-521-4121. FAX: 843-521-4198. Web Site: www.sc.edu/beaufort/library/. *Dir*, Ellen E Chamberlain; E-Mail: ellenc@sc.edu; *Librn*, Jan Longest; Tel: 843-785-3995, E-Mail: jhlonges@gwm.sc.edu; *Acq, Circ*, Geni Flowers; Tel: 843-521-4122, E-Mail: meflower@gwm.sc.edu; *ILL*, Dudley Stutz; Tel: 843-521-4126, E-Mail: ddstutz@gwm.sc.edu
Founded 1959. Enrl 1,500
1999-2000 Income $267,568. Mats Exp $66,196, Books $64,528. Sal $139,790
Library Holdings: Bk Titles 57,642; Per Subs 247
Subject Interests: SC hist
Publications: Beaufort County Union List of Periodicals & Newspapers; Library Handbook; Low Country Library Federation Brochure; South Caroliniana (bibliog)
Partic in OCLC Online Computer Library Center, Inc; SE Libr Network
Friends of the Library Group

ENNETTSVILLE

MARLBORO COUNTY LIBRARY, 200 John Corry Rd, 29512. SAN 315-4920. Tel: 843-479-5630. FAX: 843-479-5645. *Actg Dir*, Bobbie Cox; *Ch Servs*, Tammy Perkins; *Bkmobile Coordr*, Cassini Wheeler; Staff 1 (MLS 1)
Founded 1901. Pop 29,361; Circ 53,173; Highest Degree: Master
Jul 2000-Jun 2001 Income $264,079. Mats Exp $108,172, Books $45,793, Per/Ser (Incl. Access Fees) $6,500, AV Equip $5,100, Other Print Mats $48,179, Electronic Ref Mat (Incl. Access Fees) $2,600. Sal $155,907
Library Holdings: Bk Vols 48,000; Bk Titles 38,000; Per Subs 86
Subject Interests: Large print, SC
Bookmobiles: 1

ISHOPVILLE

LEE COUNTY PUBLIC LIBRARY,* 102 N Main St, 29010. SAN 315-4939. Tel: 803-484-5921. FAX: 803-484-4177. *Dir*, Dawn Ellen; *Asst Librn*, Carolyn Atkinson; *Ch Servs*, Missy Terrell; *Bkmobile Coordr*, Brenda Brisdon
Founded 1953. Pop 18,929; Circ 40,102
Library Holdings: Bk Vols 30,626; Per Subs 132
Friends of the Library Group

LACKSBURG

KINGS MOUNTAIN NATIONAL MILITARY PARK LIBRARY, 2625 Park Rd, 29702. SAN 323-7036. Tel: 864-936-7921. TDD: 864-936-7921. FAX: 864-936-9897. Web Site: www.nps.gov/kimo. *In Charge*, Chris Revels
Founded 1931
Library Holdings: Bk Titles 600
Special Services for the Deaf - TDD

AMDEN

CAMDEN ARCHIVES & MUSEUM LIBRARY, 1314 Broad St, 29020-3535. SAN 329-8582. Tel: 803-425-6050. FAX: 803-424-4021. Web Site: www.mindspring.com/~camdenarchives/index.html. *Dir*, Agnes B Corbett
Library Holdings: Bk Vols 4,000
Subject Interests: Genealogy
Special Collections: South Carolina DAR Library; South Carolina Society Colonial Dames, XVII Century
Restriction: In-house use for visitors, Non-circulating to the public
Friends of the Library Group

KERSHAW COUNTY A-TEC, Vocational-Technical Library,* 874 Vocation Lane, 29020. SAN 315-4955. Tel: 803-425-8982. FAX: 803-425-8983.
Library Holdings: Bk Vols 5,000; Per Subs 100

P KERSHAW COUNTY LIBRARY, 1304 Broad St, 29020-3595. SAN 359-9914. Tel: 803-425-1508. FAX: 803-425-7180. Web Site: www.kershaw.lib.sc.us. *Librn*, Frances M Whealton; E-Mail: fmwhealton@infoave.net; Staff 21 (MLS 4, Non-MLS 17)
Founded 1936. Pop 43,599; Circ 188,048
Library Holdings: Bk Vols 127,600
Special Collections: South Caroliniana
Automation Activity & Vendor Info: (Cataloging) epixtech, inc.; (Circulation) epixtech, inc.
Publications: Bearing News (preschool outreach newsletter); Footnotes (Friends of Library newsletter)
Friends of the Library Group
Branches: 1
BETHUNE PUBLIC, Main St, Bethune, 29009. SAN 359-9949. Tel: 843-334-8420. *Librn*, Barbara Huckabee
Library Holdings: Bk Titles 7,858
Bookmobiles: 1

CENTRAL

C SOUTHERN WESLEYAN UNIVERSITY, Claude R Rickman Library, 916 Wesleyan Dr, PO Box 1020 SWU Box 409, 29630-1020. SAN 315-4971. Tel: 864-644-5060. FAX: 864-644-5900. E-Mail: library@swu.edu. Web Site: www.swu.edu/library. *Dir Libr Serv*, Robert E Sears; Tel: 864-644-5064, E-Mail: rsears@swu.edu; *Assoc Dir*, Susan R Cooper; Tel: 864-644-5070, E-Mail: scooper@swu.edu; Staff 6 (MLS 3, Non-MLS 3)
Founded 1906. Enrl 1,332; Highest Degree: Master
Jul 1999-Jun 2000 Income Parent Institution $361,018. Mats Exp $137,469, Books $90,759, Per/Ser (Incl. Access Fees) $33,273, Presv $3,329. Sal $178,332
Library Holdings: Bk Vols 76,383; Per Subs 515
Special Collections: Genealogical Coll (upstate South Carolina families); Wesleyan Historical Coll

CHARLESTON

P CHARLESTON COUNTY PUBLIC LIBRARY, 68 Calhoun St, 29401. SAN 359-9973. Tel: 843-805-6801. Interlibrary Loan Service Tel: 843-805-6940. Circulation Tel: 843-805-6833. Reference Tel: 843-805-6930. Reference FAX: 843-727-6752. Web Site: www.ccpl.org. *Dir*, Jan Buvinger; Tel: 843-805-6821, E-Mail: buvingerj@ccpl.org; *Dep Dir*, Thomas Raines; Tel: 843-805-6821, E-Mail: rainest@ccpl.org; *Ch Servs*, Catherine Christmann; Tel: 843-805-6902, E-Mail: christmannc@ccpl.org; *Coll Develop*, Rodger Smith; Tel: 843-805-6866, E-Mail: smithr@ccpl.org; *Pub Relations*, Catherine Boykin; Tel: 843-805-6819, E-Mail: boykinc@ccpl.org; *Ref*, Ken Gibert; Tel: 843-805-6939, E-Mail: gibertk@ccpl.org; *Tech Servs*, Scott Hamiel; Tel: 843-805-6865, E-Mail: hamiels@ccpl.org; Staff 50 (MLS 50)
Founded 1930. Pop 295,035
Library Holdings: Bk Vols 941,748; Per Subs 2,187
Subject Interests: Ethnic studies, Local history
Automation Activity & Vendor Info: (Circulation) DRA
Publications: The Bridge (staff newsletter)
Partic in Coastnet; SE Libr Network
Special Services for the Deaf - Staff with knowledge of sign language; TTY machine
Friends of the Library Group
Branches: 14
COOPER RIVER MEMORIAL, 3503 Rivers Ave, Charleston Heights, 29405. SAN 360-0009. Tel: 843-744-2489. *Branch Mgr*, Linda Saylor-Marchant; Tel: 843-572-4094, Fax: 843-572-4190, E-Mail: marchantl@ccpl.org
Library Holdings: Bk Vols 51,149
DORCHESTER ROAD REGIONAL, 6325 Dorchester Rd, North Charleston, 29418. SAN 370-9140. Tel: 843-552-6466. FAX: 843-552-6775. *Branch Mgr*, Lee Relyea; E-Mail: relyeal@ccpl.org
Library Holdings: Bk Vols 83,056
EDGAR ALLAN POE BRANCH, 1921 I'On St, Sullivan's Island, 29482. SAN 360-0076. Tel: 843-883-3914. *In Charge*, Ann Melfi; Fax: 843-883-9548, E-Mail: melfia@ccpl.org
Library Holdings: Bk Vols 14,428
EDISTO BRANCH, Thomas Hall, Hwy 174, Edisto Island, 29438. SAN 360-0017. Tel: 843-869-2355.
Library Holdings: Bk Vols 4,756
FOLLY BEACH BRANCH, 45 Center St, Folly Beach, 29439. SAN 360-0025. Tel: 843-588-2001. *Librn*, Kathy Nicklaus; E-Mail: nicklausk@ccpl.org
Library Holdings: Bk Vols 4,993
JAMES ISLAND, 1248 Camp Rd, 29412. SAN 360-0033. Tel: 843-795-6679. *Branch Mgr*, Roberta Dwelley; Fax: 843-406-4850, E-Mail: dwelleyr@ccpl.org
Library Holdings: Bk Vols 46,622
JOHN L DART BRANCH, 1067 King St, 29403. SAN 360-0068. Tel: 843-722-7550. *Branch Mgr*, Cynthia Graham; Fax: 843-727-6784, E-Mail: grahamc@ccpl.org

Library Holdings: Bk Vols 50,695
MCCLELLANVILLE BRANCH, 222 Baker St, McClellanville, 29458. SAN 360-0041. Tel: 843-887-3699. *Librn*, Pat Gross; Fax: 843-887-3144, E-Mail: grossp@ccpl.org
Library Holdings: Bk Vols 12,223
MOUNT PLEASANT REGIONAL, 1133 Mathis Ferry Rd, Mount Pleasant, 29464. SAN 360-005X. Tel: 843-849-6161. FAX: 843-849-6166. *Branch Mgr*, Darlene Jackson; E-Mail: jacksond@ccpl.org
Library Holdings: Bk Vols 87,859
OTRANTO ROAD REGIONAL, 2261 Otranto Rd, North Charleston, 29406. SAN 370-9159. Tel: 843-572-4094. FAX: 843-572-4190. *Branch Mgr*, Deborah Harris; E-Mail: harrisd@ccpl.org
Library Holdings: Bk Vols 79,325
SAINT ANDREWS REGIONAL, 1735 N Woodmere Dr, 29407. SAN 370-9167. Tel: 843-766-2546. FAX: 843-766-2762. *Branch Mgr*, Vickie Gibbs; E-Mail: gibbsv@ccpl.org
Library Holdings: Bk Vols 91,210
SAINT PAUL'S BRANCH, 5153 Hwy 165, PO Box 196, Hollywood, 29449. SAN 360-0084. Tel: 843-889-3300. *In Charge*, Muffy Lee; Fax: 843-889-3605, E-Mail: leem@ccpl.org
Library Holdings: Bk Vols 7,718
VILLAGE BRANCH, 430 Whilden St, Mount Pleasant, 29464. SAN 374-5236. Tel: 843-884-9741. *In Charge*, Marvin Stewart; Fax: 843-884-5396, E-Mail: stewartm@ccpl.org
Library Holdings: Bk Vols 17,750
WEST ASHLEY, 45 Windermere Blvd, 29407. SAN 360-0092. Tel: 843-766-6635. *Branch Mgr*, Kate Dentzman; Fax: 843-769-4390, E-Mail: dentzmank@ccpl.org
Library Holdings: Bk Vols 60,630
Bookmobiles: 2

S CHARLESTON LIBRARY SOCIETY, 164 King St, 29401. SAN 315-4998. Tel: 843-723-9912. *Librn*, Catherine E Sadler; *Asst Librn*, Dedree Syracuse; *Asst Librn*, Patricia Glass Bennett; *Asst Librn*, Janice Grimes; *Asst Librn*, LeeAnn Floss; Staff 5 (MLS 2, Non-MLS 3)
Founded 1748. Pop 950; Circ 30,000
Library Holdings: Bk Titles 130,000; Per Subs 90
Subject Interests: Am Jewish hist, Charleston, Civil War, Early 20th century fiction, Literature, Revolutionary war, SC, SE Indians
Special Collections: 18th & 19th Century Manuscripts; Agriculture & Confederacy (Hinson Coll), bks, per & clippings; Architecture (Staats Coll); Horticulture (Aiken Garden Club Coll); Newspapers from 1732 to present; Timrod Scrapbooks (Courtenay Coll), bks & photog
Restriction: Members only

S CHARLESTON MUSEUM LIBRARY,* 360 Meeting St, 29403. SAN 315-5005. Tel: 843-722-2996, Ext 243. FAX: 843-722-1784. *Librn*, Sharon Bennett; Staff 3 (MLS 1, Non-MLS 2)
Founded 1773
Library Holdings: Bk Vols 16,000; Bk Titles 9,500; Per Subs 48
Subject Interests: Anthropology, Charlestonia, Decorative arts, Local natural hist, S Caroliniana, World wide natural hist
Special Collections: Gov Wm Aiken House Coll; Heyward-Washington House Coll; Manigault House Coll; Photograph Coll; Print Coll; Sheet Music Coll
Restriction: Open to public for reference only

C CHARLESTON SOUTHERN UNIVERSITY, L Mendel Rivers Library, PO Box 118087, 29423-8087. SAN 315-498X. Tel: 843-863-7940. FAX: 843-863-7947. Web Site: www.csuniv.edu/library.html. *Dir*, Enid R Causey; E-Mail: ecausey@csumv.edu
Founded 1966. Highest Degree: Master
Library Holdings: Bk Vols 188,901; Per Subs 1,172
Partic in SE Libr Network

C THE CITADEL, Daniel Library, 171 Moultrie St, 29409-6140. SAN 360-0122. Tel: 843-953-5116. Circulation Tel: 843-953-6845. Reference Tel: 843-953-2569. FAX: 843-953-5190. Web Site: www.citadel.edu/library. *Dir*, Angie W LeClercq; Tel: 843-953-1267, E-Mail: leclercqa@citadel.edu; *Acq*, Gregory J Frohnsdorff; *Bibliog Instr*, Elizabeth W Carter; *Bibliog Instr*, Kathleen Turner; *Govt Doc*, David C Heisser; *Ref*, Herbert T Nath; *Ref*, Judith Swartzel; Staff 18 (MLS 7, Non-MLS 11)
Founded 1842. Enrl 3,968; Fac 182; Highest Degree: Master
Library Holdings: Bk Vols 188,471; Per Subs 1,335
Subject Interests: Academic, General, Mil sci, South Carolina
Special Collections: Citadel Publications; German Literature (Hardin Coll)
Database Vendor: CARL, Dialog, DRA, Ebsco - EbscoHost, GaleNet, IAC - Info Trac, IAC - SearchBank, Lexis-Nexis, OCLC - First Search, ProQuest
Publications: Daniel Library Research Connections: The Newsletter of the Citadel Library (Newsletter)
Partic in Charleston Academic Libraries Consortium
Friends of the Library Group

C COLLEGE OF CHARLESTON, Robert Scott Small Library, 175 Calhoun St, 29401-3519. (Mail add: 66 George St, 29424), SAN 360-0211. Tel: 843-953-5530. Circulation Tel: 843-953-8001. Reference Tel: 843-953-8000. FAX: 843-953-8019. Web Site: www.cofc.edu/library/cofclib.html. *Dean of Libr*, David Cohen; *Coordr*, Claire Fund; E-Mail: fundc@cofc.edu; *Cat*, Katherine Bielsky; *Publ Servs*, Sheila Seaman; *Tech Servs*, Robert Neville; *Ref*, Tom Gilson; *Spec Coll*, Marie Hollings; *Coll Develop*, Katina Strauch *ILL*, Michael Phillips; Staff 43 (MLS 19, Non-MLS 24)
Founded 1785. Enrl 11,764; Fac 399; Highest Degree: Master
Jul 1999-Jun 2000 Income (Main Library and Branch Library) $3,277,662, State $2,677,744, Federal $116,551. Mats Exp $1,451,764, Books $644,01 Per/Ser (Incl. Access Fees) $653,982, Presv $44,751, Electronic Ref Mat (Incl. Access Fees) $109,015. Sal $817,712 (Prof $1,427,393)
Library Holdings: Bk Vols 479,005; Per Subs 3,194
Subject Interests: Behav sci, Marine sci, Natural science, Soc sci
Special Collections: Book Arts; College of Charleston Archives; Colonial Reading Habits (Ralph Izard Coll); John Henry Dick Ornithology Coll; South Carolina, books & per
Automation Activity & Vendor Info: (Cataloging) DRA; (Circulation) DRA
Database Vendor: DRA, Ebsco - EbscoHost, IAC - Info Trac, Lexis-Nexis OCLC - First Search, Silverplatter Information Inc.
Publications: A Catalog of the Scientific Apparatus at the College of Charleston: 1800-1940; Introduction to Bibliography & Research Methods; Proceedings of Southeastern Conferences on Bibliographic Instruction.; Tal of Charleston
Function: Archival collection
Partic in Solinet
Departmental Libraries:
MARINE RESOURCES, 217 Fort Johnson Rd, 29412. SAN 360-0246. Te 803-762-5026. Web Site: www.cofc.edu/library/cofclib.html. *Librn*, Heler Ivy

GM DEPARTMENT OF VETERANS AFFAIRS, Medical Center Library,* 109 Bee St, 29401-5799. SAN 315-5072. Tel: 843-577-5011, Ext 7274. FAX: 843-853-9167.
1997-1998 Income $50,000
Library Holdings: Bk Vols 943; Per Subs 245

S EVENING POST PUBLISHING CO, Post-Courier Library,* 134 Columbu St, 29403. SAN 315-503X. Tel: 843-937-5698. FAX: 843-937-5696. Web Site: www.charleston.net/aboutlibrary.html. *Chief Librn*, Suzanne Henderso E-Mail: henderson@postandcourier.com; *Librn*, Pam Liles
Library Holdings: Bk Vols 3,100; Per Subs 87
Subject Interests: Newsp clipping files, Newsp photogs

S GIBBES MUSEUM OF ART, Carolina Art Association Library, 135 Meeting St, 29401-2297. SAN 329-8523. Tel: 843-722-2706. FAX: 843-72 1682. E-Mail: gibbes1@charleston.net. Web Site: www.gibbes.com. *Librn*, Jean Strickland
Library Holdings: Bk Vols 5,000; Per Subs 100

S HUGUENOT SOCIETY OF SOUTH CAROLINA LIBRARY, 138 Logan St, 29401. SAN 327-0858. Tel: 843-723-3235. FAX: 843-853-8476. E-Mai huguenot@cchat.com. Web Site: www.huguenotsociety.org. *Dir*, Renee La Hue-Marshall
Library Holdings: Bk Vols 5,000
Publications: Transactions of the Huguenot Society of South Carolina

M MEDICAL UNIVERSITY OF SOUTH CAROLINA, (Formerly Medical University of South Carolina Library), 171 Ashley Ave, Ste 300, PO Box 250403, 29425-3001. SAN 360-0270. Tel: 843-792-2374. Circulation Tel: 843-792-2371. Reference Tel: 843-792-2372. FAX: 843-792-7947. Web Sit www.library.musc.edu. *Dir*, Thomas G Basler; *Assoc Dir*, Anne Robichaux; *Automation Syst Coordr*, Nancy C McKeehan; *Bibliogr*, Richard Syracuse; *Tech Servs*, Dee Boggan; *Syst Coordr*, Skip Anderson; *Publ Servs*, Peggy Mauldin; *Publ Servs*, Teri Lynn Herbert; *Publ Servs*, Bob Poyer; *Automatio Syst Coordr*, Nancy Smith; *Curator*, Jane Brown; *Publ Servs*, Doug Blansit *Publ Servs*, Lisa Boyd; *Publ Servs*, Elizabeth Connor; *Publ Servs*, Marcia Reinhardt; *Publ Servs*, Miriam Tomblin; *Tech Coordr*, Judi Wisniewski. Subject Specialists: *Chemistry*, Teri Lynn Herbert; *Chemistry*, Doug Blansit *Environ scis*, Doug Blansit; *Hist med*, Jane Brown; Staff 55 (MLS 18, Non-MLS 37)
Founded 1824. Enrl 2,366; Fac 986; Highest Degree: Doctorate
Jul 1999-Jun 2000 Income (Main Library and Branch Library) $4,751,889, State $4,751,889, Federal $71,965, Locally Generated Income $231,575, Parent Institution $202,370, Other $19,515. Mats Exp $1,216,576, Books $54,122, Per/Ser (Incl. Access Fees) $935,898, Presv $8,322, Electronic Re Mat (Incl. Access Fees) $272,356. Sal $2,754,740
Library Holdings: Bk Vols 222,970; Bk Titles 1,984; Per Subs 2,416
Subject Interests: Allied health, Behav sci, Consumer health, Dentistry, Environ sci, Medicine, Natural science, Nursing, Pharmacology, Pharmacy, Sci-tech, Science, Soc sci
Special Collections: History of Medicine (Waring Historical Library Coll), bks, mss, oral history, photog; Micro-Circulation (Melvin M Knisely Coll), bks & mss
Database Vendor: Dialog, GaleNet, IAC - Info Trac, IAC - SearchBank, Innovative Interfaces INN - View, OCLC - First Search, OVID Technologie
Publications: MUSCLS
Partic in Charleston Academic Libraries Consortium; Consortium Of Southern Biomedical Libraries (CONBLS); National Network Of Libraries Of Medicine - South Central Region

Branches:
WARING HISTORICAL Tel: 803-792-2288. FAX: 803-792-8619. *Curator*, Jane Brown; *Curator*, Kay Carter; *Archivist*, Tebalt Rachel
Subject Interests: History of medicine
Publications: Waring Library Society (Newsletter)
Friends of the Library Group

NATIONAL MARINE FISHERIES SERVICE, Charleston Laboratory-Library,* PO Box 12559, 29422-2559. SAN 315-5021. Tel: 843-762-5026. FAX: 843-762-5110. *Librn*, Helen Ivy
Aug 1997-Jul 1998 Income $44,347. Mats Exp $44,347
Library Holdings: Bk Vols 8,500; Per Subs 80

SOUTH CAROLINA HISTORICAL SOCIETY LIBRARY, Fireproof Bldg, 100 Meeting St, 29401-2299. SAN 315-5056. Tel: 843-723-3225. FAX: 843-723-8584. E-Mail: info@schistory.org. Web Site: www.schistory.org. *Exec Dir*, David O Percy; *Librn*, Ashley Yandle; *Archivist, Head of Libr*, Peter Wilkerson; *Archivist*, Karen Stokes
Founded 1855
Library Holdings: Bk Vols 35,000; Per Subs 120
Subject Interests: Culture, Local history, Photographs, State hist
Special Collections: Civil War (R Lockwood Tower Coll)
Publications: Carologue; South Carolina Historical Magazine; South Carolina Historical Society Manuscript Guide
Partic in OCLC Online Computer Library Center, Inc

TRIDENT TECHNICAL COLLEGE
BERKELEY CAMPUS LEARNING RESOURCES, LR-M, PO Box 10367, 29423-8067. SAN 324-797X. Tel: 843-899-8055. FAX: 843-899-8100. *Dean of Libr*, Dr Sandra R Winecoff; E-Mail: zpwinecoff@trident.tec.us.sc
Founded 1982
Library Holdings: Bk Vols 4,871; Bk Titles 4,025; Per Subs 67
Subject Interests: Aircraft maintainance, Cosmetology, Veterinary tech
Publications: Annual Report
MAIN CAMPUS LEARNING RESOURCES CENTER, LR-M, PO Box 118067, 29423-8067. SAN 360-036X. Tel: 843-574-6089. Interlibrary Loan Service Tel: 843-574-6316. FAX: 843-574-6484. Web Site: www.trident.tec.sc.us/lrc. *Dean of Libr*, Dr Sandra R Winecoff; E-Mail: zpwinecoff@trident.tec.us.sc; *Ref*, Dawn E S Huston; *Syst Coordr, Web Coordr*, Lisanne Hamilton; *Tech Servs*, Rose Marie Huff; *AV*, Diane Lohr; Staff 15 (MLS 8, Non-MLS 7)
Founded 1964
Special Collections: Electronics (Sam Photofact Coll)
Publications: Annual Report
PALMER CAMPUS LEARNING RESOURCES CENTER, LR-M, PO Box 118067, 29423-8067. SAN 360-0335. Tel: 843-722-5540. FAX: 843-720-5614. *Librn*, Erlene Payne; Tel: 843-722-5539, E-Mail: zppayne@trident.tec.su.us; Staff 3 (MLS 1, Non-MLS 2)
Founded 1955. Enrl 1,800
Library Holdings: Bk Vols 24,471; Bk Titles 20,492; Per Subs 101
Subject Interests: Archives, Law
Publications: Annual Report

UNITED STATES NAVY
NAVAL CONSOLIDATED BRIG LIBRARY, Bldg 3107, 1050 Remount Rd, 29406-3515. SAN 360-0459. Tel: 843-743-0306, Ext 3039. FAX: 843-743-0326. *Librn*, J Ilgenfritz
Library Holdings: Bk Vols 3,600; Per Subs 41
Commissioned November 1989
NAVAL WEAPONS STATIONS, (WPNSTA) CHASN LIBRARY, Bldg 732, 2316 Red Bank Rd, Ste 100, Goose Creek, 29445-8601. SAN 360-0513. Tel: 843-764-7900. FAX: 843-764-4138. *Librn*, Lonnie Kenny
Founded 1966
Library Holdings: Bk Vols 26,500; Per Subs 105
Subject Interests: Bks on cassettes, Children's flms, Educ flms, Large print, Self develop, Soc issues
Special Collections: CD-ROM: Help Wanted USA Classified Ads, microfiche

WESTVACO CORP, Charleston Research Information Services Center,* 5600 Virginia Ave, PO Box 118005, 29423-8005. SAN 315-5668. Tel: 843-745-3735. FAX: 803-745-3718.; Staff 2 (MLS 2)
Founded 1955
Library Holdings: Per Subs 100
Subject Interests: Chemistry, Engineering, Paper, Pulp

HARLESTON AFB

UNITED STATES AIR FORCE
CHARLESTON AIR FORCE BASE LIBRARY FL4418, 437 SVS/SVMG, 106 W McCaw St Bldg 215, 29404-4700. SAN 360-0548. Tel: 843-963-3320. FAX: 843-963-3840. *Dir*, Ann Moore; E-Mail: ann.moore@charleston.af.mil; *Tech Servs*, Anne Davis; *Cat*, Martha McLamb; *Publ Servs*, Sue Wiggins; Staff 5 (MLS 1, Non-MLS 4)
Founded 1953
Library Holdings: Bk Vols 32,000; Per Subs 160
Subject Interests: Military history, Total quality mgt
Automation Activity & Vendor Info: (Circulation) Gaylord

CHERAW

J NORTHEASTERN TECHNICAL COLLEGE LIBRARY, (Formerly Chesterfield-Marlboro Technical College Library), PO Drawer 1007, 29520-1007. SAN 315-5099. Tel: 803-921-6954. Toll Free Tel: 800-921-7399. FAX: 843-537-6148. Web Site: web.infoave.net/~cmtc/. *Chair*, Esther Brunson; Tel: 843-921-6953, E-Mail: eebrunson@chm.tee.sc.us; Staff 4 (MLS 1, Non-MLS 3)
Founded 1968. Enrl 1,067; Fac 27
Library Holdings: Bk Titles 20,000; Per Subs 155
Subject Interests: Art, Bus, Indust, Mgt, Sci, Technology

CHESTER

P CHESTER COUNTY LIBRARY,* 100 Center St, 29706-2708. SAN 360-0572. Tel: 803-377-8145. FAX: 803-377-8146. E-Mail: cheslib@infoave.net. *Ch Servs*, Beth Harris; *Ref*, Judy Bramlett; *Business*, Marsha B Lingle; E-Mail: mlcheslib@chestertel.com; Staff 11 (MLS 3, Non-MLS 8)
Founded 1900. Pop 32,170; Circ 122,188
Jul 1998-Jun 1999 Income $662,536, State $45,038, Federal $140,439, County $427,287, Other $49,772. Mats Exp $99,431, Books $87,631, Per/Ser (Incl. Access Fees) $11,425, Micro $200, AV Equip $175. Sal $342,774 (Prof $138,871)
Library Holdings: Bk Vols 66,955; Per Subs 146
Subject Interests: Local history, SC hist
Friends of the Library Group
Branches: 2
GREAT FALLS BRANCH, Great Falls, 29055. SAN 360-0602. Tel: 803-482-2149. FAX: 803-377-8146. *Librn*, Kay Evans
Library Holdings: Bk Vols 10,000
LEWISVILLE COMMUNITY LIBRARY, Richburg, 29729. Tel: 803-789-7800. FAX: 803-789-7801. *Librn*, Valerie Taylor
Library Holdings: Bk Vols 8,000
Bookmobiles: 1

CHESTERFIELD

P CHESTERFIELD COUNTY LIBRARY,* 119 W Main St, 29709-1512. SAN 360-0637. Tel: 843-623-7489. FAX: 843-623-3295. *Dir*, Darlene A Smithwick; *Asst Librn*, Myrtis Burr; *Ch Servs*, Barbara Pruitt; *Bkmobile Coordr*, Linda Helms; *Tech Servs*, Betty Moss; Staff 9 (MLS 1, Non-MLS 8)
Founded 1969. Pop 38,577
1997-1998 Income $288,661, State $52,079, City $4,000, County $203,419, Locally Generated Income $6,000, Other $13,850. Mats Exp $44,979, Books $35,979, Per/Ser (Incl. Access Fees) $6,000. Sal $162,828
Library Holdings: Bk Vols 62,000; Per Subs 84
Special Collections: South Carolina History Coll
Branches: 4
FANNIE D LOWRY MEMORIAL, PO Box 505, Jefferson, 29718. SAN 328-7149. Tel: 803-658-3966. FAX: 803-658-3966. *In Charge*, Kate Dillard
MATHESON MEMORIAL, 612 Kershaw St, Cheraw, 29520. SAN 360-0661. Tel: 803-537-3571. FAX: 803-537-1248. *In Charge*, Emily Marsh
Friends of the Library Group
MCBEE DEPOT LIBRARY, PO Box 506, McBee, 29101. SAN 328-7165. Tel: 803-335-7515. FAX: 803-335-7515. *In Charge*, Kate Dillard
PAGELAND COMMUNITY, 109 W Blakeney, Pageland, 29728. SAN 360-0696. Tel: 803-672-6930. FAX: 803-672-6670. *Librn*, Vana Middleton
Bookmobiles: 1

CLEMSON

C CLEMSON UNIVERSITY, Robert Muldrow Cooper Library, Clemson University, Box 343001, 29634-3001. SAN 360-0726. Tel: 864-656-3026. Interlibrary Loan Service Tel: 864-656-5186. Circulation Tel: 864-656-3027. Reference Tel: 864-656-3024. Toll Free Tel: 877-886-2389. TDD: 864-656-0359. FAX: 864-656-0758. E-Mail: userid@clemson.edu. Web Site: www.lib.clemson.edu. *Dean*, Joseph F Boykin, Jr; E-Mail: jboykin@clemson.edu; *Asst Dean*, Deana L Astle; Tel: 864-656-4782, E-Mail: dlast@clemson.edu; *Librn*, Sarah McCleskey; Tel: 864-656-3932, Fax: 864-656-3932, E-Mail: smccles@clemson.edu; *Mgr*, Isaac Wallace; Tel: 864-656-4336, Fax: 864-656-1792, E-Mail: wisaac@clemson.edu; *Head Ref*, Peggy Cover; Tel: 864-656-5173, Fax: 864-656-7608, E-Mail: pcover@clemson.edu; *Head, Circ*, Teri Alexander; Tel: 864-656-4622, Fax: 864-656-4622, E-Mail: tajff@clemson.edu; *Head, Cat*, Marsha McCurley; Tel: 864-656-1769, E-Mail: dylan@clemson.edu; *Head, Acq*, Emma Simmons; Tel: 864-656-1114, Fax: 864-656-7156, E-Mail: emmas@clemson.edu; *Spec Coll*, Michael Kohl; Tel: 864-656-5176, Fax: 864-656-0233, E-Mail: kohl@clemson.edu; *ILL*, Jens Holley; Tel: 864-656-3025, E-Mail: holley@clemson.edu; *Online Servs*, Gordon Cochrane; Tel: 864-656-1535, Fax: 864-656-7608, E-Mail: gmcochr@clemson.edu; *Syst Coordr*, Beth Helsel; Tel: 864-656-3039, E-Mail: bard@clemson.edu; Staff 102 (MLS 32, Non-MLS 70)
Founded 1893. Enrl 15,836; Fac 867; Highest Degree: Doctorate
Jul 1999-Jun 2000 Income (Main and Other College/University Libraries) State $7,335,970. Mats Exp $3,248,666, Books $368,928, Per/Ser (Incl.

Access Fees) $2,498,396, Electronic Ref Mat (Incl. Access Fees) $381,342. Sal $2,809,412 (Prof $1,329,620)
Library Holdings: Bk Vols 1,059,705; Per Subs 6,383
Subject Interests: Agriculture, Architecture, Engineering, Mgt, Sci
Special Collections: A Frank Lever Papers; Benjamin R Tillman Papers; Edgar A Brown Papers; James F Byrnes Papers; John C Calhoun Letters, 1805-1850; Strom Thurmond Papers; US Patent & Trademark Dep
Automation Activity & Vendor Info: (Acquisitions) NOTIS; (Cataloging) NOTIS; (Circulation) NOTIS; (OPAC) NOTIS; (Serials) NOTIS
Database Vendor: GaleNet, Lexis-Nexis, Silverplatter Information Inc.
Publications: Library Friends' Newsletter
Function: Research library
Partic in Association Of Southeastern Research Libraries (ASERL); Discus; Solinet
Friends of the Library Group
Departmental Libraries:
GUNNIN ARCHITECTURE LIBRARY, 112 Lee Hall, Clemson University, 29634-0501. SAN 360-0750. Tel: 864-656-3933. FAX: 864-656-3932. E-Mail: smccles@clemson.edu. Web Site: www.lib.clemson.edu/gunnin. *Head of Libr*, Sarah McCleskey
SPECIAL COLLECTIONS UNIT, Strom Thurmond Inst Bldg, Special Collections Box 343001, 29634-3001. SAN 373-7160. Tel: 864-656-3031. FAX: 864-656-0233.

CLINTON

C PRESBYTERIAN COLLEGE, James H Thomason Library, James H Thomason Library, 211 E Maple St, 29325. SAN 315-5102. Tel: 864-833-8299. Reference Tel: 864-833-8437. FAX: 864-833-8315. E-Mail: library@presby.edu. Web Site: www.presby.edu/library/. *Dir*, Douglas Anderson; Tel: 864-833-7028, E-Mail: danderso@presby.edu; *Head, Circ*, Teresa Inman; *Ref*, Victoria Koger; *Cat*, Tiffany Reid; *Head Tech Servs*, Diane Yarborough; *Spec Coll*, Nancy Griffith; Staff 10 (MLS 5, Non-MLS 5)
Founded 1880. Enrl 1,152; Fac 77; Highest Degree: Bachelor
Jul 1999-Jun 2000 Income $737,688. Mats Exp $267,546. Sal $347,901
Library Holdings: Bk Vols 170,167; Bk Titles 102,803; Per Subs 797
Subject Interests: Caroliniana
Special Collections: Caroliniana, Presbyterian denominational materials
Automation Activity & Vendor Info: (Acquisitions) Innovative Interfaces Inc.; (Cataloging) Innovative Interfaces Inc.; (Circulation) Innovative Interfaces Inc.; (Course Reserve) Innovative Interfaces Inc.; (OPAC) Innovative Interfaces Inc.; (Serials) Innovative Interfaces Inc.
Database Vendor: GaleNet, IAC - Info Trac, OCLC - First Search
Partic in SE Libr Network

G SOUTH CAROLINA DEPARTMENT OF DISABILITIES & SPECIAL NEEDS, Whitten Center Library & Media Resource Services, PO Box 239, 29325. SAN 315-5110. Tel: 864-938-3331. FAX: 864-938-3179. *In Charge*, Nancy Wells; E-Mail: nwells@ddsn.state.sc.us
Founded 1965
Jul 1999-Jun 2000 Income $297, State $47, Federal $250. Mats Exp $297, Per/Ser (Incl. Access Fees) $47, AV Equip $250
Library Holdings: Bk Vols 16,500; Bk Titles 15,500; Per Subs 25
Subject Interests: High interest low reading level bks for mentally handicapped, Libr toys for handicapped, Mental retardation, Psychology, Special education
Special Collections: American Journal of Mental Deficiency, (1922 to present), per; Annual Report of South Carolina State; Bibliography of Professional Materials; on Mental Retardation & Reference, (1972, 1975); Training School for the Feebleminded (1918-1968)
Publications: Subject Guide and Classification Index in Mental Retardation, 1979
Partic in SC State Libr ILL & Flm Loan Syst

COLUMBIA

C BELLE W BARUCH INSTITUTE FOR MARINE BIOLOGY & COASTAL RESEARCH LIBRARY,* University of South Carolina, 29208. SAN 372-9427. Tel: 803-777-3927. FAX: 803-777-3935.

C BENEDICT COLLEGE LIBRARY, Benjamin F Payton Learning Resources Center, 1600 Harden St, 29204. SAN 315-5137. Tel: 803-253-5181 (Library), 803-256-4220. FAX: 803-540-2528. Web Site: www.benedict.edu. *Dir*, Darlene Zinnerman-Bethea; Tel: 803-253-5182; *Cat*, Peter Rossi; *Govt Doc, Ref*, Bridget Sledge; *Circ*, Shirley Goodwin; Staff 11 (MLS 6, Non-MLS 5)
Founded 1870. Enrl 1,371; Fac 87; Highest Degree: Bachelor
Library Holdings: Bk Vols 112,821; Per Subs 279
Subject Interests: Afro-Am studies
Partic in Coop Col Libr Ctr, Inc

S CHEM-NUCLEAR SYSTEMS LIBRARY,* 140 Stoneridge Dr, 29210. SAN 329-8175. Tel: 803-758-1844. FAX: 803-758-1800. Web Site: www.chemnuclear.com. *Librn*, Amy C Gossett; E-Mail: agossett@wm.com
Library Holdings: Bk Vols 2,500; Per Subs 75
Subject Interests: Engineering, Nuclear studies, Radioactive waste

C COLUMBIA COLLEGE, J Drake Edens Library, 1301 Columbia College Dr, 29203-9987. SAN 315-5161. Tel: 803-786-3878. FAX: 803-786-3700. Web Site: www.columbiacollegesc.edu. *Dir*, John C Pritchett; Tel: 803-786-3716, E-Mail: jpritchett@colacoll.edu; *Publ Servs*, Jane Tuttle; Tel: 803-786-3371, E-Mail: jtuttle@colacoll.edu; *Publ Servs*, Alexandra Leach; Tel: 803-786-3338, E-Mail: sleach@colacoll.edu; *Media Spec*, Betty E McDonald; Tel: 803-786-3712, E-Mail: bmmcdonald@colacoll.edu; *Syst Coordr*, Mary R Cross; Tel: 803-786-3691; *Publ Servs*, Amy Fordham; Tel: 803-786-3703, E-Mail: afordham@colacoll.edu; *Circ, ILL*, Gina Dempsey; Tel: 803-786-3878, E-Mail: gdempsey@colacoll.edu; *Coll Develop*, Lin C Lake; Tel: 803-786-3042, E-Mail: linlake@colacoll.edu; Staff 10 (MLS 6, Non-MLS 4)
Founded 1854. Enrl 1,300; Fac 105; Highest Degree: Master
Jul 2000-Jun 2001 Income (Main Library Only) $196,025, Parent Institution $186,025, Other $10,000. Mats Exp $196,025, Books $73,000, Per/Ser (Incl. Access Fees) $41,100, Presv $2,000, Micro $8,000, Electronic Ref Mat (Incl. Access Fees) $25,180. Sal $328,870
Library Holdings: Bk Vols 170,185; Bk Titles 104,217; Per Subs 513
Subject Interests: Women
Special Collections: Local Authors (Peggy Parish & Barbara Johnson); Religious Literature for Children
Automation Activity & Vendor Info: (Cataloging) Innovative Interfaces Inc.; (Circulation) Innovative Interfaces Inc.; (OPAC) Innovative Interfaces Inc.; (Serials) Innovative Interfaces Inc.
Partic in SE Libr Network

CR COLUMBIA INTERNATIONAL UNIVERSITY, G Allen Fleece Library, 7435 Monticello, 29230-1599. (Mail add: PO Box 3122, 29230-3122), SAN 315-5153. Tel: 803-754-4100, Ext 3101. FAX: 803-786-4209. E-Mail: library@ciu.edu. Web Site: ciu.library.net. *Dir*, S David Mash; *Acq*, Marilyn Morrison; *AV*, Steve Pullman; *Cat*, Florida Oamil; *Circ*, Julie Jones; *Ref*, Jeannie Colson; Staff 9 (MLS 4, Non-MLS 5)
Founded 1923. Enrl 925; Fac 60; Highest Degree: Doctorate
Library Holdings: Per Subs 725
Subject Interests: Communications, Counseling, Education, Intercultural studies, Music, Psychology, Theology
Publications: Bibliotheca Nova
Partic in OCLC Online Computer Library Center, Inc; SE Libr Network

J COLUMBIA JUNIOR COLLEGE LIBRARY,* 3810 Main St, 29203. SAN 360-0815. Tel: 803-799-9082. FAX: 803-799-9005. *Librn*, Brenda Milton
Founded 1935. Enrl 425; Fac 55
1998-1999 Income $30,000
Library Holdings: Bk Titles 3,897; Per Subs 65
Subject Interests: Accounting, Behav sci, Bus, Econ, History, Med assisting, Mgt, Paralegal, Soc sci, Wordprocessing

S COLUMBIA MUSEUM OF ART, Lorick Library, Main & Hampton, PO Box 2068, 29202. SAN 315-517X. Tel: 803-343-2215. FAX: 803-343-2219. Web Site: www.colmusart.org. *Dir*, Salvatore Cilella, Jr; Tel: 803-343-2216; *Librn*, Libby Fleming; Tel: 803-343-2155, E-Mail: libby@colmusart.org; Staff 1 (MLS 1)
Founded 1980
Library Holdings: Bk Vols 13,000; Per Subs 30
Special Collections: Art Coll

GM DEPARTMENT OF VETERANS AFFAIRS DORN MEDICAL CENTER, Medical Library,* Garners Ferry Rd, 29209. SAN 315-5315. Tel: 803-776-4000, Ext 7315. FAX: 803-695-6874. *Librn*, Florence Mays; E-Mail: gayton.florence@columbia~sc.va.dov
1997-1998 Income $60,000
Library Holdings: Bk Vols 4,332; Per Subs 224

S EDUCATIONAL RESOURCES CENTER, DHEC,* 2600 Bull St, 29201. SAN 321-219X. Tel: 803-734-8505, 803-737-3923, 803-898-3804. FAX: 803-898-3800. Web Site: www.state.sc.us/dagc/. *Dir*, Marie Horton
Founded 1973
Subject Interests: Environmental studies, Public health
Special Collections: Health Education material (for distribution); Public Health related film (for loan)
Publications: Catalog

M G WERBER BRYAN PSYCHIATRIC HOSPITAL LIBRARY,* 220 Faison Dr, 29203. SAN 315-5145. Tel: 803-935-5395. FAX: 803-935-7110. *Dir*, John Fletcher; *Librn*, Frances G Young
Founded 1978
Library Holdings: Bk Vols 1,978; Per Subs 50
Subject Interests: Psychiatry, Psychology
Partic in SC Health Info Network

R LUTHERAN THEOLOGICAL SOUTHERN SEMINARY, Lineberger Memorial Library, 4201 N Main St, 29203. SAN 315-5218. Tel: 803-786-5150. FAX: 803-786-6499. *Dir*, Dr Lynn A Feider; *Asst Librn*, Leslie Walker; Staff 2 (MLS 2)
Founded 1830. Highest Degree: Master
1998-1999 Mats Exp $72,513, Books $47,058, Per/Ser (Incl. Access Fees) $24,499. Sal $152,785
Library Holdings: Bk Vols 115,967; Per Subs 474
Subject Interests: Relig studies

Special Collections: 16th through 18th Century German Pietism
Publications: The Library of the South Carolina Theological Society at Lexington, SC 1834-1852, W Richard Fritz
Partic in OCLC Online Computer Library Center, Inc; SE Libr Network

MCNAIR LAW FIRM, PA, Law Library, Nationsbank Tower, 1301 Gervais St, 29211. (Mail add: PO Box 11390, 29211), SAN 326-2685. Tel: 803-799-9800. FAX: 803-799-9804. Web Site: www.mcnair.net. *Mgr Libr Serv*, David Morgan; E-Mail: dmorgan@mcnair.net; Staff 2 (MLS 1, Non-MLS 1)
Founded 1983
Library Holdings: Bk Vols 30,000; Bk Titles 600
Automation Activity & Vendor Info: (Serials) Inmagic, Inc.
Restriction: Open to public for reference only

MUNICIPAL ASSOCIATION OF SOUTH CAROLINA, Library & Reference Center,* PO Box 12109, 29211. SAN 372-9443. Tel: 803-933-1206. FAX: 803-933-1299. Web Site: www.masc.state.sc.us.
Library Holdings: Bk Vols 350; Per Subs 45

NELSON, MULLINS, RILEY & SCARBOROUGH, Law Library,* 1330 Lady St, 3rd flr, PO Box 11070, 29201. SAN 323-6560. Tel: 803-343-5536. FAX: 803-256-7500. *Librn*, Melanie Swaby; Staff 4 (MLS 2, Non-MLS 2)
Founded 1982
Library Holdings: Bk Vols 16,000; Bk Titles 1,500; Per Subs 124
Partic in Dialog Corporation; Vutext; Westlaw
Other locations in Greenville & Myrtle Beach

PALMETTO BAPTIST MEDICAL CENTER AT COLUMBIA, Pitts Memorial Library, Taylor at Marion St, 29220. SAN 315-5242. Tel: 803-296-5281. *Dir*, Pat Stout
Founded 1954
Library Holdings: Bk Vols 1,000; Per Subs 40
Subject Interests: Allied health, Hospital administration, Medicine, Nursing
Partic in Columbia Area Med Libr; Nat Libr of Med; USC School of Med

PALMETTO RICHLAND MEMORIAL HOSPITAL, Josey Health Sciences Library, 5 Richland Medical Park, 29203. SAN 315-5234. Tel: 803-434-6312. FAX: 803-434-2651. *Dir*, Pat Stout; Staff 4 (MLS 1, Non-MLS 3)
Founded 1957
Oct 2000-Sep 2001 Mats Exp $250,000. Sal $109,405
Library Holdings: Bk Titles 4,000; Per Subs 500
Subject Interests: Health admin, Medicine, Neonatology, Orthopedics
Partic in South Carolina Ahec

RESEARCH PLANNING INC LIBRARY,* 1121 Park St, PO Box 328, 29202. SAN 372-9397. Tel: 803-256-7322. FAX: 803-254-6445. E-Mail: info@researchplanning.comm.
Special Collections: Maps

RICHLAND COUNTY PUBLIC LIBRARY, 1431 Assembly St, 29201. SAN 360-0939. Tel: 803-799-9084. Reference Tel: 803-929-3400. FAX: 803-929-3438. Interlibrary Loan Service FAX: 803-929-3439. Web Site: www.richland.lib.sc.us. *Exec Dir*, C David Warren; *Dep Dir*, Helen Ann Rawlinson; *Admin Assoc*, Linda Barker; E-Mail: lbarker@richland.lib.sc.us; *Tech Servs*, Frank Hite; *Exten Serv*, Gerda Kahn; *Info Res*, Margie Richardson; *Tech Coordr*, Bruce Heimburger; *Coordr*, Marilyn Green; *Coll Develop*, Jo Griffith
Founded 1934. Pop 285,720; Circ 2,880,826
Jul 1999-Jun 2000 Income (Main Library and Branch Library) $11,971,878, State $533,121, Federal $33,666, County $10,775,000, Other $630,091. Mats Exp $2,593,684, Books $1,913,032, Per/Ser (Incl. Access Fees) $142,503, Presv $1,267, Micro $59,027, Electronic Ref Mat (Incl. Access Fees) $477,855. Sal $7,204,027 (Prof $2,525,522)
Library Holdings: Bk Vols 1,060,060; Per Subs 2,366
Subject Interests: Local history
Automation Activity & Vendor Info: (Acquisitions) epixtech, inc.; (Cataloging) epixtech, inc.; (Circulation) epixtech, inc.; (OPAC) epixtech, inc.; (Serials) epixtech, inc.
Database Vendor: epixtech, inc.
Publications: Byline; Calendar of Events; Friendly Forum
Partic in InfoTrac; News Libr; SE Libr Network
Special Services for the Blind - Kurzweil Reading Machine
Friends of the Library Group
Branches: 9
BLYTHEWOOD BRANCH, 218 McNulty Rd, Blythewood, 29016. SAN 373-7098. Tel: 803-691-9806. FAX: 803-691-0841. *Librn*, Catherine Odom; *Admin Assoc*, Linda Barker; E-Mail: lbarker@richland.lib.sc.us
Library Holdings: Bk Vols 20,000
EASTOVER BRANCH, 608 Main St, Eastover, 29044. SAN 360-1021. Tel: 803-353-8584. FAX: 803-353-8498. *Librn*, Carolyn Flemming; *Admin Assoc*, Linda Barker; E-Mail: lbarker@richland.lib.sc.us
Library Holdings: Bk Vols 17,765
JOHN HUGHES COOPER BRANCH, 5317 N Trenholm Rd, 29206. SAN 360-0963. Tel: 803-787-3462. FAX: 803-787-8040. *Librn*, Anne Bagwell; *Admin Assoc*, Linda Barker; E-Mail: lbarker@richland.lib.sc.us
Library Holdings: Bk Vols 50,000
NORTH MAIN, 5306 Main St, 29203-6114. SAN 360-1110. Tel: 803-754-7734. FAX: 803-754-7296. *Librn*, Helen Belton
Library Holdings: Bk Vols 35,000
NORTHEAST REGIONAL, 7490 Parklane Rd, 29223. SAN 325-4372. Tel: 803-736-6575. FAX: 803-736-7853. *Librn*, Judy Geckle; *Admin Assoc*, Linda Barker; E-Mail: lbarker@richland.lib.sc.us
Library Holdings: Bk Vols 110,000
SAINT ANDREWS REGIONAL, 2916 Broad River Rd, 29210. SAN 360-1145. Tel: 803-772-6675. FAX: 803-731-2983. *Librn*, Lin Ko; *Admin Assoc*, Linda Barker; E-Mail: lbarker@richland.lib.sc.us
Library Holdings: Bk Vols 60,000
SANDHILLS, One Summit Pkwy, 29229. SAN 373-7101. Tel: 803-699-9230. FAX: 803-699-0491. *Librn*, Jacki Slight; *Admin Assoc*, Linda Barker; E-Mail: lbarker@richland.lib.sc.us
Library Holdings: Bk Vols 40,000
SOUTHEAST REGIONAL, 7421 Garners Ferry Rd, 29209. SAN 373-711X. Tel: 803-776-0855. FAX: 803-776-0216. *Librn*, Teresa Windham; *Admin Assoc*, Linda Barker; E-Mail: lbarker@richland.lib.sc.us
Library Holdings: Bk Vols 80,000
WHEATLEY, 931 Woodrow St, 29205. SAN 360-0998. Tel: 803-799-5873. FAX: 803-771-6429. *Librn*, Frances Long; *Admin Assoc*, Linda Barker; E-Mail: lbarker@richland.lib.sc.us
Library Holdings: Bk Vols 25,000
Bookmobiles: 1

S SCANA CORPORATION/SOUTH CAROLINA ELECTRIC & GAS COMPANY, Corporate Library, Palmetto Ctr, 1426 Main St, 29218. SAN 329-9317. Tel: 803-217-9942. FAX: 803-217-8310. *Coordr*, Patsy G Moss; E-Mail: pmoss@scana.com
Library Holdings: Bk Titles 2,200

S WILBUR SMITH ASSOCIATES LIBRARY,* Nationsbank Tower, 1301 Gervais St PO Box 92, 29202-0092. SAN 327-0734. Tel: 803-758-4500. FAX: 803-251-2064. *Librn*, Tammy Davis
Library Holdings: Bk Vols 16,000
Subject Interests: Engineering, Planning
Restriction: Staff use only

GL SOUTH CAROLINA ATTORNEY GENERAL'S OFFICE LIBRARY, 1000 Assembly St, Ste 742, 29201-3117. (Mail add: PO Box 11549, 29211-1549), SAN 321-7604. Tel: 803-734-3769. FAX: 803-253-6283. Web Site: www.scattorneygeneral.org. *Librn*, Susan Husman; E-Mail: agshusman@ag.state.sc.us; Staff 1 (MLS 1)
Founded 1974
Library Holdings: Bk Vols 20,000; Bk Titles 1,400; Per Subs 20
Subject Interests: Law
Special Collections: Attorney General's Opinions
Publications: Librarian Newsletter
Restriction: Open to public for reference only

S SOUTH CAROLINA COMMISSION ON HIGHER EDUCATION LIBRARY, 1333 Main St, Ste 200, 29201. SAN 371-4438. Tel: 803-737-2273. FAX: 803-737-2297. *Res*, Maryanne Braithwaite
Library Holdings: Per Subs 25

S SOUTH CAROLINA CONFEDERATE RELIC ROOM & MUSEUM LIBRARY,* 920 Sumter St, 29201. SAN 327-7895. Tel: 803-898-8095. FAX: 803-898-8099. *Dir*, Allan Roberson; Tel: 803-898-8096; *Archivist, Librn*, Dotsy Boineav; Tel: 803-898-8098, E-Mail: dboinea@crr.state.sc.com
Library Holdings: Bk Vols 1,250

GM SOUTH CAROLINA DEPARTMENT OF ALCOHOL & OTHER DRUG ABUSE SERVICES, Drugstore Information Clearinghouse, 101 Business Park Blvd, Ste 1408, 29203-9498. SAN 328-493X. Tel: 803-896-5564. Toll Free Tel: 800-942-3425. FAX: 803-896-5557. Web Site: www.daodas.state.sc.us, www.scprevents.org. *Adminr*, Elizabeth Peters; E-Mail: epeters@daodas.state.sc.us; Staff 1 (Non-MLS 1)
Library Holdings: Bk Titles 150
Special Collections: Women's Resource Center
Mem of SC State Libr LION Syst
Partic in Columbia Area Medical Librarians' Association

G SOUTH CAROLINA DEPARTMENT OF ARCHIVES & HISTORY, Division of Education Programs,* 8301 Parklane Rd, 29223. SAN 327-0777. Tel: 803-896-6100, 803-896-6189. Web Site: www.state.sc.us/scdah/homepage.htm. *Dir*, Rodger Stroup
Library Holdings: Bk Vols 2,000
Special Collections: South Carolina Government Records, 1671-present
Publications: Colonial records of South Carolina; Curriculum resource materials; Popular history booklets; South Carolina Archives micropublications; State records of South Carolina; Technical leaflets on document conservation, historic preservation, & records management

S SOUTH CAROLINA DEPARTMENT OF CORRECTIONS, Library Services, 4444 Broad River Rd, PO Box 21787, 29221. SAN 315-5250. Tel: 803-896-1567. FAX: 803-896-1513. *Mgr*, Daisy Lindler; *Librn*, Diane Austin; *Librn*, Jeanette Austin; *Librn*, Richard Boland; *Librn*, Dorothy Buxton; *Librn*, Donna Dedmondt; *Librn*, Nancy Glenn; *Librn*, Steve Gratzer; *Librn*, Sherri Green; *Librn*, Thad Hendley; *Librn*, Billy Holladay; *Librn*, Elois Jones; *Librn*, Mary McCabe; *Librn*, Grace Mitchum; *Librn*, Laurie Tamkin; *Librn*, Bill White; *Librn*, Carol Williams

Founded 1968
Library Holdings: Bk Vols 94,713; Per Subs 28
Statistics include 16 libraries, 1 bookmobile & 1 technical processing center that are all operated by South Carolina Department of Corrections

S SOUTH CAROLINA DEPARTMENT OF CORRECTIONS, Manning Correctional Institution Library,* 502 Beckman Rd, PO Box 3173, 29203-3173. SAN 371-7356. Tel: 803-935-6083. FAX: 803-935-6016. *Librn*, L Sheridan Green; Staff 1 (MLS 1)
Circ 15,000
1997-1998 Income $2,000
Library Holdings: Bk Vols 2,500; Bk Titles 2,100; Per Subs 15

G SOUTH CAROLINA PROTECTION & ADVOCACY FOR PEOPLE WITH DISABILITIES INC LIBRARY,* 3710 Landmark Dr, Ste 208, 29204. SAN 372-9435. Tel: 803-782-0639. FAX: 803-790-1946.
Library Holdings: Bk Vols 1,000; Per Subs 20

S SOUTH CAROLINA STATE HOSPITAL, Horger Library, 2100 Bull St, PO Box 119, 29202. SAN 315-5285. Tel: 803-898-2376. FAX: 803-898-2414. *Librn*, Vesta Baughman; *Coll Develop*, Theodora Richardson; Staff 2 (MLS 2)
Founded 1958
Library Holdings: Bk Titles 5,000; Per Subs 50; High Interest/Low Vocabulary Bk Vols 100; Bks on Deafness & Sign Lang 10
Subject Interests: Psychiatric rehabilitation, Psychosocial support, Recreational reading
Special Collections: Lois P Goldman Book Coll
Library serves Division of Psychiatric Rehabilitation Services of the South Carolina Department of Mental Health, as well as W.S. Hall Psychiatric Institute & Byrnes Center for Geriatric Medicine, Education & Research; it honors requests for staff support & consumer-level information & materials from mental health centers statewide.

P SOUTH CAROLINA STATE LIBRARY, 1430/1500 Senate St, 29201. (Mail add: PO Box 11469, 29211), Tel: 803-734-8666. Reference Tel: 803-734-8026. TDD: 803-734-7298. FAX: 803-734-8676. E-Mail: reference@leo.scsl.state.sc.us. Web Site: www.state.sc.us/scsl. *Dir*, James B Johnson, Jr; E-Mail: jim@leo.scsl.state.sc.us; *Dep Dir*, John H Landrum; E-Mail: john@leo.scsl.state.sc.us; *Mgr*, Margie Herron; Tel: 803-734-8650, E-Mail: margie@leo.scsl.state.sc.us; *Admin Assoc*, Deborah P Andersen; Tel: 803-734-8626, E-Mail: debbiea@leo.scsl.state.sc.us; *Senior Librn*, Mary Bull; Tel: 803-737-7736, Fax: 803-734-4757, E-Mail: mary@leo.scsl.state.sc.us; *Senior Librn*, Deborah Hotchkiss; Tel: 803-734-8646, Fax: 803-734-4757, E-Mail: deborah@leo.scsl.state.sc.us; *Senior Librn*, Libby Law; Tel: 803-734-8653, E-Mail: libby@leo.scsl.state.sc.us; *Senior Librn*, Mary M Morgan; Tel: 803-734-8866, Fax: 803-734-4757, E-Mail: marym@leo.scsl.state.sc.us; *Senior Librn*, Curtis Rogers; Tel: 803-734-8928, E-Mail: curtis@leo.scsl.state.sc.us; *Automation Syst Coordr*, Catherine B Morgan; Tel: 803-734-8651, Fax: 803-734-4757, E-Mail: catherine@leo.scsl.state.sc.us; *Cat*, Wesley Sparks; Tel: 803-734-8662, Fax: 803-734-4757, E-Mail: wesley@leo.scsl.state.sc.us; *Commun Relations*, Lucinda Kress; Tel: 803-734-8647, E-Mail: lucinda@leo.scsl.state.sc.us; *Head, Info Serv*, Anne M Schneider; Tel: 803-734-8655, Fax: 803-734-4757, E-Mail: anne@leo.scsl.state.sc.us; *Info Res*, Brenda Boyd; Tel: 803-734-8628, Fax: 803-734-4757, E-Mail: brenda@leo.scsl.state.sc.us; *Info Res*, Karen McMullen; Tel: 803-734-3208, Fax: 803-734-4757, E-Mail: karenm@leo.scsl.state.sc.us; *Info Res*, Dawn Mullin; Tel: 803-737-3762, Fax: 803-734-4757, E-Mail: dawn@leo.scsl.state.sc.us; *Info Res*, Felicia Vereen; Tel: 803-734-8645, Fax: 803-734-4757, E-Mail: feliciav@leo.scsl.state.sc.us; *Librn for Blind*, Guynell Williams; Tel: 803-734-4611, Fax: 803-734-4610, E-Mail: guynell@leo.scsl.state.sc.us; *Syst Coordr*, Lea Walsh; Tel: 803-734-8635, Fax: 803-734-4757, E-Mail: lea@leo.scsl.state.sc.us; *Head Tech Servs*, Felicia Yeh; Tel: 803-734-8663, Fax: 803-734-4757, E-Mail: felicia@leo.scsl.state.sc.us; *YA Servs*, Jane G Connor; Tel: 803-734-8658, E-Mail: janec@leo.scsl.state.sc.us; *Web Coordr*, Cheryl Kirkpatrick; Tel: 803-734-5831, Fax: 803-734-4757, E-Mail: cheryl@leo.scsl.state.sc.us. Subject Specialists: *Network*, Lea Walsh; Staff 50 (MLS 22, Non-MLS 28)
Founded 1943. Pop 3,486,703
Jul 1999-Jun 2000 Income $13,008,456, State $9,806,125, Federal $1,730,889, Other $1,471,442. Mats Exp $364,049. Sal $1,971,360 (Prof $1,249,198)
Library Holdings: Bk Vols 302,366; Per Subs 2,184
Subject Interests: Nonfiction, Southern hist
Special Collections: ERIC Coll; Foundation Center Regional Coll; Last Copy Fiction; South Carolina Coll; South Carolina Government Publications
Automation Activity & Vendor Info: (Acquisitions) DRA; (Cataloging) DRA; (Circulation) DRA; (Media Booking) DRA; (OPAC) DRA; (Serials) DRA
Database Vendor: DRA, GaleNet, OCLC - First Search
Publications: Continuing Education Opportunities, 2000-2001; Library Services & Technology Act (LSTA) PL 104-208: information & guidelines; New Resources (monthly); News About Library Services for the Blind & Physically Handicapped (quarterly); News for South Carolina Libraries (quarterly); South Carolina Connects Through Libraries Under the Library Services & Technology Act (PL, 104-208): five year plan FY1997-FY2002; South Carolina Library Standards, 1998; South Carolina Public Library Annual Statistical Summary, 1997; South Carolina State Library procurement audit report; The Great Book Feast: summer reading program librarian's manual, 1998
Friends of the Library Group
Branches: 1
DEPARTMENT FOR THE BLIND & PHYSICALLY HANDICAPPED
See Separate Entry

P SOUTH CAROLINA STATE LIBRARY, Department for the Blind & Physically Handicapped, 1430 Senate St, 29201. (Mail add: PO Box 821, 29202-0821), SAN 315-4963. Tel: 803-734-4611. Toll Free Tel: 800-922-7818. TDD: 803-734-7298. FAX: 803-734-4610. E-Mail: lbphbooks@leo.scsl.state.sc.us. Web Site: www.state.sc.us/scsl/bph.html. *Dir*, Guynell Williams; E-Mail: guynell@leo.scsl.state.sc.us; *Coll Develop*, Christopher Yates; Tel: 803-734-4618, E-Mail: chris@leo.scsl.state.sc.us; *Reader Servs*, Wendy Mullin; Tel: 803-734-4621, E-Mail: wendy@leo.scsl.state.sc.us; Sta 10 (MLS 3, Non-MLS 7)
Founded 1973. Circ 250,793
Jul 1999-Jun 2000 Income $750,204, State $599,556, Federal $140,598, Other $10,050. Mats Exp Books $11,877. Sal $325,093 (Prof $151,015)
Library Holdings: Bk Vols 315,707; Bk Titles 38,000
Special Collections: South Caroliniana, cassettes, descriptive videotapes
Database Vendor: DRA
Publications: News about Library Services for the Blind & Physically Handicapped (Newsletter)
Special Services for the Blind - Audiobooks; Bi-Folkal kits; Bks on cassett Bks/mag in Braille, on rec & on tape available by post-free mail to individuals living in New York City or on Long Island who cannot read regular print because of a visual or physical handicap; Braille; Braille Embosser; Cassette bks; Ednalite Hi-Vision scope; GEAC Advance; High interest/low vocabulary bk vols; Magnifiers; Optelek 20/20 video magnification system; Reading machine; Reference services; Talking books for the Blind; ZoomText software to enlarge computer screen

GL SOUTH CAROLINA SUPREME COURT LIBRARY, 1231 Gervais St, P(Box 11330, 29201. SAN 315-5293. Tel: 803-734-1080. FAX: 803-734-051 *Librn*, Janet F Meyer; Staff 2 (MLS 1, Non-MLS 1)
Founded 1871
Library Holdings: Bk Titles 37,884; Per Subs 115
Subject Interests: SC law
Special Collections: Court Cases (1918 to present), micro

C UNIVERSITY OF SOUTH CAROLINA, Thomas Cooper Library, 29208-0103. SAN 360-1234. Tel: 803-777-3142. Interlibrary Loan Service Tel: 803-777-4866. Circulation Tel: 803-777-3145. Web Site: www.sc.edu/librar *Spec Coll*, Allen Stokes; *Publ Servs*, Thomas McNally; *Cat*, Martha Mason *Bibliog Instr, Ref*, Virginia Weathers; *Ser*, Gail Julian; *Doc*, Lester Duncan; *Doc*, William Sudduth; *Circ*, Tucky Taylor; *Acq*, Joseph Pukl; Staff 60 (MI 60)
Founded 1801. Enrl 35,231; Fac 1,250; Highest Degree: Doctorate
Jul 1999-Jun 2000 Income (Main Library and Branch Library) $14,196,42 Mats Exp $4,764,851. Sal $6,272,179
Library Holdings: Bk Vols 2,862,896; Per Subs 15,426
Special Collections: Archaeology (19th Century), rare bks; EEC; English & American Literature, rare bks; F Scott Fitzgerald, rare bks; Ornithology (18th-20th Century), rare bks; Robert Burns & Scottish Literature, Civil W rare bks; Scottish Literature
Automation Activity & Vendor Info: (Acquisitions) NOTIS; (Circulation) NOTIS
Publications: Ex Libris; Reflections
Mem of Asn of Research Libraries
Partic in SE Libr Network
Friends of the Library Group
Departmental Libraries:

CL COLEMAN KARESH LAW LIBRARY, USC Law Ctr, 29208. SAN 360-1269. Tel: 803-777-5944. FAX: 803-777-9405. Web Site: www.law.sc.edu *Dir*, Steven Hinckley; E-Mail: hinckley@law.sc.edu; *Assoc Dir*, Joseph Cross; *Acq*, Melissa Surber; *Cat*, Diana Osbaldiston; *Cat*, Rebecca Anderson; *Circ, ILL*, Karen Taylor; Tel: 803-777-5942, E-Mail: taylork@law.sc.edu; *Ref*, Pamela Melton; *Ref*, Robert Jacoby; *Ref*, Rebekah Maxwell; *Tech Coordr*, Michael Brantley; Staff 10 (MLS 10)
Founded 1866. Enrl 708; Fac 42; Highest Degree: Doctorate
Jul 1998-Jun 1999 Income (Main Library Only) $1,816,801. Mats Exp $955,053, Books $78,159, Per/Ser (Incl. Access Fees) $656,945, Micro $36,577, AV Equip $95,838, Electronic Ref Mat (Incl. Access Fees) $87,534. Sal $710,076 (Prof $481,053)
Library Holdings: Bk Vols 453,508; Bk Vols 73,951; Per Subs 3,777; P Subs 3,166
Special Collections: Anglo-American Law; South Carolina Legal History
Automation Activity & Vendor Info: (Acquisitions) NOTIS; (Catalogin NOTIS; (Circulation) NOTIS; (OPAC) NOTIS
Publications: Guide to the Coleman Karesh Law Library
Partic in Solinet

CM SCHOOL OF MEDICINE LIBRARY, 6311 Garners Ferry Rd, 29208. (Ma add: University of South Carolina, 29208), Tel: 803-733-3344. FAX: 803-733-1509. Web Site: www.med.sc.edu. *Dir Libr Serv*, Ruth Riley; *Assoc Dir*, Sarah Gable; *Cat*, Laura Kane; *Circ*, Victor Jenkinson; *Ser*, Karen Rosati; *Syst Coordr*, Edwin Sperr; Staff 18 (MLS 6, Non-MLS 12)

Founded 1975. Enrl 289; Fac 244; Highest Degree: Doctorate
Jul 1999-Jun 2000 Income $1,138,507. Sal $559,246
Library Holdings: Bk Vols 93,130; Per Subs 913
Special Collections: Rare Medical Books
Database Vendor: Ebsco - EbscoHost
Publications: Guide; South Carolina Union List of Medical Periodicals; Southeastern Medical Periodicals Union List
Partic in Columbia Area Med Libr Consortium; SE-Atlantic Regional Med Libr Servs
SOUTH CAROLINIANA LIBRARY Tel: 803-777-3131. Interlibrary Loan Service Tel: 803-777-3132. FAX: 803-777-5747. *Dir*, Allen H Stokes; Staff 9 (MLS 9)
Founded 1801
1997-1998 Income $1,040,000. Mats Exp $84,000. Sal $653,500
Library Holdings: Bk Vols 98,092; Per Subs 325
Subject Interests: SC culture, SC hist
Special Collections: South Caroliniana & Southern Materials
Publications: Annual report; University South Caroliniana Society Annual Report of Gifts to the Collection
Friends of the Library Group

WILLIAM S HALL PSYCHIATRIC INSTITUTE, Professional Library,* 1800 Colonial Dr, PO Box 202, 29202. SAN 315-520X. Tel: 803-898-1735. FAX: 803-898-1712. E-Mail: pvw86@wshpi.dmh.state.sc.us. *Dir*, Neeta N Shah; Staff 5 (MLS 2, Non-MLS 3)
Founded 1965
1997-1998 Mats Exp $110,000. Sal $124,000
Library Holdings: Bk Vols 13,200; Per Subs 350
Subject Interests: Adjunct therapy, Behav sci, Drug abuse, Forsenic med, Genealogy, Genetics, Gerontology, Medicine, Neurology, Pastoral counseling, Psychiatry, Psychology, Psychopharma, Soc sci
Special Collections: Annual Rpt, SC Dept Mental Health (1850-present); Hist of World Asylums Coll
Publications: Psychiatric Forum (bi-annually)
Partic in BRS; Medline; SC Health Info Network
William S Hall Psychiatric Institute is a research and training facility for the South Carolina Dept of Mental Health and it is also a Dept of Neuropsychiatry and Behavioral Science of the University of South Carolina Medical School

ONWAY

COSTAL CAROLINA UNIVERSITY KIMBEL LIBRARY,* PO Box 261954, 29528-6054. SAN 315-5331. Tel: 843-349-2401. FAX: 843-349-2412. *Dean of Libr*, Dr Lynne Smith; *Bibliog Instr*, Margaret Fain; *Tech Servs*, Sallie Clarkson; *ILL, Publ Servs*, Marchita Phifer; *Publ Servs*, Michael Lackey; Staff 7 (MLS 7)
Founded 1954. Highest Degree: Master
Library Holdings: Bk Vols 202,158; Per Subs 1,006
Special Collections: Marine Science
Publications: Biblio-File
Partic in SE Libr Network

HORRY COUNTY MEMORIAL LIBRARY, 1008 Fifth Ave, 29526-5196. SAN 360-1382. Tel: 843-248-1545. TDD: 843-248-1547. FAX: 843-248-1548. Web Site: www.horry.lib.sc.us. *Dir*, John Gaumer; *Head of Libr*, Dorothy H Trautman; Tel: 843-248-1543, Fax: 843-248-1443; *Automation Syst Coordr*, Jody Jenerette-Bushee; *Coll Develop*, Anne Vaught; Tel: 843-248-1550, Fax: 843-248-1549; Staff 41 (MLS 8, Non-MLS 33)
Founded 1948. Pop 175,000; Circ 576,757
Jul 1999-Jun 2000 Income $2,086,151, State $268,711, County $1,817,150, Other $290. Mats Exp $540,229, Books $409,496, Per/Ser (Incl. Access Fees) $31,219, Presv $8,247, Micro $2,187, AV Equip $79,382, Electronic Ref Mat (Incl. Access Fees) $9,698. Sal $1,206,967
Library Holdings: Bk Vols 256,249; Per Subs 922
Special Collections: Local History
Database Vendor: epixtech, inc.
Publications: HCML Report
Partic in OCLC Online Computer Library Center, Inc; SE Libr Network
Special Services for the Deaf - Staff with knowledge of sign language
Friends of the Library Group
Branches: 9
AYNOR BRANCH, 500 Ninth Ave, Aynor, 29511. SAN 360-1412. Tel: 843-358-3324. FAX: 843-358-3324. *Branch Mgr*, Angela Hemingway
Library Holdings: Bk Titles 17,327
Friends of the Library Group
BUCKSPORT, 7657 Hwy 701 S, 29527. SAN 375-5703. Tel: 843-397-1950. FAX: 843-397-1951. *Branch Mgr*, E Ann Dion
Library Holdings: Bk Titles 11,242
Friends of the Library Group
CONWAY BRANCH Tel: 843-248-1543. FAX: 843-248-1443. *Branch Mgr*, Pat Langevin
Library Holdings: Bk Titles 57,286
Friends of the Library Group
TECHNICAL SERVICES EXTENSION SERVICES, 1603 Fourth Ave, 29526. SAN 374-4116. Tel: 843-248-1550. FAX: 843-248-1549. *Head Tech Servs*, Sue McLeod
LORIS BRANCH, 4316 Main St, Loris, 29569. SAN 360-1501. Tel: 843-756-8101. FAX: 843-756-1988. *Branch Mgr*, Frances Prince
Library Holdings: Bk Titles 22,540
Friends of the Library Group
NORTH MYRTLE BEACH, 799 Second Ave N, North Myrtle Beach, 29582. SAN 360-1471. Tel: 843-249-4164. FAX: 843-249-1700. *Librn*, Shelley Ridout
Library Holdings: Bk Titles 37,824
Special Services for the Deaf - TDD
Friends of the Library Group
SOCASTEE, 4505 Socastee Blvd, Myrtle Beach, 29588. SAN 372-7874. Tel: 843-293-1733. FAX: 843-293-2304. *Branch Mgr*, Linda Garrett
Library Holdings: Bk Titles 26,000
Friends of the Library Group
STEPHENS CROSSROAD, 107 Hwy 57 N, Little River, 29566. SAN 375-5711. Tel: 843-399-5541. FAX: 843-399-5542. *Branch Mgr*, Cindy Burgio
Library Holdings: Bk Titles 13,952
Friends of the Library Group
SURFSIDE BEACH BRANCH, 410 Surfside Dr, Surfside Beach, 29575. SAN 360-1536. Tel: 843-238-0122. FAX: 843-238-4273. *Librn*, Gwenda Hemingway
Library Holdings: Bk Titles 24,550
Friends of the Library Group
Bookmobiles: 1

J HORRY-GEORGETOWN TECHNICAL COLLEGE, Conway Campus Library, 2050 Hwy 501 E, 29526. (Mail add: PO Box 261966, 29528), Tel: 843-349-5268. FAX: 843-347-0552. Web Site: www.hor.tec.sc.us/lrc/librarywebpage.htm. *Dir*, Peggy Smith; *Acq, ILL*, John W Sharpe; *Tech Servs*, Forrest Allen; Tel: 843-349-7596, E-Mail: allen@hor.tec.sc.us; *Circ, Ser*, Melissa Coley; Tel: 843-349-7546, E-Mail: coleym@hor.tec.sc.us; Staff 5 (MLS 2, Non-MLS 3)
Founded 1966. Enrl 2,500; Fac 80
Library Holdings: Bk Vols 46,000; Bk Titles 30,000; Per Subs 350
Subject Interests: Bus, Civil engineering, Computer eng, Culinary arts, Dent hyg, Electronics tech, Forestry, Golf course maintenance, Nursing, Radiology
Automation Activity & Vendor Info: (Cataloging) DRA; (Circulation) DRA; (OPAC) DRA
Database Vendor: Ebsco - EbscoHost, GaleNet, IAC - SearchBank, Lexis-Nexis, OCLC - First Search, ProQuest, Wilson - Wilson Web
Partic in OCLC Online Computer Library Center, Inc; SE Libr Network; Solinet
Departmental Libraries:
GEORGETOWN, 4003 S Fraser St, Georgetown, 29440. SAN 372-5030. Tel: 843-546-8406. FAX: 843-546-1437.
Founded 1978. Enrl 300
Subject Interests: Bus, Licensed practical nursing
Partic in OCLC Online Computer Library Center, Inc; SE Libr Network
GRAND STRAND CAMPUS
See Separate Entry in Myrtle Beach

DARLINGTON

S DARLINGTON COUNTY HISTORICAL COMMISSION,* 204 Hewitt St, 29532. SAN 370-2103. Tel: 843-398-4710. *Dir*, Horace Fraser Rudisill
Library Holdings: Bk Vols 10,000
Subject Interests: Genealogy, Local history

P DARLINGTON COUNTY LIBRARY, 204 N Main St, 29532. SAN 360-1560. Tel: 843-398-4940. FAX: 843-398-4942. Web Site: www.geocities.com/Athens/Parthenon/2023. *Dir*, Sue Raney; E-Mail: srainey@infoave.net; *Ch Servs*, Karen E Moreau; *ILL*, Marjorie C Reason; Staff 27 (MLS 4, Non-MLS 23)
Founded 1893. Pop 61,851; Circ 206,238
Library Holdings: Bk Vols 140,000; Per Subs 422
Special Collections: NUREG
Friends of the Library Group
Branches: 3
HARTSVILLE MEMORIAL, 147 W College St, Hartsville, 29550. SAN 360-1595. Tel: 843-332-5115. TDD: 843-398-4941. FAX: 843-332-7071. Web Site: www.geocities.com/Athens/Parthenon/2023. *Librn*, Liz Watford; E-Mail: lwatford@infoave.net; Staff 4 (MLS 2, Non-MLS 2)
Founded 1930. Pop 21,000
Special Collections: Nuclear Regulatory Deposit
Friends of the Library Group
LAMAR LIBRARY, 104 S Main St, Lamar, 29069. SAN 360-1625. Tel: 803-326-5524. FAX: 803-326-5524. *Coordr*, Linda Stewart
SOCIETY HILL LIBRARY, 473 S Main St, Society Hill, 29593. SAN 360-165X. Tel: 843-378-0026. FAX: 843-378-0026. *Coordr*, Ann Morgan
Founded 1822

DENMARK

J DENMARK TECHNICAL COLLEGE, Learning Resources Center, Solomon Blatt Blvd, PO Box 327, 29042. SAN 374-6232. Tel: 803-793-5213. Circulation Tel: 803-793-5214. Reference Tel: 803-793-5215. FAX: 803-793-5942. *Dean*, Carole M Rossi; E-Mail: rossic@den.tec.sc.us; *ILL, Ref*, Lynda J Neil; *Circ*, Stephanie S Halliman; Staff 3 (MLS 2, Non-MLS 1)
Founded 1948. Enrl 1,200; Fac 36; Highest Degree: Associate
Jul 1999-Jun 2000 Income (Main Library Only) Parent Institution $750,000. Mats Exp $81,000, Books $50,000, Per/Ser (Incl. Access Fees) $11,000, AV Equip $10,000, Electronic Ref Mat (Incl. Access Fees) $6,000. Sal $84,000 (Prof $68,000)
Library Holdings: Bk Vols 14,000; Bk Titles 11,000; Per Subs 229
Automation Activity & Vendor Info: (Circulation) CASPR
Database Vendor: IAC - SearchBank, Innovative Interfaces INN - View, OVID Technologies, Wilson - Wilson Web
Publications: The Messenger (newsletter)
Function: Research library

C VOORHEES COLLEGE, Wright Potts Library, Voorhees Rd, 29042. SAN 315-534X. Tel: 803-793-3351, Ext 7095. *Librn*, Marie S Martin; *Circ*, Helen Graham; Staff 4 (MLS 4)
Founded 1935. Enrl 600; Fac 44; Highest Degree: Bachelor
Library Holdings: Bk Vols 102,299; Per Subs 472
Special Collections: Historical Papers; Ten-Year Developmental Study of Episcopal Church Book of Common Prayer; Voorhees College Documents
Partic in Coop Col Libr Ctr, Inc

DILLON

§P DILLON COUNTY LIBRARY, 600 E Main St, 29536. Tel: 843-774-0330. FAX: 843-774-0773. E-Mail: dilloncountylibrary@yahoo.com. Web Site: www.dillon.lib.sc.us. *Dir*, Barbara Henderson
Open Mon & Tues 9-8, Wed-Fri 9-5:30, Sat 9-12
Branches: 2
LAKE VIEW BRANCH, 305 S Main St, Lake View, 29563. SAN 360-294X. Tel: 803-759-2692. *Librn*, Florinette Renfrow
LATTA BRANCH, 101 N Marion St, Latta, 29565-3597. SAN 360-2885. Tel: 843-752-5389. FAX: 843-752-7457. Web Site: www.dillon.lib.sc.us. *Dir*, Yolanda McCormick; *Branch Mgr*, Christy L Berry; *Ch Servs*, Vanessa Bildon; *Bkmobile Coordr*, Shirley Coward; Staff 7 (MLS 1, Non-MLS 6)
Founded 1914. Pop 29,114; Circ 75,322
Library Holdings: Bk Vols 71,933; Per Subs 125
Automation Activity & Vendor Info: (Cataloging) Gaylord; (Circulation) Gaylord; (Course Reserve) Gaylord; (OPAC) Gaylord
Open Mon-Fri 9-5:30, Sat 9-12
Bookmobiles: 2

DUE WEST

C ERSKINE COLLEGE & THEOLOGICAL SEMINARY, McCain Library, One Depot St, 29639. SAN 315-5358. Tel: 864-379-8898. Circulation Tel: 864-379-8714. Toll Free Tel: 877-876-4348. FAX: 864-379-2900. E-Mail: library@erskine.edu. Web Site: www.erskine.edu/library. *Dir*, John F Kennerly; Tel: 864-379-8788, E-Mail: kennerly@erskine.edu; *Acq*, Shirley Adams; E-Mail: adams@erskine.edu; *Archivist, Cat*, Edith Brawley; Tel: 864-379-8763, E-Mail: ebrawley@erskine.edu; *Automation Syst Coordr*, Cathy Miller; Tel: 864-379-8789, E-Mail: cmiller@erskine.edu; *Cat, ILL*, Sara M Morrison; Tel: 864-379-8747, E-Mail: morrison@erskine.edu; *Govt Doc, Ref Serv*, Frederick W Guyette; Tel: 864-379-8784, E-Mail: fguyette@erskine.edu; Staff 7 (MLS 3, Non-MLS 4)
Founded 1837. Enrl 707; Fac 57; Highest Degree: Doctorate
Jul 1999-Jun 2000 Income Parent Institution $374,675
Library Holdings: Bk Vols 229,150; Bk Titles 152,414; Per Subs 707
Subject Interests: Erskiniana, Genealogy, History, Local history, Religion
Special Collections: Associate Reformed Presbyterian Church Records
Automation Activity & Vendor Info: (Acquisitions) Endeavor; (Cataloging) Endeavor; (Circulation) Endeavor; (Course Reserve) Endeavor; (OPAC) Endeavor; (Serials) Endeavor
Database Vendor: Dialog, GaleNet, IAC - Info Trac, OCLC - First Search
Partic in Council For Christian Colleges & Universities; Solinet; South Carolina State Library

DUNCAN

S CRYOVAC TECHNICAL LIBRARY, 100 Rogers Bridge Rd, PO Box 464, 29334-0464. SAN 315-5366. Tel: 864-433-2313. Interlibrary Loan Service Tel: 864-433-2312. FAX: 864-433-3636. *Librn*, Sherry Davis; E-Mail: sherry.davis@sealedair.com; *ILL*, Carolyn Genobles; *Mgr*, Andy Gillanders; Staff 4 (MLS 2, Non-MLS 2)
Founded 1962
Library Holdings: Bk Titles 8,000; Per Subs 225
Subject Interests: Chemistry, Engineering, Food tech, Packaging, Plastics
Special Collections: Cryovac Proprietary Documents (in-house use only)
Partic in SE Libr Network

EASLEY

P PICKENS COUNTY LIBRARY SYSTEM, 110 W First Ave, 29640-2998. SAN 360-1684. Tel: 864-850-7077. FAX: 864-850-7088. *Dir*, Marguerite D Keenan; E-Mail: margueritek@pickens.lib.sc.us; *Coll Develop*, Debra Kaniaris; *Syst Coordr*, Barbara Turner; *Tech Servs*, Anita Prien; Staff 27 (MLS 13, Non-MLS 14)
Founded 1935. Pop 93,894; Circ 351,477
Jul 1999-Jun 2000 Income (Main Library and Branch Library) $1,455,059, State $175,146, County $1,279,913. Mats Exp $185,026, Books $142,906, Per/Ser (Incl. Access Fees) $15,657, Micro $1,963, AV Equip $18,924, Electronic Ref Mat (Incl. Access Fees) $5,576. Sal $970,738
Library Holdings: Bk Vols 105,678; Bk Titles 75,000; Per Subs 339
Subject Interests: S Caroliniana
Automation Activity & Vendor Info: (Acquisitions) epixtech, inc.
Friends of the Library Group

EDGEFIELD

S TOMPKINS MEMORIAL LIBRARY,* 104 Courthouse Sq, 29824. SAN 327-8646. Tel: 803-637-4010. *Dir*, Tonya Taylor
Library Holdings: Bk Vols 17,100

FLORENCE

P FLORENCE COUNTY LIBRARY,* 319 S Irby St, 29501. SAN 360-1838. Tel: 843-662-8424. FAX: 843-661-7544. *Actg Dir, Tech Servs*, George L Hobeika; *Ad Servs*, Penny Forrester; *Ad Servs*, Timothy Anderson; *ILL, Ref* Jacqueline Brown; *Syst Coordr*, Aubrey Carroll; *Br Coordr*, Ware Martin; Staff 7 (MLS 7)
Founded 1925. Pop 114,344; Circ 329,029
Library Holdings: Bk Vols 156,835; Per Subs 380
Subject Interests: Local history
Special Collections: Caroliniana
Partic in SE Libr Network
Friends of the Library Group
Branches: 5
JOHNSONVILLE PUBLIC, Marion St, PO Box 848, Johnsonville, 29555-0004. SAN 360-1862. Tel: 843-386-2052. FAX: 843-386-2052. *Librn*, Cheryl Smith
Library Holdings: Bk Vols 8,193
LAKE CITY PUBLIC, 235 E Main St, Lake City, 29560-2114. SAN 360-1897. Tel: 843-394-8071. FAX: 843-394-8071. *Branch Mgr*, Carolyn Maci-Sims
Library Holdings: Bk Vols 10,877
OLANTA PUBLIC, PO Box 263, Olanta, 29114-0263. SAN 360-1919. Tel: 803-396-4287. FAX: 843-396-4287. *Librn*, Annis Raines
Library Holdings: Bk Vols 1,889
PAMPLICO PUBLIC, 180 Main St, Pamplico, 29583-0476. SAN 360-1927. Tel: 803-493-5441. FAX: 803-493-5441. *Librn*, Dorothy W Bostic; *Librn*, Ollie M Munn
Library Holdings: Bk Vols 6,584
TIMMONSVILLE PUBLIC, 111 S Warren St, PO Box 160, Timmonsville, 29161-0160. SAN 360-1951. Tel: 843-346-2941. FAX: 843-346-2941. *Librn*, Beverly Bell; *Librn*, Mary S Dorriety
Library Holdings: Bk Vols 6,407
Bookmobiles: 1

G FLORENCE COUNTY MUNICIPAL PLANNING DEPARTMENT LIBRARY, 218 W Evans St, 29501. SAN 372-9451. Tel: 843-676-8600. FAX: 843-676-8613. *Dir*, Elizabeth M Matthews
Library Holdings: Bk Vols 950; Per Subs 30
Subject Interests: Housing

C FRANCIS MARION UNIVERSITY, James A Rogers Library, Hwy 301 N, 29501. (Mail add: PO Box 100547, 29501-0547), SAN 315-5412. Tel: 843-661-1300. Interlibrary Loan Service Tel: 843-661-1310. Circulation Tel: 843-661-1311. Reference Tel: 843-661-1310. FAX: 843-661-1309. Web Site: alpha2.fmarion.edu. *Dean of Libr*, H Paul Dove, Jr; E-Mail: hdove@fmarion.edu; *Archivist, Spec Coll*, Suzanne Singleton; Tel: 843-661-1319, E-Mail: ssingleton@fmarion.edu; *Acq*, Joyce M Durant; Tel: 843-661-1304, E-Mail: jdurant@fmarion.edu; *Cat*, Linda D Becote; Tel: 843-661-1308, E-Mail: lbecote@fmarion.edu; *ILL*, John M Summer; Tel: 843-661-4677, E-Mail: jsummer@fmarion.edu; *Doc*, Yvette H Pierce; Tel: 843-661-1313, E-Mail: ypierce@fmarion.edu; Staff 23 (MLS 8, Non-MLS 15)
Founded 1970. Enrl 2,802; Fac 182; Highest Degree: Master
Jul 1999-Jun 2000 Income $1,590,658, State $1,569,701, Federal $10,253, Other $1,609. Mats Exp $599,003, Books $106,257, Per/Ser (Incl. Access Fees) $387,269, Presv $19,320, Micro $36,664, Electronic Ref Mat (Incl. Access Fees) $49,493. Sal $873,765 (Prof $349,538)
Library Holdings: Bk Vols 274,174; Per Subs 1,695
Special Collections: South Caroliniana especially relating to Pee Dee Area, bks & microfilm
Automation Activity & Vendor Info: (Acquisitions) DRA; (Cataloging) DRA; (Circulation) DRA; (Course Reserve) DRA; (OPAC) DRA; (Serials) DRA

Database Vendor: DRA, OCLC - First Search
Publications: The Axis
Partic in OCLC Online Computer Library Center, Inc; SE Libr Network

MCLEOD HEALTH, Pee Dee AHEC Library, 555 E Cheves St, 29506. (Mail add: PO Box 100551, 29501), SAN 315-5420. Tel: 843-777-2275. FAX: 843-777-2274. Web Site: www.ahec.net/peedee. *Mgr*, Lorraine Reiman; E-Mail: lreiman@mcleodhealth.org; Staff 1 (MLS 1)
Founded 1975
1999-2000 Income $65,000. Mats Exp $33,000, Books $15,000, Per/Ser (Incl. Access Fees) $18,000
Library Holdings: Bk Vols 500
Subject Interests: Allied health fields, Clinical medicine, Continuing educ in the health fields, Hospital operations, Mgt educ, Nursing
Special Collections: Management Materials; Publisher's Catalogs
Publications: Media List; Union list of serials
Partic in Nat Libr of Med; SC Health Info Network

WELLMAN INC, (Formerly Florence-Darlington Technical College Library), PO Box 201, 29501. SAN 315-5390. Tel: 843-661-8032. FAX: 843-661-8266. Web Site: www.flo.tec.sc.us/library. *Dir*, Jeronell W Bradley; E-Mail: bradleyj@flo.tec.sc.us; *Asst Librn*, Linda B Coe; Staff 5 (MLS 3, Non-MLS 2)
Founded 1964. Enrl 3,000; Fac 120
Jul 1999-Jun 2000 Mats Exp $147,123, Books $51,270, Per/Ser (Incl. Access Fees) $25,761. Sal $153,713
Library Holdings: Bk Vols 34,395; Bk Titles 34,258; Per Subs 300
Automation Activity & Vendor Info: (Acquisitions) DRA; (Cataloging) DRA; (Circulation) DRA; (Serials) DRA
Database Vendor: GaleNet, IAC - Info Trac, Lexis-Nexis, OCLC - First Search, ProQuest, Wilson - Wilson Web
Partic in Solinet

ORT JACKSON

UNITED STATES ARMY
FORT JACKSON MAIN POST LIBRARY, Thomas Lee Hall Main Post Library, Bldg 4679, 29207. SAN 360-1986. Tel: 803-751-4816, 803-751-5589. FAX: 803-751-1065. *Chief Librn*, John Anthony Vassallo; *Tech Servs*, Sharon Backenstose; Tel: 803-751-4816; Staff 5 (MLS 2, Non-MLS 3)
Founded 1946
Library Holdings: Bk Vols 70,115; Per Subs 65
Subject Interests: Bus and mgt, History, Mil sci
Automation Activity & Vendor Info: (Cataloging) Sagebrush Corporation
Database Vendor: OCLC - First Search
Restriction: Non-circulating to the public
Function: ILL available
Partic in Fedlink; OCLC Online Computer Library Center, Inc

M MONCRIEF ARMY HOSPITAL MEDICAL LIBRARY, 4500 Stuart St, 29207-5720. SAN 360-2044. Tel: 803-751-2149. FAX: 803-751-2734. *Librn*, Steven Leap; E-Mail: steven.leap@se.amedd.army.mil
Founded 1950
Library Holdings: Bk Vols 2,500; Per Subs 170
Subject Interests: Medicine, Nursing
Partic in Docline; Nat Libr of Med

AFFNEY

CHEROKEE COUNTY PUBLIC LIBRARY,* 300 E Rutledge Ave, 29340-2227. SAN 360-2079. Tel: 864-487-2711. FAX: 864-487-2752. Web Site: www.appnet.org/cherokee. *Dir*, Anne Moseley; *Ch Servs*, Susan Sarratt; *Bkmobile Coordr*, Wanda Howard; *ILL*, Judy Brown; Staff 1 (MLS 1)
Founded 1902. Pop 44,506; Circ 184,155
Jul 1996-Jun 1997 Income $467,383, State $60,083, County $385,500, Locally Generated Income $21,800. Mats Exp $74,700, Books $62,950, Per/Ser (Incl. Access Fees) $5,750, Presv $500. Sal $210,000
Library Holdings: Bk Vols 92,000; Bk Titles 73,000; Per Subs 141
Subject Interests: SC genealogy
Special Collections: Arthur Gettys Genealogy Coll; Gladys Coker Fort Fine Arts Coll; Heritage Room Coll; June Carr Photography Coll; Raymond & Bright Parker Story Tape Coll; Ruby Cash Garvin South Carolina Coll
Automation Activity & Vendor Info: (Circulation) epixtech, inc.
Publications: Friendly Notes; Genealogically Speaking
Friends of the Library Group
Branches: 1
BLACKSBURG BRANCH, Rutherford St, Blacksburg, 29702. SAN 360-2109. Tel: 864-839-2630. FAX: 864-839-2572. Web Site: www.appnet.org/cherokee. *Librn*, Cindy Harry
Special Collections: James M Bridges Reference Coll
Friends of the Library Group
Bookmobiles: 1

LIMESTONE COLLEGE, A J Eastwood Library, 1115 College Dr, 29340. SAN 315-5439. Tel: 864-488-4612. FAX: 864-487-4613. *Dir*, Carolyn T Hayward; Staff 5 (MLS 2, Non-MLS 3)
Founded 1845. Enrl 502; Fac 30; Highest Degree: Bachelor
Jul 1999-Jun 2000 Income $176,323. Mats Exp $83,280
Library Holdings: Bk Vols 61,000; Per Subs 253
Subject Interests: SC
Special Collections: Personal Library of Former Limestone College President (Lee Davis Lodge & Harrison Patillo Griffith)
Partic in South Carolina State Library

GEORGETOWN

P GEORGETOWN COUNTY LIBRARY SYSTEM, 405 Cleland St, 29440-3200. SAN 360-2133. Tel: 843-546-2521. FAX: 843-546-1316. E-Mail: gcldirector@infoave.net. Web Site: www.gcpl.lib.sc.us. *Dir*, Dwight McInvaill; Tel: 843-545-3304, E-Mail: dmcinvaill@georgetowncountysc.org; *Asst Dir*, Peggy Loyd; *Asst Dir*, Melanie Muller; *Mgr Libr Serv*, Trudy Bazemore; *Ch Servs*, Sheila Sullivan; *Branch Mgr*, Carlethia Rudolph; *Branch Mgr*, Donna Wade; *Tech Servs*, Vickie Jones; *Circ*, Mable Hills; Staff 26 (MLS 2, Non-MLS 24)
Founded 1799. Pop 57,000; Circ 199,551
Jul 2000-Jun 2001 Income (Main Library and Branch Library) $879,914, State $92,604, County $787,310. Mats Exp $135,089, Books $100,089, Per/Ser (Incl. Access Fees) $16,000, AV Equip $14,000, Electronic Ref Mat (Incl. Access Fees) $5,000. Sal $520,590
Library Holdings: Bk Vols 113,379; Per Subs 199
Subject Interests: Archives, Local history
Special Collections: 18th & 19th Century Library Records & Plantation Documents; Bank of Georgetown Records, 1920-1930's; Georgetown County Life 1890-1915, photos; Georgetown Library Society Materials
Automation Activity & Vendor Info: (Cataloging) Gaylord; (Circulation) Gaylord; (OPAC) Gaylord
Database Vendor: IAC - Info Trac, OCLC - First Search
Publications: A View of Our Past; Books on local history; Friends (newsletter)
Friends of the Library Group
Branches: 2
ANDREWS BRANCH, 105 N Morgan St, Andrews, 29510. SAN 360-2168. Tel: 803-264-8785. FAX: 803-264-8785. E-Mail: ablstaff@infoave.net. *Mgr*, Dale Wade
Friends of the Library Group
WACCAMAW, 24 Commerce Lane, Pawleys Island, 29585. SAN 373-1944. Tel: 803-237-4646. FAX: 803-237-4646. E-Mail: wnbstaff@infoave.net. *Mgr*, Carlethia Rudolph
Friends of the Library Group
Bookmobiles: 1

GRAMLING

S RENTAW FOUNDATION, INC LIBRARY, Hwy 176, PO Box 275, 29348-0275. SAN 321-4850. Tel: 864-472-2750. E-Mail: vlntryst@aol.com. *Librn*, Carl Watner
Founded 1981
Library Holdings: Bk Titles 1,800; Per Subs 19
Special Collections: Libertarianism (Rentaw Coll); Robert LeFevre; The Voluntaryist (Newsletter Coll)
Publications: The Voluntaryist (newsletter)

GREENVILLE

S AMERICAN LEPROSY MISSIONS INTERNATIONAL LIBRARY,* One ALM Way, 29601. SAN 372-946X. Tel: 864-271-7040. FAX: 864-271-7062. E-Mail: amlep@leprosy.org.
1998-1999 Income $300. Mats Exp $300
Library Holdings: Bk Vols 2,000

C BOB JONES UNIVERSITY, J S Mack Library, 29614. SAN 360-2192. Tel: 864-370-1800, Ext 6000. FAX: 864-232-1729. *Dir*, Joseph L Allen, Sr; Tel: 864-370-1800, Ext 6010, E-Mail: jallen@bju.edu; *Circ*, Jennifer Sackett; Staff 21 (MLS 4, Non-MLS 17)
Founded 1927. Enrl 3,860; Fac 309; Highest Degree: Doctorate
Jun 1999-May 2000 Income (Main and Other College/University Libraries) Parent Institution $764,269. Mats Exp $246,764, Books $148,350, Per/Ser (Incl. Access Fees) $63,893, Presv $9,679, AV Equip $16,342, Electronic Ref Mat (Incl. Access Fees) $8,500. Sal $461,216
Library Holdings: Bk Vols 263,310; Bk Titles 192,431; Per Subs 1,125
Subject Interests: Art, Religion
Automation Activity & Vendor Info: (Cataloging) DRA; (Circulation) DRA; (OPAC) DRA
Database Vendor: Dialog, DRA, IAC - SearchBank
Function: Reference services available
Partic in SE Libr Network
Departmental Libraries:
MUSIC Tel: 864-242-5100, Ext 2705. *Librn*, Karen Wilson
Library Holdings: Bk Vols 3,657

S FLUOR DANIEL, INC, Technical Information Center,* 100 Fluor Daniel Dr, 29607-2762. SAN 327-0793. Tel: 864-281-4799. FAX: 864-281-6480. *Librn*, Lillian Williams; E-Mail: lillian.williams@fluordaniel.com
Library Holdings: Bk Titles 3,000; Per Subs 80
Subject Interests: Engineering, Technology

C FURMAN UNIVERSITY LIBRARIES, James B Duke Library, James B Duke Library, 3300 Poinsett Hwy, 29613-0600. SAN 315-5455. Tel: 864-294-2190. Interlibrary Loan Service Tel: 864-294-2198. Circulation Tel: 864-294-2265. Reference Tel: 864-294-2195. FAX: 864-294-3004. Web Site: library.furman.edu. *Dir*, Dr Janis M Bandelin; Tel: 864-294-2191, E-Mail: janis.bandelin@furman.edu; *Assoc Dir*, John K Payne; Tel: 864-294-3098, E-Mail: john.payne@furman.edu; *Music*, Laurel Whisler; Tel: 864-294-3797, E-Mail: laurel.whisler@furman.edu; *Acq*, Betty Kelly; Tel: 864-294-2193, E-Mail: betty.kelly@furman.edu; *Spec Coll*, Dr J Glenwood Clayton; Tel: 864-294-3515, E-Mail: glen.clayton@furman.edu; *Ref*, Steve Richardson; Tel: 864-294-3227, Fax: 864-294-3230, E-Mail: steve.richardson@furman.edu; *Automation Syst Coordr*, Scott Salzman; Tel: 864-294-3204, E-Mail: scott.salzman@furman.edu; *Cat*, Nancy L Sloan; Tel: 864-294-2197, E-Mail: nancy.sloan@furman.edu; *Instrul Serv*, Mary Fairbairn; Tel: 864-294-3226, Fax: 864-294-3230, E-Mail: mary.fairbairn@furman.edu; *Govt Doc*, Libby Young; Tel: 864-294-2195, Fax: 864-294-3230, E-Mail: libby.young@furman.edu; Staff 27 (MLS 12, Non-MLS 15)
Founded 1826. Enrl 2,800; Fac 205; Highest Degree: Master
Jul 1999-Jun 2000 Income (Main and Other College/University Libraries) Parent Institution $2,023,182. Mats Exp $943,625, Books $213,756, Per/Ser (Incl. Access Fees) $566,724, Presv $22,918, Micro $38,657, AV Equip $7,783, Electronic Ref Mat (Incl. Access Fees) $85,134. Sal $797,253 (Prof $411,000)
Library Holdings: Bk Vols 395,600; Bk Titles 310,000; Per Subs 1,425
Special Collections: Furman University Archives; South Carolina Baptist History, bks, microfilm & mss
Automation Activity & Vendor Info: (Acquisitions) Innovative Interfaces Inc.; (Cataloging) Innovative Interfaces Inc.; (Circulation) Innovative Interfaces Inc.; (Course Reserve) Innovative Interfaces Inc.; (OPAC) Innovative Interfaces Inc.; (Serials) Innovative Interfaces Inc.
Database Vendor: Dialog, GaleNet, IAC - SearchBank, Innovative Interfaces INN - View, Lexis-Nexis, OCLC - First Search, Silverplatter Information Inc., Wilson - Wilson Web
Partic in Assoc Cols of the South; OCLC Online Computer Library Center, Inc; SE Libr Network
Branches: Maxwell Music Library & Ezell Science Reading Room
Departmental Libraries:
H KAY EZELL SCIENCE READING ROOM, Plyler Hall of Science, 3300 Poinsett Hwy, 29613. Tel: 864-294-2190.; Staff 1 (MLS 1)
Founded 1962
Library Holdings: Per Subs 200
ROBERT J MAXWELL MUSIC LIBRARY, Daniel Music Bldg, 3300 Poinsett Hwy, 29613. Tel: 864-294-3795. FAX: 864-294-3004. Web Site: library.furman.edu/music. *Music*, Laurel Whisler; Tel: 864-294-3797, E-Mail: laurel.whisler@furman.edu; Staff 1 (MLS 1)
Founded 1998
Library Holdings: Bk Vols 12,800; Bk Titles 12,000; Per Subs 56

P GREENVILLE COUNTY LIBRARY, 300 College St, 29601-2086. SAN 360-2257. Tel: 864-242-5000. Circulation Tel: 864-242-5000, Ext 2. Reference Tel: 864-242-5000, Ext 1. TDD: 864-271-1056. FAX: 864-235-8375. E-Mail: pritter@infoave.net. Web Site: www.greenvillelibrary.org. *Exec Dir*, Beverly A James; Tel: 864-242-5000, Ext 231, E-Mail: bajames@infoave.net; *Dir Libr Serv*, Norman Belk; Tel: 864-242-5000, Ext 238, E-Mail: normanbelk@excite.com; *Dep Dir*, Joan Sorensen; Tel: 864-242-5000, Ext 237, E-Mail: jsorenson@infoave.net; *Ref*, Roger Wellington; Tel: 864-242-5000, Ext 257, E-Mail: rwellington@infoave.net; *Ch Servs*, Susan Sponaas; Tel: 864-242-5000, Ext 249, E-Mail: susan_s@greenville.lib.sc.us; *Commun Servs*, Carolyn Cody-Fuller; Tel: 864-242-5000, Ext 235, E-Mail: cody@greenville.lib.sc.us; *Dir Info Resources & Res*, Patricia Shufeldt; Tel: 864-242-5000, Ext 219, E-Mail: pats@greenville.lib.sc.us; *Publ Servs*, Gay Nell Duckett; Tel: 864-242-5000, Ext 253, E-Mail: gay_d@greenville.lib.sc.us; *ILL*, Jimmy Smith; Tel: 864-242-5000, Ext 276, E-Mail: jsmith@infoave.net; *Business*, Helen Klemko; Tel: 864-242-5000, Ext 236, E-Mail: helen_k@greenville.lib.sc.us; *Tech Servs*, Joyce Borders; Tel: 864-242-5000, Ext 212, E-Mail: joyce_b@greenville.lib.sc.us; *Info Tech*, Ray McBride; Tel: 864-242-5000, Ext 220, E-Mail: ray_m@greenville.lib.sc.us; *Coll Develop*, Kathy Sharp; Tel: 864-242-5000, Ext 217, E-Mail: kathy_s@greenville.lib.sc.us; Staff 145 (MLS 38, Non-MLS 107)
Founded 1921. Pop 358,936; Circ 2,342,608
Jul 1999-Jun 2000 Income (Main Library and Branch Library) $8,687,905, State $597,227, County $7,668,219, Locally Generated Income $101,422, Other $210,369. Mats Exp $1,506,308, Books $800,853, Per/Ser (Incl. Access Fees) $310,611, Presv $6,215, Micro $60, AV Equip $295,089, Electronic Ref Mat (Incl. Access Fees) $93,480. Sal $4,534,385 (Prof $2,173,279)
Library Holdings: Bk Vols 823,301; Per Subs 1,570
Subject Interests: Genealogy, Law, Local history, State hist, Textile hist
Special Collections: Genealogy; Greenville County (SC) History; South Carolina History
Automation Activity & Vendor Info: (Acquisitions) DRA; (Cataloging) DRA; (Circulation) DRA; (OPAC) DRA; (Serials) DRA
Database Vendor: DRA, GaleNet, IAC - Info Trac, OCLC - First Search
Publications: Calendar of Events (monthly); Directory of Greenville Cou Clubs & Organizations (annual)
Function: Reference services available
Partic in SE Libr Network
Special Services for the Deaf - Books on deafness & sign language; High interest/low vocabulary books; Special interest periodicals; Staff with knowledge of sign language; TTY machine
Friends of the Library Group
Branches: 11
AUGUSTA, 3213 Augusta Rd, 29605. SAN 360-2281. Tel: 864-277-0161 Web Site: www.greenvillelibrary.org. *Dir Libr Serv*, F Norman Belk; Te 864-242-5000, Fax: 864-235-8375, E-Mail: normanbelk@excite.com; *Branch Mgr*, Robert Fassett
Library Holdings: Bk Vols 44,191
Friends of the Library Group
EARLE W & ELEANOR G SARGENT LIBRARY, 17 Center St, Travel Rest, 29690. SAN 360-246X. Tel: 864-834-3650. FAX: 864-834-4686. Web Site: gcl.greenville.lib.sc.us/. *Branch Mgr*, Norman Belk; Tel: 864-242-5000, Ext 238, Fax: 864-235-9375, E-Mail: normanbelk@excite.co *Mgr*, Ruth Rocap; Fax: 864-834-4686
Library Holdings: Bk Vols 53,209
Friends of the Library Group
F W SYMMES BRANCH, 1508 Pelham Rd, 29615. SAN 360-2338. Tel: 864-288-6688. FAX: 864-675-9149. Web Site: www.greenvillelibrary.or *Dir Libr Serv*, F Norman Belk; Tel: 864-242-5000, Ext 238, Fax: 864-2 8375, E-Mail: normanbelk@excite.com; *Branch Mgr*, Gwen Johnson
Library Holdings: Bk Vols 80,739
Friends of the Library Group
FOUNTAIN INN BRANCH, 400 N Main St, Fountain Inn, 29644. SAN 360-2346. Tel: 864-862-2576. Web Site: www.greenvillelibrary.org. *Dir Libr Serv*, F Norman Belk; Tel: 864-242-5000, Ext 238, Fax: 864-235-8375, E-Mail: normanbelk@excite.com; *Mgr*, Paula Jones; *In Charge*, Nancy Butler
Library Holdings: Bk Vols 24,138
Friends of the Library Group
HENDRICKS LIBRARY, 626 NE Main St, Simpsonville, 29681. SAN 3 2435. Tel: 864-963-9031. FAX: 864-228-0986. Web Site: www.greenvillelibrary.org. *Dir Libr Serv*, F Norman Belk; Tel: 864-242-5000, Ext 238, Fax: 864-235-8375, E-Mail: normanbelk@excite.com; *Branch Mgr*, Nancy Murrin
Library Holdings: Bk Vols 56,625
Friends of the Library Group
JEAN M SMITH LIBRARY, 505 Pennsylvania Ave, Greer, 29651. SAN 360-2370. Tel: 864-877-8722. FAX: 864-877-1422. Web Site: www.greenvillelibrary.org. *Business*, Joada Hiatt; *Dir Libr Serv*, F Norm Belk; Tel: 864-242-5000, Ext 238, Fax: 864-235-8375, E-Mail: normanbelk@excite.com
Library Holdings: Bk Vols 56,558
Friends of the Library Group
LAW, Greenville County Court House, 305 E North St, 29601. SAN 377-6832. Tel: 864-467-8486. *Dir Libr Serv*, F Norman Belk; Tel: 864-242-5000, Ext 238, Fax: 864-235-8375, E-Mail: normanbelk@excite.com
Library Holdings: Bk Vols 14,929
Friends of the Library Group
SARA DOBEY JONES LIBRARY OF BEREA, 111 N Hwy 25 Bypass, 29609. SAN 360-2311. Tel: 864-246-1695. FAX: 864-246-1765. Web Si gcl.greenville.lib.sc.us/. *Dir Libr Serv*, F Norman Belk; Tel: 864-242-50 Ext 238, Fax: 864-235-8375, E-Mail: normanbelk@excite.com; *Branch Mgr*, Bill Chase; Staff 7 (MLS 1, Non-MLS 6)
Library Holdings: Bk Vols 46,158
Friends of the Library Group
W JACK GREER LIBRARY OF MAULDIN, 800 W Butler Rd, 29607. SAN 360-2400. Tel: 864-277-7397. FAX: 864-246-1765. Web Site: www.greenvillelibrary.org. *Dir Libr Serv*, F Norman Belk; Tel: 864-242-5000, Ext 238, Fax: 864-235-8375, E-Mail: normanbelk@excite.com; *Branch Mgr*, Michael Evans
Library Holdings: Bk Vols 49,825
Friends of the Library Group
WADE HAMPTON-TAYLORS BRANCH, 3326 Wade Hampton Blvd, Taylors, 29687. SAN 360-2494. Tel: 864-268-5955. Web Site: www.greenvillelibrary.org. *Dir Libr Serv*, F Norman Belk; Tel: 864-242-5000, Ext 238, Fax: 864-235-8375, E-Mail: normanbelk@excite.com; *Branch Mgr*, Beth Arnold
Library Holdings: Bk Vols 80,739
Friends of the Library Group
WEST BRANCH, 1703 Easley Bridge Rd, 29611. SAN 360-2524. Tel: 86 269-5210. Web Site: www.greenvillelibrary.org. *Dir Libr Serv*, F Normar Belk; Tel: 864-242-5000, Ext 238, Fax: 864-235-8375, E-Mail: normanbelk@excite.com; *In Charge*, Gil Garrett
Library Holdings: Bk Vols 34,049
Friends of the Library Group
Bookmobiles: 2

GREENVILLE COUNTY PLANNING COMMISSION, Technical Library,* 301 University Ridge, Ste 400, 29601. SAN 325-5360. Tel: 864-467-7270. FAX: 864-467-5962. *Librn*, Wanda Johnson
Founded 1964
Library Holdings: Per Subs 35

GREENVILLE HOSPITAL SYSTEM, Health Sciences Library, 701 Grove Rd, 29605. SAN 360-2559. Tel: 864-455-7176. FAX: 864-455-5696. *Dir*, Fay Towell; E-Mail: ftowell@ghs.org; Staff 5 (MLS 3, Non-MLS 2)
Founded 1912
Library Holdings: Bk Vols 18,000; Bk Titles 4,000; Per Subs 570
Subject Interests: Allied health, Medicine, Mental health, Nursing, Psychiatry, Psychology, Rehabilitation med
Publications: Newsletter (quarterly)
Partic in SC Area Health Educ Ctr Hospital
Branches:
ROGER C PEACE HOSPITAL LIBRARY Tel: 864-455-7176. FAX: 864-455-5696. *Librn*, Deanna Black
Subject Interests: Professional material in rehabilitation med
Special Collections: Patient Education Materials

GREENVILLE MENTAL HEALTH CENTER LIBRARY,* 715 Grove Rd, 29605-4280. SAN 315-5463. Tel: 864-241-1040. FAX: 864-241-1049. E-Mail: aam34@gmhc.dmh.state.sc.us.
Founded 1969
Library Holdings: Bk Vols 3,000; Per Subs 30
Subject Interests: Counseling, Local govt publications, Mental health, Psychiatry, Psychology
Special Collections: Psychiatry & Religion (Pastoral Care Coll)
Partic in Southeastern Regional Med Libr Program
Special Services for the Deaf - Staff with knowledge of sign language; TTY machine

GREENVILLE NEWS-PIEDMONT LIBRARY,* 305 S Main St, PO Box 1688, 29602. SAN 315-5471. Tel: 864-298-4323. FAX: 864-298-4846. *Librn*, Tracey McCowan
Founded 1956
Library Holdings: Bk Vols 900; Bk Titles 600; Per Subs 12
Special Collections: South Carolina, news & photos

GREENVILLE TECHNICAL COLLEGE LIBRARY, 506 S Pleasantburg Dr, 29606. SAN 315-548X. Tel: 864-250-8319. Interlibrary Loan Service Tel: 864-250-8009. FAX: 864-250-8506. Web Site: www.greenvilletech.com. *Dir*, Dr L Gene Elliott; Tel: 864-250-8411, E-Mail: elliottlge@gvltec.edu; *Tech Servs*, Jane Mason; *Publ Servs*, Doris Jones; Staff 9 (MLS 3, Non-MLS 6)
Founded 1962. Enrl 10,785; Fac 210; Highest Degree: Associate
Jul 1999-Jun 2000 Income Parent Institution $504,121. Mats Exp $123,911, Books $91,831, Per/Ser (Incl. Access Fees) $32,080. Sal $349,790 (Prof $142,778)
Library Holdings: Bk Vols 57,219; Bk Titles 48,878; Per Subs 730
Subject Interests: Bus, Eng tech, Nursing, Sci-tech
Automation Activity & Vendor Info: (OPAC) DRA
Database Vendor: DRA, GaleNet, IAC - Info Trac, OCLC - First Search
Function: ILL available

JOHN D HOLLINGSWORTH ON WHEELS, INC, Information Services,* PO Box 516, 29602. SAN 372-9478. Tel: 864-297-1000. FAX: 864-297-2150.
Library Holdings: Bk Vols 1,000; Per Subs 29
Subject Interests: Manufacturing, Textiles

NELSON, MULLINS, RILEY & SCARBOROUGH, Law Library,* 301 N Main St, 24th flr, PO Box 10084, 29603. SAN 323-6609. Tel: 864-250-2300. FAX: 864-232-2925. *Librn*, Claire Engel
Library Holdings: Bk Vols 3,930
Other locations in Columbia & Myrtle Beach

OGLETREE, DEAKINS, NASH, SMOAK & STEWART, Law Library, 300 N Main St, 29601. (Mail add: PO Box 2757, 29602), SAN 373-5982. Tel: 864-271-1300. FAX: 864-235-4649. *Dir Info Resources & Res*, Julie Bace Luppino; E-Mail: julie.luppino@odnss.com; *Librn*, Shannon Wilson; E-Mail: shannon.wilson@odnss.com; Staff 4 (MLS 3, Non-MLS 1)
Founded 1977
Library Holdings: Bk Titles 3,000; Per Subs 100
Subject Interests: Environmental law
Database Vendor: Lexis-Nexis, ProQuest

GREENWOOD

GREENWOOD COUNTY LIBRARY, (Formerly Abbeville-Greenwood Regional Library), 106 N Main St, 29646. SAN 360-2672. Tel: 864-941-4650. FAX: 864-941-4651. Web Site: www.agrl.org. *Dir*, Prudence A Taylor; E-Mail: ptaylor81@hotmail.com; *Exten Serv*, Tracey Ouzts; *Asst Dir*, Frances A McNinch; *Coordr*, Laura Bryan; *Ch Servs*, Abby Cleland; *Tech Servs*, Rebecca Bryson; *Circ*, Deborah Dillashaw; Staff 39 (MLS 9, Non-MLS 30)
Founded 1901. Pop 62,000; Circ 238,886
2000-2001 Income (Main Library and Branch Library) $1,215,945, State $166,858, County $1,078,837, Locally Generated Income $20,000, Other $6,250. Mats Exp $219,291, Books $193,291, Per/Ser (Incl. Access Fees) $16,000, AV Equip $10,000. Sal $848,728 (Prof $299,657)
Library Holdings: Bk Vols 141,404; Per Subs 421
Special Collections: Genealogy (Star Fort Chapter DAR Coll); Local History (Abbeville District Historical Society), bks, maps, micro; Local History (Greenwood County Historical Society), bks, letters, diaries & photog
Automation Activity & Vendor Info: (Acquisitions) epixtech, inc.; (Cataloging) epixtech, inc.; (Circulation) epixtech, inc.
Database Vendor: epixtech, inc.
Publications: Library Link (children's newletter)
Function: ILL available
Friends of the Library Group
Branches: 5
ABBEVILLE COUNTY, Main & Cherry Sts, Abbeville, 29620. SAN 360-2702. Tel: 864-459-4009. FAX: 864-459-4009. *Mgr*, Doug Howard
Subject Interests: Genealogy, Local history
Friends of the Library Group
CALHOUN FALLS BRANCH, Tugaloo St, Calhoun Falls, 29628. SAN 360-2737. Tel: 864-447-8724. *Mgr*, Sara Broadwell
Friends of the Library Group
DONALDS BRANCH, Donalds, 29638. SAN 360-2761. Tel: 864-379-8568. *Mgr*, Margie Levee
Friends of the Library Group
NINETY SIX BRANCH, Ninety Six, 29666. SAN 360-2826. Tel: 864-543-4749. *Mgr*, Linda B McLane
Friends of the Library Group
WARE SHOALS BRANCH, Ware Shoals, 29692. SAN 360-2850. Tel: 864-456-2813. *Mgr*, Margaret Gowan
Friends of the Library Group

M GREENWOOD GENETIC CENTER LIBRARY,* One Gregor Mendel Circle, 29646. SAN 372-9486. Tel: 864-388-1708. FAX: 864-388-1808. *Librn*, Ellen Dewkett
Library Holdings: Bk Vols 3,000; Per Subs 60
Subject Interests: Genetics, Pediatrics
Special Collections: Genetics Rare Book Coll

C LANDER UNIVERSITY, Larry A Jackson Library, 29649-2099. SAN 315-551X. Tel: 864-388-8365. FAX: 864-388-8816. Web Site: www.lander.edu/library. *Dir*, Ann T Hare; E-Mail: ahare@lander.edu; *Tech Servs*, Susan C Going; E-Mail: sgoing@lander.edu; *Publ Servs*, Dan R Lee; E-Mail: dlee@lander.edu; *Publ Servs*, Betty H Williams; E-Mail: bwilliam@lander.edu; *Per*, Yvonne D Hudgens; E-Mail: yhudgens@lander.edu; Staff 10 (MLS 5, Non-MLS 5)
Founded 1872. Enrl 2,243; Fac 128; Highest Degree: Master
Jul 2000-Jun 2001 Income Parent Institution $754,067. Mats Exp $168,750, Books $69,705, Per/Ser (Incl. Access Fees) $78,045, Presv $4,000, Micro $17,000. Sal $417,387 (Prof $253,287)
Library Holdings: Bk Vols 169,581; Per Subs 692
Automation Activity & Vendor Info: (Acquisitions) Innovative Interfaces Inc.; (Cataloging) Innovative Interfaces Inc.; (Circulation) Innovative Interfaces Inc.; (OPAC) Innovative Interfaces Inc.; (Serials) Innovative Interfaces Inc.
Database Vendor: IAC - Info Trac, OCLC - First Search
Partic in OCLC Online Computer Library Center, Inc; Solinet

J PIEDMONT TECHNICAL COLLEGE LIBRARY,* PO Drawer 1467, 29648. SAN 315-5536. Tel: 864-941-8440. FAX: 864-941-8558. Web Site: www.piedmont.tec.sc.us/library. *Coll Develop, Dir*, Ruth Nicholson; E-Mail: nicholson@ped.tec.sc.us; *Mgr, Publ Servs*, Mary Louise Wilde; Staff 2 (MLS 2)
Founded 1966. Enrl 2,249
Jul 1996-Jun 1997 Income $161,000. Mats Exp $70,000, Books $43,000, Per/Ser (Incl. Access Fees) $20,000, Micro $2,000. Sal $125,700 (Prof $100,500)
Library Holdings: Bk Vols 26,000; Per Subs 330
Subject Interests: Allied health, Bus, Electronic engineering
Partic in Dialog Corporation; OCLC Online Computer Library Center, Inc; SE Libr Network

M SELF MEMORIAL HOSPITAL, Upper Savannah AHEC Library,* 1325 Spring St, 29646. SAN 315-5544. Tel: 864-227-4851. FAX: 864-227-4838. E-Mail: libform@ais.ais-gwd.com. Web Site: www.greenwood.net/~usahec/frame. *Librn*, Thomas W Hill; *Asst Librn*, Rachel Lewis
Founded 1976
Jul 1996-Jun 1997 Income $111,854, State $40,000, Locally Generated Income $1,000, Parent Institution $58,902. Mats Exp $39,465, Books $5,000, Per/Ser (Incl. Access Fees) $26,000, Presv $6,000, Other Print Mats $165. Sal $69,534 (Prof $56,659)
Library Holdings: Bk Titles 5,000; Per Subs 200
Subject Interests: Medicine, Nursing
Publications: Newsletter
Partic in Nat Libr of Med; SC Health Info Network; South Carolina Ahec; Upper Savannah Ahec

GREER

S MITSUBISHI POLYESTER FILM, LLC LIBRARY,* 2001 Hood Rd, PO Box 1400, 29652. SAN 324-0053. Tel: 864-879-5368. FAX: 864-879-5940.; Staff 1 (MLS 1)
Library Holdings: Bk Titles 750; Per Subs 100
Subject Interests: Chemicals, Marketing, Plastics
Partic in Dialog Corporation

HARTSVILLE

C COKER COLLEGE, James Lide Coker III Memorial Library, 300 E College Ave, 29550. SAN 315-5560. Tel: 843-383-8125. FAX: 843-383-8129. E-Mail: library@coker.edu. Web Site: www.coker.edu/library/. *Dir*, Dr David Eubanks; *Asst Librn*, Minoo Monakes; Staff 2 (MLS 2)
Founded 1908
Library Holdings: Bk Vols 87,000; Per Subs 580
Subject Interests: Music, Video
Special Collections: Arents Tobacco Coll
Publications: The Kernel
Partic in Discus; OCLC Online Computer Library Center, Inc; SE Libr Network

S SONOCO PRODUCTS CO, INC, Technical Information Center,* N Second St, PO Box 160, 29550. SAN 315-5579. Tel: 843-383-7000, Ext 7487. FAX: 843-383-3510. *Librn*, Kathleen Cooper; E-Mail: kathleencooper@sonoco.com
Library Holdings: Bk Titles 300; Per Subs 25
Subject Interests: Adhesives, Chemical technology, Coating tech, Environmental engineering, Paper tech, Plastic tech, Pulp tech
Special Collections: Chemical Abstracts; IPC Abstract Bulletins, microfiche; Standards (Federal, Military-ASTM, CCTI, TAPPI)

KINGSTREE

P WILLIAMSBURG COUNTY LIBRARY,* 215 N Jackson, 29556. SAN 315-5587. Tel: 843-354-9486. FAX: 843-354-9990. Web Site: www.wlbg.lib.sc.us. *Dir*, Cary Jones
Founded 1967. Pop 26,815; Circ 32,049
1997-1998 Income $157,444. Mats Exp $31,000. Sal $84,500
Library Holdings: Bk Vols 38,429; Bk Titles 31,529; Per Subs 74
Subject Interests: SC
Friends of the Library Group
Branches: 1
HEMINGWAY BRANCH, 306 N Main St, Hemingway, 29554. SAN 320-9695. Tel: 843-558-0743. Web Site: www.wlbg.lib.sc.us. *Librn*, Wanda Baxley
Open Mon, Wed & Fri
Bookmobiles: 1

LANCASTER

M CATAWBA-WATEREE HEALTH EDUCATION CONSORTIUM LIBRARY, 1228 Colonial Commons, PO Box 2049, 29721. SAN 370-6524. Tel: 803-286-4121. FAX: 803-286-4165. Web Site: www.c-whec.org. *Assoc Dir*, Cheri Plyler; E-Mail: cplyler@infoave.net
Founded 1978. Circ 100
Library Holdings: Bk Titles 300; Per Subs 110
Special Collections: Medicine & nursing, periodicals
Partic in SC Health Info Network

P LANCASTER COUNTY LIBRARY, 313 S White St, 29720. SAN 315-5609. Tel: 803-285-1502. FAX: 803-285-6004. E-Mail: lanclib@infoave.net. Web Site: www.lanclib.org. *Dir*, Richard A Band; *Librn*, Judy Hunter; *Asst Librn*, Nancy C Berry; *Bkmobile Coordr*, Glenda Lowery; *Ch Servs*, Brenda Parker; *Tech Servs*, Mina Gonzales; Staff 13 (MLS 3, Non-MLS 10)
Founded 1907. Pop 54,516; Circ 214,656
Jul 1998-Jun 1999 Income (Main Library and Branch Library) $624,856, State $81,775, Federal $20,140, County $480,455, Locally Generated Income $42,486. Mats Exp $623,523, Books $99,988, Per/Ser (Incl. Access Fees) $5,508, Presv $1,980, Micro $180, AV Equip $300, Electronic Ref Mat (Incl. Access Fees) $1,603. Sal $346,788
Library Holdings: Bk Vols 120,830; Per Subs 297
Subject Interests: Genealogy, Local history
Special Collections: Caroliniana
Database Vendor: IAC - Info Trac
Publications: Inventory to Perry Belle Hough Coll
Function: Research library
Partic in SC Libr Network
Branches: 1
KERSHAW MEMORIAL, 3855 Fork Hill Rd, Kershaw, 29067. SAN 325-3961. Tel: 803-475-2609. FAX: 803-475-4444. *Librn*, Pat Hinson
Bookmobiles: 1

S SPRINGS INDUSTRIES, INC, Information Systems Planning & Technology Library,* Hwy 9 & Grace Ave, PO Box 111, 29721. SAN 315-5617. Tel: 803-286-3236. FAX: 803-286-2157. *Librn*, Debbie Khoury; E-Mail: debbie.khoury@springs.com
Founded 1970
1997-1998 Income $25,000. Mats Exp $25,000
Library Holdings: Per Subs 20
Subject Interests: Data proc

C UNIVERSITY OF SOUTH CAROLINA, Medford Library, PO Box 889, 29721. SAN 315-5625. Tel: 803-285-7471. FAX: 803-289-7107. E-Mail: l70001@univscvm.scarolina.edu. *Dir*, Shari Eliades; Staff 2 (MLS 2)
Founded 1959. Enrl 1,000; Fac 36; Highest Degree: Bachelor
Library Holdings: Bk Titles 68,761; Per Subs 472
Subject Interests: Regional history
Mem of Univ of SC Regional Campus Syst
Partic in Catawba-Wateree Area Health Education Consortium; OCLC Online Computer Library Center, Inc
Friends of the Library Group

LAURENS

P LAURENS COUNTY LIBRARY, 1017 W Main St, 29360. SAN 360-297 Tel: 864-984-0596. FAX: 864-984-0598. Web Site: www.LCPL.ORG. *Dir*, William C Cooper; E-Mail: bcooper@lcpl.org; *Dep Dir*, Carol L Gaines; Tel: 864-833-1853, Fax: 864-833-9666, E-Mail: cgaines@lcpl.org; *Tech Servs*, Mary A Mundy; E-Mail: mmundy@lcpl.org; *Ch Servs*, Pam D Hartsell; E-Mail: phartsell@lcpl.org; *Publ Servs*, Margaret D Kennedy; E-Mail: pkennedy@lcpl.org; *Spec Coll*, Elaine Martin; E-Mail: emartin@lcpl.org; *Acq*, Kathryn W Johnson; E-Mail: kjohnson@lcpl.org; *Bkmobile Coordr*, Cynthia Montgomery; E-Mail: cmontgomery@lcpl.org; Staff 21 (MLS 6, Non-MLS 15)
Founded 1929. Pop 63,300; Circ 155,000
Jul 2000-Jun 2001 Income $717,927, State $116,184, City $17,000, County $543,281, Locally Generated Income $30,000, Other $11,462. Mats Exp $152,711, Books $120,211, Per/Ser (Incl. Access Fees) $17,000, Presv $3,000, Micro $500, AV Equip $10,000, Electronic Ref Mat (Incl. Access Fees) $2,000. Sal $436,329
Library Holdings: Bk Vols 108,756; Per Subs 322
Special Collections: Laurens County History and Genealogy; South Caroliniana Coll, bk & micro
Automation Activity & Vendor Info: (Acquisitions) TLC; (Cataloging) TLC; (Circulation) TLC; (OPAC) TLC
Database Vendor: GaleNet, IAC - Info Trac, OCLC - First Search
Function: Archival collection
Partic in OCLC Online Computer Library Center, Inc; SC Libr Network
Special Services for the Blind - Large print bks
Friends of the Library Group
Branches: 1
CLINTON PUBLIC, 406 N Broad St, Clinton, 29325. SAN 360-3008. Tel: 864-833-1853. FAX: 864-833-9666. *Librn*, Carol L Gaines
Library Holdings: Bk Vols 25,000
Friends of the Library Group
Bookmobiles: 1

LEXINGTON

P LEXINGTON COUNTY PUBLIC LIBRARY SYSTEM, 5440 Augusta Rd 29072. SAN 359-9671. Tel: 803-808-2600. Interlibrary Loan Service Tel: 803-808-2686. Circulation Tel: 803-808-2611. Reference Tel: 803-808-268(FAX: 803-808-2601. Web Site: www.lex.lib.sc.us. *Dir*, Daniel S MacNeill; Tel: 803-808-2640, E-Mail: dmacneill@lex.lib.sc.us; *Dep Dir*, Dee Bedenbaugh; Tel: 803-808-2643, E-Mail: dbedenbaugh@lex.lib.sc.us; *YA Servs*, Ellen Stringer; Tel: 803-808-2632, E-Mail: estringer@lex.lib.sc.us; *Tech Servs*, Barbara Remack; Tel: 803-808-2624, E-Mail: bremack@lex.lib.sc.us; *ILL, Ref*, Marie Jefferies; E-Mail: mjefferies@lex.lib.sc.us; *Bkmobile Coordr*, Mary Lott; Tel: 803-808-2649, E-Mail: mlott@lex.lib.sc.us; *Senior Librn*, Jennifer Chandler; Tel: 803-808-2614, E-Mail: jchandler@lex.lib.sc.us; *Asst Librn*, Mark Mancuso; Tel: 803-808-2673, E-Mail: mmancuso@lex.lib.sc.us; *Librn*, Kelly Poole; Tel: 803-808-2633, E-Mail: kpoole@lex.lib.sc.us. Subject Specialists: *Head*, Mark Mancuso; *Local history*, Mark Mancuso; *Servs*, Kelly Poole; *Youth*, Kelly Poole; Staff 116 (MLS 20, Non-MLS 96)
Founded 1948. Pop 195,600; Circ 1,187,522
Jul 1999-Jun 2000 Income (Main Library and Branch Library) $3,797,497, State $319,655, Federal $17,159, County $3,187,866, Locally Generated Income $148,811, Other $124,006. Mats Exp $835,069, Books $618,868, Per/Ser (Incl. Access Fees) $73,444, Presv $165, Micro $13,839, AV Equip $53,244, Electronic Ref Mat (Incl. Access Fees) $75,509. Sal $1,977,017
Library Holdings: Bk Vols 415,224; Per Subs 1,650
Subject Interests: SC genealogy, SC hist
Automation Activity & Vendor Info: (Cataloging) Gaylord; (Circulation) Gaylord; (Serials) Gaylord
Special Services for the Deaf - High interest/low vocabulary books; Special interest periodicals
Friends of the Library Group
Branches: 8
BATESBURG BRANCH, 203 Armory St, Batesburg, 29006. (Mail add: PO Box 2187, Leesville, 29070-0187), SAN 359-9760. Tel: 803-532-9223.

FAX: 803-359-0185. Web Site: www.lex.lib.sc.us. *Librn*, Kitty Warner; E-Mail: kwarner@lex.lib.sc.us; Staff 7 (MLS 1, Non-MLS 6)
Friends of the Library Group

CAYCE-WEST COLUMBIA BRANCH, 1500 Augusta Rd W, Columbia, 29169. SAN 359-9795. Tel: 803-794-6791. FAX: 803-926-5383. Web Site: www.lex.lib.sc.us. *Ref*, Jim Cheatham; E-Mail: jcheatham@lex.lib.sc.us; *Senior Librn*, Pamela Davenport; E-Mail: pdavenport@lex.lib.sc.us; *YA Servs*, Jenny Main; E-Mail: jmain@lex.lib.sc.us; Staff 19 (MLS 3, Non-MLS 16)
Friends of the Library Group

CHAPIN BRANCH, 129 NW Columbia Ave, Chapin, 29036-9423. (Mail add: PO Box 700, Chapin, 29036-0700), SAN 359-9701. Tel: 803-345-5479. Web Site: www.lex.lib.sc.us. *Librn*, Patricia Mauldin; E-Mail: pmauldin@lex.lib.sc.us; Staff 7 (MLS 1, Non-MLS 6)
Friends of the Library Group

GASTON BRANCH, 214 S Main St, Gaston, 29053. (Mail add: PO Box 479, Gaston, 29053), SAN 359-9728. Tel: 803-791-3208. Web Site: www.lex.lib.sc.us. *Branch Mgr*, Amy Shull; E-Mail: ashull@lex.lib.sc.us; Staff 3 (Non-MLS 3)
Friends of the Library Group

GILBERT BRANCH, 110 Broad St, Gilbert, 29054. (Mail add: PO Box 341, Gilbert, 29054-0341), SAN 329-5753. Tel: 803-892-5387. Web Site: www.lex.lib.sc.us. *Branch Mgr*, Leslie Meeks; E-Mail: lmeeks@lex.lib.sc.us; Staff 3 (Non-MLS 3)
Friends of the Library Group

IRMO BRANCH, 6251 St Andrews Rd, Columbia, 29212-3123. SAN 359-9736. Tel: 803-798-7880. FAX: 803-798-8570. Web Site: www.lex.lib.sc.us. *Senior Librn*, Charles E Band; E-Mail: cband@lex.lib.sc.us; *YA Servs*, Becky James; E-Mail: bjames@lex.lib.sc.us; *Ref*, Mary Gwyn; E-Mail: mgwyn@lex.lib.sc.us; Staff 23 (MLS 4, Non-MLS 19)
Friends of the Library Group

PELION BRANCH, 206 Pine St, Pelion, 29123. (Mail add: PO Box 309, Pelion, 29123-0309), SAN 359-9779. Tel: 803-894-3272. FAX: 803-894-3272. Web Site: www.lex.lib.sc.us. *Branch Mgr*, Shirley Sprenne; E-Mail: ssprenne@lex.lib.sc.us; Staff 5 (Non-MLS 5)
Founded 1986
Friends of the Library Group

SWANSEA BRANCH, 240 S Moumouth Ave, Swansea, 29160. (Mail add: PO Box 130, Swansea, 29160-0130), SAN 359-9809. Tel: 803-568-3519. Web Site: www.lex.lib.sc.us. *Branch Mgr*, Edna Terry; E-Mail: eterry@lex.lib.sc.us; Staff 3 (Non-MLS 3)
Friends of the Library Group

Bookmobiles: 1

ANNING

HARVIN CLARENDON COUNTY LIBRARY, 215 N Brooks St, 29102. SAN 373-7535. Tel: 803-435-8633. FAX: 803-435-8101. E-Mail: harcclb@ftc-i.net. Web Site: www.hccl.lib.sc.us. *Dir*, Marilyn Tsirigotis; E-Mail: marilynt@infoave.net; *Circ*, Emma Hilton; *Admin Assoc*, Carrie James; *Cat*, Patricia Ragin; *Ch Servs*, Dianne Curtain; *Ad Servs*, Bertha Wilson; Staff 6 (MLS 2, Non-MLS 4)
Founded 1977. Pop 30,198; Circ 48,000
Jul 2000-Jun 2001 Income $317,933, State $54,303, County $238,630, Locally Generated Income $25,000. Mats Exp $52,600, Books $44,000, Per/Ser (Incl. Access Fees) $4,500, Presv $600, AV Equip $500, Electronic Ref Mat (Incl. Access Fees) $3,000. Sal $147,675 (Prof $57,707)
Library Holdings: Bk Vols 35,000; Bk Titles 31,000; Per Subs 85
Special Collections: South Carolina
Automation Activity & Vendor Info: (Cataloging) Gaylord; (Circulation) Gaylord; (OPAC) Gaylord
Database Vendor: Ebsco - EbscoHost, IAC - Info Trac
Publications: Long-Range Plan
Special Services for the Deaf - Books on deafness & sign language
Friends of the Library Group

ARION

MARION COUNTY LIBRARY, 101 E Court St, 29571-3699. SAN 360-3067. Tel: 843-423-8300. FAX: 843-423-8302. E-Mail: marionlibr@infoave.net. Web Site: www.marioncountylibrary.org. *Dir*, Salley B Davidson; *Ref*, Melissa D Bowen; *Ad Servs*, Pat Koch; Staff 3 (MLS 3)
Founded 1898. Pop 33,899; Circ 86,546
Jul 1999-Jun 2000 Income (Main Library and Branch Library) $555,008, State $63,234, City $2,000, County $474,554, Locally Generated Income $15,220. Mats Exp $61,517, Books $47,197, Per/Ser (Incl. Access Fees) $7,580, Presv $517, Micro $153, AV Equip $4,220, Electronic Ref Mat (Incl. Access Fees) $1,850. Sal $202,930 (Prof $88,364)
Library Holdings: Bk Titles 71,160; Per Subs 181
Subject Interests: History
Special Collections: South Carolina, bks & micro
Automation Activity & Vendor Info: (Cataloging) Gaylord; (Circulation) Gaylord; (OPAC) Gaylord
Publications: History of Marion County
Branches: 2

MULLINS BRANCH, 210 N Main St, Mullins, 29574. SAN 360-3091. Tel: 843-464-9621. FAX: 843-464-5215. Web Site: www.marioncountylibrary.org. *Mgr*, Jayne Caesar

NICHOLS BRANCH, Floyd St, Nichols, 29581. SAN 360-3121. Tel: 843-526-2641. FAX: 843-526-2641. Web Site: www.marioncountylibrary.org. *Mgr*, Dorothy Mercier

Bookmobiles: 1

MC CORMICK

P MC CORMICK COUNTY LIBRARY, 212 Pine St, PO Box 1806, 29835-1806. SAN 315-5633. Tel: 864-465-2821. FAX: 864-465-2821. *Librn*, Dianne S Purdy; *Asst Librn*, Bruce Fisher
Founded 1953. Pop 8,868; Circ 15,074
Jul 1999-Jun 2000 Income $183,613, State $40,000, Federal $82,212, County $52,340, Locally Generated Income $3,193, Other $5,868. Mats Exp $29,844, Books $28,151, Per/Ser (Incl. Access Fees) $1,693. Sal $43,088
Library Holdings: Bk Vols 21,873; Per Subs 72
Subject Interests: Behav sci, History, Soc sci
Friends of the Library Group

MONCKS CORNER

P BERKELEY COUNTY LIBRARY,* 100 Library St, 29461. SAN 360-3156. Tel: 843-719-4223. FAX: 843-719-4226. Web Site: www.berkeley.lib.sc.us. *Dir*, Colleen L Kelley; *Dep Dir*, Judy Schmitt; *Ch Servs*, Sharon M Fashion; *Librn*, Dianne C Boersma; *Syst Coordr*, Gene Brunson; *YA Servs*, Jan Kowal; Staff 11 (MLS 11)
Founded 1936. Pop 128,776
Jul 1997-Jun 1998 Income $1,279,964, State $180,287, Federal $12,878, County $1,069,299, Locally Generated Income $17,500. Mats Exp $188,164, Books $157,873, Per/Ser (Incl. Access Fees) $10,791, Micro $5,000. Sal $632,745 (Prof $273,930)
Library Holdings: Bk Vols 110,300; Per Subs 240
Subject Interests: Berkeley County hist, Genealogy, SC hist
Friends of the Library Group
Branches: 4

GOOSE CREEK BRANCH, 325 Old Moncks Corner Rd, Goose Creek, 29445. SAN 360-3180. Tel: 843-572-1376. FAX: 843-572-1376. Web Site: www.berkeley.lib.sc.us. *Librn*, Dianne C Boersma
Friends of the Library Group

HANAHAN BRANCH, 1274 Yeamans Hall Rd, Hanahan, 29406-2627. SAN 360-3210. Tel: 843-747-5400. FAX: 843-747-5400. Web Site: www.berkeley.lib.sc.us. *In Charge*, Ramona Grimsley
Friends of the Library Group

JAMESTOWN BRANCH, PO Box 193, Jamestown, 29453. SAN 370-808X. Tel: 843-719-4231. FAX: 843-719-4231. Web Site: www.berkeley.lib.sc.us.
Friends of the Library Group

SAINT STEPHEN BRANCH, PO Box 596, Saint Stephen, 29479-0596. SAN 360-3245. Tel: 843-567-4862. FAX: 843-567-4862. Web Site: www.berkeley.lib.sc.us.
Friends of the Library Group

Bookmobiles: 1

MURRELLS INLET

S BROOKGREEN GARDENS LIBRARY,* 1931 Brookgreen Dr. (Mail add: PO Box 3368, 29585), SAN 320-5118. Tel: 843-235-6000, 843-235-6003, 843-237-4218. FAX: 843-237-1014. *Dir*, Larry Henry; *Curator*, Robin Salmon
Founded 1931
Library Holdings: Bk Vols 3,000; Bk Titles 2,800; Per Subs 75
Subject Interests: 19th Century Am sculpture, 20th Century Am sculpture, Fauna of the SE US, Flora of the SE US, Hist of SC, Horticulture, Landscape architecture
Special Collections: Brookgreen Gardens, newspapers, photogs; History (Hasell-Flagg Manuscripts), plantation rec, med accounts, personal correspondence; Sculpture archives, correspondence & clipping files on American sculptors, exhibit catalogues, photogs, taped & transcribed interviews
Restriction: Staff use only

MYRTLE BEACH

P CHAPIN MEMORIAL LIBRARY,* 400 14th Ave N, 29577-3612. SAN 329-787X. Tel: 843-918-1275. FAX: 843-918-1288. E-Mail: chapinli@sccoast.net. *Dir*, Catherine Wiggins; *Librn*, Lesta Sue Hardee; *Ch Servs*, Sue Ellen Wilson; *Ref*, Laura Floyd; Staff 3 (MLS 3)
Founded 1949. Pop 60,000; Circ 206,942
Library Holdings: Bk Vols 89,000; Per Subs 138
Friends of the Library Group

J HORRY-GEORGETOWN TECHNICAL COLLEGE, Grand Strand Campus Library,* 743 Hemlock St, 29577. SAN 372-5049. Tel: 843-477-2012. FAX: 843-477-8065. *Dir*, Peggy Smith; *Acq*, John W Sharpe; Tel: 843-349-5396,

Fax: 843-347-0552, E-Mail: sharpe@hor.tec.sc.us; *Chief Librn*, Larry Sgro; E-Mail: sgro@hor.tec.sc.us; Staff 2 (MLS 1, Non-MLS 1)
Founded 1990. Enrl 500; Highest Degree: Associate
Library Holdings: Bk Vols 11,000; Bk Titles 10,000; Per Subs 75
Subject Interests: Criminal justice, Early childhood develop, Hospitality management, Paralegal
Database Vendor: Ebsco - EbscoHost, GaleNet, IAC - SearchBank, Lexis-Nexis, OCLC - First Search, ProQuest, Wilson - Wilson Web
Partic in OCLC Online Computer Library Center, Inc; Solinet

L NELSON, MULLINS, RILEY & SCARBOROUGH, Law Library,* 2411 N Oak St, PO Box 3939, 29577-3939. SAN 323-6587. Tel: 843-448-3500. FAX: 843-448-3437. *Librn*, Claire Engel
Library Holdings: Bk Vols 10,000
Other locations in Columbia & Greenville

NEWBERRY

C NEWBERRY COLLEGE, Wessels Library, 2100 College St, 29108-2197. SAN 315-565X. Tel: 803-321-5229. FAX: 803-321-5232. Web Site: www.newberry.edu/wessels/. *Dir Libr Serv*, Lawrence E Ellis; E-Mail: lellis@newberry.edu; *Publ Servs*, Victoria Horst; E-Mail: vhorst@newberry.edu; *Tech Servs*, Cleta Dunaway; E-Mail: cdunaway@newberry.edu; Staff 6 (MLS 3, Non-MLS 3)
Founded 1858. Enrl 750; Fac 68; Highest Degree: Bachelor
Jul 1999-Jun 2000 Income $263,172. Mats Exp $106,456, Books $46,820, Per/Ser (Incl. Access Fees) $40,910, Micro $10,872, AV Equip $2,501, Electronic Ref Mat (Incl. Access Fees) $5,353. Sal $120,060
Library Holdings: Bk Vols 91,697; Bk Titles 61,857; Per Subs 398
Special Collections: Newberry College Materials; Regional Lutheran Materials; South Caroliniana
Automation Activity & Vendor Info: (Cataloging) SIRSI; (Circulation) SIRSI
Publications: (Research guide)
Partic in OCLC Online Computer Library Center, Inc; SC Found of Independent Cols Consortia; Solinet

P NEWBERRY COUNTY LIBRARY, 1300 Friend St, 29108-3400. SAN 360-330X. Tel: 803-276-0854. FAX: 803-276-7478. E-Mail: nbylib@infoave.net. *Dir*, Tucker Neel Taylor; *Asst Dir*, Elaine L Franz
Pop 33,172
2000-2001 Income $297,138, State $61,878, County $235,260. Mats Exp $36,826, Books $31,076, Per/Ser (Incl. Access Fees) $5,500, Presv $250. Sal $199,725 (Prof $67,843)
Library Holdings: Bk Vols 60,976; Per Subs 103
Friends of the Library Group
Branches: 1
WHITMIRE MEMORIAL, 1510 Church St, Whitmire, 29178. SAN 360-3369. Tel: 803-694-3961. *Mgr*, Linda Bullard
Friends of the Library Group

ORANGEBURG

C CLAFLIN COLLEGE, H V Manning Library, 400 Magnolia St, 29115. SAN 315-5676. Tel: 803-535-5307, 803-535-5309. FAX: 803-535-5091. *Dir*, Marilyn Y Gibbs-Pringle; E-Mail: mpringle@claf1.claflin.edu; *Media Spec*, Edith Frederick; Staff 9 (MLS 3, Non-MLS 6)
Enrl 633; Fac 51; Highest Degree: Bachelor
Library Holdings: Bk Vols 147,000; Per Subs 325
Subject Interests: History, Music, Relig studies
Special Collections: Black Life & History, bks, microfilm

P ORANGEBURG COUNTY LIBRARY,* 510 Louis St, PO Box 1367, 29116-1367. SAN 315-5692. Tel: 803-531-4636. FAX: 803-533-5860. *Dir*, Paula F Paul; *Ad Servs*, Capers Bull Jr; *Ch Servs*, Lorene Dennis; *Circ, Tech Servs*, Debra C Allen; Staff 7 (MLS 7)
Founded 1937. Pop 84,803; Circ 286,034
Library Holdings: Bk Vols 99,548; Per Subs 310
Subject Interests: Local history
Friends of the Library Group

J ORANGEBURG-CALHOUN TECHNICAL COLLEGE, Gressette Learning Resources Center,* 3250 Saint Matthews Rd NE, 29118. SAN 315-5684. Tel: 803-535-1262. FAX: 803-535-1388. *Dean of Libr*, Larry S Freeman; *Tech Servs*, Patti Sonefeld; *Reader Servs*, Rhonda Anderson; *Media Spec*, Robert Thomas
Founded 1968
1997-1998 Income $328,261. Mats Exp $59,500, Books $30,000, Per/Ser (Incl. Access Fees) $12,000, Presv $5,000, Micro $12,500. Sal $216,207 (Prof $102,060)
Library Holdings: Bk Vols 30,050; Per Subs 417

M REGIONAL MEDICAL CENTER OF ORANGEBURG & CALHOUN COUNTIES, Medical Library,* 3000 St Matthews Rd, 29118. SAN 371-618X. Tel: 803-533-2293. FAX: 803-533-2557. *Librn*, Barbara L Sifly; *Asst Librn*, Sue Davis; Staff 2 (Non-MLS 2)
Library Holdings: Bk Titles 218

C SOUTH CAROLINA STATE UNIVERSITY, Miller F Whittaker Library, 300 College St NE, PO Box 7491, 29117. SAN 315-5714. Tel: 803-536-7045, 803-536-7046. Interlibrary Loan Service Tel: 803-536-8637. Circulation Tel: 803-536-8645. Reference Tel: 803-536-8640. FAX: 803-5 8902. E-Mail: smallsml@alpha1.scsu.edu. Web Site: library.scsu.edu. *Asst Prof*, Mary L Smalls; Tel: 803-536-8638, E-Mail: smallsm1@alpha1.scsu.edu; *Asst Prof*, Andrew Penson; Tel: 803-536-8636, E-Mail: lbapenson@scsu.edu; *Asst Prof*, Minnie Johnson; Tel: 803-536-8642, E-M lb_mjohnson@scsu.edu; Staff 25 (MLS 8, Non-MLS 17)
Founded 1913. Enrl 4,591; Fac 238; Highest Degree: Doctorate
Jul 1999-Jun 2000 Income $1,361,422, State $970,895, Federal $107,527, Other $283,000. Mats Exp $592,752, Books $140,543, Per/Ser (Incl. Acce Fees) $208,000, Presv $509, Micro $107,700, Manuscripts & Archives $5,000, Electronic Ref Mat (Incl. Access Fees) $131,000. Sal $750,886 (F $372,450)
Library Holdings: Bk Vols 288,671; Per Subs 1,267
Subject Interests: Bus, Education, Engineering, Humanities, Soc sci
Special Collections: Black Coll-Books by & about Blacks; South Carolin State Data Center; South Carolina State University Historical Coll, bks, papers, pictures & memorabilia
Automation Activity & Vendor Info: (Cataloging) DRA; (Circulation) DRA; (Course Reserve) DRA; (OPAC) DRA
Publications: Access to Information; Alumni & Retirees of South Carolin State University; Americans with Disabilities; Building Library Skills; Collection Development Policy; Community Awareness; Computerized Information Retrieval Services; How to Locate Books; Interlibrary Loan Services; Library Databases on the World Wide Web; Library Faculty & Staff Handbook; Library Faculty Staff Handbook; Library News & Notes per semester newsletter); Library Research Skills; Library-Faculty Liaison Program; Miller F Whittaker Library - Computer & Information Services; Resources in Educational Administration; Services in the Miller F Whittak Library; South Carolina State University Historical Collection, brochure; South Carolina State University Historical Trail; Student Library Handboo The Bulldog Searcher; The Pathfinder
Partic in Dialog Corporation; Discus; OCLC Online Computer Library Center, Inc; SE Libr Network
Special Services for the Blind - Braille; Magnifying glasses/lamps

JR SOUTHERN METHODIST COLLEGE, Lynn Corbett Library, PO Box 1027, 29116-1027. SAN 315-5722. Tel: 803-534-7826. FAX: 803-534-782 E-Mail: smc@smcollege.edu. *Dir*, John Hucks
Library Holdings: Bk Vols 17,000; Per Subs 125
Special Collections: Southern Methodist, journals, publ

PARRIS ISLAND

UNITED STATES MARINE CORPS
A RECRUIT DEPOT STATION LIBRARY, PO Box 5070, 29905. SAN 36 3393. Tel: 843-525-3302, Ext 7327. FAX: 843-525-2872. *Librn*, Martha Moussatos; *Tech Servs*, Deloris Carver
Founded 1940
Sep 1997-Oct 1998 Income $37,483
Library Holdings: Bk Vols 34,000; Per Subs 93
Subject Interests: Biographies, Large print, Prof mil novels, SC
Publications: Monthly book list; weekly new books in the library

PENDLETON

S PENDLETON DISTRICT HISTORICAL, RECREATIONAL & TOURISM COMMISSION, Reference Library, 125 E Queen St, 29670. (Mail add: PO Box 565, 29670), SAN 327-0874. Tel: 864-646-3782. Toll Free Tel: 800-862-1795. FAX: 864-646-2506. E-Mail: pendtour@innova.net. *Dir*, Hurley Badders; *Librn*, Donna Roper
Founded 1966
Library Holdings: Bk Vols 1,200; Per Subs 30
Subject Interests: Genealogy
Special Collections: Black Heritage, tapes; Historic Photos of South Carolina; Records of Anderson Cotton Mill (SC, 1895-1963); Speaking of History, tapes
Publications: Friends of the Pendleton District (newsletter)
Restriction: Non-circulating to the public
Function: Photocopies available
Open Mon-Fri 9-4:30, closed holidays
Friends of the Library Group

J TRI-COUNTY TECHNICAL COLLEGE, Learning Resource Center,* PO Box 587, 29670. SAN 315-5730. Tel: 864-646-8361, Ext 2254. FAX: 864-646-8256. *Librn*, Sarah Shumpert; *AV*, Rick Bismack; Staff 7 (MLS 3, Non-MLS 4)
Founded 1963. Enrl 2,596; Fac 172
Library Holdings: Bk Vols 35,287; Per Subs 276
Subject Interests: Ethnic studies, History, Literary criticism, Sci-tech
Publications: Quarterly Report
Partic in Dialog Corporation; SE Libr Network

ROCK HILL

CLINTON JUNIOR COLLEGE LIBRARY,* 1029 Crawford Rd, 29730. SAN 315-5765. Tel: 803-327-7402, Ext 28. FAX: 803-327-3261. *Librn*, Cynthia P Roddey
Library Holdings: Bk Vols 1,300; Per Subs 33
The Clinton College Library has limited resources. It has established interlibrary loan agreement with Winthrop University, Rock Hill SC
Friends of the Library Group

MUSEUM OF YORK COUNTY, Staff Research Library,* 4621 Mount Gallant Rd, 29732-9905. SAN 326-3665. Tel: 803-329-2121. FAX: 803-329-5249. E-Mail: myco@infoave.net. *Curator*, Janis Wilkens; *Curator*, Anne Lane; Staff 1 (Non-MLS 1)
Library Holdings: Bk Titles 2,000; Per Subs 102
Subject Interests: African anthrop, African art, Arts, Crafts, Native Am of the SE, Natural science, Physical sci
Special Collections: Shikar-Safari Club Library Coll, exploration, travel & adventure bks
Publications: "Volunteer Information" (pamphlet); monthly listing of new acquisitions
Restriction: Staff use only

PIEDMONT MEDICAL CENTER LIBRARY, 222 S Herlong Ave, PO Box 11626, 29732. SAN 320-2348. Tel: 803-329-1234. FAX: 803-329-6864. *Librn*, Joyce Elder; E-Mail: joyce.elder@tenethealth.com
Library Holdings: Bk Titles 578; Per Subs 67
Subject Interests: Medicine, Nursing

ROBINSON, BRADSHAW & HINSON, Guardian Building Law Library,* One Law Pl, Ste 600, PO Drawer 12070, 29731. SAN 329-2169. Tel: 803-325-2900. FAX: 803-325-2929. *Librn*, Glenda Farrell; E-Mail: gfarrell@rbn.comm
Founded 1985
Library Holdings: Bk Vols 5,000; Bk Titles 600; Per Subs 60
Publications: Guardian Building Law Library Brief

WINTHROP UNIVERSITY, Ida Jane Dacus Library, 810 Oakland Ave, 29733. SAN 315-5781. Tel: 803-323-2131, 803-323-2530 (Acquisition), 803-323-2531 (Serial). Circulation Tel: 803-323-4502. Reference Tel: 803-323-4501. Interlibrary Loan Service FAX: 803-323-3285. Web Site: www.winthrop.edu/dacus/. *Dean of Libr*, Mark Y Herring; E-Mail: herringm@winthrop.edu; *Asst Dean*, Larry Mitlin; Tel: 803-323-2280, E-Mail: miltinl@winthrop.edu; *Head Ref*, Bob Gorman; Tel: 803-323-2259, E-Mail: gormanb@winthrop.edu; *Publ Servs*, Susan Silverman; E-Mail: silvermans@winthrop.edu; *Tech Servs*, Gloria Kelly; E-Mail: kellyg@winthrop.edu; *Archivist, Spec Coll*, Ronald J Chepesiuk; E-Mail: chepesiukr@winthrop.edu; *Doc*, Lois Walker; E-Mail: walkerl@winthrop.edu; *ILL*, D Weeks; Tel: 803-323-2322, E-Mail: weeksd@winthrop.edu; *Bibliog Instr*, Claire Clemens; Tel: 803-323-2195, E-Mail: clemensc@winthrop.edu; *Cat*, Mary Rose Adkins; Tel: 803-323-2234, E-Mail: adkinsm@winthrop.edu; *Cat*, Patricia Ballard; E-Mail: ballardp@winthrop.edu; *Web Coordr*, Jean Wells; Tel: 803-323-2330, E-Mail: wellsj@winthrop.edu; *Coll Develop*, Gloria Kelley; E-Mail: kelleyg@winthrop.edu; *Coll Develop, Ser*, Gale Teaster-Woods; E-Mail: teasterg@winthrop.edu; *Acq of Monographs*, Antje Mays; Tel: 803-323-2274, E-Mail: maysa@winthrop.edu; Staff 32 (MLS 14, Non-MLS 18)
Founded 1895. Enrl 4,417; Fac 296
Jul 1997-Jun 1998 Income $1,986,253, State $1,946,253, Federal $40,000. Mats Exp $611,315, Books $137,400, Per/Ser (Incl. Access Fees) $334,730, Presv $14,868. Sal $997,363 (Prof $573,937)
Library Holdings: Bk Vols 361,168; Per Subs 2,706
Special Collections: Catawba Indians, mss; Education (Education Resources Information Center Reports), microfiche; English Literature (Library of English Literature), ultrafiche; History (Draper Manuscript Coll), microfilm; History (Library of American Civilization), ultrafiche; Local South Carolina History, mss; Political Science (League of Nations Documents & Serial Publications, 1919-1946), microfilm; Political Science (United Nations Publications, 1946-1980), microprint; Winthrop College History, mss & archives; Women's History, mss
Database Vendor: Innovative Interfaces INN - View
Publications: A Guide to the Manuscript & Oral History Collections; A Guide to the Records Documenting the History of Winthrop College; Dacus Focus; Dacus Library Guide; Sources of Genealogical Research in the Winthrop College Archives & Special Collections; The Dean's Corner
Partic in OCLC Online Computer Library Center, Inc; SE Libr Network
Friends of the Library Group

YORK COUNTY LIBRARY, Rock Hill Public, 138 E Black St, 29731. (Mail add: PO Box 10032, 29731), SAN 360-3423. Tel: 803-324-3055, 803-324-7614. Reference Tel: 803-324-7613. FAX: 803-328-9290. Web Site: www.yclibrary.org. *Dir*, David A Lyon, IV; Tel: 803-324-7614, E-Mail: david@lyon.york.lib.sc.us; *Br Coordr, Tech Servs*, Shasta Brewer; E-Mail: shastab@lyon.york.lib.sc.us; *YA Servs*, Sarah Delaney; Tel: 803-324-7613, Fax: 803-328-9290, E-Mail: sedelaney@yahoo.com; *Coll Develop, Reader Servs*, Elizabeth Ellis; Tel: 803-324-7613, E-Mail: eellis@lyon.york.lib.sc.us; *Bkmobile Coordr, Ch Servs*, Diane Williams; Tel: 803-324-7624, E-Mail: dianew@lyon.york.lib.sc.us; *Commun Relations*, Phyllis Davis; Tel: 803-324-7615, E-Mail: phyllisd@lyon.york.lib.sc.us; *Ad Servs*, Janet Jerauld; E-Mail: janj@lyon.york.lib.sc.us; *Automation Syst Coordr*, Jessie McLaurin; Tel: 803-324-1749, E-Mail: jessie@lyon.york.lib.sc.us; *AV, Circ*, Judy Coe; E-Mail: judyc@lyon.york.lib.sc.us; *ILL*, Page Hendrix; Tel: 803-324-7613, E-Mail: pageh@lyon.york.lib.sc.us; Staff 49 (MLS 12, Non-MLS 37)
Founded 1884. Pop 131,497; Circ 799,017
Jul 2000-Jun 2001 Income (Main Library and Branch Library) $2,748,192, State $245,289, Federal $17,000, County $2,337,524, Locally Generated Income $148,379. Mats Exp $443,189, Books $315,254, Per/Ser (Incl. Access Fees) $24,636, Presv $3,844, Micro $45,609, Electronic Ref Mat (Incl. Access Fees) $53,846. Sal $1,669,079
Library Holdings: Bk Vols 244,600; Per Subs 647
Special Collections: Catawba Indian, bks, clippings & micro; Genealogical & Caroliniana (Local, State & General), bks, clippings & micro; Rock Hill & York County History, bks, clippings & micro
Automation Activity & Vendor Info: (Cataloging) epixtech, inc.; (Circulation) epixtech, inc.; (OPAC) epixtech, inc.
Database Vendor: epixtech, inc., GaleNet, IAC - Info Trac, Innovative Interfaces INN - View
Friends of the Library Group
Branches: 4
CLOVER PUBLIC, 107 Knox St, Clover, 29710. SAN 360-3458. Tel: 803-222-3474. FAX: 803-222-6695. Web Site: www.yclibrary.org. *Librn*, Mildred Elliott
FORT MILL PUBLIC, 1818 Second Baxter Crossing, Fort Mill, 29708. SAN 360-3482. Tel: 803-547-4114. FAX: 803-547-4852. Web Site: www.yclibrary.org. *Dir*, David A Lyon, IV; Tel: 803-324-7614, Fax: 803-328-9290, E-Mail: david@lyon.york.lib.sc.us; *Librn*, Mary Windell
LAKE WYLIE PUBLIC, 185 Blucher Circle, Lake Wylie, 29710. SAN 323-5548. Tel: 803-831-7774. FAX: 803-831-7943. Web Site: www.yclibrary.org. *Librn*, Nancy Monts-Rayfield
YORK PUBLIC, 120 N Congress St, York, 29745. SAN 360-3512. Tel: 803-684-3751. FAX: 803-684-6223. Web Site: www.yclibrary.org. *Librn*, Susan Dressler
Bookmobiles: 1

J YORK TECHNICAL COLLEGE LIBRARY, 452 S Anderson Rd, 29730. SAN 315-579X. Tel: 803-327-8025. FAX: 803-327-4535. Web Site: www.yorktech.com. *Librn*, Dr Elizabeth Clark-Clayton; Tel: 803-325-2883, E-Mail: eclarkclayton@york.tec.sc.us; Staff 6 (MLS 2, Non-MLS 4)
Founded 1964. Highest Degree: Associate
2000-2001 Income $350,000. Mats Exp $56,900, Books $32,200, Per/Ser (Incl. Access Fees) $15,700, Micro $9,000
Library Holdings: Bk Vols 24,211; Per Subs 475
Subject Interests: Allied health, Bus, Engineering, Industry, Liberal arts
Automation Activity & Vendor Info: (Acquisitions) DRA; (Cataloging) DRA

SAINT GEORGE

P DORCHESTER COUNTY LIBRARY, 506 N Parler Ave, 29477-2297. SAN 360-3547. Tel: 843-563-9189. FAX: 843-563-7823. Web Site: www.dcl.lib.sc.us. *Dir*, Angus M Prim; E-Mail: mprim@dcl.lib.sc.us; *Branch Mgr*, Patricia Hammond; Tel: 843-871-5075, Fax: 843-851-4811, E-Mail: phammond@dclib.sc.us; *Info Tech*, Terry G Crupe; E-Mail: tcrupe@dcl.lib.sc.us; *Mgr*, Lisa L Kling; E-Mail: lkling@dcl.lib.sx.us; *Ad Servs*, Mary Beth Reuter; E-Mail: mbreuter@dcl.lib.sc.us; *Ch Servs*, Debra B Lodge; E-Mail: dlodge@dcl.lib.sc.us; Staff 37 (MLS 6, Non-MLS 31)
Founded 1953. Pop 88,133; Circ 383,255
Jul 2000-Jun 2001 Income (Main Library and Branch Library) $1,333,843, State $154,937, Federal $767, County $1,054,907, Locally Generated Income $78,016, Other $45,216. Mats Exp $314,276, Books $250,463, Per/Ser (Incl. Access Fees) $8,785, Presv $950, Micro $2,632, AV Equip $47,587, Electronic Ref Mat (Incl. Access Fees) $3,859
Library Holdings: Bk Vols 103,928; Per Subs 233
Subject Interests: SC hist
Automation Activity & Vendor Info: (Cataloging) Gaylord; (Circulation) Gaylord; (OPAC) Gaylord
Database Vendor: GaleNet, IAC - Info Trac
Friends of the Library Group
Branches: 1
SUMMERVILLE BRANCH, 76 Old Trolley Rd, Summerville, 29485. SAN 360-3571. Tel: 803-871-5075. FAX: 803-875-4811. *Librn*, Patricia R Hammond
Circ 190,133
Friends of the Library Group
Bookmobiles: 1

SAINT MATTHEWS

P CALHOUN COUNTY LIBRARY,* 208 N Harry C Raysor Dr, 29135-1261. SAN 315-5803. Tel: 803-874-3389. FAX: 803-874-4154. *Coll Develop, Dir*, Winnie G Westbury

Pop 12,995; Circ 31,407
Library Holdings: Bk Vols 32,000; Per Subs 139
Special Collections: Julia Peterkin Coll
Partic in SE Libr Network

S CALHOUN COUNTY MUSEUM & CULTURAL CENTER, Archives & Library,* 303 Butler St, 29135. SAN 329-8507. Tel: 803-874-3964. FAX: 803-874-4790. E-Mail: calmus@oburg.net. *Dir*, Debbie Roland
Library Holdings: Bk Vols 950; Per Subs 12
Open Mon-Fri 9-4 by appointment only
Friends of the Library Group

SALUDA

P SALUDA COUNTY LIBRARY,* 101 S Main St, 29138. SAN 360-3334. Tel: 864-445-2267. FAX: 864-445-2725. *Dir*, Jill Rourke
Library Holdings: Bk Titles 14,623; Per Subs 47
Subject Interests: Folklore
Friends of the Library Group

SHAW AFB

UNITED STATES AIR FORCE

A SHAW AIR FORCE BASE LIBRARY, FL 4803, 451 Johnson St, 29152. SAN 360-3601. Tel: 803-668-3004, 803-895-9818. FAX: 803-668-4322. *Librn*, Mac Odom; Staff 6 (MLS 2, Non-MLS 4)
Library Holdings: Bk Vols 37,000; Per Subs 3,800
Subject Interests: Bus, Govt res, Mil
Special Collections: Transition Assistant Program-Military
Automation Activity & Vendor Info: (Circulation) SIRSI
Database Vendor: Dialog, Ebsco - EbscoHost, Lexis-Nexis, OCLC - First Search, Wilson - Wilson Web
Restriction: Open to department staff only

SPARTANBURG

C CONVERSE COLLEGE, Mickel Library, 580 E Main St, 29302-0006. SAN 315-5811. Tel: 864-596-9020, 864-596-9072. Interlibrary Loan Service Tel: 864-596-9074. FAX: 864-596-9075. *Dir*, Wade Woodward; *Tech Servs*, Darlene Fawver; *ILL, Per*, Becky Dalton; *Publ Servs*, Mark Collier; *Circ*, Becky Poole. Subject Specialists: *Music*, Darlene Fawver
Founded 1890. Highest Degree: Master
Library Holdings: Bk Vols 131,784; Per Subs 716
Subject Interests: Education, Music
Special Collections: School Prize Texts (A B Taylor)
Partic in SE Libr Network

S MILLIKEN & CO, Library M-470,* 920 Milliken Rd, 29304. SAN 315-5838. Tel: 864-503-1589. Interlibrary Loan Service Tel: 864-503-1588. FAX: 864-503-2769. *Librn*, Ginny Sykes
Founded 1960
Library Holdings: Bk Titles 10,000; Per Subs 300
Subject Interests: Bus, Chemistry, Textiles
Restriction: Restricted public use
Partic in Dialog Corporation

C SHERMAN COLLEGE OF STRAIGHT CHIROPRACTIC, Tom & Mae Bahan Library, 2020 Springifeld Rd, 29316-7251. (Mail add: PO Box 1452, 29304-1452), SAN 321-4842. Tel: 864-578-8770, Ext 1253. FAX: 864-599-4860. E-Mail: library@sherman.edu. *Librn*, Stephen M Whitaker; Staff 1 (MLS 1)
Founded 1973. Enrl 330; Fac 45; Highest Degree: Doctorate
Jan 2000-Dec 2000 Mats Exp $89,300, Books $23,500, Per/Ser (Incl. Access Fees) $16,800, AV Equip $49,000. Sal $48,750 (Prof $32,000)
Library Holdings: Bk Titles 9,800; Per Subs 154
Subject Interests: Biological, Chiropractic, Clinical sci
Special Collections: Chiropractic (B J Palmer Green Coll)
Automation Activity & Vendor Info: (Cataloging) Sagebrush Corporation; (Circulation) Sagebrush Corporation
Database Vendor: OCLC - First Search
Partic in Chiropractic Libr Consortium; Medline; Nat Libr of Med; OCLC Online Computer Library Center, Inc; Southeastern Regional Med Libr Program

S SOUTH CAROLINA SCHOOL FOR THE DEAF & BLIND, 355 Cedar Springs Rd, 29302-4699. SAN 315-5846. Tel: 864-585-7711. TDD: 864-577-7646. FAX: 864-577-7649. *Dir*, John D Todd; Tel: 864-577-7640, E-Mail: jtodd@scsdb.k12.sc.us; *Librn*, Galena Gaw; Tel: 864-577-7642, E-Mail: ggaw@scsdb.k12.sc.us; *Librn*, Wanda Shipman; Tel: 864-577-7651, E-Mail: wshipman@scsdb.k12.sc.us; *Librn*, Debra Wright; E-Mail: dwright@scsdb.k12sc.us. Subject Specialists: *Blindness*, Wanda Shipman; *Deafness*, Debra Wright; Staff 4 (MLS 2, Non-MLS 2)
Founded 1849. Enrl 400
Library Holdings: Bk Titles 12,882; Per Subs 110
Subject Interests: Blindness, Deafness
Special Collections: Captioned Videos; Descriptive Videos
Publications: Library School Journal
Special Services for the Deaf - Books on deafness & sign language; Staff with knowledge of sign language; TDD
Special Services for the Blind - Braille & talking book collections (print)

P SPARTANBURG COUNTY PUBLIC LIBRARIES, 151 S Church St, 29306-3241. SAN 360-3636. Tel: 864-596-3507. TDD: 864-596-3506. FA 864-596-3518. Web Site: www.infodepot.org. *Librn*, Todd Stephens; *Asst Librn*, Doris B Wright; *ILL*, Dorothy Chandler; *Acq, Ad Servs, Ref*, Stephe C Smith; *Ch Servs*, Carolyn Landrum; *Cat, Tech Servs*, Mildred Finch; *Bkmobile Coordr, Br Coordr*, Susan Grimley; *Rare Bks, Spec Coll*, Marth Dickens; *Govt Doc*, Patricia Brown; Staff 124 (MLS 24, Non-MLS 100)
Founded 1865. Pop 226,800; Circ 1,263,607
Jul 1998-Jun 1999 Income $7,913,855, State $340,201, County $7,337,86 Locally Generated Income $235,828. Mats Exp $776,678, Books $655,45 Per/Ser (Incl. Access Fees) $78,241, Presv $19,816, Electronic Ref Mat (Incl. Access Fees) $23,164. Sal $2,995,315 (Prof $618,981)
Library Holdings: Bk Vols 800,500; Bk Titles 242,000; Per Subs 800
Subject Interests: SC hist
Special Collections: County
Automation Activity & Vendor Info: (Acquisitions) DRA; (Circulation) DRA; (ILL) DRA; (OPAC) DRA; (Serials) DRA
Publications: Directory of Clubs and Organizations (Spartanburg County)
Partic in SOQUIJ
Special Services for the Deaf - Captioned film depository; High interest/lo vocabulary books; Special interest periodicals; TTY machine
Community Services Data Base
Friends of the Library Group
Branches: 9
BOILING SPRINGS, 871 Double Bridge Rd, Inman, 29349. SAN 360-36 Tel: 864-578-3365. *In Charge*, Jean Foster
Friends of the Library Group
CHESNEE BRANCH, Chesnee Shopping Ctr, 716 S Alabama Ave, Chesn 29323. SAN 360-3660. Tel: 864-461-2423. *In Charge*, Jack Underwood; *In Charge*, Mike Seagle
Friends of the Library Group
COWPINS BRANCH, 240 Battleground Rd, Cowpins, 29330. SAN 378-164X. Tel: 864-463-0430. *In Charge*, Matthew Strickland
INMAN BRANCH, 50 Mill St, Inman, 29349. SAN 360-3695. Tel: 864-472-8363. *In Charge*, Sally Culp
Friends of the Library Group
LANDRUM BRANCH, 400 E Rutherford St, Landrum, 29356. SAN 360-3725. Tel: 864-457-2218. *In Charge*, Jodie Lashua
Friends of the Library Group
MIDDLE TYGER, 65 Groce Rd, Lyman, 29365. SAN 360-375X. Tel: 864 439-4759. *In Charge*, Mike Segal
Friends of the Library Group
TRI-PACOLET BRANCH, 390 W Main St, Pacolet, 29372. SAN 375-491 Tel: 864-474-0421. *In Charge*, Peggy Hurley
Friends of the Library Group
WESTSIDE, 2400 Winchester Pl, 29301. SAN 325-4046. Tel: 864-574-681 *In Charge*, Allison Anderson
Friends of the Library Group
WOODRUFF BRANCH, 211 E Georgia St, Woodruff, 29388. SAN 360-3784. Tel: 864-476-8770. *In Charge*, Suzanne Barnes
Friends of the Library Group
Bookmobiles: 3

J SPARTANBURG METHODIST COLLEGE, Marie Blair Burgess Library, 1200 Textile Rd, 29301. SAN 315-5870. Tel: 864-587-4208. FAX: 864-587 4352. *Dir*, James Haller
Founded 1911
Library Holdings: Bk Vols 42,000; Per Subs 250
Partic in BRS; Dialog Corporation; OCLC Online Computer Library Cente Inc; Wilsonline
Friends of the Library Group

M SPARTANBURG REGIONAL MEDICAL CENTER, Health Sciences Library, 101 E Wood St, 29303. SAN 315-5862. Tel: 864-560-6220. FAX: 864-560-6791. Web Site: www.srhs.com/facilities/library.html. *Dir Libr Ser* Mary Ann Camp; E-Mail: macamp@srhs.com; Staff 2 (MLS 1, Non-MLS
Founded 1962
1998-1999 Mats Exp $115,000
Library Holdings: Bk Titles 9,600; Per Subs 275
Subject Interests: Allied health, Clinical sci, Health care admin, Medicine, Nursing
Automation Activity & Vendor Info: (Cataloging) Sagebrush Corporation (Circulation) Sagebrush Corporation; (Serials) Sagebrush Corporation
Database Vendor: OVID Technologies
Publications: Quarterly AHEC Calendar
Restriction: Non-circulating to the public
Function: Document delivery services, ILL available, Literary searches
Partic in Nat Libr of Med; SE Network of Hospital Librs on Docline; Sout Carolina Ahec

S SPARTANBURG TECHNICAL COLLEGE LIBRARY, PO Drawer 4386, 29305. SAN 315-5854. Tel: 864-591-3615. Interlibrary Loan Service Tel: 864-591-3760. FAX: 864-591-3762. Web Site: library.spt.tec.sc.us. *Dir*,

Margaret Green; E-Mail: greenm@spt.tec.sc.us; *Librn*, Gretchen Swanger; E-Mail: swangerg@spt.tec.sc.us; Staff 7 (MLS 3, Non-MLS 4)
Enrl 3,000; Highest Degree: Associate
Jul 1999-Jun 2000 Income $328,279. Mats Exp $85,000, Books $55,000, Per/Ser (Incl. Access Fees) $30,000. Sal $176,156
Library Holdings: Bk Titles 39,989; Per Subs 307; Bks on Deafness & Sign Lang 1,500
Subject Interests: Horticulture, Sensory impaired

UNIVERSITY OF SOUTH CAROLINA - SPARTANBURG LIBRARY,* 800 University Way, 29303. SAN 315-5889. Tel: 864-503-5620. FAX: 864-503-5601. Web Site: www.uscs.edu/#library. *Ref*, Karen Swetland; E-Mail: kswetland@gw.uscs.edu; *Dean of Libr*, Frieda Davidson; *Asst Dir, Tech Servs*, Holle Schneider; Tel: 864-503-5613, E-Mail: hschneider@gw.uscs.edu; *Ref*, Nancy Lambert; Tel: 864-503-5615, E-Mail: nlambert@gw.uscs.edu; *Syst Coordr*, Vicki Thompson; Tel: 864-503-5609, E-Mail: vthompson@gw.uscs.edu; *Archivist, Ref*, Jane Johnson; E-Mail: jjohnson@gw.uscs.edu; *Librn*, Karen Swetland; Staff 22 (MLS 10, Non-MLS 12)
Founded 1967. Pop 7; Enrl 4,000; Fac 238; Highest Degree: Master
Jul 1998-Jun 1999 Income (Main Library Only) $1,231,736. Mats Exp $441,818, Books $160,023, Per/Ser (Incl. Access Fees) $148,334, Presv $6,463, Micro $17,979, Electronic Ref Mat (Incl. Access Fees) $109,019. Sal $631,144 (Prof $335,432)
Library Holdings: Bk Vols 214,984; Per Subs 2,956
Automation Activity & Vendor Info: (Acquisitions) NOTIS; (Cataloging) NOTIS; (Circulation) NOTIS; (Course Reserve) NOTIS

WOFFORD COLLEGE, Sandor Teszler Library, 429 N Church St, 29303-3663. SAN 315-5897. Tel: 864-597-4300. FAX: 864-597-4329. Web Site: www.wofford.edu/library. *Dir, Rare Bks, Spec Coll*, Oakley H Coburn; E-Mail: coburnoh@wofford.edu; *Ref*, Esther Martin; *Ref*, Ellen Tillett; *Dir, Tech Servs*, Shelley Sperka; *Cat*, Timothy Brown; *ILL*, Lisa West; *Coll Develop*, Ibrahim Hanif; Staff 7 (MLS 7)
Founded 1854. Enrl 1,100; Fac 70; Highest Degree: Bachelor
Library Holdings: Bk Vols 165,276; Bk Titles 152,205; Per Subs 642
Special Collections: 16th & 17th Century Books; Book Arts; Geography & Travel; Historical Coll of Materials related to the SC Conference of the United Methodist Church; Hymns & Hymnody; Press Books; South Caroliniana
Publications: exhibit catalogs; Type Specimen Book; Wofford Bibliopolist
Partic in OCLC Online Computer Library Center, Inc; SE Libr Network
Friends of the Library Group

ULLIVAN'S ISLAND

US NATIONAL PARK SERVICE, Fort Sumter National Monument Library, 1214 Middle St, 29482. SAN 370-2898. Tel: 843-883-3123. FAX: 843-883-3910. Web Site: www.nps.gov. *Librn*, Richard W Hatcher, III; E-Mail: fosu_historian@nps.gov
Library Holdings: Bk Vols 875; Per Subs 10

UMMERVILLE

TIMROD LIBRARY,* 217 Central Ave, 29483. SAN 315-5919. Tel: 843-871-4600. *Librn*, Jane Toth
Pop 10,000; Circ 19,278
Library Holdings: Bk Vols 40,000
Subject Interests: SC

WESTVACO CORPORATION, Forest Science Laboratory Library, 180 Westvaco Rd, 29484. (Mail add: PO Box 1950, 29484), Tel: 843-851-4735. FAX: 843-875-0396. *In Charge*, Linda H O'Quinn; E-Mail: lhoquin@westvaco.com; Staff 2 (Non-MLS 2)
Founded 1982
Library Holdings: Bk Titles 3,500; Per Subs 100
Subject Interests: Bio-tech, Forestry
Automation Activity & Vendor Info: (Acquisitions) Sydney; (Cataloging) Sydney; (Circulation) Sydney; (Course Reserve) Sydney; (ILL) Sydney; (Media Booking) Sydney; (OPAC) Sydney; (Serials) Sydney
Database Vendor: Dialog
Partic in OCLC Online Computer Library Center, Inc; Solinet

UMTER

CENTRAL CAROLINA TECHNICAL COLLEGE LIBRARY,* 506 N Guignard Dr, 29150. SAN 315-5935. Tel: 803-778-6647. FAX: 803-778-7889. *Librn*, Chris Burkett; E-Mail: burkettcb@cctech.org; Staff 3 (MLS 3)
Founded 1963. Enrl 2,300; Fac 88
1997-1998 Mats Exp $70,500, Books $51,000, Per/Ser (Incl. Access Fees) $19,500. Sal $195,000 (Prof $111,470)
Library Holdings: Bk Titles 16,500; Per Subs 235
Subject Interests: Eng tech, Law, Nursing
Automation Activity & Vendor Info: (Cataloging) DRA; (Circulation) DRA; (OPAC) DRA
Partic in OCLC Online Computer Library Center, Inc; SE Libr Network

C MORRIS COLLEGE, Richardson-Johnson Learning Resources Center, 100 W College St, 29150-3599. SAN 315-5927. Tel: 803-934-3230. Interlibrary Loan Service Tel: 803-775-9371. FAX: 803-775-2580. Web Site: www.icus.org/morris/mchome.htm. *Dir Libr Serv*, Janet S Clayton; E-Mail: jclayton@morris.edu; *Asst Dir*, Margaret N Mukooza; E-Mail: mmukooza@morris.edu; *Cat*, Deborah Hadstate; E-Mail: dhadstate@morris.edu; *Circ*, Beatrice Golden; E-Mail: bgolden@morris.edu; *Ref*, Alexa Bartel; E-Mail: abartel@morris.edu; *Ser*, Mary Dow; E-Mail: mdow@morris.edu. Subject Specialists: *Curric*, Margaret N Mukooza; *Education*, Margaret N Mukooza; *Journalism*, Janet S Clayton; *Teaching*, Margaret N Mukooza; Staff 12 (MLS 3, Non-MLS 9)
Founded 1920. Enrl 889; Fac 46; Highest Degree: Bachelor
Library Holdings: Bk Vols 99,462; Bk Titles 72,409; Per Subs 415; High Interest/Low Vocabulary Bk Vols 876
Special Collections: African American Coll; Baptist Coll
Automation Activity & Vendor Info: (Cataloging) DRA; (Circulation) DRA; (ILL) DRA; (OPAC) DRA
Database Vendor: DRA, GaleNet, IAC - Info Trac, OCLC - First Search
Function: ILL available
Partic in SE Libr Network

P SUMTER COUNTY LIBRARY,* 111 N Harvin St, 29150. SAN 315-5943. Tel: 803-773-7273. FAX: 803-773-4875. E-Mail: sumtercolib@infoave.net. Web Site: www.midnet.sc.edu/sumtercls. *Librn*, Faith A Line; *Ref*, Mary Pack; *ILL*, John Calhoun; *Acq, Cat, Tech Servs*, Robert Harden; *Publ Servs*, Rudean Hill; *Bkmobile Coordr*, Jane Sanders; Staff 9 (MLS 6, Non-MLS 3)
Founded 1917. Pop 108,000; Circ 239,805
Jul 1997-Jun 1998 Income $963,630, State $153,957, County $653,726, Locally Generated Income $45,000, Other $110,947. Mats Exp $204,000, Books $154,751, Per/Ser (Incl. Access Fees) $17,000, Presv $1,500, Micro $3,000. Sal $448,212
Library Holdings: Bk Titles 135,000; Per Subs 357
Subject Interests: SC
Publications: Bibliographies; Bookings (newsletter)
Friends of the Library Group
Branches: 2
MARKET PLACE, Alice Dr at Wesmark Blvd, 29150. SAN 371-9545. Tel: 803-469-8110. FAX: 803-469-8110. Web Site: www.midnet.sc.edu/sumtercls. *Librn*, Carol Waddell
Library Holdings: Bk Vols 10,000
SOUTH SUMTER, 337 Manning Ave, 29150. SAN 374-745X. Tel: 803-775-7132. FAX: 803-775-7132. Web Site: www.midnet.sc.edu/sumtercls. *Librn*, Geneva Hogan
Library Holdings: Bk Vols 7,000
Bookmobiles: 1

C UNIVERSITY OF SOUTH CAROLINA AT SUMTER LIBRARY,* 200 Miller Rd, 29150-2498. SAN 315-596X. Tel: 803-775-6341, Ext 3234. FAX: 803-775-2180. *Librn*, Jane J Ferguson; *Asst Librn*, Susan Towery
Founded 1966. Enrl 1,500
Library Holdings: Bk Vols 60,000; Per Subs 507

TIGERVILLE

J NORTH GREENVILLE COLLEGE, Hester Memorial Library, PO Box 1892, 29688-1892. SAN 315-5978. Tel: 864-977-7093. FAX: 864-977-7021. *Dir*, John Bradshaw; *Ref*, Carol Hardin; Staff 5 (MLS 3, Non-MLS 2)
Founded 1892. Enrl 730; Fac 55
Library Holdings: Bk Vols 46,870; Per Subs 490
Special Collections: Edith Duff Miller Bible Museum Coll
Publications: Upcountry Friends Newsletter
Mem of SC Libr Network
Friends of the Library Group

UNION

P UNION COUNTY CARNEGIE LIBRARY,* 300 E South St, 29379-2392. SAN 315-5986. Tel: 864-427-7140. *Librn*, Edward G Burwell; *Circ*, Dorothy Gallman; *Commun Servs*, Sharon Rupp; *Bkmobile Coordr*, Angela Mallette; *Tech Servs*, Susan Gregory; Staff 1 (MLS 1)
Founded 1904. Pop 30,751; Circ 55,797
Library Holdings: Bk Vols 48,161; Per Subs 122
Special Collections: South Caroliniana Coll, bks & micro
Partic in SE Libr Network
Friends of the Library Group

J UNIVERSITY OF SOUTH CAROLINA AT UNION LIBRARY,* 309 E Academy St, PO Box Drawer 729, 29379. SAN 315-5994. Tel: 864-429-8728. FAX: 864-427-3682. E-Mail: r700000@vm.sc.edu. *Dir*, Susan V Smith; Staff 1 (MLS 1)
Founded 1965. Enrl 222; Fac 19
Jul 1996-Jun 1997 Income $80,779. Mats Exp $12,077. Sal $47,472 (Prof $28,203)
Library Holdings: Bk Vols 31,269
Partic in SE Libr Network

WALHALLA

P OCONEE COUNTY LIBRARY,* 501 W South Broad St, 29691. SAN 360-3814. Tel: 864-638-4133. FAX: 864-638-4132. *Dir*, Martha Baily; *Tech Servs*, Hugh Arnold; E-Mail: Hugh_A@oconee.lib.sc.us; *Mgr, Ref*, Robert McCall; *Ch Servs*, Sally Long; E-Mail: Sally_L@oconee.lib.sc.us; *Bkmobile Coordr*, Joyce Lusk; *Automation Syst Coordr*, Sue Andrus; E-Mail: Sue_A@oconee.lib.sc.us. Subject Specialists: *Reference*, Sue Andrus; Staff 28 (MLS 6, Non-MLS 22)
Founded 1948. Pop 62,000; Circ 348,500
Jul 1998-Jun 1999 Income (Main Library and Branch Library) $937,600, State $86,200, Federal $22,400, County $827,000, Locally Generated Income $2,000. Mats Exp $180,200, Books $145,200, Per/Ser (Incl. Access Fees) $14,200, AV Equip $20,800. Sal $621,200 (Prof $110,000)
Library Holdings: Bk Vols 148,500; Bk Titles 80,505; Per Subs 400
Subject Interests: Local history
Special Collections: Nuclear Reg Comm; South Carolina Coll
Automation Activity & Vendor Info: (Circulation) DRA
Database Vendor: DRA, IAC - Info Trac
Partic in Am Pub Libr Asn
Friends of the Library Group
Branches: 3
SALEM BRANCH, 5 Park Ave, Salem, 29676. SAN 360-3849. Tel: 864-944-0912. *Br Coordr*, Ramona McCoy
SENECA BRANCH, 300 E South Second St, Seneca, 29678. SAN 360-3873. Tel: 864-882-4855. *Br Coordr*, Teresa Lanford
WESTMINSTER BRANCH, 112 W North Ave, Westminster, 29693. SAN 360-3903. Tel: 864-647-3215. *Br Coordr*, Suzanne Peden
Bookmobiles: 1

WALTERBORO

P COLLETON COUNTY MEMORIAL LIBRARY, 600 Hampton St, 29488-4098. SAN 315-6001. Tel: 803-549-5621. FAX: 803-549-5122. E-Mail: ccml@infoave.com. *Dir*, Sylvia N Rowe; Staff 12 (MLS 2, Non-MLS 10)
Founded 1820. Pop 34,377; Circ 118,140
Jul 1999-Jun 2000 Income $512,559, State $64,125, City $50,000, Federal $2,850, County $374,634, Locally Generated Income $20,950. Mats Exp $81,001, Books $62,684, Per/Ser (Incl. Access Fees) $7,925, Micro $349, AV Equip $6,568, Electronic Ref Mat (Incl. Access Fees) $3,475. Sal $314,600
Library Holdings: Bk Vols 85,275; Per Subs 198
Subject Interests: SC hist
Automation Activity & Vendor Info: (Cataloging) TLC
Friends of the Library Group
Bookmobiles: 1

WEST COLUMBIA

J MIDLANDS TECHNICAL COLLEGE LIBRARY,* 1260 Lexington Dr, 29170. (Mail add: PO Box 2408, 29202), Tel: 803-822-3419. FAX: 803-822-3670. Web Site: www.mid.tec.sc.us/library. *Dir Libr Serv*, Elizabeth Haworth; Fax: 803-822-3061, E-Mail: haworthe@mtc.mid.tec.sc.us; *Tech Servs*, Ann Osborne; Tel: 803-822-3616, Fax: 803-822-3061, E-Mail: osbornea@mtc.mid.tec.sc.us; *Ref*, Laura Kerenick; *Publ Servs*, Laura Bake Tel: 803-822-3533, E-Mail: bakerl@mtc.mid.tec.sc.us; *Publ Servs*, Virginia Brooker; Tel: 803-738-7629, Fax: 803-738-7719, E-Mail: brookerv@mtc.mid.tec.sc.us; *Publ Servs*, Catherine Eckman; Tel: 803-822-3537, E-Mail: eckmanc@mtc.mid.tec.sc.us; *Publ Servs*, Erica Henning; Tel: 803-822-3674, E-Mail: hennige@mtc.mid.tec.sc.us; *Publ Servs*, Marilyn Hook; Tel: 803-822-3535, E-Mail: hookerm@mtc.mid.tec.sc.us; *Publ Servs*, Cary Lafaye; Tel: 803-738-7762, Fax: 803-738-7719, E-Mail: lafayec@mtc.mid.tec.sc.us; *Publ Servs*, Julie Roberson; Tel: 803-790-7512, Fax: 803-738-7719, E-Mail: robersonj@mtc.mid.tec.sc.us; *Tech Coordr*, Lorraine Abraham; Tel: 803-738-7734, Fax: 803-738-7719, E-Mail: abraham@mtc.mid.tec.sc.us; Staff 18 (MLS 10, Non-MLS 8)
Founded 1963
1997-1998 Income $884,157. Mats Exp $265,450
Library Holdings: Bk Titles 77,000; Per Subs 500
Automation Activity & Vendor Info: (Cataloging) DRA; (Circulation) DRA; (OPAC) DRA; (Serials) DRA
Database Vendor: Dialog, DRA, IAC - Info Trac, Lexis-Nexis, OCLC - First Search, ProQuest
Partic in Solinet
Special Services for the Deaf - Staff with knowledge of sign language
Departmental Libraries:
BELTLINE Tel: 803-738-7629. FAX: 803-738-7719. *In Charge*, Elizabeth Haworth

S SOUTH CAROLINA VOCATIONAL REHABILITATION EVALUATION CENTER LIBRARY,* 1400 Boston Ave, 29170-2138. SAN 377-3574. Tel 803-896-6040. FAX: 803-896-6148. *Librn*, Carol Teal
Library Holdings: Bk Vols 1,550; Bk Titles 1,000; Per Subs 20

WINNSBORO

P FAIRFIELD COUNTY LIBRARY, 300 Washington St, 29180. SAN 360-3938. Tel: 803-635-4971. FAX: 803-635-7715. Web Site: www.fairfield.lib.sc.us. *Dir*, Sarah D McMaster; Staff 1 (MLS 1)
Founded 1938. Pop 22,295; Circ 87,157
Jul 1999-Jun 2000 Income (Main Library and Branch Library) $364,419, State $41,588, Federal $3,665, County $303,066, Other $16,100. Mats Exp $74,951, Books $61,915, Per/Ser (Incl. Access Fees) $6,368, Micro $187, AV Equip $5,933, Electronic Ref Mat (Incl. Access Fees) $548. Sal $226,406
Library Holdings: Bk Vols 74,470; Per Subs 174
Subject Interests: History
Automation Activity & Vendor Info: (Cataloging) epixtech, inc.; (Circulation) epixtech, inc.; (OPAC) epixtech, inc.
Friends of the Library Group
Branches: 1
RIDGEWAY BRANCH, 170 S Dogwood St, Ridgeway, 29130. SAN 360-3997. Tel: 803-337-2068. Web Site: www.fairfield.lib.sc.us. *Librn*, Margo Kuebler
Automation Activity & Vendor Info: (Circulation) epixtech, inc.; (OPAC) epixtech, inc.
Bookmobiles: 1

Date of Statistics: Calendar 1998
Population, 1998 (est): 730,789
Population Served by Public Libraries: 519,409
Unserved: 211,380 (Served by mail by State Library with in-WATS telephone access)
Total Volumes in Public Libraries: 2,524,036
Volumes Per Capita: 4.86
Total Public Library Circulation: 4,576,044
Circulation Per Capita: 8.8
Total Public Library Income: $12,406,318
Source of Income: Public funds & gifts
Expenditure Per Capita: $23.89
Number of County Libraries: 20
Counties Unserved: 46
Number of Bookmobiles in State: 8 (public library)
Statistics do not include federal funds or statistics supporting public library services provided by the South Dakota State Library

BERDEEN

AVERA SAINT LUKE'S HOSPITAL, (Formerly Saint Luke's Hospital), Paul G Bunker Memorial Medical Library, 305 S State St, 57401-4590. SAN 326-4041. Tel: 605-622-5355. FAX: 605-622-5041. *Librn*, Roxie Olson; E-Mail: roxie.olson@averasaintlukes.org; Staff 1 (Non-MLS 1)
Library Holdings: Bk Vols 1,650; Bk Titles 1,500; Per Subs 230

BETHLEHEM LUTHERAN CHURCH LIBRARY,* 1620 Milwaukee Ave NE, 57401. SAN 315-6036. Tel: 605-225-9740. FAX: 605-225-6340. E-Mail: blc@hdc.net. *Librn*, Adeline Witt
Library Holdings: Bk Vols 2,139
Friends of the Library Group

DACOTAH PRAIRIE MUSEUM, Ruth Bunker Memorial Library, 21 S Main St, PO Box 0395, 57402-0395. SAN 323-6781. Tel: 605-626-7117. FAX: 605-626-4026. E-Mail: bcmuseum@midco.net. Web Site: www.brown.sd.us/museum. *Dir*, Sue Gates
Founded 1970
Library Holdings: Bk Titles 800
Special Collections: Sioux Missionary Work (Riggs Williamson Coll), papers
Restriction: By appointment only

ALEXANDER MITCHELL PUBLIC LIBRARY,* 519 S Kline St, 57401-4495. SAN 315-6060. Tel: 605-626-7097. FAX: 605-626-3506. E-Mail: ampl@sdln.net. *Dir*, Pam Lingor; *Tech Servs*, Debbie Werre; *Ch Servs*, Nancy Eckert; *Ad Servs*, Shirley Arment
Founded 1884. Pop 35,580; Circ 213,532
Jan 1999-Dec 1999 Income $652,242, City $599,125, Other $26,077. Mats Exp $71,769, Books $57,314, Per/Ser (Incl. Access Fees) $14,455. Sal $304,567 (Prof $158,385)
Library Holdings: Bk Vols 99,987; Per Subs 455
Subject Interests: Genealogy, Ref, SDak
Special Collections: AFRA (American Family Record Ass'n); Dakota Art; Dakota Maps; Genealogy; Germans from Russia; L Frank Baum; Railroad History
Publications: AMPL News
Partic in MINITEX Library Information Network; OCLC Online Computer Library Center, Inc; South Dakota Library Network
Special Services for the Deaf - High interest/low vocabulary books
Special Services - Home bound delivery; Variety Magnifiers for reading. Two telephone devices for the deaf.

C NORTHERN STATE UNIVERSITY, Beulah Williams Library & Instructional Technology Center, 1200 S Jay St, 57401-7198. SAN 315-6079. Tel: 605-626-2645. FAX: 605-626-2473. Web Site: lib.northern.edu/library. *Dir*, Dr J Philip Mulvaney; Tel: 605-626-7770, E-Mail: mulvaney@wolf.northern.edu; *Electronic Resources*, Jennifer Campbell; Tel: 605-626-7773; *Instrul Serv*, Lorena Smith; Tel: 605-626-7804; *Ref*, Steve Dixon; *Tech Servs*, Wei Ding; Tel: 605-626-7770; Staff 6 (MLS 4, Non-MLS 2)
Founded 1901. Enrl 2,634; Fac 115; Highest Degree: Master
Jul 1998-Jun 1999 Income $973,266, State $473,523, Parent Institution $499,743. Mats Exp $311,341, Books $112,616, Per/Ser (Incl. Access Fees) $127,071, Presv $7,184, Micro $3,725, AV Equip $25,381, Electronic Ref Mat (Incl. Access Fees) $35,364. Sal $480,000
Library Holdings: Bk Titles 182,000; Per Subs 1,074
Subject Interests: Bus, Education
Special Collections: Harriet Montgomery Water Resources Coll; South Dakota History
Automation Activity & Vendor Info: (Acquisitions) PALS; (Cataloging) PALS; (Circulation) PALS; (ILL) PALS; (Media Booking) PALS; (OPAC) PALS; (Serials) PALS
Partic in MINITEX Library Information Network; OCLC Online Computer Library Center, Inc; South Dakota Library Network

J PRESENTATION COLLEGE LIBRARY,* 1500 N Main, 57401-1299. SAN 360-4020. Tel: 605-229-8468. FAX: 605-229-8430. Web Site: www.presentation.edu. *Dir*, Arvyce Burns; E-Mail: burnsa@presentation.edu; Staff 1 (MLS 1)
Founded 1951. Enrl 271; Fac 43
Jun 1997-May 1998 Income $131,853. Mats Exp $17,500. Sal $60,000
Library Holdings: Bk Titles 34,831; Per Subs 351
Subject Interests: Nursing, Relig studies
Departmental Libraries:
LAKOTA CAMPUS, Eagle Butte, 57625. SAN 376-8716. Tel: 605-964-4071. FAX: 605-964-1111. Web Site: www.presentation.edu. *Librn*, Marilyn Dunn; E-Mail: dunnm@presentation.edu
Library Holdings: Bk Titles 976

G SOUTH DAKOTA SCHOOL FOR THE BLIND & VISUALLY IMPAIRED, Library Media Center,* 423 17th Ave SE, 57401-7699. SAN 325-4909. Tel: 605-626-2675. FAX: 605-626-2607. *Librn*, Lila Morris
Founded 1900
Jul 1996-Jun 1997 Income $64,533, State $56,201, Federal $8,332. Mats Exp $12,039, Books $5,531, Per/Ser (Incl. Access Fees) $2,171. Sal $42,795 (Prof $41,631)
Library Holdings: Bk Vols 18,311; Per Subs 122
Subject Interests: Blind, Deaf, Educ of the blind, Learning disabled, Mentally retarded blind, Physically handicapped, Visually handicapped
Special Collections: Local School Archive
Partic in South Dakota Library Network
Special Services for the Blind - Reading edge system; Talking book center
Cooperation with other libraries serving our clients: SDak Braille & Talking Book Library & Utah State Library

ALEXANDRIA

P ALEXANDRIA PUBLIC LIBRARY, PO Box 355, 57311-0355. SAN 315-6087. Tel: 605-239-4681. *Librn*, Shirley Letcher
Pop 598; Circ 5,852
Library Holdings: Bk Vols 9,000

ARLINGTON

P ARLINGTON COMMUNITY LIBRARY,* PO Box 345, 57212-0345. SAN 315-6095. Tel: 605-983-5241. *Librn*, Kim Myers
Pop 993; Circ 5,608
Library Holdings: Bk Vols 10,000; Per Subs 12
Mem of SDak State Libr Syst

ARMOUR

P ARMOUR PUBLIC LIBRARY, Carnegie Library, 915 Main Ave, PO Box 396, 57313-0396. SAN 315-6109. Tel: 605-724-2743. Interlibrary Loan Service Tel: 800-423-6665. *Actg Dir*, Linda Montgomery
Pop 1,200; Circ 9,350
Library Holdings: Bk Titles 10,400; Per Subs 35
Mem of SDak State Libr Syst

BELLE FOURCHE

P BELLE FOURCHE PUBLIC LIBRARY,* 905 Fifth Ave, 57717-1795. SAN 315-6117. Tel: 605-892-4407. E-Mail: pjeng@hotmail.com. *Librn*, Pat Engebretson; *Asst Librn*, Wanda Nelson; Staff 4 (MLS 1, Non-MLS 3)
Founded 1906. Pop 4,300; Circ 50,470
Jan 1999-Dec 1999 Income (Main Library Only) $164,929. Mats Exp $87,053, Books $20,000, AV Equip $2,500. Sal $84,810
Library Holdings: Bk Vols 36,386; Per Subs 90
Special Collections: Genealogy; History of South Dakota
Automation Activity & Vendor Info: (Cataloging) Sagebrush Corporation
Partic in South Dakota Library Network
Friends of the Library Group

P NORTHWEST REGIONAL LIBRARY,* 1301 Eighth, 57717. SAN 315-6125. Tel: 605-892-4420. *Dir*, Chris Durr; *Tech Servs*, Diane Bean; *Tech Servs*, Kitzan Cowendolyn
Founded 1957. Pop 5,180; Circ 23,044
Library Holdings: Bk Vols 25,000
Partic in South Dakota Library Network

BERESFORD

P BERESFORD PUBLIC LIBRARY,* 115 S Third St, 57004-1798. SAN 315-6133. Tel: 605-763-2782. FAX: 605-763-2329. *Librn*, Evelyn Hogen
Pop 1,865; Circ 23,175
Library Holdings: Bk Vols 31,000; Per Subs 78
Special Collections: South Dakota Coll
Partic in OCLC Online Computer Library Center, Inc

BOWDLE

P REVEREND MARTIN BIEBER PUBLIC LIBRARY,* PO Box 280, 57428. SAN 315-615X. *Librn*, Mona Kennedy
Founded 1971
Library Holdings: Bk Vols 10,523
Mem of SDak State Libr Syst

BRITTON

P BRITTON PUBLIC LIBRARY,* 524 Main St, PO Box 299, 57430-0299. SAN 315-6168. Tel: 605-448-2800. *Librn*, Sonia Wolf
Pop 1,589; Circ 10,725
Library Holdings: Bk Vols 11,703; Per Subs 20

BROOKINGS

M BROOKINGS HOSPITAL, Medical Library,* 300 22nd Ave, 57006-2496. SAN 328-5766. Tel: 605-696-9000. FAX: 605-697-7380. *Dir*, Judy Costar
Library Holdings: Bk Titles 400

P BROOKINGS PUBLIC LIBRARY, 515 Third St, 57006. SAN 315-6176. Tel: 605-692-9407. FAX: 605-692-9386. Web Site: www.brookingslibrary.org. *Dir*, Elvita Landau; E-Mail: elandau@sdln.net; *Tech Servs*, Cathy Enlow; E-Mail: cenlow@sdln.net; *Ch Servs*, Joyce Wrage; E-Mail: jwrage@sdln.net; *Ad Servs*, Lynn Osika; E-Mail: losida@sdln.net; *Commun Servs*, Rae Brecht; E-Mail: rbrecht@sdln.net; *Ch Servs*, Betty Ketelhut; E-Mail: bketelhu@sdln.net; Staff 17 (MLS 3, Non-MLS 14)
Founded 1913. Pop 25,207; Circ 215,318
Jan 1999-Dec 1999 Income $2,410,401, City $2,264,982, Federal $39,000, County $25,000, Locally Generated Income $84,419. Mats Exp $89,200, Books $70,019, Per/Ser (Incl. Access Fees) $8,714, AV Equip $7,911, Electronic Ref Mat (Incl. Access Fees) $31,173. Sal $418,601 (Prof $119,995)
Library Holdings: Bk Vols 83,000; Bk Titles 72,849; Per Subs 232
Special Collections: South Dakota History & Literature (South Dakota Coll)
Automation Activity & Vendor Info: (Cataloging) PALS; (Circulation) PALS; (ILL) PALS; (OPAC) PALS; (Serials) PALS
Database Vendor: GaleNet, IAC - Info Trac, ProQuest
Partic in MINITEX Library Information Network; OCLC Online Compute Library Center, Inc; South Dakota Library Network
Friends of the Library Group

C SOUTH DAKOTA STATE UNIVERSITY, Hilton M Briggs Library, N Campus Dr, PO Box 2115, 57007-1098. SAN 360-408X. Tel: 605-688-51(Circulation Tel: 605-688-5107. Reference Tel: 605-688-5572. Toll Free Tel 800-786-2038. FAX: 605-688-6133. Web Site: www.sdstate.edu/library. *De of Libr*, Dr Steve Robert Marquardt; Tel: 605-688-5557, E-Mail: steve_marquardt@sdstate.edu; *Head Tech Servs*, Bang Kim; Tel: 605-688-5560, E-Mail: bang_kim@sdstate.edu; *Acq*, Mary Caspers-Graper; Tel: 605 688-5565, E-Mail: mary_caspers_graper@sdstate.edu; *Circ*, Elizabeth Fox; Tel: 605-688-5569, E-Mail: elizabeth_fox@sdstate.edu; *Publ Servs*, Clark Hallman; Tel: 605-688-5572, E-Mail: clark_hallman@sdstate.edu; *Ser*, Carlene Aro; Tel: 605-688-5567, E-Mail: carlene_aro@sdstate.edu; *Spec C & Archives*, Liz Scott; Tel: 605-688-4906, E-Mail: elizabeth_scott@sdstate.edu; *Govt Doc*, Nancy Marshall; Tel: 605-688-5093, E-Mail: nancy_marshall@sdstate.edu. Subject Specialists: *History*, Liz Scott; Staff (MLS 13, Non-MLS 17)
Founded 1884. Enrl 7,339; Fac 446; Highest Degree: Doctorate
Jul 1999-Jun 2000 Income $3,099,169, State $1,767,560, Federal $65,817, Parent Institution $1,177,042, Other $88,750. Mats Exp $1,427,868, Books $264,079, Per/Ser (Incl. Access Fees) $857,652, Presv $32,869, Electronic Ref Mat (Incl. Access Fees) $273,268. Sal $1,268,338 (Prof $624,771)
Library Holdings: Bk Vols 575,000; Bk Titles 460,000; Per Subs 3,102
Special Collections: Marghab Rare Book Coll; South Dakota Farm Bureau & Farmers Union Locals Records
Automation Activity & Vendor Info: (Acquisitions) PALS; (Cataloging) PALS; (Circulation) PALS; (ILL) PALS; (OPAC) PALS; (Serials) PALS
Database Vendor: Dialog, IAC - Info Trac, IAC - SearchBank, Lexis-Nex OCLC - First Search, ProQuest, Silverplatter Information Inc.
Publications: Conspectus Newsletter; Index to Newspapers; Indian Countr Today Index; SDSU Collegian Index; Serials List; Sioux Falls Argus Leade Annual Index; South Dakota Farm & Home Research Index
Function: Photocopies available
Partic in MINITEX Library Information Network; South Dakota Library Network

CANTON

P CANTON PUBLIC LIBRARY,* 225 N Broadway, 57013-1715. SAN 315-6184. Tel: 605-987-5831. FAX: 605-987-5831. *Coll Develop, Librn*, Iris Schultz; Staff 5 (MLS 1, Non-MLS 4)
Founded 1912. Pop 4,000
Library Holdings: Bk Vols 35,548; Per Subs 73
Mem of SDak State Libr Syst
Friends of the Library Group

CENTERVILLE

P CENTERVILLE COMMUNITY LIBRARY, 421 Florida, PO Box C, 5701-0902. SAN 315-6192. Tel: 605-563-2540. FAX: 605-563-2615. *Dir*, Mary Ferwerda; Staff 3 (Non-MLS 3)
Founded 1935. Pop 1,500; Circ 24,600
1998-1999 Income $28,800, City $26,000, Locally Generated Income $2,000, Other $800. Mats Exp $7,550, Books $6,000, Per/Ser (Incl. Access Fees) $400, Micro $250, Other Print Mats $400, Electronic Ref Mat (Incl. Access Fees) $500. Sal $34,000
Library Holdings: Bk Vols 16,000; Per Subs 60
Subject Interests: Pioneer hist of Turner Co
Special Collections: Centennial Book - History of Centerville, 100 yrs; Centerville Journal Newspapers since 1903
Automation Activity & Vendor Info: (Acquisitions) Athena; (Cataloging) Athena; (Circulation) Athena
Publications: Weekly newspaper article
Mem of SDak State Libr Syst

CLEAR LAKE

P CLEAR LAKE CITY LIBRARY, 125 3rd Ave S, PO Box 199, 57226-0199 SAN 315-6206. Tel: 605-874-2013. *Librn*, Oriska Hover
Founded 1899. Pop 4,522; Circ 9,396
Jan 1999-Dec 1999 Income $22,200, City $2,200, Locally Generated Incom $2,200. Mats Exp $8,410, Books $4,690, Per/Ser (Incl. Access Fees) $1,020 Electronic Ref Mat (Incl. Access Fees) $2,700. Sal $11,600
Library Holdings: Bk Titles 17,300; Per Subs 48
Partic in Dewey

CRAZY HORSE

S INDIAN MUSEUM OF NORTH AMERICA LIBRARY, Crazy Horse Memorial, Avenue of the Chiefs, 57730-9506. SAN 315-6141. Tel: 605-673-4681. FAX: 605-673-2185. Web Site: www.crazyhorse.org. *Dir*, Anne Ziolkowski

Founded 1973
Library Holdings: Bk Titles 22,000
Subject Interests: History, North American Indians in all aspects
Publications: Newsletter (quarterly)

USTER

CUSTER COUNTY LIBRARY, 447 Crook St Ste 4, 57730-1509. SAN 315-6214. Tel: 605-673-8178. FAX: 605-673-8159. E-Mail: cuslib@gwtc.net. Web Site: www.gwtc.net/~cuslib/. *Dir*, Marguerite Cullum
Founded 1943. Pop 6,930; Circ 30,300
Jan 2000-Dec 2000 Income $66,261, County $57,124, Locally Generated Income $7,148, Other $1,989. Mats Exp $10,280, Books $8,577, Per/Ser (Incl. Access Fees) $1,205, AV Equip $498. Sal $44,835 (Prof $21,520)
Library Holdings: Bk Vols 15,735; Bk Titles 15,718
Special Collections: Black Hills Area History; George Armstrong Custer
Automation Activity & Vendor Info: (Acquisitions) Follett; (Cataloging) Follett; (Circulation) Follett; (OPAC) Follett

DEPARTMENT OF CORRECTIONS, Custer Youth Corrections Center Library, RR 1, Box 98, 57730-9647. SAN 326-4440. Tel: 605-673-2521. FAX: 605-673-5489. *Librn*, Sherri Reindl
Enrl 52
Library Holdings: Bk Titles 1,900
Restriction: Clients only
Friends of the Library Group

E SMET

HAZEL L MEYER MEMORIAL LIBRARY,* 114 First St, 57231. (Mail add: PO Box J, 57231-0156), Tel: 605-854-3842. E-Mail: hlmlib@dtgnet.com. *Dir*, Patricia A Coughlin; *Asst Librn*, Mary Purintun
Founded 1937. Pop 1,800; Circ 30,887
Jan 1998-Dec 1998 Income $30,877, City $29,600, Other $2,277. Mats Exp $9,721, Books $7,344, Per/Ser (Incl. Access Fees) $1,230, AV Equip $1,086, Other Print Mats $61, Electronic Ref Mat (Incl. Access Fees) $475. Sal $12,253
Library Holdings: Bk Vols 19,651; Bk Titles 19,080; Per Subs 57; High Interest/Low Vocabulary Bk Vols 50; Spec Interest Per Sub 20; Bks on Deafness & Sign Lang 10
Special Collections: Harvey Dunn Original Paintings (5); Laura Ingalls Wilder Memorabilia
Mem of SDak State Libr Syst
Special Services for the Blind - Audio-cassettes; Large print bks

EADWOOD

DEADWOOD PUBLIC LIBRARY,* 435 Williams St, 57732-1113. SAN 315-6230. Tel: 605-578-2821. FAX: 605-578-2170. E-Mail: dwd@sdln.net. Web Site: www.dwdlib.sdln.net. *Dir*, Terri Davis; E-Mail: tdavis@sdln.net; *Reader Servs*, Carol Hauck-Reif; *Ch Servs*, Nancy Berke-Hutchison; Staff 4 (MLS 1, Non-MLS 3)
Founded 1895. Pop 3,517; Circ 14,559
Jan 2000-Dec 2000 Income $114,525, City $21,050, County $65,675, Locally Generated Income $800, Other $27,000. Mats Exp Books $12,317. Sal $46,865 (Prof $30,600)
Library Holdings: Bk Vols 13,140; Per Subs 66
Subject Interests: Local history
Special Collections: Centennial Archive Coll, photogs, docs; Old Local Newspapers, files; Round Table Club scrapbooks; Round Table Club scrapbooks
Automation Activity & Vendor Info: (Cataloging) PALS; (Circulation) PALS; (ILL) PALS; (OPAC) PALS
Publications: Index to Deadwood Newspapers
Partic in South Dakota Library Network

ELL RAPIDS

CARNEGIE PUBLIC LIBRARY,* 513 N Orleans Ave, 57022-1637. SAN 315-6249. Tel: 605-428-3280. *Dir*, Deb Huska; Staff 1 (MLS 1)
Founded 1910. Pop 2,478; Circ 36,990
Jan 1997-Dec 1998 Income $69,244. Mats Exp $23,900, Books $16,543, Per/Ser (Incl. Access Fees) $1,735. Sal $33,677
Library Holdings: Bk Vols 18,465; Bk Titles 17,075; Per Subs 78
Subject Interests: SDak hist

DGEMONT

EDGEMONT PUBLIC LIBRARY,* 412 Second Ave, PO Box 449, 57735-0449. SAN 315-6257. Tel: 605-662-7712. FAX: 605-662-7922. *Librn*, Jeannee Anderson; *Asst Librn*, Agnes Reecy
Founded 1916. Pop 1,400; Circ 7,539
Jan 1997-Dec 1998 Income $22,300. Mats Exp $4,281. Sal $10,463
Library Holdings: Bk Vols 24,500; Per Subs 34
Subject Interests: Local history
Special Collections: South Dakota Coll

ELK POINT

P ELK POINT COMMUNITY LIBRARY,* 110 N Douglas, PO Box 126, 57025-0126. SAN 315-6265. *Librn*, Peg Johnson
Pop 1,600; Circ 10,500
Library Holdings: Bk Vols 15,000
Friends of the Library Group

ELLSWORTH AFB

UNITED STATES AIR FORCE
A ELLSWORTH AIR FORCE BASE HOLBROOK LIBRARY FL4690, 28 SVS/SVMG, 2650 Doolittle Dr Bldg 3910, 57706-4820. SAN 360-4144. Tel: 605-385-1688. FAX: 605-385-4467. E-Mail: library@ellsworth.af.mil. *Dir*, Cindi Mullins
Library Holdings: Bk Vols 36,000
Subject Interests: Aeronaut sci, Astronautics, Bus admin, Electronics, Mil sci, Related fields
Restriction: Not open to public
Partic in Fedlink; MINITEX Library Information Network; South Dakota Library Network

EUREKA

P KATHRYN SCHULKOSKI LIBRARY, PO Box 12, 57437-0012. SAN 315-6273. Tel: 605-284-2026. E-Mail: kslibrary@hotmail.com. *City Librn*, Virginia Greco
Founded 1932. Pop 2,500; Circ 10,214
Jan 1999-Dec 1999 Income City $8,524. Mats Exp $2,383, Books $2,034, Per/Ser (Incl. Access Fees) $26, Other Print Mats $323. Sal $5,874
Library Holdings: Bk Vols 15,396; Bk Titles 15,375

FAITH

P FAITH PUBLIC LIBRARY, 204 W Fifth St, PO Box 172, 57626-0172. SAN 326-5587. Tel: 605-967-2262. FAX: 605-967-2153. *Librn*, Betty Veit; E-Mail: betty.veit@k12.sd.us; Staff 1 (Non-MLS 1)
Founded 1924. Pop 576; Circ 24,059
2000-2000 Income $60,460, City $2,200, County $2,200, Locally Generated Income $36,260. Mats Exp $5,300, Books $2,000, Per/Ser (Incl. Access Fees) $600, AV Equip $2,200, Electronic Ref Mat (Incl. Access Fees) $500. Sal $38,378
Library Holdings: Bk Vols 13,814; Bk Titles 13,785; Per Subs 58
Special Collections: South Dakota
Automation Activity & Vendor Info: (Cataloging) Sagebrush Corporation; (Circulation) Sagebrush Corporation
Partic in South Dakota Library Network
Friends of the Library Group

FAULKTON

M FAULK COUNTY MEMORIAL HOSPITAL LIBRARY,* 911 Saint John St, PO Box 100, 57438-0426. SAN 327-8603. Tel: 605-598-6263. FAX: 605-598-4199.
Library Holdings: Bk Vols 75

FLANDREAU

P MOODY COUNTY RESOURCE CENTER LIBRARY,* 700 W Community Dr, 57028. SAN 315-6281. Tel: 605-997-3326. *Librn*, Maryll Rosheim
Founded 1915. Circ 15,025
Jan 1998-Dec 1998 Income $29,055. Mats Exp $13,880, Books $13,000, Per/Ser (Incl. Access Fees) $880. Sal $13,000 (Prof $8,000)
Library Holdings: Bk Titles 18,455; Per Subs 37
Special Collections: South Dakota Author Coll
Branches: 1
COLMAN BRANCH - SENIOR CITIZENS CENTER, Colman Senior Citizens Center, Colman, 57017. SAN 321-8740. *Librn*, Janelle Steffen

FORT MEADE

GM DEPARTMENT OF VETERANS AFFAIRS LIBRARY, VA Black Hills Health Care System, 113 Comanche Rd, 57741-1099. SAN 315-629X. Tel: 605-347-7055. FAX: 605-347-7054.
Library Holdings: Per Subs 378
Special Collections: Medical Coll
Publications: Newsletter
Partic in South Dakota Library Network; Veterans Affairs Library Network

FREEMAN

J FREEMAN ACADEMY LIBRARY,* 748 S Main St, 57029. SAN 315-6303. Tel: 605-925-4237, Ext 28. FAX: 605-925-4271. Web Site: www.freemanacademy.pvt.k12.us. *Coordr*, Cindy Graber
Founded 1904. Enrl 65; Fac 14
Jul 1998-Jun 1999 Mats Exp $1,800, Books $750
Library Holdings: Bk Titles 13,800; Per Subs 40
Publications: School Library Journal

P FREEMAN PUBLIC LIBRARY, 185 E Third St, PO Box I, 57029. SAN 315-6311. Tel: 605-925-7003. Toll Free Tel: 800-423-6665. FAX: 605-925-7127. E-Mail: frpublib@ispchannel.com. *Dir*, Berneda J Koller; Staff 1 (MLS 1)
Founded 1939. Pop 1,293; Circ 16,155
Jan 1998-Dec 1999 Income $22,055, Locally Generated Income $2,000. Mats Exp $4,800, Books $4,000, Per/Ser (Incl. Access Fees) $600, Other Print Mats $200. Sal $14,000 (Prof $8,000)
Library Holdings: Bk Vols 11,000; Bk Titles 9,900; Per Subs 40
Subject Interests: Germans in Russia from SDak, Hutterites, Mennonites, SDak hist
Special Collections: Freeman, SD materials
Partic in South Dakota Library Network

GETTYSBURG

P POTTER COUNTY FREE PUBLIC LIBRARY,* 106 E Commercial Ave, 57442-1507. SAN 315-6338. Tel: 605-765-9518. *Librn*, Peggy Williams; *Asst Librn*, Audrey Robinson
Founded 1923. Pop 4,396; Circ 21,356
Library Holdings: Bk Vols 16,145; Per Subs 42

GREGORY

P GREGORY PUBLIC LIBRARY, 112 E Fifth, 57533-1463. SAN 315-6346. Tel: 605-835-8531. *Librn*, Janice A Tilton; Tel: 605-835-8858, E-Mail: barbarianist@lycos.com
Founded 1926. Pop 1,475; Circ 14,000
Jan 1998-Dec 1999 Income $16,000. Mats Exp $2,500, Books $2,400, Per/Ser (Incl. Access Fees) $100. Sal $7,000
Library Holdings: Bk Vols 11,705; Bk Titles 10,327
Subject Interests: Local history
Mem of SDak State Libr Syst
Friends of the Library Group

HIGHMORE

P HYDE COUNTY LIBRARY,* PO Box 479, 57345-0479. SAN 315-6354. Tel: 605-852-2514. E-Mail: hydelib@sullybuttes.net. *Librn*, Tina Hamlin
Founded 1918. Pop 2,084; Circ 19,630
Jan 1998-Dec 1998 Income $44,037. Mats Exp $3,121, Books $1,953, Per/Ser (Incl. Access Fees) $1,168. Sal $28,735
Library Holdings: Bk Vols 11,957; Per Subs 53

HOT SPRINGS

GM DEPARTMENT OF VETERANS AFFAIRS LIBRARY,* 500 N Fifth St, 57747. SAN 315-6370. Tel: 605-745-2013. FAX: 605-745-2082.
Founded 1905
Library Holdings: Bk Vols 11,135; Bk Titles 11,000
Subject Interests: Hist of South Dakota, Indian, Medicine

P HOT SPRINGS PUBLIC LIBRARY,* 1543 Baltimore Ave, 57747-1631. SAN 315-6362. Tel: 605-745-3151. *Librn*, Peggy Exum
Founded 1898. Circ 16,278
Library Holdings: Bk Vols 25,000
Subject Interests: SDak hist
Friends of the Library Group

HURON

P HURON PUBLIC LIBRARY,* 521 Dacota Ave S, 57350. SAN 315-6400. Tel: 605-352-3778. FAX: 605-352-3826. *Tech Servs*, Eileen Deckert; *Librn*, Colleen Smith; E-Mail: csmith@sdln.net; *Ref*, Karen Hall; *Ch Servs*, Betty Gilchrist
Founded 1907. Pop 13,000; Circ 150,557
Jan 1999-Dec 1999 Income $324,000, City $318,000, County $6,000. Mats Exp $48,200, Books $40,000, Per/Ser (Incl. Access Fees) $8,200. Sal $195,225 (Prof $139,227)
Library Holdings: Bk Titles 84,231; Per Subs 159
Subject Interests: SDak hist
Automation Activity & Vendor Info: (Acquisitions) PALS; (Cataloging) PALS; (Circulation) PALS; (Course Reserve) PALS; (ILL) PALS; (Media Booking) PALS; (OPAC) PALS; (Serials) PALS
Publications: Academic Index; Gen Academic Index; Health Index
Mem of SDak State Libr Syst
Partic in South Dakota Library Network
Special Services for the Blind - Large print bks; Talking Books
Friends of the Library Group

C HURON UNIVERSITY, Ella McIntire Library, 749 Illinois Ave SW, 5735 2798. SAN 315-6397. Tel: 605-352-8721, Ext 58. Reference Tel: 605-352-8721, Ext 57. FAX: 605-352-1548. E-Mail: librarian@huron.edu. Web Site www.huron.edu. *Dir*, Robert E Behlke; *Asst Librn*, Nancy Bohr; Staff 2 (MLS 1, Non-MLS 1)
Founded 1883. Enrl 652; Fac 35; Highest Degree: Master
Library Holdings: Bk Vols 50,000; Per Subs 37
Subject Interests: Nursing
Special Collections: Blackburn Coll
Partic in Minn Interlibr Telecommunication Exchange

INTERIOR

S NATIONAL PARK SERVICE, Badlands National Park Library, PO Box 6 57750. SAN 315-6419. Tel: 605-433-5361. FAX: 605-433-5248. Web Site: www.nps.gov/badl. *Librn*, P Sampson
Founded 1965
Library Holdings: Bk Vols 1,300; Bk Titles 1,000; Per Subs 15
Subject Interests: Badlands, Fossils, National Park Serv, Natural history, SDak Indians

IPSWICH

P MARCUS P BEEBE MEMORIAL LIBRARY,* 120 Main St, PO Box 304 57451-0304. SAN 315-6427. Tel: 605-426-6707. *Librn*, Ruby Bosanko
Founded 1886. Pop 2,000; Circ 13,243
1998-1999 Income $11,000. Mats Exp $1,700. Sal $6,010
Library Holdings: Bk Vols 16,000; Per Subs 19

KADOKA

P JACKSON COUNTY LIBRARY,* PO Box 368, 57543. SAN 360-4381. Tel: 605-837-2689. *Librn*, Terry Stout
Founded 1962. Pop 3,437; Circ 10,783
Library Holdings: Bk Vols 16,269; Bk Titles 14,819; Per Subs 18
Branches: 3
INTERIOR BRANCH, Interior, 57750. SAN 360-4411. *Librn*, Margaret Sampson
Library Holdings: Bk Vols 4,048; Bk Titles 3,915
KADOKA, PO Box 368, 57543. SAN 360-4438. *Librn*, Terry Stout
Library Holdings: Bk Vols 6,905; Bk Titles 6,597
LONG VALLEY BRANCH, Long Valley, 57547. SAN 360-4446. *Librn*, Patty Hamar
Library Holdings: Bk Vols 1,345; Bk Titles 1,275

KENNEBEC

P KENNEBEC PUBLIC LIBRARY,* PO Box 111, 57544-0111. SAN 315-6435. Tel: 605-869-2207. *Librn*, Josephine Schoenfelder
Pop 324; Circ 415
Library Holdings: Bk Vols 5,000; Per Subs 10

KEYSTONE

G MOUNT RUSHMORE NATIONAL MEMORIAL LIBRARY, PO Box 268 57751-0268. SAN 326-2006. Tel: 605-574-2523, Ext 195. FAX: 605-574-2307. *Librn*, Susan Walter
Founded 1963
Library Holdings: Bk Titles 1,300

KYLE

J OGLALA LAKOTA COLLEGE, Learning Resources Center,* PO Box 310 57752-0310. SAN 321-2319. Tel: 605-455-2321, Ext 327. FAX: 605-455-2728. *AV*, Wilma Witt; *Circ*, Dawn Clifford; Staff 4 (MLS 1, Non-MLS 3)
Founded 1970
Library Holdings: Bk Titles 26,000; Per Subs 25
Special Collections: Indians of North America, bks, v-tapes, a-tapes, archives; Lakota Leadership Coll
Publications: Policy & Procedures Manual, library instruction & skills; Specialized Bibliographies of North American Indians & related archival materials
Mem of SDak State Libr Syst
Partic in Minn Interlibr Telecommunication Exchange; OCLC Online Computer Library Center, Inc
Departmental Libraries:
EAGLE NEST COLLEGE CENTER, PO Box 476, Wanblee, 57577. SAN 321-5407. Tel: 605-462-6274. FAX: 605-462-6105. *Librn*, Georgia Rooks

Library Holdings: Bk Vols 1,000
EAST WAKPAMNI COLLEGE CENTER, PO Box 612, Batesland, 57716. SAN 321-5857. Tel: 605-288-1834. FAX: 605-288-1828. *Dir*, Phinet Redowl
Library Holdings: Bk Vols 1,000
LACREEK COLLEGE CENTER, PO Box 629, Martin, 57551. SAN 321-5881. Tel: 605-685-6407. FAX: 605-685-6887. *Dir*, Pearl Cottier
Library Holdings: Bk Vols 1,200
MANDERSON COLLEGE CENTER, PO Box 230, Manderson, 57756. SAN 321-5873. Tel: 605-867-5352. FAX: 605-867-1245. *Dir*, Karen White Butterfly
Library Holdings: Bk Vols 900
PAHIN SINTE COLLEGE CENTER, PO Box 220, Porcupine, 57772. SAN 321-589X. Tel: 605-867-5404. FAX: 605-867-1242. *Librn*, Janet Richards
Library Holdings: Bk Vols 1,000
PASS CREEK COLLEGE CENTER, PO Box 630, Allen, 57714. SAN 321-5849. Tel: 605-455-2757. FAX: 605-455-2428. *Dir*, Dean Betteyoun
Library Holdings: Bk Vols 1,000
PEJUTA HAKA COLLEGE CENTER, PO Box 370, 57752. SAN 321-5865. Tel: 605-455-2450. FAX: 605-455-2671. *Dir*, Jaunita Scherich
Library Holdings: Bk Vols 900
PINE RIDGE VILLAGE COLLEGE CENTER, PO Box 439, Pine Ridge, 57770. SAN 321-5911. Tel: 605-867-5893. FAX: 605-867-1241. *Dir*, Evelyn (Sissy) Eagle Bull
Library Holdings: Bk Vols 2,000
SCHOOL OF NURSING, PO Box 861, Pine Ridge, 57770. SAN 321-592X. Tel: 605-867-5856. FAX: 605-867-5724. *Dir*, Margaret F Hart; E-Mail: mhart4@yahoo.com
Library Holdings: Bk Vols 2,000
WHITE CLAY COLLEGE CENTER, PO Box 19, Oglala, 57764. SAN 321-5903. Tel: 605-867-5780. FAX: 605-867-1243. *Dir*, Donna Red Ear Horse
Library Holdings: Bk Vols 1,500

AKE ANDES

LAKE ANDES CARNEGIE PUBLIC LIBRARY,* Fifth & Main St, PO Box 248, 57356-0248. SAN 315-6443. Tel: 605-487-7524. *Librn*, Mary Carda
Pop 1,500; Circ 2,567
Library Holdings: Bk Vols 11,320; Per Subs 23
Mem of SDak State Libr Syst
Open Wed & Sat 1:30-5:30

EAD

PHOEBE APPERSON HEARST LIBRARY,* 315 W Main, 57754-1604. SAN 315-6451. Tel: 605-584-2013. *Dir*, Lee Ann Paananen
Founded 1894. Pop 4,420; Circ 16,000
Jan 1997-Dec 1998 Income $57,000
Library Holdings: Bk Titles 20,000; Per Subs 30
Special Collections: Curran Coll; Foreign Language Coll; Local History & Mining Records; Ralph G Cartwright Coll

EMMON

LEMMON PUBLIC LIBRARY,* 303 First Ave W, PO Box 120, 57638. SAN 315-646X. Tel: 605-374-5611. E-Mail: lemmoulis@dacotaweb.com. *Librn*, Carole Watrous
Pop 1,800; Circ 18,884
Library Holdings: Bk Vols 33,000; Per Subs 44
Open at 2 PM

EOLA

LEOLA PUBLIC LIBRARY,* PO Box 108, 57456-0147. SAN 315-6478. Tel: 605-439-3383. *Dir*, Della Schaffner; *Asst Librn*, Jan Claggett
Founded 1968. Pop 521; Circ 57,018
Library Holdings: Bk Vols 6,392; Per Subs 10

LETCHER

P LETCHER PUBLIC LIBRARY,* PO Box 176, 57359-0176. SAN 325-0091. Tel: 605-248-2242 ((city treasurer)), 605-248-2689. *Librn*, Vera Fouberg
Founded 1924. Pop 150; Circ 2,500; Fac 134
Library Holdings: Bk Titles 2,500
Subject Interests: SDak hist

LOWER BRULE

G BUREAU OF INDIAN AFFAIRS, Lower Brule School Library, Brule Sioux High School, PO Box 245, 57548. SAN 315-6486. Tel: 605-473-5510. FAX: 605-473-0217. E-Mail: lbhs@btigate.com. *Librn*, Terry Moore
Library Holdings: Bk Vols 6,000; Per Subs 40
Subject Interests: Plains Indians
Open school hours

MADISON

C DAKOTA STATE UNIVERSITY, Karl E Mundt Library, 820 N Washington Ave, 57042-1799. SAN 315-6494. Tel: 605-256-5203. Circulation Tel: 605-256-5205. Reference Tel: 605-256-7128. FAX: 605-256-5208. Web Site: www.departments.dsu.edu/library. *Dir*, Ethelle S Bean; Tel: 605-256-5207, E-Mail: beane@pluto.dsu.edu; *Tech Servs*, Linda Stroeber; Tel: 605-256-5204, E-Mail: stoebel@pluto.dsu.edu; *Coll Develop, Publ Servs*, Rise Smith; E-Mail: smithr@pluto.dsu.edu; *Ref*, Todd Quinn; Tel: 605-256-5845, E-Mail: quinnt@pluto.dsu.edu; Staff 7 (MLS 4, Non-MLS 3)
Founded 1881. Enrl 2,003; Fac 76; Highest Degree: Master
Jul 1999-Jun 2000 Income $892,167
Library Holdings: Bk Vols 178,240; Bk Titles 77,117; Per Subs 382
Special Collections: Senator Karl E Mundt Archives; South Dakota
Automation Activity & Vendor Info: (Acquisitions) PALS; (Cataloging) PALS; (Circulation) PALS; (ILL) PALS; (Media Booking) PALS; (OPAC) PALS; (Serials) PALS
Database Vendor: Dialog, GaleNet, IAC - Info Trac, IAC - SearchBank, Lexis-Nexis, OCLC - First Search, ProQuest
Partic in MINITEX Library Information Network; OCLC Online Computer Library Center, Inc; South Dakota Library Network

M MADISON COMMUNITY HOSPITAL, Health Science Library,* 917 N Washington Ave, 57042. SAN 329-2509. Tel: 605-256-6551. FAX: 605-256-6469. *Librn*, Carol Erickson
Library Holdings: Bk Vols 44; Bk Titles 40; Per Subs 15

P MADISON PUBLIC LIBRARY,* 209 E Center St, 57042-2998. SAN 315-6508. Tel: 605-256-7525. FAX: 605-256-7526. *Dir*, Nancy Sabbe; Staff 2 (MLS 2)
Founded 1906. Pop 10,518; Circ 69,469
Jan 1998-Dec 1998 Income $277,181, City $271,811, County $1,000, Locally Generated Income $4,370. Mats Exp $50,610. Sal $72,082
Library Holdings: Bk Titles 34,000; Per Subs 184
Special Collections: South Dakota-Lake County (Dakota Coll)
Mem of SDak State Libr Syst

MARTIN

P BENNETT COUNTY PUBLIC LIBRARY,* Main St, PO Box 190, 57551-0190. SAN 315-6516. Tel: 605-685-6556. *Dir*, Ardis D Ladely
Founded 1951. Pop 4,000; Circ 11,067
Library Holdings: Bk Vols 30,000; Bk Titles 46; Per Subs 35
Friends of the Library Group

MARVIN

P BLUE CLOUD ABBEY LIBRARY,* 46561 147th St, 57251-0098. (Mail add: PO Box 98, 57251-0098), SAN 315-6524. Tel: 605-398-9200. FAX: 605-398-9201. E-Mail: abbey@bluecloud.org. Web Site: www.bluecloud.org. *Librn*, Odilo Burkhardt; Staff 2 (MLS 1, Non-MLS 1)
Founded 1950. Pop 9,500
Library Holdings: Bk Vols 35,000; Per Subs 145
Subject Interests: History, Indian studies, Scriptures, Theology

MILBANK

P GRANT COUNTY PUBLIC LIBRARY, 207 E Park Ave, 57252-2497. SAN 315-6532. Tel: 605-432-6543. FAX: 605-432-6543. E-Mail: libraryl@tnics.com. *Dir*, Robin Schrupp; Staff 13 (MLS 1, Non-MLS 12)
Founded 1978. Pop 9,304; Circ 86,661
Jan 1999-Dec 1999 Income $164,279, County $157,398, Locally Generated Income $6,881. Mats Exp $31,600, Books $23,500, Per/Ser (Incl. Access Fees) $2,391, AV Equip $5,709. Sal $101,482 (Prof $23,800)
Library Holdings: Bk Vols 49,623; Bk Titles 38,721; Per Subs 85
Subject Interests: Maps
Special Collections: Old County Newspapers on Microfilm
Automation Activity & Vendor Info: (Acquisitions) Sagebrush Corporation; (Circulation) Sagebrush Corporation
Mem of SDak State Libr Syst . Satellite Libraries: 4

MILLER

P HAND COUNTY LIBRARY, 402 N Broadway, 57362-1438. SAN 315-6540. Tel: 605-853-3693. FAX: 605-853-2201. E-Mail: hcltc@turtlecreek.net. *Librn*, Debra Bushfield
Founded 1947. Pop 4,948; Circ 57,345
2000-2000 Income $58,000
Library Holdings: Bk Vols 39,919; Per Subs 108
Subject Interests: Authors, SDak bks
Special Collections: Local Newspapers, micro
Friends of the Library Group

MISSION

J SINTE GLESKA UNIVERSITY LIBRARY,* E Hwy 18, 57555-0107. (Mail add: PO Box 107, 57555-0170), SAN 315-6559. Tel: 605-856-2355. FAX: 605-856-2011. *Coll Develop, Dir*, Rachel Lindvall; E-Mail: rachell@sinte.edu; *Cat*, Diana Dillon; *Circ*, Michelle Leneaugh; *ILL*, Donald Leader Charge; *Media Spec*, William Emery; *Ref*, Marietta Kloppel
Founded 1972. Enrl 850; Fac 60
Library Holdings: Bk Vols 45,000; Per Subs 335
Subject Interests: Ecology, Education, Environ, Law, Native Am studies
Partic in American Indian Higher Education Consortium; Minn Interlibr Telecommunication Exchange; South Dakota Library Network

MITCHELL

C DAKOTA WESLEYAN UNIVERSITY, Layne Library, 1200 W University, 57301. SAN 315-6567. Tel: 605-995-2618. FAX: 605-995-2893. Web Site: www.dwu.edu/library. *Dir*, Kevin J Kenkel; E-Mail: kekenkel@dwu.edu; *Publ Servs*, Jodie Baker; Staff 4 (MLS 2, Non-MLS 2)
Founded 1884. Enrl 715; Fac 38; Highest Degree: Master
Jun 1998-May 1999 Income $252,350. Mats Exp $89,830, Books $36,670, Per/Ser (Incl. Access Fees) $22,425, Presv $1,200, Micro $15,400, AV Equip $10,035, Electronic Ref Mat (Incl. Access Fees) $4,100. Sal $124,502 (Prof $63,588)
Library Holdings: Bk Vols 65,000; Per Subs 412
Special Collections: Senator Francis Case Coll; Senator George McGovern Coll; South Dakota & Middle Border History; Western America (Senator Francis Case Archives, Jennewein Western Library, Badger Clark Coll, Jedediah Smith Coll, Preacher Smith Coll)
Automation Activity & Vendor Info: (Acquisitions) PALS; (Cataloging) PALS; (Circulation) PALS; (Serials) PALS
Partic in Cols of Mid-Am; MINITEX Library Information Network; OCLC Online Computer Library Center, Inc; South Dakota Library Network

P MITCHELL PUBLIC LIBRARY, 221 N Duff St, 57301-2596. SAN 315-6583. Tel: 605-995-8480. FAX: 605-995-8482. *Dir*, Jackie Hess; E-Mail: jhess@sdln.net; *ILL*, Sandra Spanos; *Tech Servs*, Lajeane Jons; *Ch Servs*, Lori Wagner; *Circ*, Cindy Meinen; *Circ*, Linda Rishling; Staff 7 (MLS 1, Non-MLS 6)
Founded 1903. Pop 14,386; Circ 144,392
Jan 1999-Dec 1999 Income $354,091, City $339,574, Locally Generated Income $14,517. Mats Exp $59,498, Books $53,523, Per/Ser (Incl. Access Fees) $5,975. Sal $181,646 (Prof $34,379)
Library Holdings: Bk Vols 66,741; Per Subs 159
Special Collections: Mitchell Area Archives, newspapers; South Dakota Coll
Automation Activity & Vendor Info: (Cataloging) PALS; (Circulation) PALS; (ILL) PALS; (OPAC) PALS
Database Vendor: IAC - Info Trac, IAC - SearchBank, ProQuest
Partic in OCLC Online Computer Library Center, Inc; South Dakota Library Network
Friends of the Library Group

M QUEEN OF PEACE HOSPITAL LIBRARY,* 525 N Foster, 57301. SAN 315-6575. Tel: 605-995-2462. FAX: 605-995-2441. *Librn*, Pat Sudbeck
Founded 1918
Library Holdings: Bk Vols 1,000; Per Subs 35
Subject Interests: Nursing

MOBRIDGE

P A H BROWN PUBLIC LIBRARY,* 521 N Main St, 57601-2130. SAN 315-6591. Tel: 605-845-2808. E-Mail: ahbrown@westriv.com. *Librn*, Ione Stiles
Founded 1930. Circ 10,132
Library Holdings: Bk Vols 20,000; Per Subs 43
Subject Interests: Local history
Special Collections: South Dakota Coll

NEW HOLLAND

R CHRISTIAN REFORMED CHURCH LIBRARY, PO Box 3, 57364. SAN 315-6613. Tel: 605-243-2250. *In Charge*, Mrs Cornelius Lieuwen
Founded 1947
1998-1999 Income $500. Mats Exp Manuscripts & Archives $20
Library Holdings: Bk Vols 3,000

NEWELL

P NEWELL PUBLIC LIBRARY,* 208 Girard, PO Box 54, 57760. SAN 315-6621. Tel: 605-456-2179. *Librn*, Glynda Smith
Circ 6,046
Library Holdings: Bk Vols 12,044; Per Subs 22

ONIDA

P SULLY COUNTY LIBRARY,* PO Box 472, 57564-0472. SAN 315-663X. Tel: 605-258-2133. *Librn*, Genita deSautell; *Asst Librn*, Ann Wright
Pop 800; Circ 16,000
Library Holdings: Bk Vols 20,000

PARKER

P PARKER PUBLIC LIBRARY, 115 Main Ave, 57053-0576. (Mail add: PO Box 576, 57053-0576), SAN 315-6648. Tel: 605-297-5552. *Dir*, Linda Chaney
Founded 1904. Pop 1,005; Circ 8,000
Jan 1999-Dec 1999 Income City $30,000
Library Holdings: Bk Vols 18,000; Per Subs 30
Subject Interests: Christian fiction, Large print, SDak hist
Special Services for the Blind - Large print bks

PIERRE

P RAWLINS MUNICIPAL LIBRARY, 1000 E Church St, 57501. SAN 315-6656. Tel: 605-773-7421. FAX: 605-773-7423. Web Site: www.sdln.net/libs/rawlins/rawlins.html. *Ch Servs*, Pat Weeldreyer; E-Mail: pweeldre@sdln.net *Circ*, Judy Ulvestad
Founded 1905. Pop 14,760; Circ 101,107
Jan 1999-Dec 1999 Mats Exp $72,998, Books $51,636, Per/Ser (Incl. Access Fees) $6,562, AV Equip $14,800. Sal $198,709
Library Holdings: Bk Titles 50,988; Per Subs 106
Special Collections: History (South Dakota Coll), bks, pamphlets, pictures
Partic in South Dakota Library Network
Friends of the Library Group

M SAINT MARY'S HEALTHCARE CENTER LIBRARY, 800 E Dakota Ave 57501-3313. SAN 324-542X. Tel: 605-224-3178. FAX: 605-224-8339. E-Mail: stmarys@iw.net. *Librn*, Chris Vandenbos
Founded 1973
Library Holdings: Per Subs 180

P SOUTH DAKOTA BRAILLE & TALKING BOOK LIBRARY,* McKay Bldg, 800 Governors Dr, 57501-2294. SAN 315-6699. Tel: 605-773-3131. FAX: 605-773-4950. *State Librn*, Jane Kolbe; Staff 7 (MLS 1, Non-MLS 6)
Founded 1968. Circ 115,850
Library Holdings: Bk Vols 162,000
Special Collections: Dakota Language Coll; North Dakota & South Dakota Coll
Publications: Dakota Newsletter (quarterly, recorded on cassette, large print & Braille)

G SOUTH DAKOTA DEPARTMENT OF GAME, FISH & PARKS DIVISION OF WILDLIFE, Natural Heritage Program Library, 523 E Capitol, 57501. SAN 372-9508. Tel: 605-773-4345. FAX: 605-773-6245. *Dir*, Doug Backlund; E-Mail: doug.backlund@state.sd.us
Library Holdings: Bk Vols 4,000; Per Subs 60
Subject Interests: Natural history

G SOUTH DAKOTA STATE HISTORICAL SOCIETY, State Archives,* 900 Governors Dr, 57501-2217. SAN 315-6664. Tel: 605-773-3804. FAX: 605-773-6041. E-Mail: archref@state.sd.us. Web Site: www.state.sd.us/deca/cultural/arc_libr.htm. *Librn*, Lavera Rose; Tel: 605-773-3780
Founded 1901
Library Holdings: Bk Vols 13,770; Bk Titles 7,164; Per Subs 188
Subject Interests: Plains Indians, SDak hist, SDak Western Am
Special Collections: Dakota & Western Indians Coll, photog, newsp
Partic in OCLC Online Computer Library Center, Inc; South Dakota Library Network

P SOUTH DAKOTA STATE LIBRARY,* 800 Governors Dr, 57501-2294. SAN 360-4500. Tel: 605-773-3131. Toll Free Tel: 800-423-6665 (South Dakota only). FAX: 605-773-6962. Web Site: www.state.sd.us/state/lib. *State Librn*, Suzane Miller; *Publ Servs*, Dan Boyd; *Doc*, Ann Eichinger; *Circ, ILL*, Bellen Jacobsen; Staff 9 (MLS 9)
Founded 1913. Pop 729,034
Library Holdings: Bk Vols 160,614; Bk Titles 988; Per Subs 75
Subject Interests: Native Am
Publications: South Dakota State Government Publications
Partic in BRS; Coop Libr Agency for Syst & Servs; Dialog Corporation; MINITEX Library Information Network; OCLC Online Computer Library Center, Inc; RLIN; SDC Info Servs; South Dakota Library Network; Western Council Of State Libraries, Inc
Friends of the Library Group

GL SOUTH DAKOTA SUPREME COURT, Law Library,* State Capital, 500 E Capitol Ave, 57501-5070. SAN 315-6702. Tel: 605-773-4898. FAX: 605-773-6128. *Librn*, Sheridan Cash Anderson; *Asst Librn*, Donnis Deyo
Library Holdings: Bk Vols 40,000

NE RIDGE

THE HERITAGE CENTER LIBRARY, Red Cloud Indian School, 57770. SAN 375-6564. Tel: 605-867-5491. FAX: 605-867-1291. Web Site: www.basec.net/rcheritage/. *Dir*, Brother Simon
Library Holdings: Bk Titles 900; Per Subs 15

LANKINTON

PLANKINTON CITY LIBRARY,* PO Box 517, 57368-0517. SAN 315-6710. Tel: 605-942-7767. FAX: 605-942-7767. *Librn*, Mavis Haines
Pop 750; Circ 5,380
Library Holdings: Bk Vols 5,000

RESHO

PRESHO PUBLIC LIBRARY,* PO Box 118, 57568-0118. SAN 315-6737. Tel: 605-895-2443. *Librn*, Laverne Olson
Pop 950; Circ 4,379
Library Holdings: Bk Vols 12,000

APID CITY

NATIONAL AMERICAN UNIVERSITY, Thomas Jefferson Library, 321 Kansas City St, 57701-3692. SAN 315-6753. Tel: 605-394-4946. Interlibrary Loan Service Tel: 605-394-4943. Circulation Tel: 605-394-4912. Toll Free Tel: 800-843-8892. FAX: 605-394-4871. Web Site: www.national.edu. *Dir*, Linda Gogolin; E-Mail: lgogolin@rc.national.edu; *ILL*, Patricia Weiss; *Circ*, Suzanne Brown; Staff 3 (MLS 1, Non-MLS 2)
Founded 1964. Enrl 1,500; Fac 40; Highest Degree: Master
Library Holdings: Bk Vols 32,700; Per Subs 157
Subject Interests: Accounting, Bus, Mgt, Occupational therapy asst, Paralegal, Veterinary tech
Special Collections: Legal Resources; Veterinary Clinics of North America
Automation Activity & Vendor Info: (OPAC) PALS
Database Vendor: IAC - Info Trac, OCLC - First Search, ProQuest
Restriction: Open to student, faculty & staff, Public use on premises
Function: ILL available
Partic in MINITEX Library Information Network; OCLC Online Computer Library Center, Inc; South Dakota Library Network

RAPID CITY JOURNAL LIBRARY, 507 Main St, 57701. SAN 372-9516. Tel: 605-394-8409. FAX: 605-394-8463. E-Mail: journal@rapidnet.com. *Mgr*, Sheri Sponder
Library Holdings: Bk Vols 300

RAPID CITY PUBLIC LIBRARY, 610 Quincy St, 57701-3655. SAN 315-6761. Tel: 605-394-4171, Ext 216. FAX: 605-394-6626. Web Site: www.rapidcitypubliclibrary.org. *Dir*, Greta Chapman; E-Mail: gchapman@sdln.net; *Ad Servs, Ref*, Shari West-Twitero; *Cat, Online Servs*, Karling Abernathy; *Coll Develop, Publ Servs*, Terri Davis; *YA Servs*, Linda Wagner; Staff 27 (MLS 7, Non-MLS 20)
Founded 1903. Pop 60,000; Circ 510,000
Jan 1999-Dec 1999 Income $1,409,039, City $1,248,426, Parent Institution $160,613. Mats Exp $221,397, Books $111,821, Per/Ser (Incl. Access Fees) $28,140, Electronic Ref Mat (Incl. Access Fees) $81,436. Sal $723,374 (Prof $354,453)
Library Holdings: Bk Vols 116,831; Bk Titles 104,947; Per Subs 270
Subject Interests: Large print, SDak
Special Collections: Rapid City Society for Genealogical Research Coll
Partic in Minn Interlibr Telecommunication Exchange; OCLC Online Computer Library Center, Inc; South Dakota Library Network
Friends of the Library Group

1 RAPID CITY REGIONAL HOSPITAL, Healths Sciences Library,* 353 Fairmont Blvd, PO Box 6000, 57709-6000. SAN 315-677X. Tel: 605-341-7101. FAX: 605-348-1578. E-Mail: library@rcrh.org. Web Site: www.rcrh.org/education/libraryresources.htm. *Dir, Online Servs*, Patricia Hamilton; *Ref*, Coleen Coble; *Ref*, Michael Bossem; Staff 3 (MLS 3)
Founded 1926. Enrl 160
Library Holdings: Bk Vols 12,372; Per Subs 671
Subject Interests: Health admin, Medicine, Nursing
Special Collections: ANA Publications; Health Care, govt doc; National League for Nursing Publications
Partic in BRS; Nat Libr of Med; OCLC Online Computer Library Center, Inc

: SOUTH DAKOTA SCHOOL OF MINES & TECHNOLOGY, Devereaux Library, 501 E Saint Joseph St, 57701-3995. SAN 360-456X. Tel: 605-394-2418. FAX: 605-394-1256. E-Mail: libref@paz.sdsmt.edu. Web Site: www.sdsmt.edu/services/library. *Dir*, Patty Andersen; *Coll Develop*, Cindy Davies; Staff 3 (MLS 3)
Founded 1885. Fac 175; Highest Degree: Doctorate
1998-1999 Mats Exp $190,796, Books $36,587, Per/Ser (Incl. Access Fees) $154,209. Sal $245,980 (Prof $162,248)
Library Holdings: Bk Vols 225,854; Bk Titles 137,864; Per Subs 461
Subject Interests: Engineering, Sci, Technology
Special Collections: Black Hills & Western South Dakota Mining History, etc (Black Hills Special Coll Area), maps; School History, 1885 to date (Archives Area)
Publications: Devereaux Online
Partic in Bibliographical Center For Research, Rocky Mountain Region, Inc; MINITEX Library Information Network; OCLC Online Computer Library Center, Inc; South Dakota Library Network
Friends of the Library Group

J WESTERN DAKOTA TECHNICAL INSTITUTE LIBRARY, 800 Mickelson Dr, 57703. SAN 320-9849. Tel: 605-394-4034. Circulation Tel: 605-394-4034, Ext 218. FAX: 605-394-1789. Web Site: www.wdti.tec.sd.us/staff/alltogetherwesterndatokatec.org/inhouse/studentindex.htm. *Librn*, Debbie Arne; E-Mail: darne@wdti.tec.sd.us; Staff 2 (Non-MLS 2)
Founded 1968. Enrl 950; Highest Degree: Associate
Jul 2000-Jun 2001 Mats Exp $12,498, Books $6,598, Per/Ser (Incl. Access Fees) $3,000, Electronic Ref Mat (Incl. Access Fees) $2,900. Sal $38,438
Library Holdings: Bk Titles 3,500; Per Subs 125
Subject Interests: Agriculture, Bus mgt, Carpentry, Computer network specialist, Electronics, Law enforcement, Native Am, Nursing, Paralegal, Pharmacy, South Dakota, Vocational
Partic in South Dakota Library Network
Open Mon-Thurs 7:30-9, Fri 7:30-4, Sat 10-4

REDFIELD

P REDFIELD CARNEGIE LIBRARY,* 5 E Fifth Ave, 57469-1243. SAN 315-6788. Tel: 605-472-1710. *Librn*, Betty Baloun
Circ 14,053
Library Holdings: Bk Vols 10,643; Per Subs 54

G SOUTH DAKOTA DEVELOPMENTAL CENTER, Redfield Library,* RR 3, PO Box 410, 57469-0410. SAN 328-4786. Tel: 605-472-2400. FAX: 605-472-0922. *In Charge*, Kim Benning
Library Holdings: Bk Vols 500
Subject Interests: Special education
Partic in South Dakota Library Network

SIOUX FALLS

S ARGUS LEADER LIBRARY, 200 S Minnesota Ave, 57104. (Mail add: PO Box 5034, 57117-5034), SAN 370-6184. Tel: 605-331-2200. FAX: 605-331-2294. *Librn*, Sharon Rehfeldt
Library Holdings: Bk Vols 295; Bk Titles 170

C AUGUSTANA COLLEGE, Mikkelsen Library, 2001 S Summit Ave, 57197-0001. SAN 315-6796. Tel: 605-336-4921. FAX: 605-336-5447. Web Site: www.augie.edu/library/. *Dir Libr Serv*, Ronelle Thompson; E-Mail: rthomps@inst.augie.edu; *Tech Servs*, Deborah A Hagemeier; Tel: 605-336-5354, E-Mail: debh@inst.augie.edu; *Publ Servs*, Ann M Smith; Tel: 605-336-4383, E-Mail: asmith@inst.augie.edu; *Media Spec Ad*, Judith Howard; Tel: 605-336-4920, E-Mail: jhoward@inst.augie.edu; *Circ*, Jan Brue Enright; Tel: 605-336-4493, E-Mail: jenright@inst.augie.edu; *Cat*, Kay Christensen; Tel: 605-336-5357, E-Mail: kchriste@inst.augie.edu; *Ref*, Lisa Brunick; Tel: 605-274-4921, E-Mail: brunick@inst.augie.edu. Subject Specialists: *Govt doc*, Kay Christensen; Staff 13 (MLS 6, Non-MLS 7)
Founded 1860. Enrl 1,774; Fac 127; Highest Degree: Master
Aug 1999-Jul 2000 Income $714,165, Locally Generated Income $18,183, Parent Institution $633,589, Other $62,393. Mats Exp $326,352, Books $48,479, Per/Ser (Incl. Access Fees) $135,083, Presv $6,931, Micro $13,513, AV Equip $7,875, Electronic Ref Mat (Incl. Access Fees) $34,946. Sal $371,880 (Prof $194,807)
Library Holdings: Bk Vols 237,009; Per Subs 1,085
Special Collections: Center for Western Studies; Krause Coll; Norwegian Coll; Upper Mid-West (Dakota Coll)
Automation Activity & Vendor Info: (Acquisitions) PALS; (Cataloging) PALS; (Circulation) PALS; (Course Reserve) PALS; (ILL) PALS; (OPAC) PALS; (Serials) PALS
Database Vendor: Dialog, GaleNet, IAC - Info Trac, Lexis-Nexis, OCLC - First Search, OVID Technologies, ProQuest, Wilson - Wilson Web
Partic in MINITEX Library Information Network; OCLC Online Computer Library Center, Inc; South Dakota Library Network
Friends of the Library Group
Departmental Libraries:
CENTER FOR WESTERN STUDIES, 2001 S Summit Ave, PO Box 727, 57197. SAN 329-3033. Tel: 605-336-4007. FAX: 605-336-4999. Web Site: www.inst.augie.edu/cwsi. *Dir Info Resources & Res*, Harry F Thompson; *Exec Dir*, Arthur R Huseboe
Founded 1970
Aug 1998-Jul 1999 Income $430,000, Locally Generated Income $400,000, Parent Institution $30,000. Mats Exp $4,300, Books $3,000, Per/Ser (Incl. Access Fees) $300, Presv $450, Micro $50, Manuscripts & Archives $500. Sal $210,000 (Prof $170,000)
Library Holdings: Bk Vols 35,000; Bk Titles 29,000
Subject Interests: American West, Northern Prairie Plains
Special Collections: United Church of Christ SD Conference Archives); Upper Great Plains (Episcopal Diocese of SD Archives

Publications: CWS Newsletter; The Geography of South Dakota; Yanktonai Sioux Water Colors & other books about Plains Indians & Western History
Restriction: Non-circulating to the public
Partic in OCLC Online Computer Library Center, Inc; South Dakota Library Network
Friends of the Library Group

M AVERA MCKENNAN HOSPITAL & UNIVERSITY HEALTH CENTER, Medical Library, 800 E 21st St, 57105-1096. (Mail add: PO Box 5045, 57117-5045), SAN 315-6826. Tel: 605-322-8484. FAX: 605-322-8480.; Staff 4 (Non-MLS 4)
Library Holdings: Bk Vols 5,000; Per Subs 900
Subject Interests: Allied health, Consumer educ, Maternal child health, Medicine, Nursing
Publications: The Resource: Newsletter of McKennan Hospital's Medical Library (quarterly)
Partic in Dialog Corporation; MINITEX Library Information Network; Nat Libr of Med; OCLC Online Computer Library Center, Inc

R CHRISTIAN RESOURCE CENTER LIBRARY, 327 S Dakota, 57104. SAN 315-6818. Tel: 605-336-3734. FAX: 605-336-8370. Web Site: www.flcsf.org. *Librn*, Beth De Ruyter
Founded 1920
Library Holdings: Bk Titles 6,600; Per Subs 17
Subject Interests: Relig studies

GM DEPARTMENT OF VETERANS AFFAIRS, Center Library, 2501 W 22nd St, 57117. (Mail add: PO Box 5046, 57117-5046), SAN 315-6923. Tel: 605-336-3230, Ext 6559. FAX: 605-333-6872.
Library Holdings: Bk Titles 500; Per Subs 12
Subject Interests: Medicine, Patient educ, Recreational reading, Staff educ
Partic in Veterans Affairs Library Network

R FIRST BAPTIST CHURCH LIBRARY,* 1401 S Covell Ave, 57105. SAN 315-680X. Tel: 605-336-0966. FAX: 605-336-3294. *Librn*, Harriett Park
Library Holdings: Bk Vols 3,300; Per Subs 15
Friends of the Library Group

S GREAT PLAINS ZOO & DELBRIDGE MUSEUM, Zoo & Museum Reference Library,* 805 S Kiwanis Ave, 57104-3714. SAN 315-6869. Tel: 605-367-7003. FAX: 605-367-8340. *Exec Dir*, Ed Asper; *Dir Libr Serv*, Tyler Reid Ahnemann; E-Mail: tylera@gpzoo.org
Founded 1966. Pop 120,000
Library Holdings: Bk Vols 210; Bk Titles 185
Subject Interests: Natural history
Special Collections: Grizmik, 13 vol; International Zoo Year Book, 24 vol
Restriction: Reference only to non-staff

SR LUTHERAN CHURCH-MISSOURI SYNOD, South Dakota District Archives,* PO Box 89110, 57109. SAN 374-9398. Tel: 605-361-1514. FAX: 605-361-7959.
Library Holdings: Bk Vols 50; Per Subs 100
Special Collections: District Congregation Records

R NORTH AMERICAN BAPTIST SEMINARY, Kaiser-Ramaker Library, 1525 S Grange Ave, 57105-1526. SAN 315-6834. Tel: 605-336-6588, Ext 224. FAX: 605-335-9090. E-Mail: library@nabs.edu. Web Site: www.nabs.edu. *Dir*, Paul A Roberts; E-Mail: PARoberts@nabs.edu; Staff 3 (MLS 1, Non-MLS 2)
Founded 1858. Enrl 145; Highest Degree: Doctorate
Library Holdings: Bk Vols 66,381; Per Subs 304
Subject Interests: Biblical studies, Church history, Counseling, Theology
Special Collections: Harris Coll (preaching); North American Baptist Archives
Automation Activity & Vendor Info: (Acquisitions) PALS; (Cataloging) PALS; (Circulation) PALS; (Course Reserve) PALS; (ILL) PALS; (Media Booking) PALS; (OPAC) PALS; (Serials) PALS
Database Vendor: Ebsco - EbscoHost, IAC - Info Trac, OCLC - First Search, ProQuest
Mem of SDak State Libr Syst
Partic in MINITEX Library Information Network; Pals; South Dakota Library Network

S SIOUXLAND HERITAGE MUSEUMS, Pettigrew Museum Library, 200 W Sixth St, 57104. SAN 315-6907. Tel: 605-367-4210. FAX: 605-367-6004. *Dir*, William J Hoskins; Staff 3 (Non-MLS 3)
Founded 1926
Library Holdings: Bk Titles 10,000; Per Subs 10
Subject Interests: Especially pioneering through pre-World War II, Hist of Sioux Falls, SDak state, Surrounding region
Special Collections: Local & Regional History; Populism, Bimetalism, Maverick Politics 1880-1920; R F Pettigrew Papers & Private Library, bks, pamphlets, pvt papers
Publications: Sioxland Heritage Museums Report
Restriction: By appointment only, Not a lending library
Function: Archival collection, Photocopies available, Research library
Special Services for the Deaf - TTY machine

P SIOUXLAND LIBRARIES, 201 N Main Ave, 57104-6002. SAN 315-688 Tel: 605-367-8701. Interlibrary Loan Service Tel: 605-367-8702. Circulati Tel: 605-367-8700. Reference Tel: 605-367-8720. TDD: 605-367-7082. FA 605-367-4312. Web Site: www.siouxland.lib.sd.us. *Dir*, Jim Dertien; E-Ma jimd@siouxland.lib.sd.us; *Assoc Dir*, Joan Reddy; Tel: 605-367-8721, E-Mail: joanr@siouxland.lib.sd.us; *Librn*, Jane Goettsch; Tel: 605-367-871 Fax: 605-371-4144, E-Mail: janeg@siouxland.lib.sd.us; *Librn*, Paulette Fischer; Tel: 605-367-8714, Fax: 605-362-2816, E-Mail: pfishcer@ siouxland.lib.sd.us; *Ch Servs*, Jim Oliver; Tel: 605-367-8719, E-Mail: jimo siouxland.lib.sd.us; *AV*, Cynthia Winn; Tel: 605-367-8725, E-Mail: cwinn@ siouxland.lib.sd.us; *Res*, Doug Murdock; Tel: 605-367-8718, E-Mail: dougm@siouxland.lib.sd.us; *Circ*, Judy VanWyngarden; Tel: 605-367-8723 E-Mail: judyv@siouxland.lib.sd.us; *Cat*, Mark Bowman; Tel: 605-367-870 E-Mail: markb@siouxland.lib.sd.us; *Br Coordr*, Jodi Fick; Tel: 605-367-8713, E-Mail: jodif@siouxland.lib.sd.us; *Per*, Jane Huwe; Tel: 605-367-7444, E-Mail: janeh@siouxland.lib.sd.us; *Govt Doc*, Monique Christensen; Tel: 605-367-7436, E-Mail: moniquec@siouxland.lib.sd.us; *ILL*, Tina Irvin E-Mail: tinai@siouxland.lib.sd.us; *Tech Servs*, Donna Cranmer; Tel: 605-367-8712, E-Mail: donnac@siouxland.lib.sd.us; Staff 89 (MLS 13, Non-M 76)
Founded 1886. Pop 143,216; Circ 1,115,037
Jan 1999-Dec 1999 Income (Main Library and Branch Library) $3,446,815 City $2,827,667, County $501,890, Locally Generated Income $117,258. Mats Exp $506,207, Books $341,008, Per/Ser (Incl. Access Fees) $38,691, Micro $12,500, AV Equip $68,972, Electronic Ref Mat (Incl. Access Fees) $45,036. Sal $2,438,296
Library Holdings: Bk Vols 368,162; Bk Titles 160,878; Per Subs 587
Subject Interests: Foreign Language, Literature, SDak hist
Automation Activity & Vendor Info: (Acquisitions) epixtech, inc.; (Cataloging) epixtech, inc.; (Circulation) epixtech, inc.; (ILL) epixtech, inc. (Media Booking) epixtech, inc.; (OPAC) epixtech, inc.; (Serials) epixtech, inc.
Database Vendor: Dialog, epixtech, inc., GaleNet, IAC - Info Trac, IAC - SearchBank, OCLC - First Search
Publications: Library GROUPletter; Weekly Staff Newsletter
Partic in MINITEX Library Information Network; OCLC Online Computer Library Center, Inc; South Dakota Library Network
Special Services for the Deaf - Staff with knowledge of sign language; TD Special Services for the Blind - ADA PC (OPAC) with JAWS & Zoom Tex Kurzweil Reading Machine; Reading edge system; Telesensory screen enlarger & speech synthesis interface to the OPAC
Branches: 10
BALTIC BRANCH, PO Box 326, Baltic, 57003-0326. SAN 329-577X. Tel 605-529-5415. FAX: 605-529-5415. *In Charge*, Kathy Faith; Staff 1 (Non MLS 1)
BRANDON BRANCH, 109 N Pipestone, Brandon, 57005-1509. SAN 327-960X. Tel: 605-582-2390. FAX: 605-582-2390. *In Charge*, Peggy Lind; Staff 2 (Non-MLS 2)
CAILLE, 4100 Carnegie Circle, 57106. SAN 375-5606. Tel: 605-362-2818. FAX: 605-362-2816. *Librn*, Paulette Fischer; Tel: 605-367-7686, E-Mail: pfischer@sioux-falls.org
COLTON BRANCH, PO Box 338, Colton, 57018-0338. SAN 322-6115. Tel: 605-446-3519. FAX: 605-446-3519. *In Charge*, Sandra Bakker; Staff 1 (Non-MLS 1)
CROOKS BRANCH, 900 N West Ave, Crooks, 57020. SAN 360-4179. Tel: 605-543-5296. TDD: 605-543-5296. FAX: 605-543-5296. Web Site: www.siouxland.lib.sd.us. *In Charge*, Bev Liesinger; E-Mail: jodif@ siouxland.lib.sd.us; Staff 5 (Non-MLS 5)
Automation Activity & Vendor Info: (Cataloging) epixtech, inc.; (Circulation) epixtech, inc.; (OPAC) epixtech, inc.
Database Vendor: Ebsco - EbscoHost, epixtech, inc., IAC - SearchBank
Function: Photocopies available
GARRETSON BRANCH, PO Drawer N, Garretson, 57030-0392. SAN 322-6107. Tel: 605-594-6619. *In Charge*, Agnes Berge; Staff 3 (Non-MLS 3)
HUMBOLDT BRANCH, PO Box 166, Humboldt, 57035-0166. SAN 322-6085. Tel: 605-363-3361. FAX: 605-363-3361. *In Charge*, Marian Puthoff Staff 2 (Non-MLS 2)
RONNING, 3100 E 49th St, 57103. SAN 375-5614. Tel: 605-371-4140. FAX: 605-371-4144. *Librn*, Jane Goettsch; E-Mail: janeg@ siouxland.lib.sd.us
VALLEY SPRINGS BRANCH, PO Box 277, Valley Springs, 57068-0277. SAN 322-6123. Tel: 605-757-6555. FAX: 605-757-6730. *In Charge*, Lavon Schmitt; Staff 2 (Non-MLS 2)
WEST CENTRAL - HARTFORD BRANCH, 705 E Second St, Hartford, 57033. (Mail add: PO Box 607, Hartford, 57033-0607), Tel: 605-528-3223. Web Site: www.westcentral.edu. *In Charge*, Jo Ann Miles; Staff 1 (Non-MLS 1)
Bookmobiles: 2

S SOUTH DAKOTA STATE PENITENTIARY, Donald M Cole & Jameson Annex Library, 1600 N Dr, PO Box 5911, 57117-5911. SAN 315-6915. Tel: 605-367-5170, 605-367-5171. *Librn*, Judy Machacek; *Librn*, Julie Brandt
Enrl 180
Library Holdings: Bk Titles 18,000
Partic in South Dakota Library Network

UNITED STATES GEOLOGICAL SURVEY, Earth Resources Observation Systems, EROS Data Center Library, EROS Data Ctr, 57198. SAN 315-632X. Tel: 605-594-6565. FAX: 605-594-6529. *Librn*, Laurie Ortega
Founded 1973
Library Holdings: Bk Vols 10,000; Per Subs 75
Subject Interests: Aerial remote sensing in conjuction with geog, Computer graphics, Computer tech, Geog info systs, Geology, Hydrol, Land use planning, Satellite
Partic in OCLC Online Computer Library Center, Inc; South Dakota Library Network

UNIVERSITY OF SIOUX FALLS, Mears Library, 1101 W 22nd St, 57105-1699. SAN 315-6842. Tel: 605-331-6660. Interlibrary Loan Service Tel: 605-331-6614. FAX: 605-331-6615. Web Site: www.usioux.edu/is/library. *Dir Libr Serv*, Judy Clauson; Tel: 605-331-6661, E-Mail: judy.clauson@usiouxfalls.edu; *Circ*, Karen Scarborough; Tel: 605-331-6614, E-Mail: karen.scarborough@usiouxfalls.edu; *Cat*, Wendy Nelson; Tel: 605-331-6635, E-Mail: wendy.nelson@usiouxfalls.edu; *Per*, Katie Petzel; Tel: 605-331-6664, E-Mail: stacey.gleason@usiouxfalls.edu; Staff 5 (MLS 2, Non-MLS 3)
Founded 1883. Enrl 947; Fac 74; Highest Degree: Master
Library Holdings: Bk Vols 82,290; Bk Titles 57,395; Per Subs 364
Special Collections: Baptist, South Dakota
Partic in MINITEX Library Information Network; OCLC Online Computer Library Center, Inc; South Dakota Library Network

WEGNER HEALTH SCIENCE INFORMATION CENTER, 1400 W 22nd St, Ste 100, 57105. SAN 377-6263. Tel: 605-357-1400. FAX: 605-357-1490. Toll Free FAX: 800-521-2987. E-Mail: wegner@usd.edu. Web Site: www.usd.edu/wegner. *Dir*, Kay Wagner; *Admin Assoc*, Marcy Horkmann; *Ref Serv*, Anna Gieschen; *Outreach Serv*, Ernetta Fox; *Tech Servs*, Vicki Carlson; *Circ*, Susan Carlson; *Access Serv*, Mark Holman; *Per*, Amy Grimsley; *ILL*, Deb Taylor; Staff 13 (MLS 5, Non-MLS 8)
Founded 1998
2000-2001 Income $896,123, State $250,416, Other $645,707. Mats Exp $440,455, Books $46,003, Per/Ser (Incl. Access Fees) $160,215, Electronic Ref Mat (Incl. Access Fees) $74,220. Sal $455,668
Library Holdings: Bk Vols 30,000; Bk Titles 10,802; Per Subs 1,431
Subject Interests: Clinical medicine, Pharmacology, Psychiatry
Automation Activity & Vendor Info: (Acquisitions) PALS; (Circulation) PALS; (Course Reserve) PALS; (OPAC) PALS; (Serials) PALS
Database Vendor: Ebsco - EbscoHost, IAC - Info Trac, OCLC - First Search, OVID Technologies
Publications: Wegner Wellness (Newsletter)
Partic in MINITEX Library Information Network; National Network Of Libraries Of Medicine - South Central Region; OCLC Online Computer Library Center, Inc; South Dakota Library Network

ISSETON

SISSETON MEMORIAL LIBRARY, 305 E Maple St, 57262-1524. SAN 315-694X. Tel: 605-698-7391. E-Mail: sislib@tnics.com. *Librn*, Mary Ann Cameron
Founded 1907. Pop 11,161; Circ 26,171
Library Holdings: Bk Vols 15,000; Per Subs 72
Special Collections: Roberts County Historical Society Materials

SISSETON WAHPETON COMMUNITY COLLEGE LIBRARY, Agency Village, PO Box 689, 57262-0698. SAN 322-9483. Tel: 605-698-3966, Ext 702. FAX: 605-698-3132. Web Site: www.swcc.cc.sd.us. *Librn*, Jane Kirby; E-Mail: jkirby@swcc.cc.sd.us; Staff 1 (MLS 1)
Founded 1979. Highest Degree: Associate
Library Holdings: Bk Titles 13,000; Per Subs 145
Special Collections: Indians of North America Coll; Sisseton-Wahpeton Sioux Tribe
Database Vendor: Ebsco - EbscoHost
Restriction: Public use on premises
Friends of the Library Group

PEARFISH

GRACE BALLOCH MEMORIAL LIBRARY, Spearfish Public,* 625 N 5th St, 57783-2311. SAN 315-6958. Tel: 605-642-1330. Web Site: www.sdln.net/libs/spf/main.html. *Dir*, R Elaine Perry; E-Mail: eperry@sdln.net; *Asst Librn*, Kathy Klumb; E-Mail: kklumb@sdln.net
Founded 1945. Pop 12,170; Circ 134,839
Jan 1998-Dec 1998 Income (Main Library Only) $206,693, City $20,294, County $159,369, Locally Generated Income $19,030, Other $8,000. Mats Exp $36,267, Books $32,218, Per/Ser (Incl. Access Fees) $3,749, Micro $300. Sal $110,794
Library Holdings: Bk Vols 43,958; Bk Titles 40,648; Per Subs 142
Special Collections: South Dakota History Coll
Mem of SDak State Libr Syst
Friends of the Library Group

C BLACK HILLS STATE UNIVERSITY, E Y Berry Library-Learning Center, 1200 University ST, Unit 9676, 57799-9676. SAN 315-6966. Tel: 605-642-6833. FAX: 605-642-6298. Web Site: www.bhsu.edu/resources/library. *Dir*, W Edwin Erickson; Tel: 605-642-6355, E-Mail: eericksо@mystic.bhsu.edu; *Ref*, Barbara Chrisman; Tel: 605-642-6358; *Acq*, Linda Allbee; Tel: 605-642-6650; *Cat*, Valerie Hawkins; Tel: 605-642-6356; *Per*, Becky Cooper; Tel: 605-642-6362; *Circ*, Karen Cook; Tel: 605-642-6834; *Spec Coll*, Colleen Kirby; Tel: 605-642-6361; Staff 10 (MLS 4, Non-MLS 6)
Founded 1883. Enrl 3,029; Fac 108; Highest Degree: Master
Library Holdings: Bk Vols 232,247; Bk Titles 204,377; Per Subs 2,621
Special Collections: Arrow, Inc Coll; Congressman E Y Berry Papers; Western Historical Studies
Partic in South Dakota Library Network
Open Mon-Thurs 7-11, Fri 7-5, Sat 10-5 & Sun 2-11
Friends of the Library Group

SPENCER

P HANSON-MCCOOK COUNTY REGIONAL LIBRARY, PO Box 227, 57374. SAN 315-6974. Tel: 605-246-2740. E-Mail: hmlibrary@triotel.net. *Librn*, Cherie Schroeder
Pop 9,829; Circ 35,792
Library Holdings: Bk Vols 15,353
Bookmobiles: 1

SPRINGFIELD

S SPRINGFIELD STATE PRISON, Carl G Lawrence Library, PO Box 322, 57062. SAN 370-5412. Tel: 605-369-4418. FAX: 604-369-2813. *Librn*, Mark Stoevener
Library Holdings: Bk Vols 30,000; Per Subs 50

STURGIS

P STURGIS PUBLIC LIBRARY, 1040 Second St, 57785-1595. SAN 315-6990. Tel: 605-347-2624. FAX: 605-347-4861. *Dir*, Rita Schwartz; *Ref*, Julie Moore; *Ch Servs*, Kathy Dykstra; Staff 3 (Non-MLS 3)
Founded 1922
Jan 2000-Dec 2000 Income $210,000, City $140,000, County $20,000, Other $50,000. Mats Exp $22,000, Books $14,000, Per/Ser (Incl. Access Fees) $5,000, AV Equip $3,000. Sal $122,000
Library Holdings: Bk Vols 39,000; Bk Titles 38,000; Per Subs 140
Subject Interests: SDak-Black Hills region
Special Collections: Dakota Coll
Publications: Audiovisual Catalog
Partic in South Dakota Library Network
Friends of the Library Group
Bookmobiles: 1

TIMBER LAKE

P DEWEY COUNTY LIBRARY, 212 S Main, PO Box 68, 57656-0068. SAN 360-4624. Tel: 605-865-3541. E-Mail: dewcolib@sd.cybernex.com. *Dir*, Margaret Salzer
Pop 5,300; Circ 17,015
Jan 1998-Dec 1999 Income $34,967. Mats Exp $2,199, Books $1,450, Per/Ser (Incl. Access Fees) $749. Sal $29,718
Library Holdings: Bk Vols 23,000; Bk Titles 21,500; Per Subs 33
Subject Interests: SDak
Special Collections: Regional History
Branches: 1
ISABEL BRANCH, Isabel, 57633. SAN 360-4683. *Librn*, Violet Rost

TYNDALL

P TYNDALL PUBLIC LIBRARY, PO Box 26, 57066-0026. SAN 315-7008. Tel: 605-589-3266. *Librn*, Sue Gough
Founded 1917. Pop 1,500; Circ 14,930
Library Holdings: Bk Vols 13,098

VERMILLION

S AMERICAN INDIAN RESEARCH PROJECT, Joseph Harper Cash Memorial Library, University of South Dakota, 414 E Clark St, 12 Dakota Hall, 57069. SAN 329-9228. Tel: 605-677-5209. FAX: 605-677-6525. E-Mail: iais@usd.edu. Web Site: www.usd.edu/iais. *Dir*, Leonard R Bruguier
Library Holdings: Bk Vols 5,000; Per Subs 35
Subject Interests: Agriculture, Am Indian culture, Am Indian issues, Ethnic groups, History, Music, Politics, Rapid City flood, Religion, SDak, Veterans
Publications: Index to the American Indian Research Project; Index to the South Dakota Oral History Collection

M DAKOTA HOSPITAL LIBRARY,* 20 S Plum St, 57069-3346. SAN 327-3598. Tel: 605-624-2611. FAX: 605-624-4001.
Library Holdings: Bk Titles 100

S W H OVER STATE MUSEUM-LIBRARY,* 414 E Clark, 57069-2798. SAN 371-4446. Tel: 605-677-5228. *Dir*, Dorothy Neuhaus
Library Holdings: Bk Vols 2,000; Per Subs 10

CM UNIVERSITY OF SOUTH DAKOTA, Christian P Lommen Health Sciences Library, School of Medicine, 414 E Clark, 57069-2390. SAN 315-7016. Tel: 605-677-5347. FAX: 605-677-5124. Web Site: www.usd.edu/lhsl/. *Dir*, David Hulkonen; E-Mail: dhulkone@usd.edu; *ILL*, Deb Carlin; *Access Serv*, Heidi Nickisch Duggan; Staff 7 (MLS 2, Non-MLS 5)
Founded 1907. Enrl 860; Fac 190; Highest Degree: Doctorate
2000-2001 Income $712,000, State $510,000, Locally Generated Income $12,000, Parent Institution $190,000. Mats Exp $429,618, Books $13,286, Per/Ser (Incl. Access Fees) $384,910, Presv $8,147, Electronic Ref Mat (Incl. Access Fees) $23,275. Sal $282,382 (Prof $113,500)
Library Holdings: Bk Vols 95,281; Per Subs 809
Subject Interests: Allied health, Basic sci, Clinical medicine, Dent hyg, Nursing
Special Collections: History of Medicine Archives; Rare Books
Automation Activity & Vendor Info: (Acquisitions) PALS; (Cataloging) PALS; (Circulation) PALS; (Course Reserve) PALS; (ILL) PALS; (Media Booking) PALS; (OPAC) PALS; (Serials) PALS
Publications: Accession List; Library Handbook; SD Union List of Health Sciences Serials
Partic in MINITEX Library Information Network; South Dakota Library Network

C UNIVERSITY OF SOUTH DAKOTA, I D Weeks Library, 414 E Clark St, 57069. SAN 360-4713. Tel: 605-677-5371. FAX: 605-677-5488. E-Mail: library@usd.edu. Web Site: www.usd.edu.library. *Dir*, David Hulkonen; Fax: 605-677-6834, E-Mail: dhulkone@usd.edu; *Circ, Publ Servs*, John Van Balen; *Librn*, Yuliya Lef; *Acq, Coll Develop*, Nancy Myers; *Cat*, Joe Edelen; *Govt Doc*, Stephen Johnson; *ILL*, Theresa Gibson; *Archivist*, Amy Cooper; *Science*, Barbara Gauger; *Info Res*, Charolotte Fowles; *Librn*, Margaret Miller; Staff 32 (MLS 12, Non-MLS 20)
Founded 1882. Enrl 6,001; Highest Degree: Doctorate
Jul 1999-Jun 2000 Income $2,384,387, State $1,114,414, Parent Institution $1,249,973, Other $20,000. Mats Exp $1,029,209, Books $294,782, Per/Ser (Incl. Access Fees) $514,891, Presv $13,000, Micro $8,769, Electronic Ref Mat (Incl. Access Fees) $197,767. Sal $1,056,196 (Prof $496,740)
Library Holdings: Bk Titles 335,757; Per Subs 2,099
Special Collections: Country Schools Survey; Herman P Chilson Western Americana Coll; South Dakota History & Historical Maps (Richardson Archives)
Automation Activity & Vendor Info: (Acquisitions) PALS; (Cataloging) PALS; (Circulation) PALS; (ILL) PALS; (OPAC) PALS
Database Vendor: CARL, Dialog, Ebsco - EbscoHost, IAC - Info Trac, Lexis-Nexis, OCLC - First Search, ProQuest, Silverplatter Information Inc.
Publications: Coyote Connection Newsletter; Extension Express Newsletter; Guide to the I D Weeks Library for USD Faculty & Staff; Guide to the I D Weeks Library Resources; I D Weeks Library Serials List; USD Internet Guide: Navigating Internet Services; Volante Index
Mem of Minitex Libr Info Network
Departmental Libraries:
MCKUSICK LAW LIBRARY, 414 E Clark St, 57069-2390. SAN 360-4772. Tel: 605-677-5259. FAX: 605-677-6357. Web Site: www.usd.edu/lawlib/lib/html. *Dir*, John F Hagemann; Tel: 605-677-5041, E-Mail: hageman@mckusick.law.usd.edu; *Cat*, Delores Jorgensen; *Ser*, Karyl Knodel; *Acq*, Lynette Simonsen; *Circ, ILL*, Doris Hodgen; *Ref*, Candice Spurlin; Staff 10 (MLS 7, Non-MLS 3)
Founded 1901. Enrl 225; Fac 19; Highest Degree: Doctorate
Jul 1997-Jun 1998 Income $813,717. Mats Exp $466,389. Sal $264,050
Library Holdings: Bk Vols 183,659
Subject Interests: Agr law, Arts, Family law, Health law, Indian law, Water law
Restriction: Open to public for reference only
Partic in Mid-Am Law Sch Libr Consortium; Minn Interlibr Telecommunication Exchange; OCLC Online Computer Library Center, Inc

C UNIVERSITY OF SOUTH DAKOTA, America's Shrine to Music Museum Library, 414 E Clark St, 57069-2390. SAN 326-7695. Tel: 605-677-5306. FAX: 605-677-5073. E-Mail: smm@usd.edu. Web Site: www.usd.edu/smm. *Dir*, Andre P Larson; Staff 9 (Non-MLS 9)
Founded 1973
Library Holdings: Bk Titles 10,000; Per Subs 40
Publications: America's Shrine to Music Museum Newsletter (quarterly)
Restriction: Non-circulating to the public

S UNIVERSITY OF SOUTH DAKOTA SCHOOL OF BUSINESS, Business Research Bureau, 414 E Clark St, 57069-2390. SAN 320-8729. Tel: 605-677-5287. FAX: 605-677-5427. Web Site: www.usd.edu/brbinfo. *Dir*, Stephen Tracy
Founded 1927
Library Holdings: Bk Titles 800; Per Subs 15
Restriction: Open to public for reference only

P VERMILLION PUBLIC LIBRARY, 18 Church St, 57069-3093. SAN 315-7024. Tel: 605-677-7060. FAX: 605-677-7160. E-Mail: vpl@sdln.net. Web Site: vpl.sdln.net. *Dir*, Jane A Larson; E-Mail: jlarson@sdln.net; *Cat*, Janice Kitzler; E-Mail: jkitzler@sdln.net; *Ch Servs*, Kay Dahl; E-Mail: kdahl@sdln.net; *Commun Servs*, Mary Berglin; Staff 3 (MLS 1, Non-MLS 2)
Founded 1903. Pop 14,100; Circ 85,733
Jan 1999-Dec 1999 Income $375,011, City $337,351, County $19,500, Locally Generated Income $18,160. Mats Exp $62,000, Per/Ser (Incl. Access Fees) $3,750, Presv $600, AV Equip $150. Sal $156,737 (Prof $38,748)
Library Holdings: Bk Titles 60,869; Per Subs 160
Subject Interests: Large print, SDak
Automation Activity & Vendor Info: (Acquisitions) PALS; (Cataloging) PALS; (Circulation) PALS; (Course Reserve) PALS; (ILL) PALS; (Media Booking) PALS; (OPAC) PALS; (Serials) PALS
Publications: EAI Index, General Periodical Index, MGI, RapidCity, Journ Index, Health Index, Business Index (Index to educational materials)
Partic in South Dakota Library Network
Special Services for the Deaf - Staff with knowledge of sign language; TD
Friends of the Library Group

VIBORG

M PIONEER MEMORIAL HOSPITAL, Medical Library,* PO Box 368, 57070-0368. SAN 327-8581. Tel: 605-326-5161, Ext 30. FAX: 605-326-5734.
Library Holdings: Bk Vols 250

WAGNER

P WAGNER PUBLIC LIBRARY, 106 E Sheridan Ave, Rte 1, Box 6, 57380-9701. SAN 315-7032. Tel: 605-384-5248. FAX: 605-384-5644. E-Mail: wpublib@charles-mix.com. *Librn*, Monica Soukup
Founded 1914. Circ 1,460
Jan 1999-Dec 1999 Income $28,569, City $24,870, Federal $844, Locally Generated Income $2,135, Other $720. Mats Exp $7,600, Books $5,840, Per/Ser (Incl. Access Fees) $1,460, AV Equip $300. Sal $12,760
Library Holdings: Bk Vols 17,349; Bk Titles 16,215; Per Subs 54

WATERTOWN

S LAKE AREA TECHNICAL INSTITUTE LIBRARY, L H Timmerman Library, PO Box 730, 57201-0730. SAN 327-0955. Tel: 605-882-5284, Ext 231. FAX: 605-882-6299. *Librn*, Jeani True
Library Holdings: Bk Vols 1,500; Per Subs 113
Subject Interests: Agriculture

M PRAIRIE LAKES HEALTH CARE CENTER,* 400 Tenth Ave NW, 57201-1599. SAN 327-0912. Tel: 605-882-7000. FAX: 605-882-7819. *Librn*, Barbara Paulson
Library Holdings: Bk Vols 450

P WATERTOWN REGIONAL LIBRARY, 611 B Ave NE, 57201-2758. (Mail add: PO Box 250, 57201-0250), SAN 315-7040. Tel: 605-882-6220. FAX: 605-882-6221. E-Mail: adminwat@sdln.net. Web Site: watweb.sdln.net. *Dir*, Michael C Mullin; *Asst Librn*, Kevin Wells; *Cat*, Selma Mitchell; *Ch Servs*, Linda Bauman; *Circ*, Ellen Heisner; *Spec Coll*, Bev Moore; *YA Servs*, Dorothy Dohman; Staff 7 (MLS 2, Non-MLS 5)
Founded 1899. Pop 27,672; Circ 227,598
Jan 1999-Dec 1999 Income $530,226. Mats Exp $95,172. Sal $347,540
Library Holdings: Bk Titles 55,000; Per Subs 205
Subject Interests: SDak, Watertown hist
Special Collections: Dakota Coll
Partic in MINITEX Library Information Network; OCLC Online Computer Library Center, Inc; South Dakota Library Network

WEBSTER

P WEBSTER PUBLIC LIBRARY,* 800 Main St, 57274-1494. SAN 315-7059. Tel: 605-345-3263. *Dir*, Anne Fossum
Founded 1930. Pop 2,277; Circ 23,155
Library Holdings: Bk Vols 31,000; Per Subs 78
Special Collections: South Dakota History

WESSINGTON

P WESSINGTON PUBLIC LIBRARY,* 240 Wessington St, PO Box 108, 57381-0108. SAN 315-7067. Tel: 605-458-2596. *Dir*, Donna Runge
Founded 1937. Pop 800; Circ 4,700
Library Holdings: Bk Titles 4,665; Per Subs 16
Special Collections: South Dakota History; South Dakota Poetry, pamphlets; South Dakota State Laws

ESSINGTON SPRINGS

WESSINGTON SPRINGS CARNEGIE LIBRARY,* 109 W Main St, PO Box 336, 57382-0336. SAN 315-7075. Tel: 605-539-1803. *Dir*, Barb Horsley
Founded 1918. Pop 1,203; Circ 8,299
Library Holdings: Bk Titles 18,200; Per Subs 30
Special Collections: Books By or About South Dakotans & South Dakota; Old Newspapers (local)
Mem of SDak State Libr Syst
Friends of the Library Group

INNER

TRIPP COUNTY LIBRARY-GROSSENBURG MEMORIAL,* 442 Monroe, 57580. SAN 360-4837. Tel: 605-842-0330. FAX: 605-842-0294. *Librn*, Sandy Hansen
Founded 1921. Pop 8,171; Circ 50,747
Library Holdings: Bk Vols 30,400; Per Subs 83
Subject Interests: Agriculture, Architecture, Art, SDak Indian
Special Collections: County; South Dakota History & Tripp County History Colls, bks, pamphlets, photog
Mem of SDak State Libr Syst
Partic in Bibliographical Center For Research, Rocky Mountain Region, Inc
Friends of the Library Group
Branches: 1
COLOME BRANCH, Colome, 57528. SAN 360-4861. *Asst Librn*, Verlas Vavra
Library Holdings: Bk Vols 1,036

VOONSOCKET

WOONSOCKET PUBLIC LIBRARY,* PO Box 126, 57385-0126. SAN 315-7083. Tel: 605-796-4112. *Librn*, Pat Larson
Founded 1918. Pop 850; Circ 4,522
Library Holdings: Bk Vols 5,274; Per Subs 22

ANKTON

1 AVERA SACRED HEART HOSPITAL, Medical Library, 501 Summit St, 57078-9967. SAN 320-2356. Tel: 605-668-8384. FAX: 605-665-8840. *Librn*, Barbara Papik; E-Mail: bpapik@shhservices.com; Staff 1 (MLS 1)
Founded 1975
Library Holdings: Bk Vols 2,747; Bk Titles 2,441; Per Subs 125
Subject Interests: Allied health, Hospital administration, Medicine, Nursing

: MOUNT MARTY COLLEGE LIBRARY,* 1105 W Eighth St, 57078-3724. SAN 315-7091. Tel: 605-668-1555. FAX: 605-668-1357. Web Site: www.mtmc.edu. *Acq, Coll Develop, Dir, ILL, Ref*, Sandra Brown; E-Mail: sbrown@mtmc.edu; *Cat, Circ*, Jane Jensen; *Circ*, Krista Johnson; *Per*, Susie Schaltz; Staff 2 (MLS 2)
Founded 1936. Enrl 756; Fac 61; Highest Degree: Master
Jul 1997-Jun 1998 Income $158,460. Mats Exp $70,367, Books $18,150, Per/Ser (Incl. Access Fees) $23,688, Micro $3,569. Sal $72,488 (Prof $58,750)
Library Holdings: Bk Vols 75,000; Bk Titles 60,262; Per Subs 406
Subject Interests: Relig studies
Partic in Cols of Mid-America Consortium; MINITEX Library Information Network; OCLC Online Computer Library Center, Inc

SOUTH DAKOTA HUMAN SERVICE CENTER

M MEDICAL LIBRARY, North Hwy 81, PO Box 76, 57078-0076. SAN 360-4985. Tel: 605-668-3165. FAX: 605-668-3222. *Librn*, Mary Lou Kostel
Founded 1938
Library Holdings: Bk Vols 3,500; Per Subs 51
Subject Interests: Geriatrics, Illness, Mental health, Nursing-psychiat, Psychiatry, Psychology, Soc work
Special Collections: History (South Dakota Human Services Center Scrapbooks)

M PATIENT'S LIBRARY, North Hwy 81, PO Box 76, 57078-0076. SAN 360-5019. Tel: 605-668-3165. FAX: 605-668-3222. *Dir*, Mary Lou Kostel
Founded 1940
Library Holdings: Bk Titles 7,803; Per Subs 62
Subject Interests: Basic psychiat info for mentally handicapped, Geriatric pop, Self-help
Special Collections: Patient Education, Life Skills & Independent Living Materials; Young Adult Coll
Partic in South Dakota Library Network
Special Services - High-interest low-reading material; AV listening stations

P YANKTON COMMUNITY LIBRARY, 515 Walnut, 57078-4042. SAN 315-7121. Tel: 605-668-5276. FAX: 605-668-5277. *Ad Servs, ILL*, Joyce Brunken; *Dir*, James C Scholtz; E-Mail: jscholtz@sdln.net; *Ch Servs, YA Servs*, Lola Harens; *Tech Servs*, Irene Kolar
Founded 1902. Pop 21,000; Circ 178,344
Jan 2000-Dec 2000 Income $446,000, City $428,000, County $18,000. Mats Exp $75,200, Books $45,500, Per/Ser (Incl. Access Fees) $8,200, AV Equip $6,500, Electronic Ref Mat (Incl. Access Fees) $15,000. Sal $286,071 (Prof $74,000)
Library Holdings: Bk Vols 66,379; Bk Titles 59,941; Per Subs 160
Subject Interests: Genealogy, Local history, SDak hist
Automation Activity & Vendor Info: (Acquisitions) PALS; (Cataloging) PALS; (Circulation) PALS; (Course Reserve) PALS; (ILL) PALS; (Media Booking) PALS; (OPAC) PALS; (Serials) PALS
Partic in South Dakota Library Network
Friends of the Library Group

TENNESSEE

Date of Statistics: Fiscal 1998-99
Population, 1990 Census: 5,175,406
Population Served by Public Libraries: 5,368,198
Total Volumes in Public Libraries: 10,129,299
Volumes Per Capita: 1.89
Total Public Library Circulation: 21,543,666
Circulation Per Capita: 4.02
Total Public Library Income (including Grants-in-Aid): $69,532,115
Source of Income: Mainly public funds
Expenditures: $68,689,355
Expenditure Per Capita: $12.80
Number of County or Multi-county (Regional) Libraries: 12 multi-county, 4 metropolitan
Counties Served: 95
Number of Bookmobiles in State: 16
Grants-in-Aid to Public Libraries:
Federal (Library Services & Technology Act): $1,369,568
State Aid: $4,972,405

ADAMSVILLE

IRVING MEEK JR PUBLIC LIBRARY, 204 W Main St, PO Box 303, 38310-0303. SAN 315-713X. Tel: 901-632-3572. Interlibrary Loan Service Toll Free Tel: 800-532-6251. FAX: 901-632-3572. Web Site: www.irvingmeeklibrary.homepage.com. *Librn*, Sue Smith; E-Mail: ssmith8@mail.state.tn.us; *Asst Librn*, Mimi Tibbs
Founded 1961
Library Holdings: Bk Vols 22,600
Subject Interests: Fossils, Shells
Special Collections: Buford Pusser Memorabilia
Mem of Shiloh Regional Library

ALAMO

P CROCKETT MEMORIAL LIBRARY, 258 E Church St, 38001-1108. SAN 315-7148. Tel: 901-696-4220. FAX: 901-696-5107. *Coll Develop, Librn*, Ann Tillman; E-Mail: atillman@mail.state.tn.us
Founded 1968
Jul 1998-Jun 1999 Income $48,550, City $2,000, County $41,000. Mats Exp $3,400, Books $3,000, Per/Ser (Incl. Access Fees) $300. Sal $34,353
Library Holdings: Bk Vols 7,615
Subject Interests: Local history
Mem of Forked Deer Regional Library Center
Friends of the Library Group

ALTAMONT

P ALTAMONT PUBLIC LIBRARY, PO Box 228, 37301-0228. SAN 315-7156. Tel: 931-692-2457. FAX: 931-692-2457. E-Mail: atpublib@blomand.net. *Librn*, Brinda F Adams
Library Holdings: Bk Vols 5,000
Open Mon 8:30-12, Wed & Fri 8:30-4:30

ARDMORE

P ARDMORE COMMUNITY LIBRARY, 26347 Main St, PO Box 517, 38473-9801. SAN 376-7000. Tel: 931-427-4883. FAX: 931-427-6747. E-Mail: ardmorelib@tnii.net. *Dir*, Verlin Collins
1998-1999 Income $22,466, State $6,000, City $13,600, County $2,866. Mats Exp $5,140, Books $5,000, Per/Ser (Incl. Access Fees) $140. Sal $15,096
Library Holdings: Bk Vols 8,600; Bk Titles 8,500; Per Subs 11
Mem of Blue Grass Regional Library
Friends of the Library Group

ARNOLD AFB

UNITED STATES AIR FORCE

A ARNOLD ENGINEERING DEVELOPMENT CENTER TECHNICAL LIBRARY, FL 2804, 100 Kindel Dr, Ste C212, 37389-3212. SAN 360-5078. Tel: 931-454-4430, 931-454-5431. FAX: 931-454-5421. *In Charge*, Gay D Goethert; Tel: 931-454-4429, E-Mail: gay.goethert@arnold.af.mil; *Librn, Ref*, Sharon Butcher; E-Mail: sharon.butcher@arnold.af.mil; *Syst Coordr*, Emily Moore; Tel: 931-454-7220, E-Mail: emily.moore@arnold.af.mil; Staff 6 (MLS 3, Non-MLS 3)
Founded 1952
Library Holdings: Bk Vols 26,960; Per Subs 432
Subject Interests: Aerospace science, Astronomy, Chemistry, Engineering, Mathematics, Optics, Physics, Pollution
Special Collections: NACA Technical Reports; NACA Wartime Reports
Automation Activity & Vendor Info: (Acquisitions) SIRSI; (Cataloging) SIRSI; (Circulation) SIRSI; (OPAC) SIRSI; (Serials) SIRSI
Partic in Defense Technical Information Center; DROLS; Nasa Libraries Information System - Nasa Galaxie; OCLC Online Computer Library Center, Inc; SE Libr Network

ASHLAND CITY

P CHEATHAM COUNTY PUBLIC LIBRARY, 610 N Main St, PO Box 67, 37015-0067. SAN 315-7172. Tel: 615-792-4828. FAX: 615-792-2054. Web Site: www.members.tripod.com/cheatham_library/. *Dir*, Glenda Jacoway; *Asst Librn*, Ruth Proctor; Staff 5 (MLS 1, Non-MLS 4)
Founded 1967
Library Holdings: Bk Vols 14,033; Per Subs 15
Mem of Warioto Regional Library Center
Friends of the Library Group
Branches: 1
SOUTH CHEATHAM COUNTY PUBLIC, 358 N Main St, PO Box 310, Kingston Springs, 37082-0310. SAN 373-9317. Tel: 615-952-4752. FAX: 615-952-4752. *Dir*, Katherine Sleighter; E-Mail: ksleight@bellsouth.net; Staff 1 (MLS 1)
Founded 1986. Pop 8,796; Circ 15,500
Library Holdings: Bk Vols 14,000; Bk Titles 11,000; Per Subs 12
Special Collections: Juvenile Poetry (Brewton/Blackburn Coll)
Special Services for the Deaf - High interest/low vocabulary books; TTY machine
Friends of the Library Group

ATHENS

P EDWARD GAUCHE FISHER PUBLIC LIBRARY, 1289 Ingleside Ave, 37371. (Mail add: PO Box 1815, 37371-1815), SAN 315-7199. Tel: 423-745-7782. FAX: 423-745-1763. *Librn*, Beth Allen Mercer; E-Mail: bmercer@usit.com; Staff 1 (MLS 1)
Founded 1969. Pop 45,000
Jul 1998-Jun 1999 Income $255,176, City $115,800, County $76,276, Other $63,100. Mats Exp $33,600, Books $22,000, Per/Ser (Incl. Access Fees) $4,000, Electronic Ref Mat (Incl. Access Fees) $7,600. Sal $163,126 (Prof

$32,000)
Library Holdings: Bk Vols 45,000; Per Subs 75
Mem of Fort Loudoun Regional Library Center
Friends of the Library Group

P FORT LOUDOUN REGIONAL LIBRARY CENTER, 718 George St NW, 37303-2214. SAN 315-7180. Tel: 423-745-5194. Toll Free Tel: 800-624-1982. FAX: 423-745-8086. *Dir*, Lynette Sloan; E-Mail: lsloan@mail.state.tn.us; *Asst Dir*, David Milsaps; Staff 2 (MLS 2)
Founded 1939. Pop 338,141; Circ 1,094,162
Library Holdings: Bk Vols 264,949; Per Subs 2
Member Libraries: Audrey Pack Memorial Library; Benton Public Library; Blount County Public Library; Calhoun Public Library; Cleveland Public Library; Clyde W Roddy Library; Copperhill Public Library; Decatur-Meigs County Library; Ducktown Community Library; Edward Gauche Fisher Public Library; Englewood Public Library; Etowah Carnegie Public Library; Graysville Public Library; Greenback Public Library; Harriman Public Library; Lenoir City Public Library; Loudon Public Library; Madisonville Public Library; Niota Public Library; Oliver Springs Public Library; Philadelphia Public Library; Rockwood Public Library; Sweetwater Public Library; Tellico Plains Public Library; Vonore Public Library

C TENNESSEE WESLEYAN COLLEGE, (TWY), Merner Pfeiffer Library, 204 E College St, PO Box 40, 37371-0040. SAN 315-7202. Tel: 423-746-5250. Interlibrary Loan Service Tel: 423-746-5251. FAX: 423-744-9968. E-Mail: library@twcnet.edu. Web Site: www.twcnet.edu/library.html. *Dir*, Sandra Civils Clariday; Tel: 423-746-5249, E-Mail: sclariday@twcnet.edu; *Asst Librn*, Julie Adams; E-Mail: adamsj@twcnet.edu; *Publ Servs*, Alice Anderson; Tel: 423-746-5232, E-Mail: alice@twcnet.edu; Staff 7 (MLS 3, Non-MLS 4)
Founded 1857. Enrl 850; Fac 65; Highest Degree: Bachelor
Jul 1999-Jun 2000 Income $240,750, Parent Institution $225,750, Other $15,000. Mats Exp $110,300, Books $40,000, Per/Ser (Incl. Access Fees) $28,000, Presv $500, Micro $7,000, AV Equip $14,800, Electronic Ref Mat (Incl. Access Fees) $20,000. Sal $108,500 (Prof $55,000)
Library Holdings: Bk Vols 99,766; Bk Titles 73,359; Per Subs 448
Special Collections: Methodist Church History (Cooke Memorial Coll)
Automation Activity & Vendor Info: (Acquisitions) Endeavor; (Cataloging) Endeavor; (Circulation) Endeavor; (Course Reserve) Endeavor; (ILL) Endeavor; (Media Booking) Endeavor; (OPAC) Endeavor; (Serials) Endeavor
Database Vendor: GaleNet, IAC - Info Trac, OCLC - First Search, ProQuest, Silverplatter Information Inc.
Function: Archival collection, ILL available
Partic in Appalachian Col Asn; SE Libr Network; Tenn-Share

BEAN STATION

BEAN STATION PUBLIC LIBRARY, Old Hwy 25 E, PO Box 100, 37708-0105. SAN 361-011X. *Dir*, Ada Rhea; Tel: 865-993-3068; Staff 1 (Non-MLS 1)
Library Holdings: Bk Vols 5,000
Mem of Nolichucky Regional Library

BEERSHEBA SPRINGS

P BEERSHEBA SPRINGS PUBLIC LIBRARY, Hwy 56, PO Box 192, 37305-0192. SAN 315-7210. Tel: 931-692-3029. FAX: 931-692-3029. E-Mail: bspublib@blomand.net. *Dir*, Melissa Scruggs
Library Holdings: Bk Vols 3,000
Mem of Caney Fork Regional Library
Friends of the Library Group

BENTON

P BENTON PUBLIC LIBRARY, Polk County Courthouse, Hwy 411, 37307-0128. SAN 315-7229. Tel: 423-338-4536. *Dir*, Robin Jenkins
Library Holdings: Bk Vols 3,600
Mem of Fort Loudoun Regional Library Center

BLAINE

P NOLICHUCKY REGIONAL LIBRARY CENTER, (Formerly Blaine Public Library), Blaine Community Library, 220 Indian Ridge Rd, 37709. (Mail add: PO Box 66, Indian Cave Rd, 37709-0066), SAN 370-4394. Tel: 423-933-0845. *Librn*, Tammy Cameron
Mem of Nolichucky Regional Library

BLOUNTVILLE

J NORTHEAST STATE TECHNICAL COMMUNITY COLLEGE, Learning Resource Center, PO Box 246, 37617-0246. SAN 376-7922. Tel: 423-323-3191. FAX: 423-323-0254. Web Site: www.nstcc.tc.tn.us/lrc. *Asst Dean*, Duncan A Parsons; E-Mail: daparsons@nstcc.cc.tn.us; *Publ Servs, Tech Servs*, John Grubb; *Per, Publ Servs*, Virginia Hodges; *Acq, ILL, Publ Servs*, Annis Evans; Staff 8 (MLS 4, Non-MLS 4)
Founded 1966. Fac 95
Jul 1999-Jun 2000 Income $460,850. Mats Exp $181,200, Books $91,250, Per/Ser (Incl. Access Fees) $32,300, Presv $1,400, Micro $1,750, AV Equi $32,000, Electronic Ref Mat (Incl. Access Fees) $22,500
Library Holdings: Bk Vols 31,500; Per Subs 395
Automation Activity & Vendor Info: (Cataloging) DRA; (Circulation) DRA; (OPAC) DRA

P SULLIVAN COUNTY PUBLIC LIBRARY, 1655 Blountville Blvd, 37617-4709. (Mail add: PO Box 510, 37617-0150), SAN 360-5108. Tel: 423-279-2714. FAX: 423-279-2836. Web Site: www.wrlibrary.org/sullivan. *Dir*, Kay P Hamrick; *Asst Dir*, Linda Smith; *Librn*, Margaret Elsea; E-Mail: melsea@wrlibrary.org
Founded 1946. Pop 87,933; Circ 147,230
Jun 1999-May 2000 Income (Main Library and Branch Library) $410,771, State $6,500, County $385,675, Other $12,096. Mats Exp $74,772, Books $69,207, Per/Ser (Incl. Access Fees) $3,353, AV Equip $1,298, Other Print Mats $914. Sal $243,810 (Prof $203,702)
Library Holdings: Bk Vols 115,206; Per Subs 148
Special Collections: Genealogy Coll, bks, micro; Sullivan County History; Tennessee History
Mem of Knoxville-Knox County Pub Libr; Watauga Regional Library Center
Friends of the Library Group
Branches: 4
BLOOMINGDALE BRANCH, 3220 Van Horn St, Kingsport, 37660-2062. SAN 360-5132. Tel: 423-288-1310. FAX: 423-288-1310. Web Site: www.wrlibrary.org/sullivan/. *Mgr*, Janice Tipton; Staff 2 (Non-MLS 2)
Pop 87,933; Circ 147,230
COLONIAL HEIGHTS BRANCH, 149 Pactolus Rd, Kinsgport, 37663. SAN 360-5191. Tel: 423-239-1100. FAX: 423-239-1100. Web Site: www.wrlibrary.org/sullivan/. *Mgr*, Jo McDavid; E-Mail: jmcdavid@wrlibrary.org
Friends of the Library Group
SULLIVAN GARDENS BRANCH, 104 Bluegrass Dr, Kingsport, 37660. SAN 360-5221. Tel: 423-349-5990. FAX: 423-349-5990. Web Site: www.wrlibrary.org/sullivan/. *Mgr*, Peggy Sutherland
Friends of the Library Group
THOMAS MEMORIAL BRANCH, 481 Cedar St, Bluff City, 37618. SAN 360-5167. Tel: 423-538-1980. FAX: 423-538-1980. Web Site: www.wrlibrary.org/sullivan. *Mgr*, Kathryn Nichols
Friends of the Library Group

BOLIVAR

P BOLIVAR-HARDEMAN COUNTY PUBLIC LIBRARY, 213 N Washington St, 38008-2020. SAN 315-7237. Tel: 901-658-3436. FAX: 901-658-9045. *Dir*, Betty Taylor; E-Mail: btaylor@mail.state.tn.us; *Asst Librn*, Ann Cheshire; *Asst Librn*, Jennifer Blasingame; *Asst Librn*, Janette Tigner
Pop 22,435
Library Holdings: Bk Vols 35,000; Per Subs 91
Special Collections: Quinnie Armour Books Rare Civil War Coll, bks; Roy Black Book Coll
Mem of Shiloh Regional Library

WESTERN MENTAL HEALTH INSTITUTE
M EDWARD M LEVY PROFESSIONAL LIBRARY, 11100 Hwy 64 W, 38008. SAN 360-5310. Tel: 731-228-2000. Interlibrary Loan Service Tel: 731-528-5634. FAX: 731-658-9822.
Library Holdings: Bk Vols 3,700; Per Subs 31
Subject Interests: Behav, Clinical medicine, Dietary, Pastoral servs, Pharmacology, Psychiatric nursing, Psychiatry, Psychology, Soc servs, Therapeutic mat, Vocational rehabilitation
Mem of Memphis Area Health Sci Librs
Partic in SE-Atlantic Regional Med Libr Servs

BRENTWOOD

P THE BRENTWOOD LIBRARY & CENTER FOR FINE ARTS, 8109 Concord Rd, 37027. SAN 325-092X. Tel: 615-371-0090. Circulation Tel: 615-371-0090, Ext 807. Reference Tel: 615-371-0090, Ext 820. FAX: 615-371-2238. Web Site: library.brentwood-tn.org. *Dir*, Chuck Sherrill; E-Mail: sherrill@brentwood-tn.org; *Tech Servs*, Lisa Hamlin; E-Mail: hamlinl@brentwood-tn.org; *Ch Servs*, Missy Dillingham; *Ref*, Nina Vandewater; Staff 7 (MLS 7)
Founded 1978. Pop 30,000; Circ 315,000
2000-2001 Income $1,110,500, State $3,500, City $1,050,000, County $57,000. Mats Exp $178,000, Books $110,000, Per/Ser (Incl. Access Fees) $43,000, AV Equip $25,000. Sal $503,000 (Prof $345,315)
Library Holdings: Bk Vols 81,800; Per Subs 205
Special Collections: Brentwood Local History
Automation Activity & Vendor Info: (Acquisitions) SIRSI; (Cataloging) SIRSI; (Circulation) SIRSI; (Course Reserve) SIRSI
Mem of Blue Grass Regional Library
Partic in Tenn-Share
Friends of the Library Group

RICEVILLE

BRICEVILLE PUBLIC LIBRARY, Hwy 116, PO Box 361, 37710-0361. SAN 315-7245. Tel: 865-426-6518. FAX: 865-426-6518. *Dir*, Lynette Seeber; E-Mail: lseeber@bellsouth.net
Library Holdings: Bk Vols 3,000
Mem of Clinch-Powell Regional Library

RISTOL

1 BRISTOL REGIONAL MEDICAL CENTER LIBRARY, One Medical Park Blvd, 37621-8964. SAN 377-5410. Tel: 423-844-4440. FAX: 423-844-4443. *Librn*, Sharon Brown; E-Mail: sharon_m_brown@wellmont.org
Library Holdings: Bk Vols 1,000; Per Subs 150
Partic in Med Libr Asn, Southern Chapter; SEND Network; Tennessee Health Science Library Association

KING COLLEGE, The E W King Library, 1350 King College Rd, 37620. SAN 315-727X. Tel: 423-652-4791. Interlibrary Loan Service Tel: 423-652-4795. Circulation Tel: 423-652-4790. Reference Tel: 423-652-4790. FAX: 423-652-4871. E-Mail: library@king.edu. Web Site: www.king.edu/library. *Actg Dir*, Matthew Stuart Peltier; Tel: 423-652-4789, E-Mail: mspeltie@king.edu; *Ref*, Terrie Kay Sypolt; Tel: 423-652-6301, E-Mail: tkspyolt@king.edu; *Doc*, Crystal L Davidson; Tel: 423-652-4795, E-Mail: cldavids@king.edu; *Tech Servs*, Betty Curtis; Tel: 423-652-4792, E-Mail: becurtis@king.edu; *Acq of Monographs*, Anna P Slagle; E-Mail: apslagle@king.edu; *Actg Dir*, Matthew Stuart Peltier; Tel: 423-652-4789, E-Mail: mspeltie@king.edu; *Publ Servs*, Ann Wood; E-Mail: aawood@king.edu; Staff 6 (MLS 2, Non-MLS 4)
Founded 1867. Enrl 608; Fac 40; Highest Degree: Bachelor
Jun 2000-May 2001 Income Parent Institution $250,937. Mats Exp $108,937, Books $35,000, Per/Ser (Incl. Access Fees) $25,500, Micro $8,000, AV Equip $3,562, Electronic Ref Mat (Incl. Access Fees) $36,875. Sal $142,000 (Prof $80,000)
Library Holdings: Bk Vols 105,120; Bk Titles 80,850; Per Subs 1,653
Subject Interests: Classics, Literature, Missiology, Relig studies
Special Collections: Southern Presbyterian History Coll
Automation Activity & Vendor Info: (Acquisitions) Innovative Interfaces Inc.; (Cataloging) Innovative Interfaces Inc.; (Circulation) Innovative Interfaces Inc.; (Course Reserve) Innovative Interfaces Inc.; (ILL) Innovative Interfaces Inc.; (Media Booking) Innovative Interfaces Inc.; (OPAC) Innovative Interfaces Inc.; (Serials) Innovative Interfaces Inc.
Database Vendor: CARL, Ebsco - EbscoHost, GaleNet, IAC - Info Trac, Lexis-Nexis, OCLC - First Search
Publications: Accession list; Library brochure; Library Newsletter; Subject Bibliographies
Partic in Appalachian Libr Info Coop; Holston Associated Libr Consortium

BROWNSVILLE

P ELMA ROSS PUBLIC LIBRARY, 1011 E Main St, 38012-2652. SAN 315-7288. Tel: 901-772-9534. FAX: 901-772-5416. E-Mail: elmarosslib@pchnet.com. Web Site: www.pchnet.com. *Dir*, Ramona Anne Stevenson; E-Mail: rstevens@mail.state.tn.us; *Asst Librn*, Dortha Lynn Thomas; Staff 2 (Non-MLS 2)
Founded 1910. Pop 19,438; Circ 34,950
Jul 1999-Jun 2000 Income $124,449, State $1,300, City $46,500, Federal $13,950, County $49,098, Locally Generated Income $13,601. Mats Exp $16,684, Books $15,207, Per/Ser (Incl. Access Fees) $1,477
Library Holdings: Bk Vols 22,247; Per Subs 60
Subject Interests: West Tenn genealogy
Special Collections: Disadvantaged Grant-Core Careers; Literacy Bank for Adults
Automation Activity & Vendor Info: (Cataloging) Sagebrush Corporation; (Circulation) Sagebrush Corporation
Database Vendor: GaleNet
Mem of Forked Deer Regional Library Center
Partic in Tenn Share
Friends of the Library Group

BYRDSTOWN

P PICKETT COUNTY PUBLIC LIBRARY, Community Center Bldg, 105 S Main St, 38549-2214. SAN 315-730X. Tel: 931-864-6281. *Dir*, Ruth Moles; E-Mail: rmoles@mail.state.tn.us
Founded 1961. Circ 12,000
Library Holdings: Bk Titles 12,000; Per Subs 13
Mem of Upper Cumberland Regional Library
Friends of the Library Group

CALHOUN

P CALHOUN PUBLIC LIBRARY, Hwy 163, PO Box 115, 37309-0115. SAN 315-7318. Tel: 423-336-2348. FAX: 423-336-1527. E-Mail: calhounl@usit.net. *Dir*, Roxanna Carman
Library Holdings: Bk Titles 4,000; Per Subs 12
Mem of Fort Loudoun Regional Library Center

CAMDEN

P BENTON COUNTY PUBLIC LIBRARY, 121 S Forrest Ave, 38320-2055. SAN 315-7326. Tel: 901-584-4772. FAX: 901-584-1098. *Dir*, Virginia Whitworth; E-Mail: vwhitwor@mail.state.tn.us
Pop 14,901
Library Holdings: Bk Vols 20,000; Per Subs 40
Special Collections: Benton County Genealogy & History Coll
Mem of Reelfoot Regional Library Center
Branches: 1
BIG SANDY BRANCH, 12 Front St, PO Box 115, Big Sandy, 38221. SAN 377-7464. Tel: 731-593-0225. FAX: 731-593-0226. *Dir*, Sherry Shelton
Friends of the Library Group

CARTHAGE

P SMITH COUNTY PUBLIC LIBRARY, 215 N Main St, 37030. SAN 360-5345. Tel: 615-735-1326. FAX: 615-735-2317. Web Site: www.webman.addr.com/library/. *Dir*, Pat Bush; E-Mail: pbush@mail.state.tn.us
Pop 15,356
Library Holdings: Bk Vols 22,000; Per Subs 32
Subject Interests: Genealogy
Mem of Upper Cumberland Regional Library
Branches: 1
GORDONSVILLE LIBRARY, 63 E Main St, Gordonsville, 38563. SAN 360-537X. Tel: 615-683-8063. FAX: 615-683-8063. Web Site: www.webman.addr.com/library/gordonsville..html. *Dir*, Katheryn Dickens
Library Holdings: Bk Vols 7,000

CARYVILLE

P CARYVILLE PUBLIC LIBRARY, 4839 Old Hwy 63, Ste 2, 37714-4105. SAN 315-7334. Tel: 423-562-1108. FAX: 423-562-4373. *Dir*, Robyn Lasley; E-Mail: rlasley@icx.net
Founded 1966. Pop 1,500; Circ 9,600
Library Holdings: Bk Titles 9,000; Per Subs 16
Mem of Clinch-Powell Regional Library
Friends of the Library Group

CENTERVILLE

P HICKMAN COUNTY PUBLIC LIBRARY, 120 W Swan St, 37099-1399. SAN 315-7350. Tel: 931-729-5130. FAX: 931-729-6950. E-Mail: hclib1@centerville.net. *Dir*, Mary B Pruett; *Librn*, David Dansby
Founded 1939
Library Holdings: Bk Vols 20,306; Per Subs 70
Mem of Blue Grass Regional Library
Branches: 1
EAST HICKMAN PUBLIC LIBRARY, 4487 Hwy 100, Lyles, 37098. SAN 377-7820. Tel: 931-670-5767. FAX: 931-670-0706. E-Mail: ehbranch@mail.state.tn.us. *Librn*, Mina Dressler
Mem of Blue Grass Regional Library

CHARLESTON

S OLIN CORPORATION, Information Resource Center, 1186 Lower River Rd, PO Box 248, 37310. SAN 327-8565. Tel: 423-336-4347. Reference Tel: 423-336-4481. FAX: 423-336-4194. *Mgr Libr Serv*, Connie Jean Upton; E-Mail: cjupton@corp.olin.com; *Info Specialist*, Nancy Darlene Sneed; E-Mail: ndsneed@corp.olin.com; Staff 2 (Non-MLS 2)
Founded 1976
Library Holdings: Bk Titles 5,000; Per Subs 100
Subject Interests: Marketing, Technology
Database Vendor: Dialog
Restriction: Not open to public
Function: Research library

CHATTANOOGA

SR AMG INTERNATIONAL LIBRARY, 6815 Shallowford Rd, 37421. (Mail add: PO Box 22000, 37422-2000), Tel: 423-894-6060. FAX: 423-894-6863. E-Mail: mission@amginternational.org. Web Site: www.amginternational.org. *Librn*, Joan Belh
Library Holdings: Bk Titles 40,000

J CHATTANOOGA STATE TECHNICAL COMMUNITY COLLEGE, Augusta R Kolwyck Library, 4501 Amnicola Hwy, 37406-1097. SAN 315-7369. Tel: 423-697-4448. Interlibrary Loan Service Tel: 423-697-2584. Circulation Tel: 423-697-4448. Reference Tel: 423-697-4436. FAX: 423-697-4409. Web Site: cstcc.library.chattanooga.org/library. *Dean*, Victoria P Leather; Tel: 423-697-2576, E-Mail: leather@cstcc.cc.tn.us; *Tech Servs*, Pamela P Temple; Tel: 423-697-2574, E-Mail: temple@cstcc.cc.tn.us; *Ref*, Wilka Carter; Tel: 423-697-2571, E-Mail: carter@cstcc.cc.tn.us; *Access Serv*, Tisa Houck; Tel: 423-697-2584, E-Mail: houck@cstcc.cc.tn.us; Staff 9 (MLS 9)
Founded 1965. Highest Degree: Associate
Library Holdings: Bk Vols 74,156; Bk Titles 61,895; Per Subs 540
Subject Interests: Allied health, Environ sci, Law, Off automation
Automation Activity & Vendor Info: (Acquisitions) EOS; (Circulation) TLC; (OPAC) TLC; (Serials) EOS
Database Vendor: Ebsco - EbscoHost, GaleNet, Lexis-Nexis, OCLC - First Search
Partic in Solinet; TBR Consortium; Tenn-Share
Special Services for the Deaf - Books on deafness & sign language; Captioned film depository; High interest/low vocabulary books

P CHATTANOOGA-HAMILTON COUNTY BICENTENNIAL LIBRARY, 1001 Broad St, 37402-2652. SAN 360-540X. Tel: 423-757-5310. Interlibrary Loan Service Tel: 423-757-5415. Circulation Tel: 423-757-5315. TDD: 423-757-5053. FAX: 423-757-4994. E-Mail: library@lib.chattanooga.gov. Web Site: www.lib.chattanooga.gov. *Dir*, Jane E McFarland; Tel: 423-757-5320, E-Mail: mcfarland_j@lib.chattanooga.gov; *Asst Dir*, David F Clapp; Tel: 423-757-5323, E-Mail: clapp_david@lib.chattanooga.gov; *Govt Doc, ILL*, Robert Drake; Fax: 423-757-5341, E-Mail: drake_robert@lib.chattanooga.gov; *AV*, Barry Bradford; Tel: 423-757-5316, E-Mail: bradford_b@lib.chattanooga.gov; *Circ*, Pat Childress; *Spec Coll*, Clara Swann; Tel: 423-757-5317, E-Mail: swann_c@lib.chattanooga.gov; *Ref*, Judy Kelley; Fax: 423-757-5090, E-Mail: kelley_j@lib.chattanooga.gov; Staff 20 (MLS 19, Non-MLS 1)
Founded 1905. Pop 265,721; Circ 712,421
Jul 1999-Jun 2000 Income (Main Library and Branch Library) $4,981,531, State $200,595, City $2,165,258, Federal $66,540, County $2,235,258, Locally Generated Income $170,780, Other $143,100. Mats Exp $834,822, Books $607,291, Per/Ser (Incl. Access Fees) $92,818, Presv $3,467, AV Equip $47,202, Electronic Ref Mat (Incl. Access Fees) $84,044. Sal $2,682,948 (Prof $919,140)
Library Holdings: Bk Vols 479,857; Bk Titles 264,510; Per Subs 1,325
Special Collections: Genealogy; Interviews Chattanooga & Hamilton County History; Tennesseana (Tennessee Room Coll), bks & microflm
Automation Activity & Vendor Info: (Acquisitions) CARL; (Cataloging) CARL; (Circulation) CARL; (OPAC) CARL; (Serials) CARL
Database Vendor: Ebsco - EbscoHost, GaleNet
Publications: A Brief Guide to Genealogical Materials; and a selection of bibliographies on varying subjects; At the Library (monthly events list); Friends of the Library Newsletter
Partic in OCLC Online Computer Library Center, Inc; SE Libr Network
Special Services for the Deaf - Books on deafness & sign language; Captioned film depository; High interest/low vocabulary books
Friends of the Library Group
Branches: 4
EASTGATE, 5900 Bldg, 5705 Marlin Rd, Ste 1500, 37411. SAN 360-5434. Tel: 423-855-2685. Circulation Tel: 423-855-2689. FAX: 423-855-2696. *Librn*, Mary Helms; Tel: 423-855-2686
Library Holdings: Bk Vols 60,318
Automation Activity & Vendor Info: (Acquisitions) CARL; (Cataloging) CARL; (Circulation) CARL; (OPAC) CARL; (Serials) CARL
Database Vendor: Ebsco - EbscoHost, GaleNet
NORTHGATE, 520 Northgate Mall, 37415-6924. SAN 360-5469. Tel: 423-870-0636. Circulation Tel: 423-870-0635. FAX: 423-870-0619. *Librn*, Barbara Kreischer; Tel: 423-870-0632
Library Holdings: Bk Vols 47,570
Automation Activity & Vendor Info: (Acquisitions) CARL; (Cataloging) CARL; (Circulation) CARL; (OPAC) CARL; (Serials) CARL
Database Vendor: Ebsco - EbscoHost, GaleNet
OOLTEWAH-COLLEGEDALE, 9318 Apison Pike, Ooltewah, 37363. SAN 372-784X. Tel: 423-396-9322. Circulation Tel: 423-396-9300. FAX: 423-396-9242. *Librn*, Deborah J Meredith; Tel: 423-396-9223
Library Holdings: Bk Vols 46,167
Automation Activity & Vendor Info: (Acquisitions) CARL; (Cataloging) CARL; (Circulation) CARL; (OPAC) CARL; (Serials) CARL
Database Vendor: Ebsco - EbscoHost, GaleNet
SOUTH CHATTANOOGA, 925 W 39th St, 37410. SAN 360-5493. Tel: 423-825-7237. FAX: 423-825-7239. *Librn*, Greg DeFriese
Library Holdings: Bk Vols 27,574
Automation Activity & Vendor Info: (Acquisitions) CARL; (Cataloging) CARL; (Circulation) CARL; (OPAC) CARL; (Serials) CARL
Database Vendor: Ebsco - EbscoHost, GaleNet

S CHATTANOOGA-HAMILTON COUNTY REGIONAL PLANNING AGENCY LIBRARY, City Hall Annex, Rm 200, 100 E 11th St, 37402. SAN 327-0971. Tel: 423-757-5216. FAX: 423-757-5532. *Librn*, Yuen Lee
Library Holdings: Per Subs 30
Subject Interests: Local government, Planning

§C ELECTRONIC COMPUTER PROGRAMMING COLLEGE INC LIBRARY, 3805 Brainerd Rd, 37411. SAN 375-443X. Tel: 423-624-0077. FAX: 423-624-1575. E-Mail: ecpc@aol.com. *Librn*, Gayla C Brewer; Staff (MLS 1)
Jul 1999-Jun 2000 Income $8,000
Library Holdings: Bk Vols 3,500; Per Subs 10
Subject Interests: Computer science, Electronics, Travel tourism
Special Collections: Travel & Tourism Coll, videos

M ERLANGER HEALTH SYSTEM LIBRARY, 975 E Third St, 37403. SAN 360-5523. Tel: 423-778-7246. Interlibrary Loan Service Tel: 423-778-6525. FAX: 423-778-7247. Web Site: www.erlanger.org/library.htm. *Librn*, Virgini Cairns; E-Mail: cairnsvl@erlanger.org; Staff 4 (MLS 1, Non-MLS 3)
Founded 1940
Jul 1999-Jun 2000 Income Locally Generated Income $5,500. Mats Exp $121,000, Books $36,000, Per/Ser (Incl. Access Fees) $75,000
Library Holdings: Bk Vols 9,000; Per Subs 350
Subject Interests: Cancer, Hospital administration, Medicine, Nursing, Orthopedics, Pediatrics, Plastic surgery, Surgery
Special Collections: History of Medicine Coll
Automation Activity & Vendor Info: (Cataloging) Sagebrush Corporation; (Circulation) Sagebrush Corporation; (OPAC) Sagebrush Corporation
Publications: New Acquisitions Lists (monthly); newsletter (quarterly)
Partic in Docline; SE Libr Network; Tennessee Health Science Library Association
Open Mon-Fri 8-4

R FIRST CENTENARY UNITED METHODIST CHURCH LIBRARY, 419 McCallie Ave, 37402. (Mail add: PO Box 208, 37401), Tel: 423-756-2021. FAX: 423-266-9742. *Librn*, Elizabeth Jones
Library Holdings: Bk Vols 2,000
Partic in CSLA

GL HAMILTON COUNTY GOVERNMENTAL LAW LIBRARY, City County Courts Bldg, 600 Market St, Rm 305, 37402. SAN 315-7393. Tel: 423-209-7595. FAX: 423-209-7596. *Librn*, Martha Wilson
Founded 1953
Library Holdings: Bk Vols 13,000
Special Collections: Federal & State Codes Coll; West Reporter Coll

S HOUSTON MUSEUM OF DECORATIVE ARTS, 201 High St, 37403. SAN 315-7407. Tel: 423-267-7176. FAX: 423-756-2787. E-Mail: houston@chattanooga.net. *Dir*, Amy Frierson
Founded 1961
Library Holdings: Bk Vols 550

S HUNTER MUSEUM OF ART, Reference Library, 10 Bluff View, 37403. SAN 315-7415. Tel: 423-267-0968. FAX: 423-267-9844. *Curator*, Ellen Simak
Founded 1959
Library Holdings: Bk Vols 1,500; Bk Titles 1,300; Per Subs 38
Subject Interests: Am art, Antiques, Architecture

L MILLER & MARTIN LLP, Law Library, Volunteer Bldg Ste 1000 10th flr, 832 Georgia Ave, 37402. SAN 372-1841. Tel: 423-756-6600. FAX: 423-785-8480. Web Site: www.millermartin.com. *Librn*, Virginia Hughes; E-Mail: ghughes@millermartin.com; *Mgr*, Gail Sisson; E-Mail: gsisson@millermartin.com; *Tech Servs*, Shirley Kelly
Library Holdings: Bk Vols 10,000; Per Subs 20
Subject Interests: Real estate

MOCCASIN BEND MENTAL HEALTH INSTITUTE
M HEALTH SCIENCES LIBRARY, 100 Moccasin Bend Rd, 37405. SAN 360-5612. Tel: 865-785-3365, Ext 7722. FAX: 865-785-3364. E-Mail: icrow@mail.state.tn.us. *Librn*, Ione Crowe
Founded 1961
Library Holdings: Bk Vols 1,245; Per Subs 54
Subject Interests: Activity therapy, Nursing, Pastoral counseling, Pharmacology, Psychiatry, Psychology, Sociology
Partic in Chattanooga Health Educ Libr Prog; Southeastern Regional Med Libr Program; Tennessee Health Science Library Association
S PATIENT LIBRARY, 100 Moccasin Bend Rd. SAN 360-5647. Tel: 865-785-3365, Ext 7722. FAX: 865-785-3364. *Librn*, Ione Crowe; E-Mail: icrow@mail.state.tn.us
Library Holdings: Bk Vols 4,500

S NATIONAL MODEL RAILROAD ASSOCIATION, Kalmbach Memorial Library, 4121 Cromwell Rd, 37421-2119. SAN 373-871X. Tel: 423-894-8144. FAX: 423-899-4869. Web Site: www.nmra.org. *Dir*, Gordon T Belt; *Res*, Brent Lambert; Staff 3 (MLS 1, Non-MLS 2)
Founded 1986
Library Holdings: Bk Titles 3,500; Per Subs 251
Special Collections: Model Railroads (Walthers Coll), cat, correspondence,

kit instructions; Railroads - Locomotives (Kentlein Porter Coll), cat, docs, photos
Publications: Freight Terminals & Trains; Indexes to Major Photo Collections Held; Official Railway Equipment Register; Symposium on Railroad History

R TENNESSEE TEMPLE UNIVERSITY, Cierpke Memorial Library, 1815 Union Ave, 37404. SAN 315-7423. Tel: 423-493-4250. FAX: 423-493-4308. *Dir*, Kevin Woodruff
Founded 1946. Enrl 1,500; Fac 90; Highest Degree: Doctorate
Library Holdings: Bk Vols 196,000; Per Subs 250
Subject Interests: Arts, Relig studies, Sci
Special Collections: Rare Out of Print Books; Religious Education Materials
Partic in SE Libr Network
Special Services for the Deaf - Staff with knowledge of sign language
Friends of the Library Group

TENNESSEE VALLEY AUTHORITY, Corporate Library-Chattanooga, 1101 Market St, SP IA-C, 37402. SAN 315-7431. Tel: 423-751-4913. FAX: 423-751-4914. E-Mail: corplibchatt@tva.gov. *Librn*, Ann R Holder; Tel: 423-751-4916, E-Mail: arholder@tva.gov; *Automation Syst Coordr*, Kathy E Moree; Tel: 423-751-4915, E-Mail: kemoree@tva.gov; *Circ*, Vickie L Ragsdale; Tel: 423-751-2723, E-Mail: vlragsdale@tva.gov; Staff 3 (MLS 1, Non-MLS 2)
Founded 1957
Library Holdings: Bk Vols 35,000; Bk Titles 25,000; Per Subs 350
Subject Interests: Electric power production, Environmental studies, Nuclear energy
Special Collections: Electric Power Research Institute Reports
Automation Activity & Vendor Info: (Cataloging) EOS; (Circulation) EOS; (OPAC) EOS; (Serials) EOS
Database Vendor: Dialog, Ebsco - EbscoHost, OCLC - First Search
Publications: New EPRI Reports List; New NRC Reports List; Nuclear Power Current Awareness List; Power Current Awareness List; Utility Information Report
Function: Research library
Partic in Dialog Corporation; Fedlink; OCLC Online Computer Library Center, Inc

THE CHATTANOOGA TIMES/FREE PRESS LIBRARY, 400 E 11th St, 37403. (Mail add: PO Box 1447, 37401), SAN 324-1009. Tel: 423-757-6238. FAX: 423-757-6383. Web Site: www.timesfreepress.com. *Librn*, Jackie Punneo; E-Mail: jpunneo@timesfreepress.com
Founded 1963
Library Holdings: Bk Vols 400; Bk Titles 200
Subject Interests: Clippings dealing with local nat news, Photogs dealing with local nat news

UNIVERSITY OF TENNESSEE AT CHATTANOOGA LIBRARY, T Cartter & Margaret Rawlings Lupton Library, Vine St, 37403-2598. (Mail add: 615 McCallie Ave, 37403-2598), Tel: 423-755-4506. Circulation Tel: 423-755-4501. Reference Tel: 423-755-4510. FAX: 423-755-4775. Web Site: www.lib.utc.edu. *Dean of Libr*, Sheila A Delacroix; E-Mail: sheila-delacroix@utc.edu; *Head, Acq*, Mike Bell; E-Mail: mike-bell@utc.edu; *AV*, Kathy Breeden; E-Mail: kathy-breeden@utc.edu; *AV*, Marea Rankin; Tel: 423-755-4505, E-Mail: marea-rankin@utc.edu; *Automation Syst Coordr*, Randy Whitson; Tel: 423-755-4469, E-Mail: randy-whitson@utc.edu; *Bibliog Instr*, Laura Baker; E-Mail: laura-baker@utc.edu; *Head, Cat*, Valerie Adams; E-Mail: valarie-adams@utc.edu; *Circ*, Sherry Young; E-Mail: sherry-young@utc.edu; *Head Ref*, William Prince; E-Mail: bill-prince@utc.edu; *Spec Coll*, Frances Holly Hodges; E-Mail: holly-hodges@utc.edu; Staff 30 (MLS 14, Non-MLS 16)
Founded 1872. Enrl 7,000
Jul 1999-Jun 2000 Income $1,752,867, State $1,715,629, Other $37,238. Mats Exp $890,019, Books $174,396, Per/Ser (Incl. Access Fees) $668,357, Micro $47,266. Sal $862,848 (Prof $541,664)
Library Holdings: Bk Vols 479,007; Per Subs 2,768
Subject Interests: Civil War, Local history, Southern lit
Automation Activity & Vendor Info: (Acquisitions) VTLS; (Cataloging) VTLS; (Circulation) VTLS; (Course Reserve) VTLS; (OPAC) VTLS; (Serials) VTLS
Database Vendor: Dialog, GaleNet, IAC - Info Trac, IAC - SearchBank, Lexis-Nexis, OCLC - First Search, ProQuest, Silverplatter Information Inc.
Publications: Annual Statistical Report; Newsletter (Web)
Partic in OCLC Online Computer Library Center, Inc; SE Libr Network; Tenn Acad Libr Collaborative

CLARKSVILLE

C AUSTIN PEAY STATE UNIVERSITY, Felix G Woodward Library, 601 E College St, 37044. (Mail add: PO Box 4595, 37044), SAN 315-7474. Tel: 931-221-7618. Interlibrary Loan Service Tel: 931-221-7193. Circulation Tel: 931-221-7346. Reference Tel: 931-221-7346. FAX: 931-221-7296. Web Site: library.apsu.edu. *Publ Servs*, Anne May Berwind; Tel: 931-221-7978, E-Mail: berwinda@apsu.edu; *Dean of Libr*, Dr Donald F Joyce; E-Mail: joyced@apsu.edu; *Media Spec*, Lynda Conner; Tel: 931-221-7187, E-Mail: connerl@apsu.edu; *Acq, Coll Develop*, Sharon Johnson; Tel: 931-221-7914, E-Mail: johnsons@apsu.edu; *Cat*, Deborah Fetch; Tel: 931-221-7617, E-Mail: fetchd@apsu.edu; *Syst Coordr*, Don Carlin; Tel: 931-221-7384, E-Mail: carlind@apsu.edu; Staff 20 (MLS 12, Non-MLS 8)
Founded 1927. Enrl 5,664; Fac 280
Jul 1999-Jun 2000 Income $2,069,524, Locally Generated Income $16,132, Parent Institution $2,053,392. Mats Exp $521,042, Books $210,785, Per/Ser (Incl. Access Fees) $257,318, Presv $18,483, Micro $7,606, AV Equip $2,899, Electronic Ref Mat (Incl. Access Fees) $23,951. Sal $1,067,940 (Prof $735,298)
Library Holdings: Bk Vols 322,626; Per Subs 1,760
Automation Activity & Vendor Info: (Acquisitions) epixtech, inc.; (Cataloging) epixtech, inc.; (Circulation) epixtech, inc.; (Course Reserve) epixtech, inc.; (OPAC) epixtech, inc.; (Serials) epixtech, inc.
Publications: Notes from Felix G Woodward Library (newsletter)
Partic in Nashville Area Libr Alliance; SE Libr Network

P CLARKSVILLE-MONTGOMERY COUNTY PUBLIC LIBRARY, 350 Pageant Lane, Ste 501, 37040. SAN 320-2364. Tel: 931-648-8826. FAX: 931-648-8831. Web Site: www.clarksville.org. *Dir*, Stephen Lesnak; E-Mail: director@clarksville.org; Staff 20 (MLS 1, Non-MLS 19)
Founded 1894. Pop 109,992
Jul 1998-Jun 1999 Income $1,500,000. Mats Exp $310,000. Sal $690,000
Library Holdings: Bk Vols 110,000; Per Subs 123
Special Collections: Brown Harvey Genealogy Room; Family & Tennessee History, bks & microfilm
Publications: Friends of the Library Newsletter
Mem of Warioto Regional Library Center
Friends of the Library Group

S LEAF-CHRONICLE COMPANY LIBRARY, 200 Commerce St, 37040. SAN 327-0998. Tel: 931-552-1808 ext 274. FAX: 552-5859, 931-648-8001. E-Mail: lcnewsline@aol.com.
Library Holdings: Bk Vols 200

P WARIOTO REGIONAL LIBRARY CENTER, 1753A Alpine Dr, PO Box 886, 37041-0886. SAN 315-7482. Tel: 931-645-9531. FAX: 931-645-6695. *Dir*, John M Chapman; E-Mail: jchapman@mail.state.tn.us; *Librn*, Rebecca Bailey; E-Mail: bbailey@warioto.tsla.lib.tn.us; Staff 8 (MLS 2, Non-MLS 6)
Founded 1947. Pop 339,766; Circ 869,320
Library Holdings: Bk Titles 149,518
Publications: Word from Warioto (bi-monthly newsletter)
Member Libraries: Cheatham County Public Library; Clarksville-Montgomery County Public Library; Dickson County Public Library; Edward Ward, Carmack-Sumner County Public Library; Gorham-Macbane Public Library; Houston County Public Library; Humphreys County Public Library; Martin Curtis Hendersonville Public Library; Portland Public Library; Stewart County Public Library; White House Inn

CLEVELAND

P CLEVELAND PUBLIC LIBRARY, 795 Church St NE, 37311-5295. SAN 315-7490. Tel: 423-472-2163. FAX: 423-339-9791. E-Mail: info@clevelandlibrary.org. Web Site: www.clevelandlibrary.org. *Dir*, Andrew Hunt; E-Mail: director@clevelandlibrary.org; *Ch Servs*, Christine Gavin; *Ref*, Wilbertine Scott; *Circ*, Treasure Swanson; *Tech Servs*, Misty Eubanks; Staff 9 (MLS 4, Non-MLS 5)
Founded 1923. Pop 83,205; Circ 263,979
Jul 1999-Jun 2000 Income $718,821, City $308,000, County $308,000, Locally Generated Income $45,425, Other $57,396. Mats Exp $85,711, Books $70,528, Per/Ser (Incl. Access Fees) $5,937, AV Equip $9,246. Sal $390,045 (Prof $137,999)
Library Holdings: Bk Vols 102,802; Per Subs 112
Subject Interests: Cherokee Indians
Special Collections: Corn Cherokee Coll; Tennessee Genealogy Coll
Automation Activity & Vendor Info: (Circulation) Endeavor; (OPAC) Endeavor
Publications: Friends of the Library Newsletter; genealogical books
Mem of Fort Loudoun Regional Library Center
Friends of the Library Group

J CLEVELAND STATE COMMUNITY COLLEGE LIBRARY, PO Box 3570, 37320-3570. SAN 315-7504. Tel: 423-472-7141, Ext 209, 423-478-6209. FAX: 423-478-6255. Web Site: www.clscc.cc.tn.us/library/index.html. *Coll Develop, Dir*, Mary Evelyn Lynn; E-Mail: melynn@clscc.cc.tn.us; *Cat, Media Spec*, Sam Neas; *Acq*, Janet Caruth; *Publ Servs*, Alan Goslen
Founded 1967
Jul 1999-Jun 2000 Income $376,895, State $373,795, Other $3,100. Mats Exp $102,400, Books $58,000, Per/Ser (Incl. Access Fees) $21,600, Presv $50, Micro $13,500, AV Equip $7,500, Other Print Mats $1,700, Manuscripts & Archives $50. Sal $220,956 (Prof $141,156)
Library Holdings: Bk Titles 53,482; Per Subs 368
Subject Interests: Govt doc, Law, Local history, Medicine
Special Collections: Bradley County History, bks, flm; Polk County History
Automation Activity & Vendor Info: (Cataloging) Gaylord; (OPAC) Gaylord
Partic in SE Libr Network; Westlaw

C LEE UNIVERSITY - CHURCH OF GOD THEOLOGICAL SEMINARY, William G Squires Library, 260 11th St NE, 37311. SAN 315-7512. Tel: 423-614-8550. Circulation Tel: 423-614-8551. FAX: 423-614-8555. Web Site: www.leeuniversity.edu/library. *Dir*, Frances Arrington; E-Mail: farrington@leeuniversity.edu; *Tech Servs*, Jean Goforth; *Publ Servs*, Barbara McCullough; *Ref*, Janet Williams; *Syst Coordr*, Michael Sturrgeon; *Ser*, Allison Sharp; Staff 7 (MLS 6, Non-MLS 1)
Founded 1941. Enrl 3,365; Fac 139; Highest Degree: Master
Jul 1999-Jun 2000 Income $997,377, Locally Generated Income $33,323, Parent Institution $911,093. Mats Exp $214,283, Books $141,958, Per/Ser (Incl. Access Fees) $33,547, Presv $4,431, Micro $9,991, Electronic Ref Mat (Incl. Access Fees) $9,635. Sal $520,072 (Prof $261,341)
Library Holdings: Bk Vols 158,906; Bk Titles 147,954; Per Subs 835
Subject Interests: Education, Music, Pentecostalism, Relig studies
Special Collections: Pentecostal Research Center Coll, multi-media
Automation Activity & Vendor Info: (Acquisitions) Endeavor; (Cataloging) Endeavor; (Circulation) Endeavor; (Course Reserve) Endeavor; (OPAC) Endeavor; (Serials) Endeavor
Database Vendor: OCLC - First Search
Publications: PRC News (biannual)
Partic in OCLC Online Computer Library Center, Inc; SE Libr Network

S RED CLAY HISTORICAL PARK LIBRARY, 1140 Red Clay Park Rd SW, 37311. SAN 374-7646. Tel: 423-478-0339. FAX: 423-614-7251. *In Charge*, Lois I Osborne
Library Holdings: Bk Vols 600

CLINTON

P CLINCH-POWELL REGIONAL LIBRARY, 752 N Main St, 37716-3122. SAN 315-7539. Tel: 865-457-0931. FAX: 865-457-8546. Web Site: www.state.tn.us/sos/statelib/p&d/clinchpowell. *Dir*, Judy Greeson; E-Mail: jgreeson@mail.state.tn.us; Staff 1 (MLS 1)
Founded 1946. Pop 194,729; Circ 452,034
Jul 1999-Jun 2000 Income $427,312, State $366,287, Federal $45,067, Locally Generated Income $1,047, Other $14,911. Mats Exp $56,483, Books $51,197, Per/Ser (Incl. Access Fees) $5,286. Sal $176,944 (Prof $71,486)
Library Holdings: Bk Vols 179,712
Restriction: Not open to public
Member Libraries: Briceville Public Library; Caryville Public Library; Claiborne County Public Library; Clinton Public Library; Deer Lodge Public Library; Huntsville Public Library; Jacksboro Public Library; Jellico Public Library; La Follette Public Library; Lake City Public Library; Luttrell Public Library; Maynardville Public Library; Norris Community Library; Oakdale Public Library; Oneida County Public Library; Petros Public Library; Sunbright Public Library; Winfield Library

P CLINTON PUBLIC LIBRARY, 118 S Hicks St, 37716-2826. SAN 315-7547. Tel: 865-457-0519. FAX: 865-457-4233. *Dir*, Jane Giles; E-Mail: jgiles@usit.net; Staff 4 (MLS 1, Non-MLS 3)
Pop 34,823; Circ 96,000
Jul 1998-Jun 1999 Income $111,950, City $56,260, County $55,690. Mats Exp $15,000, Books $13,000, Per/Ser (Incl. Access Fees) $2,000
Library Holdings: Bk Titles 35,000; Per Subs 57
Special Collections: Genealogy Research Coll
Mem of Clinch-Powell Regional Library
Friends of the Library Group

COALMONT

P COALMONT PUBLIC LIBRARY, Hwy 56, 37313-9999. (Mail add: PO Box 334, 37313-0334), SAN 376-6993. Tel: 931-592-9373. FAX: 931-592-9373. E-Mail: ctpublib@blomand.net. *Dir*, Brinda Fran Adams; E-Mail: fadams@mail.state.tn.us
Library Holdings: Bk Vols 3,555
Partic in Tenn Share

COLLEGEDALE

C SOUTHERN ADVENTIST UNIVERSITY, (SAU), McKee Library, PO Box 629, 37315-0629. SAN 360-5671. Tel: 423-238-2788. Interlibrary Loan Service Tel: 423-238-2790. FAX: 423-238-3009. Web Site: www.library.southern.edu. *Dir*, Peg Bennett; E-Mail: pbennett@southern.edu; *Bibliog Instr, Publ Servs*, Marge Seifert; E-Mail: meseifrt@southern.edu; *Tech Servs*, Loranne Grace; E-Mail: kgrace@southern.edu; *Circ, Ref*, Ann Greer; E-Mail: atgreer@southern.edu; *Per*, Patricia Beaman; E-Mail: pbeaman@southern.edu; Staff 8 (MLS 5, Non-MLS 3)
Founded 1890. Enrl 2,047; Fac 113; Highest Degree: Doctorate
Jun 2000-May 2001 Income $952,782, Locally Generated Income $8,536, Parent Institution $944,246. Mats Exp $433,427, Books $150,583, Per/Ser (Incl. Access Fees) $165,425, Presv $1,050, Electronic Ref Mat (Incl. Access Fees) $87,440. Sal $504,207 (Prof $257,642)
Library Holdings: Bk Vols 126,037; Bk Titles 113,430; Per Subs 1,096; Bks on Deafness & Sign Lang 100
Subject Interests: Business, Computing, Education, Nursing, Religion
Special Collections: Abraham Lincoln (Dr Vernon Thomas Memorial Coll), bks, letters, mss, newsp, pamphlets, pictures, maps, paintings & artifacts; Civil War (Dr Vernon Thomas Memorial Coll), bks, letters, mss, newsp, pamphlets, pictures & maps; Seventh Day Adventist Church Publications, bks, per, micro & archives
Automation Activity & Vendor Info: (Cataloging) SIRSI; (Circulation) SIRSI; (OPAC) SIRSI
Database Vendor: OCLC - First Search
Publications: LNN News
Partic in Adventist Librs Info Coop; SE Libr Network
Processing center for 180 small elementary & secondary schools in the southeastern states (Ala, Fla, Ga, Ky, NC, SC & Tenn) of the Adventist Network of General Education Libraries

COLUMBIA

P BLUE GRASS REGIONAL LIBRARY, 104 E Sixth, 38401-3359. SAN 315-7555. Tel: 931-388-9282. FAX: 931-388-1762. E-Mail: bluegras@tsla.lib.tn.us. *Dir*, Marion K Bryant; E-Mail: mbryant@mail.state.tn.us; *Circ*, Jo Ann Jones; *Acq, Cat*, Vickie Thompson; Staff 8 (MLS 1, Non-MLS 7)
Founded 1954. Pop 318,693; Circ 1,277,756
Jul 1999-Jun 2000 Income $461,777, State $432,898, Federal $28,879. Mats Exp $93,523, Books $85,389, Per/Ser (Incl. Access Fees) $3,100, AV Equip $5,034. Sal $226,396 (Prof $47,000)
Library Holdings: Bk Vols 156,426
Subject Interests: Large print bks
Publications: Blue Grass Notes (bi-monthly newletter)
Member Libraries: Ardmore Community Library; Giles County Public Library; Giles County Public Library; Hickman County Public Library; Hickman County Public Library; Lawrence County Public Library; Lewis County Public Library; Marshall County Memorial Library; Maury County Public Library; Minor Hill Community Library; Perry County Public Library; Robert B Jones Memorial Library; The Brentwood Library & Center For Fine Arts; Wayne County Public Library; Williamson County Public Library
Bookmobiles: 1

J COLUMBIA STATE COMMUNITY COLLEGE, Finney Memorial Library, 1665 Hampshire Pike, 38401. (Mail add: PO Box 1315, 38402-1315), Tel: 931-540-2560. FAX: 931-540-2565. Web Site: coscc.cc.tn.us/lrc. *Dir*, Kathy Breeden; Tel: 931-540-2555, E-Mail: breeden@coscc.cc.tn.us; *Tech Servs*, Lyn Bayless; Tel: 931-540-2559, E-Mail: bayless@coscc.cc.tn.us; Staff 3 (MLS 3)
Founded 1966. Enrl 4,299
2000-2001 Mats Exp $210,000, Books $80,000, Per/Ser (Incl. Access Fees) $30,000, Micro $12,000, AV Equip $1,000, Electronic Ref Mat (Incl. Access Fees) $20,582. Sal $275,000 (Prof $150,000)
Library Holdings: Bk Vols 61,085; Per Subs 446
Special Collections: Archives; South-Central Tennessee History
Automation Activity & Vendor Info: (Cataloging) DRA; (Circulation) DRA; (OPAC) DRA
Database Vendor: Ebsco - EbscoHost, GaleNet, OCLC - First Search, Wilson - Wilson Web
Publications: LRC Handbook; LRC Policy Manual
Partic in OCLC Online Computer Library Center, Inc; SE Libr Network

P MAURY COUNTY PUBLIC LIBRARY, 211 W Eighth St, 38401. SAN 360-5701. Tel: 931-388-6332. FAX: 931-388-6371. *Coll Develop, Librn*, Elizabeth Potts
Pop 63,888
Library Holdings: Bk Vols 78,808; Per Subs 214
Subject Interests: Genealogy, Local history, Maury County, Mules, Tenn hist
Mem of Blue Grass Regional Library
Friends of the Library Group
Branches: 1
MOUNT PLEASANT BRANCH, 200 Hay Long Ave, Mount Pleasant, 38474. (Mail add: PO Box 71, Mount Pleasant, 38474-0071), SAN 360-5736. Tel: 931-379-3752. *Dir*, Janice Jones

COOKEVILLE

P PUTNAM COUNTY LIBRARY SYSTEM, 50 E Broad St, 38501. SAN 315-7571. Tel: 931-526-2416. FAX: 931-372-8517. E-Mail: pcls@usit.net. *Dir*, Diane Duncan; *Asst Dir*, Wanda H Maxwell; *Asst Dir*, Jeanne Schmitzer; *Ref*, Aimee Smith. Subject Specialists: *Children*, Wanda H Maxwell; *Ref*, Jeanne Schmitzer; Staff 3 (MLS 2, Non-MLS 1)
Founded 1939. Pop 59,735; Circ 321,525
Jul 2000-Jun 2001 Income (Main Library Only) $571,038, State $5,858, City $209,640, County $254,655, Locally Generated Income $63,628, Other $37,257. Mats Exp $67,540, Books $63,540, AV Equip $4,000. Sal $344,18
(Prof $94,705)
Library Holdings: Bk Titles 89,088; Per Subs 168
Subject Interests: Genealogy
Automation Activity & Vendor Info: (Cataloging) TLC
Database Vendor: IAC - Info Trac
Mem of Upper Cumberland Regional Library

Special Services for the Deaf - TDD
Special Services for the Blind - Bks on cassette; Braille
Dial-a-story; Daily story time for children; memorial book fund
Branches: 3
ALGOOD BRANCH, 125 Fourth Ave, Algood, 38506-5224. SAN 376-7337. Tel: 931-537-3240. FAX: 931-372-8517. E-Mail: algoodlib@yahoo.com. *Branch Mgr*, Kathy Keller
Library Holdings: Bk Vols 4,000; Bk Titles 1,390
BAXTER BRANCH, Baxter City Hall, Main St, Baxter, 38544-0335. SAN 376-8147. Tel: 931-858-1888. FAX: 931-372-8517. E-Mail: baxterlibrary@yahoo.com. *Dir*, Brinda Shanks
Library Holdings: Bk Vols 5,000; Bk Titles 2,781
MONTEREY BRANCH, 401 E Commercial Ave, Monterey, 38574. SAN 376-8155. Tel: 931-839-2103. FAX: 931-839-2103. E-Mail: mntlib@usit.net, mntlib@usit.net. *Dir*, Diane Duncan; Tel: 931-526-2416, Fax: 931-372-8517, E-Mail: pcls@usit.net; *Branch Mgr*, Doylene Farley
Income $26,972, City $25,472, County $500, Locally Generated Income $1,000
Library Holdings: Bk Titles 4,215
Friends of the Library Group

TENNESSEE TECHNOLOGICAL UNIVERSITY, University Library, 1100 N Peachtree Box 5066, 38505. SAN 315-758X. Tel: 931-372-3408. Interlibrary Loan Service Tel: 931-372-3710. Circulation Tel: 931-372-3326. FAX: 931-372-6112. E-Mail: wwalden@tntech.edu. Web Site: www2.tntech.edu/library. *Dir*, Winston A Walden; *ILL*, Linda Mulder; E-Mail: lmulder@tntech.edu; *Acq*, Georganne Burns; Tel: 931-372-3545, E-Mail: gburns@tntech.edu; *Spec Coll*, Christine Jones; Tel: 931-372-3470; *Automation Syst Coordr, Cat*, Susan LaFever; Tel: 931-372-6110, E-Mail: slafever@tntech.edu; *Coordr, Publ Servs*, Deanna Nipp; Tel: 931-372-3958, E-Mail: dnipp@tntech.edu; *Coll Develop, Coordr*, Roger Jones; Tel: 931-372-3822, E-Mail: rgjones@tntech.edu; Staff 31 (MLS 12, Non-MLS 19)
Founded 1915. Enrl 8,500; Fac 369; Highest Degree: Doctorate
Jul 1999-Jun 2000 Income $2,466,752, State $2,373,474, Federal $57,077, Locally Generated Income $36,201. Mats Exp $1,105,780. Sal $897,455 (Prof $450,223)
Library Holdings: Bk Vols 322,361; Per Subs 3,752
Subject Interests: Engineering
Special Collections: Harding Studio Coll; Joe L Evins Coll; Tennessee History Coll; Upper Cumberland History Coll
Automation Activity & Vendor Info: (Acquisitions) DRA; (Cataloging) DRA; (Circulation) DRA; (Course Reserve) DRA; (OPAC) DRA; (Serials) DRA
Database Vendor: DRA, GaleNet, IAC - Info Trac, ProQuest, Silverplatter Information Inc.
Partic in OCLC Online Computer Library Center, Inc; SE Libr Network; Tenn Share
Friends of the Library Group

UPPER CUMBERLAND REGIONAL LIBRARY, 208 E Minnear, 38501. SAN 315-7598. Tel: 931-526-4016. FAX: 931-528-3311. *Dir*, Elizabeth Jarvis; *Asst Dir*, Jennifer Cowan-Henderson; Staff 9 (MLS 2, Non-MLS 7)
Founded 1946. Pop 162,561; Circ 763,147
Jul 1999-Jun 2000 Income $437,650, State $394,999, Federal $42,651. Mats Exp $93,512, Books $80,888, Per/Ser (Incl. Access Fees) $2,200. Sal $301,487 (Prof $84,000)
Library Holdings: Bk Vols 118,960
Member Libraries: Charles Ralph Holland Memorial Library; Clay County Public Library; Fentress County Public Library; Justin Potter Public Library; Macon County Public Library; Overton County Public Library; Pickett County Public Library; Putnam County Library System; Smith County Public Library

COPPERHILL

P COPPERHILL PUBLIC LIBRARY, 160 Main St, 37317-9999. SAN 315-7601. Tel: 423-496-5141. FAX: 423-496-3617. *Dir*, Connie Workman
Mem of Fort Loudoun Regional Library Center

COSBY

P COSBY COMMUNITY LIBRARY, 3535 Adkisson Dr, 37312-2858. (Mail add: PO Box 3570, 37320-3570), SAN 376-2947. Tel: 423-487-5885. FAX: 423-487-5885. E-Mail: cosbylib@mail.state.tn.us. *Dir*, Sandra Foster
Library Holdings: Bk Vols 4,878; Per Subs 250
Mem of Nolichucky Regional Library
Friends of the Library Group

COVINGTON

P TIPTON COUNTY PUBLIC LIBRARY, 300 W Church Ave, 38019-2729. SAN 315-761X. Tel: 901-476-8289. FAX: 901-476-0008. E-Mail: tiptonpl@bellsouth.net. *Dir*, JoAnn Beatty; Staff 2 (MLS 1, Non-MLS 1)
Founded 1938. Pop 37,500
Library Holdings: Bk Vols 43,000
Subject Interests: County genealogy, State
Special Collections: MacArthur tapes; VHS tapes of local TV news 1989-93; WW II tapes
Mem of Forked Deer Regional Library Center

CROSSVILLE

P ART CIRCLE PUBLIC LIBRARY, 154 E First St, 38555-4696. SAN 315-7628. Tel: 931-484-6790. FAX: 931-484-2350. Web Site: www.artcircle.crossville.com. *Dir*, Debbie Hall; E-Mail: dhall@mail.state.tn.us; *Dep Dir*, James Houston
Founded 1898. Pop 30,000; Circ 110,000
Library Holdings: Bk Titles 28,000
Mem of Caney Fork Regional Library
Friends of the Library Group

DANDRIDGE

P DANDRIDGE MEMORIAL LIBRARY, 1235 Circle Dr, PO Box 339, 37725. SAN 315-7636. Tel: 865-397-9758. FAX: 865-397-0950. *Librn*, Billie Jean Chambers
Founded 1942. Pop 31,284; Circ 45,986
Library Holdings: Bk Vols 25,000; Per Subs 43
Subject Interests: Genealogy
Mem of Nolichucky Regional Library
Friends of the Library Group

DAYTON

C BRYAN COLLEGE LIBRARY, 130 Mercer Dr, 37321. (Mail add: PO Box 7000, 37321-7000), Tel: 423-775-7307. Interlibrary Loan Service Tel: 423-775-7228. Reference Tel: 423-775-7228. FAX: 423-775-7330. E-Mail: kaufmala@bryan.edu. *Coll Develop, Dir*, Dennis Ingolfsland; Tel: 423-775-7309, E-Mail: ingolfde@bryan.edu; *Asst Dir*, Laura Kaufman; Tel: 423-775-7196, E-Mail: kaufmala@bryan.edu; *Ref*, Lavonne Johnson; E-Mail: johnsova@bryan.edu. Subject Specialists: *Biblical studies*, Dennis Ingolfsland; Staff 4 (MLS 3, Non-MLS 1)
Founded 1930. Enrl 612; Fac 29; Highest Degree: Bachelor
Jul 1999-Jun 2000 Income $160,000. Mats Exp $90,147, Books $56,366, Per/Ser (Incl. Access Fees) $28,020, AV Equip $5,761
Library Holdings: Bk Vols 64,734
Automation Activity & Vendor Info: (OPAC) TLC
Partic in OCLC Online Computer Library Center, Inc; SE Libr Network

P CLYDE W RODDY LIBRARY, 371 First Ave, 37321-1499. SAN 315-7644. Tel: 423-775-8406. FAX: 423-775-8422. E-Mail: kmadewell@clydewroddy.org.
1999-2000 Income $264,628. Mats Exp $22,052, Books $21,788, Per/Ser (Incl. Access Fees) $264. Sal $124,271
Library Holdings: Bk Vols 32,000; Per Subs 42
Mem of Fort Loudoun Regional Library Center
Friends of the Library Group

DECATUR

P DECATUR-MEIGS COUNTY LIBRARY, PO Box 187, 37322-9999. SAN 315-7660. Tel: 423-334-3332. FAX: 423-334-1816. *Librn*, Carolyn Jones; E-Mail: cjones3@mail.state.tn.us
Pop 10,000
2000-2001 Income $35,000, City $4,000, Federal $5,000, County $26,000. Sal $15,742 (Prof $14,242)
Library Holdings: Bk Vols 10,000; Bks on Deafness & Sign Lang 10
Automation Activity & Vendor Info: (Cataloging) SIRSI
Mem of Fort Loudoun Regional Library Center
Special Services for the Deaf - TDD
Special Services for the Blind - Bks on tape
Friends of the Library Group

DECATURVILLE

P DECATUR COUNTY LIBRARY, 20 W Market St, 38329. (Mail add: PO Box 396, 38329), SAN 315-7679. Tel: 901-852-3325. FAX: 901-852-2351. Web Site: decaturpubliclibrary/homepage.com. *Dir*, Athalia Boroughs Taylor; E-Mail: ataylor@mail.state.tn.us; *Circ*, Jean Prat; *Circ*, Mildred Crawley; *Circ*, Patty Wyatt; Staff 4 (Non-MLS 4)
Founded 1955. Pop 3,111; Circ 39,630
Jul 1998-Jun 1999 Income $40,100, City $300, County $39,800. Sal $32,702
Library Holdings: Bk Titles 15,888; Per Subs 27; Bks on Deafness & Sign Lang 15
Database Vendor: Ebsco - EbscoHost, GaleNet
Function: ILL available
Mem of Shiloh Regional Library
Friends of the Library Group

DEER LODGE

P DEER LODGE PUBLIC LIBRARY, 110 Corinne Ave, PO Box 37, 37726-0037. SAN 376-7558. Tel: 423-965-3029. *Dir*, Sharon L Waschevski; E-Mail: swaschev@mail.state.tn.us
Library Holdings: Bk Vols 5,000
Mem of Clinch-Powell Regional Library

DEL RIO

P MARIE ELLISON MEMORIAL LIBRARY, 480 S Hwy 107, 37727-9625. SAN 370-6737. Tel: 423-487-5929. FAX: 423-487-5929. *Librn*, Kathy Woody; E-Mail: kwoody@mail.state.tn.us
Founded 1984. Circ 5,890
Library Holdings: Bk Titles 7,000
Mem of Nolichucky Regional Library

DICKSON

P DICKSON COUNTY PUBLIC LIBRARY, 305 E Hunt St, 37055-2098. SAN 315-7687. Tel: 615-446-8293. FAX: 615-446-9130. *Librn*, Suzanne Robinson; E-Mail: srobinso@mail.state.tn.us; *Asst Librn*, Sue Oliphant; E-Mail: oliphan@mail.state.tn.us; Staff 4 (MLS 2, Non-MLS 2)
Founded 1933. Pop 42,254; Circ 102,776
Jul 1999-Jun 2000 Income $349,542, City $15,000, County $300,675, Locally Generated Income $33,867. Mats Exp $69,369, Books $53,367, Per/Ser (Incl. Access Fees) $2,600, AV Equip $12,364, Electronic Ref Mat (Incl. Access Fees) $1,038. Sal $186,836
Library Holdings: Bk Vols 49,777; Per Subs 128
Subject Interests: Genealogy, Local history
Mem of Warioto Regional Library Center

DOVER

P STEWART COUNTY PUBLIC LIBRARY, 226 Lakeview Dr, 37058. SAN 315-7695. Tel: 931-232-5839. FAX: 931-232-3118. *Dir*, Pam Ford; E-Mail: pford@mail.state.tn.us
Library Holdings: Bk Titles 18,000; Per Subs 19
Mem of Warioto Regional Library Center
Friends of the Library Group

DRESDEN

P NED R MCWHERTER -WEAKLEY COUNTY LIBRARY, 341 Linden St, 38225-1400. SAN 315-7709. Tel: 731-364-2678. FAX: 731-364-2599. *Dir*, Candy McAdams; *Chief Librn*, Carol Tippins; *Asst Librn*, Karen Gertsch
Founded 1943. Circ 21,377
Library Holdings: Bk Vols 15,000; Per Subs 20
Mem of Reelfoot Regional Library Center
Friends of the Library Group

DUCKTOWN

P DUCKTOWN COMMUNITY LIBRARY, Main St, PO Box 369, 37326-0369. SAN 315-7717. Tel: 423-496-4004. *Librn*, Diane Meeks
Mem of Fort Loudoun Regional Library Center
Open Tues & Thurs 1:30-4:30

DUNLAP

P SEQUATCHIE COUNTY PUBLIC LIBRARY, 8 Cherry St W, 37327-5207. SAN 315-7725. Tel: 423-949-2357. FAX: 423-949-6619. *Dir*, Betty Worley; E-Mail: bworley@mail.state.tn.us
Founded 1959. Pop 8,605
Library Holdings: Bk Titles 25,000; Per Subs 9
Mem of Caney Fork Regional Library
Friends of the Library Group

DYERSBURG

J DYERSBURG STATE COMMUNITY COLLEGE, Learning Resource Center, 1510 Lake Rd, 38024. SAN 315-7733. Tel: 901-286-3225. FAX: 901-286-3228. Web Site: www.dscc.cc.tn.us. *Dean*, Robert Lhota; Tel: 901-286-3226, E-Mail: rlohta@dscc.cc.tn.us; *Librn*, Anne Reever; Tel: 901-286-3352, E-Mail: reever@dscclan.dscc.cc.tn.us; *Tech Servs*, Kari Bernier; Tel: 901-286-3272, E-Mail: bernier@dscclan.dscc.cc.tn.us; *Media Spec Ad*, Patrick Davis; Tel: 901-286-3227, E-Mail: pdavis@dscclan.dscc.cc.tn.us; *Br Coordr*, Tanga McCullough; Tel: 901-475-3100, Fax: 901-475-0008, E-Mail: mccullough@tipton.dscc.cc.tn.us; Staff 6 (MLS 3, Non-MLS 3)
Founded 1967. Enrl 1,500; Fac 50; Highest Degree: Associate
Jul 1999-Jun 2000 Income Parent Institution $247,408. Mats Exp $52,113, Books $20,903, Per/Ser (Incl. Access Fees) $23,400, Micro $4,290, Electronic Ref Mat (Incl. Access Fees) $3,520. Sal $135,117 (Prof $103,614)
Library Holdings: Bk Vols 43,839; Per Subs 296; Per Subs 252
Automation Activity & Vendor Info: (Cataloging) DRA; (Circulation) DRA; (Course Reserve) DRA; (OPAC) DRA; (Serials) DRA
Database Vendor: GaleNet, OCLC - First Search
Function: Research library
Partic in Solinet; Tenn-Share; West Tennessee Academic Library Consortium

P MCIVER'S GRANT PUBLIC LIBRARY, 204 N Mill, 38024-4631. SAN 315-7741. Tel: 901-285-5032. FAX: 901-285-9332. *Librn*, Sharon Simpson; *Asst Librn*, Gloria Carmack; *Asst Librn*, Joan Ryland
Pop 34,663
Library Holdings: Bk Vols 28,000; Per Subs 65
Special Collections: Microfilm of State Gazette; Small Genealogy Coll
Mem of Forked Deer Regional Library Center

EAGLEVILLE

P EAGLEVILLE BICENTENNIAL PUBLIC LIBRARY, 317 Hwy 99 E, PO Box 317, 37060-0317. SAN 376-7019. Tel: 615-274-2626. FAX: 615-274-2626. *Dir*, Cheryl Mathisen
Library Holdings: Bk Vols 12,000
Mem of Highland Rim Regional Library Center

EAST RIDGE

P EAST RIDGE CITY LIBRARY, 1517 Tombras Ave, 37412-2716. SAN 315-775X. Tel: 423-867-7323. *Dir*, Ann Pruett; *Acq*, Norine Bolt
Pop 25,000; Circ 15,000
Library Holdings: Bk Vols 20,000; Per Subs 12
Publications: Library Journal; Publisher's Weekly
Friends of the Library Group

ELIZABETHTON

P ELIZABETHTON-CARTER COUNTY PUBLIC LIBRARY, 201 N Sycamore St, 37643-2739. SAN 315-7768. Tel: 423-547-6360. Web Site: www.eccpl.org. *Dir*, Joyce H White; Fax: 423-542-1510, E-Mail: jwhite@eccpl.org; *Asst Dir*, Sharon Walker; *Ch Servs*, Vivian Yonkey; Staff 7 (MLS 1, Non-MLS 6)
Founded 1929. Pop 52,823; Circ 135,591
Library Holdings: Bk Titles 40,872; Per Subs 88
Special Collections: Tennessee History
Automation Activity & Vendor Info: (Acquisitions) Endeavor; (Cataloging) Endeavor; (Circulation) Endeavor; (OPAC) Endeavor
Mem of Watauga Regional Library Center
Friends of the Library Group

R MOODY BIBLE INSTITUTE OF CHICAGO, Moody Aviation Library, 415 Hwy 91, PO Box 429, 37644-0429. SAN 315-7776. Tel: 423-543-3534. FAX: 423-543-5211. Web Site: www.moodyav.org. *Mgr*, Rex Becker
Founded 1968. Enrl 81
Library Holdings: Bk Vols 500

ENGLEWOOD

P ENGLEWOOD PUBLIC LIBRARY, 103A S Niota, PO Box 834, 37329-0834. SAN 315-7792. Tel: 423-887-7152. E-Mail: engl@icx.net. *Librn*, Bennie Raper
Library Holdings: Bk Vols 6,000
Mem of Fort Loudoun Regional Library Center
Open Mon 12-5, Tues 10-6, Thurs 12-6, Fri 11-5

ERIN

P HOUSTON COUNTY PUBLIC LIBRARY, 110 Spring St, PO Box 183, 37061-0183. SAN 315-7806. Tel: 931-289-3858. FAX: 931-289-4967. *Dir*, Kay French; E-Mail: kfrench@mail.state.tn.us
Pop 6,871
Library Holdings: Bk Vols 14,500; Per Subs 10
Mem of Warioto Regional Library Center
Partic in Tenn Libr Asn
Friends of the Library Group

ERWIN

P UNICOI COUNTY PUBLIC LIBRARY, 201 Nolichucky Ave, 37650-1237. SAN 315-7814. Tel: 423-743-6533. FAX: 423-743-0275. *Dir*, Jane Garrett; E-Mail: jgarrett@wrlibrary.org
Founded 1921. Pop 16,900
Library Holdings: Bk Vols 15,000; Per Subs 14
Mem of Knoxville-Shelby County Pub Libr & Info Ctr; Watauga Regional Library Center
Open Mon, Wed, Thurs & Fri 12:30-5:30, Tues 12:30-8:30 & Sat 9-2
Friends of the Library Group

TOWAH

ETOWAH CARNEGIE PUBLIC LIBRARY, 723 Ohio Ave, 37331. SAN 315-7822. Tel: 423-263-9475. FAX: 423-263-4271. *Dir*, Joyce Ann James; E-Mail: jjjames@usit.net; Staff 1 (Non-MLS 1)
Founded 1915. Pop 10,000
Library Holdings: Bk Vols 11,000; Bk Titles 10,000
Mem of Fort Loudoun Regional Library Center
Open Mon & Wed 1-6, Fri noon-5 & Sat 11-2

AYETTEVILLE

FAYETTEVILLE-LINCOLN COUNTY PUBLIC LIBRARY, 400 Rocky Knob Lane, 37334-2558. SAN 315-7830. Tel: 931-433-3286. FAX: 931-433-0063. *Dir*, Judy Pitts; E-Mail: jpitts@mail.state.tn.us
Pop 26,483
Jul 1998-Jun 1999 Income $80,856. Mats Exp $8,000. Sal $57,000
Library Holdings: Bk Vols 36,000; Per Subs 50
Mem of Highland Rim Regional Library Center
Open Mon, Wed-Sat 9-5, Tues 9-8 (summer: Sun 2-4)
Friends of the Library Group

RANKLIN

WILLIAMSON COUNTY PUBLIC LIBRARY, 611 W Main St, 37064-2723. SAN 360-5760. Tel: 615-794-3105. FAX: 615-595-1245. Web Site: lib.williamson-tn.org. *Dir*, Janice E Keck; E-Mail: jkeck@lib.williamson-tn.org; *Asst Dir*, Jane Langston; *Ref*, Kathy Ossi; *Ch Servs*, Lesley Potts
Founded 1937
Library Holdings: Bk Titles 88,000
Special Collections: African-American Genealogy & Photograph Coll; Civil War Coll; Edythe Rucker Whitley Historical & Genealogical Coll; Local Authors Coll; Williamson County Local History & Genealogy
Publications: Community Service Directory of Williamson County
Mem of Blue Grass Regional Library
Friends of the Library Group
Branches: 5
BETHESDA, 4905 Bethesda Rd, Thompson Station, 37179-9231. SAN 372-3992. Tel: 615-790-1887. FAX: 615-790-8426. Web Site: www.lib.williamson-tn.org. *Librn*, Susan Fisher; E-Mail: sfisher@lib.williamson-tn.org
FAIRVIEW BRANCH, 2240 Fairview Blvd, Fairview, 37062-9011. SAN 360-5825. Tel: 615-799-0235. FAX: 615-799-1399. Web Site: www.lib.williamson-tn.org. *Librn*, Kathy Grimenstein
Library Holdings: Bk Vols 10,000
Friends of the Library Group
GENEALOGY, 510 Columbia Ave, 37064-2873. SAN 378-2107. Tel: 615-595-1246. FAX: 615-595-1247. Web Site: www.lib.williamson-tn.org. *Librn*, Dorris Douglass
Friends of the Library Group
LEIPER'S FORK, 5333 Old Hwy 96, 37064-9357. SAN 370-0011. Tel: 615-794-7019. FAX: 615-591-6976. Web Site: www.lib.williamson-tn.org. *Librn*, Jean Dicie
Library Holdings: Bk Vols 5,000
NOLENSVILLE BRANCH, 915 Oldham Dr, PO Box 577, Nolensville, 37135-0577. SAN 328-7181. Tel: 615-776-5490. FAX: 615-776-3626. Web Site: www.lib.williamson.tn.org. *Librn*, Janice Bobo
Friends of the Library Group

AINESBORO

CHARLES RALPH HOLLAND MEMORIAL LIBRARY, Jackson County Public Library, 205 Hull St, PO Box 647, 38562. SAN 315-7849. Tel: 615-268-9190. *Dir*, Dale Stapp; E-Mail: dstapp@mail.state.tn.us
Founded 1959. Pop 9,398
Library Holdings: Bk Vols 11,000; Per Subs 36
Special Collections: Local History
Mem of Upper Cumberland Regional Library
(Nov 15-Feb 15) Mon-Fri 9:30-4:30, Sat 10-3

ALLATIN

EDWARD WARD, CARMACK-SUMNER COUNTY PUBLIC LIBRARY, 658 Hartsville Pike, 37066-2509. SAN 315-7857. Tel: 615-452-1722. FAX: 615-451-3319. E-Mail: ewclib@bellsouth.net. *Librn*, Judy Baggett
Pop 33,400; Circ 67,766
Library Holdings: Bk Vols 30,000; Per Subs 25
Publications: College for this Community; Daniel Smith; James Winchester
Mem of Warioto Regional Library Center
Friends of the Library Group

VOLUNTEER STATE COMMUNITY COLLEGE LIBRARY, Learning Resources Center, 1480 Nashville Pike, 37066-3188. SAN 324-7783. Tel: 615-230-3400. Reference Tel: 615-230-3405. Toll Free Tel: 888-335-8722. FAX: 615-230-3410. E-Mail: vscc_librarian@vscc.cc.tn.us. Web Site: www.vscc.cc.tn.us/lib.html. *Dean*, Dr J Michael Rothacker; Tel: 615-230-3400, Ext 3414, E-Mail: mike.rothacker@vscc.cc.tn.us; *Acq*, Donna Warden; Tel: 615-230-3400, Ext 3407, E-Mail: donna.warden@vscc.cc.tn.us; *Bibliog Instr*, Louise Kelly; Tel: 615-230-3400, Ext 3412, E-Mail: louise.kelly@vscc.cc.tn.us; *Tech Servs*, Marguerite Voorhies; Tel: 615-230-3400, Ext 3404, E-Mail: marguerite.voorhies@vscc.cc.tn.us; *Selection of Gen Ref Mat*, Virginia Chambless; Tel: 615-230-3400, Ext 3438, E-Mail: virginia.chambless@vscc.cc.tn.us; *Automation Syst Coordr*, Jane Armour; Tel: 615-230-3400, Ext 3406, E-Mail: jane.armour@vscc.cc.tn.us; Staff 16 (MLS 5, Non-MLS 11)
Founded 1971. Fac 134; Highest Degree: Associate
1999-2000 Mats Exp $141,288, Books $59,339, Per/Ser (Incl. Access Fees) $28,413, Presv $3,788, Micro $8,043, Electronic Ref Mat (Incl. Access Fees) $41,705. Sal $397,366 (Prof $220,178)
Library Holdings: Bk Vols 48,430; Bk Titles 45,499; Per Subs 417
Automation Activity & Vendor Info: (Cataloging) DRA; (Circulation) DRA; (OPAC) DRA
Database Vendor: DRA, GaleNet, IAC - Info Trac, OCLC - First Search, ProQuest, Silverplatter Information Inc.
Publications: VSCC Library Newsletter
Partic in Nashville Area Libr Alliance; Tenn Acad Libr Collaborative; Tenn Share
Friends of the Library Group

GATLINBURG

P ANNA PORTER PUBLIC LIBRARY, 207 Cherokee Orchard Rd, 37738-3417. SAN 315-7873. Tel: 423-436-5588. FAX: 423-436-5588. E-Mail: appl@usit.net. Web Site: www.usit.com/appl. *Dir*, Kenton Temple; Staff 4 (MLS 1, Non-MLS 3)
Library Holdings: Bk Titles 23,000
Special Collections: Crafts; Smoky Mountain Region
Mem of Nolichucky Regional Library
Friends of the Library Group

S US NATIONAL PARK SERVICE GREAT SMOKY MOUNTAINS NATIONAL PARK LIBRARY, 107 Park Headquarters Rd, 37738. SAN 370-2863. Tel: 865-436-1296. FAX: 865-436-1220. E-Mail: grsm_library_&_archives@nps.gov. *Archivist, Librn*, Annette Hartigan
Library Holdings: Bk Vols 7,200
Special Collections: Naturalists journals

GERMANTOWN

R MID-AMERICA BAPTIST THEOLOGICAL SEMINARY, Tag Ora Byram Allison Memorial Library, 2216 Germantown Rd S, 38138-3815. SAN 321-4583. Tel: 901-751-8451. FAX: 901-751-8454. *Librn*, Terrence Neal Brown; E-Mail: tbrown@mabts.edu; Staff 6 (MLS 1, Non-MLS 5)
Founded 1972. Enrl 442; Fac 22; Highest Degree: Doctorate
Library Holdings: Bk Vols 124,011; Bk Titles 81,758; Per Subs 957
Subject Interests: Missions, Semitic lang
Partic in Dialog Corporation; OCLC Online Computer Library Center, Inc; SE Libr Network

GLEASON

P GLEASON MEMORIAL LIBRARY, 105 College St, 38229. (Mail add: 107 Richee St, 38229-9998), SAN 315-7881. Tel: 901-648-9020. *Dir*, Nina Sawyers
Library Holdings: Bk Vols 2,600; Bk Titles 2,500; Per Subs 1
Mem of Reelfoot Regional Library Center

GRAND JUNCTION

P GRAND JUNCTION COMMUNITY LIBRARY, 103 Washington Ave, PO Box 508, 38039-0508. SAN 376-7027. Tel: 901-764-2716. FAX: 901-764-2716. *Dir*, Mamie Webb
Library Holdings: Bk Vols 4,117
Mem of Shiloh Regional Library

GRAYSVILLE

P GRAYSVILLE PUBLIC LIBRARY, 151 Mill St, 37338-5044. (Mail add: PO Box 100, 37338-0100), SAN 315-789X. Tel: 423-775-0966. FAX: 423-775-8137. *Dir*, Debbie Pelfrey; E-Mail: dspelfrey@hotmail.com
Library Holdings: Bk Vols 4,080
Mem of Fort Loudoun Regional Library Center
Open Mon, Tues, Thurs & Fri 10:30-5 & Sat 11-3

GREENBACK

P GREENBACK PUBLIC LIBRARY, 6889 Morganton Rd, 37742-4142. SAN 315-7903. Tel: 423-856-2841. *Librn*, Clara Sue Hammontree; E-Mail: cshammon@esper.com

Library Holdings: Bk Titles 7,000
Mem of Fort Loudoun Regional Library Center
Open Tues, Wed & Fri 11-5, Thurs 1-7
Friends of the Library Group

GREENEVILLE

P GREENEVILLE GREEN COUNTY PUBLIC LIBRARY, 210 N Main St, 37745-3816. SAN 315-7911. Tel: 423-638-5034. FAX: 423-638-3841. E-Mail: alp7@tricon.net. *Dir*, Madge Walker; Staff 1 (MLS 1)
Founded 1908. Pop 54,406; Circ 96,608
Library Holdings: Bk Vols 50,000; Per Subs 125
Friends of the Library Group

C TATE LIBRARY OF TUSCULUM COLLEGE, Hwy 107, PO Box 5005, 37743. SAN 360-585X. Tel: 423-636-7320. FAX: 423-638-7166. E-Mail: library@tusculum.edu. Web Site: www.tusculum.edu. *Dir*, Myron J Smith, Jr; *Tech Servs*, Susan Gibson; *Tech Servs*, Carolyn Parker; *Publ Servs*, Regina Settle; *Publ Servs*, Charles Tunstall; Staff 5 (MLS 2, Non-MLS 3)
Founded 1794. Enrl 1,000; Fac 28; Highest Degree: Master
Library Holdings: Bk Vols 68,012; Per Subs 600
Special Collections: Special Education (Instructional Materials Coll), multimedia; Warren W Hobbie Civic Arts Coll
Database Vendor: IAC - Info Trac, IAC - SearchBank
Publications: Reel'n Page (monthly newsletter)
Partic in Appalachian Col Asn; OCLC Online Computer Library Center, Inc; SE Libr Network
Departmental Libraries:
INSTRUCTIONAL MATERIALS CENTER Tel: 423-638-1111.
Library Holdings: Bk Vols 850
Subject Interests: Children's literature, Education

C TUSCULUM COLLEGE, Instructional Materials Center, Edwin Hwy, 37743. (Mail add: PO Box 5001, 37743), SAN 374-7565. Tel: 423-636-7324. Toll Free Tel: 800-729-0256. FAX: 423-798-1634. Web Site: www.tusculum.edu.
Enrl 500; Fac 4; Highest Degree: Doctorate
Jul 1999-Jun 2000 Mats Exp $700, Books $500, Per/Ser (Incl. Access Fees) $100, AV Equip $100. Sal $20,000
Library Holdings: Bk Titles 1,000; Per Subs 10

G US DEPARTMENT OF THE INTERIOR, NATIONAL PARK SERVICE, Andrew Johnson National Historic Site Library, College & Depot St, PO Box 1088, 37744-1088. SAN 325-0911. Tel: 423-638-3551, 423-639-3711. FAX: 423-798-0754. *In Charge*, Jim Small
Library Holdings: Bk Vols 275
Subject Interests: 17th President of the United States, Andrew Johnson (1808-1875)
Restriction: Staff use only, Use of others with permission of librarian

GREENFIELD

P DR NATHAN PORTER PUBLIC LIBRARY, 228 N Front St, 38230-9998. SAN 376-3277. Tel: 731-235-9932. *Dir*, Patricia Mitchell
Library Holdings: Bk Vols 5,500; Bk Titles 5,000; Per Subs 28
Mem of Reelfoot Regional Library Center
Partic in Tenn Libr Asn

HALLS

P FORKED DEER REGIONAL LIBRARY CENTER, 220 N Front St, PO Box 68, 38040-0068. SAN 315-9892. Tel: 901-836-5812. FAX: 901-836-7085. E-Mail: fdeer@mail.state.tn.us. *Dir*, Robert Toth; *AV*, May Stuart; *Bkmobile Coordr*, Ellen Spain
Founded 1965. Pop 161,416; Circ 447,749
Library Holdings: Bk Titles 124,586
Subject Interests: Tennessee
Member Libraries: Crockett Memorial Library; Elma Ross Public Library; Halls Public Library; Lauderdale County Library; McIver's Grant Public Library; Munford-Tipton Memorial Library; Newbern City Library; Ridgely Public Library; Somerville-Fayette County Library; Tipton County Public Library; Tiptonville Public Library; Trimble Public Library

P HALLS PUBLIC LIBRARY, 110 N Church St, PO Box 236, 38040-0236. SAN 321-6330. Tel: 901-836-5302. *Librn*, Marie Sumrow
Founded 1980
Library Holdings: Bk Titles 10,000; Per Subs 10
Special Collections: US Tax Cases 1913-current
Mem of Forked Deer Regional Library Center
Friends of the Library Group

HARRIMAN

P HARRIMAN PUBLIC LIBRARY, 601 Walden St, 37748-2506. SAN 315-7938. Tel: 865-882-3188. FAX: 865-882-3188. *Dir*, Barbara Pelfrey; E-Mai bpelfrey@usit.net; *Ch Servs*, Tammie Edwards
Library Holdings: Bk Titles 20,000; Per Subs 45
Mem of Fort Loudoun Regional Library Center
Friends of the Library Group

J ROANE STATE COMMUNITY COLLEGE LIBRARY, 276 Patton Lane, 37748-5000. SAN 321-3412. Tel: 865-882-4553. FAX: 865-882-4562. E-Mail: librarystaff@rscc.cc.tn.us. Web Site: www.rscc.cc.tn.us/library/. *Dir* Becky Brunton; *Cat*, Rosemary Todd; Staff 7 (MLS 4, Non-MLS 3)
Founded 1971. Enrl 3,376; Fac 175
Library Holdings: Bk Vols 52,500; Bk Titles 50,000; Per Subs 560

HARROGATE

C LINCOLN MEMORIAL UNIVERSITY LIBRARY, Cumberland Gap Pkwy 37752. SAN 315-7946. Tel: 423-869-6436. FAX: 423-869-6426. Web Site: www.inetlmu.library.index. *Head Librn*, Donna Sue Bible; E-Mail: dbible@inetlmu.lmunet.edu; *Archivist*, LeAnne Garland; Tel: 423-869-6304, E-Mail: lgarland@inetlmu.lmunet.edu; *Circ*, Karen Loving; Tel: 423-869-6219, E-Mail: kloving@inetlmu.lmunet.edu; *Ser*, Kay Davis; Tel: 423-869-6218, E-Mail: kdavis@inetlmu.lmunet.edu; *Head Tech Servs*, Robin Williams; *Tec Servs*, Kathy Brunsma; Tel: 423-869-6221, E-Mail: kbrunsma@inetlmu.lmunet.edu; *Publ Servs*, Janice McDonnell; E-Mail: jmcdonnell@inetlmu.lmunet.edu; Staff 7 (MLS 3, Non-MLS 4)
Founded 1897. Enrl 1,500; Fac 45; Highest Degree: Master
Aug 1999-Jul 2000 Income $291,026. Mats Exp $128,600, Books $28,000, Per/Ser (Incl. Access Fees) $31,000, AV Equip $3,600, Other Print Mats $28,000, Electronic Ref Mat (Incl. Access Fees) $38,000. Sal $134,160
Library Holdings: Bk Vols 190,000; Bk Titles 98,636; Per Subs 833
Subject Interests: Civil War, Lincolniana
Special Collections: Jesse Stuart Coll; Lincoln Memorial University Author
Automation Activity & Vendor Info: (Cataloging) Gaylord; (Circulation) Gaylord; (OPAC) Gaylord
Database Vendor: Ebsco - EbscoHost, ProQuest
Function: For research purposes
Partic in Dialog Corporation

HARTSVILLE

P FRED A VAUGHT MEMORIAL LIBRARY, 211 White Oak St, 37074-1420. SAN 315-7954. Tel: 615-374-3677. FAX: 615-374-4553. *Librn*, Mary Carpenter; E-Mail: mcarpent@mail.state.tn.us
Founded 1961. Pop 5,952; Circ 12,500
Library Holdings: Bk Vols 9,500
Mem of Highland Rim Regional Library Center

HENDERSON

P CHESTER COUNTY PUBLIC LIBRARY, 1012 East Main St, 38340-0323. SAN 315-7962. Tel: 731-989-4673. FAX: 731-989-4673. E-Mail: ncanada@mail.tn.us. *Dir*, Nancy Canada; E-Mail: ncanada@mail.state.tn.us
Pop 12,727
Library Holdings: Bk Titles 11,000
Mem of Shiloh Regional Library
Partic in Tenn Libr Asn
Friends of the Library Group

C FREED-HARDEMAN UNIVERSITY, Loden-Daniel Library, 158 E Main St, PO Box 705, 38340-2399. SAN 315-7970. Tel: 901-989-6067. FAX: 901-989-6065. Web Site: www.fhu.edu/library. *Acq, Coll Develop, Dir, ILL*, Hope Shull; E-Mail: hshull@fhu.edu; *Per, Ref*, Mitzi Brown; *Media Spec*, Jan Sharp; *Cat, Rare Bks*, Sharon Jennette; Staff 4 (MLS 4)
Founded 1869. Enrl 1,700; Fac 106; Highest Degree: Master
Library Holdings: Bk Vols 154,800; Bk Titles 124,878
Special Collections: Religion (Restoration Library Coll), bks & tapes
Partic in OCLC Online Computer Library Center, Inc; SE Libr Network

HENDERSONVILLE

P MARTIN CURTIS HENDERSONVILLE PUBLIC LIBRARY, 116 Dunn St, PO Box 1094, 37077-1094. SAN 315-7989. Tel: 615-824-0656. FAX: 615-824-3112. *Librn*, Virginia Duffett; *Asst Librn*, Betty Orsland; Staff 10 (MLS 2, Non-MLS 8)
Founded 1965. Pop 59,600; Circ 189,740
Library Holdings: Bk Titles 46,000; Per Subs 125
Mem of Warioto Regional Library Center
Friends of the Library Group

OHENWALD

LEWIS COUNTY PUBLIC LIBRARY, 15 Kyle Ave, 38462-1434. SAN 315-7997. Tel: 931-796-5365. FAX: 931-796-5365. E-Mail: lewislib@inii.net. *Librn*, Patty Choate; Staff 1 (Non-MLS 1)
Founded 1951. Pop 11,127
Jul 1999-Jun 2000 Income $52,022. Mats Exp $8,570, Books $7,500, Per/Ser (Incl. Access Fees) $1,070. Sal $34,875
Library Holdings: Bk Vols 19,538; Per Subs 62
Mem of Blue Grass Regional Library

UMBOLDT

HUMBOLDT PUBLIC LIBRARY, 115 S 16th Ave, 38343-3403. SAN 315-8004. Tel: 731-784-2383. FAX: 731-784-0582. *Dir*, Carolyn Adams; E-Mail: cadams@mail.state.tn.us
Library Holdings: Bk Vols 20,000; Per Subs 54
Mem of Reelfoot Regional Library Center
Friends of the Library Group

UNTINGDON

CARROLL COUNTY LIBRARY, 625 High St, Ste 102, 38344-3903. SAN 315-8012. Tel: 901-986-1919. FAX: 901-986-1335. *Dir*, Karen Pierce; E-Mail: kpierce2@mail.state.tn.us
Founded 1950. Pop 28,400; Circ 64,683
Library Holdings: Bk Vols 21,000; Per Subs 29
Special Collections: Genealogy, History (Tennessee Coll), Literacy
Mem of Reelfoot Regional Library Center

UNTSVILLE

HUNTSVILLE PUBLIC LIBRARY, 314 Court House Square, PO Box 180, 37756-0098. SAN 376-2963. Tel: 423-663-9230. *Dir*, Sharon Kay Reed; E-Mail: skreed@mail.state.tn.us
Library Holdings: Bk Titles 8,794
Mem of Clinch-Powell Regional Library

ACKSBORO

JACKSBORO PUBLIC LIBRARY, 585 Main St, Ste 201, PO Box 460, 37757. SAN 315-8020. Tel: 423-562-3675. FAX: 423-562-9587. E-Mail: jlibrary@icx.net. Web Site: www.kornet.org/jlibrary. *Dir*, Margaret Southerland; E-Mail: msouther@mail.state.tn.us; *Tech Servs*, Gregory D Smith; E-Mail: jkbtech@icx.net; Staff 2 (Non-MLS 2)
Founded 1976
Jul 2000-Jun 2001 Income $34,948, City $28,873, County $6,075. Mats Exp $5,027, Books $2,478, Per/Ser (Incl. Access Fees) $593. Sal $24,321
Library Holdings: Bk Vols 13,000; Bk Titles 13,000; Per Subs 60
Automation Activity & Vendor Info: (Circulation) Sagebrush Corporation; (Serials) Sagebrush Corporation
Database Vendor: GaleNet, IAC - Info Trac
Mem of Clinch-Powell Regional Library
Friends of the Library Group

ACKSON

JACKSON STATE COMMUNITY COLLEGE LIBRARY, 2046 N Parkway, 38301. SAN 315-8047. Tel: 901-425-2615. Interlibrary Loan Service Tel: 901-425-2609. Circulation Tel: 901-425-2609. FAX: 901-425-2625. Web Site: www.jscc.cc.tn.us/users/libjscc. *Dir*, Scott Cohen; E-Mail: scohen@jscc.cc.tn.us; *Acq, Circ*, Gloria Hester; Tel: 901-424-3520, Ext 328, E-Mail: ghester@jscc.cc.tn.us; *Cat, Ref*, Jennifer Gregory; Tel: 901-424-3520, Ext 325; *Instrul Serv, Ref*, Marv Kaminsky; Tel: 901-424-3520, Ext 313, E-Mail: mkaminsky@jscc.cc.tn.us; Staff 4 (MLS 4)
Founded 1967. Enrl 2,524; Fac 101; Highest Degree: Associate
Jul 2000-Jun 2001 Mats Exp $84,600, Books $43,900, Per/Ser (Incl. Access Fees) $31,700, Presv $1,500, Micro $7,500. Sal $220,000 (Prof $149,500)
Library Holdings: Bk Vols 59,000; Bk Titles 52,000; Per Subs 272
Subject Interests: Agriculture, Bus, Careers, Eng tech, Health sciences, Technology, Tenn hist
Automation Activity & Vendor Info: (Cataloging) DRA; (Circulation) DRA; (OPAC) DRA

; JACKSON SUN LIBRARY, 245 W Lafayette, 38301. (Mail add: PO Box 1059, 38302-1059), SAN 315-8055. Tel: 901-427-3333, Ext 657. FAX: 901-425-9604. E-Mail: sun@aeneas.net. Web Site: www.jacksonsun.com. *Librn*, Debbie Morris
Founded 1974

1 JACKSON-MADISON COUNTY GENERAL HOSPITAL, Learning Center, 708 W Forest Ave, 38301-3956. SAN 320-586X. Tel: 901-425-6024. FAX: 901-425-6983. *Dir*, Linda G Farmer; E-Mail: linda.farmer@wth.org
Founded 1972
Library Holdings: Bk Titles 2,500; Per Subs 250
Subject Interests: Hospital administration, Medicine, Nursing, Nutrition, Pathology, Physical therapy, Radiology, Respiratory therapy, Surgery

P JACKSON-MADISON COUNTY LIBRARY, 433 E Lafayette, 38301-6386. SAN 315-8039. Tel: 901-425-8600. FAX: 901-425-8609. E-Mail: libjmc@erc.jscc.cc.tn.us. *Dir*, Thomas L Aud; *ILL, Ref*, Jennie Baird; *YA Servs*, Debbie Lewis; *Media Spec*, Michael Baker; *Ch Servs*, Judith Cravens; *Spec Coll*, Jack Darrell Wood; *Tech Servs*, Wanda Washburn; Staff 12 (MLS 2, Non-MLS 10)
Founded 1903. Pop 84,500; Circ 240,829
Library Holdings: Bk Vols 111,226; Per Subs 325
Special Collections: Genealogy, bks, micro; Jackson Area Business History Coll; Local & State History (Tennessee Room Coll), bks, micro
Mem of Shiloh Regional Library
Friends of the Library Group

C LAMBUTH UNIVERSITY, Luther L Gobbel Library, 705 Lambuth Blvd, 38301. SAN 315-8063. Tel: 901-425-3290. Interlibrary Loan Service Tel: 901-425-3270. Circulation Tel: 901-425-3289. Reference Tel: 901-425-3270. FAX: 901-425-3200. Web Site: www.lambuth.edu. *Dir*, Mary Roby; Tel: 901-425-3292, E-Mail: roby@lambuth.edu; *Tech Servs*, Dr Pamela Dennis; Tel: 901-425-3479, E-Mail: dennis@lambuth.edu; *Ref*, Missy Laytham; E-Mail: mlaytham@lambuth.edu; *Admin Assoc*, Cathy Finger; E-Mail: finger@lambuth.edu; *Circ*, Linda M Hayes; E-Mail: hayes@lambuth.edu; *Govt Doc*, Lyda Kowalski; Tel: 901-425-3293, E-Mail: kowalski@lambuth.edu; *Ser*, Rex West; Tel: 901-425-3448, E-Mail: west@lambuth.edu; *Coordr*, Mary Willett; Tel: 901-425-3327. Subject Specialists: *Archives*, Dr Pamela Dennis; *Education*, Mary Roby; *Fine arts*, Linda M Hayes; *Genealogy*, Dr Pamela Dennis; *Genealogy*, Lyda Kowalski; *Govt docs*, Lyda Kowalski; *Humanities*, Linda M Hayes; *Music*, Dr Pamela Dennis; *Music*, Mary Roby; Staff 8 (MLS 3, Non-MLS 5)
Founded 1843. Enrl 950; Fac 2; Highest Degree: Bachelor
Jul 1997-Jun 1998 Income $266,784. Mats Exp $44,354, Books $20,000, Per/Ser (Incl. Access Fees) $21,300, Presv $3,054. Sal $146,826
Library Holdings: Bk Vols 89,110; Per Subs 392
Subject Interests: Civil War, Methodism
Automation Activity & Vendor Info: (Acquisitions) Endeavor; (Cataloging) Endeavor; (Circulation) Endeavor; (Course Reserve) Endeavor; (OPAC) Endeavor; (Serials) Endeavor
Database Vendor: GaleNet, IAC - Info Trac, Lexis-Nexis, OCLC - First Search, ProQuest
Function: ILL available
Partic in OCLC Online Computer Library Center, Inc; Soline; Solinet; Tenn-Share; West Tennessee Academic Library Consortium

C LANE COLLEGE LIBRARY, 545 Lane Ave, 38301-4598. SAN 315-8071. Tel: 901-426-7654. Web Site: www.lane-college.edu.; Staff 5 (MLS 2, Non-MLS 3)
Founded 1882. Enrl 768; Fac 48; Highest Degree: Bachelor
Library Holdings: Bk Vols 84,000; Per Subs 339
Special Collections: Black Studies, AV, bks; Haitian Art; Juvenile
Automation Activity & Vendor Info: (Cataloging) CASPR; (Circulation) CASPR
Publications: Library Usage Manual; Staff Manual
Partic in West Tennessee Academic Library Consortium

P SHILOH REGIONAL LIBRARY, 573 Old Hickory Blvd, 38305-2901. SAN 315-808X. Tel: 901-668-0710. FAX: 901-668-6663. *Dir*, Margaret Harmon; E-Mail: mharmon3@mail.state.tn.us
Founded 1956. Pop 188,198; Circ 586,655
Library Holdings: Bk Vols 115,795
Subject Interests: Tennessee
Member Libraries: Bolivar-Hardeman County Public Library; Chester County Public Library; Decatur County Library; Everett Horn Public Library; Grand Junction Community Library; Hardin County Library; Irving Meek Jr Public Library; Jack McConnico Memorial Library; Jackson-Madison County Library; Lee Ola Roberts Public Library; Middleton Community Library; Parsons Public Library

GL TENNESSEE STATE LAW LIBRARY, Supreme Court Bldg, 6 Hwy 45 By-Pass, 38301. SAN 320-4227. Tel: 901-423-5849. *Librn*, Debbie Durham
Library Holdings: Bk Vols 30,000; Per Subs 30
Also see divisional entries in Knoxville & Nashville

JAMESTOWN

P FENTRESS COUNTY PUBLIC LIBRARY, 306 S Main St, 38556-3845. (Mail add: PO Box 178, 38556-0178), SAN 315-8101. Tel: 931-879-7512. Reference Tel: 931-879-1720. FAX: 931-879-6984. E-Mail: fentress@usit.net, fentress@usit.net. *Dir*, Leslie Pullins
Pop 14,826
Library Holdings: Bk Titles 18,000; Per Subs 28
Mem of Upper Cumberland Regional Library
Friends of the Library Group

JASPER

P JASPER PUBLIC LIBRARY, 14 W Second St, 37347-3409. SAN 315-811X. Tel: 423-942-3369. Interlibrary Loan Service Tel: 800-572-7396. FAX: 423-942-6383. *Dir*, Carolyn Stewart; E-Mail: cstewart@mail.state.tn.us; Staff 1 (Non-MLS 1)
Founded 1968. Pop 2,500; Circ 9,600
Library Holdings: Bk Vols 15,000; Per Subs 40
Mem of Caney Fork Regional Library

JEFFERSON CITY

C CARSON-NEWMAN COLLEGE, Stephens-Burnett Memorial Library, 1634 Russell Ave, 37760. SAN 315-8136. Tel: 423-471-3335. FAX: 423-471-3450. Web Site: www.library.cn.edu. *Dir*, Dr Tony Krug; E-Mail: tkrug@cn.edu; *Bibliog Instr, Ref*, Bruce Kocour; *Archivist*, Albert Lang; *Per*, Lori Thornton; *Acq*, Sylvia Sawyer; *Media Spec*, Donnie Newman; *Tech Servs*, Linda Gass; *Access Serv*, Sheila Gaines; Staff 7 (MLS 5, Non-MLS 2)
Founded 1851. Enrl 2,200; Fac 120; Highest Degree: Master
Aug 1999-Jul 2000 Income Parent Institution $521,000. Mats Exp $194,350, Books $115,000, Per/Ser (Incl. Access Fees) $43,000, Presv $4,000, Micro $10,350, Electronic Ref Mat (Incl. Access Fees) $22,000. Sal $260,000 (Prof $170,000)
Library Holdings: Bk Titles 130,000; Per Subs 1,950
Subject Interests: Baptist mat, Family counseling, Marriage
Automation Activity & Vendor Info: (Cataloging) Gaylord; (Circulation) Gaylord; (Course Reserve) Gaylord; (OPAC) Gaylord
Publications: Carson-Newman Baptist
Partic in Appalachian Libr Info Coop; OCLC Online Computer Library Center, Inc; SE Libr Network; Tenn Share

P JEFFERSON CITY PUBLIC LIBRARY, 1427 Russell Ave, 37760. SAN 315-8128. Tel: 865-475-9094. TDD: 865-9094. FAX: 865-475-1253. E-Mail: jcpl@charter.net. *Dir*, Barbara C Shelton; *Asst Librn*, Bette Disher; Staff 2 (MLS 1, Non-MLS 1)
Pop 22,905; Circ 30,748
Jul 1998-Jun 1999 Income $46,477, City $25,000, County $21,477. Mats Exp $7,910, Books $6,735, Per/Ser (Incl. Access Fees) $1,175. Sal $21,341
Library Holdings: Bk Vols 19,366; Per Subs 62
Automation Activity & Vendor Info: (Cataloging) Sagebrush Corporation; (Circulation) Sagebrush Corporation; (OPAC) Sagebrush Corporation
Mem of Nolichucky Regional Library
Special Services for the Deaf - TTY machine
Friends of the Library Group

JELLICO

P JELLICO PUBLIC LIBRARY, 104 N Main St, 37762-2004. SAN 315-8144. Tel: 423-784-7488. E-Mail: jellicbk@icx.net. *Dir*, Dorothy Potter
Library Holdings: Bk Vols 12,000; Per Subs 120
Mem of Clinch-Powell Regional Library

JOHNSON CITY

EAST TENNESSEE STATE UNIVERSITY
CM JAMES H QUILLEN MEDICAL LIBRARY, PO Box 70693, 37614-0693. (Mail add: Bldg 4, Maple St, Mountain Home, 37684), SAN 360-5949. Tel: 423-439-6252. Interlibrary Loan Service Tel: 423-439-7032. FAX: 423-439-7025. Web Site: qcom.etsu.edu/medlib. *Asst Dean*, Biddanda S Ponnappa; *Online Servs, Ref*, Ross Bowron; *Tech Servs*, Martha Whaley; *ILL*, Rick Wallace. Subject Specialists: *History of medicine*, Martha Whaley; Staff 5 (MLS 5)
Founded 1975. Fac 4; Highest Degree: Master
Library Holdings: Bk Vols 33,286; Per Subs 579
Subject Interests: Biomed
Special Collections: History of Medicine Coll; Long Coll
Publications: Actus Medicus
Partic in OCLC Online Computer Library Center, Inc

C SHERROD LIBRARY, Lake & Seehorn Dr, 37614. (Mail add: Box 70665, 37614-0665), Tel: 423-439-4337. Interlibrary Loan Service Tel: 423-439-6998. Circulation Tel: 423-439-4303. Reference Tel: 423-439-4307. TDD: 423-439-5309. FAX: 423-439-5222. E-Mail: refdesk@etsu.edu. Web Site: sherrod.etsu.edu. *Dean of Libr*, Rita Scher; E-Mail: scherr@etsu.edu; *Assoc Dir*, Jean Flanigan; Tel: 423-439-5620, Fax: 423-439-8430, E-Mail: flanigan@etsu.edu; *ILL*, Kelly Hensley; Tel: 423-439-6998, Fax: 423-439-4720, E-Mail: hensleyk@etsu.edu; *Per*, Rolly Harwell; Tel: 423-439-6996, Fax: 423-439-4410, E-Mail: harwellr@etsu.edu; *Govt Doc*, Stephen Patrick; Tel: 423-439-6994, Fax: 423-439-8430, E-Mail: patricks@etsu.edu; *Instrul Serv*, Annis Evans; *Acq*, Debbie O'Brien; Tel: 423-439-5815, Fax: 423-439-4410, E-Mail: obriend@etsu.edu; *Automation Syst Coordr*, Celia Szarejko; Tel: 423-439-4713, Fax: 423-439-8336, E-Mail: szarejko@etsu.edu; *Head Ref*, Mark Ellis; Tel: 423-439-4715, Fax: 423-439-4720, E-Mail: ellism@etsu.edu; Staff 42 (MLS 13, Non-MLS 29)
Founded 1911. Enrl 10,821; Fac 627; Highest Degree: Doctorate
Jul 1999-Jun 2000 Income State $2,792,260. Mats Exp $918,887, Books $252,865, Per/Ser (Incl. Access Fees) $450,716, Presv $24,667, Micro $23,165, AV Equip $57,894, Electronic Ref Mat (Incl. Access Fees) $109,580. Sal $1,089,867 (Prof $590,477)
Library Holdings: Bk Vols 910,462; Bk Titles 443,861; Per Subs 2,089
Subject Interests: Art, Nursing, Psychology, Sociology, Technology
Special Collections: Archives of Appalachia, Govt doc, law, maps
Automation Activity & Vendor Info: (Serials) Endeavor
Database Vendor: Dialog, GaleNet, IAC - Info Trac, OCLC - First Search, Silverplatter Information Inc.
Publications: Bibliotech (newsletter); LI Guide series
Mem of Watauga Regional Library Center
Partic in LVIS; Solinet; TBR Consortium; Tenn Share
Special Services for the Deaf - TDD
Friends of the Library Group

R EMMANUEL SCHOOL OF RELIGION LIBRARY, One Walker Dr, 3760 9438. SAN 315-8152. Tel: 423-926-1186. Interlibrary Loan Service Tel: 42 461-1543. FAX: 423-926-6198. E-Mail: library@esr.edu. Web Site: www.esr.edu/library.htm. *Librn*, Thomas E Stokes; *ILL*, Chris Quillen; *Cat*, John Mark Wade; *Tech Servs*, Deborah Powell; *Circ*, Carrie Huckaba; Staff (MLS 2)
Founded 1965. Enrl 150; Fac 10; Highest Degree: Doctorate
Jun 1999-May 2000 Income $378,383. Mats Exp $78,223, Books $47,967, Per/Ser (Incl. Access Fees) $24,006, Presv $12,741. Sal $226,636 (Prof $130,074)
Library Holdings: Bk Vols 99,750; Bk Titles 89,952; Per Subs 733
Special Collections: Discipliana Coll, historical materials pertaining to the Christian Churches & Churches of Christ
Partic in SE Libr Network; Tri-Cities Area Health Sciences Libraries Consortium

M JOHNSON CITY MEDICAL CENTER, Learning Resources Center, 400 N State of Franklin Rd, 37604-6094. SAN 371-6481. Tel: 423-431-1691. FAX 423-431-1692. *Librn*, Roberta Kahan; Staff 1 (MLS 1)
Founded 1976
Jul 1998-Jun 1999 Income $86,000. Mats Exp $54,400. Sal $32,000
Subject Interests: Cancer, Medicine, Nursing, Pediatrics, Surgery
Partic in National Network Of Libraries Of Medicine - South Central Region; Tennessee Health Science Library Association; Tri-Cities Area Health Sciences Libraries Consortium

P JOHNSON CITY PUBLIC LIBRARY, 100 W Millard St, 37604. SAN 315 8160. Tel: 423-434-4450. Circulation Tel: 423-434-4476. Reference Tel: 42 434-4454. FAX: 423-434-4469. E-Mail: info@jcpl.net. Web Site: www.jcpl.net. *Dir*, Mark A Thomas; *Assoc Dir*, Patricia H Beard; *ILL*, Alfred J Maupin; *Circ*, Gina Thayer-Coleman; *Cat*, Linda Heck Blanton; *R Serv Ad*, Phoebe Sand; *Ch Servs*, Betty Cobb; *Ch Servs*, Aryln Wattenbarge Staff 33 (MLS 9, Non-MLS 24)
Founded 1895. Pop 60,935; Circ 333,832
Jul 2000-Jun 2001 Income $1,225,000, City $1,125,000, County $100,000. Mats Exp $121,000. Sal $485,268 (Prof $297,441)
Library Holdings: Bk Vols 95,985; Bk Titles 84,299; Per Subs 286
Subject Interests: Local history
Automation Activity & Vendor Info: (OPAC) Endeavor
Database Vendor: GaleNet, IAC - Info Trac, OCLC - First Search
Mem of Watauga Regional Library Center
Special Services for the Deaf - TDD
Friends of the Library Group

L LEGAL SERVICES OF UPPER EAST TENNESSEE LIBRARY, PO Box 360, 37605-0360. SAN 320-2372. Tel: 423-928-8311. FAX: 423-928-9488. *In Charge*, Rachel Kelly
Founded 1977
Library Holdings: Bk Vols 2,000; Per Subs 37

P WATAUGA REGIONAL LIBRARY CENTER, 2700 S Roan St, Ste 435, 37601. SAN 315-8179. Tel: 423-926-2951. Toll Free Tel: 800-838-2951. FAX: 423-926-2956. Web Site: www.wrlibrary.org. *Dir*, Jud B Barry; E-Mail: judbarry@wrlibrary.org; *Asst Dir*, Stephanie Doane; *Tech Servs*, Michael L Bryant; *Tech Servs*, Linda Crain; *Tech Servs*, Joy Ketron; *Tech Servs*, Wanda Peters; Staff 7 (MLS 2, Non-MLS 5)
Pop 398,585
Jul 1998-Jun 1999 Income $436,528, State $400,185, Federal $36,343. Mats Exp $79,093. Sal $181,295
Special Collections: Local History Coll; Professional Resources Coll
Publications: Word From Watauga (annual report)
Member Libraries: East Tennessee State University; Elizabethton-Carter County Public Library; Johnson City Public Library; Johnson County Public Library; Kingsport Public Library & Archives; Mosheim Public Library; Sullivan County Public Library; Unicoi County Public Library; Washington County - Jonesborough Library; Washington County - Jonesborough Library

JONESBOROUGH

S STORYTELLING FOUNDATION INTERNATIONAL, Archives, 116 W Main St, 37659. SAN 329-8965. Tel: 423-753-2171. Toll Free Tel: 800-952-8392. FAX: 423-913-8219. Web Site: www.storytellingfestival.net. *Dir, Pres* Jimmy Neil Smith

WASHINGTON COUNTY - JONESBOROUGH LIBRARY, 200 Sabin Dr, 37659-1306. SAN 360-6007. Tel: 423-753-1800. FAX: 423-753-1802. E-Mail: alpl2@tricon.net. Web Site: wwww.wrlibrary.org. *Dir*, Emily Eddy; E-Mail: eeddy@wrlibrary.org
Founded 1896. Pop 38,964; Circ 101,870
Library Holdings: Bk Titles 50,395; Per Subs 82
Subject Interests: Genealogy, History
Mem of Watauga Regional Library Center
Friends of the Library Group
Branches: 1
GRAY BRANCH, 5026 Bobby Hicks Hwy, Gray, 37615-3461. SAN 360-6031. Tel: 423-477-1550. FAX: 423-477-1553. Web Site: www.wrlibrary.org/Libraries/washco.htm#gray. *Dir*, Lusetta Slagle Jenkins; Tel: 423-477-1559, E-Mail: ljenkins@wrlibrary.org; Staff 5 (MLS 1, Non-MLS 4)
Founded 1968. Pop 38,964
Automation Activity & Vendor Info: (Cataloging) Endeavor; (Circulation) Endeavor; (OPAC) Endeavor
Mem of Watauga Regional Library Center
Friends of the Library Group

INGSPORT

EASTMAN CHEMICAL CO, Technical Information Center, Bldg 150B, PO Box 1972, 37662-5150. SAN 371-6805. Tel: 423-224-9286. FAX: 423-229-6114. *In Charge*, Mike Cassell; Staff 19 (MLS 5, Non-MLS 14)
Founded 1944
Branches:
BUSINESS LIBRARY, Bldg 280, Lincoln St, PO Box 431, 37662-5280. SAN 360-6155. Tel: 423-229-2071. FAX: 423-224-0111. Web Site: eastmanweb/tie. *Librn*, Carl Preslar; Tel: 423-229-6117, E-Mail: gpreslar@eastman.com
Founded 1947
Library Holdings: Bk Vols 3,000; Per Subs 300
Subject Interests: Bus mgt, Economics, Indust relations, Marketing
Special Collections: Company Annual Reports; Resources for Doing Business Outside USA (culture, customs, government restrictions, etc); State Industrial Directories
RESEARCH LIBRARY, Bldg 150B, PO Box 1972, 37662-5150. SAN 360-6120. Tel: 423-229-6111. FAX: 423-229-4558. *Librn*, Karen Wehner
Founded 1944
Library Holdings: Bk Titles 24,000; Per Subs 850
Subject Interests: Agricultural chemistry, Fiber tech, Organ chem incl polymers, Pharmaceutical chem, Plastics tech, Textile tech
Special Collections: Beilstein Coll; Chemical Abstracts; Four Million US & Foreign Patents; Government Reports

1 HOLSTON VALLEY MEDICAL CENTER, Health Science Library, 130 W Ravine St, 37662. SAN 327-1013. Tel: 423-224-6870. FAX: 423-224-6014. E-Mail: br64145@ml.ebsco.com. *Librn*, Sharon M Brown; E-Mail: sharon_m_brown@wellmont.org
Library Holdings: Bk Vols 2,644; Bk Titles 2,191; Per Subs 250
Subject Interests: Allied health, Medicine, Nursing
Partic in SE-Atlantic Regional Med Libr Servs; Tennessee Health Science Library Association; Tri-Cities Area Health Sciences Libraries Consortium

KINGSPORT PUBLIC LIBRARY & ARCHIVES, (KPL), J Fred Johnson Memorial Library, 400 Broad St, 37660-4292. SAN 360-6066. Tel: 423-224-2539. FAX: 423-224-2558. E-Mail: kptlib@wlibrary.org. Web Site: www.kingsportlibrary.org. *Mgr*, Kitti Canepi; Tel: 423-229-9488, Fax: 423-224-3558, E-Mail: kcanepi@wrlibrary.org; *ILL, Ref*, June Presley; E-Mail: jpresley@wrlibrary.org; *Archivist*, Martha Avaleen Egan; Tel: 423-224-2559, Fax: 423-224-2691, E-Mail: megan@wrlibrary.org; *Spec Coll*, Helen Hamilton; E-Mail: hhamilton@wrlibrary.org; *Cat*, Lennea Hickam; Tel: 423-229-9369, E-Mail: lhickam@wrlibrary.org; *Coll Develop*, Danny Bartlett; Tel: 423-224-2588, E-Mail: dbartlett@wrilibrary.org; *Br Coordr*, Florence Maxwell; Tel: 423-229-9466, Fax: 423-224-2784, E-Mail: fmaxwell@wrlibrary.org; Staff 7 (MLS 4, Non-MLS 3)
Founded 1921. Pop 41,414; Circ 193,018
Jul 1999-Jun 2000 Income (Main Library and Branch Library) $753,808, State $7,988, City $699,968, Locally Generated Income $19,080, Other $26,772. Mats Exp $125,567, Books $83,555, Per/Ser (Incl. Access Fees) $30,981, AV Equip $11,031. Sal $397,901
Library Holdings: Bk Vols 130,118; Per Subs 418
Subject Interests: Local history
Special Collections: Archives of the City of Kingsport; First Tennessee Bank Small Business Center; Palmer Regional History Coll
Automation Activity & Vendor Info: (Cataloging) epixtech, inc.; (Circulation) epixtech, inc.; (OPAC) epixtech, inc.
Database Vendor: epixtech, inc., IAC - Info Trac, OCLC - First Search
Publications: Footnotes (Friends of Library quarterly newsletter)
Restriction: Restricted borrowing privileges
Function: Reference services available
Mem of Watauga Regional Library Center
Special Services - Books to Your Door (homebound service); Books for Babies; Even Start Family Literacy Program
Friends of the Library Group
Branches: 1
CARVER, 1013 Douglas St, 37660-4292. SAN 360-6090. Tel: 423-229-9466. *In Charge*, Florence Maxwell
Library Holdings: Bk Vols 3,961

KINGSTON

P KINGSTON PUBLIC LIBRARY, 10004 Bradford Way, No 3, 37763. SAN 315-8217. Tel: 865-376-9905. FAX: 865-376-2301. E-Mail: kingston@mail.state.tn.us. *Asst Dir*, Faye Cole; *Ch Servs*, Barbara Thorbjornsen
Founded 1947. Pop 15,000; Circ 45,000
Library Holdings: Bk Titles 18,000; Per Subs 35
Subject Interests: County genealogy, History, Tenn hist
Mem of Tenn State Regional Libr Syst
Friends of the Library Group

KNOXVILLE

S EAST TENNESSEE DISCOVERY CENTER, Chilhowee Park, 516 N Beaman St, PO Box 6204, 37914. SAN 315-8314. Tel: 865-594-1494. FAX: 865-594-1469. E-Mail: etdc@usit.net. Web Site: www.kornet.org/etdc. *Dir, Pres*, Margaret Maddox; Staff 12 (MLS 6, Non-MLS 6)
Founded 1960
Library Holdings: Bk Vols 500
Subject Interests: Anthropology, Indian artifacts, Natural science, Physical science

R FIRST CHRISTIAN CHURCH, Winona Roehl Library, 211 W Fifth Ave, 37917. SAN 315-8233. Tel: 865-522-0545. E-Mail: kfcchurch@aol.com. *In Charge*, Mary Topping
Founded 1955
Library Holdings: Bk Vols 3,514
Special Collections: Local Poetry (Elizabeth Merchant Coll); Stanley Jones Coll
Publications: Christmount Voice; Disciple; Tennessee Christian

M FORT SANDERS REGIONAL MEDICAL CENTER, Medical-Nursing Library, 1915 White Ave, 37916-2399. SAN 315-8241. Tel: 865-541-1293. Interlibrary Loan Service Tel: 865-541-1425. FAX: 865-541-1762. *Librn*, Nedra Cook; E-Mail: ncook@covhlth.com
Founded 1949
Library Holdings: Bk Titles 7,000; Per Subs 189
Subject Interests: Neurology, Nursing, Oncology, Orthopedic, Rehabilitation
Special Collections: National League for Nursing Coll
Partic in Docline; Knoxville Area Health Sciences Library Consortium

CR JOHNSON BIBLE COLLEGE, Glass Memorial Library, 7900 Johnson Dr, 37998. SAN 315-825X. Tel: 865-251-2277. FAX: 865-251-2278. E-Mail: library@jbc.edu. Web Site: www.jbc.edu/library/. *Librn*, Carolyn Lowe; Tel: 865-251-2276, E-Mail: cblowe@jbc.edu; *Asst Librn*, Jon Hale; E-Mail: jhale@jbc.edu; Staff 5 (MLS 2, Non-MLS 3)
Founded 1893. Enrl 647; Fac 27; Highest Degree: Master
Jul 1999-Jun 2000 Income $313,010. Mats Exp $107,857, Books $76,978, Per/Ser (Incl. Access Fees) $17,048, Presv $1,337, Micro $2,520, Electronic Ref Mat (Incl. Access Fees) $6,409
Library Holdings: Bk Vols 91,118; Bk Titles 61,073; Per Subs 421
Special Collections: Religion (Restoration Movement)
Automation Activity & Vendor Info: (Acquisitions) TLC; (Cataloging) TLC; (Circulation) TLC; (OPAC) TLC
Database Vendor: GaleNet, IAC - Info Trac, OCLC - First Search, Wilson - Wilson Web
Partic in Tenn Share

GL KNOX COUNTY GOVERNMENTAL LIBRARY, M47 City County Bldg, 400 Main St, 37902. SAN 327-6694. Tel: 865-215-2368. *Librn*, Katherine M Douglas
Library Holdings: Bk Vols 60,000

P KNOX COUNTY PUBLIC LIBRARY SYSTEM, Lawson McGhee Library-East Tennessee Historical Center, 500 W Church Ave, 37902-2505. SAN 360-618X. Tel: 865-215-8750. Reference Tel: 865-215-8700. TDD: 865-215-8733, 865-215-8765. FAX: 865-215-8777. Web Site: www.knoxlib.org. *Dir*, Patricia L Watson; *Admin Dir*, Glenn Selfe; *ILL*, Willa Reister; *Circ*, Beth Fredrick; *Tech Servs*, Rene Jordan; *Ref*, Janet Drumheller; *Spec Coll*, Steve Cotham; *Ch Servs*, Fredda Williams; *Archivist*, Doris Martinson; *Automation Syst Coordr*, Sally Lodico; *AV*, Dale Watermulder; *Business*, Thomas Whisman; *Coll Develop*, Nancy Petersen
Founded 1886. Pop 365,626; Circ 2,040,539
Jul 1999-Jun 2000 Income (Main Library and Branch Library) $8,289,109. Sal $4,672,879
Library Holdings: Bk Vols 865,088; Bk Titles 913,541
Special Collections: History & Genealogy of Tennessee & the Old Southwest (Calvin M McClung Historical Coll); Knox County Archives
Automation Activity & Vendor Info: (Cataloging) SIRSI; (Circulation) SIRSI; (OPAC) SIRSI

Partic in OCLC Online Computer Library Center, Inc; Solinet; Tenn-Share
Special Services for the Deaf - Captioned media; TDD
Books for the Homebound; Tennessee Resource Center (statewide ILL coordination & service)
Friends of the Library Group
Branches: 17
BURLINGTON BRANCH, 4512 Asheville Hwy, 37914. SAN 360-621X. Tel: 865-525-5431. *Mgr*, Melanie Reseigh
Library Holdings: Bk Vols 18,431
CARTER BRANCH, 9036 Asheville Hwy, 37924. SAN 360-6244. Tel: 865-933-5438. *Branch Mgr*, Jonathan Ballinger
Library Holdings: Bk Vols 13,773
CEDAR BLUFF BRANCH, 9045 Cross Park Dr, Cedar Bluff, 37923. SAN 377-6522. Tel: 865-470-7033. FAX: 865-470-0927. *Mgr*, Lee Clouse
Library Holdings: Bk Vols 51,599
CORRYTON BRANCH, 7733 Corryton Rd, Corryton, 37721-9802. SAN 360-6279. Tel: 865-688-1501. *Librn*, Patricia Sue Walker
Library Holdings: Bk Vols 9,834
FARRAGUT BRANCH, 417 N Campbell Station Rd, Farragut, 37922. SAN 360-6333. Tel: 865-777-1750. *Mgr*, Barbara Dyer
Library Holdings: Bk Vols 54,177
FOUNTAIN CITY BRANCH, 213 Hotel Ave, 37918-3227. SAN 360-6368. Tel: 865-689-2681. *Mgr*, Elizabeth Nelson
Library Holdings: Bk Vols 29,392
HALLS BRANCH, Halls S-Ctr, 7006-A Maynardville Hwy, 37918-5736. SAN 360-6392. Tel: 865-922-2552. *Branch Mgr*, Kathy Martin
Library Holdings: Bk Vols 32,578
KARNS BRANCH, 7708 Oak Ridge Hwy, 37921-3337. SAN 360-6422. Tel: 865-690-0363. *Mgr*, Karen Van Rij
Library Holdings: Bk Vols 18,294
MASCOT BRANCH, 2010 Library Rd, Mascot, 37806-9999. SAN 360-6457. Tel: 865-933-2620. FAX: 865-933-4239. *Mgr*, Ralph McGhee
Library Holdings: Bk Vols 12,495
MURPHY BRANCH, 2247 Western Ave, 37921-5756. SAN 360-649X. Tel: 865-521-7812. *Mgr*, Sandra Chandler
Library Holdings: Bk Vols 9,500
NORTH KNOXVILLE BRANCH, 2901 Ocoee Trail, 37917-3233. SAN 360-6511. Tel: 865-525-7036. *Branch Mgr*, Jeanne Cloud
Library Holdings: Bk Vols 26,425
NORWOOD BRANCH, 1110 Merchants Dr, 37912-4704. SAN 360-6546. Tel: 865-688-2454. *Mgr*, Terry Caruthers
Library Holdings: Bk Vols 25,718
POWELL, Powell Place Shopping Ctr, 3505 Emory Rd, 37938-4010. SAN 360-6570. Tel: 865-947-6210. *Mgr*, Carol Swaggerty
Library Holdings: Bk Vols 34,128
SEQUOYAH BRANCH, 1140 Southgate Rd, 37919-7646. SAN 360-6600. Tel: 865-525-1541. *Mgr*, Clara Hardin
Library Holdings: Bk Vols 21,185
SOUTH KNOXVILLE BRANCH, 4500 Chapman Hwy, 37920-4359. SAN 360-6635. Tel: 865-573-1772. *Mgr*, Kathy Martin
Library Holdings: Bk Vols 39,147
WEST KNOXVILLE BRANCH, 104 Golf Club Rd, 37919-4801. SAN 360-6724. Tel: 865-588-8813. *Branch Mgr*, Jackie Hill
Library Holdings: Bk Vols 48,921

C KNOXVILLE BUSINESS COLLEGE LIBRARY, 720 N Fifth Ave, 37917. SAN 328-5758. Tel: 865-524-3043. FAX: 865—637-0127. *Librn*, Mary McHugh
Library Holdings: Bk Titles 6,400; Per Subs 94
Subject Interests: Accounting, Tourism

C KNOXVILLE COLLEGE, Alumni Library, 901 Knoxville College Dr, 37921. SAN 315-8276. Tel: 865-524-6553. FAX: 865-524-6686. *Dir*, Naomi Williams; Staff 2 (MLS 2)
Founded 1876. Enrl 500; Fac 30; Highest Degree: Bachelor
Library Holdings: Bk Vols 95,000; Per Subs 205

G KNOXVILLE-KNOX COUNTY METROPOLITAN PLANNING COMMISSION LIBRARY, City & County Bldg Ste 403, 400 Main St, 37902-2476. SAN 326-5684. Tel: 865-215-2500. Reference Tel: 865-215-3829. FAX: 865-215-2068. E-Mail: contact@knoxmpc.org. Web Site: www.knoxmpc.org. *Dir*, Gretchen F Beal; E-Mail: gretchen.beal@knoxmpc.org; Staff 2 (MLS 1, Non-MLS 1)
Founded 1975
Library Holdings: Bk Titles 10,000; Per Subs 93
Subject Interests: Urban affairs
Publications: Catalogue of M P C Publications; Monthly Acquisitions
Restriction: Internal circulation only, Open to public for reference only, Public use on premises
Function: ILL limited, Photocopies available, Reference services available, Some telephone reference

M LAKESHORE MENTAL HEALTH INSTITUTE, Lea Earl Acuff Professional Library, 5908 Lyons View Dr, 37919-7598. SAN 373-8191. Tel: 865-584-1561, Ext 7540. FAX: 865-450-5220.
Founded 1976
Library Holdings: Bk Vols 1,600; Bk Titles 1,582; Per Subs 79
Subject Interests: Psychiatry, Psychology

Special Collections: Institute History Archive
Partic in Knoxville Area Health Sciences Library Consortium; Tennessee Health Science Library Association

G MUNICIPAL TECHNICAL ADVISORY SERVICE LIBRARY, 120 Conference Center Bldg, 37996-4105. SAN 327-6678. Tel: 865-974-0411. FAX: 865-974-0423. Web Site: www.mtas.utk.edu. *Info Res*, Frances Adam O'Brien; Tel: 865-974-9842, E-Mail: adams-obrienf@utk.edu; Staff 5 (MLS 2, Non-MLS 3)
Founded 1950
Jul 1999-Jun 2000 Income $32,000
Library Holdings: Bk Vols 14,600; Bk Titles 14,600; Per Subs 250
Subject Interests: Municipal
Special Collections: City Ordinances; Municipal Law
Automation Activity & Vendor Info: (Acquisitions) EOS; (Cataloging) EOS; (OPAC) EOS; (Serials) EOS
Database Vendor: OCLC - First Search
Publications: Directory of Tennessee Municipal Officials
Restriction: Not a lending library
Function: Research library
Partic in Solinet; Tenn-Share

S PELLISSIPPI STATE TECHNICAL COMMUNITY COLLEGE, Library Services, 10915 Harding Valley Rd, PO Box 22990, 37933-0990. SAN 327-8050. Tel: 865-694-6516. FAX: 865-694-6625. Web Site: www.pstcc.cc.tn.us/library. *Dir*, Peter Nerzak; *Ref*, Rick Bower; *Cat*, Jane Cameron; *Circ*, Jean Jackson; *Acq*, Karen Cornell
1998-1999 Mats Exp $185,000, Books $100,000, Per/Ser (Incl. Access Fees) $40,000, Micro $30,000. Sal $390,000
Library Holdings: Bk Titles 45,000; Per Subs 500
Automation Activity & Vendor Info: (Cataloging) DRA
Partic in OCLC Online Computer Library Center, Inc

GL TENNESSEE SUPREME COURT LAW LIBRARY, 719 Locust St, 37902. SAN 315-8322. Tel: 865-594-6128. *Librn*, Susan Delp
Founded 1937
Library Holdings: Bk Vols 30,000
Also see divisional entries in Jackson & Nashville

TENNESSEE VALLEY AUTHORITY
S CORPORATE LIBRARY-KNOXVILLE, 400 W Summit Hill Dr, 37902. SAN 360-6759. Tel: 865-632-3464. FAX: 865-632-4475. *Mgr*, Michael Patterson; E-Mail: mipatterson@tva.gov; *Ref*, Ed Best Jr; *Ref*, Nancy Proctor; Staff 7 (MLS 4, Non-MLS 3)
Founded 1933
Library Holdings: Bk Vols 16,685; Per Subs 335
Subject Interests: Electric power production, Engineering, Natural, Nuclear power, Water resources
Special Collections: TVA History
Publications: Environmental & Corporate Current Awareness Lists
Partic in Dialog Corporation; Fedlink; OCLC Online Computer Library Center, Inc
L LEGAL RESEARCH CENTER, 400 W Summit Hill Dr, 37999. SAN 360-6813. Tel: 865-632-6613. FAX: 865-632-3195.; Staff 5 (MLS 5)
Founded 1935
Library Holdings: Bk Vols 26,000; Per Subs 13
Subject Interests: Case law, Eminent domain, Energy, Environment, Fed practice, Fed statutory, Procedure, Procurement, Pub utilities, Water law
Restriction: Staff use only
Partic in Dialog Corporation; Vutext; Westlaw

UNIVERSITY OF TENNESSEE
CL JOEL A KATZ LAW LIBRARY, 1505 W Cumberland Ave, 37996-1800. SAN 360-6937. Tel: 865-974-4381. Circulation Tel: 865-974-3777. Reference Tel: 865-974-3771. FAX: 865-974-6571. Web Site: www.law.utk.edu/admin/library/. *Dir*, William J Beintema; Tel: 865-974-6733, E-Mail: beintema@libra.law.utk.edu; *Assoc Dir*, D Cheryn Picquet; Tel: 865-974-6729, E-Mail: picquet@libra.law.utk.edu; *Head, Cat*, Reba A Best; Tel: 865-974-6728, E-Mail: best@libra.law.utk.edu; *Ref*, Sibyl Marshall; Tel: 865-974-5906, E-Mail: marshall@libra.law.utk.edu; *Ref*, Jean E Moore; Tel: 865-974-0133, E-Mail: moore@libra.law.utk.edu; *Electronic Resources*, Cathy Cochran; Tel: 865-974-0236, E-Mail: cochran@libra.law.utk.edu; *Acq*, M Loretta Price; Tel: 865-974-9746, E-Mail: price@libra.law.utk.edu; *Info Tech*, Bill Hodges; Tel: 865-974-2547, E-Mail: hodges@libra.law.utk.edu; Staff 22 (MLS 9, Non-MLS 13)
Founded 1890. Enrl 478; Fac 35; Highest Degree: Doctorate
Jul 1999-Jun 2000 Income State $2,021,945. Mats Exp $826,912, Books $30,574, Per/Ser (Incl. Access Fees) $684,607, Micro $59,983, Electronic Ref Mat (Incl. Access Fees) $51,748. Sal $857,462 (Prof $552,872)
Library Holdings: Bk Vols 483,372; Bk Titles 95,337; Per Subs 6,363
Automation Activity & Vendor Info: (Acquisitions) Innovative Interfaces Inc.; (Cataloging) Innovative Interfaces Inc.; (Circulation) Innovative Interfaces Inc.; (Course Reserve) Innovative Interfaces Inc.; (OPAC) Innovative Interfaces Inc.; (Serials) Innovative Interfaces Inc.
Database Vendor: IAC - Info Trac, Innovative Interfaces INN - View, Lexis-Nexis, OCLC - First Search, Wilson - Wilson Web

Function: Research library
Mem of Asn of Research Libraries
Partic in Consortium Of South Eastern Law Libraries; SE Libr Network

UNIVERSITY OF TENNESSEE MEDICAL CENTER, Preston Medical Library & Learning Resource Center, 1924 Alcoa Hwy, Box U-111, 37920. SAN 315-8284. Tel: 865-544-9525. FAX: 865-544-9527. Web Site: www.utmck.edu/library. *Coll Develop, Dir*, Doris Prichard; E-Mail: doris-prichard@utk.edu; *Librn*, Shelley Paden; *Ref*, Martha Earl; Tel: 865-544-6616; Staff 4 (MLS 3, Non-MLS 1)
Founded 1969
Library Holdings: Bk Titles 3,000; Per Subs 435
Subject Interests: Biochemistry, Cancer, Clinical medicine, Dentistry, Gyn, Hematology, Immunology, OB, Perinatology, Trauma

UNIVERSITY OF TENNESSEE, KNOXVILLE, John C Hodges University Libraries, 1015 Volunteer Blvd, 37996-1000. SAN 360-6848. Tel: 865-974-4127. Interlibrary Loan Service Tel: 423-974-4240. Circulation Tel: 865-974-4351. Reference Tel: 865-974-4171. FAX: 865-974-4259. Web Site: www.lib.utk.edu. *Dean of Libr*, Barbara I Dewey; E-Mail: bdewey@utk.edu; *Assoc Dean*, Aubrey H Mitchell; Tel: 865-974-6600, E-Mail: amitchell@utk.edu; *Librn*, Tamara Miller; Tel: 865-974-4465, E-Mail: tamara-miller@utk.edu; *Head, Circ, Syst Coordr*, William Britten; Tel: 865-974-4304, Fax: 865-974-0555, E-Mail: wbritten@utk.edu; *Circ*, Deborah Thomas; *Ref*, Rita Smith; Tel: 865-974-4174, Fax: 865-974-9242, E-Mail: rsmith19@utk.edu; *Coll Develop*, Linda Phillips; Tel: 865-974-4702, Fax: 865-974-9242, E-Mail: llphillips@utk.edu; *ILL*, David Atkins; Fax: 865-974-2708, E-Mail: datkins@utk.edu; *AV*, Wm Ward; *Tech Servs*, Jill Keally; Tel: 865-974-6696, Fax: 865-974-0551, E-Mail: jill-keally@utk.edu; Staff 58 (MLS 58)
Founded 1838. Enrl 20,057; Fac 1,182; Highest Degree: Doctorate
Jul 1999-Jun 2000 Mats Exp $6,823,023, Books $1,384,747, Per/Ser (Incl. Access Fees) $5,296,218, Presv $135,034. Sal $5,879,825 (Prof $2,802,295)
Library Holdings: Bk Vols 2,425,286; Bk Titles 1,121,600; Per Subs 22,829
Special Collections: Alex Haley Coll; Cherokee Indians; Congressional Papers; Congreve; Early Imprints; Early Voyages & Travel; Nineteenth Century American Fiction; Radiation Biology; Tennessee World War II Veterans
Automation Activity & Vendor Info: (Acquisitions) GEAC; (Cataloging) epixtech, inc.; (Circulation) epixtech, inc.; (Course Reserve) epixtech, inc.; (ILL) epixtech, inc.; (OPAC) epixtech, inc.; (Serials) GEAC
Publications: Library Development Review (annual); Library Friends (biannual newsletter); Mission & Strategic Plan (annual); The UTK Librarian (biannual newsletter); The UTK Library Record (annual report)
Partic in Asn of Research Libraries; Center For Research Libraries; Digital Libr Fedn; OCLC Online Computer Library Center, Inc; SE Libr Network
Friends of the Library Group
Departmental Libraries:
ACQUISITIONS Tel: 865-974-4431. FAX: 865-974-0551.
AGRICULTURE-VETERINARY MEDICINE, Veterinary Medicine Teaching Hospital, 37996-4500. SAN 360-6902. Tel: 865-974-7338. FAX: 865-974-4732. *Branch Mgr*, Sandra Leach
GEORGE F DEVINE MUSIC LIBRARY, 301 Music Bldg, 1741 Volunteer Blvd, 37996-2600. SAN 360-6961. Tel: 865-974-3474. FAX: 865-974-0564. E-Mail: musiclib@aztec.lib.utk.edu. Web Site: www.lib.utk.edu/~music. *Librn*, Pauline S Bayne; E-Mail: pbayne@utk.edu; Staff 4 (MLS 2, Non-MLS 2)
Founded 1965
Special Collections: Barry McDonald Music Coll, scores; Canadian Composers' Information File; Opera Libretti, Programs & Ballet Programs (Earl W Quintrell Coll)
Open Mon-Thurs 8am-10pm, Fri 8-5, Sun 2pm-10pm (Spring), Mon-Thurs 8am-9pm, Fri 8-5, Sun 2pm-9pm (Summer)
MAP LIBRARY, University of Tennessee Map Library, 15 Hoskins Bldg, 37996-4006. SAN 372-7777. Tel: 865-974-4315. FAX: 865-974-3925. E-Mail: maplib@aztec.lib.utk.edu. Web Site: www.lib.utk.edu/~cic. *Branch Mgr*, James O Minton; Tel: 865-974-3878, E-Mail: minton@aztec.lib.utk.edu; Staff 2 (MLS 1, Non-MLS 1)
SERIALS Tel: 865-974-4236. FAX: 865-974-0551.
UNIVERSITY ARCHIVES & SPECIAL COLLECTIONS, Hoskins Library Bldg, 37996-4006. SAN 372-7793. Tel: 865-974-4480. FAX: 865-974-0560. *Branch Mgr*, James B Lloyd; E-Mail: jlloyd@utk.edu

LA FOLLETTE

LA FOLLETTE PUBLIC LIBRARY, 201 S Tennesee Ave, 37766-3606. SAN 315-8330. Tel: 423-562-5154. FAX: 423-562-0013. E-Mail: lpl1@icx.net. Web Site: www.kornet.org/laflib. *Librn*, Nancy J Green; E-Mail: ngreen@mail.sate.tn.us; Staff 1 (Non-MLS 1)
Library Holdings: Bk Vols 10,333
Mem of Clinch-Powell Regional Library
For holdings see library system
Friends of the Library Group

LA VERGNE

P LA VERGNE PUBLIC LIBRARY, 5089 Murfreesboro Rd, 37086-0177. SAN 322-7464. Tel: 615-793-7303. FAX: 615-793-7307. E-Mail: library@lavergne.org. Web Site: www.state.tn.us/cgi-bin/library. *Dir*, Faye Toombs
Founded 1979. Circ 106,000
Library Holdings: Bk Vols 30,000
Mem of Highland Rim Regional Library Center
Friends of the Library Group

LAFAYETTE

P MACON COUNTY PUBLIC LIBRARY, 311 Church St, 37083-1607. SAN 360-702X. Tel: 615-666-4340. Interlibrary Loan Service Tel: 800-572-7396. FAX: 615-666-8932. *Dir*, Julia Marshall
Founded 1957. Pop 20,000; Circ 40,000
Library Holdings: Bk Vols 22,000; Per Subs 28
Mem of Upper Cumberland Regional Library
Friends of the Library Group
Branches: 1
RED BOILING SPRINGS BRANCH, 335 E Main St, Red Boiling Springs, 37150-0033. SAN 360-7054. Tel: 615-699-3701. FAX: 615-699-3737. *Branch Mgr*, Linda Womack
Friends of the Library Group

LAKE CITY

P LAKE CITY PUBLIC LIBRARY, 226 N Main, PO Box 157, 37769-0157. SAN 315-8349. Tel: 423-426-6762. *Librn*, Grova Adkins-Disney
Library Holdings: Bk Titles 800; Per Subs 35
Mem of Clinch-Powell Regional Library
Open Mon & Tues 10-noon & 1-6, Thurs 11-noon & 1-6, Fri & Sat 1-6

LAWRENCEBURG

P LAWRENCE COUNTY PUBLIC LIBRARY, 519 E Gaines St, 38464-3599. SAN 315-8357. Tel: 931-762-4627. FAX: 931-766-1597. E-Mail: library7@usit.net. Web Site: www.lawrenceburg.com/library. *Dir*, Teresa Newton; E-Mail: tnewton@usit.net
Founded 1941. Pop 35,303; Circ 114,552
Library Holdings: Bk Titles 35,419; Per Subs 120
Mem of Blue Grass Regional Library
Partic in Area Resource Center, Nashville
Branches: 1
LORETTO BRANCH, 102 S Main St, Loretto, 38469-2110. (Mail add: PO Box 338, Loretto, 38469-0338), SAN 377-7847. Tel: 931-853-7323. FAX: 931-853-7324. E-Mail: llibrary@lorettotel.net. *Librn*, Judy Henkel
Library Holdings: Bk Vols 5,369

LEBANON

J CUMBERLAND UNIVERSITY, Vise Library, One Cumberland Sq, 37087. SAN 315-8365. Tel: 615-444-2562, Ext 1151. FAX: 615-444-2569. Web Site: www.cumberland.edu. *Dir*, Michelle Noel; E-Mail: mnoel@cumberland.edu; *Asst Librn*, John Boniol; Tel: 615-444-2562, Ext 1154, E-Mail: jboniol@cumberland.edu; *Tech Servs*, Vanessa Ritchie; E-Mail: vritchie@cumberland.edu
Founded 1842. Enrl 1,200; Fac 74; Highest Degree: Master
Library Holdings: Bk Vols 65,000; Per Subs 500
Subject Interests: Bus, Mgt, Tenn hist
Special Collections: Archives Coll; Tennessee Coll
Partic in SE Libr Network; Tenn Share
Friends of the Library Group

P LEBANON-WILSON COUNTY LIBRARY, 108 S Hatton Ave, 37087-3543. SAN 360-7089. Tel: 615-444-0632. FAX: 615-444-0535. Web Site: lebanonlibrary.net. *Dir*, Betty Jo Dedman; E-Mail: bdedman@tsla.lib.tn.us
Pop 60,067; Circ 203,091
Jul 1998-Jul 1999 Income $208,721, City $59,509, County $149,212. Mats Exp Books $24,000
Library Holdings: Bk Vols 40,000
Mem of Highland Rim Regional Library Center
Friends of the Library Group
Branches: 1
WATERTOWN BRANCH, Public Sq, Watertown, 37184-1422. SAN 360-7119. Tel: 615-237-9700. Web Site: lebanonlibrary.net. *Librn*, Pauline Armstrong

LENOIR CITY

P LENOIR CITY PUBLIC LIBRARY, 109 E Broadway, 37771-2909. (Mail add: PO Box 1156, 37771-1156), SAN 315-8373. Tel: 865-986-3210. E-Mail: lenoirpl@mail.state.tn.us. *Librn*, Kaye Hathcock

Founded 1928
Library Holdings: Bk Vols 13,000; Per Subs 35
Mem of Fort Loudoun Regional Library Center
Friends of the Library Group

LEWISBURG

P MARSHALL COUNTY MEMORIAL LIBRARY, 310 Old Farmington Pike, PO Box 1007, 37091-0007. SAN 315-8381. Tel: 931-359-3335. FAX: 931-359-5866. E-Mail: marshall@main.state.tn.us. *Dir*, Jan Allen
Founded 1944. Pop 19,000; Circ 133,748
Library Holdings: Bk Titles 45,000; Per Subs 110
Subject Interests: Architecture, Art, Education, Genealogy, History, Medicine, Relig studies
Mem of Blue Grass Regional Library

LEXINGTON

P EVERETT HORN PUBLIC LIBRARY, 702 W Church St, 38351-1713. SAN 315-839X. Tel: 901-968-3239. FAX: 901-968-4134. *Dir*, Lynn Lewis; E-Mail: llewis2@mail.state.tn.us
Founded 1949. Pop 21,390
Library Holdings: Bk Titles 18,000
Mem of Shiloh Regional Library

LINDEN

P PERRY COUNTY PUBLIC LIBRARY, Rte 10, Box 3A, 37096-9802. SAN 360-7178. Tel: 931-589-5011. FAX: 931-589-5011. *Dir*, Dorothy Pevahouse; E-Mail: dpevahou@mail.state.tn.us
Pop 6,111
Jul 1998-Jun 1999 Income $50,000. Mats Exp $10,000, Books $5,000, Other Print Mats $5,000. Sal $30,000
Library Holdings: Bk Titles 10,000
Mem of Blue Grass Regional Library
Open Mon, Tues, Thurs & Fri 9-5 & Sat 9-12
Branches: 1
LOBELVILLE BRANCH, PO Box 369, Lobelville, 37097-0369. SAN 360-7208. Tel: 931-593-3111. FAX: 931-593-2089. E-Mail: lobelvillelib@tnii.net. *Dir*, Betty Tucker
Library Holdings: Bk Vols 5,800
Open Mon-Fri 12-4

LIVINGSTON

P OVERTON COUNTY PUBLIC LIBRARY, 225 E Main, 38570-1959. SAN 315-8403. Tel: 931-823-1888. FAX: 931-823-1888. *Dir*, Janet W Gann; E-Mail: jgann@mail.state.tn.us
Pop 17,575
Library Holdings: Bk Vols 20,000
Special Collections: Extensive Genealogy area & support system
Mem of Upper Cumberland Regional Library
Open Mon, Tues, Thurs & Fri 9-5 & Sat 9-2
Friends of the Library Group

LOUDON

P LOUDON PUBLIC LIBRARY, 100 River Rd, 37774. SAN 315-842X. Tel: 865-458-3161. FAX: 865-458-3161. *Librn*, Tammy Smallen; E-Mail: tsmallen@mail.state.tn.us
Library Holdings: Bk Titles 5,050; Per Subs 15
Mem of Fort Loudoun Regional Library Center

LUTTRELL

P LUTTRELL PUBLIC LIBRARY, Main St, Hwy 61, 37779. (Mail add: PO Box 59, 37779-0059), SAN 315-8438. Tel: 865-992-0208. FAX: 865-992-4354. E-Mail: publicbk@icx.net. *Dir*, Gloria Fox
Library Holdings: Bk Titles 5,000; Per Subs 2
Mem of Clinch-Powell Regional Library

LYNCHBURG

P MOORE COUNTY PUBLIC LIBRARY, 17 Lynchburg Highway, PO Box 602, 37352. SAN 315-8446. Tel: 931-759-7285. FAX: 931-759-6393. *Librn*, Sara L Hope; E-Mail: shope@mail.state.tn.us; *Asst Librn*, Margaret Gold; E-Mail: mgold@mail.state.tn.us; Staff 3 (Non-MLS 3)
Founded 1953. Circ 4,140
Jul 2000-Jun 2001 Income County $50,887. Mats Exp $5,150, Books $2,000, Per/Ser (Incl. Access Fees) $350, Presv $300, AV Equip $2,500. Sal $33,789 (Prof $16,933)
Library Holdings: Bk Titles 24,876; Per Subs 17
Special Collections: Reagor Motlow Papers Coll
Database Vendor: Ebsco - EbscoHost, GaleNet, IAC - Info Trac
Function: Reference only
Mem of Highland Rim Regional Library Center
Special Services for the Deaf - TDD
Special Services for the Blind - Bks on tape

LYNNVILLE

P ROBERT B JONES MEMORIAL LIBRARY, Main St, PO Box 88, 38472 SAN 376-6918. Tel: 931-527-3103.
Library Holdings: Bk Titles 2,000
Mem of Blue Grass Regional Library

MADISONVILLE

J HIWASSEE COLLEGE, Hardwick Johnston Memorial Library, 255 Hiwassee College Dr, 37354. SAN 315-8489. Tel: 423-442-2102, 423-442-3283. Toll Free Tel: 800-356-2187. *Dir*, Adele Miller; E-Mail: millera@hiwassee.edu; *Circ*, Barbara Carringer; *Ref*, Mildred Scott; Staff 3 (MLS 1, Non-MLS 2)
Founded 1955. Enrl 350; Fac 28
Library Holdings: Bk Vols 40,000; Bk Titles 33,000; Per Subs 230
Friends of the Library Group

P MADISONVILLE PUBLIC LIBRARY, 305 College St, PO Box 99, 3735 SAN 315-8497. Tel: 423-442-6617. FAX: 423-442-8142. E-Mail: mplib@usat.net. *Librn*, Kim Hicks
Library Holdings: Bk Vols 10,381; Bk Titles 8,065
Mem of Fort Loudoun Regional Library Center
Friends of the Library Group

MANCHESTER

P COFFEE COUNTY-MANCHESTER LIBRARY, 1005 Hillsboro Hwy, 37355-2099. SAN 376-7310. Tel: 931-723-5143. FAX: 931-723-0713. *Libr* Sherryl Roberts
Library Holdings: Bk Vols 49,000; Bk Titles 46,000; Per Subs 83
Mem of Highland Rim Regional Library Center
Friends of the Library Group

MARTIN

P CE WELDON PUBLIC LIBRARY, 100 Main St, 38237-2445. SAN 315-8500. Tel: 901-587-3148. FAX: 901-587-4674. E-Mail: wlibrary@aeneas.n Web Site: www.ceweldonlibrary.org. *Librn*, Teresa Johnson; *Asst Librn*, Roberta Peacock
Founded 1925. Pop 32,896
Library Holdings: Bk Vols 45,000
Special Collections: Tennessee Genealogical Collections
Publications: C E Weldon Public Library Newsletter (Local Distibution)
Mem of Reelfoot Regional Library Center
Friends of the Library Group

P REELFOOT REGIONAL LIBRARY CENTER, Hwy 45 S, PO Box 168, 38237-0168. SAN 315-8519. Tel: 901-587-2347. FAX: 901-587-0027. *Dir*, Rogers N Susan; Staff 2 (MLS 2)
Founded 1942. Pop 179,930; Circ 873,558
Library Holdings: Bk Vols 115,000; Bk Titles 77,000; Per Subs 26
Publications: Library Lines (quarterly)
Member Libraries: Benton County Public Library; Carroll County Library CE Weldon Public Library; Dr Nathan Porter Public Library; Gibson Coun Memorial Library; Gleason Memorial Library; Humboldt Public Library; McKenzie Memorial Library; Ned R Mcwherter -Weakley County Library; Obion County Public Library; Sharon Public Library; W G Rhea Library

C UNIVERSITY OF TENNESSEE AT MARTIN, Paul Meek Library, 38237. SAN 315-8527. Tel: 901-587-7092. Interlibrary Loan Service Tel: 901-587-7068. FAX: 901-587-7074. Web Site: library.utm.edu/. *In Charge*, Steven E Rogers; Tel: 901-587-7070, E-Mail: srogers@utm.edu; *Acq*, Linda Butler; Tel: 901-587-7096, E-Mail: lbutler@utm.edu; *Ref*, John Bell; *ILL*, Earlene Moore; *Doc*, Sandra Downing; *Per*, Patricia Greer; *Spec Coll*, Richard Saunders; *Publ Servs*, James Nance; Tel: 901-587-7061, E-Mail: jimnance@utm.edu; Staff 10 (MLS 10)
Founded 1900. Enrl 5,846; Fac 224; Highest Degree: Master
Jul 1998-Jun 1999 Income $1,449,031, State $1,328,056, Locally Generatec Income $50,837, Other $70,138. Mats Exp $794,233, Books $114,573, Per/Ser (Incl. Access Fees) $290,973, Presv $13,587, Micro $56,232, AV Equip $3,777, Electronic Ref Mat (Incl. Access Fees) $49,895. Sal $731,405 (Prof $390,970)
Library Holdings: Bk Vols 350,000; Bk Titles 295,000; Per Subs 1,558
Special Collections: Congressman Ed Jones Papers; Governor Ned Ray McWherter Personal & Legislative Papers
Automation Activity & Vendor Info: (Acquisitions) Innovative Interfaces Inc.; (Cataloging) Innovative Interfaces Inc.; (Circulation) Innovative Interfaces Inc.; (Course Reserve) Innovative Interfaces Inc.; (ILL) Innovativ Interfaces Inc.; (OPAC) Innovative Interfaces Inc.; (Serials) Innovative

Interfaces Inc.
Database Vendor: Ebsco - EbscoHost, OCLC - First Search, ProQuest, Silverplatter Information Inc.
Partic in OCLC Online Computer Library Center, Inc; SE Libr Network
Friends of the Library Group

ARYVILLE

BLOUNT COUNTY PUBLIC LIBRARY, 301 McGhee St, 37801-6811. SAN 315-8535. Tel: 865-982-0981. FAX: 865-977-1142. Web Site: www.korrnet.org/bcpl. *Dir*, Kathryn Pagles; *Asst Dir*, Laura Hutchens; *Ch Servs*, Jean Closz; *Head Ref*, Jim Vevdini; Staff 12 (MLS 5, Non-MLS 7)
Founded 1919. Pop 100,000; Circ 500,000
Jul 1999-Jun 2000 Income $955,995, City $324,400, County $379,072, Locally Generated Income $176,423, Other $76,100. Mats Exp $207,696, Books $145,941, Per/Ser (Incl. Access Fees) $17,955, Presv $3,905, Micro $500, AV Equip $39,395. Sal $431,081
Library Holdings: Bk Vols 150,000; Per Subs 300
Subject Interests: Genealogy, Local history
Automation Activity & Vendor Info: (Cataloging) SIRSI; (Circulation) SIRSI; (OPAC) SIRSI
Mem of Fort Loudoun Regional Library Center
Special Services for the Deaf - TDD
Special Services for the Blind - Print scanner & software for conversion to speech; Special videos for visually handicapped
Friends of the Library Group

BLOUNT MEMORIAL HOSPITAL, L R Lingeman Memorial Medical Library, 907 E Lamar Alexander Pkwy, 37804. SAN 315-8543. Tel: 865-977-5520. FAX: 865-981-2473. *Librn*, Rebecca Marcum; Staff 1 (MLS 1)
Founded 1947
Library Holdings: Bk Titles 1,000; Per Subs 85
Subject Interests: Consumer health, Medicine, Nursing
Partic in Knoxville Area Health Sciences Library Consortium; National Network of Libraries of Medicine - Greater Midwest Region

MARYVILLE COLLEGE, Lamar Memorial Library, 502 E Lamar Alexander Pkwy, 37804-5907. SAN 315-8551. Tel: 865-981-8257. Circulation Tel: 865-981-8099. Reference Tel: 865-981-8256. FAX: 865-981-8170. Web Site: library.maryvillecollege.edu. *Dir Libr Serv*, Christine Richert Nugent; Tel: 865-981-8247, Fax: 865-981-8010, E-Mail: nugent@maryvillecollege.edu; *Cat*, Choi Park; Tel: 865-981-8258; *Ref*, Roger Myers; Tel: 865-981-8259; *Acq*, May Dori; Staff 8 (MLS 5, Non-MLS 3)
Founded 1819. Enrl 1,001; Fac 60; Highest Degree: Bachelor
Jun 1999-May 2000 Income $498,827, Locally Generated Income $30,811, Parent Institution $468,016. Mats Exp $175,705, Books $64,123, Per/Ser (Incl. Access Fees) $55,486, Presv $6,355, Micro $8,845, AV Equip $1,076, Other Print Mats $4,119, Electronic Ref Mat (Incl. Access Fees) $35,701. Sal $180,547 (Prof $107,959)
Library Holdings: Bk Vols 96,350; Bk Titles 82,955; Per Subs 1,059; Bks on Deafness & Sign Lang 258
Subject Interests: Liberal arts
Special Collections: 19th Century Hymnals, college archives
Automation Activity & Vendor Info: (Acquisitions) Innovative Interfaces Inc.; (Circulation) Innovative Interfaces Inc.; (OPAC) Innovative Interfaces Inc.; (Serials) Innovative Interfaces Inc.
Database Vendor: GaleNet, IAC - SearchBank, Lexis-Nexis, OCLC - First Search, OVID Technologies, Silverplatter Information Inc.
Publications: In4mation (Newsletter)
Restriction: Restricted access
Function: Outside services via phone, cable & mail
Partic in OCLC Online Computer Library Center, Inc; SE Libr Network; Tenn-Share; TRS
Special Services for the Blind - Kurzweil Reader

NEW PROVIDENCE PRESBYTERIAN CHURCH, Alexander-Smith Library, 703 W Broadway, 37801. SAN 315-856X. Tel: 865-983-0182. FAX: 865-681-0804. *Librn*, Peggy Thurman; *Ch Servs*, Polly McArthur
Founded 1951
Library Holdings: Bk Titles 7,110
Subject Interests: Childrens videos, Church history, Family, Fine arts, Religion, Travel

IAYNARDVILLE

MAYNARDVILLE PUBLIC LIBRARY, 296 Main St, 37807-3400. SAN 315-8578. Tel: 865-992-7106. FAX: 865-992-0202. E-Mail: mayna2bk@@icx.net. *Dir*, Chantay Collins
Pop 14,334
Library Holdings: Bk Vols 11,257
Subject Interests: Local history
Mem of Clinch-Powell Regional Library
Open Mon, Tues, Thurs & Fri 11-5 & Sat 11-3
Friends of the Library Group

MC KENZIE

C BETHEL COLLEGE, Burroughs Learning Center, 325 Cherry Ave, 38201. SAN 315-8454. Tel: 731-352-4000. FAX: 731-352-4070. Web Site: www.bethel-college.edu/library/. *Dir*, Harold Kelly; Staff 5 (MLS 2, Non-MLS 3)
Enrl 515; Fac 30; Highest Degree: Bachelor
1998-1999 Mats Exp $66,204, Books $32,000, Per/Ser (Incl. Access Fees) $31,000, Other Print Mats $3,204
Library Holdings: Bk Vols 52,004; Per Subs 340
Special Collections: Cumberland Presbyterian History
Database Vendor: Ebsco - EbscoHost, ProQuest
Partic in West Tennessee Academic Library Consortium

P MCKENZIE MEMORIAL LIBRARY, 15 N Broadway, 38201-2101. SAN 315-8462. Tel: 901-352-5741. *Librn*, Glenda Chambers
Founded 1957. Pop 10,000
Library Holdings: Bk Vols 8,000; Per Subs 32
Subject Interests: History
Mem of Reelfoot Regional Library Center

MC MINNVILLE

P MAGNESS LIBRARY, 118 W Main St, 37110. SAN 315-8470. Tel: 931-473-2428. FAX: 931-473-6778. Web Site: www.mcminnville2000.com. *Dir*, Susan Curtis; E-Mail: scurtis@mail.state.tn.us
Founded 1931. Pop 36,000; Circ 68,000
Library Holdings: Bk Vols 36,000
Special Collections: Porter Henegar Horticulture Coll; Tennessee History & Genealogy Coll
Mem of Caney Fork Regional Library

MEMPHIS

S AMERICAN BLAKE FOUNDATION, Research Library, Campus Box 526176, Dept English, Univ of Memphis, 38152-6176. SAN 370-9787. Tel: 901-678-4510. FAX: 901-678-2226. *Exec Dir*, Kay Easson
Library Holdings: Bk Vols 200

S AMERICAN CONTRACT BRIDGE LEAGUE, Albert H Morehead Memorial Library, 2990 Airways Blvd, 38116-3847. SAN 371-9464. Tel: 901-332-5586. FAX: 901-398-7754. Web Site: www.acbl.org.
Founded 1969
Jan 1998-Oct 1999 Mats Exp $30,000, Books $20,000, Per/Ser (Incl. Access Fees) $10,000. Sal $1,000
Library Holdings: Bk Titles 2,000

R ASCENSION LUTHERAN CHURCH LIBRARY, 961 Getwell Rd, 38111. SAN 315-8586. Tel: 901-327-4103.
Library Holdings: Bk Titles 275

M BAPTIST COLLEGE OF HEALTH SCIENCES, Health Sciences Library, 1003 Monroe, 38104. SAN 360-7232. Tel: 901-227-4307. FAX: 901-227-4310. *Mgr*, Richard Owen; E-Mail: richard.owen@bchs.edu
Founded 1991
1998-1999 Mats Exp $340,000, Books $150,000, Per/Ser (Incl. Access Fees) $80,000, Micro $20,000, Other Print Mats $50,000
Library Holdings: Bk Titles 8,000; Per Subs 400
Partic in Medline; OCLC Online Computer Library Center, Inc

S BUCKEYE TECHNOLOGIES INC, Cellulose & Specialties Technical Information Service, 1001 Tillman St, 38112. SAN 315-8756. Tel: 901-320-8311. FAX: 901-320-8394.
Founded 1954
Library Holdings: Bk Titles 6,000; Per Subs 354
Subject Interests: Cellulose, Polymer chemistry, Pulping tech
Special Collections: Chemistry, bk & film; Pulp & Paper Technology
Partic in Dialog Corporation; Medline

S BUCKMAN LABORATORIES INTERNATIONAL, INC, Knowledge Resource Center, 1256 N McLean Blvd, 38108. SAN 315-8608. Tel: 901-272-8585. Interlibrary Loan Service Tel: 901-272-8378. FAX: 901-272-8583. E-Mail: krc@buckman.com. Web Site: www.buckman.com. *Coll Develop, Mgr*, Cheryl Lamb; E-Mail: cmlamb@buckman.com; *Librn*, Maureen Fitzer; E-Mail: mlfitzer@buckman.com; *Librn*, Octavia Perryman; Tel: 901-272-6522, E-Mail: okperryman@buckman.com. Subject Specialists: *Chemistry*, Octavia Perryman; *Pulp and paper*, Cheryl Lamb; Staff 6 (MLS 3, Non-MLS 3)
Founded 1948
Library Holdings: Bk Titles 20,000; Per Subs 600
Subject Interests: Leather, Microbiology, Paper, Pulp, Specialty chemicals, Water treatment
Database Vendor: Dialog, Lexis-Nexis, OCLC - First Search
Partic in Memphis Area Libr Coun; Solinet

M CAMPBELL FOUNDATION LIBRARY, 910 Madison Ave, Ste 500, 38103-3433. SAN 325-5085. Tel: 901-759-3271. FAX: 901-759-3278. *Librn*, Joan Crowson
Library Holdings: Bk Vols 850; Bk Titles 714; Per Subs 54
Subject Interests: Orthopedics
Partic in Medline; SERMLP

S CENTER FOR SOUTHERN FOLKLORE, Archives & Library, 119 S Main St, 38103. (Mail add: PO Box 226, 38101), SAN 327-6651. Tel: 901-525-3655. FAX: 901-525-9965. Web Site: www.southernfolklore.com. *Exec Dir*, Judy Peiser
Subject Interests: Art
Special Collections: Folk Art Coll, quilts, baskets, sculpture; Reverend L O Taylor Coll, film, photog

CR CHRISTIAN BROTHERS UNIVERSITY, Plough Library, 650 E Pkwy S, 38104. SAN 315-8616. Tel: 901-321-3432. FAX: 901-321-3219. E-Mail: library@cbu.edu. Web Site: www.cbu.edu/library. *Actg Dir*, Floyd Csir; Tel: 901-321-3430, E-Mail: fcsir@cbu.edu; *Cat*, Jane Fleet; Tel: 901-321-3554, E-Mail: jfleet@cbu.edu; *Ref*, Kim Vassiliadis; Tel: 901-32-4355, E-Mail: kvassili@cbu.edu; *Per*, Barbara Hill; Tel: 901-321-3431, E-Mail: bhill@cbu.edu; *AV*, Jerry Swanberry; Tel: 901-321-4220, E-Mail: jswanber@cbu.edu; *Spec Coll & Archives*, Bro Robert Werle; Tel: 901-321-3243, E-Mail: rwerle@cbu.edu; *Circ*, Angelia Sparrow; Tel: 901-321-3554, E-Mail: asparrow@cbu.edu; Staff 8 (MLS 4, Non-MLS 4)
Founded 1871. Enrl 1,800; Fac 109; Highest Degree: Master
Jun 1998-May 1999 Mats Exp $171,500, Books $64,500, Per/Ser (Incl. Access Fees) $71,500, Presv $8,000, AV Equip $25,000, Manuscripts & Archives $2,500. Sal $249,300
Library Holdings: Bk Vols 151,637; Bk Titles 79,584; Per Subs 553
Subject Interests: Education, Engineering, Religion
Special Collections: De La Salle Christian Brothers Midwest Province Archives & Museum Coll; Leslie H Kuehner Napoleon Coll
Automation Activity & Vendor Info: (Acquisitions) DRA; (Cataloging) DRA; (Circulation) DRA; (OPAC) DRA
Database Vendor: DRA, Ebsco - EbscoHost, GaleNet, IAC - Info Trac, OCLC - First Search
Partic in Solinet; Tenn-Share; West Tennessee Academic Library Consortium

C CRICHTON COLLEGE, Oscar White Memorial Library, 3665 Kirby Pkwy, Ste 7, PO Box 757830, 38115. SAN 315-873X. Tel: 901-367-3880. FAX: 901-367-3897. Web Site: www.crichton.edu. *Dir*, Pam Walker; Staff 2 (MLS 1, Non-MLS 1)
Founded 1947. Enrl 850; Fac 42; Highest Degree: Bachelor
Jul 1998-Jun 1999 Mats Exp $70,100, Books $28,000, Per/Ser (Incl. Access Fees) $18,000, Micro $10,000, AV Equip $8,100. Sal $67,752
Library Holdings: Per Subs 361
Subject Interests: Biblical studies, Biology, Bus, English, Organizational mgt, Pre-nursing, Psychology, Teacher educ

GM DEPARTMENT OF VETERANS AFFAIRS, Medical Center Library, 1030 Jefferson Ave, 38104-2193. SAN 315-8861. Tel: 901-523-8990, Ext 5881. FAX: 901-577-7338. *Chief Librn*, Mary Virginia Taylor; E-Mail: taylor.mary_virginia@memphis.va.gov; Staff 3 (MLS 1, Non-MLS 2)
Founded 1941
Library Holdings: Bk Vols 1,408; Per Subs 406
Subject Interests: Medicine, Nursing, Spinal cord injury
Special Collections: Patient Health Education
Partic in Association Of Memphis Area Health Science Libraries; Veterans Affairs Library Network

S DIXON GALLERY & GARDENS LIBRARY, 4339 Park Ave, 38117. SAN 315-8624. Tel: 901-761-5250. FAX: 901-682-0943. E-Mail: adm1@dixon.org. *Coordr*, Jane W Faquin
Founded 1976
2000-2001 Income Parent Institution $5,000. Mats Exp $4,000, Books $2,500, Per/Ser (Incl. Access Fees) $1,000, AV Equip $500
Library Holdings: Bk Vols 5,750; Per Subs 15
Special Collections: Decorative Arts; French & American Impressionist Art; Horticulture; Warda S Stout German Porcelain Coll, bks
Restriction: By appointment only
Function: Archival collection, For research purposes, Photocopies available, Reference only

CR HARDING UNIVERSITY GRADUATE SCHOOL OF RELIGION, L M Graves Memorial Library, 1000 Cherry Rd, 38117. SAN 315-8659. Tel: 901-761-1354. E-Mail: hgslib@hugsr.edu. *Librn*, Don Meredith; *Asst Librn, Tech Servs*, Carisse Berryhill; Staff 4 (MLS 2, Non-MLS 2)
Founded 1958. Enrl 80
1999-2000 Mats Exp $78,429, Books $40,766, Per/Ser (Incl. Access Fees) $31,819, Micro $2,675. Sal $150,838 (Prof $95,525)
Library Holdings: Bk Vols 120,000; Per Subs 683
Subject Interests: Biblical studies, Christian doctrine, Church history, Counseling, Missions, Philosophy, Religious education
Database Vendor: Ebsco - EbscoHost
Partic in SE Libr Network

L HUMPHREYS SCHOOL OF LAW, 3715 Central Ave, 38152. SAN 360-828X. Tel: 901-678-2426. FAX: 901-678-5293. *Dir*, Gregory Laughlin; *As Dir*, Ruth Smith; Staff 15 (MLS 6, Non-MLS 9)
Founded 1963
Library Holdings: Bk Vols 180,379; Per Subs 2,513

S KRAFT FOOD INGREDIENTS CORP, Technical Center Library, 8000 Horizon Center Blvd, 38133. SAN 372-8595. Tel: 901-381-6503. FAX: 90 381-6524. *Librn*, Betty Murphy
Library Holdings: Bk Vols 4,000; Per Subs 50

M LE BONHEUR CHILDREN'S MEDICAL CENTER, Health Sciences Library, 50 N Dunlap Ave, 38103. SAN 324-6949. Tel: 901-572-3167. FA 901-572-5290. E-Mail: haysl@lebonheur.org. *Dir*, Leigh Hays
Founded 1952
Library Holdings: Bk Titles 1,200; Per Subs 140
Subject Interests: Pediatrics
Publications: Guide for users; monthly newsletter
Partic in Docline

C LE MOYNE-OWEN COLLEGE, (HFPL), Hollis F Price Library, 807 Walker Ave, 38126. SAN 315-8675. Tel: 901-942-7384. FAX: 901-942-62 Web Site: www.LeMoyne-owen.edu. *Chief Librn*, Annette C Berhe-Hunt; Staff 5 (MLS 3, Non-MLS 2)
Founded 1870. Enrl 1,050; Fac 70; Highest Degree: Master
1998-1999 Income $210,050, Parent Institution $180,000, Other $30,050. Mats Exp $85,690, Books $30,000, Per/Ser (Incl. Access Fees) $34,000, Micro $9,690, Electronic Ref Mat (Incl. Access Fees) $12,000. Sal $152,0 (Prof $106,000)
Library Holdings: Bk Vols 86,250; Bk Titles 66,000; Per Subs 350
Subject Interests: Afro-Am
Special Collections: Sweeney Coll, bks
Publications: Classified bibliography of Sweeney Coll
Partic in Coop Col Libr Ctr, Inc

G MEMPHIS & SHELBY COUNTY OFFICE OF PLANNING & DEVELOPMENT LIBRARY, City Hall, Rm 442, 125 N Main St, 38103-2084. SAN 325-8866. Tel: 901-576-6763. FAX: 901-576-7188. *Dir*, Terry Emerick
Library Holdings: Bk Titles 2,500

S MEMPHIS BOTANIC GARDEN FOUNDATION, INC, Goldsmith Civic Garden Center - Sybile Malloy Memorial Library, 750 Cherry Rd, 38117. SAN 325-8769. Tel: 901-685-1566. FAX: 901-682-1561.
Founded 1953
Jul 1998-Jun 1999 Mats Exp $700
Library Holdings: Bk Vols 2,000; Per Subs 15
Subject Interests: Horticulture
Restriction: Open to public for reference only

S MEMPHIS BROOKS MUSEUM OF ART LIBRARY, Overton Park, 193 Poplar Ave, 38104. SAN 315-8594. Tel: 901-544-6200. FAX: 901-725-407 E-Mail: brooks@brooksmuseum.org. Web Site: brooksmuseum.org.
Founded 1922
Library Holdings: Bk Vols 6,441; Per Subs 24
Subject Interests: Am Art 19th-20th Centuries, Art history
Special Collections: Decorative Arts Coll; Dr Louis Levey Coll, prints; Kress Coll; Morrie Moss Coll; The Julie Isenberg Coll

S MEMPHIS COLLEGE OF ART, G Pillow Lewis Memorial Library, 1930 Poplar Ave, 38104. SAN 315-8683. Tel: 901-272-5130, 901-272-5131. FA 901-272-6851. E-Mail: library@mca.edu. *Curator*, Bette Callow
Founded 1936. Enrl 325; Fac 39; Highest Degree: Master
1998-1999 Income $22,000. Sal $28,500
Library Holdings: Bk Titles 16,000; Per Subs 100; Spec Interest Per Sub 99
Subject Interests: Fine arts
Automation Activity & Vendor Info: (Cataloging) Sagebrush Corporation (Circulation) Sagebrush Corporation
Partic in Memphis Area Libr Coun; Tenn Share

S MEMPHIS PINK PALACE MUSEUM LIBRARY, 3050 Central Ave, 38111-3399. SAN 315-8705. Tel: 901-320-6368. FAX: 901-320-6391. Web Site: www.memphisguide.com. *Librn*, Daniel Argall; *Coll Develop*, Ron Bristr; E-Mail: rbristr@memphis.magibox.net
Founded 1967
Library Holdings: Bk Titles 5,200
Subject Interests: Archaeology, Astronom, Botany, Geology, History, Zoology
Special Collections: Burge Civil War Coll
Restriction: Open to public for reference only

R MEMPHIS THEOLOGICAL SEMINARY LIBRARY, 168 E Parkway S, 38018. SAN 315-8713. Tel: 901-458-8232. Circulation Tel: 901-458-8232, Ext. 106. Reference Tel: 901-458-8232, Ext 106. FAX: 901-452-4051. E-Mail: library@mtscampus.edu. Web Site: www.mtscampus.edu/library. *Dir*, Michael Richard Strickland; Tel: 901-458-8232, Ext 105, E-Mail: mstrickland@mtscampus.edu; *Publ Servs*, Jane Williamson; Tel: 901-458-8232, Ext 131, E-Mail: jwilliamson@mtscampus.edu; *Cat*, Sandra Leftwich

Tel: 901-458-8232, Ext 136, E-Mail: sleftwich@mtscampus.edu; *Circ*, Melissa Hamlin; Tel: 901-458-8232, Ext 106, E-Mail: mhamlin@mtscampus.edu; *Acq*, Nancy McSpadden; Tel: 901-458-8232, Ext 107, E-Mail: nmcspadden@mtscampus.edu; Staff 5 (MLS 3, Non-MLS 2)
Founded 1956. Enrl 300; Fac 13; Highest Degree: Doctorate
Library Holdings: Bk Vols 80,000; Per Subs 443
Subject Interests: Baptist, Methodism, Presbyterianism
Special Collections: Christian Missions (R Pierce Beaver Coll); Cumberland Presbyterian History; Martin Luther King, Jr., papers
Automation Activity & Vendor Info: (Cataloging) SIRSI; (Circulation) SIRSI; (Course Reserve) SIRSI; (OPAC) SIRSI
Database Vendor: IAC - Info Trac, IAC - SearchBank, OCLC - First Search
Mem of SE Libr Network

MEMPHIS-SHELBY COUNTY PUBLIC LIBRARY & INFORMATION CENTER, (MSCPLIC), 1850 Peabody Ave, 38104-4025. SAN 360-7291. Tel: 901-725-8855. Interlibrary Loan Service Tel: 901-725-8836. FAX: 901-725-8883. Web Site: www.memphislibrary.lib.tn.us. *Dir*, Judith Drescher; E-Mail: drescherj@memphis.lib.tn.us; *Dep Dir*, Sallie Johnson; E-Mail: johnsons@memphis.lib.tn.us; *Adminr*, Curtis Kittrell; Tel: 901-725-8868, E-Mail: kittrellc@memphis.lib.tn.us; *Doc, ILL*, Barbara Shultz; Tel: 901-725-8836, E-Mail: shultzb@memphis.lib.tn.us; *Acq*, Cindy Soenksen; E-Mail: soenksenc@memphis.lib.tn.us; *Cat*, Fay Levine; Tel: 901-729-3760, E-Mail: levinef@memphis.lib.tn.us; *Spec Coll*, James Johnson; Tel: 901-725-8822, E-Mail: johnsonj@memphis.lib.tn.us; *Ch Servs*, Ann Andrews; Tel: 901-725-8819; *Ref*, Ron Reid; Tel: 901-725-8895; *Ad Servs*, Heather Lawson; Tel: 901-725-8879, E-Mail: lawsonh@memphis.lib.tn.us; *Ch Servs*, Linda Gibson; Tel: 901-725-8875, E-Mail: gibsonl@memphis.lib.tn.us; *Coll Develop*, Janet Majilton; Tel: 901-725-8810, E-Mail: majiltonj@memphis.lib.tn.us; Staff 168 (MLS 132, Non-MLS 36)
Founded 1893. Pop 873,458; Circ 3,708,563
Jul 1998-Jun 1999 Income (Main Library and Branch Library) $14,436,735, City $10,125,431, County $3,998,804, Locally Generated Income $312,500. Mats Exp $2,024,939, Books $1,266,836, Per/Ser (Incl. Access Fees) $332,248, AV Equip $367,485, Other Print Mats $58,370
Library Holdings: Bk Vols 1,938,685
Subject Interests: Architecture, Art, Bus, Memphis hist, Mgt, Sci-tech
Special Collections: Afro-American Memphis (Beale Street, WC Handy, J Ashton Hayes, Blair T Hunt, George W Lee, Ethyl Venson Colls); Commerce & Industry (Rees V Downs, Henry A Montgomery Colls); Family History (Duke-Bedford, Farrow, Price-Davis, Trezevant Colls); Folk History (Morris Solomon, WW Busby, John Ogden Carley, Memphis Historical Society Colls); Louise Mercer Coll; Mary Love Coll; Memphis and Shelby County Archives; Photographs (Poland & Coovert Colls); Politics and Government (Samuel Bates, Robert Cohn, Mayer Henry Loeb, Sen Kennth McKellar, Judge John D Martin, Commissioner James Moore, Page/Lenox, Commissioner Jack W Ramsay, Tennessee Valley Authority Colls); Public Health (Memphis Crippled Childern's Hospital School, Rev George C Harris, Yellow Fever Colls); Religion (Rabbi James A Wax); The Arts (Hugh Higbee Huhn, Sarah B Kennedy, Florence McIntyre, Walter Malone, Music Miscellany, Julia Raine, Searcy Family Colls); War History (William W Goodman, Colton Greene, Memphians During War, Memphis Belle, Gideon J Pillow Colls); William Fowler Coll
Automation Activity & Vendor Info: (Acquisitions) DRA; (Cataloging) DRA; (Circulation) DRA; (Serials) DRA
Database Vendor: GaleNet
Publications: Friends Newletter; Getting Ready for Summer; Library Calendar; Library Matters; Program Highlights (channel 18); Staff Newslinc; WYPL Program Guide
Partic in Dialog Corporation; Dow Jones News Retrieval; SE Libr Network
Friends of the Library Group
Branches: 26

ARLINGTON BRANCH, 11968 Walker, Arlington, 38002. SAN 360-7569. Tel: 901-867-2561. FAX: 901-867-3661. Web Site: www.memphislibrary.lib.tn.us. *Branch Mgr*, Alethea Bragg; E-Mail: bragga@memphis.lib.tn.us
Circ 23,721
Library Holdings: Bk Vols 18,035
Database Vendor: GaleNet
Friends of the Library Group

BARTLETT BRANCH, 6382 Stage Rd, Bartlett, 38134. SAN 360-7593. Tel: 901-386-8968. FAX: 901-386-2358. *Branch Mgr*, Gay Harrist; E-Mail: harrista@memphis.lib.tn.us
Circ 397,268
Library Holdings: Bk Vols 104,400
Database Vendor: GaleNet
Friends of the Library Group

CHEROKEE, 3300 Sharpe, 38111. SAN 360-7623. Tel: 901-743-3655. FAX: 901-743-9030. *Branch Mgr*, Sidney Jackson; E-Mail: jacksons@memphis.lib.tn.us
Circ 42,246
Library Holdings: Bk Vols 36,739
Database Vendor: GaleNet

CHILDREN'S, 1850 Peabody, 38104-4025. Tel: 901-725-8819, 901-725-8895. FAX: 901-725-8883. Web Site: www.memphis.library.lib.tn.us. *Br Coordr*, Mary Seratt; E-Mail: serattm@memphis.lib.tn.us
Database Vendor: GaleNet
Friends of the Library Group

COLLIERVILLE BRANCH, 501 Poplar View Pkwy, Collierville, 38017-2635. SAN 360-7658. Tel: 901-853-2333. FAX: 901-854-5893. Web Site: www.memphislibrary.lib.tn.us. *Branch Mgr*, Chris Mitchell
Circ 182,859
Library Holdings: Bk Vols 65,188
Database Vendor: GaleNet
Friends of the Library Group

CORDOVA BRANCH, 1017 N Sanga Rd, Cordova, 38018. SAN 360-7674. Tel: 901-754-8443. FAX: 901-754-6874. *Branch Mgr*, Jane Carter; E-Mail: carterj@memphis.lib.tn.us
Library Holdings: Bk Vols 18,912
Database Vendor: GaleNet
Friends of the Library Group

CRONELIA CRENSHAW BRANCH, 531 Vance Ave, 38126-2116. SAN 360-8131. Tel: 901-525-1643. FAX: 901-525-0390. Web Site: www.memphislibrary.lib.tn.us. *Mgr*, Carmelita Broussard; E-Mail: broussardc@memphis.lib.tn.us
Circ 15,746
Library Holdings: Bk Vols 32,852
Database Vendor: GaleNet

COSSITT LIBRARY, 33 S Front, 38103-2499. SAN 360-7682. Tel: 901-526-1712. FAX: 901-526-0730. Web Site: www.memphislibrary.lib.tn.us. *Librn*, Freda Hopkins; E-Mail: hopkinf@memphis.lib.tn.us
Circ 36,871
Library Holdings: Bk Vols 16,954
Database Vendor: GaleNet

FRAYSER LIBRARY, 3712 Argonne, 38127-4414. SAN 360-7712. Tel: 901-357-4115. FAX: 901-358-0360. Web Site: www.memphislibrary.lib.tn.us. *Mgr*, Wilma Rhea; E-Mail: rheaw@memphis.lib.tn.us
Circ 93,295
Library Holdings: Bk Vols 46,789
Database Vendor: GaleNet
Friends of the Library Group

GASTON PARK, 1040 S Third, 38106-2002. SAN 360-7747. Tel: 901-942-0835. FAX: 901-942-5667. Web Site: www.memphislibrary.lib.tn.us. *Branch Mgr*, Dottie Boggan; E-Mail: boggand@memphis.lib.tn.us
Circ 16,645
Library Holdings: Bk Vols 26,043
Database Vendor: GaleNet
Friends of the Library Group

GERMANTOWN BRANCH, 1925 Exeter Rd, Germantown, 38138-2815. SAN 360-7771. Tel: 901-754-3702. FAX: 901-753-3914. *Branch Mgr*, Jane Carter; E-Mail: carterj@memphis.lib.tn.us
Circ 554,664
Library Holdings: Bk Vols 127,875
Database Vendor: GaleNet
Friends of the Library Group

HIGHLAND, 460 S Highland, 38111. SAN 360-7801. Tel: 901-452-7341. FAX: 901-452-7342. Web Site: www.memphislibrary.lib.tn.us. *Branch Mgr*, Maggie Farmer; E-Mail: farmerm@memphis.lib.tn.us
Circ 127,371
Library Holdings: Bk Vols 53,857
Database Vendor: GaleNet
Friends of the Library Group

HISTORY & TRAVEL, 1850 Peabody, 38104-4025. Tel: 901-725-8821. FAX: 901-725-8883. Web Site: www.memphislibrary.lib.tn.us. *Branch Mgr*, James Johnson; E-Mail: johnsonj@memphis.lib.tn.us
Subject Interests: Genealogy, History, Travel
Special Collections: Memphis Coll
Database Vendor: GaleNet
Friends of the Library Group

HOLLYWOOD, 1530 N Hollywood, 38108. SAN 360-7836. Tel: 901-323-6201. FAX: 901-323-5610. Web Site: www.memphislibrary.lib.tn.us. *Branch Mgr*, Debbie Stevens; E-Mail: stevensd@memphis.lib.tn.us
Circ 41,221
Library Holdings: Bk Vols 40,975
Database Vendor: GaleNet
Friends of the Library Group

HUMANITIES, 1850 Peabody, 38104-4025. Tel: 901-725-8837. FAX: 901-725-8883. Web Site: www.memphislibrary.lib.tn.us. *Branch Mgr*, Gina Milburn; E-Mail: milburng@memphis.lib.tn.us
Database Vendor: GaleNet
Friends of the Library Group

INFO BUS, 3300 Sharpe, 38111. SAN 360-7380. Tel: 901-743-3655. FAX: 901-743-9030. *Mgr*, Richard Saunders
Library Holdings: Bk Titles 30,196
Database Vendor: GaleNet
Friends of the Library Group

LEVI, 3676 S Third St, 38109-8296. SAN 360-7860. Tel: 901-789-3140. FAX: 901-789-3141. Web Site: www.memphislibrary.lib.tn.us. *Branch Mgr*, Margaret Hicks; E-Mail: hicksm@memphis.lib.tn.us
Circ 27,590
Library Holdings: Bk Vols 31,907

Database Vendor: GaleNet
MILLINGTON BRANCH, 4858 Navy Rd, Millington, 38053. SAN 360-7895. Tel: 901-872-1585. FAX: 901-873-2554. Web Site: www.memphislibrary.lib.tn.us. *Branch Mgr*, Stephanie Masin; E-Mail: masins@memphis.lib.tn.us
Circ 144,421
Library Holdings: Bk Vols 50,062
Database Vendor: GaleNet
Friends of the Library Group
NORTH, 1192 Vollintine, 38107-2899. SAN 360-7925. Tel: 901-276-6631. FAX: 901-726-0731. Web Site: www.memphislibrary.lib.tn.us. *Branch Mgr*, Inger Upchurch; E-Mail: upchurchi@memphis.lib.tn.us
Circ 30,222
Library Holdings: Bk Vols 30,159
Database Vendor: GaleNet
PARKWAY VILLAGE, 4655 Knight Arnold Rd, 38118-3234. SAN 360-795X. Tel: 901-363-8923. FAX: 901-794-2344. Web Site: www.memphislibrary.lib.tn.us. *Branch Mgr*, Brian Mitchel
Circ 215,751
Library Holdings: Bk Vols 95,817
Database Vendor: GaleNet
POPLAR-WHITE STATION, 5094 Poplar, 38117-7629. SAN 360-7984. Tel: 901-682-1616. FAX: 901-682-8975. Web Site: www.memphis.lib.tn.us. *Branch Mgr*, Caroline Barnett
Circ 223,550
Library Holdings: Bk Vols 63,322
Database Vendor: GaleNet
Friends of the Library Group
RALEIGH BRANCH, 3157 Powers Rd, 38128. SAN 360-8018. Tel: 901-386-5333. FAX: 901-371-9495. Web Site: www.memphislibrary.lib.tn.us.
Circ 174,056
Library Holdings: Bk Vols 69,640
Database Vendor: GaleNet
RANDOLPH BRANCH, 3752 Given, 38122. SAN 360-8042. Tel: 901-452-1068. FAX: 901-454-9594. Web Site: www.memphislibrary.lib.tn.us. *Branch Mgr*, Stephanie DeClue
Circ 88,915
Library Holdings: Bk Vols 65,594
Database Vendor: GaleNet
SCIENCE, BUSINESS, SOCIAL SCIENCES, 1850 Peabody, 38104-4025. Tel: 901-725-8877. FAX: 901-725-8883. Web Site: www.memphislibrary.lib.tn.us. *Branch Mgr*, Barbara Shultz; E-Mail: shultzb@memphis.lib.tn.us
Subject Interests: Business, Govt publications, Scis, Soc scis
Special Collections: Grants Information Center; Job & Career Centre; Small Business Center
Database Vendor: GaleNet
Friends of the Library Group
SOUTH, 1929 S Third St, 38109. SAN 360-8107. Tel: 901-946-8518. FAX: 901-946-1435. *Branch Mgr*, Pam Nickleberry-Brooks; E-Mail: brooksp@memphis.lib.tn.us
Circ 60,429
Library Holdings: Bk Vols 51,033
Database Vendor: GaleNet
Friends of the Library Group
WHITEHAVEN, 4122 Barton Dr, 38116. SAN 360-8166. Tel: 901-396-9700. FAX: 901-332-6150. Web Site: www.memphislibrary.lib.tn.us. *Branch Mgr*, Verjeana Hunt
Circ 101,754
Library Holdings: Bk Vols 64,970
Database Vendor: GaleNet
Friends of the Library Group
Bookmobiles: 2

M METHODIST HOSPITAL, Leslie M Stratton Medical Library, 1265 Union Ave, 38104-2499. SAN 315-8721. Tel: 901-726-7899. FAX: 901-726-8254. *Librn*, Nancy N Smith; E-Mail: smithn@methodisthealth.org; Staff 1 (MLS 1)
Founded 1951
Library Holdings: Bk Vols 5,000; Bk Titles 1,084; Per Subs 164
Subject Interests: Med sci
Partic in Association Of Memphis Area Health Science Libraries; Medical Libr Asn; Spec Libr Asn; Tennessee Health Science Library Association

S NATIONAL COTTON COUNCIL OF AMERICA LIBRARY, 1918 North Pkwy, 38112. (Mail add: PO Box 820285, 38182-0285), SAN 315-8748. Tel: 901-274-9030. FAX: 901-725-0510. Web Site: www.cotton.org.
Founded 1950
Library Holdings: Bk Vols 500
Subject Interests: Agriculture, Cotton, Econ, Government
Special Collections: History of the National Cotton Council
Publications: Cotton's Week

S NATIONAL HARDWOOD LUMBER ASSOCIATION LIBRARY, PO Box 34518, 38184-0518. SAN 372-9567. Tel: 901-377-1818. FAX: 901-382-6419. E-Mail: nhla@natl.org. Web Site: www.natl.hardwood.org.
Library Holdings: Bk Vols 2,650

A PT BOATS MUSEUM & LIBRARY, 1384 Cordova Cove, Ste 2, 38138-0070. (Mail add: PO Box 38070, 38183-0070), SAN 326-1700. Tel: 901-755-8440. E-Mail: ptboats@aol.com. Web Site: www.ptboats.org. *VPres*, Alyce N Guthrie; *Coordr*, Don Shannon; Tel: 508-678-1100
Founded 1946
Dec 1999-Nov 2000 Mats Exp $450, Books $150, Per/Ser (Incl. Access Fees) $50, Electronic Ref Mat (Incl. Access Fees) $250. Sal $102,000
Library Holdings: Bk Vols 430; Bk Titles 230; Per Subs 20
Special Collections: Two restored PT boats
Publications: The PT Boater (Newsletter)
Restriction: By appointment only
Function: Research library

C RHODES COLLEGE, Burrow Library, 2000 North Pkwy, 38112-1694. SA 315-8810. Tel: 901-843-3900. FAX: 901-843-3404. *Dir*, Lynne M Blair; E-Mail: blair@rhodes.edu; *Asst Dir, Cat*, Emily Flowers; *Acq*, Janet James; *Bibliog Instr, ILL, Ref*, William Short; *Acq, Per*, Diane Dice; *ILL*, Annette Cates; *Archivist*, Elizabeth Kesler; Staff 9 (MLS 9)
Founded 1848. Enrl 1,407; Fac 120; Highest Degree: Bachelor
Library Holdings: Bk Vols 262,000; Per Subs 1,200
Subject Interests: Architecture, Art, Humanities, Music, Relig studies
Special Collections: 19th & 20th Century English & American Literature (Walter Armstrong Rare Book Coll), autographed first editions; Art (Clougl Hansen Art Memorial for Teaching), paintings, objets d'art
Partic in Dialog Corporation; OCLC Online Computer Library Center, Inc; SE Libr Network

M SAINT JUDE CHILDREN'S RESEARCH HOSPITAL, Biomedical Librar 332 N Lauderdale, 38105-2794. SAN 315-8772. Tel: 901-495-3388. Interlibrary Loan Service Tel: 901-495-3389. FAX: 901-495-3117. E-Mail: library@st.jude.org. Web Site: www.stjude.org/library. *Dir*, Jan Orick; Staff (MLS 3, Non-MLS 2)
Founded 1962
Library Holdings: Bk Vols 2,500; Per Subs 500
Subject Interests: Bio-chem, Cancer, Immunology, Molecular biology, Pediatrics, Virology
Publications: Newsletter (quarterly)
Partic in Dialog Corporation; Nat Libr of Med; OCLC Online Computer Library Center, Inc

S SCHERING-PLOUGH HEALTH CARE, INC, Research & Development Library, PO Box 377, 38151-0001. SAN 328-624X. Tel: 901-320-2702. FAX: 901-320-3017. *Librn*, Martha Hurst; E-Mail: martha.hurst@spcorp.co
Library Holdings: Bk Titles 3,000; Per Subs 120

M SEMMES-MURPHEY CLINIC LIBRARY, 930 Madison Ave, Ste 600, 38103. SAN 315-8780. Tel: 901-227-4310, 901-522-7700. FAX: 901-227-4310. *Librn*, Patricia Irby; E-Mail: patricia.irby@bchs.edu
Founded 1961
Library Holdings: Bk Vols 857; Bk Titles 711; Per Subs 27
Subject Interests: Neurology, Neurosurgery

L SHELBY COUNTY LAW LIBRARY, Shelby County Courthouse, 140 Adams Ave, Rm 334, 38103. SAN 315-8691. Tel: 901-527-7041. FAX: 90 522-8935. E-Mail: shelbycountylawlibrary@hotmail.com. Web Site: www.co.shelby.tn.us. *Librn*, Babs Franklin Moore
Library Holdings: Bk Vols 55,000
Special Collections: Early English Law; Early Laws of North Carolina; Statutes at Large for First Congress of the United States

S SMITH & NEPHEW NORTH AMERICA, Corporate Library, 1450 Brook Rd, 38116. SAN 370-5218. Tel: 901-396-2121, Ext 5100. FAX: 901-348-6097. *Librn*, Julie Edrington
Special Collections: Orthopaedics
Partic in Dialog Corporation; SE Libr Network

CM SOUTHERN COLLEGE OF OPTOMETRY LIBRARY, 1245 Madison Av 38104. SAN 315-8802. Tel: 901-722-3237. FAX: 901-722-3292. *Dir*, Nanc Gatlin; Staff 2 (MLS 2)
Founded 1938. Enrl 485; Fac 46; Highest Degree: Doctorate
Jul 1999-Jun 2000 Income $249,234. Mats Exp $47,683, Books $20,442, Per/Ser (Incl. Access Fees) $27,241. Sal $124,762 (Prof $91,047)
Library Holdings: Bk Vols 15,559; Per Subs 174
Subject Interests: Ophthalmology, Optics, Optometry
Partic in Association Of Memphis Area Health Science Libraries; Association of Vision Science Librarians (AVSL)
Produce the Visionet online index of vision literature citations which contains citations not covered by other indices, available on the Internet at visionet.sco.edu

J SOUTHWEST TENNESSEE COMMUNITY COLLEGE, (Formerly State Technical Institute at Memphis), George E Freeman Library, 5983 Macon Cove, 38134. SAN 315-8829. Tel: 901-333-4105. FAX: 901-333-4566. *Dir* Rosa Scott Burnett; Tel: 901-333-4106, E-Mail: rburnett@mail.stim.tec.tn.u *Librn*, Stephen Beeko; E-Mail: sbeeko@mail.stim.tec.tn.us; *Assoc Librn*, Virginia Anne Howard; E-Mail: ahoward@mail.stim.tec.tn.us; *Circ*, Lisa Lumpkin; E-Mail: llumpkin@mail.stim.tec.tn.us; *Per*, Mary N Phillips; Tel: 901-333-4649, E-Mail: mphillips@mail.stim.tec.tn.us; *Cat*, Emmer T Swauncy; Tel: 901-333-4437, E-Mail: eswauncy@mail.stim.tec.tn.us. Subje

Specialists: *Pub servs tech*, Virginia Anne Howard; Staff 7 (MLS 3, Non-MLS 4)
Founded 1967. Enrl 10,500; Highest Degree: Associate
Jul 1998-Jun 1999 Income $485,583. Mats Exp $186,048, Books $90,695, Per/Ser (Incl. Access Fees) $30,698, Micro $24,186, Electronic Ref Mat (Incl. Access Fees) $40,469. Sal $244,299 (Prof $124,806)
Library Holdings: Bk Vols 42,033; Per Subs 185
Subject Interests: Computer, Engineering
Special Collections: Computer Literacy Coll; Olin F Morris Coll; Tennessee Coll
Automation Activity & Vendor Info: (Cataloging) DRA; (Circulation) DRA; (Course Reserve) DRA; (ILL) DRA; (OPAC) DRA; (Serials) DRA
Database Vendor: Lexis-Nexis, OCLC - First Search, ProQuest
Publications: Business Information Sources (library handbook)

SOUTHWEST TENNESSEE COMMUNITY COLLEGE LIBRARY, (Formerly Shelby State Community College Library), PO Box 40568, 38174-0568. SAN 315-8799. Tel: 901-333-5135. FAX: 901-333-5141. Web Site: www.stcc.cc.tn.library. *Dir*, Vivian Stewart; E-Mail: vstewart@sscc.cc.tn.us; *Ref*, Regina Massey-Hicks; Staff 5 (MLS 2, Non-MLS 3)
Founded 1972. Enrl 4,000; Fac 200
Library Holdings: Bk Vols 49,818; Bk Titles 42,493; Per Subs 426
Subject Interests: Allied health, Behav sci, Education, Ethnic studies, Soc sci
Automation Activity & Vendor Info: (Circulation) DRA
Database Vendor: DRA, IAC - Info Trac, IAC - SearchBank, Wilson - Wilson Web
Partic in TBR Consortium
Friends of the Library Group

THE COMMERCIAL APPEAL NEWS LIBRARY, 495 Union Ave, 38103. SAN 325-3627. Tel: 901-529-2781. FAX: 901-529-6460. E-Mail: library@gomemphis.com. Web Site: www.gomemphis.com. *Dir*, Rosemary Nelms; *Asst Dir*, Gregory Paraham; *Librn*, Jan Smith; *Librn*, Shirley Sykes; Staff 4 (MLS 4)
Founded 1986
Library Holdings: Bk Titles 2,000; Per Subs 200
Special Collections: Clipping Coll
Database Vendor: Dialog, Lexis-Nexis, ProQuest
Publications: The Commercial Appeal
Partic in Tenn-Share

UNITED STATES ARMY
CORPS OF ENGINEERS, MEMPHIS DISTRICT LIBRARY, 167 N Main St, 38103. SAN 360-8379. Tel: 901-544-3584, 901-544-3620. FAX: 901-544-4106.
Founded 1932
Library Holdings: Bk Titles 5,850; Per Subs 275
Subject Interests: Civil engineering, Econ, Environmental studies, Hydrol, Lower Miss Valley, Water resources
Publications: Periodical List
Restriction: Open to public for reference only
Partic in Dialog Corporation; Fedlink; OCLC Online Computer Library Center, Inc

THE UNIVERSITY OF MEMPHIS LIBRARIES, Acquisitions Department, 126 Ned R McWherter Library, 38152-3250. SAN 360-8190. Tel: 901-678-2207. Interlibrary Loan Service Tel: 901-678-2262. Circulation Tel: 901-678-2205. Reference Tel: 901-678-2208. FAX: 901-678-8218. Interlibrary Loan Service FAX: 901-678-8218. Web Site: www.lib.memphis.edu. *Dir*, Lester J Pourciau; *Dean*, Dr Sylverna V Ford; Tel: 901-678-2201, E-Mail: sford@memphis.edu; *Assoc Dean*, Annelle Ralph Huggins; Tel: 901-678-4482, E-Mail: ahuggins@memphis.edu; *Librn*, Lan-Seng Chung; Tel: 901-678-2007, E-Mail: lachung@memphis.edu; *ILL*, Elizabeth Buck; *ILL*, Wayne Key; Fax: 901-678-2511, E-Mail: wkey@memphis.edu; *Head, Acq*, Ian M Edward; Tel: 901-678-2203, E-Mail: imedward@memphis.edu; *Head, Cat*, Dr Phillip M Smith; Tel: 901-678-2214, E-Mail: psmith@memphis.edu; *Spec Coll & Archives*, Edwin G Frank; Tel: 901-678-2210, E-Mail: efrank@memphis.edu; *Bibliog Instr*, Janell Rudolph; E-Mail: nrudolph@memphis.edu; *Head, Circ*, Stacey J Smith; Tel: 901-678-2205, E-Mail: sjsmith@memphis.edu; *Head, Ser Acq*, Rita Broadway; Tel: 901-678-2204, E-Mail: rbroadway@memphis.edu; *Govt Doc*, Saundra Williams; Tel: 901-678-2206, E-Mail: swilliams@memphis.edu; *Head Ref*, Elizabeth Park; E-Mail: ehpark@memphis.edu; *Br Coordr*, Anna B Neal; Tel: 901-678-2330, E-Mail: abneal@memphis.edu; Staff 111 (MLS 29, Non-MLS 82)
Founded 1914. Enrl 15,951; Fac 735; Highest Degree: Doctorate
Jul 2000-Jun 2001 Income (Main Library and Branch Library) Parent Institution $6,856,075. Mats Exp $2,852,599, Books $414,446, Per/Ser (Incl. Access Fees) $2,096,285, Presv $52,927, Micro $135,046, Electronic Ref Mat (Incl. Access Fees) $153,895. Sal $2,590,485 (Prof $1,021,478)
Library Holdings: Bk Vols 1,085,886; Per Subs 8,005
Special Collections: 1968 Memphis Sanitation Strike Coll; 19th & 20th Century US & European Theatre History Coll; 20th Century American Circus Coll; Confederate Historical Association Coll; Edmund Orgill Coll; Edward Meeman Coll; Election Campaign Material, local, state & national; Ethnic Populations for the Mid-south; Freedman's Bureau of the US War Department; Jefferson Davis-Joel Addison Hayes Family Coll; Jesse Hill Ford Coll; John Faulkner Coll; Lower Mississippi Delta Development Center, papers; Lower Mississippi Valley History, Literature & Culture, bks, pamphlets, mss, photogs, maps, ephemera, audio & video tapes, films & sheet music; Margaret Polk Coll (Memphis Bell), scrapbks; Memphis Commercial Appeal Coll, photogs; Memphis Typographical Union Coll; Mississippi River Boatmen; Oral Histories - Blues & Jazz; Overton Park Expressway Controversy Coll; Press Scimitar, clipping file; Public Management Science Coll; Robert R Church Family Coll; Rock & Roll & Elvis Presley (Jerry Hopkins Coll); Southern Writers; Tennessee Politicians; Tennessee Valley Authority; US Regional; Watkins Overton Coll; West Tennessee Historical Society (Elizabeth Avery Meriwether Family Coll); Women Leaders of Memphis
Automation Activity & Vendor Info: (Acquisitions) DRA; (Cataloging) DRA; (Circulation) DRA; (Course Reserve) DRA; (OPAC) DRA; (Serials) DRA
Database Vendor: CARL, Dialog, DRA, GaleNet, IAC - Info Trac, Lexis-Nexis, OCLC - First Search, ProQuest, Silverplatter Information Inc.
Publications: The UOML News (Newsletter)
Partic in Association Of Southeastern Research Libraries (ASERL); OCLC Online Computer Library Center, Inc; Solinet; Tenn Acad Libr Collaborative; Tenn Share
Special Services for the Blind - Kurzweil Reading Machine
Agent for Tennessee Union List of Serials via OCLC
Friends of the Library Group
Departmental Libraries:
AUDIOLOGY & SPEECH LANGUAGE PATHOLOGY, 807 Jefferson, 38152. SAN 360-8344. Tel: 901-678-5846. FAX: 901-678-8218. *In Charge*, John Swearengen; E-Mail: jmswrngn@memphis.edu
Library Holdings: Bk Vols 7,718; Per Subs 83
CHEMISTRY, Smith Hall, Rm 316, 38152. SAN 360-8220. Tel: 901-678-2625. FAX: 901-678-8218. *In Charge*, John Barnett; E-Mail: jbarnett@memphis.edu
Library Holdings: Bk Vols 33,010; Per Subs 183
EARTH SCIENCES, Center for Earthquake Research & Information, 38152. SAN 373-5559. Tel: 901-678-2007. *Librn*, Lan-Seng Chung; E-Mail: lachung@memphis.edu
Library Holdings: Bk Vols 17,174; Per Subs 75
Subject Interests: Earthquake educ, Earthquake eng, Geology, Geophysics, Seismology
MATHEMATICS, Dunn Hall, Rm 341, 38152. SAN 373-5540. Tel: 901-678-2385. FAX: 901-678-8218. *In Charge*, Carol Washington; E-Mail: cjwshngt@memphis.edu
Library Holdings: Bk Vols 29,005; Per Subs 227
MUSIC, Music Bldg, Rm 115, 38152. SAN 360-831X. Tel: 901-678-2330. FAX: 901-678-3096. *Br Coordr, Librn*, Anna Neal; E-Mail: abneal@memphis.edu
Library Holdings: Bk Vols 40,424; Per Subs 195

CM UNIVERSITY OF TENNESSEE - MEMPHIS, Health Sciences Library & Biocommunications Center, 877 Madison Ave, 38163. SAN 360-8409. Tel: 901-448-5638. FAX: 901-448-6855. Web Site: library.utmem.edu. *Dir*, Thomas Singarella; *Spec Coll*, Susan A Selig; *Coll Develop*, Anne Carroll Bunting; *Ref*, Richard Nollan; *Ref*, Priscilla Stevenson; *Instrul Serv*, Brenda Green; *Electronic Resources*, Lois Bellamy; Staff 27 (MLS 11, Non-MLS 16)
Founded 1913. Enrl 2,600; Fac 790; Highest Degree: Doctorate
Jul 1998-Jun 1999 Mats Exp $732,000, Books $22,000, Per/Ser (Incl. Access Fees) $652,265, Presv $5,000, AV Equip $5,000, Other Print Mats $700,000. Sal $865,435
Library Holdings: Bk Vols 182,638; Bk Titles 48,760; Per Subs 1,350
Subject Interests: Allied health, Dentistry, Medicine, Nursing, Pharm, Soc work
Special Collections: History of Medicine; Tennessee Authors (Wallace Memorial Coll)
Partic in Dialog Corporation; Nat Libr of Med; SE Libr Network; Southeastern Regional Med Libr Program

L WARING COX, Law Library, 50 N Front St, Ste 1300, 38103-1190. SAN 371-5957. Tel: 901-543-8000, 901-543-8194. FAX: 901-543-8030. *Librn*, Donna Windham; E-Mail: dwindham@waringcox.com; Staff 1 (Non-MLS 1)
Library Holdings: Bk Vols 10,000; Per Subs 250

MIDDLETON

P MIDDLETON COMMUNITY LIBRARY, 100 N Main St, 38052-3403. SAN 376-7035. Tel: 731-376-0680. FAX: 731-376-0680. Web Site: www.state.tn.us/cgi-bin/library. *Dir*, Diana Hunter
1998-1999 Income $15,485, State $3,550, City $7,375, Federal $2,260, County $2,300
Library Holdings: Bk Titles 5,000; Per Subs 12
Mem of Shiloh Regional Library
Friends of the Library Group

MILAN

P MILDRED G FIELDS LIBRARY, Milan Public Library, 1075A E Vanhook St, 38358-2892. SAN 315-8888. Tel: 901-686-8268. FAX: 901-686-3207.
Dir, Dot Bruce
Founded 1950. Pop 4,500; Circ 33,425
Library Holdings: Bk Vols 40,000; Per Subs 50
Friends of the Library Group

MILLIGAN COLLEGE

C MILLIGAN COLLEGE, P H Welshimer Memorial Library, Blowers Blvd, PO Box 600, 37682. SAN 315-8896. Tel: 423-461-8703. FAX: 423-461-8984. *Dir*, Steven L Preston; E-Mail: slpreston@milligan.edu; *Ref*, Nancy McKee; Tel: 423-461-8900, E-Mail: nmckee@milligan.edu; Staff 6 (MLS 3, Non-MLS 3)
Founded 1881. Enrl 892; Fac 79; Highest Degree: Master
Jun 1998-May 1999 Income $287,107
Library Holdings: Bk Vols 109,881; Per Subs 547
Subject Interests: Education, Humanities, Relig studies
Special Collections: Restoration History (Restoration of New Testament Christianity)
Automation Activity & Vendor Info: (Acquisitions) Innovative Interfaces Inc.; (Cataloging) Innovative Interfaces Inc.; (Circulation) Innovative Interfaces Inc.; (Course Reserve) Innovative Interfaces Inc.; (ILL) Innovative Interfaces Inc.; (Media Booking) Innovative Interfaces Inc.; (OPAC) Innovative Interfaces Inc.; (Serials) Innovative Interfaces Inc.
Partic in Holston Assoc Librs, Inc; OCLC Online Computer Library Center, Inc; SE Libr Network

MINOR HILL

P MINOR HILL COMMUNITY LIBRARY, 108 Pickett Dr, 38473. SAN 315-890X. Tel: 931-565-3699. FAX: 931-565-3114. E-Mail: mhlib.l@usit.net. Web Site: www.state.tn.us/. *Dir*, Elizabeth Norwood
Circ 7,028
Library Holdings: Bk Vols 1,575
Mem of Blue Grass Regional Library
Open Mon-Fri 4-8 & Sat 9-12

MONTEAGLE

P MAY JUSTUS MEMORIAL LIBRARY, 24 Dixie Lee Ave, 37356. (Mail add: PO Box 78, 37356), SAN 315-8918. Tel: 931-924-2638. FAX: 931-924-3628. E-Mail: mayjustuslib@blomand.net. Web Site: sites.netscape.net/grundylibraries/mjml. *Librn*, Karen Tittle; Staff 1 (Non-MLS 1)
Founded 1960. Pop 1,500; Circ 18,000
Library Holdings: Bk Titles 800
Database Vendor: GaleNet
Mem of Caney Fork Regional Library
Friends of the Library Group

MORRISTOWN

P MORRISTOWN-HAMBLEN COUNTY PUBLIC LIBRARY, 417 W Main St, 37814-4686. SAN 315-8942. Tel: 423-586-6410. FAX: 615-587-6226. E-Mail: mhamblen@mail.state.tn.us. Web Site: www.state.tn.us/cgi-bin/library. *Dir*, Ann C Steffen; *Asst Librn*, Sally Inman
Founded 1925. Pop 53,132; Circ 236,000
Jul 1998-Jun 1999 Income $411,177, City $191,777, County $183,500, Other $35,900. Mats Exp $72,026. Sal $202,575
Library Holdings: Bk Titles 113,183; Per Subs 185
Special Collections: History & Genealogy (Meta Turley Goodson Room), bks, microforms & per
Mem of Nolichucky Regional Library
Special Services for the Deaf - High interest/low vocabulary books
Friends of the Library Group
Branches: 1
DAVIS HOMES BRANCH LIBRARY, 1149 Kennedy Circle, 37814-5406. SAN 324-3281. Tel: 423-581-3413. E-Mail: dhl@lcs.net. *Dir*, Nancy Mueller
Library Holdings: Bk Titles 5,000
Special Collections: Coin Coll
Special Services for the Deaf - Captioned film depository; High interest/low vocabulary books
Library has outreach program at three Headstart Centers: Morristown Hamblen Day Care Center, Life Care Center of Morristown, Girls Club, Hamblen County Jail & Heritage Center
Friends of the Library Group

P NOLICHUCKY REGIONAL LIBRARY, 315 McCrary Dr, 37814. SAN 315-8950. Tel: 423-586-6251. FAX: 423-586-7741. Web Site: www.state.tn.us/sos/statelib/p&d/nolichucky/index.htm. *Dir*, Donald B Reynolds, Jr; E-Mail: dreynolds2@mail.state.tn.us; Staff 7 (MLS 2, Non-MLS 5)
Founded 1941. Pop 270,512; Circ 818,120
Jul 1999-Jun 2000 Income $433,395, State $381,145, Federal $48,472, Oth $3,778. Mats Exp $139,108, Books $128,750, Per/Ser (Incl. Access Fees) $3,352. Sal $192,544 (Prof $82,272)
Library Holdings: Bk Vols 168,698; Per Subs 66
Special Collections: Business Coll; Head Start Resource Coll; Professiona Library Coll; Rural Coll
Restriction: Not a lending library, Not open to public
Member Libraries: Anna Porter Public Library; Bean Station Public Library; Cocke County Library System; Cosby Community Library; Dandridge Memorial Library; Grainger County Library; Grainger County Library System; H B Stamps Memorial Library; Hamblen County Library System; Hancock County Public Library; Hawkins County Library System Jefferson City Public Library; Jefferson County Library System; Marie Ellison Memorial Library; Morristown-Hamblen County Public Library; Nolichucky Regional Library Center; Parrott-Wood Memorial Library; Parrottsville Public Library; Saint Clair Library; Sevier County Library System; Sevier County Public Library; Sevier County Public Library; Stokely Memorial Library; Surgoinsville Public Library; Washburn Public Library; White Pine Public Library
Bookmobiles: 2

J WALTERS STATE COMMUNITY COLLEGE LIBRARY, 500 S Davy Crockett Pkwy, 37813-6899. SAN 315-8969. Tel: 423-585-6902. Circulatio Tel: 423-585-6903. Reference Tel: 423-585-6946. FAX: 423-585-6959. We Site: www.wscc.cc.tn.us/library. *Bibliog Instr, Dir*, Douglas Cross; E-Mail: doug.cross@wscc.cc.tn.us; *Publ Servs, Ref*, James Damewood; E-Mail: james.damewood@wscc.cc.tn.us; *Circ*, Shirley Parker; E-Mail: shirley.parker@wscc.cc.tn.us; *Ref*, Samuel Richardson; E-Mail: samuel.richardson@wscc.cc.tn.us; Staff 4 (MLS 4)
Founded 1970. Highest Degree: Associate
Jul 1999-Jun 2000 Income $477,741. Mats Exp $215,699, Books $18,698, Per/Ser (Incl. Access Fees) $22,789, Electronic Ref Mat (Incl. Access Fees $57,738. Sal $262,042 (Prof $186,200)
Library Holdings: Bk Vols 47,559; Bk Titles 41,264; Per Subs 189; Spec Interest Per Sub 189
Automation Activity & Vendor Info: (Acquisitions) TLC; (Cataloging) TLC; (Circulation) TLC; (Course Reserve) TLC; (OPAC) TLC
Database Vendor: Ebsco - EbscoHost, GaleNet, OCLC - First Search
Partic in Solinet

MOSHEIM

P MOSHEIM PUBLIC LIBRARY, 1030 Main St, 37818-0611. SAN 376-2971. Tel: 423-422-7937. FAX: 423-422-6492. Web Site: www.mosheinlib.org. *Dir*, Mary Ann Rush; E-Mail: marush@mosheimlib.o
Library Holdings: Bk Titles 9,500
Mem of Watauga Regional Library Center

MOUNT CARMEL

P MOUNT CARMEL LIBRARY, 100 Main St, 37645-9999. SAN 376-6330. Tel: 423-357-4011. FAX: 423-357-4011. *Dir*, Marsha McClellan
Library Holdings: Bk Vols 5,000
Friends of the Library Group

MOUNT JULIET

P MOUNT JULIET-WILSON COUNTY PUBLIC, 2765 N Mount Juliet Rd, 37122. (Mail add: PO Box 319, 37122-0319), SAN 360-7143. Tel: 615-754-7051. FAX: 615-754-2439. E-Mail: mjlibrary@tds.net. *Dir*, Nancy Armstrong
Library Holdings: Bk Titles 40,000
Friends of the Library Group

MOUNTAIN CITY

P JOHNSON COUNTY PUBLIC LIBRARY, 219 N Church St, PO Box 107 37683-1522. SAN 315-8977. Tel: 423-727-6544. FAX: 423-727-0319. E-Mail: aopal2i@tricon.net. Web Site: pages.preffered.com/~jcwc/. *Dir*, Linda Icenhour
Pop 13,745
Library Holdings: Bk Vols 15,000; Per Subs 15
Mem of Watauga Regional Library Center
Friends of the Library Group

MOUNTAIN HOME

GM JAMES H QUILLEN VA MEDICAL CENTER, Medical Center Library, 37684. SAN 315-8985. Tel: 423-926-1171, Ext 7454. FAX: 423-232-6940. *Librn*, Patsy Ellis
Founded 1904
Library Holdings: Bk Vols 2,946; Per Subs 238
Partic in Vets Admin Libr Network

UNFORD

MUNFORD-TIPTON MEMORIAL LIBRARY, 87 College St, 38058-1902. SAN 376-7566. Tel: 901-837-2665. E-Mail: munford@bigriver.net. *Dir*, Geraldine Simmons
Library Holdings: Bk Vols 900
Mem of Forked Deer Regional Library Center

URFREESBORO

M ALVIN C YORK VETERANS ADMINISTRATION MEDICAL CENTER, Library Service (142D), 37129. SAN 315-9019. Tel: 615-893-1360, Ext 6142. FAX: 615-867-5778. *In Charge*, Katie Burnham; Staff 2 (MLS 1, Non-MLS 1)
Library Holdings: Bk Vols 5,900; Per Subs 300
Subject Interests: Clinical medicine, Geriatrics, Nursing, Psychiatry
Partic in OCLC Online Computer Library Center, Inc; Veterans Affairs Library Network

FIRST BAPTIST CHURCH LIBRARY, 200 E Main St, 37130. SAN 315-8993. Tel: 615-893-2514. FAX: 615-895-5804. *Librn*, Juana Cates; Staff 19 (MLS 4, Non-MLS 15)
Founded 1943
Library Holdings: Bk Vols 18,398; Per Subs 31
Subject Interests: Church curriculum, Relig studies
Special Collections: Children's Coll

HIGHLAND RIM REGIONAL LIBRARY CENTER, 2118 E Main St, 37130. SAN 315-9000. Tel: 615-893-3380. FAX: 615-895-6727. E-Mail: dskousen@mail.state.tn.us. *Dir*, Diana Skousen
Founded 1945. Pop 421,663; Circ 1,943,020
Jul 1999-Jun 2000 Income $503,475, State $482,024, Federal $21,451. Mats Exp $100,698, Books $100,448, Per/Ser (Incl. Access Fees) $250
Library Holdings: Bk Vols 216,514
Member Libraries: Adams Memorial Library; Argie Cooper Public Library; Coffee County Lannom Memorial Public Library; Coffee County-Manchester Library; Eagleville Bicentennial Public Library; Fayetteville-Lincoln County Public Library; Franklin County Library; Fred A Vaught Memorial Library; La Vergne Public Library; Lebanon-Wilson County Library; Moore County Public Library; Rutherford County Library System
Bookmobiles: 1

MIDDLE TENNESSEE STATE UNIVERSITY, Central Library, MTSU, PO Box 13, 37132. SAN 360-8522. Tel: 615-898-2772. Interlibrary Loan Service Tel: 615-898-5104. Circulation Tel: 615-898-2650. Reference Tel: 615-898-2817. FAX: 615-898-5551. Web Site: www.mtsu.edu/~library/. *Dean of Libr*, J Donald Craig; E-Mail: dcraig@ulibnet.mtsu.edu; *Asst Dean*, Julie A Hight; Tel: 615-898-2521; *Acq*, Joyce Lane; *Circ*, Diane Baird; Tel: 615-898-2539; *Per*, Peggy Colflesh; *Cat*, Sue Burkheart; Tel: 615-904-8517, E-Mail: sburkheart@ulibnet.mtsu.edu; *Cat*, Molly Holland; Tel: 615-904-8518, E-Mail: mholland@ulibnet.mtsu.edu; *Govt Doc*, In MacBeth; Tel: 615-904-8519; *Automation Syst Coordr*, David Robinson; Tel: 615-898-2572, E-Mail: robinson@ulibnet.mtsu.edu; *Coll Develop*, Virginia Vesper; Tel: 615-898-2806, E-Mail: vvesper@ulibnet.mtsu.edu; *Syst Coordr*, Mike Wheaton; Tel: 615-898-5043, E-Mail: wheaton@ulibnet.mtsu.edu; Staff 25 (MLS 25)
Founded 1911. Enrl 15,455; Fac 794; Highest Degree: Doctorate
Library Holdings: Bk Vols 642,018; Bk Titles 467,957; Per Subs 3,427
Special Collections: Tennesseana
Publications: Todd Library Update
Partic in Athena; OCLC Online Computer Library Center, Inc

MIDDLE TENNESSEE STATE UNIVERSITY-CENTER FOR POPULAR MUSIC, (CPM), 140 Mass Communications Bldg, MTSU, 37132. (Mail add: PO Box 41, MTSU, 37132), SAN 323-8199. Tel: 615-898-2449. Reference Tel: 615-898-5513. FAX: 615-898-5829. E-Mail: ctrpopmu@mtsu.edu. Web Site: popmusic.mtsu.edu. *Dir*, Paul Wells; E-Mail: pfwells@mtsu.edu; *Coordr*, Mayo R Taylor; Tel: 615-898-5512, E-Mail: taylorm@mtsu.edu; *Archivist*, David J Jellema; Tel: 615-898-5900, E-Mail: djellema@mtsu.edu; *Media Spec*, Bruce Nemerov; Tel: 615-898-5509, E-Mail: bnemerov@mtsu.edu; Staff 8 (MLS 2, Non-MLS 6)
Founded 1985. Enrl 18,000; Fac 600; Highest Degree: Doctorate
Library Holdings: Bk Titles 15,800; Per Subs 316; Spec Interest Per Sub 316
Subject Interests: Am music, Popular music, Religious music
Special Collections: Alfred Moffatt Coll of Music Books; American Broadside & Songsters; Black Harmony Singing; Denominational Hymnals & gosspel songbooks; Kenneth Goldstein Coll of American Broadsides & songsters; Ray Avery (jazz, black)
Automation Activity & Vendor Info: (OPAC) Endeavor; (Serials) Endeavor
Restriction: Not a lending library
Function: For research purposes
Partic in SE Libr Network; Solinet

RUTHERFORD COUNTY LIBRARY SYSTEM, Linebaugh Public Library, 105 W Vine, 37130-3673. SAN 360-8581. Tel: 615-893-4131. FAX: 615-848-5038. Web Site: www.linebaugh.org. *Dir*, Laurel Best; E-Mail: lbest@tsla.lib.tn.us, lbest@linebaugh.org
Pop 145,000; Circ 650,000
Jul 2000-Jun 2001 Income $1,065,232, City $444,369, County $560,000, Locally Generated Income $33,600, Other $27,263. Mats Exp $161,100, Books $143,200, Per/Ser (Incl. Access Fees) $17,900. Sal $675,630
Library Holdings: Bk Titles 145,000; Per Subs 80
Subject Interests: Genealogy, Local history
Automation Activity & Vendor Info: (Acquisitions) SIRSI; (Cataloging) SIRSI; (Circulation) SIRSI; (OPAC) SIRSI
Mem of Highland Rim Regional Library Center
Friends of the Library Group
Branches: 1
SMYRNA PUBLIC LIBRARY, 400 Enon Springs Rd W, Smyrna, 37167. SAN 360-8611. Tel: 615-459-4884. FAX: 615-459-2370. Web Site: www.linebaugh.org. *Librn*, Donna George; *Ch Servs, YA Servs*, Cee Cee Doyle
Jul 2000-Jun 2001 Income $369,780, City $170,220, County $169,360, Locally Generated Income $30,200. Mats Exp $57,500, Books $50,000, Per/Ser (Incl. Access Fees) $7,500. Sal $221,395
Library Holdings: Bk Vols 50,000; Per Subs 60
Friends of the Library Group

NASHVILLE

S THE AEROSTRUCTURES CORPORATION, Technical Library, 1431 Vultee Blvd, 37217. SAN 371-5922. Tel: 615-360-4043. FAX: 615-361-2752. *Senior Librn*, Jan Haley; E-Mail: jhaley@theaerocorp.com
Library Holdings: Bk Titles 697; Per Subs 172
Subject Interests: Engineering
Automation Activity & Vendor Info: (Acquisitions) Inmagic, Inc.; (Cataloging) Inmagic, Inc.; (Circulation) Inmagic, Inc.; (Serials) Inmagic, Inc.
Publications: EDG Newsletter (monthly)
Partic in SE Libr Network

R AMERICAN BAPTIST COLLEGE OF THE AMERICAN BAPTIST THEOLOGICAL SEMINARY, TL Holcomb Library, 1800 Baptist World Center Dr, 37207-4994. SAN 315-9027. Tel: 615-228-7877. FAX: 615-226-7855. *Librn*, Ibiba Okpara; Staff 1 (MLS 1)
Founded 1924
Library Holdings: Bk Vols 40,000; Per Subs 200
Subject Interests: Ethnic studies, Relig studies
Publications: IMPRINTS
Friends of the Library Group

M BAPTIST HOSPITAL, Medical Library, 2000 Church St, 37236. SAN 315-9051. Tel: 615-284-5373. FAX: 615-284-5861. *Librn*, Marilyn Teolis; E-Mail: marilynt@baptist-hosp.org
Founded 1948
Library Holdings: Bk Vols 4,250; Per Subs 243
Subject Interests: Clinical medicine, Consumer health, Health care mgt, Nursing
Special Collections: Internal Medicine emphasis
Publications: Newsletter
Partic in Nat Libr of Med; OCLC Online Computer Library Center, Inc
Open Mon-Fri 8-5

C BEAMAN LIBRARY, Lipscomb Univ, 3901 Granny White Pike, 37204-3951. SAN 315-9094. Tel: 615-269-1793. Reference Tel: 615-279-6037. FAX: 615-269-1807. Web Site: library.lipscomb.edu. *Dir*, Carolyn T Wilson; Tel: 615-279-5837, E-Mail: carolyn.wilson@lipscomb.edu; *Bibliog Instr, Circ*, Judy M Butler; Tel: 615-279-5717, E-Mail: judy.butler@lipscomb.edu; *Ser*, David N Howard; Tel: 615-279-5763, E-Mail: david.howard@lipscomb.edu; *Tech Coordr*, Eunice F Wells; Tel: 615-279-5836, E-Mail: eunice.wells@lipscomb.edu; *Cat*, Leah P Hamrick; Tel: 615-279-5803, E-Mail: leah.hamrick@lipscomb.edu; *Ref*, Marie P Byers; Tel: 615-279-5719, E-Mail: marie.byers@lipscomb.edu; Staff 10 (MLS 6, Non-MLS 4)
Founded 1891. Enrl 2,600; Fac 133; Highest Degree: Master
Jun 1999-May 2000 Income Parent Institution $351,104. Mats Exp $322,000, Books $101,400, Per/Ser (Incl. Access Fees) $117,000, Electronic Ref Mat (Incl. Access Fees) $17,000
Library Holdings: Bk Titles 235,000; Per Subs 890
Subject Interests: Bibliog instruction, Preservation, Religion, Technology
Special Collections: Bailey Hymnology Coll (approx 2500 vols); C E W Dorris Coll; Herald of Truth videotapes
Automation Activity & Vendor Info: (Acquisitions) Innovative Interfaces Inc.; (Cataloging) Innovative Interfaces Inc.; (Circulation) Innovative Interfaces Inc.; (Course Reserve) Innovative Interfaces Inc.; (OPAC) Innovative Interfaces Inc.; (Serials) Innovative Interfaces Inc.
Database Vendor: Dialog, GaleNet, IAC - Info Trac, OCLC - First Search
Function: ILL available
Partic in Nashville Area Libr Alliance; Solinet; Tenn Share

C BELMONT UNIVERSITY, Lila D Bunch Library, 1900 Belmont Blvd, 37212-3757. SAN 315-9078. Tel: 615-460-6782. FAX: 615-460-5641. Web Site: library.belmont.edu. *Dir*, Ernest Heard; Tel: 615-460-6424, E-Mail: hearde@mail.belmont.edu; *Reader Servs*, Jane Thomas; Tel: 615-460-5498, E-Mail: thomasj@mail.belmont.edu; *Tech Servs*, Jo Williams Hall; Tel: 615-460-5496; *Circ*, Vance Wilson; Tel: 615-460-5596, E-Mail: wilsonv@mail.belmont.edu; *Per*, Rebecca Williams; Tel: 615-460-5499, E-Mail:

williamsb@mail.belmont.edu; *Music*, Timothy Gmeiner. Subject Specialists: *Music*, Timothy Gmeiner
Founded 1951. Enrl 3,026; Fac 150; Highest Degree: Master
Library Holdings: Bk Vols 219,984; Per Subs 1,445
Subject Interests: Bus, Education, Literature, Mgt, Music, Natural science, Nursing, Relig studies, Sci-tech, Soc and behav sci
Partic in OCLC Online Computer Library Center, Inc

L BOULT, CUMMINGS, CONNERS & BERRY, PLC, Law Library, 414 Union St, Ste 1600. (Mail add: PO Box 198062, 37219), SAN 371-6147. Tel: 615-252-3577. FAX: 615-248-3031. Web Site: www.bccb.com. *Dir Info Resources & Res*, Julie L Julian; E-Mail: jjulian@bccb.com; Staff 2 (MLS 1, Non-MLS 1)
Library Holdings: Bk Vols 10,000; Per Subs 81
Database Vendor: Lexis-Nexis
Restriction: Private library
Function: ILL to other special libraries
Partic in Tenn-Share

S BROWN & CALDWELL LIBRARY, 501 Great Circle Rd, Ste 150, 37228. SAN 370-4076. Tel: 615-255-2288. FAX: 615-256-8332.
Library Holdings: Bk Vols 3,000; Per Subs 20
Subject Interests: Air pollution, Ecology, Environment, Hazardous wastes mgt, Wastewater
Restriction: Not open to public

SR CATHEDRAL OF THE INCARNATION, Robert J Boyd Library, 2001 West End Ave, 37203. SAN 371-9049. Tel: 615-327-4942. FAX: 615-320-5650. *Librn*, Kathy Patten; Staff 1 (MLS 1)
Founded 1990
Library Holdings: Bk Vols 2,600
Subject Interests: Religion
Special Collections: Family Issues Coll

CHEEKWOOD-NASHVILLE'S HOME OF ART & GARDENS

S BOTANTICAL GARDENS LIBRARY, 1200 Forrest Park Dr, 37205-4242. SAN 315-9213. Tel: 615-353-2148. FAX: 615-353-2731. Web Site: www.cheekwood.org. *Chief Librn*, Ida Galehouse; Staff 3 (MLS 1, Non-MLS 2)
Founded 1971
Library Holdings: Bk Vols 4,100; Per Subs 76
Subject Interests: Botanical illustration, Environmental studies, Flower arranging, Garden design, Herbs, Horticulture, Landscape architecture, Natural history, Orchids, Plant sci, Wildflowers
Publications: The Cheekwood Calendar (newsletter)
Friends of the Library Group

S CHEEKWOOD MUSEUM OF ART, 1200 Forrest Park Dr, 37205-4242. SAN 321-6683. Tel: 615-353-6996. FAX: 615-353-2730. *Librn*, Virginia Khouri; *Curator*, Celia Walker
Library Holdings: Bk Vols 3,800; Per Subs 20
Subject Interests: Art, Art history, Contemporary Am artists, Decorative arts, Photog

S COUNTRY MUSIC HALL OF FAME & MUSEUM, Library & Media Center, 222 Fifth Ave S, 37203. SAN 315-9086. Tel: 615-416-2001. FAX: 615-255-2245. Web Site: www.countrymusichalloffame.com. *Coll Develop, Dep Dir*, John Knowles
Founded 1967
Library Holdings: Bk Titles 10,000; Per Subs 450
Subject Interests: Anglo-Am folksong, Commercial popular music in gen, Country music, Culture, Early commercial recording, Folklore, Law, Music copyright, Recorded sound tech, Southern hist
Special Collections: Country Music & The Music Industry Coll, A-tapes; Nashville Chapter Coll; National Academy of Recording Arts & Sciences; Roy Acuff Coll
Publications: Journal of Country Music
Restriction: By appointment only

S CUMBERLAND SCIENCE MUSEUM, 800 Fort Negley Blvd, 37203-4899. SAN 321-0650. Tel: 615-862-5160. FAX: 615-862-5178. Web Site: ww.csm.com. *Curator*, Joe Simon
Founded 1950
Library Holdings: Bk Titles 3,750; Per Subs 20
Subject Interests: Ornithology

GM DEPARTMENT OF VETERANS AFFAIRS, Library Service, 1310 24th Ave S, 37212-2637. SAN 315-9353. Tel: 615-327-4751, Ext 5526. FAX: 615-321-6336. *Chief Librn*, Barbara A Meadows; E-Mail: meadows.barbara@nashville.va.gov
Founded 1946
Library Holdings: Bk Vols 2,969; Per Subs 350
Partic in Medical Libr Asn; Mid-Tennessee Health Science Librarians Association; Veterans Affairs Library Network

R DISCIPLES OF CHRIST HISTORICAL SOCIETY LIBRARY, 1101 Nineteenth Ave S, 37212-2196. SAN 315-9108. Tel: 615-327-1444. FAX: 615-327-1445. E-Mail: dishistsoc@aol.com. Web Site: users.aol.com/dishistsoc. *Dir*, David Ian McWhirter; Staff 5 (MLS 1, Non-MLS 4)
Founded 1941
Library Holdings: Bk Titles 36,500
Subject Interests: Christian churches, Churches of Christ, Disciples of Christ, History, Related relig groups
Database Vendor: OCLC - First Search
Publications: Disciplina (quarterly)
Restriction: In-house use for visitors, Members only
Function: Archival collection
Partic in OCLC Online Computer Library Center, Inc; SE Libr Network

C FISK UNIVERSITY, Library & Media Center, 1000 17th Ave N, 37208-3051. SAN 315-9116. Tel: 615-329-8730. Circulation Tel: 615-329-8640. Reference Tel: 615-329-8645. FAX: 615-329-8761. E-Mail: library@dubois.fisk.edu. Web Site: www.dubois.fisk.edu/~library/. *Dir*, Dr Jessie Carney Smith; E-Mail: jcsmith@fisk.edu; *Asst Librn, ILL*, Sue P Chandler; E-Mail: schand@fisk.edu; *Spec Coll*, Beth M Howse; Tel: 615-329-8646, E-Mail: bhowse@fisk.edu; *Media Spec*, Tyrone Shelton; *Publ Servs*, Ester McShepard; Tel: 615-329-8740, E-Mail: emcshepa@fisk.edu; *Bibliogr*, Robert L Johns; Tel: 615-329-8788, E-Mail: rjohns@fisk.edu; *Info Tech*, Frederick D Smith; Tel: 615-329-8788, E-Mail: fsmith@fisk.edu; *Govt Do Publ Servs*, Susie A Harris; Tel: 615-329-8741, E-Mail: sharris@fisk.edu; *Cat*, Dixie J Jernigan; Tel: 615-329-8788, E-Mail: djerniga@fisk.edu; *Cat*, Peggy G Smith; E-Mail: psmith@fisk.edu; *Spec Coll*, Vanessa Smith; Tel: 615-329-8646, E-Mail: vsmith@fisk.edu. Subject Specialists: *African Am hist*, Beth M Howse; Staff 11 (MLS 3, Non-MLS 8)
Founded 1866. Enrl 964; Fac 85; Highest Degree: Master
May 1999-May 2000 Income $199,119. Mats Exp $93,283, Books $55,00 Per/Ser (Incl. Access Fees) $33,783, Electronic Ref Mat (Incl. Access Fees $4,500. Sal $332,235 (Prof $179,592)
Library Holdings: Bk Vols 203,600; Bk Titles 119,303; Per Subs 217
Subject Interests: Black lit, Culture, History
Special Collections: Black Literature (Charles W Chesnutt, James Weldon Johnson, Naomi Madgett, Louise Meriweather); Civil Rights & Politics (Slater King, John Mercer Langston, James Carroll Napier & William L Dawson); Music & Musical Literature (George Gershwin Coll); Music (W Handy, Scott Joplin, Fisk Jubilee Singers & John W Work); Sociology (WEB DuBois, Marcus Garvey & Charles S Johnson)
Automation Activity & Vendor Info: (Circulation) Innovative Interfaces Inc.
Partic in Coop Col Libr Ctr, Inc; Nashville Area Libr Alliance; SE Libr Network

C FREE WILL BAPTIST BIBLE COLLEGE, Welch Library, 3630 W End Ave, 37205. (Mail add: 3606 W End Ave, 37205), Tel: 615-844-5274. FAX 615-269-6028. *Mgr*, Margaret Evans Hampton; Tel: 615-844-5284, E-Mail library@fwbbc.edu; *Librn*, Carol Ketteman Reid; E-Mail: creid@fwbbc.ed Staff 3 (MLS 1, Non-MLS 2)
Founded 1942. Enrl 333; Highest Degree: Bachelor
Jun 1998-May 1999 Mats Exp $42,777, Books $31,810, Per/Ser (Incl. Access Fees) $9,092, Micro $1,875. Sal $69,460
Library Holdings: Bk Vols 57,000; Per Subs 400
Subject Interests: Bible, Theology
Special Collections: Free Will Baptist Historical Coll
Database Vendor: Ebsco - EbscoHost, IAC - Info Trac
Publications: Acquisitions (monthly)
Partic in Christian Libr Network; Nashville Area Libr Alliance; Tenn-Share

JEWISH FEDERATION LIBRARIES

R AKIVA LIBRARY, 809 Percy Warner Blvd, 37205. SAN 360-8670. Tel: 615-356-1880. FAX: 615-356-1850. *Librn*, Helen Sissel
1998-1999 Mats Exp $300
Library Holdings: Bk Vols 3,500
Special Collections: Judaica Coll

R ARCHIVES OF THE JEWISH FEDERATION OF NASHVILLE & MIDDLE TENNESSEE, 801 Percy Warner Blvd, 37205. SAN 360-8719 Tel: 615-356-3242, Ext 255. FAX: 615-352-0056. E-Mail: library@jewishnashville.org. *Dir*, Annette Ratkin
Founded 1979
1998-1999 Mats Exp $414, Per/Ser (Incl. Access Fees) $64
Special Collections: Community History; Holocaust oral histories; Manuscripts; Older Nashvillians oral histories; Record Groups; Small Co
Publications: A Guide for Teaching the History of the Jews of Nashville Tennessee

R JEWISH COMMUNITY CENTER LIBRARY, 801 Percy Warner Blvd, 37205. SAN 360-8700. Tel: 615-356-3242, Ext 255. FAX: 615-352-0056 E-Mail: library@jewishnashville.org. *Dir*, Annette Ratkin; *Asst Librn*, Leona Fleischer; Staff 2 (MLS 1, Non-MLS 1)
Founded 1902
1999-2000 Income $3,795, Locally Generated Income $2,000, Parent Institution $1,795. Mats Exp $2,400, Books $2,000, Per/Ser (Incl. Acces Fees) $400
Library Holdings: Bk Vols 8,300
Special Collections: Hebrew Coll; Holocaust Coll; Israel Coll; Judaica Coll; Large Print Coll; Russian Coll; Yiddish Coll

R TEMPLE LIBRARY, 5015 Harding Rd, 37205. SAN 360-8735. Tel: 615-352-7620. FAX: 615-352-9365.
Library Holdings: Bk Vols 5,400
Subject Interests: Am Jewish hist, Holocaust, Israel, Judaism
Special Collections: Easy Books & Young People's Coll

WEST END SYNAGOGUE LIBRARY, 3814 W End Ave, 37205. SAN 360-876X. Tel: 615-269-4592. FAX: 615-269-4695. E-Mail: nashfedlib@aol.com. *Librn*, Susan Pankowsky
1998-1999 Income $2,000. Mats Exp $2,000
Library Holdings: Bk Vols 9,700; Per Subs 5
Subject Interests: Holocaust, Israel, Judaism

JOHN A GUPTON COLLEGE, Memorial Library, 1616 Church St, 37203. SAN 315-9132. Tel: 615-327-3927. FAX: 615-321-4518. Web Site: www.guptoncollege.com. *Librn*, William P Bruce; E-Mail: pbruce@guptoncollege.com
Founded 1946. Enrl 60; Fac 14
Library Holdings: Bk Titles 3,228; Per Subs 68
Subject Interests: Mortuary science
Special Collections: Funeral Service/Grief Psychology

LIFEWAY CHRISTIAN RESOURCES OF THE SOUTHERN BAPTIST CONVENTION, E C Dargan Research Library, 127 Ninth Ave N, 37234-0142. SAN 315-906X. Tel: 615-251-2137. Interlibrary Loan Service Tel: 615-251-2126. Circulation Tel: 615-251-2133. Reference Tel: 615-251-2126. FAX: 615-251-2176. Web Site: www.library.lifeway.com. *Reader Servs, Res*, Steve Gateley; E-Mail: sgatele@lifeway.com; *Circ*, Miriam Evans; E-Mail: mevans@lifeway.com; Staff 2 (MLS 1, Non-MLS 1)
Founded 1933
Library Holdings: Bk Vols 38,000; Per Subs 595
Subject Interests: Biblical, Bus, Education, Hist Baptistiana, Mgt, Publishing, Religious education
Special Collections: Scofield Photographic Coll; Sunday School Board Press Coll
Partic in SE Libr Network

MEHARRY MEDICAL COLLEGE LIBRARY, Kresge Learning Resource Center, 1005 DB Todd Blvd, 37208. SAN 315-9140. Tel: 615-327-6318, 615-327-6862. FAX: 615-321-2932, 615-327-6448. *Dir*, Cheryl Hamberg; Tel: 615-327-6728, E-Mail: chamberg@mmc.edu; *Assoc Dir*, Mattie Lou McHollin; E-Mail: mmchollin@mmc.edu; *Tech Servs*, Marvelyn Thompson; Tel: 615-327-6394, E-Mail: mthompson@mmc.edu; *Cat*, Don Dryden; Tel: 615-327-6471, E-Mail: ddryden@mmc.edu; *Media Spec*, Bobby Bledsoe; *Ref Serv*, Jacqueline Dowdy; Tel: 615-327-6727, E-Mail: jdowdy@mmc.edu; *Ref Serv*, Charlotte Johnson; Tel: 615-327-6762, E-Mail: cjohnson@mmc.edu; *Ref Serv*, Soundaram Ranganathan; Tel: 615-327-6454; Staff 31 (MLS 11, Non-MLS 20)
Founded 1940. Enrl 924; Highest Degree: Doctorate
Jul 1998-Jun 1999 Mats Exp $1,290,616. Sal $970,328 (Prof $363,535)
Library Holdings: Bk Vols 99,273; Per Subs 1,045
Subject Interests: Biomed sci, Sciences
Special Collections: Black Medical History
Automation Activity & Vendor Info: (Cataloging) SIRSI; (Circulation) SIRSI; (ILL) CARL; (Serials) SIRSI
Database Vendor: CARL, GaleNet, OVID Technologies, Silverplatter Information Inc.
Publications: Newsletter-Dialogue
Function: Research library
Partic in Dialog Corporation; Medline; OCLC Online Computer Library Center, Inc; SE-Atlantic Regional Med Libr Servs

METROPOLITAN NASHVILLE GENERAL HOSPITAL, Health Sciences Library, 1818 Albion St, 37208. SAN 327-652X. Tel: 615-341-4417. FAX: 615-341-4501. *Librn*, Glenda L Perry; E-Mail: glenda.perry@gh.nashville.org; Staff 1 (MLS 1)
Library Holdings: Bk Titles 500; Per Subs 50
Subject Interests: Medicine, Nursing, Surgery
Partic in NLM; Tennessee Health Science Library Association

MIDDLE TENNESSEE CORRECTIONAL COMPLEX CENTER LIBRARY, 7177 Cockrill Bend Industrial Rd, 37243-0470. SAN 371-6783. Tel: 615-350-3361, Ext 1275. FAX: 615-350-3319. *Coordr*, Gary Gray
Library Holdings: Bk Titles 3,500; Per Subs 60
Subject Interests: Fiction, History, Science fiction
Branches:
MTCX ANNEX, 7466 Centennial Blvd-Extended, 32243-0466. SAN 377-7480. Tel: 615-741-6587.

NASHVILLE SCHOOL OF LAW LIBRARY, 2934 Sidco Dr, 37204. SAN 321-6144. Tel: 615-256-3684. FAX: 615-244-2383. Web Site: www.nashvilleschooloflaw.net. *Librn*, Janet W Naff; Staff 1 (MLS 1)
Founded 1911. Enrl 500; Fac 40; Highest Degree: Doctorate
Library Holdings: Bk Vols 16,500; Bk Titles 165; Per Subs 15
Special Collections: Judge Shriver Coll
Publications: Annual barrister; Annual catalog

NASHVILLE STATE TECHNICAL INSTITUTE, Educational Resource Center, 120 White Bridge Rd, 37209-4515. SAN 315-9167. Tel: 615-353-3555. FAX: 615-353-3558. Web Site: library.nsti.tec.tn.us. *Dir*, James Veatch; E-Mail: veatch_j@nsti.tec.tn.us; *Publ Servs*, Charles May; *Publ Servs, Ser*, Sally Robertson; *Reader Servs*, Ann Penuel
Founded 1969. Enrl 6,000; Fac 182
Library Holdings: Bk Vols 45,000; Bk Titles 40,538; Per Subs 325
Subject Interests: Bus accounting, Culinary, Environmental studies, Police sci-tech, Sci-tech
Publications: Annotated AV Lists, Library Guide
Partic in SE Libr Network

M NASHVILLE-DAVIDSON COUNTY METROPOLITAN DEPARTMENT OF PUBLIC HEALTH LIBRARY, 311 23rd Ave N, 37203-5220. SAN 327-6619. Tel: 615-340-2125. FAX: 615-340-5665. *Librn*, Feli Propes; E-Mail: feli_propes@mhd.nashville.org
1998-1999 Mats Exp $6,000, Books $3,700, Per/Ser (Incl. Access Fees) $2,000
Library Holdings: Bk Titles 2,600; Per Subs 102
Subject Interests: Public health
Publications: Current Serials List
Partic in Mid-Tennessee Health Science Librarians Association; Nat Libr of Med; Tenn-Share; Tennessee Health Science Library Association

S NATIONSBANK BUSINESS RESOURCE CENTER, 3401 W End Ave, 37203. SAN 327-7127. Toll Free Tel: 888-279-3121. FAX: 615-749-3685.
Library Holdings: Bk Titles 1,500; Per Subs 160
Friends of the Library Group

S PACE INTERNATIONAL UNION LIBRARY, 3340 Perimeter Hill Dr, PO Box 1475, 37202. SAN 326-1832. Tel: 615-834-8590, Ext 278. FAX: 615-831-6792. Web Site: www.paceunion.org. *In Charge*, Mary Dimoff; E-Mail: mdimoff@paceunion.org
Founded 1981
Jan 1999-Dec 1999 Mats Exp $160,000, Books $8,000, Per/Ser (Incl. Access Fees) $30,000, Presv $1,100, Micro $2,500, AV Equip $1,500, Electronic Ref Mat (Incl. Access Fees) $43,000. Sal $43,000
Library Holdings: Bk Vols 9,300; Per Subs 165
Special Collections: International Union, Allied Industrial Workers of America (AIW) Archives; Oil Chemical & Atomic Workers International Union (OCAW) Archives; UPIU Oral History Series, audio, microfilm, video cassette
Restriction: Staff use only
Partic in Westlaw

P PUBLIC LIBRARY OF NASHVILLE & DAVIDSON COUNTY, Main, 225 Polk Ave, 37203-3585. SAN 360-912X. Tel: 615-862-5760. FAX: 615-862-5771. Web Site: www.library.nashville.org. *Dir*, Donna D Nicely; *Asst Dir*, Vivian Wynn; *Publ Servs*, Pamela Reese; *Ser*, Ron Perry; *Media Spec*, Karen Byrd; *Ch Servs*, Victoria Elliott; *ILL*, Elizabeth Fisher; *Coll Develop*, Rob Pasco; *Archivist*, Ken Fieth; *Govt Doc*, Phil Krakowiak; *Br Coordr*, Elyse Adler. Subject Specialists: *Local history*, Mary Glenn Hearne; Staff 320 (MLS 77, Non-MLS 243)
Founded 1904. Pop 533,967; Circ 2,566,170
Jul 1999-Jun 2000 Income (Main Library and Branch Library) $12,423,628. Mats Exp $1,837,260, Books $1,607,920, Per/Ser (Incl. Access Fees) $229,340. Sal $8,571,547
Library Holdings: Bk Vols 1,128,077; Bk Titles 333,662; Per Subs 3,922
Subject Interests: Bus, Mgt, Tenn hist
Special Collections: Av Coll; Business Coll; Children's International Coll; Deaf Services Coll; Govt Archives; Govt Docs Coll; Grants Info Coll; Local Genealogy & History (Nashville); Naff (Drama Coll)
Automation Activity & Vendor Info: (Acquisitions) Innovative Interfaces Inc.; (Cataloging) Innovative Interfaces Inc.; (Circulation) Innovative Interfaces Inc.; (OPAC) Innovative Interfaces Inc.; (Serials) Innovative Interfaces Inc.
Database Vendor: Innovative Interfaces INN - View
Partic in Athena; OCLC Online Computer Library Center, Inc; SE Libr Network
Friends of the Library Group
Branches: 23
BELLEVUE, 650 Colice Jeanne Rd, 37221-2811. SAN 360-9146. Tel: 615-862-5854. FAX: 615-862-5758. *Branch Mgr*, Claudia Schauman
Library Holdings: Bk Vols 57,822
Friends of the Library Group
BORDEAUX, 4000 Clarksville Pike, 37218-1912. SAN 360-9154. Tel: 615-862-5856. FAX: 615-862-5748. *Branch Mgr*, Verlon Malone
Library Holdings: Bk Vols 48,570
CARNEGIE NORTH, 1001 Monroe St, 37208-2543. SAN 360-9162. Tel: 615-862-5858. FAX: 615-862-5749. *Coordr*, Amy Jordan
Library Holdings: Bk Vols 7,894
DONELSON, 2315 Lebanon Rd, 37214-3410. SAN 360-9189. Tel: 615-862-5859. FAX: 615-862-5799. *Branch Mgr*, Gloria Coleman
Library Holdings: Bk Vols 63,210
Friends of the Library Group
EAST, 206 Gallatin Rd, 37206-3240. SAN 360-9219. Tel: 615-862-5860. FAX: 615-862-5807. *Branch Mgr*, Joseph Hewgley
Library Holdings: Bk Vols 18,338
Friends of the Library Group
EDGEHILL, 1409 12th Ave S, 37203-4903. SAN 360-9243. Tel: 615-862-5861. FAX: 615-862-5840. *Branch Mgr*, Beverly Townsend
Library Holdings: Bk Vols 23,686
EDMONDSON PIKE, 5501 Edmondson Pike, 37211-5808. Tel: 615-862-5854. FAX: 615-862-5758.

Library Holdings: Bk Vols 42,189
GOODLETTSVILLE BRANCH, 106 Old Brick Church Pike, Goodlettsville, 37072-1504. SAN 360-9278. Tel: 615-862-5862. FAX: 615-862-5798. *Actg Librn*, Connie Leach
Library Holdings: Bk Vols 27,834
Friends of the Library Group
GREEN HILLS, 3701 Benham Ave, 37215-2121. SAN 360-9308. Tel: 615-862-5863. FAX: 615-862-5881. *Branch Mgr*, Carroll Miller
Library Holdings: Bk Vols 101,029
Friends of the Library Group
HADLEY PARK, 1039 28th Ave N, 37208-2809. SAN 360-9332. Tel: 615-862-5865. FAX: 615-862-5887. *Branch Mgr*, Judy Sharp
Library Holdings: Bk Vols 22,039
Friends of the Library Group
HERMITAGE BRANCH, 3700 James Kay Lane, Hermitage, 37076-3429. Tel: 615-880-3951. FAX: 615-880-3955. *Branch Mgr*, Gloria Coleman
Library Holdings: Bk Vols 49,996
INGLEWOOD, 4312 Gallatin Rd, 37216-2192. SAN 360-9367. Tel: 615-862-5866. FAX: 615-862-5888. *Branch Mgr*, Teresa Parlon
Library Holdings: Bk Vols 34,753
Friends of the Library Group
LIBRARY SERVICE FOR THE HEARING IMPAIRED, 700 Second Ave S, Rm 211, 37210-2006. SAN 328-7246. Tel: 615-862-5750. Toll Free Tel: 800-342-3262. TDD: 615-862-5750. FAX: 615-862-5494. Web Site: www.library.nashville.org. *Coordr*, Sandy Cohen
Library Holdings: Bk Vols 7,156
Special Services for the Deaf - Books on deafness & sign language; TDD
MADISON BRANCH, 610 Gallatin Pike S, Madison, 37115-4013. SAN 360-9421. Tel: 615-862-5868. FAX: 615-862-5889. *Branch Mgr*, Dianne Webb
Library Holdings: Bk Vols 58,159
Friends of the Library Group
METROPOLITAN GOVERNMENT ARCHIVES, 1113 Elm Hill Pike, 37210-3505. SAN 328-7262. Tel: 615-862-5880. FAX: 615-862-5724. *Archivist*, Kenneth Fieth
Friends of the Library Group
OLD HICKORY BRANCH, 1010 Jones St, Old Hickory, 37138-2915. SAN 360-9456. Tel: 615-862-5869. FAX: 615-862-5896. *Branch Mgr*, Ann Braden
Library Holdings: Bk Vols 32,973
Friends of the Library Group
PRUITT, 117 Charles E Davis Blvd, 37210. SAN 375-2941. Tel: 615-862-5985. FAX: 615-862-6745. *Branch Mgr*, Mike Chagunda
Library Holdings: Bk Vols 10,626
RICHLAND PARK, 4711 Charlotte Ave, 37209-3404. SAN 360-9480. Tel: 615-862-5870. FAX: 615-862-5897. *Branch Mgr*, Edward J Todd
Library Holdings: Bk Vols 40,031
Friends of the Library Group
SOUTHEAST, 2325 Hickory Highlands Dr, Antioch, 37013-2101. SAN 373-1987. Tel: 615-862-5871. FAX: 615-862-5756. *Branch Mgr*, Kerry Wallace
Library Holdings: Bk Vols 102,220
Friends of the Library Group
THOMPSON LANE, 380 Thompson Lane, 37211-2485. SAN 360-9510. Tel: 615-862-5873. FAX: 615-862-5898. *Branch Mgr*, Phyllis Jones
Library Holdings: Bk Vols 37,524
WATKINS PARK COMMUNITY, 17th Ave N, 37203-2878. SAN 375-295X. Tel: 615-862-5872. FAX: 615-862-6746. *Coordr*, Amy Jordan
Library Holdings: Bk Vols 5,995
WPLN TALKING LIBRARY, 700 Second Ave S, Rm 200, 37210-2006. SAN 328-722X. Tel: 615-862-5874. FAX: 615-862-5796. *Mgr*, Jim Stanford
Free radio reading service for blind & physically handicapped persons
Z ALEXANDER LOOBY BRANCH, 2301 Metro Center Blvd, 37228-1221. SAN 360-9391. Tel: 615-862-5867. FAX: 615-862-5797. *Branch Mgr*, Amy Jordan
Library Holdings: Bk Vols 35,316
Bookmobiles: 2

M SAINT THOMAS HOSPITAL, Julius Jacobs Health Sciences Library, 4220 Harding Rd, PO Box 380, 37202-0380. SAN 315-9175. Tel: 615-222-6658. *Head of Libr*, Dixie Fulton Williamson; Tel: 615-222-6892, E-Mail: dwilliam@stthomas.org; Staff 3 (MLS 2, Non-MLS 1)
Founded 1961
Jul 1998-Jun 1999 Income Parent Institution $149,594. Mats Exp $104,925, Books $21,000, Per/Ser (Incl. Access Fees) $65,000, Electronic Ref Mat (Incl. Access Fees) $18,925. Sal $107,656
Library Holdings: Bk Vols 3,148; Per Subs 266
Special Collections: St Thomas Hospital Archival Coll
Database Vendor: Ebsco - EbscoHost, GaleNet, OVID Technologies
Restriction: Staff use only
Function: Literary searches
Partic in Mid-Tennessee Health Science Librarians Association; Tenn Share; Tennessee Health Science Library Association
Friends of the Library Group

C SCARRITT-BENNETT CENTER, Virginia Davis Laskey Library, 1104 19 Ave S, 37212-2166. (Mail add: 1008 19th Ave S, 37212-2166), SAN 322-8177. Tel: 615-340-7479. FAX: 615-340-7463. E-Mail: library@scarrittbennett.org. Web Site: www.umc.org/scarritt/library.html. *Dir Libr Serv*, Mary Lou Moore; Tel: 615-340-7477; Staff 2 (MLS 2)
Founded 1892
Library Holdings: Bk Vols 55,297; Per Subs 153
Subject Interests: Christian educ, Church music, Spiritual formation
Special Collections: Bibles; Church & Community, United Methodist Church

SR SOUTHERN BAPTIST HISTORICAL LIBRARY & ARCHIVES, 901 Commerce St, Ste 400, 37203-3630. SAN 326-1417. Tel: 615-244-0344. FAX: 615-782-4821. *Archivist, Dir*, Bill Sumners; E-Mail: bsumners@edge.net; *Librn*, Kathy L Sylvest; E-Mail: ksylvest@edge.net; *Asst Librn*, Peggy Hester; Staff 4 (MLS 2, Non-MLS 2)
Founded 1953
Library Holdings: Bk Vols 25,300; Per Subs 280
Special Collections: SBC; Southern Baptist Convention archives depositor
Partic in OCLC Online Computer Library Center, Inc

S TENNESSEAN LIBRARY, 1100 Broadway, 37203. SAN 315-9205. Tel: 615-742-7504. FAX: 615-259-8093. Web Site: www.tennessean.com. *Librn*, Annette Morrison; *Res*, Jonathon Dees; *Res*, Nancy St Cyr; *Res*, Glenda Washam; *Archivist*, Chantay Steptoe
Founded 1940
Library Holdings: Bk Vols 1,300; Per Subs 130
Special Collections: Tennessean & Nashville Banner Coll, clippings & microfilm, 1907 Forward (Tennessean)
Partic in Data Time

S TENNESSEE DEPARTMENT OF CORRECTIONS, Tennessee Prison for Women Library, 3881 Stewarts Lane, 37243-0468. SAN 371-7364. Tel: 61 741-1255, Ext 6244. FAX: 615-880-7156. *Librn*, Pam Deak; Staff 1 (MLS 1)
Library Holdings: Bk Vols 17,000; Bk Titles 13,000; Per Subs 10
Special Collections: Children's Collection; Law Library
Special Services for the Deaf - Books on deafness & sign language; High interest/low vocabulary books; Staff with knowledge of sign language

G TENNESSEE DEPARTMENT OF ECONOMIC & COMMUNITY DEVELOPMENT LIBRARY, 312 Eighth Ave N, 37243-0405. SAN 370-7229. Tel: 615-741-1995. FAX: 615-741-7306. *Librn*, Edith Snider; E-Mail esnider@mail.state.tn.us
Library Holdings: Bk Vols 1,500; Bk Titles 1,200; Per Subs 200

G TENNESSEE DEPARTMENT OF TRANSPORTATION LIBRARY, Jame K Polk Bldg, Ste 300, 37243-0345. SAN 315-9221. Tel: 615-741-2330. FAX: 615-741-1791. *Librn*, Ruth S Letson; E-Mail: rletson@mail.state.tn.u Staff 1 (MLS 1)
Founded 1973
Oct 1999-Sep 2000 Income $72,300. Mats Exp $34,400. Sal $37,900
Library Holdings: Bk Titles 11,000; Per Subs 100
Subject Interests: Aeronautics, Hwy eng, Mass transit, Planning, Rail, Traffic eng, Transportation, Waterways
Special Collections: Photo Log
Partic in Tenn-Share; Transportation Research Information Services

G TENNESSEE HUMAN RIGHTS COMMISSION, Resource Library, Cornerstone Sq Bldg, Ste 400, 530 Church St, 37243-0745. SAN 375-2445 Tel: 615-741-5825. FAX: 615-532-2197.
Library Holdings: Bk Vols 50

P TENNESSEE REGIONAL LIBRARY FOR THE BLIND & PHYSICALL HANDICAPPED, (TSLA), 403 Seventh Ave N, 37243-0313. SAN 315-9256. Tel: 615-741-3915. Toll Free Tel: 800-342-3308. FAX: 615-532-885 *Dir*, Ruth Hemphill; E-Mail: rhemphill@mail.state.tn.us; Staff 15 (MLS 3, Non-MLS 12)
Founded 1970
Library Holdings: Bk Vols 251,994; Bk Titles 63,272

GL TENNESSEE REGULATORY AUTHORITY, Legal Department Library, 460 James Robertson Pkwy, 37243-0505. SAN 328-6266. Tel: 615-741-2904, Ext 169. FAX: 615-741-5015. Web Site: www.state.tn.us/tra/. *In Charge*, Richard Collier
Library Holdings: Bk Titles 20

GL TENNESSEE STATE LAW LIBRARY, 401 Seventh Ave N, 37219. SAN 315-9264. Tel: 615-741-2016. FAX: 615-741-7186. E-Mail: lbo1111@smtpaoc.tsc.state.tn.us. *Librn*, Stephen M Jackson
Founded 1938
Library Holdings: Bk Vols 55,000; Bk Titles 50,000; Per Subs 30
Subject Interests: Past, Present, Tenn law
Automation Activity & Vendor Info: (Cataloging) Inmagic, Inc.
Function: Research library
Also see regional entries in Jackson & Knoxville

TENNESSEE STATE LEGISLATIVE LIBRARY, G-12 War Memorial Bldg, 37243-0059. SAN 370-4181. Tel: 615-741-5816. FAX: 615-253-0177. Web Site: www.legislature.state.tn.us/. *Dir Libr Serv*, Eddie Weeks; E-Mail: eddie.weeks@legislature.state.tn.us; *Assoc Librn*, Tomi Hall; Tel: 615-741-9501; Staff 2 (MLS 1, Non-MLS 1)
Founded 1972
Library Holdings: Bk Vols 6,000; Per Subs 30; Spec Interest Per Sub 25
Subject Interests: Tenn legis mat
Special Collections: Acts of the Tennessee Legislature 1827-Present
Function: Archival collection

TENNESSEE STATE LIBRARY & ARCHIVES, (TSLA), 403 Seventh Ave N, 37243-0312. SAN 360-960X. Tel: 615-741-2451. FAX: 615-741-6471. E-Mail: reference@mail.state.tn.us. Web Site: www.state.tn.us/sos/statelib. *Asst Librn*, Jane Pinkston; Tel: 615-532-4628, E-Mail: jpinkston@mail.state.tn.us; *Asst Librn*, Jeanne D Sugg; Tel: 615-741-7996, Fax: 615-532-9293, E-Mail: jsugg@mail.state.tn.us; *Tech Servs*, Joann Blair; Tel: 615-253-3462, E-Mail: jablair@mail.state.tn.us; *Archivist, Tech Servs*, Jay Richiuso; Tel: 615-253-3468, E-Mail: jrichluso@mail.state.tn.us; *Publ Servs*, Charles A Sherrill; Tel: 615-741-2764, Fax: 615-532-2472, E-Mail: csherrill@mail.state.tn.us; *Dir Libr Serv*, Ruth Hemphill; Tel: 615-741-3915, Fax: 615-532-8856, E-Mail: rhemphill@mail.state.tn.us; *Archivist*, William W Moss; Tel: 615-253-3458, E-Mail: willmoss@mail.state.tn.us; Staff 199 (MLS 58, Non-MLS 141)
Founded 1854
Jul 1999-Jun 2000 Income $8,072,597, State $6,084,897, Federal $1,987,700. Mats Exp $4,092,000, Books $90,000, Per/Ser (Incl. Access Fees) $32,600, Presv $72,000, Micro $92,000, AV Equip $26,000, Other Print Mats $26,100, Manuscripts & Archives $8,000. Sal $3,980,597
Library Holdings: Bk Vols 653,850; Per Subs 1,582
Subject Interests: Government, SE US hist, Tenn politics
Special Collections: Genealogy Coll; Popular Sheet Music (Rose Music); Southeastern US Maps; Tennessee County & Public Records; Tennessee Newspapers
Database Vendor: GaleNet, OCLC - First Search
Publications: List of Tennessee State Publications (quarterly); Tennessee Public Library Directory & Statistics (annual); Tennessee State Library & Archives: Guide to Resources & Services; Tennessee Summer Reading Program (annual)
Partic in Solinet
Branches: 1
LIBRARY FOR THE BLIND & PHYSICALLY HANDICAPPED
See Separate Entry under Tennessee Regional Library for the Blind & Physically Handicapped
Bookmobiles: 12

TENNESSEE STATE MUSEUM LIBRARY, Polk Cultural Ctr, 505 Deaderick St, 37243-1120. SAN 321-4532. Tel: 615-741-2692. Toll Free Tel: 800-407-4324. FAX: 615-741-7231. Web Site: www.tnmuseum.org.
Founded 1977
Library Holdings: Bk Vols 1,600; Per Subs 25
Subject Interests: Am Indians, Am mat culture, Archaeology, Art, Artists, TN hist
Special Collections: Weesner Coll on Archaeology & American Indians
Restriction: Open to public for reference only
A small library for use by the staff of the Tennessee State Museum; staffed by volunteers; Books usually purchased by the Curator of Collections & other departments

TENNESSEE STATE UNIVERSITY, Brown-Daniel Library, 3500 John A Merritt Blvd, 37209-1561. SAN 315-9272. Tel: 615-963-5211. Interlibrary Loan Service Tel: 615-963-5206. Circulation Tel: 615-963-5064. Reference Tel: 615-963-5201. FAX: 615-963-5216. Web Site: www.tnstate.edu/~library/, www.tnstate.edu/library/. *Dir*, Dr Yildiz B Binkley; Tel: 615-963-5212, E-Mail: ybinkley@tnstate.edu; *Asst Dir*, Murle Kenerson; Tel: 615-963-5203, E-Mail: kenersonm@tnstate.edu; *Online Servs*, Estella Whitaker; Tel: 615-963-5213, E-Mail: ewhitaker@tnstate.edu; *Cat*, Barbara Taylor; Tel: 615-963-5235, E-Mail: btaylor@tnstate.edu; *Ref*, Fletcher Moon; Tel: 615-963-5205, Fax: 615-963-5224, E-Mail: moonf@tnstate.edu; *Circ*, Annette Pilcher; Tel: 615-963-5242, E-Mail: pilchera@tnstate.edu; *Online Servs*, Colette Bradley; Tel: 615-963-5489, E-Mail: bradleyc@tnstate.edu; *Coordr, Media Spec*, Karen Gupton; Tel: 615-963-5743, Fax: 615-963-5745, E-Mail: guptonk@tnstate.edu; *Coordr*, Dr Helen Chen; Tel: 615-963-7185, Fax: 615-963-7193, E-Mail: ChenH@tnstate.edu; *Acq*, Glenda Alvin; Tel: 615-963-5230, E-Mail: alvin001@tnstate.edu; *Spec Coll*, Sharon Hull; Tel: 615-963-5219, E-Mail: hulls@tnstate.edu; *Ser*, Georgianna Lavender; Tel: 615-963-5226, E-Mail: laven001@tnstate.edu; *Cat*, Barbara Taylor; Tel: 615-963-5236, E-Mail: taylorbj@tnstate.edu; Staff 36 (MLS 17, Non-MLS 19)
Founded 1912. Enrl 8,466; Fac 532; Highest Degree: Doctorate
Jul 1999-Jun 2000 Income (Main and Other College/University Libraries) $2,574,062, State $2,175,460, Federal $398,602. Mats Exp $1,133,581, Books $429,238, Per/Ser (Incl. Access Fees) $410,103, Presv $5,000, Micro $12,000, Manuscripts & Archives $1,000, Electronic Ref Mat (Incl. Access Fees) $276,240. Sal $1,272,243 (Prof $865,280)
Library Holdings: Bk Vols 584,412; Bk Titles 399,419; Per Subs 1,555; Bks on Deafness & Sign Lang 920
Subject Interests: Agriculture, Art, Astronomy, Biology, Business, Criminal justice, Education, Engineering, Ethnic studies, Govt affairs, History, Music, Nursing, Sociology
Special Collections: Black History; Jazz Recordings; Tennessee History; Tennessee State University History, art objects, bks, micro, pamphlets, per, pictures & newspaper files
Automation Activity & Vendor Info: (Acquisitions) DRA; (Cataloging) DRA; (Circulation) DRA; (Course Reserve) DRA; (ILL) DRA; (OPAC) DRA; (Serials) DRA
Database Vendor: CARL, Ebsco - EbscoHost, GaleNet, IAC - Info Trac, IAC - SearchBank, OCLC - First Search, ProQuest, Silverplatter Information Inc.
Publications: Annual Report; Newsletter; Student Handbooks
Restriction: Circulation limited
Partic in NALA; TBR Consortium; Tenn Acad Libr Collaborative; Tenn Share
Special Services for the Deaf - TDD
Friends of the Library Group

S TENNESSEE WESTERN HISTORY LIBRARY, PO Box 111864, 37222. SAN 323-438X. Tel: 615-834-5069. FAX: 615-832-9128. *Librn*, Steve Eng
Library Holdings: Bk Titles 300
Special Collections: Andrew Jackson; Cattle Industry; James K Polk; Jesse James; Manifest Destiny; William Walker

S THE TENNESSEEAN LIBRARY, 1100 Broadway, 37203. SAN 315-9159. Tel: 615-259-8225. FAX: 615-259-8093. *Archivist*, Annette Morrison
Founded 1939
Library Holdings: Bk Vols 500; Per Subs 10
Restriction: Staff use only

C TREVECCA NAZARENE UNIVERSITY, Waggoner Library, 333 Murfreesboro Rd, 37210-2877. SAN 315-9280. Tel: 615-248-1460. FAX: 615-248-7728. Web Site: www.maclib.trevecca.edu. *Dir*, E Ray Thrasher; E-Mail: rthrasher@trevecca.edu; *Per*, Pam Day; Tel: 615-248-1338; *Publ Servs*, Elizabeth Purtee; Tel: 615-248-1212; *Reader Servs*, Priscilla Speer; Tel: 615-248-1347; *Ref*, Judy Bivens; Tel: 615-248-1339; *Syst Coordr*, Jamen McGranahan; Tel: 615-248-7732; Staff 6 (MLS 6)
Founded 1901. Enrl 1,700; Fac 80; Highest Degree: Doctorate
Jul 1999-Jun 2000 Income Parent Institution $644,370. Mats Exp $243,138, Books $101,000, Per/Ser (Incl. Access Fees) $119,638, Presv $9,000, Micro $7,500, Other Print Mats $2,000, Manuscripts & Archives $1,000, Electronic Ref Mat (Incl. Access Fees) $3,000. Sal $274,468 (Prof $165,769)
Library Holdings: Bk Vols 101,380; Per Subs 2,586; Bks on Deafness & Sign Lang 15
Subject Interests: Bus, Education, Religion
Automation Activity & Vendor Info: (Cataloging) DRA; (OPAC) DRA
Publications: Handbook; Newsletter
Partic in Dialog Corporation; Nashville Area Libr Alliance; News Bank; ProQuest; SE Libr Network

R UNITED METHODIST PUBLISHING HOUSE LIBRARY, 201 Eighth Ave S, 37203. SAN 315-9302. Tel: 615-749-6335. FAX: 615-749-6128. *Mgr*, Rosalyn Lewis; E-Mail: r-lewis@solinet.net; Staff 3 (MLS 1, Non-MLS 2)
Founded 1945
Library Holdings: Bk Vols 40,000; Bk Titles 21,000; Per Subs 300
Subject Interests: Methodistica, Theology, United Methodist publishing
Partic in SE Libr Network

S US TOBACCO, R & D Library, 800 Harrison St, 37203. SAN 371-4454. Tel: 615-271-2200. FAX: 615-880-4692. *Librn*, Barbara Borrelli
Library Holdings: Bk Titles 2,000; Per Subs 100

G UNIVERSITY OF TENNESSEE, Center for Industrial Services Library, 226 Capitol Blvd, Ste 606, 37219-1804. SAN 326-3452. Tel: 615-532-8657. FAX: 615-532-4937.
Library Holdings: Bk Titles 150; Per Subs 50
Subject Interests: Defense procurement, Electronic commerce, Environ regulation compliance, Environmental law, Industrial engineering, Solid waste mgt
Special Collections: Military standards & specification

C UNIVERSITY OF TENNESSEE COLLEGE, Social Work Library at Nashville, 193 Polk Ave, 37203-2604. SAN 372-7785. Tel: 615-329-4851. FAX: 615-321-1869. *Librn*, Elsie Pettit; E-Mail: epettit1@utk.edu
Library Holdings: Bk Vols 19,000; Per Subs 60

SR UPPER ROOM DEVOTIONAL LIBRARY, 1908 Grand Ave, 37212. (Mail add: PO Box 340004, 37203-0004), SAN 315-9329. Tel: 615-340-7204. FAX: 615-340-7006. E-Mail: turlib@aol.com. *Librn*, Sarah Schaller-Linn; Staff 2 (MLS 1, Non-MLS 1)
Founded 1957
Jan 1999-Dec 2000 Mats Exp $7,500, Books $2,500, Per/Ser (Incl. Access Fees) $3,000, Electronic Ref Mat (Incl. Access Fees) $2,000
Library Holdings: Bk Titles 10,000; Per Subs 50
Subject Interests: Hymnals
Database Vendor: Ebsco - EbscoHost

G US COURTS OF APPEALS FOR THE SIXTH CIRCUIT, Harry Phillips Memorial Library, United States Courthouse, Rm A-810, 110 Ninth Ave S, 37203. SAN 326-7946. Tel: 615-736-7492. FAX: 615-736-2045. *Librn*, Joe

D McClure; E-Mail: jmcclure@ck6.uscourts.gov; Staff 1 (MLS 1)
Founded 1981
Subject Interests: Law
Automation Activity & Vendor Info: (Acquisitions) SIRSI; (Cataloging) SIRSI
Partic in Westlaw

C VANDERBILT UNIVERSITY, Jean & Alexander Heard Library, 419 21st Ave S, 37240-0007. SAN 360-8794. Tel: 615-322-7100. Interlibrary Loan Service Tel: 615-322-2408. FAX: 615-343-8279. Interlibrary Loan Service FAX: 615-343-7276. Web Site: www.library.vanderbilt.edu. *Librn*, Paul M Gherman; *Assoc Librn*, Flo Wilson; *Asst Librn*, John Haar; *ILL*, James Toplon; Staff 298 (MLS 89, Non-MLS 209)
Founded 1873. Highest Degree: Doctorate
Jul 1999-Jun 2000 Mats Exp $7,063,263, Books $1,510,066, Per/Ser (Incl. Access Fees) $5,341,373, Other Print Mats $211,824. Sal $7,493,822 (Prof $3,999,615)
Library Holdings: Bk Vols 2,626,630; Per Subs 22,612
Automation Activity & Vendor Info: (Acquisitions) SIRSI; (Cataloging) SIRSI; (Circulation) SIRSI
Mem of Asn of Research Libraries; Asn of Southeastern Research Libraries
Partic in OCLC Online Computer Library Center, Inc
Friends of the Library Group
Departmental Libraries:
WALKER MANAGEMENT, 401 21st Ave S, 37203. SAN 328-9737. Tel: 615-322-2970. Circulation Tel: 615-343-3340. Reference Tel: 615-322-3960. FAX: 615-343-0061. Web Site: www.library.vanderbilt.edu/walker. *Dir*, Brent Mai; *Assoc Dir*, Sylvia Graham; *Librn*, Carol McCrary; *Circ*, Rosemary Madill; Staff 12 (MLS 5, Non-MLS 7)
Jan 2000-Jan 2001 Income $1,221,040, Locally Generated Income $80,500, Parent Institution $965,540, Other $175,000. Mats Exp $432,820, Books $50,363, Per/Ser (Incl. Access Fees) $267,230, Presv $8,872, Electronic Ref Mat (Incl. Access Fees) $106,355. Sal $419,976 (Prof $288,856)
Library Holdings: Bk Vols 50,635; Per Subs 645
Subject Interests: Bus, Corp info, Mgt
Special Collections: Career Planning & Placement Resource Coll
Publications: BIS Newsletter
Friends of the Library Group
ANNE POTTER WILSON MUSIC LIBRARY, 2400 Blakemore Ave, 37212. SAN 360-9006. Tel: 615-322-7695. Circulation Tel: 615-322-7695. Reference Tel: 615-322-7696. FAX: 615-343-0050. Web Site: www.library.vanderbilt.edu/music/wilson.htm. *Dir*, Dennis Marie Clark; Staff 4 (MLS 1, Non-MLS 3)
Jul 1999-Jun 2000 Income $208,700. Mats Exp $39,400, Books $14,000, Per/Ser (Incl. Access Fees) $12,700, Other Print Mats $5,900, Electronic Ref Mat (Incl. Access Fees) $5,300. Sal $114,078
Library Holdings: Bk Vols 37,977; Per Subs 183
Special Collections: Seminar in Piano Teaching, lectures, master classes, recitals, 1970-76, cassette tapes
Publications: Newsletter (Annually)
Partic in OCLC Online Computer Library Center, Inc
Friends of the Library Group
CENTRAL, 419 21st Ave S, 37240-0007. Tel: 615-322-2800. Web Site: www.library.vanderbilt.edu. *Dir*, Paul Gherman; *Assoc Dir, Coll Develop*, John Haar; *Assoc Dir, Publ Servs*, Bill Hook; *Coll Develop*, Julie Loder; *Coll Develop*, Julie Loder; *Circ, Media Spec*, Janet Thomason; *Mgr*, Janice Adlington; *Bibliog Instr*, Christine Germino; *Head Ref*, David Carpenter; *Govt Doc*, Larry Romans; *Bibliog Instr*, Melinda Brown; *Ref Serv*, Susan Erickson. Subject Specialists: *Art*, Yvonne Boyer; *Business and management*, Melinda Brown; *Economics*, Melinda Brown; *English (language)*, Dale Manning; *French (Language)*, Yvonne Boyer; *History*, Peter Brush; *Italian (language)*, Yvonne Boyer; *Latin America*, Paula Covington; *Linguistics*, Dale Manning; *Philosophy*, Melinda Brown; *Portuguese (language)*, Paula Covington; *Spanish (language)*, Paula Covington; Staff 15 (MLS 13, Non-MLS 2)
Jul 1999-Jun 2000 Income Locally Generated Income $67,407. Mats Exp $1,663,422, Books $807,728, Per/Ser (Incl. Access Fees) $535,804, AV Equip $7,770, Electronic Ref Mat (Incl. Access Fees) $171,631. Sal $840,047 (Prof $501,137)
Library Holdings: Bk Vols 1,166,842; Per Subs 2,519
Subject Interests: Art, Humanities, Social sciences
Special Collections: Pascal Pia Coll (20th Century French Literature); WT Bandy Center for Baudelaire Studies
Automation Activity & Vendor Info: (Acquisitions) SIRSI; (Cataloging) SIRSI; (Circulation) SIRSI; (OPAC) SIRSI; (Serials) SIRSI
Partic in OCLC Online Computer Library Center, Inc
Friends of the Library Group
CR DIVINITY LIBRARY, 419 21st Ave S, 37240-0007. SAN 360-8913. Tel: 615-322-2865. FAX: 615-343-2918. E-Mail: Internet: divlib@library.vanderbilt.edu. Web Site: http://divinity.library.vanderbilt.edu/. *Dir*, William Hook; *Assoc Dir, Coll Develop*, Anne C R Womack; *Cat*, Eileen Crawford; Staff 6 (MLS 4, Non-MLS 2)
Founded 1894
Jul 1999-Jun 2000 Income $817,236. Mats Exp $236,257, Books $184,132, Per/Ser (Incl. Access Fees) $40,000, Electronic Ref Mat (Incl. Access Fees) $11,820. Sal $200,227 (Prof $148,898)
Library Holdings: Bk Vols 185,000; Per Subs 632
Subject Interests: Relig studies, Theology
Special Collections: Kelly Miller Smith Coll; Special Coll in Judaica
Publications: Guide to the Divinity Library, Franz Rosenzweig: His Li & Work; Lectionary Readings for Reference & Reflection; Vanderbilt University Library, Brief History of the Judaica Coll
Partic in OCLC Online Computer Library Center, Inc
EDUCATION, Peabody College, PO Box 325, 37203-5601. SAN 360-89 Tel: 615-322-8095. Circulation Tel: 615-322-8098. Reference Tel: 615-322-8247. FAX: 615-343-7923. Web Site: www.library.vanderbilt.edu/. *Dir*, Mary Beth Blalock; E-Mail: blalock@library.vanderbilt.edu; *Assoc Dir*, Jean Reese; Tel: 615-322-8248, E-Mail: jean.reese@vanderbilt.edu; *Ref*, Lee Ann Lannom; Tel: 615-343-2915, E-Mail: lannom@library.vanderbilt.edu; *Ref*, Leslie Boyd; Tel: 615-343-7541, E-Mail: boyd@library.vanderbilt.edu; Staff 6 (MLS 4, Non-MLS 2)
Enrl 1,546; Fac 102; Highest Degree: Doctorate
Jul 1999-Jun 2000 Mats Exp $191,343, Books $48,841, Per/Ser (Incl. Access Fees) $116,582, Electronic Ref Mat (Incl. Access Fees) $25,920. Sal $322,232 (Prof $215,854)
Library Holdings: Bk Vols 233,631; Per Subs 683
Subject Interests: Child development, Education, Human develop, Psychology
Special Collections: Child Study (Peabody Coll of Books on Children); Curriculum Laboratory; Juvenile Literature Coll
Automation Activity & Vendor Info: (Acquisitions) SIRSI; (Catalogin SIRSI; (Circulation) SIRSI; (Course Reserve) SIRSI; (OPAC) SIRSI; (Serials) SIRSI
Database Vendor: OCLC - First Search
Publications: Bibliographic guides; newsletter
Partic in OCLC Online Computer Library Center, Inc
Friends of the Library Group
CL LAW SCHOOL LIBRARY, 131 21st Ave S, 37203. SAN 315-9345. Tel: 615-322-2568. Circulation Tel: 615-343-8731. Reference Tel: 615-343-8737. FAX: 615-343-1265. Web Site: www.vanderbilt.edu/law/library. *D* Pauline M Aranas; *Assoc Dir*, Mary C Miles; *Ref*, David Bachman; *Cat*, Linda Tesar; *Acq*, William M Walker; *Publ Servs*, Martin Cerjan; *Ref*, Stephen Jordan
Founded 1874
Jul 1999-Jun 2000 Income $2,322,701, Locally Generated Income $60,000, Parent Institution $2,262,701. Mats Exp $1,036,289, Books $18,318, Per/Ser (Incl. Access Fees) $901,932, Other Print Mats $18,81 Electronic Ref Mat (Incl. Access Fees) $97,221. Sal $875,830 (Prof $429,326)
Library Holdings: Bk Vols 396,759; Per Subs 6,843
Partic in OCLC Online Computer Library Center, Inc
SCIENCE & ENGINEERING, 3205 Stevenson Center, 1225 Stevenson Lane, 37240. (Mail add: 419 21st Ave S, 37240), Tel: 615-343-1870. Circulation Tel: 615-322-2775. Reference Tel: 615-322-2717. FAX: 615-343-7239. Web Site: www.library.vanderbilt.edu/science/science.html. *Di* Sherre Harrington; Tel: 615-343-6043, E-Mail: harrington@library.vanderbilt.edu; *Tech Coordr*, Richard Stringer-Hye; Tel: 615-343-4395, E-Mail: stringer@library.vanderbilt.edu. Subject Specialists: *Astronomy*, Carlin Sappenfield; *Biology*, Jon Erickson; *Chemical engineering*, Kitty Porter; *Chemistry*, Kitty Porter; *Computer science*, Carlin Sappenfield; *Geography*, Richard Stringer-Hye; *Geology*, Richard Stringer-Hye; *Mathematics*, Carlin Sappenfield; *Molecular biology*, Jon Erickson; Staff 10 (MLS 6, Non-MLS 4)
Jan 1999-Dec 2000 Mats Exp $2,104,000, Books $251,000, Per/Ser (Inc Access Fees) $1,411,000, Electronic Ref Mat (Incl. Access Fees) $367,000. Sal $420,255
Library Holdings: Bk Vols 326,014; Per Subs 1,590
Partic in OCLC Online Computer Library Center, Inc; SE Libr Network
Friends of the Library Group
SPECIAL COLLECTIONS, 419 21st Ave S, 37240-0007. SAN 360-9065. Tel: 615-322-2807. FAX: 615-343-9832. Web Site: www.library.vanderbilt.edu/speccol/schome.html. *Librn*, Kathleen Smith; *Archivist, Librn*, Juanita Murray; *Archivist, Librn*, Sara Harwell; Staff 3 (MLS 3)
1999-2000 Income $279,140. Mats Exp $11,000, Books $10,000, Presv $1,000. Sal $237,818 (Prof $132,307)
Library Holdings: Bk Vols 40,000
Subject Interests: History, Performing arts, Politics, Southern lit
Special Collections: 20th Century Film (Delbert Mann Coll); American Literature & Criticism, 1920 to Present (Jesse E Wills Fugitive-Agrarian Coll); Sevier & Rand Coll; Theatre, Music & Dance (Francis Robinson Coll)
Partic in OCLC Online Computer Library Center, Inc
Friends of the Library Group
CM THE ANNETTE & IRWIN ESKIND BIOMEDICAL LIBRARY, 2209 Garland Ave, 37232-8340. SAN 315-9337. Tel: 615-936-1400. Interlibrar Loan Service Tel: 615-936-1405. FAX: 615-936-1407. Web Site: www.mc.vanderbilt.edu/biolib/. *Dir*, Nunzia B Giuse; Tel: 615-936-1385, Fax: 615-936-1384, E-Mail: nunzia.giuse@mcmail.vanderbilt.edu; *Assoc Dir*, Frances Lynch; Tel: 615-936-1383, Fax: 615-936-1384, E-Mail: frances.lynch@mcmail.vanderbilt.edu; *Publ Servs*, Marcia Epelbaum; Tel 615-936-1369, E-Mail: marcia.epelbaum@mcmail.vanderbilt.edu; *Coordr* Jennifer Lyon; Tel: 615-936-1418, E-Mail: jennifer.lyon@

mcmail.vanderbilt.edu; *Archivist*, Randy Jones; Tel: 615-343-7597, Fax: 615-343-5770, E-Mail: randy.jones@mcmail.vanderbilt.edu; *ILL*, Dan McCollum; Tel: 615-936-1365, E-Mail: dan.mccollum@mcmail.vanderbilt.edu; *Web Coordr*, Annette Williams; Tel: 615-936-1553, E-Mail: annette.williams@mcmail.vanderbilt.edu; *Spec Coll*, Mary H Teloh; Tel: 915-936-1406, E-Mail: mary.teloh@mcmail.vanderbilt.edu; *Coll Develop, Tech Servs*, Deborah Broadwater; Tel: 615-936-1394, E-Mail: deborah.broadwater@mcmail.vanderbilt.edu; *Instrul Serv*, Martin Senora; Tel: 615-936-1417, E-Mail: sandi.martin@mcmail.vanderbilt.edu; *Res*, Patricia Lee; Tel: 615-936-1380, E-Mail: patricia.lee@mcmail.vanderbilt.edu; *Ref*, Nila Sathe; Tel: 615-936-1905, Fax: 615-936-3508, E-Mail: nila.sathe@mcmail.vanderbilt.edu; Staff 43 (MLS 17, Non-MLS 26)
Founded 1906. Highest Degree: Doctorate
Jul 1999-Jun 2000 Income $4,332,313, Federal $95,423, Locally Generated Income $362,064, Parent Institution $3,788,923, Other $59,245. Mats Exp $1,431,809, Books $129,540, Per/Ser (Incl. Access Fees) $1,165,760, Presv $36,481, Electronic Ref Mat (Incl. Access Fees) $100,028. Sal $1,558,201
Library Holdings: Bk Vols 80,906; Per Subs 2,448
Subject Interests: Biomed, Health sci
Special Collections: History of Medicine, artifacts, bks, mss & pictures; Hypnotism (Albert Moll Coll), bks, clippings, reprints & theses; Nutrition History (Goldberger-Sebrell Coll, Helen Mitchell Coll, Franklin C Bing Coll, Neige Todhunter Culinary Coll), bks, clipping, mss & photogs
Publications: CATALIST (online newsletter); Library guide
Partic in Consortium Of Southern Biomedical Libraries (CONBLS); Nashville Area Libr Alliance; National Network Of Libraries Of Medicine - South Central Region; OCLC Online Computer Library Center, Inc
Primary information resource for the Schools of Medicine & Nursing, the Vanderbilt University Hospital/Clinic & the Bill Wilkerson Hearing & Speech Center
Friends of the Library Group

WATKINS COLLEGE OF ART & DESIGN, George B Allen Memorial Library, 100 Powell Pl, 37204. SAN 315-9361. Tel: 615-383-4848. FAX: 615-383-4849. Web Site: www.watkins.edu. *Librn*, Beverly Stark
Library Holdings: Bk Vols 7,000; Per Subs 20
Subject Interests: Architecture, Art, Film studies, Interior design
Special Collections: Tennessee History Coll

[NE]WBERN

NEWBERN CITY LIBRARY, 220 E Main St, 38059-1528. SAN 315-937X. Tel: 901-627-3153. FAX: 901-627-3129. E-Mail: newlib@pchnet.com. *Dir*, Janice Peevyhouse
Founded 1969. Pop 3,000; Circ 31,372
Library Holdings: Bk Vols 12,000; Per Subs 47
Mem of Forked Deer Regional Library Center

[NE]WPORT

STOKELY MEMORIAL LIBRARY, 383 E Broadway, 37821-3105. SAN 315-9388. Tel: 423-623-3832. FAX: 423-623-3832. *Dir*, Meschelyn Barrett; E-Mail: mbarrett@mail.state.tn.us
Library Holdings: Bk Vols 30,000
Subject Interests: Genealogy
Special Collections: James Stokely Coll
Mem of Nolichucky Regional Library
Friends of the Library Group

[NI]OTA

NIOTA PUBLIC LIBRARY, 11 E Main St, PO Box 146, 37826-0146. SAN 315-9396. Tel: 423-568-2613. FAX: 423-568-3026. E-Mail: niolib@yahoo.com. *Dir*, Eva Brakebill
Library Holdings: Bk Vols 14,091
Mem of Fort Loudoun Regional Library Center

[NO]RRIS

NORRIS COMMUNITY LIBRARY, One Town Square, 37828. SAN 315-940X. Tel: 865-494-6800. FAX: 865-494-8055. *Librn*, Melanie Paquette
Library Holdings: Bk Vols 12,000; Per Subs 32
Mem of Clinch-Powell Regional Library
Friends of the Library Group

[OA]K RIDGE

CHILDREN'S MUSEUM OF OAK RIDGE, Regional Appalachian Center - Media Library, 461 W Outer Dr, PO Box 5766, 37831-5766. SAN 326-727X. Tel: 865-482-1074. FAX: 865-481-4889. *Exec Dir*, Thelma Shapiro
Library Holdings: Bk Vols 2,520; Per Subs 20
Special Collections: Oak Ridge, Anderson & Roane Counties (personal papers, scrapbooks, photographs & oral history tapes)
Publications: An Appalachian Studies Teacher's Manual; An Encyclopedia of East Tennessee; Anderson County Tennessee: A Pictorial History; Oak Ridge and Me: From Youth to Maturity; Ridges & Valleys: A Mini-Encyclopedia of Anderson County; These Are Our Voices: The Story of Oak Ridge, Tennessee, 1943-1970
Restriction: By appointment only

SR FIRST UNITED METHODIST CHURCH, Jones Memorial Library, 1350 Oak Ridge Tpk, PO Box 4669, 37831. SAN 371-6171. Tel: 865-483-4357. FAX: 865-483-9011. E-Mail: fumc@icx.net. Web Site: www.user.icx.net/~fumc/. *Dir*, Virginia Colburn; Staff 1 (Non-MLS 1)
Founded 1967
Library Holdings: Bk Vols 9,000; Per Subs 25
Special Collections: Christians & Jews Studies (Munz Coll)
Publications: In-house bibliographies

S OAK RIDGE ASSOCIATED UNIVERSITIES, Library & Information Center, 140 Vance Rd, PO Box 117, 37831-0117. SAN 360-9901. Tel: 865-576-3490. FAX: 865-576-3070. *Librn*, Susan Ekkebus; Fax: 865-576-3070, E-Mail: ekkebuss@orau.gov; Staff 2 (MLS 2)
Founded 1974
Library Holdings: Bk Titles 1,000; Per Subs 100
Subject Interests: Biochemistry, Nuclear medicine
Special Collections: Health Sciences (Department of Energy Coll), micro
Partic in Knoxville Area Health Sciences Library Consortium; Tenn Share

S OAK RIDGE NATIONAL LABORATORY, O R N L Research Libraries, Bethel Valley Rd, 37830. (Mail add: Bldg 4500N, MS-6191, PO Box 2008, 37831-6191), SAN 360-9960. Tel: 865-574-6744. FAX: 865-574-6745. E-Mail: library@ornl.gov. Web Site: www.ornl.gov/library/. *Mgr*, Ta-Chang Liu; Tel: 865-576-7272, E-Mail: liut@ornl.gov; Staff 17 (MLS 11, Non-MLS 6)
Founded 1946
Library Holdings: Bk Vols 77,000; Bk Titles 75,000; Per Subs 1,100
Subject Interests: Biology, Ceramics, Chemistry, Climate, Computing, Ecology, Energy, Environ scis, Fusion energy, Mat sci, Metals, Neutron sci, Nuclear energy, Nuclear engineering, Physics, Robotics
Special Collections: DOE Scientific & Technical Reports
Database Vendor: Dialog, Ebsco - EbscoHost, Lexis-Nexis, OCLC - First Search
Restriction: Staff use only
Function: Research library
Partic in Knoxville Area Health Sciences Library Consortium; Oak Ridge Nat Lab Libr Coop; Tenn Valley Authority; Univ of Tenn Knoxville
Branches:

SR OAK RIDGE NATIONAL LABORATORY, Nuclear Operations Analysis Center, PO Box 2009, 37831-8065. SAN 372-9583. Tel: 865-574-0394. FAX: 865-574-0382. E-Mail: gtm@ornl.gov. *Dir*, Gary T Mays
Library Holdings: Bk Vols 1,000; Per Subs 20
Subject Interests: Nuclear energy, Physics

G OAK RIDGE PUBLIC LIBRARY, 1401 Oak Ridge Turnpike, 37830. (Mail add: Civic Center, 37830-6206), Tel: 865-425-3455. Reference Tel: 865-425-3465. FAX: 865-425-3429. Web Site: orserv01.ci.oak-ridge.tn.us/lib-html/orlib.htm. *Dir*, Kathy E McNeilly; Tel: 865-425-3456, E-Mail: kmcneilly@ci.aok-ridge.tn.us; *Asst Dir*, Marie Stooksbury; *Tech Servs*, Martha Lux; *Ref*, Ruth Dypolt; *ILL*, Catherine Miller; *Ch Servs*, Linda Bloedau; *Circ*, Maria Nathalie Farinacci; Staff 23 (MLS 6, Non-MLS 17)
Founded 1944
Jul 1999-Jun 2000 Income City $984,094. Mats Exp $159,158, Books $139,191, Per/Ser (Incl. Access Fees) $12,867, Micro $7,100. Sal $509,601
Library Holdings: Bk Vols 106,363; Per Subs 252
Subject Interests: Local authors, Local history, Small bus
Special Collections: Oak Ridge Room
Automation Activity & Vendor Info: (Acquisitions) SIRSI; (Cataloging) SIRSI; (Circulation) SIRSI; (OPAC) SIRSI; (Serials) SIRSI
Publications: Annual report; Orplines (newsletter)
Partic in Tenn-Share
Friends of the Library Group

S OFFICE OF SCIENTIFIC & TECHNICAL INFORMATION, Energy Science & Technology Center, 175 Oak Ridge Tpke, 37830. (Mail add: PO Box 1020, 37831-1020), SAN 374-8944. Tel: 865-576-2606. FAX: 865-576-6436. E-Mail: estsc@adonis.osti.gov. Web Site: www.osti.gov/estsc. *Dir*, Kim Buckner

OAKDALE

P OAKDALE PUBLIC LIBRARY, 212 Queen St, PO Box 190, 37829-0190. SAN 315-9485. Tel: 423-369-3524. *Dir*, Norma A Mathis; E-Mail: nmathis@mail.state.tn.us
Library Holdings: Bk Vols 2,250; Per Subs 2
Mem of Clinch-Powell Regional Library

OLIVER SPRINGS

P OLIVER SPRINGS PUBLIC LIBRARY, 610 Walker Ave, PO Box 303, 37840. SAN 315-9515. Tel: 865-435-2509, 865-435-7722. FAX: 865-435-5350. *Librn*, Sue St John
Library Holdings: Bk Titles 2,000
Subject Interests: Local history
Mem of Fort Loudoun Regional Library Center

ONEIDA

P ONEIDA COUNTY PUBLIC LIBRARY, Scott County Branch, 290 S Main St, 37841-2605. SAN 315-9523. Tel: 423-569-8634. *Librn*, Marilyn I Foster; E-Mail: mfoster@mail.state.tn.us
Pop 18,000
Mem of Clinch-Powell Regional Library
For holdings see library system. Open Mon, Wed & Fri 9-1, Tues 2-7, Sat 9-5

PALMER

P PALMER PUBLIC LIBRARY, Hwy 108, 37365-9999. SAN 315-9531. Tel: 931-779-5292. FAX: 931-779-5292. E-Mail: palmerlib@blomand.net. Web Site: www.state.tn.us/cgi-bin/library. *Dir*, Susan F Sissom
Founded 1956. Pop 1,027
Library Holdings: Bk Titles 1,200
Mem of Caney Fork Regional Library

PARIS

P W G RHEA LIBRARY, 400 W Washington, 38242-0456. SAN 315-954X. Tel: 901-642-1702. FAX: 901-642-1777. *Dir*, Connie McSwain; E-Mail: cmcswain@mail.state.tn.us; *Asst Dir*, Freda Reddick
Founded 1960. Pop 28,000; Circ 78,000
Library Holdings: Bk Titles 28,600; Per Subs 95
Subject Interests: Genealogy
Mem of Reelfoot Regional Library Center
Friends of the Library Group

PARSONS

P PARSONS PUBLIC LIBRARY, 105 Kentucky Ave S, 38363-2517. SAN 315-9566. Tel: 901-847-6988. FAX: 901-847-3476. Web Site: www.geocities.com/athens/troy/3469. *Librn*, Maxine Wheat
Pop 6,000
Library Holdings: Bk Vols 14,000
Mem of Shiloh Regional Library
Friends of the Library Group

PETROS

P PETROS PUBLIC LIBRARY, 208 W Main St, PO Box 147, 37845-0147. SAN 315-9574. Tel: 423-324-2825. *Dir*, Pat Chamblee
Circ 3,140
Library Holdings: Bk Vols 9,111
Mem of Clinch-Powell Regional Library

PHILADELPHIA

P PHILADELPHIA PUBLIC LIBRARY, 714 Thompson St, PO Box 129, 37846-129. SAN 376-2955. Tel: 423-458-9493. *Dir*, Kim Roberts
Library Holdings: Bk Vols 6,600; Bk Titles 7,000
Mem of Fort Loudoun Regional Library Center

PIKEVILLE

P BLEDSOE COUNTY PUBLIC LIBRARY, 102 E Cumberland Ave, PO Box 465, 37367-0465. SAN 315-9582. Tel: 423-447-2817. FAX: 423-447-3002. *Dir*, Carolyne Knight; E-Mail: cknight@mail.state.tn.us
Pop 7,643; Circ 13,000
Library Holdings: Bk Titles 10,000; Per Subs 14
Mem of Caney Fork Regional Library

PINEY FLATS

S ROCKY MOUNT HISTORICAL ASSOCIATION LIBRARY, 200 Hyder Hill Rd, 37686-4630. (Mail add: PO Box 160, 37686-0160), SAN 326-3223. Tel: 423-538-7396. FAX: 423-538-1086. E-Mail: rockymount@mindspring.com. *Exec Dir*, John Paterson
Library Holdings: Bk Vols 3,500

PORTLAND

P PORTLAND PUBLIC LIBRARY, Elmer Hinton Memorial Library, 301 Portland Blvd, 37148-1229. SAN 315-9590. Tel: 615-325-2279. Referenc Tel: 615-325-4015. FAX: 931-325-7061. Web Site: www.portlanttn.com/library.htm. *Dir*, Barbara Russell; E-Mail: brusell@bellsouth.net; *Asst Lib* Shirley Stephens; *Automation Syst Coordr*, Debra Elledge; *Ch Servs*, Lin Ackerman; Staff 4 (Non-MLS 4)
Founded 1953. Pop 19,000; Circ 49,000
Jul 1999-Jun 2000 Income $120,376, City $17,920, County $75,456, Loc Generated Income $21,500, Other $5,500. Mats Exp $17,350, Books $13,500, Per/Ser (Incl. Access Fees) $1,500, AV Equip $2,350. Sal $56,6
Library Holdings: Bk Titles 30,000; Per Subs 60; Bks on Deafness & S Lang 12
Special Collections: Civil War - Tennessee History; NASA
Database Vendor: GaleNet
Mem of Warioto Regional Library Center
Friends of the Library Group

PULASKI

P GILES COUNTY PUBLIC LIBRARY, (GCPL), 122 S Second St, 38478-2720. SAN 315-9604. Tel: 931-363-2720. FAX: 931-424-7032. E-Mail: gclib@usit.net. *Dir*, Alice Trimble; *Asst Librn*, Kathryn Cagle; *Asst Librn*, Shirley Eubank; *Circ*, Barbara Pankey; *Circ*, Betty Driscoll; Staff 1 (Non-MLS 1)
Founded 1940. Pop 29,036; Circ 80,000
Jul 1999-Jun 2000 Income (Main Library Only) $185,000, City $70,000, County $70,000, Locally Generated Income $30,000, Other $15,000. Mats Exp $39,465, Books $16,176, Per/Ser (Incl. Access Fees) $2,291, AV Equ $2,318. Sal $95,876 (Prof $32,500)
Library Holdings: Bk Titles 36,000; Per Subs 70
Subject Interests: Genealogy, History, Local history
Special Collections: Census (microfilms); Museum Coll
Database Vendor: GaleNet
Publications: Bulletin (quarterly)
Mem of Blue Grass Regional Library
Friends of the Library Group
Branches: 1
ELKTON BRANCH, 168 Main St, Elkton, 38455. (Mail add: PO Box 15 Elkton, 38455-0157), SAN 376-8082. Tel: 931-468-2506. *Librn*, Victori Costley
Library Holdings: Bk Vols 2,000
Mem of Blue Grass Regional Library

C MARTIN METHODIST COLLEGE, Warden Memorial Library, 433 W Madison St, 38478-2799. SAN 315-9612. Tel: 931-363-9844. Toll Free Te 800-467-1273. FAX: 931-363-9818. E-Mail: mmclib@usit.net. Web Site: martinlib.igiles.net, www.public.usit.net/mmclib/. *Dir*, Janet Brennan Croft E-Mail: jbcroft@hotmail.com; *Librn*, Nathalie George; Tel: 931-363-9843, E-Mail: nathgeorge@hotmail.com; Staff 6 (MLS 2, Non-MLS 4)
Founded 1870. Enrl 500; Highest Degree: Bachelor
Jul 1998-Jun 1999 Mats Exp $102,000, Books $30,000, Per/Ser (Incl. Access Fees) $24,000, AV Equip $21,000
Library Holdings: Bk Vols 38,000; Bk Titles 35,000; Per Subs 300
Subject Interests: Local history
Special Collections: Glatzer/Zimmerman Judaica; Gregory McDonald mss Methodist History; Psychology (William Fitts Coll); Senator Ross Bass Co Vachel Lindsey materials
Automation Activity & Vendor Info: (Acquisitions) SIRSI; (Circulation) SIRSI; (OPAC) SIRSI
Database Vendor: Ebsco - EbscoHost, GaleNet, OCLC - First Search, ProQuest, Silverplatter Information Inc.
Partic in Solinet; Tenn Share
Special Services for the Blind - Braille

RIDGELY

P RIDGELY PUBLIC LIBRARY, 134 N Main St, 38080-1316. SAN 315-9620. Tel: 901-264-5809. *Dir*, Wanda Richardson
Library Holdings: Bk Vols 2,565
Mem of Forked Deer Regional Library Center

RIPLEY

P LAUDERDALE COUNTY LIBRARY, 120 Lafayette St, 38063-1321. SA 315-9639. Tel: 901-635-1872. FAX: 901-635-8568. *Librn*, Marilyn Tillman
Pop 22,000
Library Holdings: Bk Titles 18,500; Per Subs 24
Subject Interests: Genealogy
Mem of Forked Deer Regional Library Center
Friends of the Library Group

CKWOOD

ROCKWOOD PUBLIC LIBRARY, 117 N Front St, 37854-2320. SAN 315-9647. Tel: 865-354-1281. FAX: 865-354-4302. Web Site: www.rockwoodlibrary.org. *Dir*, Margaret Marrs
Library Holdings: Bk Vols 36,000
Mem of Fort Loudoun Regional Library Center

GERSVILLE

H B STAMPS MEMORIAL LIBRARY, 407 E Main St, 37857. SAN 315-9655. Tel: 423-272-8710. FAX: 423-272-9261. E-Mail: hbslib@mailstate.tn.us. *Dir*, Jeannie E Davis; *Librn*, Barbara Groves; Staff 1 (MLS 1)
Founded 1954. Pop 43,000; Circ 107,838
Jul 1998-Jun 1999 Income $141,410, City $57,315, County $20,000. Mats Exp $8,513, Books $5,603, Per/Ser (Incl. Access Fees) $2,210. Sal $59,550 (Prof $26,000)
Library Holdings: Bk Vols 21,600; Bk Titles 20,000; Per Subs 76
Special Collections: Hawkins County History & Genealogy (H B Stamps Coll); Juno Altom Genealogy Room; Tennessee Valley Authority
Friends of the Library Group
Branches: 1
CHURCH HILL BRANCH, 302 E Main Blvd, PO Box 37, Church Hill, 37642-0037. SAN 315-7458. Tel: 423-357-4591. FAX: 423-357-8396. *Dir*, Maureen McDaniels; *Branch Mgr*, Phyllis Corder
Library Holdings: Bk Titles 17,289; Per Subs 42
Mem of Nolichucky Regional Library

SAINT CLAIR LIBRARY, 118 Saint Clair Park Circle, 37857. (Mail add: 746 Hwy 113, 37711), SAN 315-7296. Tel: 423-235-2900. FAX: 423-235-2900. E-Mail: stclib@onemain.com. *Dir*, Sheryl Chesnutt
Library Holdings: Bk Titles 6,500
Mem of Nolichucky Regional Library

JGBY

HISTORIC RUGBY, Thomas Hughes Free Public Library, 5517 Rugby Hwy, 37733. (Mail add: PO Box 8, 37733), SAN 324-1378. Tel: 423-628-2441. FAX: 423-628-2266. E-Mail: rugbytn@highland.net. Web Site: www.historicrugby.org. *Exec Dir*, Barbara Stagg
Founded 1881
Library Holdings: Bk Titles 7,000; Per Subs 1,010
Subject Interests: Biog, Etiquette, Poetry, Religion, Travel, Victorian-era hist
Restriction: Not a lending library
Building shown on tour. Collection available to serious researchers only.

UTLEDGE

GRAINGER COUNTY LIBRARY, Hwy 11 W, 37861. (Mail add: PO Box 100, 37861-9999), Tel: 423-828-4784. *Dir*, Rebecca Morrison; Fax: 940-720-6659, E-Mail: bmorrison@wfpl.net
Founded 1946. Pop 16,751
Library Holdings: Bk Vols 3,540; Bk Titles 3,391
Mem of Nolichucky Regional Library

VANNAH

HARDIN COUNTY LIBRARY, 1013 Main St, 38372-1903. SAN 315-9663. Tel: 901-925-4314, 901-925-6848. FAX: 901-925-7132. *Librn*, Jeanette K Smith; E-Mail: jsmith5@mail.state.tn.us; Staff 1 (Non-MLS 1)
Founded 1935. Pop 26,000
Jul 1998-Jun 1999 Income $96,681, City $10,000, County $86,681. Mats Exp $4,993, Books $2,880, Per/Ser (Incl. Access Fees) $2,113. Sal $70,574
Library Holdings: Bk Vols 31,000; Per Subs 82
Special Collections: Genealogy Coll, marriage contracts & bonds on micro; Tennessee Coll, bks, micro
Mem of Shiloh Regional Library
Friends of the Library Group

ELMER

JACK MCCONNICO MEMORIAL LIBRARY, 225 Oak Grove Rd, 38375-1879. SAN 315-9671. Tel: 901-645-5571. Interlibrary Loan Service Tel: 800-532-6251. FAX: 901-645-4874. Web Site: www.jackmcconnicolibrary.homepage.com. *Dir*, Norma Humphries; Staff 3 (MLS 1, Non-MLS 2)
Founded 1984. Pop 22,422
Library Holdings: Bk Vols 25,000
Subject Interests: Genealogy, Local, State hist
Special Collections: Historic Old Purdy; Literacy, McNairy Co hist; McNairy Co; photo; Vietnam War; Wild Flower Coll
Publications: Cemetery Records; Early Marriages; McNairy Co History
Mem of Shiloh Regional Library

SEVIERVILLE

P SEVIER COUNTY PUBLIC LIBRARY, 321 Court Ave, 37862. SAN 315-968X. Tel: 865-453-3532. FAX: 865-453-6108. E-Mail: sev1@mail.state.tn.us. Web Site: www.sevierlibrary.org. *Dir Libr Serv*, Hugh Thomas
Founded 1920. Pop 47,626; Circ 164,622
Library Holdings: Bk Vols 358,865; Per Subs 87
Subject Interests: Genealogy
Database Vendor: GaleNet, OCLC - First Search, Wilson - Wilson Web
Function: ILL available
Mem of Nolichucky Regional Library
Branches: 1
SEYMOUR BRANCH, 11560 Chapman Hwy, Seymour, 37865. SAN 320-0647. Tel: 865-573-0728. FAX: 865-573-0728. Web Site: www.sevierlibrary.org. *Head of Libr*, Virginia Borrelli
Library Holdings: Bk Titles 7,778
Mem of Nolichucky Regional Library

SEWANEE

C UNIVERSITY OF THE SOUTH, Jessie Ball DuPont Library, 735 University Ave, 37383-1000. SAN 361-0144. Tel: 931-598-1265. Interlibrary Loan Service Tel: 931-598-1612. Circulation Tel: 931-598-1664. Reference Tel: 931-598-1368. FAX: 931-598-1702. Web Site: www.library.sewanee.edu. *Dir Libr Serv*, Tom Watson; Tel: 931-598-1266, E-Mail: twatson@sewanee.edu; *Ref Serv*, Sue Armentrout; Tel: 931-598-1363, E-Mail: sarmentr@sewanee.edu; *Head, Acq*, Elizabeth Grant; Tel: 931-598-1663, E-Mail: bgrant@sewanee.edu; *Head, Cat*, Patricia Thompson; Tel: 931-598-1657, E-Mail: pthompso@sewanee.edu; *Spec Coll*, Anne Armour; Tel: 931-598-3212, E-Mail: aarmour@sewanee.edu; *Ref Serv*, Mary O'Neill; Tel: 931-598-1660, E-Mail: moneill@sewanee.edu; *Ref Serv*, Heidi Lowry; Tel: 931-598-1709, E-Mail: hlowry@sewanee.edu; *Head Ref*, Eloise Hitchcock; Tel: 931-598-1366, E-Mail: ehitchco@sewanee.edu; *Head, Ser Acq*, Joe David McBee; Tel: 931-598-1574, E-Mail: dmcbee@sewanee.edu; *Doc*, Kevin Reynolds; Tel: 931-598-1727, E-Mail: kreynold@sewanee.edu; *Automation Syst Coordr*, Penny Cowan; Tel: 931-598-1573, E-Mail: pcowan@sewanee.edu; *Head, Circ*, Barbara Dykes; Tel: 931-598-1486, E-Mail: bdykes@sewanee.edu; *ILL*, Andrew Moser; E-Mail: amoser@sewanee.edu; *Assoc Dir*, Jim Dunkly; Tel: 931-598-1267, E-Mail: jdunkly@sewanee.edu; *Ref Serv*, John Janeway; Tel: 931-598-1778, E-Mail: jjaneway@sewanee.edu; Staff 15 (MLS 9, Non-MLS 6)
Founded 1858. Enrl 1,415; Fac 137; Highest Degree: Doctorate
Jul 1999-Jun 2000 Income $2,326,278, Locally Generated Income $56,627, Parent Institution $2,269,651. Mats Exp $1,086,756, Books $322,798, Per/Ser (Incl. Access Fees) $574,069, Presv $26,996, Micro $23,680, Electronic Ref Mat (Incl. Access Fees) $139,213. Sal $812,976 (Prof $592,555)
Library Holdings: Bk Vols 488,270; Bk Titles 397,621; Per Subs 3,164
Subject Interests: Liberal arts, Theology
Special Collections: Allen Tate Coll; Anglican Prayer Book; Anglican Studies; Ayres Architecture; Episcopal Church in Southeast History; Hudson Stuck Coll; Limited Editions Club Publications; Sewaneena; Southern Literature & History; Ward Ritchie Coll
Automation Activity & Vendor Info: (Acquisitions) Innovative Interfaces Inc.; (Cataloging) Innovative Interfaces Inc.; (Circulation) Innovative Interfaces Inc.; (Course Reserve) Innovative Interfaces Inc.; (ILL) Innovative Interfaces Inc.; (Media Booking) Innovative Interfaces Inc.; (OPAC) Innovative Interfaces Inc.; (Serials) Innovative Interfaces Inc.
Publications: Friends of the Library (Newsletter)
Partic in Appalachian Col Asn; Assoc Cols of the South; OCLC Online Computer Library Center, Inc; SE Libr Network
Friends of the Library Group

SHARON

P SHARON PUBLIC LIBRARY, 133 E Main St, PO Box 235, 38255-0235. SAN 315-9698. Tel: 731-456-2707. *Dir*, Shirley Washburn
Library Holdings: Bk Titles 5,000
Mem of Reelfoot Regional Library Center

SHELBYVILLE

P ARGIE COOPER PUBLIC LIBRARY, 100 S Main St, 37160-3984. SAN 315-9701. Tel: 931-684-7323. FAX: 931-685-4848. *Dir*, Pat Hastings; E-Mail: phasting@mail.state.tn.us
Founded 1966. Pop 27,916; Circ 89,000
Library Holdings: Bk Vols 50,000; Bk Titles 36,000; Per Subs 72
Special Collections: History (Early Editions of Newspapers in Bedford County), micro
Mem of Highland Rim Regional Library Center
Friends of the Library Group

SHILOH

S NATIONAL PARK SERVICE, Shiloh National Military Park Study Library, 1055 Pittsburg Landing Rd, 38376. SAN 315-971X. Tel: 901-689-5275. FAX: 901-689-5450. *In Charge*, Stacy Allen; E-Mail: stacy_allen@nps.gov.
Subject Specialists: *Civil War*, Stacy Allen
Founded 1895
Library Holdings: Bk Vols 2,000; Bk Titles 1,600
Subject Interests: Civil War

SIGNAL MOUNTAIN

P TOWN OF SIGNAL MOUNTAIN LIBRARY, 1114 James Blvd, 37377-2509. SAN 371-7380. Tel: 423-886-7323. Web Site: www.signalmtnlibrary.org. *Dir*, Connie Pierce; E-Mail: cpierce@signalmtnlibrary.org; Staff 5 (MLS 1, Non-MLS 4)
Founded 1970. Pop 7,500; Circ 58,900
Jul 1999-Jun 2000 Income $160,901, City $115,901, Locally Generated Income $20,000, Other $25,000. Mats Exp $26,400, Books $21,000, Per/Ser (Incl. Access Fees) $1,600, AV Equip $1,400, Electronic Ref Mat (Incl. Access Fees) $2,400. Sal $76,000 (Prof $31,000)
Library Holdings: Bk Vols 18,000; Per Subs 42
Subject Interests: Local history
Automation Activity & Vendor Info: (Cataloging) Sagebrush Corporation; (Circulation) Sagebrush Corporation
Database Vendor: Ebsco - EbscoHost, IAC - Info Trac
Publications: Library Volunteer
Friends of the Library Group

SMITHVILLE

P JUSTIN POTTER PUBLIC LIBRARY, 101 S First St, 37166-1706. SAN 361-0209. Tel: 615-597-4359. FAX: 615-597-4329. *Dir*, June Close; E-Mail: jclose@mail.state.tn.us
Library Holdings: Bk Vols 28,666
Mem of Upper Cumberland Regional Library
Friends of the Library Group
Branches: 2
ALEXANDRIA BRANCH, 109 Public Square, PO Box 367, Alexandria, 37012. SAN 361-0233. Tel: 615-529-4124. FAX: 615-529-4124. *Dir*, Carolyn Walden; E-Mail: cwalden@tnii.net
Friends of the Library Group
DOWELLTOWN BRANCH, Church St, PO Box 87, Dowelltown, 37059. SAN 375-6149. Tel: 615-536-5997. FAX: 615-536-5499. *Dir*, Lawrence Bean

SNEEDVILLE

P HANCOCK COUNTY PUBLIC LIBRARY, Rte 2, Box A1, 37869. SAN 315-9736. Tel: 423-733-2020. FAX: 423-733-2847. E-Mail: hancockl@naxs.net. *Dir*, Brenda Snowden
Pop 6,887
Library Holdings: Bk Vols 3,000
Mem of Nolichucky Regional Library

SOMERVILLE

P SOMERVILLE-FAYETTE COUNTY LIBRARY, 216 W Market St, 38068-1592. SAN 315-9744. Tel: 901-465-5248. FAX: 901-465-5271. E-Mail: sfcl@mail.state.tn.us. *Dir*, Alida Gover
Founded 1931. Pop 25,599; Circ 30,849
1998-1999 Income $86,000, City $8,500, Locally Generated Income $2,000. Mats Exp $10,500, Books $8,000, Per/Ser (Incl. Access Fees) $2,500. Sal $49,500
Library Holdings: Bk Vols 26,000
Special Collections: Genealogy (Tennessee Coll); Local History (Museum Room)
Mem of Forked Deer Regional Library Center
Friends of the Library Group

SOUTH PITTSBURG

P BEENE-PEARSON PUBLIC LIBRARY, 208 Elm Ave, 37380-9998. SAN 315-9752. Tel: 423-837-6513. FAX: 423-837-6513. *Dir*, Alicia Stuart; E-Mail: astuart@tnii.net; *Asst Librn*, Wilbalene Crocker
Founded 1967. Circ 21,967
Library Holdings: Bk Titles 30,000; Per Subs 19
Mem of Caney Fork Regional Library

SPARTA

P CANEY FORK REGIONAL LIBRARY, 25 Rhea St, 38583. SAN 315-9760. Tel: 931-836-2209. FAX: 931-836-3469. *Dir*, Faith A Holdredge; E-Mail: fholdred@mail.state.tn.us; *Asst Dir*, Sarah Pellicciotti; E-Mail: spellicc@mail.state.tn.us; Staff 8 (MLS 2, Non-MLS 6)
Founded 1957. Pop 160,000
Library Holdings: Bk Vols 107,991; Per Subs 30
Member Libraries: Art Circle Public Library; Beene-Pearson Public Library; Beersheba Springs Public Library; Bledsoe County Public Library; Burritt Memorial Library; Jasper Public Library; Magness Library; May Justus Memorial Library; Orena Humphrey Public Library; Palmer Public Library; Sequatchie County Public Library; Tracy City Public Library; White County Public Library
Bookmobiles: 1

P WHITE COUNTY PUBLIC LIBRARY, 144 S Main St, 38583-2299. SAN 315-9779. Tel: 931-836-3613. Interlibrary Loan Service Toll Free Tel: 800-572-7396. FAX: 931-836-2570. E-Mail: wcpl@blomand.net. *Dir*, Cathy L Taylor; E-Mail: cathyt@blomd.net; *Asst Dir*, Lorraine Trudel
Founded 1957. Pop 20,090; Circ 65,000
Library Holdings: Bk Titles 19,000; Per Subs 25
Special Collections: Census for White County, micro 8
Mem of Caney Fork Regional Library
Friends of the Library Group

SPENCER

P BURRITT MEMORIAL LIBRARY, PO Box 18, 38585-0018. Tel: 931-946-2575. FAX: 931-946-2575. *Dir*, Donna Beck
Pop 5,200
Library Holdings: Bk Vols 1,800; Per Subs 18
Mem of Caney Fork Regional Library

SPRING CITY

P AUDREY PACK MEMORIAL LIBRARY, 114 W Rhea St, PO Box 382, 37381-0382. SAN 315-9795. Tel: 423-365-9757. FAX: 423-365-2198. *Dir*, Cathy Kincannon
Library Holdings: Bk Vols 15,000; Per Subs 20
Mem of Fort Loudoun Regional Library Center
Friends of the Library Group

SPRINGFIELD

P GORHAM-MACBANE PUBLIC LIBRARY, (GRM), 405 White St, 37172-2340. SAN 315-9809. Tel: 615-384-5123. FAX: 615-384-0106. E-Mail: gorhampl@bellsouth.net. *Librn*, Betty D Dailey; *Ch Servs*, Mary Schmidt; E-Mail: mmms1959@yahoo.com
Founded 1923. Pop 42,000; Circ 150,000
1999-2000 Income $196,500, City $90,000, County $90,000, Locally Generated Income $16,500. Mats Exp $24,500, Books $16,000, Per/Ser (Incl. Access Fees) $1,500, AV Equip $2,500, Electronic Ref Mat (Incl. Access Fees) $4,500. Sal $129,500
Library Holdings: Bk Vols 34,000; Bk Titles 33,750; Per Subs 58; High Interest/Low Vocabulary Bk Vols 400
Special Collections: Joseph Wellington Byrns Coll
Mem of Warioto Regional Library Center
Friends of the Library Group

STRAWBERRY PLAINS

P PARROTT-WOOD MEMORIAL LIBRARY, 3133 W Old Andrew Johnson Hwy, PO Box 399, 37871. SAN 315-9817. Tel: 865-933-1311. FAX: 865-932-3718. E-Mail: parro399@bellsouth.net. *Dir*, Coneen H Ailey
Founded 1955. Pop 4,000; Circ 13,184
Library Holdings: Bk Vols 7,773; Per Subs 14
Mem of Nolichucky Regional Library
Friends of the Library Group

SUNBRIGHT

P SUNBRIGHT PUBLIC LIBRARY, 8116 Morgan County Hwy, 37872. SAN 315-9825. Tel: 423-628-2439. Web Site: www.kornet.org/sunlibry. *Dir*, Lonetta Beshears; E-Mail: lbeshear@mail.state.tn.us
Jul 1998-Jun 1999 Income $5,165. Mats Exp $2,954, Books $2,325. Sal $2,120
Library Holdings: Bk Vols 6,815
Subject Interests: Civil War, Environ issues, Tenn hist, World War II
Mem of Clinch-Powell Regional Library
Open Mon, Wed & Thurs 4-6 & Sat 9:30-1:30

SURGOINSVILLE

P SURGOINSVILLE PUBLIC LIBRARY, 120 Old Stage Rd, 37873-3145. (Mail add: PO Box 115, 37873-0115), SAN 376-754X. Tel: 423-345-4805. FAX: 423-345-4805. *Dir*, Alma Williams
Library Holdings: Bk Titles 5,000; Per Subs 15
Mem of Nolichucky Regional Library

VEETWATER

SWEETWATER PUBLIC LIBRARY, 210 Mayes Ave, 37874. SAN 315-9833. Tel: 423-337-5274. FAX: 423-337-0552. E-Mail: swepltn@usit.net. *Dir*, Beverly Bollenbacher
Library Holdings: Bk Vols 43,000
Subject Interests: Genealogy, Local history
Mem of Fort Loudoun Regional Library Center
Friends of the Library Group

.ZEWELL

CLAIBORNE COUNTY PUBLIC LIBRARY, 1720 Eppes St, 37879. (Mail add: PO Box 139, 37879-0139), SAN 315-9841. Tel: 423-626-5414. FAX: 423-626-9481. *Dir*, Sandy Rosenbalm; E-Mail: srosenba@mail.state.tn.us
Pop 26,000
Library Holdings: Bk Vols 16,000; Per Subs 20
Mem of Clinch-Powell Regional Library

ELLICO PLAINS

TELLICO PLAINS PUBLIC LIBRARY, 209 Hwy 165, 37385. (Mail add: PO Box 658, 37385-0658), SAN 315-985X. Tel: 423-253-7388. E-Mail: tellicop@icx.net. *Dir*, Linda Morris
Library Holdings: Bk Vols 5,706
Mem of Fort Loudoun Regional Library Center
Friends of the Library Group

PTONVILLE

TIPTONVILLE PUBLIC LIBRARY, 126 Tipton St, 38079-1133. SAN 315-9868. Tel: 901-253-7391. *Dir*, Pam Maddox
Founded 1940. Pop 3,000
Library Holdings: Bk Vols 6,000
Mem of Forked Deer Regional Library Center
Friends of the Library Group

RACY CITY

TRACY CITY PUBLIC LIBRARY, Rte 1 Box 434, 37387-0277. SAN 315-9876. Tel: 931-592-9714. E-Mail: tcpublib@blomand.net. *Dir*, Leslie Coppinger; *Librn*, Lynn Anderson; Tel: 435-283-7366, E-Mail: lynn.anderson@snow.edu
Library Holdings: Bk Vols 2,300
Mem of Caney Fork Regional Library
All statistics included in Caney Fork Regional Libr Ctr. Open Mon & Wed noon-4:30, Fri noon-5
Friends of the Library Group

RENTON

GIBSON COUNTY MEMORIAL LIBRARY, 303 S High St, 38382-2027. SAN 315-9884. Tel: 901-855-1991. FAX: 901-855-1991. *Dir*, Connie G Bates; E-Mail: connieb@mail.state.tn.us; *Asst Librn*, Wendy Flowers; Staff 4 (MLS 4)
Founded 1945. Pop 46,315
Library Holdings: Bk Vols 26,000; Per Subs 80
Subject Interests: Formal educ support, Genealogical res, Popular mat
Special Collections: Original County Records
Mem of Reelfoot Regional Library Center
Open Nov-Dec: Mon 10:30-6:30, Tues-Fri 9- 5, Sat 9-12. Open Jan-Oct: Mon 10:30-6:30, Tues-Fri 9-5
Friends of the Library Group

RIMBLE

TRIMBLE PUBLIC LIBRARY, 90 Main St, PO Box 215, 38259-0215. SAN 376-7752. Tel: 901-297-2702. *Dir*, Neda Hinson
1998-1999 Income $10,700
Library Holdings: Bk Vols 1,800
Mem of Forked Deer Regional Library Center

ULLAHOMA

COFFEE COUNTY LANNOM MEMORIAL PUBLIC LIBRARY, 312 N Collins St, 37388-3229. SAN 315-9906. Tel: 931-454-2404, 931-455-2460. FAX: 931-454-2300. Web Site: www.lannom.org. *Dir*, Susan Stoval; E-Mail: director@lannon.org
Founded 1947. Pop 21,864; Circ 171,061
Library Holdings: Bk Vols 55,000; Per Subs 106
Subject Interests: Local history
Special Collections: Genealogy Coll
Mem of Highland Rim Regional Library Center

C MOTLOW STATE COMMUNITY COLLEGE LIBRARIES, Crouch Library, 6051 Ledford Mill Rd, 37388. (Mail add: PO Box 8500, 37352-8500), Tel: 931-393-1660. Circulation Tel: 931-393-1670. Reference Tel: 931-393-1669. Toll Free Tel: 800-654-4877. TDD: 931-393-1621. FAX: 931-393-1761. Web Site: mscc.cc.tn.us/~reference/lib,scc.html. *Dir*, J Hitchcock; E-Mail: jhitchcock@mscc.cc.tn.us; *Dir Libr Serv*, Sue Crites Szostak; Tel: 931-393-1663, Fax: 931-393-1761, E-Mail: sszostak@mscc.cc.tn.us; *ILL*, Joyce Davenport Bateman; E-Mail: jbateman@mscss.cc.tn.us; *Ref*, Mary Murphy; Tel: 931-393-1665, E-Mail: mmurphy@mscc.cc.tn.us; *Circ*, Patra Tipps Burden; E-Mail: pburden@mscc.cc.tn.us; Staff 7 (MLS 3, Non-MLS 4)
Founded 1969. Enrl 3,331; Fac 200; Highest Degree: Associate
Jul 2000-Jun 2001 Income (Main and Other College/University Libraries) $417,010. Mats Exp $85,500, Books $40,000, Per/Ser (Incl. Access Fees) $7,500, Presv $6,000, Electronic Ref Mat (Incl. Access Fees) $32,000. Sal $264,220 (Prof $131,970)
Library Holdings: Bk Vols 54,968; Bk Titles 48,575; Per Subs 114
Automation Activity & Vendor Info: (Cataloging) DRA; (Circulation) DRA; (Course Reserve) DRA; (Serials) DRA
Database Vendor: DRA, GaleNet, IAC - Info Trac, OCLC - First Search, ProQuest
Partic in SE Libr Network
Departmental Libraries:
FAYETTEVILLE CENTER, Winchester Hwy, Fayetteville, 37334. (Mail add: PO Box 618, Fayetteville, 37334), Tel: 931-438-0028. FAX: 931-438-0619. Web Site: mscc.cc.tn.us/~reference/lib,scc.html. *Dir Libr Serv*, Sue Crites Stostak; Tel: 931-393-1663, Fax: 931-393-1761, E-Mail: sszostak@mscc.cc.tn.us; *Librn*, Ann Bittel; *Librn*, Paula Standridge; E-Mail: pstandridge@mscc.cc.tn.us; Staff 3 (Non-MLS 3)
Highest Degree: Associate
Automation Activity & Vendor Info: (Circulation) DRA
Database Vendor: DRA, GaleNet, IAC - Info Trac, ProQuest
MCMINNVILLE CENTER, Cadillac Lane, McMinnville, 37110. (Mail add: PO Box 368, McMinnville, 37110), SAN 373-921X. Tel: 931-668-7010. FAX: 931-668-2172. E-Mail: sszostak@mscc.cc.tn.us. Web Site: mscc.cc.tn.us/~reference/lib,scc.html. *Dir Libr Serv*, Sue Crites Stostak; Tel: 931-393-1663, Fax: 931-393-1761, E-Mail: sszostak@mscc.cc.tn.us; *Circ*, Monica Kemper; E-Mail: mkemper@mscc.cc.tn.us; *Librn*, Roger Merritt; E-Mail: rmerritt@mscc.cc.tn.us; Staff 2 (Non-MLS 2)
Automation Activity & Vendor Info: (Circulation) DRA
Database Vendor: DRA, GaleNet, IAC - Info Trac

S TENNESSEE CORRECTION ACADEMY LIBRARY, Box 1510, 37388. SAN 373-6113. Tel: 931-461-7100. FAX: 931-454-1940. *Librn*, Scott Ulm
Founded 1984
Library Holdings: Per Subs 20
Special Collections: Corrections, bks, flm, policies

C UNIVERSITY OF TENNESSEE SPACE INSTITUTE LIBRARY, Library, MS-25, 411 B H Goethert Pkwy, 37388-9700. SAN 315-9922. Circulation Tel: 931-393-7315. Reference Tel: 931-393-7316. FAX: 931-393-7518. *Head of Libr*, Marjorie Joseph; Tel: 931-393-7316, E-Mail: mjoseph@utsi.edu; *ILL*, Brenda Brooks; E-Mail: bbrooks@utsi.edu; Staff 2 (MLS 1, Non-MLS 1)
Founded 1965. Enrl 430; Fac 42; Highest Degree: Doctorate
Jul 2000-Jan 2001 Mats Exp $184,000, Books $45,000, Per/Ser (Incl. Access Fees) $110,000, Electronic Ref Mat (Incl. Access Fees) $16,000
Library Holdings: Bk Vols 23,400; Per Subs 185
Subject Interests: Aviation, Computer science, Engineering, Mathematics, Physics
Special Collections: Artificial Intelligence Coll; Laser Coll; Propulsion (Herman Diederich Memorial Coll)
Database Vendor: Dialog
Publications: Acquisition list; Missing books list
Function: ILL available
Partic in Aerospace Res Info Network; Dialog Corporation; SE Libr Network; Solinet

UNION CITY

P OBION COUNTY PUBLIC LIBRARY, 710 S First St, 38261-5097. SAN 315-9930. Tel: 901-885-9411. FAX: 901-885-9638. *Dir*, Mary Vaughan Carpenter; E-Mail: mcarpen2@mail.state.tn.us; *Asst Dir*, Amy R Douglas. Subject Specialists: *Children's literature*, Mary Vaughan Carpenter; *Technology*, Amy R Douglas; Staff 2 (MLS 2)
Founded 1939. Pop 32,053; Circ 102,415
Jul 1999-Jun 2000 Income $259,048, City $86,349, County $172,699. Mats Exp $42,500, Books $35,500, Per/Ser (Incl. Access Fees) $3,500, AV Equip $3,500. Sal $144,062 (Prof $71,101)
Library Holdings: Bk Vols 74,998; Per Subs 170
Automation Activity & Vendor Info: (Cataloging) Sagebrush Corporation; (Circulation) Sagebrush Corporation
Database Vendor: GaleNet
Function: Reference services available
Mem of Reelfoot Regional Library Center
Friends of the Library Group

VONORE

P VONORE PUBLIC LIBRARY, 611 Church St, 37885-0308. SAN 373-6636. Tel: 423-884-6729. FAX: 423-884-6729. *Acq, Circ, Librn*, Curina Kirkland
Founded 1978. Pop 3,000; Circ 10,750
1998-1999 Income $20,000, City $10,000, County $10,000. Mats Exp $450, Books $200, Per/Ser (Incl. Access Fees) $250. Sal $10,500
Library Holdings: Bk Titles 8,500; Per Subs 14
Mem of Fort Loudoun Regional Library Center

WASHBURN

P WASHBURN PUBLIC LIBRARY, PO Box 129, 37888-0129. SAN 361-0136. Tel: 865-497-2506. *Librn*, Peggy McGhee
Library Holdings: Bk Vols 5,000; Per Subs 15
Mem of Nolichucky Regional Library

WAVERLY

P HUMPHREYS COUNTY PUBLIC LIBRARY, 201 Pavo Ave, 37185-1529. SAN 315-9957. Tel: 931-296-2143. FAX: 931-296-6520. *Dir*, Ethel Carmical; E-Mail: ecarmical@mail.state.tn.us
Pop 15,957
Library Holdings: Bk Vols 30,000; Per Subs 40
Mem of Warioto Regional Library Center
Friends of the Library Group

WAYNESBORO

P WAYNE COUNTY PUBLIC LIBRARY, Highway 64 E, 38485. (Mail add: PO Box 630, 38485-0630), SAN 315-9965. Tel: 931-722-5537. FAX: 931-722-5537. *Dir*, Katherine Motika Morris; E-Mail: kmorris@mail.state.tn.us
Pop 13,924
Library Holdings: Bk Vols 14,000
Mem of Blue Grass Regional Library

WESTMORELAND

P WESTMORELAND PUBLIC LIBRARY, 2305 Epperson Springs Rd, 37186. (Mail add: PO Box 685, 37186-0685), SAN 376-2939. Tel: 615-644-2026. FAX: 615-644-2026. *Dir*, Willie Ruth Borders; E-Mail: wborders@mail.state.tn.us
Library Holdings: Bk Vols 5,825; Per Subs 300
Friends of the Library Group

WHITE HOUSE

P WHITE HOUSE INN, Library & Museum, 412 Hwy 76, 37188. (Mail add: PO Box 1218, 37188-1218), SAN 376-3110. Tel: 615-672-0239. FAX: 615-672-9733. *Dir*, Barbara Melton; E-Mail: bmelton@acelink.net
Library Holdings: Bk Titles 16,000; Per Subs 38
Mem of Warioto Regional Library Center
Partic in Tenn Libr Asn
Friends of the Library Group

WHITE PINE

P WHITE PINE PUBLIC LIBRARY, 1708 Main St, PO Box 430, 37890. SAN 315-9973. Tel: 423-674-6313. FAX: 423-674-6313. E-Mail: wppl@usit.net. *Dir*, Betty Jo Moore
Founded 1920. Pop 8,457; Circ 19,278
1998-1999 Income $33,906, City $15,176, Locally Generated Income $2,196. Mats Exp $6,989, Books $4,383, Per/Ser (Incl. Access Fees) $602 Other Print Mats $375. Sal $17,453
Library Holdings: Bk Vols 10,500; Per Subs 36
Subject Interests: Local history
Mem of Nolichucky Regional Library
Friends of the Library Group

WHITEVILLE

P LEE OLA ROBERTS PUBLIC LIBRARY, 140 W Main St, 38075. (Mail add: PO Box 615, 38075-0615), SAN 315-9981. Tel: 731-254-8834. FAX: 731-254-8834. *Dir*, Esther Marsh; E-Mail: emarsh@mail.state.tn.us; *Tech Servs*, Bill Wernet
Library Holdings: Bk Vols 8,500
Mem of Shiloh Regional Library
Friends of the Library Group

WHITWELL

P ORENA HUMPHREY PUBLIC LIBRARY, 900 Main St, Ste 1, 37397-5249. SAN 315-999X. Tel: 423-658-6134. Interlibrary Loan Service Tel: 800-572-7396. FAX: 423-658-7726. *Dir*, Linda Powell; E-Mail: lindapowell@mail.state.tn.us; *Asst Librn*, Linda Shirley
Founded 1959. Pop 7,400
Library Holdings: Bk Vols 13,000; Per Subs 32
Mem of Caney Fork Regional Library

WINCHESTER

P FRANKLIN COUNTY LIBRARY, 105 S Porter St, 37398-1546. SAN 36 0268. Tel: 931-967-3706. FAX: 931-962-1477. *Librn*, Diane K Krauth
Pop 31,983
Library Holdings: Bk Vols 30,000
Subject Interests: Local history
Mem of Highland Rim Regional Library Center
Friends of the Library Group

WINFIELD

P WINFIELD LIBRARY, 24 961 Scott Hwy, PO Box 38, 37892-0038. SAN 376-6845. Tel: 423-569-9047. *Librn*, Darlene King
Library Holdings: Bk Vols 4,000; Per Subs 10
Mem of Clinch-Powell Regional Library

WOODBURY

P ADAMS MEMORIAL LIBRARY, 212 College St, 37190. SAN 316-0009 Tel: 615-563-5861. FAX: 615-563-2140. E-Mail: adammen@mail.state.tn.u *Dir, Librn*, Kathy Bensinger
Library Holdings: Bk Vols 31,000
Mem of Highland Rim Regional Library Center
Friends of the Library Group

Date of Statistics: Fiscal 1999
Population, 1999 Census: 20,044,141
Population Served by Public Libraries: 18,321,383
Total Volumes in Public Libraries: 46,399,153
Total Public Library Circulation: 77,450,974
Total Public Library Expenditures: $267,577,302
Expenditures Per Capita: $14.69 (population served); $13.62 (total population)
Number of Counties Served: 250
Number of Counties Unserved: 4
Number of Bookmobiles in State: 16
Appropriation for Statewide Library Development (FY 2000)
Federal (Library Services & Technology Act): $5,308,196
State Funding: $3,285,078

BERNATHY

ABERNATHY PUBLIC LIBRARY, 811 Avenue D, PO Box 686, 79311-0686. SAN 316-0017. Tel: 806-298-4138. *Librn*, Mary Furgeson; E-Mail: abnlibrary@door.net
Founded 1951. Pop 3,000
Library Holdings: Bk Titles 14,000
Automation Activity & Vendor Info: (Cataloging) Sagebrush Corporation; (ILL) VTLS
Mem of West Texas Library System

BILENE

ABILENE CHRISTIAN UNIVERSITY, Margaret & Herman Brown Library, 221 Brown Library, 79699-9208. (Mail add: ACU Box 29208, 79699-9208), SAN 361-0322. Tel: 915-674-2344. Circulation Tel: 915-674-2316. FAX: 915-674-2202. Web Site: www.acu.edu/academics/library/. *Dir*, Marsha Harper; E-Mail: harperm@acu.edu; *Cat*, Jana Davis; *Cat*, Gary Oliver; *ILL*, Ellen Schoenrock; *Per*, Mark McCallon; *Spec Coll*, Erma Jean Loveland; *Ref*, Virginia Bailey; *Ref Serv*, Melissa Johnsen; *Publ Servs*, Karen Hendrick; *Doc*, Laura Baker. Subject Specialists: *Theology*, Craig Churchill; Staff 28 (MLS 11, Non-MLS 17)
Founded 1906. Fac 249; Highest Degree: Doctorate
Jun 1999-May 2000 Income $1,569,442, Locally Generated Income $118,273, Parent Institution $1,451,169. Mats Exp $549,788, Books $251,049, Per/Ser (Incl. Access Fees) $194,348, Presv $15,532, Micro $11,450, AV Equip $3,427, Electronic Ref Mat (Incl. Access Fees) $73,982. Sal $731,675 (Prof $399,871)
Library Holdings: Bk Vols 478,831; Per Subs 2,323
Subject Interests: Education, Humanities, Relig studies
Special Collections: Austin Taylor Hymn Book Coll; Bibles; Burleson Congressional Papers; Church Historical & Archival Materials; Donner Library of Americanism; Herald of Truth Radio & Television Archives; Robbins Railroad Coll; Sewell Bible Library
Automation Activity & Vendor Info: (Acquisitions) DRA; (Cataloging) DRA; (Circulation) DRA; (Course Reserve) DRA; (OPAC) DRA; (Serials) DRA
Database Vendor: DRA, OCLC - First Search
Publications: Library Friends News; Restoration Serials Index
Partic in Abilene Library Consortium; Amigos Library Services, Inc; Llano Estacado Info Access Network; OCLC Online Computer Library Center, Inc; Tex Independent Cols & Univ Librs; TexShare
Special Services for the Blind - Reading edge system
Friends of the Library Group

ABILENE PUBLIC LIBRARY, 202 Cedar St, 79601-5793. SAN 361-0357. Tel: 915-676-6025. Interlibrary Loan Service Tel: 915-676-6021. Circulation Tel: 915-677-2474. FAX: 915-676-6024. Web Site: www.abilenetx.com/apl/. *Dir*, Ricki Brown; Tel: 915-676-6328, E-Mail: ricki.brown@alc.org; *Librn*, Dennis Miller; Tel: 915-676-6026, E-Mail: dennis.miller@alc.org; *ILL*, Linda Cavanaugh; *Publ Servs*, Margie Sanchez; E-Mail: margie.sanchez@alc.org; *Ch Servs*, Marie Noe; *Tech Servs*, E Ann Johns; *Circ*, Deborah Tarsiewicz; E-Mail: deboraht@alc.org; *Acq*, Terri L Blackwell; Staff 35 (MLS 11, Non-MLS 24)
Founded 1899. Pop 108,476; Circ 576,097
Oct 1999-Sep 2000 Income (Main Library and Branch Library) $1,802,411, City $1,759,880, Federal $42,531. Mats Exp $391,043, Books $305,022, Per/Ser (Incl. Access Fees) $16,411, Micro $16,900, AV Equip $33,667, Electronic Ref Mat (Incl. Access Fees) $19,043. Sal $1,040,500
Library Holdings: Bk Vols 244,083; Bk Titles 145,344; Per Subs 375
Subject Interests: Business, Genealogy, Science
Automation Activity & Vendor Info: (Cataloging) DRA; (Circulation) DRA; (OPAC) DRA; (Serials) DRA
Database Vendor: DRA, GaleNet, OCLC - First Search
Mem of Big Country Library System
Partic in Abilene Library Consortium
Special Services for the Deaf - Captioned film depository; Captioned media
Special Services for the Blind - Kurzweil Reading Machine
Friends of the Library Group
Branches: 1
SOUTHSIDE LOCATION, 1401 S Danville, 79605. SAN 371-3024. Tel: 915-698-7565. FAX: 915-698-7621. *Dir*, Ricki V Brown; Tel: 915-676-6328, Fax: 915-676-6024, E-Mail: ricki.brown@alc.org; *Br Coordr*, John Pecoraro; Staff 5 (MLS 1, Non-MLS 4)
Founded 1998
Friends of the Library Group

S ABILENE REPORTER NEWS LIBRARY,* 101 Cypress St, PO Box 30, 79604. SAN 326-1131. Tel: 915-673-4271. FAX: 915-670-5242. *Librn*, Wendy Shepard

P BIG COUNTRY LIBRARY SYSTEM, 202 Cedar St, 79601. SAN 316-0033. Tel: 915-676-6021. Interlibrary Loan Service Tel: 915-676-6023. FAX: 915-676-6028. *Dir*, Ricki Brown; *Coordr*, Beatrice Takacs; Staff 7 (MLS 2, Non-MLS 5)
Founded 1970. Pop 440,301
Sep 1999-Aug 2000 Income $343,753. Mats Exp $136,707. Sal $135,309
Publications: Big Country News (Newsletter)
Function: ILL available
Member Libraries: Abilene Public Library; Anson Public Library; Brownwood Public Library; Callahan County Library; Carnegie Library Of Ballinger; Clyde Public Library; Coke County Library; Coleman Public Library; Comanche Public Library; Crockett County Public Library; Cross Plains Public Library; De Leon Public Library; Eastland Centennial Memorial Library; Eden Public Library; F M (Buck) Richards Memorial Library; Haskell County Library; Irion County Library; Kent County Library; Kimble County Library; Mason County; Menard Public Library; Mitchell County Public Library; Ranger College; Reagan County Library; Rotan Public Library; Schleicher County Public Library; Scurry County Library; Shackelford County Library; Stamford Carnegie Library; Stonewall County Library; Sutton County Library; Sweetwater County-City Library; Tom Green County Library System; Western Texas College; Winters Public Library
Partic in Amigos Library Services, Inc; Texnet

R CRESCENT HEIGHTS BAPTIST CHURCH LIBRARY, 1902 N Mockingbird Lane, 79603. SAN 316-0041. Tel: 915-677-3749. FAX: 915-677-3751. *Asst Librn*, Dwanna Nichols
Founded 1959
Library Holdings: Bk Vols 2,460

C HARDIN-SIMMONS UNIVERSITY, Richardson Library, 2200 Hickey St, Box 16195, 79698-6195. SAN 316-0068. Tel: 915-670-1236. FAX: 915-677-8351. Web Site: www.hsutx.edu/library/. *Dir*, Alice Specht; *Assoc Dir, Coll Develop, Ref*, Elizabeth Norman; E-Mail: elizabethn@alcon.alc.edu; *Cat, Tech Servs*, Belinda Norvell; *Media Spec*, Gary Stephenson; *Music, Ref*, Murl Sickbert; *Doc, Per*, Carolyn McClellan; *ILL*, Pat Ferguson; Staff 7 (MLS 6, Non-MLS 1)
Founded 1892. Enrl 2,200; Fac 128; Highest Degree: Master
Jun 2000-May 2001 Income Parent Institution $805,742. Mats Exp $271,900, Books $120,000, Per/Ser (Incl. Access Fees) $91,000, Presv $4,000, Micro $12,000, AV Equip $3,000, Other Print Mats $14,900, Electronic Ref Mat (Incl. Access Fees) $27,000. Sal $433,200 (Prof $294,000)
Library Holdings: Bk Vols 212,126; Bk Titles 142,693; Per Subs 1,100
Subject Interests: Bus, Education, English, Environ, Music, Theology
Special Collections: Local historical photog archives; Printing of Carl Hertzog; Southwest History, bks & micro; Texana
Automation Activity & Vendor Info: (Acquisitions) DRA; (Cataloging) DRA; (Circulation) DRA; (Course Reserve) DRA; (ILL) DRA; (Media Booking) DRA; (OPAC) DRA; (Serials) DRA
Database Vendor: Ebsco - EbscoHost, Lexis-Nexis, OCLC - First Search
Publications: Friends of the Richardson Library imprint
Partic in Abilene Library Consortium; Amigos Library Services, Inc; Llano Estacado Info Access Network; OCLC Online Computer Library Center, Inc; TexShare
Friends of the Library Group

M HENDRICK MEDICAL CENTER, Sellers Health Sciences Library & Media Center,* 1242 N 19th, 79601. SAN 327-6821. Tel: 915-670-2375. FAX: 915-670-2422. *Coordr*, Jean Snodgrass
Library Holdings: Bk Titles 2,400; Per Subs 200
Partic in Medical Libr Asn

C MCMURRY UNIVERSITY, Jay-Rollins Library, Sayles Blvd & S 14th, Box 218, McMurry Sta, 79697-0218. SAN 316-0084. Tel: 915-793-4692. FAX: 915-793-4930. Web Site: web2.alc.org. *Dir*, Joe W Specht; E-Mail: joe.specht@alc.org; *Publ Servs, Ref*, Terry Young; *Acq*, Lynn Roberts; *Cat*, Nancy F Shanafelt; Staff 3 (MLS 3)
Founded 1923. Enrl 1,411; Fac 90; Highest Degree: Bachelor
Library Holdings: Bk Vols 145,724; Bk Titles 112,940; Per Subs 566
Subject Interests: 20th Century Am popular culture, 20th Century British, Afro-Am studies, Am, Relig studies, Spanish-Am lit
Special Collections: E L & A W Yeats Coll; Hunt Library of Texana & Southwest
Automation Activity & Vendor Info: (Acquisitions) DRA; (Cataloging) DRA; (Circulation) DRA; (Course Reserve) DRA; (OPAC) DRA; (Serials) DRA
Partic in Abilene Library Consortium; Amigos Library Services, Inc; OCLC Online Computer Library Center, Inc
Friends of the Library Group

SR JAY ROLLINS LIBRARY,* McMurry University, PO Box 218, 79697. SAN 327-6848. Tel: 915-793-4692. FAX: 915-293-4695. Web Site: www.mcm.edu. *Dir*, Joe Speck
Library Holdings: Bk Vols 130,000
Special Collections: NW Texas Conference United Methodist Church Archives
Friends of the Library Group

ALAMO

P ALAMO LALO ARCAUTE PUBLIC LIBRARY, 502 Duranta, 78516. SAN 322-7529. Tel: 956-787-6160. FAX: 956-787-5154. *Dir*, Victoria Gessaman; E-Mail: victoria.gessaman@aol.com; Staff 1 (Non-MLS 1)
Founded 1980
Library Holdings: Bk Vols 20,788; Bk Titles 20,380; Per Subs 15
Special Services for the Deaf - Books on deafness & sign language
Friends of the Library Group

ALBANY

P SHACKELFORD COUNTY LIBRARY, 400 N Second, PO Box 445, 76430. SAN 316-0092. Tel: 915-762-2672. *Librn*, Gayle Mikeska
Founded 1956. Pop 3,915
Library Holdings: Bk Vols 7,400; Per Subs 10
Mem of Big Country Library System

ALEDO

P EAST PARKER COUNTY LIBRARY,* 209 Front St, PO Box 275, 7600 SAN 372-5847. Tel: 817-441-6545. *Chair*, Peggie Herring; E-Mail: peggie tenet.edu; *Librn*, Anita Bond
Founded 1988. Pop 7,225
Library Holdings: Bk Titles 12,000
Special Collections: Parker County History Coll, bks
Mem of North Texas Regional Library System
Friends of the Library Group

ALICE

P ALICE PUBLIC LIBRARY,* 401 E Third St, 78332. SAN 361-0446. Tel: 512-664-9506. FAX: 512-668-3248. *Librn*, Alicia Salinas
Founded 1932. Pop 34,000; Circ 259,000
Library Holdings: Bk Vols 99,000; Per Subs 183
Subject Interests: Spanish lang, Tex hist
Mem of South Texas Library System
Friends of the Library Group
Branches: 2
ORANGE GROVE SCHOOL & PUBLIC LIBRARY, PO Box 534, Orang Grove, 78372. SAN 361-0470. Tel: 512-384-2461, 512-384-9363. *Librn*, Cheryl Acklen
Library Holdings: Bk Vols 16,000
PREMONT PUBLIC LIBRARY, PO Box 829, Premont, 78375. SAN 361-0500. Tel: 512-348-3815. *Librn*, Mona Wilson
Library Holdings: Bk Vols 11,000

ALLEN

P ALLEN PUBLIC LIBRARY,* 2 Allen Civic Plaza, 75013. SAN 316-0106 Tel: 972-727-0190. FAX: 972-727-0295. Web Site: www.ci.allen.tx.us. *Lib* Barbara Buehler; E-Mail: bbuehler@ci.allen.tx.us
Founded 1967. Pop 43,000; Circ 333,909
Oct 1998-Sep 1999 Income $853,818, City $838,818, County $15,000. Ma Exp $139,333, Books $114,333, Per/Ser (Incl. Access Fees) $12,000, Electronic Ref Mat (Incl. Access Fees) $13,000. Sal $563,241 (Prof $215,676)
Library Holdings: Bk Vols 83,000
Automation Activity & Vendor Info: (Acquisitions) epixtech, inc.; (Cataloging) epixtech, inc.; (Circulation) epixtech, inc.; (OPAC) epixtech, inc.; (Serials) epixtech, inc.
Mem of Northeast Texas Library System
Friends of the Library Group

ALPINE

P ALPINE PUBLIC LIBRARY,* 203 N Seventh St, 79830. SAN 361-0535. Tel: 915-837-2621. FAX: 915-837-2506. *Dir*, Richard K Zimmir
Founded 1947. Pop 7,780; Circ 51,907
1998-1999 Income $47,125, City $20,825, County $26,300. Mats Exp $2,100, Books $2,000, Per/Ser (Incl. Access Fees) $100. Sal $40,000 (Prof $19,000)
Library Holdings: Bk Vols 48,547; Bk Titles 29,551
Subject Interests: World War II
Mem of Texas Trans Pecos Library System
Branches: 1
MARATHON PUBLIC LIBRARY, PO Box 264, Marathon, 79842. SAN 361-056X.
Friends of the Library Group

C SUL ROSS STATE UNIVERSITY, Bryan Wildenthal Memorial Library,* PO Box C-109, 79832-0001. SAN 316-0114. Tel: 915-837-8123. FAX: 915 837-8400. Web Site: www.libit.sulross.edu. *Dean, Tech Servs*, Don Dowdey E-Mail: ddowdey@sulross.edu; *Coll Develop*, Eleanor Wilson; *ILL, Publ Servs*, Mike Robinson; *Publ Servs*, Pam Spooner; *AV, Coordr*, Bill Baker; Staff 17 (MLS 6, Non-MLS 11)
Founded 1920. Enrl 2,274; Fac 136; Highest Degree: Master
Sep 1997-Aug 1998 Mats Exp $326,354. Sal $625,725
Library Holdings: Bk Vols 221,000; Per Subs 1,612
Subject Interests: Big Bend region of Tex
Special Collections: Archives of the Big Bend
Automation Activity & Vendor Info: (Acquisitions) SIRSI
Partic in Amigos Library Services, Inc; OCLC Online Computer Library Center, Inc; TexShare

ALTO

P STELLA HILL MEMORIAL LIBRARY, 200 N San Antonio St, Rte 1, Bo 724, 75925. SAN 316-0122. Tel: 936-858-4343. *Dir*, Virginia Singletary
Founded 1957. Pop 1,045; Circ 4,500
Library Holdings: Bk Vols 11,001
Special Collections: Local Hist (incl negatives)

.VARADO

ALVARADO PUBLIC LIBRARY,* 200 N Spears, 76009. SAN 370-5064. Tel: 817-783-7323. *Librn*, Nina Cansler; *Asst Librn*, Leanna Cowan; Staff 2 (MLS 2)
Founded 1989. Pop 3,010
1998-1999 Income $43,546
Library Holdings: Bk Titles 19,278; Per Subs 15
Mem of North Texas Regional Library System

.VIN

ALVIN COMMUNITY COLLEGE LIBRARY, 3110 Mustang Rd, 77511. SAN 316-0130. Tel: 281-388-4645. Interlibrary Loan Service Tel: 281-388-4647. Circulation Tel: 281-388-4649. Reference Tel: 281-388-4650. FAX: 281-388-4895. Web Site: www.alvin.cc.tx.us. *Dir Libr Serv*, Gillian Callen; Tel: 281-388-4646, E-Mail: gcallen@alvin.cc.tx.us; *Asst Dir*, Tom Bates; E-Mail: tbates@alvin.cc.tx.us. Subject Specialists: *Criticism*, Tom Bates; *Literature*, Tom Bates; Staff 2 (MLS 2)
Founded 1948. Pop 45,000; Enrl 3,800; Fac 102; Highest Degree: Associate
Sep 1998-Aug 1999 Income $447,713, State $209,000, Parent Institution $238,713. Mats Exp $132,500, Books $20,000, Per/Ser (Incl. Access Fees) $12,500, Presv $300, Micro $8,000, AV Equip $77,000, Electronic Ref Mat (Incl. Access Fees) $15,000. Sal $170,500 (Prof $111,000)
Library Holdings: Bk Vols 26,000; Bk Titles 22,000; Per Subs 320; Spec Interest Per Sub 50
Subject Interests: Court reporting, Literary criticism, Shorthand
Automation Activity & Vendor Info: (Cataloging) SIRSI; (Circulation) SIRSI; (Course Reserve) SIRSI; (OPAC) SIRSI; (Serials) SIRSI
Restriction: Open to students
Partic in Amigos Library Services, Inc; TexShare
Special Services for the Deaf - TDD
Special Services for the Blind - Computers with Voice Synthesizer

.VORD

ALVORD PUBLIC LIBRARY,* 117 N Wickham, PO Box 323, 76225-0323. SAN 376-4699. Tel: 940-427-2842. FAX: 940-427-2948. E-Mail: alvordpl@wf.net. *Librn*, Brenda Moore
1997-1998 Income $16,721, City $7,700, County $7,732, Other $1,289. Mats Exp $8,600, Books $4,679, Per/Ser (Incl. Access Fees) $249. Sal $5,400
Library Holdings: Bk Vols 11,000; Per Subs 15
Mem of North Texas Regional Library System

MARILLO

AMARILLO COLLEGE, (LLLC), Lynn Library Learning Resource Center, 2201 S Washington, PO Box 447, 79178. SAN 361-0594. Tel: 806-371-5400. FAX: 806-371-5470. Web Site: www.hlc-lib.org/aclib/index.htm. *Dir*, M Karen Ruddy; Tel: 806-371-5401, E-Mail: ruddy-mk@actx.edu; *Tech Servs*, Karen F McIntosh; *Publ Servs*, Mark Hanna; E-Mail: hanna-ml@actx.edu; *Acq*, Faith Watson; *ILL*, Nancy S Klingsick; *Circ*, Marian Daniels; *Bibliog Instr*, Janice Jones; Staff 12 (MLS 4, Non-MLS 8)
Founded 1929. Enrl 8,402; Fac 500; Highest Degree: Associate
Library Holdings: Bk Vols 80,894; Per Subs 380
Automation Activity & Vendor Info: (Acquisitions) DRA; (Cataloging) DRA; (Circulation) DRA; (Course Reserve) DRA; (OPAC) DRA; (Serials) DRA
Database Vendor: DRA, OCLC - First Search
Mem of Harrington Library Consortium
Partic in Amigos Library Services, Inc; Llano Estacado Info Access Network

AMARILLO GLOBE-NEWS LIBRARY, 900 Harrison, PO Box 2091, 79166. SAN 316-0157. Tel: 806-376-4488, Ext 3347. FAX: 806-373-0810. *Librn*, Rita Leatherman; Tel: 806-345-3331
Restriction: Open to public for reference only

AMARILLO MUSEUM OF ART,* 2200 S Van Buren St, PO Box 447, 79178. SAN 316-0149. Tel: 806-371-5050. FAX: 806-373-9235. *Dir*, Patrick McCracken
Founded 1973
Library Holdings: Bk Vols 500
Subject Interests: Architecture, Art, Photog
Restriction: Open to public for reference only

AMARILLO PUBLIC LIBRARY, 413 E Fourth St, 79101. (Mail add: PO Box 2171, 79189-2171), SAN 361-0659. Tel: 806-378-3054. Interlibrary Loan Service Tel: 806-378-3053. TDD: 806-378-9328. FAX: 806-378-9327. Web Site: www.library.ci.amarillo.tx.us/library. *Dir*, Donna Littlejohn; Tel: 806-378-3050, E-Mail: dlittlejohn@visto.com; *Asst Dir*, Greg Thomas; Tel: 806-378-9330, E-Mail: aplgreg@visto.com; *Tech Servs*, Amanda Barrera; Tel: 806-378-9331, E-Mail: amandabarrera@visto.com; *Acq*, Terri Jolly; *Cat*, Marian Cole; *Ref*, Judith Sample; *AV*, Sam Jones; *Circ*, Kay Davis; *Spec Coll*, Robert Groman; Staff 72 (MLS 12, Non-MLS 60)
Founded 1902. Pop 171,149; Circ 2,030,752; Fac 72
Library Holdings: Bk Vols 700,760; Bk Titles 538,505; Per Subs 1,648
Special Collections: Genealogy; Southwestern History (William H Bush & Laurence J Fitzsimon Coll), bks, maps
Automation Activity & Vendor Info: (Cataloging) DRA; (Circulation) DRA; (OPAC) DRA; (Serials) DRA
Database Vendor: DRA, IAC - Info Trac, OCLC - First Search
Publications: Bibliography of the Bush-FitzSimon-McCarty Southwestern Collections
Function: ILL available
Mem of Texas Panhandle Library System
Partic in Harrington Library Consortium; OCLC Online Computer Library Center, Inc
Friends of the Library Group
Branches: 3
EAST, 2232 E 27th St, 79103. SAN 361-0683. Tel: 806-342-1589. FAX: 806-342-1591. Web Site: www.library.ci.amarillo.tx.us. *Librn*, Shirley Whitecotton
Library Holdings: Bk Vols 121,181
Friends of the Library Group
NORTH, 1500 NE 24th St, 79107. SAN 361-0713. Tel: 806-381-7931. FAX: 806-381-7929. Web Site: www.library.ci.amarillo.tx.us. *Librn*, Zetta Austin
Library Holdings: Bk Vols 147,374
SOUTHWEST, 4423 W 45th St, 79109. SAN 361-0748. Tel: 806-359-2094. FAX: 806-359-2096. Web Site: www.library.ci.amarillo.tx.us. *Librn*, Linda Bagwell
Library Holdings: Bk Vols 547,646
Friends of the Library Group

S AMARILLO SPEECH, HEARING & LANGUAGE CENTER LIBRARY,* 1300 Wallace Blvd, 79106. SAN 316-0173. Tel: 806-359-7681. FAX: 806-359-7755. *Dir*, S S Stephens
Library Holdings: Bk Vols 400; Per Subs 30

J AMARILLO TECHNICAL CENTER LIBRARY, (ATC), 1201 I Ave, 79111-0002. SAN 316-0238. Tel: 806-335-4257. FAX: 806-335-4270. *Librn*, Lil Withrow; E-Mail: withrow-lc@actx.edu; Staff 1 (MLS 1)
Founded 1970
Library Holdings: Bk Vols 18,131; Per Subs 190
Partic in Harrington Library Consortium

GM AMARILLO VETERANS AFFAIRS HEALTH CARE SYSTEM, (Formerly Department Of Veterans Affairs), Medical Library, 6010 Amarillo Blvd W, 79106. SAN 316-0246. Tel: 806-354-7877. FAX: 806-356-3740.
Founded 1941
Oct 1998-Sep 1999 Income $69,000. Mats Exp $57,300, Books $12,600, Per/Ser (Incl. Access Fees) $32,500. Sal $27,000
Library Holdings: Bk Vols 4,739
Subject Interests: Health mgt, Medicine, Nursing
Special Collections: Patient Education, bks, flm, pamphlet
Partic in S Cent Regional Med Libr Program; Vets Admin Libr Network

R DIOCESE OF AMARILLO, Diocesan Archives, 1800 N Spring St, PO Box 5644, 79117-5644. SAN 372-9605. Tel: 806-383-2243. FAX: 806-383-8452. *In Charge*, Sister Hildegard Varga; Tel: 806-383-2243, Ext 120; Staff 1 (Non-MLS 1)
Founded 1926
Subject Interests: Catholic studies, Religion
Special Collections: Bishop Matthiesen Coll; History of Catholic Church in Panhandle; Stanley Coll

L GIBSON, OCHSNER & ADKINS, LLP, Law Library, 701 S Taylor, Ste 500, 79101-2400. SAN 371-9456. Tel: 806-378-9739. FAX: 806-378-9797. Web Site: www.goa-law.com. *Dir*, Melissa Lockman; E-Mail: mlockman@goa-law.com; Staff 1 (MLS 1)
Library Holdings: Bk Vols 10,000; Bk Titles 150; Per Subs 20
Restriction: Private library

L POTTER COUNTY LAW LIBRARY,* 501 S Filmore, Ste 2B, 79101. SAN 327-8042. Tel: 806-379-2347. *Librn*, Susan Montgomery
Library Holdings: Bk Vols 34,000; Bk Titles 30,000

S SOUTHWESTERN PUBLIC SERVICE CO LIBRARY,* Sixth at Tyler, PO Box 1261, 79170. SAN 316-0211. Tel: 806-378-2121. FAX: 806-378-2790. *Librn*, Mary Ann Hamm
Founded 1971
Library Holdings: Bk Titles 2,000; Per Subs 75
Subject Interests: Bus, Electrical industry, Engineering, Mgt
Publications: Film catalog; promotional brochure
Restriction: Staff use only
Partic in Dialog Corporation

P TEXAS PANHANDLE LIBRARY SYSTEM, 413 E Fourth St, PO Box 2171, 79189. SAN 316-022X. Tel: 806-378-4216. FAX: 806-378-9326. E-Mail: tpls@ci.amarillo.tx.us. *Coordr*, Mary Kay Wells; *Outreach Serv*, Janice Tortoriello; Staff 4 (MLS 2, Non-MLS 2)
Founded 1969
Sep 1999-Aug 2000 Income State $321,954. Mats Exp $70,829, Books $68,640, Per/Ser (Incl. Access Fees) $294, Electronic Ref Mat (Incl. Access Fees) $1,895. Sal $92,392
Library Holdings: Bk Titles 4,970

Special Collections: Large Print; Talking Books
Publications: Directory of the Libraries in the Top 26 Counties; Saddlebags (Newsletter)
Member Libraries: Amarillo Public Library; Booker School Public Library; Canyon Public Library; Caprock Public Library; Carson County Public Library; Childress Public Library; Claude Public Library; Collingsworth Public Library; Dallam-Hartley County Library; Deaf Smith County Library; Friona Public Library; Gabie Betts Burton Memorial Library; Gruver City Library; Hansford County Library; Hemphill County Library; Higgins Public Library; Hutchinson County Library; Killgore Memorial Library; Lovett Memorial Library; Lovett Memorial Library; Memphis Public Library; Oldham County Library; Perry Memorial Library; Rhoads Memorial Library; Shamrock Public Library; Sherman County Public Library; Swisher County Library; Wheeler Public Library
Partic in Harrington Library Consortium
Headquartered at Amarillo Public Library

M TEXAS TECH HEALTH SCIENCES CENTER AT AMARILLO, Harrington Library,* 1400 Wallace Blvd, 79106. SAN 371-6996. Tel: 806-354-5448. FAX: 806-354-5430. E-Mail: libadn@ttuhsc.edu. Web Site: www.lib.ttuhsc.edu. *Assoc Dir*, Dana M Neeley; *Asst Dir*, Elizabeth Casida; *Asst Dir*, Lisa Berry; Staff 6 (MLS 3, Non-MLS 3)
Library Holdings: Bk Vols 20,596; Per Subs 630
Friends of the Library Group

ANAHUAC

P CHAMBERS COUNTY LIBRARY SYSTEM, 202 Cummings St, 77514-0520. (Mail add: PO Box 520, 77514-0520), SAN 361-0772. Tel: 409-267-8263. FAX: 409-267-3783. Web Site: www.chambers.lib.tx.us. *Librn*, Deola Miles; *Librn*, A Lynette Parsons; E-Mail: lparsons@chambers.lib.tx.us; *Tech Servs*, Emilee Nelson; Tel: 409-267-8260; Staff 19 (MLS 10, Non-MLS 9)
Founded 1950. Pop 19,907; Circ 133,729
Jan 1999-Dec 1999 Income (Main Library and Branch Library) $404,176, County $395,589, Other $8,588. Mats Exp $48,078, Books $45,843, Per/Ser (Incl. Access Fees) $2,235. Sal $400,616 (Prof $322,890)
Library Holdings: Bk Vols 85,639; Bk Titles 61,278; Per Subs 69
Subject Interests: Chambers County hist, Texana
Automation Activity & Vendor Info: (Cataloging) Sagebrush Corporation; (Circulation) Sagebrush Corporation; (OPAC) Sagebrush Corporation; (Serials) Sagebrush Corporation
Mem of Houston Area Library System
Friends of the Library Group
Branches: 3
CHAMBERS COUNTY LIBRARY, 202 Cummings St, 77514. (Mail add: PO Box 520, 77514-0520), Tel: 409-267-8261. FAX: 409-267-5181. Web Site: www.chambers.lib.tx.us. *Branch Mgr*, Deola Miles; *Asst Librn*, Peter Stines
Founded 1950
Friends of the Library Group
JUANITA HARGRAVES MEMORIAL BRANCH, 211 Broadway, Winnie, 77665. (Mail add: PO Box 597, Winnie, 77665), SAN 361-0802. Tel: 409-296-8245. FAX: 409-296-8243. Web Site: www.chambers.lib.tx.us. *Branch Mgr*, Rhonda LeBlanc; *Asst Librn*, Barbara Langlois
Friends of the Library Group
WEST CHAMBERS BRANCH, 10616 Eagle Dr, 77580-1289. (Mail add: PO Box 1289, 77514-0520), SAN 361-0829. Tel: 281-576-2246. FAX: 281-576-2496. Web Site: www.chambers.lib.tx.us. *Branch Mgr*, Susie Davis; *Asst Librn*, Valerie Jensen
Friends of the Library Group

ANDREWS

P ANDREWS COUNTY LIBRARY,* 208 NW Second St, 79714. SAN 316-0254. Tel: 915-524-1432, 915-524-1433. E-Mail: library@wtaccess.com. *Librn*, Cindy Tochterman
Founded 1950. Pop 14,353; Circ 60,981
Oct 1996-Sep 1997 Income $263,943. Mats Exp $45,000. Sal $211,907
Library Holdings: Bk Vols 57,952; Per Subs 99
Mem of West Texas Library System
Friends of the Library Group

ANGLETON

L BRAZORIA COUNTY LAW LIBRARY,* 111 E Locust St Ste 315-A, 77515. SAN 372-1914. Tel: 409-864-1225. FAX: 409-864-1226. *Librn*, Angela Wollam; E-Mail: angelaw@brazoria-county.com
Library Holdings: Bk Vols 10,000; Per Subs 20

P BRAZORIA COUNTY LIBRARY SYSTEM,* 131 E Live Oak, 77515-4641. SAN 361-0837. Tel: 409-864-1505. FAX: 409-864-1298. Web Site: bcls.lib.tx.us. *Dir*, Catherine H Threadgill; E-Mail: cthreadg@stic.lib.tx.us; *Assoc Dean*, Larry White; E-Mail: lwhite@stic.lib.tx.us; *Tech Servs*, Rita Ottum; Tel: 409-864-1544, Fax: 409-864-1273, E-Mail: rottum@stic.lib.tx.us; *Bkmobile Coordr*, Bryan Grady; Tel: 409-864-1513, Fax: 409-864-1273, E-Mail: bgrady@stic.lib.tx.us; Staff 21 (MLS 9, Non-MLS 12)
Founded 1941. Pop 220,854; Circ 1,155,419
Oct 1999-Sep 2000 Income (Main Library and Branch Library) County $2,745,620. Sal $1,411,970
Library Holdings: Bk Vols 539,696; Per Subs 1,150
Subject Interests: Genealogy
Special Collections: Brazoria County History Coll; State History (Texana Coll)
Automation Activity & Vendor Info: (Cataloging) epixtech, inc.; (Circulation) epixtech, inc.; (ILL) epixtech, inc.
Database Vendor: epixtech, inc., OCLC - First Search
Publications: Large Print Book Catalog, Library Newsletter
Mem of BRAZNET Multitype Libr Network, Houston Area Libr System
Friends of the Library Group
Branches: 10
ALVIN BRANCH, 105 S Gordon, Alvin, 77511. SAN 361-0896. Tel: 281-388-4300. FAX: 281-388-4305. *Librn*, Danna Wilson
Library Holdings: Bk Vols 67,073
Open Mon, Wed & Fri 10-6, Tues & Thurs 10-8, Sat 10-5
Friends of the Library Group
ANGLETON BRANCH, 401 E Cedar St, 77515. SAN 361-0861. Tel: 409-864-1519, Ext 1519. FAX: 409-864-1518, Ext 1518. *Librn*, Paul M Strohm
Library Holdings: Bk Vols 97,262
Open Mon & Tues 9-8, Wed-Sat 9-6
Friends of the Library Group
BRAZORIA BRANCH, 620 S Brooks, PO Drawer 1550, Brazoria, 77422. SAN 361-0926. Tel: 409-798-2372. FAX: 409-798-4013. *Librn*, Jerry Measells
Library Holdings: Bk Vols 40,257
Open Mon & Wed 10-6, Tues & Thurs 10-8, Sat 10-5
Friends of the Library Group
CLUTE BRANCH, 215 N Shanks, PO Box 517, Clute, 77531. SAN 361-0950. Tel: 409-265-4582. FAX: 409-265-8496. *Librn*, Carolyn Weatherly
Library Holdings: Bk Vols 37,078
Open Mon & Wed 10-6, Tues & Thurs 10-8, Sat 10-5
Friends of the Library Group
FREEPORT BRANCH, 410 Brazosport Blvd, Freeport, 77541. SAN 361-0985. Tel: 409-233-3622. FAX: 409-233-4300. *Librn*, Joyce Kwon
Library Holdings: Bk Vols 41,799
Open Mon & Wed 10-6, Tues & Thurs 10-8, Sat 10-5
Friends of the Library Group
LAKE JACKSON BRANCH, 250 Circle Way, Lake Jackson, 77566. SAN 361-1019. Tel: 409-297-1271. FAX: 409-297-3109. *Librn*, Nancy Hackn
Library Holdings: Bk Vols 89,532
Open Mon, Wed & Thurs 10-8, Tues & Fri 10-6, Sat 10-5
Friends of the Library Group
MANVEL BRANCH, 7402 Masters Rd, PO Box 157, Manvel, 77578. SA 361-1027. Tel: 281-489-7596. FAX: 281-489-7596. *Librn*, Kathryn Klentzman
Library Holdings: Bk Vols 20,758
Open Mon & Wed 10-6, Tues & Thurs 1-8, Sat 10-5
Friends of the Library Group
PEARLAND BRANCH, 3523 Liberty Dr, Pearland, 77581. SAN 361-104 Tel: 281-486-4876. FAX: 281-485-5576. *Librn*, Elizabeth Williams
Library Holdings: Bk Vols 84,576
Open Mon & Wed 10-8:30, Tues & Thurs 9-6, Fri 9-5 & Sat 10-5
Friends of the Library Group
SWEENY BRANCH, 205 W Ashley-Wilson Rd, PO Drawer 825, Sweeny, 77480. SAN 361-1078. Tel: 409-548-2567. FAX: 409-548-2597. *Librn*, Diane Vaclavik
Library Holdings: Bk Vols 26,052
Open Mon & Wed 10-6, Tues & Thurs 10-8, Sat 10-5
Friends of the Library Group
WEST COLUMBIA BRANCH, 518 E Brazos, West Columbia, 77486. SA 361-1108. Tel: 409-345-3394. FAX: 409-345-3652. *Librn*, Sally C Taylo
Library Holdings: Bk Vols 27,743
Open Mon & Wed 10-6, Tues & Thurs 10-8, Sat 10-5
Friends of the Library Group
Bookmobiles: 1

ANSON

P ANSON PUBLIC LIBRARY,* 1113 12th St, PO Box 528, 79501-0528. SAN 316-0262. Tel: 915-823-2711. *Librn*, Francis Thackerson
Founded 1962. Pop 2,615; Circ 5,716
Library Holdings: Bk Vols 13,800
Mem of Big Country Library System

ARANSAS PASS

P ED & HAZEL RICHMOND PUBLIC LIBRARY,* 110 N Lamont St, 78336-3698. SAN 316-0270. Tel: 512-758-2350. FAX: 512-758-6404. *Libr* James McCoy
Founded 1943. Pop 11,000; Circ 29,330

Library Holdings: Bk Vols 25,000; Bk Titles 23,000; Per Subs 10
Subject Interests: Texana
Mem of South Texas Library System

RCHER CITY

ARCHER PUBLIC LIBRARY, 103 N Center, PO Box 957, 76351. SAN 316-0289. Tel: 940-574-4954. E-Mail: apl@wf.net. *Dir*, Cheryl Beesinger
Founded 1968. Pop 7,982; Circ 9,600
1997-1998 Income $35,900, State $3,900, City $10,000, County $20,000, Locally Generated Income $2,000. Mats Exp $7,100, Books $6,550, Per/Ser (Incl. Access Fees) $200, AV Equip $350. Sal $20,000 (Prof $16,000)
Library Holdings: Bk Vols 12,200
Mem of North Texas Regional Library System

RLINGTON

ARLINGTON BAPTIST COLLEGE, Earl K Oldham Library, 3001 W Division, 76012-3425. SAN 316-0300. Tel: 817-461-8741, Ext 127. FAX: 817-274-1138. *Dir*, Marjorie R Jaeger; Staff 1 (MLS 1)
Founded 1939. Enrl 165; Fac 20; Highest Degree: Bachelor
Library Holdings: Bk Vols 27,000; Per Subs 207
Subject Interests: Elementary education, Music, Relig studies
Automation Activity & Vendor Info: (Cataloging) Sagebrush Corporation; (Circulation) Sagebrush Corporation; (OPAC) Sagebrush Corporation

ARLINGTON PUBLIC LIBRARY SYSTEM, George W Hawkes Central, 101 E Abram, 76010. SAN 361-1132. Tel: 817-459-6795. Circulation Tel: 817-459-6906. Reference Tel: 817-459-6900. TDD: 817-275-2766. FAX: 817-459-6902. Web Site: www.pub-lib.ci.arlington.tx.us. *Dir*, Betsy Burson; Tel: 817-459-6904, E-Mail: bburson@pub-lib.ci.arlington.tx.us; *Asst Dir*, Cary Siegfried; Tel: 817-459-6916, E-Mail: csiegfri@pub-lib.ci.arlington.tx.us; *Ref Serv*, Starr Krottinger; Tel: 817-459-6913, E-Mail: skrottin@pub-lib.ci.arlington.tx.us; *Coordr*, Lee Shqeir; Tel: 817-459-6903, E-Mail: lshqeir@pub-lib.ci.arlington.tx.us; *Mgr*, Sheila Smith; E-Mail: ssmith@pub-lib.ci.arlington.tx.us; *Ch Servs*, Bethany Ponder; E-Mail: bponder@pub-lib.ci.arlington.tx.us; *Circ*, James Pool; Tel: 817-459-6910, E-Mail: jpool@pub-lib.ci.arlington.tx.us; *Acq*, Phil Bacon; Tel: 817-459-6923, E-Mail: pbacon@pub-lib.ci.arlington.tx.us; *Coll Develop*, Harriet Stow; Tel: 817-459-6797, E-Mail: hstow@pub-lib.ci.arlington.tx.us. Subject Specialists: *Operations mgt*, Sheila Smith; Staff 27 (MLS 25, Non-MLS 2)
Founded 1973. Pop 320,602; Circ 1,440,328
Oct 1999-Sep 2000 Income (Main Library and Branch Library) $4,518,266, State $39,955, City $4,478,311. Mats Exp $676,294, Books $376,367, Per/Ser (Incl. Access Fees) $61,982, AV Equip $112,076, Other Print Mats $25,869, Electronic Ref Mat (Incl. Access Fees) $100,000. Sal $3,146,060
Library Holdings: Bk Vols 214,353; Bk Titles 155,613; Per Subs 1,106
Subject Interests: Careers, Deaf, Genealogy, Hearing impaired, Texana
Automation Activity & Vendor Info: (Acquisitions) Gaylord; (Cataloging) Gaylord; (Circulation) Gaylord; (OPAC) Gaylord
Database Vendor: Ebsco - EbscoHost
Mem of North Texas Regional Library System
Special Services for the Deaf - TTY machine
Special Services for the Blind - Reading edge system
Friends of the Library Group
Branches: 4
EAST ARLINGTON, 1624 New York Ave, 76010. SAN 361-1191. Tel: 817-275-3321. FAX: 817-795-0726. Web Site: www.pub-lib.ci.arlington.tx.us. *Branch Mgr*, Christopher Brown; Tel: 817-860-5816, E-Mail: cbrown@pub-lib.ci.arlington.tx.us; Staff 4 (MLS 4)
Founded 1970. Circ 126,211
Library Holdings: Bk Vols 44,188; Bk Titles 38,057; Per Subs 123
Special Collections: Children's Learning Center Coll; Multicultural Coll
Automation Activity & Vendor Info: (Circulation) Gaylord; (OPAC) Gaylord
Database Vendor: Ebsco - EbscoHost
Friends of the Library Group
NORTHEAST, 1905 Brown Blvd, 76006. SAN 361-1167. Tel: 817-277-5573. FAX: 817-276-8649. Web Site: www.pub-lib.ci.arlington.tx.us. *Branch Mgr*, Rachel Orozco; Tel: 817-277-0432, E-Mail: rorozco@pub-lib.ci.arlington.tx.us; Staff 3 (MLS 3)
Founded 1997. Circ 205,089
Library Holdings: Bk Vols 68,799; Bk Titles 55,378; Per Subs 145
Automation Activity & Vendor Info: (Circulation) Gaylord; (OPAC) Gaylord
Database Vendor: Ebsco - EbscoHost
Friends of the Library Group
SOUTHWEST, 4000 Green Oaks Blvd W, 76016. SAN 328-7289. Tel: 817-478-3762. FAX: 817-483-0895. Web Site: www.pub-lib.ci.arlington.tx.us. *Branch Mgr*, Judith Field; E-Mail: jfield@pub-lib.ci.arlington.tx.us; Staff 3 (MLS 3)
Founded 1986. Circ 367,745
Library Holdings: Bk Vols 68,733; Bk Titles 51,346; Per Subs 132
Automation Activity & Vendor Info: (Circulation) Gaylord; (OPAC) Gaylord
Database Vendor: Ebsco - EbscoHost
Friends of the Library Group

P WOODLAND WEST, 2837 W Park Row Dr, 76013. SAN 361-1221. Tel: 817-277-5265. FAX: 817-795-4741. Web Site: www.pub-lib.ci.arlington.tx.us. *Branch Mgr*, Debbie Potts; E-Mail: dpotts@pub-lib.ci.arlington.tx.us; Staff 2 (MLS 2)
Founded 1996. Circ 199,386
Library Holdings: Bk Vols 51,406; Bk Titles 44,260; Per Subs 99
Automation Activity & Vendor Info: (Circulation) Gaylord; (OPAC) Gaylord
Database Vendor: Ebsco - EbscoHost
Friends of the Library Group

R FIRST BAPTIST CHURCH, Meredith Memorial Library, 301 S Center St, Ste 500, 76010. SAN 316-0327. Tel: 817-277-6353. FAX: 817-276-6499. Web Site: www.fbca.org. *Librn*, Judy Hibbitts
Library Holdings: Bk Vols 9,000; Per Subs 15

M JOHNSON & JOHNSON MEDICAL, INC, Research Library,* 2500 Arbrook Blvd, PO Box 90130, 76004-3130. SAN 316-0297. Tel: 817-817-262-4529. FAX: 817-262-4113.
Founded 1970
Library Holdings: Bk Titles 2,500
Subject Interests: Biology, Chemistry, Health sci, Textiles
Publications: Information Bulletin (in-house)
Partic in Dallas-Tarrant County Consortium of Health Science Libraries

S RAYTHEON SYSTEMS COMPANY LIBRARY,* 2116 Arlington Downs Rd, 76011-6382. SAN 310-8708. Tel: 817-619-3579. FAX: 817-619-3590. *Librn*, Jay Dean; Staff 2 (MLS 1, Non-MLS 1)
Founded 1951
Library Holdings: Bk Vols 15,000; Per Subs 300
Subject Interests: Aeronautics, Aircraft simulators, Computers, Electrical engineering, Mechanical engineering
Partic in Amigos Library Services, Inc; BRS; Dialog Corporation; DTIC; Nasa Libraries Information System - Nasa Galaxie
Branches:
INFORMATION CENTER, PO Box 1237, Binghamton, 13902-1237. Tel: 607-721-4959. FAX: 607-721-4952. *Librn*, Robin Petrus
Library Holdings: Bk Vols 600; Per Subs 100
Partic in BRS; Dialog Corporation; DTIC; Nasa Libraries Information System - Nasa Galaxie; State University Of New York-NYLINK

C UNIVERSITY OF TEXAS AT ARLINGTON LIBRARY,* 702 College St, 76019. (Mail add: PO Box 19497, 76019-0497), SAN 316-0343. Tel: 817-272-3000. FAX: 817-272-5797. E-Mail: library@uta.edu. Web Site: www.uta.edu/library. *Dir*, Thomas L Wilding; Tel: 817-272-3390, E-Mail: wilding@library.uta.edu; *Assoc Dir*, Julie S Alexander; Tel: 817-272-5321, E-Mail: alexande@library.uta.edu; *Info Res*, Mary K Castle; Tel: 817-272-3405, E-Mail: castle@library.uta.edu; *Info Specialist*, Tommie Wingfield; Tel: 817-272-3000, Ext 2658, E-Mail: wingfield@library.uta.edu; *Info Tech*, Robert C Samson; Tel: 817-272-3728, E-Mail: samson@library.uta.edu; *Spec Coll*, Gerald Saxon; Tel: 817-272-4884, E-Mail: saxon@library.uta.edu; Staff 107 (MLS 42, Non-MLS 65)
Founded 1895. Enrl 18,662; Highest Degree: Doctorate
Sep 1998-Aug 1999 Income $6,391,213, State $4,199,806, Locally Generated Income $730,000. Mats Exp $6,391,213, Books $410,000, Per/Ser (Incl. Access Fees) $1,825,000, Presv $99,365, Manuscripts & Archives $4,133. Sal $3,230,213 (Prof $1,629,732)
Library Holdings: Bk Vols 1,076,454; Bk Titles 681,898; Per Subs 4,581
Special Collections: 19th Century American Fiction; Cartographic Library; Fort Worth Star Telegram Coll; Mexico & MesoAmerica, bks & doc; Minority Cultures Coll; Organized Labor in Texas & the Southwest doc; Photographic Archives; Robertson's colony, doc; Texas & the Mexican War, bks, cartography, doc & maps; Virginia Garrett Cartographic History Coll
Automation Activity & Vendor Info: (Cataloging) Endeavor; (Circulation) Endeavor; (OPAC) Endeavor; (Serials) Endeavor
Database Vendor: Ebsco - EbscoHost, Lexis-Nexis, OCLC - First Search, OVID Technologies, Silverplatter Information Inc., Wilson - Wilson Web
Publications: Compass Rose (special coll newsletter); Guide to Yucatan Archives & Newspapers. UTA Libraries' One Millionth Volume Celebration, April 19, 1996, UTA Library Notes: Marking a Milestone
Partic in Amigos Library Services, Inc; OCLC Online Computer Library Center, Inc; Phoenix Group; Tex Share; UT Sys Electronic Ref Ctr
Friends of the Library Group

ASPERMONT

P STONEWALL COUNTY LIBRARY,* Washington St, PO Box H, 79502-0907. SAN 324-7597. Tel: 940-989-2730. *Librn*, Donna Westbrook; *Asst Librn*, Gloria Allen; *Coll Develop*, Arnetta Cochran
Founded 1962. Pop 2,340; Circ 18,192
Library Holdings: Bk Vols 11,684; Bk Titles 11,345
Special Collections: National Geographic Coll, 1943-1987
Mem of Big Country Library System

ATHENS

P HENDERSON COUNTY, Clint W Murchison Memorial Library, 121 S Prairieville, 75751. SAN 316-0351. Tel: 903-677-7295. FAX: 903-677-7275. E-Mail: library@hendersoncotx.com. *Librn*, Sara Brown; *Asst Librn*, Terry Warren; *Ch Servs*, Thelma Metcalf
Founded 1972. Pop 49,132; Circ 79,473
Jan 1999-Dec 1999 Income (Main Library and Branch Library) $139,408, State $700, City $7,000, County $103,132, Locally Generated Income $24,326, Other $4,250. Mats Exp $25,420, Books $22,498, Per/Ser (Incl. Access Fees) $597. Sal $72,110
Library Holdings: Bk Vols 53,850; Bk Titles 45,423; Per Subs 65
Automation Activity & Vendor Info: (Circulation) Athena
Friends of the Library Group
Branches: 1
EAST, PO Box 301, Chandler, 75758. SAN 323-6994. Tel: 903-849-4122. *Librn*, Nancy Bertholf
Pop 2,000
Bookmobiles: 1

J TRINITY VALLEY COMMUNITY COLLEGE LIBRARY, Ginger Murchison Learning Resource Center, 100 Cardinal, 75751-2765. SAN 316-036X. Tel: 903-675-6229. FAX: 903-675-6292. Web Site: tvcc.cc.tx.us. *Dir*, Barbara Ruff; E-Mail: ruff@tvcc.cc.tx.us; *Ref*, Candy Dyson; Tel: 903-675-6264, E-Mail: dyson@tvcc.cc.tx.us
Founded 1946
Library Holdings: Bk Vols 28,000; Per Subs 400
Departmental Libraries:
ANDERSON COUNTY, PO Box 2530, Palestine, 75802. SAN 370-372X. Tel: 903-729-0256. *Librn*, Charles Dobroski
Library Holdings: Bk Titles 12,674; Per Subs 131
CM HEALTH OCCUPATIONAL, 800 Hwy 243 W, Kaufman, 75142. SAN 370-3738. Tel: 972-932-4309. *In Charge*, Glada Norris
Library Holdings: Bk Titles 2,013; Per Subs 41
KAUFMAN COUNTY, 1200 E I-20, PO Box 668, Terrell, 75160. SAN 370-3746. Tel: 972-563-9573. FAX: 972-563-1667. Web Site: www.tvcc.cc.tx.us. *Librn*, Deanna Thompson; Staff 1 (MLS 1)
Library Holdings: Bk Titles 7,157; Per Subs 201

ATLANTA

P ATLANTA PUBLIC LIBRARY, 101 W Hiram St, 75551. SAN 376-4451. Tel: 903-796-2112. FAX: 903-799-4067. *Librn*, Lee Hamilton
Library Holdings: Bk Vols 28,000; Per Subs 30
Mem of Northeast Texas Library System
Friends of the Library Group

AUBREY

P AUBREY AREA LIBRARY,* 109 S Main St, 76227. SAN 376-4672. Tel: 940-365-9162. FAX: 940-365-9411. *Librn*, Rene Tryling
Library Holdings: Bk Titles 17,000
Mem of North Texas Regional Library System
Friends of the Library Group

AUSTIN

SR ALL SAINTS' EPISCOPAL CHURCH, Masterson Library, 209 W 27th St, 78705-5716. SAN 371-9472. Tel: 512-476-3589, 512-476-7643. FAX: 512-476-7291. *Librn*, Nancy McCandless
Founded 1955
Library Holdings: Bk Vols 2,500; Bk Titles 1,897
Special Collections: Bishop Kinsolving (Bishop of Texas & Parish Rector - 1890's)
Publications: Saints Alive (monthly)

L ARNOLD, WHITE & DURKEE INFORMATION CENTER LIBRARY,* 600 Congress Ave, Ste 1900, 78701-3269. SAN 372-8609. Tel: 512-418-3000, Ext 3054, 512-418-3054. FAX: 512-474-7577. *Librn*, Kathy Fowler; E-Mail: kfowler@awd.com; Staff 1 (MLS 1)
Library Holdings: Bk Vols 10,600; Per Subs 65

S AUSTIN AMERICAN-STATESMAN LIBRARY,* 305 S Congress Ave, PO Box 670, 78767. SAN 316-0378. Tel: 512-445-3676. FAX: 512-445-3679. *Dir*, Denise Bortolussi; Staff 8 (MLS 2, Non-MLS 6)
Founded 1975
Library Holdings: Bk Vols 300
Subject Interests: Austin, Central Tex, State government, Travis County

J AUSTIN COMMUNITY COLLEGE, Learning Resource Services,* 1212 Rio Grande, 78701. SAN 316-0386. Tel: 512-223-3077. FAX: 512-223-3430. Web Site: lrs.austin.cc.tx.us. *Dir Libr Serv*, Richard Smith; E-Mail: rlsmith@austin.cc.tx.us; *Head of Libr*, Julie Todaro; Tel: 512-223-3071, E-Mail: jtodaro@austin.cc.tx.us; *Tech Servs*, Jeanette Mosey; Tel: 512-223-8682, Fax: 512-223-8611, E-Mail: jmosey@austin.cc.tx.us; *Automation Syst Coordr*, Melissa Airoldi; Tel: 512-223-8683, Fax: 512-223-8611, E-Mail: airoldi@austin.cc.tx.us; *Ref*, Toma Iglehart; Tel: 512-223-3066; Staff 102 (MLS 21, Non-MLS 81)
Founded 1973. Enrl 17,699; Fac 975; Highest Degree: Associate
Sep 1997-Aug 1998 Mats Exp $570,276, Books $191,150, Per/Ser (Incl. Access Fees) $219,058, Presv $1,560, Micro $44,600. Sal $2,385,063 (Pr $1,283,639)
Library Holdings: Bk Vols 133,261; Bk Titles 76,277; Per Subs 4,749; High Interest/Low Vocabulary Bk Vols 1,530; Bks on Deafness & Sign La 193
Subject Interests: Health sciences
Special Collections: Multicultural Coll
Automation Activity & Vendor Info: (Acquisitions) Innovative Interface Inc.; (Cataloging) Innovative Interfaces Inc.; (Circulation) Innovative Interfaces Inc.; (Course Reserve) Innovative Interfaces Inc.; (ILL) Innovat Interfaces Inc.; (Media Booking) Innovative Interfaces Inc.; (OPAC) Innovative Interfaces Inc.; (Serials) Innovative Interfaces Inc.
Database Vendor: Dialog, Ebsco - EbscoHost, OVID Technologies
Publications: ACC-LRS Resources (semi-annual); Library Instruction; LR Annual Report; pathfinders; strategic plan; study guides; web site
Partic in Tex Share
Special Services for the Blind - ADA terminals for visually impaired
Departmental Libraries:
CYPRESS CREEK CAMPUS LRC, 1553 Cypress Creek Rd, 78613. SAN 377-5852. Tel: 512-223-2030. *Ref*, Jonathan Buckstead
EASTRIDGE CAMPUS LRC, 4100 Ed Bluestein Blvd, 78721. SAN 377-5879. Tel: 512-223-5111.
NORTHRIDGE CAMPUS LRC, 11928 Stone Hollow Dr, 78758. SAN 32 7949. Tel: 512-223-4740. FAX: 512-223-4902. *Librn*, Cary Sowell; *Publ Servs*, Pamela Perry; *Publ Servs*, Melinda Townsel; *Publ Servs*, Theresa Ashley
PINNADE CAMPUS LRC, 7748 Hwy 290 W, 78736. SAN 377-5836. Tel 512-223-8113. FAX: 512-288-8128.
RIO GRANDE CAMPUS LRC, 1212 Rio Grande, 78701. SAN 321-7930. Tel: 512-223-3072. FAX: 512-223-3430. *Librn*, Julie Todaro; *Publ Servs*, Cherry Luedtke; *Publ Servs*, Linda Clement; *Publ Servs*, Red Wassenich *Publ Servs*, Toma Iglehart
RIVERSIDE CAMPUS LRC, 1020 Grove Blvd, 78741. SAN 321-7957. Te 512-223-6001. FAX: 512-223-6703. *Librn*, Margaret Peloquin; *Librn*, Donna Meadows; *Librn*, Steve Self

CR AUSTIN PRESBYTERIAN THEOLOGICAL SEMINARY, David L & Ja Stitt Library, 100 E 27th St, 78705-5797. SAN 316-0394. Tel: 512-472-6736. Toll Free Tel: 800-777-6127. FAX: 512-322-0901. E-Mail: library@austinseminary.edu. Web Site: www.austinseminary.edu. *Dir*, Timothy D Lincoln; *Tech Servs*, Helen Kennedy; *Tech Servs*, Ronald Reifsnider; *Asst Librn*, Genevieve Luna; *Archivist*, William Brock; *Archivist*, Kristine Toma *Publ Servs*, Lila Parrish; Staff 7 (MLS 4, Non-MLS 3)
Founded 1902. Enrl 310; Highest Degree: Doctorate
Jul 1999-Jun 2000 Income Parent Institution $505,186. Mats Exp $163,409 Books $118,864, Per/Ser (Incl. Access Fees) $28,251, Presv $8,470, Micro $196, Electronic Ref Mat (Incl. Access Fees) $7,628. Sal $207,312 (Prof $160,608)
Library Holdings: Bk Vols 157,712; Per Subs 582
Subject Interests: Biblical studies, Reformed theology
Special Collections: Rumble Communion Token Coll
Automation Activity & Vendor Info: (Cataloging) Gaylord; (Circulation) Gaylord; (Course Reserve) Gaylord; (OPAC) Gaylord; (Serials) Gaylord
Database Vendor: OCLC - First Search
Publications: Cassidorus (occasional newsletter)
Partic in OCLC Online Computer Library Center, Inc

P AUSTIN PUBLIC LIBRARY, 800 Guadalupe St, 78701. (Mail add: PO Box 2287, 78768-2287), SAN 361-1256. Tel: 512-499-7449 (Administration). FAX: 512-499-7403. Web Site: www.library.ci.austin.tx.us *Dir*, Brenda Branch; Tel: 512-499-7444, Fax: 512-499-7403; *Asst Dir*, Cynthia Kidd; Tel: 512-499-7452; *Mgr*, Donna Schiller; Tel: 512-499-7466, Fax: 512-499-7312; *Mgr*, Patricia Tuohy-Cuny; Tel: 512-499-7485, Fax: 512-499-7516; *Mgr*, Linda Vasquez; Tel: 512-499-7432, Fax: 512-499-7327 *Branch Mgr*, Anita Fudell; Tel: 512-472-3591, Fax: 512-479-8554; *ILL*, Nancy Gemmell; Tel: 512-499-7399, Fax: 512-499-7464; *Curator*, Biruta Kearl; Tel: 512-499-7479, Fax: 512-499-7483; *Coll Develop*, Valerie Anderson; Tel: 512-499-7360, Fax: 512-499-7312
Founded 1926. Pop 623,125; Circ 2,983,854
Oct 1998-Sep 1999 Income $16,138,078, City $12,678,245
Library Holdings: Bk Vols 1,767,498; Per Subs 149,724
Special Collections: Austin History Center
Automation Activity & Vendor Info: (Acquisitions) DRA; (Circulation) DRA
Partic in Amigos Library Services, Inc; Dialog Corporation; OCLC Online Computer Library Center, Inc
Special Services for the Deaf - Staff with knowledge of sign language
Special Services for the Blind - Kurzweil Reading Machine
Major Resource Ctr for Cent Texas Libr Syst
Friends of the Library Group
Branches: 20
AUSTIN HISTORY CENTER, 810 Guadalupe St, 78701. SAN 323-9306. Tel: 512-499-7480. FAX: 512-499-7483. E-Mail: ahc_reference@ci.austin.tx.us. Web Site: www.ci.austin.tx.us/library/. *Curator*, Margaret

Schlankey; *Archivist*, Biruta Celmins Kearl; Tel: 512-499-7949, E-Mail: biruta.kearl@ci.austin.tx.us; *Archivist*, Susan Soy; Staff 17 (MLS 5, Non-MLS 12)
Founded 1955. Pop 761,945
Library Holdings: Bk Vols 36,000; Bk Titles 13,500; Per Subs 200
Special Collections: Architectural Archives, drawings, blueprints; O Henry (O'Quinn - O Henry Coll), bks, mss; Travis County Historical Resource Depository; Women's Suffrage (Jane Y McCallum Coll), mss, drawings, blueprints
Publications: An Austin Album; Austin & Travis County: A Pictorial History, 1839-1939; Lucadia Pease & the Governor; Pease Porridge Hot; Waterloo Scrapbook
Restriction: Non-circulating to the public
Mem of Central Texas Library System
Open Mon-Thurs 9-9, Fri & Sat 9-6, Sun 12-6
Friends of the Library Group

CARVER, 1161 Angelina, 78702. SAN 361-1280. Tel: 512-472-8954. FAX: 512-472-0734. *Branch Mgr*, Renee Brady; Staff 7 (MLS 2, Non-MLS 5)
Pop 9,888; Circ 24,090
Library Holdings: Bk Vols 32,851
Subject Interests: Black hist
Open Mon-Thurs 10-9, Fri & Sat 10-6 & Sun 2-6

CEPEDA, 651 N Pleasant Valley Rd, 78702. SAN 361-1310. Tel: 512-499-7372. FAX: 512-499-0609. *Mgr*, Sulema Vielma; Staff 7 (MLS 2, Non-MLS 5)
Founded 1998. Pop 8,398; Circ 53,134
Library Holdings: Bk Vols 18,511
Special Collections: Adult Literacy
Open Mon-Thurs 10-9, Fri 10-6 & Sat 10-5

HOWSON, 2500 Exposition, 78703. SAN 361-1345. Tel: 512-472-3584. FAX: 512-479-8554. *Branch Mgr*, Anita Fudell; Staff 7 (MLS 2, Non-MLS 5)
Pop 21,792; Circ 116,884
Library Holdings: Bk Vols 33,570
Open Mon-Thurs 10-9, Fri 10-6 & Sat 10-5

LITTLE WALNUT CREEK, 835 W Rundberg Lane, 78758. SAN 361-137X. Tel: 512-836-8975. FAX: 512-835-0361. *Branch Mgr*, Stephanie Neely; Staff 9 (MLS 2, Non-MLS 7)
Pop 50,520; Circ 147,464
Library Holdings: Bk Vols 51,162
Open Mon-Thurs 10-9, Fri & Sat 10-6, Sun 2-6

MANCHACA ROAD, 5500 Manchaca Rd, 78745. SAN 361-140X. Tel: 512-447-6651. FAX: 512-444-5132. *Branch Mgr*, Kent Middleton; Staff 4 (MLS 4)
Founded 1974. Pop 44,858; Circ 181,329
Library Holdings: Bk Vols 74,508; Per Subs 151
Open Mon-Thurs 10-9, Fri & Sat 10-6, Sun 2-6

MILLWOOD, 12500 Amherst Dr, 78727. SAN 377-8010. Tel: 512-339-2355. *Branch Mgr*, Lexie Graham; Staff 10 (MLS 3, Non-MLS 7)
Pop 43,308; Circ 284,285
Open Mon-Thurs 10-9, Fri 10-6 & Sat 10-5

NORTH VILLAGE, 2139 W Anderson Lane, 78757. SAN 361-1493. Tel: 512-458-2239. FAX: 512-458-3432. *Branch Mgr*, Kathleen Kanarski; Staff 7 (MLS 2, Non-MLS 5)
Pop 27,676; Circ 123,511
Library Holdings: Bk Vols 33,492
Open Mon-Thurs 10-9, Fri 10-6, Sat 10-4

OAK SPRINGS, 3101 Oak Springs Dr, 78702. SAN 361-1523. Tel: 512-926-4453. FAX: 512-928-9719.; Staff 6 (MLS 3, Non-MLS 3)
Pop 12,125
Library Holdings: Bk Vols 32,808
Special Collections: Workplace Literary Coll
Open Mon-Thurs 10-9, Fri 10-6 & Sat 10-5

OLD QUARRY, 7051 Village Center Dr, 78731. SAN 361-1558. Tel: 512-345-4435. FAX: 512-794-0459. *Branch Mgr*, Patricia Campbell; Staff 7 (MLS 2, Non-MLS 5)
Pop 32,836; Circ 90,050
Library Holdings: Bk Vols 38,518
Open Mon-Thurs 10-9, Fri 10-6 & Sat 10-5

PLEASANT HILL, 211 E William Cannon Dr, 78745. SAN 361-1582. Tel: 512-441-7993. FAX: 512-444-6237. *Branch Mgr*, D J Harris; Staff 10 (MLS 2, Non-MLS 8)
Pop 46,678; Circ 184,131
Library Holdings: Bk Vols 39,317
Open Mon-Thurs 10-9, Fri 10-6 & Sat 10-5

RIVERSIDE DRIVE, 2410 E Riverside Dr, 78741. SAN 361-1566. Tel: 512-448-0776. FAX: 512-444-6280. *Branch Mgr*, Elissa Ballesteros
Pop 31,051; Circ 48,098
Library Holdings: Bk Vols 23,549
Open Mon-Thurs 10-9, Fri 10-6 & Sat 10-4

SOUTHEAST AUSTIN COMMUNITY BRANCH, 5803 Nuckols Crossing Rd, 78744. SAN 377-8037. Tel: 512-462-1452. FAX: 512-447-7639. *Mgr Libr*, Deborah Coronado; E-Mail: deborah.coronado@ci.austin.tx.us; Staff 8 (MLS 2, Non-MLS 6)
Founded 1998. Pop 25,824; Circ 66,865
2000-2001 Mats Exp Books $50,000
Open Mon-Thurs 10-9, Fri 10-6 & Sat 10-5

SPICEWOOD SPRINGS, 8637 Spicewood Springs Rd, 78759. SAN 326-8454. Tel: 512-258-9070. FAX: 512-331-4435. *Branch Mgr*, Geraldine Williams; Staff 11 (MLS 4, Non-MLS 7)
Founded 1985. Pop 59,142; Circ 265,252
Library Holdings: Bk Vols 52,519; Per Subs 104
Subject Interests: Chinese Language, Spanish language
Special Collections: Chinese (Traditional & Simplified)
Open Mon-Thurs 10-9, Fri 10-6 & Sat 10-5

TERRAZAS, 1105 E Cesar Chavez St, 78702. SAN 361-1612. Tel: 512-472-7312. FAX: 512-479-8558. *Branch Mgr*, Elva Garza; Staff 6 (MLS 2, Non-MLS 4)
Pop 11,483; Circ 32,420
Library Holdings: Bk Vols 27,690
Open Mon-Thurs 10-9, Fri 10-6 & Sat 10-5

TWIN OAKS, 2301 S Congress, No 7, 78704. SAN 361-1647. Tel: 512-442-4664. FAX: 512-448-0744. *Branch Mgr*, Kathleen Kanarski; Staff 6 (MLS 1, Non-MLS 5)
Pop 50,370; Circ 86,166
Library Holdings: Bk Vols 21,756
Open Mon-Thurs 10-9, Fri 10-6 & Sat 10-4

UNIVERSITY HILLS, 4721 Loyola Lane, 78723. SAN 328-9117. Tel: 512-929-0551. FAX: 512-929-0285. *Branch Mgr*, Frank Schmitzer; Staff 5 (MLS 3, Non-MLS 2)
Founded 1986. Pop 23,733; Circ 65,026
Library Holdings: Bk Vols 29,356
Open Mon-Thurs 10-9, Fri 10-6 & Sat 10-5

WILL HAMPTON BRANCH AT OAK HILL, 5125 Convict Hill Rd, 78749. SAN 377-7995. Tel: 512-892-6680. *Branch Mgr*, Irma Flores-Manges; Staff 14 (MLS 3, Non-MLS 11)
Founded 1997. Pop 40,166; Circ 324,220
Automation Activity & Vendor Info: (Acquisitions) DRA; (Cataloging) DRA; (Circulation) DRA
Open Mon-Thurs 10-9, Fri 10-6 & Sat 10-5

WINDSOR PARK BRANCH, 5833 Westminster Dr, 78723. SAN 361-1671. Tel: 512-928-0333. FAX: 512-929-0654. *Mgr Libr*, Jennifer Patterson; Tel: 512-928-0335, E-Mail: jennifer.patterson@ci.austin.tx.us; Staff 6 (MLS 3, Non-MLS 3)
Pop 31,832; Circ 97,529
Library Holdings: Bk Vols 54,000; Bk Titles 48,000
Mem of Central Texas Library System
Partic in Tex Share
Open Mon-Thurs 10-9, Fri 10-6, Sat 10-5

YARBOROUGH, 2200 Hancock Dr, 78756. SAN 361-1469. Tel: 512-454-7208. FAX: 512-458-3047. *Branch Mgr*, Bonita Snyder-Jones; Staff 12 (MLS 2, Non-MLS 10)
Pop 43,180; Circ 200,300
Library Holdings: Bk Vols 31,902
Open Mon-Thurs 10-9, Fri 10-6 & Sat 10-5

L BROWN MCCARROLL & OAKS HARTLINE LLP LIBRARY, 111 Congress Ave, Ste 1400, 78701-4043. SAN 329-1375. Tel: 512-472-5456. Reference Tel: 512-370-3440. FAX: 512-479-1101. *Dir*, Evan Quenon; E-Mail: equenon@bmoh.com; *Dir Info Resources & Res*, Jency J James; Tel: 512-370-3332, E-Mail: jjames@bmoh.com; *Ser*, Lisa Bailey; Tel: 512-370-3377, E-Mail: lbailey@bmoh.com; Staff 3 (MLS 1, Non-MLS 2)
Library Holdings: Bk Vols 18,000; Bk Titles 5,000; Per Subs 150
Subject Interests: Bus law, Environmental law, Litigation
Automation Activity & Vendor Info: (Acquisitions) Inmagic, Inc.; (Cataloging) Inmagic, Inc.; (Serials) Inmagic, Inc.
Function: For research purposes

SR CATHOLIC ARCHIVES OF TEXAS LIBRARY, 16th & Congress, PO Box 13124, Capitol Sta, 78711. SAN 316-0580. Tel: 512-476-6296. FAX: 512-476-3715. E-Mail: cat@onr.com. Web Site: www.onr.com/user/cat. *Archivist*, Susan Eason; *Archivist*, Kinga Perzynska; Staff 2 (MLS 2)
Founded 1924
Library Holdings: Bk Vols 1,200; Per Subs 12
Special Collections: Catholic Parishes in Texas; Catholic Texas Newspapers (1890 to present); Early Anglo & French Missionaries in Texas (Notre; general information on Texas Catholic institution, organizations, etc; Notre Dame Archives & New Orleans Diocesan Archives), photostats; Spanish Period Documents; Texas (Mexican Period); Texas Catholic Conference Rec, 1964-1990; Texas Knights of Columbus Rec, 1882-1990; Volunteers for Education & Social Services Rec, 1972-1988
Publications: Guide to the Records of Texas Catholic Conference; Guide to the Spanish & Mexican Manuscripts Collection; Our Catholic Heritage in Texas, Journal of Texas Catholic History & Culture; Texas Catholic Historical Society Newsletter
Description of records can be found on OCLC & RLIN - Archives sends them to the National Union Catalog of Manuscript Collection of the Library of Congress

P CENTRAL TEXAS LIBRARY SYSTEM, 810 Guadalupe St, PO Box 2287, 78768-2287. SAN 316-0416. Tel: 512-499-7488. FAX: 512-499-7516. Web Site: www.ctls.net. *Coordr*, Pat Tuohy; E-Mail: pat2e@ctls.net; *Dir*, Brenda Branch; *Ch Servs*, Amanda Williams; *ILL*, Nancy Gemmel; *Coll Develop*, Laurie Mahaffey; *Automation Syst Coordr*, Bob Gaines; *Syst Coordr*, Marvin

Perez; Staff 13 (MLS 6, Non-MLS 7)
Founded 1971. Pop 1,700,000
Sep 1999-Aug 2000 Income $838,138. Mats Exp $318,400, Books $282,400, Per/Ser (Incl. Access Fees) $6,000, Electronic Ref Mat (Incl. Access Fees) $30,000. Sal $372,000
Library Holdings: Bk Vols 7,756; Per Subs 72
Special Collections: Large Print Book Coll
Publications: CTLS Newsletter; Media Collection Catalog
Member Libraries: Austin Public Library; Austin Public Library; Bastrop Public Library; Blanco Library, Inc; Bryan & College Station Public Library System; Buda Public Library; Buffalo Public Library; Cameron Public Library; Cedar Park Public Library; Copperas Cove Public Library; D Brown Memorial Library; Dr Eugene Clark Library; Dripping Springs Community Library; Elgin Public Library; Fairfield Library Association, Inc; Fayette Public Library; Florence Public Library; Gatesville Public Library; Georgetown Public Library; Gibbs Memorial Library; Hamilton Public Library; Harker Heights Public Library; Harrie P Woodson Memorial Library; Herman Brown Free Library; Hewitt Community Library; Hillsboro City Library; Houston Public Library; Johnson City Library; Jonestown Community Library; Killeen Public Library; Kyle Community Library; Lake Travis Community Library; Lake Whitney Library; Lampasas Public Library; Leander Public Library; Lena Armstrong Public Library; Llano County Library System; Lucy Hill Patterson Memorial Library; Luling Public Library; Madison County Library; Maffett Memorial Library; Marlin Public Library; McGinley Memorial Public Library; Mount Calm Regional Library; Nancy Carol Roberts Memorial Library; Navasota Public Library; Pflugerville Community Library; Round Rock Public Library System; Rufus Young King Public Library; Salado Public Library; San Marcos Public Library; San Saba County Library; Schulenburg Public Library; Smith-Welch Memorial Library; Smithville Public Library; Taylor Public Library; Teague Public Library; Teinert Memorial Public Library; Village Library Of Wimberley; Waco-Mclennan County Library; West Public Library; Westbank Community Library
Partic in OCLC Online Computer Library Center, Inc

S CHICANA RESEARCH & LEARNING CENTER INCORPORATED LIBRARY,* 1502 Norris Dr, 78704. SAN 371-1978. Tel: 512-444-7595. FAX: 512-444-7597. *In Charge*, Martha P Cotera
Library Holdings: Bk Vols 4,000; Per Subs 10

L CLARK, THOMAS & WINTERS, Legal Research Center, Chase Bank Bldg, Ste 1000, 700 Lavaca St, 78701. SAN 371-0475. Tel: 512-472-8800. FAX: 512-474-1129. Web Site: www.ctw.com. *Librn*, Deborah K Meleski
Library Holdings: Bk Vols 10,000; Per Subs 45

C CONCORDIA UNIVERSITY, Founders Library, 3400 N Interregional, 78705. SAN 316-0432. Tel: 512-486-1154. Interlibrary Loan Service Tel: 512-486-1249. Reference Tel: 512-486-1150. FAX: 512-459-8517. Web Site: founders.concordia.edu. *Coll Develop, Dir*, Norman W Holmes; E-Mail: holmesn@concordia.edu; *Tech Servs*, Marcus X Fry; Tel: 512-486-1249, E-Mail: frym@concordia.edu; Staff 3 (MLS 3)
Founded 1926. Enrl 803; Fac 49; Highest Degree: Master
Jul 1999-Jun 2000 Income $111,537, Federal $7,904, Parent Institution $103,633. Mats Exp $101,206, Books $30,470, Per/Ser (Incl. Access Fees) $23,443, Micro $22,340, Electronic Ref Mat (Incl. Access Fees) $24,953. Sal $84,904 (Prof $77,000)
Library Holdings: Bk Vols 54,637; Bk Titles 50,323; Per Subs 632
Special Collections: Wm S Gray Coll in Reading
Automation Activity & Vendor Info: (Acquisitions) Endeavor; (Cataloging) Endeavor; (Circulation) Endeavor; (Course Reserve) Endeavor; (OPAC) Endeavor
Database Vendor: Ebsco - EbscoHost, GaleNet, OVID Technologies, Wilson - Wilson Web
Mem of Amigos Bibliog Coun, Inc
Partic in TexShare

S DOCUMENTATION EXCHANGE LIBRARY,* 2520 Longview Ste 408, 78705. (Mail add: PO Box 2327, 78768-2327), Tel: 512-476-9841. FAX: 512-476-0130. Web Site: www.hrde.org. *Dir*, Rebecca Hall; E-Mail: rhall@hrde.org; *Res*, Dylan Robbins; *Res*, Jan Reyes; *Res*, Faye Kolly
Library Holdings: Bk Titles 3,500; Per Subs 40

S ELISABET NEY MUSEUM LIBRARY,* 304 E 44th St, 78751. SAN 320-8745. Tel: 512-458-2255. FAX: 512-453-0638.
Founded 1911
Library Holdings: Bk Titles 310
Subject Interests: 19th Century German, Texan, US art
Special Collections: Elisabet Ney Correspondence Coll
Restriction: By appointment only
Branches:
GEORGE WASHINGTON CARVER MUSEUM LIBRARY, 1165 Angelina St, 78702. SAN 322-6042. Tel: 512-472-4809. FAX: 512-708-1639. *Curator*, Bernadette M Phifer
Library Holdings: Bk Vols 1,000
Subject Interests: Art, Culture, Ethnic minority hist, Local hist archival doc, Mus studies
Friends of the Library Group
O HENRY MUSEUM LIBRARY, 409 E Fifth St, 78701. SAN 320-8893. Tel: 512-472-1903. FAX: 512-472-7102. *Curator*, Valerie Bennett
Special Collections: O Henry Coll by William Sidney Porter; Poetry Co 19th Century
Friends of the Library Group

R EPISCOPAL CHURCH ARCHIVES, 606 Rathervue Pl, 78705. (Mail add: PO Box 2247, 78768-2247), SAN 372-9664. Tel: 512-472-6816. FAX: 512 480-0437. E-Mail: research@episcopalarchives.org. Web Site: www.episcopalarchives.org. *Archivist*, Mark J Duffy; Staff 5 (MLS 4, Non-MLS 1)
Founded 1940
1999-2000 Mats Exp Manuscripts & Archives $25,000. Sal $291,954
Library Holdings: Bk Vols 12,000; Per Subs 50
Special Collections: Book of Common Prayer
Friends of the Library Group

R EPISCOPAL THEOLOGICAL SEMINARY OF THE SOUTHWEST LIBRARY, 606 Rathervue Pl, 78705. (Mail add: PO Box 2247, 78768-2247), SAN 316-0467. Tel: 512-478-5212. FAX: 512-472-4620. E-Mail: library@etss.edu. Web Site: www.etss.edu/cs_library.html. *Dir*, Robert E Cogswell; *Circ, ILL, Publ Servs*, Mikail M McIntosh-Doty; *Cat, Tech Servs* Elizabeth Johnson; Staff 3 (MLS 3)
Founded 1951. Enrl 150; Fac 16; Highest Degree: Master
Jun 2000-May 2001 Income $330,107. Mats Exp $31,500, Books $16,500, Per/Ser (Incl. Access Fees) $14,000, Presv $1,000. Sal $198,547 (Prof $153,144)
Library Holdings: Bk Vols 101,113; Bk Titles 76,048; Per Subs 260
Subject Interests: Biblical studies, Church history, Cultural studies, Hispanic, Pastoral theology
Special Collections: History, Literature & Culture of Latin Culture (Sophie H Winterbotham Coll); Nineteenth Century English Literature-Fine Editions (Charles L Black Coll)
Automation Activity & Vendor Info: (Acquisitions) epixtech, inc.; (Cataloging) epixtech, inc.; (Circulation) epixtech, inc.; (Course Reserve) epixtech, inc.; (ILL) epixtech, inc.; (Media Booking) epixtech, inc.; (OPAC epixtech, inc.; (Serials) epixtech, inc.
Partic in Amigos Library Services, Inc

SR FIRST UNITED METHODIST CHURCH LIBRARY,* 1201 Lavaca, PO Box 1666, 78767. SAN 328-5367. Tel: 512-478-5684. FAX: 512-478-6169. Web Site: www.fumcaustin.org. *In Charge*, Sharon Doss
Library Holdings: Bk Vols 2,800; Per Subs 13

S FISHER ROSEMOUNT SYSTEMS, INC, Resource Center,* 8301 Camero Rd, 78754. SAN 374-6674. Tel: 512-834-7255. FAX: 512-832-3535. *Librn*, Marsha McGuire; E-Mail: mmcguire@frmail.frco.com; *Asst Librn*, Karen Conynghan
Founded 1984
Library Holdings: Per Subs 300
Publications: Competitive Intelligence News; Keeping Current

S JACK HENSLEY TEXAS SCHOOL FOR THE DEAF LIBRARY, 1102 S Congress, 78704. (Mail add: PO Box 3538, 78764), Tel: 512-462-5550. TDD: 512-462-5550. FAX: 512-462-5559. *Librn*, Susan A Anderson; E-Mail: susana@tsd.state.tx.us
Library Holdings: Bk Vols 14,000; Per Subs 75
Automation Activity & Vendor Info: (Cataloging) ComPanion Corp; (Circulation) ComPanion Corp

S HOGG FOUNDATION FOR MENTAL HEALTH, (RFL), Regional Foundation Library, 3001 Lake Austin Blvd, Ste 400, 78703-4200. (Mail add: PO Box 7998, University Station, 78713-7998), SAN 316-0475. Tel: 512-471-5041. FAX: 512-471-9608. Web Site: www.hogg.utexas.edu. *Librn*, Allison Supancic; Staff 1 (MLS 1)
Library Holdings: Bk Titles 800; Per Subs 30; Spec Interest Per Sub 15
Subject Interests: Evaluation, Fund raising, Grants, Volunteerism
Function: For research purposes, Reference only
Branches:
REGIONAL FOUNDATION LIBRARY *Librn*, Allison Supancic
Library Holdings: Bk Vols 350
Special Collections: Annual Reports on Private Foundations; Comprehensive Reference Coll of Materials Related to Grants; Proposal Writing: Internal Revenue Service Tax Returns for Private Foundations in Texas, microfiche; Regional Library for the Foundation Center

C HOUSTON-TILLOTSON COLLEGE, Downs-Jones Library, 900 Chicon St, 78702-3430. SAN 316-0483. Tel: 512-505-3080. FAX: 512-505-3190. Web Site: www.htc.edu. *Dir*, Patricia Quarterman; E-Mail: ppquarterman@htc.edu; *Media Spec*, Deloris C Harris; *Publ Servs*, Janelle Hedstrom; Staff 4 (MLS 4)
Founded 1891. Highest Degree: Bachelor
Library Holdings: Bk Vols 91,375; Per Subs 375
Special Collections: Afro-American History (Schomburg Coll), micro; Religion (Heinsohn Coll)
Automation Activity & Vendor Info: (Acquisitions) Endeavor; (Cataloging) Endeavor; (Circulation) Endeavor; (OPAC) Endeavor; (Serials) Endeavor

Publications: Recent Acquisitions List; Student Library Handbook
Partic in Amigos Library Services, Inc
Open Mon-Thurs 8am-10pm, Fri 8-5, Sat 10-2, Sun 3-9

IBM CORP, Library Information Resource Center, 11400 Burnet Rd, B/908, Z/9819, 78758. SAN 316-0491. Tel: 512-838-1067. *Mgr*, Bev Gerzevske; Staff 3 (MLS 1, Non-MLS 2)
Founded 1967
Library Holdings: Bk Vols 11,000; Bk Titles 9,000; Per Subs 300
Subject Interests: Bus, Computer science, Electronic engineering, Electronics, Engineering, Mathematics, Mgt
Automation Activity & Vendor Info: (Circulation) epixtech, inc.; (OPAC) epixtech, inc.; (Serials) epixtech, inc.
Restriction: Company library

INFORMATION FINDERS LIBRARY, PO Box 7519, 78713-7519. SAN 372-7432. Tel: 512-453-1449. FAX: 512-453-1353. E-Mail: infofind@earthlink.net. *Librn*, Mike Jankowski; Staff 2 (MLS 1, Non-MLS 1)
Library Holdings: Bk Vols 210; Per Subs 12
Special Collections: Texas State Documents, microfiche; Union Lists - Library Catalogs, microfiche
Restriction: Staff use only
Partic in Dialog Corporation; OCLC Online Computer Library Center, Inc

INSTITUTE FOR CHRISTIAN STUDIES LIBRARY,* 1909 University, 78705. SAN 328-3860. Tel: 512-476-2772. FAX: 512-476-3919. Web Site: www.io.com/~ics/library.html. *Librn*, Wade Osburn; E-Mail: osburn@mail.ics.edu; Staff 1 (MLS 1)
Highest Degree: Master
1998-1999 Income $45,000. Mats Exp $14,300, Books $10,000, Per/Ser (Incl. Access Fees) $3,000, Presv $1,000, Micro $300. Sal $29,000 (Prof $28,000)
Library Holdings: Bk Vols 21,000; Per Subs 90
Subject Interests: Biblical studies
Special Collections: Showalter Coll
Friends of the Library Group

JACKSON WALKER, LLP LIBRARY, (Formerly Small, Craig & Werkenthin Library), 100 Congress Ave, Ste 1100, 78701-4099. SAN 327-5426. Tel: 512-236-2306. FAX: 512-236-2002. *Librn*, Judith B Hamner; E-Mail: jhammer@jw.com; Staff 2 (MLS 1, Non-MLS 1)
Founded 1980
Library Holdings: Bk Vols 50,000; Per Subs 200
Subject Interests: Real estate
Function: Research library
Partic in Dialog Corporation; Westlaw

JENKENS & GILCHRIST, Law Library, 600 Congress Ave, Ste 2200, 78701-3278. SAN 372-1574. Tel: 512-499-3876. FAX: 512-404-3520. *Librn*, Wendy Lyon; Staff 2 (MLS 1, Non-MLS 1)
Subject Interests: Labor, Securities
Restriction: Staff use only

LADYBIRD JOHNSON WILDFLOWER CENTER LIBRARY,* 4801 LaCrosse Ave, 78739. SAN 371-5949. Tel: 512-292-4200. FAX: 512-292-4627. *Exec Dir*, Robert Brewnig; Staff 1 (MLS 1)
Library Holdings: Bk Vols 1,400
Subject Interests: Botany, Ecology, Restoration
Restriction: Non-circulating to the public

LUTHERAN SEMINARY PROGRAM IN THE SOUTHWEST, (STS), Seminex Library, 607 Rathervue Pl, PO Box 4790, 78765-4790. SAN 309-1554. Tel: 512-477-2666. FAX: 512-477-6693. E-Mail: lsps@lsps.edu. Web Site: www.lsps.edu. *Dir*, Lucille Hager
Founded 1974. Enrl 24; Fac 4; Highest Degree: Master
Jul 1999-Jun 2000 Income $23,064. Mats Exp $9,587, Books $2,885, Per/Ser (Incl. Access Fees) $1,125, Micro $3,285. Sal $13,476
Library Holdings: Bk Vols 39,421; Per Subs 130
Automation Activity & Vendor Info: (Cataloging) epixtech, inc.; (Circulation) epixtech, inc.; (ILL) epixtech, inc.; (OPAC) epixtech, inc.
Partic in Amigos Library Services, Inc

MCGINNIS, LOCHRIDGE & KILGORE, LLP, Law Library, 919 Congress Ave, Ste 1300, 78701. SAN 372-1566. Tel: 512-495-6097. FAX: 512-495-6093. *Librn*, Joan O'Mara; E-Mail: jomara@mcginnislaw.com
Library Holdings: Bk Vols 13,000; Per Subs 150

MICROELECTRONICS & COMPUTER TECHNOLOGY CORP, Information Center,* 3500 W Balcones Ctr Dr, 78759-5398. SAN 328-1647. Tel: 512-338-3526. FAX: 512-338-3808. E-Mail: Internet & Bitnet: library@mcc.com. Web Site: www.mcc.com/services/info_ctr/index.html. *Librn*, Kathy Fowler; *Mgr*, Melanie P Mack; Staff 2 (MLS 1, Non-MLS 1)
Founded 1984
Library Holdings: Bk Vols 2,500; Bk Titles 2,400; Per Subs 225
Subject Interests: Software engineering
Special Collections: MCC Technical Reports
Database Vendor: CARL, Dialog, Ebsco - EbscoHost, epixtech, inc., GaleNet, IAC - SearchBank, Lexis-Nexis, OCLC - First Search, OVID Technologies, ProQuest
Publications: MCC Non-Confidential Technical Reports
Restriction: By appointment only
Function: Research library
Partic in Dialog Corporation

S MOTOROLA, INC, Semiconductor Products Sector Global Information Center,* 3501 Ed Bluestein Blvd, 78721. SAN 300-3841. Tel: 512-933-6000. FAX: 602-413-4554. E-Mail: r31526@email.sps.mot.com. *Mgr*, Patricia Wilkins; *Coll Develop*, Donald Guy
Founded 1954
Library Holdings: Bk Vols 4,611; Bk Titles 4,500; Per Subs 161
Subject Interests: Electronics, Engineering, Physics
Restriction: Staff use only
Partic in BRS; Dialog Corporation; Medline; STN

G NATIONAL ARCHIVES & RECORDS ADMINISTRATION, Lyndon Baines Johnson Library & Museum,* 2313 Red River St, 78705-5702. SAN 361-1760. Tel: 512-916-5137. FAX: 512-916-5171. E-Mail: library@johnson.nara.gov. Web Site: www.lbjlib.utexas.edu. *Dir*, Harry J Middleton; *Asst Dir*, Patrick J Borders; *Archivist*, Christina Houston; *Coll Develop*, Allen Fisher
Founded 1971
Oct 1998-Sep 1999 Income Federal $2,957,820. Mats Exp $23,100, Books $3,000, Per/Ser (Incl. Access Fees) $200, Presv $19,000, Other Print Mats $900. Sal $1,432,200 (Prof $1,250,263)
Library Holdings: Bk Vols 17,322
Subject Interests: Career of Lyndon B Johnson, Econ, Johnson administration, Johnson family, Polit hist of the US, Presidency, Soc, US Presidency
Special Collections: Agency & Commission Records, mss, reels, audiovisual materials, & museum objects; as Wright Patman, Drew Pearson, John B Connally, William Westmoreland, etc, mss; Lyndon B Johnson (Oral History Coll), tape, transcribed; Personal Papers of Famous Individuals such
Publications: A Guide to Foreign Policy at the Lyndon B Johnson Library; Historical Materials in the Lyndon Baines Johnson Library, 1988; Lyndon B Johnson, A Bibliography (Compiled by the Staff of the Lyndon Baines Johnson Library and published by the University of Texas Press, 1984); Lyndon B Johnson, A Bibliography, Vol II (Compiled & Edited for the Lyndon Baines Johnson Library by Craig H Roell, 1988); searches of materials available for research use on subject topics
Open Mon-Sun 9-5 (Museum, except Christmas Day)
Friends of the Library Group

G PUBLIC UTILITY COMMISSION OF TEXAS LIBRARY, 1701 N Congress, 12th Flr, 78701. (Mail add: PO Box 13326, 78711-3326), SAN 327-5582. Tel: 512-936-7075, 512-936-7077, 512-936-7080. FAX: 512-936-7079. Web Site: www.puc.state.tx.us. *Mgr*, Marie D Cassens; Tel: 512-936-7075, E-Mail: marie.cassens@puc.state.tx.us; *Librn*, Helen Peeler Clements; Tel: 512-936-7075, E-Mail: clements@puc.state.tx.us; *Asst Librn*, Julie Leung; E-Mail: leung@puc.state.tx.us; *Asst Librn*, Laura Wood; Tel: 512-936-7076, E-Mail: laura.wood@puc.state.tx.us; Staff 2 (MLS 1, Non-MLS 1)
Founded 1975
1998-1999 Income $117,800. Mats Exp $50,200, Books $25,200, Per/Ser (Incl. Access Fees) $25,000. Sal $80,000
Library Holdings: Bk Vols 16,500; Per Subs 300
Special Collections: Electric Power Research Institute Research Reports
Automation Activity & Vendor Info: (Cataloging) EOS; (OPAC) EOS
Publications: PUC Library Bulletin
Library is housed with Texas Railroad Commission Library & shares their legal collection

S RADIAN INTERNATIONAL LIBRARY,* 8501 N MoPac Expressway, PO Box 201088, 78720-1088. SAN 316-0521. Tel: 512-419-5224. FAX: 512-419-5983.; Staff 3 (MLS 3)
Founded 1969
Library Holdings: Bk Vols 47,000; Per Subs 391
Subject Interests: Sci, Technology
Publications: Radian International Library Database Listing; Radian Reports (available thru NTIS); Recent Library Acquisitions

G RAILROAD COMMISSION OF TEXAS LIBRARY,* Capitol Sta, PO Drawer 12967, 78711. SAN 316-053X. Tel: 512-463-7160. FAX: 512-463-6989. *Librn*, Susan Rhyne; E-Mail: susan.rhyne@rrc.state.tx.us
Founded 1979
Library Holdings: Bk Titles 8,000; Per Subs 51
Subject Interests: Law, Texas petroleum industry statistics
Branches:
OIL & GAS DIVISION RECORDS RETENTION DEPT, William B Travis Bldg, 1701 N Congress, 78711-2967. SAN 372-9621. Tel: 512-463-6882. FAX: 512-463-7200. *Mgr*, Elsa Bosque
Library Holdings: Bk Vols 28,500,000; Per Subs 30
Subject Interests: Energy

S RESOURCE ECONOMICS INC LIBRARY,* 701 Brazos St, Ste 500, 78701. SAN 375-6734. Tel: 512-794-8511. FAX: 512-320-5973. *Pres*, Milton Holloway
Library Holdings: Bk Titles 1,000; Per Subs 25

C SAINT EDWARDS UNIVERSITY, Scarborough-Phillips Library, 3001 S Congress Ave, 78704-6489. SAN 361-1825. Interlibrary Loan Service Tel: 512-448-8768. Circulation Tel: 512-448-8469. Reference Tel: 512-448-8474. FAX: 512-448-8737. Web Site: www.libr.stewards.edu. *Dir*, Eileen Shocket; Tel: 512-448-8470, E-Mail: eileena@admin.edwards.edu; *Circ*, Fran Ebbers; Tel: 512-448-8481, E-Mail: ebbersf@libr.stedwards.edu; *Circ*, Claudine Kweder; Tel: 512-448-8448, E-Mail: kwederc@libr.stedwards.edu; *Circ*, Caroline Murphy; Tel: 512-428-1045, E-Mail: murphyc@libr.stewards.edu; *Acq, Cat*, Armando Garcia; Tel: 512-448-8471, E-Mail: gmando@ libr.stedwards.edu; *Cat*, Bernadine Reltger; Tel: 512-464-8825, E-Mail: bernar@libr.stedwards.edu; *Cat*, Mary Margaret Wells; Tel: 512-448-8477, E-Mail: mmw@libr.stedwards.edu; *Archivist, Spec Coll*, Ingrid Karklins; Tel: 512-448-8476, E-Mail: ingrid@libr.stedwards.edu; *Bibliog Instr, Ref*, Connie Cabezas; Tel: 512-448-8479, E-Mail: cabezasc@libr.stedwards.edu; *Assoc Dir, Bibliog Instr, Ref*, Carla Felsted; Tel: 512-448-8727, E-Mail: felstedc@ libr.stedwards.edu; *ILL*, Pat Phillips; Tel: 512-448-8738, E-Mail: patphil@ libr.stedwards.edu; *Ref*, Tamie Andrews; E-Mail: tamiea@ admin.stedwards.edu; *Ref*, Diane Brownlee; Tel: 512-448-8739, E-Mail: brownlee@libr.stedwards.edu; *Ref*, Jeanel Walker; E-Mail: jeanelw@ libr.stedwards.edu; *Tech Servs*, Axel Teichgraeber; Tel: 512-416-5842, E-Mail: axelt@admin.stedwards.edu; *Ser*, Rose Mason; Tel: 512-448-8473, E-Mail: mrose@libr.stedwards.edu; *ILL*, Allison K Carpenter; E-Mail: alisonc@libr.stedwards.edu; Staff 5 (MLS 5)
Founded 1889. Enrl 2,980; Fac 140; Highest Degree: Master
Library Holdings: Bk Vols 146,480; Bk Titles 105,580; Per Subs 1,185
Partic in OCLC Online Computer Library Center, Inc

SR SAINT ELIAS ORTHODOX CHURCH LIBRARY,* 408 E 11th St, 78701. SAN 328-395X. Tel: 512-476-2314. FAX: 512-476-2314. E-Mail: stelias@ juno.com. Web Site: www.st-elias.org. *Librn*, Laura Daigle; *Librn*, Tatiana Nikolova
Library Holdings: Bk Vols 1,500
Subject Interests: Theology

P TEXAS DEPARTMENT OF ECONOMIC DEVELOPMENT, Resource Center, 1700 N Congress, Ste 220-P, 78701. (Mail add: PO Box 12728, 78711), Tel: 512-936-0256. FAX: 512-936-0430. E-Mail: library@ tded.state.tx.us. *Librn*, Julie Wilbanks; E-Mail: juliel@tded.state.tx.us
Founded 1987
Library Holdings: Bk Vols 6,000; Per Subs 300
Subject Interests: Econ develop
Special Collections: Census Bureau
Restriction: Open to public for reference only

GM TEXAS DEPARTMENT OF HEALTH, Library & Information Services Program,* 1100 W 49th St, 78756-3199. SAN 316-0696. Tel: 512-458-7559. FAX: 512-458-7683. E-Mail: library@tdh.state.tx. Web Site: www.tdh.state.tx.us/library/libhome.htm. *Dir*, Cynthia Faries; Tel: 512-458-7111, Ext 6492, Fax: 512-458-7684, E-Mail: cindy.faries@tdh.state.tx.us; *Librn*, Carolyn Medina; E-Mail: carolyn.medina@tdh.state.tx.us; *AV*, Jane Hazelton; Tel: 512-458-7260, Fax: 512-458-7474, E-Mail: jane.hazelton@ tdh.state.tx.us; Staff 13 (MLS 4, Non-MLS 9)
Founded 1958
Library Holdings: Bk Vols 20,000; Bk Titles 10,400; Per Subs 465
Subject Interests: Public health
Special Collections: Tex health statistics
Publications: Funding Watch
Restriction: Open to public for reference only
Partic in Nat Libr of Med

G TEXAS DEPARTMENT OF TRANSPORTATION, Research & Tech Transfer Office Library,* PO Box 5080, 78763-5080. SAN 372-9648. Tel: 512-465-7644. FAX: 512-465-7486. *Librn*, Dana Herring
Library Holdings: Bk Vols 50,000; Per Subs 15
Subject Interests: Energy, Safety

S TEXAS DEPARTMENT OF TRANSPORTATION, Aviation Resource Center & Video Library, South Tower, Rm 1B8, 150 E Riverside Dr, 78704-2405. (Mail add: 125 E 11th St, 78701-2483), Tel: 512-416-4550. FAX: 512-416-4510. *Info Specialist, Mgr*, Marie C Peinado; Staff 1 (Non-MLS 1)
Founded 1973
Library Holdings: Per Subs 25
Subject Interests: Aeronautics, Airlines, Airport syst planning, Airports, Aviation educ, Aviation safety
Publications: Video Catalog
Video (VHS) loan library for Texas residents; Open Mon-Fri 8-12, 1-4

G TEXAS EDUCATION AGENCY, Resource Center Library, 1701 N Congress Ave, 78701-1494. SAN 321-9259. Tel: 512-463-9050. FAX: 512-475-3447. *Chief Librn*, Linda Kemp; *Librn*, Jan Anderson; Staff 2 (MLS 2)
Founded 1968
Library Holdings: Bk Vols 16,000; Per Subs 375
Subject Interests: Public school educ
Special Collections: ERIC Coll, micro

G TEXAS GENERAL LAND OFFICE, Archives & Records Division Library,* Stephen F Austin Bldg, 1700 N Congress Ave, 78701. SAN 372-9613. Tel: 512-463-5277. FAX: 512-475-4619. *Dir*, Susan Dorsey
Library Holdings: Bk Vols 200
Special Collections: Map Coll; Pub Lands Archives; Spanish Coll

G TEXAS HISTORICAL COMMISSION LIBRARY, 1510 Colorado, PO Bo 12276, 78701. SAN 326-5323. Tel: 512-463-5753. FAX: 512-463-3571. E-Mail: library@thc.state.tx.us. Web Site: www.thc.state.tx.us/library.html. *Librn*, Michelle M Mears; E-Mail: michelle.mears@thc.state.tx.us. Subject Specialists: *Archives*, Michelle M Mears; Staff 1 (MLS 1)
Founded 1998
Library Holdings: Bk Vols 5,000; Bk Titles 3,500; Per Subs 30
Subject Interests: Archaeology, Architecture
Special Collections: Archeological Surveys & Reports; National Register i Texas files; Official Texas Historical Marker Files; National Register in Texas files; Official Texas Historical Marker Files
Automation Activity & Vendor Info: (Cataloging) Athena
Restriction: Non-circulating to the public

M TEXAS MEDICAL ASSOCIATION LIBRARY,* 401 W 15th, 78701-168(SAN 316-0661. Tel: 512-370-1550. FAX: 512-370-1634. E-Mail: tma_library@texmed.org. Web Site: www.texmed.org/library/librhmpg.htm. *Dir*, Nancy Reynolds; E-Mail: nancy_r@texmed.org; *Asst Dir, Coll Develo*, Lorie Cox; *Publ Servs*, Laura Fowler
Founded 1922
Jan 1997-Dec 1998 Mats Exp $252,240, Books $24,000, Per/Ser (Incl. Access Fees) $213,440, Presv $3,000. Sal $329,100 (Prof $180,000)
Library Holdings: Per Subs 860
Subject Interests: Clinical medicine
Special Collections: History of medicine in Texas
Publications: CME Resource Catalog; Library Services Guide for Community Users; Library Services: A Guide for TMA Members; New Acquisitions List
Partic in Nat Libr of Med; S Cent Regional Med Libr Program
Friends of the Library Group

G TEXAS NATURAL RESOURCE CONSERVATION COMMISSION LIBRARY, MC-196, 12100 Park 35 Circle, PO Box 13087, 78711-3087. SAN 316-0629. Tel: 512-239-0020. FAX: 512-239-0022. Web Site: home/ tnrcc.state.tx.us/admin/pip/library/index.html. *Head Librn*, Sylvia Von Fang E-Mail: svonfang@tnrcc.state.tx.us; *Librn*, Dru Edrington; E-Mail: dedringt@tnrcc.state.tx.us; Staff 2 (MLS 2)
Founded 1964
Library Holdings: Bk Vols 65,251; Bk Titles 43,764; Per Subs 235
Subject Interests: Air, Fields of sci relating to water resources, Geology, Hazardous waste, Hydraulic eng, Hydrology, Land use, Outdoor recreation, Problems, Solid waste, Uses, Water quality, Weather modification
Special Collections: Civil Engineering (United States Corps of; Development Board Publications); Engineers & United States Bureau of Reclamation Papers); Geology (United States Geological Survey Papers); Water Resources Development (Texas Water
Automation Activity & Vendor Info: (Cataloging) SIRSI; (Circulation) SIRSI; (OPAC) SIRSI; (Serials) SIRSI
Restriction: Open to public for reference only

S TEXAS NATURAL RESOURCES INFORMATION SYSTEM LIBRARY,* Steven F Austin State Bldg, Rm B40, 1700 N Congress Ave, 78701. (Mail add: PO Box 13231, 78711-3231), Tel: 512-463-8337. FAX: 512-463-7274. Web Site: www.tnris.state.tx.us. *Mgr*, Hugh Bender

G TEXAS PARKS & WILDLIFE DEPARTMENT LIBRARY,* 4200 Smith School Rd, 78744. SAN 324-3710. Tel: 512-389-4800. FAX: 512-328-5632.
Founded 1972
Library Holdings: Bk Titles 8,500; Per Subs 50
Subject Interests: Fisheries, State park develop, Wildlife mgt
Special Collections: Federal Aid Reports in Fisheries & Wildlife

S TEXAS RESEARCH INSTITUTE-AUSTIN, INC, Nondestructive Testing Information Analysis Center,* 415 A Crystal Creek Dr, 78746-4725. SAN 372-6665. Tel: 512-263-2106. FAX: 512-263-3530. Web Site: www.ntiac.com.
Partic in Dialog Corporation; DROLS; Orbit

S TEXAS SCHOOL FOR THE BLIND, Learning Resource Center Library,* 1100 W 45th St, 78756. SAN 326-3819. Tel: 512-454-8631, Ext 108. FAX: 512-206-9450. *Librn*, Diane Nousanen; Staff 4 (MLS 1, Non-MLS 3)
Enrl 200; Fac 60
Library Holdings: Bk Vols 6,000; Per Subs 70
Special Collections: Special Education for visually handicapped

GL TEXAS STATE LAW LIBRARY,* Tom C Clark Bldg, 205 W 14th St, PO Box 12367, 78711-2367. SAN 316-0718. Tel: 512-463-1722. FAX: 512-463-1728. *Dir*, Kay Schlueter; Staff 11 (MLS 4, Non-MLS 7)
Founded 1971
Library Holdings: Bk Vols 130,000; Per Subs 275
Subject Interests: Law, Legal hist
Partic in Westlaw
Open Mon-Fri 8-5

TEXAS STATE LEGISLATIVE REFERENCE LIBRARY,* Capitol Bldg, 1100 Congress Rm 2N-3, 78701. SAN 316-0513. Tel: 512-463-1252. Toll Free Tel: 877-824-7038. FAX: 512-475-4626. Web Site: www.lrl.state.tx.us. *Dir*, Dale Propp
Founded 1969
1997-1998 Income $1,070,584
Library Holdings: Bk Vols 50,000
Subject Interests: Law, Legislation, Political science, Pub affairs
Special Collections: Texas Legislative Bills 1973-Present; Texas State Documents

TEXAS STATE LIBRARY & ARCHIVES COMMISSION, Talking Book Program,* 1201 Brazos, PO Box 12927, 78711-2927. SAN 316-0726. Tel: 512-463-5458. Toll Free Tel: 800-252-9605. FAX: 512-463-5436. E-Mail: tbp.services@tsl.state.tx.us. Web Site: www.tsl.state.tx.us/tbp. *Dir*, Jenifer Flaxbart; *Dir*, Cecil D Rudd; *Ref*, Dina Abramson; *Coll Develop*, Lisa Hendricks; Staff 30 (MLS 13, Non-MLS 17)
Founded 1931. Circ 870,836
Sep 1999-Aug 2000 Income $1,389,875
Library Holdings: Bk Titles 70,000
Special Collections: Spanish Coll, cassettes; Texana Coll, cassettes
Special Services for the Blind - Audio-cassettes; Braille; Large print bks; Large print bks
Friends of the Library Group

TEXAS STATE LIBRARY & ARCHIVES COMMISSION, 1201 Brazos, PO Box 12927, 78711-2927. SAN 361-1914. Tel: 512-463-5455. Interlibrary Loan Service Tel: 512-463-5432. FAX: 512-463-5436. E-Mail: info@tsl.state.tx.us. Web Site: www.tsl.state.tx.us. *VPres*, Michael Harper; *Dir, Librn*, Peggy D Rudd; E-Mail: peggy.rudd@tsl.state.tx.us; *Asst Librn*, Edward Seidenberg; Tel: 512-463-5460, E-Mail: edward.seidenberg@tsl.state.tx.us; *Archivist*, Chris LaPlante; Staff 78 (MLS 78)
Founded 1909. Pop 18,321,383
Sep 2000-Aug 2001 Income $23,300,000, State $13,000,000, Federal $8,500,000, Locally Generated Income $1,800,000
Library Holdings: Bk Vols 1,876,744; Per Subs 540
Subject Interests: Fed, Pub policy, State government, Texana
Special Collections: Broadside Coll); Genealogy Coll; History (Historical Manuscripts, Iconographic Maps &; Professional Librarianship Coll; Texas; Texas & Federal Government Documents Coll
Publications: Instruction Manuals; Library Developments (bimonthly newsletter); Texas Academic Library Statistics; Texas Public Library Statistics; Texas State Library & Archives Commission Biennial Report; Texas State Publications Checklist & Indexes; The Local Record (quarterly newsletter); Trails (about every 2 months)
Partic in Amigos Library Services, Inc
Special Services for the Blind - Talking book center
Friends of the Library Group

TEXAS YOUTH COMMISSION, Library of Prevention,* 4900 N Lamar Blvd, 78765-4260. SAN 375-3751. Tel: 512-424-6336. FAX: 512-424-6300. E-Mail: prevention@tyc.state.tx.us. Web Site: www.tyc.state.tx.as/prevention. *Dir*, Dr Tracy Levins; *Cat*, Rae Tregilgas
Founded 1993
Library Holdings: Bk Titles 400; Per Subs 20
Publications: Executive summaries of prevention topics
Partic in Amigos Library Services, Inc
Special Services for the Deaf - Staff with knowledge of sign language

THOMAS INVESTIGATIVE PUBLICATIONS, INC, National Association of Investigative Specialists National Trade Organization,* 9513 Burnet Rd No 101, 78758. (Mail add: PO Box 33244, 78764), SAN 372-5472. Tel: 512-719-3595. FAX: 512-719-3594. E-Mail: pim007@aol.com. Web Site: www.pimall.com/nais. *In Charge*, Ralph Thomas; E-Mail: rthomas007@aol.com; Staff 3 (MLS 3)
Library Holdings: Bk Titles 400

3M LIBRARY & INFORMATION SERVICES, Austin Information Services, Bldg 130-IN-01, 6801 Riverplace Blvd, 78726-9000. SAN 326-3673. Tel: 512-984-2124. FAX: 512-984-3237.; Staff 3 (MLS 2, Non-MLS 1)
Founded 1984
Library Holdings: Bk Titles 8,000; Per Subs 250
Subject Interests: Electronics, Telecommunications

TRAVIS COUNTY LAW LIBRARY, 314 W 11th, Rm 450, 78701-2112. (Mail add: PO Box 1748, 78767-1748), SAN 374-6070. Tel: 512-473-9519. FAX: 512-708-4560. E-Mail: tclib@cc.uts.utexas.edu. *Mgr Libr Serv*, Lisa Rush; Tel: 512-473-9290, E-Mail: lisa.rush@co.travis.tx.us; *Ref Serv*, Josie Arjona; Tel: 512-473-9519; *Ref Serv*, Judy Helms; Tel: 512-473-9045, Fax: 512-473-9082; *Ref Serv*, Geri Krohn; Tel: 512-473-9045; Staff 4 (MLS 2, Non-MLS 2)
Founded 1983
Oct 2000-Sep 2001 Income County $866,672. Mats Exp $250,340, Books $239,000, Electronic Ref Mat (Incl. Access Fees) $11,340. Sal $245,300 (Prof $172,311)
Library Holdings: Bk Titles 1,270; Per Subs 146
Special Collections: Texas & Federal Law Coll
Database Vendor: Lexis-Nexis
Restriction: Circulation limited, Non-circulating to the public
Function: For research purposes

S TTARA RESEARCH FOUNDATION, Texas Research Library,* 400 W 15th St, Ste 400, 78701. SAN 316-0688. Tel: 512-472-3127. FAX: 512-472-2636.
Founded 1952
Library Holdings: Bk Vols 2,800; Per Subs 178
Subject Interests: Local government, Res in state

C UNIVERSITY OF TEXAS LIBRARIES, Perry-Castaneda Library, 21st & Speedway, 79705. (Mail add: PO Box P, 78713-8916), SAN 361-1973. Tel: 512-495-4350, 512-495-4382. Interlibrary Loan Service Tel: 512-495-4131. FAX: 512-495-4283. Web Site: www.lib.utexas.edu. *Access Serv*, Michele Ostrow; Staff 144 (MLS 144)
Founded 1883. Enrl 49,009; Fac 2,313; Highest Degree: Doctorate
Sep 1999-Aug 2000 Mats Exp $11,022,592. Sal $16,153,431 (Prof $6,716,434)
Library Holdings: Bk Vols 7,937,574; Per Subs 50,165
Mem of Asn of Research Libraries
Partic in Amigos Library Services, Inc; Center For Research Libraries; Dialog Corporation; OCLC Online Computer Library Center, Inc; Research Libraries Group, Inc; Tex Share
Friends of the Library Group
Departmental Libraries:
ARCHITECTURE & PLANNING, Mail Code S5430, Battle Hall 200, 79705. (Mail add: PO Box P, 78713-8916), Tel: 512-495-4620. Web Site: www.lib.utexas.edu/libs/apl/. *Head Librn*, Janine Henri; Tel: 512-495-4623; *Curator*, Beth Dodd; Tel: 512-495-4621; Staff 6 (MLS 2, Non-MLS 4)
Founded 1912
Library Holdings: Bk Vols 67,700; Per Subs 180
Subject Interests: Architectural hist, Architecture, Community, Historic preservation, Interior design, Regional planning
Special Collections: Alexander Architectural Archive
BALCONES LIBRARY SERVICE CENTER, 10100 Burnet Rd, 78758. SAN 316-0742. Tel: 512-495-4644. FAX: 512-495-4643. Web Site: www.lib.utexas.edu/libs/eng/blsc/blsc.html. *Librn*, Jennifer Haas
Founded 1986
Library Holdings: Bk Vols 1,200
BUREAU OF BUSINESS RESEARCH, Red McCombs School of Business, Rm 6-400, 78705. (Mail add: PO Box 7459, 78713-7439), SAN 361-199X. Tel: 512-471-5180. Toll Free Tel: 888-212-4386. FAX: 512-471-1063. Web Site: www.utexas.edu/depts/bbr/iis/. *Librn*, Rita J Wright; E-Mail: rjwright@mail.utexas.edu; Staff 1 (MLS 1)
Founded 1926
Library Holdings: Bk Vols 25; Bk Titles 10; Per Subs 10
Subject Interests: Econ demographic data on Tex
Special Collections: Bureau of Economic Analysis Data; Economic Censuses (1980 & 1990 census); Manufacturer's Directories of Other States
Publications: Texas Trade & Professional Associations (2000)
CENTER FOR AMERICAN HISTORY, 78712. Tel: 512-495-4515. FAX: 512-495-4542. Web Site: www.cah.utexas.edu. *Dir*, Don E Carleton; *Assoc Dir*, Katherine J Adams; *Assoc Dir*, Alison M Beck
1998-1999 Income $806,580. Mats Exp $36,860, Presv $14,154. Sal $771,900 (Prof $500,000)
Library Holdings: Bk Vols 145,578; Per Subs 103
Subject Interests: Archives, Far W, Hist of old south, Imprints, Manuscripts, Music, Newsp, Oral hist, Photog, SW, Texas
Special Collections: American History Coll; Congressional History Coll; Eugene C Barker Texas History Coll; John Nance Garner House & Museum (Uvalde, Texas); Research & Collections Division; Sam Rayburn Library & Museum (Bonham, Texas); The George W Littlefield Southern History Coll; University of Texas Archives; Western Americana Coll; Winedale Historical Center (Round Top, Texas)
Publications: Newsletter
CHEMISTRY, Welch Hall 2.132, 78713. SAN 361-2422. Tel: 512-495-4600. *Librn*, David Flaxbart
Library Holdings: Bk Vols 78,342
Subject Interests: Chemical engineering, Chemistry, Nutrition
CLASSICS, Waggener Hall 1, 78713. SAN 361-2457. Tel: 512-495-4690.
Library Holdings: Bk Vols 26,555
COLLECTIONS DEPOSIT LIBRARY, PO Box P, 78713-8916. Tel: 512-495-4694.
EAST ASIAN LIBRARY PROGRAM, PO Box P, 78713-8916. Tel: 512-495-4323. *Head Librn*, Meng-fen Su; E-Mail: msu@mail.utexas.edu
Library Holdings: Bk Vols 91,254
Subject Interests: China, Japan, Korea
ENGINEERING, Cockrell Hall 1.300, 78713. SAN 361-2481. Tel: 512-495-4511. FAX: 512-495-4507. E-Mail: englib@mail.utexas.edu. *Librn*, Susan Ardis; *Asst Librn*, Larayne Dallas
Library Holdings: Bk Vols 165,000
Special Collections: Engineering Industry Standards, micro; Master

Catalog Service; Patents, micro; US Patent Office; US Patents

FINE ARTS, Fine Arts Bldg 3.200, 24th & Trinity, 78713. SAN 361-2511. Tel: 512-495-4480. FAX: 512-495-4490. Web Site: www.lib.utexas.edu/libs/fal/fal_home_page.html. *Librn*, David Hunter; Tel: 512-495-4475; *Librn*, Laura Schwartz; Tel: 512-495-4476; *AV*, Karl F Miller; Tel: 512-495-4477. Subject Specialists: *Art*, Laura Schwartz; *Music*, David Hunter

Library Holdings: Bk Vols 300,000

Subject Interests: Art, Drama, Music

Special Collections: Historical Music Recordings Coll

GEOLOGY, Geology 302, 78713-8916. SAN 361-2546. Tel: 512-495-4680. FAX: 512-471-9425. E-Mail: drtgeol@utxvm.cc.utexas.edu. *Librn*, Dennis Trombatore

Library Holdings: Bk Vols 108,000

Special Collections: Tobin Geologic Maps Coll

HARRY RANSOM HUMANITIES RESEARCH CENTER, PO Box 7219, 78713-7219. SAN 361-2724. Tel: 512-471-9119. FAX: 512-471-9646. E-Mail: info@hrc.utexas.edu, reference@hrc.utexas.edu. Web Site: www.hrc.utexas.edu. *Dir*, Thomas F Staley; *Librn*, Richard Oram; Staff 28 (MLS 28)

Founded 1957

Library Holdings: Bk Titles 400,000; Per Subs 12,775

Subject Interests: 19th Century Am lit, 19th Century British lit, French lit

Special Collections: 17th & 18th Century First Editions, T J Wise Forgeries (Wrenn Library); 17th-20th Century First Editions; 18th Century First Editions & Source Materials (Aitken Library); A A Knopf Library & Archives; Author Colls of James Agee, Maxwell Anderson, W H Auden, H E Bates, Samuel Beckett, Arnold Bennett, Edmund Blunden, E B & Robert Browning, A Burgess, Byron, J B Cabell, Conrad, Hart Crane, E E Cummings, Edward Dahlberg, J F Dobie, Norman Douglas, A C Doyle, Lord Dunsany, T S Eliot, Faulkner, Fitzgerald, C S Forester, E M Forster, John Fowles, Galsworthy, Goyen, Robert Graves, Graham Greene, D Hare, Lillian Hellman, Hemingway, Hergesheimer, W H Hudson, Huxley, Jacobson, Jeffers, Joyce, Adrienne Kennedy, D H Lawrence, T E Lawrence, Sinclair Lewis, Arthur Machen, Louis MacNeice, E L Masters, Maugham, George Meredith, James Michener, Arthur Miller, Henry Miller, Marianne Moore, Morley, Nabokov, Eugene O'Neill, Poe, Pound, Powys, Priestley, Prokosch, Purdy, Sassoon, Scott, Sexton, G B Shaw, M P Shiel, Isaac Bashevis Singer, the Sitwells, C P Snow, Steinbeck, Tom Stoppard, Dylan Thomas, Tennessee Williams, Tutuola, W C Williams, W B Yeats, Louis Zukofsky; Barrie, Eliot, Galsworthy, Shaw, Wilde, Yeats (T E Hanley Library); Currey Collection of Science Fiction; David O Selznick Archives; Edward Laroque Tinker Archives; Gernsheim Photography Coll; Grattan Collection of Southwest Pacificana; History of Science Coll; McManus-Young Magic Coll; Theatre History & Dramatic Literature, Kemble, Garrick, P T Barnum, Houdini, Norman Bel Geddes Theatre Arts Library

Friends of the Library Group

INTER-LIBRARY SERVICE DEPARTMENT, Mail Code S5462, PO Box P, 78713-8916. Tel: 512-495-4131. FAX: 512-495-4283. *Librn*, Nancy E Paine

JAMAIL CENTER FOR LEGAL RESEARCH, 727 E Dean Keeton St, 78705-3224. SAN 361-2783. Tel: 512-471-7726. Reference Tel: 512-471-6220. FAX: 512-471-0243. Web Site: tarlton.law.utexas.edu. *Dir*, Roy M Mersky; Tel: 512-471-7735; Staff 16 (MLS 15, Non-MLS 1)

Founded 1886

Sep 1999-Aug 2000 Income $2,876,076. Mats Exp $1,070,845. Sal $1,509,677 (Prof $1,075,113)

Library Holdings: Bk Vols 971,727

Subject Interests: British Commonwealth law, Constitutional law, Human rights, International law

Special Collections: ABA Gavel Committee Award entries; Holdings of Foreign Countries (Western Europe, Latin America, Middle East); Law & Popular Culture Coll; Papers of Tom C Clark, Assoc Justice, Supreme Court of the United States

Automation Activity & Vendor Info: (Acquisitions) Innovative Interfaces Inc.; (Cataloging) Innovative Interfaces Inc.; (Circulation) Innovative Interfaces Inc.; (Course Reserve) Innovative Interfaces Inc.; (ILL) Innovative Interfaces Inc.; (Media Booking) Innovative Interfaces Inc.; (OPAC) Innovative Interfaces Inc.; (Serials) Innovative Interfaces Inc.

Publications: Annual report; Tarlton Law Library Legal Bibliography Series

Partic in OCLC Online Computer Library Center, Inc; RLIN

Friends of the Library Group

LIFE SCIENCE (BIOLOGY, PHARMACY), Main Bldg 220, 78713. SAN 361-266X. Tel: 512-495-4630. FAX: 512-495-4638. Web Site: www.lib.utexas.edu/libs/lsl/lifesci/lsl.html. *Librn*, Nancy Elder; E-Mail: n.elder@mail.utexas.edu

Library Holdings: Bk Vols 192,000

Subject Interests: Biological sci, Pharm

MARINE SCIENCE, Marine Sci Inst, 750 Channelview Dr, Port Aransas, 78373. SAN 371-5965. Tel: 361-749-6723. FAX: 361-749-6725. Web Site: www.lib.utexas.edu/libs/msl/. *In Charge*, Liz DeHart; E-Mail: liz@utmsi.utexas.edu

Founded 1941

Subject Interests: Marine sci

Publications: Contributions in Marine Science

Mem of Asn of Research Libraries

MIDDLE EASTERN LIBRARY PROGRAM, PO Box P, 78713-8916. Tel: 512-495-4322. FAX: 512-495-4296. *Librn*, Abazar Sepehri; E-Mail: a.sepehri@mail.utexas.edu

Library Holdings: Bk Vols 300,500

Subject Interests: Islamic world

Publications: Arabic & Persian Periodicals in the Middle East Coll

MONOGRAPHIC ACQUISITIONS UNIT, PO Box P, 78713-8916. Tel: 512-495-4160. FAX: 512-495-4410. *In Charge*, Anita Farber

Automation Activity & Vendor Info: (Acquisitions) Innovative Interfa Inc.; (Serials) Innovative Interfaces Inc.

NETTIE LEE BENSON LATIN AMERICAN COLLECTION, Sid Richardson Hall 1-109, 78713-8916. SAN 361-2309. Tel: 512-495-4520. FAX: 512-495-4520. *Bibliogr*, Donald L Gibbs

Library Holdings: Bk Vols 632,738

Subject Interests: Latin Am studies, Mexican Am studies

Special Collections: Author collections of Sor Juana Ines de la Gruz; Central American Materials (Arturo Taracena Flores Coll); Cultural History & Literature of Brazil, Chile & the Rio de las Plata Region (Manuel Gondra, Simon Lucuix & Pedro Martinez Reales Colls); Joaqui Fernandez de Lizardi, Alfonso Reyes, Jose Angel Gutierrez, Julian Samo Library, Jose Toribio Medina & Many Literary Figures of Mexico, Argentina, Brazil, Chile & Peru; Jose Cardenas & Intercultural Development Research Association Archives; Joseph G Moore Coll of Afro-Jamaican Folklore; Julio Cortazar Literary Papers; Letters of Santa Anna & Pancho Villa; Manuscripts from 16th to 20th Century, incl 16th Century Relaciones Geograficas; Martin Fierro Coll; Media Materials of Chile, Bolivia & Peru (Diego Munoz Coll); Mexican Cultural History & Literature (Genaro Garcia, Joaquin Garcia Icazbalceta, Juan Hernandez y Davalos, Sanchez Navarro, Lazaro de la Garza, Pablo Salce Arrendondo W B Stephens Colls); Papers of Six Mexican Presidents & Other 19th Century Mexican Figures; Presidential Papers of League of United Latin American Citizens; St John d'el Rey Mining Company Archives

Publications: Biblio Noticias; Catalog of the Latin American Collection

Partic in OCLC Online Computer Library Center, Inc

PERRY-CASTANEDA LIBRARY (MAIN LIBRARY), 21st & Speedway, 79705. (Mail add: PO Box P, 78713-8916), Tel: 512-495-4350. *Circ*, Suzanne McAnna; *Ref*, John Tongate; *ILL*, Nancy Paine; *Doc*, Paul Rascoe; *Per*, William Kopplin

PHYSICS-MATH-ASTRONOMY, Robert L Moore Hall 4.200, 78713. SA 361-2635. Tel: 512-495-4610. FAX: 512-495-4611. E-Mail: pma@lib.utexas.edu. Web Site: www.lib.utexas.edu/libs/pma. *Librn*, Molly Whi

Library Holdings: Bk Vols 92,600

POPULATION RESEARCH CENTER LIBRARY, Main Bldg 1800, 7871 SAN 361-2759. Tel: 512-471-8332. FAX: 512-471-4886. Web Site: www.prc.utexas.edu. *Librn*, Diane Fisher; E-Mail: diane@prc.utexas.edu

Founded 1971

Library Holdings: Bk Vols 35,000

Subject Interests: Domestic demography, Human ecology, Int

Special Collections: World Fertility Survey, publ depository

Publications: Handbook of National Population Census: Africa & Asia; International Population Census Bibliography: 1965-68; Latin America & the Caribbean, North America, Oceania & Europe; Revision & Update: 1945-1977

PUBLICATIONS SALES OFFICE, PO Box P, 78713-8916. Tel: 512-495-4239.

SERIALS ACQUISITIONS UNIT, PO Box P, 78713-8916. Tel: 512-495-4222. FAX: 512-495-4242.

Automation Activity & Vendor Info: (Acquisitions) Innovative Interface Inc.; (Serials) Innovative Interfaces Inc.

SOUTH ASIAN LIBRARY PROGRAM, PCL 5 108, 78713. SAN 371-4985. Tel: 512-495-4329. FAX: 512-495-4296. Web Site: www.lib.utexas.edu/subject/area/asia.html. *Librn*, Merry Burlingham

Library Holdings: Bk Vols 150,000

UNDERGRADUATE, Flawn Academic Ctr 101, 78713. SAN 361-2066. Te 512-495-4444. FAX: 512-495-4340. Web Site: www.lib.utexas.edu/ugl/. *Head Librn*, Damon Jaggars; *Coll Develop, Tech Servs*, Beth Kerr

Library Holdings: Bk Vols 151,165

WASSERMAN PUBLIC AFFAIRS LIBRARY, Sid Richardson Hall 3-243, 78713-8916. Tel: 512-495-4400. FAX: 512-471-4697. Web Site: www.lib.utexas.edu/libs/pal. *Librn*, Stephen Littrell

Library Holdings: Bk Vols 70,929

Subject Interests: Pub admin, Pub policy

Special Collections: CAN (1985-Present); Canadian Documents; Governmental Financial Statements & Annual Reports; Selective US Doc Dep (since 1986)

S US GEOLOGICAL SURVEY LIBRARY,* 8027 Exchange Dr, 78754. SAN 370-2723. Tel: 512-927-3500. FAX: 512-927-3590. Web Site: tx.usgs.gov/library.

Library Holdings: Bk Vols 10,000; Per Subs 16

Restriction: Staff use only

Open Tues-Thurs 8-3

WESTBANK COMMUNITY LIBRARY, 1309 Westbank Dr, 78746. SAN 372-6789. Tel: 512-327-3045. Interlibrary Loan Service Tel: 512-314-3585. Circulation Tel: 512-314-3585. Reference Tel: 512-314-3582. FAX: 512-327-3074. Web Site: www.westbank.lib.tx.us. *Dir*, Beth Wheeler Fox; E-Mail: beth@westbank.lib.tx.us; *Cat*, Shannon Egan; E-Mail: egan@ westbank.lib.tx.us; *Coll Develop, Head Tech Servs*, Elaine Miller; E-Mail: elaine@westbank.lib.tx.us; *Head Ref, Tech Coordr*, Kate Claus; E-Mail: kate@westbank.lib.tx.us; Staff 7 (MLS 3, Non-MLS 4)
Founded 1984. Pop 21,446; Circ 180,000
Jan 2000-Dec 2000 Income $1,017,570, City $922,474, Locally Generated Income $92,721, Other $2,375. Mats Exp $36,736, Books $27,503, Per/Ser (Incl. Access Fees) $5,350, Other Print Mats $1,445, Electronic Ref Mat (Incl. Access Fees) $2,438. Sal $175,403 (Prof $114,800)
Library Holdings: Bk Vols 36,625; Bk Titles 31,829; Per Subs 97
Automation Activity & Vendor Info: (Cataloging) Sagebrush Corporation; (Circulation) Sagebrush Corporation
Database Vendor: Ebsco - EbscoHost, IAC - Info Trac, OCLC - First Search, ProQuest, Wilson - Wilson Web
Publications: Inside Story (quarterly); Newsletters (weekly & monthly)
Mem of Central Texas Library System
Friends of the Library Group

WRIGHT & GREENHILL PC, Law Library,* 221 W Sixth St, Ste 1800, 78701-3495. SAN 375-0221. Tel: 512-476-4600, Ext 371. FAX: 512-476-5382.; Staff 2 (MLS 1, Non-MLS 1)
1997-1998 Mats Exp $64,000. Sal $33,000
Library Holdings: Bk Vols 5,000; Per Subs 50
Restriction: Staff use only

ZLE

AZLE PUBLIC LIBRARY, 609 Southeast Pkwy, 76020. SAN 316-0750. Tel: 817-444-7114. FAX: 817-444-7064. Web Site: www.ci.azle.tx.us. *Librn*, Judy Whitt; E-Mail: jwhitt@ci.azle.tx.us
Founded 1964. Pop 12,000; Circ 110,744
Oct 1999-Sep 2000 Income $141,520, County $3,500. Mats Exp $14,700, Per/Ser (Incl. Access Fees) $3,209. Sal $89,583
Library Holdings: Bk Vols 39,000; Per Subs 100
Subject Interests: Holocaust, Local history
Automation Activity & Vendor Info: (Cataloging) Athena; (Circulation) Athena; (OPAC) Athena
Mem of North Texas Regional Library System
Friends of the Library Group

AIRD

CALLAHAN COUNTY LIBRARY, 100 W 4th St, B-1, 79504-5305. SAN 316-0769. Tel: 915-854-1718. FAX: 915-854-1227. E-Mail: callahancl@ bitstreet.com. *Librn*, Sonia Walker
Circ 2,331
Oct 1998-Sep 1999 Income $16,887, City $442, County $10,248, Other $697. Mats Exp $498, Books $391, Per/Ser (Incl. Access Fees) $107. Sal $9,940
Library Holdings: Bk Vols 33,000; Per Subs 16
Mem of Big Country Library System
Open Mon-Fri 1-5

ALCH SPRINGS

BALCH SPRINGS PUBLIC LIBRARY, (Formerly Balch Springs Library), 4301 Pioneer Rd, 75180. SAN 376-4478. Tel: 972-286-8856, 972-557-6096. FAX: 972-557-7531. *Dir*, Betty Rippa; E-Mail: betty@znet-tx.com; Staff 2 (Non-MLS 2)
Founded 1969. Pop 19,000; Circ 19,920
Oct 2000-Sep 2001 Income $85,367, City $83,064, Locally Generated Income $2,303. Mats Exp $19,028, Books $17,856, Per/Ser (Incl. Access Fees) $250, AV Equip $634. Sal $65,207 (Prof $29,000)
Library Holdings: Bk Vols 23,126; Bk Titles 22,880; Per Subs 26; Bks on Deafness & Sign Lang 12
Restriction: Residents only
Mem of Northeast Texas Library System

ALLINGER

CARNEGIE LIBRARY OF BALLINGER, 204 Eighth St, 76821. SAN 316-0777. Tel: 915-365-3616. FAX: 915-365-5004. *Librn*, Cindy Belden; *Asst Librn*, Margaret Strube
Founded 1909. Pop 7,157
Library Holdings: Bk Vols 13,338; Bk Titles 12,868; Per Subs 30
Mem of Big Country Library System

BALMORHEA

P BALMORHEA PUBLIC LIBRARY, 102 S Main, PO Box 355, 79718. SAN 316-0785. Tel: 915-375-2522. *Actg Librn*, Pattye Brown; Staff 1 (MLS 1)
Founded 1927. Pop 650
1998-1999 Mats Exp Books $1,500. Sal $1,800
Library Holdings: Bk Vols 3,500
Mem of Texas Trans Pecos Library System
Open Tues & Sat 11-1
Friends of the Library Group

BANDERA

P BANDERA COUNTY LIBRARY,* 515 Main St, PO Box 1568, 78003-1568. SAN 316-0793. Tel: 830-796-4213. FAX: 830-460-8201. *Dir*, Linda W Burrow; *Asst Librn*, Melanie Clark
Pop 9,025; Circ 35,000
Library Holdings: Bk Vols 27,393; Per Subs 53
Special Collections: Genealogy; Texana
Automation Activity & Vendor Info: (Cataloging) Sagebrush Corporation; (Circulation) Sagebrush Corporation
Mem of Alamo Area Library System
Friends of the Library Group

BARKSDALE

P NUECES CANYON PUBLIC LIBRARY,* PO Box 58, 78828-0058. SAN 376-4176. Tel: 830-234-3173. FAX: 830-234-3174. *Librn*, Annette Cox
Library Holdings: Bk Vols 18,000; Per Subs 35
Mem of Alamo Area Library System

BARTLETT

P TEINERT MEMORIAL PUBLIC LIBRARY,* Hwy 95 at Professor Paul Blvd, PO Box 12, 76511. SAN 316-0815. Tel: 254-527-3208. *Librn*, Pat Crawford
Founded 1976. Pop 3,789; Circ 41,667
Library Holdings: Bk Vols 20,000; Per Subs 40
Subject Interests: Local history
Mem of Central Texas Library System

BASTROP

P BASTROP PUBLIC LIBRARY, 1100 Church St, 78602. (Mail add: PO Drawer 670, 78602-0670), SAN 316-0823. Tel: 512-321-5441. FAX: 512-321-3163. E-Mail: reference@bastroplibrary.org. Web Site: www.bastroplibrary.org. *Dir*, Barbara Harris; E-Mail: barbara@ bastroplibrary.org; *Ad Servs*, Mickey DuVall; *Ch Servs*, Dana Verrall; E-Mail: danav@bastroplibrary.org; Staff 2 (MLS 2)
Founded 1972. Pop 15,000; Circ 135,000
Oct 1999-Sep 2000 Income $186,000, City $220,000, County $5,000. Mats Exp $27,000, Books $20,000, Per/Ser (Incl. Access Fees) $7,000. Sal $155,000 (Prof $67,000)
Library Holdings: Bk Titles 25,000; Per Subs 50
Subject Interests: Genealogy, Local history
Special Collections: Texana
Automation Activity & Vendor Info: (Cataloging) Sagebrush Corporation; (Circulation) Sagebrush Corporation
Database Vendor: OCLC - First Search
Mem of Central Texas Library System
Friends of the Library Group

BAY CITY

P BAY CITY PUBLIC LIBRARY, 1100 Seventh St, 77414. SAN 316-0831. Tel: 979-245-6931. FAX: 979-245-2614. *Dir*, Alan Withoff; E-Mail: abwithoff@wcnet.net; *Asst Dir*, Sue Hall; E-Mail: shall@wcnet.net; *Tech Servs*, Marjorie Carson; *Circ*, Ramona Torres; *Acq, ILL*, Janet Davis; *Ch Servs*, R Lisa Torres; Staff 10 (MLS 1, Non-MLS 9)
Founded 1913. Pop 29,258
Jan 2001-Dec 2001 Income (Main Library and Branch Library) $359,288, State $3,000, City $70,000, Federal $3,000, County $150,000, Locally Generated Income $133,288. Mats Exp $51,900, Books $40,000, Per/Ser (Incl. Access Fees) $4,000, Micro $2,000, AV Equip $5,900. Sal $185,660 (Prof $40,000)
Library Holdings: Bk Vols 64,000; Per Subs 63
Subject Interests: Genealogy, Texana
Automation Activity & Vendor Info: (Cataloging) Sagebrush Corporation; (Circulation) Sagebrush Corporation; (OPAC) Sagebrush Corporation
Publications: Friends (newsletter)
Function: ILL available
Mem of Houston Area Library System
Friends of the Library Group

Branches: 2
MATAGORDA BRANCH, 800 Fisher St, PO Box 704, Matagorda, 77457. SAN 374-4434. Tel: 979-863-7925. *Branch Mgr*, Diane Coffey; Staff 1 (Non-MLS 1)
Founded 1989
Subject Interests: Nautical
Automation Activity & Vendor Info: (Circulation) Sagebrush Corporation; (OPAC) Sagebrush Corporation
Friends of the Library Group
SARGENT BRANCH, PO Box 4007, Sargent, 77404. SAN 374-4442. Tel: 979-245-3032. *Librn*, Kate Moreland
Founded 1991
Subject Interests: Resorts
Automation Activity & Vendor Info: (Circulation) Sagebrush Corporation; (OPAC) Sagebrush Corporation

BAYTOWN

EXXON CORP
S EXXON CO USA, REFINERY INFORMATION CENTER, 2800 Decker Dr, PO Box 3950, 77522. SAN 361-2813. Tel: 281-834-4487. FAX: 281-834-4937. *In Charge*, Jeanne Davis; Staff 2 (MLS 1, Non-MLS 1)
Library Holdings: Bk Titles 6,000; Per Subs 100
Subject Interests: Accounting, Bus, Electronics, Engineering, Mgt
Partic in Dialog Corporation; Orbit

J LEE COLLEGE, Erma Wood Carlson Learning Resources Center,* 511 S Whiting St, 77522-0818. SAN 316-084X. Tel: 281-425-6380. FAX: 281-425-6557. Web Site: www.lee.edu. *Dir*, Tracey Cuellar; E-Mail: teuellar@lee.edu; *Publ Servs*, Dolores Owens; *Tech Servs*, Cordelia Inks; Staff 4 (MLS 4)
Founded 1935. Enrl 6,087; Fac 198
1997-1998 Mats Exp $627,811
Library Holdings: Bk Vols 95,000; Per Subs 610
Subject Interests: Texas gulf coast
Special Collections: Law Library Coll; Lee College Archives
Publications: Faculty Library Handbook; Instructional Media Faculty Handbook; Student & Library Handbook
Departmental Libraries:
HUNTSVILLE CENTER, One Financial Plaza, Ste 290, Huntsville, 77340. SAN 370-3711. Tel: 409-291-2583. FAX: 409-291-2583. *Dir*, Donna Zuniga
Library Holdings: Bk Vols 658; Per Subs 12

P STERLING MUNICIPAL LIBRARY, Wilbanks Ave, 77520. SAN 316-0858. Tel: 281-427-7331. FAX: 281-420-5347. E-Mail: smlib@hpl.lib.tx.us. Web Site: www.sml.lib.tx.us. *Dir*, Denise Reineke Fischer; E-Mail: dfischer@hpl.lib.tx.us; *Asst Librn, Tech Servs*, Linda Jones; E-Mail: ljones@hpl.lib.tx.us; *Asst Librn, Publ Servs*, Virginia Harrell; *Ch Servs*, Lisa S Coker; E-Mail: lcoker@hpl.lib.tx.us; *Exten Serv*, Fernando Ocegueda; E-Mail: focegued@hpl.lib.tx.us; *ILL*, Betsy Anderson; E-Mail: banderso@hpl.lib.tx.us; Staff 9 (MLS 9)
Founded 1961. Pop 93,304; Circ 533,173
Oct 1999-Sep 2000 Income $1,694,551. Mats Exp $273,292, Books $110,912, Per/Ser (Incl. Access Fees) $16,234, Electronic Ref Mat (Incl. Access Fees) $9,500. Sal $1,224,607
Library Holdings: Bk Vols 211,882; Per Subs 293
Subject Interests: Local history, Oral hist, Photographs
Automation Activity & Vendor Info: (Cataloging) Innovative Interfaces Inc.; (OPAC) Innovative Interfaces Inc.
Database Vendor: IAC - Info Trac, OCLC - First Search
Publications: Brighter Horizons, a journal of SML/Literacy Volunteers of America students
Function: ILL available
Mem of Houston Area Library System
Special Services for the Deaf - TTY machine
Adult literacy project
Friends of the Library Group

BEAUMONT

S ART MUSEUM OF SOUTHEAST TEXAS LIBRARY,* 500 Main St, 77701. SAN 316-0874. Tel: 409-832-3432. FAX: 409-832-8508. *Exec Dir*, Jeffrey York
Founded 1972
Library Holdings: Bk Vols 3,400; Bk Titles 2,650; Per Subs 20
Subject Interests: Anthropology, Archaeology, Architecture, Art, Cultural hist, Humanities

S BEAUMONT ENTERPRISE LIBRARY,* 380 Walnut St, PO Box 3071, 77704. SAN 370-4084. Tel: 409-833-3311. FAX: 409-838-2857. *Librn*, Jeanne E Walls
Library Holdings: Bk Titles 250
Subject Interests: Clip file, Ref mat
Restriction: Not open to public

P BEAUMONT PUBLIC LIBRARY SYSTEM, 801 Pearl St, 77701. (Mail add: PO Box 3827, 77704), SAN 361-2872. Tel: 409-838-6606. TDD: 40 832-1761. FAX: 409-838-6838. *Dir*, Maurine Gray; E-Mail: mgray@sparc.hpl.lib.tx.us; *Mgr*, Barbara Price; *Ch Servs*, Laureen Nock; *Ref*, Kur Woo Choi; Staff 37 (MLS 12, Non-MLS 25)
Founded 1926. Pop 114,332
Oct 1999-Sep 2000 Income City $2,606,000. Sal $1,602,900
Library Holdings: Bk Vols 332,180; Per Subs 447
Special Collections: Genealogy & Texana (Tyrrell Historical Library), bk micro
Automation Activity & Vendor Info: (Circulation) Innovative Interfaces Inc.; (OPAC) Innovative Interfaces Inc.
Friends of the Library Group
Branches: 5
LITERACY DEPOT, 1205 Franklin St, 77701. SAN 378-2123. Tel: 409-835-7924. FAX: 409-838-6734. *Librn*, Barbara Beard
R C MILLER MEMORIAL, 1605 Dowlen Rd, 77706. SAN 361-2899. Te 409-866-9487. FAX: 409-866-3720. *Librn*, Jim Shoemaker
SPINDLETOP BRANCH LIBRARY, 3199 Avenue A, 77705. SAN 375-0159. Tel: 409-832-9693. FAX: 409-832-9693. *In Charge*, Gwen Pierre
Friends of the Library Group
TYRRELL HISTORICAL, 695 Pearl St, 77701. SAN 361-2937. Tel: 409-833-2759. FAX: 409-833-5828. *Librn*, David Montgomery
Subject Interests: Genealogy, Texana
Friends of the Library Group
ELMO WILLARD BRANCH, 3590 E Lucas, 77708. SAN 378-214X. Tel: 409-892-4988. FAX: 409-898-4088. *Librn*, Cecilla Shearron-Hawkins

P JEFFERSON COUNTY LIBRARY, 7933 Viterbo Rd, 77705. SAN 316-6384. Tel: 409-727-2735. FAX: 409-722-8473. E-Mail: onwheels@co.jefferson.tx.us. Web Site: www.co.jefferson.tx.us/library/library.htm. *Lib* Emil Ciallella; Staff 5 (MLS 1, Non-MLS 4)
Founded 1930. Pop 27,892; Circ 72,089
Oct 2000-Sep 2001 Income $212,828. Mats Exp $20,150, Books $18,000, Per/Ser (Incl. Access Fees) $2,150. Sal $150,008 (Prof $41,606)
Library Holdings: Bk Vols 40,064; Per Subs 89
Mem of Houston Area Library System
Jefferson County Library is a bookmobile service, with emphasis on servic to the disadvantaged (rural residents, institutions & low-income communities)
Bookmobiles: 1

C LAMAR UNIVERSITY, Mary & John Gray Library, 211 Redbird Lane, 77705. (Mail add: Lamar University, PO Box 10021, 77710), Tel: 409-880-8118. Interlibrary Loan Service Tel: 409-880-8987. Circulation Tel: 409-88 8134. Reference Tel: 409-880-1898. FAX: 409-880-2318. Web Site: library.lamar.edu. *Actg Dir*, Kathleen Murray; Tel: 409-880-8119, E-Mail: murray@library.lamar.edu; *Syst Coordr*, Virginia Allen; Tel: 409-880-8849, E-Mail: allen@library.lamar.edu; *Acq*, Linda Dugger; Tel: 409-880-8123; *Cat*, David Carroll; Tel: 409-880-8123, E-Mail: carroll@library.lamar.edu; *Media Spec*, Mark Asteris; Tel: 409-880-8064, E-Mail: asteris@library.lamar.edu; *Publ Servs*, Karen Nichols; Tel: 409-880-8131, E-Mail: nichols@library.lamar.edu; *Circ*, Jane Gaglianella; Tel: 409-880-8133; Staff 45 (MLS 13, Non-MLS 32)
Founded 1923. Enrl 8,571; Fac 464; Highest Degree: Doctorate
Sep 1999-Aug 2000 Income $2,805,557, State $2,117,764, Locally Generated Income $687,793. Mats Exp $993,162, Books $116,559, Per/Ser (Incl. Access Fees) $730,900, Micro $53,445, Electronic Ref Mat (Incl. Access Fees) $75,799. Sal $1,294,099 (Prof $521,285)
Library Holdings: Bk Vols 436,227; Bk Titles 372,209; Per Subs 2,577; Bks on Deafness & Sign Lang 466
Subject Interests: Cookery, Education, Engineering, History
Special Collections: Cookery; Texana
Automation Activity & Vendor Info: (Acquisitions) DRA; (Cataloging) DRA; (Circulation) DRA; (OPAC) DRA; (Serials) DRA
Database Vendor: OCLC - First Search
Publications: Library Newsletter; Review of Texas Books
Partic in Amigos Library Services, Inc; E Tex Consortium of Librs; Forest Trail Library Consortium, Inc; Phoenix Group
Special Services for the Deaf - TTY machine
Special Services for the Blind - Kurzweil Reader
Friends of the Library Group

M SAINT ELIZABETH HOSPITAL, Health Science Library,* 2830 Calder Ave, PO Box 5405, 77726. SAN 316-0939. Tel: 409-899-7189. FAX: 409-899-8187. *Librn*, Joan Trahan
Founded 1957
Library Holdings: Bk Vols 1,250; Per Subs 175
Subject Interests: Allied health, Medicine, Nursing
Partic in BRS; Coop Libr Agency for Syst & Servs; Dialog Corporation; Na Libr of Med; S Cent Regional Med Libr Program

SR SAINT MARK'S PARISH LIBRARY,* 680 Calder, 77701-2398. SAN 316-0947. Tel: 409-832-3405. *Librn*, W E Krueger

EDFORD

BEDFORD PUBLIC LIBRARY, (BPL), 1805 L Don Dodson Dr, 76021. SAN 316-0955. Tel: 817-952-2335. Interlibrary Loan Service Tel: 817-952-2342. Circulation Tel: 817-952-2352. Reference Tel: 817-952-2342. FAX: 817-952-2396. Web Site: www.lib.bedford.tx.us. *Mgr*, Marleen M Watling; E-Mail: mwatling@ci.bedford.tx.us; *Ad Servs*, Susan L Neal; E-Mail: sneal@ci.bedford.tx.us; *Tech Servs*, Barbara Glassford Johnson; Tel: 817-952-2360, E-Mail: bjohnson@ci.bedford.tx.us; *YA Servs*, Carole A Blossom; Tel: 817-952-2370, E-Mail: cblossom@ci.bedford.tx.us; Staff 15 (MLS 6, Non-MLS 9)
Founded 1964. Pop 48,900; Circ 319,432
Oct 1999-Sep 2000 Income $905,225, State $3,428, City $901,797. Mats Exp $140,676, Books $89,411, Per/Ser (Incl. Access Fees) $11,523, Micro $379, AV Equip $22,632, Electronic Ref Mat (Incl. Access Fees) $16,731. Sal $685,575
Library Holdings: Bk Vols 94,239; Bk Titles 78,097; Per Subs 265
Special Collections: Bedford History Coll
Automation Activity & Vendor Info: (Acquisitions) Innovative Interfaces Inc.; (Cataloging) Innovative Interfaces Inc.; (Circulation) Innovative Interfaces Inc.; (Course Reserve) Innovative Interfaces Inc.; (ILL) Innovative Interfaces Inc.; (OPAC) Innovative Interfaces Inc.; (Serials) Innovative Interfaces Inc.
Database Vendor: OCLC - First Search
Mem of North Texas Regional Library System
Special Services for the Blind - Low vision equipment
Friends of the Library Group

CONSORTIUM FOR ADVANCE MANUFACTURING INTERNATIONAL LIBRARY,* 3301 Airport Freeway, No 324, 76021. SAN 324-0991. Tel: 817-860-1654, Ext 143. FAX: 817-275-6450. *Coordr*, Nancy Thomas
Founded 1972
Library Holdings: Bk Titles 200
Subject Interests: Advanced numerical control, CIM, Computer intergrated enterprise, Factory mgt, Geometric modeling, Process planning, Product optimization, Quality assurance
Publications: Company list of publications

EEVILLE

JOE BARNHART BEE COUNTY PUBLIC LIBRARY, 110 W Corpus Christi St, 78102-5604. SAN 316-0963. Tel: 361-362-4901. FAX: 361-358-8694. E-Mail: info@bclib.org. Web Site: www.bclib.org. *Dir*, Jo Ann Oliphant; E-Mail: joliphant@bclib.org
Founded 1939. Pop 25,400; Circ 64,571
Oct 1998-Sep 1999 Income $86,994, City $37,775, County $49,219. Mats Exp Books $27,000. Sal $48,269 (Prof $44,000)
Library Holdings: Bk Vols 28,658; Per Subs 100
Automation Activity & Vendor Info: (Acquisitions) epixtech, inc.; (Cataloging) epixtech, inc.; (Circulation) epixtech, inc.; (OPAC) epixtech, inc.; (Serials) epixtech, inc.
Mem of South Texas Library System
Friends of the Library Group

GRADY C HOGUE LEARNING RESCOURCE CENTER LIBRARY, (Formerly Bee County College Library), 3800 Charco Rd, 78102-2110. SAN 316-0971. Tel: 361-354-2740. FAX: 361-354-2719. Web Site: www.cbc.cc.tx.us. *Dir, Ref*, Sarah Milnarich; E-Mail: sarahm@cbc.cc.tx.us; *Automation Syst Coordr, Coll Develop*, Charles Thomas; E-Mail: cthomas@cbc.cc.tx.us; Staff 6 (MLS 2, Non-MLS 4)
Founded 1967. Enrl 3,016; Fac 155
Sep 2000-Aug 2001 Income $196,351, State $102,495, Provincial $72,257, Federal $21,599. Mats Exp $31,552, Books $13,050, Per/Ser (Incl. Access Fees) $16,832, Micro $1,670. Sal $135,851 (Prof $64,031)
Library Holdings: Bk Vols 40,000; Per Subs 237
Special Collections: Texana Coll
Publications: BookSampler (monthly); Recent Titles (quarterly)
Partic in Coastal Bend Health Info Network; OCLC Online Computer Library Center, Inc; Piasano Consortium; TexShare
Three bilingual staff members

BELLAIRE

S ACCESS INFORMATION ASSOCIATES, INC LIBRARY,* 4710 Bellaire Blvd Ste 140, 77401. SAN 370-3274. Tel: 713-664-4357. FAX: 713-664-4825. E-Mail: aia@ix.netcom.com. Web Site: www.aiahelp.com. *Pres*, Janice C Anderson; *VPres*, Ann M Robertson
Library Holdings: Bk Vols 400; Per Subs 20
Also a records management consulting firm

P BELLAIRE CITY LIBRARY, 5111 Jessamine, 77401-4498. SAN 316-098X. Tel: 713-662-8160. Reference Tel: 713-662-8166. FAX: 713-662-8169. Web Site: www.ci.bellaire.tx.us. *Dir*, Mary Alford; E-Mail: malford@ci.bellaire.tx.us; *Cat*, Klairon Tang; E-Mail: ktang@hpl.lib.tx.us; *Ch Servs*, Janna Miller; Tel: 713-662-8164, E-Mail: jmiller@hpl.lib.tx.us; *Ref*, Terri Mote; Tel: 713-662-8166; Staff 4 (MLS 4)
Founded 1951. Pop 14,936; Circ 181,000
Oct 1999-Sep 2000 Income $424,955, City $409,918, Other $15,037. Mats Exp $48,700, Books $30,760, Per/Ser (Incl. Access Fees) $6,200, Presv $500, AV Equip $5,040, Electronic Ref Mat (Incl. Access Fees) $6,200. Sal $295,587 (Prof $144,815)
Library Holdings: Bk Vols 69,788; Bk Titles 63,291; Per Subs 141
Subject Interests: Texas
Automation Activity & Vendor Info: (Acquisitions) Innovative Interfaces Inc.; (Cataloging) Innovative Interfaces Inc.; (Circulation) Innovative Interfaces Inc.; (Course Reserve) Innovative Interfaces Inc.; (ILL) Innovative Interfaces Inc.; (Media Booking) Innovative Interfaces Inc.; (OPAC) Innovative Interfaces Inc.; (Serials) Innovative Interfaces Inc.
Mem of Houston Area Library System
Special Services for the Deaf - TTY machine
Friends of the Library Group

BELLVILLE

P BELLVILLE PUBLIC LIBRARY,* 12 W Palm, 77418-1446. SAN 316-0998. Tel: 409-865-3731. FAX: 409-865-2060. *Librn*, Alice Neel; *Asst Librn*, Jenelle Zettel; Staff 4 (MLS 2, Non-MLS 2)
Founded 1968
Library Holdings: Bk Vols 30,987; Bk Titles 28,925; Per Subs 52
Automation Activity & Vendor Info: (Cataloging) Follett; (Circulation) Follett
Mem of Houston Area Library System

BELTON

P LENA ARMSTRONG PUBLIC LIBRARY, (Formerly Belton City Library), 301 E First St, 76513. SAN 316-1005. Tel: 254-933-5830. *Coll Develop, Dir*, Kim Adele Kroll
Founded 1904. Pop 12,376; Circ 33,214
Oct 1999-Sep 2000 Income $125,427. Mats Exp $24,762. Sal $100,665
Library Holdings: Bk Titles 52,777; Per Subs 23
Subject Interests: Genealogy, Local history
Special Collections: Local History, photogs
Mem of Central Texas Library System

C UNIVERSITY OF MARY HARDIN-BAYLOR, Townsend Memorial Library, 900 College, UMHB Sta Box 8016, 76513-2599. SAN 316-1013. Tel: 254-295-4636. FAX: 212-295-4642. Web Site: www.umhblib.umhb.edu. *Dir*, Robert A Strong; E-Mail: rstrong@umhb.edu; *Acq*, Teresa Buck; Tel: 254-295-4640, E-Mail: tbuck@umhb.edu; *Tech Servs*, Denise Karimkhani; Tel: 254-295-4639, E-Mail: dkarimkhani@umh.edu; *Head Ref*, Dorothy Planas; Tel: 254-295-4641, E-Mail: dplanas@umhb.edu; *Ref*, Jolee Miller; *Ser*, Anna Loan-Wilsey; *Ser*, Elizabeth Mallory; Tel: 254-295-4637, E-Mail: emallory@umhb.edu; *Electronic Resources*, Kathy Harden; Tel: 254-295-4637, E-Mail: kharden@umhb.edu; Staff 10 (MLS 5, Non-MLS 5)
Founded 1845. Enrl 2,700; Fac 111; Highest Degree: Master
Jun 2000-May 2001 Income Parent Institution $985,000. Mats Exp $563,000, Books $265,000, Per/Ser (Incl. Access Fees) $245,000, Micro $53,000, Electronic Ref Mat (Incl. Access Fees) $65,000. Sal $265,000
Library Holdings: Bk Vols 175,000; Bk Titles 120,000; Per Subs 1,000
Subject Interests: Baptist, Nursing
Special Collections: Baptist Coll; Local History Coll
Automation Activity & Vendor Info: (Cataloging) Innovative Interfaces Inc.; (OPAC) Innovative Interfaces Inc.
Database Vendor: Dialog, Ebsco - EbscoHost, GaleNet, Innovative Interfaces INN - View, Lexis-Nexis, OCLC - First Search, OVID Technologies, Silverplatter Information Inc.
Publications: Handbook, Library Keys
Partic in Amigos Library Services, Inc; Leian

BENBROOK

§P BENBROOK PUBLIC LIBRARY, 1065 Mercedes, 76126. (Mail add: PO Box 126467, 76126), SAN 378-3693. Tel: 817-249-6632. FAX: 817-249-6632. Web Site: www.benbrooklibrary.org. *Librn*, Michael Baldwin; E-Mail: mikeb@benbrooklibrary.org
Oct 1999-Sep 2000 Income $250,000
Library Holdings: Bk Vols 25,000; Per Subs 10
Mem of North Texas Regional Library System
Friends of the Library Group

BIG LAKE

P REAGAN COUNTY LIBRARY, County Courthouse, 76932. SAN 316-1021. Tel: 915-884-2854. *Librn*, Linda Rees; *Asst Librn*, Rosa Ramirez
Founded 1938. Pop 4,135; Circ 19,267
Library Holdings: Bk Vols 22,984; Bk Titles 22,412; Per Subs 63
Mem of Abilene Major Resources Cent; Big Country Library System

BIG SPRING

M BIG SPRING STATE HOSPITAL MEDICAL LIBRARY,* N Lamesa Hwy, PO Box 231, 79721-0231. SAN 316-1048. Tel: 915-267-8216, 915-268-7215. FAX: 915-268-7819. *Librn*, Melinda Hunter
Founded 1973
Library Holdings: Bk Vols 2,000; Per Subs 100

GM DEPARTMENT OF VETERANS AFFAIRS, Medical Center Library, 300 Veterans Blvd, 79720. SAN 316-1072. Tel: 915-263-7361, Ext 7262. FAX: 915-264-4834. *Librn*, Samie Pequeno; E-Mail: samie.pequeno@med.va.gov
Founded 1950
1999-2000 Mats Exp Per/Ser (Incl. Access Fees) $23,017
Library Holdings: Bk Vols 1,015; Bk Titles 1,000; Per Subs 66
Partic in Medline; Vets Admin Libr Network

P HOWARD COUNTY, Dora Roberts Library,* 500 Main St, 79720-2532. SAN 316-1064. Tel: 915-264-2260. FAX: 915-264-2263. *Dir*, Loraine Redman; *Ch Servs*, Martha Vierra; *Cat*, Rose Von Hassell; *Ref*, Rebbecca Taylor; *Circ*, Jennifer Price; *AV*, Milton Perkins; Staff 2 (MLS 2)
Founded 1907. Pop 31,935; Circ 161,147
Library Holdings: Bk Vols 65,000; Per Subs 120
Special Collections: Texana
Friends of the Library Group

J HOWARD COUNTY JUNIOR COLLEGE, Anthony Hunt Library & Learning Resource Center, 1001 Birdwell Lane, 79720. SAN 316-1056. Tel: 915-264-5090. FAX: 915-264-5094. Web Site: www.hc.cc.tx.us/library/hunthome.htm. *Dean of Libr*, William Luis Kincade; Tel: 915-264-5092, E-Mail: wkincade@hc.cc.tx.us; *Publ Servs*, Dr Michael Lauch; E-Mail: mlauch@hc.cc.tx.us; Staff 4 (MLS 2, Non-MLS 2)
Founded 1945. Enrl 2,236; Highest Degree: Associate
Sep 2000-Aug 2001 Income $161,293. Mats Exp $105,200, Books $16,000, Per/Ser (Incl. Access Fees) $8,500, Micro $4,000. Sal $105,200
Library Holdings: Bk Vols 33,821; Per Subs 344
Automation Activity & Vendor Info: (Circulation) Sagebrush Corporation
Database Vendor: GaleNet, IAC - Info Trac, OCLC - First Search, OVID Technologies
Function: ILL available
Departmental Libraries:
SOUTHWEST COLLEGIATE INSTITUTE FOR THE DEAF - RESOURCE CENTER, Avenue C, 79720. SAN 328-817X. Tel: 915-264-3700. FAX: 915-263-2054. Web Site: www.hc.cc.tx.us/library/xscwid.htm. *Librn*, Virginia Carter; Staff 1 (Non-MLS 1)
Founded 1980. Enrl 137; Highest Degree: Associate
Sep 2000-Aug 2001 Income $35,036. Mats Exp $9,825. Sal $20,189
Library Holdings: Bk Vols 3,262; Bk Titles 3,035; Per Subs 100; Bks on Deafness & Sign Lang 946
Special Collections: Deafness, AV mat, bks, per
Database Vendor: GaleNet, IAC - Info Trac, OCLC - First Search, OVID Technologies
Special Services for the Deaf - Books on deafness & sign language; Captioned film depository; Special interest periodicals; Staff with knowledge of sign language; TTY machine

BLANCO

P BLANCO LIBRARY, INC, 1118 N Main St, 78606. Tel: 830-833-4280. E-Mail: blanlib@moment.net. Web Site: www.blancolib.com. *Dir*, Linda F Baylis; Staff 33 (Non-MLS 33)
Founded 1938. Pop 4,659; Circ 20,242
Library Holdings: Bk Vols 18,347; Bk Titles 18,068; Per Subs 22
Automation Activity & Vendor Info: (Cataloging) Athena
Function; Photocopies available
Mem of Central Texas Library System
Friends of the Library Group

BLUE MOUND

P BLUE MOUND COMMUNITY LIBRARY,* 301 Blue Mound Rd, 76131. SAN 316-1099. Tel: 817-847-4095. FAX: 817-232-0665. *Librn*, Billie Hamilton
Pop 2,500; Circ 5,745
1997-1998 Income $11,300
Library Holdings: Bk Vols 15,000; Per Subs 10
Mem of North Texas Regional Library System

BOERNE

P BOERNE PUBLIC LIBRARY, 210 N Main St, 78006. SAN 316-1102. Tel: 830-249-3053. FAX: 830-249-8410. E-Mail: librarian@boerne.lib.tx.us. Web Site: www.boerne.lib.tx.us. *Dir*, Louise A Foster; Staff 3 (MLS 2, Non-MLS 1)
Founded 1952. Pop 10,546; Circ 78,700
Oct 1998-Sep 1999 Income $285,024, State $8,522, City $153,504, Federal $5,000, County $62,000, Locally Generated Income $31,618, Other $24,380. Mats Exp $33,232, Books $28,333, Per/Ser (Incl. Access Fees) $2,475, AV Equip $2,397, Other Print Mats $27. Sal $143,905
Library Holdings: Bk Vols 33,020; Bk Titles 31,040; Per Subs 114; High Interest/Low Vocabulary Bk Vols 125; Bks on Deafness & Sign Lang 15
Special Collections: Large Print Coll; Local History Coll; Texana Coll
Automation Activity & Vendor Info: (Cataloging) Athena
Mem of Alamo Area Library System
1614 Luneburg Low German Bible on permanent display
Friends of the Library Group

BONHAM

P BONHAM PUBLIC LIBRARY, 305 E Fifth St, 75418-4002. SAN 316-1110. Tel: 903-583-3128. FAX: 903-583-8030. E-Mail: bonhamlibrary@texoma.net. *Librn*, Barbara McCutcheon; Staff 4 (Non-MLS 4)
Founded 1901. Pop 7,338; Circ 51,788
Library Holdings: Bk Vols 35,916; Bk Titles 34,898; Per Subs 91
Mem of Northeast Texas Library System

S SAM RAYBURN LIBRARY & MUSEUM, 800 W Sam Rayburn Dr, PO Box 309, 75418-0309. SAN 316-1129. Tel: 903-583-2455. FAX: 903-583-7394. *Dir*, H G Dulaney
Founded 1957
Library Holdings: Bk Vols 20,000
Special Collections: Life & Career of Speaker Sam Rayburn, historical memorabilia, official papers, interviews, micro
Publications: Book Speak; Mr Speaker (newsletter); Sam Rayburn A Cartoon Profile

GM VETERANS AFFAIRS NORTH TEXAS HEALTH CARE SYSTEM, (Formerly Department of Veterans Affairs), Library Service - Sam Rayburn 1201 E Ninth St, 75418. SAN 316-1137. Tel: 903-583-6302. FAX: 903-583-6694. *In Charge*, Elizabeth "Deann" Hicks; E-Mail: elizabeth.hicks@med.va.gov
Library Holdings: Bk Titles 1,060; Per Subs 115

BOOKER

P BOOKER SCHOOL PUBLIC LIBRARY,* Drawer 288, 79005-0288. SAN 376-4052. Tel: 806-658-9323. FAX: 806-658-9323. E-Mail: hout@penet.ed *Librn*, Pat Hout
Library Holdings: Bk Vols 16,000; Per Subs 22
Mem of Texas Panhandle Library System

BORGER

J FRANK PHILLIPS COLLEGE, James W Dillard Library, PO Box 5118, 79008-5118. SAN 316-1145. Tel: 806-274-5311, Ext 734. FAX: 806-273-3973. Web Site: www.fpc.cc.tx.us. *Actg Librn*, Debbie Cauthon; E-Mail: dcauthon@fpc.cc.tx.us
Founded 1948
Library Holdings: Bk Vols 35,000; Bk Titles 27,078; Per Subs 138
Automation Activity & Vendor Info: (Cataloging) DRA; (Circulation) DRA; (OPAC) DRA
Partic in Harrington Library Consortium

P HUTCHINSON COUNTY LIBRARY,* 625 N Weatherly, 79007-3621. SAN 361-302X. Tel: 806-273-0126. FAX: 806-273-0128. *Dir*, Linda J Howell; *Circ*, Don Allen; *Tech Servs*, Pat Heard; Staff 2 (MLS 2)
Founded 1938. Pop 26,304; Circ 105,884
Oct 1996-Sep 1997 Income $231,126. Mats Exp $27,960, Books $16,360, Per/Ser (Incl. Access Fees) $9,055, Other Print Mats $852. Sal $147,637 (Prof $26,400)
Library Holdings: Bk Vols 58,894; Bk Titles 53,482; Per Subs 175
Subject Interests: Genealogy, Large print, Texas
Mem of Texas Panhandle Library System
Partic in Harrington Library Consortium
Friends of the Library Group
Branches: 2
FRITCH BRANCH, PO Box 430, Fritch, 79036-0430. SAN 361-3054. Tel: 806-857-3752. FAX: 806-857-3752. *Mgr*, Kim McAtee
Library Holdings: Bk Vols 8,895
Friends of the Library Group
STINNETT BRANCH, PO Box 478, Stinnett, 79083. SAN 361-3089. Tel: 806-878-4013. FAX: 806-878-4014. *Mgr*, Donna Irvin
Library Holdings: Bk Vols 11,738
Friends of the Library Group

BOWIE

P BOWIE PUBLIC LIBRARY, 301 Walnut St, 76230. SAN 316-1161. Tel: 940-872-2681. FAX: 940-872-2681. *Librn*, Diana Curry; Staff 4 (MLS 1, Non-MLS 3)
Founded 1926. Pop 6,000; Circ 60,000
Library Holdings: Bk Titles 22,000; Per Subs 62
Mem of North Texas Regional Library System
Friends of the Library Group

OYD

BOYD PUBLIC LIBRARY,* 731 E Rock Island Ave, PO Box 216, 76023-9519. SAN 376-4680. Tel: 940-433-5580. FAX: 940-433-8253. *Librn*, Doris Autry
1996-1997 Income $11,000. Mats Exp $5,400. Sal $5,000
Library Holdings: Bk Vols 10,000; Per Subs 16
Mem of North Texas Regional Library System

RACKETTVILLE

FORT CLARK HISTORICAL SOCIETY, Old Guardhouse Museum Library, Fort Clark Springs, PO Box 1061, 78832. SAN 372-9672. Tel: 830-563-9150. E-Mail: fchstex@hilconet.com. Web Site: www.hilconet.com/~fchstex/museum.
Founded 1981. Pop 3,000
Library Holdings: Bk Vols 200; Per Subs 12
Subject Interests: Local history
Restriction: Non-circulating
Function: Research library

KINNEY COUNTY PUBLIC LIBRARY,* 510 S Ellen, PO Box 975, 78832. SAN 324-1270. Tel: 830-563-2884. FAX: 830-563-2312. E-Mail: kclib1@hotmail.com. *Dir*, Sara Terrazas; *Asst Librn*, Yvette Clements; Staff 4 (MLS 3, Non-MLS 1)
Founded 1973. Pop 3,413; Circ 36,843
Oct 1999-Sep 2000 Income $50,808, County $47,683, Locally Generated Income $3,125. Mats Exp $4,000, Books $3,000, AV Equip $1,000. Sal $24,316 (Prof $18,076)
Library Holdings: Bk Vols 15,250; Bk Titles 18,000; Per Subs 13
Subject Interests: Genealogy, Local history
Automation Activity & Vendor Info: (Cataloging) Athena
Database Vendor: CARL, OVID Technologies
Mem of Alamo Area Library System
Special Services for the Blind - Talking Books
Friends of the Library Group

RADY

F M (BUCK) RICHARDS MEMORIAL LIBRARY, 1106 S Blackburn St, 76825. SAN 316-117X. Tel: 915-597-2617. E-Mail: rchmlib@centex.net. *Dir*, Ann Shuffler; Staff 4 (Non-MLS 4)
Founded 1928. Pop 8,694; Circ 53,823
Library Holdings: Bk Vols 23,222; Bk Titles 20,474; Per Subs 13
Automation Activity & Vendor Info: (Cataloging) Sagebrush Corporation; (Circulation) Sagebrush Corporation; (OPAC) Sagebrush Corporation
Mem of Big Country Library System
Open Mon, Wed-Fri 10-5:30, Tues 12-7, Sat 10-1
Friends of the Library Group

RECKENRIDGE

BRECKENRIDGE PUBLIC LIBRARY, 209 N Breckenridge Ave, 76424. SAN 316-1188. Tel: 254-559-5505. *Dir*, Mrs Grady Fox; Staff 3 (MLS 1, Non-MLS 2)
Founded 1924. Pop 9,800; Circ 16,453
Oct 1999-Nov 2000 Income $91,130, City $13,897, County $12,000, Locally Generated Income $31,877, Parent Institution $33,356. Mats Exp $7,480, Books $6,274, Per/Ser (Incl. Access Fees) $1,206. Sal $43,543 (Prof $18,285)
Library Holdings: Bk Vols 18,163; Bk Titles 17,671; Per Subs 65; High Interest/Low Vocabulary Bk Vols 50; Spec Interest Per Sub 10
Subject Interests: History
Special Collections: Texas Coll (begun in 1940's - many out-of-print titles)
Automation Activity & Vendor Info: (Cataloging) Follett; (Circulation) Follett
Restriction: Residents only
Friends of the Library Group

RENHAM

BLINN COLLEGE, W L Moody Jr Library, 902 College Ave, 77833. SAN 316-1196. Tel: 979-830-4250. FAX: 979-830-4222. Web Site: www.blinncol.edu/library/. *Dir*, Linda C Flynn; E-Mail: lflynn@mailroom.blinncol.edu; *Br Coordr*, Eugenia Hull; *Librn*, Mary Castle; *Librn*, Brad Meyer; *Cat*, Robin Osborne; *Ref*, Jeannine Bailey; *Ref*, Bernard Bennett; Staff 8 (MLS 8)
Founded 1883. Enrl 9,218; Fac 295; Highest Degree: Associate
Library Holdings: Bk Vols 150,000; Per Subs 700
Subject Interests: Germans in Tex, Local history
Special Collections: College Archives; Local History Coll
Automation Activity & Vendor Info: (Cataloging) VTLS; (Circulation) VTLS; (Course Reserve) VTLS; (OPAC) VTLS; (Serials) VTLS
Database Vendor: Ebsco - EbscoHost, Wilson - Wilson Web
Partic in Tex Share

Departmental Libraries:
BRYAN CAMPUS, Bryan. Tel: 979-821-0270. FAX: 979-821-0279. Web Site: www.blinncol.edu/library. *Br Coordr*, Eugenia Hull; *Librn*, Mary Castle; *Librn*, Brad Meyer; *Librn*, Roberta Pitts
SCHULENBURG CAMPUS, Schulenburg. Tel: 979-743-5003. Web Site: www.blinncol.edu/library/. *In Charge*, Sandy Pohlmeyer

P NANCY CAROL ROBERTS MEMORIAL LIBRARY,* 100 W Academy, 77833. SAN 316-120X. Tel: 409-277-1271. FAX: 409-277-1279. *Dir*, George Dawson; Staff 1 (MLS 1)
Founded 1901. Pop 26,500; Circ 121,286
Library Holdings: Bk Vols 57,650; Bk Titles 54,615; Per Subs 64
Subject Interests: Germans in Tex, Texana
Mem of Central Texas Library System

SR TEXAS BAPTIST HISTORICAL MUSEUM LIBRARY,* 10405 FM 50, 77833. SAN 328-0519. Tel: 409-836-5117. FAX: 409-836-5117. *Dir*, Paul Sevar
Library Holdings: Bk Titles 250
Special Collections: Tex Baptist Convention Doc
Publications: Flowers & Fruits of Texas

GM TEXAS DEPARTMENT OF MENTAL HEALTH & MENTAL RETARDATION, Brenham State School Staff Library,* 4001 Hwy 36 S, 77833-9611. SAN 372-9680. Tel: 409-277-1553. FAX: 409-277-1865. *Mgr*, Kim Littleton
Library Holdings: Bk Vols 500
Subject Interests: Mental health

BRIDGE CITY

P BRIDGE CITY PUBLIC LIBRARY,* 101 Parkside Dr, 77611. SAN 376-4079. Tel: 409-735-4242. FAX: 409-735-4242. E-Mail: bclib@exp.net. *Dir*, Mary Montgomery
Library Holdings: Bk Vols 16,000; Per Subs 31
Mem of Houston Area Library System
Friends of the Library Group

BRIDGEPORT

P JOHN A & KATHERINE G JACKSON MUNICIPAL BRIDGEPORT PUBLIC LIBRARY, 2159 Tenth St, 76426. SAN 316-1226. Tel: 940-683-4412. *Librn*, Patricia J Stegall; E-Mail: patj@wf.net
Founded 1960. Pop 12,500; Circ 63,235
Oct 1999-Sep 2000 Income $138,152, City $118,152, County $20,000. Sal $76,117 (Prof $30,000)
Library Holdings: Bk Vols 30,000; Per Subs 40
Subject Interests: Large print
Automation Activity & Vendor Info: (Cataloging) Sagebrush Corporation; (Circulation) Sagebrush Corporation
Mem of North Texas Regional Library System

BROOKS AFB

UNITED STATES AIR FORCE
A BROOKS AIR FORCE BASE LIBRARY FL2857, 311 ABG/SVMG, 8103 Outercircle Rd Ste 1, 78235-5234. SAN 361-3119. Tel: 210-536-2634. FAX: 210-536-6625. *Librn*, Joanna Hansen; E-Mail: joanna.hansen@brooks.af.mil
Oct 1999-Sep 2000 Mats Exp $33,500, Books $13,500, Per/Ser (Incl. Access Fees) $20,000. Sal $128,486
Library Holdings: Bk Vols 19,375; Per Subs 164
Subject Interests: Mil art, Sci
Publications: Annotated Video List; AWC List; Library Brochure; Project Warrior Bibliography
AM THE AEROMEDICAL LIBRARY, 2511 Kennedy Circle, 78235-5122. SAN 361-3178. Tel: 210-536-3321. FAX: 210-536-3239. Web Site: www.brooks.af.mi./afrl/daedalus. *Head of Libr*, Joseph J Franzello; E-Mail: joseph.franzello@brooks.af.mil; *Syst Coordr*, John Whitney; Tel: 210-536-3323, E-Mail: john.whitney@brooks.af.mil. Subject Specialists: *Biomedical engineering*, John Whitney; Staff 9 (MLS 3, Non-MLS 6)
Founded 1918
Oct 1999-Sep 2000 Income Federal $437,000. Mats Exp $200,200, Books $5,000, Per/Ser (Incl. Access Fees) $143,000, Presv $1,200, AV Equip $6,000, Electronic Ref Mat (Incl. Access Fees) $45,000. Sal $237,482 (Prof $126,000)
Library Holdings: Bk Vols 43,138; Bk Titles 41,613; Per Subs 431
Subject Interests: Aerospace med, Environ med, Life scis, Physiology, Psychology, Radiation sci
Special Collections: History of Aerospace Medicine Coll
Automation Activity & Vendor Info: (Cataloging) SIRSI; (Circulation) SIRSI
Database Vendor: Dialog, Ebsco - EbscoHost, Silverplatter Information Inc.
Publications: Armstrong Researcher (Newsletter)
Partic in Amigos Library Services, Inc; MLA
Serves the School of Aerospace Medicine (a medical graduate school)

BROWNFIELD

P KENDRICK MEMORIAL LIBRARY,* 301 W Tate, 79316-4387. SAN 316-1234. Tel: 806-637-3848. FAX: 806-637-7660. *Librn*, Lupe Serna
Founded 1907. Pop 13,218; Circ 70,550
Library Holdings: Bk Vols 32,500; Per Subs 53
Special Collections: Texas Heritage Resource Center
Mem of West Texas Library System
Sponsors literacy program, summer youth reading programs. Has bilingual staff member
Friends of the Library Group

BROWNSVILLE

P BROWNSVILLE PUBLIC LIBRARY, 2600 Central Blvd, 78520-8824. SAN 375-5541. Tel: 956-548-1055. TDD: 800-735-2989. FAX: 956-548-0684. Web Site: www.brownsville.lib.tx.us. *Dir*, Joe Garcia; E-Mail: jgarcia@brownsville.lib.tx.us; *Asst Dir*, Rosemary Lovely; E-Mail: rlovely@brownsville.lib.tx.us; *Ch Servs*, Gretchen Silva; E-Mail: gretchen@brownsville.lib.tx.us; *Automation Syst Coordr*, Jerry Hedgecock; *Publ Servs*, Augustin Carrera; E-Mail: acarrera@brownsville.lib.tx.us; Staff 6 (MLS 5, Non-MLS 1)
Pop 138,000; Circ 125,535
Library Holdings: Bk Vols 79,428; Bk Titles 63,967; Per Subs 226
Automation Activity & Vendor Info: (Acquisitions) SIRSI; (Cataloging) SIRSI; (Circulation) SIRSI
Mem of South Texas Library System
Special Services for the Deaf - TDD
Friends of the Library Group

C UNIVERSITY OF TEXAS AT BROWNSVILLE, (Formerly University Of Texas At Brownsville-Texas Southmost College), Texas Southmost College, 80 Fort Brown, 78520. SAN 371-4187. Tel: 956-544-8220. Reference Tel: 956-983-7206. FAX: 956-544-5495. Web Site: www.utb.edu/lib. *Dir*, Douglas M Ferrier; Tel: 956-983-7042, Fax: 956-544-3899, E-Mail: doug@utb1.utb.edu; *Senior Librn*, Mark Williams; Tel: 956-983-7108, Fax: 956-544-3899, E-Mail: mwilliams@utb1.utb.edu; *Librn*, John B Hawthorne; Tel: 956-983-7105, Fax: 956-983-3899, E-Mail: jhawthorne@utb1.utb.edu; *Head Ref*, Luisa Serna; Tel: 956-983-7281, Fax: 956-544-3899, E-Mail: lserna@utb1.utb.edu; *Cat*, Barret Havens; Tel: 956-983-7591, Fax: 956-544-3899, E-Mail: bhavens@utb1.utb.edu; *Mgr Libr Serv*, Mabel E Hockaday; Tel: 956-983-7280, Fax: 956-544-3899, E-Mail: mhockaday@utb1.utb.edu; *Outreach Serv*, Kathleen Vanderslice; Tel: 956-548-6561, Fax: 956-544-3899, E-Mail: kvanderslice@utb1.utb.edu; Staff 7 (MLS 7)
Founded 1926. Enrl 9,100; Fac 410; Highest Degree: Master
Sep 1999-Aug 2000 Income $1,177,453. Mats Exp $563,807, Books $158,035, Per/Ser (Incl. Access Fees) $154,205, Presv $35,900, Micro $17,604, AV Equip $27,234, Electronic Ref Mat (Incl. Access Fees) $170,828. Sal $340,034
Library Holdings: Bk Vols 154,800; Bk Titles 130,000; Per Subs 7,000
Subject Interests: Genealogy, Local history
Special Collections: Brownsville, Cameron County, Lower Rio Grande Valley & Northeast Mexico History
Automation Activity & Vendor Info: (Acquisitions) DRA; (Cataloging) DRA; (Circulation) DRA; (OPAC) DRA; (Serials) DRA
Database Vendor: CARL, DRA, GaleNet, IAC - SearchBank, Lexis-Nexis, OCLC - First Search, OVID Technologies, ProQuest, Wilson - Wilson Web
Publications: Annual report; newsletter; orientation manuals
Function: Some telephone reference
Partic in OCLC Online Computer Library Center, Inc; TexShare

BROWNWOOD

P BROWNWOOD PUBLIC LIBRARY,* 600 Carnegie Blvd, 76801-7038. SAN 316-1277. Tel: 915-646-0155. E-Mail: library@net. *Dir*, Mathew P McConnell; Staff 8 (MLS 1, Non-MLS 7)
Founded 1904. Pop 34,800; Circ 78,865
Oct 1998-Sep 1999 Income $224,583, City $181,383, County $30,000. Mats Exp $30,399, Per/Ser (Incl. Access Fees) $4,600, AV Equip $8,595. Sal $101,508
Library Holdings: Bk Vols 76,873; Per Subs 120
Mem of Big Country Library System

C HOWARD PAYNE UNIVERSITY, Walker Memorial Library, 1000 Fisk Ave, 76801. SAN 316-1285. Tel: 915-649-8602. Interlibrary Loan Service Tel: 915-646-2502. FAX: 915-649-8904. Web Site: www.hputx.edu. *Dir*, Nancy Anderson; E-Mail: nanderso@hputx.edu; *Syst Coordr*, Eddy Smith; Tel: 915-646-8602, Ext 5607, E-Mail: esmith@hputx.edu; *Publ Servs*, Wade Kinnin; Tel: 915-646-8602, Ext 5606, E-Mail: wkinnin@hputx.edu; *Distance Educ*, Debby Dill; E-Mail: ddill@hputx.edu; *Tech Servs*, Mary Dunham; Staff 11 (MLS 5, Non-MLS 6)
Founded 1889. Enrl 1,553; Fac 116; Highest Degree: Bachelor
Jun 1999-May 2000 Income $556,449, Locally Generated Income $30,000, Parent Institution $526,449. Mats Exp $286,659, Books $50,243, Per/Ser (Incl. Access Fees) $76,834, Presv $4,171, Micro $13,500, AV Equip $18,925, Electronic Ref Mat (Incl. Access Fees) $25,927. Sal $239,790 (Prof $107,577)
Library Holdings: Bk Vols 135,798; Per Subs 967
Subject Interests: Business, Education, Religion, Sociology
Special Collections: Burress Genealogical Coll
Database Vendor: DRA, GaleNet, Lexis-Nexis, OCLC - First Search, OVID Technologies
Mem of Abilene Libr Consortium
Partic in Amigos Library Services, Inc; Llano Estacado Info Access Network; OCLC Online Computer Library Center, Inc; Tex Independent Cols & Univ Librs; TexShare

BRYAN

P BRYAN & COLLEGE STATION PUBLIC LIBRARY SYSTEM, 201 E 26th St, 77803-5356. SAN 316-1293. Tel: 979-209-5600. FAX: 979-209-5610. Web Site: www.bcslibrary.org. *Head of Libr*, Clara B Mounce; Tel: 979-209-5611, E-Mail: cmounce@ci.bryan.tx.us; *Branch Mgr*, Kathleen Di Tel: 979-764-3416; *Branch Mgr*, Nancy M Ross; Tel: 979-209-5630; *Librn* Melissa Gililland; *Librn*, John Palmer; *Librn*, Jennifer Ulrich; *Circ*, Lucind Hill; *Circ*, Tina Swartzlander; *YA Servs*, Glenda Duncan; *YA Servs*, Robin Jones; *Cat*, Catherine Ezzell; *Archivist*, Shirley Ferguson; Tel: 979-209-563 Staff 39 (MLS 14, Non-MLS 25)
Founded 1903. Pop 140,000; Circ 460,000
Oct 1998-Sep 1999 Income (Main Library and Branch Library) City $1,370,486. Mats Exp $215,881, Books $176,045, Per/Ser (Incl. Access Fees) $27,836, Micro $2,000, Electronic Ref Mat (Incl. Access Fees) $10,000. Sal $1,006,200
Library Holdings: Bk Vols 199,131; Bk Titles 146,679; Per Subs 433
Subject Interests: Ballet, Bus, Genealogy, Humanities, Local history, Mgt, Texas, Texas poets
Special Collections: Ana Ludmilla Ballet Col
Automation Activity & Vendor Info: (Cataloging) epixtech, inc.; (Circulation) epixtech, inc.; (OPAC) epixtech, inc.
Database Vendor: epixtech, inc., IAC - Info Trac
Function: Reference services available
Special Services for the Blind - Kurzweil Reader
Open Mon, Tues & Thurs 9-9, Wed 9-6, Fri & Sat 9-5, Sun 1:30-5:30
Friends of the Library Group
Branches: 1
COLLEGE STATION PUBLIC LIBRARY, 1818 Harvey Mitchell Pkwy, College Sta, 77840. SAN 323-7702. Tel: 979-764-3416. FAX: 979-764-6379. Web Site: www.bcslibrary.org. *Branch Mgr*, Kathleen Dill; *Librn*, Amy Beck; *Librn*, Lori Hodges; *Librn*, Lou Vonn Johnson; *Librn*, Kathleen Krizek; *Librn*, Betti Small; Staff 15 (MLS 5, Non-MLS 10)
Founded 1987. Pop 140,000; Circ 460,000
Oct 1998-Sep 1999 Income City $572,288. Mats Exp $64,000, Books $55,000, Per/Ser (Incl. Access Fees) $7,000, Micro $2,000. Sal $480,792
Library Holdings: Bk Vols 55,000; Bk Titles 54,000; Per Subs 150
Automation Activity & Vendor Info: (Cataloging) epixtech, inc.; (Circulation) epixtech, inc.
Database Vendor: epixtech, inc.
Mem of Central Texas Library System
Open Mon & Wed 9-9, Tues & Thurs 10-7, Fri & Sat 10-5
Friends of the Library Group

M SAINT JOSEPH REGIONAL HEALTH CENTER LIBRARY,* 2801 Franciscan Dr, PO Box 993, 77805. SAN 316-1307. Tel: 409-776-2433, 409-776-3777. FAX: 409-776-4906. *Librn*, Barbara Thomas
Founded 1935
Library Holdings: Bk Vols 250; Bk Titles 100
Restriction: Staff use only

BUDA

P BUDA PUBLIC LIBRARY, (Formerly Moreau Memorial Library), 303 N Main St, PO Box 608, 78610-0608. SAN 376-4818. Tel: 512-295-5899. FAX: 512-295-5899. E-Mail: budalibr@hotmail.com. Web Site: www.buda.lib.tx.us. *Dir*, Marjorie Elaine Martinez; Staff 2 (MLS 1, Non-MLS 1)
Founded 1980. Pop 3,200
Library Holdings: Bk Vols 16,220; Bk Titles 15,600; Per Subs 27
Automation Activity & Vendor Info: (Cataloging) Sagebrush Corporation; (Circulation) Sagebrush Corporation; (OPAC) Sagebrush Corporation
Mem of Central Texas Library System
Friends of the Library Group

BUFFALO

P BUFFALO PUBLIC LIBRARY,* Hwy 79, PO Box 1290, 75831-1290. SA 376-4826. Tel: 903-322-4146. FAX: 903-322-3253. *Librn*, Sandra Dawkins
Library Holdings: Bk Vols 12,000
Mem of Central Texas Library System
Friends of the Library Group

ULVERDE

BULVERDE PUBLIC LIBRARY,* 30450 Cougar Bend, PO Box 207, 78163-0207. SAN 376-4184. Tel: 830-438-3666. FAX: 830-438-3666. *Dir*, Doris Haecker
Library Holdings: Bk Vols 13,000
Mem of Alamo Area Library System
Friends of the Library Group

UNA

BUNA PUBLIC LIBRARY, Hwy 62 S, PO Box 1571, 77612-1571. SAN 375-555X. Tel: 409-994-5501. FAX: 409-994-4737. *Dir*, Lena Haynes; E-Mail: lhaynes@in2000.net
Founded 1973. Pop 8,246; Circ 25,080
Library Holdings: Bk Vols 20,643; Bk Titles 18,143; Per Subs 16
Mem of Houston Area Library System
Special Services for the Deaf - Books on deafness & sign language
Friends of the Library Group

URKBURNETT

BURKBURNETT LIBRARY,* 215 E Fourth St, 76354-3446. SAN 316-1315. Tel: 940-569-2991. FAX: 940-569-1620. *Librn*, Linda Hibbard; *Asst Librn*, Corey Naranor; *Tech Servs*, Patsy J Blackmon; Staff 2 (MLS 1, Non-MLS 1)
Founded 1967. Pop 19,929; Circ 30,136
Oct 1996-Sep 1997 Income $121,031, City $119,973, Other $1,057. Mats Exp $16,885, Books $15,669, Per/Ser (Incl. Access Fees) $1,009, Micro $207. Sal $60,639 (Prof $25,579)
Library Holdings: Bk Vols 24,998; Bk Titles 24,307; Per Subs 55
Subject Interests: Genealogy, History, Texana
Special Collections: Native American History & Literature; Wordless Picture Books
Mem of North Texas Regional Library System
Friends of the Library Group

URLESON

BURLESON PUBLIC LIBRARY,* 248 SW Johnson Ave, 76028. SAN 316-1323. Tel: 817-295-6131. FAX: 817-447-5430. *Dir*, Sandra T Babb; E-Mail: sbabb@airmail.net; *Librn*, Lana Dibble; Staff 2 (MLS 2)
Founded 1971. Pop 19,550; Circ 127,321
Oct 1998-Sep 1999 Income $363,924, State $4,213, City $359,711. Mats Exp $49,200, Books $45,000, Per/Ser (Incl. Access Fees) $4,200. Sal $189,249
Library Holdings: Bk Vols 35,775; Bk Titles 35,000; Per Subs 70
Mem of North Texas Regional Library System
Friends of the Library Group

URNET

HERMAN BROWN FREE LIBRARY, Burnet County Library System,* 100 E Washington, 78611. SAN 361-3208. Tel: 512-756-2328. FAX: 512-756-2610. *Dir*, Paula Harris; *Librn*, Cookie Wallace
Founded 1948. Pop 23,000; Circ 180,622
Library Holdings: Bk Vols 87,870
Subject Interests: Genealogy, Texana
Mem of Burnet County Libr Syst; Central Texas Library System
Friends of the Library Group
Branches: 3
BERTRAM BRANCH, PO Box 243, Bertram, 78605. SAN 361-3232. Tel: 512-355-2113. FAX: 512-355-3323. *Librn*, Ann Brock
Friends of the Library Group
MARBLE FALLS BRANCH, 101 Main St, Marble Falls, 78654. SAN 361-3291. Tel: 830-693-3023. FAX: 830-693-3987. *Librn*, Diana Collins
Friends of the Library Group
OAKALLA, 100 E Washington, 78611. SAN 376-9496. *Librn*, Sue Hornsby

CALDWELL

P HARRIE P WOODSON MEMORIAL LIBRARY,* 704 W Hwy 21, 77836-1129. SAN 316-1331. Tel: 409-567-4111. FAX: 409-567-4962. *Librn*, Pat Beavers; *Asst Librn*, Mary Kuehn
Circ 17,877
Library Holdings: Bk Titles 14,825; Per Subs 15
Mem of Central Texas Library System
Open Tues & Thurs 10-8, Wed & Fri 10-6, Sat 9-12

CAMERON

P CAMERON PUBLIC LIBRARY,* 304 E Third St, 76520. SAN 316-1358. Tel: 254-697-2401. FAX: 254-697-2401. *Librn*, Mary Amerson
Founded 1953. Pop 11,890; Circ 29,035
Library Holdings: Bk Vols 35,118; Bk Titles 33,250; Per Subs 37
Special Collections: DAR Genealogy, vols, mss; Local History Coll; Texas History Coll
Mem of Central Texas Library System

CANADIAN

P HEMPHILL COUNTY LIBRARY,* 500 Main St, 79014. SAN 316-1366. Tel: 806-323-5282. FAX: 806-323-6102. E-Mail: cdn_april@hlc.actx.edu, cdn_staff@hlc.actx.edu. *Dir*, April Dillon; *Coll Develop, Librn*, Sherry Wagoner; Staff 1 (MLS 1)
Founded 1923. Pop 3,598
Oct 1997-Sep 1998 Income $109,807, City $8,000, County $100,034. Mats Exp $19,732, Books $16,135, Per/Ser (Incl. Access Fees) $2,143, Presv $855, Micro $36. Sal $60,527
Library Holdings: Bk Vols 35,538; Per Subs 68
Subject Interests: Local history
Special Collections: Local Newspaper since 1887, micro
Mem of Texas Panhandle Library System
Partic in Harrington Library Consortium
Friends of the Library Group

CANTON

P VAN ZANDT COUNTY LIBRARY,* 317 First Monday Lane, 75103. SAN 320-7498. Tel: 903-567-4276. FAX: 903-567-6981. E-Mail: vzclib@vzinet.com. *Librn*, Marti Sites
Pop 38,000
Oct 1998-Sep 1999 Income $95,000. Mats Exp $17,000, Books $16,000, Per/Ser (Incl. Access Fees) $1,000. Sal $65,000 (Prof $20,000)
Library Holdings: Bk Vols 44,697; Per Subs 60
Subject Interests: Genealogy, Local history
Special Collections: Texas Coll
Mem of Northeast Texas Library System
Friends of the Library Group

CANYON

P CANYON PUBLIC LIBRARY, 301 16th St, 79015. SAN 316-1374. Tel: 806-655-5015. FAX: 806-655-5032. *Dir*, Noreen Taylor; Staff 7 (MLS 1, Non-MLS 6)
Pop 12,000; Circ 46,000
Oct 1998-Sep 1999 Income City $90,913. Mats Exp $15,190, Books $12,000, Per/Ser (Incl. Access Fees) $890, AV Equip $2,300. Sal $53,719
Library Holdings: Bk Vols 32,000; Per Subs 56
Database Vendor: DRA
Mem of Texas Panhandle Library System
Friends of the Library Group

S PANHANDLE-PLAINS HISTORICAL MUSEUM, Research Center, 2401 Fourth Ave, WTAMU Box 60967, 79015. SAN 328-6169. Tel: 806-651-2274. FAX: 806-651-2250. Web Site: www.wtamu.edu/museum/home.html. *Dir*, Betty L Bustos
Library Holdings: Bk Vols 15,000
Special Collections: Special collection of 300,000 photographs & manuscripts of Texas, Oklahoma Panhandle & Southeast New Mexico

C WEST TEXAS A&M UNIVERSITY, Cornette Library, Second Ave & 26th St, WTAMU Box 60748, 79016-0001. SAN 316-1382. Tel: 806-651-2229. Interlibrary Loan Service Tel: 806-651-2406. Circulation Tel: 806-651-2223. Reference Tel: 806-651-2215. FAX: 806-651-2213. Web Site: www.wtamu.edu/library/libhome.html. *Dir*, Paul Coleman; Tel: 806-651-2225, E-Mail: pcoleman@mail.wtamu.edu; *Asst Dir*, Shawna Kennedy-Witthar; Tel: 806-651-2227, E-Mail: switthar@mail.wtamu.edu; *Asst Dir*, Shawna Kennedy-Witthar; Tel: 806-651-2227, E-Mail: switthar@mail.wtamu.edu; *Govt Doc*, Claire Bennett Ponsford; Tel: 806-651-2204, E-Mail: bponsford@mail.wtamu.edu; *Bibliog Instr*, Barbara Hightower; Tel: 806-651-2231, E-Mail: bhightower@mail.wtamu.edu; *ILL*, Phillip Flores; Tel: 806-651-2407, E-Mail: pflores@mail.wtamu.edu; *Coll Develop, Head, Acq*, Gonda Stayton; Tel: 806-651-2218, E-Mail: gdstayton@mail.wtamu.edu; *Head, Circ*, Carolyn Talley; Tel: 806-651-2220, E-Mail: ctalley@mail.wtamu.edu; *Head Ref*, Mary Jarvis; Tel: 806-651-2212, E-Mail: mjarvis@mail.wtamu.edu; *Head, Cat*, Mary Rausch; Tel: 806-651-2219, E-Mail: mrausch@mail.wtamu.edu; *Per*, Jana Comerford; Tel: 806-651-2208, E-Mail: jcomerford@mail.wtamu.edu; *Per*, Sidnye Johnson; Tel: 806-651-2209, E-Mail: sjohnson@mail.wtamu.edu; *Cat*, Frances Frey; Tel: 805-651-2216, E-Mail: ffrey@mail.wtamu.edu; *Ref*, Isabel Davis; Tel: 806-651-2214, E-Mail: idavis@mail.wtamu.edu; Staff 30 (MLS 11, Non-MLS 19)
Founded 1910. Enrl 6,777; Fac 208; Highest Degree: Master
Sep 1999-Aug 2000 Income $1,470,787, State $1,424,318, Locally Generated Income $10,389, Other $36,080. Mats Exp $506,699, Books $96,261, Per/Ser (Incl. Access Fees) $261,284, Presv $15,767, Micro $38,724, Other Print Mats $15,939, Electronic Ref Mat (Incl. Access Fees) $78,724. Sal $643,948 (Prof $324,472)
Library Holdings: Bk Vols 470,976; Bk Titles 300,099; Per Subs 1,773
Special Collections: American History (Library of American Civilization), micro; English History (British House of Commons Sessional Papers &

Hansard's British Parliamentary Debates), micro; English Literature (Library of English Literature, Parts 1-4), micro; Loula Grace Erdmen Papers; Sheffy Coll, regional history; Texas Panhandle & Great Plains (Dr L F Sheffy Memorial); Western Americana (Xerox UM Western Americana), micro
Database Vendor: Lexis-Nexis, OCLC - First Search, OVID Technologies
Publications: Newsletter; Quick Guides (info sheets)
Partic in Amigos Library Services, Inc; Harrington Library Consortium
Friends of the Library Group

CANYON LAKE

P TYE PRESTON MEMORIAL LIBRARY,* 1321 FM 2673, 78133-5301. SAN 324-1238. Tel: 830-964-3744. FAX: 830-964-3126. E-Mail: tyepr1lb@ink.org. *Librn*, Dora Hightower
Founded 1977. Pop 7,600; Circ 25,511
Library Holdings: Bk Vols 25,575; Bk Titles 23,920
Special Collections: Large Print Books; Texas Coll
Mem of Alamo Area Library System
Friends of the Library Group

CARRIZO SPRINGS

P DIMMIT COUNTY PUBLIC LIBRARY, (DCPL), 200 N Ninth St, 78834. SAN 376-4141. Tel: 830-876-5788. FAX: 830-876-3890. *Librn*, Mary Ellen Coleman
Library Holdings: Bk Vols 17,000; Per Subs 30
Mem of Alamo Area Library System
Friends of the Library Group

CARROLTON

P CARROLLTON PUBLIC LIBRARY,* 2001 E Jackson, 75006. SAN 319-3268. Tel: 972-466-3353. TDD: 800-643-2255. FAX: 972-466-3394. *Dir Libr Serv*, Lucile Dade; Tel: 976-466-3362, E-Mail: ldade@ci.carrollton.tx.us; *YA Servs*, Terri Allison; *Ad Servs, AV, Ref*, Jane Dillon; *Circ*, Roselyn Ware; *Automation Syst Coordr*, Sharon Castleberry; *Commun Servs*, Kathy Thompson; *Tech Servs*, Kam A Hitchcock-Mort; Tel: 972-466-4710, Fax: 972-466-4722, E-Mail: khitchco@ci.carrollton.tx.us; Staff 85 (MLS 22, Non-MLS 63)
Founded 1963. Pop 103,000; Circ 1,200,000
Oct 1998-Sep 1999 Income (Main Library and Branch Library) $3,143,674, City $2,955,111, County $81,568. Mats Exp $514,495. Sal $1,461,600
Library Holdings: Bk Vols 218,004; Bk Titles 135,162; Per Subs 422
Subject Interests: Bus, Genealogy, Large print, Tex hist
Special Collections: Local History Coll
Automation Activity & Vendor Info: (Acquisitions) epixtech, inc.; (Cataloging) epixtech, inc.; (Circulation) epixtech, inc.
Database Vendor: Ebsco - EbscoHost, epixtech, inc., GaleNet, IAC - Info Trac, OCLC - First Search, ProQuest
Function: ILL available
Mem of Northeast Texas Library System
Special Services for the Deaf - TDD
Branches: 1
FRANKFORD VILLAGE, 3030 N Josey Lane at Frankford Rd, Carrollton, 75007. SAN 374-6763. Tel: 972-466-4800. FAX: 972-394-2877. *In Charge*, Kathy Thompson

CARTHAGE

P SAMMY BROWN LIBRARY,* 522 W College St, 75633. SAN 316-1412. Tel: 903-693-6741. FAX: 903-693-4503. *Librn*, Dianne Page
Founded 1962. Pop 22,350
Library Holdings: Bk Titles 50,000; Per Subs 52
Mem of Northeast Texas Library System
Friends of the Library Group

J PANOLA COLLEGE, M P Baker Library, 1109 W Panola St, 75633. SAN 316-1404. Tel: 903-693-2052. Interlibrary Loan Service Tel: 903-693-2091. Circulation Tel: 903-693-1155. Reference Tel: 903-693-1181. FAX: 903-693-1115. Web Site: www.panola.cc.tx.us/library. *Dir*, Phyllis Reed; Tel: 903-693-2005, E-Mail: preed@panola.cc.tx.us; *Circ, ILL*, Christine Ferguson; E-Mail: cferguson@panola.cc.tx.us; *Ref, Ser*, Sherri Baker; E-Mail: ssbaker@panola.cc.tx.us; Staff 4 (MLS 3, Non-MLS 1)
Founded 1947. Enrl 1,603; Fac 70; Highest Degree: Associate
Sep 1999-Aug 2000 Income $493,898. Mats Exp $119,026, Books $53,547, Per/Ser (Incl. Access Fees) $20,012, Presv $2,166, Micro $6,000, AV Equip $2,736, Electronic Ref Mat (Incl. Access Fees) $34,565. Sal $214,559 (Prof $129,437)
Library Holdings: Bk Vols 32,721; Bk Titles 27,617; Per Subs 315
Subject Interests: Academic
Special Collections: East Texas Documents & Genealogies, oral hist
Automation Activity & Vendor Info: (Cataloging) SIRSI; (Circulation) SIRSI; (Course Reserve) SIRSI; (Media Booking) SIRSI; (OPAC) SIRSI; (Serials) SIRSI
Database Vendor: Ebsco - EbscoHost, GaleNet, Lexis-Nexis, OCLC - First Search, OVID Technologies, Wilson - Wilson Web
Publications: MP Baker Library/Learning Resource Center (Library handbook)
Restriction: Open to students
Function: ILL available, Reference services available
Partic in Amigos Library Services, Inc; Forest Trail Library Consortium, In
OCLC Online Computer Library Center, Inc; TexShare

CASTROVILLE

P CASTROVILLE PUBLIC LIBRARY, 802 London St, 78009. SAN 316-1420. Tel: 830-931-4095. FAX: 830-931-9050. E-Mail: librarian@castroville.lib.tx.us. Web Site: www.castroville.lib.tx.us. *Dir*, Carole Anne Trisler; *Asst Dir*, Doris Keller; *Asst Librn*, Dorothy Bernard; Staff 3 (Non-MLS 3)
Founded 1962. Pop 2,350
Library Holdings: Bk Vols 12,357
Subject Interests: Genealogy, Local history
Automation Activity & Vendor Info: (Cataloging) ComPanion Corp; (Circulation) ComPanion Corp
Database Vendor: CARL, GaleNet, ProQuest
Function: ILL available
Mem of Alamo Area Library System
Friends of the Library Group

CEDAR HILL

C NORTHWOOD UNIVERSITY LIBRARY, Cedar Hill Campus, 1114 W FM 1382, 75104. SAN 361-3410. Tel: 972-293-5436. FAX: 972-293-7026. *Dir*, Kaethryn Duncan
Founded 1967. Enrl 751; Fac 30; Highest Degree: Bachelor
Library Holdings: Bk Vols 10,500; Bk Titles 11,000; Per Subs 160
Subject Interests: Accounting, Bus, Econ, Fashion, Mgt
Special Collections: Advertising; Automotive Marketing; Business Management; Fashion Merchandising; Hotel & Restaurant; Management
Restriction: Staff use only, Students only

P ZULA-BRYANT-WYLIE LIBRARY,* 225 Cedar St, 75104-2655. SAN 361-4107. Tel: 972-291-7323. FAX: 972-291-5361. *Dir*, Pat Bonds; Tel: 972-291-5196, E-Mail: pbonds@airmail.net; *Ch Servs*, Carol Hanson; E-Mail: chanson@airmail.net; *Publ Servs*, Diane Rayburn; E-Mail: drayburn@airmail.net; *Tech Coordr*, Dan Watkins; E-Mail: danw01@airmail.net; Staff 22 (MLS 3, Non-MLS 19)
Founded 1948. Pop 30,000; Circ 112,030
Oct 1998-Sep 1999 Income $461,972, City $411,972, Other $50,000. Mats Exp $115,252, Books $92,125, Per/Ser (Incl. Access Fees) $23,127. Sal $275,357 (Prof $148,330)
Library Holdings: Bk Vols 66,285; Per Subs 97
Subject Interests: Local history
Automation Activity & Vendor Info: (Cataloging) epixtech, inc.; (Circulation) epixtech, inc.; (OPAC) epixtech, inc.
Database Vendor: epixtech, inc.
Function: Some telephone reference
Mem of Northeast Texas Library System
Non-residents cards: $25.00
Friends of the Library Group

CEDAR PARK

P CEDAR PARK PUBLIC LIBRARY,* 550 Discovery Blvd, 78613. SAN 325-5158. Tel: 512-259-5353. FAX: 512-259-5236. E-Mail: library@ci.cedar-park.tx.us. Web Site: www.ci.cedar-park.tx.us. *Dir*, Pauline P Lam; E-Mail: lam@ci.cedar-park.tx.us; *Ch Servs*, Melissa A Uhlhorn; E-Mail: uhlhorn@ci.cedar-park.tx.us; *Syst Coordr*, Roger K Bell; E-Mail: bell@ci.cedar-park.tx.us; Staff 11 (MLS 3, Non-MLS 8)
Founded 1981. Pop 18,000; Circ 223,594
Oct 1998-Sep 1999 Income $320,420. Mats Exp $60,000, Books $55,000, Electronic Ref Mat (Incl. Access Fees) $5,000. Sal $217,506 (Prof $74,000)
Library Holdings: Bk Vols 40,000; Bk Titles 39,000; Per Subs 103
Special Collections: Texana
Automation Activity & Vendor Info: (Circulation) Follett; (OPAC) Follett
Database Vendor: Ebsco - EbscoHost, OCLC - First Search, Wilson - Wilson Web
Mem of Central Texas Library System
Partic in Amigos Library Services, Inc
Friends of the Library Group

CELINA

P CELINA COMMUNITY LIBRARY, 710 E Pecan, 75009. (Mail add: Box 188, 75009-0188), SAN 376-4494. Tel: 972-382-3750. FAX: 972-382-3750. *Librn*, Rhonda Detro; Staff 1 (Non-MLS 1)
Founded 1992. Pop 2,000
Library Holdings: Bk Vols 10,750; Bk Titles 10,500; Per Subs 48
Subject Interests: Education

Database Vendor: GaleNet, ProQuest
Mem of Northeast Texas Library System
Open Mon-Thurs 7:45-6, Fri 7:45-4, Sat 9-12

ENTER

FANNIE BROWN BOOTH MEMORIAL LIBRARY,* 619 Tenaha St, 75935. SAN 316-1439. Tel: 409-598-5522. *Librn*, Stephen Neuville
Pop 4,970; Circ 16,832
Library Holdings: Bk Vols 13,556; Per Subs 19
Mem of Houston Area Library System
Friends of the Library Group

HANNELVIEW

EQUISTAR, Petrochemical Library,* 8280 Sheldon Rd, 77530. SAN 316-1447. Tel: 281-452-8148. FAX: 281-860-3113.
Founded 1956
Library Holdings: Bk Vols 15,000; Per Subs 32
Subject Interests: Tech info
Special Collections: Design Manuals Coll
Partic in Dialog Corporation

HARLOTTE

CHARLOTTE PUBLIC LIBRARY, 77 Yule St, 78011. (Mail add: PO Box 757, 78011), SAN 376-4206. Tel: 830-277-1212. FAX: 830-277-1212. *Librn*, Anna Estrada
Founded 1984
Jul 2000-Jun 2001 Income $31,000, City $15,000, County $4,000, Other $12,000. Mats Exp Books $14,000. Sal $10,000
Library Holdings: Bk Vols 10,100; Bk Titles 9,000
Mem of Alamo Area Library System

HICO

CHICO PUBLIC LIBRARY,* 106 W Jacksboro, PO Box 707, 76431. SAN 376-4648. Tel: 940-644-2330. FAX: 940-644-2330. *Librn*, Mary Rexin
Library Holdings: Bk Vols 10,000
Mem of North Texas Regional Library System

HILDRESS

CHILDRESS PUBLIC LIBRARY,* 117 Avenue B NE, 79201. SAN 316-1455. Tel: 940-937-8421. FAX: 940-937-8421. E-Mail: chi_judy@hlc.actx.edu. *Librn*, Judy McKeeve
Founded 1900. Pop 6,375; Circ 17,250
1998-1999 Income $24,800, City $4,000, County $4,000, Other $16,800. Mats Exp $29,801, Books $3,116, Per/Ser (Incl. Access Fees) $487. Sal $14,494
Library Holdings: Bk Titles 12,050; Per Subs 15
Mem of Texas Panhandle Library System
Friends of the Library Group

ISCO

CISCO JUNIOR COLLEGE, Maner Memorial Library, Rte 3, Box 3, 76437-9802. SAN 316-1463. Tel: 254-442-2567, Ext 182. FAX: 254-442-2546. E-Mail: library@cisco.cc.tx.us. Web Site: www.cisco.cc.tx.us. *Dir Libr Serv*, Gary Neil Fitsimmons; Tel: 254-442-2567, Ext 201, E-Mail: gfitsimmons@cisco.cc.tx.us; *Ref*, Michael Cunningham; E-Mail: mcunningham@cisco.cc.tx.us; *Acq*, Sue Endebrock; Tel: 254-442-2567, Ext 183, E-Mail: sendebrock@cisco.cc.tx.us; Staff 5 (MLS 2, Non-MLS 3)
Founded 1940. Enrl 2,600; Highest Degree: Associate
Sep 1999-Aug 2000 Income Parent Institution $1,832,055. Mats Exp $37,410, Books $19,535, Per/Ser (Incl. Access Fees) $6,940, Presv $700, Electronic Ref Mat (Incl. Access Fees) $10,235. Sal $111,496 (Prof $68,200)
Library Holdings: Bk Vols 26,000; Bk Titles 21,000; Per Subs 150
Special Collections: Randy Steffen Coll, bks, paintings; Texas & Southwest, bks, micro, paintings
Automation Activity & Vendor Info: (Cataloging) EOS; (Circulation) EOS; (Course Reserve) EOS; (Media Booking) EOS; (OPAC) EOS
Database Vendor: OCLC - First Search, OVID Technologies
Publications: (Newsletter)
Function: Reference services available
Partic in Amigos Library Services, Inc; Llano Estacado Info Access Network; Tex Share

CISCO PUBLIC LIBRARY, 600 Avenue G, 76437. SAN 316-1471. Tel: 254-442-1020. E-Mail: elibrary@txol.net. *Librn*, Louise Pryor
Circ 4,029
Library Holdings: Bk Vols 15,000

CLARENDON

J CLARENDON COLLEGE LIBRARY, 1122 College Dr, PO Box 968, 79226-0968. SAN 316-1498. Tel: 806-874-3571. FAX: 806-874-3201. Web Site: www.clarendoncollege.net. *Dir*, Austin Jewel
Founded 1898. Pop 1,500; Enrl 1,166; Fac 29; Highest Degree: Associate
2000-2001 Mats Exp $10,500, Books $6,000, Per/Ser (Incl. Access Fees) $3,600, AV Equip $900, Electronic Ref Mat (Incl. Access Fees) $8,000
Library Holdings: Bk Vols 25,000; Per Subs 125
Automation Activity & Vendor Info: (Acquisitions) DRA; (Cataloging) DRA; (Circulation) DRA; (Course Reserve) DRA; (ILL) DRA; (Media Booking) DRA; (OPAC) DRA; (Serials) DRA
Partic in Harrington Library Consortium

P GABIE BETTS BURTON MEMORIAL LIBRARY,* PO Box 783, 79226-0783. SAN 316-148X. Tel: 806-874-3685. FAX: 806-874-9750. *Librn*, Mary Green; E-Mail: cla_mary@hic.actx.edu
Founded 1923. Pop 4,100; Circ 26,393
Library Holdings: Bk Titles 30,000; Per Subs 50
Mem of Texas Panhandle Library System
Partic in Harrington Library Consortium
Friends of the Library Group

CLARKSVILLE

P RED RIVER COUNTY PUBLIC LIBRARY,* 307 N Walnut, PO Box 508, 75426. SAN 316-1501. Tel: 903-427-3991. FAX: 903-427-3991. E-Mail: rrcpl@1starnet.com. *Dir*, Betsy Tull
Founded 1961. Pop 14,298
Oct 1997-Sep 1998 Income $56,550, City $3,000, County $25,682, Other $27,868. Mats Exp $9,764, Books $7,769, Per/Ser (Incl. Access Fees) $959, Micro $76. Sal $31,413
Library Holdings: Bk Vols 36,690; Per Subs 70
Friends of the Library Group

CLAUDE

P CLAUDE PUBLIC LIBRARY,* 100 Trice St, PO Box 109, 79019. SAN 316-151X. Tel: 806-226-7881. *Librn*, June Adcock
Pop 1,895; Circ 2,049
Library Holdings: Bk Vols 7,500
Mem of Texas Panhandle Library System

CLEBURNE

P CLEBURNE PUBLIC LIBRARY,* 302 W Henderson, 76031-0486. SAN 316-1528. Tel: 817-645-0934. FAX: 817-556-8816. *Dir*, Tina Williams; Staff 1 (MLS 1)
Founded 1905. Pop 22,000; Circ 211,147
Library Holdings: Bk Vols 49,271; Bk Titles 48,687; Per Subs 4,000
Special Collections: Cleburne history; Johnson County history
Mem of North Texas Regional Library System

S LAYLAND MUSEUM, Research Library & Archives, 201 N Caddo St, 76031. SAN 370-1689. Tel: 817-645-0900, 817-645-0940. FAX: 817-645-0926. *In Charge*, Julie Baker
Founded 1963
Library Holdings: Bk Titles 800
Subject Interests: Social history
Special Collections: Texana (Layland Book Coll)

CLEVELAND

P AUSTIN MEMORIAL LIBRARY,* 220 S Bonham, 77327. SAN 316-1536. Tel: 281-592-3920. FAX: 281-593-0361. *Librn*, Sue Hayes; E-Mail: shayes@hals.lib.tx.us
Founded 1952. Pop 7,200; Circ 42,000
Library Holdings: Bk Vols 31,000
Subject Interests: Genealogy, Texas
Mem of Houston Area Library System

CLUTE

S THE BRAZOSPORT FACTS LIBRARY,* 720 S Main, PO Box 549, 77531-0549. SAN 324-1580. Tel: 409-265-7411, Ext 263. Toll Free Tel: 800-864-8340. FAX: 409-265-9052. *Librn*, Karma Lowe
Founded 1980
Library Holdings: Bk Vols 600; Bk Titles 200; Per Subs 25
Subject Interests: Local history
Special Collections: Brazoria County History
Restriction: Open to public for reference only

CLYDE

P CLYDE PUBLIC LIBRARY, 125 Oak St, 79510-4702. (Mail add: PO Box 1779, 79510-1779), SAN 324-7457. Tel: 915-893-5315. FAX: 915-893-5315. E-Mail: clydepl@bitstreet.com. *Dir*, Judith Ann Kuykendall; Staff 2 (MLS 1, Non-MLS 1)
Founded 1972. Pop 6,406
Apr 1999-Mar 2000 Income $20,792, City $6,600, County $1,800, Locally Generated Income $12,392. Mats Exp Per/Ser (Incl. Access Fees) $271. (Prof $7,800)
Library Holdings: Bk Titles 10,577; Per Subs 12
Special Collections: Texas (Callahan County Coll)
Database Vendor: OVID Technologies
Function: ILL available
Mem of Big Country Library System
Friends of the Library Group

COCKRELL HILL

P COCKRELL HILL PUBLIC LIBRARY,* 4125 W Clarendon, 75211. SAN 376-4443. Tel: 214-330-9935. FAX: 214-330-5483. *Librn*, Lisa Conley
Oct 1996-Sep 1997 Income $19,763. Mats Exp $5,000. Sal $10,957
Library Holdings: Bk Vols 8,609
Mem of Northeast Texas Library System

COLDSPRING

P COLDSPRING AREA PUBLIC LIBRARY,* 251 Slade St, PO Box 1756, 77331. SAN 329-0891. Tel: 409-653-3104. FAX: 409-653-4628. *Dir*, Dorothy Bauer
Founded 1986. Pop 789
Library Holdings: Bk Titles 17,000
Mem of Houston Area Library System
Friends of the Library Group

COLEMAN

P COLEMAN PUBLIC LIBRARY, 402 Commercial Ave, 76834-9737. SAN 316-1544. Tel: 915-625-3043. E-Mail: cpl@web-access.net. *Librn*, Sue Dossey
Pop 9,710; Circ 40,159
Jul 1999-Jun 2000 Mats Exp $11,022, Books $8,105, Per/Ser (Incl. Access Fees) $750, AV Equip $1,807, Electronic Ref Mat (Incl. Access Fees) $360. Sal $31,360
Library Holdings: Bk Vols 23,684; Bk Titles 23,275
Special Collections: Mac Woodward Texas Coll; Texana; Walter Gann Coll; World War II
Mem of Big Country Library System
Open Tues & Thurs 10-7, Wed & Fri 12-5, Sat 9-12
Friends of the Library Group

COLLEGE STATION

L RICHARDS & ASSOCIATES LIBRARY,* PO Box 10350, 77842. SAN 372-9699. Tel: 409-690-1408. FAX: 409-690-6196. *Librn*, Hoy A Richards
Library Holdings: Bk Vols 3,200
Subject Interests: Law
Publications: Monthly National Newsletter

TEXAS A&M UNIVERSITY
CUSHING LIBRARY Tel: 409-845-1951. FAX: 409-862-4761. *Head of Libr*, Donald H Dyal; E-Mail: dondyal@acs.tamu.edu; *Archivist*, David L Chapman; *Archivist*, Charles R Schultz; *Spec Coll*, Steven E Smith; Staff 6 (MLS 6)
Library Holdings: Bk Vols 77,300
Special Collections: Illustration, Military History (Ragan Coll); Literary Coll (R Kipling, S Maugham, M Arnold, Sea Fiction, R Fuller, A E Coppard, P G Wodehouse, et al); Nautical Archaeology/Naval Architecture, Botanicals, Incunables & Fore Edge Paintings (Loran Laughlin Coll); Nineteenth Century Prints (Kelsey Coll); Ornithology (Kincaid Coll); Political Papers of Texans (eg, William Clements Papers); Range Livestock (Jeff Dykes Coll); Science Fiction Coll; Texas Agriculture (TAES/TAEX Archives); Texas History (local)

C STERLING C EVANS LIBRARY Tel: 409-845-8111. Interlibrary Loan Service Tel: 409-845-5641. FAX: 409-845-6238. Web Site: library.tamu.edu. *Dean of Libr, Dir*, Fred Heath; E-Mail: fheath@tamu.edu; *Coll Develop, Tech Servs*, Stephen Atkins; *Acq*, Jeanne Harrell; *Cat*, Mary Wilson; *Bibliog Instr*, Pixie Mosley; *Syst Coordr*, William Chollett; Staff 82 (MLS 82)
Founded 1876. Enrl 43,095; Highest Degree: Doctorate
Sep 1997-Aug 1998 Income $17,071,590. Mats Exp $8,435,871, Books $1,917,392, Per/Ser (Incl. Access Fees) $5,013,295, Presv $160,591, Other Print Mats $1,344,593. Sal $7,389,988 (Prof $3,554,205)
Library Holdings: Per Subs 17,017
Subject Interests: Military history, Oceanography
Automation Activity & Vendor Info: (Acquisitions) NOTIS; (Cataloging) NOTIS
Publications: Connections
Partic in Amigos Library Services, Inc; Dialog Corporation; Greater Midwest Res Libr Consortium; Houston Area Research Library Consortium; TexShare
Friends of the Library Group

CM MEDICAL SCIENCES LIBRARY Tel: 409-845-7427. FAX: 409-845-749 Web Site: msl.tamu.edu. *Dir*, Dottie Eakin; E-Mail: deakin@tamu.edu; *Coll Develop*, Gary Ives; Staff 10 (MLS 10)
Founded 1940. Enrl 3,025; Fac 1,190; Highest Degree: Doctorate
Sep 1996-Aug 1997 Income $1,882,267, State $1,527,557, Locally Generated Income $69,010, Parent Institution $276,500, Other $9,200. Mats Exp $710,140, Books $97,624, Per/Ser (Incl. Access Fees) $612,5 Sal $766,817 (Prof $433,537)
Library Holdings: Bk Vols 113,614; Per Subs 1,712
Subject Interests: Veterinary medicine
Automation Activity & Vendor Info: (Acquisitions) NOTIS; (Catalogir NOTIS; (Circulation) NOTIS
Publications: TAMU Medical Sciences Library Newsletter
Partic in South Central Academic Medical Libraries Consortium; Tex A&M Univ Consortium of Med Librs

WEST CAMPUS, Olsen Blvd, Bldg 1511, 77843-5001. Tel: 979-845-2111. Circulation Tel: 979-862-1983. FAX: 979-862-2977. Web Site: library.tamu.edu/wcl. *Dir*, Robert B McGeachin; E-Mail: r-mcgeachin@tamu.edu; *Head of Libr*, Jane Dodd; E-Mail: janedodd@tamu.edu; Staff (MLS 8, Non-MLS 6)
Founded 1994
Library Holdings: Bk Vols 12,000; Bk Titles 4,000; Per Subs 6,000
Subject Interests: Agriculture, Business
Database Vendor: Lexis-Nexis, OCLC - First Search, OVID Technologies, ProQuest, Silverplatter Information Inc., Wilson - Wilson Web
Friends of the Library Group

COLORADO CITY

P MITCHELL COUNTY PUBLIC LIBRARY, 340 Oak St, 79512. SAN 316-1552. Tel: 915-728-3968. FAX: 915-728-3968. E-Mail: mitchelc@bitstreet.com. *Head Librn*, Nancy Mayo; *Asst Librn*, Geneva Jones
Founded 1926. Pop 9,002; Circ 27,161
Library Holdings: Bk Vols 37,476; Bk Titles 35,879; Per Subs 23
Automation Activity & Vendor Info: (Cataloging) Sagebrush Corporation (Circulation) Sagebrush Corporation
Mem of Big Country Library System
Friends of the Library Group

COLUMBUS

P NESBITT MEMORIAL LIBRARY,* 529 Washington St, 78934-2326. SA 316-1560. Tel: 409-732-3392. FAX: 409-732-3392. *Archivist, Librn*, Bill Stein; *Asst Librn*, Susan Archuletta; Staff 3 (MLS 3)
Founded 1979. Pop 6,629; Circ 44,334
Library Holdings: Bk Vols 29,979; Bk Titles 28,700; Per Subs 37
Subject Interests: Architecture, Art, History, Tex hist
Mem of Houston Area Library System

COMANCHE

P COMANCHE PUBLIC LIBRARY,* 311 N Austin, PO Box 777, 76442-0411. SAN 316-1579. Tel: 915-356-2122. FAX: 915-356-2122. *Librn*, Margaret Waring
Founded 1960. Pop 12,598; Circ 43,000
Library Holdings: Bk Vols 23,000
Subject Interests: Genealogy of Tex, Southern states
Special Collections: State & Local History, bks, micro, maps, photog
Mem of Big Country Library System
Friends of the Library Group

COMFORT

P COMFORT PUBLIC LIBRARY, 701 High St, PO Box 536, 78013. SAN 316-1587. Tel: 830-995-2398. FAX: 830-995-4068. E-Mail: library@comfort.txed.net. Web Site: www.comfortnews/library/. *Dir*, Beth Gates Bourland; *Assoc Dir*, Patti Miles; *Tech Servs*, Tracy Ahrens; Staff 3 (Non-MLS 3)
Founded 1956. Pop 7,981; Circ 18,974
Jan 1999-Dec 1999 Income $64,702, County $31,000, Locally Generated Income $33,702. Mats Exp $9,360, Books $7,967, Per/Ser (Incl. Access Fees) $1,393. Sal $30,772 (Prof $17,610)
Library Holdings: Bk Vols 19,713; Bk Titles 18,719; Per Subs 52
Subject Interests: Local history, Texana
Special Collections: Comfort Heritage Foundation Archives
Automation Activity & Vendor Info: (Cataloging) Sagebrush Corporation; (Circulation) Sagebrush Corporation

Database Vendor: CARL, Ebsco - EbscoHost, GaleNet, OCLC - First Search, ProQuest, Wilson - Wilson Web
Function: ILL available
Mem of Alamo Area Library System
Friends of the Library Group

)MMERCE

COMMERCE PUBLIC LIBRARY,* 1210 Park St, PO Box 308, 75428-0308. SAN 316-1595. Tel: 903-886-6858. E-Mail: commerce@koyote.com. Web Site: www.jesystems.com/commerce/. *Dir*, Priscilla Donovan; *Cat*, Robbie House
Pop 13,748
Jan 1997-Dec 1998 Income $63,000. Mats Exp $8,000. Sal $46,000
Library Holdings: Bk Vols 31,000; Bk Titles 30,000
Special Collections: Commerce History Coll, bks, maps, newsp, photogs; Texas History Coll
Publications: The Handbook of Commerce (1872-1985)
Mem of Northeast Texas Library System
Friends of the Library Group

TEXAS A&M UNIVERSITY-COMMERCE, James Gilliam Gee Library, 2600 S Neal St, PO Box 3011, 75429-3011. SAN 361-3534. Tel: 903-886-5731. Interlibrary Loan Service Tel: 903-886-5722. Circulation Tel: 903-886-5718. Reference Tel: 903-885-5720. FAX: 903-886-5723. Web Site: multimedia.tamu-commerce.edu/library/. *Dir*, Carolyn Kacena; Tel: 903-886-5716, E-Mail: Carolyn_Kacena@tamu-commerce.edu; *Asst Dir*, Carol Dodd; Tel: 903-886-5742, E-Mail: Carol_Dodd@tamu-commerce.edu; *Syst Coordr*, Anna Loan-Wilsey; Tel: 903-886-5727, E-Mail: Anna_Wilsey@tamu-commerce.edu; *Head Ref*, Diane Downing; Tel: 903-886-5719, E-Mail: Diane_Downing@tamu-commerce.edu; *ILL*, Scott Downing; Tel: 903-886-5741, E-Mail: Scott_Downing@tamu-commerce.edu; *Acq*, Karen Akins; Tel: 903-886-5728, E-Mail: Karen_Akins@tamu-commerce.edu; *Head, Cat*, Michael Ho; Tel: 903-886-5730, E-Mail: Michael_Ho@tamu-commerce.edu; *Archivist*, James Conrad; Tel: 903-886-5737, E-Mail: James_Conrad@tamu-commerce.edu; *Ref*, Catherine Collins; Tel: 903-886-5721, E-Mail: Catherine_Collins@tamu-commerce.edu; *Ref*, Catherine Johnston; Tel: 903-886-5721, E-Mail: Kit_Johnston@tamu-commerce.edu; *Ref*, Marsha Keenan; Tel: 903-468-6083, E-Mail: Marsha_Keenan@tamu-commerce.edu; *Ref*, Carolyn Trezevant; Tel: 903-886-5725, E-Mail: Carolyn_Trezevant@tamu-commerce.edu; *Ser*, Susan Andrews; Tel: 903-886-5733, E-Mail: Susan_Andrews@tamu-commerce.edu; *Govt Doc*, David Larkin; Tel: 903-886-5726, E-Mail: David_Larkin@tamu-commerce.edu. Subject Specialists: *Business*, Catherine Collins; *Education*, Carolyn Trezevant; *Sciences*, Catherine Johnston; Staff 41 (MLS 15, Non-MLS 26)
Founded 1894. Enrl 7,504; Fac 257; Highest Degree: Doctorate
Sep 1999-Aug 2000 Income (Main Library and Branch Library) $2,422,260. Mats Exp $684,406, Books $174,745, Per/Ser (Incl. Access Fees) $322,263, Presv $12,462, AV Equip $36,416, Other Print Mats $2,506, Electronic Ref Mat (Incl. Access Fees) $136,014. Sal $1,429,871 (Prof $686,274)
Library Holdings: Bk Vols 1,050,080; Bk Titles 620,962; Per Subs 1,754
Special Collections: Education (Curriculum Library); Foreign Diplomatic Service (Ambassador Fletcher Warren Papers); Texas Literature (Elithe Hamilton Kirkland Paper); Texas Poetry (Faye Carr Adams Coll; Texas Political History (A M Aiken, T C Chaddick & Celia M Wright Coll); US Government & Politics (Congressman Ray Roberts Papers)
Automation Activity & Vendor Info: (Acquisitions) DRA; (Cataloging) DRA; (Circulation) DRA; (Course Reserve) DRA; (OPAC) DRA; (Serials) DRA
Database Vendor: GaleNet, Lexis-Nexis, OCLC - First Search, OVID Technologies, Silverplatter Information Inc.
Partic in Amigos Library Services, Inc; OCLC Online Computer Library Center, Inc; Phoenix Group; Tex Share
Departmental Libraries:
METROPLEX COMMUTER FACILITY LIBRARY, 2600 Motley Dr, Mesquite, 75150. SAN 361-4913. Tel: 972-882-7535, 972-882-7537. FAX: 972-882-7536. Web Site: multimedia.tamu-commerce.edu/library/met.htm. *Br Coordr*, Marilyn Hoye; E-Mail: Marilyn_Hoye@tamu-commerce.edu; *Asst Dir, Tech Servs*, Carol Dodd; Tel: 903-886-5742, Fax: 903-886-5723, E-Mail: Carol_Dodd@tamu-commerce.edu
Founded 1970
Library Holdings: Bk Vols 16,776; Bk Titles 13,278
Automation Activity & Vendor Info: (Circulation) DRA; (Course Reserve) DRA; (Serials) DRA
Partic in Amigos Library Services, Inc; Dialog Corporation; OCLC Online Computer Library Center, Inc

'ONROE

MONTGOMERY COUNTY MEMORIAL LIBRARY SYSTEM, 104 I-45 N, 77301-2720. SAN 361-3593. Tel: 936-539-7814. Circulation Tel: 936-788-8360. Reference Tel: 936-788-8361. FAX: 936-788-8398. Web Site: www.countylibrary.org. *Dir*, Jerilynn A Williams; Tel: 936-788-8377, Ext 237, E-Mail: jwilliams@countylibrary.org; *Br Coordr*, Gregg Wamsley; Tel: 936-788-8377, Ext 236, E-Mail: gwamsley@countylibrary.org; *Business*, Lana Molk; Tel: 936-788-8377, Ext 238, E-Mail: lmolk@countylibrary.org; *Ad Servs*, Gregory Tramel; Tel: 936-788-8377, Ext 250, E-Mail: gtramel@countylibrary.org; *Ch Servs*, Laura Boykin; Tel: 936-788-8377, Ext 242, E-Mail: lboykin@co.montgomery.tx.us; *Ch Servs*, Laura Harper; Tel: 936-788-8377, Ext 242, E-Mail: lharper@countylibrary.org; *Circ*, Terry Melton; Tel: 936-788-8377, Ext 244, E-Mail: lharper@countylibrary.org; *Coll Develop*, Pam Morse; Tel: 936-788-8377, Ext 257, E-Mail: pmorse@countylibrary.org; *Tech Servs*, Linda Gambrill; Tel: 936-788-8377, Ext 229, E-Mail: lgambrill@countylibrary.org; Staff 92 (MLS 27, Non-MLS 65)
Founded 1948. Pop 277,503; Circ 1,057,882
Oct 1999-Sep 2000 Income (Main Library and Branch Library) $4,076,096, State $200,000, County $3,686,871, Locally Generated Income $54,225, Other $135,000. Mats Exp $852,764, Books $662,394, Per/Ser (Incl. Access Fees) $128,092, Presv $5,000, Electronic Ref Mat (Incl. Access Fees) $57,278. Sal $2,203,074 (Prof $888,838)
Library Holdings: Bk Vols 428,355
Subject Interests: Genealogy
Automation Activity & Vendor Info: (Cataloging) epixtech, inc.; (Circulation) epixtech, inc.; (OPAC) epixtech, inc.
Database Vendor: epixtech, inc.
Mem of Houston Area Library System
Friends of the Library Group
Branches: 5
MALCOLM PURVIS LIBRARY, 510 Melton St, Magnolia, 77354. SAN 326-7415. Tel: 281-259-8324. FAX: 409-788-8304. *Dir*, Jerilynn A Williams; Tel: 936-788-8377, Fax: 936-788-8398, E-Mail: jwilliams@countylibrary.org; *Branch Mgr*, Debra Ellett; E-Mail: dellett@countylibrary.org; Staff 6 (MLS 1, Non-MLS 5)
Library Holdings: Bk Vols 36,599
Mem of Montgomery County District Libr Syst
Friends of the Library Group
R B TULLIS BRANCH, 21130 US Hwy 59, Suite K, New Caney, 77357. SAN 361-3623. Tel: 281-577-8968. FAX: 281-577-8992. *Dir*, Jerilynn A Williams; Tel: 936-788-8377, Fax: 936-788-8398, E-Mail: jwilliams@countylibrary.org; *Branch Mgr*, Patricia Higgins; E-Mail: phiggins@countylibrary.org; Staff 6 (MLS 2, Non-MLS 4)
Library Holdings: Bk Vols 51,578
Friends of the Library Group
R F MEADOR BRANCH, 709 W Montgomery, Willis, 77378. SAN 371-9820. Tel: 936-856-4411. FAX: 936-856-3360. *Branch Mgr*, Twillia Liles; E-Mail: tliles@countylibrary.org; Staff 6 (MLS 1, Non-MLS 5)
Library Holdings: Bk Vols 27,646
Mem of Montgomery County District Libr Syst
Friends of the Library Group
SOUTH BRANCH, 2101 Lake Robbins Dr, The Woodlands, 77380. SAN 361-3658. Tel: 281-298-9110. FAX: 281-298-9011. *Branch Mgr*, Bonnie Boorman; E-Mail: bboorman@countylibrary.org; Staff 21 (MLS 8, Non-MLS 13)
Library Holdings: Bk Vols 128,458
Friends of the Library Group
WEST BRANCH, 511 Western Hills Plaza, Ste 507, Montgomery, 77356. SAN 329-630X. Tel: 936-788-8314. FAX: 936-788-8349. *Dir*, Jerilynn A Williams; Tel: 936-788-8377, Fax: 936-788-8398, E-Mail: jwilliams@countylibrary.org; *Branch Mgr*, Ken McKee; E-Mail: kmckee@countylibrary.org; *Branch Mgr*, Bevery Spann; Staff 5 (MLS 2, Non-MLS 3)
Library Holdings: Bk Vols 32,218
Friends of the Library Group

CONVERSE

P CONVERSE PUBLIC LIBRARY,* 502 Station St, 78109. SAN 376-4192. Tel: 210-659-4160. FAX: 210-659-4160. *Librn*, Nelda Marion
Oct 1997-Sep 1998 Income $30,000
Library Holdings: Bk Vols 10,000
Mem of Alamo Area Library System

COOPER

P DELTA COUNTY PUBLIC LIBRARY,* 300 W Dallas Ave, 75432. SAN 376-7981. Tel: 903-395-4575. FAX: 903-395-4556. *Actg Dir*, Shirley Walker
Library Holdings: Bk Vols 25,000; Per Subs 20
Mem of Northeast Texas Library System
Friends of the Library Group

COPPELL

P COPPELL PUBLIC, William T Cosby Library, 177 N Hertz Rd, 75019. SAN 361-4131. Tel: 972-304-3655. FAX: 972-304-3622. *Dir*, Kathleen Metz Edwards; *Circ*, Constance Moss; *Syst Coordr*, Sharon Castleberry; *Ch Servs*, Debbie Brightwell; *Tech Servs*, Diana Perkins; Staff 22 (MLS 9, Non-MLS 13)
Pop 34,000
Oct 2000-Sep 2001 Income City $1,256,735. Mats Exp $200,000, Books $175,000, Per/Ser (Incl. Access Fees) $5,000, Electronic Ref Mat (Incl. Access Fees) $20,000. Sal $889,145

Library Holdings: Bk Vols 81,824; Bk Titles 70,988; Per Subs 140
Automation Activity & Vendor Info: (OPAC) epixtech, inc.
Mem of Northeast Texas Library System
Friends of the Library Group

COPPERAS COVE

P COPPERAS COVE PUBLIC LIBRARY, 501 S Main St, 76522. SAN 316-1609. Tel: 254-547-3826. E-Mail: cclib@vvm.com. *Dir*, Margaret Fleet; *Asst Dir*, Kathryn Stephenson; Tel: 254-547-1863, E-Mail: kstephenson@ci.copperas-cove.tx.us; Staff 10 (MLS 1, Non-MLS 9)
Founded 1959. Pop 31,300; Circ 127,127
Oct 1998-Sep 1999 Income $306,725. Mats Exp $51,882. Sal $223,192
Library Holdings: Bk Vols 50,595; Bk Titles 43,784; Per Subs 129
Special Collections: Texana
Mem of Central Texas Library System
Friends of the Library Group

CORPUS CHRISTI

S ASIAN CULTURES MUSEUM & EDUCATION CENTER,* 1809 N Chaparral, 78401. SAN 371-2974. Tel: 512-882-2641. FAX: 512-882-5718. *Exec Dir*, Ellen Murry
Library Holdings: Bk Vols 1,100; Per Subs 3
Special Collections: Billie Chandler Coll

S CELANESE DENNIS F RIPPLE TECHNICAL INFORMATION CENTER, 1901 Clarkwood Rd, 78409. (Mail add: PO Box 9077, 78469-9077), SAN 316-1625. Tel: 361-242-4223. FAX: 361-242-4251. *Coordr*, Ruth A Umfleet; Tel: 361-242-4135, E-Mail: raumfleet@celanese.com; *Cat*, Cyndi Medina
Founded 1947
Jan 1998-Dec 1998 Mats Exp $350,000. Sal $125,000
Library Holdings: Bk Vols 13,000; Per Subs 150
Subject Interests: Chemical engineering, Chemistry
Automation Activity & Vendor Info: (Circulation) Sagebrush Corporation; (OPAC) Sagebrush Corporation
Database Vendor: OCLC - First Search
Friends of the Library Group

S CENTRAL POWER & LIGHT COMPANY, Information Research-Corporate Library,* 539 N Carancahua, 78401. SAN 327-5566. Tel: 512-881-5503. FAX: 512-880-6006. E-Mail: sdawlearn@csw.com. *Ref*, Susan Dawlearn
Library Holdings: Bk Vols 800
Special Collections: Historical Photographs, 1916

M CHRISTUS SPOHN HEALTH SYSTEM, (Formerly Spohn Memorial Hospital), Health Sciences Library, 2606 Hospital Blvd, 78405. SAN 316-1706. Tel: 361-902-4197. FAX: 361-902-4198. *Librn*, Leta Dannelley; E-Mail: leta_dannelley@iwhs.org
Founded 1972
Library Holdings: Bk Vols 50,000; Per Subs 350
Subject Interests: Allied health sci, Medicine, Nursing
Automation Activity & Vendor Info: (Cataloging) EOS; (Circulation) EOS; (Serials) EOS
Partic in Nat Libr of Med

S CORPUS CHRISTI CALLER-TIMES LIBRARY,* 820 Lower N Broadway, PO Box 9136, 78469-9136. SAN 316-1633. Tel: 512-886-4312. FAX: 512-886-3732. E-Mail: neum@scripps.com. Web Site: www.caller.com. *Librn*, Margaret J Neu
Founded 1954

S CORPUS CHRISTI MUSEUM, Library of Science & History, 1900 N Chaparral, 78401. SAN 316-1641. Tel: 361-883-2862. FAX: 361-884-7392. *Librn*, Patricia Murphy; E-Mail: pattym@ci.corpus.christi.tx.us
Founded 1957
Library Holdings: Bk Vols 20,000; Per Subs 35
Subject Interests: Anthropology, Archaeology, History, Museology, Natural history
Special Collections: 1930's pictorial history of Corpus Christi; Children's Fiction (Horatio Alger, Tom Swift & others); Law Coll-19th & 20th Centuries; library archival material (mid 19th century); Museological Coll; Natural History (Netting Periodicals Coll)

P CORPUS CHRISTI PUBLIC LIBRARIES,* 805 Comanche, 78401. SAN 361-3682. Tel: 361-880-7000. Interlibrary Loan Service Tel: 361-882-6502. FAX: 361-880-7046. Web Site: www.library.ci.corpus-christi.tx.us. *Dir*, Herbert G Canales; *Tech Servs*, Karen Van Kirk; *Spec Coll*, Margaret Rose; *Automation Syst Coordr*, Gloria Garcia; *Ch Servs*, Rose Mary Cortez; Staff 17 (MLS 17)
Founded 1909. Pop 280,000; Circ 1,400,000
Jul 1999-Jun 2000 Income $3,036,748. Mats Exp $338,000
Library Holdings: Bk Vols 380,000
Subject Interests: Genealogy, Hispanic genealogy, Local history
Mem of South Texas Library System
Partic in Amigos Library Services, Inc; Tex State Libr Communications Network
Friends of the Library Group
Branches: 4
FLOUR BLUFF, 1456 Waldron Rd, 78418. SAN 361-3712. FAX: 361-93 5222. Web Site: www.library.ci.corpus-christi.tx.us. *Librn*, Julie Shamou
GREENWOOD, 4044 Greenwood, 78416. SAN 361-3747. Tel: 361-854-2356. Web Site: www.library.ci.corpus-christi.tx.us. *Librn*, Dorothea Castenon
NORTHWEST, 3202 McKinzie Rd, 78410. SAN 361-3763. Tel: 365-241-9329. Web Site: www.library.ci.corpus-christi.tx.us. *Librn*, Lynda Whitto Henley
PARKDALE, 1230 Carmel Pkwy, 78411. SAN 361-3771. Tel: 361-853-9961. Web Site: www.library.ci.corpus-christi.tx.us. *Librn*, Eric Waggone

S CORPUS CHRISTI STATE SCHOOL,* 902 Airport Rd, PO Box 9297, 78469. SAN 316-1668. Tel: 512-888-5301, Ext 7662. FAX: 512-844-7877. *Coordr*, Judy Palmer
Library Holdings: Bk Vols 200

J DEL MAR COLLEGE, William F White Jr Library, 101 Baldwin, 78404. SAN 361-3801. Tel: 361-698-1308. Interlibrary Loan Service Tel: 361-698 1932. Circulation Tel: 361-698-1310. Reference Tel: 361-698-1311. TDD: 361-698-1174. FAX: 361-609-1182. Web Site: library.delmar.edu. *Dir*, Christine Tetzlaff-Belhasen; Tel: 361-698-1310, Fax: 361-698-1949, E-Mai chris@delmar.edu; *Br Coordr*, Dr Jenny Mohundro; Tel: 361-698-1742, Fa 361-698-1795, E-Mail: jmohundro@library.delmar.edu; *Automation Syst Coordr*, Merry Bortz; Tel: 361-698-1951, Fax: 361-698-1949, E-Mail: mbortz@library.delmar.edu; *Access Serv*, Sharon Alexander; Tel: 361-688-1932, E-Mail: salexander@library.delmar.edu; *Ref*, Noe N Guerra; E-Mail: nguerra@library.delmar.edu; *Tech Servs*, Susan Harvey; Tel: 361-698-1183, Fax: 361-698-1158, E-Mail: sharvey@library.delmar.edu; Staff 31 (MLS 9, Non-MLS 22)
Founded 1937. Enrl 9,968; Fac 390; Highest Degree: Associate
Sep 2000-Aug 2001 Mats Exp $1,859,176, Books $126,900, Per/Ser (Incl. Access Fees) $95,150, Presv $1,000, Micro $29,000, Other Print Mats $63,100, Electronic Ref Mat (Incl. Access Fees) $15,000. Sal $1,077,543
Library Holdings: Bk Vols 175,813; Per Subs 925
Database Vendor: DRA, Ebsco - EbscoHost, IAC - Info Trac, OVID Technologies
Partic in Amigos Library Services, Inc; Coastal Bend Health Info Network OCLC Online Computer Library Center, Inc; TexShare
Departmental Libraries:
TECHNICAL, 101 Baldwin, 78404. Tel: 512-698-1753. FAX: 512-698-179 *Librn*, Jenny Mohundro
Library Holdings: Bk Vols 12,000

M DRISCOLL CHILDREN'S HOSPITAL, Robert Bell Parrish Medical Library, 3533 S Alameda, PO Box 6530, 78411. SAN 316-1692. Tel: 361-694-5467. FAX: 361-694-4249. Web Site: www.driscollchildrens.org/library *Librn*, Priscilla Shontz; E-Mail: shontzp@driscollchildrens.org; *Asst Librn*, Becky Melton; E-Mail: bmelton@driscollchildrens.org; Staff 2 (MLS 2)
May 2000-Apr 2001 Mats Exp $62,000, Books $17,000, Per/Ser (Incl. Access Fees) $33,000, Electronic Ref Mat (Incl. Access Fees) $12,000. Sal $93,000 (Prof $40,000)
Library Holdings: Bk Vols 600; Bk Titles 400; Per Subs 90
Subject Interests: Pediatric med
Automation Activity & Vendor Info: (Acquisitions) Innovative Interfaces Inc.; (Cataloging) Innovative Interfaces Inc.; (Circulation) Innovative Interfaces Inc.; (Course Reserve) Innovative Interfaces Inc.; (ILL) Innovati Interfaces Inc.; (Media Booking) Innovative Interfaces Inc.; (OPAC) Innovative Interfaces Inc.; (Serials) Innovative Interfaces Inc.
Restriction: Circulates for staff only
Partic in Coastal Bend Health Info Network; Docline; Tex A&M Univ Consortium of Med Librs

S REYNOLDS METALS COMPANY, Sherwin Alumina Plant, Technical Information Center,* PO Box 9911, 78469-9911. SAN 320-121X. Tel: 512-777-2676. FAX: 512-777-2684. *Tech Servs*, Dolores Phegan; E-Mail: djphegan@sherwin.rmc.com
Founded 1979
Library Holdings: Bk Vols 800; Per Subs 68

S SOUTH TEXAS INSTITUTE FOR THE ARTS LIBRARY,* 1902 N Shoreline, 78401-1164. SAN 316-1617. Tel: 512-884-3844. FAX: 512-980-3520. *Librn*, William Otton
Founded 1965
Library Holdings: Bk Titles 1,000; Per Subs 10
Subject Interests: Art history
Restriction: Non-circulating to the public

P SOUTH TEXAS LIBRARY SYSTEM, (STLS), 805 Comanche St, 78401. SAN 316-1730. Tel: 361-880-7060. Interlibrary Loan Service Tel: 361-880-7050. Toll Free Tel: 800-659-8915. FAX: 361-883-7463. *Coordr*, Mary Thames Bundy; E-Mail: mtbundy@netrax.net; *ILL, Ref*, Alice Nixon; E-Mail: anixon@netrax.net; *Coll Develop*, Linda Erwin; E-Mail: lerwin@netrax.net; *Tech Coordr*, Elizabeth Salas; E-Mail: bsalas@netrax.net; Staff 9

(MLS 5, Non-MLS 4)
Founded 1974. Pop 1,544,875
Sep 2000-Sep 2001 Income State $764,420. Mats Exp $238,625. Sal $275,549 (Prof $182,019)
Library Holdings: Per Subs 35
Database Vendor: OCLC - First Search
Publications: Currents (newsletter)
Member Libraries: Alice Public Library; Aransas County Public Library; Bell-Whittington Public Library; Brownsville Public Library; Calhoun County Library; Carl & Mary Welhausen Library; Corpus Christi Public Libraries; Cuero Public Library; Dennis M O'Connor Public Library; Donna Public Library; Duval County-San Diego Public Library; Ed & Hazel Richmond Public Library; Edinburg Public Library; Ellis Memorial Library; Elsa Public Library; Ethel L Whipple Memorial Library; Friench Simpson Memorial Library; Goliad County Library; Harlingen Public Library; Ingleside Public Library; Jackson County Library; Jim Hogg County Public Library; Joe Barnhart Bee County Public Library; Laredo Public Library; Live Oak County Library; Mathis Public Library; McAllen Memorial Library; Mercedes Memorial Library; Odem Public Library; Pharr Memorial Library; Port Isabel Public Library; Reber Memorial Library; Rio Hondo Public Library; Robert J Kleberg Public Library; San Benito Public Library; Shiner Public Library; Sinton Public Library; Speer Memorial Library; Starr County Public Library; Taft Public Library; Victoria Public Library; Waelder Public Library; Weslaco Public Library; Yorktown Public Library; Zapata County Public Library
Partic in Tex State Libr Communications Network

TEXAS A&M UNIVERSITY CORPUS CHRISTI, Mary & Jeff Bell Library,* 6300 Ocean Dr, 78412-5501. SAN 316-1676. Tel: 361-994-2643. FAX: 361-825-5973. Web Site: www.rattler.tamucc.edu. *Assoc Dir, Publ Servs*, Nancy Cunningham; *Asst Dir*, Christine Shupala; E-Mail: christine.shupala@mail.tamucc.edu; *Archivist, Spec Coll*, Thomas Kreneck; *Govt Doc*, Bradley Meyer
Founded 1973
Library Holdings: Bk Vols 342,745; Per Subs 2,204
Special Collections: 18th, 19th & 20th Century Books (Texas-Southwest Coll); 19th Century Maps & Land Title papers of South Texas & Northern Mexico (Charles F H Von Blucher Coll); Sarita Kenedy East Estate (Turcotte Coll); South Texas bks & mss (Dan E Kilgore Coll); South Texas mss (Dr Hector P Garcia Coll); Southwest & Mexico in Fine Binding (Sanders Key Stroud II Memorial Coll); Texas Legislature (L Dewitt Hale Coll); University History; Veracruz, Mexico Archives (Archivo Notaria de Jalapa, Archivo Paroquial de Cordoba)
Automation Activity & Vendor Info: (Acquisitions) Innovative Interfaces Inc.; (Cataloging) Innovative Interfaces Inc.; (Circulation) Innovative Interfaces Inc.; (Serials) Innovative Interfaces Inc.
Partic in Amigos Library Services, Inc; Dialog Corporation; OCLC Online Computer Library Center, Inc
Friends of the Library Group

UNITED STATES NAVY
NAVAL AIR STATION LIBRARY, Bldg 5, 78419. SAN 361-395X. Tel: 512-939-3574. *Librn*, Sharon Faith Scott
Founded 1941
Library Holdings: Bk Vols 21,000; Per Subs 72
Subject Interests: Mil
Special Collections: Aviation Coll; World War II

M NAVAL HOSPITAL GENERAL MEDICAL LIBRARY, 10651 E St, 78419. SAN 361-3984. Tel: 512-961-2059, 512-961-2205. FAX: 512-961-2687. E-Mail: cch1ref@cch10.med.navy.mil. *Librn*, Robert Fanger
Library Holdings: Bk Vols 4,000; Per Subs 25
Friends of the Library Group

ORRIGAN

MICKEY REILY PUBLIC LIBRARY, (MRPL), 604 S Mathews, 75939. SAN 316-1757. Tel: 409-398-4156. FAX: 409-398-5113. *Dir*, Shirley Cockrell; E-Mail: scockrelll_409@yahoo.com; *Asst Dir*, LaDonna Ray; E-Mail: lray_409@yahoo.com; Staff 2 (Non-MLS 2)
Founded 1970. Pop 11,389
Oct 1999-Sep 2000 Income $92,231, City $89,563. Mats Exp $17,981, Books $14,175, Per/Ser (Incl. Access Fees) $1,526, AV Equip $2,280. Sal $62,906 (Prof $22,000)
Library Holdings: Bk Vols 26,038; Bk Titles 22,324; Per Subs 57
Subject Interests: Local history
Automation Activity & Vendor Info: (Cataloging) Athena
Mem of Houston Area Library System
Friends of the Library Group

ORSICANA

CORSICANA PUBLIC LIBRARY, 100 N 12th St, 75110. SAN 316-1765. Tel: 903-654-4810. FAX: 903-654-4814. E-Mail: ref@corsicana.lib.tx.us. Web Site: www.ci.corsicana.tx.us. *Dir*, Patricia Ann Spiller; *Publ Servs*, Jerre Williams; Staff 7 (MLS 2, Non-MLS 5)
Founded 1901. Pop 41,400; Circ 110,947
Oct 1999-Sep 2000 Income $397,397. Mats Exp $64,884, Books $50,000, Per/Ser (Incl. Access Fees) $6,584, AV Equip $8,300. Sal $154,689
Library Holdings: Bk Vols 55,685; Bk Titles 50,319; Per Subs 119
Subject Interests: Genealogy
Mem of Northeast Texas Library System
Friends of the Library Group

J NAVARRO COLLEGE, Gaston T Gooch Learning Resource Center, 3200 W Seventh Ave, 75110-4899. SAN 316-1773. Tel: 903-875-7442. FAX: 903-874-4636. Web Site: www.nav.cc.tx.us. *Dean*, Dr Darrell Beauchamp; E-Mail: dbeau@nav.cc.tx.us; *Asst Dir*, Tim Kevil; Staff 2 (MLS 2)
Founded 1946
1999-2000 Income $366,000. Mats Exp $150,400. Sal $198,000
Library Holdings: Bk Vols 55,400; Per Subs 290
Subject Interests: Broadcasting, Bus admin, Computer science, Electronics, Fine arts, Law enforcement, Liberal arts, Med lab tech, Sci, Soc sci, Welding
Special Collections: Indian Artifacts (R S Reading Coll)
Automation Activity & Vendor Info: (Cataloging) epixtech, inc.; (Circulation) epixtech, inc.; (OPAC) epixtech, inc.

COTULLA

P ALEXANDER MEMORIAL LIBRARY, 201 S Center St, 78014. SAN 316-179X. Tel: 830-879-2601. FAX: 830-879-2601. *Librn*, Donna Van Cleve
Founded 1936. Pop 5,000; Circ 14,000
Jan 1999-Dec 1999 Income $42,000. Mats Exp $3,580. Sal $13,400
Library Holdings: Bk Vols 19,721; Bk Titles 19,190; Per Subs 10
Mem of Alamo Area Library System

CRANE

P CRANE COUNTY LIBRARY,* 701 S Alford, 79731-2521. SAN 316-1803. Tel: 915-558-1142. FAX: 915-558-1144. E-Mail: cclibrary@apex2000.net. *Librn*, Vicki Dillard; *Asst Librn*, Paula Frymire
Founded 1950. Pop 3,500; Circ 30,000
1998-1999 Income $130,692. Mats Exp $17,200, Books $10,000, Per/Ser (Incl. Access Fees) $3,500, Presv $1,000. Sal $62,799
Library Holdings: Bk Titles 29,115; Per Subs 86
Mem of West Texas Library System

CROCKETT

S HOUSTON COUNTY HISTORICAL COMMISSION ARCHIVES, Courthouse Annex, Goliad & 54th, 2nd Flr, 75835-4035. SAN 371-6295. Tel: 409-544-3255, Ext 238. FAX: 409-544-8053. *Dir*, Eliza Bishop
Founded 1978
Library Holdings: Bk Vols 610; Per Subs 12
Subject Interests: Civil War, Indians, Texana
Special Collections: County
Publications: Mini History Brochure; Supplement to Houston County (Texas) Cemetaries, 3rd Edition

P JOHN H WOOTTERS-CROCKETT PUBLIC LIBRARY,* 708 E Goliad, PO Box 1226, 75835. SAN 316-1811. Tel: 409-544-3089. FAX: 409-544-4139. E-Mail: shofflib@lcc.com. *Librn*, Sharlene Hoffmaster; *Ch Servs*, Brooke Rains; *Circ*, Petra Rios
Founded 1904. Pop 23,700
Oct 1997-Sep 1998 Income $113,114. Mats Exp $21,070. Sal $57,780
Library Holdings: Bk Vols 68,868; Per Subs 54
Subject Interests: Genealogy, Music
Special Collections: Music Coll (early 1800's to present); Rare Books Coll; Texana; Texas History & Literature Coll
Mem of Houston Area Library System

CROSBYTON

P CROSBY COUNTY LIBRARY,* 114 W Aspen St, 79322. SAN 316-1838. Tel: 806-675-2673. *Librn*, Joy Jackson
Founded 1960. Pop 8,859; Circ 22,000
Oct 1996-Sep 1997 Income $37,000. Mats Exp $2,300, Books $2,100, Per/Ser (Incl. Access Fees) $200. Sal $22,000
Library Holdings: Bk Vols 24,034; Per Subs 15
Mem of West Texas Library System
Branches: 2
LORENZO BRANCH, PO Box 426, Lorenzo, 79343. SAN 373-9465. Tel: 806-634-5639. *Librn*, Mary Jo Smith
RALLS BRANCH, PO Box 608, Ralls, 79357. SAN 373-9473. Tel: 806-253-2755. *Librn*, Gene Reed

S CROSBY COUNTY PIONEER MEMORIAL MUSEUM LIBRARY, 101 W Main St, 79322. SAN 316-1846. Tel: 806-675-2331. E-Mail: ccpmm@door.net. Web Site: www.door.net/ccmuseum/. *Dir*, Verna Wheeler; Staff 3 (MLS 2, Non-MLS 1)
Founded 1958
Subject Interests: Genealogy, Ranch hist, Regional hist, Tex hist, Tex Indians

Special Collections: Rare Books
Publications: Aunt Hanks Rock House Kitchen; Crosby County History; Estacado, The Cradle of Culture and Civilization on the Staked Plains of Texas; Gone But Not Forgotten, The Cemetery Survey of Crosby County; McNeill Sr Ranch, 100 years in Blanco Canyon; Sun Rising on the West, the Saga of Henry Clay & Elizabeth Smith; Teachers Manuals, 3-5th Grade Level; The Bridwell Site Archaeology in Crosby County; The Crosby County Courthouse

CROSS PLAINS

P CROSS PLAINS PUBLIC LIBRARY,* PO Box 333, 76443. SAN 376-4028. Tel: 254-725-7722. FAX: 254-725-6629. E-Mail: cppl@web-access.net. *Librn*, Cherry Shults
Library Holdings: Bk Vols 10,000; Per Subs 10
Mem of Big Country Library System
Friends of the Library Group

CROWELL

P FOARD COUNTY LIBRARY, 203 N Main, PO Box 317, 79227-0317. SAN 316-1854. Tel: 940-684-1250. FAX: 940-684-1250. *Librn*, Jackie Diggs
Pop 2,211
Library Holdings: Bk Vols 15,000; Bk Titles 14,900
Mem of North Texas Regional Library System
Friends of the Library Group

CROWLEY

P CROWLEY PUBLIC LIBRARY,* 121 N Hampton Rd, PO Box 747, 76036-0747. SAN 371-7674. Tel: 817-297-6707. FAX: 817-297-6578. E-Mail: cpl@fastlane.net. *Dir*, Linda Wells; Tel: 817-297-6707, Ext 2; Staff 2 (MLS 1, Non-MLS 1)
Founded 1989
Oct 1998-Sep 1999 Income $683,839, City $681,839, Federal $2,000. Mats Exp $9,040, Books $8,040, Per/Ser (Incl. Access Fees) $1,000. Sal $50,844 (Prof $31,794)
Library Holdings: Bk Vols 22,529; Bk Titles 22,299; Per Subs 44; Bks on Deafness & Sign Lang 40
Special Collections: Deaf Education (Sign Language) Coll
Automation Activity & Vendor Info: (Acquisitions) Athena; (Cataloging) Athena; (Circulation) Athena; (OPAC) Athena; (Serials) Athena
Mem of North Texas Regional Library System
Special Services for the Deaf - Books on deafness & sign language; Videos & decoder
Open Tues & Thurs 10-8, Wed, Fri & Sat 10-5
Friends of the Library Group

CRYSTAL CITY

S CRYSTAL CITY MEMORIAL LIBRARY,* 101 E Dimmit St, 78839. SAN 375-3174. Tel: 830-374-3477, Ext 18. FAX: 830-374-9685. *Dir*, Betty Rodriguez
Founded 1948
Library Holdings: Bk Vols 9,000; Bk Titles 6,000
Special Collections: History (La Rosa Unida Coll), vf
Mem of Alamo Area Library System
Friends of the Library Group

CUERO

P CUERO PUBLIC LIBRARY,* 207 E Main St, 77954. SAN 316-1862. Tel: 512-275-2864. FAX: 512-275-2864. *Dir*, Barbara Jacob
Pop 7,100; Circ 12,788
Library Holdings: Bk Vols 19,438; Per Subs 17
Mem of South Texas Library System

CYPRESS

R WINDWOOD PRESBYTERIAN CHURCH LIBRARY,* 11735 Grant Rd, 77429. SAN 316-1870. Tel: 281-376-2017. FAX: 281-376-2713.
Founded 1971
Library Holdings: Bk Vols 650

DAINGERFIELD

P DAINGERFIELD PUBLIC LIBRARY,* 207 Jefferson St, 75638. SAN 316-1889. Tel: 903-645-2823. *Librn*, Earlene Walton
Pop 3,000; Circ 19,053
Library Holdings: Bk Vols 19,222; Per Subs 16
Mem of Northeast Texas Library System

DALHART

P DALLAM-HARTLEY COUNTY LIBRARY, 420 Denrock Ave, 79022. SAN 316-1897. Tel: 806-244-2761. FAX: 806-244-2761. *Librn*, Linda Childers; E-Mail: dal-linda@email.com; *Asst Librn*, Sandra Milanese; Staf (Non-MLS 1)
Founded 1908. Pop 10,200; Circ 35,000
Library Holdings: Bk Vols 28,000
Mem of Texas Panhandle Library System
Special Services for the Blind - Bks on tape; Large print bks
Friends of the Library Group

DALLAS

L AKIN, GUMP, STRAUSS, HAUER & FELD LIBRARY,* 1700 Pacific Ave, Ste 4100, 75201-4618. SAN 325-5395. Tel: 214-969-4628. FAX: 214-969-4343. *Librn*, Joan Hass
Library Holdings: Bk Vols 40,000; Per Subs 100

SR ALL SAINTS CATHOLIC CHURCH, (ASPRL), Parish Resource Library, 5231 Meadowcreek at Arapaho, 75248-4046. SAN 329-1383. Tel: 972-778-0327. FAX: 972-233-5401. *Librn*, Maria Bellavance; E-Mail: mbellava@mail.smu.edu; Staff 2 (MLS 2)
Founded 1979
Jul 1999-Jun 2000 Mats Exp $7,019, Books $1,285, Per/Ser (Incl. Access Fees) $834, AV Equip $314, Other Print Mats $300
Library Holdings: Bk Vols 12,400; Per Subs 81; Spec Interest Per Sub 8
Subject Interests: Catholic lit, Christian lit
Special Collections: antique Bibles; antique bks; Parish Archives
Publications: Acquisitions list; bibliographies
Restriction: Members only

S AMERICAN FIRE SPRINKLER ASSOCIATION LIBRARY, 12959 Jupit Rd, Ste 142, 75238. SAN 328-3143. Tel: 214-349-5965. FAX: 214-343-8898. E-Mail: afsainfo@firesprink.org. *Pub Relations*, Montalvo Darcy
Library Holdings: Bk Vols 40
Restriction: Staff use only

M AMERICAN HEART ASSOCIATION, National Center Library, 7272 Greenville Ave, 75231-4596. SAN 316-1900. Tel: 214-706-1408. FAX: 214-706-1211. *Mgr*, Vanessa S Perez; E-Mail: vanessap@amhrt.org; Staff 2 (MLS 2)
Founded 1954
Library Holdings: Bk Vols 2,000; Per Subs 200
Subject Interests: Bus mats, Cardiovascular health, Disease
Special Collections: Paul Dudley White Coll

A ARMY & AIR FORCE EXCHANGE SERVICE, Central Library,* 3911 S Walton Walker Blvd, PO Box 660202, 75266-0202. SAN 316-2672. Tel: 214-312-2011. FAX: 214-312-6732. *Librn*, Shirley Basa
Founded 1967
Library Holdings: Bk Vols 1,400
Subject Interests: Data systs, Engineering, Mil regulations, Personnel, Transportation

CM BAYLOR HEALTH SCIENCES LIBRARY,* 3500 Gaston Ave, 75246-2098. SAN 316-1935. Tel: 214-828-8247. FAX: 214-820-2095. Web Site: www.tambcd.edu/library. *Dir*, Cindy Scroggins; Tel: 214-828-8151, E-Mail cscroggins@tambcd.edu; *Online Servs*, Rosanna Caldwell; Staff 13 (MLS 4 Non-MLS 9)
Enrl 469
Subject Interests: Dentistry, Medicine, Nursing
Special Collections: History of Medicine; History of Music Boxes
Database Vendor: Dialog, Ebsco - EbscoHost, GaleNet, OVID Technologies
Publications: Annual Report; Newsletter; Patron Guide to the Baylor Heal Sciences Library
Partic in Amigos Library Services, Inc; Healthline

R C C CRAWFORD MEMORIAL LIBRARY, (Formerly Dallas Christian College), 2700 Christian Pkwy, 75234. SAN 316-2060. Tel: 972-241-3371. FAX: 972-241-8021. E-Mail: library@dallas.edu. *Dir*, Susan Springer; E-Mail: sspringer@dallas.edu; Staff 2 (MLS 1, Non-MLS 1)
Founded 1950. Highest Degree: Bachelor
1998-1999 Mats Exp $34,000, Books $19,000, Per/Ser (Incl. Access Fees) $15,000. Sal $36,000 (Prof $22,000)
Library Holdings: Bk Vols 28,500; Per Subs 310
Subject Interests: Biblical studies, Religion, Theology
Special Collections: History & Writings of the Restoration Movement
Database Vendor: OCLC - First Search
Function: Research library
Partic in Amigos Library Services, Inc; Christian Libr Network; OCLC Online Computer Library Center, Inc

L CARRINGTON, COLEMAN, SLOMAN & BLUMENTHAL, LLP, Law Library, 200 Crescent Ct, Ste 1500, 75201. SAN 328-6185. Tel: 214-855-3530. FAX: 214-855-1333. Web Site: www.ccsb.com. *Librn*, Sue H Johnso
Library Holdings: Bk Vols 19,000; Per Subs 50

CENTRAL & SOUTH WEST CORPORATE LIBRARY,* 1616 Woodall Rodgers Freeway, 75202. SAN 327-5442. Tel: 214-777-1000. FAX: 214-777-1763.
Library Holdings: Bk Vols 5,000
Subject Interests: Electric power
Special Collections: Electric Power Research Institute
Restriction: Company library

CHILDREN'S MEDICAL CENTER OF DALLAS, Lauren Taylor-Reardon Family Library, 1935 Motor St, 75235. SAN 327-5604. Tel: 214-456-6280. FAX: 214-456-6215.
Library Holdings: Bk Vols 2,000

CHURCH OF THE INCARNATION, Marmion Library, 3966 McKinney Ave, 75204-2099. SAN 316-2001. Tel: 214-521-5101. FAX: 214-528-7209. E-Mail: info@incarnation.org. Web Site: www.incarnation.org. *Librn,* Rebekah Mathis; Staff 2 (Non-MLS 2)
Founded 1955
Library Holdings: Bk Vols 14,700; Per Subs 25
Subject Interests: Adult fiction, Biog, Children's literature, History, Relig studies
Special Collections: Video Library (1000), CD Coll (300) & CT Coll (520)
Restriction: Members only

THE CRISWELL COLLEGE, Wallace Library, 4010 Gaston Ave, 75246. SAN 320-751X. Tel: 214-818-1348. FAX: 214-818-1310. Web Site: www.criswell.edu. *Dir,* Dr Glenn R Wittig; E-Mail: gwittig@criswell.edu; *Cat,* Vada Garner; E-Mail: vgarner@criswell.edu
Founded 1976
Library Holdings: Bk Vols 90,000; Per Subs 428
Special Collections: 17th-18th Century Religions Books & Tracts; Baptist History & Theology
Automation Activity & Vendor Info: (Cataloging) Endeavor; (Circulation) Endeavor; (OPAC) Endeavor
Partic in OCLC Online Computer Library Center, Inc

DALLAS BAPTIST UNIVERSITY, (IDA), Vance Memorial Library, 3000 Mountain Creek Pkwy, 75211-9299. SAN 316-2044. Tel: 214-333-5320. Interlibrary Loan Service Tel: 214-333-5389. Reference Tel: 214-333-5221. FAX: 214-333-5323. E-Mail: lib_circ@dbu.edu. Web Site: www.dbu.edu/library. *Dir,* Mary Pauline Fox; Tel: 214-333-5210, E-Mail: mary@dbu.edu; *Librn,* Peggy Martin; Tel: 214-333-5392, E-Mail: peggym@dbu.edu; *Acq,* Claudette Ryan; E-Mail: claudette@dbu.edu; *Ref,* Carey Moore; Tel: 214-333-5212, E-Mail: carey@dbu.edu; *Tech Servs,* Judy Srygley; Tel: 214-333-5299, E-Mail: judys@dbu.edu; *Publ Servs, Ref Serv,* Linda Stephenson; Tel: 214-333-5222, E-Mail: lindas@dbu.edu; *Archivist, Doc,* Laura Vaughn; Tel: 214-333-5211, 333-5214, E-Mail: laurav@dbu.edu; *Circ,* Sheila Rickert; E-Mail: sheilar@dbu.edu; *ILL,* Kirk Johnson; E-Mail: kirkj@@dbu.edu; *Cat,* Debbi Richard; Tel: 214-333-5225, E-Mail: debbi@dbu.edu; *Ser,* Kay Sappington; Tel: 214-333-5298, E-Mail: kays@dbu.edu; Staff 10 (MLS 6, Non-MLS 4)
Founded 1898. Enrl 4,032; Fac 85; Highest Degree: Master
Library Holdings: Bk Vols 213,072; Bk Titles 132,943; Per Subs 664
Subject Interests: Education, Music, Natural science, Religion
Special Collections: ERIC, microfiche; Library of American Literature, ultrafiche; Library of English Literature, ultrafiche
Automation Activity & Vendor Info: (Acquisitions) Endeavor; (Cataloging) Endeavor; (Circulation) Endeavor; (Course Reserve) Endeavor; (ILL) Endeavor; (OPAC) Endeavor; (Serials) Endeavor
Database Vendor: IAC - Info Trac, OCLC - First Search
Partic in Llano Estacado Info Access Network; TexShare

DALLAS COUNTY LAW LIBRARY
CRIMINAL LAW LIBRARY, Frank Crowley Bldg, 133 N Industrial, Rm A-9, 75207. SAN 370-3770. Tel: 214-653-5990. FAX: 214-653-5993. E-Mail: dcll@metronet.com. *Dir,* Mary Rankin
Library Holdings: Bk Vols 48,000
LAW LIBRARY, George Allen Courts Bldg 2nd flr, 600 Commerce St, 75202-4606. SAN 316-2087. Tel: 214-653-7481. FAX: 214-653-6103. E-Mail: dcll@metronet.com. *Dir,* Mary Rankin; *Assoc Dir,* David Wilkinson; *Cat,* Carol Washmon
Founded 1894

DALLAS HISTORICAL SOCIETY, G B Dealey Library, Hall of State at Fair Park, 3939 Grand Ave, 75210. (Mail add: PO Box 150038, 75315-0038), Tel: 214-421-4500. FAX: 214-421-7500. Web Site: www.dallashistory.org. *Coll Develop,* Alan Olson; Tel: 214-421-4500, Ext 109, E-Mail: alan@dallashistory.org; *Archivist,* Rachel Roberts; Tel: 214-421-4500, Ext 110, E-Mail: rachel@dallashistory.org; Staff 2 (Non-MLS 2)
Founded 1922
Library Holdings: Bk Vols 14,000
Special Collections: 1936 Texas Centennial Coll; Maps of Dallas & the Southwest, 1800-2000; Personal Papers of Thomas B Love, Joseph W Bailey, Hatton W Sumners, Sarah Horton Cockrell, Ann McClarmonde Chase, Margaret Scruggs Caruth, Jesse Daniel Ames, John M Moore, Elmer Scott, George W Biggs, G B Dealey & Sam Acheson; Photographs of Dallas & Texas from 1870 to 2000 (J Johnson & C E Arnold Colls); Photos of Historic Sites & Courthouses of Texas ca. 1936-40 (R M Hayes Coll); Photos of Texas, 1895-6 (Henry Stark Coll); Social & Urban History of Dallas; Spanish mss (P P Martinez Coll)
Publications: All Together: World War I Posters of the Allied Nations; Dallas Rediscovered: A Photographic Chronicle of Urban Expansion 1870-1925; Guide to Fair Park, Dallas; Legacies: A History Journal for Dallas & North Central Texas; Letters of John Milton McCoy,1870-1881; Newsletter; When Dallas Became a City
Restriction: Non-circulating to the public
Function: Archival collection
Open Wed-Fri 1-5 by appt only

S DALLAS MORNING NEWS, Reference Department, Communications Ctr, PO Box 655237, 75265. SAN 316-2117. Tel: 214-977-8302. FAX: 214-977-8957.; Staff 14 (MLS 5, Non-MLS 9)
Founded 1918
Library Holdings: Bk Titles 5,000; Per Subs 125
Special Collections: Texana, clippings; Texas Almanac, micro, photogs
Restriction: Staff use only

S DALLAS MUNICIPAL ARCHIVES, City Hall, Rm 5-D South, 1500 Marilla St, 75201. SAN 371-1900. Tel: 214-670-3738. FAX: 214-670-5029. Web Site: www.dallascityhall.org/cso/index.html. *Archivist,* John H Slate; E-Mail: jslate@ci.dallas.tx.us
Library Holdings: Per Subs 18
Function: Archival collection
Repository for official records of the City of Dallas

S DALLAS MUSEUM OF ART, Mildred R & Frederick M Mayer Library, 1717 N Harwood, 75201. SAN 316-2125. Tel: 214-922-1277. FAX: 214-954-0174. Web Site: www.dm-art.org. *Head of Libr,* Jacqui Allen; Tel: 214-922-1276, Fax: 214-954-0174, E-Mail: jallen@dm-art.org; *Ref,* Mary Leonard; *Cat,* Cathy Zisk; Staff 3 (MLS 2, Non-MLS 1)
Founded 1938
Library Holdings: Bk Vols 25,000; Per Subs 90
Subject Interests: African, Contemporary, Gen art hist, Pre-Columbian art
Automation Activity & Vendor Info: (Cataloging) Endeavor; (Circulation) Endeavor; (OPAC) Endeavor
Database Vendor: Ebsco - EbscoHost, OCLC - First Search
Publications: Exhibition Catalogues
Restriction: Non-circulating to the public
Function: Reference only
Partic in OCLC Online Computer Library Center, Inc
Friends of the Library Group

S DALLAS MUSEUM OF NATURAL HISTORY, E W Mudge Ornithology Library, 3535 Grand Ave, Fair Park, 75210-1006. (Mail add: DMNH, PO Box 150349, 75315-0349), SAN 372-6940. Tel: 214-421-3466, Ext 244. FAX: 214-428-4356. Web Site: www.dallasdino.org. *Curator,* Alex Barker
Founded 1985
Library Holdings: Bk Titles 5,000
Special Collections: Illustrated Ornithological Works from 1556 to present (Mudge Coll) bks; Travel Histories from 1600 to present (Mudge Coll) bks

P DALLAS PUBLIC LIBRARY, 1515 Young St, 75201-5499. SAN 361-4379. Tel: 214-243-2041. Interlibrary Loan Service Tel: 214-670-1741. TDD: 214-670-1716. E-Mail: porr@dallaslibrary.org. Web Site: www.dallaslibrary.org. *Dir,* Ramiro S Salazar; E-Mail: director@dallaslibrary.org; *Asst Dir,* Joe Bearden; *Asst Dir,* Laurie Evans; *Adminr,* LaVerne Brown; *Adminr,* Cindy Gray; *Adminr,* Sherry Grieb; *Adminr,* Dale McNeill; *Adminr,* Sheila Scullock; *ILL,* Sonja Hayes; *Acq,* Tish Lowrey; Staff 546 (MLS 129, Non-MLS 417)
Founded 1901. Pop 1,083,500; Circ 3,738,051
Oct 1999-Sep 2000 Mats Exp $3,900,700, Books $2,379,427, Per/Ser (Incl. Access Fees) $512,781, Micro $78,014, Other Print Mats $38,350, Electronic Ref Mat (Incl. Access Fees) $624,112. Sal $16,623,124 (Prof $5,861,313)
Library Holdings: Bk Vols 2,444,015; Bk Titles 877,896; Per Subs 5,644
Special Collections: Business Histories; Children's Literature Coll, hist & rare children's bks & per; Classical Literature (Louie N Bromberg Coll); Classical Recordings (Rual Askew Coll); Dallas Black History (John & Ethelyn M Chisum Coll), diaries, mss, photogs; Dance (Mary Bywaters Coll), dance progs, mss, pamphlets, per; Fashion (Bergdorf Goodman Coll), bks, clippings, micro, pamphlets, photogs; Genealogy, bks, micro, per; Grants (Cooperating Coll of the Foundation Center), bks, looseleaf, microfiche; History of Printing, early printing, bks; Lakewood Area History, oral hist; Standards & Specifications, bks, micro & pamphlets; Texas & Dallas, archives, bks, clippings, maps, micro, per, photogs; Theater (William Ely Hill Coll, Interstate Theatre Coll, Margo Jones Coll), bks, pamphlets, slides, disc recordings, clippings, photogs, micro, per; US Marshal Clinton T Peoples Coll, scrapbks, photogs, correspondence concerning law enforcement in Texas; US Patent; US Serial Set
Automation Activity & Vendor Info: (Circulation) DRA
Publications: Catalog of Large Type Books - Dallas Pub Libr Syst; Dallas Public Library: The First 75 Years; Dallas WPA Guide & History; In Beauty it is Finished, The McDermott Collection of Navajo Blankets; Long Range Plan for Public Library Service: A Self Study; Reminiscences, A Glimpse of Old East Dallas; The Cartoonist's Art: Editorial Cartoons by Ficklen, McClanahan, Taylor and DeOre

Mem of Northeast Texas Library System
Partic in Amigos Library Services, Inc; OCLC Online Computer Library Center, Inc; Tex State Libr Communications Network
Special Services for the Deaf - Staff with knowledge of sign language; TDD
Special Services for the Blind - CCTV (VisualTex); Kurzweil Reader
Friends of the Library Group
Branches: 22
AUDELIA ROAD, 10045 Audelia Rd, 75238-1999. SAN 361-4409. Tel: 214-670-1350. FAX: 214-670-0790. Web Site: www.dallaslibrary.org. *Librn*, Sherri Lazenby
Library Holdings: Bk Vols 89,515
Friends of the Library Group
CASA VIEW Tel: 214-670-8403. FAX: 214-670-8405. Web Site: www.dallaslibrary.org. *Librn*, Jeff Weber
Library Holdings: Bk Vols 70,170
Friends of the Library Group
DALLAS WEST, 2332 Singleton Blvd, 75212-3790. SAN 361-4468. Tel: 214-670-6445. Web Site: www.dallaslibrary.org. *Librn*, Miriam Rodriguez
Library Holdings: Bk Vols 51,502
Friends of the Library Group
FOREST GREEN, 9015 Forest Lane, 75243-4114. SAN 361-4492. Tel: 214-670-1335. FAX: 214-670-5597. Web Site: www.dallaslibrary.org. *Librn*, Peter Agbafe
Library Holdings: Bk Vols 41,391
Friends of the Library Group
FRETZ PARK, 6990 Belt Line Rd, 75240-7963. SAN 361-4522. Tel: 214-670-6421. FAX: 214-670-6621. Web Site: www.dallaslibrary.org.
Library Holdings: Bk Vols 76,048
Friends of the Library Group
HAMPTON-ILLINOIS, 2210 W Illinois Ave, 75224-1699. SAN 361-4557. Tel: 214-670-7646. FAX: 214-670-7652. Web Site: www.dallaslibrary.org. *Librn*, Annette Curtis
Library Holdings: Bk Vols 69,379
Friends of the Library Group
HIGHLAND HILLS, 3624 Simpson Stuart Rd, 75241-4399. SAN 361-4565. Tel: 214-670-0987. FAX: 214-670-0318. Web Site: www.dallaslibrary.org. *Librn*, Doris Price
Library Holdings: Bk Vols 46,100
Friends of the Library Group
KLEBERG-RYLIE, 1301 Edd Rd, 75253. SAN 376-947X. Tel: 214-670-8474. FAX: 214-670-8471. Web Site: www.dallaslibrary.org. *Librn*, Ann Shelton
Library Holdings: Bk Vols 52,978
Friends of the Library Group
LAKEWOOD, 6121 Worth St, 75214-4497. SAN 361-4611. Tel: 214-670-1376. FAX: 214-670-5701. Web Site: www.dallaslibrary.org. *Librn*, MaryAnn Kitchens
Library Holdings: Bk Vols 52,676
Friends of the Library Group
LANCASTER-KIEST, 3039 S Lancaster Rd, 75216-4448. SAN 361-4646. Tel: 214-670-1952. FAX: 214-670-0588. Web Site: www.dallaslibrary.org. *Librn*, Marcia Trent
Library Holdings: Bk Vols 48,565
Friends of the Library Group
MARTIN LUTHER KING JR LIBRARY-LEARNING CENTER, 2922 Martin Luther King Jr Blvd, 75215-2393. SAN 361-4670. Tel: 214-670-0344. FAX: 214-670-0319. Web Site: www.dallaslibrary.org. *Librn*, Osei Baffour
Library Holdings: Bk Vols 36,740
Friends of the Library Group
MOUNTAIN CREEK, 6102 Mountain Creek Pkwy, 75249. SAN 374-4477. Tel: 214-670-6704. FAX: 214-670-6780. Web Site: www.dallaslibrary.org. *Librn*, Linda Holland
Library Holdings: Bk Vols 59,196
Friends of the Library Group
NORTH OAK CLIFF, 302 W Tenth St, 75208-4617. SAN 361-4581. Tel: 214-670-7555. FAX: 214-670-7548. Web Site: www.dallaslibrary.org. *Librn*, Becky Hubbard
Library Holdings: Bk Vols 86,205
Friends of the Library Group
OAK LAWN, 4100 Cedar Springs Rd, 75219-3522. SAN 361-4700. Tel: 214-670-1359. FAX: 214-670-5703. Web Site: www.dallaslibrary.org. *Librn*, Corinne Hill
Library Holdings: Bk Vols 46,221
Friends of the Library Group
PARK FOREST, 3421 Forest Lane, 75234-7776. SAN 361-4735. Tel: 214-670-6333. FAX: 214-670-6623. Web Site: www.dallaslibrary.org. *Librn*, Jeri Baker
Library Holdings: Bk Vols 65,356
Friends of the Library Group
PLEASANT GROVE, 1125 S Buckner Blvd, 75217-4399. SAN 361-476X. Tel: 214-670-0965. FAX: 214-670-0320. Web Site: www.dallaslibrary.org. *Librn*, David Rathvon
Library Holdings: Bk Vols 53,150
Friends of the Library Group
POLK-WISDOM, 7151 Library Lane, 75232-3899. SAN 361-4794. Tel: 214-670-1947. FAX: 214-670-0589. Web Site: www.dallaslibrary.org. *Librn*, Carole Williams-Bonner
Library Holdings: Bk Vols 63,548
Friends of the Library Group
PRESTON ROYAL, 5626 Royal Lane, 75229-5599. SAN 361-4824. Tel: 214-670-7128. FAX: 214-670-7135. Web Site: www.dallaslibrary.org. *Librn*, Beth Perry
Library Holdings: Bk Vols 71,770
Friends of the Library Group
RENNER FRANKFORD LIBRARY, 6400 Frankford Rd, 75252-5747. SA 328-7300. Tel: 214-670-6100. FAX: 214-670-6090. Web Site: www.dallaslibrary.org. *Librn*, Kitty Stone
Library Holdings: Bk Vols 80,165
Friends of the Library Group
SKILLMAN SOUTHWESTERN, 5707 Skillman St, 75206. SAN 376-948 Tel: 214-670-6078. FAX: 214-670-6148. Web Site: www.dallaslibrary.org *Mgr*, Christina Worden
Library Holdings: Bk Vols 56,844
SKYLINE, 6006 Everglade, 75227-2799. SAN 361-4859. Tel: 214-670-0938. FAX: 214-670-0321. Web Site: www.dallaslibrary.org. *Librn*, Anne Harper
Library Holdings: Bk Vols 60,791
Friends of the Library Group
WALNUT HILL, 9495 Marsh Lane, 75220-4496. SAN 361-4883. Tel: 214 670-6376. FAX: 214-670-6614. Web Site: www.dallaslibrary.org. *Librn*, Kjerstine Neilson
Library Holdings: Bk Vols 48,135
Friends of the Library Group
Bookmobiles: 1

CR DALLAS THEOLOGICAL SEMINARY, Turpin Library, 3909 Swiss Ave, 75204. SAN 316-2168. Tel: 214-841-3750. Reference Tel: 214-841-3752. FAX: 214-841-3745. Web Site: www.dts.edu. *Dir*, Robert D Ibach; Tel: 214-841-3753, E-Mail: rdi@dts.edu; *Assoc Dir*, Marvin Hunn; Tel: 214-841-3751, E-Mail: mhunn@dts.edu; *Dir, Tech Serv*, Jessie Zhong; Tel: 214-841-3746, E-Mail: jzhong@dts.edu; *Coll Develop*, Jefferson Webster; Tel: 214-841-3748, E-Mail: jwebster@dts.edu; Staff 11 (MLS 4, Non-MLS 7)
Founded 1924. Pop 1,646; Enrl 934; Fac 50; Highest Degree: Doctorate
Jul 2000-Jun 2001 Income Parent Institution $298,332. Mats Exp $165,200 Books $115,800, Per/Ser (Incl. Access Fees) $42,000, Micro $3,000, Electronic Ref Mat (Incl. Access Fees) $4,400. Sal $356,922
Library Holdings: Bk Vols 178,644; Per Subs 1,053
Automation Activity & Vendor Info: (Cataloging) SIRSI; (Circulation) SIRSI
Database Vendor: OCLC - First Search
Function: Research library
Partic in Amigos Library Services, Inc

S DEGOLYER & MACNAUGHTON LIBRARY, One Energy Sq, Ste 400, 75206. SAN 316-2184. Tel: 214-368-6391. FAX: 214-369-4061. *Librn*, Deborah Buchel
Founded 1939
Library Holdings: Bk Titles 18,000; Per Subs 100
Subject Interests: Econ, Energy minerals, Engineering, Geology, Natural gas, Petroleum
Publications: 20th Century Petroleum Statistics

GM DEPARTMENT OF VETERANS AFFAIRS, VA North Texas Health Care System Library Service, 4500 S Lancaster Rd, 75216. SAN 316-2737. Tel: 214-857-1245. Interlibrary Loan Service Tel: 214-857-1248. *Chief Librn*, Nancy Clark; E-Mail: clark.nancy@dallas.va.gov; *Librn*, Shirley Campbell; Tel: 214-857-1251, E-Mail: campbell.shirley@dallas.va.gov; Staff 5 (MLS 2 Non-MLS 3)
Founded 1940
Oct 1998-Sep 1999 Income $290,000
Library Holdings: Bk Vols 4,900; Per Subs 450
Subject Interests: Medicine
Partic in Health Library Information Network; Veterans Affairs Library Network

R EAST DALLAS CHRISTIAN CHURCH, Haggard Memorial Library, 629 N Peak St, 75246. (Mail add: PO Box 710329, 75371-0329), SAN 316-2206. Tel: 214-824-8185. FAX: 214-824-8583. E-Mail: edcc1@swbell.net. *Librn*, Alfred C Grosse
Library Holdings: Bk Vols 7,000
Subject Interests: Disciples of Christ hist, Doctrine, Relig mat

J EL CENTRO COLLEGE, Learning Resources Center, Main & Lamar Sts, 75202-3604. SAN 316-2214. Tel: 214-860-2175. FAX: 214-860-2440. Web Site: www.ecc.dcccd.edu/lib/elcentro.htm. *Dir*, Dr Norman Howden; *Librn*, Linda Baker; *Librn*, Joe David; *Circ*, Garth Hill; Staff 5 (MLS 5)
Founded 1966. Enrl 4,593; Fac 137
Library Holdings: Bk Vols 83,500; Per Subs 180
Subject Interests: Allied health, Culinary arts, Ethnic studies, Nursing
Automation Activity & Vendor Info: (Cataloging) Innovative Interfaces Inc.; (Circulation) Innovative Interfaces Inc.; (OPAC) Innovative Interfaces Inc.; (Serials) Innovative Interfaces Inc.
Partic in Amigos Library Services, Inc

ENVIRONMENTAL PROTECTION AGENCY, Region 6 Library,* 1445 Ross Ave, 6MD-II, 75202-2733. SAN 316-2222. Tel: 214-665-6424, 214-665-6427. FAX: 214-665-2714. E-Mail: library-reg6@epamail.epa.gov. Web Site: www.epa.gov/earth1r6/6md/6lib.htm. *Librn*, Shari McAllister; *Tech Servs*, Sharon Martin; Staff 2 (MLS 1, Non-MLS 1)
Founded 1971
Library Holdings: Bk Vols 12,935; Per Subs 25
Subject Interests: Environmental issues
Special Collections: ATSDR Toxicological profiles; EPA Documents; Hazardous Waste; OSWER Directives; Risk Assessment; USDA Soil Surveys for Arkansas, Louisiana, Oklahoma, New Mexico & Texas
Publications: New Materials List (acquisitions list)
Partic in Fedlink; OCLC Online Computer Library Center, Inc

ERNST & YOUNG LIBRARY,* 2100 McKinney Ave Ste 800, 75201. SAN 372-9753. Tel: 214-969-8411, 214-969-8483. FAX: 214-969-9702. *In Charge*, Tommy M Yardley; E-Mail: tommy.yardley@ey.com
Library Holdings: Bk Vols 1,000; Per Subs 20
Subject Interests: Accounting, Healthcare, Real estate

FEDERAL RESERVE BANK OF DALLAS LIBRARY,* 2200 N Pearl, 75201. SAN 316-2257. Tel: 214-922-6000. FAX: 214-922-5222. *Res*, Michael Zimmerman; Staff 4 (MLS 2, Non-MLS 2)
Founded 1921
Library Holdings: Bk Titles 19,000; Per Subs 750
Subject Interests: Agriculture, Banking, Econ, Labor, Petroleum, Southwest region
Restriction: Open to public for reference only
Partic in Amigos Library Services, Inc

FIRST BAPTIST CHURCH OF DALLAS, (TML), Truett Memorial Library, 510 N Ervay, 75201. SAN 316-2273. Tel: 214-969-2442. FAX: 214-969-2471. E-Mail: truettlibrary@firstdallas.org. Web Site: www.firstdallas.org. *Dir*, Mary Anne Schmidt; *Circ, Ref*, Dr Grace E Wilson; *Assoc Dean*, Barbara Cooper
Founded 1898
Library Holdings: Bk Vols 54,000; Per Subs 210; Spec Interest Per Sub 125; Bks on Deafness & Sign Lang 36
Subject Interests: Religion
Special Collections: Hymnals; Missions History
Publications: Monthly newsletter
Mem of Novell Netware
Terminals allow patrons access to collections from three libraries (two church school libraries & one special library)

GARDERE & WYNNE, Law Library,* 1601 Elm St, Ste 3000, 75201. SAN 372-1582. Tel: 214-999-4738. FAX: 214-999-3738. E-Mail: shole@gardere.com. Web Site: www.gardere.com. *Dir*, Leslie Showalter
Library Holdings: Bk Vols 8,000; Per Subs 200

GEOTRONIC LABORATORIES LIBRARY, 1314 Ceder Hill Ave, 75208. SAN 316-232X. Tel: 214-946-7573. FAX: 214-946-7583. *Librn, Online Servs*, D S Renner
Founded 1947
Library Holdings: Bk Titles 3,000; Per Subs 10
Subject Interests: Elec, Elec eng, Physics
Restriction: Not open to public

HAYNES & BOONE, LLP, Law Library, 901 Main St, Ste 3100, 75202-3789. SAN 326-6044. Tel: 214-651-5711. Web Site: www.haynesboone.com. *Mgr*, David S Matthewson; Tel: 214-651-5712, Fax: 214-200-0527, E-Mail: matthewd@haynesboone.com; *Ref*, Judy Metcalf; E-Mail: metcalfj@haynesboone.com; Staff 7 (MLS 5, Non-MLS 2)
Library Holdings: Bk Vols 60,000; Per Subs 300
Automation Activity & Vendor Info: (Acquisitions) Inmagic, Inc.; (Cataloging) Inmagic, Inc.
Database Vendor: Dialog, Lexis-Nexis

HELLMUTH, OBATA & KASSABAUM, INC LIBRARY,* 2001 Ross Ave, Ste 2800, 75201. SAN 327-5469. Tel: 214-720-6000. FAX: 214-720-6005.
Library Holdings: Bk Vols 1,000
Subject Interests: Architecture, Engineering, Interior design, Planning

R HIGHLAND PARK PRESBYTERIAN CHURCH, Meyercord Library, 3821 University Blvd, 75205. SAN 327-5647. Tel: 214-526-7457. FAX: 214-559-5311. E-Mail: hppc@aol.com.meyercordlibrary. Web Site: www.hppc.org. *Librn*, Carolyn Brown
Library Holdings: Bk Vols 20,000
Subject Interests: Religion
Open Mon-Wed & Fri 10-3, Sun 9-12:30
Friends of the Library Group

HIGHLAND PARK UNITED METHODIST CHURCH LIBRARY, 3300 Mockingbird Lane, 75205. SAN 316-2354. Tel: 214-521-3111, Ext 273. FAX: 214-520-6451. Web Site: www.hpumc.org. *Librn*, Ann L Williams; E-Mail: williama@chpumc.org; Staff 1 (Non-MLS 1)
Founded 1950
Library Holdings: Bk Vols 18,000; Per Subs 14
Subject Interests: Arts, Education, History, Nature, Psychology, Religion, Technol, Travel
Special Collections: Large Print Books; National Geographic, 1911-1987

L HUGHES & LUCE, LLP LIBRARY,* 1717 Main St, Ste 2800, 75201. SAN 321-7906. Tel: 214-939-5510. FAX: 214-939-5849. E-Mail: dal/dalpo01/rodawav%h&l@mcimail.com. *Librn*, Thomas R Austin; Staff 5 (MLS 2, Non-MLS 3)
Library Holdings: Bk Vols 30,000; Per Subs 425
Subject Interests: Law
Partic in Dialog Corporation; IRSC; Pacer; Westlaw

L JACKSON & WALKER, Law Library, 901 Main St, Ste 6000, 75202. SAN 372-1604. Tel: 214-953-6038. FAX: 214-953-5822. Web Site: www.jw.com. *Librn*, Ann H Jeter
Library Holdings: Bk Vols 35,000; Bk Titles 5,000; Per Subs 200
Automation Activity & Vendor Info: (Acquisitions) EOS; (Cataloging) EOS; (Circulation) EOS; (OPAC) EOS; (Serials) EOS
Restriction: Not open to public

L JENKENS & GILCHRIST, Law Library, 1445 Ross Ave, Ste 3200, 75202. SAN 323-8393. Tel: 214-855-4500. FAX: 214-855-4300. Web Site: www.jenkens.com. *Mgr*, Jane Reynolds; E-Mail: jreynolds@jenkens.com; *Librn*, Wendy Lyon; *Librn*, Jennifer Till; *Librn*, Holly Watson; *Tech Servs*, Belynda Elam; *Ref*, Debbie Dollinger; *Res*, Roslyn Boateng; *Res*, Dawn Burtis; *Res*, Amanda Lefebvre; *Res*, Sean Smith; Staff 8 (MLS 6, Non-MLS 2)
Library Holdings: Bk Vols 50,000; Bk Titles 8,000; Per Subs 1,500
Automation Activity & Vendor Info: (Cataloging) EOS; (Serials) EOS

R JEWISH COMMUNITY CENTER OF DALLAS, Tycher Library, 7900 Northaven Rd, 75230. SAN 326-2820. Tel: 214-739-2737, Ext 263. FAX: 214-368-4709. Web Site: www.jccdallas.com. *Librn*, Debra Polsky; E-Mail: dpolsky@ccdallas.com
Library Holdings: Bk Vols 3,080; Per Subs 40
Subject Interests: Foreign Language
Friends of the Library Group

L JONES, DAY, REAVIS & POGUE, Law Library,* 2001 Ross Ave, Ste 2300, 75201. SAN 316-2435. Tel: 214-969-4824. FAX: 214-969-5100. *Librn*, Anne Leather; *Librn*, John L Adams
Library Holdings: Bk Vols 50,000
Partic in Data Time; Dialog Corporation; Dow Jones News Retrieval; Westlaw

S KPMG LLP INC, Information Services, 200 Crescent Ct, Ste 300, 75201. SAN 371-1765. Tel: 214-840-2000, 214-840-2778. FAX: 214-840-2051. *Librn*, Jane Whittlesey; *Coordr*, Leigh Maddox
Library Holdings: Bk Vols 4,200; Per Subs 125
Automation Activity & Vendor Info: (Cataloging) Sydney; (Serials) Sydney

L LOCKE LIDDELL & SAPP, Law Library, 2200 Ross Ave, Ste 2200, 75201-6776. SAN 316-2397. Tel: 214-740-8344. FAX: 214-740-8800. Web Site: www.lockeliddell.com. *Mgr*, Cheryl Butler; *Bibliogr*, Beth Saralegui; *Senior Info Specialist*, Elise Keller; *Info Specialist*, Angela Kubala; Staff 5 (MLS 3, Non-MLS 2)
Founded 1891
Library Holdings: Bk Vols 50,000; Per Subs 1,000
Subject Interests: Labor, Rare books, Real estate, Securities
Automation Activity & Vendor Info: (Cataloging) Inmagic, Inc.; (Serials) Inmagic, Inc.
Publications: Newsletter
Partic in OCLC Online Computer Library Center, Inc

S LOCKHEED MARTIN MISSILES & FIRE CONTROL, Technical Library, PO Box 650003, 75265-0003. SAN 316-2745. Tel: 972-603-7155. FAX: 972-603-0182. *Chief Librn*, Sherry Daniel Siler; Tel: 972-603-7155, E-Mail: sherry.siler@lmco.com; *Tech Servs*, Charlotte Duphorne; Tel: 972-603-9047, E-Mail: charlotte.duphorne@lmco.com; *Doc Delivery*, Ming-Pei Eades; Tel: 972-603-9404, E-Mail: ming-pei.eades@lmco.com; Staff 3 (MLS 2, Non-MLS 1)
Founded 1949
Library Holdings: Bk Titles 5,000; Per Subs 115
Subject Interests: Aeronautical eng, Aerospace, Defense, Electronics
Special Collections: Vought History Coll
Automation Activity & Vendor Info: (Cataloging) SIRSI; (Circulation) SIRSI; (OPAC) SIRSI; (Serials) SIRSI
Partic in Defense Technical Information Center

S MARY KAY, INC, Information Center,* 16251 Dallas Pkwy, PO Box 799045, 75379-9045. SAN 324-3613. Tel: 972-687-5527, 972-905-6451. FAX: 972-687-1600.; Staff 4 (MLS 3, Non-MLS 1)
Founded 1976
Library Holdings: Bk Vols 1,600; Bk Titles 1,500; Per Subs 500
Subject Interests: Bus, Cosmetics, Dermatology, Marketing, Skin care

S MCKINSEY & CO, INC LIBRARY, 2200 Ross Ave, Ste 5200, 75201. SAN 320-7528. Tel: 214-665-1200, 214-665-1243. FAX: 214-665-1607. Web Site: www.mckinsey.com. *In Charge*, Marjorie Williams
Library Holdings: Bk Vols 1,000; Per Subs 60

M METHODIST HOSPITALS OF DALLAS, Medical Library,* 1441 N Beckley, 75203. SAN 316-2427. Tel: 214-947-2330. FAX: 214-947-2334. *Librn*, Janet L Cowen
Library Holdings: Bk Titles 2,100; Per Subs 180
Subject Interests: Clinical medicine
Restriction: Staff use only

S MOBIL PIPE LINE COMPANY, Engineering Library,* 1201 Main St, 75270. SAN 328-4301. Tel: 214-658-2070. FAX: 214-658-2241.
Library Holdings: Bk Vols 1,200; Per Subs 44
Restriction: Staff use only

J MOUNTAIN VIEW COLLEGE, Learning Resources Center, 4849 W Illinois, 75211-6599. SAN 316-2451. Tel: 214-860-8669. Circulation Tel: 214-860-8669. Reference Tel: 214-860-8527. FAX: 214-860-8667. E-Mail: mvclibrary@dcccd.edu. Web Site: www.dcccd.edu/library. *Dir*, Dr Gwendolyn Oliver; E-Mail: glo6600@dcccd.edu; *Librn*, Cynthia Schulze; E-Mail: cls6600@dcccd.edu; *Ref*, Ted R Skinner; Staff 3 (MLS 3)
Founded 1970. Enrl 5,000; Highest Degree: Associate
2000-2001 Mats Exp $61,300, Books $32,000, Per/Ser (Incl. Access Fees) $15,600, Micro $5,000, Electronic Ref Mat (Incl. Access Fees) $8,700
Library Holdings: Bk Vols 49,000; Bk Titles 42,000; Per Subs 296
Subject Interests: Aviation
Automation Activity & Vendor Info: (Circulation) Innovative Interfaces Inc.; (Course Reserve) Innovative Interfaces Inc.; (ILL) Innovative Interfaces Inc.; (Media Booking) Innovative Interfaces Inc.; (OPAC) Innovative Interfaces Inc.
Database Vendor: Ebsco - EbscoHost
Publications: Library handbook
Partic in Amigos Library Services, Inc; TexShare

SR OAK CLIFF PRESBYTERIAN CHURCH LIBRARY,* 6000 S Hampton Rd, 75232. SAN 371-991X. Tel: 214-339-2211. FAX: 214-339-3500. *Librn*, Shirley Campbell; Staff 1 (MLS 1)
Library Holdings: Bk Vols 3,500
Subject Interests: Religion
Restriction: Members only

S OMNICOM GROUP, (Formerly Group Management Services), Omnicom Management Services - Information Services Department, 1999 Bryan St, Ste 3200, 75201. SAN 316-2656. Tel: 214-259-2500. FAX: 214-259-2508. Web Site: www.omsdal.com. *Dir*, Susan Quinn; Staff 4 (MLS 3, Non-MLS 1)
Founded 1968
Library Holdings: Bk Vols 1,800; Per Subs 200
Subject Interests: Advertising, Beverages, Consumer, Demographics, Finance, Food service, Hospitality, Marketing, Packaged goods, Petroleum, Promotions, Restaurant, Retail, Travel

SR PARK CITIES BAPTIST CHURCH, Media Library,* 3933 Northwest Pkwy, PO Box 12068, 75225-0068. SAN 378-1267. Tel: 214-860-1500, Ext 1526. FAX: 214-860-1538. Web Site: www.pcbc.org. *Librn*, Janet Fordham; E-Mail: jkfordham@pcbc.org; Staff 4 (MLS 2, Non-MLS 2)
Founded 1944. Pop 8,000; Circ 18,000
Library Holdings: Bk Vols 18,000; Per Subs 49
Subject Interests: Theology
Automation Activity & Vendor Info: (Acquisitions) Athena; (Cataloging) Athena; (Circulation) Athena

M PARKLAND HEALTH & HOSPITAL SYSTEM, Fred Bonte Library, 5201 Harry Hines Blvd, 75235. SAN 316-2486. Tel: 214-590-6601, 214-590-8655. FAX: 214-590-6985. *Dir*, Randy Blanchard
Library Holdings: Bk Vols 8,023; Per Subs 500

C PAUL QUINN COLLEGE, Zale Library, 3837 Simpson Stuart Rd, 75241. SAN 316-8328. Tel: 214-302-3565. FAX: 214-371-5889. Web Site: www.pqc.edu. *Actg Dir*, Austin Wright; Tel: 214-302-3519
Library Holdings: Bk Vols 75,000; Per Subs 250
Special Collections: Afro-American Ethnic & Cultural Coll; AME Church Archives; College Archives

R PLEASANT GROVE CHRISTIAN CHURCH LIBRARY, 1324 Pleasant Dr, 75217. SAN 316-2494. Tel: 214-391-3159. FAX: 214-391-3150. E-Mail: pgcc1324@aol.com. *Librn*, Mary Simms
Library Holdings: Bk Vols 5,300

S RAYTHEON SYSTEMS CO,* 13510 N Central Expressway, PO Box 660246, 75265. SAN 361-5367. Tel: 972-344-5036. FAX: 972-344-5042. *Librn*, Kathy Nordhaus; E-Mail: k-nordhaus@rtis.ray.com
Founded 1950
Library Holdings: Bk Vols 8,700; Bk Titles 8,400; Per Subs 190
Subject Interests: Electronics, Engineering, Mathematics
Special Collections: IEEE Periodicals from their beginning date
Partic in Amigos Library Services, Inc; Asn of Higher Educ; OCLC Onlin Computer Library Center, Inc

J RICHLAND COLLEGE LIBRARY, 12800 Abrams Rd, 75243-2199. SAN 316-2524. Tel: 972-238-6081. FAX: 972-238-6963. Web Site: www.rlc.dcccd.edu/lrc/rlclib.htm. *Dir Libr Serv*, Carole Johnson; *Adminr*, Lenni Henderson; *Info Specialist*, Joel Battle; *Tech Coordr*, Gary Duke; *W Coordr*, John Ferguson; *Instrul Serv*, Alice Fulbright; *Circ*, Pat Cullum; *P* Sharlee Jeser-Skaggs; *Prof*, Cynthia Clements; Staff 19 (MLS 8, Non-MLS 11)
Founded 1972. Enrl 13,610
Library Holdings: Bk Vols 79,600
Automation Activity & Vendor Info: (Acquisitions) Innovative Interfaces Inc.; (Cataloging) Innovative Interfaces Inc.; (Circulation) Innovative Interfaces Inc.; (Course Reserve) Innovative Interfaces Inc.; (ILL) Innovat Interfaces Inc.; (Media Booking) Innovative Interfaces Inc.; (OPAC) Innovative Interfaces Inc.; (Serials) Innovative Interfaces Inc.
Database Vendor: Innovative Interfaces INN - View
Partic in Amigos Library Services, Inc; Tex Share

M SAINT PAUL MEDICAL CENTER, C B Sacher Library, 5909 Harry Hin Blvd, 75235. SAN 316-2567. Tel: 214-879-2390, 214-879-3790. FAX: 214-879-3154. *Coordr*, Teresa Hanson; *Librn*, Marcy Schott. Subject Specialist *Medical*, Marcy Schott; Staff 2 (MLS 2)
Founded 1900
Library Holdings: Bk Titles 3,000; Per Subs 150
Subject Interests: Allied health sci, Medicine, Nursing
Restriction: Open to public for reference only
Partic in Health Library Information Network

SOUTHERN METHODIST UNIVERSITY

CR BRIDWELL LIBRARY-PERKINS SCHOOL OF THEOLOGY, 6005 Bishop Blvd, 75205. (Mail add: PO Box 750476, 75275-0476), Tel: 214-768-2363 (Methodist Studies), 214-768-3483 (Admin). Interlibrary Loan Service Tel: 214-768-1031. Circulation Tel: 214-768-3441. Reference Te 214-768-4046. FAX: 214-768-4295. E-Mail: bridadmin@mail.smu.edu. Web Site: www.smu.edu/~bridwell. *Dir*, Dr Valerie R Hotchkiss; *Assoc Dir*, Duane Harbin; Tel: 214-768-4364, E-Mail: dharbin@mail.smu.edu; *Ref*, Laura Randall; *Cat*, Linda Umoh; *ILL*, Jim Powell; *Spec Coll & Archives*, Thomas Page; *Spec Coll*, Ellen Herron; *Spec Coll*, Eric M White; *ILL*, John Wadhams; E-Mail: bridill@mail.smu.edu; *Acq*, Ellen Frost. Subject Specialists: *Methodism (religion)*, Thomas Page; Staff 23 (MLS 9, Non-MLS 14)
Founded 1915
Jun 1998-May 1999 Mats Exp $1,772,769, Books $565,902, Per/Ser (Inc Access Fees) $44,040, Presv $4,645, Micro $44,160. Sal $728,373 (Prof $556,425)
Library Holdings: Bk Vols 375,000; Per Subs 1,110
Subject Interests: Cultural hist, Methodist hist, Theology
Special Collections: 15th Century Printing; Bibles; Dance of Death/Art Dying; Fine Bindings; Fine Printing & Private Press; Methodism; Reformation; Savanarda
Automation Activity & Vendor Info: (ILL) Endeavor
Publications: The Ashendene Press; The Gehenna Press; The Reformati of the Bible/The Bible of the Reformation
Partic in Amigos Library Services, Inc; OCLC Online Computer Library Center, Inc; Phoenix Group

C CENTRAL UNIVERSITY LIBRARIES, PO Box 750135, 75275-0135. Te 214-768-2401. Interlibrary Loan Service Tel: 214-768-2328. Circulation Tel: 214-768-2329. FAX: 214-768-1842. Web Site: www.smu.edu/~cul/. *Dir*, Gillian McCombs; Fax: 214-768-3815, E-Mail: gmccombs@mail.smu.edu; *Dep Dir*, Curt Holleman; Tel: 214-768-2324, Fax: 214-76 3815, E-Mail: chollema@mail.smu.edu; *Publ Servs*, Carol Baker; Tel: 21 768-2323, E-Mail: cabaker@mail.smu.edu; Staff 78 (MLS 32, Non-MLS 46)
Founded 1915. Enrl 10,361; Fac 697; Highest Degree: Doctorate
Jun 1998-May 1999 Income $6,088,958, Locally Generated Income $588,039, Parent Institution $5,500,919. Mats Exp $2,316,387, Books $654,553, Per/Ser (Incl. Access Fees) $1,264,416, Presv $66,370, Electronic Ref Mat (Incl. Access Fees) $331,048. Sal $2,529,567 (Prof $1,335,887)
Library Holdings: Bk Vols 1,028,506; Per Subs 5,223
Subject Interests: Geology, SW art, Texana, Theatre, Transportation, Western Americana
Partic in Amigos Library Services, Inc; OCLC Online Computer Library Center, Inc; TexShare
Friends of the Library Group

C DEGOLYER LIBRARY OF SPECIAL COLLECTIONS, 6404 Hilltop Dr, 75205. (Mail add: PO Box 750396, 75275), Tel: 214-768-3231. FAX: 21 768-1565. *Dir*, David Farmer; E-Mail: dfarmer@mail.smu.edu; *Curator*, Kay Bost; E-Mail: kbost@mail.smu.edu; *Coll Develop*, Connie Vitale-Sherman; E-Mail: cvitale@mail.smu.edu; Staff 4 (MLS 4)
Library Holdings: Bk Vols 100,000; Per Subs 230
Subject Interests: Travel, Voyages
Special Collections: Horton Foote Archive; Modern Authors; Railroads (Baldwin Archives); Spanish Borderlands Coll; Stanley Marcus Archive;

Texana; Transportation; Western Americana Coll; Women of the Southwest Archives
Publications: informal publications & guides to the collections; The DeGolyer Library Publication Series
Restriction: Non-circulating
Partic in OCLC Online Computer Library Center, Inc
FONDREN LIBRARY, PO Box 750135, 75275. Tel: 214-768-2401. *Ref*, Marcella Stark; Tel: 214-768-2259, E-Mail: mstark@mail.smu.edu
HAMON ARTS LIBRARY, 6101 Bishop Blvd, 75275. Tel: 214-768-2894. Circulation Tel: 214-768-3813. Reference Tel: 214-768-1853. FAX: 214-768-1800. Web Site: www.smu.edu/ hamon.
Founded 1990
Library Holdings: Bk Vols 100,000; Per Subs 265
INDUSTRIAL INFORMATION SERVICES, Science Info Center, Rm 142, 6425 Airline Rd, 75275. (Mail add: PO Box 121, 75275), SAN 361-509X. Tel: 214-768-2271. Interlibrary Loan Service Tel: 214-768-2274. FAX: 214-768-4236. E-Mail: sicinfo@post.cis.smu.edu. Web Site: www.smu.edu/iis. *Dir*, D D Bickston; Tel: 214-768-2276, E-Mail: dbicksto@mail.smu.edu; *Librn*, Jim Quevedo; Tel: 214-768-2274, E-Mail: aquevedo@mail.smu.edu; Staff 3 (MLS 1, Non-MLS 2)
Founded 1966. Enrl 7,500; Highest Degree: Doctorate
Jun 2000-May 2001 Income Locally Generated Income $100,000. Mats Exp $100,000
Library Holdings: Bk Vols 101; Per Subs 78
Automation Activity & Vendor Info: (Acquisitions) Endeavor
Friends of the Library Group
INSTITUTE FOR STUDY OF EARTH & MAN READING ROOM, 3225 Daniels Ave, 75275. Tel: 214-768-2430. *Librn*, Paul D Metz; Tel: 540-231-5563, E-Mail: pmetz@vt.edu
Library Holdings: Bk Vols 51
SCIENCE-ENGINEERING Tel: 214-768-2271. *Librn*, Deverett D Bickston; *Online Servs*, Hank Young
Library Holdings: Bk Vols 187,451; Per Subs 1,654
Special Collections: Earth Sci (DeGolyer & MacNaughton Coll); Maps (Foscoe Coll)

SOUTHWEST MUSEUM OF SCIENCE & TECHNOLOGY, Science Place Library,* Fair Park, PO Box 151469, 75315-1469. SAN 316-2095. Tel: 214-428-5555. FAX: 214-428-2033. *Librn*, Jorge Escobar
Founded 1946
Library Holdings: Bk Vols 1,700; Per Subs 5
Subject Interests: Physical sci

SOUTHWEST RAILROAD HISTORICAL SOCIETY, Age of Steam Railroad Museum Library, Fair Park, 1105 Washington St, 75210. (Mail add: PO Box 153259, 75315-3259), SAN 372-977X. Tel: 214-428-0101. FAX: 214-426-1937. E-Mail: info@dallasrailwaymuseum.com. Web Site: www.dallasrailwaymuseum.com. *Exec Dir*, Robert H LaPrelle; *Archivist*, Kathi Loveday; Staff 1 (MLS 1)
Library Holdings: Bk Vols 700; Bk Titles 500
Subject Interests: Energy, Railroads
Special Collections: Railroad Technical Manuals
Restriction: Not a lending library
Function: Research library
Open Wed-Sun 10-5

STRASBURGER & PRICE LLP LIBRARY, 901 Main St, Ste 4300, 75202. SAN 373-6555. Tel: 214-651-4300. FAX: 214-651-4330. *Librn*, Donna Bostic
Founded 1939
Library Holdings: Bk Vols 40,000; Per Subs 1,500
Special Collections: Law; Texas Law
Automation Activity & Vendor Info: (Acquisitions) Inmagic, Inc.; (Cataloging) Inmagic, Inc.; (Serials) Inmagic, Inc.
Restriction: Staff use only

SUMMER INSTITUTE OF LINGUISTICS, Dallas Library,* 7500 W Camp Wisdom Rd, 75236-5699. SAN 326-6125. Tel: 972-708-7416. FAX: 972-708-7433. E-Mail: library_dallas@sil.org. *Dir*, Claudia Griffith; *Cat, Librn*, Ron Pappenhagen; Staff 7 (MLS 5, Non-MLS 2)
Founded 1942. Enrl 250; Fac 44; Highest Degree: Doctorate
Library Holdings: Bk Vols 28,000
Subject Interests: Linguistics
Publications: Acquisitions List

TEMPLE EMANUEL, Alex F Weisberg Library, 8500 Hillcrest Rd, 75225. SAN 361-5308. Tel: 214-706-0000. FAX: 214-706-0025. *Dir*, Nancy Austein
Founded 1957
Library Holdings: Bk Vols 12,000
Subject Interests: Judaica, Related humanities
Branches:
WILLIAM P BUDNER YOUTH LIBRARY
Subject Interests: Judaica, Youth

TEXAS HEALTH RESOURCES, Presbyterian Healthcare System Medical Library,* 8200 Walnut Hill Lane, 75231. SAN 371-8816. Tel: 214-345-2310. FAX: 214-345-2350. *Coordr*, Janet Kovatch; Staff 4 (MLS 3, Non-MLS 1)
Founded 1966
Library Holdings: Bk Vols 650; Bk Titles 311; Per Subs 181
Subject Interests: Allied health, Healthcare admin, Medicine, Nursing
Partic in Dialog Corporation

TEXAS INSTRUMENTS, INC
S S C LIBRARY, 7800 Banner Dr, MS-3954, 75251. (Mail add: PO Box 650311, MS-3954, 75265), SAN 361-5421. Tel: 972-917-1554. FAX: 972-917-1538. Web Site: www.ti.com.
Founded 1958
Library Holdings: Bk Vols 9,000; Per Subs 100
Subject Interests: Bus, Computers, Electronics, Mgt, Semi-conductor tech
Publications: Newsletter (monthly)
Restriction: Not open to public
Partic in Amigos Library Services, Inc

M TEXAS SCOTTISH RITE HOSPITAL, The Brandon Carrell Medical Library,* 2222 Welborn St, 75219-3993. SAN 329-1340. Tel: 214-521-3168. FAX: 214-559-7835. *Librn*, Mary Nelson Peters; E-Mail: mpeters@tsrh.org
Founded 1979
Library Holdings: Bk Titles 800; Per Subs 100
Subject Interests: Neurology, Orthopedics, Pediatrics
Special Collections: History of Pediatric Orthopedics
Restriction: Staff use only
Partic in Health Library Information Network; S Cent Regional Med Libr Program

S TEXAS UTILITIES, Information Resource Center, 1601 Bryan St, 75201. SAN 326-3606. Tel: 214-812-3333. FAX: 214-812-5453. *Info Res, Librn*, Ann S Midgett; Tel: 214-812-5966, E-Mail: amidget1@txu.com; *Librn*, Chris Dennis; *Librn*, Michael McDaniel; Staff 7 (MLS 3, Non-MLS 4)
Library Holdings: Bk Titles 5,500; Per Subs 450
Subject Interests: Bus, Energy, Engineering, Mgt, Utilities
Partic in Dialog Corporation; Dow Jones News Retrieval; Dun & Bradstreet Info Servs; EEI

CM TEXAS WOMAN'S UNIVERSITY, F W & Bessie Dye Memorial Library, 1810 Inwood Rd, 75235-7299. SAN 316-2621. Tel: 214-689-6580. FAX: 214-689-6583. Web Site: www.twu.edu/library. *Coordr*, Oliphant Eula; Staff 6 (MLS 2, Non-MLS 4)
Founded 1966
Library Holdings: Bk Vols 161,300; Per Subs 160
Subject Interests: Health care administration, Med rec, Nursing, Occupational therapy
Publications: Data Entries
Partic in OCLC Online Computer Library Center, Inc
Friends of the Library Group

J THE ART INSTITUTE OF DALLAS, Mildred M Kelly Learning Resources Center,* 2 North Park, 8080 Park Ln Rm 337, 75231. SAN 321-4737. Tel: 214-692-8080. FAX: 214-692-8106. Web Site: www.aid.edu. *Librn*, Bobbie Long; *Ref*, Richard Sclaudroff; Staff 1 (MLS 1)
Founded 1981. Enrl 1,100; Fac 95
Library Holdings: Bk Titles 12,482; Per Subs 227
Subject Interests: Computer aided drafting, Computer graphics, Fashion design, Graphic art, Interior design, Marketing, Music video bus, Photog
Publications: New & Of Note (quarterly)

L THOMPSON & KNIGHT, Law Library,* 1700 Pacific Ave, Ste 3300, 75201. SAN 316-263X. Tel: 214-969-1427. FAX: 214-969-1751. Web Site: www.tklaw.com. *Res*, Linda Senkas; Tel: 860-626-3290, Fax: 860-496-3632; Staff 8 (MLS 3, Non-MLS 5)
Founded 1914
Library Holdings: Bk Vols 40,000; Bk Titles 2,500
Special Collections: Extensive CLE Coll; Federal Register - 1971-Current
Automation Activity & Vendor Info: (Cataloging) Inmagic, Inc.
Database Vendor: Dialog, Ebsco - EbscoHost, Lexis-Nexis
Function: ILL limited

S UNI-BELL PVC PIPE ASSOCIATION LIBRARY, 2655 Villa Creek, Ste 155, 75234. SAN 323-5254. Tel: 972-243-3902. FAX: 972-243-3907. Web Site: www.uni-bell.org. *Exec Dir*, Robert P Walker; E-Mail: rwalker@uni-bell.org
Founded 1971
Library Holdings: Bk Vols 7,000

G US BUREAU OF THE CENSUS, Information Services Program Library,* 8700 Stamons Freeway, Ste 300, 75247. SAN 328-6045. Tel: 214-655-3050. FAX: 214-640-4431. Web Site: www.census.gov/ftp/pub/rodal/www/. *Coordr*, Michael Hall

CM UNIVERSITY OF TEXAS SOUTHWESTERN MEDICAL CENTER AT DALLAS LIBRARY, 5323 Harry Hines Blvd, 75390-9049. SAN 316-2729. Tel: 214-648-2001. FAX: 214-648-2826. Web Site: www.utsouthwestern.edu/library. *Dir*, Marty Adamson; Tel: 214-648-2626, E-Mail: marty.adamson@email.swmed.edu; *Coll Develop*, Timothy Judkins; Tel: 214-648-3415, E-Mail: timothy.judkins@email.swmed.edu; *Assoc Dir*, Brian Bunnett; Tel: 214-648-2626, E-Mail: brian.bunnett@email.swmed.edu. Subject Specialists: *Electronic resources*, Timothy Judkins; Staff 60 (MLS 22, Non-MLS 38)
Founded 1943. Pop 17,555; Enrl 1,554; Fac 1,189; Highest Degree:

Doctorate
Library Holdings: Bk Vols 262,120; Bk Titles 73,351; Per Subs 4,224
Subject Interests: Biomed sci
Special Collections: History of Health Sciences Coll
Database Vendor: Dialog, GaleNet, IAC - Info Trac, OCLC - First Search, OVID Technologies
Restriction: Not a lending library
Function: Research library
Partic in Amigos Library Services, Inc; Nat Network of Librs of Med, S Cent Res Libr Coun; OCLC Online Computer Library Center, Inc; South Central Academic Medical Libraries Consortium; Tex Share; UT-System

L WINDLE TURLEY, PC, Law Library, 6440 N Central Expressway, Ste 1000, 75206. SAN 372-1663. Tel: 214-691-4025. FAX: 214-361-5802. *Librn*, Marva Coward; Staff 1 (MLS 1)
Founded 1973
Library Holdings: Bk Vols 7,000; Per Subs 50
Subject Interests: Law
Restriction: Member organizations only

DAWSON

M WOMEN EXPLOITED BY ABORTION, INC, International Headquarters Library, PO Box 279, 76639. SAN 371-8565. Tel: 254-578-1681. FAX: 254-578-1681. *Pres*, Kathy Walker; *VPres*, Chris Hawkins; Staff 15 (Non-MLS 15)
Founded 1982
Library Holdings: Bk Titles 290
Subject Interests: Abortion
Special Collections: Pro-Life & Post Abortion Information
Publications: Newsletter

DAYTON

P EDMUND E & NIDA SMITH JONES PUBLIC LIBRARY, 307 W Houston, 77535. SAN 375-3328. Tel: 409-258-7060. FAX: 409-258-7634. *Dir*, Rose Klimitchek
Founded 1980. Pop 20,000; Circ 54,000
Library Holdings: Bk Titles 22,000; Per Subs 40
Mem of Houston Area Library System
Friends of the Library Group

DE LEON

P DE LEON PUBLIC LIBRARY,* 103 E Reynosa St, 76444-1862. SAN 316-2788. Tel: 254-893-2417. E-Mail: dllib@cctc.net. *Librn*, Bethany Sledge; *Assoc Librn*, Mary Young
Pop 4,231
1998-1999 Income $12,725, City $6,200, County $6,000. Mats Exp $1,754, Books $1,619, Per/Ser (Incl. Access Fees) $135. Sal $5,124
Library Holdings: Bk Vols 12,486
Mem of Big Country Library System

DE SOTO

P DE SOTO PUBLIC LIBRARY, 211 E Pleasant Run Rd, Ste C, 75115-3939. SAN 370-7423. Tel: 972-230-9656. Circulation Tel: 972-230-9665. Reference Tel: 972-230-9661. FAX: 972-230-5797. Web Site: www.ci.desoto.tx.us. *Dir*, Mary H Musgrave; E-Mail: mmusgrave@library.ci.desoto.tx.us; *Circ*, Marquenez Runnels; *Ref*, Erin Underhill-Eads; *Ch Servs*, Kim Boyd; Staff 9 (MLS 4, Non-MLS 5)
Founded 1943. Pop 38,000; Circ 170,000
Library Holdings: Bk Vols 70,000; Bk Titles 75,000; Per Subs 125
Automation Activity & Vendor Info: (Cataloging) epixtech, inc.; (Circulation) epixtech, inc.; (OPAC) epixtech, inc.
Database Vendor: OCLC - First Search
Mem of Northeast Texas Library System

DECATUR

P DECATUR PUBLIC LIBRARY, 1700 Hwy 51 S, 76234-9292. SAN 316-2796. Tel: 940-627-5512. FAX: 940-627-2905. *Dir*, Elizabeth Russell; E-Mail: enr@wf.net; Staff 2 (MLS 2)
Founded 1970. Pop 14,475; Circ 78,998
1999-2000 Income $233,360. Sal $129,623
Library Holdings: Bk Vols 35,011; Bk Titles 32,011; Per Subs 57
Special Collections: Texas Coll
Automation Activity & Vendor Info: (Cataloging) SIRSI; (Circulation) SIRSI; (OPAC) SIRSI
Mem of North Texas Regional Library System
Friends of the Library Group

DEER PARK

P DEER PARK PUBLIC LIBRARY,* 3009 Center St, 77536-5099. SAN 3 280X. Tel: 281-478-7208. FAX: 281-478-7212. *Dir*, Charles Suessmuth; *Servs*, Kelly Finkenbinder; *ILL*, Elizabeth Baker; *Ref*, Bonner Jones; Staff (MLS 3, Non-MLS 2)
Founded 1962. Pop 28,500; Circ 163,567
Library Holdings: Bk Vols 52,000
Subject Interests: Commun awareness, Emergency response
Special Collections: CAER Coll
Publications: Off the Shelf (quarterly newsletter)
Mem of Houston Area Library System
Friends of the Library Group

DEL RIO

P VAL VERDE COUNTY LIBRARY, 300 Spring St, 78840. SAN 316-285 Tel: 830-774-7595. FAX: 830-774-7607. E-Mail: library@delrio.com. Web Site: www.delrio.com/home/library. *Dir*, Katherine McMurrey; *ILL, Ref*, Willie Braudaway; *Ref*, Marcela Fuentes; *Circ*, Lydia Jarman; *Acq*, Elaine Neal; *Ch Servs*, Leticia Ramos; *Cat*, Rosa Martinez; Staff 10 (MLS 1, Nc MLS 9)
Founded 1940. Pop 43,313; Circ 62,027
Oct 1998-Sep 1999 Income $362,836, County $298,830, Locally Generate Income $25,106, Other $38,900. Mats Exp $68,000, Books $57,178, Per/S (Incl. Access Fees) $3,010, Other Print Mats $7,812. Sal $195,936 (Prof $33,280)
Library Holdings: Bk Vols 48,000; Bk Titles 52,309; Per Subs 152
Subject Interests: Local history, Texana
Special Collections: bks on tape; John R Brinkley Coll; Local History (D Rio Coll); Texana
Automation Activity & Vendor Info: (Cataloging) Athena; (Circulation) Athena
Database Vendor: OCLC - First Search
Mem of Alamo Area Library System
Friends of the Library Group

DELL CITY

P GRACE GREBING PUBLIC LIBRARY,* PO Box 37, 79837-0037. SAN 376-4362. Tel: 915-964-2468, 915-964-2495, Ext 3000. FAX: 915-964-24 *Librn*, Jan Lee
Oct 1997-Sep 1998 Income $26,000
Library Holdings: Bk Vols 14,000; Per Subs 28
Mem of Texas Trans Pecos Library System

DENISON

P DENISON PUBLIC LIBRARY, (DPL), 300 W Gandy, 75020-3153. SAN 316-2877. Tel: 903-465-1797. FAX: 903-465-1130. Web Site: www.barr.or *Dir*, Alvin R Bailey; *Asst Dir*, Dixie Foster; *Asst Dir, Coll Develop*, Laura Haworth; *Ch Servs*, Stephanie Coleman; *Circ*, Loretta Hall; *Tech Servs*, Steve McGowan; Staff 3 (MLS 3)
Founded 1936. Pop 21,505; Circ 162,151
Oct 1998-Sep 1999 Income $529,020, City $457,000, County $21,647, Locally Generated Income $19,073, Other $31,300. Mats Exp $35,123, Books $21,831, Per/Ser (Incl. Access Fees) $8,878, Presv $457, Micro $2,400, AV Equip $1,557. Sal $367,189 (Prof $110,572)
Library Holdings: Bk Titles 80,707; Per Subs 160
Subject Interests: Genealogy
Special Collections: Area History & Books by Area Authors (Texoma Co print, bks, pamphlet
Database Vendor: Ebsco - EbscoHost
Publications: Foundations of American Grape Culture by T V Munson; Katy's Baby by Jack Maguire
Mem of Northeast Texas Library System
Friends of the Library Group

J GRAYSON COUNTY COMMUNITY COLLEGE LIBRARY,* 6101 Grayson Dr, 75020-8299. SAN 316-2885. Tel: 903-463-8637. FAX: 903-465-4123. Web Site: www.grayson.edu. *Dir*, Gary Paikowski; E-Mail: paikowski@grayson.edu; *Asst Dir*, Lisa Harris; *Ref*, Roland Commons; Sta 4 (MLS 4)
Founded 1965. Enrl 3,843; Fac 126
Library Holdings: Bk Titles 60,000; Per Subs 96
Subject Interests: Health occupations
Partic in Barr

DENTON

S THE AMERICAN DONKEY & MULE SOCIETY LIBRARY, 2901 N El St, 76201. SAN 324-0983. Tel: 940-382-6845. FAX: 940-484-8417. E-Mai adms@juno.com. Web Site: www.admsdonkeyandmule.com. *In Charge*, Betsy Hutchins. Subject Specialists: *Donkeys*, Betsy Hutchins; *Equine*, Be Hutchins; *Mules*, Betsy Hutchins
Founded 1967

Library Holdings: Bk Titles 652
Subject Interests: Donkeys, Horses, Mules
Special Collections: Breed Association Coll (private); Historical: Studbooks
Restriction: By appointment only

DENTON PUBLIC LIBRARY, 502 Oakland St, 76201. SAN 316-2893. Tel: 940-349-8570. Circulation Tel: 940-349-7737. Reference Tel: 940-349-8569. FAX: 940-349-8560. E-Mail: library@cityofdenton.com. Web Site: www.dentonlibrary.com. *Dir Libr Serv*, Eva Poole; Tel: 940-349-7735, Fax: 940-349-8260, E-Mail: edpoole@cityofdenton.com; *Ad Servs*, Stacy Sizemore; Tel: 940-349-7740, Fax: 940-349-8260, E-Mail: ssizemore@cityofdenton.com; *Ad Servs*, Kathy Strauss; Tel: 940-349-8569, Fax: 940-349-8260, E-Mail: kgstrauss@cityofdenton.com; *Ad Servs*, Carol Weller; Tel: 940-349-8571, Fax: 940-349-8260, E-Mail: cweller@cityofdenton.com; *Branch Mgr*, Terry Vermillion; Tel: 940-349-8256, Fax: 940-349-8383, E-Mail: tdvermillion@cityofdenton.com; *Coordr, YA Servs*, Martha Edmundson; Tel: 940-349-8572, Fax: 940-349-8260, E-Mail: mmedmundson@cityofdenton.com; *Tech Servs*, Jennifer Reaves; Tel: 940-349-7297, Fax: 940-349-8260, E-Mail: jreaves@cityofdenton.com; *Automation Syst Coordr*, Mary Cresson; Tel: 940-349-7739, Fax: 940-349-8260, E-Mail: macresson@cityofdenton.com; *Coordr*, Linda Touraine; Tel: 940-349-8561, Fax: 940-349-8260, E-Mail: lstouraine@cityofdenton.com; *Ch Servs*, Stacey Irish; Tel: 940-349-8251, Fax: 940-349-8383, E-Mail: slirish@cityofdenton.com; *Ch Servs*, Nelda Nance; Tel: 940-349-8568, Fax: 940-349-8260, E-Mail: nelda.nance@cityofdenton.com; *Ch Servs*, Erin O'Toole; Tel: 940-349-8568, Fax: 940-349-8260, E-Mail: erin.o'toole@cityofdenton.com; *Ref*, Fred Kamman; Tel: 940-349-8252, E-Mail: fxkamman@cityofdenton.com; Staff 43 (MLS 13, Non-MLS 30)
Founded 1937. Pop 88,313; Circ 697,439
Oct 1999-Sep 2000 Income (Main Library and Branch Library) $1,932,542, State $82,000, City $1,643,377, County $119,199, Locally Generated Income $87,966. Mats Exp $235,505, Books $176,931, Per/Ser (Incl. Access Fees) $9,694, Presv $2,838, Micro $4,441, AV Equip $18,766, Electronic Ref Mat (Incl. Access Fees) $19,673. Sal $1,385,903 (Prof $514,503)
Library Holdings: Bk Vols 156,074; Bk Titles 115,811; Per Subs 309; High Interest/Low Vocabulary Bk Vols 21; Spec Interest Per Sub 20; Bks on Deafness & Sign Lang 75
Subject Interests: Denton hist, Genealogy, Texana
Automation Activity & Vendor Info: (Acquisitions) epixtech, inc.; (Cataloging) epixtech, inc.; (Circulation) epixtech, inc.; (OPAC) epixtech, inc.
Database Vendor: Ebsco - EbscoHost, epixtech, inc., OCLC - First Search
Function: Professional lending library
Mem of North Texas Regional Library System
Partic in Amigos Library Services, Inc
Friends of the Library Group
Branches: 1
SOUTH, 3228 Teasley Lane, 76205. SAN 376-1452. Tel: 940-349-8251. Reference Tel: 940-349-8252. FAX: 940-349-8383. E-Mail: library@cityofdenton.com. Web Site: www.dentonlibrary.com.; Staff 8 (MLS 3, Non-MLS 5)
Founded 1995
Library Holdings: Bk Vols 36,245; Bk Titles 29,753; Per Subs 90
Automation Activity & Vendor Info: (Acquisitions) epixtech, inc.; (Cataloging) epixtech, inc.; (Circulation) epixtech, inc.; (OPAC) epixtech, inc.
Mem of North Texas Regional Library System
Partic in Amigos Library Services, Inc
Friends of the Library Group

DENTON RECORD, Chronicle Library,* PO Box 369, 76202. SAN 375-7560. Tel: 940-387-3811. FAX: 940-381-9669. *Dir*, Julia Lehman

TEXAS WOMAN'S UNIVERSITY, Mary Evelyn Blagg-Huey Library, 1200 Frame St, 76209. (Mail add: PO Box 425528 TWU Sta, 76204-5528), Tel: 940-898-2665. Interlibrary Loan Service Tel: 940-898-3728. Circulation Tel: 940-898-3719. Reference Tel: 940-898-3701. FAX: 940-898-3764. Web Site: www.twu.edu/library. *Dir*, Elizabeth Snapp; Tel: 940-898-3748, E-Mail: esnapp@twu.edu; *Librn*, Eula Oliphant; Tel: 214-689-6585, E-Mail: eoliphant@twu.edu; *Coll Develop*, Marilyn Dunham; Tel: 940-898-3767, E-Mail: mdunham@twu.edu; *Distance Educ*, Stephany Compton; Tel: 940-898-3797, E-Mail: scompton@twu.edu; *Access Serv*, Linda Bixler; Tel: 940-898-3747, E-Mail: lbixler@twu.edu; *Spec Coll*, Dawn Letson; Tel: 940-898-3754, E-Mail: dletson@twu.edu; *Res*, Connie Maxwell; Tel: 940-898-3707, E-Mail: cmaxwell@twu.edu; Staff 20 (MLS 19, Non-MLS 1)
Founded 1901. Enrl 8,403; Fac 488; Highest Degree: Doctorate
Sep 1999-Aug 2000 Income $3,500,000. Mats Exp $911,300, Books $80,000, Per/Ser (Incl. Access Fees) $424,000, Presv $25,000, Micro $21,800, AV Equip $35,000, Electronic Ref Mat (Incl. Access Fees) $325,500
Library Holdings: Bk Vols 536,668; Bk Titles 323,600; Per Subs 2,097
Subject Interests: Health related professions, Health sci, Nursing, Occupational therapy, Physical therapy
Special Collections: American Fiction by Female Authors (L H Wright Coll); Cookbooks (Julie Benell & Nell Morris Coll); History of Texas Women Coll; LaVerne Harrell Clark Coll; Madeline Henrey Coll; Menu Coll; R P Tristam Coffin Coll; Woman's Coll, bks, cassettes, mss, micro; Women in the Military Coll
Automation Activity & Vendor Info: (Acquisitions) Endeavor; (Cataloging) Endeavor; (Circulation) Endeavor; (Course Reserve) Endeavor; (ILL) Endeavor; (Media Booking) Endeavor; (OPAC) Endeavor; (Serials) Endeavor
Database Vendor: CARL, Ebsco - EbscoHost, GaleNet, Lexis-Nexis, OCLC - First Search, OVID Technologies, ProQuest, Silverplatter Information Inc.
Partic in Amigos Library Services, Inc; OCLC Online Computer Library Center, Inc; TexShare
Friends of the Library Group
Departmental Libraries:
S SCHOOL OF LIBRARY & INFORMATION STUDIES, PO Box 425438, 76204-5438. SAN 361-5693. Tel: 940-898-2622. FAX: 940-898-2611. E-Mail: slis@twv.edu. Web Site: www.twu.edu/slis/lishome/about/facility/youth.htm. *Librn*, Ellen Perlow; E-Mail: s_perlow@twu.edu
Library Holdings: Bk Vols 21,525
Subject Interests: Ch, Young adult literature
Special Collections: Children's & Young Adult Coll; Historical Children's Coll; Library Science Professional Papers
Partic in Amigos Library Services, Inc

C UNIVERSITY OF NORTH TEXAS LIBRARIES, Highland Avenue & Avenue C, PO Box 305190, 76203-5190. SAN 361-5510. Tel: 940-565-2413. Interlibrary Loan Service Tel: 940-565-2495. Reference Tel: 940-565-3245. Toll Free Tel: 800-735-2989. TDD: 800-735-2989. FAX: 940-369-8760. E-Mail: circ@library.unt.edu. Web Site: www.library.unt.edu. *Dean of Libr*, B Donald Grose; Tel: 940-565-3025, E-Mail: dgrose@library.unt.edu; *Asst Dean*, Arne J Almquist; Tel: 940-565-3023, E-Mail: aalmquis@library@unt.edu; *Archivist*, Richard Himmel; Tel: 940-565-2766, E-Mail: rhimmel@library.unt.edu; *ILL*, Mark Dolive; Tel: 940-565-2493, Fax: 940-565-4949, E-Mail: mdolive@library.unt.edu; *Ad Servs, Media Spec*, Sharon Almquist; Tel: 940-565-4702, Fax: 940-369-7396, E-Mail: salmquis@library.unt.edu; *Tech Servs*, Kathryn Loafman; Tel: 940-565-2609, Fax: 940-565-2607, E-Mail: kloafman@library.unt.edu; *Rare Bks, Spec Coll*, Kenneth Lavender; Tel: 940-565-2768, E-Mail: klavende@library.unt.edu; *Online Servs*, Jo Ann Lickteig; Tel: 940-565-3955, E-Mail: jlicktei@library.unt.edu; *Head, Circ*, Lou Ann Bradley; Tel: 940-565-2415, E-Mail: lbradley@library.unt.edu; *Syst Coordr*, Robert Pierce; *Coll Develop*, Patricia Stinson-Switzer; Tel: 940-565-2770, Fax: 940-565-3695, E-Mail: pswitzer@library.unt.edu; *Head Ref*, Martha Kate Tarlton; Tel: 940-565-2762, Fax: 940-565-2599, E-Mail: tarlton@library.unt.edu; *Music*, Morris Martin; Tel: 940-565-2858, E-Mail: mmartin@library.unt.edu; *Syst Coordr*, Pamiela Hight; Tel: 940-565-3024, E-Mail: phight@library@unt.edu; *Govt Doc*, Melody Kelly; Tel: 940-565-2868, E-Mail: mkelly@library.unt.edu; *Bibliog Instr*, Suzanne Byron; Tel: 940-565-4812, Fax: 940-565-2599, E-Mail: sbyron@library.unt.edu. Subject Specialists: *Art*, Tara Carlisle; *Business*, Jeffrey Levy; *Contract law*, Doina Farkas; *Fund-raising*, Doina Farkas; *Grants*, Doina Farkas; *Humanities*, Martha Kate Tarlton; *Music*, Morris Martin; *Science/technology*, Patricia Stinson-Switzer; *Social sciences and issues*, Martha Kate Tarlton; *Theater*, Arne J Almquist; Staff 104 (MLS 33, Non-MLS 71)
Founded 1890. Enrl 25,514; Fac 1,042; Highest Degree: Doctorate
Sep 1998-Aug 1999 Income (Main Library Only) $7,964,546, Locally Generated Income $170,000, Parent Institution $7,794,546. Mats Exp $3,213,132, Books $970,348, Per/Ser (Incl. Access Fees) $2,000,314, Presv $136,767, Micro $98,964, AV Equip $6,739. Sal $3,581,934 (Prof $1,911,868)
Library Holdings: Bk Vols 1,842,879; Per Subs 9,606
Subject Interests: Music, Texana
Special Collections: Anson Jones Library; Gerontological Film Coll; Gulf Oil Company Records; Judge Sarah T Hughes Coll; Liquid Paper Corporation Records; Morrison Milling Company Records; Music (Duke Ellington, Don Gills, Lloyd Hibberd, Stan Kenton & Arnold Schoenberg Colls); Source Magazine Archives; Thomas Woody Prisoner of War Coll; WBAP Coll; Weaver Coll; WFAA Coll; World War II Coll
Automation Activity & Vendor Info: (Acquisitions) Innovative Interfaces Inc.; (Cataloging) Innovative Interfaces Inc.; (Circulation) Innovative Interfaces Inc.; (Course Reserve) Innovative Interfaces Inc.; (ILL) Innovative Interfaces Inc.; (OPAC) Innovative Interfaces Inc.; (Serials) Innovative Interfaces Inc.
Database Vendor: Dialog, Ebsco - EbscoHost, GaleNet, Innovative Interfaces INN - View, Lexis-Nexis, OCLC - First Search, OVID Technologies, ProQuest, Silverplatter Information Inc.
Publications: Friday Fragments; Friends of the Libraries Newsletter; University of North Texas Libraries Newsletter
Partic in Amigos Library Services, Inc; Center For Research Libraries; Phoenix Group; TexShare
Special Services for the Deaf - TDD
Friends of the Library Group
Departmental Libraries:
MEDIA Tel: 940-565-2480. FAX: 940-369-7396. *Head of Libr*, Sharon Almquist; Tel: 670-565-4702, E-Mail: salmquis@library.unt.edu; *Asst Dean*, Arne J Almquist; Tel: 940-565-3023, Fax: 940-369-8760, E-Mail: aalmquis@library.unt.edu
MUSIC Tel: 940-565-2860. FAX: 940-369-8760. *Head of Libr*, Morris Martin; Tel: 940-565-2858, E-Mail: mmartin@library.unt.edu; *Asst Dean*, Arne J Almquist; Tel: 940-565-3023, E-Mail: aalmquis@library.unt.edu
RARE BOOK & SPECIAL COLLECTIONS Tel: 940-565-2768. FAX: 940-369-8760. *Asst Dean*, Arne J Almquist; Tel: 940-565-3023, E-Mail:

aalmquis@library.unt.edu; *Curator*, Ken Lavender; E-Mail: klavende@library.unt.edu
Special Collections: Southern Letters (Pat Warde Coll); Texana Coll
SYSTEM CENTER AT DALLAS, 8915 S Hampton Rd, Dallas, 75232-6002. Tel: 972-780-3625. Web Site: www.library.unt.edu/scd/. *Librn*, Leora Kemp; Fax: 972-780-3676; Staff 1 (MLS 1)
Founded 1999
UNIVERSITY ARCHIVES FAX: 940-565-2766. *Archivist*, Richard Himmel

DENVER CITY

P YOAKUM COUNTY LIBRARY, 205 W Fourth St, 79323-0900. SAN 316-2907. Tel: 806-592-2754. FAX: 806-592-2439. E-Mail: dcpublib@hiplains.net. *Librn*, Opal Roberts; *Asst Librn*, Ginger Wilson
Founded 1957. Pop 8,000; Circ 63,130
Library Holdings: Bk Titles 26,370; Per Subs 88
Mem of West Texas Library System

DEVINE

P DRISCOLL PUBLIC LIBRARY, 202 E Hondo Ave, 78016. SAN 316-2915. Tel: 830-663-2993. FAX: 830-663-2993. *Dir*, Dr Kenneth Wolfe; *Asst Librn*, Katherine Johnson
Founded 1965. Pop 7,362; Circ 15,783
Library Holdings: Bk Titles 19,000; Per Subs 20
Mem of Alamo Area Library System; San Antonio Major Resource Center
Friends of the Library Group

DIBOLL

P T L L TEMPLE MEMORIAL LIBRARY, 300 Park St, 75941. SAN 316-2923. Tel: 936-829-5497, 936-829-5960. FAX: 936-829-5465. E-Mail: bcr@lcc.net. *Dir*, Brenda C Russell; Tel: 936-829-5497; Staff 6 (MLS 1, Non-MLS 5)
Founded 1961. Pop 4,341; Circ 32,436
Jan 1999-Dec 1999 Income $198,193, City $25,000, Locally Generated Income $41,973, Other $131,220. Mats Exp $12,603, Books $10,636, Per/Ser (Incl. Access Fees) $867, AV Equip $1,100. Sal $107,932 (Prof $33,475)
Library Holdings: Bk Vols 23,108; Bk Titles 20,000; Per Subs 46
Special Collections: I D Fairchild Book Coll; Large Print Coll; Latane Temple Coll; Texana Material (John S Redditt Texas Coll)
Automation Activity & Vendor Info: (Acquisitions) Athena
Mem of Houston Area Library System
Partic in Forest Trail Library Consortium, Inc
Friends of the Library Group

DICKINSON

P MARES MEMORIAL LIBRARY, 4324 Hwy 3, 77539-6801. SAN 316-2931. Tel: 281-534-3812. FAX: 281-534-3473. E-Mail: mareslib@electrotex.com. *Dir*, Beth Steiner
Founded 1966. Circ 72,834
Library Holdings: Bk Vols 47,000; Bk Titles 45,000; Per Subs 63
Automation Activity & Vendor Info: (Cataloging) Follett; (Circulation) Follett
Mem of Galveston County Libr Syst; Houston Area Library System
Partic in Houston Area Research Library Consortium; OCLC Online Computer Library Center, Inc
Friends of the Library Group

DIMMITT

P RHOADS MEMORIAL LIBRARY, 103 SW Second St, 79027. SAN 316-294X. Tel: 806-647-3532. FAX: 806-647-1038. E-Mail: rmllib@usa.net. *Dir*, Marie Howell; *Asst Dir*, Dione Steffens; Staff 2 (Non-MLS 2)
Founded 1971. Pop 10,000; Circ 28,000
Oct 1998-Sep 1999 Income $74,639, City $34,815, County $38,724, Locally Generated Income $1,100. Mats Exp $6,706, Books $5,000, Per/Ser (Incl. Access Fees) $1,706. Sal $28,560 (Prof $16,980)
Library Holdings: Bk Titles 21,000; Per Subs 20
Mem of Texas Panhandle Library System

DONNA

P DONNA PUBLIC LIBRARY,* 301 S Main, 78537. SAN 316-2958. Tel: 956-464-2221. FAX: 956-464-6951. Web Site: www.donna.lib.tx.us/. *Dir*, Bruce Kalter; E-Mail: bruce@donna.lib.tx.us; *Asst Dir*, Elodia Rios; *Tech Servs*, Lupita Hinojosa; *Circ*, Ethel Blood; Staff 1 (MLS 1)
Founded 1938. Pop 17,366; Circ 50,134
Library Holdings: Bk Vols 24,000; Per Subs 35
Special Collections: Spanish Coll; Texas Coll
Publications: Monthly Calendar, Newsletter (quarterly)
Mem of South Texas Library System
Friends of the Library Group

DRIPPING SPRINGS

P DRIPPING SPRINGS COMMUNITY LIBRARY,* PO Box 279, 78620. SAN 376-480X. Tel: 512-858-7825. FAX: 512-858-2639. Web Site: www.dscl.org. *Librn*, Nora Wouters
Oct 1997-Sep 1998 Income $48,429. Mats Exp $14,378. Sal $17,853
Library Holdings: Bk Vols 9,500; Per Subs 56
Mem of Central Texas Library System

DUBLIN

P DUBLIN PUBLIC LIBRARY,* 206 W Blackjack, 76446. SAN 316-296 Tel: 254-445-4141. FAX: 254-445-2176. E-Mail: dblinlib@eaze.net. *Coll Develop, Librn*, Sandra Thomas
Pop 2,400
Library Holdings: Bk Vols 10,799
Special Collections: Local History Archives
Mem of North Texas Regional Library System
Friends of the Library Group

DUMAS

P KILLGORE MEMORIAL LIBRARY, Moore County Library, 124 S Blis Ave, 79029-3889. SAN 361-5723. Tel: 806-935-4941. FAX: 806-935-332 *Dir*, Joe Weaver; E-Mail: dum_joe@hlc.actx.edu; *Ch Servs*, Joan Diedrichsen
Founded 1936. Pop 17,865; Circ 97,713
Library Holdings: Bk Vols 57,500; Bk Titles 54,720; Per Subs 76; High Interest/Low Vocabulary Bk Vols 45; Bks on Deafness & Sign Lang 12
Subject Interests: Native Americans
Special Collections: Texas
Publications: Newsletter
Mem of Texas Panhandle Library System
Partic in Harrington Library Consortium
Special Services - Supply materials to Jail, Discovery Center (Public Day Care), Hospital, Nursing Homes & deliver Meals-on-Wheels one day a week; proctor tests
Friends of the Library Group
Branches: 1
BRITAIN MEMORIAL, PO Box 180, Sunray, 79086-0180. SAN 361-57 Tel: 806-948-5501. FAX: 806-948-5501.

DUNCANVILLE

P DUNCANVILLE PUBLIC LIBRARY, 201 James Collins Blvd, 75116. SAN 320-8362. Tel: 972-780-5050. Circulation Tel: 972-780-4955. Reference Tel: 972-780-5052. Web Site: www.ci.duncanville.tx.us. *Librn*, Carla Wolf Bryan; E-Mail: cbryan@ci.duncanville.tx.us; *Ch Servs*, Urla Morgan; *Publ Servs*, Elaine Patrick
Founded 1955. Pop 36,000; Circ 125,000
Oct 1999-Sep 2000 Income City $551,299. Mats Exp $165,537, Books $148,537, Per/Ser (Incl. Access Fees) $17,000. Sal $354,413
Library Holdings: Bk Vols 65,776; Bk Titles 58,700; Per Subs 133
Subject Interests: Genealogy
Special Collections: Texana; Texas Heritage Resource Center
Automation Activity & Vendor Info: (Cataloging) epixtech, inc.; (Circulation) epixtech, inc.; (OPAC) epixtech, inc.
Publications: Duncanville History Tapes; Duncanville Treasures Tapes (o history tapes & transcription)
Mem of Northeast Texas Library System
Friends of the Library Group

EAGLE LAKE

P EULA & DAVID WINTERMAN LIBRARY, 101 N Walnut, 77434. SAN 316-2974. Tel: 409-234-5411. FAX: 409-234-5442. *Librn*, Charlene Rodge
Founded 1975. Pop 6,500; Circ 15,000
Library Holdings: Bk Vols 17,000; Bk Titles 16,500; Per Subs 33
Mem of Houston Area Library System
Friends of the Library Group

EAGLE PASS

P EAGLE PASS PUBLIC LIBRARY, 589 Main St, 78852. SAN 316-2982. Tel: 830-773-2516. FAX: 830-773-4202. *Dir*, Janie B Wright; E-Mail: janwrightusa@netscape.net
Founded 1939. Pop 40,000
Jan 1999-Dec 1999 Income $155,000. Mats Exp $15,000. Sal $44,500
Library Holdings: Bk Vols 42,000; Bk Titles 34,455; Per Subs 75
Special Collections: Spanish Coll; Texana Coll
Friends of the Library Group

STLAND

EASTLAND CENTENNIAL MEMORIAL LIBRARY, 210 S Lamar St, 76448-2794. SAN 316-2990. Tel: 254-629-2281. *Librn*, Kay Mabry
Founded 1904. Pop 10,838
Library Holdings: Bk Vols 12,602; Bk Titles 12,362; Per Subs 16
Mem of Big Country Library System

TEXAS STATE COURT OF APPEALS, Eleventh Supreme Judicial District Law Library,* County Courthouse, 100 W Main St, 76448. SAN 328-6088. Tel: 254-629-2638. FAX: 254-629-2191. E-Mail: appeals@eastland.net. *Librn*, Sherry Williamson

EN

EDEN PUBLIC LIBRARY,* 117 Market St, PO Box 896, 76837-0896. SAN 376-4931. Tel: 915-869-7761. FAX: 915-869-5186. *Librn*, Kathy Sellers; *Asst Librn*, Deanna Beaver
Library Holdings: Bk Vols 12,000
Mem of Big Country Library System
Friends of the Library Group

INBURG

EDINBURG PUBLIC LIBRARY, 401 E Cano St, 78539-4596. SAN 316-3008. Tel: 956-383-6246. Interlibrary Loan Service Tel: 956-383-6247. FAX: 956-318-1294. Web Site: www.edinburg.lib.tx.us. *Dir*, Noemi Garza; E-Mail: noemi@edinburg.lib.tx.us; *Asst Libr Dir*, Letty Leija; E-Mail: letty@ edinburg.lib.tx.us; *Librn*, Adolfo Evan Garcia; E-Mail: adolfo@ edinburg.lib.tx.us; *Librn*, Clemente Garcia; E-Mail: clem@edinburg.lib.tx.us; *ILL*, Raul Martinez; E-Mail: raul@edinburg.lib.tx.us; *Tech Servs*, Terry Mendoza; E-Mail: terry@edinburg.lib.tx.us; *Head, Circ*, Santa Tijerina; E-Mail: santa@edinburg.lib.tx.us; *Ch Servs*, Lupita Sanchez; E-Mail: lupita@edinburg.lib.tx.us; *Info Tech*, Juan Jose Gonzales; E-Mail: jgonzales@edinburg.lib.tx.us. Subject Specialists: *Computer tech*, Juan Jose Gonzales; *Reference*, Adolfo Evan Garcia; Staff 10 (MLS 2, Non-MLS 8)
Founded 1967. Pop 64,328; Circ 314,800
Oct 1999-Sep 2000 Income $792,404, City $781,096, County $11,308. Mats Exp $769,260, Books $58,491, Per/Ser (Incl. Access Fees) $12,827, Other Print Mats $43,606, Electronic Ref Mat (Incl. Access Fees) $6,000. Sal $633,802 (Prof $38,397)
Library Holdings: Bk Vols 104,045; Bk Titles 100,278; Per Subs 228
Subject Interests: Ethnic studies, History
Special Collections: Bilingual-Bicultural (Spanish), per, bk, flm; Literacy & Adult Basis Education, per, bk, videocassettes; Texana, per, bk, flm
Automation Activity & Vendor Info: (Circulation) SIRSI
Database Vendor: Ebsco - EbscoHost, IAC - Info Trac, IAC - SearchBank, OCLC - First Search
Mem of South Texas Library System
Partic in Hidalgo County Libr Syst
Friends of the Library Group

HIDALGO COUNTY LAW LIBRARY,* Courthouse, 100 Closner, 78539. SAN 328-4743. Tel: 956-318-2155. FAX: 956-381-4269. *Librn*, Angie Chapa
Library Holdings: Bk Titles 22,000

RIO GRANDE BIBLE INSTITUTE & LANGUAGE SCHOOL, Richard Wade & Glen Vyck McKinney Library, 4300 S Business 281, 78539. SAN 316-3016. Tel: 956-380-8138. FAX: 956-380-8256. Web Site: www.riogrande.edu. *In Charge*, Rebecca J Merrell; Tel: 956-380-8173, E-Mail: bmerrell.rgbi@juno.com; Staff 2 (MLS 1, Non-MLS 1)
Founded 1952. Enrl 90; Fac 21; Highest Degree: Doctorate
May 1998-Apr 1999 Mats Exp $15,934. Sal $55,562
Library Holdings: Bk Vols 14,711; Bk Titles 9,134; Per Subs 90
Subject Interests: Christian theol works in the Spanish language, Missions
Automation Activity & Vendor Info: (Cataloging) Sagebrush Corporation; (Circulation) Sagebrush Corporation; (OPAC) Sagebrush Corporation
Restriction: Open to students, Public use on premises
Function: Archival collection, Photocopies available, Professional lending library

THE UNIVERSITY OF TEXAS-PAN AMERICAN LIBRARY, 1201 W University Dr, 78539-2999. SAN 361-5812. Tel: 956-381-2755. Interlibrary Loan Service Tel: 956-381-2762. Circulation Tel: 956-381-3506. Reference Tel: 956-381-2752. FAX: 956-381-5396. Web Site: www.lib.panam.edu. *Dir*, Lawrence Caylor; E-Mail: caylorl@panam.edu; *Asst Dir*, Bonnie M McNeely; *Asst Dir*, Sarzaneh Razzaghi; *Spec Coll*, George R Gause, Jr; *Media Spec*, David Mizener; *Per*, Lily Torrez; *Coll Develop*, Farzaneh Razzaghi; Staff 50 (MLS 16, Non-MLS 34)
Founded 1927. Enrl 12,252; Fac 463; Highest Degree: Doctorate
Sep 2000-Aug 2001 Mats Exp $1,311,743, Books $322,000, Per/Ser (Incl. Access Fees) $642,008, Presv $25,000, Micro $58,935, AV Equip $6,300, Other Print Mats $10,000, Electronic Ref Mat (Incl. Access Fees) $247,500. Sal $1,711,706 (Prof $765,329)
Library Holdings: Bk Vols 280,319; Bk Titles 241,062; Per Subs 4,392
Subject Interests: Lower Rio Grande Valley, Mex-Ams
Special Collections: De la Gauza papers; Depository for the Texas Regional Historical Resource Depository Program, Cameron, Hidalgo, Jim Hogg, Starr, Webb, Willacy & Zapata Counties; Lower Rio Grande Valley Coll; Rare Books; Sahary papers; University Archives
Automation Activity & Vendor Info: (Acquisitions) DRA; (Cataloging) DRA; (Circulation) DRA; (Course Reserve) DRA; (ILL) DRA; (Media Booking) DRA; (OPAC) DRA; (Serials) DRA
Database Vendor: DRA
Publications: Reflections/Reflecciones (newsletter)
Partic in Amigos Library Services, Inc; OCLC Online Computer Library Center, Inc; Paisano Consortium; TexShare; UT-System
Friends of the Library Group

EDNA

P JACKSON COUNTY LIBRARY,* 411 N Wells St, 77957-2734. SAN 316-3024. Tel: 512-782-2162. FAX: 512-782-6708. *Librn*, Joyce Putnman
Pop 15,000
Jan 1997-Dec 1998 Income $69,000. Mats Exp $8,500
Library Holdings: Bk Titles 21,636; Per Subs 26
Mem of South Texas Library System

EL PASO

S DESCRIPT-LIBRARY, LR Ranch, 7328 O'Rourke Lane, 79934. SAN 370-8667. Tel: 915-821-9398.
Library Holdings: Bk Vols 5,500; Per Subs 15
Restriction: Not open to public

J EL PASO COMMUNITY COLLEGE LIBRARY,* 1111 N Oregon, PO Box 20500, 79998-0500. SAN 361-5847. Tel: 915-831-4018. FAX: 915-831-4626. Web Site: www.epcc.edu/library/library.htm. *Librn*, Charlotte Hollis
Founded 1971. Enrl 27,000; Fac 649
Library Holdings: Bk Vols 54,000; Per Subs 296
Subject Interests: Allied health fields, Mexican-American materials
Partic in Amigos Library Services, Inc; Del Norte Biosciences Library Consortium; Dialog Corporation; OCLC Online Computer Library Center, Inc

GL EL PASO COUNTY LAW LIBRARY,* 500 E San Antonio St, Rm 1202, 79901. Tel: 915-546-2245. FAX: 915-542-0440. *Librn*, Lynn Sanchez; *Asst Librn*, Sandy Galceren
Library Holdings: Bk Vols 27,000; Per Subs 49
Partic in SW Law Librs

S EL PASO MUSEUM OF ART LIBRARY,* One Art Festival Plaza, 79901. SAN 316-3067. Tel: 915-532-1707. FAX: 915-532-1010.
Library Holdings: Bk Vols 11,000; Per Subs 24
Subject Interests: Gen, Modern art
Special Collections: Renaissance & Baroque Artists Coll

S EL PASO NATURAL GAS CO, Engineering & Technical Information Center, 100 N Stanton St, PO Box 1492, 79978. SAN 316-3075. Tel: 915-496-3273. FAX: 915-496-5947. *Coordr*, Marilyn R Braithwaite; E-Mail: braithwaitem@epenergy.com; Staff 1 (Non-MLS 1)
Founded 1974
Library Holdings: Bk Titles 2,000; Per Subs 100
Subject Interests: Chemical engineering, Energy studies, Fuel, Gas pipelines, Petroleum engineering, Related topics

P EL PASO PUBLIC LIBRARY,* 501 N Oregon St, 79901. SAN 361-5901. Tel: 915-543-5401. FAX: 915-543-5410. *Dir*, Carol C Brey; Tel: 915-545-5413, E-Mail: breycx@ci.el-paso.tx.us; *Librn*, Barbara Valle; *Cat*, Glenda Roberts; Staff 33 (MLS 33)
Founded 1894. Pop 650,000; Circ 1,627,820
Sep 1997-Aug 1998 Income $7,286,779, State $259,421, City $6,643,205, Federal $263,695, Other $120,458. Mats Exp $1,242,881. Sal $3,427,728
Library Holdings: Bk Vols 648,700; Per Subs 981
Subject Interests: Genealogy, Literacy, Local archit, Local history, Local photogs, Mexican Revolutionary, Spanish, SW
Special Collections: Raza Coll
Publications: Great Constellations, Tom Lea Bibliography; Henry C Trost, Architect of the Southwest
Mem of Texas Trans Pecos Library System
Major Resource Center: Texas Trans Pecos Library System
Friends of the Library Group
Branches: 9
ARMIJO, 620 E Seventh Ave, 79901. SAN 361-5936. Tel: 915-533-1333. FAX: 915-532-1758. *Librn*, Leslie Trich Humble
Friends of the Library Group
CIELO VISTA, 8929 Viscount, 79925. SAN 361-5995. Tel: 915-591-6812. FAX: 915-591-7659. *Librn*, Anita Ruble
Friends of the Library Group
CLARDY FOX BRANCH, 5515 Robert Alva, 79905. SAN 361-6029. Tel: 915-772-0501. FAX: 915-772-7941. *Librn*, Mary Helen Michaels
Subject Interests: Spanish lang

Friends of the Library Group
IRVING SCHWARTZ BRANCH, 1865 Dean Martin, 79936. Tel: 915-857-0594. FAX: 915-857-7218. *Librn*, Penny Brewer
Friends of the Library Group
LOWER VALLEY, 7915 San Jose Rd, 79915. SAN 361-6053. Tel: 915-591-3391. FAX: 915-591-8334. *Librn*, Laurel Indalecio
Subject Interests: Spanish lang
Friends of the Library Group
MEMORIAL PARK, 3200 Copper, 79930. SAN 361-6088. Tel: 915-566-1034. FAX: 915-564-3944. *Librn*, Patricia Lang
Friends of the Library Group
RICHARD BURGES BRANCH, 9600 Diana Dr, 79924. SAN 361-5960. Tel: 915-759-2400. FAX: 915-759-2424. *Librn*, Fernando Racelis
Friends of the Library Group
WESTSIDE, 125 Belvidere, 79912. SAN 361-6118. Tel: 915-581-2024. FAX: 915-833-4785. *Librn*, Gail Haire
Friends of the Library Group
YSLETA, 9321 Alameda, 79907. SAN 361-6142. Tel: 915-858-0905. FAX: 915-860-8017. *Librn*, Margie Sanchez
Subject Interests: Spanish lang
Friends of the Library Group
Bookmobiles: 2

S EL PASO TIMES, INC LIBRARY,* 300 N Campbell, PO Box 20, 79999. SAN 326-484X. Tel: 915-546-6263. FAX: 915-546-6415. *Librn*, Julia Soles; Staff 3 (MLS 1, Non-MLS 2)
Founded 1940
Library Holdings: Bk Vols 300

R FIRST PRESBYTERIAN CHURCH LIBRARY, 1340 Murchison St, 79902. SAN 316-3083. Tel: 915-533-7551. FAX: 915-534-7167. *Librn*, Marme Davis
Founded 1957
Library Holdings: Bk Titles 3,700
Subject Interests: History, Theology

L KEMP, SMITH, PC, Law Library, 221 N Kansas, Ste 1700, 79901. SAN 372-1655. Tel: 915-546-5328. FAX: 915-546-5360. Web Site: www.kempsmith.com. *Librn*, Becky McKenzie; Staff 2 (MLS 1, Non-MLS 1)
Founded 1866
Library Holdings: Bk Vols 16,000; Per Subs 200
Automation Activity & Vendor Info: (Cataloging) EOS; (Serials) EOS
Restriction: Staff use only

L MOUNCE & GREEN, MEYERS, SAFI & GALATZAN, Law Library,* 100 N Stanton, Ste 1700, 79901. SAN 372-1647. Tel: 915-532-2000. FAX: 915-541-1597. E-Mail: mouncegreenmeyers@worldnet.att.net. *Librn*, Sylvia T Contreres
Library Holdings: Bk Vols 15,000; Per Subs 20

G NATIONAL PARK SERVICE, Chamizal National Memorial Library, 800 S San Marcial, 79905. SAN 326-3282. Tel: 915-532-7273. FAX: 915-532-7240. *Curator*, Catherine Johnson
Library Holdings: Bk Vols 1,500; Per Subs 10
Restriction: Non-circulating to the public

S SCOTT, HULSE, MARSHALL, FEUILLE, FINGER & THURMOND, Law Library, PO Box 99123, 79999. SAN 326-4513. Tel: 915-533-2493, Ext 302. FAX: 915-546-8333. *Librn*, Sharon Newson
Library Holdings: Bk Vols 15,800; Bk Titles 650; Per Subs 57
Subject Interests: Labor
Publications: Acquisitions List

P TEXAS TRANS PECOS LIBRARY SYSTEM, El Paso Public Library, 501 Oregon St N, 79901-1103. SAN 316-3121. Tel: 915-543-5418, 915-543-5464. FAX: 915-533-3556. *Coordr*, Barbara Valle; E-Mail: vallebk@ci.el-paso.tx.us; Staff 3 (MLS 2, Non-MLS 1)
Founded 1969. Pop 647,133
Sep 2000-Aug 2001 Income $434,616. Mats Exp $146,613. Sal $158,847 (Prof $130,000)
Publications: Round Up (newsletter)
Member Libraries: Alpine Public Library; Balmorhea Public Library; City Of Presidio Library; El Paso Public Library; Fort Hancock-Hudspeth County Public Library; Fort Stockton Public Library; Grace Grebing Public Library; Imperial Public Library; Iraan Public Library; Jeff Davis County Library; Marfa Public Library; Reeves County Library; Terrell County Public Library; Van Horn County Library
Partic in Amigos Library Services, Inc; Tex State Libr

UNITED STATES ARMY
AM WILLIAM BEAUMONT ARMY MEDICAL TECHNICAL LIBRARY, WBAMC/MCHM, NTL, 5005 N Piedras St, Rm 2-246, 79920-5001. SAN 361-6177. Tel: 915-569-2537, 915-569-2580. FAX: 915-569-1534. *In Charge*, William Dowdy; Staff 3 (MLS 1, Non-MLS 2)
Founded 1922
Library Holdings: Bk Vols 10,000; Per Subs 602
Subject Interests: Dentistry, Medicine, Nursing, Ortho, Surgery
Publications: Library Bulletin (quarterly)
Partic in Dialog Corporation; Nat Libr of Med; OCLC Online Compute Library Center, Inc

C UNIVERSITY OF TEXAS AT EL PASO LIBRARY, 79968-0582. SAN 361-6231. Tel: 915-747-5683. Interlibrary Loan Service Tel: 915-747-673 Circulation Tel: 915-747-5672. Reference Tel: 915-747-5643. FAX: 915-7 5345. E-Mail: admin@libr.utep.edu. Web Site: www.libraryweb.utep.edu. *Dean of Libr*, Patricia Phillips; Tel: 915-747-6710, E-Mail: pphillip@libr.utep.edu; *Assoc Dean*, Cesar Caballero; Tel: 915-747-6719, E-Mail: ccaballe@libr.utep.edu; *ILL*, Marie Reyes; *Acq*, Carol Kelley; *Cat*, Caroly Kahl; *Online Servs, Ref*, Luke Jastrzebski; *Rare Bks, Spec Coll*, Claudia Rivers; *Asst Librn, Coll Develop*, Carol M Kelley. Subject Specialists: *Children lit*, Patricia Phillips; *Education*, Cesar Caballero; Staff 85 (MLS Non-MLS 63)
Founded 1919. Enrl 14,677; Fac 792; Highest Degree: Doctorate
Sep 1998-Aug 1999 Income $4,061,783. Mats Exp $1,748,721, Books $402,874, Per/Ser (Incl. Access Fees) $1,032,619, Presv $46,456, Electron Ref Mat (Incl. Access Fees) $257,279. Sal $1,931,361 (Prof $882,105)
Library Holdings: Bk Vols 726,432; Bk Titles 580,780; Per Subs 3,108
Subject Interests: Border studies, Bus, Environmental studies, Geology, Southwest region, Southwestern anthrop, Southwestern archit
Special Collections: Art Books; Chicano Studies; Judaica; Mexican Histo (mss on micro); Mexico & Southwest; Military History (SLA Marchall); Onamastics; Printing & Bookmaking (Carl Hertzog Coll), bks & papers; Rare Books; Western Fiction
Function: Research library
Mem of Asn of Research Libraries
Partic in Amigos Library Services, Inc; TexShare
Friends of the Library Group

ELDORADO

P SCHLEICHER COUNTY PUBLIC LIBRARY,* 201 SW Main St, PO Bo 611, 76936-0611. SAN 376-4036. Tel: 915-853-3767. FAX: 915-853-2963. *Librn*, Jeri Whitten
Library Holdings: Bk Vols 10,000
Mem of Big Country Library System

ELECTRA

P ELECTRA PUBLIC LIBRARY,* 401 N Waggoner, 76360. SAN 316-314 Tel: 940-495-2208. FAX: 940-495-4143. *Dir*, Terry Holbert
Founded 1925. Pop 3,000; Circ 52,802
Oct 1997-Sep 1998 Income $55,768. Mats Exp $6,500. Sal $31,212
Library Holdings: Bk Vols 19,370; Bk Titles 14,443; Per Subs 76
Mem of North Texas Regional Library System
Friends of the Library Group

ELGIN

P ELGIN PUBLIC LIBRARY, 404 N Main St, 78621-2625. SAN 376-4842 Tel: 512-281-5678. FAX: 512-285-3015. E-Mail: elginpl@totalaccess.net. *Librn*, Sandy Ott
Pop 20,014
Oct 1998-Sep 1999 Income $49,509
Library Holdings: Bk Vols 17,984
Mem of Central Texas Library System
Friends of the Library Group

ELSA

P ELSA PUBLIC LIBRARY,* N Hidalgo St, PO Box 1447, 78543. SAN 3 3156. Tel: 956-262-3061. *Librn*, Hilda Molina
Pop 4,400; Circ 38,869
Jan 1997-Dec 1998 Income $58,744. Mats Exp $3,900. Sal $38,524
Library Holdings: Bk Vols 19,000; Per Subs 27
Mem of South Texas Library System

EMORY

P RAINS COUNTY PUBLIC LIBRARY,* 803 Lennon Dr, PO Box 189, 75440. SAN 376-4486. Tel: 903-473-2221. FAX: 903-473-1703. E-Mail: rclid@koyote.com. *Librn*, Virginia Northcutt
Oct 1996-Sep 1997 Income $45,292, City $2,000, County $41,200, Locally Generated Income $2,092. Mats Exp $2,764, Books $1,576, Per/Ser (Incl. Access Fees) $354, Micro $108. Sal $23,117 (Prof $16,565)
Library Holdings: Bk Vols 19,845
Mem of Northeast Texas Library System

NNIS

ENNIS PUBLIC LIBRARY,* 501 W Ennis Ave, 75119-3803. SAN 316-3164. Tel: 972-875-5360. FAX: 972-878-9649. E-Mail: library@ennis-tx-lib.com. Web Site: www.ennis-tx-lib.com. *Dir*, Ann Peeler; Staff 6 (Non-MLS 6)
Founded 1939. Pop 16,700; Circ 76,890
Oct 1999-Sep 2000 Income $252,000, City $240,000, Locally Generated Income $12,000. Mats Exp $21,100, Books $16,800, Per/Ser (Incl. Access Fees) $2,000, Electronic Ref Mat (Incl. Access Fees) $2,300. Sal $119,000 (Prof $37,000)
Library Holdings: Bk Vols 32,500; Bk Titles 29,000; Per Subs 105; High Interest/Low Vocabulary Bk Vols 750; Bks on Deafness & Sign Lang 15
Subject Interests: Genealogy, Tex hist
Special Collections: Ennis Historic Archives; Superconducting Super Collidor Archives
Automation Activity & Vendor Info: (OPAC) Nicholas
Database Vendor: OCLC - First Search
Function: ILL available
Mem of Northeast Texas Library System
Friends of the Library Group

ULESS

EULESS PUBLIC LIBRARY,* 201 N Ector Dr, 76039-3595. SAN 316-3172. Tel: 817-685-1679. FAX: 817-267-1979. E-Mail: library@spindle.net. *Dir*, Betty O Yarbrough; *Ch Servs*, Meredith McMannis; *Ref*, Kate Lyon; *Asst Dir*, Sheila Williams
Founded 1961. Pop 43,000; Circ 228,855
Oct 1996-Sep 1997 Income $790,632. Mats Exp $68,621, Books $38,881, Per/Ser (Incl. Access Fees) $17,366, Micro $2,145, Other Print Mats $2,205. Sal $676,917
Library Holdings: Bk Vols 68,439; Per Subs 196
Subject Interests: Genealogy
Automation Activity & Vendor Info: (Circulation) Gaylord
Mem of North Texas Regional Library System
Friends of the Library Group

VERMAN

EVERMAN PUBLIC LIBRARY,* 212 N Race St, 76140-3297. SAN 376-4621. Tel: 817-551-0726. *Librn*, Helen Johnson
Oct 1997-Sep 1998 Income $23,840
Library Holdings: Bk Vols 16,858
Mem of North Texas Regional Library System
Friends of the Library Group

BENS

EL PASO COUNTY LIBRARY,* 1331 N Fabens St, PO Drawer 788, 79838. SAN 316-3180. Tel: 915-764-3635. FAX: 915-764-3635. *Dir*, Corina Vernium
Pop 38,500
Library Holdings: Bk Vols 56,303; Bk Titles 53,772; Per Subs 70
Subject Interests: Civil rights, Cross cultural subjects, Handicraft, Southwest, Spanish
Friends of the Library Group

AIRFIELD

FAIRFIELD LIBRARY ASSOCIATION, INC,* 350 W Main, 75840. SAN 316-3199. Tel: 903-389-3574. *Librn*, Virginia Oliver
Founded 1966. Pop 8,900; Circ 37,000
Library Holdings: Bk Titles 21,707; Per Subs 56
Special Collections: Genealogy; Texas
Mem of Central Texas Library System
Friends of the Library Group

ALFURRIAS

BROOKS COUNTY LIBRARY, Ed Rachal Memorial Library, 203 S Henry St, 78355. SAN 316-3202. Tel: 512-325-2144. FAX: 512-325-3743. *Librn*, Enola Garza; E-Mail: enolagarza@yahoo.com
Founded 1960. Pop 8,005; Circ 55,068
Oct 2000-Sep 2001 Income $171,000, County $121,000, Other $50,000. Mats Exp $21,000, Books $10,000, Per/Ser (Incl. Access Fees) $6,000, Micro $1,000, AV Equip $3,000, Other Print Mats $1,000. Sal $72,000 (Prof $20,000)
Library Holdings: Bk Titles 75,000; Per Subs 28

ALLS CITY

FALLS CITY PUBLIC LIBRARY, 206 N Irvin, PO Box 220, 78113-0220. SAN 376-4214. Tel: 830-254-3361. FAX: 830-254-3954. E-Mail: librarian@fallscity.lib.tx.us. *Librn*, Dixie Mutz; E-Mail: dixiemutz@hotmail.com
Founded 1975. Pop 910
Oct 2000-Sep 2001 Income County $27,000
Library Holdings: Bk Vols 12,600; Per Subs 29
Mem of Alamo Area Library System

FARMERS BRANCH

J BROOKHAVEN COLLEGE, Learning Resources Center,* 3939 Valley View, 75244-4997. SAN 316-3210. Tel: 972-860-4854. FAX: 972-860-4675. Web Site: www.dcccd.edu/. *Mgr*, Ann Coder; *Ref*, Linda Kleen; *Ref*, Sue Crowson; *Ref*, Liz Bradford; *Coll Develop*, Lolly Archer; Staff 22 (MLS 8, Non-MLS 14)
Founded 1978. Enrl 4,233; Fac 241
Sep 1998-Aug 1999 Income $855,665. Mats Exp $93,322, Books $45,943, Per/Ser (Incl. Access Fees) $14,300, Presv $2,000, Micro $2,500, Other Print Mats $2,700. Sal $575,901 (Prof $335,546)
Library Holdings: Bk Vols 45,051; Bk Titles 43,183; Per Subs 185
Special Collections: Plotkin Holocaust Coll
Partic in Alliance For Higher Education; Amigos Library Services, Inc

P FARMERS BRANCH PUBLIC LIBRARY,* 13613 Webb Chapel, 75234-3756. SAN 316-3229. Tel: 972-247-2511. FAX: 972-247-9606. Web Site: www.ci.farmers-branch.tx.us/. *Dir*, Mary Jane Stevenson; *Asst Dir, Publ Servs*, Karel Tabor; *Tech Servs*, Gayla Bush; *Ad Servs, Ref*, Donna Gooch; *Ad Servs, Ref*, Sharon Stuart; *Media Spec, Ref*, Terry Vermillion; *Media Spec*, Jane Freeman; *Ch Servs*, Victoria Haddon; Staff 9 (MLS 9)
Founded 1961. Pop 26,000; Circ 259,341
Library Holdings: Bk Vols 83,383; Bk Titles 73,322; Per Subs 250
Subject Interests: Local, Tex hist
Automation Activity & Vendor Info: (Cataloging) Gaylord; (Circulation) Gaylord
Mem of Northeast Texas Library System
Partic in Dialog Corporation; Dow Jones News Retrieval

FARMERSVILLE

P CHARLES J RIKE MEMORIAL LIBRARY, 203 Orange, PO Box 352, 75442-0352. SAN 322-8053. Tel: 972-782-6681. FAX: 972-782-7608. E-Mail: fvillelib@texoma.net. *Coll Develop, Librn*, Pansy L Hundley
Founded 1981. Pop 3,000; Circ 22,857
Library Holdings: Bk Titles 16,727
Mem of Northeast Texas Library System

FERRIS

P FERRIS PUBLIC LIBRARY, 514 S Mable, 75125. SAN 316-3237. Tel: 972-544-3696. E-Mail: ferris1@znet-tx.com. *Librn*, Marcia K Campbell; Staff 2 (Non-MLS 2)
Founded 1971. Pop 2,600; Circ 2,700
Library Holdings: Bk Titles 13,157
Subject Interests: Genealogy, Texas hist
Special Collections: Music Coll, rec
Mem of Northeast Texas Library System

FLORENCE

P FLORENCE PUBLIC LIBRARY, 207 E Main St, PO Box 430, 76527-0430. SAN 376-4834. Tel: 254-793-2672. E-Mail: fllib@vvm.com. *Librn*, Lou Scott
Jan 2000-Dec 2000 Income $2,500
Library Holdings: Bk Vols 15,000
Mem of Central Texas Library System

FLORESVILLE

P SAM FORE JR WILSON COUNTY PUBLIC LIBRARY, One Library Lane, 78114. SAN 316-3245. Tel: 830-393-7361. FAX: 830-393-7337. *Dir*, Victoria A Duff; Staff 4 (Non-MLS 4)
Pop 22,650; Circ 47,285
Library Holdings: Bk Vols 35,600; Per Subs 35
Subject Interests: Texana
Automation Activity & Vendor Info: (Cataloging) Sagebrush Corporation; (Circulation) Sagebrush Corporation
Mem of Alamo Area Library System
Friends of the Library Group

FLOWER MOUND

P FLOWER MOUND PUBLIC LIBRARY, 3030 Broadmoor Lane, 75022. SAN 376-4702. Tel: 972-539-0120. FAX: 972-355-1393. E-Mail: fmpl@flower-mound.com. *Dir*, Gloria Frye; *Tech Servs*, Vicki Chiavetta; *YA Servs*, Marleen Watling; Staff 5 (MLS 5)
Founded 1984. Pop 51,300
1998-1999 Income $525,134, State $5,601, City $487,223, Locally Generated Income $32,310. Mats Exp $172,338, Books $107,329, Per/Ser

(Incl. Access Fees) $38,789, AV Equip $16,973. Sal $341,825
Library Holdings: Bk Vols 41,230; Bk Titles 33,803; Per Subs 102
Automation Activity & Vendor Info: (Acquisitions) epixtech, inc.; (Cataloging) epixtech, inc.; (Circulation) epixtech, inc.
Mem of North Texas Regional Library System
Friends of the Library Group

FLOYDADA

P FLOYD COUNTY LIBRARY,* Floyd County Courthouse, 79235. SAN 361-638X. Tel: 806-983-4922. *Librn*, Sandra Crawford
Pop 10,516; Circ 29,960
Library Holdings: Bk Vols 39,000
Mem of West Texas Library System
Friends of the Library Group
Branches: 1
LOCKNEY BRANCH, 224 S Main, Lockney, 79241. SAN 361-641X. Tel: 806-652-3561. *Librn*, Darlene Dipprey

FORNEY

P FORNEY PUBLIC LIBRARY,* 811 S Bois D'arc, PO Box 1794, 75126. SAN 376-4400. Tel: 972-564-7027. FAX: 972-564-7026. *Librn*, Jo Weiner
Library Holdings: Bk Vols 14,000; Bk Titles 13,000; Per Subs 145
Mem of Northeast Texas Library System

FORT BLISS

UNITED STATES ARMY

A AIR DEFENSE ARTILLERY CENTER MICKELSEN LIBRARY (SCHOOL SIDE), Bldg 2E, Sheridan Rd, 79916-3802. Tel: 915-568-1902. FAX: 915-568-5754. E-Mail: mickelsenl@bliss.army.mil. Web Site: 147.71.210.21/library/. *Chief Librn*, Richard Earl Munyon; Tel: 915-568-3089, E-Mail: munyonr@bliss.army.mil; *Publ Servs*, Trudy Ketcherside; E-Mail: ketchersidet@bliss.army.mil; *Publ Servs*, Ronald Peterson; E-Mail: petersonr@bliss.army.mil; Staff 3 (MLS 1, Non-MLS 2)
Founded 1942
Library Holdings: Bk Vols 9,586; Bk Titles 9,550; Per Subs 60
Subject Interests: Air defense artillery, Mil sci, Military history, SW
Automation Activity & Vendor Info: (Acquisitions) SIRSI; (Cataloging) SIRSI; (Circulation) SIRSI; (OPAC) SIRSI
Restriction: Circulation limited, Not open to public
Partic in Fedlink; OCLC Online Computer Library Center, Inc; Tralinet

A AIR DEFENSE ARTILLERY SCHOOL (GENERAL SIDE) MICKELSEN LIBRARY, Mickelsen Libr (Gen) Bldg 2E, Sheridan Rd, 79916-3802. SAN 361-6444. Tel: 915-568-6156. FAX: 915-568-5754. E-Mail: mickelsenl@bliss.army.mil. Web Site: 147.71.210.21/library/. *Chief Librn*, Richard Earl Munyon; Tel: 915-568-3089, E-Mail: munyonr@bliss.army.mil; *Publ Servs*, Donna E Ramsey; Tel: 915-568-1491, E-Mail: ramseyd@bliss.army.mil; *Tech Servs*, Kathryn Thomson; Tel: 915-568-6154; *ILL*, Sylvia Padillo; Tel: 915-568-6154; Staff 5 (MLS 2, Non-MLS 3)
Founded 1942
Library Holdings: Bk Vols 35,005; Bk Titles 29,829; Per Subs 65
Subject Interests: Military history, Southwest
Automation Activity & Vendor Info: (Acquisitions) SIRSI; (Cataloging) SIRSI; (Circulation) SIRSI; (Course Reserve) SIRSI; (OPAC) SIRSI
Publications: Library Handbook; Periodical Holdings List
Restriction: Circulation limited
Partic in Fedlink; OCLC Online Computer Library Center, Inc; Tralinet; United States Army Training & Doctrine Command (TRADOC)

A OTHON O VALENT LEARNING RESOURCES CENTER, Bldg 11291 Biggs Field, 79918-8002. SAN 361-6568. Tel: 915-568-8176, 915-8614. FAX: 915-568-8540. E-Mail: murraym@bliss.army.mil. *Ref, Syst Coordr*, Linda Gaunt. Subject Specialists: *Reference*, Linda Gaunt; Staff 5 (MLS 2, Non-MLS 3)
Founded 1972
Library Holdings: Bk Vols 40,000; Bk Titles 28,700; Per Subs 376
Subject Interests: Mil sci, Military history
Special Collections: Army Unit History
Automation Activity & Vendor Info: (Acquisitions) SIRSI; (Cataloging) SIRSI; (Circulation) SIRSI; (OPAC) SIRSI; (Serials) SIRSI
Database Vendor: Dialog, OCLC - First Search
Partic in Fedlink; United States Army Training & Doctrine Command (TRADOC)

FORT DAVIS

P JEFF DAVIS COUNTY LIBRARY,* 3 Woodward St, PO Box 1054, 79734-1054. SAN 376-4338. Tel: 915-426-3802. FAX: 915-426-2225. *Librn*, Carol Wolkow
1999-2000 Income $37,500
Library Holdings: Bk Vols 24,000; Per Subs 42
Mem of Texas Trans Pecos Library System
Friends of the Library Group

S NATIONAL PARK SERVICE, Fort Davis National Historic Site Library, Flipper Dr, 79734. (Mail add: PO Box 1456, 79734-1456), Tel: 915-426-3224. Reference Tel: 915-426-3224, Ext 25. FAX: 915-426-3122. *Librn*, Mary William; E-Mail: mary_(park)_williams@nps.gov. Subject Specialist: *History*, Mary William
Founded 1963
Library Holdings: Bk Titles 2,300
Special Collections: Oral History (Reminiscences of Second & Third Generation Fort Descendents); The Buffalo Soldiers & Colonel Benjamin Grierson, 10th US Cavalry; Western US Military History
Restriction: By appointment only, Open to researchers by request, Staff u only
Function: Research library

FORT HANCOCK

P FORT HANCOCK-HUDSPETH COUNTY PUBLIC LIBRARY, 101 Sch Dr, PO Box 98, 79839-0098. SAN 376-4354. Tel: 915-769-3811. FAX: 91 769-3940. E-Mail: desparza@hotmail.com. *Librn*, Daniel Esparza; Staff 1 (Non-MLS 1)
Pop 1,200
Sep 1998-Aug 1999 Income $62,729. (Prof $48,977)
Library Holdings: Bk Vols 10,000; Per Subs 21
Mem of Texas Trans Pecos Library System

FORT HOOD

UNITED STATES ARMY

AM MEDICAL LIBRARY, Bldg 36000, Darnall Army Community Hospital, 76544-5063. SAN 361-6657. Tel: 254-288-8366. FAX: 254-288-8368. *Librn*, Frank M Norton; E-Mail: nortonfm@hood_emh3.army.mil; *Asst Librn*, Jonella B Lien
Founded 1952
Library Holdings: Bk Vols 8,000; Per Subs 500
Subject Interests: Basic sci, Dentistry, Specialities, Surgical
Partic in Dialog Corporation; Docline; Nat Libr of Med; OCLC Online Computer Library Center, Inc; S Cent Regional Libr Prog

A CASEY MEMORIAL LIBRARY, 761 Tank Battalion, 76544. Tel: 254-28 0025. FAX: 254-288-4029. Web Site: hood-esd.army.mil. *Dir*, Pamela Shelton; E-Mail: sheltonp@hood-emh3.army.mil; *Cat*, Lisa Harris; Staff (MLS 3, Non-MLS 1)
Founded 1942
1998-1999 Income $370,000. Mats Exp $89,000, Books $52,000, Per/Se (Incl. Access Fees) $27,000, Micro $6,500. Sal $256,000
Library Holdings: Bk Vols 93,000; Per Subs 296
Subject Interests: Gen reading, Grad, Mil sci, Undergrad studies
Partic in Bibliog Coun; Fedlink; OCLC Online Computer Library Cente Inc

FORT SAM HOUSTON

UNITED STATES ARMY

AM BROOKE ARMY MEDICAL CENTER LIBRARY, Medical Library MCHE-CSL, 3851 Roger Brooke Dr Bldg 3600 Rm 330-19, 78234-620 SAN 361-6711. Tel: 210-916-1119. FAX: 210-916-5709. E-Mail: medicallibrary.bamc@cen.amedd.army.mil. Web Site: www.gprmc.amedd.army.mil ((BAMC)). *Librn*, Beverly Rakowitz; Tel: 210-916-0285, E-Mail: beverly.rakowitz@cen.smrff.stmy.mil; *Ser*, Janice Watt; Tel: 210-916-1219, E-Mail: watt.janice@cen.amedd.army.mil; *Cat*, Geraldine R Trumbo; E-Mail: geraldine.trumbo@cen.amedd.army.mil; *Circ*, Martin Perez, Jr; E-Mail: medicalliubrary.bamc@cen.amedd.army.mil; Staff 4 (MLS 1, Non-MLS 3)
Founded 1914. Pop 5,000; Circ 5,000
Oct 2000-Sep 2001 Income (Main Library Only) Federal $240,000
Library Holdings: Bk Vols 19,000; Per Subs 662
Subject Interests: Clinical medicine, Dentistry, Nursing
Automation Activity & Vendor Info: (Cataloging) Endeavor; (Circulation) Endeavor
Database Vendor: Dialog, IAC - Info Trac, OCLC - First Search, OVID Technologies
Restriction: Circulates for staff only
Function: Research library
Partic in Coun of Res & Acad Librs; Fedlink

A FORT SAM HOUSTON LIBRARY, Bldg 1222, 78234-5029. SAN 361-6770. Tel: 210-221-4170, 210-221-4702. FAX: 210-227-5921. *Dir*, Alfon Butcher; E-Mail: butchera@samhou-basops.army.mil; *Ref*, Susan Artiglia
Oct 1997-Sep 1998 Income $615,524. Mats Exp $59,600, Books $50,00 Per/Ser (Incl. Access Fees) $9,600. Sal $165,000 (Prof $81,000)
Library Holdings: Bk Vols 68,000; Per Subs 200
Subject Interests: Military history, Patient educ
Publications: Periodicals Holding List
Partic in Fedlink; OCLC Online Computer Library Center, Inc

AM STIMSON LIBRARY, Academy of Health Sciences, 2250 Stanley Rd, Stimson Library, Bldg 2840, Rm 106, 78234-6160. SAN 361-6746. Tel: 210-221-6900. Interlibrary Loan Service Tel: 210-221-8532. FAX: 210-221-8264. *Chief Librn*, Norma Sellers; *Coll Develop, Ref*, Kathy

Furukawa; *Cat, Doc*, Kay Livingston
Founded 1932
Library Holdings: Bk Vols 59,912; Per Subs 607
Subject Interests: Anesthesia, Behav sci, Health care admin, Mil med, Nursing, Physical therapy, Psychiatry, Public health
Special Collections: Military Medicine
Partic in Coun of Res & Acad Librs; Dialog Corporation; Health Oriented Libraries of San Antonio

RT STOCKTON

FORT STOCKTON PUBLIC LIBRARY, 500 N Water St, 79735. SAN 316-327X. Tel: 915-336-3374. FAX: 915-336-6648. E-Mail: info@fort-stockton.lib.tx.us. Web Site: www.fort-stockton.lib.tx.us. *Dir*, Dolores Flores; Tel: 915-336-3375, E-Mail: dflores@fort-stockton.lib.tx.us; *Asst Dir*, Debra Whitfield; E-Mail: dwhitfield@fort-stockton.lib.tx.us; *Tech Coordr*, Vicki Stone; E-Mail: vstone@fort-stockton.lib.tx.us; *Head, Circ*, Anne Fuentez; E-Mail: annefue@fort-stockton.lib.tx.us; *Ch Servs*, Yolanda Calzada; E-Mail: yolanda@fort-stockton.lib.tx.us; *Tech Servs*, Renee Forrister; E-Mail: renee@fort-stockton.lib.tx.us; *Circ*, Rebecca Gonzalez; E-Mail: gonzalez@fort-stockton.lib.tx.us; Staff 7 (Non-MLS 7)
Founded 1911. Pop 12,000; Circ 130,000
Library Holdings: Bk Vols 67,097; Bk Titles 66,425; Per Subs 225
Subject Interests: Genealogy, Large print, Southwest
Automation Activity & Vendor Info: (Cataloging) epixtech, inc.; (Circulation) epixtech, inc.
Database Vendor: epixtech, inc., ProQuest
Function: ILL available
Mem of Texas Trans Pecos Library System

RT WORTH

ALCON LABORATORIES, INC, Research Library R1-30,* 6201 S Freeway, 76134-2099. SAN 316-3288. Tel: 817-293-0450. *Dir*, Pency Murphy; Staff 3 (MLS 1, Non-MLS 2)
Founded 1959
Library Holdings: Bk Titles 3,500; Per Subs 500
Subject Interests: Lens care, Ophthalmology, Pharmacology
Restriction: Not open to public
Partic in Nat Libr of Med
Branches:
INTRAOCULAR LENS (IOL)
Library Holdings: Bk Titles 100; Per Subs 20

AMON CARTER MUSEUM LIBRARY, 3501 Camp Bowie Blvd, 76107-2695. SAN 316-3318. Tel: 817-738-1933. FAX: 817-377-8523. Web Site: www.cartermuseum.org. *Actg Librn*, Samuel Duncan; E-Mail: sam.duncan@cartermuseum.org; *Archivist*, Paula Stewart; E-Mail: paula.stewart@cartermuseum.org; Staff 5 (MLS 2, Non-MLS 3)
Founded 1961
Library Holdings: Bk Titles 35,000; Per Subs 110
Subject Interests: Am art, History, Photog
Special Collections: 19th Century Newspapers on Microfilm, 19th & Early 20th Century American Art, American Illustrated Books; Eliot Porter Library & Archives; History Photography; Laura Gilpin Photographic Library; M Knoedler Library
Automation Activity & Vendor Info: (Cataloging) DRA; (OPAC) DRA
Restriction: By appointment only
Partic in CDLC

BELL HELICOPTER TEXTRON, INC, Research & Engineering Library, 600 E Hurst Blvd, PO Box 482, MS 1302, 76101-0482. SAN 316-330X. Tel: 817-280-3608. FAX: 817-280-8688. *Librn*, Donald A Welch; E-Mail: dwelch@bellhelicopter.textron.com; Staff 1 (MLS 1)
Founded 1955
Library Holdings: Bk Titles 4,100; Per Subs 60
Subject Interests: Aeronautics, Astronautics, Aviation, Composite materials, Helicopters
Special Collections: Centers of Excellence for Rotary Wing Study & Technology
Database Vendor: Dialog, OCLC - First Search
Restriction: Staff use only
Branches:
LOGISTICS & TECHNICAL PUBLICATIONS, D82-Bldg 44, 600 E Hurst Blvd, PO Box 482, 76101. SAN 372-9923. Tel: 817-280-6726. FAX: 817-280-6473. *Librn*, Irene E Cordova; E-Mail: icordova@bellhelicopter.textron.com

BOTANICAL RESEARCH INSTITUTE OF TEXAS LIBRARY, 509 Pecan St, 76102-4060. SAN 374-6631. Tel: 817-332-4441. FAX: 817-332-4112. E-Mail: info@brit.org. *Librn*, Barney Lipscomb
Library Holdings: Bk Vols 72,000; Bk Titles 15,000; Per Subs 1,000
Special Collections: Botany, Taxonomy (Lloyd Shinners Coll in Systematic Botany)
Publications: SIDA Botanical Miscellaney; SIDA Contributions to Botany
Bookmobiles: 3

S CARTER & BURGESS, INC, Engineers & Planners Library,* 3880 Hulen St, 76107. SAN 328-6223. Tel: 817-735-6211. FAX: 817-877-5646. Web Site: www.c-b.com. *Librn*, James Gibbs
Library Holdings: Bk Vols 2,000; Per Subs 150

S FORT WORTH MUSEUM OF SCIENCE & HISTORY LIBRARY, 1501 Montgomery St, 76107-3079. SAN 316-3369. Tel: 817-255-9305. FAX: 817-732-7635. Web Site: www.fortworthmuseum.org. *Librn*, C Jane Dees; E-Mail: cjdees@fwmsh.org
Founded 1939
Library Holdings: Bk Vols 7,000
Subject Interests: Archaeology, Astronomy, Ethnology, Geology, Museology, Natural science, Texana
Special Collections: Institutional Archives

P FORT WORTH PUBLIC LIBRARY, 503 W Third St, 76109. SAN 361-6800. Tel: 817-871-7701. Interlibrary Loan Service Tel: 817-871-7731. Circulation Tel: 817-871-7715. TDD: 817-871-8926. FAX: 817-871-7734. E-Mail: library@fortworthlibrary.org. Web Site: www.fortworthlibrary.org. *Dir*, Dr Gleneice A Robinson; Tel: 817-871-7706, E-Mail: RobinsG@ci.fort-worth.tx.us; *Asst Dir*, Catherine A Dixon; Tel: 817-871-7708, E-Mail: cdixon@fortworthlibrary.org; *Br Coordr*, Danita Barber; Tel: 817-871-7712; *ILL*, Mary Sikes; *Govt Doc*, Carrie Gray; Tel: 817-871-7721; *Archivist*, Kenneth Hopkins; Tel: 817-871-7740; *Ref*, Robert Rankin; *Media Spec*, Eric Fry; Tel: 817-871-7991; *Cat*, Jill Blake; Tel: 817-871-7732; *Ch Servs*, Jaye McLaughlin; Tel: 817-871-7745; *Acq*, Roberta Schenewerk; Tel: 817-871-7735; *Commun Relations*, Marsha Anderson; Tel: 817-871-7720; *Humanities and Soc Sci*, Loretta Klassen; Tel: 817-871-7727; *Humanities and Soc Sci*, Thelma Stone; Tel: 817-871-7737; *Tech Coordr*, Edward McCree; Tel: 817-871-8960; *Circ*, Barbara Smith; Staff 185 (MLS 113, Non-MLS 72)
Founded 1901. Pop 504,350
Oct 1998-Sep 1999 Income (Main Library and Branch Library) $10,583,962, State $213,401, City $10,262,951, Federal $52,000, Locally Generated Income $43,025, Other $12,585. Mats Exp $1,863,725, Books $1,044,469, Per/Ser (Incl. Access Fees) $580,979, Micro $17,409, AV Equip $98,863, Electronic Ref Mat (Incl. Access Fees) $122,005. Sal $5,769,258
Library Holdings: Bk Vols 2,200,000; Bk Titles 600,000; Per Subs 2,093
Special Collections: Bookplates; Early Children's Books; Earth Science; Fort Worth History/Archives; Genealogy; Popular Sheet Music; Postcards
Automation Activity & Vendor Info: (Cataloging) epixtech, inc.; (Circulation) epixtech, inc.; (OPAC) epixtech, inc.; (Serials) epixtech, inc.
Database Vendor: Dialog, Ebsco - EbscoHost, epixtech, inc., IAC - Info Trac, Lexis-Nexis, OCLC - First Search
Restriction: Residents only
Mem of North Texas Regional Library System
Special Services for the Deaf - TDD
Special Services for the Blind - Arkenstone, a computer system for the visually handicapped
Friends of the Library Group
Branches: 11
DIAMOND HILL JARVIS BRANCH LIBRARY, 1300 NE 35th St, 76106. SAN 323-8385. Tel: 817-624-7331. FAX: 817-625-4029. Web Site: www.fortworthlibrary.org. *Librn*, Lynn Allen
Library Holdings: Bk Vols 49,977
Friends of the Library Group
EAST BERRY, 4300 E Berry St, 76105. SAN 361-6959. Tel: 817-536-1945. FAX: 817-536-6253. Web Site: www.fortworthlibrary.org. *Librn*, Larry Gainor
Library Holdings: Bk Vols 51,615
Friends of the Library Group
EAST REGIONAL, 6301 Bridge St, 76105. SAN 376-9321. Tel: 817-871-6436. FAX: 817-871-6440. Web Site: www.fortworthlibrary.org. *Librn*, Sheila Barnett
Library Holdings: Bk Vols 56,991
Friends of the Library Group
MEADOWBROOK, 5651 E Lancaster, 76112. SAN 361-6835. Tel: 817-451-0916. FAX: 817-496-8931. Web Site: ci.fort-worth.tx.us:443/. *Librn*, Jacqueline Davis
Library Holdings: Bk Vols 67,449
Friends of the Library Group
NORTHSIDE, 601 Park St, 76106. SAN 361-686X. Tel: 817-626-8241. FAX: 817-625-0702. Web Site: www.fortworthlibrary.org. *Librn*, Neva White
Library Holdings: Bk Vols 46,225
Friends of the Library Group
RIDGLEA, 3628 Bernie Anderson Ave, 76116. SAN 361-7017. Tel: 817-737-6619. FAX: 817-763-8404. Web Site: www.fortworthlibrary.org. *Librn*, Wynette Schwalm
Library Holdings: Bk Vols 95,152
Friends of the Library Group
RIVERSIDE, 2913 Yucca, 76111. SAN 361-6894. Tel: 817-838-6931. FAX: 817-838-5403. Web Site: www.fortworthlibrary.org. *Librn*, Marion Edwards
Library Holdings: Bk Vols 55,413
Friends of the Library Group
SEMINARY SOUTH, 501 E Bolt St, 76110. SAN 361-6924. Tel: 817-926-0215. FAX: 817-926-1703. Web Site: www.fortworthlibrary.org. *Librn*,

Cornelia Pim
Library Holdings: Bk Vols 66,333
Friends of the Library Group
SHAMBLEE, 959 E Rosdale, 76104. SAN 361-6916. Tel: 817-870-1330. FAX: 817-871-6624. Web Site: www.fortworthlibrary.org.
Library Holdings: Bk Vols 32,337
Friends of the Library Group
SOUTHWEST REGIONAL, 4001 Library Lane, 76109. SAN 328-7327. Tel: 817-782-9853. FAX: 817-732-8714. Web Site: www.fortworthlibrary.org. *Librn*, Lynn Seymour
Library Holdings: Bk Vols 131,489
Friends of the Library Group
WEDGEWOOD, 3816 Kimberly Lane, 76133. SAN 361-6983. Tel: 817-292-3368. FAX: 817-346-1862. Web Site: www.fortworthlibrary.org. *Librn*, Linda Bostic
Library Holdings: Bk Vols 80,583
Friends of the Library Group

S FORT WORTH STAR-TELEGRAM REFERENCE LIBRARY, 400 W Seventh, 76102. SAN 316-3385. Tel: 817-390-7742. FAX: 817-390-7255. Web Site: star-telegram.com. *Chief Librn*, Janice C Fennell; Tel: 817-390-7741, E-Mail: jfennell@star-telegram.com; *Asst Librn*, Shannon Canard; Tel: 817-390-7740; Staff 8 (MLS 2, Non-MLS 6)
Founded 1909
Jan 2000-Dec 2000 Mats Exp $99,830, Books $5,400, Per/Ser (Incl. Access Fees) $2,000, Presv $12,000, Micro $13,800, Electronic Ref Mat (Incl. Access Fees) $48,000. Sal $226,700 (Prof $78,000)
Library Holdings: Bk Vols 750; Bk Titles 750; Per Subs 20
Subject Interests: Local news

M HARRIS METHODIST HEALTH SCIENCES LIBRARY,* 1301 Pennsylvania Ave, 76104. SAN 316-3393. Tel: 817-882-2118. FAX: 817-878-5119. *Dir*, Scarlett Burchfield; E-Mail: scarlettburchfield@hmhs.com; *Librn*, Janice Johnstone
Founded 1948
Library Holdings: Bk Vols 2,200; Per Subs 325
Subject Interests: Internal medicine, Surgery
Partic in Metroplex Coun of Health Sci Libr; S Cent Regional Med Libr Program; Tarrant County Consortium of Health Sci Libr

R HEMPHILL PRESBYTERIAN CHURCH LIBRARY, 1701 Hemphill St, 76110. SAN 316-3407. Tel: 817-924-2607. FAX: 817-923-7616.
Library Holdings: Bk Vols 2,700

R INDEPENDENT BAPTIST COLLEGE LIBRARY, 5101 Western Center Blvd, 76137. (Mail add: PO Box 161309, 76161), SAN 324-1858. Tel: 817-514-6364. FAX: 817-281-8257. E-Mail: ibcsvbc@juno.com. Web Site: indbaptist.org. *Librn*, Beverly Dotson
Founded 1964. Enrl 50; Fac 10; Highest Degree: Bachelor
Library Holdings: Bk Vols 12,000; Per Subs 50
Subject Interests: Bible, Education, Music, Theology
Restriction: Students only

L KELLY, HART & HALLMAN, Law Library,* Texas Commerce Bldg, 201 Main St Ste 2500, 76102. SAN 372-1639. Tel: 817-332-2500. FAX: 817-878-9280. *Librn*, Amy E Yawn; Fax: 817-878-9822, E-Mail: amy_yawn@khh.com; Staff 3 (Non-MLS 3)
Library Holdings: Bk Vols 18,000; Per Subs 45
Subject Interests: Labor, Real estate

S KIMBELL ART MUSEUM LIBRARY, 3333 Camp Bowie Blvd, 76107. SAN 316-3415. Tel: 817-332-8451. FAX: 817-877-1264. E-Mail: ccshih@kimbellmuseum.org. *Librn*, Chia-Chun Shih; *Asst Librn*, Steve R Gassett
Founded 1967
Jan 2000-Dec 2000 Mats Exp $50,000, Books $40,000, Per/Ser (Incl. Access Fees) $10,000
Library Holdings: Bk Vols 37,000; Per Subs 135
Subject Interests: Art, Contemporary art, Excluding Am
Automation Activity & Vendor Info: (Acquisitions) DRA; (OPAC) DRA
Database Vendor: DRA
Partic in CDLC; RLIN

S LOCKHEED MARTIN TACTICAL AIRCRAFT SYSTEMS, Research Library,* PO Box 901022, MZ2246, 76101. SAN 361-7041. Tel: 817-763-1792. Interlibrary Loan Service Tel: 817-763-1793. FAX: 817-762-6761. *Chief Librn, Coll Develop*, Maxine Merriman; *Librn*, Gale Harris; *Librn*, Virginia Smith; *ILL, Ref*, Debra Johnson; *Circ*, Linda Brown
Founded 1950
Library Holdings: Bk Titles 523,000; Per Subs 850
Subject Interests: Aeronautics, Bus, Electronics, Manufacturing tech, Marketing, Mat sci, Mgt, Productivity, Quality
Special Collections: History of Aeronautics & Astronautics
Publications: For your Information Newsletter
Restriction: By appointment only

S MOTOROLA, Technical Library,* 5555 N Beach St, 76137-2794. SAN 329-2495. Tel: 817-245-6251. FAX: 817-245-6906.
Founded 1980
Library Holdings: Bk Titles 2,000
Subject Interests: Electrical engineering
Restriction: Not open to public
Partic in Dialog Corporation

G NATIONAL ARCHIVES SOUTHWEST REGION LIBRARY,* Bldg 1, 5 W Felix St, PO Box 6216, 76115. SAN 316-3423. Tel: 817-334-5525. FA 817-334-5621. Web Site: www.nara.gov. *Dir*, Kent Carter; *Asst Dir*, Bobb Hampton
Open Mon-Fri 8-4

P NORTH TEXAS REGIONAL LIBRARY SYSTEM,* 1111 Foch St Ste 1 76107-2949. SAN 316-3458. Tel: 817-335-6076. FAX: 817-335-7145. E-Mail: ntrls@onramp.net. *Exec Dir*, Lynne C Handy; *Asst Dir*, Christy L Milliot; Staff 6 (MLS 6)
Pop 2,244,225
Sep 1999-Aug 2000 Income $892,686, State $369,126, Federal $386,004. Mats Exp $197,151, Books $175,670, Per/Ser (Incl. Access Fees) $3,609, Micro $500, AV Equip $15,947, Electronic Ref Mat (Incl. Access Fees) $1,425. Sal $227,417 (Prof $186,733)
Publications: Connections (bi-monthly newsletter); Professional Library Service Catalog; Videocassette Catalog
Member Libraries: Alvarado Public Library; Alvord Public Library; Arcl Public Library; Arlington Public Library System; Aubrey Area Library; A Public Library; Baylor County Free Library; Bedford Public Library; Benbrook Public Library; Bicentennial City-County Public Library; Blue Mound Community Library; Bowie Public Library; Boyce Ditto Public Library; Boyd Public Library; Burkburnett Library; Burleson Public Libra Carnegie City-County Library; Chico Public Library; City of Justin; Cleburne Public Library; Crowley Public Library; Decatur Public Library; Denton Public Library; Denton Public Library; Dublin Public Library; Ea Parker County Library; Edwards Public Library; Electra Public Library; Euless Public Library; Everman Public Library; Flower Mound Public Library; Foard County Library; Fort Worth Public Library; Gladys Johnso Ritchie Library; Grapevine Public Library; Haltom City Public Library; Hood County Public Library; Hurst Public Library; John A & Katherine C Jackson Municipal Bridgeport Public Library; Keller Public Library; Krun Public Library; Lake Cities Library; Lewisville Public Library System; Library of Graham; Mansfield Public Library; Mary Lou Reddick Public Library; Newark Public Library; Nocona Public Library; North Richland Hills Public Library; Olney Community Library & Arts Center; Pilot Poin Community Library; Richland Hills Public Library; River Oaks Public Library; Roanoke Public Library; Saginaw Public Library; Sanger Public Library; Somervell County Library; Springtown Public Library; Stephenvi Public Library; The Colony Public Library; Thompson-Sawyer Public Library; Tom Burnett Memorial Library; Vernon Regional Junior College; Watauga Public Library; Weatherford Public Library; White Settlement Public Library; Wichita Falls Public Library
Friends of the Library Group

P RIVER OAKS PUBLIC LIBRARY,* 4900 River Oaks Blvd, 76114. SAN 316-6961. Tel: 817-624-7344. FAX: 817-624-2154. *Librn*, Joann Payne
Pop 7,800; Circ 58,207
Library Holdings: Bk Vols 28,292; Per Subs 30
Mem of North Texas Regional Library System
Friends of the Library Group

M JOHN PETER SMITH HOSPITAL, Medical Library,* 1500 S Main St, 76104. SAN 316-3490. Tel: 817-921-3431, Ext 5088. FAX: 817-923-0718
Founded 1960
Library Holdings: Bk Vols 20,000; Per Subs 300
Subject Interests: Dental surgery, Family practice, Gynecology, Internal medicine, Mgt, Nursing, Obstetrics, Othopedics, Pediatrics, Psychiatry, Radiology
Partic in Healthline; Medline; SCC/MLA
Institutional member of Medical Library Association

C SOUTHWESTERN BAPTIST THEOLOGICAL SEMINARY, Roberts Library, 4518 Stanley, 76115. (Mail add: PO Box 22490, 76122-0490), SA 361-7106. Tel: 817-923-1921, Ext 4000. FAX: 817-921-8765. Web Site: www.swbts.edu. *Dir*, Dr Berry Driver; *Asst Dir, Bibliog Instr, Coll Develo* Robert L Phillips; E-Mail: rphillips@lib.swbts.edu; *Acq*, Anna Wilson; *Ca* Barrett Border; *Archivist*, Mike Pullin; *Circ, Reader Servs*, Gene Longley; Staff 10 (MLS 10)
Founded 1908. Enrl 3,400; Fac 141; Highest Degree: Doctorate
Library Holdings: Bk Vols 430,000; Per Subs 2,200
Subject Interests: Religious education, Sacred music, Theology
Special Collections: Baptist History (James M Carroll, George W Truett M E Dodd Coll), mss files; Hymnals; Texas Baptist History, bks & mss fi
Automation Activity & Vendor Info: (Acquisitions) DRA; (Cataloging) DRA; (Circulation) DRA; (Course Reserve) DRA; (OPAC) DRA; (Serials DRA
Publications: New Titles List
Partic in OCLC Online Computer Library Center, Inc
Departmental Libraries:
AUDIOVISUAL LEARNING CENTER-COMPUTER SYSTEMS Tel: 81 923-1921, Ext 2920. FAX: 817-921-8765. *Librn*, Amy Adams
Subject Interests: Religion, Theolog media mat

Special Collections: Film Coll; Southern Baptist Convention Agencies
KATHRYN SULLIVAN BOWLD MUSIC LIBRARY Tel: 817-923-1921, Ext 2070. FAX: 817-921-8765. *Librn*, Fang-Lan Hsien
Library Holdings: Bk Titles 26,066
Subject Interests: Church, Relig scores, Sacred music
Special Collections: George Stebbins Memorial; Hymnals

TARRANT COUNTY JUNIOR COLLEGE
JENKINS GARRETT LIBRARY, 5301 Campus Dr, 76119. SAN 361-7289. Tel: 817-515-4524. FAX: 817-515-5726. E-Mail: library@tcjc.cc.tx.us. *Dir Libr Serv*, Dr Ted Drake; *Publ Servs*, Frances May; *Publ Servs*, Sue Chen; Staff 5 (MLS 5)
Founded 1967. Enrl 7,142; Fac 175
Sep 1997-Aug 1998 Mats Exp $89,000, Books $60,000, Per/Ser (Incl. Access Fees) $20,000, Micro $9,000. Sal $422,983
Library Holdings: Bk Titles 69,460; Per Subs 567
NORTHWEST CAMPUS WALSH LIBRARY, 4801 Marine Creek Pkwy, 76179. SAN 361-7254. Tel: 817-515-7725, 817-515-7765. FAX: 817-515-7720. Web Site: www.tcjc.cc.tx.us. *Dir*, Anna Holzer; E-Mail: aholzer@tcjc.cc.tx.us; *Asst Dir*, John Gonzalez; *Publ Servs*, Sandra McCurdy; Staff 4 (MLS 4)
Founded 1975. Enrl 5,240; Fac 90
1998-1999 Mats Exp $60,757, Books $36,950, Per/Ser (Incl. Access Fees) $23,807. Sal $245,279 (Prof $117,594)
Library Holdings: Bk Vols 41,024; Per Subs 250

TARRANT COUNTY LAW LIBRARY,* 100 W Weatherford, Rm 420, 76196-0800. SAN 316-3504. Tel: 817-884-1481. FAX: 817-884-1509. E-Mail: tarrant@onramp.net. *Dir*, Sharon Wayland; *Asst Dir*, Peggy Martindale; Staff 7 (MLS 4, Non-MLS 3)
Founded 1942
Library Holdings: Bk Vols 45,000; Bk Titles 3,300; Per Subs 270
Publications: Book catalog; library guide

TEXAS CHRISTIAN UNIVERSITY, Mary Couts Burnett Library, 2913 Lowden St, TCU Box 298400, 76129. SAN 361-7319. Tel: 817-257-7106. Interlibrary Loan Service Tel: 817-257-7117. Circulation Tel: 817-257-7112. Reference Tel: 817-257-7117. TDD: 817-257-7716. FAX: 817-257-7282. E-Mail: library@tcu.edu. Web Site: library.tcu.edu. *Head of Libr*, Robert A Seal; E-Mail: r.seal@tcu.edu; *Assoc Dir*, June Koelker; E-Mail: j.koelker@tcu.edu; *Librn*, James Lutz; *Librn*, Sheila Madden; *Asst Librn, Publ Servs*, Hugh MacDonald; *Cat*, Sara Dillard; *Cat*, Vinita Dobson; *Cat*, Sally Sorensen; *Per*, Janet Douglass; *Govt Doc*, Brenda Barnes; *Spec Coll*, Roger Rainwater; *Online Servs, Ref Serv*, Marianne Bobich; *ILL*, Sandy Schrag; *Circ*, Cheryl Sassman; *Automation Syst Coordr*, Kerry Bouchard; *Bibliog Instr*, Victor Baeza; *Archivist*, Glenda Stevens; *Archivist*, Laura Ruede; *Acq*, Dennis Odom; *Coll Develop*, Dennis Gibbons; *Electronic Resources*, Jennifer Duncan; Staff 54 (MLS 23, Non-MLS 31)
Founded 1873. Enrl 7,551; Fac 453; Highest Degree: Doctorate
Jun 1999-May 2000 Mats Exp $2,655,252, Books $839,115, Per/Ser (Incl. Access Fees) $1,362,092, Presv $52,720, AV Equip $24,012, Other Print Mats $6,984, Electronic Ref Mat (Incl. Access Fees) $370,329. Sal $1,518,057 (Prof $894,069)
Library Holdings: Bk Vols 1,284,100; Bk Titles 60,949; Per Subs 4,848
Subject Interests: Chemistry, English, History, Literature, Music, Psychology, Theology
Special Collections: European Union Documentation Centre; International Piano Competition (Van Cliburn Foundation Archives), AV mat; Literature (William Luther Lewis Coll); United States History (James C Wright Jr Archives)
Automation Activity & Vendor Info: (Acquisitions) DRA; (Cataloging) DRA; (Circulation) DRA; (OPAC) DRA; (Serials) DRA
Database Vendor: Dialog, DRA, GaleNet, IAC - Info Trac, OCLC - First Search, OVID Technologies, Silverplatter Information Inc.
Publications: Windows
Restriction: Restricted public use
Function: Research library
Partic in Amigos Library Services, Inc; TexShare
Special Services for the Deaf - TDD
Friends of the Library Group
Departmental Libraries:
BRITE DIVINITY SCHOOL, 2913 Lowden St, TCU Box 298400, 76129. Tel: 817-257-7668. *Librn*, Charles Bellinger

TEXAS WESLEYAN UNIVERSITY, Eunice & James L West Library,* 1201 Wesleyan St, 76105-1536. SAN 316-3512. Tel: 817-531-4800. FAX: 817-531-4806. Web Site: www.txwes.edu/library. *Dir*, Cindy Swigger; Tel: 817-531-4821, E-Mail: swiggerc@txwes.edu; *Archivist*, Louis Sherwood; Tel: 817-531-4822, E-Mail: sherwoodl@txwes.edu; *Tech Servs*, Shelley Almgren; Tel: 817-531-4804, E-Mail: almgrens@txwes.edu; *Per*, Kathy Nichols; Tel: 817-531-4816, E-Mail: nicholsk@txwes.edu; *Electronic Resources*, Andy Baker; Tel: 817-531-4808, E-Mail: bakera@txwes.edu; *Publ Servs*, Paula Sanders; Tel: 817-531-4811, E-Mail: sandersp@txwes.edu; *Coll Develop*, David Thurston; Tel: 817-531-4813, E-Mail: thurstond@txwes.edu; Staff 12 (MLS 6, Non-MLS 6)
Founded 1891. Enrl 3,049; Fac 122; Highest Degree: Master
Jun 1998-May 1999 Mats Exp $149,107, Books $53,798, Per/Ser (Incl. Access Fees) $82,725, Manuscripts & Archives $2,600, Electronic Ref Mat (Incl. Access Fees) $9,984. Sal $336,183 (Prof $194,920)
Library Holdings: Bk Vols 222,055; Bk Titles 314,716; Per Subs 693
Subject Interests: Literature
Special Collections: Joe Brown Theatre Coll, microfiche; Twyla Daniel Juvenile Coll, music scores
Automation Activity & Vendor Info: (Acquisitions) SIRSI; (Cataloging) SIRSI; (Circulation) SIRSI; (Course Reserve) SIRSI; (OPAC) SIRSI; (Serials) SIRSI
Database Vendor: Dialog, Ebsco - EbscoHost, OCLC - First Search, OVID Technologies, Silverplatter Information Inc., Wilson - Wilson Web
Partic in Amigos Library Services, Inc; OCLC Online Computer Library Center, Inc

R TRAVIS AVENUE BAPTIST CHURCH LIBRARY,* 3041 Travis Ave, 76110. SAN 316-3520. Tel: 817-924-4266. FAX: 817-921-9620. *Librn*, Cornelia Pim
Library Holdings: Bk Vols 1,250
Open Wed & Sun

S UNION PACIFIC RESOURCES CO, Technical Information Center,* 777 Main St MS 26-01, 76102. (Mail add: PO Box 7 MS26-01, 76101), SAN 321-8031. FAX: 817-321-7794. *Mgr*, Debra Lammons; Tel: 817-321-7739, E-Mail: debralammons@upr.com; *Librn*, Michele Ellis; Tel: 817-321-6395, Fax: 817-820-7269, E-Mail: micheleellis@upr.com
Library Holdings: Bk Vols 20,000; Bk Titles 16,500; Per Subs 269
Subject Interests: Geology, Geophysics, Petroleum engineering, Petroleum indust
Publications: Current Awareness Bulletin; Petroleum Abstracts, Univ of Tulsa; Tic Picks
Partic in Dialog Corporation

UNITED STATES ARMY
A CORPS OF ENGINEERS, FORT WORTH DISTRICT TECHNICAL LIBRARY, 819 Taylor St, PO Box 17300, 76102-0300. SAN 361-7408. Tel: 817-978-3585. FAX: 817-978-2472.
Founded 1950
Library Holdings: Bk Vols 35,000; Per Subs 500
Subject Interests: Engineering, Environmental studies, Soil survey
Special Collections: Civil & Military Design Reports; Law (Federal, Texas, Louisiana & New Mexico); State of Texas Water Resources Reports
Restriction: Staff use only
Partic in Fedlink; OCLC Online Computer Library Center, Inc

G UNITED STATES DEPARTMENT OF HOUSING & URBAN DEVELOPMENT, Region VI Library, 801 Cherry St, 76102. (Mail add: PO Box 2905, 76113), SAN 321-0235. Tel: 817-978-5924. FAX: 817-978-5563. *Librn*, Susan M Mann; Staff 1 (MLS 1)
Subject Interests: Housing, Law
Special Collections: Federal Reporters; Law; State Statutes for AR, LA, NM, OK & TX; Housing & Urban Affairs Coll, microfiche

G UNITED STATES DEPARTMENT OF JUSTICE, Bureau of Prisons Federal Medical Center,* 3150 Horton Rd, 76119. SAN 316-3539. Tel: 817-534-8400. *Librn*, Julia Yanez
Founded 1938
Library Holdings: Bk Vols 3,500; Per Subs 15
Subject Interests: Narcotic addiction, Psychiatry, Psychology

UNITED STATES NAVY
A NAVAL AIR STATION LIBRARY, 1500 Desert Storm Rd, NAS Fort Worth JRB, 76127. SAN 361-5480. Tel: 817-782-7735. FAX: 817-782-7219. *Librn*, Bro Bobbie Skipper; E-Mail: skipperbarb@yahoo.com; *Tech Servs*, Pat Tellman; E-Mail: alsun@yahoo.com
Oct 1999-Sep 2000 Income Federal $125,000. Mats Exp $30,260, Books $12,452, Per/Ser (Incl. Access Fees) $4,000, AV Equip $1,329, Electronic Ref Mat (Incl. Access Fees) $12,479. Sal $85,000 (Prof $85,000)
Library Holdings: Bk Vols 28,000; Per Subs 65
Subject Interests: Military history
Automation Activity & Vendor Info: (Cataloging) Follett; (Circulation) Follett; (OPAC) Follett
Restriction: Not open to public

C UNIVERSITY OF NORTH TEXAS HEALTH SCIENCE CENTER AT FORT WORTH, Lewis Health Science Library, 3500 Camp Bowie Blvd, 76107-2699. SAN 316-3466. Tel: 817-735-2380. Interlibrary Loan Service Tel: 817-735-2491. FAX: 817-735-2283. Interlibrary Loan Service FAX: 817-763-0408. Web Site: www.hsc.unt.edu/library. *Dir*, Bobby R Carter; E-Mail: brcarter@hsc.unt.edu; *Assoc Dir, Publ Servs*, Ann Brooks; Tel: 817-735-2591, E-Mail: abrooks@hsc.unt.edu; *Assoc Dir, Tech Servs*, Craig Elam; Tel: 817-735-2469, E-Mail: elamc@hsc.unt.edu; *AV*, Moira Foster; Tel: 817-735-2606, E-Mail: mfoster@hsc.unt.edu; *Tech Servs*, Tim Mason; Tel: 817-735-2466, E-Mail: tmason@hsc.unt.edu; *Ser*, Sherry White; Tel: 817-735-2467, E-Mail: shwhite@hsc.unt.edu; *Instrul Serv*, Dan Burgard; Tel: 817-735-2589, E-Mail: dburgard@hsc.unt.edu; *Ref*, Janna Ferguson; Tel: 817-735-5070, E-Mail: jferguso@hsc.unt.edu; *Ref*, Janice Johnstone; Tel: 817-735-5070, E-Mail: jjohnsto@hsc.unt.edu; *Ref*, Linda King; Tel: 817-735-2590, E-Mail: lking@hsc.unt.edu; *Info Specialist*, Lynn Johnson; Tel: 817-735-5459, E-Mail: lyjohnson@hsc.unt.edu; *Syst Coordr*, Dohn Martin; Tel:

817-735-2227, E-Mail: dhmartin@hsc.unt.edu; *Instrul Serv*, Phyllis Muirhead; Tel: 817-735-2601, E-Mail: pmuirhead@hsc.unt.edu; *Outreach Serv*, Jack Raines; Tel: 827-735-2588, E-Mail: jraines@hsc.unt.edu; Staff 46 (MLS 12, Non-MLS 34)
Founded 1970. Enrl 800; Fac 200; Highest Degree: Doctorate
Sep 1999-Aug 2000 Income $2,263,139, State $1,988,390, Locally Generated Income $240,639. Mats Exp $825,634, Books $106,483, Per/Ser (Incl. Access Fees) $639,399, Presv $21,653, Electronic Ref Mat (Incl. Access Fees) $44,437. Sal $1,271,648 (Prof $650,126)
Library Holdings: Bk Vols 63,298; Bk Titles 60,416; Per Subs 2,159
Subject Interests: Family practice, Gen, Medicine, Osteopathic med, Public health
Special Collections: History of Osteopathic Medicine; Texas Osteopathic Medical Association Archives; William G Sutherland Coll
Publications: Acquisition list; Collection Catalog; Lewis Lines; Library Guide; Library Handbook; Media Resources Guide; Newbooks; Newsletter; On-Line Services Guide; Oral History Collection CAT; Research Guide
Partic in Amigos Library Services, Inc; Healthline; Nat Libr of Med; S Cent Regional Med Libr Program; South Central Academic Medical Libraries Consortium; TexShare
Resource Library for the Texas Osteopathic Medical Association; Telefacsimile Document Delivery Network (31 machines at 22 sites)

FRANKLIN

P ROBERTSON COUNTY LIBRARY,* Hwy 79, PO Box 1027, 77856. SAN 316-3547. Tel: 409-828-4331. *Dir*, Mary Jones
Pop 1,884
Library Holdings: Bk Titles 10,000
Mem of Tex Libr Syst

FRANKSTON

P FRANKSTON DEPOT LIBRARY & MUSEUM,* Town Sq S, PO Box 639, 75763-0639. SAN 376-4435. Tel: 903-876-4463. FAX: 903-876-3226. *Librn*, Patricia Montrose; E-Mail: patm@gower.net
Library Holdings: Bk Vols 16,000; Per Subs 30
Mem of Northeast Texas Library System
Friends of the Library Group

FREDERICKSBURG

S ADMIRAL NIMITZ MUSEUM, Center for Pacific War Studies,* 328 E Main St, PO Box 777, 78624. SAN 374-4620. Tel: 830-997-4379, Ext 224. FAX: 830-997-8220. *Curator*, Paula Ussery; *Librn*, Alice LaForet; *Asst Librn*, Jessie Leigh
Founded 1978 Mats Exp Manuscripts & Archives $300
Library Holdings: Bk Vols 2,000; Bk Titles 3,000; Per Subs 30
Special Collections: Admiral Chester Nimitz Coll, bks, paper, photogs; World War II Pacific Coll, bks, maps, paper, photogs, posters; World War II Vet
Friends of the Library Group

P PIONEER MEMORIAL LIBRARY,* 115 W Main St, 78624. SAN 316-3555. Tel: 830-997-6513. FAX: 830-997-6514. E-Mail: pml@hctc.net. *Librn*, Sue Croom; Staff 1 (MLS 1)
Founded 1966. Pop 19,635; Circ 88,693
Oct 1996-Sep 1997 Income $194,273. Mats Exp $16,231, Books $11,630, Per/Ser (Incl. Access Fees) $4,343. Sal $115,973 (Prof $28,429)
Library Holdings: Bk Vols 40,619; Bk Titles 36,688; Per Subs 86
Special Collections: German Coll
Mem of Alamo Area Library System
Friends of the Library Group

FREEPORT

S DOW CHEMICAL LIBRARY, Business Intelligence Ctr, B-1210, 2301 Brazosport Blvd, 77541. SAN 316-3563. Tel: 409-238-3512. *Senior Librn*, Carl Wolfe; *Res*, Gary McNamee; *Info Specialist*, Thomas Marman; *Info Specialist*, R Martinez; *Info Specialist*, Don Maschmeyer; *Info Specialist*, Gary McNamee; Staff 6 (MLS 1, Non-MLS 5)
Founded 1944
Library Holdings: Bk Vols 12,000; Bk Titles 10,000; Per Subs 250
Subject Interests: Chemistry, Commerce, Engineering, Indust, Proprietary res
Automation Activity & Vendor Info: (OPAC) SIRSI
Database Vendor: Dialog
Partic in Amigos Library Services, Inc; OCLC Online Computer Library Center, Inc

FRIENDSWOOD

P FRIENDSWOOD PUBLIC LIBRARY, 416 S Friendswood Dr, 77546-3897. SAN 316-358X. Interlibrary Loan Service Tel: 281-482-7135. FAX: 281-482-2685. E-Mail: frpublib@friendswood.lib.tx.us. Web Site: www.friendswood.lib.tx.us. *Dir*, Mary B Perroni; *Circ, Mgr*, Mary Keeve *Ch Servs*, Monetta Houston; *Tech Servs*, Lisa Loranc; *Ref*, Donald LeBla Staff 3 (MLS 3)
Founded 1968. Pop 33,000; Circ 260,000
Oct 1998-Sep 1999 Income $599,928, City $570,928, County $26,500, O $2,500. Mats Exp $123,689, Books $85,686, Per/Ser (Incl. Access Fees) $10,951, Micro $847, AV Equip $16,492, Electronic Ref Mat (Incl. Acces Fees) $9,713. Sal $399,682 (Prof $80,000)
Library Holdings: Bk Vols 79,175; Bk Titles 70,228; Per Subs 175
Automation Activity & Vendor Info: (Cataloging) epixtech, inc.; (Circulation) epixtech, inc.; (Media Booking) epixtech, inc.
Database Vendor: Ebsco - EbscoHost, OCLC - First Search
Mem of Galveston County Libr Syst; Houston Area Library System
Friends of the Library Group

FRIONA

P FRIONA PUBLIC LIBRARY, 109 W Seventh, 79035-2548. SAN 316-35 Tel: 806-250-3200. FAX: 806-250-2185. *Librn*, Darla Bracken; *Asst Librn* Brenda Patterson
Founded 1963. Pop 3,908
Library Holdings: Bk Vols 28,700; Per Subs 75
Database Vendor: DRA
Publications: Friends of the Library (quarterly newsletter)
Mem of Texas Panhandle Library System
Partic in OCLC Online Computer Library Center, Inc
Special Services for the Blind - Kurzweil Reading Machine
Friends of the Library Group

GAINESVILLE

P COOKE COUNTY LIBRARY,* 200 S Weaver St, 76240. SAN 316-361X Tel: 940-665-2401. FAX: 940-665-5885. E-Mail: cookcountylib@texoma.r *Dir*, Ann Woods; *Circ*, Barbara Callaway; *Circ*, Dora Ward; *Tech Servs*, Helen Neu; *Tech Servs*, Kay Bishop
Founded 1893. Pop 25,000
Library Holdings: Bk Titles 56,617; Per Subs 115
Subject Interests: Genealogy, Local history
Special Collections: Local Artists Coll; Local History Coll
Mem of Northeast Texas Library System

R FIRST PRESBYTERIAN CHURCH LIBRARY, 401 S Denton St, 76240. (Mail add: PO Box 751, 76241), SAN 316-3628. Tel: 940-665-5153. *Librn* Betty Guest
Founded 1957
Library Holdings: Bk Vols 2,800
Subject Interests: Biographies, Fiction, Theology

J NORTH CENTRAL TEXAS COLLEGE LIBRARY,* 1525 W California 76240-0815. SAN 316-3601. Tel: 940-668-4283, 940-668-7731. FAX: 940 668-4203. *Dir*, Patsy Wilson; E-Mail: p.wilson@nctc.cc.tx.us; *Asst Dir, Librn*, Lee Switzer; Staff 2 (MLS 2)
Enrl 3,064; Fac 88
Library Holdings: Bk Titles 48,000; Per Subs 280
Subject Interests: Cooke County hist
Publications: Bibliographies; Faculty Handbook
Mem of Northeast Texas Library System

GALVESTON

J GALVESTON COLLEGE, David Glenn Hunt Memorial Library, 4015 Avenue Q, 77550. SAN 316-3636. Tel: 409-763-6551, Ext 240. FAX: 409-762-9367. Web Site: www.gc.edu/library. *Asst Dean*, Gary E Wilson; E-Mail: gwilson@gc.edu; *Tech Servs*, Hazel Ellis; *Ref*, Anne Brasier; Staff (MLS 2)
Founded 1967. Enrl 2,230
Sep 1999-Aug 2000 Income $294,465. Mats Exp $65,500, Books $35,000, Per/Ser (Incl. Access Fees) $22,200, Micro $4,300, AV Equip $4,000. Sal $150,825 (Prof $105,000)
Library Holdings: Bk Titles 40,220; Per Subs 205
Subject Interests: Education, Literature, Local history, Nursing
Automation Activity & Vendor Info: (Cataloging) EOS; (Circulation) EO (OPAC) EOS; (Serials) EOS

P ROSENBERG LIBRARY,* 2310 Sealy Ave, 77550-2296. SAN 316-3652. Tel: 409-763-2526 (Admin), 409-763-8854. Reference FAX: 409-763-1064 Web Site: www.geocities.com/athens/delphi/5181. *Exec Dir*, Nancy Milnor E-Mail: nlmilmor@rosenberg-library.org; *Ad Servs*, Barbara Kandt; *ILL*, Barbara Bienkowski; *Circ*, Walter Hunter; *Tech Servs*, Jessica Clarke; *Spec Coll*, Casey Greene; *Curator*, Elisabeth Darst; *Ch Servs*, Karen Stanley; Staff 12 (MLS 12)
Founded 1900. Pop 70,194; Circ 275,145
Oct 1998-Sep 1999 Income $1,932,285, City $839,134, County $435,000, Locally Generated Income $90,763, Parent Institution $562,009, Other $5,379. Mats Exp $210,951, Books $139,344. Sal $1,103,187 (Prof $496,887)
Library Holdings: Bk Vols 232,670; Bk Titles 143,975; Per Subs 603

Special Collections: Galveston & Texas History, bks, videos, mss, maps, photog, vert file, oral history; Maritime History, art, artifacts, bks, charts, mss, maps; Museum Collection, art, artifacts; Rare Books (Colonel Milo Pitcher Fox & Agness Peel Fox Rare Room), bks, mss, maps
Automation Activity & Vendor Info: (Acquisitions) epixtech, inc.; (Cataloging) epixtech, inc.; (Circulation) epixtech, inc.
Publications: A Descriptive Catalog of the Cartographic Collection of the Rosenberg Library; Fragile Empires: The Texas Correspondence of Samuel Swartwout & James Morgan, 1836-1856; Julius Stockfleth: Gulf Coast Marine & Landscape Painter; Manuscript Sources in the Rosenberg Library
Mem of Houston Area Library System
Friends of the Library Group

TEMPLE B'NAI ISRAEL, Lasker Memorial Library, 3008 Ave O, 77550. SAN 316-3660. Tel: 409-765-5796. FAX: 409-765-8302. E-Mail: tbisrael@airmail.net. *Librn*, Sophia Nussenblatt
Founded 1955
Library Holdings: Bk Vols 2,500; Per Subs 29

TEXAS A&M UNIVERSITY AT GALVESTON, Jack K Williams Library,* 200 Sea Wolf Pkwy, PO Box 1675, 77553-1675. SAN 316-3644. Tel: 409-740-4560. FAX: 409-740-4702. Web Site: www.tamug.tamu.edu/library. *Dir*, Natalie H Wiest; Tel: 409-740-4567, E-Mail: wiestn@tamug.tamu.edu; *Publ Servs*, Diane Watson; Tel: 409-740-4568, E-Mail: watsond@tamug.tamu.edu; *Tech Servs*, Gena George; Tel: 409-740-4571, E-Mail: georgeg@tamug.tamu.edu; Staff 7 (MLS 3, Non-MLS 4)
Founded 1972. Enrl 1,250; Fac 80; Highest Degree: Bachelor
Sep 1998-Aug 1999 Income $591,968, State $382,110, Locally Generated Income $169,049, Parent Institution $40,809. Mats Exp $272,972, Books $41,457, Per/Ser (Incl. Access Fees) $224,515, Electronic Ref Mat (Incl. Access Fees) $7,000. Sal $222,247 (Prof $107,600)
Library Holdings: Bk Vols 61,780; Per Subs 400
Subject Interests: Marine biology, Maritime, Oceanography, Transportation
Special Collections: Galveston Bay Information Center
Automation Activity & Vendor Info: (Acquisitions) Endeavor; (Cataloging) Endeavor; (Circulation) Endeavor; (Course Reserve) Endeavor; (ILL) Endeavor; (Media Booking) Endeavor; (OPAC) Endeavor; (Serials) Endeavor
Partic in Amigos Library Services, Inc; Tex Share

UNITED STATES ARMY
GALVESTON DISTRICT CORPS OF ENGINEERS LIBRARY, 2000 Fort Point Rd, Rm 308, 77553. (Mail add: PO Box 1229, 77553-1229), Tel: 409-766-3196. FAX: 409-766-3905. Web Site: www.swg.usace.army.mil/library.htm. *Librn*, Clark Bartee; E-Mail: clark.bartee@usace.army.mil; Staff 1 (MLS 1)
Library Holdings: Bk Vols 10,616; Per Subs 136
Subject Interests: Dredging, Ecology, Environ res, Flood control, Flood plain studies, Law, Navigation, Shoreline studies, Soils, Water resources
Special Collections: Archeological Reports; Civil Works Reports (Annual Reports of the C of E 1871-Present); Congressional Documents (1900-Present); Design Memoranda; Environmental Impact Statements & Assessments
Partic in Fedlink; OCLC Online Computer Library Center, Inc

UNIVERSITY OF TEXAS MEDICAL BRANCH, Moody Medical Library,* 301 University Blvd, 77555-1035. SAN 316-3687. Tel: 409-772-1971. FAX: 409-762-9782. Web Site: www.library.utmb.edu. *Dir*, Brett Kirkpatrick; E-Mail: bkirkpat@utmb.edu; *Assoc Dir*, Larry Wygant; E-Mail: lwygant@utmb.edu; *Asst Dir, Tech Servs*, Carol Cowan; E-Mail: ccowan@utmb.edu; *Ref*, Patricia Ciejka; E-Mail: pciejka@utmb.edu; *Cat*, Ellen Wong; E-Mail: ewong@utmb.edu; Staff 56 (MLS 11, Non-MLS 45)
Founded 1891
Sep 1998-Aug 1999 Income $3,682,028, State $3,221,018, Locally Generated Income $247,705, Other $213,305. Mats Exp $1,433,983, Books $80,131, Per/Ser (Incl. Access Fees) $1,183,630, Electronic Ref Mat (Incl. Access Fees) $170,222. Sal $1,752,378 (Prof $777,882)
Library Holdings: Bk Vols 245,650; Bk Titles 96,719; Per Subs 2,326
Subject Interests: Allied health sci, Biomedical, Medicine, Nursing
Special Collections: History of Medicine & Archives
Automation Activity & Vendor Info: (Cataloging) SIRSI; (Circulation) SIRSI; (OPAC) SIRSI
Partic in Amigos Library Services, Inc; Houston Area Research Library Consortium; Nat Libr of Med; OCLC Online Computer Library Center, Inc

ARLAND

AMBER UNIVERSITY, Library Resource Center, 1700 Eastgate Dr, 75041. SAN 316-3695. Tel: 972-279-6511, Ext 137. FAX: 972-686-5567. *Dir*, Judy M Gibson; Tel: 972-279-6511, Ext 136, E-Mail: gibson@ambernet.amberu.edu; *Asst Librn*, Don Weeks; Tel: 972-279-6511, Ext 138, E-Mail: weeks@ambernet.amberu.edu; Staff 5 (MLS 3, Non-MLS 2)
Founded 1971. Enrl 1,500; Highest Degree: Master
Library Holdings: Bk Vols 16,000; Per Subs 125
Subject Interests: Bus admin, Counseling, Ethics, Human relations
Database Vendor: OVID Technologies
Partic in Amigos Library Services, Inc; TexShare

P NICHOLSON MEMORIAL LIBRARY, 625 Austin St, 75040-6365. SAN 361-7467. Tel: 972-205-2543. Reference Tel: 972-205-2500. FAX: 972-205-2523. Web Site: www.nmls.lib.tx.us. *Dir*, Claire Bausch; *Coll Develop, Publ Servs*, Karen Ellis; Tel: 972-205-2546, E-Mail: kellis@nmls.lib.tx.us; *Coll Develop, Coordr, Publ Servs*, Betty Landon; *Tech Servs*, Robert Boyer; *Tech Servs*, Dan Cunningham; *Ch Servs*, Pat Snell; *YA Servs*, Malia Moore; *Ser*, Harry Forbes; *Govt Doc*, Sandra Reynolds; *Ref*, Brenda Bryant; *ILL*, Teresa Roberts; *Media Spec*, Fern Watson; *Syst Coordr*, Erpin Zhao; *AV*, Kathleen Cizek. Subject Specialists: *Business and management*, Walt Greening; *Fiction*, Sandra Reynolds; *Humanities*, Walt Greening; *Law*, Brenda Bryant; Staff 67 (MLS 25, Non-MLS 42)
Founded 1933. Pop 207,928
Oct 1999-Sep 2000 Income (Main Library and Branch Library) City $3,121,633. Mats Exp $470,736, Books $408,784, Per/Ser (Incl. Access Fees) $71,301, Micro $62,973, Electronic Ref Mat (Incl. Access Fees) $36,159. Sal $1,431,342
Library Holdings: Bk Vols 347,119; Per Subs 732
Subject Interests: Genealogy, Gov doc, Local history
Automation Activity & Vendor Info: (Acquisitions) epixtech, inc.; (Cataloging) epixtech, inc.; (Circulation) epixtech, inc.; (OPAC) epixtech, inc.; (Serials) epixtech, inc.
Database Vendor: Ebsco - EbscoHost, epixtech, inc., IAC - Info Trac, ProQuest
Publications: Access (newsletter)
Mem of Northeast Texas Library System
Friends of the Library Group
Branches: 3
NORTH GARLAND BRANCH, 3845 N Garland Ave, 75040. SAN 372-7920. Tel: 972-205-2801. FAX: 972-205-2808. *Mgr*, Bill Raley; *Branch Mgr*, Liza Arrendondo; *Ch Servs*, Jean Ann Kirwin; *Publ Servs*, Karen Ellis; Tel: 972-205-2546, Fax: 972-205-2523, E-Mail: kellis@nmls.lib.tx.us
Library Holdings: Bk Vols 45,357
Friends of the Library Group
RIDGEWOOD, 120 W Kingsley, 75041-3425. SAN 361-7491. Tel: 972-205-2578. FAX: 972-205-2583. *Branch Mgr*, Kathi Mehan; *Ch Servs*, Cheyrl Davenport; *Publ Servs*, Karen Ellis; Tel: 972-205-2523, E-Mail: kellis@nmls.lib.tx.us
Library Holdings: Bk Vols 41,214
Friends of the Library Group
WALNUT CREEK, 3319 Edgewood, 75042-7118. SAN 361-7521. Tel: 972-205-2587. FAX: 972-205-2589. *Mgr*, Bill Raley; *Branch Mgr*, Aurora Arthay; *Librn*, Melva Ramirez; *Publ Servs*, Karen Ellis; Tel: 972-205-2546, Fax: 972-205-2523, E-Mail: kellis@nmls.lib.tx.us; *Ch Servs*, Kelli Phelan
Library Holdings: Bk Vols 45,985
Friends of the Library Group

P NORTHEAST TEXAS LIBRARY SYSTEM,* 625 Austin, 75040-6365. SAN 316-246X. Tel: 972-205-2566. Interlibrary Loan Service Tel: 214-670-1741. FAX: 972-205-2767. Interlibrary Loan Service FAX: 214-670-1752. *Coordr*, Dale Fleeger; *Media Spec*, Barbara Rhodes; *Automation Syst Coordr*, Roy C Lewis Jr; *Coll Develop*, Charlene Edmondson; Staff 5 (MLS 5)
Founded 1969. Pop 3,435,745
Publications: Newsletter (bimonthly)
Member Libraries: A H Meadows Library; Allen Public Library; Atlanta Public Library; Balch Springs Public Library; Bonham Public Library; Cameron J Jarvis Troup Municipal Library; Carrollton Public Library; Celina Community Library; Charles J Rike Memorial Library; Cockrell Hill Public Library; Commerce Public Library; Cooke County Library; Coppell Public; Corsicana Public Library; Daingerfield Public Library; Dallas Public Library; De Soto Public Library; Delta County Public Library; Denison Public Library; Duncanville Public Library; Ennis Public Library; Farmers Branch Public Library; Ferris Public Library; Forney Public Library; Franklin County Library; Frankston Depot Library & Museum; Grand Prairie Memorial Library; Grand Saline Public Library; Highland Park Library; Howe Community Library; Irving Public Library; Jacksonville Public Library; Kaufman County Library; Kilgore Public Library; Lancaster Veterans Memorial Library; Lee Public Library; Leonard Public Library; Longview Public Library; Marshall Public Library; Maud Public Library; Melissa Public Library; Mesquite Public Library; Mesquite Public Library; Mount Pleasant Public Library; New Boston Public Library; Nicholas P Sims Library; Nicholson Memorial Library; North Central Texas College Library; Palestine Public Library; Paris Public Library; Pittsburg-Camp County Library; Plano Public Library System; Pottsboro Area Public Library; Quitman Public Library; Rains County Public Library; Red Waller Community Library; Richardson Public Library; Rita & Truett Smith Library; Rockwall County Library; Rusk County Library; Sachse Public Library; Sammy Brown Library; Sherman Public Library; Singletary Memorial Library; Sulphur Springs Public Library; Tawakoni Area Public Library; Terrell Public Library; Tri-County Library; Tyler Public Library; Upshur County Library; Van Alstyne Public Library; Van Zandt County Library; W Walworth Harrison Public Library; Whitehouse Community Library; Whitewright Public Library; Zula-Bryant-Wylie Library

GATESVILLE

P GATESVILLE PUBLIC LIBRARY, 811 Main St, 76528. SAN 316-375X. Tel: 254-865-5367. FAX: 254-248-0986. E-Mail: gpl@htcomp.net. *Librn*, Faye McCracken; Staff 4 (Non-MLS 4)
Founded 1970. Pop 16,000; Circ 40,975
Oct 1999-Sep 2000 Income City $110,000. Mats Exp $18,550, Books $14,750, Per/Ser (Incl. Access Fees) $2,800, AV Equip $1,000. Sal $48,700 (Prof $20,000)
Library Holdings: Bk Vols 23,150; Bk Titles 22,876; Per Subs 40
Special Collections: Children Coll; Genealogy; Texas Coll & Local History
Mem of Central Texas Library System
Friends of the Library Group

GEORGE WEST

P LIVE OAK COUNTY LIBRARY,* 402 Houston St, PO Box 698, 78022-0698. SAN 361-7556. Tel: 512-449-1124. *Librn*, Opal Miller; *Asst Librn*, Etainne Harrod
Founded 1955. Pop 8,500; Circ 77,967
Jan 1997-Dec 1998 Income $85,369
Library Holdings: Bk Vols 86,598; Per Subs 26
Mem of South Texas Library System
Branches: 1
THREE RIVERS BRANCH, PO Box 869, Three Rivers, 78071-0869. SAN 361-7580. Tel: 512-786-3037. *Librn*, Dorothy Matern

GEORGETOWN

P GEORGETOWN PUBLIC LIBRARY,* 808 Martin Luther King, Jr St, 78626-5527. SAN 316-3768. Tel: 512-930-3551. TDD: 512-930-3507. FAX: 512-930-3764. E-Mail: gpl@georgetowntx.org. Web Site: www.georgetowntx.org. *Dir Libr Serv*, Sheila Ross Henderson; E-Mail: srh@georgetowntx.org; *Asst Librn*, Lee Sparks; E-Mail: lees@georgetowntx.org; *Ch Servs*, Rosa Garcia; *ILL*, Ethel Barnes; *Publ Servs*, Eric P Lashley; E-Mail: epl@georgetowntx.org; Staff 18 (MLS 4, Non-MLS 14)
Founded 1968. Pop 27,000; Circ 240,000
Oct 1999-Sep 2000 Income $780,000. Mats Exp $92;000, Books $80,000, Per/Ser (Incl. Access Fees) $12,000. Sal $453,480 (Prof $157,000)
Library Holdings: Bk Vols 70,000; Bk Titles 66,000; Per Subs 118
Subject Interests: Genealogy, Tex hist
Automation Activity & Vendor Info: (Cataloging) epixtech, inc.; (Circulation) epixtech, inc.; (OPAC) epixtech, inc.
Database Vendor: epixtech, inc., IAC - Info Trac
Function: ILL available
Mem of Central Texas Library System
Special Services for the Deaf - TDD
Friends of the Library Group

C SOUTHWESTERN UNIVERSITY, A Frank Smith Jr Library Center, 1001 University Ave, PO Box 770, 78627-0770. SAN 316-3776. Tel: 512-863-1561. Interlibrary Loan Service Tel: 512-863-1638. FAX: 512-863-1155. Web Site: www.southwestern.edu/library/library-home.html. *Dir*, Lynne M Brody; E-Mail: brodyl@southwestern.edu; *Per*, Amy Anderson; *Circ*, Carol Fonken; Tel: 512-863-1550, E-Mail: fonkenc@southwestern.edu; *Spec Coll*, Kathryn Stallard; *Ref*, Joan Parks; *Acq, Automation Syst Coordr*, John Bigley; *Cat*, Therese Olson; *Coll Develop*, Dana Hendrix; Tel: 512-863-1241, E-Mail: hendrixd@southwestern.edu; Staff 19 (MLS 9, Non-MLS 10)
Founded 1840. Enrl 1,230
1998-1999 Income $1,592,473. Mats Exp $781,500, Books $442,000, Per/Ser (Incl. Access Fees) $339,500. Sal $665,643 (Prof $365,120)
Library Holdings: Bk Vols 288,010; Per Subs 1,404
Special Collections: Bertha Dobie Papers; Hymnals (Meyer Coll); J Frank Dobie Coll; John G Tower Papers; rare books (Bewick, Bible, Blake); Texana (Clark Coll)
Publications: Bibliographic series; Exhibit catalogs; Handbook; Summer Reading List
Partic in Amigos Library Services, Inc; Assoc Cols of the South; Dialog Corporation; Leian; OCLC Online Computer Library Center, Inc; TexShare

GIDDINGS

P RUFUS YOUNG KING PUBLIC LIBRARY,* 177 S Madison, 78942. SAN 316-3784. Tel: 409-542-2716. FAX: 409-542-1879. *Dir*, Pamela Hutchinson; E-Mail: pamelahutchinson@hotmail.com
Founded 1920. Pop 5,378; Circ 31,000
Oct 1996-Sep 1997 Income $98,388, City $86,682, Locally Generated Income $11,706. Mats Exp $11,192, Books $8,229, Per/Ser (Incl. Access Fees) $1,199, Micro $302. Sal $50,078 (Prof $17,493)
Library Holdings: Bk Vols 20,875; Per Subs 246
Subject Interests: Cookery, Gardening, Genealogy, Handicrafts, Local history, Texacana
Special Collections: Large Print Coll, audio cassettes
Mem of Central Texas Library System

GILMER

P UPSHUR COUNTY LIBRARY,* 702 Tyler St, 75644. SAN 316-3792. T 903-843-5001. FAX: 903-843-3995. *Librn*, Joyce Morrison; Staff 5 (MLS Non-MLS 4)
Founded 1929. Pop 31,370
Oct 1999-Sep 2000 Income $185,289, City $46,322, County $138,907. M Exp $28,093, Books $26,300, Per/Ser (Incl. Access Fees) $1,700, Micro Sal $97,692 (Prof $29,460)
Library Holdings: Bk Vols 77,651; Bk Titles 64,381; Per Subs 76
Subject Interests: Civil War, Local genealogy, Texana
Special Collections: Library of America
Mem of Northeast Texas Library System
Partic in Forest Trail Library Consortium, Inc
Friends of the Library Group

GLADEWATER

P LEE PUBLIC LIBRARY, 312 W Pacific, 75647. (Mail add: PO Box 175, 75647), SAN 316-3806. Tel: 903-845-2640. FAX: 903-845-2640. *Librn*, Janice Welton; Staff 2 (MLS 1, Non-MLS 1)
Founded 1937. Pop 8,950; Circ 51,000
Library Holdings: Bk Vols 32,213; Bk Titles 31,813; Per Subs 75
Special Collections: Texana (John Ben Shepperd Jr Coll)
Mem of Northeast Texas Library System
Friends of the Library Group

GLEN ROSE

P SOMERVELL COUNTY LIBRARY,* 108 Allen Dr, 76043. SAN 376-4583. Tel: 254-897-4582. FAX: 254-897-9882. *Librn*, Freda Whitworth; *A Librn*, Peggy Oldhan
Oct 1996-Sep 1997 Income $141,291. Mats Exp $20,355. Sal $72,481
Library Holdings: Bk Vols 19,000; Per Subs 40
Mem of North Texas Regional Library System

GOLIAD

P GOLIAD COUNTY LIBRARY,* 320 S Commercial St, PO Box 1025, 77963. SAN 316-3814. Tel: 512-645-2291. FAX: 512-645-8956. *Librn*, M Anne Welch; *Asst Librn*, Rhonda Briones
Founded 1958. Pop 6,000
Library Holdings: Bk Vols 17,000; Bk Titles 17,000; Per Subs 30
Subject Interests: Tex hist
Automation Activity & Vendor Info: (Circulation) Follett
Mem of South Texas Library System
Friends of the Library Group

GONZALES

P GONZALES PUBLIC LIBRARY,* 415 St Matthew, PO Box 220, 78629. SAN 316-3822. Tel: 830-672-6315. FAX: 830-672-8735. *Librn*, Barbara Wright
Pop 11,398; Circ 27,000
1997-1998 Income $118,500, City $118,000, County $500. Mats Exp $20,000, Books $18,000, Per/Ser (Incl. Access Fees) $2,000. Sal $73,000
Library Holdings: Bk Vols 27,000; Bk Titles 25,000; Per Subs 60
Subject Interests: Genealogy
Friends of the Library Group

GOODFELLOW AFB

UNITED STATES AIR FORCE
A FL 3030, BASE LIBRARY, Bldg 712, 17 SPTG/SVMG, 271 Fort Phanto Hill Ave, 76908-4711. SAN 361-7645. Tel: 915-654-3045. FAX: 915-65 4731. *Librn*, Elaine C Penner; Staff 8 (MLS 1, Non-MLS 7)
Founded 1942
Oct 1999-Sep 2000 Income $227,472. Mats Exp $40,134. Sal $165,448
Library Holdings: Bk Vols 24,973; Per Subs 129
Restriction: Not open to public

GRAHAM

P LIBRARY OF GRAHAM, 910 Cherry St, 76450-3547. SAN 316-3830. Te 940-549-0600. FAX: 940-549-8624. Web Site: www.libraryofgraham.org. *Coll Develop, Commun Relations, Dir*, Sherrie R Gibson; E-Mail: sherrie.gibson@escq.net; *Ch Servs*, Suzanne Holubec; Staff 7 (MLS 1, Nor MLS 6)
Founded 1911. Pop 10,000
Library Holdings: Bk Titles 46,132; Per Subs 97
Special Collections: Texana Coll; Young County Coll
Automation Activity & Vendor Info: (Cataloging) epixtech, inc.; (Circulation) epixtech, inc.; (OPAC) epixtech, inc.
Mem of North Texas Regional Library System
Friends of the Library Group

ANBURY

HOOD COUNTY PUBLIC LIBRARY,* 222 N Travis, 76048. SAN 316-3849. Tel: 817-573-3569. FAX: 817-573-3969. E-Mail: hoodcoli@itexas.net. *Librn*, Jeanell Morris
Pop 17,700; Circ 54,991
Oct 1997-Sep 1998 Income $208,680
Library Holdings: Bk Titles 34,000; Per Subs 37
Mem of North Texas Regional Library System
Friends of the Library Group

RAND PRAIRIE

GRAND PRAIRIE MEMORIAL LIBRARY,* 901 Conover Dr, 75051. SAN 316-3857. Tel: 972-264-9536. FAX: 972-264-3823. *Dir*, Kathy Ritterhouse; *Asst Librn*, Leah West; *Asst Librn*, Mel Louviere; *Ch Servs*, Jennifer Walker; *Cat*, Iris Evans; *Circ*, Anne Felix; *Ref*, Linda Stidham
Founded 1937. Pop 102,500; Circ 341,750
1997-1998 Income $1,068,820. Mats Exp $109,500, Books $86,000, Per/Ser (Incl. Access Fees) $23,500. Sal $583,990 (Prof $294,185)
Library Holdings: Bk Vols 123,000; Per Subs 230
Special Collections: Local History, bks, photogs, slides, micro, mss, doc, tapes
Automation Activity & Vendor Info: (Acquisitions) epixtech, inc.; (Cataloging) epixtech, inc.; (Circulation) epixtech, inc.
Mem of Northeast Texas Library System
Friends of the Library Group

RAND SALINE

GRAND SALINE PUBLIC LIBRARY,* 201 E Pacific Ave, 75140. SAN 320-8478. Tel: 903-962-5516. *Librn*, Catherine Jarvis
Founded 1966. Pop 2,600
Library Holdings: Bk Vols 28,000
Mem of Northeast Texas Library System
Friends of the Library Group

RAPEVINE

GRAPEVINE PUBLIC LIBRARY, 1201 Municipal Way, 76051-5545. SAN 316-3881. Tel: 817-410-3400. FAX: 817-410-3080. E-Mail: janisr1@airmail.net. Web Site: www.grapevine.lib.tx.us. *Dir*, Janis Roberson; *Ch Servs*, Leigh Burnham; *Ref*, Bruce Bumbalough; *Ref Serv*, Scott May; *Cat*, Ron Tester; *Syst Coordr*, David Coulter; *Publ Servs*, Steven Arozena; Staff 7 (MLS 7)
Founded 1923. Pop 39,190
Oct 1999-Sep 2000 Income $1,080,980. Mats Exp $202,103, Books $132,715, Per/Ser (Incl. Access Fees) $56,588, Presv $800, Micro $12,000. Sal $632,839 (Prof $320,789)
Library Holdings: Bk Titles 111,014; Per Subs 214
Subject Interests: Genealogy, Large print, Texas
Automation Activity & Vendor Info: (Acquisitions) epixtech, inc.; (Cataloging) epixtech, inc.; (Circulation) epixtech, inc.; (OPAC) epixtech, inc.
Mem of North Texas Regional Library System
Friends of the Library Group

REENVILLE

HARRIS MORGAN LAW OFFICE LIBRARY,* PO Box 556, 75403. SAN 372-9796. Tel: 903-455-3183. FAX: 903-454-4654. *Librn*, Rita Reynolds
Library Holdings: Bk Vols 5,000; Per Subs 60

W WALWORTH HARRISON PUBLIC LIBRARY, One Lou Finney Lane, 75401-3906. SAN 316-3903. Tel: 903-457-2992. FAX: 903-457-2961. *Dir*, Beth A Wright; E-Mail: bwright@ci.greenville.tx.us; Staff 3 (MLS 3)
Founded 1904. Pop 25,000
Oct 1999-Sep 2000 Income City $548,826. Mats Exp $45,000, Per/Ser (Incl. Access Fees) $6,000. Sal $418,413 (Prof $244,427)
Library Holdings: Bk Titles 39,000; Per Subs 100
Subject Interests: Genealogy, Local history
Mem of Northeast Texas Library System
Friends of the Library Group

ROESBECK

MAFFETT MEMORIAL LIBRARY, Groesbeck Public Library, 601 W Yeagua, 76642-1658. SAN 316-392X. Tel: 254-729-3667. FAX: 254-729-3501. Web Site: 198.213.140.253. *Librn*, Denise Carter; Staff 3 (MLS 1, Non-MLS 2)
Founded 1976. Pop 3,632; Circ 7,450
Library Holdings: Bk Titles 21,045; Per Subs 66
Special Collections: Large Print Books; Texas Heritage Resource Center; The History of Limestone County (Ray A Walter Coll)
Automation Activity & Vendor Info: (Cataloging) Sagebrush Corporation; (Circulation) Sagebrush Corporation
Mem of Central Texas Library System
Meeting room. Microfiche reader & 16 mm projector available. Literary classes, GED classes & ESL classes

GROVES

P GROVES PUBLIC LIBRARY,* 5600 W Washington St, 77619. SAN 325-0113. Tel: 409-962-6281. FAX: 409-962-3379. *Dir*, M Jane Millwood; *Asst Librn*, Louella Neeb; *Acq*, Sheila Martin
Founded 1930. Pop 17,008; Circ 50,000
Library Holdings: Bk Vols 38,000; Bk Titles 40,000; Per Subs 52
Special Services for the Deaf - Books on deafness & sign language; High interest/low vocabulary books; Special interest periodicals

GROVETON

P GROVETON PUBLIC LIBRARY,* PO Box 399, 75845. SAN 376-4095. Tel: 409-642-2483. FAX: 409-642-2483. *Librn*, Peggy Sullivan
Jan 1998-Dec 1999 Income $6,000
Library Holdings: Bk Vols 10,000
Mem of Houston Area Library System
Friends of the Library Group

GRUVER

P GRUVER CITY LIBRARY,* 504 King St, PO Box 701, 79040. SAN 316-3938. Tel: 806-733-2191. FAX: 806-733-2191. *Librn*, Carolyn Fletcher; E-Mail: grucarolyn@hlc.actx.edu
Founded 1961. Pop 1,631; Circ 4,218
Library Holdings: Bk Vols 18,920; Bk Titles 17,150
Mem of Texas Panhandle Library System
Open Tues-Fri 2-6

GUTHRIE

P KING COUNTY PUBLIC LIBRARY,* PO Box 1, 79236. SAN 376-4249. Tel: 806-596-4385. *Librn*, Laquita Fields
Library Holdings: Bk Vols 8,000
Mem of West Texas Library System

HALE CENTER

P HALE CENTER PUBLIC LIBRARY,* 609 Main St, PO Box 214, 79041. SAN 316-3946. Tel: 806-839-2055. *Librn*, Donna Lemons
Pop 2,000; Circ 5,234
Library Holdings: Bk Vols 10,000
Special Collections: Texas Heritage Resource Center
Mem of West Texas Library System

HALLETTSVILLE

P FRIENCH SIMPSON MEMORIAL LIBRARY, 705 E Fourth St, 77964-2828. SAN 316-3954. Tel: 361-798-3243. FAX: 361-798-5833. E-Mail: fsmlib@netrax.net. *Dir*, Carol Morisak; *Ch Servs*, Brenda Lincke-Fisseler; Staff 4 (Non-MLS 4)
Founded 1962. Pop 3,800; Circ 45,000
Library Holdings: Bk Vols 16,500; Per Subs 35
Subject Interests: Genealogy, Local history
Automation Activity & Vendor Info: (Cataloging) Follett; (Circulation) Follett; (OPAC) Follett
Mem of South Texas Library System
Friends of the Library Group

HALTOM CITY

P HALTOM CITY PUBLIC LIBRARY, (HCPL), 3201 Friendly Lane, 76117-3622. (Mail add: PO Box 14277, 76117-3622), SAN 316-3962. Tel: 817-222-7790. Interlibrary Loan Service Tel: 817-222-7787. Circulation Tel: 817-222-7785. Reference Tel: 817-222-7786. FAX: 817-834-1446. E-Mail: library@haltomcitytx.com. Web Site: www.haltomcitytx.com. *Dir Libr Serv*, Rodney L Bland; E-Mail: rbland@haltomcitytx.com; *Acq*, Diane Elrod; Tel: 817-222-7793, E-Mail: delrod@haltomcitytx.com; *Automation Syst Coordr*, Paul Waak; Tel: 827-222-7794, E-Mail: pwaak@haltomcitytx.com; *Cat*, Ann Rethard; Tel: 817-222-7792, E-Mail: arethard@haltomcitytx.com; *Ch Servs*, Becky Deaton; Tel: 817-222-7794, E-Mail: bdeaton@haltomcitytx.com; *Commun Relations*, Allison Long; Tel: 817-222-7794, E-Mail: along@haltomcitytx.com; *Publ Servs*, Lesly M Smith; Tel: 617-222-7794, E-Mail: lmsmith@haltomcitytx.com; *Publ Servs*, Grant Vaden; Tel: 617-222-7794, E-Mail: gvaden@haltomcitytx.com; Staff 15 (MLS 4, Non-MLS 11)
Founded 1961. Pop 36,000; Circ 200,000
Oct 1999-Sep 2000 Income City $731,856. Mats Exp Books $101,000. Sal $399,886 (Prof $206,092)
Library Holdings: Bk Vols 88,286; Bk Titles 78,457; Per Subs 82; Bks on

Deafness & Sign Lang 65
Subject Interests: Large-print bks, Local genealogy, Talking books, Texana
Automation Activity & Vendor Info: (Cataloging) epixtech, inc.; (Circulation) epixtech, inc.; (OPAC) epixtech, inc.
Database Vendor: epixtech, inc.
Publications: Booknotes
Mem of North Texas Regional Library System
Friends of the Library Group

HAMILTON

P HAMILTON PUBLIC LIBRARY, 201 N Pecan, 76531. SAN 376-4796. Tel: 254-386-3474. *Librn*, Linda Mentzer
Library Holdings: Bk Vols 18,550; Per Subs 23
Mem of Central Texas Library System
Friends of the Library Group

HARKER HEIGHTS

P HARKER HEIGHTS PUBLIC LIBRARY, 100 E Beeline, 76548. SAN 376-4788. Tel: 254-699-5008. FAX: 254-699-4772. *Dir*, Lisa D Youngblood; Tel: 254-699-1776, E-Mail: l_youngblood@hotmail.com; Staff 6 (MLS 1, Non-MLS 5)
Pop 18,000
Library Holdings: Bk Vols 24,000; Per Subs 10
Database Vendor: IAC - Info Trac, Wilson - Wilson Web
Function: Reference services available
Mem of Central Texas Library System
Friends of the Library Group

HARLINGEN

P HARLINGEN PUBLIC LIBRARY, 410 76th Dr, 78550. SAN 316-3997. Tel: 956-430-6650. Circulation Tel: 956-430-6610. Reference Tel: 956-430-6630. TDD: 956-430-6616. FAX: 956-430-6633. Web Site: www.ci.harlinger.tx.us/library/htm. *Dir*, Ruben Rendon; E-Mail: rendon@harlingen.lib.tx.us; Staff 26 (MLS 3, Non-MLS 23)
Founded 1920. Pop 65,552; Circ 235,635
Oct 1998-Sep 1999 Income $922,051, State $74,978, City $787,835, Locally Generated Income $59,238. Mats Exp $139,349, Books $105,432, Per/Ser (Incl. Access Fees) $17,854, Micro $5,513, Electronic Ref Mat (Incl. Access Fees) $10,550. Sal $502,961
Library Holdings: Bk Vols 129,109; Bk Titles 109,030; Per Subs 314
Subject Interests: Genealogy, Railroad hist, Spanish, Tex hist
Mem of South Texas Library System
Partic in Amigos Library Services, Inc
Special Services for the Deaf - TDD
Special Services for the Blind - Reading edge system
Non-resident fee of $10 to patrons outside of school boundaries
Friends of the Library Group

M SOUTH TEXAS HOSPITAL, Medical Library,* 1301 Rangerville Rd, 78551. (Mail add: PO Box 592, 78551), SAN 316-4004. Tel: 956-423-3420. FAX: 956-440-0521. *Librn*, Greysi Reyna; E-Mail: reynag@uthscsa.edu
Founded 1956
Library Holdings: Bk Vols 500; Per Subs 25
Subject Interests: Infectious diseases

J TEXAS STATE TECHNICAL COLLEGE, Harlingen Library, 2424 Boxwood, 78550-3697. SAN 316-4012. Tel: 956-364-4608. Reference Tel: 956-364-4623. FAX: 956-364-5149. *Dir*, David J Diehl; E-Mail: ddiehl@harlingen.tstc.edu; *Librn*, Kenneth E Partin, Jr; E-Mail: kenpartin@hotmail.com; Staff 7 (MLS 3, Non-MLS 4)
Founded 1969. Enrl 3,000; Fac 150
Sep 1999-Aug 2000 Income $479,185. Mats Exp $229,000, Books $200,000, Per/Ser (Incl. Access Fees) $22,000, AV Equip $500, Electronic Ref Mat (Incl. Access Fees) $6,500. Sal $202,356 (Prof $142,644)
Library Holdings: Bk Vols 27,200; Bk Titles 27,000; Per Subs 347; Bks on Deafness & Sign Lang 20
Subject Interests: Allied health, Sci-tech
Automation Activity & Vendor Info: (Circulation) SIRSI
Database Vendor: GaleNet, IAC - Info Trac, OVID Technologies
Partic in Paisano Consortium
Special Services for the Blind - Kurzweil Reader

HASKELL

P HASKELL COUNTY LIBRARY, 300 North Ave E, 79521-0257. SAN 316-4020. Tel: 940-864-2747. FAX: 940-864-6164. E-Mail: haskellcl@yahoo.com. *Librn*, Joan Strickland; Staff 1 (Non-MLS 1)
Circ 14,500
Sep 1999-Oct 2000 Income $31,200, State $1,200, County $28,000, Locally Generated Income $2,000
Library Holdings: Bk Vols 17,300; Per Subs 10
Subject Interests: Local county hist
Automation Activity & Vendor Info: (Cataloging) Athena; (Circulation) Athena
Mem of Big Country Library System
Friends of the Library Group

HAWKINS

P ALLEN MEMORIAL PUBLIC LIBRARY,* PO Box 329, 75765. SAN 3 7431. Tel: 903-769-2241. FAX: 903-769-2781. *Dir*, Pam McKenzie
Founded 1988. Pop 5,936
Library Holdings: Bk Vols 16,008; Per Subs 75

C JARVIS CHRISTIAN COLLEGE, Olin Library & Communication Center E Hwy 80, PO Box 1470, 75765. SAN 316-4039. Tel: 903-769-2174, Ext 820, 903-769-5820. FAX: 903-769-4842. Web Site: www.jarvis.edu. *Dir, Media Spec*, William Hampton; E-Mail: hamptonw@jarvis.edu; Staff 4 (MLS 2, Non-MLS 2)
Founded 1920. Enrl 500; Fac 53; Highest Degree: Bachelor
Library Holdings: Bk Vols 78,347; Bk Titles 69,788; Per Subs 297
Subject Interests: Bus admin, Education, Religion
Special Collections: Curriculum Library; Young Adult Coll

HEARNE

P SMITH-WELCH MEMORIAL LIBRARY,* 114 W Fourth St, 77859. SA 316-4047. Tel: 409-279-5191. FAX: 409-279-2431. *Librn*, Bonnie Miller
Pop 5,418; Circ 15,828
Library Holdings: Bk Vols 2,000
Mem of Central Texas Library System

HEBBRONVILLE

P JIM HOGG COUNTY PUBLIC LIBRARY, 210 N Smith Ave, 78361. SA 316-4055. Tel: 512-527-3421. FAX: 512-527-3421. *Librn*, Betty J Newma
Pop 5,109; Circ 8,000
Library Holdings: Bk Vols 11,000; Per Subs 42
Mem of South Texas Library System
Friends of the Library Group

HEMPSTEAD

P WALLER COUNTY LIBRARY, 2331 11th St, 77445-6724. SAN 316-406 Tel: 409-826-7658. FAX: 409-826-7657. *Dir*, Bobbye Warren
Founded 1834. Pop 35,000; Circ 70,000
Jan 2000-Dec 2000 Income Locally Generated Income $146,001. Mats Ex Books $21,700. Sal $99,626 (Prof $29,232)
Library Holdings: Bk Titles 34,662; Per Subs 21
Special Collections: Waller County Newspaper (1929-present), micro
Automation Activity & Vendor Info: (Acquisitions) Follett; (Cataloging) Follett; (Circulation) Follett
Mem of Houston Area Library System
Friends of the Library Group

HENDERSON

P RUSK COUNTY LIBRARY, 106 E Main St, 75652. SAN 361-767X. Tel: 903-657-8557. FAX: 903-657-7637. Web Site: www.rclib.org/. *Actg Dir*, Pamela Pipkin; Staff 1 (MLS 1)
Founded 1937. Pop 45,819; Circ 132,287
Jan 2000-Dec 2000 Income (Main Library and Branch Library) $565,275, County $506,646, Other $58,629. Mats Exp $59,077, Books $32,250, Per/Ser (Incl. Access Fees) $23,880, Micro $120, Electronic Ref Mat (Incl. Access Fees) $2,827. Sal $266,592 (Prof $32,600)
Library Holdings: Bk Vols 82,258; Per Subs 198
Subject Interests: History, Rusk county genealogy
Special Collections: Texas Heritage Resource Center
Automation Activity & Vendor Info: (Acquisitions) TLC; (Cataloging) TLC; (Circulation) TLC; (OPAC) TLC
Publications: The County Line (newsletter of Friends of RCML)
Mem of Northeast Texas Library System
Friends of the Library Group
Branches: 3
MCMILLAN MEMORIAL, 302 South St, Overton, 75684-1818. SAN 361 770X. Tel: 214-834-6318. Web Site: www.rclib.org/. *In Charge*, G Bisho
Library Holdings: Bk Vols 15,042
Automation Activity & Vendor Info: (Acquisitions) TLC; (Cataloging) TLC; (Circulation) TLC; (OPAC) TLC
Friends of the Library Group
MORROW, 111 W Rusk, PO Box 360, Mount Enterprise, 75681-0360. SA 361-7734. Tel: 903-822-3532. Web Site: www.rclib.org. *In Charge*, Barbara Watson
Library Holdings: Bk Vols 6,375
Automation Activity & Vendor Info: (Acquisitions) TLC; (Cataloging) TLC; (Circulation) TLC; (OPAC) TLC

Friends of the Library Group

TATUM PUBLIC, 335 Hood, PO Box 1087, Tatum, 75691-1087. SAN 361-7769. Tel: 903-947-2211. Web Site: www.rclib.org/. *In Charge*, Janet Breedlove
Library Holdings: Bk Vols 7,804
Automation Activity & Vendor Info: (Acquisitions) TLC; (Cataloging) TLC; (Circulation) TLC; (OPAC) TLC

[H]ENRIETTA

EDWARDS PUBLIC LIBRARY,* 210 W Gilbert St, 76365. SAN 316-4098. Tel: 940-538-4791. FAX: 940-538-5168, 940-538-5861. Web Site: www.edwardspl.esc9.net/. *Dir*, Norma Jean Ruiz-Hearne; E-Mail: norma.hearne@esc9.net; Staff 1 (Non-MLS 1)
Founded 1932. Pop 10,450; Circ 44,292
Oct 1998-Sep 1999 Income $58,603, County $53,196, Locally Generated Income $5,407. Mats Exp $6,284, Books $4,467, Per/Ser (Incl. Access Fees) $1,745, Micro $72. (Prof $17,317)
Library Holdings: Bk Titles 20,319; Per Subs 70
Automation Activity & Vendor Info: (OPAC) Follett
Mem of North Texas Regional Library System

[H]EREFORD

DEAF SMITH COUNTY LIBRARY, 211 E Fourth St, 79045. SAN 316-4101. Tel: 806-364-1206. FAX: 806-363-7063. E-Mail: dsh_ill@hotmail.com. Web Site: www.hlc-lib.org/hereford. *Librn*, Rebecca Walls; E-Mail: dsh_becky@hlc.actx.edu; Staff 5 (MLS 1, Non-MLS 4)
Founded 1910. Pop 19,500
Oct 1998-Sep 1999 Income County $227,799. Mats Exp $56,157, Books $45,807, Per/Ser (Incl. Access Fees) $5,961. Sal $135,196 (Prof $28,119)
Library Holdings: Bk Vols 75,885
Subject Interests: Adult basic educ, Bks on tape, Spanish, Texas hist
Mem of Texas Panhandle Library System
Partic in Harrington Library Consortium
Friends of the Library Group

HEREFORD REGIONAL MEDICAL CENTER LIBRARY,* 801 E Third St, 79045. SAN 375-7706. Tel: 806-364-2141. FAX: 806-364-1223.
Library Holdings: Bk Titles 175

[H]EWITT

HEWITT COMMUNITY LIBRARY, 105 Hewitt Dr, 76643. SAN 376-477X. Tel: 254-666-2442. FAX: 254-666-6025. *Librn*, Donna Sparks; Staff 3 (MLS 1, Non-MLS 2)
Library Holdings: Bk Vols 21,000
Automation Activity & Vendor Info: (Acquisitions) Follett; (Cataloging) Follett; (Circulation) Follett; (OPAC) Follett
Mem of Central Texas Library System
Friends of the Library Group

[H]IGGINS

HIGGINS PUBLIC LIBRARY,* 201 N Main, PO Box 250, 79046-0250. SAN 316-411X. Tel: 806-852-2214. FAX: 806-852-2214. *Librn*, Joan Smith
Pop 3,486
Dec 1998-Dec 1999 Income $7,500
Library Holdings: Bk Vols 11,500
Mem of Texas Panhandle Library System
Partic in Harrington Library Consortium
Special Services for the Blind - Talking Books

[H]IGHLAND PARK

HIGHLAND PARK LIBRARY, 4700 Drexel Dr, 75205-3198. SAN 316-1994. Tel: 214-559-9400. FAX: 214-559-9335. *Dir, Librn*, Bonnie N Case; E-Mail: bncase@home.com; Staff 5 (MLS 1, Non-MLS 4)
Founded 1930. Pop 8,800; Circ 100,323
Oct 1999-Sep 2000 Income $384,060. Mats Exp $50,000, Books $42,000, Per/Ser (Incl. Access Fees) $2,900, Micro $1,100, Electronic Ref Mat (Incl. Access Fees) $4,000. Sal $220,895
Library Holdings: Bk Titles 40,000; Per Subs 55
Automation Activity & Vendor Info: (Cataloging) epixtech, inc.; (Cataloging) epixtech, inc.; (OPAC) epixtech, inc.
Database Vendor: epixtech, inc.
Mem of Northeast Texas Library System
Friends of the Library Group

[H]ILLSBORO

HILL COLLEGE LIBRARY,* 112 Lamar, PO Box 619, 76645-0619. SAN 316-4128. Tel: 254-582-2555, Ext 240. FAX: 254-582-7591. E-Mail: library@hill-college.cc.tx.us. Web Site: www.hill-college.cc.tx.us/library. *Dir*, Joe Shaughnessy; Staff 4 (MLS 1, Non-MLS 3)
Founded 1962. Enrl 1,958; Fac 84
Library Holdings: Bk Vols 32,600; Bk Titles 32,000; Per Subs 226
Subject Interests: Behav sci, Bus, Cosmetology, Humanities, Mgt, Microelectronics, Nursing, Sci-tech, Soc sci, Vocational tech
Special Collections: Civil War Research Center
Publications: Hill Junior Coll Press-History & Civil War

P HILLSBORO CITY LIBRARY,* 118 S Waco St, 76645. SAN 316-4136. Tel: 254-582-7385. FAX: 254-582-7765. E-Mail: hillsboro.library@glade.net. *Dir*, Susan S Mann; *Asst Librn*, Russell W Keelin; Staff 3 (MLS 3)
1997-1998 Income $199,644, State $3,603, City $191,041. Mats Exp $42,353, Books $33,603, Per/Ser (Incl. Access Fees) $8,750. Sal $105,118
Library Holdings: Bk Titles 37,000; Per Subs 105
Subject Interests: Large print, Texas
Mem of Central Texas Library System
Partic in Amigos Library Services, Inc; Tex ILL Syst
Friends of the Library Group

HITCHCOCK

P GENEVIEVE MILLER HITCHCOCK PUBLIC LIBRARY,* 8005 Barry Ave, 77563-3238. SAN 376-4109. Tel: 409-986-7814. FAX: 409-986-6353. *Librn*, Kathleen Brooks
Library Holdings: Bk Vols 24,700; Per Subs 15
Mem of Houston Area Library System

HONDO

P HONDO PUBLIC LIBRARY,* 1011 19th St, 78861-2431. SAN 324-1289. Tel: 830-426-5333. FAX: 830-426-7089. E-Mail: hpl@stic.net. *Librn*, Margie Ibarra
Founded 1967. Pop 6,400
1997-1998 Income $178,830. Mats Exp $12,587, Books $10,230, Per/Ser (Incl. Access Fees) $1,546. Sal $64,697
Library Holdings: Bk Vols 10,000; Per Subs 51
Mem of Alamo Area Library System; San Antonio Major Resource Center

HONEY GROVE

P BERTHA VOYER MEMORIAL LIBRARY,* PO Box 47, 75446-0120. SAN 316-4144. Tel: 903-378-2206. FAX: 903-378-2208. *Dir*, Mary Fowler
Founded 1962. Pop 3,000; Circ 16,091
Library Holdings: Bk Vols 15,940; Per Subs 17
Automation Activity & Vendor Info: (Circulation) Sagebrush Corporation
Partic in Northeast Texas Library System
Friends of the Library Group

HOOKS

P HOOKS PUBLIC LIBRARY,* 108 W First St, PO Box 1540, 75561-1540. SAN 375-5126. Tel: 903-547-3365. *Librn*, Ava McMichael; *Asst Librn*, Betty Whitington
Founded 1990. Pop 2,650
Library Holdings: Bk Titles 11,008

HOUSTON

S ABB LUMMUS GLOBAL LIBRARY, 3010 Briarpark, 77042. (Mail add: PO Box 42833, 77242-2833), SAN 316-4632. Tel: 713-821-4616. FAX: 713-821-3564. E-Mail: rosella.r.alcala@us.abb.com. *Librn*, Rosie Alcala; Staff 1 (MLS 1)
Founded 1976
2000-2001 Mats Exp $59,300, Books $1,300, Per/Ser (Incl. Access Fees) $11,000, Other Print Mats $2,000, Electronic Ref Mat (Incl. Access Fees) $45,000
Library Holdings: Bk Vols 4,000; Bk Titles 1,400; Per Subs 75
Subject Interests: Offshore facilities, Oil, Onshore, Petrochem eng
Restriction: Company library
Branches:

S LUMMUS TECHNOLOGY DIVISION LIBRARY, 1515 Broad St, Bloomfield, 07003. SAN 310-0251. Tel: 973-893-2251. Interlibrary Loan Service Tel: 973-893-2253. FAX: 973-893-2119. *Librn*, Elizabeth A Schefler; E-Mail: elizabeth.a.schefler@us.abb.com; Staff 2 (MLS 1, Non-MLS 1)
Founded 1930
Library Holdings: Bk Vols 10,500; Per Subs 200
Subject Interests: Chemical engineering, Petrochemicals, Petroleum refining
Special Collections: Crude Oil, bks & pamphlets
Database Vendor: Dialog, Lexis-Nexis
Partic in New Jersey Library Network

S AMERADA HESS CORPORATION, US Exploration & Production - Technical Library,* 500 Dallas St, Level 2, 77002. SAN 370-9809. Tel: 713-609-5000. FAX: 713-609-5549.
Library Holdings: Bk Vols 3,000; Per Subs 30

S AMERICAN BRAHMAN BREEDERS ASSOCIATION LIBRARY,* 3003 South Loop W Ste 140, 77054. SAN 371-022X. Tel: 713-349-0854. FAX: 713-349-9795. E-Mail: abba@brahman.org. Web Site: www.brahman.org. *In Charge*, Jim E Reeves
Library Holdings: Bk Vols 4,100; Per Subs 88

S AMERICAN PRODUCTIVITY & QUALITY CENTER, APQC Information Center, 123 N Post Oak Lane, Third Flr, 77024. SAN 327-9979. Tel: 713-681-4020. FAX: 713-681-1182. E-Mail: apqcinfo@apqc.org. Web Site: www.apqc.org. *Mgr*, Anne Marsden; *Admin Assoc*, Vivian Howser; Staff 6 (MLS 6)
Library Holdings: Bk Titles 1,250; Per Subs 75
Publications: InFocus compilations; InPractice case studies

M ARNOLD, WHITE & DURKEE LIBRARY,* PO Box 4433, 77210. SAN 320-8737. Tel: 713-787-1543. FAX: 713-787-1440. *Librn*, Genel Moran; E-Mail: jgmoran@awd.com
Library Holdings: Bk Vols 9,000; Per Subs 100
Subject Interests: Copyrights, Franchises, Patents, Trademarks, Unfair competition
Partic in BRS

§S ART INSTITUTE OF HOUSTON, Resource Center, 1900 Yorktown, 77056. SAN 375-4316. Tel: 713-623-2040. FAX: 713-966-2701. Web Site: www.aii.edu. *Dir*, Patricia Garrison; *Asst Dir*, Catherine Walsh; E-Mail: garrisop@aii.edu; Staff 5 (MLS 3, Non-MLS 2)
Jul 2000-Jun 2001 Mats Exp $94,000, Books $70,000, Per/Ser (Incl. Access Fees) $24,000
Library Holdings: Bk Vols 18,000; Per Subs 225
Subject Interests: Applied art
Special Collections: Culinary Coll
Automation Activity & Vendor Info: (Cataloging) Athena; (Circulation) Athena

L BAKER & BOTTS, Law Library,* One Shell Plaza, 77002. SAN 316-4160. Tel: 713-229-1643. Interlibrary Loan Service Tel: 713-229-1412. FAX: 713-229-1522. *Acq, Assoc Librn*, Donna Joity; *Ref*, Emily Clement; *Ref*, Lynn Corbett; *Ref*, Richard Pravata; *Cat*, Suzanne Estep
Founded 1872
Library Holdings: Bk Vols 80,000
Special Collections: Corporate Law Coll; Securities Coll; Tax Coll; Utilities Coll
Publications: Library Notes (monthly); User Location Guide to Baker & Botts Library
Partic in BRS; Data Time; Dialog Corporation; Dow Jones News Retrieval; Orbit; Westlaw

S BAKER HUGHES INTEQ, Technical Library,* PO Box 670968, 77267-0968. SAN 316-4667. Tel: 713-625-6583. FAX: 713-625-6565. *Librn*, Marie Cassens; E-Mail: marie.cassens@inteq.bhi-net.com; Staff 1 (MLS 1)
Library Holdings: Bk Vols 3,500; Per Subs 30
Subject Interests: Chemistry, Drilling, Engineering, Geology, Patents petroleum

S BONNER & MOORE ASSOCIATES, INC LIBRARY,* 2727 Allen Pkwy, 77019. SAN 321-978X. Tel: 713-522-6800, 713-831-9784. FAX: 713-831-9856. E-Mail: bonmorck@bonnermoore.com. *Librn*, Jody Whittinghill
Founded 1975
Library Holdings: Bk Titles 6,000; Per Subs 200
Subject Interests: Energy, Fuels, Petrochem, Sci, Technology
Special Collections: Bonner & Moore Company Publications
Restriction: Not open to public
Partic in Dialog Corporation

S BP AMOCO, Library Information Center, 501 Westlake Park Blvd, 15-171, 77079. (Mail add: PO Box 3092, 77253), SAN 316-487X. Tel: 281-366-3387. FAX: 281-366-3117. *Info Specialist*, Donna M Cole; E-Mail: coledm@bp.com; Staff 1 (Non-MLS 1)
Founded 1972
Library Holdings: Bk Titles 40,000; Per Subs 150
Subject Interests: Earth science, Geology, Geophysics, Petroleum engineering
Special Collections: Society Publications; Special Company Reports; State Geological Survey Papers; USGS Publications
Automation Activity & Vendor Info: (Cataloging) EOS; (Circulation) EOS; (Serials) EOS
Restriction: Not open to public

L BRACEWELL & PATTERSON LLP, South Tower Pennzoil Place Law Library, 711 Louisana St, Ste 2900, 77002-2781. SAN 316-4195. Tel: 713-221-1129. FAX: 713-221-1212. *Librn*, Connie Pine; E-Mail: cpine@bracepatt.com; *ILL, Ref*, Alice Fosson
Founded 1945
Library Holdings: Bk Vols 25,000; Per Subs 2,000
Subject Interests: Corporate practice, Gen civil
Partic in Dialog Corporation; Westlaw

S BROWN & ROOT, INC, Information Resource Center,* PO Box 3, 7700 SAN 316-4209. Tel: 713-676-3373. FAX: 713-676-5715. *Mgr, Res*, Norm Urbanovsky; E-Mail: nurbanovsky@hal:burt.com; *Res*, Dell Avery; Staff 4 (MLS 3, Non-MLS 1)
Founded 1960
Jan 1997-Dec 1998 Income $900,000. Mats Exp $275,000
Library Holdings: Bk Vols 40,000
Subject Interests: Construction, Design, Engineering, Environ sci, Technology

S BROWNING-FERRIS INDUSTRIES, INC, Corporate Office Library,* PO Box 3151, 77253. SAN 372-9907. Tel: 281-870-7011. FAX: 281-584-865 *Chief Librn*, Mary F Magner; E-Mail: mary.magner@bfi.com
Library Holdings: Bk Vols 10,000; Per Subs 100

L BUTLER & BINION, Law Library,* PO Box 70649, 77270-0649. SAN 316-4217. Tel: 713-237-3655. FAX: 713-237-3202. E-Mail: cpincumbe_bbhou@msn.com. *Dir*, Colleen Pincumbe; Staff 3 (MLS 1, Non-MLS 2)
Founded 1941
Library Holdings: Bk Vols 33,000
Subject Interests: Corporate banking, Finance, Legal ref, Litigation, Natu resources, Patent, Tax, Texas
Publications: Weekly Newsletter

R CENTRAL PRESBYTERIAN CHURCH LIBRARY, 3788 Richmond Ave 77027. SAN 316-425X. Tel: 713-621-2424. FAX: 713-621-2604. *Librn*, Bruce Yaeger
Founded 1962
Library Holdings: Bk Titles 4,500; Per Subs 12
Subject Interests: Education, Relig studies

L CHAMBERLAIN, HRDLICKA, WHITE, WILLIAMS & MARTIN, Law Library,* 1200 Smith St, Ste 1400, 77002. SAN 371-6287. Tel: 713-658-2547. Toll Free Tel: 800-342-5829. FAX: 713-658-2553. E-Mail: firm@chamberlainlaw.com. *Librn*, Susan Earley; *Asst Librn*, Lydia Ramirez; Sta 2 (MLS 1, Non-MLS 1)
Library Holdings: Bk Vols 20,000; Per Subs 90

SR CHAPELWOOD UNITED METHODIST CHURCH, Chapelwood Memor Resource Library, 11140 Greenbay St, 77024-6798. SAN 328-4751. Tel: 713-354-4427, 713-465-3467. FAX: 713-365-2808. Web Site: www.chapelwood.org. *Dir*, Dona Badgett
Library Holdings: Bk Vols 13,000; Per Subs 12
Subject Interests: Religion
Special Collections: Vidio & Audio Coll

CHEVRON CHEMICAL CO

S LIBRARY & INFORMATION CENTER, 1301 McKinney, PO Box 2100, 77252-9987. SAN 361-7971. Tel: 713-754-2276. FAX: 713-754-2288. E-Mail: ctlib@chevron.com. *Res*, Nan Dubbelde; Staff 6 (MLS 4, Non-MLS 2)
Founded 1974
Library Holdings: Bk Vols 100,000; Bk Titles 50,000; Per Subs 350
Subject Interests: Bus, Exploration, Geology, Mgt, Personnel, Petrochemical bus, Petroleum engineering, Petroleum indust statistics, Production
Special Collections: Society of Petroleum Engineers, preprints
Publications: Bi-monthly Acquisitions List
Restriction: By appointment only
Partic in Dialog Corporation; Dow Jones News Retrieval

L CHEVRON LAW LIBRARY, 1301 McKinney St, Rm 2810, 77010. (Mail add: PO Box 4553, 77210), SAN 323-6536. Tel: 713-754-3330. FAX: 713-754-2288. *Librn*, Frederick A Riemann; E-Mail: fari@chevron.com
Founded 1933
Library Holdings: Bk Vols 55,000
Publications: Acquisitions List (monthly)

CITY OF HOUSTON

GL LEGAL DEPT LIBRARY, 900 Bagby, 4th flr, PO Box 1562, 77251. SAN 361-7793. Tel: 713-247-1296. FAX: 713-247-1017. *In Charge*, Evangelin Bell
Founded 1907
Library Holdings: Bk Vols 17,100; Bk Titles 11,000; Per Subs 15
Subject Interests: Municipal law
Partic in Houston Area Law Libr; Westlaw

L THE COASTAL CORP, Law Library,* 9 Greenway Plaza, 77046. SAN 327-3830. Tel: 713-877-1400. FAX: 713-877-3869. *Librn*, Jackie Pittman
Library Holdings: Bk Vols 20,000; Per Subs 10

S COMPAQ COMPUTER CORPORATION, Engineering Library,* 20555 S 249, 77070. SAN 370-6087. Tel: 281-370-0670. FAX: 281-370-0890. *Librn* Pushkala Atri
Founded 1989
Partic in Amigos Library Services, Inc

CONGREGATION BETH YESHURUN, Cantor Rubin Kaplan Memorial Library, 4525 Beechnut Blvd, 77096. SAN 316-4306. Tel: 713-666-1884. FAX: 713-666-2924. *Librn*, Monica Woolf; Staff 8 (MLS 3, Non-MLS 5)
Library Holdings: Bk Vols 30,000
Subject Interests: Holocaust, Judaica

CORE LABORATORIES, Research Library,* 6316 Windfern Rd, 77040-4916. SAN 325-2310. Tel: 972-323-3974. FAX: 972-323-3930. *Librn*, Cheryl Sheets
Library Holdings: Bk Titles 200; Per Subs 75
Subject Interests: Analytical chemistry, Geochemistry, Geology, Petroleum engineering
Restriction: Not open to public
Partic in Dialog Corporation; Orbit

DELOITTE & TOUCHE LIBRARY,* 333 Clay, Ste 2300, 77002. SAN 372-8625. Tel: 713-756-2416. FAX: 713-756-2001. *Librn*, Gail Wilson
Library Holdings: Bk Vols 4,000; Per Subs 20

M DEPARTMENT OF VETERANS AFFAIRS MEDICAL CENTER, Learning Resources Services Library,* 2002 Holcombe Blvd, 77030. SAN 316-5027. Tel: 713-794-7856. FAX: 713-794-7456. *Chief Librn*, Jerry Barrett
Library Holdings: Bk Vols 26,979

DUKE ENERGY CORP, (IRC), Information Resource Center, 5400 Westheimer Ct, 77251-1642. (Mail add: PO Box 1642, 77251-1642), SAN 372-9893. Tel: 713-627-5588. FAX: 713-989-1505. *Librn*, Donna Lucas; E-Mail: dlucas@duke-energy.com
Founded 1989
Library Holdings: Bk Vols 1,200; Bk Titles 750; Per Subs 100
Subject Interests: Energy, Natural gas
Friends of the Library Group

ELF EXPLORATION, INC, Technical & Business Library,* Wells Fargo Plaza, 1000 Louisiana, Ste 3800, 77002. SAN 326-1433. Tel: 713-739-2021. FAX: 713-739-2350. *Librn*, Elizabeth Evans
Founded 1978
Library Holdings: Bk Titles 2,000; Per Subs 57
Subject Interests: Geology, Petroleum
Publications: Daily News Summary
Restriction: By appointment only
Partic in Dialog Corporation; Dow Jones News Retrieval

ENRON CORP, Law Library,* 1400 Smith St, 77002. SAN 371-1048. Tel: 713-853-5322. FAX: 713-646-3754. *Librn*, Betty Hanchey
Library Holdings: Bk Vols 5,000; Per Subs 45

EXXON EXPLORATION CO
EXPLORATION LIBRARY, PO Box 4778, Rm 174, 77210-4778. SAN 316-4357. Tel: 281-423-7188. FAX: 281-423-7915. *Dir*, Nancy Ramirez
Founded 1971
Library Holdings: Bk Titles 8,312; Per Subs 64
Subject Interests: Geology, Geophysics, Petroleum tech
Restriction: By appointment only

EXXON MOBIL CORP, Law Library, 800 Bell, Rm 1786, 77002. (Mail add: PO Box 2180, 77252-2180), SAN 361-7947. Tel: 713-656-4383. FAX: 713-656-6770. *Librn*, Paula E Howe; E-Mail: paula.e.howe@exxon.com
Library Holdings: Bk Vols 50,000
Automation Activity & Vendor Info: (Acquisitions) Sydney; (Cataloging) Sydney; (Circulation) Sydney; (OPAC) Sydney; (Serials) Sydney

FIRST PRESBYTERIAN CHURCH, Ewing Memorial Library, 5300 Main St, 77004-6877. SAN 316-4365. Tel: 713-620-6500. FAX: 713-620-6550. Web Site: www.fpc-hou.org.
Founded 1951
Library Holdings: Bk Titles 8,300
Subject Interests: Relig studies
Publications: Presbyterian Outlook

FUGRO, INC, Corporate Library,* 6100 Hillcroft, PO Box 740010, 77274. SAN 316-4640. Tel: 713-778-5500. FAX: 713-778-5573. *Bibliog Instr, Librn, Online Servs*, Jane Vovk
Founded 1966
Library Holdings: Bk Vols 12,000; Bk Titles 8,000; Per Subs 225
Subject Interests: Geology, Geophysics, Geotech eng, Land, Offshore soil investigations
Special Collections: Geotechnics (Company Reports & Proceedings of Geotechnical Conferences); Related publications; Special technical files
Publications: McCelland Engineers Library System A to Z (handbook); New in the Library
Restriction: Staff use only
Partic in Amigos Library Services, Inc; Dialog Corporation; OCLC Online Computer Library Center, Inc

FULBRIGHT & JAWORSKI LLP, Law Library, 1301 McKinney St, 77010. SAN 316-439X. Tel: 713-651-5151, 713-651-5219. FAX: 713-651-5246. *Dir Libr Serv*, Jane D Holland; Staff 2 (MLS 2)
Founded 1919
Library Holdings: Bk Vols 55,000

L GARDERE, WYNNE, SEWELL & RIGGS LIBRARY,* 333 Clay Ave, Ste 800, 77002. SAN 372-980X. Tel: 713-308-5736. FAX: 713-308-5555. E-Mail: fabtr@gardere.com. *Librn*, Trisha Fabugais
Library Holdings: Bk Vols 10,000; Per Subs 75
Subject Interests: Law

S GULF PUBLISHING CO LIBRARY, 3301 Allen Pkwy, 77019. SAN 316-4446. Tel: 713-529-4301. FAX: 713-520-4433. E-Mail: publications@gulfpub.com. Web Site: www.gulfpub.com. *Librn*, Cheryl Curtis
Founded 1947
Library Holdings: Bk Vols 3,000; Per Subs 129
Subject Interests: Petrochem indust, Petroleum

S H O K, INC LIBRARY,* 2800 Post Oak Blvd, 77056. SAN 316-4241. Tel: 713-407-7700. FAX: 713-407-7809. *Librn*, Lorretta Fulzio
Founded 1968
Library Holdings: Bk Vols 3,000
Subject Interests: Architecture, Art, Construction, Engineering, Planning
Partic in Data Time; Dialog Corporation; SDC Search Serv; Vutext

S H O MOHR TECHNICAL LIBRARY,* 12237 FM 529, 77041. SAN 323-5130. Tel: 713-466-1527. FAX: 713-896-6807. *Mgr*, Jack Miller; *Librn*, Ann Daniel; E-Mail: adaniel@mohreng.com
Library Holdings: Bk Vols 1,000; Per Subs 50

S HALLIBURTON ENERGY SERVICES, Engineering Library,* PO Box 42800, 77242-8019. SAN 316-5043. Tel: 281-596-5495. FAX: 281-596-4279. Web Site: www.hallworld.com. *Librn*, Pat Farnell
Library Holdings: Bk Vols 1,500; Per Subs 72
Subject Interests: Applied math, Computer software, Electronics, Explosives, Geology, Geophysics, Nuclear science, Well logging
Publications: Newsletter
Partic in Dialog Corporation

S HALLIBURTON ENERGY SERVICES, Houston Technical Library, 3000 N Sam Houston Pkwy E, 77032. (Mail add: PO Box 60070, 77205), SAN 324-1866. Tel: 281-871-4544. FAX: 281-871-4018. *Librn*, Connie S Bihon; Staff 2 (MLS 1, Non-MLS 1)
Founded 1979
Library Holdings: Bk Vols 11,000; Bk Titles 9,000; Per Subs 210
Subject Interests: Chemistry, Electronics, Engineering
Special Collections: Association & Industry Standards; Military Specifications; Society of Petroleum Engineers Coll; United States Patents Coll (1972-present)
Automation Activity & Vendor Info: (Cataloging) Inmagic, Inc.
Publications: Acquisitions List (monthly); Brief Guide to the Technical Information Center; From the Sidelines (current awareness bulletin every 2 weeks); Master Serials List
Restriction: By appointment only

GL HARRIS COUNTY LAW LIBRARY, Congress Plaza, 1019 Congress, 17th flr, 77002. SAN 316-4454. Tel: 713-755-5183. *Dir*, John R Eichstadt
Founded 1913
Library Holdings: Bk Vols 100,000

P HARRIS COUNTY PUBLIC LIBRARY,* 8080 El Rio St, 77054-4195. SAN 361-8129. Tel: 713-749-9000. TDD: 281-443-4827. FAX: 713-749-9090. Web Site: www.hcpl.lib.tx.us. *Dir*, Catherine S Ensign; Tel: 713-749-9010, E-Mail: censign@stic.lib.tx.us; *Assoc Dir*, Rhoda L Goldberg; Tel: 713-749-9011, E-Mail: rgoldber@stic.lib.tx.us; *Tech Servs*, David Jones; Tel: 713-749-9040, E-Mail: djones@stic.lib.tx.us; *Cat*, Bill Jarvis; E-Mail: bjarvis@stic.lib.tx.us; *Ad Servs*, Elaine Plotkin; E-Mail: eplotkin@stic.lib.tx.us; *Acq*, Neil Campbell; E-Mail: ncampbel@stic.lib.tx.us; *Tech Coordr*, Gene Rollins; Tel: 713-749-9020, E-Mail: grollins@stic.lib.tx.us; *Coordr*, Donald Thomas; E-Mail: dthomas@stic.lib.tx.us; *Ch Servs*, Sally Goodroe; E-Mail: sgoodroe@stic.lib.tx.us; Staff 258 (MLS 81, Non-MLS 177)
Founded 1921. Pop 1,143,237; Circ 5,025,170
Mar 1998-Feb 1999 Income (Main Library and Branch Library) $11,105,412, State $200,000, County $10,705,412, Locally Generated Income $200,000. Mats Exp $10,666,941, Books $1,702,237, Per/Ser (Incl. Access Fees) $150,000. Sal $7,071,183
Library Holdings: Bk Vols 1,275,615; Bk Titles 249,674; Per Subs 2,901
Automation Activity & Vendor Info: (Acquisitions) Brodart; (Cataloging) Brodart; (Circulation) epixtech, inc.; (OPAC) epixtech, inc.
Database Vendor: epixtech, inc., IAC - Info Trac
Partic in SE Tex Libr Internet Consortium
Friends of the Library Group
Branches: 25
ALDINE BRANCH, 11331 Airline Dr, 77037. SAN 361-8153. Tel: 281-445-5560. FAX: 281-445-8625. Web Site: www.hcpl.lib.tx.us. *Librn*, Sylvia Powers
Library Holdings: Bk Vols 81,506
Friends of the Library Group
ATASCOCITA, 19520 Pinehurst Trails Dr, Humble, 77346. SAN 376-9461. Tel: 281-812-2162. FAX: 281-812-2135. Web Site: www.hcpl.lib.tx.us. *Mgr*, Linda Bryson

Friends of the Library Group
BEAR CREEK BRANCH, 16719 Clay Rd, 77084. SAN 361-8161. Tel: 281-550-0885. FAX: 281-550-3304. Web Site: www.hcpl.lib.tx.us. *Librn*, Donna Jackson
Library Holdings: Bk Vols 152,365
Friends of the Library Group
BALDWIN BOETTCHER BRANCH, 22248 Aldine Westfield Rd, Humble, 77338. SAN 322-5704. Tel: 281-821-1320. TDD: 281-443-4827. FAX: 281-443-8068. Web Site: www.hcpl.lib.tx.us. *Librn*, Karen Ellis
Library Holdings: Bk Vols 136,106
Special Services for the Deaf - TDD
Friends of the Library Group
CROSBY BRANCH, 135 Hare Rd, Crosby, 77532. SAN 361-8218. Tel: 281-328-3535. FAX: 281-328-5590. Web Site: www.hcpl.lib.tx.us. *Librn*, Diane Barker
Library Holdings: Bk Vols 83,112
Friends of the Library Group
CYPRESS CREEK BRANCH, 6815 Cypresswood Dr, Spring, 77379. SAN 361-8242. Tel: 281-376-4610. FAX: 281-376-0820. Web Site: www.hcpl.lib.tx.us. *Librn*, Nancy Agafite
Library Holdings: Bk Vols 129,138
Friends of the Library Group
EVELYN MEADOR BRANCH, 2400 N Meyer, Seabrook, 77586. SAN 329-6318. Tel: 281-474-9142. FAX: 281-474-4591. Web Site: www.hcpl.lib.tx.us. *Librn*, Greg Burns
Library Holdings: Bk Vols 72,173
Friends of the Library Group
FAIRBANKS BRANCH, 7122 N Gessner, 77040. SAN 361-8277. Tel: 281-466-4438. FAX: 281-466-9757. Web Site: www.hcpl.lib.tx.us. *Librn*, Jackie Davis
Library Holdings: Bk Vols 85,580
Friends of the Library Group
OCTAVIA FIELDS MEMORIAL BRANCH, 111 W Higgins, Humble, 77338. SAN 361-8455. Tel: 281-446-3377. FAX: 281-446-4203. Web Site: www.hcpl.lib.tx.us. *Librn*, Diane Delano
Friends of the Library Group
FREEMAN MEMORIAL BRANCH, 16602 Diana Lane, 77062. SAN 361-8307. Tel: 281-488-1906. FAX: 281-286-3931. Web Site: www.hcpl.lib.tx.us. *Librn*, Tina Russ
Library Holdings: Bk Vols 127,788
Friends of the Library Group
GALENA PARK BRANCH, 1500 Keene St, Galena Park, 77547. SAN 361-8331. Tel: 713-450-0982. FAX: 713-451-1131. Web Site: www.hcpl.lib.tx.us. *Librn*, Mila Banville
Library Holdings: Bk Vols 26,202
Friends of the Library Group
HIGH MEADOWS BRANCH, 4500 Aldine Mail Rte, 77039. SAN 361-834X. Tel: 281-590-1456. FAX: 281-987-3560. Web Site: www.hcpl.lib.tx.us.
Library Holdings: Bk Vols 70,657
Friends of the Library Group
JACINTO CITY BRANCH, 921 Akron, 77029. SAN 361-8366. Tel: 713-673-3237. FAX: 713-671-0458. Web Site: www.hcpl.lib.tx.us. *Librn*, Cynthia Lockwood
Library Holdings: Bk Vols 29,869
Friends of the Library Group
KATY BRANCH, 5702 Second St, Katy, 77493. SAN 361-8390. Tel: 281-391-3509. FAX: 281-391-1927. Web Site: www.hcpl.lib.tx.us. *Librn*, Terri Dingley
Library Holdings: Bk Vols 49,613
Friends of the Library Group
KINGWOOD BRANCH, 4102 Rustic Woods Dr, Kingwood, 77345. SAN 361-8404. Tel: 281-360-6804. FAX: 281-360-2093. Web Site: www.hcpl.lib.tx.us. *Librn*, Wendy Schneider
Library Holdings: Bk Vols 129,758
Friends of the Library Group
LAPORTE BRANCH, 526 San Jacinto, LaPorte, 77571. SAN 361-8420. Tel: 281-471-4022. FAX: 281-470-9905. Web Site: www.hcpl.lib.tx.us. *Librn*, Lorraine Jeffery
Library Holdings: Bk Vols 41,906
Friends of the Library Group
MAUD SMITH MARKS BRANCH, 1815 Westgreen Blvd, Katy, 77450. SAN 373-529X. Tel: 281-492-8592. FAX: 281-492-3480. Web Site: www.hcpl.lib.tx.us. *Librn*, Susan Green
Library Holdings: Bk Vols 101,270
Friends of the Library Group
NORTH CHANNEL BRANCH, 15741 Wallisvillle Rd, 77049. SAN 361-8633. Tel: 281-457-1631. FAX: 281-457-2305. Web Site: www.hcpl.lib.tx.us. *Librn*, Pat Lippold
Library Holdings: Bk Vols 84,356
Friends of the Library Group
NORTHWEST, 11355 Regency Green Dr, Cypress, 77429. SAN 370-0216. Tel: 281-890-2665. FAX: 281-469-4718. Web Site: www.hcpl.lib.tx.us. *Librn*, Susan Whitt
Library Holdings: Bk Vols 110,927
Friends of the Library Group
PARKER WILLIAMS BRANCH, 10851 Scarsdale Blvd, 77089. SAN 37 5281. Tel: 281-484-2036. FAX: 281-481-0729. Web Site: www.hcpl.lib.tx.us. *Librn*, Karen Ackerman
Library Holdings: Bk Vols 109,712
Friends of the Library Group
SOUTH HOUSTON BRANCH, 607 Avenue A Ave, South Houston, 7758 SAN 361-848X. Tel: 713-941-2385. FAX: 713-947-7389. Web Site: www.hcpl.lib.tx.us. *Librn*, Sandra Dies
Library Holdings: Bk Vols 26,860
Friends of the Library Group
SPRING BRANCH MEMORIAL, 930 Corbindale, 77024. SAN 361-851 Tel: 281-464-1633. FAX: 713-973-2654. Web Site: www.hcpl.lib.tx.us. *Librn*, Karen Hayes
Library Holdings: Bk Vols 104,595
Friends of the Library Group
STRATFORD BRANCH, 509 Stratford, Highlands, 77562. SAN 361-854 Tel: 281-426-3521. FAX: 281-426-4354. Web Site: www.hcpl.lib.tx.us. *Librn*, Joan Halliday
Library Holdings: Bk Vols 34,170
Friends of the Library Group
TOMBALL BRANCH, 701 James St, Tomball, 77375. SAN 361-8579. Te 281-351-7269. FAX: 281-351-6693. Web Site: www.hcpl.lib.tx.us. *Librn*, Patti Park
Library Holdings: Bk Vols 66,917
Friends of the Library Group
WEST UNIVERSITY BRANCH, 6108 Auden, 77005. SAN 361-8609. Te 713-668-8273. FAX: 713-667-2264. Web Site: www.hcpl.lib.tx.us. *Librn*, Keddy Outlaw
Library Holdings: Bk Vols 62,906
Friends of the Library Group
Bookmobiles: 2. Librn, Alan Withoff

P THE HERITAGE SOCIETY LIBRARY,* 1100 Bagby, 77002. SAN 327-5388. Tel: 713-655-1912. FAX: 713-655-7527. *Curator*, Wallace Saage
Library Holdings: Bk Vols 5,500

S HIRSCH LIBRARY MUSEUM OF FINE ARTS, HOUSTON,* 1001 Bissonnet, PO Box 6826, 77005. SAN 316-4683. Tel: 713-639-7325. FAX 713-639-7399. E-Mail: hirsch@mfah.org. Web Site: mfah.org. *Assoc Librn* Margaret Ford; *Archivist*, Lorraine Stuart; Staff 9 (MLS 5, Non-MLS 4)
1996-1997 Mats Exp Books $80,000
Library Holdings: Bk Vols 60,000; Per Subs 303
Subject Interests: Art history, Decorative arts, Fine arts, Photog
Special Collections: Bayou Bend Library; Museum Archives; Texana
Restriction: Non-circulating to the public
Partic in RLIN

M HOUSTON ACADEMY OF MEDICINE-TEXAS MEDICAL CENTER LIBRARY, 1133 MD Anderson Blvd, 77030. SAN 316-4470. Tel: 713-79 4200. FAX: 713-790-7052. Web Site: www.library.tmc.edu. *Actg Dir*, J Robert Beck; *Coll Develop*, Richard P Jasper; Tel: 713-799-7126, E-Mail: richardj@library.tmc.edu; Staff 70 (MLS 15, Non-MLS 55)
Founded 1951. Pop 16,000; Highest Degree: Doctorate
Library Holdings: Bk Vols 270,649; Per Subs 2,200
Subject Interests: Behav sci, Biochemistry, Biotech, Medicine, Nursing, Public health, Sci-tech, Soc sci
Special Collections: Arthritis, Gout & Rheumatism (Burbank Coll); Cardiovascular Surgery Coll; Hench Coll; History of Medicine (McGovern Coll); Local History (Harris County Medical Archive); Public Health (Mading Coll)
Automation Activity & Vendor Info: (Cataloging) SIRSI; (Circulation) SIRSI; (Serials) SIRSI
Publications: Library Lines
Partic in Amigos Library Services, Inc; Dialog Corporation; National Network Of Libraries Of Medicine - South Central Region; OCLC Online Computer Library Center, Inc; Tex Health Sci Libr Consortium
Friends of the Library Group

G HOUSTON AIRPORT SYSTEM TECHNICAL LIBRARY, Bush InterContinental Airport, 16930 JFK Blvd, PO Box 60106, 77032. SAN 3 4527. Tel: 281-233-1866, 281-233-3000. FAX: 281-233-1748. *Archivist*, Trudy Schindewolf
Founded 1975
Library Holdings: Per Subs 120
Subject Interests: Airport mgt, Aviation, Develop, Planning

P HOUSTON AREA LIBRARY SYSTEM,* 500 McKinney Ave, 77002-253 SAN 316-4489. Tel: 713-247-1925. FAX: 713-247-2661. Web Site: hals.lib.tx.us. *Dir*, Barbara A B Gubbin; Tel: 713-247-2700; *Automation Sy Coordr*, Vickie Phillips; Staff 4 (MLS 4)
Pop 4,923,264
Sep 1998-Aug 1999 Income $1,813,568, State $1,116,428, Federal $697,14 Mats Exp $1,039,552, Books $687,335, Per/Ser (Incl. Access Fees) $3,996, AV Equip $27,166. Sal $284,271 (Prof $161,381)
Publications: Film Catalog; Newsletter; Professional Library Science Collection Catalog; Videocassette Catalogs
Member Libraries: Allan Shivers Library; Alma M Carpenter Public

Library; Austin Memorial Library; Bay City Public Library; Bellaire City Library; Bellville Public Library; Blanche K Werner Public Library; Bridge City Public Library; Buna Public Library; Chambers County Library System; Coldspring Area Public Library; Deer Park Public Library; Edmund E & Nida Smith Jones Public Library; Effie & Wilton Hebert Public Library; Eula & David Winterman Library; Fannie Brown Booth Memorial Library; Fort Bend County Libraries; Friendswood Public Library; Genevieve Miller Hitchcock Public Library; Groveton Public Library; Helen Hall Library; Houston Public Library; Houston Public Library; Huntsville Public Library; Jasper Public Library; Jefferson County Library; John H Wootters-Crockett Public Library; Knox Memorial Library; Kountze Public Library; Kurth Memorial Library; La Marque Public Library; Liberty Municipal Library; Lumberton Public Library; Mae S Bruce Library; Mares Memorial Library; Marion & Ed Hughes Public Library; Mickey Reily Public Library; Montgomery County Memorial Library System; Moore Memorial Public Library; Murphy Memorial Library; Nacogdoches Public Library; Nesbitt Memorial Library; New Waverly Public Library; Newton County Public Library; Orange Public Library; Palacios Library, Inc; Pasadena Public Library; Port Arthur Public Library; Rosenberg Library; San Augustine Public Library; Shepherd Public Library; Sheridan Memorial Library; Sterling Municipal Library; T L L Temple Memorial Library; Vidor Public Library; Virgil & Josephine Gordon Memorial Library; Waller County Library; Weimar Public Library; Wharton County Library

HOUSTON BAPTIST UNIVERSITY, Moody Memorial Library, 7502 Fondren Rd, 77074-3298. SAN 316-4497. Tel: 281-649-3435. Interlibrary Loan Service Tel: 281-649-3000, Ext 2008. Circulation Tel: 281-649-3304. Reference Tel: 281-649-3000, Ext 2312. FAX: 281-649-3489. *Dir*, Dr Jon M Suter; E-Mail: jsuter@hbu.edu; *Assoc Dir*, Ann A Noble; Tel: 281-649-3000, Ext 2303, E-Mail: aanoble@hbu.edu; *Ref*, Kristin Fance; Tel: 281-649-3000, Ext 2356, E-Mail: kfance@hbu.edu; *Syst Coordr*, Dean Riley; Tel: 281-649-3000, Ext 2304, E-Mail: driley@hbu.edu; *Cat*, Janet Serice; Tel: 281-649-3000, Ext 2303, E-Mail: jserice@hbu.edu; Staff 12 (MLS 7, Non-MLS 5)
Founded 1963. Enrl 2,500; Fac 120; Highest Degree: Master
Jun 2000-May 2001 Income $1,027,187, Parent Institution $992,187, Other $35,000. Mats Exp $409,000, Books $151,000, Per/Ser (Incl. Access Fees) $110,000, Presv $14,000, Electronic Ref Mat (Incl. Access Fees) $134,000. Sal $385,715
Library Holdings: Bk Vols 167,866; Per Subs 1,032
Subject Interests: Baptist hist, Southwest, Texas, Victorian literature
Special Collections: Gilbert & Sullivan (Linder Coll); History & Literature (Palmer Bradley Coll); History (Hicks Memorial Coll)
Automation Activity & Vendor Info: (Cataloging) DRA; (Circulation) DRA; (ILL) DRA
Database Vendor: DRA, IAC - Info Trac, Lexis-Nexis, OCLC - First Search, OVID Technologies, ProQuest, Silverplatter Information Inc.
Restriction: Open to student, faculty & staff
Function: ILL available
Partic in Amigos Library Services, Inc; Tex Share
Friends of the Library Group

HOUSTON CHRONICLE EDITORIAL LIBRARY,* 801 Texas Ave, 77002. (Mail add: PO Box 4260, 77210), SAN 316-4500. Tel: 713-220-7312, 713-220-7313. FAX: 713-220-7275. Web Site: www.houstonchronicle.com. *Librn*, Sherry Adams; E-Mail: sherry.adams@chron.com; *Asst Librn*, Melissa Mantel
Founded 1960
Library Holdings: Bk Vols 4,000; Per Subs 14
Subject Interests: News files, Texana
Restriction: Company library
Partic in Data Time

HOUSTON COMMUNITY COLLEGE, Central Library,* 1300 Holman, 77004. SAN 316-4519. Tel: 713-718-6133. FAX: 713-718-6154. Web Site: www.hccs.cc.tx.us. *In Charge*, Ronald Homick; E-Mail: homick_r@hccs.cc.tx.us
Founded 1972. Enrl 70,000; Fac 980
Library Holdings: Bk Vols 125,000; Per Subs 500
Subject Interests: Bus, Medicine, Mgt, Sci-tech
Publications: Shelf life
Partic in Amigos Library Services, Inc; OCLC Online Computer Library Center, Inc
Fourteen branch libraries on campuses throughout the city

HOUSTON LIGHTING & POWER CO LIBRARY,* PO Box 1700, 77251. SAN 316-4535. Tel: 713-207-1111. FAX: 713-207-9960. *In Charge*, Cheryl Botts
Founded 1969
Library Holdings: Bk Vols 2,000; Per Subs 56
Subject Interests: Bus, Electricity, Engineering
Publications: Library bulletin (quarterly)
Restriction: Company library

HOUSTON MUSEUM OF NATURAL SCIENCE LIBRARY,* One Hermann Circle Dr, 77030-1799. SAN 316-4543. Tel: 713-639-4600, 713-639-4670. FAX: 713-523-4125. *Pres*, Truett Latimer
Founded 1969
Library Holdings: Bk Vols 8,000; Per Subs 80
Special Collections: Malacology

P HOUSTON PUBLIC LIBRARY, 500 McKinney Ave, 77002-2534. SAN 361-8692. Tel: 713-247-2700. Circulation Tel: 713-247-2222. Reference Tel: 713-236-1313. TDD: 713-225-3385. FAX: 713-247-1266. E-Mail: website@hpl.lib.tx.us. Web Site: www.hpl.lib.tx.us. *Dir*, Barbara Gubbin; *Dep Dir*, Alison Landers; Tel: 713-247-3263; *Dep Dir*, Abdool Sahira; Tel: 713-247-1651; *Asst Dir*, Roger Haas; Tel: 713-247-1630; *Asst Dir*, Toni Lambert; *Asst Dir*, Andrea Lapsley; *Tech Servs*, Brenda Tirrell. Subject Specialists: *Info tech*, Toni Lambert; Staff 363 (MLS 163, Non-MLS 200)
Founded 1901. Pop 1,919,390; Circ 6,234,526
Jul 1999-Jun 2000 Income City $36,642,529. Mats Exp $6,068,000. Sal $23,248,971
Library Holdings: Bk Vols 4,470,515; Bk Titles 998,776; Per Subs 17,179
Subject Interests: Architecture, Art, Genealogy, Mgt
Special Collections: Architectural Coll; Archives & Manuscripts Department (Houston Metropolitan Research Center) contains 12,000 linear ft of archival material & 1.5 million photographs & negatives related to Houston including manuscript Coll; Bibles, Civil War, Salvation Army, Milsap Coll; Early Houston & Texas Maps; Early Printing & Illuminated Manuscript (Annette Finnigan); Juvenile Literature (Norma Meldrum, Special Coll & Historical Juvenile Coll); Petroleum (Barton, Dumble, & DeWolf Coll); Posters; Sheet Music (Max Hornstein, Adele Margulies, Henry Thayer & Edna Joseph Coll); Texana (Maresh & Blake Coll)
Automation Activity & Vendor Info: (Circulation) Innovative Interfaces Inc.
Mem of Houston Area Library System
Partic in Dialog Corporation; Houston Area Research Library Consortium; NY Times Info Bank; SDC Search Serv
Special Services for the Deaf - Captioned film depository; Special interest periodicals; Staff with knowledge of sign language; TTY machine
Special Services for the Blind - Kurzweil Reading Machine
Friends of the Library Group
Branches: 47
ACRES HOMES, 8501 W Montgomery Rd, 77088. SAN 361-9176. Tel: 281-448-9841. Web Site: www.hpl.lib.tx.us. *Branch Mgr*, Jennifer Collins
Circ 52,640
Library Holdings: Bk Vols 44,473
Open Mon 12-9, Tues-Sat 10-6
ARCHIVES & MANUSCRIPTS DEPARTMENT, Julia Ideson Bldg, 500 McKinney, 77002. SAN 361-8722. Tel: 281-247-1661. Web Site: www.hpl.lib.tx.us. *Archivist*, Louis Marchiafava
Special Collections: Regional Historical Records for Texas State Depository (select records of 5 surrounding counties)
BIBLIOGRAPHIC & INFORMATION CENTER DEPARTMENT Tel: 713-236-1313. Web Site: www.hpl.lib.tx.us. *Mgr*, Carol Johnson
Library Holdings: Bk Vols 10,188
Special Collections: Center for Visually Impaired; Foundation Center
BRACEWELL BRANCH, 10115 Kleckley Dr, 77075. SAN 361-9230. Tel: 713-948-9052. Web Site: www.sparc.hpl.lib.tx.us. *Branch Mgr*, John Shults
Circ 147,589
Library Holdings: Bk Vols 88,034
Open Mon & Thurs 12-9, Tues 10-9, Wed, Fri & Sat 10-6
BUSINESS, SCIENCE & TECHNOLOGY DEPARTMENT Web Site: www.hpl.lib.tx.us. *Mgr*, Regina Stemmer
Library Holdings: Bk Vols 138,009
Special Collections: Corporate Reports; Petroleum Geology; Standards & Specifications
CARNEGIE BRANCH LIBRARY & COMMUNITY EDUCATION CENTER, 1050 Quitman, 77009. SAN 361-9265. Tel: 713-226-4445. Web Site: www.hpl.lib.tx.us. *Branch Mgr*, Diana Morales
Circ 141,114
Library Holdings: Bk Vols 110,993
Open Mon-Thurs 10-9, Fri & Sat 10-6, Sun 2-6
CHILDREN'S ROOM DEPARTMENT Tel: 713-236-1313. Web Site: www.hpl.lib.tx.us. *Mgr*, Jane McNair
Library Holdings: Bk Vols 154,116
CLAYTON LIBRARY, CENTER FOR GENEALOGICAL RESEARCH, 5300 Caroline, 77004. SAN 361-8846. Web Site: www.hpl.lib.tx.us. *Mgr*, Margaret Harris
Library Holdings: Bk Vols 53,114
Subject Interests: Genealogy
Publications: In-house Bibligraphies
Partic in OCLC Online Computer Library Center, Inc
COLLIER BRANCH, 6200 Pinemont, 77092. SAN 326-7563. Tel: 713-684-1803. Web Site: www.hpl.lib.tx.us. *Branch Mgr*, Lin Swalley
Circ 269,890
Library Holdings: Bk Vols 107,449
Open Mon-Thurs 10-9, Fri & Sat 10-6, Sun 2-6
DIXON BRANCH, 8002 Hirsch, 77016. SAN 361-929X. Tel: 713-633-2147. Web Site: www.hpl.lib.tx.us. *Branch Mgr*, Martha Mba
Circ 17,042
Library Holdings: Bk Vols 37,168

Open Mon 12-9, Tues-Sat 10-6

EVA ALICE MCCRANE-KASHMERE GARDENS BRANCH, 5411 Pardee, 77026. SAN 361-9508. Tel: 713-674-8461. Web Site: www.hpl.lib.tx.us.
Founded 1971. Circ 37,627
Library Holdings: Bk Vols 45,280
Open Mon & Thurs 12-9, Tues 10-9, Wed, Fri & Sat 10-6

FIFTH WARD, 4014 Market, 77020. SAN 361-932X. Tel: 713-238-2247. Web Site: www.hpl.lib.tx.us. *Branch Mgr*, Sarah Starling
Circ 20,949
Library Holdings: Bk Vols 37,345
Open Mon 12-9, Thurs 10-9, Tues, Wed, Fri & Sat 10-6

FINE ARTS & RECREATION DEPARTMENT Tel: 713-236-1313. Web Site: htpp://www.hpl.lib.tx.us. *Mgr*, John Harvath
Library Holdings: Bk Vols 128,004
Special Collections: Artist Information File; Auction and exhibition Catalogs; Sheet Music

FLORES BRANCH, 110 N Milby, 77003. SAN 361-9338. Tel: 713-226-4454. Web Site: www.hpl.lib.tx.us. *Branch Mgr*, Elvia Pillado
Circ 77,866
Library Holdings: Bk Vols 59,500
Open Mon & Thurs 12-9, Tues, Wed, Fri & Sat 10-6

FRANK BRANCH, 6440 W Bellfort Ave, 77035. SAN 361-9346. Tel: 713-272-3655. Web Site: www.hpl.lib.tx.us. *Branch Mgr*, Edward Osowski; Tel: 713-272-3658, E-Mail: eosowski@hpl.lib.tx.us
Founded 1984. Circ 223,198
Library Holdings: Bk Vols 106,565
Open Mon & Thurs 12-9, Tues 10-9, Wed, Fri & Sat 10-6

FREED-MONTROSE BRANCH, 4100 Montrose, 77006. Tel: 713-284-1958. Web Site: www.hpl.lib.tx.us. *Branch Mgr*, Karen Vargas
Circ 200,384
Library Holdings: Bk Vols 96,703
Open Mon & Thurs 12-9, Tues, Wed, Fri & Sat 10-6

HEIGHTS, 1302 Heights Blvd, 77008. SAN 361-9354. Tel: 713-867-0399. Web Site: www.hpl.lib.tx.us.
Circ 178,539
Library Holdings: Bk Vols 71,288
Open Mon & Thurs 12-9, Tues, Wed, Fri & Sat 10-6

HENINGTON-ALIEF BRANCH, 7979 S Kirkwood, 77072. SAN 322-5682. Tel: 281-568-3330. Web Site: www.hpl.lib.tx.us. *Branch Mgr*, Rebecca Hubert
Circ 491,440
Library Holdings: Bk Vols 134,936
Open Mon-Thurs 10-9, Fri & Sat 10-6, Sun 2-6

HILLENDAHL BRANCH, 2436 Gessner Dr, 77080. SAN 361-9419. Tel: 713-467-9090. FAX: 713-467-9049. E-Mail: hilbranc@hpl.lib.tx.us. Web Site: www.hpl.lib.tx.us. *Branch Mgr*, Alice M Depot
Circ 202,541
Library Holdings: Bk Vols 71,892
Subject Interests: African-American, Spanish (language)
Special Collections: Spanish, Vietnamese, Korean & Chinese-language books
Database Vendor: GaleNet, OCLC - First Search
Function: ILL available
Mem of Houston Area Library System
Open Mon & Thurs 12-9, Tues 10-9, Wed, Fri & Sat 10-6
Friends of the Library Group

HUMANITIES DEPARTMENT Tel: 713-236-1313. Web Site: www.hpl.lib.tx.us. *Mgr*, Beatrice Temp
Library Holdings: Bk Vols 275,060
Publications: Connections: Library Services to Hearing Impaired (newsletter)

JOHNSON BRANCH, 3517 Reed Rd, 77051. SAN 361-9443. Tel: 713-733-1983. Web Site: www.hpl.lib.tx.us. *Branch Mgr*, Hellena Stokes
Circ 55,644
Library Holdings: Bk Vols 52,119
Open Mon 12-9, Tues-Sat 10-6

JUNGMAN BRANCH, 5830 Westheimer Rd, 77057. SAN 361-9478. Tel: 713-267-0359. Web Site: www.hpl.lib.tx.us. *Actg Mgr*, Pamela Pearson
Circ 332,223
Library Holdings: Bk Vols 137,177
Open Mon-Thurs 10-9, Fri & Sat 10-6, Sun 2-6

KENDALL BRANCH, 14330 Memorial Dr, 77079. SAN 361-9532. Tel: 281-752-2202. Web Site: www.hpl.lib.tx.us. *Branch Mgr*, Linda Bryson
Circ 346,109
Library Holdings: Bk Vols 114,082
Open Mon & Thurs 12-9, Tues 10-9, Wed, Fri & Sat 10-6

LAKEWOOD, 8815 Feland, 77028. SAN 361-9591. Tel: 713-633-3725. Web Site: www.hpl.lib.tx.us.; Staff 5 (MLS 1, Non-MLS 4)
Founded 1963. Circ 37,038
Library Holdings: Bk Vols 38,011
Special Services for the Blind - ZoomText software to enlarge computer screen
Open Mon 12-9, Tues-Sat 10-6

LOOSCAN BRANCH, 2510 Willowick Rd, 77027. SAN 361-9621. Tel: 713-622-6525. Web Site: www.hpl.lib.tx.us. *Branch Mgr*, Martha Ross; E-Mail: maross@hpl.lib.tx.us
Circ 158,218
Library Holdings: Bk Vols 65,627
Open Mon & Thurs 12-9, Tues, Wed, Fri & Sat 10-6

M D ANDERSON PATIENT & FAMILY LIBRARY, 1515 Holcombe, 77030. SAN 371-9650. Tel: 713-792-2229. Web Site: www.sparc.hpl.lib.tx.us. *Mgr*, Gloria Mier-Carreno
Circ 35,559
Library Holdings: Bk Vols 16,968
Open Mon-Fri 8:30-5:30, Sat & Sun 1-4 (Vols)

MANCUSO BRANCH, 6767 Bellfort, 77087. SAN 361-963X. Tel: 713-6 1878. FAX: 713-644-1767. Web Site: www.hpl.lib.tx.us. *Branch Mgr*, Sharyn L Easterbrook; E-Mail: seasterb@hpl.lib.tx.us; *Librn*, Adela Cabillo; E-Mail: acabillo@hpl.lib.tx.us. Subject Specialists: *Children*, Adela Cabillo
Circ 47,695
Library Holdings: Bk Vols 43,689
Automation Activity & Vendor Info: (Circulation) Innovative Interfac Inc.; (OPAC) Innovative Interfaces Inc.
Function: ILL available
Open Mon & Thurs 12-9, Tues, Wed, Fri & Sat 10-6

MELCHER BRANCH, 7200 Keller, 77012. SAN 361-9656. Tel: 713-847 5141. Web Site: www.hpl.lib.tx.us. *Branch Mgr*, Amelia Juresko
Circ 89,072
Library Holdings: Bk Vols 49,779
Open Mon 12-9, Tues-Sat 10-6

MEYER BRANCH, 5005 W Bellfort, 77035. SAN 361-9680. Tel: 713-72 1630. Web Site: www.hpl.lib.tx.us. *Actg Mgr*, Darlene Dibble
Circ 257,257
Library Holdings: Bk Vols 89,447
Open Mon & Thurs 12-9, Tues 10-9, Wed, Fri & Sat 10-6

MOODY BRANCH, 9525 Irvington Blvd, 77076. SAN 361-9710. Tel: 71 697-2745. Web Site: www.hpl.lib.tx.us. *Branch Mgr*, Sandra Sadler
Circ 119,472
Library Holdings: Bk Vols 50,612
Mem of Central Texas Library System
Open Mon & Thurs 12-9, Tues, Wed, Fri & Sat 10-6

OAK FOREST, 1349 W 43rd St, 77018. SAN 361-9745. Tel: 713-688-22 Web Site: www.hpl.lib.tx.us. *Branch Mgr*, Cynthia Deitiker
Circ 136,017
Library Holdings: Bk Vols 58,082
Open Mon & Thurs 12-9, Tues, Wed, Fri & Sat 10-6

PARK PLACE REGIONAL, 8145 Park Place Blvd, 77017. SAN 361-977 Tel: 713-645-4183. Web Site: www.hpl.lib.tx.us. *Branch Mgr*, John Tug
Circ 229,617
Library Holdings: Bk Vols 100,726
Open Mon-Thurs 10-9, Fri-Sat 10-6, Sun 2-6

PLEASANTVILLE, 1520 Gellhorn Dr, 77029. SAN 361-980X. Tel: 713-676-0693. Web Site: www.hpl.lib.tx.us. *Branch Mgr*, Coleen Molden
Circ 19,019
Library Holdings: Bk Vols 30,717
Open Mon 12-9, Tues-Sat 10-6

RING BRANCH, 8835 Long Point Rd, 77055. SAN 361-9834. Tel: 713-468-2643. Web Site: www.hpl.lib.tx.us. *Branch Mgr*, Sergio Pineda
Circ 113,296
Library Holdings: Bk Vols 70,015
Open Mon & Thurs 12-9, Tues, Wed, Fri & Sat 10-6

ROBINSON WESTCHASE BRANCH, 3223 Willcrest, 77042. SAN 371-9669. Tel: 713-784-0987. Web Site: www.hpl.lib.tx.us. *Branch Mgr*, Delores Bentke
Circ 382,398
Library Holdings: Bk Vols 106,497
Open Mon & Thurs 12-9, Tues 10-9, Wed, Fri & Sat 10-6

SCENIC WOODS REGIONAL, 10677 Homestead Rd, 77016. SAN 326-758X. Tel: 713-635-8103. Web Site: www.hpl.lib.tx.us. *Branch Mgr*, Cla Russell
Circ 69,322
Library Holdings: Bk Vols 71,456
Open Mon-Thurs 10-9, Fri-Sat 10-6, Sun 2-6

SMITH BRANCH, 3624 Scott, 77004. SAN 361-9893. Tel: 713-842-3453. Web Site: www.hpl.lib.tx.us.
Circ 27,580
Library Holdings: Bk Vols 60,310
Open Mon & Thurs 12-9, Tues 10-9, Wed, Fri & Sat 10-6

SOCIAL SCIENCES DEPARTMENT, 500 McKinney, 77002. Tel: 713-24 2222. Reference Tel: 713-236-1313. Web Site: www.hpl.lib.tx.us. *Mgr*, Blaine Davis
Library Holdings: Bk Vols 162,471
Subject Interests: Afro-American hist, Biography
Database Vendor: CARL

STANAKER BRANCH, 611 Macario Garcia Dr, 77011. SAN 361-9923. Tel: 713-923-8784. Web Site: www.hpl.lib.tx.us. *Branch Mgr*, Marian Warby
Circ 103,801
Library Holdings: Bk Vols 71,968
Automation Activity & Vendor Info: (Cataloging) Innovative Interfaces Inc.; (Circulation) Innovative Interfaces Inc.
Database Vendor: IAC - Info Trac, OCLC - First Search

Open Mon & Thurs 12-9, Tues, Wed, Fri & Sat 10-6
TEXAS & LOCAL HISTORY DEPARTMENT, 500 Mckinney, 77002. Tel: 713-236-1313. Web Site: www.hpl.lib.tx.us. *Mgr*, Will Howard
Library Holdings: Bk Vols 30,752
Subject Interests: Texas
Special Collections: City Directories; Clipping files; Maps; Maresh Files; Sheet Music
TUTTLE BRANCH, 702 Kress, 77020. SAN 361-9958. Tel: 713-675-4656. Web Site: www.hpl.lib.tx.us. *Branch Mgr*, Beatriz DeAngulo
Circ 56,864
Library Holdings: Bk Vols 62,986
Open Mon & Thurs 12-9, Tues, Wed, Fri & Sat 10-6
VIDEO DEPARTMENT Tel: 281-247-1657. Web Site: www.hpl.lib.tx.us. *Mgr*, Mary Frances Townsend
Library Holdings: Bk Vols 23,889
Publications: video catalog
VINSON BRANCH, 3100 W Fuqua, 77045. SAN 361-9982. Tel: 713-433-0356. Web Site: www.hpl.lib.tx.us. *Branch Mgr*, Lon LeMaster
Circ 89,071
Library Holdings: Bk Vols 71,965
Open Mon & Thurs 12-9, Tues 10-9, Wed, Fri & Sat 10-6
WALTER BRANCH, 7660 Clarewood Dr, 77036. SAN 362-0018. Tel: 713-272-3661. Web Site: www.hpl.lib.tx.us.
Circ 180,242
Library Holdings: Bk Vols 100,655
Open Mon & Thurs 12-9, Tues, Wed, Fri & Sat 10-6
YOUNG BRANCH, 5260 Griggs Rd, 77021. SAN 362-0042. Tel: 713-643-8556. FAX: 713-847-4073. Web Site: www.hpl.lib.tx.us. *Branch Mgr*, Ola Carter Riley; E-Mail: oriley@hpl.lib.tx.us
Circ 43,099
Library Holdings: Bk Vols 46,985
Open Mon 12-9, Tues-Thurs 10-6, Fri & Sat 10-2

HOUSTON-LEARNING RESOURCE CENTER & MEDIA SERVICES,* 1130 M D Anderson Blvd, 77030. SAN 376-7930. Tel: 713-794-2161. FAX: 713-794-2162. *Head of Libr*, John Ivey
Library Holdings: Bk Titles 100

IMODCO, Business Library,* 17420 Kary Freeway, No 200, 77094. SAN 327-6260. Tel: 818-880-0300. FAX: 818-880-0333. *Librn*, Janet Pool
Library Holdings: Bk Vols 3,500; Per Subs 27

THE INSTITUTE FOR REHABILITATION & RESEARCH, T I R R Library, 1333 Moursund Ave, 77030. SAN 316-4934. Tel: 713-797-5947. FAX: 713-797-5982. *Coll Develop, Librn*, Pamela R Cornell; E-Mail: pcornell@bcm.tmc.edu
Founded 1969
Jan 1999-Dec 1999 Income Locally Generated Income $2,400. Mats Exp $1,775, Books $500, Per/Ser (Incl. Access Fees) $1,200, Other Print Mats $50. Sal $30,000
Library Holdings: Bk Vols 2,500; Per Subs 38
Subject Interests: Physical med, Rehabilitation
Special Collections: Polio & Post-Polio
Publications: Various patient information
Restriction: Reference only to non-staff
Function: Research library, Some telephone reference
Partic in HAM-TMC Libr Consortium

JACOBS ENGINEERING GROUP LIBRARY, 4848 Loop Central Dr, 77081. SAN 316-4616. Tel: 713-669-2200. FAX: 713-669-0045. *Librn*, Sara Davis; E-Mail: sara.davis@jacobs.com; Staff 1 (MLS 1)
Founded 1964
Library Holdings: Bk Titles 2,500; Per Subs 100
Subject Interests: Chemical engineering, Environmental eng
Automation Activity & Vendor Info: (Cataloging) EOS; (Circulation) EOS; (OPAC) EOS
Database Vendor: Dialog
Restriction: Open to public upon request
Partic in Dialog Corporation

KELLOGG BROWN & ROOT LIBRARY,* 601 Jefferson Ave, 77002. SAN 316-4772. Tel: 713-753-4015. FAX: 713-753-4669.; Staff 1 (MLS 1)
Library Holdings: Bk Vols 20,000; Per Subs 200
Subject Interests: Bus, Chemistry, Petrochem, Petroleum engineering, Technology
Publications: Acquisitions list (quarterly)

KPMG LLP LIBRARY, (Formerly KPMG Peat Marwick Library), 700 Louisiana St, 77002-2700. SAN 316-4721. Tel: 713-319-2000. FAX: 713-319-2102. Web Site: www.us.kpmg.com. *Librn*, Kent White
Library Holdings: Bk Titles 5,500; Per Subs 600
Subject Interests: Accounting, Mgt consult, Tax
Publications: Library Update
Restriction: Staff use only

LOCKWOOD, ANDREWS & NEWNAM, INC, Information Resource Center,* 1500 City W Blvd, Ste 900, 77042. SAN 327-3857. Tel: 713-266-6900. FAX: 281-266-2089. *Coordr*, Lorrie Beasley
Library Holdings: Bk Vols 1,500; Per Subs 40

LUNAR & PLANETARY INSTITUTE
S CENTER FOR INFORMATION & RESEARCH SERVICES, 3600 Bay Area Blvd, 77058-1113. SAN 362-0107. Tel: 281-486-2182. FAX: 281-486-2186. E-Mail: cirs2@lpi.nasa.jsc.gov, cirs2@lpi.usra.edu. Web Site: www.lpi.usra.edu/library/library.html, www.lpi.usra.edu/library/library.html. *Mgr*, Mary Ann Hager; Tel: 281-486-2136, E-Mail: hager@lpi.usra.edu; *Res*, Mary Noel; Tel: 281-486-2198, E-Mail: noel@lpi.usra.edu; *Coll Develop*, Stephen Tellier; Tel: 281-486-2191, E-Mail: tellier@lpi.usra.edu; *Tech Servs*, David Bigwood; Tel: 281-486-2134, E-Mail: bigwood@lpi.usra.edu; Staff 6 (MLS 1, Non-MLS 5)
Founded 1970
Library Holdings: Bk Vols 48,000; Bk Titles 19,500; Per Subs 140
Subject Interests: Astronomy, Geology, Space science
Special Collections: Maps & Imagery of the Solar System
Automation Activity & Vendor Info: (Cataloging) Athena
Database Vendor: OCLC - First Search
Restriction: Open to others by appointment
Function: Research library
Partic in Amigos Library Services, Inc

S M-I LLC, Technical Library, 5950 N Course Dr, 77072. SAN 316-4330. Tel: 281-561-1378. FAX: 281-561-1510. E-Mail: mdimataris@midf.com. *Librn*, Mary Dimataris
Founded 1967
Library Holdings: Bk Vols 7,000; Per Subs 75
Subject Interests: Chemical eng, Chemistry, Corrosion, Drilling, Drilling mud systs, Environ sci, Geothermal energy, Mining engineering, Petroleum geol, Petroleum production, Production practice, Reservoir eng
Special Collections: Chemische Zentralblatt Coll; Society of Petroleum Engineers Coll; US & Foreign Patents Coll
M-I Drilling Fluids is a Smith-Schlumberger joint venture

S MCKINSEY & COMPANY, INC LIBRARY, 2 Houston Ctr, Ste 3500, 909 Fannin, 77010. SAN 372-9826. Tel: 713-751-4196. FAX: 713-751-4652. Web Site: www.mckinsey.com. *Mgr*, Brian Swain
Library Holdings: Bk Vols 3,000; Per Subs 250
Subject Interests: Chemistry, Energy, Natural gas, Petroleum

S MENIL COLLECTION LIBRARY, (Formerly Menil Foundation), 1500 Branard St, 77006. (Mail add: 1511 Branard St, 77006), Tel: 713-525-9426. FAX: 713-525-9444. *Dir*, Phillip Thor Heagy; E-Mail: pheagy@menil.org; *Cat*, Anne Adler; Tel: 713-525-9424; *Archivist*, Geraldine Aramanda; Tel: 713-525-9446, E-Mail: geri@menil.org; *Publ Servs*, Stephanie Capps; Tel: 713-525-9445, E-Mail: stephanie@menil.org. Subject Specialists: *Art history*, Anne Adler; *Art history*, Phillip Thor Heagy; *Art history*, Stephanie Capps; Staff 4 (MLS 2, Non-MLS 2)
Founded 1987
Jan 1999-Dec 1999 Mats Exp $38,250, Books $15,000, Per/Ser (Incl. Access Fees) $15,000, Manuscripts & Archives $250, Electronic Ref Mat (Incl. Access Fees) $8,000. Sal $140,000 (Prof $120,000)
Library Holdings: Bk Vols 15,000; Bk Titles 11,000; Per Subs 100
Subject Interests: Art history
Special Collections: Rare Book Room (1000 titles)
Database Vendor: Dialog, Ebsco - EbscoHost, OCLC - First Search
Restriction: By appointment only
Function: Research library

S MOBIL BUSINESS RESOURCES CORP, Information Resource Center,* 12450 Greenpoint Dr, Ste 1072, 77060-1991. SAN 320-5878. Tel: 281-775-2000. FAX: 281-775-4126.; Staff 1 (MLS 1)
Founded 1979
Library Holdings: Bk Vols 5,100; Per Subs 234
Subject Interests: Earth science, Petroleum engineering, Petroleum-gas indust
Partic in Amigos Library Services, Inc; OCLC Online Computer Library Center, Inc

S NACE INTERNATIONAL LIBRARY, 1440 S Creek Dr, PO Box 218340, 77218-8340. SAN 316-0807. Tel: 281-228-6200. FAX: 281-228-6300. E-Mail: pubs@mail.nace.org. Web Site: www.nace.org. *Dir*, Gerald Shankel; *Librn*, Julia Peterlin
Founded 1945
Library Holdings: Bk Titles 2,000; Per Subs 40
Subject Interests: Corrosion
Special Collections: Corrosion Abstracts: 1962 to date; Corrosion: 1945 to date; Materials Protection/Performance: 1962 to date

G NASA, Johnson Space Center Scientific & Technical Information Center, 2101 NASA Rd One, Mail Code GP23, 77058-3696. SAN 316-4691. Tel: 281-483-4245. FAX: 281-483-2527. E-Mail: sticnter@ems.jsc.nasa.gov. Web Site: ntic.jsc.nasa.gov. *In Charge*, Jane Hultberg; Staff 19 (MLS 7, Non-MLS 12)
Founded 1962
Library Holdings: Bk Vols 68,900; Bk Titles 42,000; Per Subs 170
Subject Interests: Aeronautics, Astronautics, Computer science, Earth resources, Engineering, Geosciences, Guidance, Life sci, Mathematics, Navigation, Physics, Space med, Space science, Space shuttles, Space sta, Telemetry

Automation Activity & Vendor Info: (Acquisitions) SIRSI; (Cataloging) SIRSI; (Circulation) SIRSI; (OPAC) SIRSI
Publications: JSC Technical Library User's Guide
Partic in Amigos Library Services, Inc; Nasa Libraries Information System - Nasa Galaxie; OCLC Online Computer Library Center, Inc

J NORTH HARRIS MONTGOMERY COMMUNITY COLLEGE DISTRICT, Automated Library Services, 250 N Sam Houston Pkwy E, 77060-2000. SAN 316-4713. Tel: 281-260-3589. FAX: 281-260-3114. Web Site: www.nhmccd.cc.tx.us/lrc/als/. *Dir*, Anne Strommer; E-Mail: strommer@nhmccd.edu; *Cat*, Elizabeth Chenette; Staff 6 (MLS 2, Non-MLS 4)
Founded 1973
Automation Activity & Vendor Info: (Acquisitions) epixtech, inc.
Partic in Amigos Library Services, Inc; OCLC Online Computer Library Center, Inc
Departmental Libraries:
KINGWOOD COLLEGE LIBRARY, 20000 Kingwood Dr, Kingwood, 77339. SAN 325-352X. Tel: 281-312-1691. FAX: 281-312-1456. Web Site: www.kingwoodcollegelibrary.com. *Dir*, Elizabeth Lunden; E-Mail: elunden@nhmccd.edu; *Ref*, Charles Gillis; *Ref Serv*, Claire Gunnels; Staff 5 (MLS 5)
Founded 1984. Enrl 3,300; Fac 96
Sep 1999-Aug 2000 Income $548,720. Mats Exp $146,340, Books $68,370, Per/Ser (Incl. Access Fees) $35,270, Presv $400, AV Equip $11,300, Electronic Ref Mat (Incl. Access Fees) $31,000. Sal $371,110 (Prof $228,590)
Library Holdings: Bk Vols 36,594; Per Subs 441
Automation Activity & Vendor Info: (Acquisitions) epixtech, inc.; (Cataloging) epixtech, inc.; (Circulation) epixtech, inc.; (Course Reserve) epixtech, inc.; (OPAC) epixtech, inc.; (Serials) epixtech, inc.
Partic in Amigos Library Services, Inc; N Harris Montgomery Libr Consortium
MONTGOMERY COLLEGE LIBRARY, 3200 College Park Dr, Conroe, 77384. SAN 376-222X. Tel: 936-273-7392. FAX: 936-273-7395. Web Site: www.mc.nhmccd.edu/elc/learning_resource_center/welcome.htm. *Dir*, Janice Lucas Peyton; E-Mail: jpeyton@nhmccd.edu; *Ref*, Cheryl Mansfield-Egans; *Ref*, Deborah Cox; *Bibliog Instr*, Sue Raymond; Staff 5 (MLS 3, Non-MLS 2)
Founded 1995. Enrl 2,291; Fac 36
Library Holdings: Bk Vols 21,000; Per Subs 462
Special Collections: McKay Everett (a Children's collection)
Automation Activity & Vendor Info: (Acquisitions) epixtech, inc.; (Cataloging) epixtech, inc.; (Circulation) epixtech, inc.; (Course Reserve) epixtech, inc.; (OPAC) epixtech, inc.; (Serials) epixtech, inc.
NORTH HARRIS COLLEGE LIBRARY, 2700 W W Thorne Dr, 77073. SAN 323-6943. Tel: 281-618-5491. FAX: 281-618-5695. Web Site: www.nhclibrary.nhmccd.edu. *Dir*, Maryann Readal; E-Mail: mreadal@nhmccd.edu; *Govt Doc*, Sarah Naper; *Ref*, Pradeep Lele; *Ref*, Monica Norem; *Ref*, Olia Palmer; *Ref*, Lynn Porter; Staff 6 (MLS 6)
Founded 1973. Enrl 9,500; Fac 390
Sep 1998-Aug 1999 Income $762,458. Mats Exp $164,000, Books $90,000, Per/Ser (Incl. Access Fees) $30,000, Presv $2,000, Micro $22,000, AV Equip $20,000. Sal $564,891 (Prof $318,672)
Library Holdings: Bk Vols 101,000; Per Subs 1,041
Special Collections: ERIC Junior College Fiche Coll
Automation Activity & Vendor Info: (Acquisitions) epixtech, inc.; (Cataloging) epixtech, inc.; (Circulation) epixtech, inc.; (Course Reserve) epixtech, inc.; (OPAC) epixtech, inc.; (Serials) epixtech, inc.
Publications: Library Dateline
Partic in N Harris Montgomery Libr Consortium
TOMBALL COLLEGE LEARNING RESOURCES CENTER, 30555 Tomball Pkwy, Tomball, 77375-4036. SAN 323-696X. Tel: 281-351-3390. FAX: 281-357-3786. Web Site: wwwtc.nhmccd.cc.tx.us/bluebonnet/education/lrc/. *Dir*, Katherine Jagoe Massey; *Ref*, Mary Jean Webster; *Ref*, Ruth McDonald; Staff 11 (MLS 6, Non-MLS 5)
Founded 1988. Enrl 3,599; Fac 209
1997-1998 Income $446,323. Mats Exp $164,995, Books $63,000, Per/Ser (Incl. Access Fees) $29,000, Micro $14,000, AV Equip $35,995. Sal $157,767 (Prof $99,506)
Library Holdings: Bk Vols 24,500; Per Subs 377
Subject Interests: Human servs, Humanities, Nursing, Vet tech

S OCCIDENTAL OIL & GAS CORP LIBRARY, Five Greenway Plaza, No 16.004, 77046. SAN 357-7082. Tel: 713-215-7667. FAX: 713-215-7528. *Librn*, Cherie Colbert; E-Mail: cheriecolbert@oxy.com; *Asst Librn*, Bonita Alford; Staff 2 (MLS 1, Non-MLS 1)
Founded 1953
Library Holdings: Bk Titles 30,000; Per Subs 700
Subject Interests: Exploration, Production of Petroleum
Automation Activity & Vendor Info: (Cataloging) Inmagic, Inc.
Partic in OCLC Online Computer Library Center, Inc

S PENNZOIL EXPLORATION & PRODUCTION CO, Pepco Library,* 700 Milam, PO Box 2967, 77002. SAN 324-7961. Tel: 713-546-4000. *Librn*, Lynnette Jordan
Founded 1981
Library Holdings: Bk Vols 10,000; Bk Titles 7,000; Per Subs 125
Subject Interests: Exploration, Geology, Natural gas, Petroleum, Production eng, Reservoir eng
Publications: Journal contents pages; New books list
Restriction: Staff use only
Partic in Dialog Corporation; Dow Jones News Retrieval

S PIERCE, GOODWIN, ALEXANDER & LINVILLE LIBRARY,* 5555 S Felipe St, Ste 1000, 77056. SAN 328-4395. Tel: 713-622-1444. FAX: 713 968-9333. Web Site: www.pgal.com. *In Charge*, Michele Bowers; *Librn*, Brittany Goodpasture
Library Holdings: Bk Vols 580; Per Subs 81

S PLANNED PARENTHOOD OF HOUSTON & SE TEXAS, Hudson Thra Library, 3601 Fannin, 77004-3998. SAN 326-1158. Tel: 713-522-6363. FA 713-522-9047. Web Site: www.pphouston.org.
Library Holdings: Bk Titles 2,696; Per Subs 70

S PLANNING & FORECASTING CONSULTANTS LIBRARY, PO Box 820228, 77282-0228. SAN 372-9915. Tel: 713-467-4732. FAX: 281-497-4128. *Mgr*, Dale Steffes; E-Mail: dalestef@flash.net
Library Holdings: Bk Vols 1,000; Per Subs 38
Subject Interests: Energy, Natural gas

S RESURRECTION METROPOLITAN COMMUNITY CHURCH, (RMCC Botts Memorial Library & Archives, 2025 W 11th St, 77008. SAN 329-2916. Tel: 713-861-9149. FAX: 713-861-2520. E-Mail: mccr@neosoft.con Web Site: www.resurrectionmcc.org. *In Charge*, Ralph Lasher; E-Mail: revrl@neosoft.com
Founded 1979
Library Holdings: Bk Titles 17,902; Per Subs 200; Bks on Deafness & Sign Lang 15
Subject Interests: Homosexuality, Religion
Special Collections: Over 1000 different gay/lesbian publications
Publications: MCC Newsletter; Monthly Status Report
Religious library

C RICE UNIVERSITY, Fondren Library, 6100 Main, MS-44, 77005. (Mail add: PO Box 1892 MS44, 77251-1892), SAN 316-506X. Tel: 713-348-511 FAX: 713-348-5258. E-Mail: libr@rice.edu. Web Site: riceinfo.rice.edu/fondren/. *Librn*, Dr Charles Henry; E-Mail: chhenry@rice.edu; *Asst Librn, Coll Develop*, Kerry Keck; E-Mail: keckker@rice.edu; *Asst Librn, Cat, Te Servs*, Melinda Flannery Reagor; E-Mail: reagor@rice.edu; *Assoc Librn, Publ Servs, Ref*, Sara Lowman; E-Mail: lowman@rice.edu; *Tech Coordr*, Andrea Martin; E-Mail: andrea@rice.edu; *Acq*, Janet Lindquist; E-Mail: jlindq@rice.edu; *Spec Coll*, Nancy Boothe; E-Mail: boothe@rice.edu; *Gov Doc*, Esther Crawford; E-Mail: crawford@rice.edu; *Circ*, Virginia Martin; E-Mail: martin@rice.edu; *Doc Delivery*, Damon Camille; E-Mail: dcamille rice.edu; *Coll Develop*, Sandra Edwards; E-Mail: edwards@rice.edu; *Database Manager*, Elizabeth Baber; E-Mail: baber@rice.edu; Staff 213 (MLS 121, Non-MLS 92)
Founded 1912. Enrl 4,372; Fac 476; Highest Degree: Doctorate
Jul 1999-Jun 2000 Income $19,134,032. Mats Exp $6,707,980, Books $2,219,383, Per/Ser (Incl. Access Fees) $3,817,047, Presv $103,557, Electronic Ref Mat (Incl. Access Fees) $376,714. Sal $8,916,184 (Prof $6,252,118)
Library Holdings: Bk Vols 2,116,862; Per Subs 15,508
Special Collections: 18th & 19th Century British Navy Coll, mss; 18th Century English Drama (Axson Coll); 19th & 20th Century Texas (Judge James L Autry, William L Clayton, Walter G Hall, General William Hamman, James S Hogg, Harris Masterson, John P Osterhout, Walter B & Estelle B Sharp, Albert Thomas & J Russell Wait), mss; 19th Century Texa doc, letters, currency & diaries; Anderson Coll on the Hist of Aeronautics; Austrian History; Beethoven Coll (Bartlett Coll); Civil War Coll, imprints, doc, diaries, letters, photog & mss mil rec; Julian S Huxley Papers Coll; Larry McMurtry Papers; Maps; Maximilian & Carlota Coll, doc, letters, broadsides & memorabilia; McMurtry-Ossana Papers; Modern American Literature (William Goyen, J P Miller & David Westheimer Coll), mss; Oveta Culp Hobby Papers; Political & Public Service Papers of James A Baker III, mss; Texana (Masterson Coll), DOE Tech rpts (1958), GPO (1962), Rand, US Patents (1962); Williams Coll of Sam Houston Papers, mss
Automation Activity & Vendor Info: (Acquisitions) SIRSI; (Cataloging) SIRSI; (Circulation) SIRSI; (Course Reserve) SIRSI; (OPAC) SIRSI; (Serials) SIRSI
Database Vendor: OCLC - First Search
Publications: Flyleaf (Friends of Fondren); News from Fondren
Restriction: Public use on premises
Function: Research library
Partic in Asn of Research Libraries; Big Twelve Plus Libr Consortium; Center For Research Libraries; Coalition for Networked Info; Coun of Libr Info Resources; Houston Area Research Library Consortium; JSTOR; National Initiative for a Networked Cultural Heritage; OCLC Online Computer Library Center, Inc; Research Libraries Group, Inc; Scholarly Publ & Acad Resources Coalition; Tex Digital Libr Alliance; Tex Independent Cols & Univ Librs; Tex Share
Friends of the Library Group

ST JOSEPH HOSPITAL, Health Science Library,* 1919 LaBranch, 77002. SAN 316-4780. Tel: 713-757-1000, Ext 1296. FAX: 713-657-7208. *Coordr*, Deanna Ennis
Founded 1940
Library Holdings: Bk Vols 4,000; Bk Titles 2,000; Per Subs 184
Subject Interests: Medicine, Mgt, Nursing, Sci, Surgery
Partic in Medline

SAINT LUKE THE EVANGELIST CATHOLIC CHURCH, Community Resource Library,* 11011 Hall Rd, 77089. SAN 327-3717. Tel: 281-481-4251. FAX: 281-481-8780. *Librn*, Claudell Wert
Library Holdings: Bk Vols 750

SAINT MARTIN'S EPISCOPAL CHURCH, Parish Library, 717 Sage Rd, 77056. SAN 316-4802. Tel: 713-621-3040. FAX: 713-622-5701. Web Site: www.stmartinsepiscopal.org. *Librn*, Anne Moss
Founded 1959
Library Holdings: Bk Vols 10,893
Open wed 10-2

SAN JACINTO COLLEGE NORTH, Doctor Edwin E Lehr Library, 5800 Uvalde Rd, 77049-4589. SAN 362-0131. Tel: 281-459-7116. FAX: 281-459-7166. Web Site: www.sjcd.cc.tx.us/district/lib/ngeninfo.htm. *Dir*, Jan C Crenshaw; *Publ Servs*, Tom Rogers; *Ref*, Madelyn C Garner
Founded 1974. Enrl 4,080
Library Holdings: Bk Vols 62,000; Per Subs 349
Special Collections: Texana Coll
Automation Activity & Vendor Info: (Cataloging) epixtech, inc.; (Circulation) epixtech, inc.; (Course Reserve) epixtech, inc.; (OPAC) epixtech, inc.; (Serials) epixtech, inc.
Friends of the Library Group

SAN JACINTO COLLEGE SOUTH, Parker Williams Library, 13735 Beamer Rd, 77089-6099. SAN 362-0166. Tel: 281-922-3416. FAX: 281-922-3470. Web Site: www.sjcd.cc.tx.us/district/lib/slibhome.htm. *Per*, Jo Coleman; *Circ*, Carole Patterson; *Ref*, Richard Harper; *Ref*, Jon Luckstead; Staff 4 (MLS 4)
Founded 1979. Enrl 2,921; Fac 248; Highest Degree: Associate
Sep 1999-Aug 2000 Income State $150,331. Mats Exp $65,590, Books $25,000, Per/Ser (Incl. Access Fees) $15,700, Presv $600, Micro $11,620, Electronic Ref Mat (Incl. Access Fees) $12,670
Library Holdings: Bk Vols 60,000; Per Subs 300
Subject Interests: Am hist, American literature, British lit, Health sciences
Special Collections: Texana
Partic in TexShare

SHELL OIL COMPANY, Petro-Chemical Knowledge Center,* 3333 Hwy 6 S, PO Box 1380, 77251. SAN 320-2615. Tel: 281-544-7510. *Mgr*, Elsie T Kwok; E-Mail: kwok@shellus.com
Founded 1975
Library Holdings: Bk Vols 90,000; Bk Titles 70,000; Per Subs 600
Subject Interests: Engineering
Branches:
BUSINESS INFORMATION MANAGEMENT, One Shell Plaza, Rm 1365, PO Box 4320, 77210. SAN 362-0212. Tel: 713-241-2123. FAX: 713-241-3325. *Librn*, Trudy Companion
Founded 1947
Library Holdings: Bk Titles 20,000; Per Subs 600
Publications: Acquisitions List; Awareness Bulletin
E & T KNOWLEDGE CENTER, 3737 Bellaire Blvd, 77024. SAN 316-4829. Tel: 713-245-7288. FAX: 713-245-7108. E-Mail: libreg@shellus.com.
Founded 1947
Library Holdings: Bk Titles 30,000; Per Subs 250
Partic in Dialog Corporation
LAW LIBRARY, PO Box 2463, 77252. SAN 362-0220. Tel: 713-241-3514. FAX: 713-241-5362. E-Mail: wwwctcote@shellus.com. *Librn*, C T Cote
Founded 1975
Library Holdings: Bk Vols 45,000; Bk Titles 3,200
Publications: Library Notes
Holdings include three field location libraries

SHELL OIL COMPANY, Tax Library,* PO Box 2463, 77001. SAN 362-0247. Tel: 713-241-2155. FAX: 713-241-7029. *Librn*, C C Korkmas
Library Holdings: Bk Vols 14,000

SHRINERS' HOSPITALS FOR CHILDREN-HOUSTON, LIBRARY, 6977 Main St, 77030-3701. SAN 316-4837. Tel: 713-793-3840. FAX: 713-793-3779. *Librn*, Milton Hunt Figg; E-Mail: mfigg@shrinenet.org; Staff 1 (MLS 1)
Founded 1963
Library Holdings: Bk Vols 1,500; Per Subs 22
Restriction: Staff use only

SONAT OFFSHORE DRILLING INC, Central Records,* 4 Greenway Plaza, PO Box 2765, 77046. SAN 375-071X. Tel: 713-871-7623. FAX: 713-850-3817. *Coordr*, Rawya Resaey
Library Holdings: Bk Titles 500

CL SOUTH TEXAS COLLEGE OF LAW LIBRARY,* 1303 San Jacinto, 77002-7000. SAN 316-4845. Tel: 713-646-1711. FAX: 713-659-2217. Web Site: www.stcl.edu. *Dir Libr Serv, VPres*, David G Cowan; E-Mail: cowand@stcl.edu; *Assoc Dir*, Sally J Langston; *Ref*, Mark Lambert; *Publ Servs, Ref*, James G Durham; *Ref*, Monica Ortale; *Ref, Ser*, Mary Lippold; *Circ, Ref*, Jessica Alexander; Staff 11 (MLS 11)
Founded 1924. Enrl 1,200; Fac 59; Highest Degree: Doctorate
Library Holdings: Bk Vols 347,220; Bk Titles 36,991; Per Subs 4,083
Special Collections: Law School Archives; Rare Books; Texaco-Pennzoil
Publications: Accession list (monthly); Faculty Flash (irregular); Footnotes (monthly newsletter); journal holdings; Library Guides (series for patrons)
Partic in OCLC Online Computer Library Center, Inc; Westlaw

S TEXACO, Upstream Technology Library, 3901 Briarpark, 77042. SAN 316-442X. Tel: 713-954-6007. FAX: 713-954-6907. *Acq*, Meena Baichan; E-Mail: baichmr@texaco.com; *Online Servs*, Margy Walsh; E-Mail: walshm@texaco.com; *Ser*, Nilda Alkhoury; E-Mail: alkhonf@texaco.com; *Doc*, Louise Moyer; E-Mail: moyerel@texaco.com; *Web Coordr*, Jean Skarlos; E-Mail: sklarljs@texaco.com; *Info Specialist*, Debra J Clay; E-Mail: claydj@texaco.com; Staff 7 (MLS 4, Non-MLS 3)
Founded 1961
Library Holdings: Bk Vols 40,000; Per Subs 300
Subject Interests: Geology, Geophysics, Petroleum engineering
Special Collections: In-House reports, central files, correspondence
Automation Activity & Vendor Info: (Acquisitions) Inmagic, Inc.; (Cataloging) TechLIB; (Circulation) Inmagic, Inc.; (OPAC) TechLIB; (Serials) TechLIB
Publications: Bibliographies (upon request); In-House (monthly acquisitions list)
Restriction: Restricted access
Partic in Amigos Library Services, Inc

M TEXAS CHILDREN'S HOSPITAL, Pi Beta Phi Library for Patients & Families, 6621 Fannin St, 77030. SAN 316-490X. Tel: 713-770-1070. FAX: 713-770-1044. *Coordr*, Julia D Allison; E-Mail: jdalliso@texaschildrenshospital.org
Founded 1984
Oct 1999-Sep 2000 Mats Exp $15,000, Books $10,000
Library Holdings: Bk Vols 5,000
Subject Interests: Bks for all ages, Children's literature, Medicine, Movies, Parenting

G TEXAS DEPARTMENT OF HUMAN SERVICES LIBRARY,* 1459 E 40th St, PO Box 16017 MC 173-7, 77022. SAN 316-4918. Tel: 713-692-3236, 713-692-8028. FAX: 713-696-8081. *In Charge*, Angela Rivers
Library Holdings: Bk Vols 5,000

C TEXAS SOUTHERN UNIVERSITY LIBRARY, Robert James Terry Library,* 3100 Cleburne Ave, 77004. SAN 362-0255. Tel: 713-313-7147. Interlibrary Loan Service Tel: 713-313-1085. FAX: 313-1080, 713-313-1875. Web Site: www.tsu.edu/library/index.htm. *Dir*, Kamau Obidike; Tel: 713-313-7121; *Assoc Dir*, Norma Bean; Tel: 713-313-4420; *ILL*, Helen Tatman; *Acq*, Margaret Tunstall; Tel: 713-313-1082; *Ref*, Barbara Holliday; Tel: 713-313-4424; *Ser*, Leocadia Hooks; Tel: 713-313-4304; *Cat*, Anna Miu; Tel: 713-313-1099; *Circ*, Marion Ferguson; Tel: 713-313-4417; *Spec Coll*, Marquita Anderson; Tel: 713-313-4416; Staff 10 (MLS 10)
Founded 1947. Enrl 6,522; Fac 458; Highest Degree: Doctorate
Sep 1999-Aug 2000 Mats Exp $772,523, Per/Ser (Incl. Access Fees) $499,124. Sal $700,263 (Prof $346,999)
Library Holdings: Bk Titles 470,102; Per Subs 1,715
Special Collections: Barbara Jordan Archives; Heartman Collection; Traditional African Art Gallery; University Archives
Automation Activity & Vendor Info: (Circulation) GEAC
Publications: Catalog of the Traditional African Art Gallery
Partic in Houston Area Research Library Consortium; OCLC Online Computer Library Center, Inc; TexShare
Departmental Libraries:
THURGOOD MARSHALL SCHOOL OF LAW LIBRARY, 3100 Cleburne Ave, 77004. SAN 362-028X. Tel: 713-313-7125. FAX: 713-313-4483. Web Site: www.tsulaw.edu/lawlib. *Assoc Dir*, DeCarlous Spearman; *Librn*, Marguerite Butler; *Acq*, Cynthia Davis; *Ser*, Olu Chapman; *Ref*, Ahunanya Anga; Staff 9 (MLS 3, Non-MLS 6)
Founded 1948. Enrl 400; Fac 25; Highest Degree: Doctorate
Library Holdings: Bk Vols 371,147; Per Subs 2,448
Partic in Westlaw

S TURNER, COLLIE & BRADEN, INC LIBRARY, (AECOM), 5757 Woodway, 77057. (Mail add: PO Box 130089, 77219), SAN 316-4977. Tel: 713-267-2777. Reference Tel: 713-267-2777. FAX: 713-267-2924. Web Site: www.tcandb.com. *Mgr*, Suzette Broussard; Tel: 713-267-2826, E-Mail: broussards@tcbhou.com; *Asst Librn*, Renee Miller; E-Mail: millerr@tcbhou.com
Founded 1968
Library Holdings: Bk Titles 4,000; Per Subs 200
Subject Interests: Civil engineering
Special Collections: Environmental Protection Agency Reports Coll, micro

Restriction: Circulates for staff only
Function: Research library
Partic in Dialog Corporation; SDC Info Servs

L UNITED STATES COURTS LIBRARY,* 515 Rusk Ave, Rm 6311, 77002. SAN 372-1620. Tel: 713-250-5696. FAX: 713-250-5091. *Librn*, Ching-Cheng C Ting; E-Mail: tina_ting@ca5.uscourts.gov; *Librn*, Chou-Shia Tseng; *Librn*, Dolores Koonz
Library Holdings: Bk Vols 45,000; Per Subs 101
Automation Activity & Vendor Info: (Acquisitions) SIRSI; (Serials) SIRSI
Publications: Library guide; newsletter
Partic in Fedlink

G UNITED STATES DEPARTMENT OF COMMERCE, Houston District Office Library,* 500 Dallas St, Ste 1160, 77002. SAN 316-4993. Tel: 713-718-3062. FAX: 713-718-3060. *Dir*, James D Cook
Library Holdings: Bk Vols 200

UNIVERSITY OF HOUSTON
C M D ANDERSON LIBRARY, 4800 Calhoun, 77204. Tel: 713-743-9800. FAX: 713-743-9811. Web Site: info.lib.uh.edu. *Dean of Libr*, Dana Rooks; *Acq, Coll Develop*, Mary Beth Thomson; *Ser*, Lawrence Keating; *ILL*, Keiko Horton; *Archivist, Spec Coll*, Pat Bozeman; Staff 46 (MLS 46)
Founded 1927. Enrl 32,000; Fac 1,437; Highest Degree: Doctorate
Sep 1997-Aug 1998 Income $11,049,227. Mats Exp $3,662,571, Books $1,174,843, Per/Ser (Incl. Access Fees) $2,376,235, Presv $111,493. Sal $4,436,793 (Prof $2,148,576)
Library Holdings: Bk Vols 1,986,642; Per Subs 15,152
Subject Interests: Bus, Chemistry, Computer science, Engineering
Special Collections: American History (Israel Shreve Coll), papers; Architecture (Franzheim Memorial Coll); Bibliography & History of Printing; British & American Authors (A Huxley, Thurber, Jeffers, Patchen, Updike, Lowry & McMurtry Colls); City of Houston (George Fuermann Coll); Creative Writing & Performing Arts Archive; History of Science (Jadish Hehra Coll); James E & Miriam A Ferguson Coll, papers; James V Allred Coll of Texas gubernatorial papers; Texana & Western Americana (W B Bates Coll), bks, mss
Publications: Public-Access Computer Systems Review
Partic in Amigos Library Services, Inc; Asn of Research Libraries; Center For Research Libraries; Houston Area Research Library Consortium; Texas Council Of State University Librarians; TexShare
Friends of the Library Group

MUSIC LIBRARY, 4800 Calhoun, 77204-2091. Tel: 713-743-3197. FAX: 713-743-9918. E-Mail: musiclib@uh.edu. Web Site: info.lib.uh.edu. *Coordr*, Ericka Patillo; Tel: 713-743-3306, E-Mail: patie@uh.edu; *Librn*, Laura Snyder. Subject Specialists: *Music*, Ericka Patillo; *Theater*, Ericka Patillo
Founded 1968. Highest Degree: Doctorate
Library Holdings: Bk Vols 50,273; Per Subs 178
Partic in Asn of Research Libraries; Tex Share
Friends of the Library Group

CM OPTOMETRY LIBRARY, Rm 2225, 77204-6052. SAN 362-0441. Tel: 713-743-1910. FAX: 713-743-2001. Web Site: info.lib.uh.edu/local/optometr.htm. *Librn*, Suzanne Ferimer; E-Mail: sferimer@uhedu
Sep 1996-Aug 1997 Income $170,000. Mats Exp $65,000, Books $15,000, Per/Ser (Incl. Access Fees) $30,000. Sal $85,000
Library Holdings: Bk Vols 9,600; Per Subs 150
Subject Interests: Ophthalmology, Optometry, Physiological optics, Vision sci
Partic in Asn of Research Libraries

CM PHARMACY LIBRARY, Science & Research II, Rm 133, 3801 Cullen Blvd, 77204-5511. SAN 362-045X. Tel: 713-743-1240. Interlibrary Loan Service Tel: 713-743-9720. FAX: 713-743-1233. Web Site: www.info.lib.uh.edu/local/pharmacy.htm. *Librn*, Derral Parkin; E-Mail: dparkin@uh.edu
Library Holdings: Bk Vols 10,273; Per Subs 104
Subject Interests: Foreign drugs, Med chem, Pharmacology, Toxicology
Partic in Asn of Research Libraries; Harlic

CL THE O'QUINN LAW LIBRARY, 4800 Calhoun, 77204. Tel: 713-743-2300. FAX: 713-743-2299. *Dir*, Jon Schultz; *Asst Dir*, Gary Hartman; *Govt Doc*, Virginia Davis; *Acq*, Marek Waterstone; *Publ Servs*, Rod Borlase; *Tech Servs*, Richard Guajardo; *Archivist*, Helen Boyce; *Circ, ILL*, Helen E Boyce; *Coll Develop*, Gary R Hartman; Staff 9 (MLS 9)
Founded 1947. Enrl 1,150; Fac 46; Highest Degree: Doctorate
Library Holdings: Bk Vols 258,538; Per Subs 2,825
Subject Interests: Energy law, International trade, Taxes
Special Collections: Congressional Publications (CIS Microfiche Library); Texas Supreme Court Briefs
Automation Activity & Vendor Info: (Acquisitions) Innovative Interfaces Inc.; (Cataloging) Innovative Interfaces Inc.
Partic in Amigos Library Services, Inc; Asn of Research Libraries; Westlaw

WILLIAM R JENKINS ARCHITECTURE & ART LIBRARY, 106 Architecture Bldg, 77204-4431. SAN 362-0417. Tel: 713-743-2340. Interlibrary Loan Service Tel: 713-743-9720. FAX: 713-743-9778. Web Site: www.info.lib.uh.edu/local/arch.htm. *Librn*, Margaret Culbertson
Library Holdings: Bk Vols 70,000; Per Subs 225
Subject Interests: Architecture, Art, Landscape architecture, Photog, Urban design
Partic in Asn of Research Libraries

C UNIVERSITY OF HOUSTON - CLEAR LAKE, Neumann Library,* 270 Bay Area Blvd, 77058-1002. SAN 362-0468. Tel: 281-283-3930. FAX: 28 283-3937. Web Site: nola.cl.uh.edu. *Exec Dir*, Dr S Joe McCord; *Assoc D* Patricia Garrett; E-Mail: garrettp@cl.uh.edu; *Automation Syst Coordr*, Gar Thomson; *ILL*, Frances Roppolo; Staff 10 (MLS 10)
Founded 1973. Enrl 7,281; Fac 339; Highest Degree: Master
1997-1998 Income $1,764,187. Sal $795,742 (Prof $466,042)
Library Holdings: Bk Vols 405,797; Bk Titles 273,810; Per Subs 3,154
Subject Interests: Accounting, Environ, Software engineering, Space science
Special Collections: Early English Books (Pollard & Redgrave Coll)
Automation Activity & Vendor Info: (Circulation) VTLS
Publications: Check It Out Newsletters
Partic in Amigos Library Services, Inc

C UNIVERSITY OF HOUSTON - DOWNTOWN, William I Dykes Library, One Main St, 77002. SAN 362-0492. Tel: 713-221-8181, 713-221-8182. FAX: 713-221-8037. E-Mail: library@uh.edu. Web Site: www.dt.uh.edu/library/home.html. *Dir Libr Serv*, Pat Ensor; Tel: 713-221-8011, E-Mail: ensor@dt.uh.edu; *Admin Assoc*, Ted W Sherwin; Tel: 713-221-8468, E-Ma sherwin@dt.uh.edu; *ILL*, Charles A LeGuern; Tel: 219-284-7491, E-Mail: Cleguern@aol.com; *Coll Develop*, Henry Achee; Staff 9 (MLS 9)
Founded 1974. Pop 8,778; Enrl 8,325; Fac 410; Highest Degree: Master
Sep 1999-Aug 2000 Income $1,425,119, State $1,401,119, Other $24,000. Mats Exp $675,000, Books $258,396, Per/Ser (Incl. Access Fees) $247,00 Presv $11,076, Micro $8,339, Electronic Ref Mat (Incl. Access Fees) $41,193. Sal $637,119 (Prof $328,275)
Library Holdings: Bk Vols 238,942; Bk Titles 235,608; Per Subs 1,863
Special Collections: bks, journals, newsp clippings; Energy Information Coll
Automation Activity & Vendor Info: (Serials) Innovative Interfaces Inc.
Database Vendor: OCLC - First Search, OVID Technologies, Silverplatter Information Inc.
Publications: Library Handbook; Library Newsletter
Function: ILL available
Partic in Amigos Library Services, Inc; Dialog Corporation; Houston Area Research Library Consortium; OCLC Online Computer Library Center, Inc Tex Share
Friends of the Library Group

C UNIVERSITY OF SAINT THOMAS, Robert Pace & Ada Mary Doherty Library, 3800 Montrose, 77006. SAN 362-0522. Tel: 713-525-2192. FAX: 713-525-3886. Web Site: basil.stthom.edu/library/. *Dir*, James Piccininni; E-Mail: jpicci@basil.sttom.edu; *Ref*, Mark Landingham; Tel: 713-525-2188 E-Mail: markland@stthom.edu; *Cat*, Lilian Chen; Tel: 713-525-2183, E-Mail: chen@stthom.edu; *Acq*, Pat Gerson; *Syst Coordr*, Jane Huang; *Circ* Anne LaForge; Tel: 713-525-2180; *ILL*, George Hosko; Tel: 715-525-6926, E-Mail: loans@stthom.edu; Staff 9 (MLS 7, Non-MLS 2)
Founded 1947. Enrl 2,900; Fac 103; Highest Degree: Doctorate
Jul 1999-Jun 2000 Mats Exp $522,234, Books $241,499, Per/Ser (Incl. Access Fees) $105,624, Micro $15,000, Other Print Mats $9,390, Electroni Ref Mat (Incl. Access Fees) $150,721
Library Holdings: Bk Vols 195,722; Per Subs 3,400
Special Collections: Philosophy (Thomistic Studies Coll)
Automation Activity & Vendor Info: (Acquisitions) epixtech, inc.; (Cataloging) epixtech, inc.; (Circulation) epixtech, inc.; (OPAC) epixtech, inc.
Publications: Folio
Partic in Amigos Library Services, Inc; OCLC Online Computer Library Center, Inc; Tex Independent Cols & Univ Librs; TexShare
Friends of the Library Group
Departmental Libraries:

CR CARDINAL BERAN LIBRARY AT SAINT MARY'S SEMINARY, 9845 Memorial Dr, 77024-3498. SAN 362-0581. Tel: 713-686-4345, Ext 48. FAX: 713-681-7550. *Dir*, Laura Olejnik; E-Mail: olejnik@stthom.edu
Founded 1954
Jul 1996-Jun 1997 Income $165,000. Mats Exp $67,236, Books $45,000, Per/Ser (Incl. Access Fees) $22,000. Sal $77,544 (Prof $30,000)
Library Holdings: Bk Vols 52,000; Per Subs 370
Subject Interests: Relig studies, Theology
Partic in Amigos Library Services, Inc

UNIVERSITY OF TEXAS
CM HOUSTON HEALTH SCIENCE CENTER, SCHOOL OF PUBLIC HEALTH LIBRARY, PO Box 20186, 77225. SAN 316-5019. Tel: 713-500-9121. FAX: 713-500-9125. Web Site: utsph.sph.uth.tmc.edu/. *Dir*, Stephanie L Normann; E-Mail: snormann@utsph.sph.uth.tmc.edu; *Acq*, Marla Rosenfeld; *Publ Servs, Ref*, Martha Portree; *Tech Servs*, Barbara Breen; *ILL*, Carolyn Clark; *Cat*, Robert B Sperling; Staff 4 (MLS 4)
Founded 1969. Enrl 774; Fac 116; Highest Degree: Doctorate
Library Holdings: Bk Vols 65,000; Bk Titles 35,500; Per Subs 1,016
Subject Interests: Bio-statistics, Community health, Epidemiology, Health econ, Health promotion, HIV-AIDS, Infectious diseases, Nutrition
Special Collections: International Census Statistics; Pan American Health

Organization; World Health Organization
Automation Activity & Vendor Info: (Serials) SIRSI
Mem of Asn of Research Libraries
Partic in Amigos Library Services, Inc; National Network Of Libraries Of Medicine - South Central Region; OCLC Online Computer Library Center, Inc; S Cent Regional Med Libr Program; Tex Health Sci Libr Consortium; TexShare; UT Syst Librns

LEARNING RESOURCE CENTER Tel: 713-500-4094, 713-500-4096. FAX: 713-500-4100. *Dir*, Leah Krevit
Public access computers & resources for students & faculty of dental school. Internet access available

M D ANDERSON CANCER CENTER RESEARCH MEDICAL LIBRARY, 1515 Holcombe Blvd No 99, 77030. SAN 362-0646. Tel: 713-792-2282. FAX: 713-797-6513. Web Site: www.mdanderson.org/~library. *Exec Dir*, Kathryn J Hoffman; *Publ Servs*, Judy Willis; *ILL*, Sherry Widdoes; *Tech Servs*, Carol Steinmetz; *Coll Develop*, Ann Holliday; Staff 18 (MLS 18)
Founded 1941
Library Holdings: Bk Vols 56,820; Per Subs 875
Subject Interests: Cancer, Cell biology, Radiology
Special Collections: Leland Clayton Barbee History of Cancer Coll (600 Vol Coll of Rare Books & Early Treatises on Cancer)
Mem of Asn of Research Libraries
Partic in Amigos Library Services, Inc; National Network Of Libraries Of Medicine - South Central Region; OCLC Online Computer Library Center, Inc; Tex Health Sci Libr Consortium

DENTAL BRANCH LIBRARY, 6516 John Freeman Ave, 77030. (Mail add: PO Box 20068, 77225-0068), SAN 362-0611. Tel: 713-500-4094. FAX: 713-500-4100. E-Mail: library@mail.db.uth.tmc.edu.. Web Site: www.library.db.uth.tmc.edu. *Dir*, Leah Krevit; Staff 3 (MLS 1, Non-MLS 2)
Founded 1943. Fac 180; Highest Degree: Doctorate
Oct 1998-Sep 1999 Income $200,000. Mats Exp $50,000. Sal $120,000 (Prof $60,000)
Library Holdings: Bk Vols 31,380; Bk Titles 13,970; Per Subs 400
Subject Interests: Dentistry
Special Collections: Dentistry (Historical Coll), first editions & rare bks
Partic in Amigos Library Services, Inc; OCLC Online Computer Library Center, Inc

UNIVERSITY OF TEXAS-HOUSTON HEALTH SCIENCE CENTER, (UTP), UT Psychiatry Library, 1300 Moursund Ave, 77030-3406. SAN 316-4950. Tel: 713-500-2744. FAX: 713-500-2768. Web Site: msi.uth.tmc.edu/library/library.htm. *Bibliog Instr, Dir, Online Servs*, Felicia S Chuang; E-Mail: fchuang@mind.hcpc.uth.tmc.edu; *Tech Servs*, Nadine Bonds; Tel: 713-500-2747, E-Mail: nbonds@mind.hcpc.uth.tmc.edu; Staff 2 (MLS 2)
Founded 1959
Sep 1999-Aug 2000 Income $220,600. Mats Exp $74,700. Sal $145,900
Library Holdings: Bk Vols 20,600; Bk Titles 13,124; Per Subs 195
Subject Interests: Aging, Psychiatry, Psychopharmacol, Substance abuse
Special Collections: Psychiatry (Eugen Kahn Memorial Coll)
Database Vendor: OVID Technologies
Restriction: Public use on premises
Partic in Amigos Library Services, Inc; Tex Health Sci Libr Consortium

UNOCAL CORP, Exploration & Production Library,* 14141 Southwest Freeway, 77210. (Mail add: PO Box 4551, 77210-4551), SAN 375-0264. Tel: 281-287-5523. FAX: 281-287-5376. E-Mail: pvicars@unocal.com. *Librn*, Phyllis R Vicars; Staff 1 (MLS 1)
Library Holdings: Bk Vols 20,000
Subject Interests: Engineering
Restriction: Staff use only

VINSON & ELKINS, Law Library,* 3055 First City Tower, 1001 Fannin, 77002-6760. SAN 316-5035. Tel: 713-758-2678. FAX: 713-758-2346. *Librn*, Karl T Gruben; *Acq*, Martha White; *Cat*, Patricia Huntsman
Founded 1917
Library Holdings: Bk Vols 145,000
Partic in Westlaw

JACKSON WALKER LAW LIBRARY, 1100 Louisiana, Ste 4200, 77002. SAN 372-1612. Tel: 713-752-4479. FAX: 713-752-4221. *Librn*, Caren Zentner Luckie; E-Mail: cluckie@jw.com; Staff 1 (MLS 1)
Library Holdings: Bk Vols 15,100; Per Subs 70
Automation Activity & Vendor Info: (Cataloging) EOS; (OPAC) EOS

WEATHER RESEARCH CENTER LIBRARY, 3227 Audley St, 77098. SAN 370-3037. Tel: 713-529-3076. FAX: 713-528-3538. E-Mail: wrc@wxresearch.com. *Dir*, Jill F Hasling
Library Holdings: Bk Vols 900

WEIL, GOTSHAL & MANGES LLP, Law Library, 700 Louisiana St, Ste 1600, 77002. SAN 374-6607. Tel: 713-546-5131. FAX: 713-224-9511. *Mgr Libr*, Elizabeth Black Berry; Tel: 713-546-5055, E-Mail: elizabeth.berry@weil.com; Staff 2 (MLS 1, Non-MLS 1)
Founded 1985
Library Holdings: Bk Vols 8,000

S WESTERN GEOPHYSICAL COMPANY LIBRARY,* 10001 Richman, 77042. SAN 316-5051. Tel: 713-789-9600, Ext 2499. FAX: 281-963-2511. *Librn*, Diane Parker
Founded 1968
Partic in Dialog Corporation; Regional Info & Communication Exchange

S WILLIAM GAS PIPELINE-TRANSCO, Transcontinental Gas Pipe Line Corp Information Resource Center,* 2800 Post Oak Blvd, PO Box 1396, 77251. SAN 316-4969. Tel: 713-215-2000.
Founded 1951
Library Holdings: Bk Titles 1,000; Per Subs 250
Subject Interests: Bus, Energy, Engineering, Natural gas indust, Petroleum indust
Publications: Library Bulletin
Friends of the Library Group

S WYMAN-GORDON FORGING, INC LIBRARY,* PO Box 40456, 77240-0456. SAN 316-4225. Tel: 281-856-9900. FAX: 281-856-3315.
Founded 1969
Library Holdings: Bk Vols 2,500
Subject Interests: Alloy data, Gas, Mat, Metallurgy, Metals, Oil
Special Collections: Alloy Data & WRC Bulletins Coll (from 1955); Metals Abstracts (from 1944)
Publications: Library Bulletin
Partic in Dialog Corporation; SDC

HOWE

P HOWE COMMUNITY LIBRARY, 315 S Collins Freeway, 75459. SAN 376-4540. Tel: 903-532-5519. FAX: 903-532-9378. *Dir*, Roland H Commons; E-Mail: rhcommon@ednet10.net; Staff 3 (MLS 1, Non-MLS 2)
Founded 1982. Pop 4,500; Circ 42,000
Sep 1999-Sep 2000 Income City $16,000
Library Holdings: Bk Vols 31,500; Per Subs 75
Automation Activity & Vendor Info: (Cataloging) Follett; (Circulation) Follett; (OPAC) Follett
Mem of Northeast Texas Library System
Open Mon-Fri 8-5:30, Sat 9-12
Friends of the Library Group

HUNTSVILLE

M HUNTSVILLE MEMORIAL HOSPITAL, Medical Library Resource Center, 485 IH 45S, 77342-4001. (Mail add: PO Box 4001, 77342-4001), SAN 316-5086. Tel: 409-291-4545. FAX: 409-291-4218. *Dir*, Barbara Bohanon; Tel: 409-291-4544, Fax: 409-291-4379, E-Mail: barbarab@huntsvillememorial.com
Founded 1966
Jan 1999-Dec 1999 Mats Exp $17,726, Books $7,200, Per/Ser (Incl. Access Fees) $7,526, AV Equip $1,500, Other Print Mats $500. Sal $26,000
Library Holdings: Bk Vols 2,500; Per Subs 25
Subject Interests: Medicine, Nursing
Special Collections: CIBA, Video Coll (4000 titles)
Partic in Nat Libr of Med

P HUNTSVILLE PUBLIC LIBRARY,* 1216 14th St, 77340. SAN 316-5094. Tel: 409-291-5470. FAX: 409-291-5418. *Dir*, Judy Hunter; E-Mail: jhunter@hals.lip.px.us; *Asst Dir*, Paula Rudolph
Founded 1967. Pop 23,936; Circ 63,440
Library Holdings: Bk Vols 64,500; Bk Titles 54,000; Per Subs 125
Special Collections: Adult Education; Genealogy; Ornithology
Mem of Houston Area Library System
Friends of the Library Group

C SAM HOUSTON STATE UNIVERSITY, Newton Gresham Library, 1804 Ave H, 77340. (Mail add: PO Box 2281, 77341-2281), SAN 316-5108. Tel: 936-294-1618. Interlibrary Loan Service Tel: 936-294-1616. FAX: 936-294-3780. E-Mail: lib_ahh@shsu.edu. Web Site: www.shsu.edu. *Actg Dir*, Ann Holder; Tel: 936-294-1613; *Access Serv*, Linda Meyer; *Acq*, Teri Oparanozie; *Archivist*, Barbara Kievit-Mason; *ILL*, Ann Jerabek; *Coll Develop, Tech Servs*, Janice Lange; Tel: 936-294-1620; *Spec Coll*, Paul Culp; Staff 22 (MLS 16, Non-MLS 6)
Founded 1879. Enrl 12,700; Highest Degree: Doctorate
Library Holdings: Bk Vols 1,158,766; Bk Titles 691,035; Per Subs 3,263
Subject Interests: Criminal justice, Education, Texana
Special Collections: Col John W Thomason Coll; Criminology (Bates, Bennett, Colfield, Eliasburg & McCormirk Coll); Gertrude Stein Coll; Mark Twain Coll; Texana & the Southwest (Shettles Coll); Texana Coll; Texas (J L Clark Coll)
Automation Activity & Vendor Info: (Acquisitions) DRA; (Cataloging) DRA; (Circulation) DRA; (OPAC) DRA; (Serials) DRA
Publications: Irregular Newsletter
Mem of E Tex Libr Consortium
Partic in Amigos Library Services, Inc; Dialog Corporation; OCLC Online Computer Library Center, Inc; Westlaw

S TEXAS DEPARTMENT OF CRIMINAL JUSTICE LIBRARY,* Windham School District, PO Box 40, 77342-0040. SAN 316-5116. Tel: 409-291-5384. FAX: 409-291-5256.
Founded 1970
Library Holdings: Bk Vols 573,279

HURST

P HURST PUBLIC LIBRARY, 901 Precinct Line Rd, 76053. SAN 316-5124. Tel: 817-788-7300, 817-788-7305 (Admin). Interlibrary Loan Service Tel: 817-788-7301. FAX: 817-788-7307. Web Site: www.hurst.lib.tx.us. *Tech Servs*, Janet Young; E-Mail: jyoung@ci.hurst.tx.us; *Ch Servs*, Beverly Kirkendall; Tel: 817-788-7302, E-Mail: bkirkend@ci.hurst.tx.us; *Circ*, Brenda Stoll; Tel: 817-788-7303, E-Mail: bstoll@ci.hurst.tx.us; Staff 6 (MLS 5, Non-MLS 1)
Founded 1959. Pop 40,000; Circ 329,375
Oct 1998-Sep 1999 Income $1,348,485, State $34,046, City $1,305,439, Other $9,000. Mats Exp $166,151, Books $112,079, Per/Ser (Incl. Access Fees) $14,421, Presv $8,500, Micro $11,506, Electronic Ref Mat (Incl. Access Fees) $19,645. Sal $745,571 (Prof $54,000)
Library Holdings: Bk Vols 123,117; Bk Titles 108,980; Per Subs 392
Subject Interests: Business, Local history
Automation Activity & Vendor Info: (Acquisitions) SIRSI; (Cataloging) SIRSI; (Circulation) SIRSI; (Course Reserve) SIRSI; (OPAC) SIRSI
Mem of North Texas Regional Library System
Friends of the Library Group

J TARRANT COUNTY JUNIOR COLLEGE, Northeast Campus Learning Resource Center, 828 Harwood Rd, 76054-3219. SAN 361-722X. Tel: 817-515-6477. Reference Tel: 817-515-6629. FAX: 817-515-6275. Web Site: www.tcjc.cc.tx.us. *Dir*, Dr Steven W Hagstrom; Tel: 817-515-6637, E-Mail: steven.hagstrom@tccd.net; *Coordr*, Anne Drake; Tel: 817-515-6232, E-Mail: anne.drake@tccd.net; *Coordr*, Paul Gray; Tel: 817-515-6623, E-Mail: phgray@tccd.net; *Publ Servs*, J Paul Davidson; Tel: 817-515-6620, E-Mail: jpaul.davidson@tccd.net; *Publ Servs*, Beth Mullins; Tel: 817-515-6314, E-Mail: bmullins@tccd.net; *Publ Servs*, Dee Dee Rogers; Tel: 817-515-6626, E-Mail: deedee.rogers@tccd.net; *Publ Servs*, Judie Smith; Tel: 817-515-6625, E-Mail: judie.smith@tccd.net; Staff 17 (MLS 5, Non-MLS 12)
Founded 1968. Enrl 12,000; Fac 250; Highest Degree: Associate
Sep 2000-Aug 2001 Income $727,107. Mats Exp $151,000, Books $81,000, Per/Ser (Incl. Access Fees) $29,000, Micro $13,000, Electronic Ref Mat (Incl. Access Fees) $28,000. Sal $555,607 (Prof $267,880)
Library Holdings: Bk Vols 84,500; Per Subs 410
Subject Interests: Business, Govt docs, Humanities, Science/technology, Social sciences
Publications: Main Entry

HUTCHINS

P HUTCHINS-ATWELL PUBLIC LIBRARY,* 300 N Denton, PO Box 888, 75141. SAN 361-4042. Tel: 972-225-4711. FAX: 972-225-5559. *Librn*, Cheryl Hawkins; *Asst Librn*, Flossie White
Library Holdings: Bk Titles 24,000; Per Subs 20
Mem of Dallas County Libr Syst

IDALOU

P IDALOU PUBLIC LIBRARY,* 210 Main St, PO Box 108, 79329-0108. SAN 376-4257. Tel: 806-892-2114. *Librn*, Beth Rackley
Library Holdings: Bk Vols 14,000; Per Subs 500
Mem of West Texas Library System
Friends of the Library Group

IMPERIAL

P IMPERIAL PUBLIC LIBRARY,* 223 W Farm Rd 11, PO Box 307, 79743-0307. SAN 376-4370. Tel: 915-536-2236. FAX: 915-536-2211. *Librn*, Maxie King
Library Holdings: Bk Vols 15,000; Per Subs 15
Mem of Texas Trans Pecos Library System

INGLESIDE

P INGLESIDE PUBLIC LIBRARY,* 2775 Waco St, PO Drawer 400, 78362-0400. SAN 316-5159. Tel: 512-776-5355. FAX: 512-776-2264. *Dir*, Becky Harrell; E-Mail: bharrell@nettran.net; Staff 1 (MLS 1)
Founded 1933. Pop 8,547; Circ 25,868
Library Holdings: Bk Titles 30,000
Subject Interests: Bus, Oceanography, Ref, Texana
Special Collections: Municipal Libr Coll
Mem of San Patricio County Library System; South Texas Library System
Friends of the Library Group

IOWA PARK

P TOM BURNETT MEMORIAL LIBRARY,* 400 W Alameda, 76367. SAN 320-5134. Tel: 940-592-4981. FAX: 940-592-4664. E-Mail: tburnett@wf.n
Librn, Sue Maness
Founded 1962. Pop 6,072
Oct 1997-Sep 1998 Income $70,774. Mats Exp $8,628, Books $5,165, Per Ser (Incl. Access Fees) $1,010, Other Print Mats $1,004. Sal $34,192
Library Holdings: Bk Vols 13,854; Per Subs 33
Subject Interests: Genealogy
Mem of North Texas Regional Library System
Special Services for the Deaf - TTY machine

IRAAN

P IRAAN PUBLIC LIBRARY,* 120 W Fifth Ave, PO Box 638, 79744. SAN 316-5167. Tel: 915-639-2235. FAX: 915-639-2235. E-Mail: ira1lib@swbeu.net.
Founded 1950. Pop 1,500
Library Holdings: Bk Titles 15,000
Mem of Texas Trans Pecos Library System

IRVING

C DEVRY INSTITUTE OF TECHNOLOGY, Learning Resource Center, 480 Regent Blvd, 75063-2440. SAN 316-2192. Tel: 972-929-6777, Ext 190. FAX: 972-929-6778. Web Site: www.dal.devry.edu. *Dir*, Gale Albritton; E-Mail: galbritton@mail.dal.devry.edu; Staff 1 (MLS 1)
Founded 1969. Highest Degree: Bachelor
Library Holdings: Bk Titles 14,500; Per Subs 67
Subject Interests: Accounting, Bus operations, Computer science, Electronics, Telecommunication
Automation Activity & Vendor Info: (Cataloging) Endeavor; (Circulation Endeavor; (OPAC) Endeavor
Publications: New books lists

EXXON CORPORATION

S INFORMATION CENTER, 5959 Las Colinas Blvd, 75039-2298. SAN 353-0612. Tel: 972-444-1362, 972-444-1365. FAX: 972-444-1337. *Librn*, Lea Stewart
Library Holdings: Bk Vols 10,400; Per Subs 401
Subject Interests: Econ, Indust, Mgt, Petroleum indust, Statistics

P IRVING PUBLIC LIBRARY, 801 W Irving Blvd, PO Box 152288, 75015-2288. SAN 362-0670. Tel: 972-721-2639. Interlibrary Loan Service Tel: 972-721-2606. Circulation Tel: 972-721-2440. FAX: 972-721-2463. Web Site: www.irvinglibrary.org. *Dir*, Nancy Smith; E-Mail: nsmith@irvinglibrary.org; *Asst Dir*, Marilyn Dowell; Tel: 972-721-2628, Fax: 972-259-1171, E-Mail: mdowell@irvinglibrary.org; *Asst Dir*, James Karney; Tel 972-721-2628, Fax: 972-259-1171, E-Mail: jkarney@irvinglibrary.org; *Acq, Cat, Tech Servs*, Michael Ayres; Tel: 972-721-2764, Fax: 972-721-2329, E-Mail: mayres@irvinglibrary.org; *ILL*, Elaine Waak; E-Mail: ewaak@irvinglibrary.org; *Ch Servs*, Deborah Vaden; Tel: 972-721-2457, E-Mail: dvaden@irvinglibrary.org; *Coll Develop, Media Spec*, Michael Kirwan; Tel: 972-721-2464, E-Mail: mkirwan@irvinglibrary.org; *Ad Servs*, Lynn Baker; Tel: 972-721-2763, E-Mail: lbaker@irvinglibrary.org; *Circ*, Chris Bryan; Te 972-721-2460, E-Mail: lbyan@irvinglibrary.org; Staff 26 (MLS 26)
Founded 1961. Pop 183,350; Circ 1,288,118
Oct 1999-Sep 2000 Income (Main Library and Branch Library) City $6,875,762. Mats Exp $823,000, Books $581,690, Per/Ser (Incl. Access Fees) $41,038, Micro $18,115, Other Print Mats $68,647, Manuscripts & Archives $1,000, Electronic Ref Mat (Incl. Access Fees) $112,510. Sal $3,791,214
Library Holdings: Bk Vols 500,507; Bk Titles 214,412; Per Subs 1,294
Subject Interests: Bus, Mgt
Automation Activity & Vendor Info: (Acquisitions) epixtech, inc.; (Cataloging) epixtech, inc.; (Circulation) epixtech, inc.; (ILL) epixtech, inc.; (OPAC) epixtech, inc.; (Serials) epixtech, inc.
Mem of Northeast Texas Library System
Partic in Amigos Library Services, Inc; OCLC Online Computer Library Center, Inc
Friends of the Library Group
Branches: 4
EAST, 440 S Nursery Rd, 75060. Tel: 972-721-3722. FAX: 972-721-3724. Web Site: www.irvinglibrary.org. *Librn*, Maria Redburn; E-Mail: mredburn@irvinglibrary.org; Staff 2 (MLS 2)
Library Holdings: Bk Vols 13,183
Friends of the Library Group
NORTHWEST, 2928 N Beltline Rd, 75062. SAN 362-0700. Tel: 972-721-2691. FAX: 972-721-3637. Web Site: www.irvinglibrary.org. *Librn*, Logan Ragsdale; E-Mail: lragsdal@irvinglibrary.org; Staff 2 (MLS 2)
Library Holdings: Bk Vols 59,291
Friends of the Library Group
SOUTHWEST, 2216 W Shady Grove, 75060. SAN 362-0735. Tel: 972-721-2546. FAX: 972-721-3638. Web Site: www.irvingirving.org. *Librn*, Carol Danielson; E-Mail: cdaniels@irvinglibrary.org; Staff 2 (MLS 2)
Library Holdings: Bk Vols 55,649

Friends of the Library Group
VALLEY RANCH, 9940 W Valley Ranch Pkwy, 75063-4680. SAN 376-950X. Tel: 972-831-0669. FAX: 972-831-0672. Web Site: www.irvinglibrary.org. *Librn*, Patty Mount; E-Mail: pmount@irvinglibrary.org; Staff 3 (MLS 3)
Library Holdings: Bk Vols 54,324
Friends of the Library Group
Bookmobiles: 1

NEC AMERICA - PUBLIC SWITCHING GROUP, Technical Documents Center,* 1525 W Walnut Hill Lane, 75038. SAN 372-9931. Tel: 972-518-5233. FAX: 972-518-5285. *In Charge*, Julynn Lillard
Library Holdings: Bk Vols 1,000; Per Subs 38

NORTH LAKE COLLEGE LIBRARY,* 5001 N MacArthur Blvd, 75038-3899. SAN 324-2064. Tel: 972-273-3400. FAX: 972-273-3431. E-Mail: ekc7610@dcccd.edu. *Librn*, Enrique Chamberlain; *Librn*, Beverly Weidinger; *Asst Librn*, Jane Bell; *Circ*, Karen Fruendt; *Mgr*, Dr Lyle Vance
Library Holdings: Bk Vols 45,000; Per Subs 325
Part of Dallas County Community College District

TAPE LIBRARY OF RADIO COMMERCIALS,* 1320 Greenway, Ste 500, 75038. SAN 353-7609. Tel: 972-753-6750. FAX: 972-753-6727. *Res, VPres*, Andy Rainey
For holdings information, see entry for Radio Advertising Bureau, New York, NY

R UNIVERSITY OF DALLAS, William A Blakley Library, 1845 E Northgate Dr, 75062-4736. SAN 316-5175. Tel: 972-721-5328. Circulation Tel: 972-721-5329. Reference Tel: 972-721-5315. FAX: 972-721-4010. Web Site: www.udallas.edu/library/library1.htm. *Dir*, Robert Scott Dupree; E-Mail: scott@acad.udallas.edu; *Assoc Dir*, Nettie Baker; Tel: 972-721-4031, E-Mail: nettie@acad.udallas.edu; *ILL*, Alice Puro; Tel: 972-721-5057, E-Mail: apuro@acad.udallas.edu; *Cat*, Lely White; Tel: 972-721-5310, E-Mail: lely@acad.udallas.edu; *Circ*, Robyn Young; Tel: 972-721-5329, E-Mail: robyn@acad.udallas.edu; *Syst Coordr*, Mary Durio; Tel: 972-721-5040, E-Mail: mdurio@acad.udallas.edu; *Acq*, JoAnn Bittner; Tel: 972-721-4122, E-Mail: jbittne@acad.udallas.edu; *Ser*, Ellen Simmons; Tel: 972-721-4130, E-Mail: esimmons@acad.udallas.edu; *Ref*, Carolyn Mauzy; Tel: 972-721-5350, E-Mail: cmauzy@acad.udallas.edu. Subject Specialists: *English literature*, Robert Scott Dupree; Staff 16 (MLS 5, Non-MLS 11)
Founded 1956. Enrl 3,200; Fac 202; Highest Degree: Doctorate
Jun 1999-May 2000 Income $947,910. Mats Exp $448,190, Books $232,826, Per/Ser (Incl. Access Fees) $126,859, AV Equip $2,652, Electronic Ref Mat (Incl. Access Fees) $85,853. Sal $393,584 (Prof $160,392)
Library Holdings: Bk Vols 281,049; Bk Titles 167,089; Per Subs 688
Subject Interests: Bus, Mgt, Philosophy, Political science, Theology
Special Collections: Index Thomisticus; Jacques Migne, Patrologiae Cursus Completus, micro, index Thomisticus; Political Philosophy (Kendall Memorial Library Coll)
Automation Activity & Vendor Info: (Acquisitions) epixtech, inc.; (Cataloging) epixtech, inc.; (Circulation) epixtech, inc.; (Serials) epixtech, inc.
Database Vendor: epixtech, inc., OCLC - First Search, OVID Technologies, ProQuest
Publications: Blakley Update
Function: ILL available, Reference services available
Partic in Amigos Library Services, Inc; OCLC Online Computer Library Center, Inc; Tex Share
Friends of the Library Group

VERIZON, (Formerly GTE), Information Research Network, 700 Hidden Ridge Rd, HQWO1W60, 75038. SAN 302-377X. Tel: 972-718-7700. FAX: 972-719-0096. E-Mail: virn@verizon.com. *Mgr*, Marcia Schemper-Carlock; Staff 1 (Non-MLS 1)
Founded 1998
Subject Interests: Law, Telecommunications
Restriction: Staff use only

VERIZON MARKET INFORMATION CENTER, (Formerly GTE Telephone Operations Headquarters Library), 600 Hidden Ridge, HQE03A46, 75038. SAN 324-3834. Tel: 972-718-5263, 972-718-5549. FAX: 972-718-2399. *Mgr*, Charlotte Clark; E-Mail: charlotte.wixxclark@verizon.com. Subject Specialists: *Market res*, Charlotte Clark; Staff 1 (MLS 1)
Founded 1981
Library Holdings: Bk Titles 29,000; Per Subs 100
Subject Interests: Bus, Marketing, Soc sci, Telecommunications
Publications: Newsletter
Partic in Dialog Corporation

ITALY

P S M DUNLAP MEMORIAL LIBRARY, 300 W Main St, PO Box 390, 76651. SAN 316-5183. Tel: 972-483-6481. Interlibrary Loan Service Tel: 972-749-4341. E-Mail: dunlaplibrary@hotmail.com. *Librn*, Kathryn French
Pop 2,400
Library Holdings: Bk Vols 21,000

JACKSBORO

P GLADYS JOHNSON RITCHIE LIBRARY,* 626 W College St, 76458-1655. SAN 376-4656. Tel: 940-567-2240. FAX: 940-567-2240. E-Mail: glrlib@wf.net. Web Site: www.webfire.com. *Librn*, Juanita Damron
Library Holdings: Bk Vols 20,000; Per Subs 15
Mem of North Texas Regional Library System

JACKSONVILLE

R BAPTIST MISSIONARY ASSOCIATION THEOLOGICAL SEMINARY, Kellar Library, 1530 E Pine St, 75766-5407. SAN 316-5191. Tel: 903-586-2501, Ext 27. FAX: 903-586-0378. Web Site: www.bmats.edu. *Dir*, James C Blaylock; Staff 1 (MLS 1)
Founded 1957. Enrl 63; Fac 10; Highest Degree: Master
Aug 1999-Jul 2000 Income $109,951. Mats Exp $23,114, Books $15,057, Per/Ser (Incl. Access Fees) $7,548, Presv $509. Sal $79,507 (Prof $38,499)
Library Holdings: Bk Vols 62,100; Bk Titles 52,292; Per Subs 461
Subject Interests: History, Relig studies
Special Collections: Annuals of Baptist Yearly Meetings, bk, micro
Partic in Forest Trail Library Consortium, Inc
Friends of the Library Group

SR COMMISSION ON ARCHIVES & HISTORY, TEXAS CONFERENCE UNITED METHODIST CHURCH LIBRARY, Doornbos Historical Center, Tex Conference Archives, Lon Morris College, 75766-2900. SAN 373-7519. Tel: 903-589-4023. FAX: 903-589-4023. E-Mail: tcatxcumc@juno.com.
Library Holdings: Bk Vols 1,600
Special Collections: Texas Conference of UMC General Methodism Coll, bks, journals, mss

P JACKSONVILLE PUBLIC LIBRARY,* 502 S Jackson, 75766. SAN 316-5213. Tel: 903-586-7664. FAX: 903-586-3397. E-Mail: library@risecom.net. Web Site: www.jacksonvillelibrary.com. *Dir*, Barbara Crossman; *Tech Servs*, Ann Clampitt
Founded 1913. Pop 13,553; Circ 82,303
Library Holdings: Bk Vols 45,502; Per Subs 105
Subject Interests: Cherokee county
Database Vendor: Ebsco - EbscoHost
Mem of Northeast Texas Library System
Partic in Forest Trail Library Consortium, Inc
Friends of the Library Group

J LON MORRIS COLLEGE, Simon & Louise Henderson Library, 800 College Ave, 75766. SAN 316-5221. Tel: 903-589-4024. FAX: 903-589-4028. Web Site: library.lonmorris.edu. *Dir*, Henry Wang; Tel: 903-589-4027; *Tech Servs*, Michelle Zenor; Tel: 903-589-4025; Staff 4 (MLS 2, Non-MLS 2)
Library Holdings: Bk Vols 29,150; Per Subs 253
Partic in Forest Trail Library Consortium, Inc; Tex Share

JASPER

P JASPER PUBLIC LIBRARY, 175 E Water St, 75951. SAN 316-5248. Tel: 409-384-3791. FAX: 409-384-5881. *Dir*, Denise Milton; E-Mail: dmilton@jas.net; Staff 4 (MLS 1, Non-MLS 3)
Founded 1936. Pop 7,773
Oct 2000-Sep 2001 Mats Exp $19,300, Books $16,500, Per/Ser (Incl. Access Fees) $800, AV Equip $2,000. Sal $114,000 (Prof $32,500)
Library Holdings: Bk Vols 27,834; Bk Titles 25,734; Per Subs 103; Bks on Deafness & Sign Lang 10
Mem of Houston Area Library System

JAYTON

P KENT COUNTY LIBRARY,* PO Box 28, 79528-0028. SAN 316-5256. Tel: 806-237-3287. E-Mail: klibrary@kaprock-spur.com. *Librn*, Dana Brinkman
Founded 1961. Pop 1,110; Circ 5,179
Library Holdings: Bk Vols 25,000
Mem of Big Country Library System

JEFFERSON

P JEFFERSON CARNEGIE LIBRARY,* 301 W Lafayette, 75657. SAN 316-5264. Tel: 903-665-8911. *Librn*, Melinda Strange
Pop 9,000; Circ 12,000
Library Holdings: Bk Vols 25,000
Friends of the Library Group

S JEFFERSON HISTORICAL SOCIETY & MUSEUM, 223 W Austin St, 75657. SAN 329-8752. Tel: 903-665-2775. *Pres*, Bill McCay

JOHNSON CITY

P JOHNSON CITY LIBRARY,* 209 Nugent Ave, PO Box 332, 78636-0332. SAN 316-5272. Tel: 830-868-4469. FAX: 830-868-9195. E-Mail: jclib@moment.net. Web Site: www.moment.net/~jclib/. *Acq, Librn*, Peggy Pollock
Founded 1940. Pop 2,500; Circ 9,109
Library Holdings: Bk Titles 13,000
Special Collections: L B Johnson; Texana; Texas Poets
Mem of Central Texas Library System
Friends of the Library Group

S NATIONAL PARK SERVICE, Lyndon B Johnson National Historical Park Library, PO Box 329, 78636. SAN 316-5280. Tel: 830-868-7128, Ext 260. FAX: 830-868-7863.
Founded 1975
Library Holdings: Bk Titles 3,000; Per Subs 12
Subject Interests: Hill County hist, Life, Local, Natural hist subjects, Tex frontier, Times of Lyndon B Johnson
Restriction: Non-circulating to the public

JONESTOWN

P JONESTOWN COMMUNITY LIBRARY, 18649 FM1431, Ste 10A, 78645-3022. SAN 376-4850. Tel: 512-267-7511. FAX: 512-267-4572. E-Mail: jonestownlib@netscape.net. *Dir*, Marji Smith; *Librn*, Betty Horton; Staff 2 (Non-MLS 2)
Founded 1981
Library Holdings: Bk Vols 10,110; Bk Titles 10,000; High Interest/Low Vocabulary Bk Vols 450
Mem of Central Texas Library System

JOURDANTON

P JOURDANTON COMMUNITY LIBRARY,* 1220 Simmons St, 78026. SAN 316-5302. Tel: 830-769-3087. FAX: 830-769-4082. *Librn*, Dorothy Manning
Founded 1976
Library Holdings: Bk Vols 18,000
Special Collections: Texas Heritage Resource Center
Mem of Alamo Area Library System
Special Services for the Deaf - Books on deafness & sign language; Special interest periodicals
Friends of the Library Group

JUNCTION

P KIMBLE COUNTY LIBRARY,* 208 N Tenth St, 76849. SAN 316-5310. Tel: 915-446-2342. FAX: 915-446-3615. E-Mail: klibrary@edu.gte.com. *Librn*, Jerrie Fairchild
Founded 1933. Pop 4,063; Circ 22,642
Library Holdings: Bk Titles 20,000; Per Subs 25
Subject Interests: Texas
Mem of Big Country Library System
Friends of the Library Group

JUSTIN

P CITY OF JUSTIN, Justin Community Library, 408 N Pafford St, 76247-9442. (Mail add: PO Box 877, 76247-0877), SAN 376-4664. Tel: 940-648-3649. FAX: 940-648-3649. *Dir*, Hazel Bennett; *Coll Develop*, Ann Henderson
Founded 1986. Pop 2,000; Circ 2,200
Library Holdings: Bk Vols 26,000; Bks on Deafness & Sign Lang 10
Mem of North Texas Regional Library System

KARNES CITY

P KARNES CITY PUBLIC LIBRARY,* 302 S Panna Maria, 78118. SAN 316-5329. Tel: 830-780-2539. FAX: 830-780-3790. E-Mail: karnescitypublib@stic.mail. *Dir*, Annette Kotara
Pop 4,623; Circ 48,655
Library Holdings: Bk Titles 17,000; Per Subs 14
Mem of Alamo Area Library System; Karnes County Library System

KAUFMAN

P KAUFMAN COUNTY LIBRARY,* 3790 S Houston, 75142-2033. SAN 316-5345. Tel: 972-932-6222. FAX: 972-932-0681. *Dir*, Sue Webb; Staff 3 (MLS 1, Non-MLS 2)
Founded 1970. Pop 11,000; Circ 21,000
Library Holdings: Bk Titles 66,000
Mem of Northeast Texas Library System
Friends of the Library Group

S WES PUBLISHING LIBRARY,* 3674 E Hg 243, 75150-3355. SAN 372 9737. Tel: 972-962-6755. FAX: 972-962-5001. E-Mail: dermascope@aol.com. *Coordr*, Patricia Strunk
Library Holdings: Bk Vols 150; Per Subs 13

KEENE

C SOUTHWESTERN ADVENTIST UNIVERSITY, Chan Shun Centennial Library, 101 W Magnolia St, 76059. SAN 316-5353. Tel: 817-645-3921, E 242. FAX: 817-556-4722. Web Site: www.library.swau.edu. *Dir*, Randall Butler; Tel: 817-645-3921, Ext 732, E-Mail: butlerr@swau.edu; *Cat*, Mars Rasmussen; Tel: 817-645-3921, Ext 603, E-Mail: marshar@swau.edu; *Ref*, Sharon Wion; Tel: 817-645-3921, Ext 480, E-Mail: wions@swau.edu; Sta (MLS 3, Non-MLS 3)
Founded 1894. Pop 100,000; Enrl 1,160; Fac 60; Highest Degree: Master Jul 1998-Jun 1999 Income (Main Library Only) $17,488, Federal $3,888, Locally Generated Income $13,600. Mats Exp $139,123, Books $70,000, Per/Ser (Incl. Access Fees) $44,000, Presv $1,000, Micro $5,000, Manuscripts & Archives $2,000, Electronic Ref Mat (Incl. Access Fees) $17,123. Sal $205,464 (Prof $124,473)
Library Holdings: Bk Vols 101,540; Per Subs 450
Subject Interests: Elem educ, Nursing
Special Collections: Seventh-day Adventist Church History
Automation Activity & Vendor Info: (Acquisitions) TLC; (Cataloging) TLC; (Circulation) TLC; (Course Reserve) TLC; (OPAC) TLC; (Serials) EOS
Function: Archival collection
Partic in Tex Share
Friends of the Library Group

KELLER

P KELLER PUBLIC LIBRARY,* 640 Johnson Rd, 76248. SAN 325-1527. Tel: 817-431-9011. FAX: 817-431-3887. *Dir*, Lisa Harper Wood; Tel: 817-431-3919, E-Mail: lisa@kellerlib.org; Staff 7 (MLS 1, Non-MLS 6)
Founded 1972. Pop 19,200; Circ 151,000
Oct 1996-Sep 1997 Income $407,575. Mats Exp $62,000. Sal $264,000
Library Holdings: Bk Titles 47,500; Per Subs 40
Mem of North Texas Regional Library System
Special Services for the Deaf - Books on deafness & sign language; High interest/low vocabulary books; Special interest periodicals
Friends of the Library Group

KELLY AFB

UNITED STATES AIR FORCE
A KELLY AIR FORCE BASE LIBRARY FL2050, 76 SPTG/SVMG, 250 Goodrich Dr Ste E6, 78241-0651. SAN 362-076X. Tel: 210-925-3214. FAX: 210-925-7421. E-Mail: library1@mbpbl.afsv.af.mil. *Librn*, Earnestine R Larry
Founded 1917
Library Holdings: Bk Vols 22,000; Per Subs 491
Subject Interests: Job search, Mil educ, Transition
Special Collections: Hispanic Culture Coll; Military History; Texana

KENDALIA

P KENDALIA PUBLIC LIBRARY,* 2610-B Hwy 473, PO Box 399, 78027-0399. SAN 316-5361. Tel: 830-336-2002. FAX: 830-336-2002. E-Mail: kendlib@gvtc.com. *Librn*, Donna Jonas
Circ 2,695
Jan 1997-Dec 1998 Income $6,656. Mats Exp $1,567, Books $866, Per/Ser (Incl. Access Fees) $50, Presv $434. Sal $3,003
Library Holdings: Bk Vols 12,706; Bk Titles 10,576
Mem of Alamo Area Library System; San Antonio Major Resource Center
Mon 4-5 & Wed & Fri 1-6

KENDLETON

C BAY RIDGE CHRISTIAN COLLEGE LIBRARY,* PO Box 726, 77451. SAN 316-537X. Tel: 409-532-3982. FAX: 409-532-4352. *Dir*, Jeanette Diaz
Founded 1967
Library Holdings: Bk Vols 1,200
Special Collections: Warner Coll

KENEDY

P KARNES COUNTY LIBRARY SYSTEM,* 303 W Main, 78119. SAN 316-5388. Tel: 830-583-3313. FAX: 830-583-3270. *Dir*, Silvia Pena
Founded 1969
Library Holdings: Bk Vols 19,000
Special Collections: Holchak & McClane Coll, scrapbooks; Local History (M S Yeater Coll), biog, papers
Member Libraries: Karnes City Public Library; Runge Public Library

RMIT

WINKLER COUNTY LIBRARY,* 307 S Poplar St, 79745-4300. SAN 362-0824. Tel: 915-586-3841. FAX: 915-586-2462. *Librn*, Mary Lyn Owen
Founded 1929. Pop 8,015
Jan 1997-Dec 1998 Income $65,566, County $62,744. Mats Exp $8,125, Books $7,153, Per/Ser (Incl. Access Fees) $672, Micro $300. Sal $32,798
Library Holdings: Bk Vols 67,384; Per Subs 50
Special Collections: Geneology (coll donated by local Geneology Society)
Mem of West Texas Library System
Branches: 1
WINK BRANCH, 207 Langley Way, PO Box 457, Wink, 79789. SAN 362-0859. Tel: 915-527-3691. *Librn*, Pauline Kline

ERRVILLE

BUTT-HOLDSWORTH MEMORIAL LIBRARY,* 505 Water St, 78028. SAN 316-5396. Tel: 830-257-8422. FAX: 830-792-5552. E-Mail: kerrlib@hct.com. *Dir*, Antonio Martinez; *Ref*, Herbert Peterson; *Coll Develop, Ref*, Sherry Hiller; *Circ, ILL*, Mary L Meyers; *Publ Servs*, Pam Roberts
Founded 1967. Pop 40,000; Circ 380,000
1996-1997 Income $671,000. Mats Exp $118,000, Books $90,000, Per/Ser (Incl. Access Fees) $28,000. Sal $410,000 (Prof $200,000)
Library Holdings: Bk Titles 75,000; Per Subs 342
Special Collections: Texana Coll
Automation Activity & Vendor Info: (Circulation) Gaylord
Mem of Alamo Area Library System; San Antonio Major Resource Center
Friends of the Library Group

COWBOY ARTISTS OF AMERICA MUSEUM LIBRARY, 1550 Bandera Hwy, 78028-9547. (Mail add: PO Box 294300, 78029-4300), SAN 370-7342. Tel: 830-896-2553. FAX: 830-896-2556. E-Mail: caam@ktc.com. Web Site: www.caamuseum.com. *Librn*, Nan Stover; *Asst Librn*, Nancy Doig; *Tech Servs*, Terry Lavrendine; *Tech Servs*, Betty Syfan; *Tech Servs*, Cindy Terry; *Ref*, Gene Pope; *Ref*, Norma Richardson; *Ref*, Gordon Richardson; Staff 5 (MLS 1, Non-MLS 4)
Founded 1983
Library Holdings: Bk Titles 2,900; Per Subs 10
Publications: Newspaper & Museum Coverage of CAA Members; Special Indexes Listing Periodical

M DEPARTMENT OF VETERANS AFFAIRS, Library Service,* 3600 Memorial Blvd, 78028. SAN 316-5426. Tel: 830-896-2020, Ext 2220. FAX: 830-792-2457. *Chief Librn*, Lois A Johnson
Founded 1947
Library Holdings: Bk Vols 4,281; Per Subs 125
Subject Interests: Allied health sci, Dentistry, Hospital administration, Medicine, Nursing, Patient educ, Surgery
Partic in Health Oriented Libraries of San Antonio; OCLC Online Computer Library Center, Inc; South Central Academic Medical Libraries Consortium

KERRVILLE STATE HOSPITAL, Professional Library,* 721 Thompson Dr, 78028. SAN 316-540X. Tel: 830-896-2211, Ext 6283. FAX: 830-792-4926. *Librn*, Roxanne Frantzen; E-Mail: roxannefrantzen@mhmr.state.tx.us
Founded 1970
Library Holdings: Bk Vols 1,800
Subject Interests: Geriatrics, Psychiatry

SCHREINER COLLEGE, W M Logan Library, 2100 Memorial Blvd, 78028-5697. SAN 316-5418. Tel: 830-792-7312. FAX: 830-792-7448. Web Site: library.schreiner.edu. *Dir*, Candice Scott; Tel: 830-792-7318, E-Mail: canscott@schreiner.edu; *Ref*, Mary MacWithey; *Syst Coordr*, Conner Baldwin; Staff 3 (MLS 3)
Founded 1967. Enrl 794; Fac 47 Sal $198,520 (Prof $92,840)
Library Holdings: Bk Vols 80,000; Bk Titles 70,000; Per Subs 540
Subject Interests: Liberal arts
Special Collections: Texas Hill Country Coll
Partic in Amigos Library Services, Inc; Coun of Res & Acad Librs; OCLC Online Computer Library Center, Inc

USDA, ARS KNIPLING-BUSHLAND, US Livestock Insects Research Lab Library,* 2700 Fredricksberg Rd, 78028-9184. SAN 326-243X. Tel: 830-792-0308. FAX: 830-792-0302. *Librn*, Pat Agold; Staff 30 (MLS 30)
Library Holdings: Bk Vols 1,000; Bk Titles 1,000; Per Subs 50

ILGORE

KILGORE COLLEGE, Randolph C Watson Library, 1100 Broadway, 75662. SAN 316-5434. Tel: 903-983-8237. FAX: 903-983-8239. Web Site: www.kilgore.cc.tx.us/. *Dir*, Kathy Fair; *Acq, Circ, Ref*, Zeny Jett; Tel: 903-983-8236, E-Mail: jettz@kilgore.cc.tx.us; *Cat*, Judy Williams; Tel: 903-983-8240; *Ref*, Wade L Pipkin, Jr; Tel: 903-983-8235, E-Mail: pipkinn@hotmail.com; *Circ, Media Spec*, Barbara Murray; E-Mail: murrayb@kilgore.cc.tx.us; Staff 10 (MLS 4, Non-MLS 6)
Founded 1935. Enrl 4,148; Fac 145; Highest Degree: Associate
Sep 1999-Aug 2000 Income $368,000. Mats Exp $100,000, Books $39,000, Per/Ser (Incl. Access Fees) $30,000. Sal $261,151 (Prof $148,750)
Library Holdings: Bk Vols 120,000
Special Collections: Habenicht Texana Coll; Hill Texana Coll; Spear Coll (American & English Literature)
Partic in Forest Trail Library Consortium, Inc; OCLC Online Computer Library Center, Inc
Friends of the Library Group

P KILGORE PUBLIC LIBRARY, 301 Henderson Blvd, 75662. SAN 362-0883. Tel: 903-983-1529. FAX: 903-983-1779. E-Mail: kplib@imagineii.net. *Dir*, Linda Johnson; Staff 4 (Non-MLS 4)
Founded 1936. Pop 15,000; Circ 72,000
Library Holdings: Bk Vols 34,820; Per Subs 100
Automation Activity & Vendor Info: (Cataloging) Sagebrush Corporation; (Circulation) Sagebrush Corporation
Mem of Northeast Texas Library System
Partic in Forest Trail Library Consortium, Inc
Friends of the Library Group

KILLEEN

J CENTRAL TEXAS COLLEGE, Oveta Culp Hobby Memorial Library, 6200 W Central Texas Expressway, 76549. (Mail add: PO Box 1800, 76540-1800), Tel: 254-526-1237. Circulation Tel: 254-526-1621. Reference Tel: 254-526-1871. Toll Free Tel: 800-792-3348, Ext 1237. FAX: 254-526-1878. Web Site: www.ctcd.cc.tx.us/pg-lib.htm. *Dean of Libr*, Peg Lyons; Tel: 254-526-1475, E-Mail: plyons@ctcd.cc.tx.us; *Asst Dir*, Dana Watson; Tel: 254-526-1871, E-Mail: dwatson@ctcd.cc.tx.us; *AV*, Mark Plasterer; Tel: 254-526-1537, E-Mail: mplaster@ctcd.cc.tx.us; *Ref*, Ming Ming Swenson; Tel: 254-526-1483, E-Mail: mswenso@ctcd.cc.tx.us; Staff 18 (MLS 5, Non-MLS 13)
Founded 1967. Enrl 7,668; Fac 332; Highest Degree: Associate
Library Holdings: Bk Vols 80,381; Bk Titles 73,813; Per Subs 454
Subject Interests: Bus, Education, Law, Mgt
Automation Activity & Vendor Info: (Cataloging) SIRSI; (Circulation) SIRSI; (Course Reserve) SIRSI; (ILL) SIRSI
Database Vendor: IAC - Info Trac, OCLC - First Search, OVID Technologies, ProQuest
Partic in Amigos Library Services, Inc

P KILLEEN PUBLIC LIBRARY, 205 E Church Ave, 76541. SAN 316-5477. Tel: 254-501-8990. Circulation Tel: 254-501-8996. Reference Tel: 254-501-8991. FAX: 254-526-8737. Web Site: www.ci.killeen.tx.us. *Dir*, Deanna A Frazee; Tel: 254-501-8994, E-Mail: dfrazee@ci.killeen.tx.us; *Head Tech Servs*, Kenneth Gober; Tel: 254-501-8992, E-Mail: kgober@ci.killeen.tx.us; *Ch Servs*, Kim Miller; Tel: 254-501-8993, E-Mail: kmiller@ci.killeen.tx.us; *Head Ref*, Dawn M Blake; E-Mail: dblake@ci.killeen.tx.us; *Head, Circ*, Julie Johnson; E-Mail: jjohnson@ci.killeen.tx.us; Staff 19 (MLS 2, Non-MLS 17)
Founded 1958. Pop 84,488; Circ 165,000
Oct 1999-Sep 2000 Income City $792,000. Sal $307,287 (Prof $69,000)
Library Holdings: Bk Vols 75,000; Bk Titles 61,000; Per Subs 152
Subject Interests: Automotive repair, Children, County hist, Genealogy, Local history, Mechanics, Texana
Automation Activity & Vendor Info: (Cataloging) epixtech, inc.; (Circulation) epixtech, inc.; (OPAC) epixtech, inc.
Database Vendor: epixtech, inc.
Function: Reference services available
Mem of Central Texas Library System
Friends of the Library Group

C TARLETON STATE UNIVERSITY, Tarleton Library-Central Texas, 1901 S Clear Creek Rd, 76549. SAN 316-5450. Tel: 254-526-1244. FAX: 254-526-1993. Web Site: www.tarleton.edu/~tlct. *Circ, Dir, Ref*, Melinda Guthrie; E-Mail: mguthrie@tarleton.edu; *Ref Serv*, Lynn Schumacher; *ILL*, Stacy Ferrell; Staff 2 (MLS 2)
Founded 1973. Enrl 1,340; Fac 52; Highest Degree: Master
Jul 1999-Jun 2000 Income State $280,000. Mats Exp $85,000, Books $60,000, Per/Ser (Incl. Access Fees) $23,000. Sal $80,000 (Prof $40,000)
Library Holdings: Bk Vols 25,000; Bk Titles 23,500; Per Subs 135
Automation Activity & Vendor Info: (Acquisitions) DRA; (Cataloging) SIRSI; (Circulation) SIRSI; (Course Reserve) SIRSI; (OPAC) SIRSI
Database Vendor: Ebsco - EbscoHost, Lexis-Nexis, OCLC - First Search, OVID Technologies
Publications: Annual report; subject guides to students
Partic in Amigos Library Services, Inc; TexShare

KINGSVILLE

P ROBERT J KLEBERG PUBLIC LIBRARY, 220 N Fourth St, 78363. SAN 316-5493. Tel: 361-592-6381. *Dir*, Robert Rodriguez; *Ref*, Mary Ann Escamilla; *Per*, Albert Garcia; *Cat*, Ruth Valdez; *Acq*, Hector Vela; *Circ*, Andrea Vidaurri; *Ch Servs*, Gladys Neary; Staff 6 (MLS 6)
Founded 1927. Pop 35,600; Circ 82,135
Library Holdings: Bk Titles 80,000; Per Subs 164; Bks on Deafness & Sign Lang 20
Special Collections: Genealogy Reference; Texas Reference
Automation Activity & Vendor Info: (Cataloging) Gaylord; (Circulation)

Gaylord; (OPAC) Gaylord
Mem of South Texas Library System
Open Tues-Fri 8-6, Sat 9-1
Friends of the Library Group

C TEXAS A&M UNIVERSITY-KINGSVILLE, James C Jernigan Library,* 1050 University Ave, 78363. (Mail add: M S C 197, 78363), SAN 316-5507. Tel: 361-593-3416. FAX: 361-593-4093. Web Site: www.oasis.tamuk.edu. *Dir*, Gilda B Ortego; E-Mail: g-ortego@tamuk.edu; *Coll Develop*, Bruce Prothe; Staff 30 (MLS 13, Non-MLS 17)
Founded 1925. Enrl 6,130; Fac 225; Highest Degree: Doctorate
1998-1999 Income $1,800,000. Mats Exp $547,000. Sal $941,180
Library Holdings: Bk Vols 491,452; Bk Titles 358,466; Per Subs 2,345
Subject Interests: Bilingual studies
Special Collections: Botany (Runyon Coll); Western Americana (McGill Coll)
Publications: Newsletter, The Jernigan Journal
Partic in OCLC Online Computer Library Center, Inc

UNITED STATES NAVY
A NAVAL AIR STATION LIBRARY, 904 Dealy Ave, Ste 110, 78363-5034. SAN 362-0948. Tel: 512-516-6271. FAX: 512-516-6971. E-Mail: naslib@intcomm.com. *Mgr*, Vickie Jacobson
Founded 1943
Oct 1996-Sep 1997 Mats Exp $250,000
Library Holdings: Bk Vols 13,695; Per Subs 44
Subject Interests: Mil, Military history, Recreational

KIRBYVILLE

P KIRBYVILLE PUBLIC LIBRARY,* 210 S Elizabeth St, PO Box 567, 75956-0567. SAN 316-5515. Tel: 409-423-4653. Interlibrary Loan Service Tel: 713-224-8575. FAX: 409-423-5545. *Asst Librn*, Joyce Horn
Founded 1937. Pop 5,000; Circ 10,205
Library Holdings: Bk Vols 35,000; Per Subs 60
Friends of the Library Group

KOUNTZE

P KOUNTZE PUBLIC LIBRARY, (KPL), 835 Redwood St, 77625. SAN 316-5523. Tel: 409-246-2826. FAX: 409-246-2826. E-Mail: kpl@ruralcomm.com. Web Site: www.kountzelibrary.bizland.com. *Dir*, Deborah Childress; *Asst Dir*, Laverne Crysel
Pop 10,000; Circ 17,668
Library Holdings: Bk Titles 52,000; Per Subs 25
Mem of Houston Area Library System
Friends of the Library Group

KRUM

P KRUM PUBLIC LIBRARY,* 803 E McCart, PO Box 780, 76249-0780. SAN 376-4567. Tel: 940-482-3455. FAX: 940-482-3456. E-Mail: kplbeeb@iglobal.net. *Librn*, Becky Benedict
Oct 1999-Sep 2000 Income (Main Library Only) $25,000, City $10,000, County $12,000, Locally Generated Income $3,000
Library Holdings: Bk Vols 11,000
Mem of North Texas Regional Library System
Open Mon 9-7, Tues, Wed & Fri 9-5
Friends of the Library Group

KYLE

P KYLE COMMUNITY LIBRARY, (KCL), 409 W Blanco St, PO Box 366, 78640. SAN 316-5531. Tel: 512-268-7411. FAX: 512-268-7411. E-Mail: librarian@kyle.lib.tx.us. Web Site: www.kyle.lib.tx.us.index.html. *Dir*, Sharon S Black-Greene; Staff 2 (MLS 1, Non-MLS 1)
Founded 1963. Pop 5,200
Oct 1999-Sep 2000 Income $61,450, State $1,730, City $12,000, County $20,760, Locally Generated Income $26,560. Mats Exp $9,300, Books $8,200, Per/Ser (Incl. Access Fees) $1,100. Sal $17,000
Library Holdings: Bk Vols 13,300; Bk Titles 12,896; Per Subs 40
Special Collections: Katherine Ann Porter Coll
Automation Activity & Vendor Info: (Acquisitions) Brodart; (Circulation) Athena
Function: Some telephone reference
Mem of Central Texas Library System
Special Services for the Blind - Talking Books
Friends of the Library Group

LA GRANGE

P FAYETTE PUBLIC LIBRARY, 855 S Jefferson, 78945. SAN 316-5558. Tel: 409-968-3765. FAX: 409-968-5357. E-Mail: library@fais.net. Web Site: lagrange.fais.net/library/library.html. *Dir*, Kathy Carter; *Librn*, Annette Ruckert; Staff 4 (Non-MLS 4)
Founded 1938. Pop 5,200; Circ 50,919
1999-2000
Library Holdings: Bk Vols 22,000; Per Subs 52
Subject Interests: Local hist archives
Special Collections: Texana Coll
Automation Activity & Vendor Info: (Cataloging) Follett; (Circulation) Follett
Mem of Central Texas Library System
Friends of the Library Group

LA MARQUE

P LA MARQUE PUBLIC LIBRARY,* 1011 Bayou Rd, 77568-4195. SAN 316-5566. Tel: 409-938-9270. FAX: 409-938-9277. *Dir*, Marilee Neale; E-Mail: mneale@hals.lib.tx.us; *Asst Dir, Ref*, Irene Carstens; *Tech Servs*, Carol Hill-DeSantos; *Ch Servs*, Yvonne Brown
Founded 1946. Pop 23,691
Library Holdings: Bk Titles 39,062; Per Subs 63
Mem of Galveston County Libr Syst; Houston Area Library System

LA PORTE

S SAN JACINTO MUSEUM OF HISTORY, Albert & Ethel Herzstein Library, One Monument Circle, 77571-9744. SAN 321-8155. Tel: 281-479-2421. FAX: 281-479-2866. Web Site: www.sanjacinto-museum.org. *Exec Dir*, J C Martin; *Dir*, Lisa A Struthers; E-Mail: lstruthers@sanjacinto-museum.org; *Cat*, Kathleen S Whitsitt; E-Mail: cataloger@sanjacinto-museum.org; *Archivist*, Sarah Canby Jackson; E-Mail: archivist@sanjacinto-museum.org; Staff 4 (MLS 3, Non-MLS 1)
Founded 1939
Library Holdings: Bk Vols 15,000; Bk Titles 13,500; Bk Titles 14,000; Per Subs 35
Subject Interests: Tex hist
Database Vendor: OCLC - First Search
Restriction: By appointment only
Function: Research library
Partic in Amigos Library Services, Inc

LACKLAND AFB

A UNITED STATES DEPARTMENT OF THE AIR FORCE, Defense Language Institute, English Language Center Library, Bldg 7445, Rm 109, 2230 Andrews Ave, 78236. SAN 316-5574. Tel: 210-671-2767. FAX: 210-671-0211. *Librn*, Patricia W Henry; E-Mail: patricia.henry@lackland.af.mil
Subject Specialists: *English as a second lang*, Patricia W Henry; Staff 3 (MLS 1, Non-MLS 2)
Founded 1967
Oct 1996-Sep 1997 Income $13,419, Federal $3,419, Parent Institution $10,000. Mats Exp $8,056, Books $4,280, Per/Ser (Incl. Access Fees) $3,576
Library Holdings: Bk Vols 5,250; Bk Titles 5,000; Per Subs 86
Subject Interests: Mil sci, Teaching English as a second lang to foreign m students from various allied countries
Special Collections: English as a Second Language Coll
Database Vendor: Ebsco - EbscoHost, GaleNet, OCLC - First Search
Restriction: Open to student, faculty & staff
Function: ILL available

M WILFORD HALL MEDICAL CENTER LIBRARY, 59MDW/MSTL, 78236-5300. SAN 362-0972. Tel: 210-292-7204. Circulation Tel: 210-292-5776. FAX: 210-292-7030. Web Site: www.whmc.af.mil. *Librn*, Rita Smith E-Mail: rita.smith@59mdw.whmc.af.mil; *ILL*, Doris Perez; Tel: 210-292-5777, E-Mail: doris.perez@59mdw.whmc.af.mil; *Coll Develop*, Debra Ragan; Tel: 210-292-5770, E-Mail: debra.ragan@59mdw.whmc.af.mil; Staff 3 (MLS 3)
Founded 1950
Library Holdings: Bk Titles 11,000; Per Subs 640
Subject Interests: Clinical medicine, Dentistry, Nursing
Automation Activity & Vendor Info: (Cataloging) epixtech, inc.; (Circulation) epixtech, inc.
Database Vendor: Dialog, Ebsco - EbscoHost, GaleNet, Lexis-Nexis, OCLC - First Search, OVID Technologies, ProQuest
Restriction: Not open to public
Partic in Docline; OCLC Online Computer Library Center, Inc

LAKE DALLAS

P LAKE CITIES LIBRARY,* 302 S Shady Shores Rd, PO Box 775, 75065. SAN 376-4559. Tel: 940-497-3566. FAX: 940-497-3566. *Librn*, Vera Fingerle
1998-1999 Income $43,000
Library Holdings: Bk Vols 25,742; Per Subs 75
Mem of North Texas Regional Library System
Friends of the Library Group

AKE JACKSON

BRAZOSPORT COLLEGE LIBRARY, 500 College Dr, 77566. SAN 316-5582. Tel: 979-230-3310. Reference Tel: 979-230-3406. FAX: 409-230-3443. Web Site: www.brazosport.cc.tx.us/~lib. *Admin Dir*, Daniel R Walther; Tel: 979-230-3348, E-Mail: dwalther@brazosport.cc.tx.us; *Ser*, Tami Wisofsky; Tel: 979-230-3308, E-Mail: twisofsk@brazosport.cc.tx.us; *Ref*, Betty Prichard; Tel: 979-230-3366, E-Mail: bprichar@brazosport.cc.tx.us; *Cat*, Denise Slaydon; Tel: 979-230-3309, E-Mail: dslaydon@brazosport.cc.tx.us; Staff 6 (MLS 3, Non-MLS 3)
Founded 1968. Enrl 3,199; Fac 62
Library Holdings: Bk Vols 62,000; Bk Titles 57,500; Per Subs 350
Special Collections: Quality Coll; Small Business Development Coll; Texas Coll
Automation Activity & Vendor Info: (Cataloging) epixtech, inc.; (Circulation) epixtech, inc.; (OPAC) epixtech, inc.; (Serials) epixtech, inc.
Database Vendor: epixtech, inc., GaleNet, IAC - Info Trac, OCLC - First Search, OVID Technologies, ProQuest, Wilson - Wilson Web
Partic in Amigos Library Services, Inc; Tex Share

AKE TRAVIS

LAKE TRAVIS COMMUNITY LIBRARY,* 3322 Ranch Rd, 620 S Austin, 78734-5612. SAN 376-4737. Tel: 512-263-2885. FAX: 512-263-4446. *Librn*, Jean Johnson
Library Holdings: Bk Vols 28,000; Per Subs 40
Mem of Central Texas Library System
Friends of the Library Group

AKE WORTH

MARY LOU REDDICK PUBLIC LIBRARY, 3801 Adam Grubb Dr, 76135. SAN 316-5590. Tel: 817-237-9681. FAX: 817-237-9671. *Librn*, Lara Strother; E-Mail: laras@lake-worth.lib.tx.us
Pop 5,000; Circ 18,684
Library Holdings: Bk Vols 20,000; Per Subs 22
Automation Activity & Vendor Info: (Cataloging) Sagebrush Corporation; (Circulation) Sagebrush Corporation
Mem of North Texas Regional Library System
Friends of the Library Group

AMESA

DAWSON COUNTY LIBRARY,* 511 N Third St, 79331-1264. (Mail add: PO Box 1264, 79331), SAN 316-5604. Tel: 806-872-6502. FAX: 806-872-2435. *Coll Develop, Dir*, Jan Pendergraft; E-Mail: janp@lamesa.esa.17.net
Founded 1933. Pop 14,000; Circ 218,619
Jan 1998-Dec 1998 Income $163,731, City $7,200, County $153,331, Other $3,200
Library Holdings: Bk Titles 33,000; Per Subs 75
Special Collections: Genealogy, Texas Heritage
Automation Activity & Vendor Info: (Acquisitions) Sagebrush Corporation; (Cataloging) Sagebrush Corporation; (Circulation) Sagebrush Corporation
Mem of West Texas Library System

AMPASAS

P LAMPASAS PUBLIC LIBRARY, 201 S Main, 76550-2843. (Mail add: PO Box 308, 76550-0308), SAN 316-5612. Tel: 512-556-3251. FAX: 512-556-4065. E-Mail: library@ci.lampasas.tx.us. Web Site: www.ci.lampasas.tx.us/library. *Librn*, Sue Lilley; Staff 3 (Non-MLS 3)
Founded 1902. Pop 7,948; Circ 43,379
Oct 1998-Sep 1999 Income $81,342. Mats Exp $18,091. Sal $71,215
Library Holdings: Bk Vols 21,720; Bk Titles 17,728; Per Subs 50
Mem of Central Texas Library System
Friends of the Library Group

LANCASTER

J CEDAR VALLEY COLLEGE LIBRARY, 3030 N Dallas Ave, 75134-3799. SAN 321-3501. Tel: 972-860-8140. FAX: 972-860-8221. Web Site: www.dcccd.edu/cvc/cvc.htm. *Bibliog Instr, Coll Develop, Librn*, Kim Ross; E-Mail: kross@dcccd.edu; *Librn*, Dava Stephens; E-Mail: dstephens@dcccd.edu; *Librn*, Edna White; E-Mail: ewhite@dcccd.edu; *Circ*, Jeffrey Stagner; E-Mail: jstagner@dcccd.edu; *AV*, Judy McMullan. Subject Specialists: *History*, Jeffrey Stagner; *History*, Kim Ross; *Science*, Dava Stephens; Staff 3 (MLS 2, Non-MLS 1)
Founded 1977. Enrl 3,102; Highest Degree: Associate
Sep 1999-Aug 2000 Income $539,701. Mats Exp $46,280, Books $26,120, Per/Ser (Incl. Access Fees) $10,916, Presv $89, Micro $5,435, AV Equip $3,720. Sal $284,035 (Prof $182,167)
Library Holdings: Bk Vols 47,839; Bk Titles 41,862; Per Subs 285
Subject Interests: Commercial music, Fashion marketing, Veterinary tech
Automation Activity & Vendor Info: (Circulation) Innovative Interfaces Inc.
Database Vendor: Innovative Interfaces INN - View, OVID Technologies, ProQuest
Partic in Amigos Library Services, Inc; OCLC Online Computer Library Center, Inc; Tex Share

P LANCASTER VETERANS MEMORIAL LIBRARY, (LVML), 1600 Veterans Memorial Pkwy, 75134. SAN 376-4419. Tel: 972-227-1080. FAX: 972-227-5560. E-Mail: vmlib@onramp.net. Web Site: www.ci.lancaster.tx.us. *Mgr*, Angela Alford; *Ch Servs, Publ Servs*, Dottie Crawford
Founded 1923. Pop 23,550
Oct 1998-Sep 1999 Mats Exp $61,430
Library Holdings: Bk Vols 53,761; Bk Titles 53,088; Per Subs 99; High Interest/Low Vocabulary Bk Vols 15,314
Subject Interests: Local history
Special Collections: Genealogy Coll
Automation Activity & Vendor Info: (Acquisitions) Brodart; (Cataloging) Brodart; (Circulation) Sagebrush Corporation; (OPAC) Sagebrush Corporation
Mem of Northeast Texas Library System
Friends of the Library Group

LAPORTE

S ATOFINA PETROCHEMICALS, (Formerly Fina Oil & Chemical Company), Technical Library, 1902 Battleground Rd, 77571. (Mail add: PO Box 1200, 77536), SAN 375-3344. Tel: 281-884-0526. FAX: 281-884-0584. Web Site: www.atofina.com. *Tech Servs*, Greg Kaase; E-Mail: greg.kaase@atofina.com
Founded 1989
Library Holdings: Bk Titles 1,100; Per Subs 75
Subject Interests: Chemistry
Publications: Journal table of contents; newsletter
Partic in Dialog Corporation; RLIN

LAREDO

J LAREDO COMMUNITY COLLEGE, Harold R Yeary Library, West End Washington St, 78040-4348. SAN 316-5620. Tel: 956-721-5816. Interlibrary Loan Service Tel: 956-721-5280. Circulation Tel: 956-721-5275. Reference Tel: 956-721-5274. FAX: 210-721-5447. Web Site: www.laredo.cc.tx.us. *Dir*, Thomas LaFleur; E-Mail: tlafleur@laredo.cc.tx.us; *Ref*, William Wisner; Tel: 956-721-5281, E-Mail: bwisner@laredo.cc.tx.us; *Per*, Garry Church; Tel: 956-721-5842, E-Mail: gchurch@laredo.cc.tx.us; *Acq*, Sarah Church; Tel: 956-721-5813, E-Mail: smchurch@laredo.cc.tx.us; *Cat*, Nancy Sparks; Tel: 956-721-5271, E-Mail: nsparks@laredo.cc.tx.us; *ILL*, Albert Bustos; Tel: 956-721-5845, E-Mail: abustos@laredo.cc.tx.us; *Govt Doc*, Pedro Vasquez; Tel: 956-721-5841, E-Mail: pvasquez@laredo.cc.tx.us; *Media Spec*, Ceferino Izaguirre; Tel: 956-721-5324, Fax: 956-721-5456, E-Mail: cizaguirre@laredo.cc.tx.us; Staff 7 (MLS 6, Non-MLS 1)
Founded 1947. Enrl 5,430; Fac 300; Highest Degree: Associate
Sep 1999-Aug 2000 Income $999,441, State $18,200, Federal $15,000, Parent Institution $966,241. Mats Exp $300,242, Books $107,845, Per/Ser (Incl. Access Fees) $114,513, Presv $2,440, Micro $30,104, Electronic Ref Mat (Incl. Access Fees) $45,340. Sal $592,712 (Prof $210,661)
Library Holdings: Bk Vols 98,061; Bk Titles 78,605; Per Subs 381
Subject Interests: Behav sci, Para-med, Soc sci, Voc-tech
Special Collections: Laredo Archives; Old Fort MacIntosh Records; US Selective Govt Dep
Automation Activity & Vendor Info: (Acquisitions) DRA; (Cataloging) DRA; (Circulation) DRA; (OPAC) DRA; (Serials) DRA
Database Vendor: OCLC - First Search
Publications: Yeary Library Tidings Newsletter (irregular)
Partic in Amigos Library Services, Inc; Paisano Consortium; Tex Share

P LAREDO PUBLIC LIBRARY,* 1120 E Calton Rd, 78041. SAN 316-5639. Tel: 956-795-2400. FAX: 956-795-2403. Web Site: laredolibrary.org. *Dir*, Janice Weber; E-Mail: janice@laredolibrary.org; *Asst Dir*, Maria G Soliz; *Spec Coll*, Joe Moreno; Staff 14 (MLS 14)
Founded 1900. Pop 188,000
Oct 1997-Sep 1998 Income $2,850,023, City $2,783,406, County $5,000, Other $61,617. Mats Exp $437,743, Books $392,165, Per/Ser (Incl. Access Fees) $23,063, Micro $703. Sal $548,343
Library Holdings: Bk Vols 146,000; Per Subs 242
Subject Interests: Grantsmanship, Local authors, Webb County hist
Special Collections: Funding Information Library (Foundation Center Cooperating Coll); Laredo Historical Coll, bks, clippings
Mem of South Texas Library System
Daily classes in literacy & GED instruction, internet available
Friends of the Library Group
Branches: 1
SANTO NINO BRANCH, 2200 Zacatecas, 78043. SAN 371-9502. Tel: 956-795-2420. FAX: 956-795-2421. Web Site: laredolibrary.org. *Librn*, Rhonda Herd
Friends of the Library Group
Bookmobiles: 1

C TEXAS A&M INTERNATIONAL UNIVERSITY, Sue & Radcliffe Killam Library, 5201 University Blvd, 78041-1900. SAN 316-5647. Tel: 956-326-2400. Interlibrary Loan Service Tel: 956-326-2117. FAX: 956-326-2399. Web Site: www.tamiu.edu/library.htm. *Dir*, Rodney Webb; E-Mail: rwebb@tamiu.edu; *Cat*, John Hastings; Tel: 956-326-2114, E-Mail: jhastings@tamiu.edu; *Publ Servs*, John Maxstadt; Tel: 956-326-2116, E-Mail: jmaxstadt@tamiu.edu; *Acq, Ser*, Rogelio Hinojosa; Tel: 956-326-2123, E-Mail: rhinojosa@tamiu.edu; *Ref, Spec Coll*, Renee LaPerriere; Tel: 956-326-2404, E-Mail: rlaperriere@tamiu.edu; *Automation Syst Coordr*, Eric Elmore; Tel: 956-326-2137, E-Mail: eric@tamiu.edu; Staff 25 (MLS 8, Non-MLS 17)
Founded 1970. Enrl 3,052; Fac 138; Highest Degree: Master
Sep 1999-Aug 2000 Mats Exp $2,629,299, Books $1,627,698, Per/Ser (Incl. Access Fees) $519,107, Presv $5,165, Micro $194,427, AV Equip $30,000, Electronic Ref Mat (Incl. Access Fees) $252,902. Sal $612,843 (Prof $314,545)
Library Holdings: Bk Vols 186,227; Bk Titles 168,466; Per Subs 8,715
Subject Interests: International trade, Nursing
Special Collections: Laredo Spanish Archives on MF; Raza Unida Papers
Automation Activity & Vendor Info: (Acquisitions) Endeavor; (Cataloging) Endeavor; (Circulation) Endeavor; (Course Reserve) Endeavor; (OPAC) Endeavor; (Serials) Endeavor
Publications: Newsletter
Partic in Amigos Library Services, Inc; TexShare

LAUGHLIN AFB

UNITED STATES AIR FORCE
AM HOSPITAL MEDICAL LIBRARY, 590 Mitchell Blvd, Bldg 375, 78843-5244. SAN 362-1065. Tel: 830-298-2317, Ext 6325. FAX: 830-298-6489. *Librn*, Michele Thornton
Library Holdings: Bk Vols 703; Per Subs 19

A LAUGHLIN AIR FORCE BASE LIBRARY, 47 SPTG/SVMG, 427 Fourth St, Bldg 257, 78843-5125. SAN 362-1030. Tel: 830-298-5119. FAX: 830-298-7903. *Mgr*, Sue A Blankemeyer; Tel: 830-298-5757, E-Mail: sue.blankemeyer@laughlin.af.mil
Library Holdings: Bk Vols 18,204; Bk Titles 18,000; Per Subs 100
Special Collections: Career Transition Assistance; Military, Chief of Staff
Database Vendor: Ebsco - EbscoHost, GaleNet, OCLC - First Search
Partic in Amigos Library Services, Inc

LEAGUE CITY

P HELEN HALL LIBRARY, 100 W Walker, 77573-3899. SAN 316-5671. Tel: 281-338-4860. Reference Tel: 281-338-4867. FAX: 281-338-4143. Web Site: leaguecitylibrary.org. *Dir*, Susan Mathews; *Asst Dir*, Shelley Leader; *Ch Servs*, Mary Mills; *YA Servs*, Lynne Bose; Tel: 281-316-3434; *Ref*, Lynne Westerholm; *Spec Coll & Archives*, Becky Jeter; Tel: 281-316-3473; *Commun Relations*, Elizabeth Hopkins; Tel: 281-316-3444; *Tech Servs*, Marilynn Hopman; Tel: 281-316-3425; *Info Tech*, Weldon Horton; Tel: 281-316-3423; Staff 29 (MLS 7, Non-MLS 22)
Founded 1972. Pop 41,000; Circ 374,855
Oct 1997-Sep 1998 Income $975,093, City $928,157, County $46,936. Mats Exp $115,926, Books $104,508, Per/Ser (Incl. Access Fees) $11,418. Sal $564,338 (Prof $172,338)
Library Holdings: Bk Vols 124,607; Per Subs 235
Automation Activity & Vendor Info: (Acquisitions) epixtech, inc.; (Cataloging) epixtech, inc.; (Circulation) epixtech, inc.
Database Vendor: GaleNet, IAC - Info Trac
Publications: League City: A History from 1913-1924, vol 2
Mem of Houston Area Library System
Partic in Galveston County Libr Syst

S NATIONAL CONSERVATION FOUNDATION, (Formerly Conservation Districts Foundation), Davis Conservation Library, 408 E Main St, 77573-3741. (Mail add: PO Box 855, 77574-0855), SAN 316-5663. Tel: 281-332-3402. Toll Free Tel: 800-825-5547. FAX: 281-332-5259. Web Site: www.nacdnet.org. *Publ Servs*, Ron Francis
Founded 1962
Library Holdings: Bk Vols 1,500; Bk Titles 1,500; Per Subs 16
Subject Interests: Conserv of all natural resources, Develop of conserv districts, Environmental studies, Hist of the conserv movement in the US
Special Collections: Archives-Iowa State University, Ames
Publications: Annual Conservation Audiovisual Service Catalog

LEAKEY

P REAL COUNTY PUBLIC LIBRARY,* Main & Evergreen, PO Box 488, 78873-0557. SAN 376-4125. Tel: 210-232-5199. FAX: 830-232-5913. *Librn*, Lisa Teske
Library Holdings: Bk Vols 10,000
Mem of Alamo Area Library System

LEANDER

P LEANDER PUBLIC LIBRARY, 406 Municipal Dr, 78641. (Mail add: PO Box 410, 78646-0410), SAN 375-5118. Tel: 512-259-5259. E-Mail: lpl@eden.com. *Librn*, Rosemary Detrich; Staff 12 (MLS 1, Non-MLS 11)
Founded 1987. Pop 12,000; Circ 19,853
Oct 1999-Sep 2000 Income $44,892, City $39,348, Locally Generated Income $2,519, Other $3,025. Mats Exp $15,618, Books $13,106, Per/Ser (Incl. Access Fees) $922, AV Equip $1,590. Sal $30,142 (Prof $23,240)
Library Holdings: Bk Vols 8,093; Bk Titles 7,802; Per Subs 16
Mem of Central Texas Library System
Friends of the Library Group

LEDBETTER

S AMERICAN SUFFOLK HORSE ASSOCIATION LIBRARY, (ASHA), 4240 Goehring Rd, 78946-9707. SAN 372-9958. Tel: 979-249-5795. E-Mail: rread@cvtv.net. Web Site: www.suffolkpunch.com.
Library Holdings: Bk Vols 50

LEONARD

P LEONARD PUBLIC LIBRARY,* 109 S Connett St, PO Box 1188, 75452-0264. SAN 376-6500. Tel: 903-587-2391. FAX: 903-587-2580. *Librn*, Alice Turpin Grinstead
Library Holdings: Bk Vols 18,000
Mem of Northeast Texas Library System
Friends of the Library Group

LEVELLAND

P HOCKLEY COUNTY MEMORIAL LIBRARY,* 802 Houston St, Ste 108, 79336. (Mail add: 811 Austin St, 79336-4594), SAN 316-568X. Tel: 806-894-6750. FAX: 806-894-6917. E-Mail: hclibry@gte.net. *Dir*, Doris Baker; *Asst Librn*, Kay Daniel
Founded 1946. Pop 24,500; Circ 70,744
Jan 1997-Dec 1998 Income $98,848. Mats Exp $14,733, Books $11,998, Per/Ser (Incl. Access Fees) $1,867. Sal $67,719 (Prof $44,610)
Library Holdings: Bk Titles 37,532; Per Subs 67
Subject Interests: Tex hist
Mem of West Texas Library System
Friends of the Library Group
Branches: 2
ROPES BRANCH, 602 Hockley Main, PO Box 96, Ropesville, 79358. SAN 373-708X. Tel: 806-562-3531. *Librn*, Jean Hamby
SUNDOWN BRANCH, 207 E Richardson, PO Box 600, Sundown, 79372-0600. SAN 375-6025. Tel: 806-229-3131. *Librn*, Helen Ellison
Friends of the Library Group

J SOUTH PLAINS COLLEGE LIBRARY, 1401 College Ave, 79336. SAN 316-5698. Tel: 806-894-9611, Ext 2302. FAX: 806-894-5274. Web Site: www.spc.cc.tx.us/website/page/res/lib/index.html. *Dir*, David Drake; E-Mail ddrake@spc.cc.tx.us; *Publ Servs*, Scott Jeffries; *Publ Servs*, Carolyn Reno; *Tech Servs*, Fran Hollis; Staff 4 (MLS 4)
Founded 1958. Enrl 7,154
Sep 2000-Aug 2001 Income $471,735. Mats Exp $174,807, Books $77,000, Per/Ser (Incl. Access Fees) $41,000, Micro $6,807, AV Equip $10,000, Electronic Ref Mat (Incl. Access Fees) $40,000. Sal $243,040 (Prof $195,085)
Library Holdings: Bk Vols 75,000; Per Subs 570
Database Vendor: GaleNet, Lexis-Nexis, OVID Technologies, ProQuest
Partic in Amigos Library Services, Inc; OCLC Online Computer Library Center, Inc; Tex Share

LEWISVILLE

P LEWISVILLE PUBLIC LIBRARY SYSTEM, 1197 W Main at Civic Circle, PO Box 299002-9002, 75029. SAN 316-5701. Tel: 972-219-3570. FAX: 972-219-5094. Web Site: www.cityoflewisville.com/library. *Dir*, Ann Loggins; *Tech Servs*, Deborah Gentry; *Ch Servs*, Melissa Smith; *Automation Syst Coordr*, Carol Crumpton; *Ref*, Matt Stock; *Ref*, Erik Wilkinson; Staff 8 (MLS 8)
Founded 1968. Pop 78,150
Library Holdings: Bk Vols 170,000; Per Subs 400
Subject Interests: Bus, Local oral hist, Mgt
Special Collections: Children's Enrichment, bk, flm
Automation Activity & Vendor Info: (Acquisitions) Inlex; (Cataloging) Inlex; (Circulation) Inlex; (OPAC) Inlex
Database Vendor: DRA
Mem of North Texas Regional Library System
Open Sun 1:30-5, Mon-Thurs 9:30am-9pm, Fri 9:30-6 & Sat 9-5
Friends of the Library Group
Branches: 1
OLD TOWN, 151 Church St, 75057. SAN 376-2521. Tel: 972-219-3720. *Mgr*, Deborah Gentry
Friends of the Library Group

BERTY

SAM HOUSTON REGIONAL LIBRARY & RESEARCH CENTER, FM 1011 Governors Rd, 77575-0310. (Mail add: PO Box 310, 77575-0310), SAN 326-4505. Tel: 936-336-8821. E-Mail: samhoustoncenter@tsl.state.tx.us. Web Site: www.tsl.state.tx.us. *Archivist, Dir*, Robert L Schaadt; E-Mail: robert.schaadt@tsl.state.tx.us; *Archivist, Curator*, Lisa Meisch; *Publ Servs*, Darlene Mott; Staff 5 (MLS 3, Non-MLS 2)
Founded 1977
Sep 1999-Aug 2000 Income $168,550, Locally Generated Income $1,500, Parent Institution $154,707, Other $12,343. Mats Exp $1,266, Books $203, Per/Ser (Incl. Access Fees) $468, Presv $478, Manuscripts & Archives $117. Sal $123,029 (Prof $76,304)
Library Holdings: Bk Vols 11,418; Bk Titles 5,618; Per Subs 51
Special Collections: Jean Houston Baldwin Coll of Sam Houston Images; Papers of Martin Dies, archives; Papers of Price Daniel, archives
Restriction: Non-circulating to the public
Function: Archival collection
Friends of the Library Group

LIBERTY MUNICIPAL LIBRARY, (LML), 1710 Sam Houston Ave, 77575-4741. SAN 316-571X. Tel: 936-336-8901. FAX: 936-336-2414. E-Mail: lml@imsday.com. *Dir*, Dana Abshier
Founded 1940. Pop 7,856
Oct 1998-Sep 1999 Income $306,018, City $269,232, Other $36,786. Mats Exp $36,786, Books $31,447, Per/Ser (Incl. Access Fees) $2,500, Micro $107. Sal $149,655
Library Holdings: Bk Vols 35,696; Bk Titles 32,332; Per Subs 20
Automation Activity & Vendor Info: (Cataloging) Sagebrush Corporation; (Circulation) Sagebrush Corporation; (OPAC) Sagebrush Corporation
Database Vendor: Ebsco - EbscoHost
Mem of Houston Area Library System
Adult Literacy Program, Childrens Story Time & Lap Sit Program; English as a Second Language
Friends of the Library Group

TTLEFIELD

LAMB COUNTY LIBRARY, 232 Phelps, 79339. SAN 316-5728. Tel: 806-385-5223, 806-767-2857. Interlibrary Loan Service Tel: 800-962-7392. FAX: 806-385-5223. E-Mail: lambjo@door.net. *Librn*, JoAnn Austin; *Asst Librn*, Mary Gonzales
Pop 15,663; Circ 42,000
Oct 1999-Sep 2000 Income (Main Library Only) County $98,772. Mats Exp $8,260, Books $7,500, Per/Ser (Incl. Access Fees) $760. Sal $43,384
Library Holdings: Bk Vols 22,000; Bk Titles 12,300; Per Subs 22
Subject Interests: Texas hist
Automation Activity & Vendor Info: (Circulation) Sagebrush Corporation
Mem of West Texas Library System
Friends of the Library Group
Branches: 1
OLTON BRANCH, Box 675, Olton, 79064. SAN 321-6160. Tel: 806-285-7772. FAX: 806-385-7770. E-Mail: oltonlib@fivearea.com. *Librn*, Linda Roper
Oct 1999-Sep 2000 Mats Exp Books $3,000. Sal $15,273
Library Holdings: Bk Vols 22,000; Bk Titles 12,300
Friends of the Library Group

IVINGSTON

MURPHY MEMORIAL LIBRARY,* 601 W Church, 77351. SAN 316-5736. Tel: 409-327-4252. FAX: 409-327-4162. *Librn*, Priscilla E Emrich
Pop 23,485; Circ 64,859
Library Holdings: Bk Vols 21,098; Bk Titles 17,286; Per Subs 71
Special Collections: World War I & World War II Aviation
Mem of Houston Area Library System
Friends of the Library Group

LANO

LLANO COUNTY LIBRARY SYSTEM,* 102 E Haynie, 78643. SAN 362-109X. Tel: 915-247-5248. FAX: 915-247-5531. E-Mail: lcl@moment.net. *Librn*, Dian Ray
Founded 1939. Pop 10,144; Circ 10,147,900
Oct 1996-Sep 1997 Income $228,552. Mats Exp $26,711, Books $25,368, Per/Ser (Incl. Access Fees) $1,015, Micro $27. Sal $152,419
Library Holdings: Bk Vols 50,857; Per Subs 32
Subject Interests: Genealogy
Mem of Central Texas Library System
Friends of the Library Group
Branches: 2
KINGSLAND BRANCH, Hwy 1431, PO Box 1809, Kingsland, 78639. SAN 362-112X. Tel: 915-388-3170. *Librn*, Pam Downing
Friends of the Library Group
LAKE SHORE, Lake Shore Dr, RTI Box 379A, Buchanan Dam, 78609. SAN 376-2297. *Dir*, Verna Dick

LOCKHART

P DR EUGENE CLARK LIBRARY, 217 S Main St, PO Box 209, 78644. SAN 316-5744. Tel: 512-398-3223. FAX: 512-376-2258. E-Mail: lockhart@jump.net. Web Site: www.library.ci.lockhart.tx.us. *Dir Libr Serv*, Rose Aleta Laurell
Pop 13,000; Circ 88,000
1999-2000 Income $704,021, City $184,342, Locally Generated Income $499,679, Other $20,000. Mats Exp $32,077, Books $25,374, Per/Ser (Incl. Access Fees) $6,626, Micro $77. (Prof $35,000)
Library Holdings: Bk Vols 26,100; Per Subs 130
Subject Interests: Texas
Special Collections: Dr Eugene Clark Special Coll; Lockhart Post-Register Coll
Automation Activity & Vendor Info: (Cataloging) Brodart
Mem of Central Texas Library System
Friends of the Library Group

LONGVIEW

S EASTMAN CHEMICAL CO, Texas Eastman Div,* PO Box 7444, 75607. SAN 316-5760. Tel: 903-237-5000, 903-237-6117. FAX: 903-237-6851. *Librn*, Donna Kesterson
Library Holdings: Bk Vols 15,000; Per Subs 200
Subject Interests: Chemical engineering, Chemistry

R FIRST BAPTIST CHURCH, John L Whorton Media Center Library, 209 E South, 75601. SAN 316-5779. Tel: 903-758-0681, Ext 143. FAX: 903-753-0936. Web Site: www.fbcl.org. *Dir*, Sandra K Trippett; E-Mail: sandy@mail.fbcl.org
Founded 1942
Library Holdings: Bk Vols 20,000; Per Subs 14
Subject Interests: Biblical, Inspirational
Open Mon-Thurs 9-12
Friends of the Library Group

M GOOD SHEPHERD MEDICAL CENTER, Medical Library, 700 E Marshall Ave, 75601. SAN 375-7676. Tel: 903-236-2165. FAX: 903-236-2034. E-Mail: kboyett@gsmc.org. Web Site: www.gsmc.org. *Librn*, Karen Boyett
Library Holdings: Bk Titles 75; Per Subs 12

CR LETOURNEAU UNIVERSITY, Margaret Estes Library, 2100 S Mobberly Ave, 75602-3524. (Mail add: PO Box 7001, 75607-7001), SAN 316-5787. Tel: 903-233-3264. Circulation Tel: 903-233-3268. Reference Tel: 903-233-3271. FAX: 903-233-3263. Web Site: www.letu.edu. *Admin Dir, Coll Develop*, Henry Whitlow; Tel: 903-233-3261, E-Mail: henrywhitlow@letu.edu; *Acq*, Scotteen Mae Estes; E-Mail: scoteenestes@letu.edu; *Circ*, Linda Price; E-Mail: lindaprice@letu.edu; *Media Spec*, Paula Jean Greer; Tel: 903-233-3278, E-Mail: paulagreer@letu.edu; *Ref*, Caroline Geer; E-Mail: carolinegeer@letu.edu; *Ref Servs YA*, Jean Mathews; E-Mail: jeanmathews@letu.edu; *Ref Servs YA*, Betty Sterrett; E-Mail: bettysterrett@letu.edu; *Tech Servs*, Melissa Watson; Tel: 903-233-3805, E-Mail: melissawatson@letu.edu; *Acq, Cat, Tech Servs*, Patti Coles; E-Mail: colesp@letu.edu. Subject Specialists: *Acquisitions*, Scotteen Mae Estes; *Audio*, Paula Jean Greer; *Budgeting*, Scotteen Mae Estes; *Reference*, Jean Mathews; *Reference*, Betty Sterrett; *Research*, Caroline Geer; *Secretarial*, Scotteen Mae Estes; *Video*, Paula Jean Greer; Staff 6 (MLS 6)
Founded 1946. Enrl 2,400; Fac 51; Highest Degree: Master
Jul 2000-Jun 2001 Income $270,000. Mats Exp $110,000, Books $25,000, Per/Ser (Incl. Access Fees) $30,000, AV Equip $5,000, Electronic Ref Mat (Incl. Access Fees) $50,000. Sal $167,611 (Prof $122,753)
Library Holdings: Bk Titles 101,342; Per Subs 1,157
Subject Interests: Aviation, Biblical studies, Engineering, Humanities, Technology
Special Collections: Abraham Lincoln; Billy Sunday Coll, bks, pictures, newsp; Harmon General Hospital Coll, rpts, newsp; Rare Afro Art & Native Antiques; Robert G LeTourneau Archives & Museum, bks, flm
Database Vendor: Dialog, Ebsco - EbscoHost, Lexis-Nexis, OCLC - First Search
Partic in Alliance For Higher Education; E Tex Consortium of Librs; Forest Trail Library Consortium, Inc; TexShare

P LONGVIEW PUBLIC LIBRARY, 222 W Cotton St, 75601-6348. SAN 362-1189. Tel: 903-237-1350. FAX: 903-237-1327. Web Site: www.longview.lib.tx.us. *Mgr*, Kara Spitz; Tel: 903-237-1340, E-Mail: kspitz@longview.lib.tx.us; *Tech Servs*, Catherine Beaird; Tel: 903-237-1356, Fax: 903-237-1343, E-Mail: cbea@longview.lib.tx.us; *Head, Circ*, Beverly Matthews; Tel: 903-237-1348, E-Mail: bmat53@longview.lib.tx.us; *Ad Servs*, Steve Horton; Tel: 903-237-1354, E-Mail: s_horton@longview.lib.tx.us; *ILL*, Susan Black; Tel: 903-237-1355, Fax: 903-237-1343, E-Mail: sblack@longview.lib.tx.us; Staff 34 (MLS 4, Non-MLS 30)
Founded 1932. Pop 112,110; Circ 240,936
Oct 1999-Sep 2000 Income $1,097,688, City $1,065,188, County $32,500. Mats Exp $145,306, Books $62,500, Per/Ser (Incl. Access Fees) $59,606, Micro $13,200, AV Equip $10,000. Sal $528,616 (Prof $174,000)
Library Holdings: Bk Vols 133,197; Bk Titles 107,709; Per Subs 364
Subject Interests: Genealogy, Texana
Special Collections: East Texas; Oil Field Production Records

Database Vendor: IAC - Info Trac, OCLC - First Search, ProQuest
Function: ILL available
Mem of Northeast Texas Library System
Partic in Forest Trail Library Consortium, Inc
Friends of the Library Group

S 73RD BOMB WING ASSOCIATION LIBRARY,* 1416 Parkview, 75601. SAN 372-9974. Tel: 903-758-5727. *Librn*, Lee Gillies
Library Holdings: Bk Vols 228

LOS FRESNOS

P ETHEL L WHIPPLE MEMORIAL LIBRARY, 402 W Ocean Blvd, 78566. SAN 316-5795. Tel: 956-233-5330. FAX: 956-233-3203. *Librn*, Ann Meyn
Pop 26,000
2000-2001 Income $143,929, City $113,585, County $16,000, Locally Generated Income $14,344. Mats Exp $27,900. Sal $86,722 (Prof $26,000)
Library Holdings: Bk Vols 30,000; Bk Titles 27,699
Automation Activity & Vendor Info: (Circulation) SIRSI; (OPAC) SIRSI
Mem of South Texas Library System
Friends of the Library Group

LUBBOCK

M COVENANT MEDICAL CENTER, Medical Library,* 3615 19th St, 79410. SAN 316-5825. Tel: 806-725-0602. FAX: 806-723-7363. *Dir*, Susan Warner; E-Mail: swarner@covhs.org; Staff 2 (MLS 1, Non-MLS 1)
Library Holdings: Bk Vols 5,500; Bk Titles 3,000; Per Subs 220
Subject Interests: Allied health, Medicine, Nursing
Partic in National Network Of Libraries Of Medicine - South Central Region

R FIRST CHRISTIAN CHURCH LIBRARY, 2323 Broadway, 79401. SAN 316-5809. Tel: 806-763-1995. FAX: 806-763-5904. Web Site: www.fcclubbock.org.
Founded 1948
Library Holdings: Bk Vols 4,950

M HIGHLAND MEDICAL CENTER, INC, Health Information Library,* 2412 50th St, 79412. SAN 324-220X. Tel: 806-788-4026. FAX: 806-788-4284.
Library Holdings: Bk Titles 400; Per Subs 32
Subject Interests: Medicine, Nursing

C LUBBOCK CHRISTIAN UNIVERSITY LIBRARY,* 5601 W 19th St, 79407-2009. SAN 316-5817. Tel: 806-796-8800, Ext 270. FAX: 806-796-8917. E-Mail: library@lcu.edu. Web Site: wwwlcu.edu/library.htm. *Dir*, Rebecca Vickers; *Assoc Librn*, Paula Gannaway; Staff 3 (MLS 3)
Founded 1957. Enrl 1,200; Fac 55; Highest Degree: Master
Jul 1998-Jun 1999 Income (Main Library Only) $170,000. Mats Exp $111,719, Books $36,000, Per/Ser (Incl. Access Fees) $55,000, Micro $10,719, Electronic Ref Mat (Incl. Access Fees) $10,000. Sal $94,000
Library Holdings: Bk Vols 108,000; Bk Titles 98,829; Per Subs 550
Subject Interests: Relig studies
Partic in Leian; TexShare

G LUBBOCK CITY COUNTY LIBRARY, 1306 Ninth St, 79401. SAN 362-1278. Tel: 806-775-2834. Interlibrary Loan Service Tel: 806-775-2857. FAX: 806-775-2827. Web Site: library.ci.lubbock.tx.us. *Dir*, Jeffrey A Rippel; Tel: 806-775-2822, E-Mail: jrippel@mail.ci.lubbock.tx.us; *Publ Servs*, Jane Clausen; *Materials Manager*, Pam Waller; *Br Coordr*, James Berry; Staff 16 (MLS 16)
Founded 1966. Pop 234,479
Oct 1999-Sep 2000 Income (Main Library and Branch Library) City $2,522,347. Mats Exp $362,280, Books $323,740, Per/Ser (Incl. Access Fees) $31,054, Presv $7,486. Sal $1,577,683 (Prof $622,227)
Library Holdings: Bk Vols 323,421; Bk Titles 183,176; Per Subs 528
Subject Interests: Genealogy
Automation Activity & Vendor Info: (Circulation) SIRSI; (OPAC) SIRSI; (Serials) SIRSI
Database Vendor: OCLC - First Search
Publications: Between the Stacks; Exploring New Worlds
Mem of West Texas Library System
Partic in Amigos Library Services, Inc; Tex State Libr Communications Network; Tex State Union List
Friends of the Library Group
Branches:
GODEKE, 6601 Quaker Ave, 79413. SAN 362-1308. Tel: 806-792-6566. FAX: 806-767-3762. Web Site: library.ci.lubbock.tx.us. *Mgr*, Terri Miller
Library Holdings: Bk Vols 69,364
Friends of the Library Group
GROVES, 5520 19th St, 79416. SAN 377-662X. Tel: 806-767-3733. FAX: 806-795-9641. *Br Coordr*, James Berry
Library Holdings: Bk Vols 33,078
TJ PATTERSON BRANCH, 1836 Parkway Dr, 79403. Tel: 806-767-3300. FAX: 806-767-3302. *Dir*, Barbara Painter; *Branch Mgr*, Barbara Moreno
Library Holdings: Bk Vols 32,238
Friends of the Library Group

CM TEXAS TECH UNIVERSITY, Library of the Health Sciences,* 3601 Fo St, 79430-0001. SAN 321-2432. Tel: 806-743-2203. FAX: 806-743-2218. E-Mail: hldir@ttacs.ttu.edu. Web Site: www.lib.ttuhsc.edu. *Dir*, Richard C Wood; Tel: 806-743-2203; *Publ Servs*, Candia Thew; *Acq*, Valinda Jacks *Tech Servs*, Joe Blackburn; *Circ*, Jeanett Hearn; *Tech Servs*, JoAnn VanSchaik; *Publ Servs*, Judy Orr; Staff 59 (MLS 19, Non-MLS 40)
Founded 1971. Enrl 1,547; Fac 516; Highest Degree: Doctorate
Sep 1997-Aug 1998 Income $2,994,609, State $2,864,406, Locally Generated Income $130,203. Mats Exp $1,481,615, Books $249,286, Per (Incl. Access Fees) $1,082,969, Other Print Mats $25,512, Electronic Ref Mat (Incl. Access Fees) $123,848. Sal $1,398,524 (Prof $763,625)
Library Holdings: Bk Vols 252,355; Bk Titles 63,680; Per Subs 2,100
Subject Interests: Allied health, Medicine, Nursing
Database Vendor: Ebsco - EbscoHost, GaleNet, OVID Technologies
Publications: Newsletter
Partic in Amigos Library Services, Inc; SCAMeL
Friends of the Library Group
Departmental Libraries:
EL PASO BRANCH, 4800 Alberta Ave, El Paso, 79905. SAN 316-3113. Tel: 915-545-6653. FAX: 915-545-6656. *Assoc Dir*, Teresa Knott; *Asst Dir*, Rebecca Arthaud
Founded 1976
Library Holdings: Bk Vols 27,487
Subject Interests: Medicine
Friends of the Library Group
ODESSA BRANCH, 800 W Fourth St, Odessa, 79763. SAN 322-5739. T 915-335-5130. FAX: 915-335-5170. *Assoc Dir*, Patricia McKeown; *Asst Dir*, Barbara Whaley
Friends of the Library Group

CL TEXAS TECH UNIVERSITY, School of Law Library, School of Law Bl Box 40004, 79409-0004. SAN 362-1456. Tel: 806-742-3794. Interlibrary Loan Service Tel: 806-742-3957. FAX: 806-742-1629. Web Site: www.law.ttu.edu/library/frmain.htm. *Coll Develop*, Arturo L Torres
Founded 1967
Library Holdings: Bk Vols 251,207
Subject Interests: Commercial law
Partic in Amigos Library Services, Inc; OCLC Online Computer Library Center, Inc; Westlaw

S TEXAS TECH UNIVERSITY LIBRARIES, International Textile Center, 1001 E Loop 289, 79403-6518. (Mail add: Box 45019, 79409-5019), SAN 323-4363. Tel: 806-747-3790. FAX: 806-747-3796. E-Mail: itc@ttu.edu. Web Site: www.itc.ttu.edu. *Coordr*, Pam Alspaugh
Founded 1969
Library Holdings: Bk Titles 200; Per Subs 20
Subject Interests: Cotton, Fibers, Mohair, Synthetic fibers, Textile, Wool
Restriction: Staff use only

C TEXAS TECH UNIVERSITY LIBRARIES, 18th & Boston, 79409-0002. SAN 362-1391. Tel: 806-742-2261. Circulation Tel: 806-742-2265. Reference Tel: 806-742-2236. Toll Free Tel: 888-270-3369. FAX: 806-742-0737. E-Mail: liedc@lib.ttu.edu. Web Site: www.lib.ttu.edu. *Dean*, Dale Cluff; Tel: 806-742-2261, Ext 262, E-Mail: liedc@lib.ttu.edu; *Assoc Dean*, Douglas Birdsall; Tel: 806-742-2261, Ext 240, E-Mail: lidgb@lib.ttu.edu; *Asst Dean*, Peter Kargbo; Tel: 806-742-2236, Ext 268, Fax: 806-742-1964, E-Mail: peter.kargbo@ttu.edu; *ILL*, Carol Roberts; *Acq*, Jan Kemp; *Cat*, Jayne Sappington; *Govt Doc, Ref*, Mary Ann Higdon; *Rare Bks*, Bruce Cammack; *Automation Syst Coordr*, Geri Hutchins; *Coll Develop*, Susan McGinnis. Subject Specialists: *Africa*, Peter Kargbo; Staff 57 (MLS 51, Non-MLS 6)
Founded 1923. Enrl 24,000; Fac 871; Highest Degree: Doctorate
Sep 1998-Aug 1999 Income (Main Library Only) $8,991,843. Mats Exp $4,328,071, Books $1,084,878, Per/Ser (Incl. Access Fees) $2,540,105, Micro $108,579, AV Equip $119,465, Other Print Mats $2,361, Electronic Ref Mat (Incl. Access Fees) $403,387. Sal $3,767,297
Library Holdings: Bk Vols 2,185,245; Per Subs 22,827
Special Collections: Archive of Turkish Oral Narrative; CNN World News Report Archive; Institute for Studies in Pragmaticism; Southwest Coll; Vietnam Archive
Automation Activity & Vendor Info: (Acquisitions) Innovative Interfaces Inc.; (Cataloging) DRA; (Serials) Innovative Interfaces Inc.
Database Vendor: DRA, GaleNet, Lexis-Nexis, OCLC - First Search, OVID Technologies, Silverplatter Information Inc., Wilson - Wilson Web
Publications: ACCESS (newsletter); Guides to Library Collections; Library News; Southwest Collection (newsletter); Texas Tech University Library
Function: Research library
Partic in Amigos Library Services, Inc; Big Twelve Plus Libr Consortium; TexShare
Departmental Libraries:
SOUTHWEST COLLECTION SPECIAL COLLECTIONS LIBRARY Tel: 806-742-3676. FAX: 806-742-0496. Web Site: www.ttu.edu/~swcoll.
1997-1998 Income $811,861. Mats Exp $43,709, Books $32,923, Per/Ser (Incl. Access Fees) $4,686, Presv $2,862, Micro $2,608. Sal $531,271 (Prof $287,693)
Subject Interests: Agriculture, Education, Land colonization, Mining, Oi

Politics, Railroads, Ranching, Urban develop, Water
Special Collections: Archive of the Vietnam Conflict Coll; Rare Book Coll; Turkish Oral History Coll
Friends of the Library Group

WEST TEXAS LIBRARY SYSTEM, 1306 Ninth St, 79401-2798. SAN 316-5833. Tel: 806-775-2858. Toll Free Tel: 800-848-3146. FAX: 806-775-2856. Web Site: wtls.lib.tx.us. *Coordr*, Nancy W Hill; Tel: 806-775-2854, E-Mail: nhill@mail.ci.lubbock.tx.us; Staff 2 (MLS 2)
Founded 1969. Pop 704,540
Sep 2000-Aug 2001 Income State $419,697. Mats Exp Books $162,058. Sal $178,234 (Prof $78,977)
Library Holdings: Bk Vols 2,300
Publications: In The Wind (newsletter)
Member Libraries: Abernathy Public Library; Andrews County Library; City County Library; City Of Wolfforth Library; Cochran County Love Memorial Library; Crane County Library; Crosby County Library; Dawson County Library; Dickens County-Spur Public Library; Ector County Library; Floyd County Library; Gaines County Library; Hale Center Public Library; Hockley County Memorial Library; Idalou Public Library; Kendrick Memorial Library; King County Public Library; Lamb County Library; Lubbock City County Library; Martin County Library; Midland County Public Library; Motley County Library; Muleshoe Area Public Library; Post Public Library; Rankin Public Library; Slaton Public Library; Unger Memorial Library; Upton County Public Library; Ward County Library; Winkler County Library; Yoakum County Library; Yoakum County Library
Partic in OCLC Online Computer Library Center, Inc

UFKIN

ANGELINA COLLEGE LIBRARY, 3500 S First St, 75901-7328. (Mail add: PO Box 1768, 75902-1768), SAN 316-5841. Tel: 936-633-5219. FAX: 936-639-4299. Web Site: angelina.cc.tx.us. *Dir*, Dennis Read; Tel: 936-633-5219, Ext 217, E-Mail: dread@angelina.tx.us; *AV*, Janet Avery-Sublett; Tel: 936-633-5219, Ext 242, E-Mail: jsublett@angelina.cc.tx.us; *Tech Servs*, Barbara Fair; Tel: 936-633-5332, E-Mail: bfair@angelina.cc.tx.us; *Tech Servs*, Candace Powell; Tel: 936-633-5218, E-Mail: cpowell@angelina.cc.tx.us; Staff 4 (MLS 3, Non-MLS 1)
Founded 1968
Library Holdings: Bk Titles 38,641; Per Subs 193
Automation Activity & Vendor Info: (Acquisitions) SIRSI; (Cataloging) SIRSI; (Circulation) SIRSI; (Course Reserve) SIRSI; (ILL) SIRSI; (Media Booking) SIRSI
Partic in Forest Trail Library Consortium, Inc

FIRST UNITED METHODIST CHURCH LIBRARY, 805 E Denman Ave, 75901. SAN 328-6142. Tel: 936-639-3141. FAX: 936-639-3667. E-Mail: iheer@lufkinfumc.org. Web Site: www.lufkinfumc.org. *Librn*, Ila Heermans
Library Holdings: Bk Vols 7,000
Subject Interests: Audio bks, Religion, Religious bks, Videos
Friends of the Library Group

KURTH MEMORIAL LIBRARY, (KML), 706 S Raguet, 75904. SAN 316-585X. Tel: 936-634-7617. FAX: 936-639-2487. Web Site: kurthmemoriallibrary.com. *Ref*, Carmen Little; *Ch Servs*, Mary Grider. Subject Specialists: *Genealogy*, Cindy McMullen; Staff 4 (MLS 2, Non-MLS 2)
Founded 1932. Pop 70,000; Circ 74,413
Library Holdings: Bk Vols 43,261; Per Subs 130
Subject Interests: Genealogy, Large print, Local history
Automation Activity & Vendor Info: (Cataloging) Sagebrush Corporation; (Circulation) Sagebrush Corporation
Mem of Houston Area Library System
Partic in Forest Trail Library Consortium, Inc
Open Mon-Thur 9-8, Fri 9-5:30, Sat 9-1
Friends of the Library Group

G TEXAS FOREST SERVICE, Texas Forest Products Laboratory Library,* Hwy 59 S, PO Box 310, 75902-0310. SAN 316-5876. Tel: 409-639-8180. FAX: 409-639-8185. *Librn*, Susan Shockley; E-Mail: sshockley@inu.net; Staff 2 (MLS 1, Non-MLS 1)
Founded 1930
Library Holdings: Bk Titles 800; Per Subs 40
Subject Interests: Forest products

LULING

R FIRST BAPTIST CHURCH, EF Walker Memorial Library, PO Box 90, 78648. SAN 316-5884. Tel: 830-875-2227. Toll Free Tel: 800-846-7650. *Librn*, Lucille Matthews
Founded 1957
Library Holdings: Bk Vols 5,000

P LULING PUBLIC LIBRARY,* 215 S Pecan St, 78648. SAN 316-5892. Tel: 830-875-2813. *Librn*, Nancy Gilchrist; *Asst Librn*, Lisa Koenig
Founded 1969. Pop 4,000; Circ 38,380
Library Holdings: Bk Titles 25,000; Per Subs 17
Subject Interests: Texas
Mem of Central Texas Library System

LUMBERTON

P LUMBERTON PUBLIC LIBRARY, (LPL), 130 E Chance Cut-Off, 77657. SAN 376-4885. Tel: 409-755-7400. FAX: 409-755-6015. E-Mail: lplibrary@mailcity.com. Web Site: www.cityoflumberton.com. *Librn*, Catherine Wallis; Staff 1 (MLS 1)
Founded 1994. Circ 4,000
Library Holdings: Bk Vols 15,000; Per Subs 50
Mem of Houston Area Library System
Friends of the Library Group

LYTLE

P LYTLE PUBLIC LIBRARY,* 19325 Farm Rd, No 2790, PO Box 841, 78052. SAN 376-415X. Tel: 830-772-3142. FAX: 830-772-3675. Web Site: www.lytle_texas.org.
Library Holdings: Bk Vols 10,000
Mem of Alamo Area Library System
Friends of the Library Group

MABANK

P TRI-COUNTY LIBRARY, 132 E Market St, 75147-2307. (Mail add: PO Box 1770, 75147-1770), SAN 376-4389. Tel: 903-887-9622. *Dir*, Christine Davis
Founded 1991
Library Holdings: Bk Titles 1,600; Per Subs 25
Automation Activity & Vendor Info: (Acquisitions) Athena; (Cataloging) Athena; (Circulation) Athena
Mem of Northeast Texas Library System
Friends of the Library Group

MADISONVILLE

P MADISON COUNTY LIBRARY,* 605 S May, 77864. SAN 316-599X. Tel: 409-348-6118. E-Mail: mclib@lcc.net. *Librn*, Lynda Breeding
Pop 10,000; Circ 25,375
Library Holdings: Bk Vols 36,000; Per Subs 38
Mem of Central Texas Library System

MALAKOFF

P RED WALLER COMMUNITY LIBRARY,* 109 Mitcham St, PO Box 1177, 75148-1177. SAN 316-6007. Tel: 903-489-1818. FAX: 903-489-2517. *Coll Develop, Librn*, Peggy Julian; E-Mail: pjulian@airmail.net
Founded 1972. Pop 10,500
Oct 1996-Sep 1997 Income $23,560, City $17,014, County $5,000, Locally Generated Income $1,546. Mats Exp Books $2,431. Sal $15,305
Library Holdings: Bk Vols 28,500; Bk Titles 28,408; Per Subs 40
Special Collections: Bicentennial Package (American Issues Forum Coll); Malakoff History Coll
Publications: Library Journal
Mem of Northeast Texas Library System
Friends of the Library Group

MANSFIELD

P MANSFIELD PUBLIC LIBRARY,* 110 S Main St, 76063-3101. SAN 316-6015. Tel: 817-473-4391. FAX: 817-473-6913. *Dir*, Steven R Standefer; *Asst Dir*, Sue Owens; *Cat*, Marilyn Zaruba; *Circ*, Mollie Wiginton
Pop 27,000; Circ 80,000
Oct 1996-Sep 1997 Income $254,700, State $4,700, City $250,000. Mats Exp $59,025, Books $48,000, Per/Ser (Incl. Access Fees) $7,000, Micro $1,025. Sal $163,000
Library Holdings: Bk Vols 45,000
Mem of North Texas Regional Library System
Friends of the Library Group

MARFA

P MARFA PUBLIC LIBRARY,* 115 E Oak St, PO Drawer U, 79843-0609. SAN 316-6023. Tel: 915-729-4631. FAX: 915-729-3424. *Librn*, Ester F Sanchez; *Asst Librn*, Natalia Williams
Founded 1947. Pop 2,503; Circ 31,514
Oct 1997-Sep 1998 Income $52,758, City $52,758. Mats Exp $2,011, Books $915, Per/Ser (Incl. Access Fees) $352. Sal $44,703
Library Holdings: Bk Titles 30,453; Per Subs 32
Mem of Texas Trans Pecos Library System
Friends of the Library Group

MARION

P MARION COMMUNITY LIBRARY,* 500 Bulldog Blvd, PO Box 619, 78124-0619. SAN 376-4133. Tel: 830-914-4268, Ext 269. FAX: 830-914-2524. *Librn*, Kathy Waller
Library Holdings: Bk Vols 14,000; Per Subs 80
Mem of Alamo Area Library System
Friends of the Library Group

MARLIN

S DEPARTMENT OF VETERANS AFFAIRS MEDICAL CENTER, Library Service, 1016 Ward St, 76661. SAN 316-6058. Tel: 254-883-3511, Ext 4314. FAX: 254-883-9242.; Staff 1 (MLS 1)
Founded 1950
Library Holdings: Bk Titles 2,000; Per Subs 20
Subject Interests: Hospital administration, Internal medicine, Nursing
Restriction: Open to department staff only
Partic in Vets Admin Libr Network

P MARLIN PUBLIC LIBRARY, 301 Winter St, 76661. SAN 316-6031. Tel: 254-883-6602. *Librn*, Carolyn Contella; Staff 2 (Non-MLS 2)
Founded 1925. Pop 7,099; Circ 13,819
Oct 1999-Sep 2000 Income $26,000, City $21,000. Mats Exp $9,662, Books $8,962, Per/Ser (Incl. Access Fees) $700. Sal $12,000 (Prof $10,000)
Library Holdings: Bk Vols 13,796; Bk Titles 13,000; Per Subs 12
Mem of Central Texas Library System

MARSHALL

C EAST TEXAS BAPTIST UNIVERSITY LIBRARY,* 1209 N Grove, 75670-1498. SAN 316-6066. Tel: 903-935-7963, Ext 322. FAX: 903-935-3447. *Coll Develop, Librn*, Rose Mary Magrill; E-Mail: rmagrill@etbu.edu; *Ref*, Dorothy Meadows; E-Mail: dmeadows@etbu.edu; Staff 8 (MLS 3, Non-MLS 5)
Founded 1917. Enrl 1,350; Fac 99; Highest Degree: Bachelor
Jun 1999-May 2000 Income $559,341. Mats Exp $214,407, Books $91,970, Per/Ser (Incl. Access Fees) $95,870, Presv $4,010, Electronic Ref Mat (Incl. Access Fees) $22,557. Sal $226,475
Library Holdings: Bk Vols 114,921; Per Subs 664
Special Collections: Cope Coll of Texana; East Texas Ante-Bellum History; Lentz Coll of Texana
Automation Activity & Vendor Info: (Cataloging) DRA; (Circulation) DRA; (OPAC) DRA
Restriction: Open to faculty, students & qualified researchers
Partic in Amigos Library Services, Inc

S HARRISON COUNTY HISTORICAL MUSEUM LIBRARY,* PO Box1987, Peter Whetstone Sq, 75670. SAN 327-7992. Tel: 903-938-2680. FAX: 903-935-4379. E-Mail: museum@shreve.net. Web Site: www.rootsweb.com/~txharris/harrison/htm. *In Charge*, Martha Robb
Library Holdings: Bk Vols 3,000; Bk Titles 2,500
Subject Interests: Civil War, Genealogy, History, Law, Medicine
Special Collections: Census Records; High School Yearbooks; Marshall Telephone Books & City Directories; Pictures; Scrapbooks
Friends of the Library Group

P MARSHALL PUBLIC LIBRARY,* 300 S Alamo Blvd, 75670. SAN 316-6082. Tel: 903-935-4465. FAX: 903-935-4463. *Dir*, Patsy Harmon
Founded 1970. Pop 58,000; Circ 136,000
Jan 1997-Dec 1998 Income $290,668, City $236,206, County $28,000, Other $20,736. Mats Exp $43,434, Books $35,853, Per/Ser (Incl. Access Fees) $7,581. Sal $130,989 (Prof $54,000)
Library Holdings: Bk Vols 67,244; Per Subs 115
Special Collections: Music, tapes
Mem of Northeast Texas Library System
Partic in Forest Trail Library Consortium, Inc
Friends of the Library Group

C WILEY COLLEGE, Thomas Winston Cole, Sr Library,* 711 Wiley Ave, 75670-5151. SAN 316-6090. Tel: 903-927-3275. FAX: 903-934-9333. *Dir*, Frank Francis, Jr; E-Mail: ffrancis@wileynrts.wileyc.edu; *Asst Dir, Tech Servs*, Karen Mayfield-Hale; *Circ, Ref*, Jacqueline Read; Staff 5 (MLS 3, Non-MLS 2)
Founded 1873. Highest Degree: Bachelor
Library Holdings: Bk Vols 85,000; Per Subs 322
Special Collections: Black Studies (Schomburg Coll of Negro Literature & History), portion of the print coll on microfilm; Wiley College Memorabilia
Partic in Coop Col Libr Ctr, Inc

MASON

P MASON COUNTY, M Beven Eckert Memorial Library, 410 Post Hill, PO Drawer 780, 76856. SAN 316-6104. Tel: 915-347-5446. FAX: 915-347-6562. *Librn*, Mary Cockrell
Pop 3,356; Circ 9,884
Library Holdings: Bk Vols 10,000; Per Subs 10
Automation Activity & Vendor Info: (Cataloging) Sagebrush Corporatic (Circulation) Sagebrush Corporation
Mem of Big Country Library System
Friends of the Library Group

MATADOR

P MOTLEY COUNTY LIBRARY, 1105 Main St, 79244. (Mail add: PO Bc 557, 79244-0557), SAN 325-2922. Tel: 806-347-2717. E-Mail: biblio@caprock-spur.com. *Librn*, Suzanne Abbott
Founded 1981. Pop 1,523; Circ 4,711
Library Holdings: Bk Vols 10,583; Bk Titles 9,613
Subject Interests: Genealogy, Tex hist
Mem of West Texas Library System
Special Services for the Deaf - Books on deafness & sign language; High interest/low vocabulary books
Friends of the Library Group

MATHIS

P MATHIS PUBLIC LIBRARY,* 103 Lamar St, 78368. SAN 316-6112. Te 512-547-6201. FAX: 512-547-6201. *Librn*, Alice Bruton
Pop 5,000; Circ 8,679
Library Holdings: Bk Vols 11,000; Bk Titles 9,000
Mem of South Texas Library System
Friends of the Library Group

MAUD

P MAUD PUBLIC LIBRARY,* 134 Main St, PO Box 388, 75567-0388. SA 376-4524. Tel: 903-585-5255. FAX: 903-585-2752. *Librn*, Evelyn Horton; E-Mail: maudhorton@txk.net
Library Holdings: Bk Vols 15,000
Mem of Northeast Texas Library System
Friends of the Library Group

MC ALLEN

R FIRST BAPTIST CHURCH LIBRARY, 1200 Beech Ave, 78501. SAN 31 5914. Tel: 956-686-7418. FAX: 956-630-4940. E-Mail: fbcmcallen@cs.com Web Site: www.fbcmcallen.com. *Librn*, Mrs Hans Wells
Library Holdings: Bk Vols 6,700
Subject Interests: Biog, Children's mat, Fiction, Religion

P HIDALGO COUNTY LIBRARY SYSTEM,* 4305 N Tenth St, Ste E, 78504-3095. SAN 316-5922. Tel: 956-682-6397. FAX: 956-682-6398. Web Site: www.hcls.lib.tx.us. *Coordr*, William H J McGee; E-Mail: bill.mcgee@hcls.lib.tx.us; Staff 5 (MLS 2, Non-MLS 3)
Founded 1972. Pop 506,919
Jan 1998-Dec 1998 Income County $420,412. Mats Exp $65,000, Books $64,000, Per/Ser (Incl. Access Fees) $1,000. Sal $130,237 (Prof $85,568)
Library Holdings: Bk Vols 215; Bk Titles 190; Per Subs 12
Member Libraries: Weslaco Public Library
Associate members: Donna High School, McAllen High School, McAllen International Museum, Memorial High School, Mission High School, Weslaco High School, Nikke Rowe High School, South Texas High School, South Texas Community College

S MCALLEN INTERNATIONAL MUSEUM, Rosita C Alcorn Library, 1900 Nolana, 78504. SAN 325-4550. Tel: 956-682-1564. FAX: 956-686-1813. E-Mail: mim@hiline.net. Web Site: www.mcallenmuseum.org. *Acq, Curator*, Vernon Weckbacher; Staff 2 (MLS 2)
Founded 1979
Library Holdings: Bk Titles 2,600
Special Collections: Mexican Folk Art Culture (Rosita C Alcorn Coll), bks & pamphlets

P MCALLEN MEMORIAL LIBRARY, 601 N Main St, 78501-4666. SAN 316-5930. Tel: 956-682-4531. FAX: 956-682-1183. Web Site: www.mcallen.lib.tx.us. *Dir*, Gerard E Mittelstaedt; E-Mail: mittelst@mcallen.lib.tx.us; *Asst Dir*, Margaret Handrow; *Media Spec*, Judy Mitchell; *Acq*, Rosie Sanchez; *Cat*, Agnete Liu; *Circ*, John J Donohue; *Ch Servs*, E Beverly Kadhim; *Ref Serv*, Christine Reynolds; *AV*, Judy Perry; *ILL*, Nancy Davis; Staff 15 (MLS 12, Non-MLS 3)
Founded 1932. Pop 160,000; Circ 614,979
Library Holdings: Bk Vols 286,445; Bk Titles 252,244; Per Subs 883
Special Collections: Genealogy; Mexican-American Coll; Mexico; Spanish (Libros en Espanol); Texas
Publications: Beginnings - A First Course in Spanish
Mem of South Texas Library System
Partic in OCLC Online Computer Library Center, Inc
Special Services for the Blind - Kurzweil Reading Machine
Friends of the Library Group

Branches: 2
LARK, 2601 Lark Ave, McAllen, 78504. Tel: 956-972-7960. FAX: 956-972-7966. Web Site: www.mcallen.lib.tx.us/lark/lark.htm. *Branch Mgr*, Jose Gamez
Founded 2001
Library Holdings: Bk Vols 7,500
PALM VIEW, 3401 Jordan Ave, McAllen, 78503. Tel: 956-972-7980. FAX: 956-972-7987. Web Site: www.mcallen.lib.tx.us/palm/palm.htm. *Branch Mgr*, Kathryn Spangle
Founded 2001
Library Holdings: Bk Vols 11,000

SOUTH TEXAS COMMUNITY COLLEGE LIBRARY,* 3201 W Pecan Blvd, 78501-6661. SAN 325-0687. Tel: 956-618-8330. FAX: 956-618-8398. Web Site: www.stcc.cc.tx.us/lrc/library/libfront.html. *Dir*, Armandina A Sesin; E-Mail: sesin@stcc.cc.tx.us; *Tech Servs*, Janet Garcia; *ILL*, Noelia Gomez; Staff 2 (MLS 2)
Founded 1984
Sep 1997-Aug 1998 Income $363,737. Mats Exp $163,546, Books $138,161, Per/Ser (Incl. Access Fees) $8,817. Sal $110,612 (Prof $38,964)
Library Holdings: Bk Vols 36,000; Bk Titles 31,000; Per Subs 300
Partic in Paisano Consortium

MC CAMEY

UPTON COUNTY PUBLIC LIBRARY,* 212 W Seventh St, PO Drawer L, 79752-1112. SAN 316-5949. Tel: 915-652-8718. FAX: 915-652-3858. *Dir*, Mary Glenn
Founded 1939. Pop 2,650; Circ 22,770
Library Holdings: Bk Vols 16,500; Per Subs 18
Special Collections: Texana Coll
Mem of Lubbock Area Libr Syst; West Texas Library System

MC GREGOR

MCGINLEY MEMORIAL PUBLIC LIBRARY, 317 S Main St, 76657. SAN 372-7599. Tel: 254-840-3732. FAX: 254-840-2624. E-Mail: maclib1@aol.com. *Librn*, Betty Crelia; Staff 1 (Non-MLS 1)
Founded 1983. Pop 5,000; Circ 8,000
Library Holdings: Bk Vols 14,000; Bk Titles 13,500; Per Subs 15
Special Collections: Records (Arthur Fiedler Coll)
Mem of Central Texas Library System
Special Services for the Deaf - Books on deafness & sign language; Special interest periodicals
Friends of the Library Group

MC KINNEY

COLLIN COUNTY LAW LIBRARY,* Courthouse, Ste 203, 210 S McDonald St, 75069. SAN 372-1671. Tel: 972-548-4255. FAX: 972-547-5734, 972-548-4568. E-Mail: lawlib@co.collin.tx.us. Web Site: www.texasjudge.com. *Librn*, Judith A McCullough; *Asst Librn*, Chris Schell
Oct 1998-Sep 1999 Income $150,000. Mats Exp $85,000. Sal $73,000
Library Holdings: Bk Vols 25,000; Per Subs 15

MC KINNEY MEMORIAL PUBLIC LIBRARY, 220 N Kentucky St, 75069. SAN 316-5973. Tel: 972-547-7323. FAX: 972-542-0868. *Dir*, Susan Compton; E-Mail: scompton@mckinneytexas.org; *Librn*, John Schanot; *Librn*, Penny Trosper; *Publ Servs*, Lisa Bailey; *Ch Servs*, Gayle Travis
Founded 1928. Pop 50,000; Circ 240,000
Oct 1998-Sep 1999 Income City $913,000. Mats Exp $103,000. Sal $532,000 (Prof $38,000)
Library Holdings: Bk Vols 55,447
Subject Interests: Genealogy, Texana
Partic in Northeast Texas Library System
Friends of the Library Group

NORTH TEXAS JOB CORPS, Media Center, 1701 N Church St, PO Box 8003, 75069. SAN 371-4195. Tel: 972-542-2623, Ext 185. FAX: 972-547-0174. E-Mail: kilpatl@northtexas.ntex. Web Site: www.jobcorp.com. *Dir*, Joseph Henry Oatis, Jr; *Mgr*, Dr Kilpatrick Leon. Subject Specialists: *Education*, Dr Kilpatrick Leon

RAYTHEON, INC, McKinney Technical Library,* 2501 W University, 75070. SAN 370-0070. Tel: 972-952-2680. FAX: 972-952-2525. *Asst Librn*, Carolyn Stiltz; Staff 2 (MLS 1, Non-MLS 1)

MC LEAN

LOVETT MEMORIAL LIBRARY, 302 N Main, PO Box 8, 79057-0008. SAN 316-5981. Tel: 806-779-2851. FAX: 806-779-3241. *Librn*, Ellen Malone; E-Mail: emalone1@visto.com; Staff 1 (Non-MLS 1)
Founded 1957. Pop 1,387; Circ 19,929
Library Holdings: Bk Titles 13,160
Mem of Texas Panhandle Library System
Partic in Harrington Library Consortium

MELISSA

P MELISSA PUBLIC LIBRARY,* 1713 Cooper St, PO Box 325, 75454. SAN 376-4532. Tel: 972-837-4540. FAX: 972-837-4540. *Librn*, Jan Clark; E-Mail: jan_clark@hotmail.com
Library Holdings: Bk Vols 10,500
Mem of Northeast Texas Library System
Friends of the Library Group

MEMPHIS

P MEMPHIS PUBLIC LIBRARY, 303 S Eight St, 79245. SAN 316-6120. Tel: 806-259-2062. FAX: 806-259-2062. *Librn*, Sue Gardenhire
Pop 5,594; Circ 18,500
Library Holdings: Bk Vols 20,300; Per Subs 30
Mem of Texas Panhandle Library System

MENARD

P MENARD PUBLIC LIBRARY,* 100 E Mission, PO Box 404, 76859-0404. SAN 316-6139. Tel: 915-396-2717. *Librn*, Tommye Phillips
Pop 2,252; Circ 13,333
Library Holdings: Bk Vols 13,303
Mem of Big Country Library System

MERCEDES

P MERCEDES MEMORIAL LIBRARY,* 434 S Ohio, 78570. SAN 316-6147. Tel: 956-565-2371. FAX: 956-565-9458. *Librn*, Maria Elena Reyna; *Asst Librn*, Socorro Gracia; Staff 1 (MLS 1)
Founded 1940. Pop 11,851; Circ 54,887
Library Holdings: Bk Vols 32,293; Per Subs 85
Subject Interests: Spanish lang, Texas
Mem of South Texas Library System
Friends of the Library Group

MERTZON

P IRION COUNTY LIBRARY, Fayette & First, PO Box 766, 76941. SAN 376-4044. Tel: 915-835-2704. FAX: 915-835-2008. *Librn*, T K Hampton
Library Holdings: Bk Vols 8,000
Mem of Big Country Library System

MESQUITE

J EASTFIELD COLLEGE, Eastfield Learning Resource Center,* 3737 Motley Dr, 75150-2033. SAN 316-6163. Tel: 972-860-7168. Interlibrary Loan Service Tel: 972-860-7174. FAX: 972-860-8537. Web Site: www.efc.dcccd.edu. *Dean*, Emma Cronin; *Asst Librn*, Mary Ann Bennett; *ILL*, Ron Rollinson; *Coll Develop*, Karla Greer; E-Mail: karla_greer@dcccd.edu; Staff 27 (MLS 4, Non-MLS 23)
Founded 1970. Enrl 9,346; Fac 140
Library Holdings: Bk Vols 52,108; Per Subs 535
Special Collections: Jazz (Don Ellis Coll)
Part of Dallas County Community College District
Departmental Libraries:
TECHNICAL SERVICES CENTER, 4343 N Hwy 67, 75150-2095. SAN 324-2102. Tel: 972-860-7788. FAX: 972-860-7945. *Dir*, Paul E Dumont
Serves as a material processing center for all Dallas County Community College District libraries

P MESQUITE PUBLIC LIBRARY,* 300 W Grubb Dr, 75149. SAN 316-6171. Tel: 972-216-6220. FAX: 972-216-6740. E-Mail: mainbr@library.mesquite.tx.us. Web Site: www.library.mesquite.tx.us. *Dir*, John Williams; *ILL*, Ed Odom; *Ch Servs*, Chris Tillery; *Ch Servs*, Susan Harding; *Media Spec*, Nancy Watson; *Tech Servs*, Jeannie Johnson; *Br Coordr*, Jane Brown; *Publ Servs*, John Spinks; Staff 17 (MLS 9, Non-MLS 8)
Founded 1963. Pop 119,350; Circ 402,964
Oct 1998-Sep 1999 Income (Main Library and Branch Library) $1,690,939, City $1,651,770, Federal $30,571, Other $8,598. Mats Exp $186,411, Books $120,571, Per/Ser (Incl. Access Fees) $65,840. Sal $1,290,420
Library Holdings: Bk Vols 138,585; Bk Titles 103,939; Per Subs 343
Subject Interests: Genealogy
Mem of Northeast Texas Library System
Friends of the Library Group
Branches: 1
NORTH BRANCH, 2600 Oates Dr, 75150. SAN 328-7556. Tel: 972-681-0465. FAX: 972-613-7848. Web Site: www.northbr.library.mesquite.tx.us. *Br Coordr*, Jane Brown; *Ch Servs*, Susan Harding
Mem of Northeast Texas Library System
Friends of the Library Group

S TYCO ELECTRONICS, (Formerly Lucent Technologies), Power Systems Library, 3000 Skyline Dr, Rm 740, 75149. SAN 373-6091. Tel: 972-284-2000.

Library Holdings: Bk Titles 4,000; Per Subs 100
Subject Interests: Electronics
Publications: Power Supplies
Friends of the Library Group

MEXIA

P GIBBS MEMORIAL LIBRARY, 305 E Rusk St, 76667-2398. SAN 316-618X. Tel: 254-562-3231. FAX: 254-562-0828. Web Site: www.gibbslibrary.com. *Librn*, Carla Wilkins; E-Mail: cwilkins@gibbslibrary.com
Founded 1903. Pop 13,702; Circ 43,000
1999-2000 Income $220,000. Mats Exp $16,000, Books $15,000, Per/Ser (Incl. Access Fees) $1,000. Sal $68,000 (Prof $24,000)
Library Holdings: Bk Vols 32,500; Per Subs 60
Subject Interests: Genealogy, Local history
Special Collections: Genealogy; War of the Rebellion
Automation Activity & Vendor Info: (Cataloging) SIRSI; (Circulation) SIRSI
Mem of Central Texas Library System
Friends of the Library Group

MIAMI

P ROBERTS COUNTY LIBRARY,* PO Box 98, 79059. SAN 316-6198. Tel: 806-868-4791. *Librn*, Inez Benge
Pop 2,081; Circ 6,465
Library Holdings: Bk Vols 13,058

MIDLAND

P HALEY LIBRARY & HISTORY CENTER, Nita Stewart Haley Memorial Library, 1805 W Indiana, 79701. SAN 324-5195. Tel: 915-682-5785. FAX: 915-685-3512. Web Site: www.haley.library.com. *Librn*, Nancy Jordan; *Cat*, Norma Thurman; *Archivist*, Jim Bradshaw; Staff 3 (MLS 1, Non-MLS 2)
Founded 1976
Library Holdings: Bk Vols 24,000
Subject Interests: Cowboys, Exploration, Indust, Railroads, Ranch hist, Rodeos, Tex Indians, Tex lawmen, Tex mil, Texana, Western Americana, Western art
Special Collections: Arizona, California & N Mexico History; religion; world travel (overland & ocean); Indian wars, Native American culture, archeology; US territorial expansion (Dan L Thrapp Coll), orig files, photogs, bks; Journals & Historical Magazines for research (300 titles); Maps (500); New Mexico & El Paso History; Southwest Settlement (Robt N Mullin Coll), orig files, photogs, bks; Ranching, Cattle & Texas History (J Evetts Haley Coll), orig files, interviews, diaries, photogs; SW Texas frontier life, natural history, US military history & world travel; literary classics (Clayton W Williams Coll), orig files & books of CWW, OWW & JCW; Texas Pandle, Horses, Ranches, Buffalo & Wildlife (Harold D Bugbee Coll), orig art, files, bks; Texas Range Life & Working Cowboys (Erwin E Smith Coll), photogs, negs, bks
Automation Activity & Vendor Info: (Cataloging) Sagebrush Corporation
Publications: Haley Library Newsletter
Restriction: Open to public for reference only

J MIDLAND COLLEGE, Murray Fasken Learning Resource Center,* 3600 N Garfield, 79705. SAN 316-621X. Tel: 915-685-4557, 915-685-4560. FAX: 915-685-4721. Web Site: www.midland.cc.tx.us. *Dir*, John Deats; E-Mail: jdeats@midland.cc.tx.us; *Tech Servs*, Ellen Fino; *Automation Syst Coordr, Tech Servs*, Cecilia Miranda; *Librn*, Dan Buckley; *Media Spec*, Carlota Kellog; *Media Spec*, J Don Wallace; *Per*, Joan Williams; *Circ*, Emma King; *Publ Servs*, Aline Collins; Staff 4 (MLS 4)
Founded 1973. Enrl 4,600; Fac 185
Sep 1997-Aug 1998 Income $457,393. Mats Exp $84,624, Books $43,750, Per/Ser (Incl. Access Fees) $31,701, Presv $283, Micro $8,890. Sal $428,479
Library Holdings: Bk Vols 58,450; Bk Titles 46,000; Per Subs 311
Subject Interests: Health sci libr, Law
Publications: LRC Bulletin (semi-annual); New Acquisitions Lists
Partic in Llano Estacado Info Access Network

P MIDLAND COUNTY PUBLIC LIBRARY, 301 W Missouri, 79701. SAN 316-6228. Tel: 915-688-8991. FAX: 915-688-8996. E-Mail: reference@co.midland.tx.us/. Web Site: www.co.midland.tx.us/mcpl/library.htm. *Dir*, E Denise Johnson; E-Mail: denise_johnson@co.midland.tx.us; *Asst Dir*, J'Nevelyn White; E-Mail: white@co.midland.tx.us; *Acq, Asst Dir, Coll Develop*, Constance Roe; *Head Ref*, Debbie Wolfe; E-Mail: reference@co.midland.tx.us; *Br Coordr*, Jo Ann Clark; *ILL*, Kathy Alexander; E-Mail: alexanderk@co.midland.tx.us; *Ch Servs*, Barbara Davis; E-Mail: barbara_davis@co.midland.tx.us; *AV*, Barbara Edson; E-Mail: edson@co.midland.tx.us; *Tech Servs*, Beverly Wise; E-Mail: wise@co.midland.tx.us; *Spec Coll*, Rebecca Britton; E-Mail: britton@co.midland.tx.us; *Per*, Carole Hayter; E-Mail: periodicals@co.midland.tx.us; *Circ*, Sharon Beman; E-Mail: beman@co.midland.tx.us; Staff 41 (MLS 6, Non-MLS 35)
Founded 1903. Pop 117,000
Oct 1999-Sep 2000 Income (Main Library and Branch Library) County $1,188,445. Mats Exp $166,695, Books $124,000, Per/Ser (Incl. Access Fees) $25,250, AV Equip $17,445. Sal $923,858
Library Holdings: Bk Vols 240,000; Per Subs 675
Subject Interests: Genealogy, Petroleum
Database Vendor: Ebsco - EbscoHost, OCLC - First Search, Silverplatte Information Inc.
Publications: Friends of the Library Newsletter (semi-annual)
Mem of West Texas Library System
Partic in OCLC Online Computer Library Center, Inc
Friends of the Library Group
Branches: 1
MIDLAND CENTENNIAL, Midland Park Mall, 4511 Midkiff, 79707-32(SAN 370-4998. Tel: 915-697-8113. E-Mail: mcplbr@apex2000.net. *Lib* George Webster
Library Holdings: Bk Vols 15,216
Friends of the Library Group

S PETROLEUM MUSEUM LIBRARY & HALL OF FAME, Archives Cen 1500 Interstate 20 W, 79701. SAN 370-1905. Tel: 915-683-4403. FAX: 91 683-4509. Web Site: www.petroleummuseum.org. *Archivist, Dir*, Todd Houck
Library Holdings: Bk Titles 1,650; Per Subs 25
Subject Interests: Photographs
Publications: Museum Memo (quarterly)

MIDLOTHIAN

P A H MEADOWS LIBRARY,* 921 S Ninth St, 76065-3636. SAN 376-45 Tel: 972-775-3417. FAX: 972-775-1501. *Librn*, Gaye G Watson
Library Holdings: Bk Vols 30,000; Per Subs 60
Mem of Northeast Texas Library System

MINEOLA

P MINEOLA MEMORIAL LIBRARY, INC,* 301 N Pacific St, 75773. SAN 316-6244. Tel: 903-569-2767. FAX: 903-569-6511. E-Mail: library@mineola.com. *Dir*, Frieda Sheel; Staff 1 (MLS 1)
Founded 1950. Pop 6,000; Circ 87,330
Library Holdings: Bk Titles 42,147; Per Subs 40
Friends of the Library Group

MINERAL WELLS

P BOYCE DITTO PUBLIC LIBRARY,* 2300 SE Seventh St, 76067. SAN 316-6252. Tel: 940-328-1383. *Mgr*, Patricia Burwell; *Librn*, David Boger; *Ch Servs*, Brenda Mahaney
Founded 1907. Pop 24,062; Circ 96,000
Library Holdings: Bk Vols 41,500; Per Subs 95
Mem of North Texas Regional Library System
Friends of the Library Group

MISSION

P SPEER MEMORIAL LIBRARY,* 801 E 12th St, 78572. SAN 316-6260. Tel: 956-580-8750. FAX: 956-580-8756. *Librn*, Harold R Dove; *ILL, Ref*, Rosaura Alvarez; *Ch Servs*, Marion Mills; *Circ*, Robert Rivera; *Publ Servs*, Lynn Reynish
Pop 50,000; Circ 90,637
Library Holdings: Bk Vols 75,624; Per Subs 276
Subject Interests: Bilingual-Eng, Genealogy, Large print, Spanish, Texana
Mem of South Texas Library System
Friends of the Library Group

MONAHANS

P WARD COUNTY LIBRARY,* 409 S Dwight, 79756. SAN 316-6279. Tel: 915-943-3332. FAX: 915-943-3332. *Librn*, Bonnie Moore; Staff 3 (Non-MLS 3)
Pop 12,839; Circ 95,261
Jan 1998-Dec 1998 Income County $105,142. Mats Exp $18,605, Books $15,000, Per/Ser (Incl. Access Fees) $1,295, AV Equip $1,350, Electronic Ref Mat (Incl. Access Fees) $960. Sal $63,296 (Prof $23,280)
Library Holdings: Bk Vols 79,229; Per Subs 40
Mem of West Texas Library System
Friends of the Library Group

MORTON

P COCHRAN COUNTY LOVE MEMORIAL LIBRARY,* 318 S Main, 79346-3006. SAN 316-6287. Tel: 806-266-5051. FAX: 806-266-8057. *Librn* Nancy Key
Pop 4,338; Circ 7,129

Jan 1998-Dec 1999 Income $42,607
Library Holdings: Bk Vols 13,000; Per Subs 10
Mem of West Texas Library System

OUNT CALM

MOUNT CALM REGIONAL LIBRARY,* Allyn Ave, PO Box 84, 76673. SAN 376-4745. Tel: 254-993-2761. *Librn*, Nancy Franklin
Apr 1998-Mar 1999 Income $16,000
Library Holdings: Bk Vols 14,000; Per Subs 10
Mem of Central Texas Library System

OUNT PLEASANT

MOUNT PLEASANT PUBLIC LIBRARY,* 213 N Madison, 75455. SAN 316-6295. Tel: 903-575-4180. FAX: 903-577-8000. E-Mail: mppublib@stargate.1starnet.com. *Dir*, Leslie Sandlin; Staff 3 (MLS 1, Non-MLS 2)
Founded 1968. Pop 19,000; Circ 56,000
Library Holdings: Bk Titles 41,200; Per Subs 56
Subject Interests: Genealogy, Texana
Special Collections: County Pioneers; History (Pioneer Room), photog; Northeast Titus County Pictures Coll; Pictures & Indian Relics of Titus; Titus County, Mount Pleasant Daily Newspapers (1924-1965), photogs
Mem of Northeast Texas Library System
Partic in Tex Share
Friends of the Library Group

NORTHEAST TEXAS COMMUNITY COLLEGE, Learning Resource Center, PO Box 1307, 75456-1307. SAN 328-106X. Tel: 903-572-1911. FAX: 903-572-7017. E-Mail: lrc@ntcc.cc.tx.us. Web Site: unicorn.ntcc.cc.tx.us/lrc. *Dir*, Lonnie Beene; Tel: 903-572-1911, Ext 454, E-Mail: lbeene@ntcc.cc.tx.us; *Librn*, Jaci Walker; Tel: 903-572-1911, Ext 452, E-Mail: jwalker@ntcc.cc.tx.us; Staff 6 (MLS 3, Non-MLS 3)
Founded 1985. Enrl 2,027; Fac 71; Highest Degree: Associate
Sep 1999-Aug 2000 Mats Exp $237,813, Books $47,000, Electronic Ref Mat (Incl. Access Fees) $3,200. Sal $143,283 (Prof $70,900)
Library Holdings: Bk Vols 28,737; Bk Titles 25,804; Per Subs 270
Special Collections: Local Genealogical Coll
Automation Activity & Vendor Info: (Cataloging) SIRSI; (Circulation) SIRSI; (OPAC) SIRSI
Database Vendor: Ebsco - EbscoHost, OVID Technologies
Function: ILL available
Partic in Amigos Library Services, Inc; Tex Share
Special Services for the Deaf - High interest/low vocabulary books; Staff with knowledge of sign language

OUNT VERNON

FRANKLIN COUNTY LIBRARY,* 100 Main St, PO Box 579, 75457-0579. SAN 376-4397. Tel: 903-537-4916. *Librn*, Jean Shelby
1996-1997 Income $55,000
Library Holdings: Bk Vols 30,000; Per Subs 30
Mem of Northeast Texas Library System

UENSTER

MUENSTER PUBLIC LIBRARY,* 113 N Main St, PO Drawer E, 76252. SAN 316-6309. Tel: 940-759-4291. FAX: 940-759-2250. *Dir*, Kay Broyoes; *Asst Librn*, Mrs Clarence Fowler
Founded 1965. Pop 2,744; Circ 12,576
Library Holdings: Bk Vols 18,136; Bk Titles 19,500; Per Subs 20
Friends of the Library Group

ULESHOE

MULESHOE AREA PUBLIC LIBRARY,* 322 W Second, 79347. SAN 316-6317. Tel: 806-272-4707. FAX: 806-272-5031. *Librn*, Dyan Shipley; E-Mail: dshipley@fivearea.com; *Librn*, Linda Lopez
Founded 1964. Pop 4,624; Circ 41,409
Library Holdings: Bk Vols 23,000; Per Subs 30
Special Collections: Audio-visual Coll; Large Print Coll; Paperback Coll; Southwest Coll; Spanish Coll; Texas Coll
Mem of West Texas Library System
Friends of the Library Group

UNDAY

CITY COUNTY LIBRARY OF MUNDAY,* PO Box 268, 76371. SAN 316-6325. Tel: 940-422-4877. *Librn*, Joann Norman
Pop 5,700; Circ 9,900
Library Holdings: Bk Vols 12,791
Partic in Abilene Major Resource Syst

NACOGDOCHES

L EAST TEXAS LEGAL SERVICES, Law Library, 414 E Pillar, 75961. SAN 329-3629. Tel: 409-560-1455. FAX: 409-560-5385. *Librn*, Lana Caswell Garcia
Library Holdings: Bk Vols 20,500; Per Subs 75
Branches:
BEAUMONT BRANCH, 527 Forsythe, Beaumont, 77701. SAN 328-6207. Tel: 409-835-4971. FAX: 409-835-5783. *Librn*, LouAnn Chism
Library Holdings: Bk Vols 20,000; Per Subs 75
HUNTSVILLE BRANCH, 1502 Avenue O St, Huntsville, 77340. SAN 329-3580. Tel: 409-295-5136. FAX: 409-295-6685. *Librn*, Kim Diamond
LONGVIEW BRANCH, 140 E Tyler, Ste 150, Longview, 75601. SAN 329-3602. Tel: 903-758-9123. FAX: 903-758-1817. *Librn*, Judy Combest
PARIS BRANCH, Bank Bldg 5th flr, 115 SW First St, Paris, 75460. SAN 329-3645. Tel: 903-785-8711. FAX: 903-785-5990. *Librn*, Lometa Smith
TEXARKANA BRANCH, 1425 College Dr Ste 100, Texarkana, 75503. SAN 329-3114. Tel: 903-793-7661. FAX: 903-792-2150. *Librn*, Terri Peak
TYLER BRANCH, 320 N Glenwood, Ste 100, Tyler, 75702. SAN 329-3130. Tel: 903-595-4781. FAX: 903-595-3370. *Librn*, Lillian Davis

M MEMORIAL HOSPITAL, Mollie Sublett Tucker Memorial Medical Library, 1204 N Mound St, 75961. SAN 325-1039. Tel: 936-564-4611, Ext 505, 936-568-8505. *Coordr*, Roxanne Wheeler. Subject Specialists: *Education*, Roxanne Wheeler; Staff 1 (MLS 1)
Library Holdings: Bk Vols 300; Per Subs 15
Subject Interests: Medicine
Partic in S Cent Region of Nat Network of Libr of Med

P NACOGDOCHES PUBLIC LIBRARY,* 1112 North St, 75961-5212. SAN 316-6341. Tel: 409-569-8281. FAX: 409-560-8282. *Ad Servs*, Lillian Melton; Staff 3 (MLS 3)
Founded 1974. Pop 54,000; Circ 111,000
Library Holdings: Bk Vols 73,000; Per Subs 80
Subject Interests: Humane educ
Mem of Houston Area Library System
Friends of the Library Group

C STEPHEN F AUSTIN STATE UNIVERSITY, Ralph W Steen Library, PO Box 13055, SFA Sta, 75962-3055. SAN 316-635X. Tel: 936-468-4101. Interlibrary Loan Service Tel: 936-468-1837. Circulation Tel: 936-468-1497. Reference Tel: 936-468-4217. FAX: 936-468-4117. Web Site: libweb.sfasu.edu. *Dir*, Al Cage; Fax: 936-468-7610, E-Mail: acage@sfalib.sfasu.edu; *Dir, Spec Coll & Archives*, Virginia Rigby; Tel: 936-468-4100, E-Mail: vrigby@sfalib.sfasu.edu; *Asst Dir, Spec Coll & Archives*, Rachel Galan; Tel: 936-468-1562, E-Mail: rgalan@sfalib.sfasu.edu; *Assoc Dir*, Ann Cage; Fax: 936-468-7610, E-Mail: arcage@sfalib.sfasu.edu; *Assoc Dir, Tech Servs*, Peggy Wedgeworth; Fax: 936-468-7610, E-Mail: pwedgewo@sfalib.sfasu.edu; *Web Coordr*, Wade Carter; Tel: 936-468-1444, E-Mail: wcarter@sfalib.sfasu.edu; *Head, Cat*, Ann Ellis; Tel: 936-468-1762, Fax: 936-468-7610, E-Mail: aellis@sfalib.sfasu.edu; *Head Ref*, Karen Wielhorski; Tel: 936-468-1841, E-Mail: karenw@afalib.sfasu.edu; *Ref Serv*, Kayce Halstead; Tel: 936-468-1574, E-Mail: khalstead@sfalib.sfasu.edu; *Ref Serv*, Tina Oswald; Tel: 936-468-1861, E-Mail: toswald@sfalib.sfasu.edu; *Ref Serv*, Erin Palazzolo; Tel: 936-468-1672, E-Mail: epalazzo@sfalib.sfasu.edu; *Ref Serv*, Donald Richter; Tel: 936-468-1714, E-Mail: drichter@sfalib.sfasu.edu; *Ref Serv*, Carol Scamman; Tel: 936-468-1710, E-Mail: cscamman@sfalib.sfasu.edu; *Ref Serv*, Bernice Wright; Tel: 936-468-1528, E-Mail: bwright@sfalib.sfasu.edu; *Bibliogr*, Elaine Hackard; Tel: 936-468-1766, Fax: 936-468-7610, E-Mail: ehackard@sfalib.sfasu.edu; *Access Serv*, Phil Reynolds; Tel: 936-468-1453, E-Mail: preynold@sfalib.sfasu.edu; *Distance Educ*, Marthea Turnage; Tel: 936-468-1896, E-Mail: mturnage@sfalib.sfasu.edu. Subject Specialists: *Business*, Bernice Wright; *Doc*, Kayce Halstead; *Education*, Bernice Wright; *Humanities*, Carol Scamman; *Info servs*, Ann Cage; *Life scis*, Erin Palazzolo; *Maps*, Kayce Halstead; *Music*, Donald Richter; *Physical science*, Donald Richter; *Social sciences*, Tina Oswald; Staff 45 (MLS 17, Non-MLS 28)
Founded 1923. Enrl 11,919; Fac 646; Highest Degree: Doctorate
Sep 2000-Aug 2001 Income $3,844,804, State $62,016, Federal $49,945, Locally Generated Income $88,928, Parent Institution $3,643,915. Mats Exp $1,168,530, Books $346,147, Per/Ser (Incl. Access Fees) $531,806, Presv $34,419, Micro $1,931, Other Print Mats $10,934, Electronic Ref Mat (Incl. Access Fees) $243,293. Sal $1,396,805 (Prof $947,923)
Library Holdings: Bk Vols 932,668; Bk Titles 710,646; Per Subs 3,194
Subject Interests: Forestry
Special Collections: Business Documents & Papers of Major East Texas Lumber Companies; East Texas History, bk, mss
Automation Activity & Vendor Info: (Acquisitions) epixtech, inc.; (Circulation) epixtech, inc.; (Serials) epixtech, inc.
Database Vendor: CARL, Dialog, epixtech, inc., GaleNet, IAC - Info Trac, IAC - SearchBank, Lexis-Nexis, OCLC - First Search, OVID Technologies, Silverplatter Information Inc., Wilson - Wilson Web
Publications: Guide to Special Collections
Partic in Amigos Library Services, Inc; BRS; Dialog Corporation
Offer Academic Assistance Resource Center services & Disabled Student Resources services

P STERNE-HOYA LIBRARY & MUSEUM,* 211 S Lanana St, 75961-0012. SAN 316-6333. Tel: 409-560-5426. *Dir*, Dianna Smith
Founded 1931. Pop 32,000
Library Holdings: Bk Vols 5,000
Subject Interests: Children's literature
Special Collections: Texas Coll

NAVASOTA

P NAVASOTA PUBLIC LIBRARY,* 1411 E Washington Ave, 77868-3240. SAN 316-6376. Tel: 409-825-6744. Interlibrary Loan Service Tel: 800-252-3163. FAX: 409-825-4106. E-Mail: npl@myriad.net. *Dir*, Annette Zamberlin Main; Staff 2 (MLS 1, Non-MLS 1)
Founded 1954. Pop 7,200; Circ 54,211
Oct 1997-Sep 1998 Income $112,997, City $88,100, Locally Generated Income $14,897, Other $10,000. Mats Exp $19,125, Books $7,918, Per/Ser (Incl. Access Fees) $698, Presv $215. Sal $67,194 (Prof $32,600)
Library Holdings: Bk Vols 20,500; Per Subs 36
Subject Interests: Genealogy, Local history
Special Collections: Texanna Coll
Mem of Central Texas Library System
Houses materials for & serves as headquarters for the Grimes County Literary Council & the Archives for the Grimes County Historical Commission
Friends of the Library Group
Branches: 1
HORLOCK HOUSE HISTORY CENTER, 1215 E Washington Ave, 77868. Tel: 936-825-7055.
Subject Interests: Local genealogy, Local history

NEDERLAND

P MARION & ED HUGHES PUBLIC LIBRARY,* 2712 Nederland Ave, 77627-5099. SAN 320-2623. Tel: 409-722-1255. FAX: 409-721-5469. *Coll Develop, Dir*, Victoria L Klehn; *Circ*, Gloria Salvagio; *Tech Servs*, Wanda Lovelady; *ILL*, Bea Sticker
Founded 1930. Pop 16,721; Circ 132,451
Oct 1996-Sep 1997 Income $495,530, City $238,370, Other $257,160. Mats Exp $53,058, Books $23,590, Per/Ser (Incl. Access Fees) $2,725. Sal $104,296
Library Holdings: Bk Vols 45,072; Per Subs 86
Subject Interests: La Accadian hist, Large print, Nederland
Mem of Houston Area Library System
Friends of the Library Group

NEW BOSTON

P NEW BOSTON PUBLIC LIBRARY, 127 N Ellis St, 75570-2905. SAN 376-446X. Tel: 903-628-5414. FAX: 903-628-3565. *Librn*, Julie Woodrow
Library Holdings: Bk Vols 15,553; Per Subs 55
Mem of Northeast Texas Library System
Friends of the Library Group

NEW BRAUNFELS

P NEW BRAUNFELS PUBLIC LIBRARY, 700 E Common St, 78130-5689. SAN 316-6392. Tel: 830-608-2150. FAX: 830-608-2151. Web Site: www.nbpl.lib.tx.us. *Dir*, Vickie Hocker; *Tech Servs*, Sarah Guenther; Staff 6 (MLS 5, Non-MLS 1)
Pop 50,755; Circ 249,728
Jul 1999-Jun 2000 Income $712,393, City $649,271, County $63,122. Mats Exp $95,000. Sal $422,374
Library Holdings: Bk Vols 67,553; Per Subs 205
Special Collections: Texana Coll
Automation Activity & Vendor Info: (Cataloging) epixtech, inc.
Mem of Alamo Area Library System
Friends of the Library Group

NEW WAVERLY

P NEW WAVERLY PUBLIC LIBRARY,* 200 Gibs St, No 1, 77358. SAN 376-4117. Tel: 409-344-2198. FAX: 409-344-2198. *Librn*, Betty Smith
Library Holdings: Bk Vols 8,500; Per Subs 12
Mem of Houston Area Library System
Friends of the Library Group

NEWARK

P NEWARK PUBLIC LIBRARY,* Hudson & Ram Horn Hill Rd, PO Box 1219, 76071. SAN 376-4729. Tel: 817-489-2224. *Librn*, Peggy Taylor
Library Holdings: Bk Vols 8,000; Per Subs 10
Mem of North Texas Regional Library System

NEWCASTLE

S FORT BELKNAP ARCHIVES, INC LIBRARY,* Rte 1, Box 27, 76372. SAN 327-8549. Tel: 940-846-3222.
Library Holdings: Bk Titles 35,000
Restriction: Non-circulating to the public
Open Sat 9am-4pm

NEWTON

P NEWTON COUNTY PUBLIC LIBRARY,* 200 E High St, PO Box 657, 75966-0657. SAN 375-3727. Tel: 409-379-8300. *Dir*, Denise Milton; *Asst Librn*, Sara Davis; Staff 3 (MLS 1, Non-MLS 2)
Founded 1974
Library Holdings: Bk Vols 13,500; Bk Titles 13,000; Per Subs 26
Mem of Houston Area Library System
Special Services for the Deaf - Books on deafness & sign language; High interest/low vocabulary books

NIXON

P NIXON PUBLIC LIBRARY,* 106 W Third, 78140. SAN 316-6414. Tel: 830-582-1913. *Librn*, Cynthia McKinney
Pop 2,008; Circ 8,500
Library Holdings: Bk Vols 8,098; Bk Titles 3,898

NOCONA

P NOCONA PUBLIC LIBRARY,* Cooke St, No 10, 76255. SAN 376-459 Tel: 940-825-6373. FAX: 940-825-4587. E-Mail: noclibrary@cyberstation.net. *Librn*, Shirley Yount
Library Holdings: Bk Vols 18,000; Per Subs 15
Mem of North Texas Regional Library System
Friends of the Library Group

NORTH RICHLAND HILLS

P NORTH RICHLAND HILLS PUBLIC LIBRARY,* 6720 NE Loop 820, 76180. SAN 316-344X. Tel: 817-581-5700. FAX: 817-581-5706. Web Site 198.215.120.210. *Dir*, Steven L Brown; *Asst Dir, Tech Servs*, Elizabeth Russell; *Ch Servs*, Liz Brockman; *Ad Servs*, Dawn Anderson; *Circ*, June Brook; Staff 26 (MLS 8, Non-MLS 18)
Founded 1971. Circ 404,569
Oct 1997-Sep 1998 Income $1,089,173, City $1,050,673, Other $38,500. Mats Exp $174,685, Books $140,200, Per/Ser (Incl. Access Fees) $12,900, Micro $8,100. Sal $715,724
Mem of North Texas Regional Library System

ODEM

P ODEM PUBLIC LIBRARY, (Formerly Della Mae Baylor Public Library), 220 W Humphries St, 78370. (Mail add: PO Box 636, 78370-0636), SAN 316-6422. Tel: 361-368-7388. FAX: 361-368-7388. E-Mail: odempl@ciris.net. Web Site: odem-edroy.k12.tx.us/opl/home.html. *Librn*, Kay Janak; Tel: 361-241-1835, E-Mail: kayjanak@hotmail.com; Staff 1 (Non-MLS 1)
Founded 1934
Apr 1998-Mar 1999 Income $20,193, City $18,498, County $900, Locally Generated Income $795. Mats Exp $2,788, Books $2,765, Per/Ser (Incl. Access Fees) $23. Sal $8,900
Library Holdings: Bk Vols 7,967; Bk Titles 7,772
Mem of South Texas Library System
Friends of the Library Group

ODESSA

P ECTOR COUNTY LIBRARY, 321 W Fifth St, 79761-5066. SAN 316-643 Tel: 915-332-0633. Circulation Tel: 915-332-0633, Ext 10. Reference Tel: 915-332-0633, Ext 18. FAX: 915-337-6502. E-Mail: library@ector.lib.tx.us Web Site: www.ector.lib.tx.us. *Dir*, Kathryn J Boone; Tel: 915-332-0633, E 30, E-Mail: kboone@ector.lib.tx.us; *Ad Servs, Ref*, Rebbecca Taylor; Tel: 915-332-0633, Ext 18; *Acq, Cat*, Terri Decker; Tel: 915-332-0633, Ext 16; *Ch Servs, YA Servs*, Kathryn Boone; *Media Spec*, Ronald Roloff; Tel: 915-332-0633, Ext 13; Staff 24 (MLS 4, Non-MLS 20)
Founded 1938. Pop 122,338; Circ 606,642
Oct 2000-Sep 2001 Income $1,009,177, County $990,097, Other $19,080. Mats Exp $114,380, Books $94,080, Per/Ser (Incl. Access Fees) $19,000, Presv $300, Micro $1,000. Sal $575,141 (Prof $151,147)
Library Holdings: Bk Vols 135,051; Bk Titles 108,119; Per Subs 418
Subject Interests: Genealogy, Local history, SW hist
Automation Activity & Vendor Info: (Acquisitions) SIRSI; (Cataloging) SIRSI; (Circulation) SIRSI; (OPAC) SIRSI; (Serials) SIRSI
Mem of West Texas Library System

Special Services for the Deaf - Books on deafness & sign language; High interest/low vocabulary books
Special Services for the Blind - Bks on tape; Talking book center
Friends of the Library Group

THE LIBRARY OF THE PRESIDENTS, The Presidential Museum, 622 N Lee, 79761. SAN 316-6465. Tel: 915-332-7123. FAX: 915-498-4021. Web Site: www.presidentialmuseum.org. *Exec Dir*, Carey Behrends; *Curator*, Timothy Hewitt
Founded 1964
Library Holdings: Bk Titles 4,500
Subject Interests: The Presidency, all aspects
Special Collections: Constitutional Government; Elective Processes
Publications: Newsletter

ODESSA AMERICAN, Editorial Library, 222 E Fourth St, PO Box 2952, 79760. SAN 372-9982. Tel: 915-337-4661. Toll Free Tel: 1-800-375-4661. FAX: 915-333-7742. E-Mail: oa@link.freedom.com. Web Site: www.oaoa.com. *Mgr*, Frances Irvine; Tel: 915-333-7640, Fax: 915-334-8671
Library Holdings: Bk Vols 50; Per Subs 15
Restriction: Not open to public

ODESSA COLLEGE, Murry H Fly Learning Resources Center, 201 W University, 79764. SAN 316-6457. Tel: 915-335-6640. Reference Tel: 915-335-6645. FAX: 915-335-6610. Web Site: www.odessa.edu. *Dean of Libr*, Dr Shirley Payne; *AV*, Pamela Poindexter; *Info Tech*, David Carson; *Publ Servs*, Carolyn L Petersen; Tel: 915-335-6645, E-Mail: cpetersen@wrangler.odessa.edu; *Ser*, Patricia Quintero; *Tech Servs*, Susan Elliott; Staff 10 (MLS 2, Non-MLS 8)
Founded 1946
Sep 2000-Aug 2001 Income $471,800. Mats Exp $203,329, Books $115,500, Per/Ser (Incl. Access Fees) $30,914, Presv $2,000, Micro $10,000, AV Equip $6,915, Electronic Ref Mat (Incl. Access Fees) $38,000. Sal $233,042 (Prof $120,612)
Library Holdings: Bk Vols 58,443; Bk Titles 74,068; Per Subs 438
Automation Activity & Vendor Info: (Acquisitions) SIRSI; (Cataloging) SIRSI; (Circulation) SIRSI; (Course Reserve) SIRSI; (OPAC) SIRSI; (Serials) SIRSI
Database Vendor: GaleNet, IAC - Info Trac, OCLC - First Search, OVID Technologies
Publications: Faculty Handbook; Student Brochure (Library handbook); Student Handbook
Partic in BRS; Leian; Tex Share

UNIVERSITY OF TEXAS OF THE PERMIAN BASIN, J Conrad Dunagan Library, 4901 E University Blvd, 79762. SAN 316-6473. Tel: 915-552-2370. FAX: 915-552-2374. Web Site: www.utpb.edu/library/index. *Dir*, Charlene Shults; Tel: 915-552-2371; Staff 5 (MLS 5)
Founded 1973. Enrl 2,193; Fac 83; Highest Degree: Master
Sep 1999-Aug 2000 Income $832,545. Mats Exp $347,380, Books $120,000, Per/Ser (Incl. Access Fees) $193,000, Micro $30,380, AV Equip $1,000, Manuscripts & Archives $3,000. Sal $315,690 (Prof $169,475)
Library Holdings: Bk Vols 1,423,744; Bk Titles 257,000; Per Subs 713
Subject Interests: Education, Texana
Special Collections: J Frank Dobie Coll, bks & papers; Texas Writers Coll
Automation Activity & Vendor Info: (Cataloging) DRA; (Circulation) DRA; (Serials) DRA
Restriction: In-house use for visitors
Partic in Amigos Library Services, Inc; Leian; TexShare; Univ Tex Syst
Friends of the Library Group

LNEY

OLNEY COMMUNITY LIBRARY & ARTS CENTER, (1974), 807 W Hamilton, PO Box 67, 76374. SAN 316-6481. Tel: 940-564-5513. FAX: 940-564-3453. *Librn*, Jeanie Spivey; E-Mail: jspivey@brazosnet.com; Staff 6 (Non-MLS 6)
Pop 4,082; Circ 55,071
Library Holdings: Bk Vols 32,069; Per Subs 90
Special Collections: Paperbacks; Texas Coll; World War II Coll
Automation Activity & Vendor Info: (Cataloging) Follett; (Circulation) Follett; (OPAC) Follett
Mem of North Texas Regional Library System
Friends of the Library Group

RANGE

I DU PONT SABINE RIVER WORKS CO, INC,* 1006 Farm Rd, PO Box 1089, 77631. SAN 316-649X. Tel: 409-886-6418. FAX: 409-886-6264. *Librn*, Malia Taylor
Library Holdings: Bk Vols 8,000; Per Subs 150

LAMAR UNIVERSITY-ORANGE LIBRARY,* 410 Front St, 77630-5796. SAN 370-6982. Tel: 409-882-3352. FAX: 409-883-7552. Web Site: luolibrary.lamar.edu:8002. *Dir*, William Ryan; E-Mail: ryan@library.lamar.edu; *Publ Servs*, Jayne Kitterman; Staff 4 (MLS 2, Non-MLS 2)
Enrl 1,562; Fac 56
1997-1998 Income $363,937. Mats Exp $166,765, Books $57,606, Per/Ser (Incl. Access Fees) $23,449, Presv $20,045, Micro $6,432, AV Equip $44,180. Sal $125,301 (Prof $77,622)
Library Holdings: Bk Vols 33,680; Bk Titles 27,870; Per Subs 1,298
Partic in Dialog Corporation; OCLC Online Computer Library Center, Inc

P ORANGE PUBLIC LIBRARY, 220 N Fifth St, 77630. SAN 316-6511. Tel: 409-883-1086. Circulation Tel: 409-883-1086. Reference Tel: 409-883-1053. FAX: 409-883-1902. *Dir Libr Serv*, Karen Maddux; Fax: 409-883-1057, E-Mail: kmaddux@exp.net; *Ref Serv Ad*, Brenna Manasco; E-Mail: bmanasco@exp.net; *Ch Servs*, Marcia Conrad; *Ch Servs*, Rhonda Stanley; *Circ*, Marilyn Skeeler; *Acq*, Carol Murray; Staff 3 (MLS 2, Non-MLS 1)
Founded 1958. Pop 19,381; Circ 191,669
Library Holdings: Bk Vols 79,257; Bk Titles 68,078; Per Subs 352
Subject Interests: SE Texas, SW Louisiana genealogy
Special Collections: Large Print Children's Books; SE Texas & SW Louisiana Genealogy; Texana Coll
Mem of Houston Area Library System
Friends of the Library Group

OZONA

P CROCKETT COUNTY PUBLIC LIBRARY, 1201 Avenue G, PO Box 3030, 76943. SAN 316-652X. Tel: 915-392-3565. FAX: 915-392-2941. E-Mail: ccpl@wcc.net. Web Site: www.ozona.com. *Dir*, Louise Ledoux
Founded 1985. Pop 5,000
Jan 2000-Dec 2000 Income $84,346. Mats Exp $15,000, Per/Ser (Incl. Access Fees) $2,500, AV Equip $500, Other Print Mats $2,500. Sal $37,600 (Prof $21,000)
Library Holdings: Bk Vols 50,000; Bk Titles 35,000
Mem of Big Country Library System
Friends of the Library Group

PADUCAH

P BICENTENNIAL CITY-COUNTY PUBLIC LIBRARY,* County Courthouse, Eighth St, PO Drawer AD, 79248. SAN 372-7440. Tel: 806-492-2006. FAX: 806-492-3107. *Dir*, Mae Goodgame; Staff 1 (Non-MLS 1)
Founded 1977. Pop 2,247; Circ 8,419
Library Holdings: Bk Vols 14,000; Per Subs 15
Special Collections: Genealogy (Texas & various USA Coll); Local History (Cottle Co & Area Coll)
Mem of North Texas Regional Library System
Friends of the Library Group

PAINT ROCK

P HARRY B CROZIER MEMORIAL LIBRARY,* PO Box 173, 76866. SAN 375-4812. Tel: 915-732-4320. *Librn*, Sue Sims; *Asst Librn*, Mary Jim Currie
Founded 1971. Pop 227; Circ 1,814
Jan 1998-Dec 1999 Income $3,000
Library Holdings: Bk Titles 6,880
Special Services for the Deaf - Books on deafness & sign language; High interest/low vocabulary books
Open Tues & Thurs 1-5
Friends of the Library Group

PALACIOS

P PALACIOS LIBRARY, INC, 326 Main St, 77465. SAN 316-6538. Tel: 361-972-3234. FAX: 361-972-2142. *Librn*, Vikijane Bear; *Asst Librn*, Marsha Branscum; *Asst Librn*, Babette Adams; Staff 3 (Non-MLS 3)
Pop 9,400
Jan 1999-Dec 1999 Income $62,000, City $12,000, County $50,000
Library Holdings: Bk Titles 30,900; Per Subs 10
Mem of Houston Area Library System
Friends of the Library Group

PALESTINE

P PALESTINE PUBLIC LIBRARY, 1101 N Cedar St, 75801-7697. SAN 316-6546. Tel: 903-729-4121. FAX: 903-729-4062. E-Mail: reflib@palestine.lib.tx.us. Web Site: www.palestine.lib.tx.us. *Dir*, John D Richmond; Tel: 903-731-8438, E-Mail: johnr@palestine.lib.tx.us; *Ad Servs*, Sue Smith; *Ch Servs*, Linda Bradberry; *Spec Coll*, Brenda Ladd; Staff 15 (MLS 1, Non-MLS 14)
Pop 49,090; Circ 131,414
Oct 1999-Sep 2000 Income (Main Library Only) $554,350, City $494,350, County $60,000
Library Holdings: Bk Vols 70,800
Subject Interests: Genealogy
Special Collections: Anderson Co., TX; Civil War Coll; Texana Coll
Automation Activity & Vendor Info: (Cataloging) epixtech, inc.;

(Circulation) epixtech, inc.; (OPAC) epixtech, inc.
Database Vendor: epixtech, inc.
Mem of Northeast Texas Library System
Friends of the Library Group

PAMPA

P LOVETT MEMORIAL LIBRARY, 111 N Houston, 79065. (Mail add: PO Box 342, 79066), SAN 316-6562. Tel: 806-669-5780. FAX: 806-669-5782. E-Mail: lovettpampa@visto.com. Web Site: www.hlc-lib.org/pampa/index.html. *Dir*, Anne Stobbe; E-Mail: astobbe@visto.com; *Ch Servs*, Shanla Brookshire; Staff 11 (MLS 2, Non-MLS 9)
Founded 1954. Pop 22,000; Circ 87,000
Oct 2000-Sep 2001 Income $364,872, City $342,772, County $6,700, Locally Generated Income $16,000. Mats Exp $50,600, Books $33,000, Per/Ser (Incl. Access Fees) $5,000, AV Equip $3,000, Electronic Ref Mat (Incl. Access Fees) $9,600. Sal $237,990
Library Holdings: Bk Vols 85,000; Bk Titles 75,000; Per Subs 110
Subject Interests: Local history
Special Collections: Large Print Coll; Spanish Coll
Automation Activity & Vendor Info: (Cataloging) DRA; (Circulation) DRA; (OPAC) DRA
Database Vendor: DRA, Ebsco - EbscoHost, OCLC - First Search, Wilson - Wilson Web
Function: ILL available, Photocopies available
Mem of Texas Panhandle Library System
Partic in Harrington Library Consortium; Panhandle Library Access Network
Friends of the Library Group

PANHANDLE

P CARSON COUNTY PUBLIC LIBRARY,* 401 Main, PO Box 339, 79068. SAN 362-1510. Tel: 806-537-3742. FAX: 806-537-3780. *Librn*, Terri Koetting; *Asst Librn*, Alice Stamps; *Circ*, Ardell McAtte
Founded 1937. Pop 3,000; Circ 93,000
Library Holdings: Bk Vols 51,652; Bk Titles 43,075; Per Subs 106
Mem of Texas Panhandle Library System
Branches: 3
GROOM BRANCH, PO Box 308, Groom, 79039. SAN 362-1545. Tel: 806-248-7353. FAX: 806-248-7353. *Librn*, Karen Case
Friends of the Library Group
SKELLYTOWN BRANCH, PO Box 92, Skellytown, 79080. SAN 362-157X. Tel: 806-848-2551. FAX: 806-848-2551. *Librn*, Marcy Ruth
WHITE DEER BRANCH, PO Box 85, White Deer, 79097. SAN 362-160X. Tel: 806-883-7121. FAX: 806-883-7121. *Librn*, Catherine Martinez

PARIS

S MCCUISTION REGIONAL MEDICAL CENTER, L P McCuistion Library, 865 DeShong Dr, 75462-2097. SAN 316-6570. Tel: 903-737-1150. FAX: 903-782-2847. *In Charge*, Barbara Kyle; E-Mail: barbarakyle@texashealth.org
Founded 1923
Library Holdings: Bk Titles 12,000; Per Subs 15
Special Collections: Texana

J PARIS JUNIOR COLLEGE, Learning Center,* 2400 Clarksville St, 75460. SAN 316-6589. Tel: 903-782-0215, 903-782-0415. FAX: 903-782-0356. Web Site: www.pjc.cc.tx.us. *Dir*, LuLane Caraway; E-Mail: lcaraway@paris.cc.tx.us; *Tech Servs*, Carl Colvert; Staff 6 (MLS 2, Non-MLS 4)
Founded 1924. Enrl 2,456; Fac 84
Library Holdings: Bk Vols 54,999; Bk Titles 50,000; Per Subs 340
Special Collections: A M Aikin Archives

P PARIS PUBLIC LIBRARY, 326 S Main St, 75460-9998. SAN 316-6597. Tel: 903-785-8531. FAX: 903-784-6325. Web Site: www.paristxlibrary.com. *Dir*, Beverly Lewis; E-Mail: blewis@neto.com; *Asst Dir*, Priscilla McAnally; E-Mail: pmcnally@neto.com; Staff 14 (MLS 3, Non-MLS 11)
Founded 1926. Pop 44,200; Circ 315,700
Oct 1999-Sep 2000 Income $733,450, City $717,350, Other $16,100. Mats Exp $173,100. Sal $435,500
Library Holdings: Bk Titles 102,360; Per Subs 104
Subject Interests: Texana
Automation Activity & Vendor Info: (Cataloging) Gaylord; (Circulation) Gaylord
Mem of Northeast Texas Library System
Friends of the Library Group
Bookmobiles: 1

PASADENA

P PASADENA PUBLIC LIBRARY,* 1201 Jeff Ginn Memorial Dr, 77506-4895. SAN 362-1634. Tel: 713-477-0276. FAX: 713-473-9640. *Dir*, Ann T Clifford; E-Mail: ann@ci/pasadena.tx.us; *Asst Dir*, Earl Erickson; *ILL*, Kerry Baurax; *Ad Servs*, James Maynard; *Acq*, Sharron Ekpe; *Publ Servs*, Cynthia Saucier
Founded 1953. Pop 129,292; Circ 429,082
Oct 1996-Sep 1997 Income $1,841,461. Mats Exp $300,723, Books $197,255, Per/Ser (Incl. Access Fees) $62,017, Micro $7,865, Other Print Mats $6,974. Sal $1,303,949
Library Holdings: Bk Vols 385,900; Per Subs 1,103
Subject Interests: Local history
Publications: Booklets, brochures & bookmarks; calendar (bimonthly); newsletter (bimonthly)
Mem of Houston Area Library System
Friends of the Library Group
Branches: 1
FAIRMONT, 4330 Fairmont, 77504-3306. SAN 372-7068. Tel: 281-998-1095. FAX: 281-998-1583.
Library Holdings: Bk Vols 39,576
Bookmobiles: 1

J SAN JACINTO COLLEGE, Lee Davis Library, 8060 Spencer Hwy, 7750 SAN 362-1693. Tel: 281-476-1850. FAX: 281-478-2734. Web Site: www.sjcd.cc.tx.us/lib.htm. *Dir Libr Serv*, Jay B Clark; E-Mail: jclark@sjcd.cc.tx.us; *Publ Servs*, Terri Propes; *Per*, Judith Mayfield; *ILL*, *Ref*, Joy Hopkins; *Circ*, Nancy Cushman; *Tech Servs*, Ellen Rushing; *Online Servs*, Ron Wood; *Reader Servs*, Sue Gale Kooken; *Automation Syst Coordr*, Ka Phillips; Staff 7 (MLS 7)
Founded 1961. Enrl 7,336; Fac 500
Sep 1999-Aug 2000 Income (Main Library Only) $639,901. Mats Exp $121,000, Books $41,571, Per/Ser (Incl. Access Fees) $60,000, Electronic Ref Mat (Incl. Access Fees) $19,429. Sal $441,268 (Prof $301,120)
Library Holdings: Bk Vols 120,000; Per Subs 500
Special Collections: Pomeroy Archives on Area History
Automation Activity & Vendor Info: (Cataloging) epixtech, inc.; (Circulation) epixtech, inc.; (Course Reserve) epixtech, inc.; (OPAC) epixtech, inc.; (Serials) epixtech, inc.
Database Vendor: epixtech, inc., OVID Technologies, Wilson - Wilson W
Publications: Library handbook; Netscape guide; Newsletter for faculty; Union List of Serials for the College
Partic in Amigos Library Services, Inc; Tex Share

CM TEXAS CHIROPRACTIC COLLEGE, Mae Hilty Memorial Library, 5912 Spencer Hwy, 77505. SAN 316-6619. Tel: 281-998-6049. Interlibrary Loa Service Tel: 281-998-6052. Reference Tel: 281-998-6054. FAX: 281-487-4168. Web Site: www.txchiro.edu. *Dir*, Rebecca L McKay; E-Mail: bmckay@txchiro.edu; *Asst Dir, Tech Servs*, Carol Lynn Webb; *Tech Servs*, Kathy Foulch; *Circ*, Corina King; E-Mail: cking@txchiro.edu; *AV*, Teresa Roeder; *Publ Servs*, Theresa Hocking; E-Mail: thocking@txchiro.edu; Staf 5 (MLS 3, Non-MLS 2)
Founded 1953. Enrl 520; Fac 42; Highest Degree: Doctorate
1999-2000 Mats Exp $97,700, Books $35,000, Per/Ser (Incl. Access Fees) $30,000, Presv $2,700, AV Equip $15,000. Sal $142,000 (Prof $87,000)
Library Holdings: Bk Titles 9,000; Per Subs 186
Subject Interests: Chiropractic, Medicine, Natural science
Special Collections: Chiropractic Coll, bks
Partic in Amigos Library Services, Inc; Chiropractic Libr Consortium; Nat Libr of Med; OCLC Online Computer Library Center, Inc
Friends of the Library Group

PEARSALL

P PEARSALL PUBLIC LIBRARY,* 200 E Trinity St, 78061. SAN 316-662 Tel: 830-334-2496. FAX: 830-334-2496. *Librn*, Victor Trevino
Founded 1962. Pop 13,300; Circ 56,214
Library Holdings: Bk Titles 21,000; Per Subs 16
Mem of Alamo Area Library System; San Antonio Major Resource Center

PECOS

P REEVES COUNTY LIBRARY, 505 S Park St, 79772-3735. SAN 316-663 Tel: 915-445-5340. FAX: 915-445-5340. *Librn*, Sally Perry
Founded 1937. Pop 16,000; Circ 40,000
Jan 2000-Dec 2000 Income $83,070, County $75,820, Locally Generated Income $1,250, Other $6,000. Mats Exp $12,000. Sal $37,974 (Prof $18,714)
Library Holdings: Bk Vols 60,000; Per Subs 50; High Interest/Low Vocabulary Bk Vols 1,000
Mem of Texas Trans Pecos Library System
Friends of the Library Group

PERRYTON

P PERRY MEMORIAL LIBRARY,* 22 SE Fifth Ave, 79070. SAN 316-664 Tel: 806-435-5801. FAX: 806-435-4266. *Librn*, Celestine Thompson; *Asst Librn*, Dolores Blundell; *Asst Librn*, Sandra Sears; Staff 1 (MLS 1)
Founded 1925. Pop 10,000; Circ 72,966
Library Holdings: Bk Vols 37,500; Per Subs 10
Subject Interests: History
Special Collections: Texas Coll
Mem of Texas Panhandle Library System

LUGERVILLE

PFLUGERVILLE COMMUNITY LIBRARY, 102 S Tenth St, PO Box 1429, 78691-1429. SAN 372-5685. Tel: 512-251-9185. FAX: 512-251-9185. E-Mail: pcl@swbell.net. Web Site: www.cityofpflugerville.com. *Librn*, JoAnne A Thornton; E-Mail: joanne_t@swbell.net; Staff 6 (MLS 1, Non-MLS 5)
Founded 1981. Pop 15,000; Circ 85,611
Oct 1999-Sep 2000 Income $175,164, City $77,000, Locally Generated Income $2,094. Mats Exp $45,200, Books $44,000, Per/Ser (Incl. Access Fees) $1,200. Sal $79,802
Library Holdings: Bk Titles 25,280; Per Subs 33
Subject Interests: Texana
Automation Activity & Vendor Info: (Circulation) Nicholas
Mem of Central Texas Library System
Friends of the Library Group

IARR

PHARR MEMORIAL LIBRARY, 200 S Athol St, 78577. SAN 316-6651. Tel: 956-787-3966. FAX: 956-787-3345. E-Mail: staff@pharr.lib.tx.us. Web Site: www.pharr.lib.tx.us. *Dir*, David T Liu; *Asst Librn, Ch Servs*, Magda Elizabeth Rodriguez; Staff 12 (MLS 2, Non-MLS 10)
Founded 1960. Pop 48,836
Oct 1998-Sep 1999 Income $408,000, City $400,000, County $8,000. Mats Exp $79,500, Books $69,000, Per/Ser (Incl. Access Fees) $9,000, Electronic Ref Mat (Incl. Access Fees) $1,500. Sal $302,000 (Prof $119,000)
Library Holdings: Bk Vols 99,967; Per Subs 169; Bks on Deafness & Sign Lang 25
Special Collections: Large Print Coll; Spanish Coll (Spanish language materials); Texas Coll
Automation Activity & Vendor Info: (Cataloging) Brodart; (Circulation) Brodart
Database Vendor: Ebsco - EbscoHost, ProQuest
Mem of South Texas Library System
Friends of the Library Group

LOT POINT

PILOT POINT COMMUNITY LIBRARY,* PO Box 969, 76258-0969. SAN 376-4575. Tel: 940-686-5004. FAX: 940-686-2833. *Librn*, Phyllis Tillery
Oct 1997-Sep 1998 Income $70,000
Library Holdings: Bk Vols 18,000; Per Subs 25
Mem of North Texas Regional Library System
Friends of the Library Group

NELAND

ARTHUR TEMPLE SR MEMORIAL LIBRARY,* PO Box 847, 75968-0296. SAN 316-666X. Tel: 409-584-2546. FAX: 409-584-3206. *Dir*, Donna Nichlos; E-Mail: dnichlos@hals.lib.tx.us
Founded 1969. Pop 7,200; Circ 33,559
Library Holdings: Bk Vols 16,702; Per Subs 8
Mem of Tex Libr Syst

TTSBURG

PITTSBURG-CAMP COUNTY LIBRARY,* 613 Quitman St, 75686-1035. SAN 316-6678. Tel: 903-856-3302. FAX: 903-856-0591. E-Mail: pittlib@aol.com. *Librn*, Nancy Dunlap
Pop 10,132; Circ 50,946
1996-1997 Income $77,818. Mats Exp $6,497, Books $5,258, Per/Ser (Incl. Access Fees) $889. Sal $47,812 (Prof $20,914)
Library Holdings: Bk Vols 30,601
Subject Interests: Genealogy
Mem of Northeast Texas Library System
Friends of the Library Group

LAINS

YOAKUM COUNTY LIBRARY, 901 Ave East, PO Box 419, 79355-0419. SAN 316-6686. Tel: 806-456-8725. FAX: 806-456-7056. *Dir*, Opal Roberts; Staff 6 (MLS 3, Non-MLS 3)
Founded 1957. Pop 3,500
Library Holdings: Bk Titles 34,000; Per Subs 107
Subject Interests: Tex hist
Publications: Appraisal; Booklist; Publishers Weekly
Mem of West Texas Library System

LAINVIEW

UNGER MEMORIAL LIBRARY, (UML), 825 Austin St, 79072-7235. SAN 316-6694. Tel: 806-296-1148. FAX: 806-291-1245. Web Site: www.texasonline.net/schools/unger. *Librn*, John Sigwald; E-Mail: johnsigwald@texasonline.net; Staff 1 (MLS 1)
Founded 1960. Pop 35,000; Circ 70,000
Oct 1999-Sep 2000 Income (Main Library Only) $254,490, City $244,990, County $9,500. Mats Exp $42,852, Books $30,000, Per/Ser (Incl. Access Fees) $8,694, Presv $2,958, Micro $1,200. Sal $154,520 (Prof $37,000)
Library Holdings: Bk Vols 50,000; Per Subs 110
Subject Interests: Genealogy
Special Collections: Plainview & Hale County History
Automation Activity & Vendor Info: (Cataloging) Sagebrush Corporation; (Circulation) Sagebrush Corporation; (OPAC) Sagebrush Corporation
Database Vendor: Ebsco - EbscoHost, OCLC - First Search
Publications: Unger Ululations (monthly newsletter)
Mem of West Texas Library System
Special Services - Hale County Literacy Program
Friends of the Library Group

C WAYLAND BAPTIST UNIVERSITY, Mabee Learning Resources Center,* 1900 W Seventh, 79072-6957. SAN 316-6708. Tel: 806-296-4737. FAX: 806-296-4736. Web Site: www.wbu.edu. *Dir*, Dr Polly Lackey; E-Mail: lackep@mail.wbu.edu; *Librn*, Mark Durham; Tel: 806-291-5096, E-Mail: mdurham@mail.wbu.edu; *Coll Develop*, Donna Clark; Tel: 806-291-5080, E-Mail: clark@mail.wbu.edu; *Reader Servs*, Carol Oshel; Tel: 806-291-5086, E-Mail: oshelc@mail.wbu.edu; Staff 4 (MLS 4)
Founded 1910. Enrl 1,016; Fac 73; Highest Degree: Master
Jun 1998-May 1999 Income Parent Institution $480,559. Mats Exp $132,693, Books $80,273, Per/Ser (Incl. Access Fees) $52,420. Sal $168,343
Library Holdings: Bk Vols 110,544; Bk Titles 102,763; Per Subs 497
Database Vendor: DRA, OCLC - First Search, OVID Technologies
Partic in Harrington Library Consortium; OCLC Online Computer Library Center, Inc

PLANO

S ARCO EXPLORATION & PRODUCTION TECHNOLOGY, Technical Information Center PRC-F1100,* 2300 W Plano Pkwy, 75075. SAN 316-1927. Tel: 972-509-4492. FAX: 972-509-6502.
Founded 1942
Library Holdings: Bk Vols 15,000; Per Subs 400
Subject Interests: Chemical engineering, Chemistry, Econ, Electrical engineering, Electronics, Geology, Geophysics, Mathematics, Mech eng, Oceanography, Paleontology, Petroleum engineering, Physics, Planning, Remote sensing sci
Publications: Acquisitions list
Restriction: Staff use only
Partic in BRS; Dialog Corporation; Pergamon Orbit

J COLLIN COUNTY COMMUNITY COLLEGE DISTRICT, Richard L Ducote Learning Resource Center (Spring Creek Campus), 2800 E Spring Creek Pkwy, 75074. SAN 328-0276. Tel: 972-881-5860. Interlibrary Loan Service Tel: 972-881-5749. Reference Tel: 972-881-5985. FAX: 972-881-5911. Web Site: www.ccccd.edu. *Dean*, Michael Bell; Tel: 972-881-5831, E-Mail: mbell@ccccd.edu; *Per*, Diane Durbin; *Per*, Sneh Goyal; *Per*, Pam Tooley; *ILL*, Sandy Marton; *Tech Servs*, Jean Sobotka; Staff 48 (MLS 13, Non-MLS 35)
Founded 1985. Fac 189
1999-2000 Income $2,663,327. Mats Exp $753,614, Books $348,998, Per/Ser (Incl. Access Fees) $69,690, Presv $698, Micro $12,785, AV Equip $265,884, Electronic Ref Mat (Incl. Access Fees) $55,559. Sal $1,428,040 (Prof $509,398)
Library Holdings: Bk Vols 125,648; Bk Titles 102,224; Per Subs 940
Automation Activity & Vendor Info: (Cataloging) epixtech, inc.; (Circulation) epixtech, inc.
Partic in Amigos Library Services, Inc; OCLC Online Computer Library Center, Inc

L J C PENNEY COMPANY INC, Law Library, 6501 Legacy Dr, 75024. (Mail add: PO Box 10001, MS 1117, 75301), Tel: 972-431-1254. FAX: 972-431-1133. *Syst Coordr*, Donna Metivier; E-Mail: dmmetivi@jcpenney.com
Library Holdings: Bk Vols 25,000; Per Subs 90
Automation Activity & Vendor Info: (Cataloging) EOS; (Serials) EOS
Database Vendor: Lexis-Nexis

P PLANO PUBLIC LIBRARY SYSTEM, Library Administration, 2501 Coit Rd, 75075. SAN 316-6724. Tel: 972-964-4208. FAX: 972-964-4269. Web Site: www.planolibrary.org. *Dir*, Joyce Baumbach; E-Mail: joyceb@gwmail.plano.gov; *Cat*, Lorie Hileman; Tel: 972-941-4206, Fax: 972-941-4121, E-Mail: lorieh@gwmail.plano.gov; *Tech Coordr*, Michael Branch; Tel: 972-941-4292, Fax: 972-964-4121, E-Mail: mikeb@gwmail.plano.gov; *Acq*, Julie Torstad; Tel: 972-941-4291, Fax: 972-941-4121, E-Mail: juliet@gwmail.plano.gov; Staff 223 (MLS 74, Non-MLS 149)
Founded 1965. Pop 231,874; Circ 1,842,589
Oct 1999-Sep 2000 Income (Main Library and Branch Library) $8,270,193, City $7,904,626, County $49,900, Locally Generated Income $248,452, Other $67,215. Mats Exp $1,463,317, Books $1,179,752, Per/Ser (Incl. Access Fees) $131,829, Micro $9,435, Electronic Ref Mat (Incl. Access Fees) $59,483. Sal $4,937,728 (Prof $2,161,468)
Library Holdings: Bk Vols 558,356; Per Subs 1,104
Subject Interests: Chinese, Genealogy, Spanish, Texana
Automation Activity & Vendor Info: (Acquisitions) epixtech, inc.;

(Cataloging) epixtech, inc.; (Circulation) epixtech, inc.
Database Vendor: Ebsco - EbscoHost, epixtech, inc., GaleNet, IAC - Info Trac, OCLC - First Search
Publications: Plano, Texas: The Early Years (Local historical information)
Mem of Northeast Texas Library System
Partic in Amigos Library Services, Inc; OCLC Online Computer Library Center, Inc
The Plano Public Library Foundation, non-profit support organization
Friends of the Library Group
Branches: 6
CHRISTOPHER A PARR LIBRARY, 6200 Windhaven Pky, 75093. Tel: 972-964-4300. FAX: 972-964-4304. Web Site: www.planolibrary.org. *Mgr*, Sandy Gillman; E-Mail: sandyg@gwmail.plano.gov; Staff 38 (MLS 14, Non-MLS 24)
Founded 2001
GLADYS HARRINGTON LIBRARY, 1501 E 18th St, 75074. SAN 321-1401. Tel: 972-941-7175. FAX: 972-941-7292. Web Site: www.planolibrary.org. *Mgr*, Anne Womack; Fax: 972-941-7193, E-Mail: annew@gwmail.plano.gov; *Ref*, Marta Demaree; *Ch Servs*, Genie Hammel; E-Mail: genieh@gwmail.plano.gov; Staff 37 (MLS 12, Non-MLS 25)
Founded 1969. Circ 340,858
Oct 1999-Sep 2000 Income $9,530,765, City $1,209,831, Locally Generated Income $50,741, Parent Institution $8,270,193. Sal $959,793 (Prof $501,348)
Library Holdings: Bk Vols 137,539; Per Subs 250
Subject Interests: Arts, Genealogy, Humanities, Local history
Special Collections: Genealogy; Spanish; Texana
L E R SCHIMELPFENIG LIBRARY, 5024 Custer Rd, 75023. SAN 321-141X. Tel: 972-964-4200. FAX: 972-964-4210. Web Site: www.planolibrary.org. *Mgr*, Karen Farrell; E-Mail: karenf@gwmail.plano.gov; *Ref*, June Vanderryst; *Ch Servs*, Cindy Boatfield; E-Mail: cindybo@gwmail.plano.gov; Staff 43 (MLS 13, Non-MLS 30)
Founded 1980. Circ 475,747
Oct 1999-Sep 2000 Income $9,689,907, City $1,366,017, Locally Generated Income $53,697, Parent Institution $8,270,193. Sal $1,100,154 (Prof $478,510)
Library Holdings: Bk Vols 132,201; Per Subs 240
Subject Interests: Bus, Law, Sci
MARIBELLE M DAVIS LIBRARY, 7501 Independence Pkwy, 75025. SAN 378-0317. Tel: 972-208-8000. FAX: 972-208-8037. Web Site: www.planolibrary.org. *Mgr*, Sue Haas; E-Mail: susanh@gwmail.plano.gov; *Ch Servs*, Julie Connor; Tel: 972-208-8009, E-Mail: juliec@gwmail.plano.gov; Staff 35 (MLS 13, Non-MLS 22)
Founded 1998. Pop 462,931
Oct 1999-Sep 2000 Income $1,229,046, City $1,178,032, Locally Generated Income $51,014, Parent Institution $8,270,193. Sal $924,205 (Prof $444,335)
Library Holdings: Bk Vols 85,204; Per Subs 237
MUNICIPAL REFERENCE, 1409 Avenue K, 75074. SAN 375-5673. Tel: 972-941-7377. FAX: 972-941-7453. Web Site: www.planolibrary.org. *Librn*, Sara Mosca; E-Mail: saram@gwmail.plano.gov; Staff 2 (MLS 1, Non-MLS 1)
Founded 1991. Circ 2,025
Oct 1999-Sep 2000 Income $8,381,933, City $111,740, Parent Institution $8,270,193. Sal $71,693 (Prof $48,780)
Library Holdings: Bk Vols 3,483; Per Subs 75
W O HAGGARD JR LIBRARY, 2501 Coit Rd, 75075. SAN 370-0003. Tel: 972-964-4250. FAX: 972-964-4256. Web Site: www.planolibrary.org. *Mgr*, Cheri Gross; E-Mail: cherig@gwmail.plano.gov; *Ch Servs*, Connie Charron; E-Mail: conniec@gwmail.plano.gov; Staff 44 (MLS 16, Non-MLS 28)
Founded 1989. Circ 531,184
Oct 1999-Sep 2000 Income $9,684,091, City $1,320,874, Locally Generated Income $93,024, Parent Institution $8,270,193. Sal $1,019,374 (Prof $493,033)
Library Holdings: Bk Vols 145,720; Per Subs 302
Subject Interests: Consumer health, Sci, Technology

PLEASANTON

P PLEASANTON PUBLIC LIBRARY, 321 N Main, 78064. SAN 316-6732. Tel: 830-569-3622. FAX: 830-569-6082. Web Site: www.world-net.net/home/dguthrie. *Dir*, Diana Guthrie; E-Mail: dguthrie@world-net.net; *Ch Servs*, Julie Elliott; Staff 4 (MLS 1, Non-MLS 3)
Pop 16,700; Circ 35,316
Oct 2000-Sep 2001 Income $117,703, State $2,200, City $111,503, County $4,000. Mats Exp $12,800, Books $11,200, Per/Ser (Incl. Access Fees) $1,600. Sal $79,148 (Prof $24,354)
Library Holdings: Bk Vols 24,599; Bk Titles 25,000; Per Subs 90; Bks on Deafness & Sign Lang 20
Special Collections: Texana
Automation Activity & Vendor Info: (Cataloging) Sagebrush Corporation; (Circulation) Sagebrush Corporation
Mem of Alamo Area Library System
Friends of the Library Group

PORT ARANSAS

P ELLIS MEMORIAL LIBRARY,* 700 West Ave A, 78373. SAN 376-430 Tel: 512-749-4116. FAX: 512-749-5679. *Librn*, Sue James
Oct 1996-Sep 1997 Income $108,387. Mats Exp $54,867. Sal $53,520
Library Holdings: Bk Vols 15,000; Per Subs 50
Mem of South Texas Library System

PORT ARTHUR

C LAMAR STATE COLLEGE, Gates Memorial Library, 317 Stilwell Blvd, 77640. (Mail add: PO Box 310, 77641-0310), SAN 378-0716. Tel: 409-98 6222. Interlibrary Loan Service Tel: 409-984-6218. Circulation Tel: 409-9 6218. Reference Tel: 409-984-6220. FAX: 409-984-6008. Web Site: www.libnt4.lamarpa.edu/index.html. *Dean of Libr*, Peter B Kaatrude; Tel: 409-984-6216, E-Mail: peter.kaatrude@lamarpa.edu; *Coordr*, Jimmet G Lawrence; Tel: 409-984-6220, E-Mail: jimmet.lawrence@lamarpa.edu; *Ac* Margarita Contreras; Tel: 409-984-6225, E-Mail: margarita.contreras@lamarpa.edu; *ILL*, Myra A Thompson; E-Mail: myra.thompson@lamarpa.e *Automation Syst Coordr*, Juanita Broussard; Tel: 409-984-6219, E-Mail: juanita.broussard@lamarpa.edu; *Publ Servs*, Francis H Mosgrove; Tel: 409 984-6224, E-Mail: francis.mosgrove@lamarpa.edu; *Ser*, Jerene Marshall; T 409-984-6221, E-Mail: jerene.marshall@lamarpa.edu; Staff 9 (MLS 3, Nor MLS 6)
Founded 1909. Enrl 2,700; Fac 200; Highest Degree: Associate
Sep 1999-Aug 2000 Income State $491,920. Mats Exp $182,115, Books $90,000, Per/Ser (Incl. Access Fees) $55,800, Presv $2,315, Micro $6,000, Electronic Ref Mat (Incl. Access Fees) $28,000. Sal $242,722 (Prof $118,444)
Library Holdings: Bk Vols 42,027; Bk Titles 36,333; Per Subs 229; Bks Deafness & Sign Lang 10
Subject Interests: Business, Computer science, Cosmetology, Criminal justice, Law, Literature, Nursing, Rare books
Special Collections: Texana
Automation Activity & Vendor Info: (Acquisitions) EOS; (Cataloging) EOS; (Circulation) EOS; (Course Reserve) EOS; (ILL) EOS; (OPAC) EOS (Serials) EOS
Database Vendor: Lexis-Nexis, OVID Technologies
Partic in Amigos Library Services, Inc; TexShare

P PORT ARTHUR PUBLIC LIBRARY,* 4615 9th Ave, 77642-3136. SAN 362-1723. Tel: 409-985-8838. FAX: 409-985-5969. *Dir*, Ray Cline; *ILL, R* Katherin Lene; *Ch Servs*, Trudy Terry; *Circ*, Brenda Francis; Staff 5 (MLS 5)
Founded 1918. Pop 63,053
Library Holdings: Bk Vols 139,096; Bk Titles 120,023; Per Subs 360
Special Collections: Port Arthur History
Publications: Friends Newsletter; Juv Dept "Lagniappe" for teachers
Mem of Houston Area Library System
Friends of the Library Group

R PRESBYTERIAN CHURCH OF THE COVENANT LIBRARY, 1645 Jefferson Dr, 77642. SAN 316-6767. Tel: 409-983-1673. FAX: 409-985-8113.
Founded 1947
Library Holdings: Bk Vols 4,000
Subject Interests: Biblical commentaries, Church-related subjects, Devotionals

M ST MARY HOSPITAL, Health Science Library,* 3600 Gates Blvd, PO Bo 3696, 77643-3696. SAN 322-7537. Tel: 409-985-7431, Ext 1279. FAX: 40 989-5137.
Library Holdings: Bk Titles 22,000; Per Subs 132
Subject Interests: Dentistry, Dermatology, Pathology, Radiology

PORT ISABEL

P PORT ISABEL PUBLIC LIBRARY, 213 Yturria St, 78578. SAN 316-678 Tel: 956-943-1822. FAX: 956-943-4638. E-Mail: lvanne@port-isabel.ccls.lib.tx.us. Web Site: www.port-isabel.ccls.lib.tx.us. *Librn*, Mabel Hockaday; E-Mail: mabel@port-isabel.ccls.lib.tx.us; *Asst Librn*, Ida Tellez; *Asst Librn*, Mary Alice McCreary
Pop 8,000; Circ 19,500
Library Holdings: Bk Vols 18,100; Per Subs 36
Mem of South Texas Library System
Friends of the Library Group

PORT LAVACA

P CALHOUN COUNTY LIBRARY, 200 W Mahan, 77979. SAN 362-1782. Tel: 361-552-7323. Reference Tel: 361-552-7250. FAX: 361-552-4926. E-Mail: staff@cclibrary.org. Web Site: www.cclibrary.org. *Dir*, Noemi Cruz; Staff 4 (MLS 1, Non-MLS 3)
Founded 1962. Pop 21,300; Circ 62,602
Library Holdings: Bk Vols 56,000; Bk Titles 53,000; Per Subs 122

Automation Activity & Vendor Info: (Cataloging) Sagebrush Corporation; (Circulation) Sagebrush Corporation
Publications: Booklist; Library Journal; Public Libraries
Mem of South Texas Library System
Friends of the Library Group
Branches: 3
POINT COMFORT BRANCH, One Lamar St, Point Comfort, 77978. (Mail add: PO Box 382, Point Comfort, 77978), Tel: 361-987-2954. FAX: 361-987-2954. E-Mail: staff@cclibrary.org. Web Site: www.cclibrary.org. *Librn*, Grace Bradley; Staff 1 (Non-MLS 1)
Library Holdings: Bk Vols 11,000
Automation Activity & Vendor Info: (Circulation) Sagebrush Corporation
Friends of the Library Group
PORT O'CONNOR BRANCH, Hwy 185 & Sixth St, Port O'Connor, 77982. (Mail add: PO Box 424, Port O'Connor, 77982), Tel: 361-983-4365. FAX: 316-983-4365. E-Mail: staff@cclibrary.org. Web Site: www.cclibrary.org. *Librn*, Shirley Gordon; Staff 1 (Non-MLS 1)
Library Holdings: Bk Vols 10,000
Automation Activity & Vendor Info: (Circulation) Sagebrush Corporation
Friends of the Library Group
SEADRIFT BRANCH, 103 W Dallas, PO Box 567, Seadrift, 77983. SAN 362-1847. Tel: 512-785-4241. *Librn*, Vera Helms; Staff 1 (Non-MLS 1)
Library Holdings: Bk Vols 12,000
Friends of the Library Group

)RT NECHES

EFFIE & WILTON HEBERT PUBLIC LIBRARY, 2025 Merriman, 77651. SAN 320-5150. Tel: 409-722-4554. FAX: 409-719-4296. Web Site: www.ptn.lib.tx.us1. *Dir*, Mary Ann Carrier; E-Mail: mcarrier@hpl.lib.tx.us; *Ch Servs*, Lisa Wappler; *Tech Servs*, Nola Martin; *Admin Assoc*, Carolyn Driver; *Circ*, Mary Goldberg; Staff 7 (MLS 1, Non-MLS 6)
Founded 1934. Pop 13,944
Oct 1999-Sep 2000 Income City $340,000. Sal $131,394 (Prof $43,500)
Library Holdings: Bk Vols 50,000; Per Subs 109
Subject Interests: Acadian genealogy, Texana
Publications: Friendly Notes (quarterly) (Newsletter)
Mem of Houston Area Library System
Friends of the Library Group

)RTLAND

BELL-WHITTINGTON PUBLIC LIBRARY, 2400 Memorial Pkwy, 78374. SAN 316-6805. Tel: 361-777-0921. FAX: 361-643-6411. *Dir*, Sue Kornfuhrer; Staff 4 (MLS 4)
Founded 1934. Pop 12,000; Circ 80,000
Library Holdings: Bk Vols 30,000; Per Subs 80
Subject Interests: Architecture, Art, Bus, Education, Genealogy, Mgt
Special Collections: Antique Collecting; Genealogy Coll
Publications: Annual Report
Mem of San Patricio County Library System; South Texas Library System
Partic in Tex Share
Friends of the Library Group

)OST

POST PUBLIC LIBRARY, 105 E Main St, 79356-3299. SAN 316-6813. Tel: 806-495-2149. E-Mail: qckid@yahoo.com. *Librn*, Jeanette Edwards; Staff 2 (Non-MLS 2)
Founded 1966. Pop 5,182; Circ 16,530
Library Holdings: Bk Vols 15,018; Bk Titles 14,978
Subject Interests: Texas
Mem of West Texas Library System

)OTEET

POTEET PUBLIC LIBRARY,* 500 Avenue H, PO Box 380, 78065. SAN 316-6821. Tel: 830-742-8917. FAX: 830-742-8917. *Dir*, Mary Tondre
Library Holdings: Bk Titles 9,500; Per Subs 25
Special Collections: Texana Coll
Mem of Alamo Area Library System
Special Services for the Deaf - Books on deafness & sign language; Captioned film depository; High interest/low vocabulary books; Special interest periodicals
Friends of the Library Group

OTTSBORO

POTTSBORO AREA PUBLIC LIBRARY, 400 Hwy 120 W, PO Box 477, 75076-0477. SAN 376-4427. Tel: 903-786-8274. FAX: 903-786-5440. E-Mail: palib@texoma.com. *Librn*, Vivian Crouch
Sep 1999-Aug 2000 Income $20,000. Mats Exp $12,800
Library Holdings: Bk Vols 13,104
Mem of Northeast Texas Library System
Friends of the Library Group

PRAIRIE VIEW

J PRAIRIE VIEW A&M UNIVERSITY, John B Coleman Library, PO Box 519, 77446-0519. SAN 316-683X. Tel: 936-857-2012. Interlibrary Loan Service Tel: 936-857-2625. FAX: 936-857-2755. Web Site: www.tamu.edu/pvamu/library. *Dir*, Dr Frank Bruno; *Coll Develop*, Helen Yeh; Tel: 409-857-3192, E-Mail: helen-yeh@tamu.edu; *Per*, Mary MacWithey; Tel: 409-857-2756, E-Mail: mary-macwithey@tamu.edu; *Circ*, Juanita Walker; Tel: 409-857-2625, E-Mail: juanita-walker@tamu.edu
Founded 1878. Enrl 5,243; Fac 273; Highest Degree: Doctorate
Sep 1998-Aug 1999 Mats Exp $1,039,069, Books $50,273, Per/Ser (Incl. Access Fees) $88,997, Micro $43,190, Electronic Ref Mat (Incl. Access Fees) $29,304. Sal $534,102 (Prof $348,177)
Library Holdings: Bk Vols 314,788; Per Subs 872
Subject Interests: Biology, Business, Education, Engineering, Nursing
Special Collections: Black Heritage of the West Coll; Black Lawless Coll; Blacks in the US Military Coll
Automation Activity & Vendor Info: (Acquisitions) Endeavor; (Cataloging) Endeavor; (Circulation) Endeavor; (Course Reserve) Endeavor; (OPAC) Endeavor; (Serials) Endeavor
Partic in Amigos Library Services, Inc; Houston Area Research Library Consortium; OCLC Online Computer Library Center, Inc; TexShare

PRESIDIO

P CITY OF PRESIDIO LIBRARY,* O'Reilly St, PO Box 2440, 79845-2440. SAN 376-432X. Tel: 915-229-3317. FAX: 915-229-4640. *Librn*, Sarai Rodriquez
Library Holdings: Bk Vols 14,000; Per Subs 16
Mem of Texas Trans Pecos Library System

QUANAH

P THOMPSON-SAWYER PUBLIC LIBRARY,* 403 W Third St, 79252. SAN 376-4613. Tel: 940-663-2654. FAX: 940-663-2129. *Librn*, Janice Davis
Library Holdings: Bk Vols 30,000; Per Subs 12
Mem of North Texas Regional Library System
Friends of the Library Group

QUEMADO

P QUEMADO PUBLIC LIBRARY,* PO Drawer 210, 78877-0210. SAN 376-4168. Tel: 830-757-1313. FAX: 830-757-1313.
Library Holdings: Bk Vols 14,000; Per Subs 15
Mem of Alamo Area Library System

QUINLAN

P TAWAKONI AREA PUBLIC LIBRARY,* 340 W Hwy 276, 75474-2644. SAN 323-6668. Tel: 903-447-3445. *Librn*, Charlotte Reazes
Founded 1982. Pop 4,891; Circ 18,427
Library Holdings: Bk Vols 8,375; Bk Titles 9,000; Per Subs 1
Special Collections: American Indians (Amerindians Coll); Texas Literature (Texana Coll)
Mem of Northeast Texas Library System
Friends of the Library Group

QUITAQUE

P CAPROCK PUBLIC LIBRARY,* 104 N First, PO Box 487, 79255. SAN 376-6519. Tel: 806-455-1225. FAX: 806-455-1225. *Librn*, Arlene Hinkle
Jul 1998-Jun 1999 Income $13,000
Library Holdings: Bk Vols 9,300
Mem of Texas Panhandle Library System
Friends of the Library Group

QUITMAN

P QUITMAN PUBLIC LIBRARY,* 202 E Goode St, PO Box 77, 75783-0077. SAN 320-8486. Tel: 903-763-4191. FAX: 903-763-2532. *Dir*, Dorothy Demontigny
Founded 1975. Pop 2,000; Circ 28,955
Library Holdings: Bk Vols 21,005
Subject Interests: Bus, Genealogy
Mem of Northeast Texas Library System
Friends of the Library Group

RANDOLPH AFB

UNITED STATES AIR FORCE

A RANDOLPH AIR FORCE BASE LIBRARY, 12 SPTG/SVMG, Bldg 598 Fifth St E, 78150-4405. SAN 362-1901. Tel: 210-652-2617, 210-652-5578. FAX: 210-652-3261. Web Site: www.rafblibrary.org. *Dir*, David Ince; E-Mail: david.ince@randolph.af.mil; Staff 3 (MLS 2, Non-MLS 1)
Founded 1933
Library Holdings: Bk Vols 36,800; Bk Titles 31,200; Per Subs 125
Subject Interests: Mgt, Military history, Prof develop, Texas
Special Collections: Air War College; Project Warrior; Texana
Automation Activity & Vendor Info: (Cataloging) epixtech, inc.; (Circulation) epixtech, inc.; (Course Reserve) epixtech, inc.; (OPAC) epixtech, inc.
Database Vendor: OCLC - First Search
Partic in Coun of Res & Acad Librs; Fedlink
Friends of the Library Group

A US AIR FORCE AIR EDUCATION & TRAINING COMMAND, Library Program,* HQ AETC/SVP, 1850 First St W Ste 3, 78150-4308. SAN 370-2413. Tel: 210-652-3791. FAX: 210-652-6683. *Librn*, Darlene Price; E-Mail: darlene.price@randolph.af.mil
Library Holdings: Per Subs 7,300
Command level is office only. Air Education & Training Command totals 19 general & academic libraries

RANGER

J RANGER COLLEGE, Golemon Library, College Circle, 76470-3298. SAN 316-6880. Tel: 254-647-1414. FAX: 254-647-1656. E-Mail: ranger@cc.tx.us. Web Site: www.ranger.cc.tx.us. *Dir*, Courtney Hansen; E-Mail: chansen@ranger.cc.tx.us
Founded 1926. Highest Degree: Associate
Library Holdings: Bk Vols 32,000; Per Subs 122
Special Collections: Robert Ervin Howard Coll
Mem of Big Country Library System
Partic in TexShare

RANKIN

P RANKIN PUBLIC LIBRARY, (RPL), 310 E Tenth St, PO Box 6, 79778-0006. SAN 316-6899. Tel: 915-693-2881. FAX: 915-693-2667. E-Mail: rpl_patsy@yahoo.com. *Dir*, Patsy Northcott
Founded 1950. Pop 1,000; Circ 15,600
Library Holdings: Bk Vols 18,350; Per Subs 15
Publications: Newsletter
Mem of West Texas Library System
Open Mon-Thurs 10-5
Branches: 1

RAYMONDVILLE

P REBER MEMORIAL LIBRARY,* 193 N Fourth, 78580-1994. SAN 316-6902. Tel: 956-689-2930. FAX: 956-689-6476. *Librn*, Norma Cole
Pop 15,570; Circ 43,423
Library Holdings: Bk Vols 55,000; Per Subs 164
Mem of South Texas Library System

REFUGIO

P DENNIS M O'CONNOR PUBLIC LIBRARY,* 815 S Commerce St, 78377. SAN 316-6929. Tel: 512-526-2608. FAX: 512-526-2608. *Librn*, Nelda Blaschke; E-Mail: blaschke@netrak.net
Pop 7,980; Circ 23,668
Library Holdings: Bk Vols 23,635; Bk Titles 21,574; Per Subs 53
Special Collections: Texas Room
Mem of South Texas Library System

RICHARDSON

S ALCATEL NETWORK SYSTEMS, Information Center,* 1225 N Alma 412-120, 75081. SAN 316-6953. Tel: 972-996-6022. FAX: 972-996-6829. *Mgr*, Wanda Fox; E-Mail: wanda-g-fox@aud.alcateh.com; *Acq, Librn*, Sharon Neely
Founded 1953
Library Holdings: Bk Vols 55,000; Per Subs 300
Subject Interests: Computers, Electronics, Int bus, Marketing, Telecommunications
Restriction: Not open to public
Partic in Dialog Corporation; Dow Jones News Retrieval; Wilsonline

SR FIRST UNITED METHODIST CHURCH LIBRARY, 534 W Belt Line 75083. SAN 328-5111. Tel: 972-301-0143. Web Site: www.fumcr/library.htm. *Dir*, Janet Thompson; E-Mail: jthompson@fumcr.com
Founded 1959
Library Holdings: Bk Titles 7,000
Restriction: Members only

P RICHARDSON PUBLIC LIBRARY, 900 Civic Center Dr, 75080-5298. SAN 316-6945. Tel: 972-744-4350. Circulation Tel: 972-744-4363. Reference Tel: 972-744-4355. FAX: 972-744-5806, 972-952-0870. Web S www.cor.net/library. *Dir Libr Serv*, Julianne Lovelace; Tel: 972-744-4352, E-Mail: julianne.lovelace@cor.gov; *Asst Dir*, Jane Shelton; Tel: 972-744-4353, E-Mail: jane.shelton@cor.gov; *Librn*, Margot Burchard; Tel: 972-74 4356, E-Mail: margot.burchard@cor.gov; *Librn*, Stacey Davis; E-Mail: stacey.davis@cor.gov; *Librn*, Elizabeth Hercules; Tel: 972-744-4379, E-M elizabeth.hercules@cor.gov; *Librn*, Hanna Jurecki; E-Mail: hanna.jurecki@cor.gov; *Librn*, Peggy Keirstead; Tel: 972-744-4379, E-Mail: peggy.keirstead@cor.gov; *Librn*, Linda Lee; Tel: 972-744-4357, E-Mail: linda.lee@cor.gov; *Librn*, Ludmila Pospelova; Tel: 972-744-4379, E-Mail: ludmila.pospelova@cor.gov; *Librn*, Carol Sands; Tel: 972-744-4379, E-Ma carol.sands@cor.gov; *Tech Servs*, Steve Benson; Tel: 972-744-4368, E-Ma steve.benson@cor.gov; *Syst Coordr*, Wanda Vent; Tel: 972-744-4374, E-Mail: wanda.vent@cor.gov; *YA Servs*, Susan Allison; Tel: 972-744-4358 E-Mail: susan.allison@cor.gov; *Media Spec*, Yolanda Medina; Tel: 972-74 4359, E-Mail: yolanda.medina@cor.gov; *Cat*, Fayedene MacLeod; *Coll Develop*, Edith Reiss; *ILL*, Marilyn Comte; *Ad Servs*, Bill Pierce; Tel: 972 744-4377, E-Mail: bill.pierce@cor.gov; *Ref Serv Ad*, Elaine Klobe; Tel: 97 744-4376, E-Mail: elaine.klobe@cor.gov; *Circ*, Michael Furl; Tel: 972-74 4362, E-Mail: michael.furl@cor.gov. Subject Specialists: *Art*, Carol Sands *Fiction*, Linda Lee; *Local history*, Stacey Davis; Staff 37 (MLS 17, Non-MLS 20)
Founded 1959. Pop 91,050
Oct 1999-Sep 2000 Income $3,002,810, State $4,747, City $2,959,951, Other $38,112. Mats Exp $638,501. Sal $2,075,190
Library Holdings: Bk Vols 189,197; Bk Titles 151,881; Per Subs 450; Hi Interest/Low Vocabulary Bk Vols 511
Subject Interests: Bus ref
Special Collections: Chinese Language Materials (Dallas Chinese Lions Club Coll); History of Richardson (Richardson Public Library Coll), slides Korean Language Materials (Korean-American Breakfast Club Coll); Richardson Historical Notebook/Scrapbooks (Marilyn Floyd Coll); Richardson Wildflowers (Leonard Huffhines Coll), slides
Automation Activity & Vendor Info: (Acquisitions) epixtech, inc.; (Cataloging) epixtech, inc.; (Circulation) epixtech, inc.; (OPAC) epixtech, inc.; (Serials) epixtech, inc.
Database Vendor: GaleNet, IAC - SearchBank
Publications: Bibliographies
Mem of Northeast Texas Library System
FOL sponsors IN PERSON Author Lecture Series: KIDS IN PERSON Author Lecture Series
Friends of the Library Group

C UNIVERSITY OF TEXAS AT DALLAS, Eugene McDermott Library,* PO Box 830643, 75083-0643. SAN 362-1995. Tel: 972-883-2950. Interlibrary Loan Service Tel: 972-883-2900. FAX: 972-883-2473. Web Site: www.utdallas.edu/library. *Actg Dir, Archivist, Spec Coll*, Dr Larry D Sall; E-Mail: sall@utdallas.edu; *Cat*, Nancy S Whitt; *Ser*, Carolyn Henebry; *ILL* Vickie Bullock; *Coll Develop, Ref*, Dr Ellen D Safley
Founded 1964. Highest Degree: Doctorate
Sep 1997-Aug 1998 Income $4,243,888, State $2,199,965, Federal $4,704, Locally Generated Income $954,749, Parent Institution $846,949, Other $237,521. Mats Exp $2,197,968, Books $164,933, Per/Ser (Incl. Access Fees) $671,964, Presv $50,012, Micro $111,567, AV Equip $2,294, Other Print Mats $95,785. Sal $1,670,486 (Prof $833,819)
Library Holdings: Per Subs 3,890
Special Collections: Arnold A Jaffe Holocaust Coll; CAT/Air America Archives; General James H Doolittle Military Aviation Library; History of Aviation Coll; Louise B Belsterling Botanical Library; Translation Archives Wineburgh Philatelic Research Library
Mem of Asn of Research Libraries
Partic in Amigos Library Services, Inc; OCLC Online Computer Library Center, Inc
Departmental Libraries:
CALLIER CENTER LIBRARY, 1966 Inwood Rd, Dallas, 75235. SAN 36 2029. Tel: 972-905-3165. Interlibrary Loan Service Tel: 972-883-2900. FAX: 214-905-3143. Web Site: www.utdallas.edu/library/callier. *Librn*, D Allen L Clayton; E-Mail: aclayton@utdallas.edu
Library Holdings: Bk Vols 4,800
Subject Interests: Audiology, Deaf educ, Speech-lang pathology
Database Vendor: IAC - SearchBank, OVID Technologies, ProQuest
Function: ILL available
Partic in Alliance For Higher Education

CHLAND HILLS

RICHLAND HILLS PUBLIC LIBRARY,* 6724 Rena Dr, 76118-6297. SAN 316-3482. Tel: 817-595-6630. *Dir*, Carroll J Barrow
Founded 1960. Pop 8,500; Circ 74,084
Library Holdings: Bk Vols 33,000; Per Subs 80
Mem of North Texas Regional Library System
Friends of the Library Group

CHMOND

FORT BEND COUNTY LIBRARIES, George Memorial, 1001 Golfview Dr, 77469-5199. SAN 362-2088. Tel: 281-342-4455. Interlibrary Loan Service Tel: 281-341-2605. Circulation Tel: 281-341-2606. Reference Tel: 281-341-2604. TDD: 281-341-2669. FAX: 281-341-2688. E-Mail: dfojtik@fortbend.lib.tx.us. Web Site: www.fortbend.lib.tx.us/lib.html. *Dir*, Jane A Powell; Tel: 281-341-2618, E-Mail: jpowell@fortbend.lib.tx.us; *Asst Dir*, Carol Brown; Tel: 281-341-2653, E-Mail: ebrown@fortbend.lib.tx.us; *ILL, Ref Serv Ad*, Barbara Moren; Tel: 281-341-2627, E-Mail: bmoren@fortbend.lib.tx.us; *Cat*, Laura Calub; Tel: 281-341-2633, E-Mail: lcalub@fortbend.lib.tx.us; *Publ Servs*, Joyce Claypool Kennerly; Tel: 281-341-2611, E-Mail: jkennerly@fortbend.lib.tx.us; *Ch Servs*, Susan King; Tel: 281-341-2657, E-Mail: sking@fortbend.lib.tx.us; *Circ*, Joanne Downing; Tel: 281-341-2617, E-Mail: jdowning@fortbend.lib.tx.us; *Circ*, Maria Segura; Tel: 281-341-2666, E-Mail: msegura@fortbend.lib.tx.us; *Business*, Patty Gonzales; Tel: 281-341-2644, E-Mail: pgonzales@fortbend.lib.tx.us; *YA Servs*, Molly Krukewitt; Tel: 281-341-2634, E-Mail: mkrukewitt@fortbend.lib.tx.us; *Tech Coordr*, Jill Simpter; Tel: 281-341-2630, E-Mail: jsumpter@fortbend.lib.tx.us. Subject Specialists: *Genealogy*, Wolfram Von-Maszewski; *Local history*, Wolfram Von-Maszewski; Staff 141 (MLS 36, Non-MLS 105)
Founded 1947. Pop 362,778; Circ 1,659,665
Jan 2000-Dec 2000 Income (Main Library and Branch Library) $7,632,422, State $279,955, County $6,851,381, Parent Institution $28,382, Other $472,704. Mats Exp $420,569, Books $175,413, Per/Ser (Incl. Access Fees) $107,406, Presv $1,203, Micro $591, AV Equip $62,359, Electronic Ref Mat (Incl. Access Fees) $73,597. Sal $1,677,405 (Prof $675,304)
Library Holdings: Bk Vols 183,199; Bk Titles 135,741; Per Subs 429; Spec Interest Per Sub 28
Special Collections: Civil War; Genealogy & Local History; Regional Historial Resource Depository of Texas; Restoration (George Carriage Coll); Texana
Automation Activity & Vendor Info: (Acquisitions) epixtech, inc.; (Cataloging) epixtech, inc.; (Circulation) epixtech, inc.; (ILL) epixtech, inc.; (Media Booking) epixtech, inc.; (OPAC) epixtech, inc.; (Serials) epixtech, inc.
Database Vendor: Ebsco - EbscoHost, GaleNet, IAC - Info Trac
Publications: Annual Report; Monthly Calendar of Library Events; Quarterly Public Newsletter; Staff Newsletter
Mem of Houston Area Library System
Special Services for the Deaf - TDD
Friends of the Library Group
Branches: 8

FIRST COLONY, 2121 Austin Pkwy, Sugar Land, 77479-1219. SAN 374-4345. Tel: 281-265-4444. TDD: 281-265-4472. FAX: 281-265-4440. Web Site: www.fortbend.lib.tx.us/lib.html. *Librn*, Rosanne Burgess; E-Mail: rburgess@fortbend.lib.tx.us
Circ 561,493
Jan 2000-Dec 2000 Mats Exp $228,250, Books $193,302, Per/Ser (Incl. Access Fees) $8,397, Presv $20, AV Equip $5,705, Electronic Ref Mat (Incl. Access Fees) $20,826. Sal $340,266 (Prof $92,963)
Library Holdings: Bk Vols 110,879; Bk Titles 71,080; Per Subs 166
Automation Activity & Vendor Info: (Acquisitions) epixtech, inc.; (Cataloging) epixtech, inc.; (Circulation) epixtech, inc.; (ILL) epixtech, inc.; (Media Booking) epixtech, inc.; (OPAC) epixtech, inc.; (Serials) epixtech, inc.
Special Services for the Deaf - TDD
Friends of the Library Group

FORT BEND COUNTY LAW LIBRARY, 401 Jackson, 77469. SAN 370-9205. Tel: 281-341-3718. FAX: 281-342-0734. Web Site: www.fortbend.lib.tx.us/lib.html. *Librn*, Virginia Richards; E-Mail: vrichards@fortbend.lib.tx.us
Founded 1989
Jan 2000-Dec 2000 Income City $119,294. Mats Exp $60,000, Books $44,758, Per/Ser (Incl. Access Fees) $6,705, Electronic Ref Mat (Incl. Access Fees) $8,537. Sal $34,038
Library Holdings: Bk Vols 4,092; Bk Titles 155

ALBERT GEORGE BRANCH, 9230 Gene St, Needville, 77461-8313. SAN 362-2118. Tel: 979-793-4270. FAX: 281-342-5992. Web Site: www.fortbend.lib.tx.us/lib.html. *Librn*, Patricia Dittrich; E-Mail: pdittrich@fortbend.lib.tx.us
Founded 1974. Circ 36,240
Jan 2000-Dec 2000 Mats Exp $41,501, Books $35,037, Per/Ser (Incl. Access Fees) $2,657, Presv $22, AV Equip $1,119, Electronic Ref Mat (Incl. Access Fees) $2,666. Sal $83,767 (Prof $29,287)
Library Holdings: Bk Vols 35,670; Bk Titles 29,951; Per Subs 87
Automation Activity & Vendor Info: (Acquisitions) epixtech, inc.; (Cataloging) epixtech, inc.; (Circulation) epixtech, inc.; (ILL) epixtech, inc.; (Media Booking) epixtech, inc.; (OPAC) epixtech, inc.; (Serials) epixtech, inc.
Friends of the Library Group

MAMIE GEORGE BRANCH, 320 Dulles Ave, Stafford, 77477-4799. SAN 362-2142. Tel: 281-491-8086. FAX: 281-242-5793. Web Site: www.fortbend.lib.tx.us/lib.html. *Librn*, Susan Saunders; E-Mail: ssaunders@fortbend.lib.tx.us
Founded 1974. Circ 51,625
Jan 2000-Dec 2000 Mats Exp $35,000, Books $28,491, Per/Ser (Incl. Access Fees) $1,953, AV Equip $1,890, Electronic Ref Mat (Incl. Access Fees) $2,666. Sal $67,738 (Prof $32,654)
Library Holdings: Bk Vols 41,876; Bk Titles 33,307; Per Subs 100
Automation Activity & Vendor Info: (Acquisitions) epixtech, inc.; (Cataloging) epixtech, inc.; (Circulation) epixtech, inc.; (ILL) epixtech, inc.; (Media Booking) epixtech, inc.; (OPAC) epixtech, inc.; (Serials) epixtech, inc.
Friends of the Library Group

KATY-FORT BEND BRANCH, 23111 Cinco Ranch Blvd, Katy, 77450. Tel: 281-395-1311. FAX: 281-395-6377. Web Site: www.fortbend.lib.tx.us/lib.html. *In Charge*, Debbie Moseley; E-Mail: dmoseley@fortbend.lib.tx.us
Founded 1999. Circ 40,042
Jan 2000-Dec 2000 Mats Exp $30,000, Books $25,016, Per/Ser (Incl. Access Fees) $1,718, AV Equip $1,489, Electronic Ref Mat (Incl. Access Fees) $1,777. Sal $30,289
Library Holdings: Bk Vols 10,659; Bk Titles 5,082
Automation Activity & Vendor Info: (Acquisitions) epixtech, inc.; (Cataloging) epixtech, inc.; (Circulation) epixtech, inc.; (ILL) epixtech, inc.; (Media Booking) epixtech, inc.; (OPAC) epixtech, inc.; (Serials) epixtech, inc.
Database Vendor: epixtech, inc.

MISSOURI CITY BRANCH, 1530 Texas Pkwy, Missouri City, 77489-2170. SAN 373-2754. Tel: 281-499-4100. TDD: 281-261-5944. FAX: 281-261-5829. Web Site: www.fortbend.lib.tx.us/lib.html. *Librn*, Lorri Lessey; E-Mail: llessey@fortbend.lib.tx.us
Founded 1992. Circ 166,178
Jan 2000-Dec 2000 Mats Exp $147,250, Books $124,413, Per/Ser (Incl. Access Fees) $8,293, Presv $30, AV Equip $3,389, Electronic Ref Mat (Incl. Access Fees) $11,125. Sal $271,296 (Prof $124,794)
Library Holdings: Bk Vols 84,668; Bk Titles 59,779; Per Subs 185
Automation Activity & Vendor Info: (Acquisitions) epixtech, inc.; (Cataloging) epixtech, inc.; (Circulation) epixtech, inc.; (ILL) epixtech, inc.; (Media Booking) epixtech, inc.; (OPAC) epixtech, inc.; (Serials) epixtech, inc.
Special Services for the Deaf - TDD
Friends of the Library Group

BOB LUTTS FULSHEAR SIMONTON BRANCH, 8100 FM 359 S, Fulshear, 77441-0907. SAN 373-2762. Tel: 281-346-1432. FAX: 281-346-1265. Web Site: www.fortbend.lib.tx.us/lib.html. *Librn*, Chris Accardo; E-Mail: ccardo@fortbend.lib.tx.us
Circ 44,025
Jan 2000-Dec 2000 Mats Exp $93,700, Books $80,717, Per/Ser (Incl. Access Fees) $4,383, Presv $20, AV Equip $1,470, Electronic Ref Mat (Incl. Access Fees) $7,110. Sal $173,008 (Prof $32,897)
Library Holdings: Bk Vols 33,988; Bk Titles 22,824; Per Subs 127
Automation Activity & Vendor Info: (Acquisitions) epixtech, inc.; (Cataloging) epixtech, inc.; (Circulation) epixtech, inc.; (ILL) epixtech, inc.; (Media Booking) epixtech, inc.; (OPAC) epixtech, inc.; (Serials) epixtech, inc.
Friends of the Library Group

SUGAR LAND BRANCH, 550 Eldridge, Sugar Land, 77478. Tel: 281-277-8934. FAX: 281-277-8945. Web Site: www.fortbend.lib.tx.us/lib.html. *Mgr*, Barbara Barton; E-Mail: bbarton@fortbend.lib.tx.us; Staff 17 (MLS 4, Non-MLS 13)
Founded 1999. Circ 290,907
Jan 2000-Dec 2000 Mats Exp $224,500, Books $189,181, Per/Ser (Incl. Access Fees) $8,282, Presv $50, AV Equip $7,169, Electronic Ref Mat (Incl. Access Fees) $19,818. Sal $341,325 (Prof $116,175)
Library Holdings: Bk Vols 64,162; Bk Titles 39,485; Per Subs 115
Database Vendor: epixtech, inc.
Friends of the Library Group

RIO GRANDE CITY

P STARR COUNTY PUBLIC LIBRARY,* 700 E Canales, 78582-3588. SAN 372-7580. Tel: 956-487-4389. FAX: 956-487-7390. *Asst Dir*, Norma Gomez Fultz; E-Mail: n-fultz@netrax.net; *Asst Librn*, Leticia Guerra; *Coll Develop*, Robert Joyce; Staff 5 (MLS 1, Non-MLS 4)
Founded 1990. Pop 52,000
1996-1997 Income $109,645, County $101,575, Other $1,307. Mats Exp $26,657, Books $24,182, Per/Ser (Incl. Access Fees) $2,220. Sal $57,312 (Prof $27,500)
Library Holdings: Bk Titles 27,500; Per Subs 106
Publications: Library Update; Local newspaper column
Mem of South Texas Library System
Friends of the Library Group

Branches: 2
LAROSITA BRANCH, Hwy 83, Larosita, 78584. SAN 376-1045. Tel: 956-849-4453. *Librn*, Norma Fultz
Friends of the Library Group
ROMA BRANCH, Morelos St, Roma, 78584. SAN 376-1053. Tel: 956-849-0072. *Librn*, Angela Hinojosa
Friends of the Library Group

RIO HONDO

P RIO HONDO PUBLIC LIBRARY, N Arroyo Blvd, PO Box 740, 78583-0740. SAN 376-4311. Tel: 956-748-3322. FAX: 956-748-3322. *Librn*, Willie Montez; E-Mail: willie@riohondo.lib.ccls.tx.us
Jan 1999-Dec 1999 Income $17,500
Library Holdings: Bk Vols 13,000; Per Subs 25
Mem of South Texas Library System
Friends of the Library Group

ROANOKE

P ROANOKE PUBLIC LIBRARY, 308 S Walnut St, 76262. SAN 373-2800. Tel: 817-491-2691. FAX: 817-491-2729. E-Mail: roanpl@flash.net. Web Site: roanoke.lib.tx.us. *Dir*, Katherine Boyer; *YA Servs*, Ann Coleman; *Cat*, Vivian Henderson; *Asst City Librn*, Mollie Cummins; Staff 4 (MLS 1, Non-MLS 3)
Founded 1979. Pop 8,700; Circ 40,000
1999-2000 Income City $153,255. Mats Exp $20,400, Books $12,000, Per/Ser (Incl. Access Fees) $500, Presv $400, Micro $2,500, Electronic Ref Mat (Incl. Access Fees) $5,000. Sal $84,901 (Prof $27,000)
Library Holdings: Bk Vols 21,921; Bk Titles 21,400; Per Subs 20
Special Collections: Texana
Automation Activity & Vendor Info: (Cataloging) Athena; (Circulation) Athena; (OPAC) Athena
Database Vendor: Ebsco - EbscoHost, OCLC - First Search, Wilson - Wilson Web
Mem of North Texas Regional Library System
Special Services for the Deaf - Books on deafness & sign language; High interest/low vocabulary books
Friends of the Library Group

ROBERT LEE

P COKE COUNTY LIBRARY,* 706 Austin St, PO Box 637, 76945-0637. SAN 316-697X. Tel: 915-453-2495. *Librn*, Beth Prather
Circ 12,054
Library Holdings: Bk Vols 11,000
Mem of Big Country Library System
Open Tues & Fri 8-12, Wed 8-4, Thurs 1-5

ROBSTOWN

P NUECES COUNTY LIBRARY,* 710 E Main, 78380. SAN 362-2177. Tel: 512-767-5228. *In Charge*, Luisa Espinoza; Staff 1 (MLS 1)
Founded 1939. Pop 27,000; Circ 42,000
Library Holdings: Bk Vols 49,000; Bk Titles 48,000; Per Subs 80
Branches: 1
BISHOP BRANCH, County Bldg, Bishop, 78343. SAN 362-2207.
Library Holdings: Bk Vols 3,000
Bookmobiles: 1

ROCKDALE

P LUCY HILL PATTERSON MEMORIAL LIBRARY,* 201 Ackerman St, 76567. SAN 316-7003. Tel: 512-446-3410. FAX: 512-446-5597. E-Mail: rockdale@onr.com. Web Site: www.main.org/patlib/library.htm. *Dir*, Melanie Todd; *Assoc Librn*, Karen Newton; *Assoc Librn*, Darlene Taisler; *Asst Librn*, Bonnie George; Staff 4 (Non-MLS 4)
Founded 1953. Pop 11,691; Circ 32,368
Oct 1997-Sep 1998 Income $17,424, City $4,424, County $4,000, Locally Generated Income $9,000. Mats Exp $12,640, Books $7,500. Sal $40,680 (Prof $16,215)
Library Holdings: Bk Vols 26,333; Bk Titles 24,824; Per Subs 33
Special Collections: Dr George Hill Patterson Coll (First Editions)
Mem of Central Texas Library System
Friends of the Library Group

ROCKPORT

P ARANSAS COUNTY PUBLIC LIBRARY,* 701 E Mimosa, 78382. SAN 316-7011. Tel: 512-790-0153. FAX: 512-790-0150. *Dir*, Mary Ragsdale
Founded 1956. Pop 14,000; Circ 81,872
1997-1998 Income $86,120. Mats Exp $14,000. Sal $59,468
Library Holdings: Bk Titles 50,000; Per Subs 21
Subject Interests: Local history
Mem of South Texas Library System
Friends of the Library Group

ROCKWALL

P ROCKWALL COUNTY LIBRARY, 105 S First, 75087. SAN 316-7038. Tel: 972-882-0340. FAX: 972-882-0347. E-Mail: rocklib@znet.tx.com. W Site: www.rocklib.org. *Dir*, Kathleen Melston; *Ch Servs*, Doreen Miller; Staff 2 (MLS 1, Non-MLS 1)
Founded 1945. Pop 35,000; Circ 101,000
Library Holdings: Bk Vols 40,000; Per Subs 99
Subject Interests: Genealogy, Texana
Publications: Booklist; Library Journal; School Library Journal
Mem of Northeast Texas Library System
Friends of the Library Group

ROSEBUD

P D BROWN MEMORIAL LIBRARY,* 201 N Second St, 76570. SAN 3 7046. *Librn*, Marie Pavelka
Pop 1,600
Library Holdings: Bk Vols 14,000
Mem of Central Texas Library System
Open Mon, Wed & Fri 1:30-5:30
Friends of the Library Group

ROTAN

P ROTAN PUBLIC LIBRARY,* 404 E Sammy Baugh, 79546-3820. SAN 320-5169. Tel: 915-735-3362. FAX: 915-735-2229. E-Mail: library@bigcountry.net. *Librn*, Monica Carrillo; Staff 1 (Non-MLS 1)
Founded 1978. Pop 4,719; Circ 8,333
Library Holdings: Bk Vols 11,599; Bk Titles 10,679; Per Subs 14
Subject Interests: Genealogy, Local history
Special Collections: Texas Heritage Resource Center (Southwest Coll)
Mem of Big Country Library System
Special Services - Story hour program for children; summer reading club. Special Holdings - Literacy materials available to tutors; Charter member Texas Heritage Resource Group. Delivery of books available for persons unable to come to library

ROUND ROCK

P ROUND ROCK PUBLIC LIBRARY SYSTEM, 216 E Main St, 78664-5245. SAN 316-7054. Tel: 512-218-7000. FAX: 512-218-7061. *Dir*, Dale Ricklefs; Tel: 512-218-7005; *Coll Develop*, Linda Beebe; *Coll Develop*, Tricia Braver; *Coll Develop*, Janette Johnston; *Coll Develop*, Helen Klenz Staff 30 (MLS 5, Non-MLS 25)
Founded 1963. Pop 60,000; Circ 410,000
Library Holdings: Bk Vols 72,525; Per Subs 121
Subject Interests: Local history, Texana
Special Collections: Williamson County Genealogical Society Coll
Automation Activity & Vendor Info: (Cataloging) epixtech, inc.
Database Vendor: epixtech, inc.
Publications: Bibliographies; bibliographies
Mem of Central Texas Library System
Provides adult literacy tutoring, VITA & TCE tax consulting
Friends of the Library Group

ROUND TOP

S WINEDALE HISTORICAL CENTER LIBRARY, PO Box 11, 78954-001 SAN 327-8530. Tel: 979-278-3530. FAX: 979-278-3531. Web Site: www.cah.utexas.edu. *Mgr*, Gloria Jaster; E-Mail: g.jaster@mail.utexas.edu
Library Holdings: Bk Vols 1,000
Subject Interests: Antiques, History
Restriction: Non-circulating to the public

ROWLETT

P ROWLETT PUBLIC LIBRARY,* 3900 Main St, 75088-5075. (Mail add: PO Box 1017, 75030-1017), SAN 361-4190. Tel: 972-412-6161. FAX: 972-412-6153. *Dir Libr Serv*, Barbara Blake; *Coll Develop*, Tony New
Pop 38,700
Oct 1997-Sep 1998 Income $480,103, City $458,105, Locally Generated Income $16,033. Mats Exp $120,619, Books $75,000, Per/Ser (Incl. Access Fees) $12,000, Micro $750, AV Equip $29,869. Sal $288,911
Library Holdings: Bk Vols 34,336
Partic in Northeast Texas Library System
Friends of the Library Group

NGE

RUNGE PUBLIC LIBRARY, 311 N Helena, 78151. (Mail add: PO Box 37, 78151), SAN 316-7062. Tel: 830-239-4192. FAX: 830-239-4629. E-Mail: librarian@runge.lib.tx.us. Web Site: www.tunge.lib.tx.us. *Librn*, Catherine Jonas; Staff 1 (Non-MLS 1)
Founded 1966. Pop 1,139; Circ 17,000
Oct 2000-Sep 2001 Income $31,000, City $4,000, County $27,000. Mats Exp $7,000, Books $6,000, Per/Ser (Incl. Access Fees) $500, AV Equip $500. Sal $18,000
Library Holdings: Bk Titles 12,000; Per Subs 43
Subject Interests: Texana
Automation Activity & Vendor Info: (Acquisitions) ComPanion Corp; (Cataloging) ComPanion Corp; (Circulation) ComPanion Corp
Mem of Alamo Area Library System; Karnes County Library System

SK

RUSK STATE HOSPITAL
TEXAS DEPARTMENT OF MENTAL HEALTH & MENTAL RETARDATION MEDICAL LIBRARY, Jacksonville Hwy N, PO Box 318, 75785. SAN 316-7070. Tel: 903-683-3421, Ext 3240. FAX: 903-683-2994. *Librn*, Kathy Chancellor
Founded 1976
Library Holdings: Bk Vols 16,000; Per Subs 31
Subject Interests: Education, Recreational reading, Vocational progs
TEXAS DEPARTMENT OF MENTAL HEALTH & MENTAL RETARDATION PATIENT LIBRARY, Jacksonville Hwy N, PO Box 318, 75785. SAN 320-3581. Tel: 903-683-3421, Ext 3895. FAX: 903-683-2994.
Founded 1971
Library Holdings: Bk Vols 8,074; Per Subs 20
Subject Interests: Biographies, Fiction, Gen interest, Sports
Special Collections: Cassette Books for Visual Impaired; Large Print Coll

SINGLETARY MEMORIAL LIBRARY,* 207 E Sixth St, 75785. SAN 316-7089. Tel: 903-683-5916. *Librn*, Ruth Mather
Founded 1902. Pop 4,633; Circ 17,000
Library Holdings: Bk Vols 21,600; Per Subs 30
Special Collections: Cherokee County Genealogy; Texana
Mem of Northeast Texas Library System

BINAL

SABINAL PUBLIC LIBRARY, 412 N Center St, 78881. (Mail add: PO Box 245, 78881-0245), Tel: 830-988-2911. FAX: 830-988-2633. E-Mail: library1@ev1.net. *Dir*, Caroline Habermacher
Founded 1978. Pop 2,076
1998-1999 Income $8,500, City $7,000, County $1,500. Mats Exp Books $230. Sal $960
Library Holdings: Bk Vols 12,000; High Interest/Low Vocabulary Bk Vols 152
Automation Activity & Vendor Info: (Cataloging) epixtech, inc.; (Circulation) epixtech, inc.
Mem of Alamo Area Library System
Friends of the Library Group

CHSE

SACHSE PUBLIC LIBRARY,* 5560 Hwy 78, 75048-1545. SAN 361-4220. Tel: 972-530-8966. FAX: 972-495-7682. *Librn*, Karen Williams
Library Holdings: Bk Vols 23,000; Per Subs 10
Mem of Dallas County Libr Syst; Northeast Texas Library System
Friends of the Library Group

GINAW

SAGINAW PUBLIC LIBRARY, 355 McLeroy Blvd, PO Box 79070, 76179-0070. SAN 316-7097. Tel: 817-232-2100. FAX: 817-232-9134. E-Mail: library@ci.saginaw.tx.us. *Dir*, Yvonne Flippo; E-Mail: yflippo@ci.saginaw.tx.us
Founded 1964. Pop 12,580; Circ 91,748
Library Holdings: Bk Titles 39,374
Subject Interests: Large print, Local history, Western
Automation Activity & Vendor Info: (Cataloging) Athena; (Circulation) Athena
Mem of North Texas Regional Library System
Friends of the Library Group

SALADO

P SALADO PUBLIC LIBRARY,* 511 Main St, PO Box 706, 76571. SAN 376-4761. Tel: 254-947-9191. FAX: 254-947-9146. *Librn*, Patty Campbell
Sep 1998-Aug 1999 Income $24,000. Mats Exp $14,000. Sal $8,000
Library Holdings: Bk Vols 8,000; Per Subs 10
Mem of Central Texas Library System
Friends of the Library Group

SAN ANGELO

C ANGELO STATE UNIVERSITY, Porter Henderson Library, 2601 West Ave N, 76904. (Mail add: PO Box 11013, ASU Sta, 76909-0001), Tel: 915-942-2222. Interlibrary Loan Service Tel: 915-942-2300. Circulation Tel: 915-942-2051. Reference Tel: 915-942-2141. FAX: 915-942-2198. E-Mail: library@angelo.edu, reference@angelo.edu. Web Site: www.angelo.edu/sciences/library. *Dir*, Dr Maurice G Fortin; Tel: 915-942-2510, E-Mail: maurice.fortin@angelo.edu; *Acq*, Javad Maher; Tel: 915-942-2312, E-Mail: javad.maher@angelo.edu; *Cat*, Shirley R Richardson; Tel: 915-942-2221, E-Mail: shirley.richardson@angelo.edu; *Circ*, Angela L Skaggs; Tel: 915-942-2051, E-Mail: angela.skaggs@angelo.edu; *Doc Delivery*, Wanda Green; Tel: 915-942-2300, E-Mail: wanda.green@angelo.edu; *Media Spec*, Barbara J Bergman; Tel: 915-942-2513, E-Mail: barbara.bergman@angelo.edu; *Spec Coll*, Suzanne O Campbell; Tel: 915-942-2164, E-Mail: suzanne.campbell@angelo.edu; *Ref Serv*, Mark Allan; Tel: 915-942-2511, E-Mail: mark.allan@angelo.edu; *Doc*, Janetta Paschal; Tel: 915-942-2300, E-Mail: janetta.paschal@angelo.edu; Staff 10 (MLS 8, Non-MLS 2)
Founded 1928. Enrl 6,309; Fac 252; Highest Degree: Master
Sep 1999-Aug 2000 Income $3,257,448, State $1,605,724, Locally Generated Income $26,000, Parent Institution $1,605,724, Other $20,000. Mats Exp $702,378, Books $151,695, Per/Ser (Incl. Access Fees) $414,350, Presv $14,701, AV Equip $42,718, Electronic Ref Mat (Incl. Access Fees) $78,914. Sal $286,158 (Prof $220,474)
Library Holdings: Bk Vols 271,275; Per Subs 1,850
Subject Interests: SW hist, Tex hist, W Tex
Automation Activity & Vendor Info: (Cataloging) NOTIS
Partic in OCLC Online Computer Library Center, Inc
Friends of the Library Group

S FORT CONCHO NATIONAL HISTORIC LANDMARK, Research Library & Archives, 630 S Oakes, 76903-7099. SAN 321-0219. Tel: 915-481-2646. FAX: 915-657-4540. E-Mail: hgtrs@fortconcho.com.
Founded 1969
Library Holdings: Bk Titles 6,000; Per Subs 20
Special Collections: Architectural Coll (Oscar Ruffini Papers); Boyd Cornick Papers; Fort Concho History; Fort Concho Museum Records; George Gibson Huntt Papers; M C Ragsdale Photograph Coll; Military History; San Angelo Coll; Texas Photographers Coll, prints; William G Wedemeyer Photograph Coll; William S Veck Papers
Publications: Fort Concho Guidon (quarterly newsletter)
Restriction: Open to public for reference only
Certified Texas Heritage Resource Center

P TOM GREEN COUNTY LIBRARY SYSTEM, 113 W Beauregard, 76903-5887. SAN 362-2231. Tel: 915-655-7321. TDD: 915-659-3247. FAX: 915-659-4027. Web Site: www.co.tom-green.tx.us. *Dir*, Larry D Justiss; E-Mail: larry.justiss@co.tom-green.tx.us; *Assoc Dir*, D Karen Vavricka; *Ad Servs, ILL, Ref*, Mary Chatfield; *Ch Servs, YA Servs*, Sally Meyers; *Tech Servs*, Martha McCloskey; *Bkmobile Coordr*, Nona Williams; *Acq*, Mary Crudup; Staff 32 (MLS 5, Non-MLS 27)
Founded 1923. Pop 104,398; Circ 545,084
Oct 1999-Sep 2000 Income (Main Library and Branch Library) $1,223,694, State $2,249, County $1,070,102, Locally Generated Income $148,843, Other $2,500. Mats Exp $250,797, Books $195,233, Per/Ser (Incl. Access Fees) $16,144, Presv $3,275, Micro $3,167, Electronic Ref Mat (Incl. Access Fees) $32,978. Sal $613,313 (Prof $258,062)
Library Holdings: Bk Vols 280,006; Bk Titles 161,809; Per Subs 372
Subject Interests: Local history
Automation Activity & Vendor Info: (Acquisitions) GEAC; (Cataloging) GEAC; (Circulation) GEAC
Database Vendor: IAC - Info Trac
Mem of Big Country Library System
Special Services for the Deaf - TDD
Friends of the Library Group
Branches: 2
ANGELO WEST, 3013 Vista del Arroyo, 76904. SAN 362-2266. Tel: 915-944-1350. Web Site: www.co.tom-green.tx.us. *Librn*, Dorthy Stapleton
Library Holdings: Bk Vols 43,386
Friends of the Library Group
NORTH ANGELO, 3001 N Chadbourne, 76904. SAN 362-2290. Tel: 915-653-8412. Web Site: www.co.tom-green.tx.us. *Librn*, Rose Champlin
Library Holdings: Bk Vols 18,162
Friends of the Library Group
Bookmobiles: 1

§J HOWARD COLLEGE - SAN ANGELO, 3197 Executive Dr, 76904. Tel: 915-944-9585. FAX: 915-947-9524. Web Site: www.hc.cc.tx.us/library/xsa.htm. *Dean of Libr*, William L Kincade; Tel: 915-264-5092, Fax: 915-264-5094, E-Mail: wkincade@hc.cc.tx.us; *Librn*, Connie Kroll; E-Mail: ckroll@hc.cc.tx.us; Staff 1 (MLS 1)
Enrl 944; Highest Degree: Associate
Oct 2000-Sep 2001 Income $52,810. Mats Exp $12,350, Books $5,000, Per/Ser (Incl. Access Fees) $4,850. Sal $38,960
Library Holdings: Bk Titles 2,679; Per Subs 50
Database Vendor: GaleNet, IAC - Info Trac, OCLC - First Search, OVID Technologies

S SAN ANGELO STANDARD-TIMES NEWSPAPER,* 34 W Harris, PO Box 5111, 76902. SAN 370-2219. Tel: 915-653-1221. FAX: 915-658-7341. E-Mail: standard@texaswest.com. Web Site: www.texaswest.com. *Librn*, Edna Sedeno
Library Holdings: Bk Vols 200; Per Subs 36
Subject Interests: Newsp ref topics

M SHANNON WEST TEXAS MEMORIAL HOSPITAL LIBRARIES, 120 E Harris, PO Box 1879, 76902. SAN 316-7135. Tel: 915-657-5123, 915-657-5191. FAX: 915-657-5401. *Librn*, Austin Roseanne; E-Mail: roseanneaustin@shannonhealth.org
Library Holdings: Bk Vols 1,000; Per Subs 95
Partic in Medline; Nat Libr of Med
Holdings figures include 3 separate libraries: Doctor's Library, Nursing Library

SAN ANTONIO

L AKIN, GUMP, STRAUSS, HAUER & FELD LLP, Law Library, 300 Convent St, Ste 1500, 78205. SAN 373-6199. Tel: 210-281-7130. FAX: 210-224-2035. Web Site: www.akingump.com. *Librn*, Mary Rittgers; E-Mail: mrittgers@akingump.com
Library Holdings: Bk Vols 20,000
Restriction: Staff use only

P ALAMO AREA LIBRARY SYSTEM, 600 Soledad St, 78205-2786. SAN 316-7380. Tel: 210-207-2609. FAX: 210-207-2537. *Coordr*, Ruth Libby; Staff 6 (MLS 3, Non-MLS 3)
Sep 2000-Aug 2001 Income $775,926. Mats Exp $286,355. Sal $233,291
Library Holdings: Per Subs 148
Publications: El Nopal (bimonthly newsletter)
Member Libraries: Alexander Memorial Library; Bandera County Library; Boerne Public Library; Bulverde Public Library; Butt-Holdsworth Memorial Library; Castroville Public Library; Charlotte Public Library; Comfort Public Library; Converse Public Library; Crystal City Memorial Library; Dimmit County Public Library; Driscoll Public Library; El Progreso Memorial Library; Falls City Public Library; Hondo Public Library; Jourdanton Community Library; Karnes City Public Library; Kendalia Public Library; Kinney County Public Library; Leon Valley Public Library; Lytle Public Library; Marion Community Library; New Braunfels Public Library; Nueces Canyon Public Library; Pearsall Public Library; Pioneer Memorial Library; Pleasanton Public Library; Poteet Public Library; Quemado Public Library; Real County Public Library; Runge Public Library; Sabinal Public Library; Sam Fore Jr Wilson County Public Library; Schertz Public Library; Seguin-Guadalupe County Public Library; Tye Preston Memorial Library; Universal City Public Library; Val Verde County Library

SR ALAMO HEIGHTS UNITED METHODIST CHURCH LIBRARY, 825 E Basse Rd, 78209-1832. SAN 371-7046. Tel: 210-826-3215. *Librn*, Jody Wright
Founded 1958
Oct 1999-Sep 2000 Income $1,000
Library Holdings: Bk Vols 7,200

R ARCHDIOCESE OF SAN ANTONIO, Catholic Archives of San Antonio, 2718 W Woodlawn, 78228-5195. (Mail add: PO Box 28410, 78228-0410), SAN 329-1502. Tel: 210-734-2620, Ext 103. *Archivist*, Bro Edward J Loch; E-Mail: eloch@archdiosa.org; Staff 1 (Non-MLS 1)
Founded 1974. Highest Degree: Master
Jul 1999-Jun 2000 Income $42,000, Locally Generated Income $2,000, Parent Institution $40,000. Mats Exp $4,095, Per/Ser (Incl. Access Fees) $95, Presv $1,000, Micro $2,000, AV Equip $1,000. Sal $20,000
Library Holdings: Bk Vols 750; Bk Titles 700
Special Collections: Bexar Archives; Camargo Mexico; Chancery Papers, papers & microfilm; Orphanage (restricted); Papal Visit, papers, video; Vital Statistics, Sacramental Records, originals & microfilm, newspapers
Publications: American Archivist; Archival Outlook
Restriction: Restricted access

R ASSUMPTION SEMINARY LIBRARY,* 2600 W Woodlawn, PO Box 28240, 78228. SAN 316-7151. Tel: 210-734-5137. FAX: 210-734-2324. *Librn*, Sister Addie Walker
Founded 1952
Library Holdings: Bk Vols 20,500; Per Subs 140

M BAPTIST HEALTH SYSTEM, Bruce A Garrett Library & Media Center, 111 Dallas St, 78205-1230. SAN 327-8301. Tel: 210-297-7639. FAX: 21 297-0716. *Dir*, Dottie Jobe; E-Mail: djobe@baptisthealthsystem.org; *Asst Librn*, Dagmar Gates; *Asst Librn*, Peg Cartney
Library Holdings: Bk Titles 3,400; Per Subs 175
Subject Interests: Nursing
Branches:
VILLAGE DRIVE, 8811 Village Dr, 78217. SAN 371-3822. Tel: 210-29 2639. FAX: 210-297-0230. *Librn*, Carolyn Mueller

GL BEXAR COUNTY LAW LIBRARY,* Bexar County Courthouse, 5th flr 100 Dolorosa, 78205. SAN 316-7178. Tel: 210-227-8822. FAX: 210-271-9614. *Librn*, James M Allison
Library Holdings: Bk Vols 75,642; Per Subs 84

M BEXAR COUNTY MEDICAL LIBRARY ASSOCIATION,* 202 W Fre Pl, PO Box 12678, 78212-0678. SAN 316-7186. Tel: 210-734-6691. FAX 210-734-9556. E-Mail: bexar_md@icsi.net. Web Site: www.bcms.org. *Lib* Danna Rende
Founded 1912
Library Holdings: Per Subs 40

M CHRISTUS SANTA ROSA HEALTH CARE, (Formerly Santa Rosa He Care), Harold S Toy MD Memorial Health Science Library, 333 N Santa Rosa St, 78207-3198. SAN 316-7429. Tel: 210-704-2284. FAX: 210-704-3177. *Coordr*, Jann Guerrero
Founded 1949
Library Holdings: Bk Vols 2,000; Bk Titles 1,989; Per Subs 126
Subject Interests: Family practice, Hematology, Medicine, Nursing, Oncology, Orthopedics, Pediatrics
Partic in Docline; Medline

SR CONGREGATION AGUDAS ACHIM, Goldie & Joe Tills Library, 1655 Huebner Rd, 78248. SAN 316-7216. Tel: 210-479-0307. FAX: 210-479-0295. Web Site: www.agudas-achim.org. *Librn*, Felice Feldman
Library Holdings: Bk Vols 2,632; Bk Titles 2,529
Special Collections: Judaica Coll
Automation Activity & Vendor Info: (Cataloging) Athena; (Cataloging) Sagebrush Corporation
Self-sustaining synagogue library wholy dependent upon contributions an synagogue budget considerations. Open Mon & Wed 4-6, Sun 9-12

S DAUGHTERS OF THE REPUBLIC OF TEXAS LIBRARY, (DRTL), 3C Alamo Plaza, 78205. (Mail add: PO Box 1401, 78295-1401), SAN 316-7224. Tel: 210-225-1071, 210-225-8155. FAX: 210-212-8514. E-Mail: dr drtl.org. Web Site: www.drtl.org/. *Dir*, Elaine Davis; Tel: 210-225-1071, 16, E-Mail: edavis@drtl.org; *Asst Dir*, Martha Utterback; Tel: 210-225-10 Ext 17, E-Mail: mutterback@drtl.org; *Archivist*, Warren Stricker; Staff 8 (MLS 5, Non-MLS 3)
Founded 1945
Library Holdings: Bk Titles 17,500; Per Subs 65
Subject Interests: Texas hist: Republic period, the Alamo
Special Collections: Manuscript Coll Viceregal Mexico and early Texas; San Antonio through 1950
Restriction: Non-circulating

S EXPRESS NEWS CORP, San Antonio Express-News Library, Ave E & Third, PO Box 2171, 78297-2171. SAN 316-7364. Tel: 210-250-3274. FA 210-250-3105. Web Site: www.mysanantonio.com. *Res*, Kathy Foley
Founded 1962
Subject Interests: Current events
Special Collections: Newspaper clipping file; photos

L FULBRIGHT & JAWORSKI LIBRARY,* 300 Convent St, Ste 2200, 78205-3792. SAN 323-6269. Tel: 210-224-5575. FAX: 210-270-7205. *Lib* Kathy Craig; E-Mail: kcraig@fullbright.com; Staff 1 (MLS 1)
Library Holdings: Bk Vols 20,000; Bk Titles 2,000; Per Subs 60

R HISPANIC BAPTIST THEOLOGICAL SCHOOL LIBRARY, 8019 S Panam Expressway, 78224-1397. SAN 321-1843. Tel: 210-924-4338, Ext 230. FAX: 210-924-2701. Web Site: www.hbts.edu. *Librn*, Edith Pequeno; E-Mail: epequeno@hbts.edu; *Librn*, Teresa Martinez; E-Mail: tmartinez@hbts.edu
Founded 1955. Enrl 116; Fac 14
Library Holdings: Bk Vols 25,361; Bk Titles 16,500; Per Subs 214
Subject Interests: Theol in Spanish
Publications: Index to periodicals (1975)

S INTERCULTURAL DEVELOPMENT RESEARCH ASSOCIATION LIBRARY,* 5835 Callaghan Rd, Ste 350, 78228. SAN 329-4161. Tel: 21(684-8180. FAX: 210-684-5389. *Dir*, Sara Alemon
Library Holdings: Bk Vols 2,500; Per Subs 1,045

P LEON VALLEY PUBLIC LIBRARY,* 6425 Evers Rd, 78238-1453. SAN 372-5944. Tel: 210-684-0720. FAX: 210-684-2088. *Librn*, Joyce Miller Trent; *Asst Librn, Tech Servs*, Margaret Bissett; Staff 3 (MLS 1, Non-ML 2)
Founded 1977. Pop 10,000; Circ 64,500
Library Holdings: Bk Titles 34,000; Per Subs 80

Special Collections: Leon Valley Hist Soc
Mem of Alamo Area Library System; San Antonio Area Libr Syst
Special Services for the Deaf - Books on deafness & sign language

MARION KOOGLER MCNAY ART MUSEUM LIBRARY, 6000 N New Braunfels Ave, 78209. (Mail add: PO Box 6069, 78209-0069), SAN 316-7283. Tel: 210-824-5368. FAX: 210-824-0218. *Head Librn*, Ann Jones; *Cat*, Carl Close; Staff 3 (MLS 2, Non-MLS 1)
Founded 1954
Library Holdings: Bk Vols 30,000; Per Subs 41
Subject Interests: 19th Century art hist, 20th Century art hist
Special Collections: Tobin Theater Arts & Rare Book Coll
Friends of the Library Group

MATTHEWS & BRANSCOMB, Law Library,* One Alamo Ctr, 106 S St Mary's St, Ste 700, 78205-3692. SAN 316-7291. Tel: 210-357-9300. FAX: 210-226-0521. *Librn*, Mary Zaiontz
Library Holdings: Bk Vols 17,000; Per Subs 145
Subject Interests: Pub, Tax law

MCCAMISH SOCKS & MONTPAS, Law Library, 130 E Travis, Ste 300, 78205. (Mail add: PO Box 2999, 78299-2999), SAN 323-7001. Tel: 210-225-5500. FAX: 210-225-1283. *Librn*, Helen Hewitt; Staff 3 (MLS 1, Non-MLS 2)
Founded 1978
Library Holdings: Bk Vols 207,000; Bk Titles 25,000; Per Subs 15
Partic in Dow Jones News Retrieval; Westlaw

METHODIST HOSPITAL, Medical Nursing & Patient Library,* 7700 Floyd Curl Dr, 78229. SAN 316-7461. Tel: 210-575-4000, 210-575-4583. FAX: 210-575-1339.
Founded 1967
Special Collections: Medical
Partic in Health Oriented Libraries of San Antonio

MIND SCIENCE FOUNDATION LIBRARY,* 7979 Broadway, Ste 100, 78209. SAN 324-1874. Tel: 210-821-6094. FAX: 210-821-6199. *Librn*, Nancy Johnson
Founded 1958
Library Holdings: Bk Vols 5,000; Bk Titles 4,000; Per Subs 10
Subject Interests: Alzheimer's Disease, Creativity, Experimental parapsychol, Parapsychol, Psychokinesis, Psychoneuroimmunology, States of consciousness
Publications: Library News
Partic in Coun of Res & Acad Librs

NONPROFIT RESOURCE CENTER OF TEXAS, PO Box 15070, 78212-8270. SAN 327-8328. Tel: 210-227-4333. FAX: 210-227-0310. E-Mail: nprc@nprc.org. Web Site: www.nprc.org. *Mgr Libr Serv*, Ramona Lucius; E-Mail: rlucius@nprc.org
Library Holdings: Bk Vols 2,200; Per Subs 39
As a Foundation Center Cooperating Collection, the Nonprofit Resource Center of Texas makes available for public use all Foundation Center publications & paper copies of IRS 990 tax forms filed by most Texas foundations. The collection also contains over 3000 volumes on philanthropy (including tax regulation), fundraising & nonprofit management. The reference collection also includes files on local & national foundations, corporate philanthropy & local nonprofit agencies

NORTHEAST BAPTIST HOSPITAL, Dr Leroy & Norma Bates Memorial Library, 8811 Village Dr, 78217. SAN 372-9990. Tel: 210-297-0230, 210-297-2000, 210-297-2639. *Librn*, Carolyn Mueller
Library Holdings: Bk Vols 300
Subject Interests: Nutrition
Open Mon-Fri 7:30-11:30

NORTHWEST VISTA COLLEGE, Learning Resource Center, 3535 N Ellison Dr, LC 2nd Flr, 78251. SAN 375-4170. Tel: 210-348-2300. Web Site: www.accd.edu/nvc/lrc/index.html. *Dir*, Christine C Godin; Tel: 210-348-2062, E-Mail: cgodin@accd.edu; *Tech Servs*, Karen Weiskittel; Tel: 210-348-2065, E-Mail: kweiskit@accd.edu; *Ref*, Judy McMillan; Tel: 210-348-2061, E-Mail: jmcmilla@accd.edu; Staff 10 (MLS 5, Non-MLS 5)
Founded 1998. Enrl 4,371; Highest Degree: Associate
Sep 2000-Aug 2001 Income $385,000. Mats Exp $122,000, Books $60,000, Per/Ser (Incl. Access Fees) $15,000, AV Equip $2,000, Electronic Ref Mat (Incl. Access Fees) $45,000. Sal $190,000 (Prof $140,000)
Library Holdings: Bk Vols 4,000; Per Subs 170
Automation Activity & Vendor Info: (Acquisitions) Innovative Interfaces Inc.; (Cataloging) Innovative Interfaces Inc.; (Circulation) Innovative Interfaces Inc.; (OPAC) Innovative Interfaces Inc.
Database Vendor: Ebsco - EbscoHost, GaleNet, OVID Technologies
Partic in Amigos Library Services, Inc; Tex Share

OBLATE SCHOOL OF THEOLOGY LIBRARY, 285 Oblate, 78216-6631. SAN 316-7305. Tel: 210-341-1368. FAX: 210-341-4519. E-Mail: library@ost.edu. Web Site: www.ost.edu. *Dir*, Donald Joyce; E-Mail: donaldj@express-news.net; Staff 1 (MLS 1)
Founded 1903. Enrl 144; Fac 18; Highest Degree: Doctorate
Library Holdings: Bk Vols 85,000; Per Subs 400
Subject Interests: Mexican-American studies, Relig studies
Special Collections: Faculty Dissertations; Mission Documents
Automation Activity & Vendor Info: (Acquisitions) Endeavor; (Cataloging) Endeavor; (Circulation) Endeavor; (Course Reserve) Endeavor; (ILL) Endeavor; (Media Booking) Endeavor; (OPAC) Endeavor; (Serials) Endeavor
Partic in Amigos Library Services, Inc; Council Of Research & Academic Libraries; OCLC Online Computer Library Center, Inc

C OUR LADY OF THE LAKE UNIVERSITY LIBRARIES, Sueltenfuss Library, 411 SW 24th St, 78207-4689. SAN 362-2320. Tel: 210-434-6711, Ext 324. Circulation Tel: 210-434-6711, Ext 325. Reference Tel: 210-434-6711, Ext 8236. FAX: 210-436-1616. Web Site: library.ollusa.edu, www.ollusa.edu. *Dir*, Antoinette Garza; *Ref*, Kathleen Gallager; *Ref*, Kay Lynn Garsnett; *Acq, Tech Servs*, Linda Payne-Button; *Ref*, Judith Larson; *Ref*, Linda Bloom; *Asst Librn*, Owen Ellard; Staff 11 (MLS 9, Non-MLS 2)
Founded 1896. Enrl 2,598; Fac 181; Highest Degree: Doctorate
Jun 1999-May 2000 Income $1,447,572, State $197,311, Federal $120,539, Parent Institution $1,129,722. Mats Exp $411,011, Books $164,509, Per/Ser (Incl. Access Fees) $86,077, Presv $8,945, Micro $11,709, AV Equip $115,321, Manuscripts & Archives $700, Electronic Ref Mat (Incl. Access Fees) $23,750. Sal $654,916 (Prof $516,789)
Library Holdings: Bk Vols 153,407; Per Subs 920
Subject Interests: Education, Leadership, Mexican-Am, Psychology, Soc work
Special Collections: History of the Southwest (Texana)
Automation Activity & Vendor Info: (Acquisitions) SIRSI; (Cataloging) SIRSI; (Circulation) SIRSI; (Course Reserve) SIRSI; (ILL) SIRSI; (OPAC) SIRSI; (Serials) SIRSI
Database Vendor: OVID Technologies, Silverplatter Information Inc.
Publications: Library Guide
Partic in Amigos Library Services, Inc; Coun of Res & Acad Librs; OCLC Online Computer Library Center, Inc

J PALO ALTO COLLEGE, George Ozuna, Jr Learning Resources Center, 1400 W Villaret, 78224-2499. SAN 372-4921. Tel: 210-921-5100. Interlibrary Loan Service Tel: 210-921-5084. Circulation Tel: 210-921-5080. Reference Tel: 210-921-5087, 210-921-5450. FAX: 210-921-5461. Interlibrary Loan Service FAX: 210-921-5065. Web Site: www.accd.edu/pac/lrc/index.htm. *Dir*, Gloria E Hilario; E-Mail: hilario@accd.edu; *Acq*, Ernestina Mesa; Tel: 210-921-5074, E-Mail: tmesa@accd.edu; *Automation Syst Coordr*, Sandra Hood; Tel: 210-921-5062, E-Mail: shood@accd.edu; *Circ*, Margaret Martinez; E-Mail: mmartine@accd.edu; *Circ*, Azucena Rodriguez-Guerra; E-Mail: azrodrig@accd.edu; *Govt Doc*, Camille F Fiorillo; Tel: 210-921-5082, E-Mail: fiorillo@accd.edu; *ILL*, Michell Rodriguez; Tel: 210-921-5084, E-Mail: milopez@accd.edu; *Info Res*, Irma Sanchez; Tel: 210-921-5068, E-Mail: isanchez@accd.edu; *Info Res, Instrul Serv*, Irene F Scharf; Tel: 210-921-5452, E-Mail: scharf@accd.edu; *Web Coordr*, Colby O Glass; Tel: 210-921-5069, E-Mail: cglass@accd.edu; Staff 24 (MLS 13, Non-MLS 11)
Founded 1985. Enrl 6,200; Fac 357
Sep 1999-Aug 2000 Income $1,008,191. Mats Exp $221,041, Books $79,380, Per/Ser (Incl. Access Fees) $53,472, Micro $26,010, Electronic Ref Mat (Incl. Access Fees) $62,179. Sal $568,954 (Prof $405,740)
Library Holdings: Bk Vols 62,191; Bk Titles 55,685; Per Subs 455
Automation Activity & Vendor Info: (Acquisitions) Innovative Interfaces Inc.; (Cataloging) Innovative Interfaces Inc.; (Circulation) Innovative Interfaces Inc.; (Course Reserve) Innovative Interfaces Inc.; (ILL) Innovative Interfaces Inc.; (Media Booking) Innovative Interfaces Inc.; (OPAC) Innovative Interfaces Inc.; (Serials) Innovative Interfaces Inc.
Database Vendor: Dialog, Ebsco - EbscoHost, epixtech, inc., GaleNet, Innovative Interfaces INN - View, OCLC - First Search, ProQuest, Silverplatter Information Inc.
Partic in Amigos Library Services, Inc; Tex Share

S PLANNED PARENTHOOD OF SAN ANTONIO OF SOUTH CENTRAL TEXAS,* 104 Babcock Rd, 78201. SAN 316-7240. Tel: 210-736-2244. FAX: 210-736-0011. *Exec Dir*, Patricia Sidebottom
Founded 1939
Library Holdings: Bk Vols 1,000; Per Subs 20
Subject Interests: Birth control, Ecology, Family planning, Fertility, Human sexuality, Pop, Pregnancy, Teen sexuality, Venereal disease, World pop
Friends of the Library Group

S RESEARCH & DEVELOPMENT ASSOCIATES FOR MILITARY FOOD & PACKAGING SYSTEMS, INC, 16607 Blanco Ste 1506, 78232-1940. SAN 328-4379. Tel: 210-493-8024. FAX: 210-493-8036. E-Mail: rda50@flash.net. Web Site: www.militaryfood.org. *Exec Dir*, James F Fagan
Jan 1998-Dec 1999 Income $341,000, Federal $20,000, Parent Institution $12,000. Mats Exp $294,000, Books $10,500, Per/Ser (Incl. Access Fees) $12,000, AV Equip $8,000, Manuscripts & Archives $4,000. Sal $103,000 (Prof $103,000)
Library Holdings: Bk Titles 110

SR SAINT MARK'S EPISCOPAL CHURCH, Bishop Jones Library, 315 E Pecan St, 78205. SAN 328-5847. Tel: 210-226-2426. FAX: 210-226-2468. E-Mail: stmarks@stmarks-sa.org. Web Site: www.stmarks-sa.org. *Librn*, Dorothy Brown

Library Holdings: Bk Vols 5,600
Subject Interests: Religion
Special Collections: Jack Kent Coll, bks

SAINT MARY'S UNIVERSITY
C ACADEMIC LIBRARY, One Camino Santa Maria, 78228-8608. SAN 362-2479. Tel: 210-436-3441. Reference Tel: 210-436-3508. FAX: 210-436-3782. *Dir*, Dr H Palmer Hall; *Per*, Marcella Lesher; *Acq, Tech Servs*, Margaret Sylvia; *Cat*, Patricia Keogh; *Doc, Online Servs*, Kathleen Amen; *Bibliog Instr*, Diane Duesterhoeft; Staff 8 (MLS 8)
Founded 1852. Enrl 4,000; Fac 194; Highest Degree: Doctorate
Library Holdings: Bk Vols 270,000; Per Subs 1,100
Subject Interests: Bus, Ethnic studies, History, Law
Special Collections: Hilaire Belloc Coll & G K Chesterton Coll (complete sets of 1st editions); Peninsular Wars Coll; Political Buttons Coll; Spanish Archives of Laredo, Texas
Automation Activity & Vendor Info: (Acquisitions) epixtech, inc.; (Circulation) epixtech, inc.
Partic in Amigos Library Services, Inc; Coun of Res & Acad Librs
L SARITA KENEDY EAST LAW LIBRARY, One Camino Santa Maria, 78228-8605. SAN 362-2509. Tel: 210-436-3435. FAX: 210-436-3240, Admin. Interlibrary Loan Service FAX: 210-431-4270. Web Site: www.stmarytx.edu. *Dir*, Bernard D Reams, Jr; Tel: 210-436-5030; *Acq, Asst Prof, Cat*, Jim Bass; Tel: 210-436-1374; *Cat*, Lady Jane Hickey; Tel: 210-436-1372; *Ser*, Barbara McLaughlin; Tel: 210-436-1158; *Archivist, Govt Doc*, Christopher Anglim; Tel: 210-436-3512; *Circ, Media Spec*, Daniel McBride; Tel: 210-436-1369; *Computer Services, Ref*, Garry Stillman; Tel: 210-436-1366; *Doc Delivery, ILL, Media Spec*, Lee Unterborn; Tel: 210-436-4227; Staff 8 (MLS 8)
Founded 1927. Enrl 600; Fac 25
Library Holdings: Bk Vols 338,904; Bk Titles 32,873; Per Subs 3,474
Special Collections: Anglo American Law
Automation Activity & Vendor Info: (Cataloging) epixtech, inc.; (Circulation) epixtech, inc.; (OPAC) epixtech, inc.
Partic in Mead Data Cent; Westlaw
Friends of the Library Group

J ST PHILIP'S COLLEGE, Learning Resource Center, 1801 Martin Luther King Dr, 78203-2098. SAN 316-7321. Tel: 210-531-3359. Interlibrary Loan Service Tel: 210-531-3330. FAX: 210-531-3331. E-Mail: spcav@accd.edu. Web Site: www.accd.edu/spc/lrc/. *Dean*, Dr Adele Dendy; *Tech Servs*, Lucy E Duncan; *Automation Syst Coordr*, Jill M Zimmerman; *Cat*, Philip E Raue; *Ref*, Rita Castro; *Archivist*, Mark Barnes; *Media Spec*, Linda Cuellar; *Ser*, Lillie Turner; Staff 14 (MLS 9, Non-MLS 5)
Founded 1898. Enrl 8,644; Fac 498
Library Holdings: Bk Vols 125,000; Per Subs 1,510
Special Collections: African-American Coll
Automation Activity & Vendor Info: (Acquisitions) Innovative Interfaces Inc.; (Cataloging) Innovative Interfaces Inc.; (Circulation) Innovative Interfaces Inc.; (Course Reserve) Innovative Interfaces Inc.; (ILL) Innovative Interfaces Inc.; (Media Booking) Innovative Interfaces Inc.; (OPAC) Innovative Interfaces Inc.; (Serials) Innovative Interfaces Inc.
Publications: Basic Instruction in Word Perfect 7.0; How to Use the NOTIS OPAC; PowerPoint Library Orientation; Templates for CD-ROM Programs
Partic in Amigos Library Services, Inc; Coun of Res & Acad Librs; Tex Coun of Commun/Jr Col Librns; TexShare
Special Services for the Blind - Assistive Technology Center for Persons who are blind or physically handicapped

S SAN ANTONIO ART LEAGUE, Museum Gallery Library,* 130 King William St, 78204. SAN 316-733X. Tel: 210-223-1140. FAX: 210-223-2826. *Pres*, Louise Cantwell; *Exec Dir*, Dr Angelica Jansen-Brown
Library Holdings: Bk Vols 350
Restriction: Open to public for reference only

J SAN ANTONIO COLLEGE LIBRARY, 1001 Howard St, 78212. SAN 316-7348. Tel: 210-733-2482. FAX: 210-733-2597. Web Site: www.accd.edu/sac/lrc/. *Dean of Libr*, Dr Alice Cook; *Chairperson, Per*, Candace Peterson; *Circ*, Ralph Domas; *Doc, Tech Servs*, Christina Petimezas; *AV*, Barbara Knotts; *Ref*, Tom Kuykendall; *Instrul Serv*, Joan Alcolt; *Automation Syst Coordr*, John Hammer; *Web Coordr*, Karen Balcom; Staff 18 (MLS 16, Non-MLS 2)
Founded 1926. Enrl 20,614; Fac 948; Highest Degree: Associate
Sep 1999-Aug 2000 Income $2,448,003, State $816,001, City $816,001, Locally Generated Income $816,001. Mats Exp $524,163, Books $240,000, Per/Ser (Incl. Access Fees) $72,900, Presv $2,512, Micro $63,200, AV Equip $8,000, Other Print Mats $2,000, Electronic Ref Mat (Incl. Access Fees) $108,400. Sal $1,638,405 (Prof $906,676)
Library Holdings: Bk Vols 200,985; Per Subs 3,499; Bks on Deafness & Sign Lang 375
Special Collections: 18th Century British Literature (Morrison Coll); Los Pastores; McAllister Coll; Texana; Western Coll
Automation Activity & Vendor Info: (Acquisitions) Innovative Interfaces Inc.; (Cataloging) Innovative Interfaces Inc.; (Circulation) Innovative Interfaces Inc.; (Course Reserve) Innovative Interfaces Inc.; (Media Booking) Innovative Interfaces Inc.; (OPAC) Innovative Interfaces Inc.
Database Vendor: OCLC - First Search
Partic in Amigos Library Services, Inc; Council Of Research & Academi Libraries; TexShare
Special Services for the Blind - Kurzweil Reader

S SAN ANTONIO CONSERVATION SOCIETY FOUNDATION LIBRAR 107 King William St, 78204. SAN 316-7356. Tel: 210-224-6163. FAX: 2 224-6168. E-Mail: conserve@saconservation.org. Web Site: www.saconservation.org. *Librn*, Marianna C Jones; *Archivist*, Nelle Lee Weincek; Staff 17 (MLS 3, Non-MLS 14)
Founded 1970
Jul 2000-Jun 2001 Income Parent Institution $10,429
Library Holdings: Bk Vols 4,000; Bk Titles 3,000; Per Subs 10; High Interest/Low Vocabulary Bk Vols 10
Subject Interests: Archit hist, Hist district surveys, Preservation, Restoration techniques, San Antonio, Tex hist, Zoning
Special Collections: Dorothy Matthis Postcard Coll (early San Antonio, Galveston, Houston); Ernst Raba Photograph Coll (early San Antonio Views); Robert H H Hugman River Walk, drawings; S A Architecture History Coll, photogs, slides; Texana (John M Sr & Eleanor Freeman Bennett Coll); Texas Heritage Resource Center (Texana)
Restriction: Non-circulating to the public, Public use on premises

R SAN ANTONIO FIRST BAPTIST CHURCH, Wallace Library, 515 McCullough St, 78215. SAN 316-7259. Tel: 210-226-0363, Ext 219. FAX 210-299-2633. E-Mail: library@fbcsanan.org. *In Charge*, J O Wallace; St 5 (MLS 1, Non-MLS 4)
Founded 1939
Jan 1999-Dec 1999 Income $2,900, Parent Institution $1,700, Other $1,2 Mats Exp $1,720, Books $1,500, Per/Ser (Incl. Access Fees) $220
Library Holdings: Bk Vols 16,200; Bk Titles 13,000; Per Subs 10; Bks c Deafness & Sign Lang 10
Subject Interests: Baptist hist, Theology
Automation Activity & Vendor Info: (Cataloging) Follett; (Circulation) Follett
Restriction: Members only

P SAN ANTONIO PUBLIC LIBRARY, 600 Soledad, 78205-2786. SAN 36 2533. Tel: 210-207-2500. TDD: 210-207-2534. FAX: 210-207-2603. Web Site: www.sat.lib.tx.us. *Dir*, Laura J Isenstein; Tel: 210-207-2644, E-Mail: lisenstein@ci.sat.tx.us; *Actg Dir*, Nancy Gandara; *Adminr*, Craig Zapatos; *Automation Syst Coordr*, Martha Knott; *Br Coordr*, Sharon Soderquist; *IL* Kate Cordts; *Ch Servs*, Rose Trevino; *Automation Syst Coordr*, Roger Colunga; *Coll Develop*, Robert Beebe; Staff 201 (MLS 122, Non-MLS 79
Founded 1903. Pop 1,432,700; Circ 4,326,830
Oct 1999-Sep 2000 Income $18,494,531, State $399,916, City $16,764,14 Federal $194,068, Locally Generated Income $1,136,400, Parent Institutio $800,000, Other $31,720. Mats Exp $3,507,579, Books $2,051,121, Per/Se (Incl. Access Fees) $107,850, Presv $35,000, Micro $203,335. Sal $11,361,883
Library Holdings: Bk Vols 1,859,921; Bk Titles 485,620; Per Subs 2,000
Special Collections: Hertzberg Circus Coll; Latino Special Coll; Texana Coll
Publications: Young Pegasus (children's original poetry book)
Special Services for the Deaf - Books on deafness & sign language; Captioned film depository; High interest/low vocabulary books
Friends of the Library Group
Branches: 29
BAZAN, 2200 W Commerce St, 78207. SAN 362-2800. Tel: 210-225-161 FAX: 210-225-7461. *Branch Mgr*, Laurie Selwyv
BROOK HOLLOW, 530 Heimer Rd, 78232. SAN 362-2584. Tel: 210-496 6315. FAX: 210-495-3757. *Librn*, Beverly Jackson
CARVER, 3350 E Commerce, 78220. SAN 362-2835. Tel: 210-225-7801. FAX: 210-472-3480. *Branch Mgr*, Bell Leroy
CHILDREN'S DEPARTMENT Tel: 210-207-2500. FAX: 210-207-2555. *Librn*, Cara Waits
CIRCULATION Tel: 210-207-2500. FAX: 210-207-2553. *Circ*, Dennis Atkinson
CODY, 11441 Vance Jackson, 78230. SAN 362-2630. Tel: 210-696-6396. FAX: 210-696-6273. *Librn*, Metta Chicka
COLLINS GARDEN, 200 N Park, 78204. SAN 322-5542. Tel: 210-225-0331. FAX: 210-472-0428. *Librn*, Pam Longoria
CORTEZ, 2803 Hunter Blvd, 78224. SAN 362-2843. Tel: 210-922-7372. FAX: 210-932-1495. *Librn*, Beth Bermel
FICTION Tel: 210-207-2500. FAX: 210-207-2553. *Librn*, Wendy Friedman
FOREST HILLS, 5245 Ingram, 78228. SAN 329-6520. Tel: 210-431-2544. FAX: 210-434-3524. *Librn*, Evangeline Acosta
S GOVERNMENT DOCUMENTS Tel: 210-207-2500. FAX: 210-207-2554. *Librn*, Wilson Plunkett
GREAT NORTHWEST, 9050 Wellwood, 78251. SAN 374-6755. Tel: 210-684-5251. *Librn*, Margaret Zapatos
HERTZBERG CIRCUS MUSEUM, 210 W Market St, 78205. SAN 362-2770. Tel: 210-207-7819. FAX: 210-207-4468.
Library Holdings: Bk Vols 15,000
Subject Interests: Art, Biog, Circus hist, Costume, History, Literature, Religion
Special Collections: Circus Archives; Museum Artifacts; Photog Coll; Rare bks & mss

Publications: Guide to the Hertzberg Circus Collection
JOHNSTON, 6307 Sun Valley, 78237. SAN 362-2851. Tel: 210-674-8410. FAX: 210-675-0461. *Librn*, Lois Galbraith
LANDA, 233 Bushnell Ave, 78212. SAN 362-286X. Tel: 210-732-8369. *Librn*, Kathy Claspill
LAS PALMAS, 911 Castroville, 78237. SAN 362-2894. Tel: 210-434-6394. FAX: 210-435-5479. *Librn*, Rebecca A Alvarez
MCCRELESS, 1023 Ada, 78228. SAN 362-2924. Tel: 210-532-4254. FAX: 210-533-0041. *Librn*, Addie Armstrong
MEMORIAL, 3222 Culebra Rd, 78228. SAN 362-2932. Tel: 210-432-6783. FAX: 210-435-5471. *Librn*, Jane Malone
OAKWELL, 4134 Harry Wurzbach, 78209. SAN 362-2959. Tel: 210-828-2569. FAX: 210-821-6923. *Librn*, Peggy Mahan
PAN AMERICAN, 1122 W Pyron Ave, 78221. SAN 362-2983. Tel: 210-924-8164. FAX: 210-932-1489. *Librn*, Sherri Kyle
PERIODICALS Tel: 210-207-2500. FAX: 210-207-2556. *Librn*, Charlotte Balusek
REFERENCE Tel: 210-207-2500. FAX: 207-2552, 210-207-2556.
SAN PEDRO, 1315 San Pedro Ave, 78212. SAN 362-3017. Tel: 210-733-1454. *Librn*, Jane Forkner
TECHNICAL SERVICES Tel: 210-207-2500. FAX: 210-207-2653. *Librn*, Pat Fahrenthold
TELEPHONE REFERENCE Tel: 210-207-2500. FAX: 210-207-2557. *Librn*, Jana Prock
TEXANA & GENEALOGY Tel: 210-207-2500. FAX: 210-207-2558. *Librn*, Josephine Myler
Library Holdings: Bk Vols 108,535; Per Subs 586
Subject Interests: Education, Gen ref, Genealogy, History, Soc sci, Texana, Travel
Partic in Index to San Antonio and Texas VF
THOUSAND OAKS EL SENDERO, 4618 Thousand Oaks, 78233. SAN 328-865X. Tel: 210-657-5205. FAX: 210-657-6874. *Librn*, Sandra Neville
WESTFALL, 6111 Rosedale Ct, 78201. SAN 362-3041. Tel: 210-344-2373. FAX: 210-344-4699. *Librn*, Chris Palmer
YOUTH (WIRED) Tel: 210-207-2678. FAX: 210-207-2553. *Librn*, Jennifer Comi
Bookmobiles: 2

SAN ANTONIO STATE HOSPITAL, Staff Library,* 5900 S Presa, PO Box 23991, Highland Hills Sta, 78223-0991. SAN 362-3076. Tel: 210-531-7974. FAX: 210-531-7973. *Dir*, Dr William Johnson
Founded 1960
Library Holdings: Bk Vols 3,352; Bk Titles 2,681; Per Subs 150
Subject Interests: Medicine, Mental health, Nursing, Pastoral care, Psychiatry, Social work
Partic in Health Oriented Libraries of San Antonio; S Cent Regional Med Libr Program
Branches:
PATIENTS LIBRARY

I SOUTH TEXAS VETERANS HEALTHCARE SYSTEM, Audie L Murphy Division Library, 7400 Merton Minter Blvd, 78284-5799. SAN 316-750X. Tel: 210-617-5300, Ext 4283. FAX: 210-617-5246. E-Mail: ann.mitchell@med.va.gov. *Coll Develop*, Janean Garrett; E-Mail: janean.garrett@med.va.gov; Staff 3 (MLS 2, Non-MLS 1)
Founded 1974 Sal $147,720 (Prof $92,996)
Library Holdings: Bk Vols 5,145; Per Subs 553
Special Collections: Patients Health Education Coll, bks, videos
Publications: Staff & patient newsletters
Partic in Health Oriented Libraries of San Antonio; Vets Admin Libr Network

SOUTHWEST CRAFT CENTER TEXTILE LIBRARY,* c/o Southwest Craft Ctr, 300 Augusta, 78205. SAN 326-6133. Tel: 210-224-1848. FAX: 210-224-9337. *Librn*, Jane Dunnewald
Founded 1969. Enrl 154; Fac 16
Special Collections: American Fabrics Quarterly, 1948-1967; The Flying Needle (complete set) 1969-1991

SOUTHWEST FOUNDATION FOR BIOMEDICAL RESEARCH, Preston G Northrup Memorial Library, PO Box 760549, 78245-0549. SAN 316-7445. Tel: 210-258-9528. FAX: 210-670-3313. *Librn*, Ruth H Brooks; Tel: 210-258-9593, E-Mail: rbrooks@icarus.sfbr.org; *Asst Librn*, Alan Godin; Tel: 210-258-9426, E-Mail: agodin@icarus.sfbr.org; *Circ, ILL*, Mary Ann Smith; Tel: 210-258-9502, E-Mail: msmith@icarus.sfbr.org; Staff 3 (MLS 2, Non-MLS 1)
Founded 1947
Library Holdings: Bk Vols 48,000; Per Subs 500
Subject Interests: Basic biomed sci, Primatology, Res
Restriction: Lending to staff only, Open to public for reference only
Function: For research purposes
Partic in Amigos Library Services, Inc; Coun of Res & Acad Librs; Docline; Health Oriented Libraries of San Antonio; S Cent Regional Med Libr Program

SOUTHWEST RESEARCH INSTITUTE, Thomas Baker Slick Memorial Library, 6220 Culebra Rd, 78228. (Mail add: PO Drawer 28510, 78228-0510), SAN 316-7453. Tel: 210-522-2125, 210-522-2127. FAX: 210-522-5479. Web Site: www.swri.org. *Librn*, Robert D Armor; *Assoc Librn*, Anita E Lang; Staff 8 (MLS 4, Non-MLS 4)
Founded 1948
Library Holdings: Bk Titles 31,900; Per Subs 775
Subject Interests: Bio-eng, Environmental engineering, Sci-tech
Automation Activity & Vendor Info: (Cataloging) Endeavor; (Circulation) Endeavor; (OPAC) Endeavor
Database Vendor: Ebsco - EbscoHost
Restriction: Lending to staff only, Open to public for reference only
Partic in Coun of Res & Acad Librs

S MINNIE STEVENS PIPER FOUNDATION, Student Aid Center Library,* GPM South Tower, Ste 200, 800 N W Loop 410, 78216-5699. SAN 326-5943. Tel: 210-525-8494. FAX: 210-341-6627. E-Mail: mspf@world-net.net. *Dir*, Carlos Otero
Founded 1961
Library Holdings: Bk Vols 5,000
Publications: Compendium of Texas College & Financial Aid Calendar

S SYMPHONY SOCIETY OF SAN ANTONIO, Symphony Library,* 222 E Houston St, Ste 200, 78205. SAN 316-747X. Tel: 210-554-1000, Ext 133. FAX: 210-554-1008. Web Site: www.sasymphony.org. *Librn*, Gregory Vaught
Restriction: Open to public for reference only

M TEXAS CENTER FOR INFECTIOUS DISEASE, Library Services,* 2303 SE Military Dr, 78223-3597. SAN 316-7402. Tel: 210-534-8857, Ext 2261. FAX: 534-531-4507.
Founded 1955
Sep 1996-Aug 1997 Income $67,252, State $66,852, Federal $400. Mats Exp $23,311, Books $4,888, Per/Ser (Incl. Access Fees) $11,634, Presv $418, AV Equip $2,907. Sal $32,816
Library Holdings: Bk Titles 6,140; Per Subs 78
Subject Interests: Medicine, Nursing
Publications: The Health Science Library Newsletter

C TRINITY UNIVERSITY, Coates Library, 715 Stadium Dr, 78212-7200. SAN 362-3130. Tel: 210-999-8121. Interlibrary Loan Service Tel: 210-999-8473. Circulation Tel: 210-999-8127. FAX: 210-999-8182. Web Site: www.trinity.edu/departments/library/library.html. *Actg Dir, Online Servs, Publ Servs, Ref*, Christopher W Nolan; Tel: 210-999-8121, E-Mail: cnolan@trinity.edu; *Media Spec*, Ronnie C Swanner; Tel: 210-999-7356, E-Mail: rswanner@trinity.edu; *Ref*, Deborah Nicholl; Tel: 210-999-8160, E-Mail: dnicholl@trinity.edu; *Acq, Tech Servs*, Beatrice Caraway; Tel: 210-999-7292, E-Mail: bcaraway@trinity.edu; *Automation Syst Coordr*, Samir Iskenderov; Tel: 210-999-7473, E-Mail: samir.iskenderov@trinity.edu; *ILL*, Maria McWilliams; Tel: 210-999-8473, E-Mail: mmcwilli@trinity.edu; *Science*, Barbara MacAlpine; Tel: 210-999-7343, E-Mail: barbara.macalpine@trinity.edu; Staff 16 (MLS 15, Non-MLS 1)
Founded 1869. Enrl 2,526; Fac 239; Highest Degree: Master
Jun 1999-May 2000 Income $3,241,013. Mats Exp $1,300,624, Books $418,955, Per/Ser (Incl. Access Fees) $747,049, Presv $33,977, Micro $25,057, Electronic Ref Mat (Incl. Access Fees) $80,000. Sal $1,498,043 (Prof $544,718)
Library Holdings: Bk Vols 871,081; Bk Titles 636,498; Per Subs 2,947
Special Collections: American Literature (Helen Miller Jones Coll); Archives of Monterrey & the State of Nuevo Leon, Mexico, micro; Greek & Roman Art & Architecture (Denman Coll); Latin America (Hilton Coll); Space Exploration (Campbell Coll & Maloney Coll); Texana (Beretta Coll & Nixon Coll); Trinity University Archives
Automation Activity & Vendor Info: (Acquisitions) Endeavor; (Cataloging) Endeavor; (Circulation) Endeavor; (Course Reserve) Endeavor; (ILL) Endeavor; (Media Booking) Endeavor; (OPAC) Endeavor; (Serials) Endeavor
Partic in Amigos Library Services, Inc; Assoc Cols of the South; Coun of Res & Acad Librs

S UNITED SERVICES AUTOMOBILE ASSOCIATION, (USAA), Research Library, 9800 Fredericksburg Rd, 78288-2801. SAN 316-7488. Tel: 210-498-1524. FAX: 210-498-4776. *Dir Libr Serv*, Mary S Forman; E-Mail: mary.forman@usaa.com; *Tech Servs*, John Moreno; Tel: 210-498-3273, E-Mail: john.moreno@usaa.com; Staff 4 (MLS 3, Non-MLS 1)
Founded 1957
Library Holdings: Bk Vols 5,000; Per Subs 210
Subject Interests: Banking, Bus, Computer science, Ins, Investments, Mgt, Real estate
Partic in Amigos Library Services, Inc; Coun of Res & Acad Librs; OCLC Online Computer Library Center, Inc

UNITED STATES AIR FORCE
A RESEARCH CENTER FL7072, AFIWC/MSY, 103 Hall Blvd Ste 2 Bldg 2000, 78243-7049. SAN 320-4235. Tel: 210-977-2617. FAX: 210-977-4008. *Tech Servs*, Brenda Fraizer
Founded 1972
Library Holdings: Bk Vols 20,000
Subject Interests: Bus, Data proc, Electronic warfare, Electronics,

Engineering, Mgt
Special Collections: Air War College; Project Warrior; Total Quality Mgt & TAPS (Transition Assistance Program)

G UNITED STATES DEPARTMENT OF THE AIR FORCE, HQ Air Force Services Agency, Directorate of Programs, Air Force Libr & Info Syst HQ-AFSVA/SVPAL, 10100 Reunion Pl Ste 502, 78216-4138. SAN 316-6864. Tel: 210-652-3037, 210-652-4589. FAX: 210-652-7039. *Dir*, Barbara Wrinkle; E-Mail: barbara.wrinkle@agency.afsv.af.mil; *Asst Dir*, Margie Buchanan; *Acq*, Arthalene Gordey; Staff 8 (MLS 3, Non-MLS 5)
Subject Interests: Aeronautics, Military history
System includes 83 general, 15 technical, 10 academic & 1 special library

C UNIVERSIDAD NACIONAL AUTONOMA DE MEXICO - SAN ANTONIO, Roma Mulo Meunguia,* 600 Hemisfair Park. (Mail add: PO Box 830426, 78283-0426), SAN 329-0719. Tel: 210-222-8626. FAX: 210-225-1772. Web Site: www.usa.unam.edu. *Librn*, Lorena Ortega
Enrl 120; Fac 10
Library Holdings: Bk Vols 70,000
Partic in Amigos Library Services, Inc; OCLC Online Computer Library Center, Inc
Friends of the Library Group

C UNIVERSITY OF TEXAS AT SAN ANTONIO LIBRARY,* 6900 N Loop 1604 W, 78249-0671. SAN 316-7496. Tel: 210-458-4570. Interlibrary Loan Service Tel: 210-458-5501. FAX: 210-458-4884 (Admin). Interlibrary Loan Service FAX: 210-458-4571. Web Site: www.lib.utsa.edu. *Dir*, Michael F Kelly; E-Mail: mkelly@utsa.edu; *Tech Servs*, Sue Tyner; Tel: 210-458-4576, E-Mail: styner@utsa.edu; *Acq*, Donna Lively; *Cat*, John Conyers; *Cat*, Carolyn Ellis Gonzalez; *Ref*, Donna Hogan; *Publ Servs*, Margaret Joseph; E-Mail: mjoseph@utsa.edu; *Archivist*, Jill Jackson; *Coll Develop*, Jacquelyn Crinion; Staff 63 (MLS 22, Non-MLS 41)
Founded 1972. Enrl 18,600; Highest Degree: Doctorate
Sep 1998-Aug 1999 Income $3,497,000. Mats Exp $1,657,955, Books $292,190, Per/Ser (Incl. Access Fees) $660,410, Presv $28,994, Micro $108,923, Other Print Mats $8,991, Manuscripts & Archives $480, Electronic Ref Mat (Incl. Access Fees) $557,967. Sal $1,615,758 (Prof $834,172)
Library Holdings: Bk Vols 540,000; Bk Titles 397,386; Per Subs 2,482
Special Collections: Texana, especially San Antonio & South Texas
Database Vendor: CARL, Ebsco - EbscoHost, epixtech, inc., GaleNet, OCLC - First Search, OVID Technologies, ProQuest, Silverplatter Information Inc., Wilson - Wilson Web
Partic in Amigos Library Services, Inc; Coun of Res & Acad Libr; TexShare
Special Services - Multimedia electronic classroom
Friends of the Library Group

CM UNIVERSITY OF TEXAS HEALTH SCIENCE CENTER AT SAN ANTONIO BRISCOE LIBRARY, 7703 Floyd Curl Dr, MSC 7940, 78229-3900. SAN 362-3165. Tel: 210-567-2400. Interlibrary Loan Service Tel: 210-567-2460. Circulation Tel: 210-567-2440. Reference Tel: 210-567-2450. FAX: 210-567-2490. E-Mail: info-blis@uthscsa.edu. Web Site: www.library.uthscsa.edu. *Dir*, Dr Virginia M Bowden; E-Mail: bowden@uthscsa.edu; *Adminr*, Jonquil D Feldman; E-Mail: feldman@uthscsa.edu; *Access Serv*, Tania Bardyn; *Coll Develop*, Rajia Tobia; E-Mail: tobia@uthscsa.edu; *ILL, Syst Coordr*, Anne Comeaux; *Outreach Serv*, Mary Jo Dwyer; *Publ Servs*, Darlene Murray; *Publ Servs*, Evelyn R Olivier; E-Mail: olivier@uthscsa.edu; *Ref*, Ellen Hanks; *Ref*, Linda Levy; *Ref*, Cathy Rhodes; *Spec Coll*, Penelope Borchers; *Syst Coordr*, Sallieann Swanner; E-Mail: swanner@uthscsa.edu; *Syst Coordr*, Tim W Whisenant; *Tech Servs*, Susan Buentello; Staff 70 (MLS 22, Non-MLS 48)
Founded 1966. Enrl 2,545; Highest Degree: Doctorate
Sep 1999-Aug 2000 Income (Main Library and Branch Library) $3,486,953, State $2,982,104, Federal $45,749, Locally Generated Income $144,946, Parent Institution $250,000, Other $64,154. Mats Exp $1,202,681, Books $164,907, Per/Ser (Incl. Access Fees) $879,079, Presv $24,403, AV Equip $4,050, Electronic Ref Mat (Incl. Access Fees) $130,242. Sal $1,823,282 (Prof $961,627)
Library Holdings: Bk Vols 202,282; Bk Titles 82,341; Per Subs 2,371
Subject Interests: Allied health, Dentistry, Medicine, Nursing, Vet sci
Special Collections: History of Medicine Coll
Automation Activity & Vendor Info: (Acquisitions) Innovative Interfaces Inc.; (Circulation) Innovative Interfaces Inc.; (OPAC) Innovative Interfaces Inc.; (Serials) Innovative Interfaces Inc.
Database Vendor: Silverplatter Information Inc.
Publications: Library News; Newsletter of the Friends of the P I Nixon Medical Historical Library
Restriction: Open to public for reference only
Partic in Amigos Library Services, Inc; Coun of Res & Acad Libr; National Network Of Libraries Of Medicine - South Central Region; OCLC Online Computer Library Center, Inc; TexShare
Friends of the Library Group
Departmental Libraries:
BRADY GREEN LIBRARY, 527 N Leona, 78207. SAN 362-319X. Tel: 210-358-3939. FAX: 210-358-3880. Web Site: www.library.uthscsa.edu. *Librn*, Darlene Murray; Staff 1 (MLS 1)
Founded 1958
Library Holdings: Bk Vols 1,500; Per Subs 104
Subject Interests: Ambulatory care, Family practice, Gynecology, Inte medicine, Obstetrics, Pediatrics
Partic in Acad Press Online; Nat Libr of Med
Satellite Libr of the University of Texas Health Science Center Library San Antonio
Friends of the Library Group

CR UNIVERSITY OF THE INCARNATE WORD, JE & LE Mabee Library,* 4301 Broadway, UPO Box 297, 78209-6397. SAN 316-7275. Interlibrary Loan Service Tel: 210-829-3838. Reference Tel: 210-829-3835. FAX: 210-829-6041. Web Site: www.uiwtx.edu. *Dean*, Mendell D Morgan, Jr; Tel: 210-829-3837, E-Mail: morgan@universe.uiwtx.edu; *Tech Servs*, Mary L Jinks; Tel: 210-829-3839, E-Mail: marydig@universe.uiwtx.edu; *Cat*, Melissa Rucker; Tel: 210-829-6097, E-Mail: melissa@universe.uiwtx.edu; *Publ Servs*, Basil Aivaliotis; Tel: 210-829-6054, E-Mail: basila@universe.uiwtx.edu; *Coll Develop, Ref*, Robert Allen; *Per*, Edward D Park Tel: 210-829-3841, E-Mail: edwardp@universe.uiwtx.edu; *AV*, Diane The Tel: 210-829-3842, E-Mail: theiss@universe.uiwtx.edu; *Tech Coordr*, Lerc Bell, Jr; Tel: 210-829-3814, E-Mail: bell@universe.uiwtx.edu; *Selection o Gen Ref Mat*, Frederick Landin; Tel: 210-829-3843, E-Mail: landin@universe.uiwtx.edu; *Reader Servs*, Patricia Morris Donegan; E-Mail: donegan@universe.uiwtx.edu; Staff 15 (MLS 9, Non-MLS 6)
Founded 1897. Enrl 3,600; Fac 3; Highest Degree: Doctorate
May 1997-Jun 1999 Income $1,050,043, Federal $66,000, Locally Genera Income $38,208, Parent Institution $748,646, Other $197,189. Mats Exp $376,649, Books $201,350, Per/Ser (Incl. Access Fees) $87,210, Presv $13,500, Micro $2,400, Electronic Ref Mat (Incl. Access Fees) $72,189. S $473,641 (Prof $306,564)
Library Holdings: Bk Vols 218,911; Bk Titles 106,171; Per Subs 2,561; Bks on Deafness & Sign Lang 500
Subject Interests: Ezra Pound, Texana, Women's studies
Special Collections: Unique & Limited Editions, Rare Books
Automation Activity & Vendor Info: (Acquisitions) epixtech, inc.; (Cataloging) epixtech, inc.; (Circulation) epixtech, inc.
Database Vendor: CARL, epixtech, inc., GaleNet, IAC - SearchBank, Lexis-Nexis, OCLC - First Search, OVID Technologies, ProQuest, Silverplatter Information Inc.
Function: Reference services available
Partic in Coun of Res & Acad Libr

SAN AUGUSTINE

P SAN AUGUSTINE PUBLIC LIBRARY,* 413 E Columbia St, 75972. SA 316-7526. Tel: 409-275-5367. FAX: 409-275-5049. *Dir*, Kelly Gamble; St 1 (MLS 1)
Founded 1973. Pop 9,000
Library Holdings: Bk Titles 20,000
Special Collections: Genealogy (Tex Heritage), bk, micro
Publications: Caucasian Cemeteries of San Augustine County, Texas, 3 vols; Probate cases of San Augustine County, Texas (1828-1940)
Mem of Houston Area Library System
Open Mon-Fri 8:30-5, Sat 9-2
Friends of the Library Group

SAN BENITO

P SAN BENITO PUBLIC LIBRARY, 101 W Rose St, 78586-5169. SAN 31 7534. Tel: 956-361-3860. FAX: 956-361-3867. Web Site: www.san-benito.ccls.lib.tx.us/library.html. *Dir*, Dr Barry Mendel Cohen; E-Mail: drbarry@san-benito.ccls.lib.tx.us
Founded 1936. Pop 30,000; Circ 73,500
Oct 1998-Sep 1999 Income $205,000, City $171,000, Federal $24,000, County $10,000. Mats Exp $38,000, Books $29,000, Per/Ser (Incl. Access Fees) $9,000. Sal $140,000
Library Holdings: Bk Vols 34,000; Bk Titles 32,000; Per Subs 130
Mem of South Texas Library System
Friends of the Library Group

SAN DIEGO

P DUVAL COUNTY-SAN DIEGO PUBLIC LIBRARY, 404 S Mier, 78384 SAN 376-429X. Tel: 512-279-8201. FAX: 512-279-8201. *Librn*, Ramon Tanguma; Tel: 361-279-3341, Fax: 361-279-3401
Founded 1997
Jan 2000-Dec 2000 Income $141,500, City $12,000, County $48,000, Locally Generated Income $2,500, Other $79,000. Sal $23,500 (Prof $17,500)
Library Holdings: Bk Vols 16,000; Per Subs 26; High Interest/Low Vocabulary Bk Vols 5,000
Mem of South Texas Library System
Open Mon-Thurs 3-8, Fri 3-6 & Sat 10-5
Friends of the Library Group

N MARCOS

FIRST UNITED METHODIST CHURCH, Gertrude Callihan Memorial Library, 129 W Hutchison St, 78666. SAN 316-7542. Tel: 512-392-6001. FAX: 512-392-8001. *Librn,* Louis C Maloney
Founded 1955
Library Holdings: Bk Vols 3,200

SAN MARCOS PUBLIC LIBRARY, 625 E Hopkins, 78666. SAN 316-7550. Tel: 512-393-8200. FAX: 392-754-8131. E-Mail: smpl@ci.san-marcos.tx.us. Web Site: ci.san-marcos.tx.us/library.htm. *Dir,* Stephanie Langenkamp; *Head Tech Servs,* Arro Smith; *Head, Circ,* Diane Insley; *Commun Relations,* Robin Wood; *Outreach Serv,* Susan Smith; *Ref,* Benjamin Pensiero; *Ch Servs,* Ashley Schimelman; *Ch Servs,* Michele Scott; Staff 17 (MLS 7, Non-MLS 10)
Founded 1966. Pop 50,000; Circ 336,471
Oct 1999-Sep 2000 Income $803,960, City $741,350, County $62,610. Mats Exp $128,677, Books $96,240, Per/Ser (Incl. Access Fees) $20,628, Micro $1,470, AV Equip $10,339. Sal $454,417
Library Holdings: Bk Vols 111,557; Bk Titles 96,072; Per Subs 260
Special Collections: Local History (Tula Townsend Wyatt Coll), docs & photog; San Marcos-Hays County Coll
Automation Activity & Vendor Info: (Acquisitions) epixtech, inc.; (Cataloging) epixtech, inc.; (Circulation) epixtech, inc.; (OPAC) epixtech, inc.
Database Vendor: epixtech, inc.
Publications: Calender of events (monthly)
Mem of Central Texas Library System
Friends of the Library Group

SOUTHWEST TEXAS STATE UNIVERSITY, Albert B Alkek Library, Comanche & Talbot St, 78666-4604. (Mail add: 601 University Dr, 78666-4604), SAN 362-322X. Tel: 512-245-2133. Circulation Tel: 512-245-3681. Reference Tel: 512-245-2685. FAX: 512-245-3002. Web Site: www.library.swt.edu. *Librn,* Joan L Heath; E-Mail: jh05@swt.edu; *Acq,* Jane P Mills; E-Mail: jm23@swt.edu; *Cat,* Edward A Bergin; E-Mail: eb13@swt.edu; *Circ,* Albert M L Chang; E-Mail: ac03@swt.edu; *Ref,* Robert L Harris; E-Mail: rh01@swt.edu; *Spec Coll,* Connie Todd; E-Mail: ct03@swt.edu; *Automation Syst Coordr,* Leslie P Fatout; *Adminr,* Richard Riley; Tel: 512-245-3007, Fax: 512-245-0392, E-Mail: rr02@swt.edu; Staff 81 (MLS 30, Non-MLS 51)
Founded 1899. Enrl 21,769; Fac 992; Highest Degree: Doctorate
Sep 1999-Aug 2000 Income $6,329,779, State $3,851,788, Federal $109,817, Parent Institution $2,368,174. Mats Exp $2,540,147, Books $611,885, Per/Ser (Incl. Access Fees) $1,249,722, Presv $56,826, Electronic Ref Mat (Incl. Access Fees) $621,724. Sal $2,287,696 (Prof $1,170,521)
Library Holdings: Bk Vols 1,244,417; Bk Titles 679,762; Per Subs 6,252
Special Collections: Early Textbooks DAR; Lyndon B Johnson Coll, film, photographs; Southwestern Writers Coll, J Frank Dobie, John Graves, Preston Jones, Larry L King, Elithe Hamilton Kirkland; T E Lawrence Coll, photogs; Texana Elliott coll; Texas monthly, books, correspondence, manuscripts, screenplays & artifacts; Wittliff Gallery of Southwestern & Mexican photography, Keith Carter, Russell Lee, Mariana Yampolsky, Graciela Iturbide
Automation Activity & Vendor Info: (Acquisitions) DRA; (Cataloging) DRA; (Circulation) DRA
Database Vendor: DRA
Partic in Amigos Library Services, Inc; Coun of Res & Acad Librs; OCLC Online Computer Library Center, Inc; Tex Share

N SABA

SAN SABA COUNTY LIBRARY, Rylander Memorial Library, 103 S Live Oak, 76877. SAN 316-7569. Tel: 915-372-3079. FAX: 915-372-3079. E-Mail: rylander@centex.net. *Librn,* Christine Bessent
Pop 5,540; Circ 16,055
Library Holdings: Bk Vols 9,032
Mem of Central Texas Library System
Friends of the Library Group

NDERSON

TERRELL COUNTY PUBLIC LIBRARY,* Courthouse Sq, PO Drawer 250, 79848. SAN 376-4346. Tel: 915-345-2294. FAX: 915-345-2144. *Librn,* Christina Valles
Library Holdings: Bk Vols 25,000; Per Subs 32
Mem of Texas Trans Pecos Library System
Open Mon-Fri 1-6 & Sat 2-5
Friends of the Library Group

NGER

SANGER PUBLIC LIBRARY, 501 Bolivar, 76266. (Mail add: PO Box 1729, 76266-0017), SAN 370-7350. Tel: 940-458-3257. E-Mail: sanglib@iglobal.net. *Dir,* Victoria Elieson; Staff 2 (MLS 1, Non-MLS 1)
Founded 1970. Pop 4,708; Circ 23,763
Oct 1998-Sep 1999 Income $73,635, City $54,967, County $16,353, Locally Generated Income $2,315. Mats Exp $6,321, Books $5,179, Per/Ser (Incl. Access Fees) $916, AV Equip $226. Sal $47,760 (Prof $34,000)
Library Holdings: Bk Vols 17,908; Bk Titles 17,580; Per Subs 21
Automation Activity & Vendor Info: (Cataloging) Sagebrush Corporation; (Circulation) Sagebrush Corporation; (OPAC) Sagebrush Corporation
Mem of North Texas Regional Library System
Friends of the Library Group

SANTA ANNA

P SANTA ANNA LIBRARY,* 606 Wallas, RR 1, Box 299, 76878-9801. SAN 316-7577. Tel: 915-348-3395. *Librn,* Ovella Williams
Pop 2,250; Circ 4,500
1997-1998 Income $2,000, County $500
Library Holdings: Bk Vols 14,000
Subject Interests: Local history
Open Mon-Fri 9:30-4:30

SANTA FE

P MAE S BRUCE LIBRARY, 13302 Sixth, 77510-9148. (Mail add: PO Box 950, 77510-0950), SAN 326-1816. Tel: 409-925-5540. FAX: 409-925-8697. *Librn,* Sue McLenna; E-Mail: smclenna@yahoo.com
Pop 11,300; Circ 34,000
1998-1999 Income $116,000, Federal $3,200, County $13,800. Mats Exp $20,000, Books $19,650, Per/Ser (Incl. Access Fees) $150, Micro $200. Sal $61,741
Library Holdings: Bk Vols 19,301; Bk Titles 16,936; Per Subs 10
Automation Activity & Vendor Info: (Cataloging) Athena; (Circulation) Athena
Mem of Houston Area Library System
Special Services for the Deaf - Books on deafness & sign language; High interest/low vocabulary books

SCHERTZ

P SCHERTZ PUBLIC LIBRARY,* 608 Schertz Pkwy, 78154-1911. SAN 324-1556. Tel: 210-658-6011. FAX: 210-945-8412. *Librn,* Gail Douglas
Founded 1978. Pop 19,000; Circ 97,000
Library Holdings: Bk Titles 27,063; Per Subs 56
Special Collections: Genealogy; Texana
Mem of Alamo Area Library System; San Antonio Area Libr Syst

SCHULENBURG

P SCHULENBURG PUBLIC LIBRARY,* 700 Bohlmann Ave, 78956. SAN 316-7585. Tel: 409-743-3345. FAX: 409-743-3345. *Librn,* Cindy Lytle
Pop 2,400; Circ 12,663
Library Holdings: Bk Vols 13,463
Mem of Central Texas Library System

SEAGOVILLE

S SEAGOVILLE PUBLIC LIBRARY, 702 N Hwy 175, 75159. SAN 316-7593. Tel: 972-287-7720. E-Mail: seagolib@z-net.tx.com. *Librn,* Elizabeth Gant; E-Mail: wizzie56@aol.com
Founded 1942
Oct 1999-Sep 2000 Income $64,016, State $3,800, City $53,416, County $6,800. Sal $50,540
Library Holdings: Bk Vols 25,000; Bk Titles 23,600; High Interest/Low Vocabulary Bk Vols 100
Automation Activity & Vendor Info: (Cataloging) Sagebrush Corporation; (Circulation) Sagebrush Corporation
Mem of Dallas County Libr Syst
Open Mon & Thurs 11-7, Tues & Fri 10-5, Wed 10-6, Sat 8-1
Friends of the Library Group

SEALY

P VIRGIL & JOSEPHINE GORDON MEMORIAL LIBRARY,* 917 N Circle Dr, 77474. SAN 324-2188. Tel: 409-885-7469. FAX: 409-885-7469. *Librn,* Gloria Noy
Pop 7,269; Circ 30,173
Library Holdings: Bk Vols 22,681; Bk Titles 20,785; Per Subs 32
Mem of Houston Area Library System
Friends of the Library Group

SEGUIN

P SEGUIN-GUADALUPE COUNTY PUBLIC LIBRARY, 707 E College St, 78155-3217. SAN 316-7615. Tel: 830-401-2422. FAX: 830-401-2477. E-Mail: webmaster@seguin.lib.tx.us. Web Site: www.seguin.lib.tx.us. *Dir,* Mark Gretchen; E-Mail: mark@seguin.lib.tx.us; *Asst Dir,* Jacki Gross; *Ch*

Servs, Melissa Ronning; Staff 11 (MLS 3, Non-MLS 8)
Founded 1930. Pop 40,933; Circ 158,012
Oct 2000-Sep 2001 Income City $343,235. Mats Exp $56,000, Books $52,000, Per/Ser (Incl. Access Fees) $4,000. Sal $192,992
Library Holdings: Bk Vols 62,500
Subject Interests: Guadalupe County hist, Local history
Special Collections: Guadalupe County Land Records, micro; Historic Photographs (Kubala Coll); Old Seguin Newspapers, micro-filmed
Automation Activity & Vendor Info: (OPAC) SIRSI
Database Vendor: OCLC - First Search
Function: Reference services available
Mem of Alamo Area Library System
Friends of the Library Group

C TEXAS LUTHERAN UNIVERSITY, Blumberg Memorial Library,* 1000 W Court St, 78155-5978. SAN 316-7623. Tel: 830-372-8100. FAX: 830-372-8156. Web Site: www.txlutheran.edu. *Tech Servs*, Linda Clark; *Librn*, Patrick K Hsu; E-Mail: phsu@txlutheran.edu; *Asst Librn*, Vicki Eckhardt; *Reader Servs*, Sandra Moline; *Coordr, Reader Servs*, Martha Rinn; Staff 5 (MLS 5)
Founded 1891. Enrl 1,095; Fac 64; Highest Degree: Bachelor
Jun 1997-May 1998 Income $461,436, Federal $13,045, Parent Institution $433,770, Other $14,621. Mats Exp $133,490, Books $70,858, Per/Ser (Incl. Access Fees) $54,111, Presv $5,331, Micro $2,500, AV Equip $690. Sal $261,723 (Prof $157,651)
Library Holdings: Bk Vols 82,165; Per Subs 635
Subject Interests: Gen liberal arts, Relig studies
Special Collections: American Lutheran Church; German Literature & Culture; Rundell Rare Book Coll
Automation Activity & Vendor Info: (Cataloging) Endeavor; (Circulation) Endeavor; (OPAC) Endeavor; (Serials) Endeavor
Database Vendor: GaleNet, OCLC - First Search, OVID Technologies, Silverplatter Information Inc.
Publications: Library guide; Library newsletter
Partic in Amigos Library Services, Inc; Coun of Res & Acad Librs; OCLC Online Computer Library Center, Inc; Tex Share

SEMINOLE

P GAINES COUNTY LIBRARY,* 704 Hobbs Hwy, 79360. SAN 362-3289. Tel: 915-758-4007. FAX: 915-758-4024. *Librn*, Lupe Molinar
Founded 1957. Pop 14,123; Circ 57,784
Jan 1997-Dec 1998 Income $181,507. Mats Exp $19,958, Books $16,668, Per/Ser (Incl. Access Fees) $2,248, AV Equip $10. Sal $120,097 (Prof $29,095)
Library Holdings: Bk Vols 32,600; Per Subs 94
Subject Interests: Bks on tape, Gaines County hist, Large print, Local history, Mennonites, Spanish lang
Automation Activity & Vendor Info: (Acquisitions) Sagebrush Corporation; (Cataloging) Sagebrush Corporation; (Circulation) Sagebrush Corporation
Mem of West Texas Library System
Closed Circuit Television
Branches: 1
SEAGRAVES BRANCH, PO Box 366, Seagraves, 79359. SAN 362-3319. Tel: 806-546-3053. FAX: 806-546-3053. *In Charge*, Diana Guzman

SEYMOUR

P BAYLOR COUNTY FREE LIBRARY,* County Courthouse, 101 S Washington St, 76380-2558. SAN 316-7631. Tel: 940-888-2007. *Librn*, Ellen Arnold
Pop 5,000; Circ 13,000
Library Holdings: Bk Vols 17,360; Bk Titles 15,658; Per Subs 19
Mem of North Texas Regional Library System

SHAMROCK

P SHAMROCK PUBLIC LIBRARY,* 712 N Main St, 79079. SAN 316-764X. Tel: 806-256-3921. FAX: 806-256-3921. *Librn*, Julia Henderson
Pop 3,000; Circ 12,057
Library Holdings: Bk Vols 22,000; Per Subs 36
Mem of Texas Panhandle Library System
Open Mon-Fri 1-5
Friends of the Library Group

SHEPHERD

P SHEPHERD PUBLIC LIBRARY,* PO Box 369, 77371-0369. SAN 376-4087. Tel: 409-628-3515. FAX: 409-628-6608. *Librn*, Libby Bones
Library Holdings: Bk Vols 13,000
Mem of Houston Area Library System
Open Mon-Fri 10-5
Friends of the Library Group

SHEPPARD AFB

UNITED STATES AIR FORCE
AM 882ND TRAINING GROUP ACADEMIC LIBRARY, 882 TRG/TSOL, Missile Rd Bldg 1900, 76311-2245. SAN 362-3408. Tel: 940-676-2736. FAX: 940-676-4025. *Librn*, Patricia Boyd
Founded 1958
Library Holdings: Bk Titles 10,000; Per Subs 150
Subject Interests: Dentistry, Hosp admin, Medicine, Nursing
AM HEALTH SCIENCES LIBRARY, 82nd Medical Group, 149 Hart St, 763-3479. SAN 362-3432. Tel: 940-676-6647. FAX: 940-676-6416. *Librn*, Marilyn Lucas
Founded 1942
1999-2000 Mats Exp $45,000, Books $8,000, Per/Ser (Incl. Access Fees) $37,000. Sal $33,000
Library Holdings: Bk Vols 7,400; Per Subs 145
Subject Interests: Admin, Dentistry, Medicine, Nursing, Radiology, Surgery
Partic in S Cent Regional Med Libr Program
A SHEPPARD AIR FORCE BASE LIBRARY, 82 SVS/SVMG, 425 Third Bldg 312, 76311-3043. SAN 362-3343. Tel: 940-676-2687. FAX: 940-8854. *Librn*, Linda Fryar; E-Mail: fryar@spd.aetc.af.mil
Founded 1949
Library Holdings: Bk Vols 46,000; Per Subs 247
Subject Interests: Gen, Juv, Mil-tech

SHERIDAN

P SHERIDAN MEMORIAL LIBRARY, Logan Park W, 77475-0274. (Mail add: PO Box 274, 77475-0274), SAN 372-7335. Tel: 409-234-5154. FAX: 409-234-5950. E-Mail: sheridanlib@elc.net. *Librn*, Lillian Gohlke; Staff 1 (MLS 1)
Founded 1971. Pop 500
Jan 1999-Dec 1999 Income $5,730, County $2,930, Locally Generated Income $2,800. Mats Exp $3,240, Books $2,000, AV Equip $1,000, Electronic Ref Mat (Incl. Access Fees) $240
Library Holdings: Bk Vols 7,450; Bk Vols 7,500; High Interest/Low Vocabulary Bk Vols 50
Subject Interests: Genealogy
Automation Activity & Vendor Info: (Cataloging) Follett; (Circulation) Follett
Mem of Houston Area Library System
Open Mon-Wed 10-12 & 2-5, Thurs 10-2 & 2-6
Friends of the Library Group

SHERMAN

C AUSTIN COLLEGE, Abell Library, 900 N Grand Ave, 75090-2442. SAN 316-7658. Tel: 903-813-2518. FAX: 903-813-2297. Web Site: www.austinc.edu/abell. *Dir*, Larry Hardesty; Tel: 903-813-2490, E-Mail: lhardesty@austinc.edu; *Coll Develop*, Margaret Garner; Tel: 903-813-2369, E-Mail: mgarner@austinc.edu; *Publ Servs*, Dr Carolyn Vickrey; Tel: 903-813-2470, E-Mail: cvickrey@austinc.edu; *Assoc Librn, Syst Coordr*, John West; Tel: 903-813-2536, E-Mail: jwest@austinc.edu; Staff 5 (MLS 4, Non-MLS 1)
Founded 1849. Enrl 1,272; Fac 93; Highest Degree: Master
Jul 1999-Jun 2000 Income $1,093,518, Parent Institution $1,093,518. Mats Exp $493,465, Books $197,584, Per/Ser (Incl. Access Fees) $165,275, Presv $13,395, Micro $23,643, Manuscripts & Archives $82,965, Electronic Ref Mat (Incl. Access Fees) $10,603. Sal $351,074 (Prof $184,230)
Library Holdings: Bk Vols 201,354; Bk Titles 185,685; Per Subs 1,364
Special Collections: Alexander the Great (Berzunza Coll); Texana (Pate Texana & Hoard Texas Coll)
Automation Activity & Vendor Info: (Cataloging) SIRSI; (Circulation) SIRSI; (OPAC) SIRSI; (Serials) SIRSI
Database Vendor: Lexis-Nexis, OCLC - First Search, Wilson - Wilson W
Partic in Acad Press Online; Amigos Library Services, Inc; Britannica Online; Dialog Corporation; JSTOR; MLA; OCLC Online Computer Library Center, Inc

R NORTH PARK BAPTIST CHURCH LIBRARY, 2605 Rex Cruse Dr, 75092. SAN 362-3467. Tel: 903-892-8429. FAX: 903-893-4463. E-Mail: office@northparknet.com. Web Site: www.northparknet.com. *Dir*, Mignon Plyler; *Circ*, Doris Lee
Founded 1958
Library Holdings: Bk Titles 4,774; Per Subs 12

P SHERMAN PUBLIC LIBRARY, 421 N Travis, 75090-5975. SAN 316-7674. Tel: 903-892-7240. FAX: 903-892-7101. *Dir*, Hope Waller; E-Mail: hopecalwal@grayson.edu; *Tech Servs*, Janis Rush; *Ch Servs*, Belinda Sakowski; *Publ Servs*, Susan Banner; Staff 4 (MLS 3, Non-MLS 1)
Founded 1911. Pop 45,972; Circ 287,103
Oct 1999-Sep 2000 Income $639,574, City $612,082, County $27,492. Mats Exp $71,899, Books $57,764, Per/Ser (Incl. Access Fees) $11,038, Micro $3,097. Sal $398,333
Library Holdings: Bk Vols 111,108; Per Subs 240
Special Collections: Grayson County Historical Resources for Texas State

Library; Hilmer H Flemming Manuscripts; Mattie Davis Lucas Manuscripts
Mem of Northeast Texas Library System
Partic in Barr
Member of Bibliog Asn of the Red River
Friends of the Library Group

INER

SHINER PUBLIC LIBRARY, 115 E Wolters/Second St, PO Box 1602, 77984-0308. SAN 376-4281. Tel: 512-594-3044. FAX: 512-594-4249. E-Mail: psp@netrax.net. *Dir*, Lanelle Kasper; E-Mail: lkasper@netrax.net; *Librn*, Paula Sue Pekar
Library Holdings: Bk Vols 11,963; Per Subs 54
Mem of South Texas Library System
Friends of the Library Group

SBEE

SILSBEE PUBLIC LIBRARY,* Santa Fe Park, 77656. SAN 316-7682. Tel: 409-385-4831. FAX: 409-385-7382. *Librn*, Cathy Johnson
Pop 26,500; Circ 74,330
Library Holdings: Bk Vols 43,619; Per Subs 54
Friends of the Library Group

VERTON

SILVERTON LIBRARY,* 415 Main, PO Box 69, 79257. SAN 316-7690. Tel: 806-823-2131. FAX: 806-823-2359. *Librn*, Polly Cagle; *Asst Librn*, Diana Ivory
Pop 2,794
Library Holdings: Bk Vols 9,000

NTON

ROB & BESSIE WELDER WILDLIFE FOUNDATION LIBRARY,* PO Box 1400, 78387-1400. SAN 316-7720. Tel: 512-364-2643. FAX: 512-364-2650. *Librn*, Vaunda Davis; *Dir*, Lynn Drawe
Founded 1954
Library Holdings: Bk Titles 12,574; Per Subs 68
Subject Interests: Ecology, Environ and conserv, Nat hist, Ornithology, Range mgt, Sci, Technology, Wildlife mgt
Special Collections: Ornithology (Alexander Wetmore Coll); Rare Book Coll
Publications: Newsletter (bicennial); Student Synposiums
Restriction: By appointment only

SAN PATRICIO COUNTY LIBRARY SYSTEM,* 313 N Rachal, Rm 226, 78387-2663. SAN 316-7704. Tel: 512-364-6199. FAX: 512-364-4518. *Librn*, Kippy Edge; Staff 2 (MLS 1, Non-MLS 1)
Founded 1973. Pop 53,000
Jan 1999-Dec 1999 Income County $75,760. Mats Exp Books $1,000. Sal $41,412
Library Holdings: Bk Vols 914; Bk Titles 820
Subject Interests: Children
Member Libraries: Bell-Whittington Public Library; Ingleside Public Library
Open Mon-Fri 8-5

SINTON PUBLIC LIBRARY, (SPL), 212 E Sinton St, 78387. SAN 316-7712. Tel: 512-364-4545. FAX: 512-364-5711. *Librn*, Yolanda Bustamante; E-Mail: yabe@2fords.net; Staff 2 (Non-MLS 2)
Founded 1927. Pop 9,738; Circ 27,019
Oct 1998-Sep 1999 Income $77,211, City $72,878, County $900, Locally Generated Income $3,433. Mats Exp $15,414, Books $6,205, Per/Ser (Incl. Access Fees) $1,065, AV Equip $100, Electronic Ref Mat (Incl. Access Fees) $2,320. Sal $54,010
Library Holdings: Bk Vols 15,087; Bk Titles 13,641; Per Subs 45; Bks on Deafness & Sign Lang 10
Special Collections: Texana Coll
Automation Activity & Vendor Info: (Cataloging) Sagebrush Corporation; (Circulation) Sagebrush Corporation
Mem of South Texas Library System
Open Mon-Fri 10-6, Sat 10-2
Friends of the Library Group

ATON

SLATON PUBLIC LIBRARY,* 200 W Lynn, 79364-4136. SAN 376-4230. Tel: 806-828-2008. FAX: 806-828-2008. *Librn*, Kim Balch
1998-1999 Income $33,309. Mats Exp $4,746. Sal $20,707
Library Holdings: Bk Vols 12,500; Per Subs 30
Mem of West Texas Library System
Open Mon-Fri 9-1 & 2-5:30

SMILEY

P STELLA HART MEMORIAL PUBLIC LIBRARY, PO Box 88, 78159. SAN 316-7739. Tel: 830-587-6101. *Asst Librn*, Susy Parker
Pop 861; Circ 1,702
Library Holdings: Bk Vols 7,000

SMITHVILLE

P SMITHVILLE PUBLIC LIBRARY, (SPL), 507 Main St, 78957. SAN 316-7755. Tel: 512-237-2707. FAX: 512-237-4549. *Dir*, Karen Saunders Bell; E-Mail: kbellspl@swbell.net
Pop 3,700; Circ 33,865
Oct 1998-Sep 1999 Income $60,777, City $55,777, County $5,000. Mats Exp $13,500, Books $12,500, Per/Ser (Incl. Access Fees) $1,000. Sal $79,000 (Prof $26,000)
Library Holdings: Bk Vols 22,000; Bk Titles 20,492; Per Subs 44; Bks on Deafness & Sign Lang 20
Special Collections: Genealogy Coll; Literacy Coll; Media Library; Texian Coll; Video Coll
Automation Activity & Vendor Info: (Cataloging) Sagebrush Corporation; (Circulation) Sagebrush Corporation
Mem of Central Texas Library System
Open Mon, Wed-Fri 10-6, Tues 10-8, Sat 10-2
Friends of the Library Group

SNYDER

P SCURRY COUNTY LIBRARY, 1916 23rd St, 79549-1910. SAN 316-7763. Tel: 915-573-5572. FAX: 915-573-1060. E-Mail: scurrycl@snydertex.com. *Dir*, L Jane Romine; Staff 5 (MLS 1, Non-MLS 4)
Founded 1958. Pop 18,000; Circ 90,000
Library Holdings: Bk Vols 60,050; Per Subs 65
Subject Interests: Genealogy, Southwest
Special Collections: Genealogy; Southwest
Mem of Big Country Library System
Literacy Program

C WESTERN TEXAS COLLEGE, Learning Resource Center, 6200 College Ave, 79549. SAN 316-7771. Tel: 915-573-8511, Ext 303. FAX: 915-573-9321. Web Site: www.wtc.cc.tx.us./lrc.html. *Dir*, L V Anderson; *Tech Servs*, Donna Billingsley; E-Mail: dbillingsley@wtc.cc.tx.us; *Asst Librn*, Zelma A Irons; Tel: 915-573-8511, Ext 265, E-Mail: zirons@wtc.cc.tx.us; *AV*, Xan Harris; Tel: 915-573-8511, Ext 264, E-Mail: xharris@wtc.cc.tx.us; Staff 3 (MLS 1, Non-MLS 2)
Founded 1971
Sep 1999-Aug 2000 Income Parent Institution $172,764. Mats Exp $23,700, Books $13,000, Per/Ser (Incl. Access Fees) $9,900, Micro $800. Sal $95,500 (Prof $61,844)
Library Holdings: Bk Vols 29,980; Bk Titles 27,097; Per Subs 78
Database Vendor: Ebsco - EbscoHost
Mem of Big Country Library System
Partic in Tex Share

SONORA

P SUTTON COUNTY LIBRARY,* 306 E Mulberry St, 76950. SAN 376-401X. Tel: 915-387-2111. FAX: 915-387-9044. *Librn*, Florie Gonzalez
Library Holdings: Bk Vols 14,000
Mem of Big Country Library System
Open Mon-Fri 9-5:30
Friends of the Library Group

SOURLAKE

P ALMA M CARPENTER PUBLIC LIBRARY,* 300 S Ann, PO Box 536, 77659-0536. SAN 316-778X. Tel: 409-287-3592. *Librn*, Carolyn B Moy
Pop 5,000; Circ 10,600
Library Holdings: Bk Vols 22,000; Bk Titles 20,000
Special Collections: Texas Coll
Mem of Houston Area Library System
Open Tues 11-5:30, Wed 10-4:45 & Sat 10-12

SPEARMAN

P HANSFORD COUNTY LIBRARY, 122 Main St, 79081. SAN 316-7798. Tel: 806-659-2231. FAX: 806-659-5042. *Dir*, Sheri Benton; E-Mail: spesheri@visto.com; *Tech Servs*, Margaret Ruttman; *Circ*, Cecilia Foster; Staff 3 (Non-MLS 3)
Founded 1932. Pop 3,932; Circ 42,363
Jan 2000-Dec 2000 Income $77,403, City $9,000, County $13,200, Other $48,356. Mats Exp $13,034, Books $12,301, Per/Ser (Incl. Access Fees) $733. Sal $31,735 (Prof $19,530)
Library Holdings: Bk Vols 23,565; Per Subs 31
Automation Activity & Vendor Info: (Acquisitions) DRA; (Cataloging)

DRA; (Circulation) DRA; (Course Reserve) DRA; (ILL) DRA; (Media Booking) DRA; (OPAC) DRA; (Serials) DRA
Database Vendor: DRA
Mem of Texas Panhandle Library System
Partic in Harrington Library Consortium

SPRINGTOWN

P SPRINGTOWN PUBLIC LIBRARY, 101 S Ash Terrace, PO Box 428, 76082. SAN 376-463X. Tel: 817-523-5862. *Librn*, Barbara Ford
Library Holdings: Bk Vols 13,450
Mem of North Texas Regional Library System
Open Tues 10-5, Wed & Thurs 12-5, Fri & Sat 9-1
Friends of the Library Group

SPUR

P DICKENS COUNTY-SPUR PUBLIC LIBRARY, 415 E Hill St, PO Box 282, 79370-0282. SAN 376-4222. Tel: 806-271-3714. FAX: 806-271-3362. *Librn*, Linda Bradford
1999-2000 Income $9,609. Sal $5,230
Library Holdings: Bk Vols 10,600; Spec Interest Per Sub 15
Mem of West Texas Library System
Open Mon-Thurs 12-5
Friends of the Library Group

STAMFORD

P STAMFORD CARNEGIE LIBRARY,* 600 E McHarg St, 79553. SAN 316-7801. Tel: 915-773-2532. *Librn*, Marge Barnett
Founded 1910. Pop 5,000; Circ 12,180
Library Holdings: Bk Vols 11,000; Per Subs 12
Mem of Big Country Library System
Open Mon-Fri 12:30-6

STANTON

P MARTIN COUNTY LIBRARY,* 110 W School St, PO Box 1187, 79782. SAN 316-781X. Tel: 915-756-2472. *Librn*, Dianne Hull
Founded 1929. Pop 4,684; Circ 9,770
Library Holdings: Bk Titles 12,955
Mem of West Texas Library System
Open Mon-Fri 8:30-12 & 1-5:30

STEPHENVILLE

P STEPHENVILLE PUBLIC LIBRARY,* 174 N Columbia, 76401-3492. SAN 316-7828. Tel: 254-965-5665. Interlibrary Loan Service Tel: 940-322-1169. FAX: 254-918-1207. *Dir*, Lynn Lloyd; *Asst Librn*, Sandra Thomas
Founded 1903. Pop 26,606; Circ 66,019
Library Holdings: Bk Titles 32,329
Subject Interests: Genealogy, Texas
Mem of North Texas Regional Library System

C TARLETON STATE UNIVERSITY, Dick Smith Library, 201 Saint Felix, PO Box T-0450, 76402. SAN 316-7836. Tel: 254-968-9246. Interlibrary Loan Service Tel: 254-968-9660. FAX: 254-968-9467. Web Site: www.tarleton.edu/~library. *Dir*, Dr Kenneth W Jones; E-Mail: kjones@tarleton.edu; *Assoc Librn*, Donna Savage; E-Mail: dsavage@tarleton.edu; *Tech Servs*, Karen DeFranchi; Tel: 254-968-9934, E-Mail: franchi@tarleton.edu; *ILL*, *Ref*, Jane Dickson; E-Mail: dickson@tarleton.edu; *Cat*, Glenda Stone; E-Mail: gstone@tarleton.edu; Staff 12 (MLS 12)
Founded 1899. Enrl 7,500; Fac 300; Highest Degree: Master
Sep 1998-Aug 1999 Income $1,442,405. Mats Exp $579,492, Books $204,571, Per/Ser (Incl. Access Fees) $325,809, Presv $20,206, Micro $20,000. Sal $987,365
Library Holdings: Bk Titles 260,000; Per Subs 1,828
Subject Interests: Agriculture, Bus, Econ, Education, History, Mgt, Sci-tech
Special Collections: Agricultural, Experiment Station Reports; Texana
Automation Activity & Vendor Info: (Acquisitions) DRA; (Cataloging) DRA; (Circulation) DRA; (Course Reserve) DRA; (ILL) DRA; (Media Booking) DRA; (OPAC) DRA; (Serials) DRA
Publications: General Stacks; Library Handbook
Partic in Amigos Library Services, Inc; Tex Share
Friends of the Library Group

STRATFORD

P SHERMAN COUNTY PUBLIC LIBRARY,* 719 N Main, PO Box 46, 79084. SAN 316-7844. Tel: 806-366-2200. FAX: 806-366-7551. *Dir*, Sandra C Baskin; *Librn*, Dorothy Haile; *Asst Librn*, Doris Pleyer; Staff 2 (Non-MLS 2)
Founded 1957. Pop 2,858; Circ 9,208
Library Holdings: Bk Vols 16,479; Bk Titles 16,250; Per Subs 36
Special Collections: Texas Coll
Mem of Texas Panhandle Library System
Friends of the Library Group

SUGAR LAND

FLUOR DANIEL, INC
S LIBRARY, One Fluor Daniel Dr, 77478. (Mail add: PO Box 5014, 7748 Tel: 281-263-2244. FAX: 281-263-3777. *Librn*, Doris V Brooks; Tel: 2 263-2245, E-Mail: doris.brooks@fluordaniel.com; *Tech Servs*, David Alvarado
Founded 1973
Library Holdings: Bk Titles 4,000; Per Subs 50
Subject Interests: Chemical engineering, Civil engineering, Offshore e Petroleum engineering
Automation Activity & Vendor Info: (Cataloging) Sydney
Database Vendor: Dialog, Ebsco - EbscoHost, GaleNet
Restriction: Not open to public

S NALCO-EXXON ENERGY CHEMICALS, L P LIBRARY, 7705 Hwy 9 77478. SAN 328-8226. Tel: 281-263-7000. FAX: 281-263-7865. *Librn*, Richard Behling
Library Holdings: Bk Titles 7,000; Per Subs 130
Restriction: Not open to public

S WILLIAMS BROTHERS ENGINEERING CO, Technical Information Center,* PO Box 5014, 77487-5014. SAN 314-030X. Tel: 918-610-9500. FAX: 918-561-9510. *Dir*, Pat Clark
Founded 1971
Library Holdings: Bk Vols 4,000; Per Subs 150
Subject Interests: Bus, Engineering, Gas, Oil, Pipelines
Publications: Technical Information Center Newsletter (quarterly)

SULPHUR SPRINGS

P SULPHUR SPRINGS PUBLIC LIBRARY,* 201 N Davis St, 75482. SA 316-7852. Tel: 903-885-4926. FAX: 903-439-1052. E-Mail: publib@coyote.com. *Dir*, Katherine St Claire
Pop 25,000; Circ 54,900
Library Holdings: Bk Vols 43,500; Per Subs 95
Mem of Northeast Texas Library System
Friends of the Library Group

SUNNYVALE

P SUNNYVALE PUBLIC LIBRARY,* 402 Tower Pl, 75182. SAN 361-42 Tel: 972-226-4491. FAX: 972-226-6745. E-Mail: honeybee@flashnet. *Lib* Doris Padgett
Library Holdings: Bk Vols 20,000
Mem of Dallas County Libr Syst
Open Tues & Thurs 12-6, Fri 2-6 & Sat 11-3

SWEETWATER

P SWEETWATER COUNTY-CITY LIBRARY, 206 Elm St, 79556. SAN 316-7860. Tel: 915-235-4978. FAX: 915-235-4979. *Librn*, Bonnie McSweeney; Staff 1 (MLS 1)
Founded 1907. Pop 17,500; Circ 90,000
Library Holdings: Bk Titles 42,000
Mem of Big Country Library System
Bookmobiles: 1

J TEXAS STATE TECHNICAL COLLEGE (TSTC) LIBRARY, 300 Colle Dr, 79556. SAN 316-7879. Tel: 915-235-7406. FAX: 915-235-7369. Web Site: www.sweetwater.tstc.edu. *Dir*, Sandra C Woodman; E-Mail: sandra.woodman@sweetwater.tstc.edu; Staff 1 (MLS 1)
Library Holdings: Bk Vols 16,804; Bk Titles 14,829; Per Subs 144
Subject Interests: Computer maintenance, Computer science, Electronics, Robotics, Sci-tech, Telecommunication
Publications: New Titles List (monthly)

TAFT

P TAFT PUBLIC LIBRARY, 503 Green Ave, PO Box 416, 78390-0416. S 316-7895. Tel: 512-528-3512, Ext 15. FAX: 512-528-3515. *Librn*, Mary Griffin
Circ 19,511
Library Holdings: Bk Titles 15,817; Per Subs 14
Special Collections: Texana-Spanish Coll
Mem of South Texas Library System
Friends of the Library Group

HOKA

CITY COUNTY LIBRARY,* 1717 Main St, Box 1018, 79373. SAN 376-4273. Tel: 806-998-4050. E-Mail: librytka@gte.net. *Librn*, Shirley Draper
Library Holdings: Bk Vols 12,000
Mem of West Texas Library System
Open Mon & Wed 9-5:30, Tues & Thurs 2-7, Sat 10-1

YLOR

TAYLOR PUBLIC LIBRARY,* 721 Vance St, 76574. SAN 316-7909. Tel: 512-352-3434. FAX: 512-432-3555. *Librn*, Norma Patschke
Founded 1899. Pop 12,000; Circ 38,000
Library Holdings: Bk Vols 34,000; Per Subs 39
Mem of Central Texas Library System
Friends of the Library Group

AGUE

TEAGUE PUBLIC LIBRARY, 400 Main, 75860. SAN 316-7917. Tel: 254-739-3311. FAX: 254-739-3213. E-Mail: teague.library@mexia.com. *Librn*, Doris Herrington; Staff 2 (Non-MLS 2)
Pop 7,489; Circ 42,173
1999-2000 Income $57,639
Library Holdings: Bk Vols 30,900
Subject Interests: Tex hist
Mem of Central Texas Library System
Friends of the Library Group

MPLE

DEPARTMENT OF VETERANS AFFAIRS, (TXUOTV), Central Texas Veterans Health Care System Library Service, 1901 Veterans Memorial Dr, 76504. SAN 362-3556. Tel: 254-778-4811, Ext 4111. FAX: 254-771-4532. *Tech Servs*, Jeffery Garverick; Staff 3 (MLS 2, Non-MLS 1)
Founded 1942
Library Holdings: Bk Titles 4,900
Subject Interests: Allied health, Medicine, Nursing
Automation Activity & Vendor Info: (Cataloging) Endeavor; (Circulation) Endeavor; (OPAC) Endeavor
Database Vendor: IAC - Info Trac
Restriction: Non-circulating to the public
Function: ILL available, Photocopies available, Reference services available
Partic in Docline; National Network Of Libraries Of Medicine - South Central Region; TAMU Consortium of Med Librs; Veterans Affairs Library Network
Branches:
WACO-ICF, 4800 Memorial Dr, Waco, 76711-1397. SAN 377-001X. Tel: 254-752-6581, Ext 6609. *Chief Librn*, Joanne Greenwood
Subject Interests: Mental health, Psychiatry, Psychology
Partic in Docline; Valnet

RAILROAD & HERITAGE MUSEUM, 315 W Ave, Ste B, PO Box 2433, 76503. SAN 316-7933. Tel: 254-298-5172. FAX: 254-298-5171. E-Mail: museum@ci.temple.tx.us. *Curator*, Mary Irving; E-Mail: mirving@ci.temple.tx.us
Founded 1973
Library Holdings: Bk Titles 10,000
Subject Interests: Architecture, Area pioneer hist, Art, Employees, Railroads, Women vet
Special Collections: Santa Fe Railroad Engineer Tracings, 1896-1980; Springer Railroad Timetables & Passes
Friends of the Library Group

SCOTT & WHITE MEMORIAL HOSPITAL, Richard D Haines Medical Library,* 2401 S 31st, 76508. SAN 316-7941. Tel: 254-724-2228. FAX: 254-724-4229. *Dir*, Penny Worley; Staff 7 (MLS 4, Non-MLS 3)
Founded 1923
Library Holdings: Bk Vols 9,057; Bk Titles 6,575; Per Subs 986
Special Collections: Nursing (Laura Cole Coll)
Database Vendor: OVID Technologies
Publications: Check It Out (library newsletter); Library List of Acquisitions
Restriction: Medical staff only
Partic in Amigos Library Services, Inc; Nat Libr of Med; National Network Of Libraries Of Medicine - South Central Region; TAMU Consortium of Med Librs

SLAVONIC BENEVOLENT ORDER OF THE STATE OF TEXAS, Library & Archives Museum,* 520 N Main St, 76501. SAN 327-7984. Tel: 254-773-1575. Toll Free Tel: 800-727-7578. FAX: 254-774-7447. *Curator, Librn*, Dorothy Pechal
Library Holdings: Bk Titles 23,000
Subject Interests: Fiction, Genealogy, Geography, History
Special Collections: Czech Language Coll, bks

J TEMPLE COLLEGE, Hubert M Dawson Library, 2600 S First St, 76504-7435. SAN 316-795X. Tel: 254-298-8426. FAX: 254-298-8430. E-Mail: kf@templejc.edu. Web Site: www.templejc.edu/library/library.html. *Dir*, Kathy Fulton; *Librn*, Paul Haire; *Ref*, Todd Hively; Staff 3 (MLS 3)
Founded 1926. Enrl 2,801; Fac 152; Highest Degree: Associate
Library Holdings: Bk Vols 54,340; Per Subs 349
Automation Activity & Vendor Info: (Acquisitions) Endeavor; (Cataloging) Endeavor; (Circulation) Endeavor; (Course Reserve) Endeavor; (OPAC) Endeavor; (Serials) Endeavor
Partic in OCLC Online Computer Library Center, Inc; Tex Share

S TEMPLE DAILY TELEGRAM LIBRARY,* 10 S Third St, PO Box 6114, 76503-6114. SAN 373-000X. Tel: 254-778-4444. FAX: 254-771-3516, Ext 298. *Librn*, Mary Lopez
Library Holdings: Bk Vols 100; Per Subs 15
Subject Interests: Local history

P TEMPLE PUBLIC LIBRARY, 100 W Adams Ave, 76501-7641. SAN 316-7968. Tel: 254-298-5556. Reference Tel: 254-298-5702. TDD: 254-298-5569. FAX: 254-298-5328. Web Site: library.ci.temple.tx.us. *Dir*, Judy Duer; Tel: 254-298-5707, E-Mail: jduer@ci.temple.tx.us; *Tech Servs*, Leon Perkins; Tel: 254-298-5560, E-Mail: lperkins@ci.temple.tx.us; *Ch Servs*, Theresa Faris; Tel: 254-298-5289, E-Mail: tfaris@ci.temple.tx.us; *Cat*, Jo Ann Sudduth; *Outreach Serv*, Diane Wolfe; Tel: 254-298-5288, E-Mail: dwolfe@ci.temple.tx.us; *Circ*, Carlotta Maneice; Tel: 254-298-5706, E-Mail: cmaneice@ci.temple.tx.us; *Coll Develop*, Donna Holloman; Tel: 254-298-5295, E-Mail: dholloman@ci.temple.tx.us; *Ref Serv Ad*, Nancy Williams; Tel: 254-298-5333, E-Mail: nwilliams@ci.temple.tx.us; Staff 24 (MLS 4, Non-MLS 20)
Founded 1900. Pop 54,000; Circ 388,957
Oct 1999-Sep 2000 Income $1,143,127, City $1,019,127, Other $124,000. Mats Exp $151,039, Books $129,514, Per/Ser (Incl. Access Fees) $11,696, Micro $1,000, Electronic Ref Mat (Incl. Access Fees) $8,829. Sal $572,148 (Prof $174,979)
Library Holdings: Bk Vols 118,719; Bk Titles 96,552; Per Subs 200
Subject Interests: Temple hist
Special Collections: Adult Education; Career & Job Information; Genealogy; Large-Print; Local Authors
Automation Activity & Vendor Info: (Acquisitions) epixtech, inc.; (Cataloging) epixtech, inc.; (Circulation) epixtech, inc.
Database Vendor: epixtech, inc., OCLC - First Search, ProQuest, Wilson - Wilson Web
Special Services for the Deaf - TDD
Special Services for the Blind - Voice synthezier, online text enlargement
Outreach Bookmobile to Nursing homes & Senior citizen residential complexes & low income housing
Friends of the Library Group
Bookmobiles: 1

TERRELL

J DORIS JOHNSON LIBRARY, Hogan-Steward Learning Center,* 200 Bowser Circle, 75160. SAN 316-7984. Tel: 972-524-3341. FAX: 972-563-7133. *Librn*, Doris Johnson; *Cat*, Trinita Rollie; Staff 2 (MLS 2)
Founded 1948. Enrl 244; Fac 24; Highest Degree: Doctorate
Library Holdings: Bk Titles 29,000; Per Subs 158
Subject Interests: Arts, Black studies, Scis
Special Collections: Black Studies
Publications: A Library Handbook
Open Mon, Tues & Thurs 8am-9pm, Wed & Fri 8-5, Sat 8-1

P TERRELL PUBLIC LIBRARY, 301 N Rockwall, 75160-2618. SAN 316-7976. Tel: 972-551-6663. FAX: 972-551-6662. E-Mail: library@cityofterrell.org. Web Site: www.terrellpl.org. *Dir*, Rebecca W Sullivan; Staff 4 (MLS 3, Non-MLS 1)
Founded 1904. Pop 24,815; Circ 73,406
Oct 1998-Sep 1999 Income $301,505, City $247,955, County $53,550. Mats Exp $50,340, Books $21,155, Per/Ser (Incl. Access Fees) $14,435, Micro $1,095, AV Equip $5,602, Electronic Ref Mat (Incl. Access Fees) $8,053. Sal $212,533
Library Holdings: Bk Vols 58,269; Bk Titles 45,122; Per Subs 89
Subject Interests: Genealogy, Kaufman county hist
Automation Activity & Vendor Info: (Cataloging) Gaylord; (Circulation) Gaylord; (OPAC) Gaylord
Database Vendor: OCLC - First Search
Mem of Amigos Bibliog Coun, Inc; Northeast Texas Library System
Friends of the Library Group

TERRELL STATE HOSPITAL
M MEDICAL LIBRARY, 1200 E Brin Ave, PO Box 70, 75160. SAN 320-2631. Tel: 972-563-6452, Ext 8620. FAX: 972-551-8711. Web Site: www.mhmr.state.texas.us. *Exec Dir*, Frederick L Mobley; Tel: 972-563-6452, Ext 8635, E-Mail: Fred.Mobley@mhmr.state.tx.us; Staff 3 (MLS 1, Non-MLS 2)
Founded 1964

Library Holdings: Bk Vols 16,000; Bk Titles 7,000; Per Subs 65
Subject Interests: History, Mental health, Neurology, Psychology
Partic in S Cent Regional Libr Prog; Tex State Libr Communications Network

M PATIENT LIBRARY, 1200 E Brin Ave, PO Box 70, 75160. SAN 376-0316. Tel: 972-563-6452, Ext 8253. *Librn*, Shirley Johnson
Library Holdings: Bk Vols 11,500; Bk Titles 11,000; Per Subs 25

TEXARKANA

GL COURT OF APPEALS FOR SIXTH DISTRICT OF TEXAS, Law Library, 100 N State Line Ave, No 20, 75501. SAN 316-7992. Tel: 903-798-3046. FAX: 903-798-3034. E-Mail: 6thcourt@gte.net. *In Charge*, Tibby Hopkins
Founded 1907
Library Holdings: Bk Vols 15,530

J TEXARKANA COLLEGE, Palmer Memorial Library- John F Moss Library, 1024 Tucker St, PO Box 9150, 75599. SAN 316-8018. Tel: 903-223-3088. Interlibrary Loan Service Tel: 903-223-3094. Circulation Tel: 903-838-3215. Reference Tel: 903-223-3091. FAX: 903-831-7429. E-Mail: jimmiesue.simmons@tamut.edu. Web Site: www.tc.cc.tx.us. *Dir*, Jimmie Sue Simmons; E-Mail: jimmiesue.simmons@tamut.edu; *Govt Doc*, Katy Elkins; Tel: 903-838-3028, E-Mail: katy.elkins@tamut.edu; *Publ Servs*, Tonja Mackey; Tel: 903-838-3248, E-Mail: tonja.mackey@tamut.edu; *Head, Circ*, Vivian Osborne; E-Mail: vivian.osborne@tamut.edu; *Acq*, Mary Young; Tel: 903-223-3089, E-Mail: mary.young@tamut.edu; *ILL*, Melba Kirk; E-Mail: melba.kirk@tamut.edu; *Info Res*, Connie Brian; Tel: 903-838-3027, E-Mail: connie.brian@tamut.edu; Staff 7 (MLS 1, Non-MLS 6)
Founded 1927. Enrl 3,750; Fac 189; Highest Degree: Associate
Sep 1999-Aug 2000 Income $336,382. Mats Exp $156,960, Books $52,190, Per/Ser (Incl. Access Fees) $54,613, Presv $500, Micro $49,657. Sal $159,806 (Prof $29,500)
Library Holdings: Bk Vols 44,508; Bk Titles 38,504; Per Subs 573
Subject Interests: Nursing
Special Collections: Interstate Commerce (Transportation Coll); Rare Books
Partic in OCLC Online Computer Library Center, Inc; Tex Share; Tex State Libr Communications Network

S TEXARKANA MUSEUMS SYSTEM, Wilbur Smith Research Library & Archives, 219 State Line Ave, 75501-5606. (Mail add: PO Box 2343, 75504-2343), SAN 316-8026. Tel: 903-793-4831. FAX: 903-793-7108. Web Site: www.texarkanamuseums.org. *Dir*, Guy Vanderpool; *Coll Develop*, Jamie Simmons; *Res*, Sammy Wacasey; Staff 5 (MLS 3, Non-MLS 2)
Founded 1971
Library Holdings: Bk Vols 1,400; Per Subs 10
Subject Interests: Antiques, Local history, State
Special Collections: Local Architectural Blue Prints Coll; Local Map Coll; Wilbur Smith Coll
Restriction: Access at librarian's discretion, By appointment only, Non-circulating to the public
Function: Archival collection, Business archives, Photocopies available, Research fees apply, Research library, Some telephone reference
Open Tues-Fri

P TEXARKANA PUBLIC LIBRARY, 600 W Third St, 75501-5054. SAN 316-8034. Tel: 903-794-2149. TDD: 903-794-2149. FAX: 903-794-2139. Web Site: www.txar-publib.org. *Librn*, Alice Coleman; *Asst Librn, Coll Develop, Publ Servs*, Sandra Holmes; *Tech Servs*, Carolyn Black; Staff 15 (MLS 2, Non-MLS 13)
Founded 1925. Pop 52,500; Circ 183,169
Oct 1999-Sep 2000 Income $640,083, State $62,116, City $515,171, Locally Generated Income $51,296, Other $11,500. Mats Exp $623,121, Books $76,818, Per/Ser (Incl. Access Fees) $9,015, Micro $2,505, Other Print Mats $9,165, Electronic Ref Mat (Incl. Access Fees) $542. Sal $340,523
Library Holdings: Bk Vols 89,593; Per Subs 180
Subject Interests: Arkansas, Genealogy, Texas local hist
Special Collections: Arkansas & Texas Local History Coll; Genealogy
Automation Activity & Vendor Info: (Acquisitions) epixtech, inc.; (Cataloging) epixtech, inc.; (Circulation) epixtech, inc.; (OPAC) epixtech, inc.
Database Vendor: epixtech, inc.
Partic in Amigos Library Services, Inc; Northeast Texas Library System
Special Services for the Deaf - TTY machine
Special Services for the Blind - CCTV (VisualTex); Kurzweil Reader
Friends of the Library Group

C TEXAS A&M UNIVERSITY-TEXARKANA, John F Moss Library, 1024 Tucker St, 75501. (Mail add: PO Box 6187, 75505), SAN 321-2378. Tel: 903-223-3088. Interlibrary Loan Service Tel: 903-223-3094. Circulation Tel: 903-838-3215. Reference Tel: 903-223-3091. FAX: 903-831-7429. Web Site: www.tc.cc.tx.us/~tstover/. *Dir*, Jimmie Sue Simmons; Tel: 903-233-3088, E-Mail: jimmiesue.simmons@tamut.edu; *Asst Librn*, Arlene Kyle; Tel: 903-223-3090, E-Mail: arlene.kyle@tamut.edu; *Ref*, Teri Stover; Tel: 903-223-3091, E-Mail: teri.stover@tamut.edu; *Per*, Sibyl Carter; Tel: 903-838-3231, E-Mail: sibyl.carter@tamut.edu; Staff 10 (MLS 3, Non-MLS 7)
Founded 1971. Enrl 1,193; Fac 43; Highest Degree: Master
Sep 1999-Aug 2000 Mats Exp $207,813, Books $114,426, Per/Ser (Incl. Access Fees) $93,387. Sal $341,403 (Prof $156,639)
Library Holdings: Bk Titles 123,629; Per Subs 430
Database Vendor: OCLC - First Search
Partic in OCLC Online Computer Library Center, Inc; Tex State Libr Communications Network; TexShare

UNITED STATES ARMY

A AMC SCHOOL OF ENGINEERING & LOGISTICS, Red River Army Depot, 75507-5000. SAN 362-3580. Tel: 903-334-3210. FAX: 903-334-3696.
Founded 1970. Enrl 450
Library Holdings: Bk Vols 22,148; Per Subs 200
Subject Interests: Engineering, Industrial engineering, Industrial safety, Maintenance mgt, Manufacturing, Mgt, Mil logistics, Quality reliability, Safety eng, Software engineering, Supply mgt
Special Collections: Government Publications
Partic in Defense Logistics Studies Info Exchange; Defense Technical Information Center; Nat Tech Info Serv; OCLC Online Computer Libra Center, Inc

TEXAS CITY

J COLLEGE OF THE MAINLAND LIBRARY,* 1200 Amburn Rd, 77591-2499. SAN 316-8042. Tel: 409-938-1211, Ext 205. FAX: 409-938-8918. Web Site: www.mainland.cc.tx.us/library/index.htm. *Librn*, Robert Slaney; E-Mail: bslaney@mail.mainland.cc.tx.us; *Media Spec*, Jerry Anderson; *Bibliog Instr, Online Servs, Ref*, Kathryn Park; *Cat*, Robert Rodriguez
Founded 1967. Enrl 3,370
Sep 1998-Aug 1999 Income $384,454. Mats Exp $82,146, Books $50,63 Per/Ser (Incl. Access Fees) $14,737, Presv $682, Micro $1,532. Sal $300,288 (Prof $161,246)
Library Holdings: Bk Vols 50,504; Bk Titles 39,718; Per Subs 247
Special Collections: Black Studies, Mexican Americans & American Indi (Ethnic Coll); Texana

P MOORE MEMORIAL PUBLIC LIBRARY, 1701 Ninth Ave N, 77590. SAN 316-8069. Tel: 409-643-5979. FAX: 409-948-1106. Web Site: www.texas-city-tx.org. *Dir*, Susie Moncla; *Asst Dir*, Carol Ann Mills; *Ch Servs*, Janet Bazemore; *ILL, Ref*, Joanne Turner; Staff 6 (MLS 2, Non-ML 4)
Founded 1928. Pop 42,000; Circ 237,000
Oct 1999-Sep 2000 Income $756,000, City $700,000, County $56,000. M Exp $155,000, Books $100,000, Per/Ser (Incl. Access Fees) $23,000, Mic $1,000, AV Equip $20,000, Other Print Mats $6,000, Electronic Ref Mat (Incl. Access Fees) $5,000. Sal $450,000 (Prof $82,000)
Library Holdings: Bk Vols 108,000; Per Subs 225
Subject Interests: Genealogy, Texana
Automation Activity & Vendor Info: (Cataloging) Inlex; (Cataloging) DRA; (Circulation) Inlex; (Circulation) DRA; (OPAC) DRA; (OPAC) Inle
Database Vendor: DRA
Mem of Houston Area Library System
Friends of the Library Group

TEXLINE

P TEXLINE PUBLIC LIBRARY,* 222 N Second St, 79087. (Mail add: PO Box 356, 79087-0356), SAN 323-469X. Tel: 806-362-4849. *Librn*, Kay Hefley
Founded 1980. Pop 691; Circ 806
Library Holdings: Bk Vols 1,600
Open Mon-Fri 9-5
Friends of the Library Group

THE COLONY

P THE COLONY PUBLIC LIBRARY,* 5151 N Colony Blvd, 75056-1219. SAN 376-4605. Tel: 972-625-1900. FAX: 972-624-2245. *Librn*, Joan Sveinsson
Oct 1997-Sep 1998 Income $370,000. Mats Exp $52,000. Sal $239,000
Library Holdings: Bk Vols 71,000; Per Subs 90
Mem of North Texas Regional Library System
Open Tues & Thurs 10-9, Wed 1-9, Fri & Sat 10-5
Friends of the Library Group

TOMBALL

S CHAPARRAL GENEALOGICAL SOCIETY LIBRARY,* 310 N Live Oa PO Box 606, 77377. SAN 371-1668. Tel: 281-255-9081. *Librn*, Ella Louis Hill
Library Holdings: Bk Vols 800
Friends of the Library Group

TRINITY

P BLANCHE K WERNER PUBLIC LIBRARY,* Hwy 19 N, PO Box 1168, 75862. SAN 316-8093. Tel: 409-594-2087. FAX: 409-594-9513. *Librn*, Narceille Vaden; E-Mail: nvaden@hals.lid.tx.us

Founded 1961. Circ 37,120
Library Holdings: Bk Vols 18,034; Bk Titles 17,292
Special Collections: Texana Coll
Mem of Houston Area Library System
Friends of the Library Group

)UP

CAMERON J JARVIS TROUP MUNICIPAL LIBRARY,* 102 S Georgia, PO Box 721, 75789. SAN 375-5568. Tel: 903-842-3101. FAX: 903-842-2964. *Librn*, Bonnie Hinkle
Founded 1992. Pop 6,800
Library Holdings: Bk Titles 1,600; Per Subs 18
Automation Activity & Vendor Info: (Circulation) Sagebrush Corporation
Mem of Northeast Texas Library System
Open Tues, Wed & Fri 1-5, Thurs 3-7 & Sat 9-1
Friends of the Library Group

LIA

SWISHER COUNTY LIBRARY,* 127 SW Second St, 79088. SAN 316-8107. Tel: 806-995-3447. FAX: 806-995-2206. *Librn*, Betty Hobgood
Founded 1922. Pop 9,500
Library Holdings: Bk Vols 19,398; Bk Titles 19,073; Per Subs 49
Special Collections: Texana Coll
Mem of Texas Panhandle Library System

LER

EAST TEXAS MEDICAL CENTER, Bell-Marsh Memorial Library, PO Box 6400, 75711-6400. SAN 316-8131. Tel: 903-531-8685. FAX: 903-535-6464. *In Charge*, Sharon Motes
Founded 1951
Library Holdings: Bk Titles 725; Per Subs 18
Subject Interests: Medicine
Partic in Univ of Tex Med Br Libr

RAMEY & FLOCK, PC, Law Firm Library, 100 E Ferguson St, Ste 500, 75702. (Mail add: PO Box 629, 75710-0629), SAN 373-7403. Tel: 903-597-3301. FAX: 903-597-2413. E-Mail: ramey@ramey-flock.com. Web Site: www.ramey-flock.com.; Staff 1 (MLS 1)
Founded 1922
Library Holdings: Bk Vols 10,000; Bk Titles 1,010; Per Subs 30
Partic in Westlaw

TEXAS COLLEGE, D R Glass Library,* 2404 N Grand, 75712-4500. SAN 316-814X. Tel: 903-593-8311, Ext 207. FAX: 903-593-0588. Web Site: www.texascollege.edu. *Dir*, Adrian Weber; E-Mail: aweber@texascollege.edu; *Librn*, Mary Cleveland; *Circ, Ref*, Joyce Arps; Staff 3 (MLS 3)
Founded 1894. Enrl 500; Fac 54; Highest Degree: Bachelor
Library Holdings: Bk Vols 72,082; Per Subs 207
Subject Interests: Black studies
Partic in Coop Col Libr Ctr, Inc
Friends of the Library Group

TYLER COURIER-TIMES TELEGRAPH LIBRARY,* PO Box 2030, 75710. SAN 371-4462. Tel: 903-597-8111. FAX: 903-595-0335. *Librn*, Diane May
Special Collections: East Texas (40s-present, incomplete), news clippings; Tyler Courier Times (1985-present), microfilm; Tyler Morning Telegraph (1930-present), microfilm

TYLER MUSEUM OF ART LIBRARY, 1300 S Mahon, 75701-3499. SAN 316-8182. Tel: 903-595-1001. FAX: 903-595-1055. E-Mail: tma@etgs.com. *Dir*, Kimberley Tomio
Founded 1971
Library Holdings: Bk Vols 1,200
Subject Interests: Architecture, Art
Publications: Catalogs on selected exhibitions organized by Tyler Museum
Restriction: Non-circulating

TYLER PUBLIC LIBRARY, 201 S College Ave, 75702-7381. SAN 316-8115. Tel: 903-593-7323. Reference Tel: 903-593-4357. FAX: 903-531-1329. E-Mail: library@tylertexas.com. Web Site: www.tylertexas.com/cot/departments/library. *Dir*, Christopher Albertson; E-Mail: citylibn@tylertexas.com; *Asst City Librn*, Scherel Carver; E-Mail: asstlibn@tylertexas.com; *Circ, Media Spec, Senior Librn*, Rodney Atkins; E-Mail: circlibn@tylertexas.com; *Outreach Serv, Senior Librn, YA Servs*, Lisa Davoust; E-Mail: youthlibn@tylertexas.com; *Ad Servs, Ref, Senior Librn*, Harold J LaBorde, III; E-Mail: infolibn@tylertexas.com; *Acq, Cat, Senior Librn*, Glenn Tims; E-Mail: cataloger@tylertexas.com; *Ch Servs, YA Servs*, Lotitia Green; *Spec Coll*, Penny Reynolds; Staff 30 (MLS 6, Non-MLS 24)
Founded 1899. Pop 80,000; Circ 198,964
Oct 1999-Sep 2000 Income City $1,073,738. Mats Exp $135,555, Books $79,873, Per/Ser (Incl. Access Fees) $36,571, AV Equip $3,990. Sal $711,687
Library Holdings: Bk Vols 169,365; Bk Titles 127,615; Per Subs 472
Publications: Calendar (bi-monthly)
Mem of Northeast Texas Library System
Special Services for the Deaf - TTY machine
Friends of the Library Group

C UNIVERSITY OF TEXAS AT TYLER LIBRARY, Robert R Muntz Library, 3900 University Blvd, 75799. SAN 316-8158. Tel: 903-566-7161, 903-566-7340. Interlibrary Loan Service Tel: 903-566-7396. Circulation Tel: 903-566-7342. Reference Tel: 903-566-7343. FAX: 903-566-2513. Web Site: www.library.uttyler.edu. *Dir*, Jeanne Pyle; Tel: 903-566-7341, E-Mail: jpyle@mail.uttyl.edu; *Cat*, Vicki Betts; Tel: 905-566-7344, E-Mail: vbetts@mail.uttyl.edu; *Circ*, Joanne Buendtner; Tel: 903-566-7164, E-Mail: jbuendtn@mail.uttyl.edu; *Coll Develop*, Beth Hogan; Tel: 903-565-5614, E-Mail: bhogan@mail.uttyl.edu; *Govt Doc*, Marie Crowe; Tel: 903-566-7165, E-Mail: mcrowe@mail.uttyl.edu; *ILL*, Penny Reynolds; Tel: 903-566-7396, E-Mail: preynold@mail.uttyl.edu; *Ref*, Marilyn Green; Tel: 903-566-7167, E-Mail: mgreene@mail.uttyl.edu; *Per*, Venita McDonald; Tel: 903-566-7335, E-Mail: vmcdonal@mail.uttyl.edu; *Archivist*, Charles Harrell; Tel: 903-566-7398, E-Mail: charrell@mail.uttyl.edu; Staff 20 (MLS 7, Non-MLS 13)
Founded 1973. Enrl 3,600; Fac 160; Highest Degree: Master
Sep 1999-Aug 2000 Income State $943,193. Mats Exp $375,000, Books $108,842, Per/Ser (Incl. Access Fees) $180,568, Other Print Mats $60,500, Electronic Ref Mat (Incl. Access Fees) $25,000. Sal $474,363 (Prof $265,023)
Library Holdings: Bk Vols 216,365; Bk Titles 133,562; Per Subs 1,534
Automation Activity & Vendor Info: (Cataloging) DRA; (Circulation) DRA; (OPAC) DRA; (Serials) DRA
Database Vendor: Ebsco - EbscoHost, OCLC - First Search
Partic in Amigos Library Services, Inc; Tex Share; UT-System
Open Mon-Thurs 7:30am-10pm, Fri 7:30-5, Sat 11-5 & Sun 1-7

CM UNIVERSITY OF TEXAS HEALTH CENTER AT TYLER, Watson W Wise Medical Research Library, 11937 US Hwy 271, 75708-3154. SAN 321-6462. Tel: 903-877-2865. FAX: 903-877-2221. Web Site: library.uthct.edu/. *Dir*, Elaine Wells; Tel: 903-877-2864, E-Mail: elaine.wells@uthct.edu; *Asst Dir*, Thomas B Craig; E-Mail: tom.craig@uthct.edu; *Ser*, Mary Ball; Tel: 903-877-7355, E-Mail: mary.ball@uthct.edu; *Acq, Cat*, Sandra Holley; Tel: 903-877-7657, E-Mail: sandra.holley@uthct.edu; *Circ Ch, ILL*, Patsy Curry; Tel: 903-877-7354, E-Mail: patsy.curry@uthct.edu; *Outreach Serv*, Susan Hughes. Subject Specialists: *Administration*, Elaine Wells; *Automation*, Thomas B Craig; *Reference*, Thomas B Craig; Staff 5 (MLS 2, Non-MLS 3)
Founded 1979. Enrl 24; Fac 100; Highest Degree: Doctorate
Sep 2000-Aug 2001 Income $894,451, Federal $10,000, Locally Generated Income $20,163, Parent Institution $532,288, Other $7,450. Mats Exp $5,326,303, Books $9,700, Per/Ser (Incl. Access Fees) $5,245,000, Presv $1,000, Micro $20,000, Electronic Ref Mat (Incl. Access Fees) $50,603. Sal $206,000 (Prof $139,000)
Library Holdings: Bk Vols 3,101; Bk Titles 3,000; Per Subs 471
Subject Interests: Biochemistry, Cardiology, Cardiopulmonary med, Cell biol, Family med, Family practice, Molecular biology, Occupational med
Automation Activity & Vendor Info: (Acquisitions) Endeavor; (Cataloging) Endeavor; (Circulation) Endeavor; (OPAC) Endeavor; (Serials) Endeavor
Database Vendor: GaleNet, OCLC - First Search, OVID Technologies
Publications: Acquisitions (bimonthly), newsletter (bimonthly)
Restriction: Residents only
Partic in Amigos Library Services, Inc; Dialog Corporation; NNLM/SCR, OCLC Online Computer Libr Ctr, Inc; TexShare
Friends of the Library Group

J VAUGHN LIBRARY & LEARNING RESOURCES CENTER, (Formerly Tyler Junior College), 1327 S Baxter St, 75701. (Mail add: PO Box 9020, 75711), SAN 316-8174. Tel: 903-510-2503. Circulation Tel: 903-510-2502. Reference Tel: 903-510-2549. Toll Free Tel: 800-687-5680, Ext 2503. FAX: 903-510-2639. Web Site: www.tyler.cc.tx.us/library. *Dean*, Dr Mickey M Slimp; Tel: 903-510-2591, Fax: 903-510-2643, E-Mail: msli@tjc.tyler.cc.tx.us; *Admin Dir*, Marian D Jackson; Tel: 903-510-2759, E-Mail: mjac1@tjc.tyler.cc.tx.us; *Dir, Tech Serv*, Dr Paula V Russell; Tel: 903-510-2308, E-Mail: prus@tjc.tyler.cc.tx.us; *Dir*, Dr George Wilson; Tel: 903-510-2302, Fax: 903-510-2339, E-Mail: gwil@tjc.tyler.cc.tx.us; *Ref*, Anne Williams; E-Mail: awil@tjc.tyler.cc.tx.us; *Automation Syst Coordr*, Jim Gililand; Tel: 903-510-2577, E-Mail: jgil@tjc.tyler.cc.tx.us; *Cat*, Cynthia Deveraux; Tel: 903-510-2645, E-Mail: cdev@tjc.tyler.cc.tx.us; *ILL*, Clarice Martin; Tel: 903-510-2304, E-Mail: cmar@tjc.tyler.cc.tx.us. Subject Specialists: *Acquisitions*, Dr Paula V Russell; *Circulating per*, Marian D Jackson; *Computer*, Marian D Jackson; *Develop*, Dr Mickey M Slimp; *Distance educ*, Dr Mickey M Slimp; *Faculty*, Dr Mickey M Slimp; *Media*, Dr George Wilson; *Media*, Dr Mickey M Slimp; *Production*, Dr George Wilson; *Pub servs tech*, Marian D Jackson; *Reference*, Marian D Jackson; Staff 29 (MLS 4, Non-MLS 25)
Founded 1926
Sep 2000-Aug 2001 Mats Exp $201,458, Books $56,300, Per/Ser (Incl. Access Fees) $39,320, Presv $750, Micro $8,000, AV Equip $76,503, Electronic Ref Mat (Incl. Access Fees) $20,585. Sal $666,631 (Prof $267,929)
Library Holdings: Bk Vols 93,229; Bk Titles 68,566; Per Subs 350

Special Collections: Al Herrington Native American Indian Coll; Allied Health Sciences Coll; Dr Tom Smith Native American Indian Coll; Legal Assistant Coll; Texas History Coll
Automation Activity & Vendor Info: (Acquisitions) epixtech, inc.; (Cataloging) epixtech, inc.; (Circulation) epixtech, inc.; (OPAC) epixtech, inc.; (Serials) epixtech, inc.
Database Vendor: epixtech, inc., Lexis-Nexis, OCLC - First Search, OVID Technologies
Partic in Forest Trail Library Consortium, Inc; TexShare
Special Services for the Deaf - Captioned media; Staff with knowledge of sign language
Special Services for the Blind - Braille; Kurzweil Reader; VisualTek

UNIVERSAL CITY

P UNIVERSAL CITY PUBLIC LIBRARY,* 100 Northview Dr, 78148-4150. SAN 375-3883. Tel: 210-659-7048. FAX: 210-945-9221. E-Mail: ucpb@swbell.net. *Dir*, Ellen M Ramon; Staff 3 (MLS 1, Non-MLS 2)
Founded 1985. Pop 13,000; Circ 35,000
Library Holdings: Bk Vols 30,000; Bk Titles 26,000; Per Subs 52
Mem of Alamo Area Library System
Friends of the Library Group

UVALDE

P EL PROGRESO MEMORIAL LIBRARY,* 129 W Nopal, 78801. SAN 362-3610. Tel: 830-278-2017. FAX: 830-278-2017. *Dir*, Susan Anderson; *Asst Librn*, Olga Zamora; *Cat*, Lucy Sandoval; *Circ*, Leticia Ruiz; *Ch Servs*, Sandra Bailey
Founded 1903. Pop 25,000; Circ 78,840
Jul 1998-Jun 1999 Income $207,142, City $62,675, County $56,100, Other $88,367. Mats Exp $26,741, Books $17,990, Per/Ser (Incl. Access Fees) $2,593, Presv $2,754, AV Equip $3,404. Sal $85,538
Library Holdings: Bk Vols 39,300; Bk Titles 34,363; Per Subs 80
Special Collections: Uvalde (Uvalde Historical Coll), bks & VF mat
Automation Activity & Vendor Info: (Acquisitions) epixtech, inc.; (Cataloging) epixtech, inc.; (Circulation) epixtech, inc.; (OPAC) epixtech, inc.
Mem of Alamo Area Library System; San Antonio Major Resource Center
Friends of the Library Group

J SOUTHWEST TEXAS JUNIOR COLLEGE, Will C Miller Memorial Library, 2401 Garner Field Rd, 78801. SAN 316-8190. Tel: 830-591-7254. FAX: 830-591-4186. E-Mail: library@swtjc.cc.tx.us. Web Site: www.swtjc.cc.tx.us/ibrary. *Dir Libr Serv*, Glenda Swink; Tel: 830-591-7251, E-Mail: glenda.swink@swtjc.cc.tx.us; *Asst Librn*, Virginia Davis; Tel: 830-591-7248, E-Mail: virginia.davis@swtjc.cc.tx.us; *Tech Coordr*, Mike Mitchell; Tel: 830-591-7301, E-Mail: mike.mitchell@swtjc.cc.tx.us; Staff 8 (MLS 3, Non-MLS 5)
Founded 1945. Enrl 3,800; Fac 85; Highest Degree: Associate
Library Holdings: Bk Vols 42,000; Bk Titles 40,000; Per Subs 350
Special Collections: Archives; Education Curriculum; Texana
Automation Activity & Vendor Info: (Cataloging) epixtech, inc.; (Circulation) epixtech, inc.; (OPAC) epixtech, inc.
Database Vendor: Ebsco - EbscoHost, epixtech, inc., GaleNet, OVID Technologies

VAN ALSTYNE

P VAN ALSTYNE PUBLIC LIBRARY,* 117 N Waco St, PO Box 629, 75495. SAN 375-5576. Tel: 903-482-5991. FAX: 482-1316, 903-482-5122. E-Mail: vanalstynepl@texoma.net. Web Site: www.texoma.net/~vanalstynepl. *Librn*, Juanita L Hazelton; Staff 4 (MLS 1, Non-MLS 3)
Founded 1969. Pop 4,111; Circ 23,285
Library Holdings: Bk Vols 22,435; Bk Titles 22,041; Per Subs 29
Automation Activity & Vendor Info: (Cataloging) Sagebrush Corporation; (Circulation) Sagebrush Corporation
Mem of Northeast Texas Library System
Special Services for the Deaf - Staff with knowledge of sign language
Friends of the Library Group

VAN HORN

P VAN HORN COUNTY LIBRARY, 410 Crockett St, PO Box 129, 79855-0129. SAN 316-8204. Tel: 915-283-2855. FAX: 915-283-8316. E-Mail: vhccl410@yahoo.com.
Library Holdings: Bk Vols 18,000; Per Subs 20
Mem of Texas Trans Pecos Library System

VEGA

P OLDHAM COUNTY LIBRARY, 914 Main, PO Box 640, 79092-0640. SAN 375-4944. Tel: 806-267-2635. FAX: 806-267-2635. *Librn*, Carolyn Richardson; Staff 1 (Non-MLS 1)
Library Holdings: Bk Vols 13,134; Bk Titles 12,815
Mem of Texas Panhandle Library System
Friends of the Library Group

VERNON

P CARNEGIE CITY-COUNTY LIBRARY,* 2810 Wilbarger St, 76384. SA 316-8212. Tel: 940-552-2462. FAX: 940-552-6206. *Dir*, Beth Railsback; *Circ*, Bonnie Roberts; *Ch Servs*, Kristian Hopkins
Pop 15,355; Circ 37,000
Library Holdings: Bk Vols 24,000; Per Subs 60
Mem of North Texas Regional Library System

J VERNON REGIONAL JUNIOR COLLEGE, Wright Library, 4400 Colle Dr, 76384. SAN 329-7853. Tel: 940-552-6291, Ext 2220. FAX: 940-553-3902. Web Site: www.vrjc.cc.tx.us/libnew. *Librn*, Jim Strickland; *Tech Se* Marlene Stafford; *Tech Servs*, Stephen Stafford; E-Mail: sstafford@vrjc.cc.tx.us; *Media Spec*, Gene Frommelt; *Dir Libr Serv*, Travis Dudley; *Ref*, Patti Jouett; *Circ*, Suzanne Butler; Staff 8 (MLS 2, Non-MLS 6)
Founded 1972. Enrl 2,100; Fac 65; Highest Degree: Associate
Sep 2000-Aug 2001 Income $297,700. Mats Exp $54,000, Books $35,00 Per/Ser (Incl. Access Fees) $15,000, Electronic Ref Mat (Incl. Access Fe $4,000. Sal $199,700
Library Holdings: Bk Vols 36,000; Bk Titles 28,000; Per Subs 150
Automation Activity & Vendor Info: (OPAC) Sagebrush Corporation
Database Vendor: OVID Technologies
Mem of North Texas Regional Library System

VICTORIA

S E I DU PONT DE NEMOURS & CO, INC, Victoria Plant Technical Library,* Old Bloomington Rd, PO Box 2626, 77902. SAN 316-8239. Te 512-572-1111, Ext 1349. FAX: 512-572-1515. *Librn*, Debbie A Ganem
Founded 1951
Library Holdings: Bk Titles 2,850; Per Subs 80
Subject Interests: Chemistry, Computers, Engineering, Environmental studies, Gas chromatography, Indust hygiene, Instrumentation, Mathemati Safety

C VICTORIA COLLEGE UNIVERSITY OF HOUSTON VICTORIA LIBRARY,* 2602 N Ben Jordan St, 77901-5699. SAN 316-8247. Tel: 36 572-6421. FAX: 361-570-4155. E-Mail: dahlstromj@vic.uh.edu. Web Site www.lois.vic.uh.edu. *Dir*, Dr Joe F Dahlstrom; *Librn, Publ Servs*, Karen Locher; *Tech Servs*, Gail Crockett; *Ser*, Mitzie Stewart; *Cat, Govt Doc*, Paula Packard; *Media Spec*, Gloria Espitia; *Bibliog Instr*, David Ticen; St 23 (MLS 8, Non-MLS 15)
Founded 1925. Enrl 4,050; Fac 166; Highest Degree: Master
Library Holdings: Bk Vols 217,000; Bk Titles 157,000; Per Subs 603
Subject Interests: Behav sci, Bus, Computer science, Local history, Mgt, Science fiction, Soc sci, Texas
Special Collections: Regional Archives
Publications: Library acquisitions (monthly booklist); serials list
Partic in Amigos Library Services, Inc; Dialog Corporation; Medline; OC Online Computer Library Center, Inc; Piasano Consortium
Victoria Library is a joint operation of Victoria College and the University of Houston. It is the headquarters of the Circuit Rider Health Information Service (CRHIS) serving six hospitals and acts as agent for Piasano Unior List, ILL & Telefax consortium of 14 libraries in South Texas. It also serv as agent for the CD-ROM South Texas Union Catalog, containing holding for 32 libraries in South Texas

P VICTORIA PUBLIC LIBRARY, 302 N Main, 77901-6592. SAN 316-825 Tel: 361-572-2704. Circulation Tel: 361-572-2701. Reference Tel: 361-572 2702. FAX: 361-572-2779. E-Mail: comment@victoria.lib.tx.us. *Dir*, Jame B Stewart; *Asst Dir*, Terese M Varga; *Head Tech Servs*, Sandra Bovy; *Hea Info Serv*, Donatta Clarke; *Ch Servs*, Misti Harris; Staff 31 (MLS 9, Non-MLS 22)
Founded 1932. Pop 82,000
Oct 1998-Sep 1999 Income $1,336,121, City $730,230, County $605,891. Mats Exp $254,954, Books $161,126, Per/Ser (Incl. Access Fees) $81,637, Other Print Mats $661, Electronic Ref Mat (Incl. Access Fees) $11,530. S $657,449
Library Holdings: Bk Vols 152,485; Bk Titles 122,991; Per Subs 866
Special Collections: Great Plains-Texas, New Mexico & Arizona (Claude McCan Coll of the Great Plains)
Automation Activity & Vendor Info: (Acquisitions) epixtech, inc.; (Cataloging) epixtech, inc.; (Circulation) epixtech, inc.; (OPAC) epixtech, inc.
Database Vendor: OCLC - First Search

Mem of South Texas Library System
Partic in Amigos Library Services, Inc
Open Mon-Thurs 9-9, Fri & Sat 9-5
Friends of the Library Group

OR

VIDOR PUBLIC LIBRARY,* 440 E Bolivar, 77662. SAN 316-8263. Tel: 409-769-7148. FAX: 409-769-7148. *Librn*, Diana Hatchinson; *Asst Librn*, Cindy LoeBouel
Founded 1974. Pop 28,000; Circ 40,500
Library Holdings: Bk Vols 30,000; Per Subs 50
Subject Interests: Genealogy, Texana bks
Mem of Houston Area Library System
Friends of the Library Group

LAGE MILLS

WILDWOOD HERITAGE MUSEUM & LIBRARY,* 92 Cypress Bend Dr, PO Box 774, 77663. SAN 375-3611. Tel: 409-834-2241. FAX: 409-834-2243. *Librn*, Clara Beth Urban
Founded 1988
Library Holdings: Bk Vols 10,000

CO

ART CENTER LIBRARY,* 1300 College Dr, 76708. SAN 320-8753. Tel: 254-752-4371. FAX: 254-752-3506. *Dir*, Joseph L Kagle Jr; *Coordr*, Ann Garrett; Staff 7 (MLS 7)
Founded 1973
Library Holdings: Bk Vols 1,500; Per Subs 40
Subject Interests: Architecture, Contemporary art, Crafts, Photog
Restriction: Open to public for reference only

BAYLOR UNIVERSITY LIBRARIES, 1312 S Third, 76798-7148. SAN 362-3726. Tel: 254-710-2112. Interlibrary Loan Service Tel: 254-710-2340. FAX: 254-710-3116. Interlibrary Loan Service FAX: 254-752-5332. Web Site: www.baylor.edu/Library/. *Actg Dean*, Bill Hair; E-Mail: bill_hair@baylor.edu; Staff 113 (MLS 34, Non-MLS 79)
Founded 1845. Enrl 13,719; Fac 662; Highest Degree: Doctorate
Jun 1999-May 2000 Income (Main and Other College/University Libraries) $8,782,906. Mats Exp $4,243,175. Sal $3,557,603
Library Holdings: Bk Vols 1,215,717; Bk Titles 817,967; Per Subs 8,429
Subject Interests: 19th Century, Church-state, Fine arts, History, Law, Literature, Music, Relig studies, Sci-eng
Special Collections: Legislative Coll; Robert Browning; Texas History
Automation Activity & Vendor Info: (Acquisitions) Innovative Interfaces Inc.; (Cataloging) Innovative Interfaces Inc.; (Circulation) Innovative Interfaces Inc.; (Course Reserve) Innovative Interfaces Inc.; (ILL) Innovative Interfaces Inc.; (OPAC) Innovative Interfaces Inc.; (Serials) Innovative Interfaces Inc.
Publications: Newsletters: Armstrong Browning, Central Libraries, Texas Collection
Partic in Amigos Library Services, Inc; Big Twelve Plus Libr Consortium; OCLC Online Computer Library Center, Inc; TexShare
Financial information, holdings & library automation includes all Baylor libraries
Departmental Libraries:
BAYLOR COLLECTIONS OF POLITICAL MATERIALS, PO Box 97153, 76798-7153. SAN 372-8463. Tel: 254-710-3540. FAX: 254-710-1468. Web Site: www.baylor.edu/Library/. *Dir*, Kent Keeth; *Mgr*, Ben Rogers; Staff 1 (MLS 1)
Library Holdings: Bk Vols 10,412; Bk Titles 8,982; Per Subs 1,526
Special Collections: Archival records of Donald Adams, Charles W Barrow, Bob Bullock, O P Carrillo, John Dowdy, Chet Edwards, O C Fisher, E L Gossett, Sam Hall, Jack Hightower, Marvin Leath, Hyde Murray, Reid Murray, Thomas A Pickett, Allen Place Jr, W R Poage, Alan Steelman; Biles Editorial Cartoons Coll; Extremist Organizations; Fowler West Coll
Automation Activity & Vendor Info: (Acquisitions) Innovative Interfaces Inc.; (Cataloging) Innovative Interfaces Inc.; (Circulation) Innovative Interfaces Inc.; (Course Reserve) Innovative Interfaces Inc.; (ILL) Innovative Interfaces Inc.; (OPAC) Innovative Interfaces Inc.; (Serials) Innovative Interfaces Inc.
Database Vendor: Innovative Interfaces INN - View
ARMSTRONG BROWNING LIBRARY, PO Box 97152, 76798-7152. SAN 362-3734. Tel: 254-710-3566. FAX: 254-710-3552. Web Site: www.baylor.edu/Library/. *Dir*, Dr Mairi C Rennie; *Instr, Librn*, Cynthia Burgess; *Instr, Librn*, Rita Patterson
Library Holdings: Bk Vols 26,273; Bk Titles 20,961; Per Subs 25
Subject Interests: 19th Century Am, 19th Century British lit, Elizabeth Barrett Browing, Robert Barrett Browing
Special Collections: 19th Century American & British Literature; A Joseph Armstrong; Browning Contemporaries; Browning Family; Edward Dowden; Edward Robert Bulwer Lytton; Elizabeth Barrett Browning; John Forster; John Ruskin; Joseph Milsand; Matthew Arnold; Meynell; Ralph Waldo Emerson; Robert Browning; W Somerset Maugham
Automation Activity & Vendor Info: (Acquisitions) Innovative Interfaces Inc.; (Cataloging) Innovative Interfaces Inc.; (Circulation) Innovative Interfaces Inc.; (Course Reserve) Innovative Interfaces Inc.; (ILL) Innovative Interfaces Inc.; (OPAC) Innovative Interfaces Inc.; (Serials) Innovative Interfaces Inc.
Database Vendor: Innovative Interfaces INN - View
Publications: Armstrong Browning Library Newsletter (semiannual); Baylor Browning Interests (irregular); Studies in Browning and His Circle (annual)
Friends of the Library Group
J M DAWSON CHURCH-STATE RESEARCH CENTER, Carroll Library Bldg, PO Box 97308, 76798-7308. SAN 326-8020. Tel: 254-710-1510. FAX: 254-710-1571. *Dir*, Derek H Davis
Highest Degree: Doctorate
Library Holdings: Bk Vols 13,026; Per Subs 193
Special Collections: Church & State Coll; E S James Coll, micro & doc; Joseph Martin Dawson Coll; Leo Pfeffer Coll
Automation Activity & Vendor Info: (Acquisitions) Innovative Interfaces Inc.; (Cataloging) Innovative Interfaces Inc.; (Circulation) Innovative Interfaces Inc.; (Course Reserve) Innovative Interfaces Inc.; (ILL) Innovative Interfaces Inc.; (OPAC) Innovative Interfaces Inc.; (Serials) Innovative Interfaces Inc.
Database Vendor: Innovative Interfaces INN - View
Publications: Church & State in Scripture, History & Constitutional Law; Ecumenical Perspectives on Church & State; Jewish-Christian Relations in Today's World; Problems & Conflicts Between Law & Morality in a Free Society; Readings on Church & State; Reflections on Church & State; Religion & Politics; Religion, the State, & Education; The Contours of Church & State in the Thought of John Paul II; The First Freedom: Religion & the Bill of Rights; The Role of Government in Monitoring & Regulating Religion in Public Life; The Role of Religion in the Making of Public Policy; The Separation of Church & State Defended: Selected Writings of James E Wood, Jr
JESSE H JONES LIBRARY, PO Box 97146, 76798-7148. SAN 372-8455. Tel: 254-710-2112. FAX: 254-710-3116. Web Site: www.baylor.edu/Library/. *Actg Dean*, Bill Hair; *ILL*, Jeff Steely; *Ref Serv*, Phil Jones; *Ref Serv*, Olga Paradis
Automation Activity & Vendor Info: (Acquisitions) Innovative Interfaces Inc.; (Cataloging) Innovative Interfaces Inc.; (Circulation) Innovative Interfaces Inc.; (Course Reserve) Innovative Interfaces Inc.; (ILL) Innovative Interfaces Inc.; (OPAC) Inlex; (Serials) Innovative Interfaces Inc.
Library holdings are combined totals for Moody & Jones Libraries
CL LAW LIBRARY, PO Box 97128, 76798-7128. SAN 362-3769. Tel: 254-710-2168. FAX: 254-710-2294. Web Site: law.baylor.edu/library. *Dir*, Brandon Quarles; *Cat*, Susan Kendrick; *Ref Serv*, Matt Cordon
Library Holdings: Bk Vols 117,138; Bk Titles 20,709; Per Subs 2,156
Special Collections: Frank M Wilson Rare Book Coll
Automation Activity & Vendor Info: (Acquisitions) Innovative Interfaces Inc.; (Cataloging) Innovative Interfaces Inc.; (Circulation) Innovative Interfaces Inc.; (Course Reserve) Innovative Interfaces Inc.; (ILL) Innovative Interfaces Inc.; (OPAC) Innovative Interfaces Inc.; (Serials) Innovative Interfaces Inc.
MOODY MEMORIAL LIBRARY, PO Box 97148, 76798-7148. SAN 362-370X. Tel: 254-710-2112. FAX: 254-710-3116. Web Site: www.baylor.edu/Library/. *Actg Dean*, Bill Hair; *Access Serv*, Linda Cobbs; *Acq*, Kathy Hillman; *Cat*, Sheila Slater; *Govt Doc*, John Wilson; *Info Specialist*, Denyse Seaman; *Outreach Serv*, Billie R Peterson. Subject Specialists: *Preservation*, Kathy Sparkman
MUSIC & FINE ARTS LIBRARY, PO Box 97148, 76798-7148. SAN 362-3793. Tel: 254-710-2164. FAX: 254-710-3116. Web Site: www.baylor.edu/Library/. *Dir, Librn*, Avery Sharp; Tel: 254-710-2160; *Cat*, Beth Tice
Special Collections: 18th & 19th Century English books on music & scores; 18th Century Editions of Ensemble Music; Bob Darden Coll of contemporary Christian sound recordings; Cecil R Porter Organ Music Coll; David W Guion Coll (manuscripts); Francis G Spencer Coll of American Printed Music; J W Jennings Coll; manuscripts of Kurt Kiser; Mrs J W Jennings Coll of Medieval music manuscripts; Ouseley Library; Travis Johnson Coll
Automation Activity & Vendor Info: (Acquisitions) Innovative Interfaces Inc.; (Cataloging) Innovative Interfaces Inc.; (Circulation) Inlex; (Course Reserve) Innovative Interfaces Inc.; (ILL) Inlex; (OPAC) Inlex; (Serials) Innovative Interfaces Inc.
CM SCHOOL OF NURSING LEARNING RESOURCES CENTER, 3700 Worth St, 75246. SAN 362-3807. Tel: 214-820-2100. FAX: 214-820-4770. Web Site: www.baylor.edu/Library/. *Librn*, Johanna Guenther
Library Holdings: Bk Vols 3,973; Bk Titles 3,654; Per Subs 144
TEXAS COLLECTION, PO Box 97142, 76798-7142. SAN 362-3823. Tel: 254-710-1268. FAX: 254-710-1368. Web Site: diogenes.baylor.edu/wwwproviders/Library/home.html. *Dir*, Kent Keeth; *Librn*, Michael Toon; *Archivist*, Ellen Brown
Library Holdings: Bk Vols 106,948; Bk Titles 80,414; Per Subs 968
Special Collections: Depository for Texas State publications & documents; newsfilm archive, KWTX-TV, Waco; Regional Historical Resource Depository
Automation Activity & Vendor Info: (Acquisitions) Innovative Interfaces

Inc.; (Cataloging) Innovative Interfaces Inc.; (Circulation) Innovative Interfaces Inc.; (Course Reserve) Inlex; (ILL) Innovative Interfaces Inc.; (OPAC) Innovative Interfaces Inc.; (Serials) Innovative Interfaces Inc.
Database Vendor: Innovative Interfaces INN - View

GM DEPARTMENT OF VETERANS AFFAIRS, Medical Center Library,* 4800 Memorial Dr, 76711. SAN 316-8336. Tel: 254-752-6581, Ext 6609. FAX: 254-755-9816. *Librn*, JoAnn Greenwood
Library Holdings: Bk Vols 2,750; Per Subs 300
Mem of Valnet

R FIRST BAPTIST CHURCH, IC Anderson Library, 500 Webster St, 76706. SAN 316-8271. Tel: 254-752-3000. FAX: 254-299-0467. E-Mail: fbcwaco@aol.com. Web Site: www.fbcwaco.org. *Dir*, Victor Cooper
Founded 1945
Library Holdings: Bk Vols 20,300; Per Subs 25
Subject Interests: Biog, Children, Family studies, Philosophy, Rare books, Relig studies
Special Collections: Church History
Publications: Media Directory

M HILLCREST BAPTIST MEDICAL CENTER, Medical Reference Library, 3000 Herring Ave, 76708. SAN 316-8298. Tel: 254-202-8960. FAX: 254-202-5924.
Founded 1972
Library Holdings: Bk Titles 200; Per Subs 200
Mem of Asn of Waco Libr Adminrs

S MASONIC GRAND LODGE LIBRARY & MUSEUM OF TEXAS,* 715 Columbus, PO Box 446, 76703. SAN 316-828X. Tel: 254-753-7395. *Librn*, Barbara Mechell
Founded 1873
Library Holdings: Bk Titles 36,000; Per Subs 12
Subject Interests: Masonry, Tex hist
Partic in Am Libr Asn; Spec Libr Asn

J MCLENNAN COMMUNITY COLLEGE LIBRARY, 1400 College Dr, 76708-1498. SAN 316-8301. Tel: 254-299-8398. Reference Tel: 254-299-8159. FAX: 254-299-8062. E-Mail: jgv@mcc.cc.tx.us. Web Site: www.mcc.cc.tx.us/library. *Dir Libr Serv*, Ramona J Madewell; Tel: 254-299-8463; *Librn*, Linda K Wells; Tel: 254-299-8127, E-Mail: liw@mcc.cc.tx.us; *Librn*, Sharon K Kenan; Tel: 254-299-8127, E-Mail: skk@mcc.cc.tx.us; *Tech Servs*, Margaret A Harbaugh; Tel: 254-299-8471, E-Mail: mah@mcc.cc.tx.us; Staff 15 (MLS 5, Non-MLS 10)
Founded 1968. Enrl 6,000; Fac 200; Highest Degree: Associate
Sep 1998-Aug 1999 Income $546,240. Mats Exp $235,800, Books $89,674, Per/Ser (Incl. Access Fees) $29,616, Micro $24,500, Electronic Ref Mat (Incl. Access Fees) $45,461. Sal $310,440 (Prof $185,995)
Library Holdings: Bk Vols 78,000; Per Subs 350
Subject Interests: Law
Automation Activity & Vendor Info: (Cataloging) epixtech, inc.; (Circulation) epixtech, inc.; (Course Reserve) epixtech, inc.; (OPAC) epixtech, inc.
Database Vendor: GaleNet, OVID Technologies, Wilson - Wilson Web

GL MCLENNAN COUNTY LAW LIBRARY, 500 Washington, 76701. SAN 316-831X. Tel: 254-757-5191. *Librn*, Janet Gomez
Library Holdings: Bk Vols 11,200

S TEXAS RANGER RESEARCH CENTER, (Formerly Moody Texas Ranger Memorial Library), Texas Ranger Hall of Fame & Museum, 100 Texas Ranger Trail, 76706. (Mail add: PO Box 2570, 76702-2570), SAN 362-3971. Tel: 254-750-8631. Toll Free Tel: 877-750-8631. FAX: 254-750-8629. E-Mail: trhf@eramp.net. Web Site: www.texasranger.org.; Staff 2 (MLS 1, Non-MLS 1)
Founded 1976
Library Holdings: Bk Vols 1,700
Subject Interests: Law enforcement
Special Collections: Ex-Texas Ranger Association Papers; Frank Hamer Papers (Bonnie & Clyde); M D "Kelly" Rogers Coll; M T "Lone Wolf" Gonzaullas Papers; Texarkana Phantom Killer
Publications: Texas Ranger Annual
Friends of the Library Group

J TEXAS STATE TECHNICAL COLLEGE, Waco Library,* 3801 Campus Dr, 76705. SAN 362-3858. Tel: 254-867-4846. FAX: 254-867-2339. Web Site: www.libgate.tstc.edu. *Dir, Per*, Linda S Koepf; E-Mail: lkoepf@tstc.edu; *Cat*, Lianna Dick; *Circ, Ref*, Diane Roether; *Automation Syst Coordr*, Daniel Wang; Staff 5 (MLS 5)
Founded 1967
Library Holdings: Bk Vols 68,053
Subject Interests: Auto repairs, Aviation piloting, Computer, Electronics, Food serv, Hazardous mat, Laser mechanics, Nuclear tech, Occupational health, Occupational safety
Special Collections: Biobase College Catalogs on Fiche, Phonefiche; Children's Books; Eric Documents; FAA Aerospace Collection; Industrial & Safety Standards; Texas College Catalog; Texas Phone Books
Publications: Information Tracer; Lights, Camera, Action; Periodicals B Technology; What's New & Worth Reading?
Restriction: Staff use only

S WACO TRIBUNE-HERALD LIBRARY,* 900 Franklin, 76701. SAN 37 0018. Tel: 254-757-5757. FAX: 254-757-0302. *Librn*, Colleen Curran
Library Holdings: Bk Vols 200; Per Subs 4
Subject Interests: Local history

P WACO-MCLENNAN COUNTY LIBRARY, 1717 Austin Ave, 76701-17 SAN 362-3882. Tel: 254-750-5941. Interlibrary Loan Service Tel: 254-7 5951. Circulation Tel: 254-750-5943. Reference Tel: 254-750-5944. FAX 254-750-5940. E-Mail: library@waco-texas.com. Web Site: www.waco-texas.com. *Dir*, Pamela Bonnell; Tel: 254-750-5946, E-Mail: pbonnell@ci.waco.tx.us; *Assoc Dir*, Jackie Dodson; Tel: 254-750-5950, E-Mail: jdodson@ci.waco.tx.us; *Ch Servs*, Linda Bogusch; Tel: 254-750-5976, E-Mail: lbogusch@ci.waco.tx.us; *Circ*, Linda Shaw; E-Mail: lshaw@ci.waco.tx.us; *Per*, Bill Buckner; Tel: 254-750-5945, E-Mail: bbuckner@ci.waco.tx.us; *Head Ref*, Patricia Clark; Tel: 254-750-5958, E-Mail: pcla ci.waco.tx.us; *Tech Servs*, Linda Howell; Tel: 254-750-5993, E-Mail: lhowell@ci.waco.tx.us. Subject Specialists: *Genealogy*, Bill Buckner; Sta 19 (MLS 19)
Founded 1898. Pop 220,000; Circ 465,086
Oct 2000-Sep 2001 Income (Main Library and Branch Library) $2,384,3 Mats Exp $266,000, Books $200,000, Per/Ser (Incl. Access Fees) $25,00 Presv $6,000, Micro $10,000, Other Print Mats $10,000, Electronic Ref M (Incl. Access Fees) $15,000. Sal $1,595,853
Library Holdings: Bk Vols 259,625; Per Subs 605
Subject Interests: Branch Davidian, Genealogy, Local history, Tex hist, Texas
Special Collections: Grants Resource Center
Automation Activity & Vendor Info: (Acquisitions) epixtech, inc.; (Cataloging) epixtech, inc.; (Circulation) epixtech, inc.; (Course Reserve) epixtech, inc.; (ILL) epixtech, inc.; (Media Booking) epixtech, inc.; (OPA epixtech, inc.; (Serials) epixtech, inc.
Database Vendor: epixtech, inc.
Mem of Central Texas Library System
Friends of the Library Group
Branches: 3
EAST WACO, 901 Elm, 76704-2659. SAN 362-3912. Tel: 254-750-8620 FAX: 254-750-8611. Web Site: www.waco-texas.com/library. *Mgr*, John Peterson
1998-1999 Income $108,048. Mats Exp $22,000. Sal $127,838
Library Holdings: Bk Vols 26,064
Subject Interests: Black hist, Ethnic studies
Automation Activity & Vendor Info: (Acquisitions) epixtech, inc.; (Cataloging) epixtech, inc.; (Circulation) epixtech, inc.; (Course Reserve epixtech, inc.; (ILL) epixtech, inc.; (Media Booking) epixtech, inc.; (OPAC) epixtech, inc.; (Serials) epixtech, inc.
Friends of the Library Group
R B HOOVER LIBRARY, Lake Air Mall, 76710. SAN 362-4005. Tel: 2 776-1581. *Mgr*, Mary Ellen Wright
Library Holdings: Bk Vols 39,693
Automation Activity & Vendor Info: (Acquisitions) epixtech, inc.; (Cataloging) epixtech, inc.; (Circulation) epixtech, inc.; (Course Reserve epixtech, inc.; (ILL) epixtech, inc.; (Media Booking) epixtech, inc.; (OPAC) epixtech, inc.; (Serials) epixtech, inc.
Friends of the Library Group
SOUTH WACO, 2815 Speight, 76711-2199. SAN 362-403X. Tel: 254-75 8621. *Mgr*, Judy Horton
Library Holdings: Bk Vols 31,660
Subject Interests: Mexican Am
Automation Activity & Vendor Info: (Acquisitions) epixtech, inc.; (Cataloging) epixtech, inc.; (Circulation) epixtech, inc.; (Course Reserve epixtech, inc.; (ILL) epixtech, inc.; (Media Booking) epixtech, inc.; (OPAC) epixtech, inc.; (Serials) epixtech, inc.
Friends of the Library Group

WAELDER

P WAELDER PUBLIC LIBRARY,* 310 North Ave E, PO Box 428, 78959-0428. SAN 316-8344. Tel: 830-788-7167. *Actg Librn*, Doris Burney
Pop 904
Library Holdings: Bk Vols 5,500; Bk Titles 7,000
Mem of South Texas Library System
Open Tues-Fri 1-5

WALLIS

P KNOX MEMORIAL LIBRARY, Austin County Library System,* 6730 Railroad, PO Box 519, 77485-0519. SAN 362-4064. Tel: 409-478-6813. FAX: 409-487-6813. E-Mail: auscolib@c-com.net. *Librn*, Bernice Brast; *A Librn*, Joan Melnar
Pop 3,375
1998-1999 Income $65,860. Mats Exp $10,250, Books $8,700, Per/Ser (In

Access Fees) $975. Sal $34,416
Library Holdings: Bk Vols 15,000; Per Subs 35
Mem of Houston Area Library System
Friends of the Library Group

ASHINGTON

STAR OF THE REPUBLIC MUSEUM LIBRARY, 23200 Park Rd, No 12, PO Box 317, 77880-0317. SAN 326-2448. Tel: 936-878-2461, Ext 234. FAX: 936-878-2462. E-Mail: star@acmail.blinncol.edu. *Dir*, Houston McGaugh
Founded 1970
Library Holdings: Bk Titles 2,100; Per Subs 50
Subject Interests: Tex hist
Restriction: Non-circulating

ATAUGA

WATAUGA PUBLIC LIBRARY,* 7109 Whitley Rd, 76148-2024. SAN 375-4804. Tel: 817-428-9412. FAX: 817-581-3910. E-Mail: watglib@computek.net. *Dir*, Joanne Rodgers; *Ch Servs*, Toni Aikin; *Tech Servs*, Dorretta Hunter; *Publ Servs*, Chere Bradford; Staff 4 (MLS 2, Non-MLS 2)
Founded 1983. Pop 21,000; Circ 100,900
Library Holdings: Bk Vols 23,968; Bk Titles 22,842; Per Subs 130
Publications: Calendar (monthly)
Mem of North Texas Regional Library System
Special Services for the Deaf - Books on deafness & sign language; Captioned film depository; High interest/low vocabulary books
Friends of the Library Group

AXAHACHIE

NICHOLAS P SIMS LIBRARY,* 515 W Main, 75165-3235. SAN 316-8352. Tel: 972-937-2671. FAX: 972-937-4409. E-Mail: simslib@wisd.org. *Ad Servs, Dir*, Susan A Maxwell; *Asst Dir, Ch Servs*, Gloria Woodard; *Ch Servs*, Connie Colston; *Ref*, Lynn Davis; Staff 11 (MLS 1, Non-MLS 10)
Founded 1905. Pop 22,500; Circ 209,490
Oct 1998-Sep 1999 Income $530,520, City $443,905, Locally Generated Income $86,615. Mats Exp $82,265, Books $72,827, Per/Ser (Incl. Access Fees) $7,255, Micro $750, Electronic Ref Mat (Incl. Access Fees) $204. Sal $278,592
Library Holdings: Bk Vols 238,970; Per Subs 194
Subject Interests: Local genealogy
Mem of Northeast Texas Library System
Open Tues-Sat 9-5:30
Friends of the Library Group

SOUTHWESTERN ASSEMBLIES OF GOD UNIVERSITY, P C Nelson Memorial Library, 1200 Sycamore, 75165-2342. SAN 316-8360. Tel: 972-937-4010, Ext 1148. FAX: 972-923-0488. E-Mail: library@sagu.edu. Web Site: www.sagu.edu/library. *Dir*, Eugene Holder; *Coll Develop*, Marcy Mapes
Founded 1927. Highest Degree: Master
Library Holdings: Bk Vols 95,015; Bk Titles 90,000; Per Subs 609
Subject Interests: Education, Relig studies
Special Collections: Charismatic Authors, History & Materials (Pentecostal Alcove), bks & per
Special Services for the Deaf - Books on deafness & sign language

EATHERFORD

WEATHERFORD COLLEGE LIBRARY, (WCL), 225 College Park Dr, 76086. SAN 316-8379. Tel: 817-594-5471, Ext 252. Circulation Tel: 817-594-5471, Ext 251. TDD: 817-598-6254. FAX: 817-598-6369, 817-599-9305. Web Site: www.wc.edu/library/. *Dir*, Martha Tandy; Tel: 817-598-6252, Fax: 817-598-6369, E-Mail: tandy@wc.edu; *Publ Servs*, Mark Dolive; Tel: 817-598-6453, Fax: 817-599-9305, E-Mail: dolive@wc.edu; *Ref*, Connie Sanders; Tel: 817-598-6425, E-Mail: csanders@wc.edu; Staff 11 (MLS 3, Non-MLS 8)
Founded 1869. Enrl 2,803; Highest Degree: Associate
Sep 1999-Aug 2000 Income $297,371, Federal $5,871, Parent Institution $291,500. Mats Exp $101,670, Books $35,000, Per/Ser (Incl. Access Fees) $25,397, Presv $450, Micro $8,899, AV Equip $14,620, Manuscripts & Archives $300, Electronic Ref Mat (Incl. Access Fees) $17,004. Sal $174,000 (Prof $43,700)
Library Holdings: Bk Titles 59,830; Per Subs 421; Bks on Deafness & Sign Lang 16
Subject Interests: Texas counties hist
Special Collections: Ranching in the Southwest
Automation Activity & Vendor Info: (Cataloging) SIRSI; (Circulation) SIRSI; (OPAC) SIRSI; (Serials) SIRSI
Database Vendor: Ebsco - EbscoHost
Publications: Library Lamplighter (Newsletter to faculty & staff, irregular)
Partic in Tex Share
Special Services for the Deaf - TTY machine
Special Services for the Blind - Braille translation & printing software & equipment
Friends of the Library Group

P WEATHERFORD PUBLIC LIBRARY, 1014 Charles St, 76086-5098. SAN 316-8387. Tel: 817-598-4150. FAX: 817-598-4161. Web Site: www.weatherford.lib.tx.us. *Dir Libr Serv*, Sandra Tanner; *Asst Dir*, Cherie Kendrick; Staff 7 (MLS 7)
Founded 1959. Pop 57,500; Circ 290,000
Oct 1999-Sep 2000 Income $651,992, City $609,992, County $42,000. Mats Exp $82,500, Books $65,000, Per/Ser (Incl. Access Fees) $8,000, Micro $2,000, AV Equip $6,150, Electronic Ref Mat (Incl. Access Fees) $1,350. Sal $476,502
Library Holdings: Bk Vols 100,000; Per Subs 185
Special Collections: Mary Martin Coll; Parker County Historical & Genealogical Coll
Automation Activity & Vendor Info: (Cataloging) Sagebrush Corporation; (Circulation) Sagebrush Corporation
Function: ILL available
Mem of North Texas Regional Library System
Friends of the Library Group

WEIMAR

P WEIMAR PUBLIC LIBRARY, One Jackson Sq, 78962. SAN 316-8395. Tel: 409-725-6608. FAX: 409-725-9033. E-Mail: wpl@fais.net. *Librn*, Cindy Crutchfield
Founded 1964. Pop 3,542; Circ 18,231
Library Holdings: Bk Titles 20,000
Mem of Houston Area Library System

WELLINGTON

P COLLINGSWORTH PUBLIC LIBRARY,* 712 15th St, 79095. SAN 316-8409. Tel: 806-447-2116. FAX: 806-447-5240. *Librn*, Vicki Decker
Founded 1924. Pop 5,000; Circ 5,831
Library Holdings: Bk Titles 20,850; Per Subs 150
Mem of Texas Panhandle Library System
Special Services for the Deaf - Special interest periodicals
Friends of the Library Group

WESLACO

C TEXAS A&M UNIVERSITY KINGSVILLE CITRUS CENTER LIBRARY,* 312 N International Blvd, BO Box 1150, 78599-1150. SAN 316-8417. Tel: 956-968-2132. FAX: 956-969-0649. Web Site: www.primera.tamu.edu/kcchome. *Librn*, Marilynn Ambos; E-Mail: m-ambos@tamu.edu
Founded 1949
Library Holdings: Bk Titles 20,000; Per Subs 30
Subject Interests: Agr econ, Agr with emphasis on citrus fruits, Entomology, Horticulture, Plant pathology, Post-harvest physiology of citrus fruits, Soil sci

S USDA AGRICULTURAL RESEARCH SERVICE, USDA - TAMU Research Library,* 2413 E Hwy 83, Bldg 213, 78596. SAN 370-2480. Tel: 956-969-5005. FAX: 956-969-5033. Web Site: www.weslaco.ars.usda.gov. *Archivist, Cat, Mgr*, Deena Brandenberger; E-Mail: deena@rsru2.tamu.edu
Library Holdings: Bk Vols 8,000

P WESLACO PUBLIC LIBRARY,* 525 S Kansas St, 78596-6215. SAN 316-8425. Tel: 956-968-4533. FAX: 956-969-4069. Web Site: www.weslaco.lib.tx.us. *Dir*, Virginia Allain; E-Mail: vallain@weslaco.lib.tx.us; *Asst Dir, Ref*, Michael Fisher; *Tech Servs*, Carolyn Plank; Staff 15 (MLS 2, Non-MLS 13)
Founded 1949. Pop 37,506; Circ 183,227
Oct 1998-Sep 1999 Income $618,000, City $500,000, Federal $75,000, County $10,000, Locally Generated Income $10,000, Other $23,000. Mats Exp $73,000, Books $60,000, Per/Ser (Incl. Access Fees) $7,000, Electronic Ref Mat (Incl. Access Fees) $6,000. Sal $290,000 (Prof $81,000)
Library Holdings: Bk Vols 63,000; Bk Titles 46,200
Subject Interests: Hispanic, Spanish language
Special Collections: Texana Coll, bk & tape
Automation Activity & Vendor Info: (Circulation) SIRSI
Database Vendor: Ebsco - EbscoHost, IAC - Info Trac
Mem of Hidalgo County Library System; South Texas Library System
Partic in Amigos Library Services, Inc; Hidalgo County Libr Syst
Friends of the Library Group

WEST

P WEST PUBLIC LIBRARY, (WPL),* 209 W Tokio Rd, 76691-0513. (Mail add: PO Box 513, 76691-0513), SAN 375-3484. Tel: 254-826-3070. FAX: 254-826-4473. E-Mail: westpl@sharpsite.com. *Librn*, Henrietta Meurer; Staff 1 (Non-MLS 1)

Founded 1984
Jan 1998-Dec 1998 Income $27,946, State $2,223, City $2,500, Locally Generated Income $21,000. Mats Exp $11,000, Per/Ser (Incl. Access Fees) $70. Sal $6,600
Library Holdings: Bk Vols 28,000; Bk Titles 26,000; High Interest/Low Vocabulary Bk Vols 2,000
Automation Activity & Vendor Info: (Cataloging) Follett; (Circulation) Follett
Mem of Central Texas Library System
Special Services for the Deaf - Books on deafness & sign language
Friends of the Library Group

WHARTON

J WHARTON COUNTY JUNIOR COLLEGE, J M Hodges Library,* 911 Boling Hwy, 77488-3252. SAN 316-8441. Tel: 409-532-4560, Ext 6355. FAX: 409-532-6527. *Dir*, Patsy G Norton; *Asst Librn*, Jerry Hoke; *Circ, ILL, Ref*, Cynthia Huddleston; *Media Spec*, Mike Mills; *Librn*, Joanne Johnson; *Acq*, Jan Ammann; *Cat*, Rosie Nunez; *Ser*, Toni Copeland; Staff 2 (MLS 2)
Founded 1946. Enrl 3,962; Fac 161
Sep 1998-Aug 1999 Income $501,138. Mats Exp $136,552, Books $48,789, Per/Ser (Incl. Access Fees) $45,700, Presv $4,325. Sal $291,393 (Prof $121,468)
Library Holdings: Bk Vols 66,820; Bk Titles 57,920; Per Subs 512
Open Mon-Thurs 7:30am-9pm, Fri 7:30-4

P WHARTON COUNTY LIBRARY,* 1920 N Fulton, 77488. SAN 362-4153. Tel: 409-532-8080. Web Site: isadore.tsl.state.tx.us/w/wcl. *Dir*, Barbara J Goodell; *Asst Dir, Tech Servs*, Beverly Ermis; *ILL*, Geraldine Smaistrla; *Ch Servs*, Shelley Lott; Staff 2 (MLS 2)
Founded 1938. Pop 41,467; Circ 203,978
1997-1998 Income $554,272. Mats Exp $49,500, Books $40,103, Per/Ser (Incl. Access Fees) $4,852, Presv $700, AV Equip $767. Sal $261,498
Library Holdings: Bk Vols 81,189; Per Subs 114
Mem of Houston Area Library System
Friends of the Library Group
Branches: 3
EAST BERNARD BRANCH, 102 W Ave C, PO Box 1307, Syracuse, 67878. Tel: 409-335-6142. *Librn*, Agnes Minks
Library Holdings: Bk Vols 10,502
Friends of the Library Group
EL CAMPO BRANCH, 200 W Church, El Campo, 77437. SAN 362-4218. Tel: 409-543-2362. *Librn*, Aileen Terry
Library Holdings: Bk Vols 32,136
LOUISE BRANCH, 1002 Third St, PO Box 36, Louise, 77455. SAN 362-4242. Tel: 409-648-2018. *Librn*, Jessie Gonzales
Library Holdings: Bk Vols 5,567

WHEELER

P WHEELER PUBLIC LIBRARY,* 306 S Canadian St, PO Box 676, 79096. SAN 316-845X. Tel: 806-826-5977. FAX: 806-826-5977. *Librn*, Mary Gibson
Pop 3,000; Circ 13,808
Library Holdings: Bk Vols 22,017; Bk Titles 21,999; Per Subs 1
Mem of Texas Panhandle Library System

WHITE SETTLEMENT

P WHITE SETTLEMENT PUBLIC LIBRARY,* 8215 White Settlement Rd, 76108-1604. SAN 376-4710. Tel: 817-367-0166. FAX: 817-246-8184. *Librn*, Bethany Hills
Library Holdings: Bk Vols 56,000; Per Subs 72
Mem of North Texas Regional Library System
Open Mon 9:30-8:30, Tues & Wed 9:30-6, Thurs 9:30-8, Sat 9:30-1:30
Friends of the Library Group

WHITEHOUSE

P WHITEHOUSE COMMUNITY LIBRARY,* 107 Bascom Rd, 75791-1508. SAN 376-4508. Tel: 903-839-2949. FAX: 903-839-7228. *Librn*, Sandra Knackstedt
Library Holdings: Bk Vols 18,000
Mem of Northeast Texas Library System
Friends of the Library Group

WHITESBORO

P WHITESBORO PUBLIC LIBRARY,* 308 W Main, 76273. SAN 316-8468. Tel: 903-564-5432. FAX: 903-564-6105. *Coll Develop, Librn*, Virginia Garvin
Founded 1969. Pop 3,197; Circ 30,796
Library Holdings: Bk Vols 20,337
Subject Interests: Genealogy
Partic in Northeast Texas Library System

WHITEWRIGHT

P WHITEWRIGHT PUBLIC LIBRARY,* 200 Grand St, PO Box 984, 754 SAN 316-8476. Tel: 903-364-2955. *Librn*, Linda Brand
Circ 19,000
Library Holdings: Bk Vols 20,000; Per Subs 15
Mem of Northeast Texas Library System

WHITNEY

P LAKE WHITNEY LIBRARY,* 106 N Colorado, PO Box 2050, 76692-2050. SAN 376-4753. Tel: 254-694-4639. FAX: 254-694-0896. *Librn*, Rit Campbell
Jan 2000-Dec 2000 Mats Exp $6,000. Sal $16,143
Library Holdings: Bk Vols 10,000
Mem of Central Texas Library System
Open Tues-Fri 8-5 & Sat 8-12
Friends of the Library Group

WICHITA FALLS

C MIDWESTERN STATE UNIVERSITY, George Moffett Library, 3410 Ta Ave, 76308-2099. SAN 316-8492. Tel: 940-397-4204. Interlibrary Loan Service Tel: 940-397-4174. Circulation Tel: 940-397-4753. Reference Tel: 940-397-4758. FAX: 940-397-4689. E-Mail: msulib@nexus.mwsu.edu. W Site: mohican.mwsu.edu/~library/libraryhp.html. *Dir*, Melba S Harvill; Te 940-397-4165, E-Mail: melba.harvill@nexus.mwsu.edu; *Asst Dir*, Joan E Patterson; Tel: 940-397-4167, E-Mail: joan.patterson@nexus.mwsu.edu; *C* Robert Allen; Tel: 940-397-4176, E-Mail: robert.allen@nexus.mwsu.edu; *Cat*, John Cys; Tel: 940-397-4175, E-Mail: john.cys@nexus.mwsu.edu; *IL* Cynthia Bush; E-Mail: cynthia.bush@nexus.mwsu.edu; *Ch Servs*, Andrea Williams; Tel: 940-397-4698, E-Mail: andrea.williams@nexus.mwsu.edu; *Ser*, Sue Coffey; Tel: 940-397-4173, E-Mail: sue.coffey@nexus.mwsu.edu *Media Spec*, Scott Allen; Tel: 940-397-4686, E-Mail: scott.allens@nexus.mwsu.edu; *Head Ref*, Violet Allison Breen; Tel: 940-397-4171, E-Mail: allison.breen@nexus.mwsu.edu; *Doc*, Ryan Samuelson; Tel: 940-397-4177, E-Mail: ryan.samuelson@nexus.mwsu.edu; *Coll Develop*, Clara Latham; Tel: 940-397-4757, E-Mail: clara.latham@nexus.mwsu.edu. Subje Specialists: *Anthropology*, Joan E Patterson; *Children lit*, Andrea L Willia *Childrens educ*, Andrea L Williams; *English*, Violet Allison Breen; *Geolo* John Cys; *Govt info*, Ryan Samuelson; *History*, Violet Allison Breen; *History*, Joan E Patterson; *Humanities*, Ryan Samuelson; *Nonprint mat*, Sc Allen; *Science*, Sue Coffey; *Soc studies*, Scott Allen; *Sociology*, Clara Latham; Staff 15 (MLS 9, Non-MLS 6)
Founded 1922. Enrl 5,861; Fac 221; Highest Degree: Master
Sep 1999-Aug 2000 Income $1,210,211, State $450,000, Locally Generate Income $2,000, Parent Institution $758,211. Mats Exp $402,800, Books $153,469, Per/Ser (Incl. Access Fees) $189,751, Presv $11,000, Micro $37,805, AV Equip $2,200, Manuscripts & Archives $600, Electronic Ref Mat (Incl. Access Fees) $7,975. Sal $586,026 (Prof $342,607)
Library Holdings: Bk Vols 423,171; Bk Titles 332,740; Per Subs 1,163
Subject Interests: Education, History, US
Special Collections: Americana (Library of American Civilization), ultrafiche; English Literature (Library of English Literature to Early 20th Century), ultrafiche; Missouri-Kansas-Texas Railroad Map Coll; Nolan A Moore III Heritage of Print Coll
Automation Activity & Vendor Info: (Acquisitions) Endeavor; (Circulation) Endeavor; (Course Reserve) Endeavor; (ILL) Endeavor; (OPAC) Endeavor; (Serials) Endeavor
Database Vendor: GaleNet, OCLC - First Search, OVID Technologies
Publications: Libra (Newsletter)
Restriction: Non-circulating to the public
Function: For research purposes
Partic in Amigos Library Services, Inc; OCLC Online Computer Library Center, Inc; Tex Share
Special Services for the Deaf - TDD; TTY machine; Videos & decoder

S OIL INFORMATION LIBRARY OF WICHITA FALLS,* 100 Energy Ctr 718 Lamar, 76301-6877. SAN 316-8549. Tel: 940-322-4241. FAX: 940-32 8695. *Librn*, Gail Baldon Phillips
Founded 1966
Library Holdings: Bk Vols 1,200
Subject Interests: Gas records, Geol data, Maps, Oil records

S WICHITA FALLS MUSEUM & ART CENTER LIBRARY,* 2 Eureka Circle, 76308. SAN 316-8514. Tel: 940-692-0923. FAX: 940-696-5358.
Founded 1967
Library Holdings: Bk Titles 2,000; Per Subs 10
Subject Interests: Am art, Am hist, Print making, Sci
Restriction: Restricted public use

P WICHITA FALLS PUBLIC LIBRARY, 600 11th St, 76301-7096. SAN 316-8484. Tel: 940-767-0868. FAX: 940-720-6672. Web Site: www.wfpl.ne *Dir*, Linda Hughes; Tel: 940-767-0868, Ext 229, E-Mail: lhughes@wfpl.ne *Assoc Dir*, Jeannine Humphris; Tel: 940-767-0868, Ext 228, E-Mail: jhumphris@wfpl.net; *Assoc Dir*, Rebecca Morrison; Tel: 940-767-0868, Ex

233, E-Mail: bmorrison@wfpl.net; *Head, Circ*, Lana Horner; Tel: 940-767-0868, Ext 225, E-Mail: lhorner@wfpl.net; *Automation Syst Coordr*, Annette Britain; Tel: 940-767-0868, Ext 246, E-Mail: abritain@wfpl.net; *Tech Servs*, Rich Maruscsak; Tel: 940-767-0868, Ext 241, E-Mail: rmaruscsak@wfpl.net; *Ch Servs*, Pat Doan; Tel: 940-767-0868, Ext 245, E-Mail: pdoan@wfpl.net; *Acq, Coll Develop*, Tim Wiseman; Tel: 940-767-0868, Ext 227, E-Mail: twiseman@wfpl.net; *ILL*, Jennifer Barrera; Tel: 940-767-0868, Ext 230, E-Mail: jbarrera@wfpl.net; *Cat*, Richard Guinn; Tel: 940-767-0868, Ext 240, E-Mail: rguinn@wfpl.net; *Ref*, Lesley Daly; Tel: 940-767-0868, Ext 231, E-Mail: ldaly@wfpl.net; *Ref*, Danuta Pryzbylak; Tel: 940-767-0868, Ext 232, E-Mail: dprzbylak@wfpl.net. Subject Specialists: *Genealogy*, Andrew Jelen; Staff 24 (MLS 12, Non-MLS 12)
Founded 1918. Pop 122,378; Circ 379,410
Oct 2000-Sep 2001 Income City $1,380,996. Mats Exp $323,225, Books $200,000, Per/Ser (Incl. Access Fees) $8,133, Presv $1,000, Micro $6,000, Electronic Ref Mat (Incl. Access Fees) $16,000. Sal $785,759 (Prof $470,000)
Library Holdings: Bk Vols 133,000; Bk Titles 112,000; Per Subs 300
Special Collections: Genealogy; Texana & Southwest (Texas Coll)
Automation Activity & Vendor Info: (Acquisitions) epixtech, inc.; (Cataloging) epixtech, inc.; (Circulation) epixtech, inc.; (OPAC) epixtech, inc.
Database Vendor: Ebsco - EbscoHost, epixtech, inc., GaleNet
Publications: Check It Out (Newsletter)
Mem of North Texas Regional Library System
Friends of the Library Group

WICHITA FALLS STATE HOSPITAL, Medical & Patient's Library,* PO Box 300, 76307. SAN 316-8522. Tel: 940-689-5308, Ext 5249. FAX: 940-689-5538. *In Charge*, David Anderson
Founded 1961
1997-1998 Income $62,540
Library Holdings: Per Subs 80
Subject Interests: History, Mental health filmstrips, Nursing, Pharmacology, Philosophy, Psychiatry, Psychology
Special Collections: Clinical Neurology (Baker Coll); Harvard Classics; Medical (Ciba Coll); Nobel Prize Library; Pictures (Metropolitan Miniatures), albums; Remotivation Materials; Scientific American Medicine; Stereoscopic Atlas of Human Anatomy (Bassett Coll)
Partic in S Cent Regional Med Libr Program
Open Mon-Fri 8-5

ILMER

ELVIS MAXINE GILLIAM MEMORIAL PUBLIC LIBRARY, 205 E Beltline Rd, 75172. SAN 361-4344. Tel: 972-441-3713. FAX: 972-441-3713. *Librn*, Linda McCrory
Library Holdings: Bk Vols 11,278; Per Subs 10
Mem of Dallas County Libr Syst
Open Mon-Fri 12-6

IMBERLEY

VILLAGE LIBRARY OF WIMBERLEY,* 400 FM 2325, Box 1240, 78676-1240. SAN 320-264X. Tel: 512-847-2188. Interlibrary Loan Service Tel: 800-252-3163. E-Mail: wimlibr@ix.netcom.com. *Librn*, SuzAnne Beard
Founded 1975. Pop 12,666; Circ 18,000
Jan 1997-Dec 1998 Income $39,817, State $2,232, County $15,000, Locally Generated Income $20,585. Mats Exp Per/Ser (Incl. Access Fees) $864. Sal $15,000
Library Holdings: Bk Titles 9,887
Special Collections: History (Herrick Arnold Coll)
Publications: Wimberley - A Way of Life, 1985
Mem of Central Texas Library System
Friends of the Library Group

INNSBORO

GILBREATH MEMORIAL LIBRARY,* 916 N Main St, 75494. SAN 316-8557. Tel: 903-342-6866. FAX: 903-342-9188. *Librn*, Virginia Woodle
Pop 16,816; Circ 19,202
Library Holdings: Bk Vols 24,050; Per Subs 31
Friends of the Library Group

INTERS

WINTERS PUBLIC LIBRARY, 120 N Main, 79567. SAN 316-8565. Tel: 915-754-4251. E-Mail: winterspl@netscape.net. *Librn*, Carolyn Scarborough; Staff 1 (Non-MLS 1)
Founded 1954. Pop 4,500; Circ 8,500
Library Holdings: Bk Titles 13,000
Subject Interests: History
Publications: Big Country Major Resource News; Forecast
Mem of Big Country Library System

WOLFE CITY

P WOLFE CITY PUBLIC LIBRARY, 203 E Williams St, 75496-0109. (Mail add: PO Box 109, 75496-0109), SAN 316-8573. Tel: 903-496-7311. FAX: 903-496-7311. E-Mail: wclibrary@unicomp.net. *Dir*, James DeWitt; *Dir*, Angela Scarlett
Pop 1,500; Circ 1,692
Library Holdings: Bk Titles 12,000
Open Mon 1-8, Tues 10-12 & 12:30-6, Wed 10-12 & 12:30-3, Thurs & Fri 1-5:30
Friends of the Library Group

WOLFFORTH

P CITY OF WOLFFORTH LIBRARY,* 328 E Hwy 62-82, PO Box 36, 79382-0036. SAN 376-4265. Tel: 806-866-9280. FAX: 806-866-4217. *Librn*, Andi Youngblood
Library Holdings: Bk Vols 12,000; Per Subs 20
Mem of West Texas Library System
Open Mon-Fri 2-6 & Sat 8-12

WOODVILLE

P ALLAN SHIVERS LIBRARY,* 302 N Charlton, 75979. SAN 316-8581. Tel: 409-283-3709. FAX: 409-283-5258. *Dir*, Rosemarie Bunch
Circ 55,111
Library Holdings: Bk Vols 25,000; Per Subs 31
Mem of Houston Area Library System

WYLIE

P RITA & TRUETT SMITH LIBRARY,* 800 Thomas St, 75098. SAN 316-859X. Tel: 972-442-7566. FAX: 972-442-4075. E-Mail: library@wylietex.us. *Dir*, Mignon Morse
Founded 1970. Pop 9,200; Circ 55,105
Library Holdings: Bk Vols 32,261; Bk Titles 27,363; Per Subs 37
Publications: Library Notes (monthly)
Mem of Northeast Texas Library System
Friends of the Library Group

YOAKUM

P CARL & MARY WELHAUSEN LIBRARY,* 810 Front St, 77995. SAN 316-8603. Tel: 512-293-5001. FAX: 512-293-7091. *Librn*, Virgi Ferrell
Pop 6,000; Circ 18,519
Library Holdings: Bk Vols 20,932; Per Subs 43
Mem of South Texas Library System
Open Mon-Fri 9-6
Friends of the Library Group

YORKTOWN

P YORKTOWN PUBLIC LIBRARY,* 103 W Main, PO Box 308, 78164. SAN 316-8611. Tel: 512-564-3232. Interlibrary Loan Service Tel: 512-880-8925. FAX: 512-564-3232. *Librn*, Luellen Smiley
Founded 1939. Pop 2,498; Circ 15,043
Library Holdings: Bk Vols 15,000; Bk Titles 15,000
Mem of South Texas Library System
Friends of the Library Group

ZAPATA

P ZAPATA COUNTY PUBLIC LIBRARY,* 901 Kennedy St, Box 2806, 78076-2806. SAN 325-173X. Tel: 956-765-5351. FAX: 956-765-5351. *Librn*, Bianca E Guerrero; E-Mail: zcplibr@yahoo.com; *Asst Librn*, Sybil Singleton; *Asst Librn*, Aminta Rubio; *Asst Librn*, Maria Yanira; Tel: 956-765-4641, E-Mail: yanira7_98@yahoo.com
Founded 1983. Pop 9,000; Circ 64,000
1999-2000 Income $80,000. Mats Exp $17,000. Sal $57,000
Library Holdings: Bk Titles 30,000; Per Subs 60
Special Collections: Texas History Coll (bks)
Mem of South Texas Library System
Open Mon-Sat 10-7
Friends of the Library Group
Branches: 1
A L BENNAVIDES BRANCH, San Ygnacio, 78067. SAN 376-9879. Tel: 956-765-5611. *Librn*, Amita Rubio
Library Holdings: Bk Vols 10,000
Open Tues-Fri 3-7

UTAH

Date of Statistics: 1999
Population, 1996 Census (est): 2,099,758
Population Served by Public Libraries: 2,099,758
Total Volumes in Public Libraries: 6,357,321
Volumes Per Capita: 3.0
Total Public Library Circulation: 20,624,783
Circulation Per Capita: 9.8
Total Public Library Income (not including Grants-in-Aid): $55,092,109
Source of Income: Public funds
Expenditure Per Capita: $24.14
Number of County Libraries: 13
Number of Bookmobiles in State: 16
Grants-in-Aid to Public Libraries:
Federal (Library Services & Construction Act): $646,710
State Aid: $1,215,068

MERICAN FORK

AMERICAN FORK CITY LIBRARY,* 64 S 100 E, 84003. SAN 316-862X. Tel: 801-763-3070. FAX: 801-763-3073. Web Site: www.americanforklibrary.com. *Dir*, Christie Reimschussel
Pop 19,350; Circ 145,000
Library Holdings: Bk Vols 52,000; Bk Titles 77,000; Per Subs 105
Subject Interests: Local history
Partic in Dialog Corporation
Friends of the Library Group

NATIONAL PARK SERVICE, Timpanogos Cave National Monument Library, RR 3, Box 200, 84003-9803. SAN 321-8376. Tel: 801-756-5239. FAX: 801-756-5661. *In Charge*, Mike Gosse
Founded 1966
Library Holdings: Bk Titles 925
Subject Interests: Cave related subjs, Caves, Natural resources, The Environment

EAVER

BEAVER PUBLIC LIBRARY,* 55 W Center St, 84713. SAN 316-8638. Tel: 435-438-5274. FAX: 435-438-5826. E-Mail: jbcal@mail.state.lib.ut.us. *Librn*, Joan Beal
Pop 2,318; Circ 19,353 Sal $27,300
Library Holdings: Bk Titles 16,000; Per Subs 16
Friends of the Library Group

RIGHAM CITY

BRIGHAM CITY LIBRARY, 26 E Forest, 84302-2198. SAN 316-8646. Tel: 435-723-5850. FAX: 435-723-2813. Web Site: bcpl.lib.ut.us. *Dir*, Susan H Hill; E-Mail: sue@peachy.bcpl.lib.ut.us; *Asst Dir*, Vernetta McComb; *Ch Servs*, Connie Edwards; *Ch Servs*, Heather Bachfish; *Ref*, Susan Behring; Staff 4 (MLS 1, Non-MLS 3)
Founded 1915. Pop 15,619; Circ 172,233
Library Holdings: Bk Titles 49,312; Per Subs 128
Special Collections: Box Elder History, bks & pamphlets; Mormon History; Mormon Religion
Friends of the Library Group

THIOKOL CORP, Library Unit, PO Box 707, 84302-0707. SAN 316-8662. Tel: 435-863-6819. FAX: 435-863-6023. *Librn*, Ellen Wagstaff; E-Mail: ellen.wagstaff@thiokol.com; *Librn*, Diane Nielson; Tel: 435-863-2132, E-Mail: diane.nielson@thiokol.com; *Librn*, Martha Ward; Tel: 435-863-2477, E-Mail: martha.ward@thiokol.com
Library Holdings: Bk Vols 100,000; Per Subs 50
Subject Interests: Solid propellant rocket tech

CASTLE DALE

P EMERY COUNTY LIBRARY,* PO Box 515, 84513-0515. SAN 316-8670. Tel: 435-381-2554. *Dir*, Jerilyn Mathis; *Librn*, Odessa Jones
Pop 5,137; Circ 47,896
Library Holdings: Bk Vols 43,034
Branches: 7
CLEVELAND BRANCH, PO Box 275, Cleveland, 84518. SAN 000-0000. Tel: 435-653-2204. *Librn*, Mickey Carter
ELMO BRANCH, PO Box 217, Elmo, 84521-0217. SAN 000-0000. Tel: 435-653-2558.
EMERY BRANCH, PO Box 127, Emery, 84522-0127. SAN 000-0000. Tel: 435-286-2474. *Librn*, Vicki Jacobson
FERRON BRANCH, PO Box 850, Ferron, 84523-0818. SAN 000-0000. Tel: 435-384-2637. *Librn*, Dorothy Taylor
GREEN RIVER BRANCH, PO Box 510, Green River, 84525-0385. SAN 000-0000. Tel: 435-564-3349. *Librn*, Denise Hoffman
HUNTINGTON BRANCH, PO Box 794, Huntington, 84528-0794. SAN 000-0000. Tel: 435-687-9590. *Librn*, Gery Mortensen
ORANGEVILLE BRANCH, PO Box 628, Orangeville, 84537-0628. SAN 000-0000. Tel: 435-748-2726. *Librn*, Carole Larsen

CEDAR CITY

P CEDAR CITY PUBLIC LIBRARY,* 136 W Center St, 84720. SAN 316-8689. Tel: 435-586-6661. FAX: 435-865-7280. Web Site: www.state.lib.ut.us. *Dir*, Steven D Decker; *Ch Servs*, Pat Mills; *Ch Servs*, Crystal Bilyeu; *Tech Servs*, Sherry Bohman
Founded 1914. Pop 14,096; Circ 98,847
Jul 1996-Jun 1997 Income $220,547. Mats Exp Books $27,597. Sal $124,725
Library Holdings: Bk Vols 45,479; Per Subs 83
Subject Interests: Children, Consumer guides, History, Relig studies, Sci, Young adults
Special Collections: Local Newspaper Coll, micro; Rare Book Coll
Automation Activity & Vendor Info: (Cataloging) Follett; (Circulation) Follett
Open Mon-Thurs 9-9, Fri & Sat 9-6

C SOUTHERN UTAH UNIVERSITY, Gerald R Sherratt Library, 351 W Center St, 84720. SAN 316-8697. Tel: 435-865-8240. Interlibrary Loan Service Tel: 435-586-7938. Reference Tel: 435-865-8040. FAX: 435-865-8152. Web Site: www.li.suu.edu/. *Dean of Libr*, Diana T Graff; Tel: 435-586-7939, E-Mail: graff@suu.edu; *Assoc Dir*, Vik G Brown; Tel: 435-586-7952, E-Mail: brown_v@suu.ecu; *Librn*, John Bryner; Tel: 435-865-8081, E-Mail: bryner@suu.edu; *Librn*, Thomas H Cunningham; Tel: 435-865-8242, E-Mail: cunningham@suu.edu; *Librn*, Matthew F Nickerson; Tel: 435-586-1955, E-Mail: nickerson@suu.edu; *Tech Coordr*, Randall O Christensen; Tel: 435-586-7946, E-Mail: christensen@suu.edu; *Ser*, Suzanne Julian; Tel: 435-586-7937, E-Mail: julian@suu.edu; *Tech Servs*, Philip H Dillard; Tel: 435-586-1991, E-Mail: dillard@suu.edu; *Publ Servs*, Scott W Lanning; Tel: 435-865-8156, E-Mail: lanning@suu.edu; *Spec Coll*, Janet Burton Seegmiller;

Tel: 435-586-7945, E-Mail: seegmiller@suu.edu. Subject Specialists: *Law*, John Bryner; *Media*, John Bryner; *Spanish*, John Bryner; Staff 15 (MLS 6, Non-MLS 9)
Founded 1897. Enrl 6,025; Fac 185; Highest Degree: Master
Jul 1999-Jun 2000 Income $1,429,622. Mats Exp $544,094, Books $335,656, Per/Ser (Incl. Access Fees) $79,926, Presv $5,241, Electronic Ref Mat (Incl. Access Fees) $35,000. Sal $682,615 (Prof $581,819)
Library Holdings: Bk Vols 209,759; Bk Titles 167,526; Per Subs 7,275
Subject Interests: Music, Opera, Shakespeare, Sibelius, Utah hist
Special Collections: Opera Scores & Books of the 19th Century (Victorian Room); Shakespeare Coll; Southern Paiute Indian Coll; Southern Utah History Coll; US Geology Map
Automation Activity & Vendor Info: (Cataloging) epixtech, inc.; (Circulation) epixtech, inc.; (Course Reserve) epixtech, inc.; (OPAC) epixtech, inc.
Database Vendor: Ebsco - EbscoHost, epixtech, inc., Lexis-Nexis, OCLC - First Search, ProQuest, Silverplatter Information Inc., Wilson - Wilson Web
Publications: Annual Report; Faculty Newsletter
Partic in Utah Academic Library Consortium
Open Mon-Thurs 7-11, Fri 7-7, Sat 9-5 & Sun 2-10

CLEARFIELD

S CLEARFIELD JOB CORPS CENTER LIBRARY,* PO Box 160070, 84016-0070. SAN 316-8719. Tel: 801-774-4353. FAX: 801-774-4449. *Mgr*, Jeff Parker; E-Mail: jeffp@jcdc.jobcorps.org
Founded 1966
Library Holdings: Bk Vols 3,000; Per Subs 20
Open Mon-Fri 8-5

DELTA

P DELTA CITY LIBRARY,* 76 N 200 West, 84624-9424. SAN 316-8727. Tel: 435-864-4945. FAX: 435-864-4313. Web Site: www.deltautah.com/library.html. *Coll Develop, Librn*, Deb Greathouse; E-Mail: dgreat@inter.state.lib.ut.us
Circ 46,744
Jul 1997-Jun 1998 Income $90,307. Mats Exp $23,893, Books $22,573, Per/Ser (Incl. Access Fees) $1,320. Sal $55,032 (Prof $24,910)
Library Holdings: Bk Vols 25,000

DUGWAY

UNITED STATES ARMY
A POST LIBRARY, Dugway Proving Ground, 84022-5000. SAN 362-4277. Tel: 435-831-2178. *Librn*, Leola D Liddiard
Library Holdings: Bk Vols 23,000
S WEST DESERT TECHNICAL INFORMATION CENTER, Kuddes Bldg 4531, Rm 116, Dugway Proving Ground, 84022. (Mail add: CSTE-DTC-DP-WD-JC-L, 84022), SAN 362-4307. Tel: 435-831-3822. Reference Tel: 435-831-3822. Toll Free Tel: DSN-789-3822. FAX: 435-831-3813. Toll Free FAX: DSN-789-3813. E-Mail: jtic@dugway=emh3.army.mil. Web Site: www.cbiac.apgea.army.mil/about_us/iacs/dugway.html.; Staff 4 (MLS 2, Non-MLS 2)
Founded 1950
Library Holdings: Bk Vols 8,000; Bk Titles 20; Per Subs 46
Subject Interests: Biology, Chemistry, Ecol, Engineering, Epidemiol, Mathematics, Meteorology, Munitions, Statistics, Zoology
Database Vendor: CARL, Dialog, OCLC - First Search
Restriction: Staff use only
Partic in Defense Technical Information Center; Dialog Corporation; OCLC Online Computer Library Center, Inc

EPHRAIM

P EPHRAIM PUBLIC LIBRARY,* 30 S Main St, 84627. SAN 316-8735. Tel: 435-283-4544, 435-283-5143. FAX: 435-283-5143. *Librn*, Jackie Brown
Pop 2,500; Circ 20,726
Library Holdings: Bk Vols 15,500; Bk Titles 15,000; Per Subs 53
Partic in Utah Libr Asn
Open Tues-Thurs 3-9pm

J SNOW COLLEGE, Lucy A Phillips Library, 150 E College Ave, 84627. SAN 316-8743. Tel: 435-283-7363. FAX: 435-283-7369. E-Mail: library@snow.edu. Web Site: www.library.snow.edu. *Dir*, Russell Dean; Tel: 435-283-7361, E-Mail: russ.dean@snow.edu; *Asst Librn, Circ, ILL*, Ann Barton; Tel: 435-283-7368, E-Mail: ann.barton@snow.edu; *Acq, Cat*, Jacquelyn Beck; Tel: 435-283-7364, E-Mail: jackie.beck@snow.edu; *Circ*, Wendy Flowers; E-Mail: wendy.flowers@snow.edu; *Circ*, Kim Philips; *Circ*, Debbie Plummer; *Publ Servs, Ref Serv, Syst Coordr*, Jon Ostler; Tel: 435-283-7362, E-Mail: jon.ostler@snow.edu; *Coll Develop, Instrul Serv, Tech Servs*, Lynn Anderson; Tel: 435-283-7366, E-Mail: lynn.anderson@snow.edu; *Ser*, Denise Olson; Tel: 435-283-7367, E-Mail: denise.olson@snow.edu; *Tech Coordr*, Prescott Pratt; Tel: 435-283-7360, E-Mail: scott.pratt@snow.du. Subject Specialists: *Pub relations*, Ann Barton; Staff 7 (MLS 3, Non-MLS 4)
Founded 1888. Enrl 1,621
Library Holdings: Bk Vols 41,495; Bk Titles 34,233; Per Subs 239
Special Collections: Childrens Literature (Demont & Arlea Howell Childrens Literature Collection); Sanpete County & Snow College Histor (Ruth C Olsen Coll)
Automation Activity & Vendor Info: (Acquisitions) epixtech, inc.; (Cataloging) epixtech, inc.; (Circulation) epixtech, inc.; (Media Booking) epixtech, inc.; (OPAC) epixtech, inc.; (Serials) epixtech, inc.
Database Vendor: epixtech, inc., IAC - Info Trac, IAC - SearchBank, Lexis-Nexis, OCLC - First Search, OVID Technologies, ProQuest, Silverplatter Information Inc.
Publications: Overdue Notes (newsletter)
Partic in Utah Academic Library Consortium

FARMINGTON

P DAVIS COUNTY LIBRARY, 38 S 100 East, PO Box 115, 84025. SAN 362-4331. Tel: 801-451-2322. FAX: 801-451-9561. Web Site: www.co.davis.ut.us/library. *Dir*, Pete J Giacoma; *Asst Dir*, Jerry Meyer; *Librn*, Mary Moore; Staff 6 (MLS 6)
Founded 1946. Pop 215,000; Circ 1,300,000
Jan 2000-Dec 2000 Income (Main Library and Branch Library) $2,703,00 State $60,000, Federal $19,600, County $2,451,400, Locally Generated Income $160,000, Other $12,000. Mats Exp $499,000, Books $398,100, P Ser (Incl. Access Fees) $38,000, Presv $4,500, Micro $400, Other Print M $54,000, Electronic Ref Mat (Incl. Access Fees) $4,000. Sal $1,722,000 (Prof $410,000)
Library Holdings: Bk Vols 400,000; Per Subs 270
Automation Activity & Vendor Info: (Acquisitions) epixtech, inc.; (Cataloging) epixtech, inc.; (Circulation) epixtech, inc.
Database Vendor: epixtech, inc., OCLC - First Search
Partic in OCLC Online Computer Library Center, Inc
Friends of the Library Group
Branches: 3
CENTRAL, 155 N Wasatch Dr, Layton, 84041. SAN 329-6342. Tel: 801-547-0729. *Librn*, Marilyn Getts
Library Holdings: Bk Vols 94,000
NORTH, 562 S 1000 E, Clearfield, 84015. SAN 362-4366. Tel: 801-825-6662. *Librn*, Chris Sanford
Library Holdings: Bk Vols 88,000
SOUTH, 725 S Main St, Bountiful, 84010. SAN 362-4390. Tel: 801-295-8732. *Librn*, Bradley Maurer
Library Holdings: Bk Vols 112,000
Bookmobiles: 1. Bk vols 15,000

FILLMORE

P PRES MILLARD FILLMORE LIBRARY,* 25 S 100 West, 84631. SAN 316-8751. Tel: 435-743-5314. FAX: 435-743-5195. *Librn*, Scott Coffie; Te 360-992-2405, E-Mail: scoffie@clark.edu
Pop 2,000; Circ 14,122
Library Holdings: Bk Vols 27,000
Mon & Sat 12-5 & Tues-Fri 12-7

GARLAND

P GARLAND PUBLIC LIBRARY,* 86 W Factory St, PO Box 147, 84312. SAN 316-876X. Tel: 435-257-3117. E-Mail: garlib@utahlinx.com. *Librn*, Judy Dalton
Founded 1914. Pop 1,500
Jan 1997-Dec 1998 Income $19,597, State $4,542, City $14,114, Other $941. Mats Exp $3,159. Sal $13,652
Library Holdings: Bk Vols 9,958; Per Subs 11
Subject Interests: Agriculture, History, Literature
Open Mon-Thurs 1-6, Fri 1-4 & Sat 10-12
Friends of the Library Group

GUNNISON

P GUNNISON CIVIC LIBRARY,* PO Box 790, 84634. SAN 323-939X. Te 435-528-3104. FAX: 435-528-7958. *Acq, Librn, Publ Servs*, Barbara Reisn
Founded 1945. Pop 2,000; Circ 12,074
Library Holdings: Bk Vols 11,200; Bk Titles 11,000
Open Mon-Thurs 2-6, Sat 9-1
Friends of the Library Group

HEBER

P WASATCH COUNTY LIBRARY,* 188 S Main St, 84032-2044. SAN 31 8778. Tel: 435-654-1511. FAX: 435-654-6456. Web Site: www.shadowlink.net/~waslib. *Librn*, Kristin Bowcutt; E-Mail: kbowcutt@inter.state.lib.ut.us; Staff 8 (Non-MLS 8)
Founded 1919. Pop 13,500; Circ 75,000
Jan 2000-Dec 2000 Income $187,789, State $6,965, County $180,824. Mat Exp $21,500, Books $18,000, Per/Ser (Incl. Access Fees) $1,500, AV Equi

$2,000. Sal $91,011
Library Holdings: Bk Vols 50,000; Bk Titles 35,000; Per Subs 55; Bks on Deafness & Sign Lang 10
Friends of the Library Group

LPER

HELPER CITY LIBRARY, 19 S Main, 84526. SAN 325-1861. Tel: 435-472-5601. FAX: 435-472-5601. E-Mail: hlprlib@afnet.com. *Librn*, Debbie Peterson; *Asst Librn*, Paula Hatch; Staff 2 (MLS 1, Non-MLS 1)
Founded 1935. Circ 2,800
Library Holdings: Bk Titles 10,300; Per Subs 23
Open Tues-Fri 1-7 & Sat 9-3

LL AFB

UNITED STATES AIR FORCE
GERRITY MEMORIAL LIBRARY, FL 2020, Base Libr Bldg 440, 7415 Eighth St, 84056-5006. SAN 362-4455. Tel: 801-777-2533. FAX: 801-777-6667. *Librn*, Diana Taylor; E-Mail: diana.taylor@hill.af.mil; Staff 5 (MLS 1, Non-MLS 4)
Founded 1941
Oct 1998-Sep 1999 Income $282,310. Mats Exp $42,792, Books $26,424, Per/Ser (Incl. Access Fees) $16,368. Sal $96,146
Library Holdings: Bk Vols 35,606; Per Subs 107
Subject Interests: Aeronautical, Gen coll recreational for adults, Gen coll tech, Space, Western hist
Open Tues-Thurs 10-8, Fri & Sat 10-6

YRUM

HYRUM CITY LIBRARY, (Formerly Hyrum City - Bessie Brown Library), 83 W Main, PO Box B, 84319. SAN 316-8794. Tel: 435-245-6411. FAX: 435-245-4758. Web Site: www.hyrum.lib.ut.us. *Librn*, Virginia Tremayne; E-Mail: gtremayn@mail.state.lib.ut.us; *Asst Librn*, Jill Baxter; *Asst Librn*, Dottie Nash; *Asst Librn*, Delilah Neilsen; *Asst Librn*, Delilah Sant
Pop 10,000; Circ 200,000
Jul 2000-Jun 2001 Income $104,734. Mats Exp $22,000. Sal $42,125
Library Holdings: Bk Vols 41,000; Per Subs 21
Subject Interests: Animals, Birds
Automation Activity & Vendor Info: (Circulation) Follett
Open Mon-Fri 12-7 & Sat 2-5

NSEN

NATIONAL PARK SERVICE, Dinosaur National Monument Library,* PO Box 128, 84035-0128. SAN 316-8808. Tel: 435-789-2115. FAX: 435-781-1739. *Librn*, Donna Breslin
Founded 1960
Library Holdings: Bk Vols 15,000; Per Subs 10
Subject Interests: Archaeology, Geology, Local history, Zoology
Special Collections: Paleontology (Theodore White Coll)
Restriction: Open to public for reference only
Open Mon-Fri 8:30-4:30

AYSVILLE

KAYSVILLE CITY LIBRARY,* 44 N Main St, 84037. SAN 316-8832. Tel: 801-544-2826. *Librn*, Kay Twogood
Founded 1920. Pop 14,000; Circ 68,600
Library Holdings: Bk Vols 48,000; Per Subs 88
Automation Activity & Vendor Info: (Cataloging) Follett; (Circulation) Follett

EHI

LEHI CITY LIBRARY,* 120 N Center St, 84043. SAN 316-8840. Tel: 801-768-7150. FAX: 801-766-8856. *Librn*, Janeen Nelson Watkins; Staff 8 (MLS 1, Non-MLS 7)
Founded 1917. Pop 8,000; Circ 80,000
Library Holdings: Bk Vols 40,000; Per Subs 96
Open Mon-Thurs 9-9, Fri & Sat 10-6

EWISTON

LEWISTON PUBLIC LIBRARY,* PO Box 36, 84320-0036. SAN 316-8859. Tel: 435-258-5515. FAX: 435-258-2141. *Librn*, Vella Durrant; E-Mail: ndurrant@mail.state.lib.ut.us
Founded 1936. Pop 1,400; Circ 7,299
Library Holdings: Bk Vols 18,000; Per Subs 24
Open Mon, Tues & Thurs 12-7, Wed 9-1 & 6-9, Fri & Sat 10-3

LOGAN

P LOGAN LIBRARY, 255 N Main, 84321-3914. SAN 316-8867. Tel: 435-716-9123. Interlibrary Loan Service Tel: 435-716-9129. Circulation Tel: 435-716-9121. Reference Tel: 435-716-9120. FAX: 435-716-9145. Web Site: www.logan.lib.ut.us. *Dir*, Ronald K Jenkins; E-Mail: rjenkins@loganutah.org; *Senior Librn*, Janet Fiesinger; *Acq*, Karen Clark; *Computer Services*, Melanie Liechty; *Electronic Resources*, Kent Slade; *Ch Servs*, Becky Smith; *Ref*, Patricia Record. Subject Specialists: *Processing*, Janet Fiesinger; *Technology*, Janet Fiesinger; Staff 9 (MLS 7, Non-MLS 2)
Founded 1916. Circ 600,250
Jul 1999-Jun 2000 Income City $927,615. Mats Exp $133,600, Books $124,000, Per/Ser (Incl. Access Fees) $9,600. Sal $570,953
Library Holdings: Bk Vols 138,167; Per Subs 175
Automation Activity & Vendor Info: (Cataloging) Inlex; (Circulation) Inlex
Database Vendor: DRA
Partic in OCLC Online Computer Library Center, Inc; UNCL
Special Services - Bridgerland Literacy Program, literacy program sponsored by library, phone 435-716-9141, Brandilee Kussee, Literacy Director

C UTAH STATE UNIVERSITY LIBRARIES, 3000 Old Main Hill, 84322-3000. SAN 362-448X. Tel: 435-797-2631. Interlibrary Loan Service Tel: 435-797-2676. Circulation Tel: 435-797-2633. Reference Tel: 435-797-2678. FAX: 435-797-2880. E-Mail: maxpet@cc.usu.edu. Web Site: www.usu.edu/library/. *Actg Dir*, John A Elsweiler, Jr; *Dep Dir*, Robert Murdoch; *Head Ref*, John Elsweiler; *Head, Cat*, Cheryl Walters; *Head, Circ*, Vicki Read; *Head, Acq*, Richard Schockmel; *Govt Doc*, John Walters; *Cat*, Reed Painter; *AV*, LaDell Hoth; *Ch Servs*, Deborah Boutwell; *Spec Coll & Archives*, Ann Buttars; *Bibliog Instr*, Betty Dance; *ILL*, Carol Kochan; Staff 48 (MLS 27, Non-MLS 21)
Founded 1888. Enrl 21,000; Fac 635; Highest Degree: Doctorate
Jul 1998-Jun 1999 Income (Main and Other College/University Libraries) Parent Institution $6,652,036. Mats Exp $3,015,045, Books $652,469, Per/Ser (Incl. Access Fees) $1,894,964, Presv $108,208, Micro $11,678, AV Equip $41,863, Other Print Mats $10,863, Manuscripts & Archives $20,000, Electronic Ref Mat (Incl. Access Fees) $275,000. Sal $2,720,077 (Prof $1,649,320)
Library Holdings: Bk Vols 1,369,528; Bk Titles 941,989; Per Subs 14,732
Subject Interests: Agriculture, Environmental studies, Natural science, Sci-tech, Space studies
Special Collections: Archives of Society of American Range Management; Berten Wendell Allred Western Americana Library; Blanche Browning Rich Coll, rec; Briant H Stringham Papers, mss; Compton Photograph Coll; Cowboy Poetry Coll; Czechoslovakia (Masaryk Coll & Spencer Taggart Coll); Daryl Chase Coll; Dolly Sitton Bentley Memorial Coll; Edgar B Brossard Papers, mss; Fife Folklore Coll; Frederick P Champ Papers, mss; Gunn McKay Congressional Papers, mss; Hand Folklore Coll; Jack London Coll; Medical Artifacts & Books (Robert & Mary Ann Simmons McDill Coll); Ridgway Coll; Utah Woolgrowers Association Archives, mss; Utah, Mormons & Southern Idaho; Western American Literature (David & Beatrice C Evans Coll); Yoder Folklore Coll
Automation Activity & Vendor Info: (Acquisitions) epixtech, inc.; (Cataloging) epixtech, inc.; (Circulation) epixtech, inc.; (OPAC) epixtech, inc.; (Serials) epixtech, inc.
Database Vendor: Dialog, Ebsco - EbscoHost, epixtech, inc., Lexis-Nexis, OCLC - First Search, ProQuest, Silverplatter Information Inc., Wilson - Wilson Web
Partic in Big Twelve Plus Libr Consortium
Departmental Libraries:
EDUCATIONAL RESOURCES & TECHNOLOGY CENTER Tel: 435-797-3377. *Librn*, Nathan M Smith
ANN CARROLL MOORE CHILDREN'S LIBRARY Tel: 435-797-3091. *Librn*, Vaughn Morrison
Library Holdings: Bk Vols 20,305
QUINNEY NATURAL RESOURCES LIBRARY Tel: 435-797-2464. *Librn*, Carla G Heister
REGIONAL DEPOSITORY COLLECTION OF US GOVERNMENT DOCUMENTS Tel: 435-797-9073. *Librn*, John Walters

MAGNA

S ALLIANT TECHSYSTEMS LIBRARY, PO Box 98, 84044. SAN 316-8875. Tel: 801-251-2951, 801-251-5384. FAX: 801-251-2328. *Librn*, Nancy Hill; E-Mail: nancy_hill@atk.com; Staff 3 (MLS 1, Non-MLS 2)
Founded 1959. Pop 3,000
Library Holdings: Bk Vols 5,000; Per Subs 150
Subject Interests: Carbon fibers-reinforced composite materials, Chem rocket propulsion syst (mostly solid propellants), Composite materials, Graphite fibers, Ordnance systs
Special Collections: Active Military Standards Coll
Database Vendor: Dialog, Ebsco - EbscoHost, OCLC - First Search
Partic in BCR; Dialog Corporation; Nasa Libraries Information System - Nasa Galaxie; OCLC Online Computer Library Center, Inc

MANTI

P MANTI PUBLIC LIBRARY, 2 S Main St, 84642-1349. SAN 316-8883. Tel: 435-835-2201. FAX: 435-835-2202. Web Site: www.state.lib.ut.us. *Coll Develop, Librn*, Carolyn Bessey; E-Mail: cbessey@mail.state.lib.ut.us
Founded 1910. Pop 2,500; Circ 23,000
Jul 1998-Jun 1999 Income $63,172, State $11,267, City $44,205, Locally Generated Income $7,700. Mats Exp $44,000. Sal $24,000
Library Holdings: Bk Vols 18,700; Per Subs 55
Subject Interests: Local history
Automation Activity & Vendor Info: (Cataloging) Sagebrush Corporation; (Circulation) Sagebrush Corporation; (Course Reserve) Sagebrush Corporation; (ILL) Sagebrush Corporation
Open Mon-Sat 2-7pm
Friends of the Library Group

MIDWAY

SR CHURCH OF JESUS CHRIST OF LATTER-DAY SAINTS, Heber City Regional Branch Genealogical Library, 160 W Main St, PO Box 611, 84049. SAN 323-603X. Tel: 435-654-2760. FAX: 435-654-0599. *Dir*, Homer M LeBaron; Tel: 435-654-5821, E-Mail: homerlebaron@shadowlink.net; *Asst Dir*, Clyde Muir; *Asst Dir*, Irene Tisdale; *Asst Dir*, Robert Wren
1999-2000 Mats Exp $2,400, Books $400, Per/Ser (Incl. Access Fees) $200, Micro $500, AV Equip $600, Other Print Mats $100, Manuscripts & Archives $100, Electronic Ref Mat (Incl. Access Fees) $500
Library Holdings: Bk Titles 300; Per Subs 15
Subject Interests: Genealogy
Publications: Heber Region Family History Center Newsletter (quarterly) (Newsletter)
Open Mon-Fri 10-4 & 7-9

MOAB

P GRAND COUNTY PUBLIC LIBRARY, 25 S First E, 84532. SAN 316-8891. Tel: 435-259-5421. FAX: 435-259-1380. Web Site: www.grand.lib.ut.us. *Dir*, Sonja Plummer
Pop 8,000; Circ 69,000
Jan 1999-Dec 1999 Income $284,000, State $6,855, Federal $13,750, County $174,000, Locally Generated Income $5,000. Mats Exp $32,700, Books $30,000, Per/Ser (Incl. Access Fees) $2,700. Sal $56,326 (Prof $25,000)
Library Holdings: Bk Vols 32,000; Per Subs 74
Automation Activity & Vendor Info: (Circulation) Sagebrush Corporation
Friends of the Library Group

MONTICELLO

P SAN JUAN COUNTY LIBRARY,* 81 N Main St, PO Box 66, 84535-0066. SAN 362-4609. Tel: 435-587-2281. *Librn*, V Carroll
Pop 9,606; Circ 25,843
Library Holdings: Bk Vols 18,000
Branches: 1
BLANDING BRANCH, 25 W 300 South, Blanding, 84511-3829. SAN 362-4633. Tel: 801-678-2335. *Librn*, Barbara Roberts

MORGAN

P MORGAN COUNTY LIBRARY,* 50 W 100 North, PO Box 600, 84050-0600. SAN 316-8905. Tel: 801-829-3481. FAX: 801-845-6084. *Librn*, Jileen Boydstun; E-Mail: jboydstu@inter.state.lib.ut.us; Staff 8 (Non-MLS 8)
Pop 6,300; Circ 56,883
Jan 1999-Dec 1999 Income $67,743, State $6,500, Provincial $61,243. Mats Exp $21,811, Books $20,000, Per/Ser (Incl. Access Fees) $1,500, AV Equip $311. Sal $46,859
Library Holdings: Bk Vols 26,577; Per Subs 20
Special Collections: Morgan County Historical Society Coll
Automation Activity & Vendor Info: (Acquisitions) Follett; (Cataloging) Follett; (Circulation) Follett; (OPAC) Follett
Database Vendor: Ebsco - EbscoHost
Open Mon-Thurs 12-7, Fri & Sat 12-5
Friends of the Library Group

MOUNT PLEASANT

P MT PLEASANT PUBLIC LIBRARY,* 24 E Main St, 84647-1429. SAN 316-8913. Tel: 435-462-3240. FAX: 435-462-9115. *Librn*, Shauna Busby; E-Mail: sbusby@mail.state.lib.ut.us
Circ 60,987 Sal $25,410
Library Holdings: Bk Vols 23,000
Friends of the Library Group

MURRAY

P MURRAY PUBLIC LIBRARY,* 166 E 5300 South, 84107-6075. SAN 3[illegible] 4668. Tel: 801-264-2580. FAX: 801-264-2586. Web Site: www.murray.lib.ut.us. *Dir*, Daniel J Barr; Tel: 801-264-2575, E-Mail: dbarr@state.lib.ut.us; *Tech Servs*, Arlene Cook; *Ch Servs*, Shauna Siebers; *Ad Servs*, David Brown; *Automation Syst Coordr*, Sharon Williams; *Tech Coordr*, Danny O'Rourke; *Cat*, Helene Richardson; *Pres*, Cindy Cheney; Staff 17 (MLS 5, Non-MLS 12)
Founded 1910. Pop 33,089; Circ 281,147
Jul 1998-Jun 1999 Income $1,079,800, State $7,618, City $50,000, Locall[illegible] Generated Income $1,022,182. Mats Exp $142,170, Books $126,712, Per/[illegible] (Incl. Access Fees) $7,618, Presv $500, Electronic Ref Mat (Incl. Access Fees) $7,340. Sal $479,790
Library Holdings: Bk Vols 80,516; Bk Titles 87,038; Per Subs 290
Subject Interests: Local history
Special Collections: Utah State Historical Quarterly
Automation Activity & Vendor Info: (Circulation) epixtech, inc.; (OPAC[illegible] epixtech, inc.
Database Vendor: epixtech, inc., GaleNet, IAC - SearchBank, ProQuest
Friends of the Library Group

S TESTING ENGINEERS INTERNATIONAL LIBRARY, 4121 S 500 Wes[illegible] 84123. (Mail add: PO Box 57025, 84157-0025), SAN 316-9189. Tel: 801-262-2332. FAX: 801-262-2363. E-Mail: tei@xmission.com. *Librn*, Suzann[illegible] Turner; *Pres*, Matthew MacGregor
Founded 1963
1998-1999 Mats Exp $10,000, Books $5,000, Per/Ser (Incl. Access Fees) $5,000. Sal $14,000
Library Holdings: Bk Vols 45,000; Per Subs 25
Subject Interests: Engineering, Sci, Sci-tech
Special Collections: Standards (25,000)

NEPHI

P NEPHI PUBLIC LIBRARY, (NPL), 21 E First N, 84648-1501. SAN 316-8921. Tel: 435-623-0822. FAX: 435-623-5443. *Librn*, Barbara Lovell; E-Mail: blovell@state.lib.ut.us
Pop 4,234; Circ 54,693
Library Holdings: Bk Vols 25,000; Per Subs 34
Automation Activity & Vendor Info: (Cataloging) Sagebrush Corporation; (Circulation) Sagebrush Corporation
Open Mon-Thurs 11-7, Fri 2-6 & Sat 2-6

NORTH SALT LAKE

S HERITAGE QUEST, 669 W 900 North, PO Box 540670, 84054-0670. SA[illegible] 329-1898. Tel: 801-298-5358. FAX: 801-298-5468. E-Mail: sales@heritagequest.com. Web Site: www.heritagequest.com. *Pres*, Bradley W Steuart; *Ref*, Brad Heaton; Staff 35 (MLS 9, Non-MLS 26)
Founded 1983
Subject Interests: Genealogy, Local history
Publications: Census Indexes; Census Map Guides; Genealogical Research Guides; Marriage Indexes
Open Mon-Fri 8-6

OGDEN

M MCKAY-DEE HOSPITAL CENTER LIBRARY, 3939 Harrison Blvd, 84409. SAN 316-8948. Tel: 801-627-2800. FAX: 801-398-2032. Web Site: www.ihc.com. *Librn*, Mark Meldrum
Library Holdings: Bk Vols 1,200; Bk Titles 150
Partic in Medline
Open Mon-Fri 8-4:30

M OGDEN REGIONAL MEDICAL CENTER, Medical Center Library,* 5475 S 500 East, 84405-6978. SAN 325-1489. Tel: 801-479-2055, 801-479-2111 (Hospital). FAX: 801-479-2582. *Librn*, Kathryn Pudlock
Library Holdings: Bk Titles 700; Per Subs 120
Subject Interests: Medicine, Nursing
Partic in Nat Libr of Med; Utah Health Sciences Library Consortium
Open Mon-Thurs 8-2:30

C STEVENS HENAGER COLLEGE LIBRARY, 2168 Washington Blvd, 84401. SAN 316-8956. Tel: 801-394-7791, Ext 22. FAX: 801-393-1748. *Admin Dir*, Marjorie Anderson; E-Mail: mardawn@usa.net; *Librn*, Brad Clevenger; Staff 2 (MLS 2)
Enrl 300; Highest Degree: Bachelor
Library Holdings: Bk Titles 3,000
Subject Interests: Bus, Mgt

G UNITED STATES FOREST SERVICE, Rocky Mountain Research Station Library, 324 25th St, 84401. SAN 316-8964. Tel: 801-625-5444. FAX: 801-625-5129. E-Mail: rmas_library@fs.fed.us. *Dir*, Carol A Ayer; Tel: 801-625-5445, E-Mail: cayer@fs.fed.us; *Info Specialist*, Irene E Voit; Tel: 801-625-5446, E-Mail: ivoit@fs.fed.us; Staff 3 (MLS 3)
Founded 1966

Oct 1998-Sep 1999 Income $339,000. Mats Exp $22,000, Books $6,000, Per/Ser (Incl. Access Fees) $16,000. Sal $232,100 (Prof $159,400)
Library Holdings: Bk Vols 35,000; Per Subs 400
Subject Interests: Agriculture, Entomol, Forestry, Hydrol, Meteorol, Range mgt, Recreation, Silviculture, Watershed, Wildlife
Automation Activity & Vendor Info: (Cataloging) SIRSI; (Circulation) SIRSI; (OPAC) SIRSI
Database Vendor: Dialog, OCLC - First Search
Publications: FSLN Monthly Alert
Partic in BCR; Fed Libr & Info Network; Forest Service Library Network; OCLC Online Computer Library Center, Inc

UTAH SCHOOL FOR THE DEAF & BLIND, Educational Center,* 742 Harrison Blvd, 84404. SAN 323-7281. Tel: 801-629-4700. FAX: 801-629-4896. *Dir*, Lorrie Quigley; *Librn*, Mary Jo White
Library Holdings: Bk Vols 37,000; Bk Titles 22,000; Per Subs 15

WEBER COUNTY LIBRARY, 2464 Jefferson Ave, 84401-2464. SAN 362-4722. Tel: 801-337-2617. TDD: 801-627-6921. FAX: 801-337-2615. Web Site: www.weberpl.lib.ut.us. *Dir*, Lynnda Wangsgard; *Asst Dir*, Jeanne Bruckner; *Asst Dir, Coll Develop*, Karen Burton; *ILL*, Jane Saunders; *Circ*, Jeanne Ferrero
Founded 1903. Pop 190,716; Circ 994,016
Jan 1999-Dec 1999 Income (Main Library and Branch Library) $4,392,612, State $51,992, City $23,500, Federal $38,000, County $4,141,912, Locally Generated Income $137,200. Mats Exp $535,326, Books $431,326, Per/Ser (Incl. Access Fees) $54,200, Presv $10,400, Micro $6,800, Electronic Ref Mat (Incl. Access Fees) $32,600. Sal $2,489,520
Library Holdings: Bk Vols 382,084; Bk Titles 257,977; Per Subs 683
Special Collections: Utah & Western History (Ava J Cooper Spec Coll)
Automation Activity & Vendor Info: (Acquisitions) GEAC; (Circulation) GEAC; (OPAC) GEAC
Database Vendor: OCLC - First Search
Publications: Friends of the Library; The Rough Draft (Newsletter)
Partic in Bibliographical Center For Research, Rocky Mountain Region, Inc
Special Services for the Deaf - Books on deafness & sign language; TDD; TTY machine
Special Services for the Blind - Radio reading service
Adult literacy holdings - 3230 bks; Dial-A-Story 801-621-8181
Friends of the Library Group
Branches: 4
NORTH BRANCH, 475 E 2600 N, North Ogden, 84414. SAN 362-4765. Tel: 801-782-8800. FAX: 801-782-8801. Web Site: www.weberpl.lib.ut.us. *Librn*, Rebecca Loney; *Librn*, Randy Mueller; Staff 1 (MLS 1)
Circ 208,445
Library Holdings: Bk Vols 41,234; Bk Titles 37,328
Automation Activity & Vendor Info: (Acquisitions) GEAC; (Circulation) GEAC; (OPAC) GEAC
Database Vendor: OCLC - First Search
Friends of the Library Group
OGDEN VALLEY, 131 S 7400 East, Huntsville, 84317-9309. SAN 377-0281. Tel: 801-745-2220. FAX: 801-745-2221. Web Site: www.weberpl.lib.ut.us. *Librn*, Karen Burton; Staff 2 (MLS 2)
Circ 82,496
Library Holdings: Bk Vols 44,563; Bk Titles 40,165
Automation Activity & Vendor Info: (Acquisitions) GEAC; (Circulation) GEAC
Database Vendor: OCLC - First Search
Friends of the Library Group
SOUTHWEST BRANCH, 1950 W 4800 South, Roy, 84067-2696. SAN 362-4781. Tel: 801-773-2556. FAX: 801-773-2557. Web Site: www.weberpl.lib.ut.us. *Librn*, Ann Booth; Staff 2 (MLS 2)
Circ 189,038
Library Holdings: Bk Vols 43,378; Bk Titles 39,238
Automation Activity & Vendor Info: (Acquisitions) GEAC; (Circulation) GEAC; (OPAC) GEAC
Database Vendor: OCLC - First Search
Friends of the Library Group
WEBER COUNTY LAW LIBRARY, 2380 Washington Blvd Ste 115, 84401. SAN 323-5467. Tel: 801-337-8466. FAX: 801-337-8522. Web Site: www.weberpl.lib.ut.us. *Librn*, Nadia Lashmanova; Staff 4 (MLS 1, Non-MLS 3)
Pop 18,583
Library Holdings: Bk Vols 14,067; Bk Titles 12,713; Per Subs 17
Automation Activity & Vendor Info: (Acquisitions) GEAC; (Circulation) GEAC; (OPAC) GEAC
Database Vendor: OCLC - First Search
Partic in OCLC Online Computer Library Center, Inc
Friends of the Library Group

WEBER STATE UNIVERSITY, Stewart Library, 2901 University Circle, 84408-2901. SAN 316-8972. Tel: 801-626-6403. Interlibrary Loan Service Tel: 801-626-6384. Circulation Tel: 801-626-6545. Reference Tel: 801-626-6415. Toll Free Tel: 877-306-3140. FAX: 801-626-7045. Web Site: www.weber.edu/library/htmls/library/html. *Dean of Libr*, Joan Hubbard; E-Mail: jhubbard@weber.edu; *Syst Coordr*, John Lamborn; Tel: 801-626-6188, E-Mail: jlamborn@weber.edu; *Archivist, Spec Coll*, John Sillito; Tel: 801-626-6416, E-Mail: jsillito@weber.edu; *Govt Doc, Ref*, Kathy Payne; *Head, Cat*, Stella Chang; Tel: 801-626-6869, E-Mail: schang@weber.edu; *ILL*, Deborah Stephenson; E-Mail: dsteph2@weber.edu; *Instrul Serv*, Carol Hansen; Tel: 801-626-6071, E-Mail: chansen@weber.edu; *Head, Circ*, Sandi Andrews; Tel: 801-626-6546, E-Mail: sandrews@weber.edu. Subject Specialists: *Art*, Joan Hubbard; *Behav sci*, Wade Kotter; *Business*, Shaun Spiegel; *Economics*, Shaun Spiegel; *Education*, Evan Christensen; *Humanities*, Joan Hubbard; *Philosophy*, John Sillito; *Political science*, John Sillito; *Science/technology*, Jill Newby; *Social sciences*, Wade Kotter; Staff 46 (MLS 14, Non-MLS 32)
Founded 1924. Enrl 11,519; Fac 407; Highest Degree: Master
Jul 2000-Jun 2001 Income $3,330,800, Locally Generated Income $6,626, Parent Institution $3,020,332, Other $303,842. Mats Exp $1,406,994, Books $667,070, Per/Ser (Incl. Access Fees) $572,153, Presv $53,890, Micro $22,085, Electronic Ref Mat (Incl. Access Fees) $91,159. Sal $1,379,952 (Prof $669,901)
Library Holdings: Bk Vols 458,115; Per Subs 2,278
Special Collections: Frank Vecroft Coll (Oriental Artifacts); Hyrum & Ruby Wheelwright Coll (Mormon Literature); James A Howell Coll (Literature); Jeanette McKay Morrell Coll (Porcelain); Paul Bransom Coll (Art)
Automation Activity & Vendor Info: (Acquisitions) epixtech, inc.; (Cataloging) epixtech, inc.; (Circulation) epixtech, inc.
Database Vendor: CARL, Ebsco - EbscoHost, epixtech, inc., Lexis-Nexis, OCLC - First Search, OVID Technologies, ProQuest, Silverplatter Information Inc., Wilson - Wilson Web
Publications: Friends Newsletter
Partic in BCR; Dialog Corporation; OCLC Online Computer Library Center, Inc; Utah Academic Library Consortium
Special Services for the Deaf - TTY machine
Special Services for the Blind - Printed text enlargers
Open Mon-Thurs 7am-midnight, Fri 7am-8pm, Sat 9-8 & Sun 1-11
Friends of the Library Group

OREM

P OREM PUBLIC LIBRARY, 58 N State St, 84057-5596. SAN 316-8980. Tel: 801-229-7050. Interlibrary Loan Service Tel: 801-229-7175. Circulation Tel: 801-229-7050. Reference Tel: 801-229-7175. TDD: 801-229-7104. FAX: 801-229-7130. *Coll Develop, Dir*, Louise Wallace; *Cat*, Dale Burns; *Cat*, Dennis Clark; *Cat*, Sue Phelps; *Cat*, Evelyn Schmidt; *Ref*, Janet Low; *Media Spec*, David Koralewski; *Ad Servs*, Lanell Reeder; *Ch Servs*, Patricia Castelli; Staff 44 (MLS 8, Non-MLS 36)
Founded 1940. Pop 78,937; Circ 1,279,240 Sal $1,329,179
Library Holdings: Bk Vols 235,000; Per Subs 253
Subject Interests: Flm classics, Relig studies
Automation Activity & Vendor Info: (Acquisitions) epixtech, inc.; (Cataloging) epixtech, inc.; (Circulation) epixtech, inc.
Open Mon-Fri 9:30-9, Sat 9:30-6
Friends of the Library Group

C UTAH VALLEY STATE COLLEGE LIBRARY, 800 W University Pkwy, 84058-5999. Tel: 801-222-8751. Circulation Tel: 801-222-8058. Reference Tel: 801-222-8840. FAX: 801-764-7065. Web Site: www.uvsc.edu/library. *Dir Libr Serv*, Michael J Freeman; E-Mail: freemami@uvsc.edu; *Asst Dir*, Kim Rollins; Tel: 801-222-8752, E-Mail: rollinki@uvsc.edu; *Syst Coordr*, Tim Rowley; Tel: 801-222-8107, E-Mail: rowleyti@uvsc.edu; *Bibliog Instr*, Rama Chamberlin; Tel: 801-222-8423, E-Mail: chambera@uvsc.edu; *Media Spec*, Lori Stevens; Tel: 801-764-7421, Fax: 801-764-7064, E-Mail: stevenlo@uvsc.edu; *Ref Serv Ad*, Lesli Baker; Tel: 801-222-8286, E-Mail: bakerle@uvsc.edu; *Tech Servs*, Keith Rowley; Tel: 801-222-8780, E-Mail: rowleyke@uvsc.edu; *Ser*, Catherine McIntyre; Tel: 801-222-8821, E-Mail: mcintyca@uvsc.edu. Subject Specialists: *Arts*, Keith Rowley; *Behav sci*, Rama Chamberlin; *Business*, Lesli Baker; *Communication*, Kim Rollins; *Computer science*, Tim Rowley; *Criminal justice*, Lori Stevens; *Economic*, Lesli Baker; *Fire science*, Kim Rollins; *Health*, Kim Rollins; *History*, Catherine McIntyre; *Language*, Keith Rowley; *Literature*, Lori Stevens; *Mathematics*, Michael J Freeman; *Media*, Lori Stevens; *Music*, Keith Rowley; *Political science*, Catherine McIntyre; *Religion*, Keith Rowley; *Science*, Michael J Freeman; *Theater*, Lori Stevens; Staff 22 (MLS 8, Non-MLS 14)
Founded 1978. Pop 20,946; Circ 110,000; Enrl 21,000; Fac 238; Highest Degree: Bachelor
Jul 1999-Jun 2000 Income $1,072,114, State $1,037,114, Parent Institution $35,000. Mats Exp $260,715, Books $173,439, Per/Ser (Incl. Access Fees) $62,421, Presv $21,155, AV Equip $3,700. Sal $560,096 (Prof $337,341)
Library Holdings: Bk Vols 133,805; Bk Titles 99,341; Per Subs 3,804
Subject Interests: Bus, Computer science, Education, Literature, Trades
Special Collections: LDS Religion Coll
Automation Activity & Vendor Info: (Acquisitions) epixtech, inc.; (Cataloging) epixtech, inc.; (Circulation) epixtech, inc.; (Course Reserve) epixtech, inc.; (OPAC) epixtech, inc.; (Serials) epixtech, inc.
Database Vendor: Ebsco - EbscoHost, ProQuest, Silverplatter Information Inc., Wilson - Wilson Web
Function: Research library
Partic in Utah Academic Library Consortium

PANGUITCH

P PANGUITCH CITY-GARFIELD COUNTY LIBRARY, PO Box 75, 84759-0075. SAN 377-2780. Tel: 435-676-2431. FAX: 435-676-2758. *Librn*, Donna Osborne
Library Holdings: Bk Vols 46,000
Partic in Utah State Libr Asn

PARK CITY

P PARK CITY LIBRARY, 1255 Park Ave, PO Box 668, 84060-0668. SAN 322-6794. Tel: 435-615-5600. FAX: 435-615-4903. *Dir*, Carol E Simmons; Tel: 435-615-5605, E-Mail: csimmons@parkcity2002.com; *Online Servs*, Barbara Spruill; Tel: 435-615-5602, E-Mail: spruill@parkcity2002.com; Staff 13 (MLS 4, Non-MLS 9)
Founded 1917. Pop 7,000; Circ 92,000
Jul 1998-Jun 1999 Income $493,616, State $4,082, City $465,334, Federal $5,200, Locally Generated Income $19,000. Mats Exp $61,500, Books $39,500, Per/Ser (Incl. Access Fees) $6,000, Micro $1,000, Electronic Ref Mat (Incl. Access Fees) $15,000. Sal $196,099 (Prof $110,724)
Library Holdings: Bk Vols 51,000; Bk Titles 45,000; Per Subs 160
Subject Interests: Local history
Special Collections: Skiing and Park City History
Database Vendor: IAC - Info Trac, OCLC - First Search
Function: ILL available
Partic in Dialog Corporation; OCLC Online Computer Library Center, Inc
Open Mon-Thurs 10-9, Fri & Sat 10-6 & Sun 1-5
Friends of the Library Group

PAROWAN

P PAROWAN PUBLIC LIBRARY,* 16 S Main St, PO Box 427, 84761-0427. SAN 316-8999. Tel: 435-477-3491. FAX: 435-477-8671. E-Mail: parowlib@main.state.lib.ut.us. *Librn*, Kristen Robinson
Founded 1915. Pop 2,200; Circ 57,208
Library Holdings: Bk Titles 30,000; Per Subs 55
Subject Interests: Hist of Parowan

PAYSON

P PAYSON CITY LIBRARY,* 439 W Utah Ave, 84651-2095. SAN 316-9006. Tel: 801-465-5220. FAX: 801-465-5208. *Librn*, Linda Collard; *Asst Librn*, Sherry Gay
Founded 1878. Pop 9,776; Circ 41,413
Library Holdings: Bk Vols 26,000
Special Collections: US Constitution Materials Coll
Open Mon-Thurs 9-9, Fri & Sat 11-6
Friends of the Library Group

PLEASANT GROVE

P PLEASANT GROVE PUBLIC LIBRARY,* 30 E Center St, 84062-4247. SAN 316-9014. Tel: 801-785-3950. FAX: 801-785-9734. Web Site: www.plgrove.org/library.html. *Librn*, April H Hammer; E-Mail: aharmer@inter.state.lib.ut.us
Pop 21,000; Circ 210,000
Jul 1997-Jun 1998 Income $251,000, State $8,000, Federal $10,000. Mats Exp $28,700, Books $27,000, Per/Ser (Incl. Access Fees) $1,700. Sal $135,140 (Prof $48,300)
Library Holdings: Bk Vols 49,000
Subject Interests: Local history
Open Mon-Thurs 10-9, Sat & Sun 10-6
Friends of the Library Group

PRICE

J COLLEGE OF EASTERN UTAH LIBRARY, 451 E & 400 N, 84501. SAN 316-9030. Tel: 435-613-5209. Circulation Tel: 435-613-5278. Reference Tel: 435-613-5616. FAX: 435-613-5863. Web Site: www.ceu.edu/campus/lib.htm, www.library.ceu.edu. *Dir*, Barbara Steffee; Tel: 935-613-5283, E-Mail: bsteffee@ceu.edu; *Acq*, Aimee Lauritsen; Tel: 435-613-5608, E-Mail: alauritsen@ceu.edu; *Cat, ILL*, Sherill Shaw; Tel: 435-613-5208, E-Mail: ssjaw@ceu.edu; *Media Spec*, Cathrin Alaei; Tel: 435-613-5328, E-Mail: calaei@ceu.edu; *Ref*, Debra Petersen; E-Mail: dpetersen@ceu.edu; Staff 6 (MLS 2, Non-MLS 4)
Founded 1938. Enrl 2,029; Fac 70; Highest Degree: Associate
Jul 2000-Jun 2001 Income $380,838, State $333,838, Federal $27,000, Locally Generated Income $20,000. Mats Exp $85,204, Books $61,928, Per/Ser (Incl. Access Fees) $10,463, Presv $9,468, AV Equip $2,845, Other Print Mats $500. Sal $170,974 (Prof $85,997)
Library Holdings: Bk Vols 47,500; Per Subs 170
Subject Interests: Local history, Utah hist
Automation Activity & Vendor Info: (Acquisitions) epixtech, inc.; (Cataloging) epixtech, inc.; (Circulation) epixtech, inc.; (Course Reserve) epixtech, inc.; (OPAC) epixtech, inc.; (Serials) epixtech, inc.
Partic in Utah Academic Library Consortium
Special Services for the Deaf - TTY machine
Special Services for the Blind - Kurzweil Reading Machine
Friends of the Library Group

P PRICE CITY LIBRARY,* 159 E Main St, 84501-3033. SAN 316-9049. 435-636-3188. FAX: 435-637-2905. Web Site: www.city1.price.lib.ut.us/library/. *Librn*, Norma Rae Procarione; *Asst Librn*, Diana Burdea
Founded 1914. Pop 8,809; Circ 44,762 Sal $172,900
Library Holdings: Bk Vols 47,645; Per Subs 59
Subject Interests: Heritage, Local history

PROVO

BRIGHAM YOUNG UNIVERSITY
C HAROLD B LEE LIBRARY, 2720 HBLL, 84602. (Mail add: 2060 Lee Library, 84602), SAN 362-4811. Tel: 801-378-2927. Circulation Tel: 8(378-6061. FAX: 801-378-6708. Web Site: www.library.byu.edu. *Dir*, Sterling J Albrecht; Tel: 801-378-2905, E-Mail: sterling_albrecht@byu.edu; *Dep Dir*, Randy Olsen; Tel: 801-378-2908, E-Mail: randy_olsen@byu.edu; *Asst Librn, Publ Servs*, H Juleke Butler; *ILL*, M Smith; *Cat*, Carla Kupitz; *Asst Librn, Spec Coll*, Scott Duvall; *Circ*, Ka Hansen; *Ser*, Dennis Bernards; *Acq*, Bill Slater; *Online Servs*, Roger Fl *Govt Doc*, Larry Benson; *Coll Develop*, Susan Fales. Subject Specialist *Asia*, Gail King; *Business and management*, Gordon Casper; *Education* Tom Wright; *Engineering*, William Baer; *European history*, Richard Hacken; *Geography*, Richard Soares; *Humanities*, Christiane Ramsey; *Latin America*, Mark Grover; *Maps*, Richard Soares; *Music*, David Day *Science/technology*, John Christensen; *Science/technology*, Richard Jens *Science/technology*, Lisa Baer; *Social sciences and issues*, Marvin Wiggins; *Social sciences and issues*, Brian Champion; Staff 159 (MLS Non-MLS 72)
Founded 1875. Enrl 28,400; Fac 1,330; Highest Degree: Doctorate
Sep 1997-Aug 1998 Mats Exp $4,670,790. Sal $6,712,542 (Prof $4,058,191)
Library Holdings: Bk Vols 2,500,849; Per Subs 16,029
Special Collections: Can; Children's; Herman Melville; Incunabula; Literature; Middle American Linguistics (William Gates Coll); Modern Fine Press; Mormon & Western Americana; Robert Burns; Victorian Literature; Walt Whitman; Welsh Languages & Literature; William Wordsworth
Automation Activity & Vendor Info: (Acquisitions) SIRSI; (Catalogin SIRSI; (Circulation) SIRSI; (OPAC) SIRSI; (Serials) SIRSI
Publications: Friends Keepsake Series; Friends of the Library Newslett
Mem of Asn of Research Libraries
Partic in Center For Research Libraries; RLIN; SDC Search Serv; Utah Academic Library Consortium
Friends of the Library Group

CL HOWARD W HUNTER LAW LIBRARY, 256 JRCB, 84602-8000. SAN 362-4846. Tel: 801-378-3593. Interlibrary Loan Service Tel: 801-378-5481. FAX: 801-378-3595. Web Site: www.law.byu/law_library/. *Dir*, Constance Lundberg; *Assoc Dir*, Gary Hill; *Ref*, Dennis Sears; *Ref*, Laur Urquiaga; *Ref*, Kristin Gerdy; *Ref*, Steve Averett; *Cat*, Curt E Conklin; *Ser*, Teresa Odam; *Circ*, David Armond; *Acq*, Bonnie Geldmacher; *Govt Doc*, LeGrande Fletcher; *Coll Develop*, Lovisa Lyman; Staff 10 (MLS 1
Founded 1972. Enrl 470; Fac 26; Highest Degree: Doctorate
1998-1999 Mats Exp $804,586
Library Holdings: Bk Titles 101,321; Per Subs 5,691
Subject Interests: Am Commonwealth law, Biblical law, Brit Commonwealth law, Constitutional law, Family law, Feminist legal issue Native Am law
Automation Activity & Vendor Info: (Acquisitions) NOTIS; (Catalogin NOTIS
Mem of Asn of Research Libraries
Partic in RLIN; Utah Academic Library Consortium; Westlaw

P PROVO CITY LIBRARY,* 425 W Center, 84601. SAN 316-9057. Tel: 80 852-6661. FAX: 801-852-6670. Web Site: www.provo.lib.ut.us. *Dir*, Gene Nelson; *Circ*, Staryl Kaze; *Tech Servs*, Lynne LeBare; *Ch Servs*, Carla Morris; *Media Spec*, Marlise Brough; *Ad Servs*, Dina Wyatt; Staff 9 (MLS 9)
Founded 1904. Pop 90,000; Circ 770,723 Sal $880,000 (Prof $378,000)
Library Holdings: Bk Titles 145,000; Per Subs 481
Subject Interests: LDS relig, Utah, Utah County hist
Automation Activity & Vendor Info: (Circulation) epixtech, inc.
Publications: Calendar (monthly)
Partic in Provo City Sch Libr Network
Friends of the Library Group

J PROVO COLLEGE LIBRARY, 1450 W 820 North, 84601. SAN 378-2174 Tel: 801-375-1861, Ext 3015. FAX: 801-375-9728. Web Site: www.provocollege.org. *Coordr*, Tiffani Rytting; E-Mail: tiffanir@provocollege.org; Staff 3 (MLS 1, Non-MLS 2)
Founded 1996. Enrl 480
Jul 1998-Jun 1999 Income Parent Institution $36,943. Mats Exp $8,511, Books $3,900, Per/Ser (Incl. Access Fees) $3,611, AV Equip $1,000. Sal

$28,432 (Prof $18,432)
Library Holdings: Bk Vols 1,447; Bk Titles 1,575; Per Subs 41
Subject Interests: Accounting, Bus mgt, Computer science, Dental assisting, Medical assistant, Physical therapy

UTAH STATE HOSPITAL, Patients Library,* 1300 E Center St, PO Box 270, 84606-0270. SAN 316-9065. Tel: 801-344-4400. FAX: 801-344-4225. *Dir*, Shawna Peterson; *Librn*, Patti Ratliff
Library Holdings: Bk Vols 4,000; Per Subs 28

CHFIELD

RICHFIELD PUBLIC LIBRARY, 83 E Center St, 84701. SAN 316-9081. Tel: 435-896-5169. FAX: 435-896-6512. *Librn*, Linda Fields; E-Mail: lfields@inter.state.lib.ut.us; *Ch Servs*, Leslee Hurd
Founded 1915. Pop 7,000; Circ 52,000
2000-2001 Income $112,979, State $6,779, City $100,000, Federal $6,200. Mats Exp $17,250, Books $14,000, Per/Ser (Incl. Access Fees) $1,250, Other Print Mats $2,000. Sal $44,000 (Prof $22,400)
Library Holdings: Bk Vols 24,744; Per Subs 80
Automation Activity & Vendor Info: (Acquisitions) Sagebrush Corporation; (Cataloging) Sagebrush Corporation; (Circulation) Sagebrush Corporation
Friends of the Library Group

CHMOND

RICHMOND PUBLIC LIBRARY,* 6 W Main, PO Box 202, 84333-0202. SAN 316-909X. Tel: 435-258-5525. FAX: 435-258-2092. *Librn*, Chris Nickle; E-Mail: cnickle@mail.state.lib.ut.us
Pop 2,000; Circ 6,934 Sal $23,063
Library Holdings: Bk Vols 16,000; Per Subs 10
Open Mon 3-7, Tues-Fri 2-6 & Sat 9-1

OSEVELT

DUCHESNE COUNTY LIBRARY, 70 W Lagoon 44-4, 84066-2841. SAN 316-9103. Tel: 435-722-4441. FAX: 435-722-3386. E-Mail: rooslib@inter.state.lib.ut.us. *Librn*, Lorie Evans; *Asst Librn*, Charlene Labrum
Circ 52,209
Library Holdings: Bk Vols 52,000; Per Subs 45

INT GEORGE

BUREAU OF LAND MANAGEMENT, ARIZONA STRIP, District Office Library,* 345 E Riverside Dr, 84790. SAN 316-9111. Tel: 435-688-3200. FAX: 435-688-3252, 435-688-3258, 435-688-3358. *Librn*, Linda Barwick
Founded 1966
Library Holdings: Bk Titles 500; Per Subs 19
Subject Interests: Conservation, Grazing, Land, Range, Recreation, Wildlife management
Open Mon-Fri 7:45-4:15

DIXIE STATE COLLEGE OF UTAH, (Formerly Dixie College), Val A Browning Library, 225 S 700 East, 84770. SAN 316-912X. Tel: 435-652-7714. FAX: 435-673-1169. E-Mail: washburn@dixie.edu. Web Site: www.library.dixie.edu/library/. *Dir*, Allyson Washburn; Tel: 435-652-7711; *Syst Coordr*, Rob Snyder; Tel: 435-652-7719, E-Mail: snyder@dixie.edu; *Cat*, David Zielke; Tel: 435-652-7716, E-Mail: zielke_d@dixie.edu; *ILL*, Joyce Beazer; Tel: 435-652-7712, E-Mail: beazer_j@dixie.edu; *Acq*, Deaun Kimber; Tel: 435-652-7710, E-Mail: kimber@dixie.edu; *Acq*, Carole Williams; Tel: 435-652-7715, E-Mail: willc@dixie.edu; *Circ*, Ellen Bonadurer; Tel: 435-652-7713, E-Mail: bonadure@dixie.edu; *Spec Coll*, Percival Bonnie; Tel: 435-652-7718, E-Mail: bpercival@dixie.edu; *Ser*, Shannon Broad; Tel: 435-652-2720, E-Mail: broad@dixie.edu. Subject Specialists: *Allied health*, Allyson Washburn; *Composition*, Percival Bonnie; *Edu*, Allyson Washburn; *Fine arts*, Allyson Washburn; *Humanities*, Percival Bonnie; *Social sciences*, Percival Bonnie; Staff 9 (MLS 3, Non-MLS 6)
Founded 1912. Pop 6,000; Circ 52,902; Enrl 3,656; Highest Degree: Associate
Jul 1998-Jun 1999 Income $708,431. Mats Exp $216,911, Books $87,158, Per/Ser (Incl. Access Fees) $13,071, Presv $2,467, Micro $1,058, Manuscripts & Archives $578, Electronic Ref Mat (Incl. Access Fees) $3,950. Sal $144,439 (Prof $128,567)
Library Holdings: Bk Vols 74,230; Per Subs 343
Subject Interests: Behav sci, Humanities, Soc sci
Special Collections: Mormon & Southwest History
Automation Activity & Vendor Info: (Cataloging) epixtech, inc.; (Circulation) epixtech, inc.; (Course Reserve) epixtech, inc.; (OPAC) epixtech, inc.; (Serials) epixtech, inc.
Database Vendor: Lexis-Nexis, OCLC - First Search, ProQuest, Silverplatter Information Inc., Wilson - Wilson Web
Partic in Utah Academic Library Consortium; Western Interstate Consortium on Higher Educ

P WASHINGTON COUNTY LIBRARY,* 50 S Main, 84770-3490. SAN 316-9138. Tel: 435-634-5737. FAX: 435-634-5798. Web Site: www.washco.lib.ut.us. *Dir*, Larry L Hortin; *Ch Servs*, Dorothy Larkin; *Cat*, Sandra Sehonlaw; *Acq, Coll Develop, Librn*, Brenda Brown; *Ref*, Steve Palmer; Staff 6 (MLS 6)
Founded 1912. Pop 80,000; Circ 571,841
1997-1998 Income $1,353,000, State $60,000, County $1,190,000, Locally Generated Income $103,000. Mats Exp $156,300, Books $126,800, Per/Ser (Incl. Access Fees) $15,000, Micro $14,500. Sal $657,394 (Prof $243,984)
Library Holdings: Bk Vols 96,355; Per Subs 250
Special Collections: Local Histories & Diaries (WPA Pioneer Diary Coll), bks & pamphlets
Automation Activity & Vendor Info: (Circulation) epixtech, inc.
Publications: Newsletter
Friends of the Library Group
Branches: 3
ENTERPRISE BRANCH, 393 S 200 E, PO Box 160, Enterprise, 84725. SAN 371-3725. Tel: 435-878-2574. FAX: 435-878-2574. Web Site: www.washco.lib.ut.us. *Librn*, Susan Staheli
Library Holdings: Bk Vols 9,255
HURRICANE VALLEY BRANCH, 36 S 300 West, Hurricane, 84737-2100. SAN 325-4011. Tel: 435-635-4621. FAX: 435-635-3845. Web Site: www.washco.lib.ut.us. *Librn*, Lloyd Reid
Library Holdings: Bk Vols 30,073
SPRINGDALE BRANCH, 898 Zion Park Blvd, Springdale, 84767. SAN 371-3733. Tel: 435-772-3279. FAX: 435-778-3124. Web Site: www.washco.lib.ut.us. *Librn*, Mavis Madsen
Library Holdings: Bk Vols 10,119
Friends of the Library Group

SALINA

P SALINA PUBLIC LIBRARY, 90 W Main St, 84654. SAN 316-9146. Tel: 435-529-7753. FAX: 435-529-1235. *Librn*, Becky Lopshire; E-Mail: blopshir@inter.state.lib.ut.us
Pop 2,000; Circ 19,861
Library Holdings: Bk Vols 11,500; Bk Titles 11,250; Per Subs 30

SALT LAKE CITY

S AMERICAN EXPRESS COMPANY, SLC Info System Library,* 4315 S 2700 West, 84184. SAN 370-9760. Tel: 801-965-5559. FAX: 801-965-5535. *Librn*, Nancy Hills
Library Holdings: Bk Vols 500; Per Subs 120

CHURCH OF JESUS CHRIST OF LATTER-DAY SAINTS
R CHURCH HISTORY LIBRARY & ARCHIVES, 50 E North Temple, 84150-3800. SAN 362-4935. Tel: 801-240-2745, 801-240-3603. FAX: 801-240-1845. *Dir*, Christine Cox; *Archivist*, Steven Sorensen; Tel: 801-240-2273; *Coll Develop*, Vivian Wellman
Founded 1830
Library Holdings: Bk Vols 190,000; Per Subs 799
Subject Interests: Mormon hist, Mormon theol, Utah hist
Special Collections: Church of Jesus Christ of Latter-day Saints Coll, publications, manuscripts & records
Automation Activity & Vendor Info: (OPAC) Innovative Interfaces Inc.; (Serials) Innovative Interfaces Inc.
Restriction: Non-circulating to the public
SR STAKE FAMILY HISTORY CENTER, 1530 W Camino Real, Boca Raton, 33486. (Mail add: 1199 SW Ninth Ave, Boca Raton, 33486), SAN 375-278X. Tel: 561-395-6644. FAX: 561-395-8957. *Dir*, Donald W Jennings, Jr; E-Mail: jenningsdw@mindspring.com
Founded 1979
Library Holdings: Bk Vols 800; Per Subs 10
Subject Interests: Genealogy
Special Collections: New York Death Indexes
Open Mon & Wed 10-6, Tues 4-9
S FAMILY HISTORY LIBRARY, 35 N West Temple St, 84150-3400. SAN 362-496X. Tel: 801-240-2331. Toll Free Tel: 800-453-3860. TDD: 801-240-2616. FAX: 801-240-5551. E-Mail: fhl@ldschurch.org. Web Site: www.familysearch.org. *Dir*, David E Rencher; *Pub Relations*, Elaine Hasleton; Staff 200 (MLS 110, Non-MLS 90)
Founded 1894
Library Holdings: Bk Vols 300,000; Per Subs 4,500
Subject Interests: Family hist, Genealogy, Local history
Publications: Country & State Research Outlines; Family History Centers Address List; Family History Materials List; International Genealogical Index; International Genealogical Index (micro); Patron Aids
Special Services for the Deaf - Staff with knowledge of sign language
Provides circulation & training support to over 3400 family history centers in 65 countries

GM DEPARTMENT OF VETERANS AFFAIRS MEDICAL CENTER, Medical Library,* 500 Foothill Dr, 84148. SAN 362-577X. Tel: 801-584-1209. FAX: 801-584-1251. *Chief Librn*, Carl Worstell
Oct 1997-Sep 1998 Income $192,500. Mats Exp $146,732, Books $22,610, Per/Ser (Incl. Access Fees) $110,858, Presv $5,842

Library Holdings: Bk Vols 4,650; Per Subs 352
Subject Interests: Allied health, Medicine, Psychiatry, Related fields, Surgery
Partic in BRS; Dialog Corporation; Medline; Midcontinental Regional Med Libr Network; Vets Admin Libr Network

S DESERET NEWS PUBLISHING CO, Desert News Library, 30 E 100 South, 84111-1930. (Mail add: PO Box 1257, 84110-1257), SAN 316-9162. Tel: 801-237-2155. FAX: 801-237-2552. Web Site: www.desnews.com. *Librn*, Colleen Randall; E-Mail: colleen@desnews.com
Founded 1955
Library Holdings: Bk Titles 2,500
Open Mon-Fri 8-5

L DISTRICT ATTORNEY LAW LIBRARY,* 231 E 400 South, Ste 100, 84111. SAN 316-9243. Tel: 801-531-4152. FAX: 801-531-4176. *Librn*, Jeffrey A Lund
Library Holdings: Bk Vols 13,500
Subject Interests: Criminal law
Special Collections: Reporters & Digests

L FABIAN & CLENDENIN, Law Library,* 215 S State St, 12th flr, PO Box 510210, 84151. SAN 372-1906. Tel: 801-531-8900. FAX: 801-531-1716. *Librn*, Allyssen Rice Watkins; E-Mail: awatkins@fabclen.com
Library Holdings: Bk Vols 40,000; Per Subs 100
Open Mon-Fri 8-6

S INTERMEDIAIRE DES CASANOVISTES, The Seingalt Society Library, 555 13th Ave, 84103. SAN 372-5456. Tel: 801-532-2204. FAX: 801-539-0880. *Librn*, Tom Vitelli
Founded 1978
Library Holdings: Bk Vols 1,300; Bk Titles 1,000
Special Collections: Giacomo Casanova de Seingalt, bks, flm, microflm, microfiche, per
Restriction: By appointment only

S INTERNATIONAL SOCIETY DAUGHTERS OF UTAH PIONEERS, Museum & Library, 300 N Main St, 84103-1699. SAN 375-7811. Tel: 801-538-1050. FAX: 801-538-1119. *Librn*, Carol Dee Buchmiller
Library Holdings: Bk Titles 1,800
Restriction: Open to public for reference only

J LDS BUSINESS COLLEGE LIBRARY, 411 E South Temple St, 84111. SAN 316-9200. Tel: 801-524-8150. FAX: 801-524-1900. Web Site: www.ldsbc.edu. *Dir*, Karen Hales; E-Mail: khales@ldsbc.edu
Founded 1975. Enrl 800; Fac 18; Highest Degree: Associate
Library Holdings: Bk Vols 7,500; Per Subs 100
Subject Interests: Accounting, Bus, Computer, Computer tech, Econ, Interior design, Medical assistant, Mgt, Relig studies, Secretarial
Automation Activity & Vendor Info: (Cataloging) SIRSI; (Circulation) SIRSI; (OPAC) SIRSI
Database Vendor: ProQuest
Restriction: In-house use for visitors

M LDS HOSPITAL, Medical Library, Eighth Ave & C St, 84143. SAN 316-9219. Tel: 801-408-1054. FAX: 801-408-5287. *Dir*, Erica Lake; Staff 2 (MLS 1, Non-MLS 1)
Founded 1945
Library Holdings: Bk Vols 2,000; Per Subs 350
Subject Interests: Medicine
Database Vendor: OVID Technologies
Partic in National Network of Libraries of Medicine - Southeastern Atlantic Region; Utah Health Sciences Library Consortium
Open Mon-Fri 8:15-4:30

L LEBOEUF, LAMB, GREENE & MACRAE, Law Library,* 1000 Kearns Bldg, 136 S Main St, 84101. SAN 372-185X. Tel: 801-320-6700. FAX: 801-359-8256. *Librn*, Miki Thomas; E-Mail: mzthomas@llgm.com
Library Holdings: Bk Vols 10,000; Per Subs 30

S LORAL GOVERNMENT SYSTEMS LIBRARY,* 640 N 2200 West, MSF1J04, PO Box 16850, 84116-0850. SAN 329-9805. Tel: 801-594-2046. FAX: 801-594-2127. *Librn*, Susie Pair; E-Mail: susie.pair@L-3com.com
Library Holdings: Bk Vols 3,000; Per Subs 250

R NATIONAL SOCIETY OF SONS OF UTAH PIONEERS, Sons of Utah Pioneers Library, 3301 E 2920 S, 84109. SAN 323-7176. Tel: 801-484-4441. Toll Free Tel: 888-827-2746. FAX: 801-484-2067. E-Mail: info@sonsofutahpioneers. *Dir*, Florence Youngberg
Founded 1981
1998-1999 Mats Exp $1,200
Library Holdings: Bk Titles 2,075

M PRIMARY CHILDREN'S MEDICAL CENTER LIBRARY, 100 N Medical Dr, 84113. SAN 323-6617. Tel: 801-588-2430. FAX: 801-588-2435. E-Mail: pclwilso@ihc.com. *Librn*, Lynn Wilson; *ILL*, Dawn Carroll; Staff 2 (MLS 1, Non-MLS 1)
Library Holdings: Bk Titles 1,500; Per Subs 220
Subject Interests: Pediatrics
Partic in Utah Health Sciences Library Consortium

S QUESTAR CORP, Information Resource Library,* 180 E 100 South, PC Box 45433, 84145. SAN 370-601X. Tel: 801-324-5705. FAX: 801-324-5 *In Charge*, Marty Weed; E-Mail: martyw@qstr.com; Staff 1 (MLS 1)
Founded 1980
Library Holdings: Bk Titles 200; Per Subs 300
Subject Interests: Bus, Computers, Energy, Finance
Publications: Library catalog; New in the Library

L RAY, QUINNEY & NEBEKER, Law Library,* 79 S Main St, Ste 500, 84111. (Mail add: PO Box 45385, 84145-0385), SAN 372-1817. Tel: 801 532-1500. FAX: 801-532-7543. *Acq, Librn*, Gwendolyn Mulks; *Asst Libr* Justin McFadden
Library Holdings: Bk Vols 30,000
Open Mon-Fri 8-6

M SAINT MARK'S HOSPITAL, Library & Media Services, 1200 E 3900 South, 84124. SAN 326-2367. Tel: 801-268-7004. FAX: 801-270-3417. *Librn*, Jane Errion; E-Mail: jerrion@ut.columbia.net; Staff 1 (MLS 1)
Library Holdings: Bk Titles 600; Per Subs 75
Partic in BRS; Docline

P SALT LAKE CITY PUBLIC LIBRARY, 209 E 500 South, 84111-3280. SAN 362-4994. Tel: 801-524-8200. TDD: 801-364-4669. FAX: 801-524-8272. Web Site: www.slcpl.lib.ut.us. *Dir*, Nancy Tessman; Tel: 801-524-8250, E-Mail: ntessman@mail.slcpl.lib.ut.us; *Asst Dir*, Chip Davis; Tel: 8 524-8231; *ILL*, Jean Ann McMurrin; Tel: 801-524-8203, Fax: 801-524-82 E-Mail: jmcmurri@mail.slcpl.lib.ut.us; *Ch Servs, YA Servs*, Lisa Myron; T 801-524-8212, E-Mail: lmyron@mail.slcpl.lib.ut.us; *Circ*, Karen Johnson; Tel: 801-524-8266, Fax: 801-524-8210, E-Mail: kjohnson@mail.slcpl.lib.ut.us; *Commun Relations*, Dana Tumpowsky; Tel: 801-524-8234, E-Mail: dtumpows@mail.slcpl.lib.ut.us; *Tech Servs*, Hikmet Loe; Te 801-524-8235, E-Mail: hloe@mail.slcpl.lib.ut.us; Staff 138 (MLS 21, Non MLS 117)
Founded 1898. Pop 174,348; Circ 2,304,224
Jul 1999-Jun 2000 Income (Main Library and Branch Library) $10,046,02 State $34,627, City $9,511,396, Federal $30,000, Locally Generated Incor $420,000, Other $50,000. Mats Exp $2,293,920, Books $1,720,920, Per/S (Incl. Access Fees) $116,500, Other Print Mats $5,500, Electronic Ref Ma (Incl. Access Fees) $80,000. Sal $6,283,303
Library Holdings: Bk Vols 704,123; Bk Titles 341,484; Per Subs 1,634
Special Collections: Foundations; Grants
Database Vendor: Innovative Interfaces INN - View
Publications: Images (Newsletter); quarterly schedule of events
Partic in OCLC Online Computer Library Center, Inc
Special Services for the Deaf - TDD
Friends of the Library Group
Branches: 5
ANDERSON-FOOTHILL, 1135 S 2100 East, SLC, 84108. SAN 322-576 Tel: 801-524-8278. FAX: 801-524-8296. Web Site: www.slcpl.lib.ut.us. *Librn*, Alveeda Lauscher
Library Holdings: Bk Vols 76,561
Friends of the Library Group
CHAPMAN, 577 S 900 West, SLC, 84104-1302. SAN 362-5028. Tel: 801 524-8285. FAX: 801-524-8283. Web Site: www.slcpl.lib.ut.us. *Librn*, Ranae Pierce
Library Holdings: Bk Vols 59,626
Friends of the Library Group
DAY-RIVERSIDE, 1575 W 1000 North, SLC, 84116. SAN 362-5052. Tel 801-524-8287. FAX: 801-524-8294. Web Site: www.slcpl.lib.ut.us. *Librn* Ben Ocon
Library Holdings: Bk Vols 59,190
Friends of the Library Group
SPRAGUE, 2131 S 1100 East, SLC, 84106-2806. SAN 362-5087. Tel: 80 524-8280. FAX: 801-524-8215. Web Site: www.slcpl.lib.ut.us. *Librn*, Kathleen Daly
Library Holdings: Bk Vols 65,311
Friends of the Library Group
SWEET, 455 F St, SLC, 84103. SAN 322-5771. Tel: 801-524-8276. FAX: 801-524-8292. Web Site: www.slcpl.lib.ut.us. *Librn*, Anne-Marie Despair
Library Holdings: Bk Vols 56,876
Friends of the Library Group

J SALT LAKE COMMUNITY COLLEGE LIBRARY,* 4600 S Redwood R PO Box 30808, 84130-0808. SAN 316-9324. Tel: 801-957-4195. FAX: 80 957-4414. Web Site: www.slcc.edu/library. *Dir*, Cathleen F Partridge; *Br Coordr*, Richard Daines; Tel: 801-957-3321, Fax: 801-957-3436, E-Mail: dainesri@slcc.edu; *Tech Coordr*, Truc Tran; Tel: 801-957-4607, E-Mail: trantr@slcc.edu; *Ref*, Keith Slade; *Publ Servs*, Gordon W Young; Tel: 801-957-4963, E-Mail: younggo@slcc.edu; *Tech Servs*, Eloise G Vanderhooft; Tel: 801-957-4588, E-Mail: vanderel@slcc.edu; *AV*, William Dabbs; Tel: 801-957-4606, E-Mail: dabbswi@slcc.edu; *Circ*, Moira Lawson; Tel: 801-957-4605, E-Mail: lawsonmo@slcc.edu; Staff 37 (MLS 12, Non-MLS 25)
Founded 1948. Circ 138,850; Enrl 12,731; Fac 314
Jul 1998-Jun 1999 Income $1,330,843, State $60,000, Parent Institution $1,270,843. Mats Exp $237,175, Books $132,672, Per/Ser (Incl. Access Fees) $52,046, Presv $715, AV Equip $51,080, Electronic Ref Mat (Incl. Access Fees) $662. Sal $885,974 (Prof $390,756)
Library Holdings: Bk Vols 77,649; Bk Titles 65,235; Per Subs 692

Subject Interests: Bus, Gen educ, Indust, Nursing, Sci-tech
Special Collections: Automotive Manuals; Contractors Exams
Automation Activity & Vendor Info: (Cataloging) epixtech, inc.; (Circulation) epixtech, inc.; (Course Reserve) epixtech, inc.; (OPAC) epixtech, inc.
Database Vendor: Ebsco - EbscoHost, epixtech, inc., IAC - Info Trac, IAC - SearchBank, OCLC - First Search, ProQuest, Silverplatter Information Inc., Wilson - Wilson Web
Partic in BCR; OCLC Online Computer Library Center, Inc; Utah Academic Library Consortium

SALT LAKE COUNTY LIBRARY SYSTEM, 2197 E Fort Union Blvd, 84121-3188. SAN 362-5117. Tel: 801-943-4636. FAX: 801-942-6323. Web Site: slco.lib.ut.us. *Actg Dir*, David Wilson; Tel: 801-944-7527, E-Mail: dwilson@slco.lib.ut.us; *Dep Dir*, Marsha LeClair-Marzolf; Tel: 801-944-7511, E-Mail: mmarzolf@slco.lib.ut.us; *Dep Dir*, Stan Workman; Tel: 801-944-7513, E-Mail: sworkman@slco.lib.ut.us; Staff 76 (MLS 65, Non-MLS 11)
Founded 1938. Pop 641,152; Circ 7,738,665
2000-2001 Income $19,828,163, State $135,775, Federal $183,187, County $18,016,301, Locally Generated Income $1,425,000, Other $67,900. Mats Exp $5,252,312, Books $3,514,912, Per/Ser (Incl. Access Fees) $351,940, AV Equip $1,385,460. Sal $9,238,010 (Prof $4,053,395)
Library Holdings: Bk Vols 1,671,808; Per Subs 5,189
Automation Activity & Vendor Info: (Acquisitions) epixtech, inc.; (Cataloging) epixtech, inc.; (Circulation) epixtech, inc.; (Media Booking) epixtech, inc.; (OPAC) epixtech, inc.; (Serials) epixtech, inc.
Publications: Staff Stuff (staff newsletter)
Partic in OCLC Online Computer Library Center, Inc
Special Services for the Deaf - TTY machine
Branches: 18
ALTA READING ROOM, Alta Community Ctr, Alta, 84092-6001. SAN 362-515X. Tel: 801-742-2068. Web Site: www.slco.lib.ut.us. *Mgr*, Jo Davies
BINGHAM CREEK, 4834 W 9000 South, W Jordan, 84088. SAN 377-7413. Tel: 801-944-7684. Circulation Tel: 801-944-7685. FAX: 801-282-0943. E-Mail: binghamc@slco.lib.ut.us. Web Site: www.slco.lib.ut.us. *Mgr*, Cherly Mansen; Tel: 801-944-7688
Circ 601,441
Library Holdings: Bk Vols 148,564
CALVIN S SMITH LIBRARY, 810 E 3300 South, 84106-1534. SAN 362-5354. Tel: 801-944-7630. Circulation Tel: 801-944-7620. FAX: 801-485-3243. Web Site: www.slco.lib.ut.us. *Mgr*, Prudence Bell; Tel: 801-944-7599
Circ 194,193
Library Holdings: Bk Vols 58,480
DRAPER LIBRARY, 12441 S 900 East, Draper, 84020-9792. SAN 362-5168. Tel: 801-944-7548. Circulation Tel: 801-944-7578. FAX: 801-619-9861. Web Site: www.slco.lib.ut.us. *Mgr*, Lora Koehler; Tel: 801-944-7558
Circ 169,070
Library Holdings: Bk Vols 44,434
EAST MILLCREEK LIBRARY, 2266 E Evergreen Ave, 84109-2998. SAN 362-5176. Tel: 801-944-7622. Circulation Tel: 801-944-7623. FAX: 801-278-9016. Web Site: www.slco.lib.ut.us. *Mgr*, Suzanne Tronier; Tel: 801-944-7510
Circ 399,598
Library Holdings: Bk Vols 96,286
HOLLADAY LIBRARY, 2150 E Murray-Holladay Rd, 84117-5241. SAN 362-5230. Tel: 801-944-7627. Circulation Tel: 801-944-7629. FAX: 801-278-8947. Web Site: www.slco.lib.ut.us. *Mgr*, Steve Pierson; Tel: 801-944-7524
Circ 466,751
Library Holdings: Bk Vols 111,668
HUNTER LIBRARY, 4740 W 4100 South, 84120. SAN 374-8138. Tel: 801-944-7595. Circulation Tel: 801-944-7594. Web Site: www.slco.lib.ut.us. *Mgr*, Faye Todd; Tel: 801-944-7597
Circ 639,781
Library Holdings: Bk Vols 166,206
KEARNS LIBRARY, 5350 S 4220 West, Kearns, 84118-4391. SAN 362-5265. Tel: 801-944-7612. Circulation Tel: 801-944-7611. FAX: 801-967-8958. Web Site: www.slco.lib.ut.us. *Mgr*, Darlene Dineen; Tel: 801-944-7615
Circ 422,218
Library Holdings: Bk Vols 108,362
MAGNA LIBRARY, 8339 W 3500 South, Magna, 84044-1853. SAN 362-529X. Tel: 801-944-7547. Circulation Tel: 801-944-7626. FAX: 801-250-6927. Web Site: www.slco.lib.ut.us. *Mgr*, Ruby Cheesman; Tel: 801-944-7657
Circ 236,602
Library Holdings: Bk Vols 88,036
PARK LIBRARY, 4870 S 2700 West, Taylorsville, 84118-2128. SAN 372-0284. Tel: 801-944-7618. Circulation Tel: 801-944-7638. FAX: 801-965-3907. Web Site: www.slco.lib.ut.us. *Mgr*, Linda Frederick; Tel: 801-944-7663
Founded 1990. Circ 491,219
Library Holdings: Bk Vols 105,991
RIVERTON LIBRARY, 12860 S Redwood Rd, Riverton, 84065-7026. SAN 328-7580. Tel: 801-944-7670. Circulation Tel: 801-944-7661. FAX: 801-944-7628. Web Site: www.slco.lib.ut.us. *Mgr*, Kent Dean; Tel: 801-944-7665
Circ 400,412
Library Holdings: Bk Vols 122,302
RUTH V TYLER LIBRARY, 8041 S Wood St, Midvale, 84047-3264. SAN 362-5443. Tel: 801-944-7641. Circulation Tel: 801-944-7646. Reference Tel: 801-944-7642. FAX: 801-565-8012. Web Site: www.slco.lib.ut.us. *Mgr*, Jane Cooper; Tel: 801-944-7608
Circ 168,408
Library Holdings: Bk Vols 66,184
SANDY LIBRARY, 10100 S Petunia Way, Sandy, 84092-3624. SAN 372-0292. Tel: 801-944-7574. Circulation Tel: 801-944-7602. Reference Tel: 801-944-7601. FAX: 801-572-8247. Web Site: www.slco.lib.ut.us. *Mgr*, Susan Hamada; Tel: 801-944-7600
Circ 1,152,749
Library Holdings: Bk Vols 223,162
SOUTH JORDAN LIBRARY, 10300 Beckstead Lane, South Jordan, 84065-8801. SAN 362-5389. Tel: 801-944-7634. Circulation Tel: 801-944-7650. FAX: 801-254-9047. *Mgr*, Nannette Alderman; Tel: 801-944-7643
Circ 332,381
Library Holdings: Bk Vols 101,127
SOUTH SALT LAKE LIBRARY, 220 E Morris Ave, South Salt Lake City, 84115-3223. SAN 362-5419. Tel: 801-944-7625. Reference Tel: 801-944-7545. FAX: 801-944-7625. Web Site: www.slco.lib.ut.us. *Mgr*, Bobbie Pyron; Tel: 801-944-7606
Circ 53,830
Library Holdings: Bk Vols 25,677
WEST JORDAN LIBRARY, 1970 W 7800 South, West Jordan, 84084-4025. SAN 328-7602. Tel: 801-944-7646. Reference Tel: 801-944-7645. FAX: 801-562-8761. Web Site: www.slco.lib.ut.us. *Mgr*, Gaye Walter; Tel: 801-944-7633
Circ 453,527
Library Holdings: Bk Vols 106,652
WEST VALLEY LIBRARY, 2880 W 3650 South, West Valley City, 84119-3753. SAN 362-5206. Tel: 801-944-7621. Reference Tel: 801-944-7631. FAX: 801-969-1782. Web Site: www.slco.lib.ut.us. *Mgr*, Lynn Darrough-Walton; Tel: 801-944-7583
Circ 326,933
Library Holdings: Bk Vols 95,598
WHITMORE LIBRARY, 2197 E 7000 South, 84121-3188. SAN 362-5478. Tel: 801-944-7533. Circulation Tel: 801-944-7531. Reference Tel: 801-944-7666. FAX: 801-944-7534. Web Site: www.slco.lib.ut.us. *Mgr*, Jo Davies; Tel: 801-944-7535
Circ 857,889
Library Holdings: Bk Vols 194,391

M SALT LAKE REGIONAL MEDICAL CENTER, Medical Library,* 1050 E South Temple, 84102. SAN 329-2894. Tel: 801-350-4060. FAX: 801-350-4390.
Library Holdings: Bk Vols 990; Bk Titles 945; Per Subs 100
Subject Interests: Med ethics
Partic in Utah Health Sciences Library Consortium

S SALT LAKE TRIBUNE, Data Center,* 143 S Main St, PO Box 867, 84111. SAN 327-8344. Tel: 801-237-2001. FAX: 801-257-8956. E-Mail: datacenter@sltrib.com. *Mgr*, Ana Daraban
Special Collections: Tribune Index 1941-Aug 1991
Open Mon-Fri 1-5:30

S SPECTRUM ACOUSTICAL ENGINEERS, INC LIBRARY,* 175 S Main St Ste 5, 84111. SAN 373-0026. Tel: 801-467-4206. FAX: 801-328-5155. *Mgr*, Jim Fullmer
Jan 1997-Dec 1998 Mats Exp $2,000. Sal $45,000
Library Holdings: Bk Vols 2,000; Per Subs 30
Subject Interests: Acoustics, Sound

GL STATE OF UTAH LAW LIBRARY, 450 S State St, 84114. SAN 316-9308. Tel: 801-238-7990. FAX: 801-238-7993. *Dir*, Nancy H Cheng
Library Holdings: Bk Vols 120,000
Subject Interests: Law
Restriction: Not open to public, Staff use only

L UNITED STATES COURTS LIBRARY,* US Courthouse, Rm 201, 350 S Main St, 84101. SAN 372-1892. Tel: 801-524-3505. FAX: 801-524-3106. *Librn*, Patricia Hummel
Library Holdings: Bk Vols 15,000
Open Mon-Fri 9:30-5

UNIVERSITY OF UTAH
C MARRIOTT LIBRARY, 295 S 1500 E Rm Dock, 84112-0860. SAN 362-5532. Tel: 801-581-8558. Interlibrary Loan Service Tel: 801-581-6010. Circulation Tel: 801-581-8203. Reference Tel: 801-581-6273. FAX: 801-585-3464. Web Site: www.lib.utah.edu. *Dir*, Sarah Michalak; Tel: 801-581-8558, E-Mail: michalak@library.utah.edu; *Circ*, Daniel Lee; Tel: 801-581-8204, Fax: 801-585-3464, E-Mail: dlee@library.utah.edu; *Coll Develop*,

Margaret Landesman; Tel: 801-581-7741, E-Mail: mlandesm@library.utah.edu; *ILL*, Linda Burns; Fax: 801-585-3464, E-Mail: lburns@library.utah.edu; *Media Spec*, Linda St Clair; Tel: 801-585-9499, Fax: 801-585-3464, E-Mail: lstclair@library.utah.edu; *Asst Dir, Publ Servs*, Julianne Hinz; Tel: 801-581-5071, E-Mail: jhinz@library.utah.edu; *Ref Serv*, Leslie Haas; Tel: 801-585-9190, Fax: 801-581-3464, E-Mail: lhaas@library.utah.edu; *Doc*, Jill Moriearty; *Asst Dir, Spec Coll*, Gregory Thompson; Tel: 801-581-8864, E-Mail: gthompso@library.utah.edu; *Tech Servs*, Gary Rasmussen; Tel: 801-581-7731; Staff 349 (MLS 51, Non-MLS 298)
Founded 1850. Enrl 31,101; Fac 1,456
Jul 1999-Jun 2000 Mats Exp $5,151,193, Books $1,783,945, Per/Ser (Incl. Access Fees) $3,053,636, Electronic Ref Mat (Incl. Access Fees) $313,612. Sal $2,466,695 (Prof $7,219,692)
Library Holdings: Bk Vols 2,411,348; Per Subs 14,389
Subject Interests: Fine arts, Mathematics, Rare books, Western Americana
Special Collections: 2002 Winter Olympics; University Archives; US Patent
Automation Activity & Vendor Info: (Acquisitions) epixtech, inc.; (Cataloging) epixtech, inc.; (Circulation) epixtech, inc.
Publications: Friends of the Libraries Newsletter; Inline (library newsletter); Manuscripts Coll
Partic in Asn of Research Libraries; Bibliographical Center For Research, Rocky Mountain Region, Inc; Big Twelve Plus Libr Consortium; Center For Research Libraries; Horizon Users Group; OCLC Online Computer Library Center, Inc; Pioneer; SPARC; Utah Academic Library Consortium; Utah Libr Asn; Utah's Online Libr
Friends of the Library Group

CL S J QUINNEY LAW LIBRARY, 332 S 1400 East, 84112-0731. SAN 362-5591. Tel: 801-581-6594. Interlibrary Loan Service Tel: 801-581-3804. Circulation Tel: 801-581-6438. Reference Tel: 801-581-6184. FAX: 801-585-3033. *Dir, Prof*, Rita T Reusch; Tel: 801-581-3386, E-Mail: reuschr@aw.utah.edu; *Asst Dir, Coll Develop*, Lee Warthen; Tel: 801-581-5344, E-Mail: warthernl@law.utah.edu; *Tech Coordr*, Suzanne Miner; Tel: 801-585-3074; *Access Serv*, Linda Stephenson; Tel: 801-581-5800; *Acq, Doc*, John Bevan; Tel: 801-585-5364, E-Mail: bevanj@law.utah.edu; *Head, Circ*, John Bramble; Tel: 801-581-6438; *Head, Info Serv*, Ellen Ouyang; Tel: 801-585-5064; *ILL*, Laura Ngai; Tel: 801-581-3804; Staff 20 (MLS 7, Non-MLS 13)
Founded 1923. Enrl 365; Fac 41; Highest Degree: Doctorate
Library Holdings: Bk Vols 290,000; Per Subs 2,300
Publications: Acquisitions List (monthly); User Guide
Mem of Asn of Research Libraries
Partic in Research Libraries Group, Inc

CM SPENCER S ECCLES HEALTH SCIENCES LIBRARY, Bldg 589, 10 N 1900 E, 84112. SAN 362-5680. Tel: 801-581-8771. Interlibrary Loan Service Tel: 801-581-5282. FAX: 801-581-3632. Web Site: medstat.med.utah.edu/. *Dir*, Wayne J Peay; *Dep Dir*, Joan Stoddart; *Coll Develop*, Joan M Stoddart; Staff 10 (MLS 10)
Founded 1966. Enrl 3,000
Library Holdings: Bk Titles 51,050; Per Subs 1,903
Subject Interests: Health sci, Medicine, Nursing, Pharmacy
Special Collections: History of Medicine, bks & journals
Partic in Utah Academic Library Consortium

S UPPER COLORADO RIVER COMMISSION LIBRARY,* 355 S 400 East St, 84111. SAN 374-7662. Tel: 801-531-1150. *Exec Dir*, Wayne E Cook
Library Holdings: Bk Vols 9,000
Restriction: Open to public for reference only

S UTAH DEPARTMENT OF NATURAL RESOURCES LIBRARY,* 1594 W North Temple No 3110, 84114. SAN 372-865X. Tel: 801-537-3333. FAX: 801-537-3400. *Librn*, Mage Yonetani
Jan 1997-Dec 1998 Income $4,000
Library Holdings: Bk Vols 14,000; Per Subs 41
Subject Interests: Geology

G UTAH STATE ARCHIVES,* Archives Bldg Capitol Hill, 84114. SAN 329-9996. Tel: 801-538-3013. FAX: 801-538-3354. E-Mail: research@state.ut.us. Web Site: www.archives.state.ut.us. *Archivist*, Jeffrey O Johnson; *Acq, Cat*, Steve Wood; Staff 30 (MLS 18, Non-MLS 12)
Founded 1953
Library Holdings: Bk Titles 150

S UTAH STATE HISTORICAL SOCIETY, Utah History Information Center Library, 300 Rio Grande, 84101-1182. SAN 316-9294. Tel: 801-533-3535. FAX: 801-533-3504. Web Site: www.history.utah.org. *Coordr*, Linda Thatcher; Tel: 801-533-3574, E-Mail: thatche@history.state.ut.us; *Curator*, Susan Whetstone; Tel: 801-533-3543; Staff 4 (MLS 4)
Founded 1939
Library Holdings: Bk Vols 28,000; Per Subs 205
Subject Interests: Utah hist, Western hist
Automation Activity & Vendor Info: (Circulation) epixtech, inc.
Database Vendor: epixtech, inc.
Publications: Guide to the Women's History Holdings at the Utah State Historical Society Library; Guide to Unpublished Materials at the Utah S Historical Society
Restriction: Non-circulating
Partic in RLIN

P UTAH STATE LIBRARY DIVISION, 250 N 1950 W Ste A, 84116-790 SAN 362-5710. Tel: 801-715-6777. Toll Free Tel: 800-662-9150. FAX: 8 715-6767. Web Site: www.state.lib.ut.us. *Dir*, Amy Owen; E-Mail: aower inter.state.ut.us; *Dep Dir*, Douglas Abrams; *Doc*, Lennis Anderson; E-Ma landerso@state.lib.ut.us; *ILL*, Betti Grow; E-Mail: bgrow@state.lib.ut.us; Staff 14 (MLS 14)
Founded 1957. Pop 1,907,975
Jul 1998-Jun 1999 Income $6,190,300, State $3,556,700, Federal $1,055,000, County $946,200, Other $632,400. Mats Exp $637,200, Book $201,900, Per/Ser (Incl. Access Fees) $53,000, Electronic Ref Mat (Incl. Access Fees) $382,300. Sal $3,276,900 (Prof $1,873,554)
Library Holdings: Bk Titles 54,106; Per Subs 52
Special Collections: Local Utah History Coll
Automation Activity & Vendor Info: (Acquisitions) epixtech, inc.; (OPA epixtech, inc.
Database Vendor: OCLC - First Search
Publications: Directions for Utah Libraries; Directory of Public Libraries Utah; Utah Library Laws; Utah Public Library Service: An Annual Repor Utah Trustee Manual; Utah Under Cover (Checklist of Utah State Documents)
Partic in Bibliographical Center For Research, Rocky Mountain Region, I OCLC Online Computer Library Center, Inc; Utah Academic Library Consortium; Utah Libr Network
Branches: 1
PROGRAM FOR THE BLIND & PHYSICALLY HANDICAPPED
See Separate Entry
Bookmobiles: 4

P UTAH STATE LIBRARY DIVISION, Program for the Blind & Physicall Handicapped, 250 N 1950 West, Ste A, 84116-7901. SAN 316-9316. Tel: 801-715-6789. Toll Free Tel: 800-662-5540. FAX: 801-715-6767. Web Sit www.state.lib.ut.us. *Librn*, Gerald A Buttars; *Coll Develop*, Bessie Oakes; Staff 7 (MLS 3, Non-MLS 4)
Founded 1957. Pop 8,000
Jul 1998-Jun 1999 Income $1,254,700, State $712,900, Federal $109,200, Other $432,600. Mats Exp $20,100, Books $18,100, Per/Ser (Incl. Access Fees) $2,000. Sal $1,029,000 (Prof $365,057)
Library Holdings: Bk Vols 397,886; Bk Titles 63,451; Per Subs 140; Hig Interest/Low Vocabulary Bk Vols 1,829; Bks on Deafness & Sign Lang 30
Subject Interests: Mormon lit
Special Collections: Mormon Literature Coll; Western Books Coll
Publications: The See Note Newsletter (quarterly)
Special Services for the Blind - Bks on cassette; Braille & recorded books Descriptive videos; Large print bks; Magazines on cassette; Radio reading service; Recordings & flexible discs

C WESTMINSTER COLLEGE, Giovale Library, 1840 S 13th East, 84105. SAN 316-9340. Tel: 801-832-2250. Interlibrary Loan Service Tel: 801-832-2257. Reference Tel: 801-832-2251. FAX: 801-467-8462. Web Site: www.wcslc.edu/library/. *Dir*, David A Hales; Tel: 801-832-2256, E-Mail: d-hales@wcslc.edu; *Publ Servs*, Hildy Benham; Tel: 801-832-2252, E-Mail h-benham@wcslc.edu; *Tech Servs*, Richard Wunder; Tel: 801-832-2261, E-Mail: d-wunder@wcslc.edu; *Ser, Syst Coordr*, M Diane Raines; Tel: 801-832-2260, E-Mail: d-raines@wcslc.edu; Staff 9 (MLS 4, Non-MLS 5)
Founded 1875. Fac 100; Highest Degree: Master
Jul 1999-Jun 2000 Mats Exp $621,179, Books $168,741, Per/Ser (Incl. Access Fees) $44,925, Presv $3,986, Micro $18,439, AV Equip $500, Electronic Ref Mat (Incl. Access Fees) $47,810
Library Holdings: Bk Vols 102,632; Per Subs 406
Subject Interests: Modern women authors, Nuclear disarmament, Utah landscape
Special Collections: Archival material relating to early hist of the College early hist of the Presbyterian Church in Utah
Automation Activity & Vendor Info: (Acquisitions) epixtech, inc.; (Cataloging) epixtech, inc.; (Circulation) epixtech, inc.; (Course Reserve) epixtech, inc.; (OPAC) epixtech, inc.; (Serials) epixtech, inc.
Database Vendor: OCLC - First Search
Publications: Faculty/Staff handbook; Student guidebooks (2)
Partic in Bibliographical Center For Research, Rocky Mountain Region, Inc OCLC Online Computer Library Center, Inc; Utah Academic Library Consortium

SANDY

S BECTON-DICKINSON INFUSION THERA-PHY SYSTEMS, Information Center,* 9450 S State St, 84070. SAN 323-8083. Tel: 801-565-2309. Toll Free Tel: 800-453-4538. FAX: 801-565-2740.
Library Holdings: Bk Titles 1,000; Per Subs 200
Special Collections: Critical Medicine, Critical Care Monitoring

NTAQUIN

SANTAQUIN PUBLIC LIBRARY, 45 W 100 South, 84655. SAN 322-8606. Tel: 801-754-3211. FAX: 801-754-3526. *Librn*, Lyn Oryall; E-Mail: loryall@inter.state.lib.ut.us; Staff 1 (MLS 1)
Founded 1932. Pop 2,700; Circ 7,831
Library Holdings: Bk Titles 13,000; Per Subs 12
Mem of Utah State Libr Network
Friends of the Library Group

IITHFIELD

SMITHFIELD PUBLIC LIBRARY,* 25 N Main St, PO Box 35, 84335-0035. SAN 316-9359. Tel: 435-563-3555. *Librn*, Marilyn Benavides; *Asst Librn*, Karen Bowling
Pop 5,000; Circ 26,000 Sal $21,000
Library Holdings: Bk Vols 22,000; Per Subs 30
Open Mon-Thurs 2:30-8, Fri 2:30-5 & Sat 11-2

'ANISH FORK

SPANISH FORK CITY PUBLIC LIBRARY,* 49 S Main St, 84660-2030. SAN 316-9367. Tel: 801-798-5010. FAX: 801-798-5014. *Dir*, Louise Nuzman; *Ad Servs*, Kevin Cassel; *Ad Servs*, Sharon Lehmberg
Pop 7,284; Circ 53,294
Library Holdings: Bk Vols 40,000
Friends of the Library Group

'RINGVILLE

SPRINGVILLE PUBLIC LIBRARY, 50 S Main St, 84663. SAN 316-9391. Tel: 801-489-2720. FAX: 801-489-2709. *Ad Servs, Librn*, Lynette Catherall; E-Mail: lcathera@state.lib.ut.us; *Ch Servs*, Vivian Mileus; E-Mail: vmilius@state.lib.ut.us; Staff 4 (MLS 2, Non-MLS 2)
Founded 1916. Pop 23,000; Circ 300,669
Jul 1999-Jun 2000 Income $503,084, State $7,612, City $481,977, Federal $13,495. Mats Exp $113,344, Books $94,341, AV Equip $18,764, Other Print Mats $239. Sal $316,490
Library Holdings: Bk Vols 64,513; Per Subs 142
Special Collections: Local History Coll; Springville History Coll
Automation Activity & Vendor Info: (Cataloging) Follett; (Circulation) Follett; (OPAC) Follett
Friends of the Library Group

OOELE

TOOELE CITY PUBLIC LIBRARY,* 128 W Vine St, 84074-2059. SAN 316-9405. Tel: 435-882-2182. FAX: 435-843-2159. *Dir, Librn*, Peggy Erikson; E-Mail: perik@inter.state.lib.ut.us; *Tech Servs*, Linda Treadway; *Tech Servs*, Sharon Richards
Founded 1910. Pop 17,500; Circ 130,781
Library Holdings: Bk Vols 45,000
Open Tues-Sat 11-7
Friends of the Library Group

TREMONTON

P TREMONTON CITY LIBRARY, 210 N Tremont St, 84337-1329. SAN 316-9413. Tel: 435-257-2690. FAX: 435-257-2690. *Librn*, L H Adams; E-Mail: ladams@mail.state.lib.ut.us
Pop 5,116; Circ 28,000
Jul 1999-Jun 2000 Income $58,038. Mats Exp Books $8,100. Sal $26,895
Library Holdings: Bk Vols 22,963; Bk Titles 21,854; Per Subs 57
Automation Activity & Vendor Info: (Acquisitions) Follett; (Cataloging) Follett; (Circulation) Follett
Friends of the Library Group

VERNAL

G BUREAU OF LAND MANAGEMENT LIBRARY,* 170 S 500 East, 84078. SAN 316-9421. Tel: 435-789-1362. FAX: 435-781-4410. *Librn*, Jeanny Davis
Library Holdings: Bk Vols 2,000; Per Subs 100
Open Mon-Fri 7:45-4:30

P UINTAH COUNTY LIBRARY, 155 E Main, 84078-2695. SAN 316-943X. Tel: 435-789-0091. FAX: 435-789-6822. Web Site: www.uintah.lib.ut.us. *Dir*, Evan L Baker; E-Mail: ebaker@easilink.com; *Asst Dir, Coll Develop*, Creed Kidd; E-Mail: ckidd@easilink.com; *Librn*, Doris Burton; *Ch Servs*, Jennifer Blodgett
Founded 1908. Pop 24,500; Circ 336,080
Library Holdings: Bk Vols 77,911; Per Subs 123
Subject Interests: Local history
Automation Activity & Vendor Info: (Cataloging) epixtech, inc.; (Circulation) epixtech, inc.; (OPAC) epixtech, inc.
Publications: A History of Uintah County: Scratching the Surface; Outlaw Trail History Journal; Settlements of Uintah County: Digging Deeper
Open Mon-Thurs 10-9, Fri & Sat 10-6

S UTAH FIELD HOUSE OF NATURAL HISTORY, Scientific Library, 235 E Main, 84078. SAN 324-0339. Tel: 435-789-3799. FAX: 435-789-4883. E-Mail: ufsp@state.ut.us. *Librn*, Lu Rae Caldwell
Founded 1948
Library Holdings: Bk Titles 3,025
Subject Interests: Dinosaurs, Geology, Natural history
Restriction: Open to public for reference only

VERMONT

Date of Statistics: Fiscal 1999
Population, 1990 Census: 563,000(est.)
Population Served by Public Libraries: 545,000
Unserved: 18,000
Total Volumes in Public Libraries: 2,533,496
Volumes Per Capita: 4.64
Total Public Library Circulation: 3,745,698
Circulation Per Capita: 6.65
Total Public Library Income (not including Grants-in-Aid): $11,401,792
Source of Income: Mainly public appropriating & endowment fund interest.
Income Per Capita: $18.26

LBANY

ALBANY TOWN LIBRARY,* PO Box 512, 05820. SAN 376-4915. Tel: 802-755-6288. *Librn*, Marein Whipple
Library Holdings: Bk Vols 2,500
Mem of Northeastern Regional Libr Syst

LBURG

ALBURG PUBLIC LIBRARY, Municipal Bldg, 16 S Main St, 05440. (Mail add: PO Box 344, 05440), SAN 376-3439. Tel: 802-796-6077. FAX: 802-796-3939. E-Mail: alburg_pl@dol.state.vt.us. *Librn*, Marybelle Singer; Staff 1 (Non-MLS 1)
Founded 1917. Pop 1,500
Jan 1999-Dec 1999 Income $24,987, City $14,800, Locally Generated Income $10,187. Mats Exp Books $3,600. Sal $14,100
Library Holdings: Bk Vols 10,000
Friends of the Library Group

RLINGTON

MARTHA CANFIELD MEMORIAL FREE LIBRARY, 528 E Arlington Rd, 05250. (Mail add: PO Box 267, 05250-0267), Tel: 802-375-6153. E-Mail: arlington@dol.state.vt.us. *Dir*, Phyllis Skidmore; *Spec Coll*, John H Kennedy
Founded 1803. Pop 3,449; Circ 15,000
Library Holdings: Bk Titles 17,000; Per Subs 12
Special Collections: Vermontiana (Dr George Russell Coll), bks, mss, clipping, photog
Partic in OCLC Online Computer Library Center, Inc
Open Tues & Thurs 9-5 & 6:30-8, Wed 9-5, Fri 2-5, Sat 10-3; Special Vermontiana Collection: Tues only 9-5 or by appointment

SCUTNEY

PROCTOR LIBRARY,* PO Box 157, 05030. SAN 362-5869. Tel: 802-674-2863. *Librn*, Ruth Kelin
Founded 1902. Circ 6,844
Jul 1997-Jun 1998 Income $14,857. Mats Exp $2,591. Sal $6,539
Library Holdings: Bk Vols 6,100
Subject Interests: Local history, Vermont hist
Mem of Southeastern Library Services
Open Tues 11-5, Wed 3-8, Fri 2-8 & Sat 9-12
Friends of the Library Group

AKERSFIELD

H F BRIGHAM FREE PUBLIC LIBRARY, PO Box 5, 05441. SAN 316-9464. Tel: 802-827-4414. *Librn*, Helen Bushey; *Asst Librn*, Marian Ryel; Staff 2 (Non-MLS 2)
Pop 997
Library Holdings: Bk Titles 5,850
Partic in NW Regional Libr Coop

BARNARD

P CHARLES B DANFORTH PUBLIC LIBRARY,* PO Box 204, 05031. SAN 316-9472. Tel: 802-234-9211. *Librn*, Melanie McGovern
Pop 790; Circ 1,400
Library Holdings: Bk Vols 4,500
Mem of Midstate Regional Libr
Open Wed 7-8:30, Sat 8:30-12

BARNET

P BARNET PUBLIC LIBRARY,* PO Box 34, 05821. SAN 316-9480. Tel: 802-633-4436. E-Mail: barnet_pub@dol.state.vt.us. *Librn*, Elaine O'Hara
Founded 1900. Circ 2,596
1998-1999 Income $10,350, City $10,150, Other $200. Mats Exp $1,400, Books $1,000, Per/Ser (Incl. Access Fees) $400. Sal $6,000
Library Holdings: Bk Vols 7,500
Subject Interests: Vermont
Special Collections: Large Print Books
Mem of Northeastern Regional Libr Syst

BARRE

P ALDRICH PUBLIC LIBRARY, 6 Washington, 05641-4227. SAN 316-9499. Tel: 802-476-7550. FAX: 802-479-0450. E-Mail: aldrich@helicon.net. Web Site: www.aldrich.lib.vt.us/, www.central-vt.com/public/aldrich. *Dir*, Karen E Lane; Tel: 802-476-7550, Ext 307; *Librn*, Margaret Murray; Staff 12 (Non-MLS 12)
Founded 1907. Pop 16,893; Circ 53,172
Jul 1999-Jun 2000 Income (Main Library and Branch Library) $244,729, City $105,250, Locally Generated Income $139,479. Mats Exp $32,000, Books $28,000, Per/Ser (Incl. Access Fees) $4,000. Sal $161,648 (Prof $143,172)
Library Holdings: Bk Vols 52,168; Per Subs 135
Subject Interests: Am sculpture, Community, Ethnic hist, European sculpture, Immigration, Indust hist, Labor hist, Political movements
Special Collections: Archives of Barre History; Barre Museum; Vermont History Coll
Automation Activity & Vendor Info: (Cataloging) Follett; (Circulation) Follett
Publications: Barre Granite Heritage with Guide to the Cemeteries (1997) (Local historical information); Barre in Retrospect 1776-1995 (community hist) (Local historical information); Barre, VT; An Annotated Bibliography (1979) (Local historical information); Guide to the Manuscript Holdings of

the Archives of Barre History (1997) (Local historical information)
Special Services for the Blind - Bks on cassette; Homebound delivery; Large print bks; Optelek 20/20 video magnification system
Friends of the Library Group
Branches: 1
EAST BARRE BRANCH Tel: 802-476-5118. Web Site: www.central-vt.com/public/aldrich. *Librn*, Margaret Murray
Pop 7,000
Library Holdings: Bk Vols 3,500
Friends of the Library Group

M CENTRAL VERMONT HOSPITAL, Medical Library,* PO Box 547, 05641. SAN 316-957X. Tel: 802-371-4205. FAX: 803-371-4575. E-Mail: biomdical.reference@dartmouth.edu.
Founded 1970
Library Holdings: Bk Vols 500; Bk Titles 400; Per Subs 70
Subject Interests: Allied health lit, Medicine, Nursing

BARTON

P BARTON PUBLIC LIBRARY,* Church St, PO Box 549, 05822. SAN 316-9510. Tel: 802-525-6524. *Librn*, Cindy Karasinski
Founded 1928. Pop 1,553; Circ 15,523
Library Holdings: Bk Vols 10,000; Per Subs 15
Mem of Northeastern Regional Libr Syst; Vt State Dept of Librs
Open Mon 2-7, Wed 9-11 & 2-7, Fri 2-5, Sat 10-12

BELLOWS FALLS

P ROCKINGHAM FREE PUBLIC LIBRARY, 65 Westminster St, 05101. SAN 316-9529. Tel: 802-463-4270. FAX: 802-463-1566. E-Mail: rockingham@dol.state.vt.us. *Dir*, Becky Hollis; Staff 5 (Non-MLS 5)
Founded 1887. Pop 7,500; Circ 49,000
Jul 1999-Jun 2000 Income $245,996, City $191,360, Locally Generated Income $54,636. Mats Exp $25,136, Books $22,304, Per/Ser (Incl. Access Fees) $2,832. Sal $117,684 (Prof $104,414)
Library Holdings: Bk Titles 48,000
Subject Interests: Genealogy, Large print, Local history, Vermontania
Special Collections: Rockingham Historical Museum Coll
Mem of Southeastern Library Services
Friends of the Library Group

BELMONT

P THE MOUNT HOLLY LIBRARY,* PO Box 93, 05730. SAN 320-5177. Tel: 802-259-2333. *Librn*, Carol Ballou; Staff 1 (MLS 1)
Founded 1913. Pop 650
Library Holdings: Bk Titles 7,000
Subject Interests: Vermontiana
Mem of Vt State Dept of Librs
Friends of the Library Group

BENNINGTON

C BENNINGTON COLLEGE, Crossett Library, 05201-9992. SAN 362-5923. Tel: 802-440-4610. FAX: 802-440-4580. Web Site: bennington.edu/library. *Dir*, Robert Waldman; *Tech Servs*, Vanessa Haverkoch; *Ref*, Heather Van Inwegan; *Circ, Publ Servs*, Tim Dowgiert; Staff 4 (MLS 4)
Founded 1932. Enrl 518; Fac 60; Highest Degree: Master
1998-1999 Income $390,000. Mats Exp $102,650, Books $34,850, Per/Ser (Incl. Access Fees) $53,000, Presv $2,200, Micro $1,000, Manuscripts & Archives $500. Sal $210,000 (Prof $129,000)
Library Holdings: Bk Vols 122,000; Bk Titles 94,000; Per Subs 450
Subject Interests: Art, Dance, Literature, Theater
Special Collections: Literary Reviews; Photography
Automation Activity & Vendor Info: (Circulation) TLC; (OPAC) TLC
Database Vendor: IAC - Info Trac, Lexis-Nexis, OCLC - First Search
Publications: Acquisition List; Exhibition Flyer
Partic in OCLC Online Computer Library Center, Inc
Departmental Libraries:
MUSIC LIBRARY, Jennings Hall, 05201. SAN 362-5958. Tel: 802-440-4512. FAX: 802-447-4269. Web Site: bennington.edu/library. *Librn*, Robert Waldman
Library Holdings: Bk Vols 6,300
Subject Interests: Contemporary chamber music

P BENNINGTON FREE LIBRARY, 101 Silver St, 05201. SAN 316-9545. Tel: 802-442-9051. E-Mail: bfli@together.net. *Dir*, Anita M Gauthier; *Admin Assoc*, Anne Mook; *Cat*, Pat Quist; *Ch Servs, YA Servs*, Linda Donigan; *Ch Servs, YA Servs*, Chris Poggi; *Circ*, Joan Douglass; *Ref*, Lynne Fonteneau-McCann; *Tech Servs*, Loreen Niegoda
Founded 1865. Pop 20,500; Circ 90,336
Jul 1999-Jun 2000 Income $360,055, City $281,955, Other $78,100. Mats Exp $62,640, Books $53,358. Sal $244,057
Library Holdings: Bk Titles 56,105; Per Subs 187
Subject Interests: Town hist, Vt hist
Special Collections: Bennington Banner, 1903-present, flm
Mem of Southeastern Library Services
Friends of the Library Group

S BENNINGTON MUSEUM, Genealogy & History Research Library, W Main St, 05201. SAN 316-9553. Tel: 802-447-1571. FAX: 802-442-8305. E-Mail: bennmuse@sover.net. Web Site: www.bennington.com/museum. *Librn*, Tyler Resch
Founded 1928
Library Holdings: Bk Titles 4,500
Subject Interests: Genealogy, Regional hist
Special Collections: Bennington County Census, microfilm; Bennington Town Records & Maps; Bennington's Old First Church Records; Early V Records for Southern New England States; Essays & Data on Early Fami in New England: Cutter, Savage & Others; Genealogy Columns from Bos Transcript, Hartford Times; General resources: American Biographical & Genealogical (Rider) Index; Hemenway's Six-Volume 19th Century Verm Gazetteer: Town, County & State Histories for Vermont, New England, Many New York; Military Rosters & Data for Vermont, Nearby States: Revolution, Civil War; Mormon IGI Microfiche for New England (except Maine) & New York; Published Family Histories, New England-Oriented; Registers of New England Historic Genealogical Society, since 1847; The Day Papers: 25 Scrapbooks of Discerning News Clips, 1870-1916; The Harwood Diaries: Rich Details of Life Between 1803 & 1837; US Census Indexes, 1790-1850 for New England, New York & Others; Vermont & Bennington Regional Resources: Aldrich Histories & Child Directories of Vermont Counties, circa 1880
Open June-Oct Mon-Sat 11-5; Nov-May Mon, Thurs & Sat 11-5
Friends of the Library Group

C SOUTHERN VERMONT COLLEGE LEARNING RESOURCES CENTE 982 Mansion Dr, 05201. SAN 316-9561. Tel: 802-447-6311. FAX: 802-44 4695. E-Mail: libstaff@svc.edu. *Dir*, Cynthia Dellinger Davis; E-Mail: cydavis@svc.edu; *Res*, Constance Fritz; Tel: 802-447-6312, E-Mail: cfritz svc.edu; *ILL*, Mary VanVleck; Staff 2 (MLS 2)
Founded 1926. Enrl 524; Highest Degree: Bachelor
Library Holdings: Bk Vols 24,000
Subject Interests: Bus, Child care mgt, Communications, Criminal justice Environmental studies, Human servs, Mgt, Nursing, Soc work
Database Vendor: Dialog
Partic in Nelinet, Inc

SOUTHWESTERN VERMONT HEALTH CARE
M HEALTH SCIENCES LIBRARY, 100 Hospital Dr, 05201. SAN 362-601 Tel: 802-447-5120. FAX: 802-442-8331. E-Mail: beg@phin.org. *Librn*, Beverly E Greene
Founded 1969
Library Holdings: Bk Vols 947; Bk Titles 800; Per Subs 50
Subject Interests: Allied health, Basic sci, Biomed sci, Medicine, Nursing, Surgery
Special Collections: Consumer Health Coll
Publications: Library Newsletter
Partic in BHSL; Health Science Libraries Of New Hampshire & Vermon North Atlantic Health Sciences Libraries, Inc

G VERMONT VETERANS HOME LIBRARY,* 325 North St, 05201. SAN 321-1037. Tel: 802-442-6353. FAX: 802-447-2757. *In Charge*, Michele Burgess
Founded 1884
Library Holdings: Bk Titles 3,126; Per Subs 50
Special Collections: Civil War

BENSON

P BENSON VILLAGE LIBRARY,* PO Box 189, 05731. SAN 376-3455. Te 802-537-4181. *Librn*, Jacqueline Lussier
Library Holdings: Bk Vols 4,500
Mem of Southwest Regional Library Service System
Open Mon 6-8 & Wed 3:30-5:30

BERLIN

P VERMONT REGIONAL LIBRARY FOR THE BLIND & PHYSICALLY HANDICAPPED,* Vermont Dept of Libraries Special Services Unit, 578 Paine Turnpike N, 05602. SAN 317-0748. Tel: 802-828-3273. Toll Free Tel 800-479-1711. FAX: 802-828-2199. E-Mail: ssu@dol.state.vt.us. *Librn*, S Francis Woods; *Asst Librn*, Jennifer Hart
Founded 1976. Circ 69,962
Library Holdings: Bk Vols 200
Special Collections: Handicaps Reference Material
Publications: Newsletter (quarterly)
Special Services for the Blind - Children's Braille, Books on Cassette; Descriptive videos

THEL

BETHEL PUBLIC LIBRARY,* Main St, PO Box 354, 05032. SAN 316-9596. Tel: 802-234-9107. *Librn*, Cathy Day
Founded 1893. Pop 1,715; Circ 20,213
Library Holdings: Bk Vols 12,000; Per Subs 38
Mem of Vermont Libr Asn
Open Mon & Wed 2-5 & 7-8:30 & Sat 2-5

NDVILLE

WINHALL MEMORIAL LIBRARY,* PO Box 44A, 05340. SAN 316-960X. Tel: 802-297-9741. *Librn*, Fran Rosenthal
Pop 300; Circ 4,500
Library Holdings: Bk Vols 6,500
Special Collections: Cook & needlepoint bks
Mem of Southeastern Library Services
Open Tues 3-7 & Thurs 3-6

ADFORD

BRADFORD PUBLIC LIBRARY, 21 S Main St, PO Box 619, 05033. SAN 316-9618. Tel: 802-222-4536. *Librn*, Kathy Thibault
Founded 1796. Pop 2,800; Circ 20,330
1999-2000 Income $38,073, City $28,000, Parent Institution $10,073. Mats Exp Books $8,300. Sal $18,368 (Prof $12,168)
Library Holdings: Bk Titles 7,880; Per Subs 19
Subject Interests: Dolls, Fishing
Special Collections: Historical (Trotter Coll), bks, logs, artifacts
Friends of the Library Group

ANDON

BRANDON FREE PUBLIC LIBRARY,* Franklin & Park Sts, 05733. SAN 316-9626. Tel: 802-247-8230. E-Mail: brandon@dol.state.vt.us. *Librn*, Stephanie Choma
Founded 1901. Pop 3,697; Circ 30,800
Jul 1997-Jun 1998 Income $103,000. Mats Exp $9,000. Sal $52,000
Library Holdings: Bk Vols 31,000; Per Subs 65
Subject Interests: Vermontiana
Mem of Vermont Libr Asn
Friends of the Library Group

ATTLEBORO

AUSTINE SCHOOL LIBRARY, 130 Austine Dr, 05301-2694. (Mail add: 60 Austine Dr, 05301-2694), SAN 374-9665. Tel: 802-254-4571. TDD: 802-258-9524, Ext 524. FAX: 802-254-3921. *Librn*, Deborah Hammond; Tel: 802-258-9524, E-Mail: debbie@austine.pvt.k12.vt.us; Staff 1 (MLS 1)
Jul 2000-Jun 2001 Mats Exp $20,894, Books $1,993, Per/Ser (Incl. Access Fees) $650. Sal $17,087
Library Holdings: Bk Vols 500; Per Subs 24
Automation Activity & Vendor Info: (Acquisitions) Sagebrush Corporation; (Cataloging) Sagebrush Corporation; (Circulation) Sagebrush Corporation
Restriction: Private library
Special Services for the Deaf - Books on deafness & sign language; Captioned film depository

BRATTLEBORO MEMORIAL HOSPITAL, Medical Library, 17 Belmont Ave, 05301-6613. SAN 316-9642. Tel: 802-257-0341, Ext 8357, 802-257-8357. FAX: 802-257-8822 (Attention: Martha Fenn). E-Mail: bmhlibry@sover.net. *Librn*, Martha J Fenn; Staff 1 (MLS 1)
Founded 1970
Oct 1999-Sep 2000 Income $29,000. Mats Exp $8,800, Books $4,400, Per/Ser (Incl. Access Fees) $4,400
Library Holdings: Bk Titles 1,600; Per Subs 100
Subject Interests: Medicine, Nursing
Partic in BHSL; Health Science Libraries Of New Hampshire & Vermont; North Atlantic Health Sciences Libraries, Inc; UCMP

BRATTLEBORO RETREAT
ASA KEYES MEDICAL LIBRARY, Anna Marsh Lane, PO Box 803, 05302. SAN 321-8600. Tel: 802-258-3737, Ext 3229. FAX: 802-258-3722. *Dir Libr Serv*, Janet Perusse; E-Mail: jperusse@sover.net
1997-1998 Mats Exp $17,500, Books $4,000, Per/Ser (Incl. Access Fees) $10,000, AV Equip $500, Other Print Mats $3,000. Sal $26,000
Library Holdings: Bk Vols 4,500; Per Subs 62
Subject Interests: Behav sci, Child psychology, Eating disorders, Geriatric psychiatry, Partial hospitalization, Substance abuse, Substance treatment
Restriction: Non-circulating to the public

BROOKS MEMORIAL LIBRARY, 224 Main St, 05301. SAN 362-6040. Tel: 802-254-5290. FAX: 802-257-2309. E-Mail: brattlib@brooks.lib.vt.us. Web Site: www.brooks.lib.vt.us. *Dir*, Jerry J Carbone; E-Mail: jerry@brooks.lib.vt.us; *ILL, Ref*, Richard Shuldiner; *Ch Servs*, Sandra King; Staff 12 (MLS 4, Non-MLS 8)
Founded 1882. Pop 12,241; Circ 163,530
Jul 1999-Jun 2000 Income $479,839, City $394,446, Locally Generated Income $85,393. Mats Exp $80,930. Sal $258,439
Library Holdings: Bk Titles 68,134; Per Subs 350
Special Collections: Brattleboro & Surrounding Area (Local History Coll), mixed media; Fine Arts Coll (paintings, drawings, bronzes, sculpted marble); Genealogy (Lawson Coll); Local History (Bratteboro Photo, Porter Thayer Photo & Benjamin Crown Photo Colls); Nuclear Energy (Vermont Yankee Coll), rpt; Windam World Affairs Council Archives
Database Vendor: DRA, Ebsco - EbscoHost, OCLC - First Search
Publications: Friends of the Library (quarterly newsletter)
Friends of the Library Group

S NEW ENGLAND COALITION ON NUCLEAR POLLUTION LIBRARY,* PO Box 545, 05302. SAN 373-0034. Tel: 802-257-0336. FAX: 802-257-0336. E-Mail: necnp@sover.net.
Library Holdings: Bk Vols 300; Per Subs 75
Subject Interests: Energy, Nuclear power

C SCHOOL FOR INTERNATIONAL TRAINING, Donald B Watt Library, Kipling Rd, 05301. (Mail add: PO Box 676, 05302-0676), SAN 316-9677. Tel: 802-258-3354. FAX: 802-258-3248. E-Mail: library@sit.edu. Web Site: www.worldlearning.org. *Librn*, Indu Aggarwal; *Librn*, Shirley L Capron; *Librn*, Pamela Contakos
Founded 1967. Enrl 250; Fac 35; Highest Degree: Master
Library Holdings: Bk Vols 30,000; Bk Titles 25,000; Per Subs 356
Subject Interests: Area studies, Behav sci, Bicultural studies, Bilingual studies, Education, Environmental studies, Soc sci
Special Collections: International Organization Files; Language & Culture Coll; Masters Studies Essays

BRISTOL

P LAWRENCE MEMORIAL LIBRARY,* 40 North St, 05443. SAN 376-3358. Tel: 802-453-2366. FAX: 802-453-2569. E-Mail: bristol@do1.state.vt.us. *Librn*, Nancy Wilson
Jul 1997-Jun 1998 Income $62,217, City $48,410, Locally Generated Income $13,307. Mats Exp $11,047, Books $9,410, Per/Ser (Incl. Access Fees) $1,237. Sal $35,569 (Prof $17,935)
Library Holdings: Bk Vols 13,542; Per Subs 30
Mem of Albemarle Regional Library

BROOKFIELD

P BROOKFIELD FREE PUBLIC LIBRARY,* Ralph Rd, 05036. SAN 320-2739. Tel: 802-276-3352. FAX: 802-276-3926. *Librn*, Florence Barnum
Founded 1791. Pop 1,000; Circ 3,000
Library Holdings: Bk Titles 5,000
Special Collections: Brookfield Historical Society, Files
Friends of the Library Group

BROWNINGTON

S ORLEANS COUNTY HISTORICAL SOCIETY, INC, Old Stone House Library, Old Stone Rd. SAN 316-9723. Tel: 802-754-2022. FAX: 802-754-2022. E-Mail: osh@together.net. *Dir*, Tracy Martin
Founded 1853
Library Holdings: Bk Titles 2,000; Per Subs 10
Subject Interests: Orleans County hist
Special Collections: Nineteenth Century School Textbooks & Music Bks Coll
This library is a part of The Old Stone House Museum

BURLINGTON

M FLETCHER ALLEN HOSPITAL LIBRARY, Dana Medical Library,* University of Vermont, Given Bldg, 05405. SAN 317-185X. Tel: 802-656-2200. FAX: 802-656-0762. Web Site: www.sageunix.uvm.edu/dana/. *Dir*, Ellen Hall; *Librn*, Julie McGowen; Staff 9 (MLS 9)
Jul 1998-Jun 1999 Mats Exp $772,119, Books $63,184, Per/Ser (Incl. Access Fees) $676,261, AV Equip $889, Electronic Ref Mat (Incl. Access Fees) $31,785. Sal $680,301
Library Holdings: Bk Vols 28,688; Per Subs 1,340
Database Vendor: Dialog, GaleNet, OCLC - First Search, OVID Technologies
Publications: Briefs (quarterly)
Mem of Nat Network of Librs of Med
Partic in VT/NH Health Sci Libr

C CHAMPLAIN COLLEGE LIBRARY, (Formerly Miller Information Commons), 83 Summit St, 05401-0670. (Mail add: 163 S Willard St, 05401), SAN 316-974X. Tel: 802-860-2717. Circulation Tel: 802-865-6489. Reference Tel: 802-865-6486. FAX: 802-860-2782. Web Site: campus.champlain.edu/library/. *Access Serv, Actg Dir, Syst Coordr*, Cynthia

T Plenge; Tel: 802-865-6487, E-Mail: plenge@champlain.edu; *Actg Dir*, Paula Olsen; E-Mail: olsen@champlain.edu; *Acq*, Thomas McCaffrey; Tel: 802-865-6488, E-Mail: mccaffrey@champlain.edu; *Acq*, Lynn Rowe; *Circ*, Tammy Miller; E-Mail: millert@champlain.edu; *Ref*, Radmila Ballada; Tel: 802-860-2455, E-Mail: ballada@champlain.edu. Subject Specialists: *Children's literature*, Paula Olsen; *Political science*, Cynthia T Plenge; Staff 11 (MLS 4, Non-MLS 7)
Founded 1878. Enrl 2,300; Fac 96; Highest Degree: Bachelor
Jul 2000-Jun 2001 Income Parent Institution $320,083. Mats Exp $90,943, Books $35,000, Per/Ser (Incl. Access Fees) $25,000, Micro $9,000, AV Equip $7,760, Other Print Mats $9,000, Electronic Ref Mat (Incl. Access Fees) $5,183. Sal $157,920
Library Holdings: Bk Vols 60,000; Bk Titles 49,000; Per Subs 1,600
Subject Interests: Bus mgt, Children's literature, Computer science, Computing, Education, Travel
Special Collections: Art Book Coll; Champlain College History; College Archives; Vermontiana
Automation Activity & Vendor Info: (Cataloging) DRA; (Circulation) DRA; (Course Reserve) DRA; (OPAC) DRA
Database Vendor: Ebsco - EbscoHost, IAC - SearchBank, Lexis-Nexis, ProQuest
Function: Research library
Mem of Vt Automated Libr Syst
Partic in Nelinet, Inc

L DINSE, KNAPP & MCANDREW LIBRARY, 209 Battery St, PO Box 988, 05402-0988. SAN 323-6749. Tel: 802-864-5751. FAX: 802-862-6409. *Librn*, Trish Buckley; E-Mail: tbuckley@dinse.com
Library Holdings: Bk Vols 8,000; Bk Titles 1,000; Per Subs 50
Subject Interests: Law

R EPISCOPAL CHURCH CENTER, Bishops Library - Rock Point,* 11 Rock Point Circle, 05401. SAN 316-9774. Tel: 802-863-3431. FAX: 802-860-1562. E-Mail: bishopvt@ecunet.org.
Founded 1894
Library Holdings: Bk Vols 4,500

P FLETCHER FREE LIBRARY, 235 College St, 05401. SAN 316-9782. Tel: 802-863-3403. TDD: 802-865-7219. FAX: 802-865-7227. Web Site: www.fletcherfree.org. *Dir*, Amber Collins; Tel: 802-865-7214, E-Mail: collins@lemming.uvm.edu; *Dir*, Anita Danigelis; Tel: 802-865-7224, E-Mail: danigeli@lemming.uvm.edu; *Dir*, Robert Resnik; Tel: 802-865-7222, E-Mail: resnik@lemming.uvm.edu; *ILL*, Fred Hill; E-Mail: hill@lemming.uvm.edu; *Ch Servs*, Beth Wright; Tel: 802-865-7216; *Acq*, Susan Bevins; Tel: 802-865-7221; *Circ*, Lorrie Colburn; *Ref*, Robert Coleburn; Tel: 802-805-7218, E-Mail: coleburn@lemming.uva.edu; *Ad Servs, Outreach Serv*, Barbara Shatara; Tel: 802-865-7211, E-Mail: shatara@lemming.uvm.edu; *Ch Servs*, Rebecca Goldberg; Staff 18 (MLS 5, Non-MLS 13)
Founded 1873. Pop 39,127; Circ 270,479
Jul 1999-Jun 2000 Income $1,131,206, City $1,046,594, Other $84,612. Mats Exp $150,427, Books $128,922, Electronic Ref Mat (Incl. Access Fees) $21,505. Sal $569,529
Library Holdings: Bk Vols 107,597; Per Subs 273
Subject Interests: Local history
Automation Activity & Vendor Info: (Acquisitions) MultiLIS; (Cataloging) MultiLIS; (Circulation) MultiLIS; (OPAC) MultiLIS
Publications: BiblioFile (monthly)
Area Resource: Adult Basic Education; Consumer Health Information Center
Friends of the Library Group

S GENERAL DYNAMICS, Armament Systems Library,* 128 Lakeside Ave, Rm 1320, 05401-4985. SAN 316-9790. Tel: 802-657-6886. FAX: 802-657-6340. *Librn*, Marge Reposa; E-Mail: marge.e.reposa@gdarm.com
Library Holdings: Bk Vols 5,500; Per Subs 50

S THE LUND FAMILY CENTER,* 76 Glen Rd, 05401. SAN 316-9804. Tel: 802-864-7467, Ext 235. FAX: 802-864-1619. *Dir*, Barbara Rachelson
Library Holdings: Bk Vols 1,300
Special Collections: Adolescent Topics Coll, VF
Open Mon-Fri 8:30-5

M PLANNED PARENTHOOD OF NORTHERN NEW ENGLAND, Resource Center Library,* 23 Mansfield Ave, 05401. SAN 329-9120. Tel: 802-862-9638. FAX: 802-863-5284. E-Mail: education@ppnne.org.; Staff 1 (MLS 1)
Library Holdings: Bk Titles 600; Per Subs 25
Subject Interests: Family planning, Human sexuality
Open Mon-Fri 8:30-5

C UNIVERSITY OF VERMONT & STATE AGRICULTURAL COLLEGE, Bailey Howe Memorial Library, 05405-0036. SAN 362-6105. Tel: 802-656-2020. FAX: 802-656-4038. Web Site: sageunix.uvm.edu/. *Actg Dir*, Nancy Portnow; Tel: 802-656-1950, E-Mail: ncrane@zoo.uvm.edu; *Dean of Libr*, Mara Saule; Tel: 802-656-2003, E-Mail: msaule@zoo.uvm.edu; *Spec Coll & Archives*, Connell Gallagher; Tel: 802-656-2595, E-Mail: cbgallag@zoo.uvm.edu; *Online Servs*, Lyman Ross; *Dir Info Resources & Res*, Douglas Lehman; Tel: 802-656-0809, E-Mail: douglas.lehman@uvm.edu; *Syst Coordr*, Paul Philbin; Tel: 802-656-1369, E-Mail: pphilbin@zoo.uvm.edu; Staff 22 (MLS 22)
Founded 1800. Enrl 10,146; Fac 871; Highest Degree: Doctorate
Jul 1999-Jun 2000 Income (Main Library and Branch Library) Parent Institution $7,819,098. Mats Exp $3,091,321, Books $694,881, Per/Ser (I Access Fees) $2,021,873, Presv $69,840, AV Equip $45,157, Electronic I Mat (Incl. Access Fees) $240,700
Library Holdings: Bk Vols 1,196,350; Bk Titles 793,666; Per Subs 4,47
Special Collections: bks, mss, photog; Canadian & United States Army Serv; Civil War (Howard-Hawkins Coll); Geography, Foreign Affairs, Linguistics & Ecology (George Perkins Marsh Coll), mss; Literature & Personal Correspondence (Dorothy Canfield Fisher Coll), bks, mss; Politi & Government Coll, mss; U S Army Map Service; Vermont Local Histor Stevens Family & Bookselling (Henry Stevens Coll), mss; Vermontiana (Wilbur Coll)
Automation Activity & Vendor Info: (Acquisitions) NOTIS; (Catalogin NOTIS; (Circulation) NOTIS
Database Vendor: Dialog, Lexis-Nexis, OCLC - First Search, OVID Technologies, Silverplatter Information Inc.
Publications: A Newsletter for Friends of Special Coll; Liber
Partic in Center For Research Libraries; Nelinet, Inc; Nerl; OCLC Online Computer Library Center, Inc; Vermont Resource Sharing Network
Friends of the Library Group
Departmental Libraries:
CHEMISTRY & PHYSICS, Cook Physical Sciences Bldg, 05405. SAN 362-6164. Tel: 802-656-2268. *Librn*, Connie Israel

CM DANA MEDICAL LIBRARY, Given Bldg, 05405. SAN 362-613X. Tel: 802-656-2200. FAX: 802-656-0762. *Actg Dir*, Ellen Hall; Tel: 802-656-4396, E-Mail: ellen.hall@vtmetnet.org; *Acq*, Joy Albert; Tel: 802-656-8350, Fax: 802-656-4038, E-Mail: albert.joy@uvm.edu; Staff 22 (MLS Non-MLS 14)
Jul 1999-Jun 2000 Income Parent Institution $973,034. Mats Exp $880,124, Books $57,457, Per/Ser (Incl. Access Fees) $762,049, Presv $15,000, Electronic Ref Mat (Incl. Access Fees) $45,618
Library Holdings: Bk Vols 112,621; Per Subs 1,328
Special Collections: History of Medicine (Special Emphasis on Americ Medicine)
Automation Activity & Vendor Info: (Acquisitions) NOTIS; (Catalogi NOTIS; (Serials) NOTIS
Database Vendor: Dialog, Lexis-Nexis, OCLC - First Search, OVID Technologies, Silverplatter Information Inc.
Publications: Dana Medical Library Newsletter; Resource Library New
Partic in Nelinet, Inc; Nerl; NLM; OCLC Online Computer Library Center, Inc
Resource Library in the National Library of Medicine Regional Medical Library Network

S WCAX-TV LIBRARY, PO Box 608, 05401. SAN 373-0123. Tel: 802-65 6300. FAX: 802-652-6399. Web Site: www.wcax.com. *Librn*, Diane Landr
Library Holdings: Bk Vols 40; Per Subs 30
Special Collections: News Archives from 1950s

CABOT

P CABOT PUBLIC LIBRARY,* PO Box 6, 05647. SAN 316-9820. Tel: 80 563-2721. *Librn*, Jeanette Abbott
Pop 1,001; Circ 6,861
Library Holdings: Bk Vols 7,000; Per Subs 20
Mem of Northeastern Regional Libr Syst

CANAAN

P ALICE M WARD MEMORIAL LIBRARY, 27 Park St, 05903. (Mail add PO Box 134, 05903-0134), Tel: 802-266-7135. FAX: 802-266-7867. E-Ma ecaawml@together.net. Web Site: homepages.together.net/~ecaawml. *Librn* Gloria Bunnell
Founded 1930. Pop 1,210; Circ 10,900
Jan 1998-Dec 1998 Income $40,000. Sal $25,000
Library Holdings: Bk Vols 10,000; Bk Titles 11,000
Subject Interests: Education, History
Mem of Northeastern Regional Libr Syst
Special Services for the Blind - Homebound services
Open Mon, Tues Thurs & Fri 11-6, Wed 1-4, Sat 10-12
Friends of the Library Group

CASTLETON

P CASTLETON FREE LIBRARY,* PO Box 296, 05735. SAN 316-9847. Te 802-468-5574. *Dir*, Jan Jones; *Librn*, Meg Fitch
Pop 3,637; Circ 11,934
Library Holdings: Bk Vols 12,721
Mem of Southwest Regional Library Service System

C CASTLETON STATE COLLEGE, Calvin Coolidge Library, 178 Alumni I 05735. SAN 316-9855. Tel: 802-468-1255. FAX: 802-468-1475. *Dir*, Patric Max; *Ref*, Sandy Duling; *Doc, Tech Servs*, Nancy Luzer; *Media Spec*, Kare Sanborn; *Circ*, Virginia Johnston; *ILL, Ser*, Frances Czarnecki; Staff 4 (ML 4)
Founded 1787. Enrl 2,114; Fac 86; Highest Degree: Master

Library Holdings: Bk Vols 131,798; Bk Titles 107,720; Per Subs 512
Subject Interests: Vermontiana
Special Collections: ERIC
Publications: Serials List - Pathfinders
Partic in Nelinet, Inc
Media Center located in Library

HARLOTTE

THE CHARLOTTE LIBRARY,* 115 Ferry Rd, PO Box 120, 05445. SAN 376-4907. Tel: 802-425-3864. E-Mail: charlib@together.net. *Librn*, Diane Dolbashian
Library Holdings: Bk Vols 5,000; Per Subs 30
Friends of the Library Group

HELSEA

CHELSEA PUBLIC LIBRARY, Alden Speare Memorial Library, Main St, PO Box 67, 05038. SAN 316-9871. Tel: 802-685-2188. E-Mail: chelsea@dol.state.vt.us. *Librn*, Elizabeth Button
Founded 1894. Pop 1,091; Circ 9,036
Library Holdings: Bk Vols 10,000; Per Subs 20
Special Collections: Vermontiania Coll
Partic in Vermont State Libr Syst
Open Mon, Wed & Fri 2-6, Sat 10-12

HESTER

WHITING LIBRARY, 117 Main St, 05143. (Mail add: PO Box 68, 05143-0068), SAN 316-988X. Tel: 802-875-2277. *Librn*, Diane Lischer; Staff 3 (Non-MLS 3)
Founded 1892. Pop 2,791; Circ 20,000
Library Holdings: Bk Titles 9,953; Per Subs 20

HITTENDEN

FREDERIC D BARSTOW MEMORIAL LIBRARY,* 223 Main Rd, 05737. SAN 316-9898. Tel: 802-773-6926. FAX: 802-747-4814. *Librn*, Anne Gallivan; E-Mail: agallivan@borston.a12.vt.us
Circ 18,381
Library Holdings: Bk Vols 5,400; Per Subs 25
Mem of Southwest Regional Library Service System

OLCHESTER

BURNHAM MEMORIAL LIBRARY, 898 Main St, 05446. SAN 316-9901. Tel: 802-879-7576. FAX: 802-879-5079. E-Mail: bumeli@sover.net. Web Site: www.sover.net/~bumeli/burnham.htm. *Librn*, Carolyn Barnes; *Asst Librn*, Erica Trudeau; *Ch Servs*, Betty Ellis; Staff 2 (MLS 1, Non-MLS 1)
Founded 1902. Pop 16,500; Circ 80,000
Jul 1998-Jun 1999 Income City $168,713. Mats Exp $27,994, Books $23,514, Per/Ser (Incl. Access Fees) $2,480, Electronic Ref Mat (Incl. Access Fees) $2,000. Sal $130,339
Library Holdings: Bk Vols 38,499; Bk Titles 33,023; Per Subs 75
Subject Interests: Large print bks, Local history
Automation Activity & Vendor Info: (Cataloging) Follett; (Circulation) Follett
Mem of Vt Automated Libr Syst
Friends of the Library Group

SAINT MICHAEL'S COLLEGE, Durick Library, Winooski Pk, 05439-2525. SAN 316-991X. Tel: 802-654-2000. FAX: 802-654-2630. Web Site: www.smcvt.edu/library. *Access Serv, Instrul Serv, Publ Servs*, Mark McAteer; E-Mail: mmcateer@smcvt.edu; *ILL*, Kristen Hindes; E-Mail: khindes@smcvt.edu; *Acq*, Laura Crain; E-Mail: lcrain@smcvt.edu; *Bibliog Instr, Tech Servs*, Robert Bouchard-Hall; Tel: 802-654-2402, E-Mail: rbouchard-hall@smcvt.edu; *Tech Coordr*, Joann Trottier; E-Mail: jtrottier@smctv.edu; Staff 26 (MLS 8, Non-MLS 18)
Founded 1904. Enrl 2,600; Fac 140; Highest Degree: Master
Jul 1999-Jun 2000 Income $1,482,331. Mats Exp $451,592, Books $118,134, Per/Ser (Incl. Access Fees) $233,502, Presv $9,466, Micro $18,552, Electronic Ref Mat (Incl. Access Fees) $43,580. Sal $942,630 (Prof $769,267)
Library Holdings: Bk Vols 209,000; Bk Titles 141,000; Per Subs 1,003
Subject Interests: Education, Eng as a second language, History, Jewish studies, Psychology, Relig studies, Theology
Special Collections: Archives of the Society of St Edmund; Music (Richard Stoehr Coll); New England Culinary Institute
Automation Activity & Vendor Info: (Acquisitions) Endeavor; (Cataloging) Endeavor; (Circulation) Endeavor; (OPAC) Endeavor; (Serials) Endeavor
Database Vendor: CARL, Dialog, GaleNet, Lexis-Nexis, OCLC - First Search, ProQuest, Silverplatter Information Inc., Wilson - Wilson Web
Partic in ARIEL; Nelinet, Inc; OCLC Online Computer Library Center, Inc; Vt Automated Libr Syst

CONCORD

P CONCORD PUBLIC LIBRARY,* PO Box 188, 05824. SAN 316-9928. Tel: 802-695-2220. FAX: 802-695-2220. *Actg Librn*, Joyce Forest
Pop 1,200; Circ 2,300
Jul 1996-Jun 1997 Mats Exp $1,151
Library Holdings: Bk Vols 3,200; Per Subs 13
Mem of Northeastern Regional Libr Syst
Open Wed 2-4 & 6-8 & Sat 10-12

CORNWALL

P CORNWALL FREE PUBLIC LIBRARY,* 2629 Rte 30, 05753-9340. SAN 316-9936. Tel: 802-462-2763. FAX: 802-462-2606. *Librn*, Doris Severy
Pop 1,000; Circ 1,100
Library Holdings: Bk Vols 4,000
Subject Interests: Local authors, Local history
Mem of Southwest Regional Library Service System

CRAFTSBURY

P CRAFTSBURY PUBLIC LIBRARY,* Craftsbury Common, Box 74, 05826. SAN 376-3374. Tel: 802-586-9683. E-Mail: crastsburypl@dol.state.ut. *Librn*, Linda Wells
Library Holdings: Bk Vols 8,000; Per Subs 32
Friends of the Library Group

P JOHN WOODRUFF SIMPSON MEMORIAL LIBRARY, Rte 1, Box 1034, 05827. SAN 317-0071. Tel: 802-586-9692. *Librn*, Sherry Urie
Founded 1921. Pop 1,000; Circ 17,000
Library Holdings: Bk Titles 20,000; Per Subs 50

CUTTINGSVILLE

P SHREWSBURY PUBLIC LIBRARY,* PO Box 1115, 05738. SAN 316-9952. Tel: 802-492-3410. *Librn*, Ginny Buckley; *Librn*, Joan Aleshire
Pop 866; Circ 1,379
Library Holdings: Bk Vols 3,500; Bk Titles 4,000
Mem of Southwest Regional Library Service System
Partic in Vt Libr Asn; Vt Trustees Asn
Friends of the Library Group

DANBY

P S L GRIFFITH MEMORIAL LIBRARY,* PO Box 237, 05739-0237. SAN 316-9960. Tel: 802-293-5106. *Librn*, Joan D Bromley
Founded 1908. Pop 1,200; Circ 5,706
Library Holdings: Bk Vols 12,648; Per Subs 35
Mem of Southwest Regional Library Service System
Open Wed 2-5 & 6-8 & Sat 2-5

DANVILLE

S AMERICAN SOCIETY OF DOWSERS, Reading Library, Brainerd St, PO Box 24, 05828-0024. SAN 324-458X. Tel: 802-684-3417. FAX: 802-684-2565. E-Mail: asd@dowsers.org. Web Site: www.dowsers.org. *In Charge*, Brenda Paquin
Library Holdings: Bk Vols 600; Per Subs 30
Open Mon-Fri 9-5

P POPE MEMORIAL LIBRARY,* PO Box 260, 05828-0260. SAN 316-9979. Tel: 802-684-2256. *Librn*, Jean Ashley
Founded 1890. Pop 1,900; Circ 12,000
Jan 1997-Dec 1998 Income $25,000
Library Holdings: Bk Titles 12,500; Per Subs 12,550
Subject Interests: Genealogical res, Large print, Vt hist
Special Collections: Circulating Toy Coll; Vermont Mysteries & Westerns (fiction & nonfiction)
Home delivery to shut-ins; access to over 100 Books-on-Tape per year.
Open Mon-Wed 9-7, Fri 9-6 & Sat 9-12
Friends of the Library Group

DERBY

P DAILEY MEMORIAL LIBRARY,* PO Box 30, 05829. SAN 316-9987. Tel: 802-766-5063. *Dir*, Barbara J Whitehill; *Asst Librn*, Teresa Smith
Founded 1957. Circ 13,000
Library Holdings: Bk Titles 20,000; Per Subs 27
Subject Interests: Local history
Special Collections: Children's Coll
Mem of Vermont Libr Asn
Open Tues 12-8, Thurs 10-5 & Sat 10-3
Friends of the Library Group

DERBY LINE

P HASKELL FREE LIBRARY, INC, 93 Caswell Ave, 05830. (Mail add: PO Box 337, 05830-0337), Tel: 802-873-3022. FAX: 802-873-3634. E-Mail: haskell1@together.net. Web Site: www.haskellopera.org. *Dir*, Kim Prangley; Staff 5 (Non-MLS 5)
Founded 1905. Pop 5,000; Circ 43,331
Jan 1999-Dec 1999 Income $134,553, City $1,500, Locally Generated Income $133,053. Mats Exp $13,800, Books $12,477, Per/Ser (Incl. Access Fees) $1,323. Sal $59,327
Library Holdings: Bk Vols 20,000; Per Subs 45
Function: ILL available
Mem of Vt Automated Libr Syst
Special Services for the Blind - Bks on cassette

DORSET

P DORSET PUBLIC LIBRARY ASSOCIATION, INC,* PO Box 38, 05251. SAN 317-0004. Tel: 802-867-5774. *Librn*, Gail Bumgardner
Founded 1871. Circ 24,000
Library Holdings: Bk Vols 15,000; Per Subs 70
Mem of Southwest Regional Library Service System
Open Mon, Wed & Fri 9:30-12, Mon, Tues, Thurs & Fri 2:30-5:30, Wed 2:30-6, Sat 10-12

EAST BURKE

P EAST BURKE COMMUNITY LIBRARY,* PO Box 309, 05832. SAN 317-0047. Tel: 802-626-9823. *Librn*, Lyle Seeger
Pop 1,047; Circ 2,300
Library Holdings: Bk Vols 4,000
Mem of Northeastern Regional Libr Syst
Open Mon, Tues & Thurs 1:30-8 & Sat 9-12

EAST CORINTH

P BLAKE MEMORIAL LIBRARY,* 676 Village Rd, PO Box D, 05040. SAN 317-0063. Tel: 802-439-5338. E-Mail: blakecorinth@dol.state.vt.us. *Dir*, Janine M Moore; Tel: 802-439-5142, E-Mail: moore_janine@hotmail.com; *Librn*, Alice Thompson; *Asst Librn*, Ed Eilertsen
Pop 6,000; Circ 11,900
Library Holdings: Bk Vols 16,500; Per Subs 24
Function: Reference services available
Mem of Midstate Regional Libr
Open Mon, Wed & Fri 2-5 & 6-8 & Sat 10-12
Friends of the Library Group

EAST DOVER

P DOVER FREE LIBRARY,* 05341-0267. SAN 317-008X. Tel: 802-348-7488. FAX: 802-348-9306. E-Mail: dover_free@dol.state.vt.us. *Dir*, John G Flores
Founded 1913. Pop 990
Jul 1997-Jun 1998 Income $81,212. Mats Exp $11,500, Books $9,500, Per/Ser (Incl. Access Fees) $2,000. Sal $42,969 (Prof $28,000)
Library Holdings: Bk Vols 13,371
Subject Interests: Cookery, Early childhood educ, New England, Parenting, Vermontiana

ENOSBURG FALLS

P ENOSBURG PUBLIC LIBRARY,* PO Box 206, 05450. SAN 317-011X. Tel: 802-933-2328. *Librn*, Hildred Tatro
Pop 2,000; Circ 12,000
Library Holdings: Bk Titles 12,000; Per Subs 19
Partic in NW Regional Libr Coop
Friends of the Library Group

ESSEX

P ESSEX FREE LIBRARY, Rt 15, Jericho Rd, PO Box 8093, 05451-8093. SAN 317-0128. Tel: 802-879-0313. E-Mail: essexlib@together.net. *Librn*, Susan Overfield; Staff 6 (Non-MLS 6)
Founded 1929. Pop 9,500; Circ 96,493
Jul 2000-Jun 2001 Income Locally Generated Income $184,793. Mats Exp $27,900. Sal $104,600
Library Holdings: Bk Titles 21,516; Per Subs 77; Bks on Deafness & Sign Lang 14
Automation Activity & Vendor Info: (Acquisitions) Follett; (Cataloging) Follett; (Circulation) Follett; (Course Reserve) Follett; (ILL) Follett; (Media Booking) Follett; (OPAC) Follett; (Serials) Follett
Friends of the Library Group

ESSEX JUNCTION

P BROWNELL LIBRARY, 6 Lincoln St, 05452-3154. SAN 317-0136. Tel: 802-878-6955. TDD: 802-878-6955. FAX: 802-878-6946. E-Mail: Brownell_Library@hotmail.com. Web Site: www.together.net/wbarnes/brownell.htm. *Dir*, Penelope D Pillsbury; *Asst Dir*, Bernadette Howard; *C Servs*, Mary L Graf; Staff 5 (MLS 2, Non-MLS 3)
Founded 1897. Pop 14,392; Circ 156,986
Jul 1999-Jun 2000 Income $416,252. Mats Exp $54,561, Books $51,256, Electronic Ref Mat (Incl. Access Fees) $3,305. Sal $210,738 (Prof $165,056)
Library Holdings: Bk Vols 57,639; Per Subs 181
Subject Interests: Essex Area hist, Vermontiana
Special Collections: Vermont town histories
Automation Activity & Vendor Info: (Cataloging) Follett; (Circulation) Follett; (OPAC) Follett
Publications: Friends of Brownell Newsletter
Friends of the Library Group

S IBM CORP, Technical Library, Bldg 967B, Col M-22, 1000 River St, 05452-4299. SAN 317-0152. Tel: 802-769-6500. FAX: 802-769-6501. *Lib* Karen Lynch; E-Mail: karenlyn@us.ibm.com
Founded 1965
Library Holdings: Bk Titles 8,000; Per Subs 150
Subject Interests: Chemistry, Computer science, Mathematics, Mgt sci, Programming, Semiconductors, Solid state electronics, Solid state physics

FAIR HAVEN

P FAIR HAVEN FREE PUBLIC LIBRARY,* 107 Main, 05743. SAN 317-0160. Tel: 802-265-8011. *Librn*, Carol Scott
Founded 1906. Pop 2,819; Circ 15,132
Library Holdings: Bk Vols 15,500; Per Subs 36
Special Collections: Mystery Coll; Vermontiana Coll
Open Tues & Fri 8:30-4:30, Wed 4-8, Sat 9-1
Friends of the Library Group

FAIRFAX

P FAIRFAX COMMUNITY LIBRARY,* PO Box 168, 05454. SAN 317-0179. Tel: 802-849-2420. FAX: 802-849-6711. *Librn*, Joy M LeBaron; *Librn*, Sharon Horr; *Librn*, Suzanne Ludlam; Staff 2 (MLS 1, Non-MLS 1
Founded 1972. Pop 1,805; Circ 30,000
Jan 1996-Dec 1997 Income $103,698. Mats Exp $25,179. Sal $60,799
Library Holdings: Bk Titles 22,490; Per Subs 125
Special Collections: Local History (Fairfax Historical Society Coll)

P GEORGIA PUBLIC LIBRARY,* RD 2, Box 1060, 05454. SAN 376-3382 Tel: 802-524-4643. *Librn*, Susan Webster
Library Holdings: Bk Vols 10,000; Per Subs 55
Friends of the Library Group

FAIRFIELD

P BENT NORTHRUP MEMORIAL LIBRARY,* Rte 36, 05455. SAN 376-4893. Tel: 802-827-6639. FAX: 802-827-3604. E-Mail: fcschool@fairfield.k12.vt.us. *Librn*, Barbara Branon
Library Holdings: Bk Vols 11,166; Per Subs 10

FAIRLEE

P FAIRLEE PUBLIC LIBRARY, 25 Town Common Rd, 05045-9584. (Mail add: PO Box 125, 05045-0125), Tel: 802-333-4716. E-Mail: fairlee_pub@dol.state.vt.us. *Dir*, Debra Lee Edmands; Fax: 802-333-9214; Staff 1 (Non-MLS 1)
Founded 1898. Pop 903; Circ 7,252
Jan 1999-Dec 1999 Income $31,009, City $27,877, Locally Generated Income $3,132. Mats Exp $5,544. Sal $15,598 (Prof $15,598)
Library Holdings: Bk Vols 12,875; Per Subs 66
Function: ILL available
Mem of Vt Automated Libr Syst

FERRISBURG

S ROWLAND E ROBINSON MEMORIAL ASSOCIATION, Rokeby Museum Special Collections Library, 4334 Rte 7, 05456-9711. SAN 317-0209. Tel: 802-877-3406. E-Mail: rokeby@globalnetisp.net. Web Site: www.rokeby.org.
Founded 1962
Subject Interests: Anti-slavery, Biog, Farming, Fishing, History, Hunting, Popular lit, Quaker writings, Sch text, Spiritualism
Special Collections: Abolition, Religious History, Social History & Vermo Folklore (Robinson & Stevens family papers 1770-1960)
Restriction: By appointment only

ANKLIN

HASTON LIBRARY, Main St, PO Box 83, 05457. SAN 321-0952. Tel: 802-285-6505. *Librn*, Judy Martin
Founded 1907. Pop 1,010; Circ 1,415
Library Holdings: Bk Vols 5,269; Per Subs 10

YSVILLE

BELCHER MEMORIAL LIBRARY,* PO Box 144, 05746. SAN 376-4060. Tel: 802-234-6608. *Librn*, Linda Jagoda
Library Holdings: Bk Vols 2,500
Mem of Midstate Regional Libr

LMAN

GILMAN COMMUNITY LIBRARY,* PO Box 56, 05904. SAN 317-0233. Tel: 802-892-5969. *Librn*, Sheri Brabbury
Pop 1,138
Library Holdings: Bk Vols 15,000
Mem of Northeastern Regional Libr Syst
Open Sun & Mon 6-8:30, Wed 2-5

OVER

GLOVER PUBLIC LIBRARY,* PO Box 196, 05839. SAN 317-0241. Tel: 802-525-6612. *Librn*, Lucy Sample
Founded 1909. Pop 886
Library Holdings: Bk Vols 4,136
Mem of Northeastern Regional Libr Syst

RAFTON

GRAFTON HISTORICAL MUSEUM LIBRARY,* Main St, PO Box 202, 05146. SAN 370-8861. Tel: 802-843-2489. *Curator*, Eli Prowdy; *Pres*, Dorothy Cannon
Library Holdings: Bk Titles 30; Per Subs 50

GRAFTON PUBLIC LIBRARY, 204 Main St, PO Box 129, 05146. SAN 317-0268. Tel: 802-843-2404. *Librn*, Julie Hirschfeld
Founded 1882
Library Holdings: Bk Vols 24,000; Bk Titles 25,000; Per Subs 30
Mem of Southeastern Regional Libr Syst
Friends of the Library Group

RANBY

GRANBY TOWN LIBRARY,* Main St, 05840. SAN 317-0276. Tel: 802-328-4891. *Librn*, Barbara Brown
Pop 70; Circ 1,000
Library Holdings: Bk Vols 925
Restriction: By appointment only
Mem of Northeastern Regional Libr Syst

RAND ISLE

GRAND ISLE FREE LIBRARY,* 9 Hyde Rd, 05458. SAN 317-0284. Tel: 802-372-4797. *Librn*, Linda Smith
Library Holdings: Bk Vols 6,000

REENSBORO

GREENSBORO FREE LIBRARY, 53 Wilson St, 05841. SAN 317-0306. Tel: 802-533-2531. E-Mail: greensboro@dol.state.vt.us. *Dir*, Lisa Sammet
Pop 676; Circ 9,500
Library Holdings: Bk Titles 9,000
Subject Interests: Craft, Gardening
Special Collections: Greensboro Authors
Publications: Greensboro Free Library Newsletter (quarterly)
Mem of Northeastern Regional Libr Syst
Open Wed 1-4, Thurs 10-8, Sat 10-1 & Sun 11:30-1:30
Friends of the Library Group

ROTON

GROTON FREE PUBLIC LIBRARY,* PO Box 6, 05046. SAN 317-0314. Tel: 802-584-3358. *Librn*, Molly Easmon
Founded 1886. Pop 666; Circ 830
Library Holdings: Bk Vols 5,350
Publications: Vermont Library Trustees Publish
Mem of Northeastern Regional Libr Syst
Open Tues 1-4:30 & 6-8, Thurs 1-4:30 & 5:30-8:30 & Sat 2-4

GUILDHALL

P GUILDHALL PUBLIC LIBRARY,* PO Box 9, 05905. SAN 317-0322. Tel: 802-676-3426. *Librn*, Valerie Foy
1998-1999 Income $4,500
Library Holdings: Bk Vols 5,000
Mem of Northeastern Regional Libr Syst
Friends of the Library Group

GUILFORD

P GUILFORD FREE LIBRARY,* 4024 Guilford Center Rd, 05301. SAN 317-0330. Tel: 802-257-4603. *Librn*, Catherine Wilken
Pop 1,532; Circ 2,150
Library Holdings: Bk Vols 3,600
Subject Interests: Ch programming, Local history, Sr programming
Special Collections: Guilford, Vermont History & Biography
Publications: Newsletter (biannual)
Mem of Southeastern Regional Libr Syst
Open Tues 9:30-6 & Sat 9:30-12

HANCOCK

P HANCOCK FREE PUBLIC LIBRARY, PO Box 159, 05748. SAN 317-0349. Tel: 802-767-4651. *In Charge*, Debra McCall Frisco; Staff 1 (Non-MLS 1)
Founded 1920. Pop 340; Circ 1,469
Library Holdings: Bk Vols 2,500; Bk Titles 2,000
Mem of Midstate Regional Libr
Open Wed 3-7, Sat 10-12

HARDWICK

P JEUDEVINE MEMORIAL LIBRARY, PO Box 536, 05843. SAN 317-0357. Tel: 802-472-5948. E-Mail: hardwick_pl@dol.state.vt.us. *Librn*, Lisa Sammet; Tel: 802-586-7533; Staff 2 (MLS 1, Non-MLS 1)
Founded 1897. Pop 2,700; Circ 7,416
Jul 2000-Jun 2001 Mats Exp $3,520, Books $2,000, Per/Ser (Incl. Access Fees) $1,000, AV Equip $200, Manuscripts & Archives $120, Electronic Ref Mat (Incl. Access Fees) $200. Sal $12,000 (Prof $9,568)
Library Holdings: Bk Vols 9,575; Per Subs 20
Special Collections: Vermontiana Coll
Mem of Northeastern Regional Libr Syst

HARTFORD

P HARTFORD LIBRARY,* 1587 Maple, PO Box 512, 05047-0367. SAN 317-0373. Tel: 802-296-2568. *Librn*, Shawna Gordon
Founded 1893. Pop 1,500
Library Holdings: Bk Vols 4,900
Subject Interests: Harvard Classics, Vt hist
Mem of Midstate Regional Libr
Open Mon, Tues & Wed 2-6, Thurs 10-12 & 2-6, Sat 9-12

HARTLAND

P HARTLAND PUBLIC LIBRARIES,* Rte 12, Box 137, 05048. SAN 362-6199. Tel: 802-436-2473. FAX: 802-436-2473. *Librn*, Linda Williamson; Staff 4 (MLS 1, Non-MLS 3)
Pop 2,988; Circ 23,902
1997-1998 Income $53,080, City $52,297. Mats Exp $11,173. Sal $27,842
Library Holdings: Bk Vols 12,796; Per Subs 23
Special Collections: Vermont & Hartland Hist Coll
Open Tues & Fri 10-9, Wed 5-8 & Sat 10-3
Friends of the Library Group

HIGHGATE CENTER

P HIGHGATE PUBLIC LIBRARY, 17 Mill Hill, 05459. (Mail add: PO Box 76, 05459), SAN 317-0381. Tel: 802-868-3970. *Librn*, Lucie Fortin
Library Holdings: Bk Vols 1,500
Open Tues-Thurs 2-6

HINESBURG

P SARAH CARPENTER MEMORIAL LIBRARY, Carpenter-Carse Public Library,* Ballards-Corner Rd, 05461. (Mail add: PO Box 127, 05461), SAN 317-039X. Tel: 802-482-2878. *Dir*, Susan Barden
Founded 1947. Pop 3,700; Circ 21,000
Jul 1996-Jun 1997 Income $59,848. Mats Exp $5,700, Books $5,000, Per/Ser (Incl. Access Fees) $500. Sal $40,000 (Prof $26,000)

Library Holdings: Bk Vols 10,483; Per Subs 43
Special Collections: Vermontiana Coll
Mem of Northwest Regional Library System
Friends of the Library Group

HUBBARDTON

P HUBBARDTON COMMUNITY LIBRARY,* 1985 Rte 3, 05732. SAN 376-4877. Tel: 802-273-3303.
Library Holdings: Bk Vols 2,000
Mem of Southwest Regional Library Service System

HUNTINGTON

P HUNTINGTON PUBLIC LIBRARY, 2209 Main Rd, Ste 1, 05462. (Mail add: PO Box 98, 05462-0098), SAN 317-0403. Tel: 802-434-4583. *Dir*, Anne Dannenberg
Founded 1967. Pop 1,900; Circ 3,000
Jul 2000-Jun 2001 Income Locally Generated Income $15,000. Mats Exp Books $1,300. Sal $8,000
Library Holdings: Bk Titles 8,000; High Interest/Low Vocabulary Bk Vols 20
Subject Interests: Children's, Vermont
Friends of the Library Group

HYDE PARK

P LANPHER MEMORIAL LIBRARY,* PO Box 196, 05655. SAN 317-0411. Tel: 802-888-4628. *Librn*, Jane Nuse
Founded 1895. Pop 2,823
Library Holdings: Bk Titles 8,500; Per Subs 35
Special Collections: Art & Artist; Bound Local Newspapers 1863-1930; Vermont History, Life & Literature

IRASBURG

P LEACH PUBLIC LIBRARY,* 130 Park Ave, PO Box 87, 05845. SAN 325-0482. Tel: 802-754-6593. *Librn*, Rolinda R Chase; Staff 1 (Non-MLS 1)
Founded 1927. Pop 970
Jan 1998-Dec 1998 Income $4,250. Sal $1,959
Library Holdings: Bk Vols 10,900; Bk Titles 10,000; Per Subs 22
Open Jan-Mar, Mon 10:30-4:30, Apr-Dec, Mon 2-4 & 6-8, Fri 2-6

ISLAND POND

P ISLAND POND PUBLIC LIBRARY, PO Box 422, 05846. SAN 320-5193. Tel: 802-723-6134. *Dir, Librn*, Laura Davis
Founded 1897. Pop 1,600
Library Holdings: Bk Vols 15,600; Per Subs 12
Subject Interests: Vt
Mem of Northeastern Regional Libr Syst

ISLE LA MOTTE

P ISLE LA MOTTE FREE LIBRARY, 2238 Main St, 05463. SAN 317-042X. Tel: 802-928-4113. *Actg Librn*, Jeannine Bruley
Founded 1904
Jan 1999-Dec 1999 Income $2,693, Locally Generated Income $840, Other $1,853. Mats Exp $2,090
Library Holdings: Bk Vols 3,000
Mem of E State Regional
Open Fri 12-5, Sat 9-11
Friends of the Library Group

JACKSONVILLE

P WHITINGHAM FREE PUBLIC LIBRARY, Municipal Ctr, PO Box 500, 05342-0500. SAN 317-0438. Tel: 802-368-7506. E-Mail: whitingham@vt.state.us. *Librn*, J K Berberian
Pop 1,300; Circ 9,000
Library Holdings: Bk Vols 15,000; Per Subs 12
Mem of Southeastern Library Services

JAMAICA

P JAMAICA MEMORIAL LIBRARY,* PO Box 266, 05343. SAN 317-0446. Tel: 802-874-4010, 802-874-4901. *Librn*, Joyce Pelos
Pop 681; Circ 760
Library Holdings: Bk Vols 3,000
Special Collections: Vermont & Jamaica (VT) Histories Coll
Mem of Southeastern Library Services
Open Sat 9:30-12:30
Friends of the Library Group

JERICHO

P DEBORAH RAWSON MEMORIAL LIBRARY, 8 River Rd, 05465. SAN 329-0964. Tel: 802-899-4962. *Librn*, Jane Plarghman; Staff 1 (MLS 1)
Founded 1931. Pop 7,302; Circ 18,858
Library Holdings: Bk Titles 12,500; Per Subs 30
Automation Activity & Vendor Info: (Cataloging) Follett; (OPAC) Folle

JERICHO CENTER

P JERICHO TOWN LIBRARY, PO Box 1055, 05465. SAN 317-0470. Tel: 802-899-4686. *Librn*, Emilie Alexander
Pop 4,300
Library Holdings: Bk Vols 10,000
Partic in NW Regional Libr Coop

JOHNSON

P JOHNSON PUBLIC LIBRARY,* PO Box 601, 05656. SAN 317-0497. Te 802-635-7141. *Librn*, Jeanne Engle
Pop 2,581; Circ 4,950
Library Holdings: Bk Vols 7,500; Per Subs 38
Open Tues & Fri 3-5 & 7-8:30, Thurs 3-5 & Sat 10-12

C JOHNSON STATE COLLEGE, John Dewey Library, RR 2, Box 75, 0565 SAN 317-0500. Tel: 802-635-2356. FAX: 802-635-1294. Web Site: www.jsc.vsc.edu. *Dir*, Joseph Farara; Tel: 802-635-1272, E-Mail: fararaj@badger.jsc.vsc.edu; *ILL*, Joanne Edwards; Tel: 802-635-1277, E-Mail: joanne@scolar.vsc.edu; *Ser*, Pamela Gelineau; Tel: 802-635-1271, E-Mail: pam@scolar.vsc.edu; *Cat*, Judith Cleary; Tel: 802-635-1270, E-Mail: clearyj@badger.jsc.vsc.edu; *Publ Servs*, Linda Kramer; Tel: 802-635-1275, E-Mail: kramerl@badger.jsc.usc.edu; *Circ*, Walter Reeve; Tel: 802-635-127 E-Mail: reevew@badger.jsc.vsc.edu; *Tech Servs*, Jane Marshall; Tel: 802-635-1495, E-Mail: jane@scolar.vsc.edu; Staff 4 (MLS 4)
Founded 1866. Enrl 1,700; Fac 65; Highest Degree: Master
Library Holdings: Bk Titles 100,945; Per Subs 531
Subject Interests: Children's literature
Database Vendor: DRA
Publications: Annual Report; Pathfinders; Serials List
Partic in Nelinet, Inc; VALS

KILLINGTON

P SHERBURNE MEMORIAL LIBRARY,* PO Box 73, 05751. SAN 317-0519. Tel: 802-422-9765. E-Mail: sherburne@doll.vt.us. *Librn*, Gail Weymouth
Pop 900; Circ 9,300
Library Holdings: Bk Vols 8,000; Bk Titles 11,000
Subject Interests: Alaska, Northern territories, Vt hist
Special Collections: Sherburne Township History Coll
Open Mon 10-6, Wed 10-8, Thurs 2-6, Fri 10-6 & Sat 9-1

LINCOLN

P LINCOLN LIBRARY,* East River Rd, 05443. SAN 317-0535. Tel: 802-453-3803. *Librn*, Linda Norton
Pop 870; Circ 2,000
Library Holdings: Bk Titles 6,000; Per Subs 19
Mem of Midstate Regional Libr
Open Wed 10-4

LONDONDERRY

P LANDGROVE PUBLIC LIBRARY,* RD 1, Box 221A, 05148. SAN 317-0527. Tel: 802-824-3416, 802-824-3857. *Librn*, Marita Ott
Pop 104; Circ 140
Library Holdings: Bk Titles 2,095
Mem of Southeastern Library Services

LOWELL

P LOWELL COMMUNITY LIBRARY, Rte 100, PO Box 189, 05847. SAN 317-0543. Tel: 802-744-2447. *Librn*, Regine Griswold; Staff 1 (Non-MLS 1
Founded 1935. Pop 650; Circ 1,200
1998-1999 Income $5,000. Mats Exp $5,000, Books $3,500, Per/Ser (Incl. Access Fees) $200. Sal $1,290
Library Holdings: Bk Vols 4,500
Mem of Northeastern Regional Libr Syst
Open Tues 4-6 & Sat 10-12

LOWER WATERFORD

P DAVIES MEMORIAL LIBRARY,* PO Box 73, 05848-0073. SAN 322-8576. Tel: 802-748-9473. *Librn*, Dorothy P Morrison
Founded 1896. Pop 175; Circ 506

Jan 1997-Dec 1998 Income $1,059, City $800. Mats Exp $907, Books $367, Per/Ser (Incl. Access Fees) $540. Sal $200
Library Holdings: Bk Vols 7,804; Per Subs 11
Subject Interests: Vt

DLOW

FLETCHER MEMORIAL LIBRARY, 88 Main St, 05149. SAN 317-0551. Tel: 802-228-8921. *Librn*, Anne Wingate
Founded 1901. Pop 2,463; Circ 58,406
Library Holdings: Bk Vols 50,508; Per Subs 70
Subject Interests: Vt hist
Mem of Southeastern Library Services

TYSON LIBRARY, 46 Library Rd, 05149. (Mail add: 286 Dublin Rd, 05149), Tel: 802-228-8037. *Librn*, Betty Jarvi
Library Holdings: Bk Vols 3,000
Mem of Southeastern Library Services

NENBURG

ALDEN BALCH MEMORIAL LIBRARY,* PO Box 6, 05906. SAN 317-056X. Tel: 802-892-5365. *Librn*, Arlene Lewis; *Asst Librn*, Theresa Lewis
Founded 1904. Circ 12,517
Library Holdings: Bk Vols 4,500; Per Subs 17
Mem of Northeastern Regional Libr Syst

NDONVILLE

COBLEIGH PUBLIC LIBRARY, 14 Depot St, 0585-9715. (Mail add: PO Box 147, 05851-0147), SAN 317-0578. Tel: 802-626-5475. FAX: 802-626-1167. E-Mail: cobleigh@dol.state.vt.us. Web Site: www.cplvt.org. *Dir*, Pat Hazlehurst; E-Mail: pat@cplvt.org; *Ch Servs*, Janis Minshull; Staff 4 (Non-MLS 4)
Founded 1904. Pop 5,371; Circ 32,109
Jan 1999-Dec 1999 Income $143,000. Mats Exp $16,513, Books $14,000, Per/Ser (Incl. Access Fees) $1,900, Micro $113, Electronic Ref Mat (Incl. Access Fees) $500. Sal $85,000 (Prof $49,000)
Library Holdings: Bk Vols 20,000
Subject Interests: Vermontiania
Mem of Northeastern Regional Libr Syst
Friends of the Library Group
Bookmobiles: 1

LYNDON STATE COLLEGE, Samuel Read Hall Library, 1001 College Rd, PO Box 919, 05851-0919. SAN 317-0586. Tel: 802-626-6366. Web Site: www.lsc.vsc.edu/services/library/library.htm. *Librn*, Laurel Stanley; *Per*, Monique Morris; *Tech Servs*, Garet Nelson; *Acq*, Monique Morris; *Cat*, Patricia Webster; *Publ Servs*, David Kaunelis; *ILL*, Jean Fournier; *Circ*, Donna Edwards; Staff 7 (MLS 3, Non-MLS 4)
Founded 1911. Enrl 1,120; Fac 83; Highest Degree: Master
Jul 1999-Jun 2000 Income $475,533. Mats Exp $123,849, Books $60,382, Per/Ser (Incl. Access Fees) $42,902, Micro $14,472, AV Equip $6,093. Sal $229,366 (Prof $112,307)
Library Holdings: Bk Vols 96,342; Per Subs 568
Automation Activity & Vendor Info: (Acquisitions) DRA; (Cataloging) DRA; (Circulation) DRA; (ILL) DRA; (OPAC) DRA; (Serials) DRA
Publications: Annual report; faculty handbook; general guide; Pathfinders
Partic in Nelinet, Inc; OCLC Online Computer Library Center, Inc

ANCHESTER

THE AMERICAN MUSEUM OF FLY FISHING LIBRARY, Seminary Ave, Box 42, 05254-0042. SAN 328-1124. Tel: 802-362-3300. FAX: 802-362-3308. E-Mail: amff@together.net. Web Site: www.amff.com. *Exec Dir*, Gary Tanner
Founded 1968
Library Holdings: Bk Vols 3,000
Restriction: By appointment only
Open Mon-Fri 10-4

MARK SKINNER LIBRARY, 48 West Rd, PO Box 438, 05254-0438. SAN 317-0594. Tel: 802-362-2607. FAX: 802-362-5869. E-Mail: marklibr@souer.net. *Librn*, Gail Rice; *Asst Librn*, Cheryl Stillson; *ILL*, Laurie Jameson-Palmer; Staff 5 (Non-MLS 5)
Founded 1897. Pop 3,260; Circ 45,157
Aug 1998-Jul 1999 Income $186,005. Mats Exp $31,998, Books $27,000, Per/Ser (Incl. Access Fees) $3,726, Electronic Ref Mat (Incl. Access Fees) $1,272. Sal $109,620 (Prof $102,500)
Library Holdings: Bk Vols 43,000; Per Subs 120; Bks on Deafness & Sign Lang 25
Mem of Southwest Regional Library Service System
Partic in Southeast Regional Asn, Vermont Asn
Friends of the Library Group

MARLBORO

C MARLBORO COLLEGE, Howard & Amy Rice Library, South Road, 05344-0300. (Mail add: PO Box A, 05344-0300), Tel: 802-258-9221. FAX: 802-257-4154. E-Mail: library@marlboro.edu. Web Site: www.marlboro.edu/homepage/resources/index.html. *Dir*, Mary H White; E-Mail: mwhite@marlboro.edu; *Asst Dir*, James Fein; E-Mail: jamesfein@yahoo.com; *Asst Librn*, Heidi Welch; E-Mail: hlwelch@marlboro.edu; *Asst Librn*, Carrie Askegreen; E-Mail: cab@marlboro.edu; Staff 4 (MLS 2, Non-MLS 2)
Founded 1947. Enrl 275; Fac 38; Highest Degree: Master
Jul 2000-Jun 2001 Mats Exp $96,072, Books $44,472, Per/Ser (Incl. Access Fees) $35,280, Micro $9,180, Electronic Ref Mat (Incl. Access Fees) $7,140. Sal $101,826 (Prof $80,000)
Library Holdings: Bk Vols 54,082; Per Subs 256
Special Collections: Rudyard Kipling Coll
Database Vendor: Dialog, IAC - Info Trac, Lexis-Nexis

MARSHFIELD

P JAQUITH PUBLIC LIBRARY,* PO Box 227, 05658. SAN 317-0624. Tel: 802-426-3581. *Librn*, Mary Kasamatsu
Pop 1,441; Circ 9,175
1997-1998 Income $25,000. Mats Exp $2,356, Books $2,250. Sal $11,000
Library Holdings: Bk Vols 9,500; Per Subs 30
Subject Interests: Gen, Local history
Mem of Northeastern Regional Libr Syst

MIDDLEBURY

P ILSLEY PUBLIC LIBRARY, 75 Main St, 05753. SAN 317-0632. Tel: 802-388-4095. FAX: 802-388-4367. E-Mail: ilsley@middlebury.edu. Web Site: www.middlebury.edu/~ilsley. *Dir*, David Clark; Tel: 802-388-4098, E-Mail: dclark@myriad.middlebury.edu; *Ch Servs*, Carol Chatfield; Tel: 802-388-4097, E-Mail: cchatfield@myriad.middlebury.edu; *Ad Servs*, Brian Gyoerkoe; E-Mail: bgyoerkoe@myriad.middlebury.edu; Staff 14 (MLS 2, Non-MLS 12)
Founded 1866. Pop 8,244; Circ 160,393
Jul 2000-Jun 2001 Income $312,763, City $264,345, Locally Generated Income $48,418. Mats Exp $48,559, Books $44,499, Per/Ser (Incl. Access Fees) $3,560, Electronic Ref Mat (Incl. Access Fees) $500. Sal $128,772 (Prof $78,000)
Library Holdings: Bk Vols 54,500; Per Subs 108
Subject Interests: Local history, Vt
Special Collections: Local History
Automation Activity & Vendor Info: (Cataloging) DRA; (Circulation) DRA
Database Vendor: DRA
Publications: Ilsley Inklings
Open Mon, Wed & Fri 10-6, Tues & Thurs 10-8, Sat 10-4
Friends of the Library Group

C MIDDLEBURY COLLEGE, Egbert Starr Library, 15 Old Chapel Rd, 05753-6007. SAN 362-6318. Tel: 802-443-5391. Interlibrary Loan Service Tel: 802-443-5498. Circulation Tel: 802-443-5494. Reference Tel: 802-443-5496. FAX: 802-443-2074. Web Site: www.middlebury.edu/library.html. *Librn*, Ronald E Rucker; Tel: 802-443-5490, E-Mail: rucker@myriad.middlebury.edu; *Assoc Librn*, Hans Raum; Tel: 802-443-5493, E-Mail: raum@middlebury.edu; *Cat*, Cynthia Watters; Tel: 802-443-5499, E-Mail: cwatters@middlebury.edu; *Online Servs, Ref*, Susan Tucker; Tel: 802-443-5503; *Circ*, Judy Watts; Tel: 802-443-5798, E-Mail: watts@middlebury.edu; *Per*, William Warren; Tel: 802-443-5489, E-Mail: wwarren@middlebury.edu; *Archivist, Spec Coll*, Robert Buckeye; Tel: 802-443-5502, E-Mail: buckeye@middlebury.edu; *Syst Coordr*, Michael Lynch; Tel: 802-443-5205, E-Mail: lynch@middlebury.edu; *ILL*, Fleur Laslocky; E-Mail: laslocky@middlebury.edu; Staff 42 (MLS 15, Non-MLS 27)
Founded 1800. Enrl 2,245; Fac 203; Highest Degree: Doctorate
Jul 1999-Jun 2000 Income $3,610,787. Mats Exp $1,583,833, Books $616,849, Per/Ser (Incl. Access Fees) $845,826, Presv $61,906, Micro $59,252. Sal $1,622,859 (Prof $824,890)
Library Holdings: Bk Vols 622,497; Per Subs 2,022
Subject Interests: Am lit, Anglo-Amer Ballad, European langs
Special Collections: Abernethy American Literature Coll, bks, mss; Archives of Traditional Music Flanders Ballad Coll, bks, mss, recording; Vermont Coll.
Automation Activity & Vendor Info: (Acquisitions) DRA; (Cataloging) DRA; (Circulation) DRA; (Course Reserve) DRA; (OPAC) DRA; (Serials) DRA
Publications: Friends of the Library Newsletter; Myriad News
Partic in Dialog Corporation; Nelinet, Inc; OCLC Online Computer Library Center, Inc
Friends of the Library Group
Departmental Libraries:
ARMSTRONG LIBRARY, Science Center, 05753. SAN 362-6377. Tel: 802-443-5449. Web Site: www.middlebury.edu/~lib/. *Librn*, Louise Zipp; Tel: 802-443-5018, E-Mail: lzipp@middlebury.edu; Staff 3 (MLS 1, Non-MLS 2)
Enrl 2,245; Fac 203; Highest Degree: Doctorate

Library Holdings: Bk Vols 104,935
Database Vendor: CARL, Dialog, DRA, IAC - Info Trac, Lexis-Nexis, OCLC - First Search, ProQuest, Wilson - Wilson Web
Partic in Nelinet, Inc; OCLC Online Computer Library Center, Inc
Friends of the Library Group

MUSIC, Center for the Arts, 05753. SAN 362-6342. Tel: 802-443-5217. Circulation Tel: 802-443-5218. Reference Tel: 802-443-5785. FAX: 802-443-2074. Web Site: www.middlebury.edu/~lib/musiclib/musiclib.html. *Librn*, Jerry McBride; E-Mail: jmcbride@middlebury.edu; *Cat*, Terry Simpkins; Tel: 802-443-5045, E-Mail: tsimpkins@middlebury.edu; *Circ*, Elizabeth LaBate; Tel: 802-443-5928, E-Mail: elabate@middlebury.edu
Library Holdings: Bk Vols 11,669
Special Collections: Ethnomusicology archives, including Flanders Ballad Coll

M PORTER MEDICAL CENTER, INC, Medical Library & Information Service,* 115 Porter Dr, 05753. SAN 317-0640. Tel: 802-388-4715.
Founded 1973
Library Holdings: Bk Titles 300; Bk Titles 34,000

S SHELDON MUSEUM RESEARCH CENTER,* One Park St, 05753. SAN 317-0659. Tel: 802-388-2117. E-Mail: sheldon_mus@myriad.middlebury.edu. *Librn*, Nancy Rucker
Founded 1882
Library Holdings: Bk Titles 5,000; Per Subs 3
Subject Interests: Hist of Addison County
Special Collections: Manuscript Coll; Middlebury Newspaper Coll; Sheldon Scrapbooks
Publications: Treasures Gathered Here: A guide to the manuscript collection of the Sheldon Museum
Restriction: Open to public for reference only

MIDDLETOWN SPRINGS

P MIDDLETOWN SPRINGS PUBLIC LIBRARY,* PO Box 1250, 05757. SAN 320-5185. Tel: 802-235-2435. *Librn*, Lydia Taylor; Staff 1 (MLS 1)
Pop 603; Circ 4,340
Library Holdings: Bk Vols 5,472; Bk Titles 5,472
Mem of Southwest Regional Library Service System
Open Mon 2:30-4:30 & 7-9, Tues, Thurs & Fri 2:30-4:30 & Sat 10-2

MILTON

P MILTON PUBLIC LIBRARY,* 39 Bombadier Rd, 05468. SAN 317-0667. Tel: 802-893-4644. E-Mail: miltonpub@dol.state.vt. *Librn*, Fran Ferro
Pop 9,500; Circ 24,000
1997-1998 Income $80,000. Mats Exp Books $10,500. Sal $52,000
Library Holdings: Bk Vols 15,000; Per Subs 20
Special Collections: Antiques Coll; Cookbook Coll; Vermont Coll
Open Tues 10-8
Friends of the Library Group

MONKTON

P RUSSELL MEMORIAL LIBRARY,* Monkton Ridge, 05469. SAN 317-0675. Tel: 802-453-4471. *Librn*, Deborah Chamberlain
Pop 1,201; Circ 1,223
Library Holdings: Bk Vols 2,365
Mem of Midstate Regional Libr

MONTGOMERY CENTER

P MONTGOMERY FREE LIBRARY,* PO Box 448, 05471. SAN 317-0683. Tel: 802-326-3113. *Librn*, Chris DuRona
Pop 651; Circ 4,888
Library Holdings: Bk Vols 6,000
Open Wed 2-4 & Sat 9:30-11
Friends of the Library Group

MONTPELIER

P KELLOGG-HUBBARD LIBRARY, 135 Main St, 05602. SAN 317-0691. Tel: 802-223-3338. FAX: 802-223-3338. E-Mail: kellogg_hubb@dol.state.vt.us. Web Site: www.khl.lib.vt.us. *Dir*, Janet Nielsen; *Ch Servs*, Mary Jane Marold; *Circ*, Roberta Downey; *Tech Servs*, Diana Douglas; *Coll Develop*, Janet Nielson; *ILL, Reader Servs*, Scott Lovelette; Staff 1 (MLS 1)
Founded 1894. Pop 8,609; Circ 196,018
Jan 1999-Dec 1999 Income $334,781, City $38,000, County $7,670, Locally Generated Income $289,111. Mats Exp $50,373, Books $45,601, Per/Ser (Incl. Access Fees) $4,772. Sal $189,660
Library Holdings: Bk Titles 71,305; Per Subs 100
Automation Activity & Vendor Info: (ILL) DRA
Publications: Kellogg's Korn Flakes (monthly)
Friends of the Library Group

L NATIONAL LIFE INSURANCE CO LIBRARY,* National Life Dr, 056 SAN 317-0705. Tel: 802-229-3276. FAX: 802-229-3743.
Library Holdings: Bk Vols 17,000; Per Subs 300
Subject Interests: Econ, Ins, Investments, Law
Special Collections: Company History (Archives), bks, pictures, clipping hists, etc; Looseleaf Services in Law, Pension, Employment, Taxes, Insurance
Partic in OCLC Online Computer Library Center, Inc
Open Mon-Fri 8:15-4:30
Friends of the Library Group

G OFFICE OF THE SECRETARY OF STATE, Vermont State Archives Library, Redstone Bldg, 26 Terrace St, 05609-1103. SAN 326-2804. Tel: 802-828-2308. FAX: 802-828-2465. Web Site: www.sec.state.vt.us. *Archi Asst Librn*, Christie Carter; *Archivist*, D Gregory Sanford; E-Mail: gsanford@sec.state.vt.us
Special Collections: State Government (VT State Archives), bks, pamphl archives, photographs, film
Publications: State Papers of Vermont Series

P STATE OF VERMONT DEPARTMENT OF LIBRARIES,* 109 State St 05609-0601. SAN 322-7774. Tel: 802-828-3261. FAX: 802-828-2199. *Lil* Sybil McShane; E-Mail: smcshane@dol.state.vt.us
Subject Interests: History, Law, Newsps, Vermontaina
Special Collections: Children's Book Exhibit Center; Found Ctr; Joseph Wheeler Library Science Coll
Publications: Checklist of Vermont State Publications; Dol (newsletter)
Branches: 4
LIBRARY FOR THE BLIND & PHYSICALLY HANDICAPPED
See Separate Entry in Berlin
MIDSTATE REGIONAL, Vermont Dept of Librs, RD 4, Box 1870, 0560 SAN 316-9588. Tel: 802-828-2320. *Librn*, Marianne Kotch; *Asst Librn*, Linda Willis
NORTHEAST REGIONAL, RD 2, Box 244, Saint Johnsbury, 05819. SA 370-9434. Tel: 802-748-3428. *Librn*, Michael Roche
SOUTHEAST REGIONAL, RD 5, Box 390, Brattleboro, 05301. SAN 37 9442. Tel: 802-257-2810. *Librn*, Amy Howlett

G VERMONT AGENCY OF TRANSPORTATION LIBRARY, Vermont Policy & Planning Division,* 133 State St, 05633. SAN 317-0721. Tel: 8(828-2544. FAX: 802-828-3983. *Librn*, Sandy Aja
Founded 1960
Library Holdings: Bk Titles 3,000; Per Subs 15
Library specializes in dealing with transportation publications & reference manuals. Open to the public under most conditions

C VERMONT COLLEGE DIVISION OF NORWICH UNIVERSITY, Gary Memorial Library, College St, 05602. SAN 362-6466. Tel: 802-828-8747. FAX: 802-828-8748. Web Site: www.norwich.edu/library/gary.html. *Mgr*, Matt Pappathan; Tel: 802-828-8746, E-Mail: mattp@norwich.edu; Staff 4 (MLS 1, Non-MLS 3)
Founded 1883. Enrl 1,050; Fac 156; Highest Degree: Certificate
Jun 1999-May 2000 Income $200,000. Mats Exp $85,000, Books $50,000 Per/Ser (Incl. Access Fees) $10,000, Presv $1,000, Micro $4,000, AV Equ $4,000. Sal $91,000 (Prof $35,000)
Library Holdings: Bk Vols 45,000
Subject Interests: Applied psychol, Art therapy, Creative writing, Holistic studies, Visual arts, Women's studies
Mem of Northeastern Regional Libr Syst
Friends of the Library Group

S VERMONT HISTORICAL SOCIETY LIBRARY,* Pavilion Bldg, 109 St St, 05609-0901. SAN 317-073X. Tel: 802-828-2291. FAX: 802-828-3638. E-Mail: vhs@vhs.state.vt.us. Web Site: www.state.vt.us/vhs. *Librn*, Paul A Carnahan; *Asst Librn*, Barney Bloom
Founded 1838
Jul 1997-Jun 1998 Income $112,043, State $40,602, Locally Generated Income $15,167, Parent Institution $46,541. Mats Exp $69,080, Books $2,535, Per/Ser (Incl. Access Fees) $61,408, Presv $3,263, Manuscripts & Archives $1,874. Sal $83,659 (Prof $81,667)
Library Holdings: Bk Vols 53,000; Per Subs 220
Subject Interests: Genealogy, Lower Can hist, New England, NY hist, Vt
Special Collections: Broadsides, Photographs, Sheet Music
Restriction: Non-circulating to the public
Partic in Nelinet, Inc

C WOODBURY COLLEGE LIBRARY, 660 Elm St, 05602. Tel: 802-229-0516. FAX: 802-229-2141. E-Mail: library@woodbury-college.edu. Web Site: www.woodbury-college.edu. *Librn*, Jim Nolte; Staff 5 (MLS 1, Non-MLS 4)
Founded 1977. Enrl 200; Fac 20; Highest Degree: Bachelor
Library Holdings: Bk Vols 8,000; Per Subs 1,300
Subject Interests: Mediation, Paralegal
Partic in Nelinet, Inc

ORETOWN

MORETOWN MEMORIAL LIBRARY,* Rte 100B, 05660. SAN 317-0756. Tel: 802-496-9728. *Librn*, Stacy Sharp
Library Holdings: Bk Vols 6,000
Mem of Midstate Regional Libr
Open Thurs 5-9

ORRISVILLE

COPLEY HOSPITAL, INC, Medical Library, 528 Washington Hwy, 05661. SAN 317-0764. Tel: 802-888-4231, Ext 8347. FAX: 802-888-8361. *Librn*, Berta Barnard
Founded 1975
Library Holdings: Bk Titles 504; Per Subs 65
Subject Interests: Consumer health, Med-health sci
Publications: Medical Reference Services Q; NASHL (newsletter)
Restriction: In-house use for visitors
Function: ILL available, Literary searches, Photocopies available
Partic in New Eng Regional Med Libr Serv

MORRISTOWN CENTENNIAL LIBRARY, 7 Richmond St, 05661. (Mail add: PO Box 727, 05661-0727), Tel: 802-888-3853. E-Mail: morrisville@dol.st.vt.us. *Librn*, Mary West; *Asst Librn*, Mary Lemieux; Staff 3 (Non-MLS 3)
Founded 1890. Pop 5,000; Circ 29,167
Jul 1999-Jun 2000 Income $115,694, City $59,100, Locally Generated Income $6,912, Parent Institution $49,682. Mats Exp $18,768, Books $17,294, Per/Ser (Incl. Access Fees) $1,382, Presv $92. Sal $69,073
Library Holdings: Bk Vols 18,500; Per Subs 50
Special Collections: Cheney Civil War Coll
Friends of the Library Group

W HAVEN

NEW HAVEN COMMUNITY LIBRARY, PO Box 85, 05472. SAN 317-0780. Tel: 802-453-4015. *Librn*, N Custer Carroll; E-Mail: ncarroll@beeman.k12.vt.us
Pop 1,400; Circ 21,788
Oct 1999-Sep 2000 Income $46,700. Mats Exp Per/Ser (Incl. Access Fees) $1,000. Sal $27,494 (Prof $18,000)
Library Holdings: Bk Titles 10,000; Per Subs 40
Mem of Midstate Regional Libr
Open Tues 3-6, Thurs 3-8 & Sat 9-3
Friends of the Library Group

WBURY

TENNEY MEMORIAL LIBRARY, INC,* PO Box 85, 05051. SAN 317-0802. Tel: 802-866-5366. E-Mail: tenney@together.net. *Dir, Librn*, Marjorie Shane
Founded 1896. Pop 975; Circ 3,118
Library Holdings: Bk Vols 10,000; Per Subs 20
Special Collections: New England Coll; Town History Coll
Mem of Northeastern Regional Libr Syst
Open Tues 10-5, Thurs 3-8, Sat 10-4

EWFANE

MOORE FREE LIBRARY,* PO Box 208, 05345. SAN 317-0810. Tel: 802-365-7948. FAX: 802-365-4426. *Librn*, Cynthia W Nau
Pop 1,700; Circ 3,550
Oct 1997-Sep 1998 Income $27,265. Mats Exp $4,360. Sal $12,099 (Prof $10,212)
Library Holdings: Bk Vols 8,000; Per Subs 16
Special Collections: Civil War; Vermont Coll
Mem of Southeastern Library Services
Open Tues 3-6, Wed 8:30-5, Thurs 2-6, Fri 2-5 & Sat 9-1pm
Friends of the Library Group

EWPORT

GOODRICH MEMORIAL LIBRARY,* 202 Main St, 05855. SAN 317-0829. Tel: 802-334-7902. E-Mail: newport@col.state.us.vt. *Librn*, Louise Kennison
Pop 4,900; Circ 44,600
Library Holdings: Bk Vols 18,169; Per Subs 65
Special Collections: Vermont History Coll, bks, photogs
Mem of Northeastern Regional Libr Syst
Special Services for the Deaf - Books on deafness & sign language; Captioned film depository; High interest/low vocabulary books

NORTH COUNTRY HOSPITAL & HEALTH CENTER, Medical Library, 189 Prouty Dr, 05855. SAN 317-0837. Tel: 802-334-3256. FAX: 802-334-3240. Web Site: www.nchsi.org. *Librn*, Georgia Lee Zaveson; E-Mail: gzaveson@nchsi.org; Staff 1 (Non-MLS 1)
Pop 5,900
Oct 1998-Sep 1999 Income $46,300. Mats Exp $13,000, Books $3,800, Per/Ser (Incl. Access Fees) $9,200. Sal $17,400
Library Holdings: Bk Titles 146; Per Subs 65
Publications: Medical Reference Serves (newsletter)
Function: Research library
Partic in Health Science Libraries Of New Hampshire & Vermont; North Country Consortium

NORTH BENNINGTON

P JOHN G MCCULLOUGH FREE LIBRARY INC, 2 Main St, PO Box 339, 05257-0339. SAN 317-0845. Tel: 802-447-7121. E-Mail: nobennington@dol.state.vt.us. *Librn*, Julie Chamay
Founded 1920
Library Holdings: Bk Vols 16,000; Per Subs 84
Subject Interests: Large print, Vt hist
Special Collections: Mose Sage Coll
Mem of Southeastern Library Services
Partic in VALS
Open Tues-Fri 1-6, Sat 10-2

NORTH CLAREDON

P BAILEY MEMORIAL LIBRARY,* 11 Brookside Lane, PO Box 90, 05759. SAN 376-4869. Tel: 802-747-7743. *Librn*, Dorothy Barnes
Library Holdings: Bk Vols 9,000
Mem of Southwest Regional Library Service System

NORTH HERO

P NORTH HERO PUBLIC LIBRARY,* PO Box 187, 05474. SAN 317-0861. Tel: 802-372-5458. *Librn*, Jeanne Giard
Founded 1913. Pop 520; Circ 5,725
Library Holdings: Bk Vols 7,000
Subject Interests: Hist of Russia, Russian lit
Special Collections: Rare Book Coll; Russian Books; Vermont Coll; World War II
Open Tues 2-7, Thurs 10-3 & Sat 2-1
Friends of the Library Group

NORTH TROY

P WILLIAM H & LUCY F RAND MEMORIAL LIBRARY, 212 Main St, PO Box 509, 05859. SAN 317-0888. Tel: 802-988-4741. *Librn*, Dorothy Barlow
Founded 1925. Pop 1,600; Circ 3,526
1999-2000 Income Locally Generated Income $10,600. Mats Exp Books $1,500
Library Holdings: Bk Vols 5,200; Per Subs 30
Subject Interests: Local history, Vermont
Mem of Northeastern Regional Libr Syst
Open Mon & Wed 3-7, Tues 1-5, Thurs & Sat 9-1

NORTHFIELD

P BROWN PUBLIC LIBRARY, 93 S Main St, 05663. SAN 317-0896. Tel: 802-485-4621. FAX: 802-485-4990. E-Mail: brown@nfld.tds.net, brown@tds.net, northfield@dol.state.vt.us. Web Site: www.tds.net/brownpubliclibrary. *Dir*, Sharon V Bartram; Staff 1 (MLS 1)
Founded 1906. Pop 5,900; Circ 25,241
Jul 1999-Jun 2000 Income $60,100, City $51,000, Locally Generated Income $9,100. Mats Exp $7,400, Books $7,000, Per/Ser (Incl. Access Fees) $400. Sal $29,157
Library Holdings: Bk Vols 16,150; Per Subs 42; Bks on Deafness & Sign Lang 10
Special Collections: Vermont Coll
Automation Activity & Vendor Info: (Cataloging) Endeavor; (Circulation) Endeavor; (OPAC) Endeavor
Mem of VT State Inter-Library Loan Network
Friends of the Library Group

C NORWICH UNIVERSITY, Kreitzberg Library, 23 Harmon Dr, 05663. SAN 317-090X. Tel: 802-485-2170. FAX: 802-485-2173. Web Site: www.norwich.edu/library/kberg.html. *Actg Dir, Tech Servs*, Catherine Swenson; Tel: 802-485-2171; *Publ Servs*, Louise Murphy; Tel: 802-485-2175; *ILL*, Debbie Ahlers; Tel: 802-485-2174; *Spec Coll*, Krista Ainsworth; Tel: 802-485-2183; *Govt Doc*, Kate Burgwardt; Tel: 802-485-2168; *Info Tech*, Jennifer Fritz; Tel: 802-485-2197; Staff 13 (MLS 5, Non-MLS 8)
Founded 1819. Enrl 1,650; Fac 100; Highest Degree: Master
Jun 1998-May 1999 Income $879,166. Mats Exp $304,867, Books $166,521, Per/Ser (Incl. Access Fees) $86,456, Presv $100, Micro $12,691, AV Equip $500, Manuscripts & Archives $200, Electronic Ref Mat (Incl. Access Fees) $26,508. Sal $496,853
Library Holdings: Bk Vols 275,658; Bk Titles 190,000; Per Subs 980

Subject Interests: Architecture, Engineering, Military history, Nursing
Special Collections: Norwichian
Automation Activity & Vendor Info: (Acquisitions) Endeavor; (Cataloging) Endeavor; (Circulation) Endeavor; (Course Reserve) Endeavor; (ILL) Endeavor; (Media Booking) Endeavor
Publications: Fonul Newsletter; Library Handbook; Occasional Papers
Partic in Nelinet, Inc; OCLC Online Computer Library Center, Inc; Vt Automated Libr Syst
Friends of the Library Group

NORWICH

P NORWICH PUBLIC LIBRARY,* PO Box 290, 05055. SAN 317-0918. Tel: 802-649-1184. *Coll Develop, Librn*, Sylvia F Fraser; Staff 1 (Non-MLS 1)
Founded 1880. Pop 3,093; Circ 32,421
Jul 1996-Jun 1997 Income $73,884. Mats Exp $12,213, Books $10,391, Per/Ser (Incl. Access Fees) $778. Sal $37,048
Library Holdings: Bk Vols 15,576
Subject Interests: Local history
Mem of Midstate Regional Libr
Friends of the Library Group

ORLEANS

P JONES MEMORIAL LIBRARY,* One Water St, PO Box 38, 05860. SAN 317-0926. Tel: 802-754-6660. *Ad Servs, Librn*, Helen Leno; *Ch Servs, Librn*, Joanne Pariseau; E-Mail: newport@together.net
Founded 1873. Pop 4,170; Circ 32,578
Library Holdings: Bk Titles 22,300; Per Subs 44
Special Collections: ESP
Publications: Library Journals Adult & Children
Mem of Northeastern Regional Libr Syst
Partic in Vermont Automated Libr Syst

ORWELL

P ORWELL FREE LIBRARY,* PO Box 92, 05670. SAN 376-3463. Tel: 802-948-2041. *Librn*, Hester Phelps
Library Holdings: Bk Vols 9,250; Per Subs 25
Mem of Southwest Regional Library Service System

PAWLET

P PAWLET PUBLIC LIBRARY,* PO Box 98, 05761. SAN 317-0934. Interlibrary Loan Service Tel: 802-325-3123. *Librn*, Dolores Guarino
Pop 1,244
Library Holdings: Bk Vols 6,922; Per Subs 12
Special Collections: Pawlet History; Vermont History
Mem of Southwest Regional Library Service System
Open Mon & Thurs 1:30-6, Tues & Fri 1:30-4, Wed 12:30-3 & Sat 10-12

PEACHAM

P PEACHAM LIBRARY, 656 Bayley Hazen Rd, PO Box 253, 05862-0253. SAN 317-0942. Tel: 802-592-3216. Web Site: www.connriver.net/peachamlibrary/. *Librn*, Rebecca Lafferty; Staff 2 (Non-MLS 2)
Founded 1810. Pop 621; Circ 4,521
Jul 1999-Jun 2000 Income $32,824, City $3,500, Other $29,324. Mats Exp $11,048, Books $3,628. Sal $18,148
Library Holdings: Bk Vols 8,000; Per Subs 15
Friends of the Library Group

PITTSFIELD

P ROGER CLARK MEMORIAL LIBRARY,* PO Box 556, 05762. SAN 317-0950. Tel: 802-746-8170. *In Charge*, Susie Martin
Pop 249; Circ 2,430
Jan 1997-Dec 1998 Income $400. Mats Exp Books $300
Library Holdings: Bk Vols 2,250
Mem of Southwest Regional Library Service System
Open Tues & Thurs 2:30-4:30

PITTSFORD

P MACLURE LIBRARY,* PO Box 60, 05763. SAN 317-0969. Tel: 802-483-2972. *Librn*, Julia Reynolds; *Asst Librn*, Allison Smith
Circ 12,124
Library Holdings: Bk Vols 15,000; Per Subs 17
Special Collections: Biography Coll; History Coll
Mem of Southwest Regional Library Service System
Open Mon, Tues, Thurs & Fri 1-5, Wed 1-8 & Sat 9-12

PLAINFIELD

P CUTLER MEMORIAL LIBRARY,* High St, PO Box 186, 05667. SAN 376-799X. Tel: 802-454-8504. *Librn*, Robin Sales
Library Holdings: Bk Vols 7,000; Per Subs 12
Mem of Midstate Regional Libr
Friends of the Library Group

C GODDARD COLLEGE, Eliot D Pratt Library, 123 Pitkin Rd, 05667. SA 317-0985. Tel: 802-454-8311, Ext 208. FAX: 802-454-1451. E-Mail: library@goddard.edu. Web Site: www.goddard.edu. *Dir*, Clara Bruns; Tel: 802-454-8311, Ext 250, E-Mail: clarab@goddard.edu; *Tech Servs*, David Ferland; Tel: 802-454-8311, Ext 216, E-Mail: davidf@goddard.edu; *ILL*, Dorothy Wallace; Tel: 802-454-8311, Ext 215, E-Mail: dorothyw@goddard.edu; *Circ*, Ming Qiang; Tel: 802-454-8311, Ext 215, E-Mail: mingq@goddard.edu; Staff 4 (MLS 1, Non-MLS 3)
Founded 1938. Enrl 599
Library Holdings: Bk Vols 70,000; Bk Titles 65,000; Per Subs 280
Subject Interests: Education, Multicultural studies, Women's studies
Special Collections: BA & MA Senior Studies; Goddard Archives; Godda Authors Coll
Database Vendor: OCLC - First Search
Publications: Eliot Pratt Center Handbook
Friends of the Library Group

POULTNEY

C GREEN MOUNTAIN COLLEGE LIBRARY,* One College Circle, 0576 1199. SAN 317-0993. Tel: 802-287-8225. FAX: 802-287-8222. E-Mail: library@greenmtn.edu. *Dir*, Ruth Parlin; *ILL, Ref*, Paul Millette; Staff 2 (MLS 2)
Founded 1834. Enrl 608; Fac 38; Highest Degree: Bachelor
Jul 1997-Jun 1998 Income $266,300, State $750. Mats Exp $63,500, Book $30,000, Per/Ser (Incl. Access Fees) $25,000, Presv $2,500, Micro $4,000 AV Equip $2,000. Sal $136,900
Library Holdings: Bk Vols 55,000; Per Subs 222
Subject Interests: Environ liberal arts
Special Collections: Early American Decoration (Ramsey Coll); Library c American Civilization, ultrafiche; Welsh Coll, bks, patterns & art objects.
Publications: Student Handbook; Welsh Heritage of the Slate Belt: Workbook for elementary & middle school students
Partic in OCLC Online Computer Library Center, Inc

P POULTNEY PUBLIC LIBRARY,* 205 Main St, 05764. SAN 317-1000. Tel: 802-287-5556. *Librn*, Daphne Bartholomew
Pop 3,498; Circ 25,928
Library Holdings: Bk Vols 14,000; Per Subs 50
Special Collections: Vermont
Open Mon, Tues & Thurs 2-5 & 6:30-9, Fri 9:30-12 & Sat 2-5

POWNAL

P SOLOMON WRIGHT LIBRARY,* PO Box 400, 05261. SAN 317-1019. Tel: 802-823-5400. E-Mail: pownal_pub@bol.state.vt.us. *Dir*, Linda Hall
Pop 3,250; Circ 5,200
Jul 1997-Jun 1998 Income $10,000
Library Holdings: Bk Vols 22,000; Per Subs 25
Mem of Southwest Regional Library Service System
Open Mon & Wed 6:30-8:30, Tues 10-2, Thurs & Fri 10-12 & Sat 10-2

PROCTOR

P PROCTOR FREE LIBRARY,* 4 Main St, 05765. SAN 317-1027. Tel: 80 459-3539. E-Mail: proctor_free@dol.state.vt.us. *Librn*, Phyllis Russell
Founded 1881. Pop 1,998; Circ 29,400
Jul 1997-Jun 1998 Income $83,908, City $36,500, Other $47,408. Mats Ex $13,500, Books $10,400, Per/Ser (Incl. Access Fees) $2,500. Sal $42,898
Library Holdings: Bk Vols 28,260
Special Collections: Realia (Children); Sports Coll; Vermontiana (Papers c Four Governors from Proctor)
Mem of Southwest Regional Library Service System

PROCTORSVILLE

P CAVENDISH-FLETCHER COMMUNITY LIBRARY,* PO Box 266, 05153. SAN 376-3366. Tel: 802-226-7503. FAX: 802-226-7312. *Librn*, Joyce Fuller
Library Holdings: Bk Vols 6,500; Per Subs 16
Mem of Southeastern Library Services
Friends of the Library Group

PUTNEY

J LANDMARK COLLEGE LIBRARY,* River Rd, 05346. SAN 329-1480. Tel: 802-387-6764. *Librn*, Lisa Griest; Staff 5 (MLS 3, Non-MLS 2)
Founded 1985. Enrl 296; Fac 140

Jul 1996-Jun 1997 Income $205,658, Locally Generated Income $15,000, Parent Institution $190,658. Mats Exp $55,487, Books $25,514, Per/Ser (Incl. Access Fees) $10,720, Presv $1,284, Micro $4,685. Sal $120,522 (Prof $75,455)
Library Holdings: Bk Vols 32,717; Per Subs 187
Subject Interests: Learning disabilities
Special Collections: Learning Disabilities Coll
Publications: Holdings List Bibliography of Learning Difficulties Coll
Accredited college designed specifically for high potential students with dyslexia, attention deficit disorder or other specific learning disabilities

PUTNEY PUBLIC LIBRARY,* 90 Johnson's Curve, PO Box 193, 05346. SAN 317-1035. Tel: 802-387-4407. *Librn*, Marianne Sanders
Pop 1,850; Circ 10,116
Library Holdings: Bk Vols 10,000; Per Subs 14
Mem of Southeastern Library Services
Open Mon & Fri 1-5, Tues & Thurs 9-1, Wed 2-6, Sat 9-12

ECHEE

QUECHEE PUBLIC LIBRARY ASSOC,* 1957 Quechee Main St, PO Box 384, 05059. SAN 317-0365. Tel: 802-295-1232. FAX: 802-295-1232. E-Mail: quechee_pub@dol.state.vt.us. *Librn*, Kate Schaal
Circ 16,000
1999-2000 Income $67,620, City $46,320, Locally Generated Income $21,300. Mats Exp $11,300, Books $10,000, Per/Ser (Incl. Access Fees) $1,000, Micro $300. Sal $30,800
Library Holdings: Bk Vols 10,400; Per Subs 50
Mem of Vermont Libr Asn
Friends of the Library Group

NDOLPH

GIFFORD MEDICAL CENTER, Health Information Center,* 44 S Main, PO Box 2000, 05060. SAN 317-1043. Tel: 802-728-2244. FAX: 802-728-2367. *Librn*, Martha Howe
Library Holdings: Bk Vols 250

KIMBALL PUBLIC LIBRARY, 67 Main St, 05060. SAN 317-1051. Tel: 802-728-5073. FAX: 802-728-6735. *Librn*, Frances Inslee; Staff 3 (MLS 2, Non-MLS 1)
Founded 1903. Circ 4,900
Jan 2000-Dec 2000 Income $107,000, City $53,000, Locally Generated Income $54,000. Mats Exp $14,100, Books $13,000, Per/Ser (Incl. Access Fees) $1,100. Sal $61,400
Library Holdings: Bk Vols 22,000; Per Subs 80
Subject Interests: Hospice, Vt
Mem of Midstate Regional Libr
Open Mon & Thurs 2-8, Tues, Wed & Fri 10-5, Sat 10-1
Friends of the Library Group

NDOLPH CENTER

VERMONT TECHNICAL COLLEGE, Hartness Library, 05061. SAN 317-106X. Tel: 802-728-1237. FAX: 802-728-1506. E-Mail: library@vtc.vsc.edu. Web Site: www.vtc.vsc.edu. *Dir*, Jane U Bartlett; Staff 8 (MLS 3, Non-MLS 5)
Founded 1866. Enrl 970; Fac 67
Library Holdings: Bk Titles 60,000; Per Subs 396
Subject Interests: Agriculture, Architecture, Automotive tech, Biotech, Bus mgt, Civil engineering, Computer eng, Construction mgt, Electrical engineering, Electronic engineering, Eng tech, Horticulture, Mechanical engineering, Nursing, Vet tech
Automation Activity & Vendor Info: (Cataloging) DRA; (Circulation) DRA
Partic in Nelinet, Inc; OCLC Online Computer Library Center, Inc; Vermont Automated Libr Syst
Administrative & Reference Center for the Vermont Community & Technical Colleges Library

ADING

READING PUBLIC LIBRARY,* 717 Vermont Rte 106, PO Box 7, 05062. SAN 317-1078. Tel: 802-484-5588. *Librn*, Tina Miller
Founded 1899. Pop 647; Circ 3,200
Library Holdings: Bk Vols 64,000
Special Collections: Extensive Coll of Bound Harpers & National Geographic Magazines
Mem of Southeastern Library Services
Open Tues 1-7 & Thurs 11-7

READSBORO

P READSBORO COMMUNITY LIBRARY,* PO Box 248, 05350-0248. SAN 317-1086. Tel: 802-423-7786. *Librn*, Rumona Putnam
Founded 1874. Pop 638; Circ 4,953
Library Holdings: Bk Vols 5,910; Per Subs 35
Mem of Southeastern Library Services

RICHFORD

P ARVIN A BROWN PUBLIC LIBRARY,* 88 Main St, 05476-1133. SAN 317-1094. Tel: 802-848-3313. *Librn*, Annette Goyne
Circ 15,659
Jan 1997-Dec 1998 Income $35,000. Mats Exp $4,662. Sal $24,908
Library Holdings: Bk Vols 10,610
Subject Interests: Youth concerts, Youth programs
Special Collections: Vermont Coll

RICHMOND

P RICHMOND FREE LIBRARY, 201 Bridge St, 05477. SAN 317-1108. Tel: 802-434-3036. FAX: 802-434-3223. E-Mail: richmond@dol.state.vt.us. Web Site: www.richmond.lib.vt.us. *Librn*, Mary Ann McMaster; *Ch Servs*, L J Kopf; *Asst Librn*, Joan Cleary; Staff 4 (Non-MLS 4)
Pop 3,729; Circ 43,301
Jul 1998-Jun 1999 Income $81,306. Mats Exp $81,700. Sal $41,000
Library Holdings: Bk Vols 13,034; Per Subs 76
Mem of Midstate Regional Libr
Open Mon & Wed 10-8, Tues & Thurs 1-6, Fri 10-6 & Sat 10-2
Friends of the Library Group

ROCHESTER

P ROCHESTER PUBLIC LIBRARY,* PO Box 256, 05767. SAN 317-1124. Tel: 802-767-3927. *Librn*, Linda Kautzman
Pop 1,054; Circ 13,559
Library Holdings: Bk Vols 12,000
Mem of Midstate Regional Libr
Open Tues & Thurs 12:30-7, Sat 9-1

ROXBURY

P ROXBURY FREE LIBRARY,* PO Box 95, 05669. SAN 376-3447. Tel: 802-485-6860. *Librn*, Robert Allen
Library Holdings: Bk Vols 5,000
Mem of Midstate Regional Libr

RUTLAND

C COLLEGE OF SAINT JOSEPH LIBRARY, 71 Clement Rd, 05701. SAN 317-1140. Tel: 802-773-5900, Ext 232. FAX: 802-773-5900. *Dir*, Doreen J McCullough; E-Mail: dmccullough@csj.edu; Staff 2 (MLS 1, Non-MLS 1)
Founded 1950. Enrl 550; Fac 70; Highest Degree: Master
Jul 1999-Jun 2000 Income $151,603. Mats Exp $61,800, Books $16,000, Per/Ser (Incl. Access Fees) $39,000, Micro $6,000, AV Equip $300, Other Print Mats $500. Sal $64,742
Library Holdings: Bk Vols 67,000; Bk Titles 46,000; Per Subs 256
Subject Interests: Special education
Special Collections: Kyran McGrath Irish Studies Coll; Sister St George Vermont Coll
Automation Activity & Vendor Info: (OPAC) Sagebrush Corporation
Database Vendor: Ebsco - EbscoHost, Silverplatter Information Inc.

S MARBLE VALLEY REGIONAL CORRECTIONAL FACILITY, (Formerly Marlboro Valley Regional Correctional Facility), 167 State St, 05701. SAN 317-1159. Tel: 802-786-5830. FAX: 802-786-5843. *Librn*, Tom Giffin
Circ 3,360
Library Holdings: Bk Vols 4,362; Per Subs 16

P RUTLAND FREE LIBRARY,* 10 Court St, 05701-4058. SAN 317-1167. Tel: 802-773-1860. FAX: 802-773-1825. E-Mail: rutland_free@dol.state.vt.us. Web Site: rutlandhs.k12.vt.us/rutlandfree/rflhome.htm. *Dir*, Paula J Baker; E-Mail: paulajb@hotmail.com; *Assoc Dir*, Kathleen Naftaly; *Circ*, Deborah Higgins; *Ch Servs*, June Osowski; Staff 13 (MLS 4, Non-MLS 9)
Founded 1886. Pop 23,203; Circ 186,875
Jul 1998-Jun 1999 Income $676,714, City $489,451, Locally Generated Income $187,263. Mats Exp $91,315, Books $63,007, Per/Ser (Incl. Access Fees) $16,243, AV Equip $6,265, Electronic Ref Mat (Incl. Access Fees) $5,800. Sal $332,354
Library Holdings: Bk Vols 97,962; Per Subs 331
Special Collections: Vermont & Regional History
Automation Activity & Vendor Info: (Cataloging) MultiLIS; (Circulation) MultiLIS; (OPAC) MultiLIS
Database Vendor: IAC - Info Trac, OCLC - First Search
Friends of the Library Group

M RUTLAND REGIONAL MEDICAL CENTER, Health Science Library,* 160 Allen St, 05701. SAN 317-1175. Tel: 802-747-3777. FAX: 802-747-3955. E-Mail: claforce@rrmc.org. Web Site: www.rrmc.org. *Librn*, Claire LaForce
1999-2000 Mats Exp $31,500, Per/Ser (Incl. Access Fees) $23,500, Electronic Ref Mat (Incl. Access Fees) $8,000
Library Holdings: Bk Vols 1,000; Per Subs 130
Subject Interests: Consumer health
Database Vendor: OVID Technologies
Partic in Health Science Libraries Of New Hampshire & Vermont

RYEGATE

P RYEGATE CORNER PUBLIC LIBRARY,* PO Box 332, 05042. SAN 317-1205. Tel: 802-584-3880. *Librn*, Marsha Nelson
Pop 1,000
Library Holdings: Bk Vols 900
Publications: County Journal
Open Mon-Fri 8:30-10 & 4-5 & Sat 8:30-10

SAINT ALBANS

M NORTHWESTERN MEDICAL CENTER, Information Center,* PO Box 1370, 05478. SAN 317-1221. Tel: 802-524-5911. FAX: 802-524-1238.
Library Holdings: Bk Vols 400; Per Subs 40
Subject Interests: Medicine, Nursing
Special Collections: Allied Health Library
Restriction: Staff use only

P SAINT ALBANS FREE LIBRARY,* 11 Maiden Lane, 05478. SAN 317-1248. Tel: 802-524-1507. FAX: 802-524-1514. Web Site: www.together.net/~shell/library.htm. *Librn*, MaryPat Larrabee; *Ad Servs*, Priscilla Trombly; *Ch Servs*, Sue Wade; Staff 4 (MLS 4)
Founded 1900. Pop 11,500; Circ 42,817
Library Holdings: Bk Titles 22,000; Per Subs 100
Special Collections: Vermontiana
Publications: The Bookworm
Friends of the Library Group

SAINT JOHNSBURY

L DOWNS, RACHLIN & MARTIN, Law Library,* 90 Prospect St, 05819. SAN 372-3321. Tel: 802-748-8324. FAX: 802-748-4394. Web Site: www.drm.com. *Librn*, Wynne Browne; E-Mail: wbrowne@drm.com
Library Holdings: Bk Vols 8,000; Per Subs 100

S FAIRBANKS MUSEUM & PLANETARIUM LIBRARY,* Main & Prospect Sts, 05819. SAN 317-1256. Tel: 802-748-2372. FAX: 802-748-3347. *Curator*, Howard Reed
Library Holdings: Bk Vols 2,500
Subject Interests: Sci
Special Collections: Archives Coll; Vermont History Coll
Restriction: Not open to public
Friends of the Library Group

S NORTHEAST REGIONAL CORRECTIONAL FACILITY LIBRARY,* Rt 5 South RFD No 3, 05819. SAN 317-1299. Tel: 802-748-6633. FAX: 802-748-6604. E-Mail: annec@doc.state.vt.us, ihaworth@doc.state.vt.us. *Librn*, Anne Cote
Library Holdings: Bk Vols 8,000; Per Subs 30
Subject Interests: Literacy for adults

P NORTHEAST REGIONAL LIBRARY, Vermont Department of Libraries, 23 Tilton Rd, 05819. SAN 317-1264. Tel: 802-748-3428. E-Mail: nerl@dol.state.vt.us. *Dir*, Michael Roche; Staff 2 (MLS 2)
Founded 1936
Library Holdings: Bk Vols 65,000
Partic in Vermont Resource Sharing Network
Open Mon-Fri 8:30-5

P ST JOHNSBURY ATHENAEUM, 1171Main St, 05819-2289. Tel: 802-748-8291. FAX: 802-748-8086. E-Mail: athena@helicon.net. Web Site: www.stjathenaeum. *Dir*, Lisa Von Kann; *Ch Servs*, Dorothy Fayen; *Circ*, Peggy Little; Staff 4 (MLS 2, Non-MLS 2)
Founded 1871. Pop 7,608; Circ 86,816
Library Holdings: Bk Vols 46,000; Per Subs 110
Special Collections: Fine Art Hudson River School, 100 wks of art (orgs & reprod, incl 10 statues)

S UNITED NATIONS POPULATION FUND, Library DN-1700,* 1171 Main St, 05819-2289. SAN 317-1280. Tel: 212-297-5066. FAX: 212-297-4909. *Librn, Tech Servs*, David P Rose; Staff 4 (MLS 2, Non-MLS 2)
Founded 1973
Library Holdings: Bk Vols 5,000; Per Subs 400
Subject Interests: Dev asst, Econ develop, Family planning, Human reprod, Int orgn, Intl orgn, Pop
Publications: Acquisitions List
Partic in Consortium Of Foundation Libraries; Dialog Corporation; Medl
Accesses own database at UN headquarters

SHARON

P BAXTER MEMORIAL LIBRARY,* PO Box 87, 05065. SAN 317-1329 Tel: 802-763-2875. *Librn*, Roberta Henault
Pop 1,000; Circ 1,420
Library Holdings: Bk Titles 2,600
Mem of Midstate Regional Libr
Open Tues 3:30-7:30pm & Sat 10-12
Friends of the Library Group

SHELBURNE

S NATIONAL MUSEUM OF THE MORGAN HORSE LIBRARY, 122 Bostwick Rd, PO Box 700, 05482. SAN 375-3212. Tel: 802-985-8665. F. 802-985-5242. Web Site: member.triped.com/~nmmh.
Library Holdings: Bk Vols 750; Bk Titles 350
Restriction: Non-circulating to the public
Friends of the Library Group

P PIERSON LIBRARY, 54 Falls Rd, PO Box 475, 05482. SAN 317-1337. Tel: 802-985-5124. *Dir*, Martine Fiske; Staff 4 (MLS 1, Non-MLS 3)
Founded 1888. Pop 6,180; Circ 40,324
Jun 2000-Jun 2001 Income $116,881, City $103,366, Locally Generated Income $13,415, Other $100. Mats Exp $21,339, Books $16,506, Per/Ser (Incl. Access Fees) $3,500, AV Equip $700, Electronic Ref Mat (Incl. Ac Fees) $633. Sal $69,812 (Prof $31,622)
Library Holdings: Bk Vols 22,383; Per Subs 115
Special Collections: Doris W Maeck Coll of Vermont Material
Open Mon, Wed & Fri 10-5, Tues & Thur 2-7:30 & Sat 10-3
Friends of the Library Group

S SHELBURNE MUSEUM LIBRARY, 5555 Shelburne Rd, 05482. (Mail add: PO Box 10, 05482), SAN 317-1345. Tel: 802-985-3348, Ext 3379. FAX: 802-985-2331. Web Site: www.shelburnemuseum.org. *Archivist, Lib* Polly Darnell; E-Mail: pdarnell@shelburnemuseum.org; Staff 1 (MLS 1)
Founded 1947
Library Holdings: Bk Titles 6,000; Per Subs 66
Subject Interests: Am art, Antiques, Decorative arts, Folk art, Vermontia
Restriction: By appointment only
Function: Archival collection, Research library

SHELDON

P SHELDON PUBLIC LIBRARY, PO Box 12, 05483. SAN 376-8007. Tel. 802-933-2524. FAX: 802-933-2524. *Librn*, Yvette Severance
Circ 6,141
Library Holdings: Bk Vols 5,484; Per Subs 26

SHOREHAM

P PLATT MEMORIAL LIBRARY, 279 Main St, 05770-9759. SAN 317-13 Tel: 802-897-2647. E-Mail: shoreham@dol.state.vt.us. *Librn*, Diana Ladd; *Asst Librn*, Renee Ursitti
Founded 1906. Circ 1,959
Jan 1999-Dec 1999 Income $10,308, City $4,500, Locally Generated Inco $5,808. Mats Exp $2,238, Books $2,128, Per/Ser (Incl. Access Fees) $110 Sal $2,705
Library Holdings: Bk Vols 10,015; Per Subs 18
Mem of Northeastern Regional Libr Syst; Vermont Libr Asn

SOUTH BURLINGTON

S CHITTENDEN REGIONAL CORRECTIONAL LEARNING CENTER,* Farrell St, 05403. SAN 316-9758. Tel: 802-863-7356, Ext 149. FAX: 802-863-7473. *In Charge*, Mary Tripp
Library Holdings: Bk Vols 4,500; Per Subs 15

S NATIONAL GARDENING ASSOCIATION LIBRARY,* 1100 Dorset St. 05403-8000. SAN 371-5914. Tel: 802-863-1308. FAX: 802-863-5962. E-Mail: nga@garden.org. *Librn*, Kim Mitchell
Founded 1972
Library Holdings: Bk Titles 2,300; Per Subs 50
Subject Interests: Botany, Gardening, Horticulture

P SOUTH BURLINGTON COMMUNITY LIBRARY, 550 Dorset St, 0540 SAN 317-1361. Tel: 802-652-7080. FAX: 802-652-7013. Web Site: www.sbcl.sburl.k12.vt.us. *Dir*, Claire K Buckley
Founded 1972. Pop 14,650; Circ 62,192
Jul 1998-Jun 1999 Income $141,864. Mats Exp $133,000. Sal $79,039

Library Holdings: Bk Vols 29,000; Per Subs 123
Automation Activity & Vendor Info: (Cataloging) Follett; (Circulation) Follett; (OPAC) Follett
Friends of the Library Group

UTH HERO

SOUTH HERO COMMUNITY LIBRARY,* 75 South St, 05486. SAN 317-137X. Tel: 802-372-6209. FAX: 802-372-5188. *Librn*, Linda B Smith; Staff 2 (MLS 2)
Founded 1974. Pop 1,168; Circ 10,544
Jul 1997-Jun 1998 Income $23,000. Mats Exp $5,800. Sal $12,800
Library Holdings: Bk Vols 14,150; Per Subs 48

UTH LONDONDERRY

SOUTH LONDONDERRY FREE LIBRARY, 15 Old School St, PO Box 95, 05155-0095. SAN 317-1388. Tel: 802-824-3371. FAX: 802-824-4247. E-Mail: slondonderry@dol.vt.state.us. *Pres*, Clare Munat; *Librn*, Mary Butera; Staff 1 (Non-MLS 1)
Founded 1902. Pop 1,510; Circ 8,102
Library Holdings: Bk Vols 14,500; Per Subs 10
Subject Interests: Civil War, Classics, Vermont
Mem of Vt State Dept of Librs
Partic in Am Libr Asn; Vt Libr Asn
Open Mon & Fri 1-4:30, Wed 1-4:30 & 7-9, Sat 10-1
Friends of the Library Group

UTH POMFRET

ABBOTT MEMORIAL LIBRARY,* Stage Rd, PO Box 95, 05067. SAN 317-1396. Tel: 802-457-2236. *Librn*, Barbara Prince
Pop 874; Circ 1,382
Library Holdings: Bk Vols 4,000
Special Collections: Thomas Ware Primitive Portraits
Mem of Southeastern Library Services
Permanent exhibit of Pomfret Historical Society; Seven Thomas Ware Primitive Portraits on walls (photographs in color - 7 originals in vault for safe keeping). Open Thurs 10-9

UTH ROYALTON

ROYALTON MEMORIAL LIBRARY, 23 Alexander Pll, PO Box 179, 05068-0179. SAN 317-1418. Tel: 802-763-7094. E-Mail: royalton_mem@dol.state.vt.us. *Librn*, Elaina Griffith; Staff 2 (Non-MLS 2)
Founded 1923. Pop 2,300; Circ 14,200
Jul 2000-Jun 2001 Income $40,000, City $27,000, Locally Generated Income $5,000, Other $8,000. Mats Exp $9,300, Books $9,000, Per/Ser (Incl. Access Fees) $300. Sal $21,000 (Prof $20,000)
Library Holdings: Bk Vols 10,000; Per Subs 40
Mem of Midstate Regional Libr
Open Tues-Fri 12-6 & Sat 9-1

VERMONT LAW SCHOOL, Julien & Virginia Cornell Library, PO Box 60, 05068. SAN 317-1426. Tel: 802-763-8303. FAX: 802-763-7159. Web Site: www.vermontlaw.edu/library/library.htm. *Dir*, Carl A Yirka; Tel: 802-763-8303, Ext 2443, E-Mail: cyirka@vermonlaw.edu; *Assoc Dir*, Diane Frake; Tel: 802-763-8303, Ext 2444, E-Mail: dfrake@vermontlaw.edu; *Tech Servs*, Susan Zeigfinger; Tel: 802-763-8303, Ext 2446, E-Mail: szeigfin@vermontlaw.edu; *Ref*, Christine Ryan; Tel: 802-763-8303, Ext 2448, E-Mail: cryan@vermontlaw.edu; *Coll Develop*, Victoria Weber; Tel: 802-763-8303, Ext 2445, E-Mail: vweber@vermontlaw.edu; *Electronic Resources, Ref Serv*, Charles Papirmeister; Tel: 802-763-8303, Ext 2405; Staff 13 (MLS 6, Non-MLS 7)
Founded 1973. Enrl 500; Fac 45
Jul 1998-Jun 1999 Income $1,201,205. Mats Exp $606,840, Books $60,840, Per/Ser (Incl. Access Fees) $387,126, AV Equip $1,200, Electronic Ref Mat (Incl. Access Fees) $57,445. Sal $467,696 (Prof $301,754)
Library Holdings: Bk Vols 245,000; Per Subs 2,420
Subject Interests: Law
Special Collections: Environmental & Historic Preservation Coll
Automation Activity & Vendor Info: (Acquisitions) Innovative Interfaces Inc.; (Cataloging) Innovative Interfaces Inc.; (Circulation) Innovative Interfaces Inc.; (OPAC) Innovative Interfaces Inc.; (Serials) Innovative Interfaces Inc.
Function: ILL available, Reference services available
Partic in Nelinet, Inc; Nellco
Friends of the Library Group

UTH RYEGATE

SOUTH RYEGATE PUBLIC LIBRARY, INC,* Church St, 05069. SAN 320-5207. Tel: 603-747-2675, 603-802-584-3675. *Librn*, Margaret A Mitchell; *Asst Librn*, Deanna Arnosky
Pop 350; Circ 700
Dec 1998-Nov 1999 Income $2,100, Other $1,900. Mats Exp Books $500. Sal $500
Library Holdings: Bk Titles 4,600
Subject Interests: Ryegate hist, Vt

SPRINGFIELD

S SPRINGFIELD ART & HISTORICAL SOCIETY LIBRARY, 9 Elm St, 05156. (Mail add: PO Box 313, 05156), SAN 317-1442. Tel: 802-885-2415. *Dir*, Robert McLoughlin
Founded 1956
Library Holdings: Bk Vols 200
Subject Interests: Art, History
Open Tues & Fri 10-4, Thurs 1-4 & 7-9

M SPRINGFIELD HOSPITAL, Information Center Library,* 25 Ridgewood Rd, PO Box 2003, 05156. SAN 320-7544. Tel: 802-885-2151. FAX: 802-885-3959.
Library Holdings: Bk Vols 100; Per Subs 50

P SPRINGFIELD TOWN LIBRARY,* 43 Main St, 05156. SAN 317-1450. Tel: 802-885-3108. FAX: 802-885-4906. E-Mail: springfield@dol.state.vt.us. *Dir*, Russell Moore; *Ch Servs*, Rosemarie Ratti; *Tech Servs*, Gail Zachariah; Staff 8 (MLS 3, Non-MLS 5)
Founded 1819. Pop 9,579
Jul 1996-Jun 1997 Income $314,923, State $50, City $293,013, Locally Generated Income $11,674, Other $10,186. Mats Exp $51,618, Books $35,195, Per/Ser (Incl. Access Fees) $8,578, Presv $2,934, AV Equip $2,123. Sal $177,275 (Prof $89,964)
Library Holdings: Bk Vols 38,150; Per Subs 225
Subject Interests: Alternative tech, Machine tool, Vermontiana
Mem of Southeastern Library Services
Friends of the Library Group

STAMFORD

P STAMFORD COMMUNITY LIBRARY,* 986 Main Rd, 05352. SAN 317-1469. Tel: 802-694-1379. FAX: 802-694-1636. *Librn*, Jennifer Ward
Founded 1897. Circ 11,573
Library Holdings: Bk Vols 7,300
Mem of Southeastern Library Services
Open Mon-Fri 9am-noon & Thurs 9am-noon & 5-9pm

STARKSBORO

P STARKSBORO PUBLIC LIBRARY,* Rte 116, Box 10, 05487. SAN 376-3471. Tel: 802-453-2949. *Librn*, Judith Kessler
Library Holdings: Bk Vols 3,400
Mem of Midstate Regional Libr
Open Sat 10:30-12

STOWE

P STOWE FREE LIBRARY,* PO Box 1029, 05672. SAN 317-1485. Tel: 802-253-4808, 802-253-6145. *Dir*, Hilari Farrington; *Ch Servs*, Julie Pickett; Staff 6 (MLS 2, Non-MLS 4)
Founded 1866. Pop 3,800; Circ 40,000
Library Holdings: Bk Vols 18,000; Per Subs 70
Special Collections: Town; Vermont
Mem of Midstate Regional Libr

STRAFFORD

P MORRILL MEMORIAL & HARRIS LIBRARY, 220 Justin Morrill Memorial Hwy, 05072-9730. (Mail add: PO Box 110, 05072-0110), SAN 317-1493. Tel: 802-765-4037. E-Mail: strafford@dol.state.vt.us. *Librn*, Maureen Wilson
Pop 902; Circ 8,447
Library Holdings: Bk Vols 11,000
Special Collections: Senator Justin Smith Morrill Coll
Mem of Midstate Regional Libr

SWANTON

S NORTHWEST STATE CORRECTIONAL FACILITY,* RFD 1, Box 279-1, 05488. SAN 317-123X. Tel: 802-524-6771. FAX: 802-527-7534.
Founded 1967
Library Holdings: Bk Vols 3,500; Per Subs 20

P SWANTON PUBLIC LIBRARY,* One First St, 05488. SAN 317-1515. Tel: 802-868-7656. *Librn*, Marilyn Barney; *Asst Librn*, Darla Blondo; *Asst Librn*, Jane Bouchard; *Asst Librn*, Joann Flanagan; *Asst Librn*, Cheryl Messier; *Asst Librn*, Judy Paxman

Pop 5,636; Circ 16,707
Library Holdings: Bk Vols 15,923; Per Subs 34
Special Collections: Large Print Books; Old Vermont History Coll
Open Mon-Thurs 2-8, Fri 9-12 & 2-8, Sat 10-2

THETFORD

S THETFORD HISTORICAL SOCIETY LIBRARY, PO Box 33, 05074. SAN 325-142X. Tel: 802-785-2068. *Librn*, Charles Latham, Jr; *Asst Librn*, Marian Fifield; Staff 2 (Non-MLS 2)
Founded 1975
Library Holdings: Bk Vols 4,530
Special Collections: Charles Farnsworth Coll; Dean C Worcester Coll (Philippines); Local crafts & trades; Missionary History Coll; schoolbooks; Thetford town history, Dean C Worrcester Coll (Philippines); Town of Thetford; Vermont & New Hampshire town histories
Restriction: Not a lending library

P THETFORD TOWN LIBRARY, Latham Memorial Library, PO Box 240, 05074-0240. SAN 362-6490. Tel: 802-785-4361. *Librn*, Peter W Blodgett
Founded 1876. Pop 2,438; Circ 18,626
Jan 1998-Dec 1998 Income $31,875. Mats Exp $6,000. Sal $22,241
Library Holdings: Bk Vols 11,489; Per Subs 94
Special Collections: Peabody Coll; Thetford Authors; Vermont Coll
Mem of Midstate Regional Libr
Open Mon 2-8:30, Tues-Thurs 2-5, Fri 9-5 & Sat 10-1
Branches: 2
GEORGE PEABODY BRANCH, PO Box 190, Post Mills, 05058-0190. SAN 362-6520. Tel: 802-333-9724. *In Charge*, Peter W Blodgett
Open Tues 5-8, Wed 2-6; Summer hours: Tues 5-8, Wed 2-6 & 7-8:30 & Sat 10-12
THETFORD HISTORICAL Tel: 802-333-4613, 802-785-4361. *In Charge*, Charles Latham
Open Winter: Mon 2-4 (or by appointment); Summer: Mon 2-4 & Tues 10-12 (or by appointment)

TINMOUTH

P TINMOUTH PUBLIC LIBRARY,* 141 East Rd, 05773. SAN 376-4001. Tel: 802-446-2498. *Librn*, Ruth Drachman
Library Holdings: Bk Vols 1,000
Mem of Southwest Regional Library Service System

TOWNSHED

M OTIS HEALTH CARE CENTER, (Formerly Grace Cottage Hospital), Grace Cottage Hospital Library, 185 Graston Rd, 05353-0216. Tel: 802-365-7920, Ext 119. *Dir*, Kathleen Stover; E-Mail: stover@sover.net

TOWNSHEND

P TOWNSHEND PUBLIC LIBRARY, 1971 Rte 30, 05353. (Mail add: PO Box 252, 05353), Tel: 802-365-4039. E-Mail: townshend@dol.state.vt.us. *Librn*, Marilee Attley; Staff 1 (Non-MLS 1)
Founded 1899. Pop 1,000; Circ 8,500
Jan 1999-Dec 1999 Income $27,290, City $18,890, Locally Generated Income $8,400. Mats Exp $4,000. Sal $11,000 (Prof $8,100)
Library Holdings: Bk Vols 10,500; Per Subs 15
Subject Interests: Vt hist, W River Valley hist
Publications: ALA Booklist; Atheneum
Mem of Southeastern Library Services
Friends of the Library Group

TUNBRIDGE

P TUNBRIDGE PUBLIC LIBRARY,* 271 Vt Rte 110, PO Box 9, 05077. SAN 317-1531. Tel: 802-889-9404. E-Mail: tunbridge@dol.state.vt.us. *Librn*, Jean Wolfe
Jul 1999-Jun 2000 Income $23,465, City $12,915, Locally Generated Income $10,550. Mats Exp Books $2,510. Sal $12,330
Library Holdings: Bk Vols 7,000
Subject Interests: Vermont
Mem of Midstate Regional Libr; Vt State Dept of Librs
Friends of the Library Group

VERGENNES

P BIXBY MEMORIAL FREE LIBRARY,* 258 Main St, 05491. SAN 317-1558. Tel: 802-877-2211. *Dir*, Lois C Noonan
Founded 1912. Pop 5,500; Circ 33,969
Jul 1998-Jun 1999 Income $112,862. Mats Exp Books $13,507. Sal $495,040
Library Holdings: Bk Titles 27,175; Per Subs 20
Special Collections: American Indian Coll; Antiques (Cup Plate Coll); Paperweight Coll; Vermont History Coll

VERNON

S VERMONT YANKEE NUCLEAR POWER CORPORATION, Energy Information Center Library,* Governor Hunt Rd, PO Box 157, 05354. S. 322-8320. Tel: 802-258-5796. FAX: 802-258-5795. *Librn*, Candace Sak
Founded 1979
Library Holdings: Bk Titles 500
Subject Interests: Energy
Special Collections: Energy Coll, bks, film, videotapes, slides
Publications: Energy Educators Newsletter

P VERNON FREE PUBLIC LIBRARY,* Main Rd, PO Box 94, 05354. S/ 317-1574. Tel: 802-257-0150. *Librn*, Nancy Evans
Pop 1,854; Circ 15,494
Library Holdings: Bk Vols 14,000; Per Subs 52
Mem of Southeastern Library Services

WAITSFIELD

P JOSLIN MEMORIAL LIBRARY, 4391 Main St, PO Box 359, 05673. S 317-1590. Tel: 802-496-4205. E-Mail: waitsfield@dol.state.vt.us. *Librn*, Elizabeth Howlett; Staff 1 (MLS 1)
Founded 1913. Pop 2,300; Circ 16,700
Jan 1999-Dec 1999 Income $33,408, City $25,850, Locally Generated Income $7,558. Mats Exp $8,754, Books $8,000, Per/Ser (Incl. Access F $600, Micro $154. Sal $12,500
Library Holdings: Bk Vols 8,966; Per Subs 33; Bks on Deafness & Sig Lang 10
Special Collections: Vermont Coll
Partic in Vermont State Libr Syst
Friends of the Library Group

WALLINGFORD

P GILBERT HART LIBRARY,* 14 S Main, PO Box 69, 05773. SAN 317 1612. Tel: 802-446-2503, 802-446-2685. *Librn*, Joan Jackson
Founded 1795
Oct 1998-Sep 1999 Income $40,091, City $26,500, Locally Generated Income $6,951, Other $2,677. Mats Exp $6,435, Books $5,500, Per/Ser (Incl. Access Fees) $435, AV Equip $500. Sal $13,658 (Prof $7,188)
Library Holdings: Bk Vols 17,000; Per Subs 50
Special Collections: Vermontiana Coll
Publications: Klock-History of Wallingford, Vermont
Open Tues 10-5, Wed 10-8, Thurs-Fri 10-5 & Sat 9-12
Friends of the Library Group

WARDSBORO

P WARDSBORO FREE PUBLIC LIBRARY,* PO Box 157, 05355. SAN 1620. Tel: 802-896-6988. E-Mail: wardsboro@dol.state.vt. *Librn*, Vivian Miles
Pop 604; Circ 4,009
Library Holdings: Bk Vols 4,406
Mem of Southeastern Library Services

WARREN

P WARREN PUBLIC LIBRARY, PO Box 287, 05674. SAN 320-5215. Te 802-496-3913. E-Mail: warren@dol.state.vt.us. *Librn*, Jill Markolf; Staff (Non-MLS 4)
Pop 1,172; Circ 12,784
1998-1999 Income $35,500. Mats Exp $6,920, Books $5,700, Per/Ser (In Access Fees) $420, AV Equip $800. Sal $20,920 (Prof $17,519)
Library Holdings: Bk Titles 7,600; Per Subs 25; Bks on Deafness & Sig Lang 10
Partic in OCLC Online Computer Library Center, Inc
Friends of the Library Group
Bookmobiles: 1

WASHINGTON

P CALEF MEMORIAL LIBRARY,* PO Box 141, 05675. SAN 317-1639. Tel: 802-883-2343. *Librn*, Kay Dorsett
Pop 855; Circ 2,152
Library Holdings: Bk Vols 5,900; Per Subs 16
Mem of Midstate Regional Libr
Open Mon 10-2, Tues & Thurs 3-8
Friends of the Library Group

WATERBURY

VERMONT STATE HOSPITAL
S COMMUNITY LIBRARY, 103 S Main St, 05671-2501. SAN 362-661X. Tel: 802-241-3246. FAX: 802-241-3001.
Founded 1962

Library Holdings: Bk Vols 11,000
Subject Interests: Patient educ
Special Collections: Large Print Coll; Self-Help Books; Vermontiana Coll
Publications: Hospital Newspaper
Partic in Medline

WATERBURY VILLAGE PUBLIC LIBRARY,* 28 N Main St, 05676. SAN 317-1647. Tel: 802-244-7036, 802-244-7079. *Librn*, Donna Boring
Circ 29,000
Jan 1997-Dec 1998 Income $102,000
Library Holdings: Bk Vols 32,000
Special Collections: Vermontiana
Mem of Midstate Regional Libr
Friends of the Library Group

TERVILLE

WATERVILLE TOWN LIBRARY,* PO Box 1472, 05492. SAN 317-1663. Tel: 802-644-5683.
Pop 470; Circ 1,500
Library Holdings: Bk Vols 3,900
Open Wed 4-5

LLS

WELLS VILLAGE LIBRARY,* 5 E Wells Rd, 05774-0587. (Mail add: PO Box 587, 05774-0587), SAN 317-1671. Tel: 802-645-0611. *Librn*, Patricia M Capron
Founded 1944. Pop 900
Jan 1999-Dec 1999 Income $3,600, City $3,000, Other $600. Mats Exp Books $700. Sal $1,800
Library Holdings: Bk Vols 6,827
Subject Interests: Adult fiction, Gen juv, Nonfiction
Mem of Southwest Regional Library Service System

LLS RIVER

BALDWIN MEMORIAL LIBRARY,* PO Box 337, 05081. SAN 317-168X. Tel: 802-757-2693. E-Mail: wells_river@dol.state.vt.us. Web Site: www.wells_river@dol.state.vt.us. *Librn*, Peggy Hewes
Pop 1,440; Circ 8,076
Jan 1997-Dec 1998 Income $26,000. Mats Exp $5,500. Sal $11,000
Library Holdings: Bk Vols 9,500; Per Subs 25
Special Collections: Martin Luther King Memorial Peace Shelf
Mem of Northeastern Regional Libr Syst

ST BURKE

WEST BURKE LIBRARY,* Main St, 05871. SAN 317-1698. Tel: 802-467-3022. *Librn*, Leah Wells
Pop 338; Circ 924
Library Holdings: Bk Vols 3,200
Mem of Northeastern Regional Libr Syst
Open Wed & Sat 1:30-4:30

ST DANVILLE

WALDEN COMMUNITY LIBRARY, 135 Cahoon Farm Rd, 05873. SAN 317-1604. Tel: 802-563-3000. *Librn*, Anne Smith; *Ch Servs*, Martha E Bissell
Founded 1895. Pop 500; Circ 1,000
Jan 1999-Dec 1999 Income $2,500. Mats Exp $2,500, Books $2,000, Per/Ser (Incl. Access Fees) $500
Library Holdings: Bk Vols 7,000
Special Collections: Vermont Coll
Publications: Walden 200
Mem of Northeastern Regional Libr Syst

EST DUMMERSTON

LYDIA TAFT PRATT LIBRARY,* 05357. SAN 376-8015. Tel: 802-254-2703. *Librn*, Judy Enello
1998-1999 Income $3,200. Mats Exp $1,100. Sal $1,200
Library Holdings: Bk Vols 4,000
Mem of Southeastern Library Services

EST FAIRLEE

WEST FAIRLEE FREE PUBLIC LIBRARY,* PO Box 8, 05083. SAN 317-171X. Tel: 802-333-9696. *Librn*, Viola Farrar
Founded 1908. Pop 337; Circ 900
Library Holdings: Bk Titles 2,000
Mem of Mid State Regional Libr
Open Wed 6-8pm, Fri 2:30-5

WEST HARTFORD

P WEST HARTFORD LIBRARY, 5133 Rte 14, PO Box 26, 05084-0026. SAN 317-1728. Tel: 802-295-7992. *Librn*, Shelley Best; Staff 3 (Non-MLS 3)
Founded 1927. Pop 10,000
Jul 1999-Jun 2000 Income $38,453. Mats Exp Books $5,500. Sal $17,802 (Prof $1,300)
Library Holdings: Bk Vols 7,119; Bk Titles 7,096; Per Subs 23; High Interest/Low Vocabulary Bk Vols 10
Special Collections: Vt History
Mem of Midstate Regional Libr; Vt State Dept of Librs
Open Mon & Fri 5-7, Tues & Thurs 9-2, Wed 9-7, & Sat 10-1

WEST RUTLAND

P WEST RUTLAND FREE LIBRARY CORP, 595 Main St, 05777. SAN 317-1736. Tel: 802-438-2964. *Librn*, Mary White
Pop 2,448; Circ 7,899
Jul 1999-Jun 2000 Income $29,307, City $15,750. Mats Exp $5,125, Books $3,694, Per/Ser (Incl. Access Fees) $1,019. Sal $19,789
Library Holdings: Bk Vols 8,042; Per Subs 32
Mem of Midstate Regional Libr
Open Mon, Wed & Fri 1:30-5, Tues-Thurs 1:30-7

WEST TOWNSHEND

P WINDHAM TOWN LIBRARY,* c/o Town Clerk, RR 1 Box 109, 05359. SAN 376-334X. Tel: 802-874-4211.
Library Holdings: Bk Vols 800
Mem of Southeastern Library Services

WEST WINDSOR

P MARY L BLOOD MEMORIAL LIBRARY,* 41 Brownsville-Hartland Rd, 05089. (Mail add: PO Box 468, 05037), Tel: 802-484-7205. *Librn*, Mary Winter
Pop 932; Circ 5,960
Library Holdings: Bk Vols 4,300
Mem of Southeastern Regional Libr Syst

WESTFIELD

S HITCHCOCK MUSEUM & LIBRARY,* PO Box 87, 05874. SAN 376-3420. Tel: 802-744-2440. *Librn*, Mary Brenner; E-Mail: brenner@fcgnetworks.net
Library Holdings: Bk Vols 7,000
Mem of Northeastern Regional Libr Syst

WESTFORD

P WESTFORD LIBRARY,* PO Box 86, 05494. SAN 376-8031. Tel: 802-878-5639. *Librn*, Kit Stevenson
Library Holdings: Bk Vols 9,000
Open Mon 4-8, Wed 1-8, Thurs 10-2, Sat 9-2

WESTMINSTER

P BUTTERFIELD LIBRARY,* PO Box 123, 05158. SAN 317-1744. Tel: 802-722-4891. *Librn*, Linda Fawcett
Founded 1924. Pop 1,875; Circ 5,489
Library Holdings: Bk Vols 7,000; Per Subs 30
Open Tues & Thurs 2-8
Friends of the Library Group

WESTON

P WILDER MEMORIAL LIBRARY,* PO Box 38, 05161. SAN 317-1760. Tel: 802-824-4307. *Librn*, Carolyn Mullett
Pop 600; Circ 1,126
Library Holdings: Bk Vols 4,000
Mem of Southeastern Library Services
Open Wed & Sat 2-6

WHITE RIVER JUNCTION

GM DEPARTMENT OF VETERANS AFFAIRS MEDICAL LIBRARY,* 215 N Main St, 05009. SAN 362-6644. Tel: 802-295-9363, Ext 5236. FAX: 802-296-5150. E-Mail: va_library@dartmouth.edu. *In Charge*, Brian Grawrick
Founded 1940
Library Holdings: Bk Vols 1,300; Per Subs 250
Subject Interests: Internal medicine
Partic in Valnet

P WHITE RIVER JUNCTION-GATES MEMORIAL LIBRARY, 70 N Main St, 05001. SAN 317-1787. Tel: 802-295-7402. FAX: 802-295-7402. E-Mail: white_river@dol.state.vt.us. *Librn*, Bernadette du Tremble; Staff 2 (Non-MLS 2)
Founded 1907. Pop 10,500
Library Holdings: Bk Vols 13,485; Per Subs 40
Mem of Midstate Regional Libr
Friends of the Library Group

WHITING

P WHITING FREE LIBRARY,* 05778. SAN 376-3331. Tel: 802-623-6291. *Librn*, Kathy Coakley
Library Holdings: Bk Vols 200
Mem of Southwest Regional Library Service System
Summer hours only

WILDER

S THE BERTRAND RUSSELL SOCIETY, INC LIBRARY, 98 Gillette St, PO Box 434, 05088. SAN 371-1692. Tel: 802-295-9058. Web Site: www.geocities.com/Athens/Olympus/4268/. *Librn*, Thomas Stanley; E-Mail: tom.stanley@valley.net
Library Holdings: Bk Vols 200
Publications: Index to Newsletters of the Russell Society, 1974-1992

WILLIAMSTOWN

P AINSWORTH PUBLIC LIBRARY,* Main St, PO Box 236, 05679. SAN 322-6700. Tel: 802-433-5887. FAX: 802-433-2161. E-Mail: williamstown@dol.state.vt.us. *Dir*, Laura Phelps; *Asst Librn*, Flora O'Hara; Staff 1 (MLS 1)
Pop 3,000; Circ 6,000
1999-2000 Income $24,540. Mats Exp Books $9,000. Sal $12,622
Library Holdings: Bk Titles 8,200; Per Subs 20
Special Collections: Craft Coll, bks, periodicals
Open Mon, Tues, Thurs & Fri 2-6, Wed 9-8, Sat 9-1
Friends of the Library Group

WILLISTON

P DOROTHY ALLING MEMORIAL LIBRARY, 21 Library Lane, 05495. SAN 317-1809. Tel: 802-878-4918. FAX: 802-878-9609. Web Site: www.state.vt.us/libraries/w671/. *Librn*, Frederica M Emerson; Staff 12 (MLS 4, Non-MLS 8)
Founded 1905. Pop 6,953; Circ 75,516
Jul 1999-Jun 2000 Income $207,811. Mats Exp $30,600. Sal $144,731
Library Holdings: Bk Vols 26,741; Bk Titles 23,265; Per Subs 100; High Interest/Low Vocabulary Bk Vols 37; Bks on Deafness & Sign Lang 14
Special Collections: Local History (Williston Coll), bks, photogs, postal cards, scrapbooks, typescripts
Automation Activity & Vendor Info: (Cataloging) Follett; (Circulation) Follett; (Course Reserve) Follett; (Media Booking) Follett; (OPAC) Follett
Database Vendor: Ebsco - EbscoHost
Friends of the Library Group
Bookmobiles: 1

WILMINGTON

P PETTEE MEMORIAL LIBRARY, PO Box 896, 05363. SAN 317-1817. Tel: 802-464-8557. E-Mail: pettee2@sover.net. *Librn*, Vivian Miles; *Asst Librn*, Harriette Hamilton; Staff 1 (MLS 1)
Founded 1895. Pop 1,984; Circ 15,000
Jul 1999-Jun 2000 Income $55,451, City $49,451, Locally Generated Income $6,000. Mats Exp $7,980, Books $7,500, Electronic Ref Mat (Incl. Access Fees) $480. Sal $28,099 (Prof $19,900)
Library Holdings: Bk Titles 9,648; Per Subs 10
Special Collections: Vermont Shelf (books)
Automation Activity & Vendor Info: (Acquisitions) Follett; (Cataloging) Follett; (Circulation) Follett
Mem of Southeastern Library Services
Partic in Vt Libr Syst
Open Mon 10-2, Tues & Thurs 12-6, Fri 10-2, Sat 9:30-5, Sun 12-4
Friends of the Library Group

WINDSOR

M MOUNT ASCUTNEY HOSPITAL & HEALTH CENTER, Agatha Young Library, 289 County Rd, 05089. SAN 317-1825. Tel: 802-674-6711. FAX: 802-674-7155. E-Mail: dalegephart@dartmouth.edu. *In Charge*, Dr Dale Gephart; *Librn*, Urban Bates
Founded 1972
Library Holdings: Bk Vols 285; Bk Titles 221

S SOUTHEAST STATE CORRECTIONAL FACILITY LIBRARY,* 546 State Farm Rd, 05089. SAN 317-1833. Tel: 802-674-6717. *In Charge*, Maryanne Murphy
Library Holdings: Bk Vols 3,000; Per Subs 12
Publications: Vermont State Library Newsletter

P WINDSOR PUBLIC LIBRARY, 43 State St, 05089. SAN 317-1841. Tel 802-674-2556. *Dir*, Devik Hemmings; *Dir*, Donna Fogarty
Founded 1882. Pop 3,714; Circ 23,000
Library Holdings: Bk Vols 18,000; Per Subs 60
Special Collections: Old Vermont Newspaper Coll; Vermont History Col
Friends of the Library Group

WINOOSKI

P WINOOSKI MEMORIAL LIBRARY, 19 E Spring St, 05404. SAN 317-1868. Tel: 802-655-6424. FAX: 802-655-6414. E-Mail: winooski@dol.state.vt.us. *Dir Libr Serv*, Janet Soutiere
Founded 1930. Pop 6,800; Circ 17,250
Jul 1999-Jun 2000 Income $48,000. Mats Exp $8,000. Sal $29,500
Library Holdings: Bk Vols 13,000; Per Subs 26

WOLCOTT

S CENTER FOR NORTHERN STUDIES LIBRARY,* 479 Crossroads, 05680-9726. SAN 317-1876. Tel: 802-888-4331. FAX: 802-888-3969. E-Mail: cnsnorth@together.net. *Librn*, Victoria Hust; *Coll Develop*, Diane Holland
Founded 1971
Library Holdings: Bk Vols 4,000; Per Subs 60
Subject Interests: Arctic studies
Special Collections: North Polar Regions
Partic in OCLC Online Computer Library Center, Inc

P GLEE MERRITT KELLEY COMMUNITY LIBRARY,* PO Box 179, 05680. SAN 317-1884. Tel: 802-472-6551. *Librn*, Sally Gardner
Founded 1973. Circ 7,025
Library Holdings: Bk Vols 12,700; Per Subs 15
Special Collections: Vermont Coll

WOODBURY

P WOODBURY COMMUNITY LIBRARY,* PO Box 328, 05681. SAN 37 4923. Tel: 802-472-5715. *Librn*, Natalie Wilgoren
Library Holdings: Bk Vols 3,000; Per Subs 12
Mem of Midstate Regional Libr

WOODSTOCK

S SOUTHEAST REGIONAL COMMUNITY CORRECTIONAL CENTER LIBRARY,* 62 Pleasant St, 05091. SAN 317-1914. Tel: 802-457-2310. FAX: 802-457-4413.
Library Holdings: Bk Vols 3,000

S VERMONT INSTITUTE OF NATURAL SCIENCE LIBRARY,* Church Hill Rd, RR 2, Box 532, 05091. SAN 317-1892. Tel: 802-457-2779. FAX 802-457-1053. *Dir*, Tim Traver; *Coll Develop*, Donna Moseman
Founded 1972
Library Holdings: Bk Titles 8,500; Per Subs 90
Subject Interests: Environmental studies, Natural history, Ornithology
Special Collections: Henry Potter papers; Olin Sewall Pettingill Ornithological Library Billings - Kitteridge Herbarium
Publications: Hands on Nature - Lingelbach, Waste Away - Vins
Partic in ILL
Open Mon-Fri 9-12

P NORMAN WILLIAMS PUBLIC LIBRARY,* 10 S Park St, 05091. SAN 317-1906. Tel: 802-457-2295. FAX: 802-457-5181. E-Mail: woodstock@dol.state.vt.us. *Coll Develop, Dir*, Katherine Ludwig
Founded 1884. Pop 3,200; Circ 55,100
Jul 1998-Jun 1999 Income $187,781, City $32,000, Locally Generated Income $155,781. Mats Exp $181,373, Books $29,783. Sal $104,466
Library Holdings: Bk Vols 36,000; Per Subs 85
Subject Interests: Local history, State hist
Mem of Southeastern Regional Libr Syst
Open Mon, Tues, Wed & Fri 10-5, Sat 10-4

S WOODSTOCK HISTORICAL SOCIETY, INC, John Cotton Dana Library 26 Elm St, 05091. SAN 327-2621. Tel: 802-457-1822. FAX: 802-457-281 *Archivist, Librn*, Marie McAndrew-Taylor; E-Mail: mariemt@mail.sover.n Staff 14 (MLS 1, Non-MLS 13)
Founded 1942
Jan 1999-Dec 1999 Mats Exp Presv $500
Library Holdings: Bk Vols 2,000; Bk Titles 2,000
Subject Interests: Genealogy, Local history

Special Collections: Institutional records, family papers & diaries from Woodstock area; large photog archive
Restriction: Not a lending library
Open Tues-Thurs 10-3pm

of Statistics: Fiscal 1999-2000
lation, 1990 Census: 6,187,358
lation Served by Public Libraries: 6,686,437
Unserved: 2,361
l Volumes in Public Libraries: 21,246,782
Volumes Per Capita: 3.17
l Public Library Circulation: 51,010,198
l Public Library Expenditures (including Grants-in-Aid): $158,674,208
Source of Income: Mainly public funds
Expenditures Per Capita: $22.80
ber of County or Multi-county (Regional) Libraries: 67
Counties Served: 94
Counties Unserved: 1
Number of Independent Cities: 41
Cities Served:41
Number of Bookmobiles in State: 39
Grants-in-Aid to Public Libraries:
State Aid: $16,943,113 (state aid payments to localities - FY 2001); $20,485,543
Formula for Apportionment: Legally established libraries receive grants based on local support, population, square miles & number of government units served
Federal Aid: (Library Services & Construction Act): $2,938,963 (LSTA State Grants) Technology Act): $1,439,159 (LSTA State Grants)
Use of Funds: Grants to public libraries and statewide programs for library development

NGDON

VIRGINIA HIGHLANDS COMMUNITY COLLEGE LIBRARY, 140 Old Jonesboro Road, 24210. (Mail add: PO Box 828, 24212-0828), Tel: 540-676-5484. Toll Free Tel: 877-207-6115. FAX: 540-676-5484. Web Site: www.vh.cc.va.us/library. *Dir Libr Serv*, Dr Patricia A Hunter; Tel: 540-676-5484, Ext 312, Fax: 540-676-5598, E-Mail: phunter@vh.cc.va.us; *Ref*, Grace C Boyce; E-Mail: gboyce@vh.cc.va.us; *Ref*, Katherine M Kerns; Tel: 540-676-5484, Ext 342, E-Mail: kkerns@vh.cc.va.us; Staff 5 (MLS 3, Non-MLS 2)
Founded 1969. Enrl 2,107; Fac 66
Jul 1999-Jun 2000 Income $50,000
Library Holdings: Bk Vols 25,000; Bk Titles 20,859; Per Subs 220; Bks on Deafness & Sign Lang 13
Special Collections: VIVA (Virtual Library of Virginia)
Database Vendor: GaleNet, IAC - Info Trac, Lexis-Nexis, OCLC - First Search, OVID Technologies
Partic in SWING; VIVA-Statewide Library Resource Network

WASHINGTON COUNTY PUBLIC LIBRARY, 205 Oak Hill St, 24210. SAN 317-1949. Tel: 540-676-6222. Circulation Tel: 540-676-6233. Reference Tel: 540-676-6298. FAX: 540-676-6235. Web Site: www.wcpl.net. *Dir*, Charlotte L Parsons; Tel: 540-676-6223, E-Mail: charlotte@wcpl.net; *Mgr*, Teresa K Phillips; *Bkmobile Coordr*, Tammy Coalson; E-Mail: tcoalson@wcpl.net; *Tech Servs*, Debbie S Ledbetter; Tel: 540-676-6340, E-Mail: dledbetter@wcpl.net; *Ref*, Carol A Morgan; Tel: 540-676-6389, E-Mail: cmorgan@wcpl.net; *Ch Servs*, Shannon Bolick; Tel: 540-676-6382, E-Mail: sbolick@wcpl.net; *Publ Servs*, Ida Patton; Tel: 540-676-6390, E-Mail: ipatton@wcpl.net; *Tech Coordr*, Eric Schuler; Tel: 540-676-6246, E-Mail: eschuler@wcpl.net; Staff 21 (MLS 3, Non-MLS 18)
Founded 1954. Pop 49,900; Circ 275,124
Jul 1998-Jun 1999 Income (Main Library and Branch Library) $1,008,804, State $177,966, Federal $11,717, County $666,512, Locally Generated Income $124,209, Other $28,400. Mats Exp $164,351, Books $147,887, Per/Ser (Incl. Access Fees) $15,780. Sal $569,566 (Prof $41,004)
Library Holdings: Bk Vols 82,233; Bk Titles 92,264; Per Subs 265
Automation Activity & Vendor Info: (Acquisitions) Innovative Interfaces Inc.; (Cataloging) Innovative Interfaces Inc.; (Circulation) Innovative Interfaces Inc.; (OPAC) Innovative Interfaces Inc.; (Serials) Innovative Interfaces Inc.
Database Vendor: Ebsco - EbscoHost, OCLC - First Search
Partic in Holston Associated Librs Consortium
Friends of the Library Group
Branches: 4
DAMASCUS BRANCH, 227 Laurel Ave, PO Box 280, Damascus, 24236. SAN 329-3211. Tel: 540-475-3820. FAX: 540-475-5081. Web Site: www.wcpl.net. *Branch Mgr*, Deanna Wolfe; E-Mail: dwolfe@wcpl.net; Staff 2 (Non-MLS 2)
Automation Activity & Vendor Info: (Circulation) Innovative Interfaces Inc.
Database Vendor: Ebsco - EbscoHost, OCLC - First Search
Mem of Washington County Libr Syst
Partic in Holston Associated Librs Consortium
GLADE SPRINGS BRANCH, 212 Grace St, Glade Springs, 24340. (Mail add: PO Box 70, Glade Spring, 24340-0070), SAN 320-9504. Tel: 540-429-5626. FAX: 540-429-2740. Web Site: www.wcpl.net. *Branch Mgr*, Pamela Stallard; E-Mail: pstallard@wcpl.net; Staff 1 (Non-MLS 1)
Automation Activity & Vendor Info: (Circulation) Innovative Interfaces Inc.
Database Vendor: Ebsco - EbscoHost, OCLC - First Search
Mem of Washington County Libr Syst
Partic in Holston Associated Librs Consortium
HAYTERS GAP, 7720 Hayters Gap Rd, 24210. SAN 375-1430. Tel: 540-944-4442. FAX: 540-944-3011. Web Site: www.wcpl.net. *Branch Mgr*, Kathy Musick; E-Mail: kmusick@wcpl.net; Staff 1 (Non-MLS 1)
Automation Activity & Vendor Info: (Circulation) Innovative Interfaces Inc.
Database Vendor: Ebsco - EbscoHost, OCLC - First Search
Mem of Washington County Libr Syst
Partic in Holston Associated Librs Consortium
MENDOTA BRANCH, 2562 Mendota Rd, PO Box 99, Mendota, 24270. SAN 375-1449. Tel: 540-645-2374. FAX: 540-645-2330. Web Site: www.wcpl.net. *Branch Mgr*, Jennifer Ilowiecki; E-Mail: jilowiecki@wcpl.net; Staff 1 (Non-MLS 1)
Jul 1999-Jun 2000 Income $37,660, State $5,800, County $31,860. Mats Exp $10,300, Books $9,300, AV Equip $1,000. Sal $16,860
Automation Activity & Vendor Info: (Circulation) Innovative Interfaces Inc.
Database Vendor: Ebsco - EbscoHost, OCLC - First Search
Partic in Holston Associated Librs Consortium
Bookmobiles: 1

ACCOMAC

P EASTERN SHORE PUBLIC LIBRARY,* 23610 Front St, PO Box 360, 23301-0360. SAN 317-1957. Tel: 757-787-3400. FAX: 757-787-2241. Web Site: www.espl.org. *Dir*, W Robert Keeney; *Librn*, Brooks M Barnes; *ILL*, Sandra G Scoville; Staff 2 (MLS 2)
Founded 1957. Pop 45,200; Circ 164,451
Library Holdings: Bk Vols 110,000; Per Subs 162
Subject Interests: Boat building, Sailing
Special Collections: Local History (Eastern Shore of Virginia Coll), bks, maps, micro
Partic in SE Libr Network
Friends of the Library Group

ALBERTA

J SOUTHSIDE VIRGINIA COMMUNITY COLLEGE LIBRARIES,* 109 Campus Dr, 23821. SAN 362-6709. Tel: 804-949-1000. FAX: 804-949-0013. Web Site: www.sv.cc.va.us. *Dir*, Jack Ancell; Tel: 804-949-1066, E-Mail: jack.ancell@sv.cc.va.us
Founded 1970
1997-1998 Income $300,000. Mats Exp $35,500, Books $21,000, Per/Ser

(Incl. Access Fees) $8,500, Micro $2,000, AV Equip $4,000. Sal $160,000 (Prof $104,000)
Library Holdings: Bk Vols 30,000; Per Subs 270
Figures reported for both the Julian M Howell & John H Daniel Libraries

ALEXANDRIA

M ALEXANDRIA HOSPITAL, Medical Library,* 4320 Seminary Rd, 22304. SAN 327-2648. Tel: 703-504-3126. FAX: 703-504-3176.
Library Holdings: Bk Vols 1,000; Bk Titles 1,200
Subject Interests: Medicine, Nursing
Partic in BRS; Docline; Nat Libr of Med
Open Mon-Fri 8-4:30, Open to public 1:30-4:30

P ALEXANDRIA LIBRARY, 5005 Duke St, 22304-2903. SAN 362-6733. Tel: 703-823-5295. Interlibrary Loan Service Tel: 703-838-4555, Ext 221. TDD: 703-823-5809. FAX: 703-823-5718. Web Site: alexandria.lib.va.us. *Dir*, Patrick M O'Brien; Tel: 703-823-5295, Ext 223, E-Mail: pobrien@alexandria.lib.va.us; *Dep Dir*, Mary Randolph; Tel: 703-823-5295, Ext 228, E-Mail: mrandolph@alexandria.lib.va.us; *ILL*, Barbara Stuecker; *Tech Servs*, Ilze Cimermanis; Staff 21 (MLS 21)
Founded 1794. Pop 123,386; Circ 668,046
Jul 1999-Jun 2000 Income (Main Library and Branch Library) $4,710,944, State $244,011, City $3,902,748, Locally Generated Income $564,185. Mats Exp $670,477, Books $617,224, Per/Ser (Incl. Access Fees) $30,825, Micro $20,019, Other Print Mats $2,409. Sal $2,414,767 (Prof $1,174,481)
Library Holdings: Bk Vols 411,674; Per Subs 633
Automation Activity & Vendor Info: (Acquisitions) GEAC; (Cataloging) GEAC; (Circulation) GEAC; (Serials) GEAC
Database Vendor: Ebsco - EbscoHost, OCLC - First Search
Partic in Metro Coun of Govts; SE Libr Network
Special Services for the Blind - Braille Embosser; CCTV for print enlargement; DECTalk/JAWS for synthetic voice output of computer screen contents; Descriptive videos; Kurzweil Reader
Friends of the Library Group
Branches: 7
CHARLES E BEATLEY, JR CENTRAL, 5005 Duke St, 22304-2903. Tel: 703-519-5900. TDD: 703-823-5809. FAX: 703-823-4524. Web Site: alexandria.lib.va.us. *Branch Mgr*, Karen Russell; Tel: 703-519-5900, Ext 200, E-Mail: krussell@alexandria.lib.va.us; Staff 5 (MLS 5)
Library Holdings: Bk Vols 181,566
Special Services for the Deaf - TDD
JAMES M DUNCAN JR BRANCH, 2501 Commonwealth Ave, 22301. SAN 362-6822. Tel: 757-838-4566. FAX: 757-706-3910. *Branch Mgr*, Mary Dauphinais; E-Mail: mdauphinais@alexandria.lib.va.us; Staff 3 (MLS 3)
Library Holdings: Bk Vols 87,081
Special Services for the Deaf - TTY machine
Friends of the Library Group
KATE WALLER BARRETT HEADQUARTERS, 717 Queen St, 22314. SAN 372-8056. Tel: 703-823-5295. FAX: 703-823-5718. *Librn*, Karen Russell; Staff 7 (MLS 7)
Library Holdings: Bk Vols 128,589
Friends of the Library Group
LOCAL HISTORY BRANCH, 717 Queen St, 22314-2420. SAN 362-6857. Tel: 703-838-4577. FAX: 703-706-3912. *Branch Mgr*, Joyce McMullin; Tel: 703-838-4577, Ext 211, E-Mail: jmcmullin@alexandria.lib.va.us; Staff 4 (MLS 4)
Library Holdings: Bk Vols 14,438
Subject Interests: Genealogy, Local history, State hist
Publications: African-American History & Genealogy; African-American History Sources, (bibliography); Genealogy at Lloyd House; The Society of Friends, (bibliography)
Friends of the Library Group
TALKING BOOKS, 5005 Duke St, 22304-2903. SAN 362-6768. Tel: 703-823-6152. TDD: 703-823-5809. FAX: 703-823-9079. *Branch Mgr*, Ilze Cimermanis; Tel: 703-823-5584, Ext 229, E-Mail: icimermanis@alexandria.lib.va.us; Staff 1 (MLS 1)
Founded 1968
Special Collections: Blindness & Other Handicaps Reference Material
Publications: Hear Say (newsletter for Talking Book patrons)
Friends of the Library Group
TECHNICAL SERVICES, 5005 Duke St, 22304-2903. SAN 372-8048. Tel: 703-823-5584. FAX: 703-823-9079. *Branch Mgr*, Ilze Cimermanis; Tel: 703-823-5584, Ext 229, E-Mail: icimermanis@alexandria.lib.va.us; Staff 3 (MLS 3)
Friends of the Library Group
Bookmobiles: 1

M AMERICAN ACADEMY OF PHYSICIAN ASSISTANTS, Information Center, 950 N Washington St, 22314-1552. SAN 374-8987. Tel: 703-836-2272. FAX: 703-684-1924. E-Mail: aapa@aapa.org. Web Site: www.aapa.org.
Library Holdings: Bk Titles 500; Per Subs 20

S AMERICAN COAL ASH ASSOCIATION LIBRARY,* 6940 S Kings H Ste 207, 22310. SAN 375-9245. Tel: 703-317-2400. FAX: 703-317-2409. Web Site: www.acaa-usa.org. *Dir, Tech Servs*, Barry Stewart
Library Holdings: Bk Vols 100; Per Subs 15
Restriction: Not open to public

S AMERICAN COLLEGE OF HEALTH CARE ADMINISTRATORS (ACHCA) INFORMATION CENTER, 1800 Diagonal Rd, 22314. SAN 3 8220. Tel: 703-739-7900. FAX: 703-739-7901. E-Mail: info@achca. Web Site: www.achca.org. *In Charge*, Mary Jane Kolar
Library Holdings: Bk Titles 100; Per Subs 130
Subject Interests: Aging

S AMERICAN COUNSELING ASSOCIATION, Professional Library, 599 Stevenson Ave, 22304. SAN 302-5705. Tel: 703-823-9800, Ext 281. FAX 703-823-0252. Web Site: www.counseling.org. *Librn*, Sylvia Nisenoff; E-Mail: snisenoff@counseling.org; Staff 1 (MLS 1)
Founded 1952
Library Holdings: Bk Vols 5,000; Per Subs 25
Subject Interests: Counseling
Publications: Bibliographies

S AMERICAN DEFENSE INSTITUTE LIBRARY,* 1055 N Fairfax St, St 200, 22314. SAN 373-0042. Tel: 703-519-7000. FAX: 703-519-8627.

S AMERICAN GEAR MANUFACTURERS ASSOCIATION MEMORIAL LIBRARY, 1500 King St, Ste 201, 22314. SAN 326-5617. Tel: 703-684-0211. FAX: 703-684-0242. E-Mail: webmaster@agma.org. Web Site: www.agma.org. *Pres*, Joe T Franklin, Jr; E-Mail: franklin@agma.org
Founded 1986
Library Holdings: Bk Vols 1,250; Bk Titles 1,100; Per Subs 10
Special Collections: Mechanical Power Transmission Devices & Product
Restriction: Non-circulating to the public
Function: Reference only

S AMERICAN GEOLOGICAL INSTITUTE LIBRARY, 4220 King St, 22302-1502. SAN 317-2716. Tel: 703-379-2480, Ext 239. FAX: 703-379-7563. E-Mail: rf@agiweb.org. Web Site: www.agiweb.org. *Dir*, Sharon Tahirkheli; *Asst Dir*, Kay Yost; *Librn*, Regina Frackowiak
Founded 1967
Library Holdings: Bk Vols 1,600; Bk Titles 400
Subject Interests: Geology
Special Collections: American Geological Institute Publications

S AMERICAN HELICOPTER SOCIETY LIBRARY,* 217 N Washington 22314. SAN 329-2649. Tel: 703-684-6777. FAX: 703-739-9279. E-Mail: staff@vtol.com. Web Site: www.vtol.org. *Exec Dir*, Morris E Flater
Founded 1943
Library Holdings: Bk Titles 900; Per Subs 50
Special Collections: History of Vertical Flight (James V Liberatore Coll) archives
Restriction: Members only

S AMERICAN HORTICULTURAL SOCIETY LIBRARY,* 7931 E Boulevard Dr, 22308. SAN 317-3542. Tel: 703-768-5700, Ext 128. FAX: 703-768-8700. *Librn*, Alice Bagwill
Library Holdings: Bk Vols 4,000
Subject Interests: Botany, Gardening, Horticulture
Open Mon-Fri 8:30-8:30

S AMERICAN PHYSICAL THERAPY ASSOCIATION LIBRARY, 1111 Fairfax St, 22314. SAN 373-0050. Tel: 703-706-8534. Toll Free Tel: 800 999-2782, Ext 8534. FAX: 703-838-8910. E-Mail: inforesource@apta.org *Dir*, Tracy Temanson; Staff 2 (MLS 1, Non-MLS 1)
Library Holdings: Bk Vols 3,000; Per Subs 25
Subject Interests: Physical therapy
Automation Activity & Vendor Info: (OPAC) Inmagic, Inc.
Database Vendor: Dialog, OCLC - First Search, OVID Technologies, Silverplatter Information Inc.

S AMERICAN SOCIETY FOR TRAINING & DEVELOPMENT, Informa Center, 1640 King St, 22313-2043. SAN 372-8668. Tel: 703-683-8100. FAX: 703-683-0250. Web Site: www.astd.org.
Library Holdings: Bk Vols 2,700; Per Subs 66

S ASSOCIATION OF FUNDRAISING PROFESSIONALS, (Formerly National Society Of Fundraising Executives), AFP Fundraising Resource Center, 1101 King St, Ste 700, 22314. SAN 377-1253. Tel: 703-684-041 FAX: 703-684-0540. E-Mail: rescenter@nsfre.org. *Coordr*, Jan Alfieri; Te 703-519-8458, E-Mail: jalfieri@nsfre.org
Library Holdings: Bk Vols 3,000; Per Subs 40
Partic in Spec Libr Asn

S ASTRE CORPORATE GROUP LIBRARY,* PO Box 25766, 22313-576 SAN 370-8314. Tel: 703-548-1343. FAX: 703-548-5737. *Dir, Tech Servs*, Roy A Ackerman; E-Mail: ackerman@astrecg.com
Library Holdings: Bk Vols 76,000; Per Subs 1,500

BETH EL HEBREW CONGREGATION LIBRARY, 3830 Seminary Rd, 22304. SAN 317-1973. Tel: 703-370-9400. FAX: 703-370-7730. E-Mail: bethelhc@erols.com. *Librn*, Martin Smith
Founded 1964
Library Holdings: Bk Vols 3,600; Per Subs 70
Subject Interests: Israel, Judaica, Theology

BURNS, DOANE, SWECKER & MATHIS LIBRARY, 1737 King St, Ste 500, 22314-2756. (Mail add: PO Box 19869, 22320-0869), SAN 373-1278. Tel: 703-838-6660. FAX: 703-836-2021. Web Site: www.burnsdoane.com. *Librn*, Susan C Sutphin; E-Mail: sues@burnsdoane.com
Founded 1988
Library Holdings: Bk Vols 5,000; Bk Titles 1,800; Per Subs 20
Restriction: Not open to public

CENTER FOR NAVAL ANALYSES LIBRARY, 4825 Mark Center Dr, 22311-1846. SAN 317-1981. Tel: 703-824-2120. Interlibrary Loan Service Tel: 703-824-2096. FAX: 703-824-2200. Web Site: www.cna.org. *Dir*, Steven J Dorner; Tel: 703-824-2314; *Ref*, Greg Kaminski; Staff 8 (MLS 3, Non-MLS 5)
Founded 1962
Library Holdings: Bk Vols 19,000; Bk Titles 16,000; Per Subs 350
Subject Interests: Econ, Mathematics, Mil sci, Operations res, Political science, Statistics, Systs analysis
Publications: Acquisitions Bulletin; Items of Interest; List of Journal Holdings
Partic in Capcon Library Network; Interlibrary Users Association; OCLC Online Computer Library Center, Inc

COLLINGWOOD LIBRARY & MUSEUM OF AMERICANISM, 8301 E Blvd Dr, 22308. SAN 376-1762. Tel: 703-765-1652. FAX: 703-765-8390. Web Site: www.collingwoodlibrary.com. *Curator*, Warren Baker
Library Holdings: Bk Vols 6,000

COMMONWEALTH TECHNOLOGY INC LIBRARY,* 5875 Barclay Dr, 22315. SAN 323-4231. Tel: 703-719-6800. FAX: 703-719-6631. *In Charge*, Paul McCann
Library Holdings: Bk Vols 100; Per Subs 15

FIRST CHRISTIAN CHURCH OF ALEXANDRIA LIBRARY,* 2723 King St, 22302. SAN 317-2015. Tel: 703-549-3911, 703-549-5143. FAX: 703-549-3911.
Founded 1955
Library Holdings: Bk Vols 474
Subject Interests: Bible, Church history, Theology
Special Collections: Robin June Gustafson Children's Coll; The Martha Louise Potts Adult Coll
Friends of the Library Group

FORT WARD MUSEUM, Dorothy CS Starr Civil War Research Library, 4301 W Braddock Rd, 22304-1008. SAN 327-2486. Tel: 703-838-4848. FAX: 703-671-7350. E-Mail: fort.ward@ci.alexandria.va.us. Web Site: www.ci.alexandria.va.us./oha/fortward/index.html. *Dir*, Wanda Dowell; *Curator*, Susan Cumbey
Library Holdings: Bk Vols 2,400

HUMAN RESOURCES RESEARCH ORGANIZATION (HUMRRO),* 66 Canal Ctr Plaza, Ste 400, 22314. SAN 317-2031. Tel: 703-549-3611, Ext 693. FAX: 703-549-9025. *Librn*, Jo Hunter
Founded 1954
Library Holdings: Bk Titles 2,000; Per Subs 50
Subject Interests: Computer instruction, Education, Human eng, Psychology, Training
Special Collections: Human Resources Research Organization Technical Reports
Restriction: By appointment only

INOVA MOUNT VERNON HOSPITAL, Robert I McClaughry Health Sciences Library, 2501 Parker's Lane, 22306. SAN 377-2799. Tel: 703-664-7269. FAX: 703-664-7523. *Librn*, Veldra Jernigan-Pedrick
Library Holdings: Bk Vols 1,000; Per Subs 150
Automation Activity & Vendor Info: (Cataloging) EOS; (OPAC) EOS
Database Vendor: OVID Technologies

INSTITUTE FOR ALTERNATIVE FUTURES LIBRARY,* 100 N Pitt St, Ste 235, 22314. SAN 329-4811. Tel: 703-684-5880. FAX: 703-684-0640. E-Mail: futurist@allfutures.com. Web Site: www.allfutures.com. *Pres*, Clement Bezold
Library Holdings: Bk Vols 1,000; Per Subs 50

INSTITUTE FOR DEFENSE ANALYSES, Technical Information Services,* 1801 N Beauregard St, 22311. SAN 317-218X. Tel: 703-845-2087. FAX: 703-820-7194. *Mgr*, Dr Russell I Fries
Founded 1960
Library Holdings: Bk Titles 12,000
Subject Interests: Aeronautical eng, Chemical engineering, Econ, Mathematics, Military, Operations research, Physics, Policy analysis, Political science, Social problems
Publications: Tech Information Bulletin
Partic in Capcon Library Network

S INSTITUTE OF NAVIGATION LIBRARY,* 1800 Diagonal Rd, Ste 480, 22314. SAN 374-5406. Tel: 703-683-7101. FAX: 703-683-7105. E-Mail: publications@ion.org. Web Site: www.ion.org.
Founded 1945
Library Holdings: Bk Titles 50

S INTERNATIONAL PERSONNEL MANAGEMENT ASSOCIATION, Center for Personnel Research,* 1617 Duke St, 22314. SAN 370-5145. Tel: 703-549-7100. FAX: 703-684-0948. Web Site: www.ipma-hr.org. *Dir*, Judith Brown; Tel: 703-549-7100, Ext 242, E-Mail: jbrown@ipma-hr.org
Library Holdings: Bk Titles 300; Per Subs 30
Special Collections: Human Resource Issues
Publications: Bibliographies; information packets; surveys

S JANE'S INFORMATION GROUP, 1340 Braddock Pl Ste 300, PO Box 1436, 22314-1651. SAN 336-108X. Tel: 703-683-3700. FAX: 703-836-0029. E-Mail: info@janes.com, order@janes.com. *In Charge*, Deborah Chiao
Founded 1962
Library Holdings: Bk Titles 28

S JOHN J MCMULLEN ASSOCIATES, INC, JJMA Office Wide Library, 4300 King St Ste 400, 22302-1503. SAN 377-1520. Tel: 703-933-6645. FAX: 703-933-6291. Web Site: www.jjma.com. *Librn*, Margaret Holland; E-Mail: mholland@jjma.com; Staff 1 (Non-MLS 1)
Library Holdings: Bk Vols 20,000
Subject Interests: Marine eng, Naval archit
Special Collections: Society of Naval Architects & Marine Engineering (SNAME), journals
Database Vendor: DRA
Partic in Spec Libr Asn

S MPR ASSOCIATES, INC, Technical Library, 320 King St, 22314-3238. SAN 325-8211. Tel: 703-519-0200. FAX: 703-519-0226. *Dir*, Nancy Bladen; *Librn, Tech Servs*, Stacey Knight
Library Holdings: Bk Titles 850
Publications: Monthly bulletin

S NATIONAL ASSOCIATION OF CHAIN DRUG STORES LIBRARY, 413 N Lee St, 22314. (Mail add: PO Box 1417-D49, 22313), SAN 375-3131. Tel: 703-549-3001, Ext 898. FAX: 703-739-6079. E-Mail: library@nacds.org. *Dir*, Laura Miller; *Senior Librn*, Susan Obreski; *Librn*, Betsy Hageman; Staff 3 (MLS 2, Non-MLS 1)
Founded 1933
Library Holdings: Bk Titles 5,000; Per Subs 600
Special Collections: Chain drug store reports 1993-current
Automation Activity & Vendor Info: (Cataloging) Inmagic, Inc.
Database Vendor: Dialog, OCLC - First Search
Restriction: By appointment only
Partic in Capcon Library Network; Dialog Corporation; Dow Jones News Retrieval; OCLC Online Computer Library Center, Inc

S NATIONAL ASSOCIATION OF CONVENIENCE STORES, Information Center, 1605 King St, 22314-2792. SAN 328-5383. Tel: 703-684-3600. FAX: 703-836-4564. E-Mail: nacs@cstorecentral.com. Web Site: www.cstorecentral.com. *Dir*, Merrilynn Drews; *Mgr*, Karen Tate
Library Holdings: Bk Titles 500

M NATIONAL MENTAL HEALTH ASSOCIATION, Clifford Beers Memorial Library, 1021 Prince St, 22314-2971. SAN 373-0085. Tel: 703-684-7722. Toll Free Tel: 800-969-6642. TDD: 800-433-5959. FAX: 703-684-5968. E-Mail: infoctr@nmha.org. Web Site: www.nmha.org.
Founded 1909
Library Holdings: Bk Vols 1,350; Per Subs 12
Subject Interests: Mental health
Restriction: Not open to public

S NATIONAL SCHOOL BOARDS ASSOCIATION LIBRARY, 1680 Duke St, 22314-3493. SAN 302-7341. Tel: 703-838-6731. FAX: 703-548-5516. *Librn*, Dottie Gray; E-Mail: dgray@nsba.org; *Info Specialist*, Julie Arrighetti; E-Mail: jarrighetti@nsba.org; Staff 2 (MLS 2)
Founded 1976
Library Holdings: Bk Titles 4,000; Per Subs 150
Subject Interests: Education
Special Collections: Sample local school board policies; State School Board Associations periodicals

S NATIONAL SHERIFFS' ASSOCIATION LIBRARY, 1450 Duke St, 22314-3490. SAN 327-9049. Tel: 703-836-7827. FAX: 703-683-6541.
Library Holdings: Bk Titles 1,000

S NATIONAL SOCIETY FOR EXPERIENTIAL EDUCATION, National Resource Center for Experiential & Service Learning,* 1703 N Beauregard St, Ste 400, 2311-1714. SAN 328-5324. Tel: 703-933-0017. FAX: 703-933-1053. E-Mail: info@nsee.org. Web Site: www.nsee.org.
Library Holdings: Bk Titles 2,000
Special Collections: Action/NCSL Publications

S NATIONAL SOCIETY OF PROFESSIONAL ENGINEERS, Member Services Library,* 1420 King St, 22314. SAN 320-6289. Tel: 703-684-4811. FAX: 703-836-4875.; Staff 1 (MLS 1)
Founded 1934
Library Holdings: Bk Vols 1,500; Per Subs 60
Special Collections: Annual Salary Survey

S NATIONAL TAXPAYERS UNION LIBRARY, 108 N Alfred St, 22314. SAN 374-9932. Tel: 703-683-5700. FAX: 703-683-5722. Web Site: www.ntu.org. *VPres*, Peter Sepp; E-Mail: pressguy@ntu.org; Staff 1 (Non-MLS 1)
Founded 1990
Library Holdings: Bk Titles 100
Special Collections: Taxpayer Conference Proceedings on Audio & Video

S NICHOLS PROFESSIONAL LIBRARY, 2000 N Beauregard St, 22311. SAN 324-6035. Tel: 703-824-6670. FAX: 703-998-8299. *Dir, Tech Servs*, Kenneth Reed; Staff 2 (MLS 1, Non-MLS 1)
Founded 1968
Library Holdings: Bk Titles 9,500; Per Subs 212
Subject Interests: Education
Partic in Dialog Corporation

S OCTAMERON ASSOCIATES, INC, Research Library,* 1900 Mount Vernon Ave, 22301. SAN 321-9798. Tel: 703-836-5480. FAX: 703-836-5650. Web Site: www.octameron.com. *Librn*, Karen S Leider
Founded 1976
2000-2001 Mats Exp Books $2,000
Library Holdings: Bk Titles 2,300; Per Subs 85
Subject Interests: Higher educ
Restriction: Staff use only

M ORTHOTICS & PROSTHETICS, National Office Library,* 1650 King St, 5th flr, 22314. SAN 373-0077. Tel: 703-836-7114. FAX: 703-836-0838. Web Site: www.opoffice.org.
Library Holdings: Bk Vols 500
Restriction: Not open to public

S RAILWAY MAIL SERVICE LIBRARY, 12 E Rosemont Ave, 22301-2325. SAN 324-7996. Tel: 703-549-4095. FAX: 703-836-1955. Web Site: members.ebay.com/aboutme/fscheer@erols.com/. *Curator*, Dr Frank R Scheer; E-Mail: fscheer@erols.com; Staff 1 (Non-MLS 1)
Jan 2000-Dec 2000 Income $5,000, Locally Generated Income $3,000, Other $2,000. Mats Exp $5,000, Books $3,900, Per/Ser (Incl. Access Fees) $500, Manuscripts & Archives $600
Library Holdings: Bk Vols 1,600; Bk Titles 1,500
Subject Interests: En-route distribution, Postal markings, Transportation of mail
Special Collections: E B Bergman Schedule of Mall Routes Coll; E J Maloney Marking Device Coll; H E Rankin General Scheme Coll; J R Mundy Postal Lock Coll; L Cohen International Postal Insignia Coll; R R Schmidt Marking Device Coll
RMS library provides archival preservation of primary resources pertaining to surface mail transportation from 1864 to 1977; Up to ten photocopies are made at no charge; special ref assistance to postal history researchers

S SALVATION ARMY, Archives & Research Center, 615 Slaters Lane, PO Box 269, 22313. SAN 353-7846. Tel: 703-684-5500. FAX: 703-299-5552. E-Mail: archives@usn.salvationarmy.org. Web Site: www.salvationarmyusa.org. *Dir*, Susan Mitchem; E-Mail: susan_mitchem@usn.salvationarmy.org
Founded 1974
Library Holdings: Bk Vols 3,300
Subject Interests: Religion, Salvation Army hist, Soc serv, Women

S TECH-U-FIT CORP LIBRARY,* 400 Madison St, No 210, 22314. SAN 375-2461. Tel: 703-549-0512. FAX: 703-549-0512. *Pres*, John Molino
Library Holdings: Bk Vols 300

UNITED STATES ARMY
A HEADQUARTERS ARMY MATERIAL COMMAND TECHNICAL LIBRARY, AMCIO-I-L, 5001 Eisenhower Ave, 22333-0001. SAN 362-6881. Tel: 703-617-4115. FAX: 703-617-5588. *Librn*, Alma C Cosgrove; E-Mail: acosgrov@hqamc.army.mil; *ILL, Publ Servs*, Valerie Hicks; Staff 4 (MLS 1, Non-MLS 3)
Founded 1973
Library Holdings: Bk Titles 28,000; Per Subs 300
Subject Interests: Army, Bus, Engineering, Fed, Mgt, Mil, Procurement
Partic in Fedlink; Library of Congress
DoD, Army only
A THE INSTITUTE OF HERALDRY LIBRARY, 9325 Gunston Rd, Ste S112, Fort Belvoir, 22060-5579. SAN 362-6911. Tel: 703-806-4970. FAX: 703-806-4964. *Librn*, Roy Cornwell
Founded 1961
Library Holdings: Bk Vols 12,000; Bk Titles 9,000; Per Subs 26
Subject Interests: Art, Flags, Heraldry, Insignia, Medallic art, Medals, Military history, Seals, Symbolism, Symbols, Uniforms
Restriction: Staff use only

UNITED STATES ARMY
A HUMPHREYS ENGINEER CENTER, TECHNICAL SUPPORT LIBRA 7701 Telegraph Rd, 22315-3860. SAN 362-9074. Tel: 703-428-6386. F 703-428-6896. *Chief Librn*, Lee Porter; Staff 4 (MLS 3, Non-MLS 1)
Founded 1983
Library Holdings: Bk Vols 35,000; Bk Titles 30,000; Per Subs 539
Subject Interests: Engineering, Water resources
Publications: Accession List
Partic in Defense Technical Information Center; Dialog Corporation; Fedlink; OCLC Online Computer Library Center, Inc
A TOPOGRAPHIC ENGINEERING CENTER, 7701 Telegraph Rd, 22315-3864. SAN 362-8981. Tel: 703-428-6657. FAX: 703-428-8176. *Tech S* Peggy Diego; E-Mail: pdiego@tech.army.mil
Library Holdings: Bk Vols 5,000; Per Subs 150
Subject Interests: Cartography, Geography, Meteorology
Publications: Annual bibliography of reports; Guide to STINFO Cente Periodicals catalog
Partic in Fedlink; OCLC Online Computer Library Center, Inc

UNITED STATES DEPARTMENT OF THE ARMY
A USA COMMUNITY & FAMILY SUPPORT CENTER, Dept of the Arm CFSC-SRL-L Summit Ctr 4700 King St, 22302-4418. SAN 337-1492. 703-681-7208. FAX: 703-681-7249. Web Site: www.armymwr.com. *Ch Librn*, Barbara S Christine; E-Mail: barbara.christine@hoffman-cfsc.army.mil; *Acq, Syst Coordr*, Carla Pomager; E-Mail: carla.pomage ctsc.army.mil; *Acq*, Amy Loughran; E-Mail: amy.loughran@cfsc.army.r Staff 3 (MLS 3)
Partic in Fedlink; OCLC Online Computer Library Center, Inc
Administrative headquarters for the US Army Morale, Welfare & Recreation General Library Program. Establishes standards, policies & procedures for the administration of Army installation libraries within United States & overseas. Selects & purchases reference materials for these libraries to supplement local acquisitions & provides reading material to isolated units & maneuver areas. Army General libraries are listed under their various geographical locations & in the section Unite States Armed Forces Libraries Overseas in the back of this directory

A UNITED STATES DEPARTMENT OF THE ARMY, Office of the Chie Staff, Operational Test & Evaluation Command (OPTEC), Headley Techn Research Center,* 4501 Ford Ave, 22302-1458. SAN 317-2813. Tel: 703 681-9234. FAX: 703-681-4973. *Librn*, Marjorie Rust
Founded 1972
Oct 1997-Sep 1998 Income $60,000. Mats Exp $42,000, Books $20,000, Per/Ser (Incl. Access Fees) $22,000
Library Holdings: Bk Titles 10,000; Per Subs 300
Subject Interests: Engineering, Instrumentation-test-evaluation
Special Collections: US Dept of Army Military Publications (Administration, Organization, Training)
Publications: Catalog of OTEA/OPTEC Reports; Techinfo Bulletin (wee
Restriction: Staff use only
Partic in Dialog Corporation; Fedlink; OCLC Online Computer Library Center, Inc

UNITED STATES DEPARTMENT OF THE ARMY
A CECOM ACQUISITIONS CENTER-WASHINGTON OPERATION, Hoffman Bldg 1, Rm 960, 2461 Eisenhower Ave, 22331. SAN 374-35(Tel: 703-325-9519. FAX: 703-325-5987. *Librn*, Dianna Ford

R VIRGINIA THEOLOGICAL SEMINARY, Bishop Payne Library, 3737 Seminary Rd, 22304-5201. SAN 317-2074. Tel: 703-461-1731. Interlibra Loan Service Tel: 703-461-1733. Circulation Tel: 703-461-1733. Referen Tel: 703-461-1733. FAX: 703-370-0935. Web Site: www.vts.edu/bpl/. *Co Develop, Librn*, Mitzi J Budde; E-Mail: mjbudde@vts.edu; Staff 12 (ML Non-MLS 6)
Founded 1823. Enrl 200; Fac 26; Highest Degree: Doctorate
Jun 1999-May 2000 Income $695,432. Mats Exp $189,755, Books $124, Per/Ser (Incl. Access Fees) $50,286, Presv $8,674, Micro $110, AV Equi $165, Electronic Ref Mat (Incl. Access Fees) $5,601. Sal $411,507
Library Holdings: Bk Vols 163,954; Per Subs 990
Subject Interests: Religion, Theology
Special Collections: Anglicanism & Episcopal Church in the USA
Automation Activity & Vendor Info: (Acquisitions) epixtech, inc.; (Cataloging) epixtech, inc.; (Circulation) epixtech, inc.; (Course Reserve) epixtech, inc.; (ILL) epixtech, inc.; (Media Booking) epixtech, inc.; (OPA epixtech, inc.; (Serials) epixtech, inc.
Partic in OCLC Online Computer Library Center, Inc; Washington Theological Consortium

S VSE CORPORATION, Corporate Library, 2550 Huntington Ave, 22303-1499. SAN 317-2066. Tel: 703-329-4208. FAX: 703-960-3748.
Founded 1979
Library Holdings: Bk Vols 3,600; Per Subs 75
Subject Interests: Engineering, Mathematics, Physics
Special Collections: Military, Industry & Federal Specifications, Standar & Handbooks, micro & CD-ROM; Quality Coll; Vendor Catalogs, micro CD-ROM; VSMF Engineering Information, micro & CD-ROM
Publications: Very Special Entries (new acquisitions)

WATER ENVIRONMENT FEDERATION LIBRARY,* 601 Wythe St, 22314-1994. SAN 326-7253. Tel: 703-684-2400. FAX: 703-684-2492. Web Site: www.wef.org. *Librn*, Faith Ward
Founded 1970
Dec 1997-Nov 1998 Income $1,000. Mats Exp $500, Books $200, Per/Ser (Incl. Access Fees) $300
Library Holdings: Bk Titles 2,200; Per Subs 30
Subject Interests: Industrial wastes
Special Collections: Manuals of Practice, bks; Water Pollution Control Coll
Restriction: Non-circulating to the public

WESTMINSTER PRESBYTERIAN CHURCH LIBRARY, 2701 Cameron Mills Rd, 22302. SAN 317-2082. Tel: 703-549-4766. FAX: 703-548-1505. *Librn*, Kathy Hunter
Library Holdings: Bk Vols 2,250; Per Subs 10
Open 8-5

ELIA

AMELIA HISTORICAL SOCIETY LIBRARY, Jackson Bldg, PO Box 113, 23002. SAN 370-9817. Tel: 804-561-3180. *Chair*, Joseph O Humphreys
Library Holdings: Bk Vols 13,000; Per Subs 30

JAMES L HAMNER PUBLIC LIBRARY,* 16351 Dunn St, PO Box 610, 23002. SAN 322-6611. Tel: 804-561-4559. FAX: 804-561-3174. *Librn*, James M Bullock; *Asst Librn*, Susan Gianniny; *Asst Librn*, Annie Reyna
Founded 1972. Pop 9,200; Circ 21,793
Jul 1997-Jun 1998 Income $82,000. Mats Exp $21,000. Sal $46,000
Library Holdings: Bk Vols 26,000; Bk Titles 24,000; Per Subs 54
Partic in Virginia Library & Network Information

HERST

AMHERST COUNTY PUBLIC LIBRARY,* 382 S Main St, PO Box 370, 24521-0370. SAN 362-6946. Tel: 804-946-9388. FAX: 804-946-9348. *Dir*, Leona E Wilkins; *Asst Dir*, Judy Maxham; Staff 8 (MLS 2, Non-MLS 6)
Founded 1964. Pop 28,578; Circ 241,878
Library Holdings: Bk Vols 39,000; Per Subs 105
Special Collections: Virginia History Coll
Partic in SE Libr Network
Friends of the Library Group
Branches: 1
MADISON HEIGHTS BRANCH, River James Shopping Ctr 200 Madison Heights Sq, PO Box 540, Madison Heights, 24572. SAN 362-6970. Tel: 804-846-8171. FAX: 804-846-3102. *Librn*, Rebecca Averett
Library Holdings: Bk Vols 9,000
Friends of the Library Group

NANDALE

ANNANDALE FAMILY HISTORY CENTER LIBRARY,* 3900 Howard St, 22003-0089. SAN 377-4708. Tel: 703-256-5518. *Dir*, Linda Dunn

FAIRFAX COUNTY PUBLIC SCHOOLS, Education Library, 4414 Holborn Ave, 22003. SAN 317-2686. Tel: 703-503-7420. FAX: 703-503-7418. Web Site: www.fcps.edu/MTS/EducationLibrary. *Head Librn*, Jessica Segars Foster; E-Mail: jfoster@chapelsq.fcps.k12.va.us. Subject Specialists: *Education*, Jessica Segars Foster; Staff 2 (MLS 1, Non-MLS 1)
Founded 1968
Library Holdings: Bk Vols 17,000; Per Subs 250
Subject Interests: Education
Automation Activity & Vendor Info: (Circulation) Inlex; (OPAC) DRA
Database Vendor: Ebsco - EbscoHost, ProQuest, Wilson - Wilson Web

NORTHERN VIRGINIA COMMUNITY COLLEGE LIBRARIES, 8333 Little River Turnpike, 22003. SAN 362-7004. Tel: 703-323-3096. FAX: 703-323-3831. Web Site: www.nv.cc.va.us/library. *Coordr, Tech Servs*, Sandra J Beeson; E-Mail: sbeeson@nv.cc.va.us; Staff 22 (MLS 20, Non-MLS 2)
Founded 1965. Enrl 19,447; Fac 862; Highest Degree: Associate
Jul 1999-Jun 2000 Income (Main and Other College/University Libraries) State $3,791,967. Mats Exp $709,295, Books $349,136, Per/Ser (Incl. Access Fees) $143,627, Micro $57,297, AV Equip $71,125, Other Print Mats $13,305, Electronic Ref Mat (Incl. Access Fees) $74,805. Sal $2,674,019 (Prof $1,437,983)
Library Holdings: Bk Vols 210,220; Bk Titles 136,964; Per Subs 1,407
Automation Activity & Vendor Info: (Circulation) NOTIS; (Course Reserve) NOTIS; (OPAC) NOTIS
Database Vendor: OCLC - First Search, ProQuest
Mem of VA Community Col Syst
Partic in SE Libr Network; Virtual Libr of Va
Friends of the Library Group
Departmental Libraries:
ALEXANDRIA CAMPUS, 3001 N Beauregard St, Alexandria, 22311. SAN 362-7039. Tel: 703-845-6231. Reference Tel: 703-845-6456. FAX: 703-845-6205. Web Site: www.nv.cc.va.us/library/. *Dir*, David Williams; Tel: 703-845-6255, Fax: 703-845-6012, E-Mail: nvwilld@nv.cc.va.us; *Assoc Dir*, Margaret R Zarnosky; Tel: 703-845-6232, E-Mail: nvbruin@nv.cc.va.us
Subject Interests: Early childhood educ
Special Collections: Virginia State Child Care Media Center
Publications: Library Skill Module; LRC Handbook
Partic in VIVA-Statewide Library Resource Network
Friends of the Library Group
ANNANDALE CAMPUS Tel: 703-323-3066. FAX: 703-323-3005. Web Site: www.nv.cc.va.us/library. *Dir*, Gen Sen Chu; E-Mail: gchu@nv.cc.va.us; *Assoc Dir*, Carol Sinwell; Tel: 703-323-3004, Fax: 703-323-3005, E-Mail: asinwell@nv.cc.va.us
Subject Interests: Admin of justice, Electronics tech, Fire science, Health tech, Hotel, Marketing, Restaurant, Tourism, Travel
Special Collections: Women's History (Judy Mann DiStefano Coll)
Publications: Bibliography of the Judy Mann DiStefano Women's History Collection; LRC Student & Faculty Handbook
LOUDOUN CAMPUS, 1000 Harry Flood Byrd Hwy, Sterling, 20164-8699. SAN 362-7098. Tel: 703-450-2567. FAX: 703-450-2536. Web Site: www.nv.cc.va.us/loudoun/library. *Dir*, Agatha Taormina; Tel: 703-450-2564, E-Mail: ataormina@nv.cc.va.us; *Librn*, Jennifer Egan; Tel: 703-450-2642, E-Mail: jegan@nv.cc.va.us; *Librn*, Donatus Hayes; Tel: 703-450-2641, E-Mail: dhayes@nv.cc.va.us
Subject Interests: Communications, Horticulture, Interior design, Veterinary sci
MANASSAS CAMPUS, 6901 Sudley Rd, Manassas, 20109. SAN 362-7128. Tel: 703-257-6640. FAX: 703-368-1069. Web Site: www.nv.cc.va.us/manassas/library. *Dir*, Cathy Sabol; Tel: 703-257-6641, E-Mail: csabol@nv.cc.va.us; *Librn*, Pat Butler; Tel: 703-257-6547, E-Mail: pbutler@nv.cc.va.us; *Librn*, Sherrill Wharff; Tel: 703-257-6564, E-Mail: swharff@nv.cc.va.us; Staff 6 (MLS 3, Non-MLS 3)
Founded 1974. Enrl 2,000; Fac 150; Highest Degree: Associate
Subject Interests: Am lit, Aviation
Special Collections: Aviation
Publications: LRC Newsletter
Function: Research library
S MEDIA PROCESSING SERVICES, 8333 Little River Turnpike, 22003-3796. Tel: 703-323-3294. FAX: 703-323-3831. Web Site: www.nv.cc.va.us/depts/mps/index.htm. *Coordr, Tech Servs*, Sandra Beeson; Tel: 703-323-3096, E-Mail: sbeeson@nv.cc.va.us; *Head, Cat*, Virginia Graves; Tel: 703-323-3095, E-Mail: vagraves@nv.cc.va.us; *Cat*, Mary Price; Tel: 703-323-3470, E-Mail: mprice@nv.cc.va.us
WOODBRIDGE CAMPUS, 15200 Neabsco Mills Rd, Woodbridge, 22191. SAN 362-7152. Tel: 703-878-5727. FAX: 703-670-8433. Web Site: www.nv.cc.va.us/woodbridge/library. *Dir*, Gordon Cook; *Librn*, Ann Turpyn; *Librn*, Elza England

APPOMATTOX

S US NATIONAL PARK SERVICE APPOMATTOX COURT HOUSE LIBRARY, PO Box 218, 24522. SAN 370-2774. Tel: 804-352-8987. FAX: 804-352-8330. Web Site: www.nps.gov/apco/. *In Charge*, H Reed Johnson
1999-2000 Mats Exp Books $7,130
Library Holdings: Bk Vols 2,164

ARLINGTON

S ADVISORY GROUP ON ELECTRON DEVICES LIBRARY,* 1745 Jefferson Davis Hwy, 22202. SAN 329-8213. Tel: 703-413-1282. FAX: 703-413-1315. E-Mail: info@washington.palisades.org.
Library Holdings: Bk Vols 900; Per Subs 40

S AIR FORCE ASSOCIATION, Research Library,* 1501 Lee Hwy, 22209-1198. SAN 302-5500. Tel: 703-247-5829. FAX: 703-247-5855. *Librn*, Pearlie Draughn
Founded 1956
Library Holdings: Bk Vols 2,000
Subject Interests: Military history

A AIR FORCE COST ANALYSIS AGENCY, Technical Information Center,* 1111 Jefferson Davis Hwy, Ste 403, 22202-4306. SAN 377-1776. Tel: 703-604-0402. FAX: 703-604-6646. *Librn*, Debbie Cann
Library Holdings: Bk Vols 200; Per Subs 20

M AMERICAN COUNCIL ON ALCOHOLISM, Resource Center, 3900 N Fairfax Dr, Ste 401, 22203. SAN 323-4916. Tel: 703-248-9005. Toll Free Tel: 800-527-5344. FAX: 703-248-9007. E-Mail: aca2@earthlink.net. Web Site: www.aca-usa.org. *Exec Dir*, Charles V Pena
Library Holdings: Bk Vols 100
Restriction: Not open to public

S ANSER TECHNICAL LIBRARY,* 1215 Jefferson Davis Hwy, Ste 800, 22202-1215. SAN 317-2724. Tel: 703-416-3111. Interlibrary Loan Service Tel: 703-416-3078. FAX: 703-416-3225. *Mgr*, Deborah Brightwell; *ILL*, Karen Waddy; *Cat*, Linda Rose
Founded 1958
Library Holdings: Bk Titles 14,000; Per Subs 222
Subject Interests: Computer science, Mil, Operations res

Publications: Acessions list (monthly)
Restriction: Not open to public
Partic in Defense Technical Information Center; Dialog Corporation

P ARLINGTON COUNTY DEPARTMENT OF LIBRARIES, Arlington Public Library, 2100 Clarendon Blvd, Ste 402, 22201. SAN 362-7217. Tel: 703-228-3346, 703-228-3348. TDD: 703-228-6320, 228-4611. FAX: 703-228-3354. Web Site: www.co.arlington.va.us/lib/. *Dir*, Ann M Friedman; *Publ Servs*, Blanche Anderson; *Mgr*, Maureen Karl; *Branch Mgr*, Neil Phelps; *ILL*, Lynn Kristianson; *Ref*, Denise Kelleher; *Outreach Serv*, Javier Corredor; *YA Servs*, Margaret Brown; *Cat*, Carl Fisher; *Ch Servs*, Kristi Beavin; *Coll Develop*, Elissa Miller; *Outreach Serv*, Eileen McMurrer; *Tech Servs*, Maureen Karl; Staff 157 (MLS 52, Non-MLS 105)
Founded 1937. Pop 200,000
Jul 2000-Jun 2001 Income (Main Library and Branch Library) $9,794,000, State $260,000, County $9,534,000. Mats Exp $1,170,000. Sal $7,182,518
Library Holdings: Bk Vols 578,104; Bk Titles 315,000; Per Subs 2,230
Special Collections: Children's Illustrators (Francis & Elizabeth Booth Silver Coll); State & Local Data (Virginiana Coll)
Automation Activity & Vendor Info: (Acquisitions) CARL; (Cataloging) CARL; (Cataloging) CARL; (OPAC) CARL
Database Vendor: CARL
Publications: Library Bulletin
Partic in Capcon Library Network
Special Services for the Deaf - Captioned media; Staff with knowledge of sign language; TDD
Friends of the Library Group
Branches: 10
AURORA HILLS, 735 18th St S, 22202. SAN 362-7241. Tel: 703-228-5715. FAX: 703-228-9378. *Mgr*, Neil Phelps; *Actg Librn*, Susan Kaminow
CENTRAL LIBRARY, 1015 N Quincy St, 22201-4661. SAN 362-7276. Tel: 703-228-5990. FAX: 703-228-5962. *Mgr*, Jayne McQuade; *Librn*, Susan McCarthy
Special Collections: Art; Children's Illustrators; College (Career Coll); French; German; Italian; Local-Virginia History; Spanish; Vietnamese; Virginiana
CHERRYDALE, 2190 N Military Rd, 22207. SAN 362-7306. Tel: 703-228-6330. FAX: 703-516-4568. *Librn*, Neil Phelps; *In Charge*, Charline Rugen
COLUMBIA PIKE, 816 S Walter Reed Dr, 22204. SAN 362-7330. Tel: 703-228-5710. FAX: 703-228-5559. *Actg Mgr*, Eileen McMurrer; *Librn*, Jane McQuade
Special Collections: Vocational Coll
GLENCARLYN, 300 S Kensington St, 22204. SAN 362-7365. Tel: 703-228-6548. FAX: 703-824-3529. *Actg Mgr*, Lynn Sawyer
GOVERNMENT REFERENCE LIBRARY, Admin Off, 2100 Clarendon Blvd, 22201-4661. SAN 329-627X. Tel: 703-228-3352. FAX: 703-228-3354. *Librn*, Elizabeth Fry
Founded 1989
HOMEBOUND SERVICE, 1015 N Quincy St, 22201. SAN 329-6296. Tel: 703-228-5960. FAX: 703-228-5998. *Mgr*, Neil Phelps; *Librn*, Javier Corredor
SHIRLINGTON, 2700 S Arlington Mill Dr, 22206. SAN 362-739X. Tel: 703-228-6545. FAX: 703-379-6728. *Mgr*, Cathy Robinson; *Librn*, Roger Qualters
P TALKING BOOK SERVICE, 1015 N Quincy, 22201. SAN 362-7225. Tel: 703-228-6333. FAX: 703-228-6336. *In Charge*, Roxanne Barnes
Special Collections: Talking books, cassettes, discs
WESTOVER, 1800 N Lexington St, 22205. SAN 362-742X. Tel: 703-228-5260. FAX: 703-534-1240. *Mgr*, Susan Kaminow

S ARLINGTON COUNTY SCHOOLS PROFESSIONAL LIBRARY, 2801 Clarendon Blvd, No 204, 22201. SAN 327-246X. Tel: 703-228-6085. FAX: 703-522-3937. *Librn*, Lizette Hannegan
Library Holdings: Bk Vols 7,000; Per Subs 150
Subject Interests: Education

M ARLINGTON HOSPITAL, Medical Library, 1701 N George Mason Dr, 22205. SAN 327-3571. Tel: 703-558-6524. FAX: 703-558-6975. Web Site: www.arlhosp.org/staff.htm. *Mgr*, Sarah Wright; E-Mail: wrightst@arlhosp.org; Staff 1 (MLS 1)
Library Holdings: Bk Titles 1,600; Per Subs 385
Subject Interests: Allied health, Medicine, Nursing
Restriction: Access at librarian's discretion, Medical staff only, Open to others by appointment

M ASBESTOS INFORMATION ASSOCIATION OF NORTH AMERICA, Technical & Medical Files, 1235 Jefferson Davis Hwy, PMB 114, 22202-3283. SAN 370-3959. Tel: 703-560-2980. FAX: 703-560-2981. *Pres*, B J Pigg; E-Mail: aiabjpigg@aol.com; Staff 2 (MLS 2)
Library Holdings: Bk Titles 200; Per Subs 10
Restriction: By appointment only

S CEA MARKET INTELLIGENCE CENTER, 2500 Wilson Blvd, 22201-3834. SAN 328-1418. Tel: 703-907-7763. FAX: 703-907-7769. E-Mail: info@cea.org. Web Site: www.cea.org, www.ebrain.org. *Mgr*, Angela K Titone; *Res*, Eileen Cosgrove; Staff 3 (MLS 2, Non-MLS 1)
Founded 1984
Library Holdings: Bk Vols 2,000; Per Subs 180
Special Collections: Electronic Industries Market
Database Vendor: Lexis-Nexis
Partic in Dialog Corporation; Info Access Co; Reuters

S COLUMBIA RESEARCH CORPORATION RESPOSITORY,* 2531 Jefferson Davis Hwy, 22202. SAN 370-8993. Tel: 703-841-1445. FAX: 7 418-1139. *Librn*, Selina Smith
Library Holdings: Bk Vols 7,000; Per Subs 35
Restriction: Company library

S DRUG ENFORCEMENT ADMINISTRATION LIBRARY, 700 Army N Dr, 22202. SAN 302-6396. Tel: 202-307-8932. FAX: 202-307-8939. E-M dealibrary2@erols.com. *Librn*, Rose Mary Russo
Founded 1960
Library Holdings: Bk Vols 15,000; Per Subs 200
Subject Interests: Drug abuse, Drug laws
Publications: Monthly acquisition list
Partic in Fedlink

S EDUCATIONAL RESEARCH SERVICE LIBRARY,* 2000 Clarendon Blvd, 22201-2908. SAN 327-2664. Tel: 703-243-2100. FAX: 703-243-19 Web Site: www.ers.org. *Dir*, Josephine Franklin
Library Holdings: Bk Vols 20,000

R FIRST PRESBYTERIAN CHURCH LIBRARY, 601 N Vermont St, 222 SAN 317-2171. Tel: 703-527-4766. FAX: 703-527-2262.
Library Holdings: Bk Vols 2,334
Subject Interests: Christian Spirituality, Hebrew Bible, Hist Christianity, New Testament, Social action
Special Collections: History of First Presbyterian Church

S FORECASTING INTERNATIONAL LTD LIBRARY,* PO Box 1650, 22210. SAN 373-2568. Tel: 703-379-5600. FAX: 703-379-1999.
Library Holdings: Bk Vols 1,000

S THE FREEDOM FORUM WORLD CENTER LIBRARY, 1101 Wilson Blvd, 20th flr, 22209-2248. SAN 375-5193. Tel: 703-284-3524. Referenc Tel: 703-284-2818. FAX: 703-284-3516. *Dir*, Nancy Stewart; E-Mail: nstewart@freedomforum.org; *Mgr Libr Serv*, Jerrie Bethel; E-Mail: jbeth freedomforum.org; Staff 7 (MLS 5, Non-MLS 2)
Founded 1990
Library Holdings: Bk Titles 7,126; Per Subs 150
Special Collections: First Amendment and Journalism Coll
Automation Activity & Vendor Info: (Cataloging) Inmagic, Inc.

S INSURANCE INSTITUTE FOR HIGHWAY SAFETY LIBRARY, 1005 Glebe Rd, Ste 800, 22201. SAN 302-6760. Tel: 703-247-1500. FAX: 703 247-1678. Web Site: www.highwaysafety.org. *Librn*, Nancy Matthes
Founded 1959
Library Holdings: Bk Titles 20,000; Per Subs 175
Subject Interests: Transportation
Special Collections: US Dept of Transportation Regulatory Docket Materials

C MARYMOUNT UNIVERSITY, Emerson G Reinsch Library, 2807 N Gl Rd, 22207-4299. SAN 317-2198. Tel: 703-284-1533. FAX: 703-284-1685 Web Site: www.marymount.edu/lls. *Actg Dean*, Sister Virginia McKenna; Tel: 703-284-1535, E-Mail: sister.mckenna@marymount.edu; Staff 38 (M 22, Non-MLS 16)
Founded 1950. Enrl 2,579; Fac 368; Highest Degree: Master
Jul 1999-Jun 2000 Income $2,240,491. Mats Exp $531,516, Books $243,315, Per/Ser (Incl. Access Fees) $155,471, Presv $15,573, Micro $17,287, Electronic Ref Mat (Incl. Access Fees) $99,870. Sal $1,301,120 (Prof $661,871)
Library Holdings: Bk Vols 181,619; Bk Titles 131,731; Per Subs 1,072
Subject Interests: Art, Education, Fashion design, Interior design, Nursir Philosophy
Special Collections: Economics (Gertrude Hoyt Memorial Coll); Ireton Inspiration Reading
Automation Activity & Vendor Info: (Acquisitions) Endeavor; (Catalogi Endeavor; (Circulation) Endeavor; (Course Reserve) Endeavor; (ILL) Endeavor; (OPAC) Endeavor; (Serials) Endeavor
Publications: FACETS
Partic in Capcon Library Network; OCLC Online Computer Library Cent Inc; Washington Research Library Consortium

L WALTER T MCCARTHY LAW LIBRARY,* Court House, 1425 N Courthouse Rd, Ste 1700, 22201. SAN 317-2120. Tel: 703-228-7005. FA 703-228-7360. E-Mail: waltertmac@aol.com. *Dir, Librn*, Janet H Camillo Staff 1 (MLS 1)
Founded 1977
Jul 1997-Jun 1998 Income $114,700. Mats Exp Books $63,300. Sal $42,1
Library Holdings: Bk Vols 22,000; Per Subs 12
Subject Interests: Continuing educ
Special Collections: All Regional & Federal Reporters; Digests; Form Books; Old Codes & Acts of Assembly, Virginia; Virginia Treatises

NATHAN ASSOCIATES INC LIBRARY, 2101 Wilson Blvd, Ste 1200, 22201. SAN 302-7007. Tel: 703-516-7750. FAX: 703-351-6162. *Mgr*, Rhea C Austin; E-Mail: raustin@nathanassoc.com
Founded 1946
Library Holdings: Bk Vols 5,000; Per Subs 100
Subject Interests: Economics
Restriction: Company library, Non-circulating to the public, Not open to public
Function: Archival collection, Business archives, Document delivery services, For research purposes, ILL available, ILL to other special libraries, Literary searches, Reference services available
Partic in Dialog Corporation; Dow Jones News Retrieval; OCLC Online Computer Library Center, Inc

NATIONAL AERONAUTIC ASSOCIATION,* 1815 N Fort Myer Dr, Ste 700, 22209. SAN 329-174X. Tel: 703-527-0226. FAX: 703-527-0229. E-Mail: records@naa-usa.org. Web Site: www.naa-usa.org. *Pres*, Don Koranda
Founded 1907
Library Holdings: Bk Vols 200; Per Subs 15
Special Collections: Aviation Records (US & World)
Restriction: Not open to public

NATIONAL CENTER FOR VICTIMS OF CRIME, 2111 Wilson Blvd, Ste 300, 22201. SAN 372-4107. Tel: 703-276-2880. FAX: 703-276-2889. E-Mail: webmaster@ncvc.org. Web Site: www.ncvc.org. *In Charge*, Diane Alexander; *Res*, Bryan Criswell; *Coll Develop*, Anton Popic; Staff 2 (MLS 2)
Founded 1985
Library Holdings: Bk Titles 4,500; Per Subs 100
Special Collections: Victimization & Victim Services & Assistance
Automation Activity & Vendor Info: (Acquisitions) Inmagic, Inc.; (Cataloging) Inmagic, Inc.; (Circulation) Inmagic, Inc.; (Serials) Inmagic, Inc.
Publications: Customized bibliographies; National Organization Directory; National Victims Rights Week Kit; Publications Directory (free upon request); Rape in America; Statistical Overview
Partic in Capcon Library Network; OCLC Online Computer Library Center, Inc

NATIONAL CONFERENCE ON MINISTRY TO THE ARMED FORCES, Chaplins Memorial Library,* 4141 N Henderson Rd, Ste 13, 22203. SAN 327-2567. Tel: 703-276-7905. FAX: 703-276-7906. *Librn*, Maureen Francis; *Coordr*, Jack Williamson
Library Holdings: Bk Titles 1,100; Per Subs 40

NATIONAL GENEALOGICAL SOCIETY LIBRARY, 4527 17th St N, 22207-2399. SAN 302-7236. Tel: 703-525-0050, Ext 331. Toll Free Tel: 800-473-0060. FAX: 703-525-0052. E-Mail: library@ngsgenealogy.org. Web Site: www.ngsgenealogy.org. *Librn*, Dereka Smith; Staff 3 (MLS 2, Non-MLS 1)
Founded 1903
Library Holdings: Bk Vols 30,000; Bk Titles 20,000; Per Subs 100
Subject Interests: Genealogy, Local history
Special Collections: Genealogy & Local History (Baer, Brumbaugh, Cook, Janney, Maver, Russell, Tomlinson, Tucker, Willingham & others), mss
Partic in OCLC Online Computer Library Center, Inc

NATIONAL GRADUATE UNIVERSITY LIBRARY,* 1008 N Ranolph Rd, Ste 103, 22201. SAN 320-2704. Tel: 703-527-4800. FAX: 703-527-4804. E-Mail: nguniv@erols.com.
Founded 1967. Enrl 120
Library Holdings: Bk Vols 23,000; Per Subs 125
Subject Interests: Behav sci, Develop planning, Environ mgt, Government, Govt procurement, Mgt, Origins of democracy, Political science, Res mgt
Special Collections: American History & Government; District of Columbia Court of Appeals & District of Columbia Law Documents (Judge Godfrey Munter Coll); Government Procurement (Paul H Gantt Coll)

NATIONAL SCIENCE TEACHERS ASSOCIATION, Glenn O Blough Library, 1840 Wilson Blvd, 22201-3000. SAN 320-1325. Tel: 703-243-7100. FAX: 703-243-7177. Web Site: www.nsta.org. *Info Res*, Sue Addington
Founded 1978
Library Holdings: Bk Titles 3,600; Per Subs 50
Special Collections: Outstanding Science Tradebooks Coll

NUCLEAR WASTE TECHNICAL REVIEW BOARD LIBRARY, 2300 Clarendon Blvd, Ste 1300, 22201. SAN 374-5937. Tel: 703-235-4473. Interlibrary Loan Service Tel: 703-235-4486. Reference Tel: 703-235-4486. FAX: 703-235-4495. *Librn*, Victoria Reich; E-Mail: reich@nwtrb.gov; Staff 1 (MLS 1)
Founded 1990
Library Holdings: Bk Vols 4,200; Per Subs 50
Special Collections: Board Meeting Transcripts
Automation Activity & Vendor Info: (Cataloging) EOS; (OPAC) EOS
Restriction: Open to public for reference only
Function: ILL to other special libraries
Partic in Fedlink; OCLC Online Computer Library Center, Inc

L OBLON, SPIVAK, MCCLELLAND, MAIER & NEUSTADT, Law Library, 1755 Jefferson Davis Hwy, Ste 400, 22202-3509. SAN 374-5961. Tel: 703-412-6391. FAX: 703-413-2220. *Librn*, Jo Burke; E-Mail: jburke@oblon.com. Subject Specialists: *Patents*, Jo Burke; Staff 1 (MLS 1)
Founded 1993
Library Holdings: Bk Vols 10,000; Bk Titles 1,500; Per Subs 145
Database Vendor: Dialog, Lexis-Nexis, OCLC - First Search

S SYSTEM PLANNING CORP, Charles S Lerch Information Center,* 1000 Wilson, 22209. SAN 317-2236. Tel: 703-351-8244, Ext 8888. FAX: 703-351-8815. *Dir*, Phyllis Moon; *Librn*, Velora Jernigan-Pedrick; Staff 3 (MLS 2, Non-MLS 1)
Founded 1973
Library Holdings: Bk Vols 15,000; Per Subs 100
Subject Interests: Arms control, Eng for defense systs
Restriction: Staff use only
Partic in Dialog Corporation; OCLC Online Computer Library Center, Inc

S TELEDYNE BROWN ENGINEERING LIBRARY,* 1300 N 17th St Ste 1450, 22209. SAN 327-9537. Tel: 703-276-7900. FAX: 703-243-8950. *Librn*, GloriaDon Chambers
Library Holdings: Bk Vols 1,000; Per Subs 30

G US AGENCY FOR INTERNATIONAL DEVELOPMENT, Environmental Health Project Information Center, 1611 N Kent St, Rm 300, 22209. SAN 327-2605. Tel: 703-247-8730. FAX: 703-247-8610. E-Mail: info@ehproject.org. *Dir*, Dan Campbell
Library Holdings: Bk Titles 10,000; Per Subs 75
Subject Interests: Water resources
Partic in UN Environ Prog

GL UNITED STATES DEPARTMENT OF THE INTERIOR, Office of Hearings & Appeals Library,* 4015 Wilson Blvd, Rm 1001, 22203. SAN 317-2260. Tel: 703-235-3804. FAX: 703-235-9014. *Librn*, Theodore Richardson; E-Mail: ted_richardson@fws.gov
Founded 1970
Library Holdings: Bk Vols 20,000
Subject Interests: Environmental studies, Fed law, Indian probate, Pub lands, Surface mining
Special Collections: Congressional Record, vol 115-1969 to vol 121-1975, micro; Federal Register vol 1-1936 to vol 38-1973, micro, vol 39-1974 to present

G UNITED STATES PATENT & TRADEMARK OFFICE, Scientific & Technical Information Center,* 2021 Clark Pl, 22202. SAN 317-2287. Tel: 703-308-0810. *Mgr*, Henry C Rosicky; *Coll Develop*, Barbara T McDougald
Founded 1836
Library Holdings: Bk Vols 129,163; Per Subs 1,661
Subject Interests: Biochemistry, Biomed, Biotech, Chem eng design, Computer science, Copyright law, Electrical, Fed law, Foreign patents, Mech eng design
Special Collections: Foreign Patents
Publications: Chem/Biotechnology News; Current Serials List; New Book Acquistions List; STIC News

S USA TODAY LIBRARY, 1000 Wilson Blvd, 22229. SAN 372-8684. Tel: 703-276-5585 (Photo Resale Serv), 703-276-5588, 703-276-5864 (Pub Research). FAX: 703-247-3139. *Dir*, Barbara Maxwell; *Asst Dir*, Jeanette Brown; *Coll Develop*, Lynette Constantinedes; *Coll Develop*, Susan O'Brian
Library Holdings: Bk Vols 5,300; Per Subs 100

S VOLUNTEERS IN TECHNICAL ASSISTANCE LIBRARY,* 1600 Wilson Blvd, Ste 500, 22209. SAN 373-255X. Tel: 703-276-1800. FAX: 703-243-1865.
Library Holdings: Bk Titles 200

ASHBURN

S NATIONAL RECREATION & PARK ASSOCIATION, Joseph Lee Memorial Library & Information Center, 22377 Belmont Ridge Rd, 20148. SAN 370-6915. Tel: 703-858-2192. FAX: 703-858-0794. Web Site: www.activeparks.org. *Archivist, Librn*, Rosa Lee Furr; Fax: 703-858-0794, E-Mail: lfurr@nrpa.org
Founded 1989
Library Holdings: Bk Titles 5,000; Per Subs 20
Special Collections: American Institute of Park Executives Coll; American Park Secrets Coll; National Conference on State Parks Coll; National Recreation Association Coll; Playground Association of America Coll
Publications: Thesaurus of Park Recreation & Leisure Service Terms

ASHLAND

C RANDOLPH-MACON COLLEGE, McGraw-Page Library, 305 Henry St, PO Box 5005, 23005-5005. SAN 317-2309. Tel: 804-752-7257. Interlibrary Loan Service Tel: 804-752-5430. Reference Tel: 804-752-7323. FAX: 804-752-7345. Web Site: www.rmc.edu/library. *Dir*, Virginia E Young; Tel: 804-752-7256, E-Mail: gyoung@rmc.edu; *Tech Servs*, Elizabeth Sudduth; Staff 5 (MLS 4, Non-MLS 1)

Founded 1830. Enrl 1,118; Fac 96; Highest Degree: Bachelor
Special Collections: 18th Century European Culture (Casanova & Goudar); Henry Miller; Intellectual History of the Colonial South; Southern History; Virginia Methodism
Automation Activity & Vendor Info: (Acquisitions) SIRSI; (Cataloging) SIRSI; (Circulation) SIRSI; (ILL) SIRSI; (OPAC) SIRSI; (Serials) SIRSI
Partic in OCLC Online Computer Library Center, Inc; Richmond Academic Library Consortium; SE Libr Network; VA Independent Col & Univ Libr Asn

BEAUMONT

J BEAUMONT JUVENILE CORRECTIONAL CENTER, DCE Library,* PO Box 491, 23014. SAN 371-8220. Tel: 804-556-3316. FAX: 804-556-3316, Ext 348. *Librn*, J H Adams Jr
Enrl 245; Fac 30
Library Holdings: Bk Titles 5,100; Per Subs 32

BEDFORD

P BEDFORD PUBLIC LIBRARY SYSTEM, 321 N Bridge St, 24523-1927. SAN 317-2317. Tel: 540-586-8911. Circulation Tel: 540-586-8911, Ext 20. Reference Tel: 540-586-8911, Ext 18. FAX: 540-586-7280. Web Site: www.library.bedford.va.us. *Dir*, Thomas J Heyman; Tel: 540-586-8911, Ext 32, Fax: 540-586-8875, E-Mail: hehman@library.bedford.va.us; *Assoc Dir*, Steve Preston; Tel: 540-586-8911 Ext 29, Fax: 540-586-7280, E-Mail: preston@library.bedford.va.us; *ILL*, Christina Vito; *Ch Servs*, Chrissie Anderson; *Tech Servs*, Donna Pelcher; Tel: 540-586-8911 Ext 34, E-Mail: pletcher@library.bedford.va.us; *Ad Servs*, Bernadette Brennan; Tel: 540-586-8911, Ext 10, E-Mail: brennan@library.bedford.va.us; *Assoc Dir*, Steve Preston; Tel: 540-586-8911, Ext 29, Fax: 540-586-7280, E-Mail: preston@library.bedford.va.us; *Tech Servs*, Donna Pelcher; Tel: 540-586-8911, Ext 34, E-Mail: pletcher@library.bedford.va.us; *Circ Ch*, Leah Jasper; Staff 58 (MLS 6, Non-MLS 52)
Founded 1900. Pop 59,000; Circ 471,899
Library Holdings: Bk Vols 166,753; Per Subs 460
Subject Interests: Local history
Automation Activity & Vendor Info: (Acquisitions) TLC; (Cataloging) TLC; (Circulation) TLC
Database Vendor: Ebsco - EbscoHost
Partic in Lynchburg Area Library Cooperative; Solinet
Friends of the Library Group

BERRYVILLE

SR HOLY CROSS ABBEY LIBRARY, 901 Cool Spring Lane, 22611-2700. SAN 317-2325. Tel: 540-955-1425. FAX: 540-955-1356. *Librn*, Bro Benedict Simmonds; Staff 2 (MLS 2)
Founded 1950
Jan 1998-Dec 1998 Mats Exp $7,000
Library Holdings: Bk Vols 24,500; Per Subs 59
Automation Activity & Vendor Info: (Cataloging) TLC

BIG STONE GAP

J WAMPLER LIBRARY, Mountain Empire Community College, PO Drawer 700, 24219. SAN 317-2333. Tel: 540-523-2400, Ext 304. Circulation Tel: 540-523-7468. FAX: 540-523-8220. Web Site: www.me.cc.va.us/melrc.htm. *Dir*, W M Bullock; *Coordr*, John M Cotham; E-Mail: jcotham@me.cc.va.us; Staff 2 (MLS 2)
Founded 1972. Enrl 1,811; Fac 86
Jul 1999-Jun 2000 Income State $330,432. Mats Exp $79,887, Books $29,540, Per/Ser (Incl. Access Fees) $14,698, Presv $1,494, Micro $13,100, AV Equip $17,505, Electronic Ref Mat (Incl. Access Fees) $3,550. Sal $195,494 (Prof $124,147)
Library Holdings: Bk Vols 34,262; Bk Titles 30,318; Per Subs 220
Subject Interests: Criminal justice, Nursing, Respiratory therapy
Partic in SWING

BLACKSBURG

C VIRGINIA POLYTECHNIC INSTITUTE & STATE UNIVERSITY LIBRARIES, Drill Field Dr, PO Box 90001, 24062-9001. SAN 362-7454. Tel: 540-231-6170 (Spec Coll). Circulation Tel: 540-231-6340. Reference Tel: 540-231-6045. FAX: 540-231-7808. Web Site: www.lib.vt.edu. *Dean of Libr*, Eileen Hitchingham; Tel: 540-231-5593, E-Mail: hitch@vt.edu; *Assoc Dean*, Donald Kenney; Tel: 540-231-9257, E-Mail: kenney@vt.edu; *Dir, Tech Serv*, Leslie O'Brien; Tel: 540-231-4945, E-Mail: lobrien@vt.edu; *Branch Mgr*, Annette Burr; Tel: 540-231-9257, E-Mail: apburr@vt.edu; *Branch Mgr*, Victoria Kok; Tel: 540-231-6610, E-Mail: vkok@vt.edu; *Branch Mgr*, Edward Lener; Tel: 540-231-9201, E-Mail: lener@vt.edu; *Coll Develop*, Paul D Metz; Tel: 540-231-5563, E-Mail: pmetz@vt.edu; *Bibliog Instr*, Nancy Seamans; Tel: 540-231-2708, E-Mail: nseamans@vt.edu; *Ref*, Linda Richardson; Tel: 540-231-9224, E-Mail: lindrich@vt.edu; *Syst Coordr*, Curtis Carr; Tel: 540-231-6617, E-Mail: curtis.carr@vt.edu; *Circ*, Debra Averhart; Tel: 540-231-3608, E-Mail: averhart@vt.edu; Staff 134 (MLS Non-MLS 98)
Founded 1872. Enrl 22,500; Fac 1,466; Highest Degree: Doctorate
Jul 1999-Jun 2000 Income (Main Library and Branch Library) $11,499,3 Mats Exp $5,501,066, Books $824,607, Per/Ser (Incl. Access Fees) $3,754,463, Presv $102,592, Other Print Mats $66,504, Electronic Ref M (Incl. Access Fees) $654,642. Sal $4,931,996 (Prof $1,900,157)
Library Holdings: Bk Vols 2,057,572; Per Subs 16,803
Subject Interests: Agriculture, Architecture, Art, Behav sci, Biology, Engineering, Humanities, Physical science, Soc sci
Special Collections: Aeronautical & Space History (Archives of Americ Aerospace Exploration), including the papers of Christopher C Kraft, Jr, Samuel Herrick, John T Parsons and Melvin N Gough; American and Br Literature, 1880-1940 (Dayton Kohler Coll); Appalachian History and Fo Culture (including Patrick County Oral History Coll, Blue Ridge Parkwa Folk Life Oral History Coll); Heraldry (Harry D Temple Coll); History o Technology; History of Women's Involvement in Architecture (Internatio Archive of Women in Architecture), including the papers of Hanna Schroeder, Verena Dietrich, Ilse Koci and Elise Sundt; Late Nineteenth-Century Children's Literature (John H Barnes Coll); Nasa; Ornithology (Harold H Bailey Coll); Railroad History (Archives of the Norfolk and Western Railway and Southern Railway Systems), including archival rec for circa 300 Nineteenth-Century Railroad Companies in the South and Midwest; Sherwood Anderson; Southwest Virginia History (J Hoge Tyler papers, Preston Family papers, Black-Kent-Apperson Family papers); Western Americana
Automation Activity & Vendor Info: (Cataloging) VTLS; (Cataloging) VTLS; (Circulation) VTLS
Database Vendor: CARL, Dialog, GaleNet, IAC - Info Trac, IAC - SearchBank, Lexis-Nexis, OCLC - First Search, OVID Technologies, ProQuest, Silverplatter Information Inc., Wilson - Wilson Web
Publications: Library Friends
Partic in Consortium for Continuing Higher Educ in Northern Va; Nasa Libraries Information System - Nasa Galaxie; Nat Libr of Med; OCLC Online Computer Library Center, Inc; Virtual Libr of Va
Departmental Libraries:
ART & ARCHITECTURE Tel: 540-231-9271. *Librn*, Annette Burr
Library Holdings: Bk Vols 63,086
GEOLOGY Tel: 540-231-6101. *Librn*, Edward Lener
Library Holdings: Bk Vols 54,000
NORTHERN VIRGINIA GRADUATE CENTER, 7054 Haycock Rd, Fa Church, 22043-2311. SAN 362-7543. Tel: 703-538-8340. *Librn*, Pat Murphy
Library Holdings: Bk Vols 12,483
CM VETERINARY MEDICINE Tel: 540-231-6610. *Librn*, Victoria T Kok
Library Holdings: Bk Vols 15,627

BLUEFIELD

C BLUEFIELD COLLEGE, Easley Library, 3000 College Dr, 24605. SAN 317-235X. Tel: 540-326-4238. Circulation Tel: 540-326-4238. Reference 540-326-4269. FAX: 540-326-4288. Web Site: www.bluefield.edu/library/ *Dir*, Cynthia L Peterson; E-Mail: cpeterson@mail.bluefield.edu; *Asst Dir*, Ann Massey; Tel: 540-326-4236, E-Mail: amassey@mail.bluefield.edu; *C* Shirley Garrett; *Coll Develop*, Werner Lind; Tel: 540-326-4239, E-Mail: wlind@mail.bluefield.edu; *Tech Servs*, Nora Lockett; Tel: 540-326-4237, E-Mail: nlockett@mail.bluefield.edu; *Circ*, Lynn Bartlett; E-Mail: lbartlet mail.bluefield.edu; Staff 5 (MLS 3, Non-MLS 2)
Founded 1922. Enrl 500; Fac 46; Highest Degree: Bachelor
Jul 2000-Jun 2001 Income $94,000, State $3,000, Parent Institution $91,0 Mats Exp $35,000, Books $20,000, Electronic Ref Mat (Incl. Access Fee $15,000
Library Holdings: Bk Vols 56,000; Bk Titles 55,000; Per Subs 250
Special Collections: Barbour Coll; McKenzie Memorial Religion Coll
Automation Activity & Vendor Info: (Acquisitions) Innovative Interface Inc.; (Cataloging) Innovative Interfaces Inc.; (Circulation) Innovative Interfaces Inc.; (Course Reserve) Innovative Interfaces Inc.; (OPAC) Innovative Interfaces Inc.
Database Vendor: Ebsco - EbscoHost, GaleNet, IAC - Info Trac, Lexis-Nexis, OCLC - First Search, OVID Technologies
Publications: Easley Does It (newsletter); Library Home Pages
Restriction: Circulation limited
Function: Reference services available
Partic in Appalachian Libr Info Coop; Holston Associated Librs Consortiu SE Libr Network; SWING; VIVA/VICULA

BOYDTON

P SOUTHSIDE REGIONAL LIBRARY,* 316 Washington St, PO Box 10, 23917-0010. SAN 317-2376. Tel: 804-738-6580. FAX: 804-738-6070. E-Mail: tomtrees_1@hotmail.com. *Librn*, Thomas Emory Jr
Founded 1944. Pop 41,300; Circ 199,907
Jul 1997-Jun 1998 Income $566,366, State $131,900, Federal $8,751, County $375,498, Locally Generated Income $43,990, Other $6,227. Mats Exp $84,968, Books $62,336, Per/Ser (Incl. Access Fees) $18,436, Presv $512, Micro $3,684. Sal $303,343 (Prof $25,408)

Library Holdings: Bk Vols 93,205; Bk Titles 46,318; Per Subs 167
Subject Interests: Genealogy, Large print
Special Collections: Mecklenburg County Newspapers, late 1800s, micro
Partic in SE Libr Network
Friends of the Library Group
Branches: 5
BUTLER MEMORIAL, 515 Marshall St, Chase City, 23924. SAN 372-7084. Tel: 804-372-4286.
Library Holdings: Bk Vols 19,000
Friends of the Library Group
CLARKSVILLE PUBLIC, PO Box 1146, Clarksville, 23927. SAN 372-7092. Tel: 804-374-8692. FAX: 804-374-8692.
Library Holdings: Bk Vols 12,850
Friends of the Library Group
R T ARNOLD PUBLIC, 101 W Danville St, South Hill, 23970. SAN 372-7076. Tel: 804-447-8162. FAX: 804-447-5805.
Library Holdings: Bk Vols 19,500
Friends of the Library Group
RIPBERGER PUBLIC, PO Box 855, Kenbridge, 23944. SAN 372-7106. Tel: 804-676-3456. FAX: 804-676-3211.
Library Holdings: Bk Vols 20,000
Friends of the Library Group
VICTORIA PUBLIC, 1609 Ninth St, Victoria, 23974. SAN 372-7114. Tel: 804-696-3416. FAX: 804-696-2895.
Library Holdings: Bk Vols 12,400
Friends of the Library Group

DGEWATER

BRIDGEWATER COLLEGE, Alexander Mack Memorial Library, 22812. SAN 317-2384. Tel: 540-828-5413. FAX: 540-828-5482. Web Site: www.bridgewater.edu/departments/library/index.html. *Dir*, Ruth Greenawalt; *Cat*, Carin Teets; *Ref*, Michael Ours; *Ref*, Catherine Ruf; *Circ*, Lisa Wilson; *Archivist, Curator*, Terry Barkley; *Coll Develop*, Jennifer Keach
Founded 1880. Highest Degree: Bachelor
Library Holdings: Bk Titles 123,400; Per Subs 600
Subject Interests: Genealogy, Local history
Special Collections: Rare Bibles & Church of the Brethren Material
Partic in OCLC Online Computer Library Center, Inc; SE Libr Network

STOL

BRISTOL PUBLIC LIBRARY,* 701 Goode St, 24201-4199. SAN 362-7578. Tel: 540-645-8780. FAX: 540-669-5593. *Dir*, William A Muller, III; E-Mail: bmuller@wrlibrary.org; *Acq, Cat*, Deborah Moore; *Ch Servs, YA Servs*, Michelle Page; Staff 6 (MLS 4, Non-MLS 2)
Founded 1909. Pop 73,000; Circ 268,339
Jul 1997-Jun 1998 Income $779,591, State $162,107, City $477,995, County $50,000, Locally Generated Income $68,446, Other $21,043. Mats Exp $129,281, Books $102,571, Per/Ser (Incl. Access Fees) $14,463, Presv $272, Micro $11,975. Sal $434,922 (Prof $156,508)
Library Holdings: Bk Vols 108,141; Bk Titles 102,733
Subject Interests: Genealogy, Local history, Virginia
Friends of the Library Group
Branches: 1
AVOCA, 1550 Volunteer Pkwy, 37620. SAN 362-7608. Tel: 423-968-9663. FAX: 540-645-8795.
Library Holdings: Bk Vols 17,581; Bk Titles 17,405
Friends of the Library Group

VIRGINIA INTERMONT COLLEGE, J F Hicks Memorial Library, 1013 Moore St, 24201. SAN 317-2392. Tel: 540-466-7955, 540-466-7960. FAX: 540-466-7963. Web Site: www.vic.edu/library/index.html. *Dir*, Milton Stevenson; *Asst Dir*, Jonathan Tallman; *Ref*, William Howard; *Circ*, Nellie Dunford; *Circ*, Robert Rhea; Staff 3 (MLS 3)
Founded 1884. Enrl 562; Fac 47; Highest Degree: Bachelor
Library Holdings: Bk Vols 67,000; Bk Titles 59,500; Per Subs 300
Subject Interests: Art, Behav sci, Education, Horsemanship, Music, Photog, Soc sci

ENA VISTA

SOUTHERN VIRGINIA COLLEGE, Von Canon Library, 1 College Hill Dr, 24416. SAN 317-2406. Tel: 540-261-8440. FAX: 540-261-8496. Web Site: www.southernvirginia.edu. *Dir Libr Serv*, Michael A Beier; Tel: 541-261-4234, E-Mail: mbeier@southernvirginia.edu; *Asst Librn*, Julie Larsen; Tel: 541-261-4241, E-Mail: jlarsen@southernvirginia.edu; Staff 2 (MLS 1, Non-MLS 1)
Founded 1900. Enrl 400; Fac 40; Highest Degree: Bachelor
Nov 1998-Oct 1999 Income Parent Institution $150,000. Mats Exp $116,000, Books $77,000, Per/Ser (Incl. Access Fees) $19,000, AV Equip $20,000
Library Holdings: Bk Vols 96,000; Bk Titles 88,000; Per Subs 150; Bks on Deafness & Sign Lang 8
Subject Interests: Equine studies, Horsemanship, Women studies
Special Collections: Local History Coll; Melville Coll
Automation Activity & Vendor Info: (Cataloging) Athena; (OPAC) Athena
Database Vendor: IAC - Info Trac, Lexis-Nexis, OCLC - First Search, OVID Technologies
Publications: Von Canon Library Handbook
Function: Reference services available
Mem of OCLC ILL Subsystem
Partic in VIVA/VICULA

CAPRON

S DEERFIELD CORRECTIONAL CENTER, DCE Library, 21360 Deerfield Dr, 23829. SAN 375-4979. Tel: 804-658-4368, Ext 7232. FAX: 804-658-4371. *Librn*, Susan Gillette
Founded 1994
Library Holdings: Bk Vols 15,000; Bk Titles 12,000; Per Subs 37
Automation Activity & Vendor Info: (Circulation) Follett
Special Services for the Deaf - Books on deafness & sign language; High interest/low vocabulary books

CATAWBA

GM CATAWBA HOSPITAL, Professional Library,* PO Box 200, 24070. SAN 321-6004. Tel: 540-375-4342. FAX: 540-375-4348. *Dir*, James S Reinhard; *Dir Libr Serv*, Jane Wills; *Assoc Dir*, Jack Wood
Founded 1978
Library Holdings: Bk Vols 431; Bk Titles 420; Per Subs 52
Restriction: Staff use only

CHANTILLY

M AMERICAN MEDICAL LABORATORIES INC LIBRARY,* PO Box 10841, 20153. SAN 374-9010. Tel: 703-802-6900. FAX: 703-802-7088. *Dir*, Leslie A Weatherly; *Asst Librn*, Ronnie Weiss
Library Holdings: Bk Titles 410; Per Subs 65

S TASC, INC, 4801 Stonecroft Blvd, 20151-3822. SAN 323-7753. Tel: 703-633-8300, Ext 4654. FAX: 703-449-7648. Web Site: www.corp.tasc.com. *Librn*, Glenda Barlow; E-Mail: glbarlow@tasc.com; *Librn*, Barta McCoy; E-Mail: bkmccoy@tasc.com
Library Holdings: Bk Vols 10,000; Per Subs 200
Restriction: Staff use only
Partic in Dialog Corporation; OCLC Online Computer Library Center, Inc

CHARLOTTE COURT HOUSE

P CHARLOTTE COUNTY LIBRARY,* PO Box 788, 23923. SAN 317-2414. Tel: 804-542-5247. *Librn*, Jim Watkins
Founded 1937. Circ 50,455
Library Holdings: Bk Vols 46,000; Per Subs 130
Partic in SE Libr Network
Friends of the Library Group
Branches: 3
BACON DISTRICT, Hwy 15, Wylliesburg, 23976. SAN 373-2932. Tel: 804-735-8812.
Friends of the Library Group
KEYSVILLE BRANCH, King St, Keysville, 23947. SAN 373-2940. Tel: 804-736-0083.
Friends of the Library Group
PHENIX BRANCH, Charlotte St, Phenix, 23959. SAN 373-2959. Tel: 804-542-4654.
Friends of the Library Group

CHARLOTTESVILLE

S INSTITUTE OF TEXTILE TECHNOLOGY, Roger Milliken Textile Library, 2551 Ivy Rd, 22903-4614. SAN 317-2422. Tel: 804-296-5511. FAX: 804-977-5400. E-Mail: library@itt.edu. Web Site: www.itt.edu. *Dir Libr Serv*, Adrienne Diana Granitz; Tel: 804-296-5511, Ext 224, E-Mail: adrienneg@itt.edu; *Tech Servs*, Shelah Leake; E-Mail: shelahl@itt.edu; *Publ Servs*, Ann Carol Gatewood; E-Mail: anng@itt.edu; *Coll Develop*, Laura Painter; E-Mail: laurap@itt.edu; Staff 4 (MLS 1, Non-MLS 3)
Founded 1944. Enrl 30
Jul 2000-Jun 2001 Income Parent Institution $500,000. Mats Exp $68,500, Books $20,000, Per/Ser (Incl. Access Fees) $30,000, Micro $7,500, Other Print Mats $1,000, Electronic Ref Mat (Incl. Access Fees) $10,000. Sal $135,000
Library Holdings: Bk Vols 30,000; Bk Titles 16,000; Per Subs 302
Subject Interests: Design, Environ issues, History, Proc, Production, Textile tech
Special Collections: Callaway Coll
Database Vendor: Dialog, Ebsco - EbscoHost, GaleNet, IAC - SearchBank, OCLC - First Search, OVID Technologies, ProQuest, Silverplatter Information Inc.
Publications: Textile Technology Digest (Index to science materials)
Function: Reference services available

P JEFFERSON-MADISON REGIONAL LIBRARY, Central Library,* 201 E Market St, 22902-5287. SAN 362-7632. Tel: 804-979-7151, Ext 207 or 206. TDD: 804-293-6848. FAX: 804-971-7035. Web Site: www.jmrl.org. *Dir*, John Halliday; *Circ*, Carol Clark; *Ref*, Joyce MacDonald; *Automation Syst Coordr, Tech Servs*, Phil Williams; *Ch Servs, YA Servs*, Nancy Cook; *Coll Develop*, Andrea G Williams
Founded 1921. Pop 162,500; Circ 1,650,109
Jul 1997-Jun 1998 Income $3,881,736. Mats Exp $603,633. Sal $1,676,280
Library Holdings: Bk Vols 472,550
Special Collections: Charlottesville/Albemarle Historical Coll
Automation Activity & Vendor Info: (Circulation) Inlex
Publications: Annual Report; Friends Newsletter
Partic in Virginia Library & Information Network
Special Services for the Deaf - TDD
Friends of the Library Group
Branches: 7
CROZET BRANCH, The Old C&O Sta, PO Box 430, Crozet, 22932-0430. SAN 362-7667. Tel: 804-823-4050. FAX: 804-823-8399. Web Site: www.jmrl.org. *Head of Libr*, Mary Plum
GORDON AVE, 1500 Gordon Ave, 22903-2997. SAN 362-7691. Tel: 804-296-5544. FAX: 804-295-8737. Web Site: www.jmrl.org. *Head of Libr*, Krista Farrell
Friends of the Library Group
GREENE COUNTY, Standard St, PO Box 367, 22973-0367. SAN 362-7721. Tel: 804-985-5227. FAX: 804-985-3315. Web Site: www.jmrl.org. *Head of Libr*, Joyce Anne Stevens
Friends of the Library Group
LOUISA COUNTY, 22 Bus Garage Rd, Mineral, 23117. SAN 362-7756. Tel: 540-894-5853. FAX: 540-894-9461. Web Site: www.jmrl.org. *Head of Libr*, Virginia Reese
Friends of the Library Group
NELSON MEMORIAL, Rte 29 South, PO Box 321, Lovingston, 22949-0321. SAN 362-7780. Tel: 804-263-5904. FAX: 804-263-5988. Web Site: www.jmrl.org. *Head of Libr*, Tanith Knight
Friends of the Library Group
NORTHSIDE, Albemarle Sq, 1671 Seminole Trail, 22901-1466. SAN 371-9529. Tel: 804-973-7893. FAX: 804-973-5876. Web Site: www.jmrl.org. *Head of Libr*, Lindsay Ideson
Friends of the Library Group
SCOTTSVILLE BRANCH, Bird St, PO Box 759, Scottsville, 24590-0759. SAN 362-7810. Tel: 804-286-3541. FAX: 804-286-4744. Web Site: www.jmrl.org. *Head of Libr*, Marianne Ramsden
Friends of the Library Group
Bookmobiles: 1. Bk vols 26,980

L LEXIS LAW PUBLICATION LIBRARY,* 701 E Water St, 22902. SAN 327-2508. Tel: 804-972-7600. FAX: 804-972-7653.
Library Holdings: Bk Vols 50,000; Per Subs 50
Open Mon-Fri 8-5

S LITTON MARINE SYSTEMS, INC, (Formerly Sperry Marine, Inc), Engineering Library, 1070 Seminole Trail, 22901. SAN 329-1693. Tel: 804-974-2441. FAX: 804-974-2259. *Tech Servs*, Grace Y McKenzie; E-Mail: gym01@litton-marine.com
Library Holdings: Bk Titles 4,400; Per Subs 220
Subject Interests: Electronic engineering

L NATIONAL LEGAL RESEARCH GROUP, INC LIBRARY,* 2421 Ivy Rd, 22903. (Mail add: PO Box 7187, 22906), SAN 372-8722. Tel: 804-977-5690. FAX: 804-295-4667. E-Mail: nlrg1@aol.com. Web Site: www.nlrg.com. *Librn*, Russell T Payne
Library Holdings: Bk Vols 32,000; Per Subs 200

S NATIONAL RADIO ASTRONOMY OBSERVATORY LIBRARY, 520 Edgemont Rd, 22903-2475. SAN 317-2430. Tel: 804-296-0254. FAX: 804-296-0278. E-Mail: library@nrao.edu. Web Site: www.nrao.edu/library/. *Librn*, Ellen N Bouton; *Librn*, Mary Jo Hendricks
Founded 1959
Library Holdings: Bk Vols 17,816; Per Subs 240
Subject Interests: Astronomy, Astrophysics, Computers, Electronics, Engineering, Physics
Special Collections: ESO/SEC Atlas of the Southern Sky Coll; Observatory, Astronomical Institute & Government Agency Coll; Palomar Sky Survey
Publications: Acquisition List; Duplicate list; RAP sheet (preprint list)
Partic in Fedlink

J PIEDMONT VIRGINIA COMMUNITY COLLEGE, Betty Sue Jessup Library, 501 College Dr, 22902. SAN 317-2449. Tel: 804-961-5308. FAX: 804-977-6842. Web Site: www.pvcc.cc.va.us/library. *Dir*, Linda Cahill; Staff 4 (MLS 4)
Founded 1972. Enrl 4,337; Fac 52
Library Holdings: Bk Vols 31,308; Per Subs 304
Publications: Periodical Listing
Partic in SE Libr Network

S THOMAS JEFFERSON FOUNDATION INC, Jefferson Library, PO Box 316, 22902. SAN 327-3512. Tel: 804-984-1577. Reference Tel: 804-984-9848. FAX: 804-293-3108. Web Site: www.monticello.org. *Librn*, Jack Robertson; E-Mail: jrobertson@monticello.org; *Res*, Bryan Craig; E-Mai bcraig@monticello.org; Staff 2 (MLS 2)
Library Holdings: Bk Vols 3,500
Special Collections: 18th Century Paris, France (Howard C Rice Coll)
Partic in OCLC Online Computer Library Center, Inc

C UNIVERSITY OF VIRGINIA, University Library, PO Box 400114, 229 4114. SAN 362-7845. Tel: 804-924-3026. Interlibrary Loan Service Tel: 924-3875. Circulation Tel: 804-924-3017. FAX: 804-924-1431. Interlibra Loan Service FAX: 804-924-4337. Web Site: www.lib.virginia.edu/. *Libr* Karin Wittenborg; E-Mail: kw7g@virginia.edu; *Asst Librn*, Kendon Stub E-Mail: kls9h@virginia.edu; *Assoc Librn*, Martha Sites Blodgett; E-Mail mrs@virginia.edu; *Assoc Librn*, Gail Oltmanns; E-Mail: gvo7g@virginia.edu; *Assoc Librn*, Diane Walker; E-Mail: dpw@virginia.edu; *ILL* Douglas Hurd; E-Mail: dph9m@virginia.edu; *Cat*, Beth Camden; E-Mai bpzf@virginia.edu; *Acq*, Lynda Clendenning; E-Mail: lfc9k@virginia.edu *Ref*, Linda Lester; E-Mail: lll8g@virginia.edu; *Spec Coll*, Michael Plunk E-Mail: mfp@virginia.edu. Subject Specialists: *Preservation*, Lynda Clendenning
Founded 1819. Enrl 18,400; Fac 1,000; Highest Degree: Doctorate
Special Collections: Alfred Lord Tennyson Coll; Bret Harte Coll; Carl Sanburg Coll; Cllifton Waller Barrett Library of American Literature; Do Passos Coll; Edgar Allan Poe (Poe-Ingram Coll); Edith, Osbert & Sacheverell Sitwell Coll; Edward R Stettinius Sr & Jr Coll; Ellen Glasgo Coll; Ernest Hemingway Coll; Evolution Coll; Finance (Carter Glass Papers); Folklore; Franz Kafka Coll; French Renaissance Literature; Gar Virginia Plantation Library; GATT, European Union; General John Forbe Coll; Gothic Novels; Henry James Coll; Herman Melville Coll; Hugh Sc Coll; Industrial History of Virginia; International Law (John Bassett Moo Coll); James Madison Pamphlets & Papers; James Monroe Coll; John Moffitt Coll; John Randolph of Roanoke Coll; John Steinbeck Coll; Josep M Bruccoli Great War Coll; Labor Problems & Economics; Lafcadio He Coll; Library of Congress Overseas Acquisitions Program (Middle East & South Asia); Mark Twain Coll; Mather Family of New England (William Mather Coll); Medieval Manuscripts; Middle East Coll; Missionaries; Modern Art; Nathaniel Hawthorne; Natural History; Naval History; Orien Coll; Paul W Mellon American Coll; Poetry; Poland; Political Cartoons C Popups; Robert Frost Coll; Rudyard Kipling Coll; S S Van Dines; Sara Teasdale Coll; Sporting Books-Equestrian; Thomas Jefferson Papers; Tho W Streeter Railroad Coll; Tracy W McGregor Library of American Histo Trollope; Twin Oaks Community Papers; Typography & Printing; Univer of Virginia Archives; US Politics & Government-20th Century; Vachel Lindsay Coll; Venezuela; Virginia Authors; Virginia Family Papers, 18th-19th Centuries; Virginia History & Politics; Virginiana; Voyages & Trave Walt Whitman Coll; Washington Irving Coll; William Dean Howells Coll William Faulkner (Massey Coll & Faulkner Foundation)
Publications: Libra; Library Developments
Partic in Association Of Southeastern Research Libraries (ASERL); SE L Network
Friends of the Library Group
Departmental Libraries:
ASTRONOMY, 264 Astronomy Bldg, 22903. (Mail add: PO Box 40033 22904-4330), SAN 378-1445. Tel: 804-924-3921. FAX: 804-924-4337. Web Site: www.lib.virginia.edu/science/scilibs/astr-lib.html. *In Charge*, Chris Wiedman; E-Mail: clw@virginia.edu
Library Holdings: Bk Vols 13,486
BIOLOGY-PSYCHOLOGY, 290-A Gilmer Hall, 22903-2477. (Mail add: PO Box 400329, 22904-4329), SAN 362-8086. Tel: 804-982-5260. Web Site: www.lib.virginia.edu/science/scilibs/bio-psych-lib.html. *In Charge*, Sandra Dulaney; E-Mail: sbd2f@virginia.edu
Library Holdings: Bk Vols 30,411
CHEMISTRY, 259 Chemistry Bldg, 22903-2454. (Mail add: PO Box 400315, 22904-4315), SAN 362-790X. Tel: 804-924-3159. FAX: 804-9 4337. Web Site: www.lib.virginia.edu/science/scilibs/chem-lib.html. *In Charge*, Brenda Lambert; E-Mail: bl8w@virginia.edu
Library Holdings: Bk Vols 24,656

CM CLAUDE MOORE HEALTH SCIENCES LIBRARY, Univ Va Health Sc Ctr, Jefferson Park Ave & Lane Rd, 22908. (Mail add: PO Box 800722, 22908-0722), SAN 362-8140. Tel: 804-924-5444. Interlibrary Loan Service Tel: 804-924-0058. Reference Tel: 804-924-5591. FAX: 804-92 0379. E-Mail: law6z@virginia.edu. Web Site: www.med.virginia.edu/hs-library/. *Dir*, Linda Watson; *Assoc Dir*, Gretchen Arnold; *Syst Coordr*, Gabriel R Rios; *Coll Develop*, Jonathan M Lord; *Web Coordr*, Bart Ragon; *Ref*, Elaine Banner; *Ref*, Inhye Son; *Ref*, Patricia Vaughn; *Media Spec*, Andrea Horne; *Bibliog Instr*, Karen Grandage; *Circ, Doc Delivery* Dan WIlson; *Cat*, Nadine Ellero; Staff 14 (MLS 14)
Founded 1911. Enrl 1,362; Fac 1,256; Highest Degree: Doctorate
Jul 1999-Jun 2000 Income (Main Library Only) $3,480,320, State $2,224,543, Federal $617,698, Locally Generated Income $208,458, Par Institution $18,490, Other $411,131. Mats Exp $1,214,247, Books $97,486, Per/Ser (Incl. Access Fees) $998,473, AV Equip $3,915, Electronic Ref Mat (Incl. Access Fees) $114,373. Sal $1,404,382 (Prof $631,865)
Library Holdings: Bk Vols 188,719; Bk Titles 53,631; Per Subs 2,175
Subject Interests: Behav sci, Med hist, Medicine, Natural science, Nursing, Nursing hist, Soc sci
Special Collections: American Lung Association of Virginia Archives;

Kerr L White Health Care Coll; Philip S Hench Walter Reed/Yellow Fever Coll
Automation Activity & Vendor Info: (Acquisitions) SIRSI; (Cataloging) SIRSI; (Circulation) SIRSI; (OPAC) SIRSI; (Serials) SIRSI
Database Vendor: OVID Technologies
Publications: The Clau de Moore Health Sciences Library Annual Report; The Claude Moore Health Sciences Library Inside Information
Partic in National Network Of Libraries Of Medicine - South Central Region; OCLC Online Computer Library Center, Inc; SE Libr Network

CLEMONS LIBRARY, PO Box 400710, 22904-4710. Tel: 804-924-3684. Reference Tel: 804-924-3115. FAX: 804-924-7468. Web Site: www.lib.virginia.edu/clemons/home.html. *Dir*, Vicki Coleman; E-Mail: vc4n@virginia.edu; *Asst Librn*, Warner Granade; E-Mail: jwg2y@virginia.edu; *Publ Servs*, Elizabeth Margutti; E-Mail: eam@virginia.edu
Founded 1982
Library Holdings: Bk Vols 103,191
Subject Interests: Commerce, Film, General, Study
Special Services for the Blind - Kurzweil Reading Machine; VisualTek closed circuit TV reading aid

COLGATE DARDEN GRADUATE SCHOOL OF BUSINESS ADMINISTRATION, Graduate Business School, 22906. SAN 362-8027. Tel: 804-924-7321. FAX: 804-924-3533. *Dir*, Henry Wingate
Library Holdings: Bk Vols 115,000

EDUCATION, Ruffner Hall, 405 Emmet St, 22903-2495. (Mail add: PO Box 400278, 22904-4278), SAN 362-7934. Tel: 804-924-7040. Reference Tel: 804-924-7039. FAX: 804-924-3886. Web Site: www.lib.virginia.edu/education. *Librn*, Betsy Anthony; Tel: 804-924-0870, E-Mail: banthony@virginia.edu; *Ref*, Kay Cutter; Tel: 804-982-2664, E-Mail: cutter@virginia.edu; Staff 6 (MLS 2, Non-MLS 4)
Founded 1973
Library Holdings: Bk Vols 51,494; Per Subs 800
Subject Interests: Education
Special Collections: ERIC Microfiche Coll

FISKE KIMBALL FINE ARTS, Bayly Dr, 22903. (Mail add: PO Box 400131, 22904-4131), SAN 362-7993. Tel: 804-924-6938. FAX: 804-982-2678. Web Site: www.lib.virginia.edu/fine-arts/index.html.
Library Holdings: Bk Vols 144,211

LAW LIBRARY, 580 Massie Rd, 22903-1789. SAN 362-8051. Tel: 804-924-3384. FAX: 804-982-2232. Web Site: www.law.virginia.edu. *Dir*, Taylor Fitchett; Tel: 804-924-7725, E-Mail: tfichett@virginia.edu; *Librn*, Larry B Wenger; *Asst Librn, Syst Coordr*, Joseph Wynne; Tel: 804-924-4736, E-Mail: jjw2w@virginia.edu; *Publ Servs*, Micheal Klepper; Tel: 804-924-3495, E-Mail: mtk@virginia.edu; *Doc*, Barbara Selby; Tel: 804-924-3504, E-Mail: mbs8z@virginia.edu; *Cat*, Anne Mustain; Tel: 804-924-4730, E-Mail: am3g@virginia.edu; *Archivist*, Marsha Trimble; Tel: 804-924-3023, E-Mail: mt9c@virginia.edu; *Publ Servs*, Kent Olson; Tel: 804-924-4734, E-Mail: kco4f@virginia.edu; *Access Serv*, Cathy Palombi; Tel: 804-924-3519, E-Mail: ccp7m@virginia.edu; *Cat*, June Campbell; Tel: 804-924-3877, E-Mail: jnc@virginia.edu; *Cat*, Kip Gobin; Tel: 804-982-2232, E-Mail: krg@virginia.edu. Subject Specialists: *Foreign law*, Xinh Luu; *Intl law*, Xinh Luu; *Law*, Larry B Wenger; Staff 13 (MLS 13)
Founded 1826. Enrl 1,127; Fac 63; Highest Degree: Doctorate
Jul 1998-Jun 1999 Income $3,391,994, State $1,568, Parent Institution $3,171,251, Other $219,175. Mats Exp $1,129,591, Books $229,200, Per/Ser (Incl. Access Fees) $664,769, Presv $44,168, Micro $75,248. Sal $1,157,179 (Prof $706,486)
Library Holdings: Bk Vols 560,561; Bk Titles 232,178; Per Subs 13,022
Publications: Marine Affairs Bibliography
Partic in Solinet

MATHEMATICS, 107 Kerchof Hall, Math-Astronomy Bld, 22903. (Mail add: PO Box 400140, 22904-4140), SAN 362-8116. Tel: 804-924-7806. FAX: 804-924-4337. Web Site: www.lib.virginia.edu/science/scilibs/math-lib.html. *In Charge*, Chris Wiedman; E-Mail: cpw@virginia.edu
Library Holdings: Bk Vols 25,131

MUSIC, Old Cabell Hall, 22904-4175. (Mail add: PO Box 400175, 22904-4175), SAN 362-8175. Tel: 804-924-7041. FAX: 804-924-6033. E-Mail: musiclib@virginia.edu. Web Site: www.lib.virginia.edu/musiclib/index.html. *Dir*, Jane Penner; Tel: 804-924-7017, E-Mail: jep4f@virginia.edu; Staff 5 (MLS 2, Non-MLS 3)
Library Holdings: Bk Vols 68,534; Per Subs 273
Automation Activity & Vendor Info: (Acquisitions) SIRSI; (Cataloging) SIRSI; (Circulation) SIRSI; (Course Reserve) SIRSI; (ILL) SIRSI; (Media Booking) SIRSI; (OPAC) SIRSI; (Serials) SIRSI

PHYSICS, 323 Physics Bldg, 22903-2458. (Mail add: PO Box 400714, 22904-4714), SAN 362-8205. Tel: 804-924-6589. Web Site: www.lib.virginia.edu/science/scilibs/phys-lib.html. *In Charge*, James Shea; E-Mail: jms7n@virginia.edu
Library Holdings: Bk Vols 32,384

SCIENCE & ENGINEERING LIBRARY, Clark Hall, 22903-3188. (Mail add: PO Box 400124, 22904-4124), SAN 362-8213. Tel: 804-924-3628. FAX: 804-924-4338. Web Site: www.lib.virginia.edu/science/scilibs/SEL.html. *Dir*, Sandra Kerbel; E-Mail: ssk4k@virginia.edu; *Coordr*, Fred O'Bryant; E-Mail: jfo@virginia.edu; *Coordr*, Heather Packard; E-Mail: has8d@virginia.edu; *Coordr*, Joan Ruelle; E-Mail: jdr9d@virginia.edu
Library Holdings: Bk Vols 293,155

G VIRGINIA DIVISION OF MINERAL RESOURCES LIBRARY, 900 Natural Resource Dr, PO Box 3667, 22903. SAN 317-2481. Tel: 804-951-6354. FAX: 804-951-6365. *Info Res*, John Marr
Library Holdings: Bk Vols 1,200
Subject Interests: Forestry, Geology, Mineral resources for Va

S VIRGINIA TRANSPORTATION RESEARCH COUNCIL LIBRARY, 530 Edgemont Rd, 22903. SAN 376-1940. Tel: 804-293-1959. FAX: 804-293-1990. E-Mail: vtrcmedia@vdot.state.va.us. *Librn*, Angela Andrews
Library Holdings: Bk Vols 15,000; Per Subs 87
Special Collections: Virginia Road & Transportation History

CHATHAM

P PITTSYLVANIA COUNTY PUBLIC LIBRARY, 24 Military Dr, 24531. SAN 362-823X. Tel: 804-432-3271. FAX: 804-432-1405. E-Mail: pittslib@gamewood.net. Web Site: www4.gamewood.net/pittslib. *Dir*, Diane S Adkins; E-Mail: dsadkins@hotmail.com; *Electronic Resources*, Jonathan L Chaney; E-Mail: chaney_jon@hotmail.com; *Ch Servs*, Phyllis S Bryant; E-Mail: pbryant73@hotmail.com; *Acq*, Aubrey Davis; E-Mail: cwoard@yahoo.com; Staff 18 (MLS 1, Non-MLS 17)
Founded 1913. Pop 58,600; Circ 132,781
Jul 1998-Jun 1999 Income (Main Library and Branch Library) $501,029, State $111,571, County $389,458. Mats Exp $81,457, Books $68,783, Per/Ser (Incl. Access Fees) $7,575, AV Equip $3,309, Other Print Mats $1,790. Sal $246,873 (Prof $40,000)
Library Holdings: Bk Vols 81,000; Per Subs 133
Automation Activity & Vendor Info: (Cataloging) TLC; (Circulation) TLC; (OPAC) TLC
Database Vendor: GaleNet
Friends of the Library Group
Branches: 2

BROSVILLE CASCADE PUBLIC, 11948 Martinsville Hwy, Danville, 24541. SAN 321-9232. Tel: 804-685-1285. FAX: 804-685-3347. E-Mail: brosvlib@gamewood.net. Web Site: www4.gamewood.net/pittslib. *Dir*, Diane S Adkins; Tel: 804-432-3271, Fax: 804-432-1405, E-Mail: dsadkins@hotmail.com; *Branch Mgr*, LaVerne Campbell; E-Mail: laverne_brosville@hotmail.com; Staff 3 (Non-MLS 3)
Founded 1992
Friends of the Library Group

GRETNA BRANCH, 207 Coffey St, Gretna, 24557. SAN 362-8264. Tel: 804-656-2579. FAX: 804-656-9030. E-Mail: gretna@dellmail.com. Web Site: www4.gamewood.net/pittslib. *Dir*, Diane S Adkins; Tel: 804-432-3271, Fax: 804-432-1405, E-Mail: dsadkins@hotmail.com; *Branch Mgr*, Woodson Hughes; Staff 4 (Non-MLS 4)
Friends of the Library Group

Bookmobiles: 1

CHESAPEAKE

P CHESAPEAKE PUBLIC LIBRARY, Municipal Center, 298 Cedar Rd, 23322-5598. SAN 362-8299. Tel: 757-382-6579. Circulation Tel: 757-382-6576. Reference Tel: 757-382-6591. TDD: 757-382-8214. FAX: 757-382-8301. Web Site: www.chesapeake.lib.va.us. *Dir*, Margaret P Stillman; E-Mail: mstillma@chesapeake.lib.va.us; *Asst Dir*, Carole L King; Tel: 757-382-6717, E-Mail: cking@chesapeake.lib.va.us; *Mgr*, Charles Anderson; *Senior Librn*, Paula K Alston; Tel: 757-382-6461, Fax: 757-382-8400, E-Mail: palston@chesapeake.lib.va.us; *Ch Servs*, Martha J Cole; Tel: 757-382-8566, Fax: 757-382-8400, E-Mail: mcole@chesapeake.lib.va.us; *Coll Develop*, Debra A Lewis; Tel: 757-382-6567, Fax: 757-382-8400, E-Mail: dlewis@chesapeake.lib.va.us; *Automation Syst Coordr*, James A Pearson; Tel: 757-382-8882, Fax: 757-382-6206, E-Mail: jpearson@cheasapeake.lib.va.us; *Cat*, Joyce Burd; *Cat*, Laurel J Mancini; Tel: 757-382-8138, Fax: 757-382-8400, E-Mail: lmancini@chesapeake.lib.va.us; *Cat*, Jodie A Reha; Tel: 757-382-8588, Fax: 757-382-8400, E-Mail: jreha@chesapeake.lib.va.us; *Branch Mgr*, Stanley R Bustetter; Tel: 757-436-1185, Fax: 757-436-1884, E-Mail: sbustett@chesapeake.lib.va.us; *Branch Mgr*, Susan T Campbell; Tel: 757-382-3620, Fax: 757-382-3622, E-Mail: scampbel@chesapeake.lib.va.us; *Branch Mgr*, Jean A Carideo; Tel: 757-465-0715, Fax: 757-465-1303, E-Mail: jcarideo@chesapeake.lib.va.us; *Branch Mgr*, Janet L Forbes; Tel: 757-420-3433, Fax: 757-523-9452, E-Mail: jforbes@chesapeake.lib.va.us; *Branch Mgr*, Patricia W Jefferson; Tel: 757-545-2437, Fax: 757-545-1299, E-Mail: pjeffers@chesapeake.lib.va.us; *Bkmobile Coordr*, Gregory S Laing; Tel: 757-382-8483, Fax: 757-382-8400, E-Mail: glaing@chesapeake.lib.va.us; Staff 29 (MLS 29)
Founded 1961. Pop 204,470; Circ 1,533,411
Jul 1999-Jun 2000 Income (Main Library and Branch Library) $5,540,479, State $265,493, City $5,274,986. Mats Exp $1,072,243, Books $949,340, Per/Ser (Incl. Access Fees) $55,495, Micro $11,513, Electronic Ref Mat (Incl. Access Fees) $55,895. Sal $3,108,934 (Prof $771,531)
Library Holdings: Bk Vols 643,418; Bk Titles 220,238; Per Subs 1,164
Subject Interests: Family, History, Law
Special Collections: City Records Management; Local Hist (Wallace Memorial Libr Coll), bk, micro
Automation Activity & Vendor Info: (Cataloging) DRA; (Circulation) DRA; (OPAC) DRA

Database Vendor: DRA, Ebsco - EbscoHost, OCLC - First Search
Function: ILL available
Special Services for the Deaf - TDD
Special Services for the Blind - Arkenstone, a computer system for the visually handicapped
Friends of the Library Group
Branches: 5
GREENBRIER, 1214 Volvo Pkwy, 23320-7600. SAN 371-9553. Tel: 757-436-7400. Circulation Tel: 757-436-1080. TDD: 757-436-7400. FAX: 757-436-1884. Web Site: www.chesapeake.lib.va.us. *Branch Mgr*, Stanley R Bustetter; Tel: 757-436-1185, E-Mail: sbustett@chesapeake.lib.va.us
Founded 1992
Library Holdings: Bk Vols 86,491; Bk Titles 36,790
Special Services for the Deaf - TDD
Friends of the Library Group
INDIAN RIVER, 2320 Old Greenbrier Rd, 23325-4916. SAN 362-8353. Tel: 757-420-5804. FAX: 757-523-9452. Web Site: www.chesapeake.lib.va.us. *Branch Mgr*, Janet L Forbes; E-Mail: jforbes@chesapeake.lib.va.us
Founded 1965
Library Holdings: Bk Vols 63,240; Bk Titles 26,087
Friends of the Library Group
MAJOR HILLARD LIBRARY, 824 Old George Washington Hwy N, 23323-2214. SAN 362-8329. Tel: 757-382-3600. Circulation Tel: 757-382-3601. Reference Tel: 757-382-3606. TDD: 757-382-3606. FAX: 757-382-3610. Web Site: www.chesapeake.lib.va.us. *Branch Mgr*, Susan T Campbell; Tel: 757-382-3620, Fax: 757-382-3622, E-Mail: scampbel@chesapeake.lib.va.us; *Librn*, Paula Alston
Founded 1977
Library Holdings: Bk Vols 54,738; Bk Titles 21,652
Special Services for the Deaf - TDD
Friends of the Library Group
RUSSELL MEMORIAL, 2808 Taylor Rd, 23321-2210. SAN 362-8388. Tel: 757-488-9270. Reference Tel: 757-465-0949. TDD: 757-465-0949. FAX: 757-465-1303. Web Site: www.chesapeake.lib.va.us. *Branch Mgr*, Jean A Carideo; Tel: 757-465-0715, E-Mail: jcarideo@chesapeake.lib.va.us
Founded 1968
Library Holdings: Bk Vols 92,685; Bk Titles 33,163
Subject Interests: Family
Special Collections: Dave Smith Poetry Coll
Special Services for the Deaf - TDD
Friends of the Library Group
SOUTH NORFOLK MEMORIAL, 1100 Poindexter St, 23324-2425. SAN 362-8418. Tel: 757-545-2436. FAX: 757-545-1299. Web Site: www.chesapeake.lib.va.us. *Branch Mgr*, Patricia W Jefferson; Tel: 757-545-2437, E-Mail: pjeffers@chesapeake.lib.va.us; *Librn*, Elizabeth Evans
Founded 1958
Library Holdings: Bk Vols 46,111; Bk Titles 19,734
Subject Interests: Family
Special Services for the Blind - Arkenstone, a computer system for the visually handicapped
Friends of the Library Group

CHESTER

J JOHN TYLER COMMUNITY COLLEGE LIBRARY, 13101 Jefferson Davis Hwy, 23831-5399. SAN 317-2503. Tel: 804-796-4068. FAX: 804-796-4238. Web Site: www.jt.cc.va.us/lrtc/libweb/libweb1.htm. *Librn*, Linda Luebke; Tel: 804-796-4070, E-Mail: lluebke@jt.cc.va.us; *Ref*, Peter McTague; Staff 12 (MLS 2, Non-MLS 10)
Founded 1967. Enrl 5,349; Fac 100
Library Holdings: Bk Vols 37,500; Per Subs 104
Partic in Richmond Academic Library Consortium; Richmond Academic Library Consortium; Solinet
Departmental Libraries:
MIDLOTHIAN CAMPUS, 601 Charter Colony Pkwy, Midlothian, 23113. Tel: 804-594-1519. FAX: 804-594-1525. *Librn*, Helen McKann; Tel: 804-594-1523, E-Mail: hmckann@jt.cc.va.us; Staff 5 (MLS 1, Non-MLS 4)
Library Holdings: Bk Vols 10,879; Per Subs 44

CHESTERFIELD

P CHESTERFIELD COUNTY PUBLIC LIBRARY, 9501 Lori Rd, 23832. (Mail add: PO Box 297, 23832-0297), SAN 362-8507. Tel: 804-748-1601. Circulation Tel: 804-748-1774. Reference Tel: 804-748-1603. FAX: 804-751-4679. Web Site: library.co.chesterfield.va.us. *Dir*, Robert E Wagenknecht; E-Mail: wagenknechtr@co.chesterfield.va.us; *Asst Dir*, Hampton Auld; E-Mail: auldh@co.chesterfield.va.us; *Librn*, Barbara A Lattimer; Tel: 804-768-7433, E-Mail: lattimerb@co.chesterfield.va.us; *Mgr*, Phyllis Mortenson; *Tech Coordr*, Alanna S Graboyes; Tel: 804-748-1980, E-Mail: graboyesa@co.chesterfield.va.us; *Cat, Tech Servs*, Carolyn D Dunaway; Tel: 804-748-1763, E-Mail: dunawayc@co.chesterfield.va.us; *Outreach Serv*, Sherie P Orton; Tel: 804-748-1768, E-Mail: ortons@co.chesterfield.va.us; *Admin Assoc*, Julia Lundy; Tel: 804-748-1766, E-Mail: lundyj@co.chesterfield.va.us; *Coll Develop*, Ann C Theis; Tel: 804-748-1760, E-Mail: theisa@co.chesterfield.va.us; Staff 118 (MLS 19, Non-MLS 99)
Founded 1965. Pop 261,000; Circ 2,846,503
Jul 1999-Jun 2000 Income (Main Library and Branch Library) $5,526,3 State $282,337, County $4,782,718, Locally Generated Income $443,32 Other $8,000. Mats Exp $988,607, Books $554,414, Per/Ser (Incl. Acce Fees) $213,251, Presv $2,057, Micro $6,233, AV Equip $146,100, Elect Ref Mat (Incl. Access Fees) $66,552. (Prof $894,564)
Library Holdings: Bk Vols 746,045
Subject Interests: Civil War, Local history, Virginiana
Special Collections: Law Library Coll
Automation Activity & Vendor Info: (Acquisitions) Innovative Interfa Inc.; (Circulation) Innovative Interfaces Inc.; (Serials) Innovative Interfa Inc.
Database Vendor: Ebsco - EbscoHost, GaleNet
Billing address for branches: Central Library, PO Box 297, Chesterfield, 23832
Friends of the Library Group
Branches: 9
BON AIR, 9103 Rattlesnake Rd, Richmond, 23235. SAN 362-8531. Tel: 804-320-2461. *Mgr Libr*, Dawn C Swanson; E-Mail: swansond@co.chesterfield.va.us
Friends of the Library Group
CHESTER BRANCH, 12140 Harrowgate Rd, Chester, 23831. SAN 362-8566. Tel: 804-748-6314. *Librn*, Nancy Van Auken; E-Mail: vanauken co.chesterfield.va.us
Friends of the Library Group
CLOVER HILL, 6701 Deer Run Dr, Midlothian, 23112. SAN 374-6488. Tel: 804-739-7335. *Mgr Libr*, Polly J Duffey; E-Mail: duffeyp@co.chesterfield.va.us
Friends of the Library Group
ENON, 1801 Enon Church Rd, Chester, 23836. SAN 374-6496. Tel: 804 530-3403. *Mgr*, Clara Hart; E-Mail: hartc@co.chesterfield.va.us
Friends of the Library Group
ETTRICK-MATOACA, 4501 River Rd, Petersburg, 23803. SAN 362-85 Tel: 804-526-8087. *Mgr Libr*, Rosa Kearns-Smith; E-Mail: kearns-smit co.chesterfield.va.us
Friends of the Library Group
LA PRADE, 2730 Hicks Rd, Richmond, 23235. SAN 362-8620. Tel: 80 276-7755. *Mgr Libr*, Barbara Fischer; E-Mail: fischerb@co.chesterfield.va.us
Friends of the Library Group
LAW, 9500 Courthouse Rd, 23832. SAN 374-650X. Tel: 804-751-4986. *Librn*, Alice Milner; E-Mail: milnera@co.chesterfield.va.us; *Librn*, Her Robb; E-Mail: robbh@co.chesterfield.va.us
Jul 1999-Jun 2000 Income (Main Library and Branch Library) $138,09 County $28,620, Locally Generated Income $109,474. Mats Exp $55,1 Books $6,284, Per/Ser (Incl. Access Fees) $42,460, Electronic Ref Mat (Incl. Access Fees) $6,391
Friends of the Library Group
MEADOWDALE, 4301 Meadowdale Blvd, Richmond, 23234. SAN 373-9074. Tel: 804-743-4842. *Mgr Libr*, John Twombly; E-Mail: twomblyj co.chesterfield.va.us
Friends of the Library Group
MIDLOTHIAN BRANCH, 521 Coalfield Rd, Midlothian, 23113. SAN 3 8639. Tel: 804-794-7907. *Mgr Libr*, Yvonne Schieberl; E-Mail: schieberly@co.chesterfield.va.us
Friends of the Library Group

CHRISTIANBURG

P MONTGOMERY-FLOYD REGIONAL LIBRARY, 125 Sheltman St, 24073. SAN 319-9223. Tel: 540-382-6965, 540-382-6967 (Admin). FAX: 540-382-6964. Web Site: www.mfrl.org. *Dir*, Anne C Greene; Fax: 540-3 6965, E-Mail: agreene@mfrl.org; *Dir*, Marsha H Hertel; E-Mail: mhertel mfrl.org; *Dir*, June Sayers; E-Mail: jsayers@mfrl.org; *Mgr*, Laura Byler; 540-382-6965, Ext 14, Fax: 540-382-6965; Staff 48 (MLS 4, Non-MLS 4
Founded 1974. Pop 107,000; Circ 480,000
Jul 1998-Jun 1999 Income (Main Library and Branch Library) $1,750,00 State $260,000, County $1,490,000. Mats Exp $328,500, Books $310,000 Per/Ser (Incl. Access Fees) $12,000, Micro $3,500, Electronic Ref Mat (I Access Fees) $3,000. Sal $854,400 (Prof $345,600)
Library Holdings: Bk Vols 164,000; Per Subs 500; High Interest/Low Vocabulary Bk Vols 300; Bks on Deafness & Sign Lang 110
Subject Interests: Genealogy, Local history
Automation Activity & Vendor Info: (Cataloging) SIRSI; (Circulation) SIRSI; (OPAC) SIRSI
Database Vendor: GaleNet, OCLC - First Search
Partic in SWING; Virginia Library & Network Information
Friends of the Library Group
Branches: 2
BLACKSBURG AREA BRANCH, 200 Miller St, Blacksburg, 24060. SA 362-868X. Tel: 540-552-8246. FAX: 540-552-8265. Web Site: www.mfrl.org/. *Head Librn*, Marsha Hertel; E-Mail: mhertel@intranet.mfrl.org
Open Mon-Thurs 9-8, Fri & Sun 1-5, Sat 9-5
JESSIE PETERMAN MEMORIAL, 321 W Main St, Floyd, 24091. SAN 362-871X. Tel: 540-745-2947. FAX: 540-745-4750. Web Site:

www.mfrl.org/. *Head Librn*, Anne Greene; E-Mail: agreene@intranet.mfrl.org
Open Mon 9-5, Tues & Thurs 9-8, Wed & Sat 9-2, Fri 1-5
Bookmobiles: 2

IFTON FORGE

CHESAPEAKE & OHIO HISTORICAL SOCIETY ARCHIVES, C&O Archival Collection, 312 E Ridgeway St, PO Box 79, 24422. SAN 329-1936. Tel: 540-862-0067. FAX: 540-863-9159. E-Mail: cohs@cfw.com. Web Site: www.cohs.org. *Archivist*, Margaret T Whittington
Special Collections: Chesapeake & Ohio Railway, its predecessors, subsidiaries & successors
This is an archives facility dealing with the technological & operational history of a specific railway. The published portion of the collection is small, the archival portion large. It is run as part of a volunteer society that is national in scope with 2500 members

CLIFTON FORGE PUBLIC LIBRARY,* 535 Church St, PO Box 61, 24422-0061. SAN 317-2511. Tel: 540-863-2519. FAX: 540-863-2531. *Dir*, Michael W Armstrong; *Asst Librn*, Gertrude Gibson
Founded 1972. Pop 5,100; Circ 38,153
Library Holdings: Bk Vols 30,000; Per Subs 86

DABNEY S LANCASTER COMMUNITY COLLEGE LIBRARY,* Rte 60W, Box 1000, 24422. SAN 317-252X. Tel: 540-862-4246. FAX: 540-863-2915. Web Site: www.dl.cc.va.us/lrc-home/lrc-pg2.htm. *Dir*, Laurel Reid; E-Mail: dlreidl@dl.cc.va.us
Founded 1964
Library Holdings: Bk Vols 38,979; Bk Titles 35,822; Per Subs 376
Subject Interests: Commun col educ, Forestry, Law enforcement, Nursing
Partic in SE Libr Network

LONIAL HEIGHTS

COLONIAL HEIGHTS PUBLIC LIBRARY,* 1000 Yacht Basin Dr, 23834. SAN 317-2538. Tel: 804-520-9384. FAX: 804-524-8740. E-Mail: chlibrary@bellatlantic.net. *Dir*, Bruce N Hansen; Staff 1 (MLS 1)
Founded 1968. Pop 16,500; Circ 103,710
Library Holdings: Bk Vols 38,017; Per Subs 89

URTLAND

WALTER CECIL RAWLS LIBRARY & MUSEUM, 22511 Main St, PO Box 310, 23837-0310. SAN 362-8744. Tel: 757-653-2821. FAX: 757-653-9374. E-Mail: webmaster@rawlslib.net. Web Site: www.rawlslib.net. *Dir*, Pat Ward; *Asst Dir, Coll Develop*, Beverly B Worsham; *Ch Servs*, Debbie Sutphin; Staff 41 (MLS 3, Non-MLS 38)
Founded 1958. Pop 70,000; Circ 280,754
Jul 2000-Jun 2001 Income (Main Library and Branch Library) $1,457,000. Mats Exp $161,000. Sal $813,000
Library Holdings: Bk Vols 238,056; Per Subs 586
Subject Interests: Genealogy, Local history
Special Collections: Cary Close Memorial Coll (Civil War Reference Materials)
Friends of the Library Group
Branches: 8
SURRY PUBLIC, 11640 Rolfe Hwy, PO Box 337, Surry, 23883. SAN 322-5488. Tel: 757-294-3949. FAX: 757-294-0803. *Librn*, Faye Grandison
Subject Interests: Genealogy
Friends of the Library Group
WAVERLY PUBLIC, 352 W Main St, PO Box 597, Waverly, 23890. SAN 362-8795. Tel: 757-834-2192. FAX: 757-834-2192. *Librn*, Laurie Latham
Friends of the Library Group
CARROLLTON PUBLIC, 14362 New Towne Haven Lane, Carrollton, 23314. SAN 322-5496. Tel: 757-238-2641. FAX: 757-238-3932. *Librn*, Joyce Howard; Staff 4 (Non-MLS 4)
Founded 1984
Friends of the Library Group
CLAREMONT BRANCH, 91 Mancha Ave, Claremont, 23899. SAN 326-8136. Tel: 757-866-8627. FAX: 757-866-8628. *Librn*, Barbara Smith
Friends of the Library Group
ISLE OF WIGHT COUNTY PUBLIC, 255 James St, Smithfield, 23430. SAN 362-8779. Tel: 757-357-2264. FAX: 757-357-0883. *Librn*, Emma Jean Brady
Subject Interests: Genealogy, Local history
Friends of the Library Group
RUTH CAMP-CAMPBELL MEMORIAL, 280 N College Dr, Franklin, 23851. SAN 376-1029. Tel: 757-562-0086, 757-562-4801. FAX: 757-562-0162. *Librn*, Susan Rowsey
Friends of the Library Group
TROXLER MEMORIAL, PO Box 279, Wakefield, 23888. SAN 329-7578. Tel: 757-899-6500. FAX: 757-899-2400. *Librn*, Laurie Latham
Friends of the Library Group
WINDSOR PUBLIC, 18 Duke St, Windsor, 23487. SAN 374-8111. Tel: 757-242-3046, 757-242-3726. FAX: 757-242-3726. *Librn*, Patti Hancock
Friends of the Library Group
Bookmobiles: 1

COVINGTON

P CHARLES P JONES MEMORIAL LIBRARY,* 406 W Riverside St, 24426. SAN 317-2546. Tel: 540-962-3321. FAX: 540-962-8447. *Dir*, Thurman Pugh; *Coll Develop*, Diana Hawkins
Founded 1929. Pop 21,200; Circ 105,352
Jul 1997-Jun 1998 Income $194,000. Mats Exp $40,382, Books $33,600, Per/Ser (Incl. Access Fees) $6,200, Presv $203, Micro $97. Sal $103,177 (Prof $53,909)
Library Holdings: Bk Titles 68,971; Per Subs 119
Books-By-Mail
Friends of the Library Group

CREWE

P NOTTOWAY COUNTY PUBLIC LIBRARIES, (Formerly Nottoway Central Library), 414 Tyler St, 23930. SAN 363-1532. Tel: 804-645-9310. FAX: 804-645-8513. E-Mail: nottlib@tez.net. *Dir*, Nancy Pierce; E-Mail: npierce@tez.net; *Acq*, Lavonna Gibbs; E-Mail: lgibbs@tez.net; *Cat*, Emily Beverly; Staff 6 (MLS 1, Non-MLS 5)
Founded 1940. Pop 17,000; Circ 33,400
Jul 1999-Jun 2000 Income (Main Library and Branch Library) $114,063, State $37,524, County $76,509. Mats Exp $22,579, Per/Ser (Incl. Access Fees) $2,365, AV Equip $1,730, Electronic Ref Mat (Incl. Access Fees) $18,484. Sal $73,029 (Prof $29,612)
Library Holdings: Bk Vols 30,084; Per Subs 67
Subject Interests: Local history
Automation Activity & Vendor Info: (Cataloging) VTLS
Database Vendor: OCLC - First Search
Friends of the Library Group
Branches: 3
BLACKSTONE BRANCH, 415 S Main St, Blackstone, 23824. SAN 363-1567. Tel: 804-292-3587. FAX: 804-292-3587. *Librn*, Joyce Gallone
Friends of the Library Group
BURKEVILLE BRANCH, 116A S Agnew, Burkeville, 23922. SAN 363-1575. Tel: 804-767-4095. FAX: 804-767-2652. E-Mail: burkelib@msn.com. *Librn*, Susan Cope
Friends of the Library Group
CREWE BRANCH, 400 Tyler St, 23930. SAN 363-1591. Tel: 804-645-8688. FAX: 804-645-8688. *Librn*, Susan Howe
Friends of the Library Group

CROZIER

G VIRGINIA DEPARTMENT OF CORRECTIONS, Academy for Staff Development Library,* 1900 River Rd W, 23039. SAN 317-4662. Tel: 804-784-6841. FAX: 804-784-6999. *Librn*, Kelly Delamater; E-Mail: delamaterkc@erols.com; Staff 2 (MLS 1, Non-MLS 1)
Founded 1976
Library Holdings: Bk Vols 7,500; Per Subs 43
Subject Interests: Corrections, Inmate recovery prog, Mgmt, Staff training
Restriction: Open to department staff only
Partic in Solinet

CULPEPER

P CULPEPER COUNTY LIBRARY, 271 Southgate Shopping Ctr, 22701-3215. SAN 317-2562. Tel: 540-825-8691. FAX: 540-825-7486. Web Site: www.tlc.library.net/culpeper. *Dir*, Susan J Keller; *Asst Dir*, Margaret Williams; *Ch Servs*, Diana Cmeyla; Staff 1 (MLS 1)
Founded 1946. Pop 33,083; Circ 207,452
Jul 1999-Jun 2000 Income $548,035, State $66,599, County $371,800, Locally Generated Income $18,000. Mats Exp $82,799, Books $61,599, Per/Ser (Incl. Access Fees) $5,000, Micro $700, Other Print Mats $3,000, Electronic Ref Mat (Incl. Access Fees) $12,500. Sal $259,651 (Prof $51,000)
Library Holdings: Bk Vols 50,000; Per Subs 120
Special Collections: Art Coll; Civil War Coll; Genealogical Coll (Local History), bks, micro
Automation Activity & Vendor Info: (Cataloging) TLC; (Circulation) TLC; (OPAC) TLC
Database Vendor: Ebsco - EbscoHost
Special Services for the Deaf - TTY machine
Friends of the Library Group

CUMBERLAND

P CUMBERLAND COUNTY PUBLIC LIBRARY, 1539 Anderson Hwy, 23040-2516. (Mail add: PO Box 98, 23040-0098), SAN 373-8787. Tel: 804-492-5807. FAX: 804-492-9551. *Dir*, Ann M Kinsey; E-Mail: akinseylva@yahoo.com; *Asst Librn*, Nellie G Glenn; Staff 1 (MLS 1)
Founded 1967. Pop 8,200; Circ 19,356
Jul 1999-Jun 2000 Income $79,773, State $21,715, County $47,000, Locally Generated Income $7,444, Other $3,614. Mats Exp $15,246, Books $13,867, Per/Ser (Incl. Access Fees) $1,379. Sal $43,505 (Prof $20,000)
Library Holdings: Bk Vols 12,820; Per Subs 36
Friends of the Library Group

DAHLGREN

S NAVAL SURFACE WARFARE CENTER DAHLGREN DIVISION, Technical Library,* 17320 Dahlgren Rd Code B60, 22448-5100. SAN 329-3408. Tel: 540-653-8351. FAX: 540-663-7165, 663-2292. E-Mail: infolib@nswc.navy.mil. Web Site: www.nswc.navy.mil/smartlib/library.htm.
Library Holdings: Bk Vols 42,000; Bk Titles 28,000; Per Subs 218
Publications: Info Speak
Partic in DTIC; OCLC Online Computer Library Center, Inc

UNITED STATES NAVY
A DAHLGREN LABORATORY, GENERAL LIBRARY, Naval Surface Warfare Ctr, 22448-5000. SAN 362-8809. Tel: 540-653-7474. *Librn*, Carolyn Bradley
Founded 1954
Library Holdings: Bk Vols 18,000; Per Subs 36
Publications: General Library Newsletter (monthly)
Partic in OCLC Online Computer Library Center, Inc

DANVILLE

C AVERETT COLLEGE, Mary B Blount Library, 344 W Main St, 24541-2849. SAN 317-2570. Tel: 804-791-5691. Circulation Tel: 804-791-5690. Reference Tel: 804-791-5692. FAX: 804-791-5637. E-Mail: aclib@averett.edu. Web Site: library.averett.edu. *Dir*, Elaine L Day; Tel: 804-791-5696, E-Mail: eday@averett.edu; *Admin Assoc*, Charlotte Dodson; E-Mail: cdodson@averett.edu; *Archivist, Ref*, Clara Fountain; Tel: 804-791-5694, E-Mail: claraf@averett.edu; *ILL, Ref*, Kevin Harden; E-Mail: kharden@averett.edu; *Coll Develop*, Inja Hong; *Ref, Tech Servs*, Catherine Villyard. Subject Specialists: *Arts*, Clara Fountain; *Business*, Kevin Harden; *Electronic resources*, Kevin Harden; *Humanities*, Clara Fountain; *Sci tech*, Elaine L Day; *Social sciences*, Kevin Harden; *Systs*, Elaine L Day; Staff 10 (MLS 4, Non-MLS 6)
Founded 1859. Enrl 2,296; Fac 80; Highest Degree: Master
Jul 1999-Jun 2000 Mats Exp $189,250, Books $62,499, Per/Ser (Incl. Access Fees) $49,993, Presv $2,935, Micro $26,910, AV Equip $8,000, Electronic Ref Mat (Incl. Access Fees) $38,913
Library Holdings: Bk Vols 133,009; Bk Titles 127,715; Per Subs 502
Special Collections: Averett Coll; Dan Daniel Archives; Danville Coll
Database Vendor: GaleNet, IAC - Info Trac, IAC - SearchBank, Lexis-Nexis, OCLC - First Search, OVID Technologies, ProQuest
Partic in OCLC Online Computer Library Center, Inc; Solinet; SWING; VIVA/VICULA

S DAN RIVER INC, Research Library,* PO Box 261, 24543. SAN 317-2589. Tel: 804-799-4874, 804-799-7133. FAX: 804-799-4834.
Founded 1946
Library Holdings: Bk Vols 1,000; Per Subs 50
Subject Interests: Chemistry, Textiles

J DANVILLE COMMUNITY COLLEGE, Whittington W Clement Learning Resources Center, 1008 S Main St, 24541-4004. SAN 317-2597. Tel: 804-797-8555. FAX: 007791790415. Web Site: www.dc.cc.va.us/lrc2/lrc/lrc2.htm. *Dir*, William L Dey; E-Mail: wdey@dc.cc.va.us; Staff 8 (MLS 2, Non-MLS 6)
Founded 1968. Enrl 2,010; Fac 51
Jul 1999-Jun 2000 Mats Exp $80,000, Books $54,000, Per/Ser (Incl. Access Fees) $14,500, Presv $500, Micro $6,000, AV Equip $5,000
Library Holdings: Bk Vols 47,151; Bk Titles 42,341; Per Subs 225; Bks on Deafness & Sign Lang 50
Subject Interests: Local history
Automation Activity & Vendor Info: (Circulation) NOTIS
Database Vendor: Ebsco - EbscoHost, OCLC - First Search
Partic in OCLC Online Computer Library Center, Inc; SE Libr Network

P DANVILLE PUBLIC LIBRARY,* 511 Patton St, 24541. SAN 317-2600. Tel: 804-799-5195. FAX: 804-799-5221. E-Mail: library5@ci.danville.va.us. *Dir*, Denise Johnson; *Acq, Ref*, Florence Archer; *Ch Servs*, Carolyn Shelhorse; Staff 14 (MLS 4, Non-MLS 10)
Founded 1923. Pop 53,056; Circ 273,642 Sal $8,153
Library Holdings: Bk Vols 119,500
Subject Interests: Genealogy, Local history
Friends of the Library Group

Branches: 2
LAW Tel: 804-799-5118. FAX: 804-799-5118. *Librn*, Rebecca Webb
Founded 1987. Pop 53,056
Library Holdings: Bk Vols 25,300; Bk Titles 300
Restriction: Non-circulating to the public
WESTOVER, 3157 Westover Dr, 24541. SAN 378-1496. Tel: 804-799-5
Librn, D Johnson

M DANVILLE REGIONAL MEDICAL CENTER, Ralph R Landes Medica Library, 142 S Main St, 24541. SAN 317-2619. Tel: 804-799-4418. FAX 804-799-2255. Web Site: www.danvilleregional.org/medlib. *Librn*, Ann B Sasser; E-Mail: sassera@drmc.drhsi.org
Library Holdings: Bk Vols 1,000; Per Subs 125
Publications: RRLibrary Briefs (newsletter); Southside Virginia's Medw
Restriction: By appointment only

DAYTON

S HARRISONBURG-ROCKINGHAM HISTORICAL SOCIETY LIBRAR 382 High St, 22821. (Mail add: PO Box 716, 22821), SAN 327-8719. Te 540-879-2616. FAX: 540-879-2616. E-Mail: heritag1@shentel.net. *In Charge*, Faye Witters
Library Holdings: Bk Vols 1,100
Subject Interests: Genealogy

DILLWYN

S BUCKINGHAM CORRECTIONAL CENTER, DCE Library, Rte 20, Bo 430, 23936-0430. SAN 371-6139. Tel: 804-983-3011, Ext 329.; Staff 2 (MLS 1, Non-MLS 1)
Founded 1983
Library Holdings: Bk Titles 6,000

S DILLWYN CORRECTIONAL CENTER, DCE Library, Rte 20, Box 670 23936. SAN 375-3387. Tel: 804-983-5034, Ext 1713, 804-983-5034, Ext 1733. FAX: 804-983-1821. *Librn*, Steve Sarazin; Staff 1 (MLS 1)
Founded 1994
Library Holdings: Bk Titles 8,000; Per Subs 31

DUBLIN

J NEW RIVER COMMUNITY COLLEGE, Learning Resource Center,* R 100, PO Drawer 1127, 24084-1127. SAN 317-2627. Tel: 540-674-3600. FAX: 540-674-3626. Web Site: nr.cc.va.us/delr/lis/lishome.htm. *Circ*, Gary Bryant; *Media Spec*, Sandra Smith; *Ref*, Geraldine Mattern; *ILL, Tech Ser* Nadine Shenk; *Coll Develop*, Roberta S White; Staff 6 (MLS 3, Non-ML 3)
Founded 1968. Enrl 2,230; Fac 60
Jul 1997-Jun 1998 Income $306,846. Mats Exp $72,315, Books $38,463, Per/Ser (Incl. Access Fees) $10,884, Micro $14,691. Sal $178,694
Library Holdings: Bk Vols 34,495; Bk Titles 29,185; Per Subs 406
Subject Interests: Education, History, Humanities, Para-med
Special Holdings: High interest/low vocabulary bk vols 300; Bks on deafness & sign language 250

DUNN LORING

S NATIONAL PEST CONTROL ASSOCIATION LIBRARY,* 8100 Oak S 22027. SAN 328-3100. Tel: 703-573-8330. FAX: 703-573-4116. Web Site: www.pestworld.org. *In Charge*, Cindy Kennedy
Library Holdings: Bk Vols 2,000

EDINBURG

P SHENANDOAH COUNTY LIBRARY, 514 Stoney Creek Blvd, 22824. SAN 322-662X. Tel: 540-984-8200. Reference Tel: 540-984-8200, Ext 20 FAX: 540-984-8207. E-Mail: scl@shentel.net. Web Site: www.shenandoah.co.lib.va.us. *Dir*, David L Steinberg; Tel: 540-984-8200, Ext 206, E-Mail: dls_scl@shentel.net; *Asst Dir*, Cathy J Stuter; Tel: 540-984-8200, Ext 205, E-Mail: cjs_scl@shentel.net; *Publ Servs*, Jennifer M Heelen; Tel: 540-984-8200, Ext 207, E-Mail: jmh_scl@shentel.net; *Archiv* Karen G Cooper; Tel: 540-984-8200, Ext 208, E-Mail: kgc_scl@shentel.ne *Tech Coordr*, John R Cole; Tel: 540-984-8200, Ext 202, E-Mail: jrc_scl@schentel.net; *Asst Librn*, Carol A Fields; Tel: 540-984-8200, Ext 204, E-Mail: caf_scld@shentel.net; *Asst Librn*, Nancy R Webster; Tel: 540-984-8200, Ext 203, E-Mail: nrw_scl@shentel.net. Subject Specialists: *Automation*, John R Cole; *Genealogy*, Karen G Cooper; *Local history*, Kar G Cooper; *Programs*, Jennifer M Heelen; Staff 7 (MLS 1, Non-MLS 6)
Founded 1984. Pop 36,000; Circ 126,956
2000-2001 Income $424,244, State $87,557, County $302,156, Locally Generated Income $8,000, Other $24,531. Mats Exp $104,324, Books $47,824, Per/Ser (Incl. Access Fees) $5,000, Micro $2,000, Manuscripts & Archives $2,000, Electronic Ref Mat (Incl. Access Fees) $20,000. Sal $225,146
Library Holdings: Bk Vols 66,000; Bk Titles 60,000; Per Subs 125; Spec Interest Per Sub 15

Subject Interests: Civil War, Maryland, Shenandoah County, Shenandoah Valley, Virginia, West Virginia
Special Collections: Shenandoah Room Coll
Automation Activity & Vendor Info: (Cataloging) TLC; (Circulation) TLC; (OPAC) TLC
Database Vendor: Ebsco - EbscoHost, ProQuest
Partic in Shenandoah County Libr Syst
Special Services for the Blind - Bks on tape
Friends of the Library Group

ORY

EMORY & HENRY COLLEGE, Frederick T Kelly Library, PO Box 947, 24327. SAN 317-2643. Tel: 540-944-4121. FAX: 540-944-4592. Web Site: www.ehc.edu. *Dir*, Lorraine Abraham; *Asst Dir*, Jane Caldwell; *Tech Servs*, Janet Kirby; *ILL*, Patty Greany; *Media Spec*, Claudine Daniel; Staff 4 (MLS 4)
Founded 1836. Enrl 842; Fac 57; Highest Degree: Bachelor
Library Holdings: Bk Vols 392,000; Bk Titles 200,000; Per Subs 1,079
Subject Interests: Liberal arts
Special Collections: Appalachian Oral History Coll; Methodist Church History (I P Martin Coll); Southwestern Virginiana (Goodrich Wilson Papers)
Publications: Semaphore
Partic in Dialog Corporation; SE Libr Network

RFAX

AMERICAN MANAGEMENT SYSTEMS LIBRARY,* 4050 Legato Rd, 22033. SAN 377-5682. Tel: 703-267-5002. FAX: 703-267-5094. *Dir*, Nancy Gregory
Library Holdings: Bk Vols 4,000; Bk Titles 3,500

FAIRFAX COUNTY PUBLIC LIBRARY, Administrative Offices,* 12000 Government Ctr Pkwy, Ste 324, 22035. SAN 363-3578. Tel: 703-324-3100. Interlibrary Loan Service Tel: 703-222-3136. FAX: 703-222-3193. E-Mail: wwwlib@co.fairfax.va.us. Web Site: www.co.fairfax.va.us/library. *Dir*, Edwin S Clay III; *Dep Dir*, Judy Anderson; *Assoc Dir*, Marianne Gearhart; *Assoc Dir*, Vera Fessler; *Assoc Dir*, Jane Goodwin; *Publ Servs*, Lois Kirkpatrick; *Acq, Coll Develop*, Julie Pringle; *Cat*, Betsy Keefe; *Br Coordr*, Reed Coats. Subject Specialists: *Human resources*, Jan Prasher; *Internet*, Lydia Patrick; Staff 198 (MLS 198)
Founded 1939
Jul 1998-Jun 1999 Income $25,796,130, State $613,498, City $547,726, County $23,239,550, Locally Generated Income $1,395,356. Mats Exp $7,153,186, Books $5,385,500, Per/Ser (Incl. Access Fees) $674,639, Micro $1,089,569, Other Print Mats $3,478. Sal $15,806,521
Library Holdings: Bk Vols 2,300,000
Subject Interests: Bus, Large print bks
Special Collections: Virginia History Coll
Publications: Books & Beyond: Fairfax County Public Library's First Fifty Years; Collection Development; Fairfax County Public Library; Fairfax County Public Library Board of Trustees Policy Manual; Fairfax County Public Library User Study; Information Services Guidelines; Information Services Profile; Materials Availability Study; Page Training Manual; Problem Behavior Manual; Reference Accuracy at the Fairfax County Public Library; Training Checklist for Circulation Staff; Training Checklist for Information Services Staff
Partic in Metrop Wash Libr Coun
Special Services for the Deaf - TTY machine
Access Services for people with disabilities. Tel: 703-324-8380; Fax 703-324-8386
Friends of the Library Group
Branches: 19

RICHARD BYRD BRANCH, 7250 Commerce St, Springfield, 22150. SAN 363-3969. Tel: 703-451-8055. FAX: 703-451-2405. Web Site: www.co.fairfax.va.us/library. *Mgr*, Peggy Cope
Library Holdings: Bk Vols 61,000
Friends of the Library Group

CENTREVILLE REGIONAL BRANCH, 14200 Saint Germaine Dr, Centreville, 20121. SAN 363-3667. Tel: 703-830-2223. FAX: 703-830-0971. Web Site: www.co.fairfax.va.us/library. *Mgr*, Dave Bennett
Library Holdings: Bk Vols 143,000
Friends of the Library Group

CHANTILLY REGIONAL, 4000 Stringfellow Rd, Chantilly, 20151. SAN 374-7255. Tel: 703-502-3883. FAX: 703-817-0326. Web Site: www.co.fairfax.va.us/library. *Mgr*, Martha Ray
Library Holdings: Bk Vols 168,000
Friends of the Library Group

FAIRFAX CITY REGIONAL BRANCH, 3915 Chain Bridge Rd, 22030. SAN 363-3632. Tel: 703-246-2281. FAX: 703-385-6977. Web Site: www.co.fairfax.va.us/library. *Mgr*, Suzanne Rehder
Library Holdings: Bk Vols 194,000
Subject Interests: Genealogy, Music, Va hist
Friends of the Library Group

GREAT FALLS BRANCH, 9818A Georgetown Pike, Great Falls, 22066. SAN 363-3764. Tel: 703-759-4750. FAX: 703-759-3472. Web Site: www.co.fairfax.va.us/library. *Mgr*, Nadia Taran
Library Holdings: Bk Vols 17,000

PATRICK HENRY BRANCH, 101 Maple Ave E, Vienna, 22180. SAN 363-390X. Tel: 703-938-0405. FAX: 703-938-1612. Web Site: www.co.fairfax.va.us/library. *Mgr*, Carolyn Koehler
Library Holdings: Bk Vols 110,000
Friends of the Library Group

HERNDON FORTNIGHTLY BRANCH, 768 Center St, Herndon, 20170. SAN 363-3780. Tel: 703-437-8855. FAX: 703-707-9459. Web Site: www.co.fairfax.va.us/library. *Mgr*, DeDe Pruett
Library Holdings: Bk Vols 62,000
Friends of the Library Group

THOMAS JEFFERSON BRANCH, 7415 Arlington Blvd, Falls Church, 22042. SAN 363-4027. Tel: 703-573-1061. FAX: 703-573-0432. Web Site: www.co.fairfax.va.us/library. *Mgr*, Phyllis Ray
Library Holdings: Bk Vols 83,000
Friends of the Library Group

KINGS PARK, 9000 Burke Lake Rd, Burke, 22015. SAN 363-3845. Tel: 703-978-5600. FAX: 703-978-1745. Web Site: www.co.fairfax.va.us/library. *Mgr*, Rita Toscano
Library Holdings: Bk Vols 115,000
Friends of the Library Group

LORTON BRANCH, 9520 Richmond Hwy, Lorton, 22079. SAN 363-3853. Tel: 703-339-7385. FAX: 703-339-7415. Web Site: www.co.fairfax.va.us/library. *Mgr*, Pat White-Williams
Library Holdings: Bk Vols 56,000
Friends of the Library Group

DOLLEY MADISON BRANCH, 1244 Oak Ridge Ave, McLean, 22101. SAN 363-3691. Tel: 703-356-0770. FAX: 703-734-2758. Web Site: www.co.fairfax.va.us/library. *Mgr*, Carolyn Heyer
Library Holdings: Bk Vols 73,000
Friends of the Library Group

JOHN MARSHALL BRANCH, 6209 Rose Hill Dr, Alexandria, 22310. SAN 363-3810. Tel: 703-971-0010. FAX: 703-922-7263. Web Site: www.co.fairfax.va.us/library. *Mgr*, Evelyn Winkels
Library Holdings: Bk Vols 84,000
Friends of the Library Group

GEORGE MASON REGIONAL, 7001 Little River Tpk, Annandale, 22003. SAN 363-3756. Tel: 703-256-3800. FAX: 703-658-0961. Web Site: www.co.fairfax.va.us/library. *Mgr*, Paula Grundset
Library Holdings: Bk Vols 171,000
Friends of the Library Group

POHICK REGIONAL, 6450 Sydenstricker Rd, Burke, 22015. SAN 328-798X. Tel: 703-644-7333. FAX: 703-644-4035. Web Site: www.co.fairfax.va.us/library. *Mgr*, Elizabeth Waller
Library Holdings: Bk Vols 195,000
Friends of the Library Group

RESTON REGIONAL BRANCH, 11925 Bowman Towne Dr, Reston, 20190. SAN 363-3934. Tel: 703-689-2700. FAX: 703-787-8832. Web Site: www.co.fairfax.va.us/library. *Branch Mgr*, Nadia Taran; E-Mail: ntaran@co.fairfax.va.us; Staff 70 (MLS 14, Non-MLS 56)
Founded 1974. Pop 60,000
Library Holdings: Bk Vols 184,812
Friends of the Library Group

SHERWOOD REGIONAL, 2501 Sherwood Hall Lane, Alexandria, 22306. SAN 363-3993. Tel: 703-765-3645. FAX: 703-768-6909. Web Site: www.co.fairfax.va.us/library. *Mgr*, Liz Promen
Library Holdings: Bk Vols 162,000
Friends of the Library Group

TYSONS-PIMMIT REGIONAL, 7584 Leesburg Pike, Falls Church, 22043. SAN 363-4051. Tel: 703-790-8088. FAX: 703-448-9651. Web Site: www.co.fairfax.va.us/library. *Mgr*, Tina Cunningham
Library Holdings: Bk Vols 155,000
Friends of the Library Group

MARTHA WASHINGTON BRANCH, 6614 Fort Hunt Rd, Alexandria, 22307. SAN 363-387X. Tel: 703-768-6700. FAX: 703-768-9316. Web Site: www.co.fairfax.va.us/library. *Mgr*, Barbara Rice
Library Holdings: Bk Vols 78,000
Friends of the Library Group

WOODROW WILSON BRANCH, 6101 Knollwood Dr, Falls Church, 22041. SAN 363-4086. Tel: 703-820-8774. FAX: 703-820-6085. Web Site: www.co.fairfax.va.us/library. *Mgr*, Bonnie Worcester
Library Holdings: Bk Vols 68,000
Friends of the Library Group
Bookmobiles: 1

GL FAIRFAX LAW LIBRARY,* 4110 Chain Bridge Rd, 22030. SAN 321-8384. Tel: 703-246-2170. FAX: 703-359-6003. *Dir*, Bobbie J Denny
Founded 1970
Library Holdings: Bk Vols 35,000; Per Subs 50
Subject Interests: Law
Special Collections: Virginia Law

Publications: Brochure; Divorce PathFinder; Orientation handout with holdings
Partic in Dialog Corporation; Westlaw

C GEORGE MASON UNIVERSITY LIBRARIES, Fenwick Library, 4400 University Dr MSN 2 FL, 22030-4444. SAN 362-8833. Tel: 703-993-2250. TDD: 703-993-2210. FAX: 703-993-2200. Web Site: library.gmu.edu. *Chief Librn*, John Zenelis; Tel: 703-993-2223; *Coll Develop*, John Walsh; *Publ Servs*, Craig Gibson; *Tech Coordr*, Wally Grotophorst; *Assoc Librn*, Ruth Kifer; Staff 111 (MLS 37, Non-MLS 74)
Founded 1957. Enrl 23,408; Highest Degree: Doctorate
Jul 1999-Jun 2000 Income $8,938,500. Mats Exp $5,266,080, Books $1,641,028. Sal $4,188,324 (Prof $1,916,000)
Library Holdings: Bk Titles 702,982; Per Subs 7,187
Special Collections: Alexander Haight Civil War Coll; C Harrison Mann Papers & Map Coll; Congressional Papers of Joel T Broyhill; Early 20C Women's Magazines; Francis McNamara Papers; George Mason University Archives; Joseph E Fisher, Stanford E Parris & William L Scott; Milton C Barnes Civil War Papers; Northern Virginia Oral History Project; Papers of the Pioneer American Society; Photograph Collections of Ollie Atkins & Arthur Scott; Planned Community Archives; Rare Books; Robert Breen Papers (American National Theatre & Academy); Sophocles Papers Music Coll; The WPA Arts Project Oral History Coll; Theatre of the 1930s; Virginia & Regional History; Virginia Maps & Paints
Publications: Newsletter (Fulltext); Research Guides
Function: Research library
Partic in Association Of Southeastern Research Libraries (ASERL); CRL; OCLC Online Computer Library Center, Inc; Virtual Libr of Va
Special Services for the Deaf - TTY machine
Special Services for the Blind - VisualTek closed circuit TV reading aid
Friends of the Library Group
Departmental Libraries:
CL SCHOOL OF LAW LIBRARY, 3401 N Fairfax Dr, Arlington, 22201. SAN 362-8906. Tel: 703-993-8106. FAX: 703-993-8113. Web Site: www.law.gmu.edu/libtech. *Dir*, Deborah Keene; *Assoc Dir*, Rae Ellen Best; *Assoc Dir*, Allen Moye; *Publ Servs*, Femi Cadmus; *Publ Servs*, Marilyn Estes; *Publ Servs*, Iva Futrell; *Publ Servs*, Meghan McGee; *Publ Servs*, Ann Ribstein; *Tech Servs*, Roger Skalbeck
1999-2000 Income $1,765,800. Mats Exp $897,300, Books $50,000, Per/Ser (Incl. Access Fees) $599,685, Micro $30,000. Sal $880,150 (Prof $430,800)
Library Holdings: Bk Vols 391,771; Per Subs 5,475

S ICF CONSULTING, INC, 9300 Lee Hwy, 22031-1207. SAN 329-2843. Tel: 703-934-3088. FAX: 703-934-3101. *Mgr Libr Serv*, Susan G Press; E-Mail: susanpress@icfconsulting.com; *Online Servs*, Mary D Clark; E-Mail: maryclark@icfconsulting.com; *ILL*, Nancy E Abbott; Tel: 703-934-3091, E-Mail: nabbott@icfconsulting.com; Staff 4 (MLS 2, Non-MLS 2)
Jan 2000-Dec 2000 Income Parent Institution $169,000. Sal $167,000 (Prof $113,000)
Library Holdings: Bk Titles 3,000; Per Subs 250
Subject Interests: Econ analysis, Energy, Engineering, Environ, Health, Toxicology
Database Vendor: Dialog, Lexis-Nexis
Restriction: By appointment only
Function: ILL available
Partic in Capcon Library Network; Dialog Corporation; Dow Jones News Retrieval

S MANTECH INTERNATIONAL CORP, Information Center,* 12015 Lee Jackson Hwy, Ste 100, 22033. SAN 328-4107. Tel: 703-218-6000, 703-218-6070. FAX: 703-218-6068. Web Site: www.mantech.com. *Librn*, Eileen Ward; E-Mail: eileen.ward@mantech.com
Library Holdings: Bk Vols 800
Partic in ASIS

S MOBIL CORP, Office of General Counsel-Legal Information Center,* 3225 Gallows Rd Rm 4C110, 22037. SAN 311-8967. Tel: 703-846-2821. FAX: 703-846-1476. *Librn*, Sandra L Dokachav; *Asst Librn*, Anne Salzberg
Library Holdings: Bk Vols 50,000; Per Subs 200
Partic in Am Asn of Law Librs; Law Libr Soc of DC

S MOBIL CORPORATION, Information Services,* 3225 Gallows Rd, Rm 7D0620, 22037. SAN 377-4724. Tel: 703-846-1024. FAX: 703-846-1044.
1997-1998 Mats Exp $400,000
Library Holdings: Bk Vols 350; Per Subs 65
Partic in Spec Libr Asn

S NATIONAL INSTITUTE FOR PUBLIC POLICY LIBRARY,* 3031 Javier Rd, Ste 300, 22031. SAN 327-2443. Tel: 703-698-0563. FAX: 703-698-0566. *Librn*, Karen Lynd
Library Holdings: Bk Vols 2,500; Per Subs 70

S NATIONAL RIFLE ASSOCIATION, ILA Library,* NRA/ILA Library, 11250 Waples Mill Rd, 22030. SAN 302-7325. Tel: 703-267-3859. FAX: 703-267-3980. *Librn*, Richard Wahl
Library Holdings: Bk Vols 5,500; Per Subs 75
Restriction: Not open to public

L ODIN, FELDMAN & PITTLEMAN LIBRARY, 9302 Lee Hwy, Ste 11(22031. SAN 377-3892. Tel: 703-218-2100, 703-218-2362. FAX: 703-21 2160. *Librn*, Laura Raymond; E-Mail: lraymond@ofplaw.com
Library Holdings: Bk Vols 10,000; Per Subs 30
Partic in Am Asn of Law Librs; Law Libr Soc of DC; VA Law Librs As

S UNITED NEGRO COLLEGE FUND, INC, Department of Archives & History,* 8260 Willow Oaks Corporate Dr, PO Box 10444, 22031. SAN 374-762X. Tel: 703-205-3504. FAX: 703-205-3507.
Library Holdings: Bk Vols 100
Special Collections: African-American Information; Micro, 1944-65; Records, 1944 to present
Restriction: By appointment only

FALLS CHURCH

S CENTER FOR HEALTH, ENVIRONMENT & JUSTICE,* 150 S Washington St, 22046. SAN 374-5864. Tel: 703-237-2249. FAX: 703-23 8389. E-Mail: cchw@essential.org. Web Site: www.essential.org/cchw. *L* Barbara Sullivan; *Tech Servs*, Stephen Lester
Founded 1981
Library Holdings: Per Subs 2,000
Friends of the Library Group

S CORTANA CORP LIBRARY,* 520 N Washington St, Ste 200, 22046. SAN 373-2592. Tel: 703-534-8000. FAX: 703-534-8005. *Actg Librn*, Marjorie Moore
Library Holdings: Bk Vols 2,000; Per Subs 100

S JOHN H HAMPSHIRE RESEARCH & REFERENCE LIBRARY,* 803 Broad St Ste 600, 22046. SAN 323-4320. Tel: 703-538-1614. FAX: 703-534-8307. E-Mail: info@awci.org. Web Site: www.awci.org. *Dir, Tech Se* Lee G Jones
Library Holdings: Bk Vols 2,000; Per Subs 75
Subject Interests: Drywall, Exterior, Finishing, Fireproofing, Hist presv, Insulation, Lightweight steel, Plaster

M INOVA FAIRFAX HOSPITAL,* 3300 Gallows Rd, 22042-3300. SAN 3 2767. Tel: 703-698-3234. FAX: 703-698-3353. *Dir*, Alice J Sheridan
Founded 1966
Subject Interests: Health care, Medicine, Nursing
Partic in Dialog Corporation; Nat Libr of Med

S NORTH AMERICAN TIDDLYWINKS ASSOCIATION, Archives Libra PO Box 1701, 22041-0701. SAN 326-6168. Tel: 703-671-7098, 703-883-6731. Web Site: www.tiddlywinks.org. *Librn*, Richard W Tucker; E-Mail: ricktucker@alum.mit.edu
Founded 1978
Library Holdings: Bk Titles 50
Special Collections: Antique Games; Clippings; Patent Copies
Publications: Lexicon of Tiddlywinks; Newswink (newsletter); Tiddlywir Bibliography
Restriction: Staff use only

S RAYTHEON SYSTEMS, Falls Church Information Center,* 7700 Arling Blvd, 22042-2900. SAN 317-2759. Tel: 703-876-1972. FAX: 703-849-15
Library Holdings: Bk Vols 300; Per Subs 43
Subject Interests: Aerospace, Communications, Develop of electronic warfare, Eng res, Ordnance electronic systs, Production of electronic warfare, Sci res
Special Collections: Military Standards & Specifications, Industry Standards, on-line
Automation Activity & Vendor Info: (Acquisitions) EOS; (Cataloging) EOS; (Circulation) EOS; (Serials) EOS

L REED, SMITH, HAZEL & THOMAS, Law Library, 3110 Fairview Park Ste 1400, 22042. (Mail add: PO Box 12001, 22042-0681), SAN 372-3348 Tel: 703-641-4200, 703-641-4332. FAX: 703-641-4340. Web Site: www.reedsmith.com. *Librn*, Charles Mann; *Asst Librn*, Anne Salzberg
Library Holdings: Bk Vols 10,000; Per Subs 250

P MARY RILEY STYLES PUBLIC LIBRARY, 120 N Virginia Ave, 22046 SAN 317-2783. Tel: 703-248-5030. Reference Tel: 703-248-5035. TDD: 703-248-5009. FAX: 703-248-5144. Web Site: www.falls-church.lib.va.us. *Dir*, Mary McMahon; Tel: 703-248-5032, E-Mail: mcmahon@falls-church.falls-church.lib.va.us; *Tech Servs*, Susan Tarakemah; Tel: 703-248-5222, E-Mail: tarakemah@falls-church.falls-church.lib.va.us; *Ad Servs, Re* Josephine C Murphy; E-Mail: murphy@falls-church.falls-church.lib.va.us; *Ch Servs, YA Servs*, Julie Ramsay; E-Mail: ramsay@falls-church.falls-church.lib.va.us; *Media Spec*, Chung Ahn; E-Mail: ahn@falls-church.falls-church.lib.va.us; *Syst Coordr*, Lynn Stewart; E-Mail: stewart@falls-church.falls-church.lib.va.us; Staff 29 (MLS 8, Non-MLS 21)
Founded 1898. Pop 9,789; Circ 315,882
Jul 2000-Jun 2001 Income $1,340,892, State $252,858, City $1,088,034. Mats Exp $196,463, Books $113,870, Per/Ser (Incl. Access Fees) $18,623, Micro $8,710, AV Equip $15,000, Electronic Ref Mat (Incl. Access Fees) $40,260. Sal $833,978
Library Holdings: Bk Vols 159,514; Bk Titles 129,479; Per Subs 301

Special Collections: Falls Church Coll
Automation Activity & Vendor Info: (Acquisitions) GEAC; (Cataloging) GEAC; (Circulation) GEAC; (OPAC) GEAC; (Serials) GEAC
Function: ILL limited, Photocopies available, Some telephone reference

UNITED STATES ARMED FORCES, Office of the Army Surgeon General Medical Library, Skyline 6, Rm 670, 5109 Leesburg Pike, 22041-3258. SAN 302-7457. Tel: 703-681-8028. FAX: 703-681-8034.
Founded 1969
Library Holdings: Bk Titles 12,000; Per Subs 430
Subject Interests: Hospital administration
Special Collections: Annual Report of the Surgeon General 1818-present
Publications: Current Awareness References
Partic in Dialog Corporation; Fedlink; Medline; OCLC Online Computer Library Center, Inc

RMVILLE

CENTRAL VIRGINIA REGIONAL LIBRARY,* 217 W Third St, 23901. SAN 371-6791. Tel: 804-392-6924. FAX: 804-392-9784. *Dir*, Peggy Epperson; Staff 2 (MLS 2)
Founded 1993. Pop 30,193; Circ 70,500
Jul 1996-Jun 1997 Income $170,000. Mats Exp $36,000. Sal $91,878 (Prof $48,612)
Library Holdings: Bk Vols 49,000; Per Subs 83
Subject Interests: Local history
Automation Activity & Vendor Info: (Circulation) Sagebrush Corporation
Special Services for the Deaf - Books on deafness & sign language; Captioned film depository; High interest/low vocabulary books
Friends of the Library Group
Branches: 1
BUCKINGHAM COUNTY PUBLIC, Rte 41B, Box 530, Dillwyn, 23936. SAN 373-7063. Tel: 804-983-3848. FAX: 804-983-1587. *Librn*, Sarah Parker-Southhall
Founded 1983
Friends of the Library Group

LONGWOOD COLLEGE LIBRARY,* Redford & Pine, 23909. SAN 317-283X. Tel: 804-395-2083, 804-395-2633. FAX: 804-395-2453. Web Site: web.lwc.edu/administrative/library/library.htm. *Dir*, Dr Calvin J Boyer
Founded 1839. Enrl 3,300; Fac 157; Highest Degree: Master
Jul 1997-Jun 1998 Income $1,594,575. Mats Exp $793,795. Sal $800,800
Library Holdings: Bk Vols 305,316; Per Subs 1,925
Automation Activity & Vendor Info: (Cataloging) VTLS; (Circulation) VTLS
Partic in Alanet; BRS; Dialog Corporation; Dow Jones News Retrieval; OCLC Online Computer Library Center, Inc; SE Libr Network; Source; Specialnet; Wilsonline

RRUM

FERRUM COLLEGE, Thomas Stanley Library, PO Box 1000, 24088-9015. SAN 317-2848. Tel: 540-365-4426. Interlibrary Loan Service Tel: 540-365-4420. FAX: 540-365-4423. Web Site: www.ferrumlibrary.net. *Dir*, C I Dillon; E-Mail: cdillon@ferrum.edu; *AV*, Gary Evans; *Cat*, Peggie Barker; *ILL*, Cheryl Hundley; *Ref*, George Loveland; Staff 5 (MLS 3, Non-MLS 2)
Founded 1913. Enrl 900; Highest Degree: Bachelor
Jul 1999-Jun 2000 Income $450,000. Mats Exp $124,500, Books $65,000, Per/Ser (Incl. Access Fees) $34,000, Presv $8,500, Micro $11,000, AV Equip $8,500. Sal $191,000
Library Holdings: Bk Vols 115,000; Per Subs 550
Subject Interests: Environmental studies, History, Relig studies
Special Collections: Archives of Governor & Mrs Thomas B Stanley
Partic in OCLC Online Computer Library Center, Inc; SE Libr Network; Virginia Library & Information Network

SHERSVILLE

AUGUSTA COUNTY LIBRARY,* Rte 2, Box 600, 22939. SAN 317-2856. Tel: 540-885-3961, 540-949-6354. FAX: 540-943-5965. Web Site: www.lib.co.augusta.va.us/. *Librn*, Barbara Burdette; *Asst Librn*, Diantha McCauley; *Coll Develop, Ref*, Barbara Olsen; Staff 3 (MLS 3)
Founded 1977. Pop 60,000; Circ 391,962
Library Holdings: Bk Titles 152,000
Publications: Newsletter (quarterly)
Friends of the Library Group

RK UNION

FLUVANNA COUNTY LIBRARY,* PO Box 548, 23055. SAN 317-378X. Tel: 804-842-2230. FAX: 804-842-2230. *Librn*, Marcia Drane
Founded 1968. Pop 17,000; Circ 103,249
Library Holdings: Bk Titles 41,553; Per Subs 180
Subject Interests: Genealogy, Local history
Special Collections: Art Club Coll; Fluvanna County Historical Society Coll; Gardening & Flower Arranging (Fluvanna Garden Club)
Friends of the Library Group

FORT BELVOIR

G DEFENSE TECHNICAL INFORMATION CENTER, Inhouse Technical Library,* 8725 John J Kingman Rd, Ste 944, 22060-6218. SAN 317-199X. Tel: 703-767-8180. FAX: 703-767-8228. *Librn*, Rusty Delorie; E-Mail: rdelorie@dtic.mil; Staff 2 (MLS 1, Non-MLS 1)
Founded 1958
Oct 1998-Sep 1999 Mats Exp $91,500, Books $22,000, Per/Ser (Incl. Access Fees) $69,000, Other Print Mats $500. Sal $58,000 (Prof $36,000)
Library Holdings: Bk Vols 10,000; Per Subs 170
Subject Interests: Computer science, Indexing, Info sci, Phys scis, Sci tech
Partic in BRS; Dialog Corporation; Fedlink; Nasa Libraries Information System - Nasa Galaxie; OCLC Online Computer Library Center, Inc

S KABEISEMAN, Learning Resource Center & Technical Library, DLA Admin Support Ctr, 8725 John J Kingman Rd, Ste 4428, 22060-6220. SAN 317-2007. Tel: 703-767-4300. FAX: 703-767-4303. *Librn*, Iredell Jenkins; E-Mail: iredell_jenkins@hq.dla.mil
Founded 1962
Library Holdings: Bk Vols 3,800; Per Subs 300
Subject Interests: Automatic data processing, Mgt
Special Collections: Books In Print; Bookshelf; Encyclopedia; Industry Standards, micro; Military Handbooks & Specifications; Personnel; Ulrich's Int Periodicals
Restriction: Not open to public
Partic in Defense Technical Information Center; OCLC Online Computer Library Center, Inc

UNITED STATES ARMY
A VAN NOY LIBRARY, 5966 12th St, Ste 101, 22060-5554. SAN 362-8922. Tel: 703-806-3323. FAX: 703-806-0091. *Dir*, Linda Cheung; *Publ Servs*, Cheryl Weidner; *Ref*, Phyllis Cassler; Staff 7 (MLS 3, Non-MLS 4)
Founded 1939
Library Holdings: Bk Vols 81,259; Bk Titles 74,555; Per Subs 300
Subject Interests: Mil sci, Military history, Political science, Soc sci
Partic in Fedlink; OCLC Online Computer Library Center, Inc

FORT EUSTIS

AM MCDONALD US ARMY COMMUNITY HOSPITAL MEDICAL LIBRARY, 23604. SAN 370-243X. Tel: 757-314-7857. FAX: 757-314-7983. *Mgr*, Howard E Barton; E-Mail: howard.barton@na.amedd.army.mil
Library Holdings: Bk Vols 2,000; Per Subs 30

UNITED STATES ARMY
A AVIATION APPLIED TECHNOLOGY DIRECTORATE, TECHNICAL LIBRARY, Bldg 401, Rm 100C, 23604-5577. SAN 362-9104. Tel: 757-878-2963. FAX: 757-878-5058.
Founded 1946
Library Holdings: Bk Vols 5,100; Per Subs 200
Subject Interests: Army aircraft, Aviation safety, Composite structures, Gas turbines, Low-speed aeronaut, Propulsion systs
Partic in Fedlink; OCLC Online Computer Library Center, Inc
A GRONINGER LIBRARY, Bldg 1313, Army Transportation Ctr, 23604-5107. SAN 362-9163. Tel: 757-878-5017. FAX: 757-878-1024. *Librn*, Claudia L Levy; E-Mail: levyc@eustis.emh1.army.mil
Oct 1997-Sep 1998 Mats Exp $25,000, Books $15,000, Per/Ser (Incl. Access Fees) $10,000
Library Holdings: Bk Titles 60,000; Per Subs 70
Subject Interests: Local history, Mil sci, Transportation
Publications: Library Brochure
A TRANSPORTATION SCHOOL LIBRARY, Bldg 705 Rm 36, 23604-5450. SAN 362-9198. Tel: 757-878-5563. FAX: 757-878-6256. *Librn*, Tim Renick; E-Mail: renickt@eustis.army.mil; *Tech Servs*, Dianne Forbes; *Tech Servs*, Nancy Gordon; Staff 3 (MLS 1, Non-MLS 2)
Founded 1944
Library Holdings: Bk Titles 32,450; Per Subs 550
Subject Interests: Instrul tech, Mil regulations, Mil sci, Military history, Transportation
Publications: Acquisitions List; Bibliographies; Quarterly Newsletter
Partic in Defense Technical Information Center; Dialog Corporation; OCLC Online Computer Library Center, Inc

A US ARMY TRANSPORTATION MUSEUM LIBRARY, Besson Hall, Bldg 300, 23604-5260. SAN 370-2588. Tel: 757-878-1115. FAX: 757-878-5656. Web Site: www.eustis.army.mil/dptmsec/museum.htm. *Dir*, Barbara A Bower; *Res*, Carolyn Wright; E-Mail: wrightc@eustis.army.mil
Oct 1998-Sep 1999 Income $1,600, Federal $1,500, Other $100. Mats Exp $600, Books $350, Per/Ser (Incl. Access Fees) $250. Sal $151,000 (Prof $123,000)
Library Holdings: Bk Vols 3,600; Per Subs 30

FORT LEE

UNITED STATES ARMY
A THE ARMY LOGISTICS LIBRARY, US Army Logistics Mgmt Col, Bldg 12500, 2401 Quarters Rd, 23801-1705. SAN 362-9317. Tel: 804-765-4722. FAX: 804-765-4660. Web Site: www.almc.army.mil. *Chief Librn*, Katherine Sites; *ILL*, Virginia Gordon; *Coll Develop, Online Servs, Ref*, John Shields; E-Mail: shieldsj@lee.army.mil; Staff 6 (MLS 2, Non-MLS 4)
Founded 1971
Library Holdings: Bk Vols 39,600; Bk Titles 38,000; Per Subs 260
Subject Interests: Computer science, Logistics, Petroleum
Special Collections: US Government Publications
Publications: Accessions List (quarterly); Bibliographies; Library handbook; Periodical Listing
Partic in Defense Technical Information Center; Dialog Corporation; Fedlink; OCLC Online Computer Library Center, Inc

FORT MONROE

S CASEMATE MUSEUM LIBRARY, 20 Bernard Rd, PO Box 51341, 23651-0341. SAN 327-4047. Tel: 757-727-3935. FAX: 757-727-3886. *Dir*, Dennis Mroczkowski; E-Mail: mroczkod@monroe.army.mil; *Archivist*, David Johnson; E-Mail: johnsond@monroe.army.mil
Oct 1998-Sep 1999 Income $49,000. Mats Exp $675, Books $500, Per/Ser (Incl. Access Fees) $175. Sal $70,992
Library Holdings: Bk Vols 11,000
Subject Interests: Local history, Military history
Special Collections: Coast Artillery School
Publications: Casemate Papers; Defender of the Chesapeake; Tales of Old Fort Monroe; The Guns of Fort Monroe

UNITED STATES ARMY
A FORT MONROE GENERAL LIBRARY, Bldg 7, 23651-5123. SAN 362-9376. Tel: 757-727-2909. FAX: 757-727-3589. *Librn*, Raymond Abell; E-Mail: abellr@monroe.army.mil
Founded 1824
Library Holdings: Bk Vols 32,552; Per Subs 109
Subject Interests: Mgt

A HEADQUARTERS, US ARMY FORT MONROE TECHNICAL LIBRARY, 33 Ingalls Rd, 23651-5124. SAN 362-9341. Tel: 757-727-2821. FAX: 757-727-2931. Web Site: www-tradoc.army.mil/library. *Dir*, Frances M Doyle; Tel: 757-727-2956, E-Mail: doylef@monroe.army.mil; *Ref*, Karen J Lewis; Tel: 757-727-2967, E-Mail: lewisk@monroe.army.mil; *ILL*, Sally A Swan; Tel: 757-727-2821, E-Mail: swans@monroe.army.mil; Staff 3 (MLS 3)
Founded 1824
Library Holdings: Bk Vols 4,000
Subject Interests: Mgt, Mil sci, Military history
Special Collections: Training & Doctrine Command Technical Reports/Studies
Automation Activity & Vendor Info: (Acquisitions) TLC; (Cataloging) TLC; (Circulation) TLC; (OPAC) TLC
Database Vendor: Dialog, Ebsco - EbscoHost, IAC - Info Trac, Lexis-Nexis, OCLC - First Search, ProQuest
Partic in Dialog Corporation; Fedlink; OCLC Online Computer Library Center, Inc; Tralinet

FORT MYER

UNITED STATES ARMY
A FORT MYER POST LIBRARY, 210 McNair Rd, Bldg 469, 22211-1101. SAN 362-9406. Tel: 703-696-3555. FAX: 703-696-8587. *Dir*, Sue Thompson; E-Mail: thompsons@fmme.army.mil; *Tech Servs*, Audrey Thomas; *Publ Servs*, Pat Lambert
Library Holdings: Bk Vols 47,000; Per Subs 500
Subject Interests: Bus, Computer science, Juv, Military history, Pub admin
Special Collections: Popular Coll
Partic in Fedlink; OCLC Online Computer Library Center, Inc

FRANKLIN

J PAUL D CAMP COMMUNITY COLLEGE LIBRARY, 100 N College Dr, PO Box 737, 23851. SAN 317-2880. Tel: 757-569-6700. FAX: 757-569-6737. *Dir*, Linza M Weaver; E-Mail: lweaver@pc.cc.va.us; Staff 1 (MLS 1)
Founded 1971. Enrl 2,529; Fac 24
Library Holdings: Bk Vols 21,666; Bk Titles 21,127; Per Subs 135
Database Vendor: GaleNet, IAC - Info Trac, OCLC - First Search, OVID Technologies
Function: For research purposes, ILL available, Photocopies available, Reference services available
Mem of VA Community Col Syst
Partic in Tidewater Consortium for Continuing Higher Educ

FREDERICKSBURG

P CENTRAL RAPPAHANNOCK REGIONAL LIBRARY, Wallace Memo Library, 1201 Caroline St, 22401-3761. SAN 317-2899. Tel: 540-372-11 FAX: 540-371-7965. Web Site: www.crrl.org. *Dir*, Donna Cote; *Dep Dir* Allison Heartwell; *Ad Servs*, Ann Haley; *Ch Servs*, Caroline Parr; *Cat*, Bonnie Trahan; *Ref*, Sue Willis; *YA Servs*, Scott Phillips; Staff 100 (MLS Non-MLS 66)
Founded 1969
Jul 1999-Jun 2000 Income $8,071,065. Mats Exp $731,365, Books $684,625, Per/Ser (Incl. Access Fees) $41,655, Micro $5,085, AV Equip $280. Sal $3,705,703 (Prof $1,646,100)
Library Holdings: Bk Vols 443,984; Per Subs 836
Subject Interests: Fredericksburg, Law, Virginia
Special Services for the Deaf - TTY machine
Friends of the Library Group
Branches: 7
COOPER BRANCH, 20 Washington Ave, Colonial Beach, 22443-2337. (Mail add: PO Box 129, Colonial Beach, 22443-0129), SAN 320-0604 Tel: 804-224-0921. FAX: 804-224-0921. *Librn*, Kitty Norris
P FREDERICKSBURG SUBREGIONAL LIBRARY FOR THE BLIND & PHYSICALLY HANDICAPPED, 1201 Caroline St, 22401. Tel: 540-3 1160, ext 234. FAX: 540-373-9411. *Librn*, Nancy Buck
HAGUE BRANCH, 8047 Cople Hwy, PO Box 116, Hague, 22469-0116. SAN 326-7474. Tel: 804-472-3820. FAX: 804-472-3820. *Librn*, Jenny Hamilton
MONTROSS BRANCH, Rte 3, Montross, 22520. SAN 321-4958. Tel: 8 493-8194. FAX: 804-493-8194. *Librn*, Barbara Maines
SALEM CHURCH, 2607 Salem Church Rd, 22407. SAN 374-7247. Tel: 540-785-9267. FAX: 540-785-9443. *Librn*, Janice Black
SNOW BRANCH, 8740 Courthouse Rd, Spotsylvania, 22553. SAN 324-3087. Tel: 540-582-6900. FAX: 540-582-6900. *Librn*, Martha Mehrabi
THE JOHN MUSANTE PORTER MEMORIAL, 2001 Parkway Blvd, Stafford, 22554. SAN 320-0590. Tel: 540-659-4909. FAX: 540-659-615 *Librn*, Nelda Mohr
Bookmobiles: 1

S FREDERICKSBURG & SPOTSYLVANIA NATIONAL MILITARY PA LIBRARY,* 120 Chatham Lane, 22405. SAN 317-2902. Tel: 540-371-08 FAX: 540-371-1907. Web Site: www.nps/gov/frsp. *Chief Librn*, Robert K Krick
Founded 1927
Library Holdings: Bk Titles 6,500
Subject Interests: Am Civil War
Special Collections: Civil War Personalities, diaries, letters & related papers; Confederate & US Regimental History of Units involved in the fo battles near Fredericksburg

S INTERNATIONAL HERB ASSOCIATION LIBRARY,* 910 Charles St, 22401. SAN 375-782X. Tel: 540-368-0590. FAX: 540-370-0015. Web Site www.iherb.org. *Exec Dir*, Peggy McElgunn
Library Holdings: Bk Titles 500; Per Subs 20
Publications: Membership directory (Bimonthly)

S INTERNATIONAL PARKING INSTITUTE,* 701 Kenmore Ave, PO Box 7167, 22404-7167. SAN 373-2606. Tel: 540-371-7535. FAX: 540-371-802 *Pres*, David Ivey
Library Holdings: Bk Vols 700
Subject Interests: Law

S KENMORE PLANTATION & GARDENS,* 1201 Washington Ave, 2240 SAN 370-1441. Tel: 540-373-3381. FAX: 540-371-6066. E-Mail: mailroom@kenmore.org. Web Site: www.kenmore.org. *Curator*, Robert Leath
Library Holdings: Bk Titles 500
Special Collections: Lewis Family 18th Century Coll
Restriction: By appointment only
Plantation hours: Jan-Feb Mon-Fri reservations only, Sat 10-4 & Sun 12-4 Mar-Dec Sat 10-5 & Sun 12-5

C MARY WASHINGTON COLLEGE, Simpson Library, 1801 College Ave, 22401-4664. SAN 317-2910. Tel: 540-654-1147. Interlibrary Loan Service Tel: 654-1746. FAX: 540-654-1067. Web Site: www.library.mwc.edu. *Dir*, LeRoy S Strohl; E-Mail: lstrohl@mwc.edu; *ILL*, Carla Bailey; E-Mail: cbailey@mwc.edu; *Cat*, Charles Balthis; Tel: 540-654-1772, E-Mail: cbalthis@mwc.edu; *Instrul Serv*, Jack Bales; Tel: 540-654-1780, E-Mail: jbales@mwc.edu; *Acq*, Tina Faulconer; Tel: 540-654-1761, E-Mail: tfaulcon@mwc.edu; *Ref*, Karen Nelson; Tel: 540-654-1148, E-Mail: knelson@mwc.edu; *Spec Coll*, Brenda Sloan; Tel: 540-654-1752, E-Mail: bsloan@mwc.edu; *Instrul Serv, Syst Coordr*, Tim Newman; Tel: 540-654-1741, E-Mail: tnewman@mwc.edu; *Circ*, Beth Perkins; Tel: 540-654-1748, E-Mail: eperkins@mwc.edu; *Syst Coordr*, Robert Grattan; Tel: 540-654-1756, E-Mail: bgrattan@mwc.edu; *Coll Develop*, Rebecca Elswick; Tel: 54 654-1758, E-Mail: relswick@mwc.edu; *Ref*, Ron Comer; *Instrul Serv*, Lau Preston; Tel: 540-654-1740, E-Mail: lpreston@mwc.edu; *Instrul Serv*, Carolyn Parsons; Tel: 540-654-1742, E-Mail: cparsons@mwc.edu; Staff 8 (MLS 8)
Founded 1908. Enrl 4,040; Fac 172; Highest Degree: Master

Jul 1999-Jun 2000 Income $1,955,427. Mats Exp $657,760, Books $398,230, Per/Ser (Incl. Access Fees) $135,710, Presv $10,293, Micro $113,527. Sal $839,259 (Prof $471,837)
Library Holdings: Bk Vols 348,264; Bk Titles 340,354; Per Subs 1,587
Subject Interests: Architecture, Art, Behav sci, History, Soc sci
Special Collections: Claude Bernard Coll; James Joyce Coll; William Butler Yeats Coll
Automation Activity & Vendor Info: (Acquisitions) VTLS
Partic in SE Libr Network; VIVA-Statewide Library Resource Network

MARY WASHINGTON HOSPITAL, Medical Library,* 1001 Sam Perry Blvd, 22401-9523. SAN 317-2945. Tel: 540-899-1597. FAX: 540-899-1514. *Dir*, Jane Borland; *ILL*, Heidi Hamrick; Staff 2 (MLS 1, Non-MLS 1)
Founded 1974
Library Holdings: Bk Titles 1,000; Per Subs 130
Subject Interests: Behav sci, Biomed sci, History of medicine, Med mgt, Nursing, Soc sci
Partic in National Network Of Libraries Of Medicine

JAMES MONROE MUSEUM & MEMORIAL LIBRARY,* 908 Charles St, 22401-5810. SAN 317-2929. Tel: 540-654-1043 (Museum), 540-654-2113. FAX: 540-654-1106. *Curator*, David B Voelkel; E-Mail: dvoelkel@mwc.edu; *Dir*, John N Pearce
1997-1998 Mats Exp $2,500
Library Holdings: Bk Titles 10,000; Per Subs 10
Subject Interests: Am foreign policy, Monroe Doctrine, Virginia
Special Collections: James Monroe Coll; Monroe Correspondence
Restriction: Restricted public use

ONT ROYAL

CHRISTENDOM COLLEGE, O'Reilly Memorial Library, 134 Christendon Dr, 22630. SAN 321-6608. Tel: 540-636-2900. FAX: 540-636-1655. E-Mail: library@christendom.edu. *Librn*, Andrew Armstrong; *Coll Develop*, Andrew V Armstrong
Founded 1977. Enrl 160; Fac 15; Highest Degree: Bachelor
Library Holdings: Bk Vols 50,000; Bk Titles 42,000; Per Subs 320
Subject Interests: Hagiography, Rare books
Partic in OCLC Online Computer Library Center, Inc; SE Libr Network

HUMAN LIFE INTERNATIONAL LIBRARY, 4 Family Life Dr, 22630. SAN 371-5531. Tel: 540-635-7884. FAX: 540-636-7363. E-Mail: hli@hli.org. Web Site: www.hli.org. *Coll Develop, Dir*, Michael Schmiedicke; E-Mail: michaels@hli.org; *Head of Libr*, Stephen Philip Pilon; Tel: 520-622-5202, E-Mail: spilon@hli.org; Staff 1 (MLS 1)
Founded 1981
Library Holdings: Bk Vols 5,500; Bk Titles 4,000; Per Subs 134
Subject Interests: Abortion, Contraception, Euthanasia
Special Collections: Letters of Father Paul Marx, Founder
Automation Activity & Vendor Info: (Cataloging) Sagebrush Corporation; (Serials) Sagebrush Corporation
Function: For research purposes

SAMUELS PUBLIC LIBRARY, 538 Villa Ave, 22630. SAN 317-2953. Tel: 540-635-3153. FAX: 540-635-7229. E-Mail: samuels@shentel.net. Web Site: www.shentel.net/library/samuels/. *Dir*, Barbara Ecton; *Ref*, Nathanael Reed; *Tech Servs*, Brenda Riley
Founded 1952. Pop 29,500; Circ 231,554
Jul 1999-Jun 2000 Income $448,616, State $105,795, City $36,485, County $267,294, Other $39,042. Mats Exp $85,392, Books $80,979, Per/Ser (Incl. Access Fees) $3,413, Presv $1,000. Sal $296,387
Library Holdings: Bk Vols 79,000; Per Subs 115
Subject Interests: Local history
Special Collections: Virginia Coll
Automation Activity & Vendor Info: (Cataloging) Gaylord; (Circulation) Gaylord; (OPAC) Gaylord
Publications: Newsletter (semi-annual)
Partic in Northern Shenandoah Valley Libr Network
Friends of the Library Group

AINESVILLE

ATLANTIC RESEARCH CORP, Virginia Propulsion Division-Technical Information Center,* 5945 Wellington Rd-MS 49/07, 20155. SAN 328-3127. Tel: 703-754-5590. FAX: 703-754-5067. *Librn*, Kim Wiltshire
Library Holdings: Bk Titles 2,000; Per Subs 100
Publications: Library Bulletin (quarterly)
Partic in Dialog Corporation

ALAX

GALAX-CARROLL REGIONAL LIBRARY, BC Vaughan Memorial Library, 608 W Stuart Dr, 24333. SAN 317-2961. Tel: 540-236-2042, 540-236-2351. FAX: 540-236-5153. *Dir*, Laura A Bryant; E-Mail: lbryant@tcia.net; Staff 1 (MLS 1)
Founded 1938. Pop 34,500; Circ 159,336
Jul 1999-Jun 2000 Income (Main Library and Branch Library) $436,597, State $110,389, City $142,968, County $150,512, Locally Generated Income $24,236. Mats Exp $87,973, Books $45,012, Per/Ser (Incl. Access Fees) $5,948, AV Equip $35,413, Electronic Ref Mat (Incl. Access Fees) $1,600. Sal $261,561 (Prof $32,032)
Library Holdings: Bk Titles 52,110; Per Subs 157; Bks on Deafness & Sign Lang 10
Subject Interests: Carroll County hist, Galax City hist, Genealogy
Automation Activity & Vendor Info: (Cataloging) Gaylord; (Circulation) Gaylord; (OPAC) Gaylord
Database Vendor: OCLC - First Search
Partic in Mtn-Cat; Wythe-Grayson Regional Libr
Library Outreach Services for Senior Citizens & Preschool Centers
Branches: 1
CARROLL COUNTY PUBLIC, 101 Beaver Dam Rd, PO Box 1629, Hillsville, 24343. SAN 321-2696. Tel: 540-728-2228, 540-728-3334. FAX: 540-728-3830. *Dir*, June Pike
Library Holdings: Bk Titles 37,624

GLENNS

J RAPPAHANNOCK COMMUNITY COLLEGE LIBRARY, Glenns Campus, 12745 College Dr, 23149. SAN 362-9430. Tel: 804-758-6710. FAX: 804-758-0213. Web Site: www.rcc1.cc.va.us/public/library/library.htm. *Librn*, James E Satchell; Tel: 804-758-6714; *Actg Librn*, Melanie G Wick; Tel: 804-758-6714, E-Mail: mwick@rcc.cc.va.us; *Asst Librn*, Michelle S Pearce; *Asst Librn*, Lois Robinson; *Cat, ILL*, Bronsene Turner; E-Mail: bturner@rcc.cc.va.us; Staff 4 (MLS 1, Non-MLS 3)
Founded 1971. Enrl 800
Library Holdings: Bk Titles 25,000; Per Subs 175
Subject Interests: Bus mgr, Nursing
Database Vendor: GaleNet, IAC - Info Trac, Lexis-Nexis, OCLC - First Search, Wilson - Wilson Web
Function: ILL available

GLOUCESTER

P GLOUCESTER PUBLIC LIBRARY,* 6382 Main St, PO Box 367, 23061. SAN 317-297X. Tel: 804-693-2998. FAX: 804-693-1477. *Librn*, Nancy Dowyer
Pop 30,100; Circ 59,000
Library Holdings: Bk Vols 51,976; Per Subs 77
Friends of the Library Group

GLOUCESTER POINT

S COLLEGE OF WILLIAM & MARY, Virginia Institute of Marine Science Library, PO Box 1346, 23062. SAN 317-2996. Tel: 804-684-7000, 804-684-7114. FAX: 804-684-7113. Web Site: www.vims.edu/library. *Dir*, Charles McFadden; *Asst Librn, ILL*, Marilyn Lewis; *Publ Servs*, Diane Walker; Staff 4 (MLS 3, Non-MLS 1)
Founded 1940
Jul 1998-Jun 1999 Income $387,883. Mats Exp $219,533. Sal $124,736
Library Holdings: Bk Vols 59,208; Bk Titles 27,593; Per Subs 697
Subject Interests: Chesapeake Bay, Coastal zone, Environmental studies, Estuaries, Fisheries, Geology, Marine biology
Special Collections: Expeditions, Sport Fishing & Hunting (Ross H Walker Coll)
Publications: Chesapeake Bay Bibliography
Partic in OCLC Online Computer Library Center, Inc; SE Libr Network

GREAT FALLS

S INTERNATIONAL CADMIUM ASSOCIATION LIBRARY, PO Box 924, 22066. SAN 375-2291. Tel: 703-759-7400. FAX: 703-759-7003. *Pres*, Hugh Morrow; E-Mail: icdamorrow@aol.com
Founded 1980
Library Holdings: Bk Titles 1,000; Per Subs 12

GRUNDY

P BUCHANAN COUNTY PUBLIC LIBRARY,* Rte 2, Box 3, 24614-9613. SAN 317-302X. Tel: 540-935-6581. FAX: 540-935-6292. *Librn*, Patricia M Hatfield; E-Mail: phatfiel@usla.edu; Staff 1 (MLS 1)
Founded 1961. Pop 31,200; Circ 126,447
Library Holdings: Bk Vols 80,000; Per Subs 137
Subject Interests: History, Local history, Relig studies
Partic in SE Libr Network
Friends of the Library Group

HALIFAX

P HALIFAX COUNTY-SOUTH BOSTON REGIONAL LIBRARY,* 177 S Main St, PO Box 1729, 24558. SAN 362-9465. Tel: 804-476-3357. FAX: 804-476-3359. Web Site: www2.hal.fax.com/librny/. *Dir*, Sarah Jean Hudson; E-Mail: sarah@halifax.com

Founded 1961. Pop 37,511; Circ 124,574
Library Holdings: Bk Vols 124,915; Per Subs 224
Subject Interests: Art, Bus, Large print, Local history
Partic in OCLC Online Computer Library Center, Inc
Friends of the Library Group
Branches: 1
SOUTH BOSTON PUBLIC, 509 Broad St, South Boston, 24592. SAN 362-949X. Tel: 804-575-4228. FAX: 804-575-4229. Web Site: www2.hal.fax.com/librny/.
Friends of the Library Group
Bookmobiles: 1

HAMPDEN SYDNEY

C HAMPDEN SYDNEY COLLEGE, Eggleston Library, 12 Via Sacra, HS Box 7, 23943. SAN 317-3038. Tel: 804-223-6190. FAX: 804-223-6351. Web Site: www.hsc.edu. *Dir*, Sharon I Goad; *ILL, Ref*, Catherine Pollari; *Cat*, Sandra W Heinemann; *Media Spec*, Lori Spiro; *Publ Servs*, Chandra Gigliotti-Guridi; Staff 5 (MLS 5)
Founded 1776. Enrl 956; Fac 100; Highest Degree: Bachelor
Library Holdings: Bk Vols 200,568; Per Subs 835
Subject Interests: Audio visual mats, Humanities, Local history
Special Collections: International Video Coll; John Peter Mettauer Coll
Database Vendor: Innovative Interfaces INN - View
Partic in Southside Virginia Library Network; VIVA-Statewide Library Resource Network

HAMPTON

GM DEPARTMENT OF VETERANS AFFAIRS MEDICAL CENTER, Medical Library 142D,* 23667. SAN 317-3062. Tel: 757-722-9961, Ext 3550. FAX: 757-722-2988. *Dir*, Jacqueline Bird; E-Mail: bird.j@hampton.va.gov; Staff 4 (MLS 3, Non-MLS 1)
Founded 1870
Library Holdings: Bk Vols 12,500; Per Subs 536
Subject Interests: Acute care, Geriatrics, Gerontology, Patient educ mats, Rehabilitation med
Partic in National Network Of Libraries Of Medicine - South Central Region; Tidewater Health Scis Librs; Veterans Affairs Library Network

P HAMPTON PUBLIC LIBRARY, 4207 Victoria Blvd, 23669-4243. SAN 362-9589. Tel: 757-727-1154. FAX: 757-727-1152. Web Site: www.hamptonpubliclibrary.org. *Dir*, Douglas Perry; E-Mail: dperry@city.hampton.va.us; *Ref*, Gaynell Drummond; *Mgr, Publ Servs*, Robert Carpenter; Staff 10 (MLS 10)
Founded 1926. Pop 140,000
1999-2000 Income $1,932,862. Mats Exp $299,978. Sal $1,181,162
Library Holdings: Bk Vols 284,812
Special Collections: Grant Resources Coll; Virginia History & Genealogy
Automation Activity & Vendor Info: (Cataloging) epixtech, inc.; (Circulation) epixtech, inc.
Publications: Directory of Community Organizations (Hampton, Newport News, Poquoson & York Co)
Young Family Centers - Collections of child development & parenting materials established in the children's section of each branch of the library system
Friends of the Library Group
Branches: 4
NORTHAMPTON, 936 Big Bethel Rd, 23666. SAN 362-9619. Tel: 757-825-4559. FAX: 757-825-4646. *Librn*, Virginia L Cotter
Library Holdings: Bk Vols 56,659
PHOEBUS, One S Mallory St, 23663. SAN 362-9643. Tel: 757-727-1149. FAX: 757-727-1047. *Librn*, Mary Sue Woolard
Library Holdings: Bk Vols 29,195
P SUBREGIONAL LIBRARY FOR THE VISUALLY & PHYSICALLY HANDICAPPED, 1 S Mallony St, 23663. SAN 362-9597. Tel: 757-727-1900. *Librn*, Mary Sue Woolard
Library Holdings: Bk Vols 24,911
Function: Internet access
Toys for handicapped children, reference materials on blindness & other handicaps, Arkenstone Reader, magnifiers, PCs for handicapped
WILLOW OAKS, Willow Oaks Shopping Mall, 227 Fox Hill Rd, 23669. SAN 362-9708. Tel: 757-850-5114. FAX: 757-850-5239. *Librn*, Lorraine Bartlett
Library Holdings: Bk Vols 57,772
Bookmobiles: 2

C HAMPTON UNIVERSITY, William R & Norma B Harvey Library, 130 E Tyler St, 23668. SAN 362-952X. Tel: 757-727-5371. FAX: 757-727-5952. E-Mail: library@hamptonu.edu. Web Site: www.hamptonu.edu. *Dir*, Loretta O'Brien-Parham; E-Mail: loretta.parham@hamptonu.edu; *Tech Servs*, Naomi Rhodes; *Ref*, Greta Lowe; *Ref*, Kimberly Sargent; *Acq*, Travis Cox; *Per*, Alfred Willis; *Cat*, Xinhai Kong; Staff 31 (MLS 11, Non-MLS 20)
Founded 1868. Enrl 5,582; Highest Degree: Doctorate
Jul 1998-Jun 1999 Income $1,803,901. Mats Exp $836,200, Books $506,200, Per/Ser (Incl. Access Fees) $270,000, Micro $60,000
Library Holdings: Bk Vols 341,359; Per Subs 1,300
Subject Interests: African-American, Architecture, Education, Nursing, Pharmacy, Psychology, Sociology
Special Collections: Black Literature & History (George Foster Peabody Coll); Hampton University Archives
Database Vendor: Dialog, Ebsco - EbscoHost, IAC - Info Trac, IAC - SearchBank, Lexis-Nexis, OCLC - First Search, OVID Technologies, ProQuest, Wilson - Wilson Web
Partic in OCLC Online Computer Library Center, Inc; Solinet; VIVA/VICULA
Departmental Libraries:
ARCHITECTURE Tel: 757-727-5443. *Librn*, Norma Sellman
Library Holdings: Bk Vols 10,000
Subject Interests: Architecture
MUSIC Tel: 757-727-5411. *In Charge*, Carla Rodriquez
CM NURSING Tel: 757-727-5353. *Librn*, Cynthia Burke

G NASA, Langley Research Center Technical Library, 2 W Durand St, Mai Stop 185, 23681-2199. SAN 317-3046. Tel: 757-864-2356. FAX: 757-864-2375. E-Mail: tech-library@larc.nasa.gov. Web Site: www.larc.nasa.gov. *Head of Libr*, Mary McCaskill
Founded 1920
Library Holdings: Bk Vols 80,000; Bk Titles 70,000; Per Subs 800
Subject Interests: Aerospace science, Aerospace tech
Automation Activity & Vendor Info: (OPAC) SIRSI
Database Vendor: Dialog, OCLC - First Search, Silverplatter Informatio Inc.
Function: Some telephone reference
Partic in Fedlink; FLICC; Nasa Libraries Information System - Nasa Galaxie; OCLC Online Computer Library Center, Inc

M SENTARA HAMPTON GENERAL HOSPITAL, Medical Library,* 3120 Victoria Blvd, 23661. SAN 329-5249. Tel: 757-727-7102. FAX: 757-722-3391. *Librn*, Deborah B Linkous
Library Holdings: Bk Vols 730
Partic in Medline; SE Libr Network

C THOMAS NELSON COMMUNITY COLLEGE LIBRARY, 99 Thomas Nelson Dr, 23670. (Mail add: PO Box 9407, 23670), SAN 317-3054. Tel: 757-825-2876. Interlibrary Loan Service Tel: 757-825-3533. Circulation T 757-825-2877. Reference Tel: 757-825-2878. FAX: 757-825-2870. Web Si www.tncc.cc.va.us/administration/library/library.html. *Coordr*, Aileen Schweitzer; Tel: 757-825-2871, E-Mail: schweitzera@tncc.cc.va.us; *Circ*, Linda Dickerson; E-Mail: dikersonl@tncc.cc.va.us; *Circ*, Deborah Newma E-Mail: newmand@tncc.cc.va.us; *Acq*, Dyan Vinson; E-Mail: visond@tncc.cc.va.us; *Cat*, Susan Lawlor; E-Mail: lawlors@tncc.cc.va.us; *Ref Serv Ad*, Barbara Gibson; E-Mail: gibsonb@tncc.cc.va.us; *AV*, Ella Belch; Tel: 757-825-2875, E-Mail: belche@tncc.cc.va.us; *Ser*, Amber Oblazney Schwartzlow; Tel: 757-825-3529, Fax: 757-825-2970, E-Mail: oblazneya@tncc.cc.va.us. Subject Specialists: *Education*, Barbara Gibson; *Engineering* Barbara Gibson; *Mathematics*, Barbara Gibson; *Natural science*, Barbara Gibson; Staff 12 (MLS 4, Non-MLS 8)
Founded 1968. Enrl 4,300; Fac 103; Highest Degree: Certificate
Jul 1999-Jun 2000 Income $779,199. Mats Exp $132,100, Books $33,500, Per/Ser (Incl. Access Fees) $29,400, Presv $300, Micro $10,540, AV Equi $11,305, Electronic Ref Mat (Incl. Access Fees) $17,100. Sal $433,785 (P $130,198)
Library Holdings: Bk Vols 62,954; Bk Titles 60,500; Per Subs 29,400; High Interest/Low Vocabulary Bk Vols 80; Bks on Deafness & Sign Lang
Subject Interests: Am lit, Computer tech, English literature, Ethnic studie Instrul develop, Nursing, Soc problems
Special Collections: Accelerated Readers; Paperbacks
Automation Activity & Vendor Info: (Circulation) NOTIS
Database Vendor: GaleNet, IAC - Info Trac, IAC - SearchBank, OCLC - First Search, OVID Technologies
Partic in Educ Resources Info Ctr; OCLC Online Computer Library Cente Inc; SE Libr Network; Wilsonline

HANOVER

P PAMUNKEY REGIONAL LIBRARY, 7527 Library Dr, PO Box 119, 23069-0119. SAN 362-9732. Tel: 804-537-6211. FAX: 804-537-6389. Web Site: www.pamunkeylibrary.org. *Dir*, Fran Freimarck; E-Mail: ffreimarck@pamunkeylibrary.org; *Admin Assoc*, Renee Norman; E-Mail: rnorman@pamunkeylibrary.org; *Admin Assoc*, Carolyn G Garner; Tel: 804-537-6481, E-Mail: cgarner@pamunkeylibrary.org; *Librn*, Dr B Susan Brown; Tel: 804-537-6091, E-Mail: sbrown@pamunkeylibrary.org; *Librn*, Patricia S Franz; Tel: 804-537-6209, E-Mail: pfranz@pamunkeylibrary.org; *Librn, Web Coordr*, Deborah Lammers; Tel: 804-537-6214, E-Mail: dlammers@pamunkeylibrary.org; *Librn*, Linda Gosnell; Tel: 804-537-6074, E-Mail: lgosnell@pamunkeylibrary.org. Subject Specialists: *Adult fiction*, Patricia S Franz; *Adult non-fiction*, Dr B Susan Brown; *Audio visual mats*, Patricia S Franz; *Audio visual mats*, Linda Gosnell; *Children's fiction*, Linda Gosnell; *Info tech*, Deborah Lammers; *Non-fiction*, Dr B Susan Brown; *Young adult bks*, Linda Gosnell; Staff 6 (MLS 6)
Founded 1941. Pop 94,500; Circ 753,691
Library Holdings: Bk Vols 379,458; Bk Titles 98,529
Special Collections: Civil War; Virginiana

Automation Activity & Vendor Info: (Cataloging) VTLS; (Circulation) VTLS; (OPAC) VTLS
Database Vendor: Ebsco - EbscoHost, GaleNet, Lexis-Nexis, OCLC - First Search
Partic in Richmond Area Network; VA State Libr
Friends of the Library Group
Branches: 10
ATLEE BRANCH, 9161 Atlee Rd, Mechanicsville, 23116. SAN 378-1925. Tel: 804-559-0654. TDD: 804-730-6140. FAX: 804-559-0645. E-Mail: webmistress@pamunkeylibrary.org. Web Site: www.pamunkeylibrary.org/pamunkey/atlee.htm. *Admin Assoc*, Carolyn G Garner; Tel: 804-537-6481, Fax: 804-537-6389, E-Mail: cgarner@pamunkeylibrary.org; *Branch Mgr*, Toni M Heer; E-Mail: theer@pamunkeylibrary.org; *Ref*, Steven Hartung; E-Mail: shartung@pamunkeylibrary.org; Staff 16 (MLS 1, Non-MLS 15)
Founded 1997. Circ 200,776
Library Holdings: Bk Vols 50,000; Per Subs 108
Database Vendor: Ebsco - EbscoHost, GaleNet, OCLC - First Search
Open Mon-Thurs 10-9 & Fri-Sat 10-6
Friends of the Library Group
GOOCHLAND BRANCH, 2931 River Rd W, PO Box 207, Goochland, 23063. SAN 362-9791. Tel: 804-556-4774. TDD: 804-730-6140. FAX: 804-556-2941. Web Site: www.pamunkeylibrary.org/pamunkey/goochlan.htm. *Librn*, Laura Jurman; *Branch Mgr*, Janet Melton; E-Mail: jmelton@pamunkeylibrary.org; *Admin Assoc*, Carolyn G Garner; Tel: 804-537-6481, Fax: 804-537-6389, E-Mail: cgarner@pamunkeylibrary.org; Staff 12 (Non-MLS 12)
Founded 1977. Circ 82,017
Library Holdings: Bk Vols 22,500; Per Subs 77
Database Vendor: Ebsco - EbscoHost, GaleNet, OCLC - First Search
Friends of the Library Group
HANOVER COURTHOUSE, 7527 Library Dr, 23069. (Mail add: PO Box 119, 23069), SAN 362-9805. Tel: 804-537-6210. TDD: 804-730-6140. FAX: 804-537-5104. Web Site: www.pamunkeylibrary.org/pamunkey/hanover.htm. *Branch Mgr*, Myra Cramer; E-Mail: mcramer@pamunkeylibrary.org; *Admin Assoc*, Carolyn G Garner; Tel: 804-537-6481, Fax: 804-537-6389, E-Mail: cgarner@parmunkeylibrary.org; Staff 7 (Non-MLS 7)
Founded 1942. Circ 58,163
Library Holdings: Bk Vols 25,000; Per Subs 33
Special Collections: Virginiana
Database Vendor: Ebsco - EbscoHost, GaleNet, OCLC - First Search
KING & QUEEN, PO Box 279, Saint Stephen's Church, 23148-0279. SAN 374-5252. Tel: 804-769-1623. TDD: 804-730-6140. FAX: 804-769-9286. Web Site: www.pamunkeylibrary.org/pamunkey/king&.htm. *Branch Mgr*, Lue Dean Jackson; E-Mail: ljackson@pamunkeylibrary.org; *Admin Assoc*, Carolyn G Garner; Tel: 804-537-6481, Fax: 804-537-6389, E-Mail: cgarner@pamunkeylibrary.org; Staff 7 (Non-MLS 7)
Founded 1994. Circ 36,210
Library Holdings: Bk Vols 8,000; Per Subs 33
Database Vendor: Ebsco - EbscoHost, GaleNet, OCLC - First Search
LOIS WICKHAM JONES - MONTPELIER BRANCH, 17205 Sycamore Tavern Lane, 23192-2564. SAN 378-1909. Tel: 804-883-7116. TDD: 804-730-6140. FAX: 804-883-5165. Web Site: www.pamunkeylibrary.org/pamunkey/montpeli.htm. *Branch Mgr*, Cynthia Seay; E-Mail: cseay@pamunkeylibrary.org; Staff 10 (MLS 1, Non-MLS 9)
Founded 1996. Circ 43,378
Library Holdings: Bk Vols 10,000; Per Subs 44
Database Vendor: Ebsco - EbscoHost, GaleNet, OCLC - First Search
Special Services for the Deaf - TDD
Open Mon 9-8, Tues-Thurs 3-8, Fri 9-6 & Sat 9-2
MECHANICSVILLE BRANCH, 7179 Stonewall Pkwy, Mechanicsville, 23111. SAN 362-9821. Tel: 804-746-9615. TDD: 804-730-6140. FAX: 804-730-4292. Web Site: www.pamunkeylibrary.org/pamunkey/mechanic.htm. *Branch Mgr*, Susie Pitts; E-Mail: spitts@pamunkeylibrary.org; *Ref*, Sherida Bradby; E-Mail: sbradby@pamunkeylibrary.org; Staff 16 (MLS 1, Non-MLS 15)
Founded 1983. Circ 166,411
Library Holdings: Bk Vols 35,000; Per Subs 120
Database Vendor: Ebsco - EbscoHost, GaleNet, OCLC - First Search
Special Services for the Deaf - TDD
RICHARD S GILLIS JR - ASHLAND BRANCH, 201 S Railroad Ave, Ashland, 23005. SAN 362-9767. Tel: 804-798-4072. Circulation Tel: 804-798-6072. FAX: 804-798-6276. Web Site: www.pamunkeylibrary.org/pamunkey/ashland_branch_library.htm. *Branch Mgr*, Laurie Greene; E-Mail: lgreene@pamunkeylibrary.org; *Ref Serv*, Alyce Hackney; E-Mail: ahackney@pamunkeylibrary.org; Staff 17 (MLS 1, Non-MLS 16)
Founded 1973. Circ 207,385
Library Holdings: Bk Vols 45,000; Per Subs 100
Database Vendor: Ebsco - EbscoHost, GaleNet, OCLC - First Search
Function: Reference services available
Friends of the Library Group
ROCKVILLE BRANCH, 16600 Pouncey Tract Rd, PO Box 220, Rockville, 23146. SAN 362-9856. Tel: 804-749-3146. TDD: 804-730-6140. FAX: 804-749-3631. Web Site: www.pamunkeylibrary.org/pamunkey/rockvill.htm. *Branch Mgr*, Patricia Clowes; E-Mail: pclowes@pamunkeylibrary.org; *Mgr*, Patricia Clowes; Staff 10 (Non-MLS 10)
Founded 1985. Circ 49,267
Library Holdings: Bk Vols 18,000; Per Subs 55
Database Vendor: Ebsco - EbscoHost, GaleNet, OCLC - First Search
Special Services for the Deaf - TDD
Friends of the Library Group
UPPER KING WILLIAM, 2253 Richmond-Tappahannock Hwy, Box 459, Manquin, 23106. SAN 375-6017. Tel: 804-769-3731. TDD: 804-730-6140. FAX: 804-769-1176. Web Site: www.pamunkeylibrary.org/pamunkey/upper.htm. *Branch Mgr*, Irene Cheney; E-Mail: icheney@pamunkeylibrary.org; Staff 8 (MLS 1, Non-MLS 7)
Founded 1995. Circ 23,673
Library Holdings: Bk Vols 5,000; Per Subs 44
Database Vendor: Ebsco - EbscoHost, GaleNet, OCLC - First Search
Special Services for the Deaf - TDD
Friends of the Library Group
WEST POINT BRANCH, 721 Main St, PO Box 1680, West Point, 23181. SAN 362-9880. Tel: 804-843-3244. TDD: 804-730-6140. FAX: 804-843-4158. Web Site: www.pamunkeylibrary.org/pamunkey/westpoint.htm. *Branch Mgr*, Vickie Brizendine; E-Mail: vbrizendine@pamunkeylibrary.org; Staff 9 (Non-MLS 9)
Founded 1989. Circ 36,210
Library Holdings: Bk Vols 20,000; Per Subs 44
Database Vendor: Ebsco - EbscoHost, GaleNet, OCLC - First Search
Special Services for the Deaf - TDD
Friends of the Library Group
Bookmobiles: 2

HARRISONBURG

C EASTERN MENNONITE UNIVERSITY, Sadie A Hartzler Library, 1200 Park Rd, 22802-2462. SAN 317-3070. Tel: 540-432-4175. FAX: 540-432-4977. Web Site: www.emu.edu/lib/sadie.htm. *Media Spec*, Martin G King; *Acq*, Audrey J Shenk; *Cat*, Jennifer M Ulrich; *Rare Bks, Spec Coll*, Lois B Bowman; *Ref*, Vicky Bickerstaff; *Automation Syst Coordr*, Audrey Shenk; Staff 4 (MLS 4)
Founded 1917. Enrl 1,097; Fac 70; Highest Degree: Master
1998-1999 Mats Exp $197,219, Books $87,700, Per/Ser (Incl. Access Fees) $94,000, Presv $3,819. Sal $343,000 (Prof $164,000)
Library Holdings: Bk Titles 142,148; Per Subs 1,144
Special Collections: Anabaptist/Mennonite History, Virginiana (Menno Simons Historical Library & Archives), 16th Century bks
Partic in OCLC Online Computer Library Center, Inc; SE Libr Network

C JAMES MADISON UNIVERSITY, Carrier Library,* 22807. SAN 317-3089. Tel: 540-568-6691. FAX: 540-568-6339. Web Site: library.jmu.edu/library/. *Dir*, Ralph Alberico; E-Mail: albericor@jmu.edu; *Media Spec*, Jeff Clark; *Acq, Per*, Sharon Gasser; *ILL*, Debra Ryman; *Cat*, Judith Anderson; *Automation Syst Coordr*, Mary Ann Chappell; *Doc*, Judith Andrews; *Ref*, Sandra Maxfield. Subject Specialists: *Music*, Brian Cockburn; Staff 18 (MLS 18)
Founded 1909. Enrl 13,600; Fac 472; Highest Degree: Doctorate
Jul 1996-Jun 1997 Income $3,829,320. Mats Exp $1,339,509, Books $441,323, Per/Ser (Incl. Access Fees) $661,580, Presv $55,022, Micro $54,565, Other Print Mats $127,019. Sal $2,023,371 (Prof $770,458)
Library Holdings: Bk Vols 406,190; Per Subs 2,399
Subject Interests: Child psychology, Education, History, History of science, Philos of sci, Shenandoah Valley hist
Special Collections: American Civilization (Library of American Civilization), micro; Laird L Conrad Law Library; Science History (Landmarks of; Science), micro
Automation Activity & Vendor Info: (Cataloging) Innovative Interfaces Inc.; (Circulation) Innovative Interfaces Inc.
Partic in SE Libr Network
Friends of the Library Group

P MASSANUTTEN REGIONAL LIBRARY, (Formerly Rockingham Public Library), 174 S Main St, 22801. SAN 362-9910. Tel: 540-434-4475. FAX: 540-434-4382. Web Site: www.mrlib.org. *Dir*, Phillip T Hearne; E-Mail: phearne@rplib.org; *Asst Dir*, Nick Whitmer; *Cat*, Lora Rose; *Ad Servs*, Lois Jones; *Ch Servs*, Brenda Swannack; Tel: 715-232-2617, E-Mail: swannackb@uwstout.edu; Staff 38 (MLS 6, Non-MLS 32)
Founded 1928. Pop 119,637; Circ 545,000
Jul 2000-Jun 2001 Income (Main Library and Branch Library) $1,537,106, State $450,316, City $304,440, County $691,000. Mats Exp $268,200, Books $157,000, Per/Ser (Incl. Access Fees) $26,700, Micro $9,000, Electronic Ref Mat (Incl. Access Fees) $30,000. Sal $755,882
Library Holdings: Bk Vols 140,000; Per Subs 305
Special Collections: Virginia & Family History (Virginiana-Genealogy Coll)
Database Vendor: OCLC - First Search, ProQuest
Publications: Check-It-Out (bi-annual newsletter)
Partic in Capcon Library Network; OCLC Online Computer Library Center, Inc; SWING
Special Services for the Blind - High interest/low vocabulary bk vols
Friends of the Library Group
Branches: 6
BERGTON BRANCH, 11784 Criders Rd, Bergton, 22820. SAN 378-147X.

Tel: 540-852-3224. FAX: 540-852-3324. *Librn*, Lois Mogers
ELKTON COMMUNITY, 106 N Terrace Ave, Elkton, 22827. SAN 375-5150. Tel: 540-298-2964. FAX: 540-298-0545. *Librn*, Linda Magalis
GROTTOES BRANCH, 601 Dogwood Ave, Grottoes, 22441. Tel: 540-249-3436. FAX: 540-249-8307. *Br Coordr*, Cheryl Keeler
Founded 2000
NORTH RIVER, 118 Mount Crawford Ave, 22812. SAN 375-5169. Tel: 540-828-4492. FAX: 540-828-4492. *Librn*, Denise Madland; Tel: 715-232-2141, E-Mail: madlandd@uwstout.edu
PAGE PUBLIC, 100 Zerkel St, PO Box 734, Luray, 22835. SAN 362-9945. Tel: 540-743-6867. FAX: 540-743-7661. *Librn*, Faye Neuenfeldt; E-Mail: neuenfeldtf@uwstout.edu
Library Holdings: Bk Vols 3,474
VILLAGE, 113 S Central Ave, PO Box 1045, Broadway, 22815. SAN 372-8005. Tel: 540-896-1646. FAX: 540-896-9260. *Librn*, Elaine Taylor
Library Holdings: Bk Vols 6,147
Bookmobiles: 1

M ROCKINGHAM MEMORIAL HOSPITAL, Virginia Funkhouser Health Sciences Library, 235 Cantrell Ave, 22801-3293. SAN 317-3097. Tel: 540-433-4166. FAX: 540-433-3106. *Dir*, Ilene N Smith; E-Mail: ismith@rhcc.com; *Librn*, Mary L Addy; E-Mail: maddy@rhcc.com; Staff 2 (MLS 2)
Founded 1912
Jan 1999-Dec 1999 Income $225,737, Locally Generated Income $4,432, Parent Institution $221,305. Mats Exp $94,708, Books $23,588, Per/Ser (Incl. Access Fees) $49,839. Sal $126,597
Library Holdings: Bk Vols 5,000; Per Subs 256
Subject Interests: Allied health, Clinical medicine, Consumer health, Health care admin, Nursing
Automation Activity & Vendor Info: (Cataloging) Inmagic, Inc.; (Circulation) Inmagic, Inc.; (OPAC) Inmagic, Inc.
Publications: On the Shelf (quarterly) (Newsletter)
Partic in Docline; Nat Libr of Med; OCLC Online Computer Library Center, Inc; SE Libr Ctr

HEATHSVILLE

P NORTHUMBERLAND PUBLIC LIBRARY, 7204 Northumberland Hwy, 22473. SAN 309-9164. Tel: 804-580-5051. FAX: 804-580-5202. Web Site: www.eaglesnest.net/nulibrary. *Dir*, Alice Hershiser; E-Mail: ahershis@vsla.edu
Founded 1893. Pop 2,400; Circ 23,500
Jul 1998-Jun 1999 Income $145,000, State $23,200, County $62,300, Locally Generated Income $59,500. Mats Exp $145,000, Books $26,000, Per/Ser (Incl. Access Fees) $1,500, AV Equip $1,500, Electronic Ref Mat (Incl. Access Fees) $200. Sal $72,000 (Prof $30,000)
Library Holdings: Bk Vols 30,000; Per Subs 120
Publications: Book List; LAMA; Library Journal; Public Libraries
Mem of North Country District
Friends of the Library Group

HERNDON

S AIRLINE PILOTS ASSOCIATION INTERNATIONAL, Engineering & Air Safety Resource Center,* 535 Herndon Pkwy, PO Box 1169, 20172-1169. SAN 302-5519. Tel: 703-689-4204. FAX: 703-689-4370. *Librn*, Pablo P Santamaria; E-Mail: santamarip@alpa.org; *Asst Librn*, Marvin Ramirez
Subject Interests: Aviation
Special Collections: Federal Aviation Regulations; Jeppesen Flight Charts (worldwide); Videos

L COLUMBIA ENERGY GROUP SERVICE CORP, Law Library,* 13880 Dulles Corner Lane, 20171. SAN 302-5209. Tel: 703-561-6000. FAX: 703-561-7303. *Librn*, Penny Pinnes
Founded 1959. Pop 200
Library Holdings: Per Subs 73
Subject Interests: Corporate law, Legislation
Restriction: By appointment only

S JUSTICE FELLOWSHIP, Policy Institute, 200 Fairbrook Dr, Ste 202, 20170-5230. SAN 377-1547. Tel: 703-456-4050. Toll Free Tel: 800-217-2743. FAX: 703-478-9679. E-Mail: mail@justicefellowship.org. Web Site: www.justicefellowship.org. *Pres*, Pat Nolan
Library Holdings: Bk Vols 100

S NATIONAL ASSOCIATION OF INDUSTRIAL & OFFICE PROPERTIES, NAIOP Information Center,* 2201 Cooperative Way, 20171. SAN 328-1906. Tel: 703-904-7100. FAX: 703-904-7942. *Mgr*, Kelly Jordan
Founded 1985
Library Holdings: Bk Titles 700; Per Subs 50
Subject Interests: Real estate
Special Collections: Real Estate Marketing Coll, brochures, slides, architectural portfolios
Automation Activity & Vendor Info: (Cataloging) Inmagic, Inc.

S NATIONAL CONCRETE MASONRY ASSOCIATION LIBRARY,* 23 Horse Pen Rd, 20171-3499. SAN 328-3089. Tel: 703-713-1900. FAX: 7 713-1910. Web Site: www.ncma.org. *In Charge*, Evelyn Gilbert
Library Holdings: Bk Vols 4,000; Per Subs 80

S NATIONAL INSTITUTE OF GOVERNMENTAL PURCHASING, INC Specifications Library, 151 Spring St, No 212, 20170. SAN 373-2630. T 703-736-8900. FAX: 703-736-9644. Web Site: www.nigp.org. *In Charge* Fuad Abu-Taleb; Tel: 703-736-8900, Ext 241, E-Mail: fabutaleb@nigp.o
Founded 1944
Library Holdings: Bk Titles 80
Restriction: Members only
Open Mon-Fri 8-5

HILLSVILLE

S SOUTHWESTERN VIRGINIA TRAINING CENTER, Research & Train Library,* PO Box 1328, 24343. SAN 321-0197. Tel: 540-728-3121, Ext FAX: 540-728-3127. *Librn*, Dan Dewey
Founded 1976
Library Holdings: Bk Titles 1,000; Per Subs 20
Subject Interests: Special education

HOPEWELL

P APPOMATTOX REGIONAL LIBRARY, Maude Langhorne Nelson Lib 245 E Cawson St, 23860. SAN 317-316X. Tel: 804-458-0110. FAX: 804-452-0909. *Dir*, Charles Koutnik; E-Mail: ckoutnik@arls.org; *Asst Dir*, Sc Firestine; *Ch Servs*, Nancy Wanzong; *Ref*, Chris Wiegard; Staff 35 (MLS Non-MLS 28)
Founded 1974. Pop 71,300; Circ 255,815
Jul 1999-Jun 2000 Income (Main Library and Branch Library) $1,098,06 State $269,096, City $364,225, Federal $6,090, County $364,225, Other $94,427. Mats Exp $166,863, Books $117,747, Per/Ser (Incl. Access Fees $14,059, Presv $982, Micro $3,717, AV Equip $10,554, Electronic Ref M (Incl. Access Fees) $19,804. Sal $514,764 (Prof $138,034)
Library Holdings: Bk Vols 172,167; Bk Titles 125,537; Per Subs 371
Automation Activity & Vendor Info: (Cataloging) Gaylord; (Circulation Gaylord; (OPAC) Gaylord
Friends of the Library Group
Branches: 6
CARSON BRANCH, PO Box 428, Carson, 23830. SAN 328-9869. Tel: 804-246-2900.
Friends of the Library Group
DINWIDDIE BRANCH, 14101 Boydton Plank Rd, PO Box 480, Dinwid 23841. SAN 321-7426. Tel: 804-469-9450. FAX: 804-469-9450.
Friends of the Library Group
DISPUTANTA BRANCH, 10010 Country Dr, PO Box 59, Disputanta, 23842. SAN 324-2927. Tel: 804-991-2403. FAX: 804-991-2403.
Friends of the Library Group
MCKENNEY BRANCH, 20707 First St, McKenney, 23872. SAN 328-98 Tel: 804-478-4866. FAX: 804-478-4866.
PRINCE GEORGE BRANCH, 6402 Courthouse Rd, PO Box 368, Prince George, 23875. SAN 328-9907. Tel: 804-732-0652. FAX: 804-732-0652
Friends of the Library Group
ROHOIC, 7301 Boydton Plank Rd, Petersburg, 23803. SAN 324-2935. Te 804-732-4119. FAX: 804-732-4119.
Friends of the Library Group
Bookmobiles: 1

INDEPENDENCE

P WYTHE-GRAYSON REGIONAL LIBRARY,* 147 S Independence Ave, PO Box 159, 24348. SAN 362-997X. Tel: 540-773-3018. FAX: 540-773-3289. *Dir*, T Michael Gilley; E-Mail: mgilley@leo.vsla.edu; *Tech Servs*, Janet L Cox
Founded 1948. Pop 41,900; Circ 235,522
Library Holdings: Bk Vols 111,000; Per Subs 259
Subject Interests: Bks on tape, Civil War, Genealogy, Large print
Partic in SE Libr Network
Literacy Program; summer reading program
Friends of the Library Group
Branches: 3
FRIES PUBLIC, PO Box 325, Fries, 24330. SAN 377-7669. Tel: 540-744-3160. FAX: 540-744-3160. *Dir*, Michael Gilley
WHITETOP PUBLIC, PO Box 97, Whitetop, 24292. SAN 377-7685. Tel: 540-388-2873. FAX: 540-388-2873. *Dir*, Michael Gilley
WYTHE COUNTY PUBLIC, 300 E Monroe, Wytheville, 24382. SAN 363 0005. Tel: 540-228-4951. FAX: 540-228-6034. *Librn*, Mary Etta Clemon
Circ 141,313
Subject Interests: Bks on tape, Genealogy, Large print
Interlibrary loan; Literacy Program; summer reading program
Bookmobiles: 1

.MARNOCK

LANCASTER COMMUNITY LIBRARY,* 235 School St, PO Box 850, 22482-0850. SAN 317-3178. Tel: 804-435-1729. FAX: 804-435-0255. Web Site: www.nothernneck.com/library. *Librn*, Susanna A Collins
Pop 30,000; Circ 80,300
Jul 1998-Jun 1999 Income $338,212. Mats Exp $39,124, Books $30,179, Per/Ser (Incl. Access Fees) $3,600. Sal $104,747 (Prof $50,144)
Library Holdings: Bk Vols 35,000
Special Collections: Virginia Coll
Friends of the Library Group

NG GEORGE

LEWIS EGERTON SMOOT MEMORIAL LIBRARY,* 9533 Kings Hwy, 22485. SAN 317-3186. Tel: 540-775-7951. FAX: 540-775-5292. E-Mail: smootlib@crosslink.net. Web Site: www.smoot.org. *Dir*, Rita Schepmoes; *Asst Librn*, Linda Addair; Staff 11 (MLS 1, Non-MLS 10)
Founded 1969. Pop 16,600; Circ 61,399
Jul 1998-Jun 1999 Income $250,550, State $56,183, County $135,570, Locally Generated Income $58,797. Mats Exp $58,242, Books $45,670, Per/Ser (Incl. Access Fees) $4,684, Presv $512, AV Equip $2,436, Electronic Ref Mat (Incl. Access Fees) $4,940. Sal $120,259 (Prof $37,060)
Library Holdings: Bk Vols 52,263; Bk Titles 48,898; Per Subs 106
Subject Interests: Va hist
Special Collections: Virginiana
Friends of the Library Group

.NCASTER

MARY BALL WASHINGTON MUSEUM, Family Research Center, PO Box 97, 22503-0097. SAN 317-3194. Tel: 804-462-7280. FAX: 804-462-6107. E-Mail: history@rivnet.net. Web Site: www.mbwm.org. *Archivist, Librn*, Dr Maurice Duke
Founded 1958
Library Holdings: Bk Vols 5,010; Bk Titles 4,600; Per Subs 10
Subject Interests: Lancaster County, US hist, Va genealogy, Va state
Special Collections: Bicentennial (Governor John Garland Pollard Coll), papers, photog; Camp Meetings (Dr Henry Marvin Wharton Coll), papers, photog; Family Papers (Chilton, Chowning, Dunaway, Squires, Washington), papers, photog; Manuscripts & Research (Elizabeth Combs Peirce Coll), papers, photog; Millenback Excavation (Home of William Ball III), papers, photog & mss; Washington Family Memorabilia
Publications: 1850 Census of Lancaster County, Virginia; Ball Family Outline; Colonel James Gordon, Merchant of Lancaster County, Virginia; Historic Sites of Lancaster County, Virginia; Lancaster County Will Books (1796-1925); Map of Corotoman River; Newsletter (quarterly); The Early Thomas Carters of Lancaster County, Virginia

ANGLEY AFB

UNITED STATES AIR FORCE
LANGLEY AIR FORCE BASE LIBRARY FL4800, 1 SVS/SVMG, 62 Walnut St, 23665. SAN 363-0064. Tel: 757-764-2906. FAX: 757-764-3315. *Librn*, Esther Cornelius; Staff 2 (MLS 2)
Founded 1942
Library Holdings: Bk Vols 25,000; Per Subs 225
Subject Interests: Aeronautics, Foreign affairs, Military history, Southeast Asia
Publications: Tales of Air Warriors
Partic in Dialog Corporation; OCLC Online Computer Library Center, Inc

AWRENCEVILLE

BRUNSWICK CORRECTIONAL CENTER, DCE Library,* 1147 Planters Rd, 23868-3499. SAN 371-9448. Tel: 804-848-4131, Ext 1146. FAX: 804-848-4131, Ext 1144. *Librn*, John Kellam; Staff 1 (MLS 1)
Founded 1982
Library Holdings: Bk Vols 17,000; Bk Titles 14,000; Per Subs 61
Automation Activity & Vendor Info: (Cataloging) Follett
Special Services for the Deaf - Books on deafness & sign language; Captioned film depository; High interest/low vocabulary books; Special interest periodicals

MEHERRIN REGIONAL LIBRARY, 133 W Hicks St, 23868. SAN 363-0099. Tel: 804-848-2418. FAX: 804-848-2418. Web Site: meherrinlib.org. *Dir*, Jeann Riedl; E-Mail: jriedl@meherrinlib.org; *Tech Servs*, Margaret P Holman; *Publ Servs*, Linda Bagley; Staff 15 (MLS 2, Non-MLS 13)
Founded 1940. Pop 32,000; Circ 140,000
2000-2001 Income (Main Library and Branch Library) $529,808, State $169,913, City $76,920, County $227,507, Locally Generated Income $19,181, Other $12,621. Mats Exp $117,000, Books $85,000, Per/Ser (Incl. Access Fees) $9,000, AV Equip $8,000, Electronic Ref Mat (Incl. Access Fees) $7,000. Sal $273,632 (Prof $70,790)
Library Holdings: Bk Vols 80,000; Per Subs 200
Automation Activity & Vendor Info: (Circulation) Sagebrush Corporation; (OPAC) Sagebrush Corporation
Database Vendor: Ebsco - EbscoHost, OCLC - First Search, Wilson - Wilson Web
Partic in OCLC Online Computer Library Center, Inc
Friends of the Library Group
Branches: 1
WILLIAM E RICHARDSON JR MEMORIAL LIBRARY, One Spring St, Emporia, 23847. SAN 363-0129. Tel: 804-634-2539. FAX: 804-634-9849. *Librn*, Mary L Geist
Founded 1977
Bookmobiles: 1

C SAINT PAUL'S COLLEGE, Russell Memorial Library, 115 College Dr, 23868-1299. SAN 317-3208. Tel: 804-848-3111. FAX: 804-848-4401. *Dir*, Marc Finney; *Publ Servs*, Larry Seilhamer; *Circ*, Stacey Marshall; Staff 5 (MLS 1, Non-MLS 4)
Enrl 680; Fac 53; Highest Degree: Bachelor
Library Holdings: Bk Vols 44,690; Bk Titles 37,000; Per Subs 230
Special Collections: Black Studies (Schomburg Coll), micro; West Indies (Short Coll)
Partic in Coop Col Libr Ctr, Inc

LEBANON

P RUSSELL COUNTY PUBLIC LIBRARY,* 203 NW Main St, 24266-0247. (Mail add: PO Box 247, 24266-0247), SAN 317-3216. Tel: 540-889-8044. FAX: 540-889-8045. E-Mail: cduty@russell.lib.va.us. Web Site: www.russell.lib.va.us. *Dir*, Charlotte E Duty
Pop 29,000; Circ 71,086
Library Holdings: Bk Titles 38,758; Per Subs 70
Subject Interests: Genealogy, Local history
Automation Activity & Vendor Info: (Cataloging) TLC; (Circulation) TLC
Publications: Friends of the Library Newsletter
Friends of the Library Group

LEESBURG

P LOUDOUN COUNTY PUBLIC LIBRARY,* Admin Offices, 102 Heritage Way NE, Ste 103, 20176-3328. SAN 363-0153. Tel: 703-777-0368. Interlibrary Loan Service Tel: 703-777-0675. FAX: 703-771-5238, 703-771-5252. Web Site: www.lcpl.lib.va.us. *Dir*, Douglas A Henderson; *Automation Syst Coordr*, Marilyn Steere; *Media Spec*, Jack Frear; Staff 95 (MLS 24, Non-MLS 71)
Founded 1973. Circ 1,855,864
Jul 1997-Jun 1998 Income $4,318,388. Mats Exp $707,453, Books $571,506, Per/Ser (Incl. Access Fees) $29,081, Micro $87,689. Sal $3,396,886 (Prof $1,039,949)
Library Holdings: Bk Vols 348,815; Per Subs 415
Automation Activity & Vendor Info: (Acquisitions) epixtech, inc.; (Circulation) epixtech, inc.
Publications: An Introduction to Loudoun County Public Libraries; Calendar of Events (monthly); Community Information Referral Service; Free & Accessible: Services for Residents with Disabilities Dial Up Access Guide; Parents & Children Together; Selected Reference Sources for Small Business
Partic in Capcon Library Network
Special Services for the Deaf - TTY machine
Special Services for the Disabled - Communication Aids Room - Electronic technology for people with disabilities
Branches: 7
EASTERN LOUDOUN REGIONAL, 21020 Whitfield Pl, Sterling, 20165. SAN 371-988X. Tel: 703-444-3228. FAX: 703-444-1336. Web Site: www.lcpl.lib.va.us. *Mgr*, Carolyn Watson
Library Holdings: Bk Vols 116,500
Special Services for the Deaf - TTY machine
Special Services for the Blind - Talking book center
Special Services for the Disabled - Communications Aids Room
Friends of the Library Group
LOVETTSVILLE BRANCH, 12 N Light St, PO Box 189, Lovettsville, 20180. SAN 328-7645. Tel: 540-822-5824. FAX: 540-822-5998. Web Site: www.lcpl.lib.va.us. *Mgr*, Charles V Wood
Library Holdings: Bk Vols 11,800
Special Services for the Deaf - TTY machine
Friends of the Library Group
MIDDLEBURG BRANCH, PO Box 1823, Middleburg, 20118. SAN 328-7629. Tel: 540-687-5730. FAX: 540-687-3630. Web Site: www.lcpl.lib.va.us. *Mgr*, Sheila Whetzel; Staff 2 (MLS 1, Non-MLS 1)
Founded 1984
Library Holdings: Bk Vols 15,000
Special Services for the Deaf - TTY machine
Friends of the Library Group
OUTREACH SERVICES, 380 Old Waterford Rd, 20176. SAN 377-6506. Tel: 703-771-5621. TDD: 703-777-0323. FAX: 703-771-5620.
Special Services for the Deaf - TDD
PURCELLVILLE BRANCH, 220 E Main St, Purcellville, 20132-3167. SAN 363-0218. Tel: 540-338-7235. FAX: 540-338-2629. Web Site:

www.lcpl.lib.va.us. *Mgr*, Sharon R Hershey; E-Mail: shershey@lcpl.lib.va.us; Staff 20 (MLS 4, Non-MLS 16)
1999-2000 Mats Exp Books $65,000
Library Holdings: Bk Vols 70,000; Per Subs 100
Automation Activity & Vendor Info: (Circulation) epixtech, inc.
Special Services for the Deaf - TTY machine
Friends of the Library Group
RUST BRANCH, 380 Old Waterford Rd, 20176. SAN 371-9898. Tel: 703-777-0323. TDD: 703-777-0323. FAX: 703-771-5620. Web Site: www.lcpl.lib.va.us. *Mgr*, Ellen Henry
Library Holdings: Bk Vols 77,500
Special Services for the Deaf - TDD
Friends of the Library Group
STERLING BRANCH, 120 Enterprise St, Sterling, 20164. SAN 363-0242. Tel: 703-430-9500. TDD: 703-430-9500. FAX: 703-430-5935. Web Site: www.lcpl.lib.va.us. *Mgr*, Barbara Ecton
Library Holdings: Bk Vols 33,000
Special Services for the Deaf - TDD
Friends of the Library Group
Bookmobiles: 1

LEXINGTON

S GEORGE C MARSHALL RESEARCH FOUNDATION LIBRARY,* PO Box 1600, 24450-1600. SAN 317-3224. Tel: 540-463-7103. FAX: 540-464-5229. *Dir*, Thomas E Camden; E-Mail: camdente@vmi.edu
Founded 1964
Library Holdings: Bk Titles 25,000; Per Subs 66
Special Collections: Cryptography (William Friedman Coll), oral hist, posters, photos, Women's Army Corps; Marshall Plan; Military-Diplomatic History 1900-1950 (126 mss collections)
Publications: George C Marshall Research Library Handbook For Researchers; Manuscript Collections of the George C Marshall Library George C Marshall Papers, 1932-1960, A Guide; Posters in the George C Marshall Foundation
Partic in SE Libr Network

S STONEWALL JACKSON HOUSE - GARLAND GRAY RESEARCH CENTER & LIBRARY, Stonewall Jackson House, 8 E Washington St, 24450. SAN 327-3555. Tel: 540-463-2552. FAX: 540-463-4088. *Dir*, Michael Anne Lynn
Library Holdings: Bk Vols 11,000

P ROCKBRIDGE REGIONAL LIBRARY, 138 S Main St, 24450-2316. SAN 363-0277. Tel: 540-463-4324. FAX: 540-464-4824. Web Site: www.lib.rang.gen.va.us/. *Dir*, Linda L Krantz; E-Mail: lkrantz@lib.rang.gen.va.us; *Asst Librn*, Grace McCrowell; *Cat*, Beth Cary; *Ref*, David Gansz; *Exten Serv*, Deanie Bsullak; *Ch Servs*, Susan Milo; Staff 34 (MLS 3, Non-MLS 31)
Founded 1934. Pop 38,800; Circ 230,137
Jul 1999-Jun 2000 Income (Main Library and Branch Library) $978,189, State $233,490, City $160,050, Federal $13,563, County $452,809, Locally Generated Income $7,395, Other $110,882. Mats Exp $978,096, Books $152,422, Per/Ser (Incl. Access Fees) $12,841, AV Equip $16,062, Electronic Ref Mat (Incl. Access Fees) $50,496. Sal $461,038 (Prof $40,080)
Library Holdings: Bk Vols 160,570; Per Subs 250
Subject Interests: Local history
Automation Activity & Vendor Info: (Cataloging) Gaylord
Database Vendor: OCLC - First Search, ProQuest
Publications: Foundation annual report; Library newsletter
Function: Reference services available
Partic in SE Libr Network; SW Info Network Group
Special Services for the Blind - Printed text enlargers; Talking Books
Friends of the Library Group
Branches: 4
BATH COUNTY PUBLIC, PO Box 250, Warm Springs, 24484. SAN 363-0307. Tel: 540-839-7286. FAX: 540-839-3058. Web Site: www.lib.rang.gen.va.us. *Librn*, Jeanette Robinson; *Librn*, Sharon Lindsay
Library Holdings: Bk Vols 26,712
Friends of the Library Group
BUENA VISTA PUBLIC, 2110 Magnolia Ave, Buena Vista, 24416. SAN 363-0331. Tel: 540-261-2715. FAX: 540-261-4822. Web Site: www.lib.rang.gen.va.us. *Librn*, Anne Johnson
Library Holdings: Bk Vols 17,373
GLASGOW PUBLIC, 1015 Blueridge Rd, Glasgow, 24555. SAN 363-0366. Tel: 540-258-2509. FAX: 540-258-1400. Web Site: www.lib.rang.gen.va.us. *Librn*, Barbara Slough
Library Holdings: Bk Vols 10,726
GOSHEN PUBLIC, 1124 Virginia Ave, Goshen, 24439. SAN 323-5718. Tel: 540-997-0351. FAX: 540-997-0019. *Librn*, Anne McClung
Library Holdings: Bk Vols 6,216
Friends of the Library Group
Bookmobiles: 1

C VIRGINIA MILITARY INSTITUTE, J T L Preston Library, 24450. SAN 317-3232. Tel: 540-464-7228. FAX: 540-464-7279. Web Site: www.vmi. library/. *Dir*, Don Samdahl; *ILL*, Elizabeth Hostetter; *Tech Servs*, Linda Covington; *Doc*, Janet S Holly; *Rare Bks, Spec Coll*, Diane Jacob; *Acces Serv*, Susan Hastings; *Ref Serv*, Ken Winter; *Media Spec*, Dave Hess; St (MLS 5, Non-MLS 1)
Founded 1839. Enrl 1,300; Fac 106; Highest Degree: Bachelor
Jul 1999-Jun 2000 Income $1,121,765, State $1,044,414, Other $77,351. Mats Exp $300,625, Books $101,216, Per/Ser (Incl. Access Fees) $182,7 Presv $8,995, Micro $7,648. Sal $639,492 (Prof $224,575)
Library Holdings: Bk Vols 265,183; Per Subs 785
Special Collections: Civil War; Thomas J (Stonewall) Jackson
Database Vendor: DRA
Publications: Friends of Preston Library Newsletter; library brochure
Partic in SE Libr Network; Virtual Libr of Va
Friends of the Library Group

WASHINGTON & LEE UNIVERSITY

C JAMES GRAHAM LEYBURN LIBRARY, 24450. Tel: 540-463-8640. Interlibrary Loan Service Tel: 540-463-8644. FAX: 540-463-8964. *Dir*, Barbara J Brown; E-Mail: bbrown@wlu.edu; *ILL*, Betsy Brittigan; *Acq* Annette John; *Tech Servs*, David A Badertscher; *Ref*, Richard Grefe; *Re* Yolanda Warren; *Rare Bks, Spec Coll*, C Vaughan Stanley; *Ref*, John Tombarge; Staff 7 (MLS 7)
Founded 1749. Enrl 1,960; Fac 169; Highest Degree: Doctorate
Jul 1996-Jun 1997 Income $1,924,134. Mats Exp $961,338, Books $346,956, Per/Ser (Incl. Access Fees) $477,920, Presv $31,950, Micro $21,239. Sal $660,046 (Prof $387,087)
Library Holdings: Bk Vols 500,000
Special Collections: Classical Literature; Confederacy (Robert E Lee Coll); Franklin Society Library; Graham Society Library; W & L University & Valley of Virginia Manuscripts; Washington Society Libra
Automation Activity & Vendor Info: (Acquisitions) Innovative Interfa Inc.
Publications: Guide to the Manuscripts Coll; Rockbridge Area Union I of Serials
Partic in OCLC Online Computer Library Center, Inc; SE Libr Networ

CL WILBUR C HALL LAW LIBRARY, Lewis Hall, 24450. SAN 363-0455 Tel: 540-463-8540. Interlibrary Loan Service Tel: 540-463-8553. FAX: 540-463-8967. Web Site: www.wlu.edu/law/lib. *Dir*, Sarah K Wiant; E-Mail: wiants@wlu.edu; *Assoc Librn*, John Doyle; Tel: 540-463-8554, E-Mail: doylej@wlu.edu; *Acq*, Jean Eisenhauer; Tel: 540-463-8545, E-Mail: eisenhauerj@wlu.edu; *Doc*, Judy Stinson; Tel: 540-463-8544, E-Mail: stinsonj@wlu.edu; *Archivist*, John Jacob; Tel: 540-463-8969, E-Mail: jacobj@wlu.edu; *Cat*, John P Bissett; Tel: 540-463-8546, E-Ma bissettj@wlu.edu; *Media Spec Ad, Ref*, Tom Williams; Tel: 540-463-855 E-Mail: williamst@wlu.edu; Staff 7 (MLS 7)
Founded 1849. Enrl 374; Fac 34; Highest Degree: Doctorate
Jul 1999-Jun 2000 Income $1,051,439. Mats Exp $984,100, Books $109,327, Per/Ser (Incl. Access Fees) $795,408, Presv $14,708, Micro $18,407, AV Equip $4,008, Manuscripts & Archives $161, Electronic R Mat (Incl. Access Fees) $42,081. Sal $665,634 (Prof $394,560)
Library Holdings: Bk Vols 227,144; Bk Titles 57,865; Per Subs 4,349
Special Collections: Appellate Papers (John W Davis Coll); Bankruptcy (U S Senate Committee on the Judiciary Coll); Early Virginia Legal Materials (Burks Coll); Fourth Circuit Court of Appeals Records & Brie Impeachment Papers of President Richard M Nixon (Caldwell Butler); Lewis F Powell Jr Archives; Lewis F Powell Papers; Walter Hoffman papers; Washington & Lee Law School Archives
Automation Activity & Vendor Info: (Acquisitions) Innovative Interfa Inc.; (Cataloging) Innovative Interfaces Inc.; (Circulation) Innovative Interfaces Inc.; (OPAC) Innovative Interfaces Inc.; (Serials) Innovative Interfaces Inc.
Database Vendor: Innovative Interfaces INN - View
Publications: Acquisitions List; Current Contents; Law Library Guide; Newsletter
Partic in OCLC Online Computer Library Center, Inc

LOCUST GROVE

J GERMANNA COMMUNITY COLLEGE LIBRARY,* 2130 Germanna Hwy, 22508. SAN 317-3240. Tel: 540-727-3120. FAX: 540-727-3210. We Site: www.gc.cc.va.us. *Librn*, Linda Larkin; Staff 2 (MLS 2)
Founded 1970. Enrl 2,500
Library Holdings: Bk Titles 31,000; Per Subs 175
Subject Interests: Bus, History, Medicine, Mgt, Nursing
Special Collections: Genealogy & Local History (Germanna Foundation Society Materials & Genealogies)
Campus library located in Fredericksburg

LURAY

S SHENANDOAH NATIONAL PARK LIBRARY,* 3655 US Hwy 211 E, 22835. SAN 317-3267. Tel: 540-999-2243, Ext 3472. FAX: 540-999-3679. *Librn*, John Mitchell

Founded 1966
Library Holdings: Bk Vols 1,600; Per Subs 25
Subject Interests: Natural history

NCHBURG

BARKSDALE MEDICAL LIBRARY,* Virginia Baptist Hospital, 3300 Rivermont Ave, 24503. SAN 323-5203. Tel: 804-947-3147. FAX: 804-947-3104. *Librn*, Claire A Meissner
Jan 1999-Dec 1999 Mats Exp $27,800, Books $15,000, Per/Ser (Incl. Access Fees) $10,000, Other Print Mats $2,800
Library Holdings: Bk Titles 168; Per Subs 45
Subject Interests: Gynecology, Obstetrics, Oncology, Pediatrics, Psychiatry
Partic in Lynchburg Area Library Cooperative; National Network Of Libraries Of Medicine - South Central Region; OCLC Online Computer Library Center, Inc; Southwestern Virginia Health Information Librarians; VACOHSL

CENTRAL VIRGINIA COMMUNITY COLLEGE LIBRARY,* 3506 Wards Rd, 24502-2498. SAN 317-3283. Tel: 804-832-7750. FAX: 804-386-4677. E-Mail: cvwilla@cv.cc.va.us. Web Site: www.cv.cc.va.us/library.htm. *Ref*, James A Pollock; Staff 5 (MLS 5)
Founded 1967. Enrl 1,978; Fac 95
Library Holdings: Bk Titles 32,739; Per Subs 201
Subject Interests: Lynchburg area hist
Automation Activity & Vendor Info: (Circulation) NOTIS
Publications: Acquisitions List (quarterly)
Partic in Lynchburg Area Library Cooperative; OCLC Online Computer Library Center, Inc; SE Libr Network; Virtual Libr of Va

CENTRAL VIRGINIA TRAINING CENTER
PROFESSIONAL LIBRARY, PO Box 1098, 24505. SAN 363-051X. Tel: 804-947-6171, 804-947-6871. FAX: 804-947-2395. E-Mail: cvtc@inmind.com. *Dir*, Carolyn Robinson
Founded 1957
Library Holdings: Bk Vols 4,600; Per Subs 60
Subject Interests: Mental retardation
Database Vendor: Ebsco - EbscoHost, OCLC - First Search
Restriction: Not a lending library, Public use on premises
Function: ILL limited
Partic in Lynchburg Area Library Cooperative

FRAMATOME TECHNOLOGIES, Technical Library,* 3315 Old Forest Rd, PO Box 10935, 24506. SAN 317-3275. Tel: 804-832-2476. FAX: 804-832-2475. *Librn*, Elizabeth Boothe; E-Mail: eboothe@framatech.com
Founded 1955
Library Holdings: Bk Titles 23,000; Per Subs 50
Subject Interests: Chemistry, Computer applications, Mathematics, Nuclear science, Nuclear tech
Restriction: By appointment only
Partic in Dialog Corporation; OCLC Online Computer Library Center, Inc

GEORGE M JONES LIBRARY ASSOCIATION, Jones Memorial Library, 2311 Memorial Ave, 24501. SAN 317-3305. Tel: 804-846-0501. FAX: 804-846-1572. E-Mail: webmaster@jmlibrary.org. Web Site: www.jmlibrary.org. *Dir*, Phillip Wayne Rhodes; E-Mail: wrhodes@jmlibrary.org; *Publ Servs*, Lewis Hobgood Averett; E-Mail: laverett@jmlibrary.org; *Res*, Susan Hall Pillow; E-Mail: spillow@jmlibrary.org; *Res*, Nancy Jamerson Weiland; E-Mail: nweiland@jmlibrary.org. Subject Specialists: *Genealogical res*, Susan Hall Pillow; *Genealogical res*, Nancy Jamerson Weiland; Staff 5 (MLS 1, Non-MLS 4)
Founded 1908
Jul 1999-Jun 2000 Income $191,000. Mats Exp $219,000, Books $7,500, Per/Ser (Incl. Access Fees) $3,000, Presv $1,800, Micro $2,500. Sal $112,000
Library Holdings: Bk Titles 30,000; Per Subs 100
Subject Interests: Genealogy, Local history
Special Collections: Lynchburg Architectural Archives; Manuscript Collection, personal family papers & correspondence, records of clubs & organizations, business records
Database Vendor: OCLC - First Search
Publications: JML Report (2/yr) (Newsletter)
Partic in Lynchburg Area Library Cooperative; OCLC Online Computer Library Center, Inc
Second oldest public library in Virginia; privately-endowed public research facility specializing in genealogy & primary focus in local history of Central Virginia; collection is non-circulating; ILL requests accepted, $10 fee (ALA form or OCLC through VCQ)

R LIBERTY UNIVERSITY LIBRARY, A Pierre Guillermin Library, 1971 University Blvd, 24502. SAN 317-3313. Tel: 804-582-2220. Circulation Tel: 804-582-2506. Reference Tel: 804-582-2221. FAX: 804-582-2017. Web Site: www.liberty.edu/resources/library. *Dean*, Dr David Barnett; E-Mail: dbarnett@liberty.edu; *Assoc Dean*, Carl H Merat; E-Mail: cmerat@liberty.edu; *Coll Develop*, Tom Agee; *Electronic Resources*, Jeff Dull; E-Mail: jmdull@liberty.edu; *Librn*, Diane Sullivan; Tel: 804-582-2821, E-Mail: dssulliv@liberty.edu; *Cat*, Tom Fesmire; E-Mail: twfesmire@liberty.edu; *Distance Educ*, Diane Garber; E-Mail: dsgarber@liberty.edu; *Syst Coordr*, Michael Cobb; E-Mail: mikecobb@liberty.edu; *Ref*, Rachel Schwedt; E-Mail: resched@liberty.edu. Subject Specialists: *Educ curric*, Rachel Schwedt; *Juvenile fiction*, Rachel Schwedt; Staff 86 (MLS 9, Non-MLS 77)
Founded 1971. Enrl 5,400; Highest Degree: Doctorate
Jul 1999-Jun 2000 Income Parent Institution $942,428. Mats Exp $338,391, Books $114,283, Per/Ser (Incl. Access Fees) $90,095, Micro $300, AV Equip $21,829, Electronic Ref Mat (Incl. Access Fees) $111,884. Sal $334,917 (Prof $262,224)
Library Holdings: Bk Vols 195,881; Bk Titles 158,007; Per Subs 7,739
Subject Interests: Religion
Special Collections: Jerry Falwell Coll
Automation Activity & Vendor Info: (Cataloging) epixtech, inc.; (Circulation) epixtech, inc.; (OPAC) epixtech, inc.
Database Vendor: Ebsco - EbscoHost, GaleNet, IAC - Info Trac, Lexis-Nexis, OCLC - First Search, OVID Technologies, ProQuest, Silverplatter Information Inc.
Partic in Lynchburg Area Library Cooperative; Solinet; VIVA/VICULA

C LYNCHBURG COLLEGE, Knight-Capron Library, 1501 Lakeside Dr, 24501-3199. SAN 317-3321. Tel: 804-544-8204. Interlibrary Loan Service Tel: 804-544-8442. Reference Tel: 804-544-8575. FAX: 804-544-8499. Web Site: www.lynchburg.edu/library. *Dir Libr Serv*, Christopher Millson-Martula; Tel: 804-544-8399, E-Mail: millsonmar_c@mail.lynchburg.edu; *Ref*, Linda R Harwell; *Bibliog Instr*, Elizabeth Henderson; *ILL*, Ariel Myers; *Electronic Resources*, Linda Carder; *Tech Servs*, Rayetta Knight; Staff 10 (MLS 5, Non-MLS 5)
Founded 1903. Enrl 2,200; Fac 125; Highest Degree: Master
Jul 1999-Jun 2000 Income Parent Institution $766,542. Mats Exp $225,743, Books $60,605, Per/Ser (Incl. Access Fees) $115,240, Micro $11,603, Electronic Ref Mat (Incl. Access Fees) $38,295. Sal $357,901
Library Holdings: Bk Vols 214,893; Bk Titles 157,315; Per Subs 541
Subject Interests: Bus, Education, Mgt, Nursing
Special Collections: Iron Industry (Capron); Seventeenth, Eighteenth & Nineteenth Century Maps of North America, particularly Virginia (Capron)
Database Vendor: epixtech, inc., GaleNet, IAC - SearchBank, Lexis-Nexis, OCLC - First Search, OVID Technologies
Publications: Exhibit Catalogs; Library Handbooks
Partic in Lynchburg Area Library Cooperative; OCLC Online Computer Library Center, Inc; VIVA/VICULA

M LYNCHBURG GENERAL HOSPITAL, Health Sciences Library,* 1901 Tate Springs Rd, 24501-1167. SAN 327-3792. Tel: 804-947-3147. FAX: 804-947-3104. *Librn*, Claire A Meissner; E-Mail: claire.meissner@centrahealth.com
Jan 1997-Dec 1998 Income $56,000
Library Holdings: Bk Vols 1,300; Per Subs 65
Subject Interests: Medicine, Nursing
Partic in Lynchburg Area Library Cooperative; National Network Of Libraries Of Medicine - South Central Region; OCLC Online Computer Library Center, Inc; Southwestern Virginia Health Information Librarians; VACOHSL

P LYNCHBURG PUBLIC LIBRARY, 2315 Memorial Ave, 24501. SAN 317-333X. Tel: 804-847-1577. Interlibrary Loan Service Tel: 804-847-1566. FAX: 804-845-1479. *Dir*, Lynn L Dodge; *ILL*, Candy Thompson; *YA Servs*, Lorry Risinger; *Cat*, Jane Jobe; *Librn*, Marilyn Martin; Staff 8 (MLS 8)
Founded 1966. Pop 65,800; Circ 417,000
Jul 1999-Jun 2000 Income $1,471,020, State $217,974, City $1,178,836, Other $74,210. Mats Exp $199,356, Books $155,573, Per/Ser (Incl. Access Fees) $21,022, AV Equip $13,263. Sal $945,186 (Prof $367,784)
Library Holdings: Bk Vols 146,553; Per Subs 7,401
Database Vendor: Ebsco - EbscoHost, epixtech, inc.
Partic in Lynchburg Information Online Network
Friends of the Library Group

C RANDOLPH-MACON WOMAN'S COLLEGE, Lipscomb Library, 2500 Rivermont Ave, 24503. SAN 317-3348. Tel: 804-947-8133. FAX: 804-947-8134. Web Site: faculty.rmwc.edu/library/. *Dir*, Theodore J Hostetler; E-Mail: thostetler@rmwc.edu; *ILL, Online Servs, Ref*, Patricia DeMars; E-Mail: pdcmars@rmwc.edu; *Online Servs, Ref*, Frances Webb; E-Mail: fwebb@rmwc.edu; *Circ*, Ruth Sims; E-Mail: rsims@rmwc.edu; *Cat*, Marcia McKenzic; E-Mail: mmckenzic@rmwc.edu; *Coll Develop*, Lisa Broughman; E-Mail: llee@rmwc.edu; Staff 5 (MLS 4, Non-MLS 1)
Founded 1891. Enrl 750; Fac 90; Highest Degree: Bachelor
Jul 1999-Jun 2000 Income $720,000. Mats Exp $323,000, Books $95,000, Per/Ser (Incl. Access Fees) $145,000, Presv $3,000, Micro $30,000, AV Equip $25,000, Manuscripts & Archives $10,000, Electronic Ref Mat (Incl. Access Fees) $15,000. Sal $350,000 (Prof $190,000)
Library Holdings: Bk Vols 175,000; Per Subs 600
Special Collections: Classical Culture (Lipscomb Coll); Lininger, Children's Literature Coll; Pearl S Buck Coll; Writings by Virginia Women
Automation Activity & Vendor Info: (Acquisitions) epixtech, inc.; (Cataloging) epixtech, inc.; (Circulation) epixtech, inc.; (Course Reserve) epixtech, inc.; (OPAC) epixtech, inc.; (Serials) epixtech, inc.
Database Vendor: epixtech, inc., OCLC - First Search
Publications: Collections of Writings by Virginia Women; Lipscomb Library Guide; Quick Library Facts Sheet

Partic in Knight-Ridder Info, Inc; Lynchburg Area Library Cooperative; Lynchburg Information Online Network; SE Libr Network; Virginia Independent College & University Library Association; Virtual Libr of Va

C VIRGINIA UNIVERSITY OF LYNCHBURG, Mary Jane Cachelin Library, 2058 Garfield Ave, 24501. SAN 317-3356. Tel: 804-528-5276. FAX: 804-528-4257. *Librn*, Swannie Thompson
Founded 1887
Library Holdings: Bk Vols 18,000; Per Subs 15

MADISON

P MADISON COUNTY LIBRARY, INC, 402 N Main St, 22727. (Mail add: PO Box 243, 22727), SAN 317-3445. Tel: 540-948-4720. FAX: 540-948-4919. E-Mail: madisonlib@summit.net. *Dir*, Bonnie Utz; *Head, Acq*, Janice Douglas; *Asst Librn*, Linda Davis; Staff 7 (Non-MLS 7)
Founded 1937. Pop 12,410; Circ 45,547
Jul 1999-Jun 2000 Income $86,500, State $17,500, County $55,000, Locally Generated Income $14,000. Mats Exp Books $17,500. Sal $53,500
Library Holdings: Bk Vols 28,000; Bk Titles 27,800; Per Subs 61
Special Collections: American History (Weaver Coll)
Automation Activity & Vendor Info: (Cataloging) Sagebrush Corporation; (Circulation) Sagebrush Corporation
Friends of the Library Group

MANASSAS

S INTERNATIONAL MICROWAVE POWER INSTITUTE, Reference Library,* 10210 Leatherleaf Ct, 20111. SAN 374-9517. Tel: 703-257-1415. FAX: 703-257-0213. E-Mail: assnctr@idsonline.com. *Exec Dir*, Robert C LaGasse
Library Holdings: Bk Vols 120
Restriction: Not open to public

S LOCKHEED MARTIN, Manassas Library, Bldg 105/029, 9500 Godwin Dr, 20110. SAN 328-1019. Tel: 703-367-6161. FAX: 703-367-4698. E-Mail: manassas.library@lmco.com. *Librn*, Jennifer Hatfield; Tel: 703-367-6508
Founded 1985
Library Holdings: Bk Vols 10,000; Bk Titles 9,000; Per Subs 180
Subject Interests: Computer science, Electrical engineering, Electronic engineering, Naval sci
Restriction: By appointment only

S MANASSAS NATIONAL BATTLEFIELD PARK LIBRARY, (Formerly US National Park Service Manassas Battlefield Park Library), 12521 Lee Hwy, 20109-2005. SAN 370-2995. Tel: 703-361-1339. FAX: 703-361-7106. Web Site: www.nps.gov/mana. *In Charge*, Robert Sutton
Library Holdings: Bk Vols 1,500
Subject Interests: Manuscripts
Restriction: By appointment only

L PRINCE WILLIAM COUNTY LAW LIBRARY,* 9311 Lee Ave, 20110. SAN 372-3518. Tel: 703-792-6262. FAX: 703-792-4721. *Librn*, Robert Davis
Library Holdings: Bk Vols 10,000

S PRINCE WILLIAM COUNTY SCHOOLS, Staff Library,* 14800 Joplin Rd, 20112. (Mail add: PO Box 389, 20108), Tel: 703-791-7334. FAX: 703-791-8874. Web Site: www.pwcs.edu/staff librarian. *Librn*, Connie Murphy; E-Mail: murphyca@pwcs.edu
Library Holdings: Bk Vols 8,000; Per Subs 275
Subject Interests: Education, Research

MARION

P SMYTH-BLAND REGIONAL LIBRARY,* 118 S Sheffey St, 24354. SAN 317-3453. Tel: 540-783-2323, Ext 29. FAX: 540-783-5279. *Dir*, Bill Goodrich; E-Mail: billg@sbrl.org; *Circ*, Marie Testerman; Staff 20 (MLS 1, Non-MLS 19)
Founded 1946. Pop 39,900; Circ 219,685
Library Holdings: Bk Vols 102,253; Per Subs 173
Subject Interests: Genealogy, SW Va hist
Special Collections: Sherwood Anderson Coll
Automation Activity & Vendor Info: (Cataloging) Gaylord
Friends of the Library Group
Branches: 2
BLAND COUNTY, PO Box 480, Bland, 24315. SAN 377-6816. Tel: 540-688-3737. FAX: 540-688-3737.
SALTVILLE BRANCH, PO Box 1033, Saltville, 24370. SAN 375-4839. Tel: 540-496-5514. FAX: 540-496-5514. *Dir*, Janice S Barbrow; E-Mail: janiceb@sbrl.org; *Ch Servs*, Melissa Surber; Staff 2 (Non-MLS 2)
Founded 1985. Pop 5,000; Circ 30,732
Library Holdings: Bk Titles 10,643; Per Subs 32
Friends of the Library Group
Bookmobiles: 1

M SOUTHWESTERN VIRGINIA MENTAL HEALTH INSTITUTION, St & Patients' Library, 340 Bagley Circle, 24354. SAN 363-0633. Tel: 540-783-1200, Ext 161. FAX: 540-783-1239. E-Mail: annlib@naxs.com. *Lib* Ann E Mathews; Staff 2 (MLS 1, Non-MLS 1)
Jul 2000-Jun 2001 Income $57,623
Library Holdings: Bk Vols 6,790; Per Subs 90
Partic in Southwestern Virginia Health Information Librarians; SWING

MARTINSVILLE

P BLUE RIDGE REGIONAL LIBRARY, 310 E Church St, 24115. (Mail a PO Box 5264, 24115-5264), SAN 363-0692. Tel: 540-632-7125. FAX: 5 632-1660. Web Site: www.brrl.lib.va.us. *Dir*, Ellen Bell; *Circ*, Betty Fulc *Ch Servs, YA Servs*, Janet Boucher; *Cat*, McCluer Sherrard; *Electronic Resources*, Larry Morrison; *Tech Servs*, Jane Farley; Staff 48 (MLS 6, N MLS 42)
Founded 1923. Pop 89,736; Circ 542,130
Jul 1999-Jun 2000 Income (Main Library and Branch Library) $1,649,18 State $383,938, City $273,520, County $879,196, Locally Generated Inc $59,570, Other $30,958. Mats Exp $303,781, Books $236,725, Per/Ser (I Access Fees) $28,442, Presv $1,517, Micro $3,130. Sal $728,318 (Prof $252,460)
Library Holdings: Bk Vols 245,652; Bk Titles 230,668; Per Subs 163
Special Collections: Genealogy (Virginia Coll); Realia (toys)
Automation Activity & Vendor Info: (Acquisitions) TLC; (Cataloging) TLC; (Circulation) TLC; (OPAC) TLC
Partic in Solinet; SWING
Friends of the Library Group
Branches: 5
BASSETT BRANCH, 3969 Fairystone Park Hwy, Bassett, 24055. SAN 3 7890. Tel: 540-629-2426. FAX: 540-629-3808. *Branch Mgr*, Rebecca Bishop; Staff 1 (Non-MLS 1)
Library Holdings: Bk Vols 30,993
Friends of the Library Group
BASSETT BRANCH HISTORICAL CENTER, 3964 Fairystone Park Hw Bassett, 24055. Tel: 540-629-3078, 540-629-9191. FAX: 540-629-9840. E-Mail: baslib@hotmail.com. *In Charge*, Pat Ross; Staff 1 (Non-MLS 1
COLLINSVILLE BRANCH, 3201 Virginia Ave, Collinsville, 24078. SAN 363-0722. Tel: 540-647-1112. FAX: 540-647-1112. *Librn*, Sandra Shell
Library Holdings: Bk Vols 31,304
Friends of the Library Group
PATRICK COUNTY, 116 W Blue Ridge St, PO Box 787, Stuart, 24171. SAN 363-0757. Tel: 540-694-3352, 540-694-5427. FAX: 540-694-6744. *Librn*, Randall Glover; Staff 1 (MLS 1)
Library Holdings: Bk Vols 41,074
Friends of the Library Group
RIDGEWAY BRANCH, 900 Vista View Lane, PO Box 1210, Ridgeway, 24148. SAN 371-2990. Tel: 540-956-1828. FAX: 540-956-1828. *Librn*, Karen Parker; Staff 1 (MLS 1)
Library Holdings: Bk Vols 18,281
Friends of the Library Group
Bookmobiles: 1

M MEMORIAL HOSPITAL OF MARTINSVILLE & HENRY COUNTY, Medical Library, 320 Hospital Dr, PO Box 4788, 24115-4788. SAN 317-347X. Tel: 540-666-7467. FAX: 540-666-7816. E-Mail: mhmhclib@neocomm.net. *Librn*, Mary Alice Sherrard; Staff 1 (MLS 1)
Founded 1956
Library Holdings: Bk Titles 2,000; Per Subs 115
Subject Interests: Allied health, Hospital administration, Medicine, Nursir
Restriction: Staff use only
Partic in Southwestern Virginia Health Information Librarians

J PATRICK HENRY COMMUNITY COLLEGE, Lester Library, 645 Patrio Ave, 24112. (Mail add: PO Box 5311, 24115), SAN 317-3488. Tel: 540-63 8777, Ext 228. FAX: 540-656-0327. Web Site: www.ph.cc.va.us/library. *Di* Carolyn Byrd; Tel: 540-656-0211; *Coordr*, Barry Reynolds; E-Mail: breynolds@ph.cc.va.us; *AV*, David Dillard; Tel: 540-656-0229, E-Mail: ddillard@ph.cc.va.us; *Regional Librarian*, Becky Westfall; Tel: 540-656-0226, E-Mail: bwestfall@ph.cc.va.us; *Ref*, Beth Shrewsberry; *Tech Servs*, Aileen Martin; Tel: 540-638-8777, Ext 439; Staff 5 (MLS 2, Non-MLS 3)
Founded 1962. Enrl 1,200; Fac 32
Jul 1999-Jun 2000 Income $45,000
Library Holdings: Bk Vols 30,731; Bk Titles 31,792; Per Subs 231
Special Collections: Stone Coll (Southern History); Thomas Carter Coll (Literature)
Database Vendor: IAC - Info Trac, OCLC - First Search, OVID Technologies
Partic in VIVA-Statewide Library Resource Network

S VIRGINIA MUSEUM OF NATURAL HISTORY, Research & Collections Library, 1001 Douglas Ave, 24112. SAN 375-2194. Tel: 540-666-8600. FAX: 540-632-6487. *Dir, Res*, Dr Judith E Winston; E-Mail: jwinston@vmnh.org
Library Holdings: Bk Titles 3,900

SON NECK

GUNSTON HALL PLANTATION LIBRARY & ARCHIVES, 10709 Gunston Rd, 22079-3901. SAN 317-3259. Tel: 703-550-9220. FAX: 703-550-9480. E-Mail: library@gunstonhall. Web Site: www.gunstonhall.org. *Librn*, Kevin Shupe
Founded 1970
Library Holdings: Bk Vols 6,100; Bk Titles 5,000; Per Subs 50
Subject Interests: Am hist, Decorative arts, Genealogy, George Mason, Mason family, Va hist
Special Collections: 18th Century Library Rare Books (Robert Carter of Nomini Hall Coll)
Restriction: By appointment only
Function: Reference only, Research library

ATHEWS

MATHEWS MEMORIAL LIBRARY,* PO Box 980, 23109-0980. SAN 317-3496. Tel: 804-725-5747. FAX: 804-725-7668. *Dir*, Nicki Lynch; E-Mail: nicki@crosslink.net
Founded 1930. Pop 8,430; Circ 26,985
1998-1999 Income $171,900, State $25,900, County $111,000, Other $35,000. Mats Exp Books $25,000. Sal $60,600 (Prof $27,000)
Library Holdings: Bk Titles 35,000; Per Subs 56
Friends of the Library Group

C LEAN

BOOZ, ALLEN & HAMILTON LIBRARY,* 8283 Greensboro Dr, 22102. SAN 306-8986. Tel: 703-902-5000. FAX: 703-902-3377. *Librn*, Linda Dodson; Tel: 703-902-5913
Library Holdings: Bk Titles 2,500; Per Subs 400
Subject Interests: Computer science
Partic in Interlibrary Users Association

THE DUPUY INSTITUTE LIBRARY,* 1497 Chain Bridge Rd, Ste 100, 22101-5728. SAN 373-2797. Tel: 703-356-1151. FAX: 703-356-1152. *Librn*, Chris Lawrence
Founded 1993
Library Holdings: Bk Titles 500; Per Subs 12
Special Collections: Defense Issues; Military History (T N Dupuy Coll)

FARM CREDIT ADMINISTRATION INFORMATION CENTER,* 1501 Farm Credit Dr, 22102-5090. SAN 326-5137. Tel: 703-883-4296. FAX: 703-734-1950.
Founded 1984
1997-1998 Mats Exp $68,000, Books $8,000, Per/Ser (Incl. Access Fees) $60,000
Library Holdings: Bk Vols 10,000; Bk Titles 4,000; Per Subs 150
Publications: Newsletter (weekly)
Partic in Dialog Corporation; Fedlink; OCLC Online Computer Library Center, Inc; Westlaw

FREDDIE MAC CORPORATE INFORMATION RESOURCE CENTER, 8200 Jones Branch Dr, MS 251, 22102. SAN 375-0396. Tel: 703-903-2773. FAX: 703-903-2773. E-Mail: circ@freddiemac.com. *Mgr*, Lois Ireland; Tel: 703-903-3335, Fax: 703-903-2755, E-Mail: lois_ireland@freddiemac.com; *Ref*, Danielle Delgado; Staff 3 (MLS 2, Non-MLS 1)
Founded 1991
Library Holdings: Bk Vols 5,500; Per Subs 300
Subject Interests: Finance, Real estate
Database Vendor: CARL, Dialog, Lexis-Nexis, OCLC - First Search, ProQuest, Silverplatter Information Inc.
Partic in Solinet

LITTON INDUSTRIES, PRC Library & Information Center, 1500 PRC Dr, 22102. SAN 321-9801. Tel: 703-556-1163. FAX: 703-883-5071. *Mgr*, Pat Garman; *Circ*, Barbara Kopp; *Cat*, Patricia M Wolf; *Ref*, Alice Hill-Murray; Staff 4 (MLS 1, Non-MLS 3)
Library Holdings: Bk Titles 4,000; Per Subs 260
Subject Interests: Bus, Computer science, Govt syst, Software engineering, Telecommunications
Database Vendor: OCLC - First Search
Publications: Journal Holdings; library brochure
Restriction: Employees & their associates
Partic in Defense Technical Information Center; Dialog Corporation; Dow Jones News Retrieval; Interlibrary Users Association; OCLC Online Computer Library Center, Inc

LOGISTICS MANAGEMENT INSTITUTE LIBRARY, 2000 Corporate Ridge, 22102-7805. SAN 328-5561. Tel: 703-917-9800. Interlibrary Loan Service Tel: 703-917-7214. FAX: 703-917-7474. E-Mail: library@lmi.org. Web Site: www.lmi.org/library/html. *Dir Libr Serv*, Nancy Eichelman Handy; *Tech Servs*, Robert Kemokai; *Tech Servs*, Jim Wilson; *Librn*, Joanna Berry; *Librn*, Sara Faulk; *Librn*, Jill Hanna; *Librn*, Laura Tyler
Library Holdings: Bk Titles 8,000; Per Subs 500
Subject Interests: Mil logistics
Special Collections: LMI Reports
Automation Activity & Vendor Info: (Cataloging) Sydney; (Circulation) Sydney; (OPAC) Sydney; (Serials) Sydney

L MCGUIRE, WOODS, BATTLE & BOOTHE, Law Library, 1750 Tysons Blvd, Ste 1800, 22102. SAN 327-2540. Tel: 703-712-5000. FAX: 703-712-5050. *Librn*, Maryanne Maher
Library Holdings: Bk Titles 15,000; Per Subs 300

S MITRE CORP, Corporate Information Services, 1820 Dolly Madison Blvd, 22102. SAN 317-3399. Tel: 703-883-7667. FAX: 703-883-5684. E-Mail: infodesk@mitre.org. *Mgr*, Jean Tatalias; *Ref*, David Shumaker; *Coll Develop, Tech Servs*, B J Fisher; Staff 25 (MLS 11, Non-MLS 14)
Founded 1967
Library Holdings: Bk Vols 5,000; Bk Titles 5,000; Per Subs 300
Subject Interests: Aviation, Civil info systs, Communications, Defense communications, Energy, Environ
Automation Activity & Vendor Info: (Cataloging) TechLIB; (Circulation) TechLIB; (OPAC) TechLIB; (Serials) TechLIB
Database Vendor: OCLC - First Search
Partic in Capcon Library Network; Interlibrary Users Association

S SKC KNOWLEDGE CENTER,* 1710 Goodridge Dr, 22102-3799. SAN 324-7384. Tel: 703-749-8701. FAX: 703-821-3071. *Librn*, Rebecca Leimert; E-Mail: rebecca.a.leimert@cpmx.saic.com
Founded 1975
1997-1998 Income $450,000
Subject Interests: Energy, Environ, Health, Nat defense, Software engineering, Space, Systs eng, Transportation
Publications: Brochure
Partic in Interlibrary Users Association; OCLC Online Computer Library Center, Inc

S STRATEGIC PLANNING INTERNATIONAL, INC, Library of Strategic Assessment,* 1390 Chain Bridge Rd, 22101. SAN 373-126X. Tel: 703-356-6927. FAX: 703-883-0499. *Librn*, Robert Chandler
Founded 1992
Library Holdings: Bk Titles 400

MELFA

J EASTERN SHORE COMMUNITY COLLEGE, Learning Resources Center,* 29300 Lankford Hwy, 23410. SAN 317-3518. Tel: 757-787-5920. FAX: 757-787-5919. Web Site: www.es.cc.va.us/lrc/library.htm. *Dir*, Patricia L Phillips; *AV*, Charles W Killmon; *ILL*, Faye Ralston; Staff 1 (MLS 1)
Founded 1964. Pop 45,000
Library Holdings: Bk Vols 23,131; Per Subs 103

MERRIFIELD

G ENERGY EFFICIENCY & RENEWABLE ENERGY CLEARINGHOUSE, EREC Library, 8260 Greensboro Dr, Ste 325, 22116. (Mail add: PO Box 3048, 22116-3048), SAN 375-3581. Tel: 800-363-3732. Toll Free Tel: 800-363-3732. TDD: 800-273-2957. FAX: 703-893-0400. Web Site: www.eren.doe.gov. *Librn*, Marlene Duckworth; E-Mail: marleneduckworth@ncilnc.com
Library Holdings: Bk Titles 3,500; Per Subs 115
Special Services for the Deaf - TDD

MIDDLEBURG

S NATIONAL SPORTING LIBRARY, INC, 102 The Plains Rd, PO Box 1335, 20118-1335. SAN 317-3526. Tel: 540-687-6542. FAX: 540-687-8540. E-Mail: nsl@nsl.org. Web Site: www.nsl.org. *Curator*, Elizabeth Manierre; *Dir*, Kenneth Y Tomlinson; *Librn*, Robert K Weber; Staff 3 (MLS 1, Non-MLS 2)
Founded 1954
Library Holdings: Bk Titles 12,000
Subject Interests: Am sporting art, Am sporting mag, Breeds of horses, British sporting art, English riding, Equine hist, Field sports, Horse sports, Photographs, Vet sci
Special Collections: 16th-19th Century Books on Horses (Huth-Lonsdale-Arundel & Hunersdorf Colls); Foxhunting Papers (Harry Worcester Smith Coll); Sporting Books (John H & Martha Daniel Coll)
Automation Activity & Vendor Info: (OPAC) CASPR
Publications: NSL Newsletter
Restriction: Not a lending library, Open to public for reference only
Function: Archival collection, ILL limited, Photocopies available, Research library
Partic in OCLC Online Computer Library Center, Inc; Solinet
Friends of the Library Group

MIDDLETOWN

J LORD FAIRFAX COMMUNITY COLLEGE, Paul Wolk Library, PO Box 47, 22645. SAN 317-3534. Tel: 540-868-7000. FAX: 540-868-7171. E-Mail: lfcircd@lf.cc.va.us. *Dir*, William L Harrison; *Acq*, Jan Brown; *Circ*, Alice Seabright; *Ref*, Joyce Earhart
Founded 1970. Enrl 4,200; Fac 42; Highest Degree: Associate
Library Holdings: Bk Vols 50,000; Bk Titles 45,000; Per Subs 300
Partic in SE Libr Network

MOUNT VERNON

S MOUNT VERNON LADIES' ASSOCIATION OF THE UNION INC, Research & Reference Library, End of GW Pkwy APC Bldg, PO Box 110, 22121-0110. SAN 317-3550. Tel: 703-780-2000, Ext 290. FAX: 703-799-8698. Web Site: www.mountvernon.org. *Librn*, Barbara McMillan; Tel: 703-799-8637, E-Mail: bmcmillan@mountvernon.org; *Assoc Librn*, Lisa Odum; Staff 2 (MLS 2)
Founded 1853
Library Holdings: Bk Titles 10,000; Per Subs 40
Subject Interests: Agriculture, Colonial hist, Decorative arts, Domestic life of George Washington, Fed hist, Hist of the Asn, Historic preservation, Horticulture, Mount Vernon, Plantation crafts, Plantation industries, Slavery
Publications: Annual Report
Restriction: By appointment only
Function: For research purposes

NARROWS

P R IRIS BRAMMER PUBLIC LIBRARY, 109 Mary St, 24124. SAN 317-3569. Tel: 540-726-2884. FAX: 540-726-3050. E-Mail: narlibrary@gva.net. *Librn*, Beverly Dent; Staff 1 (Non-MLS 1)
Pop 17,646
Library Holdings: Bk Vols 24,604

NEWPORT NEWS

C CHRISTOPHER NEWPORT UNIVERSITY, Captain John Smith Library, One University Pl, 23606. SAN 317-3577. Tel: 757-594-7130. Circulation Tel: 757-594-7133. Reference Tel: 757-594-7132. TDD: 757-594-7938. FAX: 757-594-7717. Web Site: www.cnu.edu/library/libhome.html. *Dir*, Catherine Doyle; E-Mail: doyle@cnu.edu; *Head, Cat*, Andrea Kross; Tel: 757-594-8702, Fax: 757-594-7776, E-Mail: akross@cnu.edu; *Cat*, Jeanne Klesch; Tel: 757-594-7138, Fax: 757-594-7776, E-Mail: jklesch@cnu.edu; *Publ Servs*, Doris Archer; Tel: 757-594-7245, Fax: 757-594-7772, E-Mail: darcher@cnu.edu; *Publ Servs*, Deborah Dawson; Tel: 757-594-7134, Fax: 757-594-7772, E-Mail: ddawson@cnu.edu; *Ref*, Amy Boykin; Tel: 757-594-7244, Fax: 757-594-7772, E-Mail: awboykin@cnu.edu; Staff 21 (MLS 7, Non-MLS 14)
Founded 1961. Pop 4,443; Enrl 4,203; Fac 221; Highest Degree: Master
Jul 1999-Jun 2000 Income $2,623,916, State $2,592,568, Other $31,348. Mats Exp $747,655, Books $233,769, Per/Ser (Incl. Access Fees) $354,343, Presv $11,379, AV Equip $1,688, Electronic Ref Mat (Incl. Access Fees) $146,476. Sal $767,225 (Prof $281,069)
Library Holdings: Bk Vols 379,091; Per Subs 1,599
Special Collections: Alexander C Brown Nautical Coll; Josephine Hughes Music Coll; Virginia Authors Coll
Automation Activity & Vendor Info: (Acquisitions) Innovative Interfaces Inc.; (Cataloging) Innovative Interfaces Inc.; (Circulation) Innovative Interfaces Inc.; (Course Reserve) Innovative Interfaces Inc.; (ILL) Innovative Interfaces Inc.; (Media Booking) Innovative Interfaces Inc.; (OPAC) Innovative Interfaces Inc.; (Serials) Innovative Interfaces Inc.
Database Vendor: Dialog, GaleNet, IAC - Info Trac, Innovative Interfaces INN - View, Lexis-Nexis, OCLC - First Search, OVID Technologies, ProQuest, Silverplatter Information Inc., Wilson - Wilson Web
Publications: Bookends (Newsletter)
Function: Research library
Partic in Virginia Tidewater Consortium For Higher Education; Virtual Libr of Va

S THE DAILY PRESS INC LIBRARY,* 7505 Warwick Blvd, 23607. SAN 325-4666. Tel: 757-247-4882. FAX: 757-247-4881. E-Mail: news@dailypress.com. Web Site: www.dailypress.com. *Mgr*, Melissa O Simpson; Staff 1 (MLS 1)
Founded 1961
Library Holdings: Bk Vols 1,600; Bk Titles 1,580; Per Subs 60
Subject Interests: Local history
Special Collections: Journalism & current events (Raymond B Bottom Coll), bks
Partic in Tribune Co

S THOMAS JEFFERSON NATIONAL ACCELERATOR FACILITY LIBRARY, 12000 Jefferson Ave, MS-1B, 23606. SAN 317-3615. Tel: 757-269-7525. FAX: 757-269-7848. *Mgr*, Elois A Morgan; E-Mail: morgan@jlab.org; *Cat, Librn*, Tanya Lanuzo; E-Mail: tanya@jlab.org; *Ser, Tech Servs*, Carol James; Tel: 757-269-6229, E-Mail: jamesc@jlab.org
1999-2000 Mats Exp $252,000
Library Holdings: Per Subs 98
Subject Interests: Electrical engineering, Mathematics, Nuclear physics
Automation Activity & Vendor Info: (Acquisitions) Endeavor; (Catalog Endeavor; (Circulation) Endeavor; (Course Reserve) Endeavor; (ILL) Endeavor; (Media Booking) Endeavor; (OPAC) Endeavor; (Serials) Endeavor
Database Vendor: OCLC - First Search
Publications: Library Bulletin
Partic in Solinet

S THE MARINERS' MUSEUM RESEARCH LIBRARY & ARCHIVES, 1 Museum Dr, 23606-3759. SAN 317-3585. Tel: 757-591-7782. Reference 757-591-7781. FAX: 757-591-7310. E-Mail: library@mariner.org. Web Si www.mariner.org. *Dir*, Susan Berg; *Ref*, Cathy Williamson; *Archivist*, Les Weber; *Tech Servs*, Lisa DuVernay; Tel: 757-591-7788, E-Mail: lduvernay mariner.org; Staff 11 (MLS 3, Non-MLS 8)
Founded 1930
Library Holdings: Bk Vols 78,000; Bk Titles 50,000; Per Subs 175
Subject Interests: Maritime history, Naval hist
Special Collections: Naval History College Coll, architectural drawings, archival items, charts, maps, photogs
Database Vendor: OCLC - First Search
Function: Reference services available
Partic in Capcon Library Network; OCLC Online Computer Library Cent Inc
Open Mon-Sat 10-5

P NEWPORT NEWS PUBLIC LIBRARY SYSTEM,* 2400 Washington Av 23607-4300. SAN 363-0781. Tel: 757-926-8506. TDD: 757-591-4858. FA 757-926-3563. Web Site: www.ci.newport-news.va.us/library. *Dir*, Izabela Cieszynski; E-Mail: icieszyn@ci.newport-news.va.us; *Dep Dir*, Maria Patricia Anderson; E-Mail: panderso@ci.newport-news.va.us; *Tech Servs*, Frederick Robert Tench; Tel: 757-886-7893, Fax: 757-886-7974; *Admin Assoc*, Anne C Bollinger; E-Mail: anbollin@ci.newport-news.va.us; Staff 7 (MLS 12, Non-MLS 67)
Founded 1891. Pop 171,000; Circ 755,128
Jul 1998-Jun 1999 Income (Main Library and Branch Library) $3,218,571 State $223,794, City $2,671,369, Federal $6,849, Locally Generated Incon $293,304, Other $23,255. Mats Exp $480,604, Books $339,921, Per/Ser (Incl. Access Fees) $38,529, Micro $14,606, AV Equip $22,438, Electronic Ref Mat (Incl. Access Fees) $57,305. Sal $1,715,518 (Prof $428,701)
Library Holdings: Bk Vols 254,144; Per Subs 685
Subject Interests: Local genealogy, Local history
Special Collections: Martha Woodroof Hiden Virginiana Coll; Old Dominion Land Company Coll
Automation Activity & Vendor Info: (Cataloging) VTLS; (Circulation) VTLS; (OPAC) VTLS; (Serials) VTLS
Database Vendor: OCLC - First Search
Partic in OCLC Online Computer Library Center, Inc
Friends of the Library Group
Branches: 7
PEARL BAILEY BRANCH, 2510 Wickham Ave, 23607. SAN 363-096X. Tel: 757-247-8677. TDD: 757-247-8677. FAX: 757-247-2321. *Actg Libr* Sherin Henderson; Staff 8 (MLS 2, Non-MLS 6)
Pop 27,649; Circ 37,250
Library Holdings: Bk Vols 69,832
Database Vendor: OCLC - First Search
Special Services for the Deaf - TDD
Friends of the Library Group
VIRGIL I GRISSOM BRANCH, 366 DeShazor Dr, 23608. SAN 363-0900 Tel: 757-886-7896. TDD: 757-886-7896. FAX: 757-886-7899. *Chief Libr* Deedy Mason; *Librn*, James Sanderson; Staff 20 (MLS 2, Non-MLS 18)
Pop 41,875; Circ 299,898
Library Holdings: Bk Vols 131,162
Database Vendor: OCLC - First Search
Special Services for the Deaf - TDD
Friends of the Library Group
LAW LIBRARY, 2500 Washington Ave, 23607. SAN 363-0846. Tel: 757-926-8678. FAX: 757-926-8824.
Founded 1964. Pop 171,000
Jul 1998-Jun 1999 Income (Main Library Only) City $103,491. Mats Exp Books $74,229
Library Holdings: Bk Vols 17,372
Restriction: Open to public for reference only
Friends of the Library Group
MAIN STREET, 110 Main St, 23601. SAN 363-0870. Tel: 757-591-4858. TDD: 757-591-4858. FAX: 757-591-7425. *Chief Librn*, Susan Baldwin; *Librn*, Kelley Weber; Staff 22 (MLS 3, Non-MLS 19)
Circ 266,414
Library Holdings: Bk Vols 99,828
Subject Interests: Genealogy, Virginiana
Special Collections: Martha Hiden Woodroof Virginiana Coll
Database Vendor: OCLC - First Search
Special Services for the Deaf - TDD

Friends of the Library Group
MUNICIPAL REFERENCE SERVICE, 2400 Washington Ave, 23607. SAN 325-3139. Tel: 757-926-8506. FAX: 757-926-3563. *Dir*, Izabela M Cieszynski; E-Mail: icieszyn@ci.newport-news.va.us; Staff 1 (MLS 1)
Pop 171,000
Library Holdings: Bk Vols 3,864
Function: For research purposes
Friends of the Library Group
SUBREGIONAL LIBRARY FOR THE BLIND & PHYSICALLY HANDICAPPED, 110 Main St, 23601. SAN 363-0811. Tel: 757-591-4858. TDD: 757-591-4858. FAX: 757-591-7425. *Librn*, Susan Baldwin
Circ 17,874
Jul 1997-Jun 1998 Income (Main Library Only) $42,944, City (MEX) $36,095, Federal $6,849. Mats Exp AV Equip $6,849. Sal $26,546
Subject Interests: Cassette bks, Videos
Publications: Side One
Special Services for the Deaf - TDD
WEST AVENUE, 30th & West Ave, 23607. SAN 363-0935. Tel: 757-247-8505. TDD: 757-247-8505. FAX: 757-247-2344. *Assoc Librn*, Patricia Seabron; Staff 5 (Non-MLS 5)
Pop 2,399; Circ 16,471
Library Holdings: Bk Vols 67,852
Database Vendor: OCLC - First Search
Special Services for the Deaf - TDD
Friends of the Library Group
Bookmobiles: 1. Librn, Susan Baldwin

NEWPORT NEWS SHIPBUILDING & DRY DOCK CO, Library Services Department,* 4101 Washington Ave, 23607. SAN 317-3593. Tel: 757-380-2610. FAX: 757-380-7794. *Librn*, Rosetta Lamb; *Librn*, Paula Lewis
Founded 1947
Library Holdings: Bk Vols 54,000; Per Subs 800
Subject Interests: Bus, Computer science, Engineering, Marketing, Metallurgy, Mgt, Naval archit, Oceanography, Physics, Shipbuilding, Statistics

RIVERSIDE REGIONAL MEDICAL CENTER, Health Sciences Library, 500 J Clyde Morris Blvd, 23601. SAN 327-3733. Tel: 757-594-2175. FAX: 757-594-2986. *Librn*, Joan Taylor; E-Mail: joantaylor@rivhs.com; Staff 3 (MLS 1, Non-MLS 2)
Founded 1980
Library Holdings: Bk Vols 5,000; Per Subs 210
Subject Interests: Allied health, Medicine, Nursing
Special Collections: Historical Medicine & Nursing
Publications: The Library Letter

VIRGINIA WAR MUSEUM, Major George B Collings Memorial, Major George B Collings Memorial Library, 9285 Warwick Blvd, 23607. SAN 321-0200. Tel: 757-247-8523. FAX: 757-247-8627. Web Site: www.warmuseum.org. *Dir*, John V Quarstein
Founded 1923
Library Holdings: Bk Titles 25,000; Per Subs 35
Special Collections: German Language Propaganda Publications; World War I - Vietnam Film Coll; World Wars I & II, mags, photogs, scrapbks
Publications: Film Loan Catalogue
Restriction: Open to public for reference only
Function: Research library

ORFOLK

BON SECOURS DE PAUL MEDICAL CENTER, Boone Memorial Library, 150 Kingsley Lane, 23505. SAN 320-4243. Tel: 757-889-5000, 757-889-5270. FAX: 757-889-5881. *Librn*, Jeanne Morris
Library Holdings: Bk Titles 1,260; Per Subs 115
Subject Interests: Medicine

BON SECOURS DE PAUL MEDICAL CENTER, School of Nursing Library,* 150 Kingsley Lane, 23505. SAN 373-2622. Tel: 757-889-5386. FAX: 757-889-4230. *Librn*, Eileen Vaughn
Library Holdings: Bk Vols 4,229; Per Subs 65
Subject Interests: Nursing
Special Collections: Historical Coll
Publications: Audiovisuals; A-V Guide; New Books
Partic in Tidewater Health Scis Librs

CHILDREN'S HOSPITAL OF THE KING'S DAUGHTERS, Medical Library, 601 Children's Lane, 23507. SAN 328-2945. Tel: 757-668-7249. FAX: 757-668-9766. *Coordr, Res*, Peggy Loring
Library Holdings: Bk Vols 1,100; Bk Titles 700
Partic in Tidewater Health Scis Librs

CHRYSLER MUSEUM OF ART, Jean Outland Chrysler Library, 245 W Olney Rd, 23510-1587. SAN 317-364X. Tel: 757-664-6345. FAX: 757-664-6201. E-Mail: museum@chrysler.org. Web Site: www.chrysler.org. *Actg Mgr*, Matthew Wiggins; Staff 1 (MLS 1)
Founded 1929
Library Holdings: Bk Titles 30,000; Per Subs 250
Subject Interests: Am, Art history, Art nouveau, Decorative arts, Drawing, Glass, Painting, Photography, Sculpture, Textiles, Western European
Special Collections: 18th-20th century auction & exhibition catalogs; Architecture (Frank A Vanderlip Jr Coll); Knoedler Library
Partic in SE Libr Network

CM EASTERN VIRGINIA MEDICAL SCHOOL LIBRARY, 700 W Olney Rd, PO Box 1980, 23501-1980. SAN 317-3658. Tel: 757-446-5840. FAX: 757-446-5134. Web Site: www.evms.edu/evmslib. *Dir*, Judith G Robinson; *ILL*, Connie Cartoski; *Coordr, Publ Servs, Ref*, Kerrie Shaw; *Tech Servs*, Renee Mansheim; Staff 8 (MLS 8)
Founded 1972. Enrl 993; Fac 351; Highest Degree: Doctorate
Library Holdings: Per Subs 966
Subject Interests: Behav sci, Medicine, Soc sci
Partic in OCLC Online Computer Library Center, Inc
Friends of the Library Group

S HEUTTE HORTICULTURAL LIBRARY,* c/o Norfolk Botanical Garden, 6700 Azalea Garden Rd, 23518. SAN 317-3690. Tel: 757-441-5830, Ext 27. FAX: 757-853-8294. *In Charge*, Lillian Eastman
Library Holdings: Bk Vols 2,700; Per Subs 40
Subject Interests: Hort subjs, Related subjs

G JOINT FORCES STAFF COLLEGE LIBRARY, (Formerly Armed Forces Staff College Library), 7800 Hampton Blvd, 23511-1702. SAN 317-3623. Tel: 757-443-6401, 757-444-5155. Interlibrary Loan Service Tel: 757-444-5321. FAX: 757-443-6047, 757-444-2053. Web Site: www.afsc.edu/library/libindxx.htm. *Dir*, Janet Gail Nicula; Tel: 757-443-6400, Fax: 757-443-6032, E-Mail: niculag@jfsc.ndu.edu; *Reader Servs*, Carolyn B Orr; *Acq*, Mary Louise O'Brien; Tel: 757-443-6404, Fax: 757-443-6404, E-Mail: obrienm@jfsc.ndu.edu; *Syst Coordr*, Sandra Byrn; E-Mail: byrns@jfsc.ndu.edu; Staff 18 (MLS 8, Non-MLS 10)
Founded 1947
Oct 2000-Sep 2001 Income $230,000. Mats Exp $153,652
Library Holdings: Bk Vols 113,000; Per Subs 465
Subject Interests: Econ, History, Int affairs, Mgt, Mil, Military history, Nat affairs, National security, Naval hist, Science
Database Vendor: epixtech, inc., Lexis-Nexis, OCLC - First Search, ProQuest
Publications: Accessions List; AFSC Pub 2; Commandant's Professional Reading List (Research guide); Internet Sites for JFSC Researchers (Research guide); The Force of Words; Weekly Indexing; Weekly Periodical
Function: Referrals accepted
Mem of OCLC ILL Subsystem
Partic in Fedlink; OCLC Online Computer Library Center, Inc; Tidewater Consortium for Continuing Higher Educ

L KAUFMAN & CANOLES, Law Library,* One Commercial Pl Ste 2000, PO Box 3037, 23510. SAN 372-3356. Tel: 757-624-3152. FAX: 757-624-3169. Web Site: www.kaufmanandcanoles.com. *Librn*, Laurie Ann Claywell
Library Holdings: Bk Vols 10,000; Per Subs 50

S MACARTHUR MEMORIAL LIBRARY & ARCHIVES, MacArthur Sq, 23510. SAN 317-3674. Tel: 757-441-2965, 757-441-2968. FAX: 757-441-5389. E-Mail: macmem@norfolk.infi.net. Web Site: www.sites.communitylink.org/mac. *Archivist*, James W Zobel
Founded 1964. Circ 1,200
Library Holdings: Bk Titles 5,100
Subject Interests: Korean War, Occupation of Japan, Philippine Insurrection, World War I, World War II
Special Collections: D Clayton James Interviews; Facsimiles of papers of Lewis Beebe, R J Marshall, S J Chamberlain, George Grunert, Edward M Almond & Facsimiles of Richard K Sutherland; Military Intelligence & Personal Correspondence (Charles A Willougby Coll), bks, doc, plans, strategy & tactics of WWII; Military Logistics (H E Eastwood Coll), doc; Papers of Master Sergeant Paul Rogers, Wendell W Fertig, Bonner F Fellers & Philip Brougher; Philippine Guerrillas, World War II (Courtney Whitney Coll), doc
Database Vendor: OCLC - First Search
Publications: Douglas MacArthur Archives & Library (brochure); MacArthur Report
Restriction: Not a lending library
Function: Archival collection, Research library

M NORFOLK PSYCHIATRIC CENTER LIBRARY,* 860 Kempsville Rd, 23502. SAN 317-3739. Tel: 757-461-4565. FAX: 757-455-0298.
Founded 1971
Library Holdings: Bk Titles 900
Subject Interests: Psychiatry, Psychology
Restriction: Staff use only
Partic in Medline

P NORFOLK PUBLIC LIBRARY, Kirn Memorial Library, 301 E City Hall Ave, 23510-1776. SAN 363-0994. Tel: 757-664-7333. FAX: 757-664-7321. Web Site: www.npl.lib.va.us. *Dir*, Sally Reed; Tel: 757-664-7339, Fax: 757-664-7320; *ILL*, Alicia Wilson-Metzger; *Ch Servs*, Terri Raymond; Tel: 757-664-7328, Fax: 757-664-7320; *Bkmobile Coordr*, Bettie Goganious; Tel: 757-858-2044; *Ad Servs*, Melissa Malcolm; Tel: 757-664-7323, Fax: 757-664-7326; *Publ Servs*, Yvonne Hilliard-Bradley; Tel: 757-664-7352, Fax:

757-664-7320; *Acq, Tech Servs*, Deborah Folkama. Subject Specialists: *City hist*, Peggy McPhillips; Staff 25 (MLS 25)
Founded 1870. Pop 240,000; Circ 620,658
Jul 1998-Jun 1999 Income (Main Library and Branch Library) $4,801,988, State $258,266, City $4,543,722. Mats Exp $771,535, Books $540,471, Per/Ser (Incl. Access Fees) $71,360, Micro $1,114, AV Equip $86,567. Sal $2,651,812 (Prof $932,349)
Library Holdings: Bk Vols 1,019,867; Per Subs 1,249
Subject Interests: African-Am lit, Bus, Juv lit, Local history
Special Collections: Virginianna (Sargeant Memorial Room), AV, bk & micro
Database Vendor: DRA
Special Services for the Deaf - TTY machine
Friends of the Library Group
Branches: 11
BARRON F BLACK BRANCH, 6700 E Tanners Creek Rd, 23513. SAN 363-1028. Tel: 757-441-5806. FAX: 757-441-5891. Web Site: www.npl.lib.va.us. *Librn*, Margaret Hagel
Library Holdings: Bk Vols 49,166
Friends of the Library Group
BLYDEN, 879 Park Ave, 23523. SAN 363-1117. Tel: 757-441-2852. FAX: 757-441-1452. Web Site: www.npl.lib.va.us. *Librn*, Dudley Colbert
Library Holdings: Bk Vols 21,820
Friends of the Library Group
H C DOWNING, 555 E Liberty St, 23523. SAN 363-1052. Tel: 757-441-1968. FAX: 757-441-1994. Web Site: www.npl.lib.va.us. *Librn*, Barbara Munden
Library Holdings: Bk Vols 35,591
Friends of the Library Group
JANAF, 124 Janaf Shopping Ctr, 23502. SAN 363-1176. Tel: 757-441-5660. FAX: 757-441-5715. Web Site: www.npl.lib.va.us. *Branch Mgr*, Victoria Hagemeister; *Librn*, Olivia Osei-Sarfo
Library Holdings: Bk Vols 53,077
Friends of the Library Group
JORDAN-NEWBY, 961 Park Ave, 23504. SAN 363-1141. Tel: 757-441-2843. FAX: 757-441-1453. Web Site: www.npl.lib.va.us. *Librn*, Sheriden Clem; *Branch Mgr*, Rene Perez-Lopes
Library Holdings: Bk Vols 29,337
Friends of the Library Group
LAFAYETTE, 1610 Cromwell Dr, 23509. SAN 363-1206. Tel: 757-441-2842. FAX: 757-441-1454. Web Site: www.npl.lib.va.us. *Librn*, Olivia Osei-Sarfo
Library Holdings: Bk Vols 68,781
Friends of the Library Group
LARCHMONT, 6525 Hampton Blvd, 23508. SAN 363-1230. Tel: 757-441-5335. FAX: 757-441-1451. Web Site: www.npl.lib.va.us. *Librn*, Dudley Colbert
Library Holdings: Bk Vols 60,633
Friends of the Library Group
LITTLE CREEK, 7853 Tarpon Pl, 23518. SAN 363-1265. Tel: 757-441-1751. FAX: 757-441-1747. Web Site: www.npl.lib.va.us. *Librn*, Margaret Hagel
Library Holdings: Bk Vols 70,621
Friends of the Library Group
PARK PLACE, 620 W 29th St, 23508. SAN 363-1087. Tel: 757-664-7330. FAX: 757-664-7331. Web Site: www.npl.lib.va.us. *Assoc Dir*, Bettie Goganious; *Mgr*, Todd Elliott
Library Holdings: Bk Vols 26,726
Friends of the Library Group
PRETLOW, 9640 Granby St, 23503. SAN 363-129X. Tel: 757-441-1750. FAX: 757-441-1748. Web Site: www.npl.lib.va.us. *Librn*, Russell Cogar
Library Holdings: Bk Vols 63,333
Friends of the Library Group
VAN WYCK, 1368 DeBree Ave, 23517. SAN 363-132X. Tel: 757-441-2844. FAX: 757-441-1456. Web Site: www.npl.lib.va.us. *Librn*, Sheriden Clem
Library Holdings: Bk Vols 41,877
Friends of the Library Group
Bookmobiles: 1. Tel 757-858-2044. In Charge, B Goganious. Bk vols 45,940

C NORFOLK STATE UNIVERSITY, Lyman Beecher Brooks Library, 700 Park Ave, 23504-8010. SAN 317-3712. Tel: 757-823-8481. FAX: 757-823-2092, 757-823-2431. Web Site: www.nsu.edu. *Dir*, Mattie H Roane; E-Mail: m_roane@vger.nsu.edu; *Cat*, LaVerne Anderson; *Circ*, Dorothy Norfleet; *Per*, Joyce Dedmon; *Acq, Coll Develop*, Cecelia Choi; *Ref*, Cynthia Baxter-Cook; Staff 9 (MLS 9)
Founded 1935. Enrl 7,000; Fac 350; Highest Degree: Doctorate
Library Holdings: Per Subs 1,426
Subject Interests: Behav sci, Bus mgt, Chem physics, Education, Ethnic studies, Humanities, Soc sci, Soc work
Special Collections: Black Coll
Publications: Bibliographic Guides & Pathfinders; Bibliographic Instruction (handbooks)
Partic in Dialog Corporation; OCLC Online Computer Library Center, Inc; SE Libr Network

C OLD DOMINION UNIVERSITY LIBRARY,* 23529. SAN 317-3720. T 757-683-4154. Interlibrary Loan Service Tel: 757-683-4170. FAX: 757-6 5035. *Librn*, Dr Jean Major; *Ref*, Ann Pettingill; *Online Servs*, Karen Vaughan; *Cat*, Carole Kiehl; *Publ Servs*, Virginia S O'Herron; *Selection Ref Mat Business*, Amanda Wakaruk
Founded 1930. Enrl 16,686; Fac 817; Highest Degree: Doctorate
Library Holdings: Bk Vols 710,255; Per Subs 6,835
Subject Interests: Engineering, Fine arts, Oceanography, Performing arts Sci
Special Collections: Art; Historical Archives; Recordings; Scottish histor
Automation Activity & Vendor Info: (Circulation) GEAC
Publications: Departmental Guides; Instructional Guides; Miniguides for Students & Faculty
Partic in OCLC Online Computer Library Center, Inc; SE Libr Network; Virginia Tidewater Consortium For Higher Education

M SENTARA NORFOLK GENERAL HOSPITAL, Health Sciences Library 600 Gresham Dr, 23507. SAN 317-3704. Tel: 757-668-3693. FAX: 757-6 2514. *Librn*, Suzanne Duncan; E-Mail: sxduncan@sentara.com
Founded 1942
Library Holdings: Bk Vols 16,000; Per Subs 260
Subject Interests: Health admin, Medicine, Nursing
Restriction: Not open to public

TIDEWATER COMMUNITY COLLEGE LEARNING RESOURCES CENTER, Thomas W Moss Jr Campus,* 300 Granby St, 23510. SAN 37 8304. Tel: 757-822-1100. FAX: 757-822-1106. Web Site: www.tc.cc.va.us lrc. *Coordr*, Ruth Shumate; E-Mail: tcshumr@tc.cc.va.us; *Librn*, Kathleen Tilton; E-Mail: tctiltk@tc.cc.va.us; *Tech Servs*, Christie Irwin; Tel: 757-82 1103, E-Mail: tcirwic@tc.cc.va.us; *Circ*, Carolyn Roberts; E-Mail: tcrobe tc.cc.va.us; *Circ Media*, Florence Baines; Tel: 757-822-1124, E-Mail: tcbainf@tc.cc.va.us; *AV*, Debra DeMills; Tel: 757-822-1121, Fax: 757-683 9812; Staff 6 (MLS 2, Non-MLS 4)
Founded 1997
Database Vendor: Ebsco - EbscoHost, GaleNet, IAC - Info Trac, IAC - SearchBank, OCLC - First Search, OVID Technologies, Wilson - Wilson Web
Function: Reference services available

A UNITED STATES ARMED FORCES SCHOOL OF MUSIC, Reference Library, 1420 Gator Blvd, 23521-2617. SAN 370-2812. Tel: 757-462-751 FAX: 757-462-7294. *Ref*, Nancy Chiara
Library Holdings: Bk Vols 6,592; Per Subs 12
Subject Interests: Music-analysis
Restriction: Restricted public use

L UNITED STATES COURTS LIBRARY,* US Courthouse, Rm 319, 600 Granby St, 23510. SAN 372-3526. Tel: 757-222-7044. FAX: 757-222-704 *Librn*, Karen J Johnson
Library Holdings: Bk Vols 17,000

UNITED STATES NAVY
A NAVAL AMPHIBIOUS BASE LIBRARY, Bldg 3004, Little Creek, 1432 Hewitt Dr NABLC, 23521-2522. SAN 363-1419. Tel: 757-462-7691. FAX: 757-462-4593. E-Mail: nablclib@norfolk.infinet. *Coll Develop, Librn*, Tina Henry
Founded 1942
Oct 1996-Sep 1997 Income $74,000, Federal $70,000, Other $4,000. Ma Exp $42,103, Books $32,049, Per/Ser (Incl. Access Fees) $2,200, Other Print Mats $1,782
Library Holdings: Bk Vols 21,000; Per Subs 85
Subject Interests: Naval hist
Special Collections: CLEP Preparation Videos
Friends of the Library Group

C VIRGINIA WESLEYAN COLLEGE, Henry Clay Hofheimer II Library, 1584 Wesleyan Dr, 23502-5599. SAN 317-3755. Tel: 757-455-3224. Interlibrary Loan Service Tel: 757-455-3223. Reference Tel: 757-455-2132 FAX: 757-455-2129. E-Mail: library@vwc.edu. Web Site: www.vwc.edu/library_tech/library/libpage.htm. *Dir*, Jan S Pace; Tel: 757-455-3220, Fax: 757-455-2110, E-Mail: jpace@vwc.edu; *Ser*, Velma J Haley; Tel: 757-455-3221, E-Mail: vhaley@vwc.edu; *Tech Servs*, Sandra Brooks; Tel: 757-455-3262, E-Mail: ssbrooks@vwc.edu; *Coll Develop*, Mary Carole Lynch; E-Mail: mclynch@vwc.edu; Staff 8 (MLS 3, Non-MLS 5)
Founded 1966. Enrl 1,335; Fac 76; Highest Degree: Bachelor
Jul 1999-Jun 2000 Mats Exp $450,000, Books $53,000, Per/Ser (Incl. Access Fees) $61,000, Micro $4,000, AV Equip $7,000, Electronic Ref Ma (Incl. Access Fees) $12,000. Sal $261,000 (Prof $134,000)
Library Holdings: Bk Vols 111,000; Bk Titles 88,000; Per Subs 650
Automation Activity & Vendor Info: (Cataloging) TLC; (Circulation) TL (Course Reserve) TLC
Database Vendor: GaleNet, IAC - SearchBank, OVID Technologies, Silverplatter Information Inc., Wilson - Wilson Web
Publications: Discover Your Library; Periodicals Directory
Partic in Virginia Tidewater Consortium For Higher Education; Virtual Lib of Va

VIRGINIAN-PILOT LIBRARY,* 150 W Brambleton Ave, 23510. SAN 371-3040. Tel: 757-446-2242. FAX: 757-446-2974. Web Site: www.pilotonline.com. *Librn*, Ann Kinken Johnson; E-Mail: kinken@pilotonline.com
Library Holdings: Bk Vols 2,000

KWOOD

KEEN MOUNTAIN CORRECTIONAL CENTER, Department of Correctional Education Library, State Rd 629, PO Box 860, 24631-0860. SAN 373-6903. Tel: 540-498-7411, Ext 2055. *Librn*, M A Singleton
Founded 1990
Library Holdings: Bk Vols 30,000; Per Subs 51
Automation Activity & Vendor Info: (Acquisitions) Follett; (Cataloging) Follett; (Circulation) Follett
Special Services for the Deaf - Books on deafness & sign language

RANGE

ORANGE COUNTY LIBRARY, 146A Madison Rd, 22960. SAN 317-3771. Tel: 540-672-3811. FAX: 540-672-5040. *Dir*, Kathryn Hill; *Tech Servs*, Teresa Knapp; *Cat*, Caroline Bledsoe; Staff 3 (MLS 2, Non-MLS 1)
Pop 24,100; Circ 181,980
Jul 2000-Jun 2001 Income $468,681, State $103,618, County $332,680. Mats Exp $109,520, Books $104,220, Per/Ser (Incl. Access Fees) $5,300. Sal $254,424
Library Holdings: Bk Vols 99,098; Bk Titles 67,770; Per Subs 135
Automation Activity & Vendor Info: (Acquisitions) TLC; (Cataloging) TLC; (Circulation) TLC; (OPAC) TLC
Friends of the Library Group
Branches: 2
GORDONSVILLE BRANCH, 200 S Main St, PO Box 587, Gordonsville, 22942-0587. (Mail add: PO Box 587, Gordonsville, 22942), Tel: 540-832-0712. FAX: 540-832-0849. *Branch Mgr*, Jeanne Robinson
Friends of the Library Group
WILDERNESS, 6421 Flat Run Rd, Locust Grove, 22508. Tel: 540-854-5310, 540-972-1675. FAX: 540-854-5402. *Librn*, Michele B Beamer; Staff 2 (MLS 1, Non-MLS 1)
Friends of the Library Group

ARISBURG

PEARISBURG PUBLIC LIBRARY,* 209 Fort Branch Rd, 24134. SAN 317-3798. Tel: 540-921-2556. FAX: 540-921-1708. E-Mail: psbglibr@swva.net. *Librn*, Sandra V Robertson; *Asst Librn*, Birdie B Moye
Founded 1963
Library Holdings: Bk Vols 34,000
Special Collections: books on tape; Circulating art reproductions; Genealogy, including listings of Giles County cemeteries; large print books
Publications: Giles County-Virginia, History-Families

ETERSBURG

ALLIED-SIGNAL, INC, Technical Center Library,* PO Box 31, 23804. SAN 317-3801. Tel: 804-520-3617. FAX: 804-520-3377. *Librn*, R P Murphy
Library Holdings: Bk Vols 4,000; Per Subs 125
Subject Interests: Polymer sci, Synthetic fibers

CENTRAL STATE HOSPITAL
MEDICAL-PATIENTS LIBRARY, PO Box 4030, 23803. SAN 363-1621. Tel: 804-524-7235, 804-524-7517. FAX: 804-524-7308. Web Site: www.csh.state.va.us. *Librn*, Jennifer Amador; Staff 5 (MLS 1, Non-MLS 4)
Jul 1998-Jun 1999 Income $177,000, State $150,000, Federal $10,300, Other $13,000. Mats Exp $52,000, Per/Ser (Incl. Access Fees) $20,000. Sal $125,000 (Prof $32,000)
Library Holdings: Bk Vols 8,000
Subject Interests: Clinical psychiat, Clinical psychol, Mental illness, Mental retardation, Psychiat nursing, Soc work
Partic in Docline; SE Libr Network

FEDERAL CORRECTIONAL INSTITUTION, Educational Department Library,* 1100 River Rd, 23804. SAN 317-381X. Tel: 804-733-7881, Ext 380. FAX: 804-863-1504. *Librn*, Larry Joyner
Library Holdings: Bk Vols 4,000; Per Subs 16
Subject Interests: Vocational education, Vocational recreation

PETERSBURG PUBLIC LIBRARY,* 137 S Sycamore St, 23803. SAN 363-1680. Tel: 804-733-2387. FAX: 804-733-7972. Web Site: petersburg-va.com/libmain.htm. *Dir*, Wayne M Crocker; *Admin Assoc*, Kitty Hatcher; *Cat*, Carolyn T Eubanks; Staff 15 (MLS 3, Non-MLS 12)
Founded 1924. Pop 34,000; Circ 102,943
Jul 1998-Jun 1999 Income (Main Library and Branch Library) $765,792, State $176,640, City $584,857, Other $4,295. Mats Exp $102,992, Books $81,520, Per/Ser (Incl. Access Fees) $13,454. Sal $430,311 (Prof $66,677)
Library Holdings: Bk Vols 139,149; Bk Titles 96,127; Per Subs 151
Special Collections: Newspapers since 1800, bd vols & microfilm; Virginia History (Rare Virginiana & Genealogy, Civil War History Coll)
Branches: 2
A P HILL BRANCH, 1237 Halifax St, 23803. SAN 363-1710. Tel: 804-733-2391. Web Site: petersburg-va.com/libmain.htm. *In Charge*, Marion Owens
Library Holdings: Bk Vols 12,758; Bk Titles 3,774
RODOF SHOLOM BRANCH, 1865 S Sycamore St, 23805. SAN 363-1745. Tel: 804-733-2393. FAX: 804-733-2422. Web Site: petersburg-va.com/libmain.htm. *Librn*, Karen Forsyth
Library Holdings: Bk Vols 29,389; Bk Titles 9,390

J RICHARD BLAND COLLEGE LIBRARY, 11301 Johnson Rd, 23805. SAN 317-3836. Tel: 804-862-6226. Circulation Tel: 804-862-6227. Reference Tel: 804-862-6227. FAX: 804-862-6125. E-Mail: linternet@rbc.edu. Web Site: www.rbc.edu/library/. *Dir*, Dr Virginia Rose Cherry; E-Mail: vcherry@rbc.edu; *Publ Servs*, Ellen C Andes; E-Mail: eandes@rbc.edu; *Tech Servs*, Brenda Joy Galloni; Tel: 804-862-6228, E-Mail: jgalloni@rbc.edu; *Publ Servs*, Helen Quam Sherman; E-Mail: hsherman@rbc.edu; *Circ*, Karen I O'Daire; Tel: 804-862-6208, E-Mail: kodaire@rbc.edu; Staff 4 (MLS 3, Non-MLS 1)
Founded 1960. Circ 5,007; Enrl 1,200; Fac 31; Highest Degree: Associate
Jul 1999-Jun 2000 Income $95,000. Mats Exp $70,177, Books $25,743, Per/Ser (Incl. Access Fees) $15,591, Presv $4,293, Micro $2,179, Electronic Ref Mat (Incl. Access Fees) $22,371. Sal $118,790 (Prof $102,290)
Library Holdings: Bk Vols 65,163; Bk Titles 53,300; Per Subs 326
Subject Interests: Geography, History, Literature, Music, Philosophy, Psychology, Religion
Automation Activity & Vendor Info: (Cataloging) PALS; (Circulation) SIRSI; (ILL) SIRSI; (Serials) SIRSI
Database Vendor: GaleNet, IAC - SearchBank, OCLC - First Search, OVID Technologies
Restriction: Residents only
Partic in Richmond Academic Library Consortium; Virtual Libr of Va
Friends of the Library Group

M SOUTHSIDE REGIONAL MEDICAL CENTER, Medical Library,* 801 S Adams St, 23803. SAN 317-3828. Tel: 804-862-5663. FAX: 804-732-3360. *Librn*, Joan Pollard
Founded 1956
Library Holdings: Bk Vols 1,010; Per Subs 100
Subject Interests: Medicine
Partic in Mid-Atlantic Libr Asn; Nat Libr of Med

S UNITED STATES DEPARTMENT OF THE INTERIOR, Petersburg National Battlefield Library, 1539 Hickory Hill Rd, 23803-4721. SAN 317-3844. Tel: 804-732-3531. FAX: 804-732-0835. E-Mail: peteinterpretation@nps.gov. Web Site: www.mps.gov/pete/. *Librn*, Chris Calkins
Founded 1938
Library Holdings: Bk Titles 3,000
Subject Interests: Civil War history, Manuscript, Periodicals, Petersburg history, Photographs

C VIRGINIA STATE UNIVERSITY, Johnston Memorial Library, One Hayden Dr, PO Box 9406, 23806. SAN 363-177X. Tel: 804-524-5040. FAX: 804-524-5482. Web Site: www.vsu.edu/library/index.htm. *Dean of Libr*, Elsie Wetherington; Fax: 804-524-6959; *Assoc Dir*, Elizabeth Gail McClenney; Tel: 804-524-5580, Fax: 804-524-6959, E-Mail: gmcclenn@vsu.edu; *Assoc Dir*, Michael C Walker; Tel: 804-524-6946, E-Mail: mcwalker@vsu.edu; *Asst Librn*, Mary W Bailey; Tel: 804-524-5582, E-Mail: mbailey@vsu.edu; *Govt Doc*, Gloria Beck; Tel: 804-524-6945, E-Mail: gbeck@vsu.edu; *Ser*, Susan Lobaugh; Tel: 804-542-5042, Fax: 804-542-5969, E-Mail: slobaugh@vsu.edu; *Archivist*, Lucious Edwards; Tel: 804-524-5749, Fax: 804-524-6959, E-Mail: ledwards@vsu.edu; *Acq*, Gloria G Harvell; Tel: 804-524-5740, Fax: 804-524-5969, E-Mail: gharvell@vsu.edu; *Coll Develop*, Louveller Luster; E-Mail: lluster@vsu.edu. Subject Specialists: *Afro-American studies*, Michael C Walker; *Art*, Gloria Beck; *Business*, Michael C Walker; *Business*, Mary W Bailey; *Education*, Michael C Walker; *Education*, Mary W Bailey; *History*, Lucious Edwards; *History*, Gloria Beck; *History*, Gloria G Harvell; *Life sciences*, Susan Lobaugh; *Management*, Elizabeth Gail McClenney; *Psychology*, Elizabeth Gail McClenney; *Public admin*, Elizabeth Gail McClenney; *Sociology*, Gloria Beck; *Technology*, Susan Lobaugh; Staff 10 (MLS 9, Non-MLS 1)
Founded 1882. Enrl 4,303; Highest Degree: Master
Jul 1999-Jun 2000 Mats Exp $890,244, Books $197,177, Per/Ser (Incl. Access Fees) $243,373, Presv $5,721, Micro $222,717, Manuscripts & Archives $6,000, Electronic Ref Mat (Incl. Access Fees) $70,646. Sal $695,620 (Prof $374,271)
Library Holdings: Bk Vols 282,353; Bk Titles 182,958; Per Subs 1,150
Subject Interests: Black studies, Education
Automation Activity & Vendor Info: (Cataloging) VTLS; (Circulation) VTLS; (OPAC) VTLS; (Serials) VTLS
Database Vendor: IAC - SearchBank, Innovative Interfaces INN - View, OVID Technologies, ProQuest, Silverplatter Information Inc., Wilson - Wilson Web
Publications: InfoNavigator (Newsletter)
Function: Research library
Partic in Richmond Academic Library Consortium

POQUOSON

P POQUOSON PUBLIC LIBRARY, 500 City Hall Ave, 23662-1996. SAN 321-0936. Tel: 757-868-3060. FAX: 757-868-3106. E-Mail: library@ci.poquoson.va.us. Web Site: www.whro.org/cl/poquoson/. *Dir*, Elizabeth L Tai
Founded 1976. Pop 11,900; Circ 193,785
Jul 1999-Jun 2000 Income $420,359, State $86,536, City $327,326, Locally Generated Income $6,497. Mats Exp $84,792, Books $67,292, Per/Ser (Incl. Access Fees) $8,500, AV Equip $3,000, Electronic Ref Mat (Incl. Access Fees) $6,000. Sal $215,085 (Prof $52,000)
Library Holdings: Bk Vols 45,423; Per Subs 140; High Interest/Low Vocabulary Bk Vols 250
Automation Activity & Vendor Info: (Acquisitions) epixtech, inc.; (Cataloging) epixtech, inc.; (Circulation) epixtech, inc.; (Course Reserve) epixtech, inc.; (OPAC) epixtech, inc.
Database Vendor: OCLC - First Search
Publications: Book Worms; Bookmarks (Newsletter); Friends of Library Newsletter
Friends of the Library Group

PORTSMOUTH

M PINES TREATMENT CENTER, Library Media Center,* 301 Fort Lane, 23704. SAN 324-587X. Tel: 757-393-0061. FAX: 757-393-9658. *In Charge*, Edith Blake
Founded 1971
Library Holdings: Bk Vols 1,400; Bk Titles 1,200; Per Subs 70
Subject Interests: Sch libr
Partic in Dialog Corporation; Nat Libr of Med; Regional Med Libr - Region 2; Tidewater Health Scis Librs

S PORTSMOUTH NAVAL SHIPYARD MUSEUM, Marshall W Butt Library, 2 High St, PO Box 248, 23705-0248. SAN 317-3860. Tel: 757-393-8591. FAX: 757-393-5244. *Curator*, Alice C Hanes
Founded 1949
Library Holdings: Bk Titles 8,000
Subject Interests: Local history, Naval hist
Restriction: Not a lending library, Open to others by appointment
Function: Archival collection, Photocopies available, Research library

P PORTSMOUTH PUBLIC LIBRARY, 601 Court St, 23704-3604. SAN 363-1834. Tel: 757-393-8501. Reference Tel: 757-393-8973. FAX: 757-393-5107. *Dir*, Susan Burton; *Mgr, Ref*, Mary Goodman; *Cat*, Tina Scott; *Ch Servs*, Rachel Enrich; *Ad Servs*, Carolyn Hughes; Staff 30 (MLS 9, Non-MLS 21)
Founded 1914. Pop 98,500; Circ 329,263
Jul 1999-Jun 2000 Income (Main Library and Branch Library) $655,962, State $239,293, City $366,933, Other $49,736. Mats Exp $280,322, Books $205,034, Per/Ser (Incl. Access Fees) $33,288, Micro $30,000, AV Equip $12,000. Sal $942,154 (Prof $343,659)
Library Holdings: Bk Vols 311,840; Bk Titles 180,409; Per Subs 460
Special Collections: Lighthouses & Lightships; Local History Coll, bks & doc
Automation Activity & Vendor Info: (Acquisitions) epixtech, inc.; (Circulation) epixtech, inc.; (OPAC) epixtech, inc.
PULL (Portsmouth Urban Literacy Laboratory) computer based teaching. Children's computer rooms (Rapoport Room)
Friends of the Library Group
Branches: 3
CHURCHLAND, 3215 Academy Ave, 23703. SAN 363-1869. Tel: 757-686-2538. FAX: 757-686-2537. *Librn*, Carolyn L Wells
Friends of the Library Group
CRADOCK, Afton Sq, 28 Prospect Pkwy, 23702. SAN 363-1893. Tel: 757-393-8759. FAX: 757-393-5103. *Librn*, Linda Fillhart
Friends of the Library Group
MANOR, 1401 Elmhurst Lane, 23701. SAN 363-1923. Tel: 757-465-2916. FAX: 757-465-2915. *Librn*, Glenda G Richard
Friends of the Library Group

UNITED STATES NAVY
AM NAVAL REGIONAL MEDICAL CENTER, Naval Medical Ctr, 620 John Paul Jones Cir, 23708-2197. SAN 363-2040. Tel: 757-953-5530. Reference Tel: 757-953-5384. FAX: 757-953-7533. Web Site: www.nmcp.med.navy.mil/md/oob2/index.htm. *Librn*, Suad Jones; E-Mail: sfjones@pnhlo.med.navy.mil; *Ref*, Jane Pellegrino; Staff 5 (MLS 3, Non-MLS 2)
Oct 1999-Sep 2000 Income (Main Library and Branch Library) $482,786. Mats Exp $258,857, Books $42,530, Per/Ser (Incl. Access Fees) $207,000, Electronic Ref Mat (Incl. Access Fees) $9,300. Sal $195,929 (Prof $135,000)
Library Holdings: Bk Vols 27,064; Bk Titles 6,368; Per Subs 582
Subject Interests: Allied sci, Dentistry, Medicine, Nursing
Publications: Newsletter (in-house)
Restriction: By appointment only
Partic in OCLC Online Computer Library Center, Inc

A NORFOLK NAVAL SHIPYARD, TECHNICAL LIBRARY, Bldg 29, 2nd flr, Eng & Planning Dept, Code 202-3, 23709-5000. SAN 363-2016. Tel: 757-396-5674. FAX: 757-396-4103. *In Charge*, Pamela L Stevens
Library Holdings: Bk Vols 57,000; Per Subs 25
Subject Interests: Electrical, Electronics eng, Marine eng, Mgt
Special Collections: Technical Manuals Coll

POWHATAN

P POWHATAN COUNTY PUBLIC LIBRARY,* 3908 Old Buckingham Rd, Ste 3, 23139. SAN 375-8710. Tel: 804-598-5670. FAX: 804-598-5671. *Dir & Librn*, Kim Armentrout; E-Mail: director@richmond.net
Founded 1975. Pop 13,062
Library Holdings: Bk Titles 17,000; Per Subs 20
Open Mon & Wed 10-8, Tues & Thurs 9-5 & Sat 10-2

PRINCE WILLIAM

P PRINCE WILLIAM PUBLIC LIBRARY SYSTEM,* 13083 Chinn Park Dr, 22192-5073. SAN 363-0544. Tel: 703-792-6100. TDD: 703-792-6163. FAX: 703-792-4875. Web Site: www.co.prince-william.va.us. *Dir*, Richard Murphy; *Dep Dir*, Virginia Dorkey; *Tech Servs*, Marcia Kolb; Staff 198 (MLS 55, Non-MLS 143)
Founded 1952. Pop 287,489; Circ 3,506,500
Jul 1996-Jun 1997 Income $11,969,800, State $552,571, City $1,488,852, County $9,593,595, Locally Generated Income $334,782. Mats Exp $1,906,359, Books $1,104,939, Per/Ser (Incl. Access Fees) $706,150, Pres $1,490. Sal $6,800,695 (Prof $1,616,839)
Library Holdings: Bk Vols 735,000
Subject Interests: Govt of Prince William County, Local history, Manass
Special Collections: Management & Government Information Center
Automation Activity & Vendor Info: (Circulation) epixtech, inc.
Partic in BRS; Capcon Library Network; Dialog Corporation; Login; OCLC Online Computer Library Center, Inc
Special Services for the Deaf - TDD
Friends of the Library Group
Branches: 10
BULL RUN REGIONAL, 8051 Ashton Ave, Manassas, 20109-2892. SAN 374-6887. Tel: 703-792-4500. TDD: 704-792-4524. FAX: 703-792-4520. Web Site: www.co.prince-william.va.us.
Special Services for the Deaf - TDD
Friends of the Library Group
CENTRAL, 8601 Mathis Ave, Manassas, 20110-5229. SAN 329-644X. Tel: 703-361-8211. TDD: 703-361-7572. FAX: 703-335-2956. Web Site: www.co.prince-william.va.us.
Special Services for the Deaf - TDD
Friends of the Library Group
CHINN PARK REGIONAL, 13065 Chinn Park Dr, 22192-5073. SAN 37-4361. Tel: 703-792-4800. TDD: 703-792-4876. FAX: 703-792-4612. Web Site: www.co.prince-william.va.us.
Special Services for the Deaf - TDD
Friends of the Library Group
DALE CITY MINI, 4249 Dale Blvd, Woodbridge, 22193-2414. SAN 326-8284. Tel: 703-680-4716. FAX: 703-670-6152. Web Site: www.co.prince-william.va.us.
DUMFRIES MINI, 261-A S Fraley Blvd, Dumfries, 22026-2411. SAN 32-8306. Tel: 703-221-2268. FAX: 703-221-7814. Web Site: www.co.prince-william.va.us.
GAINESVILLE MINI, 4603 James Madison Hwy, Haymarket, 22069-252 SAN 328-963X. Tel: 703-754-8862. FAX: 703-754-2494. Web Site: www.co.prince-william.va.us.
INDEPENDENT HILL MINI, 14418 Bristow Rd, Manassas, 20112-3932. SAN 328-9656. Tel: 703-791-4469. FAX: 703-791-2721. Web Site: www.co.prince-william.va.us.
LAKE RIDGE MINI, 12964 Harbor Dr, Woodbridge, 22192-3012. SAN 326-8322. Tel: 703-491-2218. FAX: 703-491-6661. Web Site: www.co.prince-william.va.us.
NOKESVILLE MINI, 12993 Fitzwater Dr, Nokesville, 20181-2229. SAN 326-8349. Tel: 703-594-2124. FAX: 703-594-2250. Web Site: www.co.prince-william.va.us.
POTOMAC, 2201 Opitz Blvd, Woodbridge, 22191-3309. SAN 363-0579. Tel: 703-494-8126. FAX: 703-491-2593. Web Site: www.co.prince-william.va.us. *Librn*, Trudi Sommerfield
Friends of the Library Group

PROVIDENCE FORGE

P CHARLES CITY-NEW KENT HERITAGE FOUNDATION, INC, Heritage Public Library, 9001 Blvd, PO Box 8, 23140-0008. SAN 324-5780. Tel: 804-966-2480. FAX: 804-966-5982. *Librn*, Alan M Bernstein
Founded 1980. Pop 20,000
Jul 1999-Jun 2000 Income $147,000, State $48,000, County $96,000, Parent Institution $3,000. Mats Exp $35,947, Books $35,000, Per/Ser (Incl. Access Fees) $947. Sal $62,000 (Prof $34,000)
Library Holdings: Bk Titles 47,000
Special Collections: Religion (Charles Jeffery Smith Coll)

LASKI

PULASKI COUNTY LIBRARY, 60 W Third St, 24301. SAN 317-3887. Tel: 540-980-7770. FAX: 540-980-7775. *Dir*, Dot M Ogburn; Tel: 540-980-7772, E-Mail: dogburn@pc-va.org; *Ch Servs*, Rachael DeHaven; Tel: 540-980-7843, E-Mail: rdehaven@pc-va.org; *Tech Coordr*, Carol Smith; E-Mail: csmith@pc-va.org; *Business*, Becky Palmer; Tel: 540-980-7842, E-Mail: bpalmer@pc-va.org; *Outreach Serv*, Sally Warburton; Tel: 540-980-7855, E-Mail: swarburton@pc-va.org; *Circ*, Wanda Saunders; E-Mail: wsaunders@pc-va.org; *Ref*, Sharon Rupe; E-Mail: srupe@pc-va.org; *Tech Servs*, Teresa Jones; Tel: 540-980-7773, E-Mail: tjones@pc-va.org; Staff 10 (MLS 1, Non-MLS 9)
Founded 1937. Pop 35,000
Jul 2000-Jun 2001 Income (Main Library and Branch Library) $462,430, State $138,879, County $323,551, Locally Generated Income $8,000. Mats Exp $74,532, Books $57,432, Per/Ser (Incl. Access Fees) $8,900, Presv $1,200, Electronic Ref Mat (Incl. Access Fees) $7,000. Sal $277,790 (Prof $100,000)
Library Holdings: Bk Vols 71,000; Per Subs 175
Subject Interests: Pulaski County local hist
Automation Activity & Vendor Info: (Circulation) Sagebrush Corporation; (OPAC) Sagebrush Corporation
Database Vendor: ProQuest
Friends of the Library Group
Branches: 1
CHARLES & ONA B FREE MEMORIAL, 300 Giles Ave, Dublin, 24084. SAN 374-5295. Tel: 540-674-2856. FAX: 540-674-2907. *Branch Mgr*, Mia Catron; E-Mail: mcatron@pc-va.org; Staff 3 (Non-MLS 3)
Founded 1990
Friends of the Library Group

RCELLVILLE

PURCELLVILLE LIBRARY,* 220 E Main St, 20132. *In Charge*, Melody A Blaney; Tel: 540-554-8708, E-Mail: bearden@crosslink.net

ANTICO

FEDERAL BUREAU OF INVESTIGATION, Academy Library, MCB No 4, 22135. SAN 317-3895. Tel: 703-632-3200, 703-632-3201. FAX: 703-632-3214. *Librn*, Eugenia B Ryner; Tel: 702-632-3215, E-Mail: eryner@fbiacademy.edu; *Librn, Tech Servs*, Linda A Cranston; Tel: 703-632-3203, E-Mail: lcranston@fbiacademy.edu; *Librn, Publ Servs*, Jane Garrison; Tel: 703-632-3204, E-Mail: jgarrison@fbiacademy.edu; *Coll Develop, Librn*, Bertha A Scott; Tel: 703-632-3217, E-Mail: bscott@fbiacademy.edu; *Tech Servs*, Veronica Sacra; Tel: 703-632-3213, E-Mail: vsacra@fbiacademy.edu; *Info Tech, Tech Servs*, Marian Allen; Tel: 703-623-3212, E-Mail: mallen@fbiacademy.edu; *Tech Servs*, Jean Caddy; Tel: 703-632-3211, E-Mail: jcaddy@fbiacademy.edu; Staff 12 (MLS 4, Non-MLS 8)
Founded 1972
Library Holdings: Bk Vols 40,000; Per Subs 327
Subject Interests: Criminal justice, Law enforcement, Police
Automation Activity & Vendor Info: (Cataloging) Sydney
Publications: Subject Bibliographies
Restriction: Restricted access
Partic in OCLC Online Computer Library Center, Inc

UNITED STATES MARINE CORPS
MARINE CORPS UNIVERSITY LIBRARY, 2040 Broadway St, 22134-5207. SAN 363-2105. Tel: 703-784-4409. Reference Tel: 703-784-4411. FAX: 703-784-4306. E-Mail: reference@tecom.usmc.mil. Web Site: www.mcu.usmc.mil/mcrcweb/index.html. *Dir*, Carol Ellis Ramkey; Tel: 703-784-4764, E-Mail: ramkeyce@tecom.usmc.mil; *Ref*, Patricia Lane; *Tech Servs*, Linda Resler; Tel: 703-784-4838, E-Mail: reslerlm@tecom.usmc.mil; *Publ Servs*, Jane A Watson; E-Mail: watsnja1@tecom.usmc.mil; Staff 15 (MLS 8, Non-MLS 7)
Founded 1928. Enrl 4,000; Fac 200; Highest Degree: Master
Library Holdings: Bk Vols 140,000; Per Subs 700
Subject Interests: International relations, International studies, Marine corps hist, Mil art, Mil sci, Military hist
Special Collections: Marine Corps History; Military Operations
Automation Activity & Vendor Info: (Acquisitions) epixtech, inc.; (Cataloging) epixtech, inc.; (Circulation) epixtech, inc.; (OPAC) epixtech, inc.; (Serials) epixtech, inc.
Database Vendor: Dialog, epixtech, inc., Lexis-Nexis, OCLC - First Search, ProQuest
Function: ILL available
Partic in Consortium of Navy Librs; Fedlink; Military Educ Coordination Conf Libr Consortium
QUANTICO FAMILY LIBRARY, 2040 Broadway St, 22134-5107. SAN 363-213X. Tel: 703-784-4353. Reference Tel: 703-784-4348. FAX: 703-784-4306. Web Site: www.mcu.usmc.mil/mcrcweb/library6.html. *Dir*, Carol E Ramkey; Tel: 703-784-4764, E-Mail: ramkeyce@tecom.usmc.mil; *Librn*, Adam Yantorn; E-Mail: yantornra@tecom.usmc.mil; Staff 3 (MLS 1, Non-MLS 2)
Library Holdings: Bk Vols 30,000; Per Subs 100
Subject Interests: Col educ support, Mil fiction, Military history
Database Vendor: epixtech, inc., ProQuest
Partic in Fedlink

A UNITED STATES MARINE CORPS, Technical Library,* Marine Corp Systems Command Program Support Directorate, Code PSD, 2033 Barnett Ave, Ste 315, 22134-5010. SAN 337-2502. Tel: 703-784-2286, 703-784-4206. FAX: 703-784-4271. *Librn*, Dotty Canada
Library Holdings: Bk Vols 1,500; Per Subs 46
Special Collections: Marine Corps Technical Publications

RADFORD

P RADFORD PUBLIC LIBRARY, 30 First St, 24141. SAN 317-3917. Tel: 540-731-3608. Circulation Tel: 540-731-3621. FAX: 540-731-4857. Web Site: www.radford.va.us/library. *Dir*, Ann H Fisher; E-Mail: afisher@roanokemail.com; Staff 10 (MLS 3, Non-MLS 7)
Founded 1941. Pop 15,940; Circ 155,456
1999-2000 Income $322,053, State $34,059, City $287,994. Mats Exp $76,407, Books $62,483, Per/Ser (Incl. Access Fees) $5,003, Micro $518, AV Equip $8,403
Library Holdings: Bk Vols 76,562; Bk Titles 66,514; Per Subs 109
Subject Interests: Genealogy, Local history
Special Collections: Adult Low Reading Level Coll
Automation Activity & Vendor Info: (Circulation) TLC; (OPAC) TLC
Friends of the Library Group

C RADFORD UNIVERSITY, John Preston McConnell Library, 24142-6881. SAN 317-3909. Tel: 540-831-5471. FAX: 540-831-6138. Web Site: www.lib.runet.edu/lib-web/. *Actg Librn*, Linda Farynk; E-Mail: lfarynk@radford.edu; *Cat, Coll Develop*, Gerald Gordon; *Coordr*, Mary Wilson; Staff 14 (MLS 14)
Founded 1913. Enrl 8,600; Fac 395
Library Holdings: Bk Vols 305,321; Bk Titles 204,469; Per Subs 3,289
Subject Interests: Bus, Education, History, Music, Nursing, Soc work
Special Collections: Southwestern Virginia Regional History
Publications: McConnell Columns (library newsletter)
Partic in SE Libr Network
Special Services for the Blind - Kurzweil Reading Machine; Printed text enlargers; VIEW (Visually Impaired Educational Workstation)

RESTON

S BRICK INDUSTRY ASSOCIATION LIBRARY,* 11490 Commerce Park Dr, 20191. SAN 323-6080. Tel: 703-620-0010. FAX: 703-620-3928. E-Mail: brickinfo@bia.org.
Founded 1934
Library Holdings: Bk Titles 3,000; Per Subs 50
Subject Interests: Masonry

A DYNCORP, Information & Engineering Technology,* 11710 Plaza America Dr, No 500, 20190-4741. SAN 322-7847. Tel: 703-222-1500. FAX: 703-222-1552. *Librn*, Alan Gardner
Founded 1984
Library Holdings: Bk Vols 1,500; Per Subs 200
Subject Interests: Air tech, Automated info systs, Engineering, Space tech
Special Collections: Naval Regulations (Military Specifications & Standards Coll), bks
Restriction: Staff use only
Partic in Dialog Corporation

S HARDWOOD PLYWOOD & VENEER ASSOCIATION LIBRARY,* 1825 Michael Faraday Dr. (Mail add: PO Box 2789, 20195-0789), SAN 320-8761. Tel: 703-435-2900. FAX: 703-435-2537.
Founded 1921
Library Holdings: Bk Titles 300; Per Subs 50
Publications: How to Sell & Install Hardwood Plywood Manual; Inspection Testing & Listed Products Manual; Labor Survey; Members Bulletin (monthly); Prefinished Survey; Where to Buy Hardwood Plywood & Veneer (annual)

S METRON INC, Scientific Library,* 11911 Freedom Dr, Ste 800, 20190-5602. SAN 375-6858. Tel: 703-787-8700. FAX: 703-787-3518. *Librn*, Mary Beth Dwyer; E-Mail: dwyer@mctsci.com
Library Holdings: Bk Titles 3,000

S NATIONAL COUNCIL OF TEACHERS OF MATHEMATICS, Teacher Learning Center,* 1906 Association Dr, 20191. SAN 328-5278. Tel: 703-620-9840. FAX: 703-476-2970. *Dir*, Dr John Thorpe
Library Holdings: Bk Titles 1,000; Per Subs 712
Subject Interests: Education, Mathematics

S NATIONAL GROCERS ASSOCIATION LIBRARY,* 1825 Samuel Morse Dr, 20190. SAN 327-3539. Tel: 703-437-5300. FAX: 703-437-7768.
Library Holdings: Bk Vols 1,500

S TRW, Information Resources Center, 10211 Sunset Hills Rd, 20190. SAN 370-7768. Tel: 703-968-1000. Web Site: www.trw.com. *Mgr*, Norma C Draper
Founded 1982
Library Holdings: Bk Titles 6,000; Per Subs 125

G UNITED STATES GEOLOGICAL SURVEY LIBRARY,* 12201 Sunrise Valley Dr, National Ctr, Mail Stop 950, 20192. SAN 317-3968. Tel: 703-648-4302. TDD: 703-648-4105. FAX: 703-648-6373. E-Mail: library@usgs.gov. Web Site: library.usgs.gov. *Chief Librn*, Edward H Liszewski; *Acq*, Margaret Merryman; *Circ, Coll Develop, Ref*, Carol Messick
Founded 1882
Library Holdings: Per Subs 7,000
Subject Interests: Cartography, Chemistry, Environmental studies, Geology, Geothermal energy, Mineral resources, Mineralogy, Oceanography, Paleontology, Petrology, Physics, Planetary geology, Remote sensing, Soil science, Surveying, Water resources, Zoology
Special Collections: Gems & Minerals (Geroge F Kunz Coll); Russian Geology Books (Alverson)
Automation Activity & Vendor Info: (Cataloging) epixtech, inc.; (Serials) epixtech, inc.
Partic in Dialog Corporation; Fed Libr & Info Network; OCLC Online Computer Library Center, Inc
Special Services for the Deaf - TDD

RICHLANDS

J SOUTHWEST VIRGINIA COMMUNITY COLLEGE LIBRARY, (SVCC), PO Box SVCC, 24641. SAN 317-3976. Tel: 540-964-2555. Interlibrary Loan Service Tel: 540-964-7265. Circulation Tel: 540-964-7265. FAX: 540-964-7259. Web Site: www.sw.cc.va.us/library/. *Dir*, Sue W Captain; Tel: 540-964-7266, E-Mail: sue_captain@sw.cc.va.us; *Ref Serv*, Diane Phillips; Tel: 540-964-7617, E-Mail: diane_phillips@sw.cc.va.us; Staff 3 (MLS 3)
Founded 1968. Enrl 2,200; Fac 162; Highest Degree: Associate
Library Holdings: Bk Vols 38,000; Per Subs 225; Bks on Deafness & Sign Lang 25

RICHMOND

S ASSOCIATION FOR THE PRESERVATION OF VIRGINIA ANTIQUITIES LIBRARY, 204 W Franklin St, 23220. SAN 317-3984. Tel: 804-648-1889. FAX: 804-775-0802. *Dir*, Louis J Malon; E-Mail: lmalon@apva.org
Founded 1970
1999-2000 Mats Exp $1,500, Books $500, Per/Ser (Incl. Access Fees) $1,000
Library Holdings: Bk Vols 3,300; Per Subs 40
Subject Interests: Architecture, Art, Decorative arts, Va hist
Restriction: Staff use only

SR BETH ABABAH MUSEUM & ARCHIVES, 1109 W Franklin St, 23220. SAN 373-8396. Tel: 804-353-2668. FAX: 804-358-3451. Web Site: www.bethahabah.org. *Dir*, Shirley Belkowitz; *Asst Dir*, Bonnie Ersenman; *Publ Servs, Ref*, Lillian D M Kelsey; Staff 3 (Non-MLS 3)
Founded 1977
Library Holdings: Bk Titles 500
Subject Interests: Genealogy
Special Collections: Genealogy Coll; Jefferson Lakeside Country Club; Jewish Community Center; Jewish Community Federation of Richmond; Jewish Family Servs, Beth Shalom Home; National Council of Jewish Women; Rabbi Ariel Goldberg Coll; Rabbi Edward N Calisch Coll
Publications: Generations (triannual)
Restriction: Non-circulating

CM BON SECOURS RICHMOND HEALTH SYSTEM, Bon Secours Memorial School of Nursing Library, Bon Secours Memorial School of Nursing, 8550 Magellan Pkwy, Ste 1100, 23227. SAN 317-4115. Tel: 804-915-8013. FAX: 804-915-8281. E-Mail: rmhlibra@richmond.infi.net. Web Site: rmhlibra@richmond.infi.net. *Librn*, Merle L Colglazier, Jr; Staff 1 (MLS 1)
Founded 1963. Enrl 90; Fac 16
Library Holdings: Bk Vols 2,400; Per Subs 65
Subject Interests: Nursing
Automation Activity & Vendor Info: (Cataloging) Sagebrush Corporation; (Circulation) Sagebrush Corporation; (OPAC) Sagebrush Corporation
Database Vendor: Ebsco - EbscoHost
Function: For research purposes
Partic in Nat Libr of Med

M BON SECOURS-SAINT MARY'S HOSPITAL, Health Sciences Library, 5801 Bremo Rd, 23226. SAN 322-9017. Tel: 804-281-8247. FAX: 804-285-2448. *Librn, Online Servs*, Damon Persiani; E-Mail: bssmh.damon@erols.com
Library Holdings: Bk Vols 750; Bk Titles 737; Per Subs 125

S BRAILLE CIRCULATING LIBRARY, INC, 2700 Stuart Ave, 23220. SAN 317-400X. Tel: 804-359-3743. FAX: 804-359-4777. E-Mail: www.braillecl@aol.com. *Exec Dir*, R C Roberts; Tel: 804-359-3771
Founded 1925
Library Holdings: Bk Vols 25,000; Bk Titles 9,900
Subject Interests: Religion
Publications: Insight (bimonthly publication)
Special Services for the Blind - Braille

L CHRISTIAN & BARTON, LLP ATTORNEYS AT LAW, Law Library, 9 E Main St, 23219. SAN 372-350X. Tel: 804-697-4100. FAX: 804-697-41[illegible] Web Site: www.cblaw.com/. *Librn*, Jane V Bowe
Library Holdings: Bk Vols 20,000; Per Subs 200

S CHRISTIAN CHILDREN'S FUND LIBRARY, 2821 Emerywood Pkwy, Box 26484, 23261-6484. SAN 373-9171. Tel: 804-756-2700 Ext 2112. FA 804-756-2732. *In Charge*, Joan Losen; E-Mail: joanl@ccfusa.org; Staff 1 (MLS 1)
Founded 1990
Library Holdings: Bk Vols 3,000; Per Subs 50
Special Collections: International Child & Community Development (CC Archives)
Restriction: By appointment only
Friends of the Library Group

P COUNTY OF HENRICO PUBLIC LIBRARY, 1001 N Laburnum Ave, 23223. SAN 363-2199. Tel: 804-222-1643. FAX: 804-222-5566. Web Site www.co.henrico.va.us/library. *Dir*, Gerald M McKenna; E-Mail: gmckenn henrico.lib.va.us; *Tech Coordr*, Bob Sweet; *Cat*, Toni Hamlett; *Ch Servs*, Joyce Antrim; *Commun Relations*, Courtney Melchor; *Automation Syst Coordr*, Lisa Gaza; *Coll Develop*, Judith Atlas; Staff 137 (MLS 44, Non-MLS 93)
Founded 1966. Pop 254,194; Circ 2,239,975
Jul 1999-Jun 2000 Income $6,904,876
Partic in OCLC Online Computer Library Center, Inc
Friends of the Library Group
Branches: 10
DUMBARTON AREA, 6800 Staples Mill, 23228. SAN 363-2229. Tel: 8(262-6507. FAX: 804-266-8986. Web Site: www.co.henrico.va.us/library. *Mgr*, Marianne White
Friends of the Library Group
FAIRFIELD AREA, 1001 N Laburnum Ave, 23223. Tel: 804-222-1559. FAX: 804-222-1958. Web Site: www.co.henrico.va.us/library.
Library Holdings: Bk Vols 116,033
Friends of the Library Group
GAYTON, 10600 Gayton Rd, 23233. SAN 329-6288. Tel: 804-740-2747. FAX: 804-741-3523. Web Site: www.co.henrico.va.us/library. *Librn*, Tor Bruno
Library Holdings: Bk Vols 69,253
Friends of the Library Group
GLEN ALLEN BRANCH, 10501 Staples Mill Rd, Glen Allen, 23060. SA 375-5754. Tel: 804-756-7523. FAX: 804-755-1702. Web Site: www.co.henrico.va.us/library. *Librn*, Ingrid Whaley
Library Holdings: Bk Vols 28,085
Friends of the Library Group
INNSBROOK, 4060 Innslake Dr, Glen Allen, 23060. SAN 373-5265. Tel: 804-747-8140. FAX: 804-747-1117. Web Site: www.co.henrico.va.us/library. *Librn*, Ahmed Tabib
Library Holdings: Bk Vols 49,717
Friends of the Library Group
MUNICIPAL GOVERNMENT & LAW, PO Box 27032, 23273. SAN 36: 2288. Tel: 804-501-4780. FAX: 804-501-1948. Web Site: www.co.henrico.va.us/library. *Librn*, Isabel Paul
NORTH PARK, 8141 Brook Rd, 23227. SAN 323-813X. Tel: 804-262-4876. FAX: 804-264-7035. Web Site: www.co.henrico.va.us/library. *Libr* Louise Perry
Friends of the Library Group
SANDSTON BRANCH, 23 E Williamsburg Rd, Sandston, 23150. SAN 3(2318. Tel: 804-737-3728. FAX: 804-328-1041. Web Site: www.co.henrico.va.us/library. *Librn*, Charles W Sohn
Friends of the Library Group
TUCKAHUE AREA, 1700 Parham Rd, 23229. SAN 363-2342. Tel: 804-270-9578. FAX: 804-346-0985. Web Site: www.co.henrico.va.us/library. *Librn*, Janet Woody
Friends of the Library Group
VARINA, 2001 Library Rd, 23231. SAN 363-2377. Tel: 804-222-3414. FAX: 804-222-4244. Web Site: www.co.henrico.va.us/library. *Librn*, Jean Burchill
Friends of the Library Group
Bookmobiles: 1

GM DEPARTMENT OF VETERANS AFFAIRS, Medical Center Library Service,* 1201 Broad Rock Blvd, 23249. SAN 317-4220. Tel: 804-675-5000, Ext 5142. FAX: 804-675-5252. *Librn*, Susana Hernandez-Kurtulus
Library Holdings: Bk Vols 4,650; Per Subs 300

L DIVISION OF LEGISLATIVE SERVICES REFERENCE CENTER, General Assembly Bldg, 910 Capitol St 2nd flr, 23219. SAN 372-3496. Tel 804-786-3591. FAX: 804-371-0169. Web Site: www.dls.state.va.us/lrc.htm. *Info Res*, Cheryl Jackson; E-Mail: cjackson@leg.state.va.us
Library Holdings: Bk Vols 8,000; Per Subs 150

DU PONT COMPANY, Spruance Technical Library, PO Box 27001, 23261. SAN 317-4018. Tel: 804-383-4107. FAX: 804-383-4544. *Info Specialist*, Brett Crouse; E-Mail: brett.a.crouse@usa.dupont.com; Staff 2 (MLS 1, Non-MLS 1)
Founded 1943
Library Holdings: Bk Titles 2,350; Per Subs 150
Subject Interests: Chemistry, Engineering, Nonwovens, Polymer sci, Polymer tech, Synthetic fibers
Publications: Library Bulletin
Restriction: Not open to public
Affiliated with the Du Pont Technical Library Network, headquartered in Wilmington, Delaware

ECPI TECHNICAL COLLEGE, Richmond Campus Library, 800 Moorefield Park Dr, 23236. SAN 375-5398. Tel: 804-330-5533. FAX: 804-330-5577. Web Site: www.ecpi.edu. *Chief Librn*, Robert Christopher; E-Mail: rchristopher@ecpi.edu
Library Holdings: Bk Vols 7,300; Per Subs 145
Subject Interests: Computer science

FEDERAL RESERVE BANK OF RICHMOND, Research Library,* 701 E Byrd St, 23261. (Mail add: PO Box 27622, 23261-7622), SAN 317-4026. Tel: 804-697-8125. FAX: 804-697-8134. E-Mail: reslib@richmond.infi.net. Web Site: www.rich.frb.org/. *Mgr*, Anne R Hallerman; E-Mail: anne.hallerman@rich.frb.org; *Acq, Purchasing, Ser*, Charlene Fenner; *Cat*, Veronica Cummings; *Ref*, Christian Pascasio; Staff 8 (MLS 4, Non-MLS 4)
Founded 1920
Library Holdings: Bk Vols 29,000; Bk Titles 20,000; Per Subs 325
Subject Interests: Banking, Econ, Finance
Special Collections: Federal Reserve System Publications
Automation Activity & Vendor Info: (Acquisitions) Innovative Interfaces Inc.; (Cataloging) Innovative Interfaces Inc.; (Circulation) Innovative Interfaces Inc.; (OPAC) Innovative Interfaces Inc.; (Serials) Innovative Interfaces Inc.
Database Vendor: Dialog, Ebsco - EbscoHost, Silverplatter Information Inc.
Publications: Recent Acquisitions (monthly)
Partic in Capcon Library Network; OCLC Online Computer Library Center, Inc

FIRST BAPTIST CHURCH LIBRARY,* 2709 Monument Ave, 23220. SAN 370-2367. Tel: 804-355-8637. FAX: 804-359-4000. Web Site: www.fbcrichmond.org. *Chairperson*, Rob Blackmore
Library Holdings: Bk Vols 14,500; Per Subs 45

FORT JAMES CORP, Corporate Information Center,* PO Box 2218, 23217. SAN 301-3944. Tel; 804-662-8000, Ext 8407. FAX: 804-662-8779.
Founded 1952
Library Holdings: Bk Titles 5,000; Per Subs 300
Subject Interests: Business and management
Partic in Dialog Corporation; RLIN

GRAND LODGE OF VIRGINIA, Allen E Roberts Masonic Library & Museum, 4115 Nine Mile Rd, 23223-4926. SAN 326-0585. Tel: 804-222-3110. FAX: 804-222-4253. E-Mail: glova@erols.com, glva@web-span.com. *Librn*, Marie M Barnett; Staff 1 (Non-MLS 1)
Founded 1778
Jan 1999-Dec 1999 Income $1,250. Mats Exp $240, Books $50, Per/Ser (Incl. Access Fees) $40, Manuscripts & Archives $150. Sal $10,000
Library Holdings: Bk Vols 8,790; Bk Titles 4,290; Per Subs 64
Special Collections: Masonic Archival Materials (hist, transactions, bylaws); Museum objects
Publications: The Virginia Masonic Herald
Restriction: Members only, Open to public for reference only
Function: Research library

HENRICO DOCTORS HOSPITAL, Medical Library,* 1602 Skipwith Rd, 23229-5298. SAN 371-6163. Tel: 804-289-4728. FAX: 804-289-4960. *Librn*, Sarah Raible
Founded 1980
Library Holdings: Bk Vols 224; Bk Titles 163; Per Subs 54
Restriction: Staff use only

HUNTON & WILLIAMS, Law Library, East Tower River Front Plaza, 951 E Byrd St, PO Box 1535, 23219. SAN 317-4042. Tel: 804-788-8272. FAX: 804-788-8218. *Librn*, Frosty Owen
Founded 1901
Library Holdings: Bk Vols 65,000; Per Subs 150
Subject Interests: Accounting, Antitrust, Environ, Fed law, Labor law, Real estate, Utilities, Virginia Law
Special Collections: Law Memoranda; Records & Briefs; Speeches of Henry W Anderson
Restriction: Staff use only
Partic in Dialog Corporation

INTERNATIONAL MISSION BOARD, SOUTHERN BAPTIST CONVENTION

R ARCHIVES CENTER, 3806 Monument Ave, PO Box 6767, 23230. SAN 321-8619. Tel: 804-219-1296. FAX: 804-254-8980. Web Site: www.imb.org. *Archivist*, Edith M Jeter; E-Mail: edie.jeter@imb.org
Subject Interests: Missions hist, Southern Baptist Convention hist
Special Collections: Country Files from Mid-19th Century, missionary hist

R JENKINS RESEARCH LIBRARY, 3806 Monument Ave, 23230-0767. (Mail add: PO Box 6767, 23230-0767), SAN 317-4158. Tel: 804-219-1429. FAX: 804-254-8980. E-Mail: jenkins.library@imb.org. *Dir*, Kathryn K Purks; Tel: 804-219-1435, E-Mail: kathy.purks@imb.org; *Librn*, Nancy Michael; Tel: 804-219-1824, Fax: 804-219-1850, E-Mail: nancy.michael@imb.org; *Librn*, Judith Bernicchi; Tel: 804-219-1352, E-Mail: judith.bernicchi@imb.org; Staff 7 (MLS 4, Non-MLS 3)
Founded 1960
Library Holdings: Bk Vols 22,000; Per Subs 800
Subject Interests: Anthropology, Cross-cultural communication, Econ, Ethnolinguistic people groups, Future studies, Hist of missions, History, Missiology, Politics
Special Collections: Southern Baptist Missions History
Database Vendor: Dialog, Ebsco - EbscoHost, Lexis-Nexis, OCLC - First Search
Partic in OCLC Online Computer Library Center, Inc; SE Libr Network

R MISSIONARY LEARNING CENTER LIBRARY, 16492 MLC Lane, Rockville, 23146. SAN 321-8627. Tel: 804-219-1824. FAX: 804-219-1850.
Founded 1967
Library Holdings: Bk Vols 6,000; Per Subs 200

J SARGEANT REYNOLDS COMMUNITY COLLEGE LIBRARY

J DOWNTOWN CAMPUS-LEARNING RESOURCES CENTER, 700 E Jackson St, PO Box 85622, 23285-5622. SAN 363-2407. Tel: 804-786-5638. FAX: 804-786-6200. *Dir*, Dr Abdul J Miah; E-Mail: amiah@jsr.cc.va.us; *Media Spec*, Cynthia Sugg; *Ref*, Khalil Ahmed; Staff 4 (MLS 4)
Founded 1973. Enrl 2,000
Library Holdings: Bk Vols 33,825; Bk Titles 26,505; Per Subs 215
Special Collections: Business Administration, AV, bks; Health Science, AV, bks
Partic in VIVA-Statewide Library Resource Network
Financial information includes all campuses

MEDIA PROCESSING CENTER, PO Box 85622, 23285-5622. SAN 363-2431. Tel: 804-371-3022. FAX: 804-371-3091.; Staff 1 (MLS 1)
Founded 1974
Library Holdings: Bk Vols 647; Bk Titles 100; Per Subs 17
Special Collections: Bibliographic aids for cataloging book & non-book media
Automation Activity & Vendor Info: (Cataloging) NOTIS; (Circulation) NOTIS
Partic in Richmond Academic Library Consortium; VIVA-Statewide Library Resource Network

J PARHAM CAMPUS LEARNING RESOURCES CENTER, 1651 E Parham Rd, 23228. (Mail add: PO Box 85622, 23285-5622), SAN 363-2466. Tel: 804-371-3220. Circulation Tel: 804-371-3016. Reference Tel: 804-371-3017. FAX: 804-371-3086. Web Site: www.jsr.cc.va.us/lrc/index.htm. *Actg Dir, Tech Servs*, Charles Lewis; Tel: 804-371-3026, Fax: 804-371-3091, E-Mail: clewis@jsr.cc.va.us; *Actg Dir, Publ Servs*, Tim Williams; Tel: 804-371-3403, E-Mail: twilliams@jsr.cc.va.us; *Ref*, Lisa Bishop; E-Mail: lbishop@jsr.cc.va.us; *Ref*, Kathy Hierholzer; E-Mail: khierholzer@jsr.cc.va.us; *Bibliog Instr, Ref*, Hong Wu; Tel: 804-371-3436, E-Mail: hwu@jsr.cc.va.us; *Acq, Circ*, Jill Brown; Tel: 804-371-3891, E-Mail: jbbrown@jsr.cc.va.us; *Circ, ILL*, Barbara Campeau; Tel: 804-371-3892, E-Mail: bcampeau@jsr.cc.va.us; *Circ*, Catherine Geissler; Tel: 804-371-3222, E-Mail: cgeissler@jsr.cc.va.us; *Acq, Tech Servs*, Kate Cooke; Tel: 804-371-3022, Fax: 804-371-3091, E-Mail: kcooke@jsr.cc.va.us; *Tech Servs*, Patsy VanSickle; Tel: 804-371-3221, Fax: 804-371-3091, E-Mail: pvansickle@jsr.cc.va.us; *AV*, Celeste Gaines; Tel: 804-371-3221, E-Mail: cgaines@jsr.cc.va.us; *AV*, Eric Meyer; E-Mail: emeyer@jsr.cc.va.us. Subject Specialists: *Media*, Patsy VanSickle; *Reserve syst*, Catherine Geissler; Staff 11 (MLS 5, Non-MLS 6)
Founded 1974. Enrl 10,725; Fac 120; Highest Degree: Associate
Jul 1999-Jun 2000 Income (Main Library Only) $69,614, State $66,614, Federal $3,000. Mats Exp $71,114, Books $34,314, Per/Ser (Incl. Access Fees) $16,000, Micro $11,000, AV Equip $1,500, Electronic Ref Mat (Incl. Access Fees) $8,300. Sal $411,000 (Prof $202,000)
Library Holdings: Bk Vols 56,000; Bk Titles 32,000; Per Subs 220; High Interest/Low Vocabulary Bk Vols 175; Spec Interest Per Sub 10; Bks on Deafness & Sign Lang 25
Subject Interests: CAD, Electronics, Info systs, Legal assisting, Liberal arts, Semiconductors
Database Vendor: Ebsco - EbscoHost, GaleNet, IAC - Info Trac, IAC - SearchBank, Lexis-Nexis, OCLC - First Search, OVID Technologies
Publications: Off the Shelf
Mem of VA Community Col Syst
Partic in Richmond Academic Library Consortium; Solinet; SWING; VA Tech Libr Syst; VIVA-Statewide Library Resource Network

J WESTERN CAMPUS, PO Box 85622, 23285-5622. SAN 370-3525. Tel: 804-786-3316. FAX: 804-371-8938. *Tech Servs*, Shirley Hughes; E-Mail: shughes@jsr.cc.va.us
Library Holdings: Bk Vols 3,000; Bk Titles 2,565; Per Subs 38
Subject Interests: Automotive, Horticulture

P LIBRARY & RESOURCE CENTER, 395 Azalea Ave, 23227-3623. SAN 317-4298. Tel: 804-371-3661. FAX: 804-371-3508. *Dir*, Barbara McCarthy; E-Mail: mccartbn@dvh.state.va.us; *Librn*, Randy French; Staff 5 (MLS 5)
Founded 1958
Library Holdings: Bk Vols 203,000; Per Subs 16
Special Collections: Print Research Material on Blindness
Publications: Newsletter (quarterly)
Special Services for the Blind - Braille; Braille & cassetes; Braille & recorded books; Textbooks on audiocassettes, variable speed cassette players
Friends of the Library Group

L MAYS & VALENTINE LLP, Law Library, 1111 E Main St, 23219. (Mail add: PO Box 1122, 23218), SAN 372-3925. Tel: 804-697-1200. FAX: 804-697-1339. *Librn*, Bonnie K Gates; *Librn*, Carol Goodman
Library Holdings: Bk Vols 10,000

L MCGUIRE, WOODS, BATTLE & BOOTHE LIBRARY, One James Ctr, 23219. SAN 317-4050. Tel: 804-775-1070. FAX: 804-775-1061. *Librn*, David Mason; Tel: 804-775-7863
Library Holdings: Bk Titles 80,000; Per Subs 250
Subject Interests: Law
Partic in Dialog Corporation; Westlaw

S MUSEUM OF THE CONFEDERACY, Eleanor S Brockenbrough Library, 1201 E Clay St, 23219. SAN 317-4069. Tel: 804-649-1861. FAX: 804-644-7150. E-Mail: library@moc.org. Web Site: www.moc.org. *Dir*, John Coski; *Mgr*, Ruth Ann Coski; Staff 3 (Non-MLS 3)
Founded 1890
Library Holdings: Bk Vols 11,000; Per Subs 15
Subject Interests: Confederacy, Southern hist
Special Collections: Archives of the Museum; Confederate Financial Instruments (bonds & currency); Confederate Imprints; Confederate Military Unit Records; Jefferson Davis Coll; Letters of Southern Soldiers & Civilians; Maps; Newspapers; Records of Confederate Monument Association; Records of the United Confederate Veterans Association; Records of United Daughters of the Confederacy Association
Restriction: By appointment only

S NATIONAL PARK SERVICE, Richmond National Battlefield Park Headquarters Library, 3215 E Broad St, 23223. SAN 317-4077. Tel: 804-226-1981. FAX: 804-771-8522. Web Site: www.nps.gov/rich. *In Charge*, Michael Andrus
Founded 1948
Library Holdings: Bk Vols 1,000
Subject Interests: The Civil War
Special Services for the Deaf - Captioned film depository

L OFFICE OF THE ATTORNEY GENERAL LIBRARY, 900 E Main St, 23219. SAN 372-3941. Tel: 804-786-0084. FAX: 804-786-1904. *Librn*, Georgiana Gekas Wellford
Library Holdings: Bk Vols 10,000; Per Subs 50
Restriction: Not open to public

S PHILIP MORRIS USA LIBRARY, 4201 Commerce Rd, PO Box 26583, 23261. SAN 317-4085. Tel: 804-274-2877. FAX: 804-274-2160. *Ser*, Cynthia Church; *Doc Delivery*, Lynn Larson; Staff 6 (MLS 4, Non-MLS 2)
Founded 1959
Library Holdings: Bk Titles 40,000; Per Subs 300
Subject Interests: Tobacco
Restriction: Staff use only
Partic in Dialog Corporation; Dow Jones News Retrieval; Questal Orbit; Solinet; STN

L PUBLIC LAW LIBRARY,* 400 N Ninth St, 23219. SAN 372-3976. Tel: 804-646-6500. *Librn*, Theresa H Schmid
Library Holdings: Bk Vols 12,000; Per Subs 12

SR REVEILLE UNITED METHODIST CHURCH LIBRARY, 4200 Cary Street Rd, 23221. SAN 317-4093. Tel: 804-359-6041. FAX: 804-359-6090. *Librn*, Mrs William B Guthrie; *Ch Servs*, Barbara Inge; *Ch Servs*, Diane Hall; Staff 7 (MLS 2, Non-MLS 5)
Library Holdings: Bk Titles 9,527

REYNOLDS METALS CO
L LAW LIBRARY, 6601 W Broad St, 23230. SAN 363-2520. Tel: 804-281-4708. FAX: 804-281-3740. *Librn*, Martha P Clampitt; E-Mail: mpclampi@rmc.com
Founded 1957
Library Holdings: Bk Vols 20,800
Subject Interests: Antitrust, Commercial, Corporate, Environ, Intellectual prop, Labor, Real estate, Securities law, Tax
Restriction: By appointment only

S RICHMOND NEWSPAPERS, INC LIBRARY,* 333 E Grace St, 23219. SAN 317-4123. Tel: 804-649-6283, 804-649-6286. FAX: 804-775-8059. Web Site: www.timesdispatch.com. *Librn*, Charles D Saunders
Library Holdings: Bk Titles 2,300
Special Collections: Newspapers Back to 1852, microfilm

P RICHMOND PUBLIC LIBRARY, 101 E Franklin St, 23219-2193. SAN 363-261X. Tel: 804-646-4867. FAX: 804-646-4757. Web Site: www.richmondpubliclibrary.org. *Dir*, Robert D Rieffel; Tel: 804-646-4550, Fax: 804-646-7685, E-Mail: rieffero@ci.richmond.va.us; *Asst Dir*, Alvin Andersom; Tel: 804-646-4257, Fax: 804-646-7685, E-Mail: andersom@ci.richmond.va.us; *Asst Dir*, Patricia W McKay; Tel: 805-646-4514, Fax: 804-646-7685; *Coll Develop*, Beth Morelli; Tel: 804-646-3410; *Ch Servs*, Gloria Nottingham; *Automation Syst Coordr*, Robert Barbie; Staff 72 (MLS 16, Non-MLS 56)
Founded 1924. Pop 194,100; Circ 1,058,137
Jul 1999-Jun 2000 Income $4,147,195, State $263,886, City $3,776,471, Locally Generated Income $106,838. Mats Exp $345,311, Books $250,89[illegible], Per/Ser (Incl. Access Fees) $51,483, Presv $2,021, Micro $12,628, Electronic Ref Mat (Incl. Access Fees) $23,308. Sal $3,193,178
Library Holdings: Bk Vols 923,699; Per Subs 846
Special Collections: Rare Children's Books; Richmond Authors
Automation Activity & Vendor Info: (Acquisitions) DRA; (Cataloging) DRA; (Circulation) DRA
Library holdings includes all branches
Friends of the Library Group
Branches: 8
BELMONT BRANCH, 3100 Ellwood Ave, 23221. SAN 363-2644. Tel: 804-646-1139. *Branch Mgr*, Helen Ogden; Tel: 804-646-1239; *Librn*, Ellen Anderson; *Librn*, Robert Rieffel; Tel: 804-646-4550, Fax: 804-646-7685, E-Mail: rieffero@ci.richmond.va.us; Staff 5 (MLS 1, Non-MLS 4)
Library Holdings: Bk Vols 51,769
Friends of the Library Group
BROAD ROCK, 4820 Warwick Rd, 23224. SAN 363-2679. Tel: 804-780-4488. Web Site: www.homepages.go.com/homepages/b/r/o/broadrocklibrary/. *Librn*, Lindia Porter
Library Holdings: Bk Vols 43,436
EAST END, 25th & R St, 23223. SAN 363-2709. Tel: 804-780-4474. Web Site: www.homepages.go.com/homepages/e/a/s/eastendlibrary/. *Librn*, Mary Terry
Library Holdings: Bk Vols 31,787
GINTER PARK, 1200 Westbrook Ave, 23227. SAN 363-2733. Tel: 804-78[illegible]-6236. Web Site: www.cydom.com/ginterparklibrary/. *Librn*, Marie Martinelli; E-Mail: mariemartinelli@yahoo.com
Library Holdings: Bk Vols 43,019
HULL STREET, 1400 Hull St, 23224. SAN 328-7173. Tel: 804-780-4676. *Librn*, Letitia Conyers
Library Holdings: Bk Vols 32,996
NORTH AVENUE, 2901 North Ave, 23222. SAN 363-275X. Tel: 804-780-8675. E-Mail: northavenuelibrary@planetaccess.com. Web Site: www.homepages.go.com/homepages/n/o/r/northavenuelibrary. *Librn*, Joan Goode
Library Holdings: Bk Vols 26,375
Friends of the Library Group
WEST END, 5420 Patterson Ave, 23226. SAN 363-2768. Tel: 804-780-8677. E-Mail: westendlib@xoom.com. Web Site: www.members.xoom.com/westendlib/. *Librn*, Barbara L Gregory
Library Holdings: Bk Vols 55,447
Friends of the Library Group
WESTOVER HILLS, 1408 Westover Hills Blvd, 23225. SAN 363-2792. Tel: 804-646-8833. E-Mail: wh_library@hotmail.com. Web Site: www.homepages.go.com/homepages/w/e/s/westoverhillslibrary/. *Librn*, Patricia Gordinier
Library Holdings: Bk Vols 45,177
Friends of the Library Group
Bookmobiles: 2

R SAINT PAUL'S EPISCOPAL CHURCH LIBRARY, 815 E Grace St, 23219. SAN 317-414X. Tel: 804-643-3589. FAX: 804-649-3283. Web Site: www.saintpauls-episcopal.org.
Founded 1963
Library Holdings: Bk Vols 3,300; Per Subs 12
Subject Interests: Childrens bks, Relig studies

S SUNTRUST BANK, (Formerly Crestar Bank), Information Center, 919 E Main St, 23219. (Mail add: PO Box 26665, 23261-6665), SAN 363-2881. Tel: 804-782-7452. FAX: 804-782-5262. *VPres*, Sue Miller; *Tech Servs*, Tim Schmitt; Staff 3 (MLS 2, Non-MLS 1)
Founded 1970
Library Holdings: Bk Vols 9,000; Per Subs 600
Subject Interests: Accounting, Bank operations, Corporate finance, Econ, Electronic data proc, Eurobanking, Leasing, Mgt, Personnel
Publications: Books 'n Things
Restriction: By appointment only

THE LIBRARY OF VIRGINIA, 800 E Broad St, 23219-8000. SAN 363-3128. Tel: 804-692-3592. Interlibrary Loan Service Tel: 804-692-3993. Circulation Tel: 804-692-3547. Reference Tel: 804-692-3777. TDD: 804-692-3976. FAX: 804-692-3594. Web Site: www.lva.lib.va.us. *State Librn*, Nolan T Yelich; Tel: 804-692-3535, E-Mail: nyelich@lva.lib.va.us; *Archivist*, Conley L Edwards, III; Tel: 804-692-3554, Fax: 804-692-3556, E-Mail: cedwards@lva.lib.va.us; *Info Tech*, Paul Casalaspi; Tel: 804-692-3756, E-Mail: pcasalaspi@lva.lib.va.us; Staff 172 (MLS 40, Non-MLS 132)
Founded 1823. Pop 6,686,437
Jul 1999-Jun 2000 Income $32,558,128, State $27,555,664, Federal $3,017,648, Other $1,984,816. Mats Exp $1,226,488, Books $322,500, Per/Ser (Incl. Access Fees) $125,500, Presv $498,488, Other Print Mats $70,000, Manuscripts & Archives $150,000, Electronic Ref Mat (Incl. Access Fees) $60,000. Sal $9,754,709 (Prof $7,316,032)
Library Holdings: Bk Vols 748,485; Per Subs 980
Subject Interests: Architecture, Art, Engraving, Government, Local history, Photographs, Politics, Prints, Rare books, Sheet music, Southern hist
Special Collections: Confederate Imprints; Genealogy Coll; Government and Politics; Virginia & Southern History; Virginia Broadsides; Virginia Maps; Virginia Newspapers; Virginia Picture Coll; Virginia Public Records; Virginia State Documents; Virginia-related Sheet Music
Automation Activity & Vendor Info: (Cataloging) VTLS; (Circulation) VTLS; (ILL) VTLS; (OPAC) VTLS; (Serials) VTLS
Database Vendor: OCLC - First Search
Publications: bibliographical resources; documentary editions & monographs; facsimilies; historical & genealogical research notes & guides; library statistics; newsletters
Restriction: Residents only, Restricted loan policy
Function: Reference services available
Partic in Solinet; VIVA-Statewide Library Resource Network
Non-Virginia residents may use materials only in library reading rooms; archival agency of the Commonwealth; records management authority for state & local government; administrator of the State Aid to local libraries; certification of librarians; operates state records center for non-current goverment records
Branches: 1

UNION THEOLOGICAL SEMINARY & PRESBYTERIAN SCHOOL OF CHRISTIAN EDUCATION, William Smith Morton Library, 3401 Brook Rd, 23227. SAN 317-4166. Tel: 804-278-4310. FAX: 804-278-4375. Web Site: www.library.union-psce.edu. *Bibliog Instr, Coll Develop, Dir*, John B Trotti; E-Mail: jtrotti@union-psce.edu; *Assoc Librn*, Robert Benedetto; *ILL, Online Servs, Ref*, Patsy Verreault; *Acq*, Hobbie Carlson; *Cat*, Dorothy G Thomason; *Media Spec*, Ann Knox
Founded 1806. Enrl 220; Fac 27; Highest Degree: Doctorate
Library Holdings: Bk Vols 315,636; Per Subs 1,358
Subject Interests: Education, History, Relig studies, Theology
Special Collections: Religion (Records of Synod of Virginia), micro; Social Science; William Blake (Norfleet)
Publications: Pettee Matters; Scholars Choice
Partic in BRS; SE Libr Network

UNION-PSCE, Center on Aging Library,* 3401 Brook Rd, 23227-4597. SAN 371-8603. Tel: 804-254-8045. FAX: 804-254-8060. *Dir*, Henry Simmons; E-Mail: hsimmons@utsva.edu; Staff 1 (MLS 1)
Library Holdings: Bk Titles 1,600
Restriction: Open to public for reference only

UNITED DAUGHTERS OF THE CONFEDERACY, Caroline Meriwether Goodlett Library, 328 North Blvd, 23220-4057. SAN 317-4174. Tel: 804-355-1636. FAX: 804-353-1396. E-Mail: hqudc@rcn.com. Web Site: www.hqudc.org. *Librn*, Ann Baker; *Librn*, Barbara Dunn
Founded 1957
1998-1999 Income $1,500, Other $1,000. Mats Exp Books $200
Library Holdings: Bk Vols 2,000
Special Collections: Confederacy letters, diaries, documents, other unpublished material & published books

UNITED NETWORK FOR ORGAN SHARING, National Transplantation Resource Center, 1100 Boulders Pkwy, Ste 500, PO Box 13770, 23225-8770. SAN 374-6658. Tel: 804-330-8546. FAX: 804-330-8593. Web Site: www.unos.org. *Librn*, Lorraine C Sitler; E-Mail: librarian@unos.org. Subject Specialists: *Transplantation*, Lorraine C Sitler; Staff 1 (MLS 1)
Founded 1987
Library Holdings: Bk Titles 450; Per Subs 75
Partic in Docline; Medline; National Network of Libraries of Medicine - Southeastern Atlantic Region

UNITED STATES COURT OF APPEALS, Fourth Circuit Library, United States Courthouse, 1000 E Main St, 23219-3517. SAN 317-4182. Tel: 804-916-2319. FAX: 804-916-2364. *Librn*, Alyene McClure; Tel: 804-916-2322; *Librn*, Peter A Frey; Tel: 804-916-2321; *Librn*, Elaine Woodward; Tel: 804-916-2323
Library Holdings: Bk Vols 70,000; Per Subs 300
Automation Activity & Vendor Info: (Acquisitions) SIRSI; (Cataloging) SIRSI; (OPAC) SIRSI
Partic in Fedlink; OCLC Online Computer Library Center, Inc; Westlaw
Open Mon-Fri 8:30-5

C UNIVERSITY OF RICHMOND, Boatwright Memorial Library, 28 Westhampton Way, 23173. SAN 363-2946. Tel: 804-289-8454. Interlibrary Loan Service Tel: 804-289-8672. Circulation Tel: 804-289-8876. Reference Tel: 804-289-8669. FAX: 804-287-1840. Interlibrary Loan Service FAX: 804-289-8757. Web Site: www.richmond.edu/is/library. *Librn*, James R Rettig; Tel: 804-289-8456, E-Mail: jrettig@richmond.edu; *Librn*, Marcia Whitehead; Tel: 804-289-8829, E-Mail: mwhitehe@richmond.edu; *Librn*, Bonlyn Hall; Tel: 804-287-6849, Fax: 804-287-6899, E-Mail: bhall@richmond.edu; *Librn*, Littleton Maxwell; *Librn*, Melanie Hillner; Tel: 804-289-8262, Fax: 804-289-8482, E-Mail: mhillner@richmond.edu; *Librn*, Keith Weimer; Tel: 804-289-8851; *ILL*, Nancy Vick; E-Mail: nvick@richmond.edu; *Instrul Serv, Outreach Serv*, Lucretia McCulley; Tel: 804-289-8670, E-Mail: lmcculle@richmond.edu; *Access Serv, Bibliog Instr*, Jean Lenville; Tel: 804-289-8942, E-Mail: jlenvill@richmond.edu; *Media Spec*, Paul Porterfield; Tel: 804-289-8453, E-Mail: pporterf@richmond.edu; *Coll Develop*, James E Gwin; Tel: 804-289-8458, E-Mail: jgwin@richmond.edu; *Business*, Maxwell Littleton; Tel: 804-289-8666, E-Mail: lmaxwell@richmond.edu; *Syst Coordr*, Nancy Woodall; Tel: 804-289-8853, E-Mail: nwoodall@richmond.edu. Subject Specialists: *Business*, Littleton Maxwell; *Govt info*, Keith Weimer; *Humanities*, Marcia Whitehead; *Music*, Bonlyn Hall; *Science/technology*, Melanie Hillner; Staff 17 (MLS 14, Non-MLS 3)
Founded 1830. Enrl 3,891; Fac 296; Highest Degree: Master
Jul 1999-Jun 2000 Income (Main Library and Branch Library) $3,370,899. Mats Exp $1,641,616, Books $437,353, Per/Ser (Incl. Access Fees) $811,781, Presv $33,153, AV Equip $47,152, Manuscripts & Archives $31,990, Electronic Ref Mat (Incl. Access Fees) $280,187. Sal $1,361,341 (Prof $739,126)
Library Holdings: Bk Vols 402,589; Per Subs 3,579
Subject Interests: Confederacy, Leadership studies, Religion
Special Collections: 19th-20th Century American Literature; Virginia Baptists (Virginia Baptist Historical Society); Virginia History
Automation Activity & Vendor Info: (Acquisitions) Endeavor; (Cataloging) Endeavor; (Circulation) Endeavor; (Course Reserve) Endeavor; (ILL) Endeavor; (Media Booking) Endeavor; (OPAC) Endeavor; (Serials) Endeavor
Publications: UR Librarian (occasional online newsletter)
Partic in Richmond Academic Library Consortium; Richmond Academic Library Consortium; SE Libr Network
Friends of the Library Group
Departmental Libraries:

S GOTTWALD SCIENCE CENTER LIBRARY, 23173. SAN 317-4271. Tel: 804-289-8261. FAX: 804-289-8482. Web Site: www.richmond.edu/is/library/science. *Librn*, Melanie M Hillner; Tel: 804-289-8262, E-Mail: mhillner@richmond.edu; Staff 3 (MLS 1, Non-MLS 2)
Founded 1949
Jul 1999-Jun 2000 Income $493,520. Mats Exp $453,750, Books $50,000, Per/Ser (Incl. Access Fees) $403,750
Library Holdings: Per Subs 557
Subject Interests: Biology, Chemistry, Computer science, Mathematics, Physics
Friends of the Library Group

PARSONS MUSIC LIBRARY, Modlin Center for the Arts, Webb Tower, 23173. SAN 363-3004. Tel: 804-289-8286. FAX: 804-287-6899. Web Site: www.richmond.edu/is/library/music/musiclib.html. *Librn*, Bonlyn Hall; Tel: 804-287-6849, E-Mail: bhall@richmond.edu; Staff 2 (MLS 1, Non-MLS 1)
Jul 1999-Jun 2000 Mats Exp $42,248, Books $7,172, Per/Ser (Incl. Access Fees) $4,417, Micro $6,809, AV Equip $7,450, Other Print Mats $10,370, Electronic Ref Mat (Incl. Access Fees) $6,030
Library Holdings: Bk Vols 8,119; Per Subs 54
Subject Interests: Asian-African music, Musicology, World music
Database Vendor: epixtech, inc.

L LAW LIBRARY, 28 Westhampton Way, 23173. Tel: 804-289-8225. Circulation Tel: 804-289-8217. Reference Tel: 804-289-8685. FAX: 804-289-8683. E-Mail: refdesk@uofrlaw.richmond.edu. Web Site: law.richmond.edu/library/musehome.htm. *Dir*, Timothy L Coggins; Tel: 804-289-8218, E-Mail: tcoggins@richmond.edu; *Dep Dir*, Joyce Manna Janto; Tel: 804-289-8223, E-Mail: janto@uofrlaw.richmond.edu; *Head Tech Servs*, Sally H Wambold; Tel: 804-289-8226, E-Mail: wambold@uofrlaw.richmond.edu; *Ref*, John R Barden; Tel: 804-289-8727, E-Mail: jbarden@richmond.edu; *Ref*, Gail F Zwirner; Tel: 804-287-6555, E-Mail: gzwirner@richmond.edu; *Info Tech*, Paul M Birch; Tel: 289-804-8222, E-Mail: birch@uofrlaw.richmond.edu; *Publ Servs*, James R Wirrell; Tel: 804-289-8217, E-Mail: jwirrell@richmond.edu; Staff 17 (MLS 7, Non-MLS 10)
Founded 1870. Enrl 465; Fac 25; Highest Degree: Doctorate
Jul 1999-Jun 2000 Income Parent Institution $2,060,978. Mats Exp $986,674, Books $151,887, Per/Ser (Incl. Access Fees) $765,497, Presv $1,014, Other Print Mats $18,282, Electronic Ref Mat (Incl. Access Fees) $49,994. Sal $671,895 (Prof $374,631)
Library Holdings: Bk Vols 294,542; Bk Titles 132,409; Per Subs 4,265
Subject Interests: Environment, Law, Legal hist, Taxation (government)
Special Collections: Robert R Merhige (Retired Federal District Judge) Papers
Automation Activity & Vendor Info: (Acquisitions) Endeavor; (Cataloging) Endeavor; (Circulation) Endeavor; (Course Reserve) Endeavor; (OPAC) Endeavor; (Serials) Endeavor

Database Vendor: Lexis-Nexis, OCLC - First Search
Publications: Museletter; Research Guides; Research Guides Series; Technology Tidbits
Function: Research library
Partic in SE Libr Network

S VALENTINE MUSEUM,* 1015 E Clay St, 23219-1590. SAN 317-4212. Tel: 804-649-0711. FAX: 804-643-3510. Web Site: www.valentinemuseum.com.
Founded 1898
Library Holdings: Bk Vols 7,300; Per Subs 35
Subject Interests: 19th Century advertising art, Artists, Hist of Richmond, Life of Richmond, Tobacco manufacture
Special Collections: Advertising Art (American Tobacco Co Scrapbooks), lithographs; Art Coll, pen, pencil, watercolor & oil; Engravings (Views of Richmond, Scenic & Historical); Photog (Cook-Lancaster-Scott-Minton-Colonial Studios Coll), negatives & prints
Publications: In Bondage & Freedom: Antebellum Black Life in Richmond, Virginia; Old Richmond Neighborhoods; Valentine News (bi-monthly)
Restriction: By appointment only

SR VIRGINIA BAPTIST HISTORICAL SOCIETY LIBRARY, University of Richmond, PO Box 34, 23173. SAN 326-5986. Tel: 804-289-8434. FAX: 804-289-8953. *Acq, Librn*, Fred Anderson; *Publ Servs, Ref*, Darlene Slater; Staff 3 (MLS 3)
Founded 1876
Library Holdings: Bk Vols 25,000
Special Collections: VA Baptist Church
Publications: The Virginia Baptist Register (annual journal)
Friends of the Library Group

C VIRGINIA COMMONWEALTH UNIVERSITY, University Library Services,* 901 Park Ave, 23284-9056. (Mail add: PO Box 842033, 23284-2033), SAN 363-3071. Tel: 804-828-1110, 804-828-9136. FAX: 804-828-0151. Web Site: www.library.vcu.edu/. *Tech Servs*, John Duke; *Humanities and Soc Sci, Science*, Steve Stratton; *Acq*, Diane Hollyfield; *Automation Syst Coordr*, Chengren Hu; *Cat*, Barbara Anderson; *Govt Doc*, Louveller Luster; *Archivist, Spec Coll*, Jodi Koste; *Coll Develop*, John McDonald; Staff 38 (MLS 38)
Founded 1838. Enrl 23,125; Fac 1,955; Highest Degree: Doctorate
Jul 1997-Jun 1998 Mats Exp $4,802,491, Books $1,207,255, Per/Ser (Incl. Access Fees) $2,753,613, Presv $127,983. Sal $3,510,002 (Prof $1,422,625)
Publications: Library Online (Friends newsletter)
Partic in Association Of Southeastern Research Libraries (ASERL); Center For Research Libraries; OCLC Online Computer Library Center, Inc; Richmond Academic Library Consortium; Richmond Academic Library Consortium; SE Libr Network; Virtual Libr of Va
Friends of the Library Group
Departmental Libraries:
JAMES CABELL BRANCH LIBRARY, Academic Campus, 901 Park Ave, 23284-2033. SAN 363-3063. Tel: 804-828-1110. Interlibrary Loan Service Tel: 804-828-1115. FAX: 804-828-0151. E-Mail: Bitnet: ulsjbcref@ gems.vcu.edu, Internet: ulsjbcref@vcuvax.
1997-1998 Mats Exp $3,073,339, Books $939,553, Per/Ser (Incl. Access Fees) $1,514,098, Presv $95,987, Micro $34,502
Library Holdings: Bk Vols 979,392; Per Subs 15,538
Subject Interests: Art, Art history, Behav sci, Biol sci, Education, Humanities, Journalism, Music, Physical sci, Social work, Society sci, Urban planning
Special Collections: Adele Clark Papers; Book Art; Comics & Cartoon Coll; James Branch Cabell Coll; John Clark Jazz (Record Archives); Richmond Area Development Archives (Richmond Symphony, Richmond YWCA, United Way of Greater Richmond, Richmond Urban Institute); US Patent; Va Writers Coll (Helena Caperton, Dabney Stuart, Paul Nagel)
Friends of the Library Group
CM TOMPKINS-MCCAW LIBRARY, Medical College of Virginia Campus, 509 N 12th St, 23298-0582. SAN 363-3098. Tel: 804-828-0636. Interlibrary Loan Service Tel: 804-828-0630. FAX: 804-828-6089. E-Mail: Bitnet: ulstmlref@vcuvax, Internet: ulstmlref@gems.vcu.edu. *In Charge*, Phyllis C Self
1997-1998 Mats Exp $1,803,028, Books $221,697, Per/Ser (Incl. Access Fees) $1,305,413, Presv $31,996, Micro $11,501
Library Holdings: Bk Vols 297,918; Per Subs 2,777
Subject Interests: Allied health, Dentistry, Med tech, Medicine, Nursing, Pharm
Special Collections: Medical Artifacts Coll; Virginia Health Sciences Archives (Harry Warthen, Harry Lyons, Virginia Nurses Association, Virginia Dental Association & Virginia League for Nursing Colls); Walther Riese Papers; William H Hodgkin Papers; William T Sanger Papers

G VIRGINIA DEPARTMENT OF CRIMINAL JUSTICE SERVICES LIBRARY, 805 E Broad St, 23219. SAN 317-4247. Tel: 804-786-8478. FAX: 804-371-8981. *Librn*, Stephen E Squire; E-Mail: ssquire@ dcjs.state.va.us
Founded 1974
Library Holdings: Bk Titles 8,000; Per Subs 200
Subject Interests: Crime prevention, Criminal justice, Juvenile justice, Program evaluation, Program planning
Publications: List of current subscriptions
Restriction: By appointment only

G VIRGINIA DEPARTMENT OF HISTORIC RESOURCES, Archives-Research Library,* 2801 Kensington Ave, 23221. SAN 323-6722. Tel: 8(367-2323. TDD: 804-367-2386. FAX: 804-367-2391. *Archivist*, Suzanne Durham; Staff 3 (MLS 1, Non-MLS 2)
Library Holdings: Bk Titles 4,200; Per Subs 80
Special Collections: Gilmer Confederate Engineer Maps, Wood's Maps Virginia
Publications: various indexes; Virginia Unpublished Archaeological Rep
Special Services for the Deaf - TDD

G VIRGINIA DEPARTMENT OF MENTAL HEALTH, MENTAL RETARDATION & SUBSTANCE ABUSE SERVICES LIBRARY, 122 Bank St, 23219-3645. (Mail add: PO Box 1797, 23219-1797), SAN 321-5326. Tel: 804-371-8915. FAX: 804-692-0060. *Asst Librn*, Leslie Hartzog E-Mail: lhartzog@dmhmrsas.state.va.us; Staff 1 (MLS 1)
Founded 1977
Library Holdings: Bk Titles 500; Per Subs 25
Subject Interests: Mental health, Mental retardation, Nursing, Psychiatry, Psychology, Substance abuse
Automation Activity & Vendor Info: (Cataloging) Follett; (Circulation) Follett
Database Vendor: Ebsco - EbscoHost, OCLC - First Search
Function: ILL available

S VIRGINIA HISTORICAL SOCIETY LIBRARY, 428 North Blvd, PO B 7311, 23221-0311. SAN 317-4263. Tel: 804-358-4901. Interlibrary Loan Service Tel: 804-342-9688. FAX: 804-355-2399. Web Site: www.vahistorical.org. *Dir*, Charles F Bryan Jr; *Assoc Dir*, Robert F Strob *Archivist*, E Lee Shepard; *Tech Servs*, Paulette Schwurming; *Publ Servs*, Pamela R Seay
Founded 1831
Jan 1999-Dec 1999 Income $3,081,000, State $300,000, City $5,000, Co $13,000, Locally Generated Income $1,635,000, Other $1,128,000. Mats $288,557, Books $105,734, Per/Ser (Incl. Access Fees) $2,025, Presv $115,633, Micro $87, AV Equip $26,000, Other Print Mats $3,425, Manuscripts & Archives $27,653, Electronic Ref Mat (Incl. Access Fees) $8,000. Sal $2,134,000 (Prof $1,280,000)
Library Holdings: Bk Vols 144,000; Per Subs 350
Subject Interests: Colonial hist, Confederate hist, Early Amer hist, Local history, State hist
Special Collections: Confederate Imprints, newsp, sheet music; Maryland Steuart Coll, Confederate Weaponry & Military; Virginia Portraiture & Museum Objects
Publications: Document Monograph Series; Virginia History Notes; Virgi Magazine of History & Biography
Partic in Solinet

S VIRGINIA MUSEUM OF FINE ARTS LIBRARY, 2800 Grove Ave, 232 2466. SAN 317-428X. Tel: 804-340-1498. Reference Tel: 804-340-1495. FAX: 804-340-1548. Web Site: www.vmfa.state.va.us. *Chief Librn, Coll Develop*, Dr Suzanne Hill Freeman; E-Mail: sfreeman@vmfa.state.va.us; *Assoc Librn*, Douglas A Litts; Tel: 804-340-1496, E-Mail: dlitts@ vmfa.state.va.us; *Asst Librn*, Sarah Falls; Tel: 804-340-1497, E-Mail: sfall vmfa.state.va.us; Staff 4 (MLS 2, Non-MLS 2)
Founded 1954
Jul 2000-Jun 2001 Income $267,196, State $203,296, Locally Generated Income $63,900. Mats Exp $89,200, Books $63,200, Per/Ser (Incl. Access Fees) $26,000. Sal $150,862
Library Holdings: Bk Vols 70,000; Bk Titles 63,500; Per Subs 234
Subject Interests: 20th Century art, African art, Am decorative arts, Anci art, East Asian arts, European arts, Indian arts, Numismatics
Special Collections: American Arts (McGlothlin Coll); Art Deco, Art Nouveau (Lewis Coll); Contemporary Art (Geldzahler Coll); East Asian A (Maxwell Coll); Faberge Coll; Numismatics (St John Tucker Coll); Orient Arts (Weedon Coll & Coopersmith Coll); Paul Mellon Pre-1850 British A Coll
Automation Activity & Vendor Info: (OPAC) SIRSI
Database Vendor: Ebsco - EbscoHost, OCLC - First Search
Restriction: Not a lending library, Open to public for reference only
Function: Reference services available
Partic in SE Libr Network

S VIRGINIA POWER RESEARCH, Research-Records Services,* 701 E Ca St, PO Box 26666, 23261. SAN 317-4255. Tel: 804-771-3657. Interlibrary Loan Service Tel: 804-771-3659. FAX: 804-771-3168. *Res*, Linda G Royal Staff 8 (MLS 4, Non-MLS 4)
Founded 1937
Library Holdings: Bk Titles 10,000; Per Subs 350
Subject Interests: Bus, Electricity, Engineering, Environ, Fuel, Gas, Mgt, Nuclear power, Wellness
Restriction: By appointment only

VIRGINIA STATE CRIME COMMISSION LIBRARY,* General Assembly Bldg, 910 Capitol St, Ste 915, 23219. SAN 323-7214. Tel: 804-225-4534. FAX: 804-786-7872. *Dir*, Rich Savage

VIRGINIA STATE DEPARTMENT OF GENERAL SERVICES, Division of Consolidated Laboratory Services Library,* One N 14th St, Rm 231, 23219. SAN 327-4217. Tel: 804-786-7905. FAX: 804-371-7973.
Library Holdings: Bk Titles 1,500; Per Subs 10
Subject Interests: Biology, Chemistry

VIRGINIA STATE LAW LIBRARY, (Formerly Supreme Court Of Virginia), Supreme Court Bldg, 100 N Ninth St, 2nd flr, 23219-2335. SAN 363-2822. Tel: 804-786-2075. FAX: 804-786-4542. E-Mail: lawlibrary@courts.state.va.us. *Dir*, Gail Warren; E-Mail: gwarren@courts.state.va.us; *Asst Librn*, Terry E Long; *Asst Librn*, Cecile C Taylor; *Circ*, Marquitta N Joyce; Staff 4 (MLS 2, Non-MLS 2)
Founded 1899
Library Holdings: Bk Vols 100,000; Per Subs 336
Subject Interests: Anglo-Am law
Special Collections: 18th Century Legal Treatises; English Reports (Nominative Reports, Mostly Originals)
Database Vendor: IAC - Info Trac, OCLC - First Search
Restriction: Restricted public use
Function: ILL limited
Partic in Westlaw
Special Services for the Deaf - TDD

VIRGINIA STATE POLICE ACADEMY LIBRARY, 7700 Midlothian Tpke, 23235. (Mail add: PO Box 27472, 23261-7472), Tel: 804-674-2258. FAX: 804-674-2089. *Librn*, Joan Jacobs; Staff 1 (MLS 1)
Founded 1989
Library Holdings: Bk Vols 3,000; Per Subs 25
Subject Interests: Law enforcement

VIRGINIA UNION UNIVERSITY, L Douglas Wilder Library & Learning Resource Center, 1500 N Lombardy St, 23220. SAN 317-431X. Tel: 804-257-5820. Interlibrary Loan Service Tel: 804-257-5822. FAX: 804-257-5818. Web Site: www.vuu.edu. *Dir*, Dr Vonita W Foster; E-Mail: vfoster@vuu.edu; *Acq, ILL*, Ronald A Shelton; Tel: 804-278-4119, E-Mail: rshelton@vuu.edu; *Cat*, Michelle Taylor; Tel: 804-257-5823; *Per*, Shanda Lemon; Tel: 804-278-4112; *Archivist*, Suzanne Durham; Tel: 804-278-4124; *Electronic Resources*, Pamela Foreman; Staff 12 (MLS 7, Non-MLS 5)
Founded 1997. Enrl 1,233; Fac 82; Highest Degree: Bachelor
Jul 1998-Jun 1999 Mats Exp $360,000, Books $41,217, Presv $4,028, Micro $47,539, AV Equip $6,661, Electronic Ref Mat (Incl. Access Fees) $117,741. Sal $387,000 (Prof $213,700)
Library Holdings: Bk Vols 144,000; Bk Titles 80,000; Per Subs 330
Subject Interests: Bus, Education, Mathematics, Natural scis, Philosophy, Psychology, Religion
Special Collections: Black Studies (L Douglas Wilder Coll); Black Studies (Schomberg Coll), micro
Database Vendor: GaleNet, IAC - Info Trac, IAC - SearchBank, Lexis-Nexis, OCLC - First Search, ProQuest
Function: Professional lending library
Partic in OCLC Online Computer Library Center, Inc

DANOKE

ART MUSEUM OF WESTERN VIRGINIA, Fine Arts Library, Center in the Sq, One Market Sq, 2nd flr, 24011. SAN 317-4352. Tel: 540-342-5760. FAX: 540-342-5798.
Founded 1952
Library Holdings: Bk Vols 2,500
Subject Interests: Fine arts

BOTETOURT COUNTY LIBRARY,* 2220 Blue Ridge Blvd, 24012. SAN 324-5179. Tel: 540-473-8339. Interlibrary Loan Service Tel: 540-977-3433. FAX: 540-977-2407. *Dir*, Stephen C Vest; E-Mail: svest@vsla.edu; *Librn*, Paige Ware; *Per, Tech Servs*, Nancy Bloomer; *ILL*, Janet Buttram
Founded 1979. Pop 24,270; Circ 183,052
Jul 1997-Jun 1998 Income $494,103. Mats Exp $75,702. Sal $282,503
Library Holdings: Bk Vols 29,000; Per Subs 220
Friends of the Library Group
Branches: 2
BUCHANAN BRANCH, 852 Main St, PO Box 799, Buchanan, 24066. SAN 324-6248. Tel: 540-254-2538. FAX: 703-254-1793. *Librn*, Debra Newcomb
Library Holdings: Bk Vols 10,000
Friends of the Library Group
FINCASTLE BRANCH, Academy St, PO Box 129, Fincastle, 24090. SAN 324-623X. Tel: 540-473-8339. FAX: 540-473-1107. *In Charge*, Paige Ware
Library Holdings: Bk Vols 28,000
Friends of the Library Group
Bookmobiles: 1

M CARILION ROANOKE MEMORIAL HOSPITAL, Health Sciences Library,* Belleview at Jefferson St, PO Box 13367, 24033. SAN 324-6329. Tel: 540-981-8039. FAX: 540-981-8666.
Library Holdings: Bk Titles 2,289; Per Subs 284
Restriction: Staff use only

CM COLLEGE OF HEALTH SCIENCES, Learning Resource Center,* 920 S Jefferson St, 24016. SAN 327-9146. Tel: 540-985-8273. FAX: 540-224-4404. Web Site: www.chs.edu/lrchome.htm. *Tech Servs*, Crystal Dent; *ILL*, Dottie Beck; *Coll Develop*, Jose Elacate; Staff 7 (MLS 1, Non-MLS 6)
Enrl 481; Fac 57
Oct 1996-Sep 1997 Income $158,279. Mats Exp $32,822, Books $9,073, Per/Ser (Incl. Access Fees) $17,967, Micro $800, AV Equip $1,482. Sal $152,831 (Prof $32,510)
Library Holdings: Bk Titles 8,006; Per Subs 226
Subject Interests: Allied health, Medicine, Nursing

C ECPI COMPUTER INSTITUTE, Roanoke Campus Library, 5234 Airport Rd, 24012-1603. SAN 375-5401. Tel: 540-563-8000. FAX: 540-362-5400. Web Site: www.ecpi.edu. *Dir*, Walter Anthony Neuron; Tel: 540-563-8000, Ext 35, E-Mail: wneuron@ecpi.edu; Staff 2 (Non-MLS 2)
Library Holdings: Bk Vols 3,915; Bk Titles 3,346; Per Subs 70
Subject Interests: Computer science
Automation Activity & Vendor Info: (Circulation) Athena
Partic in Libr Info Res Network
Library Advisory Committee is staffed by school librarians from the community

S ETS, INC LIBRARY, 1401 Municipal Rd NW, 24012-1309. SAN 373-2673. Tel: 540-265-0004. FAX: 540-265-0131. E-Mail: etsi@roanoke.infi.net. *Librn*, Art Nunn
Library Holdings: Bk Vols 1,500; Per Subs 40

L GENTRY, LOCKE, RAKES & MOORE LIBRARY,* 800 Crestar Plaza, 10 Franklin Rd, 24011. SAN 323-7559. Tel: 540-983-9357. FAX: 540-983-9400. E-Mail: lawlibrary@gentrylocke.com. *Dir*, Yvonne Powell

S HAYES, SEAY, MATTERN & MATTERN, INC LIBRARY,* 1315 Franklin Rd, PO Box 13446, 24034. SAN 317-4336. Tel: 540-857-3244. FAX: 540-857-3180. *Librn*, Cynthia Humphries; E-Mail: chumphries@hsmm.com
Founded 1958
Library Holdings: Bk Vols 13,802; Bk Titles 10,428; Per Subs 284
Subject Interests: Architecture, Civil engineering, Construction, Elect eng, Environmental engineering, Mech eng, Planning, Structural engineering
Restriction: Staff use only

S HISTORY MUSEUM & HISTORICAL SOCIETY OF WESTERN VIRGINIA LIBRARY, One Market Sq Center in the Sq, PO Box 1904, 24008. SAN 329-093X. Tel: 540-342-5770. FAX: 540-224-1256. E-Mail: history@roanoke.infi.net. Web Site: www.history-museum.org. *Librn*, Alice Roberts
Library Holdings: Bk Vols 1,400; Bk Titles 1,300
Special Collections: Breckinridge, Preston, Trout, Borden, Grant, Tayloe, Deyerle, Campbell, Roanoke Hist, Roanoke Photos, Watts, Eubank

C HOLLINS UNIVERSITY, Wyndham Robertson Library, 7950 E Campus Dr, Hollins University, 24020-1000. (Mail add: PO Box 9000, Hollins University, 24020-1000), SAN 317-3143. Tel: 540-362-6591. Interlibrary Loan Service Tel: 540-362-6592. Reference Tel: 540-362-7465. FAX: 540-362-7493. Web Site: www.hollins.edu/academics/library/libtoc.htm. *Dean of Libr*, Diane J Graves; Tel: 540-362-6240, Fax: 540-362-6756, E-Mail: dgraves@hollins.edu; *Dir Info Resources & Res*, Elizabeth M Doolittle; Tel: 540-362-6234, Fax: 540-362-7493, E-Mail: edoolittle@hollins.edu; *Dir, Tech Serv*, James Redwine; Tel: 540-362-6592, E-Mail: jredwine@hollins.edu; *Tech Coordr*, Michael Mansfield; Tel: 540-362-6569, Fax: 540-362-6756, E-Mail: mmansfield@hollins.edu; *Acq*, Lee C Rose; Tel: 540-362-6240, Fax: 540-362-6756, E-Mail: lrose@hollins.edu; *Spec Coll & Archives*, Beth S Harris; Tel: 540-362-6237, Fax: 540-362-6756, E-Mail: bharris@hollins.edu; *Automation Syst Coordr*, Tammy K Baker; Tel: 540-362-6082, E-Mail: tbaker@hollins.edu; *Circ*, Margaret Airey; Tel: 540-362-6591, E-Mail: mairey@hollins.edu; *Cat*, Lilla Thompson; Tel: 540-362-7467, Fax: 540-362-6756, E-Mail: lthompson@hollins.edu; *Govt Doc*, Candance Mills; Tel: 540-362-6328, Fax: 540-362-6756, E-Mail: cmills@hollins.edu; *Govt Doc*, Jill Pigeon; Tel: 540-362-6238, Fax: 540-362-6756, E-Mail: jpigeon@hollins.edu; *Per*, Amanda B Hurst; Tel: 540-362-6239, E-Mail: ahurst@hollins.edu; *Per*, Kathryn Smith; Tel: 540-362-6239, Fax: 540-362-6756, E-Mail: psmith@hollins.edu; *AV*, Jennifer Ehalt; Tel: 540-362-6235, Fax: 540-362-6756, E-Mail: jehalt@hollins.edu; Staff 14 (MLS 5, Non-MLS 9)
Founded 1842. Enrl 1,100; Fac 91; Highest Degree: Master
Jul 2000-Jun 2001 Income $812,640. Mats Exp $313,200, Books $102,000, Per/Ser (Incl. Access Fees) $190,200, Presv $4,500, AV Equip $4,500. Sal $424,040 (Prof $208,720)
Library Holdings: Bk Vols 257,000; Bk Titles 187,997; Per Subs 6,500
Subject Interests: Art, Behav sci, Literature, Music, Philosophy, Religion, Soc sci, Women studies
Special Collections: Benjamin Franklin Coll; Canadiana; Children's Literature (Margaret Wise Brown Coll); French Symbolist Literature (Enid Starkie Coll); Hollins Authors; Incunabula; Paper-Making; Printing; Private

Presses; Robert Frost (McVitty Coll)
Automation Activity & Vendor Info: (Acquisitions) Innovative Interfaces Inc.; (Cataloging) Innovative Interfaces Inc.; (Circulation) Innovative Interfaces Inc.; (Course Reserve) Innovative Interfaces Inc.; (OPAC) Innovative Interfaces Inc.; (Serials) Innovative Interfaces Inc.
Database Vendor: CARL, Ebsco - EbscoHost, GaleNet, IAC - SearchBank, Lexis-Nexis, OCLC - First Search, OVID Technologies, Silverplatter Information Inc., Wilson - Wilson Web
Restriction: Circulation limited
Partic in Solinet; VA Independent Col & Univ Libr Asn; VIVA-Statewide Library Resource Network

R ROANOKE CHURCH OF CHRIST, Elgin E Altizer Library, 2740 Derwent Dr SW, 24015-2620. SAN 324-0975. Tel: 540-343-8596. FAX: 540-772-3793. *Librn*, Pamela Wieringo; Staff 1 (Non-MLS 1)
Founded 1980
Jan 1999-Dec 1999 Income Parent Institution $200. Mats Exp $200, Books $140, AV Equip $60
Library Holdings: Bk Vols 1,148; Bk Titles 982
Subject Interests: Restoration movement, Theology
Special Services for the Deaf - Captioned film depository; Staff with knowledge of sign language

P ROANOKE CITY PUBLIC LIBRARY SYSTEM, 706 S Jefferson St, 24016-5104. SAN 363-3330. Tel: 540-853-2473. Interlibrary Loan Service Tel: 540-853-2477. Reference Tel: 540-853-2477. TDD: 540-853-2641. FAX: 540-853-1781. E-Mail: library@ci.roanoke.va.us. Web Site: www.ci.roanoke.va.us/depts/library/index.html. *Tech Servs*, Sheila Umberger; *Ref*, Lucy Glenn; *YA Servs*, Demetria Tucker; *Circ*, Susan Ewald; Staff 16 (MLS 12, Non-MLS 4)
Founded 1921. Pop 100,600
Jul 1998-Jun 1999 Income (Main Library and Branch Library) $3,033,978, State $225,211, City $2,776,441, Locally Generated Income $32,326. Mats Exp $315,930, Books $237,482, Per/Ser (Incl. Access Fees) $46,238, Presv $5,091, Micro $7,171, AV Equip $19,948. Sal $2,182,876 (Prof $619,597)
Library Holdings: Bk Vols 339,685; Per Subs 905
Subject Interests: Civil War, Genealogy, Local history, Virginiana
Automation Activity & Vendor Info: (Acquisitions) DRA; (Circulation) DRA; (Serials) DRA
Special Services for the Deaf - TDD
Friends of the Library Group
Branches: 6
GAINSBORO, 15 Patton Ave NW, 24016. SAN 363-3365. Tel: 540-853-2540. FAX: 540-853-1155. *Librn*, Caralene Lewis; Staff 1 (Non-MLS 1)
Library Holdings: Bk Vols 25,866
Subject Interests: Black hist
JACKSON PARK, 1101 Morningside St SE, 24013. SAN 363-339X. Tel: 540-853-2640. FAX: 540-853-1156. *Librn*, Jessie Craig; Staff 1 (Non-MLS 1)
Library Holdings: Bk Vols 30,248
Friends of the Library Group
LAW, 315 Church Ave SW, 24016. SAN 320-2720. Tel: 540-853-2268. FAX: 540-342-8664.; Staff 1 (Non-MLS 1)
Founded 1925
Library Holdings: Bk Vols 19,195
Special Collections: Federal Taxation Coll
MELROSE, 2607 Salem Tpk NW, 24017. SAN 363-342X. Tel: 540-853-2648. FAX: 540-853-1030. *Librn*, Rebecca Cooper; Staff 1 (MLS 1)
Library Holdings: Bk Vols 27,500
RALEIGH COURT, 2112 Grandin Rd SW, 24015. SAN 363-3454. Tel: 540-853-2240. FAX: 540-853-1783. *Librn*, Elizabeth Stewart; Staff 1 (MLS 1)
Library Holdings: Bk Vols 49,989
WILLIAMSON ROAD, 3837 Williamson Rd NW, 24012. SAN 363-3489. Tel: 540-853-2340. FAX: 540-853-1065. *Librn*, Sarah Rubush; Staff 1 (MLS 1)
Library Holdings: Bk Vols 41,886
Bookmobiles: 1

P ROANOKE COUNTY PUBLIC LIBRARY, 3131 Electric Rd, 24018-6496. SAN 363-3187. Tel: 540-772-7507. FAX: 540-772-2131. Web Site: www.co.roanoke.va.us./library/rclibhp.htm. *Dir*, Diana Rosapepe; *ILL*, Alan Hale; *Tech Servs*, Ellen Hylton; *Ref*, Ruth Lipnik; *Acq*, Robin Walters; Staff 9 (MLS 9)
Founded 1945. Pop 83,100; Circ 840,179
Jul 1997-Jun 1998 Income $1,817,000. Mats Exp $332,000. Sal $1,118,000
Library Holdings: Bk Vols 347,002; Per Subs 1,016
Subject Interests: Virginiana
Special Collections: Kirkwood Professional Coll; Local History
Friends of the Library Group
Branches: 6
BENT MOUNTAIN BRANCH, 10148 Tinsley Lane, Bent Mountain, 40475. Tel: 540-929-4700. *Librn*, Gladys Walters
Library Holdings: Bk Vols 7,994
Open Mon & Fri 1-5, Wed & Sat 1-9
Friends of the Library Group
CATAWBA BOOK STATION, Catawba Community Ctr, Catawba, 24070.
Open Tues & Thurs 9-12
GLENVAR, 3917 Daugherty Rd, Salem, 24153. SAN 363-3241. Tel: 54(387-6163. FAX: 540-380-3951. *Librn*, John Vest
Library Holdings: Bk Vols 41,710
Database Vendor: DRA
Open Mon-Thurs 9-6, Fri & Sat 9-5
Friends of the Library Group
HOLLINS, 6624 Peters Creek Rd, 24019. SAN 363-3276. Tel: 540-561-8024. FAX: 540-563-8902. *Librn*, Terri Walker
Library Holdings: Bk Vols 73,864
Database Vendor: DRA
Open Mon-Thurs 9-9, Fri & Sat 9-5
Friends of the Library Group
MOUNT PLEASANT BLVD, 3218 Mount Pleasant Blvd, 24014. SAN 3 8292. Tel: 540-427-3130. *Librn*, Sherry Pearson
Library Holdings: Bk Vols 5,273
Open Mon-Thurs 1-5
Friends of the Library Group
VINTON BRANCH, 800 E Washington Ave, Vinton, 24179. SAN 363-3 Tel: 540-857-5043. FAX: 540-344-3285. *Librn*, Sherry Pearson
Library Holdings: Bk Vols 61,793
Open Mon-Thurs 9-9, Fri & Sat 9-5
Friends of the Library Group

S ROANOKE TIMES LIBRARY, 201 W Campbell Ave, PO Box 2491, 24010-2491. SAN 317-4360. Tel: 540-981-3279. FAX: 540-981-3346. We Site: www.archives.com. *Librn*, Belinda Harris; E-Mail: harrisb@ roanoke.infi.net; Staff 1 (Non-MLS 1)
Library Holdings: Bk Vols 1,000; Per Subs 10
Subject Interests: Local newspaper data
Restriction: Not open to public
Function: Newspaper reference library
Partic in Dow Jones News Retrieval

J VIRGINIA WESTERN COMMUNITY COLLEGE, Brown Library, 3095 Colonial Ave SW, PO Box 40012, 24022-0012. SAN 317-4379. Tel: 540-857-7303. FAX: 540-857-7544. Web Site: www.vw.cc.va.us/library. *Coord* David Hillman; *ILL*, Judy Moreth; *Cat, Ref*, Lynn Carter; Staff 3 (MLS 3)
Founded 1966
Library Holdings: Bk Vols 69,622; Per Subs 245
Automation Activity & Vendor Info: (Cataloging) NOTIS; (Circulation) NOTIS

L WOODS, ROGERS & HAZLEGROVE, PLC, Law Library, First Union Tower, Ste 1400, 10 S Jefferson St, 24011. SAN 372-333X. Tel: 540-983-7531. FAX: 540-983-7711. *Librn*, Jane Roth Baugh; E-Mail: baugh@ woodsrogers.com; Staff 1 (MLS 1)
2000-2001 Mats Exp $250,000
Library Holdings: Bk Vols 10,000; Per Subs 150

ROCKY MOUNT

P FRANKLIN COUNTY PUBLIC LIBRARY, 120 E Court St, 24151. SAN 317-4387. Tel: 540-483-3098. FAX: 540-483-1568. *Dir*, David E Bass, III E-Mail: dbass@cablenet-va.com; Staff 3 (MLS 1, Non-MLS 2)
Founded 1975. Pop 43,000; Circ 186,000
Library Holdings: Bk Vols 90,000; Per Subs 220
Subject Interests: Local history

RUSTBURG

P CAMPBELL COUNTY PUBLIC LIBRARY, 684 Village Hwy (Lower Level), 24588. (Mail add: PO Box 310, 24588), Tel: 804-332-9560. FAX: 804-332-9697. Web Site: tlc.library.net/campbell. *Actg Dir*, Linda Owen; E-Mail: lowen@campbell.k12.va.us; *Dep Dir*, Myra Runge; E-Mail: mrunge@campbell.k12.va.us; Staff 16 (MLS 3, Non-MLS 13)
Founded 1968. Pop 49,900; Circ 253,914
Jul 1999-Jun 2000 Income (Main Library and Branch Library) $725,011. S $325,660
Library Holdings: Bk Vols 150,000; Per Subs 222
Subject Interests: Genealogy
Automation Activity & Vendor Info: (Circulation) TLC
Database Vendor: OCLC - First Search
Publications: Newsletter (quarterly)
Function: Literary searches
Partic in Lynchburg Area Library Cooperative
Friends of the Library Group
Branches: 3
PATRICK HENRY MEMORIAL BRANCH, 204 Lynchburg Ave, Brookneal, 24528. SAN 377-0540. Tel: 804-376-3363. FAX: 804-376-1111. *Branch Mgr*, Gale Seamster
Founded 1938. Pop 4,000; Circ 15,576
Automation Activity & Vendor Info: (Circulation) TLC
Friends of the Library Group
STAUNTON RIVER MEMORIAL BRANCH, 500 Washington St, AltaVista, 24517. SAN 328-7343. Tel: 804-369-5140. FAX: 804-369-172 *Branch Mgr*, Patrice Owen

Founded 1956. Pop 5,000; Circ 47,726
Friends of the Library Group
TIMBROOK BRANCH, 9201-F Timberlake Rd, Lynchburg, 24502. SAN 325-3988. Tel: 804-239-1190. FAX: 804-237-6784. *Mgr*, Mary Rogers
Founded 1968. Pop 25,000; Circ 72,627
Friends of the Library Group
Bookmobiles: 1

..EM

DEPARTMENT OF VETERANS AFFAIRS
MEDICAL CENTER LIBRARY, 1970 Roanoke Blvd, 24153. SAN 363-3519. Tel: 540-982-2463, Ext 2380. FAX: 540-983-1079. *Chief Librn*, Jean Kennedy; Staff 3 (MLS 2, Non-MLS 1)
Founded 1946
Oct 1999-Sep 2000 Income Federal $74,578. Mats Exp $89,823, Books $9,475, Per/Ser (Incl. Access Fees) $41,006, AV Equip $820. Sal $120,000
Library Holdings: Bk Titles 4,771; Per Subs 122
Subject Interests: Behav sci, Biomed sci, Hospital administration, Nursing, Soc sci
Partic in Medline; OCLC Online Computer Library Center, Inc; Valpac
MEDICAL CENTER PATIENT'S LIBRARY, 1970 Roanoke Blvd, 24153. SAN 363-3543. Tel: 540-982-2463, Ext 2381. FAX: 540-983-1079. *Chief Librn*, Jean Kennedy; *Librn*, Susan DuGrenier
Oct 1998-Sep 1999 Income (Main Library Only) Federal $603. Mats Exp $603, Books $319, Per/Ser (Incl. Access Fees) $284
Library Holdings: Bk Titles 6,360
Subject Interests: Gen, Patient health educ
Special Collections: Patient Health Education Coll; World War II (Military History Coll)

LEWIS-GALE MEDICAL CENTER, Medical Library,* 1900 Electric Rd, 24153. SAN 320-5894. Tel: 540-776-4159, 540-776-4442. FAX: 540-776-4597. *Librn*, Robin Barnhill
Jan 1998-Dec 1999 Mats Exp Books $1,500
Library Holdings: Bk Titles 15
Subject Interests: Medicine, Surgery

NATIONAL COLLEGE OF BUSINESS & TECHNOLOGY, Roanoke Valley Campus Library, 1813 E Main St, 24153-4598. (Mail add: PO Box 6400, 24017-0400), SAN 317-4344. Tel: 540-986-1800. Toll Free Tel: 800-664-1886. FAX: 540-986-1344. *Librn*, Betty W Johnson; E-Mail: bjohnson@educorp.edu; Staff 2 (MLS 1, Non-MLS 1)
Founded 1886. Enrl 259; Fac 29; Highest Degree: Bachelor
Dec 1998-Nov 1999 Income $12,500. Mats Exp $12,500, Books $6,500, Per/Ser (Incl. Access Fees) $1,500
Library Holdings: Bk Vols 20,877
Subject Interests: Accounting, Bus, Computers, Hospitality, Medicine, Travel
Publications: Newsletter
Restriction: Open to student, faculty & staff
Partic in SWING

ROANOKE COLLEGE, Fintel Library, 220 High St, 24153. SAN 317-4417. Tel: 540-375-2295. Interlibrary Loan Service Tel: 540-375-2298. Circulation Tel: 540-375-2294. Reference Tel: 540-375-2295. FAX: 540-375-2083. E-Mail: library@roanoke.edu. Web Site: www.roanoke.edu/library. *Dir*, Stan Umberger; Tel: 540-375-2293, E-Mail: umberger@roanoke.edu; *Cat, Tech Servs*, Patricia Powell; Tel: 540-375-2292, E-Mail: ppowell@roanoke.edu; *Circ, Per*, William T Davidson; E-Mail: davidson@roanoke.edu; *Media Spec*, David Mulford; Tel: 540-375-2290, E-Mail: mulford@roanoke.edu; *Ref*, Rebecca Heller; E-Mail: rheller@roanoke.edu; *Archivist*, Linda Miller; Tel: 540-375-2490, E-Mail: lmiller@roanoke.edu; *Info Specialist*, Michael Santoroski; E-Mail: santoros@roanoke.edu; Staff 7 (MLS 4, Non-MLS 3)
Founded 1842. Enrl 1,654; Fac 119; Highest Degree: Bachelor
Jul 1999-Jun 2000 Income $831,803, Locally Generated Income $55,805, Parent Institution $775,998. Mats Exp $355,957, Books $161,212, Per/Ser (Incl. Access Fees) $182,627, Presv $8,900, Electronic Ref Mat (Incl. Access Fees) $3,218. Sal $428,874 (Prof $290,642)
Library Holdings: Bk Vols 147,727; Bk Titles 121,929; Per Subs 759
Special Collections: Henry F Fowler Coll; Roanoke College Coll
Automation Activity & Vendor Info: (Acquisitions) Innovative Interfaces Inc.; (Cataloging) Innovative Interfaces Inc.; (Circulation) Innovative Interfaces Inc.; (Course Reserve) Innovative Interfaces Inc.; (ILL) Innovative Interfaces Inc.; (Media Booking) Innovative Interfaces Inc.; (OPAC) Innovative Interfaces Inc.; (Serials) Innovative Interfaces Inc.
Database Vendor: Innovative Interfaces INN - View
Partic in SE Libr Network

SALEM BAPTIST CHURCH LIBRARY, 103 N Broad St, 24153. SAN 317-4425. Tel: 540-387-0416. FAX: 540-375-6412. E-Mail: sbc24153@lwol.com. *Dir*, Lisa Bond
Library Holdings: Bk Vols 4,000

SALEM PUBLIC LIBRARY, 28 E Main St, 24153. SAN 317-4433. Tel: 540-375-3089. TDD: 540-375-4064. FAX: 540-389-7054. Web Site: www.co.roanoke.va.us/library/salemhp.htm. *Dir*, Janis C Augustine; E-Mail: jaugustine@ci.salem.va.us; *Cat*, Vickie M Anway; E-Mail: vanway@ci.salem.va.us; *Ch Servs*, Maureen G Harrill; E-Mail: mharrill@ci.salem.va.us; *Circ*, Benita Van Cleave; E-Mail: bvanclea@vsla.edu; *Res*, Nancy C Collins; E-Mail: ncollins@ci.salem.va.us; Staff 12 (MLS 5, Non-MLS 7)
Founded 1969. Pop 23,895; Circ 194,315
Jul 1999-Jun 2000 Income $665,333, State $150,014, City $515,319
Library Holdings: Bk Vols 107,179; Per Subs 140
Subject Interests: Literacy Vols of Am reading prog
Special Collections: Literature for Visually Handicapped (Listening Library), cassettes, phonodiscs
Automation Activity & Vendor Info: (Acquisitions) DRA; (Cataloging) DRA; (Circulation) DRA; (OPAC) DRA; (Serials) DRA
Database Vendor: Ebsco - EbscoHost, OCLC - First Search, ProQuest
Function: ILL available
Friends of the Library Group

SPOTSYLVANIA

S SPOTSYLVANIA HISTORICAL ASSOCIATION, Research Museum & Library,* PO Box 64, 22553. SAN 328-3372. Tel: 540-582-7167. *Pres*, John Pruitt Jr; *Dir*, Martha C Carter
Library Holdings: Bk Titles 2,500
Subject Interests: Civil War, County hist, Genealogy

SPRINGFIELD

S ARMY TIMES PUBLISHING CO LIBRARY,* 6883 Commercial Dr, 22159. SAN 373-2681. Tel: 703-750-8696. FAX: 703-750-8622. *Dir*, Neff Hudson
Restriction: Not open to public

G BUREAU OF LAND MANAGEMENT, Eastern States Office Library,* 7450 Boston Blvd, 22153-3121. SAN 307-0301. Tel: 703-440-1561, 703-440-1562. FAX: 703-440-1599. *Librn*, Bernadine White
Library Holdings: Bk Vols 10,000; Per Subs 50

S ENSCO, INC, Information Resource Center, 5400 Port Royal Rd, 22151-2312. SAN 317-445X. Tel: 703-321-4604. FAX: 703-321-4565. *Librn*, Irene Minich; E-Mail: minich@ensco.com
Founded 1972
Library Holdings: Bk Titles 2,500; Per Subs 150
Subject Interests: Computer science, Highway design, Highway transportation, Railroad tech, Seismic detection, Signal processing, Underwater acoustics
Special Collections: Seismology; Track-Train Dynamics
Publications: In-house Newsletter
Partic in Defense Technical Information Center; Dialog Corporation

S VERSAR, INC, Information Services,* 6850 Versar Ctr, PO Box 1549, 22151. SAN 329-1103. Tel: 703-750-3000, Ext 255. FAX: 703-642-6809. Web Site: www.versar.com.
Special Collections: EPA Technical Reports; Versar Reports
Publications: Library monthly bulletin
Partic in OCLC Online Computer Library Center, Inc
Field library, Versar, Inc, Columbia, MD

S VIETNAM REFUGEE FUND LIBRARY, 6433 Northanna Dr, 22150. SAN 372-8714. Tel: 703-971-9178. FAX: 703-719-5764. *Librn*, Dao Thi Hoi
Library Holdings: Bk Vols 2,000; Per Subs 35
Restriction: By appointment only

S WASHINGTON GAS CORP LIBRARY,* 6801 Industrial Rd, 22151. SAN 302-8240. Tel: 703-750-5503. FAX: 703-750-7915.
Founded 1934
Library Holdings: Bk Vols 300; Per Subs 58
Subject Interests: Natural gas
Publications: Clipping Service; Library Bulletin; New in the Library
Partic in BRS; Dialog Corporation; Dow Jones News Retrieval; OCLC Online Computer Library Center, Inc

STAFFORD

S AMERICAN LIFE LEAGUE LIBRARY,* PO Box 1350, 22555. SAN 373-269X. Tel: 540-659-4171. FAX: 540-659-2586. E-Mail: sysop@all.org. *Actg Librn*, Rosann Frields
Library Holdings: Bk Vols 1,800
Restriction: Open to public for reference only

STATE FARM

S DEPARTMENT OF CORRECTIONAL EDUCATION, Powhatan, James River & Deep Meadow Correctional Center Library,* 23160-9998. SAN 317-4492. Tel: 804-784-3551, Ext 2345. FAX: 804-784-2480. *Librn*, James Riley
Founded 1968

1997-1998 Mats Exp $18,000
Library Holdings: Bk Vols 12,800; Bk Titles 12,000; Per Subs 325
Special Collections: Black Studies (Paul Robeson Memorial Coll)
System includes main library & 9 branches

STAUNTON

C MARY BALDWIN COLLEGE, Martha S Grafton Library, New & Frederick Sts, 24401-9983. SAN 317-4506. Tel: 540-887-7085. Circulation Tel: 540-887-7317. Reference Tel: 540-887-7310. FAX: 540-887-7297. E-Mail: lib4u@mbc.edu. Web Site: www.mbc.edu/resources/library/library.html. *Dir*, Lisabeth Chabot; Tel: 540-887-7299, E-Mail: lchabot@mbc.edu; *Publ Servs*, Carol Creager; E-Mail: ccreager@mbc.edu; *ILL*, Charlene M Plunkett; Tel: 540-887-7311, E-Mail: cplunket@mbc.edu; *Acq*, Elaine King-McCarrick; Tel: 540-887-7087, E-Mail: emccarri@mbc.edu; *Archivist*, William Pollard; Tel: 540-887-7239; *AV*, Alan Moye; Tel: 540-887-7267, E-Mail: amoye@mbc.edu; *Ser*, Lucy Crews; Tel: 540-887-7088, E-Mail: lcrews@mbc.edu; *Cat*, Jennifer Davison; Tel: 540-887-7316, E-Mail: jdavison@mbc.edu; *Circ*, Heather Bischof; Tel: 540-887-7317, E-Mail: hbischof@mbc.edu; Staff 8 (MLS 4, Non-MLS 4)
Founded 1842. Enrl 1,172; Fac 113; Highest Degree: Master
Jul 1999-Jun 2000 Income $353,355. Mats Exp $148,701, Books $57,878, Per/Ser (Incl. Access Fees) $58,454, Presv $6,130, Micro $9,704, Electronic Ref Mat (Incl. Access Fees) $16,535. Sal $203,911 (Prof $127,244)
Library Holdings: Bk Vols 171,797; Bk Titles 106,057; Per Subs 514
Subject Interests: Women's studies
Special Collections: College History; Mary Julia Baldwin Coll
Automation Activity & Vendor Info: (Acquisitions) epixtech, inc.; (Cataloging) epixtech, inc.; (Circulation) epixtech, inc.; (Course Reserve) epixtech, inc.; (ILL) epixtech, inc.; (OPAC) epixtech, inc.; (Serials) epixtech, inc.
Database Vendor: Dialog, Ebsco - EbscoHost, epixtech, inc., GaleNet, IAC - Info Trac, Lexis-Nexis, OCLC - First Search, OVID Technologies
Function: Archival collection
Partic in Solinet; VIVA/VICULA

M EZRA POUND INSTITUTE OF CIVILIZATION, National Council for Medical Research Library,* 126 Madison Pl, PO Box 1105, 24401. SAN 371-5906. Tel: 540-886-5580. *Librn*, Eustace Mullins; Staff 1 (MLS 1)
Library Holdings: Bk Vols 40,000; Bk Titles 1,800
Branches:
NATIONAL COMMISSION FOR JUDICIAL REFORM *Librn*, Eustace Mullins
Founded 1989
Library Holdings: Bk Vols 30,000; Bk Titles 1,500; Per Subs 10

P STAUNTON PUBLIC LIBRARY, One Churchville Ave, 24401. SAN 317-4514. Tel: 540-332-3902. TDD: 540-332-3902. FAX: 540-332-3906. Web Site: www.staunton.va.us/library/spinlibr.htm. *Dir*, Ruth S Arnold; E-Mail: arnoldrs@ci.staunton.va.us; *Ad Servs*, Diane Devoy; E-Mail: devoydh@ci.staunton.va.us; *Ch Servs*, Denise Brady; E-Mail: bradydl@ci.staunton.va.us; *Tech Servs*, Beth Horn; E-Mail: hornea@ci.staunton.va.us; Staff 22 (MLS 3, Non-MLS 19)
Founded 1930. Pop 24,100; Circ 402,253
Jul 1999-Jun 2000 Income (Main Library Only) $898,960, State $215,996, City $682,964. Mats Exp $143,396, Books $119,283, Per/Ser (Incl. Access Fees) $15,309, Micro $2,249, AV Equip $350, Electronic Ref Mat (Incl. Access Fees) $6,205. Sal $478,195 (Prof $87,697)
Library Holdings: Bk Vols 150,053; Per Subs 255; High Interest/Low Vocabulary Bk Vols 790; Bks on Deafness & Sign Lang 200
Subject Interests: Local genealogy, Local history
Database Vendor: Ebsco - EbscoHost, OCLC - First Search, ProQuest
Publications: Books & Your Baby
Special Services for the Deaf - Books on deafness & sign language; High interest/low vocabulary books; TDD
Friends of the Library Group
Branches: 1

P TALKING BOOK CENTER, One Churchville Ave, 24401-3229. SAN 321-6519. Tel: 540-885-6215. Toll Free Tel: 800-995-6215. FAX: 540-332-3906. E-Mail: talkingbooks@ci.staunton.ca.us. *Librn*, Oakley Pearson; E-Mail: pearsonjo@ci.staunton.va.us; Staff 2 (MLS 1, Non-MLS 1)
Founded 1982. Pop 225,025
Library Holdings: Bk Vols 18,000
Subregional library of the National Library System for the Blind & Physically Handicapped

WESTERN STATE HOSPITAL
M MEDICAL-PROFESSIONAL LIBRARY, 1301 Richmond Rd, PO Box 2500, 24402-2500. SAN 363-4116. Tel: 540-332-8307. FAX: 540-332-8065. *Librn*, Kathy Mohler
Founded 1830
Library Holdings: Bk Vols 2,800; Per Subs 64
Subject Interests: Psychiatry, Psychology
Partic in VA Med Info Syst

S STRIBLING LIBRARY, PO Box 2500, 24402. SAN 363-4140. Tel: 540-332-8340. FAX: 540-332-8014.
Library Holdings: Bk Vols 5,000
Subject Interests: Basic living skills, Bibliotherapy, Mental health
Special Collections: Large Type Fiction & Non-fiction Coll, bks, per

S WOODROW WILSON BIRTHPLACE FOUNDATION, Research Librar 18 N Coalter St, PO Box 24, 24402-0024. SAN 317-4522. Tel: 540-885-0897. FAX: 540-886-9874. E-Mail: woodrow@woodrowwilson.org. Web Site: www.woodrowwilson.org. *Exec Dir*, Patrick Clarke; *Librn*, Jean Sm
Founded 1973
Library Holdings: Bk Vols 2,000; Per Subs 20
Subject Interests: 19th-20th Centuries, Accomplishments of Foundation since 1925, Decorative arts, Hist of Foundation since 1925
Special Collections: (President Woodrow Wilson); Edith Bolling Wilson papers; Emily Smith papers; Historic Photograph Coll; Katherine Brand Coll; Wilson Manuscript Coll; Wilson-McClure Coll
Restriction: By appointment only

STERLING

S LAW ENGINEERING & ENVIRONMENTAL SERVICES LIBRARY,* 22455 Davis Dr, Ste 100, 20164. SAN 326-6087. Tel: 703-404-7000. FA: 703-404-7070.
Founded 1980
Library Holdings: Bk Titles 2,000; Per Subs 35
Subject Interests: Environmental engineering
Restriction: By appointment only
Partic in Dialog Corporation; STN

STRATFORD

S JESSIE BALL DUPONT MEMORIAL LIBRARY, Stratford Hall Plantat 22558. SAN 321-4753. Tel: 804-493-8572. FAX: 804-493-8006. Web Site www.stratfordhall.org. *Archivist*, Judith S Hynson; E-Mail: jhynson@stratfordhall.org; *Asst Librn*, Patsy Childs
Founded 1980
Library Holdings: Bk Vols 10,000; Bk Titles 7,000; Per Subs 25
Special Collections: 18th Century America (Shippen Coll), antiquarian b 18th Century England (Ditchley Coll), antiquarian bks; Lee Family Manuscripts
Restriction: By appointment only

SUFFOLK

M LOUISE OBICI MEMORIAL HOSPITAL, Health Science Library,* 190 Main St, PO Box 1100, 23430. SAN 328-5987. Tel: 757-934-4865. FAX: 757-934-4867. E-Mail: hslibrary@obici.com. *Librn*, Janet Beyer Daum; E-Mail: jdaum@obici.com
Oct 1998-Sep 1999 Income $101,900. Mats Exp $41,000, Books $12,000, Per/Ser (Incl. Access Fees) $18,000, AV Equip $5,000, Electronic Ref Ma (Incl. Access Fees) $6,000. Sal $58,800 (Prof $38,000)
Library Holdings: Bk Vols 1,200; Per Subs 137
Subject Interests: Nursing
Partic in Medical Libr Asn; Tidewater Health Scis Librs

P SUFFOLK PUBLIC LIBRARY SYSTEM, 443 W Washington St, 23434. SAN 317-4530. Tel: 757-934-7686. FAX: 757-539-7155. E-Mail: library@suffolk.lib.va.us. *Dir*, Elliot A Drew; *Asst Dir*, Janice Felker; *Asst Dir*, Ka Ferrill; *Asst Dir, Tech Servs*, Beverly Kay Hill; *Ref*, Ruth Smith; *Ch Servs* Cathy Scott; Staff 16 (MLS 4, Non-MLS 12)
Founded 1959. Pop 67,195; Circ 248,013
Jul 1998-Jun 1999 Income $1,166,915, State $218,869, City $948,046. M Exp $284,802, Books $261,823, Per/Ser (Incl. Access Fees) $13,998, Pres $1,252, Micro $538, AV Equip $7,191. Sal $481,770 (Prof $161,229)
Library Holdings: Bk Vols 115,960; Bk Titles 93,875; Per Subs 225
Special Collections: Black Arts & Literature (Reid Coll)
Automation Activity & Vendor Info: (Circulation) Gaylord
Database Vendor: Ebsco - EbscoHost, OCLC - First Search
Mem of Suffolk County Libr Syst
Friends of the Library Group

SWEET BRIAR

C SWEET BRIAR COLLEGE LIBRARY, PO Box 1200, 24595-1200. SAN 363-4175. Tel: 804-381-6138. FAX: 804-381-6173. Web Site: www.cochra sbc.edu. *Dir*, John G Jaffe; E-Mail: jgjaffe@sbc.edu; *Assoc Dir, Publ Serv* Lisa Johnston; E-Mail: lujohnston@sbc.edu; *Br Coordr*, L Joseph Malloy; E-Mail: ljmalloy@sbc.edu; *Head, Cat*, Betty Evans; E-Mail: baevans@sbc.edu; *Circ*, Shirley Reid; E-Mail: spreid@sbc.edu; *Coll Develop*, Joyce Kramar; *ILL*, Thelma Jordan; E-Mail: tbjordan@sbc.edu; *Per*, Liz Linton; E-Mail: melinton@sbc.edu; *Head Tech Servs*, Marge M Freeman; E-Mail: mmfreeman@sbc.edu; *Tech Servs*, Melinda Wheeler; E-Mail: mqwheeler@sbc.edu; Staff 12 (MLS 5, Non-MLS 7)
Founded 1901. Enrl 583; Fac 90; Highest Degree: Bachelor
Library Holdings: Bk Vols 164,818; Per Subs 1,092

Special Collections: Evelyn D Mullen T E Lawrence Coll; Fletcher Williams Founders Coll; George Meredith Coll; Incunabula; Kellogg Childrens Coll; Vincent Chinese Coll; Virginia Woolf Coll; Wystan Hugh Auden Coll
Automation Activity & Vendor Info: (Acquisitions) epixtech, inc.; (Cataloging) epixtech, inc.; (Circulation) epixtech, inc.; (Serials) epixtech, inc.
Publications: Friends of the Library Gazette
Partic in Lynchburg Area Library Cooperative; Lynchburg Information Online Network; VA Independent Col & Univ Libr Asn; Virtual Libr of Va
Friends of the Library Group
Departmental Libraries:
FANNY B FLETCHER SCIENCE LIBRARY, Connie M Guion Science Bldg, 24595. SAN 363-423X. Tel: 804-381-6297.
Founded 1964
Library Holdings: Bk Vols 21,400
JUNIUS P FISHBURN MUSIC LIBRARY, Babcock Fine Arts Bldg, 24595. SAN 363-4191. Tel: 804-381-6250. FAX: 804-381-6173.
Founded 1961
Library Holdings: Bk Vols 8,562
MARTIN C SHALLENBERGER ART LIBRARY, Anne Gary Pannell Ctr, 24595. SAN 363-4205. Tel: 804-381-6294. *In Charge*, Caressa Talley
Founded 1961
Library Holdings: Bk Vols 14,738

ZEWELL

TAZEWELL COUNTY PUBLIC LIBRARY,* 310 E Main St, PO Box 929, 24651-0929. SAN 363-4264. Tel: 540-988-2541. FAX: 540-988-5980. *Dir*, Laurie Roberts; E-Mail: lroberts@vsla.edu; *Ch Servs*, Jill Gates; *Ref*, Nora Lockett; *Tech Servs*, Lindsey Martin; Staff 20 (MLS 3, Non-MLS 17)
Founded 1964. Pop 47,700; Circ 140,545
Jul 1998-Jun 1999 Income $623,264, State $147,000, County $427,917, Locally Generated Income $24,347. Mats Exp $65,370, Books $46,000, Per/Ser (Incl. Access Fees) $14,000. Sal $328,628 (Prof $89,709)
Library Holdings: Bk Vols 116,000; Bk Titles 59,418; Per Subs 393
Subject Interests: Genealogy, Local history
Branches: 2
BLUEFIELD BRANCH, 108 Huffard Dr, Bluefield, 24605. SAN 363-4299. Tel: 540-326-1577. FAX: 540-322-5705. *Librn*, Michael Pettry
RICHLANDS BRANCH, 102 Suffolk Ave, PO Box 806, Richlands, 24641. SAN 325-3252. Tel: 540-964-5282. FAX: 540-963-1107. *Librn*, Charlotte Sayers
Bookmobiles: 1

BANNA

MIDDLESEX COUNTY PUBLIC LIBRARY, (MCPL), Urbanna Branch, 150 Grace St, PO Box 189, 23175-0189. SAN 317-4557. Tel: 804-758-5717. FAX: 804-758-5910. Web Site: www.mcpl.middlesex.lib.va.us/. *Coll Develop, Exec Dir*, Sherry Inabinet; E-Mail: inabinet@mcpl.middlesex.lib.va.us; Staff 5 (MLS 1, Non-MLS 4)
Founded 1927. Pop 9,600; Circ 45,000
Jul 1999-Jun 2000 Income $163,302, State $42,802, City $5,500, County $67,000, Locally Generated Income $30,000, Other $18,000. Mats Exp $30,700, Books $23,000, Per/Ser (Incl. Access Fees) $1,700, Presv $1,000, Electronic Ref Mat (Incl. Access Fees) $5,000. Sal $86,000 (Prof $35,000)
Library Holdings: Bk Vols 27,000; Bk Titles 31,000; Per Subs 150
Special Collections: Chesapeake Bay; Virginia Reference
Automation Activity & Vendor Info: (Cataloging) TLC; (Circulation) TLC; (OPAC) TLC
Friends of the Library Group

ENNA

CENTER FOR CHINESE RESEARCH MATERIALS, Information Center,* 10415 Willow Crest Ct, 22182-1852. SAN 370-9639. Tel: 703-715-2688. FAX: 703-715-7913. *Dir*, Pingfeng Chi
Publications: Newsletter

KELLEY, DRYE & WARREN, Law Library, Tyson's Corner, 8000 Tower Crescent Dr, 12th flr, 22182. Tel: 202-955-9601.

KOREAN SCIENTISTS & ENGINEERS ASSOCIATION IN AMERICA LIBRARY,* 1952 Gallows Rd Ste 300, 22182. SAN 374-9355. Tel: 703-748-1221. FAX: 703-748-1331. *Pres*, H Thomas Hahn; E-Mail: pres@ksea.org
Library Holdings: Bk Vols 500

NATIONAL SUDDEN INFANT DEATH SYNDROME RESOURCE CENTER,* 2070 Chain Bridge Rd, Ste 450, 22182-2536. SAN 373-2614. Tel: 703-821-8955, Ext 249. FAX: 703-821-2098.
Library Holdings: Bk Vols 250
Restriction: Open to public for reference only
Specialized resource center - with comprehensive collection on SIDS & related subjects - including infant mortality, apnea, grief & bereavement associated with a SIDS & other infant loss

S NATIONAL WILDLIFE FEDERATION LIBRARY, 8925 Leesburg Pike, 22184-0001. SAN 302-7384. Tel: 703-790-4446. FAX: 703-790-4354. E-Mail: levy@nwf.org, liblist@nwf.org. *Coll Develop, Librn*, Sharon Levy; Staff 1 (MLS 1)
Founded 1961
Library Holdings: Bk Vols 3,000; Per Subs 250
Subject Interests: Animals, behavior of, Natural resources, Pollution
Partic in Capcon Library Network; Dialog Corporation

S NEWSPAPER ASSOCIATION OF AMERICA, Information Resource Center, 1921 Gallows Rd, Ste 600, 22182. SAN 317-3925. Tel: 703-902-1692. FAX: 703-902-1691. E-Mail: irc@naa.org. Web Site: www.naa.org. *Mgr*, Paul Yachnes; Tel: 703-902-1694, E-Mail: yachp@naa.org; Staff 4 (MLS 2, Non-MLS 2)
Founded 1887
Library Holdings: Bk Titles 8,000; Per Subs 400
Subject Interests: Newsp advertising, Newsp indust hist, Newsp publ indust
Special Collections: ANPA Bulletins; Presstime
Automation Activity & Vendor Info: (Cataloging) Inmagic, Inc.; (OPAC) Inmagic, Inc.

L WICKWIRE GAVIN PC LIBRARY, 8100 Boone Blvd, Ste 700, 22182. SAN 377-4015. Tel: 703-790-8750. FAX: 703-448-1801. *Librn*, Millie Cronin
Library Holdings: Bk Vols 2,500; Per Subs 40
Partic in Am Asn of Law Librs; Law Libr Soc of DC

VIRGINIA BEACH

S ASSOCIATION FOR RESEARCH & ENLIGHTENMENT, Edgar Cayce Foundation Library,* 215 67th St, 23451. SAN 317-459X. Tel: 757-428-3588 Ext 7141. FAX: 757-422-4631. E-Mail: are@webartisans.com. Web Site: www.are.cayce.com. *Mgr*, Stephen Jordan; *Circ*, Claudeen Cowell; *Ref*, Wayne Emley; *Tech Servs*, Marcia Nolle
Founded 1940
1998-1999 Income $58,589. Mats Exp $19,563, Books $7,452; Per/Ser (Incl. Access Fees) $2,228
Library Holdings: Bk Vols 65,800; Per Subs 85
Subject Interests: Archaeology, Astrology, Comparative relig, Death, Dying, ESP, Future life, Health, Metaphysics, Parapsychology, Psychic res, Reincarnation, Theosophy, Transpersonal psychology
Special Collections: Atlantis (Egerton Sykes Coll); Metaphysics (Andrew Jackson Davis Coll); Readings (Edgar Cayce Coll); San Francisco Metaphysical Library Coll
Publications: New Millennium; Perspective; Perspective on Consciousness & Psi Research; Venture Inward (ARE magazine)
Friends of the Library Group

P COMMONWEALTH COLLEGE LIBRARY SYSTEM,* 301 Centre Pointe Dr, 23462. SAN 372-5146. Tel: 757-499-7900. FAX: 757-499-9977. Web Site: www.commonwealthcollege.com. *Dir Libr Serv*, April Adams-Pace; E-Mail: apace@leo.vsla.edu; *Publ Servs*, Cheryl Zebrowski; *Online Servs*, Lindsey Van Sicklen; Staff 13 (MLS 9, Non-MLS 4)
Founded 1982. Enrl 1,700
Library Holdings: Bk Vols 26,000; Bk Titles 23,500; Per Subs 565
Subject Interests: Medicine
Friends of the Library Group
Branches: 1
RICHMOND CAMPUS, 8141 Hull Street Rd, Richmond, 23235. SAN 372-5332. Tel: 804-745-2444. *Librn*, Lindsay Van Sicklen

C ECPI COLLEGE OF TECHNOLOGY, Virginia Beach Main Campus Library, 5555 Greenwich Rd, 23462. SAN 373-8620. Tel: 757-671-7171. Interlibrary Loan Service Tel: 757-671-7171, Ext 215. Circulation Tel: 757-671-7171, Ext 382. Reference Tel: 757-671-7171, Ext 215. FAX: 757-671-8661. Web Site: www.ecpi.edu. *Coordr*, Rebecca Tabakin; E-Mail: rtabakin@ecpi.edu; Staff 2 (MLS 2)
Founded 1984. Circ 4,093; Enrl 800; Fac 75; Highest Degree: Associate
Library Holdings: Bk Titles 11,891; Per Subs 230
Subject Interests: Computer science, Data processing
Special Collections: Computer Technology
Automation Activity & Vendor Info: (Cataloging) Sagebrush Corporation; (Circulation) Sagebrush Corporation; (OPAC) Sagebrush Corporation
Database Vendor: Ebsco - EbscoHost, GaleNet, IAC - Info Trac
Partic in Libr & Info Resources Network
Departmental Libraries:
CHARLOTTE CAMPUS, 4800 Airport Center Pkwy, Charlotte, 28208. Tel: 704-399-1010. *Librn*, Lewis Herman; E-Mail: lherman@ecpi.edu; Staff 2 (MLS 1, Non-MLS 1)
Enrl 500; Fac 30; Highest Degree: Associate
Library Holdings: Bk Vols 6,109; Bk Titles 5,461
Subject Interests: Computer science, Computer tech
Automation Activity & Vendor Info: (Cataloging) Sagebrush Corporation; (Circulation) Sagebrush Corporation; (OPAC) Sagebrush Corporation
Database Vendor: Ebsco - EbscoHost, GaleNet, IAC - Info Trac

Partic in Libr & Info Resources Network

GREENSBORO CAMPUS, 7015-G Albert Pick Rd, Grennsboro, 27409. Tel: 336-665-1400. *Librn*, Ann Benson; Staff 2 (MLS 1, Non-MLS 1)
Enrl 380; Fac 30; Highest Degree: Associate
Library Holdings: Bk Vols 4,848; Bk Titles 3,844
Subject Interests: Computer science, Computer tech
Automation Activity & Vendor Info: (Cataloging) Sagebrush Corporation; (Circulation) Sagebrush Corporation; (OPAC) Sagebrush Corporation
Database Vendor: Ebsco - EbscoHost, GaleNet, IAC - Info Trac
Partic in Libr & Info Resources Network

GREENVILLE CAMPUS, 15 Brendan Way No 120, Greenville, 29615-3514.; Staff 1 (MLS 1)
Founded 1999. Enrl 200; Fac 12; Highest Degree: Associate
Library Holdings: Bk Vols 528; Bk Titles 456
Subject Interests: Computer tech
Automation Activity & Vendor Info: (Cataloging) Sagebrush Corporation; (Circulation) Sagebrush Corporation; (OPAC) Sagebrush Corporation
Database Vendor: Ebsco - EbscoHost, GaleNet, IAC - Info Trac
Partic in Libr & Info Resources Network

HAMPTON CAMPUS, 1919 Commerce Dr, Hampton, 23666. SAN 377-0664. Tel: 757-838-9191, Ext 234. Web Site: www.ecpi.edu. *Librn*, Anthony Di Tommaso; E-Mail: aditommaso@ecpi.edu; Staff 2 (MLS 1, Non-MLS 1)
Fac 30; Highest Degree: Associate
2000-2001 Mats Exp $142,338
Library Holdings: Bk Vols 4,450; Bk Titles 3,707
Automation Activity & Vendor Info: (Acquisitions) Sagebrush Corporation; (Circulation) Sagebrush Corporation; (OPAC) Sagebrush Corporation
Database Vendor: Ebsco - EbscoHost, GaleNet, IAC - Info Trac
Partic in Libr & Info Resources Network

S PROVIDENCE PRESBYTERIAN CHURCH LIBRARY,* 5497 Providence Rd, 23464. SAN 328-123X. Tel: 757-420-6159. FAX: 757-420-7553. *In Charge*, Karen Cagni
Founded 1985
Library Holdings: Bk Titles 1,600

C REGENT UNIVERSITY LIBRARY, 1000 Regent University Dr, 23464. SAN 321-6314. Tel: 757-226-4185. Circulation Tel: 757-226-4159. Reference Tel: 757-226-4159. FAX: 757-226-4167. E-Mail: refer@regent.edu. Web Site: www.regent.edu/lib. *Dean of Libr*, Albert Liu; E-Mail: albeliu@regent.edu; *Assoc Librn*, Karen Robinson; Tel: 757-226-4457, E-Mail: karerob@regent.edu; *Assoc Librn*, Robert J Sivigny; Tel: 757-226-4184, E-Mail: robesiv@regent.edu; *Assoc Librn*, Sandra Yaegle; Tel: 757-226-4165, E-Mail: sandyae@regent.edu; *Asst Librn*, Barbara Burd; Tel: 757-226-4183, E-Mail: barbur@regent.edu; *Asst Librn*, Amanda Hankins; Tel: 757-226-4187, E-Mail: amanhan@regent.edu; *Asst Librn*, Marta Lee; Tel: 757-226-4174, E-Mail: martlee@regent.edu; *Govt Doc, Ref*, Cindy Cabia; *Automation Syst Coordr, Distance Educ*, Leanne Strum; Tel: 757-226-4172, E-Mail: leangar@regent.edu; *ILL*, Luwana Baker. Subject Specialists: *Business*, Barbara Burd; *Communication*, Karen Robinson; *Counseling*, Amanda Hankins; *Education*, Sandra Yaegle; *Government*, Marta Lee; *Psychology*, Amanda Hankins; Staff 34 (MLS 9, Non-MLS 25)
Founded 1978. Enrl 2,123; Highest Degree: Doctorate
Jul 1999-Jun 2000 Income (Main Library Only) $1,795,994. Mats Exp $656,239, Books $258,958, Per/Ser (Incl. Access Fees) $259,611, Presv $17,137, Micro $18,229, AV Equip $9,000, Other Print Mats $16,910, Electronic Ref Mat (Incl. Access Fees) $76,394. Sal $974,705
Library Holdings: Bk Vols 209,815; Bk Titles 207,192; Per Subs 1,484; Bks on Deafness & Sign Lang 56
Subject Interests: Biblical studies, Bus, Communications, Counseling, Education, Government, Hymnology, Leadership studies, Psychology
Special Collections: Animated Films; Baptista Film Mission Archives; Christian Films Research Coll; Clark Hymnology Coll; Scott Ross Cultural Coll
Automation Activity & Vendor Info: (Acquisitions) Innovative Interfaces Inc.; (Cataloging) Innovative Interfaces Inc.; (Circulation) Innovative Interfaces Inc.; (OPAC) Innovative Interfaces Inc.; (Serials) Innovative Interfaces Inc.
Database Vendor: GaleNet, IAC - Info Trac, IAC - SearchBank, Lexis-Nexis, OCLC - First Search, OVID Technologies, ProQuest, Silverplatter Information Inc., Wilson - Wilson Web
Function: Research library
Partic in OCLC Online Computer Library Center, Inc; SE Libr Network; Tidewater Consortium; Virginia Tidewater Consortium For Higher Education
Regent University is a free-standing graduate only institution
Departmental Libraries:

CL LAW LIBRARY, 1000 Regent University Dr, 23464. SAN 329-8108. Tel: 757-226-4450. Circulation Tel: 757-226-4450. Reference Tel: 757-226-4145. FAX: 757-226-4451. Web Site: www.regent.edu/acad/schlaw/library/. *Dir*, Charles H Oates; Tel: 757-226-4452, E-Mail: charoat@regent.edu; *Asst Dir*, Margaret Christiansen; Tel: 757-226-4463, E-Mail: margchr@regent.edu; *Head Tech Servs*, Teresa A Parker-Bellamy; Tel: 757-226-4370, E-Mail: terepar@regent.edu; *Head Ref*, Eric L Welsh; Tel: 757-226-4454, E-Mail: ericwel@regent.edu; *Ref*, Kaaren Jurack; Tel: 757-226-4145, E-Mail: kaarjur@regent.edu; *Ref*, Marie Summerlin-Hamm; Tel: 757-2 4233, E-Mail: mariham@regent.edu; *Cat*, Ann Cannon; Tel: 757-226-4 E-Mail: anncann@regent.edu; *Info Tech*, Vicki Boggs; Tel: 757-226-4 E-Mail: vickbog@regent.edu; *Ref*, William Magee; Tel: 757-226-4098, E-Mail: willmag@regent.edu. Subject Specialists: *Legal res*, Marie Summerlin-Hamm; *Legislative mat*, Eric L Welsh; *Taxation*, William Magee; *Writing*, Marie Summerlin-Hamm; Staff 15 (MLS 6, Non-ML
Founded 1986
Jul 1999-Jun 2000 Income (Main Library Only) $2,070,822, Locally Generated Income $1,073, Parent Institution $2,069,749. Mats Exp $1,283,352, Books $163,060, Per/Ser (Incl. Access Fees) $775,987, Pr $5,874, Micro $86,917, AV Equip $1,510, Electronic Ref Mat (Incl. Access Fees) $250,004. Sal $594,155 (Prof $338,785)
Library Holdings: Bk Vols 354,351; Bk Titles 41,726; Per Subs 4,51
Subject Interests: Biblical law, Constitutional law, Environmental law taxation, Int trade law, Intellectual property law, International law, Leg hist, Virginia Law
Special Collections: Amendment & Civil rights Coll; Early US Law Library Founder's Coll; Founders Coll, more than one thousand volum John Brabner-Smith Library & papers; Ralph Bunche Coll, contains 2 pieces; Roscoe Pound Papers
Automation Activity & Vendor Info: (Acquisitions) Innovative Interf Inc.; (Cataloging) Innovative Interfaces Inc.; (Circulation) Innovative Interfaces Inc.; (Course Reserve) Innovative Interfaces Inc.; (OPAC) Innovative Interfaces Inc.; (Serials) Innovative Interfaces Inc.
Database Vendor: CARL, Dialog, Ebsco - EbscoHost, GaleNet, IAC - Info Trac, Lexis-Nexis, OCLC - First Search, Wilson - Wilson Web
Publications: Testimony (Newsletter)
Function: Research library
Partic in Virginia Tidewater Consortium For Higher Education; VIVA-Statewide Library Resource Network

UNITED STATES ARMY

A FORT STORY LIBRARY, Bldg T-530, Solomons Rd, Fort Story, 23459 5067. SAN 320-9563. Tel: 757-422-7548. Circulation Tel: 757-422-75 FAX: 757-422-7773. *Librn*, Valerie D Fashion; E-Mail: fashionv@eustis.army.mil; Staff 2 (MLS 1, Non-MLS 1)
Library Holdings: Bk Titles 34,000; Per Subs 60
Subject Interests: Mil
Automation Activity & Vendor Info: (Circulation) Sagebrush Corporation
Partic in Fedlink; Tralinet

P VIRGINIA BEACH DEPARTMENT OF PUBLIC LIBRARIES, Bldg 1 Municipal Ctr, 2nd flr, 2416 Courthouse Dr, 23456. SAN 363-4329. Tel: 757-427-4321. Interlibrary Loan Service Tel: 757-431-3047. FAX: 757-4 4220. Web Site: www.virginia-beach.va.us/services/library/vbpls.htm. *Dir* Martha J Sims; *Mgr*, John D Stewart; Staff 52 (MLS 52)
Founded 1959. Pop 421,517; Circ 3,142,609
Library Holdings: Bk Vols 1,256,754
Special Collections: Princess Anne County (Princess Anne Historical Co bks, microfilm & microcards
Automation Activity & Vendor Info: (Circulation) VTLS
Publications: The Beach: A History of Virginia Beach; Update (Virginia Beach Public Library newsletter, bi-monthly)
Partic in Dialog Corporation; OCLC Online Computer Library Center, In
Friends of the Library Group
Branches: 15

AUTOMATED SERVICES DIV, Central Library, 4100 Virginia Beach Blvd, 23452. SAN 363-4361. Tel: 757-437-6451.
Founded 1985

BAYSIDE AREA, 936 Independence Blvd, 23455. SAN 363-4590. Tel: 7 460-7518. FAX: 757-464-6741. Web Site: www.virginia-beach.va.us/services/library/system/bayside.htm. *Librn*, Carolyn Caywood; E-Mail: ccaywood@city.virginia-beach.va.us; Staff 17 (MLS 1, Non-MLS 16)
Founded 1967

CENTRAL LIBRARY, 4100 Virginia Beach Blvd, 23452. SAN 377-056 Tel: 757-437-6450. FAX: 757-431-3082. *Librn*, Carolyn Barkley

COLLECTION MANAGEMENT, 4100 Virginia Beach Blvd, 23452. SA 322-614X. Tel: 757-437-6451. *Librn*, Toni Lohman

GREAT NECK AREA, 1251 Bayne Dr, 23454. SAN 363-4620. Tel: 757-496-6868. FAX: 757-481-1587. *Librn*, Jacqueline Lewis; E-Mail: jackie.lewis@city.virginia-beach.va.us

INTERLIBRARY LOAN DIV, 4100 Virginia Beach Blvd, 23452. SAN 3 4434. Tel: 757-431-3047. FAX: 757-431-3018. *Coordr*, Jennifer Thalm

KEMPSVILLE AREA, 832 Kempsville Rd, 23464-2793. SAN 363-4655. Tel: 757-495-1016. FAX: 757-495-5401. *Librn*, Judy Pate

LIBRARY CATALOGING SERVICES, 4100 Virginia Beach Blvd, 2345 SAN 363-4442. Tel: 757-437-6451. FAX: 757-431-3018.
Library Holdings: Bk Vols 467

MUNICIPAL REFERENCE DIV, Municipal Ctr, Bldg 17, 23456. SAN 3 4477. Tel: 757-427-4644. FAX: 757-427-8240. *Coordr*, Kathy Beavers

OCEANFRONT AREA, 1811 Arctic Ave, 23451. SAN 363-468X. Tel: 75 437-4821. FAX: 757-428-0566. *Librn*, Mary Appelberg

OUTREACH SERVICES DIV BOOKMOBILE, 3612 S Plaza Trail, 2345 SAN 363-4418. Tel: 757-340-7798. *Librn*, Susan Head; Staff 7 (MLS 1

Non-MLS 6)

PUNGO-BLACKWATER LIBRARY, 922 Princess Anne Rd, 23457. SAN 370-9426. Tel: 757-426-5194. FAX: 757-426-5537. *Librn*, Liz Lett

SUBREGIONAL LIBRARY FOR THE BLIND & HANDICAPPED, SPECIAL SERVICES LIBRARY, 930 Independence Blvd, 23455. SAN 363-4353. Tel: 757-464-9175. TDD: 757-464-9175. FAX: 757-460-7606. Web Site: www.virginia-beach.va.us/services/library. *In Charge*, Aleene Wicher; Staff 6 (MLS 1, Non-MLS 5)
Founded 1972
Library Holdings: Bk Vols 8,169
Special Services for the Deaf - TDD

WAHAB PUBLIC LAW LIBRARY, Municipal Ctr, Judicial Ctr, Court Support Bldg 10B, 23456. SAN 363-4507. Tel: 757-427-4419. FAX: 757-427-8742. *Coordr*, Jill Burr

WINDSOR WOODS AREA, 3612 S Plaza Trail, 23452. SAN 363-471X. Tel: 757-340-1043. FAX: 757-431-3746. *In Charge*, Josephine Schaffer

VIRGINIA MARINE SCIENCE MUSEUM LIBRARY, 717 General Booth Blvd, 23451. SAN 328-3631. Tel: 757-437-6020. FAX: 757-437-4976. Web Site: www.vmfm.org. *Coordr*, Kathleen Reed; E-Mail: kreed@city.virginia-beach.va.us
Library Holdings: Bk Vols 1,000; Per Subs 25

LLOPS ISLAND

NASA, Goddard Space Flight Center, Wallops Flight Facility Library, Tech Lib E-105, 292 W, 23337. SAN 317-4611. Tel: 757-824-1065. FAX: 757-824-1716. Web Site: www.library.gsfc.nasa.gov/. *Librn*, Roberta Eddy; Staff 3 (MLS 1, Non-MLS 2)
Founded 1959
Library Holdings: Bk Vols 10,000; Bk Titles 7,800; Per Subs 345
Subject Interests: Aerospace, Applied sci, Mathematics, Phys
Special Collections: Balloon Library
Publications: Booster
Partic in Nasa Libraries Information System - Nasa Galaxie

RRENTON

FAUQUIER COUNTY PUBLIC LIBRARY, 11 Winchester St, 20186-2825. SAN 317-462X. Tel: 540-347-8750, Ext 24. Interlibrary Loan Service Tel: 540-347-8750, Ext 26. Circulation Tel: 540-347-8750, Ext 10. Reference Tel: 540-347-8750, Ext 25. FAX: 703-349-3278. Web Site: www.co.fauquier.va.us/services/libraries. *Dir, Librn*, Maria Del Rosso; *Asst Librn*, Ava K Lee; *Tech Servs*, Linda Yowell; *Ref*, Dawn Sowers; *Per*, Mary McGee; *Br Coordr*, Deborah Cosby; *Br Coordr*, Muriel McCabe; Staff 36 (MLS 9, Non-MLS 27)
Founded 1922. Pop 53,167; Circ 403,200
Jul 1999-Jun 2000 Income $950,261. Mats Exp $218,227, Books $198,938, Per/Ser (Incl. Access Fees) $10,796, Presv $791, Micro $7,702. Sal $890,122 (Prof $384,361)
Library Holdings: Bk Vols 111,520; Bk Titles 87,522; Per Subs 845
Subject Interests: Genealogy, Local history, Virginia
Automation Activity & Vendor Info: (Acquisitions) Innovative Interfaces Inc.; (Cataloging) Innovative Interfaces Inc.; (Circulation) Innovative Interfaces Inc.; (OPAC) Innovative Interfaces Inc.; (Serials) Innovative Interfaces Inc.
Database Vendor: OCLC - First Search
Partic in SWING
Friends of the Library Group
Branches: 2

BEALETON BRANCH, Bealeton Village Center, 6346 Village Center Dr, Bealeton, 22712. SAN 371-9294. Tel: 540-439-9728. FAX: 540-439-9731. Web Site: www.co.fauquier.va.ux/services/libraries. *Mgr*, Muriel C McCabe; Staff 6 (MLS 2, Non-MLS 4)
Library Holdings: Bk Vols 26,010
Friends of the Library Group

JOHN MARSHALL BRANCH, 4133 Rectortown Rd, Marshall, 20115. SAN 375-5487. Tel: 540-364-4910. FAX: 540-364-4911. Web Site: co.fauquier.va.us/services/libraries. *Mgr*, Deborah Cosby; Staff 3 (MLS 1, Non-MLS 2)
Library Holdings: Bk Vols 16,848
Friends of the Library Group

RSAW

RAPPAHANNOCK COMMUNITY COLLEGE, Library Center, 52 Campus Dr, 22572. SAN 363-4833. Tel: 804-333-6700. Circulation Tel: 804-333-6710. FAX: 804-333-0589. *Dir Libr Serv*, Tracy Elliott; Tel: 804-333-6716, E-Mail: telliott@rcc.cc.va.us; *ILL*, Betsy Garland; Tel: 804-333-6714; Staff 3 (MLS 3)
Founded 1973. Pop 157,000; Enrl 1,600; Fac 29; Highest Degree: Associate
Jul 1999-Jun 2000 Income $80,500, State $22,000, City $5,000, County $36,000, Locally Generated Income $17,500. Mats Exp $75,968, Books $28,518, Per/Ser (Incl. Access Fees) $10,800, Presv $250, AV Equip $18,000, Electronic Ref Mat (Incl. Access Fees) $18,400. Sal $225,038 (Prof $126,096)
Library Holdings: Bk Vols 30,000; Bk Titles 25,000; Per Subs 203
Special Collections: Children's Library; Cooperative Law Library; Virginiana Coll
Automation Activity & Vendor Info: (Cataloging) NOTIS; (Circulation) NOTIS; (OPAC) NOTIS
Database Vendor: OCLC - First Search
Partic in Solinet; VIVA-Statewide Library Resource Network
Friends of the Library Group

WASHINGTON

P RAPPAHANNOCK COUNTY LIBRARY,* Rte 211, PO Box 55, 22747-0055. SAN 317-4646. Tel: 540-675-3780. FAX: 540-675-1290. *Dir, Librn*, David Shaffer; *Ch Servs*, Jennifer Glenn
Founded 1963. Circ 16,783
Library Holdings: Bk Vols 25,000
Friends of the Library Group

WAYNESBORO

S DU PONT DE NEMOURS & CO, INC, Benger Laboratory Library, DuPont Co, 400 Du Pont Blvd, 22980. SAN 317-4654. Tel: 540-949-2000, 540-949-2485. FAX: 540-949-2949. *Librn*, Becky Moomau
Founded 1947
Library Holdings: Bk Titles 10,000; Per Subs 90

P WAYNESBORO PUBLIC LIBRARY, 600 S Wayne Ave, 22980. SAN 363-4868. Tel: 540-942-6746. FAX: 540-942-6753. *Coll Develop, Dir*, Dorothy Anne Reinbold; *Asst Dir*, M Zahir Mahmoud; *Ref*, Dee Collins; Staff 12 (MLS 3, Non-MLS 9)
Founded 1915. Pop 18,549; Circ 492,842
Library Holdings: Bk Vols 164,828
Subject Interests: Local history
Special Collections: Charles Smith Art Coll; George Speck Art Coll, prints; Waynesboro Local History, bks, micro
Automation Activity & Vendor Info: (Cataloging) DRA; (Circulation) DRA; (OPAC) DRA
Publications: Bookmark (newsletter)
Assistive workstation with Zoom Text for the physically challenged patrons
Friends of the Library Group

WEYERS CAVE

J BLUE RIDGE COMMUNITY COLLEGE, Houff Library, One College Lane, 24486-2205. (Mail add: PO Box 80, 24486-0080), Tel: 540-234-9261. Toll Free Tel: 888-750-2722 (only in VA). FAX: 540-234-9598. E-Mail: bralexd@br.cc.va.us. Web Site: www.br.cc.va.us. *Dir Libr Serv*, Frank Moran; Tel: 540-453-2269, E-Mail: brmoraf@br.cc.va.us; *Librn*, Sheila Newman; Tel: 540-453-2357, E-Mail: brnewms@br.cc.va.us; *Librn*, Connie Shewmake; Tel: 540-453-2390, E-Mail: brshewc@br.cc.va.us; *ILL*, Donna S Alexander; Tel: 540-453-2247; *Media Spec*, Ruth Blakenship; Tel: 540-453-2275, E-Mail: brblanr@br.cc.va.us; *Circ*, Laura Moyers; Tel: 540-453-2256, E-Mail: brmoyel@br.cc.va.us; *Ref*, Sue Ellen Church; Tel: 540-453-2278, E-Mail: brchurs@br.cc.va.us; Staff 5 (MLS 2, Non-MLS 3)
Founded 1967. Pop 203,000; Enrl 1,630; Highest Degree: Associate
Jul 1999-Jun 2000 Income $276,911. Mats Exp $69,700, Books $34,565, Per/Ser (Incl. Access Fees) $16,281, Presv $253, Micro $655, AV Equip $8,561, Other Print Mats $6,435, Electronic Ref Mat (Incl. Access Fees) $2,950. Sal $207,484 (Prof $110,484)
Library Holdings: Bk Vols 48,085; Bk Titles 45,681; Per Subs 220
Subject Interests: Veterinary tech
Special Collections: Virginia Regional Historical Coll
Automation Activity & Vendor Info: (Circulation) NOTIS; (OPAC) NOTIS
Publications: AV Guide; New Accessions; Periodical Listing
Function: ILL available
Partic in OCLC Online Computer Library Center, Inc; VIVA-Statewide Library Resource Network

WILLIAMSBURG

COLLEGE OF WILLIAM & MARY IN VIRGINIA

CL MARSHALL-WYTHE LAW LIBRARY, S Henry St, PO Box 8795, 23187-8795. SAN 363-504X. Tel: 757-221-3255. Circulation Tel: 757-221-3255. Reference Tel: 757-221-3257. FAX: 757-221-3175. Toll Free FAX: 757-221-3075. Web Site: www.wm.edu/law/law_library. *Dir*, James Heller; Tel: 757-221-3252; *Ref*, Catherine Marshall; *Tech Servs*, Sue Welch; *Ref*, Christopher Byrne; *Circ*, Steven Blaiklock; *AV*, Mary Grace Hune; *Res*, William Cooper; Staff 6 (MLS 6)
Enrl 540; Fac 30; Highest Degree: Doctorate
Jul 2000-Jun 2001 Income $2,150,000. Mats Exp $982,000, Books $120,000, Per/Ser (Incl. Access Fees) $750,000, Presv $12,000, Micro $30,000, Electronic Ref Mat (Incl. Access Fees) $70,000. Sal $939,000 (Prof $450,000)
Library Holdings: Bk Vols 365,000; Bk Titles 65,000; Per Subs 5,300
Subject Interests: Constitutional law, Environmental law, Legal hist,

Roman law
Special Collections: Thomas Jefferson Law Books
Partic in Dialog Corporation; OCLC Online Computer Library Center, Inc; SE Libr Network; Westlaw

C EARL GREGG SWEM LIBRARY, PO Box 8794, 23187-8794. SAN 363-4922. Tel: 757-221-3050. Interlibrary Loan Service Tel: 757-221-3089. FAX: 757-221-2635. Web Site: www.swem.wm.edu. *Dean*, Connie K McCarthy; E-Mail: cmccarthy@janus.swem.wm.edu; *Access Serv*, Mary S Molineux; *Assoc Dean*, John D Haskell, Jr; *Assoc Dean*, Berma L Heyman; *Coll Develop*, James Deffenbaugh; *Asst Dean*, Kay J Domine; *Acq*, Stephen D Clark; *Govt Doc*, Alan F Zoellner; *ILL*, John R M Lawrence; *Rare Bks*, Margaret C Cook; *Ref Serv*, Donald J Welsh; *Ser*, Merle A Kimball. Subject Specialists: *Academic*, Berma L Heyman; *Automation*, Berma L Heyman; *Manuscripts*, John D Haskell, Jr; *Manuscripts*, Margaret C Cook; *Preservation*, James Deffenbaugh; *Rare books*, John D Haskell, Jr; Staff 25 (MLS 25)
Founded 1693. Enrl 7,553; Fac 575; Highest Degree: Doctorate
Jul 1999-Jun 2000 Income $5,948,080. Mats Exp $5,682,516, Books $815,719, Per/Ser (Incl. Access Fees) $1,764,331, Presv $69,101. Sal $2,202,079 (Prof $1,140,134)
Library Holdings: Bk Vols 1,186,489; Per Subs 5,724
Special Collections: Books with fore-edge Paintings (Ralph Wark Coll); Dogs (Peter Chapin, Murray & Shirley Horowitz Colls) History of Books & Printing; Seed Catalogs; Tucker-Coleman Papers (Virginia Family), 1675-1956; United States History 17th-19th Centuries, Warren E Burger Collection; Virginia History, 17th-20th Centuries, mss
Automation Activity & Vendor Info: (Acquisitions) SIRSI; (Cataloging) SIRSI; (Circulation) SIRSI; (Course Reserve) SIRSI; (ILL) SIRSI; (OPAC) SIRSI; (Serials) SIRSI
Publications: Guide to Special Collections in the Earl Gregg Swem Library (1993); Treasures of the College of William & Mary Library (1988)
Partic in Association Of Southeastern Research Libraries (ASERL); Center For Research Libraries; SE Libr Network
Friends of the Library Group

S COLONIAL WILLIAMSBURG FOUNDATION, John D Rockefeller Jr Library, 313 First St, PO Box 1776, 23187. SAN 363-5139. Tel: 757-565-8500. Circulation Tel: 757-565-8512. Reference Tel: 757-565-8510. FAX: 757-565-8518. Web Site: www.colonialwilliamsburg.org. *Actg Dir*, Mary Haskell; Tel: 757-565-8501, Fax: 757-565-8508, E-Mail: mhaskell@cwf.org; *Publ Servs*, Juleigh Clark; Tel: 757-565-8511, E-Mail: jclark@cwf.org; *Circ*, Joann Proper; E-Mail: jproper@cwf.org; *Acq*, Annette Parham; Tel: 757-565-8532, Fax: 757-565-8538, E-Mail: aparham@cwf.org; Staff 15 (MLS 8, Non-MLS 7)
Founded 1933
Library Holdings: Bk Vols 72,334; Per Subs 400
Subject Interests: African-Am, Architecture, Customs, Decorative arts, Early Am periods, Economics, Government, Hist of Williamsburg-Va-Chesapeake region in Colonial, Hist presv, Mat culture, Mus studies, Music, Soc life
Special Collections: House Histories; Research Query File, 1927 to present; Research Reports
Database Vendor: OCLC - First Search
Publications: Colonial Williamsburg: The Journal of the Colonial Williamsburg Foundation (quarterly); Early American History Research Reports from the Colonial Williamsburg Foundation Library, microfiche
Open 9-5; Reference Service 9-4
Branches:
ABBY ALDRICH ROCKEFELLER FOLK ART MUSEUM LIBRARY, 307 S England St, 23185-4266. (Mail add: PO Box 1776, 23187-1776), SAN 363-5228. Tel: 757-220-7668. FAX: 757-565-8915. Web Site: www.history.org. *In Charge*, Anne Motley; E-Mail: amotley@cwf.org
Library Holdings: Bk Vols 10,000; Bk Titles 5,548; Per Subs 32
Subject Interests: Coverlets, Decoys, Folk paintings, Needlework pictures, Quilts, Sculptures in metal, Sculptures in wood, Theorems, Weathervanes
Special Collections: 19th Century Children's Books
Database Vendor: OCLC - First Search
Publications: Exhibition Catalogues
Restriction: By appointment only
JOHN D ROCKEFELLER, JR LIBRARY - SPECIAL COLLECTIONS Tel: 757-565-8520. FAX: 757-565-8528. Web Site: www.history.org. *Spec Coll*, Gail Greve; Tel: 757-565-8501, E-Mail: ggreve@cwf.org; Staff 3 (MLS 2, Non-MLS 1)
Founded 1929
Library Holdings: Bk Vols 12,500
Subject Interests: Early Am periods, Hist of Williamsburg, Va and Chesapeake region in colonial
Special Collections: A Lawrence Kocher Architecture Coll; Alden Hopkins Landscape Architecture Coll; Colonial Virginia & Chesapeake History Coll; Colonial Williamsburg Foundation Coll (1993); Eighteenth Century Music; Eighteenth Century Williamsburg Imprints; Francis Nicholson Papers; John Norton & Sons Papers; Robert Anderson Papers; Shirley Plantation Research Coll; Virginia Colonial Records Project; Webb-Prentis 18th Century Williamsburg Coll; William Blathwayt Papers; Wolcott Coll
Database Vendor: OCLC - First Search
Publications: Collections at the Colonial Williamsburg Foundation Library; Guide to the Manuscript; The Colonial Williamsburg Research Collections in Microform; The William Blathwayt Papers at Colonial Williamsburg, 1631-1722
Open 9-5; Reference Service 9-4
JOHN D ROCKEFELLER, JR LIBRARY - VISUAL RESOURCES Tel: 757-565-8540. FAX: 757-565-8548. Web Site: www.colonialwilliamsburg.org. *AV*, Marianne Martin; Tel: 757-565-854[illegible] E-Mail: mmartin@cwf.org; Staff 3 (MLS 1, Non-MLS 2)
Founded 1946
Subject Interests: 18th Century archit, 18th Century decorative arts, 1[illegible] Century furnishing, 19th Century folk art, Am decorative arts, Colonial life, Colonial period, English decorative arts, Mat culture, Va-Chesapea[illegible] region archit
Special Collections: Colonial Williamsburg Foundation Restoration & Programs; Museum Programs; Williamsburg Activities, History, Person & Collections; Williamsburg's African-American Community in 1940s-1950s (Albert W Durant Coll)
Restriction: By appointment only
Open Mon-Fri 10-5 by appointment

M EASTERN STATE HOSPITAL, Library Services,* 4601 Ironbound Rd, 23187-8791. (Mail add: PO Box 8791, 23187), SAN 317-4700. Tel: 757-253-5387. FAX: 757-253-5192. Web Site: www.easternstatehospital.org. *Head of Libr*, Judy B Belle; Tel: 757-253-4310, E-Mail: jbelle@esh.state.va.us; *Head of Libr*, Sandra Kochersperger; Tel: 757-253-5457, Fax: 757-253-7078, E-Mail: slamendola@esh.state.va.us; Staff 4 (MLS 1, Non-MLS 3)
Founded 1843
Library Holdings: Bk Vols 17,800; Bk Titles 17,000; Per Subs 343
Subject Interests: Nursing, Psychiatry, Psychology, Soc work
Special Collections: Galt Papers, mss
Automation Activity & Vendor Info: (Cataloging) Follett; (Circulation) Follett
Database Vendor: Dialog, Ebsco - EbscoHost, OCLC - First Search, Silverplatter Information Inc.
Publications: Inflow
Function: Outside services via phone, cable & mail
Partic in Dialog Corporation; OCLC Online Computer Library Center, In[illegible] Tidewater Health Scis Librs; Virginia Library & Information Network
First Patients' Library in a Public Psychiatric Hospital

L NATIONAL CENTER FOR STATE COURTS LIBRARY,* 300 Newpor[illegible] Ave. (Mail add: PO Box 8798, 23187-8798), SAN 317-4719. Tel: 757-25[illegible] 1819. FAX: 757-220-0449. *Dir*, Erick Baker Low; E-Mail: elow@ncsc.dni.us; *Cat*, Ruth Etheredge; *Acq, Coll Develop*, Peggy W Rogers; S[illegible] 3 (MLS 3)
Founded 1973
Library Holdings: Bk Vols 30,000; Bk Titles 20,000; Per Subs 430
Subject Interests: Court improvement, Court mgt, Judicial admin
Special Collections: National Center for State Courts Reports
Publications: Acquisitions List (quarterly); video catalog
Partic in Capcon Library Network; OCLC Online Computer Library Cent[illegible] Inc
Special Serivices - Consulting provided to court libraries
Branches:
DENVER BRANCH, 1331 17th St, Ste 402, Denver, 80202-1554. SAN 375-6661. Tel: 303-293-3063. FAX: 303-296-9007. *VPres*, James Thom[illegible]
Library Holdings: Per Subs 50

S OMOHUNDRO INSTITUTE OF EARLY AMERICAN HISTORY & CULTURE, Kellock Library, 109 Cary St, 23185-4061. (Mail add: PO B[illegible] 8781, 23187-8781), SAN 327-8832. Tel: 757-221-1126. FAX: 757-221-10[illegible] Web Site: www.wm.edu/oieahc. *Librn*, Patricia Higgs; E-Mail: pvhigg@wm.edu
Jan 1999-Dec 1999 Mats Exp $1,705, Books $917, Per/Ser (Incl. Access Fees) $788. Sal $3,250
Library Holdings: Bk Titles 8,060; Per Subs 31

P WILLIAMSBURG REGIONAL LIBRARY SYSTEM, 7770 Croaker Rd, 23188. SAN 317-4727. Tel: 757-259-7720. FAX: 757-259-4079, 757-259-7798. Web Site: www.wrl.org. *Dir*, John A Moorman; Tel: 757-259-7777, E-Mail: jmoorman@mail.wrl.org; *Dep Dir*, Kirstin Steele; *YA Servs*, Nore[illegible] Bernstein; *Bkmobile Coordr*, Eletha Davis; *Coll Develop*, Peg Bradshaw; *Acq*, Cela Schmidt; *Ref*, Jordan Davis; *Ref*, Jeff Kempe; *Ref*, Bonita Stockmeyer; *Ref*, Barry Trott
Founded 1908. Pop 55,676
Jul 1999-Jun 2000 Income $4,202,406, State $450,148, City $595,881, County $2,981,193, Locally Generated Income $175,184. Mats Exp $534,982. Sal $3,084,148
Library Holdings: Bk Vols 258,082; Per Subs 562
Special Collections: Local Documents
Database Vendor: epixtech, inc.
Publications: Newsletter (monthly)
Partic in Capcon Library Network
Special Services for the Deaf - TDD

Special Services for the Blind - VisualTek closed circuit TV reading aid
Theater seating 266; 6 meeting rooms available
Friends of the Library Group
Bookmobiles: 1

NCHESTER

HANDLEY REGIONAL LIBRARY,* 100 W Picadilly St, PO Box 58, 22601. SAN 317-4735. Tel: 540-662-9041. FAX: 540-722-4769. E-Mail: handley@shentel.net. Web Site: www.shentel.net/handley-library/index.html. *Dir*, Trish Ridgeway; *Tech Servs*, Sara Holloway; *Ref*, Kim Bean
Founded 1913. Pop 88,800; Circ 372,756
Jul 1997-Jun 1998 Income $1,185,021, State $260,554, City $243,160, County $522,663, Locally Generated Income $61,142, Other $97,502. Mats Exp $170,532, Books $122,079, Per/Ser (Incl. Access Fees) $15,029, Presv $1,531, Micro $9,261. Sal $705,500 (Prof $206,678)
Library Holdings: Bk Vols 132,814; Per Subs 316
Special Collections: Civil War Coll; Rare Local Newspapers; Virginiana Coll
Automation Activity & Vendor Info: (Cataloging) epixtech, inc.
Publications: The Friend
Mem of VA State Regional Librs
Closed for renovation
Friends of the Library Group
Branches: 1
CLARKE COUNTY, 36 E Main St, Berryville, 22611. SAN 375-5665. Tel: 540-955-5144. FAX: 540-955-4928. Web Site: ccl@shentel.net. *Mgr*, Charlene Allen
Friends of the Library Group

SHENANDOAH UNIVERSITY, Alson H Smith Jr Library, 1460 University Dr, 22601. SAN 317-4743. Tel: 540-665-5424. Reference Tel: 540-665-5421. Toll Free Tel: 877-289-4611. FAX: 540-665-4609. E-Mail: library@su.edu. Web Site: www.su.edu/library/. *Dir*, Christopher A Bean; Tel: 540-665-4553, E-Mail: cbean@su.edu; *Tech Servs*, Megan Williams; Tel: 540-665-4638, E-Mail: mwilliam@su.edu; *Media Spec*, Russell Courter; Tel: 540-665-4551, E-Mail: rcourter@su.edu; *Publ Servs*, David McKinney; Tel: 540-665-4634, E-Mail: dmckinne@su.edu; Staff 14 (MLS 6, Non-MLS 8)
Founded 1875. Enrl 2,400; Fac 185; Highest Degree: Doctorate
Jul 1999-Jun 2000 Income Parent Institution $813,684. Mats Exp $409,181, Books $70,150, Per/Ser (Incl. Access Fees) $177,686, Presv $3,949, Micro $22,992, AV Equip $20,000, Electronic Ref Mat (Incl. Access Fees) $29,186. Sal $397,344 (Prof $195,000)
Library Holdings: Bk Vols 116,571; Per Subs 1,173
Subject Interests: Civil War, Dance, Education, Music, Nursing, Pharmacy, Physical therapy, Theater
Special Collections: Religion (Evangelical United Brethren Church Historical Room); Shenandoah University Archives; Shenandoah Valley History
Automation Activity & Vendor Info: (Acquisitions) SIRSI; (Cataloging) SIRSI; (Circulation) SIRSI; (Course Reserve) SIRSI; (Media Booking) SIRSI; (OPAC) SIRSI; (Serials) SIRSI
Database Vendor: IAC - Info Trac, Lexis-Nexis, OCLC - First Search, OVID Technologies
Partic in Northern Shenandoah Valley Libr Network; SE Libr Network; Shenandoah Valley Independent Cols Libr Coop; VA Independent Col & Univ Libr Asn
Friends of the Library Group

WINCHESTER MEDICAL CENTER, (Formerly Valley Health System - Winchester Medical Center), Health Sciences Library, 1840 Amherst St, 22601-2808. SAN 324-5721. Tel: 540-536-8040. Interlibrary Loan Service Tel: 540-536-4091. FAX: 540-536-8844. Web Site: www.valleyhealthlink.com. *Dir*, Joellynn Wilner; E-Mail: jwilner@valleyhealthlink.com; *Librn*, Barbara Adams; E-Mail: badams2@valleyhealthlink.com; Staff 2 (MLS 1, Non-MLS 1)
Jan 2001-Dec 2001 Income $235,720. Mats Exp $138,520. Sal $74,500
Library Holdings: Bk Titles 1,410; Per Subs 300
Subject Interests: Allied health, Consumer health, Medicine, Nursing
Database Vendor: Ebsco - EbscoHost, GaleNet, OVID Technologies
Publications: Health Resource Handbook: Support & Community Groups, 2000-2001
Partic in NNLM/SCR, OCLC Online Computer Libr Ctr, Inc

SE

CLINCH VALLEY COLLEGE OF THE UNIVERSITY OF VIRGINIA, John Cook Wyllie Library, 1 College Ave, 24293-4412. SAN 317-4751. Tel: 540-328-0150. Circulation Tel: 540-328-0158. Reference Tel: 540-328-0157. FAX: 540-328-0105. E-Mail: ecn2y@wise.virginia.edu. Web Site: www.lib.wise.virginia.edu/. *Dir Libr Serv*, Robin Paul Benke; Tel: 540-328-0151, E-Mail: rpb@wise.virginia.edu; *Cat*, Karen S Chafin; Tel: 540-328-0153; *Publ Servs*, Kelly McBride; Tel: 540-328-0159, E-Mail: krm3e@wise.virginia.edu; *Ref*, J J Cromer; E-Mail: jjc5r@wise.virginia.edu; *Tech Servs*, Amelia C VanGundy; Tel: 540-328-0154, E-Mail: acv6d@wise.virginia.edu; *Outreach Serv*, Ann Duesing; Tel: 540-328-0168, E-Mail: cad4n@wise.virginia.edu; Staff 14 (MLS 6, Non-MLS 8)
Founded 1954. Enrl 1,426; Fac 112; Highest Degree: Bachelor
Jul 1999-Jun 2000 Income $689,879. Mats Exp $267,328, Books $38,630, Per/Ser (Incl. Access Fees) $57,972, Presv $5,821, Micro $10,843, AV Equip $5,138, Electronic Ref Mat (Incl. Access Fees) $46,761. Sal $423,698 (Prof $195,950)
Library Holdings: Bk Vols 148,548; Bk Titles 95,861; Per Subs 1,251
Subject Interests: Appalachian studies
Special Collections: Archives of Southwest Virginia Folklore Society Coll; Beaty-Flannary Papers Coll; Bruce Crawford Papers Coll; Elihu Jasper Sutherland Papers Coll; Emory L Hamilton Papers Coll; James Taylor Adams Papers Coll; Southwest Virginia (Archives of Southwest Virginia Historical Society; Trigg Floyd Papers; Virginia Coal Operators Coll)
Automation Activity & Vendor Info: (Acquisitions) SIRSI; (Cataloging) SIRSI; (Circulation) SIRSI; (Course Reserve) SIRSI; (OPAC) SIRSI; (Serials) SIRSI
Database Vendor: OCLC - First Search
Publications: Information Guides; Periodicals & Newspaper Holdings List
Partic in OCLC Online Computer Library Center, Inc; Solinet; VIVA-Statewide Library Resource Network

P LONESOME PINE REGIONAL LIBRARY, 124 Library Rd SW, PO Box 1379, 24293-1379. SAN 363-5287. Tel: 540-328-8325. FAX: 540-328-1739. E-Mail: lprlibraryusa@netscape.net. Web Site: www.lprlibrary.org. *Dir*, Virginia Adams; Staff 66 (MLS 3, Non-MLS 63)
Founded 1958. Pop 108,200; Circ 816,860
Jul 1999-Jun 2000 Income $2,346,302, State $552,393, City $43,050, County $1,301,160, Other $449,699. Mats Exp $273,146, Books $190,623, Per/Ser (Incl. Access Fees) $39,184, Presv $929, Micro $3,432, Other Print Mats $15,616, Electronic Ref Mat (Incl. Access Fees) $23,362. Sal $1,031,247 (Prof $66,619)
Library Holdings: Bk Vols 419,774; Per Subs 836
Subject Interests: Genealogy, SW Va hist
Automation Activity & Vendor Info: (Acquisitions) GEAC; (Cataloging) GEAC; (Circulation) GEAC; (OPAC) GEAC
Branches: 9
COEBURN COMMUNITY, 111 Third St, PO Box 2169, Coeburn, 24230. SAN 363-5317. Tel: 540-395-6152. FAX: 540-395-3563. E-Mail: ccllibrary@naxs.net. Web Site: www.lprlibrary.org. *Mgr*, Candess Hylton; Staff 7 (Non-MLS 7)
Circ 79,818
Jul 1999-Jun 2000 Income (Main Library Only) $154,994, State $22,321, County $104,220, Other $28,453. Mats Exp $16,261, Books $13,547, Per/Ser (Incl. Access Fees) $2,714. Sal $74,322
Library Holdings: Bk Vols 38,382
Automation Activity & Vendor Info: (Acquisitions) GEAC; (Cataloging) GEAC; (Circulation) GEAC; (OPAC) GEAC
Friends of the Library Group
HAYSI PUBLIC, 527 Main St, PO Box CC, Haysi, 24256. SAN 363-5376. Tel: 540-865-4851. FAX: 540-865-5441. E-Mail: hpllibrary@naxs.net. Web Site: www.lprlibrary.org. *Mgr*, Shirley Hawkins; Staff 3 (Non-MLS 3)
Circ 32,125
Jul 1999-Jun 2000 Income (Main Library Only) $87,034, State $13,054, County $59,619, Other $14,361. Mats Exp $8,163, Books $5,911, Per/Ser (Incl. Access Fees) $2,154, Presv $98. Sal $43,862
Library Holdings: Bk Vols 17,711
Automation Activity & Vendor Info: (Acquisitions) GEAC; (Cataloging) GEAC; (Circulation) GEAC; (OPAC) GEAC
J FRED MATTHEWS MEMORIAL, 16552 Wise St, PO Box 1976, Saint Paul, 24283. SAN 363-5430. Tel: 540-762-9702. FAX: 540-762-0528. E-Mail: spblibrary@naxs.net. Web Site: www.lprlibrary.org. *Mgr*, Charles Engle; Staff 5 (Non-MLS 5)
Circ 56,199
Jul 1999-Jun 2000 Income (Main Library Only) $237,305, State $23,808, County $95,718, Other $117,779. Mats Exp $15,288, Books $12,044, Per/Ser (Incl. Access Fees) $3,244. Sal $59,432
Library Holdings: Bk Vols 27,805
Automation Activity & Vendor Info: (Acquisitions) GEAC; (Cataloging) GEAC; (Circulation) GEAC; (OPAC) GEAC
Friends of the Library Group
JONNIE B DEEL MEMORIAL, PO Box 650, Chase St, Clintwood, 24228. SAN 363-5309. Tel: 540-926-6617. FAX: 540-926-6795. E-Mail: jbdlibrary@naxs.net. Web Site: www.lprlibrary.org. *Mgr*, Sheila Phipps; Staff 7 (Non-MLS 7)
Founded 1963. Circ 82,801
Jul 1999-Jun 2000 Income (Main Library Only) $162,898, State $31,960, County $109,098, Other $21,840. Mats Exp $22,018, Books $18,064, Per/Ser (Incl. Access Fees) $3,658, Presv $157, Micro $139. Sal $72,580
Library Holdings: Bk Vols 63,239
Automation Activity & Vendor Info: (Acquisitions) GEAC; (Cataloging) GEAC; (Circulation) GEAC; (OPAC) GEAC
Friends of the Library Group
LEE COUNTY PUBLIC, 406 Joslyn Ave, Pennington Gap, 24277. SAN 363-5341. Tel: 540-546-1141. FAX: 540-546-5136. E-Mail: lcplibrary@naxs.net. Web Site: www.lprlibrary.org. *Mgr*, Norma Ferguson; Staff 6 (Non-MLS 6)
Founded 1965. Circ 92,743

Jul 1999-May 2000 Income (Main Library Only) $186,313, State $42,888, County $114,381, Other $29,044. Mats Exp $24,798, Books $19,962, Per/Ser (Incl. Access Fees) $4,150, Presv $202, Micro $84. Sal $89,649
Library Holdings: Bk Vols 71,169
Automation Activity & Vendor Info: (Acquisitions) GEAC; (Cataloging) GEAC; (Circulation) GEAC; (OPAC) GEAC

ROSE HILL COMMUNITY, Main St, PO Box 280, Rose Hill, 24281. SAN 363-5422. Tel: 540-445-5329. FAX: 540-445-5329. E-Mail: rhplibrary@naxs.net. Web Site: www.lprlibrary.org. *Mgr*, Lela Johnson; Staff 1 (Non-MLS 1)
Circ 14,249
Jul 1999-Jun 2000 Income (Main Library Only) $35,457, State $14,444, County $15,233, Other $5,780. Mats Exp $7,025, Books $5,334, Per/Ser (Incl. Access Fees) $1,676, Presv $15. Sal $11,787
Library Holdings: Bk Vols 8,659
Automation Activity & Vendor Info: (Acquisitions) GEAC; (Cataloging) GEAC; (Circulation) GEAC; (OPAC) GEAC

SCOTT COUNTY PUBLIC, 131 W Jackson St, Gate City, 24251. SAN 363-5406. Tel: 540-386-3302. FAX: 540-386-2977. E-Mail: scplibrary@naxs.net. Web Site: www.lprlibrary.org. *Mgr*, Lisa Edwards; Staff 6 (MLS 1, Non-MLS 5)
Founded 1972. Circ 121,439
Jul 1999-May 2000 Income (Main Library Only) $214,130, State $57,731, County $100,016, Other $56,383. Mats Exp $33,282, Books $26,250, Per/Ser (Incl. Access Fees) $5,070, Presv $29, Micro $1,933. Sal $96,782 (Prof $8,639)
Library Holdings: Bk Vols 80,648
Automation Activity & Vendor Info: (Acquisitions) GEAC; (Cataloging) GEAC; (Circulation) GEAC; (OPAC) GEAC
Friends of the Library Group

C BASCOM SLEMP MEMORIAL, 11 Proctor St N, Big Stone Gap, 24219. SAN 363-549X. Tel: 540-523-1334. FAX: 540-523-5306. E-Mail: cbslibrary@naxs.net. Web Site: www.lprlibrary.org. *Mgr*, Donna Miller; Staff 7 (Non-MLS 7)
Founded 1974. Circ 96,473
Jul 1999-Jun 2000 Income (Main Library Only) $238,440, State $29,761, County $125,540, Other $83,139. Mats Exp $24,072, Books $18,932, Per/Ser (Incl. Access Fees) $5,004, Presv $57, Micro $79. Sal $90,795
Library Holdings: Bk Vols 60,502
Automation Activity & Vendor Info: (Acquisitions) GEAC; (Cataloging) GEAC; (Circulation) GEAC; (OPAC) GEAC
Friends of the Library Group

WISE COUNTY PUBLIC, 124 Library Rd SW, PO Box 1379, 24293. SAN 363-552X. Tel: 540-328-8061. FAX: 540-328-8022. E-Mail: lprlwise@compunet.net. Web Site: www.lprlibrary.org. *Mgr*, Linda Scarborough; Staff 10 (MLS 1, Non-MLS 9)
Founded 1958. Circ 197,096
Jul 1999-Jun 2000 Income (Main Library Only) $367,694, State $72,913, City $43,050, County $183,313, Other $68,418. Mats Exp $67,912, Books $55,386, Per/Ser (Incl. Access Fees) $10,958, Presv $371, Micro $1,197. Sal $158,356 (Prof $5,471)
Library Holdings: Bk Vols 136,437
Automation Activity & Vendor Info: (Acquisitions) GEAC; (Cataloging) GEAC; (Circulation) GEAC; (OPAC) GEAC
Friends of the Library Group

WOODBRIDGE

M POTOMAC HOSPITAL, Richard P Immerman Memorial Library, 2300 Opitz Blvd, 22191. Tel: 703-670-1331. FAX: 703-878-1619. *Librn*, Debr Scarborough
Founded 1974
Library Holdings: Bk Vols 1,000; Bk Titles 750; Per Subs 175
Partic in National Network Of Libraries Of Medicine - South Central Re

WYTHEVILLE

J WYTHEVILLE COMMUNITY COLLEGE LIBRARY, 1000 E Main St, 24382-3397. SAN 317-476X. Tel: 540-223-4743. FAX: 540-223-4745. W Site: www.wc.cc.va.us/visitors/library. *In Charge*, Anna Ray Roberts; *Ass Librn*, George Mattis; Staff 3 (MLS 2, Non-MLS 1)
Founded 1963. Enrl 2,400; Fac 68; Highest Degree: Associate
Library Holdings: Bk Vols 28,000; Per Subs 260
Special Collections: Local History (F B Kegley Library), bks, maps, ms
Database Vendor: epixtech, inc.
Partic in VIVA-Statewide Library Resource Network

YORKTOWN

S NATIONAL PARK SERVICE, Colonial National Historical Park Library, PO Box 210, 23690. SAN 317-4778. Tel: 757-898-3400. FAX: 757-898-6346. *Info Res*, Jane M Sundberg; Tel: 757-898-2415, E-Mail: jane_sundberg@nps.gov
Founded 1930
Library Holdings: Bk Vols 1,200
Subject Interests: Colonial hist, Revolutionary war history
Restriction: By appointment only

P YORK COUNTY PUBLIC LIBRARY, 100 Long Green Blvd, 23693. SA 317-3003. Tel: 757-890-5100. FAX: 757-890-5127. Web Site: www.yorkcounty.gov/library. *Dir*, Beverly Dudley; Tel: 757-890-5107, E-Mail: dudleyb@yorkcounty.gov; *Asst Dir*, Norma Colton; Tel: 757-890-5104, E-Mail: coltonn@yorkcounty.gov; *Mgr Libr*, Kevin W Smith; Tel: 757-890-5134, E-Mail: smithk@yorkcounty.gov; Staff 61 (MLS 3, Non-M 58)
Founded 1968. Pop 57,900
Jul 2000-Jun 2001 Income $1,636,023, State $260,444, County $1,375,57 Mats Exp $344,584, Books $281,148, Per/Ser (Incl. Access Fees) $22,58 Electronic Ref Mat (Incl. Access Fees) $40,852. Sal $818,507 (Prof $143,353)
Library Holdings: Bk Vols 143,353; Bk Titles 84,290; Per Subs 450
Subject Interests: Virginia
Special Collections: Virginia & Local History
Automation Activity & Vendor Info: (Cataloging) TLC; (Circulation) epixtech, inc.; (OPAC) epixtech, inc.
Database Vendor: epixtech, inc., Lexis-Nexis, OCLC - First Search, ProQuest
Mem of York County Library System
Friends of the Library Group

WASHINGTON

Date of Statistics: 1998
Population: 5,685,300
Population Served by Public Libraries: 5,495,933
Unserved: 189,367
Population figures & statistics below (Volumes, Circulation & Income) based on Washington State tabulations & estimates of 1998
Total Volumes in Public Libraries: 19,355,962
Volumes Per Capita: $3.52
Total Public Library Circulation: 53,533,342
Circulation Per Capita: $ 9.74
Total Public Library Income: $196,785,296
Expenditures Per Capita: $35.18
Source of Income: Mainly local public funds
Number of County or Multi-county (Regional) Libraries: 21
Counties Served: 29
Number of Mobile Units in State: 19

ERDEEN

GRAYS HARBOR COLLEGE, John Spellman Library, 98520-7599. SAN 317-4786. Interlibrary Loan Service Tel: 360-538-4050. Circulation Tel: 360-538-4050. Reference Tel: 360-538-4054. Toll Free Tel: 800-562-4830, Ext 4050 (in state) (in state). FAX: 360-538-4294. E-Mail: lib_ref@ghc.ctc.edu. Web Site: spellman.ghc.ctc.edu. *Dir*, Stanley Horton; E-Mail: shorton@ghc.ctc.edu; *Librn*, Adrienne Julius; *Librn*, Elaine Holster; *Coll Develop*, Don Cates; Staff 3 (MLS 3)
Founded 1930. Enrl 1,857; Highest Degree: Associate
Jul 1999-Jun 2000 Mats Exp $81,766, Books $37,202, Per/Ser (Incl. Access Fees) $21,360, AV Equip $8,169, Electronic Ref Mat (Incl. Access Fees) $15,035. Sal $108,096
Library Holdings: Bk Vols 38,559; Bk Titles 33,527; Per Subs 241
Subject Interests: Careers
Special Collections: Pacific Northwest; Small Business; Water/Fisheries
Automation Activity & Vendor Info: (Acquisitions) Endeavor
Partic in OCLC; Western Libr Network

ACORTES

ANACORTES PUBLIC LIBRARY, 1209 Ninth St, 98221. SAN 317-4794. Tel: 360-293-1910. FAX: 360-293-1929. Web Site: www.library.anacortes.wa.us. *Dir*, Doug Everhart; Tel: 360-293-1926, E-Mail: douge@cityofanacortes.org; *Ad Servs*, Regina VanHess; Tel: 360-293-1910, Ext 24, E-Mail: ginav@cityofanacortes.org; *Ch Servs*, Rae Kozloff; Tel: 360-293-1910, Ext 27, E-Mail: raek@cityofanacortes.org; *ILL*, Esther Noyes; Staff 3 (MLS 3)
Founded 1911. Pop 11,500; Circ 144,331
Library Holdings: Bk Titles 60,000; Per Subs 126
Partic in OCLC; OCLC Online Computer Library Center, Inc
Friends of the Library Group

BURN

GREEN RIVER COMMUNITY COLLEGE, Holman Library, 12401 SE 320th St, 98092-3699. SAN 317-4824. Tel: 253-833-9111. FAX: 253-288-3436. Web Site: www.ivygreen.ctc.edu/library. *Dir*, Kimberly Nakano; *Librn*, Jennifer Dysart; *Librn*, Wendy Graham; *Librn*, Rachel MacDonald; *Librn*, Lee Semsen; *Media Spec*, Steve Carkeek; Staff 14 (MLS 5, Non-MLS 9)
Founded 1965
Library Holdings: Bk Vols 40,000; Per Subs 300

WHITE RIVER VALLEY HISTORICAL SOCIETY MUSEUM LIBRARY,* 918 H St SE, 98002. SAN 370-3215. Tel: 253-939-2783. FAX: 253-939-4523. *Dir*, Patricia Cosgrove
Library Holdings: Bk Titles 2,000
Subject Interests: Local history
Special Collections: Newpapers - Auburn & Kent 1890s-1982, photographs
Open Wed-Sun 12-4

BELLEVUE

J BELLEVUE COMMUNITY COLLEGE, Library Media Center,* 3000 Landerholm Circle SE, 98007-6484. SAN 317-4832. Tel: 425-641-2252. FAX: 425-562-6186. E-Mail: zzreference@bcc.ctc.edu. Web Site: is.bcc.ctc.edu/library. *Dir*, Myra Van Vactor; *Acq*, Kate Bradley; *Tech Servs*, Shahla Rowhani; *ILL*, Xinhang Hu
Founded 1966
Jul 1997-Jun 1998 Income $592,730. Mats Exp $103,514, Books $40,000, Per/Ser (Incl. Access Fees) $38,600, AV Equip $12,504. Sal $400,639 (Prof $225,360)
Library Holdings: Bk Vols 45,000; Per Subs 400
Partic in OCLC

S SECOND AMENDMENT FOUNDATION LIBRARY,* 12500 NE Tenth Pl, 98005. SAN 377-4465. Tel: 425-454-7012. FAX: 425-451-3959. Web Site: www.saf.org. *Dir*, John Barnett
Library Holdings: Bk Vols 70

BELLINGHAM

S BELLINGHAM HERALD LIBRARY,* 1155 N State St, PO Box 1277, 98227. SAN 373-272X. Tel: 360-715-2283. FAX: 360-647-9260.
Library Holdings: Bk Vols 500; Per Subs 20
Special Collections: Pacific Northwest History (particularly Whatcom County, Wash)

P BELLINGHAM PUBLIC LIBRARY,* 210 Central Ave, PO Box 1197, 98227-1197. SAN 363-5589. Tel: 360-676-6860. FAX: 360-676-7795. E-Mail: cobweb@cob.org. Web Site: www.cob.org/bplhome.htm. *Ref*, Margaret Ziegler; *ILL*, Fay Fenske; *Ch Servs*, Scott Blume; *AV, Media Spec*, Linda Hodge; *Tech Servs*, Emma De la Cruz; *Circ*, Gayle Helgoe; *Acq*, Cathy Coldren; *Dir*, Julie Carterson; Staff 12 (MLS 12)
Founded 1904. Pop 58,000; Circ 1,044,820
Jan 1998-Dec 1998 Income $2,370,315, State $16,192, City $2,102,735, Locally Generated Income $153,984. Mats Exp $242,071, Books $212,071, Per/Ser (Incl. Access Fees) $30,000. Sal $1,591,419
Library Holdings: Bk Vols 275,000; Per Subs 500
Special Collections: Local History Coll
Automation Activity & Vendor Info: (Cataloging) epixtech, inc.
Partic in OCLC; OCLC Online Computer Library Center, Inc
Friends of the Library Group
Branches: 1
FAIRHAVEN, 1117 12th, 98226. SAN 363-5619. Tel: 360-676-6877. FAX: 360-676-6996. Web Site: www.cob.org/bplhome.htm. *In Charge*, Donna Grasdock
Library Holdings: Bk Vols 15,362
Friends of the Library Group . Outreach Van 1

S GEORGIA-PACIFIC WEST, INC, Bellingham Div Library,* PO Box 1236, 98227-1236. SAN 317-4859. Tel: 360-733-4410. FAX: 360-676-7217. E-Mail: sjlafeen@gapac.com. *Librn*, Shirley Lafeen
Library Holdings: Bk Vols 1,200; Per Subs 30
Subject Interests: Chemical engineering, Chemistry, Paper, Pulp, Wood sci, Wood tech

C HUXLEY COLLEGE OF ENVIRONMENTAL STUDIES, Resource Library,* Huxley College, ES 539 MS 9079, 98225. SAN 373-2738. Tel: 360-650-3520. FAX: 360-650-2842. E-Mail: library@lib.huxley.edu. *Dean of Libr*, Bradley Smith
1997-1998 Income $117,000. Mats Exp $100,000. Sal $45,000 (Prof $45,000)
Library Holdings: Bk Vols 2,000; Per Subs 20
Friends of the Library Group
Departmental Libraries:
MAP LIBRARY, MS 9085, 98225. SAN 375-3077. Tel: 360-650-3272. FAX: 360-650-7284. *Librn*, Janet Collins
Library Holdings: Bk Vols 1,200

M ST JOSEPH HOSPITAL LIBRARY, 2901 Squalicum Pkwy, 98225. SAN 317-4867. Tel: 360-738-6786. FAX: 360-715-4106. Web Site: www.sjhbell.com. *Librn*, Bea Hellis; E-Mail: bhellis@peacehealth.org
Founded 1975
Library Holdings: Bk Vols 1,500; Per Subs 250
Subject Interests: Consumer health, Health sci
Restriction: Open to others by appointment, Staff & members only
Partic in Pacific NW Regional Health Sci Libr; Wash State Libr Network

C WESTERN WASHINGTON UNIVERSITY, Mabel Zoe Wilson Library, 516 High St, 98225. SAN 363-5643. Tel: 360-650-3050. Interlibrary Loan Service Tel: 360-650-3076. FAX: 360-650-3044. Web Site: www.library.wwu.edu. *Actg Dir*, Marian Alexander; Tel: 360-650-3051, E-Mail: marian.alexander@wwu.edu; *Librn*, Dr Jeanne Armstrong; Tel: 360-650-7667, Fax: 360-650-7996, E-Mail: jeanne.armstrong@wwu.edu; *Librn*, Margaret Fast; Tel: 360-650-3174, Fax: 360-650-7996, E-Mail: margaret.fast@wwu.edu; *Librn*, Raymond McInnis; Tel: 360-650-3194, Fax: 360-650-7996, E-Mail: ray.mcinnis@wwu.edu; *Librn*, Donna Packer; Tel: 360-650-3335, Fax: 360-650-7996, E-Mail: donna.packer@wwu.edu; *Librn*, Diane Parker; Tel: 360-650-3274, E-Mail: diane.parker@wwu.edu; *Librn*, Paul Piper; Tel: 360-650-3097, Fax: 360-650-7996, E-Mail: paul.piper@wwu.edu; *Librn*, Cecilia Poon; *Librn*, Jeff Purdue; Tel: 360-650-7750, Fax: 360-650-7996, E-Mail: jeffery.purdue@wwu.edu; *Librn*, Dr Judith Segal; Tel: 360-650-7583, E-Mail: judith.segal@wwu.edu; *Librn*, Peter Smith; Tel: 360-650-3175, Fax: 360-650-7996, E-Mail: peter.smith@wwu.edu; *Librn*, Sylvia Tag; Tel: 360-650-7992, E-Mail: sylvia.tag@wwu.edu; *Automation Syst Coordr*, Andrea Peterson; Tel: 360-650-3894, Fax: 360-650-3954, E-Mail: andrea.peterson@wwu.edu; *Govt Doc*, Robert Lopresti; Tel: 360-650-3342, Fax: 360-650-6563, E-Mail: robert.lopresti@wwu.edu; *Cat*, Karen Rice; Tel: 360-650-3303, Fax: 360-650-3954, E-Mail: karen.rice@wwu.edu; *Librn*, Cecilia Poon. Subject Specialists: *Music*, Marian Ritter; Staff 58 (MLS 15, Non-MLS 43)
Founded 1899. Enrl 11,600; Highest Degree: Master
Jul 1998-Jun 1999 Income (Main Library and Branch Library) Parent Institution $4,356,704. Mats Exp $1,586,324, Books $367,036, Per/Ser (Incl. Access Fees) $999,935, AV Equip $60,034, Electronic Ref Mat (Incl. Access Fees) $159,319. Sal $2,095,920 (Prof $722,129)
Library Holdings: Bk Vols 800,000; Bk Titles 650,000; Per Subs 4,900
Special Collections: Canadian; Mongolia-Russian Far East Coll
Automation Activity & Vendor Info: (Cataloging) Innovative Interfaces Inc.; (Circulation) Innovative Interfaces Inc.; (Course Reserve) Innovative Interfaces Inc.; (Media Booking) Innovative Interfaces Inc.; (OPAC) Innovative Interfaces Inc.; (Serials) Innovative Interfaces Inc.
Database Vendor: Innovative Interfaces INN - View
Function: ILL available
Partic in Wash Coop Libr Project
Departmental Libraries:
MUSIC Tel: 360-650-3716. *Librn*, Marian Ritter
Friends of the Library Group

J WHATCOM COMMUNITY COLLEGE LIBRARY, 237 W Kellogg Rd, 98226. SAN 317-4875. Tel: 360-647-3266. FAX: 360-738-6165. E-Mail: wcc-irc@wln.com. *Assoc Dean*, Dal Symes; Tel: 360-676-2170, Ext 3312; *Assoc Dir*, Linda Lambert; Tel: 360-676-2170, Ext 3268; *Publ Servs*, Jo Dereske; Tel: 360-676-2170, Ext 3439; *Tech Servs*, Gillian McCloud; Tel: 360-676-2170, Ext 3446; Staff 9 (MLS 4, Non-MLS 5)
Founded 1972. Enrl 2,600; Fac 220; Highest Degree: Associate
Library Holdings: Bk Vols 21,000; Bk Titles 20,000; Per Subs 132

P WHATCOM COUNTY PUBLIC LIBRARY,* 5205 Northwest Rd, 98226-9092. SAN 363-5732. Tel: 360-384-3150. FAX: 360-384-4947. Web Site: www.wcls.lib.wa.us. *Dir*, Andrew Waters; E-Mail: awaters@wln.com; *Mgr*, Kathryn Frank; *ILL*, Jo Ann Gebhart; *Publ Servs*, Sigrid Brorson; *Ch Servs*, Catherine Sarette; *YA Servs*, Sally Kintner; *Ch Servs*, Theresa Gormley; *Coll Develop*, Robin Barker; Staff 61 (MLS 10, Non-MLS 51)
Founded 1945. Pop 92,000; Circ 900,000
Jan 1997-Dec 1998 Income $3,571,614. Mats Exp $414,000, Books $380,000, Per/Ser (Incl. Access Fees) $30,000. Sal $1,774,467
Library Holdings: Bk Vols 224,421; Bk Titles 109,334; Per Subs 1,036
Automation Activity & Vendor Info: (Circulation) epixtech, inc.
Partic in OCLC; OCLC Online Computer Library Center, Inc
Friends of the Library Group
Branches: 9
BLAINE BRANCH, 610 Third St, PO Box Y, Blaine, 98230. SAN 363-5767. Tel: 360-332-8146. FAX: 360-332-8146. Web Site: www.wcls.lib.wa.us. *Librn*, Kathy Richardson
Friends of the Library Group
DEMING BRANCH, PO Box 357, Deming, 98244. SAN 363-5791. Tel: 360-592-2422. Web Site: www.wcls.lib.wa.us. *Librn*, Frances Barbaga; E-Mail: fbarbaga@sttl.uswest.net
Friends of the Library Group
EVERSON COMMUNITY, PO Box 250, Everson, 98247. SAN 363-58 Tel: 360-966-5100. FAX: 360-966-5100. Web Site: www.wclr.lib.wa.us *Librn*, Diane Thorn
Friends of the Library Group
FERNDALE BRANCH, 2222 Main St, PO Box 1209, Ferndale, 98248. SAN 363-5759. Tel: 360-384-3647. FAX: 360-384-6224. Web Site: www.wcls.lib.wa.us. *Librn*, Dave Menard
Friends of the Library Group
ISLAND, PO Box 1, Lummi Island, 98262. SAN 363-5740. Tel: 360-75 7145. FAX: 360-758-7145. Web Site: www.wcls.lib.wa.us. *Librn*, Karl Tucker
Friends of the Library Group
LYNDEN BRANCH, Fourth & Grover Sts, Lynden, 98264. SAN 363-59 Tel: 360-354-4883. FAX: 360-354-3149. Web Site: www.wcls.lib.wa.us *Librn*, Lizz Roberts
Friends of the Library Group
MAPLE FALLS BRANCH, PO Box 316, Maple Falls, 98266. SAN 363 5848. Tel: 360-599-2020. FAX: 360-599-2020. Web Site: www.wcls.lib.wa.us. *Librn*, Georgina Furlong-Head
Friends of the Library Group
POINT ROBERTS BRANCH, Community Center, PO Box 970, Point Roberts, 98281. SAN 363-6003. Tel: 604-945-5424. FAX: 604-945-542 Web Site: www.wcls.lib.wa.us. *Librn*, Kris Lomedico
Friends of the Library Group
SUMAS BRANCH, PO Box 215, Sumas, 98295. SAN 363-6062. Tel: 36 988-2501. FAX: 360-988-2501. Web Site: www.wcls.lib.wa.us. *Librn*, Penny Leenders
Friends of the Library Group
Bookmobiles: 1

BOTHELL

S ADVANCED TECHNOLOGY LABORATORIES LIBRARY,* 22100 Bothell Everett Hwy, PO Box 3003, 98041-3003. SAN 323-5645. Tel: 42 487-7476. FAX: 425-485-6080. *Librn*, Theresa Men; Staff 1 (MLS 1)
Library Holdings: Bk Titles 2,000; Per Subs 300

BREMERTON

L HARRISON MEMORIAL HOSPITAL, Robert S Frech Health Science Library, 2520 Cherry Ave, 98310. SAN 327-7062. Tel: 360-792-6500. FA 360-792-6515. *Librn*, Dan Nolan; Staff 2 (MLS 1, Non-MLS 1)
Apr 1998-Mar 1999 Mats Exp $65,000, Books $5,000, Per/Ser (Incl. Acc Fees) $30,000, Micro $10,000. Sal $44,984 (Prof $27,984)
Library Holdings: Bk Vols 1,300; Bk Titles 900; Per Subs 185

S KITSAP COUNTY HISTORICAL SOCIETY, Museum Library, 280 Fou St, PO Box 903, 98337. SAN 327-4292. Tel: 360-479-6226. FAX: 360-4 9294. E-Mail: kchsm@telebyte.net. Web Site: www.waynes.net/kchsm/. *Adminr*, Pamela Buckingham; *Archivist*, Carolyn McClurkan; Staff 4 (ML 1, Non-MLS 3)
Founded 1948
Library Holdings: Bk Titles 2,000
Special Collections: Kitsap County; Washington State

P KITSAP REGIONAL LIBRARY, (KRL), 1301 Sylvan Way, 98310-3498. SAN 363-6097. Tel: 360-405-9100, 360-405-9158. FAX: 360-405-9128. E-Mail: admin@krl.org. Web Site: www.krl.org. *Dir*, Ellen Newberg; *Cat*, Anne Ross; *Coll Develop*, Gail Goodrick; *Ch Servs*, Carol Schuyler; *Coll Develop*, Martha Knappe; *Br Coordr*, Robin Cameron; *Head, Info Serv, Head Ref*, Sara Scribner
Founded 1955. Pop 229,400; Circ 1,925,361
Library Holdings: Bk Vols 452,103; Bk Titles 203,277; Per Subs 1,270; High Interest/Low Vocabulary Bk Vols 193; Bks on Deafness & Sign Lan 115
Subject Interests: Consumer health, Gardening, How-to, Local history, Pacific Northwest
Automation Activity & Vendor Info: (Acquisitions) epixtech, inc.; (Cataloging) epixtech, inc.; (Circulation) epixtech, inc.; (OPAC) epixtech, inc.; (Serials) epixtech, inc.
Database Vendor: epixtech, inc.
Publications: KRL News (weekly newsletter)
Partic in OCLC Online Computer Library Center, Inc
Friends of the Library Group

Branches: 8
BAINBRIDGE ISLAND BRANCH, 1270 Madison Ave N, Bainbridge Island, 98110. SAN 363-6127. Tel: 206-842-4162. FAX: 206-780-5310. Web Site: www.krl.org. *Librn*, Cynthia Harrison
Circ 338,292
Friends of the Library Group
BREMERTON BRANCH, 612 Fifth St, 98337. SAN 363-6135. Tel: 360-377-3955. FAX: 360-479-8206. Web Site: www.krl.org. *Librn*, Karen Liljegren
Circ 89,995
Friends of the Library Group
CENTRAL LIBRARY (HQ), 1301 Sylvan Way, 98310. Tel: 360-377-7601. FAX: 360-405-9128. Web Site: www.krl.org. *Librn*, Sandra Carlson
Circ 488,927
Friends of the Library Group
KINGSTON BRANCH, 11212 State Hwy 104, PO Box 519, Kingston, 98346. SAN 363-6240. Tel: 360-297-3330. FAX: 360-297-3330. Web Site: www.krl.org. *Librn*, Arlene Thompson
Circ 72,034
Friends of the Library Group
MANCHESTER BRANCH, 8067 E Main St, Manchester, 98353. SAN 363-6275. Tel: 360-871-3921. FAX: 360-871-3236. Web Site: www.krl.org. *Librn*, Cheryl McCulloch
Circ 59,748
Friends of the Library Group
PORT ORCHARD BRANCH, 87 Sidney St, Port Orchard, 98366. SAN 363-6151. Tel: 360-876-2224. FAX: 360-876-9588. Web Site: www.krl.org. *Librn*, Linda Thompson
Circ 300,888
Friends of the Library Group
POULSBO BRANCH, 700 N E Lincoln St, Poulsbo, 98370. SAN 363-6186. Tel: 360-779-2915. FAX: 360-779-1051. Web Site: www.krl.org. *Librn*, Susan Lavin
Circ 243,961
Friends of the Library Group
SILVERDALE BRANCH, 3450 NW Carlton, PO Box 1068, Silverdale, 98383. SAN 363-6305. Tel: 360-692-2779. FAX: 360-698-7702. Web Site: www.krl.org. *Librn*, Cheri Mathisen
Circ 235,685
Friends of the Library Group
Bookmobiles: 1

OLYMPIC COLLEGE, (HL), Haselwood Library, 1600 Chester Ave, 98337. SAN 317-4891. Tel: 360-475-7250. Reference Tel: 360-475-7252. FAX: 360-475-7261. Web Site: www.oc.ctc.edu. *Dean of Libr*, Ruth M Ross; E-Mail: rross@oc.ctc.edu; *Cat, Tech Servs*, Judy Cunneen; E-Mail: jcunneen@oc.ctc.edu; *ILL, Ref*, Dianne Moore; Staff 6 (MLS 6)
Founded 1946. Highest Degree: Associate
Library Holdings: Bk Vols 59,281; Bk Titles 53,267; Per Subs 392
Special Collections: Mountaineering & Outdoor Literature (George W Martin Coll)
Automation Activity & Vendor Info: (Acquisitions) Endeavor; (Cataloging) Endeavor; (Circulation) Endeavor; (Course Reserve) Endeavor; (ILL) Endeavor; (OPAC) Endeavor; (Serials) Endeavor
Database Vendor: ProQuest
Partic in OCLC

UNITED STATES NAVY
ENGINEERING LIBRARY, Puget Sound Naval Shipyard, Code 1143, 98314-5001. SAN 363-6399. Tel: 360-476-2767. FAX: 360-476-4667. *Librn*, Marilyn A Drengson
Founded 1936
Library Holdings: Bk Titles 20,000; Per Subs 150
Subject Interests: Bus, Electrical, Electronic, Marine, Mechanical engineering, Metallurgy, Mgt, Naval archit, Navy hist, Navy policy
NAVAL HOSPITAL LIBRARY, Boone Rd, 98312-1898. SAN 363-6429. Tel: 360-475-4316. FAX: 360-475-4324. *Librn*, Jane Easley; E-Mail: easleym@pnw.med.navy.mil
Founded 1947
Library Holdings: Bk Vols 1,600; Per Subs 220
Partic in Dialog Corporation; OCLC
RESOURCE CENTER, Naval Station Bremerton, 120 S Dewey St, 98314-5000. SAN 363-6364. Tel: 360-476-3178. FAX: 360-476-2908. E-Mail: resource@psnsmwr.org. Web Site: www.psnsmwr.org.
Library Holdings: Bk Vols 7,900; Per Subs 70
Subject Interests: Naval hist

EWSTER

BREWSTER PUBLIC LIBRARY,* 17 S Third St, PO Box 280, 98812-0280. SAN 317-4905. Tel: 509-689-4046. FAX: 509-689-4046. *Librn*, Judy Johnston
Pop 1,000; Circ 8,050
Library Holdings: Bk Vols 15,000; Per Subs 10
Friends of the Library Group

BURLINGTON

P BURLINGTON PUBLIC LIBRARY, 900 E Fairhaven Ave, 98233-1998. SAN 317-4913. Tel: 360-755-0760. FAX: 360-755-0717. Web Site: www.ci.burlington.wa.us/library/bpublib.htm, www.sos.net/home/burlpl/bplib.htm. *Librn*, M Darlene Maloy; E-Mail: darlene@ci.burlington.wa.us; *Ch Servs*, Lisa Anderson; *Circ, Syst Coordr*, Janet Baize; E-Mail: janet@ci.burlington.wa.us; *ILL, Ref*, Barbara Bostrom; *Info Res*, Janice Burwash; *Tech Servs*, Virginia Crandall
Founded 1910. Pop 5,700; Circ 72,500
Jan 2000-Dec 2000 Income Locally Generated Income $273,700. Mats Exp $29,000. Sal $162,500 (Prof $43,000)
Library Holdings: Bk Vols 32,000; Per Subs 121
Subject Interests: NW mat
Automation Activity & Vendor Info: (Cataloging) epixtech, inc.; (Circulation) epixtech, inc.
Partic in OCLC; OCLC Online Computer Library Center, Inc
Friends of the Library Group

CAMAS

P CAMAS PUBLIC LIBRARY, 421 NE Franklin St, 98607. SAN 317-4921. Tel: 360-834-4692. FAX: 360-834-0199. Web Site: www.swwcn.org/clark/camas/home. *Dir*, David Zavortink; E-Mail: dzavor@pacifier.com; *Assoc Dir*, Sharon Stack; Staff 9 (MLS 1, Non-MLS 8)
Founded 1929. Pop 11,300; Circ 184,000
Jan 1999-Dec 1999 Income (Main Library Only) City $674,400. Mats Exp $87,150, Books $65,730, Per/Ser (Incl. Access Fees) $8,520, Presv $300, Other Print Mats $1,600, Electronic Ref Mat (Incl. Access Fees) $11,000. Sal $338,180 (Prof $57,900)
Library Holdings: Bk Vols 62,500; Bk Titles 52,500; Per Subs 200
Subject Interests: Pacific Northwest
Automation Activity & Vendor Info: (Cataloging) epixtech, inc.; (Circulation) epixtech, inc.; (OPAC) epixtech, inc.
Database Vendor: epixtech, inc., IAC - Info Trac, ProQuest
Function: Some telephone reference
Partic in OCLC
Friends of the Library Group

CASTLE ROCK

P CASTLE ROCK PUBLIC LIBRARY, 137 Cowlitz St W, PO Box 1350, 98611. SAN 317-4948. Tel: 360-274-6961. FAX: 360-274-4876. E-Mail: rocklib@hotmail.com. *Dir*, Vicki Velander; *Asst Librn, Assoc Dir*, Connie Amsbury
Founded 1912. Pop 2,500; Circ 21,000
Jan 1999-Dec 1999 Mats Exp Books $26,400
Library Holdings: Bk Vols 16,300
Subject Interests: Genealogy, Local history
Database Vendor: ProQuest
Function: Photocopies available
Friends of the Library Group

CATHLAMET

P CATHLAMET CITY LIBRARY, 100 Main St, PO Box 335, 98612-0335. SAN 321-463X. Tel: 360-795-3254. *Librn*, Noreen Holten
Founded 1929. Pop 2,000; Circ 10,129
Library Holdings: Bk Titles 10,300; Per Subs 25

CENTRALIA

J CENTRALIA COLLEGE, 600 W Locust St, 98531. SAN 317-4956. Tel: 360-736-9391, Ext 241. Circulation Tel: 360-736-9391, Ext 241. FAX: 360-330-7509. E-Mail: reference@centralia.ctc.edu. Web Site: www.library.centralia.ctc.edu. *Dir*, Philip A Meany; E-Mail: pmeany@centralia.ctc.edu; *Librn*, Stephanie Carter; Tel: 360-736-9391, Ext 615, E-Mail: scarter@centralia.ctc.edu; *Librn*, Judith V Metcalf; Tel: 360-736-9391, Ext 423, E-Mail: jmetcalf@centralia.ctc.edu; *Librn*, Margaret Snyder; E-Mail: msnyder@centralia.ctc.edu; *Tech Servs*, Hyesoo Albright; Tel: 360-736-9391, Ext 421, E-Mail: halbright@centralia.ctc.edu; *Tech Servs*, Darlene J Rahn; Tel: 360-736-9391, Ext 350, E-Mail: drahn@centralia.ctc.edu; Staff 6 (MLS 4, Non-MLS 2)
Founded 1925. Enrl 1,803; Fac 63; Highest Degree: Associate
Jul 1999-Jun 2000 Income State $359,521. Mats Exp $92,031, Books $24,731, Per/Ser (Incl. Access Fees) $31,650, AV Equip $13,800, Electronic Ref Mat (Incl. Access Fees) $21,850. Sal $201,501 (Prof $142,818)
Library Holdings: Bk Vols 34,156; Bk Titles 32,581; Per Subs 1,868
Special Collections: Centralia Massacre Coll
Automation Activity & Vendor Info: (Cataloging) Endeavor; (Circulation) Endeavor; (Course Reserve) Endeavor; (ILL) Endeavor; (Media Booking) Endeavor; (OPAC) Endeavor; (Serials) Endeavor
Database Vendor: Ebsco - EbscoHost, OCLC - First Search, ProQuest
Partic in OCLC; OCLC Online Computer Library Center, Inc

S THE CHRONICLE LIBRARY, 321 N Pearl, 98531-4387. (Mail add: PO Box 580, 98531-0580), SAN 375-3085. Tel: 360-736-3311. FAX: 360-736-4796. *Chief Librn*, Linda Stewart; Tel: 360-807-8225, E-Mail: lstewart@chronline.com
Library Holdings: Bk Vols 100
Special Collections: Fiche & film dating back to 1890

CHEHALIS

S LEWIS COUNTY HISTORICAL MUSEUM LIBRARY,* 599 NW Front Way, 98532. SAN 370-3754. Tel: 360-748-0831. E-Mail: lchm@myhome.net. *Librn*, Margaret Langus; *Librn*, Margaret Shields
Library Holdings: Bk Vols 150
Subject Interests: Artifacts, Directories, Displays, Genealogy, Local county hist, Local newspaper data, Photographs, Tools

GL LEWIS COUNTY LAW LIBRARY,* County Courthouse, 360 NW North St, 98532. SAN 317-4964. Tel: 360-748-9121. *Librn*, Louise Amell
Library Holdings: Bk Titles 12,000

CHENEY

C EASTERN WASHINGTON UNIVERSITY, John F Kennedy Memorial Library, 816 F St, 100LIB, 99004-2453. SAN 363-6453. Tel: 509-359-2264. Interlibrary Loan Service Tel: 509-359-2492. Circulation Tel: 509-359-7884. Reference Tel: 509-359-2263. FAX: 509-359-6456. Web Site: www.library.ewu.edu. *Dean of Libr*, Patricia M Kelley; Tel: 509-359-2264, Fax: 509-359-4840, E-Mail: patricia.kelley@mail.ewu.edu; *Head, Info Serv, Publ Servs*, Dave Nelson; Tel: 509-359-7909, Fax: 509-359-6456, E-Mail: dnelson@ewu.edu; *Head Tech Servs*, Carolynne Myall; Tel: 509-359-6967, Fax: 509-359-2476, E-Mail: cmyall@ewu.edu; *Coll Develop*, Theophil Otto; Tel: 509-359-7895, E-Mail: totto@ewu.edu; *Adminr*, Pat Ryan; Tel: 509-359-2306, Fax: 509-359-4840, E-Mail: pat.ryan@mail.ewu.edu; Staff 45 (MLS 12, Non-MLS 33)
Founded 1890. Enrl 8,419; Fac 560; Highest Degree: Master
Jul 1999-Jun 2000 Income (Main Library and Branch Library) $3,655,695. Mats Exp $1,052,310, Books $315,181, Per/Ser (Incl. Access Fees) $731,560, Presv $31,563. Sal $2,062,346 (Prof $768,380)
Library Holdings: Bk Vols 541,327; Bk Titles 357,276; Per Subs 6,429
Subject Interests: Applied sci, Behav sci, Bus educ, Education, Music, Sci, Soc sci
Special Collections: Northwest History, bks, micro
Automation Activity & Vendor Info: (Cataloging) Innovative Interfaces Inc.; (Circulation) Innovative Interfaces Inc.; (Media Booking) Innovative Interfaces Inc.; (OPAC) Innovative Interfaces Inc.; (Serials) Innovative Interfaces Inc.
Database Vendor: OCLC - First Search, ProQuest, Silverplatter Information Inc.
Partic in Wash Coop Libr Project
Special Services for the Blind - Kurzweil Reading Machine
Friends of the Library Group
Departmental Libraries:
COOPERATIVE ACADEMIC LIBRARY SERVICES (CALS), 668 N Riverpoint Blvd, Box C, 1RPT, Spokane, 99202-1677. SAN 328-9834. Tel: 509-358-7930. Circulation Tel: 509-358-7930. Reference Tel: 509-358-7930. FAX: 509-358-7928. Web Site: www.library.ewu.edu. *Head of Libr*, Kathleen Ann Schwanz; Tel: 509-358-7925, E-Mail: schwanz@wsu.edu; *Librn*, Henrietta Pew; Tel: 509-358-7929, E-Mail: hpew@ewu.edu; *Publ Servs*, Lydia M McNulty; Tel: 509-358-7926, E-Mail: mcnulty@wsu.edu; *Publ Servs*, Michelanne Adams; Tel: 509-358-7931, E-Mail: madams@ewu.edu; *ILL*, Dee J Rodgers; Tel: 509-358-7927, E-Mail: rodgers@wsu.edu; *Ser*, Lavada J Smith; E-Mail: ljsmith@mail.wsu.edu; Staff 2 (MLS 1, Non-MLS 1)
Founded 1993. Highest Degree: Master
Library Holdings: Per Subs 200
Subject Interests: Architecture, Business, Health sciences, Health servs admin, Public admin
Database Vendor: Lexis-Nexis, OCLC - First Search, ProQuest
Function: ILL limited, Reference services available, Research library
Partic in Wash Coop Libr Project
Friends of the Library Group

CHEWELAH

P CHEWELAH PUBLIC LIBRARY,* E 301 Clay Ave, PO Box 87, 99109-0087. SAN 317-4972. Tel: 509-935-6805. FAX: 509-935-4564. E-Mail: chewlib@theofficenet.com. *Librn*, Pat Thompson; *Asst Librn*, J Andrews
Founded 1914. Pop 2,012; Circ 57,000
Library Holdings: Bk Vols 33,000; Per Subs 70
Special Collections: State History
Friends of the Library Group

CLARKSTON

P ASOTIN COUNTY LIBRARY, 417 Sycamore St, 99403-2666. SAN 31 4980. Tel: 509-758-5454. FAX: 509-751-1460. E-Mail: admin@aclibrary *Dir*, Gail Hanowell; Staff 11 (MLS 2, Non-MLS 9)
Founded 1902
Library Holdings: Bk Titles 44,000; Per Subs 111
Subject Interests: NW hist
Database Vendor: GaleNet, ProQuest
Partic in Valnet
Friends of the Library Group

CLE ELUM

P CARPENTER MEMORIAL LIBRARY,* 302 Pennsylvania Ave, 98922-1196. SAN 317-4999. Tel: 509-674-2313. FAX: 509-674-2313. E-Mail: cml@cleelum.com. Web Site: www.eburg.com/~cml. *Librn*, Debby DeSc
Founded 1978. Pop 4,500; Circ 18,400
Jan 1997-Dec 1998 Income $37,300, City $24,000, County $13,000, Loc Generated Income $300. Mats Exp $3,500, Books $3,000, Per/Ser (Incl. Access Fees) $500. Sal $18,706
Library Holdings: Bk Titles 12,500; Per Subs 12
Subject Interests: Health, Nutrition, Wash State facts
Special Collections: Pacific Northwest History (Northwest Book Coll)
Partic in OCLC
Friends of the Library Group

COLFAX

P WHITMAN COUNTY RURAL LIBRARY, (WCL), S 102 Main St, 991 1892. SAN 317-5006. Tel: 509-397-4366. FAX: 509-397-6156. Web Site www.whitco.lib.wa.us. *Dir*, Kristie Kirkpatrick; E-Mail: kirkpatr@colfax.com; *Publ Servs*, Cindy Wigen; *Ch Servs, YA Servs*, Jeana Obom; Staff 5 (Non-MLS 5)
Founded 1945. Pop 15,297; Circ 150,000
Jan 1999-Dec 1999 Income $507,070. Mats Exp $50,000, Books $33,70 Per/Ser (Incl. Access Fees) $3,500. Sal $272,000
Library Holdings: Bk Vols 78,000; Bk Titles 72,000
Subject Interests: Local history
Database Vendor: epixtech, inc.
Partic in Palouse Area Library Information Services
Friends of the Library Group

COLLEGE PLACE

CR WALLA WALLA COLLEGE, (PML), Peterson Memorial Library, 104 S Adams, 99324. SAN 317-5014. Tel: 509-527-2133. Reference Tel: 509-5 2142. FAX: 509-527-2001. Web Site: dewey.wwc.edu/. *Dir Libr Serv*, Carolyn Gaskell; Tel: 509-527-2107, E-Mail: gaskca@wwc.edu; *Branch Mgr*, Bruce McClay; Tel: 503-251-7306, E-Mail: mcclbr@wwc.edu; *Ref*, Violet Maynard-Reid; Tel: 509-527-2142, Fax: 509-527-2192, E-Mail: maynvi@wwc.edu; *Per*, Carol Morse; Tel: 509-527-2684, E-Mail: morsca wwc.edu; *Publ Servs*, Carolyn Clark; Tel: 509-527-2169, E-Mail: clarshe wwc.edu; *Tech Servs*, Mark Copsey; Tel: 509-527-2203, E-Mail: copsma wwc.edu; Staff 11 (MLS 6, Non-MLS 5)
Founded 1892. Enrl 1,616; Fac 128; Highest Degree: Master
Jul 1999-Jun 2000 Income Parent Institution $972,170. Mats Exp $356,9 Books $123,218, Per/Ser (Incl. Access Fees) $150,459, Presv $5,027, Mi $24,954, Electronic Ref Mat (Incl. Access Fees) $51,309. Sal $533,355 ($217,301)
Library Holdings: Bk Vols 191,584; Bk Titles 128,747; Per Subs 1,000
Subject Interests: Behav sci, Business, Education, History, Music, Natur science, Soc sci
Special Collections: Denominational History
Automation Activity & Vendor Info: (Acquisitions) Innovative Interface Inc.; (Cataloging) Innovative Interfaces Inc.; (Circulation) Innovative Interfaces Inc.; (Course Reserve) LS 2000; (Media Booking) Innovative Interfaces Inc.; (OPAC) LS 2000; (Serials) MultiLIS
Database Vendor: Ebsco - EbscoHost, OCLC - First Search, ProQuest, Silverplatter Information Inc.
Publications: Idea Starters; InfoQuest (self-guided tours); Peterson Parchment (Newsletter); PML LIbrary Information (booklet); Term Paper Sources (leaflets)
Function: Business archives
Partic in Adventist Librs Info Coop; Northwest Association of Private Colleges & Universities Libraries; OCLC Online Computer Library Cente Inc
See also Portland, OR

COLVILLE

P COLVILLE PUBLIC LIBRARY,* 195 S Oak, 99114-2845. SAN 317-50 Tel: 509-684-6620. FAX: 509-684-3911. E-Mail: colville.library@plix.cor *Librn*, Beth E Carr
Pop 4,760; Circ 77,531
1997-1998 Income $140,119. Mats Exp $28,175. Sal $74,962

Subject Interests: Northwest
Special Collections: Genealogy
Partic in OCLC
Open Tues & Wed 11-8, Thurs & Fri 11-6, Sat 11-4

CRETE

CONCRETE PUBLIC LIBRARY, 45672 D St & Main St, PO Box 28, 98237-0028. SAN 317-5030. Tel: 360-853-8950. FAX: 360-853-8002. *Librn*, Robin Wood
Circ 6,968
1998-1999 Income $15,694, City $7,694, County $4,000, Other $115. Mats Exp Books $1,482. Sal $6,720
Library Holdings: Bk Vols 8,873

ENPORT

DAVENPORT PUBLIC LIBRARY,* 411 Morgan St, PO Box 1169, 99122. SAN 317-5049. Tel: 509-725-4355. E-Mail: davenportlibrary@sisna.com. *Librn*, Sharon Brower
Founded 1926. Pop 1,739; Circ 13,101
1998-1999 Income $33,948, City $20,022, Locally Generated Income $721, Other $2,098. Mats Exp $6,500, Books $5,162, Per/Ser (Incl. Access Fees) $409
Library Holdings: Bk Vols 28,000; Per Subs 15
Special Collections: Area Newspapers, 1893-present, micro & hardcopy

TON

DAYTON MEMORIAL LIBRARY,* 111 S Third, PO Box 74, 99328-0074. SAN 317-5057. Tel: 509-382-4131. E-Mail: dml@bmi.net. *Librn*, Lynn Williams; *Asst Librn*, Sue Hagfeldt
Founded 1925. Circ 18,574
1997-1998 Income $27,200. Mats Exp $15,000
Library Holdings: Bk Vols 16,500; Bk Titles 14,341; Per Subs 52
Open Mon-Thurs 3-5 & 7-9, Sat 10-2
Friends of the Library Group

MOINES

HIGHLINE COMMUNITY COLLEGE LIBRARY,* 2400 S 240th St, MS 25-4 PO Box 98000, 98198-9800. SAN 317-5456. Tel: 206-878-3710, Ext 3230. FAX: 206-870-3744. Web Site: www.flightline.highline.ctc.edu/library/. *Dean*, Marie Zimmermann; Tel: 206-870-3714, E-Mail: mzimmerm@hcc.ctc.edu; *Librn*, Karen Fernandez; Tel: 206-878-3710, Ext 3809, Fax: 206-870-3776, E-Mail: kfernand@hcc.ctc.edu; *Librn*, Dana Franks; Tel: 206-878-3710, Ext 3240, Fax: 206-870-3776, E-Mail: dfranks@hcc.ctc.edu; *Coll Develop*, Monica Luce; Staff 16 (MLS 5, Non-MLS 11)
Founded 1961. Circ 41,500; Enrl 5,000; Fac 132; Highest Degree: Associate
Jul 1998-Jun 1999 Income State $604,030. Mats Exp $111,400, Books $27,000, Per/Ser (Incl. Access Fees) $38,000, Micro $5,600, AV Equip $12,000, Other Print Mats $12,700, Electronic Ref Mat (Incl. Access Fees) $16,100. Sal $510,375 (Prof $213,354)
Library Holdings: Bk Vols 91,000; Bk Titles 76,000; Per Subs 450; High Interest/Low Vocabulary Bk Vols 160; Spec Interest Per Sub 30; Bks on Deafness & Sign Lang 100
Subject Interests: Law, Native Americans
Automation Activity & Vendor Info: (Acquisitions) Endeavor; (Cataloging) Endeavor; (Circulation) Endeavor; (Course Reserve) Endeavor; (OPAC) Endeavor; (Serials) Endeavor
Partic in OCLC Online Computer Library Center, Inc

STSOUND

ORCAS ISLAND LIBRARY DISTRICT, 500 Rose St, 98245-9453. Tel: 360-376-4985. FAX: 360-376-5750. Web Site: www.orcaslibrary.org. *Dir*, Victoria Paker; E-Mail: v.paker@orcaslibrary.org
Library Holdings: Bk Vols 30,000; Per Subs 50
Automation Activity & Vendor Info: (Acquisitions) epixtech, inc.; (Cataloging) epixtech, inc.; (Circulation) epixtech, inc.

MONDS

PUGET SOUND CHRISTIAN COLLEGE LIBRARY, 410 Fourth Ave N, 98020. SAN 317-5073. Tel: 425-775-8686. Reference Tel: 425-775-8686, Ext 256. FAX: 425-775-8688. Web Site: www.pscc.edu. *Librn*, Thomas Joseph; E-Mail: tjoseph@pscc.edu; *Ref*, Gunvor K Olson; E-Mail: golson@pscc.edu; Staff 7 (MLS 2, Non-MLS 5)
Founded 1950. Enrl 210
Sep 1999-Aug 2000 Mats Exp $13,000, Per/Ser (Incl. Access Fees) $5,500, Presv $500, Other Print Mats $7,500. Sal $71,032 (Prof $57,772)
Library Holdings: Bk Vols 37,000; Bk Titles 36,000; Per Subs 134
Subject Interests: Religion
Partic in Christian Libr Asn

ELLENSBURG

C CENTRAL WASHINGTON UNIVERSITY LIBRARY, (CWU), 400 E Eighth Ave, 98926-7548. SAN 317-5081. Tel: 509-963-1901. Interlibrary Loan Service Tel: 509-963-1033. Circulation Tel: 509-963-3662. Reference Tel: 509-963-1021. FAX: 509-963-3684. E-Mail: library@www.lib.cwu.edu. Web Site: www.lib.cwu.edu. *Dean of Libr*, Dr Gary A Lewis; *Cat*, Daniel CannCasciato; *Circ*, Zilpha Nickerson; *Coll Develop*, Patrick McLaughlin; *Doc*, Thomas Yeh; *ILL*, *Ref*, Gerard Hogan; *Per*, *Ser*, Kirsten Tozer; *Syst Coordr*, John Creech; Staff 14 (MLS 14)
Founded 1891. Enrl 7,123; Fac 327; Highest Degree: Master
Jul 1998-Jun 1999 Mats Exp $771,830, Books $229,855, Per/Ser (Incl. Access Fees) $448,576, Presv $16,966, Electronic Ref Mat (Incl. Access Fees) $76,433. Sal $1,466,876 (Prof $680,745)
Library Holdings: Bk Vols 536,583; Per Subs 1,667
Automation Activity & Vendor Info: (OPAC) Innovative Interfaces Inc.
Friends of the Library Group

P ELLENSBURG PUBLIC LIBRARY, 209 N Ruby St, 98926-3338. SAN 317-509X. Tel: 509-962-7250. FAX: 509-962-7295. E-Mail: epl@eburg.com. Web Site: epl.eburg.com. *Dir*, Celeste Kline; Tel: 509-962-7252, E-Mail: klinec@epl.eburg.com; *Ch Servs*, Jennifer Merry; E-Mail: merryj@epl.eburg.com; *Ch Servs*, Josephine Yaba; E-Mail: yabaj@epl.eburg.com; *Circ*, Ken Paschen; E-Mail: paschenk@epl.eburg.com; Staff 13 (MLS 2, Non-MLS 11)
Founded 1910. Pop 15,000
Jan 2000-Dec 2000 Income $464,692, City $371,492, County $59,000, Locally Generated Income $34,200. Mats Exp $76,500, Books $49,070, Per/Ser (Incl. Access Fees) $8,030, Micro $500, AV Equip $13,400, Electronic Ref Mat (Incl. Access Fees) $5,500. Sal $254,311 (Prof $81,000)
Library Holdings: Bk Vols 58,700; Bk Titles 52,500; Per Subs 190
Subject Interests: Local history
Special Collections: Local History
Automation Activity & Vendor Info: (Cataloging) epixtech, inc.; (Circulation) epixtech, inc.
Database Vendor: OCLC - First Search, ProQuest
Function: ILL available
Friends of the Library Group

ENUMCLAW

P ENUMCLAW PUBLIC LIBRARY,* 1700 First St, 98022. SAN 317-5103. Tel: 360-825-2938. FAX: 360-825-0825. E-Mail: epl@tx3.com. Web Site: enumclawpubliclibrary.org. *Dir*, Robert Baer; Staff 1 (MLS 1)
Founded 1922. Pop 8,200; Circ 158,000
Library Holdings: Bk Vols 45,000; Per Subs 145
Subject Interests: Local history
Friends of the Library Group

EPHRATA

P EPHRATA PUBLIC LIBRARY,* 45 Alder NW, 98823-1663. SAN 317-5111. Tel: 509-754-3971. FAX: 509-754-3971. E-Mail: ephrata@ncrl.org. *In Charge*, Kay Dirks
Pop 5,326; Circ 57,725
Library Holdings: Bk Vols 25,000; Per Subs 74
Subject Interests: Local history
Special Collections: Grant County Genealogical Society
Partic in OCLC
Branch of North Central Regional Library
Friends of the Library Group

EVERETT

S AGILENT TECHNOLOGIES, (Formerly Hewlett-Packard Company), Lake Stevens Library, 8600 Soper Hill Rd, 98205-1209. SAN 327-4233. Tel: 425-335-2406. FAX: 425-335-2113. E-Mail: lake-stevens_library@agilent.com. *Librn*, Ruth L Van Dyke; E-Mail: ruth_vandyke@agilent.com
Founded 1984
Library Holdings: Bk Vols 2,000
Subject Interests: Electrical engineering
Partic in OCLC Online Computer Library Center, Inc

J EVERETT COMMUNITY COLLEGE, John N Terrey Library - Media Center, 2000 Tower, 98201-1352. SAN 317-5138. Tel: 425-388-9501. Circulation Tel: 425-388-9353. Reference Tel: 425-388-9354. FAX: 425-388-9144. Web Site: www.evcc.ctc.edu/depts/library. *Dean of Libr*, Jeanne Leader; Tel: 425-388-9502, E-Mail: jleader@ctc.edu; *Tech Servs*, Christie Nelson; Tel: 425-388-9489, E-Mail: cnelson@ctc.edu; *Ad Servs, Media Spec*, Jeanie Goodhope; Tel: 425-388-9348, E-Mail: jgoodhop@ctc.edu; *Publ Servs*, David Rash; Tel: 425-388-9494, E-Mail: drash@ctc.edu; *Coll Develop*, Helen Feeney; Tel: 425-388-9492, E-Mail: hfeeney@ctc.edu
Founded 1948
1998-1999 Mats Exp $88,937, Books $45,496, Per/Ser (Incl. Access Fees) $27,366, Electronic Ref Mat (Incl. Access Fees) $16,075. Sal $541,269 (Prof $241,020)

Library Holdings: Bk Vols 42,281; Bk Titles 37,492
Automation Activity & Vendor Info: (OPAC) Endeavor
Database Vendor: ProQuest
Publications: Bookmarks; Brochure; Campus Newsletter; Search Guides
Partic in OCLC Online Computer Library Center, Inc

P EVERETT PUBLIC LIBRARY, 2702 Hoyt Ave, 98201-3556. SAN 317-5162. Tel: 425-257-8010. FAX: 425-257-8017. Web Site: www.epls.org. *Dir*, Mark A Nesse; E-Mail: mnesse@ci.everett.wa.us; *Asst Dir, Coll Develop, Ref*, Eileen Simmons; E-Mail: esimmons@ci.everett.wa.us; *ILL*, Joan Blacker; E-Mail: jblacker@ci.everett.wa.us; *Ch Servs*, Dorothy Matsui; E-Mail: dmatsui@ci.everett.wa.us; *Tech Servs*, Pat Bennett; E-Mail: pbennett@ci.everett.wa.us; *Doc*, Sue Selmer; E-Mail: sselmer@ci.everett.wa.us; *Bkmobile Coordr*, Theresa Gemmer; E-Mail: tgemmer@ci.everett.wa.us; *Circ*, Fran Habicht; E-Mail: fhabicht@ci.everett.wa.us; Staff 21 (MLS 18, Non-MLS 3)
Founded 1894. Pop 84,330
Jan 2000-Dec 2000 Income (Main Library and Branch Library) $3,663,411, State $15,324, City $3,602,087, Locally Generated Income $46,000. Mats Exp $472,130, Books $355,630, Per/Ser (Incl. Access Fees) $56,950, AV Equip $50,850, Electronic Ref Mat (Incl. Access Fees) $8,700. Sal $2,811,821
Library Holdings: Bk Vols 361,221; Bk Titles 153,873; Per Subs 933; Bks on Deafness & Sign Lang 192
Subject Interests: Architecture, Art, Bus, Mgt
Special Collections: City of Everett; Fore Edge Books (Baker Coll); Pacific Northwest (Northwest Coll), bk, photo, rec
Automation Activity & Vendor Info: (Acquisitions) epixtech, inc.; (Cataloging) epixtech, inc.; (Circulation) epixtech, inc.
Publications: Annual reports; Journal of Everett & Snohomish County History
Friends of the Library Group
Branches: 1
EVERGREEN, 9512 Evergreen Way, 98204. SAN 375-5916. Tel: 425-257-8260. FAX: 425-257-8265. Web Site: www.epls.org. *Mgr*, Liz Hawkins
Circ 307,543
Bookmobiles: 1

M PROVIDENCE GENERAL HOSPITAL MEDICAL CENTER, Health Sciences Library,* PO Box 1147, 98206. SAN 317-5197. Tel: 425-261-4090. FAX: 425-261-4092. E-Mail: pgmclib@halcyon.com. Web Site: www.halcyon.com/pgmclib. *Librn*, Sue Innes
Founded 1974
Library Holdings: Bk Titles 1,500; Per Subs 250
Subject Interests: Admin, Allied health, Medicine, Nursing
Partic in BRS; Nat Libr of Med; OCLC

GL SNOHOMISH COUNTY LAW LIBRARY,* 3000 Rockefellar, 98201. SAN 317-5200. Tel: 425-388-3010. FAX: 425-388-3020. E-Mail: snocll@wln.com. *Librn*, Carol Best
Founded 1932
Library Holdings: Bk Vols 21,700
Subject Interests: Case law, Statute law

FAIRCHILD AFB

UNITED STATES AIR FORCE
A FAIRCHILD BASE LIBRARY, 2 W Castle St, 99011-9401. SAN 363-6518. Tel: 509-247-5228, 509-247-5556. FAX: 509-247-3365. *Librn*, Sherry Hokanson; E-Mail: sherry.hokanson@fairchild.af.mil; *Ref*, Lisa Love; Staff 6 (MLS 2, Non-MLS 4)
Founded 1950
2000-2000 Income $161,489
Library Holdings: Bk Vols 30,000; Per Subs 200
Subject Interests: Mil sci, Military history, Northwest
Automation Activity & Vendor Info: (Cataloging) EOS; (Circulation) EOS; (OPAC) EOS
Database Vendor: OCLC - First Search
Restriction: Members only
Partic in OCLC Online Computer Library Center, Inc

FEDERAL WAY

S BERGER-ABAM ENGINEERS, Technical Library,* 33301 Ninth Ave S, Ste 300, 98003-2600. SAN 370-8187. Tel: 206-241-2040. FAX: 206-431-2250. Web Site: www.abam.com. *Tech Servs*, Ann Kennedy
Library Holdings: Bk Vols 1,200; Per Subs 20

L BOGLE & GATES LIBRARY & RESEARCH SERVICES,* PO Box 3979, 98063-3979. SAN 317-5928. Tel: 206-682-5151, Ext 3291. FAX: 206-621-2660. E-Mail: bdacres@bogle.com. *Librn*, Bridget E Dacres; *Asst Librn*, Amy Padfield; *Asst Librn*, Curt Robbins; *Asst Librn*, Jan Lawrence; *Asst Librn*, Sandra Edmunds; Staff 7 (MLS 5, Non-MLS 2)
Library Holdings: Bk Vols 36,000
Partic in OCLC

S RHODODENDRON SPECIES FOUNDATION, Lawrence J Pierce Lib 2525 S 336th St, 98003. (Mail add: PO Box 3798, 98063-3798), Tel: 2 838-4646. FAX: 253-838-4686. E-Mail: rsf@halcyon.com. *Librn*, Fran Harrison
Library Holdings: Bk Titles 2,000; Per Subs 15

S WEYERHAEUSER LIBRARY, 32901 Weyerhaeuser Way S, 98003. SA 317-5219. Interlibrary Loan Service Tel: 253-924-3030. FAX: 253-924- *Mgr*, Linda Martinez; Tel: 253-924-6263, E-Mail: linda.martinez@weyerhaeuser.com
Library Holdings: Bk Vols 10,500; Per Subs 692
Subject Interests: Forestry, Paper, Printing, Pulp, Wood
Special Collections: Annual Reports; Trade Publications
Automation Activity & Vendor Info: (Acquisitions) epixtech, inc.; (Cataloging) epixtech, inc.; (Circulation) epixtech, inc.; (OPAC) epixtec inc.; (Serials) epixtech, inc.
Publications: Library Bulletin; New Book List; Quality Improvement Stories Report
Restriction: Not open to public
Partic in OCLC Online Computer Library Center, Inc
Branches:
TECHNICAL INFORMATION CENTER, WTC - TIC, PO Box 2999, Tacoma, 98477-2999. SAN 325-0865. Tel: 253-924-6267. FAX: 253-9 6870. *Publ Servs*, K Ewing; *Mgr*, Linda Martinez; *Publ Servs*, L Parr; *Publ Servs*, S Smith; *Acq*, C S Kartanas; *Cat*, J Baldwin; Staff 11 (MI Non-MLS 4)
Library Holdings: Bk Titles 70,000; Per Subs 475
Subject Interests: Forestry, Graphic art, Logging, Paper, Pulp, Solid products
Publications: Current Awareness List; Patent Digest
Partic in OCLC Online Computer Library Center, Inc

FORT LEWIS

S FORT LEWIS MILITARY MUSEUM,* PO Box 331001, 98433-1001. 317-5235. Tel: 253-967-7206. FAX: 253-966-3029. Web Site: www.lewis.army.mil/. *Curator*, Alan Archambault
Founded 1973
Library Holdings: Bk Vols 600
Subject Interests: Northwest
Special Collections: Development & History of the Military in the Northwest, bks, doc & pers; United States & Foreign Military Artifacts Identification
Reference Library supports our artifact collection & answers questions relevant to Northwest military history

UNITED STATES ARMY
A FORT LEWIS LIBRARY SYSTEM, Bldg 2109, Box 339500, 98433-95 SAN 363-6542. Tel: 253-967-7736. FAX: 253-967-3922. E-Mail: flls@lewis.army.mil. Web Site: www.lewis.army.mil/community/dpca/crd/lib *Dir*, Bonnie Tucker; *Tech Servs*, Marganne Weathers; *Publ Servs*, Catherine Kargacin; Tel: 253-966-1314, E-Mail: kargaci@lewis.army.m *Ref*, Jeremy Marshall; Tel: 253-966-1300, E-Mail: marshal@lewis.army.mil; Staff 30 (MLS 5, Non-MLS 25)
Founded 1942
Library Holdings: Bk Vols 130,000; Per Subs 450
Subject Interests: History, Mil sci
Special Collections: Military Science; Videos, Korean, German, Spani language
Partic in Dialog Corporation; OCLC Online Computer Library Center,

FRIDAY HARBOR

P SAN JUAN ISLAND PUBLIC LIBRARY,* 1010 Guard St, 98250-9612 SAN 317-5243. Tel: 360-378-2798. FAX: 360-378-2706. E-Mail: child@sanjuan.lib.wa.us, info@sanjuan.lib.wa.us, sjlib@rockisland.com. Web Sit www.sanjuan.lib.wa.us. *Asst Librn*, Carrie Eldridge; *Dir*, Kathleen McHa Staff 2 (MLS 2)
Founded 1922. Pop 6,000; Circ 132,000
Jan 1998-Dec 1999 Income $590,000, Federal $31,500, County $6,000, Locally Generated Income $37,500, Other $19,850. Mats Exp $67,700, Books $47,300, Per/Ser (Incl. Access Fees) $9,500, AV Equip $6,900. Sa $210,000 (Prof $96,000)
Library Holdings: Bk Vols 42,000; Per Subs 170
Subject Interests: NW local hist, San Juan Islands
Automation Activity & Vendor Info: (Circulation) epixtech, inc.
Friends of the Library Group

S WHALE MUSEUM, Manfred C Vernon Library, 62 First St N, PO Box 945, 98250. SAN 329-3041. Tel: 360-378-4710. FAX: 360-378-5790. *Exe Dir*, Clark Gilbert McAlpine; *Librn*, Rowann Tallman; *Curator*, Albert Shepard; Staff 1 (Non-MLS 1)
Founded 1979
Library Holdings: Bk Titles 550; Per Subs 10
Subject Interests: Marine mammals, Pacific Northwest
Restriction: Not a lending library

NDVIEW

BLEYHL COMMUNITY LIBRARY,* 311 Division, 98930-1398. SAN 317-5251. Tel: 509-882-9217. E-Mail: grandlib@televar.com. *Librn*, Linda Dunham; *Asst Librn*, Ruth Dirk; Staff 1 (MLS 1)
Founded 1914. Pop 7,169; Circ 41,399
Jan 2000-Dec 2000 Income $178,408, Locally Generated Income $178,408. Mats Exp $19,400, Books $13,000, Per/Ser (Incl. Access Fees) $3,000, AV Equip $1,320, Electronic Ref Mat (Incl. Access Fees) $2,080. Sal $102,583
Library Holdings: Bk Titles 39,803; Per Subs 69; Bks on Deafness & Sign Lang 29
Subject Interests: Agriculture, Spanish
Special Collections: Blanche McLane Cook Art Coll; Local History (Special History of Grandview), bks, pamphlets

NGER

YAKIMA VALLEY REGIONAL LIBRARY, Granger Library, 508 Sunnyside Ave, 98932. Tel: 509-854-1446. Web Site: www.yvrls.lib.wa.us/Granger.html. *Librn*, Nell Barrett
Library Holdings: Bk Vols 12,800; Per Subs 19
Open Mon & Wed 9:30-5, Tues & Thurs 2-8, Sat 2-5

RRINGTON

HARRINGTON PUBLIC LIBRARY,* S 11 Third St, PO Box 496, 99134. SAN 317-5278. Tel: 509-253-4345. FAX: 509-253-4370. E-Mail: library@harrington-wa.com. *Librn*, Vivienne Schultz
Pop 509; Circ 3,677
Library Holdings: Bk Titles 4,731

AQUAH

KING COUNTY LIBRARY SYSTEM, 960 NW Newport Way, 98027. SAN 317-6061. Tel: 206-684-6604 (Admin), 425-369-3200. TDD: 206-684-4494. FAX: 425-369-3255. Web Site: www.kcls.org. *Dir*, Bill Ptacek; Tel: 425-369-3232; *Acq*, Julie Ben-Simon; Tel: 425-369-3205; *Business*, Debbie Nagasawa; Tel: 425-369-3260; *Cat*, Sally Smith; Tel: 425-369-3340; *Ch Servs, YA Servs*, Sally Porter; Tel: 425-369-3224; *Coll Develop*, Barbara Tolliver; Tel: 425-369-3203; *Commun Relations*, Jeanne Thorsen; Tel: 425-369-3450; *Govt Doc*, Linda Fredericks; Tel: 425-450-1782; *Publ Servs*, Bruce Adams; Tel: 206-296-5290; *Publ Servs*, Claudia McCain; Tel: 253-838-3491; *Publ Servs*, Denise Siers; Tel: 425-482-9281; *Reader Servs*, Chapple Langemack; Tel: 425-369-3318
Founded 1943. Pop 1,000,000; Circ 13,000,000
Library Holdings: Bk Vols 3,139,812; Per Subs 10,483
Publications: King County Library System News & Events (monthly newsletter); Omnibus (quarterly materials review)
Member Libraries: King County Library System
Special Services for the Deaf - TDD
Friends of the Library Group
Branches: 47

ALGONA-PACIFIC LIBRARY, 255 Ellingson Rd, Pacific, 98047. SAN 328-9567. Tel: 253-833-3554. FAX: 206-296-5019. Web Site: www.kcls.org. *Mgr*, Donna McMillen
Jan 2000-Dec 2000 Mats Exp $76,159. Sal $229,180
Library Holdings: Bk Titles 55,649; Per Subs 131
Friends of the Library Group

AUBURN BRANCH, 1102 Auburn Way S, Auburn, 98002. SAN 317-4816. Tel: 253-931-3018. FAX: 206-205-6773. Web Site: www.kcls.org. *Mgr Libr*, Fran Wendtland; *YA Servs*, Bonnie Cline; *Ch Servs*, Anita Sheneberger; *Ch Servs*, Terry Hendershott; *Coll Develop, Ref*, Greg Rathbone; *Outreach Serv*, Mary Douglas; Staff 6 (MLS 6)
Founded 1905. Pop 36,000; Circ 250,000
Jan 2000-Dec 2000 Mats Exp $217,602. Sal $217,602
Library Holdings: Bk Vols 95,000; Bk Titles 124,464; Per Subs 369
Subject Interests: Local history, Pac NW hist
Partic in Western Libr Network
Friends of the Library Group

BELLEVUE REGIONAL LIBRARY, 1111 110th NE, Bellevue, 98004. SAN 303-528X. Tel: 425-450-1765. FAX: 425-450-2468. Web Site: www.kcls.org. *Mgr*, Jim King
Jan 2000-Dec 2000 Mats Exp $726,357. Sal $1,816,267
Library Holdings: Bk Titles 642,588; Per Subs 1,047
Friends of the Library Group

BLACK DIAMOND LIBRARY, 24301 Roberts Rd, PO Box 306, Black Diamond, 98010. SAN 328-9583. Tel: 360-886-1105. FAX: 206-296-5042. Web Site: www.kcls.org. *Mgr*, Linda Scoggin
Jan 2000-Dec 2000 Mats Exp $34,347. Sal $155,489
Library Holdings: Bk Titles 22,508; Per Subs 84
Friends of the Library Group

BOTHELL REGIONAL LIBRARY, 18215 98th Ave NE, Bothell, 98011. SAN 328-0837. Tel: 425-486-7811. FAX: 206-296-5043. Web Site: www.kcls.org. *Mgr*, Ruth Bacharach
Jan 2000-Dec 2000 Mats Exp $410,977. Sal $866,918
Library Holdings: Bk Titles 217,257; Per Subs 578
Friends of the Library Group

BOULEVARD PARK, 12015 Roseberg Ave S, Seattle, 98168. SAN 322-7138. Tel: 206-242-8662. FAX: 206-296-5044. Web Site: www.kcls.org. *Mgr*, Gretchen Furber
Jan 2000-Dec 2000 Mats Exp $90,808. Sal $220,049
Library Holdings: Bk Titles 53,035; Per Subs 124
Friends of the Library Group

BURIEN, 14700 Sixth SW, Seattle, 98166. SAN 328-9605. Tel: 206-243-3490. FAX: 206-296-5045. Web Site: www.kcls.org. Mats Exp $282,669
Library Holdings: Bk Titles 195,780; Per Subs 544
Friends of the Library Group

CARNATION LIBRARY, 4804 Tolt Ave, PO Box 1298, Carnation, 98014. SAN 328-9621. Tel: 425-333-4398. TDD: 206-296-5046. FAX: 206-296-5046. Web Site: www.kcls.org. *Mgr Libr*, Darcy L Newman; E-Mail: danewman@kcls.org; Staff 5 (MLS 2, Non-MLS 3)
Founded 1924. Pop 2,000
Jan 2000-Dec 2000 Mats Exp $34,810. Sal $169,829
Library Holdings: Per Subs 80
Database Vendor: epixtech, inc., IAC - Info Trac, IAC - SearchBank, ProQuest
Special Services for the Deaf - TDD
Friends of the Library Group

CEDAR HILLS ALCOHOLISM TREATMENT CENTER, 15900 227th Ave SE, Maple Valley, 98038. SAN 317-5448. Tel: 206-205-6631. FAX: 206-296-8707. *In Charge*, Katie Jones
Library Holdings: Bk Titles 2,043

COVINGTON LIBRARY, 27100 164th Ave SE, Covington, 98042. SAN 373-8485. Tel: 253-630-8761. FAX: 253-205-0787. Web Site: www.kcls.org. *Mgr*, Georgia Lomax
Jan 2000-Dec 2000 Mats Exp $260,666. Sal $667,398
Library Holdings: Bk Titles 148,398; Per Subs 467
Friends of the Library Group

DES MOINES LIBRARY, 21620 11th Ave S, Des Moines, 98198. SAN 328-9648. Tel: 206-824-6066. FAX: 206-296-5047. Web Site: www.kcls.org. *Mgr*, Mike McNamara
2000-2001 Mats Exp $136,819. Sal $412,547
Library Holdings: Bk Titles 85,929; Per Subs 269
Friends of the Library Group

DUVALL LIBRARY, 15619 NE Main St, PO Box 339, Duvall, 98019. SAN 328-9664. Tel: 425-788-1173. FAX: 206-296-7429. Web Site: www.kcls.org. *Mgr*, Ruth McGlauflin
Jan 2000-Dec 2000 Mats Exp $43,651. Sal $103,004
Library Holdings: Bk Titles 38,849; Per Subs 77
Friends of the Library Group

FAIRWOOD, 17009 140th SE, Renton, 98058. SAN 328-9680. Tel: 425-226-0522. FAX: 206-296-8115. Web Site: www.kcls.org. *Mgr*, Bruce Schauer
Jan 2000-Dec 2000 Mats Exp $259,634. Sal $668,980
Library Holdings: Bk Titles 180,640; Per Subs 454
Friends of the Library Group

FALL CITY LIBRARY, 33415 SE 42nd Pl, Fall City, 98024. SAN 328-9702. Tel: 425-222-5951. FAX: 206-296-5048. Web Site: www.kcls.org. *Mgr*, Nan Palmer
Jan 2000-Dec 2000 Mats Exp $37,269. Sal $98,303
Library Holdings: Bk Titles 29,179; Per Subs 95
Friends of the Library Group

FEDERAL WAY 320TH LIBRARY, 848 S 320th St, Federal Way, 98003. SAN 373-8493. Tel: 253-839-0257. FAX: 206-296-5053. Web Site: www.kcls.org. *Mgr*, Marie Metsker
Jan 2000-Dec 2000 Mats Exp $149,459. Sal $388,843
Library Holdings: Bk Titles 94,765; Per Subs 233
Friends of the Library Group

FEDERAL WAY REGIONAL LIBRARY, 34200 First Way S, Federal Way, 98003. SAN 372-0306. Tel: 253-838-3668. FAX: 253-838-3008. Web Site: www.kcls.org. *Mgr*, Judy Renzema
Jan 2000-Dec 2000 Mats Exp $419,668. Sal $885,913
Library Holdings: Bk Titles 218,297; Per Subs 547
Friends of the Library Group

FOSTER LIBRARY, 4060 S 144th, PO Box 68697, Tukwila, 98168. SAN 328-9214. Tel: 206-242-1640. FAX: 206-296-5055. *Mgr*, Sharon Kidd; Staff 12 (MLS 3, Non-MLS 9)
Jan 2000-Dec 2000 Mats Exp $72,645. Sal $227,588
Library Holdings: Bk Titles 50,840; Per Subs 119
Friends of the Library Group

ISSAQUAH LIBRARY, 300 Eighth Ave N, Seattle, 98109. SAN 328-7874. Tel: 425-392-5430. FAX: 206-296-5041. Web Site: www.kcls.org. *Reader Servs*, Chris Livingston; Tel: 206-373-7007, Fax: 206-205-5112
Jan 2000-Dec 2000 Mats Exp $129,537. Sal $490,488
Library Holdings: Bk Titles 89,667; Per Subs 210
Friends of the Library Group

KENMORE, 18138 73rd NE, Bothell, 98011. SAN 328-9230. Tel: 425-486-8747. FAX: 206-296-5056. Web Site: www.kcls.org. *Mgr*, Colleen Brazil
Jan 2000-Dec 2000 Mats Exp $48,296. Sal $173,111
Library Holdings: Bk Titles 26,412; Per Subs 81
Friends of the Library Group

KENT REGIONAL LIBRARY, 212 Second Ave N, Kent, 98032. SAN 328-9257. Tel: 253-859-3330. FAX: 206-296-5060. Web Site: www.kcls.org.

Mgr, Judy Zelter
Jan 2000-Dec 2000 Mats Exp $400,482. Sal $891,624
Library Holdings: Bk Titles 174,088; Per Subs 551
Friends of the Library Group

KING COUNTY JAIL, 500 Fifth Ave, Seattle, 98104. SAN 317-6045. Tel: 206-296-1250. *Head of Libr*, Barbara Massey
Library Holdings: Bk Titles 1,790

KINGSGATE, 12315 NE 143rd, Kirkland, 98034. SAN 328-9273. Tel: 425-821-7686. FAX: 206-296-5061. *Mgr*, Paul Jensen
Jan 2000-Dec 2000 Mats Exp $143,942. Sal $466,914
Library Holdings: Bk Titles 91,819; Per Subs 265
Friends of the Library Group

KIRKLAND LIBRARY, 308 Kirkland Ave, Kirkland, 98033. SAN 328-929X. Tel: 425-822-2459. FAX: 206-296-5062. Web Site: www.kcls.org. *Mgr*, Mary Jane Vinella
Pop 42,000; Circ 500,000
2000-2001 Mats Exp $249,201. Sal $667,019
Library Holdings: Bk Titles 147,628; Per Subs 421
Database Vendor: epixtech, inc.
Friends of the Library Group

LAKE FOREST PARK, 17171 Bothell Way NE, Seattle, 98155. SAN 328-9192. Tel: 206-362-8860. FAX: 206-296-5054. Web Site: www.kcls.org. *Mgr*, Judy Weathers
2000-2001 Mats Exp $68,213. Sal $251,755
Library Holdings: Bk Titles 44,931; Per Subs 113
Friends of the Library Group

LAKE HILLS, 15228 Lake Hills Blvd, Bellevue, 98007. SAN 328-9311. Tel: 425-747-3350. FAX: 206-296-5063. Web Site: www.kcls.org. *Mgr*, Robin Rothschild
2000-2001 Mats Exp $139,532. Sal $449,628
Library Holdings: Bk Titles 87,190; Per Subs 212
Friends of the Library Group

MAPLE VALLEY LIBRARY, 23730 Maple Valley Hwy, Maple Valley, 98038. SAN 328-9338. Tel: 425-432-4620. FAX: 206-296-5018. Web Site: www.kcls.org. *Mgr*, Michele Drovdahl
2000-2001 Mats Exp $68,995. Sal $264,683
Library Holdings: Bk Titles 69,620; Per Subs 214
Friends of the Library Group

MERCER ISLAND, 4400 88th Ave SE, Seattle, 98040. SAN 328-9354. Tel: 206-236-3537. FAX: 206-296-5064. Web Site: www.kcls.org. *Mgr*, Susan Wheeler
2000-2001 Mats Exp $189,079. Sal $397,600
Library Holdings: Bk Titles 102,207; Per Subs 258
Friends of the Library Group

MUCKLESHOOT, 38811 172nd Ave SE, Auburn, 98002. SAN 328-9370. Tel: 253-931-6779. FAX: 206-296-0215. Web Site: www.kcls.org. *Mgr*, Berlinda Adair
2000-Dec 2001 Mats Exp $34,828. Sal $77,948
Library Holdings: Bk Titles 20,665; Per Subs 55
Friends of the Library Group

NEWPORT WAY, 14250 SE Newport Way, Bellvue, 98006. SAN 328-9397. Tel: 425-747-2390. FAX: 206-296-5065. Web Site: www.kcls.org. *Mgr*, Marilee Cogswell
2000-2001 Mats Exp $133,522. Sal $416,807
Library Holdings: Bk Titles 85,916; Per Subs 198
Friends of the Library Group

NORTH BEND LIBRARY, 115 E Fourth, North Bend, 98045. SAN 328-9419. Tel: 425-888-0554. FAX: 206-296-0216. Web Site: www.kcls.org. *Mgr*, Keitha Owen
2000-2001 Mats Exp $135,892. Sal $420,602
Library Holdings: Bk Titles 97,151; Per Subs 229
Friends of the Library Group

NORTH REHABILITATION FACILITY - FIRLANDS, 2002 NE 150th, Seattle, 98155. SAN 328-9613. Tel: 206-296-7671, Ext 225. *Head of Libr*, Ginelle Dickson
Library Holdings: Bk Titles 1,071

REDMOND LIBRARY, 15810 NE 85th, Redmond, 98052. SAN 328-9451. Tel: 425-885-1861. FAX: 206-296-5067. Web Site: www.kcls.org. *Mgr*, Louise Blain
2000-2001 Mats Exp $485,000. Sal $844,629
Library Holdings: Bk Titles 192,112; Per Subs 571
Friends of the Library Group

REGIONAL JUSTICE CENTER, 620 W James, Kent, 98032. SAN 376-933X. Tel: 206-205-2201. FAX: 206-205-2199. *Mgr*, Merry Titus; E-Mail: merry.titus@metrokc.gov; Staff 3 (Non-MLS 3)
Founded 1997
Library Holdings: Bk Titles 296
Restriction: Internal circulation only, Not open to public

RICHMOND BEACH, 2402 NW 195th Pl, Seattle, 98177. SAN 328-9478. Tel: 206-546-3522. FAX: 206-296-5068. Web Site: www.kcls.org. *Mgr*, Anina Sill
2000-2001 Mats Exp $37,273. Sal $126,890
Library Holdings: Bk Titles 28,353; Per Subs 82
Friends of the Library Group

SAMMAMISH LIBRARY, 825 228th Ave NE, Redmond, 98053. SAN 375-6041. Tel: 425-836-8793. FAX: 206-205-9095. Web Site: www.kels.org/samm/sammhome.html. *Mgr*, John Sheller; E-Mail: johnsh@kcls.org; Staff 19 (MLS 4, Non-MLS 15)
Founded 1998
2000-2001 Mats Exp $157,559. Sal $443,047
Library Holdings: Bk Titles 90,117; Per Subs 212
Mem of King County Library System
Friends of the Library Group

SHORELINE, 345 NE 175th, Seattle, 98155. SAN 328-9494. Tel: 206-3 7550. FAX: 206-296-5069. Web Site: www.kcls.org. *Mgr*, Lynda Lock
2000-2001 Mats Exp $314,479. Sal $741,984
Library Holdings: Bk Titles 206,420; Per Subs 467
Friends of the Library Group

SKYKOMISH LIBRARY, 100 Fifth St, Skykomish, 98288. SAN 328-9 Tel: 360-677-2660. FAX: 206-296-0217. Web Site: www.kcls.org. *Mg* Linda Cyrus
2000-2001 Mats Exp $28,253. Sal $46,934
Library Holdings: Bk Titles 12,535; Per Subs 29

SKYWAY, 7614 S 126th, PO Box 78039, Seattle, 98178. SAN 325-119 Tel: 206-772-5541. FAX: 206-296-5070. Web Site: www.kcls.org. *Mg* Barbara Reich
2000-2001 Mats Exp $71,278. Sal $227,690
Library Holdings: Bk Titles 51,246; Per Subs 109
Friends of the Library Group

SNOQUALMIE LIBRARY, 38580 SE River St, PO Box 968, Snoqualm 98065. SAN 328-9532. Tel: 425-888-1223. FAX: 206-296-0218. Web www.kcls.org. *Mgr*, Loretta Herman
2000-2000 Mats Exp $34,808. Sal $99,271
Library Holdings: Bk Vols 72; Bk Titles 24,805
Friends of the Library Group

TUKWILA, 14475 59th S, Tukwila, 98168. SAN 328-9559. Tel: 206-24 5140. FAX: 206-296-5071. Web Site: www.kcls.org. *Mgr*, Sharon Kid
2000-2001 Mats Exp $35,342. Sal $120,454
Library Holdings: Bk Titles 23,111; Per Subs 85
Friends of the Library Group

VALLEY VIEW, 17850 Military Rd S, Seattle, 98188. SAN 328-9575. T 206-242-6044. TDD: 206-242-4335. FAX: 206-296-5072. Web Site: www.kcls.org. *Mgr*, Karen Hardiman
2000-2001 Mats Exp $74,091. Sal $219,697
Library Holdings: Bk Titles 61,016; Per Subs 176
Special Services for the Deaf - TDD
Friends of the Library Group

VASHON ISLAND LIBRARY, 17210 Vashon Hwy SW, Vashon Island, 98070. SAN 328-0853. Tel: 206-463-2069. FAX: 206-296-5073. Web S www.kcls.org. *Mgr*, Hester Kremer; E-Mail: hkremer@kcls.org; Staff 1 (MLS 3, Non-MLS 11)
Founded 1946. Pop 10,800
2000-2001 Mats Exp $122,414. Sal $300,052
Library Holdings: Bk Titles 70,863; Per Subs 221
Friends of the Library Group

WHITE CENTER, 11220 Sixteenth SW, Seattle, 98146. SAN 328-9591. 206-243-0233. FAX: 206-296-5074. Web Site: www.kcls.org. *Mgr*, Pau Warden
2000-2001 Mats Exp $89,669. Sal $254,863
Library Holdings: Bk Titles 76,547; Per Subs 166
Friends of the Library Group

WOODINVILLE LIBRARY, 17105 Avondale Rd NE, Woodinville, 9807 SAN 373-8507. Tel: 425-788-0733. FAX: 206-296-8297. Web Site: www.kcls.org. *Mgr*, Don Julien
2000-2001 Mats Exp $262,071. Sal $611,860
Library Holdings: Bk Titles 137,175; Per Subs 410
Friends of the Library Group

WOODMONT LIBRARY, 26809 Pacific Hwy S, Des Moines, 98198. Te 253-839-0121. *Mgr*, Laurel Steiner
2000-2001 Mats Exp $78,775. Sal $211,084
Library Holdings: Bk Titles 45,666; Per Subs 130

YOUTH SERVICE CENTER, 1211 E Alder, Seattle, 98122. SAN 327-733X. Tel: 206-205-9641. *Mgr*, Jill Morrison

R TRINITY LUTHERAN COLLEGE, (Formerly Lutheran Bible Institute Library), 4221 228th Ave SE, 99299. SAN 317-610X. Tel: 425-392-0400 Ext 241. FAX: 425-392-0404. E-Mail: lbi-libr@lbi.edu. *Dir*, Elliott Ohan *Cat*, Steve Lukasiak
Founded 1944. Highest Degree: Bachelor
Library Holdings: Bk Vols 30,000; Per Subs 216
Special Collections: Bible Study; Bible Versions; Christian Education; Li of Christ; Theology Coll; Youth Work
Partic in OCLC

KALAMA

P KALAMA PUBLIC LIBRARY,* 312 N First, PO Box 576, 98625. SAN 317-5286. Tel: 360-673-4568. FAX: 360-673-4560. E-Mail: kalamalibrary kalama.com. *Librn*, Jan Hoffmann; *Asst Librn*, Marlene Sidwell; *Asst Lib* Molly Ciancibelli
Founded 1927. Circ 6,176
Library Holdings: Bk Vols 9,624
Special Collections: Classics; National Geographic

.SO

KELSO PUBLIC LIBRARY, 314 Academy St, 98626-4196. SAN 317-5294. Tel: 360-423-8110. FAX: 360-425-5195. Web Site: www.kelso.gov/library.htm. *Actg Dir*, Hope Koistinen; E-Mail: hopek@kelsogov; *ILL*, Cindy Donaldson
Founded 1916. Pop 11,950; Circ 61,330
Jan 1999-Dec 1999 Income $260,555, City $250,348, Locally Generated Income $10,207. Mats Exp $20,233, Books $14,265, Per/Ser (Incl. Access Fees) $4,040, Presv $241, Micro $60, Other Print Mats $1,627. Sal $140,765
Library Holdings: Bk Vols 34,975; Per Subs 104
Automation Activity & Vendor Info: (Circulation) PALS
Database Vendor: ProQuest
Publications: New Book List (monthly)
Friends of the Library Group

.MORE

BASTYR UNIVERSITY LIBRARY, 14500 Juanita Dr NE, 98028. SAN 323-7664. Tel: 425-602-3020. FAX: 425-602-3188. E-Mail: library@bastyr.edu. Web Site: www.bastyr.edu/library. *Dir Libr Serv*, Jane D Saxton; Tel: 425-602-3024; *Librn*, Susan Banks; Tel: 425-602-3022, E-Mail: sbanks@bastyr.edu; Staff 5 (MLS 2, Non-MLS 3)
Founded 1981. Enrl 1,000; Fac 95; Highest Degree: Doctorate
Library Holdings: Bk Titles 11,000; Per Subs 270
Subject Interests: Alternative med, Exercise, Homeopathy, Nutrition, Spirituality
Special Collections: Alternative Medical Coll; Bauervic Coll of Homeopathy; Naturopathic Medicine Historical Coll
Automation Activity & Vendor Info: (Cataloging) Sagebrush Corporation; (Circulation) Sagebrush Corporation
Database Vendor: Ebsco - EbscoHost
Publications: Library Letter (Newsletter)
Function: Research library
Partic in Nat Network of Librs of Med, S Cent Res Libr Coun

.NEWICK

MID-COLUMBIA LIBRARY, 405 S Dayton, 99336. SAN 363-6577. Tel: 509-582-4745. FAX: 509-734-7446. Web Site: www.mcl-lib.org. *Dir*, Phelps Shepard; *Mgr Libr*, Inez Freeman; *Mgr Libr*, John Hill; *Mgr Libr*, Tom Moak; *Mgr Libr*, Susan Towne; *Publ Servs*, Brian Soneda; Staff 17 (MLS 12, Non-MLS 5)
Founded 1949. Pop 150,000; Circ 763,710
Jan 1999-Dec 1999 Income (Main Library and Branch Library) $5,275,582. Mats Exp Books $511,846. Sal $1,487,177
Library Holdings: Bk Vols 424,328; Per Subs 600
Subject Interests: Bus, Econ, Mexican-Am studies
Automation Activity & Vendor Info: (Acquisitions) Gaylord; (Cataloging) Gaylord; (Circulation) Gaylord; (Course Reserve) Gaylord; (ILL) Gaylord; (Media Booking) Gaylord; (OPAC) Gaylord; (Serials) Gaylord
Partic in OCLC Online Computer Library Center, Inc
Friends of the Library Group
Branches: 10
BASIN CITY BRANCH, 50-A N Canal Blvd, Basin City, 99343. SAN 373-5273. Tel: 509-269-4201. FAX: 509-269-4201. Web Site: www.mcl-lib.org. *Librn*, Shirley Patton
Friends of the Library Group
BENTON CITY BRANCH, PO Box 369, Benton City, 99320. SAN 326-7458. Tel: 509-588-6471. FAX: 509-588-6471. Web Site: www.mcl-lib.org. *Librn*, Cheryle Kielrulff
CONNELL BRANCH, 118 N Columbia, PO Box 657, Connell, 99326. SAN 363-6631. Tel: 509-234-4971. FAX: 509-234-4971. Web Site: www.mcl-lib.org. *Librn*, Helen Tobin
Friends of the Library Group
KENNEWICK BRANCH, 1620 S Union, 99337. SAN 329-3343. Tel: 509-586-3156. FAX: 509-586-8887. Web Site: www.mcl-lib.org. *Mgr Libr*, Tom Moak; *Ch Servs*, Karen Recher
Subject Interests: Automotive repair, Genealogy
Friends of the Library Group
MERRILL'S CORNER BRANCH, 5240 Eltopia W, Eltopia, 99330. SAN 370-4254. Tel: 509-297-4341. Web Site: www.mcl-lib.org. *Librn*, Sharon Hunter
OTHELLO BRANCH, 101 E Main St, Othello, 99344. SAN 374-8170. Tel: 509-488-9683. FAX: 509-488-5321. Web Site: www.mcl-lib.org. *Mgr Libr*, Inez Freeman
Friends of the Library Group
PASCO BRANCH, 1320 W Hopkins, Pasco, 99301. SAN 363-6666. Tel: 509-545-1019. FAX: 509-547-5416. Web Site: www.mcl-lib.org. *Mgr Libr*, John Hill; *Ch Servs*, Bev Stubbles
Subject Interests: Railroads
Friends of the Library Group
WEST BENTON BRANCH, 614 Sixth St, West Richland, 99350. SAN 370-4270. Tel: 509-786-3777. FAX: 509-786-3777. Web Site: www.mcl-lib.org. *Librn*, Joanne Porter
WEST RICHLAND BRANCH, 3803 W Van Giesen, West Richland, 99353. SAN 363-6682. Tel: 509-967-3191. FAX: 509-967-3191. Web Site: www.mcl-lib.org. *Mgr Libr*, Susan Towne
Friends of the Library Group
Bookmobiles: 1

KETTLE FALLS

P KETTLE FALLS PUBLIC LIBRARY, 605 Meyers St, PO Box 478, 99141. SAN 326-2995. Tel: 509-738-6817. FAX: 509-738-2787. *Librn*, Joan G Nullet; Staff 1 (Non-MLS 1)
Founded 1950. Pop 2,000; Circ 14,000
Jan 1999-Dec 1999 Income $26,515. Mats Exp $7,540. Sal $7,250
Library Holdings: Bk Titles 12,236; Per Subs 45
Special Collections: Photo Collection of Old Kettle Falls
Automation Activity & Vendor Info: (Cataloging) Follett; (Circulation) Follett
Database Vendor: ProQuest
Partic in OCLC
Friends of the Library Group

KIRKLAND

CR NORTHWEST COLLEGE, Hurst Library, 5520 108th Ave NE, 98033-0579. (Mail add: PO Box 579, 98083-0579), SAN 363-6720. Tel: 425-889-5266. FAX: 425-889-7801. Web Site: www.nwcollege.edu/library. *Tech Servs*, Leslie Engelson; Tel: 425-889-5339, E-Mail: leslie.engelson@ncag.edu; *Publ Servs*, Lynette Sorenson; Tel: 425-889-5302, E-Mail: lynette.sorenson@ncag.edu; *Acq*, Jim Morris; Tel: 425-889-5265, E-Mail: jim.morris@ncag.edu; *Cat*, Phyllis Kimball; Tel: 425-889-5267, E-Mail: phyllis.kimball@ncag.edu; *Ser*, Marian Hansen; Tel: 425-889-5301, E-Mail: marian.hansen@ncag.edu; *Circ*, Kari Hagihara; E-Mail: kari.hagihara@ncag.edu; *Circ*, Becky Paulson; E-Mail: becky.paulson@ncag.edu; Staff 7 (MLS 4, Non-MLS 3)
Founded 1934. Enrl 973; Fac 48; Highest Degree: Bachelor
Library Holdings: Bk Vols 156,769; Bk Titles 67,867; Per Subs 810
Subject Interests: Relig studies, Teacher educ
Special Collections: Messianic Jewish Coll; Pacific Rim; Pentecostal Movement
Automation Activity & Vendor Info: (Cataloging) Endeavor; (Circulation) Endeavor; (Course Reserve) Endeavor; (OPAC) Endeavor; (Serials) Endeavor
Database Vendor: Ebsco - EbscoHost, OCLC - First Search, ProQuest, Silverplatter Information Inc.
Function: ILL available
Partic in Northwest Association of Private Colleges & Universities Libraries; Puget Sound Acad Independent Librs

LA CONNER

P LA CONNER REGIONAL LIBRARY, 614 Morris St, 98257. (Mail add: PO Box 370, 98257), SAN 317-5324. Tel: 360-466-3352. FAX: 360-466-9178. E-Mail: lclib@cnw.net. *Dir*, Linda V Malone; *Publ Servs*, Stephanie Lafferty; Staff 4 (MLS 1, Non-MLS 3)
Pop 5,000; Circ 20,216
Library Holdings: Bk Titles 16,000
Automation Activity & Vendor Info: (Cataloging) Sagebrush Corporation
Database Vendor: ProQuest
Friends of the Library Group

S SKAGIT COUNTY HISTORICAL MUSEUM LIBRARY,* 501 S Fourth, PO Box 818, 98257. SAN 317-5332. Tel: 360-466-3365. FAX: 360-466-1611. Web Site: www.skagit.home. *Dir*, James G Barmore; *Librn*, Mari Anderson-Densmore; *Curator*, Pat Doran; *Curator*, Janet Oakley; *Pub Relations*, Janet Saunders-Smith
Library Holdings: Bk Vols 1,639; Bk Titles 1,528
Subject Interests: County hist, Genealogy, Local history, State hist

LACEY

G PUGET SOUND WATER QUALITY ACTION TEAM, 300 Desmond Dr SE, Area E. (Mail add: PO Box 40900, 98504-0900), SAN 373-8345. Tel: 360-407-7314. FAX: 360-407-7333. *Librn*, Cindy Snow; E-Mail: csnow@psat.wa.gov
Founded 1987
Library Holdings: Bk Vols 8,000; Bk Titles 5,000; Per Subs 15
Special Collections: Puget Sound Coll, docs & rpts; Water Quality & Pollution Coll, docs & rpts
Restriction: Staff use only

C SAINT MARTIN'S COLLEGE, O'Grady Library, 5300 Pacific Ave SE, 98503. SAN 317-5340. Tel: 360-486-8800. Circulation Tel: 360-486-8802. Reference Tel: 360-486-8803. FAX: 360-486-8810. Web Site: www.stmartin.edu/library. *Dir*, Dalia L Hagan; Tel: 360-486-8808, E-Mail: dhagan@stmartin.edu; *Publ Servs*, Andrea J Kueter; Tel: 360-486-8812,

E-Mail: akueter@stmartin.edu; *Tech Servs*, Kirsti Thomas; Tel: 360-486-8827, Fax: 360-486-8825, E-Mail: kthomas@stmartin.edu; Staff 11 (MLS 3, Non-MLS 8)
Founded 1895. Enrl 974; Fac 64; Highest Degree: Master
Jul 1999-Jun 2000 Income Parent Institution $545,216. Mats Exp $276,838, Books $81,059, Per/Ser (Incl. Access Fees) $105,580, AV Equip $459, Electronic Ref Mat (Incl. Access Fees) $32,500. Sal $268,378 (Prof $117,000)
Library Holdings: Bk Vols 76,486; Per Subs 868
Special Collections: Catholic Theology; Children's Literature; History (Frederick J Lorden Coll); Lobor History
Automation Activity & Vendor Info: (Acquisitions) Innovative Interfaces Inc.; (Cataloging) Innovative Interfaces Inc.; (Circulation) Innovative Interfaces Inc.; (Course Reserve) Innovative Interfaces Inc.; (ILL) Innovative Interfaces Inc.; (Media Booking) Innovative Interfaces Inc.; (OPAC) Innovative Interfaces Inc.; (Serials) Innovative Interfaces Inc.
Database Vendor: Ebsco - EbscoHost, GaleNet, Lexis-Nexis, OCLC - First Search, ProQuest
Function: ILL available
Partic in Coop Libr in Olympia; Northwest Association of Private Colleges & Universities Libraries; OCLC Online Computer Library Center, Inc; Puget Sound Acad Independent Librs

LAKEWOOD

J PIERCE COLLEGE LIBRARY, 9401 Farwest Dr SW, 98498. SAN 317-6835. Tel: 253-964-6547. Interlibrary Loan Service Tel: 253-964-7349. FAX: 253-964-6713. E-Mail: dgilchri@pierce.ctc.edu. Web Site: www.pierce.ctc.edu/users.old/depts/library/library.htm. *Dir*, Debra Gilchrist; Tel: 253-964-6553; *Tech Servs*, Patti Semsen; Tel: 253-840-8306; *Instrul Serv, Ref*, Lynn Olson; Tel: 253-964-6366; *Instrul Serv, Ref*, Christie Flynn; Tel: 253-840-8304; *Instrul Serv, Ref*, Sue Cole; Tel: 253-964-6305; *Instrul Serv, Ref*, Kathy Swart; Tel: 253-840-8305; *Instrul Serv, Ref*, Mary Hammond; Tel: 253-964-6303; Staff 15 (MLS 9, Non-MLS 6)
Founded 1967. Enrl 13,500; Fac 300; Highest Degree: Associate
1998-1999 Income $650,000. Mats Exp $213,000, Books $165,000, Per/Ser (Incl. Access Fees) $48,000
Library Holdings: Bk Titles 120,000; Per Subs 525
Partic in OCLC Online Computer Library Center, Inc; Washington Libr Network
Departmental Libraries:
PUYALLUP CAMPUS, 1601 39th Ave SE, Puyallup, 98374. Circulation Tel: 253-840-8300. *Ref*, Christie Flynn; Tel: 253-840-8304; *Ref*, Kathy Swart; Tel: 253-840-8305; *Tech Servs*, Patricia Semsen; Tel: 253-840-8306; *Circ*, Laurie White; Tel: 253-840-8308; *Acq*, Susan Pinkis; Tel: 253-840-8310

LONGVIEW

S THE DAILY NEWS LIBRARY, 770 11th Ave, PO Box 189, 98632-0017. SAN 317-5367. Tel: 360-577-2511. E-Mail: library@tdn.com. *Chief Librn*, Donna Yardley
Founded 1923
Special Collections: Clip files of the Daily News
Restriction: Not open to public

P LONGVIEW PUBLIC LIBRARY,* 1600 Louisiana St, 98632-2993. SAN 317-5375. Tel: 360-577-3380. FAX: 360-577-2037. Web Site: www.ci.longview.wa.us. *Dir*, Marion J Otteraaen; E-Mail: marion@ci.longview.wa.us; *Acq*, Carol Wood; *Ad Servs*, Judith Fuller; *Ch Servs, YA Servs*, Karen Dennis; *Circ*, Bruce Holmes; *ILL*, Marian Steely; *Media Spec*, Jerry Ritchie; *Ref*, Chris Skaugset; *Tech Servs*, Edith Uthmann; Staff 17 (MLS 7, Non-MLS 10)
Founded 1926. Pop 34,140; Circ 376,648
Jan 1998-Dec 1998 Income $1,544,780. Mats Exp $248,330, Books $156,160, Per/Ser (Incl. Access Fees) $29,990. Sal $912,230
Library Holdings: Bk Vols 185,971; Per Subs 491
Special Collections: '23 Club Oral History Coll, cassettes; Construction of Longview (Long Bell Files), letters; Early Longview History (S M Morris Coll), pictures; Fed; Rudolph Steiner Coll
Automation Activity & Vendor Info: (Circulation) epixtech, inc.; (Course Reserve) epixtech, inc.; (ILL) epixtech, inc.; (Media Booking) epixtech, inc.; (OPAC) epixtech, inc.; (Serials) epixtech, inc.
Publications: In Review (newsletter)
Partic in Western Libr Network
Special Services for the Deaf - Captioned film depository; High interest/low vocabulary books; Special interest periodicals
Other Special Services - Children's Department has an educational/literacy learning computer; Adult & Family Literacy Program: Project Read-one on one tutoring of adults 18 years & older; Share A Book: Outreach parental/pre-school home visits; Family Search (Genius System) Magazine Index, Telephone Index of US & Special Business telephone index, Health Reference Index
Friends of the Library Group

J LOWER COLUMBIA COLLEGE, Alan Thompson Library, 1600 Mapl 98632-3907. (Mail add: PO Box 3010, 98632-0310), SAN 317-5383. Te 360-577-2310. FAX: 360-578-1400. *Dir*, Mike Gabriel; *Librn*, J Carmen Robinson; Staff 5 (MLS 2, Non-MLS 3)
Founded 1934. Enrl 2,150; Fac 90
Library Holdings: Bk Vols 41,000; Per Subs 150
Automation Activity & Vendor Info: (Cataloging) epixtech, inc.; (Circulation) epixtech, inc.
Database Vendor: epixtech, inc.
Partic in OCLC

M SAINT JOHN MEDICAL CENTER, Herbert H Minthorn Memorial Lib 1615 Delaware St, PO Box 3002, 98632-9973. SAN 317-5391. Tel: 360 414-7462. Circulation Tel: 360-414-2000, Ext 7144. FAX: 360-414-746 E-Mail: sjmc_library@peacehealth.org. *Dir*, Barbara A Sherry; Staff 2 (M 1, Non-MLS 1)
1998-1999 Mats Exp $60,000, Books $30,000, Per/Ser (Incl. Access Fee $30,000
Library Holdings: Bk Vols 2,000; Per Subs 150
Subject Interests: Medicine, Pathology
Database Vendor: GaleNet, OVID Technologies, ProQuest

LOON LAKE

P STEVENS COUNTY RURAL LIBRARY DISTRICT, 4000 Cedar St, 99148-9676. (Mail add: PO Box 744, 98148-0744), SAN 375-4111. Tel: 509-233-9621. Interlibrary Loan Service Tel: 509-738-3033. Toll Free Te 877-251-3300. Web Site: www.stevcolib.org. *Dir*, Regan Robinson; E-M regan@stevcolib.org; Staff 10 (MLS 6, Non-MLS 4)
Founded 1998. Pop 30,000
Jan 2000-Dec 2000 Income $770,000
Automation Activity & Vendor Info: (Cataloging) DRA; (Circulation) DRA
Database Vendor: DRA, OCLC - First Search, ProQuest
Friends of the Library Group

LOPEZ ISLAND

P LOPEZ ISLAND LIBRARY, 2225 Fisherman Bay Rd, PO Box 770, 98 0770. SAN 326-7105. Tel: 360-468-2265. *Librn*, Aimee Hirschel; Staff 2 (MLS 1, Non-MLS 1)
Founded 1982. Pop 2,100
Jan 1999-Dec 1999 Income County $234,800. Mats Exp Books $31,000. $81,300 (Prof $39,900)
Library Holdings: Bk Titles 18,000; Per Subs 64
Friends of the Library Group

LYNNWOOD

J EDMONDS COMMUNITY COLLEGE LIBRARY, 20000 68th Ave W, 98036. SAN 317-543X. Tel: 425-640-1529. FAX: 425-775-0690. Web Si www.edcc.edu/library. *Publ Servs*, David Doctor; *Publ Servs*, Monica To *Tech Servs*, Dale Burke; Staff 13 (MLS 4, Non-MLS 9)
Founded 1967. Enrl 4,500
2000-2001 Mats Exp $80,000, Books $38,000, Per/Ser (Incl. Access Fees $38,000, Micro $4,000
Library Holdings: Bk Vols 46,000; Bk Titles 38,000; Per Subs 385
Subject Interests: Horticulture, Legal assisting
Automation Activity & Vendor Info: (Acquisitions) Endeavor; (Catalog Endeavor; (Circulation) Endeavor; (Course Reserve) Endeavor; (OPAC) Endeavor; (Serials) Endeavor
Database Vendor: OCLC - First Search
Partic in OCLC Online Computer Library Center, Inc

MARYSVILLE

P SNO-ISLE REGIONAL LIBRARY SYSTEM,* 7312 35th Ave NE, 9827 7417. SAN 363-681X. Tel: 360-651-7000, 360-659-8447. Toll Free Tel: 8 342-1936. FAX: 360-651-7151. Web Site: www.sno-isle.org. *Dir*, Arthur Weeks; Tel: 360-651-7001, E-Mail: aweeks@sno-isle.org; *Dep Dir*, Jonal Woolf-Ivory; Tel: 360-651-7008, E-Mail: jwoolf-ivory@sno-isle.org; *Tech Servs*, Sarah Schwartz; Tel: 360-651-7070, E-Mail: sschwartz@sno-isle.o *Commun Relations*, Mary K Kelly; Tel: 360-651-7030, E-Mail: mkelly@s isle.org; *Ch Servs*, Kay O'Connell; Tel: 360-651-7017, E-Mail: koconnell sno-isle.org; *Ad Servs, YA Servs*, Penni Vogel; Tel: 360-651-7018, E-Mail pvogel@sno-isle.org; *Coll Develop*, Michael Levine; Tel: 360-651-7025, E-Mail: mlevine@sno-isle.org; Staff 236 (MLS 55, Non-MLS 181)
Founded 1945. Pop 542,430; Circ 4,717,313
Jan 1999-Dec 1999 Income (Main Library and Branch Library) $15,790,(State $270,000, City $2,355,623, County $12,855,805, Locally Generated Income $119,641, Other $189,023. Mats Exp $2,975,000, Books $1,887,0 Per/Ser (Incl. Access Fees) $103,563, AV Equip $245,326, Other Print M $1,718. Sal $7,804,022 (Prof $3,462,009)
Library Holdings: Bk Vols 899,541

Automation Activity & Vendor Info: (Acquisitions) CARL; (Cataloging) CARL; (Circulation) CARL
Database Vendor: CARL
Partic in OCLC Online Computer Library Center, Inc
Friends of the Library Group
Branches: 18
ARLINGTON BRANCH, 135 N Washington Ave, Arlington, 98223. SAN 363-6844. Tel: 360-435-3033. FAX: 360-435-3854. *Librn*, Maggie Buckholz
Library Holdings: Bk Vols 46,580
Open Mon-Thurs 10-9, Fri & Sat 10-5, Sun (Sept-June) 1-5
BRIER BRANCH, 23303 Brier Rd, Brier, 98036. SAN 363-6860. Tel: 425-483-0888. FAX: 425-487-1880. *Librn*, Eric Spencer
Library Holdings: Bk Vols 20,060
Open Mon-Wed 12-8, Fri & Sat 12-6
Friends of the Library Group
COUPEVILLE BRANCH, 788 NW Alexander, PO Box 745, Coupeville, 98239. SAN 363-6879. Tel: 360-678-4911. FAX: 360-678-5261. *Librn*, Leslie Franzen
Library Holdings: Bk Vols 25,269
Open Mon & Wed 11-9, Tues, Thurs, Fri & Sat 11-5
Friends of the Library Group
DARRINGTON BRANCH, 1005 Cascade St, PO Box 25, Darrington, 98241. SAN 363-6909. Tel: 360-436-1600. FAX: 360-436-1659. *Librn*, Linda McPherson
Library Holdings: Bk Vols 21,284
Open Mon & Wed 11-8, Tues, Fri & Sat 11-5
Friends of the Library Group
EDMONDS BRANCH, 650 Main St, Edmonds, 98020. SAN 363-6933. Tel: 425-771-1933. FAX: 425-771-1977. *Librn*, Evie Wilson-Lingbloom
Library Holdings: Bk Vols 110,317
Open Mon-Thurs 10-9, Fri 10-6, Sat 10-5 & Sun (Sept-June) 1-5
Friends of the Library Group
FREELAND BRANCH, 1695 Layton Rd, PO Box 1357, Freeland, 98249. SAN 363-6968. Tel: 360-331-7323. FAX: 360-331-1572. *Librn*, Joanne Harmon
Library Holdings: Bk Vols 25,259
Open Tues & Thurs 11-8, Wed 11-6, Fri & Sat 11-5, Sun (Sept-June) 1-5
Friends of the Library Group
GRANITE FALLS BRANCH, 101 E Pioneer, PO Box 599, Granite Falls, 98252. SAN 363-6992. Tel: 360-691-6087. FAX: 360-691-5533. *Librn*, Lynette Howard
Library Holdings: Bk Vols 21,067
Open Mon & Wed 11-8, Tues, Fri & Sat 11-5
Friends of the Library Group
LAKE STEVENS BRANCH, 1804 Main St, PO Box 217, Lake Stevens, 98258. SAN 363-7026. Tel: 425-334-1900. FAX: 425-334-9487. *Librn*, Gredel Schilling
Library Holdings: Bk Vols 24,508
Open Mon-Wed 12-9, Fri & Sat 10-5
Friends of the Library Group
LANGLEY BRANCH, 104 Second St, Langley, 98260. (Mail add: PO Box 365, Langley, 98260), Tel: 360-221-4383. FAX: 360-221-3067. Web Site: www.sno-isle.org. *Branch Mgr*, Vicky Welfare; E-Mail: vwelfare@sno-isle.org; *Ch Servs*, Laurie Barker-Perez; E-Mail: lbarker-perez@sno-isle.org; Staff 8 (MLS 1, Non-MLS 7)
Founded 1922. Circ 141,000
Library Holdings: Bk Vols 28,004; Bk Titles 28,000; Per Subs 75
Database Vendor: CARL, IAC - Info Trac, IAC - SearchBank, ProQuest
Function: ILL available
Open Mon-Wed 11-8, Thurs-Sat 11-5
Friends of the Library Group
LYNNWOOD BRANCH, 19200 44th Ave W, Lynnwood, 98036. SAN 363-7085. Tel: 425-778-2148. Reference Toll Free Tel: 800-645-7596. FAX: 425-774-3434. *Librn*, Judy Sasges
Library Holdings: Bk Vols 137,970
Special Services for the Deaf - TTY machine
Open Mon-Thurs 10-9, Fri 10-6, Sat 10-5, Sun 1-5
Friends of the Library Group
MARYSVILLE BRANCH, 6120 Grove St NE, 98270. SAN 363-7115. Tel: 360-658-5000. FAX: 360-659-5050. *Librn*, Eileen McDonnell
Library Holdings: Bk Vols 122,389
Open Mon-Thurs 10-9, Fri 10-6, Sat 10-5 & Sun 1-5
Friends of the Library Group
MILL CREEK BRANCH, 15429 Bothell-Everett Hwy, Mill Creek, 98012. SAN 328-9044. Tel: 425-337-4822; 425-743-5544, 425-743-5544. FAX: 425-337-3567. Web Site: www.sno-isle.org.; Staff 3 (MLS 3)
Founded 1987. Pop 60,000
Library Holdings: Bk Vols 62,093
Database Vendor: CARL, IAC - Info Trac, OCLC - First Search, ProQuest
Function: Reference services available
Open Mon-Thurs 10-9, Fri & Sat 10-6
Friends of the Library Group
MONROE BRANCH, 201 W Hill St, Monroe, 98272. SAN 363-714X. Tel: 360-794-7851. FAX: 360-794-0292. *Librn*, Betsy Lewis
Library Holdings: Bk Vols 44,806
Open Mon-Thurs 10-9, Fri & Sat 10-5
Friends of the Library Group
MOUNTLAKE TERRACE BRANCH, 23300 58th Ave W, Mountlake Terrace, 98043. SAN 363-7174. Tel: 425-776-8722. FAX: 425-776-3411. *Librn*, Cindy Lyons
Library Holdings: Bk Vols 56,359
Open Mon-Thurs 10-9, Fri & Sat 10-5, Sun (Sept-June) 1-5
Friends of the Library Group
OAK HARBOR BRANCH, 1000 SE Regatta Dr, Oak Harbor, 98277. SAN 363-7263. Tel: 360-675-5115. FAX: 360-679-3761. *Librn*, Becky Bolte
Library Holdings: Bk Vols 107,670
Open Mon-Thurs 10-9, Fri & Sat 10-5, Sun (Sept-June) 1-5
Friends of the Library Group
SNOHOMISH BRANCH, 105 Cedar St, Snohomish, 98290. SAN 363-7328. Tel: 360-568-2898. FAX: 360-568-1922. *Librn*, Jane Appling
Library Holdings: Bk Vols 74,371
Open Mon-Thurs 10-9, Fri & Sat 10-5, Sun (Sept-June) 1-5
Friends of the Library Group
STANWOOD BRANCH, 9701 271st St NW, PO Box 247, Stanwood, 98292. SAN 363-7352. Tel: 360-629-3132. FAX: 360-629-3516. *Librn*, Icle Crow
Library Holdings: Bk Vols 47,742
Open Mon-Thurs 10-9, Fri & Sat 10-5
Friends of the Library Group
SULTAN BRANCH, 515 Main St, PO Box 580, Sultan, 98294. SAN 363-7417. Tel: 360-793-1695. FAX: 360-793-9634. *Librn*, Jackie McCluskey
Library Holdings: Bk Vols 21,482
Open Mon-Thurs 11-8, Fri & Sat 11-5
Friends of the Library Group
Bookmobiles: 2

MC CHORD AFB

UNITED STATES AIR FORCE
A MC CHORD AIR FORCEBASE LIBRARY FL4479, 62 SVS/SVMG, 851 Lincoln Blvd, 98438-1317. SAN 363-678X. Tel: 253-984-3454. FAX: 253-984-3944. *Librn*, David English; E-Mail: david.english@mcchord.af.mil; *Ref*, Cindy Spano; Staff 7 (MLS 2, Non-MLS 5)
Founded 1941
Library Holdings: Bk Vols 30,000; Per Subs 193
Subject Interests: Aviation, Military history

MONTESANO

GL GRAYS HARBOR COUNTY, Law Library,* 102 W Broadway, Rm 203, 98563. SAN 317-5472. Tel: 360-249-5311. FAX: 360-249-6391. *Librn*, Elaine Urguhart
Library Holdings: Bk Vols 15,000

MOSES LAKE

J BIG BEND COMMUNITY COLLEGE LIBRARY, 7662 Chanute St, 98837. SAN 317-5480. Tel: 509-762-6246. Reference Tel: 509-762-6247. FAX: 509-762-2402. Web Site: library.bb.cc.wa.us. *Dir Libr Serv*, Tim Fuhrman; *Coll Develop, Ref*, Lance Wyman
Founded 1963. Enrl 4,622; Fac 50
Jul 1999-Jun 2000 Income $344,620. Mats Exp $90,048. Sal $183,872 (Prof $100,232)
Library Holdings: Bk Titles 33,323; Per Subs 225
Subject Interests: Grant County hist, Pacific Northwest
Special Collections: Chinese Art Coll
Automation Activity & Vendor Info: (Circulation) Follett; (OPAC) Follett
Database Vendor: Ebsco - EbscoHost, ProQuest
Partic in Western Libr Network
Special Services for the Blind - Closed circuit television

MOUNT VERNON

P MOUNT VERNON CITY LIBRARY, 315 Snoqualmie St, 98273. SAN 317-5499. Tel: 360-336-6209. FAX: 360-336-6259. E-Mail: library@ci.mount-vernon.wa.us. Web Site: www.mount-vernon.wa.us/reclib/wp.htm. *Dir*, Mary Ann Grimm; Tel: 360-336-6249, Fax: 360-336-6259, E-Mail: anng@ci.mount-vernon.wa.us; *Dep Dir*, Donna P Wineman; E-Mail: donnaw@ci.mount-vernon.wa.us; *Ch Servs*, Lisa Webster; *ILL, Tech Servs*, Rebecca Taylor; *Circ*, Ellen Christilaw; *Ad Servs*, Janna Gage; *Acq*, Anita Thornton; *Automation Syst Coordr*, Kathleen O'Neill; Staff 26 (MLS 1, Non-MLS 25)
Founded 1908. Pop 23,020; Circ 302,697
Jan 2000-Dec 2000 Income City $850,284. Mats Exp $89,500, Books $75,000, Per/Ser (Incl. Access Fees) $14,500. Sal $118,284
Library Holdings: Bk Vols 81,000; Bk Titles 65,433; Per Subs 315
Subject Interests: Architecture, Art, Aviation, History
Special Collections: Spanish Language Coll, includes 774 titles & 6538 non-print titles
Automation Activity & Vendor Info: (Acquisitions) epixtech, inc.; (Cataloging) epixtech, inc.; (Circulation) epixtech, inc.

Database Vendor: GaleNet, IAC - Info Trac, ProQuest
Partic in Wash State Libr Network
Children's Summer Reading Program
Friends of the Library Group

S PACCAR, INC, Technical Center Library, 12479 Farm to Market Rd, 98273. SAN 329-1405. Tel: 360-757-5234. FAX: 360-757-5370. *Res*, Betsy Aldridge; E-Mail: betsy.aldridge@paccar.com; *Mgr*, Maryanne Ward; *Doc*, Sharon Bowen
Founded 1985
Library Holdings: Bk Titles 4,000; Per Subs 120
Subject Interests: Automotive engineering
Partic in OCLC Online Computer Library Center, Inc

GL SKAGIT COUNTY LAW LIBRARY, County Courthouse, 205 W Kincaid, No 104, 98273. SAN 375-0337. Tel: 360-336-9324. FAX: 360-336-9336. *Librn*, Patti Worl; E-Mail: pattiw@co.skagit.wa.us
Library Holdings: Bk Vols 8,000

J SKAGIT VALLEY COLLEGE, Norwood Cole Library, 2405 E College Way, 98273. SAN 317-5510. Tel: 360-416-7761. Interlibrary Loan Service Tel: 360-416-7659. Circulation Tel: 360-416-7837. Reference Tel: 360-416-7847. FAX: 360-416-7698. E-Mail: library@skagit.ctc.edu. Web Site: svclib.ctc.edu. *Assoc Dean*, Mindy Coslor; Tel: 360-416-7761, E-Mail: coslor@skagit.ctc.edu; *Cat, Tech Servs*, Gary Payne; Tel: 360-416-7624, E-Mail: payne@skagit.ctc.edu; *Ref*, Margret Mills; Tel: 360-416-7760, E-Mail: mills@skagit.ctc.edu; *Br Coordr*, Owais Jafrey; Staff 5 (MLS 5)
Founded 1926. Enrl 3,000; Fac 170
Library Holdings: Bk Vols 75,943; Bk Titles 44,118; Per Subs 250
Subject Interests: Skagit County
Automation Activity & Vendor Info: (Acquisitions) Innovative Interfaces Inc.; (Cataloging) Innovative Interfaces Inc.; (Circulation) Innovative Interfaces Inc.; (Course Reserve) Innovative Interfaces Inc.; (ILL) Innovative Interfaces Inc.; (Media Booking) Innovative Interfaces Inc.; (OPAC) Innovative Interfaces Inc.
Departmental Libraries:
WHIDBEY, Library Media Ctr, 1900 SE Pioneer Way, Oak Harbor, 98277. SAN 376-2068. Tel: 360-679-5322. FAX: 360-679-5341. *Librn*, Owais Jafrey; Tel: 360-679-5321

NESPELEM

S COLVILLE CONFEDERATED TRIBE LIBRARY,* PO Box 150, 99155. SAN 373-6881. Tel: 509-634-4711, Ext 2791. FAX: 509-634-2790. E-Mail: alhtrc@televar.com, alhtrc@theofficenet.com. *Librn*, Adrian Holm
Founded 1983
Library Holdings: Bk Titles 5,000
Special Collections: Construction of Grand Conlee Dam & Chief Joseph Dam, 1938-1978, log, notebooks, res data, surveys
Special Services for the Deaf - Special interest periodicals
Branches:
INCHELIUM RESOURCE CENTER, PO Box 156, Inchelium, 99138. SAN 373-8108. Tel: 509-722-7037. FAX: 509-533-7040. E-Mail: alhtrc@theofficenet.com. *Tech Servs*, Adrian Holm
Library Holdings: Bk Vols 3,500
KELLER LIBRARY, Keller, 99140. SAN 373-8116. Tel: 509-634-2802. *Librn*, Adrian Holm
Library Holdings: Bk Vols 1,500

NEWPORT

P PEND OREILLE COUNTY LIBRARY DISTRICT, 116 S Washington Ave, 99156. SAN 326-1735. Tel: 509-447-2111. FAX: 509-447-2806. Web Site: www.pocld.org. *Dir*, Janet Marie Lyon; E-Mail: jlyon@pocld.org; *Br Coordr*, Georgia Rier; E-Mail: grier@pocld.org; *Br Coordr*, Pam Thompson; Tel: 509-445-1215, Fax: 509-445-1215, E-Mail: pamt@pocld.org; *Br Coordr*, Johnnee Curtiss; Tel: 509-442-3030, Fax: 509-442-3030, E-Mail: jcurtiss@pocld.org; *Br Coordr*, Lynn Barnes; Tel: 509-446-3232, Fax: 509-446-2302, E-Mail: lbarnes@pocld.org; *Tech Servs*, Kevin Paulus; E-Mail: lpaulus@pocld.org; Staff 8 (Non-MLS 8)
Founded 1980. Pop 11,200; Circ 63,842
Library Holdings: Bk Vols 40,760; Bk Titles 40,760; Per Subs 194
Subject Interests: Local history
Database Vendor: Ebsco - EbscoHost, GaleNet, ProQuest
Publications: People Yellow Pages, A Computer based Community Information and Referral Directory covering three Washington counties & one Idaho county
Special Services for the Deaf - High interest/low vocabulary books
Friends of the Library Group
Branches: 4
CALISPEL VALLEY, 105 First Ave, PO Box 227, Cusick, 99119. SAN 326-3754. Tel: 509-445-1215. FAX: 509-445-1215. *In Charge*, Pam Thompson
Library Holdings: Bk Vols 3,200
IONE PUBLIC, 112 Central Ave, Ione, 99139. SAN 326-3770. Tel: 509-442-3030. FAX: 509-442-3030. *In Charge*, Johnnee Curtiss
Library Holdings: Bk Vols 4,200
Friends of the Library Group
MAIN Tel: 509-447-2111, 509-447-3711. FAX: 509-447-2806.
Friends of the Library Group
METALINES BRANCH, 302 Park, PO Box 111, Metaline Falls, 99153 SAN 326-3797. Tel: 509-446-3232. FAX: 509-446-2302. *In Charge*, I Barnes
Library Holdings: Bk Vols 4,500
Friends of the Library Group

OAK HARBOR

UNITED STATES NAVY
A NOR'WESTER ACTIVITIES CENTER-RESOURCE CENTER, NAS Whidbey Island, 3675 N Saratoga Blvd, 98278-2200. SAN 363-7476. 360-257-2702. FAX: 360-257-3963.
Founded 1944
Library Holdings: Bk Titles 7,000; Per Subs 90
Subject Interests: Acad support, Recreational reading
Special Collections: Transition Assistance Management Program (TA US Navy Professional Reading Program
Publications: Monthly annotated new booklists; Newsletters
Partic in OCLC
Special Services - Annual short story contest; acts as a distribution po for IRS forms & information; lends Polaroid cameras & public domai software; offers weekly traveling library with two stops; offers childre summer reading club; weekly preschool storytime; monthly evening storyhour; exhibits local artists' work; offers public access FAX servic

OCEAN SHORES

P OCEAN SHORES PUBLIC LIBRARY,* 573 Point Brown Ave NW, PO Box 669, 98569-0669. SAN 317-5529. Tel: 360-289-3919. FAX: 360-28 4318. E-Mail: oslib@techline.com. *Dir*, Judith E Stull; Staff 3 (MLS 1, MLS 2)
Founded 1973. Pop 3,300; Circ 46,515
Jan 1998-Dec 1998 Income City $156,511. Mats Exp $156,511. Sal $80, (Prof $36,360)
Library Holdings: Bk Titles 18,778; Per Subs 77
Subject Interests: Local history
Special Collections: Local History (Pacific Northwest Coll)
Automation Activity & Vendor Info: (Cataloging) Follett; (Circulation) Follett
Publications: History of Ocean Shores
Friends of the Library Group

ODESSA

P ODESSA PUBLIC LIBRARY,* 21 E First Ave, PO Box 218, 99159. SA 317-5537. Tel: 509-982-2654. FAX: 509-982-2410. E-Mail: odessapublib odessaoffice.com. *Librn*, Mila E Carozzi; Tel: 403-691-4070
Founded 1942. Pop 1,009; Circ 8,063
Library Holdings: Bk Titles 15,000
Subject Interests: US hist

OLYMPIA

L ATTORNEY GENERAL'S OFFICE, Law Library, 1101 Washington St S Ste 260, PO Box 40115, 98504-0115. SAN 327-7046. Tel: 360-753-2681. FAX: 360-753-3490. *Mgr*, Jane Halligan; Staff 7 (MLS 4, Non-MLS 3)
Library Holdings: Bk Titles 11,000

G DEPARTMENT OF INFORMATION SERVICES, Computer Services D 1310 Jefferson St SE, PO Box 42445, 98504-2445. SAN 374-4728. Tel: 360-902-3037. FAX: 360-586-7454.
Library Holdings: Bk Vols 4,346; Per Subs 250

C EVERGREEN STATE COLLEGE, Daniel J Evans Library, Library 2300 98505. SAN 317-5545. Tel: 360-866-6000, Ext 6250. FAX: 360-866-679 Web Site: www.evergreen.edu. *Dean of Libr*, William Bruner; *ILL*, Miko Francis; *Cat*, Tim Markus; *Acq*, Shelley Swelland; *Media Spec*, Alley Hinkle; *Per*, Brian Gerheim; Staff 10 (MLS 5, Non-MLS 5)
Founded 1969. Enrl 3,715; Fac 170; Highest Degree: Master
Jul 1999-Jun 2000 Income $3,177,472. Mats Exp $819,612, Books $256,101, Per/Ser (Incl. Access Fees) $373,308, Presv $851, AV Equip $20,298, Electronic Ref Mat (Incl. Access Fees) $87,101. Sal $1,931,206 (Prof $746,496)
Library Holdings: Bk Vols 473,386; Bk Titles 438,736; Per Subs 2,559
Special Collections: Chicano & Latino Art Culture of the Pacific Northw archives; Evergreen State Authors Project & Special Microfilm Coll; Japanese Culture (Beckman Colls), rare bks; Nisqually Delta Association Archives; TESC Archives; Washington State Folklife Council Archives; Washington Worm Growers Assoc Archives
Automation Activity & Vendor Info: (Acquisitions) Innovative Interface Inc.; (Cataloging) Innovative Interfaces Inc.; (Circulation) Innovative Interfaces Inc.; (Course Reserve) Innovative Interfaces Inc.; (ILL) Innovat

Interfaces Inc.; (Media Booking) Innovative Interfaces Inc.; (OPAC) Innovative Interfaces Inc.; (Serials) Innovative Interfaces Inc.
Partic in Coop Libr in Olympia
Friends of the Library Group

PROVIDENCE SAINT PETER HOSPITAL, Library Services,* 413 Lilly Rd NE, 98506. SAN 329-4269. Tel: 360-493-7222. FAX: 360-493-7924. *Mgr*, Edean Berglund
Library Holdings: Bk Titles 1,100; Per Subs 350

SOUTH PUGET SOUND COMMUNITY COLLEGE LIBRARY,* 2011 Mottman Rd SW, 98512. SAN 317-5553. Tel: 360-754-7711. FAX: 360-664-0780. *Dir*, W Russell Rose; *Librn*, Susan Jones; *Ch Servs*, Steve Willis; Staff 6 (MLS 3, Non-MLS 3)
Founded 1972. Enrl 1,800
Library Holdings: Bk Vols 35,000; Bk Titles 30,000; Per Subs 300
Partic in Western Libr Network

TIMBERLAND REGIONAL LIBRARY,* 415 Airdustrial Way SW, 98501-5799. SAN 363-7506. Tel: 360-943-5001. FAX: 360-586-6838. Web Site: www.timberland.lib.wa.us. *Dir*, Thelma Kruse; *Dep Dir, Publ Servs*, Tina Roose; *Coll Develop*, Judith Covell; *Coll Develop, YA Servs*, Barbara Winfree; *YA Servs*, Ellen Duffy; *Coll Develop*, Jan Sterner; *Automation Syst Coordr*, Gwen Culp; Staff 192 (MLS 48, Non-MLS 144)
Founded 1968. Pop 395,429
Library Holdings: Bk Vols 895,595; Bk Titles 355,674; Per Subs 3,206
Subject Interests: Genealogy, Sheet music
Automation Activity & Vendor Info: (Acquisitions) epixtech, inc.; (Circulation) epixtech, inc.
Partic in OCLC; OCLC Online Computer Library Center, Inc
Special Services for the Deaf - High interest/low vocabulary books
Branches: 27
W H ABEL MEMORIAL, 125 Main St S, Montesano, 98563-3794. SAN 363-7530. Tel: 360-249-4211. FAX: 360-249-4203. Web Site: www.timberland.lib.wa.us. *Librn*, Valerie Jester
Friends of the Library Group
ABERDEEN BRANCH, 121 E Market St, Aberdeen, 98520-5292. SAN 363-7565. Tel: 360-533-2360. FAX: 360-532-2953. Web Site: www.timberland.lib.wa.us. *Librn*, Christine Peck
Friends of the Library Group
AMANDA PARK BRANCH, 6118 US Hwy 101, PO Drawer K, Amanda Park, 98526-0089. SAN 363-7573. Tel: 360-288-2725. FAX: 360-288-2725. Web Site: www.timberland.lib.wa.us. *In Charge*, Kathy Clayton
Friends of the Library Group
CENTRALIA BRANCH, 110 S Silver St, Centralia, 98531-4218. SAN 363-759X. Tel: 360-736-0183. FAX: 360-736-2714. Web Site: www.timberland.lib.wa.us. *Librn*, Virginia Burns
Friends of the Library Group
CHEHALIS BRANCH, 76 NE Park St, PO Box 419, Chehalis, 98532-0419. SAN 363-762X. Tel: 360-748-3301. FAX: 360-748-0914. Web Site: www.timberland.lib.wa.us. *Librn*, Kitty Schiltz
Friends of the Library Group
ELMA BRANCH, 118 N First, PO Box Q, Elma, 98541-0547. SAN 363-7689. Tel: 360-482-3737. FAX: 360-482-3047. Web Site: www.timberland.lib.wa.us. *In Charge*, Nancy Alconcel
Friends of the Library Group
HOODSPORT BRANCH, N 40 Schoolhouse Hill Rd, PO Box 847, Hoodsport, 98548-0847. SAN 372-512X. Tel: 360-877-9339. FAX: 360-877-9695. Web Site: www.timberland.lib.wa.us. *In Charge*, Nancy Triplett
Friends of the Library Group
HOQUIAM BRANCH, 420 Seventh St, Hoquiam, 98550-3616. SAN 363-7719. Tel: 360-532-1710. FAX: 360-533-4123. Web Site: www.timberland.lib.wa.us. *Librn*, Roberta Holmes
Friends of the Library Group
ILWACO BRANCH, 158 First Ave N, PO Box 520, Ilwaco, 98624-0520. SAN 363-7743. Tel: 360-642-3908. FAX: 360-642-8417. Web Site: www.timberland.lib.wa.us. *Librn*, Kristine Pointer
Friends of the Library Group
LACEY BRANCH, 500 College St SE, Lacey, 98503-1240. SAN 363-7778. Tel: 360-491-3860. FAX: 360-459-6714. Web Site: www.timberland.lib.wa.us. *Librn*, Ruta Maeda
Friends of the Library Group
MCCLEARY BRANCH, 100 Third St, PO Box 660, McCleary, 98557-0660. SAN 329-6792. Tel: 360-495-3368. FAX: 360-495-3368. Web Site: www.timberland.lib.wa.us. *In Charge*, Mary Thornton
Friends of the Library Group
MOUNTAIN VIEW, 210 Silverbrook Rd, PO Box 340, Randle, 98377-0340. SAN 328-7114. Tel: 360-497-2665. FAX: 360-497-2665. Web Site: www.timberland.lib.wa.us. *In Charge*, Nancy Sawyer
Friends of the Library Group
NASELLE BRANCH, 4 Parpala Rd, Naselle, 98638-0190. (Mail add: PO Box 190, Naselle, 98638), SAN 328-7092. Tel: 360-484-3877. FAX: 360-484-3445. Web Site: www.timberland.lib.wa.us. *In Charge*, Ann Musche
Library Holdings: Bk Vols 14,000
Friends of the Library Group
NORTH MASON, 23081 NE State Rte 3, PO Box 1179, Belfair, 98528-1179. SAN 363-7867. Tel: 360-275-3232. FAX: 360-275-6999. Web Site: www.timberland.lib.wa.us. *Librn*, Victoria Rexford
Friends of the Library Group
OAKVILLE BRANCH, 204 Main St, PO Box G, Oakville, 98568-0079. SAN 363-7891. Tel: 360-273-5305. FAX: 360-273-7446. Web Site: www.timberland.lib.wa.us. *In Charge*, Deborah Baker
Friends of the Library Group
OCEAN PARK BRANCH, 1308 256th Pl, PO Box 310, Ocean Park, 98640-0310. SAN 363-7905. Tel: 360-665-4184. FAX: 360-665-5983. Web Site: www.timberland.lib.wa.us. *Librn*, Iver Matheson
Friends of the Library Group
OLYMPIA BRANCH, 313 Eighth Ave SE, 98501-9300. SAN 363-7921. Tel: 360-352-0595. FAX: 360-586-3207. Web Site: www.timberland.lib.wa.us. *Librn*, Bette Anderson
Subject Interests: Genealogy, Music
Friends of the Library Group
PACKWOOD BRANCH, 109 W Main St, PO Box 589, Packwood, 98361-0589. SAN 363-8103. Tel: 360-494-5111. FAX: 360-494-9237. Web Site: www.timberland.lib.wa.us. *In Charge*, Virginia Squires
Friends of the Library Group
RAYMOND BRANCH, 507 Duryea St, Raymond, 98577-1829. SAN 363-7956. Tel: 360-942-2408. Toll Free Tel: 800-562-6022. FAX: 360-942-5670. Web Site: www.timberland.lib.wa.us. *Commun Servs*, Robert Stalder; *Librn*, Emily Popovich; E-Mail: epopovic@timberland.lib.wa.us; Staff 6 (MLS 2, Non-MLS 4)
Pop 7,000
Database Vendor: GaleNet, IAC - SearchBank, ProQuest
Friends of the Library Group
WILLIAM G REED PUBLIC, 710 W Alder St, Shelton, 98584-2571. SAN 363-7972. Tel: 360-426-3512. FAX: 360-426-2959. Web Site: www.timberland.lib.wa.us. *Librn*, Tim Mallory; Tel: 360-426-1362, E-Mail: tmallory@timberland.lib.wa.us; *Librn*, Michael Potts; E-Mail: mpotts@timberland.lib.wa.us; *Ch Servs, YA Servs*, Brenda Pierce; E-Mail: bpierce@timberland.lib.wa.us; *Ref*, Cindy Buhi; E-Mail: cbuhi@timberland.lib.wa.us; Staff 18 (MLS 4, Non-MLS 14)
Founded 1989. Pop 25,000; Circ 350,000
Library Holdings: Bk Vols 85,000; Per Subs 279
Database Vendor: epixtech, inc., IAC - SearchBank, ProQuest
Friends of the Library Group
SALKUM BRANCH, 2480 US Hwy 12, PO Box 120, Salkum, 98582-0120. SAN 328-7130. Tel: 360-985-2148. FAX: 360-985-7704. Web Site: www.timberland.lib.wa.us. *In Charge*, Cherie Rusk
Friends of the Library Group
SOUTH BEND BRANCH, First & Pacific, PO Box 368, South Bend, 98586-0368. SAN 363-7980. Tel: 360-875-5532. FAX: 360-875-5532. Web Site: www.timberland.lib.wa.us. *In Charge*, Joann Rucker
Friends of the Library Group
TENINO BRANCH, 172 Central Ave W, PO Box 4017, Tenino, 98589-0510. SAN 363-8006. Tel: 360-264-2369. FAX: 360-264-2369. Web Site: www.timberland.lib.wa.us. *In Charge*, Kristina Kauffman
Friends of the Library Group
TUMWATER BRANCH, 7023 New Market St, Tumwater, 98501-6563. SAN 363-8014. Tel: 360-943-7790. FAX: 360-943-6753. Web Site: www.timberland.lib.wa.us. *In Charge*, Sally Nash
Friends of the Library Group
WESTPORT BRANCH, 506 N Montesano St, PO Box 1410, Westport, 98595-1408. SAN 363-8049. Tel: 360-268-0521. FAX: 360-268-0558. Web Site: www.timberland.lib.wa.us. *In Charge*, Kathleen Ringenberg
Friends of the Library Group
WINLOCK BRANCH, 322 First St, PO Box 428, Winlock, 98596-0428. SAN 363-8073. Tel: 360-785-3461. FAX: 360-785-3461. Web Site: www.timberland.lib.wa.us. *In Charge*, Harriet Whisler
Friends of the Library Group
YELM BRANCH, 105 Yelm Ave W, Yelm, 98597-0940. (Mail add: PO Box 940, Yelm, 98597-0940), SAN 363-8138. Tel: 360-458-3374. FAX: 360-458-5172. Web Site: www.timberland.lib.wa.us. *Librn*, Kristin Blalack; Staff 6 (MLS 1, Non-MLS 5)
Friends of the Library Group

S WASHINGTON STATE CAPITAL MUSEUM, Library & Photo Archives, 211 W 21st Ave, 98501. SAN 328-3259. Tel: 360-753-2580. FAX: 360-586-8322. Web Site: www.wshs.wa.gov. *Dir*, Derek R Valley; *Curator*, Lynette Miller; E-Mail: lmiller@wshs.wa.gov
Library Holdings: Bk Vols 300
Subject Interests: Anthropology, Art, History, Natural history, Washington
Partic in Capcon Library Network

G WASHINGTON STATE DEPARTMENT OF NATURAL RESOURCES, Division of Geology & Earth Resources Library, 1111 Washington St SE, MS 47007, 98504-7007. SAN 317-5561. Tel: 360-902-1472. FAX: 360-902-1785. *Librn*, Connie J Manson; E-Mail: connie.manson@wadnr.gov
Founded 1935
Library Holdings: Bk Vols 42,000; Per Subs 100
Subject Interests: Geology, Maps, Mineral resources, Mining
Special Collections: geologic maps; Theses
Publications: 1996 County Bibliographies; Bibliography & Index of Washington Geology & Mineral Resources, 1963-1980, 1981-1985, 1986-1990, 1991-1995; Index to Geologic & Geophysical Mapping of Washington; Landslides of Western Washington; Mount St Helens - A

Bibliography of Geoscience Literature, 1882-1986; Seismic Hazards of Western Washington; Theses of Washington Geology
Restriction: Open to public for reference only

GL WASHINGTON STATE LAW LIBRARY, Temple of Justice, PO Box 40751, 98504-0751. SAN 317-5588. Tel: 360-357-2136. FAX: 360-357-2143. E-Mail: law.library@courts.wa.gov. Web Site: www.courts.wa.gov/library.; Staff 15 (MLS 4, Non-MLS 11)
Founded 1889
Library Holdings: Bk Vols 344,000; Per Subs 915
Subject Interests: Legal res
Special Collections: Legal Periodicals
Automation Activity & Vendor Info: (Acquisitions) Innovative Interfaces Inc.; (Cataloging) Innovative Interfaces Inc.; (Circulation) Innovative Interfaces Inc.; (OPAC) Innovative Interfaces Inc.; (Serials) Innovative Interfaces Inc.
Database Vendor: OCLC - First Search
Publications: Books Recently Cataloged List (quarterly)
Partic in OCLC

P WASHINGTON STATE LIBRARY, PO Box 42460, 98504-2460. SAN 363-8162. Tel: 360-753-5590. Interlibrary Loan Service Tel: 360-753-4028. FAX: 360-586-7575. Interlibrary Loan Service FAX: 360-753-3546. Web Site: www.statelib.wa.gov. *State Librn*, Nancy Zussy; Staff 62 (MLS 62)
Founded 1853
Jul 1999-Jun 2000 Income (Main Library Only) $10,407,045, State $7,276,055, Federal $3,130,990. Mats Exp $564,184
Library Holdings: Bk Titles 339,194
Subject Interests: Behav sci, Ecology, Energy, Environmental studies, Health, Hwys, Local government, Medicine, Political science, Soc sci, State government, Transportation
Special Collections: Washington Authors; Washington Newspapers, microflm; Washington State Documents
Automation Activity & Vendor Info: (Circulation) Innovative Interfaces Inc.
Publications: Directory of Washington Libraries; Public Administration (monthly bibliography); Tuesday News (staff newsletter); Washington Public Library Statistics; Washington State Publications (monthly list)
Partic in Dialog Corporation; Medline; Westlaw
Special Services for the Deaf - Captioned film depository
Branches: 16
AIRWAY HEIGHTS CORRECTIONAL CENTER, PO Box 1899, Airway Heights, 99001-1899. SAN 378-2115. Tel: 509-244-6700, Ext 6239. FAX: 509-244-6727. *Librn*, Robert Fendler; E-Mail: rfendler@statelib.wa.gov
Jul 1999-Jun 2000 Income $108,930, State $79,723, Federal $29,207. Mats Exp $29,207
Open Tues & Wed 12:50-4 & 5:30-8:30, Thurs-Sat 7:50-11 & 12:50-4
CLALLAM BAY CORRECTION CENTER, 1830 Eagle Crest Way, Clallam Bay, 98326-9775. SAN 328-2287. Tel: 360-963-2000, Ext 3005. FAX: 360-963-3247. *In Charge*, Ben Newbold; E-Mail: bnewbold@statelib.wa.gov
Jul 1999-Jun 2000 Income $116,416, State $96,990, Federal $19,426. Mats Exp $19,426
Library Holdings: Bk Vols 8,027; Per Subs 62
Partic in OCLC
Open Mon, Tues & Fri 7:45-4:30, Wed & Thurs 12:30-9
DEPARTMENT OF LABOR & INDUSTRIES, 7273 Linderson Way SW, PO Box 44606, Tumwater, 98504-4606. SAN 363-8359. Tel: 360-902-5498. FAX: 360-902-6335. E-Mail: wsl-li@wln.com. *In Charge*, Bruce West; Tel: 360-902-5497, E-Mail: wesb235@lni.wa.gov; *Librn*, Lisa Engvall; E-Mail: ganl235@lni.wa.gov; *Asst Librn*, Claire Hall; Tel: 360-902-5421, E-Mail: hacl235@lni.wa.gov; Staff 3 (MLS 2, Non-MLS 1)
Library Holdings: Bk Vols 7,000; Bk Titles 6,000; Per Subs 140
Subject Interests: Occupational health, Occupational safety, Workmen's comp ins
Database Vendor: Dialog, Ebsco - EbscoHost, Innovative Interfaces INN - View, Lexis-Nexis, OVID Technologies, Silverplatter Information Inc.
Partic in Wash State Libr Network
DEPARTMENT OF TRANSPORTATION, Department & Transportation, PO Box 47425, 98504-7425. SAN 363-8588. Tel: 360-705-7750, 360-705-7751. FAX: 360-705-6831. *Senior Librn*, Claudia Devlin; E-Mail: devlinc@wsdot.wa.gov
Library Holdings: Per Subs 300
Subject Interests: Hwy construction, Hwy eng, Tech innovation, Tech transfer, Transportation planning
Publications: Accessions List
Partic in OCLC; OCLC Online Computer Library Center, Inc
EASTERN STATE HOSPITAL, PO Box A, B32-23, Medical Lake, 99022-0045. SAN 363-8251. Tel: 509-299-4276. FAX: 509-299-4555. *Librn*, Cathy Miller; E-Mail: cmiller@statelib.wa.gov; *Librn*, Nancy White; E-Mail: nwhite@statelib.wa.gov
Jul 1999-Jun 2000 Income State $131,265. Mats Exp $17,438
Library Holdings: Bk Vols 6,363; Per Subs 64
Subject Interests: Mental health
Partic in Dialog Corporation; OCLC
Open Mon-Thurs 8-11:30 & 12:30-4:30, Fri 8-11 & 1-4:30
MCNEIL ISLAND CORRECTION CENTER, PO Box 88900, WT-01, Steilacoom, 98388-0900. SAN 363-8448. FAX: 253-512-6587. *Librn*, Dungey; E-Mail: wdungey@statelib.wa.gov; *Librn*, Regina Joseph; Te 253-588-5281, Ext 1509, E-Mail: rjoseph@statelib.wa.gov; *Librn*, Lau Sherbo; Tel: 253-512-6586, E-Mail: lsherbo@statelib.wa.gov
Jul 1999-Jun 2000 Income $175,259, State $146,197, Federal $29,062 Mats Exp $29,062
Partic in OCLC
Open Mon, Thurs & Fri 8-4, Tues & Wed 8-8
NATURAL RESOURCES BLDG, PO Box 47000, 98504-7000. SAN 3 2131. Tel: 360-902-2992. *In Charge*, Diane Mitchell; E-Mail: dmitche statelib.wa.gov
RAINIER SCHOOL, PO Box 600, B27-20, Buckley, 98321-0600. SAN 8529. Tel: 360-829-1111, Ext 4367. FAX: 360-829-3008. *Librn*, Carol Estep; E-Mail: cestep@statelib.wa.gov; *Librn*, Beverly Hosford; E-Ma bhosford@statelib.wa.gov; *Librn*, Lynn Red; E-Mail: lred@statelib.wa
Jul 1999-Jun 2000 Income State $168,156. Mats Exp $33,292
Special Collections: Developmental Disabilities
Partic in OCLC
Open Mon-Fri 8-4:30 (closed for lunch 12-1)
STAFFORD CREEK CORRECTIONAL CENTER, 191 Constantine Wa WA-39, Aberdeen, 98520. SAN 363-8197. Tel: 360-537-1800, Ext 450 FAX: 360-537-2501. *In Charge*, Connie Blackman; E-Mail: cblackmar statelib.wa.gov
Jul 1999-Jun 2000 Income State $255,090. Mats Exp $174,238
TWIN RIVERS UNIT BRANCH LIBRARY OF THE MONROE CORRECTIONAL COMPLEX, 16774 170th Dr. SE, Monroe, 98272. (M add: PO Box 888, NM-85, Monroe, 98272-0888), Tel: 360-794-2481. FAX: 360-794-2417. *Librn*, Doug Olson; E-Mail: dolson@statelib.wa.g Staff 2 (MLS 1, Non-MLS 1)
Founded 1984
Jul 1999-Jun 2000 Income $123,252, State $105,366, Federal $17,886. Mats Exp $17,886
Library Holdings: Bk Titles 17,000; Per Subs 25
Subject Interests: Popular fiction
Automation Activity & Vendor Info: (Circulation) Sagebrush Corporation; (OPAC) Sagebrush Corporation
Partic in OCLC Online Computer Library Center, Inc; Washington Lib Network
Open Mon, Wed & Fri 7-3:30, Tues & Thurs 12-8:30
UTILITIES & TRANSPORTATION COMMISSION, PO Box 47250, 98504-7425. SAN 327-9375. Tel: 360-664-1199. FAX: 360-586-1145. *Librn*, Mary Lu White; E-Mail: mwhite@wutc.wa.gov
Library Holdings: Bk Vols 3,400; Per Subs 400
Subject Interests: Micro econ, RR, Transportation regulation, Truckin Utility mgt
Partic in OCLC
WASHINGTON CORRECTIONS CENTER FOR WOMEN, PO Box 17, Gig Harbor, 98335-0017. SAN 378-2158. Tel: 253-858-4230. FAX: 25 858-4271. *Librn*, Lori Smith Thornton; E-Mail: lthornton@statelib.wa.g *Publ Servs*, Douglas Andre Gelis; E-Mail: dgelis@statelib.wa.gov; Staf (MLS 1, Non-MLS 1)
Jul 1999-Jun 2000 Income $113,946, State $97,312, Federal $16,634. M Exp $16,634
Automation Activity & Vendor Info: (Cataloging) Innovative Interfac Inc.; (Circulation) Sagebrush Corporation; (ILL) Innovative Interfaces (OPAC) Sagebrush Corporation
Database Vendor: Ebsco - EbscoHost, OVID Technologies
Function: Reference services available
Open Mon-Fri 8-4:30
WASHINGTON STATE PENITENTIARY BRANCH LIBRARY-MAXIMUM, 1313 N 13th Ave, Walla Walla, 99362-1065. Tel: 509-526-6408. FAX: 509-626-6469. *Librn*, Tim Brown; E-Mail: tbrown@statelib.wa.gov; *Librn*, Judy Price; E-Mail: jprice@statelib.wa.gov
Jul 1999-Jun 2000 Income $156,540, State $132,056, Federal $24,484. Mats Exp $24,484
Open Mon-Thurs 8am-9pm, Fri 8-4
WASHINGTON STATE PENITENTIARY BRANCH LIBRARY-MEDIU 1313 N 13th Ave, Walla Walla, 99362-1065. SAN 363-8618. Tel: 509-5 3610, Ext 2088. FAX: 509-526-6453. *Librn*, Elizabeth Jahnke; E-Mail: ejahnke@statelib.wa.gov; Staff 2 (MLS 1, Non-MLS 1)
Jul 1999-Jun 2000 Income $127,425, State $102,913, Federal $24,512. Mats Exp $24,512. Sal $90,000
Library Holdings: Bk Titles 10,000; Per Subs 108; High Interest/Low Vocabulary Bk Vols 75
Automation Activity & Vendor Info: (Cataloging) Sagebrush Corporation; (Circulation) Sagebrush Corporation; (OPAC) Sagebrush Corporation
Open Mon 9-5, Tues-Fri 9:30-11, 12-3:30 & 4-8:30
WASHINGTON STATE REFORMATORY, PO Box 777, NM-83, Monro 98272-0777. SAN 363-8499. Tel: 360-794-2872. FAX: 360-794-2648. *Librn*, Rodney Askelson; E-Mail: raskelson@statelib.wa.gov; *Librn*, Virginia Persak; E-Mail: vpersak@statelib.wa.gov
Jul 1999-Jun 2000 Income $147,324, State $127,827, Federal $19,497. Mats Exp $19,497
Partic in OCLC

Open Mon, Wed & Thurs 12:30-4 & 5:30-8:30, Tues & Fri 7:30-11 & 12:30-4

WESTERN STATE HOSPITAL, 9601 Steilacoom Blvd SW, W27-19, WSH 08-300, Tacoma, 98498-7213. SAN 363-8677. Tel: 253-756-2715. FAX: 253-756-2598. Web Site: www.stategov.wa.gov. *Librn*, Kathleen Benoun; E-Mail: kbenoun@statelib.wa.gov; *Librn*, Sharon Brewer; E-Mail: sbrewer@statelib.wa.gov; *Librn*, Neal VanDerVoorn; E-Mail: nvandervoorn@statelib.wa.gov; Staff 3 (MLS 1, Non-MLS 2)
Pop 3,000
Jul 1999-Jun 2000 Income State $200,902. Mats Exp $55,205
Library Holdings: Bk Titles 6,000; Per Subs 230; High Interest/Low Vocabulary Bk Vols 300; Spec Interest Per Sub 200
Subject Interests: Consumer health, Geriatrics, Mental health, Mental illness, Nursing, Psychiatric nursing, Psychiatry, Psychology, Soc work, Substance abuse
Database Vendor: Innovative Interfaces INN - View, OVID Technologies
Function: ILL available
Partic in OCLC
Open Mon-Thurs 9-11 & 12-4, Fri 1:30-4

WASHINGTON STATE OFFICE OF SECRETARY OF STATE, Division Archives & Records Management,* 1129 Washington St SE, 98504-0238. SAN 326-1174. Tel: 360-586-1492. FAX: 360-664-8814. E-Mail: wa-arch@wln.com. *Archivist*, Wayne Lawson; *Tech Servs*, Everett Evans; *Cat*, David Hastings; *Ref*, Pat Hopkins; *Archivist*, Richard Hobbs; *Archivist*, James Moore; *Archivist*, Tim Eckert; *Archivist*, Michael Saunders; Staff 11 (MLS 11)
Special Collections: Washington State History (Washington State Archives Coll), unbound & bound recs

WASHINGTON STATE SUPERINTENDENT OF PUBLIC INSTRUCTION, Educational Materials Center,* Old Capitol Bldg, PO Box 47200, 98504-7200. SAN 317-557X. Tel: 360-753-6731. FAX: 360-664-0372.
Library Holdings: Bk Vols 800; Per Subs 350
Subject Interests: Education
Special Collections: Reavis Coll
Publications: SPI Publication
Partic in OCLC

WASHINGTON STATE UNIVERSITY COOPERATIVE EXTENSION, Energy Program Library, 925 Plum St SE, PO Box 43169, 98504-3169. SAN 374-4787. Tel: 360-956-2076. FAX: 360-236-2076. E-Mail: library@energy.wsu.edu. Web Site: www.energy.wsu.edu/library/. *Mgr*, Angela Santamaria; E-Mail: santamariaa@energy.wsu.edu; *ILL*, Martha Parsons; E-Mail: parsonsm@energy.wsu.edu; Staff 4 (MLS 2, Non-MLS 2)
Library Holdings: Bk Vols 17,000; Bk Titles 13,000; Per Subs 400
Subject Interests: Alternative energy, Energy conservation, Energy policy
Automation Activity & Vendor Info: (Cataloging) Innovative Interfaces Inc.; (OPAC) Innovative Interfaces Inc.
Database Vendor: Dialog, Lexis-Nexis, OCLC - First Search, ProQuest
Function: ILL available
Partic in OCLC; OCLC Online Computer Library Center, Inc; OCLC Western Service Center

SCO

COLUMBIA BASIN COLLEGE, Library Services, 2600 N 20th Ave, 99301. SAN 317-5618. Tel: 509-547-0511, Ext 2287. Reference Tel: 509-547-0511, Ext 2290. FAX: 509-547-5293. *Dean*, Katie Foley; Tel: 509-547-0511, Ext 2294, E-Mail: kfoley@cbc2.org; *ILL, Ref*, Stephen Badalamente; *Bibliog Instr, Cat, Tech Servs*, Drew Proctor
Founded 1955. Enrl 4,300; Fac 170; Highest Degree: Associate
Jul 1997-Jun 1998 Income $519,991. Mats Exp $117,349, Books $40,422, Per/Ser (Incl. Access Fees) $65,000, Micro $6,067. Sal $345,811 (Prof $154,828)
Library Holdings: Bk Vols 53,317; Bk Titles 38,286; Per Subs 266
Subject Interests: Community college curric, Nursing
Special Collections: Benton-Franklin County Law Library
Automation Activity & Vendor Info: (Circulation) Endeavor
Database Vendor: Ebsco - EbscoHost, ProQuest, Silverplatter Information Inc.
Function: Research library
Partic in Orbis; Western Libr Network

RT ANGELES

CLALLAM COUNTY LAW LIBRARY, County Courthouse, 223 E Fourth St, PO Box 863, 98362-0149. SAN 373-742X. Tel: 360-417-2287. *Librn*, Patricia Metcalf; E-Mail: pmetcalf@olypen.com
Library Holdings: Bk Vols 6,800

NATIONAL PARK SERVICE, Olympic National Park Library, Olympic National Park Visitor Ctr, 3002 Mount Angeles Rd, 98362-6798. SAN 317-5650. Tel: 360-452-0330. FAX: 360-452-0307. *In Charge*, Polly Angelakis; Tel: 360-452-0330, Ext 234
Founded 1938
Library Holdings: Bk Vols 2,000
Subject Interests: Natural history, Northwest Coast Indian culture, Papers of early pioneers, Papers of early settlers, Park history
Partic in OCLC Online Computer Library Center, Inc

P NORTH OLYMPIC LIBRARY SYSTEM, 2210 S Peabody, 98362-6536. SAN 363-8790. Tel: 360-417-8500. Interlibrary Loan Service Tel: 360-417-8501. Reference Tel: 360-417-8501. FAX: 360-457-4469. Web Site: www.nols.org. *Dir*, George Stratton; Tel: 360-417-8525, E-Mail: gstratton@nols.org; *Ch Servs*, Colleen Cunningham; *Asst Dir, Exten Serv*, Leslie Spotkov; *ILL*, Margaret Ritchie; *Publ Servs*, Susan Skaggs; Staff 8 (MLS 8)
Founded 1919. Pop 66,400; Circ 695,935
2000-2001 Mats Exp $375,000, Books $194,000, Per/Ser (Incl. Access Fees) $169,000, Electronic Ref Mat (Incl. Access Fees) $12,000
Library Holdings: Bk Vols 245,992; Bk Titles 129,915; Per Subs 607; Bks on Deafness & Sign Lang 152
Special Collections: Clallam County History (Bert Kellogg Coll), photog, slides; Pacific Northwest History, bks, maps, oral hist
Automation Activity & Vendor Info: (Acquisitions) epixtech, inc.; (Cataloging) epixtech, inc.; (Circulation) epixtech, inc.
Database Vendor: OCLC - First Search
Partic in OCLC Online Computer Library Center, Inc
Friends of the Library Group
Branches: 4
CLALLAM BAY BRANCH, PO Box 106, Clallam Bay, 98326. SAN 363-8812. Tel: 360-963-2414. FAX: 360-963-2260. *Mgr*, Cheryl Pelletier
Friends of the Library Group
FORKS BRANCH, PO Box 1817, Forks, 98331. SAN 363-8820. Tel: 360-374-6402. FAX: 360-374-6499. *Mgr*, Frances Henneke
PORT ANGELES BRANCH, 2210 S Peabody St, 98362. SAN 363-8855. Tel: 360-417-8500. Interlibrary Loan Service Tel: 360-417-8501. FAX: 360-457-2581.
Friends of the Library Group
SEQUIM BRANCH, 630 N Sequim Ave, Sequim, 98382. SAN 363-888X. Tel: 360-683-1161. FAX: 360-681-7811. *Mgr*, Jola Nicola
Friends of the Library Group

J PENINSULA COMMUNITY COLLEGE, John D Glann Library, 1502 E Lauridsen Blvd, 98362-6698. SAN 317-5669. Tel: 360-452-9277. FAX: 360-417-6295. Web Site: www.pc.ctc.edu/lmc/. *Dir*, Paula B Doherty; Tel: 360-417-6275, E-Mail: pdohrt@ctc.edu; Staff 2 (MLS 2)
Founded 1961
1999-2000 Mats Exp $96,494, Per/Ser (Incl. Access Fees) $17,413, Micro $43,838, Other Print Mats $35,243. Sal $267,328
Library Holdings: Bk Titles 34,000; Per Subs 343
Special Collections: Chamber music
Automation Activity & Vendor Info: (Cataloging) Endeavor; (Circulation) Endeavor; (Course Reserve) Endeavor; (Media Booking) Endeavor; (OPAC) Endeavor; (Serials) Endeavor

S PENINSULA DAILY NEWS LIBRARY,* 305 W First St, PO Box 1330, 98362. SAN 373-3580. Tel: 360-452-2345. Toll Free Tel: 800-826-7714. FAX: 360-417-3521. Web Site: www.peninsuladailynews.com/. *Librn*, Geri Zanon
Subject Interests: Economics

PORT HADLOCK

P JEFFERSON COUNTY RURAL LIBRARY DISTRICT,* 620 Cedar Ave, PO Box 990, 98339-0990. SAN 321-4818. Tel: 360-385-6544. FAX: 360-385-7921. *Dir*, Bill Mitchell; *Librn*, Judith B Gunter; *Librn*, Lorraine Jackson; *Publ Servs*, Meredith Wagner; *Bkmobile Coordr*, Judith Lucia; *ILL*, Shery Hart; *Circ*, Jeanne Mahan; *Ref*, Brad Collier; Staff 12 (MLS 2, Non-MLS 10)
Founded 1980. Pop 17,500; Circ 217,000
Jan 1997-Dec 1998 Income $739,000. Mats Exp $84,000, Books $65,000, Per/Ser (Incl. Access Fees) $7,000. Sal $337,660
Library Holdings: Bk Vols 51,000; Per Subs 240
Partic in OCLC
Friends of the Library Group

PORT ORCHARD

GL KITSAP COUNTY LAW LIBRARY, 614 Division St, 98366. SAN 323-6471. Tel: 360-337-5788. E-Mail: library@kitsapbar.com. Web Site: www.kitsapbar.com/library. *Librn*, Paul Fjelstad
Library Holdings: Bk Vols 10,000

PORT TOWNSEND

S JEFFERSON COUNTY HISTORICAL SOCIETY MUSEUM, 210 Madison, 98368. SAN 329-8795. Tel: 360-385-1003. FAX: 360-385-1042. E-Mail: jchsmuseum@olympus.net. Web Site: www.jchsmuseum.org. *Dir*, Dr Niki R Clark; Staff 4 (Non-MLS 4)
Founded 1951
Library Holdings: Bk Vols 750

Subject Interests: Local history, Local photos, Maritime history, Victorian archit, Victorian decoration
Restriction: Non-circulating
Partic in Cooperating Libraries Automated Network (CLAN)

P PORT TOWNSEND PUBLIC LIBRARY, 1220 Lawrence St, 98368-6527. SAN 317-5677. Tel: 360-385-3181. FAX: 360-385-5805. E-Mail: ptlib10@olympus.net. Web Site: www.wlo.statelib.lib.wa.us/ptpl. *Dir*, Linnea R Patrick; Tel: 360-344-3054; *Ch Servs*, Beth de Jarnette; *Automation Syst Coordr, Ref*, Carol Cahill. Subject Specialists: *Adult fiction*, Linnea R Patrick; *Pac NW hist*, Linnea R Patrick; Staff 8 (MLS 3, Non-MLS 5)
Founded 1898. Pop 8,440; Circ 185,000
Jan 2000-Dec 2000 Income $465,499, City $445,297, Federal $20,220. Mats Exp $40,189, Books $25,505, Per/Ser (Incl. Access Fees) $7,500, AV Equip $1,684, Electronic Ref Mat (Incl. Access Fees) $5,000. Sal $274,835 (Prof $134,000)
Library Holdings: Bk Vols 38,000; Per Subs 135
Subject Interests: Folklore jungian psychol, Jungian psychol, Maritime, Mythology, Pac NW hist
Special Collections: Maritime Resource Center
Automation Activity & Vendor Info: (OPAC) epixtech, inc.
Database Vendor: Dialog, epixtech, inc., GaleNet, IAC - SearchBank, ProQuest
Partic in Cooperating Libraries Automated Network (CLAN)
Also have a Library Foundation
Friends of the Library Group

PROSSER

P PROSSER PUBLIC LIBRARY,* 902 Seventh St, 99350-1454. SAN 317-5685. Tel: 509-786-2533. FAX: 509-786-7341. E-Mail: proslib3@bentonrea.com. *Librn*, Margaret Klover; *Asst Librn*, Ruby Michner; *Tech Servs*, Nancy Martinez
Founded 1910. Circ 40,235
Jan 1999-Dec 1999 Income City $185,000. Sal $74,800
Library Holdings: Bk Vols 27,097; Per Subs 75
Subject Interests: Wine
Automation Activity & Vendor Info: (Cataloging) Sagebrush Corporation; (Circulation) Sagebrush Corporation
Database Vendor: OCLC - First Search
Friends of the Library Group

PULLMAN

P NEILL PUBLIC LIBRARY, (NPL), Pullman Public Library, 210 N Grand Ave, 99163-2693. SAN 317-5693. Tel: 509-334-3595, 509-334-4555. FAX: 509-334-6051. E-Mail: library@neill-lib.org. Web Site: www.neill-lib.org. *Dir*, Michael Pollastro; *Commun Servs*, Andriette Pieron; *YA Servs*, Nancy Collins-Warner; Staff 5 (MLS 4, Non-MLS 1)
Founded 1921. Pop 25,630; Circ 249,349
Jan 1999-Dec 1999 Income City $757,866. Mats Exp $108,636, Books $76,191, Per/Ser (Incl. Access Fees) $5,562, AV Equip $23,648, Electronic Ref Mat (Incl. Access Fees) $3,235. Sal $344,645
Library Holdings: Bk Vols 57,695; Per Subs 163
Special Collections: English as a Second Language Coll; Local History (Northwest)
Automation Activity & Vendor Info: (Cataloging) TLC; (Circulation) epixtech, inc.; (OPAC) epixtech, inc.
Database Vendor: GaleNet, ProQuest
Friends of the Library Group

C WASHINGTON STATE UNIVERSITY LIBRARIES,* PO Box 64510, 99164-5610. SAN 363-891X. Tel: 509-335-9671. FAX: 509-335-6721. Interlibrary Loan Service FAX: 509-335-0934. Web Site: www.wsulibs.wsu.edu/. *Dir*, Nancy Baker; *Tech Servs*, Sharon Walbridge; *ILL*, Kay Vyhnanek; *Bibliogr*, Ingrid Mifflin; *Acq*, Robert Ferguson; Staff 153 (MLS 49, Non-MLS 104)
Founded 1892. Highest Degree: Doctorate
Jul 1997-Jun 1998 Income $11,916,852. Mats Exp $4,564,575, Books $931,887, Per/Ser (Incl. Access Fees) $3,449,705, Presv $95,015. Sal $5,512,109 (Prof $1,911,649)
Library Holdings: Bk Vols 1,966,516; Per Subs 27,377
Special Collections: Angling; ERDA; Ethnic History (Germans From Russia); Hispanic Americana; Leonard & Virginia Woolf Libr:& Bloomsbury Coll, (The Sitwells); Moldenhalier (music) Archives; Pacific Northwest History; Pacific Northwest Agricultural History Archives; Pacific Northwest Publishers Archives; Pierre-Jean Desmet; School Archives; music scores; sound recordings; moving image materials; Veterinary History; Wildlife & Outdoor Recreation
Automation Activity & Vendor Info: (Acquisitions) Innovative Interfaces Inc.; (Circulation) Innovative Interfaces Inc.
Partic in Asn of Research Libraries; Center For Research Libraries; Coop Libr Agency for Syst & Servs; Dialog Corporation; Eric Processing & Reference Facility; Medline; Wash Coop Libr Project
Friends of the Library Group
Departmental Libraries:
ARCHITECTURE, PO Box 642210, 99164-2210. SAN 376-9569. Tel: 509-335-4967.
EDUCATION, PO Box 642112, 99164-2112. SAN 363-8944. Tel: 509-1591. FAX: 507-335-6425. *Librn*, Cindy Kaag
OWEN SCIENCE & ENGINEERING, PO Box 643200, 99164-3200. S. 363-8979. Tel: 509-335-4181. FAX: 509-335-2534. *Librn*, Darlene Hildebrandt

CM VETERINARY MEDICAL & PHARMACY, 170 Wegner Hall, PO Box 646512, 99164-6512. SAN 363-9002. Tel: 509-335-9556. FAX: 509-3 5158. Web Site: www.wsulibs.swu.edu/vet/vethmpag.htm. *Head of Lib* Vicki Croft; Tel: 509-335-5544, E-Mail: croft@wsu.edu; Staff 5 (MLS Non-MLS 3)
Founded 1963
Library Holdings: Bk Vols 65,000; Per Subs 580
Subject Interests: Pharmacology, Pharmacy, Toxicology, Veterinary medicine
Database Vendor: Dialog, Innovative Interfaces INN - View, Lexis-N OCLC - First Search, ProQuest, Silverplatter Information Inc.
Function: Research library
Partic in Wash Coop Libr Project

PUYALLUP

P CHIEF LESCHI LIBRARY, Chief Leschi Schools,* 5625 52nd St E, 98 SAN 370-5307. Tel: 253-445-6000. *Librn*, Ronald W Simchen
Founded 1972
Library Holdings: Bk Titles 80,000; Per Subs 12
Special Collections: Archival (Puyallup Tribe) papers, notes; Puyallup T

S NIXON & BACCUS FAMILY ASSOCIATION CLEARINGHOUSE, 58 144th St E, 98375-5221. SAN 373-3009. Tel: 253-537-8288. *Mgr*, Janet Baccus; E-Mail: janetgb@worldnet.att.net
Founded 1981
Library Holdings: Bk Vols 1,150
Subject Interests: Genealogy, Local history

P PUYALLUP PUBLIC LIBRARY,* 324 S Meridian, 98371. SAN 317-57 Tel: 253-841-5454. FAX: 253-841-5483. Web Site: www.ci.puyallup.wa.u *Dir*, Catherine G Uhl; Staff 3 (MLS 3)
Founded 1912. Pop 30,000; Circ 390,000
Jan 2000-Dec 2000 Income $800,000, City $770,000, Locally Generated Income $30,000. Mats Exp $164,800, Books $100,000, Per/Ser (Incl. Acc Fees) $7,000, Micro $500, Electronic Ref Mat (Incl. Access Fees) $25,0 Sal $418,000 (Prof $169,000)
Library Holdings: Bk Vols 78,000; Per Subs 121
Subject Interests: Local hist (Puyallup Valley)
Open Mon-Thurs 10-8, Fri & Sat 10-5
Friends of the Library Group

REARDAN

P REARDAN PUBLIC LIBRARY,* S 120 Oak, PO Box 227, 99029. SAN 317-5715. Tel: 509-796-3921. FAX: 509-796-3925. *Librn*, Lisa Moore
Pop 450; Circ 3,395
Library Holdings: Bk Vols 9,700
Special Collections: Davenport Times Coll
Friends of the Library Group

REDMOND

S ALLIED-SIGNAL AVIONICS LIBRARY,* Bldg 1, 15001 NE 36th St, P Box 97001, 98073-9701. SAN 317-5758. Tel: 425-885-3711. FAX: 425-8 2061.
Founded 1957
Library Holdings: Bk Titles 1,200; Per Subs 100
Subject Interests: Accelerometers, Airborne annunciators, Avionic flight control systs, Cockpit voice recorders, Flight data recorders, Passenger entertainment systs, Pressure transducers, Servo pressure gauges, Temperature controls, Thermal switches, Vibration transducers
Special Collections: Airbus Industries; Arinc Standards; ASTM Standards CCITT & ISO Standards; EIA/Jedec Standards; FAA Documents; IEEE Standards; IPC Standards; Military/Federal Standards & Specifications; World Maps
Partic in Dialog Corporation; OCLC; OCLC Online Computer Library Center, Inc

S GOLDER ASSOCIATES, INC, Seattle Library, 18300 NE Union Hill Rd, Ste 200, 98052-3333. SAN 373-8922. Tel: 425-883-0777. FAX: 425-882-5498. *Mgr*, Fern Honore; E-Mail: fhonore@glolder.com; *Librn*, Colleen Kellerman; Staff 2 (MLS 2)
Founded 1979
2000-2001 Mats Exp $35,000, Books $3,400, Per/Ser (Incl. Access Fees) $31,000, Electronic Ref Mat (Incl. Access Fees) $600. Sal $74,960
Library Holdings: Bk Titles 15,000; Per Subs 275
Automation Activity & Vendor Info: (Cataloging) Inmagic, Inc.; (Circulation) Inmagic, Inc.

NTON

CITY UNIVERSITY LIBRARY, 919 SW Grady Way, 98055. SAN 321-7191. Tel: 206-204-3760. Toll Free Tel: 800-526-4269. FAX: 425-204-3865. E-Mail: library@cityu.edu. Web Site: www.cityu.edu/library/lib-svcs.htm. *Dean, Mgr Libr Serv*, Verla Peterson; *Br Coordr*, Daria Lall; *Br Coordr*, Barbara Williams; *Librn*, Theresa Gehrig; *Librn*, Karen Harrison; *Librn*, Yvette Olson; *Librn*, Laura Staley; Staff 8 (MLS 8)
Founded 1973. Enrl 6,500; Highest Degree: Master
Jul 1999-Jun 2000 Income $980,000. Mats Exp $490,800. Sal $350,000
Library Holdings: Bk Vols 33,000; Bk Titles 25,000; Per Subs 1,100
Subject Interests: Bus mgt, Education
Automation Activity & Vendor Info: (Acquisitions) Endeavor; (Circulation) Endeavor; (Course Reserve) Endeavor; (OPAC) Endeavor; (Serials) Endeavor
Partic in OCLC Online Computer Library Center, Inc

RENTON PUBLIC LIBRARY, 100 Mill Ave S, 98055-2126. SAN 363-9037. Tel: 425-430-6610. TDD: 425-430-6612. FAX: 425-430-6833. Web Site: www.ci.renton.wa.us. *Dir*, Clark H Petersen; Tel: 425-430-6820; *Asst Dir, Tech Servs*, Marilyn Pederson; Tel: 425-430-6832; *Ch Servs, YA Servs*, Jerene Battisti; Tel: 425-430-6825; *Bibliog Instr, Online Servs, Ref*, Barbara Pozner; Tel: 425-430-6824; Staff 6 (MLS 6)
Founded 1914. Pop 48,270; Circ 334,619
Jan 2000-Dec 2000 Income (Main Library and Branch Library) City $1,338,300. Mats Exp $198,000, Books $158,280, Per/Ser (Incl. Access Fees) $11,580, AV Equip $9,120, Electronic Ref Mat (Incl. Access Fees) $19,020. Sal $1,037,111
Library Holdings: Bk Titles 112,000; Per Subs 365
Special Collections: Pacific Northwest (Washington State Coll), bks, per
Automation Activity & Vendor Info: (Acquisitions) epixtech, inc.; (Circulation) epixtech, inc.; (OPAC) epixtech, inc.; (Serials) epixtech, inc.
Database Vendor: OCLC - First Search
Publications: Homeschooling
Friends of the Library Group
Branches: 1
HIGHLANDS, 2902 NE 12th St, 98056. SAN 363-9061. Tel: 425-430-6790.
Library Holdings: Bk Vols 32,000

RENTON TECHNICAL COLLEGE, Library Resource Center,* 3000 NE Fourth St, 98056-4195. SAN 373-6318. Tel: 425-235-2331. FAX: 425-235-7832. Web Site: renton.library.ctc.edu. *Librn*, Eric Palo; E-Mail: epalo@rtc.ctc.edu; Staff 3 (MLS 1, Non-MLS 2)
Founded 1991. Enrl 3,416; Fac 178; Highest Degree: Associate
Jul 1999-Jun 2000 Income $200,000. Mats Exp $45,000
Library Holdings: Bk Titles 13,000; Per Subs 130
Automation Activity & Vendor Info: (Acquisitions) Endeavor; (Cataloging) Endeavor; (Circulation) Endeavor; (Course Reserve) Endeavor; (OPAC) Endeavor; (Serials) Endeavor
Partic in OCLC
Special Services for the Deaf - TTY machine

VALLEY MEDICAL CENTER LIBRARY, 400 S 43rd St, 98055. SAN 317-5774. Tel: 425-251-5194. FAX: 425-656-5429. Web Site: www.valleymed.org (click on services). *Librn*, Barbara Ivester; E-Mail: barbara_ivester@valleymed.org; *Librn*, Nancy Turrentine; E-Mail: nancy_turrentine@valleymed.org; Staff 1 (MLS 1)
Founded 1978
Jan 1999-Dec 1999 Income Parent Institution $95,341. Mats Exp $28,600, Per/Ser (Incl. Access Fees) $28,000, Micro $600. Sal $44,383
Library Holdings: Bk Vols 800; Bk Titles 750; Per Subs 138
Subject Interests: Medical
Automation Activity & Vendor Info: (Serials) EOS
Partic in Docline

CHLAND

ENERGY NORTHWEST LIBRARY, WNP-2 N Power Plant Loop, PO Box 968, 99352. SAN 317-5855. Tel: 509-377-6145. FAX: 509-377-8250. *Librn*, Betty Hodges; E-Mail: bjhodges@wnp2.com
Founded 1973
Library Holdings: Bk Vols 9,375; Per Subs 35
Subject Interests: Electrical power, Energy, Indust standards, Nuclear power

FLUOR FEDERAL SERVICES LIBRARY, (Formerly Fluor Daniel Northwest Library), Library E6-13, 1200 Jadwin, 99352. (Mail add: PO Box 1050, 99352), SAN 370-1425. Tel: 509-372-2000, 509-376-6941. FAX: 509-372-1742. *Librn*, Patricia A Davis; E-Mail: patricia_a_davis@rl.gov; *Librn*, Janice L McMullin; E-Mail: janice_l_mcmmullin@rl.gov
Library Holdings: Bk Vols 100,000
Function: Reference only

PACIFIC NORTHWEST NATIONAL LABORATORY, Hanford Technical Library, 2770 University Dr, 99352. (Mail add: PO Box 999, 99352), SAN 317-5804. Tel: 509-372-7430. Circulation Tel: 509-372-7440. Reference Tel: 509-372-7430. FAX: 509-372-7431. E-Mail: pnl.techlib@pnl.gov. Web Site: www.pnl.gov/tech_lib/home.html. *Dir*, Erik N Anderson; Tel: 509-372-7448, Fax: 509-372-7459, E-Mail: erik.anderson@pnl.gov; *Asst Dir*, Melissa K McBurney; Tel: 509-372-7434; *Coll Develop*, Nancy Doran; Tel: 509-372-7434; *ILL*, Cheryl A Wiborg; Tel: 509-372-7432; Staff 27 (MLS 8, Non-MLS 19)
Founded 1948
Library Holdings: Bk Vols 38,000; Per Subs 1,170
Subject Interests: Biology, Chemistry, Engineering, Environmental studies, Metallurgy, Nuclear tech, Physica, Sci-tech
Special Collections: Department of Energy Contractor Reports
Automation Activity & Vendor Info: (Cataloging) epixtech, inc.; (Circulation) epixtech, inc.; (OPAC) epixtech, inc.; (Serials) epixtech, inc.
Database Vendor: epixtech, inc.
Partic in OCLC
Merged with Washington State University at Tri-Cities Library
Branches:
LEGAL LIBRARY, Federal Bldg, Rm 431, PO Box 800, 99352. SAN 329-3203. Tel: 509-376-6807. FAX: 509-376-9039. *Librn*, Margaret Dagle
Library Holdings: Bk Vols 9,000
Subject Interests: Environ regulations, Environmental law

S PACIFIC NORTHWEST NATIONAL LABORATORY, Department of Energy's Public Reading Room,* 2770 University Dr, CIC Rm 101L, 99352. SAN 373-3017. Tel: 509-372-7443. FAX: 509-372-7444. E-Mail: doe.reading.room@pnl.gov. Web Site: www.hanford.gov/doe/reading.htm or rrcatalog.pnl.gov.
Publications: Reading Room Catalog

P RICHLAND PUBLIC LIBRARY,* 955 Northgate Dr, 99352-3539. SAN 317-5839. Tel: 509-942-7450. FAX: 509-942-7447. Web Site: richland.lib.wa.us. *Tech Servs*, Judy McMakin; Tel: 509-942-7445; *Dir*, Wayne L Suggs; *Ch Servs*, Sheila Dickinson; Tel: 509-942-7452; *Ref*, Kathy Knutson; Tel: 509-942-7457; Staff 34 (MLS 8, Non-MLS 26)
Founded 1951. Pop 36,500; Circ 470,981
Jan 1998-Dec 1998 Income $1,286,078, City $1,184,692, Federal $4,528, Other $96,965. Mats Exp $216,018, Books $162,879, Per/Ser (Incl. Access Fees) $53,139. Sal $827,380
Library Holdings: Bk Vols 116,540; Per Subs 576
Special Collections: Nuclear Regulatory Commission; Repository (WPPSS Documents), micro, print; Richland & Tri-City Area History (Local History), bk, micro
Automation Activity & Vendor Info: (Acquisitions) epixtech, inc.; (Cataloging) epixtech, inc.; (Circulation) epixtech, inc.; (Course Reserve) epixtech, inc.; (ILL) epixtech, inc.; (Media Booking) epixtech, inc.; (OPAC) epixtech, inc.; (Serials) epixtech, inc.
Database Vendor: IAC - Info Trac, ProQuest
Special Services for the Blind - VisualTek closed circuit TV reading aid
Fee charged for non-residents
Friends of the Library Group

C WASHINGTON STATE UNIVERSITY TRI-CITIES, Consolidated Information Center, 2710 University Dr, 99352. SAN 317-5820. Tel: 509-372-7000. Circulation Tel: 509-372-7440. Reference Tel: 509-372-7430. FAX: 509-372-7281. Web Site: www.tricity.wsu.edu. *Dir*, Barbara Burrows; Tel: 780-492-5562, E-Mail: barbara.burrows@ualberta.ca; Staff 5 (MLS 2, Non-MLS 3)
Founded 1990. Enrl 640; Fac 50; Highest Degree: Master
Library Holdings: Bk Titles 15,000
Partic in Western Libr Network
Friends of the Library Group

RITZVILLE

P RITZVILLE PUBLIC LIBRARY,* 302 W Main, 99169. SAN 317-5863. Tel: 509-659-1222. FAX: 509-659-0253. E-Mail: ritzlib@ritzcom.net. *Dir*, Sandra Fitch
Founded 1903. Circ 22,484
Library Holdings: Bk Vols 14,722; Per Subs 51
Partic in OCLC
Friends of the Library Group

ROSLYN

P ROSLYN PUBLIC LIBRARY,* 201 S First, PO Box 451, 98941-0451. SAN 317-5871. Tel: 509-649-3420. FAX: 509-649-3420. E-Mail: rpl@inlandnet.com. *Librn*, Erin Krake
Founded 1898. Pop 1,200
Jan 1997-Dec 1997 Mats Exp $24,088, Books $6,669, Per/Ser (Incl. Access Fees) $100, Other Print Mats $100. Sal $16,000
Library Holdings: Bk Titles 16,800; Per Subs 12
Subject Interests: Genealogy, Pacific Northwest
Partic in Kittitas Regional Libr Syst
Friends of the Library Group

SEATTLE

M ARNOLD DIGITAL LIBRARY, 1100 Fairview Ave N, B-010, PO Box 19024, 98109-1024. SAN 317-6037. Tel: 206-667-4314. Interlibrary Loan Service Tel: 206-667-6852. Reference Tel: 202-667-6850. FAX: 206-667-4737. E-Mail: library@fhcrc.org. Web Site: www.fhcrc.org/library. *Coll Develop, Dir*, Ann Marie Clark; Staff 10 (MLS 5, Non-MLS 5)
Founded 1975
Library Holdings: Bk Titles 2,300; Per Subs 340
Subject Interests: Biochemistry, Biology, Biostatistics, Epidemiology, Genetics, Hematology, Immunology, Medicine, Molecular biology, Oncology, Pathology, Pharmacology, Pub health med, Radiology, Surgery, Virology
Publications: Line-Up (newsletter)
Partic in Nat Libr of Med/Docline; OCLC Online Computer Library Center, Inc

§S ART INSTITUTE OF SEATTLE LIBRARY, 2323 Elliott Ave, 98121. SAN 375-4448. Tel: 206-239-2359. FAX: 206-441-3475. *Dir*, Cathy Donaldson
Library Holdings: Bk Vols 16,500; Bk Titles 16,000; Per Subs 290
Subject Interests: Applied art, Design
Automation Activity & Vendor Info: (Cataloging) Athena; (Circulation) Athena
Open Mon-Thurs 7:15am-10pm, Fri 7:15am-6pm, Sat 10-4:30 (during school session)

S BATTELLE-SEATTLE RESEARCH CENTER, Library & Information Services, 4500 Sand Point Way NE, Ste 1000, 98105-3949. SAN 317-591X. Tel: 206-528-3370. FAX: 206-528-3553. E-Mail: schuelle@battelle.org. *Mgr*, Janette Schueller; Tel: 206-528-3372, E-Mail: schuelle@battelle.org; Staff 3 (MLS 1, Non-MLS 2)
Founded 1968
Library Holdings: Per Subs 150
Subject Interests: Environment, Public health, Transportation
Database Vendor: CARL, Dialog, OCLC - First Search, ProQuest
Partic in Dialog Corporation; Docline; Nat Libr of Med; OCLC; OCLC Online Computer Library Center, Inc

S BOEING CO, Technical Libraries,* M/S 62-LC, PO Box 3707, 98124-2207. SAN 363-9185. Tel: 425-237-8311. FAX: 237-4582, 425-237-3491. *Mgr*, Corinne A Campbell; Staff 51 (MLS 25, Non-MLS 26)
Founded 1938
Library Holdings: Bk Vols 120,000; Per Subs 5,500
Subject Interests: Aeronautics, Bus, Chemistry, Computers, Economics, Electronics, Eng tech, Engineering, Government, Industrial medicine, Mgt, Missile tech, Physics, Transportation
Special Collections: International Data Bank
Publications: Boeing Documents Bulletin (monthly); Library Announcement Bulletin (monthly); Specialized Newsletters
Restriction: Staff use only
Partic in Aerospace Res Info Network; Defense Technical Information Center; Dialog Corporation; OCLC Online Computer Library Center, Inc
Libraries located in Bellevue, Kent & Renton, Wash

S BROWN & CALDWELL (ENGINEERING) SEATTLE LIBRARY,* 999 Third Ave, Ste 500, 98104-4012. SAN 326-1182. Tel: 206-624-0100. FAX: 206-749-2200. *Librn*, Marilyn Burwell; E-Mail: mburwell@brwncald.com; Staff 2 (MLS 1, Non-MLS 1)
Founded 1978
1999-2000 Income $21,400. Mats Exp $18,500, Books $2,400, Per/Ser (Incl. Access Fees) $9,100, Manuscripts & Archives $7,000

G THE BUSINESS ENTERPRISE CENTER, Information Center,* 1200 Sixth Ave, Ste 1700, 98101-1128. SAN 373-6059. Tel: 206-553-7311. FAX: 206-553-7044. E-Mail: score55@aol.com. Web Site: www.sba.gov/region5/wa/seat.htm. *Mgr*, Tina Bradley; Staff 1 (MLS 1)
Founded 1991
Library Holdings: Bk Vols 3,000; Per Subs 20
Special Collections: TQM Coll, bks & v-tapes

L CARNEY, BADLEY, SMITH & SPELLMAN LIBRARY, (Formerly Carney, Badley, Smith & Spellman), Law Library, 701 Fifth Ave No 2200, 98104. SAN 372-3313. Tel: 206-607-4149. FAX: 206-467-8215. Web Site: www.carneylaw.com. *Librn*, Susan Beebe; E-Mail: beebe@carneylaw.com
Library Holdings: Bk Vols 10,000; Per Subs 30

S CENTER FOR URBAN HORTICULTURE, Elisabeth C Miller Horticulture Library, University of Washington, PO Box 354115, 98195-4115. SAN 328-0918. Tel: 206-543-0415. FAX: 206-685-2692. E-Mail: hortlib@u.washington.edu. Web Site: www.depts.washington.edu/hortlib. *Mgr*, Valerie Easton; Staff 2 (MLS 2)
Founded 1985
Library Holdings: Bk Vols 7,000; Per Subs 300
Subject Interests: Horticulture
Special Collections: Seed Catalogs
Restriction: Non-circulating to the public
Partic in OCLC Online Computer Library Center, Inc

M CHILDREN'S HOSPITAL & REGIONAL MEDICAL CENTER, Hospi Library, 4800 Sand Point Way NE CH-38, PO Box 5371, 98105. SAN 3 5944. Tel: 206-526-2098. Reference Tel: 206-526-2118. FAX: 206-527-3 E-Mail: library@chmc.org. *Librn*, Susan Lee Klawansky; E-Mail: sklaw chmc.org; *Librn*, Kathleen McCrory; E-Mail: kmccro@chmc.org. Subjec Specialists: *Pediatrics*, Kathleen McCrory; *Pediatrics*, Susan Lee Klawansky; Staff 3 (MLS 2, Non-MLS 1)
Founded 1946
Library Holdings: Bk Vols 2,600; Bk Titles 2,500; Per Subs 350
Subject Interests: Child psychiat, Child psychology, Pediatric med
Database Vendor: Dialog, OVID Technologies

C CORNISH COLLEGE OF THE ARTS LIBRARY, Cornish North Camp 1501 Tenth Ave E, 98102. (Mail add: 710 E Roy St, 98102), SAN 317-5 Tel: 206-726-5041. FAX: 206-726-5055. E-Mail: library@cornish.edu. W Site: www.cornish.edu/information/library.htm. *Dir Libr Serv*, Hollis P N Tel: 206-726-5040, E-Mail: hnear@cornish.edu; *Librn*, Melinda P Olson E-Mail: molson@cornish.edu; *Curator*, Steven M Vromm; Tel: 206-726-5126, E-Mail: svroom@cornish.edu; Staff 3 (MLS 2, Non-MLS 1)
Founded 1973. Enrl 700; Highest Degree: Bachelor
Library Holdings: Bk Vols 17,500; Bk Titles 15,000; Per Subs 110
Subject Interests: Art, Dance, Design, Music, Performance, Theatre
Special Collections: Slide Coll
Automation Activity & Vendor Info: (Cataloging) CASPR; (Circulatio CASPR; (OPAC) CASPR; (Serials) CASPR

S DAMES & MOORE LIBRARY,* 2025 First Ave, Ste 500, 98121. SAN 317-5960. Tel: 206-728-0744. FAX: 206-727-3350.
Founded 1974
Library Holdings: Bk Titles 3,500; Per Subs 100
Subject Interests: Aquatic biol of Pacific NW, Geology of Puget Sound, Hazardous wastes mgt, Marine biol of Pacific NW, Solid wastes mgt
Partic in OCLC Online Computer Library Center, Inc

L DAVIS, WRIGHT & TREMAINE, Law Library, 2600 Century Sq, 1501 Fourth Ave, 98101-1688. SAN 372-3631. Tel: 206-622-3150. FAX: 206-(7699. *Librn*, Christy Leith; *Assoc Librn*, Fred Hanson; Tel: 206-628-760(*Assoc Librn*, Connelly Johnson
Library Holdings: Bk Vols 40,000
Partic in OCLC Online Computer Library Center, Inc

GM DEPARTMENT OF VETERANS AFFAIRS, Puget Sound Health Care System Seattle Division Medical Library, 1660 S Columbian Way, 98108 1597. SAN 317-6525. Tel: 206-764-2065. FAX: 206-764-2816. *Dir*, Elizabeth S Visconti; E-Mail: elizabeth.visconti@med.va.gov; *Librn*, Ted Hamilton; Tel: 206-277-6107, E-Mail: theodore.hamilton@med.va.gov; *Librn*, Mia Hammula; Tel: 206-277-3255, E-Mail: mia.hannula@med.va.g Staff 5 (MLS 3, Non-MLS 2)
Founded 1951
Library Holdings: Bk Vols 4,400; Bk Titles 3,327; Per Subs 338
Subject Interests: Alcohol abuse, Clinical medicine, Drug abuse, Gerontology, Metabolism, Psychia, Psychology, Spinal cord injury
Database Vendor: OCLC - First Search, OVID Technologies, ProQuest, Silverplatter Information Inc.
Partic in Nat Libr of Med; Vets Admin Libr Network

SR DIOCESE OF OLYMPIA, Diocesan Resource Center, 1551 Tenth Ave E, PO Box 12126, 98102. SAN 326-5277. Tel: 206-325-4200. Toll Free Tel: 800-488-4978 ((WA state)). FAX: 206-325-4631. *Dir*, Tovi Harris; E-Mai tharris@olympia.anglican.org
Library Holdings: Bk Titles 6,800; Per Subs 100
Subject Interests: Religious education, Theology
Special Collections: Episcopal Church in Western WA

L FOSTER, PEPPER & SHEFELMAN PLLC, Research Center, 1111 Third Ave, Ste 3400, 98101. SAN 327-4314. Tel: 206-447-6474. FAX: 206-447-9700. E-Mail: researchcenter@foster.com. *Dir*, Barbara Rothwell; Tel: 20(447-2811, Fax: 206-749-2049, E-Mail: rothb@foster.com; Staff 6 (MLS 3, Non-MLS 3)
Library Holdings: Bk Vols 13,000
Database Vendor: Dialog, Lexis-Nexis
Function: Research library

S FRYE ART MUSEUM LIBRARY,* 704 Terry Ave, 98104. SAN 317-599 Tel: 206-622-9250. FAX: 206-223-1707. *Dir*, Richard V West; E-Mail: richard@fryemuseum.org
Oct 1996-Sep 1997 Mats Exp $4,100, Books $3,500, Presv $600
Library Holdings: Bk Vols 1,000
Special Collections: 19th & 20th Century American & German Art

L GARVEY, SCHUBERT & BARER, Law Library,* 1191 Second Ave, Ste 1800, 98101-2939. SAN 372-3968. Tel: 206-464-3939. FAX: 206-464-012 Web Site: www.gsblaw.com. *Librn*, Jill Allyn; E-Mail: jallyn@gsblaw.com
Library Holdings: Bk Vols 10,000

L GRAHAM & DUNN, Law Library, 1420 Fifth Ave, 33rd flr, 98101-2390. SAN 317-6010. Tel: 206-624-8300. Reference Tel: 206-903-4801. FAX: 2(340-9599. *Librn*, Katie Drake; E-Mail: kdrake@grahamdunn.com; Staff 2 (MLS 1, Non-MLS 1)

Library Holdings: Bk Vols 10,000
Subject Interests: Banking, Securities, Tax law
Partic in Dialog Corporation; Dow Jones News Retrieval; Westlaw

GROUP HEALTH COOPERATIVE OF PUGET SOUND, Medical Library, 200 15th Ave E, 98112. SAN 363-924X. Tel: 206-326-3393. FAX: 206-326-2629. *Dir*, Jackie Morton; Staff 3 (MLS 2, Non-MLS 1)
Founded 1969
Library Holdings: Bk Titles 3,000; Per Subs 200
Subject Interests: Allied health care, Clinical medicine, Health care mgt, Health maintenance orgns, Nursing, Pharmacy
Database Vendor: Dialog, OVID Technologies
Branches:
KATHLEEN HILL MEMORIAL LIBRARY, 521 Wall St, ACC-2, 98121. SAN 370-7164. Tel: 206-448-5643. FAX: 206-448-2792. *Librn*, Arlene McBride; Staff 3 (MLS 2, Non-MLS 1)
Library Holdings: Bk Titles 1,400; Per Subs 200
Subject Interests: Computers, Gen mgt, Healthcare admin, Networks
Partic in Coop Libr Agency for Syst & Servs; OCLC Online Computer Library Center, Inc

HISTORICAL SOCIETY OF SEATTLE & KING COUNTY, Sophie Frye Bass Library of Northwest Americana,* 2700 24th Ave E, 98112. SAN 317-6363. Tel: 206-324-1126. FAX: 206-324-1346. E-Mail: library@seattlehistory.org. Web Site: www.seattlehistory.org. *Librn*, Carolyn Marr; *Librn*, Mary Montgomery
Founded 1952
1997-1998 Income $70,856
Library Holdings: Bk Titles 10,000
Subject Interests: Alaska, History, Maritime, Pacific Northwest, Seattle
Special Collections: PEMCO Webster & Stevens Photography Coll; PSMHS Williamson Maritime Photography Coll; Seattle Post-Intelligence Photography Coll
Restriction: Non-circulating to the public, Open to public for reference only
Library includes the holdings of the Puget Sound Maritime Historical Society & the Black Heritage Society of Washington State (information)

K C M INC, Info Center Library,* 1917 First Ave, 98101. SAN 317-6088. Tel: 206-443-5300. FAX: 206-443-5372. *Librn*, Mary Jo Aegerter
Founded 1975
Subject Interests: Lake restoration, Waste water treatment
Publications: Monthly Acquisitions List

KARR TUTTLE CAMPBELL, Law Library, 1201 Third Ave, Ste 2900, 98101-3028. SAN 321-8163. Tel: 206-223-1313. FAX: 206-682-7100. Web Site: www.karrtuttle.com. *Mgr*, Dana Gaddy; Tel: 206-224-8187, E-Mail: dgaddy@karrtuttle.com; Staff 2 (Non-MLS 2)
Founded 1904
Library Holdings: Bk Titles 2,300; Per Subs 420
Subject Interests: Civil law, General law, Trial practice law
Partic in OCLC Online Computer Library Center, Inc

KELLER & ROHRBACK, Law Library,* 1201 Third Ave, Ste 3200, 98101. SAN 372-3623. Tel: 206-623-1900. FAX: 206-623-3384. *Librn*, Mort Brinchmann
Library Holdings: Bk Vols 5,000; Per Subs 40

KING COUNTY HAZARDOUS WASTE LIBRARY, 130 Nickerson St, Ste 100, 98109-1658. SAN 373-6563. Tel: 206-263-3051. FAX: 206-263-3070. Web Site: www.metrokc.gov/hazwaste/hwl/. *Head Librn*, Anne K Moser; E-Mail: anne.moser@metrokc.gov; Staff 2 (MLS 2)
Founded 1992
Library Holdings: Bk Titles 4,500; Per Subs 300
Special Collections: Hazardous Waste Management for Small Business & Households
Automation Activity & Vendor Info: (Cataloging) EOS; (Circulation) EOS; (OPAC) EOS
Database Vendor: OCLC - First Search

KING COUNTY LAW LIBRARY, W 621 King County Courthouse, 516 Third Ave, 98104. SAN 317-6053. Tel: 206-296-0940. FAX: 206-205-0513. E-Mail: kcll@metrokc.gov. Web Site: www.kcll.org. *Dir*, Jean M Holcomb; Tel: jean.holcomb@ metrokc.gov; *Head Tech Servs*, Rita Dermody; *Publ Servs*, Richard Stroup; *Ref*, Kerry Fitz-Gerald; *Head Ref*, Rita Kaiser; *Ref*, Vicki Valleroy
Jan 1998-Dec 1999 Income $913,637. Mats Exp $466,000. Sal $395,282
Library Holdings: Bk Vols 87,000; Per Subs 200

LANE POWELL SPEARS LUBERSKY LLP LIBRARY, 1420 Fifth Ave, Ste 4100, 98101-2388. SAN 321-7663. Tel: 206-223-6245. FAX: 206-223-7107. Web Site: www.lanepowell.com. *Dir Info Resources & Res*, Denyse McFadden; Tel: 206-223-7139, E-Mail: mcfaddend@lanepowell.com; Staff 6 (MLS 3, Non-MLS 3)
Subject Interests: Law
Partic in OCLC

S LAWRENCE ELECTRONICS CO LIBRARY,* 14636 Ambaum Blvd SW, PO Box 66556, 98166. SAN 373-3033. Tel: 206-243-7310. FAX: 206-243-7588. *Mgr*, Bill Grant
Library Holdings: Bk Vols 1,500; Bk Titles 1,000; Per Subs 30

M VIRGINIA MASON MEDICAL CENTER LIBRARY, 925 Seneca, 98101. SAN 371-1331. Tel: 206-223-6733. FAX: 206-223-2376.
Library Holdings: Bk Vols 4,500
Restriction: Staff use only

L REED MCCLURE LIBRARY,* 601 Union St, No 4800, 98101-3900. SAN 373-6601. Tel: 206-292-4900. FAX: 206-223-0152. *Librn*, Sue Sorensen; E-Mail: ssorensen@rmlaw.com; Staff 1 (MLS 1)
1997-1998 Mats Exp $130,000. Sal $45,000
Library Holdings: Bk Vols 10,000

S MOUNTAINEERS, Mountaineer Library, 300 Third Ave W, 98119. SAN 317-6126. Tel: 206-284-6310. FAX: 206-284-4977. Web Site: www.mountaineers.org. *Librn*, LoAnne Larson; Tel: 206-284-6310, Ext 3014, E-Mail: loannel@mountaineers.org
Founded 1915
Library Holdings: Bk Vols 6,000; Per Subs 40
Subject Interests: Climbing, Environmental studies, Exploration mountaineering biog, Exploration mountaineering hist, Natural history
Special Collections: Conservation (Mountaineer Foundation Libr)
Automation Activity & Vendor Info: (Cataloging) TLC

G MUNICIPAL RESEARCH & SERVICES CENTER OF WASHINGTON LIBRARY,* 1200 Fifth Ave, Ste 1300, 98101-1159. SAN 317-6134. Tel: 206-625-1300. FAX: 206-625-1220. E-Mail: mrsc@mrsc.org. Web Site: www.mrsc.org. *Mgr*, Fred Ward; *Librn*, Andrew Derby; Staff 5 (MLS 2, Non-MLS 3)
Founded 1970
Library Holdings: Per Subs 300
Special Collections: Municipal Government Documents

S MUSEUM OF FLIGHT LIBRARY, 9404 E Marginal Way S, 98108-4097. SAN 370-6028. Tel: 206-764-5700. FAX: 206-764-5707. E-Mail: library@museumofflight.org. Web Site: www.museumofflight.org. *Curator*, Dennis Parks; Staff 3 (MLS 3)
Founded 1985
Library Holdings: Bk Vols 30,000; Bk Titles 20,000; Per Subs 85
Subject Interests: Aerospace, Aviation
Special Collections: Aviation-Aerospace (G S Williams Photographic Coll); D D Hatfield Aviation History Coll; E B Jeppesen Aviation History & Navigation Coll
Restriction: Non-circulating to the public, Open to public for reference only
Function: Archival collection, For research purposes, Photocopies available, Reference services available, Research fees apply, Research library, Some telephone reference
Open Mon, Wed & Fri 1-5, Thurs 1-9, or by appointment

G NATIONAL ARCHIVES & RECORDS ADMINISTRATION, Pacific Alaska Region (Seattle),* 6125 Sand Point Way, 98115-7999. Tel: 206-526-6501. FAX: 206-526-6575. E-Mail: center@seattle.nara.gov. Web Site: www.nara.gov/regional/seattle.html. *Archivist*, Susan Karren
Special Collections: Archival Records of Federal Agencies & Courts in Idaho, Oregon & Washington State; Indian Affairs Records, microfilm; Passenger Arrival & Naturalization Records, microfilm; Population Censuses for All States, 1790-1920, microfilm; Pre-Federal & Early Federal History, microfilm; Pre-World War I Military Service Records, microfilm; US Diplomacy Records, microfilm
Restriction: Reference only to non-staff
Open for public services: Mon-Fri 7:45-4 & 1st & 2nd Tues each month 4pm-9pm (microfilm research only); federal agency services: Mon-Fri 7:45-4:15

G NATIONAL ENVIRONMENTAL SATELLITE DATA & INFORMATION SERVICES, NOAA Library Seattle,* Bldg 3, 7600 Sand Point Way NE, 98115. SAN 373-8647. Tel: 206-526-6241. FAX: 206-526-4535. Web Site: www.wrclib.noaa.gov/. *Librn*, Maureen Woods; E-Mail: mwoods@wrclib.noaa.gov
1997-1998 Income $250,000. Mats Exp $100,000
Library Holdings: Bk Titles 13,000
Subject Interests: Meteorology, Oceanography
Partic in Fedlink

G NATIONAL MARINE FISHERIES SERVICE, Northwest Fisheries Science Center,* 2725 Montlake Blvd E, 98112. SAN 317-6568. Tel: 206-860-3210. Web Site: www.mwffc.noah.gov/library. *Librn*, Patricia Cook
Founded 1931
Library Holdings: Bk Titles 26,000; Per Subs 250
Subject Interests: Aquatic sci, Biochemistry, Fisheries biol, Fisheries mgt, Food, Marine sci
Partic in OCLC Online Computer Library Center, Inc

S NORDIC HERITAGE MUSEUM, Gordon Ekvall Tracie Music Library, 3014 NW 67th St, 98117. SAN 326-4920. Tel: 206-789-5707, 206-789-5708. FAX: 206-789-3271. E-Mail: nordic@intelistep.com. Web Site:

www.nordicmuseum.com. *Dir*, Marianne Forssblad; *Archivist*, Mary Mohler; Staff 1 (Non-MLS 1)
Founded 1995
Library Holdings: Bk Vols 13,000; Per Subs 50
Special Collections: Gordon Tracie History Archive; Skandia Folkdance Society Archives
Restriction: By appointment only

NORDIC HERITAGE MUSEUM, Walter Johnson Memorial Library, 3014 NW 67th St, 98117. Tel: 206-789-5707, 206-789-5708. FAX: 206-789-3271. E-Mail: nordic@intelistep.com. Web Site: www.nordicmuseum.com. *Dir*, Marianne Forssblad; *Curator*, Lisa Hill-Festa; Staff 1 (Non-MLS 1)
Founded 1986
Library Holdings: Bk Vols 15,500
Subject Interests: Danish (Language), Films, Finnish (language), Norwegian (language), Sound recordings, Swedish (language)
Special Collections: Vanishing Generations Project
Restriction: By appointment only
Function: Reference only

J NORTH SEATTLE COMMUNITY COLLEGE, Library Media Center,* 9600 College Way N, 98103. SAN 317-6169. Tel: 206-527-3607. FAX: 206-527-3614. Web Site: www.sccd.ctc.edu/~library/.
Founded 1970. Enrl 9,000
Library Holdings: Bk Vols 46,000; Per Subs 491
Automation Activity & Vendor Info: (Cataloging) Inlex; (Circulation) Inlex
Partic in OCLC

M NORTHWEST HOSPITAL, Library & Information Resources, 1550 N 115th St, D-101, 98133. SAN 317-6185. Tel: 206-368-1642. FAX: 206-368-1501. *Librn*, Pamela Murray; E-Mail: pmurray@nwhsea.org; Staff 1 (MLS 1)
Founded 1975
Library Holdings: Bk Vols 500; Per Subs 80
Subject Interests: Bus, Medicine, Mgt, Nursing

P NORTHWEST LIBRARY ON DEAF CULTURE & HISTORY, Community Service Center for the Deaf & Hard of Hearing, 1609 19th Ave, 98122. SAN 371-7127. Tel: 206-322-4996. FAX: 206-720-3251. E-Mail: cscdhh@aol.com. Web Site: www.deafwebwashington.com. *Librn*, Mildred Johnson
Founded 1983
Library Holdings: Bk Titles 250
Special Services for the Deaf - Books on deafness & sign language; Special interest periodicals; Staff with knowledge of sign language; TTY machine
Friends of the Library Group

S PACIFIC COAST BANKING SCHOOL LIBRARY,* 1601 Second Ave, Ste 410, 98101. SAN 317-6193. Tel: 206-447-4141. FAX: 206-448-4799. *Librn*, Judy Brunsdon
Founded 1938
Library Holdings: Bk Vols 500; Bk Titles 300
Subject Interests: Econ, Finance

L PERKINS COIE LIBRARY,* 1201 Third Ave Ste 4800, 98101. SAN 317-6215. Tel: 206-583-8444. FAX: 206-583-8500. E-Mail: librt@perkinscoie.com. *Dir Libr Serv*, Barbara Cornwell Holt; E-Mail: holtb@perkinscole.com; *Librn*, Catherine Horan; *Librn*, Karen Braucht; *Librn*, Betsy Chessler; *Librn*, Carol Warner; *Librn*, Sandra Edmunds; Staff 9 (MLS 6, Non-MLS 3)
Founded 1912
Jan 1998-Dec 1999 Mats Exp $1,500,000. Sal $412,000 (Prof $308,000)
Library Holdings: Bk Vols 50,000; Per Subs 1,000
Subject Interests: Aviation, Bus, Corp, Environmental law, Estate planning, Intellectual property, Labor law, Litigation, Probate, Pub utilities, Real estate, Securities, Taxation
Automation Activity & Vendor Info: (Acquisitions) Inmagic, Inc.
Database Vendor: Dialog, Lexis-Nexis, OCLC - First Search
Restriction: Private library
Partic in Western Libr Network

PLYMOUTH CONGREGATIONAL CHURCH, Vida B Varey Library, 1217 Sixth Ave, 98101-3199. SAN 317-6223. Tel: 206-622-4865. FAX: 206-622-8726. *Coordr*, Barbara Baker; Staff 1 (MLS 1)
Founded 1948
Jan 2000-Dec 2000 Mats Exp $2,135, Books $2,000, Per/Ser (Incl. Access Fees) $135. (Prof $2,500)
Library Holdings: Bk Vols 5,000; Bk Titles 5,000; Per Subs 10
Subject Interests: Children's books, Relig studies
Special Collections: Forums on audio cassette; Sermons on audio cassette
Automation Activity & Vendor Info: (Cataloging) CASPR

L PRESTON GATES & ELLIS LIBRARY, 5000 Bank of America Tower, 701 Fifth Ave, 98104-7078. SAN 317-624X. Tel: 206-623-7580. FAX: 206-623-7022. E-Mail: info@prestongates.com. Web Site: www.prestongates.com. *Dir*, Bridget Dacres; E-Mail: bridgetd@prestongates.com; Staff 7 (MLS 4, Non-MLS 3)
Library Holdings: Bk Vols 28,000; Bk Titles 4,400
Subject Interests: Law
Automation Activity & Vendor Info: (Acquisitions) Sydney; (Catalogi Sydney; (OPAC) Sydney; (Serials) Sydney
Partic in OCLC Online Computer Library Center, Inc

S PUGET SOUND REGIONAL COUNCIL, Information Center, 1011 We Ave Ste 500, 98104-1035. SAN 317-6266. Tel: 206-464-7532. FAX: 20 587-4825. E-Mail: infoctr@psrc.org. Web Site: www.psrc.org. *Mgr*, Dea McLaughlin; *Ref*, Margaret Warwick; *Cat*, Doris Dungan; Staff 3 (MLS
Founded 1967
Library Holdings: Bk Titles 3,000; Per Subs 60
Subject Interests: Growth mgt, Transportation
Special Collections: Census; Small Area Regional Forecasts (population households, employment)

L RIDDLE WILLIAMS PS, Law Library, 1001 Fourth Ave Plaza, Ste 450 98154. SAN 372-3658. Tel: 206-624-3600. FAX: 206-389-1708. Web Si www.riddlewilliams.com. *Librn*, Crystal Sherman
Library Holdings: Bk Vols 2,000; Per Subs 80
Subject Interests: Labor, Securities

S SAFECO INSURANCE CO LIBRARY,* Safeco Plaza, 98185. SAN 31 6282. Tel: 206-545-5505. FAX: 206-545-6088. *Librn*, Kimberly S Anick
Founded 1965
Library Holdings: Bk Titles 6,000; Per Subs 300
Subject Interests: Bus, Ins, Mgt
Special Collections: Company Archives; Insurance Periodical, back issu
Partic in OCLC Online Computer Library Center, Inc
Computer training for employees

L SCHROETER, GOLDMARK & BENDER LIBRARY,* Central Bldg, 8 Third Ave, Ste 500, 98104. SAN 323-8156. Tel: 206-622-8000. FAX: 20 682-2305. E-Mail: sgb-lib@wln.com. *Librn*, Mark Gardner
Library Holdings: Bk Vols 3,000; Bk Titles 2,000; Per Subs 150

S SEATTLE AQUARIUM, Staff Library,* Pier 59, Waterfront Park, 98101 (Mail add: 1483 Alaskan Way, 98101), SAN 371-4497. Tel: 206-386-430 206-386-4320. FAX: 206-386-4328. *In Charge*, Marty Morris; *In Charge* Mary Carlson
Library Holdings: Bk Vols 300; Per Subs 15

SEATTLE ART MUSEUM

S DOROTHY STIMSON BULLITT LIBRARY, 100 University St, 98101-2902. (Mail add: PO Box 22000, 98101-9900), SAN 317-6320. Tel: 20 654-3220. FAX: 206-654-3135. *Coll Develop, Librn*, Elizabeth deFato; Staff 4 (MLS 3, Non-MLS 1)
Founded 1933
Library Holdings: Bk Titles 18,500; Per Subs 50
Subject Interests: Archaeology, Art history
Special Collections: Northwest Artists Files, clippings
Restriction: Non-circulating to the public
Function: Reference only
Partic in OCLC Online Computer Library Center, Inc

S MCCAW FOUNDATION LIBRARY OF ASIAN ART, Volunteer Park, 98112. (Mail add: 100 University St, 98101-2902), SAN 375-538X. Tel 206-654-3202. FAX: 206-654-3191. *Librn*, Jan Hwang
Founded 1983
Library Holdings: Bk Vols 4,200; Bk Titles 3,500; Per Subs 44
Partic in OCLC Online Computer Library Center, Inc
Open Thurs 1-8 & Fri-Sat 1-5

J SEATTLE CENTRAL COMMUNITY COLLEGE, Instructional Resource Services Library,* 1701 Broadway, 98122. SAN 317-6339. Tel: 206-587-4050, 206-587-5420. FAX: 206-587-3878. *Librn*, Lynn Kanne; Tel: 206-5 4072; *Librn*, Ian Chan; Tel: 206-587-6336. Subject Specialists: *Food industry and trade*, Karen Michaelson; *Humanities*, Karen Michaelson; *Mathematics*, Ian Chan; *Science*, Ian Chan; Staff 6 (MLS 6)
Founded 1966. Enrl 7,886; Fac 174
Library Holdings: Bk Titles 60,575; Per Subs 595
Subject Interests: Architecture, Art, Ethnic studies, Sci-tech
Partic in OCLC

S SEATTLE GENEALOGICAL SOCIETY LIBRARY,* 8511 15th Ave NE, 98115. (Mail add: PO Box 75388, 98125-0388), Tel: 206-522-8658. *In Charge*, Sara Little
Founded 1923
Library Holdings: Bk Vols 7,000; Per Subs 400
Subject Interests: Genealogy, Local history
Special Collections: British Isles (British Isles Coll); New Jersey (George Kent Coll), bks, cards; Scandinavian Coll
Publications: Bulletin (quarterly), Newsletter (monthly)

M SEATTLE INSTITUTE FOR PSYCHOANALYSIS, Edith Buxbaum Library, 4020 E Madison St, Ste 230, 98112. SAN 373-3025. Tel: 206-328 5315. FAX: 206-328-5879.
Library Holdings: Bk Vols 5,000; Per Subs 10
Friends of the Library Group

SEATTLE METAPHYSICAL LIBRARY, 1000 E Madison, Ste B, 98122. SAN 326-2049. Tel: 206-329-1794. E-Mail: metaphysical@mindspring.com. Web Site: www.hometown.aol.com/library14U/welcome.Seattle.html. *Dir*, Philip Bruce Lipson; Staff 11 (MLS 1, Non-MLS 10)
Founded 1961
Library Holdings: Bk Vols 10,000; Bk Titles 10,000; Per Subs 10
Subject Interests: Alternative med, Ancient history, Astrology, Holistic health, New Age, Occult, Religion, UFO phenomenon
Special Collections: Rare Parapsychology Coll
Publications: As-You-Like-It (newsletter) (Newsletter)
Mail order & internet memberships via website http://asyoulikeit.ml.org

SEATTLE PACIFIC UNIVERSITY LIBRARY, 3307 Third Ave W, 98119. SAN 363-9363. Tel: 206-281-2228. FAX: 206-281-2936. Web Site: www.spu.edu/depts/library/. *Dir*, J Ray Doerksen; Tel: 206-281-2414, E-Mail: doerksen@spu.edu; *Asst Dir*, Ann Hill; Tel: 206-281-2422, E-Mail: annhill@spu.edu; *Info Specialist*, Gary Fick; *Info Specialist*, Linda Lambert; *Info Specialist*, Aileen Maddox. Subject Specialists: *Science/technology*, Gary Fick; Staff 10 (MLS 9, Non-MLS 1)
Founded 1891. Enrl 4,290; Fac 156; Highest Degree: Doctorate
Jul 1999-Jun 2000 Mats Exp $567,460. Sal $869,673 (Prof $540,582)
Library Holdings: Bk Vols 169,527; Bk Titles 138,165; Per Subs 1,336
Subject Interests: Education, Nursing, Psychology, Religion
Special Collections: Free Methodism
Automation Activity & Vendor Info: (Cataloging) Innovative Interfaces Inc.; (Circulation) Innovative Interfaces Inc.; (Course Reserve) Innovative Interfaces Inc.; (OPAC) Innovative Interfaces Inc.; (Serials) Innovative Interfaces Inc.
Restriction: Public use on premises
Function: ILL available, Newspaper reference library, Photocopies available, Reference services available, Some telephone reference
Partic in OCLC; Orbis; Puget Sound Acad Independent Librs

SEATTLE POST-INTELLIGENCER LIBRARY, 101 Elliott Ave W, 98119-4220. SAN 317-638X. Tel: 206-448-8537. *Librn*, Lytton Smith; E-Mail: lyttonsmith@seattle-pi.com
Subject Interests: News
Special Collections: Index to Seattle Post-Intelligencer
Partic in Dialog Corporation; Dow Jones News Retrieval; News Bank

SEATTLE PUBLIC LIBRARY, 1000 Fourth Ave, 98104-1193. SAN 363-9398. Tel: 206-386-4636. Interlibrary Loan Service Tel: 206-386-4601. Circulation Tel: 206-386-4190. TDD: 206-386-4697. FAX: 206-386-4685. E-Mail: infospl@spl.org. Web Site: www.spl.org. *City Librn*, Deborah Jacobs; Tel: 206-386-4100, Fax: 206-386-4119, E-Mail: deborah.jacobs@spl.org; *Dir Libr Serv*, Jill Jean; Tel: 206-386-4678, Fax: 206-386-4119, E-Mail: jill.jean@spl.org; *Assoc Dir*, Jan Ames; Tel: 206-615-0400, Fax: 206-615-0437, E-Mail: jan.ames@wtbbl.org; *Assoc Dir*, Laurie Brown; Tel: 206-388-4110, Fax: 206-386-4108, E-Mail: laurie.brown@spl.org; *Assoc Dir*, Terry Collings; Tel: 206-386-4130, Fax: 206-386-4132, E-Mail: terry.collins@spl.org; *Assoc Dir*, Lois Fenker; Tel: 206-386-4657, Fax: 206-386-4119, E-Mail: lois.fenker@spl.org; *Assoc Dir*, Bob Goldstein; Tel: 206-386-4648, Fax: 206-386-4108, E-Mail: bob.goldstein@spl.org; *Assoc Dir*, Alex Harris; Tel: 206-386-4145, E-Mail: alex.harris@spl.org; *Assoc Dir*, Gloria Leonard; Tel: 206-386-4133, Fax: 206-386-4107, E-Mail: gloria.leonard@spl.org; *Assoc Dir*, Nancy Pearl; Tel: 206-386-4184, Fax: 206-386-4119, E-Mail: nancy.pearl@spl.org; *Assoc Dir*, Lin Schnell; Tel: 206-386-4125, Fax: 206-386-4119, E-Mail: lin.schnell@spl.org; *Assoc Dir*, Ray Serebrin; Tel: 206-386-4662, Fax: 206-386-4119, E-Mail: ray.serebrin@spl.org; *Ch Servs*, Chance Hunt; Tel: 206-386-4097, Fax: 206-386-4635, E-Mail: chance.hunt@spl.org; *YA Servs*, Jeff Katz; Tel: 206-386-4151, Fax: 206-386-4167, E-Mail: jeff.katz@spl.org; *ILL*, Tom Horne; Tel: 206-615-1624, Fax: 206-386-4185, E-Mail: tom.horne@spl.org; *Info Tech*, Marilyn Sheck; Tel: 206-386-4637, Fax: 206-386-4108, E-Mail: marilyn.sheck@spl.org; *Coll Develop*, Sybil Harrison; Tel: 206-615-1625, Fax: 206-386-4185, E-Mail: sybil.harrison@spl.org; *Commun Relations*, Andra Addison; Tel: 206-386-4103, Fax: 206-386-4119, E-Mail: andra.addison@spl.org; Staff 455 (MLS 141, Non-MLS 314)
Founded 1891. Pop 534,732; Circ 4,993,099
Jan 2000-Dec 2000 Income (Main Library and Branch Library) $31,654,017. Mats Exp $3,675,546. Sal $24,116,510
Library Holdings: Bk Vols 981,221; Bk Titles 689,740
Subject Interests: Aviation hist, Genealogy, Seattle hist
Automation Activity & Vendor Info: (Acquisitions) epixtech, inc.; (Cataloging) epixtech, inc.; (Circulation) epixtech, inc.; (OPAC) epixtech, inc.
Database Vendor: epixtech, inc.
Partic in OCLC Online Computer Library Center, Inc
Special Services for the Deaf - Staff with knowledge of sign language; TDD
Special Services for the Blind - Magnifiers
Provide materials for literacy services & information regarding business, trade, industry & technology for the Asia/Pacific region. Computer learning lab (at main library); adult book discussion groups
Friends of the Library Group
Branches: 25

BALLARD, 5711 24th Ave NW, 98107. SAN 363-972X. Tel: 206-684-4089. FAX: 206-684-4022. E-Mail: ballard@spl.org. Web Site: www.spl.org/neighborhoodlibs/ballard/. *Branch Mgr*, Sibyl deHaan; E-Mail: sibyl.dehaan@spl.org
Library Holdings: Bk Vols 58,608
Friends of the Library Group

BEACON HILL, 2519 15th Ave S, 98144. SAN 363-9665. Tel: 206-684-4711. FAX: 206-684-4726. E-Mail: beaconhill@spl.org. Web Site: www.spl.org/neighborhoodlibs/beaconhill/. *Branch Mgr*, Julie Anne Oiye; E-Mail: julieann.oiye@spl.org
Library Holdings: Bk Vols 26,971
Friends of the Library Group

BROADVIEW, 12755 Greenwood Ave N, 98133. SAN 363-9754. Tel: 206-684-7519. FAX: 206-684-4981. E-Mail: broadview@spl.org. Web Site: www.spl.org/neighborhoodlibs/broadview/. *Branch Mgr*, Bob Hageman; E-Mail: bob.hageman@spl.org
Library Holdings: Bk Vols 51,911

COLUMBIA, 4721 Rainier Ave S, 98118. SAN 363-9932. Tel: 206-386-1908. FAX: 206-386-1947. E-Mail: columbia@spl.org. Web Site: www.spl.org/neighborhoodlibs/columbia/. *Branch Mgr*, Mary Jo Torgeson; E-Mail: maryjo.torgenson@spl.org
Library Holdings: Bk Vols 34,243

DELRIDGE (SELF-SERVICE), 4555 Delridge Way SW, 98106. SAN 377-7502. Tel: 206-937-7680. E-Mail: delridge@spl.org. Web Site: www.spl.org/neighborhoodlibs/delridge/. *Branch Mgr*, Karen Spiel; Tel: 206-684-7467, E-Mail: karen.spiel@spl.org
Library Holdings: Bk Vols 1,398

DOUGLASS-TRUTH, 2300 E Yesler Way, 98122. SAN 363-9967. Tel: 206-684-4704. FAX: 206-684-4346. E-Mail: douglass-truth@spl.org. Web Site: www.spl.org/neighborhoodlibs/douglass/. *Branch Mgr*, Carolyn Head; E-Mail: carolyn.head@spl.org
Library Holdings: Bk Vols 47,606
Special Collections: African-American Coll

FREMONT, 731 N 35th St, 98103. SAN 363-9789. Tel: 206-684-4084. FAX: 206-684-4020. E-Mail: fremont@spl.org. Web Site: www.spl.org/neighborhoodlibs/fremont/. *Branch Mgr*, Valerie Frye; E-Mail: val.frye@spl.org
Library Holdings: Bk Vols 20,838

GREEN LAKE, 7364 E Green Lake Dr N, 98115. SAN 363-9541. Tel: 206-684-7547. FAX: 206-684-4982. E-Mail: greenlake@spl.org. Web Site: www.spl.org/neighborhoodlibs/greenlake/. *Branch Mgr*, Toni Myers; E-Mail: toni.myers@spl.org
Founded 1910
Library Holdings: Bk Vols 40,618
Friends of the Library Group

GREENWOOD, 8016 Greenwood Ave N, 98103. SAN 363-9819. Tel: 206-684-4086. FAX: 206-684-4024. E-Mail: greenwood@spl.org. Web Site: www.spl.org/neighborhoodlibs/greenwood/. *Branch Mgr*, Francesca Wainwright; E-Mail: francesca.wainwright@spl.org
Library Holdings: Bk Vols 40,116
Friends of the Library Group

HENRY, 425 Harvard Ave E, 98102. SAN 363-9576. Tel: 206-684-4715. FAX: 206-684-4724. E-Mail: henry@spl.org. Web Site: www.spl.org/neighborhoodlibs/henry/. *Branch Mgr*, Rae Charlton; E-Mail: rae.charlton@spl.org
Library Holdings: Bk Vols 32,425
Friends of the Library Group

HIGH POINT, 6338 32nd Ave SW, 98126. SAN 323-9942. Tel: 206-684-7454. FAX: 206-684-7465. E-Mail: highpoint@spl.org. Web Site: www.spl.org/neighborhoodlibs/highpoint. *Branch Mgr*, Christy Tyson; E-Mail: christy.tyson@spl.org
Library Holdings: Bk Vols 12,544

LAKE CITY, 12501 28th Ave NE, 98125. SAN 363-9606. Tel: 206-684-7518. FAX: 206-684-7517. E-Mail: lakecity@spl.org. Web Site: www.spl.org/neighborhoodlibs/lakecity/. *Branch Mgr*, Beth de la Fuente; E-Mail: beth.delafuente@spl.org
Library Holdings: Bk Vols 68,845
Friends of the Library Group

MADRONA-SALLY GOLDMARK, 1134 33rd Ave, 98122. SAN 323-9888. Tel: 206-684-4705. FAX: 206-684-4729. E-Mail: madrona@spl.org. Web Site: www.spl.org/neighborhoodlibs/madrona/. *Branch Mgr*, Carolyn Head; E-Mail: carolyn.head@spl.org
Library Holdings: Bk Vols 16,099

MAGNOLIA, 2801 34th Ave W, 98199. SAN 363-9843. Tel: 206-386-4225. FAX: 206-386-4281. E-Mail: magnolia@spl.org. Web Site: www.spl.org/neighborhoodlibs/magnolia/. *Branch Mgr*, Irene Haines; E-Mail: irene.haines@spl.org
Library Holdings: Bk Vols 29,754
Friends of the Library Group

MOBILE SERVICES, 2025 Ninth Ave, 98121. SAN 363-9452. Tel: 206-684-4713. FAX: 206-615-0049. E-Mail: mobile.services@spl.org. Web Site: www.spl.org/mobileserv/mobserv.html. *Branch Mgr*, Marilyn Ring-Nelson; E-Mail: marilyn.ring-nelson@spl.org
Library Holdings: Bk Vols 80,234

MONTLAKE, 2300 24th Ave E, 98112. SAN 323-9985. Tel: 206-684-4720. FAX: 206-684-4350. E-Mail: montlake@spl.org. Web Site: www.spl.org/neighborhoodlibs/montlake/. *Branch Mgr*, Rae Charlton; E-Mail: rae.charlton@spl.org

Library Holdings: Bk Vols 15,543
NEWHOLLY, 7058 32nd Ave S, 98118. SAN 323-9969. Tel: 206-386-1905. FAX: 206-386-1946. E-Mail: newholly@spl.org. Web Site: www.spl.org/neighborhoodlibs/newholly. *Branch Mgr*, Roberta Daniel; E-Mail: bobbie.daniel@spl.org
Library Holdings: Bk Vols 16,669
NORTH EAST, 6801 35th Ave NE, 98115. SAN 363-9630. Tel: 206-684-7539. FAX: 206-684-4980. E-Mail: northeast@spl.org. Web Site: www.spl.org/neighborhoodlibs/northeast/. *Branch Mgr*, Elizabeth Yee; E-Mail: elizabeth.yee@spl.org
Library Holdings: Bk Vols 63,060
Friends of the Library Group
QUEEN ANNE, 400 W Garfield St, 98119. SAN 363-9878. Tel: 206-386-4227. FAX: 206-386-4270. E-Mail: queenanne@spl.org. Web Site: www.spl.org/neighborhoodlibs/queenanne/. *Branch Mgr*, Valerie Frye; E-Mail: val.frye@spl.org
Library Holdings: Bk Vols 20,897
Friends of the Library Group
RAINIER BEACH, 9125 Rainier Ave S, 98118. SAN 363-9983. Tel: 206-386-1906. FAX: 206-386-1948. E-Mail: rainierbeach@spl.org. Web Site: www.spl.org/neighborhoodlibs/rainierbeach/. *Branch Mgr*, Roberta Daniel; E-Mail: bobbie.daniel@spl.org
Library Holdings: Bk Vols 44,448
SOUTHWEST, 9010 35th Ave SW, 98126. SAN 363-9991. Tel: 206-684-7455. FAX: 206-684-7462. E-Mail: southwest@spl.org. Web Site: www.spl.org/neighborhoodlibs/southwest/. *Branch Mgr*, Christy Tyson; E-Mail: christy.tyson@spl.org
Library Holdings: Bk Vols 43,854
Friends of the Library Group
UNIVERSITY, 5009 Roosevelt Way NE, 98105. Tel: 206-684-4063. FAX: 206-684-4083. E-Mail: university@spl.org. Web Site: www.spl.org/neighborhoodlibs/university/. *Branch Mgr*, Michael Delury; E-Mail: michael.delury@spl.org
Library Holdings: Bk Vols 33,951
WALLINGFORD, 1501 N 45th Ave N, 98103. SAN 323-9926. Tel: 206-684-4088. FAX: 206-684-4025. E-Mail: wallingford@spl.org. Web Site: www.spl.org/neighborhoodlibs/wallingford/. *Branch Mgr*, Michael Delury; E-Mail: michael.delury@spl.org
Library Holdings: Bk Vols 12,420
WASHINGTON TALKING BOOK & BRAILLE
See Separate Entry , 2021 Ninth Ave, 98121-2737.
WEST SEATTLE, 2306 42nd Ave SW, 98116. SAN 364-0027. Tel: 206-684-7444. FAX: 206-684-7466. E-Mail: westseattle@spl.org. Web Site: www.spl.org/neighborhoodlibs/westseattle/. *Branch Mgr*, Karen Spiel; E-Mail: karen.spiel@spl.org
Library Holdings: Bk Vols 40,133
Bookmobiles: 4. To child care centers, retirement & nursing homes, & to individuals who are homebound because of age or disability

P SEATTLE PUBLIC LIBRARY, Washington Talking Book & Braille Library, 2021 Ninth Ave, 98121-2783. SAN 317-655X. Tel: 206-615-0400. Toll Free Tel: 800-542-0866. TDD: 206-615-0419. FAX: 206-615-0441. E-Mail: wtbbl@wtbbl.org. Web Site: www.spl.org/wtbbl/wtbbl.html. *Dir*, Jan Ames; Tel: 206-386-1255, E-Mail: jan.ames@wtbbl.org; *Outreach Serv, Reader Servs*, Phyllis Cairns; Tel: 206-615-0412, Fax: 206-615-0437, E-Mail: phyllis@wtbbl.org; *Coll Develop*, Beth Eisenhood; Tel: 206-615-0436, Fax: 206-615-0436, E-Mail: beth@wtbbl.org; Staff 19 (MLS 3, Non-MLS 16)
Founded 1931
Jul 2000-Jun 2001 Income $1,381,610, State $1,053,610, Federal $328,000. Sal $800,723 (Prof $235,471)
Library Holdings: Bk Vols 277,000
Special Collections: Northwest Coll; Reference Materials on Blindness & Other Disabilities; Volunteer Produced Braille & Tapes
Database Vendor: DRA
Publications: Catalog of locally produced titles; large print calendar; various newsletters
Special Services for the Blind - CCTV's for print disabled; Radio reading service

S SEATTLE TIMES LIBRARY,* Fairview Ave N & John St, PO Box 70, 98111. SAN 317-6398. Tel: 206-464-2307. FAX: 206-464-3258. Web Site: www.seattletimes.com. *In Charge*, Tom Boyer
Library Holdings: Bk Vols 6,000; Per Subs 100

C SEATTLE UNIVERSITY, A A Lemieux Library,* 900 Broadway, 98122-4340. SAN 317-6401. Tel: 206-296-6222. FAX: 206-296-2572. Web Site: www.seattleu.edu/lemlib/llhomepg.htm. *Librn*, John Popko; *Online Servs, Ref*, Robert Novak; *Circ*, Holly Sturgeon; Staff 11 (MLS 11)
Enrl 4,909; Highest Degree: Doctorate
Jul 1996-Jun 1997 Income $1,599,653. Mats Exp $655,733, Books $320,112, Per/Ser (Incl. Access Fees) $267,902, Presv $6,431, Micro $37,733. Sal $679,544 (Prof $318,523)
Library Holdings: Bk Vols 216,677; Per Subs 1,604
Subject Interests: Bus, Education, Mgt, Relig studies, Software engineering
Automation Activity & Vendor Info: (Acquisitions) SIRSI
Publications: Serials List
Partic in American Theological Library Association; Asn Jesuit & Univ; Northwest Association of Private Colleges & Universities Libraries; OC Online Computer Library Center, Inc; Puget Sound Acad Independent L

CL SEATTLE UNIVERSITY SCHOOL OF LAW LIBRARY, Sullivan Ha 900 Broadway, 98122-4340. SAN 364-2429. Tel: 206-398-4221. Interlib Loan Service Tel: 206-398-4227. Reference Tel: 206-398-4225. FAX: 2(398-4194. Web Site: www.law.seattleu/library/. *Actg Dir*, Kristin Chene *Coll Develop*, Kara Phillips; *Ref*, Terry Cullen; *Ref*, Kelly Kunsch; *Ref*, Menanteaux; *Ref*, Brendan Starkey; *Tech Servs*, Suzanne Harvey; Staff 1 (MLS 7, Non-MLS 9)
Founded 1972. Enrl 935; Fac 40; Highest Degree: Doctorate
Jul 1999-Jun 2000 Income Parent Institution $1,474,721. Mats Exp $779,170, Books $65,325, Per/Ser (Incl. Access Fees) $578,501, Presv $6,851, Micro $41,003, Electronic Ref Mat (Incl. Access Fees) $87,490. $642,282 (Prof $356,203)
Library Holdings: Bk Vols 138,922; Bk Titles 42,752; Per Subs 3,806
Special Collections: Int
Automation Activity & Vendor Info: (Acquisitions) Innovative Interfac Inc.; (Cataloging) Innovative Interfaces Inc.; (Circulation) Innovative Interfaces Inc.; (OPAC) Innovative Interfaces Inc.; (Serials) Innovative Interfaces Inc.
Database Vendor: OCLC - First Search
Publications: Faculty Bibliographies; Faculty Guide to the Library; Pathfinders; Student Library Handbook
Partic in OCLC Online Computer Library Center, Inc; RLIN

S SHANNON & WILSON, INC, Technical Library, 400 N 34th St, Ste 10 98103-8636. (Mail add: PO Box 300303, 98103-9703), SAN 317-6428. 206-695-6821. FAX: 206-695-6777. *Mgr Libr Serv*, Judith Bloch; E-Mai jab@shanwill.com; Staff 1 (MLS 1)
Founded 1965
Library Holdings: Bk Vols 4,000; Bk Titles 2,800; Per Subs 300
Subject Interests: Applied geophysics, Earthquake effects on soil, Environmental engineering, Geology, Ground water, Rock mechanics, So mechanics, Wash State, Waste mgt
Partic in OCLC; OCLC Online Computer Library Center, Inc

J SHORELINE COMMUNITY COLLEGE, Ray W Howard Library Medi Center, 16101 Greenwood Ave N, 98133-5696. SAN 317-6436. Tel: 206-546-4663. Interlibrary Loan Service Tel: 206-546-4556. Circulation Tel: 546-4556. Reference Tel: 206-546-6939. FAX: 206-546-4604. Web Site: oscar.ctc.edu/library. *Dir*, John Backes; Tel: 206-546-4558, E-Mail: jbackes@ctc.edu; *Circ, Ref*, Elena Bianco; Tel: 206-546-5820, E-Mail: ebianco@ctc.edu; *Media Spec*, Lawrence Cheng; Tel: 206-546-4592, E-M lcheng@ctc.edu; *Acq, Cat*, John James; Tel: 206-546-6937, E-Mail: jjame ctc.edu; *Ref*, Leslie Potter-Henderson; Tel: 206-546-4554, E-Mail: lhende ctc.edu; *Ref*, Tom Moran; Tel: 206-546-4774, E-Mail: tmoran@ctc.edu; S 22 (MLS 6, Non-MLS 16)
Founded 1963. Enrl 5,200; Fac 150; Highest Degree: Associate
Library Holdings: Bk Titles 70,000; Per Subs 360; High Interest/Low Vocabulary Bk Vols 1,650
Subject Interests: Canadian studies, Ethnic studies
Database Vendor: OCLC - First Search

L SHORT, CRESSMAN & BURGESS, Law Library,* 999 Third Ave, Ste 3000, 98104-4008. SAN 323-5785. Tel: 206-682-3333, Ext 5935. FAX: 2 340-8856. *Librn*, Vivienne C Burke; E-Mail: vburke@scblaw.com; *Tech Servs*, Pat Lowe Pi; E-Mail: ppi@scblaw.com; Staff 2 (MLS 1, Non-MLS
Library Holdings: Bk Vols 6,000; Per Subs 140
Subject Interests: Real estate
Database Vendor: Dialog, Lexis-Nexis

SR SISTERS OF PROVIDENCE, Mother Joseph Province, 4800 37th Ave S 98126. SAN 329-5087. Tel: 206-937-4600. FAX: 206-938-6193. E-Mail: archives@providence.org. Web Site: www.providence.org/archives. *Archiv* Loretta Zwolak Greene; E-Mail: lgreene@providence.org
Library Holdings: Bk Titles 3,000
Subject Interests: Catholic Church, Education, Health care, Sisters of Providence, Soc welfare in the NW
Special Collections: Mother Joseph, a Sister of Providence (1823-1902), represents Washington State in Statuary Hall, Washington, DC
Publications: Past Forward (quarterly newsletter)

J SOUTH SEATTLE COMMUNITY COLLEGE, Instructional Resources Center,* 6000 16th Ave SW, 98106. SAN 317-6444. Tel: 206-764-5395, 206-768-6400. FAX: 206-763-5155. Web Site: www.sccd.ctc.edu/sccdlib/. *Dir*, Mary Jo White; *Librn*, Pamela Wilkins; *Ref*, Esther Sunde; *Ref*, John Ashford; *Ref*, Randy Nelson; Staff 4 (MLS 4)
Founded 1971. Enrl 6,000; Fac 170
Library Holdings: Bk Vols 33,081; Per Subs 650
Subject Interests: Automotive, Aviation, Bus, Food servs, Mgt, Sci-tech, Secretarial
Special Collections: Landscape-Horticulture, bk, flm, micro & pamphlets
Partic in OCLC
Special Services for the Blind - Brailling & large print projects; VisualTek closed circuit TV reading aid

STOEL, RIVES, BOLEY, JONES & GREY, Law Library,* One Union Sq, 600 University St, Ste 3600, 98101. SAN 372-3615. Tel: 206-386-7502. FAX: 206-386-7500. E-Mail: srb-lib@wln.com. *Librn*, Marina Parascenzo-Brush
Library Holdings: Bk Vols 1,500
Partic in OCLC

SWEDISH MEDICAL CENTER, Reference Library,* 747 Broadway, 98122. SAN 317-6452. Tel: 206-386-2484. FAX: 206-386-3570. *Mgr*, Shannon Goodwin
Founded 1949
Library Holdings: Bk Vols 3,500; Per Subs 375
Subject Interests: Hospital administration, Medicine, Nursing, Surgery
Special Collections: CIBA Coll, slides; Gower Coll, slides
Publications: Pacific Northwest Library Identifier Codes: Directory and Key
Partic in Dialog Corporation

SWEDISH MEDICAL CENTER, (Formerly Providence Medical Center), Providence Campus, 500 17th Ave, PO Box 34008, 98124. SAN 317-6258. Tel: 206-320-2423. FAX: 206-324-5871. *Dir*, Cheryl Goodwin
Founded 1940
Library Holdings: Bk Titles 2,000; Per Subs 300
Subject Interests: Cardiovascular med, Hospital administration, Nursing, Psychiatry, Rehabilitation, Surgery
Publications: Newsletter
Partic in BRS; Dialog Corporation; Medline; OCLC

TEMPLE DE HIRSCH SINAI LIBRARY, 1511 E Pike, 98122. SAN 326-7199. Tel: 206-323-8486. FAX: 206-324-6772. E-Mail: library@tdhs-nw.org. Web Site: www.tdhs-nw.org. *Coll Develop, Librn*, Rebecca Alexander; Staff 1 (MLS 1)
Founded 1908
Jul 2000-Jun 2001 Income $2,500. Mats Exp Books $2,000. Sal $18,000
Library Holdings: Bk Vols 9,500; Bk Titles 9,200; Per Subs 37
Subject Interests: History, Holocaust, Judaism
Special Collections: Benjamin Zukor Children's Libr; Historical Collection; Music Collection
Free to synagogue members, voluntary membership fee $5 annually for all others.

UNITED STATES ARMY
CORPS OF ENGINEERS, SEATTLE DISTRICT LIBRARY, PO Box 3755, 98124-2255. SAN 364-0051. Tel: 206-764-3728. FAX: 206-764-3796, 764-6529.
Founded 1940
Library Holdings: Bk Vols 30,000; Bk Titles 12,000; Per Subs 300
Subject Interests: Engineering, Law
Partic in Defense Technical Information Center; Dialog Corporation; OCLC Online Computer Library Center, Inc

US CENSUS BUREAU, Seattle Regional Office Reference Center, 700 Fifth Ave, Ste 5100, 98104-5018. SAN 327-4276. Tel: 206-553-5835. FAX: 206-553-5860. E-Mail: mcintosh@census.gov. Web Site: www.census.gov. *In Charge*, Cam McIntosh; Staff 2 (MLS 1, Non-MLS 1)
Library Holdings: Bk Vols 5,000

UNITED STATES COURTS LIBRARY, 1018 US Courthouse, 1010 Fifth Ave, 98104-1149. SAN 317-6460. Tel: 206-553-4475. FAX: 206-553-4385. *Librn*, Timothy Sheehy; *Asst Librn*, Sarah Joan Griffith; *Asst Librn*, Janice Olson; *Asst Librn*, Jean Pasche; Staff 4 (MLS 3, Non-MLS 1)
Founded 1939
Library Holdings: Bk Vols 41,800; Bk Titles 2,400; Per Subs 1,400
Subject Interests: Law-fed states, Ninth circuit states
Automation Activity & Vendor Info: (Acquisitions) SIRSI; (Cataloging) SIRSI; (OPAC) SIRSI
Restriction: Circulation limited
Function: ILL limited

UNITED STATES DEPARTMENT OF LABOR, Occupational Safety & Health Administration Library - Region X (WA, OR, AK, ID), 1111 Third Ave, Ste 715, 98101-3212. SAN 322-709X. Tel: 206-553-5930. FAX: 206-553-6499. *Librn*, Laura Tippetts
Founded 1971
Library Holdings: Bk Titles 1,600
Subject Interests: Engineering, Safety, Toxicology
Publications: Standards Interpretations Index
Partic in Fedlink

UNITED STATES ENVIRONMENTAL PROTECTION AGENCY, Region 10 Library, 1200 Sixth Ave, Mail-Stop OMP-104, 98101. SAN 317-5987. Tel: 206-553-1289. FAX: 206-553-0404. E-Mail: library-reg10@epa.gov. Web Site: www.epa.gov/r10earth/. *Head Librn*, Alison M Keyes; Staff 5 (MLS 2, Non-MLS 3)
Library Holdings: Bk Vols 8,000; Per Subs 165
Subject Interests: Air pollution, Ecosystems, Environ mgt, Environmental law, Hazardous mat, Solid waste mgt, Toxic substances, Water pollution
Special Collections: EPA Coll, rpts, working papers
Partic in Fed Libr & Info Network; OCLC Online Computer Library Center, Inc

R UNIVERSITY CHRISTIAN CHURCH LIBRARY, 4731 15th Ave NE, 98105. SAN 317-6517. Tel: 206-522-0169. FAX: 206-527-2995. *Librn*, Hope McFadden
Founded 1960
Library Holdings: Bk Vols 1,775
Subject Interests: Gen relig
Publications: Accessions list (semiannual)

CL UNIVERSITY OF WASHINGTON, Marian Gould Gallagher Law Library, 1100 NE Campus Pkwy, 98105-6617. SAN 364-0531. Tel: 206-543-4086. Interlibrary Loan Service Tel: 206-543-4262. Reference Tel: 206-543-6794. FAX: 206-685-2165. Web Site: lib.law.washington.edu. *Librn*, Penny A Hazelton; *Asst Librn, Tech Servs*, Richard Jost; *Asst Librn*, Jonathan Franklin; *Ref*, Cheryl Nyberg; *Ref*, Nancy McMurrer; *Doc, Ref*, Peggy Jarrett; *Cat, Online Servs*, Laura Mahoney; *Cat*, Patricia Hart; *Ser*, Ann Nez; *Circ*, Mary Ann Hyatt; *Coll Develop*, Reba Turnquist; *ILL*, Judy Ann Davis; *Ref*, Ann Hemmens. Subject Specialists: *East Asia*, William McCloy; Staff 17 (MLS 16, Non-MLS 1)
Founded 1899. Enrl 630; Fac 45; Highest Degree: Doctorate
Jul 2000-Jun 2001 Mats Exp $1,305,263, Books $70,157, Per/Ser (Incl. Access Fees) $768,351. Sal $1,424,170 (Prof $802,415)
Library Holdings: Bk Vols 529,265; Bk Titles 109,248; Per Subs 5,510
Subject Interests: Indian law, Librarianship, Water law
Special Collections: (East Asian Legal Materials);
Automation Activity & Vendor Info: (Acquisitions) Innovative Interfaces Inc.; (Cataloging) Innovative Interfaces Inc.; (Circulation) Innovative Interfaces Inc.; (OPAC) Innovative Interfaces Inc.; (Serials) Innovative Interfaces Inc.
Database Vendor: IAC - Info Trac, IAC - SearchBank, Lexis-Nexis, OCLC - First Search
Publications: Current Index to Legal Periodicals; Marian Gould Gallagher Library Publication Series
Partic in OCLC Online Computer Library Center, Inc; RLIN

C UNIVERSITY OF WASHINGTON LIBRARIES, Allen Library, Rm 482, Box 352900, 98195-2900. SAN 364-0086. Tel: 206-543-1760. Interlibrary Loan Service Tel: 206-543-1878. FAX: 206-685-8727. Interlibrary Loan Service FAX: 206-685-8049. Web Site: www.lib.washington.edu/. *Dir*, Lizabeth G Wilson; *Dep Dir*, Charles E Chamberlin; *Doc*, Eleanor L Chase; *Ref*, Nancy Huling; *Circ*, Kirsten Spillum; *Ser*, James Stickman; *Acq of Monographs*, Joseph Kiegel; *Spec Coll*, Carla Rickerson. Subject Specialists: *East Asia*, Min-Chih Chou; *Manuscripts*, Karyl Winn; *Scandinavia*, A Gerald Anderson; *Slavic history and literature*, Michael Biggins; *South Asia*, Alan M Grosenheider; *Southeast Asia*, Judith Henchy; Staff 138 (MLS 138)
Founded 1862. Highest Degree: Doctorate
Library Holdings: Bk Vols 6,000,000; Per Subs 50,245
Special Collections: 19th Century American Literature; Architectural Drawings (Seattle & Puget Sound); Book Arts; Can & European Communities; Early Recorded Vocal Music (Eric Offenbacher Mozart Coll); Hans Christian Anderson; Historical Children's Literature; Historical Photography (particularly western Washington, Alaska & Yukon); Pacific Northwest & Alaska; Pacific Northwest Native Americans; Pacific Northwest Poets; Papers of Richard Hugo, Theodore Roethke, Anna Louise Strong, Mark Tobey, Senator Henry M Jackson, Senator Warren G Magnuson & other 20th Century Senators & Representatives from Washington State; Rowing Books; Seattle Jewish Archives; Seattle Theater Programs; Travel & Exploration; William Blake; William Butler Yeats; Wind Instrument Records (Melvin Harris Coll)
Automation Activity & Vendor Info: (Acquisitions) Innovative Interfaces Inc.; (Cataloging) Innovative Interfaces Inc.; (Circulation) Innovative Interfaces Inc.; (Serials) Innovative Interfaces Inc.
Database Vendor: Innovative Interfaces INN - View
Publications: Library Directions
Mem of Asn of Research Libraries
Partic in National Network Of Libraries Of Medicine - Pacific Northwest Region; OCLC; OCLC Online Computer Library Center, Inc
Includes Allen/Suzzallo Libraries (main libraries), Odegaard Undergraduate Library, Health Sci Library, Law Library, Bothell & Tacoma Branch Campus Libraries, East Asia Library & 15 branch libraries
Friends of the Library Group
Departmental Libraries:
ARCHITECTURE-URBAN PLANNING, 334 Gould Hall, Box 355730, 98195-5730. SAN 364-0175. Tel: 206-543-4067. E-Mail: arch@lib.washington.edu. Web Site: www.lib.washington.edu. *Librn*, Betty L Wagner
Library Holdings: Bk Vols 41,357
Subject Interests: Architecture, Construction mgt, Landscape architecture, Urban design, Urban planning
ART, Art Bldg, Box 353440, 98195. SAN 364-0205. Tel: 206-543-0648. E-Mail: art@lib.washington.edu. Web Site: www.lib.washington.edu. *Librn*, Connie T Okada
Library Holdings: Bk Vols 43,035
CHEMISTRY, Chemistry Libr Bldg, Box 351700, 98195. SAN 364-0264. Tel: 206-543-1603. E-Mail: chemlib@u.washington.edu. Web Site: www.lib.washington.edu. *Librn*, Susanne J Redalje; Tel: 206-543-2070, Fax: 206-543-3863, E-Mail: curie@u.washington.edu

Library Holdings: Bk Vols 62,312
DRAMA, Hutchinson Hall, Box 353950, 98195. SAN 364-0299. Tel: 206-543-5148. FAX: 206-543-8512. E-Mail: drama@lib.washington.edu. Web Site: www.lib.washington.edu. *Librn*, Elizabeth Fugate
Library Holdings: Bk Vols 29,600
Special Collections: Acting Editions of Plays
EAST ASIA, Gowen Hall, Box 353527, 98195. SAN 364-0329. Tel: 206-543-4490. FAX: 206-685-8049. E-Mail: eal@lib.washington.edu. Web Site: www.lib.washington.edu. *Librn*, Min-chih Chou; Staff 12 (MLS 6, Non-MLS 6)
Highest Degree: Doctorate
Jul 1998-Jun 1999 Mats Exp $405,561
Library Holdings: Bk Vols 450,811; Per Subs 2,728
ENGINEERING, Engineering Library Bldg, Box 352170, 98195. SAN 364-0353. Tel: 206-543-0740. FAX: 206-543-3305. E-Mail: englib@u.washington.edu. Web Site: www.lib.washington.edu. *Librn*, Charles Lord
Library Holdings: Bk Vols 141,669
Special Collections: ACM Depository Coll; Technical Reports; United States Patent & Depository Library
FISHERIES-OCEANOGRAPHY, Oceanography Teaching Bldg, Box 357952, 98195. SAN 364-0388. Tel: 206-543-4279. E-Mail: fishlib@u.washington.edu. Web Site: www.lib.washington.edu. *Librn*, Pamela A Mofjeld
Library Holdings: Bk Vols 66,834
FOREST RESOURCES, Bloedel Hall, Box 352112, 98195-2112. SAN 364-0418. Tel: 206-543-2758. FAX: 206-543-8375. E-Mail: forlib@u.washington.edu. Web Site: www.lib.washington.edu. *Librn*, Carol C Green
Library Holdings: Bk Vols 52,840
FOSTER BUSINESS, 013 Seafirst Exec Educ Ctr, Box 353224, 98195-3224. SAN 364-023X. Tel: 206-543-4360. FAX: 206-616-6430. Web Site: www.lib.washington.edu. *Librn*, Gordon Aamot
Library Holdings: Bk Vols 59,812
FRIDAY HARBOR, 620 University Rd, Friday Harbor, 98250. (Mail add: c/o Natural Sciences Library, Box 352900, 98195-2900), Tel: 206-543-1484. FAX: 206-543-1273. E-Mail: frihar@u.washington.edu. Web Site: www.lib.washington.edu/fhl. *Librn*, Maureen D Nolan; Tel: 206-685-2126, Fax: 206-685-3892, E-Mail: nolan@u.washington.edu; Staff 2 (MLS 1, Non-MLS 1)
Library Holdings: Bk Vols 18,000
Database Vendor: Innovative Interfaces INN - View, Lexis-Nexis, ProQuest, Silverplatter Information Inc.
Function: For research purposes
CM HEALTH SCIENCES, Box 357155, 98195. SAN 364-0507. Tel: 206-543-5531. Interlibrary Loan Service Tel: 206-543-3441. FAX: 206-543-8066. Web Site: healthlinks.washington.edu/hsl/. *Dir*, Sherrilynne S Fuller; *Dep Dir*, Debra Ketchell; *Acq*, Colleen M Weum; *Coll Develop*, Lorraine M Raymond; Staff 22 (MLS 22)
Founded 1949
Library Holdings: Bk Vols 351,624; Per Subs 3,856
Subject Interests: Allied health, Dentistry, Medicine, Nursing, Pharm, Public health, Soc work
Special Collections: History of Medicine
Publications: Books & Bytes
Partic in BRS; Dialog Corporation; Nat Libr of Med; OCLC Online Computer Library Center, Inc
K K SHERWOOD LIBRARY, Harborview Medical Ctr, 325 Ninth Ave, Box 359902, 98104. SAN 364-0779. Tel: 206-731-3360. FAX: 206-731-8673. Web Site: www.healthlinks.washington.edu. *Librn*, Ellen Howard; Staff 2 (MLS 1, Non-MLS 1)
Founded 1964
Library Holdings: Bk Titles 350; Per Subs 180
Subject Interests: Clinical medicine
Restriction: Clients only, Not a lending library, Staff use only, Students only
MAP COLLECTION & CARTOGRAPHIC INFORMATION RESOURCES, Basement, Suzzallo Library, Box 352900, 98195-2900. SAN 329-3556. Tel: 206-543-9392. FAX: 206-685-8049. E-Mail: maplib@u.washington.edu. Web Site: www.lib.washington.edu. *Librn*, Jennifer Stone; *Librn*, Kathryn Womble
Library Holdings: Bk Vols 3,966
Subject Interests: Atlases, Geog info systs
Special Collections: Aerial Photography of Washington State, 1944 to present; US Geological Survey Topographic Maps
MATHEMATICS RESEARCH LIBRARY, C306 Padelford Hall, 98195-4350. (Mail add: Box 354350, 98195-4350), SAN 364-0566. Tel: 206-543-7296. FAX: 206-543-5222. E-Mail: mathlib@u.washington.edu. Web Site: www.lib.washington.edu/math. *Librn*, Martha Tucker; Staff 2 (MLS 1, Non-MLS 1)
Library Holdings: Bk Vols 48,900
Subject Interests: Mathematics, Statistics
Friends of the Library Group
MEDIA CENTER Tel: 206-543-6051. FAX: 206-685-8484. Web Site: www.lib.washington.edu.
MUSIC, Music Bldg, Box 353450, 98195. SAN 364-0590. Tel: 206-543-1168. E-Mail: muslib@u.washington.edu. Web Site: www.lib.washington.edu.
Library Holdings: Bk Vols 60,437
Subject Interests: Music
Special Collections: American Music Coll; Harris Wind Instrument Recordings Coll; Offenbacher Mozart Coll
NATURAL SCIENCES, Allen Library, Box 352900, 98195. SAN 364-0 Tel: 206-543-1243. FAX: 206-685-1665. E-Mail: natsci@u.washington.edu. *Librn*, Nancy G Blase
Library Holdings: Bk Vols 205,847
ODEGAARD UNDERGRADUATE LIBRARY, Box 353080, 98195. S 364-0116. Tel: 206-543-1947. FAX: 206-685-8485. Web Site: www.lib.washington.edu. *Head of Libr*, Jill McKinstry
Library Holdings: Bk Vols 180,118
PHYSICS-ASTRONOMY, C-620 Physics Astronomy Bldg, Box 35156 98195-1560. SAN 364-068X. Tel: 206-543-2988, 206-616-2750. FAX: 206-685-0635. E-Mail: phylib@u.washington.edu. Web Site: www.lib.washington.edu. *Librn*, Pamela Yorks
Library Holdings: Bk Vols 29,331
Subject Interests: Astronomy, Astrophysics, Physics
Special Collections: Sky Atlases
SOCIAL WORK, Social Work-Speech & Hearing Sci Bldg, Box 354900 98195. SAN 364-0744. Tel: 206-685-2180. FAX: 206-685-7647. Web www.lib.washington.edu. *Librn*, Angela Lee
Library Holdings: Bk Vols 32,180; Per Subs 247
Subject Interests: Family, Marriage, Soc policy, Soc welfare, Soc wo

S WOODLAND PARK ZOOLOGICAL GARDENS LIBRARY, 5500 Phir Ave N, 98103. SAN 328-3453. Tel: 206-233-7076. FAX: 206-233-2663. *Librn*, Barbara Glicksberg
Library Holdings: Bk Titles 2,000; Per Subs 33
Subject Interests: Animal behavior, Birds, Endangered species, Environ, Mammals, Zoology, Zoos
Special Collections: audiotapes, slides, videotapes; Information on Spec Zoos in the United States & Foreign Countries; Species Vertical File

SEDRO-WOOLLEY

P SEDRO WOOLLEY PUBLIC LIBRARY,* 802 Ball Ave, 98284-2008. S 317-6576. Tel: 360-855-1166. FAX: 360-855-0636. *Librn*, Debra D Peter *Asst Librn*, Teresa J Johnson
Pop 7,500; Circ 75,000
Jan 1998-Dec 1998 Income $168,350, City $155,350. Mats Exp $25,500. $78,700
Library Holdings: Bk Vols 34,000; Per Subs 130
Friends of the Library Group

SHAW ISLAND

SR OUR LADY OF THE ROCK LIBRARY, Order of Saint Benedict, PO B 425, 98286. SAN 317-6592. Tel: 206-468-2321. FAX: 206-468-2319. *In Charge*, Mother Dilecta
Founded 1977
2000-2001 Mats Exp Books $500
Library Holdings: Bk Titles 4,000; Per Subs 10
Subject Interests: History, Judaica, Northwest Coast hist, Theology
Restriction: Not open to public

SHELTON

M MASON GENERAL HOSPITAL LIBRARY, PO Box 1668, 98584. SAN 317-6614. Tel: 360-427-3609. FAX: 360-427-1921. E-Mail: tdidonna@masongeneral.com. Web Site: www.pugetsoundwa.net/mgh/.
1999-2000 Mats Exp $3,750, Books $2,000, Per/Ser (Incl. Access Fees) $500, AV Equip $500, Other Print Mats $500, Manuscripts & Archives $250. Sal $42,500
Library Holdings: Bk Vols 427

SKAMOKAWA

P SKAMOKAWA LIBRARY, 11 Schoolhouse Rd, PO Box 83, 98647. SAN 317-6630. Tel: 360-795-8605. *Librn*, Irene Martin
Founded 1974. Pop 750
Library Holdings: Bk Vols 3,500
Special Collections: Wahkiakum County History
Publications: Grays River Builder; History of the Wahkiakum Indians; Index to the Skamokawa Eagle; Skamokawa Library Welcomes You; Skamokawa National Historic District; Skamokawa: Sad Years, Glad Years
Partic in Washington Libr Network

SPOKANE

CM BETTY M ANDERSON LIBRARY, Intercollegiate Center for Nursing Education,* 2917 W Fort George Wright Dr, 99224-5290. SAN 324-6183. Tel: 509-324-7344. FAX: 509-324-7349. Web Site: www.icne.wsu.edu/library/index.html. *Librn*, Robert M Pringle, Jr; E-Mail: rpringle@wsu.edu; *ILL*, Nancy Wagner; *Cat, Ref*, Mary Wood; *Ref*, Jeanne Wagner; *Ref*, Babs

Hachey; Staff 6 (MLS 2, Non-MLS 4)
Founded 1969. Enrl 325; Fac 50; Highest Degree: Master
Jul 1999-Jun 2000 Mats Exp $55,350, Books $21,000, Per/Ser (Incl. Access Fees) $32,000, Presv $1,100, Other Print Mats $1,250. Sal $210,000
Library Holdings: Bk Vols 11,000; Bk Titles 10,000; Per Subs 225
Subject Interests: Nursing practice, Nursing res
Automation Activity & Vendor Info: (Acquisitions) Innovative Interfaces Inc.; (Circulation) Innovative Interfaces Inc.; (Course Reserve) Innovative Interfaces Inc.; (OPAC) Innovative Interfaces Inc.; (Serials) Innovative Interfaces Inc.
Database Vendor: OCLC - First Search
Publications: Indexes to ANA/NLN
Partic in Inland Northwest Health Sciences Libraries
Jointly operated by Eastern Washington University, Washington State University, Whitworth College & Gonzaga University

CATHOLIC DIOCESAN ARCHIVES, 1023 W Riverside Ave, 99201. SAN 328-1450. Tel: 509-358-7349. FAX: 509-358-7302. *Archivist*, Rev Ted Bradley
Library Holdings: Bk Vols 2,000
Special Collections: Church; Eastern Washington Catholic Church History Coll; Western American Coll
Open Tues 9-12

DEPARTMENT OF VETERANS AFFAIRS, Hospital Library,* N 4815 Assembly St, 99205-6197. SAN 317-6770. Tel: 509-327-0258. FAX: 509-325-7922. *Librn*, Mary Curtis-Kellett; E-Mail: curtis-kellett.mary@forum.va.gov
Founded 1951
Oct 1996-Sep 1997 Income $61,743. Mats Exp $56,213, Books $14,704, Per/Ser (Incl. Access Fees) $31,373, Micro $3,603
Library Holdings: Bk Titles 3,282; Per Subs 233
Subject Interests: Medicine, Mgt develop, Patient education, Patient recreation
Restriction: Staff use only
Partic in Vets Admin Libr Network

EMPIRE HEALTH SERVICES, Health Information Center, 800 W Fifth Ave, 99204. (Mail add: PO Box 248, 99210-0248), SAN 317-6657. Tel: 509-473-7398. Reference Tel: 509-473-7343. FAX: 509-473-7790. E-Mail: hic@empirehealth.org. *Mgr*, Robin E Braun; Tel: 509-473-7342, E-Mail: braunr@empirehealth.org. Subject Specialists: *Medical*, Robin E Braun; Staff 3 (MLS 2, Non-MLS 1)
Founded 1937
Jan 2000-Dec 2000 Income $242,874, Locally Generated Income $5,701, Parent Institution $237,173. Mats Exp $66,219, Books $13,500, Per/Ser (Incl. Access Fees) $45,396, AV Equip $750, Other Print Mats $3,000, Electronic Ref Mat (Incl. Access Fees) $3,573. Sal $155,453
Library Holdings: Bk Titles 2,378; Per Subs 378
Subject Interests: Medicine
Database Vendor: Ebsco - EbscoHost, OCLC - First Search, ProQuest
Partic in Inland Northwest Health Sciences Libraries

GONZAGA UNIVERSITY, Foley Library, E 502 Boone Ave, 99258-0095. SAN 364-0868. Tel: 509-323-6532. Circulation Tel: 509-323-5803. Reference Tel: 509-323-5931. FAX: 509-323-5904. Web Site: www.foley.gonzaga.edu. *Dean of Libr*, Robert L Burr; *Actg Dean*, Eileen Bell-Garrison; Tel: 509-323-6535, E-Mail: bellgarrison@its.gonzaga.edu; *Cat*, Sydney Chambers; Tel: 509-323-6537, E-Mail: chambers@its.gonzaga.edu; *Publ Servs*, Kathleen O'Connor; Tel: 509-323-6545, E-Mail: oconnor@its.gonzaga.edu; *Spec Coll*, Stephanie Plowman; Tel: 509-323-3847, E-Mail: plowman@its.gonzaga.edu; *Materials Manager*, Konny Thompson; Tel: 509-323-6546, E-Mail: thompson@its.gonzaga.edu; *Coll Develop*, Linda Pierce; Tel: 509-323-3834, Fax: 509-323-5806, E-Mail: pierce@its.gonzaga.edu; *Archivist*, Pamela Moffett Padley; Tel: 509-323-3872, Fax: 509-323-5030, E-Mail: padley@its.gonzaga.edu; Staff 28 (MLS 12, Non-MLS 16)
Founded 1992. Enrl 4,000; Fac 286; Highest Degree: Doctorate
Jun 1999-May 2000 Income (Main Library Only) $1,720,000, Federal $100,000, Parent Institution $1,620,000. Mats Exp $639,500, Books $160,000, Per/Ser (Incl. Access Fees) $420,000, Presv $17,000, Manuscripts & Archives $2,500, Electronic Ref Mat (Incl. Access Fees) $40,000. Sal $820,000 (Prof $400,000)
Library Holdings: Bk Vols 363,688; Bk Titles 217,089; Per Subs 1,514
Subject Interests: Behav sci, Philosophy, Relig studies, Soc sci
Special Collections: Bing Crosby Coll, bks, memorabilia, papers & rec; Jesuitica; Labor Unions (Jay Fox Coll); Pacific Northwest History, bks & mss; Victorian Poetry (Gerard Manley Hopkins Coll)
Automation Activity & Vendor Info: (Acquisitions) Endeavor; (Cataloging) Endeavor; (Circulation) Endeavor; (ILL) Endeavor; (Serials) Endeavor
Publications: ITS News (Newsletter)
Partic in Inland Northwest Library Automation Network; Northwest Association of Private Colleges & Universities Libraries
Friends of the Library Group
Departmental Libraries:
LAW LIBRARY, 721 N Cincinnati Ave, 99202. (Mail add: PO Box 3528, 99220-3528), SAN 364-0892. Tel: 509-323-5792. Reference Tel: 509-323-3758. FAX: 509-323-5733. Web Site: law.gonzaga.edu/library/index.htm. *Dir Libr Serv*, June L Stewart; Tel: 509-323-3782, E-Mail: jstewart@lawschool.gonzaga.edu; *Asst Prof, Assoc Dir*, Kevin P Gray; Tel: 509-323-3750, E-Mail: kevin@lawschool.gonzaga.edu; *Tech Servs*, Lynn R Robinson; Tel: 509-323-3749, E-Mail: lrobinson@lawschool.gonzaga.edu; *Res*, Buck C Sterling; Tel: 509-323-3753, E-Mail: bsterling@lawschool.gonzaga.edu; *Coll Develop*, Elizabeth Thweatt; Tel: 509-323-3754, E-Mail: ethweatt@lawschool.gonzaga.edu; Staff 18 (MLS 5, Non-MLS 13)
Founded 1912. Enrl 503; Fac 37; Highest Degree: Doctorate
Jun 1999-May 2000 Income $820,893, Federal $38,319, Locally Generated Income $4,854, Parent Institution $777,720. Mats Exp $542,148, Books $53,978, Per/Ser (Incl. Access Fees) $458,918, Presv $1,791, Micro $16,814, Other Print Mats $10,087, Electronic Ref Mat (Incl. Access Fees) $560. Sal $669,816 (Prof $431,893)
Library Holdings: Bk Vols 149,965; Bk Titles 30,336; Per Subs 2,784
Special Collections: ABA Archive Files; American Law Institute Coll; Butler Labor & Tax Library Coll; Canon Law Coll; Faculty Library Coll; Hein's Federal Legislative History; Hein's Legal Thesis; Karl Llewellyn Papers; Native American Legal Materials; Selective 19th Century Legal Treatises
Automation Activity & Vendor Info: (Acquisitions) CARL; (Cataloging) CARL; (Circulation) CARL; (ILL) CARL; (Serials) CARL
Database Vendor: CARL, Dialog, IAC - Info Trac, Lexis-Nexis, OCLC - First Search
Publications: Bibliographic Series I & II; New Books Cataloged; On Point Newsletter
Restriction: Circulation limited, In-house use for visitors
Partic in Inland Northwest Library Automation Network; OCLC Online Computer Library Center, Inc

M HOLY FAMILY HOSPITAL, Medical Library, 5633 N Lidgerwood St, 99207. SAN 317-6673. Tel: 509-482-0111. FAX: 509-482-2808. *Librn*, Gail W Fielding
Library Holdings: Bk Titles 700; Per Subs 55
Subject Interests: Continuing educ mgt, Med info, Nursing

SR JESUIT OREGON PROVINCE ARCHIVES & LIBRARY,* Gonzaga University, Special Coll, Foley Ctr, 99258-0001. SAN 326-0119. Tel: 509-323-3814. FAX: 509-324-5904. E-Mail: jopa@foley.gonzaga.edu. Web Site: www.foley.gonzaga.edu/spcoll/jopa.html. *Archivist*, David Kingma; *Archivist, Asst Librn*, Edward Jennings; Staff 2 (MLS 1, Non-MLS 1)
Founded 1934
Library Holdings: Bk Titles 5,000; Per Subs 12
Special Collections: Indian & Eskimo Languages (Indian Language Coll), bks, mss, microfilm; Jesuit Missions of the NW (Jesuit Missions Coll), docs, letters, photogs, microfilm
Friends of the Library Group

S NORTHWEST MUSEUM OF ART & CULTURE/EASTERN WASHINGTON STATE HISTORICAL SOCIETY, (MAC), (Formerly Eastern Washington State Historical Society), Research Library & Archives, 715 E Sprague, 99202. (Mail add: 2316 W First Ave, 99204), Tel: 509-456-2703, Ext 114. FAX: 509-456-7690. Web Site: www.northwestmuseum.org. *Curator*, Karen DeSeve; E-Mail: karend@ztc.net
Founded 1916
Library Holdings: Bk Titles 12,000; Per Subs 20
Subject Interests: Architecture, Bus hist, Hist of mining, Inland NW hist, Plateau Indian cultures, Plateau Indian hist, Women's hist
Special Collections: Manuscript Coll; Photographic Coll
Publications: (Nolan) A Guide to the Cutter Coll 1984; (Nolan) A Night of Terror, Devastation, and Awful Woe: the Spokane Fire of 1889 (1989); (Nolan) Frank Palmer, Scenic Photographer 1987; (Nolan) Guide to Manuscript Coll 1987; Libbys' Spokane: A Visual Retrospect 1980

M SACRED HEART MEDICAL CENTER, Health Sciences Library, W 101 Eighth Ave, 99204. (Mail add: PO Box 2555, 99220-2555), SAN 317-669X. Tel: 509-474-3094. FAX: 509-474-4475. *Librn*, Sandy Keno; E-Mail: kenos@shmc.org; *Tech Servs*, Gail Leong
Library Holdings: Bk Vols 2,500; Per Subs 270

J SPOKANE COMMUNITY COLLEGE, N 1810 Greene St, Mailstop 2160, 99217-5399. SAN 317-6711. Tel: 509-533-7045. Circulation Tel: 509-533-7055. Reference Tel: 509-533-8821. FAX: 509-533-7276. Web Site: www.scc.spokane.cc.wa.us/lrc/library. *Dean of Libr*, Mary M Carr; E-Mail: mcarr@scc.spokane.cc.wa.us; *Publ Servs*, Carlyn Quinton; *Ref*, Timothy Aman; Tel: 509-533-7054, Fax: 509-533-8818, E-Mail: taman@scc.spokane.cc.wa.us; *Media Spec*, John Wesley; Tel: 509-533-7059, Fax: 509-533-8060, E-Mail: jwesley@scc.spokane.cc.wa.us; *Tech Servs*, Claudia Parkins; Tel: 509-533-7046, Fax: 509-533-8818, E-Mail: cparkins@scc.spokane.cc.wa.us; *Web Coordr*, Bob Nelson; Tel: 509-533-8161, Fax: 509-533-8060, E-Mail: bnelson@scc.spokane.cc.wa.us; *ILL*, Ginny Toland; Tel: 509-533-8170, Fax: 509-533-8818, E-Mail: gtoland@scc.spokane.cc.wa.us; Staff 25 (MLS 8, Non-MLS 17)
Founded 1963. Enrl 5,982; Fac 245
Library Holdings: Bk Vols 45,000; Bk Titles 30,000; Per Subs 340
Subject Interests: Agriculture, Health sciences, Law, Nursing, Sci-tech
Special Collections: Career Center
Automation Activity & Vendor Info: (Acquisitions) Endeavor; (Cataloging)

Endeavor; (Circulation) Endeavor; (OPAC) Endeavor
Database Vendor: ProQuest
Partic in Spokane Coop Libr Info Syst; Washington Libr Network

GL SPOKANE COUNTY LAW LIBRARY, 1020 Paulsen Bldg, W 421 Riverside Ave, 99201-0402. SAN 317-6738. Tel: 509-477-4680. FAX: 509-477-4722. E-Mail: spolaw@foxinternet.net. Web Site: www.spokanecounty.org.
Founded 1920
1998-1999 Income $186,000
Library Holdings: Bk Vols 25,000; Bk Titles 1,000; Per Subs 50

P SPOKANE COUNTY LIBRARY DISTRICT, (SCLD), 4322 N Argonne Rd, 99212-1853. SAN 364-0922. Tel: 509-924-4122. Interlibrary Loan Service Tel: 509-926-6283. TDD: 509-927-4126. FAX: 509-928-4157. Interlibrary Loan Service FAX: 509-926-7139. E-Mail: admin@scld.lib.wa.us. Web Site: www.scld.org. *Dir*, Michael J Wirt; E-Mail: mwirt@scld.lib.wa.us; *Asst Dir*, Lyn W Dedas; E-Mail: ldedas@scld.lib.wa.us; *Regional Manager*, Priscilla Ice; Tel: 509-926-6283, Fax: 509-926-7139, E-Mail: pice@scld.lib.wa.us; *Mgr*, William H Sargent; E-Mail: wsargent@scld.lib.wa.us; *Mgr*, Mary Tarrer; E-Mail: mtarrer@scld.lib.wa.us; *Regional Manager*, Ellen Miller; Tel: 509-467-5250, Fax: 509-467-5932, E-Mail: emiller@scld.lib.wa.us; *Ch Servs, Coll Develop, YA Servs*, Eva-Maria Lusk; E-Mail: elusk@scld.lib.wa.us; *Ad Servs, Coll Develop*, Steward Robbins; E-Mail: srobbins@scld.lib.wa.us; *Info Tech*, David Girshick; Tel: 509-922-1371, Fax: 509-892-5570, E-Mail: dgirshick@scld.lib.wa.us; *Tech Servs*, Linda Dunham; E-Mail: lpdunham@scld.lib.wa.us; *Outreach Serv*, Doug Stumbough; Tel: 509-924-4123, Fax: 509-892-5570, E-Mail: dstumbough@scld.lib.wa.us; Staff 161 (MLS 23, Non-MLS 138)
Founded 1942. Pop 225,542; Circ 1,837,797
Jan 1999-Dec 1999 Income (Main Library and Branch Library) $5,874,069, County $4,957,743, Locally Generated Income $340,766, Other $575,560. Mats Exp $913,211, Books $699,032, Per/Ser (Incl. Access Fees) $55,617, Presv $1,669, Electronic Ref Mat (Incl. Access Fees) $20,842. Sal $3,053,604
Library Holdings: Bk Vols 410,531; Per Subs 1,384
Subject Interests: Local history
Automation Activity & Vendor Info: (Acquisitions) DRA; (Cataloging) DRA; (Circulation) DRA; (ILL) DRA; (OPAC) DRA; (Serials) DRA
Database Vendor: Dialog, DRA, Ebsco - EbscoHost, GaleNet, ProQuest
Partic in OCLC Online Computer Library Center, Inc
Special Services for the Deaf - TTY machine
Friends of the Library Group
Branches: 10
AIRWAY HEIGHTS COMMUNITY LIBRARY, 1213 S Lundstrom, PO Box 760, Airway Heights, 99001-0760. SAN 370-1026. Tel: 509-244-5510. FAX: 509-244-5253. E-Mail: ahcirc@scld.lib.wa.us. Web Site: www.scld.org. *Asst Dir*, Lyn W Dedas; Tel: 509-928-4122, Fax: 509-924-4157, E-Mail: idedas@scld.lib.wa.us; *Regional Manager*, Ellen Miller; Tel: 509-467-5250, E-Mail: emiller@scld.lib.wa.us; *Mgr*, Sandy Pratt
Library Holdings: Bk Vols 14,299
Friends of the Library Group
ARGONNE, 4322 N Argonne Rd, 99212-1853. SAN 364-1074. Tel: 509-926-4334. FAX: 509-926-9671. E-Mail: arcirc@scld.lib.wa.us. Web Site: www.scld.org. *Asst Dir*, Lyn W Dedas; Tel: 509-924-4122, Fax: 509-928-4157, E-Mail: ldedas@scld.lib.wa.us; *Regional Manager*, Priscilla Ice; Tel: 509-926-6283, E-Mail: pice@scld.lib.wa.us; *Mgr*, Ellen Miller
Library Holdings: Bk Vols 56,232
Friends of the Library Group
CHENEY LIBRARY, 610 First St, Cheney, 99004-1652. SAN 364-0957. Tel: 509-235-7333. FAX: 509-235-7239. E-Mail: chcirc@scld.lib.wa.us. Web Site: www.scld.org. *Asst Dir*, Lyn W Dedas; Tel: 509-92-4122, Fax: 509-928-4157, E-Mail: ldedas@scld.lib.wa.us; *Regional Manager*, Ellen Miller; Tel: 509-467-5250, E-Mail: emiller@scld.lib.wa.us
Library Holdings: Bk Vols 46,538
Friends of the Library Group
DEER PARK COMMUNITY LIBRARY, 208 S Forest, PO Box 729, Deer Park, 99006-0729. SAN 364-0981. Tel: 509-276-2985. FAX: 509-276-6768. E-Mail: dpcirc@scld.lib.wa.us. Web Site: www.scld.org. *Asst Dir*, Lyn W Dedas; Tel: 509-924-4122, Fax: 509-928-4157, E-Mail: ldedas@scld.lib.wa.us; *Regional Manager*, Ellen Miller; Tel: 509-467-5250, E-Mail: emiller@scld.lib.wa.us
Library Holdings: Bk Vols 35,724
Friends of the Library Group
FAIRFIELD COMMUNITY LIBRARY, 303 W Main, Fairfield, 99012-0048. SAN 364-1015. Tel: 509-283-2512. FAX: 509-283-2512. E-Mail: ffcirc@scld.lib.wa.us. Web Site: www.scld.org. *Asst Dir*, Lyn W Dedas; Tel: 509-924-4122, Fax: 509-928-4157, E-Mail: ldedas@scld.lib.wa.us; *Regional Manager*, Priscilla Ice; Tel: 509-926-6283, E-Mail: pice@scld.lib.wa.us
Library Holdings: Bk Vols 12,699
Friends of the Library Group
MEDICAL LAKE COMMUNITY LIBRARY, 321 E Herb, PO Box 249, Medical Lake, 99022-0249. SAN 364-104X. Tel: 509-299-4891. FAX: 509-299-7126. E-Mail: mlcirc@scld.lib.wa.us. Web Site: www.scld.org. *Asst Dir*, Lyn W Dedas; Tel: 509-924-4122, Fax: 509-928-4157, E-Mail: ldedas@scld.lib.wa.us; *Regional Manager*, Ellen Miller; Tel: 509-467-5250, E-Mail: emiller@scld.lib.wa.us
Library Holdings: Bk Vols 17,480
Friends of the Library Group
MORAN PRAIRIE, 3022 E 57th Ave, Ste 19, 99223. Tel: 509-443-6663. FAX: 509-443-6665. E-Mail: mpcirc@scld.lib.wa.us. Web Site: www.scld.org. *Regional Manager*, Priscilla Ice; Tel: 509-926-6283, E-Mail: pice@scld.lib.wa.us
Library Holdings: Bk Vols 10,315
Friends of the Library Group
NORTH SPOKANE LIBRARY, 44 E Hawthorne Rd, 99218-1513. SAN 364-1104. Tel: 509-467-5250. FAX: 509-466-5932. E-Mail: nscirc@scld.lib.wa.us. Web Site: www.scld.org. *Asst Dir*, Lyn W Dedas; Tel: 5 924-4122, Fax: 509-928-4157, E-Mail: ldedas@scld.lib.wa.us; *Regiona Manager*, Ellen Miller; Tel: 509-467-5250, E-Mail: emiller@scld.lib.w
Library Holdings: Bk Vols 114,557
Friends of the Library Group
OTIS ORCHARDS LIBRARY, 22324 E Wellesley Ave, Otis Orchards, 99027-9336. SAN 371-9723. Tel: 509-921-1500. FAX: 509-921-1183. E-Mail: otcirc@scld.lib.wa.us. Web Site: www.scld.org. *Asst Dir*, Lyn Dedas; Tel: 509-924-4122, Fax: 509-928-4157, E-Mail: ldedas@scld.lib.wa.us; *Regional Manager*, Priscilla Ice; Tel: 509-926-6283, E-Mail: pice@scld.lib.wa.us
Library Holdings: Bk Vols 35,090
Friends of the Library Group
VALLEY LIBRARY, 12004 E Main Ave, 99206-5114. SAN 364-1139. T 509-926-6283. TDD: 509-924-4598. FAX: 509-926-7139. E-Mail: vlcir scld.lib.wa.us. Web Site: www.scld.lrg. *Regional Manager*, Priscilla Ice E-Mail: pice@scld.lib.wa.us; *Asst Dir*, Lyn W Dedas; Tel: 509-924-412 Fax: 509-928-4157, E-Mail: ldedas@scld.lib.wa.us
Library Holdings: Bk Vols 157,160
Special Services for the Deaf - TDD
Friends of the Library Group

J SPOKANE FALLS COMMUNITY COLLEGE, Library Media Services, 3410 Ft W Wright Dr, MS 3020, 99224-5288. SAN 317-6754. Tel: 509-5 3800. FAX: 509-533-3144. Web Site: library.sfcc.spokane.cc.wa.us. *Circ, Tech Servs*, Susan Anderson; Tel: 509-533-3818, E-Mail: suea@sfcc.spokane.cc.wa.us; *Asst Dean, Cat*, Mary Ann Goodwin; Tel: 509-537 3820, Fax: 509-533-3820, E-Mail: maryanng@sfcc.spokane.cc.wa.us; *Mec Spec*, Diane Lloyd; Tel: 509-533-3806, E-Mail: dianel@sfcc.spokane.cc.wa.us; *Ref*, Robert Schroeder; Tel: 509-533-3802, E-Mail: roberts@sfcc.spokane.cc.wa.us; *Ref*, Janet Wingerroth; Tel: 509-533-3224, E-Mail: janw@sfcc.spokane.cc.wa.us; *Media Spec, Tech Coordr*, John McCollom; Tel: 509-533-3835; *Ref Serv*, George Suttle; Tel: 509-533-380 E-Mail: georges@sfcc.spokane.cc.wa.us. Subject Specialists: *Media*, John McCollom; Staff 8 (MLS 7, Non-MLS 1)
Founded 1967. Enrl 4,500; Fac 150; Highest Degree: Associate
Library Holdings: Bk Vols 54,000; Bk Titles 50,000; Per Subs 619
Automation Activity & Vendor Info: (Acquisitions) Endeavor; (Catalogi Endeavor; (Circulation) Endeavor; (Course Reserve) Endeavor; (OPAC) Endeavor; (Serials) Endeavor
Database Vendor: OCLC - First Search
Partic in OCLC Online Computer Library Center, Inc

P SPOKANE PUBLIC LIBRARY, 906 W Main Ave, 99201-0976. SAN 364-1163. Tel: 509-444-5300. Circulation Tel: 509-444-5333. Reference Tel: 5(444-5336. FAX: 509-444-5365. Web Site: www.spokanelibrary.org. *Dep D* Janice Bradley; Tel: 509-444-5330, E-Mail: jbradley@spokanelibrary.org; *Dep Dir*, Rip Strautman; Tel: 509-444-5320, E-Mail: rstrautman@spokanelibrary.org; *Commun Relations*, Dolly Richendrfer; Staff 110 (MLS 28, Non-MLS 82)
Founded 1891. Pop 190,000; Circ 1,916,722
Jan 2000-Dec 2000 Income (Main Library and Branch Library) $7,003,448 City $6,638,987, Locally Generated Income $364,461. Mats Exp $1,019,22 Sal $3,794,529
Library Holdings: Bk Vols 654,616; Per Subs 1,400
Special Collections: Adult Literacy Coll; Genealogy, (clippings, bks, mags microfilms, microcards); Government Documents; History of the Book Col Large-type Coll; Northwest History Room
Automation Activity & Vendor Info: (Acquisitions) DRA; (Cataloging) DRA; (Circulation) DRA; (OPAC) DRA
Database Vendor: DRA, GaleNet, IAC - Info Trac, OCLC - First Search, ProQuest
Publications: Annual Report; brochures; weekly & monthly newsletters
Friends of the Library Group
Branches: 4
EAST SIDE, 524 S Stone, 99202. SAN 364-1228. Tel: 509-626-5375. FAX 509-626-5369. *Mgr*, Merrie Hortse; *Ch Servs*, Jennifer Meyer
HILLYARD, 4005 N Cook, 99207. SAN 364-1252. Tel: 509-626-5380. FAX: 509-626-5370. Web Site: splnet.spokpl.lib.wa.us/spl.html. *Librn*, Patricia A Bonner; *Ch Servs*, Sally Blackman
SHADLE BRANCH, 2111 W Wellesley, 99205. SAN 364-1376. Tel: 509-626-5390. FAX: 509-626-5372. Web Site: splnet.spokpl.lib.wa.us/spl.html

Librn, Andrea Sharps; *Ch Servs*, Janet Eddy
SOUTH HILL, 3324 S Perry, 99203. SAN 364-1317. Tel: 509-626-5385. FAX: 509-626-5371. Web Site: splnet.spokpl.lib.wa.us/spl.html. *Librn*, Michael Sierra; *Ch Servs*, Kristen Snyder
Bookmobiles: 2

SPOKESMAN-REVIEW, Newspaper Reference Library, PO Box 2160, 99210. SAN 317-6762. Tel: 509-459-5526. Toll Free Tel: 800-789-0029, Ext 5526. FAX: 509-459-3815. Web Site: www.spokesmanreview.com/news/archives.asp. *In Charge*, Jackie Van Allen
Founded 1928
Library Holdings: Bk Titles 3,000; Per Subs 15
Special Collections: Newspaper Clipping & Photographs
Restriction: Private library

UNITED STATES DEPARTMENT OF THE INTERIOR
US GEOLOGICAL SURVEY, MINERAL RESOURCES LIBRARY, W 904 Riverside Ave, Rm 202, 99201. SAN 364-1406. Tel: 509-353-3174. FAX: 509-353-0505. *Librn*, Dave Frank
Founded 1946
Library Holdings: Bk Vols 11,000; Per Subs 25
Subject Interests: Geology, Related sci
Special Collections: United States Geological Survey Publications
Restriction: Open to public for reference only
Open Mon-Fri 9-4

UNITED STATES GEOLOGICAL SURVEY, Spokane Library,* W 904 Riverside Ave, Rm 202, 99201. SAN 374-7921. Tel: 509-353-2649, 509-353-3174. FAX: 509-353-0505.
Library Holdings: Bk Vols 1,000; Per Subs 15
Subject Interests: Geology, Mining, Water resources
Special Collections: US Bureau of Mines Publications Coll; US Geological Survey Publications Coll

WHITWORTH COLLEGE, Harriet Cheney Cowles Memorial Library, 300 W Hawthorne Rd MS 0901, 99251-0001. SAN 364-1465. Tel: 509-777-3260. Interlibrary Loan Service Tel: 509-777-4488. FAX: 509-777-3221. Web Site: www.whitworth.edu. *Dir*, Dr Hans E Bynagle; Tel: 509-777-4482, E-Mail: hbynagle@whitworth.edu; *Publ Servs*, Nancy Bunker; Tel: 509-777-4481, E-Mail: nbunker@whitworth.edu; *Circ*, Barbara Carden; Tel: 509-777-3767, E-Mail: bcarden@whitworth.edu; *ILL*, Gail Fielding; Tel: 509-777-4488, E-Mail: gfielding@whitworth.edu; *Tech Servs*, Dr Virgil A Dedas; Tel: 509-777-4480, E-Mail: vdedas@whitworth.edu; *Tech Servs*, Debi Kaufman; *Tech Servs*, Jeanette Langston; Tel: 509-777-4226, Fax: 509-777-3231, E-Mail: jlangston@whitworth.edu; *Archivist*, Janet Hauck; Tel: 509-777-4751, E-Mail: jhauck@whitworth.edu; *Acq*, Debi Kaufman; Tel: 509-777-4485, E-Mail: dkaufman@whitworth.edu; *Coordr*, Tami Echavarria; Tel: 509-777-4483, E-Mail: techavarria@whitworth.edu; Staff 9 (MLS 4, Non-MLS 5)
Founded 1890. Circ 30,000; Enrl 1,856; Highest Degree: Master
Jul 1999-Jun 2000 Income $724,466, Parent Institution $711,157, Other $13,309. Mats Exp $226,653, Books $72,603, Per/Ser (Incl. Access Fees) $90,131, Presv $4,424, Micro $19,500, AV Equip $5,215, Electronic Ref Mat (Incl. Access Fees) $34,780. Sal $406,219 (Prof $233,161)
Library Holdings: Bk Vols 180,129
Subject Interests: Education, Liberal arts, Sciences
Special Collections: Daniel Photography Coll; Protestantism in Pacific NW
Automation Activity & Vendor Info: (Cataloging) CARL; (Circulation) CARL; (OPAC) CARL; (Serials) CARL
Database Vendor: CARL, GaleNet, Lexis-Nexis, OCLC - First Search, ProQuest
Partic in Inland Northwest Library Automation Network; OCLC Online Computer Library Center, Inc

ACOMA

AMERICAN INSTITUTE FOR BIOSOCIAL & MEDICAL RESEARCH INC LIBRARY, PO Box 1174, 98401-1174. SAN 372-8757. Tel: 253-286-2888. FAX: 253-286-2886. Web Site: www.aibmr.com. *Librn*, Lesley Loch
Library Holdings: Bk Vols 23,000; Per Subs 125

APA - THE ENGINEERED WOOD ASSOCIATION, Records Department Library, 7011 S 19th St, 98466-5333. (Mail add: PO Box 11700, 98411-0700), SAN 317-6797. Tel: 253-565-6600, Ext 461. FAX: 253-565-7265. Web Site: www.apawood.org. *In Charge*, Barbara Embrey
Library Holdings: Bk Vols 300; Per Subs 200
Subject Interests: Forestry, Wood tech
Restriction: Not a lending library

CLOVER PARK TECHNICAL COLLEGE, F V Miner Resource Center, 4500 Steilacoom Blvd SW, 98499-4098. SAN 324-5160. Tel: 253-589-5544. FAX: 253-589-5726. Web Site: www.cptc.ctc.edu/cptc/. *Dean of Libr*, Laurie Clary; Tel: 253-589-5586, E-Mail: lclary@cptc.ctc.edu; *Admin Assoc*, Vicki Harter; Tel: 253-589-5571, E-Mail: vharter@cptc.ctc.edu; *Librn*, Buff Hirko; Tel: 253-589-5628, E-Mail: bhirko@cptc.ctc.edu; *Tech Servs*, Gladys Fillman; Tel: 253-589-6068, E-Mail: gfillman@cptc.ctc.edu; *Ref*, Rose Altig; Tel: 253-589-5764, E-Mail: raltig@cptc.ctc.edu; *Acq*, Jackie Hayter; Tel: 253-589-6067, E-Mail: jhayter@cptc.ctc.edu; Staff 6 (MLS 1, Non-MLS 5)
Library Holdings: Bk Titles 15,000; Per Subs 30
Subject Interests: Vocational education
Special Collections: Technical college materials
Automation Activity & Vendor Info: (Acquisitions) epixtech, inc.; (Cataloging) epixtech, inc.; (Circulation) epixtech, inc.; (Course Reserve) epixtech, inc.; (ILL) epixtech, inc.; (Media Booking) epixtech, inc.; (OPAC) epixtech, inc.; (Serials) epixtech, inc.
Database Vendor: epixtech, inc., ProQuest

GM DEPARTMENT OF VETERANS AFFAIRS, Puget Sound Health-American Lake Division Library, American Lake, 98493-5000. SAN 317-6924. Tel: 253-582-8440, Ext 6357. FAX: 253-589-4029. *Librn*, Karen Lowman; Staff 3 (MLS 2, Non-MLS 1)
Founded 1924
Library Holdings: Per Subs 103
Subject Interests: Medicine, Nursing, Psychology, Recreation
Partic in Vets Admin Libr Network

CR FAITH EVANGELICAL LUTHERAN SEMINARY LIBRARY, 3504 N Pearl, 98407-2607. (Mail add: PO Box 7186, 98406-0186), SAN 317-6827. Tel: 253-752-2020. FAX: 253-759-1790. *Dean of Libr*, Michael Adams
Founded 1969. Enrl 39; Fac 7; Highest Degree: Doctorate
1998-1999 Mats Exp $25,500, Books $2,000, Per/Ser (Incl. Access Fees) $2,000. Sal $21,000
Library Holdings: Bk Vols 20,000; Per Subs 90
Partic in Puget Sound Area Libr Tech

C PACIFIC LUTHERAN UNIVERSITY, Robert AL Mortvedt Library, Park & 121st St, 98447-0013. SAN 317-6843. Tel: 253-535-7500. FAX: 253-535-7315. Interlibrary Loan Service FAX: 253-536-5110. Web Site: www.plu.edu/libr/library.html. *Dean*, Dr Leon Reisberg; *ILL*, Sue Golden; *Online Servs*, Francesca Lane Rasmus; *Tech Servs*, Jeanine Barndt; Tel: 253-535-7510, E-Mail: barndtje@plu.edu; *Media Spec*, Layne Nordgren; *Archivist, Spec Coll*, Kerstin Ringdahl; *Circ*, Sharon Chase; Staff 8 (MLS 8)
Founded 1894. Enrl 3,172; Highest Degree: Master
Library Holdings: Bk Vols 602,000; Bk Titles 356,513; Per Subs 1,869
Special Collections: Scandinavian Immigrant Experience Coll
Automation Activity & Vendor Info: (Circulation) epixtech, inc.
Database Vendor: Ebsco - EbscoHost, epixtech, inc., Lexis-Nexis, OCLC - First Search, ProQuest
Partic in OCLC Online Computer Library Center, Inc

GL PIERCE COUNTY LAW LIBRARY,* 930 Tacoma Ave S Rm 1A - 105, 98402-2174. SAN 317-6851. Tel: 253-798-7494. FAX: 253-798-2989. *Asst Librn*, Tina Aure; E-Mail: taure@co.pierce.wa.us; *Dir*, Laurie B Miller; Tel: 253-798-2973, E-Mail: lmiller@co.pierce.wa.us; Staff 4 (MLS 2, Non-MLS 2) Sal $100,000
Library Holdings: Bk Vols 35,000; Per Subs 20
Partic in Westlaw
Friends of the Library Group

P PIERCE COUNTY LIBRARY SYSTEM, 3005 112th St E, 98446-2215. SAN 364-1589. Tel: 253-536-6500. FAX: 253-537-4600. Web Site: www.pcl.lib.wa.us. *Dir*, Neel Parikh; E-Mail: neelp@pcl.lib.wa.us; *Dep Dir*, Diane Thompson; E-Mail: dianet@pcl.lib.wa.us; *Dep Dir*, Sharon Winters; E-Mail: swinters@pcl.lib.wa.us; *Br Coordr*, David Kennicott; E-Mail: davidk@pcl.lib.wa.us; *Coll Develop*, Sharon Ufer; E-Mail: sufer@pcl.lib.wa.us; *YA Servs*, Elise Debuiseppi; E-Mail: elised@pcl.lib.wa.us; *Tech Servs*, Becky Hester; E-Mail: beckyh@pcl.lib.wa.us; *Outreach Serv*, Bruce Weathers; E-Mail: brucew@pcl.lib.wa.us; *Ref*, Bill Christiansen; E-Mail: williamc@pcl.lib.wa.us; Staff 209 (MLS 30, Non-MLS 179)
Founded 1946. Pop 447,000; Circ 4,692,918
Jan 2000-Dec 2000 Income (Main Library and Branch Library) $12,682,889, County $11,914,932, Locally Generated Income $170,957, Other $597,000. Mats Exp $1,958,433, Books $1,209,173, Per/Ser (Incl. Access Fees) $166,000, AV Equip $360,000, Other Print Mats $98,260, Electronic Ref Mat (Incl. Access Fees) $125,000. Sal $8,393,994
Library Holdings: Bk Titles 304,792
Automation Activity & Vendor Info: (Circulation) epixtech, inc.
Partic in OCLC Online Computer Library Center, Inc
Friends of the Library Group
Branches: 17
BONNEY LAKE BRANCH, 18501 90th St E, Bonney Lake, 98390. SAN 364-1643. Tel: 253-863-5867. FAX: 253-863-6016. Web Site: www.pcl.lib.wa.us. *Librn*, Linda Bembenek
Library Holdings: Bk Titles 48,678
Friends of the Library Group
BUCKLEY BRANCH, 123 S River Ave, PO Box 167, Buckley, 98321. SAN 364-1708. Tel: 360-829-0300. FAX: 360-829-2874. Web Site: www.pcl.lib.wa.us.
Library Holdings: Bk Titles 28,550
Friends of the Library Group
EATONVILLE BRANCH, 205 Center St, PO Box 69, Eatonville, 98328. SAN 364-1732. Tel: 360-832-6011. FAX: 360-832-7201. Web Site: www.pcl.lib.wa.us. *Librn*, Cindy Dargan
Library Holdings: Bk Titles 27,636
Must reside in Pierce County or Annex/contrated cities

Friends of the Library Group
GRAHAM BRANCH, 9202 224th St E, PO Box 1267, Graham, 98338. SAN 373-5656. Tel: 253-847-4030. FAX: 253-846-5174. Web Site: www.pcl.lib.wa.us. *Librn*, Juanita Bennett
Library Holdings: Bk Titles 47,940
Friends of the Library Group
KEY CENTER, 8905 KPN, Lakebay, 98349. SAN 364-1791. Tel: 253-884-2242. FAX: 253-884-3706. Web Site: www.pcl.lib.wa.us. *Librn*, Dory Myers
Library Holdings: Bk Titles 32,659
Friends of the Library Group
LAKEWOOD, 6300 Wildaire Rd SW, 98499. SAN 364-197X. Tel: 253-582-6040. FAX: 253-589-7377. Web Site: www.pcl.lib.wa.us. *Librn*, Rose Jetler
Library Holdings: Bk Titles 178,157
Friends of the Library Group
MILTON BRANCH, 1000 Laurel St, Milton, 98354-8852. SAN 317-5464. Tel: 253-922-2870. FAX: 253-922-2385. *Circ*, Pat McKenna
Library Holdings: Bk Titles 21,917
Partic in OCLC
Friends of the Library Group
ORTING BRANCH, 202 Washington Ave S, PO Box 1060, Orting, 98360. SAN 364-1821. Tel: 360-893-2661. FAX: 360-893-4149. Web Site: www.pcl.lib.wa.us. *Circ*, Susan Crum
Library Holdings: Bk Titles 25,267
Friends of the Library Group
PARKLAND-SPANAWAY, 13718 Pacific Ave S, 98444. SAN 364-1856. Tel: 253-531-4656. FAX: 253-536-3789. Web Site: www.pcl.lib.wa.us. *Librn*, Diane Kerlon
Library Holdings: Bk Titles 120,678
Friends of the Library Group
PENINSULA, 4424 Point Fosdick Dr NW, Gig Harbor, 98335. SAN 364-1767. Tel: 253-851-3793. FAX: 253-851-8002. Web Site: www.pcl.lib.wa.us. *Librn*, Lynne Zeiher
Library Holdings: Bk Titles 131,309
Friends of the Library Group
SOUTH HILL, 15420 Meridian E, Puyallup, 98375. SAN 364-1880. Tel: 253-848-8686. FAX: 253-841-4692. Web Site: www.pcl.lib.wa.us. *Librn*, Kathleen Wolf
Library Holdings: Bk Titles 143,397
Friends of the Library Group
STEILACOOM BRANCH, 2950 Steilacoom Blvd SW, PO Box 88636, Steilacoom, 98388. SAN 364-1910. Tel: 253-588-1452. FAX: 253-589-7095. Web Site: www.pcl.lib.wa.us. *Librn*, Maryann Wiitala
Library Holdings: Bk Titles 30,512
Friends of the Library Group
SUMMIT, 5107 112th St E, 98446. SAN 373-9090. Tel: 253-536-6186. FAX: 253-536-6009. Web Site: www.pcl.lib.wa.us. *Circ*, Patti Cox
Library Holdings: Bk Titles 47,112
Friends of the Library Group
SUMNER BRANCH, 1116 Fryar Ave, Sumner, 98390. SAN 364-1945. Tel: 253-863-0441. FAX: 253-863-0650. Web Site: www.pcl.lib.wa.us. *Mgr Libr*, Carol Bell; Tel: 253-863-0441, Ext 216, E-Mail: bellcm@pcl.lib.wa.us
Library Holdings: Bk Titles 82,694
Friends of the Library Group
TILLICUM BRANCH, 14916 Washington Ave SW, Lakewood, 98498. SAN 364-2003. Tel: 253-588-1014. FAX: 253-588-2095. Web Site: www.pcl.lib.wa.us. *Circ*, Justine Robb
Library Holdings: Bk Titles 23,373
Friends of the Library Group
UNIVERSITY PLACE, 3605 Bridgeport Way W, 98466. SAN 364-2038. Tel: 253-565-9447. FAX: 253-565-2913. Web Site: www.pcl.lib.wa.us. *Librn*, Cindy Bonaro
Library Holdings: Bk Titles 91,821
Friends of the Library Group
WILKESON BRANCH, 540 Church Ave, PO Box 379, Wilkeson, 98396. SAN 364-2062. Tel: 360-829-0513. FAX: 360-829-0513. Web Site: www.pcl.lib.wa.us. *Circ*, Janet Barclay
Library Holdings: Bk Titles 12,734
Friends of the Library Group
Bookmobiles: 3

M SAINT JOSEPH MEDICAL CENTER LIBRARY, 1717 South J St, PO Box 2197, 98401. SAN 317-6878. Tel: 253-591-6778. FAX: 253-779-6260. *Librn*, Brynn Beals; E-Mail: brynnbeals@chiwest.com; Staff 1 (MLS 1)
Founded 1920
Library Holdings: Bk Vols 1,120; Per Subs 124
Subject Interests: Hospitals, Medicine, Nursing, Related subjects
Partic in Medline; Pacific NW Regional Health Sci Libr; Washington Libr Network

S TACOMA ART MUSEUM REFERENCE LIBRARY,* 1123 Pacific Ave, 98402-4399. SAN 328-0497. Tel: 253-272-4258. FAX: 253-627-1898. Web Site: www.tacomaartmuseum.org. *Dir*, Janeanne Upp; *Librn*, Donna Marie Garcia
Founded 1971
Library Holdings: Bk Titles 2,995; Per Subs 40
Special Collections: Japanese Prints (Lyon Coll); Tacoma & Northwest Artists
Publications: Exhibit Catalogues (occasionally)

J TACOMA COMMUNITY COLLEGE LIBRARY, (Formerly Tacoma Community College), 6501 S 19th St, 98466. SAN 317-6894. Tel: 253-5 5087. Reference Tel: 253-566-5134. TDD: 253-566-5130. FAX: 253-566 5398. Web Site: www.tacoma.ctc.edu/library. *Head Librn*, Rebecca L Sp E-Mail: bsproat@tcc.tacoma.ctc.edu; Staff 13 (MLS 5, Non-MLS 8)
Founded 1965
Library Holdings: Bk Vols 60,000; Per Subs 1,200
Subject Interests: NW hist
Database Vendor: epixtech, inc., IAC - Info Trac, ProQuest
Partic in OCLC
Friends of the Library Group

S TACOMA FAMILY HISTORY CENTER,* 5915 S 12th, 98465. SAN 3 6819. Tel: 253-564-1103. *Dir*, Clyde E Brown; *Dir*, Marie Brown
Library Holdings: Bk Vols 3,000

P TACOMA PUBLIC LIBRARY,* 1102 Tacoma Ave S, 98402-2098. SAN 364-2097. Tel: 253-591-5666. FAX: 253-591-5470. Web Site: www.tpl.lib.wa.us. *Actg Dir*, Susan Odencrantz; *Asst Dir*, Darrell Matz; *Automation Syst Coordr*, Lare Mischo; *Spec Coll*, Gary Fuller Reese; *AV* Bob Schuler; Staff 73 (MLS 23, Non-MLS 50)
Founded 1886. Pop 182,950; Circ 2,696,342
Library Holdings: Bk Vols 1,005,354; Per Subs 2,002
Special Collections: City Archives; Lincoln Coll, bks & VF; Northwest History Coll, mss, doc, bks & pamphlets; Photography Coll, prints & negatives; Richards Coll (historic Tacoma, photos 1923-1980); World Wa (John B Kaiser Coll), bks & posters
Publications: Bibliographies; Pioneer (journals & histories)
Partic in OCLC Online Computer Library Center, Inc
Special Services for the Deaf - High interest/low vocabulary books; TTY machine
Friends of the Library Group
Branches: 9
CHARLOTTE MOTTET BRANCH, 3523 East G St, 98404. SAN 364-2240. Tel: 253-591-5660. FAX: 253-594-7821. *Librn*, Pat Miraldi
Library Holdings: Bk Vols 44,782
FERN HILL, 765 S 84th St, 98444. SAN 364-2127. Tel: 253-591-5620. FAX: 253-591-5729. *Librn*, Barbara Scott
Library Holdings: Bk Vols 89,125
GEORGE O SWASEY BRANCH, 7001 Sixth Ave, 98406. SAN 364-230 Tel: 253-591-5680. FAX: 253-594-7827. *Librn*, Joan Bregger
Library Holdings: Bk Vols 96,959
GRACE R MOORE BRANCH, 215 S 56th St, 98408. SAN 364-2216. Te 253-591-5650. FAX: 253-474-2531. *Librn*, Pat Miraldi
Library Holdings: Bk Vols 97,430
KOBETICH MEMORIAL, 212 Brown's Point Blvd NE, 98422. SAN 364 2151. Tel: 253-591-5630. FAX: 253-594-7815. *Librn*, Ruie Miller
Library Holdings: Bk Vols 52,216
MARTIN LUTHER KING JR BRANCH, 1902 S Cedar St, 98405. SAN 329-6660. Tel: 253-591-5166. FAX: 253-591-5179. *Librn*, Joan Bregger
Library Holdings: Bk Vols 45,461
SOUTH TACOMA, 3411 S 56th St, 98409. SAN 364-2275. Tel: 253-591-5670. FAX: 253-591-5085. *Librn*, Barbara Scott
Library Holdings: Bk Vols 58,717
SWAN CREEK, 3828 Portland Ave, 98404. SAN 329-6687. Tel: 253-594-7805. FAX: 253-594-7808. *Librn*, Pat Miraldi
Library Holdings: Bk Vols 40,415
ANNA LEMON WHEELOCK BRANCH, 3722 N 26th St, 98407. SAN 364-2186. Tel: 253-591-5640. FAX: 253-594-7834. *Librn*, Vicki Armstrong
Library Holdings: Bk Vols 113,847

S THE NEWS TRIBUNE LIBRARY, PO Box 11000, 98411-0008. SAN 31 6916. Tel: 253-597-8626, 253-597-8629. FAX: 253-597-8274. E-Mail: tntinfo@p.tribnet.com. Web Site: www.tribnet.com. *In Charge*, Pilivam Britton; Staff 3 (MLS 1, Non-MLS 2)
Library Holdings: Bk Vols 500; Per Subs 150
Subject Interests: Local news
Special Collections: Newspaper clip file by subject (1955-87)

UNITED STATES ARMY
AM MADIGAN ARMY MEDICAL CENTER, MEDICAL LIBRARY, Attn: MCHJ EDML, 98431. SAN 364-2364. Tel: 253-968-0118. FAX: 253-96 0958. E-Mail: mamcmedlib@nw.amedd.army.mil. Web Site: www.mamc.amedd.army.mil/medlib/medlib.htm. *In Charge*, Marcia I Batchelor; E-Mail: marcia.batchelor@nw.amedd.army.mil; Staff 4 (MLS Non-MLS 2)
Founded 1944
Library Holdings: Bk Titles 9,450; Per Subs 419
Subject Interests: Health admin, Medicine, Nursing
Database Vendor: Dialog, Ebsco - EbscoHost, OCLC - First Search,

OVID Technologies
Restriction: Lending to staff only
Partic in OCLC Online Computer Library Center, Inc

UNIVERSITY OF PUGET SOUND, Collins Memorial Library, 1500 N Warner St, 98416. SAN 364-2399. Tel: 253-879-3243. Circulation Tel: 253-879-3669. Reference Tel: 253-879-3216. FAX: 253-879-3670. Web Site: www.ups.edu/library/home/htm. *Dir*, Marilyn Mitchell; Tel: 253-879-3118, E-Mail: mitchell@ups.edu; *Assoc Dir, Bibliog Instr*, Lori Ricigliano; Tel: 253-879-3229, E-Mail: ricigliano@ups.edu; *Head Tech Servs*, Peggy Firman; Tel: 253-879-3615, E-Mail: firman@ups.edu; *Head Ref, Online Servs*, Maureen Kelly; Tel: 253-879-3512, E-Mail: kelly@ups.edu; *Archivist, Head, Circ*, Donna Bachmann; Tel: 253-879-3619, E-Mail: bachmann@ups.edu; *Automation Syst Coordr*, Michael Dekoven; *Coll Develop*, Suzanne Schreiner; Tel: 253-879-3646, E-Mail: schreiner@ups.edu; *Syst Coordr*, Jon Mark Bolthouse; Tel: 253-879-2875, E-Mail: jbolthouse@ups.edu; *Tech Coordr*, Michael Nanfito; Staff 27 (MLS 8, Non-MLS 19)
Founded 1888. Enrl 2,760; Fac 228; Highest Degree: Master
Sep 1999-Aug 2000 Income $2,644,083, Locally Generated Income $18,847, Parent Institution $2,625,236. Mats Exp $1,020,662, Books $357,014, Per/Ser (Incl. Access Fees) $357,259, Presv $9,960, Micro $73,389, AV Equip $56,476, Other Print Mats $16,100, Electronic Ref Mat (Incl. Access Fees) $150,464. Sal $1,045,392 (Prof $387,468)
Library Holdings: Bk Vols 544,528; Bk Titles 326,438; Per Subs 4,510
Subject Interests: Liberal arts
Special Collections: Music Recordings & Scores Coll
Automation Activity & Vendor Info: (Acquisitions) Innovative Interfaces Inc.; (Cataloging) Innovative Interfaces Inc.; (Circulation) Innovative Interfaces Inc.; (ILL) Innovative Interfaces Inc.; (Media Booking) Innovative Interfaces Inc.; (OPAC) Innovative Interfaces Inc.; (Serials) Innovative Interfaces Inc.
Database Vendor: Ebsco - EbscoHost, GaleNet, Innovative Interfaces INN - View, Lexis-Nexis, OCLC - First Search, OVID Technologies, ProQuest, Silverplatter Information Inc., Wilson - Wilson Web
Publications: Faculty Library Handbook
Partic in OCLC Online Computer Library Center, Inc; Orbis; Puget Sound Acad Independent Librs

WASHINGTON STATE HISTORICAL SOCIETY RESEARCH CENTER, Special Collections Div, 315 N Stadium Way, 98403. SAN 317-6932. Tel: 253-798-5914. FAX: 253-597-4186. E-Mail: jwerlink@wshs.wa.gov. *Curator*, Edward W Nolan; E-Mail: enolan@wshs.wa.gov; *Ref Serv*, Elaine Miller; Tel: 253-798-5915, E-Mail: emiller@wshs.wa.gov; *Ref Serv*, Joy Werlink; Tel: 253-798-5916, E-Mail: jwerlink@wshs.wa.gov
Founded 1941
2000-2001 Mats Exp Manuscripts & Archives $7,500
Library Holdings: Bk Vols 12,000
Subject Interests: Pac NW hist
Special Collections: mss; Washington State (Asahel Curtis Coll), photogs
Restriction: By appointment only
Open Tues, Wed & Thurs 12:30-4:30 by appointment only

)PPENISH

HERITAGE COLLEGE, Donald K C North Library, 3240 Fort Rd, 98948. SAN 324-0541. Tel: 509-865-2244. FAX: 509-865-4144. Web Site: www.heritage.edu. *Dir*, Ella M Melik; Tel: 509-865-2244, Ext 1827, E-Mail: melik_e@heritage.edu; *Circ*, Neomie Olson; Staff 4 (MLS 2, Non-MLS 2)
Founded 1982. Enrl 1,200; Fac 150; Highest Degree: Master
Jul 1999-Jun 2000 Income $260,000, Parent Institution $260,000. Mats Exp $61,708, Books $20,000, Per/Ser (Incl. Access Fees) $32,708, Other Print Mats $1,000, Electronic Ref Mat (Incl. Access Fees) $8,000. Sal $132,871 (Prof $88,336)
Library Holdings: Bk Titles 32,000; Per Subs 200
Subject Interests: Bilingual Education, Social work
Automation Activity & Vendor Info: (Acquisitions) Endeavor; (Cataloging) Endeavor; (Circulation) Endeavor; (Course Reserve) Endeavor; (OPAC) Endeavor
Partic in Ore Pvt Acad Libr Link
Departmental Libraries:
OMAK CAMPUS, 17 S Ash, 98841. SAN 324-2080. Tel: 509-826-1064. FAX: 509-826-4749. *Librn*, Jim Deters

YAKAMA NATION LIBRARY, Yakama Nation Cultural Ctr, Hwy 97 at Fort Rd, 98948. (Mail add: PO Box 151, 98948), SAN 324-0312. Tel: 509-865-2800, Ext 6, 509-865-5121, Ext 4723 & 4721. FAX: 509-865-6101. Web Site: www.wolfe.net/~yingis/chc/timash.html, www.wolfenet.com/~yingis/timash.html. *Head Librn*, Colleen M Veomett; E-Mail: colleen@yakama.com; *Tech Servs*, Georgette Abrahamson; *Tech Servs*, Jolena Umtuch; *Tech Servs*, Katrina Walsey; Staff 4 (MLS 1, Non-MLS 3)
Founded 1980. Pop 1,144; Circ 2,972
Library Holdings: Bk Vols 17,894; Per Subs 91; Spec Interest Per Sub 88
Subject Interests: Am Indian
Special Collections: American Indian; Strongheart Archives; Yakama Tribal
Automation Activity & Vendor Info: (Acquisitions) Athena; (Cataloging) Athena; (Circulation) Athena; (Course Reserve) Athena
Database Vendor: OCLC - First Search
Restriction: Residents only, Use of others with permission of librarian
Partic in OCLC; OCLC Online Computer Library Center, Inc
Branches: 1
ENVIRONMENTAL RESTORATION WASTE MANAGEMENT Tel: 509-452-2502. FAX: 509-452-2503.
Library Holdings: Bk Vols 3,000

TRI CITIES

S TRI-CITY HERALD LIBRARY,* PO Box 2608, 99302. SAN 317-5634. Tel: 509-582-1530. FAX: 509-582-1510. E-Mail: librarian@tri-cityherald.com. Web Site: www.tri-cityherald.com. *Librn*, Debra Carver

VANCOUVER

J CLARK COLLEGE, Lewis D Cannell Library, 1800 E McLoughlin Blvd, MS No 26, 98663-3598. SAN 317-6975. Tel: 360-992-2151. FAX: 360-992-2869. *Dir Libr Serv*, Leonoor Ingraham-Swets; Tel: 360-992-2472, E-Mail: lingraham-swets@clark.edu; *Librn*, Joan Carey; Tel: 360-992-2826, E-Mail: jcarey@clark.edu; *Media Spec Ad*, Scott Coffie; Tel: 360-992-2405, E-Mail: scoffie@clark.edu; *Circ*, Amy Waite; Tel: 360-992-2152, E-Mail: awaite@clark.edu; *Tech Servs*, Pam Smith; Tel: 360-992-2443, E-Mail: psmith@clark.edu. Subject Specialists: *Reference*, Joan Carey; *Reference*, Joan Carey; Staff 16 (MLS 6, Non-MLS 10)
Founded 1933. Enrl 6,100
Jul 1998-Jun 1999 Mats Exp $214,381, Books $56,004, Per/Ser (Incl. Access Fees) $46,680, Presv $3,285, Micro $14,141, Electronic Ref Mat (Incl. Access Fees) $7,310. Sal $458,308 (Prof $182,541)
Library Holdings: Bk Vols 52,660; Bk Vols 60,060; Per Subs 574
Special Collections: Mushrooms
Partic in OCLC Online Computer Library Center, Inc; PORTALS

L CLARK COUNTY LAW LIBRARY,* 1200 Franklin, PO Box 5000, 98666. SAN 370-5188. Tel: 360-397-2268. *Librn*, Rosemary Lewin
1997-1998 Income $120,000. Mats Exp $85,000
Library Holdings: Bk Vols 17,000; Bk Titles 200; Per Subs 50
Special Collections: Washington Law

S COLUMBIAN NEWSPAPER INFORMATION RESOURCE CENTER, 701 W Eighth St, PO Box 180, 98666. SAN 317-6983. Tel: 360-694-3391. FAX: 360-699-6033. Web Site: www.columbian.com. *Librn*, Diane Gibson; E-Mail: diane.gibson@columbian.com
Founded 1890
Library Holdings: Bk Titles 300
Subject Interests: Entertainers, Govt agency rpts, Hist info, Statistical data

P FORT VANCOUVER REGIONAL LIBRARY DISTRICT, 1007 E Mill Plain Blvd, 98663. SAN 364-2453. Tel: 360-695-1561. TDD: 360-695-1560. FAX: 360-693-2681. Web Site: www.fvrl.org. *Exec Dir*, Bruce Ziegman; *Assoc Dir*, Patty Duitman; *Assoc Dir*, Carly Morgan; *Assoc Dir*, Doreen Turpen; *Tech Servs*, Yvonne Iverson; Staff 161 (MLS 38, Non-MLS 123)
Founded 1910. Pop 358,935; Circ 2,722,517
Jan 1999-Dec 1999 Income $11,800,569, Federal $103,166, Locally Generated Income $11,109,596, Other $587,707. Mats Exp $1,415,544, Books $1,086,160, Per/Ser (Incl. Access Fees) $212,014, Electronic Ref Mat (Incl. Access Fees) $117,370. Sal $6,670,377
Library Holdings: Bk Vols 602,895; Bk Titles 235,721; Per Subs 2,046
Automation Activity & Vendor Info: (Cataloging) epixtech, inc.; (Circulation) epixtech, inc.; (OPAC) epixtech, inc.
Partic in OCLC; OCLC Online Computer Library Center, Inc
Branches: 11
BATTLE GROUND COMMUNITY, 12 W Main St, Battle Ground, 98604. SAN 364-2488. Tel: 360-687-2322. FAX: 360-687-1573. Web Site: www.fvrl.org. *Librn*, Barbara Micheel; Staff 9 (MLS 2, Non-MLS 7)
Pop 32,800; Circ 336,265
Library Holdings: Bk Vols 45,222; Per Subs 1,887
Automation Activity & Vendor Info: (Circulation) epixtech, inc.; (OPAC) epixtech, inc.
Database Vendor: epixtech, inc.
Open Mon-Wed 10-8, Thurs-Sat 10-6
Friends of the Library Group
CASCADE PARK COMMUNITY, 301 SE Hearthwood Blvd, 98684. SAN 377-0397. Tel: 360-256-7782. FAX: 360-256-7987. Web Site: www.fvrl.org. *Librn*, Teresa Torres; Staff 6 (MLS 1, Non-MLS 5)
Pop 32,600; Circ 213,933
Library Holdings: Bk Vols 26,923; Per Subs 1,100
Automation Activity & Vendor Info: (Circulation) epixtech, inc.; (OPAC) epixtech, inc.
Database Vendor: epixtech, inc.
Open Tues-Thurs 10-8, Fri & Sat 10-6
Friends of the Library Group
GOLDENDALE COMMUNITY, 131 W Burgen, Goldendale, 98620. SAN 364-2518. Tel: 509-773-4487. FAX: 509-773-3345. Web Site: www.fvrl.org. *Librn*, Naomi Fisher; Staff 5 (MLS 1, Non-MLS 4)
Pop 10,300; Circ 100,106
Library Holdings: Bk Vols 32,916; Per Subs 6,619

Automation Activity & Vendor Info: (Circulation) epixtech, inc.; (OPAC) epixtech, inc.
Database Vendor: epixtech, inc.
Open Mon-Wed 12-8, Thurs-Sat 10-6
Friends of the Library Group

NORTH BONNEVILLE COMMUNITY, M-17 Cascade Dr, PO Box 99, North Bonneville, 98639. SAN 364-2542. Tel: 509-427-4439. Web Site: www.fvrl.org. *Librn*, Mara Reynolds
Pop 596; Circ 1,719
Library Holdings: Bk Vols 2,645; Per Subs 753
Automation Activity & Vendor Info: (Circulation) epixtech, inc.; (OPAC) epixtech, inc.
Database Vendor: epixtech, inc.
Open Tues 1-5 & Thurs 9-12

RIDGEFIELD COMMUNITY, 210 N Main Ave, PO Box 547, Ridgefield, 98642. SAN 364-2577. Tel: 360-887-8281. FAX: 360-887-4833. Web Site: www.fvrl.org. *Librn*, Tina Smith; Staff 3 (MLS 1, Non-MLS 2)
Pop 7,200; Circ 58,907
Library Holdings: Bk Vols 18,373; Per Subs 726
Automation Activity & Vendor Info: (Circulation) epixtech, inc.; (OPAC) epixtech, inc.
Database Vendor: epixtech, inc.
Open Tues & Wed 10-8, Thurs-Sat 10-5
Friends of the Library Group

STEVENSON COMMUNITY, 120 NW Vancouver Ave, PO Box 818, Stevenson, 98648. SAN 364-2607. Tel: 509-427-5471. FAX: 509-427-4830. Web Site: www.fvrl.org. *Librn*, Mara Reynolds; Staff 6 (MLS 1, Non-MLS 5)
Pop 9,253; Circ 82,086
Library Holdings: Bk Vols 28,487; Per Subs 3,640
Automation Activity & Vendor Info: (Circulation) epixtech, inc.; (OPAC) epixtech, inc.
Database Vendor: epixtech, inc.
Open Mon 10-5, Tues & Wed 10-8, Thurs-Sat 10-5
Friends of the Library Group

VANCOUVER COMMUNITY LIBRARY, 1007 E Mill Plain Blvd, 98663. SAN 364-2631. Circulation Tel: 360-695-1564. Reference Tel: 360-695-1566. TDD: 360-695-1560. FAX: 360-699-8823. Web Site: www.fvrl.org. *Librn*, Doreen Turpen; Staff 54 (MLS 17, Non-MLS 37)
Pop 171,300; Circ 1,274,011
Library Holdings: Bk Vols 259,882
Automation Activity & Vendor Info: (Circulation) epixtech, inc.; (OPAC) epixtech, inc.
Database Vendor: epixtech, inc.
Special Services for the Deaf - TDD
Open Mon-Thurs 10-9, Fri & Sat 10-6, Sun 1-9
Friends of the Library Group

VANCOUVER MALL COUMMUNITY, 8700 NE Vancouver Mall Dr, Ste 183, 98662. SAN 364-264X. Tel: 360-892-8256. FAX: 360-896-1767. Web Site: www.fvrl.org. *Librn*, Jane Miller; Staff 12 (MLS 3, Non-MLS 9)
Pop 68,581; Circ 327,902
Library Holdings: Bk Vols 50,647
Automation Activity & Vendor Info: (Circulation) epixtech, inc.; (OPAC) epixtech, inc.
Database Vendor: epixtech, inc.
Open Mon-Sat 10-9, Sun 11-6
Friends of the Library Group

WASHOUGAL COMMUNITY, 1661 C St, Washougal, 98671. SAN 364-2666. Tel: 360-835-5393. FAX: 360-835-9011. Web Site: www.fvrl.org. *Librn*, Sean McGill; Staff 3 (MLS 1, Non-MLS 2)
Pop 12,600; Circ 78,232
Library Holdings: Bk Vols 18,394
Automation Activity & Vendor Info: (Circulation) epixtech, inc.; (OPAC) epixtech, inc.
Database Vendor: epixtech, inc.
Open Tues 10-8, Wed-Sat 10-6
Friends of the Library Group

WHITE SALMON VALLEY COMMUNITY, 142 E Jewett Blvd, PO Box 316, White Salmon, 98672. SAN 364-2690. Tel: 509-493-1132. FAX: 509-493-2943. Web Site: www.fvrl.org. *Librn*, Jennifer Hull; E-Mail: jhull@fvrl.org; Staff 3 (MLS 1, Non-MLS 2)
Pop 9,600; Circ 64,902
Library Holdings: Bk Vols 14,550
Automation Activity & Vendor Info: (Circulation) epixtech, inc.; (OPAC) epixtech, inc.
Database Vendor: epixtech, inc.
Open Tues & Wed 10-6, Thurs 10-8, Fri & Sat 10-6
Friends of the Library Group

WOODLAND COMMUNITY, 770 Park St, Woodland, 98674. Tel: 360-225-2115. *Librn*, Geraldine Veenstra; Staff 3 (MLS 1, Non-MLS 2)
Pop 4,105; Circ 44,718
Library Holdings: Bk Vols 13,976
Automation Activity & Vendor Info: (Circulation) epixtech, inc.; (OPAC) epixtech, inc.
Database Vendor: epixtech, inc.
Open Tues & Wed 11-8, Thurs & Fri 10-6, Sat 10-4
Friends of the Library Group

Bookmobiles: 3

M SOUTHWEST WASHINGTON MEDICAL CENTER
LIBRARY SERVICES, 400 NE Mother Joseph Pl. (Mail add: PO Box 1600, 98668), SAN 364-2720. Tel: 360-514-2045. FAX: 360-514-646 *Librn*, Patsy Bacon; E-Mail: pbacon@swmedctr.com; *Librn*, Madelyn E-Mail: mhall@swmedctr.com; Staff 2 (MLS 1, Non-MLS 1)
Library Holdings: Bk Vols 2,500; Per Subs 200

S UNITED STATES NATIONAL PARK SERVICE-FORT VANCOUVE NATIONAL HISTORIC SITE-LIBRARY, 612 E Reserve St, 98661-38 SAN 317-6991. Tel: 360-696-7659, Ext 18. FAX: 360-696-7657. E-Mail fova_library@nps.gov. *Librn*, Scott Langford
Founded 1948
Library Holdings: Bk Vols 1,300; Per Subs 4
Subject Interests: Hudson's Bay Co, Pac NW fur trade
Special Collections: Fort Vancouver National Historic Site Archaeologic Documents

S WASHINGTON SCHOOL FOR THE DEAF, Learning Resource Center, McGill Library, 611 Grand Blvd, 98661-4498. SAN 317-7017. Tel: 360-6525. FAX: 360-418-0418. Web Site: www.wsdeaf.wednet.edu. *Librn*, Tommy Meehan
Founded 1886
Library Holdings: Bk Vols 10,978; Per Subs 73
Special Collections: Professional Coll for Educators of the Deaf
Special Services for the Deaf - Books on deafness & sign language; Captioned film depository; TTY machine; Videos & decoder

WALLA WALLA

A UNITED STATES ARMY
CORPS OF ENGINEERS, WALLA WALLA DISTRICT LIBRARY, 201 Third, 99362-1876. SAN 364-278X. Tel: 509-527-7427. FAX: 509-527-7816. Web Site: www.nww.usace.army.mil. *Tech Servs*, Barbara Hacket
Founded 1948
Library Holdings: Bk Vols 19,000; Per Subs 300
Subject Interests: Army field law libr, Civil works constr, Engineering Fish, Hydrol, Water resources, Wildlife
Special Collections: Law Coll
Partic in Dialog Corporation; OCLC Online Computer Library Center,

GM JONATHAN V WAINWRIGHT MEMORIAL MEDICAL VA MEDICAL CENTER LIBRARY, 77 Wainwright Dr, 99362-3994. SAN 317-7041. Te 509-525-5200, Ext 2834. FAX: 509-527-6106. *Chief Librn*, Darlene Fleming; E-Mail: darlenefleming@med.va.gov; Staff 1 (MLS 1)
Library Holdings: Bk Vols 2,500; Per Subs 85
Subject Interests: Medicine, Nursing materials
Partic in Coop Libr Agency for Syst & Servs; Nat Libr of Med; Vets Adr Libr Network; Wash State Libr Network

J WALLA WALLA COMMUNITY COLLEGE LIBRARY,* 500 Tausick Way, 99362-9267. SAN 317-705X. Tel: 509-527-4294. Interlibrary Loan Service Tel: 509-527-4297. FAX: 509-527-4480. Web Site: www.ww.cc.wa.us/wwcclib.html. *Dir*, Charlene Grass; *Asst Dir, Tech Serv* Ann Daly; E-Mail: adaly@mail.ww.cc.wa.us; *Ref*, Jim Rice; Staff 3 (MLS
Founded 1967
Jul 1996-Jun 1997 Income $720,330. Mats Exp $102,251, Books $36,436, Per/Ser (Incl. Access Fees) $19,900, Presv $100, Micro $7,876, AV Equip $8,000. Sal $408,350 (Prof $110,756)
Library Holdings: Bk Vols 42,444; Bk Titles 37,172; Per Subs 787
Automation Activity & Vendor Info: (Circulation) Inlex
Partic in OCLC

GL WALLA WALLA COUNTY LAW LIBRARY, County Courthouse, 315 W Main St, 99362. SAN 317-7068. Tel: 509-527-3229. FAX: 509-527-3214. *Librn*, Tina Driver; E-Mail: tdriver@co.walla-walla.wa.us
Library Holdings: Bk Vols 14,530

P WALLA WALLA COUNTY LIBRARY,* 37 Jade Ave, 99362-1628. SAN 373-8272. Tel: 509-527-3284. Toll Free Tel: 800-547-7349. FAX: 509-527-3740. Web Site: www.walnet.walla-walla.wa.us/walrld/burbank.html. *In Charge*, Jean Adams
Founded 1972. Pop 16,000; Circ 73,000
Library Holdings: Bk Titles 29,000; Per Subs 50
Automation Activity & Vendor Info: (Cataloging) Inlex; (Circulation) Inlex; (OPAC) Inlex
Database Vendor: Ebsco - EbscoHost, OCLC - First Search, ProQuest
Partic in OCLC; WALNET
Special Services for the Deaf - Books on deafness & sign language; Video & decoder
Friends of the Library Group

P WALLA WALLA PUBLIC LIBRARY,* 238 E Alder, 99362. SAN 317-7076. Tel: 509-527-4550. FAX: 509-527-3748. Web Site: www.ci.walla-walla.wa.us. *Dir*, Martha A Van Pelt; Tel: 509-527-4388, Ext 511, E-Mail: nvanpelt@walnet.walla-walla.wa.us; *Tech Servs*, Stephen Towery; Tel: 509-527-4550, Ext 514; *Librn*, Beth Hudson; Tel: 509-527-4550, Ext 505; *Ch Servs*, Mary Ann Gilpatrick; Tel: 509-527-4550, Ext 510; Staff 12 (MLS 4,

Non-MLS 8)
Founded 1897. Pop 30,000; Circ 250,000
Library Holdings: Bk Vols 120,000; Per Subs 253
Subject Interests: Local history
Database Vendor: ProQuest
Partic in OCLC Online Computer Library Center, Inc; WALNET
Friends of the Library Group

WALLA WALLA UNION-BULLETIN LIBRARY, First & Poplar, PO Box 1358, 99362. SAN 317-7084. Tel: 509-525-3300, Ext 281. Toll Free Tel: 800-423-5617. FAX: 509-525-1232. Web Site: www.union-bulletin.com. *Librn*, Janet G Collins; E-Mail: jcollins@ubnet.com
Special Collections: Back issues, micro

WHITMAN COLLEGE, Penrose Library, 345 Boyer, 99362-9982. SAN 317-7092. Tel: 509-527-5191. FAX: 509-526-4785, 509-527-5900. Web Site: www.whitman.edu/departments/penrose/index.html. *Dir*, H M Yaple; E-Mail: yaple@whitman.edu; *Asst Dir*, D Shorey; *ILL*, B Martonick; *Ref*, L Keene; *Cat*, C Carr; *Archivist*, L Dodd; *Circ*, B Huntington; *Coll Develop*, J Drazan
Founded 1882. Enrl 1,372; Fac 105; Highest Degree: Bachelor
Jul 1999-Jun 2000 Income $1,889,723. Mats Exp $889,695, Books $388,732, Per/Ser (Incl. Access Fees) $410,000, Presv $17,563, Micro $5,000, AV Equip $4,400, Electronic Ref Mat (Incl. Access Fees) $64,000. Sal $450,812 (Prof $294,735)
Library Holdings: Bk Vols 375,911; Bk Titles 339,700; Per Subs 2,000
Special Collections: Dogwood Press Coll; McFarlane Coll, early illustrated bks; Stuart Napoleon Coll
Automation Activity & Vendor Info: (Circulation) Innovative Interfaces Inc.; (Course Reserve) Innovative Interfaces Inc.; (OPAC) Innovative Interfaces Inc.
Publications: Penrose Impressions: The Newsletter of Penrose Library
Partic in OCLC; Orbis
Friends of the Library Group

SHINGTON DC

MORRIS, MANNING & MARTIN LIBRARY, (Formerly Morris, Manning, Martin & Player Library), 1341 G St NW, 10th Flr, 20005. SAN 377-4368. Tel: 202-408-5153. FAX: 202-408-5146. *Librn*, Jordis Kruger; E-Mail: jsk@mmmlaw.com
Library Holdings: Bk Vols 70

ENATCHEE

CENTRAL WASHINGTON HOSPITAL, Ross A Heminger Health Library, 1201 S Miller St, PO Box 1887, 98807-1887. SAN 317-7106. Tel: 509-662-1511, Ext 2446. FAX: 509-665-6145. Web Site: www.cwhs.com. *Info Specialist*, Susan Marshall; E-Mail: smarshall@cwhs.com; Staff 1 (MLS 1)
Founded 1972
Library Holdings: Bk Titles 1,000; Per Subs 100
Subject Interests: Consumer health, Health, Hospital mgt, Hospital services, Medicine, Nursing
Partic in Docline; Nat Libr of Med

CHELAN COUNTY LAW LIBRARY,* 350 Orondo Ave, No 10, 98801-2885. SAN 317-7114. Tel: 509-664-5213. FAX: 509-664-5588.
Library Holdings: Bk Vols 10,000; Per Subs 10
Subject Interests: Regional reporters, Washington law

NORTH CENTRAL REGIONAL LIBRARY, (NCRL), 238 Olds Station Rd, 98801-8103. SAN 364-281X. Tel: 509-662-5021, 509-663-1117. Interlibrary Loan Service Tel: 509-662-5021, Ext 28. Toll Free Tel: 800-426-7323. FAX: 509-662-8060. Web Site: www.ncrl.org. *Dir*, Dean Marney; Tel: 509-663-1117, Ext 227, E-Mail: dmarney@ncrl.org; *Asst Dir*, Marilyn Neumiller; Tel: 509-663-1117, Ext 236, E-Mail: mneumiller@ncrl.org; *Acq*, Lisa Bell; Tel: 509-663-1117, Ext 244; *Cat*, Rita Keller; Tel: 509-663-1117, Ext 243; *Ref*, Joy C Neal; *Head, Info Serv*, Sandra Purcell; Tel: 509-662-5021, Ext 23, E-Mail: spurcell@ncrl.org; Staff 4 (MLS 4)
Founded 1961. Pop 210,153; Circ 1,341,897
Jan 1999-Dec 1999 Income $5,871,362, State $3,592, City $209,488, Federal $19,014, County $5,482,093, Locally Generated Income $36,195, Other $120,980. Mats Exp $1,238,534, Books $886,332, Other Print Mats $306,034, Electronic Ref Mat (Incl. Access Fees) $46,168. Sal $2,272,859
Library Holdings: Bk Vols 655,641; Bk Titles 154,559; Per Subs 1,339
Subject Interests: Audio visual mats, Compact discs, NW hist, Video cassettes
Publications: Mail Order Library Catalogs
Mem of North Central Regional Library System
Partic in OCLC Online Computer Library Center, Inc
Friends of the Library Group

WENATCHEE VALLEY COLLEGE, John A Brown Library Media Center,* 1300 Fifth St, 98801. SAN 317-7130. Tel: 509-664-2520. FAX: 509-664-2542. *Dir*, Bruce P Swenson; *Librn*, Meredith Patterson; *Media Spec*, Sharon Thompson; Staff 11 (MLS 3, Non-MLS 8)
Founded 1939. Enrl 6,179; Fac 57
Library Holdings: Bk Titles 33,500; Per Subs 290
Subject Interests: Architecture, Art, Behav sci, Nursing, Soc sci
Special Collections: Northwest Indian History; Pacific Northwest History
Partic in OCLC

WILBUR

P HESSELTINE PUBLIC LIBRARY, 14 NW Division, 99185-0214. (Mail add: PO Box 185, 99185-0185), SAN 317-7149. Tel: 509-647-5828. FAX: 509-647-2047. *Librn*, Cathy Miller
Founded 1900. Circ 12,728
Library Holdings: Bk Vols 10,665; Per Subs 40
Publications: Library Journal (weekly)
Open Mon, Fri & Sat 3-5 & Wed 7-9
Friends of the Library Group

YACOLT

S LARCH CORRECTIONS CENTER,* 15314 NE Dole Valley Rd, 98675. SAN 317-7173. Tel: 360-260-6300, Ext 270. FAX: 360-686-3892. *Dir*, Marty Martinez
Founded 1975
Library Holdings: Bk Titles 850
Part of Washington State Libr

YAKIMA

R FIRST PRESBYTERIAN CHURCH LIBRARY, 9 S Eighth Ave, 98902. SAN 317-7181. Tel: 509-248-7940. FAX: 509-248-0937. *Librn*, Rondi Downs
Founded 1927
Library Holdings: Bk Vols 2,000
Subject Interests: Autobiographies, Bible study, Biographies, Christian life
Special Collections: Cassette tapes of sermons; Video Classes
Partic in Pac NW Asn Church Librs
Open Mon-Fri 9-5, Sun 8-1

GL YAKIMA COUNTY LAW LIBRARY,* County Courthouse, 98901. SAN 317-7203. Tel: 509-574-2692. *Librn*, Letha Hammer
Founded 1923
Library Holdings: Bk Vols 20,000

J YAKIMA VALLEY COMMUNITY COLLEGE LIBRARY, 16th Ave at Nob Hill Blvd, PO Box 22520, 98907-2520. SAN 317-7211. Tel: 509-574-4991. FAX: 509-574-4989. *Dir Libr Serv, Media Spec*, Joan L Weber; Staff 8 (MLS 3, Non-MLS 5)
Founded 1929. Enrl 3,200; Fac 106
Library Holdings: Bk Titles 32,000; Per Subs 80
Automation Activity & Vendor Info: (Acquisitions) Endeavor; (Cataloging) Endeavor; (Circulation) Endeavor; (Course Reserve) Endeavor; (OPAC) Endeavor; (Serials) Endeavor
Partic in OCLC; OCLC Online Computer Library Center, Inc

S YAKIMA VALLEY GENEALOGICAL SOCIETY LIBRARY, PO Box 445, 98907. SAN 326-7830. Tel: 509-248-1328. *Librn*, Ellen Brzoska; *Publ Servs*, Maxine Bissell; *Asst Librn, Per*, Irene Minicozzi; *ILL*, Wilbur Helm; *Bibliog Instr*, Lorna Borman; Staff 5 (MLS 1, Non-MLS 4)
Founded 1969
1998-1999 Income $10,000. Mats Exp $10,000
Library Holdings: Bk Vols 5,000; Bk Titles 3,800; Per Subs 222
Subject Interests: Genealogy
Publications: Bulletin

S YAKIMA VALLEY MUSEUM ARCHIVES, 2105 Tieton Dr, 98902. SAN 326-4432. Tel: 509-248-0747. FAX: 509-453-4890. E-Mail: archives@yakimavalleymuseum.org. Web Site: yakimavalleymuseum.org. *Archivist*, Martin M Humphrey
Library Holdings: Bk Vols 7,000
Subject Interests: Local history
Special Collections: Betty Edmondson, Mayor of Yakima; Marjorie Lynch Coll (HEW State Legislator); Martha Wiley, Missionary to China 1900-1946, artifacts, correspondence; William O Douglas Coll, bks, photos, slides, stills, tapes
Publications: 100 Years 100 Women - 1889-1989
Restriction: Non-circulating to the public

P YAKIMA VALLEY REGIONAL LIBRARY, 102 N Third St, 98901-2759. SAN 364-2879. Tel: 509-452-8541. FAX: 509-575-2093. *Dir*, Anne Haley; *Dep Dir*, Monica Weyhe; *ILL*, Lois Collett; *Ad Servs*, Linda McCracken; *Ch Servs*, Karen Spence; *Ref*, Cynthia Garrick; *YA Servs*, Deborah Stilson; Staff 9 (MLS 9)
Founded 1951. Pop 202,000; Circ 895,137
Library Holdings: Bk Vols 318,455; Per Subs 581
Subject Interests: Agriculture, Architecture, Art, Wash hist
Special Collections: Northwest Americans & Indians of Pacific Northwest

(Relander Coll), bks, clippings, letters, maps, negatives, photog & prints
Publications: Annual Report; large print book catalogs; Local Bibliography of Yakima Valley History; Relander Collection Index; Washington State Phone Book Index
Branches: 19
BUENA LIBRARY, 813 Buena Rd, Buena, 98921. Tel: 509-865-3390. Web Site: www.yvrls.lib.wa.us/Buena.html. *Librn*, Karla Marshall
Library Holdings: Bk Vols 4,000; Per Subs 11
Open Tues-Thurs 2-7, Sat 9-2
HARRAH LIBRARY, 21 E Pioneer, Harrah, 98933. Tel: 509-848-3458. Web Site: www.yvrls.lib.wa.us/Harrah.html. *Librn*, Lisa Whitefoot
Library Holdings: Bk Vols 4,700
Special Collections: Scrapbooks on Harrah History (dating back to the 1940's)
Open Mon-Thurs 2-7
MABTON LIBRARY, 415 B St, Mabton, 98935. Tel: 509-894-4128. Web Site: www.yvrls.lib.wa.us/Mabton.html. *Librn*, Linda Lee Bales
Library Holdings: Bk Vols 7,000; Per Subs 26
Open Mon-Wed 1-5 & 7-9, Thurs-Sat 1-5
MARY L GOODRICH PUBLIC LIBRARY, One S Elm, Toppenish, 98948. SAN 317-6959. Tel: 509-865-3600. *Librn*, Alice Fleming
Pop 6,420; Circ 23,720
Library Holdings: Bk Vols 20,000; Per Subs 100
Friends of the Library Group
MOXEE LIBRARY, 255 W Seattle, Moxee, 98936. Tel: 503-575-8854. Web Site: www.yvrls.lib.wa.us/Moxee.html. *Librn*, Delores Bowden
Library Holdings: Bk Vols 8,000; Per Subs 19
Open Mon & Fri 9-12 & 1-6, Tues-Thurs 11-3 & 4-8, Sat 9-2
NACHES LIBRARY, 306 naches Ave, Naches, 98937. Tel: 509-653-2005. Web Site: www.yvrls.lib.wa.us/Naches.html. *Librn*, Joan Laughery
Library Holdings: Bk Vols 3,700; Per Subs 14
Open Tues-Thurs 2-7, Sat 10-3
NILE LIBRARY, 1891 Nile Rd, 10020 State Route 410, Naches, 98937-9129. Tel: 509-658-2660. Web Site: www.yvrls.lib.wa.us/Nile.html. *Librn*, Judy Will
Library Holdings: Bk Vols 2,600
Open Tues 10-5, Wed 12-7, Sat 10-4
RICHARD E OSTRANDER SUMMITVIEW LIBRARY, 5709 Summitview Ave, 98908. SAN 364-2909. Tel: 509-966-7070. Web Site: www.yvrls.lib.wa.us. *Librn*, Cathy Rathbone
SELAH PUBLIC LIBRARY, 115 W Naches, Selah, 98942. SAN 317-6584. Tel: 509-698-7345. *Librn*, Clara Eustis
Pop 5,000; Circ 44,069
Library Holdings: Bk Vols 19,400; Per Subs 35
SOUTHEAST YAKIMA LIBRARY, 1211 S Seventh St, 98901. SAN 373-1413. Tel: 509-576-0723. *Librn*, Florien Williams
SUNNYSIDE LIBRAY, 621 Grant, Saunnyside, 98944. Tel: 509-537-32 Web Site: www.yvrls.lib.wa.us/Sunyside.html. *Librn*, Kay Saunders
Library Holdings: Bk Vols 37,000; Per Subs 67
Subject Interests: Bks on cassettes, Large print bks, Reference, Span language, Videos
Function: Photocopies available
Open Mon-Thurs 9:30-9, Fri & Sat 9:30-6
TERRACE HEIGHTS LIBRARY, 4011 Commonwealth Dr, 98901. Tel: 509-457-5319. Web Site: www.yvrls.lib.wa.us/Terhghts.html. *Librn*, Te Walker
Library Holdings: Bk Vols 5,000; Per Subs 20
Open Mon & Wed 1-8, Thurs & Fri 10-4
TIETON LIBRARY, 418 Maple, Tieton, 98947. Tel: 509-673-2621. Web Site: www.yvrls.lib.wa.us/Tieton.html. *Librn*, Delores Parsley
Library Holdings: Bk Vols 3,500
Open Mon & Wed 2-6, Tues & Thurs 12-6
TOPPENISH LIBRARY, One South Elm, Toppenish, 98948. Tel: 509-8(3600. Web Site: www.yvrls.lib.wa.us/Topenish.html. *Librn*, Alice Flem
Library Holdings: Bk Vols 15,000; Per Subs 66
Subject Interests: Spanish language
Function: Photocopies available
Open Mon-Thurs 9:30-6, Fri & Sat 2-6
UNION GAP LIBRARY, 3104 S First St, Union Gap, 98903. Tel: 509-4 4252. Web Site: www.yvrls.lib.wa.us/Uniongap.html. *Librn*, Lorinda Bowden
Library Holdings: Bk Vols 8,900; Per Subs 27
Open Mon-Thurs 10-5:30 & 7-9, Fri-Sat 10-5
WAPATO LIBRARY, 119 E Third St, Wapato, 98951. Tel: 509-877-288 Web Site: www.yvrls.ib.wa.us/Wapato.html. *Librn*, Mickey Wittner
Library Holdings: Bk Vols 5,100; Per Subs 32
Subject Interests: Large print bks, Spanish language
Function: Photocopies available
Open Mon-Sat 9-5 & Wed evenings 6-8
WHITE SWAN LIBRARY, 391 First St, PO Box 151, Whie Swan, 9895 0151. Tel: 509-874-2060. Web Site: www.yvrls.lib.wa.us/Whiteswn.htm *Librn*, Jennifer L Lewis
Library Holdings: Bk Vols 4,400; Per Subs 16
Open Mon-Thurs 12-6, Fri 9-3
ZILLAH LIBRARY, 109 Seventh St, Zillah, 98953. Tel: 509-829-6707. Site: www.yvrls.lib.wa.us/Zillah.html. *Librn*, Fern Greene
Library Holdings: Bk Vols 7,500; Per Subs 18
Open Mon-Thurs 2-7, Sat 2-5
Bookmobiles: 1

Date of Statistics: Fiscal 1999-2000
Population, 1990 Census: 1,793,477
Population Served by Public Libraries: 1,793,477
Total Volumes in Public Libraries: 4,844,404
Total Public Library Expenditures (including Grants-in-Aid): $24,666,990
Source of Income: Public & private funds
Expenditure Per Capita: $13.75
Number of Regional & Service Center Libraries: 15
Grants-in-Aid to Public Libraries: $6,838,883
Federal & State: $7,153,196

DERSON

ALDERSON LIBRARY,* 308 Walnut Ave, RR 1, Box 147, 24910. SAN 376-7787. Tel: 304-445-7221. FAX: 304-445-7221. *Librn*, Phyllis Auvil
Library Holdings: Bk Vols 10,000; Bk Titles 8,000

HENS

CONCORD COLLEGE, J Frank Marsh Library, PO Box 1000, 24712-1000. SAN 317-722X. Tel: 304-384-5371. FAX: 304-384-7955. E-Mail: library@concord.edu. Web Site: library.concord.edu. *Dir*, Stephen D Rowe; Tel: 304-384-5366, E-Mail: rowe@concord.edu; *Reader Servs*, Robert Turnbull; Tel: 304-384-5374, E-Mail: turnbull@concord.edu; *Cat*, Virginia Rubinstein; Tel: 304-384-5368, E-Mail: rubenstein@concord.edu; Staff 6 (MLS 3, Non-MLS 3)
Founded 1872. Enrl 2,800; Fac 101; Highest Degree: Bachelor
Jul 1998-Jun 1999 Income Parent Institution $385,000. Mats Exp $133,100, Books $102,000, Per/Ser (Incl. Access Fees) $12,000, Presv $3,500, Micro $4,000, Manuscripts & Archives $3,600, Electronic Ref Mat (Incl. Access Fees) $8,000. Sal $200,000 (Prof $140,000)
Library Holdings: Bk Vols 137,000; Bk Titles 124,000; Per Subs 535
Special Collections: Holographs (F Wells Goodykoontz Holograph Coll), photog
Database Vendor: Dialog, IAC - Info Trac, OCLC - First Search
Partic in PALINET & Union Library Catalogue of Pennsylvania; WV Libr Comm

EAVER

UNITED STATES DEPARTMENT OF LABOR, National Mine Health & Safety Academy, Technical Information Center & Library,* 1301 Airport Rd, 25813-9426. SAN 317-7262. Tel: 304-256-3267. FAX: 304-256-3299. *Ref*, Ronald L Minor; *AV*, Jane M DeMarchi
Founded 1976
Library Holdings: Bk Vols 16,000; Per Subs 150
Subject Interests: Earth science, Industrial safety, Mgt, Mining, Occupational diseases
Special Collections: Bureau of Mines Publications; Mine Accident Reports; MSHA Publications
Partic in Dialog Corporation; Fed Libr & Info Network; OCLC Online Computer Library Center, Inc; SDC Info Servs

UNITED STATES DEPARTMENT OF LABOR - MSHA, Technical Information Center Library, 1301 Airport Rd, 25813-9426. SAN 320-1279. Tel: 304-256-3531. FAX: 304-256-3372. E-Mail: library@msha.gov. Web Site: www.msha.gov. *Librn*, Merle Moore; Staff 6 (MLS 1, Non-MLS 5)
Founded 1976. Pop 1,200
Oct 1998-Sep 1999 Mats Exp $150,000. Sal $300,000
Library Holdings: Bk Vols 20,000; Bk Titles 12,000; Per Subs 150
Subject Interests: Mine safety
Special Collections: Bureau of Mines (1910-present); Mine Accident Reports (Middle 1800-present)
Publications: Journal holdings list; new publications; new services
Partic in Nat Libr of Med; OCLC Online Computer Library Center, Inc

BECKLEY

M APPALACHIAN REGIONAL HOSPITAL, Medical Library,* 306 Stanaford Rd, 25801-3186. SAN 317-7238. Tel: 304-255-3394, 304-255-3420. FAX: 304-255-3422. *Dir*, Barbara Cook
Library Holdings: Bk Vols 1,927; Per Subs 80

J COLLEGE OF WEST VIRGINIA LIBRARY,* 609 S Kanawha St, 25802. SAN 317-7246. Tel: 304-253-7351, Ext 368. FAX: 304-253-0789. *Dir*, Judy Altis; E-Mail: jaltis@cwv.edu
Library Holdings: Bk Vols 65,000; Per Subs 104
Subject Interests: Behav sci, Bus, Computers, Econ, Interdiciplinary studies, Medical, Mgt, Nursing, Soc sci
Special Collections: Child lit, West Virginia
Publications: Library Examiner (in-house newsletter)

GM DEPARTMENT OF VETERANS AFFAIRS, Medical Center Library,* 200 Veterans Ave, 25801. SAN 317-7270. Tel: 304-255-2121, Ext 4342. FAX: 304-256-5455. *Librn*, Lois Watson
Founded 1952
Library Holdings: Bk Vols 3,100; Per Subs 117

P RALEIGH COUNTY PUBLIC LIBRARY, 221 N Kanawha St, 25801-4716. SAN 364-2933. Tel: 304-255-0511. Web Site: raleigh.lib.wv.us/rcpl. *Dir*, Danny McMillion; E-Mail: mcmillid@raleigh.lib.wv.us; *Ref*, Louise Hoyle; *Bkmobile Coordr*, Valerie Hartling; Staff 2 (MLS 2)
Founded 1935. Pop 76,819; Circ 305,755
Jul 2000-Jun 2001 Income (Main Library and Branch Library) $1,271,142, State $353,356, City $42,400, Federal $4,720, County $744,000, Locally Generated Income $43,000, Other $88,396. Mats Exp $186,500, Books $155,500, Per/Ser (Incl. Access Fees) $26,000, Micro $3,000, Other Print Mats $2,000. Sal $742,297
Library Holdings: Bk Vols 191,258; Per Subs 221
Subject Interests: Bus, Mgt, Sci-tech
Special Collections: Business Corral; Coal Mining; History (Tams Coll); West Virginia History (West Virginia Heritage Coll)
Friends of the Library Group
Branches: 3
MARSH FORK, PO Box 70, Naoma, 25140. SAN 364-2968. Tel: 304-854-2677. FAX: 304-854-2666. Web Site: www.raleigh.lib.wv.us. *Librn*, Kay Daniel; Staff 3 (Non-MLS 3)
Friends of the Library Group
SOPHIA BRANCH, Gen Delivery, Sophia, 25921. SAN 364-2992. Tel: 304-683-5990. FAX: 304-683-3124. Web Site: www.raleigh.lib.wv.us/sophia. *Librn*, Johnnie King
Friends of the Library Group
STRALIE WALKER BRANCH, PO Drawer 1299, Shady Springs District, 25918. SAN 322-5933. Tel: 304-763-2681. FAX: 304-763-3940. Web Site:

www.raleigh.lib.wv.us/shady. *Librn*, Carol Sponaugle; Staff 2 (Non-MLS 2)
Friends of the Library Group
Bookmobiles: 2

BELINGTON

P BELINGTON PUBLIC LIBRARY,* 512 Elliott Ave, PO Box 878, 26250. SAN 325-0458. Tel: 304-823-1026. FAX: 304-823-1026. Web Site: www.clark.lib.wv.us/bel/default.htm.htm. *Librn*, Janice Coontz
Founded 1980. Pop 6,672; Circ 17,621
Library Holdings: Bk Titles 12,491; Per Subs 4
Special Collections: Genealogical books; Language cassettes; Large Print books
Special Services for the Deaf - Books on deafness & sign language; High interest/low vocabulary books; Special interest periodicals

BERKELEY SPRINGS

P MORGAN COUNTY PUBLIC LIBRARY,* 204 N Washington, 25411. SAN 317-7289. Interlibrary Loan Service Tel: 304-258-3350. FAX: 304-258-3350. *In Charge*, Karen Dawson
Pop 8,085; Circ 56,334
Library Holdings: Bk Vols 34,088; Per Subs 37
Special Collections: West Virginia Historical & Genealogical Collection
Mem of Martinsburg Serv Ctr
Open Mon, Thurs & Fri 9-6, Tues 9-9, Wed & Sat 9-12
Friends of the Library Group

BETHANY

CR BETHANY COLLEGE, T W Phillips Memorial Library, 300 Main St, 26032. SAN 317-7297. Tel: 304-829-7321. Reference Tel: 304-829-7335. FAX: 304-829-7333. Web Site: www.bethanywv.edu/resources/library. *Acq, Coll Develop, Dir*, Mary-Bess Halford; Tel: 304-829-7334, E-Mail: m.halford@mail.belthanywv.edu; *Bibliog Instr, ILL, Ref*, Heather May; Tel: 304-829-7335, E-Mail: h.may@mail.bethanywv.edu; *Archivist*, Jeanne Cobb; Tel: 304-829-7898, E-Mail: j.cobb@mail.bethanywv.edu; *Media Spec*, Sachiko Wood; *Automation Syst Coordr, Tech Servs*, Willette Stinson; Tel: 304-829-7508, E-Mail: w.stinson@mail.bethanywv.edu; *Bibliog Instr, ILL, Publ Servs*, Heather May; Tel: 304-829-7335, E-Mail: h.may@mail.bethanywv.edu; *AV*, Curtis Bischoff; Tel: 304-829-7541, E-Mail: c.bischoff@mail.bethanywv.edu; Staff 4 (MLS 2, Non-MLS 2)
Founded 1841. Enrl 750; Fac 56; Highest Degree: Bachelor
Jul 1999-Jun 2000 Income Parent Institution $23,000,000. Mats Exp $429,237, Books $52,958, Per/Ser (Incl. Access Fees) $89,780, Presv $19,203, Micro (CAN) $19,203, AV Equip $5,293, Manuscripts & Archives $9,293, Electronic Ref Mat (Incl. Access Fees) $22,984. Sal $167,391 (Prof $120,777)
Library Holdings: Bk Titles 190,000; Per Subs 525
Subject Interests: Regional history, Relig studies
Special Collections: Alexander Campbell & Christian Church-Disciples of Christ (Alexander Campbell Archives), bk, mss, per; Hazlett-Cummins Civil War Collections, bks; Ornithology (Brooks Bird Club Coll), per; Upper Ohio Valley Coll, bks, mss, per
Automation Activity & Vendor Info: (Acquisitions) SIRSI; (Circulation) SIRSI; (Course Reserve) SIRSI; (ILL) SIRSI; (OPAC) SIRSI; (Serials) SIRSI
Database Vendor: GaleNet, Lexis-Nexis, ProQuest, Silverplatter Information Inc.
Publications: Friends of the Library Newsletter (Newsletter)
Function: Archival collection, ILL available
Partic in OCLC Online Computer Library Center, Inc; PALINET & Union Library Catalogue of Pennsylvania
Friends of the Library Group

BLUEFIELD

S BLUEFIELD DAILY TELEGRAPH LIBRARY, 928 Bluefield Ave, 24701-2744. SAN 373-1510. Tel: 304-327-2801. FAX: 304-327-6179. E-Mail: editor@bdtonline.com.

C BLUEFIELD STATE COLLEGE, Wendell G Hardway Library, 219 Rock St, 24701. SAN 364-3026. Tel: 304-327-4055. Interlibrary Loan Service Tel: 304-327-4054. Circulation Tel: 304-327-4054. Reference Tel: 304-327-4056. FAX: 304-327-0278. Web Site: www.bluefield.wvnet.edu/library.htm. *Govt Doc, Ser*, Peggy Turnbull; Tel: 304-327-4053, E-Mail: pturnbull@bluefield.wvnet.edu; *Ref*, Joanna M Thompson; Tel: 304-327-4050, E-Mail: jthompson@bluefield.wvnet.edu; *Syst Coordr*, Robin Shapiro; Tel: 304-327-4052, E-Mail: rshapiro@bluefield.wvnet.edu; Staff 3 (MLS 3)
Founded 1895. Enrl 1,582; Highest Degree: Bachelor
Library Holdings: Bk Titles 72,011; Per Subs 225
Partic in OCLC Online Computer Library Center, Inc; PALINET & Union Library Catalogue of Pennsylvania

P CRAFT MEMORIAL LIBRARY, Mercer County Service Center,* 600 Commerce St, 24701. SAN 317-7319. Tel: 304-325-3943. FAX: 304-325-3702. *Dir*, Nancy H Moore; E-Mail: mooren@raleigh.lib.wv.us; *Asst Dir*, Eva McGuire; *Cat*, Delois Carter; *Acq*, Shirley Stringfellow; *Circ*, Nancy Siggelkow; *Archivist*, C Stuart McGehee; Staff 2 (MLS 2)
Founded 1972. Pop 64,980; Circ 116,829
Library Holdings: Bk Vols 78,000; Bk Titles 85,000; Per Subs 150
Subject Interests: Architecture, Art, Bus, Econ, Education, History, Mgt
Special Collections: Eastern Regional Coal Archives; West Virginia & Virginia History Coll
Automation Activity & Vendor Info: (Cataloging) VTLS; (Circulation) VTLS
Mem of Mercer County Serv Ctr
Partic in Southern West Virginia Library Automation Corporation
Open Mon-Thurs 9:30-8, Fri 9:30-5, Sat 12-5 & Sun 3-6
Friends of the Library Group

BRADLEY

CR JOHN VAN PUFFELEN LIBRARY OF THE APPALACHIAN BIBLE COLLEGE, (Formerly Appalachian Bible College Library), 100 N Sand Branch Rd, 25818. (Mail add: PO Box ABC, 25818), SAN 317-7327. Tel: 304-877-6428, Ext 3210. FAX: 304-877-5983. E-Mail: each100@aol.com. Web Site: www.abc.edu. *Mgr Libr Serv*, Bonita Gayle Haynes; E-Mail: ghaynes@abc.edu; *Librn*, Ed Arnold Chesley; Tel: 304-877-6428, Ext 32
Subject Specialists: *English*, Ed Arnold Chesley; *History*, Ed Arnold Chesley; *Science*, Ed Arnold Chesley; Staff 3 (MLS 1, Non-MLS 2)
Founded 1950. Enrl 257; Fac 14; Highest Degree: Master
Jul 1999-Jun 2000 Income Parent Institution $63,000. Mats Exp $30,000, Books $15,000, Per/Ser (Incl. Access Fees) $10,500, Electronic Ref Mat (Incl. Access Fees) $4,000. Sal $72,000 (Prof $39,000)
Library Holdings: Bk Vols 45,000; Bk Titles 38,000; Per Subs 200; High Interest/Low Vocabulary Bk Vols 300; Spec Interest Per Sub 70; Bks on Deafness & Sign Lang 20
Subject Interests: Missions, Theology, West Virginia
Special Collections: Archives Reference Coll (books 100 years old or more); Cults & Christian Counterfeits Coll; Judiaca Coll
Automation Activity & Vendor Info: (OPAC) Sagebrush Corporation
Database Vendor: Ebsco - EbscoHost, Silverplatter Information Inc.
Function: Research library
The library will be moving into expanded quarters over the next two year

BRIDGEPORT

P BRIDGEPORT PUBLIC LIBRARY, 1200 Johnson Ave, 26330. SAN 317-7335. Tel: 304-842-8248. FAX: 304-842-4018. Web Site: www.bridgeportwv.com. *Dir*, Sharon R Saye; Staff 15 (MLS 1, Non-MLS 14)
Founded 1956. Pop 6,739; Circ 218,195
Jul 1999-Jun 2000 Income $379,896, State $27,050, City $313,414, Coun $25,819, Locally Generated Income $13,613. Mats Exp $77,849, Books $51,125, Presv $760, AV Equip $11,853, Electronic Ref Mat (Incl. Access Fees) $8,533. Sal $174,358
Library Holdings: Bk Vols 78,269; Bk Titles 67,915; Per Subs 127
Special Collections: Michael Benedum Coll, bks, clippings, memorabilia, per, scrapbks; West Virginia Coll, bk, pamphlets
Automation Activity & Vendor Info: (Cataloging) Follett; (Circulation) Follett; (OPAC) Follett
Publications: Bridgeport: The Town & Its People
Open Mon-Fri 10-8 & Sat 12-5
Friends of the Library Group

BUCKHANNON

P CHARLES W GIBSON PUBLIC LIBRARY,* 105 E Main, 26201. SAN 317-7343. Tel: 304-472-2339. FAX: 304-472-2339. *Librn*, Denise Weese
Founded 1942. Circ 28,319
Library Holdings: Bk Vols 28,319
Mem of Upshur County Public Library

P UPSHUR COUNTY PUBLIC LIBRARY, Rte 6, Box 480, 26201. SAN 317-7351. Tel: 304-473-4219. FAX: 304-473-4221. *Acq, Actg Dir, Asst Dir, Tech Servs*, Sandra Bumgardner; Staff 1 (MLS 1)
Founded 1956. Circ 89,924
Jul 1999-Jun 2000 Income $249,260, State $68,068, County $31,500, Locally Generated Income $56,226. Mats Exp $41,443, Books $26,503, Per/Ser (Incl. Access Fees) $3,488, AV Equip $5,982, Electronic Ref Mat (Incl. Access Fees) $5,470. Sal $125,428 (Prof $57,016)
Library Holdings: Bk Vols 63,753; Bk Titles 42,077; Per Subs 83
Automation Activity & Vendor Info: (Cataloging) VTLS; (Circulation) VTLS; (OPAC) VTLS
Member Libraries: Burnsville Library; Charles W Gibson Public Library; Five Rivers Public Library; Gassaway Public Library; Mountaintop Library; Philippi Public Library; Pioneer Memorial Library; Sutton Public Library
Administrative headquarters for 6 state institutional libraries
Friends of the Library Group

WEST VIRGINIA WESLEYAN COLLEGE, Annie Merner Pfeiffer Library, 59 College Ave, 26201. SAN 317-736X. Tel: 304-473-8059. FAX: 304-473-8888. *Dir Libr Serv*, Kathleen Parker; E-Mail: parker_k@wvwc.edu; *Cat*, Judith R Martin; *Bibliog Instr, Ref*, Ben F Crutchfield; Staff 9 (MLS 3, Non-MLS 6)
Founded 1890. Enrl 1,520; Fac 88; Highest Degree: Master
Jun 1999-May 2000 Income Parent Institution $306,345. Mats Exp $292,359, Books $53,137, Per/Ser (Incl. Access Fees) $53,249, Presv $1,525, Micro $14,413, Electronic Ref Mat (Incl. Access Fees) $95,434
Library Holdings: Bk Vols 120,186; Bk Titles 102,874; Per Subs 674
Subject Interests: Civil War hist, Relig studies, WV Methodist Hist
Special Collections: Jones Lincoln Coll; Pearl S Buck Manuscripts; West Virginia Historical Archives
Automation Activity & Vendor Info: (Acquisitions) Innovative Interfaces Inc.; (Cataloging) Innovative Interfaces Inc.; (Circulation) Innovative Interfaces Inc.; (Serials) Innovative Interfaces Inc.
Function: ILL available
Partic in Mountain States Consortium; PALINET & Union Library Catalogue of Pennsylvania

RLINGTON

BURLINGTON LIBRARY,* PO Box 61, 26710. SAN 376-6608. Tel: 304-289-3690. FAX: 304-289-3233. *Dir*, Eleanor Spanburgh
Library Holdings: Bk Vols 5,000; Bk Titles 3,000
Mem of Potomac Valley Regional Libr Syst

RNSVILLE

BURNSVILLE LIBRARY,* General Delivery, 26335. SAN 376-6071. Tel: 304-853-2338. FAX: 304-853-2338. *Librn*, Mary S Black
Library Holdings: Bk Vols 9,000; Bk Titles 5,000; Per Subs 10
Mem of Upshur County Public Library

PON BRIDGE

CAPON BRIDGE PUBLIC LIBRARY,* PO Box 88, 26711. SAN 317-7378. Tel: 304-856-3777. FAX: 304-856-3777. *Librn*, Cathy Haines
Founded 1969. Pop 3,000; Circ 9,414
Library Holdings: Bk Vols 23,000; Bk Titles 20,000; Per Subs 25
Mem of Potomac Valley Regional Libr Syst
Friends of the Library Group

APMANVILLE

CHAPMANVILLE PUBLIC LIBRARY,* Box 4586, 25508. SAN 321-0057. Tel: 304-855-3405. FAX: 304-855-8590. *Librn*, Carolyn Bell; E-Mail: cbell@cabell.lib.wv.us; *Asst Librn*, Joanne Bevino; Staff 2 (Non-MLS 2)
Founded 1977. Circ 46,521
Library Holdings: Bk Titles 19,439; Per Subs 43
Special Collections: AV Coll, bks, vf; Logan County Hist Special Coll; Video cassettes; West Virginia, bks, vf
Publications: Library Paper (newsletter)
Partic in VA Tech Libr Syst
Open Mon, Wed & Fri 10-5, Tues & Thurs 10-7
Friends of the Library Group

IARLES TOWN

OLD CHARLES TOWN LIBRARY, 200 E Washington St, 25414. SAN 317-7386. Tel: 304-725-2208. FAX: 304-725-6618. *Librn*, Marcia Lance
Founded 1927. Pop 35,000; Circ 115,000
Library Holdings: Bk Vols 95,000; Per Subs 150
Special Collections: Civil War History, Genealogy (Perry Room); Large Type Coll, West Virginia History

HARLESTON

CHARLESTON NEWSPAPERS LIBRARY,* 1001 Virginia St E, 25301. SAN 326-3878. Tel: 304-348-4888. *Librn*, Ron Miller; *Asst Librn*, Pamela Moles
Founded 1940
Special Collections: Charleston Gazette & Charleston Daily Mail Coll, per

COLUMBIA GAS TRANSMISSION CORP, Law Library,* PO Box 1273, 25325-1273. SAN 364-3050. Tel: 304-357-2554. FAX: 304-357-3206. *Librn*, Sandra K Neylon; Staff 2 (MLS 1, Non-MLS 1)
Library Holdings: Bk Titles 11,000; Per Subs 50
Subject Interests: All reported cases, Digests, Texts, To the Fed Power Comm in a seven state area, Treatises applicable to gen operating practices of gas indust

R FIRST PRESBYTERIAN CHURCH OF CHARLESTON LIBRARY, 16 Leon Sullivan Way, 25301. SAN 317-7408. Tel: 304-343-8961. FAX: 304-343-8970. *Librn*, Helen Thomas; Staff 1 (MLS 1)
Library Holdings: Bk Vols 9,000
Subject Interests: Bible, Religion
Friends of the Library Group

L JACKSON & KELLY, Law Library, 1600 Laidley Tower, 25322. (Mail add: PO Box 553, 25322), SAN 317-7416. Tel: 304-340-1000. FAX: 304-340-1093. *Librn*, Pat Link; E-Mail: pmlink@jacksonkelly.com
Library Holdings: Bk Vols 20,000
Partic in Am Asn of Law Librs; SE Asn of Law Librs

P KANAWHA COUNTY PUBLIC LIBRARY,* 123 Capitol St, 25301. SAN 364-314X. Tel: 304-343-4646. FAX: 304-348-6530. Web Site: kanawha.lib.wv.us. *Dir*, Linda Wright; *Circ*, Barbara Straughter; *Ch Servs*, Terri McDougal; *Media Spec*, Julie Spiegler; *Ref*, Linda Miller; *ILL*, Elizabeth Fraser; *Publ Servs*, Ginger Miloserny; *Automation Syst Coordr*, Karen Arnett; *Tech Servs*, Jane Hughes; Staff 25 (MLS 25)
Founded 1909. Pop 208,713; Circ 1,148,704
Jul 1998-Jun 1999 Income $5,305,816, State $742,734, City $650,159, County $1,743,893. Mats Exp $773,350, Books $620,530, Per/Ser (Incl. Access Fees) $40,520, Micro $8,500. Sal $2,666,358 (Prof $1,020,501)
Library Holdings: Bk Vols 628,308
Special Collections: Local History (West Virginia)
Publications: West Virginia Foundation Directory
Member Libraries: Nitro Public Library
Friends of the Library Group
Branches: 9
CLENDENIN, 104 Cardinal St, Clendenin, 25045. SAN 377-0583. Tel: 304-548-6370. *Librn*, Tammy Parker
CROSS LANES, 5451 Big Tyler Rd, 25313. SAN 364-3204. Tel: 304-776-5999. *Librn*, Alice Riecks
DUNBAR PUBLIC, 301 Twelfth Street Mall, Dunbar, 25064. SAN 364-3239. Tel: 304-766-7161. *Librn*, Sandra Turner
ELK VALLEY, 4636 Pennsylvania Ave, 25302. SAN 364-3263. Tel: 304-965-3636. *Librn*, Susanna Holstein
GLASGOW BRANCH, 129 Fourth Ave, PO Box 317, Glasgow, 25086. SAN 364-3298. Tel: 304-595-3131. *Librn*, Traletta Wallace
MARMET BRANCH, 9303 Oregon Ave, Marmet, 25315. SAN 364-3301. Tel: 304-949-6628. *Librn*, Traletta Wallace
SAINT ALBANS BRANCH, Sixth Ave & Fourth St, Saint Albans, 25177. SAN 364-3328. Tel: 304-722-4244. FAX: 304-722-4245. *Librn*, Judy Duncan
SISSONVILLE, 601 Clearview Heights, 25320. SAN 364-3336. Tel: 304-984-2244. *Librn*, Pat Abbott
P SUBREGIONAL LIBRARY FOR THE BLIND & PHYSICALLY HANDICAPPED *Coordr*, Dixie Smith
Special Collections: West Virginia, cassettes
Bookmobiles: 1

L ROBINSON & MCELWEE LLP, Law Library, 500 Virginia St E, 25301. (Mail add: PO Box 1791, 25326), SAN 372-3933. Tel: 304-344-5800. FAX: 304-344-9566. E-Mail: mda@ramlaw.com. Web Site: www.ramlaw.com. *Librn*, Mary Aldridge; Tel: 304-347-8325
Dec 1999-Nov 2000 Mats Exp $206,000, Books $140,000, Per/Ser (Incl. Access Fees) $6,000, Electronic Ref Mat (Incl. Access Fees) $60,000
Library Holdings: Bk Vols 10,000; Bk Titles 600
Automation Activity & Vendor Info: (Acquisitions) Inmagic, Inc.; (Cataloging) Inmagic, Inc.; (Circulation) Inmagic, Inc.; (Course Reserve) Inmagic, Inc.; (ILL) Inmagic, Inc.; (Media Booking) Inmagic, Inc.; (OPAC) Inmagic, Inc.; (Serials) Inmagic, Inc.
Restriction: By appointment only
Open Mon-Fri 9-5

S SUNRISE MUSEUMS, INC LIBRARY,* 746 Myrtle Rd, 25314. SAN 376-1886. Tel: 304-344-8035. FAX: 304-344-8038. E-Mail: sunrise@citynet.net. *Curator*, Ric Ambrose
Library Holdings: Bk Vols 3,000
Restriction: Not open to public

L UNITED STATES COURTS LIBRARY, US Court House, 300 Virginia St E Rm 7400, 25301. SAN 372-3488. Tel: 304-347-3420. FAX: 304-347-3423. *Librn*, Marjorie Price; E-Mail: marjorie_price@wvsd.uscourts.gov; Staff 2 (MLS 1, Non-MLS 1)
Library Holdings: Bk Vols 25,000; Per Subs 20
Open Mon-Fri 8:30-5

C UNIVERSITY OF CHARLESTON, Schoenbaum Library, 2300 Maccorkle Ave SE, 25304-1099. SAN 317-7440. Tel: 304-357-4780. Reference Tel: 304-357-4913. FAX: 304-357-4715. Web Site: www.uchaswv.edu/library/index.html. *Dir Libr Serv*, Donna Lewis; E-Mail: dlewis@ucwv.edu; *Head Tech Servs*, Lynn Sheehan; Tel: 304-357-4918, E-Mail: lsheehan@ucwv.edu; *Tech Servs*, Ingrid Smith; Tel: 304-357-4918, E-Mail: ismith@uchaswv.edu; *Bibliog Instr*, Susan Foster-Harper; Tel: 304-357-4779, E-Mail: sfoster@ucwv.edu; *ILL*, Janet Hill; Tel: 304-357-4782, E-Mail: jhill@ucwv.edu; *Ser*, Emily Garnett; Tel: 304-357-4917, E-Mail: egarnett@ucwv.edu; *Circ*, Judy Fortner; E-Mail: jfortner@ucwv.edu; *Circ*, Rebecca Harris; E-Mail: rharris@

ucwv.edu; *Circ*, Marc Via; E-Mail: mvia@ucwv.edu; Staff 12 (MLS 4, Non-MLS 8)
Founded 1888. Enrl 1,064; Highest Degree: Master
Jul 1999-Jun 2000 Income Parent Institution $331,519. Mats Exp $131,000, Books $50,000, Per/Ser (Incl. Access Fees) $50,000, Presv $6,000, Electronic Ref Mat (Incl. Access Fees) $25,000. Sal $187,495
Library Holdings: Bk Vols 114,954; Per Subs 404
Subject Interests: Am hist, Architecture, Art, Design, Political science, Religion
Special Collections: Appalachian Culture Coll; Art (Thomas Coll); Civil War (Gorman Coll); Early American History (John Allen Kinnaman Circulating Coll); James Swann Etchings; Kendall Vintroux Political Cartoons; Presidential Biographies (James David Barber Coll); Rare Book Coll; West Virginia Coll
Automation Activity & Vendor Info: (Cataloging) VTLS; (Circulation) VTLS; (Serials) VTLS
Database Vendor: GaleNet, IAC - Info Trac, Lexis-Nexis, Wilson - Wilson Web
Publications: Library Leaves
Restriction: Not open to public
Function: Reference services available
Partic in PALINET & Union Library Catalogue of Pennsylvania

J WEST VIRGINIA CAREER COLLEGE LIBRARY,* 1000 Virginia St E, 25301. SAN 375-3158. Tel: 304-345-2820, Ext 33. FAX: 304-345-1425. *Librn*, Patricia Link; Staff 1 (MLS 1)
Founded 1992. Fac 20
Library Holdings: Bk Vols 2,900; Bk Titles 2,500; Per Subs 40
Partic in WVa Network for Educ Telecomputing

G WEST VIRGINIA DIVISION OF CULTURE & HISTORY, Archives & History Library,* Cultural Ctr, 1900 Kanawha Blvd E, 25305-0300. SAN 317-7475. Tel: 304-558-0230. FAX: 304-558-2779. Web Site: www.wvlc.wvnet.edu/history/historyw.html. *Dir*, Fredrick Armstrong
Founded 1905
1996-1997 Income $401,354, State $351,117, Locally Generated Income $50,237. Mats Exp $26,000, Books $2,490, Per/Ser (Incl. Access Fees) $670, Presv $2,500, Micro $10,500, AV Equip $1,500, Other Print Mats $2,860, Manuscripts & Archives $150. Sal $799,895
Library Holdings: Bk Vols 63,540; Per Subs 326
Subject Interests: Appalachia, Civil War, Colonial hist, Genealogy, Mid-Atlantic region, Ohio Valley, WVa hist
Special Collections: State Printed Doc 35,290
Publications: Checklist of State Publications (biannual)

G WEST VIRGINIA LEGISLATIVE REFERENCE LIBRARY, Capitol Bldg, Rm MB 27, 25305. SAN 317-7505. Tel: 304-348-2153. FAX: 304-347-4919.
Library Holdings: Bk Vols 3,150; Per Subs 37

P WEST VIRGINIA LIBRARY COMMISSION, Cultural Center, 1900 Kanawha Blvd, State Capitol Complex, 25305. SAN 364-3417. Tel: 304-558-2041. Reference Tel: 304-558-2045. Toll Free Tel: 800-642-9021, WV only. FAX: 304-558-2044. E-Mail: mcilvain@wvlc.lib.wv.us. Web Site: wvlc.lib.wv.us. *Exec Dir*, David Michael Price; E-Mail: dprice@wvlc.wvnet.edu; *Dir*, Donna B Calvert; E-Mail: calvertd@wvlc.lib.wv.us; *Dir*, Karen Goff; Tel: 304-558-3978, Fax: 304-558-4066, E-Mail: goffk@wvlc.lib.wv.us; *Dir*, David McIlvain; Tel: 304-558-2531, Fax: 304-558-1612, E-Mail: mcilvain@wvlc.lib.wv.us; *Dep Dir*, R D Childers; E-Mail: childers@wvlc.wvnet.edu; *Dep Dir*, J D Waggoner; E-Mail: waggoner@wvlc.lib.wv.us; *Admin Assoc*, Jonnie Blackburn; *YA Servs*, David H Shouldis; *Res*, Stephen L Fesenmaier; Tel: 304-558-3978, Ext 2015, Fax: 304-558-4066, E-Mail: fesenms@wvlc.lib.wv.us. Subject Specialists: *AV*, Donna B Calvert; *Blind*, Donna B Calvert; *Physical handicaps*, Donna B Calvert; *Physical med*, Donna B Calvert; *Radar*, Donna B Calvert; *Ref*, Donna B Calvert; Staff 65 (MLS 15, Non-MLS 50)
Founded 1929. Pop 1,793,477; Circ 1,793,477
Jul 1997-Jun 1998 Income $13,884,943, State $12,642,056, Federal $1,237,739. Mats Exp Electronic Ref Mat (Incl. Access Fees) $112,595. Sal $2,152,475
Library Holdings: Bk Vols 92,844; Per Subs 600
Subject Interests: Libr sci, Political science, Pub admin
Special Collections: Government Documents; UNESCO PGI Documents
Automation Activity & Vendor Info: (Cataloging) VTLS
Database Vendor: Dialog, ProQuest
Publications: Annual Report; Annual Statistical Report
Function: Outside services via phone, cable & mail
Partic in Dialog Corporation
Headquarters for four Regional Libraries & nine Service Centers
Branches: 2
REFERENCE LIBRARY, Cultural Center, 1900 Kanawha Blvd E, 25305-0620. SAN 327-5574. Tel: 304-558-2045. FAX: 304-558-2044. Web Site: www.wvlc.wvnet.edu/. *Librn*, Karen E Goff; *Doc*, Robin Chesnex
Library Holdings: Bk Titles 92,844
Subject Interests: Libr sci, Political science, Pub admin
Special Collections: Gov Docs (US); UNESCO PGI Doc
Partic in Dialog Corporation

P SERVICES FOR THE BLIND & PHYSICALLY HANDICAPPED, Cu Ctr, 1900 Kanawha Blvd E, 25305-0620. SAN 317-7513. Tel: 304-55 4061. Toll Free Tel: 800-642-8674. FAX: 304-558-6016. *Dir*, Donna Calvert
Radio reading service

G WEST VIRGINIA RESEARCH INFORMATION CENTER LIBRARY,* West Virginia Developmental Office, State Capital Complex, Bldg 6, Rm B553, 25305-0311. SAN 317-7424. Tel: 304-558-4010. FAX: 304-558-0 *Librn*, Mary Ellen Warkentin
Library Holdings: Bk Vols 500
Special Collections: Census Data Center
Open Mon-Fri 8-5

GL WEST VIRGINIA STATE SUPREME COURT, Law Library,* Bldg 1, E-404, 1900 Kanawha Blvd E, 25305-0833. SAN 317-7521. Tel: 304-55 2607, 304-558-3637. FAX: 304-558-3673. Web Site: www.wvlc.wvnet.e lawlib/menu.html. *Librn*, Marjorie Price; E-Mail: pricem@wvnvm.wvnet
Founded 1867
Library Holdings: Bk Vols 137,107
Subject Interests: Government, Law
Partic in OCLC Online Computer Library Center, Inc; PALINET & Unic Library Catalogue of Pennsylvania
Maintains 31 judicial circuit law libraries in WVa

CM WEST VIRGINIA UNIVERSITY, Robert C Byrd Health Science Center, 3110 MacCorkle Ave SE, 25304. SAN 317-753X. Tel: 304-347-1285. FA 304-347-1288. Web Site: www.hsc.wvu.edu/charleston. *Librn*, Patricia Dawson; Staff 7 (MLS 1, Non-MLS 6)
Founded 1974
Library Holdings: Bk Vols 32,000; Bk Titles 22,000; Per Subs 431
Subject Interests: Clinical medicine
Partic in Dialog Corporation; Medline; OCLC Online Computer Library Center, Inc

CHESTER

P LYNN MURRAY MEMORIAL LIBRARY, 601 Railroad St, 26034. SA 317-7548. Tel: 304-387-1010. FAX: 304-387-1010. *Dir*, Linda Clark; E-Mail: linda.clark@eudoramail.com; Staff 2 (Non-MLS 2)
Founded 1971. Pop 7,998; Circ 22,807
Jul 1999-Jun 2000 Income $62,560. Mats Exp $13,349. Sal $32,788
Library Holdings: Bk Titles 16,081; Per Subs 42

CLARKSBURG

P CLARKSBURG-HARRISON PUBLIC LIBRARY,* 404 W Pike St, 263 SAN 317-7556. Tel: 304-627-2236. FAX: 304-627-2239. Web Site: www.clark.lib.wv.us. *Dir*, Beth Nicholson; E-Mail: nicholsb@clark.lib.wv. *Ch Servs*, Mary Loomis; E-Mail: loomis@clark.lib.wv.us; *Commun Relations*, Regina Hardman; E-Mail: hardmang@clark.lib.wv.us; *YA Servs* Charley Hively; E-Mail: hivelyc@clark.lib.wv.us; *Curator*, David Houchi E-Mail: houchin@clark.lib.wv.us; *Circ*, Rebecca Lafferty; E-Mail: lafferty clark.lib.wv.us; *Tech Servs*, Tammy Richards; E-Mail: richards@clark.lib.wv.us; *Cat*, Fred Spring; E-Mail: spring@clark.lib.wv.us. Subject Specialists: *Genealogy*, David Houchin; *Local history*, David Houchin; St 20 (MLS 2, Non-MLS 18)
Founded 1907. Pop 57,857; Circ 115,513
Jul 1998-Jun 1999 Income (Main Library Only) $575,000, State $107,191 City $118,000, Federal $72,000, County $73,000, Locally Generated Inco $74,000. Mats Exp $83,000, Books $72,000, Per/Ser (Incl. Access Fees) $4,500, Micro $3,500. Sal $245,000 (Prof $64,500)
Library Holdings: Bk Vols 81,973; Bk Titles 69,000; Per Subs 137
Subject Interests: Genealogy, Local history
Special Collections: UFO (Gray Barker Coll)
Automation Activity & Vendor Info: (Cataloging) VTLS; (Circulation) VTLS; (OPAC) VTLS
Database Vendor: OCLC - First Search, ProQuest, Wilson - Wilson Web
Function: ILL available
Friends of the Library Group

GM LOUIS A JOHNSON VA MEDICAL CENTER LIBRARY, One Medical Center Dr, 26301. SAN 317-7580. Tel: 304-623-7635. FAX: 304-623-7618 *Tech Servs*, Mary McCloud
Founded 1950
Library Holdings: Bk Vols 880; Bk Titles 800; Per Subs 379
Subject Interests: Dentistry, Medicine, Nursing, Psychiatry, Surgery
Partic in Nat Libr of Med; Veterans Affairs Library Network

M UNITED HOSPITAL CENTER, Health Science Library,* 3 Hospital Plaz 26302. SAN 317-7572. Tel: 304-624-2230. FAX: 304-624-2909.
Founded 1973
Library Holdings: Bk Vols 2,200; Per Subs 220

WEN

COWEN LIBRARY, PO Box 187, 26206. SAN 376-7795. Tel: 304-226-5332. FAX: 304-226-5332. *Librn*, Mary L Miller; Staff 2 (Non-MLS 2)
Founded 1978. Pop 5,010
1999-2000 Income $25,000. Mats Exp $2,000, Books $2,000
Library Holdings: Bk Vols 18,000; Bk Titles 16,000

AIGSVILLE

CRAIGSVILLE LIBRARY, School St, HC 59 Box 314, 26205. SAN 376-7809. Tel: 304-742-3532. FAX: 304-742-3532. Web Site: www.raleigh.lib.wv.us/nicholas/craigsville. *Dir*, Nancy Chapman; E-Mail: nancyc@wvlc.wvnet.edu
Founded 1978. Pop 8,925; Circ 34,000
Jul 1999-Jun 2000 Income $60,574, State $45,824, Locally Generated Income $9,750, Other $5,000. Mats Exp Books $10,200. Sal $34,310
Library Holdings: Bk Vols 28,000; Bk Vols 35,000; Bk Titles 34,000; Bks on Deafness & Sign Lang 12
Mem of WVa Libr Comn

LBARTON

MINGO COUNTY LIBRARY,* PO Box 10, 25670. SAN 317-7610. Tel: 304-475-2749. FAX: 304-475-3970. *Librn*, Pam Warden; E-Mail: pwarden@cabell.lib.wv.us
Pop 26,949
Library Holdings: Bk Vols 22,000; Per Subs 18
Mem of Western Counties Regional Libr Syst
Branches: 3
GILBERT BRANCH, PO Box 266, Gilbert, 25621. SAN 324-2641. Tel: 304-664-8886. FAX: 304-664-8886. *Librn*, Elberta Allen
Library Holdings: Bk Titles 4,200; Per Subs 10
KERMIT BRANCH, PO Box 577, Kermit, 25674. SAN 324-265X. Tel: 304-393-4553. FAX: 304-393-4553. *Librn*, Dorothy Linville
Library Holdings: Bk Titles 4,000; Per Subs 10
MATEWAN BRANCH, PO Box 111, Matewan, 25678. SAN 324-2668. Tel: 304-426-6306. FAX: 304-426-6306. *Librn*, Sharon Star
Library Holdings: Bk Titles 4,000; Per Subs 10

IZABETH

DORA BEE WOODYARD MEMORIAL LIBRARY, Mulberry St, PO Box 340, 26143. SAN 317-7629. Tel: 304-275-4295. FAX: 304-275-4295. *Librn*, Karen Ancrile; E-Mail: ancrilek@hp9k.park.lib.wv.us
Founded 1962. Pop 5,192; Circ 32,466
Library Holdings: Bk Vols 16,655; Per Subs 50
Special Collections: West Virginia History
Publications: Book News
Mem of Alpha Regional Library
Open Mon & Thurs 8-8, Tues, Wed & Fri 8-5

KINS

DAVIS & ELKINS COLLEGE, Booth Library, 100 Campus Dr, 26241. SAN 317-7637. Tel: 304-637-1200. Reference Tel: 304-637-1359. FAX: 304-637-1415. *Asst Dir*, Jacqueline D Schneider; Tel: 304-637-1359, E-Mail: jds@euclid.dne.wvnet.edu; *Head Librn*, Thomas Ellis Hodgin; Tel: 304-637-1233, E-Mail: ehodgin@euclid.dne.wvnet.edu; *Circ*, Paula Taylor; E-Mail: ptaylor@euclid.dne.wvnet.edu; *Syst Coordr*, Patrick Johnson; *Ref*, Kathy Doig; E-Mail: kdoig@euclid.dne.wvnet.edu; *Tech Servs*, Susan Bunner; Tel: 304-637-1358, E-Mail: susb@euclid.dne.wvnet.edu; *AV*, Debbie Shaffer; Tel: 304-637-1232, E-Mail: shafferd@educlid.dne.wvnet.edu; Staff 6 (MLS 3, Non-MLS 3)
Founded 1904. Enrl 647; Fac 65; Highest Degree: Bachelor
Library Holdings: Bk Vols 116,000; Per Subs 689
Special Collections: Traditional Music Archives Coll
Automation Activity & Vendor Info: (Cataloging) epixtech, inc.; (Circulation) epixtech, inc.; (Course Reserve) epixtech, inc.; (OPAC) epixtech, inc.; (Serials) epixtech, inc.
Database Vendor: OCLC - First Search, ProQuest
Partic in Appalachian Libr Info Coop; PALINET & Union Library Catalogue of Pennsylvania

ELKINS-RANDOLPH COUNTY PUBLIC LIBRARY,* 416 Davis Ave, 26241. SAN 317-7645. Tel: 304-637-0287. FAX: 304-637-0288. *Librn*, Audrey Taylor
Founded 1922. Pop 28,734; Circ 60,124
Library Holdings: Bk Vols 35,000; Per Subs 70
Mem of Stonewall Jackson Regional Libr Syst
Friends of the Library Group

FAIRMONT

C FAIRMONT STATE COLLEGE, Ruth Ann Musick Library, 1201 Locust Ave, 26554. SAN 317-767X. Tel: 304-367-4123. Interlibrary Loan Service Tel: 304-367-4622. FAX: 304-367-4016. E-Mail: U5355@wvnvm.wvnet.edu. Web Site: www.fscwv.edu/library. *Dir*, Thelma Hutchins; *ILL*, Sharon Maguire; *Publ Servs*, William Grubb; E-Mail: wgrubb@mail.fscwv.edu; Staff 8 (MLS 8)
Founded 1867. Highest Degree: Bachelor
Jul 1998-Jun 1999 Income $1,013,168. Mats Exp $216,734, Books $93,317, Per/Ser (Incl. Access Fees) $118,136, Presv $5,261. Sal $533,808
Library Holdings: Bk Vols 217,050; Per Subs 848
Automation Activity & Vendor Info: (Acquisitions) NOTIS; (Cataloging) NOTIS; (Circulation) NOTIS; (ILL) NOTIS; (OPAC) Nicholas
Publications: Handbook
Partic in OCLC Online Computer Library Center, Inc; PALINET & Union Library Catalogue of Pennsylvania

P MARION COUNTY PUBLIC LIBRARY, 321 Monroe St, 26554-2952. SAN 317-7688. Tel: 304-366-1210. FAX: 304-366-4831. Web Site: www.wvlc.wvnet.edu/marion/marionhp.html/. *Dir*, Jeannette Martin; *Dir*, Jill Dotts; Tel: 304-366-1210, Fax: 304-366-4831, E-Mail: dotts@clark.lib.wv.us; *Ch Servs*, Christian Cox; *Media Spec*, Chriss Russell; *Cat*, Barbara Satterfield; *Circ*, Kresta Harris; *Ref*, Dan Gurash; Staff 23 (MLS 2, Non-MLS 21)
Founded 1941. Pop 58,367; Circ 167,498
Jul 1998-Jun 1999 Income (Main Library and Branch Library) $681,727, State $229,793, City $21,000, County $368,104, Locally Generated Income $41,330, Other $21,500. Mats Exp $646,370, Books $104,806, Per/Ser (Incl. Access Fees) $14,700, AV Equip $21,200, Electronic Ref Mat (Incl. Access Fees) $4,871. Sal $351,762
Library Holdings: Bk Vols 104,588; Per Subs 184
Special Collections: Genealogy Coll
Automation Activity & Vendor Info: (Cataloging) VTLS; (Circulation) VTLS
Database Vendor: GaleNet, ProQuest
Friends of the Library Group
Branches: 2
FAIRVIEW PUBLIC LIBRARY, 318 Main St, PO Box 296, Fairview, 26570. SAN 324-4717. Tel: 304-449-1021. FAX: 304-449-1021. *Dir*, Jill Dotts; Tel: 304-366-1210, Fax: 304-366-4831, E-Mail: dottsj@clark.lib.wv.us; *Librn*, Oneita Opyoke
Library Holdings: Bk Vols 12,344; Per Subs 44
Friends of the Library Group
MANNINGTON PUBLIC LIBRARY, 109 Clarksburg St, Mannington, 26582. SAN 324-4725. Tel: 304-986-2803. FAX: 304-986-3425. *Librn*, Catherine Eastman
Library Holdings: Bk Vols 31,186; Per Subs 56
Friends of the Library Group

FRANKLIN

P PENDLETON COUNTY PUBLIC LIBRARY,* PO Box 519, 26807. SAN 364-3476. Tel: 304-358-7038. FAX: 304-358-7038. *Librn*, Virginia Bates
Pop 695; Circ 35,045
Library Holdings: Bk Vols 17,000; Per Subs 15
Mem of Potomac Valley Regional Libr Syst
Friends of the Library Group

GASSAWAY

P GASSAWAY PUBLIC LIBRARY, 536 Elks, 26624-1216. SAN 317-770X. Tel: 304-364-8292. TDD: 55-049-2808-001. FAX: 304-364-8292. *Dir*, Ann Friend; E-Mail: friendl@clark.lib.wv.us; *Librn*, Paula Shuman; Staff 2 (Non-MLS 2)
Founded 1967. Pop 4,833; Circ 8,172
Library Holdings: Bk Vols 15,500; Per Subs 20
Database Vendor: GaleNet, ProQuest
Function: Photocopies available
Mem of Upshur County Public Library
Friends of the Library Group

GLENVILLE

P GILMER PUBLIC LIBRARY,* 214 Walnut St, 26351. SAN 320-9822. Tel: 304-462-5620. FAX: 304-462-5620. *Librn*, Louise Galenza; E-Mail: galenza@wvlc.wvnet.edu
Founded 1979. Pop 8,334; Circ 24,500
Library Holdings: Bk Vols 18,142; Bk Titles 17,482; Per Subs 21
Subject Interests: Crafts, Local history, Medicine, Religion, WVa
A West Virginia Library Commission Instant Library
Friends of the Library Group

C GLENVILLE STATE COLLEGE, Robert F Kidd Library, 100 High St, 26351. SAN 317-7718. Tel: 304-462-4109. FAX: 304-462-4049. Web Site: www.glenville.edu/library2000.htm. *Dir*, Ed Messenger; Tel: 304-462-4109,

Ext311, E-Mail: messenger@glenville.edu; *Ref*, Ben Bruton; Tel: 304-462-4109, Ext 314, E-Mail: brutonb@glenville.edu; *Tech Servs*, Prem Verma; Tel: 304-462-4109, Ext 312, E-Mail: verma@glenville.edu; Staff 9 (MLS 3, Non-MLS 6)
Founded 1930. Enrl 2,708; Fac 81; Highest Degree: Bachelor
Jul 1999-Jun 2000 Income $651,923. Mats Exp $126,485, Books $28,722, Per/Ser (Incl. Access Fees) $72,063, Micro $7,421, AV Equip $14,053, Other Print Mats $4,226. Sal $126,485
Library Holdings: Bk Titles 115,892; Per Subs 1,893
Subject Interests: West Virginia
Special Collections: Berlin B Chapman - Special Collection Room
Automation Activity & Vendor Info: (Cataloging) VTLS
Database Vendor: Ebsco - EbscoHost

GRAFTON

P TAYLOR COUNTY PUBLIC LIBRARY, 200 Beech St, 26354. SAN 317-7726. Tel: 304-265-6121. FAX: 304-265-6122. E-Mail: ourlibrary@hotmail.com. Web Site: taylor.clark.lib.wv.us. *Dir*, Erika Reed; E-Mail: reed@westvirginia.net; *Tech Servs*, Marli Jenkins; *Circ*, Joyce Coombs; Staff 4 (MLS 1, Non-MLS 3)
Founded 1979. Pop 15,144
Jul 1999-Jun 2000 Income $140,000, State $67,000, County $54,000, Locally Generated Income $19,000. Mats Exp $18,375, Books $12,000, Per/Ser (Incl. Access Fees) $3,000, AV Equip $3,000, Electronic Ref Mat (Incl. Access Fees) $375. Sal $57,000 (Prof $24,000)
Library Holdings: Bk Vols 24,066; Bk Titles 21,798; Per Subs 35
Subject Interests: Genealogy, Local history
Special Collections: West Virginia Coll
Automation Activity & Vendor Info: (Cataloging) Follett; (Circulation) Follett; (OPAC) Follett
Database Vendor: GaleNet, IAC - Info Trac, ProQuest, Wilson - Wilson Web
Publications: Monthly newsletter
Special Services - Outreach programs to nursing facilities & local schools

GRANTSVILLE

P CALHOUN COUNTY PUBLIC LIBRARY,* Mill St N, PO Box 918, 26147. SAN 317-7734. Tel: 304-354-6300. FAX: 304-354-6300. Web Site: www.hp9k.park.lib.wv.us/calhoun/calhoun.html. *Librn*, Glada Stump
Pop 7,877; Circ 20,685
Library Holdings: Bk Vols 16,500; Per Subs 21
Mem of Alpha Regional Library

GREEN BANK

S NATIONAL RADIO ASTRONOMY OBSERVATORY LIBRARY,* PO Box 2, 24944. SAN 317-7742. Tel: 304-456-2011, Ext 223. FAX: 304-456-2229. Web Site: www.cv.nrao.edu/html/library/library.html. *In Charge*, Alesia Wayne; E-Mail: awayne@nrao.edu
Founded 1959
Library Holdings: Bk Vols 2,926; Per Subs 65
Subject Interests: Astronomy, Astrophysics, Electronics
Special Collections: Observatory Publications Coll; Palomar Sky Survey Coll
Branch of main library in Charlottesville, Virginia Open Mon-Fri 8-4:30

HAMLIN

P HAMLIN-LINCOLN COUNTY PUBLIC LIBRARY,* 7999 Lynn Ave, 25523. SAN 364-3654. Tel: 304-824-5481. FAX: 304-824-7014. *Dir*, Margaret Smith; E-Mail: smithm@wvlc.wvnet.edu; *Asst Librn*, Alma Cummings; Staff 1 (MLS 1)
Founded 1972. Pop 21,382; Circ 56,986
Library Holdings: Bk Titles 30,000; Per Subs 20
Special Collections: Genealogical Coll; West Virginia Historical Coll
Branches: 2
ALUM CREEK PUBLIC, PO Box 530, Alum Creek, 25003. SAN 364-3662. Tel: 304-756-9211. FAX: 304-756-9211. *Librn*, Kathy Cummings
Circ 19,807
Library Holdings: Bk Vols 16,633
Special Collections: West Virginia Coll
Friends of the Library Group
BRANCHLAND OUTPOST LIBRARY, PO Box 278, Branchland, 25506. SAN 364-3689. Tel: 304-778-7315. FAX: 304-778-7315. *Librn*, Edith Clay
Circ 23,065
Library Holdings: Bk Vols 20,246

HARMAN

P PIONEER MEMORIAL LIBRARY, (PML), PO Drawer 13, Rte 33E, 26270-0013. SAN 376-6020. Tel: 304-227-4788. FAX: 304-227-4788. *L.* Maureen Judy; E-Mail: judyma@clark.lib.wv.us; Staff 1 (Non-MLS 1)
Library Holdings: Bk Vols 22,000; Bk Titles 20,000
Mem of Upshur County Public Library
Friends of the Library Group

HARPERS FERRY

P BOLIVAR-HARPERS FERRY PUBLIC LIBRARY, 600 Polk St, 25425 SAN 326-3622. Tel: 304-535-2301. FAX: 304-535-2301. *Librn*, Nancy Manuel; *Ad Servs*, Mary Mahan; *Ch Servs*, Judy Grabill; Staff 3 (MLS 1 Non-MLS 2)
Founded 1977. Pop 15,000
Jul 1999-Jun 2000 Income $65,000. Mats Exp $12,000
Library Holdings: Bk Titles 20,743; Per Subs 30
Special Collections: Civil War Coll; Harpers Ferry Coll, bks; Simon Bo Coll
Automation Activity & Vendor Info: (Cataloging) VTLS; (Circulation) VTLS

S NATIONAL PARK SERVICE, Harpers Ferry Center Library, Fillmore S 25425-0050. SAN 364-3719. Tel: 304-535-6261. FAX: 304-535-6492. *Li* David Nathanson; *ILL*, Nancy Flanagan; *Ser*, Diann McCoy; Staff 3 (ML 1, Non-MLS 2)
Founded 1973
Library Holdings: Bk Vols 36,000; Bk Titles 33,000; Per Subs 400
Subject Interests: Am hist, Decorative arts, Historic sites, Material cultu Mil art, Museology, Nat parks, Natural history, NPS oral hist coll, Sci
Special Collections: Cultural Resources Bibliography Coll; Evelyn Walla Domestic Economy Coll; Harold L Peterson Military Art & Science Coll National Park Service History Coll; National Park Service Technical Rep Coll; NPS Museum Coll; Rare Book Coll; Trade Catalogs; Vera Craig Pictorial Archive of Interiors
Publications: A Survey of Oral History in the NPS; Accessions (newslet Index to the Courier (News Magazine of the National Park Service, 1982 92); information sheets on rare book administration & park library management; NPS Oral History Manual; Preliminary Inventory Series (fc archival coll); Sunshine & Shadows: A Catalog of Civil War Unit Histori & Personal Narratives in NPS Libraries; Trade Catalog Guide (on disk)
Partic in Fedlink; OCLC Online Computer Library Center, Inc
Branches:
CONSERVATION LABORATORIES LIBRARY FAX: 304-535-6055.
Library Holdings: Bk Vols 1,500
Subject Interests: Museology
Special Collections: Ralph Lewis Coll
GRAPHIC RESEARCH CENTER LIBRARY
Library Holdings: Bk Vols 1,500
Special Collections: Harpers Weekly Magazine
HISTORIC FURNISHINGS LIBRARY
Library Holdings: Bk Vols 3,700
Subject Interests: Decorative arts, Domestic econ, Mat culture, Social history
Special Collections: Domestic Science (Wallace Coll); Trade Catalog Coll; US Patent Label Coll, 1872-1940
NATIONAL PARK SERVICE HISTORY COLLECTION
Library Holdings: Bk Vols 3,000
Subject Interests: Hist sites, Monuments, Nat parks, The Nat Park Ser
Special Collections: Museum Coll (uniforms & insignia of the NPS); NPS Oral Hist Coll; Original Artwork
Publications: Index to the Courier-Newsmagazine of the National Park Service; NPS Uniforms & Insignia (vol 1, 1992, vol 2, 1994, vol 3, 199

HARRISVILLE

P RITCHIE COUNTY PUBLIC LIBRARY, 130 Court St, 26362. SAN 317-7750. Tel: 304-643-2717. FAX: 304-643-2717. Web Site: www.hp9k.park.lib.wv.us/alpha/ritchi.html. *Head Librn*, Janice White; *Asst Librn*, Thresa Prunty
Founded 1931. Pop 10,233; Circ 49,398
Jul 1999-Jun 2000 Income (Main Library and Branch Library) $173,000, State $41,000, County $114,000, Locally Generated Income $18,000. Mats Exp $32,233, Books $27,000, Per/Ser (Incl. Access Fees) $2,133, Micro $100, Electronic Ref Mat (Incl. Access Fees) $3,000. Sal $74,000 (Prof $43,000)
Library Holdings: Bk Titles 34,580; Per Subs 87; Bks on Deafness & Sig Lang 30
Special Collections: The Minnie Kendall Lowther Memorial Coll, oral his West Virginia History & Ritchie County History Coll, bks, rec, micro, slid A-tapes
Mem of Alpha Regional Library
Branches: 1
PENNSBORO BRANCH, 411 Main St, Pennsboro, 26415. SAN 376-897X Tel: 304-659-2197. FAX: 304-659-2197. Web Site:

www.hp9k.park.lib.wv.us/alpha/penn.html. *Librn*, Jane Hearne
Founded 1984. Pop 4,093; Circ 11,000
Library Holdings: Bk Vols 15,000; Per Subs 28

LVETIA

HELVETIA LIBRARY,* Main St, PO Box 15, 26224. SAN 376-6128. Tel: 304-924-5063. FAX: 304-924-5063. *Librn*, Darlene Lucas; E-Mail: lucasd@hp9k.clark.lib.wv.us
Library Holdings: Bk Titles 4,000

LSBORO

PEARL S BUCK BIRTHPLACE FOUNDATION, Historic House Museum Library, PO Box 126, 24946. SAN 377-5003. Tel: 304-653-4430. Web Site: www.wvnet.edu. *Mgr*, Anita Withrow
Library Holdings: Bk Titles 400
Restriction: Non-circulating to the public

POCAHONTAS COUNTY FREE LIBRARY,* PO Box 132, 24946. SAN 364-3565. Tel: 304-653-4936. FAX: 304-653-4936. E-Mail: pocahontaslib@yahoo.com. *Dir*, Charlene Beverage
Pop 9,917; Circ 30,000
Library Holdings: Per Subs 23
Branches: 4
DURBIN BRANCH, PO Box 333, Durbin, 26264-0333. SAN 376-2416. Tel: 304-456-3142. *Librn*, Maria Tenney
Library Holdings: Bk Vols 6,209
GREEN BANK BRANCH, PO Box 1, Green Bank, 24944-0001. SAN 376-2424. Tel: 304-456-4507. FAX: 304-456-4500. *Librn*, Jane Mospan
Library Holdings: Bk Vols 24,230
HILLSBORO BRANCH, PO Box 132, 24946. SAN 364-359X. Tel: 304-653-4936. FAX: 304-653-4936. *Librn*, Junida Strader
Circ 4,800
Library Holdings: Bk Vols 19,675
MCCLINTIC, Rte 2, Box 526, Buckeye, 24924. SAN 364-362X. Tel: 304-799-4165. FAX: 304-799-4165.
Circ 5,700
Library Holdings: Bk Vols 11,914

NTON

SUMMERS COUNTY PUBLIC LIBRARY, 201 Temple St, 25951. SAN 329-9384. Tel: 304-466-4490. FAX: 304-466-5260. *Librn*, Myra Ziegler; E-Mail: zieglerm@raleigh.lib.wv.us; *Asst Librn*, Sharon Gill; *Asst Librn*, Sherry Whitaker; Staff 3 (MLS 1, Non-MLS 2)
Founded 1977
Jul 1998-Jun 1999 Income $112,874, State $48,747, City $4,000, County $6,000, Locally Generated Income $2,100, Other $42,027. Mats Exp $26,667, Books $25,183, Per/Ser (Incl. Access Fees) $1,484. Sal $54,440 (Prof $22,000)
Library Holdings: Bk Titles 19,373; Per Subs 42
Automation Activity & Vendor Info: (Circulation) VTLS
Friends of the Library Group

NDRED

HUNDRED PUBLIC LIBRARY,* PO Box 453, 26575. SAN 364-4731. Tel: 304-775-5161. FAX: 304-775-5161. *Librn*, Ruth Satterfield
Pop 1,590; Circ 20,365
Library Holdings: Bk Vols 5,000
Mem of Miracle Valley Regional Library System
Friends of the Library Group

NTINGTON

CABELL COUNTY PUBLIC LIBRARY, Western Counties Regional Library System, 455 Ninth Street Plaza, 25701. SAN 364-3832. Tel: 304-528-5700. FAX: 304-528-5701. E-Mail: library@cabell.lib.wv.us. Web Site: cabell.lib.wv.us. *Dir*, Judy K Rule; E-Mail: jrule@cabell.lib.wv.us; *Asst Dir*, G Steve Christo; E-Mail: schristo@cabell.lib.wv.us; *Dir Info Resources & Res*, Francie Buchanan; E-Mail: fbuchanan@cabell.lib.wv.us; *Syst Coordr*, Geraldine Smith; E-Mail: gsmith@cabell.lib.wv.us; *Ref*, Karen Bremer; E-Mail: kbremer@cabell.lib.wv.us; *Ref*, Mary Lou Pratt; E-Mail: mpratt@cabell.lib.wv.us; *Ch Servs*, Barbara Gilbert; E-Mail: bgilbert@cabell.lib.wv.us; *Ch Servs*, Mary Jane Howard; E-Mail: mhoward@cabell.lib.wv.us; *AV*, Margot Durbin; E-Mail: mdurbin@cabell.lib.wv.us; *Cat*, Deborah Musser; E-Mail: dmusser@cabell.lib.wv.us; Staff 54 (MLS 11, Non-MLS 43)
Founded 1902. Pop 96,827
Jul 2000-Jun 2001 Income (Main Library and Branch Library) $2,503,915, State $551,984, City $7,000, Federal $18,500, County $964,700, Locally Generated Income $136,000, Other $825,731. Mats Exp $435,500, Books $383,500, AV Equip $2,000, Other Print Mats $40,000, Electronic Ref Mat (Incl. Access Fees) $10,000. Sal $1,632,217
Library Holdings: Bk Vols 356,160; Bk Titles 133,945; Per Subs 312
Special Collections: Regional History
Automation Activity & Vendor Info: (Cataloging) SIRSI; (Circulation) SIRSI; (OPAC) SIRSI
Database Vendor: ProQuest
Special Services for the Deaf - Books on deafness & sign language
Branches: 7
BARBOURSVILLE BRANCH, 728 Main St, Barboursville, 25504. SAN 364-3867. Tel: 304-736-4621. *Librn*, Karen Fields
Library Holdings: Bk Vols 26,108
GALLAHER VILLAGE, 368 Norway Ave, 25705. SAN 364-3956. Tel: 304-528-5696. FAX: 304-528-5696. *Librn*, Donna McCoy
Library Holdings: Bk Vols 28,142
GUYANDOTTE, 203 Richmond St, 25702. SAN 364-3980. Tel: 304-528-5698. FAX: 304-528-5698. *Librn*, Elwin Layman
Library Holdings: Bk Vols 11,091
MILTON BRANCH, 1140 Smith St, Milton, 25541. SAN 364-4014. Tel: 304-743-6711. FAX: 304-743-6747. *Librn*, Georgina Doss
Library Holdings: Bk Vols 20,045
SALT ROCK PUBLIC, Salt Rock Community School, RFS No 1, Salt Rock, 25559. SAN 364-4049. Tel: 304-736-1956. *Librn*, Beverly Harbour
Library Holdings: Bk Vols 4,315
P SERVICES FOR THE BLIND & PHYSICALLY HANDICAPPED *Librn*, Suzanne Marshall
Friends of the Library Group
WEST HUNTINGTON, 428 W 14th St, 25704. SAN 364-4073. Tel: 304-528-5697. FAX: 304-528-5697. *Librn*, Lola Miller
Library Holdings: Bk Vols 18,162
Bookmobiles: 2

L HUDDLESTON, BOLEN, BEATTY, PORTER & COPEN, Law Library, 611 Third Ave, 25701. (Mail add: PO Box 2185, 25722-2185), SAN 372-3461. Tel: 304-529-6181. FAX: 304-522-4312. *Librn*, Elizabeth L Bennett; E-Mail: ebennett@huddlestonbolen.com; Staff 2 (Non-MLS 2)
Library Holdings: Bk Vols 25,000
Database Vendor: Lexis-Nexis
Open Mon-Fri 9-5

S HUNTINGTON MUSEUM OF ART LIBRARY,* 2033 McCoy Rd, 25701. SAN 317-7793. Tel: 304-529-2701. FAX: 304-529-7447. E-Mail: hma@ianet.net. *Librn*, Christopher Hatten
Library Holdings: Bk Vols 11,200; Bk Titles 12,000; Per Subs 55
Subject Interests: Am glass, Antique firearms, Antique to contemporary, Fine arts, Tapestries
Special Collections: Fastoria Glass Catalogs & Price Lists 1897-1980; Fine Arts Coll; Fire Arms History & Manufacture Coll; Glass History & Technology Coll
Microfiche reader located in libr; special coll of Fostoria glass catalogs and price lists 1897-1980

L JENKINS, FENSTERMAKER, PLLC, Law Library, PO Box 2688, 25726. SAN 372-347X. Tel: 304-523-2100. FAX: 304-523-2347. *Mgr Libr*, Clara J Sheets; *Actg Librn*, Jacqueline S Burns; Staff 2 (Non-MLS 2)
Library Holdings: Bk Vols 5,000
Open Mon-Fri 8:30am-5:30pm

M MARSHALL UNIVERSITY, Health Science Libraries,* 1600 Medical Center Dr, 25701. SAN 322-6972. Tel: 304-691-1752. FAX: 304-691-1766. *Librn*, Edward Dzierzak; E-Mail: dzierzak@marshall.edu; *Online Servs, Ref*, Robert Williams; Staff 7 (MLS 3, Non-MLS 4)
Founded 1976. Enrl 200; Fac 175; Highest Degree: Doctorate
Jul 1997-Jun 1998 Income $354,000, State $305,000, Locally Generated Income $24,000, Other $25,000. Mats Exp $293,000, Books $14,000, Per/Ser (Incl. Access Fees) $277,000. Sal $278,000 (Prof $103,000)
Library Holdings: Bk Titles 15,620; Per Subs 423
Partic in Medline

C MARSHALL UNIVERSITY LIBRARIES, 400 Hal Greer Blvd, 25755-2060. SAN 317-7815. Tel: 304-696-2320. Interlibrary Loan Service Tel: 304-696-4011. FAX: 304-696-5858. E-Mail: library@marshall.edu. Web Site: www.marshall.edu/library/. *Dean*, Barbara A Winters; *Assoc Dean*, Monica G Brooks; Tel: 304-696-6613, Fax: 304-696-3597, E-Mail: brooks@marshall.edu; *Assoc Dean*, Dr Celene Seymour; Tel: 304-746-8901, Fax: 304-746-8905, E-Mail: seymour@marshall.edu; *Dir*, Edward Dzierzak; Tel: 304-691-1753, Fax: 304-696-1766, E-Mail: dzierzak@marshall.edu; *Ref*, Timothy Balch; Tel: 304-696-2335, E-Mail: balch@marshall.edu; *Ref*, Stephen Tipler; Tel: 304-696-2907, E-Mail: tipler@marshall.edu; *Spec Coll*, Kathleen Bledsoe; Tel: 304-696-3174, Fax: 304-696-2361, E-Mail: bledsoek@marshall.edu; *Curator*, Lisle Brown; Tel: 304-696-2344, Fax: 304-696-2361, E-Mail: brown@marshall.edu; *Exten Serv*, Judith Arnold; Tel: 304-696-3627, E-Mail: arnold@marshall.edu; *Publ Servs*, Karen Curtis; Tel: 304-691-1761, Fax: 304-696-1766, E-Mail: curtisk@marshall.edu; *Publ Servs*, Lynne Edington; Tel: 304-746-8902, Fax: 304-746-8905, E-Mail: edington@marshall.edu; *Publ Servs*, Robert Williams; Tel: 304-691-1760, Fax: 304-696-1766, E-Mail: williamr@marshall.edu; *Cat*, Pamela Ford; Tel: 304-696-2312, Fax: 304-696-5228, E-Mail: ford@marshall.edu; *Coll Develop*, David Gray; Tel: 304-696-4356, Fax: 304-696-5228, E-Mail: grayd@marshall.edu; *Govt Doc*, Dr Majed Khader; Tel: 304-696-3121, Fax:

304-696-2361, E-Mail: khader@marshall.edu; *Access Serv*, Wendy Moorhead; Tel: 304-696-2336, E-Mail: moorhead@marshall.edu; *Access Serv*, Paris E Webb; Tel: 304-696-2852, Fax: 304-696-2361, E-Mail: webb@marshall.edu; *Instrul Serv*, Jennifer Sias; Tel: 304-696-6577, E-Mail: sias3@marshall.edu; *Archivist*, Cora Teel; Tel: 304-696-2346, Fax: 304-696-2361, E-Mail: teel@marshall.edu; *Electronic Resources*, Ron Titus; Tel: 304-696-6575, E-Mail: titus@marshall.edu; *Electronic Resources*, Jingping Zhang; Tel: 304-696-2326, Fax: 304-696-6579, E-Mail: zhangj@marshall.edu; *Ser*, Peter Washkevich; Tel: 304-696-6567, E-Mail: washkevich@marshall.edu; *Music*, Kay Wildman; Tel: 304-696-2509, E-Mail: wildman@marshall.edu; Staff 53 (MLS 21, Non-MLS 32)
Founded 1929. Pop 13,748; Circ 70,774; Enrl 13,748; Fac 579; Highest Degree: Doctorate
Jul 1998-Jun 1999 Income $3,446,373. Mats Exp $1,174,845, Books $143,050, Per/Ser (Incl. Access Fees) $724,358, Presv $22,210, Micro $39,692, AV Equip $31,698, Other Print Mats $3,065, Electronic Ref Mat (Incl. Access Fees) $207,649. Sal $2,054,028
Library Holdings: Bk Vols 395,163; Per Subs 2,644
Subject Interests: Tri-state, W Va
Special Collections: Anthropology (Human Relations Area Files), microfiche; Civil War Newspapers; Congress of Racial Equality Papers; Historic Literature (Pollard, Redgrave & Wing Books, published in England & Scotland, 1400-1700), microfilm; Hoffman History of Medicine Library; Sociology; The Rosanna Blake Library of Confederate History
Automation Activity & Vendor Info: (Circulation) VTLS
Database Vendor: Dialog, Ebsco - EbscoHost, OCLC - First Search, ProQuest, Silverplatter Information Inc., Wilson - Wilson Web
Publications: Bibliobillboard; Carlton D Weaver Transallegheny Map Collection; Guide to Local History & Genealogy; Guide to the Marshall University Libraries; James E Morrow Library Associates Brochure, Library Connection; Library Information Brochure; WVa: Historical Guide
Function: Research library
Partic in PALINET & Union Library Catalogue of Pennsylvania
Friends of the Library Group

M MILDRED MITCHELL BATEMAN HOSPITAL LIBRARY, 1530 Norway Ave, PO Box 448, 25709-0448. SAN 328-0365. Tel: 304-525-7801, Ext 305. FAX: 304-525-7249. *Librn*, Barbara Vance
Founded 1968
Library Holdings: Bk Vols 4,519; Per Subs 15
Special Collections: high interest-low vocabulary bks; Special interest periodicals

M SAINT MARY'S HOSPITAL, Medical Library 6-East, Saint Mary's Hospital, 2900 First Ave, 25702-1271. SAN 317-7823. Tel: 304-526-1814. FAX: 304-526-1314. *Actg Librn*, Thelma Nicely; Staff 1 (MLS 1)
Founded 1924
Library Holdings: Bk Vols 617; Bk Titles 515; Per Subs 141
Subject Interests: Clinical, Preclinical med, Surgery
Publications: Listing of book holdings (author & subject); Listing of periodical holdings (title & subject)
Partic in Medline

S SPECIAL METALS CORP, Technology Information Services, 3200 Riverside Dr, 25705-1771. SAN 317-7785. Tel: 304-526-5433. FAX: 304-526-5973. *Admin Dir*, Connie Back; E-Mail: cback@smcwv.com
Founded 1964
Library Holdings: Bk Titles 4,500; Per Subs 100
Subject Interests: Analytical chemistry, Ferrous metallurgy, Gen mgt, Nonferrous
Automation Activity & Vendor Info: (Acquisitions) EOS; (Cataloging) EOS; (Circulation) EOS; (OPAC) EOS; (Serials) EOS
Restriction: By appointment only
Partic in PALINET & Union Library Catalogue of Pennsylvania

UNITED STATES ARMY
A HUNTINGTON DISTRICT CORPS OF ENGINEERS LIBRARY, 502 Eighth St, 25701-2070. SAN 364-4103. Tel: 304-529-5435, 304-529-5713. FAX: 304-529-5591. *Librn*, Sandra McCallister; E-Mail: sandram@mail.lrh.usace.army.mil; *Tech Servs*, Judy Daniels
Founded 1974
Library Holdings: Bk Vols 6,500; Per Subs 83
Subject Interests: Civil engineering, Water quality
Partic in Fedlink

HURRICANE

P PUTNAM COUNTY LIBRARY, 4219 State Rte 34, 25526. SAN 364-4138. Tel: 304-757-7308. FAX: 304-757-7384. E-Mail: putnam@cabell.lib.wv.us. Web Site: 129.71.124.2/putnam/. *Dir*, Peggy Bias; E-Mail: pbias@cabell.lib.wv.us; *Ch Servs*, Christie A Cook; E-Mail: ccook@cabell.lib.wv.us. Subject Specialists: *Early childhood develop*, Christie A Cook; Staff 8 (MLS 1, Non-MLS 7)
Founded 1959. Pop 54,000; Circ 238,455
Jul 2000-Jun 2001 Income (Main Library and Branch Library) $382,318, State $171,768, City $8,750, County $190,800, Locally Generated Income $6,000, Other $5,000. Mats Exp Books $54,000. Sal $299,413 (Prof $44,500)
Library Holdings: Bk Vols 93,000; Per Subs 125
Database Vendor: ProQuest
Publications: Friends of Putnam County Library Newsletter
Mem of Western Counties Regional Libr Syst
Friends of the Library Group
Branches: 4
BUFFALO BRANCH, PO Box 366, Buffalo, 25033. SAN 364-4154. Te 304-937-3538. FAX: 304-937-3538. *Librn*, Kimberly Moore
ELEANOR BRANCH, 203 Eleanor Circle, Eleanor, 25070. SAN 364-4 Tel: 304-586-4295. FAX: 304-586-4295. Web Site: www.cabell.lib.wv. putnam. *Librn*, Tretha Savilla
Friends of the Library Group
HURRICANE BRANCH, 410 Midland Trail, 25526. SAN 364-4197. Te 304-562-6711. FAX: 304-562-6711. *Librn*, Elaine Childs
POCA BRANCH, PO Box 606, Poca, 25159. SAN 364-4200. Tel: 304-7 3241. FAX: 304-755-3241. *Librn*, LuAnn Raynes

HUTTONSVILLE

S HUTTONSVILLE CORRECTIONAL CENTER LIBRARY,* PO Box 1 26273. SAN 317-784X. Tel: 304-335-2291, Ext 244. *Librn*, Robert Char
Founded 1968
Library Holdings: Bk Titles 5,000; Per Subs 77
Special Collections: ABA Recommended Material; Huttonsville Correcti Center Coll; Law (State & Federal) Coll
Special Services for the Deaf - Captioned film depository; High interest/ vocabulary books

INDUSTRIAL

G WEST VIRGINIA INDUSTRIAL HOME FOR YOUTH LIBRARY, 15 Industrial Blvd, 26375. SAN 329-3246. Tel: 304-782-1128. FAX: 304-78 1379. *In Charge*, Robert Daquilante
Enrl 50; Fac 9
Books supplied by Clarksburg & Harrison Libraries

INSTITUTE

S WEST VIRGINIA DEPARTMENT OF EDUCATION & THE ARTS, Division of Rehabilitation Services, Staff Library, West Virginia Rehabilitation Ctr, PO Box 1004, 25112-1004. SAN 317-7858. Tel: 304- 4644. FAX: 304-766-4913. *Librn*, Kellie Booton
Founded 1968
Library Holdings: Bk Vols 14,600
Subject Interests: Behav sci, Medicine, Soc sci
Publications: AV Catalog

C WEST VIRGINIA STATE COLLEGE, Drain-Jordan Library, Campus 16 PO Box 102, 25112-1002. SAN 317-7866. Tel: 304-766-3116. FAX: 304-766-4103. Web Site: www.library.wvsc.edu/index.html. *Dir*, Dr Ravindra Sharma; Tel: 304-766-3117, E-Mail: sharmarn@mail.wvsc.edu; *Archivist*, Ellen Ressmeyer; E-Mail: eressmeyer@mail.wvsc.edu; *Automation Syst Coordr*, Deborah Jean Wells; E-Mail: wells@mail.wvsc.edu; *Cat*, Ronald Wiley; E-Mail: wileylr@mail.wvsc.edu; *Coll Develop*, John Michael Kist *Doc, Ref, Res*, Irmin Allner; *Ser*, Janet Bosley; Tel: 304-766-2162; Staff 1 (MLS 9, Non-MLS 9)
Founded 1891. Enrl 3,446; Fac 142; Highest Degree: Bachelor
Jul 1998-Jun 1999 Income $1,022,804, State $610,360, Locally Generated Income $10,213, Other $402,231. Mats Exp $451,057, Books $79,460, Pe Ser (Incl. Access Fees) $84,105, Presv $2,484, Micro $14,500, AV Equip $112,737, Electronic Ref Mat (Incl. Access Fees) $13,418. Sal $505,430 (Prof $255,053)
Library Holdings: Bk Vols 204,801; Bk Titles 160,000; Per Subs 792
Subject Interests: African-American hist
Special Collections: College Archives, correpondence, photog, rpts; John Davis Papers
Automation Activity & Vendor Info: (Acquisitions) VTLS; (Cataloging) VTLS; (Circulation) VTLS; (Serials) VTLS
Database Vendor: Ebsco - EbscoHost, IAC - Info Trac, IAC - SearchBan OCLC - First Search, Silverplatter Information Inc., Wilson - Wilson Web
Publications: Library Timesavers; Periodical Holding List
Partic in Dialog Corporation; OCLC Online Computer Library Center, Inc PALINET & Union Library Catalogue of Pennsylvania

KEARNEYSVILLE

G UNITED STATES GEOLOGICAL SURVEY-BIOLOGICAL RESOURCE DIVISION, Technical Information Services, 1700 Leetown Rd, 25430. SA 317-7874. Tel: 304-724-4447. FAX: 304-724-4435. Web Site: lsc-tis.library.net. *Librn*, Vi Catrow; E-Mail: vi_catrow@usgs.gov; *Tech Servs*, Lora McKenzie
Founded 1959
Library Holdings: Bk Titles 22,000; Per Subs 200
Subject Interests: Aquaculture, Culture, Diseases, Fish bacteriology,

Genetics, Histology, Immunology, Nutrition, Parasitology, Physiology, Virology
Partic in Dialog Corporation; OCLC Online Computer Library Center, Inc
Branches:
NORTHERN APPALACHIAN RESEARCH LABORATORY, PO Box 63, Wellsboro, 16901-9217. SAN 377-0605. Tel: 717-724-3322. FAX: 717-724-2525. Web Site: lsc-tis.library.net. *Tech Servs*, Betsy Driebelbies
Founded 1978
Library Holdings: Bk Titles 3,600; Per Subs 120
Special Collections: Community Ecology; Fish Genetics; Materials on Aquaculture Engineering; Specialized materials on Fish Culture
Partic in Fedlink; Susquehanna Library Cooperative

NOVA

CEREDO-KENOVA MEMORIAL PUBLIC LIBRARY,* 1200 Oak St, 25530. SAN 317-7882. Tel: 304-453-2462. FAX: 304-453-2462. *Dir*, Susan McComas
Library Holdings: Bk Titles 35,000; Per Subs 44
Mem of Western Counties Regional Libr Syst
Friends of the Library Group
Branches: 2
FORT GAY PUBLIC, PO Box 457, Fort Gay, 25514. SAN 324-2625. Tel: 304-648-5338. FAX: 304-648-5338. *Librn*, Sheila Salmons
Circ 27,605
Library Holdings: Per Subs 33
WAYNE PUBLIC, PO Box 567, Wayne, 25570. SAN 317-851X. Tel: 304-272-3756. FAX: 304-272-3756. *Librn*, Lana Smith

YSER

KEYSER-MINERAL COUNTY PUBLIC LIBRARY, 105 N Main St, 26726. SAN 317-7890. Tel: 304-788-3222. FAX: 304-788-3222. *Exec Dir*, Connie Sutton; E-Mail: sutton_c@martin.lib.wv.us; *Dir Libr Serv*, Mary E Keepers; E-Mail: keepers_m@martin.lib.wv.us; *Asst Librn*, Mary Beth Mowen; E-Mail: mowen_m@martin.lib.wv.us; *Circ*, Betty Myers; E-Mail: myers_em@martin.lib.wv.us42; Staff 4 (MLS 2, Non-MLS 2)
Founded 1937. Pop 25,440; Circ 53,571
Jul 2000-Jun 2001 Income (Main Library and Branch Library) $188,675
Library Holdings: Bk Vols 47,522; Per Subs 31
Automation Activity & Vendor Info: (Circulation) VTLS; (ILL) VTLS; (OPAC) VTLS
Friends of the Library Group
Branches: 2
BURLINGTON PUBLIC, PO Box 61, Burlington, 26710. Tel: 304-289-3690. FAX: 304-289-3233. *Librn*, Lea Spanburgh; *Asst Librn*, Catherine Weaver; Staff 2 (Non-MLS 2)
Founded 1981
Library Holdings: Bk Vols 6,500
Automation Activity & Vendor Info: (Circulation) VTLS; (OPAC) VTLS
Open Tues & Thurs 10-5, Wed 1-6, Sat 10-3
FORT ASHBY PUBLIC, PO Box 64, Fort Ashby, 26719. SAN 329-7446. Tel: 304-298-4493. FAX: 304-298-4014. *Librn*, Jane E Howser; *Asst Librn*, Anne S Hyde; Staff 2 (Non-MLS 2)
Founded 1974
Library Holdings: Bk Vols 18,080; Per Subs 15
Automation Activity & Vendor Info: (Circulation) VTLS; (OPAC) VTLS
Open Mon & Fri 12-5, Tues, Wed & Thurs 12-5 & 6-8, Sat 9-12 & 1-4
Friends of the Library Group

POTOMAC STATE COLLEGE LIBRARY OF WEST VIRGINIA UNIVERSITY,* 26726. SAN 317-7904. Tel: 304-788-6901. FAX: 304-788-6946. E-Mail: lib001@pscvax.wvnet.edu. Web Site: www.pscvax.psc.wynet.edu/~library. *Acq, Tech Servs*, Kathleen Weber; *Media Spec*, Patricia McGuire
Founded 1901. Enrl 1,121; Fac 36
Jul 1997-Jun 1998 Income $75,000. Mats Exp $36,927, Books $17,649, Per/Ser (Incl. Access Fees) $2,960, Presv $300, Micro $8,576, AV Equip $7,051. Sal $134,137 (Prof $61,470)
Library Holdings: Bk Vols 43,406; Per Subs 156
Subject Interests: Local history, World War II

NGWOOD

KINGWOOD PUBLIC LIBRARY, 205 W Main St, 26537-1418. SAN 317-7912. Tel: 304-329-1499. FAX: 304-329-1499. *Bibliog Instr, Coll Develop, Dir*, Joel W Beane; E-Mail: beanejo@hp9k.clark.lib.wv.us; Staff 1 (MLS 1)
Founded 1941. Pop 30,000
Jul 2001-Jun 2002 Income $162,856, State $67,981, City $50,875, Locally Generated Income $44,000. Mats Exp $20,985, Books $18,000, Per/Ser (Incl. Access Fees) $2,700. Sal $65,200 (Prof $26,000)
Library Holdings: Bk Vols 43,000; Bk Titles 41,095; Per Subs 100; Bks on Deafness & Sign Lang 50
Subject Interests: Relig studies
Special Collections: Preston County (Local History Coll); West Virginia Coll
Automation Activity & Vendor Info: (Circulation) VTLS
Publications: Highlights (monthly newsletter)
Special Services for the Deaf - Books on deafness & sign language; High interest/low vocabulary books
Friends of the Library Group

LESAGE

P COX LANDING LIBRARY,* RFD 1 Box 75, 25537. SAN 376-6942. Tel: 304-733-3022. FAX: 304-733-3022. E-Mail: rhetakeefer@cabell.lib.wv.us. *Librn*, Rheta Keefer
Library Holdings: Bk Titles 5,000

LEWISBURG

J GREENBRIER COMMUNITY COLLEGE CENTER LIBRARY, 101 Church St, 24901-0151. SAN 317-7920. Tel: 304-647-7514. FAX: 304-647-7512. *Librn*, Robert Coston; E-Mail: rcoston@bluefield.wvnet.edu
Library Holdings: Bk Titles 13,000; Per Subs 50
Special Collections: West Virginia Coll
Automation Activity & Vendor Info: (Cataloging) VTLS

P GREENBRIER COUNTY LIBRARY,* 301 Courtney Dr, 24901. SAN 317-7939. Tel: 304-647-7568. FAX: 304-647-7569. *Librn*, Ann Farr; *Asst Librn*, Christy Grim
Pop 8,143; Circ 64,000
Library Holdings: Bk Vols 29,000; Per Subs 52
Friends of the Library Group

S GREENBRIER HISTORICAL SOCIETY ARCHIVES, 301 W Washington St, 24901. SAN 329-0379. Tel: 304-645-3398. FAX: 304-645-5201. E-Mail: omb00701@mail.wvnet.edu. Web Site: web.mountain.net/ghs/ghs.html. *Archivist*, James E Talbert
Founded 1963
Library Holdings: Bk Vols 1,165; Bk Titles 795; Per Subs 17
Subject Interests: Local history
Special Collections: Dime Novelist (Mrs Alex McVeigh Miller Coll), autobiography, poems, stories; Original drawings used in Mrs Arthur Dayton's books on local West Virginia subjects; West Virginia Artists (Ashton Reniers & Naomi Hosterman Colls)
Publications: Appalachian Springs (quarterly); GHS Annual Journal; Greenbrier County Cemetaries; The History of Greenbrier County; The History of Monroe County
Open Mon, Thurs & Sat 1-4 or by appointment

CM WEST VIRGINIA SCHOOL OF OSTEOPATHIC MEDICINE LIBRARY,* 400 N Lee St, 24901. SAN 317-7947. Tel: 304-647-6261. FAX: 304-645-4443. *Dir*, Mary Frances Bodemuller; E-Mail: mbodemuller@wvsom.edu; Staff 1 (MLS 1)
Founded 1973. Enrl 260; Fac 29; Highest Degree: Doctorate
1998-1999 Income $216,689. Mats Exp $151,716, Books $5,000, Per/Ser (Incl. Access Fees) $128,146, AV Equip $7,570, Electronic Ref Mat (Incl. Access Fees) $11,000. Sal $159,913 (Prof $42,000)
Library Holdings: Bk Vols 18,277; Bk Titles 11,671; Per Subs 455
Subject Interests: Medicine
Partic in Medline; OCLC Online Computer Library Center, Inc

LOGAN

M LOGAN GENERAL HOSPITAL, Medical Library,* 20 Hospital Dr, 25601. SAN 317-7955. Tel: 304-792-1556, 304-792-1655. FAX: 304-792-1654. *Librn*, Teresa McNeely
Library Holdings: Bk Vols 1,206; Per Subs 59
Publications: Abridged Index Medieus; Hospital Literature Index & Cumulative Index to Nursing & Allied Health
Partic in Medline

P WOMAN'S CLUB OF LOGAN LIBRARY,* 581 Main St, 25601. SAN 317-7963. Tel: 304-752-6508. *Librn*, Sydney Thacker
Pop 3,311; Circ 3,727
Library Holdings: Bk Vols 4,858; Per Subs 15
Open Mon-Fri 2-5

LOST CREEK

P SOUTHERN AREA LIBRARY, Old Bank Bldg, Main St, PO Box 282, 26385. SAN 376-7760. Tel: 304-745-4865. FAX: 304-745-4865. *Dir*, Diane West; Staff 2 (Non-MLS 2)
Founded 1972
Jul 1998-Jun 1999 Income $17,070, State $1,575, City $500, County $12,272, Other $2,723. Mats Exp $2,362, Books $1,394, Per/Ser (Incl. Access Fees) $249, Other Print Mats $719. Sal $11,512
Library Holdings: Bk Vols 10,000; Per Subs 12
Mem of Clarksburg-Harrison County Serv Ctr
Open Mon-Fri 12-5 & Sat 10-2
Friends of the Library Group

MADISON

P BOONE-MADISON PUBLIC LIBRARY,* 375 Main St, 25130. SAN 364-4286. Tel: 304-369-7842. FAX: 304-369-7842. *Dir*, Renee Schwarz; Staff 1 (MLS 1)
Founded 1974. Pop 25,870; Circ 72,550
Jul 1997-Jun 1998 Income $218,998, State $98,647, City $5,000, Federal $6,379, County $40,500, Other $8,472. Mats Exp $23,986, Books $20,460, Per/Ser (Incl. Access Fees) $3,526. Sal $79,230 (Prof $20,500)
Library Holdings: Bk Titles 50,865; Per Subs 75
Subject Interests: County hist
Special Collections: Genealogy (Boone County & Southern West Virginia Coll)
Automation Activity & Vendor Info: (Cataloging) VTLS; (Circulation) VTLS
Partic in Southern West Virginia Library Automation Corporation
Branches: 3
BARRETT-WHARTON BRANCH, SC 78, Box 4, Wharton, 25208. SAN 364-4316. Tel: 304-247-6530.
COAL RIVER, Star Rte 425, Racine, 25165. SAN 364-4324. Tel: 304-837-8437. *In Charge*, Marilyn Kay Ferrell
WHITESVILLE BRANCH, PO Box 747, Whitesville, 25209. SAN 322-5992. Tel: 304-854-0196. *In Charge*, Marilyn Kay Ferrell

MAN

P BUFFALO CREEK MEMORIAL LIBRARY,* 511 E McDonald Ave, 25635. SAN 317-7971. Tel: 304-583-7887. FAX: 304-583-7887. *Librn*, Vickie Johnson; *Asst Librn*, Anita Grimmett
Founded 1973. Circ 36,000
Library Holdings: Bk Titles 27,000; Per Subs 40
Subject Interests: Cookbooks, Diet, Exercise, Nutrition, WVa
Special Collections: Cookbooks-Coal Mining Towns, photos, diet, exercise, nutrition; West Virginia Code
Open Mon & Thurs 10-6, Tues, Wed & Fri 10-5 & Sat 10-1

MARTINSBURG

M CITY HOSPITAL, INC, Medical Staff Library,* Dry Run Rd, PO Box 1418, 25402. SAN 317-798X. Tel: 304-264-1000, Ext 1246. FAX: 304-264-1381. *Librn*, Carol Davis
Library Holdings: Bk Vols 260

GM DEPARTMENT OF VETERANS AFFAIRS, LRS Library Section (142D),* Rte 9, 25401. SAN 317-7998. Tel: 304-263-0811, Ext 3820. FAX: 304-262-4847. *Chief Librn*, Jim Haines; *Coll Develop*, Eileen Southerly; *Coll Develop*, Sally Van Metre; Staff 3 (MLS 1, Non-MLS 2)
Founded 1946
Oct 1998-Sep 1999 Mats Exp $95,036, Books $25,171, Per/Ser (Incl. Access Fees) $58,485, Electronic Ref Mat (Incl. Access Fees) $5,000. Sal $127,830 (Prof $107,830)
Library Holdings: Bk Vols 3,977; Per Subs 245
Subject Interests: Medicine, Patient educ
Publications: Acquisitions List; AV Listing; Special Subj Listing
Partic in Valnet
Library section includes a general/patient library & a medical library

P MARTINSBURG-BERKELEY COUNTY PUBLIC LIBRARY,* 101 W King St, 25401. SAN 364-4340. Tel: 304-267-8933. FAX: 304-267-9720. Web Site: www.tlc.library.net/martin. *Dir*, Peggy Young Batten; *Asst Dir*, Lois Brady; *Ref*, Keith Hammersla; *Ch Servs*, Sharon Morris; *Ad Servs*, Elizabeth Gunnoe
Founded 1926. Pop 59,276; Circ 336,051
Jul 1999-Jun 2000 Income $891,975, City $61,413, County $266,045, Locally Generated Income $25,000. Mats Exp $105,000, Books $80,992, Per/Ser (Incl. Access Fees) $10,994, Presv $3,469. Sal $509,448 (Prof $149,000)
Library Holdings: Bk Titles 156,314; Per Subs 279
Automation Activity & Vendor Info: (Acquisitions) VTLS; (Cataloging) VTLS; (Circulation) VTLS
Friends of the Library Group
Branches: 3
MUSSELMAN-SOUTH BERKELEY COMMUNITY LIBRARY, Rte 2, Box 124, Inwood, 25428. SAN 364-443X. Tel: 304-229-2220.
Library Holdings: Bk Titles 3,000
NAYLOR MEMORIAL, PO Box 265, Hedgesville, 25427. SAN 364-4375. Tel: 304-754-3949. *Librn*, Hope Miller
Library Holdings: Bk Titles 4,000
NORTH BERKELEY, PO Box 786, Falling Waters, 25419. SAN 364-4405. Tel: 304-274-3443. *Librn*, Hope Miller
Library Holdings: Bk Titles 3,000
Friends of the Library Group

MIDDLEBOURNE

P TYLER COUNTY PUBLIC LIBRARY,* Main & Broad Sts, PO Box 1 26149. SAN 317-8005. Tel: 304-758-4304. FAX: 304-758-4304. *Librn*, Cantwell; *Librn*, Gilda Neese
Pop 814; Circ 11,320
Library Holdings: Bk Vols 10,200
Mem of Miracle Valley Regional Library System

MONTGOMERY

C WEST VIRGINIA UNIVERSITY INSTITUTE OF TECHNOLOGY, Vir Library, Fayette Pike, 25136. SAN 317-8013. Tel: 304-442-3141. Interli Loan Service Tel: 304-442-3082. Circulation Tel: 304-442-3230. FAX: 3 442-3091. Web Site: www.wvit.wvnet.edu/library. *Actg Dir*, Mitch Casto *Acq*, Jane Elliott; *Per*, Jewel Rucker; *Ref*, Joy Humphries; Staff 2 (MLS
Founded 1897. Enrl 2,593; Fac 131; Highest Degree: Master
Jul 1999-Jun 2000 Income $613,485, State $609,228, Federal $4,257. M Exp $159,713, Books $13,000, Per/Ser (Incl. Access Fees) $118,491, Electronic Ref Mat (Incl. Access Fees) $28,222. Sal $330,756 (Prof $62,750)
Library Holdings: Bk Vols 144,442; Bk Titles 112,223; Per Subs 605
Special Collections: West Virginia
Automation Activity & Vendor Info: (Circulation) VTLS
Publications: Acquisitions List; Cataloging Manual; Periodical Directory
Partic in OCLC Online Computer Library Center, Inc; WVNET

MOOREFIELD

P HARDY COUNTY PUBLIC LIBRARY,* 102 N Main St, 26836. SAN 364-4464. Tel: 304-538-6560. FAX: 304-538-2639. *Librn*, Marjorie Zirk
Founded 1939. Pop 2,400; Circ 81,482
Library Holdings: Bk Vols 55,520; Per Subs 75
Subject Interests: Local genealogy, Local history
Mem of Potomac Valley Regional Libr Syst
All figures include main library & branch
Friends of the Library Group
Branches: 1
EAST HARDY COUNTY BRANCH, PO Box 98, Baker, 26801. SAN 3 4499. Tel: 304-897-5544. FAX: 304-897-5544. *Librn*, Catherine Smith

MORGANTOWN

S AACE INTERNATIONAL LIBRARY, 209 Prairie Ave, Ste 100, 26501. SAN 327-6465. Tel: 304-296-8444. Toll Free Tel: 800-858-2678. FAX: 3 291-5728. E-Mail: info@aacei.org. Web Site: www.aacei.org.
Founded 1958
Library Holdings: Bk Vols 6,000

S FEDERAL CORRECTIONAL INSTITUTION - MORGANTOWN LIBRARY,* PO Box 1000, 26507. SAN 317-8021. Tel: 304-296-4416. FAX: 304-296-7549. *Librn*, Eleni Turner
Library Holdings: Bk Vols 11,000; Per Subs 62
Special Collections: Prisoner Rights

P MORGANTOWN PUBLIC LIBRARY, Morgantown Service Center, 373 Spruce St, 26505. SAN 364-4529. Tel: 304-291-7425. FAX: 304-291-742 Web Site: www.clark.lib.wv.us/morg/morg.html. *Dir*, Sharon Turner; *Hea Ref*, Mary Schmezer; E-Mail: schmezem@clark.lib.wv.us; *Ch Servs*, Ruth Godfrey; *Circ*, Donna Balderson; *Coll Develop*, Ellen Hathaway; E-Mail: hathaway@clark.lib.wv.us; Staff 2 (MLS 2)
Founded 1929. Pop 75,509; Circ 623,328
Jul 1998-Jun 1999 Income (Main Library and Branch Library) $906,449, State $295,239, City $332,817, County $175,500, Locally Generated Inc $64,007. Mats Exp $109,632, Books $75,718, Per/Ser (Incl. Access Fees) $10,500. Sal $643,387 (Prof $445,059)
Library Holdings: Bk Vols 133,378; Per Subs 100
Subject Interests: WVa hist
Automation Activity & Vendor Info: (Cataloging) VTLS; (Circulation) VTLS
Member Libraries: Terra Alta Public Library
Friends of the Library Group
Branches: 3
CHEAT AREA, 121 Crosby Rd, 26508. SAN 364-4545. Tel: 304-594-10 *Librn*, Nancy Gallagher; Staff 5 (MLS 1, Non-MLS 4)
Library Holdings: Bk Vols 12,039; Per Subs 15
Friends of the Library Group
CLAY-BATTELLE PUBLIC LIBRARY, Rte 7, Box 68, 26521. SAN 36 4561. Tel: 304-432-8531. *Librn*, Jan Stiles; Staff 2 (Non-MLS 2)
Library Holdings: Bk Vols 13,418; Per Subs 28
Friends of the Library Group
CLINTON DISTRICT LIBRARY, 2005 Grafton Rd, 26508. SAN 364-45 Tel: 304-291-0703. *Librn*, Jean Wilburn; Staff 2 (Non-MLS 2)
Library Holdings: Bk Vols 7,881; Per Subs 17

NATIONAL INSTITUTE FOR OCCUPATIONAL SAFETY & HEALTH, NIOSH Morgantown Library, 1095 Willowdale Rd, 26505-2888. SAN 317-8048. Tel: 304-285-5886. FAX: 304-285-6085. E-Mail: morg-libraryrequestse@cdc.gov. *Librn*, Barbara B Landreth; Staff 4 (MLS 1, Non-MLS 3)
Founded 1972
Library Holdings: Bk Titles 6,000; Per Subs 220
Subject Interests: Occupational lung diseases, Worker safety
Special Collections: NIOSHTIC microfiche
Partic in Fedlink; Medlars

UNITED STATES DEPARTMENT OF ENERGY, Federal Energy Technology Center Library,* PO Box 880, 26507-0880. SAN 317-803X. Tel: 304-285-4183. FAX: 304-285-4188. *Ref*, Matt Marsteller; E-Mail: mmarst@fetc.doe.gov; *Tech Servs*, Hilary Fredette; E-Mail: hfrede@fetc.doe.gov
Founded 1953
Library Holdings: Bk Titles 30,000; Per Subs 150
Subject Interests: Chemistry, Environ mgt, Environ remediation, Fossil fuels, Geology, Petroleum
Special Collections: DOE Fossil Energy Reports; Energy (US Dept of Energy); Mines Open File Reports); Mining (US Bureau of; Mining (US Bureau of Mines, Reports of Investigations, Information Circulars)
Partic in Dialog Corporation; Fedlink; OCLC Online Computer Library Center, Inc

UNITED STATES ENVIRONMENTAL PROTECTION AGENCY, National Small Flows Clearinghouse Library, West Virginia Univ, PO Box 6064, 26506-6064. SAN 373-3041. Toll Free Tel: 800-624-8301. FAX: 304-293-3161.
Library Holdings: Bk Titles 180

WEST VIRGINIA UNIVERSITY LIBRARIES,* Wise Library, PO Box 6069, 26506-6069. SAN 364-4588. Tel: 304-293-4040. Interlibrary Loan Service Tel: 304-293-5440. FAX: 304-293-6638. Web Site: www.libraries.wvu.edu. *Ref*, Myra Lowe; *Per*, Anna Schein; *Cat*, Donna Cook; *Circ*, Carroll Wilkinson; *Dean*, Frances O'Brien; *Curator*, John Cuthbert
Founded 1867. Enrl 22,500; Fac 1,617; Highest Degree: Doctorate
Library Holdings: Per Subs 7,453
Subject Interests: Africa, Appalachia, Coal
Departmental Libraries:
AUDIOVISUAL, PO Box 6462, 26506-6462. SAN 377-7294. Tel: 304-293-4019. *Head of Libr*, Charles Burkart
COLLEGE OF LAW, PO Box 6135, 26505-6135. SAN 364-4618. Tel: 304-293-5300. FAX: 304-293-6020. *Dir*, Camille Riley; *Publ Servs*, Kevin Fredette; *Tech Servs*, Carol Davis; Staff 4 (MLS 4)
Library Holdings: Per Subs 909
COLSOM RESERVE LIBRARY, PO Box 6464, 26506-6464. SAN 377-7316. Tel: 304-293-2640. *Head of Libr*, Carroll Wilkinson
EVANSDALE LIBRARY, PO Box 6105, 26506-6105. SAN 377-7332. Tel: 304-293-4696. FAX: 304-293-7330. *Librn*, Jo Ann Calzonetti; Staff 17 (MLS 6, Non-MLS 11)
HEALTH SCIENCES CENTER, Health Sciences Ctr N, PO Box 9801, 26506. SAN 364-4642. Tel: 304-293-2113. FAX: 304-293-7319.; Staff 5 (MLS 5)
Founded 1959. Enrl 1,425; Highest Degree: Doctorate
Library Holdings: Per Subs 2,227
Special Collections: Occupational Respiratory Diseases
Publications: What's New
Mem of WVa Univ Libr
Partic in Dialog Corporation; Nat Libr of Med; OCLC Online Computer Library Center, Inc
MATHEMATICS, 453 Armstrong Hall, PO Box 6468, 26506. SAN 328-8072. Tel: 304-293-6011. FAX: 304-295-6638. *Head of Libr*, Mary Strife
Library Holdings: Bk Vols 18,587; Per Subs 18,587
Open Mon-Wed 8:30am-10pm, Thurs & Fri 8:30-5
MUSIC, PO Box 6111, 26506-6111. SAN 328-8641. Tel: 304-293-4505, Ext 3199. FAX: 304-293-7491.
Library Holdings: Bk Vols 30,501; Per Subs 130
Subject Interests: Renaissance musicology
Special Collections: Jazz recordings, 1920-45 (Fry Jazz Archives Coll), rec
Partic in Pittsburgh Regional Libr Consortium
PHYSICAL SCIENCES, PO Box 6470, 26506-6470. SAN 377-7359. *Head of Libr*, Mary Strife
WEST VIRGINIA & REGIONAL HISTORY COLLECTION, Colson Hall, PO Box 6464, 26506. SAN 328-8609. Tel: 304-293-3536. FAX: 304-293-3981. *Curator, Spec Coll*, John Cuthbert
Library Holdings: Bk Vols 31,602
Subject Interests: Archives, Cent Appalachian hist, Coal mining hist, Culture, WVa hist, WVa mss

OUNDSVILLE

MIRACLE VALLEY REGIONAL LIBRARY SYSTEM, City-County Public Library, Headquarters,* 700 Fifth St, 26041-1993. SAN 364-4677. Tel: 304-845-6911. FAX: 304-845-6912. *Dir*, Susan Reilly; *ILL*, Mildred Ulman; *Tech Servs*, Judi White; *Acq*, Susan Shaw; *Ch Servs*, Diane Walters; Staff 5 (MLS 5)
Founded 1917. Pop 74,802; Circ 378,473
Library Holdings: Bk Vols 174,989; Per Subs 462
Subject Interests: Career info, Child safety, Computers, Cookery, Crafts, Health, Home-repairs
Special Collections: West Virginia Coll
Automation Activity & Vendor Info: (Cataloging) VTLS; (Circulation) VTLS
Publications: Newsletter (bi-monthly)
Member Libraries: Hundred Public Library; New Martinsville Public Library; Paden City Public Library; Pine Grove Public Library; Sistersville Public Library; Tyler County Public Library
Friends of the Library Group
Branches: 4
BENWOOD-MCMECHEN PUBLIC, 201 Marshall St, McMechen, 26040. SAN 364-4766. Tel: 304-232-9720. *Librn*, Virginia Benham
CAMERON PUBLIC, Benedum Bldg, 44 Main St, Cameron, 26033. SAN 364-4707. Tel: 304-686-2140. FAX: 304-686-2140. *Librn*, Mary Evelyn Garey
SAINT JOSEPH PUBLIC, RD 1, Proctor, 26055. SAN 364-4790. Tel: 304-455-2950. *Librn*, Debbie Frohnapfel; *Librn*, Joan Estep; *Librn*, Linda Franklin
SAND HILL PUBLIC, c/o Sandy Hill Elementary, 700 Fifth St, Dallas, 26036. SAN 364-4804. Tel: 304-547-5754. *Librn*, Cathy Rohm. Van 1

S NORTHERN REGIONAL JAIL CORRECTIONAL FACILITY,* RD 2, Box 1, 26041. SAN 317-8056. Tel: 304-843-4067. FAX: 304-843-4089. *Dir*, Leonard Wellman
Library Holdings: Bk Vols 3,995

MOUNT GAY

J SOUTHERN WEST VIRGINIA COMMUNITY & TECHNICAL COLLEGE, Harless Library, Dempsey Branch Rd, 25637. (Mail add: PO Box 2900, 25637-2900), SAN 364-4251. Tel: 304-792-7098, Ext 294. TDD: 304-792-7054. FAX: 304-752-2837. Web Site: www.southern.wvnet.edu. *Mgr Libr Serv*, Kimberly Maynard; Tel: 304-792-7098, Ext 202, E-Mail: kimm@southern.wvnet.edu; Staff 1 (Non-MLS 1)
Founded 1971. Enrl 1,291; Fac 30; Highest Degree: Associate
Jul 1999-Jun 2000 Income State $221,587. Mats Exp $80,738, Books $33,838, Per/Ser (Incl. Access Fees) $14,205, Micro $3,413, Electronic Ref Mat (Incl. Access Fees) $14,164. Sal $140,849 (Prof $25,548)
Library Holdings: Bk Vols 33,431; Bk Titles 30,088; Per Subs 152
Special Collections: West Virginia Coll (local hist & genealogy)
Automation Activity & Vendor Info: (Acquisitions) epixtech, inc.; (Cataloging) epixtech, inc.; (Circulation) epixtech, inc.; (Course Reserve) epixtech, inc.; (Media Booking) epixtech, inc.; (OPAC) epixtech, inc.; (Serials) epixtech, inc.
Database Vendor: epixtech, inc.
Function: ILL available, Photocopies available, Reference services available
Partic in OCLC Online Computer Library Center, Inc; PALINET & Union Library Catalogue of Pennsylvania
Special Services for the Deaf - TDD
Special Services for the Blind - Kurzweil Reader
Friends of the Library Group

NEW CUMBERLAND

P SWANEY MEMORIAL LIBRARY,* 601 Court St, 26047. (Mail add: PO Box 608, 26047-0608), SAN 317-8064. Tel: 304-564-3471. FAX: 304-564-3471. *Librn*, Jane Mehaffey
Pop 1,865; Circ 14,098
Library Holdings: Bk Vols 14,103; Per Subs 27
Subject Interests: Genealogy, Local history
Mem of Mary H Weir Public Library

NEW MARTINSVILLE

S BAYER, INC, Research Library,* State Rte 2, 26155. SAN 317-8072. Tel: 304-455-4400, Ext 2272. FAX: 304-455-5134. *Librn*, Kimberly S Adkins; E-Mail: kimberly.adkins.b@bayer.com; *Asst Librn*, Kathy McGuire; Staff 2 (MLS 1, Non-MLS 1)
Founded 1956
Library Holdings: Bk Titles 3,500; Per Subs 100
Subject Interests: Chemical engineering, Chemistry
Special Collections: Chemistry (Houben-Weyl Coll); Organic Chemistry (Beilsteins Handbuch Coll)

P NEW MARTINSVILLE PUBLIC LIBRARY,* 160 Washington St, 26155. SAN 317-8080. Tel: 304-455-4545. FAX: 304-455-4545. *Dir*, Barbara V Stewart; Staff 8 (MLS 1, Non-MLS 7)
Founded 1946. Pop 9,577; Circ 62,636
Library Holdings: Bk Titles 25,000; Per Subs 1,106

Subject Interests: Genealogy, Local history, West Virginia
Mem of Miracle Valley Regional Library System
Open Mon-Wed 10-8, Fri, Sat 10-5
Friends of the Library Group

NITRO

P NITRO PUBLIC LIBRARY,* 1700 Park Ave, 25143. SAN 317-8110. Tel: 304-755-4432. FAX: 304-755-5130. Web Site: www.kanawha.lib.wv.us. *Librn*, Karen Miller
Founded 1964. Circ 40,978
Library Holdings: Bk Vols 24,257
Mem of Kanawha County Public Library
Open Mon & Thurs 11-7, Tues, Wed & Fri 9-5

NUTTER FORT

P NUTTER FORT LIBRARY,* 1300 Buckhannon Pike, 26301-4406. SAN 376-7779. Tel: 304-622-7563. FAX: 304-622-7563. *Librn*, Crystal Hamrick
1997-1998 Income $30,000. Mats Exp $12,000. Sal $18,000
Library Holdings: Bk Vols 25,000; Bk Titles 12,000; Per Subs 20
Mem of Clarksburg-Harrison County Serv Ctr
Friends of the Library Group

OAK HILL

P FAYETTE COUNTY PUBLIC LIBRARIES,* 531 Summit St, 25901. SAN 364-4820. Tel: 304-465-0121. FAX: 304-465-5664. E-Mail: gunsaulj@raleigh.lib.wv.us. Web Site: www.fayette.lib.wv.us. *Dir*, Judy Gunsaulis
Founded 1959. Pop 47,952; Circ 213,170
Library Holdings: Bk Vols 83,000; Per Subs 26
Special Collections: Books About West Virginia & by West Virginia Authors (West Virginia Room Coll); Books-by-Mail Coll
Automation Activity & Vendor Info: (Cataloging) VTLS; (Circulation) VTLS
Books-by-Mail Coll - Vols 12,800. Bk storage at Headquarters - Vols 3581
Friends of the Library Group
Branches: 7
ANSTED PUBLIC, Oak St, PO Box 428, Ansted, 25812. SAN 364-4944. Tel: 304-658-5472. FAX: 304-658-5472. *Librn*, Helen Cole
Library Holdings: Bk Vols 7,240
FAYETTEVILLE BRANCH, 200 W Maple Ave, Fayetteville, 25840. SAN 364-4855. Tel: 304-574-0070. FAX: 304-574-0070. *Librn*, Debrah Arrington
Library Holdings: Bk Vols 23,318
Special Collections: West Virginia Coll
GAULEY BRIDGE BRANCH, PO Box 487, Gauley Bridge, 25085. SAN 364-4898. Tel: 304-632-2172. FAX: 304-632-2172. *Librn*, Connie Fryer
Library Holdings: Bk Vols 2,590
HERBERT JONES LIBRARY, 611 Main St, 25901. SAN 364-491X. Tel: 304-469-9890. FAX: 304-469-9890. *Librn*, Paula Carter
Library Holdings: Bk Vols 17,982
MEADOW BRIDGE BRANCH, PO Box 354, Meadow Bridge, 25976. SAN 326-8314. Tel: 304-484-7942. FAX: 304-484-7942. *Librn*, Janet Kincaid
Library Holdings: Bk Vols 3,113
MONTGOMERY BRANCH, 507 Ferry St, Montgomery, 25136. SAN 364-4979. Tel: 304-442-5665. FAX: 304-442-5665. *Librn*, Linda Beal
Library Holdings: Bk Vols 9,506
PATRICK C GRANEY JR, LIBRARY, 500 Main St, Mount Hope, 25880. SAN 364-488X. Tel: 304-877-3260. FAX: 304-877-3260. *Librn*, Teresa White
Library Holdings: Bk Vols 6,800

PADEN CITY

P PADEN CITY PUBLIC LIBRARY, 114 S Fourth Ave, 26159. SAN 317-8129. Tel: 304-337-9333. FAX: 304-337-9333. Web Site: www.weirton.lib.wv.us/wetzel/paden/padenlib.html. *Dir*, Sharon K Kastigar; E-Mail: kastigar@weirton.lib.wv.us; *Asst Librn*, Elizabeth Martin; *Asst Librn*, Judith McAnarney; Staff 3 (Non-MLS 3)
Founded 1947. Pop 4,989; Circ 9,754
Jul 1999-Jun 2000 Income $37,195, State $16,020, City $12,420, Locally Generated Income $8,755. Mats Exp $32,888, Books $4,813, Per/Ser (Incl. Access Fees) $987. Sal $17,044
Library Holdings: Bk Vols 11,821; Bk Titles 11,821; Per Subs 31
Mem of Miracle Valley Regional Library System

PARKERSBURG

M CAMDEN-CLARK MEMORIAL HOSPITAL, Medical Library, 800 Garfield Ave, 26101. SAN 317-8137. Tel: 304-424-2450. FAX: 304-424-2861. *Librn*, Jessica Srogi; E-Mail: jsrogi@ccmh.org; Staff 1 (Non-MLS 1)
Founded 1900
Library Holdings: Bk Titles 2,700; Per Subs 237
Subject Interests: Allied health, Medicine, Nursing
Partic in Nat Libr of Med

P PARKERSBURG & WOOD COUNTY PUBLIC LIBRARY, Wood Cou Service Center,* 3100 Emerson Ave, 26104-2414. SAN 364-5002. Tel: 3 420-4587. FAX: 304-420-4589. Web Site: www.park.lib.wv.us. *Dir*, Ann Lorentz; E-Mail: lorentza@wvlc.wvnet.edu; *ILL*, Nalini Mehta; *Tech Ser* Jo Ellen Dennis; *Ref*, Lindsay Roseberry; *Media Spec*, Lynn Roberts; *Ch Servs*, Brenda Taylor; *Librn for Blind*, Mike Hickman; Staff 3 (MLS 3)
Founded 1905. Pop 76,053; Circ 387,584
Jul 1997-Jun 1998 Income $977,413, State $290,007, City $149,472, Fe $16,652, County $170,322, Locally Generated Income $75,501. Mats Ex $183,864, Books $120,809, Per/Ser (Incl. Access Fees) $25,486, Presv $5,729, Micro $1,200. Sal $391,111 (Prof $87,600)
Library Holdings: Bk Vols 177,979
Special Collections: West Virginia History & Genealogical Coll, bks & microfilm
Friends of the Library Group
Branches: 4
P SERVICES FOR THE BLIND & PHYSICALLY HANDICAPPED Tel: 304-420-4587. FAX: 304-420-4589. *Librn*, Mike Hickman
Founded 1970
Friends of the Library Group
SOUTH PARKERSBURG, 1713 Blizzard Dr, 26101. SAN 364-5061. Te 304-428-7041. FAX: 304-428-7041. *Librn*, Teresa Dulaney
Friends of the Library Group
WAVERLY, Rte 1, Box 287, 26184. SAN 377-8215. Tel: 304-464-5668 FAX: 304-464-5668. *Librn*, Nesta Morrison
Friends of the Library Group
WILLIAMSTOWN BRANCH, 201 W Fifth St, Williamstown, 26187. SA 364-5096. Tel: 304-375-6052. FAX: 304-375-6502. *Librn*, Edith Lindl
Friends of the Library Group
Bookmobiles: 1

M SAINT JOSEPH'S HOSPITAL, Educational Resources Center,* 1824 Murdoch Ave, PO Box 327, 26102-0327. SAN 317-8188. Tel: 304-424-4607. FAX: 304-424-4951. *Dir Libr Serv*, Else Lamba
Founded 1967
Library Holdings: Bk Titles 3,000; Per Subs 190
Subject Interests: Hospital administration, Medicine, Nursing
Partic in WVa Health Sci Asn

R TEMPLE B'NAI ISRAEL LIBRARY, 1703 20th St, 26101. SAN 317-8 Tel: 304-428-1192. *Pres*, Robert Ellison; Tel: 304-428-0898; Staff 2 (ML Non-MLS 1)
Founded 1949
Library Holdings: Bk Vols 1,530; Bk Titles 1,030
Subject Interests: Judaica
Special Collections: Jewish Authors

J WEST VIRGINIA UNIVERSITY AT PARKERSBURG LIBRARY,* 30 Campus Dr, 26101. SAN 317-8161. Tel: 304-424-8260. FAX: 304-424-8 Web Site: www.wvup.wvnet.edu. *Dir*, Bruce Arrowood; *Assoc Librn*, Lis Gianettino
Founded 1971. Enrl 3,329; Fac 119
Jul 1997-Jun 1998 Income $230,480. Mats Exp $58,900, Books $22,000, Per/Ser (Incl. Access Fees) $12,000, Other Print Mats $7,600. Sal $160,1 (Prof $82,970)
Library Holdings: Bk Vols 48,006; Bk Titles 43,483; Per Subs 122
Subject Interests: Children's literature
Partic in OCLC Online Computer Library Center, Inc; PALINET & Unio Library Catalogue of Pennsylvania

PARSONS

P FIVE RIVERS PUBLIC LIBRARY, 301 Walnut St, 26287. SAN 317-82 Tel: 304-478-3880. FAX: 304-478-3880. *Librn*, Nancy Moore; E-Mail: moore_na@clark.lib.wv.us; *Asst Librn*, Kathy Phillips; E-Mail: phillipk@clark.lib.wv.us
Founded 1974. Pop 4,366; Circ 19,956
Library Holdings: Bk Vols 15,200; Per Subs 125
Mem of Upshur County Public Library

PAW PAW

P PAW PAW PUBLIC LIBRARY, 437 Moser Ave, 25434-9500. (Mail add PO Box 9, 25434-0009), SAN 317-8218. Tel: 304-947-7013. FAX: 304-9 7013. *Librn*, Betty L Weaver; E-Mail: weaver_be@martin.lib.wv.us; *Librn* Mary Jane Bradford
Founded 1971. Pop 4,043; Circ 10,000
Jul 2000-Jun 2001 Income $47,228, State $16,228, City $500, County $8,000, Locally Generated Income $15,500, Other $7,000. Mats Exp $9,0 Books $6,107, Per/Ser (Incl. Access Fees) $335, AV Equip $2,600. Sal $13,341

Library Holdings: Bk Vols 16,830; Per Subs 50
Subject Interests: Audio, Large print bks
Mem of Martinsburg Serv Ctr
Special Services for the Blind - Audio-cassettes; Large print bks
Friends of the Library Group

ERSBURG

GRANT COUNTY LIBRARY,* 18 Mountain View St, 26847-1524. SAN 317-8226. Tel: 304-257-4122. FAX: 304-257-4122. *Librn*, Betty S McCartney; *Asst Librn*, Barbara Carr
Founded 1963. Pop 10,210; Circ 36,988
Library Holdings: Bk Vols 23,000; Per Subs 31
Mem of Potomac Valley Regional Libr Syst
Open Mon, Tues, Thurs & Fri 9-5, Wed 9-9 & Sat 9-12
Branches: 1
ALLEGHENY-MOUNTAIN TOP, PO Box 161, Mount Storm, 26739. SAN 324-2544. Tel: 304-693-7504. FAX: 304-693-7504. *Chief Librn*, Dana Carr
Friends of the Library Group

LIPPI

ALDERSON-BROADDUS COLLEGE, Pickett Library, College Hill Rd, 26416. SAN 317-8234. Tel: 304-457-6229. FAX: 304-457-6239. Web Site: www.ab.edu/library. *Dir*, David E Hoxie; Staff 2 (MLS 2)
Enrl 702; Fac 58; Highest Degree: Master
Jul 1998-Jun 1999 Income $253,685. Mats Exp $82,048, Books $40,907, Per/Ser (Incl. Access Fees) $41,141. Sal $138,601 (Prof $70,157)
Library Holdings: Bk Vols 100,000; Per Subs 1,200
Subject Interests: Education, Health sci
Special Collections: Baptist Archives Coll; Civil War Coll
Partic in OCLC Online Computer Library Center, Inc; PALINET & Union Library Catalogue of Pennsylvania

PHILIPPI PUBLIC LIBRARY,* 102 S Main St, 26416-1317. SAN 317-8242. Tel: 304-457-3495. FAX: 304-457-5569. *Librn*, Mary Ellen Weekley; E-Mail: maryellen@10linc.net; *Asst Librn*, Debbie McLean
Founded 1966. Pop 16,639; Circ 28,998
Library Holdings: Bk Vols 40,000
Special Collections: Library of America
Mem of Upshur County Public Library
Open Mon-Fri 9-8 & Sat 10-1
Friends of the Library Group

DMONT

PIEDMONT PUBLIC LIBRARY,* Child's Ave, 26750. SAN 317-8250. Tel: 304-355-2757. FAX: 304-355-2757. *Librn*, Paula Boggs
Founded 1960. Pop 1,397; Circ 18,096
1997-1998 Income $18,846, State $6,803, County $2,725, Other $9,318. Mats Exp $2,736, Books $2,111, Per/Ser (Incl. Access Fees) $281, Other Print Mats $344. Sal $5,980
Library Holdings: Bk Vols 19,295
Mem of Potomac Valley Regional Libr Syst

E GROVE

PINE GROVE PUBLIC LIBRARY, PO Box 416, 26419-0416. SAN 317-8269. Tel: 304-889-3288. FAX: 304-889-3288. *Librn*, Cathy Brown
Founded 1975. Pop 1,200; Circ 20,190
Library Holdings: Bk Vols 12,000; Per Subs 15
Subject Interests: WVa
Mem of Miracle Valley Regional Library System

EVILLE

WYOMING COUNTY LIBRARY SYSTEM, Castle Rock Ave, PO Box 130, 24874-0130. SAN 364-5126. Tel: 304-732-6228. FAX: 304-732-6899. *Actg Dir*, Joyce Cain; Tel: 304-732-6899, E-Mail: lee_rod@raleigh.lib.wv.us. Subject Specialists: *Gov doc*, Joyce Cain; *Reference*, Joyce Cain; Staff 11 (MLS 1, Non-MLS 10)
Founded 1966. Pop 28,990; Circ 104,164
Jul 1998-Jun 1999 Income (Main Library and Branch Library) $176,993, State $110,545, City $5,500, Federal $4,616, County $20,000, Locally Generated Income $24,332, Other $12,000. Mats Exp $34,344, Books $29,961, Per/Ser (Incl. Access Fees) $3,337, Other Print Mats $1,046. Sal $109,004 (Prof $28,000)
Library Holdings: Bk Vols 67,182; Bk Titles 64,317; Per Subs 128; High Interest/Low Vocabulary Bk Vols 200
Special Collections: West Virginia History & Literature; Wyoming County, WV Genealogy & History
Friends of the Library Group
Branches: 3
MULLENS AREA PUBLIC LIBRARY, 102 Fourth St, Mullens, 25882. SAN 364-5215. Tel: 304-294-6687. FAX: 304-294-6687. *Librn*, Cindy Nuekolls
Friends of the Library Group
OCEANA PUBLIC, PO Box 1768, Oceana, 24870. SAN 364-5185. Tel: 304-682-6784. FAX: 304-682-6784. *Librn*, Glenna Brown
Friends of the Library Group
PINEVILLE BRANCH, PO Box 130, 24874. SAN 364-5150. Tel: 304-732-6228. FAX: 304-732-6899. *Librn*, Sandra Tucker; *Asst Librn*, Ella Price; E-Mail: tuckers@raleigh.lib.wv.us; Staff 2 (Non-MLS 2)
Pop 28,990
Library Holdings: Bk Vols 21,190; Bk Titles 20,280; Per Subs 37
Friends of the Library Group

POINT PLEASANT

P MASON COUNTY LIBRARY SYSTEM, 508 Viand St, 25550-1199. SAN 364-524X. Tel: 304-675-0894. FAX: 304-675-0895. E-Mail: mcpllib@hp9k.park.lib.wv.us. *Dir*, Mary Horn; E-Mail: maryhorn@hp9k.park.lib.wv.us; *Cat*, Carolyn Sayre; *Circ*, Tammy Crinfield; Staff 9 (MLS 1, Non-MLS 8)
Founded 1930. Pop 25,178; Circ 151,613
Jul 1999-Jun 2000 Income (Main Library and Branch Library) $171,314, State $101,063, City $10,251, County $60,000. Mats Exp $29,294, Books $27,912, Per/Ser (Incl. Access Fees) $5,253, AV Equip $1,382. Sal $80,714
Library Holdings: Bk Vols 52,000; Per Subs 148
Special Collections: Local History Coll; Riverboat Coll
Automation Activity & Vendor Info: (Cataloging) Athena
Database Vendor: ProQuest
Branches: 3
HANNAN, 6760 Ashton-Upland Rd, Ashton, 25503. SAN 326-7539. Tel: 304-743-6200. FAX: 304-743-6200. *Librn*, Sharon Holley
Library Holdings: Bk Vols 7,232
Friends of the Library Group
MASON CITY PUBLIC, 8 Brown St, Mason, 25260. SAN 364-5274. Tel: 304-773-5580. FAX: 304-773-5580. *Librn*, Pamela Thompson
Library Holdings: Bk Vols 10,006
Friends of the Library Group
NEW HAVEN PUBLIC, 106 Main St, New Haven, 25265. SAN 364-5304. Tel: 304-882-3252. FAX: 304-882-3252. *Librn*, Marian Batey; *Librn*, Susan Howard; *Librn*, Sarah Gibbs
Library Holdings: Bk Vols 10,970
Friends of the Library Group

PRINCETON

M PRINCETON COMMUNITY HOSPITAL LIBRARY,* PO Box 1369, 24740-1369. SAN 317-8277. Tel: 304-487-7000, 304-487-7246. FAX: 304-487-7772.
Founded 1970
Library Holdings: Bk Titles 600; Per Subs 44

P PRINCETON PUBLIC LIBRARY, Mercer Memorial Library, 205 Center St, 24740-2932. SAN 317-8285. Tel: 304-487-5045. FAX: 304-487-5046. E-Mail: ppl@raleigh.lib.wv.us. *Dir*, Connie L Clay
Founded 1922. Pop 15,000; Circ 79,180
Library Holdings: Bk Titles 83,000; Per Subs 149
Special Collections: Genealogy Coll; Local History Coll; Print Coll; West Virginia Coll
Mem of Mercer County Serv Ctr
Open Mon, Tues & Thurs 9-8, Wed, Fri & Sat 9-5
Friends of the Library Group

QUINWOOD

P QUINWOOD COMMUNITY LIBRARY,* PO Box 157, 25981. SAN 328-0802. Tel: 304-438-3011. FAX: 304-438-3011. *Librn*, Kimberley Spencer; E-Mail: spencerk@wvlc.wvnet.edu; Staff 1 (Non-MLS 1)
Founded 1982. Pop 1,500; Circ 15,000
Library Holdings: Bk Titles 12,000
Friends of the Library Group

RAINELLE

P RAINELLE MUNICIPAL PUBLIC LIBRARY,* 312 Seventh St, 25962-1649. SAN 328-0675. Tel: 304-438-3008. FAX: 304-438-3008. *Dir*, Debra Goddard; E-Mail: dgoddard@raleigh.lib.wv.us
Founded 1973. Pop 7,334; Circ 48,083
Library Holdings: Bk Titles 24,000; Per Subs 12
Automation Activity & Vendor Info: (Circulation) VTLS
Open Mon 1-7, Tues-Thurs 11-7, Fri 10-5 & Sat 10-3
Friends of the Library Group

RICHWOOD

P RICHWOOD PUBLIC LIBRARY,* 8 White Ave, 26261. SAN 317-8307. Tel: 304-846-6222. FAX: 304-846-6222. Web Site: www.wvlc.wvnet.edu/nicholas/rchwdhp.html. *Librn*, Linda Lindsey; E-Mail: lindseyl@wvlc.wvnet.edu; *Asst Librn*, Judy Davis
Founded 1942. Circ 40,503
Jul 1997-Jun 1998 Income $73,032, State $34,033, City $8,800, Locally Generated Income $25,199. Mats Exp $11,059, Books $10,210, Per/Ser (Incl. Access Fees) $849. Sal $42,671 (Prof $24,000)
Library Holdings: Bk Vols 34,412; Per Subs 95
Mem of WVa Libr Comn

RIPLEY

P JACKSON COUNTY LIBRARY, 208 N Church St, 25271-1204. SAN 364-5339. Tel: 304-372-5343. FAX: 304-372-7935. E-Mail: ripleypl@hp9k.park.lib.wv.us. *Dir*, Ed Rauh; *ILL*, Lynn Pauley; *Br Coordr*, Mary Woolever; Staff 3 (MLS 1, Non-MLS 2)
Founded 1949. Pop 25,938; Circ 121,630
Jul 1999-Jun 2000 Income $335,827, State $104,113, City $8,500, County $42,171, Locally Generated Income $181,043. Mats Exp $39,338, Books $33,466, Per/Ser (Incl. Access Fees) $3,235, Presv $1,045, Other Print Mats $1,592. Sal $172,707 (Prof $45,600)
Library Holdings: Bk Vols 52,885; Per Subs 88
Subject Interests: Genealogy, Local history
Automation Activity & Vendor Info: (Cataloging) VTLS; (Circulation) VTLS; (OPAC) VTLS
Database Vendor: ProQuest
Friends of the Library Group
Branches: 1
RAVENSWOOD BRANCH, 323 Virginia St, Ravenswood, 26164. SAN 364-5363. Tel: 304-273-5343. FAX: 304-273-5395. E-Mail: ravenspl@hp9k.park.lib.wv.us. *Librn*, Mary Woolever
Library Holdings: Bk Vols 34,221
Automation Activity & Vendor Info: (Cataloging) VTLS; (Circulation) VTLS; (OPAC) VTLS
Database Vendor: ProQuest

ROMNEY

P HAMPSHIRE COUNTY PUBLIC LIBRARY,* 153 W Main St, 26757. SAN 317-8315. Tel: 304-822-3185. FAX: 304-822-3955. *Pres*, Robert Shilling; *Librn*, Brenda Riffle
Founded 1942
Library Holdings: Bk Vols 38,030; Per Subs 69
Special Collections: Census of the County 1810-1920, mocro; Local History Coll; Local Newspaper Coll (1884-1994), micro
Mem of Potomac Valley Regional Libr Syst
Friends of the Library Group

P WEST VIRGINIA SCHOOL FOR THE BLIND LIBRARY,* 301 E Main St, 26757. SAN 317-8323. Tel: 304-822-4894. FAX: 304-822-4896. *Librn*, Cynthia Johnson; E-Mail: cjohnson@access.mountain.net
Special Collections: Visual Impairment & Blindness Coll

S WEST VIRGINIA SCHOOL FOR THE DEAF & BLIND LIBRARY, (WVSD), 301 E Main St, 26757. SAN 317-8331. Tel: 304-822-4860, Ext 862. TDD: 304-822-4560, Ext 862. FAX: 304-822-3370. *Librn*, Norma Czernicki; Staff 1 (MLS 1)
Founded 1870. Enrl 91; Fac 27; Highest Degree: Doctorate
2000-2001 Mats Exp $1,800, Per/Ser (Incl. Access Fees) $1,600, Presv $200
Library Holdings: Bk Vols 9,000; Bk Titles 11,195; Per Subs 59; High Interest/Low Vocabulary Bk Vols 1,000
Subject Interests: Educ of the deaf, West Virginia
Special Collections: Deaf & Deafness
Restriction: Open to students, Reference only to non-staff, Staff & members only
Special Services for the Deaf - Captioned film depository; High interest/low vocabulary books; Staff with knowledge of sign language; TDD

RONCEVERTE

P RONCEVERTE LIBRARY,* 712 W Main St, 24970. SAN 376-7345. Tel: 304-647-7400. *Librn*, Valerie O'Brien
Library Holdings: Bk Vols 19,000; Bk Titles 5,000
GED Adult Education classes held at library

RUPERT

P RUPERT COMMUNITY PUBLIC LIBRARY,* Rte 60, Nicholas St, PO Box 578, 25984. SAN 328-0659. Tel: 304-392-6158. FAX: 304-392-5460. *Librn*, Cherie Davis
Founded 1977. Pop 4,239; Circ 39,115
Library Holdings: Bk Titles 17,000
Automation Activity & Vendor Info: (Cataloging) VTLS; (Circulation) VTLS

SAINT MARYS

P PLEASANTS COUNTY PUBLIC LIBRARY,* 101 Lafayette St, 26170-1025. SAN 317-834X. Tel: 304-684-7494. FAX: 304-684-7495. *Coll Develop, Librn*, Judy Lawhon
Pop 7,546
1998-1999 Income $67,316
Library Holdings: Bk Vols 25,332; Per Subs 25
Mem of Wood County Serv Ctr

SALEM

C SALEM-TEIKYO UNIVERSITY, Benedum Library, University Ave, 26- SAN 364-5398. Tel: 304-782-5390. FAX: 304-782-5244. *Dir*, Dr Phyllis Freedman; E-Mail: freedman@salemiu.org; *ILL*, Jacquelyn Isaacs; *Per*, Ann Casey; *Cat*, Christian F Langer; *Govt Doc*, James Rogers; *Circ*, Ch Rogers; E-Mail: crogers@wired-university.org. Subject Specialists: *Administration*, Dr Phyllis D Freedman; Staff 5 (MLS 2, Non-MLS 3)
Founded 1888. Enrl 785
Sep 1999-Aug 2000 Income (Main Library and Branch Library) Parent Institution $46,000. Mats Exp $39,595, Books $5,960, Per/Ser (Incl. Acc Fees) $3,119, Electronic Ref Mat (Incl. Access Fees) $2,000
Library Holdings: Bk Vols 112,000; Bk Titles 100,000; Per Subs 630; Interest Per Sub 17
Subject Interests: Aviation, Education, Equestrian studies, Japanese stu Natural science, WVa
Special Collections: Jennings Randolph Materials; Local History
Automation Activity & Vendor Info: (Cataloging) DRA; (Circulation) DRA; (Course Reserve) DRA; (OPAC) DRA
Database Vendor: DRA, IAC - Info Trac
Function: ILL available
Partic in PALINET & Union Library Catalogue of Pennsylvania

SHEPHERDSTOWN

C SHEPHERD COLLEGE, Scarborough Library, 301 King St, 25443. (Ma add: PO Box 3210, 25443-3210), SAN 317-8358. Tel: 304-876-5312. Interlibrary Loan Service Tel: 304-876-5217. Circulation Tel: 304-876-5 Reference Tel: 304-876-5420. FAX: 304-876-0731. Web Site: www.shepherd.edu/libweb. *Asst Dir, Tech Servs*, Barbara A Maxwell; *Go Doc*, Ann W Henriksson; *Syst Coordr*, Laura A Neal; Staff 14 (MLS 5, MLS 9)
Founded 1872. Enrl 4,597; Fac 137; Highest Degree: Bachelor
Jul 1999-Jun 2000 Income $812,318, Locally Generated Income $32,628 Parent Institution $779,690. Mats Exp $240,551, Books $105,272, Per/S (Incl. Access Fees) $83,296, Presv $5,209, Micro $29,418, Electronic Re Mat (Incl. Access Fees) $17,356. Sal $429,404 (Prof $157,767)
Library Holdings: Bk Vols 162,298; Per Subs 918
Subject Interests: Art, Bus, Econ, Education, History, Literature, Mgt, Music
Special Collections: West Virginia Coll, bk, doc, per
Automation Activity & Vendor Info: (Cataloging) Endeavor; (Circulati Endeavor; (OPAC) Endeavor
Database Vendor: Ebsco - EbscoHost
Partic in OCLC Online Computer Library Center, Inc; PALINET & Unic Library Catalogue of Pennsylvania

P SHEPHERDSTOWN PUBLIC LIBRARY, German & Kings Sts, PO Bo 278, 25443. SAN 329-7012. Tel: 304-876-2783. FAX: 304-876-6213. We Site: www.lib.shepherdstown.wv.us. *Librn*, Margaret Didden; *Ch Servs*, Taylor; Staff 4 (MLS 2, Non-MLS 2)
Founded 1922
Library Holdings: Bk Titles 20,000; Per Subs 18
Special Collections: Jefferson County Oral & Visual History Association Photograph Coll
Partic in WV Libr Comm
Friends of the Library Group

SHINNSTON

P LOWE PUBLIC LIBRARY, 40 Bridge St, 26431. SAN 317-8366. Tel: 3 592-1700. FAX: 304-592-1700. *Librn*, Deborah Starkey
Pop 3,059; Circ 20,850
Library Holdings: Bk Vols 22,000; Bk Titles 20,000; Per Subs 10
Affiliate of Clarksburg-Harrison Public Library, Clarksburg

TERSVILLE

SISTERSVILLE PUBLIC LIBRARY, 518 Wells St, 26175. SAN 317-8374. Tel: 304-652-6701. FAX: 304-652-6701. *Dir*, Janet Hadley
Founded 1907. Pop 11,320; Circ 13,101
Library Holdings: Bk Vols 18,000; Per Subs 35
Mem of Miracle Valley Regional Library System

TH CHARLESTON

MARSHALL UNIVERSITY, Graduate College Library, 100 Angus E Peyton Dr, 25303-1600. SAN 364-4227. Tel: 304-746-8900. FAX: 304-746-8905. Web Site: www.marshall.edu/library. *Dir*, Celene Seymour; *Publ Servs*, Lynne Edington; Staff 7 (MLS 2, Non-MLS 5)
Founded 1972. Enrl 2,314; Highest Degree: Master
Jul 1999-Jun 2000 Income State $591,658. Mats Exp $111,205, Books $7,018, Per/Ser (Incl. Access Fees) $67,023, Presv $1,031, Micro $11,367, Electronic Ref Mat (Incl. Access Fees) $24,766. Sal $275,951 (Prof $126,664)
Library Holdings: Bk Vols 6,888; Per Subs 374
Subject Interests: Bus, Education
Special Collections: ERIC Coll
Automation Activity & Vendor Info: (Circulation) VTLS
Partic in OCLC Online Computer Library Center, Inc; PALINET & Union Library Catalogue of Pennsylvania

SOUTH CHARLESTON PUBLIC LIBRARY,* 312 Fourth Ave, 25303-1297. SAN 317-8382. Tel: 304-744-6561. FAX: 304-744-8808. E-Mail: info@zeus.scpl.wvnet.edu. Web Site: www.scpl.wvnet.edu. *Dir*, Pamela Coyle; *Asst Dir*, Linda Heddinger; *Cat*, Cheryl Jeanne Shelton; Staff 4 (MLS 2, Non-MLS 2)
Founded 1966. Circ 224,083
Jan 1997-Dec 1998 Income $523,037, State $51,652, City $409,421, Federal $4,533, Locally Generated Income $57,431. Mats Exp $92,652, Books $70,416, Per/Ser (Incl. Access Fees) $10,433. Sal $315,991 (Prof $103,500)
Library Holdings: Bk Vols 80,000; Per Subs 139
Subject Interests: WVa hist
Open Mon-Thurs 9-9, Fri & Sat 9-5 (Oct-Apr Fri 9-7, Sun 1-5)
Friends of the Library Group

THOMAS MEMORIAL HOSPITAL LIBRARY,* 4605 MacCorkle Ave SW, 25309. SAN 317-8390. Tel: 304-766-3791. FAX: 304-766-3796.
Library Holdings: Bk Vols 250; Per Subs 50

UNION CARBIDE CORPORATION,* Bldg 791, PO Box 8361, 25303-0361. SAN 364-5428. Tel: 304-747-4308. FAX: 304-747-4969. *Ref*, Terrie Crum; Staff 7 (MLS 1, Non-MLS 6)
Library Holdings: Bk Vols 5,000; Per Subs 300
Subject Interests: Chemical engineering, Chemistry
Partic in Pittsburgh Regional Libr Consortium

WEST VIRGINIA DEPARTMENT OF HEALTH & HUMAN RESOURCES, Office of Laboratory Services, 167 11th Ave, 25303. SAN 327-6716. Tel: 304-558-3530. FAX: 304-558-2006. *In Charge*, Jennifer Graley
Library Holdings: Bk Vols 325

NCER

ALPHA REGIONAL LIBRARY,* PO Box 149, 25276. SAN 317-8412. Tel: 304-927-1770. FAX: 304-927-1779. Web Site: www.wvlc.wvnet.edu/alpha/alphareg.html. *ILL*, Carol Hall; E-Mail: hallcj@wvlc.wvnet.edu; Staff 2 (MLS 2)
Founded 1949. Pop 55,407; Circ 203,249
Library Holdings: Bk Titles 119,114
Publications: Books-by-Mail Catalog
Member Libraries: Calhoun County Public Library; Clay County Public Library; Doddridge County Public Library; Dora Bee Woodyard Memorial Library; Ritchie County Public Library; Roane County Public Library; Walton Public Library

ROANE COUNTY PUBLIC LIBRARY, 110 Parking Plaza, 25276. SAN 317-8420. Tel: 304-927-1130. FAX: 304-927-1196. *Librn*, Suzette Lowe; *Asst Librn*, Arlene Boggess
Founded 1952. Pop 15,952; Circ 48,968
Library Holdings: Bk Vols 39,000
Special Collections: West Virginia History, bks, per, memorabilia
Mem of Alpha Regional Library
Branches: 1
GEARY LIBRARY-HEALTH CARE FACILITY, 98 Library Lane, Ste 1, Left Hand, 25251-9744. (Mail add: PO Box 90, Left Hand, 25251-0090), Tel: 304-565-4608. FAX: 304-565-4608. *Librn*, Tammy Cone

SUGAR GROVE

UNITED STATES NAVY
A NSGA SUGAR GROVE, WV BASE LIBRARY, Bldg 63, NSGA, 26815. Tel: 304-249-6321. FAX: 304-249-6385. E-Mail: mwr@mountain.net. Web Site: www.mountain.net/~mwr/library.html. *Mgr*, Dudley James Gregory; *Librn*, Lisa Franklin
Founded 1977
Library Holdings: Bk Titles 5,000

SUMMERSVILLE

P SUMMERSVILLE PUBLIC LIBRARY,* 85 Scenic Hwy, 26651. SAN 317-8447. Tel: 304-872-0844. FAX: 304-872-0845. *Librn*, Imagene Clackler
Pop 8,925; Circ 53,906
Jul 1997-Jun 1998 Income $90,410, State $33,535, City $12,000. Mats Exp $21,351, Books $18,444, Per/Ser (Incl. Access Fees) $2,061. Sal $32,911
Library Holdings: Bk Vols 29,502; Per Subs 90

SUMMIT POINT

P SOUTH JEFFERSON PUBLIC LIBRARY, Rt 13 & Shirley Rd, 25446. (Mail add: PO Box 17, 25446), SAN 328-1205. Tel: 304-725-6227. FAX: 304-725-6227. *Librn*, Dana S Jenkins
Founded 1984. Pop 4,170
Library Holdings: Bk Titles 7,145; Per Subs 16
Mem of Martinsburg Serv Ctr

SUTTON

P SUTTON PUBLIC LIBRARY, 450 Fourth St, No C, 26601. SAN 317-8455. Tel: 304-765-7224. FAX: 304-765-7224. *Librn*, Patricia Long; E-Mail: longpat@wvlc.wvnet.edu; *Asst Librn*, Mary Jane Stewart
Founded 1968. Pop 4,833; Circ 40,949
1999-2000 Mats Exp $5,200, Books $5,000, Per/Ser (Incl. Access Fees) $200. Sal $13,339
Library Holdings: Bk Vols 15,000; Per Subs 30; High Interest/Low Vocabulary Bk Vols 50
Mem of Upshur County Public Library
Partic in WV Libr Comm
Friends of the Library Group

TERRA ALTA

P TERRA ALTA PUBLIC LIBRARY, 701-B E State Ave, 26764-1423. SAN 317-8463. Tel: 304-789-2724. FAX: 304-789-2724. *Librn*, Ima Thomas; *Asst Librn*, Sharon Haskiell
Founded 1972. Pop 12,500; Circ 37,136
Jul 1999-Jun 2000 Income $52,722
Library Holdings: Bk Vols 37,179; Per Subs 88
Subject Interests: Local history
Restriction: Members only
Function: ILL available, Newspaper reference library, Photocopies available, Reference services available, Some telephone reference
Mem of Morgantown Public Library
Friends of the Library Group

THOMAS

P MOUNTAINTOP LIBRARY,* Grant St, PO Box 217, 26292. SAN 376-611X. Tel: 304-463-4582. FAX: 304-463-4582. *Librn*, Inza E Wilcox
Library Holdings: Bk Vols 15,000
Mem of Upshur County Public Library

UNION

P MONROE COUNTY PUBLIC LIBRARY,* 103 South St, PO Box 558, 24983. SAN 317-8471. Tel: 304-772-3038. FAX: 304-772-4052. *Librn*, Doris McCurdy; E-Mail: mccurdy@raleigh.lib.wv.us; *Asst Librn*, Gary Ballard
Founded 1947. Pop 11,272; Circ 22,125
Library Holdings: Bk Titles 30,000; Per Subs 16
Friends of the Library Group

VALLEY HEAD

P VALLEY HEAD PUBLIC LIBRARY,* PO Box 98, 26294. SAN 317-848X. Tel: 304-339-6071. FAX: 304-339-6071. *Librn*, Edna Mae Wood; E-Mail: wood-mae@clark.lib.wv.us
Founded 1975. Pop 2,000; Circ 5,987
Library Holdings: Bk Vols 9,000
Partic in WVa Asn
Friends of the Library Group

VIENNA

C OHIO VALLEY COLLEGE, (Formerly Icy Belle Library), Icy Belle Library, One Campus View Dr, 26105-8000. SAN 317-8153. Tel: 304-485-7384. FAX: 304-485-3106. Web Site: www.ovc.edu. *Dir*, Allie Keller; Tel: 304-485-7384, Ext 138, E-Mail: aekeller@ovc.edu; *Librn*, John Foust; Tel: 304-485-7384, Ext 139, E-Mail: jfoust@ovc.edu; Staff 2 (MLS 2)
Founded 1960. Circ 7,169; Enrl 426; Fac 23; Highest Degree: Bachelor
Jun 1999-May 2000 Mats Exp $36,984, Books $2,382, Per/Ser (Incl. Access Fees) $20,918, Micro $13,684. Sal $61,780 (Prof $30,890)
Library Holdings: Bk Vols 30,052; Per Subs 273
Subject Interests: Relig studies
Automation Activity & Vendor Info: (OPAC) VTLS
Database Vendor: Ebsco - EbscoHost, GaleNet, IAC - Info Trac, OCLC - First Search
Partic in Appalachian Col Asn; Midwest Libr Consortium
Friends of the Library Group

P VIENNA PUBLIC LIBRARY, 2300 River Rd, 26105. SAN 317-8498. Tel: 304-295-7771. FAX: 304-295-7776. E-Mail: viennapl@hp9k.park.lib.wv.us. Web Site: vienna.park.lib.wv.us. *Dir*, Alice C Thomas; *Ch Servs*, Holly Van Camp; *Tech Servs*, Judy Stemple; Staff 4 (MLS 1, Non-MLS 3)
Founded 1959. Pop 10,862; Circ 151,200
Jul 1999-Jun 2000 Income $270,502, State $40,733, City $141,877, Federal $6,436, County $39,897, Other $41,559. Mats Exp $63,950, Books $47,000, Per/Ser (Incl. Access Fees) $4,500. Sal $184,267
Library Holdings: Bk Vols 49,400; Per Subs 88
Special Collections: Local History; West Virginia History
Open Mon-Thurs 10-8, Fri 10-5, Sat 10-4 & Sun 2-5

WALTON

P WALTON PUBLIC LIBRARY,* PO Box 217, 25286. SAN 376-6101. Tel: 304-577-6071. FAX: 304-577-6071. *Librn*, Debbie Greathouse
Library Holdings: Bk Vols 8,000; Bk Titles 4,000; Per Subs 20
Mem of Alpha Regional Library

WAR

P WAR PUBLIC LIBRARY,* Berwind Lake Rd, PO Box 68, 24892. SAN 320-4278. Tel: 304-875-4622. FAX: 304-875-4622. *Librn*, Frances Blankenship; E-Mail: francesb@raleighpub.lib.wv.us
Library Holdings: Bk Vols 34,000; Per Subs 25

WASHINGTON

S E I DU PONT DE NEMOURS & CO, Washington Laboratory Library, Rte 892 Dupont Rd, 26181. (Mail add: PO Box 1217, 26102-1217), Tel: 304-863-4528. FAX: 304-863-2681. *Librn*, Donna Siebold
Subject Interests: Chemistry, Polymerization, Polymers

S GE PLASTICS TECHNICAL INFORMATION CENTER, (TIC), Plastics Technical, Rte 892 S, 26181. SAN 317-8501. Tel: 304-424-7741. FAX: 304-863-7481.
Founded 1960
1999-2000 Mats Exp $165,000, Books $10,000, Per/Ser (Incl. Access Fees) $150,000, Micro $2,000, Other Print Mats $3,000
Library Holdings: Bk Titles 10,000; Per Subs 250
Subject Interests: Chemical engineering, Organic chemistry, Polymer chemistry
Special Collections: Safety films & tapes; US & Foreign Patent Files
Publications: Articles of Interest; New Library Materials Bulletin; TOC
Restriction: Staff use only
Partic in OCLC Online Computer Library Center, Inc; Pittsburgh Regional Libr Consortium

WEBSTER SPRINGS

P WEBSTER-ADDISON PUBLIC LIBRARY,* 331 S Main St, 26288. SAN 317-8528. Tel: 304-847-5764. FAX: 304-847-5764. *Dir*, Bobbi Martin
Founded 1972. Pop 9,000
Library Holdings: Bk Vols 21,000
Special Collections: West Virginia Coll

WEIRTON

P MARY H WEIR PUBLIC LIBRARY,* 3442 Main St, 26062. SAN 317-8544. Tel: 304-797-8510. FAX: 304-797-8526. Web Site: www.weirton.lib.wv.us. *Dir*, Richard G Rekowski; *Govt Doc, Ref*, Lois Aleta Fundis; E-Mail: fundisl@weirton.lib.wv.us; Staff 23 (MLS 3, Non-MLS 20)
Founded 1958. Pop 38,000
Library Holdings: Bk Vols 121,241; Bk Titles 110,000; Per Subs 212
Subject Interests: Local history
Database Vendor: IAC - Info Trac, ProQuest
Publications: The Way Toward Literary
Member Libraries: Swaney Memorial Library
Special Services for the Deaf - High interest/low vocabulary books; Sta with knowledge of sign language; TTY machine
Friends of the Library Group

WELCH

P MCDOWELL PUBLIC LIBRARY, Welch Library, 90 Howard St, 2480 SAN 364-5517. Tel: 304-436-3070. FAX: 304-436-8079. Web Site: www.raleigh.lib.wv.us/mcdowell. *Actg Dir, ILL*, Rebecca Moore; *Ch Ser* Judy Richardson; Staff 7 (MLS 1, Non-MLS 6)
Founded 1954. Pop 35,233
Library Holdings: Bk Vols 49,331; Bk Titles 34,000; Per Subs 123
Subject Interests: Medicine
Special Collections: Medical Coll; Southern Appalachian Culture Coll; Virginiana Coal Mining Coll
Automation Activity & Vendor Info: (Cataloging) VTLS; (Circulation) VTLS
Partic in Southern West Virginia Library Automation Corporation
Branches: 3
BRADSHAW BRANCH, PO Box 498, Bradshaw, 24817. SAN 364-554 Tel: 304-967-5140. FAX: 304-967-5140. *Librn*, Iris Shelton
Library Holdings: Bk Vols 5,491
IAEGER BRANCH, PO Box 2640, Iaeger, 24844. SAN 364-5630. Tel: 938-3825. *Librn*, Marilyn Fain
Library Holdings: Bk Vols 4,554
NORTHFORK BRANCH, PO Box 229, Northfork, 24868. SAN 364-57 Tel: 304-862-4541. *Librn*, Don Graham
Library Holdings: Bk Vols 2,790
Friends of the Library Group

WELLSBURG

P BROOKE COUNTY PUBLIC LIBRARY,* 945 Main St, 26070. SAN 3 5754. Tel: 304-737-1551. FAX: 304-737-1010. Web Site: weirton.lib.wv. index_34.html. *Dir*, Mary Kay Wallace
Founded 1962. Pop 22,989; Circ 96,000
Library Holdings: Bk Vols 30,000; Per Subs 81
Subject Interests: Genealogy, Local history
Friends of the Library Group
Branches: 1
FOLLANSBEE BRANCH, 844 Main St, Follansbee, 26037. SAN 364-5 Tel: 304-527-0860. Web Site: www.weirton.lib.wv.us/index_n34.html. *Librn*, Faye Long; *Librn*, Joyce McAlpine
Pop 3,900
Library Holdings: Bk Vols 6,480; Per Subs 29
Friends of the Library Group

WEST LIBERTY

C WEST LIBERTY STATE COLLEGE, Paul N Elbin Library, 26074. SA 317-8579. Tel: 304-336-8035. Interlibrary Loan Service Tel: 304-336-835 FAX: 304-336-8186. Web Site: vms.wlsc.wvnet.edu. *Dir*, Cheryl Harshm E-Mail: harshmac@wisc.wvnet.edu; *Acq*, Lu Ann P Johnson; *Cat, ILL*, Jennifer D Cross; *Ref*, Jeanne V Schramm; *Bibliog Instr*, Ted Nesbitt
Founded 1932. Highest Degree: Bachelor
Library Holdings: Bk Vols 205,000; Per Subs 758
Subject Interests: Education, Music
Special Collections: Nelle Krise Rare Book Room
Partic in Dialog Corporation; OCLC Online Computer Library Center, In PALINET & Union Library Catalogue of Pennsylvania
Friends of the Library Group

WEST UNION

P DODDRIDGE COUNTY PUBLIC LIBRARY, 117 Court St, 26456. SA 364-5819. Tel: 304-873-1941. FAX: 304-873-1941. *Librn*, Cathy J Ash; *A Librn*, Sheila McCutchan
Founded 1952. Pop 6,994; Circ 61,678
Library Holdings: Bk Titles 29,818; Per Subs 54
Special Collections: Doddridge County History; Farm Women Reading Coll; Local Genealogy; West Virginia History
Publications: Booklines (newsletter)
Mem of Alpha Regional Library
Mail-a-Book Service
Branches: 1
CENTER POINT BRANCH, General Delivery, Center Point, 26339. SA 364-5843. Tel: 304-782-2461. FAX: 304-782-2461. *Librn*, Jeanie Taylo
Founded 1978
Library Holdings: Bk Titles 5,146

:TON

LOUIS BENNETT PUBLIC LIBRARY,* 148 Court Ave, 26452. SAN 317-8587. Tel: 304-269-5151. FAX: 304-269-7332. *Dir*, Karen H Enderle
Founded 1923. Pop 17,223; Circ 32,390
Library Holdings: Bk Vols 23,310; Per Subs 20
Special Collections: Bennett Family Archive; West Virginia Coll
Open Mon-Fri 10-6, Sat 10-2
Friends of the Library Group

WILLIAM SHARP JR, HOSPITAL, Patients' Library,* PO Drawer 1127, 26452. SAN 317-8595. Tel: 304-269-1210, Ext 399. FAX: 304-269-6235. *Librn*, Carl Anderson
Founded 1969
Library Holdings: Bk Vols 4,000; Per Subs 33

EELING

BETHLEHEM UNITED PRESBYTERIAN CHURCH LIBRARY,* 45 Chapel Rd Bethlehem, 26003. SAN 317-8609. Tel: 304-242-4407.
Library Holdings: Bk Vols 300
Friends of the Library Group

OGLEBAY INSTITUTE MANSION MUSEUM LIBRARY,* Oglebay Park, Burton Center, 26003. SAN 317-8617. Tel: 304-242-7272. FAX: 304-242-4203. *Dir*, Holly H McCluskey
Founded 1934
Library Holdings: Bk Titles 750
Subject Interests: Decorative arts, Local history
Special Collections: Brown Coll of Wheeling History, photogs; Wheeling & Belmont Bridge Company Papers; Wheeling City Directories

OHIO COUNTY LAW LIBRARY,* City-County Bldg, Rm 406, 1500 Chapline St, 26003. SAN 317-8625. Tel: 304-234-3780. FAX: 304-234-3827. *Librn*, Nancy Coughlan
Founded 1919
Library Holdings: Bk Titles 35,000
Special Collections: Supreme Court Records & Briefs
Restriction: Open to public for reference only

OHIO COUNTY PUBLIC LIBRARY, 52 16th St, 26003-3696. SAN 364-5878. Tel: 304-232-0244. FAX: 304-232-6848. E-Mail: ocplweb@weirton.lib.wv.us. Web Site: wheeling.weirton.lib.wv.us. *Dir*, Dottie Thomas; *Asst Dir, Head Tech Servs*, Louis Horacek; *Ad Servs, Ref*, Amy Kastigar; *Ref, Tech Servs*, Christina George; Staff 27 (MLS 4, Non-MLS 23)
Founded 1882. Pop 50,871; Circ 246,097
Jul 1999-Jun 2000 Income $867,394, State $204,192, County $584,412, Other $78,790. Mats Exp $155,684, Books $111,146, Per/Ser (Incl. Access Fees) $29,714, Presv $1,824, Micro $10,000, Electronic Ref Mat (Incl. Access Fees) $3,000. Sal $499,798 (Prof $121,887)
Library Holdings: Bk Vols 115,916; Bk Titles 95,778; Per Subs 285
Special Collections: Wheeling-Ohio County History (Wheeling Coll)
Database Vendor: IAC - Info Trac, ProQuest
Publications: Blind & Physically Handicapped Newsletter; First Look at Books (Newsletter); OCPL Newsletter
Subregional library of the National Library Service for the Blind & Physically Handicapped
Friends of the Library Group
Branches: 1
HILDEBRAND MEMORIAL, 99 N 17th St, 26003. SAN 364-5908. Tel: 304-277-1800. *Librn*, Nancy Viewig
Friends of the Library Group
Bookmobiles: 1

OHIO VALLEY MEDICAL CENTER, Hupp Medical Library,* 2000 Eoff St, 26003. SAN 317-8633. Tel: 304-234-8771. FAX: 304-234-8330. Web Site: www.web.mountain.net/~klc. *Dir*, Bradley A Long; E-Mail: blong@ovrh.org; Staff 2 (MLS 1, Non-MLS 1)
Founded 1955
Jan 1998-Dec 1998 Income $47,500. Mats Exp $41,200, Books $11,000, Per/Ser (Incl. Access Fees) $29,000
Library Holdings: Bk Vols 6,500; Per Subs 139
Subject Interests: Med hist, Medicine, Nursing, Psychiatry
Special Collections: Medical Classics; Osterman Psychiatric Coll
Automation Activity & Vendor Info: (OPAC) TLC
Publications: Access (quarterly newsletter)
Restriction: Non-circulating to the public

WEST VIRGINIA NORTHERN COMMUNITY COLLEGE LIBRARY, Learning Resources Center, 1704 Market St, 26003-3699. SAN 364-5932. Tel: 304-233-5900, Ext 4252. FAX: 304-232-0965. Web Site: www.northern.wvnet.edu/~library. *Dir*, Mary Salony; Staff 6 (MLS 3, Non-MLS 3)
Founded 1972. Enrl 1,473; Fac 64; Highest Degree: Associate
Jul 1999-Jun 2000 Income (Main Library and Branch Library) $217,848. Mats Exp $55,342, Books $6,590, Per/Ser (Incl. Access Fees) $16,812, Micro $1,081, AV Equip $593, Electronic Ref Mat (Incl. Access Fees) $10,782. Sal $162,506 (Prof $94,282)
Library Holdings: Bk Vols 36,958; Bk Titles 30,464; Per Subs 180
Partic in PALINET & Union Library Catalogue of Pennsylvania
Departmental Libraries:
NEW MARTINSVILLE CAMPUS, 141 Main St, New Martinsville, 26155. SAN 317-8102. Tel: 304-455-4684, Ext 4727. FAX: 304-455-4681. *Librn*, Janet Corbitt
WEIRTON CAMPUS, 150 Park Ave, Weirton, 26062. SAN 317-8552. Tel: 304-723-2210. FAX: 304-723-6704. *Librn*, Patricia Stroud; Tel: 304-723-2210, Ext 4609
Library Holdings: Bk Vols 35,000; Per Subs 254

M WHEELING HOSPITAL, INC, Henry G Jepson Memorial Library, One Medical Park, 26003. SAN 317-865X. Tel: 304-243-3308. FAX: 304-243-3329. E-Mail: dlibwh34@whghosp.com. *Librn*, Karen Leach
Founded 1966
Library Holdings: Bk Titles 1,400; Per Subs 75
Open Mon-Fri 7:30-4

C WHEELING JESUIT UNIVERSITY, (WWV), Bishop Hodges Library, 316 Washington Ave, 26003-0759. SAN 317-8641. Tel: 304-243-2226. FAX: 304-243-2466. E-Mail: library@wju.edu. Web Site: library@wju.edu. *Dir*, Eileen Carpino; E-Mail: ecarppino@wju.edu; *Bibliog Instr, Online Servs, Ref Serv, Syst Coordr*, Robert Behary; *Cat, Online Servs*, Mary Moore; *ILL*, Barbara Julian; Staff 7 (MLS 3, Non-MLS 4)
Founded 1955. Enrl 1,497; Fac 87; Highest Degree: Master
Jul 1999-Jun 2000 Income $621,933, Other $6,440. Mats Exp $270,063, Books $98,825, Per/Ser (Incl. Access Fees) $91,016, Presv $2,342, Micro $12,488, AV Equip $10,051, Electronic Ref Mat (Incl. Access Fees) $55,341. Sal $263,282 (Prof $176,102)
Library Holdings: Bk Vols 154,094; Bk Titles 120,100; Per Subs 473
Subject Interests: Local history
Automation Activity & Vendor Info: (Acquisitions) SIRSI; (Cataloging) SIRSI; (Circulation) SIRSI; (Course Reserve) SIRSI; (ILL) SIRSI; (Media Booking) SIRSI; (OPAC) SIRSI; (Serials) SIRSI
Database Vendor: Dialog, Ebsco - EbscoHost, GaleNet, Lexis-Nexis, OCLC - First Search
Partic in Appalachian Col Asn; OCLC Online Computer Library Center, Inc; OHIONET

WHITE SULPHUR SPRINGS

P WHITE SULPHUR SPRINGS PUBLIC LIBRARY,* 203 W Main St, 24986-2411. SAN 317-8676. Tel: 304-536-1171. FAX: 304-536-3801. *Asst Dir*, Kimberly Bierer
Pop 6,689; Circ 24,000
Library Holdings: Bk Vols 22,000; Per Subs 40
Mem of WVa Libr Comn
Friends of the Library Group

WILLIAMSON

J SOUTHERN WEST VIRGINIA COMMUNITY & TECHNICAL COLLEGE, Williamson Campus Library, 1601 Armory Dr, 25661. SAN 364-5967. Tel: 304-235-6046 Ext 353. FAX: 304-235-6043. Web Site: www.southern.wvnet.edu. *Dir Libr Serv*, Carol Lee Carlton; Tel: 304-235-6046, Ext 356, E-Mail: carolc@southern.wvnet.edu; Staff 1 (MLS 1)
Founded 1971. Enrl 1,009; Fac 22; Highest Degree: Associate
Jul 1999-Jun 2000 Income State $246,464. Mats Exp $80,738, Books $33,838, Per/Ser (Incl. Access Fees) $14,964, Micro $4,305, Electronic Ref Mat (Incl. Access Fees) $14,164. Sal $165,726 (Prof $62,138)
Library Holdings: Bk Vols 27,777; Bk Titles 24,999; Per Subs 181
Special Collections: Appalachian Coll; Children's Coll
Automation Activity & Vendor Info: (Acquisitions) epixtech, inc.; (Cataloging) epixtech, inc.; (Circulation) epixtech, inc.; (Course Reserve) epixtech, inc.; (Media Booking) epixtech, inc.; (OPAC) epixtech, inc.; (Serials) epixtech, inc.
Database Vendor: epixtech, inc.
Restriction: Open to student, faculty & staff
Function: ILL available, Photocopies available, Reference services available
Partic in OCLC Online Computer Library Center, Inc; PALINET & Union Library Catalogue of Pennsylvania
Special Services for the Deaf - TDD
Special Services for the Blind - Kurzweil Reader
Friends of the Library Group

P WILLIAMSON PUBLIC LIBRARY,* General Delivery, 25661. SAN 317-8684. Tel: 304-235-6029. FAX: 304-235-6029. E-Mail: william@cabell.lib.wv.us. Web Site: www.williamsonlibrary.org. *Librn*, Lola Henry
Pop 5,831; Circ 27,818
Library Holdings: Bk Vols 23,966; Per Subs 16
Mem of Western Counties Regional Libr Syst

WISCONSIN

of Statistics: 1999
lation, 1999 Census: 5,274,827
lation Served by Public Libraries: 5,274,827
Volumes in Public Libraries: 18,360,488
olumes Per Capita: 3.48
Public Library Circulation: 46,720,568
irculation Per Capita: 8.86
Public Library Income (including Grants-in-Aid): $158,900
verage Income: (382 public libraries) $395,136
ource of Income: Local & county (87.3%), state (3.3%), federal (.4%); Other (9.0%)
xpenditures Per Capita: $28.62

Number of Bookmobiles in State: 13
Grants and Services to Public Libraries:
Federal (LSTA): (FY 2000) $2,623,955
State Aid:
Public Library Systems: $14,748,800 (FY 2001);
Services to Blind & Physically Handicapped (through contract with the Milwaukee Public Library): $736,400 (FY 2001) Milwaukee Public Library (Interlibrary Loan Contract): $65,000 (FY 2001)
Wisconsin Interlibrary Loan Service: $180,900 (FY 2001). This and the Milwaukee Public Library contract above augment the ability of the State Reference & Loan Library to serve the needs of its statewide clientele

OTSFORD

ABBOTSFORD PUBLIC LIBRARY,* Birch & Second, PO Box 506, 54405-0506. SAN 317-8692. Tel: 715-223-3920. FAX: 715-223-8891. E-Mail: ablib@pcpros.net. *Librn*, Jane Medenwaldt
Founded 1903. Pop 1,900; Circ 15,500
Jan 1998-Dec 1999 Income $40,000, State $500, City $35,000, County $4,500. Mats Exp $7,500, Books $6,000, Per/Ser (Incl. Access Fees) $1,000. Sal $15,000 (Prof $12,000)
Library Holdings: Bk Vols 12,000; Per Subs 26
Mem of Wisconsin Valley Library Service

MS

ADAMS COUNTY LIBRARY, 101 S Main St, PO Box 850, 53910-0850. SAN 317-8706. Tel: 608-339-4250. FAX: 608-339-4250. *Dir*, Dan C Calef; Staff 1 (MLS 1)
Founded 1974. Pop 18,000; Circ 52,812
Library Holdings: Bk Titles 20,000; Per Subs 68
Friends of the Library Group

ANY

ALBANY PUBLIC LIBRARY, 203 Oak St, PO Box 329, 53502-0329. SAN 317-8714. Tel: 608-862-3491. FAX: 608-862-3505. E-Mail: albpl@tds.net. *Dir*, Hillary Bauman; *Asst Dir*, Rosie Hart; Staff 5 (MLS 1, Non-MLS 4)
Founded 1964. Pop 1,180
Library Holdings: Bk Vols 15,000; Per Subs 80
Mem of South Central Library System
Friends of the Library Group

OMA

ALGOMA PUBLIC LIBRARY,* 406 Fremont St, 54201. SAN 317-8722. Tel: 920-487-2295. *Dir*, Ann Schmitz; Staff 4 (Non-MLS 4)
Founded 1922. Pop 3,348; Circ 69,476
Jan 1999-Dec 1999 Income $206,678, State $2,161, City $125,855, County $68,389, Locally Generated Income $10,273. Mats Exp $24,661, Books $19,161, Per/Ser (Incl. Access Fees) $5,300, Presv $200. Sal $86,867 (Prof $81,246)
Library Holdings: Bk Titles 29,000; Per Subs 100
Subject Interests: Local history
Mem of Nicolet Federated Library System
Friends of the Library Group

MA

ALMA PUBLIC LIBRARY,* 312 Main St N, 54610-0277. SAN 325-3775. Tel: 608-685-3823. FAX: 608-685-4935. *Librn*, Linda Torgerson
Pop 896
Jan 1998-Dec 1999 Income $26,000. Mats Exp $8,300, Books $7,500, Per/Ser (Incl. Access Fees) $800. Sal $11,500
Library Holdings: Bk Vols 11,500; Bk Titles 11,500; Per Subs 32
Mem of Winding Rivers Library System

ALTOONA

P ALTOONA PUBLIC LIBRARY, (APL), 1303 Lynn Ave, 54720-0278. SAN 324-7198. Tel: 715-839-5029. FAX: 715-839-5119. *Dir*, Mary Vernau; E-Mail: maryvernau@yahoo.com; *Librn*, Carol Hillman; *Asst Librn*, Dianne Dunn; Staff 4 (MLS 1, Non-MLS 3)
Pop 8,691; Circ 34,764
Jan 1998-Dec 1998 Income $108,709, State $246, City $84,410, Federal $6,818, County $17,235. Mats Exp $24,392. Sal $49,047
Library Holdings: Bk Vols 40,000; Per Subs 135
Mem of Indianhead Federated Library System
Friends of the Library Group

AMERY

P AMERY PUBLIC LIBRARY,* 801 Keller Ave S, 54001-1096. SAN 376-673X. Tel: 715-268-9340. FAX: 715-268-8659. E-Mail: amerypl@spacestar.net. *Librn*, Barbara Sorenson
Library Holdings: Bk Vols 40,000; Bk Titles 10,000; Per Subs 40
Mem of Indianhead Federated Library System
Friends of the Library Group

AMHERST

P LETTIE W JENSEN PUBLIC LIBRARY, 278 N Main St, 54406-9101. Tel: 715-824-5510. E-Mail: amherstlibrary@wi-net.com. *Librn*, Kristi Pennebecker
Library Holdings: Bk Vols 20,000; Bk Titles 9,000; Per Subs 84
Mem of South Central Library System
Friends of the Library Group

ANTIGO

P ANTIGO PUBLIC LIBRARY, 617 Clermont, 54409-1894. SAN 317-8749. Tel: 715-623-3724. FAX: 715-627-2317. *Ch Servs*, Helen McNamara
Founded 1900. Pop 20,618; Circ 164,237
1999-2000 Income $550,160. Mats Exp $51,900, Books $39,000, Per/Ser (Incl. Access Fees) $6,569, Micro $900, AV Equip $500, Other Print Mats $1,700. Sal $263,109
Library Holdings: Bk Vols 59,891; Per Subs 125
Mem of Wisconsin Valley Library Service

APPLETON

S AID ASSOCIATION FOR LUTHERANS, (IRC), Information Resource Center, 4321 N Ballard Rd, 54919. SAN 317-8757. Tel: 920-734-5721, Ext 4007. FAX: 920-730-4821. *Dir*, Kathleen Brandel; E-Mail: kathy_brandel@

aal.org
Library Holdings: Bk Vols 5,000; Per Subs 200
Subject Interests: Business
Partic in Fox Valley Library Council

P APPLETON PUBLIC LIBRARY, 225 N Oneida St, 54911-4780. SAN 317-8765. Tel: 920-832-6170. Circulation Tel: 920-832-6179. Reference Tel: 920-832-6173. TDD: 920-832-6173. FAX: 920-832-6182. E-Mail: apl@apl.org. Web Site: www.apl.org. *Dir*, Terry P Dawson; E-Mail: tdawson@apl.org; *Asst Dir*, Barbara J Kelly; Tel: 920-832-6168, Fax: 920-832-6422, E-Mail: bkelly@apl.org; *Tech Servs*, Michael Nitz; Tel: 920-832-6185, E-Mail: mnitz@apl.org; *Business*, Tim Muench; E-Mail: tmuench@apl.org; *Ch Servs*, Carole De Jardin; Tel: 920-832-6187, E-Mail: cdejardin@apl.org; *Circ*, Vicki Lenz; E-Mail: vienz@apl.org; *Ref*, Margaret Shriver; E-Mail: mshriver@apl.org; *Tech Coordr*, Kurt Riechers; E-Mail: kriechers@apl.org; *Commun Relations*, Cecilia Wiltzius; Tel: 920-832-6195, E-Mail: cwiltzius@apl.org; *ILL*, Karen Probst; Staff 53 (MLS 17, Non-MLS 36)
Founded 1897. Pop 70,000; Circ 867,936
Jan 1999-Dec 1999 Income $2,992,073, City $2,484,296, County $467,265, Other $40,512. Mats Exp $354,191, Books $244,263, Per/Ser (Incl. Access Fees) $48,987, Micro $8,621, AV Equip $39,075, Other Print Mats $6,942, Electronic Ref Mat (Incl. Access Fees) $6,303. Sal $1,044,945 (Prof $725,204)
Library Holdings: Bk Vols 280,253; Bk Titles 238,092; Per Subs 524
Subject Interests: Local history
Automation Activity & Vendor Info: (Cataloging) GEAC; (Circulation) GEAC; (OPAC) GEAC
Database Vendor: Dialog, Ebsco - EbscoHost, IAC - Info Trac, IAC - SearchBank, OCLC - First Search
Function: Some telephone reference
Mem of Outagamie Waupaca Library System
Partic in OCLC Online Computer Library Center, Inc; OWLSnet
Special Services for the Deaf - TDD; TTY machine
Special Services for the Blind - Braille; Talking Books
Friends of the Library Group

J FOX VALLEY TECHNICAL COLLEGE, William M Sirek Educational Resource Center,* 1825 N Bluemound Dr, PO Box 2277, 54913-2277. SAN 317-8773. Tel: 920-735-5600. FAX: 920-735-4870. Web Site: www.foxvalley.tec.wi.us/library/. *Dir*, Karen Parson
Founded 1967. Enrl 4,405; Fac 285
Jul 1997-Jun 1998 Income $341,681. Mats Exp $48,150, Books $24,078, Per/Ser (Incl. Access Fees) $24,072. Sal $186,798 (Prof $91,596)
Library Holdings: Bk Vols 52,313; Per Subs 303
Subject Interests: Agriculture, Bus, Environmental studies, Medicine, Mgt, Sci-tech

S INTEGRATED PAPER SERVICES, INC LIBRARY,* PO Box 446, 54912-0446. SAN 377-9599. Tel: 920-749-3046. FAX: 920-749-3046. Web Site: www.integratedpaperservices.com.
Library Holdings: Bk Titles 25; Per Subs 20

C LAWRENCE UNIVERSITY, Seeley G Mudd Library, 113 S Lawe St, 54911-5683. (Mail add: PO Box 599, 54912-0599), SAN 364-5991. Tel: 920-832-6750. FAX: 920-832-6967. E-Mail: reference@lawrence.edu. Web Site: www.lawrence.edu/library. *Dir*, Susan Richards; E-Mail: susan.l.richards@lawrence.edu; *Music*, Jennifer Bollerman; *Head Tech Servs*, Corinne Wocelka; *Archivist*, Carol Butts; *Syst Coordr*, Kathy Isaacson; *Media Spec*, Thomas Sykes; *Ref*, Gretchen Revie; *Head, Circ*, Cynthia Patterson; *Ref*, Charles Morris; Staff 14 (MLS 6, Non-MLS 8)
Founded 1850. Enrl 1,242; Fac 125; Highest Degree: Bachelor
Jul 1999-Jun 2000 Income Parent Institution $1,362,792. Mats Exp $650,534, Books $246,152, Per/Ser (Incl. Access Fees) $353,012, Presv $29,103, Micro $201, AV Equip $8,997. Sal $41,414
Library Holdings: Bk Vols 365,612; Per Subs 1,406
Database Vendor: DRA
Partic in Fox River Valley Area Library Consortium; NE Wis Intertype Librs, Inc; OCLC Online Computer Library Center, Inc; Wisconsin Library Services

L OUTAGAMIE COUNTY LAW LIBRARY,* 320 S Walnut St, 54911. SAN 327-8360. Tel: 920-832-5149. FAX: 920-832-5115. *Librn*, Lynn Driessen
Library Holdings: Bk Vols 4,000

P OUTAGAMIE WAUPACA LIBRARY SYSTEM,* 225 N Oneida, 54911-4780. SAN 317-879X. Tel: 920-832-6190. FAX: 920-832-6422. Web Site: www.owls.lib.wi.us. *Dir*, Richard Krumwiede; *Asst Dir*, Greta Thompson; Staff 12 (MLS 5, Non-MLS 7)
Founded 1975
Jan 1998-Dec 1999 Income $2,263,196. Sal $351,051
Member Libraries: Appleton Public Library; Black Creek Village Library; Clintonville Public Library; Ellison Public Library; Hortonville Public Library; Iola Village Library; Kaukauna Public Library; Kimberly-Little Chute Public Library; Lakes Country Public Library; Marion Public Library; Muehl Public Library; Neuschafer Community Library; New London Public Library; Shiocton Public Library; Sturm Memorial Library; Waupaca Area Public Library; Weyauwega Public Library

M SAINT ELIZABETH HOSPITAL, Health Science Library, 1506 S One St, 54915. SAN 317-8803. Tel: 920-738-2324. FAX: 920-731-0562. *Dir Serv*, Mary M Bayorgeon; E-Mail: mbayorgeon@affinityhealth.org; Staf (MLS 1, Non-MLS 2)
Founded 1968
Library Holdings: Bk Vols 3,150; Bk Titles 3,000; Per Subs 350
Subject Interests: Consumer health, Hospital administration, Medicine, Nursing
Automation Activity & Vendor Info: (Acquisitions) EOS; (Cataloging EOS; (Circulation) EOS; (OPAC) EOS; (Serials) EOS
Database Vendor: Silverplatter Information Inc.
Mem of Affinity Health Syst, Inc
Partic in Fox River Valley Area Library Consortium; Fox Valley Library Council; Nat Libr of Med

ARCADIA

P ARCADIA FREE PUBLIC LIBRARY,* 406 E Main St, 54612-1396. S 317-8811. Tel: 608-323-7505. *Asst Dir*, Carol Krett
Founded 1899. Pop 2,159; Circ 38,035
Library Holdings: Bk Vols 13,666; Per Subs 80
Mem of Winding Rivers Library System
Open Mon & Thurs 12-8, Tues, Wed & Fri 9-5, Sat 9-12 during school

ARGYLE

P ARGYLE PUBLIC LIBRARY,* PO Box 250, 53504-0250. SAN 317-8 Tel: 608-543-3113. *Librn*, Jacqueline A Whitmar
Pop 713; Circ 6,407
Library Holdings: Bk Vols 7,500; Per Subs 35
Special Collections: Argyle Atlas Newspaper Coll (bound issues beginn in 1885)
Mem of Southwest Wisconsin Library System

ARPIN

P ARPIN PUBLIC LIBRARY,* 8095A Church Rd, 54410-9607. SAN 31 8838. Tel: 715-652-2273. E-Mail: arpinpl@tznet.com. *Dir*, Rebecca Ass
Founded 1951
Library Holdings: Bk Vols 8,500; Per Subs 40
Mem of South Central Library System

ASHLAND

L ASHLAND COUNTY LAW LIBRARY,* 201 W Main St, Courthouse 304, 54806. Tel: 715-682-7016. FAX: 715-682-7919. *In Charge*, Rosalir Wilhelm
Library Holdings: Bk Vols 6,500; Bk Titles 6,500; Per Subs 15

M HEALTH SCIENCE LIBRARY, Memorial Medical Center,* 1615 Map Lane, 54806. Tel: 715-682-4563, Ext 247. FAX: 715-682-4022. *Dir*, Su Bendapudi; E-Mail: yesbendapudi@ashlandmmc.com
Library Holdings: Bk Vols 1,500; Bk Titles 1,500; Per Subs 62

P NORTHERN WATERS LIBRARY SERVICE, 3200 E Lakeshore Dr, 54806-2510. SAN 317-8854. Tel: 715-682-2365. FAX: 715-685-2704. E-Mail: nwls@nwls.lib.wi.us. Web Site: www.nwls.lib.wi.us. *Dir*, Joan Airoldi; *ILL*, Carol Kane; E-Mail: ckane@nwls.lib.wi.us
Founded 1972. Pop 140,000; Circ 65,081
Library Holdings: Bk Vols 44,000
Database Vendor: Innovative Interfaces INN - View
Publications: Rivers
Member Libraries: Bad River Public Tribal Library; Bayfield Carnegie Library; Ben Guthrie-Lac Du Flambeau Public Library; Boulder Junctio Public Library; Burnett Community Library; Drummond Public Library; Eleanor Ellis Public Library; Forest Lodge Library; Frank B Koller Memorial Library; Grantsburg Public Library; Hayward Carnegie Librar Hurley Public Library; Irma Stein Memorial Library; Lac Courte Oreille Ojibwa College Community Library; Land O'Lakes Public Library; Leg Memorial Library; Madeline Island Public Library; Mercer Public Librar Plum Lake Public Library; Shell Lake Public Library; Spooner Memoria Library; Superior Public Library; Tice Public Library; Vaughn Public Library; Walter E Olson Memorial Library; Washburn Public Library; Winchester Public Library
Books by mail program; Literacy Services

C NORTHLAND COLLEGE, Dexter Library, 1411 Ellis Ave, 54806-3999 SAN 317-8846. Tel: 715-682-1279. FAX: 715-682-1693. Web Site: library.northland.edu. *Dir*, Julia Trojanowski; *Admin Assoc*, Karlan Willi *Cat*, Sharon Youngberg; Staff 3 (MLS 2, Non-MLS 1)
Founded 1892. Enrl 760; Fac 42; Highest Degree: Bachelor
Jul 2000-Jun 2001 Income $291,650. Mats Exp $58,386, Books $32,450 Per/Ser (Incl. Access Fees) $34,550, Presv $1,200, Micro $12,000, AV E $300, Electronic Ref Mat (Incl. Access Fees) $26,270. Sal $93,106 (Prof $70,000)
Library Holdings: Bk Vols 71,868; Bk Titles 62,000; Per Subs 335

Subject Interests: Environmental studies, Native Americans
Automation Activity & Vendor Info: (Acquisitions) Endeavor; (Cataloging) Endeavor; (Circulation) Endeavor; (Course Reserve) Endeavor; (OPAC) Endeavor; (Serials) Endeavor
Database Vendor: Ebsco - EbscoHost, OCLC - First Search, Silverplatter Information Inc.
Partic in Wisconsin Library Services

VAUGHN PUBLIC LIBRARY, 502 W Main St, 54806. SAN 317-8862. Tel: 715-682-7027, 715-682-7060. FAX: 715-682-7185. Web Site: www.ci.ashland.wi.us/dept/library/. *Librn*, Jim Trojanowski; E-Mail: jtrojano@coawi.org; Staff 6 (MLS 1, Non-MLS 5)
Founded 1888. Pop 13,650; Circ 127,500
Jan 1999-Dec 1999 Income $339,966, State $1,100, City $297,301, County $23,115, Other $18,450. Mats Exp $324,385, Books $40,789, Per/Ser (Incl. Access Fees) $5,597, AV Equip $4,029. Sal $166,121 (Prof $38,873)
Library Holdings: Bk Vols 28,480; Bk Titles 26,964; Per Subs 155
Automation Activity & Vendor Info: (Cataloging) TLC; (Circulation) TLC; (OPAC) TLC
Mem of Northern Waters Library Service
Friends of the Library Group

USTA

AUGUSTA MEMORIAL PUBLIC LIBRARY, 113 N Stone St, PO Box 474, 54722-0474. SAN 326-1204. Tel: 715-286-2070. FAX: 715-286-5367. E-Mail: augustalibrary@ifls.lib.wi.us. *Dir*, Deborah Klossner; *Asst Librn*, Nancy Lein; *Asst Librn*, Eileen Stensen; Staff 1 (Non-MLS 1)
Pop 1,550; Circ 18,394
Library Holdings: Bk Titles 15,000; Per Subs 40
Mem of Indian Head Federated Libr Syst
Open Tues, Fri & Sat 11-5, Wed & Thurs 11-6:30
Friends of the Library Group

DWIN

BALDWIN PUBLIC LIBRARY,* 400 Cedar St, 54002-0465. SAN 317-8870. Tel: 715-684-3813. FAX: 715-684-5115. *Dir*, Cheryl Moe
Founded 1941. Pop 2,575; Circ 18,200
Library Holdings: Bk Titles 14,000; Per Subs 77
Mem of Indianhead Federated Library System

SAM LAKE

BALSAM LAKE PUBLIC LIBRARY,* 404 Main St, PO Box 340, 54810-0340. SAN 317-8889. Tel: 715-485-3215. FAX: 715-485-3215. *Dir*, Patricia Olson; *Asst Dir*, Lorraine McKenzie
Founded 1946. Pop 1,000; Circ 12,779
Library Holdings: Bk Titles 17,000; Per Subs 40
Special Collections: Native American Materials Coll; Wisconsin Coll
Mem of Indianhead Federated Library System

POLK COUNTY LIBRARY FEDERATION,* 215 Main St, PO Box 217, 54810-0217. SAN 376-6683. Tel: 715-485-8680. FAX: 715-485-8601. *Dir*, Marlene M Janssen; E-Mail: marlenej@co.polk.wi.us
1998-1999 Income $157,746, State $11,203, County $146,543. Mats Exp $21,000, Books $17,000, Per/Ser (Incl. Access Fees) $500, Micro $3,500. Sal $83,000 (Prof $40,000)
Library Holdings: Bk Vols 42,500; Bk Titles 21,000
Mem of Indianhead Federated Library System

:ABOO

BARABOO PUBLIC LIBRARY,* 230 Fourth Ave, 53913. SAN 317-8897. Tel: 608-356-6166. FAX: 608-355-3779. E-Mail: barlib@scls.lib.wi.us. *Dir*, Josephine Zipsie; *Ch Servs*, Miriam Thompson; *Tech Servs*, Nancy McFarland; *Circ*, Ann Adkins; *ILL*, Nijole Etzwiler; Staff 16 (MLS 3, Non-MLS 13)
Founded 1903. Pop 19,836; Circ 228,798
Jan 1998-Dec 1998 Income $515,106, State $9,190, City $365,933, County $94,490, Other $29,255. Mats Exp $63,629, Books $56,080, Per/Ser (Incl. Access Fees) $6,574, Micro $975. Sal $252,204
Library Holdings: Bk Vols 58,926; Per Subs 212
Database Vendor: epixtech, inc.
Mem of South Central Library System

CIRCUS WORLD MUSEUM, Robert L Parkinson Library & Research Center, 415 Lynn St. (Mail add: 550 Water St, 53913-2597), SAN 317-8900. Tel: 608-356-8341. FAX: 608-355-7959. E-Mail: library.cwm@baraboo.com. *Archivist*, Erin Foley; E-Mail: efoley.cwm@baraboo.com; *Asst Librn*, Meg Allen
Founded 1966
Library Holdings: Bk Vols 3,659; Bk Titles 3,300; Per Subs 29
Subject Interests: Circus, Wild West
Publications: Current Circus Activity; loan lists for books, serials, films & videos; USA & Canada List
Restriction: Not a lending library
Owned by The State Historical Society of Wisconsin

S INTERNATIONAL CRANE FOUNDATION, Ron Sauey Memorial Library for Bird Conservation, Int Crane Found, E-11376 Shady Lane Rd, PO Box 447, 53913-0447. SAN 321-902X. Tel: 608-356-9462, Ext 124. FAX: 608-356-9465. E-Mail: library@savingcranes.org. Web Site: www.savingcranes.org/library/library.htm. *Librn*, Betsy Didrickson
Founded 1973
Library Holdings: Bk Titles 3,000; Per Subs 200; Spec Interest Per Sub 50
Subject Interests: Biology, Conservation, Ornithology, Wetlands
Partic in Wisconsin Library Services

S SAUK COUNTY HISTORICAL SOCIETY, Museum Library, 531 Fourth Ave, 53913. (Mail add: PO Box 651, 53913), SAN 317-8919. Tel: 608-356-1001. E-Mail: schist@shopstop.net. Web Site: www.saukcounty.com/schs. *Pres*, Mona Larsen; *Exec Dir*, Peter Shrake; *Archivist*, Kathy Waddell. Subject Specialists: *Genealogy*, Kathy Waddell; *Local history*, Kathy Waddell; Staff 2 (Non-MLS 2)
Founded 1905
Library Holdings: Bk Vols 2,000
Subject Interests: Genealogy, Local history
Special Collections: H E Cole; Local family history; W H Canfield
Restriction: Not a lending library
Function: Archival collection
Library opens in May, closes Sept 15

GL SAULK COUNTY LAW LIBRARY,* 515 Oak St, 53913. SAN 377-9874. Tel: 608-355-3401. FAX: 608-355-3514.
Library Holdings: Bk Vols 3,000

J UNIVERSITY OF WISCONSIN BARABOO-SAUK COUNTY, Savides Library, 1006 Connie Rd, 53913. SAN 317-8927. Tel: 608-356-8351, Ext 249. FAX: 608-356-4074. Web Site: baraboo-sauk.uwc.edu/library. *Dir*, Jim Bredeson; E-Mail: jbredeso@uwc.edu; *ILL*, Stacey Burkart; Tel: 608-356-8351, Ext 251, E-Mail: sburkart@uwc.edu; *ILL*, Jane Whitney; Tel: 608-356-8351, Ext. 251, E-Mail: mjwhitne@uwc.edu; Staff 2 (MLS 2)
Founded 1968. Enrl 390; Fac 31
Jul 2000-Jun 2001 Income $134,000. Mats Exp $28,500. Sal $85,000 (Prof $76,000)
Library Holdings: Bk Vols 32,200; Per Subs 171
Automation Activity & Vendor Info: (Circulation) Endeavor
Partic in OCLC Online Computer Library Center, Inc; S Cent Libr Syst; Wisconsin Library Services

BARNEVELD

P BARNEVELD PUBLIC LIBRARY,* W Orbison St, PO Box 92, 53507-0092. SAN 317-8935. Tel: 608-924-3711. *In Charge*, Earlene O'Keefe
Founded 1955. Pop 715; Circ 2,916
Jan 1998-Dec 1999 Income $37,688. Mats Exp $2,201. Sal $11,744
Library Holdings: Bk Titles 4,000
Mem of Southwest Wisconsin Library System

BARRON

P BARRON PUBLIC LIBRARY,* 10 N Third St, 54812-1119. SAN 317-8943. Tel: 715-537-3881. FAX: 715-537-5080. E-Mail: barronpl@yahoo.com. *Dir*, Nancy Ausman-Dhatt; *Circ*, LeAnn Clausen; *Ch Servs*, Nancy Hanaman; Staff 7 (MLS 2, Non-MLS 5)
Founded 1909
Library Holdings: Bk Vols 26,000; Per Subs 70
Automation Activity & Vendor Info: (Circulation) epixtech, inc.
Mem of Indianhead Federated Library System
Partic in Barron County Libr Servs
Friends of the Library Group

BAYFIELD

P BAYFIELD CARNEGIE LIBRARY,* 37 N Broad St, PO Box 727, 54814-0727. SAN 317-8951. Tel: 715-779-3953. *Librn*, Roberta Baggerley
Founded 1903. Pop 786; Circ 12,000
Library Holdings: Bk Vols 9,000; Per Subs 28
Mem of Northern Waters Library Service; Northwest Wis Libr Syst

S NATIONAL PARK SERVICE, Apostle Islands National Lakeshore Library,* Rte 1 Box 4, 54814. SAN 328-1779. Tel: 715-779-3397. FAX: 715-779-3049. *In Charge*, Myra Dec
Founded 1975
Library Holdings: Bk Vols 1,500; Per Subs 30
Subject Interests: Local history
Restriction: Staff use only

BEAVER DAM

M BEAVER DAM COMMUNITY HOSPITALS,* 707 S University Ave, 53916. Tel: 920-887-7181. *Librn*, Diane Fashun
Library Holdings: Bk Vols 800; Bk Titles 250; Per Subs 45

P BEAVER DAM COMMUNITY LIBRARY, 311 N Spring St, 53916-2174. SAN 317-8978. Tel: 920-887-4631, Ext 12. FAX: 920-887-4633. E-Mail: bdref@mwfls.org. Web Site: www.beaverdam.lib.wi.us. *Dir*, Susan Mary Mevis; E-Mail: mevis@mwfls.org; Staff 12 (MLS 4, Non-MLS 8)
Founded 1884. Circ 288,894
Jan 2000-Dec 2000 Income $702,632, City $520,739, County $181,893. Mats Exp $193,189, Books $137,773, Per/Ser (Incl. Access Fees) $10,441, Presv $3,900, Micro $575, AV Equip $21,500, Electronic Ref Mat (Incl. Access Fees) $19,000. Sal $305,806 (Prof $146,000)
Library Holdings: Bk Titles 94,539; Per Subs 183
Database Vendor: Ebsco - EbscoHost, epixtech, inc., GaleNet, IAC - Info Trac, Wilson - Wilson Web
Mem of Mid-Wisconsin Federated Library System
Friends of the Library Group

P DODGE COUNTY LIBRARY SERVICE, 311 N Spring St, 53916-2043. SAN 364-605X. Tel: 920-885-4571. FAX: 920-887-4633. *Dir*, Susan Mevis; E-Mail: mevis@mwfls.org
Founded 1964. Pop 74,747; Circ 29,532
Jan 2000-Dec 2000 Income County $574,568. Mats Exp $29,700, Per/Ser (Incl. Access Fees) $1,200, AV Equip $27,000, Electronic Ref Mat (Incl. Access Fees) $1,500. Sal $25,778
Database Vendor: Ebsco - EbscoHost, epixtech, inc., GaleNet, IAC - Info Trac, Wilson - Wilson Web
Mem of Mid-Wisconsin Federated Library System
Branches: 1
NEOSHO PUBLIC, Hwy 67, Neosho, 53059. SAN 328-736X. *Librn*, Krista Becker
Library Holdings: Bk Vols 3,579

J MORAINE PARK TECHNICAL COLLEGE LIBRARY, Beaver Dam Campus, 700 Gould St, 53916. SAN 317-896X. Tel: 920-887-4406. FAX: 920-887-4473. *Librn*, Mary Janice Powers; Staff 3 (Non-MLS 3)
Library Holdings: Bk Vols 4,000; Per Subs 80

BELLEVILLE

P BELLEVILLE PUBLIC LIBRARY,* 130 S Vine St, PO Box 140, 53508-0140. SAN 317-8986. Tel: 608-424-1812. FAX: 608-424-3545. E-Mail: jcblvlib@scls.lib.wi.us. *Ch Servs, Dir*, Jean Christensen; *Asst Librn*, Ginny Nichols
Founded 1878
Library Holdings: Bk Vols 14,000; Per Subs 51
Subject Interests: Local history
Mem of Southcentral Libr Syst
Friends of the Library Group

BELMONT

P JOHN TURGESON PUBLIC LIBRARY,* 220 Mound Ave, 53510-9622. SAN 317-8994. Tel: 608-762-5137. *Dir*, Sylvia Henry
Pop 1,800; Circ 3,300
1998-1999 Income $21,091. Mats Exp $5,310. Sal $10,700
Library Holdings: Bk Vols 10,000
Mem of Southwest Wisconsin Library System

BELOIT

C BELOIT COLLEGE, Colonel Robert H Morse Library, 731 College St, 53511-5595. SAN 364-6238. Tel: 608-363-2483. Interlibrary Loan Service Tel: 608-363-2544. Circulation Tel: 608-363-2230. Reference Tel: 608-363-2544. FAX: 608-363-2487. Web Site: beloit.edu/~libhome. *Dir*, Dennis W Dickinson; *Tech Servs*, Dianne Witte; *Archivist*, Fred Burwell; *Bibliog Instr, Publ Servs*, Chris Nelson; Staff 7 (MLS 4, Non-MLS 3)
Founded 1849. Enrl 1,192; Fac 103; Highest Degree: Master
Jun 1999-May 2000 Income $1,007,174. Mats Exp $362,398, Books $139,583, Per/Ser (Incl. Access Fees) $156,091, Presv $8,212, Micro $8,086, AV Equip $12,040. Sal $365,400 (Prof $240,699)
Library Holdings: Bk Vols 242,417; Bk Titles 168,726; Per Subs 845
Special Collections: Beloit Poetry Journal Coll; Pacifism & Nonviolence (M L King Coll); World Order (Cullister Coll)
Automation Activity & Vendor Info: (Acquisitions) DRA; (Cataloging) DRA
Mem of Arrowhead Library System
Partic in Coun of Wis Librs, Inc; OCLC Online Computer Library Center, Inc; Wisconsin Library Services
Friends of the Library Group

P BELOIT HISTORICAL SOCIETY, Arthur L Luebke Memorial Librar[y], Lincoln Ctr, 845 Hackett St, 53511. SAN 371-1641. Tel: 608-365-7835. FAX: 608-365-5999. *Dir*, Paul Kerr
Library Holdings: Bk Vols 200; Per Subs 2
Collection of Old Books for research and general use

P BELOIT PUBLIC LIBRARY, 409 Pleasant St, 53511. SAN 317-9001. 608-364-2908. Circulation Tel: 608-364-2911. Reference Tel: 608-364-[...] TDD: 608-364-2913. FAX: 608-364-2907. Web Site: www.als.lib.wi.us. *Dir*, Peg Bredeson; E-Mail: bredeson@als.lib.wi.us; *Ch Servs*, Amber McCrea; *Ref Serv Ad*, Elizabeth Cook; *Circ*, Vicki Cogswell; *Info Tech* Scott Conrad; *Cat*, Linda Beyer; *Automation Syst Coordr*, Roger Dutch Staff 27 (MLS 7, Non-MLS 20)
Founded 1902. Pop 48,000; Circ 362,276
Jan 1999-Dec 1999 Income $1,580,131, City $1,276,863, Federal $17,4[...] County $241,131, Locally Generated Income $44,679. Mats Exp $222,[...] Books $153,799, Per/Ser (Incl. Access Fees) $21,702, AV Equip $39,4[...] Electronic Ref Mat (Incl. Access Fees) $7,501. Sal $1,109,837 (Prof $342,310)
Library Holdings: Bk Vols 131,938; Per Subs 379
Subject Interests: Genealogy, Local history
Automation Activity & Vendor Info: (Cataloging) Innovative Interfac[es] Inc.; (Circulation) Innovative Interfaces Inc.
Database Vendor: Ebsco - EbscoHost, ProQuest
Function: Some telephone reference
Mem of Arrowhead Library System
Special Services for the Deaf - TTY machine
Friends of the Library Group

S COLTEC INDUSTRIES, FM Engine Division Library,* 701 White Ave 53511. SAN 317-9028. Tel: 608-364-8168. FAX: 608-364-8233.
Library Holdings: Bk Titles 2,000; Per Subs 40
Subject Interests: Controls, Diesel engines, Electrical engineering, Pol[...] controls, Related eng, Sewage treatment

BENET LAKE

SR SAINT BENEDICT'S ABBEY, Benet Library, 12605 224th Ave, 53102-0333. SAN 317-9044. Tel: 262-396-4311. FAX: 262-396-4365. *Librn*, Barbara Konitzer; *Asst Librn*, Bro Vincent Wedig
Founded 1945
Library Holdings: Bk Titles 19,000; Per Subs 45
Subject Interests: Behav sci, Biblical studies, History, Psychology, Rel studies, Soc sci
Partic in Tri-County Libr Council, Inc

BENTON

P BENTON PUBLIC LIBRARY, 48 W Main St, PO Box 26, 53803-002[6] SAN 317-9052. Tel: 608-759-2665. FAX: 608-759-3212. Web Site: ci.benton.wi.us/bpl. *Dir*, Stephen J Calvert; E-Mail: scalvert@mhtc.net; 1 (MLS 1)
Founded 1922. Pop 2,146
Jan 2000-Dec 2000 Income $30,250, City $25,000, Other $5,250. Mats $8,250, Books $6,400, Per/Ser (Incl. Access Fees) $350, AV Equip $1,5[...] Sal $9,000
Library Holdings: Bk Titles 6,000; Per Subs 30
Special Collections: Local history
Function: ILL available
Mem of Southwest Wisconsin Library System
Open Mon & Thurs 10-12 & 1-5, Tues 10-12 & 1-7

BERLIN

M BERLIN MEMORIAL HOSPITAL, Health Science Library,* 225 Mem[...] Dr, 54923. Tel: 920-361-5502. FAX: 920-361-5517. *Dir*, Shirley Forst
Library Holdings: Bk Vols 100; Bk Titles 10; Per Subs 5

P BERLIN PUBLIC LIBRARY, (BPL), 121 W Park Ave, 54923. SAN 31[...] 9060. Tel: 920-361-5420. FAX: 920-361-5424. Web Site: www.berlinlibrary.org. *Ch Servs*, Christine Carroll; E-Mail: carroll@winnefox.org; *Tech Servs*, Diane Disterhaft; E-Mail: disterhaft@winnefox.org; Staff 3 (MLS 1, Non-MLS 2)
Founded 1903. Pop 9,000; Circ 112,993
Jan 2000-Dec 2000 Income $340,200, City $242,000, County $66,000, Locally Generated Income $7,200, Other $25,000. Mats Exp $47,200, B[...] $41,000, Per/Ser (Incl. Access Fees) $5,000, Micro $1,200. Sal $104,00[...] (Prof $88,867)
Library Holdings: Bk Vols 42,424; Per Subs 110; High Interest/Low Vocabulary Bk Vols 100; Bks on Deafness & Sign Lang 30
Subject Interests: Large print, Literacy, Local history
Special Collections: Large Print Coll; Literacy Coll; Local History Coll Spanish Language Materials Coll
Automation Activity & Vendor Info: (Circulation) DRA
Database Vendor: DRA

Mem of Winnefox Library System
Special Services for the Deaf - TTY machine
Special Services for the Blind - Magnifiers; Printed text enlargers
Friends of the Library Group

BEND

BIG BEND VILLAGE LIBRARY,* W230 S90175 Nevins St, 53103-9722. SAN 324-7880. Tel: 414-662-3571. FAX: 414-662-3751. *Coll Develop, Dir*, Sadie Soneberg; Staff 4 (MLS 1, Non-MLS 3)
Pop 1,299; Circ 15,307
Dec 1997-Jan 1998 Income $38,000. Mats Exp $7,000, Books $6,000, Per/Ser (Incl. Access Fees) $1,000. Sal $24,650 (Prof $13,745)
Library Holdings: Bk Vols 600; Per Subs 32
Subject Interests: Local history
Mem of Waukesha County Federated Library System
Open Mon & Thurs 3-9, Tues & Wed 9:30-12 & 6-9, Sat 9:30-12

CK CREEK

BLACK CREEK VILLAGE LIBRARY,* 507 S Maple St, 54106-9304. SAN 317-9087. Tel: 920-984-3094. FAX: 920-984-3559. *Librn*, Diane Wendt
Pop 18,000
Library Holdings: Bk Vols 10,200
Mem of Outagamie Waupaca Library System

CK EARTH

BLACK EARTH PUBLIC LIBRARY, 1210 Mills St, 53515. (Mail add: PO Box 347, 53515), SAN 317-9095. Tel: 608-767-2400. FAX: 608-767-2064. E-Mail: berlib@scls.lib.wi.us. *Dir*, Margaret E Koeller; E-Mail: mkoeller@midplains.net; Staff 3 (Non-MLS 3)
Pop 1,400; Circ 20,000
Jan 2000-Dec 2000 Income $58,429. Mats Exp $9,409, Books $7,500, Per/Ser (Incl. Access Fees) $774, AV Equip $1,135. Sal $29,873
Library Holdings: Bk Titles 9,163; Per Subs 48
Mem of South Central Library System
Open Mon - Fri 10-12 & 2-7, Sat 10-2

CK RIVER FALLS

BLACK RIVER FALLS PUBLIC LIBRARY,* 222 Fillmore St, 54615. SAN 364-6386. Tel: 715-284-4112. FAX: 715-284-5369. *Librn*, Mary Lent
Founded 1872. Circ 75,772
1998-1999 Income $121,920. Mats Exp $15,750, Books $13,000, Per/Ser (Incl. Access Fees) $2,500, Micro $250. Sal $58,000
Library Holdings: Bk Titles 24,155; Per Subs 61
Subject Interests: Indians, Local history
Mem of Winding Rivers Library System
Branches: 1
CHILDRENS ROOM *Librn*, Nancy Oldham

IR

BLAIR-PRESTON PUBLIC LIBRARY, 122 S Urberg Ave, 54616-0165. (Mail add: PO Box 165, 54616-0165), SAN 317-9109. Tel: 608-989-2502. *Librn*, Elaine Angst
Founded 1916. Pop 2,500; Circ 15,000
Library Holdings: Bk Vols 8,368
Subject Interests: Rural
Publications: Book List
Mem of Winding Rivers Library System

NCHARDVILLE

BLANCHARDVILLE PUBLIC LIBRARY,* PO Box 104, 53516-0104. SAN 317-9117. Tel: 608-523-2055. FAX: 608-523-4321. *Dir*, Gretchen Dieterich
Pop 1,084; Circ 3,217
1997-1998 Income $8,425, City $8,325, Other $100. Mats Exp $1,856, Books $1,294, Per/Ser (Incl. Access Fees) $164, Other Print Mats $398. Sal $3,668
Library Holdings: Bk Vols 5,500; Per Subs 22
Subject Interests: Local history
Mem of Southwest Wisconsin Library System

OOMER

G E BLESKACEK MEMORIAL LIBRARY, Bloomer Public Library, 1519 17th Ave, 54724. SAN 317-9125. Tel: 715-568-2384. FAX: 715-568-2387. E-Mail: maindesk@bloomerlibrary.org. *Dir*, Lowell Walters; E-Mail: lwalters@bloomerlibrary.org; Staff 4 (MLS 1, Non-MLS 3)
Founded 1917. Pop 4,711; Circ 44,468
Jan 1999-Dec 1999 Income $126,871, State $505, City $79,600, Federal $1,531, County $32,259, Locally Generated Income $12,976. Mats Exp $14,750, Books $10,500, Per/Ser (Incl. Access Fees) $2,250, Micro $150. Sal $64,500 (Prof $30,500)
Library Holdings: Bk Vols 25,153; Bk Titles 18,975; Per Subs 75
Automation Activity & Vendor Info: (Cataloging) Athena; (Circulation) Athena
Mem of Indianhead Federated Library System

BLOOMINGTON

P BLOOMINGTON PUBLIC LIBRARY,* Municipal Bldg, 453 Canal St, 53804-9999. SAN 317-9133. Tel: 608-994-2531. E-Mail: bpublib@grant.tds.net. *Librn*, Jim Warczak
Founded 1905
Library Holdings: Bk Vols 6,381; Per Subs 10
Mem of Southwest Wisconsin Library System
Open Wed 9-12 & 2-5, Sat 9-12

BOSCOBEL

P HILDEBRAND MEMORIAL LIBRARY, Boscobel Public, 1033 Wisconsin Ave, 53805-1597. SAN 317-9141. Tel: 608-375-5723. *Dir*, Janean Miller
Founded 1906
Library Holdings: Bk Vols 21,000; Per Subs 52
Special Collections: Boscobel Dial Newspaper Coll, micro
Automation Activity & Vendor Info: (Circulation) epixtech, inc.
Mem of Southwest Wisconsin Library System
Partic in OCLC Online Computer Library Center, Inc

§S SUPERMAX CORRECTIONAL INSTITUTION LIBRARY, 1101 Morrison Dr, PO Box 1000, 53805-1000. SAN 378-3774. Tel: 608-375-5656. FAX: 608-375-5434. *Librn*, Linda Lane; E-Mail: linda.lane@doc.state.wi.us; Staff 1 (MLS 1)
Library Holdings: Bk Vols 3,000; Per Subs 20
Automation Activity & Vendor Info: (Circulation) Sagebrush Corporation

BOULDER JUNCTION

P BOULDER JUNCTION PUBLIC LIBRARY,* 5386 Park St, PO Box 9, 54512-0009. SAN 324-7414. Tel: 715-385-2050. FAX: 715-385-2586. *Librn*, Janet Blair; E-Mail: jsblair@centuryinter.net
Founded 1976. Pop 1,200; Circ 4,601
Library Holdings: Bk Vols 11,000; Per Subs 20
Mem of Northern Waters Library Service
Friends of the Library Group

BOYCEVILLE

P BOYCEVILLE PUBLIC LIBRARY,* 501 Main St, PO Box 127, 54725-0127. SAN 317-915X. Tel: 715-643-2106. E-Mail: boycepl@discover-net.net. *Dir*, Rundi Myklebust
Founded 1900. Pop 954; Circ 11,012
1998-1999 Income $38,080, State $496, County $16,792. Mats Exp $6,097, Books $4,434, Per/Ser (Incl. Access Fees) $634, Micro $1,029. Sal $18,705
Library Holdings: Bk Vols 9,089; Per Subs 30
Mem of Indianhead Federated Library System
Open Tues & Thurs 10:30-5, Wed & Fri 3-7, Sat 10-12
Friends of the Library Group

BRANDON

P BRANDON PUBLIC LIBRARY,* 117 E Main St, 53919-0208. SAN 317-9168. Tel: 920-346-2350. FAX: 920-346-5895. E-Mail: cen23660@centuryinter.net. Web Site: host.pc.centuryinter.net/brandonpl. *Dir*, Nancy L Paul
Jan 1998-Dec 1999 Income $31,748, State $752, County $3,272. Mats Exp $3,900, Books $2,800, Per/Ser (Incl. Access Fees) $1,100. Sal $14,464 (Prof $10,504)
Library Holdings: Bk Vols 7,085; Per Subs 56

BRILLION

P BRILLION PUBLIC LIBRARY, (BPL), 326 N Main St, 54110. SAN 317-9176. Tel: 920-756-3215. FAX: 920-756-3874. E-Mail: brref@esls.lib.wi.us. Web Site: www.ci.brillion.wi.us. *Dir*, Christine Moede; E-Mail: cmoede@esls.lib.wi.us
Founded 1928. Pop 3,000; Circ 78,100
Jan 1999-Dec 1999 Income $153,304, City $126,194, County $21,110, Locally Generated Income $6,000. Mats Exp $21,154, Books $14,609, Per/Ser (Incl. Access Fees) $3,170, Micro $578, AV Equip $2,797. Sal $78,353
Library Holdings: Bk Titles 31,237; Per Subs 171
Mem of Manitowoc-Calumet Library System

BRODHEAD

P MEMORIAL PUBLIC LIBRARY,* 902 W Second Ave, 53520-1308. SAN 317-9184. Tel: 608-897-4070. *Dir*, Gloria Rosa
Founded 1909. Pop 3,153; Circ 32,122
Library Holdings: Bk Titles 28,000; Per Subs 67

BROOKFIELD

P BROOKFIELD PUBLIC LIBRARY, 1900 N Calhoun Rd, 53005. SAN 317-9192. Tel: 262-782-4140. FAX: 262-796-6696. *Tech Servs*, Ron Knipple; *Circ*, Sue Brown; Staff 8 (MLS 8)
Founded 1960. Pop 36,877; Circ 545,072
Jan 1998-Dec 1999 Income $1,732,658. Mats Exp $302,885, Books $184,378, Per/Ser (Incl. Access Fees) $96,987, Electronic Ref Mat (Incl. Access Fees) $21,520. Sal $926,112
Library Holdings: Bk Vols 129,331; Bk Titles 105,843; Per Subs 361
Subject Interests: Bus, Fine arts, Home improvement, Pre-sch children, Ref, Travel
Special Collections: Adult Literacy; Books on Tape, Interactive Multimedia; Large Print Books
Publications: BrookBytes (Newsletter)
Mem of Waukesha County Federated Library System

M COVENANT HEALTHCARE SYSTEM - ELMBROOK MEMORIAL HOSPITAL, Mary Beth Curtis Health Science Library, 19333 W North Ave, 53045. SAN 317-9206. Tel: 414-785-2091. FAX: 414-785-2425. Web Site: www.covlibrary.org. *Librn*, Vicki Kuenzi; E-Mail: vkuenzi@covenantlibrary.org
Founded 1969
Subject Interests: Health sci, Medicine, Mgt, Nursing, Women's health
Restriction: Open to public for reference only
Partic in Covenant Libr Syst; Midwest Health Sci Libr Network; Southeastern Wisconsin Health Science Library Consortium; Wis Health Sci Libr Asn

S FUNERAL SERVICE EDUCATIONAL FOUNDATION, Howard C Raether Library, 13625 Bishops Dr, 53005. SAN 325-691X. Tel: 262-789-1880. FAX: 262-789-6977. *Mgr*, Kathleen Ann Walczak; Tel: 262-814-1556, E-Mail: kwalczak@nfda.org. Subject Specialists: *Funeral service*, Kathleen Ann Walczak; Staff 1 (MLS 1)
Founded 1998
1998-1999 Income $35,000
Library Holdings: Bk Vols 3,000
Restriction: In-house use for visitors
Function: Research library
Comprehensive collection of funeral service related books & periodicals

S INTERNATIONAL FOUNDATION OF EMPLOYEE BENEFIT PLANS, Information Center, 18700 W Blue Mound Rd, 53045. (Mail add: PO Box 69, 53008-0069), SAN 317-9214. Tel: 262-786-6700, Ext 8350. FAX: 262-786-8780. E-Mail: infocenter@ifebp.org. Web Site: www.ifebp.org. *Dir Info Resources & Res*, Dee B Birschel; E-Mail: deeb@ifebp.org; *Dir Info Resources & Res*, Patricia Krajnak; E-Mail: patk@ifebp.org; *Senior Info Specialist*, Kelli Kolsrud; E-Mail: kellik@ifebp.org; *Senior Info Specialist*, Julie Stich; E-Mail: julies@ifebp.org; *Info Specialist*, Christina Chiu; E-Mail: christinac@ifebp.org; *Dir, Tech Serv*, Julia E Miller; E-Mail: juliem@ifebp.org; *Tech Servs*, Sharon Olecheck; E-Mail: sharono@ifebp.org; Staff 10 (MLS 7, Non-MLS 3)
Founded 1970
Dec 1999-Nov 2000 Mats Exp $95,000, Books $25,000, Per/Ser (Incl. Access Fees) $70,000. Sal $350,000
Library Holdings: Bk Vols 13,000; Per Subs 600
Subject Interests: Employee benefits, Ins, Pensions
Publications: Bibliographies
Restriction: Lending to staff only, Members only, Open to others by appointment
Function: Document delivery services, Outside services via phone, cable & mail, Reference services available, Research library
Partic in Dialog Corporation; Library Council Of Metropolitan Milwaukee, Inc; OCLC Online Computer Library Center, Inc

S NATIONAL FUNERAL DIRECTORS ASSOCIATION LIBRARY, Howard C Raether Library, 13625 Bishop's Dr, 53005-6607. SAN 328-3062. Tel: 262-814-1556. Toll Free Tel: 877-402-5900. FAX: 262-789-6977. *Mgr*, Kathleen Ann Walczak; E-Mail: kwalczak@nfda.org. Subject Specialists: *Funeral service*, Kathleen Ann Walczak; Staff 1 (MLS 1)
Founded 1998
Library Holdings: Bk Vols 2,000
Subject Interests: Death, Funeral service
Special Collections: Books on Dying, Death & Grief Dating Back to the Early 1400's through the 1900's
Database Vendor: OCLC - First Search
Restriction: Not a lending library
Function: Research library

BROWN DEER

P BROWN DEER PUBLIC LIBRARY, 5600 W Bradley Rd, 53223-351(SAN 317-9230. Tel: 414-357-0106. FAX: 414-357-0156. *Dir*, Arnold Gutkowski; *Ad Servs, Ref*, Mary Dunn; *Ch Servs*, Terry Wilson; *Ref*, N Champe; Staff 4 (MLS 4)
Founded 1969. Pop 14,000; Circ 311,563
Jan 1999-Dec 1999 Income $559,000. Mats Exp $94,368, Books $73,1 Per/Ser (Incl. Access Fees) $7,648, AV Equip $13,618. Sal $282,437 (P $143,454)
Library Holdings: Bk Titles 77,382; Per Subs 200; High Interest/Low Vocabulary Bk Vols 50
Automation Activity & Vendor Info: (Circulation) Innovative Interfac Inc.; (OPAC) Innovative Interfaces Inc.; (Serials) Innovative Interfaces
Mem of Milwaukee County Federated Library System
Friends of the Library Group

BROWNSVILLE

P BROWNSVILLE PUBLIC LIBRARY,* 379 Main, 53006-0248. SAN 3 9249. Tel: 920-583-4325. FAX: 920-583-4325. *Dir*, Janis Johnson
Founded 1949. Pop 457; Circ 25,529
Library Holdings: Bk Vols 16,000; Per Subs 63
Mem of Mid-Wisconsin Federated Library System

BRUCE

P BRUCE AREA PUBLIC LIBRARY,* 834 N Main St, PO Box 277, 54 0277. SAN 376-6721. Tel: 715-868-2005. *Librn*, Kathleen Voss
Library Holdings: Bk Titles 15,000; Per Subs 24
Mem of Indianhead Federated Library System
Friends of the Library Group

BURLINGTON

P BURLINGTON PUBLIC LIBRARY, 166 E Jefferson St, 53105. SAN 3 9257. Tel: 262-763-7623. FAX: 262-763-1938. E-Mail: pburling@burlington.lib.wi.us. Web Site: www.burlington.lib.wi.us. *Dir*, Gayle A F E-Mail: gafalk@burlington.lib.wi.us; *Head Ref*, Judy Rockwell; E-Mail: jrockwel@burlington.lib.wi.us; *Ch Servs*, Ruhama Kordatzky; E-Mail: rkordatz@burlington.lib.wi.us; *Ch Servs*, Rhonda Puntney; *Ad Servs*, Jennifer Einwalter; Staff 6 (MLS 4, Non-MLS 2)
Founded 1908. Pop 16,800; Circ 198,000
Jan 2000-Dec 2000 Income $522,451, City $260,224, County $229,122, Locally Generated Income $33,105. Mats Exp $83,000. Sal $353,694 (P $122,373)
Library Holdings: Bk Titles 62,257; Per Subs 222
Special Collections: Church of the Latter Day Saints - Strangite (Strang Mormon Newspapers & Chronicles)
Automation Activity & Vendor Info: (Cataloging) SIRSI; (Circulation) SIRSI; (OPAC) SIRSI
Database Vendor: Ebsco - EbscoHost, ProQuest
Publications: Friend to Friend (newsletter)
Mem of Lakeshores Library System
Friends of the Library Group

BUTLER

P BUTLER PUBLIC LIBRARY, 12621 W Hampton Ave, 53007-1705. SA 317-9273. Tel: 262-783-2535. FAX: 262-783-9900. *Dir*, Kathryn Barbasiewicz
Founded 1964. Pop 2,055
Jan 1997-Dec 1998 Income $40,000. Mats Exp $8,000. Sal $26,890
Library Holdings: Bk Titles 21,000; Per Subs 55
Mem of Waukesha County Federated Library System

CABLE

P FOREST LODGE LIBRARY,* PO Box 176, 54821-0176. SAN 317-928 Tel: 715-798-3189. E-Mail: cablelib@win.bright.net. Web Site: www.win.bright.net/~cablelib/. *Dir*, Margaret Eggers
Pop 1,000; Circ 7,500
Jan 1998-Dec 1999 Income $29,000, City $10,483, Federal $500, County $9,500. Mats Exp $9,000, Books $2,500, Per/Ser (Incl. Access Fees) $30 Sal $17,000
Library Holdings: Bk Titles 8,000; Per Subs 30
Subject Interests: Local history, Native Americans, Natural history
Mem of Northern Waters Library Service
Open Tues 10-5, Wed 3-8, Thurs 10-5, Sat 10-1 (Sept 1-May 31); Tues 1 Wed 10-8, Thurs 10-5, Sat 10-4 (June 1-Aug 31)
Friends of the Library Group

OTT

CADOTT COMMUNITY LIBRARY, 331 Main St, PO Box 68, 54727-0068. SAN 317-929X. Tel: 715-289-4950. FAX: 715-289-3149. E-Mail: cadcomlb@discover-net.net. *Dir*, Dorothy Kaiser
Founded 1955. Pop 2,500; Circ 25,855
Jan 1999-Dec 1999 Income $62,550, City $43,477, County $11,773, Other $7,000. Mats Exp $11,005, Books $9,055, Per/Ser (Incl. Access Fees) $1,950. Sal $34,735 (Prof $15,912)
Library Holdings: Bk Vols 12,833; Per Subs 67
Automation Activity & Vendor Info: (Acquisitions) SIRSI; (Cataloging) SIRSI; (Circulation) SIRSI; (OPAC) SIRSI
Mem of Indianhead Federated Library System

IBRIA

JANE MORGAN MEMORIAL LIBRARY,* 109 W Edgewater St, PO Box 477, 53923-0477. SAN 324-7902. Tel: 920-348-4030. *Librn*, Jeanne Radke
Pop 680
Library Holdings: Bk Vols 6,000; Per Subs 25
Subject Interests: Local community, Welsh
Mem of South Central Library System

IBRIDGE

CAMBRIDGE COMMUNITY LIBRARY,* 200 Spring St, PO Box 390, 53523-0390. SAN 325-1934. Tel: 608-423-3900. *Librn*, Joan Behm; Staff 4 (MLS 1, Non-MLS 3)
Founded 1978. Pop 4,800
Jan 1997-Dec 1998 Income $86,000. Mats Exp $13,200. Sal $46,000
Library Holdings: Bk Titles 1,500; Per Subs 93
Subject Interests: Local history
Automation Activity & Vendor Info: (Circulation) epixtech, inc.
Partic in S Cent Libr Syst

IERON

CAMERON PUBLIC LIBRARY, 603 Main St, PO Box 343, 54822-0343. SAN 377-9300. Tel: 715-458-2267. FAX: 715-458-2267. E-Mail: cameronpl@mail.ifls.lib.wi.us:8383/. *Librn*, Patricia S Becker
Pop 1,425
Jan 2000-Dec 2000 Income $36,000, City $32,000, County $4,000. Mats Exp $6,500, Books $6,000, Per/Ser (Incl. Access Fees) $500. Sal $19,000 (Prof $16,000)
Library Holdings: Bk Titles 8,000; Per Subs 24; Bks on Deafness & Sign Lang 12
Automation Activity & Vendor Info: (Acquisitions) epixtech, inc.; (Cataloging) epixtech, inc.; (Circulation) epixtech, inc.; (OPAC) epixtech, inc.; (Serials) epixtech, inc.
Database Vendor: epixtech, inc.
Mem of Indianhead Federated Library System
Partic in Barron County Libr Servs

IPBELLSPORT

CAMPBELLSPORT PUBLIC LIBRARY,* 220 N Helena St, 53010-0405. SAN 317-9303. Tel: 920-533-8534. FAX: 920-533-8712. E-Mail: csportpl@thesurf.net. *Dir*, Suellen Bladek
Founded 1929. Pop 1,700; Circ 19,421
Library Holdings: Bk Vols 12,000; Per Subs 33

HTON

TORKELSON MEMORIAL LIBRARY,* 809 Main St, PO Box 234, 54619-0234. SAN 377-9610. Tel: 608-654-5465. E-Mail: cashtonlibrary@centuryinter.net. *Librn*, Darla Schroeder
Library Holdings: Bk Titles 7,000; Per Subs 15
Mem of Winding Rivers Library System
Open Mon & Fri 12:30-5:30, Tues 12:30-7, Wed 9-1:30

SVILLE

ECKSTEIN MEMORIAL LIBRARY, 1034 E Dewey St, PO Box 450, 53806. SAN 317-9311. Tel: 608-725-5838. E-Mail: casspl@swls.org. *Dir*, Susan Uppena; *Asst Librn*, Bae Ruth Kirschbaum
Library Holdings: Bk Vols 7,950; Per Subs 29
Mem of Southwest Wisconsin Library System
Open Mon & Thurs 10-5, Wed 12-8 & Sat 9-12

AR GROVE

CEDAR GROVE PUBLIC LIBRARY,* 131 Van Altena, 53013-0287. SAN 317-932X. Tel: 920-668-6834. FAX: 920-668-8744. Web Site: bratsheedu./2cgrove/. *Dir*, Diana Nett
Founded 1944
1997-1998 Income $100,533. Mats Exp $15,298, Books $12,172, Per/Ser (Incl. Access Fees) $1,902. Sal $45,298
Library Holdings: Bk Vols 18,000; Per Subs 54
Special Collections: Small Dutch Heritage Coll
Mem of Eastern Shores Library System
Friends of the Library Group

CEDARBURG

P CEDARBURG PUBLIC LIBRARY, W63 N583 Hanover Ave, 53012. SAN 317-9338. Tel: 262-375-7640. FAX: 262-375-7618. *Dir*, Mary Marquardt; Staff 13 (MLS 4, Non-MLS 9)
Founded 1911. Pop 16,495; Circ 164,195
Jan 2000-Dec 2001 Income $401,327, State $1,173, City $266,818, Federal $165, County $4,073, Other $129,098. Mats Exp $62,125, Books $46,150, Per/Ser (Incl. Access Fees) $8,000, AV Equip $6,625, Electronic Ref Mat (Incl. Access Fees) $1,350. Sal $227,301
Library Holdings: Bk Vols 64,000; Bk Titles 62,200; Per Subs 241
Subject Interests: Civil War, Historic preservation, Large print, Popular fiction
Automation Activity & Vendor Info: (Circulation) epixtech, inc.; (OPAC) epixtech, inc.
Publications: Informational Brochure
Mem of Eastern Shores Library System
Friends of the Library Group

CENTURIA

P CENTURIA PUBLIC LIBRARY,* 409 Fourth St, PO Box 370, 54824-0370. SAN 376-6713. Tel: 715-646-2630. *Librn*, Jane Johnson
Library Holdings: Bk Vols 8,000; Bk Titles 3,000; Per Subs 20
Mem of Indianhead Federated Library System

CHETEK

P CALHOUN MEMORIAL LIBRARY,* 321 Moore St, PO Box 25, 54728-0025. SAN 317-9346. Tel: 715-924-3195. *Librn*, Judy Bishop
Founded 1888. Pop 4,000; Circ 25,270
Library Holdings: Bk Vols 17,147; Per Subs 47
Mem of Indianhead Federated Library System

CHILTON

P CHILTON PUBLIC LIBRARY, 221 Park St, 53014. SAN 317-9354. Tel: 920-849-4414. FAX: 920-849-2370. E-Mail: clibrary@fdl.net.com. *Dir*, Kathy Garton; *Asst Librn*, Patti Sabo; *Asst Librn*, Joyce Sell; *Asst Librn*, Lynn Michels
Founded 1933. Pop 6,859; Circ 116,294
Jan 1999-Dec 1999 Income $141,687, City $87,175, Federal $149, County $46,825, Locally Generated Income $7,538. Mats Exp $27,631, Books $18,631, Per/Ser (Incl. Access Fees) $3,951, AV Equip $5,049. Sal $64,547 (Prof $30,000)
Library Holdings: Bk Vols 41,204; Per Subs 134
Special Collections: Parent/Teachers Coll; Wis Coll
Automation Activity & Vendor Info: (Cataloging) Sagebrush Corporation; (Circulation) Sagebrush Corporation
Mem of Manitowoc-Calumet Library System
Friends of the Library Group

CHIPPEWA FALLS

P CESA NO 10 - INSTRUCTIONAL MEDIA CENTER, Instructional Materials Center,* 725 W Park Ave, 54729. SAN 327-8387. Tel: 715-720-2067. FAX: 715-720-2070. E-Mail: imccirc@cesio.k12.wi.us. *Librn*, Susan Olson
Library Holdings: Bk Titles 9,000; Per Subs 30

P CHIPPEWA FALLS PUBLIC LIBRARY, 105 W Central, 54729-2397. SAN 317-9362. Tel: 715-723-1146. Reference Tel: 715-723-1146, Ext 106. FAX: 715-720-6922. E-Mail: cflib@chippewa.library.org. Web Site: www.chippewalibrary.org. *Dir*, Rosemary Kilbridge; E-Mail: kilbriro@discover-net.net; *Ch Servs*, Cindy Tackett; *Tech Servs*, Julie Woodruff; *Circ*, Lynn Kuechenmeister; *ILL*, *Ref*, Terri Anderson; *Business*, Karen Grothe; Staff 6 (MLS 6)
Founded 1893. Pop 31,851; Circ 324,457
Jan 2001-Dec 2001 Income $824,265, City $576,112, County $248,153. Mats Exp $135,938, Books $99,591, Per/Ser (Incl. Access Fees) $17,488, Presv $1,000, Micro $500, AV Equip $9,109, Electronic Ref Mat (Incl. Access Fees) $8,250. Sal $560,696
Library Holdings: Bk Vols 92,281; Per Subs 225; High Interest/Low Vocabulary Bk Vols 200
Special Collections: Wisconsin (Historical Coll), bk, microfilm, fs

Automation Activity & Vendor Info: (Cataloging) epixtech, inc.; (Circulation) epixtech, inc.; (OPAC) epixtech, inc.
Mem of Indianhead Federated Library System
Friends of the Library Group

M SAINT JOSEPH'S HOSPITAL LIBRARY,* 2661 County Rd I, 54729. SAN 327-8409. Tel: 715-726-3292. FAX: 715-726-3426.
Library Holdings: Bk Vols 400

CLEAR LAKE

P CLEAR LAKE PUBLIC LIBRARY,* PO Box 365, 54005-0365. SAN 376-6705. Tel: 715-263-2802. FAX: 715-263-2666. E-Mail: cllib@bucky.win.bright.net. *Librn*, Evelyn Humphrey
Library Holdings: Bk Vols 8,000
Mem of Indianhead Federated Library System

CLEVELAND

J LAKESHORE TECHNICAL COLLEGE LIBRARY, 1290 North Ave, 53015. SAN 317-9389. Tel: 920-458-4183. FAX: 920-693-8966. *Mgr*, Linda McCabe; Staff 5 (MLS 1, Non-MLS 4)
Founded 1965. Enrl 2,000; Fac 85; Highest Degree: Associate
Jul 1999-Jun 2000 Income $170,000. Mats Exp $167,380, Books $11,900, Per/Ser (Incl. Access Fees) $3,540, Electronic Ref Mat (Incl. Access Fees) $31,940. Sal $120,000
Library Holdings: Bk Vols 16,000; Per Subs 220
Subject Interests: Hazardous mat, Legal assts, Nursing
Mem of Manitowoc-Calumet Library System
Partic in Fox River Valley Area Library Consortium; OCLC Online Computer Library Center, Inc

CLINTON

P CLINTON PUBLIC LIBRARY,* 214 Mill St, PO Box 487, 53525-0487. SAN 317-9397. Tel: 608-676-5569. *Dir*, Michelle Dennis
Founded 1913
Jan 1997-Dec 1998 Income $97,263. Mats Exp $14,688, Per/Ser (Incl. Access Fees) $1,800. Sal $46,185
Library Holdings: Bk Vols 20,000; Per Subs 50
Mem of Arrowhead Library System
Friends of the Library Group

CLINTONVILLE

P CLINTONVILLE PUBLIC LIBRARY,* 75 Hemlock St, 54929-1461. SAN 317-9400. Tel: 715-823-4563. FAX: 715-823-7134. *Dir*, Harriet McCauley; *Asst Librn*, Kathleen Mitchell; Staff 2 (MLS 2)
Founded 1905. Pop 4,478; Circ 93,010
Jan 1998-Dec 1999 Income $271,519, City $206,297, County $65,222. Mats Exp $41,770. Sal $106,760
Library Holdings: Bk Titles 42,247; Per Subs 146
Mem of Outagamie Waupaca Library System
Friends of the Library Group

COBB

P COBB PUBLIC LIBRARY,* 109 Mifflin St, PO Box 249, 53526-0249. SAN 317-9419. Tel: 608-623-2554.
Founded 1930
Library Holdings: Bk Vols 4,000; Bk Titles 3,700
Mem of Southwest Wisconsin Library System
Friends of the Library Group

COLBY

P COLBY PUBLIC LIBRARY, 211 W Spence St, PO Box 318, 54421-0318. SAN 317-9427. Tel: 715-223-2000. *Librn*, Carol Wilhelmi; E-Mail: cwilhelm@wvls.lib.wi.us; Staff 3 (Non-MLS 3)
Founded 1879. Pop 1,660
Jan 1999-Dec 1999 Income $65,323. Mats Exp $61,722. Sal $24,545
Library Holdings: Bk Vols 12,900; Per Subs 75
Mem of Wisconsin Valley Library Service
Friends of the Library Group

COLFAX

P COLFAX PUBLIC LIBRARY,* 613 Main St, PO Box 525, 54730-0525. SAN 317-9435. Tel: 715-962-4334. *Dir*, Mary Larson
Founded 1901. Pop 1,166; Circ 23,032
Library Holdings: Bk Vols 12,600; Per Subs 40
Mem of Indianhead Federated Library System
Open Mon & Thurs 1-8, Tues, Wed & Fri 1-5

COLOMA

P COLOMA PUBLIC LIBRARY,* 155 Front St, PO Box 99, 54930-028 Tel: 715-228-2530. FAX: 715-228-2532. Web Site: asp.winnefox.org/w copl/. *Dir*, Sandy Zuehlke
Library Holdings: Bk Vols 9,000; Bk Titles 9,000; Per Subs 45

COLUMBUS

M COLUMBUS COMMUNITY HOSPITAL-MEDICAL LIBRARY, Med Library,* 1515 Park Ave, 53925. SAN 377-9637. Tel: 920-623-2200, E 1490. FAX: 920-623-3546.
Library Holdings: Bk Titles 400; Per Subs 40
Partic in S Cent Wis Consortia

P COLUMBUS PUBLIC LIBRARY,* 223 W James, 53925-1572. SAN 9443. Tel: 920-623-5910. FAX: 920-623-5928. E-Mail: colpl@centuryinter.net. *Dir*, Peggy Kindschi
Founded 1877. Pop 7,000; Circ 56,649
Library Holdings: Bk Vols 22,454
Subject Interests: Local history
Special Collections: Local Newspapers Coll 1850-present, microfilm
Mem of South Central Library System
Friends of the Library Group

CORNELL

P CORNELL PUBLIC LIBRARY, 117 N Third St, PO Box 796, 54732. 317-9451. Tel: 715-239-3709. *Dir*, Sharon Shepard
Pop 3,500; Circ 8,912
Library Holdings: Bk Titles 9,000; Per Subs 32
Mem of Indianhead Federated Library System

CRANDON

P CRANDON PUBLIC LIBRARY, 10 W Polk St, 54520-1458. SAN 317 946X. Tel: 715-478-3784, 715-847-5535 (Interlibrary Loan Services Tel *Dir*, Karen Guth
Founded 1910. Pop 9,044; Circ 18,364
Library Holdings: Per Subs 33
Mem of Wisconsin Valley Library Service
Friends of the Library Group

CROSS PLAINS

P ROSEMARY GARFOOT PUBLIC LIBRARY,* 2107 Julius St, 53528-9499. SAN 317-9478. Tel: 608-798-3881. FAX: 608-798-0196. *Dir*, Pam Bosben; *Asst Dir*, Fran Garn
Founded 1964. Pop 2,840
Library Holdings: Bk Titles 18,000; Per Subs 67
Mem of South Central Library System
Friends of the Library Group

CUBA CITY

P CUBA CITY PUBLIC LIBRARY,* 108 N Main, 53807-1538. SAN 31 9486. Tel: 608-744-2613. FAX: 608-744-2151. *Dir*, Nancy Kunkel
Pop 2,119; Circ 26,000
Library Holdings: Bk Vols 23,000; Per Subs 60
Mem of Southwest Wisconsin Library System

CUDAHY

P CUDAHY MEMORIAL PUBLIC LIBRARY, 4665 S Packard Ave, 531 1441. SAN 317-9494. Tel: 414-769-2244. Interlibrary Loan Service Tel: 414-769-2245. FAX: 414-769-2252. Web Site: www.ci.cudahy.wi.us/libra default.htm. *Dir Libr Serv*, Rebecca Roepke; E-Mail: rebecca.roepke@mcfls.org; Staff 4 (MLS 4)
Founded 1906. Pop 19,019; Circ 220,487
1999-1999 Income City $553,831. Mats Exp $89,154, Books $70,382, P Ser (Incl. Access Fees) $8,249, Electronic Ref Mat (Incl. Access Fees) $6,130. Sal $268,694
Library Holdings: Bk Vols 79,775; Per Subs 200
Special Collections: Local History Coll
Database Vendor: Innovative Interfaces INN - View
Mem of Milwaukee County Federated Library System
Partic in Library Council Of Metropolitan Milwaukee, Inc
Friends of the Library Group

S LADISH CO, Technical Information Center,* 5481 S Packard Ave, 5311 SAN 373-305X. Tel: 414-747-3063. FAX: 414-747-3036. *Mgr, Res*, Dave Furrer
Library Holdings: Bk Vols 2,000; Per Subs 12

ST LUKES SOUTH SHORE HOSPITAL LIBRARY,* 5900 S Lake Dr, 53110. SAN 317-9516. Tel: 414-489-4028. FAX: 414-489-4154. E-Mail: sstthh@mixcom.com. *Librn*, Stephanie Hanus
Founded 1967
Library Holdings: Bk Titles 1,500; Per Subs 50
Subject Interests: Health care admin, Medicine, Nursing
Publications: Newsletter
Partic in Dialog Corporation; Library Council Of Metropolitan Milwaukee, Inc; Medline; Southeastern Wisconsin Health Science Library Consortium

IBERLAND

CUMBERLAND PUBLIC LIBRARY,* 1305 Second Ave, PO Box 97, 54829-0097. SAN 317-9524. Tel: 715-822-2767. FAX: 715-822-5427.
Founded 1905. Pop 2,000; Circ 45,506
Library Holdings: Bk Vols 19,635; Per Subs 61
Subject Interests: Geography, Wis hist
Mem of Barron County Libr Syst; Indianhead Federated Library System
Open Summer June 1-Labor Day: Mon, Tues, Thurs 1-6, Wed & Fri 10-6, Sat 9-1; Winter Hours Tues after Labor Day-May 31: Mon 1-6, Tues & Thurs 1-8, Wed & Fri 10-6, Sat 9-3
Friends of the Library Group

LAS

DALLAS PUBLIC LIBRARY,* PO Box 84, 54733-0084. SAN 317-9532. Tel: 715-837-1186. *Librn*, Beatrice Amdall; *Asst Librn*, Shirley Jenson
Pop 450; Circ 4,200
Library Holdings: Bk Vols 5,012; Bk Titles 4,937
Mem of Indianhead Federated Library System

RIEN

DARIEN PUBLIC LIBRARY,* 24 E Beloit St, PO Box 465, 53114-0465. SAN 317-9540. Tel: 414-724-5155. *Librn*, Betty Blanke
Founded 1922. Pop 2,000
Library Holdings: Bk Vols 7,000
Mem of Lakeshores Library System
Friends of the Library Group

RLINGTON

JOHNSON PUBLIC LIBRARY, City of Darlington, 131 E Catherine St, 53530. SAN 317-9559. Tel: 608-776-4171. FAX: 608-776-8832. *Dir*, Carol McDaniel; E-Mail: cjmd@swls.org; Staff 1 (Non-MLS 1)
Pop 2,400; Circ 35,402
Jan 2001-Dec 2001 Income $104,460, City $80,873, County $19,963, Locally Generated Income $3,624. Sal $47,740 (Prof $24,400)
Library Holdings: Bk Vols 30,000; Bk Titles 25,000; Per Subs 90
Special Collections: Darlington Newspapers (1865-present), micro; Lafayette County Newspaper on micro; Parenting Coll in Parent's Place area in library
Automation Activity & Vendor Info: (Acquisitions) epixtech, inc.
Function: ILL available, Photocopies available
Mem of Southwest Wisconsin Library System
Special Services for the Blind - Printed text enlargers
Friends of the Library Group

FOREST

DEFOREST PUBLIC LIBRARY,* 605 S Main, 53532. SAN 317-9567. Tel: 608-846-5482. FAX: 608-846-6875. *Dir*, Jan Berg; Staff 4 (MLS 1, Non-MLS 3)
Founded 1964. Pop 7,424; Circ 69,643
Library Holdings: Bk Vols 26,185; Per Subs 95
Subject Interests: Popular mat
Mem of South Central Library System
Friends of the Library Group

PERE

GREEN EARTH BRANCH LIBRARY,* W1273 Redtail Dr, 54155-9423. SAN 375-4766. Tel: 920-833-7226. *Asst Dir*, Eleanore Danforth
Founded 1996. Pop 4,232
Library Holdings: Bk Titles 1,300

SAINT NORBERT ABBEY, Augustine Library, 1016 N Broadway, 54115-2697. SAN 317-9575. Tel: 920-337-4311. FAX: 920-337-4328. *Librn*, Sally V Cubitt; E-Mail: cubisa@mail.snc.edu; Staff 1 (MLS 1)
Founded 1898
Jul 1999-Jun 2000 Income $3,900. Mats Exp $1,400, Books $1,000. Sal $2,500
Library Holdings: Bk Vols 11,200; Bk Titles 8,000
Subject Interests: Archives, Bible, Canon law, Church history, Monasticism, Philosophy, Premonstratensian hist, Religious orders, Theology
Restriction: By appointment only
Function: Archival collection

CR SAINT NORBERT COLLEGE, Todd Wehr Library, 100 Grant St, 54115-2099. SAN 317-9583. Tel: 920-403-4090. Interlibrary Loan Service Tel: 920-403-3283. FAX: 920-403-4064. Web Site: www.snc.edu/library/. *Dir*, Jerome I VanLom; Tel: 920-403-3290, E-Mail: lomjea@mail.snc.edu; *Librn*, Sally V Cubitt; E-Mail: cubisa@mail.snc.edu; *Archivist*, Donald L Pieters; Tel: 920-403-4045, E-Mail: pietdl@mail.snc.edu; *Cat*, Carol Cain; Tel: 920-403-3296, E-Mail: caincj@mail.snc.edu; *Publ Servs*, Sally L Hansen; Tel: 920-403-3453, E-Mail: hanssl@mail.snc.edu; *Ref*, Kimberly M Boldt; Tel: 920-403-3282, E-Mail: boldkm@mail.snc.edu; *Tech Servs*, Anthony LaLuzerne; Tel: 920-403-3291, E-Mail: laluaj@mail.snc.edu; *ILL*, Lynn Orlowski; Tel: 920-403-3283, E-Mail: orlorm@mail.snc.edu; Staff 17 (MLS 8, Non-MLS 9)
Founded 1898. Enrl 1,871; Fac 158; Highest Degree: Master
Jun 1999-May 2000 Income (Main Library Only) $878,091. Mats Exp $437,699, Books $197,627, Per/Ser (Incl. Access Fees) $124,229, Micro $29,860, Other Print Mats $2,515, Electronic Ref Mat (Incl. Access Fees) $13,030. Sal $389,785 (Prof $231,297)
Library Holdings: Bk Vols 196,440; Bk Titles 140,314; Per Subs 690
Subject Interests: Humanities, Religion, Soc scis, Theology
Special Collections: College Archives; Papers of John F Bennett
Automation Activity & Vendor Info: (Acquisitions) Innovative Interfaces Inc.; (Cataloging) Innovative Interfaces Inc.; (Circulation) Innovative Interfaces Inc.; (Serials) Innovative Interfaces Inc.
Departmental Libraries:
MEDIA SERVICES, John Minahan Science Hall, Rm 223, 100 Grant St, 54115. SAN 373-899X. Tel: 920-403-3244. FAX: 920-403-1341. Web Site: www.snc.edu/media/. *Dir*, Tom Smith; Staff 3 (MLS 1, Non-MLS 2)
1997-1998 Income $196,255. Mats Exp $51,787, AV Equip $26,730. Sal $154,769

DEER PARK

P DEER PARK PUBLIC LIBRARY,* 112 Front St W, 54007. SAN 377-9882. Tel: 715-269-5464. FAX: 715-269-5664. *Librn*, Kathleen Setter; E-Mail: kmsetter@arr.bright.net
Jan 1997-Dec 1998 Income $21,400. Mats Exp $14,928. Sal $6,472
Library Holdings: Bk Titles 7,400; Per Subs 32
Mem of Indianhead Federated Library System
Partic in Wis Libr Asn
Open Tues 2-8, Wed & Sat 10-1, Thurs 4-8
Friends of the Library Group

DEERFIELD

P DEERFIELD PUBLIC LIBRARY,* 12 W Nelson St, PO Box 408, 53531. SAN 317-9591. Tel: 608-764-8102. *Librn*, Kaia Fry; *Asst Librn, Ch Servs*, Marsha Dunlap
Founded 1974. Pop 1,617; Circ 31,477
Jan 1998-Dec 1999 Income $91,553, County $23,442, Locally Generated Income $2,800. Mats Exp $10,450, Books $6,750, Per/Ser (Incl. Access Fees) $1,700. Sal $63,530
Library Holdings: Bk Titles 11,417; Per Subs 63
Mem of South Central Library System
Friends of the Library Group

DELAFIELD

P DELAFIELD PUBLIC LIBRARY,* 500 N Genessee St, 53018-1895. SAN 317-9605. Tel: 414-646-6230. FAX: 414-646-6232. *Dir*, Polly Gropen
Founded 1907
Library Holdings: Bk Vols 45,000; Per Subs 117
Subject Interests: Art, Cooking, Detective fiction, Needlecrafts, Parenting
Mem of Waukesha County Federated Library System
Friends of the Library Group

DELAVAN

P ARAM PUBLIC LIBRARY,* 404 E Walworth Ave, 53115-1208. SAN 317-9613. Tel: 414-728-3111. FAX: 414-728-3111. *Dir*, Peggy Fleck
Founded 1908. Pop 10,000; Circ 90,000
Jan 1997-Dec 1998 Income $266,000, City $210,000, County $56,000. Mats Exp $20,000. Sal $96,000 (Prof $32,000)
Library Holdings: Bk Vols 35,000
Mem of Lakeshores Library System
Friends of the Library Group

S WISCONSIN SCHOOL FOR THE DEAF, John R Gant Library, 309 W Walworth Ave, 53115. SAN 317-9621. Tel: 262-728-7127, Ext 7133. FAX: 262-728-7129. *Actg Librn*, Shelly McDowell; Staff 1 (MLS 1)
Founded 1930

Library Holdings: Bk Vols 11,250
Mem of Columbia Libr System
Special Services for the Deaf - Collection on deaf education; Deaf publications

DESOTO

P DESOTO PUBLIC LIBRARY,* Houghton St, PO Box 187, 54624-0187. SAN 376-6632. Tel: 608-648-3593. E-Mail: despl@mwt.net. *Dir*, Lennie Mayer
Jan 1998-Dec 1999 Income $10,319, City $6,478, County $1,920, Other $993. Mats Exp $1,487, Books $952, Per/Ser (Incl. Access Fees) $535. Sal $5,346
Library Holdings: Bk Vols 11,000; Bk Titles 5,000; Per Subs 39
Mem of Winding Rivers Library System

DODGEVILLE

P DODGEVILLE PUBLIC LIBRARY, 139 S Iowa St, 53533. SAN 317-963X. Tel: 608-935-3728. *Dir*, Krista Ross; E-Mail: rossk@swls.org; Staff 7 (MLS 1, Non-MLS 6)
Founded 1900. Pop 4,200; Circ 86,316
Library Holdings: Bk Vols 18,000; Per Subs 74
Subject Interests: Large print
Automation Activity & Vendor Info: (Cataloging) epixtech, inc.; (Circulation) epixtech, inc.
Mem of Southwest Wisconsin Library System
Friends of the Library Group

LANDS END
S CORPORATE LIBRARY, 5 Lands End Lane, 53595. SAN 378-0902. Tel: 608-935-4175. FAX: 608-935-4260, Web Site: www.landsend.com. *Librn*, Kimberly Boughton; E-Mail: kmbough@landsend.com
Library Holdings: Bk Titles 2,000; Per Subs 60
S FILM LIBRARY, One Lands End Lane, 53595. SAN 378-0929. Web Site: www.landsend.com. *Coordr*, Jean Thousand

DORCHESTER

P DORCHESTER PUBLIC LIBRARY, 155 N 2nd St, PO Box 198, 54425. SAN 317-9648. Tel: 715-654-5959. FAX: 715-654-5802. *Dir*, Susan Wild
Pop 698; Circ 10,671
Library Holdings: Bk Vols 11,566; Per Subs 32
Mem of Wisconsin Valley Library Service
Friends of the Library Group

DRESSER

P DRESSER VILLAGE LIBRARY,* 117 S Central Ave, PO Box 547, 54009-0547. SAN 376-6691. Tel: 715-755-2944. FAX: 715-755-2944. E-Mail: drpublib@century.net. *Librn*, Linda Ellefson
Library Holdings: Bk Titles 5,000; Per Subs 15
Mem of Indianhead Federated Library System

DRUMMOND

P DRUMMOND PUBLIC LIBRARY,* Owen Ave, PO Box 23, 54832. SAN 317-9656. Tel: 715-739-6290. E-Mail: drumlib@win.bright.net. *Dir*, Val Cane
Library Holdings: Bk Vols 7,200
Mem of Northern Waters Library Service; Northwest Wis Libr Syst

DURAND

P DURAND PUBLIC LIBRARY,* 604 Seventh Ave E, 54736. SAN 317-9664. Tel: 715-672-8730. *Ad Servs, Dir*, Patti Blount; *Ch Servs*, Avonelle Lamphere
Founded 1886. Circ 40,536
Library Holdings: Bk Vols 39,000; Per Subs 54
Subject Interests: Local history
Special Collections: Local Newspaper 1889-present
Mem of Indianhead Federated Library System

EAGLE

P ALICE BAKER MEMORIAL PUBLIC LIBRARY, 820 E Main, 53119-0520. (Mail add: PO Box 520, 53119-0520), SAN 376-6640. Tel: 414-594-2800. FAX: 414-594-5126. E-Mail: eaglepl@eagle.lib.wi.us. Web Site: www.wcfls.lib.wi.us/eagle. *Dir*, Barbara Jatczak; E-Mail: bjatczak@eagle.lib.wi.us
Library Holdings: Bk Vols 20,000; Bk Titles 17,000; Per Subs 80
Mem of Waukesha County Federated Library System
Friends of the Library Group

EAGLE RIVER

M EAGLE RIVER MEMORIAL HOSPITAL LIBRARY,* 201 Hospital 54521. SAN 377-9491. Tel: 715-479-7411. FAX: 715-479-0321.
Library Holdings: Bk Titles 100

P WALTER E OLSON MEMORIAL LIBRARY, 203 N Main St, 54521. (Mail add: PO Box 69, 54521-0069), SAN 317-9672. Tel: 715-479-807 FAX: 716-479-2435. E-Mail: olson@olson.nwls.lib.wi.us. *Dir Libr Serv* Diana B Anderson; E-Mail: danderson@olson.nwls.lib.wi.us; *Asst Libr* Kecia Hoeger; Tel: 715-479-8070, Ext 22, E-Mail: khoger@olson.nwls.lib.wi.us; *ILL*, Martha Cahill; *ILL*, Pat Mueller; Tel: 715-479-8070, Ext 23, E-Mail: pmueller@olson.nwls.lib.wi.us; *Ch Servs*, Connie Hill; *Ch Servs*, Cyndy Thomas; Tel: 715-479-8070, Ext 24, E-Mail: cthomas@olson.nwls.lib.wi.us; *Publ Servs*, Katrina Champeny; Staff 5 (MLS 5)
Founded 1915. Pop 8,000; Circ 77,000
Jan 1999-Dec 1999 Income $160,690, State $100, City $111,208, Coun $10,500, Locally Generated Income $38,882. Mats Exp $28,487, Books $17,388, Per/Ser (Incl. Access Fees) $4,374, AV Equip $3,890, Electron Ref Mat (Incl. Access Fees) $2,835. Sal $77,471 (Prof $73,543)
Library Holdings: Bk Vols 35,156; Bk Titles 35,138; Per Subs 118
Special Collections: Kalmar Financial
Automation Activity & Vendor Info: (Cataloging) Innovative Interfaces Inc.; (Circulation) Innovative Interfaces Inc.
Database Vendor: Innovative Interfaces INN - View
Publications: Newsletter (bi-monthly)
Function: ILL available
Mem of Northern Waters Library Service
Friends of the Library Group

L VILAS COUNTY LAW LIBRARY, 330 Court St, 54521. SAN 377-96 Tel: 715-479-3632. FAX: 715-479-3740.
Library Holdings: Bk Vols 2,000; Per Subs 10

EAST TROY

P EAST TROY LIONS PUBLIC LIBRARY, 3094 Graydon Ave, 53120. S 317-9680. Tel: 414-642-6262. FAX: 414-642-6264. Web Site: www.easttroy.k12.wi.us/library. *Dir*, Jackie Gotz; E-Mail: gotz@easttroy.k12.wi.us
Founded 1895. Pop 3,300; Circ 46,000
1998-1999 Income $150,169, City $77,521, County $72,648. Mats Exp $22,370, Books $13,486, Per/Ser (Incl. Access Fees) $1,952, AV Equip $4,142, Electronic Ref Mat (Incl. Access Fees) $2,790. Sal $78,190
Library Holdings: Bk Vols 24,000; Bk Titles 20,000; Per Subs 93
Mem of Lakeshores Library System

EAU CLAIRE

S CHIPPEWA VALLEY MUSEUM, INC,* 1204 Carson Park Dr, PO Box 1204, 54702-1204. SAN 327-8425. Tel: 715-834-7871. FAX: 715-834-6 E-Mail: cvmuseum@discover-net.net. *Coll Develop, Librn*, Eldbjorg Tob
Library Holdings: Bk Vols 45,000

J CHIPPEWA VALLEY TECHNICAL COLLEGE LIBRARY,* 620 W Clairemont Ave, 54701-6162. SAN 317-9699. Tel: 715-833-6285. FAX: 833-6470. Web Site: www.chippewa.tec.wi.us/library.; Staff 8 (MLS 1, N MLS 7)
Founded 1965
1997-1998 Income $395,520. Mats Exp $90,008, Books $49,858, Per/Se (Incl. Access Fees) $40,150. Sal $213,026
Library Holdings: Bk Vols 36,425; Bk Titles 24,109
Subject Interests: Allied health, Bus, Culinary, Indust, Paralegal
Automation Activity & Vendor Info: (Acquisitions) Innovative Interfac Inc.; (Cataloging) Innovative Interfaces Inc.; (Circulation) Innovative Interfaces Inc.; (Course Reserve) Innovative Interfaces Inc.; (OPAC) Innovative Interfaces Inc.; (Serials) Innovative Interfaces Inc.
Mem of Indianhead Federated Library System
Partic in OCLC Online Computer Library Center, Inc

S EAU CLAIRE LEADER-TELEGRAM NEWSROOM LIBRARY,* 701 S Farwell St, PO Box 570, 54702. SAN 377-9327. Tel: 715-833-9200. FAX 715-833-9244. E-Mail: leadertelegram@ecol.net. Web Site: www.cvol.net
Library Holdings: Bk Titles 70

CR IMMANUEL LUTHERAN COLLEGE LIBRARY, 501 Grover Rd, 5470 SAN 377-9505. *Librn*, Barbara Gullerud
Founded 1959. Enrl 180; Fac 14
Library Holdings: Bk Titles 10,000; Per Subs 70
Mem of Indianhead Federated Library System

P INDIANHEAD FEDERATED LIBRARY SYSTEM,* 1538 Truax Blvd, 54703. SAN 317-9729. Tel: 715-839-5082. Interlibrary Loan Service Tel: 715-839-5151. FAX: 715-839-5151. Web Site: ifls.lib.wi.us. *Dir*, Milton Mitchell; Staff 5 (MLS 5)
Founded 1978. Pop 390,000
Jan 1998-Dec 1999 Income $1,022,569, State $960,528, Federal $5,000,

Other $57,041. Sal $373,001
Publications: Directions; Directly
Member Libraries: Altoona Public Library; Amery Public Library; Baldwin Public Library; Balsam Lake Public Library; Barron Public Library; Boyceville Public Library; Bruce Area Public Library; Cadott Community Library; Calhoun Memorial Library; Cameron Public Library; Carleton A Friday Memorial Library; Centuria Public Library; Chippewa Falls Public Library; Chippewa Valley Technical College Library; Clarella Hackett Johnson Library; Clear Lake Public Library; Colfax Public Library; Cornell Public Library; Cumberland Public Library; D R Moon Memorial Library; Dallas Public Library; Deer Park Public Library; Dresser Village Library; Durand Public Library; Ellsworth Public Library; Fairchild Public Library; Fall Creek Public Library; Frederic Public Library; G E Bleskacek Memorial Library; Glenwood City Public Library; Hammond Community Library; Hawkins Area Library; Hazel Mackin Community Library; Hudson Public Library; Immanuel Lutheran College Library; L E Phillips Memorial Public Library; Luck Public Library; Menomonie Public Library; Milltown Public Library; Ogema Public Library; Osceola Public Library; Park Falls Public Library; Phillips Public Library; Plum City Public Library; Polk County Library Federation; Prescott Public Library; Rice Lake Public Library; Rusk County Community Library; Somerset Public Library; Spring Valley Public Library; St Croix Falls Public Library; Turtle Lake Public Library; University Of Wisconsin-Eau Claire; Wisconsin Indianhead Technical College; Woodville Community Library

L E PHILLIPS MEMORIAL PUBLIC LIBRARY,* 400 Eau Claire St, 54701. SAN 317-9710. Tel: 715-839-1648. Interlibrary Loan Service Tel: 715-839-5006. TDD: 715-839-1689. FAX: 715-839-3822. *Dir*, Mark Morse; *Assoc Dir, Tech Servs*, Mildred Larson; *Ch Servs, Circ*, Helen Mabrey; *AV, Ref*, John Stoneberg; *Coll Develop*, Mary Tlusty; Staff 40 (MLS 7, Non-MLS 33)
Founded 1875. Pop 89,461; Circ 872,572
Library Holdings: Bk Vols 211,389; Per Subs 555
Subject Interests: History
Mem of Indianhead Federated Library System
Partic in OCLC Online Computer Library Center, Inc
Special Services for the Deaf - High interest/low vocabulary books; Special interest periodicals; TDD
Friends of the Library Group

LUTHER HOSPITAL LIBRARY SERVICES,* 1221 Whipple St, 54702-4105. SAN 317-9737. Tel: 715-838-3248. FAX: 715-838-3289. *Dir Libr Serv*, Virginia Wright; E-Mail: wright.ginny@mayo.edu
Founded 1930
Library Holdings: Bk Vols 4,260; Per Subs 300
Subject Interests: Allied health, Hospital administration, Medicine, Nursing
Special Collections: Consumer Health Information Center Coll
Publications: Newsletter
Partic in Mayo Clinic Regional Health Syst

SACRED HEART HOSPITAL, Medical Library,* 900 W Clairemont Ave, 54701. SAN 317-9745. Tel: 715-839-4330. FAX: 715-839-8417. *Librn*, Bruno Warner
Founded 1964
Library Holdings: Bk Titles 5,000; Per Subs 264
Subject Interests: Dentistry, Hospital administration, Medicine, Neurology, Nursing
Partic in Greater Midwest Regional Medical Libr Network; Northwestern Wisconsin Health Science Library Consortium

UNIVERSITY OF WISCONSIN-EAU CLAIRE, William D McIntyre Library, 105 Garfield Ave, 54702-4004. SAN 317-9761. Tel: 715-836-3715. Interlibrary Loan Service Tel: 715-836-5377. Circulation Tel: 715-836-3856. Reference Tel: 715-836-3858. FAX: 715-836-2949. Web Site: www.uwec.edu/admin/library/. *Dir*, Robert Rose; E-Mail: roserf@uwec.edu; *Media Spec*, Cleo Powers; Tel: 715-836-5820, E-Mail: powerscj@uwec.edu; *Acq*, Janice Bogstad; Tel: 715-836-6032, E-Mail: bogstajm@uwec.edu; *ILL*, Mary Finseth; E-Mail: finsetma@uwec.edu; *Per*, Linda Cecchini; Tel: 715-836-3508, E-Mail: cecchilr@uwec.edu; *Online Servs*, Dan Norstedt; *Ref Servs YA*, Janet Patterson; Tel: 715-836-4362, E-Mail: patterjl@uwec.edu; *Cat*, Cheryl Cutsforth; Tel: 715-836-3304, E-Mail: cutsfocl@uwec.edu; *Automation Syst Coordr*, Stephen Elfstrand; Tel: 715-836-4962, E-Mail: elfstrsf@uwec.edu; *Govt Doc*, Leslie Foster; Tel: 715-836-3247, E-Mail: fosterla@uwec.edu; *Ref*, Mimi King; Tel: 715-836-4958, E-Mail: kingm@uwec.edu; Staff 34 (MLS 16, Non-MLS 18)
Founded 1916. Enrl 10,549; Fac 482; Highest Degree: Master
Jul 1999-Jun 2000 Income $2,723,027, State $2,568,737, Federal $69,000, Locally Generated Income $85,290. Mats Exp $810,413, Books $321,490, Per/Ser (Incl. Access Fees) $315,178, Presv $8,804, Micro $64,583, Electronic Ref Mat (Incl. Access Fees) $100,358. Sal $1,587,910 (Prof $897,937)
Library Holdings: Bk Vols 537,469; Bk Titles 443,628; Per Subs 1,580
Subject Interests: Bus, Education, Nursing
Special Collections: Area Research Center; Campus Evolution Records (reflecting change from normal school to university); Chippewa Valley Historical Manuscripts & Local Government Records; Early Settlement, Lumbering, Labor, Genealogy & Politics; Uniroyal Management & Labor Union Records; Wood Family Farm Diaries
Automation Activity & Vendor Info: (Acquisitions) Endeavor; (Cataloging) Endeavor; (Circulation) Endeavor; (Course Reserve) Endeavor; (ILL) Endeavor; (OPAC) Endeavor; (Serials) Endeavor
Publications: Off the Shelf (Newsletter)
Mem of Indianhead Federated Library System
Partic in OCLC Online Computer Library Center, Inc; Wisconsin Library Services

EDGERTON

P EDGERTON PUBLIC LIBRARY,* 101 Albion St, 53534-1836. SAN 317-977X. Tel: 608-884-4511. FAX: 608-884-7575. *Librn*, Marylou Fox
Jan 1998-Dec 1999 Income $142,000. Mats Exp $15,000. Sal $68,000
Library Holdings: Bk Vols 22,000; Per Subs 88
Mem of Arrowhead Library System
Friends of the Library Group

ELKHART LAKE

P ELKHART LAKE PUBLIC LIBRARY,* 84 N Lake St, PO Box R, 53020-0367. SAN 376-6624. Tel: 920-876-2554. *Dir*, JoAnn Dent
Library Holdings: Bk Vols 10,000; Bk Titles 5,000; Per Subs 24
Mem of Eastern Shores Library System
Friends of the Library Group

ELKHORN

J GATEWAY TECHNICAL COLLEGE, Elkhorn Campus,* 400 S Hwy H, 53121-2020. SAN 317-9788. Tel: 414-741-6124. FAX: 414-741-6148.
Library Holdings: Bk Vols 5,900; Per Subs 70
Subject Interests: Computer aided design, Desktop publ, Graphic design, Office tech
Partic in OCLC Online Computer Library Center, Inc

M LAKELAND MEDICAL CENTER, Medical Library,* W3985 County Ra NN, PO Box 1002, 53121. SAN 317-980X. Tel: 414-741-2475. FAX: 414-741-2482. *Librn*, Brenda Schneider
Founded 1974
Library Holdings: Bk Titles 330; Per Subs 50
Partic in Southeastern Wisconsin Health Science Library Consortium

P MATHESON MEMORIAL LIBRARY, 101 N Wisconsin, 53121. SAN 317-9818. Tel: 262-723-2678. FAX: 262-723-2870. Toll Free FAX: 262-723-2870. Web Site: www.elknet.net/library, www.elknet.net/library. *Coll Develop, Dir*, Valerie Lapicola; E-Mail: vlapicol@elkhorn.lib.wi.us; *Ref Serv*, Jennifer Einwalter; E-Mail: jeinwalt@elkhorn.lib.wi.us; *YA Servs*, Melissa Kuiper; E-Mail: mkuiper@elkhorn.lib.wi.us; Staff 3 (MLS 3)
Founded 1931. Pop 6,500; Circ 95,000
Jan 2000-Dec 2000 Income $278,000, State $1,000, City $173,000, County $104,000. Mats Exp $67,500, Books $48,500, Per/Ser (Incl. Access Fees) $9,000, Micro $1,000. Sal $204,500 (Prof $94,500)
Library Holdings: Bk Titles 37,000; Per Subs 170; High Interest/Low Vocabulary Bk Vols 400; Spec Interest Per Sub 20; Bks on Deafness & Sign Lang 15
Special Collections: Robert Burns (Matheson Coll)
Automation Activity & Vendor Info: (ILL) Brodart
Database Vendor: Ebsco - EbscoHost
Publications: Booklist; Library Journal; School LJ; VOYA
Mem of Lakeshores Library System

ELLSWORTH

P ELLSWORTH PUBLIC LIBRARY, 312 W Main, 54011. SAN 317-9826. Tel: 715-273-3209. FAX: 715-273-3209. *Dir*, Margaret Levenhagen; E-Mail: margaret.levenhagen@ifls.lib.wi.us; Staff 1 (Non-MLS 1)
Founded 1924. Pop 2,706; Circ 57,000
Jan 1999-Dec 1999 Income $148,000, City $106,000, County $42,000. Mats Exp $14,394, Books $5,969, Per/Ser (Incl. Access Fees) $1,245, Other Print Mats $5,851, Electronic Ref Mat (Incl. Access Fees) $1,329. Sal $56,202 (Prof $28,631)
Library Holdings: Bk Titles 15,751; Per Subs 50
Subject Interests: History
Publications: Booklist
Mem of Indianhead Federated Library System

ELM GROVE

S ALDRIAN, GUSZKOWSKI, LTD, Architects Library,* 12958 W Blue Mound, 53122. SAN 328-2848. Tel: 262-789-6060. FAX: 262-789-6066. E-Mail: postmaster@agarch.com. *Librn*, Steve Alexander
Library Holdings: Bk Vols 400

P ELM GROVE PUBLIC LIBRARY, 13600 W Juneau Blvd, 53122-0906. SAN 317-9834. Tel: 414-782-6717. FAX: 414-780-4827. Web Site: www.execpc.com/~elmgrove, www.wcfls.lib.wi.us/elmgrove. *Dir*, Timothy Dirks; *Ad Servs, Tech Servs*, Karen Wood; *Ad Servs, ILL*, Susan Freitag;

Staff 6 (MLS 5, Non-MLS 1)
Founded 1962. Pop 6,261; Circ 115,000
Jan 2000-Dec 2000 Income $276,000. Mats Exp $314,218, Books $46,344, Per/Ser (Incl. Access Fees) $6,156, AV Equip $3,800. Sal $181,000
Library Holdings: Bk Titles 32,809
Subject Interests: Gen popular
Mem of Waukesha County Federated Library System
Friends of the Library Group

S FLUID POWER CONSULTANTS INTERNATIONAL LIBRARY,* 1000 Grandview Dr, PO Box 106, 53122-0106. SAN 370-8675. Tel: 414-782-0410. FAX: 414-782-0410. *Pres*, Russell W Henke
Library Holdings: Bk Vols 200; Per Subs 30

ELROY

P ELROY PUBLIC LIBRARY,* 501 Second Main St, 53929-1255. SAN 317-9842. Tel: 608-462-2407. *Dir*, Barbara Delong
Pop 1,500; Circ 27,760
Library Holdings: Bk Vols 14,000; Per Subs 60
Mem of Winding Rivers Library System
Friends of the Library Group

ENDEAVOR

P ENDEAVOR PUBLIC LIBRARY, 413 Academy Blvd, PO Box 80, 53930-0176. SAN 322-8525. Tel: 608-587-2111. FAX: 608-587-2111. *Dir*, Suellen Peterson; *Librn*, Juanita McDowell; Staff 2 (Non-MLS 2)
Library Holdings: Bk Vols 9,145; Per Subs 38
Mem of Winnefox Library System
Friends of the Library Group

EVANSVILLE

P EAGER FREE PUBLIC LIBRARY,* 39 W Main St, 53536. SAN 317-9850. Tel: 608-882-2260. FAX: 608-882-2261. Web Site: als.lib.wi.us/efpl. *Dir*, Ruth Montgomery
Founded 1898. Circ 50,167
Jan 1998-Dec 1999 Income $150,731, City $93,858, County $27,981. Mats Exp $27,897, Books $24,149, Per/Ser (Incl. Access Fees) $2,270. Sal $77,034 (Prof $43,364)
Library Holdings: Bk Titles 18,246; Per Subs 100
Special Collections: Evansville Historical Materials Coll; Wisconsin Writers Coll
Mem of Arrowhead Library System
Friends of the Library Group

EXELAND

P EXELAND PUBLIC LIBRARY,* 1563 N Hwy 40, 54835. SAN 317-9869. Tel: 715-943-2723. *Librn*, Phyllis Sander; Staff 1 (MLS 1)
Library Holdings: Bk Vols 7,000
Special Collections: Local History
Mem of Northwest Wis Libr Syst

FAIRCHILD

P FAIRCHILD PUBLIC LIBRARY, 200 Huron St, PO Box 149, 54741-0149. SAN 377-9904. Tel: 715-334-2803. *Librn*, Mary Ligman
Library Holdings: Bk Vols 11,813; Per Subs 20
Mem of Indianhead Federated Library System
Open Mon, Tues, Thurs & Fri 9-5, Wed 9-1

FALL CREEK

P FALL CREEK PUBLIC LIBRARY,* 122 E Lincoln, PO Box 426, 54742. SAN 324-1548. Tel: 715-877-3334. FAX: 715-877-2392. *Dir*, Marian Smith
Library Holdings: Bk Titles 12,000; Per Subs 42
Mem of Indianhead Federated Library System
Friends of the Library Group

FENNIMORE

P DWIGHT T PARKER PUBLIC LIBRARY,* 925 Lincoln Ave, 53809-1743. SAN 317-9877. Tel: 608-822-6294. *Dir*, Trudi Freymiller; *Ch Servs*, Cathy Smith
Library Holdings: Bk Vols 24,588; Per Subs 78
Special Collections: National Geographics Coll
Publications: A History of Fennimore
Mem of Southwest Wisconsin Library System

P SOUTHWEST WISCONSIN LIBRARY SYSTEM, 1775 Fourth St, 53809-1137. SAN 317-9885. Tel: 608-822-3393. FAX: 608-822-6251. *Actg Dir*, Jo Don Anderson; Tel: 608-822-2050, E-Mail: joma@swis.org; *Automation Syst Coordr*, Steve T Platteter; Tel: 608-822-2053, E-Mail: sepp@swis.org; *Head Tech Servs*, Kim F Streif; Tel: 608-822-2055, E-Mail: kstreif@swis.org; *Circ*, Peggy S Freymiller; Tel: 608-822-2052, E-Mail: pfrymllr@swls.o[r]
Subject Specialists: *Continuing educ mgt*, Jo Don Anderson; Staff 17 (M[LS] 3, Non-MLS 14)
Founded 1959. Pop 120,000
Jan 2000-Dec 2000 Income $671,778, State $332,775, County $288,99[2] Locally Generated Income $49,811. Mats Exp $9,000, Books $5,000, P[er/] Ser (Incl. Access Fees) $4,000. Sal $365,956 (Prof $219,984)
Library Holdings: Bk Vols 72,447; Bk Titles 65,950; Per Subs 15
Subject Interests: Regional hist
Automation Activity & Vendor Info: (Cataloging) epixtech, inc.; (Circulation) epixtech, inc.
Publications: Stepping Stones, Stepping Stones for Children (Newslette[r])
Member Libraries: Argyle Public Library; Barneveld Public Library; Benton Public Library; Blanchardville Public Library; Bloomington Pub[lic] Library; Brewer Public Library; Cobb Public Library; Cuba City Public Library; Dodgeville Public Library; Dwight T Parker Public Library; Eckstein Memorial Library; Gays Mills Public Library; Hildebrand Memorial Library; John Turgeson Public Library; Johnson Public Librar[y]; Lone Rock Community Library; Martin Allen Library; Mineral Point Pu[blic] Library; Montfort Public Library; Muscoda Public Library; Platteville P[ublic] Library; Schreiner Memorial Library; Shullsburg Public Library; Soldie[rs] Grove Public Library; Viola Public Library; Wachuta Memorial Library
Partic in OCLC Online Computer Library Center, Inc; Wisconsin Librar[y] Services

J SOUTHWEST WISCONSIN TECHNICAL COLLEGE LIBRARY,* 18[00] Bronson Blvd, 53809-9778. SAN 317-9893. Tel: 608-822-3262, Ext 23[3] FAX: 608-822-6019. *Librn*, Patricia L Payson; Tel: 608-822-3262, Ext 2[ ] E-Mail: ppayson@southwest.tec.wi.us; *Asst Librn*, Edith Hunter; Tel: 60[8-] 822-3262, Ext 2337, E-Mail: ehunter@southwest.tec.wi.us; Staff 2 (MLS [1,] Non-MLS 1)
Founded 1971
Jul 1999-Jun 2000 Mats Exp $49,000, Books $28,000, Per/Ser (Incl. Ac[cess] Fees) $21,000. Sal $79,300 (Prof $50,000)
Library Holdings: Bk Titles 28,220; Per Subs 372
Special Collections: A-V Coll
Automation Activity & Vendor Info: (Cataloging) Sagebrush Corporati[on] (Circulation) Sagebrush Corporation; (OPAC) Sagebrush Corporation
Database Vendor: Ebsco - EbscoHost
Function: Mail loans to members

FLORENCE

P FLORENCE COUNTY LIBRARY,* 400 Olive Ave, PO Box 440, 5412[1-] 0440. SAN 376-6616. Tel: 715-528-3094. FAX: 715-528-5338. *Dir*, Mar[ ] Seggelink
Library Holdings: Bk Titles 11,000; Per Subs 40
Mem of Nicolet Federated Library System
Friends of the Library Group

FOND DU LAC

GL FOND DU LAC CIRCUIT COURT, Law Library,* PO Box 1355, 5493[6-] 1355. SAN 317-9907. FAX: 920-929-3933. *Librn*, Carol Marx
Library Holdings: Bk Vols 13,000

S FOND DU LAC COUNTY HISTORICAL SOCIETY-FAMILY HERIT[AGE] CENTER, Adams House Resource Center, 336 Old Pioneer Rd, 54935-6[ ] (Mail add: PO Box 1284, 54936-1284), SAN 326-4912. Circulation Tel: 920-922-1166. Reference Tel: 920-922-0991. FAX: 920-922-9099. *Dir*, J[ ] Ebert; *Chair*, Sally Albertz; Staff 3 (MLS 1, Non-MLS 2)
Mar 1999-Feb 2000 Income $650, Locally Generated Income $300, Pare[nt] Institution $350. Mats Exp $650, Books $400, Presv $50, Other Print Ma[ts] $200
Library Holdings: Bk Vols 10,000
Subject Interests: Local history
Adams House Resource Center is located on the grounds of Galloway H[ouse] & Village Park

P FOND DU LAC PUBLIC LIBRARY,* 32 Sheboygon St, 54935. SAN 3[17-] 9915. Tel: 920-929-7080. FAX: 920-929-7082. *Dir*, Leslyn Shires; *Asst D[ir]*, Cheryl Gage; *Ad Servs*, Cheryl Bornemann; *Ch Servs, YA Servs*, Lillian Nolan; *Cat, Tech Servs*, Lucinda Ward; *Cat*, Marge Brashier; *Ref*, Kay Conrad; *Doc*, Marge Albert; *Ch Servs*, Shelly Armstrong; *ILL*, Debbie Rosenberg; Staff 33 (MLS 10, Non-MLS 23)
Founded 1876. Pop 61,925; Circ 509,058
Library Holdings: Bk Vols 219,520; Per Subs 402
Subject Interests: Architecture, Art
Special Collections: Mertes Children's Folk & Fairy Tale Coll; Municipa[l]
Publications: Ex Libris (newsletter)
Partic in Wisconsin Library Services
Friends of the Library Group

C MARIAN COLLEGE OF FOND DU LAC, Cardinal Meyer Library, 45 S National Ave, 54935. SAN 317-9923. Tel: 920-923-7641, 920-923-8725. FAX: 920-923-7154. E-Mail: refdesk@mariancollege.edu. Web Site:

www.mariancollege.edu. *Dir*, Mary Ellen Gormican; E-Mail: mgormican@mariancollege.edu; *Bibliog Instr*, Carolyn Colwell; Tel: 920-923-8099, E-Mail: ccolwell@mariancollege.edu; *Archivist*, Sister Sharon McEnery; Tel: 920-923-8747, E-Mail: smcenery@mariancollege.edu; *Ref*, Nima Ingle; Tel: 920-923-8096, E-Mail: ningle@mariancollege.edu; *Circ*, Jane McGovern; *ILL*, Connie Conrad; E-Mail: cconrad@mariancollege.edu; *Acq, Cat, Syst Coordr*, Paul Koch; Staff 9 (MLS 6, Non-MLS 3)
Founded 1936. Enrl 1,794; Highest Degree: Master
Jul 1999-Jun 2000 Mats Exp $125,350, Books $39,000, Per/Ser (Incl. Access Fees) $62,000, AV Equip $4,350, Electronic Ref Mat (Incl. Access Fees) $20,000. Sal $179,000 (Prof $144,800)
Library Holdings: Bk Vols 93,261; Bk Titles 91,368; Per Subs 669
Subject Interests: Education, Nursing
Automation Activity & Vendor Info: (Cataloging) Innovative Interfaces Inc.; (Circulation) Innovative Interfaces Inc.; (OPAC) Innovative Interfaces Inc.
Partic in Fox River Valley Area Library Consortium; Fox Valley Library Council; OCLC Online Computer Library Center, Inc; Wisconsin Library Services

MERCURY MARINE, Information Resource Center,* W6250 W Pioneer Rd, PO Box 1939, 54936-1939. SAN 374-5120. Tel: 920-929-5447. FAX: 920-929-4950. *Librn*, Sharon Gebhardt; Staff 2 (MLS 1, Non-MLS 1)
Library Holdings: Bk Titles 5,000; Per Subs 200
Partic in Fox Valley Library Council

MORAINE PARK TECHNICAL COLLEGE LIBRARY, 235 N National Ave, PO Box 1940, 54936-1940. SAN 364-6440. Tel: 920-924-3112, 920-924-3117. Interlibrary Loan Service Tel: 920-924-3118. Circulation Tel: 920-929-2470. Reference Tel: 920-924-3108. FAX: 920-924-3117. Web Site: www.morainepark.com. *Mgr*, Charlene Petti; E-Mail: cpettit@moraine.tec.wi.us; *Tech Servs*, Gary Flynn; E-Mail: gflynn@moraine.tec.wi.us; *ILL*, Joely Brennan; E-Mail: jbrennan@moraine.tec.wi.us
Founded 1965. Enrl 2,400; Fac 134
Library Holdings: Bk Vols 30,000; Bk Titles 25,000; Per Subs 390
Partic in Fox River Valley Area Library Consortium; Fox Valley Library Council; Wis PALS Libr Consortium

SAINT AGNES HOSPITAL, Health Sciences Library, 430 E Division St, 54935. SAN 317-994X. Tel: 920-926-4559. FAX: 920-926-4306. *Librn*, Lisa Smith; Staff 1 (MLS 1)
Founded 1918
Library Holdings: Bk Vols 1,500; Per Subs 111

TAYCHEEDAH CORRECTIONAL INSTITUTION LIBRARY,* 751 Hwy K, 54935-9099. SAN 318-4110. Tel: 920-929-3800, Ext 3899. FAX: 920-929-2067. *Actg Librn*, Roger Brimeyer
Founded 1967
Library Holdings: Bk Vols 14,000; Per Subs 45
Special Collections: Legal Coll - Women's Issues

NTANA

FONTANA PUBLIC LIBRARY,* 166 Second Ave, PO Box 437, 53125. SAN 317-9966. Tel: 414-275-5107. E-Mail: fontana@idcnet.com. *Dir*, Chris Van Voorhees
Founded 1931
Library Holdings: Bk Vols 23,200; Per Subs 54
Subject Interests: Circus, Craft, Gardening, Local history, Medicine
Mem of Lakeshores Library System

RT ATKINSON

DWIGHT FOSTER PUBLIC LIBRARY,* 102 E Milwaukee Ave, 53538-2049. SAN 317-9974. Tel: 920-563-7790. FAX: 920-563-7774. E-Mail: reference@mail.fort.lib.wi.us. Web Site: www.fort.lib.wi.us. *Dir*, Connie Meyer; E-Mail: cmeyer@mail.fort.lib.wilus; *Asst Dir*, Amy Lutzke; E-Mail: alutzko@mail.fort.lib.wi.us; *Ch Servs*, Shelly Menzer; E-Mail: smenzer@mail.fort.lib.wi.us; Staff 3 (MLS 2, Non-MLS 1)
Founded 1890. Pop 16,236; Circ 226,488
Jan 2000-Dec 2000 Income $514,950, City $338,894, County $176,056. Mats Exp $119,390, Books $65,000, Per/Ser (Incl. Access Fees) $6,140, Micro $250, AV Equip $42,000, Electronic Ref Mat (Incl. Access Fees) $6,000. Sal $252,059 (Prof $174,805)
Library Holdings: Bk Vols 78,511; Bk Titles 70,035; Per Subs 237
Special Collections: Local History, bks & clippings; Lorine Niedecker Coll
Automation Activity & Vendor Info: (Cataloging) epixtech, inc.; (Circulation) epixtech, inc.; (OPAC) epixtech, inc.
Friends of the Library Group

FORT ATKINSON MEMORIAL HOSPITAL, Medical Library,* 611 E Sherman Ave, 53538. Tel: 920-568-5194. FAX: 920-568-5194. *Coordr*, Carrie Garity; E-Mail: carrie.garity@famhs.org
Library Holdings: Bk Vols 75; Bk Titles 75; Per Subs 50

HIGHSMITH, INC, Corporate Library, W5527 Hwy 106, PO Box 800, 53538-0800. SAN 329-7683. Tel: 920-563-9571. FAX: 920-563-7395. Web Site: www.highsmith.com. *Dir*, Lisa Guedea Carreno; E-Mail: iguedea@highsmith.com; *Librn*, Genevieve Foskett; E-Mail: gfoskett@highsmith.com; *Asst Librn*, Genevieve Mecherly; *Tech Servs*, Oma Dixon; E-Mail: odixon@highsmith.com; Staff 2 (MLS 1, Non-MLS 1)
Founded 1986
Library Holdings: Bk Titles 3,050; Per Subs 700
Subject Interests: Education, Libr sci
Special Collections: Company Archive Materials; Highsmith Cat
Automation Activity & Vendor Info: (Cataloging) Inmagic, Inc.; (OPAC) Inmagic, Inc.; (Serials) Inmagic, Inc.
Database Vendor: Dialog, Lexis-Nexis, OCLC - First Search
Publications: Acquisitions List (in-house); Regular column in in-house company newsletter
Restriction: Not open to public
Partic in Library Council Of Metropolitan Milwaukee, Inc

S HOARD HISTORICAL MUSEUM LIBRARY, 407 Merchants Ave, 53538. SAN 373-3068. Tel: 920-563-7769. FAX: 920-568-3203. E-Mail: infohoardmuseum@compufort.com. Web Site: www.hoardmuseum.org. *Dir*, Sue Hartwick; E-Mail: hartwick@hoardmuseum.org
Library Holdings: Bk Vols 5,000
Subject Interests: Civil War, Local history
Restriction: Not a lending library

FOX LAKE

S FOX LAKE CORRECTIONAL INSTITUTION LIBRARY,* PO Box 147, 53933. SAN 364-6475. Tel: 920-928-3151, Ext 240. FAX: 920-928-6229. *Senior Librn*, Bob Zabkowicz; Staff 1 (MLS 1)
Founded 1962. Pop 1,000; Circ 52,000
Library Holdings: Bk Titles 20,000; Per Subs 50
Subject Interests: Fiction, Legal
Automation Activity & Vendor Info: (Cataloging) Sagebrush Corporation; (Circulation) Sagebrush Corporation; (Course Reserve) Sagebrush Corporation; (ILL) Sagebrush Corporation; (Media Booking) Sagebrush Corporation; (OPAC) Sagebrush Corporation; (Serials) Sagebrush Corporation
Branches:
L LAW LIBRARY *Librn*, Bob Zabkowicz
Library Holdings: Bk Vols 1,629

P FOX LAKE PUBLIC LIBRARY,* 117 W State, 53933. SAN 317-9982. Tel: 920-928-3223. FAX: 920-928-3810. E-Mail: flpl@centuryinter.net. *Dir*, Julie Flemming
Founded 1910. Pop 3,000
1997-1998 Mats Exp $14,000, Books $8,000, Per/Ser (Incl. Access Fees) $1,700
Library Holdings: Bk Titles 12,000; Per Subs 100
Mem of Mid-Wisconsin Federated Library System
Friends of the Library Group

FRANKLIN

P FRANKLIN PUBLIC LIBRARY, 9229 W Loomis Rd, 53132. SAN 324-0916. Tel: 414-425-8214. FAX: 414-425-9498. *Dir*, Barbara Roark; E-Mail: barbara.roark@mcfls.org; *Ad Servs*, Darlene Blakely; *Ch Servs*, Kim Heikkinen; *Ref*, Roselie Rentz; Staff 6 (MLS 5, Non-MLS 1)
Founded 1980. Pop 27,780; Circ 200,000
Jan 2000-Dec 2000 Mats Exp $503,007, Books $83,559, Per/Ser (Incl. Access Fees) $9,250. Sal $285,287 (Prof $138,135)
Library Holdings: Bk Vols 48,000; Bk Titles 52,000; Per Subs 161
Database Vendor: Innovative Interfaces INN - View
Mem of Milwaukee County Federated Library System
Friends of the Library Group

FREDERIC

P FREDERIC PUBLIC LIBRARY,* 107 Oak St E, PO Box 700, 54837-0700. SAN 377-9920. Tel: 715-327-4979. FAX: 715-327-4455. E-Mail: fredlibr@centuryinter.net.
Jan 1997-Dec 1998 Income $50,000. Mats Exp $18,531. Sal $27,817
Library Holdings: Bk Titles 13,000; Per Subs 49
Mem of Indianhead Federated Library System
Open Mon & Wed 1-8, Thurs & Fri 1-5, Sat 10-12, Sun 12-3
Friends of the Library Group

FREMONT

P NEUSCHAFER COMMUNITY LIBRARY, 317 Wolf River Dr, PO Box 498, 54940-0498. SAN 375-0469. Tel: 920-446-2474. FAX: 920-446-2480. Web Site: www.owls.lib.wi.us/fpl/. *Dir*, Carol A Toepke; E-Mail: ctoepke@mail.owls.lib.wi.us; *Asst Librn*, Beth Edwards
Pop 735; Circ 1,829
Jan 1999-Dec 1999 Income $10,335, County $8,024, Locally Generated

Income $2,311. Mats Exp $3,924. Sal $19,193
Library Holdings: Bk Vols 4,000; Bk Titles 1,530; Per Subs 44
Mem of Outagamie Waupaca Library System
Friends of the Library Group

FRIENDSHIP

M ADAMS COUNTY MEMORIAL HOSPITAL,* PO Box 40, 53934. Tel: 608-339-3331. FAX: 608-339-9385. *Syst Coordr*, Diane Roekle
Library Holdings: Bk Vols 400; Bk Titles 400; Per Subs 20

GALESVILLE

P GALESVILLE PUBLIC LIBRARY, 16787 Main St, 54630-0697. (Mail add: PO Box 697, 54630-0697), SAN 317-9990. Tel: 608-582-2552. *Dir*, Judy Gautsch; *Asst Librn*, Meredith Houge
Founded 1912. Pop 1,600; Circ 15,223
Library Holdings: Bk Titles 8,740; Per Subs 45
Mem of Winding Rivers Library System
Open Mon, Wed & Fri 2-7, Tues 10-9, Thurs 12-9, Sat 9-12
Friends of the Library Group

GAYS MILLS

P GAYS MILLS PUBLIC LIBRARY, 205 Main St, PO Box 215, 54631-0217. SAN 318-000X. Tel: 608-735-4331. E-Mail: gmbooks@mwt.net. Web Site: www.mwt.net/~gmbooks. *Dir*, Maura Jean Otis; E-Mail: gmbooks@mwt.net
Founded 1941. Pop 1,000; Circ 4,000
Jan 1999-Dec 1999 Income $15,101, City $15,000, Other $2,625. Mats Exp $4,346, Books $2,914, Per/Ser (Incl. Access Fees) $254, AV Equip $400. Sal $11,142 (Prof $8,978)
Library Holdings: Bk Titles 8,000; Per Subs 31
Mem of Southwest Wisconsin Library System
Open Mon 6-9, Wed 9-2, Fri 3-6 & Sat 9-1

GENOA CITY

P GENOA CITY PUBLIC LIBRARY,* 126 Freeman St, PO Box 727, 53128-0727. SAN 318-0018. Tel: 414-279-6188. FAX: 414-279-5923. E-Mail: genoa@idcnet.com. *Dir*, Marie Hatcher
Founded 1900. Pop 1,356; Circ 15,280
1997-1998 Income $30,747, State $132, City $21,000, County $5,769, Locally Generated Income $800, Other $1,405. Mats Exp $8,800, Books $7,800, Per/Ser (Incl. Access Fees) $1,000. Sal $16,722 (Prof $10,000)
Library Holdings: Bk Titles 11,000
Friends of the Library Group

GERMANTOWN

P DUERRWAECHTER MEMORIAL LIBRARY, N 112 W 16879 Mequon Rd, 53022. SAN 318-0026. Tel: 414-253-7760. FAX: 414-253-7763. E-Mail: duer@hnet.net. Web Site: www.hnet.net/~duer. *Dir*, Roberta Olson; *Ch Servs*, Judy Farrow-Busack; Staff 10 (MLS 3, Non-MLS 7)
Founded 1963. Pop 18,000; Circ 185,000
Jan 1998-Dec 1999 Income $535,400, City $363,400, County $148,000, Locally Generated Income $24,000. Mats Exp $109,487, Books $100,487, Per/Ser (Incl. Access Fees) $9,000. Sal $263,368
Library Holdings: Bk Vols 85,000; Per Subs 225
Database Vendor: Ebsco - EbscoHost
Friends of the Library Group

GILLETT

P GILLETT PUBLIC LIBRARY,* 200 E Main St, PO Box 109, 54124-0109. SAN 318-0034. Tel: 920-855-6224. FAX: 920-855-6533. *Librn*, Alice Gudowicz
Founded 1927. Pop 3,000; Circ 8,858
Library Holdings: Bk Vols 8,553; Per Subs 25
Mem of Nicolet Federated Library System
Friends of the Library Group

GILMAN

P WESTERN TAYLOR COUNTY PUBLIC LIBRARY,* Fourth & Main St, PO Box 87, 54433-0087. SAN 318-0042. Tel: 715-447-5486. *Dir*, Marilyn Newman
Library Holdings: Bk Vols 7,500; Per Subs 22
Mem of Wisconsin Valley Library Service

GLENDALE

P NORTH SHORE LIBRARY,* 6800 N Port Washington Rd, 53217. SAN 324-7201. Tel: 414-351-3461. FAX: 414-351-3528. Web Site: www.mclfls.org. *Dir*, Richard Nelson; *Ch Servs*, Linda Madlung; *Ref*, Svetlana Foley; Staff 6 (MLS 6)
Founded 1980. Pop 28,000; Circ 274,000
Library Holdings: Bk Vols 73,000; Per Subs 237
Mem of Milwaukee County Federated Library System
Partic in Library Council Of Metropolitan Milwaukee, Inc
Joint library - operated by 4 municipalities
Friends of the Library Group

GLENWOOD CITY

P GLENWOOD CITY PUBLIC LIBRARY, 127 Pine St, PO Box 247, 54 8554. SAN 318-0050. Tel: 715-265-7443. FAX: 715-265-7307. *Dir*, Ly Barringer; Staff 2 (MLS 1, Non-MLS 1)
Founded 1931. Pop 2,741; Circ 12,871
Library Holdings: Bk Vols 7,500; Per Subs 45
Subject Interests: Audio bks, Large-print bks, Videos
Automation Activity & Vendor Info: (Acquisitions) Innovative Interfa Inc.; (Cataloging) Innovative Interfaces Inc.; (Circulation) Innovative Interfaces Inc.; (OPAC) Innovative Interfaces Inc.; (Serials) Innovative Interfaces Inc.
Mem of Indianhead Federated Library System

GRAFTON

P USS LIBERTY MEMORIAL PUBLIC LIBRARY, 1620 11th Ave, 530 2404. SAN 318-0069. Tel: 262-375-5315. FAX: 262-375-5317. Web Sit www.grafton.lib.wi.us. *Dir*, John Hanson; E-Mail: jhanson@esls.lib.wi.u Staff 11 (MLS 2, Non-MLS 9)
Founded 1958. Pop 15,000; Circ 182,000
2000-2001 Mats Exp $77,000, Books $70,000, Per/Ser (Incl. Access Fe $6,000, AV Equip $1,000
Library Holdings: Bk Vols 70,000; Per Subs 130
Subject Interests: Biography
Mem of Eastern Shores Library System

GRANTON

P SAMSON MEMORIAL LIBRARY,* 107 Second St, PO Box 70, 5443 0070. SAN 318-0077. Tel: 715-238-7339, 715-238-7598. FAX: 715-238-8605. *Dir*, Donna Dachel; *Asst Dir*, Connie Alexander
Pop 425; Circ 4,772
Library Holdings: Bk Vols 7,542; Per Subs 24
Mem of Wisconsin Valley Library Service

GRANTSBURG

P GRANTSBURG PUBLIC LIBRARY,* 416 S Pine St, 54840-7423. SA 318-0085. Tel: 715-463-2244. FAX: 715-463-5555. *Dir*, Maude Dahlber
Pop 1,200; Circ 14,510
Library Holdings: Bk Vols 6,000; Per Subs 37
Subject Interests: Local authors, Local history
Mem of Northern Waters Library Service

GREEN BAY

M BELLIN HOSPITAL, Health Science Library,* 744 S Webster Ave, PO 23400, 54305-3400. SAN 318-0093. Tel: 920-433-3693. FAX: 920-433-7498. E-Mail: roselibr@bellin.org. *Librn*, Cynthia Reinl; Staff 2 (MLS 1, Non-MLS 1)
Founded 1910
Library Holdings: Bk Vols 2,800; Per Subs 197
Subject Interests: Allied health, Medicine, Nursing
Partic in Fox River Valley Area Library Consortium; Nat Libr of Med; N Wis Intertype Librs, Inc

P BROWN COUNTY LIBRARY, 515 Pine St, 54301. SAN 364-653X. Te 920-448-4400. Interlibrary Loan Service Tel: 920-448-4417. TDD: 920-4 4350. FAX: 920-448-4364. Web Site: www.browncountylibrary.org. *Dir*, Patricia LaViolette; Tel: 920-448-4400, Ext 351, E-Mail: laviolette_cp@ co.brown.wi.us; *Asst Dir*, Pamela Nyberg Kiesner; Tel: 920-448-4400, E 365, E-Mail: kiesner_pn@co.brown.wi.us; *Ch Servs*, Clare Kindt; Tel: 92 448-4400, Ext 392, Fax: 920-448-6253, E-Mail: kindt_ca@co.brown.wi.u *Tech Servs*, Emily Wilson; Tel: 920-448-4400, Ext 366, Fax: 920-448-44 E-Mail: wilson_eh@co.brown.wi.us; *Ad Servs, Branch Mgr*, Rosalie Shie Tel: 920-448-4400, Ext 373
Founded 1968. Pop 220,773; Circ 1,710,790
Jan 1999-Dec 1999 Income (Main Library and Branch Library) $5,500,7 State $127,650, Federal $26,808, County $4,628,743, Other $717,519. M Exp $514,779, Books $393,624, Per/Ser (Incl. Access Fees) $36,370, Mic $9,463, AV Equip $19,660, Electronic Ref Mat (Incl. Access Fees) $55,6 Sal $2,455,095
Library Holdings: Bk Vols 276,959; Per Subs 1,260
Subject Interests: Spanish language
Special Collections: Brown County History; Genealogy; Hmong Langua Coll; Wisconsin History

Automation Activity & Vendor Info: (Acquisitions) epixtech, inc.; (Circulation) epixtech, inc.
Database Vendor: epixtech, inc., OCLC - First Search
Publications: Newsletter (quarterly)
Mem of Nicolet Federated Library System
Partic in NE Wis Intertype Librs, Inc
Special Services for the Deaf - Captioned media; TDD; Videos & decoder
Special Services for the Blind - Large print bks
Friends of the Library Group
Branches: 8
ASHWAUBENON, 1060 Orlando Dr, 54304. SAN 364-6599. Tel: 920-492-4913. FAX: 920-492-4914. *Librn*, Eileen Below
Friends of the Library Group
DE PERE BRANCH, 380 Main Ave, De Pere, 54115. SAN 364-6653. Tel: 920-448-4407. FAX: 920-448-4406. Web Site: www.browncountylibrary.org. *Librn*, Caroline Haskin
Friends of the Library Group
DENMARK BRANCH, 450 N Wall St, Denmark, 54208. SAN 364-6629. Tel: 920-863-6613. FAX: 920-863-5169. Web Site: www.browncountylibrary.org. *Librn*, Charlotte Franke; *Librn*, Melody Urban; Staff 2 (Non-MLS 2)
Friends of the Library Group
EAST BRANCH, 2255 Main St, 54302-3743. SAN 364-6742. Tel: 920—391-4600. FAX: 920-391-4601. Web Site: www.browncountylibrary.org. *Librn*, Louanne Crowder; Staff 6 (MLS 1, Non-MLS 5)
Circ 220,000
Automation Activity & Vendor Info: (Cataloging) epixtech, inc.; (Circulation) epixtech, inc.; (OPAC) epixtech, inc.; (Serials) epixtech, inc.
Database Vendor: Ebsco - EbscoHost, epixtech, inc., ProQuest
Mem of Nicolet Federated Library System
Friends of the Library Group
HOWARD, 2680 Riverview Dr, 54313. SAN 364-6718. Tel: 920-448-4405. FAX: 920-448-4404. Web Site: www.browncountylibrary.org. *Librn*, Kasha Kerwin; Staff 1 (MLS 1)
Friends of the Library Group
PULASKI BRANCH, 222 W Pulaski St, Pulaski, 54162. SAN 364-6777. Tel: 920-822-3220. FAX: 920-822-5589. *Librn*, Anne Mead
Friends of the Library Group
SOUTHWEST, 974 Ninth St, 54304. SAN 364-6807. Tel: 920-492-4910. FAX: 920-492-4911. Web Site: www.browncountylibrary.org. *Librn*, Sandy Kallunki
Friends of the Library Group
WRIGHTSTOWN BRANCH, 529 Main St, Wrightstown, 54180. (Mail add: PO Box 96, Wrightstown, 54180), SAN 364-6831. Tel: 920-532-4011. FAX: 920-532-4199. Web Site: www.browncountylibrary.org. *Librn*, Jan Grall; Staff 1 (Non-MLS 1)
Automation Activity & Vendor Info: (Acquisitions) epixtech, inc.; (Cataloging) epixtech, inc.; (Circulation) epixtech, inc.; (OPAC) epixtech, inc.; (Serials) epixtech, inc.
Database Vendor: epixtech, inc.
Mem of Nicolet Federated Library System
Friends of the Library Group
Bookmobiles: 1

BROWN COUNTY MENTAL HEALTH CENTER STAFF LIBRARY,* 2900 Saint Anthony Dr, 54311-9962. SAN 327-8468. Tel: 920-391-4839. FAX: 920-391-4870.
Library Holdings: Bk Vols 1,800; Per Subs 45
Subject Interests: Psychiatry, Psychology
Publications: Happenings of the Week (weekly newsletter)
Partic in Fox River Valley Area Library Consortium

FIRST UNITED METHODIST CHURCH LIBRARY, 501 Howe St, 54301. SAN 318-0107. Tel: 920-437-9252. FAX: 920-437-0991. Web Site: www.firstumcgb.org. *Ad Servs*, David Wilkinson; *Ch Servs*, Barbara Hayes
Founded 1959
Library Holdings: Bk Vols 1,550; Bk Titles 1,500; Per Subs 10

FOTH & VAN DYKE, Engineering Architecture Library, 2737 S Ridge Rd, PO Box 19012, 54304-5590. SAN 324-3745. Tel: 920-497-2500, Ext 6623. FAX: 920-497-8516. *Librn*, Bart Voskuil; E-Mail: bvoskuil@foth.com; Staff 1 (MLS 1)
Founded 1980
Library Holdings: Bk Vols 6,000; Bk Titles 5,000; Per Subs 150
Subject Interests: Architecture, Engineering
Restriction: By appointment only
Partic in NE Wis Intertype Librs, Inc

GREEN BAY CORRECTIONAL INSTITUTION LIBRARY,* PO Box 19033, 54307. SAN 318-0115. Tel: 920-432-4877, Ext 473. FAX: 920-432-5388. *Librn*, Karen Juckem
Enrl 850
Library Holdings: Bk Vols 6,100; Per Subs 110
Subject Interests: Law
Restriction: Not open to public

S GREEN BAY PRESS-GAZETTE LIBRARY,* PO Box 19430, 54307-9430. SAN 329-7993. Tel: 920-431-8362. FAX: 920-431-8379. *Librn*, Diane L Robb
Library Holdings: Bk Vols 500; Per Subs 20

S NEVILLE PUBLIC MUSEUM OF BROWN COUNTY LIBRARY,* 210 Museum Pl, 54303-2780. SAN 329-2568. Tel: 920-448-4460. FAX: 920-448-4458. *Head of Libr*, Mary K Huelsbeck; Tel: 920-448-4499, Ext 210, E-Mail: huelsbeck_mk@co.brown.wi.us; Staff 1 (Non-MLS 1)
Library Holdings: Bk Titles 4,500; Per Subs 20
Subject Interests: Art, Dolls, Local history, Museum practice, Nat sci, Textiles
Special Collections: Private & Business Mss
Restriction: Not a lending library
Function: Photocopies available

P NICOLET FEDERATED LIBRARY SYSTEM, (NFLS), 515 Pine St, 54301. SAN 318-0123. Tel: 920-448-4410. FAX: 920-448-4420. Web Site: www.nfls.lib.wi.us. *Dir*, Mark D Merrifield; E-Mail: mmerrifi@owls.lib.wi.us; Staff 10 (MLS 3, Non-MLS 7)
Founded 1976. Pop 359,533
Jan 1998-Dec 1999 Income $966,752. Mats Exp $6,200, Books $5,000, Per/Ser (Incl. Access Fees) $1,200. Sal $312,218
Publications: Nicolet Compass (newsletter)
Member Libraries: Algoma Public Library; Brown County Library; Brown County Library; Brown County Library; Door County Libraries; Farnsworth Public Library; Florence County Library; Gillett Public Library; Kewaunee Public Library; Lena Public Library; Marinette County Consolidated Public Library Service; Menominee Tribal County Library; Oconto Falls Community Library; Oneida Community Library; Shawano City-County Library
Partic in NE Wis Intertype Librs, Inc

J NORTHEAST WISCONSIN TECHNICAL COLLEGE, Learning Resource Center, 2740 W Mason, PO Box 19042, 54307-9042. SAN 318-0131. Tel: 920-498-5490. FAX: 920-498-6910. *Mgr Libr Serv*, Mary Parrott; *Ref*, Kim Laplante; Tel: 920-498-5487
Founded 1966. Enrl 4,500
Jul 1999-Jun 2000 Income $449,000. Mats Exp $217,438, Books $116,350, Per/Ser (Incl. Access Fees) $46,000, Electronic Ref Mat (Incl. Access Fees) $55,088. Sal $190,000
Library Holdings: Bk Vols 20,118; Bk Titles 11,508; Per Subs 450
Publications: New staff orientation handbooks; online catalog instruction handbook; student usage brochures
Partic in Fox River Valley Area Library Consortium; NE Wis Intertype Librs, Inc

M SAINT MARY'S HOSPITAL MEDICAL CENTER, Staff Library, 1726 Shawano Ave, 54303. SAN 327-9693. Tel: 920-498-4616. FAX: 414-498-3537. *Librn*, Julie Baeten
Library Holdings: Bk Titles 500; Per Subs 20
Subject Interests: Develop, Education, Medicine, Personal growth

M SAINT VINCENT HOSPITAL, Medical Library, 835 S Van Buren St, 54301. (Mail add: PO Box 13508, 54307), SAN 318-014X. Tel: 920-433-8171. FAX: 920-431-3171. E-Mail: mlibrary@stvgb.org. *Librn*, Patricia Nieland; *Librn*, Lori Francar; Staff 3 (MLS 2, Non-MLS 1)
Founded 1982
Library Holdings: Bk Titles 736; Per Subs 150
Partic in Fox River Valley Area Library Consortium; NE Wis Intertype Librs, Inc; Nicolet Federated Libr Syst

S SCHREIBER FOODS, INC LIBRARY,* PO Box 19010, 54307-9010. SAN 327-8506. Tel: 920-437-7601, Ext 6134. FAX: 920-437-1308. *Librn*, Margi Kvitek
Library Holdings: Bk Vols 1,500

C UNIVERSITY OF WISCONSIN-GREEN BAY, Cofrin Library, 2420 Nicolet Dr, 54311-7001. SAN 318-0158. Tel: 920-465-2333. Circulation Tel: 920-465-2530. Reference Tel: 920-465-2303. FAX: 920-465-2388. Web Site: www.uwgb.edu/~library/index.html. *Dir*, Kathy Pletcher; Tel: 920-465-2383, E-Mail: pletchek@uwgb.edu; *Asst Dir*, Leanne Hansen; Tel: 920-465-2537, E-Mail: hansenl@uwgb.edu; *Head, Circ*, John N Jax; Tel: 920-465-2304, Fax: 920-465-2136, E-Mail: jaxj@uwgb.edu; *Head Ref*, Anne Kasuboski; Tel: 920-465-2543, E-Mail: kasubosa@uwgb.edu; *Head Tech Servs*, Judy Nelson; Tel: 920-465-2154, E-Mail: nelsonj@uwgb.edu; *Archivist, Spec Coll*, Debra Anderson; Tel: 920-465-2539, E-Mail: andersod@uwgb.edu; *Coll Develop, Govt Doc*, Joan Robb; *Info Tech*, Marlys Brunsting; Tel: 920-465-2893, E-Mail: brunstim@uwgb.edu; *Ref*, Holly Egebo; Tel: 920-465-2764, E-Mail: egeboh@uwgb.edu; *Bibliog Instr*, Paula Ganyard; Tel: 920-465-2666, E-Mail: ganyardp@uwgb.edu; *ILL*, Mary Naumann; Tel: 920-465-2385, Fax: 920-465-2136, E-Mail: naumannm@uwgb.edu; *Cat*, Debra Strelka; Tel: 920-465-2541, E-Mail: strelkad@uwgb.edu; Staff 19 (MLS 8, Non-MLS 11)
Founded 1967. Enrl 5,500; Fac 160; Highest Degree: Master
Jul 1999-Jun 2000 Income $475,217. Mats Exp $468,265, Books $118,025, Per/Ser (Incl. Access Fees) $272,530, Presv $10,000, Micro $12,410, Other Print Mats $4,180, Electronic Ref Mat (Incl. Access Fees) $51,120. Sal $567,034 (Prof $350,671)

Library Holdings: Bk Vols 282,432; Bk Titles 238,466; Per Subs 1,327
Subject Interests: Environmental studies, Humanities, Music, Natural science
Special Collections: Belgian-American Ethnic Coll; Local History (Area Research Center), bks, mss & micro; University Archives
Automation Activity & Vendor Info: (Acquisitions) Endeavor; (Cataloging) Endeavor; (Circulation) Endeavor; (Course Reserve) Endeavor; (OPAC) Endeavor; (Serials) Endeavor
Database Vendor: Ebsco - EbscoHost, Lexis-Nexis, OCLC - First Search, OVID Technologies, ProQuest, Silverplatter Information Inc.
Partic in NE Wis Intertype Librs, Inc; OCLC Online Computer Library Center, Inc; Wisconsin Library Services
Friends of the Library Group

GREEN LAKE

P CAESTECKER PUBLIC LIBRARY,* 518 Hill St, 54941. SAN 318-0166. Tel: 920-294-3572. FAX: 920-294-6055. Web Site: axpwinnefox.org/wwn/wls/greenlake.html. *Dir*, Tasha Saecker; E-Mail: saecker@winnefox.org
Pop 2,662; Circ 42,713
Library Holdings: Bk Vols 12,000; Per Subs 70
Mem of Winnefox Library System
Friends of the Library Group

GREENDALE

P GREENDALE PUBLIC LIBRARY,* 5647 Broad St, 53129-1887. SAN 318-0174. Tel: 414-423-2136. FAX: 414-423-2139. Web Site: www.greendale.org. *Dir*, Gary Warren Niebuhr; E-Mail: gary.niebuhr@mcfls.org; *Librn*, Jennifer Loeffel; E-Mail: jennifer.loeffel@mcfls.org; *Librn*, Betty Grypp; E-Mail: betty.gryppe@mcfls.org
Founded 1938. Pop 15,500; Circ 183,251
Jan 1999-Dec 1999 Income $387,293. Mats Exp $65,000, Books $52,000, Per/Ser (Incl. Access Fees) $6,000. Sal $189,435 (Prof $101,475)
Library Holdings: Bk Vols 55,540; Per Subs 100
Subject Interests: Local history
Automation Activity & Vendor Info: (Acquisitions) Innovative Interfaces Inc.; (Cataloging) Innovative Interfaces Inc.; (Circulation) Innovative Interfaces Inc.
Mem of Milwaukee County Federated Library System
Partic in Library Council Of Metropolitan Milwaukee, Inc
Friends of the Library Group

GREENFIELD

P GREENFIELD PUBLIC LIBRARY,* 7215 W Coldspring, 53220. SAN 325-1578. Tel: 414-321-9595. FAX: 414-321-8595. Web Site: www.greenfieldlibrary.org. *Dir*, Terri Delke; *Ref*, Chris Helm; Staff 11 (MLS 3, Non-MLS 8)
Library Holdings: Bk Vols 97,631; Per Subs 175
Mem of Milwaukee County Federated Library System
Friends of the Library Group

GREENWOOD

P GREENWOOD PUBLIC LIBRARY,* 102 N Main St, PO Box 100, 54437. SAN 318-0190. Tel: 715-267-7103. FAX: 715-267-6636. *Librn*, Pat Braun; E-Mail: plbraun@mail.badgerdial.net
Founded 1913. Pop 3,400; Circ 54,164
Library Holdings: Bk Titles 17,496; Per Subs 82
Subject Interests: History
Special Collections: National Geographic from 1916-1987
Publications: Booklist; CCBC; Library Journal
Mem of Wisconsin Valley Library Service

HALES CORNERS

S BOERNER BOTANICAL GARDENS, Horticultural Reference Library, 5879 S 92nd St, 53130-0429. SAN 328-3526. Tel: 414-425-1130. FAX: 414-425-8679. Web Site: www.countyparks.com.
Library Holdings: Bk Vols 10,000

P HALES CORNERS LIBRARY, 5885 S 116th St, 53130-1707. SAN 318-0204. Tel: 414-529-6150. FAX: 414-529-6154. *Dir*, Patricia Laughlin; E-Mail: pat.laughlin@mcfls.org; Staff 4 (MLS 4)
Founded 1976. Pop 7,850; Circ 140,500
Jan 2000-Dec 2000 Income $388,548. Mats Exp $48,080, Books $39,280, Per/Ser (Incl. Access Fees) $4,650, AV Equip $3,450, Electronic Ref Mat (Incl. Access Fees) $700. Sal $261,848
Library Holdings: Bk Titles 41,771; Per Subs 125
Mem of Milwaukee County Federated Library System
Friends of the Library Group

R SACRED HEART SCHOOL OF THEOLOGY, Leo Dehon Library, 7335 S Hwy 100, PO Box 429, 53130-0429. SAN 318-0212. Tel: 414-425-8300, Ext 7278. FAX: 414-529-6992. E-Mail: shstlib@switchinc.org. *Dir*, Kathleen Harty; E-Mail: kharty@switchinc.org; Staff 3 (MLS 2, Non-MLS 1)
Founded 1932. Enrl 105; Fac 32; Highest Degree: Master
Jul 1998-Jun 1999 Income Parent Institution $181,943. Mats Exp $37,5 Books $17,027, Per/Ser (Incl. Access Fees) $16,253, Presv $1,491, Electronic Ref Mat (Incl. Access Fees) $2,800. Sal $93,846 (Prof $78,9
Library Holdings: Bk Vols 89,357; Per Subs 451
Subject Interests: Canon law, Church history, Liturgy, Sacred scripture
Special Collections: Religious Americana; Sacred Heart Coll
Automation Activity & Vendor Info: (Cataloging) Innovative Interface Inc.; (Circulation) Innovative Interfaces Inc.; (OPAC) Innovative Interfa Inc.; (Serials) Innovative Interfaces Inc.
Database Vendor: Ebsco - EbscoHost
Publications: Library Policies & Procedures (Library handbook)
Partic in Southeastern Wisconsin Information Technology Exchange, Inc

HAMMOND

P HAMMOND COMMUNITY LIBRARY, 850 Davis St, PO Box 120, 54015-0120. SAN 318-0220. Tel: 715-796-2281. FAX: 715-796-2332. E-Mail: hamlib@scecnet.net. Web Site: www.scecnet.net/~hamlib. *Dir*, Michelle Johnson
Founded 1968. Pop 1,072; Circ 18,000
Jan 2000-Dec 2000 Income $75,785, City $64,385, County $11,400. Ma Exp $64,385. Sal $26,260
Library Holdings: Bk Titles 10,000; Per Subs 70
Mem of Indianhead Federated Library System

HANCOCK

P HANCOCK PUBLIC LIBRARY,* 114 S Main St, PO Box 217, 54943-0217. SAN 318-0239. Tel: 715-249-5817. FAX: 715-249-5815. Web Site telnetzaxp.winnefox.org. *Dir*, Sandra Zuehlke
Pop 1,664; Circ 26,551
Library Holdings: Bk Vols 6,000; Per Subs 40
Subject Interests: Local history
Special Collections: Census, microfilm; Hancock-Coloma News; Plainfie Sun Newsp; Waushara Argus
Mem of Winnefox Library System
Open Mon, Thurs & Fri 1-6, Sat 10-12
Friends of the Library Group

HARTFORD

M HARTFORD MEMORIAL HOSPITAL, INC, Medical Staff Library, 103 Sumner St, 53027. SAN 318-0247. Tel: 262-673-2300, Ext 266. FAX: 26 670-7620. *Librn*, Debbi Groves
Library Holdings: Bk Vols 150; Per Subs 20
Subject Interests: Health specialties, Medicine, Nursing

P HARTFORD PUBLIC LIBRARY,* 115 N Main St, 53027-1596. SAN 3 0255. Tel: 262-673-8240. FAX: 262-673-8300. E-Mail: hpl@hnet.net. We Site: www.hnet.net/~hpl. *Dir*, Michael J Gelhausen; Tel: 262-673-8241, E-Mail: mikeg@hnet.net; *Ch Servs*, Audrey Wolter; Tel: 262-673-8242, E-Mail: awol@hnet.net; Staff 12 (MLS 2, Non-MLS 10)
Pop 20,000; Circ 207,129
Jan 1998-Dec 1998 Income $655,731, State $8,405, City $415,157, Coun $204,201, Locally Generated Income $27,968. Mats Exp $108,145, Book $87,396, Per/Ser (Incl. Access Fees) $8,504, Micro $25. Sal $251,069 (Pr $83,000)
Library Holdings: Bk Vols 90,680; Per Subs 201
Special Collections: All US Census Records for Wisconsin-Washington & Dade County, micro; History Room Coll; Local History, micro; Local Pa (1864-1994), micro
Automation Activity & Vendor Info: (Cataloging) epixtech, inc.; (Circulation) epixtech, inc.; (OPAC) epixtech, inc.
Mem of Mid-Wisconsin Federated Library System
Partic in Library Council Of Metropolitan Milwaukee, Inc
Outreach service for institutions & homebound

HARTLAND

P HARTLAND PUBLIC LIBRARY, 110 E Park Ave, 53029. SAN 318-026 Tel: 262-367-3350. FAX: 262-369-2251. E-Mail: info@hartland.lib.wi.us. Web Site: www.hartland.lib.wi.us/index.htm. *Dir*, Nancy Massnick; *Ref Se* Priscilla Bohacheck; *Tech Servs*, Villa Johnson; *Ch Servs*, Lin Pohl; Staff (MLS 4, Non-MLS 12)
Founded 1897. Pop 12,000; Circ 130,000
Jan 1999-Dec 1999 Income $456,250. Mats Exp $93,340, Books $42,600, Per/Ser (Incl. Access Fees) $4,550, AV Equip $18,300. Sal $300,570
Library Holdings: Bk Titles 60,000; Per Subs 118
Subject Interests: Local history
Special Collections: Parenting, bks, prints
Mem of Waukesha County Federated Library System
Friends of the Library Group

/KINS

HAWKINS AREA LIBRARY,* 522 Grand Ave, 54530-9702. SAN 324-1246. Tel: 715-585-2311. *Dir*, Dolores Krings
Founded 1979. Pop 800; Circ 2,582
Library Holdings: Bk Titles 5,112
Mem of Indianhead Federated Library System
Partic in OCLC Online Computer Library Center, Inc

'WARD

HAYWARD AREA MEMORIAL HOSPITAL, Health Sciences Library,* 11040 N State Rt 77, 54843. SAN 324-0959. Tel: 715-634-1120. FAX: 715-634-2515.
Founded 1975
Library Holdings: Bk Titles 200; Per Subs 22

HAYWARD CARNEGIE LIBRARY, 10538 Main, PO Box 512, 54843-0512. SAN 318-0271. Tel: 715-634-2161. FAX: 715-634-5257. E-Mail: hlibrary@win.bright.net. *Dir*, Molly Lank-Jones; *Librn*, Roxanne Breitwish; *Asst Librn*, Carol Soulier
Founded 1904. Circ 63,462
1999-2000 Income $157,908, State $100, County $112,000, Locally Generated Income $31,240, Other $33,325. Mats Exp $22,519, Books $15,612, Per/Ser (Incl. Access Fees) $2,944, Other Print Mats $3,963. Sal $89,553
Library Holdings: Bk Vols 24,184; Per Subs 82
Subject Interests: Wis hist
Automation Activity & Vendor Info: (Acquisitions) Follett; (Cataloging) Follett; (Circulation) Follett
Mem of Northern Waters Library Service
Friends of the Library Group

LAC COURTE OREILLES OJIBWA COLLEGE COMMUNITY LIBRARY,* 13466 W Trepania Rd, 54843-2186. SAN 377-967X. Tel: 715-634-4790, Ext 108. FAX: 712-634-5049. E-Mail: capfoff@win.bright.net. *Librn*, Caryl Pfaff; *Asst Librn*, David Bisonette
Library Holdings: Bk Titles 16,000; Per Subs 100
Mem of Northern Waters Library Service
Partic in Am Indian Libr Asn; Am Libr Asn; American Indian Higher Education Consortium; Wis Libr Asn

.LSBORO

HILLSBORO PUBLIC LIBRARY,* 819 High Ave, 54634-0468. SAN 318-0298. Tel: 608-489-2192. E-Mail: hlibrary@mwt.net. *Librn*, Debra K Lambert
Pop 1,273; Circ 35,100
Library Holdings: Bk Vols 19,800; Per Subs 45
Mem of Winding Rivers Library System

LMEN

LA CROSSE COUNTY LIBRARY,* Administration Ctr 103 State St, PO Box 220, 54636-0220. SAN 364-7196. Tel: 608-526-4198. FAX: 608-526-3299. Web Site: www.centuryinter.net/countylibrary. *Dir*, Marcia K Matheson; Tel: 608-526-9600, E-Mail: matmar@mail.holmen.k12.wi.us; *Cat*, Eileen Paudler; *Ch Servs*, Carol Knapmiller; Tel: 608-526-4641, E-Mail: knacar@mail.holmen.k12.wi.us; *Ch Servs*, Karen Kroll; Tel: 608-526-4641, E-Mail: karkro@mail.holmen.k12.wi.us; *Ch Servs*, Diane Richards; Tel: 608-526-4641, E-Mail: ricdia@mail.holmen.k12.wi.us; *Automation Syst Coordr, Ref*, Susanne Stranc; Tel: 608-526-3311, E-Mail: strasue@mail.holmen.k12.wi.us; *Reader Servs, Ref*, Rebecca Dandrea; Tel: 608-781-9599, Fax: 608-781-9594, E-Mail: danre@mail.onalaska.k12.wi.us; *Reader Servs, Ref*, Carol Petrowski; Tel: 608-781-9599, Fax: 608-781-9594, E-Mail: petca@mail.onalaska.k12.wi.us; Staff 42 (MLS 3, Non-MLS 39)
Founded 1898. Pop 53,670; Circ 306,565
Jan 1999-Dec 1999 Income (Main Library and Branch Library) $946,525, County $928,035, Locally Generated Income $18,490. Mats Exp $107,800, Books $72,000, Per/Ser (Incl. Access Fees) $9,300, Presv $512. Sal $596,407
Database Vendor: epixtech, inc.
Mem of Winding Rivers Library System
Friends of the Library Group
Branches: 5
CAMPBELL, Campbell Town Hall, 2219 Bainbridge, LaCrosse, 54603. SAN 364-7250. Tel: 608-783-0052. Web Site: www.centuryinter.net/countylibrary. *Librn*, Sarah Stuber
Friends of the Library Group
HOLMEN AREA Tel: 608-526-4198. Web Site: www.centuryinter.net/countylibrary.
JOHN BOSSHARD MEMORIAL LIBRARY, 1720 Henry Johns Blvd, Bangor, 54614. SAN 364-7226. Tel: 608-486-4408. Web Site: www.centuryinter.net/countylibrary. *Librn*, Katewin Peterson
ONALASKA PUBLIC, 741 Oak Ave S, PO Box 248, Onalaska, 54650. SAN 364-7315. Tel: 608-781-9568. Web Site: www.centuryinter.net/countylibrary.
Friends of the Library Group
WEST SALEM BRANCH, 175 S Leonard, West Salem, 54669. SAN 364-734X. Tel: 608-786-1505. Web Site: www.centuryinter.net/countylibrary. *Librn*, Susan Rotering
Friends of the Library Group

HORICON

P HORICON PUBLIC LIBRARY,* 404 E Lake St, 53032-1297. SAN 318-0301. Tel: 920-485-3535. FAX: 920-485-3536. E-Mail: horiconlib@horicon.org. *Dir*, Geri Feucht
Founded 1899. Pop 3,782; Circ 40,000
Library Holdings: Bk Vols 24,000; Per Subs 55
Mem of Mid-Wisconsin Federated Library System
Friends of the Library Group

HORTONVILLE

P HORTONVILLE PUBLIC LIBRARY,* 102 W Main St, 54944. SAN 318-031X. Tel: 920-779-4279. FAX: 920-779-4279. *Dir*, Carolyn R Habeck; E-Mail: chabeck@owlsnet.owls.lib.wi.us; Staff 1 (MLS 1)
Founded 1920
Jan 1997-Dec 1998 Income $65,472, City $41,747, County $23,725. Mats Exp $11,200, Books $9,000, Per/Ser (Incl. Access Fees) $1,300. Sal $33,297 (Prof $31,349)
Library Holdings: Bk Vols 12,458; Per Subs 61
Mem of Outagamie Waupaca Library System
Friends of the Library Group

HUDSON

P HUDSON PUBLIC LIBRARY,* 911 Fourth St, 54016. SAN 318-0336. Tel: 715-386-3101. Web Site: www.pressenter.com/~hupublib. *Dir*, Kathleen Norden
Pop 20,000; Circ 140,894
Library Holdings: Bk Vols 39,246; Per Subs 102
Mem of Indianhead Federated Library System
Friends of the Library Group

HURLEY

P HURLEY PUBLIC LIBRARY,* 405 Fifth Ave N, 54534-1170. SAN 318-0344. Tel: 715-561-5707. FAX: 715-561-3222. E-Mail: hupl@portup.com. *Librn*, Lynne Pedri
Library Holdings: Bk Vols 9,500; Per Subs 22
Publications: Booklist
Mem of Northern Waters Library Service; Northwest Wis Libr Syst

HUSTISFORD

P HUSTISFORD PUBLIC LIBRARY, (HPL), 210 S Lake St, PO Box 386, 53034-0386. SAN 370-6591. Tel: 920-349-3463. FAX: 920-349-4540. E-Mail: hust@mwfls.org. Web Site: www.hustisford.com/library.htm. *Dir*, Candace Graulich; E-Mail: graulich@mwfls.org; *Ch Servs*, Lois Braemer; E-Mail: lbraemer@mwfls.org; Staff 3 (Non-MLS 3)
Founded 1986. Pop 2,350; Circ 30,000
Jan 2001-Dec 2001 Income $73,630, State $750, City $58,380, County $12,000, Locally Generated Income $2,500. Mats Exp $13,900, Books $12,500, Per/Ser (Incl. Access Fees) $1,400. Sal $40,000
Library Holdings: Bk Vols 14,000; Bk Titles 13,500; Per Subs 60
Automation Activity & Vendor Info: (Cataloging) Sagebrush Corporation; (Circulation) Sagebrush Corporation; (OPAC) Sagebrush Corporation
Function: ILL available
Mem of Mid-Wisconsin Federated Library System
Friends of the Library Group

INDEPENDENCE

P INDEPENDENCE PUBLIC LIBRARY,* 23688 Adams St, PO Box 98, 54747-0098. SAN 318-0352. Tel: 715-985-3616. FAX: 715-985-2530. *Dir*, Cathy Kruckenberg
Founded 1908. Pop 1,174; Circ 18,760
Library Holdings: Bk Vols 13,532; Per Subs 55
Mem of Winding Rivers Library System

IOLA

P IOLA VILLAGE LIBRARY,* 180 S Main St, 54945-9689. SAN 324-6965. Tel: 715-445-4330. FAX: 715-445-2917. E-Mail: ivl@owlsnet.owls.lib.wi.us. Web Site: www.gglbbs.com/iolalib/index.htm. *Dir*, Robyn Grove; E-Mail: rgrove@owlsnet.owls.lib.wi.us

Pop 1,109; Circ 17,976
Library Holdings: Bk Vols 17,820; Per Subs 58
Mem of Outagamie Waupaca Library System
Friends of the Library Group

IRON RIDGE

P IRON RIDGE PUBLIC LIBRARY,* 205 Park St, 53035. SAN 364-6114. Tel: 920-387-3637. FAX: 920-387-3637. E-Mail: iridge@nconnect.net. *Dir*, Jerilyn Papenfuss
Library Holdings: Bk Vols 13,332
Mem of Mid-Wisconsin Federated Library System

JANESVILLE

P ARROWHEAD LIBRARY SYSTEM, 210 Dodge St, 53545-3809. SAN 318-0360. Tel: 608-758-6690. FAX: 608-758-6689. Web Site: als.lib.wi.us. *Dir*, Gary Silver; E-Mail: gsilver@als.lib.wi.us; Staff 2 (MLS 2)
Founded 1974. Pop 139,771
Jan 1998-Dec 1999 Income $1,046,358, State $343,194, County $703,164. Mats Exp $21,118, Books $8,015, Per/Ser (Incl. Access Fees) $2,200. Sal $160,453 (Prof $75,000)
Member Libraries: Beloit College; Beloit Public Library; Blackhawk Technical College Library; Clinton Public Library; Eager Free Public Library; Edgerton Public Library; Hedberg Public Library; Milton Public Library; Orfordville Public Library; University of Wisconsin-Rock County Library; Wisconsin Center for the Blind & Visually Impaired
Partic in OCLC Online Computer Library Center, Inc

J BLACKHAWK TECHNICAL COLLEGE LIBRARY, 6004 Prairie Rd, 53547. SAN 318-0379. Tel: 608-757-7671. Reference Tel: 608-757-7705. FAX: 608-758-6914. *Librn*, Janet Laura White; E-Mail: jwhite@blackhawk.tec.wi.us; Staff 3 (MLS 1, Non-MLS 2)
Founded 1966. Enrl 1,527; Fac 100
1999-2000 Mats Exp $125,767, Books $24,466, Per/Ser (Incl. Access Fees) $23,650, Micro $6,300, Electronic Ref Mat (Incl. Access Fees) $11,351. Sal $104,142 (Prof $57,604)
Library Holdings: Bk Titles 21,000; Per Subs 350; High Interest/Low Vocabulary Bk Vols 839
Special Collections: Child Care; High/Low; Professional
Database Vendor: Ebsco - EbscoHost, GaleNet, ProQuest
Mem of Arrowhead Library System
Partic in South Central Wisconsin Health Science Library Cooperative

P HEDBERG PUBLIC LIBRARY, (HPL), 316 S Main St, 53545-3971. SAN 318-0387. Tel: 608-758-6588. Interlibrary Loan Service Tel: 608-758-6598. Circulation Tel: 608-758-6582. Reference Tel: 608-758-6581. TDD: 608-758-6604. FAX: 608-758-6583. E-Mail: hpl@als.lib.wi.us. Web Site: als.lib.wi.us/hpl. *Dir*, Karen Krueger; Tel: 608-758-6600, E-Mail: kkrueger@als.lib.wi.us; *Asst Dir*, Patricia Dwyer Wanninger; Tel: 608-758-6600; *Circ*, Barbara Ertl; *Coll Develop, Tech Servs*, Carol Kuntzelman; *ILL*, Jeanne Motsinger; *Pub Relations*, Linda Belknap; *YA Servs*, Catherine Norris; Staff 51 (MLS 13, Non-MLS 38)
Founded 1884. Pop 80,133; Circ 988,178
Jan 1999-Dec 1999 Income $2,901,214, State $95,023, City $2,232,173, County $333,855, Locally Generated Income $225,303, Other $14,860. Mats Exp $358,652, Books $235,841, Per/Ser (Incl. Access Fees) $26,434, AV Equip $56,836, Electronic Ref Mat (Incl. Access Fees) $39,541. Sal $1,510,008
Library Holdings: Bk Vols 254,110; Per Subs 651
Subject Interests: Local history
Automation Activity & Vendor Info: (Acquisitions) epixtech, inc.; (Circulation) epixtech, inc.; (OPAC) epixtech, inc.; (Serials) epixtech, inc.
Database Vendor: OCLC - First Search
Publications: Library Matters (bi-monthly)
Mem of Arrowhead Library System
Partic in OCLC Online Computer Library Center, Inc
Special Services for the Deaf - TDD
Special Services for the Blind - Descriptive videos
Friends of the Library Group

M MERCY HOSPITAL, Medical Library,* 1000 Mineral Point Ave, 53545. SAN 364-6920. Tel: 608-756-6000, 608-756-6749. FAX: 608-756-6512.
Founded 1925
Library Holdings: Bk Vols 800; Bk Titles 700; Per Subs 85
Subject Interests: Gen med, Nursing, Surgical
Partic in South Central Wisconsin Health Science Library Cooperative

GM ROCK COUNTY HEALTH CARE CENTER, Staff Library, 3530 N County Hwy F, PO Box 351, 53547-0351. SAN 318-0417. Tel: 608-757-5000. FAX: 608-757-5010.
Founded 1971
Jan 1999-Dec 1999 Income County $3,700. Mats Exp Per/Ser (Incl. Access Fees) $3,000
Library Holdings: Bk Titles 1,000; Per Subs 52
Subject Interests: Alcohol, Counseling, Drugs, Geriatrics, Group work, Nursing, Psychiatry
Publications: Intersect
Restriction: Not a lending library, Not open to public

S ROCK COUNTY HISTORICAL SOCIETY, Archives of Rock County History, 933 Mineral Point Ave, 53545-2970. (Mail add: PO Box 8096, 53547-8096), Tel: 608-756-4509. Toll Free Tel: 800-577-1859. FAX: 60 741-9596. E-Mail: rchs@ticon.net. Web Site: www.lincolntallman.org.
Founded 1948
Library Holdings: Bk Titles 8,385; Per Subs 19
Subject Interests: Archit studies of local hist sites, Hist of Rock county Survey of all hist sites
Special Collections: Carrie Jacobs Bond Coll; Frances Willard Coll; Historic Materials (Samson Tractor Company), papers; Land Speculatio (Tallman Family), papers; Local History, diaries & family papers; Local Organizations Coll; Rock County Industrial Development Coll; Women' Christian Temperance Union Coll
Restriction: Not a lending library
Function: Research fees apply

R SEVENTH-DAY BAPTIST HISTORICAL SOCIETY LIBRARY, 3120 Kennedy Rd, PO Box 1678, 53547. SAN 310-4311. Tel: 608-752-5055. FAX: 608-752-7711. E-Mail: sdbgen@inwave.com, sdbhist@inwave.co Web Site: www.seventhdaybaptist.org. *In Charge*, Don A Sanford; Staff (MLS 1, Non-MLS 1)
Founded 1916
Jan 1999-Dec 1999 Income $40,000. Mats Exp $1,500, Books $300, Pe (Incl. Access Fees) $200, AV Equip $1,000. Sal $25,000 (Prof $20,000)
Library Holdings: Bk Vols 4,500; Bk Titles 2,600; Per Subs 25
Subject Interests: Hist of the Sabbath, Seventh Day Baptists
Special Collections: 17th-20th Century English Seventh Day Baptist Churches (Mill Yard Church & Sabbatarian Literature Coll), bks & mss; Archives of Seventh Day Baptist General Conference, USA & Canada; China Mission Coll, 1847-1945, mss & ephemera; Early African Sevent Day Baptist Missions (Nyasaland Missions Coll), 1895-1914; Ephrata, P. Cloister (Julius F Sachse Coll), bks, mss, ephemera, realia
Publications: Annual Report; books & pamphlets on Seventh Day Bapti history; occasional newsletter
Restriction: By appointment only, Not a lending library
Function: Research library

C UNIVERSITY OF WISCONSIN-ROCK COUNTY LIBRARY, 2909 Kellogg Ave, 53546-5699. SAN 318-0433. Tel: 608-758-6531. FAX: 608 758-6560. Web Site: rock.uwc.edu/library.htm. *Acq, Librn, Ref*, Evelyn Payson; E-Mail: epayson@uwc.edu; *Asst Librn*, Sue Kitto; E-Mail: skitto uwc.edu; Staff 2 (MLS 1, Non-MLS 1)
Founded 1966. Enrl 875; Fac 50; Highest Degree: Associate
Jul 1999-Jun 2000 Income $130,000, State $111,000, Federal $19,000. M Exp $37,000, Books $15,000, Per/Ser (Incl. Access Fees) $20,000, AV E $2,000. Sal $97,000 (Prof $50,000)
Library Holdings: Bk Titles 65,000; Per Subs 200
Automation Activity & Vendor Info: (Acquisitions) Endeavor; (Catalog Endeavor; (Circulation) Endeavor; (Course Reserve) Endeavor; (ILL) Endeavor; (OPAC) Endeavor; (Serials) Endeavor
Mem of Arrowhead Library System
Partic in OCLC Online Computer Library Center, Inc

S WISCONSIN CENTER FOR THE BLIND & VISUALLY IMPAIRED WISCONSIN SCHOOL FOR THE VISUALLY HANDICAPPED LIBRARY, 1700 W State St, 53546. SAN 318-0441. Tel: 608-758-611 FAX: 608-758-6161.; Staff 1 (Non-MLS 1)
Library Holdings: Bk Vols 12,000; Per Subs 90
Automation Activity & Vendor Info: (Circulation) epixtech, inc.
Mem of Arrowhead Library System

JEFFERSON

G COUNTRYSIDE HOME STAFF LIBRARY, 1425 Wisconsin Dr, 53549-1999. SAN 324-0894. Tel: 920-674-5903. FAX: 920-674-6075. *Librn*, Ca Rueth
Founded 1967
1998-1999 Income $100. Mats Exp $200, Books $50, Per/Ser (Incl. Acce Fees) $150
Library Holdings: Bk Titles 1,046; Per Subs 31
Subject Interests: Crafts, Medicine, Nursing

P JEFFERSON PUBLIC LIBRARY,* 321 S Main St, 53549-1772. SAN 32 2161. Tel: 920-674-7733. FAX: 920-674-7735. E-Mail: jeffpubl@intaccess.com. Web Site: www.jefnet.com/library/. *Dir*, Kate Crowley Lorenz; *Tech Servs*, Hazel Rooker; *Ch Servs*, Jane Besel; *Automation Syst Coordr, ILL*, Sue McKechnie; *Ad Servs*, Leann Schwanat-Lehner; Staff 6 (MLS 1, Non-MLS 5)
Founded 1871. Pop 11,647; Circ 78,327
Library Holdings: Bk Titles 37,359; Per Subs 130
Mem of Mid-Wisconsin Federated Library System

NSON CREEK

JOHNSON CREEK PUBLIC LIBRARY,* 125 Lincoln St, PO Box 130, 53038-0130. SAN 324-1254. Tel: 920-699-3741. FAX: 920-699-3741. E-Mail: jcplibrary@jefnet.com. *Librn*, Luci Bledsoe; Staff 2 (MLS 1, Non-MLS 1)
Founded 1902. Pop 2,153; Circ 20,648
Library Holdings: Bk Titles 13,000; Per Subs 50
Friends of the Library Group

EAU

JUNEAU PUBLIC LIBRARY,* 250 N Fairfield Ave, 53039-1323. SAN 318-045X. Tel: 920-386-4805. FAX: 920-386-4806. *Dir*, Barbara Smith
Founded 1949
Library Holdings: Bk Vols 25,000; Per Subs 49
Mem of Mid-Wisconsin Federated Library System
Open Mon-Thurs 11-8, Fri 11-4, Sat 9-12; summer closed Sat
Friends of the Library Group

JKAUNA

KAUKAUNA PUBLIC LIBRARY,* 111 Main Ave, PO Box 530, 54130-0530. SAN 318-0468. Tel: 920-766-6340. FAX: 920-766-6343. *Dir*, Craig A Lahm; E-Mail: clahm@owlsnet.owls.lib.wi.us
Founded 1899. Pop 12,397; Circ 168,613
1998-1999 Income $438,573, City $372,796, County $65,777. Mats Exp $56,575, Books $39,205, Per/Ser (Incl. Access Fees) $7,305, Micro $8,119. Sal $241,725
Library Holdings: Bk Vols 59,756; Per Subs 206
Subject Interests: Wis hist
Mem of Outagamie Waupaca Library System

NDALL

KENDALL PUBLIC LIBRARY,* 110 ES Railroad St, 54638-9999. SAN 318-0476. Tel: 608-463-7103. *Dir*, Helen Zunlke
Founded 1946. Pop 468
Library Holdings: Bk Vols 5,373; Per Subs 20
Mem of Winding Rivers Library System

NOSHA

CARTHAGE COLLEGE, John Mosheim Ruthrauff Library, 2001 Alford Park Dr, 53140-1900. SAN 318-0492. Tel: 262-551-5900. FAX: 262-551-5904. Web Site: www.carthage.edu. *Dir*, Eugene A Engeldinger; *Tech Servs*, Richard Hren; *ILL*, Jane Dorf; *Ref*, Tina Eger; *Archivist*, Dennis Unterholzner; *Publ Servs*, Angela Quick; Staff 9 (MLS 7, Non-MLS 2)
Founded 1847
Library Holdings: Bk Vols 155,000; Bk Titles 120,000; Per Subs 450
Special Collections: Civil War (Palumbo Coll); English & American Literature 1890-1950 (Dawe Coll); Historiography (Wilde Coll); Religion & Sociology (Evjen Coll)
Publications: BiblioNews
Partic in Coun of Wis Librs, Inc; OCLC Online Computer Library Center, Inc; Tri-County Libr Council, Inc; Wis Libr Consortium; Wisconsin Library Services
Repository for Archives of Carthage College & Wis-Upper Mich Synod of the Lutheran Church in America

GATEWAY TECHNICAL COLLEGE, Learning Resources Center Library, 3520 30th Ave, 53144-1690. SAN 364-7013. Tel: 262-564-2786. Interlibrary Loan Service Tel: 262-564-2640. FAX: 262-564-2787. Web Site: www.gateway.tec.wi.us/library. *Librn*, Gerald Perona; Tel: 262-564-2640, E-Mail: peronaj@gateway.tec.wi.us; *Acq*, Linda Nielsen; Tel: 262-564-2604, E-Mail: nielsenl@gateway.tec.wi.us; *Cat*, Judy Quinn; Tel: 262-564-2654, E-Mail: quinnj@gateway.tec.wi.us; *Circ*, Linda Cate; Tel: 262-564-2540, E-Mail: catel@gateway.tec.wi.us
Founded 1964. Fac 201
Library Holdings: Bk Vols 90,000; Bk Titles 35,000; Per Subs 365; Bks on Deafness & Sign Lang 417
Subject Interests: Aviation, Computer science, Horticulture, Interior design, Law enforcement, Nursing, Physical therapy
Automation Activity & Vendor Info: (Acquisitions) Endeavor; (Cataloging) Endeavor; (Circulation) Endeavor; (Course Reserve) Endeavor; (OPAC) Endeavor; (Serials) Endeavor
Database Vendor: Ebsco - EbscoHost, IAC - Info Trac, ProQuest, Wilson - Wilson Web
Partic in Library Council Of Metropolitan Milwaukee, Inc; Wis PALS Libr Consortium
Special Services for the Deaf - Videos & decoder

KENOSHA COUNTY HISTORICAL SOCIETY, Kenosha History Center Archives, 6300 Third Ave, 53143. SAN 318-0530. Tel: 262-654-5770. FAX: 262-654-1730. *Dir*, Robert Fuhrman; E-Mail: kchs@acronet.net; *Archivist*, Catherine Dallas
Founded 1878
Library Holdings: Bk Titles 3,000
Subject Interests: City of Kenosha, Kenosha county, Local history, State of Wisc
Restriction: Open to public for reference only

M KENOSHA HOSPITAL & MEDICAL CENTER, Health Sciences Library,* 6308 Eighth Ave, 53143. SAN 318-0549. Tel: 414-656-2120. FAX: 414-653-5780. *Librn*, Patty Westrich
Founded 1970
Library Holdings: Bk Vols 2,000; Bk Titles 1,700; Per Subs 120
Subject Interests: Cardiology, Hosp admin, Medicine, Nursing, Oncology
Partic in Southeastern Wisconsin Health Science Library Consortium

S KENOSHA NEWS, Newspaper Library, 715 58th St, 53140. SAN 371-1498. Tel: 262-656-6297. FAX: 262-657-8455. E-Mail: library@kenoshanews.com. Web Site: www.kenoshanews.com. *Librn*, Michelle M Laycock; Staff 2 (MLS 1, Non-MLS 1)
Library Holdings: Bk Titles 200
Subject Interests: Local news
Restriction: Not open to public, Staff use only
Function: Newspaper reference library

P KENOSHA PUBLIC LIBRARY,* PO Box 1414, 53141-1414. SAN 364-7048. Tel: 414-605-2160, Ext 1020. Interlibrary Loan Service Tel: 414-605-2160, Ext 1015. FAX: 414-605-2170. Web Site: www.kenosha.lib.wi.us. *Dir*, Douglas Baker; E-Mail: dbaker@kenosha.lib.wi.us; *Publ Servs*, Lin Swartz-Truesdell; *Publ Servs*, Susan Siewert; *Ch Servs*, Kathleen Thomson; *Media Spec*, Esther Puhek; *Acq, Cat, Coll Develop, ILL*, Ellen Melyon; *Bkmobile Coordr*, Therese O'Halloran; Staff 116 (MLS 26, Non-MLS 90)
Founded 1900. Pop 86,535; Circ 1,069,699
Jan 1997-Dec 1998 Income $3,799,473, City $2,733,894, County $873,879, Other $191,700. Mats Exp $384,124, Books $311,311, Per/Ser (Incl. Access Fees) $45,623. Sal $2,686,280
Library Holdings: Per Subs 1,400
Subject Interests: Kenosha county hist
Special Collections: Reading Readiness Resource Coll
Automation Activity & Vendor Info: (Circulation) GEAC
Publications: Guide to Genealogy; Job Search Information; Kenosha Organization Directory; Local Historical Resources; Newsnotes
Mem of Kenosha County Libr Syst
Partic in OCLC Online Computer Library Center, Inc; Wisconsin Library Services
Friends of the Library Group
Branches: 4
NORTHSIDE, 1500 27th Ave, PO Box 1414, 53141-1414. SAN 364-7137. Tel: 414-595-3740. FAX: 414-595-3746. *Librn*, Linda Anderson
Library Holdings: Bk Vols 122,441
GILBERT M SIMMONS BRANCH, 711 59th Pl, PO Box 1414, 53141-1414. SAN 364-7072. Tel: 414-942-3700. FAX: 414-942-3708.
Library Holdings: Bk Vols 35,488
Special Collections: Local History & Genealogy
SOUTHWEST, 7979 38th Ave, 53142-2199. (Mail add: PO Box 1414, 53141-1414), SAN 364-7080. Tel: 414-942-3710. FAX: 414-942-3705. Web Site: www.kenosha.lib.wi.us/southwest.html. *Librn*, Esther Puhek
Founded 1981
Library Holdings: Bk Vols 121,156
UPTOWN, 2419 63rd St, PO Box 1414, 53141-1414. SAN 364-7161. Tel: 414-942-3703. FAX: 414-942-3707. *Librn*, Laura Henry
Library Holdings: Bk Vols 21,398 . Librn, Therese OHalloran. Bk vols 11,802

S KENOSHA PUBLIC MUSEUM LIBRARY, 5500 First Ave, 53140. SAN 318-0557. Tel: 262-653-4140. FAX: 262-653-4143. *Dir*, Paula Touhey; *Curator*, Dan Joyce; *Curator*, Nancy Mathews; E-Mail: mnancym@kenosha.org. Subject Specialists: *Anthropology*, Nancy Mathews
Founded 1936
Jan 2000-Dec 2000 Income City $3,445. Mats Exp $3,445, Books $1,850, AV Equip $1,595
Library Holdings: Bk Vols 3,800
Subject Interests: Anthropology, Art, Mus, Natural history
Special Collections: Art Reference; Natural History Reference
Restriction: Open to public for reference only
Function: Research library
Friends of the Library Group

M SAINT CATHERINE'S HOSPITAL, Medical Library, 3556 Seventh Ave, 53140. SAN 318-0565. Tel: 262-656-3011. FAX: 262-656-3443.
Founded 1962
Library Holdings: Bk Vols 1,500; Per Subs 60
Subject Interests: Anatomy, Behav serv, Family practice, Oncology, Surgery
Publications: Bibliographies; Statistics; Surveys
Partic in Greater Midwest Regional Medical Libr Network; Southeastern Wisconsin Health Science Library Consortium

S SPEBSQSA, INC, Old Songs Library, 6315 Third Ave, 53143. SAN 318-0514. Tel: 414-653-8440. FAX: 414-654-4048. E-Mail: library@spebsqsa.org. *Librn*, Tom Barr; E-Mail: tbarr@spebsqsa.org

Founded 1965
Library Holdings: Bk Titles 150,000
Subject Interests: Old lyrical sheet music
Special Collections: 78 RPM Barbershop Records, (Lou Reed & William; Old Music (Edison & Columbia Cylinder Records); Spengler Colls)
Partic in Tri-County Libr Council, Inc

C UNIVERSITY OF WISCONSIN-PARKSIDE LIBRARY, 900 Wood Rd, PO Box 2000, 53141-2000. SAN 318-0573. Tel: 262-595-2221. Interlibrary Loan Service Tel: 262-595-2595. FAX: 262-595-2545. Web Site: www.uwp.edu/info-services/library. *Dir*, Thomas Peischl; Tel: 262-595-2273, E-Mail: thomas.peischl@uwp.edu; *Assoc Dir*, Barbara Baruth; Tel: 262-595-2167, E-Mail: barbara.baruth@uwp.edu; *Instrul Serv*, Linda Piele; Tel: 262-595-2642, E-Mail: linda.piele@uwp.edu; *Ref*, Cynthia Bryan; Tel: 262-595-2730, E-Mail: cynthia.bryan@uwp.edu; *Ref Serv*, Judith Pryor; Tel: 262-595-2730, E-Mail: judith.pryor@uwp.edu; *Online Servs*, Sylvia Beardsley; Tel: 262-595-2190, E-Mail: sylvia.beardsley@uwp.edu; *Media Spec*, Kate Pietri; Tel: 262-595-2546, E-Mail: kate.pietri@uwp.edu; *Ser*, Luellen Breed; Tel: 262-595-2274, E-Mail: luellen.breed@uwp.edu; *Cat*, Dina Kaye; Tel: 262-595-2215, E-Mail: dina.kaye@uwp.edu; *Archivist*, Nicholas Weber; Tel: 262-595-2077, E-Mail: webern@uwp.edu; Staff 17 (MLS 11, Non-MLS 6)
Founded 1967. Enrl 4,700; Fac 175; Highest Degree: Master
Library Holdings: Bk Vols 408,000; Bk Titles 280,000; Per Subs 1,641
Special Collections: 18th & 19th Century American Drama (Teisberg & Perishable Press Coll); Irving Wallace Papers
Automation Activity & Vendor Info: (Acquisitions) Endeavor; (Cataloging) Endeavor; (Circulation) Endeavor; (Course Reserve) Endeavor; (ILL) Endeavor; (Media Booking) Endeavor; (OPAC) Endeavor; (Serials) Endeavor
Partic in Coun of Wis Librs, Inc; OCLC Online Computer Library Center, Inc; Wisconsin Library Services
Friends of the Library Group

KESHENA

P MENOMINEE TRIBAL COUNTY LIBRARY,* PO Box 1090, 54135-1090. SAN 318-0581. Tel: 715-799-5212. FAX: 715-799-6516. *Dir*, Sally Kitson
Founded 1964. Pop 450; Circ 5,000
Library Holdings: Bk Vols 10,000; Per Subs 44
Mem of Nicolet Federated Library System

KEWASKUM

P KEWASKUM PUBLIC LIBRARY, 206 First St, PO Box 38, 53040. SAN 318-059X. Tel: 414-626-4312. FAX: 414-626-4861. E-Mail: kewaskumlib@hnet.net. *Dir*, Shellie Anderson
Founded 1913. Pop 2,600; Circ 30,863
Library Holdings: Bk Vols 20,000; Per Subs 68
Mem of Mid-Wisconsin Federated Library System

KEWAUNEE

P KEWAUNEE PUBLIC LIBRARY,* 822 Juneau St, 54216-1200. SAN 318-0603. Tel: 920-388-5015. FAX: 920-388-5016. E-Mail: kews@uwlsnet.owls.lib.wi.us. *Coll Develop, Dir*, Susan Grosshuesch; *Coll Develop*, Laurie Kuchl
Founded 1906. Pop 20,103; Circ 63,931
Library Holdings: Bk Vols 34,804; Per Subs 130
Mem of Nicolet Federated Library System
Friends of the Library Group

KIEL

P KIEL PUBLIC LIBRARY,* 511 Third St, 53042. SAN 318-0611. Tel: 920-894-7122. FAX: 920-894-4023. E-Mail: kielpl@esis.lib.wi.us. *Dir*, Aileen Fitzgerald; *Asst Librn*, Eileen Walsdorf; *Ch Servs*, Joie Baldock; Staff 3 (MLS 1, Non-MLS 2)
Founded 1925. Pop 4,500; Circ 80,000
Jan 2000-Dec 2000 Income (Main Library Only) $178,000, City $134,000, County $42,000, Locally Generated Income $2,000. Mats Exp $26,270, Books $23,142, Per/Ser (Incl. Access Fees) $3,128. Sal $84,400 (Prof $31,050)
Library Holdings: Bk Titles 35,000
Special Collections: Career; Wisconsin
Automation Activity & Vendor Info: (Cataloging) Sagebrush Corporation; (Circulation) Sagebrush Corporation
Mem of Manitowoc-Calumet Library System

KIMBERLY

P KIMBERLY-LITTLE CHUTE PUBLIC LIBRARY,* 515 W Kimberly Ave, 54136-1399. SAN 318-062X. Tel: 920-7825, 920-788-7515. FAX: 7827, 920-788-7516. *Dir*, Barbara Wentzel; E-Mail: bwentzel@owls.lib.wi.us
Founded 1907. Pop 16,500; Circ 300,000
Library Holdings: Bk Vols 82,000; Bk Titles 77,000; Per Subs 150
Special Collections: Toys, Hand Puppets 300
Mem of Outagamie Waupaca Library System
Partic in Fox River Valley Area Library Consortium
Joint public library operating a second facility in Little Chute, Wisconsi
Statistics reported are for both of these facilities combined

KING

S WISCONSIN VETERANS' HOME LIBRARY,* Hwy QQ, 54946. SAN 377-9696. Tel: 715-258-5586, Ext 2366. FAX: 715-258-5736. *Librn*, Li Hager
Library Holdings: Bk Titles 10,000; Per Subs 20
Subject Interests: Civil War, Wars
Special Collections: War History Coll, Civil War to Present

KINGSTON

P MILLPOND PUBLIC LIBRARY,* 151 N South St, PO Box 98, 53939 0098. SAN 318-0638. Tel: 920-394-3281. FAX: 920-394-3281. *Dir*, Sar Wilson; E-Mail: slwilson@dotnet.com
Founded 1964. Circ 10,531
Mem of Winnefox Library System
Friends of the Library Group

KOHLER

P KOHLER SCHOOL & PUBLIC LIBRARY,* 230 School St, 53044. SA 318-0646. Tel: 920-459-2920, 920-459-2923. FAX: 920-459-2930. *Librn* Ann Graumann
Pop 1,651; Circ 20,130
Library Holdings: Bk Vols 9,450; Per Subs 60
Mem of Eastern Shores Library System; Sheboygan County Libr Syst
Friends of the Library Group

LA CROSSE

S ASBURY UNITED METHODIST CHURCH LIBRARY,* 1818 Redfiel 54601. Tel: 608-782-2526. FAX: 608-782-8450.
Library Holdings: Bk Vols 500; Bk Titles 350; Per Subs 4

S DAIRYLAND POWER COOPERATIVES, 3200 East Ave S, PO Box 8 54602-0817. SAN 370-209X. Tel: 608-787-1218. FAX: 608-787-1290. W Site: www.dairynet.com. *Mgr Libr Serv*, Janet Nelson; E-Mail: jln@dairynet.com
Library Holdings: Bk Vols 600; Per Subs 580
Subject Interests: Bus, Elec cooperatives, Mgt, Pub utilities, Rural electrification
Restriction: Company library

SR DIOCESE OF LA CROSSE ARCHIVES, PO Box 4004, 54602-4004. SA 373-3076. Tel: 608-788-7700. FAX: 608-788-8413. E-Mail: chancery@dioceseoflacrosse.com. *In Charge*, Sister Marlene Weisenbeck; *Archivist*, Robert Altmann; Staff 2 (Non-MLS 2)
Library Holdings: Bk Vols 100
Subject Interests: Canon law, Church history
Special Collections: Local Church history (Catholic)

R ENGLISH LUTHERAN CHURCH LIBRARY, 1509 King St, 54601. SA 318-0662. Tel: 608-784-9335. FAX: 608-784-8936. *Librn*, Nancy Mills
Founded 1953
Library Holdings: Bk Titles 3,500
Subject Interests: Bible ref, Children's relig studies, Christian novels, Re studies
Partic in La Crosse Libr

S FRANCISCAN SKEMP HEALTHCARE-MAYO HEALTH SYSTEM, Health Sciences Library, 700 West Ave S, 54601. SAN 318-0697. Tel: 60 785-0940, Ext 2685. FAX: 608-791-9495.
Founded 1945
Library Holdings: Bk Titles 3,000; Per Subs 352
Subject Interests: Dentistry, Health science, Medicine, Nursing

M GUNDERSEN-LUTHERAN LA CROSSE, Health Science Library,* 1910 South Ave, 54601-9980. SAN 318-0689. Tel: 608-791-5406. FAX: 608-79 6343.
Founded 1965
Library Holdings: Bk Vols 10,000; Bk Titles 3,000; Per Subs 850
Subject Interests: Hospital-health sci, Medical, Nursing, Soc servs
Publications: Library Bulletin
Partic in BRS; Dialog Corporation; Medline

S HSR ARCHITECTS, INCORPORATED LIBRARY, 100 Milwaukee St, 54601-9880. SAN 377-9718. Tel: 608-784-1830. FAX: 608-782-5844. We Site: www.hsrassociates.com.
Library Holdings: Bk Titles 400

LA CROSSE PUBLIC LIBRARY,* 800 Main St, 54601-4122. SAN 364-7374. Tel: 608-789-7100. FAX: 608-789-7106. Web Site: www.lacrosse.lib.wi.us. *Dir*, Thomas R Strange; Tel: 608-789-7123, E-Mail: trs@lacrosse.lacrosse.lib.wi.us; *Mgr*, Peg M Zappen; Tel: 608-789-7142, E-Mail: mmz@lacrosse.lib.wi.us; *Mgr*, Jane E Radloff; Tel: 608-789-1733, E-Mail: jer@lacrosse.lib.wi.us; *Reader Servs*, Janet J Munson; Tel: 608-789-7118, E-Mail: jjm@lacrosse.lib.wi.us; *Archivist*, Anita Taylor Doering; Tel: 608-789-7156, E-Mail: atd@lacrosse.lib.wi.us; *Coll Develop*, Madeline Anderson; Staff 84 (MLS 8, Non-MLS 76)
Founded 1888. Pop 52,368; Circ 804,816
Jan 1999-Dec 2000 Income (Main Library and Branch Library) $3,158,509. Mats Exp $448,300, Books $356,940, Per/Ser (Incl. Access Fees) $61,360, Electronic Ref Mat (Incl. Access Fees) $30,000. Sal $2,279,774
Library Holdings: Bk Vols 212,985; Per Subs 539
Subject Interests: Local history
Automation Activity & Vendor Info: (Cataloging) epixtech, inc.; (Circulation) epixtech, inc.; (Serials) epixtech, inc.
Database Vendor: Ebsco - EbscoHost, OCLC - First Search, OVID Technologies
Function: Reference services available
Mem of Winding Rivers Library System
Special Services for the Deaf - TDD
Special Services for the Blind - Bks on cassette
Friends of the Library Group
Branches: 2
NORTH, 1552 Kane St, 54603-2229. SAN 364-7404. Tel: 608-789-7102. FAX: 608-789-7104. Web Site: www.lacrosse.lib.wi.us. *Librn*, Janet Munson
Friends of the Library Group
SOUTH, 1307 S 16th St, 54601-4122. SAN 364-7439. Tel: 608-789-7103. FAX: 608-789-7105. Web Site: www.lacrosse.lib.wi.us. *Librn*, Janet Munson
Friends of the Library Group

LA CROSSE TRIBUNE LIBRARY,* 401 N Third St, 54601. SAN 325-058X. Tel: 608-782-9710, Ext 232. FAX: 608-782-9723. *Librn*, Janet Erickson

OUR SAVIOR'S LUTHERAN CHURCH LIBRARY, 612 Division St, 54601. SAN 328-5928. Tel: 608-782-3468. FAX: 608-782-3468.
Library Holdings: Bk Vols 300

TRANE CO, Technical Library,* 3600 Pammel Creek Rd, 54601. SAN 318-0700. Tel: 608-787-3583. FAX: 608-787-4622. *Librn*, Janet Lukas; E-Mail: jlukas@trane.com
Library Holdings: Bk Vols 3,800
Special Collections: Engineering Coll
Restriction: Staff use only
Partic in Dialog Corporation; OCLC Online Computer Library Center, Inc

UNIVERSITY OF WISCONSIN - LA CROSSE
MURPHY LIBRARY RESOURCE CENTER, 1631 Pine St, 54601-3792. SAN 318-0727. Tel: 608-785-8505. Interlibrary Loan Service Tel: 608-785-8636. Circulation Tel: 608-785-8507. Reference Tel: 608-785-8508. Web Site: www.perth.uwlax.edu/MurphyLibrary/. *Dir Libr Serv*, Anita Evans; Tel: 608-785-8805, Fax: 608-785-8639, E-Mail: evans.anit@uwlax.edu; *Spec Coll & Archives*, Paul Beck; Tel: 608-785-8511, Fax: 608-785-8639, E-Mail: beck.paul@uwlax.edu; *Cat*, Charles Marx; Tel: 608-758-8402, Fax: 608-785-8639, E-Mail: marx@mail.uwlax.edu; *Acq of Monographs*, Karin Sandvik; Tel: 608-785-8397, Fax: 608-785-8639, E-Mail: sandvick.kari@uwlax.edu; *Circ Ch*, Mary Esten; Tel: 608-785-8651, Fax: 608-785-8639, E-Mail: esten.mary@uwlax.edu; *Acq of New Ser*, Jennifer Holman; Tel: 608-785-8395, Fax: 608-785-8634, E-Mail: holman.jeni@uwlax.edu; *Automation Syst Coordr*, Bill Doering; Tel: 608-785-8399, E-Mail: doering.will@uwlax.edu; *Circ*, Michele Strange; *Cat*, Analisa Lee; Tel: 608-785-8740, Fax: 608-785-8639, E-Mail: lee.ana@uwlax.edu. Subject Specialists: *Curric*, Mary Esten; *Oral hist*, Analisa Lee; Staff 27 (MLS 12, Non-MLS 15)
Enrl 9,142; Fac 753; Highest Degree: Master
Jul 1999-Jun 2000 Income $2,189,917. Mats Exp $792,926, Books $262,469, Per/Ser (Incl. Access Fees) $383,643, Presv $11,373, Micro $58,208, Other Print Mats $450, Manuscripts & Archives $1,726, Electronic Ref Mat (Incl. Access Fees) $64,050. Sal $1,087,828 (Prof $547,126)
Library Holdings: Bk Vols 385,769; Bk Titles 297,281; Per Subs 1,605
Subject Interests: Allied health, Bus, Education, Phys educ
Special Collections: Contemporary Poetry; Gothic Literature (Arkham House & Skeeters Coll); Inland River Steamboats, photog; Regional History Coll, photographs; Small Presses Coll
Automation Activity & Vendor Info: (Acquisitions) Endeavor; (Cataloging) Endeavor; (Circulation) Endeavor; (Course Reserve) Endeavor; (ILL) Endeavor; (Media Booking) Endeavor; (OPAC) Endeavor; (Serials) Endeavor
Database Vendor: CARL, Ebsco - EbscoHost, GaleNet, Lexis-Nexis, OCLC - First Search, ProQuest, Silverplatter Information Inc.
Publications: Fine Print
Partic in Coun of Wis Librs, Inc; OCLC Online Computer Library Center, Inc; Wisconsin Library Services
Special Services for the Blind - Adapted computers & special software with speech output to assist learning disabled, mentally retarded & uneducated
Friends of the Library Group

G USGS, Upper Midwest Environmental Sciences Center, 2630 Fanta Reed Rd, 54603-1223. SAN 318-0719. Tel: 608-781-6215. FAX: 608-783-6066. *Librn*, Kathy Mannstedt; E-Mail: kathy_mannstedt@usgs.gov
Founded 1959
Library Holdings: Bk Titles 5,000; Per Subs 60
Subject Interests: Chem registration, Chemistry, Ecology of large river systs, Fish culture, Limnology, Pharmacol, Physiol, Toxicol
Special Collections: Bulletin of United States Fish Commission
Automation Activity & Vendor Info: (Cataloging) EOS; (OPAC) EOS
Partic in Fedlink

C VITERO UNIVERSITY, Todd Wehr Memorial Library, 815 S Ninth St, 54601. SAN 318-0743. Tel: 608-796-3260. FAX: 608-796-3275. E-Mail: reference@viterbo.edu. Web Site: www.viterbo.edu/library. *Dir*, Dr John Hempstead; Tel: 608-796-3265, E-Mail: johempstead@viterbo.edu; *Tech Servs*, Sister Jeanine Luger; Tel: 608-796-3263, E-Mail: sjluger@viterbo.edu; *Circ, ILL*, Christie Krueger; Tel: 608-796-3269; *Circ, ILL*, Jonathan Hinck; Tel: 608-796-3269; *Ref*, Nancy Steinhoff; Tel: 608-796-3278, E-Mail: ncsteinhoff@viterbo.edu; *Ser*, David Wambold; Tel: 608-796-3262, E-Mail: djwambold@viterbo.edu; *Cat*, Rita Magno; Tel: 608-796-3267, E-Mail: rmmagno@viterbo.edu; *Circ, ILL*, Susan Spiker; Tel: 608-796-3269; Staff 8 (MLS 5, Non-MLS 3)
Founded 1890. Enrl 1,478; Fac 91; Highest Degree: Master
Jul 1999-Jun 2000 Income Parent Institution $583,573. Mats Exp $98,887, Books $66,188, Presv $4,608, Micro $4,137, AV Equip $2,313, Other Print Mats $4,082, Electronic Ref Mat (Incl. Access Fees) $16,776. Sal $261,855 (Prof $207,934)
Library Holdings: Bk Vols 90,700; Bk Titles 70,171; Per Subs 824
Subject Interests: Bus, Education, Fine arts, Health sci, Liberal arts, Nursing, Relig studies
Special Collections: Catholic History; Music Scores
Automation Activity & Vendor Info: (Acquisitions) Innovative Interfaces Inc.; (Cataloging) Innovative Interfaces Inc.; (Circulation) Innovative Interfaces Inc.; (Course Reserve) Innovative Interfaces Inc.; (ILL) Innovative Interfaces Inc.; (OPAC) Innovative Interfaces Inc.; (Serials) Innovative Interfaces Inc.
Database Vendor: Innovative Interfaces INN - View
Restriction: Open to faculty, students & qualified researchers
Partic in Wis Libr Consortium

R WESLEY UNITED METHODIST CHURCH LIBRARY, 721 King St, 54601. SAN 318-0751. Tel: 608-782-3018. FAX: 608-782-3018.; Staff 8 (MLS 1, Non-MLS 7)
Founded 1965
Jan 2000-Dec 2000 Income $50. Mats Exp $50
Library Holdings: Bk Titles 2,500
Subject Interests: Behav sci, Biog, Fiction, Relig studies, Soc sci
Friends of the Library Group

S WESTERN WISCONSIN TECHNICAL COLLEGE LIBRARY, 400 N Seventh St, 54602-0908. SAN 318-076X. Tel: 608-785-9142. Reference Tel: 608-785-9406. FAX: 608-789-6212. Web Site: www.western.tec.wi.us/library/. *Mgr*, Patrick J Brunet; E-Mail: brunetp@western.tec.wi.us; Staff 6 (MLS 2, Non-MLS 4)
Founded 1967. Enrl 3,300; Fac 185; Highest Degree: Associate
Jul 2000-Jun 2001 Income $270,755. Mats Exp $47,000, Books $24,500, Per/Ser (Incl. Access Fees) $15,000, Other Print Mats $7,500. Sal $226,565 (Prof $99,854)
Library Holdings: Bk Vols 31,000; Per Subs 325
Automation Activity & Vendor Info: (Cataloging) Sagebrush Corporation; (Circulation) Sagebrush Corporation; (OPAC) Sagebrush Corporation

P WINDING RIVERS LIBRARY SYSTEM, 800 Main St, 54601-4122. SAN 318-0778. Tel: 608-789-7151. FAX: 608-789-7106. *Dir*, David Polodna; Tel: 608-789-7119, E-Mail: dlp@lacrosse.lib.wi.us
Founded 1967
Jan 2000-Dec 2000 Income $969,151, State $703,102, Federal $53,280, County $172,469, Locally Generated Income $25,000, Other $15,300. Mats Exp Books $186,200. Sal $460,900
Library Holdings: Bk Vols 22,416
Automation Activity & Vendor Info: (Cataloging) epixtech, inc.; (Circulation) epixtech, inc.; (ILL) epixtech, inc.; (OPAC) epixtech, inc.
Publications: Whirlpools (bi-monthly newsletter)
Member Libraries: Alma Public Library; Arcadia Free Public Library; Bekkum Memorial Library; Black River Falls Public Library; Blair-Preston Public Library; Desoto Public Library; Elroy Public Library; Galesville Public Library; Hauge Memorial Library; Hettie Pierce Public Library; Hillsboro Public Library; Independence Public Library; Kendall Public Library; La Crosse County Library; La Crosse Public Library; Lawton Memorial Library; Mauston Public Library; McIntosh Memorial Library; Mondovi Public Library; Necedah Memorial Library; New Lisbon Memorial Library; Ontario Public Library; Readstown Public Library; Sparta Free Library; Strum Public Library; Taylor Memorial Library; Tomah Public

Library; Torkelson Memorial Library; Whitehall Public Library; Wilton Public Library; Wonewoc Public Library
Partic in OCLC Online Computer Library Center, Inc

LA FARGE

P LAWTON MEMORIAL LIBRARY,* 118 N Bird St, PO Box 38, 54639-0038. SAN 318-0786. Tel: 608-625-2015. FAX: 608-625-2800. E-Mail: lml@mwt.net. *Librn*, Jean Muller
Founded 1923. Pop 829; Circ 6,272
Library Holdings: Bk Titles 15,000; Per Subs 40
Special Collections: Arrowheads
Mem of Winding Rivers Library System
Open Mon 1-5, Tues 10-5, Wed 1-8, Fri 3-8, Sat 9-4

LA POINTE

P MADELINE ISLAND PUBLIC LIBRARY,* Library St, PO Box 65, 54850-0065. SAN 318-0794. Tel: 715-747-3662. E-Mail: madlib@win.bright.net. *Dir*, Connie Ross
Founded 1960. Pop 180; Circ 4,636
Library Holdings: Bk Vols 4,200; Per Subs 50
Mem of Northern Waters Library Service; Northwest Wis Libr Syst

LA VALLE

P LA VALLE PUBLIC LIBRARY,* 101 W Main, PO Box 7, 53941-0007. SAN 318-0808. Tel: 608-985-8383. FAX: 608-985-8383. E-Mail: lavlib@mwt.net. *Dir*, David Doering
Pop 414; Circ 3,000
Jan 1998-Dec 1999 Income $8,750. Mats Exp $2,000. Sal $3,100
Library Holdings: Bk Vols 7,100
Mem of South Central Library System
Open Tues 3-5 & Sat 2-5
Friends of the Library Group

LAC DU FLAMBEAU

P BEN GUTHRIE-LAC DU FLAMBEAU PUBLIC LIBRARY,* Peace Pipe Rd, PO Box 368, 54538-0368. SAN 376-6586. Tel: 715-588-7001. E-Mail: ldlib@newnorth.net. *Librn*, Mary Mann
Library Holdings: Bk Vols 10,000; Bk Titles 4,000; Per Subs 24
Mem of Northern Waters Library Service

LADYSMITH

C MOUNT SENARIO COLLEGE RESOURCE LIBRARY, 1500 College Ave W, 54848-2196. SAN 318-0824. Tel: 715-532-5511, Ext 1150. FAX: 715-532-7690. Web Site: www.mountsenario.edu. *Dir*, Eileen J Emberson; Tel: 715-532-5511, Ext 1152, E-Mail: emberson@mountsenario.edu; Staff 4 (MLS 1, Non-MLS 3)
Founded 1962. Enrl 722; Highest Degree: Bachelor
Library Holdings: Bk Vols 40,682; Bk Titles 37,068
Special Collections: Native American; Wisconsin History
Automation Activity & Vendor Info: (Acquisitions) epixtech, inc.; (Cataloging) epixtech, inc.; (Circulation) epixtech, inc.; (OPAC) epixtech, inc.; (Serials) epixtech, inc.

P RUSK COUNTY COMMUNITY LIBRARY, Ladysmith Public Library,* 418 Corbett Ave, 54848-1396. SAN 318-0816. Tel: 715-532-2604. FAX: 715-532-2658. *Librn*, Mary Bloedow; *Ch Servs*, Nancy Reidner; Staff 1 (MLS 1)
Founded 1907. Pop 15,047; Circ 64,171
Library Holdings: Bk Vols 21,104; Bk Titles 20,886; Per Subs 121
Mem of Indianhead Federated Library System
Friends of the Library Group

LAKE GENEVA

P LAKE GENEVA PUBLIC LIBRARY, 918 W Main St, 53147-1890. SAN 318-0840. Tel: 262-249-5299. Reference Tel: 262-249-5299. FAX: 262-249-5284. E-Mail: lgpl3@genevaonline.com. Web Site: www.genevaonline.com/~lgpl. *Dir*, Linda A Bendix; E-Mail: lindabendix@genevaonline.com; *Ad Servs*, Diane Neverman-Bailey; E-Mail: dianenb@genevaonline.com; *Ref Serv*, Andrea Peterson; E-Mail: andreap@genevaonline.com; *Tech Coordr*, Tom Wham; E-Mail: lgpl3@genevaonline.com; *YA Servs*, Gail Pachucki; E-Mail: gchooky@genevaonline.com; Staff 4 (MLS 3, Non-MLS 1)
Founded 1895. Pop 15,665; Circ 101,990
Jan 2000-Dec 2000 Income $541,343, City $307,726, Federal $2,539, County $152,296
Library Holdings: Bk Vols 34,871; Per Subs 230
Special Collections: Local History, Large Print
Automation Activity & Vendor Info: (Circulation) Follett
Publications: Lakeside Reader (Newsletter)
Mem of Lakeshores Library System
Friends of the Library Group

LAKE MILLS

P L D FARGO PUBLIC LIBRARY, 120 E Madison St, 53551-1644. SA 318-0867. Tel: 920-648-2166. FAX: 920-648-5561. *Dir*, Susan Kreager 5 (MLS 1, Non-MLS 4)
Founded 1902. Pop 5,400; Circ 86,000
1998-1999 Income $223,000, City $160, County $63,000. Mats Exp $31,300, Books $25,000, Per/Ser (Incl. Access Fees) $6,300. Sal $122,
Library Holdings: Bk Titles 30,000; Per Subs 111
Special Collections: Aztalan Historical Society (Lake Mills) Print & Pi Coll; Local History (Lake Mills Leader 1902-present)
Automation Activity & Vendor Info: (Circulation) epixtech, inc.
Friends of the Library Group

LAKEWOOD

P LAKES COUNTRY PUBLIC LIBRARY,* 15235 Hwy 32, PO Box 22 54138-0220. SAN 377-9947. Tel: 715-276-9020. FAX: 715-276-7151. E-Mail: lak@owls.lib.wi.us. Web Site: www.ez-net/~lepl/index.html. *Di* Pamela F Ellingson
Library Holdings: Bk Titles 11,000; Per Subs 60
Mem of Outagamie Waupaca Library System

LANCASTER

P SCHREINER MEMORIAL LIBRARY, Lancaster Public Library, 113 W Elm St, 53813-1202. SAN 318-0875. Tel: 608-723-7304. *Dir*, JoAnne Halferty; *Ch Servs*, Mary O'Leary; Staff 2 (MLS 2)
Founded 1901. Pop 4,000; Circ 52,000
Library Holdings: Bk Titles 30,000; Per Subs 65
Mem of Southwest Wisconsin Library System
Friends of the Library Group

LAND O'LAKES

P LAND O'LAKES PUBLIC LIBRARY,* 4242 County Hwy B, PO Box 54540-0450. SAN 318-0883. Tel: 715-547-6006. FAX: 715-547-6006. *D* Judy Franz; E-Mail: jfranz@newnorth.net
Pop 794; Circ 3,866
Library Holdings: Bk Vols 12,000
Mem of Northern Waters Library Service; Northwest Wis Libr Syst
Friends of the Library Group

LAONA

P EDITH EVANS COMMUNITY LIBRARY,* 111 Forest Ave, PO Box 1 54541-0127. SAN 318-0891. Tel: 715-674-4751. FAX: 715-674-5904. *Li* Cynthia M Lemerande
Founded 1917. Pop 2,000
Mem of Wisconsin Valley Library Service

LENA

P LENA PUBLIC LIBRARY, 117 E Main, PO Box 179, 54139-0179. SAN 377-9963. Tel: 920-829-5335. *Dir*, Lea Ann Pillath; E-Mail: lpillath@mail.nfls.lib.wi.us Sal $10,500
Library Holdings: Bk Titles 6,455; Per Subs 70
Mem of Nicolet Federated Library System

LIVINGSTON

P MARTIN ALLEN LIBRARY,* 220 W Barber Ave, 53554. SAN 318-090 Tel: 608-943-6800. FAX: 608-943-6800.
Library Holdings: Bk Vols 2,700
Mem of Southwest Wisconsin Library System
Open Tues 3-5 & Wed 6:30-8:30
Friends of the Library Group

LODI

P LODI WOMAN'S CLUB PUBLIC LIBRARY, 130 Lodi St, 53555-1217. SAN 318-0913. Tel: 608-592-4130. FAX: 608-592-2327. *Dir*, Peggy Hilli
Pop 2,600; Circ 69,710
1999-2000 Income $163,000, City $110,700, County $35,000, Other $17,300. Mats Exp $163,000
Library Holdings: Bk Vols 25,000

Automation Activity & Vendor Info: (Acquisitions) epixtech, inc.; (Course Reserve) epixtech, inc.; (OPAC) epixtech, inc.
Mem of South Central Library System
Friends of the Library Group

›IIRA

LOMIRA PUBLIC LIBRARY,* 1038 Main St, 53048-1108. SAN 318-0921. Tel: 920-269-4115. FAX: 920-269-4115. E-Mail: lpljane@spiritusa.net. *Dir*, Jane Kietzer; *Librn*, Darlene Robbins; *Asst Librn*, Ann Kohli
Founded 1938. Pop 1,732; Circ 18,996
Jan 1999-Dec 1999 Income $42,859, County $1,400, Other $500. Mats Exp $11,500, Books $10,200, Per/Ser (Incl. Access Fees) $1,100. Sal $25,159
Library Holdings: Bk Vols 17,675; Bk Titles 17,255; Per Subs 52
Special Collections: Commemorative Stamps Coll, 1972-1988; Local Genealogy Coll, church & cemetary rec; Local Newspaper, micro
Mem of Mid-Wisconsin Federated Library System

›E ROCK

LONE ROCK COMMUNITY LIBRARY, 234 N Broadway, 53556-0007. SAN 318-093X. Circulation Tel: 608-583-2034 (patrons only). *Librn*, Marian Copus; E-Mail: mcopus_99@yahoo.com
Founded 1972. Pop 741; Circ 4,875
Library Holdings: Bk Vols 4,500
Mem of Southwest Wisconsin Library System

WELL

LOWELL PUBLIC LIBRARY,* 105 N River St, PO Box 6, 53557-0006. SAN 364-6149. Tel: 920-927-5700. FAX: 920-927-5700. E-Mail: lowellib@internetwis.com. *Librn*, Karen Christianson
Library Holdings: Bk Vols 7,000
Mem of Mid-Wisconsin Federated Library System

YAL

LOYAL PUBLIC LIBRARY, 288 N Main St, 54446-0087. (Mail add: PO Box 87, 54446-9495), SAN 318-0948. Tel: 715-255-8189. FAX: 715-255-8348. *Librn*, Judy Bobrofsky; Tel: 715-255-8064, E-Mail: jbobrofsky@hotmail.com; *Asst Librn*, Lori Larson; Tel: 715-255-9967; *Asst Librn*, Kathy Lyons; Tel: 715-255-9281; Staff 3 (Non-MLS 3)
Founded 1901. Pop 4,184; Circ 25,114
Jan 1999-Jan 2000 Income $55,700, City $41,500, County $12,900, Locally Generated Income $1,300. Mats Exp $7,800, Books $6,600, Per/Ser (Incl. Access Fees) $1,200. Sal $20,900
Library Holdings: Bk Titles 13,000; Per Subs 55
Mem of Wisconsin Valley Library Service

CK

LUCK PUBLIC LIBRARY,* 21 Second Ave W, PO Box 500, 54853-0500. SAN 318-0956. Tel: 715-472-2770. FAX: 715-472-4312. *Dir*, Helga Konopacki; Staff 2 (Non-MLS 2)
Founded 1938. Pop 1,025; Circ 21,000
Library Holdings: Bk Titles 8,000; Per Subs 13
Special Collections: County & Local History; Wisconsin
Mem of Indianhead Federated Library System

PROGRESSIVE FOUNDATION, Nukewatch Library, 740 Round Lake Rd, 54653-2017. (Mail add: PO Box 649, 54853-0649), SAN 370-1980. Tel: 715-472-4185. FAX: 715-472-4184. Web Site: www.nukewatch.com. *Dir*, Bonnie Urfer; *Asst Dir*, John LaForge
Founded 1979
Library Holdings: Bk Titles 150
Publications: Pathfinder (newsletter quarterly)

ADISON

AMERICAN FAMILY MUTUAL INSURANCE GROUP, Corporate Library,* 6000 American Pkwy, 53783. SAN 370-3983. Tel: 608-249-2111, Ext 30457. FAX: 608-243-4916. *Librn*, Lee A Weinberger; Staff 2 (MLS 1, Non-MLS 1)
Library Holdings: Bk Titles 3,500
Subject Interests: Employment

AMERICAN SOCIETY OF AGRONOMY, Information Center,* 677 S Segoe Rd, 53711-1086. SAN 370-971X. Tel: 608-273-8080. FAX: 608-273-2021.
Library Holdings: Bk Vols 1,000; Per Subs 30

BJORKSTEN RESEARCH LABORATORIES LIBRARY,* PO Box 259444, 53725-9444. SAN 370-811X. Tel: 608-271-6900. FAX: 608-271-6930.
Library Holdings: Bk Vols 500; Per Subs 10

S CENTERS FOR PREVENTION & INTERVENTION LIBRARY, 2000 Fordem Ave, 53704. SAN 328-266X. Tel: 608-246-7606. FAX: 608-246-7610. E-Mail: cpicenters@aol.com.
Library Holdings: Bk Vols 3,500; Per Subs 28

S COVANCE LABORATORIES, INC, Library-08, 3301 Kinsman Blvd, PO Box 7545, 53707-7545. SAN 318-1197. Tel: 608-242-2712, Ext 2491. FAX: 608-241-7227. *Librn*, Sandra Thompson; E-Mail: sandra.thompson@covance.com; Staff 3 (MLS 1, Non-MLS 2)
Founded 1948
Library Holdings: Bk Titles 4,000; Per Subs 500
Subject Interests: Analytical chemistry, Nutrition, Toxicology
Automation Activity & Vendor Info: (Cataloging) Inmagic, Inc.; (Serials) EOS
Mem of South Central Library System

S CREDIT UNION NATIONAL ASSOCIATION, INC, Information Resource Center, 5710 Mineral Point Rd, 53701-4493. (Mail add: PO Box 431, 53701-0431), SAN 318-1391. Tel: 608-231-4308. FAX: 608-232-8024. Web Site: www.cuna.org. *Mgr*, Eva Cry; E-Mail: ecry@cuna.com; *Archivist*, Gabriel Kirkpatrick; E-Mail: gkirkpatrick@cuna.com; *Res*, Lora Kloth; E-Mail: lkloth@cuna.com; Staff 3 (MLS 2, Non-MLS 1)
Founded 1958
Oct 1999-Sep 2000 Income $338,000. Mats Exp $43,000, Books $7,000, Per/Ser (Incl. Access Fees) $9,000, Manuscripts & Archives $2,000, Electronic Ref Mat (Incl. Access Fees) $25,000. Sal $154,000
Library Holdings: Bk Vols 3,000; Bk Titles 2,500; Per Subs 150
Subject Interests: Econ, Finance, Hist of coop banking
Special Collections: Caisses Populaires (Papers of Alphonse Desjardins, 1854-1920); Credit Unions (Papers of Edward A Filene, 1860-1936 & Papers of Roy F Bergengren, 1879-1955)
Publications: Acquisition List (monthly); Periodical Holding List
Restriction: By appointment only

GL DANE COUNTY LAW LIBRARY, 315 City-County Bldg, 210 Martin Luther King Jr Blvd, 53709. SAN 321-9941. Tel: 608-266-6316. FAX: 608-266-5988.; Staff 2 (MLS 1, Non-MLS 1)
Founded 1886
Library Holdings: Bk Vols 6,400
Subject Interests: Wis law

P DANE COUNTY LIBRARY SERVICE, 201 W Mifflin St, 53703-2597. SAN 318-1014. Tel: 608-266-6388. TDD: 608-266-6389. E-Mail: dcljac@scls.lib.wi.us. Web Site: www.scls.lib.wi.us/dcl. *Dir*, Julie Anne Chase; Staff 10 (MLS 3, Non-MLS 7)
Founded 1966
Jan 2000-Dec 2000 Income $2,728,447, County $2,693,447, Other $35,000. Mats Exp $86,600. Sal $532,600
Library Holdings: Bk Vols 55,000; Per Subs 34
Automation Activity & Vendor Info: (Acquisitions) epixtech, inc.; (Cataloging) epixtech, inc.; (Circulation) epixtech, inc.; (OPAC) epixtech, inc.; (Serials) epixtech, inc.
Member Libraries: Monona Public Library
Bookmobiles: 1

S DANE COUNTY REGIONAL PLANNING COMMISSION LIBRARY, 217 S Hamilton St, Ste 403, 53703. SAN 318-1030. Tel: 608-266-4137. FAX: 608-266-9117.
Founded 1967
Library Holdings: Bk Vols 3,900; Per Subs 30
Subject Interests: Census, Environmental studies, Housing, Land use planning, Master plans, Pop, Transportation, Water resources mgt

GM DEPARTMENT OF VETERANS AFFAIRS, Hospital Library, 2500 Overlook Terrace, 53705-2286. SAN 318-1286. Tel: 608-256-1901, 608-280-7173. FAX: 608-280-7108. *Mgr*, Jill Everson; E-Mail: jill.everson@med.va.gov; Staff 1 (Non-MLS 1)
Founded 1951
Library Holdings: Bk Vols 12,450
Special Collections: General Medicine, AV
Partic in Nat Libr of Med; South Central Wisconsin Health Science Library Cooperative; Veterans Affairs Library Network
Open Mon-Fri 8-4:30

L DEWITT, ROSS & STEVENS, Law Library, 2 E Mifflin St, Ste 600, 53703. SAN 372-3593. Tel: 608-283-5504. FAX: 608-252-9243. *Dir*, Richard D Hendricks; E-Mail: rdh@dewittross.com; Staff 2 (MLS 1, Non-MLS 1)
Mem of South Central Library System

C EDGEWOOD COLLEGE LIBRARY, Oscar Rennebohm Library, 1000 Edgewood College Dr, 53711-1997. SAN 364-7463. Tel: 608-663-3300. FAX: 608-663-6778. E-Mail: library@edgewood.edu. Web Site: www.library.edgewood.edu. *Dir*, Mary Jane Scherdin; Tel: 608-663-3305, E-Mail: scherdin@edgewood.edu; Staff 5 (MLS 5)
Founded 1941. Enrl 1,581; Highest Degree: Master
Jul 1999-Jun 2000 Income Parent Institution $504,802. Mats Exp $149,448, Books $76,905, Per/Ser (Incl. Access Fees) $38,204, Presv $2,539, Micro $8,521, Electronic Ref Mat (Incl. Access Fees) $23,279. Sal $321,815 (Prof $211,000)

Library Holdings: Bk Vols 89,653; Bk Titles 69,331; Per Subs 437
Subject Interests: Education, Religion
Database Vendor: Ebsco - EbscoHost, IAC - Info Trac, Lexis-Nexis, OCLC - First Search, ProQuest, Silverplatter Information Inc.
Mem of South Central Library System
Partic in WILS
Friends of the Library Group

L FOLEY & LARDNER, Law Library,* 150 E Gilman St. (Mail add: PO Box 1497, 53701), SAN 372-3607. Tel: 608-257-5035. FAX: 608-258-4258. Web Site: www.foleylardner.com. *Librn*, Pamela Noyd; E-Mail: pnoyd@foleylaw.com
Library Holdings: Bk Vols 2,000; Per Subs 225

C HERZING COLLEGE LIBRARY, 5218 E Terrace Dr, 53718-8340. SAN 378-0597. Tel: 608-249-6611. FAX: 608-249-8593. *Librn*, Beth Huwe; Tel: 608-663-0816, E-Mail: bethhuwe@msn.herzing.edu; Staff 1 (MLS 1)

L LIBRARY OF THE US COURTS, US Courthouse, Rm 550, 120 N Henry St, 53703. SAN 371-6473. Tel: 608-264-5448. FAX: 608-264-5930. *Librn*, Sylvia A Brown; E-Mail: sylvia_a_brown@wiwd.uscourts.gov
Founded 1981
Library Holdings: Bk Titles 1,200; Per Subs 45
Automation Activity & Vendor Info: (Acquisitions) SIRSI; (Cataloging) SIRSI; (OPAC) SIRSI; (Serials) SIRSI
Partic in OCLC Online Computer Library Center, Inc; Westlaw

J MADISON AREA TECHNICAL COLLEGE, Information Resource Center,* 3550 Anderson St, 53704. SAN 318-1073. Tel: 608-246-6640. FAX: 608-246-6644.; Staff 32 (MLS 5, Non-MLS 27)
Founded 1965. Enrl 7,600; Fac 360
Library Holdings: Bk Vols 62,000; Bk Titles 55,000; Per Subs 900
Publications: Bibliographies; Library Guide
Also have satellite campus libraries at Fort Atkinson, Portage, Reedsburg & Watertown; Downtown Education Center, Madison

S MADISON METROPOLITAN SCHOOL DISTRICT, Educational Reference Library,* 545 W Dayton St, 53703. SAN 327-8484. Tel: 608-266-6188. FAX: 608-267-1634. Web Site: danenet.wicip.org/lms/. *Librn*, Joanne Lenburg; E-Mail: jlenburg@madison.k12.wi.us
Library Holdings: Bk Vols 11,000; Bk Titles 10,000; Per Subs 150
Subject Interests: Education

P MADISON PUBLIC LIBRARY, 201 W Mifflin St, 53703. SAN 364-7617. Tel: 608-266-6300. Circulation Tel: 608-266-6357. Reference Tel: 608-266-6350. TDD: 608-266-6314. FAX: 608-266-4338. Reference FAX: 608-266-4230. Web Site: madison.scls.lib.wi.us. *Dir*, Barbara Dimick; *Circ*, Harriet Anderson; *AV, Coordr*, Ann Michalski; *Coll Develop*, Vada Mayfield; Staff 46 (MLS 46)
Founded 1875. Pop 200,814; Circ 2,710,334
Jan 1999-Dec 1999 Income (Main Library and Branch Library) $7,547,351, State $24,521, City $6,366,624, Federal $39,639, County $524,049, Locally Generated Income $592,518. Mats Exp $987,437, Books $687,490, Per/Ser (Incl. Access Fees) $72,210, Presv $9,206, Micro $17,048, AV Equip $178,924, Other Print Mats $13,199, Electronic Ref Mat (Incl. Access Fees) $9,360. Sal $5,790,689 (Prof $2,822,428)
Library Holdings: Bk Vols 857,844; Bk Titles 365,264; Per Subs 1,981
Special Collections: City; Local Materials; Music
Automation Activity & Vendor Info: (Acquisitions) epixtech, inc.; (Cataloging) epixtech, inc.; (Circulation) epixtech, inc.; (OPAC) epixtech, inc.; (Serials) epixtech, inc.
Database Vendor: Ebsco - EbscoHost, GaleNet, IAC - Info Trac, ProQuest
Publications: Film Catalog; Periodical Directory
Mem of South Central Library System
Partic in Multitype Libr Coun
Special Services for the Deaf - Books on deafness & sign language; Special interest periodicals; TDD
Friends of the Library Group
Branches: 7
HAWTHORNE, 2707 E Washington Ave, 53704. SAN 364-7641. Tel: 608-246-4548. FAX: 608-246-4549. Web Site: madison.scls.lib.wi. *Br Coordr*, Jane Roughen
Library Holdings: Bk Vols 35,213
Friends of the Library Group
LAKEVIEW, 2845 N Sherman Ave, 53704. SAN 364-7706. Tel: 608-246-4547. FAX: 608-246-4699. Web Site: madison.scls.lib.wi.us. *Br Coordr*, Jane Roughen
Library Holdings: Bk Vols 49,376
Friends of the Library Group
MEADOWRIDGE, 5740 Raymond Rd, 53711. SAN 364-7730. Tel: 608-288-6160. FAX: 608-288-6162. Web Site: madison.scls.lib.wi.us. *Br Coordr*, Jane Roughen
Library Holdings: Bk Vols 61,069
Friends of the Library Group
MONROE, 1705 Monroe St, 53711. SAN 364-7765. Tel: 608-266-6390. FAX: 608-266-6396. Web Site: madison.scls.lib.wi.us. *Br Coordr*, Jane Roughen
Library Holdings: Bk Vols 27,652
Friends of the Library Group
PINNEY, 204 Cottage Grove Rd, 53716. SAN 364-782X. Tel: 608-224-7100. FAX: 608-224-7102. Web Site: madison.scls.lib.wi.us. *Br Coor*, Jane Roughen
Library Holdings: Bk Vols 79,137
Friends of the Library Group
SEQUOYA, 513 S Midvale Blvd, 53711. SAN 364-7854. Tel: 608-266-6385. FAX: 608-266-7353. Web Site: madison.scls.lib.wi.us. *Br Coor*, Jane Roughen
Library Holdings: Bk Vols 113,167
Friends of the Library Group
SOUTH MADISON, 2222 S Park St, 53713. SAN 364-7889. Tel: 608-2 6395. FAX: 608-266-6303. Web Site: madison.scls.lib.wi.us. *Br Coor*, Jane Roughen
Library Holdings: Bk Vols 34,551
Friends of the Library Group

M MENDOTA MENTAL HEALTH INSTITUTE, Library-Media Center,* Troy Dr, 53704. SAN 318-1146. Tel: 608-243-2615. FAX: 608-243-273 Staff 2 (MLS 1, Non-MLS 1)
Founded 1955
Jul 1997-Jun 1998 Income $25,000
Library Holdings: Bk Vols 15,000; Per Subs 60
Special Collections: High Interest/Low vocabulary Materials; Mental Health; Patient's Library: Self Help Materials; Staff Library: Forensics, Mental Health, Psychiatry & Psychology
Mem of South Central Library System
Partic in Madison Area Libr Coun; Southeastern Wisconsin Health Scien Library Consortium

M MERITER HOSPITAL, Medical Library,* 202 S Park St, 53715. SAN 3 7587. Tel: 608-267-6234. FAX: 608-267-6007. *Librn*, Robert Koehler; E-Mail: rkoehler@meriter.com
Library Holdings: Bk Titles 3,000; Per Subs 302
Subject Interests: Dentistry, Hospital administration, Medicine, Nursing
Partic in Regional Med Libr - Region 3

S OSCAR MAYER FOODS CORP, Research Information Center,* 910 M Ave, 53704. SAN 318-1170. Tel: 608-285-4025. FAX: 608-285-6010.
Library Holdings: Bk Vols 2,000; Per Subs 180
Subject Interests: Food sci, Meat, Poultry proc, Technology
Friends of the Library Group

S PROMEGA CORPORATION INFORMATION RESOURCE CENTER,* 2800 Woods Hollow Rd, 53711. Tel: 608-274-4331. FAX: 608-277-2601. Web Site: www.promega.com. *Info Tech*, Adriana Dino; E-Mail: adino@promega.com
Library Holdings: Bk Vols 5,000; Bk Titles 700; Per Subs 300

L PUBLIC SERVICE COMMISSION OF WISCONSIN, Information Reference Center,* 610 N Whitney Way, PO Box 7854, 53707-7854. SA 318-1189. Tel: 608-266-2935. FAX: 608-266-3957. *In Charge*, Martha Jelinski; *Asst Librn*, Elizabeth Hogensen
Library Holdings: Bk Vols 4,000; Per Subs 175
Subject Interests: Electric, Energy conserv, Energy efficiency, Environ analysis, Natural gas, Pub utilities regulation, Telecommunications
Special Collections: Attorney General Opinions; Federal Reporter; Wisconsin Reports; Wisconsin Statistics Annotated
Partic in Dialog Corporation
Friends of the Library Group

S RAYOVAC CORP, Technology Center Library,* 630 Forward Dr, 53711. SAN 318-1049. Tel: 608-275-4714. FAX: 608-275-4992. *Librn*, Sandra Plisch; E-Mail: splisch@rayovac.com
Founded 1967
Library Holdings: Bk Titles 2,500; Per Subs 100
Subject Interests: Batteries, Chemistry, Electrochem, Engineering, Flashlights, Mgt
Special Collections: Company & Government Reports (Uniterm Coll), paper & micro; Patents
Partic in Madison Area Libr Coun

S RMT, INC LIBRARY, 744 Heartland Trail, 53717. SAN 322-7812. Tel: 608-831-4444. FAX: 608-831-3334. *Head Tech Servs*, Mary Janeck; Tel: 608-662-5385, E-Mail: mary.janeck@rmtinc.com; Staff 2 (MLS 1, Non-M 1)
Founded 1978
Library Holdings: Bk Vols 10,000; Per Subs 200
Subject Interests: Environmental engineering
Restriction: Staff use only
Mem of South Central Library System

SR SAINT MARIA GORETTI PARISH, (Formerly Saint Maria Goretti Churc Library), Saint Maria Goretti Catholic Parish School Library, 5405 Flad A 53711. SAN 318-1200. Tel: 608-271-7551. FAX: 608-271-7551. *Librn*, Michele Ruth; E-Mail: mbruth@yahoo.com; Staff 1 (Non-MLS 1)
Founded 1962. Pop 210; Enrl 210; Fac 15
Library Holdings: Bk Vols 3,700
Restriction: Open to student, faculty & staff

ST MARY'S HOSPITAL, Medical Library, 707 S Mills St, 53715. SAN 318-1219. Tel: 608-258-6533. FAX: 608-258-6119. E-Mail: library@ssmhc.com. *Head of Libr*, Leslie A Christiansen; Tel: 608-258-6532, E-Mail: leslie_christensen@ssmhc.com; *ILL*, Jodi Burgess; Tel: 608-258-6535, E-Mail: jodi_burgess@ssmhc.com; *Ser*, Lori Bakken; Tel: 608-258-6161, E-Mail: lory_bakken@ssmhc.com; Staff 3 (MLS 1, Non-MLS 2)
Founded 1951
Library Holdings: Bk Titles 4,000; Per Subs 250
Subject Interests: Hospital administration, Medicine, Mgt, Nursing
Database Vendor: Dialog, Ebsco - EbscoHost, IAC - Info Trac, OCLC - First Search, OVID Technologies
Mem of South Central Library System
Partic in Docline; Greater Midwest Regional Medical Libr Network; Wis Health Sci Libr Asn

SOUTH CENTRAL LIBRARY SYSTEM, 5250 E Terrace Dr Ste A, 53718-8345. SAN 364-7919. Tel: 608-246-7970. FAX: 608-246-7958. Web Site: www.scls.lib.wi.us/.; Staff 25 (MLS 12, Non-MLS 13)
Founded 1975. Pop 711,067
Jan 1999-Dec 1999 Income $4,122,526, State $1,463,190, Federal $119,490, County $442,581, Locally Generated Income $1,309,652, Other $787,613. Mats Exp $44,354, Books $4,021, Per/Ser (Incl. Access Fees) $40,333. Sal $1,288,626 (Prof $586,645)
Library Holdings: Bk Vols 675; Per Subs 66
Subject Interests: Libr sci
Automation Activity & Vendor Info: (Circulation) epixtech, inc.
Database Vendor: Ebsco - EbscoHost, IAC - Info Trac, ProQuest
Publications: Horizons
Member Libraries: Albany Public Library; Arpin Public Library; Baraboo Public Library; Black Earth Public Library; Columbus Public Library; Covance Laboratories, Inc; Deerfield Public Library; Deforest Public Library; Dewitt, Ross & Stevens; Edgewood College Library; Jane Morgan Memorial Library; Kilbourn Public Library; La Valle Public Library; Lettie W Jensen Public Library; Lodi Woman's Club Public Library; Madison Public Library; Marshall Community Library; Marshfield Public Library; Mazomanie Free Library; McFarland Public Library; McMillan Memorial Library; Mendota Mental Health Institute; Mid-State Technical College Library; Monona Public Library; Monroe Public Library; Monticello Public Library; Mount Horeb Public Library; New Glarus Public Library; North Freedom Public Library; Oregon Public Library; Plain Public Library; Portage County Public Library; Portage Public Library; Poynette Public Library; Prairie Du Sac Public Library; Reedsburg Public Library; Rio Community Library; RMT, Inc Library; Rock Springs Public Library; Rosemary Garfoot Public Library; Sauk City Public Library; Spring Green Community Library; St Mary's Hospital; Stoughton Public Library; Sun Prairie Public Library; University Of Wisconsin-Madison; Verona Public Library; Vesper Public Library; Waunakee Public Library; Wisconsin Department Of Employee Trust Funds Library; Wisconsin Department of Workforce Development Library; Wisconsin State Department Of Natural Resources
Members also include over 200 other libraries - school, academic, special & state agency

STATE HISTORICAL SOCIETY OF WISCONSIN LIBRARY,* 816 State St, 53706. SAN 318-1227. Tel: 608-264-6534. FAX: 608-264-6520. Web Site: www.wisc.edu/shs-library/index.html. *Dir*, J Kevin Graffagnino; *Acq*, James Buckett; *Cat*, Jonathan D Cooper; *Govt Doc*, M Elizabeth Cowell; *Publ Servs*, Michael Edmonds; Staff 34 (MLS 19, Non-MLS 15)
Founded 1847
Jul 1997-Jun 1998 Income $1,824,800. Mats Exp $336,000, Books $112,000, Per/Ser (Incl. Access Fees) $66,000, Micro $138,000, AV Equip $7,000, Other Print Mats $10,000, Manuscripts & Archives $3,000. Sal $1,145,640
Library Holdings: Bk Vols 3,600,000
Subject Interests: Ethnic hist, Labor hist, Military history, Minority hist, Newspapers, Numismatics, Philately, Radical, Reform movements, Relig hist, Religion, Women's hist
Publications: Clio's Tracings; Wisconsin Public Documents
Partic in Center For Research Libraries; Coun of Wis Librs, Inc; OCLC Online Computer Library Center, Inc
Special Services for the Deaf - TTY machine

STATE MEDICAL SOCIETY OF WISCONSIN LIBRARY, 330 E Lakeside St, PO Box 1109, 53701-1109. SAN 318-1235. Tel: 608-257-6781. FAX: 608-283-5401. Web Site: www.wismed.com.
Founded 1841
Library Holdings: Bk Vols 100; Per Subs 50
Restriction: Not open to public

TRINITY LUTHERAN CHURCH LIBRARY, 1904 Winnebago St, 53704. SAN 318-1251. Tel: 608-249-8527. FAX: 608-249-9070. *Librn*, Sharon Kenyon
Founded 1944
Library Holdings: Bk Vols 4,500
Subject Interests: Relig studies

G UNITED STATES FOREST SERVICE, Forest Products Laboratory Library, One Gifford Pinchot Dr, 53705-2398. SAN 318-126X. Tel: 608-231-9313. TDD: 608-231-9544. FAX: 608-231-9311. Web Site: www.fpl.fs.fed.us. *Head of Libr*, Julie Blankenburg; Tel: 608-231-9491, E-Mail: jblankenburg@fs.fed.us; *Acq*, Shelley Minier; *ILL*, Mary Kemp; E-Mail: mkemp@fs.fed.us. Subject Specialists: *Forest products*, Julie Blankenburg; Staff 3 (MLS 1, Non-MLS 2)
Founded 1910
Oct 2000-Sep 2001 Income $205,000. Mats Exp $92,500, Books $7,500, Per/Ser (Incl. Access Fees) $67,000, Other Print Mats $3,500, Electronic Ref Mat (Incl. Access Fees) $14,500. Sal $110,000
Library Holdings: Bk Vols 99,000; Bk Titles 44,000; Per Subs 470
Subject Interests: Adhesives, Biotechnology, Drying, Energy from wood, Fire science, Mycology, Paint and coatings, Pulp and paper, Recycling, Solid wood products, Technology, Wood eng
Restriction: In-house use for visitors, Non-circulating to the public, Open to public for reference only
Function: ILL limited
Partic in FS-Info; OCLC Online Computer Library Center, Inc; Wisconsin Library Services
Special Services for the Deaf - TDD

UNIVERSITY OF WISCONSIN-MADISON

S INSTITUTE FOR ENVIRONMENTAL STUDIES LIBRARY, 15 Science Hall, 550 N Park St, 53706-1491. SAN 318-1278. Tel: 608-263-3064. FAX: 608-262-0014. E-Mail: sjschul2@facstaff.wisc.edu. *Librn*, Samuel Schultz
Library Holdings: Bk Vols 1,000; Per Subs 180
Subject Interests: Conservation, Ecol, Energy, Int envion concern, Water resources, Wildlife

S WATER RESOURCES INSTITUTE LIBRARY, 1975 Willow Dr, 2nd Flr, 53706-1177. SAN 321-981X. Tel: 608-262-3069. FAX: 608-262-0591. E-Mail: askwater@wri.wisc.edu. Web Site: www.wri.wisc.edu/library. *Coll Develop, Librn*, JoAnn Savoy; E-Mail: josavoy@wri.wisc.edu; Staff 2 (MLS 1, Non-MLS 1)
Founded 1966
Library Holdings: Bk Titles 22,000; Per Subs 35
Subject Interests: Ground water, Wastewater treatment, Water pollution, Water quality, Water res planning, Water treatment
Automation Activity & Vendor Info: (Cataloging) Endeavor; (OPAC) Endeavor
Publications: Recent Acquisitions
Mem of South Central Library System
Partic in Univ of Wis Spec Campus Libr Group

C UNIVERSITY OF WISCONSIN-MADISON, General Library System & Memorial Library, 728 State St, 53706. SAN 364-8036. Tel: 608-262-3193. Interlibrary Loan Service Tel: 608-262-2571. Circulation Tel: 608-263-7360. Reference Tel: 608-262-3242. FAX: 608-265-2754. Web Site: www.library.wisc.edu. *Tech Servs*, Richard Reeb; *Ref*, David Null; *Publ Servs*, Edward Van Gemert; *Automation Syst Coordr*, Nolan Pope; *Spec Coll*, Robin Rider; *ILL*, Judy Tuohy. Subject Specialists: *Africa*, David Henige; *East Asia*, Thomas Hahn; *Education*, Marilyn Hicks; *Europe*, John Dillon; *European history*, Barbara Walden; *History of science*, John A Neu; *Latin America*, Luis Villar; *Psychology*, Marilyn Hicks; *Slavic history and literature*, Alexander J Rolich; *Social sciences and issues*, Victoria Hill; *Southeast Asia*, Carol Mitchell; *Women's studies*, Phyllis Weisbard
Founded 1850. Fac 2,078; Highest Degree: Doctorate
Library Holdings: Bk Vols 6,057,201; Per Subs 39,802
Special Collections: 17th & 18th Century European Theology (Chwalibog Coll); 20th Century English & American Literature; Alchemy (Duveen Coll); American Gift Books & Annuals; Balcanica Coll; Book Plates; Brazilian Positivism; Brodhead Manuscripts; Buddhism; Burgess Collection of Children's Literature; C S Lewis Letters; Calvinist Theology & Dutch History (Tank Coll); Carol von Linee Coll; Chess (Peter G Toepfer Coll); Civil War Band Books; Classical & 19th Century German Literature (George B Wild Coll); Cossack Coll; Dalton Trumbo Coll; Deryck Collection of Belgian Congo Archival Materials; Dutch Pamphlets; Early American Women Authors (William Cairns Coll), English Grammars (Berry Coll); English 19th Century Free Thought; English 19th Century Social & Economic Pamphlets; English Manor Rolls; English Romantic Poetry (Arthur Beatty Coll); English Temperance (Guy Hayler Coll); Eugene O'Neill Coll; European & American Student Publications; European Socialism (Herman Schlueter Library & William English Walling Coll); Ferber Coll; French 18th Century Literature & Culture (Tucker Coll); French Political Pamphlets, 1560-1648; French Protestantism (Montauban Coll); French Revolutionary Pamphlets; French Socialist Congresses; French Student Revolt, 1968; German 18th Century Theater; German Expressionism; German Philology; Grotius Coll; Herald Coll (Leon Srabian Herald, Poet & Philosopher); History of Chemistry (Cole Duveen Coll); History of Science; Icelandic History & Literature; Irish History & Literature; Italian 16th Century Imprints (Giolito Coll); Joseph Priestly Coll; Judaica (Joseph L Baron Coll); Juridical Materials, 15th & 16th Century; Latimer Coll (Matthias Collection of the Letters of Marjorie Latimer); Lithuanian History & Literature (Alfred Senn Coll); Little Magazines (Marvin Sukov Coll); Lutheran Theology (Hoyer Coll); Madras History Sources; Mark Twain (George H Brownell & Norman Bassett Colls);

Mazarinades Coll; Medieval History; Medieval Spanish Literature; Mesmer Coll; Mexican Pamphlets; Mottey Coll; National Socialism; Natural History & English Literature (Chester H Thordarson Coll); Norwegian Local History; O Henry Coll; Papyri Coll; Polish Literature & History; Private Press Coll; Renaissance Epic Coll; Robert Boyle Coll; Rousseau Coll; Russian Culture (Romanovskii Coll); Russian Revolutionary Movement (Russian Free Press Coll); Russian Satirical Journals; Saint Simon Coll; Scandinavian Literature & Language (Olson Coll); Scandinavian Literature (Mimers Coll); Swift (Teerink Coll); Swiss Literature Romande; Tams-Witmark Coll (American Music); The Lost Dauphin (William W Wight Coll); Theater (Thomas H Dickinson Coll); Tibetan Coll; Welsh Theology (Jones-Roberts Coll)
Friends of the Library Group
Departmental Libraries:

ARTHUR H ROBINSON MAP LIBRARY, 310 Science Hall, 550 N Park St, 53706-1491. SAN 364-8451. Tel: 608-262-1471. E-Mail: maplib@macc.wisc.edu. *Librn*, Mary Galneder; E-Mail: galneder@macc.wisc.edu
Library Holdings: Bk Vols 963
Subject Interests: Aerial photos, Maps
Special Collections: Wisconsin Aerial Photographs

BIOLOGY LIBRARY, 430 Lincoln Dr, 53706. SAN 364-815X. Tel: 608-262-2740. FAX: 608-262-9003. *Librn*, Elsa Althen
Library Holdings: Bk Vols 48,920
Subject Interests: Botany, Conserv biol, Ecol, Natural history, Zoology

BUSINESS LIBRARY, 2200 Grainger Hall, 975 University Ave, 53706-1343. SAN 364-8184. Tel: 608-262-5935. FAX: 608-262-9001. *Librn*, Michael Enyart
Library Holdings: Bk Vols 51,282

CENTER FOR DEMOGRAPHY LIBRARY, 1180 Observatory Dr, 53706. SAN 323-9993. Tel: 608-263-6372. FAX: 608-262-8400. E-Mail: library@ssc.wisc.edu. Web Site: www.ssc.wisc.edu/cde/library/home.htm. *Dir*, Wendy Brand; Tel: 608-262-4879, E-Mail: brand@ssc.wisc.edu; *Librn*, John Carlson; Staff 2 (MLS 1, Non-MLS 1)
Founded 1970
Library Holdings: Bk Vols 21,000; Bk Titles 19,000; Per Subs 214
Subject Interests: Population studies
Database Vendor: Silverplatter Information Inc.
Restriction: Circulation limited
Function: Document delivery services, Reference services available, Research library

CENTER FOR INSTRUCTIONAL MATERIALS & COMPUTING, 225 N Mills St, 53706. SAN 364-8303. Tel: 608-263-4750. Reference Tel: 608-263-4751. FAX: 608-262-6050. Web Site: www.cimc.soemadison.wisc.edu. *Dir*, JoAnn Carr; Tel: 608-263-4755, E-Mail: carr@education.wisc.edu; Staff 8 (MLS 4, Non-MLS 4)
Founded 1848. Highest Degree: Doctorate
Jul 1998-Jun 1999 Income (Main Library Only) Parent Institution $764,678. Mats Exp $92,718, Books $36,693, Per/Ser (Incl. Access Fees) $35,913, Per/Ser (Incl. Access Fees) $451, Micro $4,307, AV Equip $9,046, Electronic Ref Mat (Incl. Access Fees) $6,308. Sal $435,591 (Prof $256,742)
Library Holdings: Bk Vols 50,265; Per Subs 413
Subject Interests: Teacher educ
Partic in WILS

CHEMISTRY LIBRARY, 1101 University Ave, 53706. SAN 364-8214. Tel: 608-262-2942. FAX: 608-262-9002. *Librn*, Kendall Rouse
Library Holdings: Bk Vols 44,166

COLLEGE (UNDERGRADUATE) LIBRARY, 600 N Park St, 53706. SAN 364-8060. Tel: 608-262-3245. FAX: 608-265-2193. *Dir*, Donna Senzig
Library Holdings: Bk Vols 106,554

COOPERATIVE CHILDREN'S BOOK CENTER, 600 N Park St, 53706. SAN 323-9977. Tel: 608-263-3720. FAX: 608-262-4933. E-Mail: ccbcinfo@mail.soemadison.wisc.edu. *Librn*, Virginia Moore Kruse

GEOGRAPHY, 280 Science Hall, 550 N Park St, 53706. SAN 364-8249. Tel: 608-262-1706. *Librn*, Thomas Tews; E-Mail: ttews@library.wisc.edu; Staff 2 (MLS 1, Non-MLS 1)
Library Holdings: Bk Vols 61,422

GEOLOGY & GEOPHYSICS LIBRARY, 1215 W Dayton St, 53706-1692. SAN 364-8273. Tel: 608-262-8956. FAX: 608-262-0693. *Librn*, Marie Dvorzak
Library Holdings: Bk Vols 61,032
Subject Interests: Geology, Geophysics

NIEMAN GRANT JOURNALISM READING ROOM, 821 University Ave, 53706. SAN 364-8516. Tel: 608-263-3387. *Librn*, Linda Barnicket

KOHLER ART LIBRARY, 800 University Ave, 53706. SAN 364-8338. Tel: 608-263-2258. FAX: 608-263-2255. Web Site: www.library.wisc.edu/libraries/art/. *Dir*, Lynette Korenic
Library Holdings: Bk Vols 140,839
Subject Interests: Architecture, Art, Artists bks, Decorative arts, Photography
Special Collections: Artists Books

CL LAW SCHOOL, 975 Bascom Mall, 53706. SAN 364-8397. Tel: 608-262-1128. FAX: 608-262-2775. *Librn*, Steven Barkan
Library Holdings: Bk Vols 346,464
Subject Interests: Criminal justice, Environmental law

MATHEMATICS LIBRARY, 480 Lincoln Dr, 53706. SAN 364-8486. Tel: 608-262-3596. FAX: 608-263-8891. *Librn*, Shirley Shen
Library Holdings: Bk Vols 48,679
Subject Interests: Computer science, Mathematics, Physics, Statistic

MILLS MUSIC LIBRARY, 728 State St, 53703. SAN 364-8575. Tel: 6 263-1884. FAX: 608-265-2754. *Librn*, Geraldine Laudati
Library Holdings: Bk Vols 55,370
Special Collections: 19th Century American Music Imprints; Civil W Band Books

PHYSICS LIBRARY, 4220 Chamberlin Hall, 1150 University Ave, 537 SAN 364-863X. Tel: 608-262-9500. FAX: 608-265-2754. E-Mail: physlib@library.wisc.edu. Web Site: www.library.wisc.edu/libraries/Physics. *Head of Libr*, Kerry L Kresse; Tel: 608-262-8696, E-Mail: kkresse@library.wisc.edu. Subject Specialists: *Physics*, Kerry L Kress Staff 2 (MLS 1, Non-MLS 1)
Founded 1972
Library Holdings: Bk Vols 42,611
Database Vendor: Lexis-Nexis, OCLC - First Search, OVID Technologies, ProQuest, Silverplatter Information Inc., Wilson - Wilsc Web
Function: Research library
Partic in CIC; WILS

PLANT PATHOLOGY MEMORIAL, 1630 Linden Dr, 53706. SAN 32 8277. Tel: 608-262-8698. FAX: 608-263-2626. *Librn*, Steve Cloyd; E-Mail: scloyd@library.wisc.edu
Library Holdings: Bk Vols 13,630; Per Subs 75
Subject Interests: Plant pathology, Plant virology
Special Collections: Virus Literature (Johnson-Hoggan-Fulton Virus C abstracts on cards, bks
Automation Activity & Vendor Info: (Acquisitions) Endeavor; (Cataloging) Endeavor; (Circulation) Endeavor; (Course Reserve) Endeavor; (ILL) Endeavor; (OPAC) Endeavor; (Serials) Endeavor
Database Vendor: OVID Technologies, Silverplatter Information Inc., Wilson - Wilson Web
Function: For research purposes, Reference services available

F B POWER PHARMACY LIBRARY, 425 N Charter St, 53706. SAN 8605. Tel: 608-262-2894. *Librn*, Heidi Marleau
Founded 1890

PRIMATE CENTER LIBRARY, 1220 Capitol Ct, 53715. SAN 364-866 Tel: 608-263-3512. FAX: 608-263-4031. Web Site: www.primate.wisc. pin/. *Dir*, Larry Jacobsen; E-Mail: jacobsen@primate.wisc.edu; *Librn*, Joanne Brown; E-Mail: brown@primate.wisc.edu; *Spec Coll*, Ray Ham E-Mail: hamel@primate.wisc.edu
Library Holdings: Bk Vols 19,680
Subject Interests: Aging, Animal welfare, Neurobiol, Primatology, Reproductive biol, Veterinary medicine, Virology
Special Collections: Primatology Coll, audiovisuals, bks, per Manage Primate-Science, An Electronic Forum for over 500 primatologists; Primate Info Net (PIN) a website for primatologists worldwide, Ask-Primate, an international reference service, the International Directory of Primatology, a web directory to primatologist & Primate Jobs, a job listing service
Friends of the Library Group

SCHOOL OF LIBRARY & INFORMATION STUDIES LIBRARY, 600 Park St Rm 4191, 53706. SAN 364-8427. Tel: 608-263-2960. FAX: 60 263-4849. *Librn*, Cecily Lehman; Staff 1 (MLS 1)
Library Holdings: Bk Vols 65,054
Subject Interests: Children's literature, Info sci, Libr

SOCIAL SCIENCE REFERENCE LIBRARY, 1180 Observatory Dr, 537 SAN 364-8729. Tel: 608-262-6195. *Librn*, Mary Folster; E-Mail: mfolster@library.wisc.edu
Library Holdings: Bk Vols 14,618
Subject Interests: Econ, Ind rels
Special Collections: Industrial Relations; Poverty; Social Systems

SOCIAL WORK LIBRARY, 1350 University Ave, Rm 236, 53706. SAN 364-8753. Tel: 608-263-3840. FAX: 608-265-2754. *Librn*, Jane Linzmey
Library Holdings: Bk Vols 21,073
Subject Interests: Child welfare, Family issues, Gerontology

SPACE SCIENCE & ENGINEERING CENTER, 1225 W Dayton St, 537 SAN 323-9845. Tel: 608-262-0987. FAX: 608-262-5974. Web Site: www.ssec.wisc.edu/library/library.htm. *Librn*, Jean Phillips; Tel: 608-262 8164, E-Mail: jean.phillips@ssec.wisc.edu; Staff 2 (MLS 1, Non-MLS 1
Subject Interests: Atmospheric sci, Space science

STEENBOCK MEMORIAL AGRICULTURAL LIBRARY, 550 Babcock Dr, 53706. SAN 364-8095. Tel: 608-262-9635. FAX: 608-263-3221. *Dir* Jean Gilbertson
Library Holdings: Bk Vols 196,306

KURT WENDT ENGINEERING LIBRARY, 215 N Randall Ave, 53706. SAN 364-8788. Tel: 608-262-3493. FAX: 608-262-4739. E-Mail: kfwlib doit.wisc.edu. *Dir*, Thomas Murray
Library Holdings: Bk Vols 304,609
Subject Interests: Atmospheric, Computer science, Engineering, Oceani sci

CM WILLIAM S MIDDLETON HEALTH SCIENCES LIBRARY, 1305 Lind Dr, 53706. SAN 364-8540. Tel: 608-262-2371. FAX: 608-262-4732. *Dir*, Karen Dahlen
Library Holdings: Bk Vols 326,894
Subject Interests: Allied health, Cancer res, Hospital administration, Neurosci, Nursing

Special Collections: History of Medicine, especially Anatomical Works
WISCONSIN CENTER FOR FILM & THEATER RESEARCH, 821 University Ave, 53706. SAN 323-9861. Tel: 608-264-6466. FAX: 608-264-6472. *Librn*, Maxine Fleckner Ducey
WOODMAN ASTRONOMICAL LIBRARY, 6521 Sterling Hall, 475 N Charter St, 53706. SAN 364-8842. Tel: 608-262-1320. FAX: 608-265-2754. *Librn*, Andrew Wertheimer

VESTERHEIM GENEALOGICAL CENTER, Naeseth Library, 415 W Main St, 53703-3116. SAN 326-0038. Tel: 608-255-2224. FAX: 608-255-6842. *Dir*, Blaine Hedberg; Staff 3 (MLS 1, Non-MLS 2)
Library Holdings: Bk Vols 1,303; Bk Titles 1,220
Publications: Norwegian Tracks (quarterly)

WISCONSIN DEPARTMENT OF EMPLOYEE TRUST FUNDS LIBRARY, 801 W Badger Rd, PO Box 7931, 53707-7931. SAN 324-7376. Tel: 608-267-2926. FAX: 608-267-4549. Web Site: www.badger.state.wi.us/agencies/etf. *Senior Librn*, Margery Katz; E-Mail: margery.katz@etf.state.wi.us; Staff 1 (MLS 1)
Founded 1972. Highest Degree: Doctorate
Library Holdings: Bk Titles 3,000; Per Subs 200
Subject Interests: Pensions, Pub employee retirement
Publications: Acquisitions list
Mem of South Central Library System
Partic in OCLC Online Computer Library Center, Inc

WISCONSIN DEPARTMENT OF HEALTH & FAMILY SERVICES LIBRARY, One W Wilson St, Rm 630, 53702. SAN 327-4071. Tel: 608-266-7473. FAX: 608-267-0358. *Librn*, B J Kraemer; E-Mail: kraembj@dhfs.state.wi.us
Library Holdings: Bk Vols 7,000; Per Subs 100

WISCONSIN DEPARTMENT OF JUSTICE, Law Library,* 123 W Washington Ave, Rm 349, PO Box 7857, 53707. SAN 318-1324. Tel: 608-266-0325. FAX: 608-267-2223. *Librn*, Michael F Bemis; E-Mail: bemismf@doj.state.wi.us; *Librn, Online Servs*, Sara J Paul
Founded 1969
Library Holdings: Bk Vols 40,000; Bk Titles 16,000; Per Subs 30
Subject Interests: Wis law
Special Collections: Consumer Protection Material; Forensics, per; Wisconsin Attorney General Material
Publications: Citations to the Wisconsin Administration Code; Index Digest to Opinions of the Attorney General of the State of Wisconsin, 1845-1972, 1973-current; Library News (periodic news memo)
Partic in Westlaw

WISCONSIN DEPARTMENT OF PUBLIC INSTRUCTION, Division for Libraries, Technology & Community Learning, 125 S Webster St, PO Box 7841, 53707-7841. SAN 364-8877. Tel: 608-266-2205. FAX: 608-267-1052. Web Site: www.dpi.state.wi.us/dpi/dltcl/. *In Charge*, Cal Potter; E-Mail: calvin.potter@dpi.state.wi.us; Staff 1 (Non-MLS 1)
Branches: 4
DEPARTMENT OF PUBLIC INSTRUCTION LIBRARY & STATISTICAL INFORMATION CENTER, 125 S Webster St, PO Box 7841, 53707. SAN 364-8990. Tel: 608-266-3108. FAX: 608-266-2529. Web Site: www.dpi.state.wi.us/dpi/dltcl/libstat/. *Librn*, Kay Ihlenfeldt; E-Mail: kay.ihlenfeldt@dpi.state.wi.us; Staff 5 (MLS 2, Non-MLS 3)
Founded 1968. Circ 3,500
Jul 1999-Jun 2000 Income $347,700, State $69,200, Federal $167,700, Parent Institution $110,800. Mats Exp $12,800, Books $2,000, Per/Ser (Incl. Access Fees) $8,000, Micro $2,800. Sal $213,800
Library Holdings: Bk Vols 2,666; Per Subs 190
Subject Interests: Educ statistics, Education, Libr sci
Special Collections: Eric Coll, microfiche
Automation Activity & Vendor Info: (ILL) Brodart; (OPAC) Brodart
Database Vendor: Dialog, Lexis-Nexis, OCLC - First Search
Partic in S Cent Libr Syst
INSTRUCTIONAL MEDIA & TECHNOLOGY TEAM, 125 S Webster St, PO Box 7841, 53707. SAN 364-8931. Tel: 608-267-3856. FAX: 608-267-1052. Web Site: www.dpi.state.wi.us/dpi.dltcl/imt/. *Dir*, Neah Lohr; E-Mail: neah.lohr@dpi.state.ui.us; Staff 7 (MLS 2, Non-MLS 5)
INTERLIBRARY LOAN & RESOURCE SHARING, 2109 S Stoughton, 53716-2899. SAN 364-9059. Tel: 608-224-6167. Toll Free Tel: 888-542-5543. FAX: 608-224-6178. Web Site: www.dpi.state.wi.us/dpi/dltcl/rll/index.html. *Dir*, Sally Drew; Tel: 608-224-6161, E-Mail: sally.drew@dpi.state.wi.us; *ILL*, Terry Wilcox; *Media Spec*, Willeen Tretheway; *Ref*, Mary Struckmeyer; Staff 12 (MLS 11, Non-MLS 1)
Circ 25,564
Jul 1999-Jun 2000 Income $3,514,384, State $1,627,727, Federal $1,777,652, Other $109,005. Mats Exp $66,777, Books $33,777, Per/Ser (Incl. Access Fees) $13,000, Micro $20,000. Sal $889,912
Library Holdings: Bk Vols 151,096; Bk Titles 133,000; Per Subs 117
Automation Activity & Vendor Info: (Circulation) Brodart; (ILL) Brodart; (OPAC) Brodart
Database Vendor: OCLC - First Search
Partic in Dialog Corporation; OCLC Online Computer Library Center, Inc
Special Services for the Blind - Newsline for the Blind
PUBLIC LIBRARY DEVELOPMENT TEAM, 125 S Webster St, PO Box 7841, 53707. SAN 364-9024. Tel: 608-266-7270. FAX: 608-267-1052. Web Site: www.dpi.state.wi.us/dpi/dltcl/pld. *Dir*, Larry T Nix; E-Mail: larry.nix@dpi.state.wi.us; Staff 6 (MLS 6)
Founded 1968

S WISCONSIN DEPARTMENT OF VETERAN AFFAIRS, (Formerly Wisconsin Veterans Museum Research Center), Museum Research Center, 30 W Mifflin St, 53703. SAN 325-4992. Tel: 608-267-1790. FAX: 608-264-7615. E-Mail: museum@mail.state.wi.us. *Actg Dir*, Richard Harrisson; *Archivist, Coll Develop*, Gayle Martinson; E-Mail: gayle.martinson@dva.state.wi.us; Staff 2 (MLS 1, Non-MLS 1)
Library Holdings: Bk Titles 7,000; Per Subs 40
Subject Interests: Mil hist mus
Special Collections: GAR National & Dept Records, bks, mss; Manuscript Coll, over 100 ln ft
Publications: Old Abe the War Eagle (1986); USS Wisconsin: Story of the Battleships (1988)
Partic in Wiscat

G WISCONSIN DEPARTMENT OF WORKFORCE DEVELOPMENT LIBRARY, 201 E Washington Ave, Rm 407, PO Box 7946, 53707. SAN 325-0296. Tel: 608-266-2832. FAX: 608-261-7979. *Librn*, Janet D Pugh; Staff 2 (MLS 1, Non-MLS 1)
Founded 1972
Library Holdings: Bk Titles 4,500; Per Subs 100
Subject Interests: Employment program info, Labor market info, Training program info
Mem of South Central Library System

M WISCONSIN HOSPITAL ASSOCIATION, Memorial Library,* 5721 Odana Rd, 53719. SAN 327-4608. Tel: 608-274-1820. FAX: 608-274-8554. *Librn*, Jenny Boudreau; E-Mail: jboudreau@wha.org
Library Holdings: Per Subs 50
Subject Interests: Hospital administration
Mem of S Cent Wis Health Planning Coop

G WISCONSIN LEGISLATIVE REFERENCE BUREAU, Reference & Library Sections,* 100 N Hamilton St, PO Box 2037, 53701-2037. SAN 318-1332. Tel: 608-266-0341. FAX: 608-266-5648.
Founded 1901
Library Holdings: Bk Titles 100,000
Subject Interests: Conservation, Constitutional revision, Crime, Econ dev, Education, Energy, Fed govt relating to state legislation, Judiciary, Labor relations, Legislation, Local govt relating to state legislation, Pollution control, Public admin, State finance, State govt: legislative process, Taxation, Transportation, Welfare
Special Collections: Bill Drafting Records, files, micro; Bill Index, 1897-present; Clipping Coll, 1900-present; Wisconsin Bills, 1897-present; Wisconsin State Government Documents
Publications: Index to Bulletin of Proceedings; Informational Bulletins, Wisconsin Briefs (on assorted topics relating to state government & state legislation); Wisconsin Blue Book (biennial)
Income figures reported are for entire bureau of which forty percent is library & reference

WISCONSIN STATE DEPARTMENT OF NATURAL RESOURCES
GL BUREAU OF LEGAL SERVICES LIBRARY, 101 S Webster St, PO Box 7921, 53707-7921. SAN 364-9172. Tel: 608-266-7524. Interlibrary Loan Service Tel: 608-266-8933. FAX: 608-266-6983.
Library Holdings: Bk Vols 5,000
Subject Interests: Legal ref mat pertaining to Wis law
G DEPARTMENT LIBRARY, 101 S Webster St, PO Box 7921, 53707-7921. Tel: 608-266-8933. FAX: 608-264-8943. Web Site: www.dnr.state.wi.us. *In Charge*, Dreux J Watermolen; Tel: 608-266-8931, Fax: 608-267-5231, E-Mail: waterd@dnr.state.wi.us
Founded 1978
Jul 1999-Jun 2000 Income (Main Library and Branch Library) State $145,000. Mats Exp $74,000, Books $2,000, Per/Ser (Incl. Access Fees) $16,000, Electronic Ref Mat (Incl. Access Fees) $18,000. Sal $109,000 (Prof $69,000)
Library Holdings: Bk Vols 33,000; Per Subs 300
Subject Interests: Air quality, Conservation, Environ qual, Fish, Natural resources, Pollution, Pollution control, Water quality, Wetlands, Wildlife
Database Vendor: OCLC - First Search, ProQuest
Function: For research purposes, ILL available
Partic in S Cent Libr Syst
G RESEARCH LIBRARY, 1350 Femrite Dr, Monona, 53716. SAN 364-9202. Tel: 608-221-6325. FAX: 608-221-6353. *Librn*, Chloe Keefer; E-Mail: keefee@dnr.state.wi.us
Founded 1964
Library Holdings: Bk Titles 10,000; Per Subs 200
Subject Interests: Fish, Water resources, Wildlife
Special Collections: Fish (Dr Schneberger, Lyle Christensen & Warren Churchill Coll), Richard Hunt and Carroll D Besadny Coll, Uncataloged Materials
Publications: Library Acquisition List (quarterly); Periodical Holding List;

Research Bureau Staff Publications List; Serials List
Mem of South Central Library System
Partic in Coun of Wis Librs, Inc; OCLC Online Computer Library Center, Inc; Wisconsin Library Services

G WISCONSIN STATE DEPARTMENT OF TRANSPORTATION LIBRARY,* 4802 Sheboygan Ave, Rm 803, PO Box 7957, 53707. SAN 364-9296. Tel: 608-266-0724. FAX: 608-267-0294. Web Site: www.dot.state.wi.us/dtid/library/library.html. *Librn*, John Cherney; E-Mail: john.cherney@dot.state.wi.us; Staff 3 (MLS 1, Non-MLS 2)
Founded 1968
1998-1999 Income $70,500. Mats Exp $18,500, Books $2,500, Per/Ser (Incl. Access Fees) $11,000. Sal $33,000 (Prof $22,000)
Library Holdings: Bk Vols 25,000; Per Subs 380
Subject Interests: Air transportation, Construction, Engineering, Evaluation, Highway transportation, Rail transportation, Transportation
Special Collections: Regional Planning Commission Reports; Transportation (Transportation Research Board)
Publications: From the Top Shelf (quarterly newsletter)
Partic in OCLC Online Computer Library Center, Inc; Wisconsin Library Services

S WISCONSIN STATE JOURNAL - CAPITAL TIMES LIBRARY, 1901 Fish Hatchery Rd, 53713. (Mail add: PO Box 8058, 53708), SAN 318-1367. Tel: 608-252-6412. FAX: 608-252-6119. Web Site: www.madison.com. *Librn*, Ronald J Larson; E-Mail: rlarson@madison.com; *Asst Librn*, Dennis McCormick; Staff 1 (MLS 1)
Library Holdings: Bk Vols 700
Subject Interests: Current events
Partic in Dialog Corporation; Dow Jones News Retrieval; Infonautics; News Libr; ProQuest

L WISCONSIN STATE LAW LIBRARY, (Formerly Wisconsin Supreme Court), One E Main, 53703. (Mail add: PO Box 7881, 53703-7881), Tel: 608-266-1600. Circulation Tel: 608-266-1600. Reference Tel: 608-267-9696. FAX: 608-267-2319. Web Site: wsll.state.wi.us. *Dir*, Marcia J Koslov; Tel: 608-266-1424, E-Mail: marcia.koslov@courts.state.wi.us; *Dir, Publ Servs*, Jane Colwin; Tel: 608-261-2340, E-Mail: jane.colwin@courts.state.wi.us; *Tech Servs*, Elaine Sharp; Staff 14 (MLS 8, Non-MLS 6)
Founded 1836
Library Holdings: Bk Vols 140,000; Per Subs 675
Subject Interests: Court decisions, Fed govt, Govt doc, Legal per, Legal texts, Statutes
Special Collections: Wisconsin Appendices & Briefs, 1836-present; Wisconsin Court of Appeals Unpublished Opinions, 1978-present
Automation Activity & Vendor Info: (Acquisitions) Innovative Interfaces Inc.; (Cataloging) Innovative Interfaces Inc.; (Circulation) Innovative Interfaces Inc.; (OPAC) Innovative Interfaces Inc.; (Serials) Innovative Interfaces Inc.
Database Vendor: Lexis-Nexis
Publications: Directory of County Law Libraries; Wisconsin State Law Library, Information Brochure; WSLL Newsletter; WSLL Serials List; WSLL WSLL Manual (1992)
Partic in Dialog Corporation; OCLC Online Computer Library Center, Inc; Westlaw; WILS

MANAWA

P STURM MEMORIAL LIBRARY,* 130 N Bridge St, PO Box 20, 54949-0020. SAN 318-1405. Tel: 920-596-2252. FAX: 920-596-2234. E-Mail: man@owls.lib.wi.us. *Dir*, Ellen L Connor; *Asst Librn*, Lyn Hokenstad; *Asst Librn*, Pat Wegener
Founded 1910. Pop 2,582; Circ 29,000
Library Holdings: Bk Titles 18,000; Per Subs 50
Subject Interests: Fishing, Hunting, Rodeos, Wisconsin, World War II
Mem of Outagamie Waupaca Library System

MANITOWISH WATERS

P FRANK B KOLLER MEMORIAL LIBRARY,* Hwy 51, PO Box 100, 54545-0100. SAN 376-6659. Tel: 715-543-2700. Web Site: www.centuryinter.net/kml. *Dir*, Janelle M Kohl; E-Mail: jkohl@centuryinter.net
Circ 18,464
Jan 1998-Dec 1998 Income $109,904, State $608, City $42,140, Federal $877, County $2,000, Other $17,416. Mats Exp $62,806, Books $12,060, Per/Ser (Incl. Access Fees) $1,898, AV Equip $5,079, Electronic Ref Mat (Incl. Access Fees) $1,085. Sal $23,434
Library Holdings: Bk Vols 20,170; Bk Titles 20,000; Per Subs 56
Subject Interests: Arts and crafts, Cooking, Popular fiction, World War II
Automation Activity & Vendor Info: (Circulation) Sagebrush Corporation
Database Vendor: Ebsco - EbscoHost
Mem of Northern Waters Library Service
Summer story hour.
Friends of the Library Group

MANITOWOC

M HOLY FAMILY MEMORIAL, Health Sciences Library, 2300 Western 54220-3712. (Mail add: PO Box 1450, 54221-1450), SAN 318-1413. Te 920-684-2260. FAX: 920-684-2009. *Librn*, Dan Eckert; E-Mail: deckert hfmhealth.org; Staff 2 (MLS 1, Non-MLS 1)
Founded 1975
Library Holdings: Bk Vols 3,000; Bk Titles 2,500; Per Subs 150
Subject Interests: Clinical medicine, Hospital administration, Nursing
Publications: Newsletter
Mem of Manitowoc-Calumet Library System
Partic in Docline; Fox River Valley Area Library Consortium; Medline

P MANITOWOC PUBLIC LIBRARY, 707 Quay, 54220. SAN 318-143X. 920-683-4863. TDD: 920-683-4872. FAX: 920-683-4873. Web Site: www.manitowoc.lib.wi.us. *Dir*, Alan Engelbert; *Publ Servs*, Hallie Yundt Silver; *Circ*, Connie Willems; *Tech Servs*, Dale Gort; *Ad Servs, Info Res*, Kathy Schmidt; *YA Servs*, Hazel Dahlke; *Head Tech Servs*, Lisa Bruere; Staff 9 (MLS 9)
Founded 1900. Pop 58,213; Circ 655,291
Jan 1999-Dec 1999 Income $1,731,430, City $1,238,512, County $449,0 Other $43,905. Mats Exp $274,592, Books $159,511, Per/Ser (Incl. Acce Fees) $58,956, Micro $8,400, AV Equip $43,954, Electronic Ref Mat (In Access Fees) $2,351
Library Holdings: Bk Vols 177,429; Per Subs 392
Subject Interests: Submarines
Special Collections: Art & Gardening (Ruth West Library of Beauty); Behnke Historic Photo Coll; World War II Personal Narratives
Automation Activity & Vendor Info: (Acquisitions) epixtech, inc.; (Circulation) epixtech, inc.; (Serials) epixtech, inc.
Publications: Newsletter
Mem of Manitowoc-Calumet Library System
Partic in BRS; Dialog Corporation; Fox River Valley Area Library Consortium; OCLC Online Computer Library Center, Inc
Friends of the Library Group

P MANITOWOC-CALUMET LIBRARY SYSTEM,* 707 Quay St, 54220. SAN 318-1421. Tel: 920-683-4863. FAX: 920-683-4873. *Dir*, Alan Engelbert; *Coordr*, Carol Gibson; Staff 2 (MLS 2)
Founded 1977. Pop 106,679; Circ 9,100
Library Holdings: Bk Vols 190,000
Special Collections: Story Wagon Service Coll
Publications: System Newsletter (bi-monthly)
Member Libraries: Brillion Public Library; Chilton Public Library; Holy Family Memorial; Kiel Public Library; Lakeshore Technical College Libr Lester Public Library; Manitowoc Public Library; New Holstein Public Library
Open Mon-Thurs 9-9, Fri 9-6, Sat 9-5 & Sun 12-4
Friends of the Library Group

CR SILVER LAKE COLLEGE, Zigmunt Library, 2406 S Alverno Rd, 54220 SAN 318-1448. Tel: 920-686-6174. FAX: 920-684-7082. E-Mail: slclibrary@silver.sl.edu. Web Site: www.sl.edu. *Coll Develop, Dir*, Sister Mary Gabriel Van Dreel; *Dir Libr Serv*, Sister Ritarose Stahl; Tel: 920-68 6134, E-Mail: elasta@silver.sl.edu; *Acq*, Diane Draheim; Tel: 920-686-61 E-Mail: ddraheim@silver.sl.edu; *ILL*, Lisa Kliment; E-Mail: kliment@silver.sl.edu; *Publ Servs*, Sister Mary Peter Harvey; E-Mail: harvey@silver.sl.edu; *Librn*, Sister Barbara Hadbavny; E-Mail: hadbavny@silver.sl.edu; Staff 5 (MLS 1, Non-MLS 4)
Founded 1939. Enrl 938; Highest Degree: Master
Jul 1999-Jun 2000 Income $146,969, Parent Institution $145,034, Other $1,935. Mats Exp $36,011, Books $20,968, Per/Ser (Incl. Access Fees) $10,918, AV Equip $3,075, Electronic Ref Mat (Incl. Access Fees) $1,050 Sal $81,748 (Prof $80,014)
Library Holdings: Bk Vols 59,043; Bk Titles 54,017; Per Subs 294
Subject Interests: Bus, Education, Juv lit, Music, Rare books
Special Collections: Kodaly Music
Automation Activity & Vendor Info: (Cataloging) Innovative Interfaces Inc.; (Circulation) Innovative Interfaces Inc.; (OPAC) Innovative Interfaces Inc.; (Serials) Innovative Interfaces Inc.
Database Vendor: Innovative Interfaces INN - View
Publications: Scoop (intra-college newsletter) (Newsletter); Scoop (intra-college newsletter)

S WISCONSIN MARITIME MUSEUM, Resource Center Library,* 75 Maritime Dr, 54220. SAN 326-5129. Tel: 920-684-0218. FAX: 920-684-0219. E-Mail: maritime@dataplusnet.com. *Curator*, Jay Martin; *In Charge*, Molly A Biddle
Founded 1969
Library Holdings: Bk Titles 7,000; Per Subs 100
Subject Interests: Great Lakes
Special Collections: Great Lakes Vessels (Carus Coll), photogs; Photograp Coll

:RINETTE

MARINETTE COUNTY CONSOLIDATED PUBLIC LIBRARY SERVICE, Stephenson Public Library, 1700 Hall Ave, 54143-1798. SAN 318-1480. Tel: 715-732-7570. FAX: 715-732-7575. E-Mail: mrt@owls.lib.wi.us. *Dir*, Nancy Krei
Pop 42,000; Circ 378,319
Library Holdings: Bk Vols 200,000; Per Subs 550
Special Collections: Marinette history
Mem of Nicolet Federated Library System
Mon-Fri 9:30am-9pm & Sat 9am-5pm
Friends of the Library Group
Branches: 6
COLEMAN-POUND BRANCH, PO Box 262, Coleman, 54112-0262. SAN 329-6466. Tel: 920-897-2400. FAX: 920-897-2400. *Librn*, Dorothy Kaminski
CRIVITZ BRANCH, PO Box 100, Crivitz, 54114-0100. SAN 324-038X. Tel: 715-854-7562. FAX: 715-854-7562. *Librn*, Janet King
GOODMAN-DUNBAR BRANCH, PO Box 160, Goodman, 54125. SAN 323-5637. Tel: 715-336-2576. *Librn*, Susan Strope
NIAGARA BRANCH, PO Box 108, Niagara, 54151-1417. SAN 318-2940. Tel: 715-251-3236. *Librn*, Lisa St Ours
Friends of the Library Group
PESHTIGO BRANCH, PO Box 155, Peshtigo, 54157. SAN 318-3203. Tel: 715-582-4905. *Librn*, Dorothy Wolverton
WAUSAUKEE BRANCH, PO Box 139, Wausaukee, 54177. SAN 324-0398. Tel: 715-856-5995. *Librn*, Joellen Simpson
Friends of the Library Group
Bookmobiles: 1

MARINETTE COUNTY LAW LIBRARY,* Court House, 1926 Hall Ave, PO Box 320, 54143-0320. SAN 327-6724. Tel: 715-732-7449, 715-732-7450.
Library Holdings: Bk Vols 1,000

UNIVERSITY OF WISCONSIN, Marinette Library, 750 W Bay Shore, 54143-1299. SAN 318-1502. Tel: 715-735-4306. FAX: 715-735-4307. Web Site: www.uwc.edu/mnt. *Dir*, Constance V Scofield; E-Mail: cscofiel@uwc.edu; Staff 1 (MLS 1)
Founded 1965. Enrl 551; Fac 30; Highest Degree: Associate
1998-1999 Income State $96,338. Mats Exp $18,124, Books $3,152, Per/Ser (Incl. Access Fees) $13,402, AV Equip $605, Other Print Mats $454, Electronic Ref Mat (Incl. Access Fees) $511. Sal $71,949
Library Holdings: Bk Vols 28,011; Bk Titles 24,697; Per Subs 189
Special Collections: Naval Architecture & Boating (Clinton F DeWitt Coll)
Automation Activity & Vendor Info: (Acquisitions) Endeavor; (Cataloging) Endeavor; (Circulation) Endeavor; (Course Reserve) Endeavor; (OPAC) Endeavor; (Serials) Endeavor
Database Vendor: Ebsco - EbscoHost, ProQuest, Wilson - Wilson Web
Partic in OCLC Online Computer Library Center, Inc; Wisconsin Library Services

:ARION

MARION PUBLIC LIBRARY,* 402 N Main, PO Box 267, 54950-0267. SAN 318-1510. Tel: 715-754-5368. FAX: 715-754-4610. *Dir*, Ellen Rineck; *Asst Dir*, Sharon Stuhr
Founded 1924. Pop 1,300; Circ 35,000
Library Holdings: Bk Titles 17,000; Per Subs 54
Mem of Outagamie Waupaca Library System
Friends of the Library Group

:ARKESAN

MARKESAN PUBLIC LIBRARY, 75 N Bridge St, PO Box 160, 53946-0160. SAN 318-1529. Tel: 920-398-3434. FAX: 920-398-2364. *Dir*, Lucy Hazlewood
Pop 1,500; Circ 25,700
2001-2001 Income $95,650, City $60,000, County $28,000, Other $7,650. Mats Exp $15,300. Sal $50,000
Library Holdings: Bk Vols 12,000; Per Subs 40
Mem of Winnefox Library System
Friends of the Library Group

:ARSHALL

MARSHALL COMMUNITY LIBRARY,* PO Box 778, 53559. SAN 318-1537. Tel: 608-655-3123. E-Mail: marlbstf@scls.lib.wi.us. *Dir*, Diana Skalitzky; Staff 2 (MLS 1, Non-MLS 1)
Founded 1956
Jan 1997-Dec 1998 Income $78,881, City $63,500, County $12,381, Locally Generated Income $3,000. Mats Exp $7,600, Books $6,000, Per/Ser (Incl. Access Fees) $1,100. Sal $48,600 (Prof $28,000)
Library Holdings: Bk Vols 16,670; Per Subs 72
Mem of South Central Library System
Friends of the Library Group

MARSHFIELD

M MARSHFIELD CLINIC, George E Magnin Medical Library, 1000 N Oak Ave, 54449-5777. SAN 318-1545. Tel: 715-387-5183. FAX: 715-389-5366. *Mgr*, Alana Ziaya; E-Mail: ziayaa@mfldclin.edu; *Ref*, Barbara Bartkowiak; Staff 2 (MLS 2)
Founded 1916
Library Holdings: Bk Vols 2,451; Per Subs 449
Subject Interests: Clinical medicine, Supporting sci
Special Collections: Biostatistics; Technical Writing
Partic in Regional Med Libr - Region 3

P MARSHFIELD PUBLIC LIBRARY, 211 E Second St, 54449. SAN 318-1553. Tel: 715-387-8494. FAX: 715-387-6909. E-Mail: refmfld@wctc.net. Web Site: ci.marshfield.wi.us.li. *Dir*, Dale Bartkowick; *Ad Servs, Asst Dir*, Lori Belongia; *Tech Servs*, Kathleen Jones; *Ch Servs*, Kim Ropson; *Circ*, Jodi Carlson; Staff 5 (MLS 5)
Founded 1864. Pop 35,270; Circ 400,116
Jan 1999-Dec 1999 Income $936,993, State $9,934, City $788,319, County $114,714, Locally Generated Income $43,791, Other $10,279. Mats Exp $125,674, Books $94,485, Per/Ser (Incl. Access Fees) $13,483, Micro $1,491, Electronic Ref Mat (Incl. Access Fees) $2,333. Sal $206,330 (Prof $479,066)
Library Holdings: Bk Vols 113,000; Per Subs 300
Subject Interests: Genealogy, Local history
Automation Activity & Vendor Info: (Acquisitions) epixtech, inc.; (Cataloging) epixtech, inc.; (Circulation) epixtech, inc.
Mem of South Central Library System
Partic in OCLC Online Computer Library Center, Inc
Friends of the Library Group

J MID-STATE TECHNICAL COLLEGE, Marshfield Campus Library,* 2600 W Fifth St, 54449. SAN 318-1561. Tel: 715-387-2538. FAX: 715-389-2864. *Librn*, Diane Andres; E-Mail: dandres@midstate.tec.wi
Library Holdings: Bk Titles 4,500
For holdings see parent entry in Wisconsin Rapids

M SAINT JOSEPH'S HOSPITAL, Learning Resource Center,* 611 Saint Joseph Ave, 54449. SAN 318-157X. Tel: 715-387-7271. FAX: 715-389-3977. *Librn*, Cindy Herzog; E-Mail: herzogc@mfldclin.edu; Staff 3 (MLS 1, Non-MLS 2)
Founded 1918
Library Holdings: Bk Vols 7,889; Bk Titles 7,300; Per Subs 161
Subject Interests: Consumer health, Large print, Nursing
Special Collections: Nursing (Historical Coll)
Publications: Bi-weekly Current Acquisitions List
Partic in Greater Midwest Regional Medical Libr Network; Northern Wis Health Sci Libr Coop; Wisconsin Valley Library Service

J UNIVERSITY OF WISCONSIN, Marshfield-Wood County Library, 2000 W Fifth St, PO Box 150, 54449-0150. SAN 318-1588. Tel: 715-389-6531. FAX: 715-389-6539. Web Site: www.marshfield.edu. *Dir*, Ruth V Elberbrook; E-Mail: relderbr@uwc.edu; Staff 2 (MLS 2)
Founded 1964. Enrl 600; Highest Degree: Associate
Jul 1998-Jun 1999 Mats Exp $23,545, Books $3,616, Per/Ser (Incl. Access Fees) $9,619, Micro $1,922, AV Equip $5,137, Other Print Mats $843, Electronic Ref Mat (Incl. Access Fees) $2,408. Sal $51,274 (Prof $40,770)
Library Holdings: Bk Vols 31,954; Bk Titles 29,156; Per Subs 145
Database Vendor: CARL, Ebsco - EbscoHost, OCLC - First Search, ProQuest, Wilson - Wilson Web
Partic in OCLC Online Computer Library Center, Inc

MAUSTON

P MAUSTON PUBLIC LIBRARY,* 133 E State St, 53948-1344. SAN 318-1596. Tel: 608-847-4454. FAX: 608-847-2306. *Dir*, Kathy Manders
Founded 1897. Pop 3,466; Circ 87,738
Library Holdings: Bk Vols 27,344
Subject Interests: Juneau County hist
Mem of Winding Rivers Library System

M MILE BLUFF MEDICAL CENTER, 1050 Division St, 53948. Tel: 608-847-6161. FAX: 608-847-6017. *Librn*, Marthy Airth-Kindree; E-Mail: hessmem5@mwt.net
Library Holdings: Bk Vols 300; Bk Titles 50; Per Subs 150

MAYVILLE

P MAYVILLE PUBLIC LIBRARY,* 111 N Main St, 53050. SAN 318-160X. Tel: 920-387-7910. FAX: 920-387-7917. E-Mail: maylibrary@powerweb.net. *Dir*, Karen S Harris
Pop 4,515
Jan 1997-Dec 1998 Income $135,000. Mats Exp $36,000. Sal $60,000 (Prof $32,000)
Library Holdings: Bk Vols 46,000; Per Subs 105
Mem of Mid-Wisconsin Federated Library System

P MID-WISCONSIN FEDERATED LIBRARY SYSTEM, 201 N Main St, 53050-1238. (Mail add: PO Box 267, 53050-0267), SAN 317-9931. Tel: 920-387-7284. FAX: 920-387-7288. Web Site: www.mwfls.org. *Dir*, Shannon Lang; E-Mail: langs@mwfls.org; *Asst Dir*, Matthew Bollerman; E-Mail: bollerman@mwfls.org; *Admin Assoc*, Cathy Duehring; E-Mail: duehring@mwfls.org; *ILL*, Sharon Webb; E-Mail: webbs@mwfls.org; *Publ Servs*, Judi Jones; E-Mail: jjones@mwfls.org; *Tech Coordr*, Steve Scarbrough; E-Mail: steves@mwfls.org; Staff 6 (MLS 2, Non-MLS 4)
Founded 1974. Pop 286,755
Jan 2001-Dec 2001 Income $1,069,094, State $741,190, Federal $22,300, Other $305,604. Mats Exp $3,000, Books $1,700, Per/Ser (Incl. Access Fees) $1,300. Sal $237,413 (Prof $106,934)
Special Collections: Professional materials
Publications: Elan (Newsletter)
Member Libraries: Beaver Dam Community Library; Brownsville Public Library; Dodge County Library Service; Fox Lake Public Library; Hartford Public Library; Horicon Public Library; Hustisford Public Library; Hutchinson Memorial Library; Iron Ridge Public Library; Jefferson Public Library; Juneau Public Library; Kewaskum Public Library; Lomira Public Library; Lowell Public Library; Mayville Public Library; Reeseville Public Library; Slinger Community Library; Theresa Public Library; Watertown Public Library; Waupun Public Library; West Bend Community Memorial Library
Partic in OCLC Online Computer Library Center, Inc; Wisconsin Library Services

MAZOMANIE

P MAZOMANIE FREE LIBRARY, 102 Brodhead St, 53560-0458. SAN 318-1618. Tel: 608-795-2104. FAX: 608-795-2102. Web Site: www.scls.lib.wi.us/maz. *Dir*, Mary Morris Hutnik; E-Mail: mmhutnik@scls.lib.wi.us; Staff 3 (MLS 1, Non-MLS 2)
Founded 1899
Jan 2000-Dec 2000 Mats Exp $12,500, Books $9,000, Per/Ser (Incl. Access Fees) $1,000, AV Equip $2,500. Sal $40,000
Library Holdings: Bk Vols 15,000; Per Subs 54
Subject Interests: Genealogy, Local history
Mem of South Central Library System
Friends of the Library Group

MCFARLAND

P MCFARLAND PUBLIC LIBRARY, 5114 Farwell St, 53558. SAN 377-9343. Tel: 608-838-4590. E-Mail: mcflib@scls.lib.wi.us. *Dir*, Patricia Chevis; Tel: 608-838-4589; *Ch Servs*, Susan Herr-Hoyman
Founded 1997
Library Holdings: Bk Vols 22,752; Per Subs 118
Mem of South Central Library System
Friends of the Library Group

MEDFORD

P FRANCES L SIMEK MEMORIAL LIBRARY-MEDFORD,* 400 N Main, 54451. SAN 318-1626. Interlibrary Loan Service Tel: 715-748-2505. FAX: 715-748-4160. Web Site: www.sws-wis.com/medfordpubliclibrary/. *Dir*, Shirley Lemke; E-Mail: slemke@wvls.lib.wi.us
Founded 1916. Pop 4,000; Circ 60,000
Library Holdings: Bk Vols 24,340; Per Subs 87
Mem of Wisconsin Valley Library Service
Friends of the Library Group

MELLEN

P LEGION MEMORIAL LIBRARY, 102 E Bennett St, PO Box 47, 54546-0447. SAN 318-1642. Tel: 715-274-8331. *Librn*, Judy Goeckermann
Founded 1929. Pop 2,000; Circ 18,000
Library Holdings: Bk Vols 6,040; Bk Titles 7,000; Per Subs 24
Publications: Booklist
Mem of Northern Waters Library Service
Friends of the Library Group

MENASHA

G EAST CENTRAL WISCONSIN REGIONAL PLANNING COMMISSION LIBRARY, 132 Main St, 54952. SAN 324-735X. Tel: 920-751-4770. FAX: 920-751-4771. *Mgr*, Vicky Johnson
Library Holdings: Bk Titles 10,000
Special Collections: US Census Coll, bks, micro

P ELISHA D SMITH PUBLIC LIBRARY,* 440 First St, 54952-3191. SAN 318-1650. Tel: 920-751-4795, 920-751-5168. FAX: 920-751-5159. *Dir*, Jack Fry; *Ad Servs*, Karen Phillips; *Ch Servs*, Marge Loch-Wouters; *Ref*, De Dalum; *Ref*, Katheline Hannah; *Ref*, Barbara LaFontaine; *Ref*, Patricia Nieland; *Circ*, Catherine Brandt
Founded 1898. Pop 23,000; Circ 275,000
Library Holdings: Bk Titles 110,000; Per Subs 300
Subject Interests: Local history
Mem of Winnefox Library System
Partic in Fox Valley Library Council
Friends of the Library Group

J UNIVERSITY OF WISCONSIN-FOX VALLEY LIBRARY, Fox Valley 1478 Midway Rd, 54952-1297. SAN 318-1669. Tel: 920-832-2672. Interlibrary Loan Service Tel: 920-832-2673. Reference Tel: 920-832-26 FAX: 920-832-2874. Web Site: www.uwfoxvalley.uwc.edu. *Dir*, April K Breese; E-Mail: akain@uwcmail.uwc.edu; *ILL*, Patricia Warmbrunn; *Bib Instr*, Christine Chamness; *Circ*, Kathryn Bloomer; Tel: 920-832-2672; 4 (MLS 2, Non-MLS 2)
Founded 1937. Enrl 1,400; Fac 63; Highest Degree: Associate
Jul 1999-Jun 2000 Income $166,000. Mats Exp $43,178, Books $24,114 Per/Ser (Incl. Access Fees) $18,964, Presv $100. Sal $113,447 (Prof $79,060)
Library Holdings: Bk Vols 33,614; Bk Titles 29,230; Per Subs 200
Automation Activity & Vendor Info: (Acquisitions) Endeavor; (Catalog Endeavor; (Circulation) Endeavor; (Course Reserve) Endeavor; (ILL) Endeavor; (Media Booking) Endeavor; (OPAC) Endeavor
Database Vendor: Ebsco - EbscoHost, OCLC - First Search
Partic in Fox Valley Library Council; OCLC Online Computer Library Center, Inc; Wisconsin Library Services

MENOMONEE FALLS

M COMMUNITY MEMORIAL HOSPITAL, McKay Memorial Library, W N8085 Town Hall Rd, PO Box 408, 53051. SAN 324-721X. Tel: 262-25 3440. FAX: 262-253-7169. *Librn*, B Keppel
Library Holdings: Bk Titles 360; Per Subs 200
Subject Interests: Hospital administration, Medicine, Nursing
Publications: Acquisitions list (annual); serial holdings list; VC list
Restriction: Staff use only
Partic in Greater Midwest Regional Medical Libr Network; Southeastern Wisconsin Health Science Library Consortium

P MAUDE SHUNK PUBLIC LIBRARY, Menomonee Falls Public Library 156th N, 8446 Pilgrim Rd, 53052-3140. SAN 318-1677. Tel: 262-255-83 FAX: 262-532-8900. *Dir*, Richard A Crane; *Ch Servs*, Chris Stabo; *Ad Se* Anne Reid; *Syst Coordr*, Robert Rapp; *Cat, Tech Servs*, Jane Schall; *ILL*, Mari Schmidt; *Circ*, Judi Sommerville
Founded 1906. Pop 28,700; Circ 460,000
Library Holdings: Bk Vols 107,642; Per Subs 362
Special Collections: Historical Photograph Coll; Menomonee Falls Local History
Mem of Waukesha County Federated Library System
Partic in OCLC Online Computer Library Center, Inc
Friends of the Library Group

MENOMONIE

P MENOMONIE PUBLIC LIBRARY, 600 Wolske Bay Rd, 54751. SAN 3 1685. Tel: 715-232-2164. FAX: 715-232-2324. *Dir*, Dianne Lueder; *Asst Dir*, Helen Hullberg
Founded 1986. Pop 17,000; Circ 377,515
Jan 1998-Dec 1998 Income $426,010, City $218,217, County $138,886, Locally Generated Income $68,907. Mats Exp $67,882, Books $53,926, P Ser (Incl. Access Fees) $6,077, AV Equip $7,879. Sal $73,819 (Prof $41,200)
Library Holdings: Bk Vols 85,794; Per Subs 192
Automation Activity & Vendor Info: (Cataloging) Sagebrush Corporatio (Circulation) Sagebrush Corporation
Mem of Indianhead Federated Library System
Friends of the Library Group

C UNIVERSITY OF WISCONSIN-STOUT, Library Learning Center, 315 Tenth Ave, 54751-0790. SAN 318-1693. Tel: 715-232-1215. Interlibrary Loan Service Tel: 715-232-1112. TDD: 715-232-1333. FAX: 715-232-178 Interlibrary Loan Service FAX: 715-232-2618. Web Site: www.uwstout.ed lib. *Dir*, John J Jax; Tel: 715-232-1184, E-Mail: jaxj@uwstout.edu; *ILL*, Faye Neuenfeldt; E-Mail: neuenfeldtf@uwstout.edu; *Automation Syst Coordr*, Philip Schwarz; Tel: 715-232-2363, E-Mail: schwarzp@uwstout.e *Cat*, Mary Richards; Tel: 715-232-2094, E-Mail: richardsm@uwstout.edu; *Electronic Resources*, Lelah Lugo; Tel: 715-232-1552, E-Mail: lugola@uwstout.edu; *Archivist*, Kevin Thorie; Tel: 715-232-2300, E-Mail: thoriek@uwstout.edu; *Instrul Serv*, Denise Madland; Tel: 715-232-2141, E-Mail: madlandd@uwstout.edu; *Ref, Ser*, Theresa Muraski; Tel: 715-232-1160, E-Mail: muraskit@uwstout.edu; *Coll Develop*, Susan J Strehl; Tel: 715-23 2363, E-Mail: strehls@uwstout.edu; *Ref Serv*, Jana Reeg-Steidinger; Tel: 715-232-1553, E-Mail: reegj@uwstout.edu; *Access Serv*, Diana Slater; Tel: 715-232-1402, E-Mail: slaterd@uwstout.edu; *Ref Serv*, Carol Hagness; Tel 715-232-1892, E-Mail: hagnessc@uwstout.edu; *Instrul Serv*, Brenda Swannack; Tel: 715-232-2617, E-Mail: swannackb@uwstout.edu; Staff 29 (MLS 12, Non-MLS 17)
Founded 1891. Enrl 7,800; Fac 551; Highest Degree: Master
Jul 1999-Jun 2000 Income $2,343,051, State $2,210,050, Federal $62,947,

Locally Generated Income $62,054, Parent Institution $8,000. Mats Exp $603,697, Books $191,033, Per/Ser (Incl. Access Fees) $191,499, Micro $4,669, AV Equip $93,703, Other Print Mats $1,553, Manuscripts & Archives $3,500. Sal $1,079,942 (Prof $500,171)
Library Holdings: Bk Vols 219,270; Bk Titles 219,270; Per Subs 6,205
Subject Interests: Consumer studies, Family studies, Hospitality, Indust tech, Manufacturing eng, Tourism, Vocational rehabilitation
Automation Activity & Vendor Info: (Acquisitions) Endeavor; (Cataloging) Endeavor; (Circulation) Endeavor; (Course Reserve) Endeavor; (ILL) Endeavor; (Media Booking) Endeavor; (OPAC) Endeavor; (Serials) Endeavor
Partic in OCLC Online Computer Library Center, Inc; Wisconsin Library Services
Special Services for Students with Disabilities - Arkenstone Readers, DecTalk, Large Print CRT screens, TDD

QUON

CONCORDIA UNIVERSITY WISCONSIN, Rincker Memorial Library, 12800 N Lake Shore Dr, 53097. SAN 318-1901. Tel: 414-243-4330. Circulation Tel: 414-243-4420. FAX: 414-243-4424. Web Site: topcat.switchinc.org. *Per*, Karen Nimz; Tel: 262-243-4402, E-Mail: karen.nimz@cuw.edu; *Dir*, Richard L Wohlers; E-Mail: richard.wohlers@cuw.edu; *Distance Educ*, sarah Rohrer; Tel: 262-243-4397, E-Mail: sarah.rohrer@cuw.edu; *Ref*, Thomas Krenzke; Tel: 262-243-4534, E-Mail: thomas.krenzke@cuw.edu; *Head, Circ*, Carol Mittag; E-Mail: carol.mittag@cuw.edu; Staff 11 (MLS 5, Non-MLS 6)
Founded 1881. Enrl 4,603; Highest Degree: Master
Library Holdings: Bk Vols 110,000; Per Subs 810
Subject Interests: Bus, Church music, Education, Nursing, Physical therapy, Theology
Special Collections: 16th & 17th Century Lutheran Theology; German Hymnals
Automation Activity & Vendor Info: (OPAC) Innovative Interfaces Inc.
Database Vendor: Ebsco - EbscoHost, IAC - Info Trac, Lexis-Nexis, OCLC - First Search, OVID Technologies, ProQuest, Silverplatter Information Inc., Wilson - Wilson Web
Publications: Library Communique (Newsletter)
Partic in Library Council Of Metropolitan Milwaukee, Inc; OCLC Online Computer Library Center, Inc; Southeastern Wisconsin Information Technology Exchange, Inc

FRANK L WEYENBERG LIBRARY OF MEQUON-THIENSVILLE,* 11345 N Cedarburg Rd, 53092-1998. SAN 318-1715. Tel: 262-242-2593. FAX: 262-242-1220. Web Site: www.flwlib.org. *Ad Servs, Asst Dir, Coll Develop*, Gail Skiff; E-Mail: bethb@flwlib.org; *Tech Servs*, Gwen Kuske; *Govt Doc, Media Spec, Ref*, David Nimmer; E-Mail: davidn@flwlib.org; *Ad Servs*, Beth Beecher; E-Mail: bethb@flwlib.org; *Ch Servs*, Jennie Stoltz; E-Mail: jennies@flwlib.org; *Circ*, Pat Bluhm; E-Mail: patb@flwlib.org; Staff 6 (MLS 5, Non-MLS 1)
Founded 1954. Pop 25,000; Circ 280,000
Jan 1999-Dec 1999 Income $894,569, City $829,569, Locally Generated Income $65,000. Mats Exp $114,345, Books $90,845, Per/Ser (Incl. Access Fees) $7,500, Electronic Ref Mat (Incl. Access Fees) $16,000. Sal $417,527
Library Holdings: Bk Vols 120,000; Per Subs 350; High Interest/Low Vocabulary Bk Vols 100
Special Collections: Local History of Mequon & Thiensville
Automation Activity & Vendor Info: (Cataloging) epixtech, inc.; (Circulation) epixtech, inc.; (OPAC) epixtech, inc.
Publications: Columns (newsletter)
Mem of Eastern Shores Library System
Partic in Library Council Of Metropolitan Milwaukee, Inc
Friends of the Library Group

MILWAUKEE AREA TECHNICAL COLLEGE LIBRARY, North Campus, 5555 W Highland Rd, 53092. SAN 318-1707. Tel: 414-238-2212, 414-238-2301. FAX: 414-238-2306. *Librn*, Steven Heser; Tel: 262-238-2212, E-Mail: hesers@gwise1.matc.edu
Library Holdings: Bk Vols 18,051; Bk Titles 15,880; Per Subs 175

HORACE J & IDABELL ROSEN LIBRARY, 2909 W Mequon Rd, 53092. SAN 318-1863. Tel: 262-242-6900. FAX: 262-242-3952. *Librn*, Maggi Treager
Library Holdings: Bk Titles 2,000
Subject Interests: Jewish hist, Jewish lit, Judaism
Special Services for the Blind - Bks on cassette; Braille

SAINT MARY'S HOSPITAL, OZAUKEE, 13111 N Port Washington Rd, 53097. SAN 324-6981. Tel: 262-243-7300. FAX: 262-243-7416. *In Charge*, Gayle Wellenstein
Library Holdings: Bk Titles 1,000; Per Subs 70
Restriction: Staff use only
Partic in Greater Midwest Regional Medical Libr Network; Southeastern Wisconsin Health Science Library Consortium

WISCONSIN LUTHERAN SEMINARY LIBRARY,* 6633 W Wartburg Circle, 53092-1530. SAN 318-1723. Tel: 414-257-8813. FAX: 414-257-8818. E-Mail: library@wls.wels.net. *Bibliog Instr, Dir, Ref*, John P Hartwig; *Cat, Per, Tech Servs*, Lynn Whittenberger; Staff 2 (MLS 2)
Founded 1878. Enrl 224; Fac 16; Highest Degree: Master
Library Holdings: Bk Vols 43,000; Per Subs 400
Subject Interests: Bible, Church history, Doctrinal, Lutheran Church, Practical theol, Relig studies

MERCER

P MERCER PUBLIC LIBRARY,* PO Box 561, 54547. SAN 318-1731. Tel: 715-476-2366. FAX: 715-476-2366. E-Mail: mercerlib@mercer.baysat.net. *Coll Develop, Dir*, Debbie Hohner
Founded 1940. Pop 3,000; Circ 10,300
Library Holdings: Bk Vols 6,756; Per Subs 26
Mem of Northern Waters Library Service

MERRILL

SR OUR SAVIOUR'S LUTHERAN CHURCH LIBRARY, 300 Logan, 54452. SAN 324-7228. Tel: 715-536-5813. FAX: 715-536-3658. *Librn*, Brenda Mueller
Library Holdings: Bk Vols 763; Bk Titles 753

P T B SCOTT LIBRARY, Merrill Public Library, 106 W First St, 54452-2398. SAN 318-174X. Tel: 715-536-7191. FAX: 715-536-1705. Web Site: library.ci.merrill.wi.us/. *Dir*, Beatrice Lebal; E-Mail: blebal@mail.wiscnet.net; *Asst Libr Dir*, Stacy Stevens; E-Mail: stevens@mail.wiscnet.net; *Ad Servs*, Doreen Bashore; E-Mail: dbashore@wvls.lib.wi.us; *Ch Servs*, Karen Algire; Tel: 715-536-7909; *Circ*, Donna Hertel; *Tech Coordr*, Eleanor Schwartz; Staff 20 (MLS 2, Non-MLS 18)
Founded 1891. Pop 20,000; Circ 291,716
Jan 1998-Dec 1998 Income $691,903, City $377,233, Federal $3,935, County $292,935, Locally Generated Income $9,188, Other $8,612. Mats Exp $76,878, Books $61,018, Per/Ser (Incl. Access Fees) $13,150, Micro $475, Other Print Mats $215, Electronic Ref Mat (Incl. Access Fees) $2,070. Sal $366,581 (Prof $47,320)
Library Holdings: Bk Vols 75,905; Per Subs 255
Special Collections: Wisconsin & Local History
Automation Activity & Vendor Info: (Circulation) epixtech, inc.; (ILL) Brodart
Database Vendor: epixtech, inc.
Mem of Wisconsin Valley Library Service
Friends of the Library Group

R TRINITY CHURCH LIBRARY, 107 N State St, 54452. SAN 325-111X. Tel: 715-536-5482. FAX: 715-539-2911. E-Mail: trinluth@dwave.net. *Librn*, Sandy Frank
Library Holdings: Bk Vols 150

MIDDLETON

S AGRACETUS LIBRARY,* 8520 University Green, 53562. SAN 329-1146. Tel: 608-821-3440. FAX: 608-836-9710. *Info Specialist*, Cheryl Scadlock; E-Mail: cheryl.b.scadlock@monsanto.com
Founded 1982
Library Holdings: Bk Vols 2,000; Bk Titles 1,050
Subject Interests: Agriculture, Genetics, Molecular biology
Restriction: By appointment only

P MIDDLETON PUBLIC LIBRARY, 7425 Hubbard Ave, 53562-3117. SAN 318-1758. Tel: 608-831-5564. FAX: 608-836-5724. E-Mail: mid@scls.lib.wi.us. Web Site: www.scls.lib.wi.us/middleton. *Dir*, Paul Nelson; *YA Servs*, Eve Robillard; *Ad Servs*, Liz Cohen; *Circ*, Elizabeth Bauer; *Tech Servs*, Christine Smith; *Computer Services*, Patrick Williams; Staff 21 (MLS 3, Non-MLS 18)
Founded 1926. Pop 15,200; Circ 466,989
Library Holdings: Bk Vols 68,871; Per Subs 267
Friends of the Library Group

MILLTOWN

P MILLTOWN PUBLIC LIBRARY,* 89 W Main St, PO Box 68, 54858-0068. SAN 318-1766. Tel: 715-825-2313. *Librn*, Mary Lee Johnson
Pop 742; Circ 10,607
Library Holdings: Bk Vols 12,000; Per Subs 25
Mem of Indianhead Federated Library System

MILTON

P MILTON PUBLIC LIBRARY, 430 E High St Ste 100, 53563-0337. SAN 318-1782. Tel: 608-868-7462. FAX: 608-868-6926. Web Site: www.als.lib.wi.us/MPL. *Dir*, Patricia Conrad; E-Mail: pconrad@als.lib.wi.us; Staff 5 (MLS 1, Non-MLS 4)
Founded 1967. Pop 6,177; Circ 44,926
Jan 2000-Dec 2000 Income $149,263, City $110,910, County $38,353. Mats Exp $28,248, Books $26,000, Per/Ser (Incl. Access Fees) $2,248. Sal $47,222 (Prof $36,800)

Library Holdings: Bk Titles 26,083; Per Subs 116
Automation Activity & Vendor Info: (Acquisitions) Follett; (Cataloging) Follett; (Circulation) Follett
Mem of Arrowhead Library System
Friends of the Library Group

MILWAUKEE

S ACDRICH CHEMICAL CO, INC LIBRARY,* 940 W Saint Paul Ave, PO Box 355, 53201. SAN 318-1790. Tel: 414-273-3850. FAX: 414-273-4979. *Librn*, Bethany Wolf
Founded 1950
Library Holdings: Bk Vols 2,674; Bk Titles 1,300; Per Subs 51
Subject Interests: Chemistry

C ALVERNO COLLEGE LIBRARY, 3400 S 43rd St, 53234-3922. (Mail add: PO Box 343922, 53234-3922), SAN 318-1820. Tel: 414-382-6052. Interlibrary Loan Service Tel: 414-382-6173. Circulation Tel: 414-382-6060. Reference Tel: 414-382-6062. FAX: 414-382-6354. Web Site: www.depts.alverno.edu/library. *Dir*, Kathleen Beaver; Tel: 414-382-6054, E-Mail: kathleen.beaver@alverno.edu; *Adminr*, Holly Morse; E-Mail: holly.morse@alverno.edu; *Librn*, Linda Romm; Tel: 414-382-6184, E-Mail: linda.romm@alverno.edu; *Acq*, Diane Klajbor; Tel: 414-382-6056, E-Mail: diane.klajbor@alverno.edu; *Archivist*, Debra Butz; Tel: 414-382-6059, E-Mail: debra.butz@alverno.edu; *Archivist*, Sara Shutkin; Tel: 414-382-6202, E-Mail: sara.shutkin@alverno.edu; *Bibliog Instr*, Amy Panenteau; *Bibliog Instr*, Jennifer Schmidt; Tel: 414-382-6355, E-Mail: jennifer.schmidt@alverno.edu; *Cat*, Cathy Carey; Tel: 414-382-6180, E-Mail: catherine.carey@alverno.edu; *Cat*, MaryAnn Schmidt; Tel: 414-382-6063, E-Mail: maryann.schmidt@alverno.edu; *Head, Circ*, Charles Elftmann; Tel: 414-382-6193, E-Mail: charles.elftmann@alverno.edu; *Circ*, Kathy Bailey; Tel: 414-382-6174, E-Mail: kathy.bailey@alverno.edu; *Circ*, Susan Radaj; Tel: 414-382-6174, E-Mail: susan.radaj@alverno.edu; *ILL*, Rebecca Bissell; Tel: 414-382-6089, E-Mail: rebecca.bissell@alverno.edu; *ILL*, Anne Pach; Tel: 414-382-6173, E-Mail: anne.pach@alverno.edu; *Head Ref*, Jacqueline Rice; Tel: 414-382-6057, E-Mail: jacqueline.rice@alverno.edu; *Ser*, Marcia Boyer; Tel: 414-382-6059, E-Mail: marcia.boyer@alverno.edu; *Ser*, Melisa Peters; Tel: 414-382-6058, E-Mail: melisa.peters@alverno.edu; *Syst Coordr*, Robin Zalben; Tel: 414-382-6397, E-Mail: robin.zalben@alverno.edu; *Tech Servs*, Mary Nemmer; Tel: 414-382-6175; Staff 19 (MLS 10, Non-MLS 9)
Founded 1936. Enrl 1,876; Fac 133; Highest Degree: Master
Library Holdings: Bk Vols 89,643; Per Subs 1,407
Subject Interests: Education, Ethnicity, Feminism, Music, Nursing
Special Collections: Children's Literature Coll; Faculty Resource Center (Higher Education); Teaching Materials Coll
Automation Activity & Vendor Info: (Acquisitions) Innovative Interfaces Inc.; (Cataloging) Innovative Interfaces Inc.; (Circulation) Innovative Interfaces Inc.; (Course Reserve) Innovative Interfaces Inc.; (ILL) Innovative Interfaces Inc.; (Media Booking) Innovative Interfaces Inc.; (OPAC) Innovative Interfaces Inc.; (Serials) Innovative Interfaces Inc.
Database Vendor: Ebsco - EbscoHost, IAC - Info Trac, IAC - SearchBank, OCLC - First Search, OVID Technologies, ProQuest, Silverplatter Information Inc.
Partic in Library Council Of Metropolitan Milwaukee, Inc; OCLC Online Computer Library Center, Inc; Southeastern Wisconsin Information Technology Exchange, Inc; Wis Asn Of Independent Cols & Univs; Wisconsin Library Services

S AMERICAN ASSOCIATION OF HANDWRITING ANALYSTS LIBRARY, 3352 S Indiana Ave, 53207. SAN 376-0847. Tel: 414-481-9198. FAX: 414-481-9999. E-Mail: wryte4me@aol.com. *Librn*, Alice M Steuck-Konkel
Library Holdings: Bk Titles 850
Restriction: Access at librarian's discretion, By appointment only
Function: Mail loans to members

S AMERICAN SOCIETY FOR QUALITY, Quality Information Center, PO Box 3005, 53201. SAN 328-5944. Tel: 414-272-8575, Ext 8917. FAX: 414-765-8660. E-Mail: qic@asq.org. Web Site: www.asq.org. *Mgr*, Marylee Kastelie
Library Holdings: Bk Vols 3,500
Special Collections: ASQ & Quality Press Publications; ASQ Standards
Restriction: By appointment only

R ASCENSION LUTHERAN CHURCH LIBRARY, 1236 S Layton Blvd, 53215-1653. SAN 318-1847. Tel: 414-329-8813.
Founded 1954
Library Holdings: Bk Titles 13,000
Subject Interests: Art, Biography, Cinema, Fiction, Religion
Special Collections: Movie Books (Richard Krueger Coll); Old Bibles; Sheet Music Coll (organ); The Dewey 200's

AURORA HEALTH CARE LIBRARIES
M SAINT LUKE'S MEDICAL CENTER LIBRARY, 2900 W Oklahoma Ave, PO Box 2901, 53201-2901. SAN 318-2452. Tel: 414-649-7357. FAX: 414-649-7037. *Mgr*, Kathleen Strube; E-Mail: kathleen.strube@mixcom.com; Staff 5 (MLS 3, Non-MLS 2)
Founded 1967
Library Holdings: Per Subs 476
Publications: Table of Contents for Administrators; The Knowledge Network (newsletter)
Partic in BRS; Dialog Corporation; Docline; Medline; Southeastern Wisconsin Health Science Library Consortium

M SINAI SAMARITAN MEDICAL CENTER HURWITZ MEDICAL LIBRARY, 945 N 12th St, 53233. SAN 318-2258. Tel: 414-219-6710 Interlibrary Loan Service Tel: 414-219-6709. FAX: 414-219-6708. *Lib* Mary Jo Koenen; E-Mail: mjknen@mixcom.com; Staff 3 (MLS 1, No MLS 2)
Founded 1957
Library Holdings: Bk Titles 4,000; Per Subs 350
Subject Interests: Cardiology, Clinical medicine, Consumer health, Geriatrics, Obstetrics, Orthopedics, Sports med, Surgery
Partic in Southeastern Wisconsin Health Science Library Consortium

M BLOOD CENTER OF SOUTHEASTERN WISCONSIN, INC, Stratton Library, PO Box 2178, 53201-2178. SAN 318-210X. Tel: 414-937-6112. FAX: 414-937-6332. *Librn*, Mary L Rice; E-Mail: mlrice@bcsew.edu
Founded 1951
Library Holdings: Bk Vols 925; Per Subs 125
Subject Interests: Hematology, Immunology
Mem of SE Wis Health Sci Libr Consortium

C BRYANT & STRATTON COLLEGE LIBRARY-MILWAUKEE,* 1300 Jackson St, 53202-2602. SAN 377-936X. Tel: 414-276-5200. FAX: 414-3930. Web Site: www.bryantstratton.edu. *Dir*, Lloyd G Daub
Library Holdings: Bk Titles 1,000; Per Subs 100
Partic in Library Council Of Metropolitan Milwaukee, Inc; Wis Libr Asn

C CARDINAL STRITCH UNIVERSITY LIBRARY, 6801 N Yates Rd, 53207-3985. SAN 364-9326. Tel: 414-410-4261, 414-410-4263. FAX: 41 410-4268. Web Site: www.stritch.edu/~csclib/. *Dir*, David Wineberg-Kins *AV*, Sherina Venable; *Tech Servs*, Louise Diodato; *Publ Servs*, Sister Margaret Ruddy; Staff 34 (MLS 7, Non-MLS 27)
Founded 1937. Fac 76
Aug 1998-Jul 1999 Income $629,497. Mats Exp $164,748, Books $75,3 Per/Ser (Incl. Access Fees) $75,989, Presv $5,707, AV Equip $7,745. Sal $345,170 (Prof $272,570)
Library Holdings: Bk Vols 130,065; Bk Titles 96,864; Per Subs 688
Subject Interests: Bus and mgt, Education, Nursing
Database Vendor: Ebsco - EbscoHost, Innovative Interfaces INN - View OCLC - First Search, OVID Technologies, ProQuest, Wilson - Wilson W Partic in Library Council Of Metropolitan Milwaukee, Inc; OCLC Online Computer Library Center, Inc; Southeastern Wisconsin Information Technology Exchange, Inc; Wis Asn Of Independent Cols & Univs

CM COLUMBIA COLLEGE OF NURSING LIBRARY,* 2121 E Newport A 53211. SAN 364-9563. Tel: 414-961-3533. FAX: 414-961-4121. *Librn*, Shirley S Chan; E-Mail: schan@carroll.cc.edu; *Asst Librn*, Cindy Taylor; Staff 3 (MLS 1, Non-MLS 2)
Founded 1901
Library Holdings: Bk Titles 6,700; Per Subs 214
Special Collections: ANA Monograph Series; History of Nursing Coll; N Publications
Publications: Audiovisual Software List; New Materials List (monthly); Serials List
Partic in Library Council Of Metropolitan Milwaukee, Inc; Southeastern Wisconsin Health Science Library Consortium; Wis Health Sci Libr Asn

COLUMBIA HOSPITAL
CM MEDICAL LIBRARY, 2025 E Newport Ave, 53211. SAN 364-9539. Tel: 414-961-3858. FAX: 414-961-3813. *Mgr Libr Serv*, Ruth Holst; Tel: 41 961-3856, E-Mail: rholst@columbia-stmarys.org
Founded 1950
Jul 2000-Jun 2001 Income $181,982. Mats Exp $63,190, Books $9,500, Per/Ser (Incl. Access Fees) $40,000, Presv $2,100, Electronic Ref Mat (Incl. Access Fees) $11,590. Sal $110,022 (Prof $97,961)
Library Holdings: Bk Titles 2,500; Per Subs 200
Subject Interests: Allied health, Health admin, Medicine, Nursing
Special Collections: Consumer Health Coll
Automation Activity & Vendor Info: (Cataloging) Inmagic, Inc.; (OPA Inmagic, Inc.
Database Vendor: Ebsco - EbscoHost, OVID Technologies
Restriction: Circulates for staff only
Function: Photocopies available
Partic in Library Council Of Metropolitan Milwaukee, Inc; Southeastern Wisconsin Health Science Library Consortium

R CONGREGATION EMANU-EL B'NE JESHURUN LIBRARY, Rabbi Dudley Weinberg Library, 2020 W Brown Deer Rd, 53217. SAN 318-191X Tel: 414-228-7545. *Librn*, Paula H Fine; Staff 2 (MLS 1, Non-MLS 1)
Founded 1929
Library Holdings: Bk Vols 8,500; Per Subs 30
Subject Interests: Judaica

R CONGREGATION SHALOM, Sherman Pastor Memorial Library, 7630 N Santa Monica Blvd, 53217. SAN 318-1928. Tel: 414-352-9288. FAX: 414-352-9280. Web Site: www.cong-shalom.org. *Librn*, Elaine Friedman

Founded 1970
Library Holdings: Bk Titles 6,000
Subject Interests: Children's fiction, Holocaust, Israel, Jewish fiction, Judaica, Non-fiction
Partic in Library Council Of Metropolitan Milwaukee, Inc
Friends of the Library Group

DEPARTMENT OF VETERANS AFFAIRS, Medical Center Library Service,* 5000 W National Ave, 53295. SAN 365-0316. Tel: 414-384-2000, Ext 2340. FAX: 414-382-5334. *ILL, Online Servs*, Janice Curnes; Staff 5 (MLS 3, Non-MLS 2)
Library Holdings: Bk Vols 24,400; Per Subs 672
Automation Activity & Vendor Info: (Cataloging) EOS; (Circulation) EOS; (OPAC) EOS
Partic in Southeastern Wisconsin Health Science Library Consortium; Valnet
Branches:
HOSPITAL PATIENTS LIBRARY *Librn*, Jill Gennari
Library Holdings: Bk Vols 16,070; Per Subs 162
Subject Interests: Bibliotherapy, GED programs, Historic preservation, Military history, Recreational reading for patients, Rehabilitation
MEDICAL LIBRARY, VA Medical Ctr, 5000 W National Ave, 53295. SAN 365-0375. *Librn*, Janice Curnes
Library Holdings: Bk Vols 5,500; Per Subs 503
Subject Interests: Allied health, Dentistry, Medicine, Nursing, Psychology, Rehabilitation, Surgery
Partic in BRS; Dialog Corporation; Medline; Nat Libr of Med; OCLC Online Computer Library Center, Inc
PATIENT HEALTH EDUCATION LIBRARY *Librn*, Jill Gennari
Library Holdings: Bk Vols 1,253; Per Subs 20
Subject Interests: Alcoholism, Bibliotherapy, Develop-mgt for employees, Disease information for the layman, Patient education, Recreational reading for patients, Rehabilitation, Self care, Vocational rehabilitation, Wellness

ENDOMETRIOSIS ASSOCIATION LIBRARY, 8585 N 76th Pl, 53223-2692. SAN 374-5104. Tel: 414-355-2200. Toll Free Tel: 800-992-3636. FAX: 414-355-6065. E-Mail: endo@endometriosisassn.org. Web Site: www.endometriosisassn.org.
Library Holdings: Bk Vols 300
Restriction: Circulates for staff only, Non-circulating to the public

ERNST & YOUNG LIBRARY,* 111 E Kilbourn Ave, 53202. SAN 375-1228. Tel: 414-274-8778. FAX: 414-273-7200.
Library Holdings: Bk Titles 1,200; Per Subs 35

FOLEY & LARDNER, Law Library,* 777 E Wisconsin Ave, 53202-5367. SAN 318-1960. Tel: 414-271-2400, Ext 2011. Interlibrary Loan Service Tel: 414-297-2011. FAX: 414-297-4900. *Dir*, Susan O'Toole; E-Mail: sotoole@foleylaw.com; *Asst Librn*, Linda A Mariske; Staff 7 (MLS 2, Non-MLS 5)
Founded 1842
Library Holdings: Bk Vols 32,000; Per Subs 450
Subject Interests: Corporate finance, Employment law, Intellectual property, Securities, Tax

FROEDTERT MEMORIAL LUTHERAN HOSPITAL LIBRARY,* 9200 W Wisconsin Ave, 53226. SAN 321-4648. Tel: 414-259-3051.; Staff 2 (MLS 1, Non-MLS 1)
Founded 1981
Library Holdings: Bk Vols 283
Subject Interests: Clinical medicine
Partic in OCLC Online Computer Library Center, Inc
Branch library of the Medical College of Wisconsin

HOPE LUTHERAN CHURCH LIBRARY, 1115 N 35th St, 53208. SAN 327-4586. Tel: 414-342-0471. *Librn*, Beverly Bischeff
Library Holdings: Bk Titles 3,246
Subject Interests: Religion
Publications: Lutheran Church Library mazazine; Media magazine

JOHNSON CONTROLS, INC
CORPORATE LIBRARY SERVICES, 507 E Michigan St, 53202. SAN 318-1995. Tel: 414-524-4687. FAX: 414-524-4596. *Mgr Libr Serv*, Mary F Kaczmarek; Tel: 414-524-4446, E-Mail: mary.f.kaczmarek@jci.com; *Info Specialist*, Kay J Goodwin; Tel: 414-524-5742, E-Mail: kay.j.goodwin@jci.com; *Info Specialist*, Patricia A Riese; Tel: 414-524-4694, E-Mail: patricia.a.riese@jci.com; Staff 3 (MLS 3)
Founded 1973
Library Holdings: Bk Titles 10,000; Per Subs 500
Subject Interests: Air conditioning, Applied scis, Bldg control tech, Bus, Electronics, Heating-ventilating, Mats scis, Mgt
Special Collections: American Society of Heating, Refrigeration & Air-Conditioning Engineers Material, dating back to 1900s
Automation Activity & Vendor Info: (OPAC) TechLIB
Database Vendor: Dialog, Ebsco - EbscoHost, Lexis-Nexis, OCLC - First Search
Publications: Serials list
Partic in Coun of Wis Librs, Inc; Library Council Of Metropolitan Milwaukee, Inc

S JOURNAL SENTINEL INC, News Information Center, PO Box 661, 53201-0661. SAN 318-2169. Tel: 414-224-2376. FAX: 414-224-2388. *Coll Develop, Mgr*, Rosemary Jensen
Founded 1922
Library Holdings: Bk Vols 5,000
Subject Interests: Milwaukee, Wisconsin
Special Collections: Milwaukee Journal Sentinel, micro, newsp clippings, photogs
Partic in Data Time

G LEGISLATIVE REFERENCE BUREAU, City Hall, Rm B-11, 200 E Wells St, 53202-3567. SAN 318-2177. Tel: 414-286-2295. Reference Tel: 414-286-2297. FAX: 414-286-3004. Web Site: www.ci.mil.wi.us/citygov/council. *In Charge*, Eileen Lipinski; *Librn*, Mary Lohmeier; Staff 5 (MLS 4, Non-MLS 1)
Founded 1908
Jan 2000-Dec 2000 Mats Exp $26,700. Sal $151,180 (Prof $138,425)
Library Holdings: Per Subs 180
Subject Interests: Municipal admin, Urban affairs
Special Collections: City Government Documents; United States Census
Automation Activity & Vendor Info: (Acquisitions) EOS; (Cataloging) EOS; (Serials) EOS
Partic in Library Council Of Metropolitan Milwaukee, Inc

C MARQUETTE UNIVERSITY LIBRARIES, Main Library, 1415 W Wisconsin Ave, PO Box 3141, 53201-3141. SAN 364-9652. Tel: 414-288-7214. Interlibrary Loan Service Tel: 414-288-7257. FAX: 414-288-5324. Web Site: www.marquette.edu/library. *Dean of Libr*, Dr Nicholas Burckel; E-Mail: nicholas.burckel@marquette.edu; *Assoc Dir*, Michael B Pate; E-Mail: michael.pate@marquette.edu; *Ser*, Alice Gormley; Tel: 414-288-7252, Fax: 414-288-3123, E-Mail: alice.gormley@marquette.edu; *Outreach Serv*, Susan Hopwood; Tel: 414-288-5995, Fax: 414-288-5324, E-Mail: susan.hopwood@marquette.edu; *Circ*, Tom Holberg; Tel: 414-288-7555, Fax: 414-288-5324, E-Mail: tom.holberg@marquette.edu; *Rare Bks, Spec Coll*, Charles Elston; Tel: 414-288-7256, Fax: 414-288-6709, E-Mail: charles.elston@marquette.edu; *Online Servs*, James Lowrey; Tel: 414-288-6043, E-Mail: james.lowrey@marquette.edu; *ILL*, Joan Sommer; Tel: 414-288-1997, E-Mail: sommerj@marquette.edu; *Coll Develop*, Jay Kirk; Tel: 414-288-3396, Fax: 414-288-1633, E-Mail: jay.kirk@marquette.edu; *Ref*, Anne Reuland; Tel: 414-288-2140, E-Mail: anne.reuland@marquette.edu; Staff 72 (MLS 30, Non-MLS 42)
Founded 1907. Enrl 10,892; Highest Degree: Doctorate
Jul 1999-Jun 2000 Income (Main Library and Branch Library) $6,706,072, Federal $175,172, Parent Institution $6,530,900. Mats Exp $3,584,465, Books $1,208,655, Per/Ser (Incl. Access Fees) $1,908,481, Presv $68,363, Electronic Ref Mat (Incl. Access Fees) $398,966. Sal $2,724,580 (Prof $1,415,049)
Library Holdings: Bk Vols 1,083,179; Bk Titles 741,752; Per Subs 6,248
Subject Interests: Mathematics, Nursing, Philosophy, Theology
Special Collections: Catholic Conference on; Catholic Indian Mission Records-Bureau of Catholic Indian Missions (Washington, DC); Citizens for Educational Freedom; Council on Urban Life (Milwaukee); Dorothy Day & the Catholic Worker Movement; Elizabeth W Houghton, mss; H Herman Rauch Labor Arbitration Files; Holy Rosary Mission & St Francis Mission; Industrial Problems; J R R Tolkien, mss; Jesuiticia; Justice & Peace Center; Lincoln Room (Lester W Olson, Fred Holmes); Madonna Center (Chicago); National Catholic Conference for Interracial Justice; National Catholic Rural Life Conference; National Coalition of American Nuns; National Sisters Vocation Conference; Personal Papers (Charles J Kersten, Michael Collins, Brother Leo V Ryan CSV, Sister Margaret Ellen Traxler SSND, Don McNeill, John O Riedl, Msgr Luigi G Ligutti, Karl J Priebe, Clement J Zablocki); Philanthropy & Fundraising (Foundation Center Regional Reference Coll), bks, current per, pamphlets, microfiche; President's Committee on Employment of the Handicapped; Project Equality, Inc (National Office); Sister Formation/Religious Formation Conference; Social Justice Papers-Catholic Association for International Peace
Automation Activity & Vendor Info: (Acquisitions) Innovative Interfaces Inc.; (Cataloging) Innovative Interfaces Inc.; (Circulation) Innovative Interfaces Inc.; (Course Reserve) Innovative Interfaces Inc.; (ILL) Innovative Interfaces Inc.; (Media Booking) Innovative Interfaces Inc.; (OPAC) Innovative Interfaces Inc.; (Serials) Innovative Interfaces Inc.
Publications: Foundations in Wisconsin A Directory, Library Acquisitions, Marqcat report, C Lamb, VP Finance Rept 10/25/2000, Include all titles & all volumes, Library stats, report from Bib Control
Partic in Center For Research Libraries; Library Council Of Metropolitan Milwaukee, Inc; Midwest Health Sci Libr Network; OCLC Online Computer Library Center, Inc; Wisconsin Library Services
Departmental Libraries:
CL LAW LIBRARY, Sensenbrenner Hall, PO Box 3137, 53201-3137. SAN 364-9687. Tel: 414-288-7092. FAX: 414-288-5914. Web Site: www.mu.edu/law/library/research.html. *Dir*, Sumiye Sugawara; *Assoc Dir*, Theodore Potter; *Tech Servs*, Lois O'Brien; *Cat*, Angelina G Joseph; *Acq, Ser*, James Mumm; *Per*, Julia Jaet; *Per*, Lynn Hartke
Founded 1908
Jul 1997-Jun 1998 Income $1,229,059. Mats Exp $641,701
Library Holdings: Bk Vols 262,568; Bk Titles 6,131; Per Subs 3,077

Publications: Monthly Acquisitions List; Weekly Contents Pages Service
SCIENCE LIBRARY, 560 N 16th St, PO Box 3141, 53201-3141. SAN 364-9695. Tel: 414-288-3396. FAX: 414-288-1633. Web Site: www.mu.edu/library/html. *Chief Librn, Coll Develop*, Jay Kirk; E-Mail: kirkj@vms.csd.mu.edu; *Bibliog Instr*, Martha Jerome; *Bibliog Instr*, Pat Berge; Staff 6 (MLS 6)
Library Holdings: Bk Vols 238,000; Per Subs 2,476
Subject Interests: Chemistry, Dentistry, Engineering, Life sci, Mathematics, Nursing

M MEDICAL COLLEGE OF WISCONSIN, (Formerly Children's Hospital Of Wisconsin), Children's Hospital Of Wisconsin Medical Library, 9000 W Wisconsin Ave, PO Box 1997, 53201. (Mail add: 8701 Watertown Plank Rd, 53226), SAN 327-6767. Tel: 414-456-8323. FAX: 414-456-6532. E-Mail: asklib@mcw.edu. Web Site: www.mcw.edu/lib/. *Librn*, Jane Walczak; Staff 1 (MLS 1)
Library Holdings: Bk Titles 1,200; Per Subs 65
Subject Interests: Pediatrics

CM MEDICAL COLLEGE OF WISCONSIN LIBRARIES,* 8701 Watertown Plank Rd, 53226-0509. SAN 320-541X. Tel: 414-456-8323. Interlibrary Loan Service Tel: 414-456-8310. FAX: 414-456-6532. Web Site: www.mcw.edu. *Dir*, Mary B Blackwelder; E-Mail: blackwel@mcw.edu; *Cat*, Shantha Jhansale; *Bibliog Instr, Online Servs, Ref*, Karen Hanus; *Bibliog Instr, Online Servs, Ref*, Rita Sieracki; *Bibliog Instr, Online Servs, Ref*, Jane Walczak; *Bibliog Instr, Online Servs, Ref*, Linda Backus; *Per*, Diane Eichholz; *Publ Servs*, Barbara Jamieson; *ILL*, Julie Gores; *Tech Servs*, Alfred Kraemer; Staff 31 (MLS 14, Non-MLS 17)
Founded 1913. Enrl 1,370; Fac 923; Highest Degree: Doctorate
Library Holdings: Bk Vols 250,000; Per Subs 2,134
Subject Interests: Basic sciences, Clinical medicine, Nursing
Special Collections: Medical History (Horace Manchester Brown Coll)
Publications: Annual Report; Library Guide & Service Brochure; NEWSLINE; Pronto; Recent Acquisitions
Partic in Dialog Corporation; Nat Libr of Med; OCLC Online Computer Library Center, Inc
Departmental Libraries:
CHILDREN'S HOSPITAL OF WISCONSIN HEALTH SCIENCES LIBRARY
See Separate Entry
FROEDTERT MEMORIAL LUTHERAN HOSPITAL
See Separate Entry

M FRANCIS D MURPHY LIBRARY, FMLH E Clinic Bldg, 9200 W Wisconsin Ave, 53226. SAN 318-2142. Tel: 414-257-5898. FAX: 414-456-6532. *In Charge*, Linda K Backus; Staff 2 (MLS 1, Non-MLS 1)
Founded 1958
Library Holdings: Bk Vols 4,500; Per Subs 110
Subject Interests: Clinical medicine, Consumer health, Hospital administration, Nursing
Automation Activity & Vendor Info: (Acquisitions) Innovative Interfaces Inc.; (Cataloging) Innovative Interfaces Inc.; (Circulation) Innovative Interfaces Inc.; (Course Reserve) Innovative Interfaces Inc.; (ILL) Innovative Interfaces Inc.; (Media Booking) Innovative Interfaces Inc.; (OPAC) Innovative Interfaces Inc.; (Serials) Innovative Interfaces Inc.
Database Vendor: OVID Technologies
Partic in OCLC Online Computer Library Center, Inc
Medical College of Wisconsin, Inc satellite library

G METROPOLITAN MILWAUKEE FAIR HOUSING COUNCIL LIBRARY, 600 E Mason St, Ste 401, 53202. SAN 324-1599. Tel: 414-278-1240. FAX: 414-278-8033. *Exec Dir*, William Tisdale; *In Charge*, Margaret Bowitz
Founded 1977
Library Holdings: Bk Titles 2,500; Per Subs 32
Subject Interests: Civil rights, Fair housing, Landlord-tenant relations
Publications: brochures in English & Spanish; Case study reports; Fair Housing Keys (newsletter); Your move, Your choice (Milwaukee Neighborhoods)
Partic in Library Council Of Metropolitan Milwaukee, Inc

S MGIC INVESTMENT CORP, Corporate Library, MGIC Plaza, 53202. SAN 318-207X. Tel: 414-347-6409. FAX: 414-347-6959. *Librn*, Christine Peterson
Founded 1973
Subject Interests: Finance, Ins

L MICHAEL, BEST & FRIEDRICH LLP, Law Library, 100 E Wisconsin Ave, 53202-4108. SAN 318-2088. Tel: 414-271-6560. FAX: 414-277-0656. *Dir Info Resources & Res*, Jane B Moberg; E-Mail: jbmoberg@mbf-law.com; Staff 3 (MLS 2, Non-MLS 1)
Founded 1848
Library Holdings: Bk Vols 25,000
Special Collections: Law (taxation, corporate, labor, antitrust, patent, trademark, copyright, Wisconsin)
Partic in Library Council Of Metropolitan Milwaukee, Inc

S MILLER BREWING COMPANY, Research & Technical Library,* 3939 W Highland Blvd, 53201-0482. SAN 327-456X. Tel: 414-931-3640. FAX: 414-931-2818. *Librn*, Julie Baldwin; E-Mail: baldwin.julie@mbco.com
Library Holdings: Bk Vols 9,000; Bk Titles 7,000
Subject Interests: Brewing
Special Collections: Brewing Journals (US & foreign)
Publications: Acquisitions list (weekly); patent bulletin; research bullet technical center checklist
Restriction: By appointment only

M MILWAUKEE ACADEMY OF MEDICINE LIBRARY, 8701 Watertov Plank Rd, 53226. SAN 327-408X. Tel: 414-456-8249. FAX: 414-456-65 *In Charge*, Amy John; E-Mail: amyjohn@execpc.com
Library Holdings: Bk Vols 1,500
Restriction: By appointment only

J MILWAUKEE AREA TECHNICAL COLLEGE, Rasche Memorial Libr 700 W State St, 53233-1443. SAN 364-9717. Tel: 414-297-7030. Refere Tel: 414-297-7559. E-Mail: library@milwaukee.tec.wi.us. Web Site: www.milwaukee.tec.wi.us. *Dir*, Jeff Jackson; Tel: 414-297-6946; Staff 3 (MLS 3)
Founded 1935. Enrl 70,000; Fac 811
2000-2001 Mats Exp $95,000, Books $62,500, Per/Ser (Incl. Access Fee $32,500. Sal $530,000 (Prof $390,000)
Library Holdings: Bk Vols 70,000; Bk Titles 52,000; Per Subs 380
Automation Activity & Vendor Info: (Acquisitions) SIRSI; (Cataloging SIRSI; (Circulation) SIRSI; (Course Reserve) SIRSI; (OPAC) SIRSI; (Serials) SIRSI
Partic in Library Council Of Metropolitan Milwaukee, Inc

S MILWAUKEE ART MUSEUM LIBRARY,* 750 N Lincoln Memorial 53202. SAN 318-2096. Tel: 414-224-3270. FAX: 414-271-7588. *Librn*, Elizabeth Schmoeger; E-Mail: schmoeger@mam.org
Founded 1965
Subject Interests: 19th Century art, 20th Century art, Architecture, Contemporary art, Decorative arts, Early art, European old masters, Folk Haitian art, Medieval, Modern, Photos, Renaissance art
Special Collections: Marily Kroening Coll

P MILWAUKEE COUNTY FEDERATED LIBRARY SYSTEM,* 709 N Eighth St, 53233-2414. SAN 318-2118. Tel: 414-286-3210. FAX: 414-28 3209. *Dir*, Doris Nix; E-Mail: doris.nix@mcfls.o; *Tech Coordr*, James Gingery; Staff 4 (MLS 4)
Founded 1973. Pop 933,067
Jan 1997-Dec 1998 Income $2,878,000, State $2,319,000, County $66,96 Other $184,000. Sal $435,000 (Prof $148,000)
Member Libraries: Brown Deer Public Library; Cudahy Memorial Pub Library; Franklin Public Library; Greendale Public Library; Greenfield Public Library; Hales Corners Library; Milwaukee Public Library; North Shore Library; Oak Creek Public Library; Shorewood Public Library; So Milwaukee Public Library; St Francis Public Library; Wauwatosa Public Library; West Allis Public Library; Whitefish Bay Public Library
Partic in Coun of Wis Librs, Inc; Library Council Of Metropolitan Milwaukee, Inc

S MILWAUKEE COUNTY HISTORICAL SOCIETY, Library & Archives 910 N Old World Third St, 53203. SAN 318-2126. Tel: 414-273-8288. *Librn*, Steven Daily; *Asst Librn*, Michael Jacobs; Staff 2 (MLS 2)
Founded 1935
Library Holdings: Bk Vols 11,000
Subject Interests: Ethnic hist, Milwaukee, Socialism, Wisconsin

GM MILWAUKEE COUNTY MENTAL HEALTH COMPLEX, Michael Kas Library, 9455 Watertown Plank Rd, 53226. SAN 318-2150. Tel: 414-257-7381. FAX: 414-257-5374. *Librn*, Anna M Green
Founded 1941
Library Holdings: Bk Vols 11,875; Bk Titles 6,650; Per Subs 270
Subject Interests: Mental health, Psychiatry, Psychoanalysis, Psychology
Partic in Dialog Corporation; Docline; Southeastern Wisconsin Health Science Library Consortium; Wis Health Sci Libr Asn

S MILWAUKEE INSTITUTE OF ART & DESIGN LIBRARY,* 273 E Eri St, 53202-6003. SAN 318-2215. Tel: 414-276-7889. FAX: 414-291-8077. Web Site: topcat.switchinc.org. *Librn*, Nancy Blank-Eahr; *Curator*, Annik Lott; Staff 2 (MLS 2)
Founded 1977. Enrl 460
Library Holdings: Bk Titles 20,000; Per Subs 75
Subject Interests: Advertising, Aesthetics, Art history, Artists' monograph Behav sci, Decorative arts, Drama, Drawing, Eng design, Fiction, Graphic design, History, Industrial design, Interior design, Natural science, Paintin Photog, Poetry, Psychology, Rhetoric, Sculpture, Soc sci, Typography
Special Collections: Art slides & postcards
Publications: Acquisitions List (quarterly)
Partic in Library Council Of Metropolitan Milwaukee, Inc

R MILWAUKEE JEWISH COUNCIL FOR COMMUNITY RELATIONS LIBRARY, 1360 N Prospect Ave, 2nd flr, 53202-3091. SAN 371-7925. Te 414-390-5777. FAX: 414-390-5787. E-Mail: mjccr@aol.com. *Coordr*, Kat Heilbronner; Tel: 414-390-5736, Fax: 414-390-5736; Staff 2 (MLS 1, Non MLS 1)

Library Holdings: Bk Vols 1,000; Per Subs 10
Subject Interests: Holocaust, Israel, Religion
Partic in Library Council Of Metropolitan Milwaukee, Inc

MILWAUKEE PUBLIC LIBRARY, (MPL), 814 W Wisconsin Ave, 53233-2385. SAN 364-9741. Tel: 414-286-3000. Interlibrary Loan Service Tel: 414-286-3082. FAX: 414-286-2794. E-Mail: mailbox@mpl.org. Web Site: www.mpl.org. *City Librn*, Kathleen M Huston; *Asst Librn*, Sandra Lockett; *Head Tech Servs*, Lynn Bellehuneur; *Business*, Taj Schoening; *Ch Servs*, Kelly Hughbanks. Subject Specialists: *Business*, Ted Cebula; *Fine arts*, Thomas Altmann; *Humanities*, Virginia Schwartz; *Local history*, Paul Woehrmann; *Science*, Ted Cebula; Staff 110 (MLS 110)
Founded 1878. Pop 612,740; Circ 3,156,330
Jan 1999-Dec 1999 Income (Main Library and Branch Library) $21,132,203, State $550,960, City $20,008,877, Federal $38,686, Other $533,680. Mats Exp $2,610,038, Books $1,209,041, Per/Ser (Incl. Access Fees) $1,113,997, Micro $1,000, AV Equip $260,000, Other Print Mats $26,000. Sal $11,442,958
Library Holdings: Bk Vols 2,504,461; Per Subs 6,469
Subject Interests: Railroad hist, Trans-Miss Am
Special Collections: Alexander Mitchell Coll; American Maps; Art & Motion Picture Posters; Charles King (King Coll); City Archives, bk & pamphlet; Cookery (Breta Greim Coll); Current Trade Books for Children (Historical Reference Coll 1976 to date); Early American Imprints, microfiche; Eastman Fairy Tale Coll; Great Lakes Ships & Shipping (Runge Marine Memorial), photog bk & pamphlets; H G Wells Coll; Historical Popular Children's Literature Coll (1850-1940); Historical Recordings; Literature (Definitive Editions of British & American Writers); Milwaukee Artists; Milwaukee Road Railroad Archives; Rare Bird Prints (Audubon Folio Prints), pictures; Significant Publishers Series; United States, British & Canadian Patents; US Patent Office, US Geol Survey, US Dept of Defense Maps; Wisconsin Architectural Archives
Publications: Milwaukee Reader; Miscellaneous Booklists & Brochures; Staff News (staff newsletter); Weekly Accessions List
Mem of Milwaukee County Federated Library System
Partic in HQ-WIS Reg Libr for Blind & Physically Handicapped; Library Council Of Metropolitan Milwaukee, Inc; OCLC Online Computer Library Center, Inc
Special Services for the Deaf - Staff with knowledge of sign language; TTY machine
Friends of the Library Group
Branches: 12
ATKINSON, 1960 W Atkinson Ave, 53209. SAN 364-9806. Tel: 414-286-3068. FAX: 414-286-8469. Web Site: www.mpl.org. *Branch Mgr*, Mary Milinkovich
Library Holdings: Bk Vols 59,976
Friends of the Library Group
BAY VIEW, 2566 S Kinnickinnic, 53207. SAN 373-9244. Tel: 414-286-3019. FAX: 414-286-8459. Web Site: www.mpl.org. *Branch Mgr*, Linda Vincent
Library Holdings: Bk Vols 58,332
Friends of the Library Group
CAPITOL, 3969 N 74th St, 53216. SAN 364-9830. Tel: 414-286-3006. FAX: 414-286-8432. Web Site: www.mpl.org. *Branch Mgr*, Acklen Banks
Library Holdings: Bk Vols 80,256
Friends of the Library Group
CENTER STREET, 2727 W Fond Du Lac Ave, 53210. SAN 364-9865. Tel: 414-286-3090. FAX: 414-286-8467. Web Site: www.mpl.org. *Branch Mgr*, Lois Redic
Library Holdings: Bk Vols 56,194
Friends of the Library Group
EAST, 1910 E North Ave, 53202. SAN 364-989X. Tel: 414-286-3058. FAX: 414-286-8431. Web Site: www.mpl.org. *Branch Mgr*, Christine Arkenberg
Library Holdings: Bk Vols 85,313
Friends of the Library Group
FINNEY, 4243 W North Ave, 53208. SAN 364-992X. Tel: 414-286-3066. FAX: 414-286-8471. Web Site: www.mpl.org. *Branch Mgr*, Nancy Torphy
Library Holdings: Bk Vols 57,914
Friends of the Library Group
FOREST HOME, 1432 W Forest Home Ave, 53204. SAN 364-9954. Tel: 414-286-3083. FAX: 414-286-8461. Web Site: www.mpl.org. *Branch Mgr*, Florence Nelson
Library Holdings: Bk Vols 83,853
Friends of the Library Group
MARTIN LUTHER KING BRANCH, 310 W Locust St, 53212. SAN 365-0014. Tel: 414-286-3098. TDD: 414-286-2419. FAX: 414-286-8465. Web Site: www.mpl.org. *Branch Mgr*, Jean Ross; Staff 8 (MLS 4, Non-MLS 4)
Library Holdings: Bk Vols 68,219
Friends of the Library Group
MILL ROAD, 6431 N 76th St, 53223. SAN 365-0049. Tel: 414-286-3088. FAX: 414-286-8454. Web Site: www.mpl.org. *Branch Mgr*, Dawn Lauber
Library Holdings: Bk Vols 72,292
Friends of the Library Group
TIPPECANOE, 3912 S Howell Ave, 53207. SAN 365-0138. Tel: 414-286-3085. FAX: 414-286-8405. Web Site: www.mpl.org. *Branch Mgr*, Ceci Chapple
Library Holdings: Bk Vols 89,379
Friends of the Library Group
VILLARD AVENUE, 3310 W Villard Ave, 53209. SAN 365-0073. Tel: 414-286-3079. FAX: 414-286-8473. Web Site: www.mpl.org. *Branch Mgr*, Carol Gordon
Library Holdings: Bk Vols 74,127
Friends of the Library Group
ZABLOCKI, 3501 W Oklahoma Ave, 53215. SAN 365-0103. Tel: 414-286-3055. FAX: 414-286-8430. Web Site: www.mpl.org. *Branch Mgr*, Patricia Kennedy
Library Holdings: Bk Vols 78,072
Friends of the Library Group
Bookmobiles: 1. Librn, Chris Prevetti. Bk vols 113,336, AV Total 3001. Tel No.: 414-286-3076

MILWAUKEE PUBLIC MUSEUM
S REFERENCE LIBRARY, 800 W Wells St, 53233. SAN 318-2193. Tel: 414-278-2736. FAX: 414-278-6100. E-Mail: libarc@mpm.edu. Web Site: www.mpm.edu/collect/libmenu.html. *Dir*, Judith Campbell Turner; Tel: 414-278-2730, E-Mail: jct@mpm.edu; *Ser*, Ruth King; Tel: 414-278-2798, E-Mail: ruth@mmp.edu; Staff 2 (MLS 2)
Founded 1883
Library Holdings: Per Subs 1,200
Subject Interests: Anthropology, Archaeology, Botany, Decorative arts, Ecology, Geology, Museology, Paleontology, Zoology
Special Collections: Milwaukee Public Museum Archives
Restriction: By appointment only, Non-circulating to the public
Partic in Library Council Of Metropolitan Milwaukee, Inc; OCLC Online Computer Library Center, Inc; Wisconsin Library Services

C MILWAUKEE SCHOOL OF ENGINEERING, Walter Schroeder Library, 500 E Kilbourn Ave, 53202. (Mail add: 1025 N Broadway, 53202-3109), Tel: 414-277-7180. Circulation Tel: 414-277-7180. Reference Tel: 414-277-7180. FAX: 414-277-7186. Web Site: www.msoe.edu/library. *Dir*, Mary Ann Perdue; E-Mail: perduem@msoe.edu; *Actg Dir*, Gary S Shimek; Tel: 414-277-7181, E-Mail: shimek@msoe.edu; *Ref*, Pam Gorzalski; Tel: 414-277-7471, E-Mail: gorzalsk@msoe.edu; *AV*, William Krajnak; Tel: 414-277-7179, E-Mail: krajnak@msoe.edu; *Acq, Cat, Coll Develop*, Laura Kazmierczak; *Ser*, Karen Bolton; Tel: 414-277-7183, E-Mail: bolton@msoe.edu; *Circ*, Annette Ronowski; E-Mail: ronowsk@msoe.edu; *ILL*, Anne Mosgaller; Tel: 414-277-7184, E-Mail: mosgalle@msoe.edu; Staff 6 (MLS 4, Non-MLS 2)
Founded 1903. Enrl 2,100; Fac 108; Highest Degree: Master
Jul 1999-Jun 2000 Mats Exp $472,326, Books $18,121, Per/Ser (Incl. Access Fees) $99,697, Micro $5,342, Electronic Ref Mat (Incl. Access Fees) $68,507. Sal $230,036 (Prof $161,946)
Library Holdings: Bk Vols 45,638; Bk Titles 41,927; Per Subs 430
Subject Interests: Archit eng, Biomedical eng, Bus, Computer eng, Electrical engineering, Fluid power, Indust mgt, Mechanical engineering, Nursing
Automation Activity & Vendor Info: (Acquisitions) epixtech, inc.; (Cataloging) epixtech, inc.; (Circulation) epixtech, inc.; (Course Reserve) epixtech, inc.; (OPAC) epixtech, inc.; (Serials) epixtech, inc.
Database Vendor: Dialog, Ebsco - EbscoHost, epixtech, inc., IAC - Info Trac, OCLC - First Search, OVID Technologies, ProQuest
Restriction: Circulation limited, In-house use for visitors, Non-circulating to the public
Function: ILL available
Partic in Library Council Of Metropolitan Milwaukee, Inc; OCLC Online Computer Library Center, Inc; Wisconsin Library Services

R MOUNT CARMEL LUTHERAN CHURCH LIBRARY, 8424 W Center St, 53222. SAN 318-2231. Tel: 414-771-1270. FAX: 414-771-1616. *Librn*, Sue Basham
Founded 1947
Library Holdings: Bk Vols 4,500; Per Subs 10
Subject Interests: Religion
Special Collections: Bibles; Norwegian Heritage

R MOUNT MARY COLLEGE, Patrick & Beatrice Haggerty Library, 2900 N Menomonee River Pkwy, 53222-4597. SAN 318-224X. Tel: 414-258-4810, Ext 190. FAX: 414-256-1205. *Dir*, Volker Kriegisch; Staff 8 (MLS 3, Non-MLS 5)
Founded 1913. Enrl 1,169
Library Holdings: Bk Vols 107,695; Per Subs 550
Subject Interests: Art, Art therapy, Behav sci, Dietetics, Education, Fashion design, Humanities, Occupational therapy, Soc sci, Soc work
Publications: Haggerty Happenings (newsletter)
Partic in Library Council Of Metropolitan Milwaukee, Inc; OCLC Online Computer Library Center, Inc; Wisconsin Library Services

M NORTHWEST GENERAL HOSPITAL, Health Science Library,* 5310 W Capitol Dr, 53216. SAN 318-2282. Tel: 414-447-8543. FAX: 414-447-8589. *Librn*, Martin Liddy
Founded 1975
Library Holdings: Per Subs 91
Restriction: Medical staff only
Partic in Docline; Southeastern Wisconsin Health Science Library Consortium

NORTHWESTERN MUTUAL LIFE INSURANCE CO

S CORPORATE INFORMATION CENTER, 720 E Wisconsin Ave, 53202-4797. SAN 365-0197. Tel: 414-665-2492. FAX: 414-665-7022.; Staff 7 (MLS 4, Non-MLS 3)
Founded 1951
Library Holdings: Bk Vols 10,000; Per Subs 350
Subject Interests: Bus, Financial serv, Life ins, Management
Publications: NEWSCAN
Partic in Library Council Of Metropolitan Milwaukee, Inc; Wisconsin Library Services

L LAW LIBRARY, 720 E Wisconsin Ave, 53202-4797. SAN 365-0162. Tel: 414-299-2422. FAX: 414-299-7016. *Librn*, Patricia A Ellingson; E-Mail: patriciaellingson@northwesternmutual.com
Founded 1892
Library Holdings: Bk Vols 20,000; Bk Titles 2,500; Per Subs 40
Subject Interests: Ins, Investing, Law, Taxes

R PALLOTTI HOUSE LIBRARY, 5424 W Blue Mound Rd, 53208. SAN 318-2320. Tel: 414-258-0653. FAX: 414-258-9314. *In Charge*, Leon Martin
Founded 1923
Library Holdings: Bk Titles 3,297; Per Subs 20
Subject Interests: Philosophy, Theology
Special Collections: Hagiography (St Vincent Pallotti Coll), bk, slides

S PHARMACIA BIOTECK, INC, Library,* 2202 N Bartlett Ave, 53202. SAN 318-2312. Tel: 414-227-3600, 414-227-3663. FAX: 414-227-3759. *Librn*, Marge Tilch
Founded 1954
Library Holdings: Bk Titles 4,255; Per Subs 150
Subject Interests: Biochemistry, Chemistry, Molecular biology
Restriction: By appointment only
Partic in Library Council Of Metropolitan Milwaukee, Inc

S PLANNED PARENTHOOD OF WISCONSIN, Ritz Family Resource Center, 302 N Jackson St, 53202. SAN 318-2355. Tel: 414-271-7930. FAX: 414-271-1935. *Librn*, Ann H McIntyre; E-Mail: annmac@execpc.com
Founded 1972
Library Holdings: Bk Titles 3,400; Per Subs 110
Subject Interests: Family planning, Human sexuality, Population, Reproductive health, Sex educ
Publications: Audiovisual Bibliography; Literature Bibliography
Partic in Asn of Population Librs & Info Centers; Library Council Of Metropolitan Milwaukee, Inc; Southeastern Wisconsin Health Science Library Consortium

R PRINCE OF PEACE LUTHERAN CHURCH LIBRARY, 4419 S Howell Ave, 53207. SAN 318-2363. Tel: 414-483-3828. *Librn*, Mrs Robert Heinritz
Founded 1963
Library Holdings: Bk Vols 2,600
Special Collections: Martin Luther Coll

G PUBLIC POLICY FORUM, Researching Community Issues,* 633 W Wisconsin Ave, Ste 406, 53203. SAN 326-0445. Tel: 414-276-8240. FAX: 414-276-9962. E-Mail: ppf@execpc.com. *Exec Dir*, David G Meissner; Staff 2 (MLS 2)
Founded 1913
Library Holdings: Bk Titles 3,000; Per Subs 100
Publications: Bulletin (monthly); Special Reports
Restriction: By appointment only
Friends of the Library Group

L QUARLES & BRADY, Law Library,* 411 E Wisconsin Ave, 53202-4491. SAN 318-2371. Tel: 414-277-5000. FAX: 414-271-3552. E-Mail: aeb@quarels.com.; Staff 6 (MLS 4, Non-MLS 2)
Founded 1910
Library Holdings: Bk Vols 40,000; Per Subs 100
Subject Interests: Banking, Bankruptcy, Environmental law, Estate planning, Health care, Hospital, Immigration, Labor, Litigation, Patents, Pensions, Real estate, School law, Securities, Taxation, Trademarks

L REINHART, BOERNER, VAN DEUREN, NORRIS & RIESELBACH, Information Resource Center, 1000 N Water St, Ste 2100, 53203-3400. SAN 324-0177. Tel: 414-298-8253. FAX: 414-298-8097. Web Site: www.reinhartlaw.com. *Mgr*, Carol Bannen; E-Mail: cbannen@reinhartlaw.com; Staff 7 (MLS 4, Non-MLS 3)
Founded 1975
Library Holdings: Bk Vols 20,000; Bk Titles 6,000; Per Subs 460
Subject Interests: Employee benefits
Automation Activity & Vendor Info: (Acquisitions) EOS; (Cataloging) EOS; (Circulation) EOS; (OPAC) EOS; (Serials) EOS
Partic in Library Council Of Metropolitan Milwaukee, Inc

S ROCKWELL AUTOMATION LIBRARY,* 1201 S Second St, 53204. SAN 318-1804. Tel: 414-382-2342. FAX: 414-382-2462. *Head of Libr*, Randy Bell
Founded 1942
Library Holdings: Bk Titles 10,000; Per Subs 425
Subject Interests: Bus, Electrical, Electronic engineering, Indust automation, Mechanical engineering, Mgt, Physics
Special Collections: Military standards & specifications
Restriction: Not open to public
Partic in Library Council Of Metropolitan Milwaukee, Inc

M SAINT FRANCIS HOSPITAL, Library-Audiovisual Center,* 3237 S 1[illegible] St, 53215. SAN 318-2428. Tel: 414-389-2931. Interlibrary Loan Service 414-647-5156. FAX: 414-647-5195. Web Site: www.covenantlibrary.org Debra Hagen
Founded 1974
Library Holdings: Bk Titles 2,500; Per Subs 300
Subject Interests: Allied health, Medicine, Nursing
Partic in Library Council Of Metropolitan Milwaukee, Inc; Medline; Southeastern Wisconsin Health Science Library Consortium

M SAINT JOSEPH'S HOSPITAL, Samuel Rosenthal Memorial Library, 5[illegible] W Chambers St, 53210. SAN 318-2444. Tel: 414-447-2174. FAX: 414-2128. E-Mail: clf@iswi.net. Web Site: www.covlibrary.org. *Librn*, Sunja Shaikh
Founded 1967
Library Holdings: Bk Titles 4,200
Subject Interests: Admin, Cancer care, Candicare, Gynecology, Health Medicine, Neonatal, Nursing, Obstetrics
Publications: Newsletter
Partic in Southeastern Wisconsin Health Science Library Consortium

M SAINT MARY'S HOSPITAL, Health Sciences Library, 2323 N Lake D[illegible] PO Box 503, 53201-0503. SAN 318-2460. Tel: 414-291-1278. FAX: 41[illegible] 291-1281. E-Mail: swochos@outreach.its.mcw.edu. *Librn*, Sharon Woch[illegible] Staff 1 (MLS 1)
Founded 1959
Library Holdings: Bk Vols 2,900; Per Subs 340
Subject Interests: Nursing, Rehabilitation

S A O SMITH CORPORATION, Corporate Technology Library, 12100 W Park Pl, 53224-3029. (Mail add: PO Box 245012, 53224-9512), SAN 32[illegible] 1243. Tel: 414-359-4234. FAX: 414-359-4248. *Info Res*, Judith Sayrs; E-Mail: jsayrs@aosmith.com; Staff 1 (MLS 1)
Founded 1930
Library Holdings: Bk Vols 1,780; Per Subs 250
Subject Interests: Electrical engineering, Metallurgy

S SOCIAL DEVELOPMENT COMMISSION, Office of Planning, Researc[illegible] Evaluation Library,* 231 W Wisconsin Ave, 53203. SAN 318-1898. Tel: 414-272-5600, Ext 2301. FAX: 414-272-7982. *Dir*, Terry Williams
Founded 1965
Library Holdings: Bk Vols 1,100; Per Subs 20
Subject Interests: Aging, Education, Employment, Health, Housing, Juvenile justice, Poverty, Training, Urban develop
Publications: Community Service Bulletins

S THE ALLIANCE FOR CHILDREN & FAMILIES, Severson National Information Center, 11700 W Lake Park Dr, 53224. SAN 311-757X. Tel: 414-359-1040. Toll Free Tel: 800-221-3726. FAX: 414-359-1074. E-Mail severson@alliance1.org. Web Site: www.alliance1.org. *Dir*, Susan Hornu[illegible] *Librn*, Georgia Bouda; *Librn*, Debra Conlin; *Tech Servs*, Mary Jo Gehrki[illegible] Staff 5 (MLS 3, Non-MLS 2)
Founded 1945
2000-2001 Income $400,000. Mats Exp $26,000, Books $7,000, Per/Ser (Incl. Access Fees) $9,000, Electronic Ref Mat (Incl. Access Fees) $10,0[illegible]
Library Holdings: Bk Vols 3,100; Per Subs 200
Subject Interests: Behav sci, Family studies, Nonprofit mgt, Psychology, Soc sci, Soc work
Special Collections: Administration & Programs of Family Service Agen[illegible] & child residential care institutions, ephemeral material
Restriction: Staff & members only
Partic in Library Council Of Metropolitan Milwaukee, Inc; Wis Health S[illegible] Libr Asn

L UNITED STATES COURTS LIBRARY,* 517 E Wisconsin Ave, Rm 48[illegible] 53202. SAN 372-364X. Tel: 414-297-1698. FAX: 414-297-1695. *Librn*, Mary B Jones
Library Holdings: Bk Vols 20,000

S UNIVERSAL FOODS CORP, Technical Information Center,* 6143 N 60 St, 53218-1696. SAN 318-2533. Tel: 414-535-4307. FAX: 414-535-4358. E-Mail: 1drives@execpc.com.
Library Holdings: Bk Vols 4,400
Subject Interests: Bacteriology, Biochemistry, Biotech, Chemistry, Food tech, Genetic eng, Microbiology

C UNIVERSITY OF WISCONSIN-MILWAUKEE, Golda Meir Library, 23[illegible] E Hartford Ave, PO Box 604, 53201-0604. SAN 365-0227. Tel: 414-229-6202. Interlibrary Loan Service Tel: 414-229-4493. Circulation Tel: 414-2[illegible] 4132. Reference Tel: 414-229-4659. TDD: 800-947-3529. FAX: 414-229-4380. Web Site: www.uwm.edu/library. *Dir*, Peter Watson-Boone; *Assoc D[illegible]* Ewa Barczyk; *Tech Servs*, Janet Padway; *Archivist*, Timothy Ericson; *Pub[illegible] Servs*, Vanaja Menon; *Branch Mgr, Coll Develop*, R James Tobin; Staff 92 (MLS 54, Non-MLS 38)

Founded 1956. Enrl 23,000; Fac 970; Highest Degree: Doctorate
1999-2000 Income $7,106,805. Mats Exp $2,476,907, Books $776,178, Per/Ser (Incl. Access Fees) $1,609,281, Presv $10,005, AV Equip $39,343, Electronic Ref Mat (Incl. Access Fees) $42,100. (Prof $2,144,241)
Library Holdings: Bk Vols 1,544,869; Bk Titles 1,102,816; Per Subs 7,923
Subject Interests: Am lit, Architecture, Art, Behav sci, Bus, Cartography, Econ, Education, Engineering, Geography, Geol sci, History, Mgt, Related fields, Soc sci, Urban studies
Special Collections: 17th Century Literature Coll; Area Research Center of the State Historical Soc of Wisconsin, bks, mss; Blatz Brewing Company Records; Camus Bibliography Res Coll; Education, Children's Literature (Curriculum Coll), bks & non-print media; Franklin Delano Roosevelt (Jagodzinski); George Hardie Aerospace Coll; Harrison Forman Photograph Coll; Institutional History (University of Wisconsin-Milwaukee Archives), mss; Layton School of Art Library Coll; Little Review Papers, mss; Milwaukee Polish & the Roman Kwasniewski Photo Archive; Milwaukee Press Club Records; Shakespeare Research; Social Justice (Fromkin Memorial); Wisconsin Legislation Reference Bureau Clippings File, micro
Publications: AGS Collection Special Publications Series; Current Geographical Publications; Golda Meir Library Newsletter
Partic in Dialog Corporation; Library Council Of Metropolitan Milwaukee, Inc; Nat Libr of Med; OCLC Online Computer Library Center, Inc; SDC Info Servs; Wisconsin Library Services
Special Services for the Deaf - TDD
Special Services for the Blind - Adapted computers & special software with speech output to assist learning disabled, mentally retarded & uneducated; Braille books on tape; Braille Webster's Dictionary; Kurzweil Reader; Magna Cam (machine) print enlargers; ZoomText software to enlarge computer screen
Friends of the Library Group
Departmental Libraries:
AMERICAN GEOGRAPHICAL SOCIETY COLLECTION, 2311 E Hartford Ave, 53211. (Mail add: PO Box 399, 53201-0399), SAN 365-0251. Tel: 414-229-6282. FAX: 414-229-3624. Web Site: leardo.lib.uwm.edu. *Dir*, Peter Watson-Boone; *Curator*, Christopher Baruth; Staff 3 (Non-MLS 3)
Founded 1852
Subject Interests: Cartography, Exploration, Geography, Photographs
Publications: Current Geographical Publications
Partic in OCLC Online Computer Library Center, Inc
Friends of the Library Group

VON BRIESEN PURTELL & ROPER SC, Law Library, 411 E Wisconsin Ave, No 700, 53202. SAN 373-8876. Tel: 414-276-1122. FAX: 414-276-6281. *Dir*, Susan M Janik; E-Mail: sjanik@vonbriesen.com; Staff 4 (MLS 1, Non-MLS 3)
Library Holdings: Bk Vols 10,000
Publications: Serials List; Special Bibliographies

WISCONSIN CONSERVATORY MUSIC LIBRARY,* 1584 N Prospect Ave, 53202. SAN 318-2576. Tel: 414-276-5760. FAX: 414-276-6076. *Chief Librn*, Raymond Mueller
Founded 1969. Enrl 1,000; Fac 70
Library Holdings: Per Subs 35
Special Collections: Late 19th & Early 20th Century Music; Music for Classical Guitar; Music for the Violin (Hatzi Coll)
Publications: Twelve Landler for Two Guitars (facsimile reprint of 19th-century music)
Partic in Library Council Of Metropolitan Milwaukee, Inc

WISCONSIN DEPARTMENT OF NATURAL RESOURCES, Southeast District Library,* 2300 N Martin Luther King Jr Dr, PO Box 12436, 53212-0436. Tel: 414-263-8493. FAX: 414-263-8483. *Librn*, Kathleen Schultz; E-Mail: schulk@dnr.state.wi.us
Founded 1979
Library Holdings: Bk Vols 2,950; Bk Titles 3,000; Per Subs 135
Subject Interests: Forestry
Special Collections: Department Publications; EPA Documents
Restriction: Open to public for reference only

WISCONSIN ELECTRIC POWER COMPANY LIBRARY, 231 W Michigan St, PO Box 2046, 53201. SAN 328-8382. Tel: 414-221-2580. FAX: 414-221-2282. *Librn*, Mary Ann Barragry
Library Holdings: Bk Titles 17,000; Per Subs 650
Subject Interests: Engineering
Partic in Library Council Of Metropolitan Milwaukee, Inc

WISCONSIN GAS CO, Corporate Library,* 626 E Wisconsin Ave, 53202. SAN 318-2592. Tel: 414-291-6454. FAX: 414-291-6672. *Librn*, Pat Jankowski; Staff 3 (MLS 2, Non-MLS 1)
Founded 1930
Library Holdings: Bk Vols 3,000; Per Subs 300
Subject Interests: Energy, Engineering, Mgt, Natural gas, Pub utilities, Utility regulation
Publications: Information Resource Update

C WISCONSIN LUTHERAN COLLEGE, Marvin M Schwan Library, 8800 W Bluemound Rd, 53226. SAN 324-7236. Tel: 414-443-8864. FAX: 414-443-8505. E-Mail: library@wlc.edu. Web Site: www.wlc.edu/campus/buildings/library.html. *Dir Libr Serv*, Starla C Siegmann; *Ref*, Jenny Baker; E-Mail: jenny_baker@wlc.edu; *Cat*, Sarah Parlier; E-Mail: sarah_parlier@wlc.edu; Staff 4 (MLS 3, Non-MLS 1)
Founded 1978. Enrl 530; Fac 50; Highest Degree: Bachelor
Jul 1998-Jun 1999 Mats Exp $132,783, Books $45,345, Per/Ser (Incl. Access Fees) $57,604, AV Equip $19,802, Other Print Mats $10,032. Sal $109,492 (Prof $86,647)
Library Holdings: Bk Vols 64,000; Bk Titles 59,000; Per Subs 600
Subject Interests: Liberal arts, Lutheran theol
Automation Activity & Vendor Info: (Cataloging) Innovative Interfaces Inc.; (Circulation) Innovative Interfaces Inc.; (Course Reserve) Innovative Interfaces Inc.; (Media Booking) Innovative Interfaces Inc.; (OPAC) Innovative Interfaces Inc.; (Serials) Innovative Interfaces Inc.
Database Vendor: Ebsco - EbscoHost, IAC - SearchBank, OCLC - First Search, Silverplatter Information Inc.
Partic in OCLC Online Computer Library Center, Inc; Southeastern Wisconsin Information Technology Exchange, Inc

P WISCONSIN REGIONAL LIBRARY FOR THE BLIND & PHYSICALLY HANDICAPPED, 813 W Wells St, 53233-1436. SAN 318-2614. Tel: 414-286-3045. Toll Free Tel: 800-242-8822. TDD: 414-286-3548. FAX: 414-286-3102. E-Mail: cpirtl@mpl.org. Web Site: www.dpi.state.wi.us/dpi/dict/rll/bphinfo.html. *Dir*, Marsha J Valance; Tel: 414-286-3010, E-Mail: mvalan@mpl.org; *Dep Dir*, Constance Pirtle; Tel: 414-286-3153; Staff 16 (MLS 3, Non-MLS 13)
Founded 1960. Pop 13,127; Circ 285,598
Jul 1999-Jun 2000 Income State $711,411. Mats Exp $12,354, Books $7,979, Per/Ser (Incl. Access Fees) $2,375, AV Equip $2,000. Sal $645,071
Library Holdings: Bk Vols 192,031; Bk Titles 85,011; Per Subs 10; Spec Interest Per Sub 10
Special Collections: Wisconsin Subjects & Authors, braille & cassettes
Automation Activity & Vendor Info: (Cataloging) DRA; (Circulation) DRA; (OPAC) DRA; (Serials) DRA
Database Vendor: DRA
Publications: Quarterly newsletter
Special Services for the Deaf - TDD
Special Services for the Blind - Talking bks & player equipment

MINERAL POINT

S MINERAL POINT HISTORICAL SOCIETY ARCHIVES,* Gundry House, 234 Madison St, PO Box 188, 53565. SAN 329-9023. Tel: 608-987-2884. *Pres*, Mark Breseman

P MINERAL POINT PUBLIC LIBRARY, 137 High St, 53565. SAN 318-2622. Tel: 608-987-2447. FAX: 608-987-3885. *Dir*, Barbara Polizzi; E-Mail: bpolizzi@swls.org; Staff 1 (Non-MLS 1)
Founded 1893. Pop 2,428; Circ 33,396
Jan 1999-Dec 1999 Income $97,064, City $92,337, Other $4,727. Mats Exp $12,468, Books $10,915, Per/Ser (Incl. Access Fees) $1,388, Micro $165. Sal $43,173 (Prof $31,673)
Library Holdings: Bk Vols 16,642; Per Subs 51; Bks on Deafness & Sign Lang 10
Special Collections: Mineral Point Room of Local History; Natural History (Loraine Nohr Memorial Library of Natural History)
Automation Activity & Vendor Info: (Circulation) epixtech, inc.
Mem of Southwest Wisconsin Library System
Friends of the Library Group

MINOCQUA

P MINOCQUA PUBLIC LIBRARY, 415 Menominee St, 54548-1087. (Mail add: PO Box 1087, 54548-1087), SAN 318-2630. Tel: 715-356-4437. FAX: 715-358-2873. *Dir*, Karen J Augitto; E-Mail: kaugitto@wvls.lib.wi.us
Founded 1933
Library Holdings: Bk Vols 26,281
Automation Activity & Vendor Info: (Cataloging) epixtech, inc.; (Circulation) epixtech, inc.
Mem of Wisconsin Valley Library Service
Friends of the Library Group

MONDOVI

P MONDOVI PUBLIC LIBRARY, 146 W Hudson St, 54755. SAN 318-2649. Tel: 715-926-4403. FAX: 715-926-6176. E-Mail: mondovpl@frontiernet.net. *Dir*, Patricia Ellen Berglund; Staff 3 (Non-MLS 3)
Founded 1902. Pop 5,000; Circ 22,000
Jan 2000-Dec 2000 Income $63,327, City $46,827, County $5,000, Locally Generated Income $3,500, Other $8,000. Mats Exp $15,777, Books $12,977, Per/Ser (Incl. Access Fees) $1,800, AV Equip $1,000. Sal $35,200
Library Holdings: Bk Vols 23,200; Per Subs 55
Automation Activity & Vendor Info: (Circulation) Follett; (OPAC) Follett

Database Vendor: Ebsco - EbscoHost
Mem of Winding Rivers Library System
Open Mon 10-8, Tues-Thurs 2-8, Sat 9-12
Friends of the Library Group

MONONA

P MONONA PUBLIC LIBRARY,* 1000 Nichols Rd, 53716-2531. SAN 318-2657. Tel: 608-222-6127. FAX: 608-222-8590. E-Mail: monona@scls.lib.wi.us. Web Site: www.scls.lib.wi.us/monona. *Dir*, John DeBacher; *Asst Dir, Coll Develop*, Carol Anderson
Founded 1964. Pop 11,000; Circ 280,100
Jan 1997-Dec 1998 Income $408,580, State $2,503, City $252,224, Federal $5,523, County $130,321, Other $17,953. Mats Exp $47,201, Books $36,115, Per/Ser (Incl. Access Fees) $5,013. Sal $210,169
Library Holdings: Bk Vols 60,672; Per Subs 76
Special Collections: Living History of Historic Blooming Grove
Mem of Dane County Library Service; South Central Library System
Friends of the Library Group

MONROE

M MONROE CLINIC, Medical Library,* 515 22nd Ave, 53566. SAN 322-7634. Tel: 608-324-1244. FAX: 608-324-1113. *Librn*, Carol Hasse; Staff 1 (MLS 1)
Founded 1973
Library Holdings: Bk Titles 700; Per Subs 120
Subject Interests: Medicine, Nursing
Partic in Medline; South Central Wisconsin Health Science Library Cooperative

P MONROE PUBLIC LIBRARY,* 925 16th Ave, 53566-1497. SAN 318-2665. Tel: 608-325-3016. FAX: 608-329-4657. *Dir*, Lisa J Cihlar
Founded 1904. Pop 18,515; Circ 224,034
1998-1999 Income $457,449. Mats Exp $59,351, Books $50,957, Per/Ser (Incl. Access Fees) $7,477, Presv $200, Micro $717. Sal $217,737 (Prof $38,489)
Library Holdings: Bk Vols 64,540; Per Subs 192
Subject Interests: Green County, Wis hist
Automation Activity & Vendor Info: (Circulation) epixtech, inc.
Mem of South Central Library System
Resource Library for Green County, WI
Friends of the Library Group

MONTELLO

P MONTELLO PUBLIC LIBRARY,* 128 Lake Ct, PO Box 457, 53949-0457. SAN 325-2892. Tel: 608-297-7544. FAX: 608-297-2673. *Dir*, Bruce Dethlefsen; E-Mail: dethlefsen@winnefox.org; *Coll Develop, Librn*, Linda Tanner; Staff 1 (MLS 1)
Founded 1936. Pop 1,500; Circ 24,591
Jan 1998-Dec 1998 Income $49,430, City $29,896, County $19,534. Mats Exp $7,200, Books $6,500, Per/Ser (Incl. Access Fees) $700. Sal $28,971 (Prof $15,600)
Library Holdings: Bk Titles 10,240; Per Subs 60
Special Collections: John Muir Coll, bks & magazines
Mem of Winnefox Library System
Friends of the Library Group

MONTFORT

P MONTFORT PUBLIC LIBRARY,* 102 E Park St, 53569-0157. SAN 318-2673. Tel: 608-943-6265. *Dir*, Della M Norby
Founded 1885. Pop 668
1998-1999 Income $9,265. Mats Exp $1,875, Books $1,620, Micro $200, Other Print Mats $55. Sal $4,269
Library Holdings: Bk Vols 2,718
Mem of Southwest Wisconsin Library System

MONTICELLO

P MONTICELLO PUBLIC LIBRARY,* 140 N Main St, PO Box 149, 53570-0149. SAN 377-998X. Tel: 608-938-4011. *Dir*, Sharon Briggs; *Librn*, Ruth Wittingwyler
Library Holdings: Bk Titles 14,000; Per Subs 50
Mem of South Central Library System
Open Tues & Thurs 2-7:30, Wed 9-12 & 2-5:30, Fri 2-5:30, Sat 9-12
Friends of the Library Group

MONTREAL

P MONTREAL PUBLIC LIBRARY,* City Hall, 53 Wisconsin Ave, 545[illegible] SAN 318-2681. Tel: 715-561-4955. FAX: 715-561-4964. *Dir*, Karen Te[illegible]
Pop 877; Circ 7,650
Library Holdings: Bk Vols 13,349
Mem of Northwest Wis Libr Syst

MOUNT CALVARY

R SAINT LAWRENCE HIGH SCHOOL SEMINARY LIBRARY,* 301 Church St, 53057. SAN 327-6740. Tel: 920-753-3911. FAX: 920-753-2[illegible] *Dir*, Oliver Bambenek; *Asst Librn*, Kay Seibel; Staff 2 (MLS 1, Non-M[illegible] 1)
Jun 1997-May 1998 Income $10,295, Federal $815. Mats Exp $7,943, Books $4,829, Per/Ser (Incl. Access Fees) $2,159, Other Print Mats $84[illegible]
Library Holdings: Bk Vols 15,210; Per Subs 70

MOUNT HOREB

P MOUNT HOREB PUBLIC LIBRARY,* 105 N Grove St, 53572-1909. 318-2711. Tel: 608-437-5021. FAX: 608-437-6264. *Coll Develop, Dir*, Lysianne Unruh; *Tech Servs*, Kirsten Houtman; *Ch Servs, Circ*, Linda C[illegible] *Reader Servs*, Donna Stevenson; *Per*, Kathy Glover
Founded 1877. Pop 4,700; Circ 64,000
Library Holdings: Bk Vols 27,000; Per Subs 166
Special Collections: Girl & Boy Scout Coll; Mount Horeb Mail Newsp[illegible] July 17, 1883-1992
Mem of South Central Library System
Friends of the Library Group

MUKWONAGO

P MUKWONAGO COMMUNITY LIBRARY,* 300 Washington Ave, 53[illegible] 1909. SAN 318-272X. Tel: 414-363-6411. FAX: 414-363-6457. E-Mail: lib@wauknet.com. *Dir*, Kathleen McBride
Jan 1998-Dec 1999 Income $456,751
Library Holdings: Bk Vols 40,731; Per Subs 60
Subject Interests: History
Mem of Waukesha County Federated Library System
Friends of the Library Group

MUSCODA

P MUSCODA PUBLIC LIBRARY,* 206 N Wisconsin Ave, PO Box 138, 53573-0138. SAN 318-2738. Tel: 608-739-3182. FAX: 608-739-3183. *D*[illegible] Jean M Benson
Founded 1926. Pop 2,300; Circ 14,000
Library Holdings: Bk Titles 8,000; Per Subs 25
Subject Interests: Local history
Mem of Southwest Wisconsin Library System
Open Mon & Wed 9-12, 2-5 & 7-8:30, Fri 9-12 & 2-5 & Sat 9-12

MUSKEGO

P MUSKEGO PUBLIC LIBRARY, S73 W16663 Janesville Rd, PO Box 8[illegible] 53150-0810. SAN 318-2746. Tel: 262-971-2100. Interlibrary Loan Servic[illegible] Tel: 262-971-2112. Reference Tel: 262-971-2101. FAX: 262-971-2115. W[illegible] Site: www.ci.muskego.wi.us. *Dir*, Holly Sanhuber; Tel: 262-971-2119, E-Mail: hsanhuber@ci.muskego.wi.us; *Asst Dir*, Charlene Lenzen; Tel: 2[illegible] 971-2107, E-Mail: clenzen@ci.muskego.wi.us; *Tech Servs*, Linda Brown; Tel: 262-971-2108, E-Mail: lbrown@ci.muskego.wi.us; *Publ Servs*, Penny Halle; Tel: 262-971-2106, E-Mail: phalle@ci.muskego.wi.us; *Ref Serv*, Ja[illegible] Genzel; Tel: 262-971-2105, E-Mail: jgenzel@ci.muskego.wi.us; Staff 18 (MLS 3, Non-MLS 15)
Founded 1960. Pop 26,000; Circ 106,533
Jan 1999-Dec 1999 Income $670,798, City $610,407, County $25,482, Locally Generated Income $9,724, Other $10,764. Mats Exp $83,367, Bo[illegible] $63,182, Per/Ser (Incl. Access Fees) $9,220, Presv $1,000, AV Equip $9,[illegible] Electronic Ref Mat (Incl. Access Fees) $150. Sal $321,094 (Prof $111,81[illegible]
Library Holdings: Bk Vols 81,816; Bk Titles 70,000; Per Subs 425
Mem of Waukesha County Federated Library System
Partic in Wiscat
Friends of the Library Group

NASHOTAH

SR NASHOTAH HOUSE LIBRARY, 2777 Mission Rd, 53058-9793. SAN 3[illegible] 2754. Tel: 262-646-6535. FAX: 262-646-6504. E-Mail: librarian@library.nashotah.edu. Web Site: www.nashotah.edu/library. *Librn*, Thomas Osterfield; Staff 5 (MLS 1, Non-MLS 4)
Founded 1842
Library Holdings: Bk Vols 88,705; Per Subs 299
Subject Interests: Anglicana, Bks of common prayer, Especially Bibles, Pre-1800 imprints

Special Collections: Archives of Nashotah House; National Altar Guild Coll; Prayer Books (Underwood Coll)
Database Vendor: OCLC - First Search, ProQuest
Partic in Library Council Of Metropolitan Milwaukee, Inc; OCLC Online Computer Library Center, Inc; Wisconsin Library Services

EDAH

NECEDAH MEMORIAL LIBRARY, 216 S Main St, PO Box 279, 54646. SAN 318-2762. Tel: 608-565-7979. E-Mail: necmem@tde.net. *Librn*, Rose Marie Carter; Staff 1 (MLS 1)
Founded 1914
Library Holdings: Bk Vols 10,329; Per Subs 26
Subject Interests: Cookbooks
Mem of Winding Rivers Library System
Open Mon-Wed & Fri 1-5, Sat 9-1

NAH

BERGSTROM MAHLER MUSEUM LIBRARY,* 165 N Park Ave, 54956-2994. SAN 327-4500. Tel: 920-751-4658. FAX: 920-751-4755. *Exec Dir*, Alex Vance
Library Holdings: Bk Titles 1,300
Open Sat & Sun 1-4:30, Tues-Fri 10-4:30

FORT JAMES CORP, Technical Information Center,* 1915 Marathon Ave, PO Box 899, 54956. SAN 318-2770. Tel: 920-729-8170. FAX: 920-729-8597.; Staff 2 (MLS 1, Non-MLS 1)
Founded 1943
Library Holdings: Bk Titles 15,000; Per Subs 600
Subject Interests: Paper chem, Pulp, Technology
Special Collections: US Patent (1978-present)
Publications: Information Update; James River in the News
Partic in Fox Valley Library Council; Wisconsin Library Services

J J KELLER & ASSOCIATES, INC, Editorial Resource Center, Research & Technical Library,* 3003 W Breezewood Lane, PO Box 368, 54957-0368. SAN 318-2797. Tel: 920-722-2848. FAX: 920-727-7519. E-Mail: library@jjkeller.com. Web Site: www.jjkeller.com. Subject Specialists: *Business and management*, Lisa Zwickey; *Legislation*, Kim Laabs; *Transportation*, Marie Beede
Founded 1958
Library Holdings: Bk Vols 6,500; Per Subs 510
Subject Interests: Distribution, Hazardous mat, Hazardous waste, Occupational safety, Regulatory law, Transportation
Publications: Acquisitions Update
Restriction: Staff use only
Partic in Fox River Valley Libr Coop

KIMBERLY-CLARK CORP LIBRARY,* 2100 Winchester Rd, PO Box 999, 54957-0999. SAN 318-2800. Tel: 920-721-5261. FAX: 920-721-6394. *Librn*, M E Sutliff
Library Holdings: Bk Vols 10,000; Per Subs 400
Subject Interests: Chemistry, Paper, Pulp sci, Technology, Textiles

NEENAH PUBLIC LIBRARY, (NPL), 240 E Wisconsin Ave, 54956. (Mail add: PO Box 569, 54957-0569), SAN 318-2819. Tel: 920-751-4722. Interlibrary Loan Service Tel: 920-751-4722, Ext 204. Circulation Tel: 920-751-4722, Ext 300. Reference Tel: 920-751-4722, Ext 250. FAX: 920-751-4931. Web Site: www.neenahlibrary.org. *Dir*, Stephen Proces; Tel: 920-751-4722, Ext 100, E-Mail: proces@winnefox.org; *Ch Servs*, Patricia H Hewitt-McNichols; *Ad Servs*, Gretchen Raab; Tel: 920-751-4722, Ext 200, E-Mail: raab@winnefox.org; *Cat, Tech Servs*, Jane Laswell; *Circ*, Nancy Britten; *Ref*, Desiree Fahrenkrug; *Ref*, Melissa Kazmer; Tel: 920-751-4722, Ext 203, E-Mail: kazmer@winnefox.org; Staff 8 (MLS 8)
Founded 1884. Pop 37,872; Circ 550,000
Jan 2000-Dec 2000 Income $1,400,000, City $1,027,470, County $332,530, Locally Generated Income $40,000. Mats Exp $200,000, Books $120,000, Per/Ser (Incl. Access Fees) $18,000, Micro $5,000, AV Equip $52,000, Electronic Ref Mat (Incl. Access Fees) $5,000. Sal $750,000
Library Holdings: Bk Vols 185,704; Per Subs 362
Subject Interests: Local history, Naval hist
Automation Activity & Vendor Info: (Acquisitions) DRA; (Cataloging) DRA; (Circulation) DRA; (OPAC) DRA; (Serials) DRA
Database Vendor: DRA
Publications: Newsletters
Mem of Winnefox Library System
Friends of the Library Group

THEDA CLARK MEDICAL CENTER, ThedaCare Library, 130 Second St, PO Box 2021, 54957-2021. SAN 318-2789. Tel: 920-729-2190. FAX: 920-729-2321.; Staff 2 (MLS 1, Non-MLS 1)
Founded 1970
Library Holdings: Bk Vols 1,800; Bk Titles 1,300; Per Subs 350
Subject Interests: Cardiology, Critical care, Maternal fetal med, Neonatal intensive care, Trauma
Partic in Fox River Valley Area Library Consortium; Fox Valley Library Council

NEILLSVILLE

P NEILLSVILLE FREE LIBRARY,* 409 Hewett St, 54456-1923. SAN 318-2827. Tel: 715-743-2558. FAX: 715-743-6213. *Dir*, Kent Hatlestad
Pop 6,900; Circ 79,358
Library Holdings: Bk Vols 19,887; Per Subs 71
Mem of Wisconsin Valley Library Service
Friends of the Library Group

NEKOOSA

P CHARLES & JOANN LESTER LIBRARY, 100 Park St, 54457. SAN 318-2835. Tel: 715-886-7879. FAX: 715-886-7879. *Dir*, Linda Overbey
Founded 1939. Pop 2,794; Circ 48,340
Library Holdings: Bk Vols 35,000; Per Subs 70

NESHKORO

P NESHKORO PUBLIC LIBRARY,* 132 S Main St, PO Box 196, 54960-0196. SAN 378-0007. Tel: 920-293-4026. FAX: 920-293-4026. *Dir*, Cheryl Milbrandt
Library Holdings: Bk Titles 10,000; Per Subs 20
Mem of Winnefox Library System
Open Wed 12-7, Thurs 9:30-5:30, Fri 12-6

NEW BERLIN

P NEW BERLIN PUBLIC LIBRARY, 14750 W Cleveland Ave, 53151. SAN 318-2851. Tel: 414-785-4980. FAX: 414-785-4984. Web Site: www.wcfls.lib.wi.us/newberlin. *Dir*, Katie Schulz; E-Mail: kgschulz@wcfls.lib.wi.us; *Head, Circ*, Joanne Anderson; *Ch Servs*, Elizabeth Fox; *Ref*, Barbara Draeger; *Ref*, Peg Schellin; *Ch Servs*, Mary Flag; Staff 18 (MLS 5, Non-MLS 13)
Founded 1969. Pop 38,000; Circ 378,000
Jan 1999-Dec 2000 Income City $758,000. Mats Exp $380,000, Books $110,000, Electronic Ref Mat (Incl. Access Fees) (MEX) $15,000. Sal $380,000
Library Holdings: Bk Vols 119,211; Bk Titles 97,681; Per Subs 210
Subject Interests: Am hist, Bus, Cookery, History, Indust, Mgt
Special Collections: State Selected Depository Library
Database Vendor: epixtech, inc., Innovative Interfaces INN - View, OCLC - First Search
Publications: Annotated Bibliographies for Young Readers & Their Parents; Annotated Bibliographies of Business Resources; Library Info Brochure
Mem of Waukesha County Federated Library System
Friends of the Library Group

NEW GLARUS

P NEW GLARUS PUBLIC LIBRARY,* 319 Second St, PO Box 35, 53574-0035. SAN 318-286X. Tel: 608-527-2003. FAX: 608-527-5126. E-Mail: ngpl@scls.lib.wi.us. Web Site: www.scls.lib.wi.us. *Dir*, Virginia Bryan
Founded 1934. Pop 2,731; Circ 67,487
Jan 1998-Dec 1999 Income $135,211. Mats Exp $40,237, Books $17,300, Per/Ser (Incl. Access Fees) $2,070. Sal $63,916 (Prof $31,200)
Library Holdings: Bk Titles 15,316; Per Subs 94
Mem of South Central Library System
Friends of the Library Group

NEW HOLSTEIN

P NEW HOLSTEIN PUBLIC LIBRARY, 2115 Washington St, 53061-1098. SAN 318-2878. Tel: 920-898-5165. FAX: 920-898-9022. E-Mail: nhref@esls.lib.wi.us. Web Site: newholstein@lib.wi.us. *Dir*, Barbara A Weber
Founded 1955. Pop 9,300; Circ 90,000
Jan 2000-Dec 2000 Income $176,600, City $151,000, County $18,500, Locally Generated Income $7,100. Mats Exp $29,839, Books $23,139, Per/Ser (Incl. Access Fees) $3,200, AV Equip $3,500. Sal $90,000 (Prof $31,000)
Library Holdings: Bk Vols 35,000; Per Subs 120
Automation Activity & Vendor Info: (Cataloging) epixtech, inc.; (Circulation) epixtech, inc.; (OPAC) epixtech, inc.
Mem of Manitowoc-Calumet Library System

NEW LISBON

P NEW LISBON MEMORIAL LIBRARY,* 115 W Park St, 53950-1250. SAN 318-2886. Tel: 608-562-3213. FAX: 608-562-3213. E-Mail: nlploff@nwt.net. *Dir*, Mary Crawford

Founded 1931
Library Holdings: Bk Vols 29,765; Per Subs 97
Special Collections: Indian Artifacts (Harry Mortenson Coll), bks
Mem of La Crosse Area Libr Syst; Winding Rivers Library System

NEW LONDON

M NEW LONDON FAMILY MEDICAL CENTER, Health Science Library,* 1405 Mill St, PO Box 307, 54961. SAN 318-2894. Tel: 920-982-5330, Ext 3240. FAX: 920-982-8742. *In Charge*, Kathleen Mielke; Tel: 920-982-8725, E-Mail: kmielke@ahsfv.org
Founded 1974
Library Holdings: Bk Titles 350; Per Subs 30
Partic in Fox River Valley Area Library Consortium
Figures include departmental libraries

P NEW LONDON PUBLIC LIBRARY, 406 S Pearl St, 54961-1441. SAN 318-2908. Tel: 920-982-8519. FAX: 920-982-8617. E-Mail: nlp@owls.lib.wi.us. *Dir*, Ann Hunt; *Ch Servs*, Jane Friess; *Ad Servs*, Janet Reidenbach; Staff 7 (MLS 2, Non-MLS 5)
Founded 1895. Pop 12,000; Circ 137,000
1999-2000 Income $335,000. Mats Exp $52,100, Books $39,000, Per/Ser (Incl. Access Fees) $4,500, Micro $100, AV Equip $8,500. Sal $204,000 (Prof $166,000)
Library Holdings: Bk Vols 43,500; Per Subs 150
Special Collections: Historical Coll
Automation Activity & Vendor Info: (Cataloging) GEAC; (Circulation) GEAC; (OPAC) GEAC
Database Vendor: Ebsco - EbscoHost, IAC - Info Trac, OCLC - First Search
Mem of Outagamie Waupaca Library System

NEW RICHMOND

P CARLETON A FRIDAY MEMORIAL LIBRARY, New Richmond Public Library, 155 E First St, PO Box 179, 54017-0179. SAN 318-2916. Tel: 715-246-2364. FAX: 715-246-2691. E-Mail: nrpublib@presscenter.com. *Publ Servs, Tech Servs*, Mildred Hendrickson; *Publ Servs*, Leanne A Koepke; *Ch Servs, Publ Servs*, Mary Ellen Westerlund; *ILL*, Sandra Venhor; Staff 5 (MLS 1, Non-MLS 4)
Founded 1883. Pop 13,773
Library Holdings: Bk Vols 36,817; Per Subs 114
Special Collections: New Richmond Historical Coll
Mem of Indianhead Federated Library System
Friends of the Library Group

J WISCONSIN INDIANHEAD TECHNICAL COLLEGE, New Richmond Campus Learning Resources Center,* 1019 S Knowles Ave, 54017. SAN 318-2924. Tel: 715-246-6561, Ext 4362. FAX: 715-246-2777.; Staff 2 (MLS 1, Non-MLS 1)
Founded 1968. Enrl 1,000; Fac 52
Library Holdings: Bk Vols 7,000; Bk Titles 4,600; Per Subs 160
Subject Interests: Agriculture, Bus, Health, Indust, Mgt, Nursing, Trade
Mem of Indianhead Federated Library System

NORTH FOND DU LAC

P SPILLMAN LIBRARY,* 719 Wisconsin Ave, 54937-1335. SAN 318-2959. Tel: 920-929-3771. FAX: 920-929-3669. E-Mail: spillman@spiritusa.net. *Dir*, Lois Potratz
Library Holdings: Bk Vols 19,500; Per Subs 50

NORTH FREEDOM

P NORTH FREEDOM PUBLIC LIBRARY,* 103 N Maple St, PO Box 60, 53951-0300. SAN 318-2967. Tel: 608-522-4571. E-Mail: nflibrary@baraboo.com. Web Site: www.scls.lib.wi.us. *Librn*, Darlene Cox
Founded 1898. Circ 6,500
Library Holdings: Bk Vols 4,600; Bk Titles 4,500; Per Subs 14
Subject Interests: History, Natural science, Sci-tech
Mem of South Central Library System

NORTH LAKE

P TOWN HALL LIBRARY, N 76 W 31429 Hwy VV, PO Box 158, 53064-0158. SAN 318-2975. Tel: 414-966-2933. FAX: 414-966-3365. *Dir*, Martha Riel; E-Mail: mlriel@wcfls.lib.wi.us; Staff 13 (MLS 1, Non-MLS 12)
Founded 1964. Pop 7,900; Circ 80,000
Jan 2000-Dec 2000 Income $222,000, County $15,000, Locally Generated Income $207,000. Mats Exp $49,000. Sal $105,000
Library Holdings: Bk Vols 28,000; Bk Titles 25,000; Per Subs 80
Automation Activity & Vendor Info: (Cataloging) Gaylord; (Cataloging) Gaylord
Function: ILL available, Reference services available
Mem of Waukesha County Federated Library System
Friends of the Library Group

OAK CREEK

J MILWAUKEE AREA TECHNICAL COLLEGE, South Campus Cente Library, 6665 S Howell Ave, 53154. SAN 318-2991. Tel: 414-571-460 E-Mail: slibrary@matc.edu. *Librn*, Jeffrey Grossman; Tel: grossmaj@matc.edu; Staff 3 (MLS 2, Non-MLS 1)
Library Holdings: Bk Vols 14,500; Bk Titles 12,300; Per Subs 100
Subject Interests: Air conditioning, Computer programming, Compute science, Fire, Police sci
Automation Activity & Vendor Info: (Acquisitions) SIRSI; (Catalogin SIRSI; (Circulation) SIRSI; (Course Reserve) SIRSI; (OPAC) SIRSI; (Serials) SIRSI
Database Vendor: Ebsco - EbscoHost, IAC - Info Trac, ProQuest

P OAK CREEK PUBLIC LIBRARY, 8620 S Howell Ave, 53154. SAN 3 3009. Tel: 414-764-4400. FAX: 414-768-6583. Web Site: www.mcfls.or ocpl. *Librn*, Ross Talis; *Asst Librn*, Jonathan Bloy; *Ch Servs, YA Servs*, Jenny Wegener; *Ref*, Susan Kaczmarek; Staff 4 (MLS 4)
Founded 1972. Pop 26,400; Circ 221,480
1999-2000 Income $562,935. Mats Exp $76,500, Books $52,000, Per/S (Incl. Access Fees) $8,700, Micro $3,800, AV Equip $12,000. Sal $290, (Prof $148,765)
Library Holdings: Bk Vols 76,212; Per Subs 160
Subject Interests: Bus, Cookbooks
Automation Activity & Vendor Info: (Circulation) Innovative Interfac Inc.
Publications: Bookmark; monthly calendar
Mem of Milwaukee County Federated Library System
Partic in Library Council Of Metropolitan Milwaukee, Inc
Friends of the Library Group

OAKFIELD

P OAKFIELD PUBLIC LIBRARY, 111 N Main St, PO Box 278, 53065. 318-3017. Tel: 920-583-4552. FAX: 920-583-4552. E-Mail: oakslib@spiritusa.net. *Dir*, Dianne Bilitz; Tel: 920-583-3218; *Asst Librn*, Eleanor Fendley
Founded 1898
1999-2000 Income $31,646, State $710, County $8,240, Locally Genera Income $22,696. Mats Exp $6,655, Books $5,900, Per/Ser (Incl. Access Fees) $755. Sal $17,916
Library Holdings: Bk Titles 15,000; Per Subs 39
Mem of Winnefox Library System

OCONOMOWOC

M OCONOMOWOC MEMORIAL HOSPITAL, Health Science Library, 79 Summit Ave, 53066. SAN 318-3025. Tel: 414-569-9400, Ext 1240. *Librn* Donna Dunham; Staff 1 (MLS 1)
Founded 1970
Library Holdings: Bk Vols 1,795; Bk Titles 1,080; Per Subs 200
Subject Interests: Dental, Hospital departments, Medical, Nursing
Partic in Library Council Of Metropolitan Milwaukee, Inc; Nat Libr of M Southeastern Wisconsin Health Science Library Consortium

P OCONOMOWOC PUBLIC LIBRARY, (OPL), 200 South St, 53066-521 SAN 318-3033. Tel: 262-569-2193. FAX: 262-569-2176. *Dir*, Ray McKenna; E-Mail: rmckenna@cooney.lib.wi.us; Staff 30 (MLS 6, Non-M 24)
Founded 1893. Pop 26,342; Circ 199,602
Jan 2000-Dec 2000 Income $806,821. Mats Exp $103,586, Books $80,82 Per/Ser (Incl. Access Fees) $17,261, Micro $5,500. Sal $532,489
Library Holdings: Bk Vols 85,000; Per Subs 275
Subject Interests: Art, Biog
Automation Activity & Vendor Info: (Cataloging) Gaylord; (Circulatior Gaylord; (OPAC) Gaylord
Mem of Waukesha County Federated Library System
Friends of the Library Group

OCONTO

P FARNSWORTH PUBLIC LIBRARY,* 715 Main St, 54153-1795. SAN 318-3041. Tel: 920-834-7730. *In Charge*, Dwaine Konshak
Founded 1903. Pop 4,446; Circ 50,000
Library Holdings: Bk Vols 20,000
Subject Interests: Local history
Mem of NE Wis Intertype Librs Inc; Nicolet Federated Library System
Partic in Wiscat
Friends of the Library Group

OCONTO FALLS

P OCONTO FALLS COMMUNITY LIBRARY, 251 N Main St, 54154-10 SAN 318-305X. Tel: 920-846-2673. FAX: 920-846-9946. *Dir*, Jeannie Waschbisch; E-Mail: jwaschbi@mail.nfls.lib.wi.us
Pop 2,700; Circ 25,197

Library Holdings: Bk Vols 17,852; Per Subs 46
Automation Activity & Vendor Info: (Cataloging) GEAC; (Circulation) GEAC; (OPAC) GEAC
Database Vendor: IAC - Info Trac
Mem of Nicolet Federated Library System
Friends of the Library Group

NAH

BAD RIVER PUBLIC TRIBAL LIBRARY, PO Box 39, Blackbird Center, 54861. SAN 377-9386. Tel: 715-682-7111. FAX: 715-682-7118. E-Mail: biizhoo@ncis.net. *Librn*, Norma J Soulier
Library Holdings: Bk Vols 10,000; Bk Titles 9,000; Per Subs 31
Subject Interests: Native Am
Mem of Northern Waters Library Service
Partic in Wis Libr Asn
Friends of the Library Group

:MA

OGEMA PUBLIC LIBRARY, W 5005 State Rd 86, PO Box 603, 54459-0603. SAN 322-838X. Tel: 715-767-5130. FAX: 715-767-5130. E-Mail: ogemapl@centurytel.net. *Librn*, Lavonne Mattson
Founded 1973. Pop 1,000; Circ 7,673
2000-2001 Mats Exp $21,102, Books $500. Sal $7,997
Library Holdings: Bk Titles 11,669
Mem of Indianhead Federated Library System

RO

CARTER MEMORIAL LIBRARY,* 405 E Huron St, 54963-1405. SAN 324-7244. Tel: 920-685-7016. FAX: 920-685-7011. *Librn*, Theo Knigge; *Asst Librn*, Debra Esch; Staff 5 (MLS 1, Non-MLS 4)
Pop 2,909; Circ 33,208
Library Holdings: Bk Titles 18,677; Per Subs 61
Special Collections: Local History Coll
Mem of Winnefox Library System
Friends of the Library Group

EIDA

ONEIDA COMMUNITY LIBRARY,* 201 Elm St, PO Box 365, 54155-0365. SAN 324-7791. Tel: 920-869-2210. FAX: 920-869-1299. E-Mail: onelib@netnet.net. Web Site: www.owlsnet.com. *Dir*, Brian Doxtator; *Asst Librn*, Dan Metoxen; *Asst Librn*, Eleanore Dansforth; *Ref*, Karen Kuhn
Founded 1968. Pop 4,232; Circ 10,000
Library Holdings: Bk Titles 12,000; Per Subs 42
Special Collections: Iroquois-Oneida Indian Coll, bks, flms; Native American Coll, bks, flms, reels, fiche
Mem of Nicolet Federated Library System

TARIO

ONTARIO PUBLIC LIBRARY,* PO Box 69, 54651-0069. SAN 318-3068. Tel: 608-337-4651. *Dir*, Margaret Murphy
Circ 18,000
Jan 1997-Dec 1998 Income $24,532, City $16,535, County $1,858, Other $1,316. Mats Exp $5,680, Books $4,468, Per/Ser (Incl. Access Fees) $743. Sal $10,001
Library Holdings: Bk Vols 900; Per Subs 60
Mem of Winding Rivers Library System
Friends of the Library Group

STBURG

OOSTBURG PUBLIC LIBRARY,* 213 N Eighth St, 53070-0187. SAN 318-3076. Tel: 920-564-2934. *Librn*, Mary Lou DuMez; *Asst Librn*, Colleen Swart; *Ch Servs*, Trixine Tahtinen
Founded 1941. Pop 3,500
Library Holdings: Bk Titles 13,100; Per Subs 65
Mem of Eastern Shores Library System
Friends of the Library Group

EGON

OREGON PUBLIC LIBRARY, 256 Brook St, 53575. SAN 318-3084. Tel: 608-835-3656. FAX: 608-835-2856. E-Mail: orelib@scls.lib.wi.us. *Dir*, Victoria Cothroll; E-Mail: cothrolv@scls.lib.wi.us; *Ch Servs*, Ruth Doran; E-Mail: recd@scls.lib.wi.us; Staff 8 (MLS 2, Non-MLS 6)
2000-2000 Income $324,456, City $227,677, County $80,161, Other $16,618. Mats Exp $37,400, Books $31,100, AV Equip $6,300. Sal $211,300 (Prof $70,000)
Library Holdings: Bk Titles 52,416; Per Subs 147
Database Vendor: Ebsco - EbscoHost, epixtech, inc., IAC - Info Trac
Mem of South Central Library System; Southcentral Libr Syst
Friends of the Library Group

ORFORDVILLE

P ORFORDVILLE PUBLIC LIBRARY,* 203 W Beloit St, PO Box 249, 53576-0249. SAN 318-3092. Tel: 608-879-9229. FAX: 608-879-2022. *Librn*, Angie Stelter; E-Mail: astelter@als.lib.wi.us
Founded 1905. Pop 1,136; Circ 6,149
Library Holdings: Bk Vols 12,295
Mem of Arrowhead Library System
Friends of the Library Group

OSCEOLA

P OSCEOLA PUBLIC LIBRARY,* PO Box 596, 54020. SAN 376-608X. Tel: 715-294-2310. FAX: 715-755-3510. E-Mail: ospublib@centuryinter.net. *Dir*, Margaret Tomfohrde
Library Holdings: Bk Vols 12,000; Bk Titles 6,000; Per Subs 25
Mem of Indianhead Federated Library System
Friends of the Library Group

OSHKOSH

S BOEING AERONAUTICAL LIBRARY, PO Box 3065, 54903-3065. SAN 324-7252. Tel: 920-426-4848. FAX: 920-426-4828. E-Mail: library@eaa.org. Web Site: www.eaa.org/museum. *Mgr Libr Serv*, Susan A Lurvey; E-Mail: slurvey@eaa.org. Subject Specialists: *Aviation*, Susan A Lurvey; Staff 1 (MLS 1)
Founded 1972
Library Holdings: Bk Titles 10,000; Per Subs 30
Subject Interests: Aircraft, Amateur construction, Aviation, Aviation hist
Special Collections: Dwiggins Coll
Publications: Index to EAA pubs-Sport Aviation, Experimenter, Vintage Airplane; Photo Archives Catalog; Scale Aircraft Drawing Index
Restriction: Not a lending library
Function: ILL available

C FORREST R POLK LIBRARY, (Formerly University Of Wisconsin-Oshkosh), Information Technology Division, 800 Algoma Blvd, 54901. SAN 365-0529. Tel: 920-424-3334. Circulation Tel: 920-424-3320. Reference Tel: 920-424-4333. FAX: 920-424-7338. E-Mail: infodesk@uwosh.edu. Web Site: www.uwosh.edu/library/. *Assoc Dir*, Patrick Wilkinson; Tel: 920-424-2147, E-Mail: wilkinso@uwosh.edu; *Head Tech Servs*, Barbara Fahey; Tel: 920-424-0291, E-Mail: fahey@uwosh.edu; *Head, Circ*, Jeanne Foley; Tel: 920-424-7315, E-Mail: foley@uwosh.edu; *Head, Info Serv*, Sarah Neises; Tel: 920-424-0401, E-Mail: neises@uwosh.edu; *Govt Doc*, Mike Watkins; Tel: 920-424-7305; *ILL*, Erin Czech; Tel: 920-424-3348; *Coll Develop*, Cynthia Huebschen; Tel: 920-424-7327; *Archivist*, Joshua Ranger; Tel: 920-424-0828; *Bibliog Instr*, Marisa Finkey; Tel: 920-424-3436. Subject Specialists: *Education*, Mary Keefer; Staff 26 (MLS 13, Non-MLS 13)
Founded 1871. Enrl 10,783; Fac 534; Highest Degree: Master
Jul 1999-Jun 2000 Mats Exp $950,000, Books $375,000, Per/Ser (Incl. Access Fees) $560,000. Sal $898,041 (Prof $537,999)
Library Holdings: Bk Vols 425,000; Per Subs 1,850
Subject Interests: Business, Education, Nursing, Undergrad studies
Special Collections: Pare Lorenz Coll; University Archives Coll; Wisconsin Area Research Center Coll
Automation Activity & Vendor Info: (Cataloging) Endeavor; (Circulation) Endeavor; (Course Reserve) Endeavor; (OPAC) Endeavor; (Serials) Endeavor
Database Vendor: Ebsco - EbscoHost, GaleNet, Lexis-Nexis, OCLC - First Search, ProQuest, Silverplatter Information Inc., Wilson - Wilson Web
Publications: Polk Library News (Newsletter)
Partic in Fox Valley Library Council; OCLC Online Computer Library Center, Inc
Departmental Libraries:
HALSEY RESOURCE CENTER, Halsey Science Ctr, 800 Algoma Blvd, 54901. SAN 374-3527. Tel: 920-424-4979. *In Charge*, Judy Nord

M MERCY MEDICAL CENTER, The Clark Family Health Science Library, 500 S Oakwood Rd, PO Box 3370, 54903. SAN 318-3106. Tel: 920-223-0342. FAX: 920-223-0343. *Dir*, Mary Bayorgeon; Tel: 920-223-0341; *Librn*, Michele Matucheski; Tel: 920-223-0340; *ILL*, Regina Uerkwitz; Tel: 920-223-0341; Staff 3 (MLS 2, Non-MLS 1)
Founded 1906
Library Holdings: Bk Vols 2,100; Per Subs 200
Subject Interests: Consumer health, Medicine, Nursing, Surgery
Automation Activity & Vendor Info: (Cataloging) EOS; (OPAC) EOS; (Serials) EOS
Database Vendor: Ebsco - EbscoHost, IAC - Info Trac, ProQuest, Silverplatter Information Inc.

Mem of Affinity Health Syst, Inc
Partic in Fox River Valley Area Library Consortium; Fox Valley Library Council; Greater Midwest Regional Medical Libr Network

P OSHKOSH PUBLIC LIBRARY, 106 Washington Ave, 54901-4985. SAN 365-0405. Tel: 920-236-5200. Reference Tel: 920-236-5205. FAX: 920-236-5228. Web Site: www.axp.winnefox.org. *Dir*, John V Nichols; E-Mail: nichols@winnefox.org; *Asst Dir*, Joan Mueller; Tel: 920-236-5231, E-Mail: mueller@winnefox.org; *Ch Servs*, Laurie Magee; E-Mail: magee@winnefox.org; *Automation Syst Coordr*, Karen Boehning; E-Mail: boehring@winnefox.org; *Circ*, Victoria O'Rourke; E-Mail: orourke@winnefox.org; *Acq*, Kathleen Grace; Tel: 920-236-5232, E-Mail: grace@winnefox.org; *Ref Serv Ad*, Janice Dibble; Fax: 920-236-5227, E-Mail: dibble@winnefox.org; *Ch Servs*, Laurie Magee; Tel: 920-236-5208, E-Mail: magee@winnefox.org; Staff 48 (MLS 13, Non-MLS 35)
Founded 1895. Pop 87,358; Circ 1,051,607
Jan 1999-Dec 1999 Income $3,065,768, City $1,828,749, Federal $13,295, County $704,410, Other $360,827. Mats Exp $414,227, Books $271,004, Per/Ser (Incl. Access Fees) $30,491, Micro $938, AV Equip $75,439, Other Print Mats $8,834, Electronic Ref Mat (Incl. Access Fees) $27,521. Sal $1,307,019 (Prof $507,115)
Library Holdings: Bk Vols 282,443; Per Subs 615
Subject Interests: Genealogy, Local history
Special Collections: US Census Coll
Automation Activity & Vendor Info: (Acquisitions) DRA; (Cataloging) DRA; (Circulation) DRA; (OPAC) DRA
Publications: Library Lines (Newsletter); Tid Bits
Mem of Winnefox Library System
Partic in Fox Valley Library Council; OCLC Online Computer Library Center, Inc; Wisconsin Library Services
Special Services for the Deaf - TDD
Friends of the Library Group
Bookmobiles: 1

S OSHKOSH PUBLIC MUSEUM LIBRARY, 1331 Algoma Blvd, 54901-2799. SAN 318-3114. Tel: 920-424-4735. FAX: 920-424-4738. *Archivist*, Scott Cross; E-Mail: cross@publicmuseum.oshkosh.net
Founded 1924
Library Holdings: Bk Titles 6,000
Subject Interests: Archaeology, Architecture, Art, Local history, Logging, Lumbering, Meteorites, Natural history
Special Collections: Local History (Oshkosh Pioneers), bks, doc & photogs
Restriction: Not a lending library
Function: Research library

S PAINE ART CENTER & ARBORETUM, George P Nevitt Library, 1410 Algoma Blvd, 54901-7708. SAN 318-3122. Tel: 920-235-6903, Ext 32. FAX: 920-235-6303. *In Charge*, Corinne H Spoo; Staff 1 (MLS 1)
Founded 1975
Library Holdings: Bk Vols 5,748
Subject Interests: Am painters, Architecture, Art, Barbizon, Decorative art, Eng archit, Fine arts, Horticulture
Restriction: Open to public for reference only
Bookmobiles: 1

GL WINNEBAGO COUNTY LAW LIBRARY,* Court House, 415 Jackson St, PO Box 2808, 54903-2808. SAN 318-3130. Tel: 920-236-4808.
Library Holdings: Bk Vols 22,150

P WINNEFOX LIBRARY SYSTEM,* 106 Washington Ave, 54901-4985. SAN 318-3149. Tel: 920-236-5220. FAX: 920-236-5228. Web Site: axp.winnefox.org. *Dir*, John V Nichols; *Coordr*, Ken Hall; E-Mail: hall@axp.winnefox.org; *ILL*, Joy Schwarz; Staff 10 (MLS 4, Non-MLS 6)
Founded 1977. Pop 205,522
Jan 1999-Dec 1999 Income $3,795,787, State $532,056, Federal $27,596, County $1,873,316, Other $814,865. Mats Exp $30,204, Books $24,712, Per/Ser (Incl. Access Fees) $942. Sal $496,543
Library Holdings: Bk Vols 10,685; Per Subs 31
Publications: Fox Tale Newsletter; Tell-A-Tale Treasures; Winnefox Library System Directory; Winnefox Library System Interlibrary Loan Manual; WLS Business Video Cassette Catalog
Member Libraries: Berlin Public Library; Caestecker Public Library; Carter Memorial Library; Elisha D Smith Public Library; Endeavor Public Library; Hancock Public Library; Leon-Saxeville Township Library; Markesan Public Library; Millpond Public Library; Montello Public Library; Neenah Public Library; Neshkoro Public Library; Oakfield Public Library; Oshkosh Public Library; Oxford Public Library; Packwaukee Pulic Library; Patterson Memorial Library; Plainfield Public Library; Poy Sippi Public Library; Princeton Public Library; Redgranite Public Library; Ripon Public Library; Wautoma Public Library; Westfield Public Library; Winneconne Public Library
Partic in Fox Valley Library Council
Special Services for the Deaf - TTY machine

OSSEO

P HAUGE MEMORIAL LIBRARY,* 50655 Charles St, PO Box 659, 54
SAN 318-3157. Tel: 715-597-3444. *Dir*, Arlie J Schwoch
Pop 1,500; Circ 25,000
Library Holdings: Bk Vols 12,000; Per Subs 38
Mem of Winding Rivers Library System
Friends of the Library Group

M OSSEO AREA HOSPITAL & NURSING HOME, Medical Library,* P
Box 70, 54758. SAN 324-6973. Tel: 715-597-3121. FAX: 715-597-312

OWEN

P OWEN PUBLIC LIBRARY,* 414 Central Ave, PO Box 130, 54460. S
318-3165. Tel: 715-229-2939. FAX: 715-229-2939. *Dir*, Shirley Lehr
Pop 1,000; Circ 29,000
Library Holdings: Bk Vols 19,000; Per Subs 45
Mem of Wisconsin Valley Library Service

OXFORD

P OXFORD PUBLIC LIBRARY,* 129 S Franklin St, PO Box 32, 53952-0032. SAN 376-6594. Tel: 608-586-4458. FAX: 608-586-4558. E-Mail: oxlib@mags.net. *Dir*, Sandra Eberlin
Library Holdings: Bk Vols 7,500; Bk Titles 4,000; Per Subs 20
Mem of Winnefox Library System

PACKWAUKEE

P PACKWAUKEE PULIC LIBRARY,* W5960 Walnut St, PO Box 406, 53953-0403. SAN 377-9734. Tel: 608-589-5202. FAX: 608-589-5202. E-Mail: palib@mail.maqs.net. *Dir*, Sharon H McDowell
Library Holdings: Bk Titles 7,000; Per Subs 30
Mem of Winnefox Library System
Partic in Fox Valley Library Council
Open Mon & Thurs 10:30-5:30, Tues & Wed 4-7, Fri 3-6, Sat 9-11

PALMYRA

P POWERS MEMORIAL LIBRARY,* 115 Main St, PO Box O, 53156-09
SAN 318-3173. Tel: 414-495-4605. FAX: 414-495-8617. *Librn*, Ann Fri
Founded 1927. Pop 2,500; Circ 25,124
Library Holdings: Bk Vols 19,000; Per Subs 86
Special Collections: Local Newspaper-Palmyra Enterprise, 1874-present, vols & micro

PARDEEVILLE

P ANGIE WILLIAMS COX PUBLIC LIBRARY,* 119 N Main St, 53954-0370. SAN 318-3181. Tel: 608-429-2354. FAX: 608-429-4308. Web Site www.par.scls.lib.wi.us/par. *Dir*, Karin A Thomas
Founded 1925
Jan 1999-Dec 1999 Income $67,824, City $42,704, County $14,052, Parc Institution $6,000. Mats Exp $9,000, Books $7,300, Per/Ser (Incl. Access Fees) $1,700. Sal $44,333 (Prof $23,060)
Friends of the Library Group

PARK FALLS

P PARK FALLS PUBLIC LIBRARY,* 121 N Fourth Ave, 54552. SAN 31 319X. Tel: 715-762-3121. FAX: 715-762-2286. *Dir*, Gary Olson; *Ad Serv* Deb Hyde; *Ch Servs*, Sherry Ryther; Staff 3 (MLS 3)
Founded 1906. Pop 15,000; Circ 60,080
Library Holdings: Bk Titles 36,000; Per Subs 130
Subject Interests: Local history, Lumber, Lumbering
Mem of Indianhead Federated Library System
Headquarters for Price County Books-By-Mail Service
Friends of the Library Group

PEPIN

P PEPIN PUBLIC LIBRARY,* 510 Second St, PO Box 248, 54759. SAN 374-5465. Tel: 715-442-4932. FAX: 715-442-3038. E-Mail: pepinlib@cannon.net. *Librn*, Christy Rundquist; Staff 4 (MLS 1, Non-MLS 3)
Jan 1998-Dec 1998 Income $23,306, City $11,928, County $11,378. Mats Exp $6,200, Books $4,027, Per/Ser (Incl. Access Fees) $703. Sal $20,500
Library Holdings: Bk Titles 12,323; Per Subs 38
Friends of the Library Group

AUKEE

INSTRUCTIONAL MEDIA SERVICES INC LIBRARY, 1291 Hickory St, Ste E, 53072. SAN 374-7840. Tel: 262-691-1200. FAX: 262-691-1622. E-Mail: imsinfo@imseducates.com. Web Site: www.imseducates.com. *Pres*, Dorinne S Geldon; Tel: 262-691-1200, Fax: 262-691-1622
Jul 1999-Jun 2000 Income $80,000. Sal $30,000
Subject Interests: Video cassettes

BARBARA SANBORN PUBLIC LIBRARY,* 302 Oakton Ave, 53072-3596. SAN 318-3211. Tel: 414-691-5670. FAX: 414-691-5673. *Dir*, Cheryl Schoenhaar
Founded 1904. Pop 7,000; Circ 55,185
Library Holdings: Bk Vols 37,405; Per Subs 92
Mem of Waukesha County Federated Library System
Friends of the Library Group

WAUKESHA COUNTY TECHNICAL COLLEGE LIBRARY, 800 Main St, 53072. SAN 318-322X. Tel: 262-691-5316. Interlibrary Loan Service Tel: 262-691-5108. Circulation Tel: 262-691-5316. Reference Tel: 262-691-7877. FAX: 262-695-3402. Web Site: www.waukesha.tec.wi.us/library.html. *Dir*, Ruth Ahl; Tel: 262-691-5311, E-Mail: rahl@waukesha.tec.wi.us; *Ref*, Colleen Cullen; E-Mail: ccullen@waukesha.tec.wi.us; Staff 11 (MLS 2, Non-MLS 9)
Founded 1965. Enrl 3,263; Fac 235; Highest Degree: Associate
Jul 2000-Jun 2001 Income $698,585. Mats Exp $212,547. Sal $355,843 (Prof $87,635)
Library Holdings: Bk Vols 19,266; Bk Titles 22,988; Per Subs 426; Bks on Deafness & Sign Lang 34
Subject Interests: Electronics, Financial planning, Fire science, Hospitality mgt, International trade, Marketing, Nursing, Police, Printing, Publishing, Retail mgt, Sci
Special Collections: Career Materials; Company Files; Educational Resources Information Center Coll (ERIC); International Trade; Newsbank
Automation Activity & Vendor Info: (Acquisitions) Endeavor; (Cataloging) Endeavor; (Circulation) Endeavor; (Course Reserve) Endeavor; (OPAC) Endeavor; (Serials) Endeavor
Partic in Library Council Of Metropolitan Milwaukee, Inc; Wis PALS Libr Consortium; Wisconsin Library Services

ELPS

ELEANOR ELLIS PUBLIC LIBRARY,* Town Hall Rd, PO Box 8, 54554-0008. SAN 318-3238. Tel: 715-545-2887. *Dir*, June Franzen; E-Mail: jfranzen@newnorth.net
Founded 1934
Library Holdings: Bk Vols 9,000; Per Subs 21
Subject Interests: Wisconsin
Mem of Northern Waters Library Service
Friends of the Library Group

ILLIPS

PHILLIPS PUBLIC LIBRARY, 286 Cherry St, 54555-1240. SAN 374-6046. Tel: 715-339-2868. FAX: 715-339-6603. *Dir*, John F Hendricks; E-Mail: jfhendri@win.bright.net; *Cat*, Joel Meyers; *Cat*, Diane Soul; *Circ, ILL*, Barb Schaumberg; *Circ*, Kate Puckhaber; *Ad Servs, Circ*, Nancy Genisio; *Ch Servs*, Jo Hick; *Ad Servs*, Eileen Zielinski; Staff 5 (MLS 1, Non-MLS 4)
Pop 4,000
Jan 1999-Dec 1999 Income $206,687, City $90,316, County $111,267, Locally Generated Income $5,104. Mats Exp $25,758, Books $21,750, Per/Ser (Incl. Access Fees) $1,498, AV Equip $1,970, Electronic Ref Mat (Incl. Access Fees) $540. Sal $105,745
Library Holdings: Bk Titles 24,000; Per Subs 107
Automation Activity & Vendor Info: (Cataloging) Athena; (Circulation) Athena; (OPAC) Athena
Mem of Indianhead Federated Library System
Friends of the Library Group

NE RIVER

LEON-SAXEVILLE TOWNSHIP LIBRARY,* N4715 Main St, PO Box 247, 54965-0247. SAN 318-3246. Tel: 920-987-5110. FAX: 920-987-5110. *Dir*, Sherry Attoe; *Asst Dir*, Linda Forseth
Pop 1,800
Library Holdings: Bk Vols 8,000
Subject Interests: Pine river hist
Special Collections: Wisconsin - V-tapes
Mem of Winnefox Library System
Open Mon 9-7, Tues 2-7, Wed 10-7, Fri 4-7, Sat 8-1
Friends of the Library Group

PITTSVILLE

P PITTSVILLE COMMUNITY LIBRARY,* 5291 Third Ave, 54466-0911. SAN 318-3254. Tel: 715-884-6500. *Librn*, Diane Creola
Founded 1975. Pop 2,000; Circ 11,163
Library Holdings: Bk Vols 14,000; Per Subs 80
Friends of the Library Group

PLAIN

P PLAIN PUBLIC LIBRARY,* 1015 Cedar St, PO Box 309, 53577-0252. SAN 318-3262. Tel: 608-546-4201. E-Mail: pllbry@mhtc.net. *Dir*, Elsie D Haas; *Asst Librn*, Linda Paulus
Founded 1964. Pop 680
Library Holdings: Bk Vols 7,000; Per Subs 40
Mem of South Central Library System

PLAINFIELD

P PLAINFIELD PUBLIC LIBRARY,* 126 S Main St, PO Box 305, 54966-0305. SAN 318-3270. Tel: 715-335-4523. Interlibrary Loan Service Tel: 920-236-5218. FAX: 715-335-6712. *Dir*, Linda Helmrick
Founded 1915. Pop 902; Circ 16,558
Library Holdings: Bk Vols 10,000
Subject Interests: Local history
Mem of Winnefox Library System
Friends of the Library Group

PLATTEVILLE

P PLATTEVILLE PUBLIC LIBRARY,* 65 S Elm, 53818. SAN 318-3289. Tel: 608-348-7441. FAX: 608-348-9923. *Dir*, Kathy Scheetz; *Ch Servs*, Erin Isabell; Staff 4 (MLS 4)
Founded 1906. Pop 18,000; Circ 150,000
Library Holdings: Bk Titles 40,000; Per Subs 150
Subject Interests: Large type, Wisconsin
Special Collections: Wisconsin Coll
Mem of Southwest Wisconsin Library System
Homebound Delivery Program; Serves local nursing homes

C UNIVERSITY OF WISCONSIN-PLATTEVILLE, Elton S Karrmann Library, 1 University Plaza, 53818. SAN 318-3297. Tel: 608-342-1688. Interlibrary Loan Service Tel: 608-342-1648. Circulation Tel: 608-342-1679. Reference Tel: 608-342-1668. FAX: 608-342-1645. E-Mail: reference@uwplatt.edu. Web Site: www.uwplatt.edu/~library. *Dir*, Paul V Moriarty; E-Mail: moriarty@uwplatt.edu; *Senior Librn*, Judy Moriarty; Tel: 608-342-1099, E-Mail: moriartj@uwplatt.edu; *Acq, Coll Develop*, Judith Wurtzler; Tel: 608-342-1077, E-Mail: wurtzler@uwplatt.edu; *Archivist*, Mary Freymiller; Tel: 608-342-1719, E-Mail: freymilm@uwplatt.edu; *Archivist*, James Hibbard; Tel: 608-342-1229, E-Mail: hibbardj@uwplatt.edu; *Automation Syst Coordr*, Marie Erdman; Tel: 608-342-1052, E-Mail: erdmanm@uwplatt.edu; *Cat*, Susan Riehl; Tel: 608-342-1192, E-Mail: riehl@uwplatt.edu; *Circ, Ref*, John Leonard Berg; Tel: 608-342-1355, E-Mail: bergjo@uwplatt.edu; *Govt Doc, ILL*, Bryan Schwark; Tel: 608-342-1649, E-Mail: schwark@uwplatt.edu; *Ref, Web Coordr*, Jessica Donahoe; Tel: 608-342-1348, E-Mail: donahoej@uwplatt.edu; *Ref*, Kay Young; Tel: 608-342-1134, E-Mail: young@uwplatt.edu; *Tech Servs*, Tonya Stappert; Tel: 608-342-1792, E-Mail: stappert@uwplatt.edu; *Tech Coordr*, Anthony Valentine; Tel: 608-342-1708, E-Mail: valentia@uwplatt.edu; Staff 9 (MLS 8, Non-MLS 1)
Founded 1866. Enrl 5,432; Fac 213; Highest Degree: Master
Jul 2000-Jun 2001 Income $1,753,066, State $1,625,681, Federal $50,291, Locally Generated Income $36,500, Other $40,220. Mats Exp $576,191, Books $99,956, Per/Ser (Incl. Access Fees) $268,073, Presv $6,656, Micro $34,051, AV Equip $14,758, Other Print Mats $498, Electronic Ref Mat (Incl. Access Fees) $20,535. Sal $962,292 (Prof $487,966)
Library Holdings: Bk Vols 230,019; Bk Titles 200,017; Per Subs 1,422
Subject Interests: Bus, Engineering, Indust, Middle-level educ
Special Collections: Archives (Area Research Center), mss; Regional History
Automation Activity & Vendor Info: (Acquisitions) Endeavor; (Cataloging) Endeavor; (Course Reserve) Endeavor; (Media Booking) Endeavor; (OPAC) Endeavor; (Serials) Endeavor
Database Vendor: Ebsco - EbscoHost, Lexis-Nexis, OCLC - First Search, Wilson - Wilson Web

PLEASANT PRAIRIE

S RUST-OLEUM CORPORATION, Technical Library,* PO Box 581906, 53158-0906. SAN 326-9450. Tel: 414-947-7220, Ext 810. FAX: 414-947-6855. *Admin Assoc*, Lorraine Fernandes
Library Holdings: Bk Vols 2,000

PLUM CITY

P PLUM CITY PUBLIC LIBRARY,* 611 Main St, PO Box 203, 54761. SAN 378-0023. Tel: 715-647-2373. FAX: 715-647-2373. E-Mail: plumlib@ win.brightnet. *Dir*, Judith Ann Anderson
Jan 1998-Dec 1998 Income $21,000
Library Holdings: Bk Titles 8,000; Per Subs 55
Subject Interests: Local history
Mem of Indianhead Federated Library System
Partic in Pierce County Libr Servs
Open Tues & Fri 12:30-5, Wed 12:30-9, Thurs 10-5, Sat 10-1 (sch yr)

PLYMOUTH

S KETTLE MORAINE CORRECTIONAL INSTITUTION LIBRARY,* PO Box 31, 53073. SAN 324-1734. Tel: 920-526-3244, Ext 309. FAX: 920-526-3989. *Librn*, Conrad Reedy
Library Holdings: Bk Titles 15,000; Per Subs 50

P PLYMOUTH PUBLIC LIBRARY,* 130 Division St, 53073-1802. SAN 318-3300. Tel: 920-892-4416. FAX: 920-892-6295. *Coll Develop, Dir*, Martha Suhfras; *Ch Servs*, Carol Langkabel
Founded 1909. Pop 10,860; Circ 126,610
Library Holdings: Bk Vols 56,832; Per Subs 180
Subject Interests: Local city (Plymouth) hist
Mem of Eastern Shores Library System
Friends of the Library Group

PORT WASHINGTON

P W J NIEDERKORN PUBLIC LIBRARY,* 316 W Grand Ave, 53074-2293. SAN 318-3319. Tel: 414-284-5031. FAX: 414-284-7680. *Dir*, Judy Kirsch
Pop 9,000; Circ 125,773
Library Holdings: Bk Vols 63,000; Per Subs 127
Mem of Eastern Shores Library System

PORTAGE

L COLUMBIA CORRECTIONAL INSTITUTION LIBRARY, 2925 Columbia Dr, PO Box 950, 53901-0950. SAN 370-7407. Tel: 608-742-9100, Ext 247. FAX: 608-742-9111. *Librn*, Glen W Singer; E-Mail: glen.singer@ doc.state.wi.us; Staff 2 (MLS 1, Non-MLS 1)
Founded 1986
Library Holdings: Bk Vols 24,500; Bk Titles 18,500; Per Subs 35
Partic in Wisconsin Library Services

GL COLUMBIA COUNTY LAW LIBRARY,* 400 DeWitt, PO Box 587, 53901. SAN 324-1602. Tel: 608-742-9624. FAX: 608-742-9601. *Librn*, Donna Purvis
Library Holdings: Bk Titles 9,500
Subject Interests: Basic demands of judges, Basic demands of local attorneys

P PORTAGE PUBLIC LIBRARY, 253 W Edgewater St, 53901. SAN 318-3335. Tel: 608-742-4959. FAX: 608-742-3819. E-Mail: porill@scls.lib.wi.us. Web Site: www.scls.lib.wi.us/portage. *Dir*, Hans W Jensen; Staff 4 (MLS 1, Non-MLS 3)
Founded 1902. Pop 15,515; Circ 188,278
Jan 1999-Dec 1999 Income $435,630, State $8,300, City $279,657, Federal $669, County $90,848, Locally Generated Income $50,965, Other $5,191. Mats Exp $79,644, Books $64,157, Per/Ser (Incl. Access Fees) $7,068, Micro $854, AV Equip $6,095, Electronic Ref Mat (Incl. Access Fees) $1,470
Library Holdings: Bk Vols 51,337; Bk Titles 45,633; Per Subs 151
Special Collections: Zona Gale Coll
Automation Activity & Vendor Info: (Acquisitions) epixtech, inc.; (Cataloging) epixtech, inc.; (Circulation) epixtech, inc.; (ILL) epixtech, inc.; (OPAC) epixtech, inc.; (Serials) epixtech, inc.
Mem of South Central Library System
Friends of the Library Group

POY SIPPI

P POY SIPPI PUBLIC LIBRARY,* 1003 Commercial St, PO Box 345, 54967-0345. SAN 318-3343. Tel: 920-987-5737. FAX: 920-987-5737. *Chief Librn, Dir*, Sherrie Attoe
Founded 1963. Pop 2,734
Library Holdings: Bk Titles 3,929; Per Subs 9
Mem of Winnefox Library System

POYNETTE

P POYNETTE PUBLIC LIBRARY,* 118 N Main, PO Box 368, 53955-0368. SAN 318-3351. Tel: 608-635-7577. E-Mail: ppl@chorus.net. *Dir*, Linda A Kohl
Founded 1941. Pop 5,000; Circ 10,000
Library Holdings: Bk Titles 14,000; Per Subs 25
Mem of South Central Library System
Friends of the Library Group

G WISCONSIN STATE DEPARTMENT OF NATURAL RESOURCES, MacKenzie Environmental Education Center, W 7303 County Hwy CS, 53955. SAN 327-4780. Tel: 608-635-8105, 608-635-8110. FAX: 608-635-8107. Web Site: www.naturenet.com/mackenzie. *Mgr*, Derek Duane
Library Holdings: Bk Vols 400
Special Collections: Photographic Slides Coll
Library used by visitors to our center & by on sight staff & staff throughout state

PRAIRIE DU CHIEN

P WACHUTA MEMORIAL LIBRARY, Prairie du Chien Memorial Library, 125 S Wacouta Ave, 53821-1632. SAN 318-336X. Tel: 608-326-6211. FAX: 608-326-7069. *Dir*, Lois Gilbert; E-Mail: lgilbert@swls.org
Founded 1897. Pop 6,000; Circ 48,894
1998-1999 Income $212,177. Mats Exp $39,500, Books $25,000, Per/Ser (Incl. Access Fees) $11,400. Sal $93,471
Library Holdings: Bk Vols 34,000; Per Subs 68
Subject Interests: Local history, Wisconsin
Special Collections: Newspapers from 1864-1995
Mem of Southwest Wisconsin Library System
Friends of the Library Group

PRAIRIE DU SAC

P PRAIRIE DU SAC PUBLIC LIBRARY,* 560 Park Ave, 53578-1199. SAN 318-3378. Tel: 608-643-8318. FAX: 608-643-4897. E-Mail: jtpdslib@ scls.lib.wi.us. Web Site: www.scls.lib.wi.us/pds. *Librn*, John T Thompson; *Ch Servs*, Stacy Alt
Jan 1998-Dec 1999 Income $179,091, State $300, City $149,514, County $24,577, Locally Generated Income $4,700. Mats Exp $29,820, Books $18,500, Per/Ser (Incl. Access Fees) $4,000. Sal $171,747
Library Holdings: Bk Vols 25,230; Per Subs 134
Subject Interests: Local history
Mem of South Central Library System
Friends of the Library Group

PRESCOTT

P PRESCOTT PUBLIC LIBRARY,* 800 Borner St N, 54021-1703. SAN 3394. Tel: 715-262-5555. FAX: 715-262-4229. E-Mail: amberlit@ pressenter.com. *Dir*, Ann Hokanson; *Asst Dir*, Anne LeBlanc
Founded 1900. Pop 3,500
Library Holdings: Bk Vols 19,000; Per Subs 35
Subject Interests: Local history, Wis hist
Automation Activity & Vendor Info: (Circulation) Sagebrush Corporation
Publications: Cover to Cover Newsletter
Mem of Indianhead Federated Library System; Pierce County Library Service
Friends of the Library Group

PRESQUE ISLE

P IRMA STEIN MEMORIAL LIBRARY,* School Loop Rd, 54557. (Mail add: PO Box 115, 54557-0115), SAN 376-6667. Tel: 715-686-7613. FAX: 715-686-2473. E-Mail: isml@centuryinter.net. *Librn*, Pam Eschenbauch
Library Holdings: Bk Vols 6,000; Bk Titles 6,000; Per Subs 22
Mem of Northern Waters Library Service

PRINCETON

P PRINCETON PUBLIC LIBRARY,* 424 W Water St, 54968-9147. SAN 318-3416. Tel: 920-295-6777. FAX: 920-295-3303. *Dir*, Vicki Duhr
Founded 1933
Library Holdings: Bk Vols 8,145; Per Subs 33
Special Collections: Wis, bks, authors
Mem of Winnefox Library System
Partic in Waushara & Green Lake Coop Syst
Friends of the Library Group

RACINE

M ALL SAINTS HEALTHCARE SYSTEM INC,* c/o Saint Mary's Medical Ctr, 3801 Spring St, 53405. SAN 318-3483. Tel: 414-636-4300. FAX: 414-636-4175. Web Site: www.execpc.com/allsaintshealthcare. *Dir*, Vicki Budzisz; E-Mail: vbudzisz@execpc.com; Staff 3 (MLS 1, Non-MLS 2)
Founded 1932
Library Holdings: Bk Titles 175; Per Subs 175
Subject Interests: Medicine, Nursing
Partic in Docline; Medline; Regional Med Libr - Region 3

CHARLES A WUSTUM MUSEUM OF FINE ARTS,* 2519 Northwestern Ave, 53404. SAN 318-3505. Tel: 262-636-9177. FAX: 262-636-9231. *Dir*, Bruce W Pepich
Founded 1941
Library Holdings: Per Subs 12
Subject Interests: Art, Art history, Out-of-print
Special Collections: Art History Coll; Exhibition Catalogues; Out-of-Print
Partic in Tri-County Library Consortium

DEKOVEN FOUNDATION, Dekoven Center Library,* 600 21st St, 53403. SAN 374-6194. Tel: 414-633-6401. FAX: 414-633-6401. *Librn*, Kathleen Cloyd
Founded 1852
Library Holdings: Bk Titles 7,000

GATEWAY TECHNICAL COLLEGE, Learning Resources Center Library, 1001 S Main St, 53403-1582. SAN 324-3362. Tel: 262-619-6220. Interlibrary Loan Service Tel: 262-619-6340. FAX: 262-619-6221. Web Site: www.gateway.tec.wi.us//library. *Head Librn*, Linda M Pulera; Tel: 262-619-6598, E-Mail: puleral@gatway.tec.wi.us; *Circ*, Pati Dill; Tel: 262-619-6370, E-Mail: dillp@gateway.tec.wi.us; Staff 3 (MLS 1, Non-MLS 2)
Enrl 2,200; Fac 85
Library Holdings: Bk Vols 15,000; Per Subs 150
Subject Interests: Electronics, Fire science, Food servs, Med assisting, Word processing
Automation Activity & Vendor Info: (Acquisitions) Endeavor; (Cataloging) Endeavor; (Circulation) Endeavor; (Course Reserve) Endeavor; (OPAC) Endeavor; (Serials) Endeavor
Database Vendor: Ebsco - EbscoHost, IAC - SearchBank, ProQuest, Wilson - Wilson Web
Partic in Library Council Of Metropolitan Milwaukee, Inc; Wis PALS Libr Consortium

INTERNATIONAL BANK NOTE SOCIETY LIBRARY,* PO Box 1642, 53401. SAN 374-9509. Tel: 414-554-6255.
Library Holdings: Bk Vols 600

JOURNAL TIMES, Newsroom Library, 212 Fourth St, 53403. SAN 326-3096. Tel: 262-631-1712. FAX: 262-634-9194. Web Site: www.journaltimes.com, www.racinecounty.com. *Librn*, Peggy Anderson; E-Mail: peganderson@journaltimes.com
Library Holdings: Bk Vols 300
In-house use only

RACINE COUNTY LAW LIBRARY,* 730 Wisconsin Ave, 53403-1247. SAN 318-3475. Tel: 414-636-3773. FAX: 414-636-3341. *In Charge*, Theresa Wheary
Library Holdings: Bk Vols 16,000

RACINE HERITAGE MUSEUM, Reference Archive of County History & Genealogy,* 701 S Main St, 53403-1211. SAN 318-3467. Tel: 414-636-3926. FAX: 414-636-3940. Web Site: www.racine.org/rcmuseum.html. *Archivist*, Richard E Ammann
Founded 1969
1997-1998 Income $2,400. Mats Exp $1,892
Library Holdings: Bk Titles 300
Subject Interests: Few bks on Wisconsin hist, Genealogy, Racine Co hist
Special Collections: 1790 Census Books; Card Index of Surnames; Cemetery & Marriage records; Century Family Charts; County Histories; Genealogical Books; Military Histories; Pictorial Coll; Racine City Directories, 1850 through 1998; Wisconsin Historical Coll (Draper)
Publications: Society & Museum Newsletter
Friends of the Library Group

RACINE PUBLIC LIBRARY,* 75 Seventh St, 53403-1200. SAN 365-0588. Tel: 414-636-9251. FAX: 414-636-9260. Web Site: www.racinecounty.com. *Librn*, Jay J Chung; E-Mail: jchung@racinelib.lib.wi.us; *Ad Servs*, Jill Hartmann; *Ch Servs*, Darcy Mohr; *Tech Servs*, Mary Lou Nordstrom; *Cat*, Mary Luedtke; *Circ*, Robert Margis; Staff 14 (MLS 14)
Founded 1897. Pop 149,195; Circ 997,095
Jan 2000-Dec 2000 Income $2,642,396, State $156,536, City $1,823,631, County $640,811, Other $14,019. Mats Exp $414,019, Books $308,152, Per/Ser (Incl. Access Fees) $33,475. Sal $1,902,489 (Prof $682,955)
Library Holdings: Bk Vols 225,561; Per Subs 647
Special Collections: Early Childhood Resource Coll; Racine City & County Historical Material, bks, pamphlets & clippings
Automation Activity & Vendor Info: (Circulation) epixtech, inc.
Mem of Lakeshores Library System
Partic in OCLC Online Computer Library Center, Inc
Friends of the Library Group

S C JOHNSON & SON INC, Research Information Center, 1525 Howe St, MS152, 53403. SAN 318-3440. Tel: 414-260-4022. FAX: 414-260-2044.; Staff 2 (MLS 2)
Founded 1946
Library Holdings: Bk Vols 10,000
Subject Interests: Biology, Bus, Chemistry, Mgt, Physics
Restriction: Not open to public, Private library

M SAINT MARY'S MEDICAL CENTER LIBRARY, 3801 Spring St, 53405. SAN 328-3429. Tel: 262-636-8914. FAX: 262-636-4175. *Librn*, Vicki Budzisz; E-Mail: vbudzisz@execpc.com
Library Holdings: Bk Titles 575
Subject Interests: Cardiology, Nursing, Orthopedics, Pediatrics, Surgery

RANDOLPH

P HUTCHINSON MEMORIAL LIBRARY, 228 N High St, 53956. SAN 318-3521. Tel: 920-326-4640. FAX: 920-326-4642. *Dir*, Ione Deich; E-Mail: ione@randolph.lib.wi.us; *Asst Librn*, Paulette Miller; *Asst Librn*, Darlene Missall
Founded 1906. Pop 1,700
1998-1999 Income $97,900. Mats Exp $12,800, Books $8,900, Per/Ser (Incl. Access Fees) $2,400, AV Equip $1,500. (Prof $48,600)
Library Holdings: Bk Vols 22,000; Per Subs 40
Special Collections: Randolph Advance Newspapers (1890-Present), micro
Automation Activity & Vendor Info: (Cataloging) Sagebrush Corporation; (Circulation) Sagebrush Corporation
Mem of Mid-Wisconsin Federated Library System
Friends of the Library Group

RANDOM LAKE

P LAKEVIEW COMMUNITY LIBRARY, 112 Butler St, PO Box 326, 53075-0326. SAN 318-353X. Tel: 920-994-4825. FAX: 920-994-2230. E-Mail: raref@esls.lib.wi.us. Web Site: randomlake.lib.wi.us. *Librn*, Darla Jean Kraus; Staff 4 (MLS 4)
Founded 1957. Pop 5,000; Circ 46,916
Jan 1999-Dec 1999 Income $177,882, State $827, Federal $1,447, County $19,721, Locally Generated Income $106,672, Other $49,215. Mats Exp $20,206, Books $13,305, Per/Ser (Incl. Access Fees) $2,839, Micro $449, AV Equip $2,383, Electronic Ref Mat (Incl. Access Fees) $1,230. Sal $70,086
Library Holdings: Bk Titles 22,203; Per Subs 100
Subject Interests: Large print
Mem of Eastern Shores Library System
Friends of the Library Group

REDGRANITE

P REDGRANITE PUBLIC LIBRARY, 135 W Bannerman Ave, PO Box 291, 54970-0291. SAN 318-3548. Tel: 920-566-0176. FAX: 920-566-0176. E-Mail: rpl@dotnet.com. *Librn*, Joann Borchardt; Staff 2 (MLS 1, Non-MLS 1)
Library Holdings: Bk Vols 10,000
Mem of Waushara-Green Lake Coop Libr Serv; Winnefox Library System

REEDSBURG

P REEDSBURG PUBLIC LIBRARY,* 370 Vine St, 53959-1917. SAN 318-3556. Tel: 608-524-3316. FAX: 608-524-9024. E-Mail: rplstf@scls.lib.wi.us. Web Site: www.scls.lib.wi.us/ree. *Dir*, Susan Steiner; *Asst Dir*, Nancy Lukes; *Ch Servs*, Maureen Palmer; Staff 3 (MLS 3)
Founded 1898. Pop 11,000; Circ 100,000
Jan 1998-Dec 1998 Income $283,822, City $227,568, County $56,254. Mats Exp $44,170, Books $27,800, Per/Ser (Incl. Access Fees) $5,000. Sal $182,131
Library Holdings: Bk Titles 43,200; Per Subs 143
Subject Interests: Large print
Mem of South Central Library System
Friends of the Library Group

REESEVILLE

P REESEVILLE PUBLIC LIBRARY,* 206 S Main St, 53579-0286. SAN 364-6173. Tel: 920-927-5243. FAX: 920-927-5245. *Dir*, Karen Christianson
Library Holdings: Bk Vols 9,675
Mem of Mid-Wisconsin Federated Library System

RHINELANDER

J NICOLET AREA TECHNICAL COLLEGE, Richard J Brown Library, Lake Julia Campus, Hwy G, PO Box 518, 54501. SAN 318-3572. Interlibrary Loan Service Tel: 715-365-4479 (.). Reference Tel: 715-365-4429. FAX: 715-365-4404. Web Site: www.nicolet.tec.wi.us/libry/index.html. *Dir*, Allan A Mussehl; Tel: 715-365-4489, E-Mail: amussehl@nicolet.tec.wi.us; *Coll Develop, Ref*, Susan L Brant; E-Mail: slbrant@nicolet.tec.wi.us; *Cat*, Barbara Heiffner; Tel: 715-365-4486, E-Mail: heiffner@nicolet.tec.wi.us; *ILL*, Maureen McCloskey; Tel: 715-365-4606, E-Mail: mmcclosk@nicolet.tec.wi.us; *AV*, Roger Davis; Tel: 715-365-4428, E-Mail: rdavis1@nicolet.tec.wi.us; *Web Coordr*, Brian Vaughn; Tel: 715-365-4437, E-Mail: bvaugh@nicolet.tec.wi.us; *Acq*, Terri Cable; Tel: 715-365-4436, Fax: 715-365-4551, E-Mail: tcable@nicolet.tec.wi.us; Staff 9 (MLS 4, Non-MLS 5)
Founded 1969. Enrl 1,200; Fac 75; Highest Degree: Associate

Jul 1999-Jun 2000 Income $737,654. Mats Exp $256,153, Books $57,500, Per/Ser (Incl. Access Fees) $45,000, Presv $2,000, AV Equip $55,520. Sal $450,901 (Prof $242,296)
Library Holdings: Bk Vols 56,000; Per Subs 350
Subject Interests: Art, Native Am, Nursing
Automation Activity & Vendor Info: (Cataloging) Sagebrush Corporation; (Circulation) Sagebrush Corporation; (OPAC) Sagebrush Corporation
Publications: handbook; subject bibliographies & pathfinders
Partic in OCLC Online Computer Library Center, Inc; Wisconsin Library Services

P RHINELANDER DISTRICT LIBRARY, 106 N Stevens St, 54501-3193. SAN 318-3580. Tel: 715-365-1070. FAX: 715-365-1076. *Dir*, Steven Kenworthy; *Ch Servs*, Kris Adams Wendt; Tel: 715-365-1050; Staff 9 (MLS 2, Non-MLS 7)
Founded 1898. Pop 20,000; Circ 205,525
Library Holdings: Bk Vols 72,000; Per Subs 201
Subject Interests: Architecture, Art
Special Collections: Art (Ruth Smith Bump Coll); Genealogy Coll; Wisconsin Coll
Mem of Wisconsin Valley Library Service
Friends of the Library Group

G UNITED STATES DEPARTMENT OF AGRICULTURE, North Central Forest Experiment Station, Forestry Sciences Laboratory Library, 5985 Hwy K, 54501. SAN 327-9952. Tel: 715-362-7474. FAX: 715-362-1166. *Adminr*, Elaine Boanshick
Founded 1960
Library Holdings: Bk Vols 3,010; Per Subs 100
Subject Interests: Biology, Botany, Ecology, Genetics, Physiology

RIB LAKE

P RIB LAKE PUBLIC LIBRARY,* Landall & Pearl, PO Box 188, 54470. SAN 318-3599. Tel: 715-427-5769. Interlibrary Loan Service Tel: 715-847-5549. FAX: 715-427-5368. E-Mail: riblakpl@newnorth.net. *Dir*, Aimee Hein; *Dir*, Mary Hebda
Founded 1900. Pop 19,000
Library Holdings: Bk Titles 14,000; Per Subs 83
Subject Interests: Arts, Crafts, Wisconsin
Mem of Wisconsin Valley Library Service

RICE LAKE

P RICE LAKE PUBLIC LIBRARY, 2 E Marshall, 54868. SAN 318-3602. Tel: 715-234-4861. FAX: 715-234-5026. E-Mail: rlpublib@discover-net.net. *Dir*, Tom Hurlburt; *Ad Servs*, Nancy Zabel; *Tech Servs*, Liz Davis; *Tech Servs*, Linda Meyers; *Ch Servs*, JoAnn Erickson; Staff 5 (MLS 1, Non-MLS 4)
Founded 1897. Pop 7,960; Circ 170,000
Library Holdings: Bk Vols 46,859; Per Subs 218
Mem of Indianhead Federated Library System
Friends of the Library Group

J UNIVERSITY OF WISCONSIN-BARRON COUNTY LIBRARY, Barrow County, 1800 College Dr, 54868-2497. SAN 318-3610. Tel: 715-234-8176, Ext 5448. FAX: 715-234-1975. Web Site: 143.235.10.10. *Dir*, Zora Sampson; E-Mail: zsampson@uwc.edu; *Assoc Librn*, Gail Piotrowski; E-Mail: gpiotrow@uwc.edu
Founded 1966. Enrl 430; Fac 26
Library Holdings: Bk Vols 30,984; Bk Titles 27,006; Per Subs 310
Partic in OCLC Online Computer Library Center, Inc; WILS

J WISCONSIN INDIANHEAD TECHNICAL COLLEGE, Learning Resource Center,* 1900 College Dr, 54868. SAN 318-3629. Tel: 715-234-7082. FAX: 715-234-5172.
Library Holdings: Bk Vols 3,053

RICHLAND CENTER

P BREWER PUBLIC LIBRARY,* 325 N Central Ave, 53581-1802. SAN 318-3637. Tel: 608-647-6444. *Dir*, Tom Bachman
Founded 1900. Pop 20,000; Circ 170,000
Library Holdings: Bk Vols 91,000; Per Subs 111
Special Collections: Richland County History Coll
Mem of Southwest Wisconsin Library System
Friends of the Library Group

J UNIVERSITY OF WISCONSIN-RICHLAND, Miller Memorial Library, 1200 US Hwy 14 W, 53581-1399. SAN 318-3645. Tel: 608-647-6186, Ext 220. FAX: 608-647-6225. *Dir*, James A Gollata; E-Mail: jgollata@uwcmail.uwc.edu
Enrl 275
Library Holdings: Bk Vols 44,000
Partic in OCLC Online Computer Library Center, Inc; Wisconsin Library Services

RIO

P RIO COMMUNITY LIBRARY,* PO Box 306, 53960-0306. SAN 318-
Tel: 920-992-3206. *Dir*, Shirley Jean Nelson
Founded 1917. Pop 784; Circ 24,000
Library Holdings: Bk Vols 11,261; Per Subs 57
Mem of South Central Library System
Friends of the Library Group

RIPON

C RIPON COLLEGE, Lane Library, 300 Seward St, PO Box 248, 54971-
SAN 318-3661. Tel: 920-748-8747. Circulation Tel: 920-748-8175. Reference Tel: 920-748-9751. FAX: 920-748-7243. Web Site: www.ripon.edu/library. *Dir*, Michele M Reid; Tel: 920-748-8750, E-Ma reidm@ripon.edu; *Coll Develop*, Karen Williams; E-Mail: williamsk@ripon.edu; *Syst Coordr*, Marc Boucher; E-Mail: boucherm@mail.ripon.e *Acq*, Kathleen Bradenburg; E-Mail: bradenburgk@ripon.edu; *Ref*, Charl Burr; E-Mail: burrc@ripon.edu; *Circ*, Jeanne Chaney; Tel: chaneyj@ripon.edu; *ILL*, Don Shankman; E-Mail: shankmand@ripon.edu; *Cat*, C Ziebell; E-Mail: ziebellc@ripon.edu; Staff 9 (MLS 6, Non-MLS 3)
Founded 1851. Enrl 750; Fac 74; Highest Degree: Bachelor
Jul 1999-Jun 2000 Income Parent Institution $546,213. Mats Exp $154, Per/Ser (Incl. Access Fees) $69,475, Presv $7,138, Micro $14,441, Manuscripts & Archives $2,642. Sal $221,424 (Prof $159,962)
Library Holdings: Bk Vols 162,710; Bk Titles 123,912; Per Subs 794
Subject Interests: Liberal arts
Special Collections: ColisLotory; Local History (Pedrick Coll),
Automation Activity & Vendor Info: (Acquisitions) Innovative Interfa Inc.; (Cataloging) Innovative Interfaces Inc.; (Circulation) Innovative Interfaces Inc.; (Course Reserve) Innovative Interfaces Inc.; (ILL) Innov Interfaces Inc.; (OPAC) Innovative Interfaces Inc.; (Serials) Innovative Interfaces Inc.
Database Vendor: CARL, Dialog, Ebsco - EbscoHost, IAC - Info Trac, Innovative Interfaces INN - View, Lexis-Nexis, OCLC - First Search
Publications: Bibliographic guides
Function: ILL available
Partic in Fox Valley Library Council; OCLC Online Computer Library Center, Inc; Wisconsin Library Services

P RIPON PUBLIC LIBRARY, 120 Jefferson St, 54971-1395. SAN 318-36
Tel: 920-748-6160. FAX: 920-748-6298. Web Site: www.riponlibrary.org *Dir*, Alan Jorgenson; E-Mail: jorgenson@winnefox.org; *Ch Servs*, Linda DeCramer; E-Mail: decramer@winnefox.org; *ILL*, Karen Larson; E-Mail larson@winnefox.org; Staff 3 (MLS 2, Non-MLS 1)
Founded 1885. Pop 11,500
Jan 1999-Dec 1999 Income $306,814, City $261,573, County $31,839, Locally Generated Income $13,402. Mats Exp $24,445, Books $17,913, Ser (Incl. Access Fees) $3,494, AV Equip $3,038. Sal $176,558 (Prof $92,968)
Library Holdings: Bk Vols 56,800; Bk Titles 56,227; Per Subs 170
Automation Activity & Vendor Info: (Cataloging) DRA; (Circulation) DRA; (OPAC) DRA
Database Vendor: DRA
Publications: Ripon Public Library (Newsletter)
Mem of Winnefox Library System
Friends of the Library Group

RIVER FALLS

P RIVER FALLS PUBLIC LIBRARY, 140 Union St, 54022. (Mail add: P Box 45, 54022), SAN 318-3688. Tel: 715-425-0905. FAX: 715-425-0914 E-Mail: rfpublib@ifls.lib.wi.us. Web Site: www.rfcity.org/library. *Dir*, Na Miller; *Ch Servs*, Susan Pesheck; *Ref*, Kim Kiiskinen; *Tech Servs*, Jon George
Jan 1999-Dec 1999 Income $430,329. Mats Exp $50,000, Books $40,000 Per/Ser (Incl. Access Fees) $5,000. Sal $264,479 (Prof $109,593)
Library Holdings: Bk Vols 62,206; Per Subs 201
Subject Interests: Hist of River Falls
Library has River Falls Public Library Foundation
Friends of the Library Group

C UNIVERSITY OF WISCONSIN-RIVER FALLS, Chalmer Davee Library 410 S Third St, 54022. SAN 318-3696. Tel: 715-425-3321. Interlibrary L Service Tel: 715-425-4286. FAX: 715-425-3590. Web Site: www.uwrf.edu library. *Dir*, Christina D Baum; Tel: 715-425-3222; *Coll Develop*, Curt Lemay; Staff 22 (MLS 9, Non-MLS 13)
Founded 1875. Enrl 5,200; Fac 340; Highest Degree: Master
Library Holdings: Bk Vols 300,000; Per Subs 1,290
Subject Interests: Agriculture, Education, History
Special Collections: Frontier History, bks, flm
Automation Activity & Vendor Info: (Acquisitions) Endeavor
Publications: UW-RF Library News
Partic in OCLC Online Computer Library Center, Inc; Wisconsin Library Services

ERTS

HAZEL MACKIN COMMUNITY LIBRARY, 107 W Main St, PO Box 88, 54023. SAN 318-370X. Tel: 715-749-3849. E-Mail: rlibrary@pressenter.com. Web Site: www.pressenter.com/%7erlibrary/. *Librn*, Beverly Jacobson; *Asst Librn*, Kathy Miller; Staff 1 (Non-MLS 1)
Founded 1975. Pop 1,500; Circ 21,429
1999-2000 Income $65,000, Provincial $20,000, Locally Generated Income $45,000. Mats Exp $19,000, Books $15,000, Per/Ser (Incl. Access Fees) $1,000, Electronic Ref Mat (Incl. Access Fees) $3,000. Sal $28,500 (Prof $28,000)
Library Holdings: Bk Titles 12,000; Per Subs 44
Special Collections: Civil War
Automation Activity & Vendor Info: (Cataloging) SIRSI; (Circulation) SIRSI; (OPAC) SIRSI; (Serials) SIRSI
Mem of Indianhead Federated Library System

HESTER

ROCHESTER PUBLIC LIBRARY,* 208 W Spring St, PO Box 245, 53167-0245. SAN 318-3718. Tel: 414-534-3533. *Dir*, Hanne Grammins
Founded 1890
Library Holdings: Bk Vols 10,000; Per Subs 50
Mem of Lakeshores Library System
Friends of the Library Group

K SPRINGS

ROCK SPRINGS PUBLIC LIBRARY,* 108 W Broadway, PO Box 56, 53961-0056. SAN 318-3726. Tel: 608-522-5050. *Dir*, Meg Allen
Founded 1957. Pop 480; Circ 5,352
Library Holdings: Bk Titles 6,021
Subject Interests: Local history
Mem of South Central Library System
Open Mon & Wed 3-7, Tues, Thurs & Sat 9-1

HSCHILD

LIGNOTECH (US) INC, Lignin Chemical Research Library, 100 Hwy 51 S, 54474-1198. SAN 318-3734. Tel: 715-359-6544, Ext 600. FAX: 715-355-3648. *Librn*, Tina Nickel
Founded 1928
Library Holdings: Bk Vols 500; Per Subs 70
Subject Interests: Cellulose, Chem products, Lignin

US FILTER-ZIMPRO INC LIBRARY, 301 W Military Rd, 54474. SAN 318-3742. Tel: 715-359-7211. FAX: 715-355-3219. *Librn*, Lois Sirvio
Founded 1962
Library Holdings: Bk Vols 2,500; Per Subs 155
Subject Interests: Indust pollution control eng, Municipal

NT CROIX FALLS

ST CROIX FALLS PUBLIC LIBRARY,* 210 Washington St, PO Box 549, 54024-0549. SAN 378-004X. Tel: 715-483-1777. *Dir*, Jill Glover; *Asst Dir*, Eloise Anderson
Jan 1998-Dec 1998 Income $34,600. Mats Exp $11,000. Sal $17,000
Library Holdings: Bk Titles 12,000; Per Subs 32
Special Collections: Wisconsin History Coll; Wisconsin Newspapers 1872-
Mem of Indianhead Federated Library System
Open Mon 10-12 & 2-8, Wed 1-8, Fri 10-12 & 2-7, Sat 10-1

NT FRANCIS

ST FRANCIS PUBLIC LIBRARY, 4230 S Nicholson Ave, 53235. SAN 323-4738. Tel: 414-481-7323. TDD: 414-481-7323. FAX: 414-481-8949. Web Site: www.mcfls.org/stfrancislib. *Dir*, Maggie Luczywko; *Ch Servs*, Suzanne Doyle; *Ref*, Constance Sheehan; Staff 4 (MLS 3, Non-MLS 1)
Pop 9,893; Circ 100,254
Library Holdings: Bk Vols 41,681; Per Subs 114
Special Collections: Literacy: Teacher, Tutor & Students
Publications: Annual Report
Mem of Milwaukee County Federated Library System
Special Services for the Deaf - TDD
Friends of the Library Group

SAINT FRANCIS SEMINARY, Salzmann Library, 3257 S Lake Dr, 53235-0905. SAN 318-2436. Tel: 414-747-6479. Interlibrary Loan Service Tel: 414-747-6478. Circulation Tel: 414-747-6479. Reference Tel: 414-747-6476. FAX: 414-747-6442. Web Site: www.sfs.edu/salzmann.html. *Dir*, Colleen McHale O'Connor; Tel: 414-747-6477; *Ref Serv*, Mary Carian; Staff 2 (MLS 2)
Founded 1845. Enrl 152; Fac 18
Library Holdings: Bk Vols 84,120; Bk Titles 80,000; Per Subs 508
Subject Interests: Biblical works, Bioethics, Canon law, Church history, Milwaukee, Patristics, Scripture, Theology, Wisconsin, Women's studies
Special Collections: Bibles; Religion (Catholic Americana Coll), missals; Weakland
Automation Activity & Vendor Info: (Acquisitions) Endeavor; (Cataloging) Endeavor; (Circulation) Endeavor; (Course Reserve) Endeavor; (OPAC) Endeavor; (Serials) Endeavor
Partic in OCLC Online Computer Library Center, Inc; Wisconsin Library Services
Friends of the Library Group

SALEM

P SALEM COMMUNITY LIBRARY, 24615 89th St, 53168. SAN 377-9521. Tel: 262-843-3348. FAX: 262-843-3144. *Librn*, Mary Ellen Close; E-Mail: meclose@kenosha.lib.wi.us; *Publ Servs*, Ivan Schoen
Library Holdings: Bk Titles 59,000; Per Subs 225
Mem of Kenosha County Libr Syst
Open Mon-Thurs 9-9, Fri-Sat 9-4
Branches: 2
SILVER LAKE COMMUNITY, 313 E Lake St, Silver Lake, 53170. SAN 377-9777. Tel: 262-889-4606.
Library Holdings: Bk Titles 2,000
Subject Interests: Children's literature
Mem of Kenosha County Libr Syst
Open Mon, Tues & Thurs 3:30-7, Wed 1:30-5, Sat 9-1
TWIN LAKES COMMUNITY, 110 S Lake Ave, Twin Lakes, 53181. SAN 377-9815. Tel: 262-877-4281. FAX: 262-877-2682. *Branch Mgr*, Ivan Shoren; Tel: 262-877-4281, Fax: 262-877-2682
Library Holdings: Per Subs 125
Mem of Kenosha County Libr Syst
Open Mon-Thurs 10-8, Sat 10-4, Sun 12-5

SAND CREEK

P CLARELLA HACKETT JOHNSON LIBRARY,* NE 9311 13-45th Ave, PO Box 656, 54765. SAN 378-0066. Tel: 715-658-1269. E-Mail: chjohnson@cliboardun.net. *Librn*, Inez Anderson; *Asst Librn*, Merline Rufledt
Library Holdings: Bk Titles 8,000; Per Subs 20
Mem of Indianhead Federated Library System
Open Mon & Fri 1-5, Wes 1-8, Sat 8-12

SAUK CITY

P SAUK CITY PUBLIC LIBRARY,* 515 Water St, 53583-1159. SAN 318-3750. Tel: 608-643-8346. *Dir*, Peggy Heidenreich; *Asst Librn*, Sheryl Adank
Founded 1924
Library Holdings: Bk Vols 28,000; Per Subs 96
Mem of South Central Library System
Special Services for the Blind - Audio-cassettes; Large print bks
Homebound delivery for the elderly

SAUKVILLE

P OSCAR GRADY LIBRARY,* 151 S Main St, 53080-1930. SAN 324-7988. Tel: 414-284-6022. FAX: 414-284-1933. *Librn*, Helen Mehring
Founded 1972. Pop 3,700
Library Holdings: Bk Titles 14,000; Per Subs 90
Mem of Eastern Shores Library System

SAYNER

P PLUM LAKE PUBLIC LIBRARY, 239 Hwy 155, PO Box 99, 54560-0099. (Mail add: PO Box 99, 54560), SAN 318-3769. Tel: 715-542-2020. FAX: 715-542-2627. E-Mail: plumlib@newnorth.net. *Dir*, Ida Nemac; *Dir*, Ida Nemec
Founded 1939. Pop 800; Circ 23,242
Jan 1999-Dec 1999 Income $51,700, State $1,000, City $20,271, Federal $6,005, County $2,100, Locally Generated Income $21,530. Mats Exp $8,321, Books $6,300, Per/Ser (Incl. Access Fees) $1,121, AV Equip $900. Sal $22,371
Library Holdings: Bk Titles 17,930; Per Subs 53
Subject Interests: Local history
Special Collections: Memorial Coll
Automation Activity & Vendor Info: (Circulation) Sagebrush Corporation; (ILL) Brodart
Mem of Northern Waters Library Service
Friends of the Library Group

SCANDINAVIA

P ELLISON PUBLIC LIBRARY, 349 N Main St, PO Box 117, 54977-0117. SAN 377-9750. Tel: 715-467-4636. E-Mail: sca@owls.lib.wi.us. *Librn*, Dorothy Youngblood; E-Mail: yngblood@athenet.net; Staff 1 (Non-MLS 1)
Pop 642

Jan 2000-Dec 2000 Income $16,500, City $6,800, County $9,700
Library Holdings: Bk Titles 6,500; Per Subs 25
Mem of Outagamie Waupaca Library System
Open Mon, Wed & Fri 12-6, Sat 10-12

SEYMOUR

P MUEHL PUBLIC LIBRARY, 436 N Main, 54165-1512. SAN 318-3777. Tel: 920-833-2725. FAX: 920-833-9804. E-Mail: sey@owlsnet.owls.lib.wi.us. Web Site: www.owls.lib.wi.us/sey. *Dir*, Bryan J McCormick; E-Mail: bmccormi@mail.owls.lib.wi.us; Staff 3 (MLS 1, Non-MLS 2)
Founded 1901. Pop 4,990; Circ 60,525
Jan 2000-Dec 2000 Income $148,290, City $97,478, County $41,812, Locally Generated Income $5,500, Other $3,500. Mats Exp $31,700, Books $30,000, AV Equip $1,700. Sal $67,492 (Prof $28,500)
Library Holdings: Bk Titles 23,580; Per Subs 114; High Interest/Low Vocabulary Bk Vols 90; Bks on Deafness & Sign Lang 10
Automation Activity & Vendor Info: (Circulation) GEAC; (OPAC) GEAC
Mem of Outagamie Waupaca Library System
Friends of the Library Group

SHARON

P BRIGHAM MEMORIAL LIBRARY,* 131 Plain St, PO Box 510, 53585-0510. SAN 318-3785. Tel: 414-736-4249. FAX: 414-736-2181. *Librn*, Janet Zimmerman
Founded 1927. Pop 1,280; Circ 14,500
Library Holdings: Bk Vols 10,000; Per Subs 40
Special Collections: Large Print
Mem of Lakeshores Library System
Friends of the Library Group

SHAWANO

P SHAWANO CITY-COUNTY LIBRARY,* 128 S Sawyer St, 54166-2496. SAN 365-0642. Tel: 715-526-3829. FAX: 715-526-6772. *Br Coordr, Dir*, Michael Hille; *Circ*, Bobbie Sager; *Cat, ILL*, Sue Porath; *Ch Servs*, Penny Habeck; *Bkmobile Coordr*, Barbara Coollnow
Founded 1899. Pop 39,000; Circ 245,000
1998-1999 Income $510,254, City $95,045, County $383,680, Locally Generated Income $23,000. Mats Exp $85,400, Books $62,000, Per/Ser (Incl. Access Fees) $8,700, Micro $500, AV Equip $1,000, Other Print Mats $6,000. Sal $311,186
Library Holdings: Bk Vols 112,426; Per Subs 167
Subject Interests: Architecture, Art
Special Collections: Menominees (American Indian)
Mem of Nicolet Federated Library System
Friends of the Library Group
Branches: 5
BIRNAMWOOD PUBLIC, 531 Maple St, Birnamwood, 54414-9799. SAN 365-0669. Tel: 715-449-3120. *Librn*, Karen Dickman
Library Holdings: Bk Vols 2,000
BONDUEL PUBLIC, 117 1/2 W Green Bay St, Bonduel, 54107. SAN 365-0677. Tel: 715-758-2267. *Librn*, Carol Luepke
Library Holdings: Bk Vols 7,959
MATTOON BRANCH, PO Box 266, Mattoon, 54450. SAN 329-3505. Tel: 715-489-3333.
Library Holdings: Bk Vols 1,500
TIGERTON PUBLIC, PO Box 166, Tigerton, 54486-0166. SAN 365-0707. Tel: 715-535-2194. *Librn*, Peggy Slicer
Library Holdings: Bk Vols 7,059
WITTENBERG PUBLIC, 803 Cherry St, Wittenberg, 54499. SAN 365-0715. Tel: 715-253-2936. *Librn*, Alene Newcomb
Library Holdings: Bk Vols 6,598
Bookmobiles: 1

SHEBOYGAN

P EASTERN SHORES LIBRARY SYSTEM, 4932 S Taylor Dr, 53081-1107. SAN 318-3831. Tel: 920-208-4900. FAX: 920-208-4901. Web Site: www.esls.lib.wi.us. *Dir*, David J Weinhold; E-Mail: weinhold@esls.lib.wi.us; *Automation Syst Coordr*, Paul Onufrak; E-Mail: ponufrak@esls.lib.wi.us; *Tech Servs*, Alison Hoffman; Staff 11 (MLS 3, Non-MLS 8)
Founded 1979. Pop 192,000
Jan 2001-Dec 2001 Income $2,008,355, State $568,398, Federal $17,200, County $908,812, Locally Generated Income $30,889, Other $483,056. Mats Exp Books $26,584. Sal $338,786 (Prof $145,900)
Library Holdings: Bk Vols 31,783; Bk Titles 30,931; Per Subs 38
Automation Activity & Vendor Info: (Cataloging) Sagebrush Corporation; (Circulation) Sagebrush Corporation
Database Vendor: Ebsco - EbscoHost
Publications: The Library Connection (Newsletter)
Member Libraries: Cedar Grove Public Library; Cedarburg Public Library; Elkhart Lake Public Library; Frank L Weyenberg Library Of Mequon-Thiensville; Kohler School & Public Library; Lakeland College; Lakev Community Library; Mead Public Library; Oostburg Public Library; O Grady Library; Plymouth Public Library; Sheboygan Falls Memorial Library; University Of Wisconsin Sheboygan; USS Liberty Memorial I Library; W J Niederkorn Public Library
Partic in Wis PALS Libr Consortium; Wisconsin Library Services
Bookmobiles: 1. Carries 5000 items

S JOHN MICHAEL KOHLER ARTS CENTER, Resource Center, 608 N York Ave, 53081-4507. (Mail add: PO Box 489, 53082-0489), SAN 31 3793. Tel: 920-458-6144. FAX: 920-458-4473. *Dir*, Ruth DeYoung Ko *Actg Librn*, Heather Stuart; Tel: 920-458-6144, Ext 147, E-Mail: hstuar jmkac.org
Founded 1967
Library Holdings: Bk Vols 3,500; Bk Titles 3,000; Per Subs 75
Subject Interests: Contemporary Am crafts, Contemporary art, Photog Self-taught artists
Publications: Newsletters, calendars of events, exhibition catalogues & related publications, annual reports

C LAKELAND COLLEGE, John Esch Library, PO Box 359, 53082-035 SAN 318-3807. Tel: 920-565-1238. FAX: 920-565-1206. *Dir*, Ann Penk Tel: 920-565-1242, E-Mail: penkea@lakelamd.edu; *Per*, Robert Schuric *ILL*, Charles Romaine; Staff 4 (MLS 3, Non-MLS 1)
Founded 1940. Enrl 779; Fac 57; Highest Degree: Master
Jul 1999-Jun 2000 Income $250,142. Mats Exp $250,142, Books $37,0 Per/Ser (Incl. Access Fees) $44,700, Electronic Ref Mat (Incl. Access F $10,000. Sal $86,000
Library Holdings: Bk Vols 63,890; Bk Titles 53,725; Per Subs 300
Subject Interests: Jewish holocaust, Modern American poetry
Publications: Lakeland College Library Skills Workbook (Library handbook)
Mem of Eastern Shores Library System
Partic in WILS

P MEAD PUBLIC LIBRARY, 710 N Eighth St, 53081-4563. SAN 318-3 Tel: 920-459-3400. Interlibrary Loan Service Tel: 920-459-3422. Circula Tel: 920-459-3400, Ext 3401. Reference Tel: 920-459-3400, Ext 3422. T 920-459-3436. FAX: 920-459-0204. Web Site: www.sheboygan.lib.wi.us *Libr Serv*, Sharon L Winkle; Tel: 920-459-3400, Ext 3414, E-Mail: swinkle@esls.lib.wi.us; *Asst Dir*, Rick E Gustafson; Tel: 920-459-3400, 3410, E-Mail: rgustaf@esls.lib.wi.us; *Asst Dir*, Kay L Knauer; Tel: 920-3400, Ext 3407, E-Mail: kknauer@esls.lib.wi.us; *Ref*, Debbra L Voss; Te 920-459-3400, Ext 3420, E-Mail: dvoss@esls.lib.wi.us; *Ch Servs*, Kathl S Hofschield; Tel: 920-459-3400, Ext 3433, E-Mail: khofshld@esls.lib.w *Reader Servs*, Barbara J Voight; Tel: 920-459-3400, Ext 3434, E-Mail: bvoight@esls.lib.wi.us; *Tech Coordr*, Mary Ellen Petzold; Tel: 920-459-3400, Ext 3415, E-Mail: mpetzold@esls.lib.wi.us; *Circ*, Susan C Mathev Tel: 920-459-3400, Ext 3403, E-Mail: smathews@esls.lib.wi.us; Staff 55 (MLS 14, Non-MLS 41)
Founded 1897. Pop 70,000; Circ 727,956
Jan 1999-Dec 1999 Income $3,873,254, State $34,546, City $2,506,149, Federal $3,597, County $369,721, Locally Generated Income $243,032, Other $716,209. Mats Exp $391,644, Books $289,844, Per/Ser (Incl. Ac Fees) $40,851, Other Print Mats $3,156, Electronic Ref Mat (Incl. Acces Fees) $12,332. Sal $1,847,734
Library Holdings: Bk Vols 279,639; Per Subs 517
Subject Interests: Furniture
Special Collections: Local History; United States & State Census Coll
Database Vendor: epixtech, inc., OCLC - First Search, ProQuest
Publications: Footnotes (bi-monthly); Mead Sheet (monthly); Union Lis Periodicals; VHS Catalog
Mem of Eastern Shores Library System
Partic in OCLC Online Computer Library Center, Inc
Special Services for the Deaf - TDD
Friends of the Library Group
Bookmobiles: 1

M SAINT NICHOLAS HOSPITAL, Health Sciences Library,* 1601 N Tayl Dr, 53081-2496. SAN 318-3823. Tel: 920-459-4713. FAX: 920-452-2499
Founded 1975
Library Holdings: Bk Titles 1,000; Per Subs 150
Subject Interests: Communications, Management, Medicine, Nursing, Pathology, Radiology, Wellness
Restriction: Medical staff only
Partic in Fox River Valley Area Library Consortium; Greater Midwest Regional Medical Libr Network; Medline; Regional Med Libr - Region 3 Southeastern Wisconsin Health Science Library Consortium

S SHEBOYGAN PRESS LIBRARY,* 632 Center Ave, 53081. SAN 375-0 Tel: 920-457-7711. FAX: 920-457-3573. E-Mail: spress@excel.net. Web Site: www.shebpress.com. *Librn*, Sue Dempster; Tel: 920-457-7711, Ext E-Mail: suzanne.dempster@thomnews.com
Library Holdings: Bk Vols 500
Special Collections: Sheboygan Press (1856-present) bd vols

UNIVERSITY OF WISCONSIN SHEBOYGAN, Battig Memorial Library, One University Dr, 53081-4789. SAN 318-3858. Tel: 920-459-6625. Reference Tel: 920-459-6680. FAX: 920-459-6602, 920-459-6615. Web Site: www.sheboygan.uwc.edu/library. *Dir*, Jeffrey A Ellair; Tel: 920-459-6679, E-Mail: jellair@uwc.edu; *Ref*, Amy M Mussell; Tel: 920-459-6680, E-Mail: amussell@uwc.edu; *ILL*, Karen L McArdle; Tel: 920-459-6681, E-Mail: kmcardle@uwc.edu; Staff 3 (MLS 2, Non-MLS 1)
Founded 1965. Enrl 750; Fac 32; Highest Degree: Associate
Jul 1999-Jun 2000 Income $129,475, State $126,136, Federal $3,339. Mats Exp $24,024, Books $8,390, Per/Ser (Incl. Access Fees) $15,634. Sal $99,677 (Prof $80,174)
Library Holdings: Bk Vols 40,342; Bk Titles 34,938; Per Subs 183
Automation Activity & Vendor Info: (Cataloging) Endeavor; (Circulation) Endeavor; (OPAC) Endeavor
Database Vendor: CARL, Ebsco - EbscoHost, GaleNet, OCLC - First Search, ProQuest, Silverplatter Information Inc., Wilson - Wilson Web
Mem of Eastern Shores Library System
Partic in OCLC Online Computer Library Center, Inc; Wisconsin Library Services

BOYGAN FALLS

SHEBOYGAN COUNTY HISTORICAL RESEARCH CENTER LIBRARY, (SCHRC), 518 Water St, 53085. SAN 325-5557. Tel: 920-467-4667. FAX: 920-467-1395. E-Mail: schrc@execpc.com. Web Site: www.schrc.org. *Dir*, Rose Rumpff; *Librn*, Janice Hildebrand; *Librn*, Carol Shaffer; Staff 21 (Non-MLS 21)
Founded 1983
Subject Interests: Sheboygan County hist
Special Collections: Sheboygan County
Publications: The Researcher
Friends of the Library Group

SHEBOYGAN FALLS MEMORIAL LIBRARY,* 330 Buffalo St, PO Box 140, 53085. SAN 318-3866. Tel: 920-467-7908. FAX: 920-467-7912. *Dir*, Scott Gehrig
Founded 1924. Pop 10,000; Circ 112,000
1998-1999 Income $214,750. Mats Exp $32,800. Sal $113,775
Library Holdings: Bk Vols 32,000; Per Subs 156
Subject Interests: Biog, Crafts, History
Mem of Eastern Shores Library System
Friends of the Library Group

LL LAKE

SHELL LAKE PUBLIC LIBRARY,* 501 First St, PO Box 318, 54871-0318. SAN 318-3874. Tel: 715-468-2074. FAX: 715-468-7638. E-Mail: shellpbl@syslan.net. *Dir*, Beth Owens
Circ 11,194
Jan 1999-Dec 1999 Income $42,651. Mats Exp $4,600. Sal $31,893
Library Holdings: Bk Vols 9,000
Special Collections: Holiday Coll; Hunting Fishing Coll; Wisconsin Coll
Mem of Northern Waters Library Service
Friends of the Library Group

WASHBURN COUNTY LAW LIBRARY, Courthouse, PO Box 339, 54871. SAN 328-3569. Tel: 715-468-4677. FAX: 715-468-4678. *In Charge*, Karen Nord
Jan 1999-Dec 1999 Mats Exp $8,000

OCTON

SHIOCTON PUBLIC LIBRARY,* W7740 Pine St, 54170. SAN 378-0082. Tel: 920-986-3933. FAX: 920-986-3743. *Librn*, Betty Rickel; E-Mail: brickel@owls.lib.wi.us
Jan 1998-Dec 1998 Income $36,505. Mats Exp $10,000. Sal $17,154
Library Holdings: Bk Titles 10,000; Per Subs 20
Mem of Outagamie Waupaca Library System
Open Mon & Wed 1-7, Tues & Thurs 10-5, Fri 11-5:30, Sat 10-2

OREWOOD

SHOREWOOD PUBLIC LIBRARY, 2030 E Shorewood Blvd, 53211-2385. SAN 318-3882. Tel: 414-963-6984. FAX: 414-961-2820. *Dir*, Elizabeth Carey; *Ch Servs*, Heide Piehler; *Ad Servs*, Bonnie Poquette; *Tech Servs*, Nancy Shimon; *Circ*, Pete Loeffel; Staff 5 (MLS 5)
Founded 1932. Pop 14,121; Circ 250,000
Library Holdings: Bk Vols 40,000; Per Subs 110
Database Vendor: Innovative Interfaces INN - View
Mem of Milwaukee County Federated Library System
Friends of the Library Group

SHULLSBURG

P SHULLSBURG PUBLIC LIBRARY,* 112 S Gratiot St, 53586-9999. SAN 318-3890. Tel: 608-965-4424. *Dir*, Peg Roberts
Pop 1,526; Circ 5,170
Library Holdings: Bk Vols 6,100; Per Subs 12
Mem of Southwest Wisconsin Library System

SLINGER

P SLINGER COMMUNITY LIBRARY,* 220 Slinger Rd, 53086. SAN 378-0104. Tel: 414-644-6171. FAX: 414-644-6171. E-Mail: slingerlib1@nconnect.net. Web Site: www.nconnect-net/~slingerlib1/. *Dir*, Judith A Heft
Jan 1998-Dec 1998 Income $122,885. Mats Exp $34,190. Sal $70,733
Library Holdings: Bk Titles 17,779
Mem of Mid-Wisconsin Federated Library System
Partic in Am Libr Asn; Wis Libr Asn
Open Mon, Tues & Thurs 12-7, Wed 9-5, Fri 9:30-12:30 (summer); Mon, Tues & Thurs 2-7, Wed 9-5, Sat 9:30-12:30 (winter)
Friends of the Library Group

SOLDIERS GROVE

P SOLDIERS GROVE PUBLIC LIBRARY,* 123 Passive Sun Dr, PO Box 6, 54655-0006. SAN 318-3912. Tel: 608-624-5815. *Dir*, Cele Wolf; E-Mail: cwolf@swlf.org
Founded 1970. Pop 1,500; Circ 6,209
Library Holdings: Bk Vols 12,000
Mem of Southwest Wisconsin Library System

SOMERSET

P SOMERSET PUBLIC LIBRARY,* 208 Hud St, PO Box 129, 54025-0129. SAN 318-3920. Tel: 715-247-5228. FAX: 715-247-5141. *Librn*, Norma Scott
Founded 1974. Pop 2,972; Circ 27,933
Library Holdings: Bk Vols 6,000; Per Subs 37
Special Collections: Somerset History
Mem of Indianhead Federated Library System
Friends of the Library Group

SOUTH MILWAUKEE

P SOUTH MILWAUKEE PUBLIC LIBRARY, 1907 Tenth Ave, 53172. SAN 318-3939. Tel: 414-768-8195. FAX: 414-768-8072. *Dir*, Bob Pfeiffer; E-Mail: bpfeif@mcfls.org; *Ref*, James Lewis; *YA Servs*, Denise Herr; Staff 4 (MLS 3, Non-MLS 1)
Founded 1899. Pop 21,367; Circ 245,187
Jan 1999-Dec 1999 Income $691,194, State $40,500, City $629,972, Locally Generated Income $20,722. Mats Exp $110,407, Books $73,364, Per/Ser (Incl. Access Fees) $10,002, AV Equip $11,930, Other Print Mats $3,232, Electronic Ref Mat (Incl. Access Fees) $5,000. Sal $393,981 (Prof $139,271)
Library Holdings: Bk Vols 112,732; Per Subs 281
Automation Activity & Vendor Info: (Cataloging) Innovative Interfaces Inc.; (Circulation) Innovative Interfaces Inc.; (OPAC) Innovative Interfaces Inc.; (Serials) Innovative Interfaces Inc.
Mem of Milwaukee County Federated Library System
Friends of the Library Group

SPARTA

S MONROE COUNTY LOCAL HISTORY ROOM & LIBRARY,* 200 W Main St, 54656-2141. SAN 326-6192. Tel: 608-269-8680. FAX: 608-269-8921.
Library Holdings: Bk Vols 2,000; Bk Titles 2,000; Per Subs 30
Special Collections: 30,000 cards; Andres Coll; Monroe Co Coll, 3000 photographs

P SPARTA FREE LIBRARY,* 124 W Main St, PO Box 347, 54656-0347. SAN 318-3947. Tel: 608-269-2010. FAX: 608-269-1542. E-Mail: spartalibrary@centurytel.net. Web Site: www.wi.centuryinter.net/spartalib. *Dir*, Marge Fromm
Founded 1861. Pop 15,000
Library Holdings: Bk Vols 51,201; Per Subs 136
Subject Interests: Bicycles, Bicycling
Publications: Sparta Free Library Newsletter (printed 6 times a year)
Mem of Winding Rivers Library System

UNITED STATES ARMY
A FORT MCCOY POST LIBRARY, B 2000 11th Ave, Fort McCoy, 54656-5161. SAN 320-5223. Tel: 608-388-2410. FAX: 608-388-2690. *Librn*, Mary Limp
Library Holdings: Bk Vols 10,000; Per Subs 20
Subject Interests: Military history, World War I, World War II
Special Collections: Encyclopaedia Britannica Coll, ninth ed circa 1892; Military Insignia & Memorabilia & Patch Coll

SPOONER

P SPOONER MEMORIAL LIBRARY,* 421 High St, 54801-1431. SAN 318-3955. Tel: 715-635-2792. FAX: 715-635-2147. *Dir*, Jane Frankiewicz; *Acq*, Sharlene Parish; *Ch Servs*, Jane Hvizdak; *ILL*, Bonnie Brandt
Founded 1915. Pop 2,500; Circ 42,640
Library Holdings: Bk Vols 17,000; Per Subs 160
Subject Interests: Architecture, Art
Mem of Northern Waters Library Service; Northwest Wis Libr Syst
Friends of the Library Group

SPRING GREEN

P SPRING GREEN COMMUNITY LIBRARY, 230 E Monroe St, 53588-8035. (Mail add: PO Box 520, 53588-0520), SAN 318-3971. Tel: 608-588-2276. Web Site: www.scls.lib.wi.us/sgr. *Dir*, Mary Jo Warnke
Founded 1955. Pop 1,441; Circ 50,000
Library Holdings: Bk Vols 19,890; Per Subs 70
Special Collections: Frank Lloyd Wright Coll; Wisconsin Authors Coll; Wisconsin History Coll
Mem of South Central Library System
Friends of the Library Group

SPRING VALLEY

P SPRING VALLEY PUBLIC LIBRARY,* E 121 S Second St, PO Box 217, 54767-0217. SAN 376-6675. Tel: 715-778-4590. FAX: 715-778-4589. *Librn*, Doris Ronnander
Library Holdings: Bk Titles 9,000; Per Subs 33
Mem of Indianhead Federated Library System

STANLEY

P D R MOON MEMORIAL LIBRARY, 154 Fourth Ave, 54768. SAN 318-398X. Tel: 715-644-2004. FAX: 715-644-2941. E-Mail: librarypl@yahoo.com. *Coll Develop, Dir*, Susan Anderson
Founded 1901
Jan 1999-Dec 1999 Income $90,638. Mats Exp $13,878, Books $11,602, Per/Ser (Incl. Access Fees) $2,276. Sal $44,000 (Prof $28,000)
Library Holdings: Bk Vols 34,000; Per Subs 77
Mem of Indianhead Federated Library System
Friends of the Library Group

STETSONVILLE

P JEAN M THOMSEN MEMORIAL LIBRARY, 105 N Gershwin St, PO Box 99, 54480-0099. SAN 318-3998. Tel: 715-678-2892. FAX: 715-678-2032. Web Site: geocities.com/athens/forum/2594/index.html. *Dir*, Patricia Reich; E-Mail: preich@wvis.lib.wi.us
Pop 715; Circ 9,569
Jan 1999-Dec 1999 Income $49,484, City $25,273, Federal $700, County $15,010, Other $8,501. Mats Exp $11,162, Books $7,826, Per/Ser (Incl. Access Fees) $974, AV Equip $854, Other Print Mats $1,272, Electronic Ref Mat (Incl. Access Fees) $236. (Prof $18,608)
Library Holdings: Bk Vols 14,000; Per Subs 45
Special Collections: Handicrafts & Cookery
Automation Activity & Vendor Info: (Cataloging) epixtech, inc.; (Circulation) epixtech, inc.
Publications: Booklist; Library Journal
Mem of Wisconsin Valley Library Service

STEVENS POINT

J MID-STATE TECHNICAL COLLEGE, Stevens Point Campus Library,* 933 Michigan Ave, 54481. SAN 318-4005. Tel: 715-342-3129, 715-344-3063. FAX: 715-342-3134. *Dir*, Sharon Peters
Founded 1974. Enrl 200; Fac 15
Library Holdings: Bk Titles 4,750

P PORTAGE COUNTY PUBLIC LIBRARY, 1001 Main St, 54481-2860. SAN 318-403X. Tel: 715-346-1545. FAX: 715-346-1239. Web Site: library.uwsp.edu/pcl/. *Dir*, Robert J Stack; E-Mail: bstack@uwsp.edu; *Asst Dir*, Janice J Doxtator; E-Mail: jdoxtato@uwsp.edu; *Br Coordr*, Darla Engwall; E-Mail: Darla.Engwall@uwsp.edu; *Ch Servs*, Mary Whittington; E-Mail: mwhittin@uwsp.edu; *Publ Servs*, Deborah M McCabe; E-Mail: dmccabe@uwsp.edu; *Tech Servs*, Victoria A Billings; E-Mail: vbillings@uwsp.edu; Staff 6 (MLS 6)
Founded 1895. Pop 67,378; Circ 425,120
Jan 2000-Dec 2000 Income $1,327,503, State $8,240, County $1,273,413, Locally Generated Income $45,850. Mats Exp $118,747, Books $103,290, Per/Ser (Incl. Access Fees) $13,161, Micro $2,296. Sal $727,054 (Prof $231,208)
Library Holdings: Bk Vols 157,918; Per Subs 391
Mem of South Central Library System
Friends of the Library Group

L SAINT MICHAEL'S HOSPITAL, Health Science Library, 900 Illinois 54481. SAN 328-5553. Tel: 715-346-5091. FAX: 715-346-5077. *Librn*, Melinda LaBonte; Staff 2 (MLS 1, Non-MLS 1)
Library Holdings: Bk Vols 350
Subject Interests: Medicine, Nursing
Partic in Greater Midwest Regional Medical Libr Network; NW Hospi Consortium

S SENTRY INSURANCE LIBRARY, 1800 N Point Dr, 54481. SAN 31 4013. Tel: 715-346-6787. FAX: 715-346-7028. *Coordr*, Elaine Momsen Staff 3 (MLS 2, Non-MLS 1)
Founded 1930
Subject Interests: Bus, Ins, Law, Mgt
Special Collections: Investments, Legal; Loss Control
Publications: Periodical Holdings List

C UNIVERSITY OF WISCONSIN-STEVENS POINT, University Library Reserve St, 54481-1985. SAN 318-4021. Tel: 715-346-3038. FAX: 715 3857. *Dir*, A Arneson; E-Mail: aarneson@uwsp.edu; *Automation Syst Coordr, Cat*, Carol Van Horn; *Per*, Theresea Chao; *Doc*, Marg Whalen; L Schuler
Founded 1894
Library Holdings: Bk Vols 313,588; Per Subs 1,668
Subject Interests: Education, Environmental studies, Ethnic studies, Hi
Special Collections: Censorship; John F Kennedy Assassination; Native Americans
Automation Activity & Vendor Info: (Cataloging) Endeavor
Partic in Wisconsin Library Services

STOUGHTON

S NELSON INDUSTRIES, INC, Corporate Technical Library, 1801 Hwy 138, PO Box 428, 53589-0428. SAN 374-5015. Tel: 608-873-4370. FAX 608-873-1550. *Tech Servs*, Jayne Fischer
Library Holdings: Bk Titles 1,500; Per Subs 60
Subject Interests: Acoustics

P STOUGHTON PUBLIC LIBRARY, 304 S Fourth St, 53589-0191. SAN 318-4048. Tel: 608-873-6281. FAX: 608-873-0108. *Dir*, Pat Erickson; E-Mail: erickson@scls.lib.us.wi; *Librn*, Sue Freedman; *Tech Servs*, Mari Granrud; *Ch Servs*, Bonny Labno; Staff 2 (MLS 2)
Founded 1901
Jan 1999-Dec 1999 Income $484,834, City $307,104, County $124,195, Other $53,535. Mats Exp $67,333, Books $49,226, Per/Ser (Incl. Access Fees) $6,130, Electronic Ref Mat (Incl. Access Fees) $11,977. Sal $243,
Library Holdings: Bk Vols 82,255; Per Subs 196
Automation Activity & Vendor Info: (Circulation) epixtech, inc.; (OPA epixtech, inc.
Database Vendor: OCLC - First Search
Mem of South Central Library System
Special Services for the Deaf - TDD
Friends of the Library Group

STRUM

P STRUM PUBLIC LIBRARY,* 202 Fifth Ave S, PO Box 10, 54770. SA 318-4056. Tel: 715-695-3848. FAX: 715-695-3510. *Dir*, Kathy Wezyk
Pop 6,000; Circ 9,000
Library Holdings: Bk Titles 10,000; Per Subs 22
Mem of Winding Rivers Library System
Open Fri 12-4:30, closed Thurs & Sat

STURGEON BAY

P DOOR COUNTY LIBRARIES, 107 S Fourth Ave, 54235. SAN 318-406 Tel: 920-743-6578. FAX: 920-743-6697. Web Site: www.dcl.lib.wi.us. *Di* Rebecca Berger; E-Mail: rberger@mail.nfls.lib.wi.us; *Tech Servs*, Joseph Clabots; *Acq*, Dorothy Bruckner; *Coll Develop*, Nancy Emery
Founded 1950. Circ 283,143
Library Holdings: Bk Vols 135,143; Per Subs 458
Subject Interests: Local history
Special Collections: Door County Authors
Publications: Friends of Door County Libraries
Mem of Nicolet Federated Library System
Partic in OWLSnet
Friends of the Library Group
Branches: 8
BAILEYS HARBOR BRANCH, PO Box 313, Baileys Harbor, 54202. S 324-3095. Tel: 920-839-2210. *Librn*, Kaye Maher
Library Holdings: Bk Vols 8,717
CENTRAL LIBRARY *Coll Develop*, Nancy Emery; *YA Servs*, Beth Lokk *Circ*, Judy Ellenbecker
Library Holdings: Bk Vols 64,604
Subject Interests: Door County hist, Local history
Friends of the Library Group
EGG HARBOR BRANCH, PO Box 207, Egg Harbor, 54209. SAN 324-3109. Tel: 920-868-3334. *Librn*, Jeanne Majeski

Library Holdings: Bk Vols 7,490
Friends of the Library Group
EPHRAIM BRANCH, PO Box 97, Ephraim, 54211. SAN 324-3117. Tel: 920-854-2014. *Librn*, Linda Malmgren
Library Holdings: Bk Vols 9,052
Subject Interests: Ephraim hist
Friends of the Library Group
FISH CREEK BRANCH, PO Box 7, Fish Creek, 54212. SAN 324-3125. Tel: 920-868-3471. *Librn*, Holly Somerhalder
Library Holdings: Bk Vols 10,170
Friends of the Library Group
FORESTVILLE BRANCH, PO Box 308, Forestville, 54213. SAN 324-3133. Tel: 920-856-6886. *Librn*, Barbara Gigot
Library Holdings: Bk Vols 10,314
Friends of the Library Group
SISTER BAY BRANCH, PO Box 347, Sister Bay, 54234. SAN 324-3141. Tel: 920-854-2721. *Librn*, Betty Ann Curzon
Library Holdings: Bk Vols 11,226
Friends of the Library Group
WASHINGTON ISLAND BRANCH, Rte 1, Box 3, Washington Island, 54246. SAN 324-315X. Tel: 920-847-2323. *Librn*, Marcia Carr
Library Holdings: Bk Vols 13,788

RTEVANT

GOLDEN BOOKS PUBLISHING, INC LIBRARY, 10101 Science Dr, 53177. SAN 318-3491. Tel: 414-631-5261. FAX: 414-635-1533. *Archivist, Mgr Libr*, Mary Janaky; E-Mail: mjanaky@goldenbooks.com
Founded 1907
Library Holdings: Bk Titles 7,500
Restriction: Company library
Function: Archival collection, Business archives

PRAIRIE

SUN PRAIRIE PUBLIC LIBRARY, 1350 Linnerud Dr, 53590-2631. SAN 318-4072. Tel: 608-837-5644. FAX: 608-825-3936. Web Site: www.scls.lib.wi.us/sunprairie/home.html. *Dir*, Sharon Zindars; E-Mail: szindars@scls.lib.wi.us; *Ad Servs*, Beverly Kennedy; *Ch Servs*, Amy Brandt; *Tech Servs*, Debra Bird; Staff 17 (MLS 4, Non-MLS 13)
Pop 24,000; Circ 285,000
1999-1999 Income $647,480, State $600, City $454,000, County $110,000, Other $82,880. Mats Exp $111,650. Sal $413,000
Library Holdings: Bk Vols 63,211; Per Subs 265
Subject Interests: Local history
Automation Activity & Vendor Info: (Acquisitions) epixtech, inc.; (Cataloging) epixtech, inc.; (Circulation) epixtech, inc.; (ILL) epixtech, inc.; (OPAC) epixtech, inc.; (Serials) epixtech, inc.
Database Vendor: IAC - Info Trac
Mem of South Central Library System
Partic in Link
Special Services for the Blind - Talking Books
Friends of the Library Group

WISCONSIN CONFERENCE UNITED METHODIST CHURCH, Historical Library,* 750 Windsor St, PO Box 620, 53590-0620. SAN 323-6358. Tel: 608-837-7328, Ext 243. FAX: 608-837-8547. E-Mail: archives@wisconsinumc.org. *Librn*, Mary Schroeder
Library Holdings: Bk Titles 2,000
Special Collections: Diaries of William Ames 1857-98, Michael Benson 1832-1919 & Joseph Austin 1838-85
Restriction: By appointment only

ERIOR

DOUGLAS COUNTY LAW LIBRARY,* 1313 Belknap St, 54880. SAN 318-4080. Tel: 715-395-1207. *In Charge*, Sandy Picard
Library Holdings: Bk Vols 10,500

SUPERIOR PUBLIC LIBRARY, 1530 Tower Ave, 54880-2532. SAN 365-0731. Tel: 715-394-8860. TDD: 715-394-8878. FAX: 715-394-8870. E-Mail: library@ci.superior.wi.us. Web Site: ci.superior.wi.us. *Dir*, Janet I Jennings; E-Mail: jenningsj@ci.superior.wi.us; *Ad Servs, Archivist*, Julie M Zachau; E-Mail: zachauj@superior.nwls.lib.wi.us; *Circ*, Sandra M Henning; E-Mail: hennings@superior.mwls.lib.wi.us; *Ch Servs*, Linda M Olson; E-Mail: olsonl@superior.mwls.lib.wi.us; *Doc*, Miina Helske; *ILL*, Linda G Moe; *Online Servs*, Wanita D Anderson; *Per*, Susan M Mattson; *Tech Servs*, Carla J Powers; E-Mail: powerse@superior.nwls.lib.wi.us; *Admin Assoc*, Nancy C Roulston; E-Mail: roulstonn@ci.superior.wi.us; Staff 13 (MLS 4, Non-MLS 9)
Founded 1888. Pop 27,294; Circ 309,589
Jan 1999-Dec 1999 Income $1,037,728, State $21,604, City $860,874, Federal $1,786, County $100,000, Locally Generated Income $31,423, Other $22,041. Mats Exp $140,942, Books $85,122, Per/Ser (Incl. Access Fees) $9,912, Micro $1,876, AV Equip $20,414, Other Print Mats $2,325, Electronic Ref Mat (Incl. Access Fees) $21,293. Sal $590,340
Library Holdings: Bk Vols 116,756; Per Subs 284
Subject Interests: Architecture, Art, Genealogy, Great Lakes area hist, Heraldry, History, Labor hist, Music
Special Collections: Art (Anna B Butler Coll), photogs; City of Superior and Douglas County, Wisconsin, archives (State Historical Society of Wisconsin Area Research Center); Learning Disabilities (Burton Ansell Memorial Coll), bks, pamphlets, film; Rare Books (Henry S Butler Coll); Superior, Wisconsin, Newspapers from 1855; Wisconsin History (Henry E Legler Coll), bks, docs, micro, mss, film, photogs, A-tapes, V-tapes, pamphlets
Automation Activity & Vendor Info: (Acquisitions) Innovative Interfaces Inc.; (Cataloging) Innovative Interfaces Inc.; (Circulation) Innovative Interfaces Inc.; (OPAC) Innovative Interfaces Inc.
Database Vendor: OCLC - First Search
Publications: "Remembering the Globe" video (Local historical information)
Mem of Northern Waters Library Service
Partic in OCLC Online Computer Library Center, Inc; Wisconsin Library Services
Special Services for the Deaf - TDD
Special Services for the Blind - Kurzweil Personal Reader
Open Mon-Thurs 9:30-8:30, Fri 9:30-5:30, Sat & Sun 1-4:30 (Winter)
Friends of the Library Group

CR UNIVERSITY OF WISCONSIN-SUPERIOR, Jim Dan Hill Library, PO Box 2000, Belknap & Catlin, 54880. SAN 318-4099. Tel: 715-394-8343. Interlibrary Loan Service Tel: 715-394-8130. Reference Tel: 715-394-8341. FAX: 715-394-8462. Web Site: www.uwsuper.edu. *Head of Libr*, Bob Carmack; Tel: 715-394-8346, E-Mail: bcarmack@staff.uwsuper.edu; *Bk Coordr*, Laura Jacobs; Tel: 715-394-8359, E-Mail: ljacobs@staff.uwsuper.edu; *Govt Doc*, Ella Cross; Tel: 715-394-8512, E-Mail: ecross@staff.uwsuper.edu; *Info Tech*, Jeneen LaSee-Willemssen; Tel: 715-394-8342, E-Mail: jwillems@staff.uwsuper.edu; *Tech Servs*, Deb Nordgren; Tel: 715-394-8233, E-Mail: dnorgre@staff.uwsuper.edu; Staff 11 (MLS 5, Non-MLS 6)
Founded 1896. Enrl 2,350; Fac 135; Highest Degree: Master
Jul 1999-Jun 2000 Income $747,912, State $737,133, Other $10,779. Mats Exp $220,186, Books $39,845, Per/Ser (Incl. Access Fees) $129,035, Presv $2,689, Micro $9,211, Other Print Mats $14, Electronic Ref Mat (Incl. Access Fees) $16,141. Sal $399,378 (Prof $186,216)
Library Holdings: Bk Vols 250,468; Bk Titles 198,569; Per Subs 1,894
Subject Interests: Education, Government
Special Collections: Lake Superior Marine Museum Association Coll; Literature (John W R Beecroft); Regional History
Database Vendor: Dialog, Ebsco - EbscoHost, IAC - Info Trac, IAC - SearchBank, OCLC - First Search, Silverplatter Information Inc., Wilson - Wilson Web
Publications: IITC Connections
Partic in Coun of Wis Libs, Inc; OCLC Online Computer Library Center, Inc; Wisconsin Library Services
Special Services for the Blind - Computers with Voice Synthesizer

J WISCONSIN INDIANHEAD TECHNICAL COLLEGE, Learning Resource Center,* 600 N 21st St, 54880-5296. SAN 318-4102. Tel: 715-394-6677, Ext 6268. Toll Free Tel: 800-243-9484. FAX: 715-394-3771. *Librn*, Judy Lyons; E-Mail: jlyons@wite.tec.wi.us
Founded 1965
Library Holdings: Bk Vols 8,300; Bk Titles 7,900; Per Subs 190

SUSSEX

P PAULINE HAASS PUBLIC LIBRARY, N64 W23820 Main St, 53089-3120. SAN 324-1300. Tel: 262-246-5180. Reference Tel: 262-246-5181. FAX: 262-246-5236. Web Site: www.wcfls.lib.wi.us/phpl/. *Dir*, Joy Botts; E-Mail: mjbotts@phpl.lib.wi.us; *Ad Servs, Ref*, Kathy Klager; *Ch Servs*, Beth Brendler; Tel: 262-246-5182; *Tech Servs*, Janet Soofi; Staff 16 (MLS 5, Non-MLS 11)
Founded 1980. Pop 17,000; Circ 219,392
Jan 1999-Dec 1999 Income $631,607, City $287,930, County $307,791, Locally Generated Income $35,886. Mats Exp $78,544, Books $60,855, Per/Ser (Incl. Access Fees) $5,098, AV Equip $10,179, Electronic Ref Mat (Incl. Access Fees) $2,412. Sal $316,267 (Prof $162,090)
Library Holdings: Bk Vols 56,085; Bk Titles 55,855; Per Subs 158
Database Vendor: epixtech, inc.
Publications: Newsletter
Mem of Waukesha County Federated Library System
Friends of the Library Group

THERESA

P THERESA PUBLIC LIBRARY,* 290 Mayville St, 53091-0307. SAN 364-6203. Tel: 920-488-2342. FAX: 920-488-2342. *Coll Develop, Librn*, Nancy Wiedmeyer; *Ch Servs*, Elizabeth Bodden; *Ch Servs*, Margaret Giese
Jan 1998-Dec 1999 Income $34,641, State $2,060, County $2,000. Mats Exp $7,975, Books $6,775, Per/Ser (Incl. Access Fees) $500. Sal $16,224 (Prof $10,400)

Library Holdings: Bk Vols 8,058; Per Subs 30
Subject Interests: Collectibles, Local history
Mem of Mid-Wisconsin Federated Library System
Open Mon, Wed & Thurs 1-8, Fri 1-5, closed Tues
Friends of the Library Group

THIENSVILLE

S EDUCATIONAL LEADERSHIP INSTITUTE LIBRARY, 424 Susan Lane, 53092. SAN 373-3084. Tel: 262-512-2875. *Dir*, Dr Jeremy Lietz
Library Holdings: Bk Vols 920; Per Subs 61
Special Collections: Regional Demographic Data; School Law; School Organization & Routines; Special Education Adminstration

THORP

P THORP PUBLIC LIBRARY,* 401 S Conway Dr, 54771. (Mail add: PO Box 407, 54771), SAN 318-4129. Tel: 715-669-5953. FAX: 715-669-7319. *Dir*, Renee Hermsen; E-Mail: rhermsen@wvls.lib.wi.us; *Asst Librn*, Melva Jaskot
Founded 1898. Pop 1,650; Circ 30,184
Library Holdings: Bk Vols 23,000; Per Subs 73
Mem of Wisconsin Valley Library Service

THREE LAKES

P EDWARD U DEMMER MEMORIAL LIBRARY,* 6961 W School St, 54562. SAN 318-4137. Tel: 715-546-3391. FAX: 715-546-2930. *Coll Develop, Librn*, Michelle Gobert
Founded 1949. Pop 2,000; Circ 40,892
Library Holdings: Bk Titles 28,643; Per Subs 72
Publications: Demmer Library Newsletter (monthly)
Mem of Wisconsin Valley Library Service
Friends of the Library Group

P ONEIDA COUNTY MAILBOX LIBRARY,* 6169 W School St, PO Box 375, 54562-0375. SAN 377-9793. Tel: 715-546-3450. FAX: 715-546-3450. *Librn*, Deanne S Evensen
Library Holdings: Bk Titles 50,000
Partic in Wisconsin Valley Library Service

TOMAH

GM DEPARTMENT OF VETERAN AFFAIRS, VA Medical Center Library, 500 E Veterans St, 54660. SAN 318-4153. Tel: 608-372-1716. FAX: 608-372-1670. *In Charge*, Kathy Sasbender; Tel: 608-372-1270; Staff 2 (MLS 1, Non-MLS 1)
Founded 1947
Oct 1998-Sep 1999 Income Federal $116,000. Mats Exp $116,052, Books $30,887, Per/Ser (Incl. Access Fees) $62,094, Electronic Ref Mat (Incl. Access Fees) $4,157
Library Holdings: Bk Titles 7,796; Per Subs 316
Subject Interests: Clinical medicine, Large print, Nursing, Patient health educ, Psychiatry, Psychology
Automation Activity & Vendor Info: (Acquisitions) Sagebrush Corporation; (Cataloging) Sagebrush Corporation; (Circulation) Sagebrush Corporation; (Course Reserve) Sagebrush Corporation; (ILL) Sagebrush Corporation; (Media Booking) Sagebrush Corporation; (OPAC) Sagebrush Corporation
Partic in Greater Midwest Regional Medical Libr Network; Northwestern Wisconsin Health Science Library Consortium; Vets Admin Libr Network
Includes Health Sciences & General libraries & Institution's Historical Archives; Supports patients, staff, volunteers & visitors to the Tomah VA Medical Center

P TOMAH PUBLIC LIBRARY,* 716 Superior Ave, 54660-2098. SAN 318-4145. Tel: 608-374-7470. FAX: 608-374-7471. E-Mail: tomah_pl@tomah.com. Web Site: www.tomah.com/tomahpl. *Dir*, Jeanne Rice; *Ch Servs*, Geraldine Wells
Founded 1876. Pop 16,325
Jan 1999-Dec 1999 Income $300,525. Mats Exp $44,789, Books $34,436, Per/Ser (Incl. Access Fees) $6,878, Micro $99, AV Equip $3,376. Sal $129,843 (Prof $32,566)
Library Holdings: Bk Vols 42,838
Automation Activity & Vendor Info: (Cataloging) Follett; (Circulation) Follett; (OPAC) Follett
Mem of Winding Rivers Library System
Friends of the Library Group

TOMAHAWK

P TOMAHAWK PUBLIC LIBRARY,* 300 W Lincoln Ave, 54487. SAN 318-4161. Tel: 715-453-2455. FAX: 715-453-1630. *Dir*, Paula Steurnagel
Jan 1998-Dec 1998 Income $313,750, State $2,023, City $133,079, Federal $1,500, County $150,068, Other $27,080. Mats Exp $52,511. Sal $168
Library Holdings: Bk Vols 54,383; Per Subs 156
Mem of Wisconsin Valley Library Service

TREMPEALEAU

P HETTIE PIERCE PUBLIC LIBRARY,* 24455 Third St, PO Box 383, 54661. SAN 318-417X. Tel: 608-534-6197. *Librn*, Judy Grant
Founded 1913. Pop 1,100; Circ 8,000
Jan 1999-Dec 1999 Income $41,000
Library Holdings: Bk Vols 11,000; Per Subs 36
Mem of La Crosse Area Libr Syst; Winding Rivers Library System

TURTLE LAKE

P TURTLE LAKE PUBLIC LIBRARY,* 114 Martin Ave, 54889-0272. S 376-6748. Tel: 715-986-4618. *Librn*, Marsha Gehrman
Jan 2000-Dec 2000 Income $30,000. Mats Exp $5,600. Sal $20,463
Library Holdings: Bk Vols 10,000; Bk Titles 9,000; Per Subs 103
Mem of Indianhead Federated Library System
Open Tues & Thurs 10-6, Wed 12-8 & Sat 10-12

TWO RIVERS

P LESTER PUBLIC LIBRARY, (LPL), 1001 Adams, 54241. SAN 318-4 Tel: 920-793-8888. Interlibrary Loan Service Tel: 920-793-7105. Refere Tel: 920-793-7114. FAX: 920-793-7150. E-Mail: lesref@esls.lib.wi.us. Nicholas Niederlander; Tel: 920-793-7104, E-Mail: nicholas@esls.lib.w *Circ*, Betty VanDer Vaart; Staff 6 (MLS 1, Non-MLS 5)
Founded 1891. Pop 19,045; Circ 186,636
Jan 2000-Dec 2000 Income $686,000, City $505,000, County $131,000 Locally Generated Income $50,000. Mats Exp $77,326, Books $52,950, Ser (Incl. Access Fees) $9,451, Micro $150. Sal $288,296 (Prof $70,90
Library Holdings: Bk Vols 52,531; Per Subs 203
Subject Interests: Genealogy, Local history
Automation Activity & Vendor Info: (Acquisitions) epixtech, inc.; (Cataloging) epixtech, inc.; (Circulation) epixtech, inc.; (Course Reserve epixtech, inc.; (ILL) epixtech, inc.; (Media Booking) epixtech, inc.; (OP epixtech, inc.; (Serials) epixtech, inc.
Mem of Manitowoc-Calumet Library System
Friends of the Library Group

UNION GROVE

P GRAHAM PUBLIC LIBRARY, 1215 Main St, 53182-1303. SAN 318- Tel: 262-878-2910. FAX: 262-878-0213. Web Site: www.uniongrove.lib.wi.us. *Dir*, Kathryn A Hanson; Staff 2 (Non-MLS 2
Pop 6,700; Circ 58,138
2000-2001 Income $193,598, City $123,798, County $55,200, Other $7, Mats Exp $28,800, Books $24,000, Per/Ser (Incl. Access Fees) $4,800. $84,499 (Prof $26,000)
Library Holdings: Bk Titles 33,946; Per Subs 103
Subject Interests: Am hist, Art, Local genealogy, Popular psychol
Automation Activity & Vendor Info: (Cataloging) Follett; (Circulation Follett; (OPAC) Follett
Mem of Lakeshores Library System
Partic in OCLC Online Computer Library Center, Inc

VERONA

P VERONA PUBLIC LIBRARY,* 130 N Franklin St, 53593-1202. SAN 4218. Tel: 608-845-7180. FAX: 608-845-8917. E-Mail: verona@scls.lib.wi.us. *Dir*, Mary Griffith; *Ch Servs*, Jan Gessler
Founded 1959. Pop 10,000; Circ 149,672
Library Holdings: Bk Titles 34,741; Per Subs 105
Special Collections: Local History
Mem of South Central Library System
Friends of the Library Group

VESPER

P VESPER PUBLIC LIBRARY, 6553 Cameron St, 54489-9999. SAN 318 4226. Tel: 715-569-4669. E-Mail: vespl@tznet.com. *Dir*, Arlene Marti
Founded 1950. Circ 12,500
Library Holdings: Bk Vols 9,426; Per Subs 52
Subject Interests: Children, Christian bks, Crafts
Special Collections: World War II
Mem of South Central Library System

VIOLA

P VIOLA PUBLIC LIBRARY, 137 S Main St, 54664-7037. SAN 318-423 Tel: 608-627-1850. FAX: 419-828-6156. *Dir*, Lynette Owens; E-Mail: lowens@swls.org; Staff 1 (Non-MLS 1)

Founded 1918. Pop 1,790; Circ 6,321
Jan 1999-Dec 1999 Income $33,823, City $32,639, County $1,150. Mats Exp $4,651, Books $3,200, Per/Ser (Incl. Access Fees) $826, AV Equip $625. Sal $11,963
Library Holdings: Bk Titles 8,475; Per Subs 57
Special Collections: 1891-1987 Issues of Local Newspaper, microfilm
Automation Activity & Vendor Info: (Cataloging) epixtech, inc.; (Circulation) epixtech, inc.; (ILL) epixtech, inc.
Database Vendor: Ebsco - EbscoHost
Mem of Southwest Wisconsin Library System

)QUA

MCINTOSH MEMORIAL LIBRARY, 118 E Jefferson St, PO Box 821, 54665-0821. SAN 318-4242. Tel: 608-637-7151. E-Mail: mcintlib@frontier.net.net. *Dir*, Lisa Solverson
1998-1999 Income $121,000, City $110,000, County $8,000, Locally Generated Income $3,000. Mats Exp $15,900, Books $12,000, Per/Ser (Incl. Access Fees) $3,000, Micro $900. Sal $79,500 (Prof $26,200)
Library Holdings: Bk Vols 35,000; Bk Titles 10,000; Per Subs 100
Mem of Winding Rivers Library System

ɜENO

WABENO PUBLIC LIBRARY,* 4556 Branch St, 54566. SAN 318-4250. Tel: 715-473-4131. FAX: 715-473-4131. *Dir*, Diane D Johnson; *Asst Librn*, Terry Glasl
Founded 1910. Pop 1,200; Circ 16,799
Jan 1999-Dec 1999 Income $16,000. Mats Exp $3,860. Sal $8,100
Library Holdings: Bk Titles 8,500; Per Subs 22
Mem of Wisconsin Valley Library Service

.WORTH

WALWORTH MEMORIAL LIBRARY,* 101 Maple Ave, PO Box 280, 53184-0280. SAN 318-4277. Tel: 414-275-6322. *Librn*, Jan Peterson
Pop 1,750; Circ 35,000
Library Holdings: Bk Vols 12,500; Per Subs 33
Mem of Lakeshores Library System

SHBURN

WASHBURN PUBLIC LIBRARY, 307 Washington Ave, 54891. (Mail add: PO Box 248, 54891), SAN 318-4285. Tel: 715-373-6172. FAX: 715-373-6186. E-Mail: washlib@win.bright.net. Web Site: www.win.bright.net/~washlib. *Dir*, Cheryl A Michalski; Staff 6 (Non-MLS 6)
Founded 1904. Pop 6,000; Circ 45,000
Jan 2000-Dec 2000 Income (Main Library Only) $107,210, City $70,210, County $34,000, Locally Generated Income $3,000. Mats Exp $17,500. Sal $49,213
Library Holdings: Bk Titles 30,000; Per Subs 60
Automation Activity & Vendor Info: (OPAC) Innovative Interfaces Inc.
Database Vendor: Innovative Interfaces INN - View
Function: ILL available
Mem of Northern Waters Library Service
Partic in Merlin
Open Tues 9-5, Wed & Thurs 1-8, Fri 9-5, Sat 10-2
Friends of the Library Group

TERFORD

LAKESHORES LIBRARY SYSTEM, 106 W Main St, 53185. SAN 318-3459. Tel: 262-636-9211. FAX: 262-636-3710. Web Site: www.lakeshores.lib.wi.us. *Syst Coordr*, Bernard Bellin; E-Mail: bbellin@wi.net; Staff 6 (MLS 3, Non-MLS 3)
Founded 1983. Pop 232,304
Publications: Lake Shore Lines
Member Libraries: Aram Public Library; Barrett Memorial Library; Brigham Memorial Library; Burlington Public Library; Darien Public Library; East Troy Lions Public Library; Fontana Public Library; Graham Public Library; Lake Geneva Public Library; Matheson Memorial Library; Racine Public Library; Rochester Public Library; Walworth Memorial Library; Waterford Public Library
Partic in OCLC Online Computer Library Center, Inc
Lakeshores Library System is a two-county federated library system serving the 15 libraries in Racine & Walworth Counties

WATERFORD PUBLIC LIBRARY,* 123 N River St, 53185-4149. SAN 318-4307. Tel: 414-534-3988. FAX: 414-534-5373. *Dir*, Pam Beldon; Staff 2 (MLS 2)
Founded 1967. Pop 10,000
Jan 1998-Dec 1998 Income $147,458. Mats Exp $17,825. Sal $111,274
Library Holdings: Bk Vols 25,000; Per Subs 71
Mem of Lakeshores Library System
Friends of the Library Group

WATERLOO

P KARL JUNGINGER MEMORIAL LIBRARY,* 625 N Monroe St, 53594-1183. SAN 318-4315. Tel: 920-478-3344. FAX: 920-478-2351. *Dir*, Cynthia Taylor; *Asst Librn, Coll Develop*, Joel Zibell; Staff 3 (MLS 2, Non-MLS 1)
Founded 1901. Pop 2,216; Circ 24,913
Jan 1999-Dec 1999 Income $276,909, State $1,168, City $125,529, County $8,387, Locally Generated Income $2,500, Other $139,325. Mats Exp $23,580, Books $15,660, Per/Ser (Incl. Access Fees) $1,800, Other Print Mats $1,350. Sal $106,601 (Prof $67,577)
Library Holdings: Bk Vols 23,615
Subject Interests: Children lit, Genealogy, Local history
Special Collections: American Wood Carvings (Leon Wood Coll); German Language Books
Publications: newsletters; Off the Shelves (newspaper column)
Special Services for the Deaf - High interest/low vocabulary books; Special interest periodicals
Friends of the Library Group

WATERTOWN

SR BETHESDA LUTHERAN HOMES & SERVICES, INC, (NCRC), National Christian Resource Center, 700 Hoffmann Dr, 53094. SAN 328-025X. Tel: 920-261-3050, Ext 416. Toll Free Tel: 800-369-4636. FAX: 920-262-6513. E-Mail: ncrc@blhs.org. Web Site: www.blhs.org. *Coordr*, Thomas Heuer; Staff 5 (Non-MLS 5)
Library Holdings: Bk Vols 3,000
Subject Interests: Special education
Partic in South Central Wisconsin Health Science Library Cooperative
Special religious education & ministry with persons who have disabilities & their families

CR MARANATHA BAPTIST BIBLE COLLEGE, Cedarholm Library & Resource Center,* 745 W Main St, 53094. SAN 370-6206. Tel: 920-206-2375. FAX: 920-261-9109. *Dir*, Stephan Mattsen; Staff 5 (MLS 2, Non-MLS 3)
Founded 1967. Enrl 810
Jul 1997-Jun 1998 Mats Exp $71,915, Books $34,972, Per/Ser (Incl. Access Fees) $19,500, Micro $5,537. Sal $123,601 (Prof $47,872)
Library Holdings: Bk Vols 95,664; Bk Titles 85,000; Per Subs 515

M WATERTOWN MEMORIAL HOSPITAL, Quirk Resource Center,* 125 Hospital Dr, 53098-3384. SAN 374-4841. Tel: 920-262-4278. FAX: 920-262-4266. *Librn*, Bonnie O'Leske; E-Mail: boleske@wahs.com
Founded 1988
Oct 1996-Sep 1997 Income $53,915, Locally Generated Income $6,700, Parent Institution $13,640, Other $9,965. Mats Exp $10,139, Books $3,520, Per/Ser (Incl. Access Fees) $4,919. Sal $11,440
Library Holdings: Bk Titles 300; Per Subs 100
Subject Interests: Medicine, Nursing

P WATERTOWN PUBLIC LIBRARY, 100 S Water St, 53094-4320. SAN 318-4331. Tel: 920-262-4090. FAX: 920-261-8943. E-Mail: askrefwt@mwfls.org. Web Site: www.watertown.lib.wi.us. *Dir*, Matthew Williams; Tel: 920-262-4090, Ext 12, E-Mail: williamm@mwfls.org; *Asst Dir*, Hans Baierl; Tel: 920-262-4090, Ext 13, E-Mail: baierlh@mwfls.org; *Ch Servs*, Leah Fritsche; Tel: 920-262-4090, Ext 24, E-Mail: fritschl@mwfls.org; *Ch Servs*, Chris Ticknor; *Cat*, Dan Cawley; *Coll Develop*, Sharry Lueck; Tel: 920-262-4090, Ext 18, E-Mail: luecks@mwfls.org; Staff 4 (MLS 4)
Founded 1907
Jan 2000-Dec 2000 Income $755,882, City $572,324, County $146,456, Locally Generated Income $40,200. Mats Exp $99,850, Books $92,080, Per/Ser (Incl. Access Fees) $7,500, AV Equip $9,500. Sal $566,268
Library Holdings: Bk Vols 83,723
Subject Interests: Local history
Mem of Mid-Wisconsin Federated Library System
Friends of the Library Group

WAUKESHA

CR CARROLL COLLEGE, Todd Wehr Memorial Library, 100 N East Ave, 53186. SAN 318-434X. Tel: 262-524-7175, 262-524-7177. Reference Tel: 262-650-4892. FAX: 262-524-7377. Web Site: www.cc.edu/library. *Dir*, Dr Lelan McLemore; Tel: 262-524-7377, E-Mail: lmclemor@cc.edu; *Assoc Dir*, Becky Steffes; Tel: 262-524-7176, 524-7372, E-Mail: bsteffes@cc.edu; *Mgr*, Allison Reeves; Tel: 262-524-7180, E-Mail: areeves@cc.edu; *Ref*, James Van Ess; Tel: 262-524-7178, E-Mail: jvaness@cc.edu; *Acq, Cat*, Dr Linda Hartig; Tel: 262-524-7179, E-Mail: lhartig@cc.edu; *Circ*, Carole Winrich; Tel: 262-524-7307, E-Mail: cwinrich@cc.edu; *Ser*, Kristin Edenharder; Tel: 262-951-3022, E-Mail: kedenhar@cc.edu; *Info Specialist*, Kristin Miller; Tel: 262-524-7674, E-Mail: krismil@cc.edu; *Info Res*, Mary Hickey; Tel: 262-650-3008, E-Mail: mhickey@cc.edu; *ILL*, Joanne Hemb; Tel: 262-650-4832, E-Mail: jhemb@cc.edu. Subject Specialists: *Archives*, James Van Ess; *Business*, Mary Hickey; *Civil War*, Becky Steffes; *Music*, Dr Linda Hartig; *Politics*, Dr Lelan McLemore; Staff 10 (MLS 5, Non-MLS 5)
Founded 1851. Enrl 2,521; Fac 88; Highest Degree: Master
Library Holdings: Bk Vols 188,000; Per Subs 641

Subject Interests: History, Relig studies
Special Collections: English & Scottish 19th Century Literature; History (W Norman FitzGerald Civil War Coll), bks, maps; Welsh Literature & Language
Automation Activity & Vendor Info: (Acquisitions) Innovative Interfaces Inc.; (Cataloging) Innovative Interfaces Inc.; (Circulation) Innovative Interfaces Inc.; (Course Reserve) Innovative Interfaces Inc.; (ILL) Innovative Interfaces Inc.; (OPAC) Innovative Interfaces Inc.; (Serials) Innovative Interfaces Inc.
Database Vendor: Ebsco - EbscoHost, GaleNet, IAC - SearchBank, Lexis-Nexis, OCLC - First Search, ProQuest, Silverplatter Information Inc.
Restriction: Private library
Partic in Library Council Of Metropolitan Milwaukee, Inc; WILS; Wis Asn Of Independent Cols & Univs
Friends of the Library Group

R FIRST BAPTIST CHURCH LIBRARY-WAUKESHA, 247 Wisconsin Ave, 53186. SAN 318-4358. Tel: 262-542-7233. *Librn*, Sandra Cope
Library Holdings: Bk Vols 3,000
Subject Interests: Religion
Special Collections: Christian Education Materials

S KALMBACH PUBLISHING CO LIBRARY, PO Box 1612, 53187. SAN 318-2002. Tel: 414-796-8776, Ext 423. FAX: 414-796-6468. *Librn*, Nancy L Bartol
Founded 1949
Library Holdings: Bk Titles 7,500; Per Subs 175
Subject Interests: Dollhouses, Railroads

J UNIVERSITY OF WISCONSIN COLLEGES, Waukesha Library & Media Services,* 1500 University Dr, 53188. SAN 318-4382. Tel: 414-521-5471. Interlibrary Loan Service Tel: 414-521-5531. FAX: 414-521-5116. *Bibliog Instr, Dir*, Faye Flesia; E-Mail: fflesia@uwc.edu; *ILL, Librn, Publ Servs*, Ann O'Hara; *ILL, Librn, Publ Servs*, Jane Cavanaugh; *AV*, Denise Spleas; *AV*, Linda Wilson
Founded 1966. Enrl 2,500
Library Holdings: Bk Vols 39,000
Partic in Library Council Of Metropolitan Milwaukee, Inc; Wisconsin Library Services

P WAUKESHA COUNTY FEDERATED LIBRARY SYSTEM, 831 N Grand Ave, Ste 220, 53186-4822. SAN 321-1061. Tel: 262-896-8080. TDD: 262-896-8089. FAX: 262-896-8086. E-Mail: wcfls@wcfls.lib.wi.us. Web Site: www.wcfls.lib.wi.us. *Dir*, Thomas J Hennen, Jr; E-Mail: thennen@wcfls.lib.wi.us; *Ad Servs*, Jocelyn Bubolz; E-Mail: bubolz@wcfls.lib.wi.us; *Automation Syst Coordr*, Mellanie Mercier; E-Mail: mmercier@wcfls.lib.wi.us; *ILL*, Laurie Freund; E-Mail: ljfreund@wcfls.lib.wi.us; *Ch Servs*, Claudia Backus; E-Mail: clbackus@wcfls.lib.wi.us; *Ref*, Nancy Fletcher; E-Mail: nsfletch@wcfls.lib.wi.us; Staff 6 (MLS 6)
Founded 1981. Pop 345,440
Jan 1999-Dec 1999 Income $3,211,294, State $846,043, Federal $576,436, County $1,788,815
Publications: Expression (Newsletter)
Member Libraries: Alice Baker Memorial Public Library; Barbara Sanborn Public Library; Big Bend Village Library; Brookfield Public Library; Butler Public Library; Delafield Public Library; Elm Grove Public Library; Hartland Public Library; Maude Shunk Public Library; Mukwonago Community Library; Muskego Public Library; New Berlin Public Library; Oconomowoc Public Library; Pauline Haass Public Library; Town Hall Library; Waukesha Public Library

S WAUKESHA COUNTY MUSEUM, Research Center,* 101 W Main St, 53186. SAN 318-4390. Tel: 414-548-7186. FAX: 414-896-6862.; Staff 5 (MLS 3, Non-MLS 2)
Founded 1914
Library Holdings: Bk Titles 7,000; Per Subs 37
Special Collections: Waukesha County Family & Local History Coll
Publications: limestone book; Publications list; research guides; walking tour guides

M WAUKESHA MEMORIAL HOSPITAL, Medical Library, 725 American Ave, 53188-9982. SAN 318-4404. Tel: 262-928-2150. FAX: 262-928-2514. *Librn, Online Servs*, Linda Oddan; E-Mail: linda.oddan@phci.org; Staff 1 (MLS 1)
Founded 1959
Library Holdings: Bk Vols 2,604; Per Subs 287
Subject Interests: Hospital administration, Medicine, Nursing, Paramed
Publications: Adlibs (newsletter)
Partic in Midwest Health Sci Libr Network; Southeastern Wisconsin Health Science Library Consortium

P WAUKESHA PUBLIC LIBRARY, 321 Wisconsin Ave, 53186-4786. SAN 318-4412. Tel: 262-524-3680. Circulation Tel: 262-524-3684. Reference Tel: 262-524-3682. TDD: 262-524-3696. FAX: 262-524-3677. Web Site: www.waukesha.lib.wi.us. *Dir*, Jane Ameel; Tel: 262-524-3681, E-Mail: jameel@waukesha.lib.wi.us; *Ad Servs*, Davie Brostrom; Tel: 262-524-3746, E-Mail: dbrostrom@waukesha.lib.wi.us; *Tech Coordr*, Shawn Carlson; Tel: 262-524-3691, E-Mail: scarlson@waukesha.lib.wi.us; *Ref*, Shirley Chilson; Tel: 262-524-3904, E-Mail: schilson@waukesha.lib.wi.us; *Ch Servs*, Sandra Cope; *Ch Servs*, Kate FitzGerald-Fleck; Tel: 262-524-3692, E-Mail: kfitzger@waukesha.lib.wi.us; *Circ*, Marsha Martin; Tel: 262-524-3903, E-Mail: mmartin@waukesha.lib.wi.us; *Automation Syst Coordr*, J How Pringle; Tel: 262-524-3688, E-Mail: hpringle@waukesha.lib.wi.su; *Tech Servs*, Mary Wegener; Tel: 262-524-3690, E-Mail: mwegener@waukesha.lib.wi.us; Staff 38 (MLS 14, Non-MLS 24)
Founded 1896. Pop 102,856; Circ 1,144,983
Jan 1999-Dec 1999 Income $2,800,672, State $54,449, City $1,681,37[illegible] County $811,800, Locally Generated Income $77,033, Other $176,015. Exp $380,524, Books $327,261, Per/Ser (Incl. Access Fees) $29,513, Electronic Ref Mat (Incl. Access Fees) $23,750. Sal $1,819,216 (Prof $843,270)
Library Holdings: Bk Vols 269,952; Bk Titles 248,756; Per Subs 541
Automation Activity & Vendor Info: (Acquisitions) DRA; (Catalogin[illegible] DRA; (Circulation) DRA; (OPAC) DRA
Mem of Waukesha County Federated Library System
Partic in Library Council Of Metropolitan Milwaukee, Inc
Friends of the Library Group

G WISCONSIN DEPARTMENT OF TRANSPORTATION, District Two Library, 141 NW Barstow, District 2, PO Box 798, 53187-0798. SAN [illegible] 2584. Tel: 262-548-5917. FAX: 262-521-5357. *Librn*, Jean Trumpy; E-[illegible] jean.trumpy@dot.state.wi.us
Founded 1975
Library Holdings: Per Subs 80
Subject Interests: Construction, Hwy admin, Maintenance, Operations, Traffic control, Urban transportation
Publications: Acquisitions List (monthly)
Partic in Library Council Of Metropolitan Milwaukee, Inc

WAUNAKEE

P WAUNAKEE PUBLIC LIBRARY,* 710 South St, 53597-1638. SAN [illegible] 4420. Tel: 608-849-4217. FAX: 608-849-7817. Web Site: www.scis.lib.[illegible] wau/home.html. *Dir*, Louise Bauer; *Librn*, Agnes Steichen; *Librn*, Kath[illegible] Spahn; *Librn*, Karla Stafford; *Librn*, Kathy Vogt; *Librn*, Sandra Esse; *Li[illegible]* Kris Semler; *Librn*, Gay Strandemo; *Librn*, Susan McComb; *Librn*, Kat[illegible] Sperry
Pop 8,023; Circ 127,738
Jan 1998-Dec 1998 Income $309,316, State $319, City $258,492, Coun[illegible] $41,504, Locally Generated Income $9,001. Mats Exp $33,068, Books $18,247, Per/Ser (Incl. Access Fees) $3,132, Micro $165, AV Equip $4,[illegible] Other Print Mats $5,093, Electronic Ref Mat (Incl. Access Fees) $1,541 $224,368
Library Holdings: Bk Vols 38,000; Bk Titles 37,415; Per Subs 128
Automation Activity & Vendor Info: (Acquisitions) epixtech, inc.; (Cataloging) epixtech, inc.; (Circulation) epixtech, inc.; (OPAC) epixtec[illegible] inc.; (Serials) epixtech, inc.
Mem of South Central Library System
Friends of the Library Group

WAUPACA

M RIVERSIDE MEDICAL CENTER, Health Science Library,* 800 Rivers[illegible] Dr, 54981. SAN 371-652X. Tel: 715-258-1065. FAX: 715-256-2030. *In Charge*, Andrea Crane
Library Holdings: Bk Titles 650; Per Subs 70
Partic in Fox River Valley Area Library Consortium

P WAUPACA AREA PUBLIC LIBRARY,* 107 S Main St, 54981-1521. [illegible] 318-4447. Tel: 715-258-4414. FAX: 715-258-4418. *Dir*, Gerald A Brow[illegible] *Asst Librn*, Kristen Anderson; *Ch Servs*, Sandra Grambsch; *Ref*, Stephan[illegible] Thomas
Founded 1900
Jan 1999-Dec 1999 Income $411,000. Mats Exp $57,625, Books $47,00[illegible] Per/Ser (Incl. Access Fees) $5,600, Presv $25, Micro $5,000. Sal $216,3[illegible]
Library Holdings: Bk Vols 64,000; Per Subs 120
Special Collections: Large Print Coll; Susan Christenson Memorial Women's Studies Coll; Wisconsin Coll
Mem of Outagamie Waupaca Library System

WAUPUN

S DODGE CORRECTIONAL INSTITUTION LIBRARY, One W Lincoln PO Box 661, 53963-0661. SAN 365-0855. Tel: 920-324-5577, Ext 6570. FAX: 920-324-6297. *Senior Librn*, William Hession; *Coll Develop, ILL*, John Lungren; Staff 8 (MLS 2, Non-MLS 6)
Library Holdings: Bk Titles 8,700; Per Subs 130
Subject Interests: Criminal justice, Law
Automation Activity & Vendor Info: (Cataloging) Sagebrush Corporati[illegible] (Circulation) Sagebrush Corporation; (OPAC) Sagebrush Corporation

S WAUPUN CORRECTIONAL INSTITUTION LIBRARY, 200 S Madiso[illegible] St, PO Box 351, 53963-0351. SAN 318-4463. Tel: 920-324-5571, Ext 15[illegible] FAX: 920-324-7250. *Librn*, Nevin B Webster; E-Mail: nevin.webster@

doc.state.wi.us; Staff 1 (Non-MLS 1)
Founded 1890
Library Holdings: Bk Vols 12,000; Per Subs 90
Automation Activity & Vendor Info: (Circulation) Sagebrush Corporation; (ILL) Brodart; (OPAC) Sagebrush Corporation

WAUPUN PUBLIC LIBRARY, 120 S Mill St, 53963-0391. (Mail add: PO Box 391, 53963), SAN 318-4455. Tel: 920-324-7925. FAX: 920-324-7933. E-Mail: wpl@mwfls.org. Web Site: www.waupunpubliclibrary.org. *Dir*, Bret Jaeger; E-Mail: wpldir@mwfls.org; *Asst Dir*, Pam Eichstadt; E-Mail: wplad@mwfls.org; *Circ*, Kathy Jensen; E-Mail: wplcirc@mwfls.org; *Ch Servs*, kay Hansen; E-Mail: wplchild@mwfls.org; *ILL*, Lynda Lagodney; E-Mail: wplill@mwfls.org; Staff 14 (MLS 2, Non-MLS 12)
Founded 1857. Pop 14,000; Circ 86,488
Jan 1999-Dec 1999 Income $387,845, State $821, City $332,164, Federal $9,000, County $41,062, Locally Generated Income $4,798. Mats Exp $50,950, Books $39,295, Per/Ser (Incl. Access Fees) $7,970, Micro $651, AV Equip $3,685, Other Print Mats $407. Sal $174,925 (Prof $41,200)
Library Holdings: Bk Vols 46,359; Bk Titles 45,973; Per Subs 156
Subject Interests: Wis hist
Automation Activity & Vendor Info: (Cataloging) epixtech, inc.; (Circulation) epixtech, inc.; (OPAC) epixtech, inc.
Database Vendor: epixtech, inc.
Mem of Mid-Wisconsin Federated Library System
Friends of the Library Group

SAU

DR JOSEPH F SMITH MEDICAL LIBRARY, 333 Pine Ridge Blvd, 54401. SAN 328-3038. Tel: 715-847-2184. FAX: 715-847-2183. Web Site: www.wausauhospital.org. *Dir*, Jan Kraus; E-Mail: jank@waushosp.org
Library Holdings: Bk Vols 1,400; Per Subs 200
Partic in Northern Wis Health Sci Libr Coop

LEIGH YAWKEY WOODSON ART MUSEUM LIBRARY, 700 N 12th St, 54403-5007. SAN 326-5161. Tel: 715-845-7010. FAX: 715-845-7103. E-Mail: museum@lywam.org. Web Site: www.lywam.org. *Librn*, Kathryn Piffl
Library Holdings: Bk Titles 1,800; Per Subs 30
Subject Interests: Birds, Decorative arts
Restriction: By appointment only

MARATHON COUNTY HISTORICAL SOCIETY LIBRARY, 410 McIndoe St, 54403. SAN 324-1572. Tel: 715-848-0378. FAX: 715-848-0576. *Dir, Librn*, Mary Jane Uecker-Hettinga; Staff 1 (MLS 1)
Founded 1980
Library Holdings: Bk Vols 6,800; Per Subs 20
Subject Interests: County hist, Genealogy, Logging
Special Collections: Marathon County (James Colby Coll), glass neg
Function: Research library
Hours Tues-Thurs 9-3:30

MARATHON COUNTY PUBLIC LIBRARY, 300 N First St, 54403-5405. SAN 365-0944. Tel: 715-261-7200. Interlibrary Loan Service Tel: 715-261-7238. Reference Tel: 715-261-7230. TDD: 715-261-7241. FAX: 715-261-7210. E-Mail: refques@mcpl.lib.wi.us. Web Site: www.mcpl.lib.wi.us. *Dir*, Mary Bethke; Tel: 715-261-7211, E-Mail: mjbethke@mcpl.lib.wi.us; *Br Coordr*, Inese Christman; Tel: 715-261-7242, Fax: 715-261-7249, E-Mail: ineserc@mcpl.lib.wi.us; *Ad Servs*, Michael O'Connor; Tel: 715-261-7234, Fax: 715-261-7232, E-Mail: mikeloconnor@yahoo.com; *Ch Servs*, Sonja Ackerman; Tel: 715-261-7222, E-Mail: snacker@mcpl.lib.wi.us; *Tech Servs*, Elizabeth Scully; Tel: 715-261-7270, Fax: 715-261-7278, E-Mail: elscully@mcpl.lib.wi.us; *Circ*, Gary Gisselman; Tel: 715-261-7205, E-Mail: glgiss@mcpl.lib.wi.us; Staff 55 (MLS 11, Non-MLS 44)
Founded 1905. Pop 126,393; Circ 755,307
Jan 1999-Dec 1999 Income (Main Library and Branch Library) County $3,060,446. Mats Exp $261,550, Books $188,756, Per/Ser (Incl. Access Fees) $50,401, Micro $9,493, Other Print Mats $3,500, Electronic Ref Mat (Incl. Access Fees) $9,400. Sal $2,175,304
Library Holdings: Bk Vols 290,199; Bk Titles 174,309; Per Subs 836
Special Collections: Old Popular Sheet Music; Wisconsin History
Database Vendor: epixtech, inc.
Mem of Wisconsin Valley Library Service
Partic in OCLC Online Computer Library Center, Inc; WILS; Wisconsin Valley Library Service
Friends of the Library Group
Branches: 7
ATHENS BRANCH, Athens Community Hall, 221 Caroline St, Athens, 54411-0910. SAN 365-0979. Tel: 715-257-7292. FAX: 715-257-7292. Web Site: www.mcpl.lib.wi.us. *Br Coordr*, Deborah Balz; E-Mail: debabalz@yahoo.com
Library Holdings: Bk Vols 18,879
Database Vendor: epixtech, inc.
Friends of the Library Group
JOSEPH DESSERT BRANCH, 123 Main St, Mosinee, 54455-1441. SAN 365-1037. Tel: 715-693-2144. FAX: 715-693-2144. Web Site: www.mcpl.lib.wi.us. *Br Coordr*, Nancy Dahlke; E-Mail: njdahlke@yahoo.com
Library Holdings: Bk Vols 19,191
Database Vendor: epixtech, inc.
Friends of the Library Group
EDGAR BRANCH, 224 S Third Ave, Edgar, 54426-0228. SAN 365-1061. Tel: 715-352-3155. FAX: 715-352-3155. Web Site: www.mcpl.lib.wi.us. *Br Coordr*, Debbie Gauerke; E-Mail: ed_debb@yahoo.com
Library Holdings: Bk Vols 14,814
Database Vendor: epixtech, inc.
Friends of the Library Group
MARATHON CITY BRANCH, 704 Third St, PO Box 245, Marathon, 54448. SAN 365-1126. Tel: 715-443-2775. FAX: 715-443-2775. Web Site: www.mcpl.lib.wi.us. *Br Coordr*, Lavone Runge; E-Mail: lrunge14@yahoo.com
Library Holdings: Bk Vols 11,722
Database Vendor: epixtech, inc.
Friends of the Library Group
ROTHSCHILD AREA BRANCH, 211 Grand Ave, Rothschild, 54474-1122. SAN 365-1150. Tel: 715-359-6208. FAX: 715-359-6208. Web Site: www.mcpl.lib.wi.us. *Br Coordr*, Carol Oslage; E-Mail: coslage@yahoo.com
Library Holdings: Bk Vols 30,835
Database Vendor: epixtech, inc.
Friends of the Library Group
SPENCER BRANCH, 105 Park St, PO Box 398, Spencer, 54479-0398. SAN 365-1215. Tel: 715-659-3996. FAX: 715-659-3996. Web Site: www.mcpl.lib.wi.us. *Br Coordr*, Judy Berger; E-Mail: mustangjeb@yahoo.com
Library Holdings: Bk Vols 15,577
Database Vendor: epixtech, inc.
Friends of the Library Group
STRATFORD BRANCH, 400 N Fourth Ave, PO Box 74, Stratford, 54484. SAN 365-124X. Tel: 715-687-4420. FAX: 715-687-4420. Web Site: www.mcpl.lib.wi.us. *Br Coordr*, Janice Pankratz; E-Mail: pankyjan@yahoo.com
Library Holdings: Bk Vols 19,125
Database Vendor: epixtech, inc.
Friends of the Library Group
Bookmobiles: 2

C NORTHCENTRAL TECHNICAL COLLEGE LIBRARY, 1000 W Campus Dr, 54401. SAN 318-448X. Tel: 715-675-3331. Circulation Tel: 715-675-3331 Ext 4054. Reference Tel: 715-675-3331 Ext 4053. FAX: 715-675-9776. Web Site: www.northcentral.tec.wi.us/library.htm. *Dir*, Barbara Cummings; Tel: 715-675-3331, Ext 4056, E-Mail: cummings@northcentral.tec.wi.us; *Librn*, Tatiana B Miller; Tel: 715-675-3331, Ext 4115, Fax: 715-675-1832, E-Mail: miller@northcentral.tec.wi.us; *Tech Servs*, Liz Jacobson; Tel: 715-675-3331, Ext 4053, E-Mail: jacobson@northcentral.tec.wi.us; *Admin Assoc*, Jayne Skrzypchak; Tel: 715-675-3331, Ext 4055, E-Mail: skrzypch@northcentral.tec.wi.us; *Admin Assoc*, Helen Wisneski; Tel: 715-675-3331 Ext, 4054, E-Mail: wisneski@northcentral.tec.wi.us; Staff 6 (MLS 2, Non-MLS 4)
Founded 1969. Enrl 2,500
Jul 1999-Jun 2000 Income $268,000. Mats Exp $67,259, Books $27,359, Per/Ser (Incl. Access Fees) $39,900. Sal $133,692 (Prof $80,741)
Library Holdings: Bk Vols 35,000; Per Subs 300
Subject Interests: Dental hygiene, Nursing, Sci-tech
Special Collections: American Sign Language
Database Vendor: Ebsco - EbscoHost, IAC - SearchBank, ProQuest
Function: Some telephone reference
Partic in Wis PALS Libr Consortium

C UNIVERSITY OF WISCONSIN CENTER-MARATHON COUNTY LIBRARY, 518 S Seventh Ave, 54401-5396. SAN 318-4498. Tel: 715-261-6220. Circulation Tel: 715-261-6220. Reference Tel: 715-261-6218. FAX: 715-261-6330. Web Site: www.uwmc.uwc.edu. *Dir*, Judy Palmateer; Tel: 715-261-6219, E-Mail: jpalmate@uwc.edu; *Ref*, Todd Roll; Tel: 715-261-6218, E-Mail: troll@uwc.edu; *Circ*, Betty Osswald; Tel: 715-261-6202, E-Mail: bosswald@uwc.edu; *Tech Coordr*, Paul Henfer; Tel: 715-261-6208, E-Mail: phenfer@uwc.edu; Staff 4 (MLS 2, Non-MLS 2)
Founded 1938. Enrl 1,100; Fac 45; Highest Degree: Associate
Jul 1998-Jun 1999 Mats Exp $29,665, Books $15,860, Per/Ser (Incl. Access Fees) $13,805. Sal $141,503 (Prof $128,537)
Library Holdings: Bk Vols 38,625; Bk Titles 30,643; Spec Interest Per Sub 141
Automation Activity & Vendor Info: (Cataloging) Endeavor; (Circulation) Endeavor; (Course Reserve) Endeavor; (Media Booking) Endeavor; (OPAC) Endeavor; (Serials) Endeavor
Database Vendor: Dialog, Ebsco - EbscoHost, GaleNet, OCLC - First Search, ProQuest, Wilson - Wilson Web
Partic in OCLC Online Computer Library Center, Inc; Wisconsin Library Services

P WISCONSIN VALLEY LIBRARY SERVICE, (WVLS), 300 N First St, 54403. SAN 318-4501. Tel: 715-261-7250. FAX: 715-261-7259. Web Site: wisvalley.lib.wi.us. *Dir*, Heather Ann Eldred; Tel: 715-261-7251, E-Mail: heldred@wvls.lib.wi.us; *Admin Assoc*, Marla Sepnafski; Tel: 715-261-7252; *Automation Syst Coordr*, Linda Orcutt; Tel: 715-261-7253; *ILL*, Ellen Buchberger; Tel: 715-261-7255; *YA Servs*, Beth Sillars; Staff 10 (MLS 5,

Non-MLS 5)
Founded 1961. Pop 272,550
Jan 2000-Dec 2000 Income $904,672, State $780,256, Federal $49,850, County $31,566, Other $43,000. Mats Exp $72,438, Books $29,347, Per/Ser (Incl. Access Fees) $16,641, Micro $3,950, AV Equip $15,850, Electronic Ref Mat (Incl. Access Fees) $6,650. Sal $393,765 (Prof $241,133)
Automation Activity & Vendor Info: (Acquisitions) epixtech, inc.; (Cataloging) epixtech, inc.; (Circulation) epixtech, inc.; (ILL) Brodart; (Media Booking) epixtech, inc.; (OPAC) epixtech, inc.; (Serials) epixtech, inc.
Publications: Directory of Libraries & Librarians; Lamplighter; Wisconsin Valley Library Service
Member Libraries: Abbotsford Public Library; Antigo Public Library; Colby Public Library; Crandon Public Library; Dorchester Public Library; Edith Evans Community Library; Edward U Demmer Memorial Library; Frances L Simek Memorial Library-Medford; Greenwood Public Library; Jean M Thomsen Memorial Library; Loyal Public Library; Marathon County Public Library; Minocqua Public Library; Neillsville Free Library; Owen Public Library; Rhinelander District Library; Rib Lake Public Library; Samson Memorial Library; T B Scott Library; Thorp Public Library; Tomahawk Public Library; Wabeno Public Library; Westboro Public Library; Western Taylor County Public Library; Withee Public Library
Partic in Dialog Corporation; OCLC Online Computer Library Center, Inc
Special Services for the Blind - Audio-cassettes; Large print bks; Talking books (cassettes & rec)

WAUTOMA

P WAUTOMA PUBLIC LIBRARY, 410 W Main St, PO Box 269, 54982. SAN 318-451X. Tel: 920-787-2988. *Dir*, Mary Elizabeth Knuth; E-Mail: knuth@winnefox.org; Staff 4 (Non-MLS 4)
Pop 7,299; Circ 60,993
Library Holdings: Bk Vols 9,576; Per Subs 74
Automation Activity & Vendor Info: (OPAC) DRA
Database Vendor: DRA
Mem of Winnefox Library System

WAUWATOSA

S BEIHOFF MUSIC CORPORATION, Sheet Music Department Library,* 12040 W Feerick St, Unit H, 53222. SAN 377-3639. Tel: 414-438-3920. FAX: 414-438-3939. *Mgr*, Kenneth Kunz
Library Holdings: Bk Titles 20,000; Per Subs 15

R BETHANY-CALVARY UNITED METHODIST CHURCH LIBRARY, 7265 W Center St, 53210-1129. SAN 318-4528. Tel: 414-258-2868. FAX: 414-258-4171. *Librn*, Leslie Karabon
Library Holdings: Bk Titles 460
Subject Interests: Relig studies

S HARLEY-DAVIDSON, INC, Engineering Library,* Capitol Dr, PO Box 25527, 53225-5527. SAN 370-887X. Tel: 414-616-1213. FAX: 414-616-1213. *Mgr*, Tom Pietrzak
Library Holdings: Bk Titles 250; Per Subs 50

§L LEGAL HORIZONS, LLC LIBRARY, 7412 W State St, 53213. SAN 378-3812. Tel: 414-476-5700. FAX: 414-476-5407. Web Site: www.legalhorizons.com. *In Charge*, Michelle Fitzgerald; E-Mail: mfitzgerald@legalhorizons.com
Library Holdings: Bk Vols 2,000; Per Subs 100

SR WAUWATOSA PRESBYTERIAN CHURCH LIBRARY, 2366 N 80th St, 53213. SAN 328-445X. Tel: 414-774-5005. FAX: 414-774-5320. *Librn*, Ruth Timeus
Library Holdings: Bk Titles 1,000

P WAUWATOSA PUBLIC LIBRARY, 7635 W North Ave, 53213-1718. SAN 318-4544. Tel: 414-471-8484. FAX: 414-479-8984. Web Site: www.//tpublib.fp.execpc.com. *Dir*, Mary Mulroy; *Asst Dir*, Shawn Duffy; *Ch Servs*, Mary Krueger; *Ref*, Gloria Goller; Staff 12 (MLS 9, Non-MLS 3)
Founded 1886. Pop 49,300; Circ 718,577
Jan 1999-Dec 1999 Income $1,623,560, City $1,203,189, Federal $30,500, Locally Generated Income $307,481. Mats Exp $231,908, Per/Ser (Incl. Access Fees) $35,000, AV Equip $44,111, Other Print Mats $152,797. Sal $1,216,499
Library Holdings: Bk Vols 181,889; Per Subs 344
Automation Activity & Vendor Info: (Acquisitions) Innovative Interfaces Inc.; (Cataloging) Innovative Interfaces Inc.; (Circulation) Innovative Interfaces Inc.; (OPAC) Innovative Interfaces Inc.
Database Vendor: OCLC - First Search
Mem of Milwaukee County Federated Library System
Friends of the Library Group

WEBSTER

P BURNETT COMMUNITY LIBRARY, 7451 W Main St, PO Box 510 54893-0510. SAN 376-6136. Tel: 715-866-7697. E-Mail: nwls@nwls.lib.wi.us. *Librn*, Maxine Peterson; E-Mail: maxine@webster.nwls.lib.wi.us
Founded 1992. Pop 5,250; Circ 15,000
1999-2000 Income $35,680, City $20,000, County $15,680. Mats Exp $2,800, Books $2,000, Per/Ser (Incl. Access Fees) $300, AV Equip $50 $21,632
Library Holdings: Bk Titles 10,600; Per Subs 26
Function: Internet access
Mem of Northern Waters Library Service
Friends of the Library Group

WEST ALLIS

R HOLY TRINITY LUTHERAN CHURCH LIBRARY, 11709 W Cleve Ave, 53227-2901. SAN 318-4552. Tel: 414-321-0700. *Librn*, Donald Jorgensen
Founded 1960
Jan 2000-Dec 2000 Income $200. Mats Exp Books $150
Library Holdings: Bk Titles 4,348
Subject Interests: Lutheran Church statements on social issues, Teachi pictures

J MILWAUKEE AREA TECHNICAL COLLEGE, West Region Campus Library,* 1200 S 71st, 53214. SAN 318-4560. Tel: 414-456-5393. FAX 414-456-5413. *Librn*, Elizabeth Conrad; Staff 2 (Non-MLS 2)
Library Holdings: Bk Vols 13,258; Bk Titles 12,265; Per Subs 100
Subject Interests: Bus, Design, Electronic systs, Funeral serv, Hotel, Interior design, Liberal arts, Motel mgt, Sci
Partic in Library Council Of Metropolitan Milwaukee, Inc

M WEST ALLIS MEMORIAL HOSPITAL, Medical Library, 8901 W Lin Ave, 53227. SAN 318-4579. Tel: 414-328-7910. FAX: 414-328-7912. *L* Joan Clausz
Library Holdings: Bk Titles 600; Per Subs 100
Partic in Southeastern Wisconsin Health Science Library Consortium

P WEST ALLIS PUBLIC LIBRARY, 7421 W National Ave, 53214-4699 SAN 365-1304. Tel: 414-302-8501. Circulation Tel: 414-302-8503. Reference Tel: 414-302-8500. TDD: 414-302-8540. FAX: 414-302-8545 Web Site: www.wawm.k12.wi.us/wapl. *Dir*, Dennis Mulvey; Staff 8 (M 8)
Founded 1898. Pop 63,221; Circ 747,463
Jan 1999-Dec 1999 Income $2,082,411. Mats Exp $223,755, Books $146,931, Per/Ser (Incl. Access Fees) $19,125, Presv $4,581, Micro $6, AV Equip $29,702, Electronic Ref Mat (Incl. Access Fees) $16,547. Sal $1,118,843
Library Holdings: Bk Vols 203,237; Per Subs 542
Automation Activity & Vendor Info: (Acquisitions) Innovative Interfa Inc.; (Cataloging) Innovative Interfaces Inc.; (Circulation) Innovative Interfaces Inc.; (OPAC) Innovative Interfaces Inc.; (Serials) Innovative Interfaces Inc.
Database Vendor: Ebsco - EbscoHost, GaleNet
Mem of Milwaukee County Federated Library System
Partic in OCLC Online Computer Library Center, Inc
Special Services for the Deaf - TTY machine
Special Services for the Blind - Access to internet through assistive technology is offered
Friends of the Library Group

WEST BEND

J MORAINE PARK TECHNICAL COLLEGE, West Bend Campus Librar 2151 N Main St, 53090-1598. SAN 318-4587. Tel: 414-334-3413, Ext 5 FAX: 414-335-5829. *Librn*, Vickie Stangel
Founded 1969
Library Holdings: Bk Vols 12,000; Bk Titles 5,000; Per Subs 150
Subject Interests: Adult basic educ, Bus, Computer science, Indust, Marketing, Nursing, Trade
Partic in Fox River Valley Area Library Consortium; Mid-Wis Multi-typ Libr

J UNIVERSITY OF WISCONSIN, Washington County Library, 400 University Dr, 53095-3619. SAN 318-4595. Tel: 262-335-5206. FAX: 26 335-5220. Web Site: washington.uwc.edu/library/. *Dir*, Tom Fitz; Tel: 26 335-5214, E-Mail: tfitz@uwc.edu; Staff 3 (MLS 2, Non-MLS 1)
Founded 1968. Enrl 900; Fac 28; Highest Degree: Associate
Jul 1999-Jun 2000 Income $141,975, State $141,441, Locally Generated Income $534. Mats Exp $30,174, Books $15,237, Per/Ser (Incl. Access Fees) $9,394, Micro $538, AV Equip $1,751, Electronic Ref Mat (Incl. Access Fees) $3,254. Sal $111,198 (Prof $96,342)
Library Holdings: Bk Titles 43,124; Per Subs 192
Special Collections: Indians of North America Coll; International Folk Music Coll

Automation Activity & Vendor Info: (Acquisitions) Endeavor; (Cataloging) Endeavor; (Circulation) Endeavor; (Course Reserve) Endeavor; (OPAC) Endeavor
Database Vendor: Ebsco - EbscoHost
Partic in Coun of Univ of Wis Librs; Library Council Of Metropolitan Milwaukee, Inc; OCLC Online Computer Library Center, Inc; Wisconsin Library Services

WASHINGTON COUNTY LAW LIBRARY,* 432 E Washington St, Rm 3096, 53095-7986. SAN 318-4609. Tel: 414-335-4341. FAX: 414-335-4776.
Library Holdings: Bk Titles 257

WEST BEND COMMUNITY MEMORIAL LIBRARY, 630 Poplar St, 53095-3380. SAN 318-4617. Tel: 262-335-5151. Reference Tel: 262-335-5152. FAX: 262-335-5150. E-Mail: libref@hnet.net. Web Site: www.hnet.net/~wbcml/. *Dir*, Michael Tyree; Tel: 262-335-5151, Ext 125, E-Mail: mtyree@hnet.net; Staff 25 (MLS 7, Non-MLS 18)
Founded 1901. Pop 50,000; Circ 432,209
Library Holdings: Bk Vols 120,858; Bk Titles 100,500; Per Subs 360
Database Vendor: epixtech, inc.
Mem of Mid-Wisconsin Federated Library System

TBORO

WESTBORO PUBLIC LIBRARY,* PO Box 100, 54490-0100. SAN 318-4641. Tel: 715-427-5864. FAX: 715-427-5354. E-Mail: wlibrary@newnorth.net. *Librn*, Betsy Koch
Founded 1947. Pop 900; Circ 9,000
Library Holdings: Bk Titles 6,000; Per Subs 18
Mem of Wisconsin Valley Library Service

TBY

BEKKUM MEMORIAL LIBRARY,* 206 N Main St, 54667-1108. SAN 318-465X. Tel: 608-634-4419. *Dir*, Joanne Dahlen
Pop 3,000; Circ 35,000
Library Holdings: Bk Vols 14,000; Per Subs 89
Mem of Winding Rivers Library System

TFIELD

WESTFIELD PUBLIC LIBRARY, Ethel Everhard Memorial Library, 117 E Third St, PO Box 355, 53964-0355. SAN 318-4668. Tel: 608-296-2544. FAX: 608-296-2622. *Dir*, Marty Kaszar
Pop 2,669; Circ 12,284
Library Holdings: Bk Vols 13,000; Per Subs 38
Subject Interests: Wisconsin
Mem of Winnefox Library System

YAUWEGA

WEYAUWEGA PUBLIC LIBRARY, 301 S Mill St, PO Box 6, 54983-0006. SAN 318-4676. Tel: 920-867-3742. FAX: 920-867-3741. *Dir*, Lucie A Erickson; E-Mail: lerickso@owls.lib.wi.us; *Ch Servs*, Linda Streyle
Founded 1912
Library Holdings: Bk Vols 13,000; Per Subs 85
Mem of Outagamie Waupaca Library System

ITEFISH BAY

WHITEFISH BAY PUBLIC LIBRARY, 5420 N Marlborough Dr, 53217. SAN 318-2568. Tel: 414-964-4380. FAX: 414-964-5733. Web Site: www.mcfls.org/wfbay. *Dir*, Tracy Blaschka; E-Mail: tracy.blaschka@mcfls.org; *Librn*, Bernard Bellin; E-Mail: bernie.bellin@mcfls.org; *Ch Servs*, Ann Piehl; E-Mail: ann.piehl@mcfls.org; *Ref*, Jessica Rehbaum; *Ad Servs*, Mary McIntyre; E-Mail: mary.mcintyre@mcfls.org; *Reader Servs*, Elke Saylor; E-Mail: elke.saylor@mcfls.org; *Circ*, Jennifer Williams; E-Mail: jennifer.williams@mcfls.org; Staff 10 (MLS 4, Non-MLS 6)
Founded 1936. Pop 13,999; Circ 214,000
Jan 2000-Dec 2000 Income City $500,000. Mats Exp $65,000. Sal $278,000
Library Holdings: Bk Vols 58,000; Per Subs 144
Subject Interests: Local history, Ref
Automation Activity & Vendor Info: (Circulation) Innovative Interfaces Inc.
Database Vendor: Ebsco - EbscoHost, ProQuest
Publications: Newsletter
Function: Reference services available
Mem of Milwaukee County Federated Library System
Friends of the Library Group

ITEHALL

WHITEHALL PUBLIC LIBRARY,* 36245 Park, PO Box 36, 54773-0036. SAN 318-4684. Tel: 715-538-4107. *Dir*, Gitta Rice; Tel: 416-325-1254, E-Mail: riceg@gov.on.ca
Pop 3,415; Circ 14,243
Jan 1998-Dec 1998 Income $23,816, City $20,000, County $1,305, Locally Generated Income $1,011. Mats Exp $3,674, Books $2,100, Per/Ser (Incl. Access Fees) $600, Micro $729, AV Equip $180. Sal $13,892
Library Holdings: Bk Vols 11,637
Mem of Winding Rivers Library System

WHITEWATER

C UNIVERSITY OF WISCONSIN-WHITEWATER, Andersen Library, 800 W Main St, 53190-0900. SAN 365-1398. Tel: 262-472-5511. Circulation Tel: 262-472-5511. Reference Tel: 262-472-1032. FAX: 262-472-5727. E-Mail: library@uww.edu. Web Site: library.uww.edu. *Head, Circ*, Sherry Hofer; Tel: 262-472-5673, E-Mail: hofers@uww.edu; *Automation Syst Coordr*, Allan Davis; E-Mail: davisa@uww.edu; *Archivist*, Karen Weston; Tel: 262-472-5520, E-Mail: westonk@uww.edu; *Coll Develop*, Barbara Bren; Tel: 262-472-5521, E-Mail: brenb@uww.edu; *ILL*, Joe Jaquess; Tel: 262-472-5524, E-Mail: jaquessj@uww.edu; *Coll Develop*, Joyce Huang; Tel: 262-472-5516, E-Mail: huangj@uww.edu; *Ref*, Catherine Hansen; Tel: 262-472-5519; *Ref*, Joe Schneider; Tel: 262-472-5525, E-Mail: schneidj@uww.edu; *Ref*, Martha Stephenson; Tel: 262-472-4366, E-Mail: stephenm@uww.edu; *Ref*, Vicky Topp; Tel: 262-472-5751, E-Mail: toppv@uww.edu. Subject Specialists: *Accounting*, Catherine Hansen; *Art*, Catherine Hansen; *Bus law*, Joe Schneider; *Communication*, Catherine Hansen; *Dance*, Catherine Hansen; *Economics*, Joe Schneider; *Education*, Vicky Topp; *Ethnicity*, Vicky Topp; *Finance*, Joe Schneider; *Govt docs*, Barbara Bren; *Law*, Barbara Bren; *Marketing*, Joe Schneider; *Medicine*, Vicky Topp; *Philosophy*, Joe Schneider; *Political science*, Catherine Hansen; *Psychology*, Vicky Topp; *Religious*, Joe Schneider; *Science*, Martha Stephenson; *Theater*, Catherine Hansen; *Women studies*, Vicky Topp; Staff 24 (MLS 11, Non-MLS 13)
Founded 1868. Enrl 9,780; Fac 381; Highest Degree: Master
Jul 1999-Jun 2000 Income $1,847,903, State $1,783,179, Locally Generated Income $64,724. Mats Exp $816,478, Books $177,295, Per/Ser (Incl. Access Fees) $439,025, Presv $13,379, Micro $29,028, AV Equip $59,927, Other Print Mats $4,287, Electronic Ref Mat (Incl. Access Fees) $93,537. Sal $869,512 (Prof $396,810)
Library Holdings: Bk Vols 386,575; Bk Titles 309,769; Per Subs 1,862
Subject Interests: Bus, Education, Finance
Special Collections: Criminology (Steinmetz Coll); George A Custer (Kenneth Hammer Coll); Local History (Area Research Center Coll), bks, mss & archives
Automation Activity & Vendor Info: (Acquisitions) Endeavor; (Cataloging) Endeavor; (Circulation) Endeavor; (OPAC) Endeavor; (Serials) Endeavor
Database Vendor: CARL, Ebsco - EbscoHost, GaleNet, Lexis-Nexis, OCLC - First Search, OVID Technologies, ProQuest, Silverplatter Information Inc.
Partic in Coun of Wis Librs, Inc; CUWL; Wisconsin Library Services
Friends of the Library Group

P IRVIN L YOUNG MEMORIAL LIBRARY, 431 W Center St, 53190-1915. SAN 318-4692. Tel: 262-473-0530. FAX: 262-473-0539. E-Mail: vpfollst@idcnet.com. *Dir*, Virginia P Follstad; *Ad Servs, Asst Dir, Ref*, Sally Mason; *Ch Servs*, Cathy Bloom; Staff 3 (MLS 2, Non-MLS 1)
Founded 1899. Pop 19,000; Circ 171,639
Jan 2000-Dec 2000 Income $662,497, City $446,867, County $190,630, Locally Generated Income $25,000. Mats Exp $81,700, Books $58,000, Per/Ser (Incl. Access Fees) $10,200, Micro $1,000, Other Print Mats $500, Electronic Ref Mat (Incl. Access Fees) $12,000. Sal $264,503 (Prof $113,235)
Library Holdings: Bk Vols 65,500; Bk Titles 63,000; Per Subs 287; High Interest/Low Vocabulary Bk Vols 100; Bks on Deafness & Sign Lang 20
Subject Interests: Local history, Spanish
Special Collections: Achen Photographs; Whitewater history
Automation Activity & Vendor Info: (Cataloging) epixtech, inc.; (Circulation) epixtech, inc.; (OPAC) epixtech, inc.
Mem of Contract with Lakeshores Libr Syst & Arrowhead Libr Syst
Friends of the Library Group

WILD ROSE

P PATTERSON MEMORIAL LIBRARY, 500 Wisconsin St, PO Box 305, 54984-0305. SAN 318-4706. Tel: 920-622-3835. FAX: 920-622-5140. *Dir*, Linda R Steffen; E-Mail: steffen@winnefox.org; Staff 3 (Non-MLS 3)
Founded 1930. Pop 3,500; Circ 45,000
Jan 2001-Dec 2001 Mats Exp $84,100. Sal $50,700
Library Holdings: Bk Vols 13,005; Bk Titles 14,000; Per Subs 50; High Interest/Low Vocabulary Bk Vols 200; Bks on Deafness & Sign Lang 10
Special Collections: Local Oral History on Audio Cassette & CD
Mem of Winnefox Library System
Friends of the Library Group

WILLIAMS BAY

P BARRETT MEMORIAL LIBRARY, 65 W Geneva St, 53191-0190. SAN 318-4714. Tel: 262-245-2709. FAX: 262-245-2719. *Dir*, Marleen Rogers; Staff 4 (MLS 1, Non-MLS 3)
Founded 1903. Pop 2,200; Circ 33,000

Jan 2000-Dec 2000 Income $94,200, City $66,450, County $22,412, Locally Generated Income $5,338. Mats Exp $14,214, Books $10,420, Per/Ser (Incl. Access Fees) $1,397, AV Equip $1,000, Other Print Mats $1,397. Sal $83,079 (Prof $30,160)
Library Holdings: Bk Vols 18,350; Bk Titles 18,006; Per Subs 64
Automation Activity & Vendor Info: (Cataloging) Follett; (Circulation) Follett; (OPAC) Follett
Mem of Lakeshores Library System
Friends of the Library Group

C UNIVERSITY OF CHICAGO, Yerkes Observatory Library, 373 W Geneva St, 53191-0258. SAN 318-4722. Tel: 262-245-5555, Ext 30. FAX: 262-245-9805. *Librn*, Judith A Bausch; E-Mail: jab@yerkes.uchicago.edu; Staff 1 (MLS 1)
Founded 1897
Library Holdings: Bk Vols 25,000
Subject Interests: Astronomy, Astrophysics
Special Collections: Star Atlases & Charts

WILTON

P WILTON PUBLIC LIBRARY,* PO Box 280, 54670-9998. SAN 318-4730. Tel: 608-435-6710. *Dir*, Karen Carr
Circ 10,130
Library Holdings: Bk Titles 11,000; Per Subs 55
Mem of Winding Rivers Library System

WINCHESTER

P WINCHESTER PUBLIC LIBRARY, HCR 2, Box 625, 54557. SAN 370-7008. Tel: 715-686-2926. FAX: 715-686-2926. *Librn*, Barbara Bull; E-Mail: bbull@centurytel.net; Staff 2 (MLS 1, Non-MLS 1)
Founded 1986. Pop 392; Circ 7,630
1999-2000 Income $23,175, State $241, City $11,077, County $2,100, Locally Generated Income $9,757. Mats Exp $4,971, Books $4,280, Per/Ser (Incl. Access Fees) $330, AV Equip $361. Sal $6,787
Library Holdings: Bk Vols 9,334; Per Subs 35; Bks on Deafness & Sign Lang 500
Mem of Northern Waters Library Service
Friends of the Library Group

WINNEBAGO

M DCTF LIBRARY INFORMATION NETWORK, PO Box 9, 54985-0009. SAN 325-7924. Tel: 920-235-4910, Ext 2443. FAX: 920-235-3807. E-Mail: kotscmc@dhfs.state.wi.us. *Dir*, Mary Campfield Kotschi; Staff 3 (MLS 1, Non-MLS 2)
Founded 1893
Library Holdings: Bk Vols 7,500; Per Subs 160
Subject Interests: Mental health, Psychiatry, Soc work
Database Vendor: Dialog, ProQuest
Function: ILL to other special libraries
Partic in Fox River Valley Area Library Consortium; Fox Valley Library Council
Branches:
JOYCE MARSH MEMORIAL LIBRARY, PO Box 9, 54985-0009. Tel: 920-235-4910, Ext 2444. FAX: 920-235-3807. *Librn*, Ellen Roemer
Library Holdings: Bk Titles 7,740; Per Subs 23
Subject Interests: Adult reading skills, Functional daily living skills, Music, Poetry, Sex educ
WATERWOOD SCHOOL, PO Box 9, 54985-0009. Tel: 920-235-4910, Ext 2384. FAX: 920-235-3807. *Asst Librn*, Karen Stedl
Library Holdings: Bk Vols 5,500
Subject Interests: Fiction, Non-fiction support of sch curriculum pre K thru 12th grade

WINNECONNE

P WINNECONNE PUBLIC LIBRARY, 31 S Second St, 54986-9347. (Mail add: PO Box 5002, 54986-5002), Tel: 920-582-7091. FAX: 920-582-9426. E-Mail: winnepl@vbe.com. *Librn*, Edith Phillips; Staff 3 (MLS 1, Non-MLS 2)
Founded 1913. Pop 2,360; Circ 22,000
Jan 2000-Dec 2000 Income $91,799, County $36,705, Locally Generated Income $55,094. Mats Exp $24,700, Books $13,000, Per/Ser (Incl. Access Fees) $1,600. Sal $37,656 (Prof $30,000)
Library Holdings: Bk Vols 22,000; Per Subs 82
Subject Interests: Local history
Automation Activity & Vendor Info: (Acquisitions) DRA; (Cataloging) DRA; (Circulation) DRA; (Course Reserve) DRA; (ILL) DRA; (Media Booking) DRA; (OPAC) DRA; (Serials) DRA
Mem of Winnefox Library System
Friends of the Library Group

WINTER

P TICE PUBLIC LIBRARY,* 6593 W Hazel St, PO Box 340, 54896. SA 318-4757. Tel: 715-266-2144. FAX: 715-266-3101. *Dir*, Susan Johnsor
E-Mail: sjohnso1@mail.wiscnet.net
Pop 1,980; Circ 28,000
1998-1999 Income $47,000, County $39,700
Library Holdings: Bk Vols 9,300; Per Subs 35
Mem of Northern Waters Library Service

WISCONSIN DELLS

P KILBOURN PUBLIC LIBRARY, 620 Elm St, 53965. SAN 318-4765. 608-254-2146. E-Mail: dells@scls.lib.wi.us. Web Site: www.scls.lib.wi. wid. *Dir*, Charlotte Walch Davies
Founded 1897. Pop 2,500; Circ 52,463
Jan 1999-Dec 1999 Income $144,990. Mats Exp $25,030. Sal $73,000
Library Holdings: Bk Titles 22,148; Per Subs 63
Subject Interests: History
Special Collections: Local Newspapers from 1856 to Date, micro
Automation Activity & Vendor Info: (Acquisitions) epixtech, inc.; (Cataloging) epixtech, inc.; (Circulation) epixtech, inc.; (OPAC) epixtec inc.; (Serials) epixtech, inc.
Mem of South Central Library System
Partic in S Cent Libr Syst
Friends of the Library Group

WISCONSIN RAPIDS

S CONSOLIDATED PAPERS, INC, Research & Development Library, 3 Biron Dr, 54494. SAN 318-4773. Tel: 715-422-2368. FAX: 715-422-22 *Librn*, Cynthia Van Ert; E-Mail: cindy.vanert@conpapers.com
Library Holdings: Bk Vols 10,000; Per Subs 700
Subject Interests: Computer science, Engineering, Graphic arts, Mgt, F sci, Pulp
Automation Activity & Vendor Info: (Cataloging) EOS; (Circulation) (OPAC) EOS; (Serials) EOS
Publications: From the Stacks (quarterly newsletter)
Partic in Dialog Corporation; Sci & Tech Info Network

P MCMILLAN MEMORIAL LIBRARY, 490 E Grand Ave, 54494-4898. 318-4781. Tel: 715-423-1040. FAX: 715-423-2665. E-Mail: mcmweb@ scls.lib.wi.us. Web Site: www.scls.lib.wi.us/mcm. *Dir*, Ronald McCabe; *Dir*, Andrew Barnett; *Ad Servs*, Donald Litzer; *Ch Servs*, Eric Norton; S 25 (MLS 5, Non-MLS 20)
Founded 1889. Pop 45,000; Circ 407,661
Jan 1999-Dec 1999 Income $1,218,996, State $10,311, City $829,777, County $194,782, Other $184,126. Mats Exp $117,815, Other Print Mat $223. Sal $549,107
Library Holdings: Bk Vols 139,348; Per Subs 338
Subject Interests: Bus, Genealogy, Local history, Paper indust
Automation Activity & Vendor Info: (Circulation) epixtech, inc.
Publications: At McMillan (bimonthly newsletter); Genealogical Resour
Mem of South Central Library System
Friends of the Library Group

J MID-STATE TECHNICAL COLLEGE LIBRARY, 500 32nd St N, 544 SAN 365-1576. Tel: 715-422-5469. FAX: 715-422-5466. *Dir*, Harriet Broom; Staff 1 (MLS 1)
Founded 1967. Enrl 1,792; Fac 90; Highest Degree: Associate
Jul 2000-Jun 2001 Mats Exp Books $43,506. Sal $63,000
Library Holdings: Bk Titles 19,200; Per Subs 450
Subject Interests: Bus, Mgt, Nursing, Sci-tech
Automation Activity & Vendor Info: (Acquisitions) Endeavor; (Catalog Endeavor; (Circulation) Endeavor; (OPAC) Endeavor; (Serials) Endeavor
Mem of South Central Library System
Partic in Wisconsin Library Services

WITHEE

P WITHEE PUBLIC LIBRARY,* 504 Division, PO Box 147, 54498-0147 SAN 318-479X. Tel: 715-229-2010. FAX: 715-229-2010. E-Mail: witlib badger.tds.net. *Actg Dir*, Sheila Harledans
Pop 1,590; Circ 11,000
Library Holdings: Bk Vols 6,400; Per Subs 24
Mem of Wisconsin Valley Library Service

WONEWOC

P WONEWOC PUBLIC LIBRARY,* 305 Center St, PO Box 116, 53968-0116. SAN 318-4803. Tel: 608-464-7625. Interlibrary Loan Service Tel: 784-3151. E-Mail: wonewocpl@mwt.net. Web Site: www.mwt.net/ ~wonewocpl. *Librn*, Sally A Byington
Founded 1910. Pop 1,500; Circ 24,357

Library Holdings: Bk Titles 9,322; Per Subs 34
Special Collections: Wonewoc Genealogy; Wonewoc History
Mem of Winding Rivers Library System
Open Mon, Wed & Fri 10-12 & 1-5

)DRUFF

HOWARD YOUNG MEDICAL CENTER, Health Science Library,* 240 Maple St, PO Box 470, 54568. SAN 327-4926. Tel: 715-356-8070. FAX: 715-356-8561.
Library Holdings: Bk Titles 1,200; Per Subs 100
Subject Interests: Orthopedics, Surgery
Partic in Greater Midwest Regional Medical Libr Network; Medline; Northwestern Wisconsin Health Science Library Consortium

WOODVILLE

P WOODVILLE COMMUNITY LIBRARY,* 102 Main St, PO Box 204, 54028-0204. SAN 318-4811. Tel: 715-698-2430. FAX: 715-698-2697. *Librn*, Lissa List; E-Mail: lalist@win.bright.net
Founded 1970. Pop 3,000
Library Holdings: Bk Titles 8,000; Per Subs 30
Special Collections: Norwegian Coll
Mem of Indianhead Federated Library System
Partic in St Croix Libr Syst

WYOMING

Date of Statistics: Fiscal 2000
Population, 1999 (est): 479,541
Population Served by Public Libraries: 479,541
Total Volumes in Public Libraries: 2,509,645
Volumes Per Capita: 5.23
Total Public Library Circulation: 3,699,600
Circulation Per Capita: 7.71
Total Public Library Income (not including Grants-in-Aid, nor Capital Construction): $14,573,389
Source of Income: Public funds
Expenditure Per Capita: $27.93
Number of County Libraries: 23 systems
Number of Bookmobiles in State: 4
Grants-in-Aid to Public Libraries:
Federal: (Library Services & Technology Act): $62,068

IN

BIG HORN COUNTY LIBRARY, 430 West C St, 82410. (Mail add: PO Box 231, 82410), SAN 365-1606. Tel: 307-568-2388. Toll Free Tel: 877-768-2388. FAX: 307-568-2011. Web Site: www.wsl.state.wy.us/bighorn. *Dir*, Sandra Munger; E-Mail: smunger@will.state.wy.us; Staff 4 (MLS 1, Non-MLS 3)
Founded 1903. Pop 11,000; Circ 69,130
Jul 1999-Jun 2000 Income (Main Library and Branch Library) $234,122, State $18,374, Federal $201, County $212,390, Locally Generated Income $3,157. Mats Exp $22,122, Books $15,745, Micro $150, Electronic Ref Mat (Incl. Access Fees) $6,227. Sal $76,649 (Prof $23,000)
Library Holdings: Bk Vols 42,000; Per Subs 63
Subject Interests: Wyoming
Automation Activity & Vendor Info: (Cataloging) DRA; (Circulation) DRA; (ILL) DRA; (Serials) DRA
Partic in WYLD Network
Friends of the Library Group
Branches: 7
BURLINGTON BRANCH SCHOOL LIBRARY, 109 N Nineth St, Burlington, 82411. (Mail add: PO Box 9, Burlington, 82411), SAN 370-8071. Tel: 307-762-3334. *Librn*, Judy Morris; E-Mail: judybm@tetwest.net
Pop 250; Circ 250
Library Holdings: Bk Vols 10,000; Bk Titles 10,000; Per Subs 25; Spec Interest Per Sub 10
Subject Interests: Teacher
Open Mon-Fri 8-4, School Library - rotating collection only
BYRON BRANCH SCHOOL LIBRARY, 30 E Main, PO Box 176, Byron, 82412. SAN 365-1630. Tel: 307-548-2723. FAX: 307-548-6453. *Librn*, John Bernhisel
Library Holdings: Bk Vols 11,000; Bk Titles 5,000; Per Subs 25
Occassional rotating collection - School Library
DEAVER BRANCH, 180 W First St, PO Box 202, Deaver, 82421. SAN 365-169X. Tel: 307-664-2770. *Librn*, Molly Yates; Staff 1 (MLS 1)
Pop 150
Jul 1999-Jun 2000 Mats Exp Books $100. Sal $1,239
Library Holdings: Bk Vols 6,000
FRANNIE BRANCH, 311 Fourth St, Box 23, Frannie, 82423. SAN 365-172X. *Librn*, Paula Steiger; Staff 1 (Non-MLS 1)
Pop 150
Jul 1999-Jun 2000 Mats Exp Books $35. Sal $1,239
Library Holdings: Bk Vols 8,000
GREYBULL BRANCH, PO Box 226, Greybull, 82426. SAN 365-1754. Tel: 307-765-2551. *Librn*, Karen Amend; Staff 2 (Non-MLS 2)
Pop 1,800
Jul 1999-Jun 2000 Mats Exp Books $4,486. Sal $17,131
Library Holdings: Bk Vols 15,000; Per Subs 20
Automation Activity & Vendor Info: (Circulation) DRA; (Serials) DRA
Partic in WYLD Network
Friends of the Library Group
HYATTVILLE LIBRARY, 119 N Main, Box 77, Hyattville, 82428. SAN 373-9252. Tel: 307-469-2218. *Librn*, Gay Tharp; Staff 1 (Non-MLS 1)
Pop 50
Library Holdings: Bk Vols 3,000
LOVELL LIBRARY, 300 Oregon Ave, Lovell, 82431. Tel: 307-548-7228. *Librn*, Sharalyn Nicholls; Staff 2 (Non-MLS 2)
Pop 2,000
Jul 1999-Jun 2000 Mats Exp Books $4,500. Sal $18,958
Library Holdings: Bk Vols 15,000; Per Subs 37
Automation Activity & Vendor Info: (Circulation) DRA; (Serials) DRA
Partic in WYLD Network
Friends of the Library Group

BUFFALO

P JOHNSON COUNTY LIBRARY,* 171 N Adams, 82834. SAN 318-4846. Tel: 307-684-5546. FAX: 307-684-7888. Web Site: www.will.state.wy.us/johnson/index.htm. *Dir*, Cynthia R Twing; E-Mail: ctwing@will.state.wy.us; Staff 11 (Non-MLS 11)
Founded 1909. Pop 6,500; Circ 72,000
Jul 1999-Jun 2000 Income (Main Library and Branch Library) $232,055, City $12,000, County $192,055, Locally Generated Income $28,000. Mats Exp $38,000, Books $25,000, Per/Ser (Incl. Access Fees) $4,000, Manuscripts & Archives $1,000, Electronic Ref Mat (Incl. Access Fees) $8,000. Sal $136,100
Library Holdings: Bk Titles 35,000; Per Subs 125
Subject Interests: Wyo hist
Special Collections: Local History Coll; Western History Coll
Database Vendor: DRA, OCLC - First Search
Partic in Wyo Libr Database
Friends of the Library Group
Branches: 2
KAYCEE BRANCH, Kaycee, 82639-0226. SAN 325-3198. *Librn*, Bonnie Ross
Friends of the Library Group
LINCH BRANCH, Linch, 82640. SAN 323-8059. *Librn*, Cathy Andreen

CASPER

J CASPER COLLEGE, Goodstein Foundation Library, 125 College Dr, 82601. SAN 318-4870. Tel: 307-268-2269. FAX: 307-268-2682. Web Site: www.cc.whecn.edu. *Dir*, R Lynnette Anderson; *ILL*, Laurie Lye; *Spec Coll*, Kevin Anderson; Staff 4 (MLS 4)
Founded 1945. Enrl 2,297; Fac 160
Jul 1998-Jun 1999 Income $90,000
Library Holdings: Bk Vols 80,869; Per Subs 653
Special Collections: History of Wyoming, Natrona & Casper County, bks, maps, per, VF
Partic in OCLC Online Computer Library Center, Inc

M COMMUNITY HEALTH CENTER OF CENTRAL WYOMING, (Formerly University Of Wyoming Family Practice Residency Program Library At Casper), 1522 East A St, 82601. SAN 370-517X. Tel: 307-233-6055. FAX: 307-235-6202. Web Site: www.uwyo.edu/hs/casfamprac/hmpg.htm. *In Charge*, Mary Humphrey; Tel: 307-266-3076, E-Mail: humphrey@uwyo.edu;

Staff 1 (Non-MLS 1)
Founded 1978
2000-2001 Income $18,000, State $17,000, Federal $1,000. Mats Exp $17,000
Library Holdings: Bk Titles 1,000; Per Subs 54
Subject Interests: Family med, Geriatric, Obstetrics-gynecology, Pediatrics, Primary health care, Sports med
Special Collections: Geriatric; Obstetrics and Gynecology; Pediatrics; Sports Medicine
Automation Activity & Vendor Info: (ILL) Gateway
Database Vendor: Ebsco - EbscoHost
Restriction: Restricted borrowing privileges
Function: Document delivery services
Partic in Colorado Council Of Medical Librarians; National Network Of Libraries Of Medicine - South Central Region

P NATRONA COUNTY PUBLIC LIBRARY, 307 E Second St, 82601. SAN 365-1843. Tel: 307-237-4935. FAX: 307-266-3734. Web Site: www.library.natrona.net. *Dir*, Bill Nelson; Tel: 307-237-4935, Ext 15, E-Mail: bnelson@will.state.wy.us; *Br Coordr*, Cathy Bodenhamer; E-Mail: cboden@will.state.wy.us; *Head Tech Servs*, Mary Lou Walker; Tel: 307-237-4935, Ext 20, E-Mail: mlwalker@will.state.wy.us; *Librn*, John Wright; E-Mail: jwright@will.state.wy.us; *ILL*, Lida Vollin; *Ad Servs, Head, Info Serv*, Becky Sheller; Tel: 307-237-4925, Ext 11, E-Mail: bsheller@will.state.wy.us; *Govt Doc, Spec Coll*, Susan Stanton; E-Mail: sstanton@will.state.wy.us; *Ref Servs YA*, Glenda Williams; *Head, Circ*, Shelly Padilla; E-Mail: spadilla@will.state.wy.us; *Ch Servs*, Jerry Jones; E-Mail: jjones@will.state.wy.us. Subject Specialists: *Government publications*, Susan Stanton; Staff 28 (MLS 4, Non-MLS 24)
Founded 1910. Pop 65,160; Circ 338,945
Jul 1999-Jun 2000 Income (Main Library and Branch Library) $749,000, County $618,000, Other $123,000. Mats Exp Books $134,000. Sal $469,000
Library Holdings: Bk Vols 200,000; Per Subs 352
Subject Interests: County hist, Genealogy, Geol, Govt docs, Grants, Literacy, Literacy for adults, Local history, Petroleum
Special Collections: Patent & Trademark Depository; Selective Government Documents
Automation Activity & Vendor Info: (Cataloging) DRA; (Circulation) DRA; (ILL) DRA; (OPAC) DRA; (Serials) DRA
Database Vendor: CARL, DRA, Ebsco - EbscoHost, OCLC - First Search, Wilson - Wilson Web
Publications: Monthly calendar of events; monthly newsletter
Partic in Bibliographical Center For Research, Rocky Mountain Region, Inc; Wyo Libr Network
Friends of the Library Group
Branches: 2
MARK J DAVIS, JR MEMORIAL BRANCH, Second & Cottonwood, Edgerton, 82635. SAN 365-1878. Tel: 307-437-6617. FAX: 307-437-6617. *Librn*, Michelle Butler
Library Holdings: Bk Vols 2,438
P MILLS BRANCH, 425 Morgan Ave, Mills, 82644. Tel: 307-265-6017. *Mgr*, Tanise Lavering
Library Holdings: Bk Vols 2,711
Automation Activity & Vendor Info: (OPAC) DRA
Bookmobiles: 1

M WYOMING MEDICAL CENTER, Health Sciences Library,* 1233 E Second St, 82601. SAN 325-0547. Tel: 307-577-2450. FAX: 307-577-2265. *Dir*, Susan Craft
Library Holdings: Bk Titles 1,000; Per Subs 135
Subject Interests: Health sciences

CHEYENNE

GM DEPARTMENT OF VETERANS AFFAIRS, Medical Center,* 2360 E Pershing Blvd, 82001. SAN 318-4927. Tel: 307-778-7321. FAX: 307-778-7356. *Librn*, Kerry Skidmore; E-Mail: skidmore.kerry@forum.va.gov
Library Holdings: Per Subs 515
Partic in National Network Of Libraries Of Medicine - South Central Region
Friends of the Library Group

S GRAND LODGE OF ANCIENT FREE & ACCEPTED MASONS OF WYOMING LIBRARY,* 1820 Capitol Ave, 82001. SAN 327-7690. Tel: 307-634-1655. FAX: 307-637-7160. *Librn*, Paul Fisher
Library Holdings: Bk Titles 3,500

J LARAMIE COUNTY COMMUNITY COLLEGE LIBRARY,* 1400 E College Dr, 82007. SAN 318-4900. Tel: 307-778-1205. FAX: 307-778-1399. *Dir*, Sandra J Donovan; *Tech Servs*, Crystal Stratton; *Circ*, Veronica Murray; *Ref*, Mary Coffin; *Media Spec*, Lori Mares; Staff 13 (MLS 2, Non-MLS 11)
Founded 1969. Enrl 5,031; Fac 88
Library Holdings: Bk Vols 40,000; Per Subs 398
Subject Interests: Nursing
Special Collections: Children's Literature; Foundation Center Materials; Wyoming History Coll
Publications: Wyoming Foundation Directory

P LARAMIE COUNTY LIBRARY SYSTEM, 2800 Central Ave, 82001-SAN 365-1908. Tel: 307-635-1032. TDD: 307-634-0105. FAX: 307-63 2082. Web Site: www.lclsonline.org. *Dir*, Lucie P Osborn; Tel: 307-63 3561, E-Mail: losborn@larm.lib.wy.us; *Asst Dir*, Carey Hartmann; Tel: 635-1032, Ext 124, E-Mail: chartmann@larm.lib.wy.us; *Mgr*, Alan D Harrington; Tel: 307-635-1032, Ext 121, E-Mail: aharrington@larm.lib.wy.us; *Ref*, Elizabeth Cuckow; Tel: 307-635-1032, Ext 141, E-ecuckow@larm.lib.wy.us; *Circ*, Sidney Stanfill; *ILL*, Janice McCraken; 307-635-1032, Ext 145; *Bkmobile Coordr*, Lynn Erickson; Tel: 307-63 1032, Ext 131; *Ch Servs, Mgr*, Amy Shelley; Tel: 307-635-1032, Ext 1 *Mgr, Tech Servs*, Scott Kinney; Tel: 307-635-1032, Ext 138; *Media Sp* Kim West; Tel: 307-635-1032, Ext 168; Staff 52 (MLS 6, Non-MLS 4
Founded 1886. Pop 80,000; Circ 610,218
Jul 1999-Jun 2000 Income (Main Library and Branch Library) $2,044, Federal $5,121, County $1,386,122, Locally Generated Income $653,4 Mats Exp $315,538, Books $254,410, Per/Ser (Incl. Access Fees) $10, Presv $936, Micro $4,373, Electronic Ref Mat (Incl. Access Fees) $44, Sal $804,479 (Prof $135,844)
Library Holdings: Bk Vols 253,962; Per Subs 413
Subject Interests: Genealogy
Special Collections: Elk of North America; Western History (Carpente of Western Americana)
Automation Activity & Vendor Info: (Acquisitions) DRA; (Catalogin DRA; (Circulation) DRA; (ILL) DRA; (OPAC) DRA; (Serials) DRA
Publications: Annual Report; Library Newsletter
Special Services for the Deaf - TDD
Branches: 2
BURNS BRANCH, 112 Main St, PO Box 220, Burns, 82053. SAN 36 1932. Tel: 307-547-2249. FAX: 307-547-9253. Web Site: www.lclsonline.org. *Librn*, Cathy Metzger
Circ 10,287
Library Holdings: Bk Vols 7,515
Database Vendor: DRA
PINE BLUFFS BRANCH, 110 E Second St, PO Box 646, Pine Bluffs, 82082. SAN 365-1967. Tel: 307-245-3646. FAX: 307-245-3029. Web www.lclsonline.org. *Librn*, Mary Cushing
Library Holdings: Bk Vols 17,779
Database Vendor: DRA
Bookmobiles: 1

M UNIVERSITY OF WYOMING AT CHEYENNE, Family Practice Resi Program Library, 821 E 18th St, 82001-4775. SAN 321-7922. Tel: 307-7911. FAX: 307-638-3616. *Librn*, Barbara Fortune; E-Mail: bfortune@uwyo.edu
Founded 1950
Library Holdings: Bk Titles 500; Per Subs 70
Subject Interests: Clinical medicine
Special Collections: Medical Society
Open Mon-Fri 8-5

G WYOMING GAME & FISH DEPARTMENT LIBRARY, 5400 Bishop Blvd, 82006-0001. SAN 329-1685. Tel: 307-777-4541. Toll Free Tel: 80 548-9453. FAX: 307-777-4610. *Librn*, Mary E Link; E-Mail: mlink@state.wy.us
Library Holdings: Bk Titles 100; Per Subs 40
Subject Interests: Conservation, Fisheries, Wildlife
Special Collections: Wyoming Game & Fish Publications; Wyoming Wildlife Magazine
Function: ILL available
Special Services for the Deaf - Special interest periodicals
Special Services for the Blind - Bks on tape

S WYOMING STATE ARCHIVES, Historical Research Library,* Barrett Bldg, 2301 Central Ave, 82002. SAN 365-2025. Tel: 307-777-7826. FAX 307-777-7044. E-Mail: wyarchive@state.wy.us. Web Site: www.spacr.state.wy.us/cr/archives. *Dir*, Tony Adams
Library Holdings: Bk Vols 15,000
Special Collections: WPA Federal Writers Project, maps, newspapers, or histories

G WYOMING STATE DEPARTMENT OF HEALTH, Audio-Visual Resou Library, Hathaway Bldg, 4th Flr, Rm 430, 2300 Capitol, 82002-0480. SA 323-6730. Tel: 307-777-7363. FAX: 307-777-7278. Web Site: www.wdhfs.state.wy.us/wy_nursing/. *Librn*, Ria Brownlow; E-Mail: rbrown@state.wy.us
Library Holdings: Bk Titles 1,500
Subject Interests: Adolescence, Health educ
Special Collections: HIV/AIDS

P WYOMING STATE LIBRARY, (WSL), 2301 Capitol Ave, 82002-0060. SAN 365-2084. Tel: 307-777-7281. Interlibrary Loan Service Tel: 307-77 6333. FAX: 307-777-6289. E-Mail: wslref@wyld.state.wy.us. Web Site: www-wsl.state.wy.us. *State Librn*, Lesley Boughton; E-Mail: lbough@missc.state.wy.us; *In Charge*, Jerry Krois; Tel: 307-777-6496, E-Mail: jkrois@missc.state.wy.us; *Automation Syst Coordr*, Brian Greene; Tel: 30 777-3634, E-Mail: bgreen@missc.state.wy.us; *Ref*, Venice Beske; Tel: 307 777-7982, E-Mail: vbeske@missc.state.wy.us; Staff 14 (MLS 11, Non-ML 3)

Founded 1871. Pop 480,000
Jul 1999-Jun 2000 Income $1,832,155, State $1,383,284, Federal $448,871. Mats Exp Books $35,000. Sal $1,155,214
Library Holdings: Bk Vols 142,720; Per Subs 348
Subject Interests: Am Indians, Bus, Libr sci, Mgt, Western hist, Wyoming authors
Automation Activity & Vendor Info: (Acquisitions) DRA; (Cataloging) DRA; (Circulation) DRA; (OPAC) DRA; (Serials) DRA
Database Vendor: OCLC - First Search
Publications: Catalog of Wyoming State Grants; Coming Attractions; Equality State Almanac; Outrider (newsletter); WYGIAC Newsletter; Wyoming Annual Report; Wyoming Library Directory; Wyoming Library Laws
Partic in Bibliographical Center For Research, Rocky Mountain Region, Inc; WYLD Network

WYOMING SUPREME COURT, Wyoming State Law Library, Supreme Court & Library Bldg, 2301 Capitol Ave, 82002-0450. SAN 320-4286. Tel: 307-777-7509. FAX: 307-777-7240. Web Site: courts.state.wy.us/lawlib.htm. *Dir, Librn*, Kathleen Carlson; E-Mail: kcarls@state.wy.us; *Asst Librn*, Ann Harrington; *Electronic Resources*, Jessica Rehbaum; E-Mail: jrehba@state.wy.us. Subject Specialists: *Law*, Kathleen Carlson; Staff 6 (MLS 3, Non-MLS 3)
Founded 1871
Jul 2000-Jun 2001 Income State $438,500. Mats Exp $250,000, Books $211,000, Per/Ser (Incl. Access Fees) $24,000, Presv $5,000, Micro $10,000. Sal $187,000 (Prof $167,000)
Library Holdings: Bk Vols 96,000; Bk Titles 2,000; Per Subs 240
Automation Activity & Vendor Info: (Acquisitions) EOS; (Cataloging) DRA; (OPAC) DRA; (Serials) EOS
Publications: Quick Index to Wyoming Statutes Annotated
Partic in OCLC Online Computer Library Center, Inc

DY

BUFFALO BILL HISTORICAL CENTER, McCracken Research Library, 720 Sheridan Ave, 82414. SAN 318-4943. Tel: 307-578-4059. FAX: 307-527-6042. E-Mail: hmrl@bbhc.org. Web Site: www.bbhc.org/library.htm. *Librn*, Frances B Clymer; *Curator*, Nathan E Bender
Founded 1927
Library Holdings: Bk Vols 20,000; Per Subs 96
Subject Interests: Firearms, Mus ref mat, Native Am studies, Photog, Western Am natural hist, Western art, Western hist, Western lit
Special Collections: Archives, photogs; Buffalo Bill Coll, mss; Dude Ranching; W H D Koerner Coll; William F Cody; Winchester Repeating Arms Company Archives; Wyoming Territorial Imprints, 1866-1890; Yellowstone National Park Coll
Publications: Annotated Bibliographies
Partic in BCR; OCLC Online Computer Library Center, Inc; WYLD Network
Friends of the Library Group

PARK COUNTY BAR ASSOCIATION, Law Library,* Court House, 1002 Sheridan Ave, 82414. SAN 370-1867. Tel: 307-587-6291. FAX: 307-587-5547. *Pres*, Diane Walsh
Library Holdings: Bk Vols 10,700

PARK COUNTY LIBRARY SYSTEM, 1057 Sheridan Ave, 82414. SAN 365-2149. Tel: 307-587-6204. FAX: 307-587-6205. Web Site: will.state.wy.us/park. *Dir*, Arlene Ott; *AV*, Gloria Gutierrez
Founded 1906. Pop 23,000; Circ 230,000
Library Holdings: Bk Titles 60,000; Per Subs 112
Friends of the Library Group
Branches: 2
MEETEETSE BRANCH, 2107 Idaho, PO Box 129, Meeteetse, 82433-0129. SAN 365-2173. Tel: 307-868-2248. FAX: 307-868-2249. *Librn*, Diane Chapman
Circ 25,165
Library Holdings: Bk Vols 18,000
POWELL BRANCH, 217 E Third, Powell, 82435-1903. SAN 365-2203. Tel: 307-754-8828. E-Mail: powlill@wyld.state.wy.us. Web Site: www-wsl.state.wy.us/park. *Librn*, Janet Meury
Circ 87,300
Library Holdings: Bk Vols 54,800; Per Subs 75
Automation Activity & Vendor Info: (Acquisitions) DRA; (Cataloging) DRA; (Circulation) DRA; (ILL) DRA; (OPAC) DRA; (Serials) DRA
Database Vendor: DRA
Partic in Mountain Plains Libr Asn; Wyo Libr Database
Special Services for the Blind - Cassette bks; Large print bks
Friends of the Library Group

UGLAS

CONVERSE COUNTY LIBRARY, 300 Walnut, 82633. SAN 365-2238. Tel: 307-358-3644. FAX: 307-358-6743. Web Site: will.state.wy.us/converse. *Dir*, Karen Hopkins; E-Mail: khopkins@will.state.wy.us; *Ch Servs*, Brenda Hemberry; E-Mail: bhemberr@will.state.wy.us; *Tech Servs*, Donna Rusk; E-Mail: drusk@will.state.wy.us; *Circ*, Paul Pidde; E-Mail: ppidde@will.state.wy.us; *ILL*, Kirk Hissam; E-Mail: khissam@will.state.wy.us; Staff 11 (Non-MLS 11)
Founded 1905. Pop 12,000; Circ 91,552
Jul 1999-Jun 2000 Income (Main Library and Branch Library) $365,941, Federal $2,916, County $345,495, Locally Generated Income $17,530. Mats Exp $46,101, Books $30,485, Per/Ser (Incl. Access Fees) $5,046, Presv $210, Micro $30, Electronic Ref Mat (Incl. Access Fees) $10,570. Sal $153,318
Library Holdings: Bk Vols 54,708; Per Subs 131
Subject Interests: Large print, Quilting, Vietnam conflict
Special Collections: Western American Coll
Database Vendor: CARL, Ebsco - EbscoHost, OCLC - First Search, Wilson - Wilson Web
Publications: Bridges (newsletter)
Partic in WYLD Network
Branches: 1
GLENROCK BRANCH, 518 S Fourth St, PO Box 1000, Glenrock, 82637. SAN 365-2262. Tel: 307-436-2573. FAX: 307-436-8525. Web Site: will.state.wy.us/glenrock. *Branch Mgr*, Carol A Thomas; E-Mail: cthomas@will.state.wy.us; *Ch Servs*, Eileen Nugent; E-Mail: enugent@will.state.wy.us; *Circ*, Trudy Martinez; E-Mail: tmsrtine@will.state.wy.us; Staff 4 (Non-MLS 4)
Founded 1939. Pop 2,100; Circ 28,223
Library Holdings: Bk Vols 15,566; Per Subs 58
Automation Activity & Vendor Info: (Cataloging) DRA; (Circulation) DRA; (ILL) DRA; (Serials) DRA
Database Vendor: CARL, Ebsco - EbscoHost, OCLC - First Search, Wilson - Wilson Web
Function: ILL available
Partic in Wyo Libr Database

ENCAMPMENT

S GRAND ENCAMPMENT MUSEUM, INC LIBRARY,* PO Box 43, 82325. SAN 373-3092. Tel: 307-327-5308. *Pres*, Doug Tieszen
Library Holdings: Bk Titles 100
Restriction: Open to public for reference only
Closed in winter

EVANSTON

P UINTA COUNTY LIBRARY, 701 Main St, 82930. SAN 365-2297. Tel: 307-789-2770. Interlibrary Loan Service Tel: 307-789-1328. Reference Tel: 307-789-1328. FAX: 307-789-0148. Web Site: www-wsl.state.wy.us/uinta/. *Dir*, Dale Collum; E-Mail: dcollum@will.state.wy.us; *ILL, Ref*, Claire Francis; *Ch Servs*, Leslie Carlson; *Circ*, Kathy Kallas; E-Mail: kallas98@hotmail.com; Staff 7 (MLS 3, Non-MLS 4)
Founded 1904. Pop 20,490; Circ 111,336
Jul 1999-Jun 2000 Income (Main Library and Branch Library) $573,943, Federal $13,650, County $544,908, Locally Generated Income $15,385. Mats Exp $53,815, Books $41,672, Per/Ser (Incl. Access Fees) $10,993, Micro $1,150. Sal $244,100 (Prof $83,365)
Library Holdings: Bk Vols 62,075; Per Subs 122
Subject Interests: Nat parks of western US, Western Americana
Partic in OCLC Online Computer Library Center, Inc; Wyo Libr Database
Branches: 2
LYMAN BRANCH, 204 E Sage, PO Box 839, Lyman, 82937-0839. Tel: 307-787-6556. FAX: 307-787-6339. E-Mail: lymanlib@bvea.net. *Branch Mgr*, Susan Worthen; Staff 1 (Non-MLS 1)
Founded 1916. Pop 1,700; Circ 18,727
Jul 1999-Jun 2000 Mats Exp $5,385, Books $3,235, Per/Ser (Incl. Access Fees) $2,150
Library Holdings: Bk Vols 13,810; Per Subs 80
MOUNTAIN VIEW BRANCH, Second & Cedar St, PO Box 530, Mountain View, 82939-0530. SAN 365-2351. Tel: 307-782-3161. FAX: 307-782-6640. E-Mail: mtnviewlib@bvea.net. *Branch Mgr*, Nita Duncan; Staff 1 (Non-MLS 1)
Founded 1940. Pop 1,182; Circ 16,756
Jul 1999-Jun 2000 Mats Exp $5,285, Books $3,235, Per/Ser (Incl. Access Fees) $2,050
Library Holdings: Bk Vols 12,752; Per Subs 65

M WYOMING STATE HOSPITAL LIBRARY,* 831 Hwy 150 S, PO Box 177, 82931-0177. SAN 318-496X. Tel: 307-789-3464, Ext 785. FAX: 307-789-7373. *Librn*, William L Matchinski; E-Mail: will@wsh.state.wy.us
Founded 1890
Jan 1998-Dec 1999 Income $8,000
Library Holdings: Bk Titles 5,000; Per Subs 50
Subject Interests: Medicine, Psychiatry, Psychology

F E WARREN AFB

UNITED STATES AIR FORCE

A FRANCIS E WARREN AIR FORCE BASE LIBRARY, Bldg 214, 7205 Randall Ave, 82005-2988. SAN 365-2386. Tel: 307-773-3416. FAX: 307-773-4515.; Staff 2 (MLS 2)
Library Holdings: Bk Vols 50,000; Per Subs 127

GILLETTE

M CAMPBELL COUNTY MEMORIAL HOSPITAL LIBRARY, 501 S Burma, PO Box 3011, 82717. SAN 371-8239. Tel: 307-687-5183. FAX: 307-687-5182. E-Mail: odm@ccmh.net. *Librn*, Michlene D Mankin; E-Mail: mmd@ccmh.net; Staff 1 (Non-MLS 1)
Jul 1999-Jun 2000 Income $55,000
Library Holdings: Bk Titles 3,000; Per Subs 150
Subject Interests: Mental health
Restriction: Staff use only
Partic in NE Wyo Med Libr Consortium

P CAMPBELL COUNTY PUBLIC LIBRARY, (CCPL), 2101 4J Rd, 82718-5205. SAN 365-2416. Tel: 307-687-0009. Interlibrary Loan Service Tel: 307-682-3223. Circulation Tel: 307-682-3223. Reference Tel: 307-687-0115. FAX: 307-686-4009. Web Site: www.ccg.co.campbell.wy.us/library/. *Dir*, Marcia Wright; E-Mail: mwright@will.state.wy.us; *Asst Dir*, Pam Boger; E-Mail: pboger@will.state.wy.us; *Ch Servs*, Deb Bruse; Tel: 307-687-9225, E-Mail: dbruse@will.state.wy.us; *Tech Servs*, Lori Kirchoff; E-Mail: lkirchoff@will.state.wy.us; *Ref*, Ara Anderson; Tel: 307-687-0115, E-Mail: aanderso@will.state.wy.us; *Circ*, Jackie Darnall; Tel: 307-687-3223, E-Mail: jdarnall@will.state.wy.us; *YA Servs*, Susan Knesel; Tel: 307-687-9227, E-Mail: sknesel@will.state.wy.us; *Exten Serv*, Pat Brose; Tel: 307-687-9228, E-Mail: pbrose@will.state.wy.us; Staff 8 (MLS 1, Non-MLS 7)
Founded 1928. Pop 32,663; Circ 340,355
Jul 1998-Jun 1999 Income (Main Library and Branch Library) $1,538,983, Federal $1,420, County $1,492,849, Locally Generated Income $5,000, Other $3,439. Mats Exp $35,800, Books $20,000, Per/Ser (Incl. Access Fees) $15,800. Sal $866,492
Library Holdings: Bk Vols 106,480; Per Subs 256
Special Collections: US Geological Survey Map Depository; Western Art
Automation Activity & Vendor Info: (Acquisitions) DRA; (Cataloging) DRA; (Circulation) DRA; (OPAC) DRA; (Serials) DRA
Publications: Newsline (bi-monthly) (Newsletter)
Partic in BCR; OCLC Online Computer Library Center, Inc; WYLD Network
Special Services for the Deaf - High interest/low vocabulary books
Branches: 1
WRIGHT BRANCH, Wright, 82732-0600. SAN 365-2475. Tel: 307-464-0500. FAX: 307-464-0500.
Founded 1978
Library Holdings: Bk Vols 6,593
Automation Activity & Vendor Info: (Acquisitions) DRA; (Cataloging) DRA; (Circulation) DRA; (OPAC) DRA; (Serials) DRA

GREEN RIVER

P SWEETWATER COUNTY LIBRARY SYSTEM,* 300 N First East, PO Box 550, 82935-4221. SAN 365-2505. Tel: 307-875-3615. FAX: 307-872-3203. *Dir*, Helen Higby; E-Mail: hhigby@wyld.state.wy.us; *Bkmobile Coordr*, Leanna Bunderman; *ILL*, Judy McPhie; *Tech Servs*, Julie Farr; *Br Coordr*, Harold Hayes; *Publ Servs*, Vicki Roth
Founded 1907. Pop 42,000
Jul 1997-Jun 1998 Income $2,078,349. Mats Exp $251,746. Sal $1,476,581
Library Holdings: Bk Vols 204,994; Per Subs 669
Subject Interests: Spanish Am, Western Am, Women's studies
Automation Activity & Vendor Info: (Acquisitions) DRA; (Cataloging) DRA; (Circulation) DRA; (Serials) DRA
Publications: The Library Link (newsletter)
Branches: 7
BAIROIL BRANCH, 501 Paintbrush Ave, PO Box 40, Bairoil, 82322-0040. SAN 365-253X. Tel: 307-328-0239. *Librn*, Sylvia McCain
FARSON BRANCH, PO Box 400, Farson, 82932. SAN 365-2564. Tel: 307-273-9301. FAX: 307-273-9313. *Librn*, Dolores McGowan
GRANGER BRANCH, PO Box 38, Granger, 82934. SAN 365-2572. Tel: 307-875-8038. FAX: 307-875-8038. *Librn*, Gloria Andrews
RELIANCE BRANCH, 1329 Main St, PO Box 330, Reliance, 82943. SAN 365-2610. Tel: 307-352-6670. FAX: 307-352-6670. *Librn*, Cindy Camacho
ROCK SPRINGS BRANCH, 400 C St, Rock Springs, 82901. SAN 365-2629. Tel: 307-352-6667. FAX: 307-352-6657. *Librn*, Vivian Hurley; *Ch Servs*, Terri M Larsen; *ILL*, Ernestine Gamble
SUPERIOR BRANCH, PO Box 99, Superior, 82945. SAN 365-2653. Tel: 307-352-6671. FAX: 307-352-6671. *Librn*, Teri Robert
Friends of the Library Group
WHITE MOUNTAIN, 2935 Sweetwater Dr, Rock Springs, 82901-4331. SAN 329-6814. Tel: 307-362-2665. FAX: 307-352-6655. *Librn*, Julie Farr; *Ch Servs*, Vickie Riley; *ILL*, Pam Hiltner
Bookmobiles: 1

JACKSON

GM ST JOHN'S HOSPITAL, Medical Library, PO Box 428, 83001. SAN 6145. Tel: 307-739-7371. FAX: 307-739-7372. *Librn*, Doreen Ward; E-dvward@teton.hospital.org; *Librn*, Maureen O'Leary
Library Holdings: Bk Titles 825; Per Subs 90

P TETON COUNTY LIBRARY, Huff Memorial Library, PO Box 1629, 83001-1629. SAN 365-2688. Tel: 307-733-2164. FAX: 307-733-4568. Site: will.state.wy.us/teton/home/. *Dir*, Betsy Bernfeld; E-Mail: bbernfe will.state.wy.us
Founded 1940. Pop 12,500; Circ 217,695
Jul 1999-Jun 2000 Income $1,500,000
Library Holdings: Bk Titles 71,627
Subject Interests: Mountaineering, Outdoor sports, Western hist
Special Collections: American Alpine Club Branch
Friends of the Library Group
Branches: 1
ALTA BRANCH, Rte 1, Box 3480, Driggs, 83422. SAN 365-2718. Te 307-353-2472. Web Site: will.state.wy.us-teton-home. *Librn*, Gretche Notzold; E-Mail: gnotzold@will.state.wy.us

KELLY

S TETON SCIENCE SCHOOL LIBRARY,* One Ditch Creek Rd, PO B 68, 83011. SAN 327-8379. Tel: 307-733-4765. FAX: 307-739-9388. E-info@tetomscience.org. Web Site: www.tetomscience.org. *Librn*, Jack S
Library Holdings: Bk Vols 2,000
Restriction: Non-circulating to the public

KEMMERER

P LINCOLN COUNTY LIBRARY, 519 Emerald, 83101. SAN 365-2742. 307-877-6961. FAX: 307-877-4147. Web Site: www-wsl.state.wy.us/linc *Dir*, Mary Lynn Corbett; *Admin Assoc*, Karyl Montgomery; E-Mail: kmontgom@will.state.wy.us; Staff 29 (MLS 1, Non-MLS 28)
Founded 1983. Pop 14,500; Circ 192,786
Jul 1998-Jun 1999 Income (Main Library and Branch Library) $517,68 County $468,905, Locally Generated Income $30,412, Other $18,364. M Exp $99,126, Books $64,000, Per/Ser (Incl. Access Fees) $8,331, AV E $10,500, Manuscripts & Archives $105, Electronic Ref Mat (Incl. Acces Fees) $16,190. Sal $288,364 (Prof $30,000)
Library Holdings: Bk Vols 114,658; Per Subs 240
Database Vendor: Dialog, OCLC - First Search
Function: ILL available
Mem of Lincoln County Libr Syst
Branches: 3
COKEVILLE BRANCH, 240 E Main St, PO Box 69, Cokeville, 83114. SAN 365-2807. Tel: 307-279-3213. FAX: 307-279-3263. *Librn*, Gayle Chadwick
LABARGE BRANCH, 262 Main St, PO Box 57, LaBarge, 83123. SAN 365-2815. Tel: 307-386-2571. FAX: 307-386-2569. *Librn*, Marika Tha
Founded 1981
STAR VALLEY, 261 Washington, PO Box 849, Afton, 83110. SAN 365 2777. Tel: 307-885-3158. FAX: 307-885-9651. *Librn*, Myrna Galloway
Bookmobiles: 1

LANDER

P FREMONT COUNTY LIBRARY SYSTEM, 451 N Second St, 82520-2. SAN 365-2831. Tel: 307-332-5194. FAX: 307-332-3909. *Dir*, Ada Howa E-Mail: ahoward@will.state.wy.us; *Ch Servs*, Linda Willenbrecht; *Tech Servs*, June Cleveland; *Ad Servs*, Barbara Oakleaf; Staff 1 (MLS 1)
Founded 1907. Pop 36,000
Jul 1999-Jun 2000 Income (Main Library and Branch Library) $653,642. Mats Exp $38,000, Books $25,000, Per/Ser (Incl. Access Fees) $9,000, A Equip $4,000. Sal $458,742
Library Holdings: Bk Vols 166,000; Per Subs 255
Subject Interests: Architecture, Art, Fishing, Large print, Outdoors, Wes Americana
Database Vendor: DRA
Partic in WYLD Network
Friends of the Library Group
Branches: 2
DUBOIS BRANCH, PO Box 787, Dubois, 82513-0787. SAN 365-2866. 307-455-2992. FAX: 307-455-2992. *Branch Mgr*, Sandra Leseberg; E-Mail: sleseber@wyoming.com
Library Holdings: Bk Vols 15,000
Friends of the Library Group
RIVERTON BRANCH, 1330 W Park, Riverton, 82501. SAN 365-3048. 307-856-3556. FAX: 307-857-3722. E-Mail: riverton@will.state.wy.us. Web Site: www.will.state.wy.us/fremont/index.html. *Branch Mgr*, Gloria Brodle; *Ch Servs*, Dorothy Phelps

Library Holdings: Bk Vols 77,000
Subject Interests: Small bus
Database Vendor: DRA
Friends of the Library Group

LANDER VALLEY REGIONAL MEDICAL CENTER, Medical Library,* 1320 Bishop Randall Dr, 82520. SAN 321-9836. Tel: 307-332-4420, Ext 213. FAX: 307-332-0347. Web Site: www.landerhospital.com. *Librn*, Sylvia Sala
Library Holdings: Bk Vols 400; Per Subs 2

NATIONAL OUTDOOR LEADERSHIP SCHOOL, Wilderness Education Resource Library,* 288 Main St, 82520-3140. SAN 373-3106. Tel: 307-332-1264. FAX: 307-332-8811. E-Mail: library@nols.edu. Web Site: www.nols.edu/.
Library Holdings: Bk Vols 6,500; Bk Titles 6,000; Per Subs 40
Restriction: Staff use only

WYOMING STATE TRAINING SCHOOL MEDICAL LIBRARY, 8204 State Hwy 789, 82520-9499. SAN 329-0646. Tel: 307-335-6804. FAX: 307-335-6990. *Librn*, Shirley Townsend
Library Holdings: Bk Titles 500; Per Subs 11
Subject Interests: Pediatrics
Restriction: Staff use only
Special Services for the Deaf - Books on deafness & sign language; High interest/low vocabulary books; Special interest periodicals; Staff with knowledge of sign language

RAMIE

ALBANY COUNTY PUBLIC LIBRARY, 310 S Eighth St, 82070-3969. SAN 365-3102. Tel: 307-721-2580. Circulation Tel: 307-721-2580, Ext 12. Reference Tel: 307-721-2580, Ext 6. FAX: 307-721-2584. E-Mail: albyref@wyld.state.wy.us. Web Site: acpl.lib.wy.us. *Dir*, Susan M Simpson; Tel: 307-721-2580, Ext 15, E-Mail: ssimpson@will.state.wy.us; *Circ*, Jennifer Ingram; Tel: 307-721-2580, Ext 10, E-Mail: jingram@will.state.wy.us; *ILL*, Stacey Wiegand; E-Mail: albyill@wyld.state.wy.us; *Tech Servs*, Sandra Frazier; Tel: 307-721-2580, Ext 18, E-Mail: albylibmgr@wyld.state.wy.us; *Outreach Serv*, Janet Gray; *Outreach Serv*, Ann Horan; *Ch Servs*, Debbie Sims; E-Mail: dsims@will.state.wy.us; Staff 4 (MLS 1, Non-MLS 3)
Founded 1887. Pop 31,000
Jul 1999-Jun 2000 Income (Main Library and Branch Library) $411,623, City $24,750, Federal $839, County $371,716, Locally Generated Income $14,318. Mats Exp $30,157. Sal $267,344
Library Holdings: Bk Vols 144,000; Per Subs 259
Subject Interests: Local history
Automation Activity & Vendor Info: (Cataloging) DRA; (Circulation) DRA; (OPAC) DRA; (Serials) DRA
Database Vendor: Ebsco - EbscoHost, OCLC - First Search, Wilson - Wilson Web
Partic in Wyo Libr Database
Friends of the Library Group
Branches: 2
CENTENNIAL VALLEY BRANCH, PO Box 188, Centennial, 82055-0188. SAN 365-3137. *Librn*, Deb Shogren
Jul 1999-Jun 2000 Mats Exp $771
Library Holdings: Bk Vols 3,000
Partic in Wyo Libr Database
Friends of the Library Group
ROCK RIVER BRANCH, 386 Ave D, Rock River, 82083. (Mail add: PO Box 213, Rock River, 82083-0213), SAN 365-3161. *Librn*, Sherri Winton
Jul 1999-Jun 2000 Mats Exp $1,181
Library Holdings: Bk Vols 4,000

AMERICAN HERITAGE CENTER, Toppan Rare Books Library, Centennial Complex, Willett Dr, PO Box 3924, 82071-3924. SAN 377-0591. Tel: 307-766-2565. FAX: 307-766-5511. Web Site: www.uwyo.edu/ahc/depts/toppan/toppan.htm. *Librn*, Ann Marie Lane; E-Mail: amlane@uwyo.edu
Library Holdings: Bk Titles 40,000

IVINSON MEMORIAL HOSPITAL LIBRARY, 255 N 30th St, 82072. SAN 324-377X. Tel: 307-742-2141, Ext 5390. FAX: 307-721-9804. E-Mail: imhlib@vcn.com. *In Charge*, Wendye Ware; E-Mail: wendyew@ivinsonhospital.org
Founded 1964
Library Holdings: Bk Titles 350; Per Subs 110
Restriction: Staff use only

LARAMIE PLAINS MUSEUM ASSOCIATION INC LIBRARY,* 603 Ivinson Ave, 82070-3299. SAN 326-1220. Tel: 307-742-4448. *Dir*, Daniel A Nelson
Founded 1972
Library Holdings: Bk Vols 1,000

LARAMIE SOILS SERVICE LIBRARY,* 209 Grand Ave, Ste 408, PO Box 255, 82073. SAN 373-3114. Tel: 307-742-4185. FAX: 307-742-2090. E-Mail: geomorph@compuserve.com.
Library Holdings: Bk Vols 600
Special Collections: Soil Samples; Volcanic Ash
Partic in Colorado Alliance Of Research Libraries

UNIVERSITY OF WYOMING
CL LAW LIBRARY, University Sta, PO Box 3035, 82071-3035. SAN 365-3374. Interlibrary Loan Service Tel: 307-766-2210. FAX: 307-766-4044. *Librn*, Tim Kearley; *Tech Servs*, Joan Binder; E-Mail: jebinder@corral.uwyo.edu; *Publ Servs*, Mary Jenny; Staff 7 (MLS 3, Non-MLS 4)
Founded 1920 Mats Exp Per/Ser (Incl. Access Fees) $259,155
Library Holdings: Bk Vols 186,643
Subject Interests: US law
Special Collections: Roman Law (Blume Coll)
Publications: In-house Newsletter; Self-Help Guides
Partic in Dialog Corporation; OCLC Online Computer Library Center, Inc; Westlaw

S UNIVERSITY MEDIA SERVICES, University Sta, PO Box 3334, 82071. SAN 365-334X. Tel: 307-766-2035. FAX: 307-766-4822. *Dir*, Andrew Bryson; Staff 3 (MLS 3)
Founded 1966. Enrl 1,339; Fac 114; Highest Degree: Doctorate
Subject Interests: Education, Instrucl tech

C UNIVERSITY OF WYOMING LIBRARIES, 13th & Ivinson, PO Box 3334, 82071-3334. SAN 365-3196. Tel: 307-766-3279. Interlibrary Loan Service Tel: 307-766-5168. Circulation Tel: 307-766-3190. Reference Tel: 307-766-2070. FAX: 307-766-2510, 307-766-3062. Web Site: www-lib.uwyo.edu, www.uwyo.edu/lib/home.htm. *Dir*, Keith M Cottam; E-Mail: kcottam@uwyo.edu; *Asst Dir*, Sandra M Barstow; Tel: 307-766-5621, E-Mail: sbarstow@uwyo.edu; *Ref*, Diana Shelton; Tel: 307-766-6216, E-Mail: dshelton@uwyo.edu; *Cat*, Carol J White; Tel: 307-766-6402, E-Mail: cwhite@uwyo.edu; *Coll Develop*, William Van Arsdale; Tel: 307-766-4296, E-Mail: arsdale@uwyo.edu; *Doc*, Katherine Powell; Tel: 307-766-3845, E-Mail: kpowell@uwyo.edu; Staff 110 (MLS 31, Non-MLS 79)
Founded 1887. Enrl 11,126; Fac 680; Highest Degree: Doctorate
Jul 1999-Jun 2000 Income (Main and Other College/University Libraries) $5,292,931. Mats Exp $2,992,729, Books $733,848, Per/Ser (Incl. Access Fees) $2,115,889, Presv $71,916. Sal $2,300,202
Library Holdings: Bk Vols 1,252,596; Per Subs 13,296
Automation Activity & Vendor Info: (Acquisitions) Endeavor; (Cataloging) Endeavor; (Circulation) Endeavor; (OPAC) Endeavor; (Serials) Endeavor
Publications: The Library Associate
Partic in Bibliographical Center For Research, Rocky Mountain Region, Inc; Center For Research Libraries; Colorado Alliance Of Research Libraries; Mid-Continental Regional Med Librs Asn; OCLC Online Computer Library Center, Inc
Departmental Libraries:
AV FILM Tel: 307-766-3184.
BRINKERHOFF EARTH RESOURCES INFORMATION CENTER, University Sta, PO Box 3006, 82071-3006. SAN 365-3250. Tel: 307-766-3374. Reference Tel: 307-766-3328. FAX: 307-766-6679. *Librn*, Sally Scott; Tel: 307-766-6538, E-Mail: sscott@uwyo.edu; *Asst Dir, Tech Servs*, Sandra Barstow; Tel: 307-766-5621, Fax: 307-766-2510, E-Mail: sbarstow@uwyo.edu
Subject Interests: Geochemistry, Geology, Geomorphology, Geophysics, Paleontology, Remote sensing, Sedimentology
LEARNING RESOURCE CENTER, University Sta, PO Box 3374, 82071. SAN 328-7270. Tel: 307-766-2527. *Librn*, Laurn Wilhelm
ROCKY MOUNTAIN HERBARIUM REFERENCE COLLECTION, University Sta, PO Box 3262, 82071. SAN 328-7297. Tel: 307-766-5165. *Librn*, Janis Leath
SCIENCE-TECHNOLOGY, PO Box 3262, 82071. SAN 365-3285. Tel: 307-766-5165. FAX: 307-766-6757. *Admin Assoc, Tech Servs*, Sandra Barstow; Tel: 307-766-5621, Fax: 307-766-2510, E-Mail: sbarstow@uwyo.edu; *Librn*, Lori Phillips; Tel: 307-766-3859, E-Mail: lphil@uwyo.edu
Subject Interests: Ecology, Environ sci, Health sci, Psychology

G UNIVERSITY OF WYOMING LIBRARY, The Learning Resources Center, 15th & Lewis St, PO Box 3374 University Sta, 82071-3374. SAN 321-4443. Tel: 307-766-2527. FAX: 307-766-2018. *Head of Libr*, Laurn Wilhelm
Library Holdings: Bk Vols 16,300; Per Subs 15
Subject Interests: Practical educ
Special Collections: NASA Regional Teachers Resource Center
Provide software to Wyoming educators for preview purposes

G WYOMING STATE GEOLOGICAL SURVEY LIBRARY, Geological Survey Bldg, 11th & Lewis St, 82071-3008. (Mail add: PO Box 3008, 82071-3008), SAN 321-7655. Tel: 307-766-2286. FAX: 307-766-2605. E-Mail: sales@wsgs.uwyo.edu. Web Site: www.wsgs.uwyo.edu.
Founded 1933
2000-2000 Mats Exp $2,250, Per/Ser (Incl. Access Fees) $1,500, Other Print Mats $500, Manuscripts & Archives $250
Library Holdings: Bk Vols 25,000; Bk Titles 600; Per Subs 10
Subject Interests: Environ impact statements for Wyo projects, Geology, Mineral resources, Mining rec, Wyoming
Special Collections: Oil & Gas Records (Wyoming Electric Log Files Coll & Wyoming Petroleum Information Cards Coll); US Geological Survey

Open-File Reports for Wyoming
Restriction: Circulates for staff only, Lending to staff only, Not a lending library, Open to public for reference only, Public use on premises
Function: Archival collection

LOVELL

SR CHURCH OF JESUS CHRIST OF LATTER-DAY SAINTS, Lovell Wyoming Family History Center, 50 W Main, PO Box 575, 82431. SAN 329-8388. Tel: 307-548-2963. *Dir*, Billie Hudspeth
Library Holdings: Bk Titles 360
Special Collections: Census Index

LUSK

P NIOBRARA COUNTY LIBRARY, 425 S Main, PO Box 510, 82225. SAN 318-4994. Tel: 307-334-3490. FAX: 307-334-3490. E-Mail: niobill@wyld.state.wy.us. Web Site: will.state.wy.us/niobrara. *Dir*, Debbie Sturman
Founded 1913. Pop 2,499; Circ 17,945
Library Holdings: Bk Titles 30,000; Per Subs 34
Friends of the Library Group

S WYOMING WOMEN'S CENTER LIBRARY, 1000 W Griffith, PO Box WWC-20, 82225-0020. SAN 320-9881. Tel: 307-334-3693, Ext 244. FAX: 307-334-2254. *Librn*, Virginia Pullen
Founded 1980
Library Holdings: Bk Titles 4,000; Per Subs 10

MOOSE

S NATIONAL PARK SERVICE, Grand Teton National Park Library, PO Box Drawer 170, 83012. SAN 321-0189. Tel: 307-739-3399. FAX: 307-739-3438. Web Site: www.nps.gov/grte. *In Charge*, Eileen Andes
Founded 1929
Library Holdings: Bk Titles 3,000; Per Subs 15
Subject Interests: Botany, Geology, Local history, Natural history, Zoology

NEWCASTLE

S ANNA MILLER MUSEUM LIBRARY,* 401 Delaware, PO Box 698, 82701. SAN 326-5757. Tel: 307-746-4188. FAX: 307-746-4629. E-Mail: annamm@trib.com. *Dir*, Angelil Cregger; *Curator*, Bobbie Jo Tysdal
Library Holdings: Bk Vols 5,000
Special Collections: Newcastle History; Newsletter Journal, newsp
Friends of the Library Group

P WESTON COUNTY PUBLIC LIBRARY,* 23 W Main St, 82701. SAN 365-3404. Tel: 307-746-2206. FAX: 307-746-2218. E-Mail: westill@wyld.state.wy.us.
Founded 1911
Library Holdings: Bk Vols 38,000; Per Subs 128
Special Collections: Wyoming Coll
Branches: 1
UPTON BRANCH, 722 Fourth St, PO Box 605, Upton, 82730-0605. SAN 365-3439. Tel: 307-468-2324. FAX: 307-468-2324. *Librn*, Sherri Kay Boothroyd; *Mgr*, Sherri Randall; E-Mail: sbooth@will.state.wy.us; Staff 2 (Non-MLS 2)
Founded 1969. Pop 950
Library Holdings: Bk Titles 9,250; Per Subs 19
Automation Activity & Vendor Info: (Cataloging) DRA; (Circulation) DRA; (OPAC) DRA; (Serials) DRA
Database Vendor: CARL, Ebsco - EbscoHost, OCLC - First Search, Wilson - Wilson Web

PINEDALE

P SUBLETTE COUNTY LIBRARY,* 1551 S Tyler Ave, PO Box 489, 82941-0489. SAN 318-5001. Tel: 307-367-4115. FAX: 307-367-6722. *Dir*, Daphne Platts; *Asst Dir*, Linda Baker; Staff 4 (Non-MLS 4)
Founded 1967. Pop 5,000; Circ 55,000
Library Holdings: Bk Titles 53,183; Per Subs 211
Special Collections: Film books; Rocky Mountain Fur Trade, photogs
Partic in Health Sci Libr & Info Coop
Friends of the Library Group
Branches: 1
BIG PINEY BRANCH, 346 Fish St, PO Box 768, Big Piney, 83113. SAN 321-7396. Tel: 307-276-3515. FAX: 307-276-3516. *Dir*, Carrie Anderson
Friends of the Library Group

POWELL

J NORTHWEST COLLEGE, Hinckley Library, 231 W Sixth St, 82435. SAN 318-501X. Tel: 307-754-6207. FAX: 307-754-6010. Web Site: www.nwc.cc.wy.us/area/library/. *Dir*, Kay Carlson; E-Mail: carlsonk@nwc.cc.wy.us; Staff 6 (MLS 2, Non-MLS 4)
Founded 1948. Enrl 1,600; Fac 95; Highest Degree: Associate
Jul 1998-Jun 1999 Income $180,000. Mats Exp $82,000, Books $50,0C Per/Ser (Incl. Access Fees) $32,000. Sal $125,000 (Prof $60,000)
Library Holdings: Bk Vols 45,000; Per Subs 435
Subject Interests: Country music, Heart Mountain
Database Vendor: DRA
Partic in Wyo Libr Database

RAWLINS

P CARBON COUNTY LIBRARY SYSTEM,* 215 W Buffalo St, 82301. 365-3463. Tel: 307-328-2618. FAX: 307-328-2615. *Dir*, Vicki Hitchcoc *Servs, Mgr*, Douglas Wolfe; *Coll Develop, Tech Servs*, Vicky Baunach
Founded 1925. Circ 74,280
Jul 1997-Jun 1998 Income $318,283, State $692, County $287,830, Lo Generated Income $29,761. Mats Exp $61,267. Sal $203,220
Library Holdings: Bk Vols 78,079; Per Subs 30
Special Collections: Rare Western Americana
Friends of the Library Group
Branches: 7
ELK MOUNTAIN BRANCH, PO Box 156, Elk Mountain, 82324. SAN 365-351X. Tel: 307-348-7421. FAX: 307-348-7421. *Mgr*, Linda Runy
ENCAMPMENT BRANCH, PO Box 712, Encampment, 82325. SAN 3 3528. Tel: 307-327-5775. FAX: 307-327-5775.
Friends of the Library Group
HANNA BRANCH, PO Box 189, Hanna, 82327. SAN 365-3552. Tel: 3 325-9357. FAX: 307-325-9357.
LITTLE SNAKE RIVER VALLEY BRANCH, PO Box 370, 82321. SA 365-3498. Tel: 307-383-7323. FAX: 307-383-7323.
Friends of the Library Group
MEDICINE BOW BRANCH, PO Box 279, Medicine Bow, 82329. SAN 365-3587. Tel: 307-379-2888. FAX: 307-379-2888.
SARATOGA BRANCH, PO Box 27, Saratoga, 82331. SAN 365-3617. 307-326-8209. FAX: 307-326-8209.
Friends of the Library Group
SINCLAIR BRANCH, PO Box 8, Sinclair, 82334. SAN 365-3633. Tel: 324-6231. FAX: 307-324-6231.

S WYOMING STATE PENITENTIARY LIBRARY,* PO Box 400, 8230 0400. SAN 318-5036. Tel: 307-328-1441, Ext 284. FAX: 307-328-2179. *Charge*, Donna Erickson
Founded 1924
Library Holdings: Bk Vols 10,000; Bk Titles 9,000
Subject Interests: Adventure, Science fiction, Western stories
Special Collections: National Geographic 1916-present

RIVERTON

J CENTRAL WYOMING COLLEGE LIBRARY, 2660 Peck Ave, 82501. SAN 318-5044. Tel: 307-855-2141. Interlibrary Loan Service Tel: 307-85 2178. Reference Tel: 307-855-2178. Toll Free Tel: 800-735-8418, Ext 21 FAX: 307-855-2094. *Dir Libr Serv*, Carol L Deering; Tel: 307-855-2232, E-Mail: cdeering@cwc.cc.wy.us; *Circ*, Kathleen Holbert; *Tech Servs*, Kri Hardtke; Tel: 307-855-2109, E-Mail: khardtke@cwc.cc.wy.us; *ILL, Ref*, Elaine Ray; E-Mail: eray@cwc.cc.wy.us; Staff 3 (MLS 1, Non-MLS 2)
Founded 1967
Subject Interests: Am Indians, Geology, Wyoming
Special Collections: American Indian Coll; Wyoming Coll
Automation Activity & Vendor Info: (Acquisitions) DRA; (Cataloging) DRA; (Circulation) DRA
Database Vendor: Ebsco - EbscoHost, Wilson - Wilson Web
Publications: Acquisitions Bulletins; Specialized Subject Bibliographies
Partic in Wyo Libr Database

M RIVERTON MEMORIAL HOSPITAL, (Formerly Columbia HCA-Rivert Memorial Hospital), Medical Library, 2100 W Sunset, 82501. SAN 370-890X. Tel: 307-856-4161. FAX: 307-857-3586. Web Site: www.riverton-hospital.com. *Librn*, Jody McConnaughey
Library Holdings: Bk Titles 500; Per Subs 20

ROCK SPRINGS

J HAY LIBRARY,* 2500 College Dr, PO Box 428, 82902-0428. SAN 318-5079. Tel: 307-382-1701. FAX: 307-382-7665. Web Site: www.wwcc.cc.wy.us/college/library/. *Dir*, Robert Kalabus; E-Mail: rkalabus@wwcc.cc.wy.us; *Publ Servs*, Fern Stringham; *Tech Servs*, Deann LeBarron; *Coll Develop*, Agnes Kelly
Founded 1959. Enrl 3,200; Fac 81
Library Holdings: Bk Vols 47,000; Bk Titles 41,000; Per Subs 420
Special Collections: Local Newspaper (Rock Springs Rocket), micro, (Green River Star), micro
Partic in Bibliographical Center For Research, Rocky Mountain Region, Ir

MEMORIAL HOSPITAL OF SWEETWATER LIBRARY,* 1200 College Dr, PO Box 1359, 82902-1359. SAN 377-0575. Tel: 307-362-3711, Ext 433. FAX: 307-362-8391. *Librn*, Kathy Tacke
Library Holdings: Bk Titles 800; Per Subs 160
Partic in Medical Libr Asn

RIDAN

DEPARTMENT OF VETERANS AFFAIRS, Medical Center Library,* 1898 Fort Rd, 82801. SAN 318-5095. Tel: 307-672-1661. FAX: 307-672-1652. *Dir*, Pat Carlson; Staff 2 (MLS 1, Non-MLS 1)
Founded 1922
Library Holdings: Bk Vols 8,000; Per Subs 418
Subject Interests: Dentistry, Medicine, Nursing, Psychiatry, Psychology
Partic in Vets Admin Libr Network

SHERIDAN COLLEGE, Instructional Resource Center,* 82801. SAN 318-5087. Tel: 307-674-6446, Ext 6200. FAX: 307-674-4874. E-Mail: diverson@radar.sc.whecn.edu. Web Site: www.sc.whecn.edu. *Librn*, Deborah Iverson; *Circ*, Peg Parkison; *Media Spec*, Pamela See; *Ref*, Harold Huber; *Tech Servs*, Lisa Smith; *ILL*, Carrol Geisler
Founded 1948. Enrl 2,500; Fac 70
1997-1998 Income $226,375, State $201,375, County $25,000. Mats Exp $55,000. Sal $122,000
Library Holdings: Bk Vols 34,096; Bk Titles 26,008; Per Subs 300
Special Collections: Western Americana (Reynolds Memorial Coll)
Partic in Bibliographical Center For Research, Rocky Mountain Region, Inc

SHERIDAN COUNTY FULMER PUBLIC LIBRARY, (Formerly Sheridan County Public Library System), 335 W Alger St, 82801-3899. SAN 365-3676. Tel: 307-674-8585, Ext 15. Reference Tel: 307-674-8585, Ext 15. FAX: 307-674-7374. Web Site: www.sheridanwyolibrary.org. *Dir*, Cathleen M Butler; E-Mail: cbutler@will.state.wy.us; *Ch Servs*, Michelle Havenga; E-Mail: mhavenga@will.state.wy.us; *Circ*, Marci Mock; *Spec Coll & Archives*, Karen Woinoski; E-Mail: kwoinosk@will.state.wy.us; *Ref*, Lynn Friesner; E-Mail: lfriesne@will.state.wy.us; Staff 13 (MLS 3, Non-MLS 10)
Founded 1903. Pop 26,700; Circ 313,572
Jul 1999-Jun 2000 Income (Main Library and Branch Library) $628,804, Federal $7,747, County $557,112, Locally Generated Income $63,945. Mats Exp $63,828, Books $41,893, Per/Ser (Incl. Access Fees) $6,694, Other Print Mats $3,419, Electronic Ref Mat (Incl. Access Fees) $15,241. Sal $459,128 (Prof $90,929)
Library Holdings: Bk Titles 150,649; Per Subs 183
Subject Interests: Regional history
Special Collections: Folklore & Storytelling (Spell-Spinner Coll)
Automation Activity & Vendor Info: (Acquisitions) DRA; (Cataloging) DRA; (Circulation) DRA; (OPAC) DRA
Database Vendor: DRA
Partic in WYLD Network
Special Services for the Deaf - TTY machine
Friends of the Library Group
Branches: 3
CLEARMONT BRANCH LIBRARY, PO Box 26, Clearmont, 82835. SAN 365-3706. Tel: 307-758-4331. FAX: 307-758-4331. E-Mail: cbl@mcn.net. Web Site: www.sheridanwyolibrary.org. *Mgr*, Barbara Carlock; Staff 1 (Non-MLS 1)
Library Holdings: Bk Vols 5,000
Friends of the Library Group
STORY BRANCH LIBRARY, Story, 82842. SAN 365-3730. Tel: 307-683-2922. FAX: 307-683-2922. E-Mail: sherstor@fiberpipe.net. Web Site: www.sheridanwyolibrary.org. *Mgr*, Joyce Hoffman
Library Holdings: Bk Titles 14,206
Friends of the Library Group
TONGUE RIVER BRANCH LIBRARY, PO Box 909, Ranchester, 82839-0909. SAN 365-3765. Tel: 307-655-9726. FAX: 307-655-9726. E-Mail: shertong@fiberpipe.net. Web Site: www.sheridanwyolibrary.org. *Mgr*, Connie Fiedor
Library Holdings: Bk Vols 8,600 . Home delivery for homebound patrons

WHEDON CANCER FOUNDATION LIBRARY,* 30 S Scott St, PO Box 683, 82801-0683. SAN 328-1299. Tel: 307-672-2941. FAX: 307-672-7273. Web Site: www..uwyo.edu/~whedon. *Coll Develop, Dir*, Nancy E Peterson; E-Mail: nanpeter@uwyo.edu
Founded 1981
Library Holdings: Bk Vols 400; Per Subs 50
Special Collections: Breast Cancer Coll, Hospice & ACS (lending library of videos)
Partic in Docline; Midcontinental Regional Med Libr Program

NDANCE

CROOK COUNTY LIBRARY,* 414 Main St, PO Box 910, 82729-0910. SAN 365-379X. Tel: 307-283-1006, 307-283-1008. FAX: 307-283-1006. *Dir*, Jill A Mackey; *Ad Servs*, Violet Smith; *Tech Servs*, Tanya Brekke; *Ch Servs*, Bonnie Stahla
Founded 1937
Jul 1998-Jun 1999 Income (Main Library and Branch Library) $180,775, County $178,655, Locally Generated Income $187, Other $1,552. Mats Exp $24,960, Books $21,199, Per/Ser (Incl. Access Fees) $2,091, Presv $301, Other Print Mats $866. Sal $128,294
Library Holdings: Bk Vols 49,000
Special Collections: Wyomingana
Partic in Wyo Libr Database
Friends of the Library Group
Branches: 2
HULETT LIBRARY, 401 Sager, PO Box 127, Hulett, 82720. SAN 365-382X. Tel: 307-467-5947. FAX: 307-467-5280. *Librn*, Rod Knudson
MOORCROFT BRANCH, 105 E Converse, PO Box 10, Moorcroft, 82721-0010. SAN 365-3854. Tel: 307-756-3232. FAX: 307-756-3232. *Librn*, Maureen Farrier

THERMOPOLIS

P HOT SPRINGS COUNTY LIBRARY,* 344 Arapahoe, 82443-0951. (Mail add: PO Box 951, 82443-0951), SAN 318-5109. Tel: 307-864-3104. FAX: 307-864-5416. E-Mail: aderomedi@will.state.wy.us. *Dir*, Ann Deromedi; Staff 2 (Non-MLS 2)
Pop 3,200; Circ 44,069
Jul 1998-Jun 1999 Income $101,000. Mats Exp $6,266. Sal $55,440
Library Holdings: Bk Vols 49,505
Subject Interests: Behav sci, Natural science, Soc sci
Special Collections: Local Newspapers from 1905, micro; Wyoming History Coll
Database Vendor: DRA
Friends of the Library Group

S WYOMING PIONEER HOME LIBRARY, 141 Pioneer Home Dr, 82443-2451. SAN 372-8781. Tel: 307-864-3151. FAX: 307-864-2934. E-Mail: wypionr@trib.com. *Librn*, Julie Miller
Library Holdings: Bk Vols 900; Per Subs 30
Subject Interests: Fiction, History, Large print, Reference
Restriction: Staff use only

TORRINGTON

M COMMUNITY HOSPITAL, Medical Library,* 2000 Campbell Dr, 82240. SAN 326-1247. Tel: 307-532-4181. FAX: 307-532-3783. *Librn*, Valerie Lamb
Founded 1978
Library Holdings: Bk Vols 143; Bk Titles 125; Per Subs 35
Subject Interests: Cardiology, Pathology
Partic in OCLC Online Computer Library Center, Inc; SE Wyo Health Sci Libr Consortium

C EASTERN WYOMING COLLEGE LIBRARY, 3200 West C, 82240. SAN 318-5117. Tel: 307-532-8210. FAX: 307-532-8225. Web Site: 137.86.16.2/library.htm, ewcweb.ewc.whecn.edu/library.htm. *Dir*, Marilyn Miller; E-Mail: mmiller@ewcl.ewc.whecn.edu; *Asst Dir*, Becky Lorenz; Staff 2 (MLS 2)
Founded 1948. Enrl 1,040; Fac 60
1998-1999 Mats Exp $26,111, Books $5,006, Per/Ser (Incl. Access Fees) $5,500, Micro $2,500, Other Print Mats $11,933. Sal $73,230 (Prof $60,376)
Library Holdings: Bk Vols 30,694; Bk Titles 26,300; Per Subs 105
Subject Interests: Agriculture, Bus, Education, History, Mgt, Veterinary tech

P GOSHEN COUNTY LIBRARY, 2001 East A St, 82240-2898. SAN 318-5125. Tel: 307- 532-3411. FAX: 307-532-2169. *Dir*, Isabel M Hoy; E-Mail: ihoy@will.state.wy.us; *ILL*, Judith M Hunter; Staff 6 (Non-MLS 6)
Founded 1922. Pop 12,500; Circ 47,845
Jul 1999-Jun 2000 Income County $156,000. Mats Exp $33,700, Books $25,000, Per/Ser (Incl. Access Fees) $2,100, Presv $1,500, Micro $100, AV Equip $1,000, Electronic Ref Mat (Incl. Access Fees) $4,000. Sal $30,600 (Prof $25,800)
Library Holdings: Bk Vols 30,100; Bk Titles 30,100; Per Subs 82
Automation Activity & Vendor Info: (Circulation) DRA
Database Vendor: DRA, Ebsco - EbscoHost, IAC - Info Trac, IAC - SearchBank, OCLC - First Search, Wilson - Wilson Web
Function: ILL available
Partic in Wyo Libr Database
Friends of the Library Group

WHEATLAND

P PLATTE COUNTY PUBLIC LIBRARY,* 904 Ninth St, 82201-9711. SAN 365-3889. Tel: 307-322-2689. FAX: 307-322-3540. E-Mail: plat@wyld.state.wy.us. Web Site: will.state.wy.us/wyld/libraries/plat. *Dir*, Patty Myers; *Asst Dir*, Ruth Vaughn
Founded 1894. Pop 8,145; Circ 85,779
Jul 1997-Jun 1998 Income $221,515, City $5,959, Federal $1,770, County $206,626, Locally Generated Income $5,867, Other $1,293. Mats Exp $42,214. Sal $119,232

Library Holdings: Bk Titles 56,297
Special Collections: Western Americana
Partic in Bibliographical Center For Research, Rocky Mountain Region, Inc
Friends of the Library Group
Branches: 3
CHUGWATER BRANCH, Chugwater, 82210. SAN 365-3919. Tel: 307-422-3666. *Librn*, Beth Vaughn
Friends of the Library Group
GLENDO BRANCH, 213 Second St, Glendo, 82213. (Mail add: PO Box 295, Glendo, 82213), Tel: 307-735-4480. *Librn*, Betty Amick
Library Holdings: Per Subs 5
Friends of the Library Group
GUERNSEY BRANCH, PO Box 607, Guernsey, 82214. SAN 365-3978. Tel: 307-836-2816. *Librn*, Pat Carpenter

WORLAND

P WASHAKIE COUNTY LIBRARY SYSTEM, 1019 Coburn Ave, 82401. SAN 365-4001. Tel: 307-347-2231. FAX: 307-347-2248. Web Site: www-wsl.state.wy.us/washakie/. *Dir*, Tobi Liedes-Bell; E-Mail: tliedes-bell@will.state.wy.us; *Asst Dir*, Dolores Koch; E-Mail: dkoch@will.state.wy.us; *Br Coordr*, Dorothy Dillard; Tel: 307-366-2348, E-Mail: ddillard@wyld.state.wy.us; Staff 1 (MLS 1)
Founded 1999. Pop 8,000; Circ 95,791
Jul 1999-Jun 2000 Income (Main Library and Branch Library) $197,050, County $76,000, Locally Generated Income $37,500, Other $83,550. Mats Exp $9,852, Books $3,332, Electronic Ref Mat (Incl. Access Fees) $6,520. Sal $77,475
Library Holdings: Bk Titles 58,000; Per Subs 166
Automation Activity & Vendor Info: (Circulation) DRA
Database Vendor: CARL, DRA, Ebsco - EbscoHost, IAC - SearchBa[illegible], OCLC - First Search, Wilson - Wilson Web
Function: ILL available
Open Mon-Fri 8-5, Tues & Thurs 7pm-9pm, Sat 9-1
Friends of the Library Group
Branches: 1
TEN SLEEP BRANCH, 401 Fir St, Ten Sleep, 82442. SAN 365-4036. 307-366-2348. *Br Coordr*, Dorothy Dillard; *Asst Librn*, Karen Fund
Circ 33,159
Open Mon-Fri 8am-12pm (Summer/June-Aug), Mon 8am-12pm & 1[illegible] 6pm, Tues-Fri 8am-12pm & 1pm-4pm (Fall/Winter)
Friends of the Library Group

YELLOWSTONE NATIONAL PARK

S NATIONAL PARK SERVICE-YELLOWSTONE ASSOCIATION, Yellowstone Research Library & Archives, Albright Visitor Center, Mammoth Hot Springs, 82190. (Mail add: PO Box 168, 82190), SAN [illegible] 515X. Tel: 307-344-2264. FAX: 307-344-2323. E-Mail: yell_research_library@nps.gov. *Assoc Librn*, Kathryn Lancaster; *Assoc Librn*, Barbara Zafft
Founded 1933
Library Holdings: Bk Titles 10,700; Per Subs 55
Subject Interests: Yellowstone National Park
Special Collections: Montana Historical Society Coll (1876-present); Yellowstone Area (Rare Bks Coll)
Restriction: Open to public for reference only

LIBRARIES IN PUERTO RICO AND REGIONS ADMINISTERED BY THE UNITED STATES

ɜO PAGO

AMERICAN SAMOA OFFICE OF LIBRARY SERVICES, PO Box 1952, 96799. SAN 365-463X. Tel: 684-633-1181. Interlibrary Loan Service Tel: 684-633-1182. *Dir*, Emma F C Pen; *AV*, Uluao Tilei; *Rare Bks, Spec Coll*, Arieta Thompson; *Asst Librn*, Paulo Atafua; Staff 1 (MLS 1)
Founded 1913. Pop 35,000; Circ 201,000
Library Holdings: Bk Vols 124,000; Bk Titles 120,000; Per Subs 100
Special Collections: Pacific Islands, bks, flm, recs, & VF; Territory
Branches: 13
ALATAUA LUA SCHOOL LIBRARY, 96799. SAN 326-8276.
Library Holdings: Bk Vols 650
FAGA'ITUA BRANCH, Faga'itua Village, 96799. SAN 365-4699. Tel: 684-622-7528. *Librn*, Mata Peters
Library Holdings: Bk Titles 5,650
FELETI PACIFIC, Fagatogo Village, 96799. SAN 365-4729. Tel: 684-633-1181. *In Charge*, Salamina Taunuu
Library Holdings: Bk Vols 5,900
LEONE MIDKIFF BRANCH, Leone Village, 96799. SAN 365-480X. *Librn*, Florentine Peo
Library Holdings: Bk Vols 5,450
LEONE SCHOOL - COMMUNITY, Vailoa Village, 96799. SAN 365-4753. Tel: 684-688-7119. *Librn*, Debbie Duilefano
Library Holdings: Bk Vols 6,670
LUPELELE, Iliili Village, 96799. SAN 322-6395. *Librn*, Mata Tilito
MANU'A, Tau Community School, Manu'a Island, 96799. SAN 365-4818. Tel: 684-732-3512. *Librn*, Alofa Veligitone
Library Holdings: Bk Titles 4,350
Additionally, 24 library-media centers are located in elementary schools
MANULELE, Nuiuuli Village, 96799. SAN 322-6409. Tel: 684-699-9617. *Librn*, Agapapalagi Malofie; *Asst Librn*, Meleane Savusa
MATAFAO SCHOOL COMMUNITY LIBRARY, Fagaalu Village, 96799. SAN 365-4796. *Librn*, Matavaine O'Brien
Library Holdings: Bk Vols 3,555
OLOSEGA SCHOOL LIBRARY, 96799. SAN 326-825X. *Librn*, Evelini Puletasi
Library Holdings: Bk Vols 1,770
PAGO PAGO BRANCH *Librn*, Lomi Bali
Library Holdings: Bk Vols 4,756
PAVAIAI BRANCH, Pavaiai Village, 96799. SAN 365-4834. Tel: 684-639-9605. *Librn*, Kopa Siatunuu
Library Holdings: Bk Vols 4,300
TAUFUNA HIGH SCHOOL - COMMUNITY, Taufuna Village, 96799. SAN 365-4842. Tel: 684-699-1303. *Librn*, Ruth Apulu
Library Holdings: Bk Vols 2,000

J COMMUNITY COLLEGE OF AMERICAN SAMOA, Learning Resource Center, PO Box 2609, 96799. SAN 365-4605. Tel: 684-699-4673, 684-699-9155. FAX: 684-699-2062. *Cat, Dir, Ref*, Steven Yi-hsin Lin; *Publ Servs, Tech Servs*, Ave Sualoa; Staff 2 (MLS 2)
Founded 1974. Enrl 1,000; Fac 50
Oct 1998-Sep 1999 Income $115,500. Mats Exp $5,000, Books $1,000, Per/Ser (Incl. Access Fees) $3,000. Sal $105,000 (Prof $58,000)
Library Holdings: Bk Vols 30,000; Bk Titles 24,500; Per Subs 100
Subject Interests: Anthropology, Archaeology, Creative writing, Ethnography, Forests, Geography, Geology, Indigenous art, Lang, Marine biology, Meteorology, Natural marine resources, Oceanography, Pac lit, Samoan hist
Special Collections: Govt & Territory; Pacific & Samoa Coll

GUAM

Date of Statistics: 1994
Population, 1990 Census: 133,152 (including military)
Population Served by Public Libraries: All island residents
Total Volumes in Public Libraries: 187,864
Total Public Library Circulation: 101,474
Total Public Library Income (including Grants-in-Aid): $873,166
Number of Extension Libraries: 4
Number of Bookmobiles in Territory: 1
Grants-in-Aid to Public Libraries:
Federal (Library Services & Construction Act): $77,066 (Title I & Title III)
Local: $826,946
Special Uses of These Two Funds: Augmenting main library collection, basic collection for extension libraries, institutional library collection, Union Catalog & Union List of Serials of Libraries in Guam.

ANA

GUAM LAW LIBRARY,* 141 San Ramon Rd, 96910. SAN 324-8011. Tel: 671-472-8062, 671-477-7623. FAX: 671-472-1246. E-Mail: gtll@ite.net. Web Site: www.justice.gov.gu/tll.htm.
1997-1998 Income $372,383, State $290,333, Locally Generated Income $62,437, Other $19,613. Mats Exp $535,558, Books $140,121. Sal $175,359 (Prof $69,025)
Library Holdings: Bk Vols 36,965; Bk Titles 4,678
Special Collections: Guam; Pacific Islands
Partic in Dialog Corporation; Westlaw

DERSEN AFB

UNITED STATES AIR FORCE
ANDERSEN AIR FORCE BASE LIBRARY, 36 SVS/SVMG (FL 5240), Unit 14004, PO Box 28, APO AP, 96543-4004. SAN 365-4575. Tel: 671-366-4294. FAX: 671-366-2728.
1998-1999 Income $311,478, Federal $308,478, Other $3,000. Mats Exp $52,028, Books $16,411, Per/Ser (Incl. Access Fees) $35,028. Sal $204,700
Library Holdings: Bk Vols 33,500; Per Subs 125
Subject Interests: Air War College, Micronesia, Project warrior, Southeast Asia, The Pacific
Partic in Guam Libr Asn

ANGILAO

GUAM COMMUNITY COLLEGE LIBRARY,* PO Box 23069, 96921. SAN 318-5303. Tel: 671-735-5578. FAX: 671-734-4356. Web Site: guam.gcc.edu.gu.; Staff 3 (MLS 3)
Founded 1967. Enrl 2,500; Fac 186
Library Holdings: Bk Vols 18,000; Per Subs 120
Special Collections: Pacific Coll
Publications: Newsletters

UNIVERSITY OF GUAM, Robert F Kennedy Memorial Library, UOG Station, 96923. SAN 318-5281. Tel: 671-735-2330, 671-735-2333. FAX: 671-734-6882. Web Site: uog2.uog.edu.rfk/. *Actg Dean*, Suzanne T Bell; E-Mail: stbell@uog9.uog.edu; *Acq, Coll Develop*, Nick Goetzfridt; E-Mail: ngoetzfr@uog9.uog.edu; *Cat*, Rick Castro; *Circ, Outreach Serv*, Arlene Cohen; E-Mail: acohen@uog9.uog.edu; *Bibliog Instr, Ref*, Mark C Goniwiecha; E-Mail: goniwiec@uog9.uog.edu; *Syst Coordr*, Joanne Crotts; Staff 9 (MLS 9)
Founded 1952. Circ 54,411; Enrl 3,346; Fac 218; Highest Degree: Master
Oct 1999-Sep 2000 Income $2,176,837, State $2,025,022, Locally Generated Income $53,315, Other $52,000. Mats Exp $696,652, Books $205,221, Per/Ser (Incl. Access Fees) $420,781, Micro $43,210, AV Equip $12,090. Sal $1,303,462
Library Holdings: Bk Vols 103,273; Per Subs 715
Subject Interests: Agriculture, Arts, Bus, Education, Humanities, Literature, Sci, Soc sci
Special Collections: Agriculture & Life Sciences Coll; Curriculum Resources Center; East Asian Coll
Publications: Annual Report; LR Newsletter; new acquisitions, bibliog guides
Partic in Dialog Corporation; OCLC Online Computer Library Center, Inc; Pac S Regional Med Libr s
The Learning Resources program consists of Library Services (Robert F Kennedy Memorial Library) & Instructional Media Services

C UNIVERSITY OF GUAM, Micronesian Area Research Center (MARC) Guam & Micronesia Collections,* University of Guam, 303 University Dr, UOG Sta, 96923. SAN 321-9887. Tel: 671-735-2160. FAX: 671-734-7403. Web Site: uog.2uog.edu. *Ref*, Monique Carriveau-Storey; E-Mail: moniquec@uog9.uog.edu; *Tech Servs*, Carmen F Quintanilla; *Tech Servs*, Lourdes Nededog; *Tech Servs*, John P Sablan
Oct 1997-Sep 1998 Income $370,000. Mats Exp $8,000. Sal $275,000
Library Holdings: Bk Vols 40,000; Bk Titles 25,000
Subject Interests: Micronesia, Oceania
Special Collections: Manuscripts Coll; Reference Coll; South Pacific Commission; Spanish Documents Coll
Friends of the Library Group

PAN, MARIANA ISLANDS

JOETEN-KIYU PUBLIC LIBRARY, Beach Rd, Susupe, PO Box 1092, 96950. SAN 377-0419. Tel: 670-235-7322. FAX: 670-235-7550. E-Mail: jklibrary@saipan.com. Web Site: www.saipan.com/gov/library/. *Dir*, Joseph McElory; *Actg Dir, Ch Servs*, Susan Becton; *Tech Coordr*, Greg Folta; *Coordr, Outreach Serv*, Roy Rechebei; Staff 12 (MLS 4, Non-MLS 8)
Founded 1992. Pop 58,846; Circ 102,685
Oct 1999-Sep 2000 Income $574,873, State $386,110, Federal $87,465, Other $33,800. Mats Exp $80,950, Books $67,679, Per/Ser (Incl. Access Fees) $6,875. Sal $281,628 (Prof $184,029)
Library Holdings: Bk Vols 30,089; Bk Titles 26,890; Per Subs 1,793
Special Collections: Pacific Area & World War II Pacific (Pacific Reference Coll); Saipan, Tinian & Rota History, 1972-1994 (Marianas Variety Newspaper Coll), microflm
Automation Activity & Vendor Info: (Cataloging) epixtech, inc.; (Circulation) epixtech, inc.
Friends of the Library Group
Branches: 2
ROTA PUBLIC, c/o Office of Mayor, PO Box 537, Rota, 96951. SAN 376-835X. Tel: 670-532-9433. FAX: 670-532-9454. *In Charge*, Josephine Cabrera
Library Holdings: Bk Vols 2,000
TINIAN PUBLIC, c/o Northern Marianas Col, Campus Box 459, Tinian, 96952. SAN 376-8368. Tel: 670-433-0504. *Librn*, Richard B L Creecy Jr
Library Holdings: Bk Vols 3,200; Per Subs 10
Bookmobiles: 1

J NORTHERN MARIANAS COLLEGE, Olympiot Borja Memorial Library,* As Terlaje Campus Rd, Bldg O, 96950. (Mail add: Borja Memorial Library, PO Box 1250, 96950), SAN 378-0848. Tel: 670-234-5498, Ext 1121. *Dir Libr Serv*, Paul J Steere; E-Mail: pauls@nmcnet.edu; *Publ Servs*, Craig Ballian; *Govt Doc*, Rosamond H Rice; Staff 7 (MLS 4, Non-MLS 3)
Enrl 1,239; Fac 91
Oct 1997-Sep 1998 Income $288,131. Mats Exp $82,627, Books $47,228, Per/Ser (Incl. Access Fees) $14,340, AV Equip $9,564. Sal $175,394 (Prof $90,590)
Library Holdings: Bk Vols 42,039; Bk Titles 39,618; Per Subs 461
Special Collections: Asian Develop Bank
Departmental Libraries:
CURRICULUM RESOURCES CENTER, School of Education, PO Box 1250, 96950. SAN 378-1844. Tel: 670-234-5498, Ext 1901. *Librn*, Laurel Davis
PACIFIC & SPECIAL COLLECTIONS, PO Box 1250, 96950. SAN 378-1860. Tel: 670-234-5498, Ext 1110. FAX: 670-234-0759. *Curator*, Martin L Gerbens

Date of Statistics: Fiscal Year 1998-99
Population, 1990 Census: 3,522,037
Population Served by Public Libraries: 1,907,603
Unserved: 1,614,434
Total Volumes in Public Libraries: 731,269
Total Public Library Circulation: 574,960
Total Public Library Income (including Federal Aid): $5,110,250
Source of Income: State and Federal LSCA
Number of Bookmobiles: 3
Grants-in-Aid to Public Libraries:
Federal Library Services & Technology Act: $1,877,250
State Funds: $3,233,000
Special Uses of These Funds: To improve public library services in the Commonwealth of Puerto Rico including major urban resources libraries, Regional Library for the Blind and Physically Handicapped, and libraries in correctional institutions, among others. To improve library services to people with limited English speaking ability & to implement (RICOPUR), the technological capacity of libraries for interlibrary cooperation and resource sharing.

JADILLA

INTER-AMERICAN UNIVERSITY OF PUERTO RICO, Aguadilla Campus Library, PO Box 20000, 00905. SAN 318-5346. Tel: 787-891-0925. FAX: 787-882-3020. E-Mail: inter@edu.nyulfo. *Dir*, Monserrate Yulfososa; *Librn*, Lazaratte Lopez; *Per*, Miranda Valle; Staff 14 (MLS 3, Non-MLS 11)
Founded 1968. Fac 138
Jul 1998-Jun 1999 Income $570,444. Mats Exp $119,000, Books $67,000, Per/Ser (Incl. Access Fees) $50,000, Micro $2,000. Sal $298,487 (Prof $96,239)
Library Holdings: Bk Vols 53,000; Per Subs 342
Special Collections: Manuel Mendez Ballister Coll
Publications: faculty catalog; periodical catalog; Student catalog
Partic in Davis-Louven

ECIBO

INTER-AMERICAN UNIVERSITY OF PUERTO RICO, Center for Access to Information - Biblioteca Rene Marques, Barrio San Daniel, Sector Las Canelas, 00614-4050. (Mail add: PO Box 4050, 00614-4050), Tel: 787-878-5475, Ext 2321. FAX: 787-880-1624. Web Site: www.arecibo.inter.edu. *Dir*, Sara Abreu; E-Mail: sabreu@ns.inter.edu; Staff 14 (MLS 2, Non-MLS 12)
Founded 1958. Enrl 3,500; Fac 100; Highest Degree: Master
Library Holdings: Bk Vols 67,960; Bk Titles 57,389; Per Subs 315
Subject Interests: Anesthesia, Biology, Census, Criminal justice, Doc, Education, Microbiology, Nursing, Social work
Automation Activity & Vendor Info: (Acquisitions) SIRSI; (Cataloging) SIRSI; (Circulation) SIRSI; (Course Reserve) SIRSI; (ILL) SIRSI; (Media Booking) SIRSI; (OPAC) SIRSI; (Serials) SIRSI

PONTIFICIA CATHOLIC UNIVERSITY OF PUERTO RICO, ARECIBO,* PO Box 144045, 00614-4045. SAN 318-5354. Tel: 787-881-1212. FAX: 787-881-0777. *Librn*, Nora Garcia; *Asst Librn, Ref*, Lydia Ortega; *AV*, Radames Trujillo; Staff 7 (MLS 1, Non-MLS 6)
Founded 1973. Enrl 1,300
Library Holdings: Bk Vols 31,855; Bk Titles 28,260; Per Subs 642
Special Collections: Puerto Rican Coll, bks & printed mat

UNIVERSITY OF PUERTO RICO, Arecibo Technological University College Library,* PO Box 4010, 00614. SAN 318-5370. Tel: 787-878-9363. FAX: 787-878-9363. *Librn*, Luis Concepcion; *Cat*, Aixa Morales; *Acq*, Hector Ranos; *Ref*, Luis Rios
Founded 1967. Enrl 3,537; Fac 198
Library Holdings: Bk Vols 7,665; Per Subs 2,460
Subject Interests: Computer science, Education, Nursing, Sci
Special Collections: Arecibo Region Historical Coll; Juvenile Coll
Mem of University Of Puerto Rico Library System

BARRANQUITAS

C INTER-AMERICAN UNIVERSITY OF PUERTO RICO, Barranquitas Campus Library, Bo Helechal, Carr 156 Intersiccion 719, 00794. (Mail add: PO Box 517, 00794), SAN 318-5389. Tel: 787-857-2585, 787-857-3600, Ext 2063. Reference Tel: 787-857-3600, Ext 2075. FAX: 787-857-2244. Web Site: www.br.inter.edu. *Dir*, Maribel Lopez; E-Mail: mlopez@br.inter.edu; Staff 2 (MLS 1, Non-MLS 1)
Founded 1959. Enrl 1,502
Library Holdings: Bk Vols 33,024; Bk Titles 27,246; Per Subs 223
Automation Activity & Vendor Info: (Circulation) SIRSI; (Course Reserve) SIRSI
Database Vendor: IAC - SearchBank, Innovative Interfaces INN - View, ProQuest
Mem of Inter Am Univ of PR Syst
Partic in OCLC Online Computer Library Center, Inc

S LUIS MUNOZ RIVERA LIBRARY & MUSEUM,* Calle Luis Munoz Rivera, No 10, 00794. SAN 318-5397. Tel: 787-857-0230. *Librn*, Maria L Valencia; Staff 2 (MLS 1, Non-MLS 1)
Founded 1959
1998-1999 Income $25,500. Mats Exp $2,500, Books $1,500, Per/Ser (Incl. Access Fees) $500, Presv $500. Sal $20,000 (Prof $14,000)
Library Holdings: Bk Titles 3,000
Subject Interests: Barranquitas, Luis Munoz Rivera, Puerto Rico
Special Collections: Puerto Rican Authors, Culture, History & Folklore
Publications: Cultural Bulletin
Library affilated with the General Library of Puerto Rico at San Juan, PR
Friends of the Library Group

BAYAMON

INTER-AMERICAN UNIVERSITY OF PUERTO RICO
C RECINTO DE BAYAMON, Hwy 830, No 500, 00957. SAN 318-5400. Tel: 787-279-1912. FAX: 787-279-2205. *Dir*, Carmen Ortega; *Ref*, Maria E Villamil; Staff 4 (MLS 4)
Founded 1967. Enrl 4,701
Library Holdings: Bk Vols 57,880; Per Subs 1,000
Subject Interests: Sci, Technology
Special Collections: Interamerican Press; Puerto Rico

C UNIVERSIDAD CENTRAL DE BAYAMON LIBRARY, Learning Resources Center,* PO Box 1725, 00960. SAN 318-5427. Tel: 787-786-3030. FAX: 787-740-2200. E-Mail: alousoaltamirarano@usa.net. *Librn*, Carlos Altamirarano; Staff 13 (MLS 7, Non-MLS 6)
Founded 1961. Enrl 2,700; Fac 127; Highest Degree: Master
1998-1999 Income $425,192. Mats Exp $164,885, Books $40,000, Per/Ser (Incl. Access Fees) $101,975. Sal $257,053 (Prof $134,940)
Library Holdings: Bk Vols 45,000
Subject Interests: Catholic theol, Philosophy
Special Collections: Cesareo Rosa Nieves Coll; Puerto Rican Literature Coll

M UNIVERSIDAD CENTRAL DEL CARIBE, Caribe Medical Library, Ave Laurel Sta Juanita, 00956. (Mail add: PO Box 60327, 00960), SAN 370-7288. Tel: 787-798-3001, Ext 290. FAX: 787-785-3425. Web Site: www.uccaribe.edu. *Dir*, Juan Melenez; *Librn*, Mildred Rivera; Tel: 787-798-3001, Ext 309, E-Mail: mildredrivera@uccaribe.edu; *Asst Librn*, Juanita Lopez; Tel: 787-798-3001, Ext 308, E-Mail: jlopez@uccaribe.edu; *Asst Librn*, Rosa M Sanchez; E-Mail: rsanchez@uccaribe.edu; Staff 5 (MLS 1, Non-MLS 4)
Founded 1976. Fac 40
Library Holdings: Bk Vols 30,000; Bk Titles 1,700; Per Subs 409
Database Vendor: Ebsco - EbscoHost
Publications: Library newsletter (local circulation)
Function: ILL available
Partic in BRS

J UNIVERSITY OF PUERTO RICO - BAYAMON TECHNOLOGICAL UNIVERSITY COLLEGE, Learning Resources Center,* 174 Minillas Industrial Park, 170 Rd, 00959. SAN 318-5435. Tel: 787-786-2885. FAX: 787-798-1595. *Dir*, Pilar Aponte; *Tech Servs*, Nellie Perez; *Per*, Loida Correa; *Circ*, Delia Colon; *Ref*, Jesus Gonzalez; *Cat*, Alba Osorio; *Cat*, Norma Padilla; *Publ Servs*, Mildred Perez; Staff 35 (MLS 8, Non-MLS 27)
Founded 1971. Enrl 5,856; Fac 339
Library Holdings: Bk Vols 61,603; Bk Titles 45,257; Per Subs 541
Subject Interests: Education, Phys educ for handicapped, Sci-tech
Special Collections: Children's Literature; Puerto Rican Coll
Publications: Library Week Memoirs-1992; New Acquisitions List
Partic in Biblionet
The LRC participates in the Cooperative Indexing Project which indexes Puerto Rican periodicals in Spanish & also participates in another project which indexes Puerto Rican newspapers

CAROLINA

J COLEGIO UNIVERSITARIO DEL ESTE LIBRARY,* PO Box 2010, 00984-2010. SAN 320-0515. Tel: 787-257-7373, Ext 2500. FAX: 787-252-0070. *Dean of Libr*, Carmen Laura Hernandez; Staff 10 (MLS 7, Non-MLS 3)
Founded 1949. Enrl 4,535; Fac 84
Library Holdings: Bk Titles 60,000; Per Subs 2,030
Publications: Biblio-Notas; La Revista Informa; Lista de nuevas Adquisiciones; Manual del CRA para la Facultad; Manual del CRA para los Estudiantes
Partic in Atlas

CAYEY

C UNIVERSITY OF PUERTO RICO, Cayey University College Library, Antonio R Barcelo Ave, 00736. SAN 318-5443. Tel: 787-738-2161, Ext 2021, 787-738-5651. FAX: 787-263-2760. E-Mail: biblioteca@cayey1.upr.clu.edu. Web Site: www.cuc.upr.clu.edu/biblioteca/index.html. *Dir*, Dr Hector Maymi; *Ref*, David Castro; *Cat*, Nilda Aponte; *Ch Servs*, Ariel Aponte; *Spec Coll*, Eliam Alvarado; *Automation Syst Coordr*, Eddei Burgos; *Acq*, Luis Munoz; *Music*, Jose Estrada; *Info Res*, Juan Barria; *Circ*, Mariano Guetierrez. Subject Specialists: *Puerto Rico*, Eliam Alvarado; Staff 42 (MLS 7, Non-MLS 35)
Founded 1967. Enrl 3,400; Fac 225
Jul 1998-Jun 1999 Income $952,046. Mats Exp $171,000, Per/Ser (Incl. Access Fees) $100,000, Micro $1,000, AV Equip $16,000, Manuscripts & Archives $53,000, Electronic Ref Mat (Incl. Access Fees) $1,000. Sal $782,046 (Prof $282,951)
Library Holdings: Bk Vols 420,000; Bk Titles 202,414; Per Subs 1,108
Subject Interests: Bus admin, Education, Humanities, Natural science, Soc sci, Women
Special Collections: Juvenile Coll; Miguel Melendez Munoz Coll; Music Coll; Puerto Rican Coll; Women Coll
Publications: Acquisition list; bibliographies
Academic Computer Laboratory

FAJARDO

C INTER-AMERICAN UNIVERSITY-FAJARDO CAMPUS, Centro de Acceso a la Informacion, Calle Union, Batey Central, 00738. (Mail add: Call Box 70003, 00738-7003), SAN 365-4966. Tel: 787-863-2390. FAX: 787-860-3470. E-Mail: fajardo@inter.edu/cai. *Dir*, Angie E Colon; Tel: 787-863-2390, Ext 2213, E-Mail: acolon@inter.edu; Staff 9 (MLS 3, Non-MLS 6)
Founded 1961. Enrl 1,860; Fac 35; Highest Degree: Bachelor
Jul 2000-Jun 2001 Mats Exp $51,000, Books $40,000, AV Equip $3,000, Electronic Ref Mat (Incl. Access Fees) $8,000
Library Holdings: Bk Vols 34,000; Bk Titles 27,000; Per Subs 675
Subject Interests: Recycling
Special Collections: Puerto Rico Data Census Center
Database Vendor: IAC - Info Trac, OVID Technologies

FORT BUCHANAN

UNITED STATES ARMY

A FORT BUCHANAN POST LIBRARY, US Army - Post Library, Bldg PO Box 34000, 00934. SAN 365-5024. Tel: 787-273-3208. FAX: 78 3210. E-Mail: jtp@coqui.net. *Librn*, Eva Cabanas; Tel: 787-707-381 *Librn*, John Tejera-Perez; E-Mail: jtp@coqui.net; Staff 6 (MLS 2, No MLS 4)
2000-2001 Mats Exp $39,000, Books $15,000, Per/Ser (Incl. Access $6,000, AV Equip $4,000, Electronic Ref Mat (Incl. Access Fees) $1 Sal $240,000
Library Holdings: Bk Vols 28,400; Bk Titles 27,000; Per Subs 165
Special Collections: Children's Coll
Database Vendor: OCLC - First Search
Partic in Fedlink; OCLC Online Computer Library Center, Inc

GUAYAMA

C CATHOLIC UNIVERSITY OF PUERTO RICO, Guayama Branch Lib Calle Valmer, Esquina Ashford, PO Box 809, 00784. SAN 318-546X. T 787-864-0570. FAX: 787-864-0640. *Dir*, Julia Sanchez Mevina; *Asst L* Celia Casiano; *Ref, Spec Coll*, Maria Teresa Colon; *Res*, Jose Rivera; S (Non-MLS 5)
Founded 1968. Enrl 929; Fac 49
Library Holdings: Bk Vols 34,000; Per Subs 215
Special Collections: Puerto Rico

C INTER-AMERICAN UNIVERSITY OF PUERTO RICO, Guayama Ca Library, PO Box 10004, 00785. SAN 318-5478. Tel: 787-864-2222. FA 787-864-8232. Web Site: www.guayama.inter.edu/cai.html. *Dir*, Angel Rivera; E-Mail: briveras@ns.inter.edu; *Librn*, Myrna Rosario Santiago; 10 (MLS 3, Non-MLS 7)
Founded 1958. Fac 46
Jul 1999-Jun 2000 Income $192,035. Mats Exp $47,000, Books $25,00 Per/Ser (Incl. Access Fees) $15,000, AV Equip $5,000, Electronic Ref M (Incl. Access Fees) $12,000. Sal $145,098 (Prof $54,805)
Library Holdings: Bk Vols 21,000; Bk Titles 21,000; Per Subs 130
Subject Interests: Bus, Education, Humanities, Nursing, Sci
Special Collections: Afro-antillian Poetry Coll; Luis Palis Matos Coll
Automation Activity & Vendor Info: (Cataloging) SIRSI; (Circulation) SIRSI
Database Vendor: IAC - Info Trac, OVID Technologies
Publications: Infocai Bulletin
Friends of the Library Group

GURABO

C UNIVERSIDAD DEL TURABO, Learning Center,* PO Box 3030, 0077 SAN 321-611X. Tel: 787-743-7979, Ext 4500. FAX: 787-744-5427. *Dea Libr*, Julio Gonzalez; Staff 16 (MLS 7, Non-MLS 9)
Founded 1969. Enrl 7,000; Highest Degree: Master
1998-1999 Income $720,461. Mats Exp $208,946, Books $60,000, Per/S (Incl. Access Fees) $96,000, Presv $1,000, Micro $4,500. Sal $437,110 $155,000)
Library Holdings: Bk Vols 43,406; Bk Titles 35,000; Per Subs 470
Publications: Acquisitions List
Partic in Atlas

HATO REY

S AMAURY VERAY MUSIC LIBRARY,* 350 Rafael Lamar, 00918. SAN 318-5672. Tel: 787-751-0160, Ext 256. FAX: 787-758-8268. E-Mail: libramus@caribe.net. *Coll Develop, Dir*, Keila Garcia; *Cat*, Damaris Cordero; *Circ, Ref*, Juanita Melendez
Founded 1962. Enrl 260; Fac 60; Highest Degree: Bachelor
Jun 1998-Jul 1999 Income $213,200. Mats Exp $14,650, Books $5,300, P Ser (Incl. Access Fees) $4,750, Other Print Mats $4,600. Sal $149,637 (P $70,837)
Library Holdings: Bk Titles 6,000; Per Subs 62
Subject Interests: Music
Special Collections: Music (Puerto Rican & Latin American Composers)
Automation Activity & Vendor Info: (Cataloging) Sagebrush Corporatio (Circulation) Sagebrush Corporation; (OPAC) Sagebrush Corporation

G ECONOMIC DEVELOPMENT ADMINISTRATION LIBRARY,* 355 Roosevelt Ave, PO Box 362350, 00936. SAN 318-5486. Tel: 787-758-474 Ext 2450. FAX: 787-751-9924. *Librn*, Aleida Guadeloupe
Library Holdings: Bk Vols 15,000
Subject Interests: Economy-industrialization, Related fields

C INTER-AMERICAN UNIVERSITY OF PUERTO RICO, Metropolitan Campus Library, Carr PR 1, Esq Calle Francisco Sein, PO Box 1293, 00919-1293. SAN 365-5059. Tel: 787-250-1912, Ext 2160. FAX: 787-751 3915. Web Site: metro.inter.edu. *Dir*, Rosa Pimentel; *ILL*, Pilar Ortiz del Valle; *Online Servs*, Eric Morales; Staff 25 (MLS 9, Non-MLS 16)
Founded 1961. Enrl 12,156; Fac 693; Highest Degree: Doctorate
Jun 1999-May 2000 Mats Exp $385,040, Books $185,040, Per/Ser (Incl. Access Fees) $200,000. Sal $464,550 (Prof $210,800)

Library Holdings: Bk Vols 111,560; Per Subs 2,771
Special Collections: Benitez Coll; Juvenile Coll; Puerto Rican Coll
Mem of Inter Am Univ of PR Syst

MCCONNELL VALDES, 270 Munoz Rivera Ave, 00918. SAN 371-9316. Tel: 787-250-5147, 787-759-9292. FAX: 787-759-9225. E-Mail: bv@mcvpr.com. *Dir, Librn*, Betsaida Velez-Natal; Staff 5 (MLS 1, Non-MLS 4)
Founded 1947
Jun 2000-May 2001 Mats Exp $597,000, Books $50,000, Per/Ser (Incl. Access Fees) $259,000, Electronic Ref Mat (Incl. Access Fees) $288,000. Sal $100,000 (Prof $50,400)
Library Holdings: Bk Vols 58,000; Bk Titles 4,000; Per Subs 124
Subject Interests: Corporate law, Labor laws, Taxes
Automation Activity & Vendor Info: (Cataloging) Sagebrush Corporation; (OPAC) Sagebrush Corporation; (Serials) Inmagic, Inc.
Database Vendor: Lexis-Nexis
Restriction: Staff use only
Partic in Dialog Corporation; Westlaw

OFFICE OF COURT ADMINISTRATION, Library Services Division,* Zequerra Bldg, Vela St, Stop 35 1/2, PO Box 190917, Hato Rey Sta, 00919-0917. SAN 324-1513. Tel: 787-751-8670. Interlibrary Loan Service Tel: 787-763-1362. FAX: 787-767-7757. *Chief Librn*, Manuela O Martinez; *Circ, Publ Servs*, Hector Nieves; *Acq*, Jorge Domenech; *Bibliog Instr*, Juan Matos; Staff 5 (MLS 2, Non-MLS 3)
Library Holdings: Bk Vols 155,000; Bk Titles 5,000; Per Subs 300
Subject Interests: Court admin, Fed jurisprudence, Fed law, Local jurisprudence, Local law, Spain civil law
Special Collections: Law Administration, Spanish Civil & US Law, Puerto Rican Law & Management
Publications: List of Recent Acquisitions

PUBLIC LIBRARY SERVICES, Department of Education,* Cesar Gonzalez Ave, PO Box 190759, 00919-0759. SAN 318-5494. Tel: 787-759-2000, Ext 2822. FAX: 787-282-6312. *Dir*, Sandra Castro; *Coll Develop*, Carmen L Martinez
Library Holdings: Bk Vols 920,213
Special Collections: Blind & Physically Handicapped Coll (856 titles); Puerto Rican Authors & Themes About Puerto Rican Culture
Publications: Union Catalogue of Puerto Rican Materials
Library Program - State Advisory Council on Libraries

UNITED STATES COURT OF APPEALS FIRST CIRCUIT SATELLITE LIBRARY,* Federal Bldg, Rm 121, 150 Chardon Ave, 00918. SAN 372-3585. Tel: 787-772-3096. FAX: 787-766-5747. *Librn*, Ana Milagros Rodriguez; *Tech Servs*, Jose Garcia
Library Holdings: Bk Vols 25,000; Per Subs 50
Partic in OCLC Online Computer Library Center, Inc; Westlaw

ANA DIAZ

UNIVERSITY OF PUERTO RICO, Fortuna R&D Center,* HC-04 Box 7115, 00795-9998. SAN 325-3090. Tel: 787-837-3905. FAX: 787-837-6823.
Founded 1983. Fac 10
Library Holdings: Bk Vols 100

YAGUEZ

PONTIFICAL CATHOLIC UNIVERSITY OF PUERTO RICO, Mayaguez Branch Library,* Post ST 482, PO Box 1326, 00681-1326. SAN 318-5540. Tel: 787-834-5151, Ext 5008. FAX: 787-831-7155. E-Mail: catolica@coqui.net. *Librn*, Edwin Ramos
1997-1998 Income $92,000, Parent Institution $90,000. Mats Exp $108,500, Books $45,000, Per/Ser (Incl. Access Fees) $45,000, Presv $2,000, AV Equip $5,000, Other Print Mats $1,000, Manuscripts & Archives $500. Sal $111,850 (Prof $87,168)
Library Holdings: Bk Vols 127,000; Per Subs 5,645
Subject Interests: Gen (encyclopedias), Religion, Sci
Special Collections: Puerto Rico Coll

STEY-NEVANT PUBLIC LIBRARY,* PO Box 118, 00681-0118. SAN 318-5532. Tel: 724-983-2714. FAX: 724-983-2710. E-Mail: muggs-snpl@juno.com. *Librn*, Margaret Orchard
Founded 1935. Pop 9,777; Circ 21,314
Library Holdings: Bk Vols 35,332; Per Subs 75
Special Collections: Black Studies Coll
Database Vendor: Ebsco - EbscoHost
Partic in Access Pa

UNIVERSIDAD ADVENTISTA DE LAS ANTILLAS LIBRARY,* Carr 106 Km 2 Interior, Bo La Quinta, 00680. (Mail add: PO Box 118, 00681), Tel: 787-834-9595. FAX: 787-834-6015. E-Mail: uaalib@coqui.net. Web Site: dsm-uaa.library.net. *Tech Servs*, Noelle Cook; Tel: 517-265-5161, Ext 4229, E-Mail: ncook@adrian.edu; *Dir*, Aixa Vega; *Circ*, Isabel Escobar; Staff 6 (MLS 1, Non-MLS 5)
Founded 1957. Pop 1,000; Circ 26,607; Enrl 767; Fac 72; Highest Degree: Master
Aug 1997-Jul 1998 Income $225,077. Mats Exp $45,000, Books $20,000, Per/Ser (Incl. Access Fees) $25,000. Sal $154,741
Library Holdings: Bk Vols 84,842; Per Subs 440
Subject Interests: Theology
Special Collections: Puerto Rico; Theology
Automation Activity & Vendor Info: (Cataloging) TLC; (Circulation) TLC
Database Vendor: Ebsco - EbscoHost
Publications: Biblio revista (Bibliographic & instructional newsletter)
Partic in SE Libr Network

C UNIVERSITY OF PUERTO RICO, Mayaguez Campus General Library, N Post St, 00681. (Mail add: PO Box 9022, 00681-9022), SAN 365-5172. Tel: 787-265-3810. FAX: 787-265-5483. E-Mail: library@rumlib.uprm.edu. Web Site: www.uprm.edu/library. *Dir*, Isabel Ruiz; E-Mail: isabel@rumlib.uprm.edu; *Coordr, Publ Servs*, Irma Ramirez; E-Mail: irma@rumlib.uprm.edu; *Coordr*, Jeanette Valentin; E-Mail: jeanette@rumlib.uprm.edu
Founded 1911. Highest Degree: Doctorate
Jul 1999-Jun 2000 Mats Exp $4,500,000, Books $200,000, Per/Ser (Incl. Access Fees) $1,500,000, Micro $10,000, AV Equip $20,000, Electronic Ref Mat (Incl. Access Fees) $300,000. Sal $2,500,000
Library Holdings: Bk Vols 1,500,000; Bk Titles 323,654; Per Subs 2,800
Subject Interests: Applied tech, Business, Census data, Chemical engineering, Civil engineering, Computer eng, Electrical engineering, Electronic resources, Electronics eng, Industrial engineering, Marine sci, Mechanical engineering, Natural science, Patents-trademarks, Soc sci, Visually impaired
Special Collections: Puerto Rican Coll (Sala Manuel Maria Sama)
Automation Activity & Vendor Info: (Acquisitions) DRA; (Cataloging) DRA; (Circulation) DRA; (OPAC) DRA; (Serials) DRA
Database Vendor: DRA, Ebsco - EbscoHost, OCLC - First Search, ProQuest, Silverplatter Information Inc., Wilson - Wilson Web
Publications: BiblioRum; Boletin de la Coleccion de Referencia
Partic in Associated Cols of the Midwest; OCLC Online Computer Library Center, Inc; Solinet
Electronic Resources Center, Census Data Center & Research & Development Center
Departmental Libraries:
CENTER FOR RESEARCH & DEVELOPMENT FOR THE CARRIBEAN Tel: 787-832-4040, Ext 2080. *In Charge*, Lirio I Lorenzo
Library Holdings: Bk Titles 4,527; Per Subs 1,277
Subject Interests: Atomic energy, Marine sci, Nuclear science
MARINE SCIENCE Tel: 787-832-4040, Ext 2513. *In Charge*, Sheila Dunstan
Library Holdings: Bk Titles 1,200
Subject Interests: Aquaculture, Chem oceanography, Fisheries biol, Marine biology, Phys

MERCEDITA

J INTER-AMERICAN UNIVERSITY OF PUERTO RICO, Ponce Campus Library, 104 Parque Industrial Turpo, 00715-2201. SAN 318-5575. Tel: 787-284-1912. Interlibrary Loan Service Tel: 787-284-2119. Circulation Tel: 787-284-2119. Reference Tel: 787-284-2119. FAX: 787-841-0103. Web Site: ponce.inter.edu. *Dean*, Sharon Clampitt; Tel: 787-284-2127, E-Mail: sclampit@ponce.inter.edu; *Head Librn*, Maria C Varela; E-Mail: mcvarela@ponce.inter.edu; *Info Specialist*, Brunilda Figueroa; Tel: 787-284-2114, E-Mail: bfiguero@ponce.inter.edu; *Coll Develop*, Idalia Molina; E-Mail: imolina@ponce.inter.edu; Staff 10 (MLS 2, Non-MLS 8)
Founded 1966. Enrl 4,200; Fac 76; Highest Degree: Bachelor
Library Holdings: Bk Vols 50,767; Bk Titles 44,153; Per Subs 576
Subject Interests: Applied sci, Bus, Computers, Econ, Education, Mgt
Special Collections: Puerto Rican Coll
Automation Activity & Vendor Info: (Acquisitions) SIRSI; (Cataloging) SIRSI; (Circulation) SIRSI; (Course Reserve) SIRSI; (ILL) SIRSI; (Media Booking) SIRSI; (OPAC) SIRSI
Database Vendor: IAC - Info Trac, ProQuest, Silverplatter Information Inc.
Restriction: Not open to public, Open to students
Function: Reference services available
Partic in Dobis-Leuven

PONCE

M PONCE SCHOOL OF MEDICINE, Fundacion Angel Ramos Library, Ana Dolores Perez-Marchand St, 00732. (Mail add: PO Box 7004, 00732), SAN 371-425X. Tel: 787-840-2575. Reference Tel: 787-840-2575, Ext 2225. FAX: 787-844-3865. E-Mail: psmlib@caribe.net. Web Site: psm.edu. *Dir*, Carmen G Malavet; Staff 9 (MLS 3, Non-MLS 6)
Founded 1977. Enrl 298; Highest Degree: Doctorate
Jul 1999-Jun 2000 Mats Exp $209,706, Books $98,293, Per/Ser (Incl. Access Fees) $102,413, Presv $9,000, AV Equip $9,000. Sal $145,018 (Prof $69,365)
Library Holdings: Bk Vols 29,830; Bk Titles 17,068
Database Vendor: Ebsco - EbscoHost
Partic in Nat Libr of Med

PONTIFICAL CATHOLIC UNIVERSITY OF PUERTO RICO
C ENCARNACION VALDES LIBRARY, 2250 Las Americas, Ste 509, 00731-6382. SAN 365-5261. Tel: 787-841-2000. FAX: 787-284-0235. E-Mail: eirizarry@pucpr.edu. Web Site: www.pucpr.edu. *Dir*, Esther Irizarry Vazquez; *Acq, ILL*, Isabel Mayol; *Automation Syst Coordr*, Edna Ramirez; *Ref*, Dr Cirilo Toro; *Per*, Rosaura Romero; *Circ*, Ramon Folch; *Bibliog Instr*, Mildred Lopez; Staff 19 (MLS 10, Non-MLS 9)
Founded 1950. Enrl 7,586
1998-1999 Mats Exp $432,389, Books $75,000, Books $150,000, Per/Ser (Incl. Access Fees) $140,000, Presv $820, Micro $6,000, AV Equip $59,069. Sal $548,116 (Prof $227,232)
Library Holdings: Bk Vols 232,957; Per Subs 5,046
Special Collections: Monsignor Vincent Murga Coll; Puerto Rico Census Data Center, Strategiv Publications Center of the PHO
Database Vendor: Ebsco - EbscoHost, epixtech, inc., OCLC - First Search, ProQuest, Silverplatter Information Inc., Wilson - Wilson Web
Publications: Faculty handbook; Student handbook
Function: Research library

L MONSEIGNOR FREMIOT TORRES OLIVER LEGAL INFORMATION & RESEARCH CENTER, 2250 Avenida Las Americas Ste 544, 00717-0777. SAN 365-5296. Tel: 787-841-2000, Ext 1850, 1851. Circulation Tel: 787-841-2000, Ext 1853. FAX: 787-841-5354. E-Mail: bib_derecho@pucpr.edu. Web Site: www.pucpr.edu. *Dir*, Noelia Padua; Tel: 787-841-2000, Ext 1852, E-Mail: npadua@pucpr.edu; *Automation Syst Coordr, Cat*, Tammy Martinez; Tel: 787-841-2000, Ext 1858, E-Mail: tmartinez@pucpr.edu; *Circ, Ref*, Miguel Alvarez; E-Mail: malvarez@pucpr.edu; *Circ, Ref*, Teresita Colon; E-Mail: tguillemard@pucpr.edu; *Acq*, Ileana Amil; E-Mail: iamill@pucpr.edu; Staff 9 (MLS 4, Non-MLS 5)
Founded 1961. Enrl 536; Fac 42
Library Holdings: Bk Vols 193,714; Bk Titles 25,529; Per Subs 2,449
Subject Interests: Civil, Constitutional, Criminal, Int, Law, Roman
Special Collections: Puerto Rico Coll
Publications: Boletin Informativo (Publicacion Trimestral); Sumario de Revistas en Espanol
Partic in OCLC Online Computer Library Center, Inc; SE Libr Network

RIO PIEDRAS

G USDA FOREST SERVICE, International Institute of Tropical Forestry Library, PO Box 25000, 00928-2500. SAN 322-7944. Tel: 787-766-5335. FAX: 787-766-6302.; Staff 4 (MLS 1, Non-MLS 3)
Founded 1939
Library Holdings: Bk Titles 5,200; Per Subs 200
Subject Interests: Tropical forestry, Ttropical ecology
Special Collections: Tropical Forestry
Publications: General Technical Reports; IITF Annual Letter; Research Papers; Resource Bulletins
Partic in Forest Service Library Network

SAN GERMAN

C INTER AMERICAN UNIVERSITY OF PUERTO RICO, Juan Cancio Ortiz Library, PO Box 5100, 00603-9801. SAN 318-5648. Tel: 787-264-1912, Ext 7521. Interlibrary Loan Service Tel: 787-264-1912. Circulation Tel: 787-264-1912, Ext 75. Reference Tel: 787-264-1912, Ext 7534. FAX: 787-264-2544, 787-264-2544. Web Site: www.sg.inter.edu/cai. *Dir*, Doris Asencio-Toro; Tel: 787-892-5115, 264-1912, Ext 7520, E-Mail: dasencio@sg.inter.edu; *Librn*, Clara Torres; Tel: 787-264-1912, Ext 7534; *Asst Libr Dir*, Carlos Garcia-Hernandez; Tel: 787-264-1912, Ext 7528, E-Mail: cgarcia@sg.inter.edu; *Bibliog Instr*, Mirna Bonilla-Hernandez; Tel: 787-264-1912, Ext 7529, E-Mail: mibonill@sg.inter.edu; *Spec Coll*, Angelita Laguillo; Tel: 787-264-1912, Ext 7536, E-Mail: dorlag@sg.inter.edu; *Per*, Jenny Salazar; Tel: 787-264-1912, Ext 7537, E-Mail: jsmallor@sg.inter.edu; *Ref*, Felipa Pabon; Tel: 787-264-1912, Ext 7534, E-Mail: felipa@sg.inter.edu; Staff 16 (MLS 6, Non-MLS 10)
Founded 1923. Enrl 6,600; Fac 168; Highest Degree: Master
Jun 2000-Jul 2001 Mats Exp $228,545, Books $90,000, Per/Ser (Incl. Access Fees) $125,000, Presv $1,000, AV Equip $10,500, Other Print Mats $2,045. Sal $677,198
Library Holdings: Bk Vols 151,138; Bk Titles 112,803; Per Subs 3,015
Subject Interests: Education, History, Literature, Soc sci
Special Collections: Arturo Morales Carrion Historical Coll; Puerto Rican Coll, print
Automation Activity & Vendor Info: (Acquisitions) SIRSI; (Cataloging) SIRSI; (Circulation) SIRSI; (Media Booking) SIRSI; (Serials) SIRSI
Database Vendor: IAC - Info Trac, IAC - SearchBank, OVID Technologies, ProQuest, Silverplatter Information Inc., Wilson - Wilson Web
Publications: Bibliographic Instruction Series; Faculty Manual; Library Newsletter (irregular); Orientation Series; Recent Acquisitions Lists; Student Manual; Subject Bibliographies (irregular)
Restriction: In-house use for visitors, Open to public for reference only
Function: Research library
Partic in Dialog Corporation
Special Services for the Blind - Braille; Reading room

SAN JUAN

S CARIBBEAN CENTER FOR ADVANCED STUDIES LIBRARY, Ca Albizu Miranda Library, Old San Juan Sta, 00902. (Mail add: PO Box 9023711, 009023711), SAN 372-879X. Tel: 787-725-6500, Ext 68, 26. Circulation Tel: 787-725-6500, Ext 25. Reference Tel: 787-725-6500, E FAX: 787-721-7187. *Dir, Librn*, Julio Yamil Mercado-Avila; E-Mail: jmercado@prip.edu; Staff 4 (MLS 1, Non-MLS 3)
Founded 1966. Enrl 800; Fac 80
Jan 2000-Dec 2000 Income Parent Institution $120,000. Mats Exp $12(Books $14,000, Per/Ser (Incl. Access Fees) $40,000, AV Equip $4,000, Electronic Ref Mat (Incl. Access Fees) $4,000. Sal $51,000 (Prof $24,0
Library Holdings: Bk Vols 12,000; Bk Titles 10,000; Per Subs 180; B Deafness & Sign Lang 100
Subject Interests: Behav sci, Psychology
Special Collections: Dissertations; Drugs
Automation Activity & Vendor Info: (OPAC) Sagebrush Corporation
Database Vendor: OCLC - First Search, ProQuest, Silverplatter Inform Inc.
Publications: Ciencias de la Conducta

C CENTRO DE ESTUDIOS AVANZADOS DE PUERTO RICO Y EL CARIBE BIBLIOTECA,* Calle Cristo NUN 52, Apartado S 9023970, 00902. SAN 321-7329. Tel: 787-723-4481. FAX: 787-723-4481. E-Mail: centro@prtc.net. Web Site: www.patc.net/~centro. *Librn*, Carmen S Arr Staff 3 (MLS 2, Non-MLS 1)
Founded 1976
Library Holdings: Bk Titles 13,000; Per Subs 50
Subject Interests: Archaeology, Puerto Rico, The Caribbean cultures
Special Collections: Puerto Rican Art & Theater Coll
Publications: Bibliography of books received; duplicate exchange list

COMMONWEALTH OF PUERTO RICO
GL DEPT OF JUSTICE, OFFICE OF THE ATTORNEY GENERAL LAW LIBRARY, PO Box 192, 00902. SAN 365-5741. Tel: 787-721-2900, E 238. Reference Tel: 787-724-6869. FAX: 787-724-4770. E-Mail: bibliotecalegal@justicemail.com, henieves@justica.prstar.net.; Staff 7 (MLS 2, Non-MLS 5)
Founded 1936
Jul 2000-Jun 2001 Mats Exp $240,500, Books $97,000, Per/Ser (Incl. Access Fees) $4,000, Presv $1,000, AV Equip $25,000, Other Print Ma $4,000, Manuscripts & Archives $2,000, Electronic Ref Mat (Incl. Acc Fees) $107,500
Library Holdings: Bk Vols 110,556; Bk Titles 20,000; Per Subs 310; Spec Interest Per Sub 10
Subject Interests: Common law, Puerto Rican law, Spanish civil law
Special Collections: Puerto Rico History & Government; Puerto Rico Rules & Regulations Archives

GL LEGISLATIVE REFERENCE LIBRARY, Office of Legislative Servs, Capitol Bldg, PO Box 3986, 00902-3986. SAN 365-589X. Tel: 787-72 5200, Ext 285. FAX: 787-724-7252. *Dir*, Jose A Figueroa; *Cat*, Ivonne Quintero
Founded 1964
Library Holdings: Bk Vols 60,000; Per Subs 300
Subject Interests: Econ, Law, Political science
Partic in Westlaw

G OFFICE OF MANAGEMENT & BUDGET, 254 Tetuan & Cruz Sts, PO Box 9023228, 00902-3228. SAN 365-5776. Tel: 787-725-9420, Ext 21 FAX: 809-721-8329. Web Site: presupuerto.prstar.net. *Librn*, Isaias Pec E-Mail: ipecho@06p.prstar.net
Founded 1942
Library Holdings: Bk Vols 4,600; Per Subs 140
Subject Interests: Econ, Law, Political science, Pub admin
Special Collections: Public Documents; Puerto Rican Budget
Restriction: Restricted public use

L PUERTO RICO DEPARTMENT OF JUSTICE LAW LIBRARY, Olimpo Ave & Lindberg St, PO Box 9020-192, 00902-0192. SAN 328-4581. Te 787-724-6869. FAX: 787-721-3937, 787-721-3977. E-Mail: bibliotccalegal@justicemail.com. *Dir*, Hector Nieves Vera; *Librn*, Ivette Lopez Jusino
Library Holdings: Bk Titles 85,000; Per Subs 100
Friends of the Library Group

GL SUPREME COURT LIBRARY, PO Box 9022392, 00902-2392. SAN 36 5806. Tel: 787-723-3863, 787-723-6033, Ext 2152. FAX: 787-724-5090 E-Mail: deptreferencia@microjuris.com. *Dir*, Ivette Torres-Alvarez; E-Mail: torresalvarezi@microjuris.com; *Circ*, Nimia Perez; *Cat*, Marma Eugenia Montijo-Lizardi
Founded 1832
Jul 1998-Jun 1999 Mats Exp $363,060, Books $83,000, Per/Ser (Incl. Access Fees) $280,060
Library Holdings: Bk Vols 151,850; Per Subs 350
Subject Interests: Civil law, Common law
Special Collections: Rare Books Coll
Publications: Nuevas Adquisiciones
Partic in Westlaw

DEPARTMENT OF VETERANS AFFAIRS, Hospital Library, VA Medical Center, 10 Calle Casia, 00921-3201. SAN 318-5745. Tel: 787-641-7582, Ext 12227. Circulation Tel: 787-641-7582, Ext 12226. Reference Tel: 787-641-7582, Ext 12392. FAX: 787-641-4550. *Chief Librn*, Elsa M Lopez-Mertz; Tel: 787-641-3639, E-Mail: elsa.lopez@med.va.gov; *Librn*, Jose Quinones-Figueroa; E-Mail: jose.quinones@va.med.gov; *Librn*, Debbie A Quintana; Tel: 787-641-7582, Ext 12163. Subject Specialists: *Medical*, Jose Quinones-Figueroa; *Patient information*, Debbie A Quintana; Staff 7 (MLS 3, Non-MLS 4)
Founded 1947. Circ 13,621
Oct 1999-Sep 2000 Income Federal $275,000
Library Holdings: Bk Vols 20,311; Bk Titles 20,311; Per Subs 544
Subject Interests: Health sciences
Function: Research library
Mem of Valnet
Special Services for the Blind - Large print bks

EVANGELICAL SEMINARY OF PUERTO RICO LIBRARY, 776 Ponce de Leon Ave, 00925-9907. SAN 328-5162. Tel: 787-763-6700, Ext 233. FAX: 787-751-0847. *Dir, Publ Servs*, Maricarmen Laureano; *Asst Librn*, Velma Sosa; Staff 3 (MLS 2, Non-MLS 1)
Founded 1919
Library Holdings: Bk Titles 53,733
Subject Interests: Religion, Theology
Special Collections: Historical Archives of Protestantism in Puerto Rico; Puerto Rican Coll of Protestantism; Spanish Reformers

INTER-AMERICAN UNIVERSITY OF PUERTO RICO, School of Law Library, Federico Costa St No 170, Tres Monjitas Industrial Sector, 00918-1303. (Mail add: PO Box 70351, 00936-8351), SAN 318-5818. Tel: 787-751-1912. FAX: 787-763-6301. *Dir*, Ivette Rossello; *Cat*, Maria Cordona; *Acq*, Evelyn Ortiz; *Ref Serv*, Odila Collazo; *Ref Serv*, Alberto Guzman; *Circ*, Delia Cruz; *Per*, Lourdes Dorrios; Staff 18 (MLS 7, Non-MLS 11)
Founded 1961. Enrl 725; Fac 24; Highest Degree: Doctorate
Library Holdings: Bk Vols 135,000; Per Subs 650
Subject Interests: Civil law
Special Collections: Domingo Toledo Alamo Coll; Jose Echeverria Coll
Automation Activity & Vendor Info: (Acquisitions) SIRSI
Database Vendor: Lexis-Nexis
Publications: Acquisitions list; bibliographies

PRESBYTERIAN COMMUNITY HOSPITAL, INC, Learning Resources Center,* 1451 Ashford Ave, PO Box 32, 00907. SAN 318-5826. Tel: 787-721-2160. *In Charge*, Arnaldo Quinonez
Library Holdings: Bk Vols 600; Per Subs 35
Subject Interests: Hospital administration, Medicine, Nursing

PUERTO RICO CENTRAL OFFICE OF PERSONNEL ADMINISTRATION LIBRARY,* Ponce de Leon Ave, PO Box 8476, Fernandez Juncos Sta, 00910-0476. SAN 318-5834. Tel: 787-721-4300, Ext 3050. FAX: 787-721-4891. *Librn*, Lydia Mulero
Founded 1945
Library Holdings: Bk Vols 2,000; Per Subs 20
Subject Interests: Law, Personnel, Pub admin

PUERTO RICO DEPARTMENT OF HEALTH, Medical Library,* A Building Barrio Monacillos, PO Box 70184, 00936-8184. SAN 328-557X. Tel: 787-274-7646, 787-274-7647, 787-274-7676. FAX: 787-250-6547.
Library Holdings: Bk Vols 800

PUERTO RICO ELECTRIC POWER AUTHORITY LIBRARY,* PO Box 364267, 00936-3928. SAN 372-3542. Tel: 787-289-4497. FAX: 787-289-4430. *Librn*, Maria Serrano
Library Holdings: Bk Vols 16,000
Subject Interests: Law

PUERTO RICO MUNICIPAL SERVICES, Law Library, PO Box 70167, 00936-8167. SAN 323-6420. Tel: 787-754-1601, Ext 207. FAX: 787-753-6080. *Dir*, Johnny Colon; Staff 2 (MLS 2)
Founded 1978. Pop 500
Library Holdings: Bk Titles 500
Special Collections: Federal Register, bks; McGuillings, bks
Special Services for the Deaf - High interest/low vocabulary books; Special interest periodicals; Staff with knowledge of sign language

PUERTO RICO REGIONAL LIBRARY FOR THE BLIND & PHYSICALLY HANDICAPPED, Biblioteca Regional para Ciegos y Fisicamente Impedidos de Puerto Rico, 520 Ponce De Leon Ave, 00901. SAN 320-4294. Tel: 787-723-2519. Toll Free Tel: 800-981-8008. FAX: 787-721-8177. E-Mail: bibciego@tld.net. *Dir*, Igri S Enriquez; Staff 10 (MLS 1, Non-MLS 9)
Founded 1975. Pop 1,600; Circ 71,128
Subject Interests: Braille mat in Spanish incl rec, Cassettes
Special Collections: Braille bks and magazines in Spanish; Cassette bks & magazines in English & Spanish
Publications: Enfoque & Carta Informativa; Fact Sheet
Function: Mail loans to members
Special Services for the Blind - Assistive Technology Center for Persons who are blind or physically handicapped; Braille bks & record players; Closed circuit television; Recordings & flexible discs; Spanish Braille magazines & books; Volunteer books production program
Friends of the Library Group

UNIVERSITY OF PUERTO RICO

CL LAW SCHOOL LIBRARY, PO Box 23310, 00931-3310. SAN 365-5474. Tel: 787-763-6820, 787-763-7199. FAX: 787-764-2660. *Dir*, P Michael Whipple; E-Mail: pwhipple@upracd.upr.clu.edu; Staff 42 (MLS 10, Non-MLS 32)
Founded 1913. Enrl 511
Library Holdings: Per Subs 4,800
Subject Interests: Rare books
Publications: Boletin Bibliografico

CM MEDICAL SCIENCES CAMPUS LIBRARY, PO Box 365067, 00936-5067. SAN 318-5737. Tel: 787-751-8199. FAX: 787-759-6713. Web Site: www.rcm.upr.clu.edu. *Dir*, Francisca Corrada; E-Mail: f_corrada@rcmaca.upr.clu.edu; *Ref*, Margarita Gonzalez
Founded 1950
Jul 1997-Jun 1998 Income $1,487,902. Mats Exp $785,415. Sal $800,361
Library Holdings: Bk Vols 121,436
Subject Interests: Health sci professions
Special Collections: History of Medicine (Dr Bailey K Ashford); Puerto Rican Coll
Partic in Greater NE Regional Med Libr Program; SE-Atlantic Regional Med Libr Servs

C UNIVERSITY OF PUERTO RICO LIBRARY SYSTEM,* Rio Piedras Campus, PO Box 23302, 00931-3302. SAN 365-5385. Tel: 787-764-0000, Ext 3296. FAX: 764-0270, 787-763-5685. Web Site: upracd.upr.clu.edu/9090/sisbib. *Dir*, Dr Jorge Encarnacion; *Assoc Librn*, Marilyn Montalvo; *Tech Servs*, Ileana Rosa; Staff 60 (MLS 60)
Founded 1903. Enrl 31,635; Fac 1,390; Highest Degree: Doctorate
1998-1999 Income $11,473,469, Locally Generated Income $412,802, Parent Institution $11,060,492, Other $175. Mats Exp $2,768,160, Books $688,150, Per/Ser (Incl. Access Fees) $2,012,710, Presv $67,300. Sal $5,935,005 (Prof $1,944,052)
Library Holdings: Bk Titles 611,982; Per Subs 5,599
Special Collections: Arts Coll; Caribbean & Latin American Studies Coll; El Mundo Newspaper Photographs; Literature (Puerto Rican Coll & Zenobia Y Juan Ramon Jimenez Coll); Rare Book (Josefina del Toro Fulladosa Coll); Services for the Blind Coll
Automation Activity & Vendor Info: (Acquisitions) NOTIS; (Circulation) NOTIS
Publications: Al Dia (newsletter); collections description brochures; Lumbre (newsletter); Perspectiva (journal); services description brochures; subject bibliographies
Member Libraries: University Of Puerto Rico
Partic in Dialog Corporation; OCLC Online Computer Library Center, Inc; SE Libr Network
Departmental Libraries:
ARTS COLLECTION, Recinto de Rmo Piedras, PO Box 23302, 00931-3302. SAN 327-9871. Tel: 787-764-0000, Ext 3492. FAX: 787-763-5685. Web Site: www.upracd.upr.clu.edu:9090/sisbib. *Librn*, Iris Rodriguez-Parrilla; Tel: 787-764-0000, Ext 5156, E-Mail: irodrigu@rrpac.upr.clu.edu; Staff 4 (MLS 1, Non-MLS 3)
Founded 1953
Library Holdings: Bk Vols 34,667
Subject Interests: Fine, Graphic, Visual arts
Special Collections: Artist Illustrated Books; Arts Exhibition Catalogs; Catalogos de Expos de Arte Sebastian Gonzalez Garcia; Dance Archives Collection; Rare Art Books
Publications: Lista anotada de recursos de la Coleccion de las Artes, Serie: indices; Manual de Instruccion Bibliotecaria: Las artes sus recursos y serv ARTES (information sheet of organized exhibitions)
Function: Research library
BUSINESS ADMINISTRATION LIBRARY, PO Box 23302, 00931-3302. SAN 365-5466. Tel: 787-764-0000, Ext 2146. FAX: 787-763-5685. *Librn*, Magda Rivera
Library Holdings: Bk Vols 54,980
Subject Interests: Accounting, Computer science, Finance, Marketing, Mgt, Statistics
CARIBBEAN & LATIN AMERICAN STUDIES COLLECTION, PO Box 23302, 00931-3302. SAN 327-9855. Tel: 787-764-0000, Ext 3319. FAX: 787-763-5685. *Librn*, Almaluces Figueroa
Library Holdings: Bk Vols 142,004
Subject Interests: Caribbean-demography, Economics, Education, Statistics, Tourism, Trade
Special Collections: Latin American Pamphlets from the Yale University Library Coll; Peron's Documents Coll; Rare Books and Carribean Organizations Documents; The Latin American Documents Project A & B
Publications: ACURIL (newsletter)
CIRCULATION & RESERVE COLLECTION, PO Box 23302, 00931-3302. SAN 376-2327. Tel: 787-764-0000, Ext 3335. FAX: 787-763-5685. *Librn*, Carmen A Orlandi
Library Holdings: Bk Vols 394,406

Subject Interests: Humanities, Soc sci
JOSEFINA DEL TORO FULLADOSA COLLECTION, PO Box 23302, 00931-3302. SAN 327-9898. Tel: 787-764-0000, Ext 3043. FAX: 787-763-5685. *Librn*, Natividad Torres
Library Holdings: Bk Vols 9,594
Subject Interests: Hist (Americana), Literature, Religion
Special Collections: Genaro Cautino Coll; Nemours Coll, (Haiti)
DOCUMENTS & MAPS COLLECTION, PO Box 23302, 00931-3302. SAN 376-2335. Tel: 787-764-0000, Ext 3514. FAX: 787-763-5410. *Librn*, Carmen Concepcion
Subject Interests: Caribbean area, Econ, Latin area, Polit
EDUCATION LIBRARY, PO Box 23302, 00931-3302. SAN 365-5482. Tel: 787-764-0000, Ext 4149. FAX: 787-763-5685. Web Site: upracd.upr.clu.edu:9090/sisbib. *Librn*, Carlos Torres
Library Holdings: Bk Vols 40,648
Subject Interests: Counseling, Curric, Educ philos, Educ sociol, Education, Guidance, Psychology
GENERAL STUDIES LIBRARY, PO Box 23302, 00931-3302. SAN 365-5490. Tel: 787-764-0000, Ext 2223. FAX: 787-763-5685. *Librn*, Aurelio Huertas; Tel: 787-764-0000, Ext 5196, E-Mail: ahuertas@rrpac.up.clu.edu
Founded 1971. Enrl 6,554; Fac 260; Highest Degree: Bachelor Mats Exp Books $10,000
Library Holdings: Bk Vols 22,691; Per Subs 27
Subject Interests: Academic
Publications: Servicio de Alerta
LIBRARY & INFORMATION SCIENCES, PO Box 23302, 00931-3302. SAN 365-5504. Tel: 787-764-0000, Ext 3482, 787-764-0270. FAX: 787-763-5685. *Librn*, Carmen D Alequin
Library Holdings: Bk Vols 101,494
Subject Interests: Info, Libr sci
Special Collections: Juvenile Coll
Publications: Egebiana (journal); Servicio de alerta
LIBRARY SERVICES FOR THE PHYSICALLY HANDICAPPED, PO Box 23302, 00931-3302. SAN 327-9790. Tel: 787-764-0000, Ext 5173. FAX: 787-763-5685. *Asst Librn*, Ludim Diaz
Library Holdings: Bk Vols 9,272
Subject Interests: Blind-educ, History, Lang, Literature, Printing, Rehabilitation, Writing systs
Special Collections: Books in Braille; Large Print; Talking Books
MONSERRATE SANTANA DE PALES LIBRARY, PO Box 23302, 00931-3302. SAN 365-5652. Tel: 787-764-0000, Ext 5835. *Librn*, Lillian Oliveras
Library Holdings: Bk Vols 28,242
Subject Interests: Child abuse, Counseling, Family relations, Med soc work, Psychopathology, Rehabilitation, Soc servs, Soc work
MUSIC LIBRARY, Agustin Stahl Bldg Rio Piedras Campus, PO Box 23302, 00931-3302. SAN 327-9812. Tel: 787-764-0000, Ext 5204. FAX: 787-763-5685. *Librn*, Doris Rivera; E-Mail: drivera@upracd.upr.clu.edu
Founded 1953
Library Holdings: Bk Vols 72,228; Bk Titles 42,663; Per Subs 231
NATURAL SCIENCES LIBRARY, PO Box 22446, 00931-2246. SAN 365-5539. Tel: 787-764-0000, Ext 2359. FAX: 787-764-2890. Web Site: www.cnnet.upr.clu.edu/bcn/. *Dir*, Evangelina Perez; Tel: 787-764-0000, Ext 4760, E-Mail: evperez@rrpac.upr.clu.edu; *Coll Develop*, Julia Y Velez; Staff 13 (MLS 5, Non-MLS 8)
Founded 1954. Highest Degree: Doctorate
Library Holdings: Per Subs 1,200
Subject Interests: Astronomy, Biology, Botany, Chemistry, Geology, Mathematics, Physics, Pure sci, Zoology
Special Collections: Puerto Rico Science Coll
Automation Activity & Vendor Info: (OPAC) epixtech, inc.
Database Vendor: Ebsco - EbscoHost, epixtech, inc., OVID Technologies, Silverplatter Information Inc., Wilson - Wilson Web
Function: Reference services available
PERIODICALS COLLECTION, PO Box 23302, 00931-3302. SAN 376-2343. Tel: 787-764-0000, Ext 3487. FAX: 787-763-4611. Web Site: www.upr.clu.edu. *Per*, Rafael Encarnacion
Library Holdings: Bk Vols 117,805
Subject Interests: Humanities, Soc sci
PLANNING LIBRARY, PO Box 23302, 00931-3302. SAN 365-5563. 787-764-0000, Ext 3186. FAX: 787-763-5605. *Librn*, Bethel Rodrigu
Library Holdings: Bk Vols 36,907
Subject Interests: Environ, Planning-econ, Regional, Soc urban
PUBLIC ADMINISTRATION LIBRARY, PO Box 23302, 00931-3302 SAN 365-5598. Tel: 787-764-0000, Ext 3290. FAX: 787-763-5685. *Librn*, Aracelis Sosa
Library Holdings: Bk Vols 68,558
Subject Interests: Administrative law, Labor legislation, Organizatio theory, Personnel admin, Public admin, Public policy
PUERTO RICAN COLLECTION, PO Box 23302, 00931-3302. SAN 991X. Tel: 787-764-0000, Ext 3463. FAX: 787-763-5685. *Librn*, Mar Ordonez
Library Holdings: Bk Titles 39,244
Subject Interests: Puerto Ricans, Puerto Rico
Special Collections: Antonio S Pedreira Coll; Emilio J Pasarell Coll; Gerardo Selles Sola Coll; Miguel Guerra Mondragon Coll; Sociedad Economica de Amigos del Pais
REFERENCE COLLECTION, PO Box 23302, 00931-3302. SAN 376- Tel: 787-764-0000, Ext 3327. FAX: 787-763-5685. *Librn*, Ena Huyke Carlo
Library Holdings: Bk Vols 675,071
Subject Interests: Humanities, Soc sci
SOCIAL SCIENCES RESERVE ROOM, PO Box 23302, 00931-3302. 365-544X. Tel: 787-764-0000, Ext 2483. FAX: 787-763-5685. *Asst L* Gregorio Cordova
Library Holdings: Bk Vols 13,582
Subject Interests: Soc sci
ZENOBIA & JUAN RAMON JIMENEZ ROOM, PO Box 22933, 0093 2933. SAN 327-9936. Tel: 787-764-0000 Ext 3475. FAX: 787-763-56 *Librn*, Herminia Reinat
Library Holdings: Bk Vols 104,937
Subject Interests: Spanish lit
Special Collections: Bernardo G Candamo Coll; Juan Guerrero Ruiz Personal Library; Rafael Cansinos Assens Coll; Zenobia & Juan R Jimenez Personal Library & Documents

SANTURCE

CR UNIVERSITY OF THE SACRED HEART, Madre Maria Teresa Gueva Library, Rosales St, PO Box 12383, 00914-0383. SAN 318-5788. Tel: 7 728-1515, Ext 4353. FAX: 787-268-8868. Web Site: www.biblioteca.sagrado.edu/. *Dir*, Maria A Morales deGarin; *Assoc Dir*, Sonia Dmaz Latorre; Tel: 787-728-1515, Ext 4356, E-Mail: sdiaz@ sagrado.edu; *Ref*, Holanda Rendon; *Spec Coll*, Carlos M Gonzalez; *Spec Coll*, Andres Lopez; *Media Spec*, Carlos Perez; *Cat, Tech Servs*, Dolores Barreras; *Bibliog Instr*, Yoshira Castro; Staff 24 (MLS 11, Non-MLS 13)
Founded 1936. Enrl 5,300; Fac 417; Highest Degree: Master
1999-2000 Income (Main Library Only) $797,944. Mats Exp $238,110, Books $100,000, Per/Ser (Incl. Access Fees) $125,296, Presv $1,400. Sal $539,888
Library Holdings: Bk Vols 204,296; Bk Titles 120,563; Per Subs 1,500
Subject Interests: Para-med
Special Collections: Historical Archives of the Institution
Automation Activity & Vendor Info: (Cataloging) SIRSI; (Circulation) SIRSI; (Course Reserve) SIRSI; (OPAC) SIRSI; (Serials) SIRSI
Database Vendor: Dialog, ProQuest
Publications: Delfilinea (quarterly); Guia para la presentacion y aprobacionde una Tesis de Grado; Library Guides; Manual para la Preparacion de un Trabajo de Invesitgacion; Tapia Ayer y Hoy
Partic in Dialog Corporation
Friends of the Library Group

VIRGIN ISLANDS

Date of Statistics: 2000
Population, 1998: 110,000
Total Volumes in Public Libraries: 172,240
Total Library Circulation: 32,105
Source of Income: Public funds appropriated by legislation
Number of Bookmobiles: 1
Grants-in-Aid to Public Libraries:
Federal LSTA (Library Services & Technology Act): $96,000

ISTIANSTED

GOVERNOR JUAN F LUIS HOSPITAL & MEDICAL CENTER LIBRARY,* 4007 Estate Diamond Ruby, 00820-4421. SAN 318-5877. Tel: 340-778-6311, Ext 2610. FAX: 340-778-5500.
Library Holdings: Bk Vols 800; Per Subs 68

DERIKSTED

UNIVERSITY OF THE VIRGIN ISLANDS, Saint Croix Campus Library, 2 Golden Grove, 00840. (Mail add: RR 02, Box 10000, 00851), Tel: 340-692-4133. Circulation Tel: 340-692-4130. Reference Tel: 340-692-4138. FAX: 340-692-4135. Web Site: library.uvi.edu. *Dir Libr Serv*, Jennifer Jackson; Tel: 340-692-4000, Fax: 340-692-4005, E-Mail: jjackso@uvi.edu; *Librn, Mgr*, Judith V Rogers; Tel: 340-692-4132, E-Mail: jrogers@uvi.edu; *Cat*, Wenda Stephenson; Tel: 340-692-4136, E-Mail: wstephe@uvi.edu; Staff 7 (MLS 3, Non-MLS 4)
Founded 1969. Enrl 1,200; Fac 85; Highest Degree: Master
Oct 1998-Sep 1999 Income $344,490. Mats Exp $56,484. Sal $288,006 (Prof $139,000)
Library Holdings: Bk Vols 33,553; Bk Titles 28,857; Per Subs 155
Special Collections: Caribbean materials; ERIC, Virgin Island; VI documents
Automation Activity & Vendor Info: (Cataloging) epixtech, inc.; (Circulation) epixtech, inc.; (Course Reserve) epixtech, inc.; (OPAC) epixtech, inc.
Database Vendor: epixtech, inc., GaleNet, IAC - SearchBank, OCLC - First Search, Silverplatter Information Inc.
Publications: Acquisitions List; Library Handbook; Library Newsletter
Partic in NNLM/SCR, OCLC Online Computer Libr Ctr, Inc; Solinet; Virgin Islands Libr & Info Network

NT CROIX

GOOD HOPE SCHOOL, Ward M Canaday Library, Frederiksted, 170 Estate Whim, 00840. SAN 318-5869. Tel: 340-772-0022. FAX: 340-772-4626. *Chief Librn, Online Servs*, Cynthia J Mault; *Asst Librn*, Peg Waniewski; Staff 2 (MLS 1, Non-MLS 1)
Founded 1970. Enrl 400; Fac 40
Library Holdings: Bk Titles 15,000; Per Subs 78
Special Collections: Caribbeana (John C & Gene H Heatherston; Endowment); Marine Science (Tarbert, plus several minor contributors); Rare Books (Dewitt Wallace Coll)
Library serves students from 20 different countries in grades K through 12. The building features include closed-circuit TV, attached mini-theater & a rare book room. Middle States Association Accreditation

ATHALIE MCFARLANE PETERSEN PUBLIC LIBRARY, 604 Strand St, Frederiksted, 00840. SAN 318-5850. Tel: 340-772-0315. FAX: 340-772-2699. *Librn*, Sylvie Renaud; *Asst Librn*, Veronica DeLeon
Founded 1920. Circ 13,000
Library Holdings: Bk Vols 16,000
Subject Interests: Caribbean culture, History
Branch of Bureau of Libraries, Museums & Archaeological Services, Saint Thomas
Friends of the Library Group

S VIRGIN ISLANDS ENERGY OFFICE LIBRARY,* 200 Strand St, Frederiksted, 00840. SAN 371-4470. Tel: 340-772-2616. FAX: 340-772-0063. E-Mail: vieo0441@viaccess.net. *Librn*, Jamal Nielsen
Library Holdings: Bk Vols 100

P FLORENCE A S WILLIAMS PUBLIC LIBRARY,* 1122 King St Christiansted, 00820-4951. SAN 318-5885. Tel: 340-773-5715. FAX: 340-773-5327. *Librn*, Wallace Williams; *Doc*, Denice Ellis
Founded 1920
Library Holdings: Bk Vols 20,000; Per Subs 15
Special Collections: Virgin Islands & Caribbean Materials
Branch of Bureau of Libraries, Museums & Archaelogical Services, Saint Thomas

SAINT JOHN

P ELAINE IONE SPRAUVE LIBRARY & MUSEUM, Enighed Estate, Cruz Bay, PO Box 30, 00831. SAN 318-5893. Tel: 340-776-6359. FAX: 340-693-7375. E-Mail: friendsprlib@att.net. Web Site: www.library.gov.vi/sprauve. *Librn*, Carol McGuinness; E-Mail: cmcguin@att.net; Staff 2 (MLS 1, Non-MLS 1)
Founded 1959. Pop 3,800
2000-2000 Mats Exp $20,000, Books $19,000, Per/Ser (Incl. Access Fees) $1,000
Library Holdings: Bk Vols 12,000; Per Subs 37
Special Collections: West Indies
Branch of Bureau of Libraries, Museums & Archaeological Services, Saint Thomas
Friends of the Library Group

SAINT THOMAS

P DIVISION OF LIBRARIES, ARCHIVES & MUSEUMS,* 23 Dronningens Gade, 00802. SAN 365-592X. Tel: 340-774-3407. FAX: 340-775-1887. *Asst Dir, Br Coordr*, Simon C Caines; *Tech Servs*, Shirley Lincoln; *Spec Coll*, Beverly Smith; Staff 24 (MLS 24)
Founded 1920. Pop 100,000
Library Holdings: Bk Vols 220,000; Per Subs 125
Special Collections: Virgin Islands; Von Scholten Coll, Founded 1920: Danish West Indies, Virgin Islands & Caribbean, bks, doc, local newsp, mss, maps, pamphlets, per, photogs, VF
Publications: Annual Report; Caribbeana: Recent Acquisitions of Caribbean Materials in Virgin Islands Libraries; Checklist of Virgin Islands Government Documents; Information (newsletter); Occasional Papers Series;

Union Catalog of 16mm Motion Pictures; Union List of Periodicals and Newspapers; Virgin Islands Govt Blou bks; Virgin Islands Govt Calendar for 1985; Virgin Islands Newspaper Index
Partic in Vilinet
Branches: 5
ATHALIE MCFARLANE PETERSEN PUBLIC LIBRARY
See Separate Entry in Saint Croix
ELAINE IONE SPRAUVE LIBRARY & MUSEUM
See Separate Entry in Saint John
ENID M BAA LIBRARY & ARCHIVES
See Separate Entry
FLORENCE A WILLIAMS PUBLIC LIBRARY
See Separate Entry in Saint Croix

P REGIONAL LIBRARY FOR THE BLIND & PHYSICALLY HANDICAPPED, 3012 Golden Rock, Christiansted, Saint Croix, 00820. SAN 365-5989. Tel: 340-772-2250. FAX: 340-772-3545. *Librn*, Wallace Williams; Staff 1 (MLS 1)
Founded 1968. Circ 7,559
Special Services - Free home & mail delivery of materials; serves eligible patrons throughout the territory. In St Thomas, distributes materials through the Outreach Dept of Enid M Baa Public Library
Friends of the Library Group

P ENID M BAA LIBRARY & ARCHIVES,* 20 Dronningen Gade, 00802. SAN 365-5954. Tel: 340-774-0630. FAX: 340-775-1887.
Founded 1920. Pop 51,000
Library Holdings: Bk Vols 40,000; Per Subs 20
Special Collections: Building Houses Von Scholten; UN & VI Documents Coll
Branch of Division of Libraries, Archives & Museums, U.S. Virgin Islands
Friends of the Library Group

S ISLAND RESOURCES FOUNDATION LIBRARY,* 6292 Estate Nazareth No 100, 00802-1104. SAN 318-5907. Tel: 340-775-6225. FAX: 340-779-2022. Web Site: www.irf.org. *Pres*, Bruce Potter
Founded 1972
Library Holdings: Bk Titles 10,000
Subject Interests: Coastal zone mgt, Develop planning, Environ impa assessment, Maritime history, Park planning, Resource mgt, Tourism d
Special Collections: Geographic Information Systems & Applications
Publications: Bulletin (semi-annual)
Branches:
WASHINGTON DC BRANCH, 1718 P St NW Ste T-4, Washington, 2 SAN 327-9391. Tel: 202-265-9712. FAX: 202-232-0748. Web Site: www.irf.org. *Librn*, Jean-Pierre Bacle
Library Holdings: Per Subs 3,000

C UNIVERSITY OF THE VIRGIN ISLANDS, Ralph M Paiewonsky Lib 2 John Brewers Bay, 00802-9990. SAN 365-6012. Tel: 340-693-1360. Reference Tel: 340-693-1367. FAX: 340-693-1365. E-Mail: reflib@uvi Web Site: library.uvi.edu. *Mgr Libr*, Linda Robinson Barr; Tel: 340-69 1361, E-Mail: lbarr@uvi.edu; *Syst Coordr*, Sharlene Harris; Tel: 340-6 1368, E-Mail: sharris@uvi.edu; *Publ Servs*, Cynthia Perry Richards; Te 340-693-1369, E-Mail: crichar@uvi.edu. Subject Specialists: *Govt docs* Sharlene Harris; Staff 10 (MLS 5, Non-MLS 5)
Founded 1962. Enrl 2,500; Fac 82; Highest Degree: Master
Library Holdings: Bk Vols 91,673; Bk Titles 83,000; Per Subs 530
Subject Interests: Caribbean hist, Caribbean lit, Caribbean politics, Government
Special Collections: Caribbean Area Coll, VF; Melchior Center for Re Virgin Islands History
Automation Activity & Vendor Info: (Cataloging) epixtech, inc.; (Circulation) epixtech, inc.; (ILL) epixtech, inc.; (OPAC) epixtech, inc.
Database Vendor: epixtech, inc., GaleNet, IAC - Info Trac, OCLC - F Search, Silverplatter Information Inc.
Publications: Acquisitions list; Library handbooks; Periodical List
Partic in SE Libr Network; Solinet; Virgin Islands Libr & Info Network